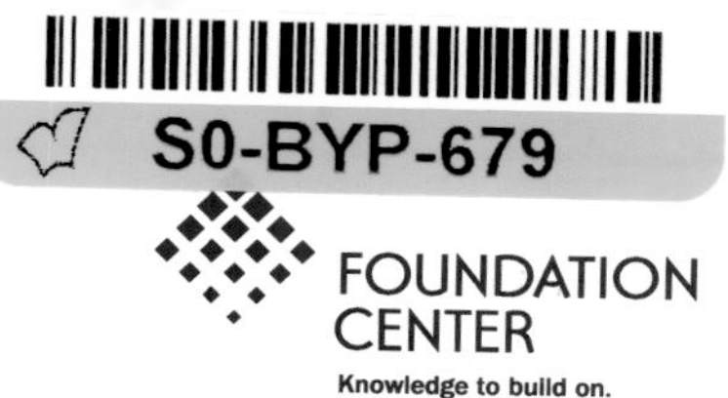

WHAT'S IN THE FOUNDATION DIRECTORY?

The Foundation Directory provides information on the finances, governance, and giving interests of the nation's 10,000 largest grantmaking foundations—those foundations who were among the top 10,000 in terms of awards made in the latest fiscal year of record. The information in The Foundation Directory is based either on reports received directly from the foundations or on the most current public records available.

The Foundation Directory is arranged alphabetically by state and, within states, by foundation name. Each entry includes the foundation's name and address, financial data for the latest available year of record, a description of funding interests, a list of officers and trustees, and the foundation's IRS Employer Identification Number. Where applicable, additional information is provided on the types of grants or other forms of support awarded, restrictions on the giving program by geographic or subject area, application procedures and deadlines, and the number of staff members the foundation employs. When available, a selected list of up to ten grants reported during a given fiscal year is included.

When using *The Foundation Directory* to identify potential funding sources, grantseekers are urged to read each foundation description carefully to determine the nature of the grantmaker's interests and to note any restrictions on giving that would prevent the foundation from considering their proposal. Some foundations limit their giving to a particular subject field or geographic area; others are unable to provide certain types of support, such as funds for buildings and equipment or for general operating budgets. Even when a foundation has not provided an explicit limitations statement, restrictions on giving may exist. This is often the case with entries updated from public records. Further research into the giving patterns of these foundations is necessary before applying for funds.

INDEXES

Seven indexes to the descriptive entries are provided to assist grantseekers and other users of *The Foundation Directory*:

- The **Index to Donors, Officers, Trustees** is an alphabetical list of individual and corporate donors, officers, and members of governing boards whose names appear in *The Foundation Directory* entries.
- The **Geographic Index** lists foundations by the states and cities in which they are located, with cross-references to foundations located elsewhere that have made substantial grants in a particular state.
- The **International Giving Index** provides access to foundations whose giving interests extend beyond the United States. A complete alphabetical list of countries, continents, and regions is provided at the beginning of the index. Under each country, continent, or region, entry numbers are listed by the state location and abbreviated name of the foundation.
- The **Types of Support Index** provides access to foundation entries by the specific types of support the foundation awards. A glossary of the forms of support included appears at the beginning of this index. Under each type of support term, entry numbers are listed by the state location and abbreviated name of the foundation.
- The **Subject Index** provides access to giving interests of foundations based on the "Fields of Interest" section of their entries. A list of the subject terms used is provided at the beginning of this index. Under each subject term, entry numbers are listed by the state location and abbreviated name of the foundation.
- The index of **Foundations New to the Edition** is a listing of foundations that appear in the current edition of *The Foundation Directory* but had not met criteria for inclusion in the previous edition. The descriptive entries for these foundations are highlighted with a star (☆).
- **The Foundation Name Index** is an alphabetical list of all foundations with entries in *The Foundation Directory*. Former names of foundations appear with "see" references to the appropriate entry numbers. This index also provides references to Appendix A, which lists foundations that appeared in the previous edition but have since terminated or otherwise become ineligible for inclusion.

In the Geographic Index, Types of Support Index, and Subject Index, foundations that award grants on a national, regional, or international basis are listed in boldface type. The other foundations generally limit their giving to the city or state in which they are located.

APPENDIXES

- **Appendix A** lists foundations described in the previous edition of *The Foundation Directory* that do not have entries in the current edition because they have terminated operations, merged with another foundation, ceased grantmaking, or changed their legal status.
- **Appendix B** lists foundations that have made a significant amount of grants, but are excluded because they contribute only to a few specified beneficiaries or to the support of a single institution.

Knowledge to build on.

THE FOUNDATION DIRECTORY

37th Edition
2015

CONTRIBUTING STAFF

Vice President for Data and Technology Strategy	Jake Garcia
Vice President for Data Architecture	Jeffrey A. Falkenstein
Director, Foundation Information Management	David G. Jacobs
Director, Grants Information Management	Jeannine Corey
Coordinator, Grant Analysis and Collection	Denise McLeod
Data Integration Liaison	Chuck Bartelt
Coordinator, Large Foundations	Cindy B. Martinez
Senior Editorial Associates	Regina Judith Faighes
	William Giles
	Elia S. Glenn
	Joseph W. Guastella
	Cynthia Y. Manick
Editorial Associate	Lakesha Spiegel-Reneau
Editorial Assistants	Carlos Edwin Estremera
	Michele Kragalott
	Casey Robbins
Data Entry Clerk	Willean Baldwin
Manager, Corporate Philanthropy	Andrew N. Grabois
Community Foundations Liaison	David Rosado
Application Developer	Kathye Giesler
System Administrator	Emmy So
Production Manager	Christine Innamorato
Graphic Designer	Betty Saronson
Senior Programmer/Analyst	Mirek Drozdzowski

The editor gratefully acknowledges the many other Foundation Center staff who contributed support, encouragement, and information that was indispensable to the preparation of this volume. Special mention should also be made of the staff members of the New York, Washington, DC, Cleveland, San Francisco, and Atlanta libraries who assisted in tracking changes in foundation information. We would like to express our appreciation as well to the many foundations that cooperated fully in updating information prior to the compilation of *The Foundation Directory*.

ISBN 978-1-59542-499-0
Printed and bound in the United States of America.

CONTENTS

INTRODUCTION

The Foundation Directory is the definitive annual reference source for information about private and community grantmaking foundations in the United States. It is used by fundseekers, foundation and government officials, scholars, journalists, and others generally interested in giving by U.S. foundations.

THE 2015 EDITION

The 2015 Edition is the thirty-seventh complete revision of *The Foundation Directory* since the volume was first published by the Foundation Center in 1960. This year's edition of the *Directory* contains information on the 10,000 largest grantmaking foundations in the U.S. These foundations awarded the most dollars in total giving during the most current fiscal year of record.[1] (Entries for the next 10,000 largest grantmaking foundations in the U.S. during the most current fiscal year of record can be found in a companion volume, *Foundation Directory Part 2*). Entries in this volume hold a combined total assets value of more than $672.4 billion (84.2 percent of all foundation assets) and awarded grants totaling over $49.2 billion (89.2 percent of all foundation giving) in the latest year of record (Table 1).

SELECTED GRANTS

To illustrate a foundation's giving pattern, selected grants to recipient organizations have been provided whenever possible. Up to ten selected grants have been included for foundations where applicable. Grants to individuals are not listed. Of the 10,000 entries in this volume, 4,682 (46.8 percent) include lists of selected grants. In all, 31,080 grants are included, totaling over $10.7 billion in support to organizations. These grants may serve to illustrate fields of interest and geographic preferences. In general, however, the selected grants represent large awards and may not reveal the full spectrum of programs and giving interests of a foundation. The complete descriptive entry should always be carefully examined to determine a foundation's current funding emphasis, and, where available, the "average" grant amount noted in the fiscal information section should be consulted to ascertain the typical range of grants awarded.

FOUNDATIONS NEW TO THE FOUNDATION DIRECTORY

There are 1,342 foundations in the 2015 edition that were not listed in the 2014 edition (Table 2). Of these, 1,185 (88.3 percent) are independent foundations, 77 (5.7 percent) are company-sponsored foundations, 38 (2.8 percent) are community foundations, and 42 (3.1 percent) are grantmaking operating foundations. One hundred and fifty-two of the newly-added foundations hold assets of $20 million or more (Table 6), but, like other foundations in *The Foundation Directory*, the majority fall into the $1 million to $10 million asset range. Foundations new to *The Foundation Directory* can be identified by a star (☆) in their descriptive entries. Users with a particular interest in these newly qualifying foundations will find them listed separately in the index of Foundations New to the Edition.

WHAT IS A FOUNDATION?

The Center defines a foundation as a nongovernmental, nonprofit organization with its own funds (usually from a single source, either an individual, family, or corporation) and program managed by its own trustees and directors that was established to maintain or aid educational, social, charitable, religious, or other activities serving the common welfare, primarily by making grants to other nonprofit organizations.

The Foundation Directory includes those organizations meeting the Foundation Center's definition of a private or community foundation and are included in the second tier of the largest foundations by total giving in the U.S.

The Foundation Directory does not include organizations whose giving is restricted by charter to one or more specified organizations; foundations that function as endowments for special purposes within and under the governance of a parent institution, such as a college or church; operating foundations that do not maintain active grantmaking programs; organizations that act as associations for industrial or other special groups; or organizations that make general appeals to the public for funds. Lists of private foundations that meet the criteria for *The Foundation Directory* but which are excluded for the reasons cited above are provided in the Appendixes.

---

[1] In addition, *The Foundation Directory* includes entries for 3 large organizations that are not private foundations, but closely resemble them in form and function: Howard Hughes Medical Institute, classified by the IRS as a Medical Research Organization, The California HealthCare Foundation, which is classified as a public charity, and The Pew Charitable Trusts, which was reorganized as a public charity in 2004. These organizations resemble private foundations in that they do not make appeals to the public for donations, and aid charitable purposes through grantmaking in accordance with an IRS payout requirement. These entries are omitted from the statistical tables and summaries in this edition.

TYPES OF FOUNDATIONS

Foundations included in this volume fall into one of four categories:

Independent Foundation: A fund or endowment designated by the Internal Revenue Service (IRS) as a private foundation under the law, the primary function of which is the making of grants. The assets of most independent foundations are derived from the gift of an individual or family. Some function under the direction of family members and are known as "family foundations." Depending on their range of giving, independent foundations may also be known as "general purpose" or "special purpose" foundations.

Company-Sponsored Foundation: A private foundation under the tax law deriving its funds from a profit-making company or corporation but independently constituted, the purpose of which is to make grants, usually on a broad basis although not without regard for the business interests of the corporation. Company-sponsored foundations are legally distinct from contributions programs administered within the corporation directly from corporate funds. Direct corporate giving programs are not listed in *The Foundation Directory*. The Foundation Center's *National Directory of Corporate Giving*, Nineteenth Edition, published in 2013, includes complete giving profiles on nearly 4,200 companies.

Operating Foundation: A fund or endowment designated under the tax law by the Internal Revenue Service as a private operating foundation, the primary purpose of which is to operate research, social welfare, or other programs determined by its governing body or charter. Most operating foundations award few or no grants to outside organizations, and therefore do not appear in *The Foundation Directory*.

Community Foundation: In its general charitable purposes, a community foundation is much like a private foundation; its funds, however, are derived from many donors rather than a single source, as is usually the case with private foundations. Further, community foundations are usually classified under the tax law as public charities and are therefore subject to different rules and regulations than those which govern private foundations. Public charities other than community foundations are not included in *The Foundation Directory*.

FIGURE A. General Characteristics of Four Types of Foundations

Foundation Type	Description	Source of Funds	Decision-Making Activity	Grantmaking Requirements	Reporting
Independent Foundation	An independent grant-making organization established to aid social, educational, religious, or other charitable activities.	Endowment generally derived from a single source such as an individual, a family, or a group of individuals. Contributions to endowment limited as to tax deductibility.	Decisions may be made by donor or members of the donor's family; by an independent board of directors or trustees; or by a bank or trust officer acting on the donor's behalf.	Broad discretionary giving allowed but may have specific guidelines and give only in a few specific fields. About 70% limit their giving to local area.	Annual information returns (990-PF) filed with IRS must be made available to public. A small percentage issue separately printed annual reports.
Company-Sponsored Foundation	Legally an independent grantmaking organization with close ties to the corporation providing funds.	Endowment and annual contributions from a profit-making corporation. May maintain small endowment and pay out most of contributions received annually in grants, or may maintain endowment to cover contributions in years when corporate profits are down.	Decisions made by board of directors often composed of corporate officials, but which may include individuals with no corporate affiliation. Decisions may also be made by local company officials.	Giving tends to be in fields related to corporate activities or in communities where corporation operates. Usually give more grants but in smaller dollar amounts than independent foundations.	Same as above.
Operating Foundation	An organization that uses its resources to conduct research or provide a direct service.	Endowment usually provided from a single source, but eligible for maximum deductible contributions from public.	Decisions generally made by independent board of directors.	Makes few, if any grants. Grants generally related directly to the foundation's program.	Same as above.
Community Foundation	A publicly sponsored organization that makes grants for social, educational, religious, or other charitable purposes in a specific community or region.	Contributions received from many donors. Usually eligible for maximum tax deductible contributions from public.	Decisions made by board of directors representing the diversity of the community.	Grants generally limited to charitable organizations in local community.	IRS 990 return available to public. Many publish full guidelines or annual reports.

SOURCES OF INFORMATION

The entries in *The Foundation Directory* are revised and updated on an ongoing basis, using the newest and most complete information available. This information is either provided by the foundation itself, or it comes from available public records. The main source of information are the foundations' tax returns, the form 990-PF. Other public sources of information used in this edition include updates from foundation web sites, annual reports, press releases and newspaper articles. In addition, the Foundation Center offers private foundations several ways to share newer and more current information. Entries in the book are prepared and sent to the individual foundations for verification. In 2014, 760 foundations responded to these requests. In addition, 644 foundations sent either full or partial information updates via Foundation Center electronic reporting applications (*Foundation Finder* and *Foundation Center Updater*) available on the Foundation Center's web site (foundationcenter.org). For grantmakers who do not respond to our requests for information, entries were prepared from the most recent IRS tax return available as of January 2015. These entries are indicated in *The Foundation Directory*, by the symbol (✧) following the foundation name.

The Internet is an important and effective research tool, enabling staff to learn more about foundations and their most current grantmaking activities. This edition contains 3,146 entries with a URL (Internet web site address), and an additional 3,496 that report having an e-mail address.

A breakdown of the 10,000 foundations by fiscal year-end date reveals the following: 172 foundations (1.7 percent) with 2014 fiscal data, 7,422 (74.2 percent) with 2013 fiscal data, 2,331 (23.3 percent) with 2012 fiscal data, and 73 foundations (.73 percent) with 2011 fiscal data. Thus, 2014 and 2013 fiscal information is reported for 75.9 percent of the foundations listed. Of the 100 largest foundations, 92 percent are represented by 2014 or 2013 fiscal data (Tables 4 and 5). Even when more recent financial information was not available, foundation addresses, contacts, program information, and application procedures reflect the latest updates received by the Center through January 2015.

TABLE 1. Aggregate Fiscal Data by Foundation Type (All dollar figures expressed in thousands)

Foundation Type	Number of Foundations	%	Assets	%	Gifts Received	%	Total Giving*	%	Qualifying Distributions	%	Loans
Independent	8,367	83.7	$550,279,360	81.8	$25,092,288	54.1	$31,666,721	64.3	$35,815,609	64.9	$259,502
Company-Sponsored	866	8.7	23,325,464	3.5	6,012,548	13.0	5,200,958	10.6	5,413,511	9.8	9049
Community	511	5.1	72,230,348	10.7	8,165,973	17.6	5,178,304	10.5	5,570,680	10.1	9866
Operating	256	2.6	26,640,528	4.0	7,111,667	15.3	7,236,888	14.7	8,413,121	15.2	36,796
Total	**10,000**	**100.0**	**$672,475,700**	**100.0**	**$46,382,476**	**100.0**	**$49,282,870**	**100.0**	**$55,212,921**	**100.0**	**$315,214**

Note: Figures may not add up due to rounding.
*Throughout this introduction, "Total Giving" figures include grants, scholarships, employee matching gifts, and other amounts reported as "Grants and Contributions Paid During the Year" on the 990-PF reporting form. Loan amounts including program-related investments (PRIs) are indicated separately. Total giving does not include all qualifying distributions under the tax law, e.g., loans, PRIs, and program or other administrative expenses.

TABLE 2. Aggregate Fiscal Data for Foundations New to *The Foundation Directory* by Foundation Type
(All dollar figures expressed in thousands)

Foundation Type	Number of Foundations	%	Assets	%	Gifts Received	%	Total Giving*	%	Qualifying Distributions	%	Loans
Independent	1,185	88.3	$14,114,292	85.0	$2,229,125	89.9	$1,232,810	86.8	$1,450,788	83.3	$554
Company-Sponsored	77	5.7	371,142	2.2	114,443	4.6	115,119	8.1	119,110	6.8	0
Community	38	2.8	468,619	2.8	53,404	2.2	29,511	2.1	36,211	2.1	0
Operating	42	3.1	1,642,848	9.9	81,431	3.3	42,296	3.0	135,521	7.8	0
Total	**1,342**	**100.0**	**$16,596,902**	**100.0**	**$2,478,404**	**100.0**	**$1,419,736**	**100.0**	**$1,741,630**	**100.0**	**$554**

Note: Figures may not add up due to rounding.
*Throughout this introduction, "Total Giving" figures include grants, scholarships, employee matching gifts, and other amounts reported as "Grants and Contributions Paid During the Year" on the 990-PF reporting form. Loan amounts including program-related investments (PRIs) are indicated separately. Total giving does not include all qualifying distributions under the tax law, e.g., loans, PRIs, and program or other administrative expenses.

TABLE 3. Fiscal Data of Foundations by Region and State (All dollar figures expressed in thousands)

Region	Number of Foundations	%	Assets	%	Gifts Received	%	Expenditures	%	Total Giving	%
NORTHEAST	**3,167**	**31.7**	**$197,570,725**	**29.4**	**$14,632,758**	**31.5**	**$20,203,248**	**33.9**	**$17,133,330**	**34.8**
New England	**804**	**8.0**	**34,396,407**	**5.1**	**2,814,280**	**6.1**	**3,173,770**	**5.3**	**2,635,508**	**5.3**
Connecticut	203	2.0	9,037,394	1.3	1,264,880	2.7	997,070	1.7	893,745	1.8
Maine	35	0.4	2,273,615	0.3	57,769	0.1	141,367	0.2	117,521	0.2
Massachusetts	419	4.2	17,359,374	2.6	1,213,540	2.6	1,573,356	2.6	1,229,345	2.5
New Hampshire	28	0.3	1,751,235	0.3	125,885	0.3	188,172	0.3	166,381	0.3
Rhode Island	100	1.0	3,561,308	0.5	122,628	0.3	237,885	0.4	199,699	0.4
Vermont	19	0.2	413,480	0.1	29,579	0.1	35,919	0.1	28,817	0.1
Middle Atlantic	**2,363**	**23.6**	**163,174,319**	**24.3**	**11,818,477**	**25.5**	**17,029,478**	**28.6**	**14,497,822**	**29.4**
New Jersey	322	3.2	20,207,143	3.0	2,965,598	6.4	3,683,539	6.2	3,191,720	6.5
New York	1,593	15.9	118,187,290	17.6	7,357,222	15.9	10,986,450	18.5	9,251,752	18.8
Pennsylvania	448	4.5	24,779,886	3.7	1,495,658	3.2	2,359,489	4.0	2,054,350	4.2
MIDWEST	**2,184**	**21.8**	**135,904,986**	**20.2**	**8,947,697**	**19.3**	**11,635,638**	**19.6**	**9,869,245**	**20.0**
East North Central	**1,563**	**15.6**	**96,519,198**	**14.4**	**6,646,582**	**14.3**	**8,318,422**	**14.0**	**7,116,354**	**14.4**
Illinois	604	6.0	29,234,750	4.3	2,471,805	5.3	3,096,147	5.2	2,709,392	5.5
Indiana	158	1.6	15,667,822	2.3	1,211,458	2.6	1,550,532	2.6	1,399,632	2.8
Michigan	265	2.7	26,947,659	4.0	1,105,140	2.4	1,825,839	3.1	1,459,729	3.0
Ohio	363	3.6	17,763,062	2.6	1,221,791	2.6	1,301,027	2.2	1,081,498	2.2
Wisconsin	173	1.7	6,905,905	1.0	636,388	1.4	544,876	0.9	466,102	0.9
West North Central	**621**	**6.2**	**39,385,788**	**5.9**	**2,301,114**	**5.0**	**3,317,216**	**5.6**	**2,752,891**	**5.6**
Iowa	83	0.8	2,687,865	0.4	208,168	0.4	211,779	0.4	178,975	0.4
Kansas	65	0.7	2,340,757	0.3	121,759	0.3	153,119	0.3	126,745	0.3
Minnesota	214	2.1	15,824,942	2.4	418,854	0.9	1,072,444	1.8	834,484	1.7
Missouri	154	1.5	10,755,533	1.6	856,842	1.8	925,155	1.6	724,240	1.5
Nebraska	79	0.8	6,840,095	1.0	629,849	1.4	897,258	1.5	840,907	1.7
North Dakota	12	0.1	291,196	0.0	12,035	0.0	18,377	0.0	15,218	0.0
South Dakota	14	0.1	645,400	0.1	53,607	0.1	39,085	0.1	32,323	0.1
SOUTH	**2,690**	**26.9**	**145,426,272**	**21.6**	**8,515,275**	**18.4**	**11,935,515**	**20.1**	**9,878,870**	**20.0**
South Atlantic	**1,543**	**15.4**	**78,950,858**	**11.7**	**4,348,634**	**9.4**	**6,284,875**	**10.6**	**5,164,000**	**10.5**
Delaware	144	1.4	4,780,670	0.7	306,811	0.7	382,368	0.6	326,396	0.7
District of Columbia	84	0.8	7,283,411	1.1	462,001	1.0	506,405	0.9	390,540	0.8
Florida	437	4.4	16,961,885	2.5	1,224,031	2.6	1,332,600	2.2	1,107,507	2.2
Georgia	187	1.9	12,807,182	1.9	559,936	1.2	1,071,287	1.8	936,823	1.9
Maryland	199	2.0	13,086,879	1.9	542,918	1.2	893,234	1.5	636,112	1.3
North Carolina	219	2.2	13,912,394	2.1	671,185	1.4	1,184,958	2.0	1,041,110	2.1
South Carolina	57	0.6	1,803,543	0.3	121,252	0.3	155,510	0.3	130,495	0.3
Virginia	185	1.9	7,427,956	1.1	386,801	0.8	709,567	1.2	554,034	1.1
West Virginia	31	0.3	886,938	0.1	73,700	0.2	48,945	0.1	40,984	0.1
East South Central	**292**	**2.9**	**11,128,811**	**1.7**	**584,566**	**1.3**	**944,289**	**1.6**	**790,722**	**1.6**
Alabama	78	0.8	1,906,052	0.3	110,494	0.2	151,507	0.3	128,294	0.3
Kentucky	52	0.5	2,145,202	0.3	87,332	0.2	156,227	0.3	132,573	0.3
Mississippi	40	0.4	1,081,484	0.2	73,297	0.2	97,453	0.2	75,640	0.2
Tennessee	122	1.2	5,996,073	0.9	313,443	0.7	539,102	0.9	454,215	0.9
West South Central	**855**	**8.6**	**55,346,603**	**8.2**	**3,582,075**	**7.7**	**4,706,350**	**7.9**	**3,924,147**	**8.0**
Arkansas	35	0.4	3,962,022	0.6	827,915	1.8	655,184	1.1	613,376	1.2
Louisiana	68	0.7	2,670,842	0.4	104,146	0.2	260,124	0.4	205,685	0.4
Oklahoma	97	1.0	12,731,377	1.9	366,899	0.8	561,781	0.9	442,334	0.9
Texas	655	6.6	35,982,361	5.4	2,283,115	4.9	3,229,261	5.4	2,662,752	5.4
WEST	**1,955**	**19.6**	**193,511,090**	**28.8**	**14,280,983**	**30.8**	**15,733,934**	**26.4**	**12,396,650**	**25.2**
Mountain	**470**	**4.7**	**23,175,803**	**3.4**	**1,253,719**	**2.7**	**1,796,370**	**3.0**	**1,458,620**	**3.0**
Arizona	89	0.9	3,476,351	0.5	177,467	0.4	287,746	0.5	229,631	0.5
Colorado	168	1.7	9,684,813	1.4	445,423	1.0	730,760	1.2	576,214	1.2
Idaho	22	0.2	1,213,293	0.2	73,582	0.2	89,342	0.2	73,804	0.1
Montana	16	0.2	971,701	0.1	75,169	0.2	41,757	0.1	32,607	0.1
Nevada	63	0.6	3,181,130	0.5	132,324	0.3	328,525	0.6	291,722	0.6
New Mexico	28	0.3	1,185,448	0.2	91,184	0.2	100,685	0.2	73,641	0.1
Utah	56	0.6	2,187,857	0.3	46,874	0.1	135,026	0.2	114,611	0.2
Wyoming	28	0.3	1,275,210	0.2	211,696	0.5	82,528	0.1	66,391	0.1
Pacific	**1,485**	**14.9**	**170,335,287**	**25.3**	**13,027,264**	**28.1**	**13,937,564**	**23.4**	**10,938,030**	**22.2**
Alaska	11	0.1	819,316	0.1	64,048	0.1	49,760	0.1	29,820	0.1
California	1,148	11.5	109,902,376	16.3	7,941,316	17.1	8,411,892	14.1	6,686,884	13.6
Hawaii	40	0.4	1,526,383	0.2	47,643	0.1	120,788	0.2	93,358	0.2
Oregon	81	0.8	5,879,786	0.9	332,548	0.7	380,106	0.6	290,405	0.6
Washington	205	2.1	52,207,426	7.8	4,641,709	10.0	4,975,018	8.4	3,837,563	7.8
CARIBBEAN	**4**	**0.0**	**62,627**	**0.0**	**5,763**	**0.0**	**7,478**	**0.0**	**4,776**	**0.0**
Puerto Rico	2	0.0	40,262	0.0	3,820	0.0	4,688	0.0	2,452	0.0
Virgin Islands	2	0.0	22,364	0.0	1,943	0.0	2,790	0.0	2,324	0.0
TOTAL:	**10,000**	**100.0**	**$672,475,700**	**100.0**	**$46,382,476**	**100.0**	**$59,515,812**	**100.0**	**$49,282,870**	**100.0**

Note: Figures may not add up due to rounding.

TABLE 4. 100 Largest Foundations by Assets

Name	Assets	Total Giving	Fiscal Date
1. Bill & Melinda Gates Foundation	$41,310,207,525	$3,320,725,374	12/31/13
2. Ford Foundation	12,259,961,589	560,335,883	12/31/13
3. J. Paul Getty Trust	11,110,918,337	12,778,308	6/30/13
4. The Robert Wood Johnson Foundation	10,173,403,442	337,561,658	12/31/13
5. W. K. Kellogg Foundation	8,621,183,526	294,891,874	8/31/14
6. The William and Flora Hewlett Foundation	8,607,073,000	240,100,000	12/31/13
7. Lilly Endowment Inc.	7,699,211,116	270,300,000	12/31/13
8. The David and Lucile Packard Foundation	6,902,501,278	295,015,267	12/31/13
9. Gordon and Betty Moore Foundation	6,417,833,620	272,332,512	12/31/13
10. The John D. and Catherine T. MacArthur Foundation	6,323,307,217	218,542,721	12/31/13
11. The Andrew W. Mellon Foundation	6,188,229,000	234,372,144	12/31/13
12. Bloomberg Philanthropies	5,402,611,056	204,007,709	12/31/13
13. Silicon Valley Community Foundation	4,723,897,000	362,390,000	12/31/13
14. The Leona M. and Harry B. Helmsley Charitable Trust	4,241,501,002	210,352,475	3/31/13
15. The Rockefeller Foundation	4,121,465,814	137,817,790	12/31/13
16. Tulsa Community Foundation	3,729,789,000	110,512,000	12/31/12
17. The California Endowment	3,668,459,217	182,809,047	3/31/14
18. The Kresge Foundation	3,543,405,167	130,183,827	12/31/13
19. The Duke Endowment	3,367,128,863	127,729,045	12/31/13
20. Foundation to Promote Open Society	3,330,839,478	380,512,799	12/31/13
21. Robert W. Woodruff Foundation, Inc.	3,119,096,039	155,816,887	12/31/13
22. Margaret A. Cargill Foundation	3,094,112,687	38,269,750	12/31/13
23. Carnegie Corporation of New York	3,033,694,178	130,380,545	9/30/13
24. The Susan Thompson Buffett Foundation	2,731,731,558	450,319,788	12/31/13
25. The Annie E. Casey Foundation	2,666,068,266	98,681,016	12/31/12
26. Charles Stewart Mott Foundation	2,587,788,238	114,442,289	12/31/13
27. John Templeton Foundation	2,555,855,497	105,248,596	12/31/12
28. Walton Family Foundation, Inc.	2,480,825,574	311,719,212	12/31/13
29. The New York Community Trust	2,443,372,250	144,241,100	12/31/13
30. Conrad N. Hilton Foundation	2,430,703,442	92,000,000	12/31/13
31. John S. and James L. Knight Foundation	2,395,608,862	107,825,135	12/31/13
32. Richard King Mellon Foundation	2,343,064,597	99,152,041	12/31/13
33. The JPB Foundation	2,318,642,200	78,051,333	12/31/13
34. Charles and Lynn Schusterman Family Foundation	2,291,018,311	64,025,508	12/31/13
35. The William Penn Foundation	2,283,164,256	80,099,460	12/31/13
36. The McKnight Foundation	2,239,101,229	86,598,229	12/31/13
37. The Simons Foundation	2,170,686,615	179,640,382	12/31/13
38. Greater Kansas City Community Foundation	2,151,222,919	234,274,371	12/31/13
39. The Cleveland Foundation	2,132,806,744	81,368,990	12/31/13
40. The Harry and Jeanette Weinberg Foundation, Inc.	2,127,938,700	96,929,767	2/28/14
41. Ewing Marion Kauffman Foundation	2,125,039,000	17,666,000	12/31/13
42. The Wyss Foundation	2,115,965,902	19,014,335	12/31/13
43. The Chicago Community Trust	2,087,011,848	150,313,429	9/30/13
44. Casey Family Programs	2,061,764,408	3,528,325	12/31/12
45. The James Irvine Foundation	1,953,184,048	69,000,000	12/31/13
46. Eli & Edythe Broad Foundation	1,889,617,384	111,692,581	12/31/13
47. Alfred P. Sloan Foundation	1,888,720,791	82,091,585	12/31/13
48. Doris Duke Charitable Foundation	1,859,405,732	75,080,723	12/31/13
49. Houston Endowment Inc.	1,727,247,300	64,484,305	12/31/13
50. The Oregon Community Foundation	1,698,892,336	66,052,201	12/31/13
51. Annenberg Foundation	$1,690,604,187	$70,030,812	12/31/13
52. Laura and John Arnold Foundation	1,648,587,004	80,519,024	12/31/13
53. The Heinz Endowments	1,601,995,851	61,162,789	12/31/13
54. Barr Foundation	1,555,580,555	52,102,925	12/31/13
55. The Moody Foundation	1,530,491,198	54,796,543	12/31/13
56. The Columbus Foundation and Affiliated Organizations	1,520,768,529	95,963,350	12/31/12
57. The Wallace Foundation	1,514,962,198	61,462,148	12/31/13
58. Joseph B. Whitehead Foundation	1,432,190,285	36,345,000	12/31/13
59. Daniels Fund	1,388,360,517	46,406,291	12/31/13
60. The Brown Foundation, Inc.	1,375,012,451	74,487,624	6/30/14
61. The Starr Foundation	1,371,638,088	83,168,245	12/31/13
62. The Samuel Roberts Noble Foundation, Inc.	1,322,307,756	1,989,149	12/31/13
63. California Community Foundation	1,315,930,000	164,428,000	6/30/13
64. Marin Community Foundation	1,300,134,779	62,536,631	6/30/13
65. Foundation For The Carolinas	1,276,583,309	180,272,727	12/31/13
66. Lumina Foundation	1,258,939,683	51,847,439	12/31/13
67. W. M. Keck Foundation	1,254,540,000	54,992,000	12/31/13
68. The San Francisco Foundation	1,183,262,000	86,830,000	6/30/13
69. George Lucas Family Foundation	1,141,488,469	7,527,500	12/31/12
70. Bat Hanadiv Foundation No. 3	1,134,111,098	23,119,943	12/31/13
71. The Anschutz Foundation	1,126,706,872	50,069,897	11/30/13
72. The Carl Victor Page Memorial Foundation	1,119,754,597	40,355,326	12/31/13
73. The Ahmanson Foundation	1,108,002,312	50,359,404	10/31/13
74. Cummings Foundation, Inc.	1,085,901,102	769,155	12/31/13
75. The Pittsburgh Foundation	1,073,171,203	42,569,107	12/31/13
76. M. J. Murdock Charitable Trust	1,048,190,889	33,944,270	12/31/13
77. Shimon ben Joseph Foundation	1,041,590,492	31,387,034	12/31/13
78. The Brin Wojcicki Foundation	1,033,586,191	25,428,560	12/31/13
79. The J. E. and L. E. Mabee Foundation, Inc.	1,015,687,642	46,240,322	8/31/14
80. Communities Foundation of Texas, Inc.	982,331,000	82,493,000	6/30/13
81. Druckenmiller Foundation	971,517,239	74,469,500	11/30/13
82. The Edna McConnell Clark Foundation	965,338,606	43,155,001	9/30/13
83. The California Wellness Foundation	939,762,194	43,330,286	12/31/13
84. The Broad Art Foundation	937,124,622	576,693	12/31/12
85. The Joyce Foundation	936,451,953	35,081,737	12/31/13
86. Surdna Foundation, Inc.	929,596,379	34,643,450	6/30/13
87. The Community Foundation for Greater Atlanta	929,200,310	134,633,871	12/31/13
88. The Lynde and Harry Bradley Foundation, Inc.	922,303,709	34,178,862	12/31/13
89. Otto Bremer Foundation	898,842,764	38,321,048	12/31/13
90. Boston Foundation, Inc.	896,216,000	105,365,000	6/30/13
91. Bush Foundation	888,876,731	28,609,015	12/31/13
92. Hall Family Foundation	880,600,000	38,152,716	12/31/13
93. The Ford Family Foundation	877,924,758	21,319,479	12/31/13
94. Rockefeller Brothers Fund, Inc.	870,572,218	27,399,104	12/31/13
95. The Henry Luce Foundation, Inc.	867,417,767	34,554,143	12/31/13
96. The Michael and Susan Dell Foundation	841,658,316	72,785,040	12/31/13
97. Hartford Foundation for Public Giving	810,709,993	29,828,016	12/31/12
98. Hess Foundation, Inc.	807,050,408	29,281,120	11/30/13
99. The Seattle Foundation	802,875,771	65,653,979	12/31/13
100. Weingart Foundation	798,922,695	32,665,578	6/30/14

[1]J. Paul Getty Trust is an operating foundation and most of its qualifying distributions are paid out for administration of operating programs and not for grants. Total giving includes only grants and grant-related expenses as reported. In 2013, program amounts totaled over $272 million.

[2]Casey Family Programs is an operating foundation and most of its qualifying distributions are paid out for administration of its operating programs and not for grants. Total giving includes only grants and grant-related expenses as reported. In 2012, program amounts totaled over $110 million.

[3]The Broad Art Foundation is an operating foundation and most of its qualifying distributions are paid out for administration of its operating programs and not for grants. Total giving includes only grants and grant-related expenses as reported. In 2012, program amounts totaled over $14 million.

TABLE 5. 100 Largest Foundations by Total Giving

	Name	Total Giving	Assets	Fiscal Date
1.	Bill & Melinda Gates Foundation	**$3,320,725,374**	$41,310,207,525	12/31/13
2.	The Bristol-Myers Squibb Patient Assistance Foundation, Inc.	**811,433,684**	17,738,435	12/31/13
3.	The Abbvie Patient Assistance Foundation	**783,366,952**	53,271,158	12/31/13
4.	Lilly Cares Foundation, Inc.	**697,004,928**	0	12/31/13
5.	Merck Patient Assistance Program, Inc.	**686,800,564**	11,124,231	12/31/13
6.	Genentech Access To Care Foundation	**680,278,040**	56,516,388	12/31/13
7.	Johnson & Johnson Patient Assistance Foundation, Inc.	**611,680,261**	69,921,484	12/31/12
8.	GlaxoSmithKline Patient Access Programs Foundation	**599,953,667**	47,877,145	12/31/12
9.	Ford Foundation	**560,335,883**	12,259,961,589	12/31/13
10.	Pfizer Patient Assistance Foundation, Inc.	**515,726,553**	17,817,709	12/31/12
11.	Open Society Institute	**455,863,798**	685,871,435	12/31/12
12.	Novartis Patient Assistance Foundation, Inc.	**452,745,445**	31,616,576	12/31/12
13.	The Susan Thompson Buffett Foundation	**450,319,788**	2,731,731,558	12/31/13
14.	Foundation to Promote Open Society	**380,512,799**	3,330,839,478	12/31/13
15.	Silicon Valley Community Foundation	**362,390,000**	4,723,897,000	12/31/13
16.	The Robert Wood Johnson Foundation	**337,561,658**	10,173,403,442	12/31/13
17.	Walton Family Foundation, Inc.	**311,719,212**	2,480,825,574	12/31/13
18.	The David and Lucile Packard Foundation	**295,015,267**	6,902,501,278	12/31/13
19.	W. K. Kellogg Foundation	**294,891,874**	8,621,183,526	8/31/14
20.	Sanofi Foundation for North America	**284,044,399**	2,559,174	12/31/12
21.	Gordon and Betty Moore Foundation	**272,332,512**	6,417,833,620	12/31/13
22.	Lilly Endowment Inc.	**270,300,000**	7,699,211,116	12/31/13
23.	International Medical Outreach, Inc.	**247,416,601**	788,111	12/31/12
24.	The William and Flora Hewlett Foundation	**240,100,000**	8,607,073,000	12/31/13
25.	The Andrew W. Mellon Foundation	**234,372,144**	6,188,229,000	12/31/13
26.	Greater Kansas City Community Foundation	**234,274,371**	2,151,222,919	12/31/13
27.	The John D. and Catherine T. MacArthur Foundation	**218,542,721**	6,323,307,217	12/31/13
28.	The Leona M. and Harry B. Helmsley Charitable Trust	**210,352,475**	4,241,501,002	3/31/13
29.	Bloomberg Philanthropies	**204,007,709**	5,402,611,056	12/31/13
30.	Wells Fargo Foundation	**186,775,875**	488,707,083	12/31/13
31.	The Wal-Mart Foundation, Inc.	**182,859,236**	21,162,257	1/31/13
32.	The California Endowment	**182,809,047**	3,668,459,217	3/31/14
33.	Foundation For The Carolinas	**180,272,727**	1,276,583,309	12/31/13
34.	Boehringer Ingelheim Cares Foundation, Inc.	**179,977,010**	30,640,335	12/31/13
35.	The Simons Foundation	**179,640,382**	2,170,686,615	12/31/13
36.	The Bank of America Charitable Foundation, Inc.	**175,299,789**	32,075,548	12/31/12
37.	California Community Foundation	**164,428,000**	1,315,930,000	6/30/13
38.	Robert W. Woodruff Foundation, Inc.	**155,816,887**	3,119,096,039	12/31/13
39.	The Chicago Community Trust	**150,313,429**	2,087,011,848	9/30/13
40.	The New York Community Trust	**144,241,100**	2,443,372,250	12/31/13
41.	The Rockefeller Foundation	**137,817,790**	4,121,465,814	12/31/13
42.	Camp Foundation	**135,600,000**	140,335,032	6/30/13
43.	The Community Foundation for Greater Atlanta	**134,633,871**	929,200,310	12/31/13
44.	Carnegie Corporation of New York	**130,380,545**	3,033,694,178	9/30/13
45.	The Kresge Foundation	**130,183,827**	3,543,405,167	12/31/13
46.	The Duke Endowment	**127,729,045**	3,367,128,863	12/31/13
47.	GE Foundation	**124,512,065**	24,057,981	12/31/13
48.	The JPMorgan Chase Foundation	**115,516,001**	328,377,669	12/31/12
49.	Charles Stewart Mott Foundation	**114,442,289**	2,587,788,238	12/31/13
50.	Eli & Edythe Broad Foundation	111,692,581	1,889,617,384	12/31/13
51.	Tulsa Community Foundation	**$110,512,000**	$3,729,789,000	12/31/12
52.	John S. and James L. Knight Foundation	**107,825,135**	2,395,608,862	12/31/13
53.	Boston Foundation, Inc.	**105,365,000**	896,216,000	6/30/13
54.	John Templeton Foundation	**105,248,596**	2,555,855,497	12/31/12
55.	Howard G. Buffett Foundation	**103,284,879**	275,916,946	12/31/13
56.	The Sherwood Foundation	**101,964,342**	184,904,318	12/31/13
57.	Jerome L. Greene Foundation, Inc.	**100,947,352**	315,308,325	12/31/13
58.	Robertson Foundation	**99,597,042**	732,721,762	11/30/13
59.	Richard King Mellon Foundation	**99,152,041**	2,343,064,597	12/31/13
60.	Greater Houston Community Foundation	**98,934,435**	438,701,314	12/31/13
61.	The Annie E. Casey Foundation	**98,681,016**	2,666,068,266	12/31/12
62.	The Harry and Jeanette Weinberg Foundation, Inc.	**96,929,767**	2,127,938,700	2/28/14
63.	The Columbus Foundation and Affiliated Organizations	**95,963,350**	1,520,768,529	12/31/12
64.	The Community Foundation for the National Capital Region	**95,397,756**	334,979,789	3/31/13
65.	Conrad N. Hilton Foundation	**92,000,000**	2,430,703,442	12/31/13
66.	The San Francisco Foundation	**86,830,000**	1,183,262,000	6/30/13
67.	The McKnight Foundation	**86,598,229**	2,239,101,229	12/31/13
68.	The Starr Foundation	**83,168,245**	1,371,638,088	12/31/13
69.	Communities Foundation of Texas, Inc.	**82,493,000**	982,331,000	6/30/13
70.	Edward C. Johnson Fund	**82,350,200**	300,564,418	12/31/13
71.	Alfred P. Sloan Foundation	**82,091,585**	1,888,720,791	12/31/13
72.	The Cleveland Foundation	**81,368,990**	2,132,806,744	12/31/13
73.	Dr. Miriam & Sheldon G. Adelson Charitable Trust	**80,729,814**	335,679,305	12/31/13
74.	Laura and John Arnold Foundation	**80,519,024**	1,648,587,004	12/31/13
75.	The William Penn Foundation	**80,099,460**	2,283,164,256	12/31/13
76.	Genzyme Charitable Foundation, Inc.	**78,603,357**	11,036	12/31/13
77.	Citi Foundation	**78,372,150**	50,165,877	12/31/13
78.	The JPB Foundation	**78,051,333**	2,318,642,200	12/31/13
79.	Omaha Community Foundation	**75,638,463**	654,375,931	12/31/12
80.	Doris Duke Charitable Foundation	**75,080,723**	1,859,405,732	12/31/13
81.	The Brown Foundation, Inc.	**74,487,624**	1,375,012,451	6/30/14
82.	Druckenmiller Foundation	**74,469,500**	971,517,239	11/30/13
83.	The Michael and Susan Dell Foundation	**72,785,040**	841,658,316	12/31/13
84.	ExxonMobil Foundation	**72,747,966**	106,013,353	12/31/13
85.	Annenberg Foundation	**70,030,812**	1,690,604,187	12/31/13
86.	The Coca-Cola Foundation, Inc.	**69,658,157**	191,508,505	12/31/12
87.	The Greater Cincinnati Foundation	**69,133,479**	539,645,114	12/31/13
88.	The James Irvine Foundation	**69,000,000**	1,953,184,048	12/31/13
89.	The Oregon Community Foundation	**66,052,201**	1,698,892,336	12/31/13
90.	The Seattle Foundation	**65,653,979**	802,875,771	12/31/13
91.	Houston Endowment Inc.	**64,484,305**	1,727,247,300	12/31/13
92.	The Denver Foundation	**64,306,537**	606,066,260	12/31/12
93.	Charles and Lynn Schusterman Family Foundation	**64,025,508**	2,291,018,311	12/31/13
94.	Marin Community Foundation	**62,536,631**	1,300,134,779	6/30/13
95.	The Wallace Foundation	**61,462,148**	1,514,962,198	12/31/13
96.	The Heinz Endowments	**61,162,789**	1,601,995,851	12/31/13
97.	S.D. Bechtel, Jr. Foundation	**59,422,815**	339,549,608	12/31/12
98.	Donald W. Reynolds Foundation	**58,939,931**	175,552,668	12/31/13
99.	Community Foundation of Greater Memphis	**58,341,057**	314,940,599	4/30/13
100.	NoVo Foundation	**56,715,829**	264,168,686	12/31/12

TABLE 6. Foundations New to *The Foundation Directory* with Assets Over $20 Million (All dollar figures expressed in thousands)

Name	State	Established Year	Type of Foundation*	Fiscal Date	Assets	Gifts Received	Total Giving
1. Joseph B. Whitehead Foundation	GA	1937	IF	12/31/13	$1,432,190	$0	$36,345
2. Cummings Foundation, Inc.	MA	1986	OP	12/31/13	1,085,901	1,004	769
3. GHR Foundation	MN	2011	IF	12/31/12	294,168	0	14,024
4. Henderson-Wessendorff Foundation	TX	1956	IF	12/31/12	186,538	74,384	3,485
5. The Hagan Trust	MO		IF	12/31/13	175,958	0	552
6. The Hagan Scholarship Foundation	MO		IF	12/31/13	173,080	27,459	736
7. National Endowment for Financial Education	CO	1972	OP	12/31/13	166,170	444	441
8. Overdeck Family Foundation, Inc.	NY		IF	12/31/13	164,296	0	3,839
9. Vera and Joseph Dresner Foundation	MI		IF	12/31/13	140,258	51,392	2,122
10. Elliotsville Plantation Inc	ME	2002	OP	12/31/11	129,195	0	569
11. The D. Dan and Betty Kahn Foundation	MI	1986	IF	03/31/13	121,183	119,696	2,337
12. The Donald Bren Foundation	CA	1986	IF	11/30/13	115,656	94,478	2,115
13. Satterberg Foundation	WA	1990	FM	12/31/13	106,171	100,668	2,370
14. Robert W. Deutsch Foundation	MD	1991	IF	12/31/12	96,576	13,000	3,710
15. The Pindaros Foundation, Inc.	NY	2002	IF	12/31/13	94,229	845	548
16. The Lynch Foundation	MA	1988	IF	12/31/12	91,915	0	6,807
17. The Community Foundation of Northwest Connecticut, Inc.	CT	1970	CM	12/31/13	80,715	1,336	2,858
18. New Tamarind Foundation, Inc.	NY		IF	06/30/13	77,343	63,740	2,162
19. The Vibrant Village Foundation	OR		IF	12/31/12	76,214	32,643	1,149
20. Lauritzen Foundation	NE	1973	IF	12/31/13	75,373	68,152	2,058
21. Richard W. Goldman Family Foundation	DC		IF	12/31/13	74,565	2,688	2,863
22. The Carl A. and Lois E. Davis Foundation	TX	2011	IF	12/31/13	73,572	0	4,000
23. The Derfner Foundation	NY	1992	IF	12/31/12	72,087	2,335	1,838
24. Foundation for Research in Cell Biology Cancer and Cardiology	MA	1996	IF	12/31/13	68,803	2	4,382
25. Martha Dana Mercer Trust	RI		IF	12/31/13	64,226	0	2,937
26. The Valley Foundation	CA	1984	IF	09/30/13	61,414	0	1,000
27. The Erwin Rautenberg Foundation	CA		IF	11/30/13	58,441	50,691	1,749
28. The John and Polly Sparks Foundation	CT		IF	11/30/13	55,906	16,738	1,570
29. Newport Restoration Foundation	RI	1968	OP	12/31/13	55,617	2,523	496
30. The Butters Foundation	NY		IF	12/31/12	54,393	7,000	2,000
31. BCLF Managed Assets Corporation	MA		IF	12/31/12	53,925	0	1,250
32. B.A. and Esther Greenheck Foundation	WI		IF	12/31/13	53,395	500	1,833
33. The Hamer Foundation	PA	1989	IF	12/31/13	52,303	3,742	2,010
34. The Community Foundation, Inc.	MS	1963	IF	12/31/13	48,215	0	5,060
35. Joseph and Vera Zilber Charitable Foundation, Inc.	WI	2008	IF	06/30/13	47,869	48,935	1,492
36. Porter B. Byrum Charitable Trust	NC		IF	12/31/13	47,846	5,353	4,121
37. CHDI Foundation, Inc.	NJ	2004	IF	10/31/13	46,428	150,018	538
38. JRS Biodiversity Foundation	WA		IF	12/31/13	45,262	0	1,313
39. Carolands Preservation Foundation	CA		IF	11/30/13	44,722	0	1,930
40. Building Healthy Lives Foundation	OH		IF	12/31/12	43,946	342	430
41. Henry E. Haller, Jr. Foundation	FL	2000	FM	12/31/13	43,924	32,064	1,610
42. Cabin Road Foundation	NJ		IF	11/30/13	43,164	0	2,319
43. Swain Barber Foundation	NJ		IF	11/30/13	43,046	0	2,157
44. Maddox Foundation	MS	1968	IF	12/31/13	42,506	0	1,683
45. The Stanley E. Hanson Foundation	CA		IF	12/31/13	42,238	0	3,043
46. MSJ Foundation	MI	1992	IF	12/31/13	42,224	17,032	1,754
47. The Foley Family Charitable Foundation	FL	1997	IF	12/31/12	42,026	0	1,265
48. The McConnell Educational Foundation	OH	1992	IF	12/31/13	41,976	204	1,404
49. The Paiko Foundation	FL		IF	12/31/12	41,631	17,000	1,000
50. Stifler Family Foundation	MA	2001	IF	12/31/13	40,965	30,000	548
51. Esther B. O'Keeffe Charitable Foundation	FL	1990	FM	12/31/13	40,881	0	1,920
52. Bacchetta Foundation	NJ		IF	12/31/13	40,874	0	1,666
53. The Gilbert J. Martin Foundation	CA	1983	IF	12/31/12	40,633	3,078	439
54. Lunda Charitable Fund, Inc.	WI		IF	12/31/13	40,438	0	2,204
55. Harman Family Foundation	CA		IF	12/31/13	39,319	1,000	2,454
56. Taubman Foundation for the Arts	VA		IF	12/31/12	38,873	3,890	3,815
57. Teach A Man To Fish Foundation	CA		IF	12/31/12	38,522	34,938	1,918
58. Inmaat Foundation	NY		IF	12/31/13	38,464	0	2,012
59. The Brookby Foundation	WI	1994	FM	12/31/13	37,825	25,845	937
60. Frances Bean Vair Trust	OH		IF	12/31/13	37,801	0	1,665
61. The Foundation for Global Sports Development	CA		IF	12/31/13	37,482	53	1,030
62. Many Voices Foundation	NY	2000	IF	12/31/13	36,505	5,430	9,442
63. The Auen Foundation	CA	1992	IF	12/31/13	36,393	0	463
64. The Barnett and Annalee Newman Foundation	NY	1996	IF	12/31/13	36,358	0	1,235
65. Harry E. Bovay, Jr. Foundation	TX	2001	IF	12/31/12	36,313	1,438	1,396
66. David & Carol Myers Foundation	MI	1989	IF	12/31/13	35,985	0	1,914
67. Owsley Brown Ii Cockayne Fund, Inc.	KY		IF	12/31/13	35,408	0	1,278
68. Leducq Foundation for Cardiovascular Research	TX	2012	IF	12/31/12	35,017	53,178	18,493
69. Rapier Family Foundation	TX		IF	12/31/13	34,965	8	1,567
70. Jacques & Natasha Gelman Foundation Inc.	NY		IF	11/30/13	34,418	32,130	924
71. Elgin Foundation	TN	2003	FM	06/30/13	33,719	0	1,267
72. The Ressler Family Foundation	CA	1994	IF	12/31/13	33,666	527	4,634
73. The Robert and Michelle Cooke Atchinson Foundation	MA	1998	IF	12/31/13	33,253	2,532	645
74. Philip E. and Carole R. Ratcliffe Foundation, Inc.	FL	2003	IF	12/31/13	32,995	39	1,435
75. Eleanor Crook Foundation	TX		IF	12/31/13	32,971	2,316	2,005
76. Isaac W. Bernheim Trust	PA		IF	12/31/13	32,939	0	1,411
77. Brickstreet Foundation, Inc.	WV		IF	12/31/13	31,463	0	3,811
78. Clements Foundation	TX	1968	IF	12/31/13	31,254	11,059	1,036

*Type of foundation codes: OP=Operating foundation; IF=Independent foundation; CS=Company-sponsored foundation; CM=Community foundation

TABLE 6. Foundations New to *The Foundation Directory* with Assets Over $20 Million, continued

	Name	State	Established Year	Type of Foundation*	Fiscal Date	Assets	Gifts Received	Total Giving
79.	Shaffer Family Foundation	CA		IF	12/31/13	$31,059	$615	$1,344
80.	The Armstrong Foundation, Inc.	NY		IF	10/31/13	31,044	27,917	518
81.	Wayne D. & Joan E. Kuni Foundation	WA	2005	IF	12/31/12	30,851	4,431	2,658
82.	Head Family Charitable Foundation	PA		IF	12/31/13	30,591	0	1,247
83.	J. Craig and Page T. Smith Scholarship Foundation, Inc.	AL	2005	OP	12/31/12	30,546	23,785	574
84.	Joel F. Gemunder Foundation	FL	1997	IF	12/31/12	30,162	0	442
85.	Eugenie and Joseph Jones Family Foundation	LA	1955	IF	12/31/13	29,565	0	1,008
86.	The Carl C. Icahn Foundation	NY	1980	IF	11/30/13	29,033	35	731
87.	Clark Foundation	OR	1968	FM	12/31/13	28,836	0	1,260
88.	Dew Foundation	IL		IF	12/31/13	28,747	184	1,108
89.	Robert T. Keeler Foundation	OH	2001	FM	12/31/13	28,380	0	937
90.	Kane Family Foundation, Inc.	CO		IF	10/31/13	27,957	0	1,255
91.	Vijay and Marie Goradia Charitable Foundation	TX	2006	IF	12/31/13	27,742	3,853	482
92.	Rothberg Family Charitable Foundation for Children's Diseases	FL		IF	12/31/13	27,052	0	1,070
93.	The George F. Jewett Foundation	MN	2010	IF	12/31/13	26,937	0	1,076
94.	Gustavus and Louise Pfeiffer Research Foundation	NJ	1942	FM	12/31/13	26,568	0	622
95.	W. Duncan and Nivin MacMillan Foundation	MN		IF	12/31/13	26,471	512	1,027
96.	Steven J. and Melissa C. Kean Charitable Foundation Inc.	TX		IF	07/31/13	26,267	24,415	1,030
97.	The Macbea Foundation	OH	2010	IF	12/31/13	26,187	0	2,892
98.	Cares Foundation	CA		IF	12/31/12	25,944	23,935	1,096
99.	Fotsch Family Foundation	WI		IF	12/31/13	25,418	14,509	586
100.	Caxambas Foundation Inc.	WI	1995	IF	12/31/12	25,380	273	571
101.	The Kors Le Pere Foundation	DE		IF	12/31/12	25,329	5,063	812
102.	Thomas W. Pangborn Trust	PA		IF	12/31/13	25,247	0	1,038
103.	Hancock County Community Foundation, Inc.	IN	1992	CM	12/31/13	25,205	1,041	530
104.	The Arthur M. Sackler Foundation	NY	1965	OP	12/31/13	25,188	0	1,123
105.	G.A. Ackermann Memorial Fund	IL	1937	IF	12/31/13	25,183	0	700
106.	Abe and Ida Cooper Foundation	IL	1982	IF	12/31/13	25,169	0	1,169
107.	Alice Rosenwald Fund	NY	1982	IF	04/30/13	25,000	6,541	585
108.	Weitzman Family Foundation	NJ		IF	12/31/13	24,905	0	2,076
109.	William S. & Ina Levine Foundation Inc.	AZ	1997	IF	05/31/13	24,502	0	752
110.	Gilmore & Golda Reynolds Foundation	IN	1990	IF	12/31/13	24,268	0	721
111.	Richard C. Seaver Charitable Trust	CA	1978	IF	12/31/13	24,263	0	810
112.	The Wilma S. and Laurence A. Tisch Foundation	NY	2011	IF	12/31/13	24,070	15,242	17,553
113.	Galesburg Community Foundation	IL	1984	CM	12/31/13	23,863	1,885	650
114.	Mary K. Oxley Foundation	OK		IF	12/31/13	23,770	0	932
115.	Yot Full Circle Foundation	OK		IF	12/31/13	23,712	0	936
116.	Debby Durham Family Foundation	NE	2000	IF	12/31/13	23,708	226	871
117.	Donald Levin Family Foundation	IL	1984	IF	09/30/13	23,697	20,000	1,252
118.	The Kerr Foundation Inc.	OK	1963	IF	12/31/12	23,493	0	423
119.	The Moxie Foundation, Inc.	CA	1998	IF	12/31/12	23,473	0	1,261
120.	The Sara Blakely Foundation Inc.	GA		IF	12/31/13	23,342	4,006	614
121.	Smithville Charitable Foundation	IN		IF	10/31/13	23,245	33	975
122.	The John A. Moran Charitable Trust	FL	1988	IF	12/31/13	23,218	0	4,019
123.	Hintz Family Fund, Inc.	IL		IF	12/31/13	23,139	2,082	826
124.	Zatkoff Family Foundation	MI	2000	CS	12/31/13	23,008	7,000	482
125.	Bacca Foundation	IL		IF	12/31/13	22,973	3,000	4,047
126.	The Morby Family Charitable Foundation, Inc.	FL	1986	IF	11/30/13	22,953	1,007	1,089
127.	Steven H. Durham Family Charitable Foundation	TX	2000	IF	12/31/12	22,521	500	439
128.	John K. & Lynne D. Boyer Foundation	NE	2000	IF	12/31/13	22,455	500	667
129.	The Jack Miller Center for Teaching America's Founding Principles and History	PA		IF	12/31/13	22,415	23,901	1,271
130.	The LeVecke Family Foundation	CA		IF	12/31/13	22,383	718	1,105
131.	B. H. Homan, Jr. Trust	IL	1978	IF	05/31/13	22,212	0	1,000
132.	William A. Brookshire Foundation	TX	1998	IF	06/30/13	22,082	6,000	470
133.	John C. Hench Foundation	CA	1990	IF	11/30/13	21,964	0	430
134.	Lewis Foundation	TN		IF	12/31/13	21,573	0	1,400
135.	Fox Family Foundation	CO	2007	IF	06/30/13	21,498	3,352	621
136.	R. C. Baker Foundation	CA		IF	12/31/13	21,414	0	970
137.	Adeline & George McQueen Foundation	IL	1960	IF	06/30/13	21,352	0	431
138.	Tauck Family Foundation, Inc.	CT		IF	12/31/13	21,347	60	474
139.	The Kahlert Foundation, Inc.	MD	1996	IF	06/30/13	21,202	16,497	1,254
140.	Rossin Foundation	PA	1989	CS	12/31/13	21,197	1,045	601
141.	The Martino Family Foundation	CT		IF	12/31/13	21,009	9,988	540
142.	Blue Cross of Idaho Foundation for Health, Inc.	ID	2001	CS	12/31/13	20,927	62	495
143.	Foundation for Arts Initiatives	NY		IF	08/31/13	20,868	0	838
144.	Robert "Aqqaluk" Newlin, Sr. Memorial Trust	AK	1990	IF	12/31/12	20,721	3,949	768
145.	The Charlesmead Foundation, Inc.	RI	1987	FM	12/31/13	20,576	0	1,215
146.	Institute of Mental Hygiene of the City of New Orleans	LA	1937	IF	12/31/12	20,533	375	997
147.	MKM Foundation	PA	1998	IF	12/31/13	20,459	10,000	446
148.	Schmitz Family Foundation	CO	2001	IF	12/31/13	20,366	8	682
149.	Stuart Rose Family Foundation	OH	1988	FM	11/30/13	20,273	791	2,967
150.	The Story Garschina Foundation	NY		IF	12/31/13	20,219	9,988	1,191
151.	The Gamble Foundation	CA	1968	FM	12/31/13	20,052	450	700
152.	The ETZ Chaim Charitable Trust	NY	1997	IF	12/31/13	20,043	5,887	1,016

*Type of foundation codes: OP=Operating foundation; IF=Independent foundation; CS=Company-sponsored foundation; CM=Community foundation

TABLE 7. Foundations by Asset Categories (All dollar figures expressed in thousands)

Asset Category	Number of Foundations	%	Assets	%	Gifts Received	%	Total Giving	%	Grants*	%
$100 million and over	968	9.7	$491,617,632	73.1	$24,800,658	53.5	$25,608,375	52	$25,237,648	60
$50 to $100 million	871	8.7	61,091,924	9.1	6,031,769	13	5,907,294	12	3,763,842	8.9
$25 to $50 million	1,560	15.6	55,192,837	8.2	5,069,097	10.9	5,119,506	10.4	3,800,245	9
$10 to $25 million	3,219	32.2	51,563,713	7.7	5,245,720	11.3	6,222,831	12.6	4,145,444	9.9
$5 to $10 million	1,211	12.1	9,329,500	1.4	1,065,342	2.3	1,581,581	3.2	1,535,540	3.7
$1 to $5 million	1,208	12.1	3,410,151	0.5	1,670,601	3.6	2,101,836	4.3	1,746,161	4.2
Under $1 million	963	9.6	269,944	0	2,499,289	5.4	2,741,448	5.6	1,833,694	4.4
Total	10,000	100	$672,475,700	100	$46,382,476	100	$49,282,870	100	$42,062,576	100

Note: Figures may not add up due to rounding.
*"Grants" figures represent grants paid to organizations

TABLE 8. Foundations New to *The Foundation Directory* by Asset Categories (All dollar figures expressed in thousands)

Asset Category	Number of Foundations	%	Assets	%	Gifts Received	%	Total Giving	%	Grants*	%
$100 million and over	13	1.0	$4,290,765	25.9	$469,526	18.9	$69,706	4.9	$69,706	5.1
$50 to $100 million	20	1.5	1,391,013	8.4	265,936	10.7	47,220	3.3	47,220	3.5
$25 to $50 million	73	5.4	2,534,781	15.3	608,976	24.6	133,589	9.4	131,949	9.7
$10 to $25 million	348	25.9	5,118,709	30.8	494,089	19.9	291,569	20.5	284,403	21.0
$5 to $10 million	305	22.7	2,312,711	13.9	177,763	7.2	227,964	16.1	224,885	16.6
$1 to $5 million	313	23.3	876,120	5.3	288,851	11.7	349,597	24.6	313,102	23.1
Under $1 million	270	20.1	72,803	0.4	173,262	7.0	300,091	21.1	282,396	20.9
Total	1,342	100.0	$16,596,902	100.0	$2,478,404	100.0	$1,419,736	100.0	$1,353,660	100.0

Note: Figures may not add up due to rounding.
*"Grants" figures represent grants paid to organizations

TABLE 9. Independent Foundations by Asset Categories (All dollar figures expressed in thousands)

Asset Category	Number of Foundations	%	Assets	%	Gifts Received	%	Total Giving	%	Grants*	%
$100 million and over	760	9.1	$397,972,518	72.3	$15,415,620	61.4	$19,324,939	61.0	$19,148,080	61.1
$50 to $100 million	693	8.3	48,802,304	8.9	2,369,194	9.4	2,641,866	8.3	2,611,531	8.3
$25 to $50 million	1,336	16.0	47,216,254	8.6	2,591,943	10.3	2,876,424	9.1	2,846,072	9.1
$10 to $25 million	2,833	33.9	45,294,014	8.2	2,019,009	8.0	3,099,879	9.8	3,055,471	9.7
$5 to $10 million	1,044	12.5	8,040,549	1.5	769,365	3.1	1,227,976	3.9	1,217,823	3.9
$1 to $5 million	976	11.7	2,751,943	0.5	945,624	3.8	1,293,997	4.1	1,281,428	4.1
Under $1 million	725	8.7	201,776	0.0	981,532	3.9	1,201,638	3.8	1,189,298	3.8
Total	8,367	100.0	$550,279,360	100.0	$25,092,288	100.0	$31,666,721	100.0	$31,349,702	100.0

Note: Figures may not add up due to rounding.
*"Grants" figures represent grants paid to organizations

TABLE 10. Company-Sponsored Foundations by Asset Categories (All dollar figures expressed in thousands)

Asset Category	Number of Foundations	%	Assets	%	Gifts Received	%	Total Giving	%	Grants*	%
$100 million and over	50	5.8	$10,487,287	45.0	$2,098,777	34.9	$1,094,706	21.0	$964,523	23.6
$50 to $100 million	69	8.0	4,745,155	20.3	731,190	12.2	740,351	14.2	728,163	17.8
$25 to $50 million	102	11.8	3,568,943	15.3	1,232,552	20.5	1,201,165	23.1	711,452	17.4
$10 to $25 million	203	23.4	3,284,389	14.1	797,529	13.3	791,545	15.2	733,333	18.0
$5 to $10 million	93	10.7	709,214	3.0	177,440	3.0	264,491	5.1	237,494	5.8
$1 to $5 million	172	19.9	480,791	2.1	652,710	10.9	738,055	14.2	398,429	9.8
Under $1 million	177	20.4	49,685	0.2	322,349	5.4	370,644	7.1	308,737	7.6
Total	866	100.0	$23,325,464	100.0	$6,012,548	100.0	$5,200,958	100.0	$4,082,131	100.0

Note: Figures may not add up due to rounding.
*"Grants" figures represent grants paid to organizations

TABLE 11. Community Foundations by Asset Categories (All dollar figures expressed in thousands)

Asset Category	Number of Foundations	%	Assets	%	Gifts Received	%	Total Giving	%	Grants*	%
$100 million and over	128	25.0	$59,921,996	83.0	$6,869,442	84.1	$4,356,235	84.1	$4,312,684	85.0
$50 to $100 million	86	16.8	6,005,370	8.3	562,943	6.9	366,473	7.1	347,305	6.8
$25 to $50 million	100	19.6	3,672,895	5.1	384,947	4.7	232,092	4.5	216,455	4.3
$10 to $25 million	134	26.2	2,225,353	3.1	260,514	3.2	164,647	3.2	150,963	3.0
$5 to $10 million	43	8.4	342,054	0.5	67,576	0.8	44,355	0.9	35,571	0.7
$1 to $5 million	20	3.9	62,681	0.1	20,552	0.3	14,502	0.3	13,245	0.3
Total	511	100.0	$72,230,348	100.0	$8,165,973	100.0	$5,178,304	100.0	$5,076,222	100.0

Note: Figures may not add up due to rounding.
*"Grants" figures represent grants paid to organizations

TABLE 12. Operating Foundations by Asset Categories (All dollar figures expressed in thousands)

Asset Category	Number of Foundations	%	Assets	%	Total Giving*	%	Program Amount	%
$100 million and over	30	11.7	$23,235,831	87.2	$832,494	11.5	$688,344	79.2
$50 to $100 million	23	9.0	1,539,095	5.8	2,158,603	29.8	53,564	6.2
$25 to $50 million	22	8.6	734,745	2.8	809,825	11.2	11,059	1.3
$10 to $25 million	49	19.1	759,955	2.9	2,166,759	29.9	85,267	9.8
$5 to $10 million	31	12.1	237,683	0.9	44,759	0.6	5,044	0.6
$1 to $5 million	40	15.6	114,736	0.4	55,282	0.8	8,946	1.0
Under $1 million	61	23.8	18,482	0.1	1,169,165	16.2	16,536	1.9
Total	256	100.0	$26,640,528	100.0	$7,236,888	100.0	$868,760	100.0

Note: Figures may not add up due to rounding.
*Throughout this introduction "Total Giving" figures include grants, scholarships, employee matching gifts, and other amounts reported as "Grants and Contributions Paid During the Year" on the 990-PF reporting form. Loan amounts including program-related investments (PRIs) are indicated separately. Total giving does not include all qualifying distributions under the tax law, e.g., loans, PRIs, and program or other administrative expenses.

HOW TO USE THE FOUNDATION DIRECTORY

The Foundation Directory is designed to help grantseekers identify foundations that might be interested in funding their project or organization. It provides basic descriptions and current fiscal data for the nation's largest foundations—those foundations that were among the top 10,000 in terms of awards made in the latest fiscal year record. In addition, indexes help to identify foundations that may have giving interests in particular subject fields or geographic areas, or that provide specific types of support.

Researchers, journalists, grantmakers, and others interested in the philanthropic field also use *The Foundation Directory* to get a broad overview of current foundation activities nationally or within a particular geographic region, or to gather facts about one or more specific foundations.

When using *The Foundation Directory* to identify potential funding sources, grantseekers are urged to read each foundation description carefully to determine the nature of the grantmaker's interests and to note any restrictions on giving that would prevent the foundation from considering their proposal. Many foundations limit their giving to a particular subject field or geographic area; others are unable to provide certain types of support, such as funds for buildings and equipment or for general operating budgets. Even when a foundation has not provided an explicit limitations statement, restrictions on giving may exist. This is often the case with entries updated from public records. Further research into the giving patterns of these foundations is necessary before applying for funds.

ARRANGEMENT

The Foundation Directory is arranged alphabetically by state and, within states, by foundation name. Each descriptive entry is assigned a sequence number; references in the indexes are to these entry numbers.

WHAT'S IN AN ENTRY?

There are 34 basic data elements that could be included in a *Foundation Directory* entry. The content of entries varies widely due to differences in the size and nature of foundation programs and the availability of information from foundations. Specific data elements that could be included are:

1. The full legal **name of the foundation.**
2. The **former name** of the foundation.
3. The **street address, city,** and **zip code** of the foundation's principal office.
4. The **telephone number** of the foundation.
5. The name and title of the **contact person** of the foundation.
6. Any **additional address** (such as a separate application address) supplied by the foundation. Additional telephone or fax numbers as well as e-mail and/or URL addresses also may be listed here.
7. **Establishment data**, including the legal form (usually a trust or corporation) and the year and state in which the foundation was established.
8. The **donor(s)** or principal contributor(s) to the foundation, including individuals, families, and corporations. If a donor is deceased, the symbol † follows the name.
9. **Foundation type:** community, company-sponsored, independent, or operating.
10. The **year-end date** of the foundation's accounting period for which financial data is supplied.
11. **Assets:** the total value of the foundation's investments at the end of the accounting period. In a few instances, foundations that act as "pass-throughs" for annual corporate or individual gifts report zero assets.
12. **Asset type:** generally, assets are reported at market value (M) or ledger value (L).
13. **Gifts received:** the total amount of new capital received by the foundation in the year of record.
14. **Expenditures:** total disbursements of the foundation, including overhead expenses (salaries; investment, legal, and other professional fees; interest; rent; etc.) and federal excise taxes, as well as the total amount paid for grants, scholarships, and matching gifts.
15. The total amount of **qualifying distributions** made by the foundation in the year of record. This figure includes all grants paid, qualifying administrative expenses, loans and program-related investments, set-asides, and amounts paid to acquire assets used directly in carrying out charitable purposes.

16. The dollar value and number of **grants paid** during the year, with the largest grant paid **(high)** and smallest grant paid **(low)**. When supplied by the foundation, the average range of grant payments is also indicated. Grant figures generally do not include commitments for future payment or amounts spent for grants to individuals, employee matching gifts, loans, or foundation-administered programs.
17. The total dollar value of **set-asides** made by the foundation during the year. Although set-asides count as qualifying distributions toward the foundation's annual payout requirement, they are distinct from any amounts listed as grants paid.
18. The total amount and number of **grants made directly to or on behalf of individuals,** including scholarships, fellowships, awards, and medical payments. When supplied by the foundation, high, low, and average range are also indicated.
19. The dollar amount and number of **employee matching gifts** awarded, generally by company-sponsored foundations.
20. The total dollars expended for **programs administered by the foundation** and the number of foundation-administered programs. These programs can include museums or other institutions supported exclusively by the foundation, research programs administered by the foundation, etc.
21. The dollar amount and number of **loans** made to nonprofit organizations by the foundation. These can include program-related investments, emergency loans to help nonprofits that are waiting for grants or other income payments, etc. When supplied by the foundation, high, low, and average range are also indicated.
22. The number of **loans to individuals** and the total amount loaned. When supplied by the foundation, high, low, and average range are also indicated.
23. The monetary value and number of **in-kind gifts**.
24. The **purpose and activities**, in general terms, of the foundation. This statement reflects funding interests as expressed by the foundation or, if no foundation statement is available, an analysis of the actual grants awarded by the foundation during the most recent two-year period for which public records exist. Many foundations leave statements of purpose intentionally broad, indicating only the major program areas within which they fund. More specific areas of interest can often be found in the "Fields of Interest" section of the entry.
25. The **fields of interest** reflected in the foundation's giving program. The terminology used in this section conforms to the Foundation Center's Grants Classification System (GCS). The terms also provide access to foundation entries through the Subject Index at the back of the volume.
26. The **international giving interests** of the foundation.
27. The **type of support** (such as endowment funds, building/renovation, equipment, fellowships, etc.) offered by the foundation. Definitions of the terms used to describe the forms of support available are provided at the beginning of the Types of Support Index at the back of this volume.
28. Any stated **limitations** on the foundation's giving program, including geographic preferences, restrictions by subject focus or type of recipient, or specific types of support the foundation cannot provide. It is noted here if a foundation does not accept unsolicited applications.
29. **Publications** or other printed materials distributed by the foundation that describe its activities and giving program. These can include annual or multi-year reports, newsletters, corporate giving reports, informational brochures, grant lists, etc.
30. **Application information**, including the preferred form of application, the number of copies of proposals requested, application deadlines, frequency and dates of board meetings, and the general amount of time the foundation requires to notify applicants of the board's decision. Some foundations have indicated that their funds are currently committed to ongoing projects.
31. The names and titles of **officers, principal administrators, trustees,** or **directors,** and members of other governing bodies. An asterisk (*) following the individual's name indicates an officer who is also a trustee or director.
32. The number of professional and support **staff** employed by the foundation, and an indication of part-time or full-time status of these employees, as reported by the foundation.
33. **EIN:** the Employer Identification Number assigned to the foundation by the IRS for tax purposes. This number can be useful when ordering or searching for the foundation's annual information return, Form 990-PF.
34. A list of **selected grants.** Up to ten grants reported during a given fiscal year may be provided. Grants to individuals are not included.

INDEXES

Seven indexes to the descriptive entries are provided at the back of the book to assist grantseekers and other users of *The Foundation Directory:*

1. The **Index to Donors, Officers, Trustees** is an alphabetical list of individual and corporate donors, officers, and members of governing boards whose names appear in *The Foundation Directory* entries. Many grantseekers find this index helpful in determining whether current or prospective members of their own governing boards, alumni of their schools, or current contributors are affiliated with any foundations.
2. The **Geographic Index** references foundation entries by the state and city in which the foundation maintains its principal office. The index includes "see also" references at the end of each state section to indicate foundations that have made substantial grants in that state but are located elsewhere. Foundations that award grants on a national, regional, or international basis are indicated in bold type. The remaining foundations generally limit their giving to the state or city in which they are located.
3. The **International Giving Index** provides access to foundations whose giving interests extend beyond the

United States. A complete alphabetical list of countries, continents, and regions is provided at the beginning of the index. Under each country, continent, or region, entry numbers are listed by the state location and abbreviated name of the foundation. Organizations whose programs benefit foreign countries should use this index to identify funders with similar geographic interests.

4. The **Types of Support Index** provides access to foundation entries by the specific types of support the foundation awards. A glossary of the forms of support listed appears at the beginning of the index. Under each type of support term, entry numbers are listed by the state location and abbreviated name of the foundation. Foundations that award grants on a national, regional, or international basis are indicated in bold type. When using this index, grantseekers should focus on foundations located in their own state that offer the specific type of support needed, or on foundations listed in bold type if their program has national impact.
5. The **Subject Index** provides access to the giving interests of foundations based on the "Fields of Interest" sections of their entries. The terminology in the index conforms to the Foundation Center's Grants Classification System (GCS). A complete alphabetical list of the subject headings in the current edition is provided at the beginning of the index as well as "see also" references to related subject areas included in this volume. Under each subject term, entry numbers are listed by the state location and abbreviated name of the foundation. As in the Types of Support Index, foundations that award grants on a national, regional, or international basis are indicated in bold type. Again, grantseekers should focus on foundations located in their own state that have shown an interest in their subject area, or on foundations listed in bold type if their program is national in scope.
6. The index of **Foundations New to the Edition** is a listing of foundations that appear in the current edition of *The Foundation Directory* but had not met criteria for inclusion in the previous edition. The descriptive entries for these foundations are highlighted with a star (☆).
7. The **Foundation Name Index** is an alphabetical list of all foundations appearing in the *Directory*. Former names of foundations appear with "see" references to the appropriate entry numbers. This index also provides references to Appendix A, which lists foundations that appeared in the previous edition but have since terminated or otherwise become ineligible for inclusion.

APPENDIXES

In addition to the descriptive entries and indexes, *The Foundation Directory* includes two appendixes. Appendix A lists foundations described in the previous edition of *The Foundation Directory* that do not have entries in the current edition because they have terminated operations, merged with another foundation, ceased grantmaking, or changed their legal status. Appendix B lists those foundations that are excluded because they contribute only to a few specified beneficiaries or to the support of a single institution.

RESEARCHING FOUNDATIONS

Foundations receive many thousands of requests each year. Most of these requests are declined because there are never enough funds to go around or because the application clearly falls outside the foundation's fields of interest. Sometimes the qualifications of the staff are not well established; the budget or the means of evaluating the project may not be presented convincingly; or the organization may not have asked itself whether it is especially suited to make a contribution to the solution of the problem, whether it can provide the service proposed, or whether others are not already effectively engaged in the same activity.

The first step in researching foundation funding support, then, is to analyze your own program and organization to determine the need you plan to address, the audience you will serve, and the amount and type of support you need. Become familiar with the basic facts about foundations in general as well as how they operate. Consider other sources of funding, such as individual contributors, government grants, earned income possibilities, and so on. Although foundations are an important source of support for nonprofit organizations, their giving represents a relatively small percentage of the total philanthropic dollars contributed annually, and an even smaller percentage of the total when government grants and earned income are included.

Once you have determined the amount and type of support you need and the reasons why you are seeking foundation support, *The Foundation Directory* can help you to develop an initial list of foundations that might be interested in funding your project. In determining whether or not it is appropriate to approach a particular foundation with a grant request, keep in mind the following questions:

1. Has the foundation demonstrated a real commitment to funding in your subject area?
2. Does it seem likely that the foundation will make a grant in your geographic area?
3. Does the amount of money you are requesting fit within the foundation's grant range?
4. Does the foundation have any policy prohibiting grants for the type of support you are requesting?
5. Does the foundation prefer to make grants that cover the full cost of a project or does it favor projects where other foundations or funding sources share the cost?

6. What types of organizations does the foundation tend to support?
7. Does the foundation have specific application deadlines and procedures or does it review proposals continuously?

Some of these questions can be answered from the information provided in *The Foundation Directory*, but grantseekers will almost always want to consult a few additional resources before submitting a request for funding. If the foundation issues an annual report, application guidelines, or other printed materials describing its program, it is advisable to obtain copies and study them carefully before preparing your proposal. If the foundation has a web site, studying it is essential. The foundation's annual information return (Form 990-PF) includes a list of all grants paid by the foundation, as well as basic data about its finances, officers, and giving policies.

THE FOUNDATION DIRECTORY PART 2

The Foundation Directory Part 2 provides information on the second tier of U.S. grantmaking foundations, those among the next 10,000 largest annual givers. *The Foundation Directory Part 2* serves as a guide to smaller but significant grantmakers whose charitable giving often supports local organizations. Together, *The Foundation Directory* and *The Foundation Directory Part 2* constitute the standard reference work for information on 20,000 of the largest active grantmaking foundations in the United States.

THE FOUNDATION DIRECTORY SUPPLEMENT

The Foundation Directory Supplement, published six months after *The Foundation Directory* and *The Foundation Directory Part 2*, contains entries that have had substantial changes since the publication of those volumes. New information is highlighted in boldface type in the entries.

GLOSSARY

The following list includes important terms used by grantmakers and grantseekers. A number of sources have been consulted in compiling this glossary, including *The Handbook on Private Foundations*, 3rd Edition, by David F. Freeman, John A. Edie, Jane C. Nober, and the Council on Foundations (Washington, DC, 2005); *The Law of Tax-Exempt Organizations*, 9th Edition, by Bruce R. Hopkins (Hoboken, NJ: John Wiley & Sons, 2007); and the *AFP Fund-Raising Dictionary*, (2003).

Annual Report: A *voluntary* report issued by a foundation or corporation that provides financial data and descriptions of grantmaking activities. Annual reports vary in format from simple typewritten documents listing the year's grants to detailed publications that provide substantial information about the grantmaking program.

Assets: The amount of capital or principal—money, stocks, bonds, real estate, or other resources—controlled by the foundation or corporate giving program. Generally, assets are invested and the income is used to make grants.

Beneficiary: In philanthropic terms, the donee or grantee receiving funds from a foundation or corporate giving program is the beneficiary, although society benefits as well. Foundations whose legal terms of establishment restrict their giving to one or more named beneficiaries are not included in this publication.

Bricks and Mortar: An informal term for grants for buildings or construction projects.

Capital Support: Funds provided for endowment purposes, buildings, construction, or equipment, and including, for example, grants for "bricks and mortar."

Challenge Grant: A grant awarded that will be paid only if the donee organization is able to raise additional funds from another source(s). Challenge grants are often used to stimulate giving from other donors. (*See also* **Matching Grant**)

Community Foundation: A 501(c)(3) organization that makes grants for charitable purposes in a specific community or region. Funds are usually derived from many donors and held in an endowment independently administered; income earned by the endowment is then used to make grants. Although a few community foundations may be classified by the IRS as private foundations, most are classified as public charities eligible for maximum income tax-deductible contributions from the general public. (*See also* **501(c)(3)**; **Public Charity**)

Community Fund: An organized community program which makes annual appeals to the general public for funds that are usually not retained in an endowment but are used for the ongoing operational support of local social and health service agencies. (*See also* **Federated Giving Program**)

Company-Sponsored Foundation (also referred to as Corporate Foundation): A private foundation whose grant funds are derived primarily from the contributions of a profit-making business organization. The company-sponsored foundation may maintain close ties with the donor company, but it is an independent organization with its own endowment and is subject to the same rules and regulations as other private foundations. (*See also* **Private Foundation**)

Cooperative Venture: A joint effort between or among two or more grantmakers (including foundations, corporations, and government agencies). Partners may share in funding responsibilities or contribute information and technical resources.

Corporate Giving Program: A grantmaking program established and administered within a profit-making company. Corporate giving programs do not have a separate endowment and their annual grant totals are generally more directly related to current profits. They are not subject to the same reporting requirements as private foundations. Some companies make charitable contributions through both a corporate giving program and a company-sponsored foundation.

Distribution Committee: The board responsible for making grant decisions. For community foundations, it is intended to be broadly representative of the community served by the foundation.

Donee: The recipient of a grant. (Also known as the grantee or the beneficiary.)

Donor: The individual or organization that makes a grant or contribution. (Also known as the grantor.)

Employee Matching Gift: A contribution to a charitable organization by a company employee that is matched by a similar contribution from the employer. Many corporations have employee matching gift programs in higher education that stimulate their employees to give to the college or university of their choice.

Endowment: Funds intended to be kept permanently and invested to provide income for continued support of an organization.

Expenditure Responsibility: In general, when a private foundation makes a grant to an organization that is not classified by the IRS as a "public charity," the foundation is required by law to provide some assurance that the funds will be used for the intended charitable purposes. Special reports on such grants must be filed with the IRS. Most grantee organizations are public charities and many foundations do not make "expenditure responsibility" grants.

Family Foundation: An independent private foundation whose funds are derived from members of a single family. Family members often serve as officers or board members of the foundation and have a significant role in grantmaking decisions. (*See also* **Operating Foundation**; **Private Foundation**; **Public Charity**)

Federated Giving Program: A joint fundraising effort usually administered by a nonprofit "umbrella" organization which in turn distributes contributed funds to several nonprofit agencies. United Way and community chests or funds, the United Jewish Appeal and other religious appeals, the United Negro College Fund, and joint arts councils are examples of federated giving programs. (*See also* **Community Fund**)

501(c)(3): The section of the Internal Revenue code that defines nonprofit, charitable (as broadly defined), tax-exempt organizations; 501(c)(3) organizations are further defined as public charities, private operating foundations, and private non-operating foundations. (*See also* **Operating Foundation**; **Private Foundation**; **Public Charity**)

Form 990-PF: The annual information return that all private foundations must submit to the IRS each year and which is also filed with appropriate state officials. The form requires information on the foundation's assets, income, operating expenses, contributions and grants, paid staff and salaries, program funding areas, grantmaking guidelines and restrictions, and grant application procedures.

General Purpose Foundation: An independent private foundation that awards grants in many different fields of interest. (*See also* **Special Purpose Foundation**)

General Purpose Grant: A grant made to further the general purpose or work of an organization, rather than for a specific purpose or project. (*See also* **Operating Support Grant**)

Grantee Financial Report: A report detailing how grant funds were used by an organization. Many corporations require this kind of report from grantees. A financial report generally includes a listing of all expenditures from grant funds as well as an overall organizational financial report covering revenue and expenses, assets and liabilities.

Grassroots Fundraising: Efforts to raise money from individuals or groups from the local community on a broad basis. Usually an organization's own constituents— people who live in the neighborhood served or clients of the agency's services—are the sources of these funds. Grassroots fundraising activities include membership drives, raffles, auctions, benefits, and a range of other activities.

Independent Foundation: A grantmaking organization usually classified by the IRS as a private foundation. Independent foundations may also be known as family foundations, general purpose foundations, special purpose foundations, or private non-operating foundations. The Foundation Center defines independent foundations and company-sponsored foundations separately; however, federal law normally classifies both as private, non-operating foundations subject to the same rules and requirements. (*See also* **Private Foundation**)

In-Kind Contributions: Contributions of equipment, supplies, or other property as distinguished from monetary grants. Some organizations may also donate space or staff time as an in-kind contribution.

Matching Grant: A grant that is made to match funds provided by another donor. (*See also* **Challenge Grant**; **Employee Matching Gift**)

Operating Foundation: A 501(c)(3) organization classified by the IRS as a private foundation whose primary purpose is to conduct research, social welfare, or other programs determined by its governing body or establishment charter. Some grants may be made, but the sum is generally small relative to the funds used for the foundation's own programs. (*See also* **501(c)(3)**)

Operating Support Grant: A grant to cover the regular personnel, administrative, and other expenses of an existing program or project. (*See also* **General Purpose Grant**)

Payout Requirement: The minimum amount that private foundations are required to expend for charitable purposes (includes grants and, within certain limits, the administrative cost of making grants). In general, a private foundation must meet or exceed an annual payout requirement of five percent of the average market value of the foundation's assets.

Private Foundation: A nongovernmental, nonprofit organization with funds (usually from a single source, such as an individual, family, or corporation) and program managed by its own trustees or directors that was established to maintain or aid social, educational, religious or other charitable activities serving the common welfare, primarily through the making of grants. "Private foundation" also means an organization that is tax-exempt under code section 501(c)(3) and is classified by the IRS as a private foundation as defined in the code. The code definition usually, but not always, identifies a foundation with the characteristics first described. (*See also* **501(c)(3)**; **Public Charity**)

Program Amount: Funds that are expended to support a particular program administered internally by the foundation or corporate giving program.

Program Officer: A staff member of a foundation who reviews grant proposals and processes applications for the board of trustees. Only a small percentage of foundations have program officers.

Program-Related Investment (PRI): A loan or other investment (as distinguished from a grant) made by a foundation or corporate giving program to another organization for a project related to the grantmaker's stated charitable purpose and interests. Program-related investments are often made from a revolving fund; the foundation generally expects to receive its money back with interest or some other form of return at less than current market rates, and it then becomes available for further program-related investments.

Proposal: A written application, often with supporting documents, submitted to a foundation or corporate giving program in requesting a grant. Preferred procedures and formats vary. Consult published guidelines.

Public Charity: In general, an organization that is tax-exempt under code section 501(c)(3) and is classified by the IRS as a public charity and not a private foundation. Public charities generally derive their funding or support primarily from the general public in carrying out their social, educational, religious, or other charitable activities serving the common welfare. Some public charities engage in grantmaking activities, although most engage in direct service or other tax-exempt activities. Public charities are eligible for maximum income tax-deductible contributions from the public and are not subject to the same rules and restrictions as private foundations. Some are also referred to as "public foundations" or "publicly supported organizations" and may use the term "foundation" in their names. (*See also* **501(c)(3)**; **Private Foundation**)

Qualifying Distributions: Expenditures of private foundations used to satisfy the annual payout requirement. These can include grants, reasonable administrative expenses, set-asides, loans and program-related investments, and amounts paid to acquire assets used directly in carrying out exempt purposes.

Query Letter: A brief letter outlining an organization's activities and its request for funding sent to a foundation or corporation to determine whether it would be appropriate to submit a full grant proposal. Many grantmakers prefer to be contacted in this way before receiving a full proposal.

RFP: Request For Proposal. When the government issues a new contract or grant program, it sends out RFPs to agencies that might be qualified to participate. The RFP lists project specifications and application procedures. A few foundations occasionally use RFPs in specific fields, but most prefer to consider proposals that are initiated by applicants.

Seed Money: A grant or contribution used to start a new project or organization. Seed grants may cover salaries and other operating expenses of a new project.

Set-Asides: Funds set aside by a foundation for a specific purpose or project that are counted as qualifying distributions toward the foundation's annual payout requirement. Amounts for the project must be paid within five years of the first set-aside.

Special Purpose Foundation: A private foundation that focuses its grantmaking activities in one or a few special areas of interest. For example, a foundation may only award grants in the area of cancer research or child development. (*See also* **General Purpose Foundation**)

Technical Assistance: Operational or management assistance given to nonprofit organizations. It can include fundraising assistance, budgeting and financial planning, program planning, legal advice, marketing, and other aids to management. Assistance may be offered directly by a foundation or corporate staff member, or be offered in the form of a grant to pay for the services of an outside consultant. (*See also* **In-Kind Contributions**)

Trustee: A member of a governing board. A foundation's board of trustees meets to review grant proposals and make decisions. Often also referred to as a "director" or "board member."

ABBREVIATIONS

The following lists contain standard abbreviations frequently used by the Foundation Center's editorial staff. These abbreviations are used most frequently in the addresses of grantmakers and the titles of corporate and grantmaker officers.

STREET ABBREVIATIONS

1st	First*	N.E.	Northeast
2nd	Second*	N.W.	Northwest
3rd	Third*	No.	Number
Apt.	Apartment	Pkwy.	Parkway
Ave.	Avenue	Pl.	Place
Bldg.	Building	Plz.	Plaza
Blvd.	Boulevard	R.R.	Rural Route
Cir.	Circle	Rd.	Road
Ct.	Court	Rm.	Room
Ctr.	Center	Rte.	Route
Dept.	Department	S.	South
Dr.	Drive	S.E.	Southeast
E.	East	S.W.	Southwest
Expwy.	Expressway	Sq.	Square
Fl.	Floor	St.	Saint
Ft.	Fort	St.	Street
Hwy.	Highway	Sta.	Station
Ln.	Lane	Ste.	Suite
M.C.	Mail Code	Terr.	Terrace
M.S.	Mail Stop	Tpke.	Turnpike
Mt.	Mount	Univ.	University
N.	North	W.	West

*Numerics used always

TWO LETTER STATE AND TERRITORY ABBREVIATIONS

AK	Alaska	NC	North Carolina
AL	Alabama	ND	North Dakota
AR	Arkansas	NE	Nebraska
AZ	Arizona	NH	New Hampshire
CA	California	NJ	New Jersey
CO	Colorado	NM	New Mexico
CT	Connecticut	NV	Nevada
DC	District of Columbia	NY	New York
DE	Delaware	OH	Ohio
FL	Florida	OK	Oklahoma
GA	Georgia	OR	Oregon
HI	Hawaii	PA	Pennsylvania
IA	Iowa	PR	Puerto Rico
ID	Idaho	RI	Rhode Island
IL	Illinois	SC	South Carolina
IN	Indiana	SD	South Dakota
KS	Kansas	TN	Tennessee
KY	Kentucky	TX	Texas
LA	Louisiana	UT	Utah
MA	Massachusetts	VA	Virginia
MD	Maryland	VI	Virgin Islands
ME	Maine	VT	Vermont
MI	Michigan	WA	Washington
MN	Minnesota	WI	Wisconsin
MO	Missouri	WV	West Virginia
MS	Mississippi	WY	Wyoming
MT	Montana		

ABBREVIATIONS USED FOR OFFICER TITLES

Acctg.	Accounting
ADM.	Admiral
Admin.	Administration
Admin.	Administrative
Admin.	Administrator
Adv.	Advertising
Amb.	Ambassador
Assn.	Association
Assoc(s).	Associate(s)
Asst.	Assistant
Bro.	Brother
C.A.O.	Chief Accounting Officer
C.A.O.	Chief Administration Officer
C.E.O.	Chief Executive Officer
C.F.O.	Chief Financial Officer
C.I.O.	Chief Information Officer
C.I.O.	Chief Investment Officer
C.O.O.	Chief Operating Officer
Capt.	Captain
Chair.	Chairperson
Col.	Colonel
Comm.	Committee
Comms.	Communications
Commo.	Commodore
Compt.	Comptroller
Cont.	Controller
Contrib(s).	Contribution(s)
Coord.	Coordinator
Corp.	Corporate, Corporation
Co(s).	Company(s)
Dep.	Deputy
Devel.	Development
Dir.	Director
Distrib(s).	Distribution(s)
Div.	Division
Exec.	Executive
Ext.	External
Fdn.	Foundation
Fr.	Father
Genl.	General
Gov.	Governor
Govt.	Government
Hon.	Judge
Inf.	Information
Int.	Internal
Intl.	International
Jr.	Junior
Lt.	Lieutenant
Ltd.	Limited
Maj.	Major
Mfg.	Manufacturing
Mgmt.	Management
Mgr.	Manager
Mktg.	Marketing
Msgr.	Monsignor
Mt.	Mount
Natl.	National
Off.	Officer
Opers.	Operations
Org.	Organization
Plan.	Planning
Pres.	President
Prog(s).	Program(s)
RADM.	Rear Admiral
Rels.	Relations
Rep.	Representative
Rev.	Reverend
Rt. Rev.	Right Reverend
Secy.	Secretary
Secy.-Treas.	Secretary-Treasurer
Sen.	Senator
Soc.	Society
Sr.	Senior
Sr.	Sister
Supt.	Superintendent
Supvr.	Supervisor
Svc(s).	Service(s)
Tech.	Technology
Tr.	Trustee
Treas.	Treasurer
Univ.	University
V.P.	Vice President
VADM.	Vice Admiral
Vice-Chair.	Vice Chairperson

ADDITIONAL ABBREVIATIONS

E-mail	Electronic mail
FAX	Facsimile
LOI	Letter of Inquiry
RFP	Request for Proposals
SASE	Self-Addressed Stamped Envelope
TDD, TTY	Telecommunication Device for the Deaf
Tel.	Telephone
URL	Uniform Resource Locator (web site)

Jan.	January
Feb.	February
Mar.	March
Apr.	April
Aug.	August
Sept.	September
Oct.	October
Nov.	November
Dec.	December

RESOURCES OF THE FOUNDATION CENTER

Established in 1956 and today supported by close to 550 foundations, Foundation Center is the leading source of information about philanthropy worldwide. Through data, analysis, and training, it connects people who want to change the world to the resources they need to succeed. Foundation Center maintains the most comprehensive database on U.S. and, increasingly, global grantmakers and their grants — a robust, accessible knowledge bank for the sector. It also operates research, education, and training programs designed to advance knowledge of philanthropy at every level. Thousands of people visit Foundation Center's website each day and are served in its five library/learning centers and at more than 470 Funding Information Network locations nationwide and around the world.

ONLINE DATABASES

Foundation Directory Online

Which grantmaker is most likely to fund your organization? *Foundation Directory Online* (FDO) will help you answer this question, making it an essential tool for any grantseeker.

With detailed profiles on 120,000+ grantmakers — including U.S. and international foundations, corporations, and grantmaking public charities — FDO eliminates the guesswork from finding the right funder.

Foundation Directory Online includes:

- **Grantmaker profiles:** Get application information and deadlines, grant limitations, fields of interest, and geographic focus to help narrow your search.
- **Grants information:** Discover grants awarded to organizations similar to yours, with in-depth descriptions.
- **Visualization tools:** Easily map and chart a grantmaker's funding patterns by location and subject area.
- **Workspace:** Get the tools you need to quickly evaluate foundations, manage projects, track deadlines, and streamline your workflow.

Monthly and annual plans are available to fit your research needs.

LEARN MORE: foundationcenter.org/fdo

Foundation Grants to Individuals Online

Need a scholarship, fellowship or award? Visit the new *Foundation Grants to Individuals Online* built specifically for students, artists, researchers, and individuals like you!

$19.95: ONE MONTH
$36.95: THREE MONTHS
$59.95: SIX MONTHS
$99.95: ONE YEAR

TO SUBSCRIBE, VISIT gtionline.foundationcenter.org

TRASI (Tools and Resources for Assessing Social Impact)

Browse or search the TRASI database for proven approaches to social impact assessment, guidelines for creating and conducting an assessment, and ready-to-use tools for measuring social change. TRASI also features a community page where individuals can connect with peers and experts.

FREE

PLEASE VISIT trasi.foundationcenter.org

Foundation Maps

Foundation Maps brings to life data about U.S. and global philanthropy through extensive mapping, charting, and analytic capabilities. This interactive tool for funders is designed to facilitate more transparent, effective, and collaborative philanthropy.

LEARN MORE: maps@foundationcenter.org

Nonprofit Collaboration Database

This database provides hundreds of real-life examples of how nonprofits are working together.

PLEASE VISIT foundationcenter.org/gainknowledge/collaboration

GRANTMAKER DIRECTORIES

The Foundation Directory, 2015 Edition

Key facts include fields of interest, contact information, financials, names of decision makers, and over 31,000 sample grants. Convenient indexes are provided for all *Foundation Directories*.

MARCH 2015 / ISBN 978-1-59542-499-0 / $215 / PUBLISHED ANNUALLY

The Foundation Directory Part 2, 2015 Edition

Thorough coverage for the next 10,000 largest foundations, with over 20,000 sample grants.

MARCH 2015 / ISBN 978-1-59542-500-3 / $185 / PUBLISHED ANNUALLY

The Foundation Directory Supplement, 2015 Edition

This single volume provides updates for thousands of foundations in *The Foundation Directory* and the *Directory Part 2*. Changes in foundation status, contact information, and giving interests are highlighted in new entries.

SEPTEMBER 2015 / ISBN 978-1-59542-501-0 / $125 / PUBLISHED ANNUALLY

Guide to Funding for International & Foreign Programs, 11th Edition

Profiles of more than 2,200 grantmakers that provide international relief, disaster assistance, human rights, civil liberties, community development, and education.

MAY 2012 / ISBN 978-1-59542-408-2 / $125

The Celebrity Foundation Directory
5th Digital Edition

This downloadable directory (PDF) includes detailed descriptions of more than 1,880 foundations started by VIPs in the fields of business, entertainment, politics, and sports.

NOVEMBER 2013 / ISBN 978-1-59542-456-3 / $59.95

Foundation Grants to Individuals, 23rd Edition

The only publication devoted entirely to foundation grant opportunities for qualified individual applicants, this directory features more than 10,000 entries with current information including foundation name, address, program description, and application guidelines.

JULY 2014 / ISBN 978-1-59542-410-5 / $75 / PUBLISHED ANNUALLY

The PRI Directory, 3rd Edition
Charitable Loans and Other Program-Related Investments by Foundations

This *Directory* lists leading funders, recipients, project descriptions, and includes tips on how to secure and manage PRIs. Foundation listings include funder name and state; recipient name, city, and state (or country); and a description of the project funded.

PUBLISHED IN PARTERNSHIP WITH PRI MAKERS NETWORK.

JULY 2010 / ISBN 978-1-59542-214-9 / $95

Grant Guides

Designed for fundraisers who work within specific areas, 15 digital edition *Grant Guides* list actual foundation grants of $10,000 or more. *Guides* include a keyword search tool and indexes to pinpoint grants of interest to you. As a special bonus, each grantmaker entry contains a link to its *Foundation Directory Online Free* profile for even more details, all in a convenient PDF format.

2014 EDITIONS / $39.95 EACH

TO ORDER, VISIT foundationcenter.org/grantguides

FUNDRAISING GUIDES

After the Grant
The Nonprofit's Guide to Good Stewardship

An invaluable and practical resource for anyone seeking funding from foundations, this *Guide* will help you manage your grant to ensure you get the next one.

MARCH 2010 / ISBN 978-1-59542-301-6 / $39.95

Foundation Fundamentals, 8th Edition
Expert advice on fundraising research and proposal development.

A go-to resource in academic programs on the nonprofit sector. *Foundation Fundamentals* describes foundation funding provides advice on research strategies, including how to best use *Foundation Directory Online*.

MARCH 2008 / ISBN 978-1-59542-156-2 / $39.95

Foundation Center's Guide to Proposal Writing, 6th Edition

Author Jane Geever provides detailed instructions on preparing successful grant proposals, incorporating the results of interviews with 40 U.S. grantmakers.

MAY 2012 / ISBN 978-1-59542-404-4 / $39.95

Guía Para Escribir Propuestas

The Spanish-language translation of *Foundation Center's Guide to Proposal Writing*, 5th edition.

MARCH 2008 / ISBN 978-1-595423-158-6 / $39.95

The Grantseeker's Guide to Winning Proposals

A collection of 35 actual proposals submitted to international, regional, corporate, and local foundations. Each includes remarks by the program officer who approved the grant.

AUGUST 2008 / ISBN 978-1-59542-195-1 / $39.95

Securing Your Organization's Future
A Complete Guide to Fundraising Strategies, Revised Edition

Author Michael Seltzer explains how to strengthen your nonprofit's capacity to raise funds and achieve long-term financial stability.

FEBRUARY 2001 / ISBN 0-87954-900-9 / $39.95

NONPROFIT MANAGEMENT GUIDES

America's Nonprofit Sector
A Primer

The third edition of this publication, by Lester Salamon, is ideal for people who want a thorough, accessible introduction to the nonprofit sector—as well as the nation's social welfare system.

MARCH 2012 / ISBN 978-1-59542-360-3 / $24.95

The 21st Century Nonprofit
Managing in the Age of Governance

This book details the significant improvements in nonprofit management practice that have taken place in recent years.

SEPTEMBER 2009 / ISBN 978-1-59542-249-1 / $39.95

Foundations and Public Policy

This book presents a valuable framework for foundations as they plan or implement their engagement with public policy.

Published in partnership with The Center on Philanthropy & Public Policy.

MARCH 2009 / ISBN 978-1-59542-218-7 / $34.95

Local Mission-Global Vision
Community Foundations in the 21st Century

This book examines the new role of community foundations, exploring the potential impact of transnational evolution on organized philanthropy.

Published in partnership with Transatlantic Community Foundations Network.

AUGUST 2008 / ISBN 978-1-59542-204-0 / $34.95

Wise Decision-Making in Uncertain Times
Using Nonprofit Resources Effectively

This book highlights the critical challenges of fiscal sustainability for nonprofits, and encourages organizations to take a more expansive approach to funding outreach.

AUGUST 2006 / ISBN 1-59542-099-1 / $34.95

Effective Economic Decision-Making by Nonprofit Organizations

Editor Dennis R. Young offers practical guidelines to help nonprofit managers advance their mission while balancing the interests of trustees, funders, government, and staff.

DECEMBER 2003 / ISBN 1-931923-69-8 / $34.95

The Board Member's Book
Making a Difference in Voluntary Organizations, 3rd Edition

Written by former Independent Sector President Brian O'Connell, this is the perfect guide to the issues, challenges, and possibilities facing a nonprofit organization and its board.

MAY 2003 / ISBN 1-931923-17-5 / $29.95

Philanthropy's Challenge

Building Nonprofit Capacity Through Venture Grantmaking

Author Paul Firstenberg explores the roles of grantmaker and grantee within various models of venture grantmaking. He outlines the characteristics that qualify an organization for a venture grant, and outlines the steps a grantmaker can take to build the grantees' organizational capacity.

FEBRUARY 2003 / SOFTBOUND: ISBN 1-931923-15-9 / $29.95
HARDBOUND: ISBN 1-931923-53-1 / $39.95

Investing in Capacity Building

A Guide to High-Impact Approaches

Author Barbara Blumenthal helps grantmakers and consultants design better methods to help nonprofits, while showing nonprofit managers how to get more effective support.

NOVEMBER 2003 / ISBN 1-931923-65-5 / $34.95

ASSOCIATES PROGRAM

For just $995 a year or $695 for six months, the Associates Program experts will answer all of your questions about foundation giving, corporate philanthropy, and individual donors.

You will receive online access to several lists that are updated monthly, including new grantmakers and grantmaker application deadlines. In addition, you will receive most results within the next business day.

JOIN NOW AT foundationcenter.org/associates

ADDITIONAL ONLINE RESOURCES

foundationcenter.org

- *Philanthropy News Digest* is a daily digest of philanthropy-related articles. Read interviews with leaders, look for RFPs, learn from the experts, and share ideas with others in the field.
- Foundation Stats is a web-based tool that provides free and open access to a wealth of data on the U.S. foundation community. The intuitive platform can be used by anyone to generate thousands of custom tables and charts on the size, scope, and giving priorities of the U.S. foundation community.
- Access research studies to track trends in foundation growth and giving in grantmaker policies and practices.
- To stay current on the latest research trends visit foundationcenter.org/gainknowledge.

grantspace.org

GrantSpace, Foundation Center's learning community for the social sector, features resources organized under the 13 most common subject areas of funding research — including health, education, and the arts.

- Dig into the GrantSpace knowledge base for answers to more than 150 questions asked about grantseeking and nonprofits.
- Stay up-to-date on classes and events happening in person and online with the GrantSpace training calendar.
- Add your voice and help build a community-driven knowledge base: share your expertise, rate content, ask questions, and add comments.

glasspockets.org

Glasspockets provides the data, resources, examples, and action steps foundations need to understand the value of transparency, be more open in their own communications, and help shed more light on how private organizations are serving the public good.

- Learn about the online transparency and accountability practices of the largest foundations, and see who has "glass pockets."
- Transparency Talk, the Glasspockets blog and podcast series, highlights strategies, findings, and best practices related to foundation transparency.
- The Giving Pledge is an effort that encourages the world's wealthiest individuals and families to commit the majority of their assets to philanthropic causes. Eye on the Giving Pledge offers an in-depth picture of Giving Pledge participants, their charitable activities, and the potential impact of the Giving Pledge.
- Learn more about the Reporting Commitment, an initiative aimed at developing more timely, accurate, and precise reporting on the flow of philanthropic dollars.

grantcraft.org

GrantCraft combines the practical wisdom of funders worldwide with the expertise of Foundation Center to improve the practice of philanthropy. Since 2001, GrantCraft has delivered the knowledge funders need to be strategic and effective in their work, addressing questions funders face across various strategies and issue areas.

- Search the 13 content types including guides, takeaways, discussions, infographics, and videos to find real-life examples from funders.
- Register for free access to the monthly newsletter, personal dashboard, and to share content and comment.
- All content is free to use and share.

issuelab.org

IssueLab provides free access to resources that analyze the world's most pressing social, economic, and environmental challenges and their potential solutions. The platform contains thousands of case studies, evaluations, white papers, and issue briefs, and represents one the largest collections of social sector knowledge.

- Search and browse the database by social issue area, author, publishing organization, or geography.
- Learn how to add resources to the IssueLab collection.

DESCRIPTIVE DIRECTORY

ALABAMA

1
Alabama Power Foundation, Inc. ✧
600 N. 18th St.
P.O. Box 2641
Birmingham, AL 35291-0011 (205) 257-2508
Contact: Alisa Summerville, Dir. of Charitable Giving
FAX: (205) 257-1860;
E-mail: info@powerofgood.com; Tel. and e-mail for Alisa Summers: (205) 257-4722, atsummer@southernco.com; Contact for Gateway Grants and Good Roots: Peggy Burnett, Prog. Dir., tel.: (205) 257-2357, e-mail: peburnet@southernco.com; Main URL: http://powerofgood.com/

Established in 1989 in AL.
Donors: The Charles D. McCrary Family; Alabama Power Co.; Elmer Harris; Glenda Harris; Bruce Hutchins; Priscilla Hutchins.
Foundation type: Company-sponsored foundation.
Financial data (yr. ended 12/31/12): Assets, $126,827,859 (M); gifts received, $17,581; expenditures, $7,503,207; qualifying distributions, $6,480,549; giving activities include $5,823,451 for 787 grants (high: $578,447; low: $100).
Purpose and activities: The foundation supports programs designed to promote education; health and human services; arts and culture; the environment; and programs that promote future growth and neighborhood betterment in underserved communities.
Fields of interest: Arts, cultural/ethnic awareness; Visual arts; Performing arts; Arts; Elementary school/education; Higher education; Teacher school/education; Education, services; Education; Environment, natural resources; Environment, water resources; Landscaping; Environment, beautification programs; Environment; Animals/wildlife; Health care; Recreation, parks/playgrounds; YM/YWCAs & YM/YWHAs; Human services; Civil/human rights, equal rights; Community development, neighborhood development; Urban/community development; Community/economic development; United Ways and Federated Giving Programs; Minorities; Economically disadvantaged.
Type of support: Employee-related scholarships; General/operating support; Continuing support; Capital campaigns; Building/renovation; Endowments; Program development; Seed money; Scholarship funds; Matching/challenge support.
Limitations: Applications accepted. Giving limited to areas of company operations in central and south AL. No support for discriminatory organizations, churches or religious organizations not of direct benefit to the entire community, fraternal, athletic, or veterans' organizations, private or secondary private schools, or political organizations. No grants to individuals (except for employee-related scholarships), or for fundraising, general operating support for United Way-supported organizations, athletic tournaments, band trips, research trips, field trips, or other similar events.
Publications: Application guidelines; Informational brochure (including application guidelines); Newsletter.
Application information: Support is limited to 2 years in length. Video and audio submissions are not accepted. Organizations receiving support are asked to submit a completion report. Application form required.
Initial approach: Complete online application
Deadline(s): None for requests under $50,000; Feb. 22, May 24, Aug. 23, and Nov. 15 for requests over $50,000; Apr. 22 to June 17 for Gateway Grant Program; June 3 to July 29 for Good Roots
Board meeting date(s): Mar. 14, June 13, Sept. 12, and Dec. 2
Final notification: 8 weeks; Aug. 2 for Gateway Grant Program; Sept. 12 for Good Roots
Officers and Directors:* Zeke W. Smith,* Chair.; John O. Hudson III, Pres.; William E. Zales, Jr., V.P. and Secy.; Christopher R. Blake, Treas.; Gregory J. Barker; Mathew W. Bowden; Mark S. Crews; Daniel K. Glover; Bobbie J. Knight; Gordon G. Martin; Donna D. Smith; Steve R. Spencer.
Number of staff: 4 full-time professional; 1 full-time support.
EIN: 570901832
Selected grants: The following grants are a representative sample of this grantmaker's funding activity:
$531,448 to United Way of Central Alabama, Birmingham, AL, 2012. For general operating support.
$390,871 to Birmingham Urban Revitalization Partnership, Birmingham, AL, 2012. For general operating support.
$302,732 to Auburn University Foundation, Auburn, AL, 2012. For general operating support.
$206,900 to Alabama Childrens Hospital Foundation, Birmingham, AL, 2012. For general operating support.
$100,000 to Birmingham Museum of Art Foundation, Birmingham, AL, 2012. For general operating support.
$12,885 to Alabama Power Service Organization, Southeast Division, Eufaula, AL, 2012. For general operating support.
$6,180 to United Way of Lee County, Opelika, AL, 2012. For general operating support.
$5,750 to Easter Seals of Alabama, Birmingham, AL, 2012. For general operating support.
$5,000 to Birmingham Historical Society, Birmingham, AL, 2012. For general operating support.
$4,000 to Alabama Southern Community College Foundation, Monroeville, AL, 2012. For general operating support.

2
Alfa Foundation ✧
P.O. Box 11189
Montgomery, AL 36111-0189 (334) 613-4498
Contact: David R. Proctor

Established in 1996 in AL.
Donors: Alfa Mutual Insurance Co.; Alfa Mutual Fire Insurance Co.
Foundation type: Company-sponsored foundation.
Financial data (yr. ended 10/31/12): Assets, $16,271,929 (M); expenditures, $692,708; qualifying distributions, $578,500; giving activities include $578,500 for 20 grants (high: $200,000; low: $500).
Purpose and activities: The foundation supports organizations involved with secondary, higher, and engineering education, pollution control, health, cancer, equestrianism, and children services.
Fields of interest: Education; Human services; Religion.
Limitations: Applications accepted. Giving limited to AL. No grants to individuals.
Application information: Application form not required.
Initial approach: Proposal
Deadline(s): None
Officers: Jerry A. Newby, Pres.; C. Lee Ellis, V.P.; Ralph Forsythe, C.F.O.; H. Al Scott, Secy.; Stephen G. Rutledge, Treas.
EIN: 721373145

3
Alpha Foundation, Inc.
c/o John R. Wynn
P.O. Box 2087
Huntsville, AL 35804
E-mail: info@alphafoundationhsv.org; Main URL: http://alphafoundationhsv.org

Donor: Lonnie S. McMillian.
Foundation type: Operating foundation.
Financial data (yr. ended 12/31/12): Assets, $43,853,927 (M); expenditures, $2,899,626; qualifying distributions, $2,485,000; giving activities include $2,485,000 for 18 grants (high: $890,000; low: $5,000).
Purpose and activities: Giving primarily for education, youth development, and human services.
Fields of interest: Education; Medical research; Youth development; Human services; Homeless, human services; Protestant agencies & churches.
Limitations: Applications accepted. Giving primarily in Huntsville, AL. No support for churches and religious organizations for projects that primarily benefit their own members or adherence. No grants to individuals, or for event tickets, productions, performances, dinners, conferences or seminars, or for debt.
Publications: Application guidelines.
Application information: Application form not required.
Initial approach: Letter
Copies of proposal: 2
Deadline(s): None
Directors and Officers:* Lonnie M. McMillian,* Pres.; Hellen W. McMillian, V.P.; Glynda Cavalcanti, Treas.; Barbara M. Fisk; Kelly Fisk; Lonnie Key; Robert Key; Emily M. Robertson; Andy Whitehead; Susan M. Whitehead; John R. Wynn.
EIN: 631188643

4
Altec/Styslinger Foundation ✧
210 Inverness Center Dr.
Birmingham, AL 35242-4834

Established in 1997 in AL.
Donors: Lee J. Styslinger, Jr.; Altec Industries, Inc.; Global Rental Co.
Foundation type: Company-sponsored foundation.
Financial data (yr. ended 12/31/13): Assets, $43,626,674 (M); gifts received, $20,170,000; expenditures, $2,064,347; qualifying distributions, $1,971,876; giving activities include $1,970,885 for 86 grants (high: $540,000; low: $500).
Purpose and activities: Giving primarily for arts and culture, education, health associations, human services, children and youth services, the United Way, and religion.
Fields of interest: Arts; Education; Animals/wildlife.

Limitations: Applications not accepted. Giving primarily in AL. No grants to individuals.
Application information: Contributes only to pre-selected organizations.
Officers: Lee J. Styslinger, Jr., Chair.; Lee J. Styslinger III, Pres. and C.E.O.; Allen W. Ritchie, Secy.
EIN: 721372302

5
The Charlie & Moll Anderson Foundation ✧
(formerly The Charlie and Beth Anderson Family Foundation)
c/o Martin R. Abroms, C.P.A.
P.O. Box 1426
Florence, AL 35631-1426

Established in 1999 in TN.
Donors: Charles C. Anderson, Jr.; Beth B. Anderson; Charles C. Anderson; Anderson Media; Anderson Merchandisers.
Foundation type: Independent foundation.
Financial data (yr. ended 12/31/13): Assets, $5,497,788 (M); gifts received, $2,105,945; expenditures, $1,503,021; qualifying distributions, $1,502,696; giving activities include $1,468,124 for 36 grants (high: $500,000; low: $1,000).
Purpose and activities: Giving primarily for education and the arts.
Fields of interest: Arts; Higher education; Education; Human services; Children, services; United Ways and Federated Giving Programs.
Limitations: Applications not accepted. Giving primarily in Knoxville, TN. No grants to individuals.
Application information: Contributes only to pre-selected organizations.
Directors: Martin R. Abroms; Charles C. Anderson, Jr.
EIN: 621795976

6
Arlington Partners Charitable Foundation Inc. ✧
(formerly Founders Charitable Foundation, Inc.)
2000 Morris Ave., Ste. 1300
Birmingham, AL 35203-4163 (205) 488-4300
Contact: Kenneth H. Polk, Dir.

Established in 2001 in AL.
Donors: Steve Bell; Carl O. Black; Marilyn S. Black; Steven L. Hines; William B. Israel; Steve McKeehan; Michael B. Patton; Kenneth H. Polk; William Nicrosi; Timothy R. Smith; Brian Snoddy; Rhett Bennett; Greg Logan; Jon Moody; Vann Russell; Arlington Assocs.; Arlington Capital Advisors; Jones Family Fund; Max Bessie Bakal; Joe Mac Smith; Sarah Smith; Ken Jennifer Smith.
Foundation type: Independent foundation.
Financial data (yr. ended 12/31/13): Assets, $1,250,807 (M); gifts received, $256,011; expenditures, $1,892,849; qualifying distributions, $1,874,102; giving activities include $1,874,102 for grants (high: $1,200,000; low: $50).
Purpose and activities: Giving primarily to Christian churches and ministries; support also for health associations and education.
Fields of interest: Higher education; Education; Health organizations; Human services; Children/youth, services; Christian agencies & churches; Protestant agencies & churches.
Type of support: General/operating support.
Limitations: Applications accepted. Giving primarily in AL; some funding also in NC.
Application information: Application form required.
Initial approach: Completed application form
Deadline(s): None
Directors: Rhett C. Bennett; Kenneth H. Polk.
EIN: 631263667

7
Bashinsky Foundation, Inc. ✧
3432 E. Briarcliff Rd.
Birmingham, AL 35223-1309

Established in 1988 in AL.
Donors: SYB, Inc.; Joann F. Bashinsky; Sloan Y. Bashinsky, Sr.
Foundation type: Company-sponsored foundation.
Financial data (yr. ended 12/31/12): Assets, $10,436,968 (M); gifts received, $200,000; expenditures, $593,583; qualifying distributions, $531,721; giving activities include $531,721 for 8 grants (high: $173,996; low: $2,500).
Purpose and activities: The foundation supports hospitals and organizations involved with education and equestrianism; and awards scholarships to children of employees of Golden Flakes and to students attending the University of Alabama.
Fields of interest: Education; Human services; Religion.
Type of support: General/operating support; Employee-related scholarships; Scholarships—to individuals.
Limitations: Applications accepted. Giving primarily in AL. No grants to individuals (except for employee-related scholarships).
Application information: Application form required.
Initial approach: Completed application form
Deadline(s): None
Officers: Joann Bashinsky, Chair. and C.E.O.; John S. Stein, Pres.; John P. McKleroy, Jr., Secy.
EIN: 630968201

8
BBVA Compass Charity ✧
P.O. Box 10566, M/C: AL BI CH TXA
Birmingham, AL 35296

Established in 2007 in AL.
Donor: Compass Bank.
Foundation type: Independent foundation.
Financial data (yr. ended 12/31/13): Assets, $814,180 (M); gifts received, $1,325,522; expenditures, $913,600; qualifying distributions, $913,000; giving activities include $913,000 for 2,511 grants (high: $900; low: $10).
Fields of interest: Health organizations, association; Human services; United Ways and Federated Giving Programs.
Limitations: Applications not accepted. Giving primarily in AL; some funding also in FL and TX.
Application information: Unsolicited requests for funds not accepted.
Officers and Trustee:* James G. Heslop,* Chair.; Tiffany Dunne, Pres.; J. Reymundo Ocanas, V.P.; Joseph B. Cartee, Secy.; Kirk Pressley, Treas.
EIN: 261615917

9
BBVA Compass Foundation ✧
(formerly Compass Bank Foundation)
P.O. Box 10566, M.C. AL/BI/CH/ACT
Birmingham, AL 35296-0002 (205) 297-3464
Contact: Reymundo Ocanas, V.P. and Exec. Dir.
E-mail: grants@bbvacompass.com; Additional contact: Joye Hehn, Mgr., Corp. Responsibility and Reputation; Application address: 2001 Kirby Dr., Ste. C110, Houston, TX 77019, tel.: (713) 831-5705; Main URL: http://www.bbvacompass.com/compass/responsibility/foundations.cfm

Established in 1981 in AL.
Donor: Compass Bank.
Foundation type: Company-sponsored foundation.
Financial data (yr. ended 12/31/12): Assets, $85,929 (M); gifts received, $4,050,000; expenditures, $4,607,990; qualifying distributions, $4,606,800; giving activities include $4,606,800 for 600 grants (high: $150,000; low: $100).
Purpose and activities: The foundation supports organizations involved with arts and culture, education, the environment, health, housing, human services, diversity and inclusion, community development, minorities, and economically disadvantaged people.
Fields of interest: Museums; Arts; Elementary/secondary education; Higher education; Teacher school/education; Education; Environment, natural resources; Environment, energy; Environmental education; Environment; Health care, equal rights; Public health; Health care; Housing/shelter; Children/youth, services; Human services, financial counseling; Human services; Civil rights, race/intergroup relations; Community development, neighborhood development; Business/industry; Community/economic development; United Ways and Federated Giving Programs; Leadership development; Minorities; Economically disadvantaged.
Type of support: General/operating support; Management development/capacity building; Annual campaigns; Program development; Curriculum development; Scholarship funds; Research; Sponsorships; Employee-related scholarships; Matching/challenge support.
Limitations: Applications accepted. Giving primarily in areas of company operations in AL, AZ, CA, CO, FL, NM, NY, PR, and TX. No support for political committees or candidates, veterans' or fraternal organizations, alumni organizations, religious organizations not of direct benefit to the entire community, discriminatory organizations, individual pre-college schools including private, parochial, charter, or home schools, or individual schools in public school systems. No grants for sponsorships, golf tournaments, tables at events, fundraising activities that includes tickets, meals, or other benefits, general operating support for organizations supported by the United Way, or political causes.
Publications: Application guidelines; Program policy statement.
Application information: All applicants are encouraged to attend the semi-monthly Charitable Contributions Process conference calls and webinar presentations. Application form required.
Initial approach: Complete online eligibility quiz and application
Deadline(s): Jan. 20 to Sept. 30
Officers and Trustees:* Manolo Sanchez,* Chair.; Tiffany Dunne, Pres.; J. Reymundo Ocanas, V.P. and

Exec. Dir.; Joseph B. Cartee, Secy.; Kirk Pressley, Treas.; Rafael Bustillo; William Helms; James G. Heslop; Angel Regiero; Sandy Salgado; Jeffery Talpas.
EIN: 630823545
Selected grants: The following grants are a representative sample of this grantmaker's funding activity:
$150,000 to United Way of Central Alabama, Birmingham, AL, 2012.
$125,000 to Museum of Fine Arts, Houston, Houston, TX, 2012.
$75,000 to Innovation Depot, Birmingham, AL, 2012.
$75,000 to Rebuilding Together Houston, Houston, TX, 2012.
$50,000 to American Red Cross, Pikes Peak Chapter, Colorado Springs, CO, 2012.
$40,000 to Teach for America, Phoenix, AZ, 2012.
$30,000 to Big Brothers Big Sisters Lone Star, Irving, TX, 2012.
$10,000 to Westside Development Corporation, San Antonio, TX, 2012.
$5,000 to Better Basics, Birmingham, AL, 2012.
$5,000 to Holocaust Museum Houston, Houston, TX, 2012.

10
A. H. Bean Foundation, Inc. ✧ ☆
2222 9th St.
Tuscaloosa, AL 35401-2318 (205) 391-5720

Established in 1985 in AL.
Donor: A.H. Bean.
Foundation type: Independent foundation.
Financial data (yr. ended 12/31/13): Assets, $10,918,755 (M); expenditures, $559,317; qualifying distributions, $538,370; giving activities include $491,000 for 15 grants (high: $105,000; low: $5,000).
Purpose and activities: Giving primarily for higher education, health and medical purposes, and Christian and Protestant churches.
Fields of interest: Education; Health organizations; Christian agencies & churches; Protestant agencies & churches.
Limitations: Applications accepted. Giving primarily in AL.
Application information: Application form required.
Initial approach: Letter
Deadline(s): None
Board Members: Tommy Knight; Connie Oswalt; Scott Ridings.
EIN: 636134142

11
The J. L. Bedsole Foundation ✧
P.O. Box 1137
Mobile, AL 36633-1137 (251) 432-3369
Contact: Christopher L. Lee, Exec. Dir.
FAX: (251) 432-1134;
E-mail: info@jlbedsolefoundation.org; E-mail for Christopher Lee: chrislee@jlbedsolefoundation.org; Main URL: http://www.jlbedsolefoundation.org
Contact for scholarships: Scott A. Morton, Dir., e-mail: scott@jlbedsolefoundation.org

Established in 1949.
Donor: J.L. Bedsole†.
Foundation type: Independent foundation.
Financial data (yr. ended 12/31/12): Assets, $64,134,957 (M); gifts received, $500; expenditures, $3,783,502; qualifying distributions, $3,106,041; giving activities include $1,885,210 for 63 grants (high: $225,000; low: $500), $747,500 for 152 grants to individuals (high: $6,000; low: $1,500), and $473,331 for foundation-administered programs.
Purpose and activities: Giving primarily to improve the quality of life for the citizens of Southwest AL and to strengthen the communities in which they live. Specifically, the foundation funds projects that serve: 1) Education, arts and culture, health and human services and economic development; 2) Projects where there is potential for permanent, enduring benefits that will provide value to the community and the residents of Southwest AL; 3) Diverse groups that collaborate on projects to achieve common goals; 4) Organizations and projects that clearly demonstrate sound fiscal management and accountability; 5) Organizations that attract multiple sources of support for projects; and 6) Projects that address underserved segments of the population, the economically disadvantaged or citizens of rural communities.
Fields of interest: Arts; Elementary/secondary education; Higher education; Human services; Economic development.
Type of support: General/operating support; Capital campaigns; Building/renovation; Publication; Scholarship funds; Scholarships—to individuals.
Limitations: Applications accepted. Giving limited to Mobile, Baldwin, Clarke, Monroe, and Washington counties, AL. No support for political organizations. No grants to individuals (except for J.L. Bedsole Scholarships and awards), or for endowment funds, or multiple year pledges.
Publications: Application guidelines.
Application information: Grant and scholarship application guidelines available on foundation web site. Requests from non-resident applicants not considered or acknowledged. Videotapes, audiotapes, photographs, artwork or other bulky items are not accepted. Application form not required.
Initial approach: Proposal on 8 1/2 x 11-inch paper, printed on one side only (for grants); scholarship applicants use online application
Copies of proposal: 1
Deadline(s): None
Board meeting date(s): Feb., Apr., June, Sept., and Dec.
Final notification: Following distribution committee meetings
Officers and Distribution Committee:* T. Bestor Ward III,* Chair.; Christopher L. Lee, Exec. Dir.; Patty Patton, Secy.; Travis M. Bedsole, Jr.; John M. Turner, Jr.; John White-Spunner; Robert J. Williams.
Trustee: Regions Bank.
Number of staff: 1 full-time support; 4 part-time support.
EIN: 237225708

12
Herman and Emmie Bolden Charitable ✧ ☆
P.O. Box 360028
Birmingham, AL 35236-0028 (205) 988-8989
Application address: c/o Herman D. Bolden, Tr., P.O. Box 360025, Birmingham, AL 35236

Donor: Herman D. Bolden.
Foundation type: Independent foundation.
Financial data (yr. ended 06/30/13): Assets, $3,047,269 (M); gifts received, $100,000; expenditures, $527,160; qualifying distributions, $512,750; giving activities include $512,750 for 19 grants (high: $200,000; low: $200).
Fields of interest: Education; Health organizations; Human services.
Limitations: Applications accepted. Giving primarily in Birmingham, AL.
Application information: Application form required.
Initial approach: Proposal
Deadline(s): None
Trustees: Emmie C. Bolden; Herman D. Bolden.
EIN: 455585842

13
The Harry B. & Jane H. Brock Foundation ✧ ☆
(formerly The Brock Foundation)
P.O. Box 11643
Birmingham, AL 35202

Established in 1985 in AL.
Donor: Harry B. Brock, Jr.
Foundation type: Independent foundation.
Financial data (yr. ended 12/31/13): Assets, $7,898,312 (M); expenditures, $571,603; qualifying distributions, $526,697; giving activities include $507,222 for 36 grants (high: $108,050; low: $500).
Fields of interest: Higher education; Education; Environment, natural resources; Human services; Children/youth, services; Women, centers/services; Community/economic development; Voluntarism promotion; United Ways and Federated Giving Programs.
Type of support: General/operating support; Annual campaigns; Capital campaigns; Endowments; Program development; Research.
Limitations: Applications not accepted. Giving primarily in AL. No grants to individuals.
Application information: Unsolicited request for funds not accepted.
Officers and Directors:* Harry B. Brock, Jr.,* Pres.; Jane H. Brock,* V.P.; Stanley M. Brock,* Secy.
EIN: 630926012
Selected grants: The following grants are a representative sample of this grantmaker's funding activity:
$20,000 to Samford University, School of Arts, Birmingham, AL, 2012. For educational.
$8,000 to YWCA of Birmingham, Birmingham, AL, 2012. For general and adm.

14
Brooke Family Foundation ✧
4325 Altamont Rd.
Birmingham, AL 35213 (205) 987-5612
Contact: William W. Brooke Sr., Dir.

Established in AL.
Donors: William W. Brooke, Sr.; Williamson, Martin, Brooke Family Foundation.
Foundation type: Independent foundation.
Financial data (yr. ended 12/31/13): Assets, $2,945,601 (M); gifts received, $3,950; expenditures, $870,236; qualifying distributions, $841,155; giving activities include $839,180 for 8 grants (high: $450,000; low: $20,000).

Fields of interest: Higher education; Human services; United Ways and Federated Giving Programs; Religion.
Limitations: Applications accepted. Giving primarily in Birmingham, AL; some funding also in Anaheim, CA.
Application information: Application form required.
Initial approach: Letter
Deadline(s): None
Directors: Margaret W. Brooke; William W. Brooke, Sr.; William W. Brooke, Jr.
EIN: 270373823

15
The Joseph S. Bruno Charitable Foundation ✧
P.O. Box 530727
Birmingham, AL 35253-0727 (205) 879-0799
Contact: Jera G. Stribling, Exec. Dir.
FAX: (205) 879-4899; E-mail: jstribling@jsbcf.org; Main URL: http://www.jsbcf.org/

Established in 1985 in AL.
Foundation type: Independent foundation.
Financial data (yr. ended 11/30/13): Assets, $10,696,472 (M); expenditures, $1,013,571; qualifying distributions, $968,735; giving activities include $828,500 for 45 grants (high: $250,000; low: $1,500).
Purpose and activities: Giving primarily for 1) education, particularly to prepare children for success in school, as well as to support school readiness, quality early childhood development and early intervention, and working with families and youth service organizations to insure academic success and prevent school dropout; and 2) community health and services, particularly to promote healthy behavior, wellness, and prevention; and to improve access to health care for vulnerable populations, and provide opportunities for families that encourage healthy lifestyles and improved mental and physical health. The foundation also has secondary focus areas in: basic services for at-risk families and children, family literacy and adult education, community improvement and nonprofit capacity building, culture and increasing accessibility to the arts, and philanthropy and volunteerism. The foundation considers programs that have matching or other funds from government, other foundations, corporate or private funding. Organizations and programs that show collaboration and sharing of ideas and resources are strongly encouraged.
Fields of interest: Arts; Education; Health care; Human services; Community/economic development.
Type of support: Capital campaigns; Program development; Seed money; Technical assistance; Matching/challenge support.
Limitations: Giving primarily in the greater Birmingham, AL, area. No support for fraternal, sports, of religious organizations, or for organizations outside of the Greater Birmingham, AL, area. No grants to individuals, or for fundraising, dinners, advertising, endowments, scholarships, recurring operating expenses (unless for a start-up project) or for program expenses that occur on a regular basis.
Publications: Informational brochure (including application guidelines).
Application information: Any organization that has been awarded 3 consecutive grants may not apply for another grant until 1-year after the last grant. Application form not required.
Initial approach: Use application process on foundation web site
Copies of proposal: 1
Deadline(s): Mar. 15 (for Apr. board meeting), Sept. 15 (for Oct. board meeting)
Board meeting date(s): Apr. and Oct.
Officer: Jera G. Stribling, Exec. Dir.
Trustees: Norm Davis; Anne B. LaRussa; Benny LaRussa, Jr.; Marian Phillips; Robert A. Sprain, Jr.
Number of staff: 1 full-time professional; 1 part-time support.
EIN: 630936234

16
The Lee Bruno Foundation ✧
4112 Autumn Ln.
Birmingham, AL 35243-5208

Established in AL.
Donor: Vincent Bruno & Carol Ann Bruno Trust.
Foundation type: Independent foundation.
Financial data (yr. ended 12/31/13): Assets, $11,687,886 (M); expenditures, $607,695; qualifying distributions, $514,167; giving activities include $459,500 for 23 grants (high: $75,000; low: $1,000).
Fields of interest: Catholic agencies & churches.
Limitations: Applications not accepted. Giving primarily in Birmingham, AL. No grants to individuals.
Application information: Unsolicited requests for funds not accepted.
Officers: Vincent John Bruno, Pres. and Treas.; Paul Bruno, V.P.; Mary Ann Bruno, Secy.; Vincent Joseph Bruno, Exec. Dir.
EIN: 260300148

17
Bruno-Rumore Foundation ✧
2664 Vesclub Cir.
Birmingham, AL 35216-1358

Established in AL.
Donor: Vincent A. Bruno & Carol Ann Rumore Trust.
Foundation type: Independent foundation.
Financial data (yr. ended 12/31/13): Assets, $10,521,145 (M); expenditures, $624,759; qualifying distributions, $528,647; giving activities include $527,890 for 39 grants (high: $66,000; low: $250).
Fields of interest: Education; Catholic agencies & churches.
Limitations: Applications not accepted. Giving primarily in AL, with emphasis on Birmingham. No grants to individuals.
Application information: Unsolicited requests for funds not accepted.
Directors: Christina M. Hare; Carol Ann Bruno Rumore; Phillip Rumore.
EIN: 260300098

18
The Caring Foundation ✧
450 Riverchase Pkwy. E.
Birmingham, AL 35244-2858 (205) 220-9194
Contact: Tim King, Mgr., The Caring Fdn & Corporate Giving
E-mail: TheCaringFoundation@bcbsal.org; Main URL: https://www.bcbsal.org/web/the-caring-foundation-and-corporate-giving.html

Established in 1990 in AL.
Donor: Blue Cross and Blue Shield of Alabama, Inc.
Foundation type: Company-sponsored foundation.
Financial data (yr. ended 12/31/12): Assets, $43,253,103 (M); gifts received, $972; expenditures, $4,462,393; qualifying distributions, $4,318,044; giving activities include $4,318,044 for 275 grants (high: $1,000,000; low: $250).
Purpose and activities: The foundation supports programs designed to promote health, wellness, and education, with a special interest in assisting children.
Fields of interest: Education; Hospitals (general); Health care; Safety, education; Boy scouts; Salvation Army; Children/youth, services; Human services; United Ways and Federated Giving Programs; Children.
Type of support: General/operating support; Program development.
Limitations: Applications accepted. Giving primarily in AL. No support for political organizations or provide foundations or charities. No grants to individuals, or for capital campaigns.
Publications: Application guidelines.
Application information: Application form required.
Initial approach: Complete online application
Copies of proposal: 1
Deadline(s): None
Board meeting date(s): 4th Wed. in Apr.
Final notification: 1 to 2 months
Officers and Directors:* M. Eugene Moor, Jr.,* Chair.; Terry D. Kellogg, Pres.; Timothy L. Kirkpatrick, V.P.; Cynthia M. Vice, Treas.; James M. Aycock; L. Keith Granger; Kenneth E. Hubbard; Fred D. Hunker, M.D.; Donald L. Large, Jr.; William J. Stevens.
EIN: 631035261
Selected grants: The following grants are a representative sample of this grantmaker's funding activity:
$255,000 to United Way of Central Alabama, Birmingham, AL, 2011.
$225,000 to Salvation Army of Birmingham, Birmingham, AL, 2011.
$210,000 to Childrens Hospital of Alabama, Birmingham, AL, 2011.
$169,000 to University of Alabama, Tuscaloosa, AL, 2011.
$40,000 to Multiple Sclerosis Society, National, Birmingham, AL, 2011.
$30,000 to Alabama Shakespeare Festival, Montgomery, AL, 2011.
$15,000 to KID One Transport System, Birmingham, AL, 2011.
$10,000 to United Way of Etowah County, Gadsden, AL, 2011.
$3,000 to John Carroll Catholic High School, Birmingham, AL, 2011.
$2,500 to Discovery Clubs of Alabama, Birmingham, AL, 2011.

19
Central Alabama Community Foundation, Inc. ✧
(formerly Montgomery Area Community Foundation, Inc.)
35 S. Court St.
Montgomery, AL 36104 (334) 264-6223
Contact: Burton Ward, Pres.; For grants: Lynn Broach, V.P., Community Svcs.
FAX: (334) 263-6225;
E-mail: burton.ward@cacfinfo.org; Grant inquiry e-mail: lynne.broach@cacfinfo.org; Main URL: http://www.cacfinfo.org
E-Newsletter: http://www.cacfinfo.org/newsletter.html
Facebook: https://www.facebook.com/cacfinfo?ref=ts
Twitter: https://twitter.com/CACFinfo

Established in 1987 in AL.
Foundation type: Community foundation.
Financial data (yr. ended 12/31/13): Assets, $45,117,034 (M); gifts received, $5,864,233; expenditures, $4,454,878; giving activities include $3,417,325 for 97+ grants (high: $722,000).
Purpose and activities: The foundation was created by and for the people of central Alabama. Individuals and corporate donors make gifts and bequests of any size for the betterment of the community. Through the grants program, the foundation addresses a wide variety of needs and opportunities, supporting programs and projects in education, human services, health, cultural arts, and other civic concerns.
Fields of interest: Arts; Education; Health care; Agriculture/food; Housing/shelter; Children/youth, services; Family services; Family services, domestic violence; Human services; Nonprofit management; Community/economic development; Children/youth.
Type of support: Income development; Management development/capacity building; Program development; Seed money; Scholarship funds; Technical assistance; Scholarships—to individuals; Matching/challenge support.
Limitations: Applications accepted. Giving limited to Autauga, Elmore, Lowndes, Macon, and Montgomery counties, AL. No grants to individuals (except for designated scholarship funds limited to local area residents), or for fundraising events or capital campaigns.
Publications: Application guidelines; Annual report; Financial statement; Grants list; Newsletter.
Application information: Visit foundation web site for online applications and guidelines per grant type. Application form required.
Initial approach: Create online profile
Copies of proposal: 1
Deadline(s): Aug. 29 for CACF grants; varies for geographic affiliates
Final notification: Dec. for CACF grants; varies for geographic affiliates
Officers and Directors:* Kyle Johnson,* Chair.; Burton Ward,* Pres.; David Allred; Rita O. Brown; Milton C. Davis; Laura Harmon; Evette Hester; Louise Jennings; Jennifer McDonald; Riley Roby; William J. Scanlan; Shannon G. Speir; K. Roger Teel, Jr.; Daniel Thompson; Clay Torbert.
Number of staff: 4 full-time professional; 1 full-time support.
EIN: 630842355

20
The Comer Foundation ✧
400 Office Park Dr., Ste. 240
Birmingham, AL 35223-3409 (205) 802-2700
Contact: Jane B. Selfe, Tr.

Incorporated in 1945 in AL.
Donors: Avondale Mills; Comer-Avondale Mills, Inc.; Cowikee Mills.
Foundation type: Independent foundation.
Financial data (yr. ended 12/31/13): Assets, $14,841,545 (M); expenditures, $806,973; qualifying distributions, $738,373; giving activities include $672,500 for 27 grants (high: $150,000; low: $2,500).
Purpose and activities: Emphasis on higher and other education; support also for health, recreation, human services, and cultural programs.
Fields of interest: Arts; Elementary/secondary education; Higher education; Health care; Human services; YM/YWCAs & YM/YWHAs; Children; Youth; Adults; Women; Girls; Young adults, female; Boys; Young adults, male; Terminal illness, people with; Economically disadvantaged.
Type of support: Program development; Scholarship funds.
Limitations: Applications accepted. Giving primarily in AL. No grants to individuals.
Application information: Application form required.
Initial approach: Letter
Copies of proposal: 1
Deadline(s): None
Trustees: Richard J. Comer, Jr.; Francis H. Crockard, Jr.; Gillian C. Goodrich; Hugh Comers Nabers, Jr.; Jane B. Selfe.
Number of staff: 1 full-time professional.
EIN: 636004424
Selected grants: The following grants are a representative sample of this grantmaker's funding activity:
$122,891 to Auburn University, Auburn, AL, 2011.
$82,326 to University of Alabama, Tuscaloosa, AL, 2011.
$40,000 to State of Alabama Ballet, Birmingham, AL, 2010.
$21,000 to Troy University, Troy, AL, 2011.
$20,000 to Alabama Archives and History Foundation, Montgomery, AL, 2010.
$20,000 to Alabama Symphony Association, Birmingham, AL, 2010.
$5,000 to Wildlife Rescue Service, Pelham, AL, 2010.

21
Community Foundation of Greater Birmingham
(formerly The Greater Birmingham Foundation)
2100 First Ave. N., Ste. 700
Birmingham, AL 35203-4223 (205) 327-3800
Contact: Kate Nielsen, Pres.; For grants: James McCrary, V.P., Grants and Evaluation
FAX: (205) 328-6576;
E-mail: info@foundationbirmingham.org; Grant inquiry tel.: (205) 327-3812; Grant inquiry e-mail: jmccrary@foundationbirmingham.org; Scholarship inquiry e-mail: swilkerson@foundationbirmingham.org; Main URL: http://www.foundationbirmingham.org
Blog: http://www.foundationbirmingham.org/news-media/blog/
Community Foundation of Greater Birmingham's Philanthropy Promise: http://www.ncrp.org/philanthropys-promise/who
Facebook: http://www.facebook.com/pages/Birmingham-AL/Community-Foundation-of-Greater-Birmingham/37101947449
LinkedIn: http://www.linkedin.com/groups?home=&gid=1894200&trk=anet_ug_hm
RSS Feed: http://feeds.feedburner.com/cfgb
Twitter: http://twitter.com/comfoundbham
YouTube: http://www.youtube.com/user/comfoundbham

Established in 1959 in AL by resolution and declaration of trust; corporate side established in 1997.
Foundation type: Community foundation.
Financial data (yr. ended 12/31/12): Assets, $169,336,538 (M); gifts received, $23,947,276; expenditures, $20,058,050; giving activities include $17,384,477 for 279+ grants (high: $5,585,022), and $317,950 for 99 grants to individuals.
Purpose and activities: The foundation leverages gifts and bequests from many people to drive positive change, bring people together to address community issues, build on opportunities and achieve measurable results, and work in partnership with others to improve the life of the local region.
Fields of interest: Arts, artist's services; Arts; Higher education; Libraries/library science; Education, drop-out prevention; Education, reading; Education; Environment, toxics; Environment, beautification programs; Environment; Animal welfare; Reproductive health, prenatal care; Health care; Substance abuse, prevention; Housing/shelter, development; Disasters, preparedness/services; Recreation, parks/playgrounds; Youth development, services; Neighborhood centers; Family services; Family services, parent education; Family services, adolescent parents; Human services, emergency aid; Aging, centers/services; Human services; Nonprofit management; Community/economic development; Foundations (community); Public affairs; Economically disadvantaged.
Type of support: Capital campaigns; Building/renovation; Equipment; Program development; Publication; Seed money; Curriculum development; Matching/challenge support.
Limitations: Applications accepted. Giving limited to Blount, Jefferson, Shelby, St. Clair, and Walker counties, AL. No support for religious organizations for religious purposes. No grants to individuals (except for scholarships), or for national fundraising drives, sponsorships of fundraising events, endowment funds, debt reduction or replacements of government fund cuts.
Publications: Application guidelines; Annual report; Financial statement; Grants list; Informational brochure; Newsletter; Occasional report.
Application information: The foundation uses a results-based approach to grantmaking with a focus on four results most important to the community's well-being and identified by data and community input. The Results Framework includes four results, each with targeted strategies and objectives, as well as separate RFPs and application guidelines. Full proposals are accepted by invitation only based on brief proposals; visit foundation web site for complete application information. Application form required.
Initial approach: Complete online brief proposal

Deadline(s): January date for brief proposals and March date for full proposals for Cycle 1; July date for brief proposals and September date for full proposals for Cycle 2
Board meeting date(s): Quarterly
Final notification: February date for full proposal invitations and May for grant determination for Cycle 1; August date for full proposal invitations and Dec. for grant determination for Cycle 2
Officers and Directors:* Robert Holmes, Jr.,* Chair.; Kate Nielsen, Pres.; Marguerite Johnson, Sr. V.P., Grants and Initiatives; Kathryn Corey, V.P., Donor Rels.; James McCrary, V.P., Grants and Evaluation; Erin Kendrick Stephenson, V.P., Devel.; Wendy Rodde, C.F.O.; Neal R. Berte; H. Corbin Day; John Alex Floyd, Jr.; Gillian White Goodrich; Jay Grinney; Kathryn D. Harbert; Ronne M. Hess; Michael D. Luce; Carl E. Miller III; Kathryn Miree; G. Ruffner Page, Jr.; Yolanda N. Sullivan; Larry D. Thornton, Sr.; Ray Watts; Lloyd R. Wilson; Denise "Dee" A. Woodham; Cameron M. Vowell, Ph.D.
Trustee Banks: Canterbury Trust Company; Compass Bank; CB&T; National Bank of Commerce; Regions Bank; The Trust Co. of Sterne, Agee and Leach; Wachovia Bank, N.A.
Number of staff: 10 full-time professional; 2 part-time professional; 4 full-time support; 1 part-time support.
EIN: 631209631

22
Community Foundation of Huntsville/ Madison County ✧

225 Church St.
P.O. Box 332
Huntsville, AL 35804 (256) 535-2065
Contact: Stuart Obermann, C.E.O.
E-mail: info@communityfoundationhsv.org; Additional e-mail: stuart@communityfoundationhsv.org; Main URL: http://communityfoundationhsv.org/
Facebook: https://www.facebook.com/CFHuntsville

Established in 2009 in AL.
Foundation type: Community foundation.
Financial data (yr. ended 12/31/13): Assets, $10,311,487 (M); gifts received, $1,472,532; expenditures, $1,646,299; giving activities include $1,413,456 for 41+ grants (high: $183,150).
Purpose and activities: The foundation fulfills its mission by: 1) encouraging donors to partner with us in fulfilling their financial and charitable goals; 2) ensuring that gifts made to the Community Foundation grow and have lasting impact both now and into the future; 3) convening people to work on relevant community challenges and issues; 4) providing cumulative community knowledge about this area; 5) catalyzing community involvement and philanthropic commitment to improve the quality of life in Huntsville and Madison County; and making grants to fund responses to important needs in Huntsville, Madison County, and beyond.
Limitations: Applications accepted. Giving primarily in Huntsville and Madison County, AL.
Application information: The foundation is currently establishing the Community Catalyst Fund and will conduct an across-the-board critical community needs assessment when target balance of $250,000 is achieved. When those critical needs are identified, the foundation will issue a request for proposals to address those needs. Visit foundation web site for updates.
Officers and Directors:* Bob Ludwig,* Chair.; Sarah Savage,* Vice-Chair.; Stuart Obermann, C.E.O. and Pres.; Melissa Thompson, V.P., Opers.; Dianne Reynolds,* Secy.; Bill Fleming,* Treas.; Margaret Anne Goldsmith, Emeritus; John Baggette; Ken Barnett; Bobby Bradley; Frank Caprio; Elizabeth Dotts Fleming; James Gilbert, M.D.; Pam Hudson; Jeremiah Knight; Bill Roark; Anne Marie Reidy, M.D.; Chris Russell.
EIN: 263750673

23
Community Foundation of Northeast Alabama ✧

(formerly Calhoun County Community Foundation)
1130 Quintard Ave., Ste. 100
Anniston, AL 36201 (256) 231-5160
Contact: Jennifer S. Maddox, C.E.O.
FAX: (256) 231-5161;
E-mail: info@yourcommunityfirst.org; Additional e-mail: jmaddox@yourcommunityfirst.org; Mailing address: PO Box 1826, Anniston, AL 36202-1826; Main URL: http://www.yourcommunityfirst.org/
Facebook: http://www.facebook.com/pages/Community-Foundation-of-Northeast-Alabama/212407278799983

Established in 1997 in AL; reorganized as a community foundation in 1999.
Foundation type: Community foundation.
Financial data (yr. ended 09/30/13): Assets, $34,488,973 (M); gifts received, $2,277,226; expenditures, $1,789,000; giving activities include $1,118,005 for 25+ grants (high: $250,000), and $409,345 for foundation-administered programs.
Purpose and activities: The foundation is a permanent philanthropic resource dedicated to enhancing the quality of life in nine counties in Northeast Alabama including Calhoun, Cherokee, Clay, Cleburne, DeKalb, Etowah, Randolph, St. Clair, and Talladega. The foundation's mission is to wisely assess needs and channel donor resources to maximize community well-being, by using donor gifts to grow funds that benefit the community.
Fields of interest: Arts; Child development, education; Education; Health care; Mental health, treatment; Human services.
Type of support: Seed money; Program evaluation; Management development/capacity building; Curriculum development; General/operating support; Building/renovation; Equipment; Emergency funds; Program development; Conferences/seminars; Publication; Scholarship funds; Research; Technical assistance; Matching/challenge support.
Limitations: Applications accepted. Giving to organizations who provide services to residents of Calhoun County, AL. No support for religious organizations for religious purposes or to influence elections. No grants to individuals (except for scholarships), or for organizations operating less than one year, endowments, special events or fundraising campaigns, or capital campaigns.
Publications: Application guidelines; Annual report; Financial statement; Grants list; Informational brochure; Newsletter; Occasional report; Program policy statement.
Application information: Visit foundation web site for online application forms and guidelines. Application form required.
Initial approach: Varies, see website
Deadline(s): Varies
Board meeting date(s): Quarterly
Officers and Trustees:* Tommie J. Goggans III,* Chair.; Cheryl Potts,* Vice-Chair.; Jennifer Maddox,* C.E.O. and Pres.; Eula Tatman,* V.P., Grants, Scholarships and Initiatives; Susan Williamson,* V.P., Advancement, Comms.; Martha G. Lavender,* Secy.; Newman R. Nowlin,* Treas.; Matt Akin; Gloria K. Bennett; Anne S. Carruth; Terry Graham, Ed.D.; James S. Nolen; Thomas S. Potts, Jr.; Manju Purohit; Albert L. Shumaker; Brenda S. Stedham; Jack Swift.
Number of staff: 4 full-time professional; 1 part-time professional; 1 part-time support.
EIN: 630308398

24
The Community Foundation of South Alabama ✧

(formerly The Mobile Community Foundation)
212 St. Joseph Rd.
Mobile, AL 36602 (251) 438-5591
Contact: Rebecca Byrne, Pres.
FAX: (251) 438-5592;
E-mail: info@communityendowment.com; Grant inquiry e-mail: program@communityendowment.com; Mailing address: P.O. Box 990, Mobile, AL 36601-0990; Main URL: http://www.communityendowment.com
Blog: http://thecommunityfoundationofsouthalabma.blogspot.com/
Twitter: https://twitter.com/CFSouthAlabama
YouTube: http://www.youtube.com/user/CFSouthAlabama?feature=mhee

Incorporated in 1976 in AL.
Foundation type: Community foundation.
Financial data (yr. ended 09/30/13): Assets, $59,266,751 (M); gifts received, $1,792,248; expenditures, $4,729,919; giving activities include $2,993,361 for 96+ grants (high: $225,230).
Purpose and activities: The foundation works to improve the quality of life in South Alabama by promoting philanthropy. Through wise investments, they help build the financial resources necessary to make effective grants that positively impact our community. They are committed to providing the effective leadership that is necessary to help solve tough problems in their communities. By building strategic partnerships with community leaders, corporations and volunteers we bring the community together to share ideas and identify issues to strengthen South Alabama.
Fields of interest: Arts; Higher education; Adult education—literacy, basic skills & GED; Education; Environment; Animal welfare; Health care, insurance; Health care; Substance abuse, prevention; Crime/violence prevention; Crime/violence prevention, abuse prevention; Disasters, preparedness/services; Recreation, parks/playgrounds; Recreation; Youth development, services; Neighborhood centers; Children, day care; Family services; Human services, emergency aid; Aging, centers/services; Human services; Community/economic development; Children/youth; Youth; Aging; Young adults; Mentally disabled; Minorities; Asians/Pacific Islanders; African Americans/Blacks; Girls; Boys; AIDS, people with; Single parents; Economically disadvantaged; Homeless.
Type of support: Program evaluation; General/operating support; Management development/

capacity building; Building/renovation; Equipment; Emergency funds; Program development; Publication; Seed money; Curriculum development; Scholarship funds; Program-related investments/ loans; In-kind gifts; Matching/challenge support.
Limitations: Applications accepted. Giving primarily limited to an eight county region in Southwest AL, including Baldwin, Choctaw, Clarke, Conecuh, Escambia, Mobile, Monroe, and Washington counties. No support for religious activities. No grants to individuals, or for national fundraising campaigns, conferences or seminar expenses, tickets for charity benefits, or budget deficits.
Publications: Application guidelines; Annual report; Annual report (including application guidelines); Financial statement; Informational brochure (including application guidelines); Newsletter.
Application information: Visit the foundation's web site for application form and guidelines. Unsolicited applications are not accepted. Application form required.
Initial approach: Submit application form and attachments
Copies of proposal: 1
Deadline(s): Varies
Board meeting date(s): Quarterly
Final notification: Varies
Officers and Directors:* Norman D. Pitman, Jr.,* Chair.; Bob Higgins,* Vice-Chair.; Rebecca Byrne, C.E.O. and Pres.; Mary Kathleen Miller,* Secy.; Linette Clausman, C.F.O.; Mark Hieronymus,* Treas.; Tom Bates; Jennifer Jenkins; Robert "Bob" Jones; Douglas M. Littles, Ph.D.; Champ Meyercord; Samford T. Myers; Eric Nager; Ashley Ramsay-Naile; A.J. Rudnick; Mary M. Tucker; Susan Turner; Marietta Urquhart; Cynthia H. Zipperly.
Number of staff: 5 full-time professional; 1 part-time professional; 2 full-time support; 1 part-time support.
EIN: 630695166

25
Community Foundation of West Alabama ✧

700 Energy Center Blvd., Ste. 406
Northport, AL 35473 (205) 366-0698
Contact: Glenn Taylor, C.E.O.
FAX: (205) 366-0813; E-mail: glenn@thecfwa.org; Mailing address: P.O. Box 3033, Tuscaloosa, AL 35403; Main URL: http://www.thecfwa.org

Established in 1999 in AL as an initiative of the Tuscaloosa Estate Planning Council.
Foundation type: Community foundation.
Financial data (yr. ended 12/31/13): Assets, $9,366,557 (M); gifts received, $1,808,587; expenditures, $1,978,572; giving activities include $1,165,932 for 38+ grants (high: $275,000), and $553,576 for grants to individuals.
Purpose and activities: The foundation seeks to connect people and resources to the real needs of the community. The foundation strives to help build partnerships between donors, nonprofit organizations and the community at large in order to strengthen and enhance the quality of life of the people of western AL.
Fields of interest: Humanities; Arts; Education; Environment; Health care; Disasters, Hurricane Katrina; Recreation; Residential/custodial care, hospices; Aging, centers/services; Human services; Community/economic development; United Ways and Federated Giving Programs; Infants/toddlers; Children/youth; Youth; Disabilities, people with; Physically disabled; Blind/visually impaired; Mentally disabled; Single parents; Crime/abuse victims; Terminal illness, people with; Economically disadvantaged.
Limitations: Applications accepted. Giving limited to western AL, including Bibb, Fayette, Green, Hale, Lamar, Marengo County, Pickens, Sumter, and Tuscaloosa. No support for religious organizations for religious purposes. No grants to individuals (except for scholarships), or for dinners, balls, or other ticketed events, or endowments.
Publications: Application guidelines; Annual report; Annual report (including application guidelines); Financial statement; Grants list; Informational brochure; Newsletter; Program policy statement.
Application information: Visit foundation web site for application form and guidelines. Application form required.
Initial approach: Submit application form and attachments
Copies of proposal: 1
Deadline(s): Apr. 1 and Oct. 1
Board meeting date(s): May and Nov.
Final notification: May and Nov.
Officers and Directors:* Thomas A. Nettles IV,* Chair.; Glenn Taylor,* C.E.O. and Pres.; Joseph D. Blackburn,* V.P.; William A. Tate,* V.P.; Anne Moman,* Secy.; Pierce Boyd,* Treas.; Davis S. Burton; Claude D. Edwards; Hon. John England; Sam Faucett; James I. Harrison III; Shelley Jones; Dr. Barry Mason; Gina Miers; Lin Moore; Mary Bess Paluzzi; Pam Parker; Leah Ann Sexton; Dr. Hugh H. Stegall; William W. Walker, Jr.
Number of staff: 2 part-time professional.
EIN: 631225003

26
Crampton Trust ✧

c/o Regions Bank
P.O. Box 1628
Mobile, AL 36633-1628 (251) 431-8309
Contact: Roger Cole

Established in 1993 in AL.
Donor: Katharine C. Cochrane‡.
Foundation type: Independent foundation.
Financial data (yr. ended 12/31/13): Assets, $20,369,655 (M); expenditures, $1,012,580; qualifying distributions, $870,579; giving activities include $867,734 for 44 grants (high: $100,000; low: $3,000).
Fields of interest: Arts; Education; Hospitals (general); Human services.
Type of support: General/operating support; Capital campaigns; Building/renovation; Equipment; Endowments.
Limitations: Applications accepted. Giving primarily limited to southwestern AL, including Baldwin, Clarke, Escambia, Mobile, Monroe and Washington counties. No grants to individuals.
Application information: Application form not required.
Initial approach: Proposal
Deadline(s): None
Trustee: Regions Bank.
EIN: 636181261
Selected grants: The following grants are a representative sample of this grantmaker's funding activity:
$125,000 to Waterfront Rescue Mission, Pensacola, FL, 2011.
$10,000 to YMCA of South Alabama, Mobile, AL, 2011.

27
The Daniel Foundation of Alabama ✧

510 Office Park Dr., Ste. 210
Birmingham, AL 35223-2414 (205) 874-3523
Contact: Joyce Brasher, Admin. Asst.
FAX: (205) 874-3526; E-mail: info@df-al.com; E-mail for Joyce Brasher: joyce@df-al.com, E-mail for guidelines requests: guidelines@df-al.com; Main URL: http://danielfoundationofalabama.com/ Photo Gallery: http://danielfoundationofalabama.com/photo_gallery.htm

Established in 1978 in AL as partial successor to the Daniel Foundation.
Foundation type: Independent foundation.
Financial data (yr. ended 12/31/13): Assets, $138,136,595 (M); expenditures, $7,171,373; qualifying distributions, $6,671,950; giving activities include $6,671,950 for 459 grants (high: $500,000; low: $250).
Purpose and activities: The foundation's mission is to strengthen communities within Alabama and improve the quality of life for citizens from all regions of Alabama through the support of quality educational programs, arts and culture, civic and community programs, and medical care and research.
Fields of interest: Arts; Higher education; Education; Health care; Human services.
Type of support: General/operating support; Capital campaigns; Equipment; Endowments; Scholarship funds.
Limitations: Applications accepted. Giving primarily in AL. No grants to individuals, or for fundraising events or start-up costs and/or seed money for new organizations.
Publications: Application guidelines; Annual report.
Application information: Guidelines must be requested each time prior to submitting a proposal. Guidelines are only given to organizations after their eligibility has been established. Only one proposal may be submitted during a 12 month period. Application form required.
Initial approach: Guideline request by mail or e-mail
Deadline(s): See foundation website for current deadlines
Board meeting date(s): Jan., Apr., July and Oct.
Final notification: Varies
Officers and Directors:* Charles W. Daniel,* Chair.; Lyndra P. Daniel,* Pres.; Marion Daniel Head,* V.P.; Maria S. Kennedy,* Secy.-Treas. and Exec. Dir.; Dr. Jack Hawkins; James F. Hughey, Jr.; Lucy C. McVay.
Number of staff: 1 part-time professional; 1 part-time support.
EIN: 630736444
Selected grants: The following grants are a representative sample of this grantmaker's funding activity:
$200,000 to Troy University, Troy, AL, 2012. For Phenix City Riverfront Development Project.
$150,000 to Samford University, Birmingham, AL, 2012. For Campaign for Samford.
$100,000 to Alabama Historical Commission, Montgomery, AL, 2012. For Construction of Old Cahawba Visitor's Complex.
$50,000 to Childrens Harbor, Alexander City, AL, 2012. For Capital Campaign for Facilities Expansion.
$50,000 to Freedom Rain Outreach Ministries, Birmingham, AL, 2012. For Operating Support and Program Upgrades.
$25,000 to Main Street Alabama, Birmingham, AL, 2012. For Start-Up for MSA operations over 3 years.

$20,000 to Restoration Academy, Fairfield, AL, 2012. For Tuition for students from the Lovelady Center and Grace Center.
$15,000 to Birmingham Boys Choir Foundation, Birmingham, AL, 2012. For Satellite Programs / Capacity Building Programs.
$15,000 to Carmel Health Network, Mobile, AL, 2012. For Salary Support for New Pediatrician.
$15,000 to One Place Family Justice Center, Montgomery, AL, 2012. For Operating expenses.

28
Davenport-Spiva Charitable Educational Trust ✧
c/o Regions Bank
P.O. Box 2886
Mobile, AL 36652-2886

Established in MS.
Foundation type: Independent foundation.
Financial data (yr. ended 12/31/13): Assets, $15,022,716 (M); expenditures, $752,330; qualifying distributions, $673,158; giving activities include $655,677 for 8 grants (high: $163,919; low: $6,557).
Fields of interest: Education; Health care; Human services.
Limitations: Applications not accepted. Giving primarily in MS.
Application information: Unsolicited requests for funds not accepted.
Trustee: Regions Bank.
EIN: 646183870

29
Ernest G. DeBakey Charitable Foundation ✧
33561 Boardwalk Dr.
Spanish Fort, AL 36527-9064 (251) 621-1344
Contact: Marsha Debakey, Pres.

Established in 1997 in AL.
Foundation type: Independent foundation.
Financial data (yr. ended 12/31/12): Assets, $17,802,976 (M); gifts received, $303,224; expenditures, $1,133,484; qualifying distributions, $1,012,297; giving activities include $969,137 for 17 grants (high: $490,464; low: $600).
Purpose and activities: Giving primarily for education and health.
Fields of interest: Higher education; Education; Health care; Human services.
Limitations: Applications accepted. Giving primarily in AL, with emphasis on Mobile.
Application information: Application form not required.
Initial approach: Letter
Deadline(s): None
Officers and Directors:* Marsha L. DeBakey,* Pres. and Treas.; John H. Martin,* Secy.; Kermit Bishop; F.T. Boudreau III, M.D.; Leigh Anne Fleming; Frank L. McPhillips, M.D.
Trustee: BankTrust.
EIN: 721374786

30
Solon & Martha Dixon Foundation ✧
P.O. Drawer 990
Andalusia, AL 36420-1219
Contact: Gordon S. Jones, Exec. V.P.
FAX: (334) 222-3140; E-Mail: gsjones@alaweb.com

Established in 1981 in AL.
Donors: Solon Dixon; Martha B. Dixon.
Foundation type: Independent foundation.
Financial data (yr. ended 06/30/13): Assets, $19,144,661 (M); expenditures, $1,141,993; qualifying distributions, $880,334; giving activities include $803,758 for 41 grants (high: $364,934; low: $250).
Purpose and activities: The foundation seeks to support and promote the cultivation and growth of forests as a natural resource, and to support and promote educational activities which develop and implement systemic forest management information for the production of timber products, and at the same time, promote conservation of such natural resources, and to foster ecological development of co-existence between timber resources and distributions of human, social and cultural patterns. Priority is given to Auburn University's School of Forestry and Wildlife Sciences, Lyman Ward Military Academy, and government and related agencies, education systems and charitable entities within Covington County, AL.
Fields of interest: Higher education; Education; Environment, natural resources; Environment, forests; Human services; Public affairs, government agencies.
Type of support: Building/renovation; Equipment; Program development; Research.
Limitations: Giving primarily in Covington County, AL. No grants to individuals.
Application information:
Initial approach: Letter
Deadline(s): Feb. 2, Sept. 1, and Nov. 30
Officers and Directors:* Doris B. Tyler, Pres.; Phillip G. Jones, Exec. V.P.; Frank McGuire, V.P.; Louisa Mann, Secy.; Martha B. Dixon,* Dir. Emerita.
Number of staff: 1 part-time professional.
EIN: 630812726
Selected grants: The following grants are a representative sample of this grantmaker's funding activity:
$125,000 to Lyman Ward Military Academy, Camp Hill, AL, 2011.
$100,380 to Covington County Board of Education, Andalusia, AL, 2011.
$75,000 to Auburn University Foundation, Auburn, AL, 2011.
$50,000 to Andalusia, City of, Andalusia, AL, 2011.
$50,000 to Discovering Alabama, Tuscaloosa, AL, 2010.
$50,000 to Opportunity House, Opp, AL, 2011.
$25,000 to CrossOver Ministry, Richmond, VA, 2010.
$20,000 to Childrens Hospital of Alabama, Birmingham, AL, 2010.
$15,000 to American Red Cross, Andalusia, AL, 2011.
$11,043 to Covington County Commission, Andalusia, AL, 2011.
$10,000 to Florala, City of, Florala, AL, 2010.
$10,000 to Florala, City of, Florala, AL, 2011.
$5,000 to Andalusia Ballet Association, Andalusia, AL, 2010.
$5,000 to Andalusia, City of, Andalusia, AL, 2011.
$2,750 to Covington County Commission, Andalusia, AL, 2011.

31
Dove Family Foundation ✧ ☆
(formerly The G. Mack and Nancy R. Dove Foundation)
P.O. Box 6827
Dothan, AL 36302-6827 (334) 793-2284
Contact: G. Mack Dove, Pres.

Established in 1982 in AL.
Donors: G. Mack Dove; Nancy R. Dove; Reid B. Dove.
Foundation type: Independent foundation.
Financial data (yr. ended 12/31/13): Assets, $1,299,098 (M); gifts received, $404,189; expenditures, $543,642; qualifying distributions, $530,721; giving activities include $530,721 for 33 grants (high: $250,000; low: $50).
Purpose and activities: Giving for educational and religious purposes.
Fields of interest: Arts; Education; Health organizations, association; Diabetes research; Youth development; Children/youth, services; Christian agencies & churches.
Type of support: General/operating support; Capital campaigns.
Application information: Application form not required.
Initial approach: Proposal
Deadline(s): None
Officers: G. Mack Dove, Pres.; Reid B. Dove, V.P.; J. Steven Roy, Secy.-Treas.
EIN: 630836253

32
Energen Foundation ✧
605 Richard Arrington Jr. Blvd. N.
Birmingham, AL 35203-2707
Contact: Lindsay Reddick
E-mail: EGNFoundation@energen.com; Main URL: http://www.energen.com/Community-Relations/Community-Investment/Energen-Foundation-491.html

Donors: Energen Corporation; Energen Resource Corp.
Foundation type: Company-sponsored foundation.
Financial data (yr. ended 12/31/13): Assets, $2,430,276 (M); gifts received, $16,870; expenditures, $889,964; qualifying distributions, $884,870; giving activities include $882,870 for 215 grants (high: $290,000; low: $25).
Purpose and activities: The foundation supports organizations involved with arts and culture, education, health, human services, community development, and civic affairs.
Fields of interest: Museums (science/technology); Arts; Higher education; Business school/education; Hospitals (general); Health care; Youth development, business; Salvation Army; YM/YWCAs & YM/YWHAs; Human services; Community/economic development; United Ways and Federated Giving Programs; Public affairs.
Type of support: Employee matching gifts; General/operating support.
Limitations: Applications accepted. Giving primarily in areas of company operations in AL, LA, NM, and TX. No support for public or private schools with grades K-12, churches, public facilities, state organizations, or state-supported organizations, political candidates or organizations, individual collegiate Greek organizations, or other foundations. No grants to individuals or for sporting events, walks, or runs.
Publications: Application guidelines.

Application information: Application form required.
Initial approach: Download application form and e-mail or mail to foundation
Deadline(s): Before the end of Aug.
Officers and Directors:* James T. McManus II,* Pres.; Robert S. Mcannally,* V.P.; Dudley C. Reynolds,* Secy.; Charles W. Porter, Jr.,* Treas.; William K. Bibb; Russell E. Lynch, Jr.
EIN: 261678215
Selected grants: The following grants are a representative sample of this grantmaker's funding activity:
$317,069 to United Way of Central Alabama, Birmingham, AL, 2011.
$22,749 to United Way, San Juan, Farmington, NM, 2011.
$20,000 to Birmingham Civil Rights Institute, Birmingham, AL, 2011.
$12,500 to Jefferson County Committee for Economic Opportunity, Birmingham, AL, 2011.
$10,000 to American Gas Foundation, Washington, DC, 2011.
$10,000 to Petroleum Museum, Midland, TX, 2011.
$5,520 to United Way of Etowah County, Gadsden, AL, 2011.
$5,000 to Nonprofit Resource Center of Alabama, Birmingham, AL, 2011.
$3,000 to Civic Club Foundation, Birmingham, AL, 2011.
$2,500 to Birmingham Childrens Theater, Birmingham, AL, 2011.

33
Curtis Finlay Foundation Inc. ✧
P.O. Box 298
Brewton, AL 36427-0298 (251) 867-7706
Contact: Richard D. Finlay, Dir.

Established in AL.
Donor: Curtis Finlay†.
Foundation type: Independent foundation.
Financial data (yr. ended 12/31/13): Assets, $14,230,930 (M); expenditures, $754,813; qualifying distributions, $661,696; giving activities include $566,000 for 45 grants (high: $50,000; low: $450), and $59,000 for 10 grants to individuals (high: $14,000; low: $5,000).
Purpose and activities: Scholarships only to residents of Escambia County, AL, attending accredited preparatory schools, four-year colleges or universities, or Jefferson Davis Community College, AL; giving also for the arts and human services.
Fields of interest: Arts, government agencies; Arts; Secondary school/education; Higher education; Education; Human services; Community development, neighborhood development.
Type of support: General/operating support; Scholarship funds; Scholarships—to individuals.
Limitations: Applications accepted. Giving limited to AL. Scholarships limited to residents of Escambia County, AL; giving to organizations primarily in Brewton, AL.
Application information: Application form not required.
Initial approach: Proposal
Deadline(s): None
Directors: Richard D. Finlay; Sally Finlay; Paul D. Owens, Jr.
EIN: 631080992
Selected grants: The following grants are a representative sample of this grantmaker's funding activity:
$25,000 to Brewton Public Library, Brewton, AL, 2011. For unrestricted support.

34
J. Hunter Flack Foundation, Inc. ✧
7550 Halcyon Summit Dr.
Montgomery, AL 36117-7010

Established in 1979 in AL.
Donors: J. Hunter Flack†; Eleanor E. Flack.
Foundation type: Independent foundation.
Financial data (yr. ended 01/31/13): Assets, $10,966 (M); gifts received, $420,000; expenditures, $434,775; qualifying distributions, $434,000; giving activities include $434,000 for 6 grants (high: $248,000; low: $1,000).
Purpose and activities: Giving primarily for Anglican and other Protestant churches and educational organizations.
Fields of interest: Higher education; Protestant agencies & churches.
Limitations: Applications not accepted. Giving limited to North America. No grants to individuals.
Application information: Unsolicited requests for funds not accepted.
Officer: Eleanor E. Flack, Pres.
EIN: 636009500

35
The Frank & Fred Friedman Family Foundation ✧
(formerly The Frank and Fred Friedman Foundation)
P.O. Box 430229
Birmingham, AL 35243-1229
E-mail: fredf3443@aol.com

Established in 1990 in AL.
Donor: Frank Friedman.
Foundation type: Independent foundation.
Financial data (yr. ended 03/31/13): Assets, $10,778,068 (M); expenditures, $763,528; qualifying distributions, $438,234; giving activities include $438,234 for 97 grants (high: $105,000; low: $100).
Fields of interest: Education; Health care; Health organizations, association; Human services; Jewish federated giving programs; Jewish agencies & synagogues.
Type of support: Annual campaigns; Capital campaigns; Building/renovation; Curriculum development; Matching/challenge support.
Limitations: Applications not accepted. Giving limited to Birmingham, AL, and the surrounding counties. No grants to individuals.
Application information: Contributes only to pre-selected organizations.
Board meeting date(s): Biannually
Officers: Fred H. Friedman, Pres. and Treas.; Brenda Friedman, Secy.
Directors: Jeremy Cohen; Leah Cohen; Jordan Friedman.
EIN: 630921651
Selected grants: The following grants are a representative sample of this grantmaker's funding activity:
$105,000 to Birmingham Jewish Foundation, Birmingham, AL, 2010.
$90,126 to Knesseth Israel Congregation, Birmingham, AL, 2010.
$80,572 to Temple Beth El, 2010.
$30,000 to YWCA, 2010.
$14,080 to Temple Emanu-El, 2010.
$4,000 to American Cancer Society, Atlanta, GA, 2011.
$1,850 to Muscular Dystrophy Association, Tucson, AZ, 2011.
$1,650 to American Heart Association, Dallas, TX, 2011.

36
Mike and Gillian Goodrich Foundation ✧
(formerly Mike and Gillian Goodrich Charitable Foundation)
3800 Colonnade Pkwy., Ste. 430
Birmingham, AL 35243-3369 (205) 443-7809
Main URL: http://www.mggoodrichfoundation.org/

Established in 2008 in AL.
Donors: T. Michael Goodrich; Gillian W. Goodrich.
Foundation type: Independent foundation.
Financial data (yr. ended 12/31/13): Assets, $81,999,409 (M); gifts received, $2,000,000; expenditures, $3,551,232; qualifying distributions, $3,362,924; giving activities include $2,959,922 for 93 grants (high: $291,522; low: $400), and $250,000 for 1 loan/program-related investment.
Purpose and activities: Giving primarily for education, neighborhood revitalization, the environment, arts and culture, and positioning strategic community assets. Grant applications must be geared toward achieving specific results in these focus areas.
Fields of interest: Arts; Education; Environment, natural resources; Community development, neighborhood development.
Limitations: Giving primarily in the Birmingham metro, and Woodlawn areas of AL, as well as the Black Belt, AL, area (particularly Hale and Greene counties). No support for individual school classrooms or programs, private schools, or mission trips or ambassador programs. No grants to individuals, or for scholarships, private awards, health-related research, or fundraising events that are not 100% deductible for charitable purposes.
Publications: Application guidelines.
Application information: Full proposals for Leadership Grants are by invitation only, upon consideration of Letter of Intent. Grants to faith-based organizations may be made to support programs that address the focus areas. See foundation web site for specific application guidelines.
Initial approach: For Leadership Grants: use Letter of Intent process on foundation web site; use online application process for Community Support Grants
Deadline(s): See foundation web site for current deadlines
Officers and Directors:* Gillian W. Goodrich,* Chair. and Pres.; T. Michael Goodrich,* V.P.; T. Michael Goodrich II,* Secy.; Carol W. Butler, Exec. Dir.; Alexandra D. Goodrich; Gillian G. Goodrich; Mary B. Goodrich.
EIN: 263587489
Selected grants: The following grants are a representative sample of this grantmaker's funding activity:
$400,000 to Woodlawn Foundation, Birmingham, AL, 2012. To support Neighborhood Revitalization Efforts.
$260,000 to McWane Science Center, Birmingham, AL, 2012. To support the Children's Museum.

$150,000 to Birmingham Education Foundation, Birmingham, AL, 2012. To support Aspire Professional Development Program.
$100,000 to Alabama Archives and History Foundation, Montgomery, AL, 2012. For construction of the Museum of Alabama.
$100,000 to Alabama Historical Commission, Montgomery, AL, 2012. For construction of the Visitors' Complex at Old Cahawba Archaeological Park.
$80,000 to Main Street Alabama, Birmingham, AL, 2012. For Start Up Funds for Organization.
$50,000 to Jefferson County Schools Public Education Foundation, Birmingham, AL, 2012. To support Stellar Teaching Program.
$40,000 to Community Foundation of Greater Birmingham, Birmingham, AL, 2012. To support Roads to Recovery.
$25,861 to United Way of Central Alabama, Birmingham, AL, 2012. To support Success By Six Program.
$25,000 to Alabama School of Fine Arts Foundation, Birmingham, AL, 2012. To fund the purchase of a Wenger Acoustical Shell.

37
The James I. Harrison Family Foundation ✧

3925 Rice Mine Rd.
Tuscaloosa, AL 35406-1523
Contact: James I. Harrison, Jr., Pres.

Established in 1997 in GA.
Donor: James I. Harrison, Jr.
Foundation type: Independent foundation.
Financial data (yr. ended 12/31/13): Assets, $12,990,499 (M); expenditures, $1,958,939; qualifying distributions, $1,895,227; giving activities include $1,894,227 for 29 grants (high: $1,053,771; low: $250).
Purpose and activities: Giving primarily to charitable organizations in Tuscaloosa County, AL. Most grants are awarded based on the proactive efforts of the foundation president.
Fields of interest: Elementary/secondary education; Higher education; Health organizations, association; Youth development, centers/clubs; Human services.
Limitations: Applications not accepted. Giving generally limited to Tuscaloosa County, AL.
Application information: Unsolicited requests for funds not accepted.
Officer: James I. Harrison, Jr., Pres. and Secy.-Treas.
Director: Peggy T. Harrison.
Trustee: Lazard Freres & Co.
EIN: 582327810

38
Hearin-Chandler Foundation ✧

(formerly Chandler Foundation)
P.O. Box 450
Mobile, AL 36601-0450 (251) 694-1957
Contact: Thomas B. Van Antwerp, Tr.

Established in 1963 in AL.
Donors: Ralph B. Chandler†; William J. Hearin†.
Foundation type: Independent foundation.
Financial data (yr. ended 12/31/13): Assets, $42,299,592 (M); expenditures, $2,096,756; qualifying distributions, $1,643,153; giving activities include $1,521,000 for 55 grants (high: $100,000; low: $100).
Purpose and activities: Giving primarily to cultural institutions; giving also for education, the environment, and human services.
Fields of interest: Museums; Performing arts; Arts; Higher education; Libraries (public); Environment, beautification programs; Medical care, in-patient care; Human services; Community/economic development; Christian agencies & churches; Women.
Type of support: General/operating support; Capital campaigns; Building/renovation; Equipment; Endowments; Program development; Scholarship funds; Matching/challenge support.
Limitations: Applications accepted. Giving primarily in Mobile County, AL. No grants to individuals.
Application information: Application form not required.

Initial approach: Letter
Copies of proposal: 1
Deadline(s): Oct. 1
Board meeting date(s): Dec.
Final notification: Jan. of the next calendar year

Trustee: Thomas B. Van Antwerp.
Number of staff: 1 part-time professional.
EIN: 636075470

39
The Ronne & Donald Hess Foundation ✧

(formerly Ronne & Donald Hess Charitable Foundation)
505 20th St. N., Ste. 1015
Birmingham, AL 35203-2607 (205) 328-3120
Contact: Ronne Hess, Pres. and Dir.

Established in 1985 in AL.
Donors: Donald E. Hess; Ronne Hess; Emily Ruth Hess Levine.
Foundation type: Independent foundation.
Financial data (yr. ended 12/31/13): Assets, $1,400,941 (M); gifts received, $422,595; expenditures, $684,985; qualifying distributions, $674,836; giving activities include $673,802 for 65 grants (high: $100,926; low: $100).
Fields of interest: Arts; Higher education; Human services; Jewish agencies & synagogues.
Type of support: Annual campaigns; Capital campaigns; Building/renovation.
Limitations: Applications accepted. Giving primarily in AL. No grants to individuals.
Application information: Application form required.

Initial approach: Proposal
Deadline(s): None
Board meeting date(s): Varies

Officers and Directors:* Ronne Hess,* Pres.; Donald E. Hess, V.P. and Secy.; Emily Ruth Hess Levine, V.P. and Treas.; Alan Z. Engel,* V.P.; David R. Nelson, Jr., V.P.
Number of staff: 1 part-time support.
EIN: 630916545
Selected grants: The following grants are a representative sample of this grantmaker's funding activity:
$2,400 to Alabama Symphony Association, Birmingham, AL, 2011. For general support.

40
Hill Crest Foundation, Inc. ✧

P.O. Box 530507
Mountain Brook, AL 35253-0507
Contact: Charles R. Terry Sr., Chair.

Established in 1967 in AL.
Foundation type: Independent foundation.
Financial data (yr. ended 06/30/13): Assets, $45,340,991 (M); expenditures, $2,186,397; qualifying distributions, $1,936,403; giving activities include $1,866,000 for 94 grants (high: $200,000; low: $1,000).
Purpose and activities: Giving primarily for health associations, human services and education; some funding also for the arts.
Fields of interest: Arts; Elementary/secondary education; Higher education; Health organizations, association; Human services; Children/youth, services.
Type of support: Capital campaigns; Building/renovation; Equipment; Endowments; Program development; Professorships; Publication; Seed money; Scholarship funds; Research; Technical assistance; Matching/challenge support.
Limitations: Giving limited to AL. No grants to individuals.
Application information: Application form not required.

Initial approach: Letter
Copies of proposal: 4
Deadline(s): None
Board meeting date(s): Quarterly

Officer and Trustees:* Charles R. Terry, Sr.,* Chair.; Bill D. Eddleman; Ann Hightower; Willard L. Hurley; Charles R. Terry, Jr.; William W. Walker III.
Number of staff: 2 full-time professional.
EIN: 630516927
Selected grants: The following grants are a representative sample of this grantmaker's funding activity:
$10,000 to Birmingham Botanical Gardens, Birmingham, AL, 2013. For Support.

41
International Retinal Research Foundation, Inc. ✧

1720 University Blvd., Ste. 124
Birmingham, AL 35233-1816 (205) 325-8103
Contact: Sandra Blackwood, Exec. Dir.
FAX: (205) 325-8394;
E-mail: sblackwood@irrfonline.org; Main URL: http://www.IRRFonline.org
E-Newsletter: http://www.irrfonline.org/newsletters.html

Established in 1997 in AL.
Foundation type: Independent foundation.
Financial data (yr. ended 12/31/13): Assets, $32,300,336 (M); gifts received, $3,635; expenditures, $1,698,666; qualifying distributions, $1,373,357; giving activities include $1,373,357 for 22 grants (high: $455,500; low: $125).
Purpose and activities: The foundation supports scientific research on the diseases of the human eye, especially its center, the macula, and peripheral retinal research that ultimately will accelerate the outcome of discovery. Specific consideration will be given to those scientists who are actively working toward discovering the causes, preventions, and cures of macular degeneration and diabetic retinopathy. Limited funding is available for

postdoctoral training in the area of vision research and for educational and scientific exchange.
Fields of interest: Eye research.
Type of support: Equipment; Conferences/seminars; Fellowships; Research; Matching/challenge support.
Limitations: Applications accepted. Giving on a national and international basis. No support for capital building programs. No grants to individuals, or for building construction, or salary of the Principal Investigator except when matching funds are committed from another funding agency.
Publications: Application guidelines; Grants list; Informational brochure; Newsletter.
Application information: Applications sent by e-mail are not accepted. Application form required.
Initial approach: Download application form from foundation web site, or telephone requesting it
Copies of proposal: 2
Deadline(s): May 1 (for regular grants); Mar. 1 (for Postdoctoral Scholar nominations)
Board meeting date(s): Mar., May, Aug., and Nov.
Officers and Directors:* Michael A. Callahan, M.D.*, Pres.; John S. Parker, M.D.*, V.P.; Victor Hugo Marx III, M.D.*, Treas.; Sandra Blackwood, Exec. Dir.; Larry A. Donoso, M.D., Ph.D., Scientific Dir.; Paul Sternberg, Jr., M.D., Scientific Advisor.
Number of staff: 2 full-time professional; 1 part-time support.
EIN: 721342841

42
The Thomas E. Jernigan Foundation ✧
2000 Morris Ave., Ste. 1500
Birmingham, AL 35203-4178

Established in 1986 in AL.
Donors: Thomas E. Jernigan; Marathon Corp.
Foundation type: Independent foundation.
Financial data (yr. ended 03/31/13): Assets, $15,949,473 (M); expenditures, $921,809; qualifying distributions, $672,035; giving activities include $672,035 for grants.
Fields of interest: Museums; Elementary/secondary education; Health organizations; Youth development; Foundations (community); Protestant agencies & churches.
Type of support: General/operating support.
Limitations: Applications not accepted. Giving primarily in AL, with emphasis on Birmingham. No grants to individuals.
Application information: Contributes only to pre-selected organizations.
Officer: Lisa R. Jernigan, Pres.
EIN: 630935852
Selected grants: The following grants are a representative sample of this grantmaker's funding activity:
$159,485 to Mountain Brook High School, Mountain Brook, AL, 2013. To fund athletic programs.
$15,000 to Alabama Wildlife Federation, Millbrook, AL, 2013. For Promotes the Conservation of Alabama's Wildlife.
$15,000 to American Cancer Society, Birmingham, AL, 2013. To fund cancer research.
$10,000 to Birmingham Botanical Gardens, Birmingham, AL, 2013. For Antiques at the Garden.
$5,000 to American Heart Association, Birmingham, AL, 2013. To Fund Cardiovascular Disease Research.

43
The Hugh Kaul Foundation ✧
c/o Regions Bank
P.O. Box 11426
Birmingham, AL 35202-1426 (205) 326-5382
Contact: Carla B. Gale, V.P. and Trust Off., Regions Bank

Established in 1989 in AL.
Donor: Hugh Kaul†.
Foundation type: Independent foundation.
Financial data (yr. ended 12/31/13): Assets, $59,629,646 (M); expenditures, $3,208,287; qualifying distributions, $3,022,495; giving activities include $2,993,000 for 52 grants (high: $550,000; low: $3,000).
Purpose and activities: Giving primarily for arts, education, children and youth services, family services, and community development.
Fields of interest: Arts; Education; Environment; Health care; Human services; Children/youth, services; Family services; Economic development; Community/economic development; Infants/toddlers; Children/youth; Children; Youth; Adults; Aging; Young adults; Disabilities, people with; Physically disabled; Blind/visually impaired; Deaf/hearing impaired; Mentally disabled; Minorities; Asians/Pacific Islanders; African Americans/Blacks; Hispanics/Latinos; Native Americans/American Indians; Indigenous peoples; Women; Infants/toddlers, female; Girls; Adults, women; Young adults, female; Men; Infants/toddlers, male; Adults, men; Young adults, male; Military/veterans; Offenders/ex-offenders; Substance abusers; AIDS, people with; Single parents; Crime/abuse victims; Terminal illness, people with; Immigrants/refugees; Economically disadvantaged; Homeless; Migrant workers.
Type of support: Fellowships; General/operating support; Continuing support; Management development/capacity building; Annual campaigns; Capital campaigns; Building/renovation; Equipment; Land acquisition; Program development; Professorships; Film/video/radio; Publication; Seed money; Curriculum development; Scholarship funds; Research; Technical assistance; Program evaluation; Matching/challenge support.
Limitations: Applications accepted. Giving limited to Jefferson, Clay and Coosa counties, and the greater metropolitan Birmingham, AL, area. No support for religious or political organizations. No grants to individuals.
Publications: Application guidelines.
Application information: Please write or telephone for application guidelines. Application form required.
Initial approach: Proposal
Copies of proposal: 11
Deadline(s): Mar. 1 and Sept. 1
Board meeting date(s): May and Nov.
Final notification: May 31 and Dec. 15
Distribution Committee: H. Corbin Day; Nancy Dunlap; John Kaul Greene; Beverly P. Head III; Don James; John McMahon, Jr.; Hillery Head Perkins; Sam Yates.
Trustee: Regions Bank.
EIN: 636158725

44
Annie Graham King Trust ✧ ☆
P.O. Box 2450
Montgomery, AL 36102-2450

Established in 2009 in AL.
Foundation type: Independent foundation.
Financial data (yr. ended 12/31/13): Assets, $6,808,614 (M); expenditures, $501,289; qualifying distributions, $429,281; giving activities include $420,000 for 13 grants (high: $84,000; low: $3,360).
Fields of interest: Education; Health care; YM/YWCAs & YM/YWHAs; Human services; Protestant agencies & churches.
Limitations: Applications not accepted. Giving primarily in Selma, AL. No grants to individuals.
Application information: Contributes only to pre-selected organizations.
Trustee: Regions Bank Trust Dept.
EIN: 636102496

45
The J. K. Lowder Family Foundation ✧
(formerly James K. and Margaret Lowder Foundation)
5251 Hampstead High St., Ste. 205
Montgomery, AL 36116-6745
Contact: Emily Lowder Wootten, Managing Dir.
FAX: (334) 270-6566; Main URL: http://www.jklowderfamilyfoundation.com

Established in 1995 in AL.
Donors: James K. Lowder; Catherine Lowder; Colonial Company; Servisfirst Bank.
Foundation type: Independent foundation.
Financial data (yr. ended 12/31/12): Assets, $17,177,332 (M); expenditures, $985,917; qualifying distributions, $817,236; giving activities include $775,460 for 51 grants (high: $150,000; low: $160).
Purpose and activities: Giving primarily for arts and culture, education, youth and family programs, community development and revitalization, and human services.
Fields of interest: Arts; Education; Human services; Youth, services; Family services; Community/economic development.
Limitations: Giving primarily in AL. No grants to individuals; no loans.
Publications: Application guidelines; IRS Form 990 or 990-PF printed copy available upon request.
Application information: Unsolicited proposals are not accepted. Full proposals are by invitation only, upon review of application request.
Initial approach: Use application request form on foundation web site
Board meeting date(s): 3 times a year (usually in Apr. Aug., and Dec.)
Officers and Directors:* James K. Lowder,* Pres.; Margaret B. Lowder,* V.P.; Emily L. Wootten, Managing Dir.; Joshua K. Lowder.
EIN: 631139499
Selected grants: The following grants are a representative sample of this grantmaker's funding activity:
$50,000 to Tigers Unlimited Foundation, Auburn, AL, 2012. To support Athletic Program.
$42,000 to Reformed Theological Seminary, Atlanta, GA, 2012. For funding for General Program Expenditures.
$15,000 to Cloverdale Playhouse, Montgomery, AL, 2012. For capital campaign contribution.
$1,000 to Hospice of Montgomery, Montgomery, AL, 2012. For Hospice Fund Raising.

46
The Jane K. Lowe Charitable Foundation ✧
P.O. Box 348
Huntsville, AL 35804-0348 (256) 536-1231
E-mail: janelowe@hiwaay.net; Additional address: 307 Clinton Ave. W., Ste. 305, Huntsville, AL 35801; Main URL: http://www.lowefoundation.org

Established in 1998 in AL.
Donor: Jane K. Lowe†.
Foundation type: Independent foundation.
Financial data (yr. ended 12/31/13): Assets, $35,307,862 (M); expenditures, $1,817,950; qualifying distributions, $1,501,821; giving activities include $1,501,821 for 22 grants (high: $525,636; low: $20,073).
Purpose and activities: Giving primarily for education and youth organizations.
Fields of interest: Higher education; Education; Health care; Boys & girls clubs; Human services; Children/youth, services.
Type of support: General/operating support; Program development; Scholarship funds.
Limitations: Applications accepted. Giving primarily in Madison County, AL. No support for religious organizations for projects that primarily benefit their own members or adherence. No grants to individuals, or for conferences, seminars, special events, productions, performances, research, debt, multi-year grants, or for administrative, program or operating support.
Publications: Application guidelines.
Application information: Telephone inquiries are accepted Mon., Tue., and Thurs., 9:00am-3:00pm. Application form not required.
Initial approach: Proposal
Copies of proposal: 3
Deadline(s): June 1
Final notification: On or before July 15
Trustees: W.F. Sanders, Jr.; Richard J. Smith; John R. Wynn.
Number of staff: 1 full-time professional.
EIN: 636203439
Selected grants: The following grants are a representative sample of this grantmaker's funding activity:
$76,883 to Randolph School, Huntsville, AL, 2012. To provide education.
$21,506 to American Heart Association, Huntsville, AL, 2012. For funding for CPR Anytime Program.
$21,506 to Huntsville Chamber Music Guild, Huntsville, AL, 2012. For funding for Cultural Enrichment Program.
$21,506 to Huntsville Symphony Orchestra, Huntsville, AL, 2012. For funding for Youth Violin Program.

47
The Mapp Family Foundation ✧
P.O. Box 1031
Fairhope, AL 36533-1031 (251) 929-2228
E-mail: info@themappfamilyfoundation.org; Main URL: http://www.themappfamilyfoundation.org

Established in 2002 in AL.
Donors: Mary Elizabeth Faulkner Mapp; Louis Mapp; Mary E.F. Mapp Trust.
Foundation type: Independent foundation.
Financial data (yr. ended 12/31/13): Assets, $11,055,174 (M); gifts received, $456,578; expenditures, $569,100; qualifying distributions, $533,931; giving activities include $491,836 for 59 grants (high: $20,000; low: $2,000).
Purpose and activities: Giving primarily for programs which help people and animals at risk or in need due to unfortunate circumstances, neglect or abuse.
Fields of interest: Arts; Animal welfare; Human services; United Ways and Federated Giving Programs.
Limitations: Applications accepted. Giving primarily in Baldwin County, AL; some giving also in southern AL and in MS. No grants to individuals.
Application information: Application guidelines and form available on foundation web site. Completed applications should be e-mailed or mailed (please do not fax). Application form required.
Initial approach: Download application from web site
Deadline(s): None
Board meeting date(s): Varies
Trustees: Louis E. Mapp.
Agent: Citicorp Trust, N.A.
Number of staff: None.
EIN: 137349796
Selected grants: The following grants are a representative sample of this grantmaker's funding activity:
$5,000 to American Cancer Society, Atlanta, GA, 2011.

48
The Ben May Charitable Trust ✧
c/o Regions Bank
P.O. Box 1628
Mobile, AL 36633-1628 (251) 438-8260
Contact: Kenneth E. Niemeyer
E-mail: ken.niemeyer@regions.com; Main URL: http://benmaycharitable.org

Established in 1971 in Mobile, AL.
Donor: Ben May Trust.
Foundation type: Independent foundation.
Financial data (yr. ended 12/31/13): Assets, $31,971,541 (M); expenditures, $1,467,695; qualifying distributions, $1,330,175; giving activities include $1,158,713 for 72 grants (high: $250,000; low: $1,000).
Purpose and activities: Giving primarily for education, as well as for the arts, human services, and religion.
Fields of interest: Museums; Arts; Secondary school/education; Higher education; Education; Human services; Christian agencies & churches; Protestant agencies & churches; Jewish agencies & synagogues.
Limitations: Applications accepted. Giving primarily in South AL; some giving nationally. No grants to individuals.
Application information: Application form not required.
Initial approach: Letter
Deadline(s): Nov. 1
Distribution Committee: Martin Perlman, M.D., Chair.; Vivian G. Johnston III; Vivian G. Johnston V; Lynette P. Koppel; Allison H. Peebles; John D. Peebles.
Trustee: Regions Bank.
EIN: 237145009
Selected grants: The following grants are a representative sample of this grantmaker's funding activity:
$35,000 to Stanford University, School of Medicine, Stanford, CA, 2012. For general purposes.
$18,000 to University of South Alabama, Mobile, AL, 2012. For Ben May History Project.

49
Mayer Electric Supply Foundation, Inc. ✧
P.O. Box 1328
Birmingham, AL 35201-1328

Established about 1966.
Donors: Charles A. Collat; Mayer Electric Supply Co., Inc.
Foundation type: Company-sponsored foundation.
Financial data (yr. ended 11/30/13): Assets, $11,729,569 (M); gifts received, $1,845,609; expenditures, $1,016,328; qualifying distributions, $916,108; giving activities include $916,108 for 11 grants (high: $400,000; low: $2).
Purpose and activities: The foundation supports hospitals and community foundations and organizations involved with higher education, neurology, children's services, and Judaism.
Fields of interest: Education; Human services; Religion.
Type of support: General/operating support.
Limitations: Applications accepted. Giving primarily in Birmingham, AL. No grants to individuals.
Application information: Application form required.
Initial approach: Letter
Deadline(s): None
Officers and Directors:* Charles A. Collat,* Pres.; Nancy Collat Goedecke,* V.P.; Wes Smith,* V.P.; Charles A. Collat, Jr., Secy.-Treas.
EIN: 630505982

50
D. W. McMillan Foundation ✧
P.O. Box 867
Brewton, AL 36427-0867 (251) 867-4881
Contact: Daniel W. McMillan, Tr.

Established in 1956 in AL.
Donor: D.W. McMillan Trust.
Foundation type: Independent foundation.
Financial data (yr. ended 12/31/13): Assets, $29,347,560 (M); expenditures, $1,579,035; qualifying distributions, $1,316,277; giving activities include $1,220,850 for 61 grants (high: $220,000; low: $3,500).
Purpose and activities: Aid to poor and needy people, including welfare and medical aid, through grants to local health and welfare organizations; limited to programs giving direct aid.
Fields of interest: Hospitals (general); Health care; Health organizations, association; Human services; Children/youth, services; Homeless, human services; Economically disadvantaged.
Type of support: Continuing support; Emergency funds.
Limitations: Applications accepted. Giving limited to Escambia County, AL, and Escambia County FL.
Application information: Application form required.
Initial approach: Proposal
Copies of proposal: 1
Deadline(s): None
Board meeting date(s): Dec. 1
Final notification: Dec. 31
Trustees: John David Finlay, Jr.; Michael N. Hoke; Daniel W. McMillan; Allison R. Sinrod; Robert R. Smith.
Number of staff: 2 part-time support.
EIN: 636044830
Selected grants: The following grants are a representative sample of this grantmaker's funding activity:
$30,000 to Baptist Hospital, Pensacola, FL, 2011.

$10,000 to Covenant Hospice, Pensacola, FL, 2011.
$10,000 to Habitat for Humanity, Pensacola, Pensacola, FL, 2011.
$10,000 to Manna Food Bank, Pensacola, FL, 2011.
$5,000 to Volunteers of America, Alexandria, VA, 2011.

51
McWane Foundation ✧
P.O. Box 43327
Birmingham, AL 35243-0327 (205) 414-3400
Contact: C. Phillip McWane, Tr.
Main URL: http://www.mcwane.com/community/charitable-giving-guidelines/

Established in 1961.
Donor: McWane, Inc.
Foundation type: Company-sponsored foundation.
Financial data (yr. ended 12/31/13): Assets, $712,363 (M); gifts received, $1,493,000; expenditures, $1,516,637; qualifying distributions, $1,504,169; giving activities include $1,504,169 for 50 grants (high: $1,000,000; low: $250).
Purpose and activities: The foundation supports programs designed to promote arts and culture; education; environmental stewardship; heath and safety; and children.
Fields of interest: Museums (science/technology); Arts; Higher education; Education; Health care; Safety/disasters; YM/YWCAs & YM/YWHAs; Children, services.
Type of support: Scholarship funds; General/operating support; Capital campaigns; Matching/challenge support.
Limitations: Applications accepted. Giving primarily in areas of company operations, with emphasis on Birmingham, AL. No support for discriminatory organizations, political organizations, or athletic teams, fraternal orders, sectarian religious or veterans' organizations, or labor associations. No grants to individuals, or for telephone or mass mail appeals.
Publications: Application guidelines.
Application information: Application form not required.
Initial approach: Proposal to the nearest company facility
Copies of proposal: 1
Deadline(s): Mar. 15, June 15, Sept. 14, and Dec. 15
Board meeting date(s): Quarterly
Trustees: John McMahon; C. Phillip McWane.
EIN: 636044384

52
Erie Hall Meyer Charitable Fund, Inc. ✧
P.O. Drawer 2527
Mobile, AL 36652-2527 (251) 432-5511
Application address: c/o Kenneth E. Niemeyer, Pres., 11 N. Water St., 28th Fl., Mobile, AL 36602; (251) 690-1535,
e-mail: ken.niemeyer@regions.com

Established in 1991 in AL.
Donor: Erie H. Meyer†.
Foundation type: Independent foundation.
Financial data (yr. ended 09/30/13): Assets, $13,464,161 (M); expenditures, $790,287; qualifying distributions, $699,703; giving activities include $686,750 for 16 grants (high: $457,500; low: $500).
Fields of interest: Education; Environment; Health organizations; Human services; Community/economic development.
Type of support: General/operating support.
Limitations: Giving primarily in the South Baldwin County, AL, area. No grants to individuals.
Application information: Application form not required.
Initial approach: Letter
Deadline(s): None
Officers and Directors:* Herbert J. Malone, Jr.,* Chair.; Kenneth E. Niemeyer,* Pres.; Neil C. Johnston,* V.P.; Norman D. Pitman III,* Secy.-Treas.
EIN: 631055074

53
Robert R. Meyer Foundation ✧
c/o Regions Bank
P.O. Box 11426
Birmingham, AL 35202-1426 (205) 326-5382
Contact: Carla B. Gale, V.P. and Trust Off., Regions Bank

Trust established in 1942 in AL.
Donors: Robert R. Meyer†; John E. Meyer†.
Foundation type: Independent foundation.
Financial data (yr. ended 12/31/13): Assets, $42,744,169 (M); expenditures, $2,159,874; qualifying distributions, $1,967,332; giving activities include $1,922,142 for 84 grants (high: $100,000; low: $1,000).
Purpose and activities: Aid largely to local health and welfare organizations, educational institutions, and cultural organizations selected by an advisory committee.
Fields of interest: Arts; Education; Environment; Hospitals (general); Health care; Health organizations, association; Human services; Infants/toddlers; Children/youth; Children; Youth; Adults; Aging; Young adults; Disabilities, people with; Physically disabled; Blind/visually impaired; Deaf/hearing impaired; Mentally disabled; Minorities; African Americans/Blacks; Hispanics/Latinos; Women; Infants/toddlers, female; Girls; Young adults, female; Men; Infants/toddlers, male; Boys; Adults, men; Young adults, male; Military/veterans; Offenders/ex-offenders; Substance abusers; AIDS, people with; Single parents; Crime/abuse victims; Terminal illness, people with; Economically disadvantaged; Homeless.
Type of support: General/operating support; Continuing support; Management development/capacity building; Capital campaigns; Building/renovation; Equipment; Land acquisition; Program development; Film/video/radio; Publication; Curriculum development; Scholarship funds; Research; Technical assistance; Program evaluation; Matching/challenge support.
Limitations: Applications accepted. Giving limited to the greater Birmingham, AL, area. No grants to individuals, or for endowment funds.
Publications: Application guidelines.
Application information: Grant guidelines are available upon request. Application form required.
Initial approach: Proposal (no more than 4 pages)
Copies of proposal: 7
Deadline(s): Mar. 1 and Sept. 1
Board meeting date(s): May and Dec.
Final notification: Mid June and mid Dec.
Advisory Committee: Beverly Baker; Sharon L. Blackburn; Raymond Harbert; Elmer E. Harris.
Trustee: Regions Bank.
EIN: 636019645

54
Abraham A. Mitchell Charitable Foundation ✧
P.O. Box 16006
Mobile, AL 36616-0006

Established in 1986 in AL.
Donor: Abraham A. Mitchell.
Foundation type: Independent foundation.
Financial data (yr. ended 12/31/13): Assets, $3,167,731 (M); expenditures, $1,664,813; qualifying distributions, $1,644,771; giving activities include $1,644,771 for 14 grants (high: $991,500; low: $500).
Fields of interest: Business school/education; Theological school/education; Health organizations, association; Medical research, institute; Aging, centers/services; Jewish agencies & synagogues; Aging.
Limitations: Applications not accepted. Giving primarily in AL, Washington, DC, GA, and NY. No grants to individuals.
Application information: Unsolicited requests for funds not accepted.
Officers: Abraham A. Mitchell, Pres.; Jay Weber, V.P.; Robert Weber, Secy.-Treas.
EIN: 630935457
Selected grants: The following grants are a representative sample of this grantmaker's funding activity:
$77,864 to Congregation Ahavas Chesed, Mobile, AL, 2011.
$50,000 to American Israel Education Foundation, Washington, DC, 2010.
$50,000 to American Israel Education Foundation, Washington, DC, 2011.
$50,000 to Camp Ramah Darom, Atlanta, GA, 2011.
$3,000 to University of South Alabama, Mobile, AL, 2011.

55
A. S. Mitchell Foundation, Inc. ✧
(formerly The Mitchell Foundation, Inc.)
P.O. Box 1126
Mobile, AL 36633-1126

Incorporated in 1957 in AL.
Donors: A.S. Mitchell†; Mrs. A.S. Mitchell†.
Foundation type: Independent foundation.
Financial data (yr. ended 01/31/13): Assets, $16,095,583 (M); expenditures, $985,656; qualifying distributions, $600,000; giving activities include $600,000 for grants.
Purpose and activities: Giving primarily for education, as well as for historical preservation, human services, health associations, and for United Methodist Church support.
Fields of interest: Historic preservation/historical societies; Higher education; Education; Environment, natural resources; Health organizations, association; Human services; Protestant agencies & churches.
Limitations: Applications not accepted. Giving in the U.S., primarily in AL and GA. No grants to individuals.

Application information: Contributes only to pre-selected organizations.
Board meeting date(s): Quarterly
Officers and Directors:* Augustine Meaher III,* Pres.; Frank B. Vinson, Jr.,* V.P.; David D. Dukes,* Secy.-Treas.; Joanna Vinson Blythe; Jane Dukes; Joseph L. Meaher; Margaret Meaher; Benjamin Vinson; Kenneth G. Vinson.
Number of staff: 1 full-time support.
EIN: 630368954
Selected grants: The following grants are a representative sample of this grantmaker's funding activity:
$10,000 to Tulane University, New Orleans, LA, 2010.
$10,000 to Tulane University, New Orleans, LA, 2011.
$5,000 to Cystic Fibrosis Foundation, Bethesda, MD, 2010.
$5,000 to Saint Jude Childrens Research Hospital, Memphis, TN, 2011.

56
The Nabers Charitable Foundation ✧
800 Lakeshore Dr., Brooks Hall 227
Birmingham, AL 35229

Established in 1998 in AL.
Donor: Drayton Nabers, Jr.
Foundation type: Independent foundation.
Financial data (yr. ended 12/31/13): Assets, $13,686,746 (M); gifts received, $151,670; expenditures, $803,466; qualifying distributions, $729,433; giving activities include $729,433 for 13 grants (high: $510,000; low: $200).
Purpose and activities: Giving primarily to Christian churches and agencies, and for education.
Fields of interest: Arts; Education; Human services; Children/youth, services; Christian agencies & churches; Protestant agencies & churches.
Limitations: Applications not accepted. Giving primarily in AL, with emphasis on Birmingham. No grants to individuals.
Application information: Contributes only to pre-selected organizations.
Officers: Drayton Nabers, Jr., Pres.; Fairfax Smathers Nabers, Secy.; Mary Nabers Doyle, Treas.
EIN: 631189714
Selected grants: The following grants are a representative sample of this grantmaker's funding activity:
$190,000 to National Christian Foundation, Alpharetta, GA, 2011.
$5,000 to Alabama Policy Institute, Birmingham, AL, 2010.

57
The Hermoine & Glen Nelson Foundation ✧
c/o Regions Bank Trust Dept.
P.O. Box 2886
Mobile, AL 36652-2886

Established in 1987 in TN.
Donor: Hermoine Corlew Adkisson.
Foundation type: Independent foundation.
Financial data (yr. ended 12/31/13): Assets, $12,513,963 (M); expenditures, $818,187; qualifying distributions, $742,012; giving activities include $740,000 for 10 grants (high: $500,000; low: $10).
Purpose and activities: Support primarily for health care, education, including Protestant schools and colleges, and children, youth and social services.
Fields of interest: Elementary/secondary education; Higher education; Hospitals (specialty); Health organizations, association; Human services; Children/youth, services; Protestant agencies & churches.
Limitations: Applications not accepted. Giving primarily in TN. No grants to individuals.
Application information: Contributes only to pre-selected organizations.
Officers: Barbara Nelson Lamberson, Pres.; Nelson Lamberson, V.P.; Thomas Lamberson, V.P.
Directors: Mike Childree; Claudia Lamberson.
EIN: 621317088
Selected grants: The following grants are a representative sample of this grantmaker's funding activity:
$25,000 to Empower Me Day Camp, Lebanon, TN, 2012. To support Educational and Healthcare Activities.

58
Pleiad Foundation ✧
2140 Warwick Dr.
Birmingham, AL 35209-1362 (205) 322-3302
Contact: Carrie C. McMahon, Pres.
Main URL: http://pleiadfoundation.org/

Established in 1995 in AL.
Donors: Betty T. McMahon; John J. McMahon, Jr.; David A. McMahon; Joel W. McMahon; John J. McMahon III; Buffalo News, Inc.; McCloud Investments; MacCloud Investment Company, LLC; Pleiad Partners, L.P.
Foundation type: Independent foundation.
Financial data (yr. ended 12/31/13): Assets, $8,788,771 (M); gifts received, $161,150; expenditures, $931,882; qualifying distributions, $811,500; giving activities include $811,500 for 30 grants (high: $300,000; low: $1,000).
Fields of interest: Arts; Higher education; Education; Human services.
Limitations: Applications accepted. Giving in Birmingham, AL.
Application information: Application form not required.
Initial approach: Proposal
Deadline(s): None
Officer: Carrie C. McMahon, Pres.
Directors: Ashley R. McMahon; Betty T. McMahon; David A. McMahon; Joel W. McMahon; John J. McMahon, Jr.; John J. McMahon III.
EIN: 631159236

59
Protective Life Foundation ✧
P.O. Box 2606
Birmingham, AL 35202-2606 (205) 268-4434
Contact: Kate H. Cotton, Exec. Dir.
FAX: (205) 268-5547;
E-mail: kate.cotton@protective.com; Main URL: http://www.protective.com/giving-back.aspx

Established in 1994 in AL.
Donor: Protective Life Insurance Co.
Foundation type: Company-sponsored foundation.
Financial data (yr. ended 12/31/13): Assets, $27,440 (M); gifts received, $2,520,000; expenditures, $2,611,602; qualifying distributions, $2,524,303; giving activities include $2,394,508 for 181 grants (high: $420,725; low: $50), and $29,795 for 45 grants to individuals (high: $2,500; low: $150).
Purpose and activities: The foundation supports organizations involved with arts and culture, education and literacy, health and human services, and the environment and community revitalization.
Fields of interest: Performing arts, orchestras; Historical activities; Arts; Elementary school/education; Higher education; Education, reading; Education; Environment; Hospitals (general); Health care; Food banks; Recreation, parks/playgrounds; YM/YWCAs & YM/YWHAs; Children/youth, services; Human services; Civil/human rights; Community/economic development; United Ways and Federated Giving Programs.
Type of support: General/operating support; Continuing support; Annual campaigns; Capital campaigns; Program development; Scholarship funds; Research; Sponsorships; Employee matching gifts; Employee-related scholarships.
Limitations: Applications accepted. Giving primarily in areas of company operations in the metro Birmingham, AL, area. Generally, no support for K-12 public or private schools, churches, public facilities, or state organizations, or other corporate or private foundations. Generally, no grants for animal-related causes, sporting events, walks, or runs, or start-up costs.
Publications: Application guidelines; Annual report.
Application information: Proposals should be submitted using organization letterhead and should be no longer than 4 pages. Support is limited to 1 contribution per organization during any given year. Application form not required.
Initial approach: Proposal
Copies of proposal: 1
Deadline(s): Feb. 17, May 15, Aug. 15, and Nov. 17
Board meeting date(s): Mar., June, Sept., and Dec.
Final notification: Varies
Officers: John D. Johns,* Pres.; Kate H. Cotton,* Secy. and Exec. Dir.
Advisory Council: Holly Brown; Sallie Bryant; Aldrich Callins; Patty Cobb; Rita E. Fulton; Ben W. Ingram; Ellen A. Michael; Kevin Sullivan; Sherri D. Swickard.
Number of staff: 1 full-time professional; 1 part-time professional.
EIN: 631129596

60
The Psalm 67 Foundation ✧ ☆
2500 Acton Rd.
Birmingham, AL 35243

Donors: David J. Platt; Heather B. Platt.
Foundation type: Independent foundation.
Financial data (yr. ended 12/31/13): Assets, $2,179,130 (M); expenditures, $489,600; qualifying distributions, $489,600; giving activities include $489,600 for 11 grants (high: $297,500; low: $5,000).
Fields of interest: Environment; Human services; Religion.
Limitations: Applications not accepted. Giving primarily in AL, CO and TX.
Application information: Unsolicited requests for funds not accepted.
Officer: James A. Warren, Exec. Dir.
Trustees: David J. Platt; Heather B. Platt.
EIN: 452041448

61
Regions Financial Corporation Foundation ✧
(formerly Regions Bancorporation Foundation)
c/o Regions Bank
P.O. Box 2886
Mobile, AL 36652-2886

Established in 1997 in AL.
Donors: AmSouth Bank; AmSouth Bancorporation; Regions Financial Corp.; Regions Morgan Keegan Trust; Regions Bank.
Foundation type: Company-sponsored foundation.
Financial data (yr. ended 12/31/13): Assets, $46,856 (M); gifts received, $500,000; expenditures, $968,273; qualifying distributions, $967,373; giving activities include $967,373 for 440 grants (high: $200,000; low: $25).
Purpose and activities: The foundation supports organizations involved with health, housing, and human services. Special emphasis is directed toward education and arts and culture.
Fields of interest: Arts; Education; Health care.
Type of support: General/operating support; Continuing support; Employee matching gifts.
Limitations: Applications accepted. Giving primarily in AL and FL; some giving also in GA and TN. No support for religious organizations not of direct benefit to the entire community, political organizations, or alumni groups. No grants to individuals, or for cultural or social events.
Application information: Application form required.
Initial approach: Completed application form
Deadline(s): None
Officers and Directors:* Fournier J. Gale III,* Pres.; Douglas J. Jackson,* V.P.; Dale M. Herbert, Secy.; Ann W. Forney, Treas.; David B. Edmonds; William D. Ritter.
Trustee: Regions Bank.
EIN: 631144265
Selected grants: The following grants are a representative sample of this grantmaker's funding activity:
$200,000 to University of Alabama, Tuscaloosa, AL, 2011.
$4,960 to University of Alabama, Tuscaloosa, AL, 2011.
$3,705 to University of Alabama, Tuscaloosa, AL, 2011.
$3,350 to University of Tennessee, Knoxville, TN, 2011.
$2,960 to University of Alabama, Tuscaloosa, AL, 2011.
$2,684 to University of Alabama, Tuscaloosa, AL, 2011.
$2,055 to University of Alabama, Tuscaloosa, AL, 2011.
$1,100 to University of North Carolina, Chapel Hill, NC, 2011.
$1,050 to University of North Carolina, Chapel Hill, NC, 2011.
$1,030 to University of Tennessee, Knoxville, TN, 2011.

62
W. Earl Richards Charitable Foundation, Inc. ✧
2000 Morris Ave., Ste. 1300
Birmingham, AL 35203-4163

Established in 2005 in AL.
Donors: William Earl Richards†; Association of Related Churches; Vapor Thrift Stores; Kenneth H. Polk; Kenworth of Birmingham; TP Land, LLC.
Foundation type: Independent foundation.
Financial data (yr. ended 12/31/13): Assets, $18,403,807 (M); gifts received, $1,004,126; expenditures, $1,960,383; qualifying distributions, $1,196,993; giving activities include $1,196,993 for 10 grants (high: $460,000; low: $72).
Fields of interest: Christian agencies & churches.
Limitations: Applications not accepted. Giving primarily in AL. No grants to individuals.
Application information: Contributes only to pre-selected organizations.
Officers: Mark J. Brown, Pres. and Secy.; Kenneth H. Polk, V.P. and Treas.
EIN: 201939160

63
Benjamin & Roberta Russell Foundation, Inc. ✧
(formerly Benjamin and Roberta Russell Educational and Charitable Foundation, Inc.)
P.O. Box 369
Alexander City, AL 35011-0369
Contact: James D. Nabors, Secy.-Treas.

Incorporated in 1944 in AL.
Donor: Benjamin Russell.
Foundation type: Independent foundation.
Financial data (yr. ended 12/31/13): Assets, $15,708,608 (M); expenditures, $787,788; qualifying distributions, $623,500; giving activities include $444,000 for 15 grants (high: $184,000; low: $3,000), and $179,500 for grants to individuals.
Purpose and activities: Giving for higher and public education, youth programs, and a hospital.
Fields of interest: Higher education; Education; Hospitals (general); Youth development, services; Children/youth, services.
Type of support: General/operating support; Scholarship funds.
Limitations: Applications not accepted. Giving limited to AL; scholarship funds limited to Tallapoosa and Coosa counties. No grants to individuals (except for scholarships).
Application information: Unsolicited requests for funds not accepted.
Directors: Earl C. Baumgardner; James W. Brown, Jr.; Julia Goree; Nancy R. Gwaltney; Adelia R. Hendrix; James D. Nabors; Benjamin Russell.
EIN: 630393126

64
Scott Foundation, Inc. ✧
2641 Interstate Dr.
Opelika, AL 36804 (334) 749-5045
Contact: I.J. Scott III, Dir.

Established in 2005 in AL.
Donors: Scott Bridge Company, Inc.; Ike Scott; Coye Yeager.
Foundation type: Company-sponsored foundation.
Financial data (yr. ended 12/31/12): Assets, $11,472,591 (M); gifts received, $1,819,116; expenditures, $808,673; qualifying distributions, $751,002; giving activities include $704,900 for 14 + grants (high: $88,000).
Purpose and activities: The foundation supports organizations involved with human services and religion.
Fields of interest: Education; Human services; Religion.
Type of support: General/operating support.
Limitations: Applications accepted. Giving primarily in AL, CO, FL, and MA, and in Honduras.
Application information: Application form not required.
Initial approach: Proposal
Deadline(s): None
Directors: I.J. Scott III; William M. Scott; Gerard Swarthout III.
EIN: 161744259

65
Louise Maytag Smith Charitable Trust ✧
P.O. Box 2450
Montgomery, AL 36102-2450

Established in 1964; supporting organization of The Berry Schools, Boy Scouts Service Center, Huntington College, Salvation Army, School of the Ozarks, Southern Research Institute, United Appeal, and YMCA.
Foundation type: Independent foundation.
Financial data (yr. ended 12/31/13): Assets, $15,228,836 (M); expenditures, $729,966; qualifying distributions, $611,179; giving activities include $611,179 for 8 grants (high: $111,846; low: $37,282).
Fields of interest: Higher education; Human services; Salvation Army; YM/YWCAs & YM/YWHAs; United Ways and Federated Giving Programs.
Limitations: Applications not accepted. Giving primarily in AL; funding also in GA and MO.
Application information: Contributes only to pre-selected organizations; unsolicited requests for funds not considered or acknowledged.
Trustee: Regions Trust Dept.
EIN: 636050879
Selected grants: The following grants are a representative sample of this grantmaker's funding activity:
$126,069 to Southern Research Institute, Birmingham, AL, 2012. For Life Sciences Research.

66
Sybil H. Smith Charitable Trust ✧
6 Saint Joseph St.
Mobile, AL 36602-3502 (251) 432-0208
Contact: Mary L. Cousar
FAX: (251) 432-0209;
E-mail: smthtrst@bellsouth.net

Established in 1983 in AL.
Donor: Sybil H. Smith†.
Foundation type: Independent foundation.
Financial data (yr. ended 07/31/13): Assets, $26,020,211 (M); expenditures, $1,288,302; qualifying distributions, $1,256,689; giving activities include $1,002,725 for 35 grants (high: $145,000; low: $2,500).
Purpose and activities: Giving primarily for education and human services; some emphasis on funding for the arts.
Fields of interest: Arts councils; Performing arts; Arts; Elementary/secondary education; Higher education; Education; Human services; Children/

youth, services; Community/economic development.
Type of support: Annual campaigns; Capital campaigns; Building/renovation; Equipment; Consulting services; Matching/challenge support.
Limitations: Giving primarily in the 1st Congressional District of Mobile, AL. No support for political organizations. No grants to individuals or for higher education.
Publications: Annual report; Grants list.
Application information: Application form not required.
Initial approach: Letter
Copies of proposal: 5
Deadline(s): 15th of the month prior to meetings
Board meeting date(s): 1st Mon. in Feb., May, Aug., and Nov.
Final notification: Varies
Committee Members: Ann Smith Bedsole, Chair.; Lorraine B. Demas; John H. Martin III; Mary Martin Riser.
Trustee: Iberia Bank.
Number of staff: 1 full-time professional.
EIN: 636128407

67
J. Craig and Page T. Smith Scholarship Foundation, Inc. ✧ ☆
400 Caldwell Trace Park
Indian Springs, AL 35242 (205) 202-4076
Contact: Ahrian Tyler Dudley, C.E.O.

Established in 2005 in AL.
Foundation type: Operating foundation.
Financial data (yr. ended 12/31/12): Assets, $30,545,848 (M); gifts received, $23,785,249; expenditures, $1,281,428; qualifying distributions, $986,945; giving activities include $573,587 for grants to individuals.
Purpose and activities: The foundation funds college scholarships for deserving students throughout Alabama, with special consideration given to applicants who would be the first in their mother's and/or father's families to attend college.
Fields of interest: Higher education.
Type of support: Scholarships—to individuals.
Limitations: Applications accepted. Giving limited to AL.
Application information: Application form required.
Initial approach: Letter
Deadline(s): Jan. 15
Officer and Directors:* Ahrian Tyler Dudley,* Exec. Dir.; Lewis G. Burks, Jr.; June Cunniff; C.R. Dudley, Jr.; Stewart R. Dudley; Helen Crow Mills.
Trustees: Barbara J. Belisle; Michael K.K. Choy, Esq.; Deivid Delgado; Richard H. Gill, Esq.; Jason Leger; Fred Phillips; Stephen Powell; Kenneth O. Simon, Esq.; Keith Walker; and 4 additional trustees.
EIN: 202224138

68
Snook Foundation ✧
P.O. Box 1267
Foley, AL 36536 (251) 952-5810
Contact: Brenda Lee, Exec. Dir.
Main URL: http://www.thesnookfoundation.com/

Established in AL.
Donor: Marjorie Y. Snook.
Foundation type: Independent foundation.
Financial data (yr. ended 12/31/13): Assets, $38,816,734 (M); expenditures, $2,240,693; qualifying distributions, $2,326,268; giving activities include $1,677,470 for 40 grants (high: $400,000; low: $3,000).
Fields of interest: Education, single organization support; Education, fund raising/fund distribution; Education; United Ways and Federated Giving Programs.
Limitations: Applications accepted. Giving primarily in AL. No grants to individuals.
Application information: Application form required.
Initial approach: Request application form
Deadline(s): None
Trustees: Rosemary Johnston; William L. Lambert; Lester Smith; Marjorie Y. Snook; M. Mort Swaim.
EIN: 237250795

69
Stephens Foundation ✧
P.O. Box 1943
Birmingham, AL 35201-1943

Established in 1991.
Donors: Elton B. Stephens†; Dell S. Brooke.
Foundation type: Independent foundation.
Financial data (yr. ended 12/31/13): Assets, $8,349,016 (M); expenditures, $1,106,586; qualifying distributions, $1,074,000; giving activities include $1,074,000 for 71 grants (high: $500,000; low: $250).
Purpose and activities: Giving primarily for the arts, education, health associations, and to a United Methodist church.
Fields of interest: Arts education; Performing arts centers; Performing arts, orchestras; Arts; Education; Health organizations, association; Protestant agencies & churches.
Type of support: General/operating support.
Limitations: Applications not accepted. Giving primarily in AL, with some emphasis on Birmingham and Huntsville. No grants to individuals.
Application information: Contributes only to pre-selected organizations.
Officers: James T. Stephens, Pres.; Jane S. Comer, V.P.; Dell S. Brooke, Secy.; Elton B. Stephens, Jr., Treas.
EIN: 631035698

70
The Thompson Foundation, Inc. ✧
P.O. Box 10367
Birmingham, AL 35202-0367

Established in 1997 in AL.
Donors: Lisa Thompson-Smith; Michael D. Thompson; Thompson Tractor Co.
Foundation type: Independent foundation.
Financial data (yr. ended 12/31/13): Assets, $7,195,731 (M); gifts received, $3,500,000; expenditures, $1,310,581; qualifying distributions, $1,225,492; giving activities include $1,186,844 for 191 grants (high: $200,000; low: $200).
Purpose and activities: Giving for art and cultural programs, education, youth services, and health associations; funding also for health and social services.
Fields of interest: Arts; Higher education; Education; Environment; Zoos/zoological societies; Health organizations; Human services; Children/youth, services; United Ways and Federated Giving Programs; Christian agencies & churches.
Limitations: Applications not accepted. Giving primarily in AL. No grants to individuals.
Application information: Contributes only to pre-selected organizations.
Officers: Michael D. Thompson, Pres.; Lucy Thompson Marsh, V.P.; Benjamin H. Thompson, Secy.-Treas.
Directors: Jacob Marsh; Hall W. Thompson, Jr.; Netagene R. Thompson; Patricia A. Thompson; Lisa Thompson-Smith.
EIN: 721389140

71
The Joseph Treadwell Charitable Foundation ✧
c/o Trustmark National Bank
P.O. Box 3067
Mobile, AL 36652-3067

Established in 1988 in AL.
Donor: Joseph Treadwell†.
Foundation type: Independent foundation.
Financial data (yr. ended 12/31/13): Assets, $9,898,203 (M); expenditures, $892,154; qualifying distributions, $766,554; giving activities include $766,554 for 19 grants (high: $237,318; low: $5,000).
Fields of interest: Higher education; Human services; Salvation Army.
Type of support: General/operating support.
Limitations: Applications not accepted. Giving primarily in Mobile, AL. No grants to individuals.
Application information: Contributes only to pre-selected organizations.
Managers: Vincent F. Kilborn; Ralph "Sonny" Middleton; John H. Wilson.
Trustee: Trustmark National Bank.
EIN: 570880131

72
Dr. W.H. Turner and Sara Elizabeth Turner Medical Trust ✧
c/o Regions Morgan Keegan Trust
P.O. Box 11426
Birmingham, AL 35202-1426
Contact: Carla B. Gale, Sr. V.P. and Dir., Endowments and Foundations
Application address: c/o Jill Smith, Exec. Dir., Houston County Medical Society, P.O. Box 5527, Dothan, AL 36302-5527

Established in 2000.
Foundation type: Independent foundation.
Financial data (yr. ended 10/31/13): Assets, $15,525,280 (M); expenditures, $822,590; qualifying distributions, $737,973; giving activities include $720,888 for 6 grants (high: $386,646; low: $17,604).
Purpose and activities: The foundation grants scholarships to students from the Dothan, AL, area who are attending medical school, or who are engaged in a full-time course of study leading ultimately to a Doctor of Medicine degree. Scholarships are not paid directly to the individuals.
Fields of interest: Medical school/education.
Limitations: Applications accepted. Giving primarily in the Dothan, AL, area (for medical school scholarships). No grants to individuals directly.
Publications: Annual report.

Application information: Application form required.
Initial approach: Request application form from Jill W. Smith, Exec. Dir., HCMS
Copies of proposal: 2
Deadline(s): May 1
Board meeting date(s): May
Final notification: 2 months
Trustee: Regions Bank.
EIN: 636219873
Selected grants: The following grants are a representative sample of this grantmaker's funding activity:
$54,607 to University of South Alabama, College of Medicine, Mobile, AL, 2012.
$52,167 to Des Moines University Osteopathic Medical Center, Des Moines, IA, 2012.
$51,841 to University of South Alabama, College of Medicine, Mobile, AL, 2012.
$51,841 to University of South Alabama, School of Medicine, Mobile, AL, 2012.
$49,094 to University of South Carolina, School of Medicine, Columbia, SC, 2012.
$45,793 to University of Alabama, School of Medicine, Tuscaloosa, AL, 2012.
$45,577 to University of Alabama, School of Medicine, Tuscaloosa, AL, 2012.
$45,577 to University of Alabama, School of Medicine, Tuscaloosa, AL, 2012.
$45,577 to University of Alabama, School of Medicine, Tuscaloosa, AL, 2012.
$45,577 to University of Alabama, School of Medicine, Tuscaloosa, AL, 2012.
$45,577 to University of Alabama, School of Medicine, Tuscaloosa, AL, 2012.
$45,564 to University of Alabama, Tuscaloosa, AL, 2012.
$45,564 to University of Alabama, School of Medicine, Tuscaloosa, AL, 2012.
$26,642 to Auburn University, Auburn, AL, 2012.
$22,780 to University of Alabama, School of Medicine, Tuscaloosa, AL, 2012.
$22,642 to Auburn University, Auburn, AL, 2012.

73
Vulcan Materials Company Foundation ✧

P.O. Box 385014
Birmingham, AL 35238-5014 (205) 298-3222
Contact: Carol B. Maxwell, Secy.-Treas.
E-mail: giving@vmcmail.com; Additional tel.: (205) 298-3229; Main URL: http://www.vulcanmaterials.com/sustainability/community/vulcan-foundation

Established in 1987 in AL.
Donors: Vulcan Materials Co.; Vulcan Lands Inc.; Calmat Co.; Legacy Vulvan Corp.-Western.
Foundation type: Company-sponsored foundation.
Financial data (yr. ended 11/30/13): Assets, $4,848,236 (M); gifts received, $1,658,050; expenditures, $1,690,138; qualifying distributions, $1,650,227; giving activities include $1,650,224 for 510 grants (high: $144,000).
Purpose and activities: The foundation supports programs designed to work with schools; support environmental stewardship; and encourage employee involvement.
Fields of interest: Education, reform; Elementary/secondary education; Higher education; Engineering school/education; Environment, natural resources; Environment; Animals/wildlife, preservation/protection; Animals/wildlife; Recreation, parks/playgrounds; Business/industry; Science, formal/general education; Mathematics.
Type of support: General/operating support; Continuing support; Annual campaigns; Capital campaigns; Endowments; Program development; Seed money; Scholarship funds; Employee volunteer services; Employee-related scholarships; Matching/challenge support.
Limitations: Applications accepted. Giving primarily in areas of company operations, with emphasis on Birmingham, AL. No support for political organizations, athletic, labor, fraternal, or veterans' organizations, discriminatory organizations, or private foundations. No grants to individuals (except for employee-related scholarships), or for telephone or mass mail appeals, testimonial dinners, or sectarian religious activities.
Publications: Application guidelines; Annual report (including application guidelines).
Application information: E-mail foundation for local Charitable Contributions Officer contact information. Proposals should be no longer than 1 to 2 pages. Application form not required.
Initial approach: Proposal to nearest Charitable Contributions Officer; proposal to foundation for organizations located in the Birmingham, AL, area
Copies of proposal: 1
Deadline(s): None
Board meeting date(s): Quarterly
Officers and Trustees:* Donald M. James,* Chair.; Michael R. Mills,* Pres.; David A. Donaldson, V.P.; Carol B. Maxwell, Secy.-Treas.; Daniel F. Sansone; Danny R. Shepherd; J. Wayne Houston.
Number of staff: 1 full-time professional; 1 part-time support.
EIN: 630971859

74
Walker Area Community Foundation ✧

611 8th Ave.
Jasper, AL 35501 (205) 302-0001
Contact: Cristy Moody, Prog. Off.; For grants: Sandy Vaughn, Admin. Coord.
FAX: (205) 302-0424; E-mail: mhudson@wacf.org; Additional E-mail: contact@wacf.org; Grant application E-mail: svaughn@wacf.org; Mailing address: Post Office Box 171 Jasper, Alabama 35502-0171; Main URL: http://www.wacf.org
Facebook: https://www.facebook.com/pages/Walker-Area-Community-Foundation/161387217212292
LinkedIn: http://www.linkedin.com/company/walker-area-community-foundation?trk=tyah&trkInfo=tarId%3A1406047951980%2Ctas%3Awalker+area%2Cidx%3A3-1-5
Twitter: https://twitter.com/wacf

Established in 1995 from a portion of sale of local hospital.
Foundation type: Community foundation.
Financial data (yr. ended 12/31/13): Assets, $23,900,783 (M); gifts received, $1,190,813; expenditures, $3,672,171; giving activities include $3,065,770 for 40+ grants (high: $1,474,882).
Purpose and activities: The mission of the foundation is to serve as a nonprofit dedicated to the nurture and advancement of the community through forming and preserving charitable capital and using the proceeds of that capital to better the community as a whole. Grants may be made in the following areas: arts and humanities, children and youth, education, elder care, the environment, health and medicine, recreation, and social welfare.
Fields of interest: Humanities; Arts; Education; Environment; Health care; Recreation; Children/youth, services; Aging, centers/services; Human services; Community/economic development; Children/youth.
Type of support: General/operating support; Management development/capacity building; Capital campaigns; Building/renovation; Equipment; Emergency funds; Program development; Conferences/seminars; Seed money; Curriculum development; Technical assistance; Program evaluation; In-kind gifts; Matching/challenge support.
Limitations: Applications accepted. Giving limited to Walker County, AL. No support for religious organizations for religious purposes. No grants to individuals, or for endowments, ticketed events, or for replacement of government funding.
Publications: Application guidelines; Annual report; Financial statement; Grants list; Informational brochure; Newsletter.
Application information: Visit foundation web site for application form and guidelines. Applications may be mailed or e-mailed to the foundation. Application form required.
Initial approach: Submit application form and attachments
Copies of proposal: 1
Deadline(s): Mar. 1 and Sept. 1
Board meeting date(s): Distribution Comm. meets in Apr. and Oct.
Final notification: Within 2 weeks of board meetings
Officers and Directors:* Edward R. Jackson,* Chair.; W. Haig Wright II,* Vice-Chair.; Paul W. Kennedy,* Pres.; Russell B. Robertson,* Secy.-Treas.; Jack G. Allen; Robbin Allen; Abbie Drummond; Steven Globetti; John T. Oliver, Jr.; Barbara D. Thorne Stukes; Doug Warren.
Number of staff: 1 full-time professional; 2 part-time professional.
EIN: 631154984

75
Warner Foundation, Inc. ✧

2705 Battlement Dr. N.E.
Tuscaloosa, AL 35406-1103

Established in AL.
Donor: Jack Warner Foundation, Inc.
Foundation type: Independent foundation.
Financial data (yr. ended 12/31/12): Assets, $5,644,502 (M); gifts received, $1,445,570; expenditures, $2,194,968; qualifying distributions, $1,980,000; giving activities include $1,980,000 for grants.
Purpose and activities: Giving primarily for art history preservation.
Fields of interest: Museums (art).
Limitations: Applications not accepted. Giving primarily in NY.
Application information: Unsolicited requests for funds not accepted.
Directors: Susan G. Austin; Janet Dill; Andreae Lemaistre; Charles Lemaistre; Vaughan Morrissette; Jerry Phillips; Jonathan W. Warner.
EIN: 263311211

76
Susan Mott Webb Charitable Trust ✧
P.O. Box 2886
Mobile, AL 36652-2886
Application address: c/o Barbara Hays Watson, Regions Bank, P.O. Box 1688, Birmingham, AL 35202-1688, tel.: (205) 264-5754

Established in 1978 in AL.
Donor: Susan Mott Webb†.
Foundation type: Independent foundation.
Financial data (yr. ended 12/31/13): Assets, $16,646,419 (M); expenditures, $926,711; qualifying distributions, $850,269; giving activities include $833,500 for 77 grants (high: $50,000; low: $3,000).
Purpose and activities: Emphasis on supporting charitable organizations in the Birmingham, Alabama, area only.
Fields of interest: Arts; Education; Animals/wildlife; Health care; Human services; Youth, services; Urban/community development; Christian agencies & churches; General charitable giving; Homeless.
Type of support: General/operating support; Continuing support; Annual campaigns; Capital campaigns; Building/renovation; Equipment; Endowments; Emergency funds; Program development; Publication; Curriculum development; Internship funds; Technical assistance.
Limitations: Applications accepted. Giving limited to the greater Birmingham, AL, area. No grants to individuals, or for scholarships or fellowships; no loans.
Publications: Application guidelines.
Application information: Application form required.
Initial approach: Completed application form
Deadline(s): Mar. 1 and Sept. 1
Trustees: Suzanne Dansby Bollman; Nina Botsford; Stewart M. Dansby; Regions Bank.
EIN: 636112593
Selected grants: The following grants are a representative sample of this grantmaker's funding activity:
$25,000 to Alabama School of Fine Arts, Birmingham, AL, 2011.
$20,000 to Alabama Symphony Association, Birmingham, AL, 2011.
$15,000 to Alabama Humanities Foundation, Birmingham, AL, 2011.
$10,000 to Alcohol and Drug Abuse Council, Birmingham, AL, 2011.
$5,000 to Alabama Appleseed Center for Law and Justice, Montgomery, AL, 2011.
$5,000 to Nonprofit Resource Center of Alabama, Birmingham, AL, 2011.

77
Wiregrass Foundation
1532 Whatley Dr.
Dothan, AL 36303-1984 (334) 699-1031
Contact: Cindy Bedsole, V.P., Admin. and Grants; Dr. Barbara Alford, Pres.
FAX: (334) 669-2472;
E-mail: Barbara@wiregrassfoundation.org; E-mail address for Cindy White, V.P., Admin. and Grants: cindy@wiregrassfoundation.org; Main URL: http://www.wiregrassfoundation.org
Grants List: http://www.wiregrassfoundation.org/grants-1/

Established in 2003 in AL.
Foundation type: Independent foundation.
Financial data (yr. ended 12/31/13): Assets, $105,065,826 (M); expenditures, $5,559,028; qualifying distributions, $4,600,357; giving activities include $3,951,563 for 83 grants (high: $1,000,000; low: $750).
Purpose and activities: Giving primarily to make grants that have a significant, measurable impact on the health, education and quality of life of the Dothan, Alabama area.
Fields of interest: Education; Health care.
Limitations: Applications accepted. Giving primarily in Houston, Henry, Dale and Geneva counties, AL.
Publications: Application guidelines; Annual report; Financial statement.
Application information: Any application (including micro-grant applications) for projects that will operate in schools, request services from school personnel, or involve students during the school day or in connection with their school-sponsored activities, must include written endorsements by the principal(s) and the superintendent of that school and system. The endorsements will not affect the foundation's funding decision, but are intended to insure that the school and system are aware of the proposed project. All proposals must comply with grant application guidelines which are available on foundation web site. Application form required.
Initial approach: See foundation web site for guidelines and eligibility quiz
Copies of proposal: 2
Deadline(s): Applications accepted between Mar. 1, May 1, July 1, and Sept. 1
Board meeting date(s): Apr. 19, June 21, Aug. 16 and Oct. 18
Officers and Directors:* Steve McCarroll,* Chair.; Mary Julia Lee,* Chair.-Elect; Barbara Alford, Pres.; Cindy Besole, V.P., Admin. and Grant Mgmt.; Steve Shaw,* Secy.; John Dunn; John H. Edge; Bobby Hewes; G. David Johnston; Addie McKinzie; David W. Parsons.
EIN: 200897153

78
Working Woman's Home Association, Inc. ✧
7526 Lakeridge Dr.
Montgomery, AL 36117-8511 (334) 263-5308
E-mail: president@wwhassn.org; Application address: c/o Winifred Stakeley, 3116 Southview Ave., Montgomery, AL 36106 tel: (334) 263-5308; Main URL: http://wwhassn.org/

Established in AL.
Foundation type: Independent foundation.
Financial data (yr. ended 01/31/14): Assets, $8,321,174 (M); expenditures, $496,993; qualifying distributions, $428,550; giving activities include $428,550 for 28 grants (high: $40,000; low: $2,000).
Purpose and activities: Giving to aid and assist distressed and abused women and their children; to aid in the education of women to the end that they may become self sufficient; to aid and assist women in providing emergency housing; and to aid and assist elderly persons, particularly women in meeting their basic needs.
Fields of interest: Arts; Health care; Boys & girls clubs; Human services; Salvation Army; Children/youth, services; Family services; Women, centers/services; Christian agencies & churches.
Limitations: Applications accepted. Giving primarily in Montgomery, AL. No grants to individuals.
Application information: Applicants submitting a printed proposal should submit completed proposal plus two stapled copies, (not to exceed 7 pages in length each). Application form required.
Initial approach: Proposal
Deadline(s): July 31
Officers: Menelle Weiss, Pres.; Helen Wells, V.P.; Susan Patton, Treas.; Catherine Davis, Secy.
Directors: Martha Allen; Nancy Bradford; Catherine Davis; Beth Dubina; Carol Hodges; Emilie Reid; Alice Reynolds; Carol Rickard; Tutter Rogers; Winifred Stakeley.
EIN: 630302186
Selected grants: The following grants are a representative sample of this grantmaker's funding activity:
$8,000 to Unity Wellness Center, Auburn, AL, 2012.

ALASKA

79
The Alaska Community Foundation ✧
3201 C St., Ste. 110
Anchorage, AK 99503 (907) 334-6700
Contact: Candace Winkler, C.E.O.; For grants: Anne Remick, Prog. Off.
FAX: (907) 334-5780; E-mail: info@alaskacf.org; Additional e-mail: cwinkler@alaskacf.org; Grant application tel.: (907) 274-6705; Grant application e-mail: aremick@alaskacf.org; Main URL: http://www.alaskacf.org
Facebook: http://www.facebook.com/pages/The-Alaska-Community-Foundation/97080836858
Pinterest: https://www.pinterest.com/AlaskaCF/
Twitter: http://twitter.com/AKCommunity
YouTube: http://www.youtube.com/user/AlaskaCF
Scholarship inquiry tel.: (907) 274-6710; Scholarship e-mail: adalton@alaskacf.org

Incorporated in 1995 in AK.
Foundation type: Community foundation.
Financial data (yr. ended 12/31/13): Assets, $68,631,626 (M); gifts received, $6,097,164; expenditures, $6,957,115; giving activities include $3,858,529 for 59+ grants (high: $441,325), and $280,783 for 54 grants to individuals.
Purpose and activities: The foundation is a nonprofit public charity promoting personal philanthropy and providing financial management, strategic development and donor development services to communities, organizations and donors across AK.
Fields of interest: Philanthropy/voluntarism.
Type of support: General/operating support; Equipment; Program development; Scholarship funds; Matching/challenge support.
Limitations: Applications accepted. Giving generally limited to AK. No support for religious organizations for religious purposes. No grants for individuals (except for scholarships) fundraising activities, endowments, construction or the purchase of real property, sponsorships, membership solicitations, debt reduction, or funding after the fact.
Publications: Annual report; Grants list; Informational brochure; Newsletter.
Application information: Visit foundation web site for application forms and guidelines per grant type. Application form required.
Initial approach: Telephone
Copies of proposal: 1
Deadline(s): Varies
Board meeting date(s): Quarterly
Officers and Directors:* Blythe Campbell,* Chair.; Alex Slivka,* Vice-Chair.; Don Zoerb,* 1st Vice-Chair.; Candace Winkler,* C.E.O. and Pres.; Beth Rose, V.P., Philanthropy and External Rels.; Kris Norosz,* Secy.; Karen Griffin, C.F.O.; Lane Tucker,* Treas.; Angela Cox; Kathryn Dodge; Susan Behlke Foley; Diane Kaplan; Peter Michalski; Penny Pedersen; John Rubini; Bill Sheffield; Kate Slyker; Andy Teuber.
Number of staff: 4 full-time professional; 1 part-time professional.
EIN: 920155067

80
The Aleut Foundation ✧
703 W. Tudor Rd., Ste. 102
Anchorage, AK 99503-6650 (907) 646-1929
Contact: Cynthia H. Lind, Exec. Dir.
FAX: (907) 646-1949;
E-mail: taf@thealeutfoundation.org; Main URL: http://thealeutfoundation.org

Established in 1987.
Donors: The Aleut Corp.; Space Mark Inc.; Aleutian Pribilof Islands Restitution Trust.
Foundation type: Company-sponsored foundation.
Financial data (yr. ended 03/31/13): Assets, $272,954 (M); gifts received, $939,225; expenditures, $895,733; qualifying distributions, $643,374; giving activities include $643,374 for 2 + grants.
Purpose and activities: The foundation awards grants and college scholarships to original enrollees and the descendants of original enrollees of the Aleut Corporation, beneficiaries and the descendants of beneficiaries of the Aleutian Pribilof Islands Restitution Trust, and original enrollees and the descendants of original enrollees of the Isanotski Corporation.
Fields of interest: Arts, cultural/ethnic awareness; Vocational education, post-secondary; Higher education; Education; Native Americans/American Indians.
Type of support: Scholarships—to individuals.
Limitations: Applications not accepted. Giving limited to AK.
Application information: Unsolicited requests for funds not accepted.
Board meeting date(s): Quarterly
Officers: Kathy Griesbaum, Chair.; Cynthia H. Lind, Exec. Dir.
Directors: Jessica Borenin; Gary Ferguson; Kathy Greisbaum; Debra Mack; Thomas Mack; Boris Merculief.
Number of staff: 2 full-time professional.
EIN: 920124517

81
Arctic Education Foundation ✧
3900 C. St., Ste. 1002
Anchorage, AK 99503 (907) 852-9456
Contact: Muriel Brower, Mgr.
FAX: (907) 852-2774; E-mail: arcticed@asrc.com; Tel. and e-mail for Carolyn M. Edwards: (907) 852-8633, cmedwards@asrc@com; Additional address: P.O. Box 129, Barrow, AK 99723, tel.: (800) 770-2772; Main URL: http://www.arcticed.com

Established in 1978 in AK.
Donors: Arctic Slope Regional Corp.; Chevron U.S.A., Inc.; BP Alaska; Shell Oil Co.; Amoco Corp.; Piqunik Management Corp.; UIC Construction LLC.
Foundation type: Company-sponsored foundation.
Financial data (yr. ended 12/31/13): Assets, $38,780,709 (M); gifts received, $947,216; expenditures, $1,606,356; qualifying distributions, $1,487,390; giving activities include $1,448,163 for 420 grants to individuals (high: $23,100; low: $29).
Purpose and activities: The foundation awards scholarships for training and higher education to Northern Alaska Inupiat Natives currently residing in the Artic Slope Region, original 1971 shareholders of the Artic Slope Regional Corporation, and lineal descendants of original 1971 shareholders of the Arctic Slope Regional Corporation.
Fields of interest: Vocational education; Higher education; Education; Native Americans/American Indians.
Type of support: Scholarships—to individuals.
Limitations: Applications accepted. Giving limited to AK.
Publications: Application guidelines.
Application information: Application form required.
Initial approach: Complete online application or download application form and mail to foundation
Deadline(s): Mar. 1, May 1, Aug. 1, and Dec. 1 for scholarships and training; Apr. 15 for Anagi Leadership Award
Board meeting date(s): Jan. and Aug.
Officers: George Sielak, Chair. and Pres.; Eddie Ahyakak, V.P.; Lucinda Stackhouse, Secy.
Directors: Patsy Aamodt; Paul Bodfish, Sr.
Number of staff: 1 full-time professional.
EIN: 920068447

82
Atwood Foundation, Inc. ✧
301 W. Northern Lights Blvd., Ste. 440
Anchorage, AK 99503-2648 (907) 274-4900
Contact: Edward Rasmuson, Chair.
FAX: (907) 274-2415;
E-mail: atwoodfoundation@gci.net; Application address: c/o Natasha Vonimhof, Latash Investments, 301 Northern Lights Blvd., Ste. 412, Anchorage, AK 99503; tel.: (907) 274-4900; Main URL: http://www.atwoodfoundation.org

Established in 1962 in AK.
Donors: Robert B. Atwood; Elaine Atwood†; Anchorage Times Publishing Co.
Foundation type: Independent foundation.
Financial data (yr. ended 12/31/12): Assets, $27,300,349 (M); gifts received, $33,741; expenditures, $1,504,840; qualifying distributions, $1,028,852; giving activities include $851,200 for 30 grants (high: $250,000; low: $1,500).
Fields of interest: Performing arts; Higher education.
Limitations: Applications accepted. Giving primarily in Anchorage, AK. No grants to individuals.
Publications: Annual report; Grants list.
Application information: Application form available on foundation web site. Application form required.
Initial approach: Application via U.S. Mail, e-mail, or hand delivery
Copies of proposal: 1
Deadline(s): See foundation web site for current deadlines
Board meeting date(s): Quarterly in Mar., June, Sept., and Dec.
Final notification: 90 days
Officers: Edward Rasmuson, Chair.; David J. Tobin, Vice-Chair.; Ira Perlman, Secy.; Nancy Harbour, Treas.
Directors: Gloria Allen; Maria Downey; Carolyn Heyman-Layne.
Number of staff: 1 full-time professional; 1 part-time support.
EIN: 926002571
Selected grants: The following grants are a representative sample of this grantmaker's funding activity:
$250,000 to University of Alaska Foundation, Fairbanks, AK, 2012. To support of the Programs.

83

The Carr Foundation, Inc. ✧ ☆
935 W. 3rd Ave.
Anchorage, AK 99501-3567

Established in 1990 in AK.
Donors: L.J. Carr; Wilma Carr Administrative Trust.
Foundation type: Independent foundation.
Financial data (yr. ended 12/31/13): Assets, $11,227,388 (M); gifts received, $5,000,000; expenditures, $680,192; qualifying distributions, $631,498; giving activities include $629,100 for 42 grants (high: $193,100; low: $500).
Purpose and activities: Giving primarily for Roman Catholic organizations; funding also for education, the arts, and social services.
Fields of interest: Performing arts, music; Performing arts, opera; Arts; Higher education; Education; Human services; Catholic agencies & churches.
Limitations: Applications not accepted. Giving primarily in AK. No grants to individuals.
Application information: Contributes only to pre-selected organizations.
Officers and Directors:* Lauren A. Blanchett,* Pres.; Nathan K. Carr,* V.P.; Jacqueline Carr,* Secy.-Treas.; Gregory M. Carr.
EIN: 920135110
Selected grants: The following grants are a representative sample of this grantmaker's funding activity:
$168,100 to Alaska Pacific University, Anchorage, AK, 2012. For This grant was to a public charity to support its general charitable purposes.
$10,000 to Clare House, Anchorage, AK, 2012. For The grant is to a public charity for use in its general charitable purpose.

84

Chugach Heritage Foundation ✧
3800 Centerpoint Dr., Ste. 601
Anchorage, AK 99503-4196 (907) 563-8866
FAX: (907) 550-4147;
E-mail: scholarships@chugach-ak.com; Main URL: http://www.chugachheritagefoundation.org/

Established in 1994 in AK.
Donors: Chugach Alaska Regional Corp.; Chugach Alaska Corp.
Foundation type: Company-sponsored foundation.
Financial data (yr. ended 12/31/13): Assets, $2,272,183 (M); gifts received, $2,874,978; expenditures, $849,479; qualifying distributions, $844,270; giving activities include $6,000 for 2 grants (high: $5,000; low: $1,000), and $753,396 for 226 grants to individuals (high: $16,000; low: $94).
Purpose and activities: The foundation awards college scholarships, vocational certificates, and job training to shareholders and the descendants of shareholders of Chugach Alaska Corporation, and works to utilize, preserve, and promote the tradition and cultural heritage of the Chugach region.
Fields of interest: Vocational education; Higher education; Education; Health care; Employment, training; Human services; Native Americans/American Indians.
Type of support: Scholarships—to individuals.
Limitations: Applications accepted. Giving primarily in AK and WA.
Publications: Application guidelines.
Application information: Application form required.
Initial approach: Download application form or contact corporate office
Deadline(s): June 30 for Barney Uhart Memorial Scholarship
Officer: Michael McCanna,* Chair. and Pres.
Trustee: Sheri D. Buretta; Marchell Espe; Gabriel Kompkoff.
EIN: 920116128

85

The CIRI Foundation ✧
(also known as The Cook Inlet Region, Inc. Foundation)
3600 San Jeronimo Dr., Ste. 256
Anchorage, AK 99508-2870 (907) 793-3575
FAX: (907) 793-3585;
E-mail: tcf@thecirifoundation.org; Additional tel.: (800) 764-3382; Main URL: http://www.thecirifoundation.org
Education and Heritage Project Grant Recipients: http://www.thecirifoundation.org/project_grants_Awards_2011.html
Facebook: http://www.facebook.com/#!/pages/The-CIRI-Foundation/124737080941125
The Ciri Foundation: Making A Difference Video: http://www.thecirifoundation.org/TCF_Video.html

Established in 1982 in AK.
Donors: CIRI, Inc.; CITC; Salamatof Native Association; AK Villiage Initiatives; Tyonek Native Corp.; Southcentral Foundation.
Foundation type: Company-sponsored foundation.
Financial data (yr. ended 12/31/12): Assets, $50,389,113 (M); gifts received, $309,360; expenditures, $3,895,457; qualifying distributions, $3,376,290; giving activities include $121,869 for 5 grants (high: $43,869; low: $9,000), and $2,494,575 for 682 grants to individuals (high: $10,000; low: $250).
Purpose and activities: The foundation supports organizations involved with Alaska Native heritage and education, and awards scholarships, grants, and fellowships to Alaska Natives to promote individual self-development and economic self-sufficiency.
Fields of interest: Arts, cultural/ethnic awareness; Visual arts; Performing arts; History/archaeology; Literature; Philosophy/ethics; Historic preservation/historical societies; Arts; Vocational education; Higher education; Graduate/professional education; Business school/education; Engineering school/education; Health sciences school/education; Scholarships/financial aid; Education; Employment, services; Employment, training; Employment; Mathematics; Native Americans/American Indians.
Type of support: General/operating support; Continuing support; Program development; Conferences/seminars; Fellowships; Internship funds; Scholarship funds; Research; Grants to individuals; Scholarships—to individuals.
Limitations: Applications accepted. Giving primarily in the Cook Inlet Region, AK. No grants for endowments, buildings or equipment, completed projects, re-granting, or lobbying or propaganda efforts; no loans.
Publications: Application guidelines; Grants list; Program policy statement.
Application information: Visit website for scholarship endowment funds and named scholarship funds. Additional information may be requested at a later date for project grants. Organizations receiving project grants are asked to submit a final report. Application form required.
Initial approach: Complete online application; download application form and mail proposal and application to foundation for General and Cultural Heritage Fellowships and project grants
Copies of proposal: 1
Deadline(s): Mar. 1, June 1, Sept. 1, and Nov. 1 for project grants; Mar. 31, June 30, Sept. 30, and Dec. 1 for Vocational Training, General and Cultural Heritage Fellowships, and internships; June 1 for Achievement, Excellence, and Special Excellence Annual Scholarships; and June 1 and Dec. 1 for General Semester Scholarships
Board meeting date(s): Quarterly
Final notification: 30 to 60 days for project grants
Officers and Directors:* Jeff Gonnason,* Chair.; Louis Nagy, Jr.,* Vice-Chair.; Susan A. Anderson, C.E.O. and Pres.; Tamara Pickett, MD, Secy.-Treas.; Hallie Bissett; Jessica Greiner; Rayna Hartz; Deanna Sackett; Jaclyn Sallee; Susan Wells; David Wright.
Number of staff: 6
EIN: 920087914
Selected grants: The following grants are a representative sample of this grantmaker's funding activity:
$35,000 to Koahnic Broadcast Corporation, Anchorage, AK, 2012. For Grants to Other Organizations.

86

The Doyon Foundation ✧
615 Bidwell, Ste. 101
Fairbanks, AK 99701-7580 (907) 459-2048
Contact: Doris Miller, Exec. Dir.
FAX: (905) 459-2065;
E-mail: foundation@doyon.com; E-mail for Doris Miller: millerd@doyon.com; Additional tel.: (888) 478-4755; Main URL: http://www.doyonfoundation.com/
Doyon Foundation Blog: http://doyonfoundation.wordpress.com/
Facebook: http://www.facebook.com/doyonfoundation
Tel. for Tonya. Garnett; (907) 459-2049, e-mail: garnett@doyon.com

Established in 1988 in AK.
Donor: Doyon Ltd. and Affiliates.
Foundation type: Company-sponsored foundation.
Financial data (yr. ended 06/30/13): Assets, $16,359,338 (M); gifts received, $1,492,633; expenditures, $1,066,680; qualifying distributions, $629,392; giving activities include $426,630 for 597 grants to individuals (high: $2,500; low: $299).
Purpose and activities: The foundation supports programs designed to improve educational, career, and cultural opportunities for Dayan shareholders. Special emphasis is directed toward programs designed to strengthen Native culture and heritage through education.
Fields of interest: Arts, cultural/ethnic awareness; Elementary/secondary education; Vocational education; Higher education; Education; Native Americans/American Indians.
Type of support: General/operating support; Internship funds; Scholarships—to individuals.
Limitations: Applications accepted. Giving primarily in AK.
Publications: Application guidelines; Annual report; Informational brochure; Newsletter.

Application information: Application form required.
Initial approach: Complete online application or download application and mail
Deadline(s): Apr. 15 for Competitive Scholarships; Mar. 15, Apr. 15, and Nov. 15 for Basic Scholarships; Mar. 15, Apr. 15, Sept. 15, and Nov. 15 for Vocational Scholarships
Board meeting date(s): Quarterly
Officers and Board Members:* Lanien Livingston, Pres.; Allan Hayton, V.P.; Julie Anderson, Secy.-Treas.; Doris Miller, Exec. Dir.; Paul Mountain; Victor Nicholas; Joshua Peter; Teisha Simmons.
Number of staff: 2 full-time professional.
EIN: 943089624

87
Benito and Frances C. Gaguine Foundation ✧

2551 Vista Dr., Ste. D101
Juneau, AK 99801 (907) 789-2986
Contact: John Gaguine, Pres.

Established in AK.
Foundation type: Independent foundation.
Financial data (yr. ended 12/31/13): Assets, $13,971,682 (M); expenditures, $730,265; qualifying distributions, $702,900; giving activities include $702,900 for 11 grants (high: $250,000; low: $500).
Fields of interest: Human services; International relief.
Limitations: Applications accepted. Giving in the U.S., with some emphasis on AK, CA, and NY.
Application information: Application form not required.
Initial approach: Proposal
Deadline(s): None
Officers and Directors:* John Gaguine,* Pres.; Mary Alice McKeen,* V.P.; Cynthia Gaguine,* Secy.; Robert Storer,* Treas.
EIN: 111792380

88
Robert "Aqqaluk" Newlin, Sr. Memorial Trust ✧ ☆

333 Shore Ave., Ste. 202
P.O. Box 509
Kotzebue, AK 99752-0509 (907) 442-1607
Contact: Erica Nelson, Pres.
FAX: (907) 442-2289;
E-mail: aqqaluk.trust@aqqaluktrust.com; Toll-free tel.: (866) 442-1607; Main URL: http://www.aqqaluktrust.com/

Established in 1990 in AK; status changed to a public charity in 2002.
Foundation type: Independent foundation.
Financial data (yr. ended 12/31/12): Assets, $20,721,237 (M); gifts received, $3,948,829; expenditures, $2,094,014; qualifying distributions, $1,418,916; giving activities include $767,848 for 337 grants to individuals (high: $6,000; low: $280), and $571,594 for foundation-administered programs.
Purpose and activities: The trust awards scholarships to NANA shareholders, their descendents and dependents who are interested in pursuing college and post-graduate degrees, and post-secondary education.
Fields of interest: Indigenous peoples.
Type of support: Scholarships—to individuals.
Limitations: Applications accepted. Giving limited to the Northwest Arctic Borough of AK.
Publications: Application guidelines; Informational brochure (including application guidelines).
Application information: Application form required.
Initial approach: Download application form on foundation web site
Officers and Trustees:* Dood Lincoln,* Chair.; Linda Lee,* Vice-Chair.; Erica Nelson,* Pres.; Levi Cleveland; Cheryl Edenshaw; Raymond Hawley; Diana Ramoth; Helvi Sandvik.
EIN: 943116762

89
Rasmuson Foundation ✧

301 W. Northern Lights Blvd., Ste. 400
Anchorage, AK 99503-2648 (907) 297-2700
Contact: Diane S. Kaplan, C.E.O. and Pres.; Ian Dutton, V.P. and C.O.O.; Sammye Pokryfi, V.P., Prog (s).
FAX: (907) 297-2770;
E-mail: rasmusonfdn@rasmuson.org; Toll free tel. within Alaska: (877) 366-2700; Main URL: http://www.rasmuson.org
Facebook: http://www.facebook.com/pages/Anchorage-AK/Rasmuson-Foundation/50072648161
Flickr: http://www.flickr.com/photos/rasmusonfoundationgallery
Grants Database: http://www.rasmuson.org/PastAwards/Search/search.php
MySpace: http://www.myspace.com/rasmusonfoundation
Rasmuson Foundation Gallery (Second Life): http://www.rasmuson.org/index.php?switch=viewpage&pageid=195
RF Blog: http://www.rasmuson.org/blog/
Twitter: http://www.twitter.com/rasmuson
YouTube: http://www.youtube.com/user/rasmusonfoundation

Established in 1955 in AK.
Donors: Elmer E. Rasmuson†; Jenny Rasmuson†; Mary Louise Rasmuson†.
Foundation type: Independent foundation.
Financial data (yr. ended 12/31/12): Assets, $569,389,107 (M); gifts received, $42,404,890; expenditures, $29,480,222; qualifying distributions, $22,474,459; giving activities include $16,546,129 for 436 grants (high: $1,000,000; low: $500), $263,200 for 37 grants to individuals (high: $25,000; low: $2,800), $404,385 for 4 foundation-administered programs and $2,050,000 for 3 loans/program-related investments (high: $1,100,000; low: $450,000).
Purpose and activities: The foundation is a catalyst to promote a better life for Alaskans.
Fields of interest: Arts; Education; Health care; Recreation; Human services; Children/youth, services; Aging, centers/services; Women, centers/services; Community/economic development; Native Americans/American Indians.
Type of support: Research; Publication; Program evaluation; Grants to individuals; Fellowships; Capital campaigns; Building/renovation; Curriculum development; Equipment; Land acquisition; Management development/capacity building; Matching/challenge support; Mission-related investments/loans; Program development; Program-related investments/loans; Seed money; Technical assistance.
Limitations: Applications accepted. Giving limited to organizations based in and providing services to Alaska. For religious organizations, only projects with a broad community impact are considered. For units of government and tribes, only projects with a broad community impact beyond traditional government functions are considered. No support for organizations or foundations for redistribution of funds to entities of their own selection; or organizations that, as a major purpose, influence legislation or support candidates for public office, or organizations that discriminate by reason of race, religion, sex, or national origin, or other private foundations. No grants generally for general operations, administrative, indirect, or overhead costs, or for deficits or debt reduction, endowments, scholarships, fund-raising events or sponsorships, reimbursement for items already purchased, or for electronic health records and other emerging technologies.
Publications: Application guidelines; Annual report; Grants list; Informational brochure (including application guidelines); Newsletter; Occasional report.
Application information: All application forms available on web site. Application form required.
Initial approach: The foundation encourages applicants to call or meet with staff to discuss proposals prior to submission. Hard copy of forms can be mailed, or use online application.
Copies of proposal: 2
Deadline(s): Some programs open year round for applications; others have specific due dates
Board meeting date(s): Summer and winter
Final notification: Varies.
Officers and Directors:* Edward B. Rasmuson,* Chair.; Cathryn Rasmuson,* Vice-Chair.; Diane S. Kaplan, C.E.O. and Pres.; Ian Dutton, C.O.O. and V.P.; Sammye Pokryfki, V.P., Prog(s).; Natasha von Imhof,* Secy.-Treas.; Jeff Cook; Adam Gibbons; Lile R. Gibbons; Matthew Hirschfeld; Linda Leary; Anthony Mallott; Kris Norosz; Judy Rasmuson; Aaron Schutt.
Trustee: Wells Fargo Financial Alaska, Inc.
Number of staff: 16 full-time professional.
EIN: 916340739
Selected grants: The following grants are a representative sample of this grantmaker's funding activity:
$2,775,000 to Anchorage Park Foundation, Anchorage, AK, 2012. To implement strategies to grow public and private support for Anchorage parks and trails.
$40,000 to Alaska Network on Domestic Violence and Sexual Assault, Juneau, AK, 2013. For sabbatical program.
$25,000 to Alaska Pacific University, Anchorage, AK, 2013. To develop Master Plan for Kellogg farm campus in Palmer.
$24,975 to Women in Safe Homes, Ketchikan, AK, 2013. To upgrade security and electrical system in Ketchikan.
$20,000 to Rural Alaska Community Action Program, Anchorage, AK, 2013. For tools and equipment for self-help owner built homeownership program on the Kenai Peninsula.
$16,000 to Kenai Peninsula Borough, Seldovia, AK, 2013. To renovate Sea Otter Community Center in Seldovia.

ARIZONA

90
Anderson Family Foundation ✧
P.O. Box 32677
Phoenix, AZ 85064-2677

Established in 2002 in AZ.
Donors: Joseph P. Anderson; Bob Ramsey.
Foundation type: Independent foundation.
Financial data (yr. ended 12/31/13): Assets, $24,735 (M); gifts received, $2,875,000; expenditures, $2,922,056; qualifying distributions, $2,922,056; giving activities include $2,922,056 for 21 grants (high: $800,000; low: $5,000).
Fields of interest: Education; Health care; Catholic agencies & churches.
Type of support: General/operating support.
Limitations: Applications not accepted. Giving primarily in AZ, CA, and MD. No grants to individuals.
Application information: Contributes only to pre-selected organizations.
Officers and Directors:* Joseph P. Anderson,* Pres.; Jacob V. Anderson,* V.P.; Monica Rose Anderson,* V.P.; Deborah Margaret Matwijkow,* Secy.; Patricia J. Davis.
EIN: 421561494

91
APS Foundation, Inc. ✧
P.O. Box 53999, M.S. 8657
Phoenix, AZ 85072-3999 602-250-4736
Contact: Julie Coleman, Exec. Dir.
FAX: 602-250-4492;
E-mail: corporategiving@aps.com; E-mail for Julie Coleman: julie.coleman@aps.com; Main URL: http://www.aps.com/en/communityandenvironment/charitablegiving/ourgivingprograms/Pages/home.aspx

Established in 1981 in AZ.
Donor: Arizona Public Service Co.
Foundation type: Company-sponsored foundation.
Financial data (yr. ended 12/31/13): Assets, $30,349,680 (M); expenditures, $3,220,309; qualifying distributions, $3,121,997; giving activities include $3,023,685 for 25 grants (high: $1,000,000; low: $5,000).
Purpose and activities: The foundation supports education programs designed to promote science, technology, engineering, and math to nurture's tomorrow's leader and create a more educated workforce.
Fields of interest: Elementary/secondary education; Higher education; Education; Environment; Children/youth, services; Foundations (community); Mathematics; Engineering/technology; Science.
Type of support: Building/renovation; General/operating support; Program development.
Limitations: Applications accepted. Giving primarily in APS service territories in AZ. No support for charter or private schools, religious, political, fraternal, legislative, or lobbying organizations, civic service clubs, private or family foundations, start-up organizations, discriminatory organizations, sports teams, scouting troops, or advocacy organizations. No grants to individuals, or for fundraising events, sponsorships, endowments, debt reduction, or capital or building campaigns.
Publications: Application guidelines.
Application information: Support is limited to 1 contribution per organization during any given year. Organizations receiving support are asked to provide a final report. Application form not required.
Initial approach: Complete online application
Deadline(s): Mar. 1 and Sept. 1
Final notification: 30 to 60 days
Officers and Directors:* Donald E. Brandt,* Chair. and Pres.; David P. Falck,* Secy.; Tommy D. McLeod,* Treas.; Julie Coleman, Exec. Dir.; Linda R. Fisker; John S. Hatfield; Donald G. Robinson; Mark A. Schiavoni.
Number of staff: 2 full-time professional; 1 part-time support.
EIN: 953735903

92
Arizona Community Foundation ✧
2201 E. Camelback Rd., Ste. 405B
Phoenix, AZ 85016-3431 (602) 381-1400
FAX: (602) 381-1575;
E-mail: info@azfoundation.org; Grant application e-mail: grants@azfoundation.org; Main URL: http://www.azfoundation.org
E-Newsletter: http://www.azfoundation.org/About/NewsEvents/E-NewsSignup.aspx
Facebook: http://www.facebook.com/pages/Arizona-Community-Foundation/40029502243?v=wall
LinkedIn: http://www.linkedin.com/companies/arizona-community-foundation
Twitter: http://twitter.com/AZFoundation

Incorporated in 1978 in AZ.
Donors: L. Dilatush†; Bert A. Getz; G.R. Herberger; R. Kieckhefer; Newton Rosenzweig†.
Foundation type: Community foundation.
Financial data (yr. ended 03/31/13): Assets, $556,710,301 (M); gifts received, $60,339,973; expenditures, $55,409,581; giving activities include $38,633,992 for grants.
Purpose and activities: The foundation's mission is to lead, serve and collaborate to mobilize enduring philanthropy for a better Arizona.
Fields of interest: Visual arts, architecture; Performing arts; Arts; Education, public education; Education, early childhood education; Child development, education; Higher education; Adult education—literacy, basic skills & GED; Education, reading; Education; Environment, natural resources; Environment; Health care; Substance abuse, services; Mental health/crisis services; Health organizations, association; AIDS; AIDS research; Legal services; Employment; Housing/shelter, development; Housing/shelter; Disasters, Hurricane Katrina; Boys & girls clubs; Children/youth, services; Child development, services; Family services; Homeless, human services; Human services; Rural development; Community/economic development; Engineering/technology; Science; Government/public administration; Public affairs; Aging; Disabilities, people with; Minorities; Economically disadvantaged; Homeless.
Type of support: General/operating support; Continuing support; Building/renovation; Equipment; Emergency funds; Program development; Publication; Seed money; Scholarship funds; Research; Technical assistance; Matching/challenge support.
Limitations: Applications accepted. Giving limited to AZ. No support for religious organizations for religious purposes. No grants to individuals (except for scholarships), travel to or support of conferences, fundraising campaigns and expenses, debt reduction, or capital grants; generally, no loans.
Publications: Application guidelines; Annual report; Financial statement; Informational brochure; Newsletter; Program policy statement.
Application information: Visit foundation web site for application and guidelines per grant type. Application form required.
Initial approach: Complete online grant application
Deadline(s): Varies
Board meeting date(s): Quarterly
Final notification: 60 days
Officers and Directors:* Jack Davis,* Chair.; Ron Butler,* Vice-Chair.; Steven G. Seleznow,* C.E.O. and Pres.; Jacky Alling, Chief Philanthropic Svcs. Off.; Megan Brownell, Chief Business Devel. and Brand Off.; Ellen Steele Allare,* Secy.; Melissa Hangsleben, Cont.; John Gogolak,* Treas.; Bert A. Getz,* Chair. Emeritus; Dr. William V. Andrew; Tony Astorga; Betsey Bayless; Gwen Calhoun; Sue Clark-Johnson; Shelly Cohn; W. David Connell; Robbin M. Coulon; Stephen O. Evans; Carol Parry Fox; Charley Freericks; Neil H. Hiller; William J. Hodges; Herbert M. Kaufman, Ph.D.; Michael E. Kelly; Leezie Kim; Paul J. Luna; Mary Martuscelli; Marjorie McClanahan; Jodi O. Padgett; Frederick M. Pakis; Barbara Poley; Denise Resnik; Julia Rosen; James W. Ryan; Hal Tashman; Lisa Urias; John O. Whiteman.
Number of staff: 33 full-time professional; 13 full-time support; 2 part-time support.
EIN: 860348306
Selected grants: The following grants are a representative sample of this grantmaker's funding activity:
$1,439,700 to Transition Zone Horticultural Institute, Arboretum, Flagstaff, AZ, 2012.
$1,019,182 to Thunderbirds Charities, Phoenix, AZ, 2012. For Local Maricopa County 501(c)(3) Charities.
$846,231 to Chicago Community Foundation, Chicago, IL, 2012. For Panson Family Foundation.
$526,566 to Wickenburg Unified School District, Wickenburg, AZ, 2012. For Move On When Ready Program.
$400,000 to Memoir Journal, Emeryville, CA, 2012. For Literary Journal memoir (and) and (in)visible memoir projects.
$375,000 to Aspen Institute, Washington, DC, 2012. For general program support.
$20,000 to Catholic Charities Community Services, Phoenix, AZ, 2012. For My Sisters Place and Pathways.
$20,000 to United Way, Valley of the Sun, Phoenix, AZ, 2012. For general support.
$10,000 to Helping Hands for Single Moms, Glendale, AZ, 2012. For Scholarship Plus Program.
$10,000 to STEP Student Expedition Program, Tucson, AZ, 2012. For unrestricted support.

93
Arizona Foundation for Educational Advancement ✧
P.O. Box 10417
Phoenix, AZ 85064-0417

Established in AZ.

Foundation type: Independent foundation.
Financial data (yr. ended 12/31/13): Assets, $14,954,712 (M); expenditures, $780,488; qualifying distributions, $651,092; giving activities include $460,000 for 35 grants (high: $75,000; low: $1,000).
Purpose and activities: The foundation supports educational advancement.
Fields of interest: Education.
Limitations: Applications not accepted. Giving primarily in AZ.
Application information: Unsolicited requests for funds not accepted.
Officers: Clancy Woods, Chair.; Richard J. Emerine II, Vice-Chair. and Treas.; John C. Muessle, Pres. and Secy.
Director: Leo V. Valdez.
EIN: 860664560
Selected grants: The following grants are a representative sample of this grantmaker's funding activity:
$25,000 to University of Portland, Portland, OR, 2012. To Fund the Father Pruzynski Endowed Accounting Scholarship and the E-Scholars Program.
$24,000 to Jesuit High School, Portland, OR, 2012. For Tuition Assistance for Economically Disadvantaged Students and E-Scholar Program.
$15,000 to Lodestar Day Resource Center, Phoenix, AZ, 2012. For Serve As Gateway to Self-Sufficiency and Success for Homeless Individuals.
$10,000 to Southwest Human Development, Phoenix, AZ, 2012. For Using Technology to Provide Successful Instruction to Students with Physical and Cognitive Problems.
$5,000 to Arizona Grantmakers Forum, Phoenix, AZ, 2012. For Membership Association and Assistance for Grantmakers in Arizona.
$5,000 to McCurdy School, Espanola, NM, 2012. For Funding Scholarships, Financial Aid and Operations of This Mission School.
$3,000 to Be a Leader Foundation, Phoenix, AZ, 2012. To increase the Number of College-Going Students by Empowering Them to Be College Bound, Focused and Prepared.
$2,500 to Regional Center for Border Health, Somerton, AZ, 2012. For Supporting Environmental Health Education.
$2,500 to Stepping Stone Foundation, Phoenix, AZ, 2012. For at risk preschool children and family literacy.

94
Aurora Foundation ✧
4835 E. Exeter Blvd.
Phoenix, AZ 85018-2940 (602) 557-1790

Established in 1997 in AZ.
Donor: John G. Sperling.
Foundation type: Independent foundation.
Financial data (yr. ended 12/31/13): Assets, $33,191,474 (M); expenditures, $1,305,675; qualifying distributions, $1,305,675; giving activities include $1,275,000 for 3 grants (high: $1,000,000; low: $25,000).
Fields of interest: Higher education; Medical research, institute; Agriculture/food; Community/economic development; Foundations (community).
Type of support: General/operating support.
Limitations: Applications not accepted. Giving primarily in CA and OR. No grants to individuals.
Application information: Contributes only to pre-selected organizations.
Trustee: John G. Sperling.
EIN: 860873239
Selected grants: The following grants are a representative sample of this grantmaker's funding activity:
$5,000,000 to Civic Duty Coalition, Las Vegas, NV, 2012. For general support.
$4,000,000 to Stanford University, Stanford, CA, 2012. For general support.
$1,073,680 to Kronos Longevity Research Institute, Phoenix, AZ, 2012. For medical research.
$1,000,000 to Nexus Research and Policy Center, Tempe, AZ, 2012. For education research.
$350,000 to Memoir Journal, Emeryville, CA, 2012. For general support.
$208,182 to Lasallian Education Fund, Mill Valley, CA, 2012. For general support.
$5,000 to Literacy Volunteers of Maricopa County, Phoenix, AZ, 2012. For general support.
$500 to Love House Kids Program, Phoenix, AZ, 2012.

95
The Baird Foundation Inc. ✧
933 N. Cherry Ave.
Tucson, AZ 85721-0009

Established in 2006 in AZ.
Foundation type: Independent foundation.
Financial data (yr. ended 12/31/13): Assets, $5,960,852 (M); expenditures, $448,920; qualifying distributions, $426,546; giving activities include $426,546 for 1 grant.
Fields of interest: Higher education; Scholarships/financial aid.
Limitations: Applications not accepted. Giving primarily in AZ. No grants to individuals.
Application information: Unsolicited requests for funds not accepted.
Directors: Stephanie Adamson; David Butler; Helen D. Day; Stephen H. Lesher; David McEvoy; Gary M. Munsinger; James S. Sakrison; John P. Schaefer; Robert S. Svob; David L. Windsor.
EIN: 866050315
Selected grants: The following grants are a representative sample of this grantmaker's funding activity:
$416,546 to University of Arizona, Tucson, AZ, 2011. For scholarships.

96
Craig and Barbara Barrett Foundation ✧
4617 E. Ocotillo Rd.
Paradise Valley, AZ 85253-4032

Established in 2004 in AZ.
Donors: Barbara Barrett; Craig Barrett.
Foundation type: Independent foundation.
Financial data (yr. ended 12/31/13): Assets, $1,360,196 (M); gifts received, $997,240; expenditures, $922,677; qualifying distributions, $894,204; giving activities include $894,204 for 90 grants (high: $250,000; low: $15).
Purpose and activities: Giving primarily for higher education; funding also for animal and wildlife protection, environmental conservation, and social services.
Fields of interest: Higher education; Engineering school/education; Education; Environment, natural resources; Animals/wildlife; Human services; Children/youth, services; International affairs; Engineering/technology.
Limitations: Applications not accepted. Giving primarily in AZ.
Application information: Contributes only to pre-selected organizations.
Officers: Craig Barrett, Pres.; Barbara Barrett, V.P.
EIN: 201539507
Selected grants: The following grants are a representative sample of this grantmaker's funding activity:
$83,200 to Horatio Alger Association of Distinguished Americans, Alexandria, VA, 2011.
$10,000 to Horatio Alger Association of Distinguished Americans, Alexandria, VA, 2011.

97
Thomas R. Brown Family Private Foundation ✧
6720 E. Camino Principal, Ste. 203
Tucson, AZ 85715-3900
Main URL: http://www.brownfoundation.org/

Established in 2005 in AZ.
Donors: Mary B. Brown; Sarah B. Smallhouse; Mary B. Bernal.
Foundation type: Independent foundation.
Financial data (yr. ended 12/31/12): Assets, $42,329,682 (M); expenditures, $2,224,738; qualifying distributions, $2,040,000; giving activities include $2,040,000 for 7 grants (high: $2,000,000; low: $5,000).
Fields of interest: Higher education, university; Foundations (public).
Limitations: Applications not accepted. Giving primarily in AZ. No grants to individuals.
Application information: Contributes only to pre-selected organizations.
Officers: Mary B. Bernal, C.E.O. and Secy.; Sarah B. Smallhouse, Pres. and Treas.
EIN: 550899701

98
Canyon Institute ✧
(formerly Grand Canyon University Institute for Advanced Studies)
3101 N. Central Ave., No. 1490
Phoenix, AZ 85012-2644

Established in AZ.
Donors: Richard MacLeod; Hines Memorial; California Baptist Foundation; A.L. Swanson Revocable Trust; All-In Ministries; Helms Family Foundation.
Foundation type: Independent foundation.
Financial data (yr. ended 06/30/13): Assets, $30,621,528 (M); gifts received, $3,432; expenditures, $2,013,299; qualifying distributions, $1,533,564; giving activities include $1,266,671 for 22 grants (high: $150,000; low: $10,828).
Fields of interest: Higher education; Children, services; Homeless, human services; Christian agencies & churches.
Limitations: Applications not accepted. Giving primarily in AZ, CA, TX, and WA.
Application information: Unsolicited requests for funds not accepted.
Officers: Donald Pewitt, Chair.; Brian Middleton, C.E.O. and Pres.; Mitchell C. Laird, C.O.O.; Jerry Sowell, Secy.; Bruce McNaught, C.F.O.

Trustees: William Brotherton; Steve Hayes; Robin Hintze Kreutzberg; Kenneth Miller; Bonnie Muir; Jeff Pettett; Michael Rochelle.
EIN: 860977269

99
Shirley C. Caris Family Foundation ✧
P.O. Box 14315
Scottsdale, AZ 85267-4315

Established in 1999 in AZ.
Donors: Shirley C. Caris†; The Shirley C. Caris Revocable Trust.
Foundation type: Operating foundation.
Financial data (yr. ended 12/31/13): Assets, $12,723,982 (M); expenditures, $667,187; qualifying distributions, $510,000; giving activities include $510,000 for 24 grants (high: $100,000; low: $1,000).
Fields of interest: Higher education, university; Human services; Children, services; Catholic agencies & churches.
Limitations: Applications not accepted. Giving primarily in AZ, with emphasis on Scottsdale and Phoenix. No grants to individuals.
Application information: Contributes only to pre-selected organizations.
Officers: Catherine Ann Hart, Pres.; Sherry Lynn Cowan, Secy.-Treas.
EIN: 860965394
Selected grants: The following grants are a representative sample of this grantmaker's funding activity:
$30,000 to Medicine Horse Center, Mancos, CO, 2011.
$25,000 to Xavier Foundation, Phoenix, AZ, 2011.
$15,000 to Children's Hospital Corporation, Boston, MA, 2011.
$10,000 to American Heart Association, Tempe, AZ, 2011.
$5,000 to Brophy College Preparatory, Phoenix, AZ, 2011.
$5,000 to University of Arizona Foundation, Tucson, AZ, 2011.

100
Click Family Foundation ✧
P.O. Box 12399
Tucson, AZ 85732-2399 (520) 570-7340

Established in 1998 in AZ.
Donors: James H. Click, Jr.; Vicki M. Click; Click Charitable Lead Annuity Trust; James H. Click.
Foundation type: Independent foundation.
Financial data (yr. ended 12/31/13): Assets, $2,133,047 (M); gifts received, $280,240; expenditures, $635,718; qualifying distributions, $599,116; giving activities include $599,116 for 15 grants (high: $100,000; low: $20,000).
Purpose and activities: Giving primarily for education, and for human services and families in need.
Fields of interest: Secondary school/education; Zoos/zoological societies; Boys & girls clubs; Human services; Family services.
Limitations: Applications accepted. Giving primarily in AZ. No grants to individuals.
Application information: Application form required.
Initial approach: Letter
Deadline(s): None
Officers: James H. Click, Pres.; Carrie W. Click, V.P.; Christian J. Click, V.P.; Christopher B. Cotter, Secy.
EIN: 860933752

101
Community Foundation for Southern Arizona ✧
2250 E. Broadway Blvd.
Tucson, AZ 85719-6014 (520) 770-0800
Contact: J. Clint Mabie, C.E.O.
FAX: (520) 770-1500;
E-mail: philanthropy@cfsoaz.org; Additional e-mail: cmabie@cfsoaz.org; Main URL: http://www.cfsoaz.org
Community Matters: http://www.cfsoaz.blogspot.com/
Facebook: http://www.facebook.com/communityfoundationfor.southernarizona
Twitter: http://twitter.com/SoAZCommunityFd
Scholarship and award inquiries: mmaley@cfsaz.org

Established in 1980 in AZ.
Foundation type: Community foundation.
Financial data (yr. ended 06/30/13): Assets, $107,311,858 (M); gifts received, $6,138,141; expenditures, $8,962,787; giving activities include $6,582,078 for grants.
Purpose and activities: The mission of the foundation is to work with charitably minded individuals and organizations to strengthen southern AZ communities, now and for generations to come. The foundation also administers a variety of donor-initiated funds and conducts competitive scholarship and grant rounds.
Fields of interest: Arts; Education; Environment; Health care; AIDS; Recreation; Children/youth, services; Human services; Community/economic development.
International interests: Mexico.
Type of support: Program development; Scholarship funds; Research; Scholarships—to individuals; Matching/challenge support.
Limitations: Applications accepted. Giving limited to southern AZ, with particular emphasis on Pima and Santa Cruz counties. No support for sectarian organizations or individual schools (except for special literacy grants). No grants to individuals (except for scholarships), or for operating expenses, endowment building, capital campaigns, debt retirement, research or fundraising events.
Publications: Application guidelines; Annual report; Financial statement; Informational brochure.
Application information: Visit foundation web site for guidelines per grant type. Application form required.
Deadline(s): Varies
Board meeting date(s): Bimonthly
Final notification: 60 days
Officers and Trustees:* R. Michael Sullivan,* Chair.; Fred Chaffee,* Vice-Chair.; J. Clinton Mabie, C.E.O. and Pres.; Barbara L. Brown, V.P., Prog. Svcs. and Community Initiatives; Cande Grogan,* Secy.; Missy Bowden, C.F.O.; Craig Wisnom,* Treas.; Joseph Blair; Carrie Brennan; Tony Dabdoub; Darryl Dobras; Robert Friesen; Bill Holmes; Marian Lalonde; Natalie Fernandez Lee; Jan Lesher; Paul Lindsey; Don Luria; Karen McCloskey; Richard Mundinger; Chinwe Mary Okoye; Anne Roediger; Jim Rowley; Barbara Smith; Jody Summerset Roll.
Number of staff: 5 full-time professional; 10 full-time support; 2 part-time support.
EIN: 942681765

102
Cooper Family Foundation ✧
8912 E. Pinnacle Peak Rd., Ste. F9-663
Scottsdale, AZ 85255-3615 (602) 909-4173
Contact: Mary I Cooper, Dir.

Established in 1998 in AZ.
Donors: John Cooper; Mary Cooper; John and Mary Logser Charitable Lead Trust; John and Mary Cooper Charitable Lead Annuity Trust.
Foundation type: Independent foundation.
Financial data (yr. ended 12/31/12): Assets, $1,277,121 (M); expenditures, $439,573; qualifying distributions, $426,724; giving activities include $426,724 for 30 grants (high: $103,200; low: $1,000).
Purpose and activities: Giving primarily for children, youth, and social services and to Christian organizations.
Fields of interest: Youth development; Human services; Children/youth, services; Christian agencies & churches.
Limitations: Applications accepted. Giving primarily in NY.
Application information: Application form required.
Initial approach: Letter
Deadline(s): None
Directors: Christine Cooper; Gary Cooper; John Cooper; Mary Cooper.
EIN: 860905824

103
Frederick Gardner Cottrell Foundation ✧
5210 E. Williams Cir., Ste. 240
Tucson, AZ 85711-4410

Established in 1998 in AZ.
Donor: Research Corporation Technologies, Inc.
Foundation type: Independent foundation.
Financial data (yr. ended 12/31/13): Assets, $12,684,712 (M); gifts received, $2,654,552; expenditures, $1,952,372; qualifying distributions, $1,935,385; giving activities include $1,932,840 for 13 grants (high: $750,000; low: $1,000).
Purpose and activities: Giving primarily for research on solar energy.
Fields of interest: Higher education; Environment, energy.
Limitations: Applications not accepted. Giving primarily in Tucson, AZ. No grants to individuals.
Application information: Unsolicited requests for funds not accepted.
Officers and Directors:* Gary M. Munsinger,* Pres.; Rebecca Buescher, Secy.; Christopher Martin,* Treas.; Lyle Bootman; Shaun A. Kirkpatrick; John Schaefer.
EIN: 860940147

104
J. & C. Davis Foundation Inc. ✧
2403 E. Sentry Ridge Ct.
Tucson, AZ 85718-7867

Established in 2000 in IN.
Donors: Henry C. Davis; Jeannine M. Davis; H. Coleman Davis III.
Foundation type: Independent foundation.
Financial data (yr. ended 12/31/13): Assets, $10,299,869 (M); expenditures, $546,075; qualifying distributions, $537,372; giving activities

include $530,000 for 11 grants (high: $125,000; low: $10,000).
Fields of interest: Education; Boys & girls clubs; Human services; Children/youth, services.
Limitations: Applications not accepted. Giving primarily in Tucson, AZ. No grants to individuals.
Application information: Contributes only to pre-selected organizations.
Officers: Jeannine M. Davis, Pres.; H. Coleman Davis III, Secy.-Treas.
EIN: 352118361
Selected grants: The following grants are a representative sample of this grantmaker's funding activity:
$175,000 to San Miguel of Tucson Corporation, Tucson, AZ, 2012. To support Its College and Career Preparatory High School and Capital Campaign.
$50,000 to Therapeutic Riding of Tucson, Tucson, AZ, 2012. For Therapeutic Riding Lessons for Children W/Special Ne.
$45,000 to Casa de los Ninos, Tucson, AZ, 2012. To support Its Crisis Center Program.
$40,000 to Child and Parent Services, Elkhart, IN, 2012. For Endowment and Service Support.
$10,000 to El Rio Foundation, Tucson, AZ, 2012. For Public Charity Teenage Parenting Program.

105
Timothy T. Day Foundation, Inc. ✧
3219 E. Camelback Rd., Ste. 841
Phoenix, AZ 85018-2307

Established in 1997 in AZ.
Donor: Timothy T. Day.
Foundation type: Independent foundation.
Financial data (yr. ended 12/31/13): Assets, $73,689,494 (M); expenditures, $2,900,677; qualifying distributions, $2,641,000; giving activities include $2,641,000 for 41 grants (high: $1,300,000; low: $300).
Fields of interest: Education; Animal welfare; Human services; Children/youth, services; United Ways and Federated Giving Programs; Military/veterans' organizations.
Type of support: General/operating support.
Limitations: Applications not accepted. Giving primarily in AZ, MA, VA, and WY. No grants to individuals.
Application information: Contributes only to pre-selected organizations.
Officers and Directors:* Timothy T. Day,* Pres.; Sandra R. Day,* V.P.; Richard Mallery, Secy.; Stacy Tucker,* Treas.; Bryan W. Day; Timothy T. Day, Jr.; William Eric Christopher Gleason; Leslie Day Pellillo.
EIN: 860870436

106
Delta Dental of Arizona Charitable Foundation and Trust ✧
5656 W. Talavi Blvd.
Glendale, AZ 85306-1876 (602) 588-3922
Contact: Dawn Lorenzo, Dir., Philanthropy
FAX: (602) 548-5023;
E-mail: dlorenzo@deltadentalaz.com; Contact for Community Grants Program: Dr. Sandi Perez, Ph.D., V.P., Communications and Community Benefit, E-mail: sperez@deltadentalaz.com; Main URL: http://www.deltadentalaz.com/foundation/index.asp
Facebook: https://www.facebook.com/DeltaDentalAZ
Twitter: http://twitter.com/DeltaDentalAZ
YouTube: http://www.youtube.com/user/DeltaDentalAZ?feature=mhee

Established in 1996 in AZ.
Donor: Arizona Dental Insurance Services, Inc.
Foundation type: Company-sponsored foundation.
Financial data (yr. ended 12/31/12): Assets, $4,173,221 (M); gifts received, $1,779,232; expenditures, $803,067; qualifying distributions, $701,951; giving activities include $462,233 for 41 grants (high: $101,591; low: $75).
Purpose and activities: The foundation supports organizations involved with dental care, oral health, and human services. Special emphasis is directed toward underserved and uninsured populations.
Fields of interest: Health care, clinics/centers; Dental care; Children/youth, services; Human services; Economically disadvantaged.
Type of support: Matching/challenge support; Program development; Seed money; Sponsorships; Donated products; In-kind gifts.
Limitations: Applications accepted. Giving primarily in areas of company operations in Phoenix, AZ. No support for religious organizations not of direct benefit to the entire community or lobbying organizations. No grants to individuals, or sponsorships or attendance at conferences, debt reduction, or fundraising.
Publications: Application guidelines; Newsletter.
Application information: Letters of inquiry should be no longer than 1 page. A full application may be requested for Community Grants Program. Additional information and a site visit may be requested. Application form required.
Initial approach: E-mail letter of inquiry for Community Grants Program; contact foundation for Fluoride Varnish Program
Deadline(s): Oct. 1 to Nov. 1 for letters of inquiry for Community Grants Program; Dec. 1 for full application for Community Grants Program; None for Fluoride Varnish Program
Board meeting date(s): Quarterly
Final notification: Feb. for Community Grants Program
Officers and Directors:* James P. Davis, D.D.S.*, Chair.; Karen Berrigan, D.M.D.*, Vice-Chair.; Rebecca Kenyon,* Secy.; Felix Durazo,* Treas.; Allan Allford; Alisa Diggs; Susan Fry; Keith Guazza; Don Henninger; Kathy LaVoy; Alison Lund; Kendis Muscheid; Fred Olson; Xavier Ortega; Philip Stoker; Tim Wilson, D.D.S.
EIN: 860842694
Selected grants: The following grants are a representative sample of this grantmaker's funding activity:
$15,000 to Central Arizona Shelter Services, Phoenix, AZ, 2012. For Community Grant - Murphy Dental Clinic.
$15,000 to Chicanos Por La Causa, Phoenix, AZ, 2012. For Community Grant - Children's Oral Health Services.
$15,000 to Midwestern University, Glendale, AZ, 2012. For Community Grant - Super Sealant Saturday.
$14,188 to Southwest Human Development, Phoenix, AZ, 2012. For Community Grant - Oral Health Education Program.
$10,000 to Arizona Community Foundation, Phoenix, AZ, 2012. For community grant.
$10,000 to International Rescue Committee, Phoenix, AZ, 2012. For Community Grant - Prenatal and Postnatal Oral Health.
$10,000 to Wellcare Foundation, Phoenix, AZ, 2012. For Community Grant - Oral Health Prevention and Education.
$6,000 to Noraz Poets, Sedona, AZ, 2012. For Community Grant - You Can't Be Heard Without a Healthy Mouth Education Campaign.
$2,500 to Association for Supportive Child Care, Tempe, AZ, 2012. For sponsorship - clinical.

107
Dorrance Family Foundation ✧
7600 E. Doubletree Ranch Rd., Ste. 300
Scottsdale, AZ 85258-2137 (480) 367-7000

Established in 1991 in AZ.
Donor: Bennett Dorrance.
Foundation type: Independent foundation.
Financial data (yr. ended 12/31/12): Assets, $53,793,078 (M); expenditures, $4,577,504; qualifying distributions, $4,314,106; giving activities include $4,110,100 for 89 grants (high: $1,436,707; low: $500).
Purpose and activities: Giving primarily for education and national resource conservation.
Fields of interest: Museums (science/technology); Arts; Elementary/secondary education; Higher education, college; Environment, natural resources.
Limitations: Applications not accepted. Giving primarily in AZ. No grants to individuals.
Application information: Contributes only to pre-selected organizations.
Officers and Directors:* Bennett Dorrance,* Pres.; Bennett Dorrance, Jr.,* V.P.; Jacquelynn W. Dorrance,* Secy.; Ashley Dorrance Kaplan,* Treas.
Number of staff: 1 full-time professional; 1 part-time professional.
EIN: 860691863
Selected grants: The following grants are a representative sample of this grantmaker's funding activity:
$1,436,707 to Arizona Community Foundation, Phoenix, AZ, 2012. For Dorrance Scholarship Program.
$1,386,707 to Arizona Community Foundation, Phoenix, AZ, 2012. For Dorrance Scholarship Program.
$100,000 to Ballet Arizona, Phoenix, AZ, 2012. For general operating support.
$100,000 to Translational Genomics Research Institute Foundation, Phoenix, AZ, 2012. To hire Patient Care Coordinator in Center for Rare Childhood Disorders.
$74,000 to Arizona Community Foundation, Phoenix, AZ, 2012. For Dorrance Scholarship Program.
$60,000 to POPSICLE Center, Feeding Matters, Scottsdale, AZ, 2012. To upgrade website.
$50,000 to Barrow Neurological Foundation, Phoenix, AZ, 2012. For Barrow Neurological Society's Grand Ball event.
$25,000 to Arizona Centennial 2012 Foundation, Phoenix, AZ, 2012. For general program support.
$25,000 to Not My Kid, Scottsdale, AZ, 2012. For Be The Ball Event.
$20,000 to Kahilu Theater Foundation, Kamuela, HI, 2012. For Kahilu Theater Youth Summer Arts.

108
The Emerald Foundation ✧
c/o Phil Giltner, Shamrock Foods
3900 E. Camelback Rd., Ste. 300
Phoenix, AZ 85018-2615

Established in 2006 in AZ.
Donor: Frances McClelland†.
Foundation type: Independent foundation.
Financial data (yr. ended 12/31/13): Assets, $2,428,875 (M); expenditures, $1,934,902; qualifying distributions, $1,927,000; giving activities include $1,927,000 for 13 grants (high: $500,000; low: $10,000).
Fields of interest: Higher education; Education; Hospitals (specialty); Human services; Children/youth, services; Foundations (private grantmaking).
Limitations: Applications not accepted. Giving primarily in Phoenix and Tucson, AZ. No grants for individuals.
Application information: Contributes only to pre-selected organizations.
Directors: John Christian; F. Philips Giltner; Pricilla Kuhn; Joan Parker Schuerman; William Voigt.
EIN: 203820912

109
Every Voice In Action Foundation ✧ ☆
1300 S. Belvedere Ave.
Tucson, AZ 85711-5701 (520) 615-2100
Contact: Judith Anderson, C.E.O.; Ruth Marblestone, Oper. Mgr.
MySpace: http://www.myspace.com/everyvoiceaz
Tumblr: http://everyvoiceaz.tumblr.com/
Twitter: http://twitter.com/everyvoiceaz

Established in 2001 in AZ.
Foundation type: Independent foundation.
Financial data (yr. ended 06/30/13): Assets, $7,048,790 (M); expenditures, $1,172,574; qualifying distributions, $1,071,800; giving activities include $887,668 for 2 grants (high: $785,015; low: $102,653).
Purpose and activities: Every Voice in Action is a small, private foundation supporting Youth Voice-focused nonprofit programs in Tucson and Pima County, Arizona. The mission of the foundation is to ignite and support youth voice, infusing the community with the unique perspectives of young people. The foundation supports Youth Voice programs, including those focused on youth activism, youth media, youth as resources and youth philanthropy.
Fields of interest: Youth development, services; Youth.
Type of support: General/operating support; Equipment; Program development; Film/video/radio; Technical assistance; Matching/challenge support.
Limitations: Giving limited to Tucson and Pima County, AZ. No support for religious programs and any program that practices or promotes discrimination against people. No grants to individuals or for government services, public school services required by law, and projects that jeopardize an organization's tax-exempt status; no loans or deficit funding.
Publications: Grants list.
Application information:
Board meeting date(s): Jan.
Officers and Directors:* Scott Lunn,* Chair.; Judith Anderson, C.E.O. and Pres.; Rofaidah Al Shamir, Secy.; Daniel Arellano,* Treas.; David Aquino; Andres Cano; Rosie Garcia; Massie Gebedou; Jose Hoyos; Manny Leon; Trey Spiece.
Number of staff: 3 full-time professional; 1 part-time support.
EIN: 860988206

110
Alberta B. Farrington Foundation ✧
5825 E. Pinnacle Vista Dr.
Scottsdale, AZ 85266-8745

Established in 1992 in AZ.
Donor: Alberta B. Farrington†.
Foundation type: Independent foundation.
Financial data (yr. ended 12/31/13): Assets, $11,629,888 (L); expenditures, $726,837; qualifying distributions, $577,913; giving activities include $505,558 for 39 grants (high: $55,000; low: $400).
Purpose and activities: Giving primarily to Roman Catholic agencies, churches, and schools, as well as for higher education, health associations, children, youth, and social services, and to a junior golf association.
Fields of interest: Higher education; Health organizations, association; Food banks; Recreation, association; Human services; Children/youth, services; Foundations (private grantmaking); Catholic agencies & churches.
Limitations: Applications not accepted. Giving primarily in AZ, with some emphasis on Phoenix. No grants to individuals.
Application information: Unsolicited requests for funds not accepted.
Officers: Geri J. Cavanagh, Pres.; Michael Cavanagh, Secy.-Treas.
Directors: Harry J. Cavanagh, Jr.; Jamie Hufford.
Number of staff: 1 part-time professional.
EIN: 860717723
Selected grants: The following grants are a representative sample of this grantmaker's funding activity:
$10,000 to Sun Angel Foundation, Tempe, AZ, 2012. For All of the Contributions Are to Public Charities and Are Generally Not Restricted As to Use.

111
The Flinn Foundation ✧
1802 N. Central Ave.
Phoenix, AZ 85004-1506 (602) 744-6800
Contact: Jack B. Jewett, C.E.O.
FAX: (602) 744-6815; E-mail: info@flinn.org; Main URL: http://www.flinn.org
Arizona Biosciences Feed: http://www.flinn.org/feed.rss
Bioscience Roadmap: http://www.flinn.org/bio-roadmap/reports-and-multimedia
E-Newsletter: http://www.flinn.org/newsletter-signup
Twitter: http://www.twitter.com/biozonanews
Scholarship tel.: (602) 744-6802, e-mail: fscholars@flinn.org

Established in 1965 in AZ.
Donors: Irene Flinn†; Robert S. Flinn, M.D.†.
Foundation type: Independent foundation.
Financial data (yr. ended 12/31/12): Assets, $194,755,468 (M); gifts received, $172,814; expenditures, $10,138,784; qualifying distributions, $8,937,578; giving activities include $5,250,603 for 61 grants (high: $2,500,000; low: $1,620), and $2,470,177 for foundation-administered programs.
Purpose and activities: Giving to improve the quality of life in Arizona to benefit future generations, by improving the competitiveness of Arizona's biomedical/research enterprise; by strengthening universities through an undergraduate scholarship program for outstanding high school students; and by furthering the artistic mission and strengthening the institutional capacity of principal visual and performing arts organizations.
Fields of interest: Arts; Higher education; Medical research, institute; Biology/life sciences.
Type of support: Program development; Seed money; Scholarship funds; Research.
Limitations: Applications accepted. Giving limited to AZ. No grants for building projects, purchase of equipment, endowment projects, annual fundraising campaigns, ongoing operating expenses or deficit needs; requests to support conferences and workshops, publications, or the production of films and video are considered only when these activities are an integral component of a larger foundation initiative.
Publications: Annual report; Financial statement; Newsletter; Occasional report.
Application information: Applications accepted for Flinn Scholarship only. Application form required.
Initial approach: See foundation web site for scholarship information and application form procedures
Deadline(s): Oct. 19 for scholarships
Board meeting date(s): Quarterly
Officers and Directors:* David J. Gullen, M.D.*, Chair.; Steven M. Wheeler,* Vice-Chair.; Jack B. Jewett, C.E.O. and Pres.; Cathy McGonigle, Exec. V.P.; William A. Read, Ph.D., Sr. V.P., Research and Special Programs; Don P. Snider, V.P. and C.F.O.; Bradley W. Halvorsen, V.P., Comms.; Nancy Welch, V.P., Arizona Center for Civic Leadership; Eric M. Reiman, M.D.*, Secy.; Rosellen C. Papp,* Treas.; Robert A. Brooks, M.D., Honorary Dir.; David R. Frazer, Honorary Dir.; Merlin W. Kampfer, M.D., Honorary Dir.; Edward V. O'Malley, Jr., Honorary Dir.; Lisa Wilkinson-Fannin, M.D., Honorary Dir.; Linda J. Blessing, Ph.D.; Drew M. Brown; Richard J. Caselli, M.D.; Shaun A. Kirkpatrick; W. Scott Robertson, M.D.
Number of staff: 10 full-time professional; 7 full-time support.
EIN: 860421476

112
Freeport-McMoRan Copper & Gold Foundation ✧
(formerly Phelps Dodge Foundation)
333 N. Central Ave.
Phoenix, AZ 85004-2189 (602) 366-8116
Contact: Angie Harmon, Social Investment Mgr.
FAX: (602) 366-7305; E-mail: foundation@fmi.com; E-mail for Angie Harmon: Angie_Harmon@fmi.com; Additional tel.: (800) 528-1182, ext. 8116; fax: (602) 366-7323; e-mail: communitydevelopment@fmi.com; Main URL: http://www.freeportinmycommunity.com/
Grants Database: http://www.freeportinmycommunity.com/nonprofits/search-our-grants
Contact for Scholarship Program: Brittany Watkins, e-mail: brittany_watkins@fmi.com

Incorporated in 1953 in NY.

Donor: Phelps Dodge Corp.
Foundation type: Company-sponsored foundation.
Financial data (yr. ended 12/31/13): Assets, $4,099,021 (M); gifts received, $17,000,000; expenditures, $20,132,946; qualifying distributions, $20,132,309; giving activities include $15,114,051 for 175+ grants (high: $1,300,000), and $5,018,258 for employee matching gifts.
Purpose and activities: The foundation supports organizations involved with arts and culture, education, the environment, health, mental health, crime and violence prevention, employment, nutrition, housing, safety, recreation, human services, community development, science, civic affairs, and economically disadvantaged people.
Fields of interest: Arts, cultural/ethnic awareness; Arts; Elementary/secondary education; Education, early childhood education; Vocational education; Higher education; Teacher school/education; Adult/continuing education; Education, reading; Education; Environment, natural resources; Environment, water resources; Environment, land resources; Environment, forests; Environmental education; Environment; Hospitals (general); Public health, physical fitness; Health care; Substance abuse, prevention; Mental health/crisis services; Crime/violence prevention, domestic violence; Crime/violence prevention, child abuse; Employment, training; Employment; Nutrition; Housing/shelter; Disasters, preparedness/services; Safety/disasters; Recreation; Youth development, adult & child programs; Children/youth, services; Family services; Family services, domestic violence; Human services; Economic development; Economic development, visitors/convention bureau/tourism promotion; Business/industry; Community development, small businesses; Community/economic development; United Ways and Federated Giving Programs; Science, formal/general education; Physical/earth sciences; Mathematics; Geology; Engineering/technology; Science; Transportation; Leadership development; Public affairs; Native Americans/American Indians; Women; Girls; Economically disadvantaged.
Type of support: General/operating support; Continuing support; Management development/capacity building; Annual campaigns; Equipment; Curriculum development; Internship funds; Scholarship funds; Research; Employee volunteer services; Employee matching gifts; Employee-related scholarships; Scholarships—to individuals; Matching/challenge support.
Limitations: Applications accepted. Giving primarily in areas of company operations in Ajo, Bagdad, Bisbee Area, Clarkdale, Globe, Graham County, Green Valley, Greenlee County, Jerome, Miami, Phoenix, Sahuarita, Tucson, AZ, Chafee County, Clear Creek County, Denver, Eagle County, Grand County, Lake County, and Summit County, CO, Norwich, CT, Ft. Madison, IA, Jefferson Parish, Lafayette Parish, New Orleans, Plaquemines Parish, St. Bernard Parish, St. Charles Parish, St. John the Baptist Parish, St. Tammany Parish, and Tangipahoa Parish, LA, Elizabeth, NJ, Grant County, NM, and El Paso and Houston, TX; also serving Native American Communities of Hualapai, San Carlos Apache, Tohono O'odham, and White Mountain Apache. No support for discriminatory organizations, fraternal, veterans', or labor organizations, churches or religious organizations not of direct benefit to the entire community, political or lobbying organizations, pass-through foundations, or auxiliary organizations. No grants to individuals (except for scholarships), or for travel, conference fees, medical procedures, advertising, religious activities, or debt reduction or operational deficits.
Publications: Application guidelines; Grants list; Informational brochure (including application guidelines); Program policy statement.
Application information: Organizations receiving STEM Innovation Grants are required to submit a final report. Application form required.
Initial approach: Complete online application; download application form and mail to participating schools for scholarships
Copies of proposal: 1
Deadline(s): Mar. 1 to Aug. 30 for Genl. Social Investment Prog.; May 1 to Oct. 1 for Mini-Grants for Education; Dec. 1 to Mar. 15 for STEM Innovation Grants; Mar. 30, June 30, and Sept. 30 for Native American Partnership Fund; Aug. 1 to Oct. 1 for Women's Development; Varies for Community Investment Funds
Board meeting date(s): May
Final notification: Jan. for Genl. Social Investment Prog.; May 30, Aug. 30, and Nov. 30 for Native American Partnership Fund; Oct. 1 for Mini-Grants for Education; Nov. 15 for Women's Development
Officers and Directors:* Tracy L. Bame,* Pres.; Michael J. Arnold,* V.P.; Dean T. Falgoust, V.P.; Douglas N. Currault II, Secy.; Kathleen L. Quirk,* Treas.; Pamela Q. Masson, Exec. Dir.; Richard C. Adkerson; Suzanne G. Lebaron; L. Richards McMillan II.
Number of staff: 2 part-time professional; 1 part-time support.
EIN: 136077350
Selected grants: The following grants are a representative sample of this grantmaker's funding activity:
$1,300,000 to National World War II Museum, New Orleans, LA, 2013.
$1,089,300 to Thunderbird, The Garvin School of International Management, Glendale, AZ, 2013. For Women's Business Training.
$1,000,000 to LSU Foundation, Baton Rouge, LA, 2013. For Taylor Hall/Chemical Engineering Building Project.
$700,000 to Science Foundation Arizona, Phoenix, AZ, 2013. For Science, Technology, Engineering and Math Initiative/Network.
$500,000 to Arizona Youth Partnership, Marana, AZ, 2013.
$500,000 to Phoenix Childrens Hospital, Phoenix, AZ, 2013.
$500,000 to Women for Women International, Washington, DC, 2013. For Agriculture Training Program for women in DRC.
$222,000 to Graham County Community Investment Fund, Phoenix, AZ, 2013.
$35,000 to Owens-Whitney Elementary School, Wikieup, AZ, 2013.
$35,000 to W Y E S Greater New Orleans Educational Television Foundation, New Orleans, LA, 2013.

113
Fulton Family Foundation ✧
9140 S. Kyrene Rd., Ste. 202
Tempe, AZ 85284-2929 (480) 753-6789
Contact: Ira A. Fulton, C.E.O. and Dir.

Established in 1986 in CA.
Donor: Ira A. Fulton.
Foundation type: Independent foundation.
Financial data (yr. ended 12/31/13): Assets, $5,469,077 (M); expenditures, $2,028,272; qualifying distributions, $2,000,000; giving activities include $2,000,000 for 1 grant.
Fields of interest: ALS research.
Limitations: Applications accepted. Giving in the U.S., with emphasis on AZ. No grants to individuals.
Application information: Application form required.
Initial approach: Letter
Deadline(s): None
Officer and Directors:* Ira A. Fulton,* C.E.O.; Mary Lou Fulton,* Secy.; Douglas S. Fulton; Lorie Ann Nicholls.
EIN: 954080516
Selected grants: The following grants are a representative sample of this grantmaker's funding activity:
$1,500,000 to Barrow Neurological Foundation, Phoenix, AZ, 2012. For Barrow Neurological Institute - AL's Research.

114
Giving Hope Worldwide Foundation ✧
7175 E. Camelback Rd., Ste. 503
Scottsdale, AZ 85251-1296
Main URL: http://www.givinghopeworldwide.com/

Donors: Kelly C. Park; Michelle M. Park; Park Corporation.
Foundation type: Independent foundation.
Financial data (yr. ended 12/31/13): Assets, $13,448,068 (M); gifts received, $100,000; expenditures, $1,120,532; qualifying distributions, $1,073,742; giving activities include $1,053,036 for 35 grants (high: $157,905; low: $500).
Fields of interest: Education; Health care; Housing/shelter.
Limitations: Applications not accepted. Giving primarily in AZ and CA.
Application information: Unsolicited requests for funds not accepted.
Directors: Kelly C. Park; Michelle M. Park.
EIN: 274201354

115
Globe Foundation ✧
6730 N. Scottsdale Rd., Ste. 250
Scottsdale, AZ 85253-4424

Established in 1958 in IL.
Donors: Bert A. Getz; George F. Getz, Jr.†.
Foundation type: Independent foundation.
Financial data (yr. ended 12/31/13): Assets, $29,454,893 (M); expenditures, $2,832,832; qualifying distributions, $1,976,333; giving activities include $1,976,056 for 67 grants (high: $572,000; low: $500).
Purpose and activities: Giving primarily for education, as well as for children, youth and social services.
Fields of interest: Higher education; Education; Zoos/zoological societies; Hospitals (general); Human services; Children/youth, services; Foundations (private grantmaking).
Type of support: General/operating support; Continuing support; Annual campaigns; Capital campaigns; Building/renovation; Equipment; Endowments; Program development; Professorships; Curriculum development; Research;

Employee matching gifts; Matching/challenge support.
Limitations: Applications not accepted. Giving primarily in AZ and IL. No support for privately supported groups. No grants to individuals.
Application information: Unsolicited requests for funds not accepted.
Officers and Directors:* Bert A. Getz,* Pres.; Bert A. Getz, Jr.,* V.P.; Lynn Getz-Schmidt,* V.P.; George F. Getz,* Secy.; Michael J. Olsen, Treas.; James L. Johnson; Rock S. Edwards.
EIN: 366054050

116
William M. & Ann K. Grace Foundation ✧
c/o William Matt Grace Development Co.
7575 N. 16th St., Ste. 1
Phoenix, AZ 85020-4625 (602) 956-8254
Contact: Ron Richards, Dir.
FAX: (602) 943-3548;
E-mail: ronrichards@wmgracefoundation.com; Main URL: http://www.wmgracefoundation.com

Established in 2005 in AZ.
Donor: Ann K. Grace Charitable Lea Ann Trust.
Foundation type: Independent foundation.
Financial data (yr. ended 12/31/13): Assets, $11,851,826 (M); gifts received, $1,875,100; expenditures, $752,728; qualifying distributions, $736,857; giving activities include $736,857 for 43 grants (high: $155,750; low: $1,000).
Purpose and activities: The foundation provides individual scholarships directly to students (for all levels of school, including private grade schools, high schools, colleges, universities) with scholarships given for merit or need. The foundation also makes grants for existing scholarship funds, as well as grants directly to schools for facilities, scholarships or general support. The foundation strongly encourages and gives preference to matching funds where it concerns grants to organizations.
Fields of interest: Higher education.
Type of support: General/operating support; Scholarship funds; Scholarships—to individuals; Matching/challenge support.
Limitations: Applications accepted. Giving primarily in AZ and northwest MO.
Application information: Application form required.
Initial approach: Submit application form (which can be downloaded from foundation web site) via U.S. mail, fax or e-mail
Deadline(s): Nov. 15
Officers and Board Members:* Howard T. Grace,* Pres.; Barb Grace; Matt Grace; Heather G. Kaiser.
Directors: Kate Kaiser; Ron Richards.
EIN: 562529760

117
The George Mason and Lois C. Green Foundation ✧
2440 E. Broadway
Tucson, AZ 85719-6008 (520) 791-3939
Contact: Linda Lohse, Secy.
FAX: (520) 791-3995; Main URL: http://www.tucsonfoundations.org

Established in 1986 in AZ.
Donors: Lois C. Green†; G.M. Green Unitrust; George Mason Green†.
Foundation type: Independent foundation.
Financial data (yr. ended 12/31/13): Assets, $14,433,573 (M); gifts received, $134,545; expenditures, $1,019,961; qualifying distributions, $965,110; giving activities include $857,430 for 12 grants (high: $371,000; low: $1,500).
Fields of interest: Arts; Human services; Children/youth, services.
Type of support: General/operating support; Annual campaigns; Capital campaigns; Building/renovation; Endowments; Emergency funds.
Limitations: Giving primarily in Tucson, AZ. No grants to individuals.
Application information: Unsolicited requests for funds are not currently accepted. Refer to foundation web site for updates.
Officers: Robert Lohse, Pres.; Jennifer Lohse, V.P.; Linda Lohse, Secy.; Patricia Lohse, Treas.
Director: Jason DePizzo.
Number of staff: 3
EIN: 742379340
Selected grants: The following grants are a representative sample of this grantmaker's funding activity:
$375,600 to University of Arizona Foundation, Tucson, AZ, 2012. For Community Education and Capital.
$100,000 to TMC Foundation, Tucson, AZ, 2012. For health capital funds.
$8,898 to University of Arizona, Tucson, AZ, 2012. For education scholarships.

118
Bruce T. Halle Family Foundation ✧
20225 N. Scottsdale Rd.
Scottsdale, AZ 85255-6456 (480) 515-7500
Contact: Diane M. Halle, Pres.
E-mail: info@hallefamilyfoundation.org; Main URL: http://hallefamilyfoundation.org

Established in 2002 in AZ.
Donors: Bruce T. Halle, Sr.; Diane M. Halle; Richard Kuipers; Laura Kuipers; Susan Halle Lyle; Dean Muglia; Chris Pedersen; Lisa Pedersen; Bruce T. Halle, Jr.; Michael Zuieback; Sheila Zuieback; Reinalt-Thomas Corporation; Preisman-Beriro; Pirelli Tire North America; Yokohama Tire Corporation; The Continental Tire America, LLC; Michelin North America, Inc.; Cooper Tire and Rubber Foundation; Rosenbaum Advisors; Wheels Pros; Colony Cabinets, Inc.; Nitto Tire USA, Inc.; CKGH Law, PC.
Foundation type: Independent foundation.
Financial data (yr. ended 12/31/13): Assets, $84,438 (M); gifts received, $8,735,250; expenditures, $8,663,584; qualifying distributions, $8,663,584; giving activities include $8,627,033 for 70+ grants (high: $2,000,000).
Purpose and activities: Giving primarily for health care including health organizations, education, the arts, children, youth, women, and social services.
Fields of interest: Museums (art); Museums (specialized); Performing arts; Arts; Elementary/secondary education; Higher education; Education; Hospitals (specialty); Health care, infants; Health organizations, association; Medical research, association; Food banks; Human services; Children/youth, services; Foundations (community); Catholic agencies & churches; Women.
Limitations: Giving primarily in AZ; some funding also in CA and CO. No grants to individuals.
Application information: Application form not required.
Initial approach: Letter
Deadline(s): Mar. 15 and Sept. 15
Officers and Directors:* Diane M. Halle,* Chair. and Pres.; Nikki Halle,* V.P.; Lisa Pedersen,* Secy.; Chris Pederson,* Treas.; Bruce T. Halle, Jr.; Susan Halle-Lyle; Michael S. Zuieback; Sheila Zuieback.
EIN: 460469787

119
Herberger Foundation ✧
10881 N. Scottsdale Rd., Ste. 200
Scottsdale, AZ 85254-6715

Established in 1961 in AZ.
Donors: G.R. Herberger†; Mrs. G.R. Herberger†; Gary K. Herberger; G.R. Herberger Revocable Trust; Herberger Enterprises, Inc.
Foundation type: Independent foundation.
Financial data (yr. ended 12/31/13): Assets, $8,588,279 (M); expenditures, $2,476,249; qualifying distributions, $2,460,134; giving activities include $2,445,000 for 9 grants (high: $1,200,000; low: $10,000).
Purpose and activities: Giving primarily for the arts and education.
Fields of interest: Performing arts; Arts; Higher education; Children/youth, services.
Limitations: Applications not accepted. Giving primarily in AZ, with emphasis on Phoenix. No grants to individuals; no loans or program-related investments.
Application information: Contributes only to pre-selected organizations.
Officers and Directors:* Gary K. Herberger,* C.E.O.; Judd R. Herberger,* Pres.; Michael J. Dempsey,* V.P.; Billie Jo Herberger,* V.P.; Jeanne L. Herberger,* V.P.; Denise K. Hornbaker,* Secy.-Treas.
EIN: 866050190

120
The Hermundslie Foundation ✧
3762 N. Harrison Rd.
Tucson, AZ 85749-8942 (520) 749-8501
Contact: Gerold D. Hermundslie, Dir.

Established in 1968 in AZ.
Foundation type: Independent foundation.
Financial data (yr. ended 12/31/13): Assets, $13,484,669 (M); expenditures, $1,914,768; qualifying distributions, $1,914,768; giving activities include $1,593,376 for 7 grants (high: $1,137,646; low: $2,000).
Fields of interest: Education; Health organizations, association; Youth development, services; Pregnancy centers; Christian agencies & churches.
Type of support: Research.
Limitations: Applications accepted. Giving primarily in Tucson, AZ. No grants to individuals.
Application information: Application form required.
Initial approach: Proposal
Deadline(s): None
Directors: Gloria Fitzgerald; Carol Hermundslie; Gerold D. Hermundslie; John Hibbard.
EIN: 237001359
Selected grants: The following grants are a representative sample of this grantmaker's funding activity:
$942,721 to Desert Christian Schools, Tucson, AZ, 2011.

121
Hickey Family Foundation ✧
530 E. Huber St.
Mesa, AZ 85203-3648
Contact: Nancy E. Baldwin, Tr.
FAX: (480) 461-8398;
E-mail: hickeyfamilyfoundation@cox.net; Main URL: http://www.hickeyfoundation.org/

Established in 2004 in AZ.
Donors: Francis G. Hickey, Jr.‡; Frank Hickey Trust.
Foundation type: Independent foundation.
Financial data (yr. ended 12/31/12): Assets, $134,617,275 (M); gifts received, $4,465; expenditures, $6,601,256; qualifying distributions, $5,857,256; giving activities include $5,360,724 for 33 grants (high: $384,639; low: $20,000), and $150,000 for 1 employee matching gift.
Purpose and activities: The foundation's mission is to support the rescue of youth projects, medical technology development and medical training center development projects.
Fields of interest: Higher education; Medical research; Youth development, services; Youth, services; Children/youth; Youth; Young adults; Homeless.
International interests: Africa; Dominican Republic; Haiti; Philippines; West Bank/Gaza (Palestinian Territories).
Type of support: General/operating support; Management development/capacity building; Capital campaigns; Building/renovation; Program development; Research; Matching/challenge support.
Limitations: Applications not accepted. Giving on a world wide basis.
Application information: Unsolicited requests for funds not accepted.
Board meeting date(s): Quarterly
Trustees: Nancy E. Baldwin; Eljay B. Bowron; Christopher J. McNaughton; Kenneth L. Naiff; Gary S. Stein.
Agent: Deutsche Bank AG; US Trust, N.A.
Number of staff: 1 full-time professional.
EIN: 866331657
Selected grants: The following grants are a representative sample of this grantmaker's funding activity:
$750,000 to International Medical Corps, Los Angeles, CA, 2012. For hurricane and cholera epidemic relief in Haiti, medical training in South Sudan, DRC.
$244,000 to Indiana University-Purdue University Indianapolis, School of Medicine, Indianapolis, IN, 2012. To develop new medicine for treatment of Lou Gehrig's Disease or Amyotrophic Lateral Sclerosis (ALS).
$200,000 to NPH USA, Chicago, IL, 2012. For Shinsky Matamoros Orphanage Project.
$115,000 to NPH USA, Chicago, IL, 2012. To education orphans in Mexico.

122
Hill Foundation ✧
c/o Wells Fargo Bank Arizona, N.A.
P.O. Box 53456, MAC S4101-22G
Phoenix, AZ 85072-3456
Application address: c/o Wells Fargo Bank West, N.A., 1740 Broadway, Denver, CO 90274, tel.: (720) 947-6725

Established in 1955 in CO.
Donor: Virginia W. Hill‡.
Foundation type: Independent foundation.
Financial data (yr. ended 04/30/13): Assets, $37,096,414 (M); expenditures, $2,594,366; qualifying distributions, $1,982,299; giving activities include $1,887,450 for 172 grants (high: $100,000; low: $3,000).
Purpose and activities: Grants largely for health care for the medically indigent, higher education, services for the elderly, and cultural programs; support also for social service agencies and the disabled, as well as the arts, particularly the opera.
Fields of interest: Performing arts, opera; Arts; Higher education; Education; Hospitals (general); Health care, financing; Health organizations, association; Human services; Catholic federated giving programs; Catholic agencies & churches; Homeless.
Type of support: Program development; Scholarship funds; Matching/challenge support.
Limitations: Giving primarily in CO and WY. No grants to individuals, or for capital improvements other than equipment acquisition for health care and related purposes.
Publications: Informational brochure; Program policy statement.
Application information:
Initial approach: Letter
Deadline(s): None
Final notification: Within 5 weeks
Trustees: Francis W. Collopy; John R. Moran; Margaret L. Toal; Wells Fargo Bank West, N.A.
EIN: 846081879
Selected grants: The following grants are a representative sample of this grantmaker's funding activity:
$30,000 to Colorado State University, Fort Collins, CO, 2012.
$10,000 to Habitat for Humanity of Colorado, Lakewood, CO, 2012.
$10,000 to SET of Colorado Springs, Colorado Springs, CO, 2012.
$10,000 to Urban Peak Colorado Springs, Colorado Springs, CO, 2012.
$10,000 to Volunteers of America, Alexandria, VA, 2012.
$5,000 to Adoption Exchange, Aurora, CO, 2012.
$5,000 to American Indian College Fund, Denver, CO, 2012.
$5,000 to Book Trust, Fort Collins, CO, 2012.
$5,000 to Colorado Springs Ecumenical Social Ministries, Colorado Springs, CO, 2012. For general operating support.
$5,000 to Urban Peak Colorado Springs, Colorado Springs, CO, 2012.

123
Ben and Catherine Ivy Foundation ✧
6710 N. Scottsdale Rd., Ste. 235
Scottsdale, AZ 85253-4407 (480) 659-9621
FAX: (480) 659-9651;
E-mail: info@ivyfoundation.org; Main URL: http://www.ivyfoundation.org
E-Newsletter: http://www.ivyfoundation.org/news/ivy
Facebook: https://www.facebook.com/IvyFoundation
Google Plus: https://plus.google.com/105982076267406579679/posts#105982076267406579679/posts
LinkedIn: http://www.linkedin.com/company/the-ben-&-catherine-ivy-foundation
Twitter: http://twitter.com/ivyfoundation
Wordpress: http://ivyfoundation.wordpress.com/
YouTube: http://www.youtube.com/IvyFoundationGBM

Established in 2005 in CA.
Donors: Ben F. Ivy‡; Ben F. Ivy Trust; Catherine Ivy.
Foundation type: Independent foundation.
Financial data (yr. ended 12/31/13): Assets, $214,214,189 (M); gifts received, $68; expenditures, $10,559,465; qualifying distributions, $10,040,677; giving activities include $9,046,278 for 24 grants (high: $3,684,000; low: $100).
Purpose and activities: Giving primarily for patient-focused gliomas research and development of better diagnostics and treatment that offer long-term survival and high-quality of life for patients with brain tumors.
Fields of interest: Cancer research; Brain research.
Limitations: Applications not accepted. Giving primarily in CA and Washington, DC.
Application information: Unsolicited requests for funds are currently not accepted. Refer to foundation web site for updates on this matter.
Officers and Directors:* Catherine E. Ivy,* Pres.; Stephanie McRae, Esq.*, Secy.; Megan Edwards,* Treas.
EIN: 203968546
Selected grants: The following grants are a representative sample of this grantmaker's funding activity:
$3,684,000 to Translational Genomics Research Institute, Phoenix, AZ, 2013. For Ivy Genomics-Based Medicine Research Project on specific and optimal therapy for GlioBlastoma Multiforme (GBM).
$3,000,000 to Translational Genomics Research Institute, Phoenix, AZ, 2012. For Ivy Genomics-Based Medicine Research Project on specific and optimal therapy for GlioBlastoma Multiforme (GBM).
$2,800,000 to Stanford University, Stanford, CA, 2012. For Next Generation Neuro-Oncological Imaging Strategies which will make it possible to visualize GlioBlastoma Multiforme (GBM) at molecular level in detail revealing rate at which tumor cells multiply and die, growth of new blood vessels on which tumor enlargement depends, and receptors on tumor cells that could receive chemical signals useful for intervening against the disease.
$1,606,132 to University of California, San Francisco, CA, 2012. For research project, Ivy Foundation Early Phase Clinical Trials Consortium: Identifying Combination Targeted Therapies and Dosing Schedules.
$1,481,548 to University of California, San Francisco, CA, 2013. For research project, Ivy Foundation Early Phase Clinical Trials Consortium: Identifying Combination Targeted Therapies and Dosing Schedules.
$1,000,000 to Stanford University, Stanford, CA, 2013. For Next Generation Neuro-Oncological Imaging Strategies which will make it possible to visualize GlioBlastoma Multiforme (GBM) at molecular level in detail revealing rate at which tumor cells multiply and die, growth of new blood vessels on which tumor enlargement depends, and receptors on tumor cells that could receive chemical signals useful for intervening against the disease.
$750,000 to University of California, Los Angeles, CA, 2013. For Brain Cancer Molecular Diagnostic Translational Medicine Laboratory.
$634,060 to Swedish Medical Center Foundation, Seattle, WA, 2013. To support an integrated

approach using large-scale chemical screens to identify therapeutic agents against turmor initiating cells derived from individual patients. Candidates are evaluated in VIVO in matching patient-derived Xenograft models to allow patient-specific therapeutic agents.
$500,000 to Dana-Farber Cancer Institute, Boston, MA, 2013. For research project, Preclinical Evaluation of Patient-Specific Neoantigen Vaccination Strategy, An Implantable Vaccine Device and Combinatorial Regimens to Enhance Anti-Tumor Immune Responses.
$500,000 to Swedish Medical Center Foundation, Seattle, WA, 2012. To support an integrated approach using large-scale chemical screens to identify therapeutic agents against turmor initiating cells derived from individual patients. Candidates are evaluated in VIVO in matching patient-derived Xenograft models to allow patient-specific therapeutic agents.
$400,000 to Allen Institute for Brain Science, Seattle, WA, 2012. For comprehensive 3D map of gene activity in cancerous brain tumor tissue, specifically glioblastoma, potential to help match patients to best treatments and accelerate discovery of new brain cancer treatments.
$283,776 to Mayo Clinic, Rochester, MN, 2013. For research project, Combining a Patient's Optimized Dendritic Cells (Potent Immune Stimulators) with Pooled and Well-Characterized Lysates from Other Patients' Brain Tumor Cultures to Generate Anti-Tumor Vaccine Incorporating New Methods for Monitoring Changes in the Immune System.
$248,050 to University of Texas M.D. Anderson Cancer Center, Houston, TX, 2013. For research project, Development of Oral Formulation and Toxicity Studies for Inhibitor WP1066, of Signal Transducer ADN Activator or Transcription 3-A Pathway That Drives the Development of Malignant Brain Tumors and Immune Suppression.
$237,160 to Dignity Health, Barrow Neurological Institute at Saint Joseph's Hospital, Phoenix, AZ, 2013. For research project, Phase O Clinical Trial of A Novel Moleculary-Targeted Therapy for Recurrent Glioblastoma Patients.
$75,000 to Massachusetts General Hospital, Boston, MA, 2012. For research which will circulate biomarkers that predict response to an irreversible pan-her kinase inhibitor in EGFR-Amplified GlioBlastoma Multiforme (GBM).
$45,000 to Translational Genomics Research Institute Foundation, Phoenix, AZ, 2012. For Ivy Neurological Sciences Internship Program.
$25,000 to Saint Vincent de Paul Society, Phoenix, AZ, 2012. For general support.
$10,000 to Arizona State University, Tempe, AZ, 2012. For scholarships.
$10,000 to University of Washington, Seattle, WA, 2012. For scholarships.

124
Jasam Foundation Fund B ✧

286 N. Fenceline Dr.
Tucson, AZ 85748-3726

Established in 2002 in AR.
Foundation type: Independent foundation.
Financial data (yr. ended 12/31/12): Assets, $7,763,700 (M); expenditures, $568,834; qualifying distributions, $506,655; giving activities include $485,000 for 25 grants (high: $75,000; low: $5,000).
Purpose and activities: Giving primarily for education, hospitals and health organizations, Christian organizations, human services and U.S. troop support.
Fields of interest: Education; Hospitals (general); Health organizations, association; Human services; Children/youth, services; Christian agencies & churches.
Limitations: Applications not accepted. Giving limited to western MI, and the greater Tucson, AZ, area. No grants to individuals.
Application information: Contributes only to pre-selected organizations.
Board meeting date(s): Varies
Officer: Joan D. Guylas, Admin.
Number of staff: 1 part-time support.
EIN: 383637370
Selected grants: The following grants are a representative sample of this grantmaker's funding activity:
$25,000 to Navy-Marine Corps Relief Society, Arlington, VA, 2011.
$25,000 to Operation Homefront, San Antonio, TX, 2011.
$10,000 to Literacy Volunteers of Tucson, Tucson, AZ, 2011.
$10,000 to Smile Train, New York, NY, 2011.
$10,000 to TMC Foundation, Tucson, AZ, 2011.

125
The Jazzbird Foundation ✧

c/o Robert Ravenscroft
P.O. Box 3410
Carefree, AZ 85377-3410

Established in 1994 in AZ.
Donors: Gretchen F. Ravenscroft; Robert B. Ravenscroft.
Foundation type: Independent foundation.
Financial data (yr. ended 12/31/13): Assets, $187,596 (M); gifts received, $1,499,267; expenditures, $1,471,191; qualifying distributions, $1,127,825; giving activities include $1,127,825 for grants (high: $127,000; low: $1,000).
Purpose and activities: Giving primarily for education, and to Lutheran and other Christian organizations and churches.
Fields of interest: Higher education; Theological school/education; Christian agencies & churches; Protestant agencies & churches.
Limitations: Applications not accepted. Giving primarily in AZ and CA. No grants to individuals.
Application information: Contributes only to pre-selected organizations.
Officers and Directors:* Robert B. Ravenscroft,* Pres.; Gretchen F. Ravenscroft,* V.P.; Lori Geare,* Secy.; Steve F. Buel, Treas.
EIN: 860745156
Selected grants: The following grants are a representative sample of this grantmaker's funding activity:
$53,000 to Arizona State University, Tempe, AZ, 2012. To foster education.

126
Arthur L. "Bud" Johnson in Memory of Elaine V. Johnson Foundation ✧

(also known as Arthur L. & Elaine V. Johnson Foundation)
3881 E. Birchwood Pl.
Chandler, AZ 85249-5570 (480) 632-8693
Contact: David Hammerslag, Managing Tr.
FAX: (480) 545-8949;
E-mail: info@aljfoundation.org; Contacts for Letter of Inquiry: David Hammerslag e-mail: david@aljfoundation.org; Send 1 additional copy of Letter of Inquiry to: Sally Mode, Sr. Tr., 815 Dorr Ave., Rhinelander, WI 54501, e-mail: sally@aljfoundation.org; Main URL: http://www.aljfoundation.org

Established in 1990 in IL.
Donor: Arthur L. Johnson†.
Foundation type: Independent foundation.
Financial data (yr. ended 12/31/13): Assets, $17,374,902 (M); expenditures, $890,826; qualifying distributions, $779,674; giving activities include $673,725 for 20 grants (high: $165,000; low: $725).
Purpose and activities: Giving aid to organizations which provide for the care, benefit, support and preservation of seeing eye dogs or other animals trained to assist the sight impaired or otherwise handicapped individuals, (or that facilitate the use of such animals by sight-impaired or otherwise handicapped individuals); funding also for nature conservancy.
Fields of interest: Environment; Animals/wildlife, training; Animals/wildlife; Physically disabled; Blind/visually impaired.
Type of support: Management development/capacity building; Capital campaigns; Building/renovation; Equipment; Land acquisition; Program development; Conferences/seminars; Seed money; Research; Consulting services; Program evaluation; Matching/challenge support.
Limitations: Applications accepted. Giving on a national basis. No support for the therapeutic use of animals. No grants to individuals.
Publications: Application guidelines; Grants list; IRS Form 990 or 990-PF printed copy available upon request.
Application information: Organizations that do not submit a Letter of Inquiry may still submit a grant application, however the limited time available for due diligence may significantly reduce the likelihood of the grant being funded. Completed application forms may be e-mailed to grants@aljfoundation.org. See foundation web site for further information and forms. Application form required.
Initial approach: Letter of Inquiry (via e-mail if possible) to David Hammerslag and 1 additional copy to Sally Mode
Copies of proposal: 2
Deadline(s): May 1 (for letters of inquiry); Aug. 1 (for grant application)
Board meeting date(s): Various
Trustees: David Hammerslag; Sally Mode.
EIN: 363739494
Selected grants: The following grants are a representative sample of this grantmaker's funding activity:
$45,000 to Southeastern Guide Dogs, Palmetto, FL, 2012. For handicap assistance animals.
$25,000 to Yellowstone Park Foundation, Bozeman, MT, 2012. For nature conservation.

127
Emma Eccles Jones Foundation ✧
c/o Wells Fargo Bank, N.A.
P.O. Box 53456 MAC S4101-22G
Phoenix, AZ 85072-3456 (888) 730-4933

Established in 1972 in UT.
Donor: Emma Eccles Jones†.
Foundation type: Independent foundation.
Financial data (yr. ended 08/31/13): Assets, $99,554,260 (M); expenditures, $4,652,966; qualifying distributions, $4,112,363; giving activities include $4,037,000 for 37 grants (high: $2,000,000; low: $2,000).
Purpose and activities: Giving primarily to education. Giving also to human services and arts and culture.
Fields of interest: Arts; Education; Human services; YM/YWCAs & YM/YWHAs.
Type of support: General/operating support; Continuing support; Building/renovation.
Limitations: Applications not accepted. Giving primarily in UT.
Application information: Unsolicited requests for funds not accepted.
Board meeting date(s): 3 times per year
Directors: Spencer F. Eccles; Clark P. Giles; Robert A. Hatch; Frederick Q. Lawson.
Trustee Bank: Wells Fargo Bank Northwest, N.A.
EIN: 876155073
Selected grants: The following grants are a representative sample of this grantmaker's funding activity:
$2,000,000 to Utah State University, College of Education, Logan, UT, 2013. For general support.
$1,000,000 to Utah State University, College of Education, Logan, UT, 2013. For general support.
$200,000 to Utah State University, Early Childhood Education Center, Logan, UT, 2013. For general support.
$150,000 to University of Utah, College of Nursing, Salt Lake City, UT, 2013. For building renovations.
$100,000 to Utah Symphony and Opera, Salt Lake City, UT, 2013. For general support.
$50,000 to Ballet West, Salt Lake City, UT, 2013. For general support.
$50,000 to University of Utah, KUED, Salt Lake City, UT, 2013. For general support.
$50,000 to University of Utah, Pioneer Memorial Theater, Salt Lake City, UT, 2013. For general support.
$50,000 to Utah Museum of Natural History, Salt Lake City, UT, 2013. For general support.
$30,000 to Utah Shakespearean Festival, Cedar City, UT, 2013. For general support.

128
JSC Foundation, Inc. ✧
60 E. Rio Salado Pkwy., Ste. 1012
Tempe, AZ 85281-9501

Donors: Holland H. Coors IV; John Coors; Sharna Coors; Holland H. Coors, IV Charitable Lead Annuity Trust.
Foundation type: Independent foundation.
Financial data (yr. ended 12/31/12): Assets, $6,456,870 (M); gifts received, $2,611,964; expenditures, $2,675,350; qualifying distributions, $2,624,369; giving activities include $2,616,340 for 2 grants (high: $2,608,628; low: $7,712).
Fields of interest: Christian agencies & churches.
Limitations: Applications not accepted. Giving primarily in GA.
Application information: Contributes only to pre-selected organizations.
Officers: John Coors, Pres.; Sharna Coors, Secy.; Michael Coors, Treas.
Directors: Jonathan Coors; Heidi Robbins.
EIN: 263802494

129
J. W. Kieckhefer Foundation ✧
116 E. Gurley St.
P.O. Box 1151
Prescott, AZ 86301-3821
Contact: John I. Kieckhefer, Tr.; Eugene P. Polk, Tr.

Trust established in 1953 in AZ.
Donor: John W. Kieckhefer†.
Foundation type: Independent foundation.
Financial data (yr. ended 12/31/13): Assets, $41,099,697 (M); expenditures, $2,125,073; qualifying distributions, $1,930,075; giving activities include $1,930,075 for 77 grants (high: $200,000; low: $75).
Fields of interest: Arts; Higher education; Health organizations; Human services; Children/youth, services.
Type of support: General/operating support; Continuing support; Annual campaigns; Building/renovation; Equipment; Land acquisition; Endowments; Emergency funds; Program development; Conferences/seminars; Publication; Research; Matching/challenge support.
Limitations: Applications not accepted. Giving on a national basis. No loans or grants to individuals.
Application information: Contributes mostly to pre-selected organizations. Internally initiated grants comprise virtually all of the current grantmaking of the foundation.
Board meeting date(s): Quarterly, and as required
Trustees: John I. Kieckhefer; Eugene P. Polk.
EIN: 866022877
Selected grants: The following grants are a representative sample of this grantmaker's funding activity:
$200,000 to University of Nebraska Foundation, Omaha, NE, 2012. For the Medical School-toward diabetes research.
$75,000 to Circle the City, Phoenix, AZ, 2012. Toward renovation of a building for use as a Medical Respite Center for the homeless.
$75,000 to Sharlot Hall Museum, Prescott, AZ, 2012. Toward completion of the Trades Building.
$45,000 to Coalition for Compassion and Justice, Prescott, AZ, 2012. For general purposes ($20,000), Endowment at Yavapai County Community Foundation ($25,000).
$35,000 to CALA Alliance, Scottsdale, AZ, 2012. Toward 2013 CALA Arts and Culture Festival.
$35,000 to Grand Canyon Association, Grand Canyon, AZ, 2012. Toward endowment of summer intern Program.
$30,000 to Heard Museum, Phoenix, AZ, 2012. Toward the Centennial Fund campaign.
$25,000 to Adult Care Services, Prescott, AZ, 2012. Toward updates and modernization of restrooms at The Susan B. Rheem Center in Prescott.
$15,000 to Musical Instrument Museum, Phoenix, AZ, 2012. Toward admission and transportation costs for students of financially struggling schools.
$15,000 to Sedona Arts Center, Sedona, AZ, 2012. Toward the art barn renovation project.

130
The Kiita Foundation ✧ ☆
8600 N. 64th Pl.
Paradise Valley, AZ 85253-1828

Established in 2001 in AZ.
Donors: James D. Armstrong; Jo-Ann Armstrong.
Foundation type: Independent foundation.
Financial data (yr. ended 12/31/12): Assets, $7,496,496 (M); gifts received, $1,793,855; expenditures, $803,110; qualifying distributions, $778,392; giving activities include $778,392 for grants.
Purpose and activities: Giving primarily to organizations that provide assistance to indigent people.
Fields of interest: Crime/violence prevention, domestic violence; Human services; Family services; Philanthropy/voluntarism; Economically disadvantaged.
Limitations: Applications not accepted. Giving primarily in AZ. No grants to individuals.
Application information: Unsolicited requests for funds not accepted.
Officers: James D. Armstrong, Pres. and Treas.; Jo-Ann Armstrong, V.P. and Secy.
Director: Andrew M. Armstrong.
EIN: 860994439

131
KMB Charitable Foundation ✧ ☆
5968 E. Sapphire Ln.
Paradise Valley, AZ 85253-2205

Donor: George W. Podd Survivor's Trust.
Foundation type: Independent foundation.
Financial data (yr. ended 12/31/13): Assets, $257,918 (M); gifts received, $595,203; expenditures, $500,345; qualifying distributions, $500,000; giving activities include $500,000 for 1 grant.
Fields of interest: Philanthropy/voluntarism.
Limitations: Applications not accepted. Giving primarily in Evanston, IL.
Application information: Unsolicited requests for funds not accepted.
Officer: Greg Podd, Exec. Dir.
EIN: 800174574

132
Least Indeed Foundation ✧ ☆
5015 W. Echo Ln.
Glendale, AZ 85302-6316

Established in 2005 in AZ.
Donors: Karsten L. Solheim; Barbara R. Solheim.
Foundation type: Independent foundation.
Financial data (yr. ended 12/31/13): Assets, $134 (M); gifts received, $1,428; expenditures, $1,125,451; qualifying distributions, $1,125,451; giving activities include $1,123,800 for 36 grants (high: $650,000; low: $200).
Fields of interest: Human services; Children/youth, services; United Ways and Federated Giving Programs; Christian agencies & churches.
Limitations: Applications not accepted. Giving primarily in AZ, CA, FL and GA. No grants to individuals.
Application information: Contributes only to pre-selected organizations.

Officers: Karsten L. Solheim, Pres.; Barbara R. Solheim, Secy.
EIN: 202330700
Selected grants: The following grants are a representative sample of this grantmaker's funding activity:
$12,000 to Food for the Hungry, Phoenix, AZ, 2011.
$12,000 to Wonders of Science, Whittier, CA, 2011.
$9,000 to Phoenix Gospel Mission, Phoenix, AZ, 2011.
$6,000 to Neighborhood Ministries, Phoenix, AZ, 2011.
$3,000 to Billy Graham Evangelistic Association, Charlotte, NC, 2011.
$3,000 to Haggai Institute for Advanced Leadership Training, Norcross, GA, 2011.
$3,000 to Neighborhood Christian Clinic, Phoenix, AZ, 2011.
$3,000 to Teen Challenge of Arizona, Tucson, AZ, 2011.

133
William S. & Ina Levine Foundation Inc. ✧ ☆
2201 E. Camelback Rd., Ste. 650
Phoenix, AZ 85016-4666

Established in 1997 in AZ.
Donor: Levine Investments Limited Partnership.
Foundation type: Independent foundation.
Financial data (yr. ended 05/31/13): Assets, $24,502,081 (M); expenditures, $816,288; qualifying distributions, $752,450; giving activities include $752,450 for 40 grants (high: $465,000; low: $200).
Purpose and activities: Giving primarily to Jewish organizations, temples, and schools; some funding for the arts, particularly museums.
Fields of interest: Museums (specialized); Arts; Education; Human services; Jewish federated giving programs; Jewish agencies & synagogues.
Limitations: Applications not accepted. Giving primarily in AZ. No grants to individuals.
Application information: Contributes only to pre-selected organizations.
Officer and Directors:* William S. Levine,* Pres.; Jay David Levine; Jonathan L. Levine; Julie Schoen.
EIN: 860866703
Selected grants: The following grants are a representative sample of this grantmaker's funding activity:
$50,000 to American Israel Education Foundation, Washington, DC, 2011.
$50,000 to Jewish Community Association of Greater Phoenix, Scottsdale, AZ, 2011.
$50,000 to Jewish Community Association of Greater Phoenix, Scottsdale, AZ, 2011.
$50,000 to UMOM New Day Centers, Phoenix, AZ, 2011.
$25,000 to Childrens Museum of Phoenix, Phoenix, AZ, 2011.
$12,000 to Valley of the Sun Jewish Community Center, Scottsdale, AZ, 2011.
$5,000 to Career Concepts for Youth, Phoenix, AZ, 2011.
$5,000 to National Kidney Foundation, New York, NY, 2011.
$5,000 to Yeshiva of Flatbush, Brooklyn, NY, 2011.
$3,500 to Saint Marys Food Bank, Phoenix, AZ, 2011.

134
T. W. Lewis Foundation ✧
850 W. Elliot Rd.
Tempe, AZ 85284-1202 (480) 820-0807
FAX: (480) 820-1445;
E-mail: twlfoundation@twlewis.com; Main URL: http://www.twlewisfoundation.org/

Established in 2000 in AZ.
Donors: Janet R. Lewis; Thomas W. Lewis.
Foundation type: Independent foundation.
Financial data (yr. ended 12/31/12): Assets, $16,714,743 (M); gifts received, $1,004,683; expenditures, $604,006; qualifying distributions, $521,329; giving activities include $400,700 for 26 grants (high: $205,000; low: $100), and $101,205 for 38 grants to individuals (high: $4,683; low: $1,665).
Purpose and activities: Giving primarily to programs that improve the quality of life for people in need, with a special focus on the needs and education of children. The foundation also offers a scholarship program, designed to assist outstanding Maricopa County, AZ, high school students, (who have a minimum SAT score of 1800, a minimum high school cumulative GPA of 3.0, and academically rank in the top twenty percent of their graduating class) in attending college and furthering their education.
Fields of interest: Higher education; Education; Children, services.
Type of support: Scholarships—to individuals.
Limitations: Applications accepted. Giving in the U.S., with emphasis on AZ for grants; scholarships are limited to Maricopa County, AZ, high school students.
Publications: Grants list.
Application information: Application form required.
Initial approach: Proposal
Deadline(s): None
Officers: Thomas W. Lewis, Pres. and Treas.; Janet R. Lewis, V.P. and Secy.
Director: Thomas W. Lewis, Jr.
EIN: 860989236
Selected grants: The following grants are a representative sample of this grantmaker's funding activity:
$20,000 to ANASAZI Foundation, Mesa, AZ, 2012. For Anasazi Scholarship Fund.
$1,000 to Sigma Chi Foundation, Evanston, IL, 2012. For White Cross Trust.

135
The Ronald and Maxine Linde Foundation ✧
c/o Maxine Linde
3300 E. Stanford Dr.
Paradise Valley, AZ 85253-7527

Established in 1989 in IL.
Donors: Ronald K. Linde; Maxine H. Linde.
Foundation type: Independent foundation.
Financial data (yr. ended 02/28/13): Assets, $20,268,315 (M); expenditures, $1,320,152; qualifying distributions, $873,971; giving activities include $868,500 for 3 grants (high: $848,000; low: $500).
Purpose and activities: Giving primarily for higher education.
Fields of interest: Higher education; Engineering school/education; Scholarships/financial aid; Philanthropy/voluntarism.
Type of support: General/operating support; Capital campaigns; Building/renovation; Endowments; Publication; Scholarship funds; Research; Matching/challenge support.
Limitations: Applications not accepted. Giving primarily in CA. No grants to individuals.
Application information: Contributes only to pre-selected organizations.
Board meeting date(s): 1st Mon. in May
Officers and Directors:* Ronald K. Linde,* Chair. and Treas.; Maxine H. Linde,* Pres.; Jennings J. Newcom; Lester G. Traub.
EIN: 363635349
Selected grants: The following grants are a representative sample of this grantmaker's funding activity:
$500 to USA Projects, Los Angeles, CA, 2013. For Urban Srts Project.

136
The Lodestar Foundation ✧
4455 E. Camelback Rd., Rm. 215A
Phoenix, AZ 85018

Established in AZ.
Donors: I. Jerome Hirsch; Hirsch Investment Co LLC.
Foundation type: Independent foundation.
Financial data (yr. ended 12/31/12): Assets, $104,305 (M); gifts received, $1,439,536; expenditures, $1,554,385; qualifying distributions, $1,548,638; giving activities include $1,488,476 for 64 grants (high: $125,000; low: $1,250).
Fields of interest: Human services; Philanthropy/voluntarism, fund raising/fund distribution; Foundations (community); Philanthropy/voluntarism.
Limitations: Applications not accepted. Giving primarily in AZ and NY. No grants to individuals.
Application information: Contributes only to pre-selected organizations.
Officers: Lois Savage, Pres.; I. Jerome Hirsch, Secy.
EIN: 204480084

137
John F. Long Foundation, Inc. ✧
5035 W. Camelback Rd.
Phoenix, AZ 85031-1331 (602) 272-0421
Contact: Jacob F. Long, Pres. and Dir.
FAX: (623) 846-7208;
E-mail: foundation@jflong.com; Main URL: http://www.jflong.com/foundation.htm

Established in 1959.
Donor: John F. Long†.
Foundation type: Independent foundation.
Financial data (yr. ended 04/30/13): Assets, $8,754,766 (M); expenditures, $471,347; qualifying distributions, $440,762; giving activities include $430,198 for 142 grants (high: $30,000; low: $162).
Purpose and activities: Giving primarily for groups who are working to help themselves, their own communities, and help others like themselves through self-empowering, community organizing efforts. The foundation's approach to grant requests focuses on fostering local neighborhood vitality and excellence.
Fields of interest: Arts; Elementary/secondary education; Human services; Children/youth, services; Family services; Community/economic

development; Christian agencies & churches; Protestant agencies & churches.
Limitations: Applications accepted. Giving primarily in Phoenix, AZ. No grants to individuals.
Application information: Application guidelines and questionnaire available on foundation web site. Grant requests exceeding $1,000 must be accompanied by financial reports for the past and current fiscal year, and a list of past donors going back no more than 2 years. Application form required.
Initial approach: Letter
Deadline(s): None
Officer and Directors:* Jacob F. Long,* Pres.; Shirley Long Lewis; James J. Miller.
EIN: 866052431
Selected grants: The following grants are a representative sample of this grantmaker's funding activity:
$30,000 to Arizona Zoological Society, Phoenix, AZ, 2012.
$20,000 to West-MEC Alliance, Phoenix, AZ, 2012.
$7,700 to Maryvale Revitalization Corporation, Phoenix, AZ, 2012.
$6,000 to Saint Marys Food Bank, Phoenix, AZ, 2012.
$5,000 to Camp Colley Foundation, Phoenix, AZ, 2012.
$5,000 to Homeward Bound, Phoenix, AZ, 2012.
$3,500 to Make-A-Wish Foundation of America, Phoenix, AZ, 2012.
$3,161 to Arizona Science Center, Phoenix, AZ, 2012.
$2,780 to Boys and Girls Clubs of Metropolitan Phoenix, Phoenix, AZ, 2012.
$2,500 to Mission of Mercy, Phoenix, AZ, 2012.

138
The Lord's Fund ✧
60 E. Rio Salado Pkwy., Ste. 1012
Tempe, AZ 85281-9501
Contact: Lance Berkman
E-mail: LARGENT@Texas.NET; TX tel.: (210) 593-1012, TX fax: (210) 614-8033

Established in 1997 in TX.
Donors: William Lance Berkman; Cara Berkman; Josh Hamilton; Lance Berkman.
Foundation type: Independent foundation.
Financial data (yr. ended 12/31/13): Assets, $4,027,627 (M); gifts received, $1,200,000; expenditures, $1,470,649; qualifying distributions, $1,470,649; giving activities include $1,469,353 for 24 grants (high: $171,460; low: $500).
Purpose and activities: Support for missionary and charitable programs.
Fields of interest: Christian agencies & churches.
Type of support: General/operating support.
Limitations: Applications not accepted. Giving primarily in TX; some funding in IL.
Application information: Unsolicited requests for funds not accepted.
Officers: William Lance Berkman, Pres.; Cynthia Ann Berkman, V.P.; Larry G. Berkman, Secy.-Treas.
Directors: Jason Baker; Jason Walton.
EIN: 742879125
Selected grants: The following grants are a representative sample of this grantmaker's funding activity:
$113,362 to Pro Athletes Outreach, Issaquah, WA, 2011. For general support.

139
Marco Foundation ✧
4431 E. Sunset Dr.
Phoenix, AZ 85028-6112 (480) 367-7367
Contact: Mark N. Sklar, Pres. and Dir.

Established in 2000 in AZ.
Donors: Mark N. Sklar; Jo Ann Sklar; Ruth S. Coleman Living Trust.
Foundation type: Independent foundation.
Financial data (yr. ended 12/31/13): Assets, $13,378,977 (M); expenditures, $846,390; qualifying distributions, $683,000; giving activities include $683,000 for 22 grants (high: $125,000; low: $5,000).
Fields of interest: Arts; Education; Health care; Jewish federated giving programs; Jewish agencies & synagogues.
Limitations: Applications accepted. Giving primarily in AZ, with emphasis on Phoenix.
Application information: Application form required.
Initial approach: Letter
Deadline(s): None
Officers and Directors:* Mark N. Sklar,* Pres.; Jo Ann Sklar,* V.P. and Secy.
EIN: 860969412

140
The Kemper and Ethel Marley Foundation ✧
P.O. Box 10392
Phoenix, AZ 85064-0392
Contact: Daniel Corrigan, V.P.

Established in 1990 in AZ.
Donors: Ethel Marley†; Kemper Marley Trust.
Foundation type: Independent foundation.
Financial data (yr. ended 12/31/12): Assets, $221,262,246 (M); gifts received, $147,363; expenditures, $13,879,734; qualifying distributions, $10,641,854; giving activities include $10,317,408 for 77 grants (high: $1,200,000; low: $1,000).
Purpose and activities: Giving primarily for higher education, human service organizations, the arts, and a zoo.
Fields of interest: Museums; Historic preservation/historical societies; Higher education; Zoos/zoological societies; Youth, services.
Type of support: General/operating support.
Limitations: Applications not accepted. Giving limited to AZ. No support for animal welfare organizations. No grants to individuals.
Application information: Contributes only to pre-selected organizations.
Officers and Directors:* Stephen M. Corrigan,* Pres.; Nancy Elitharp Ball,* V.P. and Treas.; Daniel Corrigan,* V.P.
EIN: 860653091
Selected grants: The following grants are a representative sample of this grantmaker's funding activity:
$2,500,000 to Mayo Foundation, Scottsdale, AZ, 2012. For endowment.
$1,200,000 to University of Arizona Foundation, Tucson, AZ, 2012. For endowment.
$850,000 to Arizonans for Children, Tempe, AZ, 2012. For capital support.
$300,000 to University of Arizona Foundation, Tucson, AZ, 2012. For endowment.
$250,000 to Circle the City, Phoenix, AZ, 2012. For capital support.
$250,000 to Phoenix Theater, Phoenix, AZ, 2012. For capital support.
$150,000 to Saint Josephs Foundation, Phoenix, AZ, 2012. For capital support.
$100,000 to CALA Alliance, Scottsdale, AZ, 2012. For operating support.
$85,000 to Adult Care Services, Prescott, AZ, 2012. For capital support.
$50,000 to Central Arizona College Foundation, Coolidge, AZ, 2012. For operating support.

141
Marshall Foundation ✧
814 E. University Blvd.
P.O. Box 3306
Tucson, AZ 85722-3306 (520) 622-8613
Contact: Jane McCollum
FAX: (520) 622-0124;
E-mail: jane@marshallfoundation.com; Application contact: Jen Dang, Secy., e-mail: jendang@email.arizona.edu; Main URL: http://www.marshallfoundation.com

Incorporated in 1930 in AZ.
Donor: Louise F. Marshall†.
Foundation type: Independent foundation.
Financial data (yr. ended 12/31/12): Assets, $31,144,882 (M); expenditures, $3,794,437; qualifying distributions, $1,069,806; giving activities include $945,394 for 67 grants (high: $197,539; low: $25).
Purpose and activities: Giving primarily for higher education, children and youth programs, cultural organizations and programs, community service organizations, and medical research.
Fields of interest: Arts; Higher education; Scholarships/financial aid; Education; Health organizations, association; Medical research, institute; Human services; Children/youth, services; Foundations (private grantmaking).
Type of support: Capital campaigns; Building/renovation; Scholarship funds.
Limitations: Giving limited to Tucson and Pima County, AZ. No grants to individuals, or for operational support, or annual support.
Publications: Application guidelines; Annual report; Informational brochure.
Application information: Funding to new recipients is limited due to large-scale commitments to the University of Arizona Scholarship Fund and the University Medical Center Artificial Heart Laboratory as well as other long-term commitments. Application form required.
Initial approach: Use online application form via foundation web site
Copies of proposal: 2
Deadline(s): Mar. 15, May 15 and Sept. 15
Board meeting date(s): Monthly
Officers: Charles Jackson, Pres.; Bruce Shelton, Secy.; George Steele, V.P.; Anne Nelson, Treas.
Directors: Francisco Aguilar; Bruce Burke.
Number of staff: 2 full-time professional; 1 part-time professional; 4 full-time support.
EIN: 860102198
Selected grants: The following grants are a representative sample of this grantmaker's funding activity:
$300 to Sam Hughes Elementary School, Tucson, AZ, 2012. For various functions of the qualified organizations.

142
Matricaria Family Foundation ✧ ☆
9674 E. Taos Dr.
Scottsdale, AZ 85262-5187

Established in MN.
Donor: Ronald Matricaria.
Foundation type: Independent foundation.
Financial data (yr. ended 12/31/13): Assets, $6,856,822 (M); expenditures, $1,036,409; qualifying distributions, $1,036,409; giving activities include $1,007,200 for 6 grants (high: $1,000,000; low: $200).
Purpose and activities: Giving primarily for education.
Fields of interest: Education; Hospitals (general); Health care.
Type of support: General/operating support; Scholarship funds.
Limitations: Applications not accepted. Giving primarily in Boston, MA. No grants to individuals.
Application information: Contributes only to pre-selected organizations.
Trustees: Andrew S. Matricaria; Lee M. Matricaria; Lucille E. Matricaria; Ronald Matricaria; Ronald A. Matricaria, Jr.
EIN: 416510809

143
McCain Institute Foundation ✧ ☆
4702 N. Dromedary Rd.
Phoenix, AZ 85018-2939

Foundation type: Independent foundation.
Financial data (yr. ended 12/31/13): Assets, $8,701,207 (M); expenditures, $522,124; qualifying distributions, $500,000; giving activities include $500,000 for 1 grant.
Fields of interest: Education, fund raising/fund distribution.
Limitations: Applications not accepted. Giving primarily in Tempe, AZ.
Application information: Unsolicited requests for funds not accepted.
Trustees: Philip Handy; William J. Post; Richard S. Williamson.
EIN: 454556648

144
Armstrong McDonald Foundation ✧
3420 E. Sunrise Dr., Ste. 200
Tucson, AZ 85718 (520) 878-9627
FAX: (520) 797-3866;
E-mail: info@ArmstrongMcDonaldFoundation.org; Application address: P.O. Box 70110, Tucson, AZ 85737-0110; Main URL: http://www.armstrongmcdonaldfoundation.org
Grant History: http://www.armstrongmcdonaldfoundation.org/5year.html

Established in 1986 in NE.
Donor: J.M. McDonald, Sr.‡.
Foundation type: Independent foundation.
Financial data (yr. ended 12/31/13): Assets, $18,480,838 (M); expenditures, $1,028,356; qualifying distributions, $940,266; giving activities include $928,217 for 19 grants (high: $285,000; low: $2,500).
Purpose and activities: Giving primarily for higher education, animal welfare organizations that perform endangered species reproduction research, the training of guide dogs for the visually impaired, and for the training of dogs to be companions for the physically challenged or for mobility restricted seniors; funding also for scouting or boys and girls club-type children and youth services, health organizations, and social services, including community outreach programs, shelters for the homeless as well as abused women and children, veteran related projects, services to seniors, purchase of vans for various transportation needs and transitional living programs.
Fields of interest: Higher education; Animal welfare; Animals/wildlife, endangered species; Health care; Health organizations, association; Human services; Children/youth, services; Disabilities, people with.
Type of support: General/operating support; Continuing support; Building/renovation; Equipment; Program development; Research.
Limitations: Applications accepted. Giving to states west of the Mississippi River and MN or LA for organizations that have received previous grants; AZ or NE for organizations that have not received a previous grant. No support for multi-year projects. No grants to individuals, or for salaries or capital campaigns.
Publications: Application guidelines; Financial statement.
Application information: The foundation only accepts unsolicited grant requests from non-profits listed on the Pre-Approved for Grant Submission List, which can be viewed on foundation web site. See foundation web site for specific application instructions and information. Faxed or mailed grant requests which require a signature for retrieval of the package at the post office will not be considered. Application form required.
Copies of proposal: 1
Deadline(s): Sept. 15
Board meeting date(s): Nov.
Officers and Trustees:* Laurie L. Bouchard,* Pres.; Ryan M. Bouchard,* V.P.; Corby L. Lust,* V.P.; Todd McDonald,* V.P.; Michael J. Bouchard,* Secy.-Treas.
EIN: 363458711

145
Joe and Mary Moeller Foundation ✧
27437 N. 97th Pl.
Scottsdale, AZ 85262-8432

Established in 2004 in KS.
Donors: Joseph W. Moeller; Mary Moeller.
Foundation type: Independent foundation.
Financial data (yr. ended 12/31/13): Assets, $8,610,408 (M); expenditures, $478,863; qualifying distributions, $447,390; giving activities include $447,390 for grants.
Fields of interest: Higher education; Youth development; Human services; Catholic agencies & churches.
Type of support: General/operating support.
Limitations: Applications not accepted. Giving primarily in CO, FL, GA, KS, OK and VA. No grants to individuals.
Application information: Contributes only to pre-selected organizations.
Officers: Joseph W. Moeller, Pres.; Mary F. Moeller, Secy.
Director: Margaret Sharon Walker.
EIN: 830411709

146
Margaret E. Mooney Foundation ✧
2440 E. Broadway
Tucson, AZ 85719-6008 (520) 791-3939

Established in 1991 in AZ.
Donor: Margaret E. Mooney‡.
Foundation type: Independent foundation.
Financial data (yr. ended 12/31/13): Assets, $21,860,933 (M); expenditures, $1,621,478; qualifying distributions, $1,212,388; giving activities include $1,184,539 for 14 grants (high: $739,800; low: $375).
Fields of interest: Arts; Higher education; Animals/wildlife; Housing/shelter, development; Human services.
Type of support: Annual campaigns; Emergency funds; Program development.
Limitations: Applications accepted. Giving limited to Tucson, AZ. No grants to individuals.
Application information: Application form not required.
Initial approach: Letter
Copies of proposal: 1
Deadline(s): None
Officers: Linda Lohse, Pres.; Patricia Lohse, V.P.; Jennifer Lohse, Secy.; Robert Lohse, Treas.
Number of staff: 2
EIN: 860647807
Selected grants: The following grants are a representative sample of this grantmaker's funding activity:
$935,400 to University of Arizona Foundation, Tucson, AZ, 2012. For Education - Endowment and Capital Funds.
$51,000 to Arizona Opera Company, Tucson, AZ, 2012. For Music - Unrestricted Funds.
$33,000 to Arizona Theater Company, Tucson, AZ, 2012. For Community Theater - Capital Funds.
$25,000 to Angel Charity for Children, Tucson, AZ, 2012. For Youth Activities - Capital Funds.
$25,000 to Pima Community College Foundation, Tucson, AZ, 2012. For Education - Endowed Funds.
$3,000 to Tucson Museum of Art, Tucson, AZ, 2012. For Community - Unrestricted Use Or Sale of Donated Items.

147
Moreno Family Foundation ✧
4455 E. Camelback Rd., Ste. D-145
Phoenix, AZ 85018-2847

Established in 1998 in AZ.
Donors: Arturo Moreno; Carole Moreno.
Foundation type: Independent foundation.
Financial data (yr. ended 12/31/12): Assets, $17,351,028 (M); gifts received, $3,994,744; expenditures, $556,059; qualifying distributions, $493,500; giving activities include $491,890 for 55 grants (high: $100,000; low: $500).
Purpose and activities: Giving primarily for education, as well as for youth, health, and human services.
Fields of interest: Higher education; Education; Health organizations, association; Boys & girls clubs; Human services; Children/youth, services; Foundations (private grantmaking); Foundations (community).
Limitations: Applications not accepted. Giving primarily in Phoenix and Tucson, AZ, and Anaheim, CA. No grants to individuals.
Application information: Contributes only to pre-selected organizations.

Officer: Fernando Pacheco, Mgr.
Directors: Arturo Moreno; Carole Moreno.
EIN: 860918198

148
Margaret T. Morris Foundation ✧
P.O. Box 592
Prescott, AZ 86302-0592 (928) 445-4010
Contact: Thomas E. Polk, Tr.

Established in 1967.
Donor: Margaret T. Morris‡.
Foundation type: Independent foundation.
Financial data (yr. ended 12/31/13): Assets, $20,607,257 (M); expenditures, $1,072,587; qualifying distributions, $999,779; giving activities include $979,083 for 85 grants (high: $67,000; low: $250).
Purpose and activities: Support for the performing arts and other cultural programs, education, with emphasis on higher education, youth and child welfare, family planning, medical research and education, the environment and animal welfare, and social services, primarily those benefiting the handicapped.
Fields of interest: Museums; Performing arts; Performing arts, music; Arts; Higher education; Medical school/education; Education; Environment; Animal welfare; Reproductive health, family planning; Mental health/crisis services; Medical research, institute; Human services; Children/youth, services; Residential/custodial care, hospices; Homeless, human services; Marine science; Disabilities, people with; Economically disadvantaged; Homeless.
Type of support: General/operating support; Capital campaigns; Building/renovation; Land acquisition; Endowments; Debt reduction; Program development; Scholarship funds; Matching/challenge support.
Limitations: Applications accepted. Giving primarily in AZ. No support for religious organizations or their agencies. No grants to individuals; no loans.
Application information: Application form required.
Initial approach: Letter
Deadline(s): None
Officer: Eugene P. Polk, Exec. Dir.
Trustee: Thomas E. Polk.
EIN: 866057798
Selected grants: The following grants are a representative sample of this grantmaker's funding activity:
$42,500 to Arizona Community Foundation, Phoenix, AZ, 2012. Toward the 2013 Summer Youth Program Fund ($10,000); Arizona Women's Education and Employment/Endowment of Annual Volunteerism Award ($7,500); Prescott Fund, ($25,000).
$25,000 to Coalition for Compassion and Justice, Prescott, AZ, 2012. For Endowment at Yavapai County Community Foundation ($15,000), general purposes ($10,000).
$25,000 to Grand Canyon Association, Grand Canyon, AZ, 2012. Toward endowment of Intern Program.
$22,500 to Adult Care Services, Prescott, AZ, 2012. For Updates and modernization of restroom facilities ($7,500), Scholarship Fund ($15,000).
$22,000 to Yavapai College Foundation, Prescott, AZ, 2012. For Scholarship endowment, ($10,000), Jewish Community Foundation Healthcare Scholarship Program, ($12,000).
$15,000 to Arizona Friends of Foster Children Foundation, Phoenix, AZ, 2012. Toward permanent endowment fund.
$15,000 to CALA Alliance, Scottsdale, AZ, 2012. Toward the 2013 CALA Arts and Cultural Festival.
$15,000 to Desert Caballeros Western Museum, Wickenburg, AZ, 2012. Toward the 2012 capital campaign.
$10,000 to Phoenix Art Museum, Phoenix, AZ, 2012. Toward West Select exhibit.
$7,500 to Project Aware, Prescott, AZ, 2012. Toward affordable housing for the homeless.

149
Otto & Edna Neely Foundation ✧
325 S Higley Rd.,
Gilbert, AZ 85296
Main URL: http://www.ottoandednaneelyfoundation.org/

Established in 1988 in AZ.
Foundation type: Independent foundation.
Financial data (yr. ended 12/31/12): Assets, $14,356,618 (M); expenditures, $859,319; qualifying distributions, $681,630; giving activities include $554,498 for 55 grants (high: $86,600; low: $500).
Purpose and activities: Giving primarily for higher and other education, as well as for children, youth and social services, and for Presbyterian and United Methodist churches.
Fields of interest: Arts; Higher education; Scholarships/financial aid; Education; Human services; Children/youth, services; Protestant agencies & churches.
Limitations: Applications accepted. Giving primarily in AZ.
Application information: Application form required.
Initial approach: Completed application form
Deadline(s): None
Officers and Directors:* Clifford W. Saylor,* Pres.; Logan W. Stillwell,* V.P.; Harley Christian,* Secy. and Treas.; Gregory L. Bamford; Steve Haase; Norman L. Knox.
EIN: 860581770

150
The Ottosen Family Foundation ✧
105 S. 28th St.
Phoenix, AZ 85034-2619

Established in AZ.
Donors: Donald R. Ottosen; Barbara Ottosen.
Foundation type: Independent foundation.
Financial data (yr. ended 12/31/13): Assets, $11,550,693 (M); gifts received, $300,000; expenditures, $447,308; qualifying distributions, $438,654; giving activities include $438,654 for 11 grants (high: $261,850; low: $365).
Fields of interest: Museums (art); Higher education; Botanical gardens; Hospitals (specialty); Human services; Community/economic development.
Limitations: Applications not accepted. Giving primarily in AZ. No grants to individuals.
Application information: Unsolicited requests for funds not accepted.
Officers: Barbara J. Ottosen, Pres.; Diann C. Henderson, Secy.; Donald R. Ottosen, Treas.
EIN: 860778785
Selected grants: The following grants are a representative sample of this grantmaker's funding activity:
$162,000 to Phoenix Childrens Hospital, Phoenix, AZ, 2011.
$122,500 to Arizona State University Foundation for a New American University, Tempe, AZ, 2011.
$51,234 to Desert Botanical Garden, Phoenix, AZ, 2011.
$40,000 to Nature Conservancy, Arlington, VA, 2011.

151
The Bob and Renee Parsons Foundation ✧
(formerly Parsons Foundation)
15475 N. 84th St.
Scottsdale, AZ 85260-1827 (480) 398-2535
Contact: Renee Labelle Parsons, V.P.
E-mail: info@tbrpf.org; Main URL: http://tbrpf.org/
Bob and Renee Parsons' Giving Pledge Profile: http://glasspockets.org/philanthropy-in-focus/eye-on-the-giving-pledge/profiles#p
Facebook: https://www.facebook.com/TheParsonsFoundation
Twitter: https://www.twitter.com/WeDealInHope

Established in 2011 in AZ.
Donors: Robert Parsons; Renee Labelle Parsons.
Foundation type: Independent foundation.
Financial data (yr. ended 12/31/13): Assets, $9,679,657 (M); gifts received, $23,003,697; expenditures, $13,328,403; qualifying distributions, $13,328,403; giving activities include $13,053,341 for 34 grants (high: $4,264,814; low: $5,000).
Purpose and activities: The foundation believes every person is entitled to an education, good nutrition, medical care, a stress free happy environment, and the hope that they too, will share in the American Dream. It provides funding to non-profit organizations that are successfully addressing these essential needs. The foundation is also committed to the people of Haiti, helping to grow and improve schools, medical services, and overall well-being for communities in rural Haiti through the organization, Hope for Haiti.
Fields of interest: Education; Health care; Nutrition; Human services; International relief.
International interests: Haiti.
Limitations: Applications accepted. Giving primarily in the greater Phoenix, AZ, area.
Application information: Application form required.
Initial approach: Online application form
Deadline(s): None
Officers: Robert Parsons, Pres.; Renee Labelle Parsons, V.P.; Anne O' Moore, Treas.; Laura Mitchell, Exec. Dir.
EIN: 452713666

152
The Virginia G. Piper Charitable Trust ✧
1202 E. Missouri Ave.
Phoenix, AZ 85014-2921 (480) 948-5853
Contact: Judy Jolley Mohraz Ph.D., C.E.O. and Pres.
FAX: (480) 348-1316; E-mail: info@pipertrust.org;
Main URL: http://www.pipertrust.org
E-Newsletter: http://visitor.constantcontact.com/manage/optin/ea?v=001lQ4Q15knkjMpZ2OUGVSlcA%3D%3D

Grants Database: http://www.pipertrust.org/our-grants/search-grants/
Knowledge Center: http://www.pipertrust.org/nonprofit-support/piper-academy/
Twitter: https://twitter.com/pipertrust

Established in 1995.
Donor: Virginia G. Piper†.
Foundation type: Independent foundation.
Financial data (yr. ended 03/31/13): Assets, $533,033,849 (M); gifts received, $22; expenditures, $23,682,862; qualifying distributions, $19,891,992; giving activities include $15,016,997 for 399 grants (high: $1,127,364; low: $35), $39,256 for 111 employee matching gifts, and $1,373,729 for 4 foundation-administered programs.
Purpose and activities: The trust seeks to enhance and strengthen the quality of life for the people in Maricopa County through support of healthcare and medical research, children, older adults, arts and culture, education and religious organizations.
Fields of interest: Arts; Youth development, adult & child programs; Aging, centers/services; Youth.
Type of support: Building/renovation; Capital campaigns; Continuing support; Employee matching gifts; Endowments; Equipment; Fellowships; General/operating support; Management development/capacity building; Matching/challenge support; Program development; Technical assistance.
Limitations: Applications accepted. Giving primarily to organizations that serve residents of Maricopa County, AZ, have operated as a Section 501(c)(3) organization or governmental entity for at least three years, and not be a private foundation or ineligible Type III supporting organization. No support for private foundations, or for start-ups. No grants to individuals, or for endowments.
Publications: Biennial report; Financial statement; Grants list; Newsletter; Occasional report.
Application information: The letter of inquiry and Grant Summary Form can be submitted online from the foundation's web site. Applications should be directed to the Grants Manager. An organization must serve residents of Maricopa County, have operated as a Section 501(c)(3) organization or governmental entity for at least three years, and not be a private foundation or ineligible Type III supporting organization. An additional requirement is the adoption of eight best practices listed on the website. Online application form required.
Application form required.
Initial approach: Online Grant Summary Form and attach a two-page letter of inquiry.
Copies of proposal: 1
Deadline(s): None
Board meeting date(s): 12 times per year
Final notification: 3 to 6 months
Officers and Trustees:* Susan M. Pepin, C.E.O. and Pres.; Mary Jane Rynd, Exec. V.P. and C.F.O.; Marilee L. Dal Pra, V.P., Programs; James D. Bruner; Jose A. Cardenas; Paul N. Critchfield; Art DeCabooter; Laura R. Grafman; Sharon C. Harper; Judy Jolley Mohraz, Ph.D.; Steven J. Zabilski.
Number of staff: 13 full-time professional; 3 full-time support.
EIN: 866247076
Selected grants: The following grants are a representative sample of this grantmaker's funding activity:
$1,127,364 to Arizona State University Foundation for a New American University, Tempe, AZ, 2013. To create Virginia G. Piper Center for Personalized Diagnostics in partnership with TGen.
$1,000,000 to Arizona State University Foundation for a New American University, Tempe, AZ, 2013. For university-wide strategic initiative to improve health care delivery and outcomes.
$700,000 to Experience Matters Consortium, Phoenix, AZ, 2013. To create scalable business model that connects social sector organizations and experienced adults focused on civic service.
$500,000 to John C. Lincoln Health Foundation, Phoenix, AZ, 2013. For new geriatric trauma unit.
$461,506 to Saint Vincent de Paul Society, Phoenix, AZ, 2013. To develop pilot project designed to transform marketing and fundraising.
$300,000 to Phoenix Symphony Association, Phoenix, AZ, 2013. For marketing initiative to strengthen client base and support new musical director search.
$256,000 to Roman Catholic Church of Phoenix, Phoenix, AZ, 2013. For a sustainability assessment of all Catholic elementary schools in the Diocese of Phoenix.
$15,000 to Arizona State University Foundation for a New American University, Tempe, AZ, 2013. For Center for Sustainable Health at the BioDesign Institute for the Initiatives of Dr Birt and Dr Hartwell.
$10,000 to Adelante Healthcare, Phoenix, AZ, 2013. For Piper Fellow and related staff development.
$5,000 to Neighbors Who Care, Sun Lakes, AZ, 2013. To Recognize exemplary efforts in engaging people age 50+ in social purpose work.

153
Pivotal Foundation ✧
(formerly F. Francis Najafi Family Foundation)
3200 E. Camelback Rd., Ste. 295
Phoenix, AZ 85018-2343

Established in 2005 in AZ.
Donor: F. Francis Najafi.
Foundation type: Independent foundation.
Financial data (yr. ended 12/31/13): Assets, $6,074,992 (M); expenditures, $1,179,294; qualifying distributions, $1,166,267; giving activities include $1,166,100 for 35 grants (high: $510,000; low: $250).
Purpose and activities: Giving primarily for education, human services, and to U.S.-based Iranian causes.
Fields of interest: Arts; Education, fund raising/fund distribution; Education; Health organizations; Human services; Children/youth, services; Science.
Limitations: Applications not accepted. Giving primarily in AZ. No grants to individuals.
Application information: Contributes only to pre-selected organizations.
Officers and Director:* F. Francis Najafi,* Pres.; Jackie Reed, Secy.; Richard Garner, Treas.
EIN: 203959093

154
The Pocono Charitable Foundation ✧ ☆
P.O. Box 65929
Tucson, AZ 85728-5929 (520) 297-3243

Established in 2001 in AZ.
Donors: James D. Toole; Molly C. Toole; Sarah Toole Cottingham; Timothy J. Toole; Two Springs, LLC; Summit Investors; James D. Toole II; James D. Toole III; Molly Toole Roman; Elizabeth Toole Goodrow; Thomas D. Toole.
Foundation type: Independent foundation.
Financial data (yr. ended 12/31/13): Assets, $1,723,132 (M); expenditures, $449,238; qualifying distributions, $446,000; giving activities include $446,000 for 41 grants (high: $150,000; low: $500).
Fields of interest: Elementary/secondary education; Education; Human services; Children/youth, services; Catholic agencies & churches.
Limitations: Applications accepted. Giving in the U.S., with emphasis on AZ.
Application information: Application form not required.
Initial approach: Proposal
Deadline(s): None
Officers and Directors:* James D. Toole II,* Pres.; Molly C. Toole,* V.P.; Elizabeth Toole Goodrow,* Secy.; Thomas D. Toole,* Treas.; Sarah Toole Cottingham; Molly Toole Roman; James D. Toole III; Timothy J. Toole.
EIN: 861045072

155
Raymond Family Foundation ✧
c/o Wells Fargo Bank N.A., Trust Tax Dept.
P.O. Box 53456, MAC S4101-22G
Phoenix, AZ 85072-3456
Application address: c/o David L. Buchman, Wells Fargo Bank, 299 S. Main St., 5th Fl., Salt Lake City, UT 84111, tel.: (801) 246-1436

Established in 1996 in UT.
Donors: Mary R. Raymond; Mary R. Raymond Charitable Lead Trust; Robert Raymond Foundation, Inc.
Foundation type: Independent foundation.
Financial data (yr. ended 12/31/13): Assets, $15,584,512 (M); gifts received, $62,500; expenditures, $745,120; qualifying distributions, $670,822; giving activities include $638,050 for 142 grants (high: $60,000; low: $300).
Fields of interest: Museums; Performing arts; Higher education; Education; Animals/wildlife; Health organizations, association; Food banks; Human services.
Limitations: Applications accepted. Giving in the U.S., with emphasis on CA and UT.
Application information: Application form not required.
Initial approach: Proposal
Deadline(s): None
Directors: Daniela Megan Kerrigan; Elizabeth K. Raymond; Robert Raymond.
Trustee: Wells Fargo Bank, N.A.
EIN: 566502391
Selected grants: The following grants are a representative sample of this grantmaker's funding activity:
$25,000 to San Francisco Chamber Orchestra, San Francisco, CA, 2011.
$22,500 to Santa Sabina Center, San Rafael, CA, 2011.
$17,000 to U.S. Ski and Snowboard Team Foundation, Park City, UT, 2011.
$15,000 to People for the Ethical Treatment of Animals, Norfolk, VA, 2011.
$15,000 to Planned Parenthood of Central North Carolina, Chapel Hill, NC, 2011.
$10,000 to Gay Mens Health Crisis, New York, NY, 2011.

$10,000 to Heifer Project International, Little Rock, AR, 2011.
$10,000 to Jesuit Volunteer Corps Northwest, Portland, OR, 2011.
$8,600 to University of Utah, Salt Lake City, UT, 2011.
$3,000 to Oregon Public Broadcasting, Portland, OR, 2011.

156
David E. Reese Family Foundation ✧
7748 N. 54th St.
Paradise Valley, AZ 85253-3056

Established in 1994 in AZ.
Donors: David E. Reese; Caleb F. Reese; Everett D. Reese II; Everett Reese†; Louise F. Reese.
Foundation type: Independent foundation.
Financial data (yr. ended 12/31/13): Assets, $14,690,401 (M); expenditures, $1,467,966; qualifying distributions, $1,400,100; giving activities include $1,400,100 for 24 grants (high: $625,000; low: $100).
Fields of interest: Higher education; Education; Human services; Independent living, disability; Foundations (private grantmaking).
Limitations: Applications not accepted. Giving in the U.S., with emphasis on Phoenix, AZ and Granville, OH. No grants to individuals.
Application information: Contributes only to pre-selected organizations.
Officers: David E. Reese, Pres.; Louise R. Reese, V.P. and Secy.; Everett D. Reese, Treas.
EIN: 860763892
Selected grants: The following grants are a representative sample of this grantmaker's funding activity:
$100,000 to Wheaton College, Norton, MA, 2012. To support Scholarship and Educational Programs.
$50,000 to Ohio State University Foundation, Columbus, OH, 2012. To provide Funds for College Scholarships.
$5,000 to Arizona Science Center, Phoenix, AZ, 2012. To promote Science and Education.
$5,000 to Musical Instrument Museum, Phoenix, AZ, 2012. To promote Education and Cultural Programs Promote Education And.
$1,000 to A Call to College, Newark, OH, 2012. To provide College Scholarships.

157
Research Corporation for Science Advancement ✧
4703 E. Camp Lowell Dr., Ste. 201
Tucson, AZ 85712-1292 (520) 571-1111
Contact: Daniel Gasch, C.F.O.
FAX: (520) 571-1119; E-mail: awards@rescorp.org; Main URL: http://www.rescorp.org
Facebook: http://www.facebook.com/pages/Research-Corporation-for-Science-Advancement/166231769296?ref=ts
Grants Database: http://www.rescorp.org/grants-and-awards/awards-database
Twitter: http://twitter.com/ResearchCorp

Incorporated in 1912 in NY.
Donors: Rachel Brown†; Frederick Gardner Cottrell†; Elizabeth Hazen†; Donald F. Jones†; Edward C. Kendall†; Paul C. Mangelsdorf; Charles H. Townes; Robert E. Waterman†; Robert R. Williams†; Robert B. Woodward†.
Foundation type: Operating foundation.
Financial data (yr. ended 12/31/13): Assets, $160,741,837 (M); gifts received, $217,327; expenditures, $6,689,563; qualifying distributions, $8,056,240; giving activities include $3,019,998 for 119 grants (high: $72,500; low: $600), and $8,056,240 for foundation-administered programs.
Purpose and activities: Giving to advance academic science research and teaching. The awards programs include the Cottrell College Science Awards, Cottrell Scholars Awards, and Scialog Awards and are open to U.S. colleges and universities to support basic research in the physical sciences (physics, chemistry, and astronomy).
Fields of interest: Astronomy; Chemistry; Physics; Science.
Type of support: Program development; Research.
Limitations: Applications accepted. Giving limited to the U.S. No grants to individuals directly, or for building or endowment funds, indirect costs, common supplies and services, tuition, research leave to start new projects, faculty academic year salaries, post-doctoral or graduate student stipends, secretarial assistance, general support, scholarships, fellowships, publications, travel expenses to scientific meetings, or matching gifts; no loans.
Publications: Application guidelines; Annual report; Newsletter; Occasional report.
Application information: Only online applications will be accepted. Application form required.
Initial approach: Fill out application request form on foundation web site
Deadline(s): Deadlines vary from year to year
Board meeting date(s): Feb., Apr., and Nov.
Final notification: Differs by program
Officers and Directors:* G. Scott Clemons,* Chair.; Robert Shelton, Ph.D., Pres.; Robert B. Hallock,* Secy.; Daniel Gasch, C.F.O.; Patricia C. Barron, Dir. Emeritus; Stuart B. Crampton, Dir. Emeritus; Robert Holland, Jr., Dir. Emeritus; Suzanne D. Jaffe,* Dir. Emeritus; Patrick S. Osmer, Ph.D., Dir. Emeritus; John P. Schaefer, Dir. Emeritus; Lars Bildsten, Ph.D..; Peter K. Dorhout; Jonathan Hook; Brent Iverson; Gayle P.W. Jackson; Elizabeth P.W. McCormack, Ph.D.; David L. Wenner; Joan B. Woodard.
Science Advisory Committee: Bert Chandler; Mike Dennin; Jordan Gerton; Martin Gruebele; Peter Iovine; Nicola Pohl; Veronika Szalai.
Number of staff: 9 full-time professional; 5 full-time support.
EIN: 131963407

158
The Rodel Foundation ✧
6720 N. Scottsdale Rd., Ste. 310
Scottsdale, AZ 85253-4471

Established in 1999 in AZ; reorganized in 2004.
Donors: William D. Budinger; Donald V. Budinger.
Foundation type: Independent foundation.
Financial data (yr. ended 12/31/13): Assets, $61,311,321 (M); expenditures, $3,150,485; qualifying distributions, $2,899,091; giving activities include $2,449,600 for 24 grants (high: $650,000; low: $2,500).
Fields of interest: Higher education; Foundations (private grantmaking); Social sciences, public policy; Public policy, research; Leadership development.
Limitations: Applications not accepted. Giving primarily in AZ and CO; some funding also in CA and Washington, DC. No grants to individuals.
Application information: Contributes only to pre-selected organizations.
Officers and Directors:* Donald V. Budinger,* Pres.; Susan B. Lonki,* Secy.; William D. Budinger.
EIN: 861015598
Selected grants: The following grants are a representative sample of this grantmaker's funding activity:
$400,000 to Third Way Institute, Washington, DC, 2012. For Community Concern.

159
William and Mary Ross Foundation ✧
4729 E. Sunrise Dr.
P.O. Box 501
Tucson, AZ 85718-4535

Established in 1997 in AZ.
Donor: Mary June Ross†.
Foundation type: Operating foundation.
Financial data (yr. ended 12/31/13): Assets, $17,236,111 (M); expenditures, $1,105,284; qualifying distributions, $808,261; giving activities include $805,500 for 26 grants (high: $100,000; low: $1,000).
Fields of interest: Education; Cancer; Human services; Christian agencies & churches.
Limitations: Applications not accepted. Giving primarily in AZ. No grants to individuals.
Application information: Contributes only to pre-selected organizations.
Officers: Jane Garigan, Pres., V.P., and Co-Secy.-Treas.; Tim Garigan, V.P. and Co-Treas.; Robert Struse, Co-Secy.
EIN: 860891827
Selected grants: The following grants are a representative sample of this grantmaker's funding activity:
$151,500 to University of Arizona Foundation, Tucson, AZ, 2011. For program support.
$50,000 to Carondelet Foundation, Tucson, AZ, 2011. For program support.
$50,000 to Critical Path Institute, Tucson, AZ, 2011. For program support.
$50,000 to Saint Jude Childrens Research Hospital, Memphis, TN, 2010. For program support.
$50,000 to Salpointe Catholic High School, Tucson, AZ, 2011. For program support.
$50,000 to Teach for America, New York, NY, 2011. For program support.
$25,000 to American Cancer Society, Tucson, AZ, 2011. For program support.
$25,000 to PIMA Air and Space Museum, Tucson, AZ, 2011. For program support.
$25,000 to Tohono Chul Park, Tucson, AZ, 2011. For program support.
$25,000 to UNICEF, New York, NY, 2010. For program support.
$20,000 to Arts for All, Tucson, AZ, 2011. For program support.
$20,000 to Saint Lukes Home, Tucson, AZ, 2011. For program support.
$10,000 to United Way of Tucson and Southern Arizona, Tucson, AZ, 2010. For program support.

160
Rouha Education & Welfare Foundation Inc. ✧ ☆
1739 E. Beverly Ave., Ste. 220
Kingman, AZ 86409-3593 (928) 757-5889
Contact: Ahmad S. Khan, Pres. and Dir.

Established in 2001 in AZ.
Donors: Ahmad Saeed Khan; Manzhar Javaid.
Foundation type: Operating foundation.
Financial data (yr. ended 12/31/13): Assets, $1,582,410 (M); gifts received, $281,020; expenditures, $465,796; qualifying distributions, $465,000; giving activities include $465,000 for 4 grants (high: $380,000; low: $5,000).
Fields of interest: Education; Human services; Religion.
Limitations: Applications accepted. Giving primarily in IL.
Application information: Application form not required.
Initial approach: Letter
Deadline(s): None
Officer and Directors:* Ahmad S. Khan,* Pres.; Manzhar Javaid; Hamid Mahmud.
EIN: 861008594
Selected grants: The following grants are a representative sample of this grantmaker's funding activity:
$1,000 to Montclair State University Foundation, Montclair, NJ, 2011.

161
Ken & Carol Schultz Foundation ✧ ☆
13771 N. Fountain Hills Blvd.
P.O. Box 613
Fountain Hills, AZ 85268-5939
Main URL: http://kcschultzfoundation.org/

Donors: Kenneth M. Schultz; Carol Schultz.
Foundation type: Independent foundation.
Financial data (yr. ended 12/31/13): Assets, $1,837,703 (M); gifts received, $3,000; expenditures, $591,639; qualifying distributions, $576,750; giving activities include $576,750 for 5 grants (high: $288,750; low: $7,000).
Fields of interest: Media, film/video; Higher education; Animals/wildlife; Health care.
Limitations: Applications not accepted. Giving primarily in CA.
Application information: Unsolicited requests for funds not accepted.
Officers: Kenneth M. Schultz, Pres.; Carol Schultz, V.P.
EIN: 263863383

162
The Jess & Sheila Schwartz Family Foundation ✧
15 Biltmore Estates Dr.
Phoenix, AZ 85016-2821
Contact: Sheila Schwartz, Pres. and Dir.

Established in 1999 in AZ.
Donors: Sheila Schwartz; Sheila Schwartz Charitable Remainder Trust.
Foundation type: Independent foundation.
Financial data (yr. ended 12/31/13): Assets, $2,637 (M); gifts received, $645,000; expenditures, $645,000; qualifying distributions, $633,995; giving activities include $633,995 for 16 grants (high: $300,000; low: $3,000).
Fields of interest: Secondary school/education; Education; Jewish federated giving programs; Jewish agencies & synagogues.
Limitations: Applications accepted. Giving primarily in AZ.
Application information: Application form not required.
Initial approach: Proposal
Deadline(s): None
Officers and Directors:* Sheila Schwartz,* Pres.; Frank L. Schwartz,* Secy.-Treas.; Lesley Schwartz Hammer; Abby I. Schwartz.
EIN: 860942313

163
Solheim Foundation ✧
P.O. Box 84558
Phoenix, AZ 85071-4558

Established in 1985 in AZ.
Donors: Karsten Solheim†; Louise C. Solheim; Karsten Manufacturing Corp.
Foundation type: Independent foundation.
Financial data (yr. ended 06/30/13): Assets, $687,325 (M); expenditures, $1,089,464; qualifying distributions, $1,078,254; giving activities include $1,078,013 for 23 grants (high: $250,000; low: $5,000).
Purpose and activities: Giving primarily for Christian education, missions, and other related activities.
Fields of interest: Human services; International affairs; Christian agencies & churches.
Limitations: Applications not accepted. Giving primarily in AZ, CA, CO, MD and TX. No grants to individuals.
Application information: Contributes only to pre-selected organizations.
Trustees: Allan Solheim; Allan Solheim, Jr.; Andrew Solheim; David Solheim; Joy Solheim; Karsten Louis Solheim; Louise Solheim.
EIN: 742378207

164
Stardust Foundation, Inc. ✧
6730 N. Scottsdale Rd., Ste. 230
Scottsdale, AZ 85253-4416
E-mail: contact@stardustco.com; Main URL: http://www.stardustfoundation.org

Established in 1993 in AZ as successor to the Bisgrove Foundation.
Donors: Gerald Bisgrove; Debra Bisgrove†; Bisgrove Foundation.
Foundation type: Company-sponsored foundation.
Financial data (yr. ended 12/31/13): Assets, $27,016,914 (M); expenditures, $758,237; qualifying distributions, $755,180; giving activities include $750,700 for 15 grants (high: $395,000; low: $100).
Purpose and activities: The foundation supports community foundations and organizations involved with arts and culture, health, human services, and community development. Special emphasis is directed toward programs designed to link concepts of family and neighborhood stability.
Fields of interest: Museums; Performing arts, theater; Performing arts, orchestras; Arts; Higher education; Health care; Children/youth, services; Family services; Homeless, human services; Human services; Community/economic development; Foundations (community); United Ways and Federated Giving Programs.
Type of support: General/operating support; Endowments; Program development; Scholarship funds.
Limitations: Applications not accepted. Giving primarily in Phoenix and Scottsdale, AZ.
Application information: Contributes only to pre-selected organizations.
Officers and Trustee:* Gerald Bisgrove,* Pres.; Jon Munson, Secy.-Treas.
EIN: 860735230
Selected grants: The following grants are a representative sample of this grantmaker's funding activity:
$5,000 to UMOM New Day Centers, Phoenix, AZ, 2012. For community engagement.

165
The Steele Foundation, Inc. ✧
702 E. Osborn Rd., Ste. 190
Phoenix, AZ 85014-5215
Contact: Marianne Cracchiolo Mago, Pres.
E-mail: grants@steele-foundation.com; Additional address: P.O. Box 1112, Phoenix, AZ 85001

Established in 1980 in AZ.
Donors: Horace Steele†; Ethel Steele†.
Foundation type: Independent foundation.
Financial data (yr. ended 12/31/13): Assets, $75,116,968 (M); expenditures, $4,009,651; qualifying distributions, $3,659,085; giving activities include $3,106,095 for 61 grants (high: $200,000; low: $250).
Purpose and activities: Primary areas of interest are education, holistic health, and community enrichment.
Fields of interest: Education; Holistic medicine; Infants/toddlers; Children/youth; Children; Youth; Economically disadvantaged; Homeless.
Type of support: Technical assistance; Matching/challenge support; Income development; Curriculum development; General/operating support; Management development/capacity building; Program development; Scholarship funds; Research; Consulting services; Program evaluation.
Limitations: Applications not accepted. Giving primarily in AZ. No support for political or religious organizations, or for universities outside of AZ. No grants to individuals, or for events.
Application information: Contributes only to pre-selected organizations.
Board meeting date(s): Nov.
Officers and Directors:* Daniel Cracchiolo,* C.E.O. and Chair.; Marianne Cracchiolo Mago,* Pres.; Andy Abraham; Andrea Cracchiolo III, M.D.; Bryant Stooks.
Number of staff: 3 full-time professional.
EIN: 953466880

166
Stewart Education Foundation ✧
(formerly Donnell B. and Elizabeth Dee Shaw Stewart Educational Foundation)
c/o Wells Fargo Bank Arizona, N.A., Trust Tax Dept.
P.O. Box 53456, MAC S4101-22G
Phoenix, AZ 85072-3456
Application address: c/o Mary Barker, Wells Fargo Bank, N.A., 2389 Washington Blvd., 2nd Fl., Ogden, UT 84401-1971

Established in 1977 in UT.
Donor: Elizabeth D.S. Stewart†.
Foundation type: Independent foundation.
Financial data (yr. ended 12/31/13): Assets, $66,935,159 (M); expenditures, $2,787,305;

qualifying distributions, $2,658,833; giving activities include $2,445,500 for 3 grants (high: $2,415,500; low: $5,000).
Purpose and activities: Giving primarily for the arts, education, health organizations, and social services.
Fields of interest: Media, television; Museums; Performing arts; Arts; Higher education; Education; Health organizations, association; Human services; Children/youth, services; Foundations (private grantmaking); United Ways and Federated Giving Programs.
Type of support: Annual campaigns; Capital campaigns; Building/renovation; Equipment; Endowments; Professorships; Scholarship funds; Research; Matching/challenge support.
Limitations: Applications accepted. Giving primarily in UT, with emphasis on Ogden.
Application information: Application form required.
Initial approach: Letter
Copies of proposal: 1
Deadline(s): None, but prior to Sept. 30 is preferred
Officers: Jack D. Lampros, Chair.; Dean W. Hurst, Co-Vice-Chair.; William C. Stromberg, Co-Vice-Chair.
Directors: Mary L. Barker; Kristen Hurst-Hyde; Jamie Lampros Shenefelt; Bernice Stromberg; Richard Stromberg.
Trustee: Wells Fargo Bank, N.A.
EIN: 876179880
Selected grants: The following grants are a representative sample of this grantmaker's funding activity:
$11,500 to Youth Impact, Ogden, UT, 2012. For Weber State University in kind contribution of 75,000 shares of General Electric Company stock was gifted on January 9, 2012 Mean value of $1,407,000.

167
The Surplus Line Association of Arizona Foundation ✧
c/o Kierland Business Center
15849 71St., Ste. 100
Scottsdale, AZ 85254-2179

Established in 2003 in AZ.
Donor: The Surplus Line Association of Arizona.
Foundation type: Independent foundation.
Financial data (yr. ended 12/31/12): Assets, $6,337,570 (M); gifts received, $751,500; expenditures, $455,430; qualifying distributions, $455,153; giving activities include $426,000 for 37 grants (high: $75,000; low: $2,500).
Fields of interest: Food banks; Human services; United Ways and Federated Giving Programs; Christian agencies & churches.
Limitations: Applications not accepted. Giving primarily in AZ and PA. No grants to individuals.
Application information: Unsolicited requests for funds not accepted.
Officers: Timothy Downey, Pres.; T. Curtis Anderson, V.P.; Larry Beach, Secy.-Treas.; J. Scott Wede, Exec. Dir.
Directors: Marc Adler; Karla Burt; Lanny Hair; Konnie Keaschall-Kiser; Gerald L. Silver.
EIN: 866320000
Selected grants: The following grants are a representative sample of this grantmaker's funding activity:
$25,000 to Samaritans Purse, Boone, NC, 2012. For Disaster Relief for the Tornado Victims.
$5,000 to Arizona Bridge to Independent Living, Phoenix, AZ, 2012. For Virginia Piper Disability S and A Center.

168
SVL Foundation ✧ ☆
P.O. Box 17917
Tucson, AZ 85731-7917

Donors: Susan LaFave; Victor LaFave.
Foundation type: Independent foundation.
Financial data (yr. ended 06/30/13): Assets, $2,150,801 (M); gifts received, $605,696; expenditures, $449,696; qualifying distributions, $449,500; giving activities include $444,000 for 20 grants (high: $150,000; low: $1,000).
Fields of interest: Education; Animals/wildlife; Human services.
Limitations: Applications not accepted. Giving primarily in Tucson, AZ. No grants to individuals.
Application information: Contributes only to pre-selected organizations.
Officers: Victor LaFave, Pres.; Susan LaFave, Secy.-Treas.
EIN: 455145898

169
Ruth McCormick Tankersley Charitable Trust ✧
3430 E. Sunrise Dr., Ste. 200
Tucson, AZ 85718-3236 (520) 792-1181
Contact: Richard Duffield, Tr.

Established in 1994 in AZ.
Donors: Tiffany T. Wolfe Charitable Remainder Unitrust 1999; Tiffany T. Wolfe Charitable Remainder Unitrust 1997; Ruth McC Tankersley Trust.
Foundation type: Independent foundation.
Financial data (yr. ended 12/31/13): Assets, $43,321,897 (M); gifts received, $32,118,250; expenditures, $2,373,253; qualifying distributions, $2,176,055; giving activities include $2,176,055 for 29 grants (high: $500,000; low: $2,100).
Purpose and activities: Giving primarily for education, including a literacy program; funding also for human services, animal welfare, and to a children's hospital.
Fields of interest: Secondary school/education; Higher education; Education; Animal welfare; Hospitals (specialty); Human services.
Limitations: Applications accepted. Giving primarily in the U.S., with emphasis on AZ, FL, and TX.
Application information: Application form required.
Initial approach: Proposal
Deadline(s): None
Trustees: Richard Duffield; Michael Halle; Kristie Miller; Mark McCormick Miller; Burton Rubin.
EIN: 866224242

170
The Thomarie Foundation ✧
20225 N. Scottsdale Rd.
Scottsdale, AZ 85255-6456 (480) 502-9462
Contact: Diane M. Halle, Pres.

Established in 2007 in AZ.
Donors: Bruce T. Halle; Diane M. Halle; Reinalt-Thomas Corp.
Foundation type: Independent foundation.
Financial data (yr. ended 12/31/12): Assets, $128 (M); gifts received, $18,100; expenditures, $613,797; qualifying distributions, $595,000; giving activities include $595,000 for grants.
Fields of interest: Museums (art).
Limitations: Applications accepted. Giving primarily in New York, NY and Phoenix, AZ. No grants to individuals.
Application information: Application form not required.
Initial approach: Letter
Deadline(s): None
Officers: Bruce T. Halle, Chair.; Diane M. Halle, Pres.; Lisa Pedersen, Secy.; Michael Zuieback, Treas.
EIN: 261477416
Selected grants: The following grants are a representative sample of this grantmaker's funding activity:
$450,000 to Museum of Modern Art, New York, NY, 2011. For general support.
$173,000 to Phoenix Art Museum, Phoenix, AZ, 2011. For general support.

171
The Gary and Diane Tooker Family Foundation ✧
15802 N. 71st St., Ste. 657
Scottsdale, AZ 85254-7115

Established in 2007 in AZ.
Donor: The Gary L. Tooker Charitable Lead Annuity Trust.
Foundation type: Independent foundation.
Financial data (yr. ended 12/31/12): Assets, $1,495,797 (M); gifts received, $244,676; expenditures, $560,155; qualifying distributions, $531,500; giving activities include $531,500 for 12 grants (high: $200,000; low: $3,000).
Fields of interest: Education; Genetic diseases and disorders research; Human services; Christian agencies & churches.
Limitations: Applications not accepted. Giving primarily in AZ. No grants to individuals.
Application information: Contributes only to pre-selected organizations.
Trustees: Lisa J. Hickie; Diane R. Tooker; Gary L. Tooker; Michael R. Tooker.
EIN: 860975172

172
University of Phoenix Foundation ✧
4025 S. Riverpoint Pkwy., Stop CF-K815
Phoenix, AZ 85040-0723
E-mail: upxfoundation@phoenix.edu; Main URL: http://www.upxfoundation.org

Established in 2006 in AZ.
Donors: Apollo Group, Inc.; Liberty Mutual; Inmart Group; Herff Jones, Inc.
Foundation type: Company-sponsored foundation.
Financial data (yr. ended 08/31/13): Assets, $1,710,546 (M); gifts received, $1,250,000; expenditures, $1,464,049; qualifying distributions, $1,464,049; giving activities include $1,464,049 for 4 grants (high: $614,049; low: $100,000).
Purpose and activities: The foundation supports programs designed to increase access to education, with emphasis on underrepresented and low-income students.

Fields of interest: Education, research; Higher education; Education, services; Education; Youth, services; Economically disadvantaged.
Type of support: Scholarship funds; Sponsorships; Program development; General/operating support; Research.
Limitations: Giving primarily in AZ, CA, and Washington, DC.
Application information: The foundation is in the process of revising its application guidelines. Please visit website for updated information.
Officers and Director:* Nina Munson,* Chair.; Nancy Hennigan, Secy.; Mathew Beckler, Treas.; Pat Gottfried, Exec. Dir.; Charlotte Saylors.
EIN: 205964568
Selected grants: The following grants are a representative sample of this grantmaker's funding activity:
$560,504 to Boys and Girls Clubs of America, Long Beach, CA, 2011.
$150,000 to MIND Research Institute, Irvine, CA, 2011.
$150,000 to WestEd, San Francisco, CA, 2011.
$100,000 to College Track, Oakland, CA, 2011.
$83,333 to Everybody Wins! USA, Boston, MA, 2011.
$50,000 to East Bay Zoological Society, Oakland, CA, 2011.
$47,000 to Ohio Literacy Network, Columbus, OH, 2011.
$46,800 to Junior Achievement Worldwide, Colorado Springs, CO, 2011.
$25,000 to Daily Dose of Reading, South Euclid, OH, 2011.
$25,000 to Point Foundation, Los Angeles, CA, 2011.

173
The Weatherup Family Foundation ✧
10343 E. Pinnacle Peak Rd.
Scottsdale, AZ 85255-3747

Established in 1998 in CT.
Donors: Craig E. Weatherup; Constance K. Weatherup.
Foundation type: Independent foundation.
Financial data (yr. ended 12/31/13): Assets, $5,706,794 (M); gifts received, $5,000; expenditures, $1,098,727; qualifying distributions, $1,056,000; giving activities include $1,056,000 for 56 grants (high: $250,000; low: $1,000).
Fields of interest: Museums (art); Higher education; Education; Environment, natural resources; Human services.
Limitations: Applications not accepted. Giving primarily in AZ and NY. No grants to individuals.
Application information: Contributes only to pre-selected organizations.
Trustees: Constance K. Weatherup; Craig E. Weatherup.
EIN: 066469433

174
Del E. Webb Foundation ✧
P.O. Box 2427
Prescott, AZ 86302-2427 (928) 445-9699
Contact: Lawrence A. Johnson, Pres.
FAX: (928) 445-1584; E-mail: Larry@DEWF.org; Main URL: http://www.DEWF.org
Grants List: http://www.dewf.org/TFM/$WebStatus/AppsApprDateSort.asp

Incorporated in 1960 in AZ.
Donor: Del E. Webb‡.
Foundation type: Independent foundation.
Financial data (yr. ended 12/31/13): Assets, $54,948,229 (M); expenditures, $2,795,034; qualifying distributions, $2,476,621; giving activities include $2,119,487 for 30 grants (high: $500,000; low: $2,400).
Purpose and activities: Giving to support organizations that are primarily involved in providing formal medical services, medical research, or medical education and are located in the states of Arizona, California or Nevada.
Fields of interest: Education; Health care; Infants/toddlers; Children/youth; Children; Youth; Adults; Aging; Young adults; Disabilities, people with; Physically disabled; Blind/visually impaired; Deaf/hearing impaired; Mentally disabled; Minorities; Asians/Pacific Islanders; African Americans/Blacks; Hispanics/Latinos; Native Americans/American Indians; Indigenous peoples; Women; Infants/toddlers, female; Girls; Adults, women; Young adults, female; Men; Infants/toddlers, male; Boys; Adults, men; Young adults, male; Military/veterans; Offenders/ex-offenders; Substance abusers; AIDS, people with; Single parents; Crime/abuse victims; Terminal illness, people with; Immigrants/refugees; Economically disadvantaged; Homeless; Migrant workers; LGBTQ.
Type of support: General/operating support; Continuing support; Capital campaigns; Building/renovation; Equipment; Land acquisition; Emergency funds; Program development; Seed money; Curriculum development; Scholarship funds; Research; Matching/challenge support.
Limitations: Applications accepted. Giving limited to AZ, CA, and NV. No support for government agencies, sectarian or religious organizations, or pass-through organizations. No grants to individuals, or for deficit financing or indirect costs.
Publications: Application guidelines.
Application information: Application guidelines and form available on foundation web site. Formal proposals are by invitation only, after review of letter of intent. Application form required.
Initial approach: 1-page letter of intent with foundation Contact Information Form which can be downloaded from foundation web site
Deadline(s): None, for letters of intent. Formal grant applications are due 1-month prior to the foundation's next board meeting. (Refer to meeting calendar on foundation web site)
Board meeting date(s): Jan., Apr., July and Oct.
Final notification: Within 1-week for letters of intent
Officers and Directors:* Lawrence A. Johnson,* Pres.; John B. Lees, V.P.; Shielia Johnson, Treas.; Nicole Aubin; Jean Canoose; John W. Smith.
Number of staff: 2 full-time professional; 2 part-time support.
EIN: 866052737

175
The Weil Foundation ✧
(formerly Polaris Foundation)
P.O. Box 13006
Tucson, AZ 85732-3006
Contact: Nancy Olmstead, Recording Secy.
E-mail: info@weilfoundation.org; Proposal e-mails: James Dalen: jdalenmd@gmail.com, and Nancy Olmstead: nancy@x9ranch.com; Express package address: c/o Nancy Olmstead, The Weil Foundation, 1670 N. Kolb Rd., Ste. 240, Tucson, AZ 85715; Main URL: http://www.weilfoundation.org/
Facebook: http://www.facebook.com/WeilFoundation
Twitter: https://twitter.com/WeilFoundation
Vimeo: http://vimeo.com/weilfoundation

Established in 2002 in AZ.
Donors: Andrew Weil; Custom Nutrition Services, LLC; drugstore.com, inc.
Foundation type: Independent foundation.
Financial data (yr. ended 12/31/12): Assets, $654,418 (M); gifts received, $582,849; expenditures, $506,858; qualifying distributions, $435,000; giving activities include $435,000 for 12 grants (high: $200,000; low: $5,000).
Purpose and activities: Support for the advancement of integrative medicine. The foundation's current strategic focus is the training and education of medical students, physicians and other health care professionals in integrative medicine.
Fields of interest: Higher education; Medical school/education; Holistic medicine.
Limitations: Applications accepted. Giving primarily in AZ; some giving also in ME and NM.
Publications: Application guidelines.
Application information: Grants are funded from July 1 until June 30. If any material that is to be submitted does not exist in electronic form, indicate in e-mail that such material is being sent by regular mail. Specific instructions available on foundation web site. Application form required.
Initial approach: Proposal (5-10 pages, to be e-mailed to both James Dalen and Nancy Olmstead), along with cover page which is located on foundation web site
Deadline(s): Jan. 31
Final notification: Mar.
Officers: Andrew Weil, Chair.; Lura M. Lovell, Vice-Chair.; Richard Baxter, Secy.-Treas.; Nancy Olmstead, Recording Secy.; James Dalen, M.D., Exec. Dir.
Directors: Donald Abrams, M.D.; Janet Lang; Humberto S. Lopez; Daria Myers; Robert G. Sarver; Adele Simmons.
EIN: 861049023

176
Whale Beach Foundation ✧
(formerly Edgecliff Foundation)
3133 N. Meadowbrook Dr.
Flagstaff, AZ 86004-7411

Established in 1994 in CA.
Donors: Douglas Otto; Rex Licklider.
Foundation type: Independent foundation.
Financial data (yr. ended 12/31/13): Assets, $3,678,690 (M); expenditures, $1,167,734; qualifying distributions, $1,165,000; giving activities include $1,165,000 for 17 grants (high: $500,000; low: $5,000).
Fields of interest: Elementary/secondary education; Higher education.
Limitations: Applications not accepted. Giving primarily in CA; some giving also in GA and MA. No grants to individuals.
Application information: Contributes only to pre-selected organizations.
Officers: Rex A. Licklider, Pres.; John Kalinich, C.F.O.
EIN: 770386216

177
Homa & Irene Wood Foundation ✧
1222 E. Baseline Rd., Ste. 200
Tempe, AZ 85283-1434

Established in 2002 in AZ.
Donor: Irene Wood†.
Foundation type: Independent foundation.
Financial data (yr. ended 05/31/13): Assets, $10,325,219 (M); expenditures, $749,825; qualifying distributions, $637,122; giving activities include $637,122 for 15+ grants (high: $371,548).
Fields of interest: Higher education.
Limitations: Applications not accepted. No grants to individuals.
Application information: Contributes only to pre-selected organizations.
Officer: Jeffrey C. McMullin, Treas.
Directors: Douglas K. Cook; Lynette Peterson.
EIN: 860788519
Selected grants: The following grants are a representative sample of this grantmaker's funding activity:
$405,351 to Arizona State University, Tempe, AZ, 2011. For scholarships.
$100,061 to University of Arizona, Tucson, AZ, 2011. For scholarships.
$69,005 to Northern Arizona University, Flagstaff, AZ, 2011. For scholarships.
$30,750 to Mesa Community College, Mesa, AZ, 2011. For scholarships.
$20,000 to Eastern Arizona College, Thatcher, AZ, 2011. For scholarships.
$5,000 to University of San Francisco, San Francisco, CA, 2011. For scholarships.
$4,000 to Southwestern Illinois College, Belleville, IL, 2011. For scholarships.
$2,500 to New York University, New York, NY, 2011. For scholarships.
$2,500 to Utah Valley University, Orem, UT, 2011. For scholarships.
$2,000 to Colby College, Waterville, ME, 2011. For scholarships.

178
Zuckerman Family Foundation ✧
8600 E. Rockcliff Rd.
Tucson, AZ 85750-9733 (520) 749-9655
Contact: Jay Zuckerman, V.P.; Amy Zuckerman, Dir.

Established in 2005 in AZ.
Donors: Jay Zuckerman; Amy Zuckerman; Zuckerman Investments, LLC.
Foundation type: Independent foundation.
Financial data (yr. ended 12/31/13): Assets, $7,746,059 (M); expenditures, $770,730; qualifying distributions, $719,665; giving activities include $719,665 for 37 grants (high: $200,000; low: $500).
Fields of interest: Arts; Higher education; Education; Medical research, institute; Children/youth, services; Foundations (community); Jewish federated giving programs; Jewish agencies & synagogues.
Limitations: Applications accepted. Giving primarily in AZ and MA.
Application information: A site visit will be required of applicants. Application form required.
Initial approach: Letter of inquiry
Deadline(s): None
Officers: Mel Zuckerman, Pres.; Enid Zuckerman, V.P.; Jay Zuckerman, V.P.; Jerrold Cohen, Secy.-Treas.
Director: Amy Zuckerman.
EIN: 202955094
Selected grants: The following grants are a representative sample of this grantmaker's funding activity:
$2,500 to AOPA Foundation, Frederick, MD, 2012. To support General Aviation.
$500 to AIDS/LifeCycle, San Francisco, CA, 2012. For Donation on Behalf of Charlie Pinkowski.

ARKANSAS

179

Arkansas Community Foundation, Inc. ✧

1400 W. Markham St., Ste. 206
Little Rock, AR 72201-1843 (501) 372-1116
Contact: Heather Larkin, C.E.O.
FAX: (501) 372-1166; E-mail: arcf@arcf.org; Additional tel.: (888) 220-2723; Additional e-mail: hlarkin@arcf.org; Main URL: http://www.arcf.org
Facebook: http://www.facebook.com/ArkansasCommunityFoundation
LinkedIn: http://www.linkedin.com/company/arkansas-community-foundation
YouTube: http://www.youtube.com/user/ARCFvideo

Established in 1976 in AR.
Foundation type: Community foundation.
Financial data (yr. ended 06/30/13): Assets, $190,174,811 (M); gifts received, $33,341,011; expenditures, $12,517,488; giving activities include $11,136,960 for grants.
Purpose and activities: The foundation seeks to inspire people and communities to build and distribute charitable funds for Good, for Arkansas, for Ever.
Fields of interest: Humanities; Arts; Higher education; Libraries/library science; Education; Environment; Animal welfare; Health care; Youth development; Human services; Community/economic development; Religion.
Type of support: General/operating support; Continuing support; Endowments; Program development; Conferences/seminars; Publication; Seed money; Scholarship funds; Research; Technical assistance.
Limitations: Applications accepted. Giving limited to AR. No grants for operating expenses, debt elimination, capital improvements, building, property, computer systems or emergencies.
Publications: Annual report; Financial statement; Grants list; Informational brochure; Newsletter; Occasional report.
Application information: Visit foundation web site for application information.
Initial approach: Contact Prog. Dir.
Copies of proposal: 2
Deadline(s): Varies
Board meeting date(s): Feb., May, Sept., and Nov.
Officers and Directors:* Ted Belden,* Chair.; Carolyn Blakely, Ph.D.*, Vice-Chair.; Heather Larkin, C.E.O. and Pres.; Kim Evans, V.P., Devel. and Client Svcs.; David E. Johnson, V.P., Community Investment; Sara Kinser, V.P., Comm. Strategy; Corey Moline, C.F.O.; Charlotte Brown, Governance Chair.; Mary Elizabeth Eldridge, Community Investment Chair.; Eric Hutchinson, Finance Chair.; Jackson Farrow; Dennis Hunt; Dr. Mahlon Maris; George E. McLeod; Steve Nipper; Sam Scruggs; Angela Shirey; Philip Tappan; Robert Thompson; Estella Tullgren; Robert Zunick.
Number of staff: 9 full-time professional; 4 full-time support.
EIN: 521055743
Selected grants: The following grants are a representative sample of this grantmaker's funding activity:
$675,000 to Arkansas Single Parent Scholarship Fund, Springdale, AR, 2014. For general operating support to the Arkansas Single Parent Scholarship Fund.
$625,000 to Arkansas Single Parent Scholarship Fund, Springdale, AR, 2013. For the Arkansas Single Parent Scholarship Fund Program.
$285,914 to Single Parent Scholarship Fund of Benton County, Bentonville, AR, 2014. For general operating support to the Single Parent Scholarship Fund of Benton County.
$196,422 to East Arkansas Family Health Center, West Memphis, AR, 2013. To fund contractual services for indigent patients at the Helena Community Health Center.
$150,000 to Boys and Girls Club of Phillips County, Helena, AR, 2014. For development of athletic facility.
$125,000 to Alliance for Affordable Energy, New Orleans, LA, 2014. For pursuit of energy efficient and renewable energy policy goals in Louisiana.
$125,000 to Alliance for Affordable Energy, New Orleans, LA, 2013. For pursuit of energy efficiency and renewable energy policy goals in Louisiana.
$100,000 to Saint Marks Episcopal Church, Little Rock, AR, 2014. For church support.
$100,000 to TEDX, Inc., Paonia, CO, 2014. For research and personnel.
$100,000 to University of Arkansas for Medical Sciences, Arkansas Aging Initiative, Little Rock, AR, 2014. For general operating support.
$96,000 to Wind Coalition, Austin, TX, 2013. To increase transmission resources for renewable wind and solar power within Arkansas, Texas, Oklahoma and Louisiana.
$83,333 to Walton Arts Center, Fayetteville, AR, 2014. For renovations to the Fayetteville facility.
$80,000 to United States Marshals Museum Foundation, Fort Smith, AR, 2013. For the pledge of funds to be used for building and exhibits.
$60,000 to First United Methodist Church, Little Rock, AR, 2013. For gift to the church.
$5,000 to Arkansas Country Doctor Museum, Lincoln, AR, 2013. For general operating support.
$5,000 to Center for Art and Education, Van Buren, AR, 2014. For sponsorship of the River Valley Student Art Competition.
$4,950 to Campus Crusade for Christ International, Orlando, FL, 2013. For the Jesus Project Network Acct and other uses.
$3,000 to Christian Health Center of Heber Springs, Heber Springs, AR, 2013. For clinic services for poor and uninsured persons.
$2,000 to Pulaski Technical College, North Little Rock, AR, 2013. For scholarship.
$2,000 to Southern Arkansas University, Magnolia, AR, 2014. For scholarship.

180

Bailey Family Foundation ✧ ☆

1400 W. Markham St., Ste. 202
Little Rock, AR 72201-1843

Established in 2006 in AR.
Donors: John Bailey; Patricia Bailey.
Foundation type: Independent foundation.
Financial data (yr. ended 12/31/13): Assets, $28,871 (M); gifts received, $420,375; expenditures, $432,822; qualifying distributions, $432,822; giving activities include $432,822 for 39 grants (high: $253,000; low: $25).
Fields of interest: Higher education; Education; Boys & girls clubs; Youth development; Human services.
Limitations: Applications not accepted. Giving primarily in AR.
Application information: Unsolicited requests for funds not accepted.
Officers: John Bailey, Pres.; Patricia Bailey, V.P.; Rachel Oberste, Secy.
EIN: 208350641

181

Blue & You Foundation for a Healthier Arkansas ✧

(formerly ABC Foundation)
USAble Corporate Ctr.
320 W. Capitol, Ste. 200
Little Rock, AR 72201-3506 (501) 378-3300
Contact: Patrick O'Sullivan, Exec. Dir.; Suzanne Baldwin, Admin. Asst.
FAX: (501) 378-2051;
E-mail: posullivan@arkbluecross.com; Tel. for Patrick O'Sullivan: (501) 378-2221; Additional contact: Suzanne Baldwin, Admin. Asst., tel. (501) 378-2223, e-mail: lsbaldwin@arkbluecross.com; Main URL: http://www.blueandyoufoundationarkansas.org
Grants List: http://www.blueandyoufoundationarkansas.org/grants_awarded/

Established in 2001 in AR.
Donor: Arkansas Blue Cross and Blue Shield.
Foundation type: Company-sponsored foundation.
Financial data (yr. ended 12/31/13): Assets, $55,658,098 (M); expenditures, $3,210,151; qualifying distributions, $2,725,346; giving activities include $2,725,346 for 97 grants (high: $150,000; low: $1,000).
Purpose and activities: The foundation supports programs designed to improve health in Arkansas. Special emphasis is directed towards programs designed to affect health care delivery, health care policy, and health care economics in Arkansas.
Fields of interest: Health care, public policy; Health care, reform; Hospitals (general); Health care, clinics/centers; Health care, infants; Dental care; Health care, patient services; Health care; Diabetes; Children/youth, services; Family services.
Type of support: General/operating support; Program development; Research; Program evaluation.
Limitations: Applications accepted. Giving limited to AR. No support for private foundations, organizations with a contractual relationship with Arkansas Blue Cross and Blue Shield, political or lobbying organizations, fraternal, athletic, or social organizations, or religious organizations not of direct benefit to the entire community. No grants to individuals, or for fundraising events or celebrations, capital campaigns or endowments, facilities or equipment, conferences, indirect costs, or tobacco-related programs.
Publications: Application guidelines; Grants list.
Application information: Mini-Grants are for requests of $1,000. Regular grants are for requests of $5,000 to $150,000. Regular grant recipients file 6-month and 12-month reports and receive a site visit. Mini-Grant recipients file a one-page report within six months. Application form required.
Initial approach: Complete online application
Deadline(s): Jan. 1 to Mar. 31 for Mini-Grants; July 15 for Regular Grants
Final notification: 10 days for Mini-Grants; Dec. 31 for Regular Grants

Officers and Directors:* Robert D. Cabe,* Chair.; Lee Douglass, Secy.; Gray Dillard, Treas.; Patrick O'Sullivan, Exec. Dir.; Carolyn Blakely, Ph.D.; Marla Johnson; Mahlon Maris, M.D.; J. Thomas May; George K. Mitchell, M.D.; Sherman Tate.
Number of staff: 2 full-time professional.
EIN: 710862108
Selected grants: The following grants are a representative sample of this grantmaker's funding activity:
$150,000 to Community Clinic at Saint Francis House, Springdale, AR, 2011.
$150,000 to University of Arkansas for Medical Sciences, Little Rock, AR, 2011.
$138,500 to Arkansas Childrens Hospital Foundation, Little Rock, AR, 2011.
$80,000 to Monticello School District, Monticello, AR, 2011.
$76,400 to Pulaski Technical College, North Little Rock, AR, 2011.
$55,000 to Arkansas Community Foundation, Little Rock, AR, 2011.
$52,785 to Our House, Little Rock, AR, 2011.
$50,000 to Northwest Arkansas Free Health Center, Fayetteville, AR, 2011.
$40,341 to PACES, Jonesboro, AR, 2011.
$14,795 to The Jones Trust, Springdale, AR, 2011.

182
Horace C. Cabe Foundation ✧
108 N. Front St.
Gurdon, AR 71743-1010 (903) 794-2223
Contact: Paul Harris
TX tel.: (903) 794-2223; Main URL: http://horaceccabefoundation.org/

Established in 1991 in TX.
Donor: Horace C. Cabe†.
Foundation type: Independent foundation.
Financial data (yr. ended 06/30/13): Assets, $34,280,761 (M); expenditures, $2,041,313; qualifying distributions, $1,787,462; giving activities include $1,697,347 for 100 grants (high: $113,750; low: $100).
Purpose and activities: Giving primarily for education, health care and hospitals, including children's hospitals, and children and youth services.
Fields of interest: Arts; Higher education; Education; Hospitals (general); Hospitals (specialty); Health care; Youth development; Human services; Children/youth, services; Protestant agencies & churches; Children; Youth; Aging; Young adults; Physically disabled; Terminal illness, people with; Economically disadvantaged; Homeless.
Type of support: Annual campaigns; Building/renovation; Capital campaigns; Conferences/seminars; Continuing support; Curriculum development; Debt reduction; Emergency funds; Endowments; Equipment; General/operating support; Land acquisition; Management development/capacity building; Matching/challenge support; Program development; Program-related investments/loans; Research; Scholarship funds; Seed money.
Limitations: Applications accepted. Giving primarily in southwest AR and northeast TX. No grants to individuals.
Publications: Biennial report (including application guidelines); Newsletter.
Application information: Applications should be sent unbound and without folders or binders. Application form required.
Initial approach: Use application form on foundation web site
Copies of proposal: 1
Deadline(s): Jan. 1, Apr. 1, and Sept. 1
Board meeting date(s): Sept. 30, Jan. 31, and May 31
Final notification: 1 week
Officers: Charles Lee "Sandy" Cabe, Pres.; JJ Barto, V.P.; Lucille T. Cook, Secy.
Directors: Charles L. Cabe, Jr.; Thomas H. Cabe; John K. Slicker.
Number of staff: 1 part-time professional; 1 part-time support.
EIN: 752402852

183
Tom J. and Edna Mae Carson Foundation ✧
c/o Ken Rossi
5000 Rogers Ave., Ste. 700
Fort Smith, AR 72903-2079

Established in 1989 in AR.
Donors: Tom J. Carson; Mary Carson.
Foundation type: Independent foundation.
Financial data (yr. ended 12/31/13): Assets, $17,727,779 (M); expenditures, $690,438; qualifying distributions, $622,393; giving activities include $622,393 for 35 grants (high: $400,000; low: $50).
Fields of interest: Museums; Historical activities; Higher education; Education; Health organizations, association; Human services; Community/economic development; Christian agencies & churches.
Limitations: Applications not accepted. Giving primarily in OK. No grants to individuals.
Application information: Contributes only to pre-selected organizations.
Trustees: Drew T. Carson; James F. Carson; Tom J. Carson; Rita Kay Fowlkes.
EIN: 581880469
Selected grants: The following grants are a representative sample of this grantmaker's funding activity:
$1,664 to Oklahoma State University Foundation, Stillwater, OK, 2011. For general use.
$1,500 to Boy Scouts of America, Tulsa, OK, 2011. For general use.
$1,100 to Admiral Nimitz Foundation, Fredericksburg, TX, 2011. For general use.

184
Delta Dental of Arkansas Foundation, Inc. ✧
c/o Edie Arey
1513 Country Club Rd.
Sherwood, AR 72120-5076 (501) 992-1602
E-mail: earey@ddpar.com; Application contact: Kelly Caldwell, Mgr., tel.: (501) 992-1698, toll-free tel.: (800) 462-5410, e-mail: kcaldwell@deltadentalar.com; Main URL: http://www.ddarfoundation.com

Established in AR.
Donor: Delta Dental Plan of Arkansas, Inc.
Foundation type: Independent foundation.
Financial data (yr. ended 12/31/12): Assets, $2,574,749 (M); gifts received, $1,765,956; expenditures, $1,391,282; qualifying distributions, $1,380,370; giving activities include $1,380,370 for 24 grants (high: $400,000; low: $3,389).
Fields of interest: Hospitals (specialty); Health care, clinics/centers; Dental care.
Type of support: Equipment.
Limitations: Applications accepted. Giving primarily in AR.
Publications: Application guidelines.
Application information: See foundation web site for specific application form and instructions. Application form required.
Initial approach: E-mail grant request to Kelly Caldwell, Mgr.
Deadline(s): See foundation web site for current deadline
Officers: James Johnston, Chair.; Weldon Johnson, Vice-Chair.; Ed Choate, Pres.; Dr. Paul Fitzgerald, Secy.; Billy Tarpley, Treas.
Directors: Joyce Dees; Dr. Bob Mason; Ron Ownbey; Dr. Jim Phillips; Dr. Michael Zweifler.
EIN: 261569324
Selected grants: The following grants are a representative sample of this grantmaker's funding activity:
$15,000 to CARTI Foundation, Little Rock, AR, 2012. For Dental service for cancer patients.
$5,000 to Northwest Arkansas Radiation Therapy Institute, Springdale, AR, 2012. For Dental Care-High Risk Patients.
$5,000 to River Valley Christian Clinic, Dardanelle, AR, 2012. For Supplies and Maintenance.

185
El Dorado Promise, Inc. ✧
200 Peach St.
El Dorado, AR 71730-5836 (870) 864-5128
Additional address: 2000 Wildcat Dr., El Dorado, AR 71730; Main URL: http://www.eldoradopromise.com/
Facebook: http://www.facebook.com/pages/El-Dorado-Promise/13193968839
Twitter: http://twitter.com/eldoradopromise
YouTube: http://www.youtube.com/user/eldopromise

Established in 2007 in AR.
Donor: Murphy Oil Corp.
Foundation type: Company-sponsored foundation.
Financial data (yr. ended 12/31/13): Assets, $26,705,407 (M); gifts received, $5,000,000; expenditures, $3,294,027; qualifying distributions, $3,044,434; giving activities include $3,044,434 for grants to individuals.
Purpose and activities: The foundation awards college scholarships to graduates of El Dorado High Schools in El Dorado, Arkansas.
Fields of interest: Scholarships/financial aid; Education.
Type of support: Scholarships—to individuals.
Limitations: Applications accepted. Giving primarily in El Dorado, AR.
Publications: Application guidelines.
Application information: Application form required.
Initial approach: Download application form and mail to application address or participating high school counseling office
Deadline(s): Student's senior year of high school
Officers and Directors:* Roger W. Jenkins,* Pres.; Kelli M. Hammock,* V.P.; E. Ted Botner, Secy.; John B. Gardner, Treas.; Walter K. Compton.
EIN: 208303418

186
Endeavor Foundation ✧
800 Founders Park Dr. E.
Springdale, AR 72762 (479) 361-4624
Contact: Anita Scism, C.E.O.
FAX: (479) 361-5094;
E-mail: anita@endeavorfoundation.net; Main URL: http://www.endeavorfoundation.net
Blog: http://endeavorfoundation.net/blog/
Facebook: https://www.facebook.com/EndeavorFoundation

Established in 1999 in AR.
Foundation type: Community foundation.
Financial data (yr. ended 12/31/13): Assets, $172,611,380 (M); gifts received, $6,670,142; expenditures, $12,499,961; giving activities include $11,460,273 for grants.
Purpose and activities: The foundation seeks to impact Northwest Arkansas by identifying community issues, engaging key stakeholders, making grants and leveraging resources to address the issues.
Fields of interest: Education; Human services; Civil/human rights, immigrants; Community/economic development.
Type of support: General/operating support; Annual campaigns; Capital campaigns; Building/renovation; Equipment; Endowments; Program development; Conferences/seminars; Seed money; Curriculum development; Scholarship funds; Program evaluation; Scholarships—to individuals.
Limitations: Applications not accepted. Giving limited to Benton, Carroll, Madison and Washington counties in northwest AR. No support for religious organizations. No grants to individuals (except for scholarships).
Publications: Annual report; Biennial report; Financial statement; Informational brochure; Occasional report.
Application information:
Board meeting date(s): Bimonthly
Officers and Directors:* Lisa Ray,* Chair.; Debi Havner,* Vice-Chair.; Anita Scism,* C.E.O. and Pres.; Lisa McCullough,* C.F.O. and C.O.O.; Rick Parsons,* Treas.; Victoria Bossler; Roger Collins; Alan Dranow; Steven Lane; Katie Papasan; Charles Rateliff; Guillermo Rosales; Brad Sikorski; Terry Smith; Michael Stewart; Celia Swanson; Warren Wheat; Walter Turnbow.
Number of staff: 5 full-time professional; 2 full-time support.
EIN: 311682365

187
The Fox Family Charitable Trust ✧
5300 Edgewood Rd.
Little Rock, AR 72207-5308

Established in 2007 in AR.
Donor: Jeffrey Fox.
Foundation type: Independent foundation.
Financial data (yr. ended 12/31/13): Assets, $1,997,930 (M); gifts received, $1,018,500; expenditures, $1,103,405; qualifying distributions, $1,099,110; giving activities include $1,096,700 for 6 grants (high: $500,000; low: $10,000).
Fields of interest: Higher education; Education; Cancer; Medical research, institute; Diabetes research; Children/youth, services.
Limitations: Applications not accepted. Giving primarily in AR and NC. No grants to individuals.
Application information: Contributes only to pre-selected organizations.
Trustee: Jeffrey Fox.
EIN: 261375654

188
Charles A. Frueauff Foundation, Inc. ✧
200 River Market Ave., Ste. 100
Little Rock, AR 72201-1762 (501) 324-2233
Contact: Alma Willett, Office Mgr.; Anna Kay F. Frueauff, V.P., Comms. and Prog.
FAX: (501) 324-2236; Main URL: http://www.frueauff.org
Grants Database: http://www.frueauff.org/index.php?fuseaction=p0004.&mod=25

Incorporated in 1950 in NY.
Donor: Charles A. Frueauff†.
Foundation type: Independent foundation.
Financial data (yr. ended 12/31/13): Assets, $111,220,900 (M); expenditures, $6,100,113; qualifying distributions, $5,267,030; giving activities include $4,632,000 for 165 grants (high: $65,000; low: $5,000), and $38,209 for foundation-administered programs.
Purpose and activities: The mission of the foundation is to improve the lives of those in need by awarding grants to nonprofits in the areas of social services, health and hospitals, and higher education.
Fields of interest: Higher education; Hospitals (general); Health care; Human services; Children/youth, services.
Type of support: Annual campaigns; Building/renovation; Capital campaigns; Continuing support; Emergency funds; Endowments; Equipment; General/operating support; Matching/challenge support; Program development; Scholarship funds; Technical assistance.
Limitations: Applications accepted. Giving limited to the U.S. with emphasis on east of the Rockies, the South, and Northeast. No support for international projects, state supported colleges of universities, primary and secondary schools, or churches. No grants to individuals, or for multi-year grants, fundraising drives, or special events.
Publications: Grants list.
Application information: The foundation is not considering proposals from first time grant seekers. Grantseekers are encouraged to visit the foundation's web site for additional information prior to calling or submitting a letter of inquiry. Please re-visit the foundation's website periodically for an update on the funding status. Application form not required.
Copies of proposal: 1
Board meeting date(s): May and Nov.
Final notification: After May and Nov. meetings
Officers and Trustees:* David A. Frueauff,* Pres.; Anna Kay Frueauff,* V.P., Comms. and Progs.; James P. Fallon,* C.F.O.; Sue M. Frueauff,* C.A.O.; A.C. McCully, M.D.*, Pres. Emeritus.
Number of staff: 3 full-time professional; 1 part-time professional; 1 full-time support.
EIN: 135605371
Selected grants: The following grants are a representative sample of this grantmaker's funding activity:
$100,000 to City Harvest, New York, NY, 2012. For general support and disaster relief.
$63,000 to Boys and Girls Clubs of the Big Bend, Tallahassee, FL, 2012. For general operating support.
$60,000 to Arkansas Childrens Hospital Foundation, Little Rock, AR, 2012. For pediatric dentistry chair endowment.
$60,000 to Arkansas Single Parent Scholarship Fund, Springdale, AR, 2012. For scholarships.
$60,000 to Boys Choir of Tassahassee, Tallahassee, FL, 2012. For general program support.
$55,000 to Big Bend Hospice Foundation, Tallahassee, FL, 2012. For expansion campaign.
$47,700 to Good Shepherd Services, New York, NY, 2012. For disaster relief, summer and after-school programs.
$45,000 to Arkansas Rice Depot, Little Rock, AR, 2012. For programming support.
$30,000 to Christian Brothers University, Memphis, TN, 2012. For scholarship endowment fund.
$25,000 to Safe Horizon, New York, NY, 2012. For Streetwork support and disaster relief.

189
Conway & Margaret George Charitable Trust ✧ ☆
11412 Huron Ln.
Little Rock, AR 72211

Classified as a private foundation in 2001 in AR.
Donor: James Conway George†.
Foundation type: Independent foundation.
Financial data (yr. ended 08/31/13): Assets, $19,693 (M); expenditures, $3,571,399; qualifying distributions, $2,275,500; giving activities include $2,275,500 for 11 grants (high: $601,000; low: $25,000).
Fields of interest: Education; Health care; Health organizations; Protestant agencies & churches.
Limitations: Applications not accepted. Giving primarily in AR. No grants to individuals.
Application information: Unsolicited requests for funds not accepted.
Trustees: David Hardke; Johnny K. Hudson.
EIN: 756641221

190
Glass Family Foundation ✧
17 Glenbrook
Bentonville, AR 72712-3840
Contact: David D. Glass, Dir.

Established in 2000 in AR.
Donor: David D. Glass.
Foundation type: Independent foundation.
Financial data (yr. ended 12/31/13): Assets, $12,442,308 (M); expenditures, $758,104; qualifying distributions, $751,430; giving activities include $749,430 for 15 grants (high: $306,430; low: $1,000).
Purpose and activities: Giving primarily for education and Christian organizations; funding also for an institute for preventive medicine research.
Fields of interest: Higher education; Medical research, institute; Human services; Christian agencies & churches.
Limitations: Applications accepted. Giving primarily in AR and TX. No grants to individuals.
Application information: Application form not required.
Initial approach: Proposal
Deadline(s): None

Officers and Directors:* Ruth A. Glass,* Pres.; Dayna A. Martz,* Secy.-Treas.; David D. Glass.
EIN: 710848400

191
The Jesus Fund ✧
1901 Napa Valley Dr.
Little Rock, AR 72212-3913

Established in 2004 in AR.
Donors: Mountaire Corp.; Ronald M. Cameron.
Foundation type: Company-sponsored foundation.
Financial data (yr. ended 12/31/12): Assets, $38,525,335 (M); gifts received, $5,250,000; expenditures, $5,637,084; qualifying distributions, $5,075,600; giving activities include $5,075,600 for grants.
Purpose and activities: The foundation supports various public charities.
Fields of interest: General charitable giving.
Limitations: Applications not accepted. No grants to individuals.
Application information: Contributes only to pre-selected organizations.
Trustees: Ronald M. Cameron; Genevieve R. Couch.
EIN: 861108441

192
The Philip R. Jonsson Foundation ✧
c/o Signal Media Corporation
P.O. Box 251304
Little Rock, AR 72205
Application address: c/o Terri Mahan, 2400 Cottonsdale Ln., Little Rock, AR 72202; tel.: (501) 664-9410

Established in 1977 in TX.
Donors: Philip R. Jonsson; The Jonsson Foundation.
Foundation type: Independent foundation.
Financial data (yr. ended 12/31/13): Assets, $6,107,099 (M); expenditures, $708,948; qualifying distributions, $581,159; giving activities include $500,000 for 38 grants (high: $40,000; low: $3,500).
Purpose and activities: Giving primarily for education, health, and children, youth and social services.
Fields of interest: Arts; Higher education; Education; Reproductive health, family planning; Health organizations; Cancer research; Human services; Children/youth, services.
Type of support: General/operating support; Continuing support; Annual campaigns; Capital campaigns; Building/renovation; Equipment; Curriculum development; Scholarship funds; Research; Matching/challenge support.
Application information: Include cover letter detailing amount requested and what the money will be used for. Application form required.
Initial approach: Proposal
Copies of proposal: 1
Deadline(s): None
Board meeting date(s): Annually in the fall
Officers: Steven W. Jonsson, Pres.; Suzanne E. Jonsson, V.P.; Christina A. Jonsson, Secy.; Eileen J. Lewis, Treas.
EIN: 751552642

193
The Murphy Foundation ✧
200 N. Jefferson Ave., Ste. 400
El Dorado, AR 71730-5854 (870) 862-4961
Contact: Brett Williamson, Secy.-Treas.

Incorporated in 1958 in AR.
Donors: Charles H. Murphy, Jr.; members of the Murphy family.
Foundation type: Independent foundation.
Financial data (yr. ended 04/30/13): Assets, $62,120,303 (M); expenditures, $3,262,642; qualifying distributions, $3,042,109; giving activities include $2,231,148 for 59+ grants (high: $600,000), and $677,749 for 164 grants to individuals (high: $19,000; low: $786).
Purpose and activities: Emphasis on higher education, including scholarships; grants also for the arts and human services.
Fields of interest: Arts; Higher education; Education; Human services; Children/youth, services; United Ways and Federated Giving Programs.
Type of support: Annual campaigns; Endowments; General/operating support; Scholarships—to individuals.
Limitations: Giving primarily in southern AR for grants to organizations; giving limited to the southern AR area for grants to individuals.
Application information: Application form, including a copy of applicant's scholastic record, required for educational grants to individuals.
Initial approach: Letter
Copies of proposal: 1
Deadline(s): Aug. 1 for educational grants
Board meeting date(s): Semiannually
Officers and Directors:* R. Madison Murphy,* Pres.; Jerry W. Watkins,* V.P.; Brett Williamson, Secy.-Treas.
EIN: 716049826

194
Nabholz Charitable Foundation ✧
P.O. Box 2090
Conway, AR 72033 (501) 327-7781
Contact: Charles Nabholz, Dir.

Established in 1987 in AR.
Donors: Charles Nabholz; Nabholz Construction Corp.; Nabholz, Inc.; Nabhloz Mechanical & Electrical, Inc.; Nabholz Propoerties Inc.; Robert D. Nabholz.
Foundation type: Independent foundation.
Financial data (yr. ended 03/31/13): Assets, $1,144,220 (M); gifts received, $598,510; expenditures, $476,247; qualifying distributions, $472,538; giving activities include $472,538 for 76 grants (high: $48,338; low: $100).
Fields of interest: Performing arts, opera; Higher education; Health care, association; Hospitals (general); Hospitals (specialty); Health care, clinics/centers; Human services; Youth, services; Catholic agencies & churches.
Limitations: Applications accepted. Giving primarily in AR.
Application information: Application form not required.
Initial approach: Proposal
Deadline(s): None
Directors: Bill Hannah; Charles Nabholz; Greg Williams.
EIN: 581748037

Selected grants: The following grants are a representative sample of this grantmaker's funding activity:
$40,350 to Arkansas Childrens Hospital, Little Rock, AR, 2011.
$20,000 to Hendrix College, Conway, AR, 2011.
$11,750 to Arkansas Food Bank Network, Little Rock, AR, 2011.
$10,000 to Arkansas Prostate Cancer Foundation, Little Rock, AR, 2011.
$10,000 to Missouri State University, Springfield, MO, 2011.
$5,000 to Arkansas Baptist College, Little Rock, AR, 2011.
$5,000 to Arkansas State University, Mountain Home, AR, 2011.
$5,000 to Walton Arts Center, Fayetteville, AR, 2011.
$3,000 to Magnolia Hospital Foundation, Magnolia, AR, 2011.
$2,500 to Arkansas Symphony Orchestra, Little Rock, AR, 2011.

195
Oliver Charitable Corporation ✧
P.O. Box 3417
Little Rock, AR 72203-3417

Donors: Bess Chisum Stephens; Elizabeth Stephens Campbell; Craig Dobbs Campbell.
Foundation type: Independent foundation.
Financial data (yr. ended 12/31/13): Assets, $6,123,753 (M); gifts received, $600,000; expenditures, $1,044,205; qualifying distributions, $1,042,000; giving activities include $1,042,000 for 17 grants (high: $500,000; low: $1,000).
Purpose and activities: Giving primarily for education and the arts.
Fields of interest: Performing arts, orchestras; Secondary school/education; Foundations (community).
Limitations: Applications not accepted. Giving primarily in Little Rock, AR.
Application information: Contributes only to pre-selected organizations.
Directors: Rebecca Carr; Kathy Conley; Robert L. Schulte.
EIN: 204399824
Selected grants: The following grants are a representative sample of this grantmaker's funding activity:
$200,000 to Hip Knee Arkansas Foundation, Little Rock, AR, 2011. For general fund.
$150,000 to Anthony School, Little Rock, AR, 2011. For general fund.
$50,000 to Mayo Clinic, Rochester, MN, 2011. For general fund.
$20,000 to Arkansas Game and Fish Foundation, Little Rock, AR, 2011. For general fund.
$15,000 to Razorback Foundation, Fayetteville, AR, 2011. For general fund.
$10,000 to Tulane University, New Orleans, LA, 2011. For general fund.

196
Riggs Benevolent Fund ✧
P.O. Box 1399
Little Rock, AR 72203 (501) 570-3100

Trust established in 1959 in AR.

Donors: Robert G. Cress; Lamar W. Riggs Trust; J.A. Riggs Tractor Co.; Jack Riggs III; Lamar W. Riggs.
Foundation type: Company-sponsored foundation.
Financial data (yr. ended 12/31/13): Assets, $8,235,158 (M); gifts received, $279,388; expenditures, $507,110; qualifying distributions, $460,721; giving activities include $433,350 for 48 grants (high: $85,000; low: $1,000).
Purpose and activities: The fund supports museums and hospitals and organizations involved with education, cancer, youth development, children services, and Christianity.
Fields of interest: Museums; Elementary/secondary education; Higher education; Education; Hospitals (general); Cancer; Youth development, agriculture; Youth development; Children, services; United Ways and Federated Giving Programs; Christian agencies & churches.
Type of support: General/operating support; Scholarship funds.
Limitations: Applications accepted. Giving primarily in Little Rock, AR. No grants to individuals.
Application information: Application form required.
Initial approach: Proposal
Deadline(s): None
Trustees: Robert G. Cress; Edwin Keith Riggs; John A. Riggs III; Bank of America Private Client Group.
EIN: 716050130

197
The Winthrop Rockefeller Foundation

225 E. Markham St., Ste. 200
Little Rock, AR 72201-1636 (501) 376-6854
Contact: Prog. Staff
FAX: (501) 374-4797;
E-mail: programstaff@wrfoundation.org; Main URL: http://www.wrfoundation.org
Facebook: http://www.facebook.com/pages/Winthrop-Rockefeller-Foundation/133363867787?ref=ts
Grants Database: http://www.wrfoundation.org/grants/recent-grantees/search-grantees.html
Grants List: http://www.wrfoundation.org/grants/recent-grantees/recent-grantees-listing.html
The Winthrop Rockefeller Foundation's Philanthropy Promise: http://www.ncrp.org/philanthropys-promise/who
Twitter: http://twitter.com/wrf_arkansas
YouTube: http://www.youtube.com/user/WinthropRockefeller

Incorporated in 1956 in Arkansas as Rockwin Fund, Inc.; renamed in 1974.
Donor: Winthrop Rockefeller†.
Foundation type: Independent foundation.
Financial data (yr. ended 12/31/13): Assets, $147,122,064 (M); gifts received, $89,000; expenditures, $6,566,411; qualifying distributions, $5,427,176; giving activities include $3,106,129 for grants.
Purpose and activities: From inception, the Winthrop Rockefeller Foundation (WRF) has made grants with the explicit mission of improving the lives of Arkansans. Over time, WRF has developed a more targeted approach that focuses resources on three substantive areas: 1) Economic Development; 2) Education; and 3) Economic, Racial, and Social Justice. In 2008, WRF adopted Moving the Needle, a strategic plan that refined the Foundation's mission and has four specific goals that guide their work through 2013: 1) Reduce the number of Arkansas families living below 200 percent of the federal poverty line. This will be achieved with targeted funding of policy advocacy, workforce development, financial literacy, and asset development initiatives; 2) Increase high school and college graduation rates in the state. This will be achieved through funding initiatives to create a culture of high aspiration and educational achievement, reduce the achievement gap, and decrease both dropout rates and levels of post-secondary remediation; 3) Increase educational attainment and economic mobility in select communities in Arkansas. This will be achieved by supporting communities and providing technical assistance and increasing funding for civic engagement, policy advocacy, and community organizing on behalf of people and communities that have the least wealth and opportunity; 4) Show that strategic support and good grantmaking practices can help selected grantees achieve goals within the parameters of their missions. This means WRF grants may include general operating support, multi-year funding commitments, and other recognized best practices that improve the sustainability and effectiveness of grantees.
Fields of interest: Education, early childhood education; Higher education; Youth development, citizenship; Civil/human rights; Rural development; Community/economic development; Economics; Public policy, research; Children/youth; Adults; Young adults; Minorities; African Americans/Blacks; Hispanics/Latinos; Immigrants/refugees; Economically disadvantaged.
Type of support: Management development/capacity building; Program development; Research; Technical assistance; Program evaluation; Program-related investments/loans; Matching/challenge support; Mission-related investments/loans.
Limitations: Applications accepted. Giving limited to Arkansas, or for projects that benefit Arkansas. No grants to individuals, or for capital expenditures, fundraising campaigns, scientific research, operating support to cover budget shortfalls, or endowments; no loans (except program-related investments).
Publications: Annual report; Financial statement; Grants list; Informational brochure.
Application information: The Winthrop Rockefeller Foundation (WRF) receives online applications via e-mail. The online application can be accessed on WRF's web site. The application begins with a short eligibility quiz. If basic eligibility is met, the applicant will be given the opportunity to complete the application and attach a line item project budget, organization budget, and a board of directors list. Applicant may save a partial application and return to it at a later time. Applications accepted on an ongoing basis. An initial review by WRF program staff determines fit with WRF's vision, mission, and funding priorities. The review and selection process takes an average of three to six months from the time the completed application and related documents are received. Grant seekers are encouraged to begin the application process at least six months before the proposed funding would go into effect. Organizations whose applications receive favorable initial review may be invited to submit more detailed proposals and can receive guidance in the subsequent proposal preparation process from WRF program staff. Funding recommendations are presented to the WRF Board of Directors at their quarterly meetings. All funding decisions are made by the WRF Board, which may decide to award all, none, or some portion of the requested funds.
Initial approach: Online application
Copies of proposal: 1
Deadline(s): None
Board meeting date(s): Mar., June, Sept., and Dec.
Final notification: Immediately after board approves funding. Applicants should expect approximately six months from initial inquiry to approval
Officers and Directors:* Toyce Newton,* Chair.; Phillip N. Baldwin,* Vice-Chair.; Sherece Y. West-Scantlebury, Ph.D., C.E.O. and Pres.; Andrea M. Dobson, C.P.A., C.O.O. and C.F.O.; Corey S. Anderson, V.P.; Jerry Adams; Helen Dorado Alessi; Frederick Black; Rene Bryce-Laporte; Andre Guerrero, Ed.D; Susan Harriman; Pledger E. Monk III; S. Yvette Murphy-Erby, Ph. D.; David Rainey, Ed.D; Lisenne Rockefeller; Vicki Saviers; Calvin White; Diana Gonzalez Worthen, Ph.D.
Number of staff: 4 full-time professional; 2 full-time support.
EIN: 710285871
Selected grants: The following grants are a representative sample of this grantmaker's funding activity:
$933,868 to University of Arkansas for Medical Sciences, Little Rock, AR, 2012. To design and construct new cancer treatment center for Winthrop P. Rockefeller Cancer Institute.
$150,000 to Jobs for the Future, Boston, MA, 2012. To enable four Arkansas two-year institutions to participate in Achieving the Dream national demonstration project to measurably improve student outcomes.
$145,000 to Arkansas State University, Mountain Home, AR, 2012. For expansion of Volunteer Income Tax Assistance (VITA) sites.
$143,000 to Arkansas Public Policy Panel, Little Rock, AR, 2012. To support APPP's mission to engage low wealth communities in community development and public policy advocacy.
$125,000 to Arkansas Advocates for Children and Families, Little Rock, AR, 2012. To support AACF's mission to support low-income children and families through research, education, communications, coalition-building, and policy advocacy.
$110,000 to University of Arkansas, Fayetteville, AR, 2012. To support a pilot of the Arkansas Teacher Corps program, in partnership with the School of Social Work and School of Journalism, to supply high-quality teachers for high-needs public schools across the state.
$105,500 to Boys, Girls, Adults Community Development Center, Marvell, AR, 2012. To support BGACDC's mission to build community competency in youth development, intergenerational community development, economic development, housing, and leadership development.
$75,000 to Arkansas State University, Mountain Home, AR, 2012. For expansion of Volunteer Income Tax Assistance (VITA) sites in Baxter, Jefferson, Mississippi, Polk and Pulaski Counties.
$61,500 to alt.Consulting, Pine Bluff, AR, 2012. To support small business lending operations in the Arkansas Delta.
$50,000 to University of Arkansas, Fayetteville, AR, 2012. To support, in partnership with the School of Social Work and School of Journalism, a pilot demonstration of independent qualitative and quantitative data gathering tools in support of the WRF Grantee Outcomes Assessment Learning System (GOALS).

198
Winthrop Rockefeller Trust ✧
2230 Cottondale Ln., Ste. 6
Little Rock, AR 72202-2048 (501) 661-9294
Contact: Marion Burton, Tr.

Established in 1973 in AR.
Donor: Winthrop Rockefeller†.
Foundation type: Independent foundation.
Financial data (yr. ended 06/30/13): Assets, $120,788,880 (M); expenditures, $6,504,446; qualifying distributions, $4,926,324; giving activities include $4,716,241 for 13 grants (high: $4,500,000; low: $1).
Purpose and activities: Support primarily for an agricultural development institute and a historic preservation foundation.
Fields of interest: Historic preservation/historical societies; Higher education, university; Agriculture.
Type of support: General/operating support.
Limitations: Applications accepted. Giving limited to AR. No grants to individuals.
Application information: Application form not required.
Deadline(s): None
Officer: Donna Huckabee, C.E.O.
Trustees: Bruce Bartley; Marion Burton; Wilson Jones; Donal C. O'Brien; Robert Schults; John W. Ward.
EIN: 716082655
Selected grants: The following grants are a representative sample of this grantmaker's funding activity:
$4,500,000 to University of Arkansas Winthrop Rockefeller Center, Winthrop Rockefeller Institute, Morrilton, AR, 2012. For operating support.
$4,500,000 to University of Arkansas Winthrop Rockefeller Center, Winthrop Rockefeller Institute, Morrilton, AR, 2013. For operating support.
$290,084 to University of Arkansas Winthrop Rockefeller Center, Winthrop Rockefeller Institute, Morrilton, AR, 2012. For capital support.
$100,000 to Museum of Automobiles, Morrilton, AR, 2012. For matching grant.
$100,000 to University of Arkansas, Institute on Race and Ethnicity, Little Rock, AR, 2012. For operating support.
$89,000 to Winthrop Rockefeller Foundation, Little Rock, AR, 2012. For general support.
$89,000 to Winthrop Rockefeller Foundation, Little Rock, AR, 2013. For general support.
$73,234 to University of Arkansas Winthrop Rockefeller Center, Morrilton, AR, 2013. For Winthrop Rockefeller Centennial Celebration, partnership celebrating Governor Winthrop Rockefeller's ongoing impact in Arkasas and the world.
$25,000 to University of Arkansas Winthrop Rockefeller Center, Morrilton, AR, 2013. For Nanotechnology for Health Care Conference.
$23,769 to University of Arkansas, Little Rock, AR, 2013. For library system archives.
$5,100 to Governor Winthrop Rockefeller Charitable Corporation, Little Rock, AR, 2012. For operating support.
$5,100 to Governor Winthrop Rockefeller Charitable Corporation, Little Rock, AR, 2013. For operating support.

199
The Ross Foundation ✧
P.O. Box 335
Arkadelphia, AR 71923-0335 (870) 246-9881
Contact: Mary Elizabeth Eldridge, Dir. of Progs.
FAX: (870) 246-9674;
E-mail: info@rossfoundation.us; Main URL: http://rossfoundation.us

Established in 1966 in Arkadelphia, AR.
Donors: Esther C. Ross†; Jane Ross†.
Foundation type: Independent foundation.
Financial data (yr. ended 12/31/13): Assets, $94,231,153 (M); expenditures, $2,022,854; qualifying distributions, $1,386,773; giving activities include $602,955 for 25 grants (high: $351,684; low: $300), and $575,864 for foundation-administered programs.
Purpose and activities: Giving primarily for education, arts and cultural enrichment, community beautification and improvement, historical preservation, mental health and people who are developmentally disabled, and forestry research and conservation management.
Fields of interest: Arts; Higher education; Education; Environment, natural resources; Environment, forests; Children/youth, services; Community/economic development; Foundations (community); United Ways and Federated Giving Programs; Children/youth; Adults; Disabilities, people with.
Type of support: Scholarship funds; Capital campaigns; General/operating support; Building/renovation; Equipment; Endowments; Emergency funds; Program development; Publication; Seed money; Research; Consulting services; Matching/challenge support.
Limitations: Applications accepted. Giving limited to Arkadelphia and Clark County, AR. No support for political organizations. No grants to individuals, or for scholarships or fellowships; no loans.
Publications: Application guidelines; Informational brochure (including application guidelines).
Application information: Full proposals are by invitation only, upon review of pre-proposal. Application form required.
Initial approach: Pre-proposal
Copies of proposal: 6
Deadline(s): None for pre-proposals; Jan. 1, May 1, and Sept. 1 for full proposals
Board meeting date(s): Monthly
Final notification: Within 1 month for pre-proposals; Mar. 31, July 31, and Nov. 30 for full proposals
Officers and Trustees:* Ross M. Wipple,* Chair.; Mary Whipple,* Secy.; Peggy Clark; Mary Elizabeth Eldridge; Mark Karnes; Clark Tennyson.
Number of staff: 4 full-time professional; 4 full-time support; 1 part-time support.
EIN: 716060574
Selected grants: The following grants are a representative sample of this grantmaker's funding activity:
$351,684 to Arkadelphia Promise Foundation, Arkadelphia, AR, 2012. For scholarships for graduating seniors of Arkadelphia High School.
$51,731 to Arkansas Game and Fish Foundation, Little Rock, AR, 2012. For unrestricted support.
$32,726 to Arkansas Forestry Association Education Foundation, Little Rock, AR, 2012. For unrestricted support.
$32,726 to Nature Conservancy, Arlington, VA, 2012. For Arkansas Nature Conservancy programs.
$20,950 to University of Arkansas Foundation, Fayetteville, AR, 2012. For Garvan Woodland Gardens.
$16,000 to United Way of Clark County, Arkadelphia, AR, 2012. For annual campaign.
$15,000 to Arkansas Childrens Hospital Foundation, Little Rock, AR, 2012.
$15,000 to Dawson Education Cooperative, Arkadelphia, AR, 2012. For mini-grant program.
$10,800 to University of Arkansas Foundation, Fayetteville, AR, 2012. For School for Mathematics, Sciences and Arts.
$10,000 to Arkansas Food Bank Network, Little Rock, AR, 2012.
$10,000 to Boy Scouts of America, Quapaw Area Council, Little Rock, AR, 2012.

200
The Schmieding Foundation ✧
P.O. Box 369
Springdale, AR 72765-0369
Contact: Gilda Underwood, Pres.

Established in 1990 in AR.
Donors: H.C. Schmieding†; L.H. Schmieding; H.C. Schmieding Produce Co., Inc.; Northwest Arkansas Community Foundation; L.H. Schmieding Revocable Trust.
Foundation type: Independent foundation.
Financial data (yr. ended 12/31/13): Assets, $24,420,429 (M); gifts received, $257,560; expenditures, $2,099,943; qualifying distributions, $1,575,266; giving activities include $1,471,163 for 52 grants (high: $823,357; low: $13).
Purpose and activities: Giving primarily for higher education, human services, health organizations, and to a Lutheran church.
Fields of interest: Higher education; Education; Health organizations, association; Human services; Children/youth, services; Residential/custodial care, hospices; Protestant agencies & churches.
Type of support: General/operating support; Continuing support; Building/renovation; Program development.
Limitations: Applications accepted. Giving primarily in Washington and Benton counties, AR.
Application information: Application form required.
Initial approach: Request application form
Deadline(s): None
Officers: Gilda Underwood, Pres.; Lance Taylor, V.P. and Secy.-Treas.
Directors: Pam English; Bob Rokeby; Helen Schmieding; Patricia Williams; Robby Zink.
Number of staff: 2 part-time professional.
EIN: 237262279

201
Stella B. Smith Charitable Trust ✧
1911 Country Club Ln.
Little Rock, AR 72207-2035 (501) 376-0504
Contact: Michael R. Mayton, Tr.; Catherine H. Mayton, Tr.

Established around 1974 in AR.
Donor: Stella B. Smith.
Foundation type: Independent foundation.
Financial data (yr. ended 12/31/13): Assets, $15,590,925 (M); expenditures, $860,516; qualifying distributions, $777,815; giving activities include $587,073 for 21 grants (high: $130,840; low: $1,000).

Purpose and activities: Giving primarily for the performing arts, education, human services, and to a children's hospital.
Fields of interest: Performing arts; Performing arts, orchestras; Higher education; Hospitals (specialty); Health organizations, association; Human services; Protestant agencies & churches.
Limitations: Applications accepted. Giving primarily in Little Rock, AR. No grants to individuals.
Application information: Application form not required.
Initial approach: Proposal
Deadline(s): None
Trustees: Kay Kelley Arnold; Catherine H. Mayton; Michael R. Mayton.
EIN: 237365134

202
The Soderquist Family Foundation ✧
c/o Donald G. Soderquist
201 S. 19th St., Ste. P
Rogers, AR 72758-1123

Established in 2001 in AR.
Donors: Donald G. Soderquist; M. David Sloane; Soderquist Charitable Lead Annuity Trust.
Foundation type: Independent foundation.
Financial data (yr. ended 12/31/12): Assets, $19,724,556 (M); gifts received, $1,177,459; expenditures, $923,963; qualifying distributions, $788,770; giving activities include $788,770 for grants.
Purpose and activities: Giving primarily for education, children, youth, and social services, and Christian organizations and churches.
Fields of interest: Higher education; Human services; Children/youth, services; Christian agencies & churches.
Limitations: Applications not accepted. Giving in the U.S., with emphasis on AR and IL. No grants to individuals.
Application information: Contributes only to pre-selected organizations.
Officers and Directors:* Donald G. Soderquist,* Pres.; Sandra Ford,* V.P.; Jeffrey Soderquist,* V.P.; Mark Soderquist,* V.P.; Wendy Soderquist-Togami,* V.P.; Joann Soderquist,* Secy.-Treas.
EIN: 731621266

203
Carol and Witt Stephens Charitable Foundation ✧
P.O. Box 3417
Little Rock, AR 72203-3417

Established in 2001 in AR.
Donors: W.R. Stephens, Jr.; Bess C. Stephens.
Foundation type: Independent foundation.
Financial data (yr. ended 12/31/13): Assets, $8,710,309 (M); expenditures, $2,344,155; qualifying distributions, $2,332,268; giving activities include $2,332,268 for 20 grants (high: $1,500,000; low: $250).
Purpose and activities: Giving primarily to a children's hospital, as well as for education and human services.
Fields of interest: Education; Hospitals (specialty); Human services; Children/youth, services.
Limitations: Applications not accepted. Giving primarily in AR.
Application information: Unsolicited requests for funds not accepted.
Trustee: W.R. Stephens, Jr.
EIN: 311740109
Selected grants: The following grants are a representative sample of this grantmaker's funding activity:
$500,000 to Arkansas Childrens Hospital, Little Rock, AR, 2011. For general fund.
$300,000 to Anthony School, Little Rock, AR, 2011. For general fund.
$50,000 to Arkansas Baptist College, Little Rock, AR, 2011. For general fund.
$50,000 to Nature Conservancy, Little Rock, AR, 2011. For general fund.
$10,000 to Boy Scouts of America, Little Rock, AR, 2011. For general fund.
$2,500 to Arkansas Commitment, Little Rock, AR, 2011. For general fund.
$1,500 to Plantation Wildlife Arts Festival, Thomasville, GA, 2011. For general fund.
$1,000 to Arkansas State University, State University, AR, 2011. For general fund.
$1,000 to Soaring Wings Ranch, Conway, AR, 2011. For general fund.

204
Harriet and Warren Stephens Family Foundation ✧
P.O. Box 3507
Little Rock, AR 72203-3507

Established in 2007 in AR.
Donors: Warren A. Stephens; Harriet Stephens.
Foundation type: Independent foundation.
Financial data (yr. ended 12/31/13): Assets, $17,738,108 (M); gifts received, $7,769,223; expenditures, $462,275; qualifying distributions, $433,000; giving activities include $433,000 for 2 grants (high: $383,000; low: $50,000).
Fields of interest: Historic preservation/historical societies.
Limitations: Applications not accepted. Giving primarily in Stratford, VA. No grants to individuals.
Application information: Contributes only to pre-selected organizations.
Trustees: Harriet C. Stephens; Warren A. Stephens.
EIN: 261634531

205
The Roy and Christine Sturgis Charitable and Educational Trust ✧
P.O. Box 7599
Little Rock, AR 72217-7599 (501) 664-8525
Contact: Barry Findley II

Established about 1979.
Donors: Roy Sturgis†; Christine Sturgis.
Foundation type: Independent foundation.
Financial data (yr. ended 12/31/13): Assets, $12,389,816 (M); expenditures, $735,145; qualifying distributions, $707,578; giving activities include $605,538 for 25 grants (high: $115,000; low: $5,000).
Purpose and activities: Giving primarily for Baptist and Roman Catholic organizations and churches; funding also for education.
Fields of interest: Higher education; Education; Human services; Protestant agencies & churches; Catholic agencies & churches.
Limitations: Applications accepted. Giving limited to AR. No grants to individuals.
Application information: Application form required.
Initial approach: Letter
Deadline(s): None
Trustees: Barry B. Findley; Brian Findley; Lisa Speer.
EIN: 710495345
Selected grants: The following grants are a representative sample of this grantmaker's funding activity:
$87,840 to Easter Seals Arkansas, Little Rock, AR, 2012. For kitchen equipment.
$30,000 to Catholic High School for Boys, Little Rock, AR, 2012. For school equipment.
$20,000 to Arkansas State University, State University, AR, 2012. For Equipment For Accounting Department.

206
Tenenbaum Foundation ✧ ☆
P.O. Box 15128, GMF
Little Rock, AR 72231-5128 (501) 945-0881
Contact: Tim McGrath

Established about 1967 in AR.
Donors: J.M. Tenenbaum; A. Tenenbaum Co., Inc.; Arkansas Aluminum Alloys, Inc.
Foundation type: Independent foundation.
Financial data (yr. ended 12/31/13): Assets, $2,355,327 (M); expenditures, $476,537; qualifying distributions, $471,939; giving activities include $471,939 for 29 grants (high: $151,000; low: $100).
Fields of interest: Education; Human services; Foundations (private grantmaking); Jewish federated giving programs; Jewish agencies & synagogues.
Limitations: Applications accepted. Giving primarily in Little Rock, AR. No grants to individuals.
Application information: Application form required.
Initial approach: Letter
Deadline(s): None
Trustees: Jack D. Grundfest; Cori T. McGrath; Harold Tenenbaum.
EIN: 716061727
Selected grants: The following grants are a representative sample of this grantmaker's funding activity:
$50,000 to Tenenbaum Educational Trust, North Little Rock, AR, 2012. For Scholarships for College Students.
$44,780 to American Heart Association, Little Rock, AR, 2012. For Educational - Medical and Research Awareness.
$25,000 to Argenta Downtown Council, North Little Rock, AR, 2012. For Sponsorship of Downtown Area Awareness.
$8,333 to Pulaski Technical College, North Little Rock, AR, 2012. For Educational and Fellowship Events.
$1,000 to Reach Out and Read, Boston, MA, 2012. For Non Profit Way for Pediatrician to Intervene in the Developmental Problems in Children Living In.

207
Tyson Family Foundation, Inc. ✧
P.O. Box 2020
Springdale, AR 72765-2020
FAX: (479) 290-7984; Application address: c/o Roberta Gonzales, 2200 Don Tyson Pkwy., Springdale, AR 72762; tel.: (479) 290-5180

Established in 1970 in AR.
Donors: Don Tyson†; Barbara Tyson; Tyson Limited Partnership; Tyson Foods, Inc.
Foundation type: Independent foundation.
Financial data (yr. ended 12/31/13): Assets, $29,419,208 (M); gifts received, $700,000; expenditures, $2,451,905; qualifying distributions, $2,149,309; giving activities include $2,104,500 for 6+ grants.
Purpose and activities: Giving primarily for education, including scholarships available to individuals majoring in certain areas of agriculture, business, engineering, computer science, and nursing. Scholarships awarded only to employees of Tyson Foods, Inc. and their dependents.
Fields of interest: Higher education; Education.
Type of support: Scholarships—to individuals.
Limitations: Giving primarily in AR.
Application information: Application form required.
Initial approach: Letter requesting pre-printed application with instructions
Deadline(s): None
Board meeting date(s): Biannually
Officers: Harry C. Erwin III, Pres.; James B. Blair, V.P.; W.H. Taylor, Secy.
Number of staff: 1 full-time professional; 1 part-time professional; 1 part-time support.
EIN: 237087948

208
Union County Community Foundation, Inc. ✧ ☆
P.O. Box 148
El Dorado, AR 71731-0148 (870) 862-8223
Contact: Rodney Landes, Chair.

Established in 1996 in AR.
Foundation type: Community foundation.
Financial data (yr. ended 09/30/13): Assets, $16,626,464 (M); gifts received, $215,584; expenditures, $761,705; giving activities include $336,571 for 40+ grants (high: $93,000; low: $500), and $94,530 for 56 grants to individuals.
Purpose and activities: The foundation provides a charitable vehicle that accepts, invests and distributes resources according to the donors' wishes. Giving also to individuals for scholarships.
Fields of interest: Historic preservation/historical societies; Scholarships/financial aid; Education; Human services; Community/economic development; Protestant agencies & churches.
Type of support: Scholarships—to individuals; Employee matching gifts; In-kind gifts.
Limitations: Applications not accepted. Giving limited to the El Dorado, AR, area.
Publications: Financial statement; Grants list; Newsletter.
Officers and Board Members:* Rodney Landes,* Chair.; John McFarland,* Vice-Chair.; Ginger Bullard,* Secy.; Mike Murphy,* Treas.; Gill Colvin; Lynn Landers; Lois Meekins; Tandy Menefee; Lenora Newsome; Bob Risor; Mary Jo Scott; Stacy Scroggins; Matthew Shepherd; Scott Simpson; Kenna Williams.
Number of staff: 1 full-time professional; 1 full-time support.
EIN: 311500805

209
Willard and Pat Walker Charitable Foundation, Inc. ✧
P.O. Box 10500
Fayetteville, AR 72703-2857 (479) 582-2310
Contact: John M. Walker, Pres.
FAX: (479) 582-2292;
E-mail: walkerfamily1@sbcglobal.net

Established in 2003 in AR; funded in 2004 from the transfer of assets from Willard and Pat Walker Charitable Foundation Trust.
Donors: Amy S. Walker; Willard and Pat Walker Charitable Foundation Trust.
Foundation type: Independent foundation.
Financial data (yr. ended 12/31/13): Assets, $19,972,077 (M); expenditures, $7,503,460; qualifying distributions, $7,423,698; giving activities include $7,276,548 for 70 grants (high: $1,000,000; low: $150).
Purpose and activities: The foundation seeks to honor the legacy of its founders through charitable giving and promoting the virtues of integrity and generosity.
Fields of interest: Higher education; Education; Health organizations; Children/youth, services; Residential/custodial care, hospices.
Type of support: Continuing support; Capital campaigns; Building/renovation; Equipment; Endowments; Program development; Scholarship funds; Matching/challenge support.
Limitations: Applications accepted. Giving primarily in AR, KS, MO and OK. No grants to individuals.
Application information: Audio and videotapes will not be accepted. Only 1 application per organization per year. Application form not required.
Initial approach: Letter (not to exceed 3 pages)
Copies of proposal: 1
Deadline(s): Semi-annually: Jan. 15 - Mar. 1 and Aug. 15 - Oct. 1
Board meeting date(s): Apr. and Nov.
Final notification: Within one month following board meeting
Officers: John M. Walker, Pres.; Amy S. Walker, Treas.
Number of staff: 2 full-time professional.
EIN: 200235689
Selected grants: The following grants are a representative sample of this grantmaker's funding activity:
$1,000,000 to Crystal Bridges Museum of American Art, Bentonville, AR, 2013. For endowment.
$1,000,000 to New School, Fayetteville, AR, 2013. For challenge grant.
$625,000 to Razorback Foundation, Fayetteville, AR, 2013. For capital campaign.
$625,000 to University of Arkansas for Medical Sciences, Winthrop Rockefeller Cancer Institute, Little Rock, AR, 2013. For capital campaign.
$500,000 to Washington Regional Medical Foundation, Fayetteville, AR, 2013. For capital campaign.
$250,000 to Circle of Life, Springdale, AR, 2013. For capital campaign.
$100,000 to University of Arkansas for Medical Sciences, Winthrop Rockefeller Cancer Institute, Little Rock, AR, 2013.
$50,000 to Fayetteville Public Library, Fayetteville, AR, 2013. For program support.
$50,000 to Northwest Arkansas Free Health Center, Fayetteville, AR, 2013. For challenge grant.
$15,000 to Theater Squared, Fayetteville, AR, 2013. For program support.

210
The Wal-Mart Foundation, Inc.
(also known as The Walmart Foundation)
(formerly Wal-Mart Foundation)
702 S.W. 8th St., Dept. 8687, No. 0555
Bentonville, AR 72716-0555 (800) 530-9925
Contact: Julie Gehrki, Sr. Dir., Business Integration
FAX: (479) 273-6850; Main URL: http://foundation.walmart.com
RSS Feed: http://walmartstores.com/RSS/FeaturedTopics/rss.ashx?id=11
Twitter: https://twitter.com/WalmartGiving
Walmart Blog: http://blog.walmart.com/giving

Established in 1979 in AR.
Donor: Wal-Mart Stores, Inc.
Foundation type: Company-sponsored foundation.
Financial data (yr. ended 01/31/13): Assets, $21,162,257 (M); gifts received, $182,566,130; expenditures, $182,860,304; qualifying distributions, $182,859,236; giving activities include $182,859,236 for 13,225 grants (high: $7,721,220; low: $30).
Purpose and activities: The foundation supports programs designed to promote hunger relief and healthy eating; sustainability; women's economic empowerment; and career opportunity. The foundation also funds disaster relief, women, military and veterans, and economically disadvantaged people.
Fields of interest: Arts; Middle schools/education; Elementary school/education; Secondary school/education; Higher education; Education, reading; Education; Environment, recycling; Environment, natural resources; Environment, energy; Health care, equal rights; Hospitals (general); Health care, clinics/centers; Dental care; Public health; Health care; Crime/law enforcement; Employment, services; Employment, training; Employment, retraining; Goodwill Industries; Employment; Agriculture, sustainable programs; Agriculture, farmlands; Food services; Food banks; Food distribution, meals on wheels; Nutrition; Housing/shelter; Disasters, preparedness/services; Recreation, parks/playgrounds; Recreation; Boys & girls clubs; Youth development, business; American Red Cross; Salvation Army; Children, services; Human services, financial counseling; Human services, mind/body enrichment; Aging, centers/services; Human services; Civil/human rights, equal rights; Community development, business promotion; Community development, small businesses; Community/economic development; United Ways and Federated Giving Programs; Military/veterans' organizations; Minorities; Women; Military/veterans; Economically disadvantaged.
Type of support: Management development/capacity building; Emergency funds; Program development; Scholarship funds; Employee volunteer services; Sponsorships; Employee matching gifts; Employee-related scholarships; Grants to individuals; Matching/challenge support.
Limitations: Applications accepted. Giving on a national basis in areas of company operations, with emphasis on AR, Washington, DC, DE, GA, MA. MD, NY, TN, TX, UT, and VA. No support for faith-based organizations not of direct benefit to the entire community, political candidates or organizations, athletic teams, or discriminatory organizations. No grants to individuals (except for scholarships), or for multi-year funding, annual meetings, contests or pageants, political causes or campaigns, advertising, film, or video projects, research, athletic

sponsorships or events, tickets for contests, raffles, or any other activities with prizes, travel, capital campaigns, endowments, association or chamber memberships, or registration fees, research, salaries, stipends, trips, rewards, construction costs, or projects that send products or people to a foreign country.
Publications: Application guidelines; Program policy statement.
Application information: Applications for State Giving Program are accepted designated periods or cycles only and all states have two cycles a year. Visit website for State Giving Program for deadlines. A full proposal may be requested at a later date for National Giving Program. Organizations receiving support are asked to submit an impact report detailing what outcomes were achieved.
Initial approach: Complete online application for State Giving Program, Walmart U.S. Manufacturing Innovation Fund, Northwest Arkansas Giving Program, Community Grant Program, and Legal Department Strategic Partners Sponsorship Program; complete online letter of inquiry for National Giving Program
Deadline(s): Varies per cycle and state for State Giving Program; Varies for Walmart U.S. Manufacturing Innovation Fund and Legal Department Sponsorship Program; Feb. 1, Feb. 10, Apr. 1, May 15, June 1, Aug. 1, Aug. 4, Oct. 1, Nov. 20 and Dec. 1 for Northwest Arkansas Giving Program; Dec. 31 for Community Grant Program; None for National Giving Program
Board meeting date(s): Mar., May, Aug., and Nov.
Final notification: 90 days for Local Giving Program; 6 to 8 weeks for National Giving Program
Officers and Directors:* Michael T. Duke, Chair.; Kathleen McLaughlin, Pres.; M. Susan Chambers; Cindy Davis; Gisel Ruiz; Cathy Smith.
Number of staff: 31 full-time professional.
EIN: 205639919
Selected grants: The following grants are a representative sample of this grantmaker's funding activity:
$7,721,220 to Feeding America, Chicago, IL, 2013.
$6,508,555 to YMCA of the U.S.A., Chicago, IL, 2013.
$5,910,071 to United Way Worldwide, Alexandria, VA, 2013.
$4,256,498 to National Summer Learning Association, Baltimore, MD, 2013.
$2,183,302 to International Youth Foundation, Baltimore, MD, 2013.
$2,067,250 to American Cancer Society, Atlanta, GA, 2013.
$1,500,000 to Alliance for a Healthier Generation, Portland, OR, 2013.
$36,500 to Community Food Bank of Eastern Oklahoma, Tulsa, OK, 2013.
$25,000 to Northwest New Mexico Seniors, Farmington, NM, 2013.
$10,000 to Bentonville Public Schools Foundation, Bentonville, AR, 2013.

211
Walton Family Foundation, Inc.

P.O. Box 2030
Bentonville, AR 72712-2030 (479) 464-1570
Contact: Buddy D. Philpot, Exec. Dir.
FAX: (479) 464-1580; E-mail: info@wffmail.com;
Main URL: http://www.waltonfamilyfoundation.org
Facebook: https://www.facebook.com/waltonfamilyfoundation
Twitter: https://mobile.twitter.com/waltonfamilyfdn
Walton Family Foundation Education Reform: https://www.facebook.com/wffeducation
YouTube: http://www.youtube.com/user/wfamilyfoundation
Application address for environment projects: The Walton Family Foundation, Attn.: Letter of Inquiry, 919 18th St., N.W., Ste. 650, Washington, DC 20006

Established in 1987 in AR.
Donors: Sam M. Walton‡; Helen R. Walton‡; John T. Walton‡; Walton Enterprises, LLC.
Foundation type: Independent foundation.
Financial data (yr. ended 12/31/13): Assets, $2,480,825,574 (M); gifts received, $500,676,062; expenditures, $336,040,265; qualifying distributions, $341,261,654; giving activities include $311,719,212 for 1,142 grants (high: $20,426,136; low: $500), and $13,457,382 for 2 loans/program-related investments.
Purpose and activities: Giving is focused in three areas: 1) Systemic reform of primary education (K-12); 2) The environment, specifically marine and freshwater conservation; and 3) The foundation's home region of Northwest Arkansas and the delta region of Arkansas and Mississippi.
Fields of interest: Elementary/secondary education; Child development, education; Elementary/secondary school reform; Environment, natural resources.
Type of support: General/operating support; Continuing support; Management development/capacity building; Equipment; Program development; Curriculum development; Technical assistance; Program evaluation; Program-related investments/loans; Matching/challenge support.
Limitations: Applications accepted. Giving through two of four funding areas is limited to northwest AR and the Mississippi River's delta region of AR and MS. Educational funding is limited to target school districts. No support for non-established medical research programs. No grants to individuals, or for endowments for operations, church-related construction projects, travel expenses for groups to compete or perform, or business-related activities such as start-up costs, or expenses related to groups or individuals participating in non-curricular programs.
Publications: Annual report; Grants list.
Application information: Proposals by invitation only. See web site for more information.
Initial approach: Letter of inquiry
Officer and Directors:* Buddy D. Philpot,* Exec. Dir.; Carrie W. Penner; Alice A. Proietti; Alice L. Walton; Benjamin S. Walton; Jim C. Walton; Lukas T. Walton; S. Robson Walton; Samuel R. Walton; Steuart L. Walton; Thomas L. Walton.
Number of staff: 6 full-time professional.
EIN: 133441466
Selected grants: The following grants are a representative sample of this grantmaker's funding activity:
$109,744,500 to Walton Family Charitable Support Foundation, Bentonville, AR, 2012. For additional endowment funding to the Walton Family Charitable Support Foundation for the support of the Walton International Scholarship Program and other charitable activities.
$22,658,644 to Conservation International, Arlington, VA, 2012.
$16,900,000 to Charter Fund, Broomfield, CO, 2012.
$11,445,000 to Teach for America, New York, NY, 2012.
$8,374,000 to KIPP Foundation, San Francisco, CA, 2012.
$275,000 to Oxfam America, Boston, MA, 2012.
$220,000 to Empower College Prep, Phoenix, AZ, 2012.
$200,000 to Winrock International, Arlington, VA, 2012.
$110,000 to Trust for Public Land, New Orleans, LA, 2012.

212
Bob White Memorial Foundation ✧

(also known as BWMF Farm)
P.O. Box 537
Eudora, AR 71640-9419

Established in 1982 in AR.
Donor: J. Austin White.
Foundation type: Independent foundation.
Financial data (yr. ended 12/31/13): Assets, $8,961,241 (M); expenditures, $580,194; qualifying distributions, $443,158; giving activities include $443,158 for 20 grants (high: $85,000; low: $1,200).
Purpose and activities: Giving to improve the standard of living in Eudora and Chicot County, Arkansas.
Fields of interest: Human services; Community/economic development.
Type of support: General/operating support; Building/renovation; Endowments; Scholarship funds.
Limitations: Applications not accepted. Giving primarily in Chicot County, AR and the immediate area of the southeast AR geographical region. No grants to individuals.
Application information: Contributes only to pre-selected organizations.
Trustees: Alvin Reynold Meyer; Craig Stephenson; Stephen Tisdale.
Number of staff: 1 full-time support.
EIN: 311041899
Selected grants: The following grants are a representative sample of this grantmaker's funding activity:
$15,000 to Arkansas Childrens Hospital Foundation, Little Rock, AR, 2011.

213
Windgate Charitable Foundation, Inc. ✧

P.O. Box 826
Siloam Springs, AR 72761-0826
Contact: John E. Brown, III, Exec. Dir.
FAX: (479) 524-3550;
E-mail: windgate@cox-internet.com

Established in 1993 in AR.
Donor: Dorothea W. Hutcheson‡.
Foundation type: Independent foundation.
Financial data (yr. ended 12/31/13): Assets, $174,284,603 (M); gifts received, $79,520,000; expenditures, $42,742,711; qualifying distributions, $90,241,127; giving activities include $41,741,431 for 342 grants (high: $3,000,000; low: $1,500).

Purpose and activities: Giving primarily to promote art and craft education, and projects that strengthen marriage and family relationships. Limited giving also to programs that serve children and Christian higher education.
Fields of interest: Arts education; Children/youth, services; Family services.
Type of support: Program development; Matching/challenge support.
Limitations: Applications accepted. Giving on a national basis with emphasis on the Midwest and Southwest. No support for private religious schools or churches. No grants to individuals, or for undesignated annual funds, debt retirement, completed projects, or group travel for performance or competition.
Publications: Application guidelines; Program policy statement.
Application information: Application form not required.
Initial approach: 2-page letter
Copies of proposal: 1
Deadline(s): Mar. 1, July 1 and Oct. 1
Board meeting date(s): Varies
Final notification: 3 to 4 months
Officer: John E. Brown III, Exec. Dir.
Directors: Robyn Horn; Karen Hutcheson; Mary E. Hutcheson; Richard Hutcheson; William L. Hutcheson.
Number of staff: 2
EIN: 710723781
Selected grants: The following grants are a representative sample of this grantmaker's funding activity:
$2,000,000 to Penland School of Crafts, Penland, NC, 2012. For 2013 Programs and Projects and Capital Campaign.
$1,980,625 to John Brown University, Siloam Springs, AR, 2012. For Five Year Challenge Grant.
$1,000,000 to North Bennet Street School, Boston, MA, 2012. For New North Street Facility.
$850,060 to First Assembly of God Church, Van Buren, AR, 2012. For Challenge Grant.
$647,632 to Penland School of Crafts, Penland, NC, 2012. For Core Program Student Endowment Fund.
$260,000 to A World for Children, Round Rock, TX, 2012. To foster Child Transition Program.
$50,000 to Kinship Center, Salinas, CA, 2012. For Family Finding Program.
$50,000 to Morris Ministries, Nashville, TN, 2012. For Ministry Programs.
$50,000 to University of Arkansas, Little Rock, AR, 2012. For Art Programs and Metals Resident Artist.
$2,500 to Colorado Christian University, Lakewood, CO, 2012. For Marriage and Family Relationships Conference 2011-2012.

CALIFORNIA

214
1011 Foundation, Inc. ✧
3435 Ocean Park Blvd., No. 107
PMB K
Santa Monica, CA 90405-3320

Donors: Robert Kotick; Nina Kotick.
Foundation type: Independent foundation.
Financial data (yr. ended 12/31/13): Assets, $19,310,823 (M); gifts received, $584,173; expenditures, $2,049,552; qualifying distributions, $2,046,313; giving activities include $2,046,313 for 26 grants (high: $831,172; low: $250).
Fields of interest: Arts; Education; Health care; Human services.
Limitations: Applications not accepted. Giving primarily in CA. No grants to individuals.
Application information: Contributes only to pre-selected organizations.
Officers and Directors:* Robert Kotick,* Pres.; Judith Hans,* V.P.; Deborah Gruber, Secy.-Treas.
EIN: 912168491
Selected grants: The following grants are a representative sample of this grantmaker's funding activity:
$25,000 to Cystic Fibrosis Foundation, Bethesda, MD, 2012. For Efforts to Find a Cure for Cystic Fibrosis.

215
2005 Tomchin Family Charitable Trust ✧
727 Lilac Dr.
Santa Barbara, CA 93108-1436

Established in 2005 in CA.
Foundation type: Independent foundation.
Financial data (yr. ended 12/31/12): Assets, $7,238,647 (M); expenditures, $615,953; qualifying distributions, $516,500; giving activities include $516,500 for grants.
Fields of interest: Arts; Education; Environment; Human services.
Limitations: Applications not accepted. Giving primarily in CA.
Application information: Contributes only to pre-selected organizations.
Trustee: Cheryl Tomchin.
EIN: 206708205

216
AAM Foundation ✧
7110 Redwood Blvd., Ste. A
Novato, CA 94945-4141 (415) 898-9528
E-mail: info@aamf.org; Main URL: http://www.aamf.org

Established in 1999.
Donors: Deepak Chopra, M.D.; Eckhart Corp.; Solanova, LLC.
Foundation type: Independent foundation.
Financial data (yr. ended 12/31/12): Assets, $834,747 (M); gifts received, $1,208,535; expenditures, $659,689; qualifying distributions, $659,689; giving activities include $648,000 for 2 grants (high: $600,000; low: $48,000).
Purpose and activities: Giving to provide underprivileged children with adequate nutrition, medication and education, giving them the chance to learn, grow and live with good health and dignity.
Fields of interest: Children; Economically disadvantaged.
Limitations: Applications accepted. Giving primarily in India.
Application information: Application form required.
Initial approach: Completed application form
Deadline(s): None
Officers: Deepak Chopra, M.D., Pres.; Sandeep Chopra, Secy.
EIN: 943352261

217
The McGrath Abrams Family Foundation ✧ ☆
16000 Ventura Blvd., Ste. 900
Encino, CA 91436-2760

Established in CA.
Donors: Kathleen McGrath; Jeffrey Abrams.
Foundation type: Independent foundation.
Financial data (yr. ended 12/31/12): Assets, $2,164,516 (M); gifts received, $1,900,000; expenditures, $1,726,395; qualifying distributions, $1,662,876; giving activities include $1,571,445 for grants.
Fields of interest: Education; Human services.
Limitations: Applications not accepted. Giving in the U.S., with emphasis on CA.
Application information: Unsolicited requests for funds not accepted.
Officers and Directors:* Kathleen McGrath,* Pres.; Jeffrey Abrams,* Secy.-Treas.
EIN: 453682112

218
Achieving America Family Foundation ✧ ☆
450 San Rafael Ave.
Pasadena, CA 91105-1528

Established in 1998.
Donor: Charles Munger.
Foundation type: Independent foundation.
Financial data (yr. ended 12/31/13): Assets, $1,081,836 (M); expenditures, $830,424; qualifying distributions, $829,500; giving activities include $829,500 for 29 grants (high: $564,500; low: $500).
Fields of interest: Education; Community/economic development; Catholic agencies & churches.
Type of support: General/operating support.
Limitations: Applications not accepted. Giving primarily in CA and DC. No grants to individuals.
Application information: Contributes only to pre-selected organizations.
Trustees: Stephen R. English; Molly Munger.
EIN: 957053032

219
Agarwal Family Foundation ✧
15 Crest Rd. W.
Rolling Hills, CA 90274

Donors: Avadhesh Agarwal; Uma Rani.
Foundation type: Independent foundation.
Financial data (yr. ended 08/31/13): Assets, $5,186,966 (M); expenditures, $742,505; qualifying distributions, $711,119; giving activities include $709,453 for 70 grants (high: $125,000; low: $500).
Fields of interest: Education; United Ways and Federated Giving Programs.
Limitations: Applications not accepted. Giving primarily in CA and TX.
Application information: Contributes only to pre-selected organizations.
Officers: Avadhesh Agarwal, Pres.; Uma Rani, Treas.
EIN: 263901520
Selected grants: The following grants are a representative sample of this grantmaker's funding activity:
$21,000 to Pratham USA, Houston, TX, 2013. For Free education for poor children in India.
$10,000 to Anaheim Community Foundation, Anaheim, CA, 2013. For Free medical camp in city of Anaheim.
$10,000 to Lestonnac Free Clinic, Orange, CA, 2013. Toward the free health clinic for the disadvantaged.
$1,500 to AARP, Washington, DC, 2013. For helping seniors.

220
Agilent Technologies Foundation ✧
5301 Stevens Creek Blvd., MS 1B-07
Santa Clara, CA 95051-7201
E-mail: foundation@agilent.com; Main URL: http://www.agilent.com/contributions/foundation.html

Established in 2001 in CA.
Donor: Agilent Technologies, Inc.
Foundation type: Company-sponsored foundation.
Financial data (yr. ended 10/31/12): Assets, $8,779,274 (M); gifts received, $3,000,000; expenditures, $3,530,058; qualifying distributions, $3,497,567; giving activities include $2,337,466 for 64 grants (high: $150,000; low: $671), and $892,879 for employee matching gifts.
Purpose and activities: The foundation supports programs designed to increase student interest and achievement in science education, with an emphasis directed towards populations underrepresented in the technology industry. It also funds university research at the frontiers of measurement in electronics and biosciences.
Fields of interest: Elementary/secondary education; Higher education; Employment, services; Disasters, preparedness/services; Science, formal/general education; Chemistry; Engineering/technology; Biology/life sciences; Science; Minorities; Women.
Type of support: General/operating support; Building/renovation; Program development; Conferences/seminars; Seed money; Curriculum development; Research; Employee volunteer services; Sponsorships; Program evaluation; Employee matching gifts.
Limitations: Applications not accepted. Giving primarily in areas of company operations, with emphasis on CA, CO, DE, Canada, China, Germany, India, Japan, and Taiwan. No support for home schools, sectarian or denominational organizations, discriminatory organizations, or health or human services organizations. No grants to individuals, or for luncheons, dinners, or auctions, annual campaigns, endowments or capital campaigns, political activities, television or radio productions, or personal websites.
Publications: Corporate giving report; Financial statement.

Application information: Unsolicited applications are not accepted.
Board meeting date(s): Apr.
Officers and Directors: William P. Sullivan, Chair. and Pres.; Marie Oh Huber, V.P. and Secy.; Neil Dougherty, V.P. and Treas.; Cynthia D. Johnson, V.P.; Laurie Nichol, Exec. Dir.; Didier Hirsch; Darlene Solomon.
Number of staff: 2 full-time professional; 1 full-time support.
EIN: 770532250
Selected grants: The following grants are a representative sample of this grantmaker's funding activity:
$576,895 to JK Group, Plainsboro, NJ, 2011.
$310,894 to American Red Cross, San Jose, CA, 2011.
$150,000 to Broad Institute, Cambridge, MA, 2011.
$125,000 to Society for Science and the Public, Washington, DC, 2011.
$98,753 to Princeton University, Princeton, NJ, 2011.
$68,313 to Arizona State University, Tempe, AZ, 2011.
$30,000 to Brigham Young University, Provo, UT, 2011.
$28,482 to United Way Worldwide, Alexandria, VA, 2011.
$25,000 to Society of Women Engineers, Chicago, IL, 2011.
$11,212 to United Way of Taiwan, Taipei, Taiwan, 2011.

221
The Agouron Institute ✧
1055 E. Colorado Blvd., Ste. 250
Pasadena, CA 91106-2359 (626) 744-5100
E-mail: info@agi.org; Main URL: http://www.agi.org/
Knowledge Center: http://www.agi.org/publications.html

Established in 1978.
Foundation type: Independent foundation.
Financial data (yr. ended 06/30/13): Assets, $34,061,692 (M); expenditures, $3,110,191; qualifying distributions, $2,756,444; giving activities include $1,831,337 for 21 grants (high: $629,261; low: $3,000).
Purpose and activities: Giving primarily for scientific research and education.
Fields of interest: Higher education; Education; Science, research; Biology/life sciences.
Limitations: Applications not accepted. Giving primarily in the U.S, with some emphasis on CA; some funding also internationally, particularly in Canada and Denmark.
Application information: Contributes only to pre-selected organizations.
Officers and Directors:* Melvin Simon, Ph.D.*, Chair.; John Abelson, Ph.D.*, Pres. and Exec. Dir.; Willis Wood, Ph.D.*, V.P.; Gary Friedman,* Exec. V.P. and Secy.; Gustaf Arrhenius, Ph.D.; Dr. Theodore Friedmann, M.D.; Gordon Gill, M.D.; John Grotzinger, Ph.D.; David Hirsch, Ph.D.; Peter Johnson; Deborah Spector, Ph.D.; Edward Stolper, Ph.D.
EIN: 953248387

222
The Ahmanson Foundation
9215 Wilshire Blvd.
Beverly Hills, CA 90210-5501 (310) 278-0770
Contact: Yvonne deBeixedon, Grants Admin.
E-mail: info@theahmansonfoundation.org; Main URL: http://www.theahmansonfoundation.org

Incorporated in 1952 in CA.
Donors: Howard F. Ahmanson†; Dorothy G. Sullivan†; William Hayden Ahmanson†; Robert H. Ahmanson†.
Foundation type: Independent foundation.
Financial data (yr. ended 10/31/13): Assets, $1,108,002,312 (M); expenditures, $52,416,048; qualifying distributions, $52,530,907; giving activities include $50,359,404 for 525 grants (high: $3,000,000; low: $1,000).
Purpose and activities: Emphasis on education at all levels, the arts and humanities, health and medicine, and a broad range of human service programs.
Fields of interest: Visual arts; Museums; Performing arts; Humanities; Arts; Elementary school/education; Secondary school/education; Higher education; Adult education—literacy, basic skills & GED; Libraries/library science; Education, reading; Education; Health care; Crime/violence prevention, domestic violence; Recreation, public policy; Human services; Youth, services; Homeless, human services; Children/youth; Adults; Aging; Young adults; Disabilities, people with; Physically disabled; Minorities; Substance abusers; Economically disadvantaged; Homeless.
Type of support: Building/renovation; Capital campaigns; Debt reduction; Equipment; General/operating support; Land acquisition; Matching/challenge support; Program-related investments/loans; Scholarship funds; Technical assistance.
Limitations: Applications accepted. Giving primarily in southern CA, with emphasis on the Los Angeles area. No support for religious organizations for sectarian purposes, or advocacy or political organizations. No grants to individuals, or generally for continuing support, endowed chairs, annual campaigns, deficit financing, professorships, internships, film production, media projects, general research and development, workshops, studies, surveys, operational support of regional and national charities, underwriting, or exchange programs.
Publications: Application guidelines.
Application information: Fax or e-mail requests will not be accepted. Application form not required.
Initial approach: Letter of inquiry (following review of guidelines)
Copies of proposal: 1
Deadline(s): None
Board meeting date(s): 4 times annually
Final notification: 60 to 90 days
Officers and Trustees:* William Howard Ahmanson,* Pres.; Karen A. Hoffman,* Secy. and Managing Dir.; Kristen K. O'Connor, C.F.O. and Treas.; Lloyd E. Cotsen, Trustee Emeritus; Leonard E. Walcott, Jr., Managing Dir., Emeritus; Howard F. Ahmanson, Jr.; Mark A. Brooks; Robert M. DeKruif; Stephen D. Rountree; John Wagner; Stephen D. Yslas.
Number of staff: 11 full-time professional; 1 full-time support; 1 part-time support.
EIN: 956089998
Selected grants: The following grants are a representative sample of this grantmaker's funding activity:
$750,000 to Loyola Marymount University, Los Angeles, CA, 2013. Toward construction of new Life Sciences Building.
$450,000 to Saint Johns Well Child and Family Center, Los Angeles, CA, 2013. Toward renovations for expansion of Chronic and Environmental Disease Center.
$200,000 to Library Foundation of Los Angeles, Los Angeles, CA, 2013. Toward equipment and supplies for Student Zones program, which gives students in grades K-12 access to basic school supplies; laptops equipped with Internet access, basic word processing and links to Los Angeles Public Library's digital database resources. Students also receive free online one-on-one tutoring via Live Homework Help and homework related printouts are free-of-charge to eligible students during Student Zone hours.
$195,000 to Montrose Search and Rescue Team, Montrose, CA, 2013. To acquire customized Search and Rescue replacement truck.
$85,000 to Childrens Dental Center, Inglewood, CA, 2013. For facility and equipment upgrades.
$50,000 to Art Center College of Design, Pasadena, CA, 2013. For Ahmanson Veterans Scholarship Initiative.
$50,000 to Good Shepherd Center for Homeless Women and Children, Los Angeles, CA, 2013. Toward Languille Emergency Shelter services.
$30,000 to El Centro de Accion Social, Pasadena, CA, 2013. Toward Youth Education Programs.
$29,500 to Inside Out Community Arts, Venice, CA, 2013. For furnishings, equipment, technology and moving support.

223
Akonadi Foundation
436 14th St., No. 1417
Oakland, CA 94612-2703 (510) 663-3867
Contact: Quinn Delaney, Pres.
FAX: (510) 663-3860; E-mail: info@akonadi.org;
Main URL: http://www.akonadi.org
Akonadi Foundation's Philanthropy Promise: http://www.ncrp.org/philanthropys-promise/who
Facebook: https://www.facebook.com/akonadifoundation?ref=hl
LinkedIn: https://www.linkedin.com/company/akonadi-foundation
Twitter: https://twitter.com/akonadi_oakland

Established in 1999 in CA.
Donors: Quinn Delaney; Wayne Jordan; The California Endowment.
Foundation type: Independent foundation.
Financial data (yr. ended 12/31/13): Assets, $27,751,910 (M); gifts received, $3,000,000; expenditures, $1,941,230; qualifying distributions, $1,676,837; giving activities include $1,257,924 for 66 grants (high: $85,000; low: $100).
Purpose and activities: The mission of the foundation is to work with others to eliminate racism, with a focus on structural and institutional racism.
Fields of interest: Civil rights, race/intergroup relations.
Limitations: Applications not accepted. Giving primarily in the San Francisco Bay Area, CA. No support for organizations which provide local programming in areas outside of northern CA. No grants to individuals.
Publications: Grants list.

Application information: Contributes only to pre-selected organizations. Proposals are by invitation only.
Officers and Directors:* Quinn Delaney,* Pres.; Wayne Jordan,* Secy.-Treas.
Number of staff: 1 part-time support.
EIN: 943329873

224
Alalusi Foundation ✧

1975 National Ave.
Hayward, CA 94545-1709 (510) 887-2374
E-mail: info@alalusifoundation.org; Main URL: http://www.alalusifoundation.org/
Facebook: https://www.facebook.com/pages/Alalusi-Foundation/497928536916586?ref=br_tf

Established in 2001 in CA.
Donors: Hesham Al-Alusi; Ayam Alshar; Mirza Baig; Patricia Baig; Mohammed Raheemuddin Ahmed; Husam Shuayb; Ahd Shuayb; Syed K. Raza; Nabeela Sajjad.
Foundation type: Independent foundation.
Financial data (yr. ended 03/31/13): Assets, $0 (M); gifts received, $576,325; expenditures, $753,871; qualifying distributions, $752,727; giving activities include $659,530 for 8 grants (high: $253,200; low: $3,200), and $65,734 for grants to individuals.
Purpose and activities: Giving primarily for Muslim and Islamic relief and affairs, as well as for humanitarian assistance in other regions.
Fields of interest: International relief; International human rights; Islam; Religion.
International interests: Africa; Asia; China; Middle East.
Type of support: General/operating support; Grants to individuals.
Limitations: Applications accepted. Giving on an international basis with emphasis on China; some giving also in CA.
Application information:
Initial approach: Letter
Deadline(s): None
Director: Hesham Al-Alusi.
EIN: 912158518

225
The Al-Ameen Foundation ✧

c/o Jean & Associates
1301 Ocean Ave.
Santa Monica, CA 90401-1019

Established in 1998 in CA.
Donors: Ahmad Adaya; Adaya Family Trust.
Foundation type: Independent foundation.
Financial data (yr. ended 12/31/12): Assets, $5,933,704 (M); expenditures, $485,983; qualifying distributions, $466,350; giving activities include $466,350 for grants.
Fields of interest: Education; Hospitals (general); Health care; Human services; Family services, domestic violence; Islam.
International interests: Pakistan.
Limitations: Applications not accepted.
Application information: Contributes only to pre-selected organizations.
Officers: Gazala Shauk, C.F.O.; Tehmina Adaya, Secy.
Directors: Amina Adaya; Salim Adaya; Nargis Dada; Nasreen Haroon; Ruksana Mohammed.
EIN: 954698812

226
Albatross Foundation ✧

2865 Albatross St.
San Diego, CA 92103-6101

Established in 2007 in CA.
Donors: Brent V. Woods; Laurie C. Mitchell.
Foundation type: Independent foundation.
Financial data (yr. ended 12/31/13): Assets, $24,818,558 (M); gifts received, $510,350; expenditures, $1,313,948; qualifying distributions, $1,225,000; giving activities include $1,225,000 for 7 grants (high: $925,000; low: $10,000).
Purpose and activities: Giving primarily to a children's museum; some funding also for an art museum and for higher education and an independent K-12 school.
Fields of interest: Museums (art); Museums (children's); Elementary/secondary education; Higher education.
Limitations: Applications not accepted. Giving primarily in San Diego, CA. No grants to individuals.
Application information: Contributes only to pre-selected organizations.
Officers: Brent V. Woods, Pres.; Laurie C. Mitchell, Secy.-Treas.
Director: Marilyn J. Woods.
EIN: 208064368
Selected grants: The following grants are a representative sample of this grantmaker's funding activity:
$500,000 to New Childrens Museum, San Diego, CA, 2011.
$450,000 to San Diego Public Library, San Diego, CA, 2011.
$50,000 to Barrio Logan College Institute, San Diego, CA, 2011.

227
The Isabel Allende Foundation ✧

116 Caledonia St.
Sausalito, CA 94965-1925 (415) 289-0992
Contact: Lori Barra, Exec. Dir.
FAX: (415) 289-1154;
E-mail: lori@isabelallendefoundation.org; Tel. for Lori Barra: (415) 332-1313; E-mail: lori@isabelallendefoundation.org; Main URL: http://www.isabelallendefoundation.org

Established in 1996 in CA.
Donors: Isabel Allende; William C. Gordon.
Foundation type: Independent foundation.
Financial data (yr. ended 11/30/13): Assets, $10,151,378 (M); gifts received, $139,425; expenditures, $947,522; qualifying distributions, $862,353; giving activities include $663,621 for 78 grants (high: $80,000; low: $500).
Purpose and activities: Giving primarily to organizations whose missions are to provide women and girls with reproductive self-determination, healthcare, education, and protection from violence, exploitation and/or discrimination.
Fields of interest: Education; Crime/violence prevention, domestic violence; Youth development; Women, centers/services; Women; Girls.
Type of support: General/operating support; Program development.
Limitations: Applications accepted. Giving primarily in CA and Chile. No support for political, religious and/or military organizations. No grants to individuals, or for capital campaigns, trips, tours, conferences or events.
Publications: Application guidelines.
Application information: New organization proposals for Esperanza Grants are not being accepted at this time. Unsolicited requests for Espiritu Awards and Paula Scholarships are not accepted. Information sent to the foundation by e-mail or U.S. mail is not considered unless the foundation requests such information from an applicant. Complete application policies and guidelines available on foundation web site. Application form required.
Board meeting date(s): Jan.
Officers: Isabel Allende, Pres.; William C. Gordon, Secy.; Lori Barra, Exec. Dir.
Number of staff: 1 full-time professional.
EIN: 911748486
Selected grants: The following grants are a representative sample of this grantmaker's funding activity:
$40,000 to Global Fund for Women, San Francisco, CA, 2013. For Health, Education, Protection and Literacy for Women.
$35,000 to Center for Reproductive Rights, New York, NY, 2013. For health and empowerment.
$30,826 to Homeless Prenatal Program, San Francisco, CA, 2013. For assisting homeless pregnant women.
$29,500 to 10,000 Degrees, San Rafael, CA, 2013. For Scholarship for Latino Women.
$22,750 to Mujeres Unidas y Activas, San Francisco, CA, 2013. For Empowerment of Women and Their Rights.
$8,970 to 826 Valencia, San Francisco, CA, 2013. For education, literacy, empowerment of children.
$8,500 to San Jose State University, San Jose, CA, 2013. For Scholarships for Low Income Youth.
$8,000 to Canal Alliance, San Rafael, CA, 2013. To support the Development of Leadership Skills for You.
$7,500 to Circulo de Vida Cancer Support and Resource Center, San Francisco, CA, 2013. For Health, Education, Advocacy, Counseling for Latinas.
$5,000 to Legal Aid of Marin, San Rafael, CA, 2013. To provide Legal Aid to Immigrants and Those Underserved Communities.

228
The Allergan Foundation ✧

2525 Dupont Dr., T1-4D
P.O. Box 19534
Irvine, CA 92623-9534 (714) 246-2077
Contact: Vanessa Ryan, Dir., Community Rels.
E-mail: AllerganFoundation@Allergan.com; E-mail for Vanessa Ryan: ryan_vanessa@allergan.com; Main URL: http://www.allerganfoundation.org

Established in 1998 in GA.
Donor: Allergan, Inc.
Foundation type: Company-sponsored foundation.
Financial data (yr. ended 12/31/12): Assets, $45,991,841 (M); expenditures, $6,456,144; qualifying distributions, $6,298,482; giving activities include $5,954,809 for 308 grants (high: $1,000,000; low: $150).
Purpose and activities: The foundation supports programs designed to enhance and strengthen the communities where Allergan employees live or work,

focusing on the areas of health and human services, education, civic and community, and the arts. Special emphasis is directed toward programs designed to serve vulnerable and at-risk populations including children, the elderly, and the infirm.
Fields of interest: Arts; Education; Hospitals (general); Public health; Health care, patient services; Health care; Housing/shelter; Disasters, preparedness/services; Human services; Community/economic development; United Ways and Federated Giving Programs; Public affairs; Children; Aging; Women; Economically disadvantaged.
Type of support: Equipment; Program development; Scholarship funds; Employee volunteer services; Sponsorships.
Limitations: Applications accepted. Giving primarily in areas of company operations in Orange and Santa Barbara counties, CA, and McLennan County, TX, area; giving also to regional and national organizations. No support for religious groups not of direct benefit to the entire community, fraternal, labor, political, or veterans' organizations, discriminatory organizations, athletic leagues, school-affiliated orchestras, bands, or choirs, private K-12 schools, pass-through organizations, consumer interest groups, or agencies normally financed by government sources. No grants to individuals, or for family requests for scholarships, fellowship assistance, or other types of support, matching gifts, university administrative, management, or indirect fees, golf tournaments, athletic events, or team sponsorships, student trips or tours, fundraising activities or advertising sponsorships, conferences, workshops, exhibits, surveys, films, or publishing activities, endowments, capital, or building campaigns, general operating support, debt reduction, or contributions in the name of a memorial tribute; no in-kind gifts.
Publications: Application guidelines; Annual report (including application guidelines).
Application information: Community Grants range from $5,000 to $10,000. Support is limited to 1 contribution per organization during any given year. Videos, faxed, or e-mailed applications are not accepted. Application form required.
Initial approach: Complete online application
Deadline(s): May 1 through July 1
Final notification: Sept.
Officers and Directors:* David E.I. Pyott,* Chair. and C.E.O.; James M. Hindman,* Pres.; Terilea J. Wielenga,* C.F.O.; Matthew J Maletta, Secy. and Genl. Counsel; Daryn A. Martin, Treas.; Gwyn L. Grenrock, Exec. Dir.; Julian S. Gangolli; Gavin S. Herbert; Lynn D. Salo; Scott D. Sherman; Scott M. Whitcup, M.D.
EIN: 330794475

229
Alliance Healthcare Foundation ✧
5060 Shoreham Pl., Ste. 350
San Diego, CA 92122-5977 (877) 820-9410
FAX: (858) 202-1698;
E-mail: info@alliancehealthcarefoundation.org; Contact for Responsive Grants: Sylvia Barron, Prog. Off., e-mail: sbarron@alliancehealthcarefoundation.org; contact for assistance with grant application: Selina Forte, Grants Mgr., tel.: (858) 875-3330; contact for additional questions: Nancy Sasaki, Exec. Dir., tel.: (858) 875-3304, e-mail: nsasaki@Alliancehealthcarefoundation.org; Main URL: http://www.alliancehealthcarefoundation.org/
Blog: http://www.alliancehealthcarefoundation.org/blog/
E-Newsletter: http://alliancehealthcarefoundation.us4.list-manage.com/subscribe/post?u=574b820f9f8b6ef24b4602059&id=85350a06b2
Facebook: http://www.facebook.com/pages/Alliance-Healthcare-Foundation-Community-Forum/215457288468198
Grants List: http://www.alliancehealthcarefoundation.org/grants/grantees/
LinkedIn: http://www.linkedin.com/company/alliance-healthcare-foundation?goback=.cps_1286141702340_1
Twitter: https://twitter.com/#!/AllianceHF
YouTube: http://www.youtube.com/user/AllianceFoundation?ob=0

Established in 1988 in CA; converted to Independent foundation as a result of sale of Community Care Network, Inc. to Value Health in 1994.
Donors: Kathleen Briggs; National AIDS Fund; AIDS Walk San Diego, Inc.
Foundation type: Independent foundation.
Financial data (yr. ended 06/30/13): Assets, $68,357,370 (M); expenditures, $3,529,952; qualifying distributions, $3,260,691; giving activities include $2,339,024 for 53+ grants (high: $622,689).
Purpose and activities: Giving to promote quality health care in the San Diego, CA, region, with special emphasis on the medically underserved. The foundation seeks to accomplish this through collaborative grantmaking, advocacy and education. Funding includes people who are under 250 percent of the Federal Poverty Level, children, and homeless individuals and families.
Fields of interest: Health care; Mental health/crisis services, public policy; AIDS; Crime/violence prevention; Children; Economically disadvantaged; Homeless.
Type of support: General/operating support; Management development/capacity building; Program development; Seed money; Curriculum development; Technical assistance; Program evaluation.
Limitations: Applications accepted. Giving limited to San Diego and Imperial counties, CA. No support for research, costly equipment, fundraising events, capital campaigns or annual fund drives. No grants to individuals, lobbying, capital campaigns, or construction or renovation or for the underwriting of medical expenses.
Publications: Application guidelines; Financial statement; Grants list; Informational brochure; Newsletter.
Application information: The foundation prefers application to be filed online. Application form as well as additional application information is available on foundation web site.
Initial approach: Use online application process on foundation web site
Deadline(s): None for Responsive Grants; May 23 for Innovations Initiative; Mission Support is generally launched in Jan./Feb. annually. Applications for this are due 1-month following the announcement
Board meeting date(s): Feb., May, Aug., and Nov.
Final notification: 4-6 weeks
Officers and Trustees:* Robert B. McCray,* Chair.; Rosemarie Marshall Johnson, M.D.*, Secy.; Atul Patel,* Treas.; Arthur Roke, C.F.O.; Nancy L. Sasaki, Exec. Dir.; Elizabeth Dreicer; Donald Jones; Stan Lewis; B. Kathlyn Mead; Joe Ramsdell, M.D.; Dwight Smith; Jeffrey Willman.
Number of staff: 7 full-time professional; 2 part-time professional.
EIN: 330340635

230
The Alpert & Alpert Foundation ✧
1815 S. Soto St.
Los Angeles, CA 90023-4210

Established in 1974 in CA.
Donors: Raymond Alpert; Jake J. Farber; Alpert & Alpert Iron & Metal, Inc.; Vista Metals Corp.; V.S. Trading.
Foundation type: Company-sponsored foundation.
Financial data (yr. ended 06/30/14): Assets, $4,647,789 (M); gifts received, $1,050,000; expenditures, $802,382; qualifying distributions, $800,100; giving activities include $800,100 for 49 grants (high: $350,000; low: $1,000).
Purpose and activities: The foundation supports family foundations and organizations involved with arts and culture, cancer, human services, and Judaism.
Fields of interest: Arts; Cancer; Human services; Foundations (private grantmaking); Jewish federated giving programs; Jewish agencies & synagogues; Religion.
Type of support: General/operating support.
Limitations: Applications not accepted. Giving primarily in CA. No grants to individuals.
Application information: Unsolicited requests for funds not accepted.
Officers and Directors:* Jake J. Farber,* Pres.; Alan Alpert,* V.P.; Howard Farber,* V.P.; Raymond Alpert,* Secy.-Treas.
EIN: 237388729
Selected grants: The following grants are a representative sample of this grantmaker's funding activity:
$2,750 to Adat Ari El Temple, North Hollywood, CA, 2011. For general charitable use.

231
The Herb Alpert Foundation ✧
c/o Rona Sebastian, Pres.
1414 6th St.
Santa Monica, CA 90401-2510
Main URL: http://www.herbalpertfoundation.org

Established in 1988 in CA.
Donor: Herb Alpert.
Foundation type: Independent foundation.
Financial data (yr. ended 12/31/12): Assets, $17,229,852 (M); gifts received, $46,788; expenditures, $8,262,832; qualifying distributions, $7,079,757; giving activities include $7,079,757 for 72 grants (high: $3,150,000; low: $500).
Purpose and activities: Support primarily for arts, with focus on arts education, jazz and support to professionals, as well as compassion and well being.
Fields of interest: Arts education; Performing arts, music; Arts; Children/youth; Youth; Adults; Young adults; Minorities.

Type of support: Fellowships; General/operating support; Grants to individuals; Management development/capacity building; Matching/challenge support; Program development; Scholarship funds; Seed money.
Limitations: Applications not accepted. Giving on a national basis, with an emphasis on Los Angeles, CA. No grants to individuals (except for awards and scholarship programs).
Application information: Contributes only to pre-selected organizations.
Officers: Herb Alpert, Chair.; Lani Hall Alpert, Vice-Chair.; Rona Sebastian, Pres.; Ian Wiener, Secy.; Paul Frimmer, C.F.O.
Number of staff: 2 full-time professional; 1 full-time support.
EIN: 954191227
Selected grants: The following grants are a representative sample of this grantmaker's funding activity:
$3,150,000 to Harlem School of the Arts, New York, NY, 2012.
$588,340 to California Institute of the Arts, Valencia, CA, 2012.
$500,000 to Community Arts Partnership of Tompkins County, Ithaca, NY, 2012.
$340,800 to California State Summer School for the Arts, Sacramento, CA, 2012.
$300,000 to Modest Needs Foundation, New York, NY, 2012.
$100,000 to Good People Fund, Millburn, NJ, 2012.
$75,000 to Communities in Schools of California, Sacramento, CA, 2012.
$50,000 to California State University at Northridge Foundation, Northridge, CA, 2012.
$25,000 to REDCAT, Los Angeles, CA, 2012.

232
Raymond and Barbara Alpert Foundation ✧ ☆
5521 La Pasada
Long Beach, CA 90815-4320

Established in 1996 in CA.
Donors: Raymond Alpert; Barbara Alpert; Philip Waldman; Teri Alpert.
Foundation type: Independent foundation.
Financial data (yr. ended 12/31/13): Assets, $5,875,207 (M); gifts received, $400,000; expenditures, $1,341,965; qualifying distributions, $1,339,363; giving activities include $1,339,363 for grants.
Fields of interest: Health organizations, association; Jewish agencies & synagogues.
Limitations: Applications not accepted. Giving primarily in Long Beach, CA. No grants to individuals.
Application information: Unsolicited requests for funds not accepted.
Officers: Raymond Alpert, Pres.; Barbara Alpert, C.F.O. and Treas.
EIN: 954541253

233
The Lisa & Steve Altman Family Foundation ✧
9696 La Jolla Farms Rd.
La Jolla, CA 92037-1131

Established in CA.
Donors: Steve R. Altman; Lisa J. Altman.
Foundation type: Independent foundation.
Financial data (yr. ended 12/31/13): Assets, $3,468,446 (M); gifts received, $3,816,511; expenditures, $583,353; qualifying distributions, $568,208; giving activities include $568,208 for 50 grants (high: $200,500; low: $200).
Purpose and activities: Giving primarily for education, medical research, and social services.
Fields of interest: Arts; Elementary/secondary education; Higher education; Education; Medical research, institute; Diabetes research; Human services; Children/youth, services.
Limitations: Applications not accepted. Giving primarily in CA. No grants to individuals.
Application information: Contributes only to pre-selected organizations.
Officers: Steve R. Altman, Pres.; Lisa J. Altman, V.P.
EIN: 582667016

234
The Jenifer Altman Foundation ✧
c/o Thoreau Center for Sustainability
Presidio Bldg. 1016, 1st Fl.
San Francisco, CA 94129-0209
FAX: (415) 561-6480; E-mail: info@jaf.org; Main URL: http://www.jaf.org

Established in 1991 in CA.
Donors: Jenifer Altman†; Pinewood Foundation; Avalon Trust.
Foundation type: Independent foundation.
Financial data (yr. ended 06/30/13): Assets, $5,920,277 (M); gifts received, $10,000; expenditures, $944,594; qualifying distributions, $709,832; giving activities include $489,750 for 19 grants (high: $440,000; low: $1,000).
Purpose and activities: Giving primarily for: 1) Environmental Health and Justice (grants to address the impact of chemicals on human and ecological health, and to develop and strengthen an integrated global environmental health and justice movement); 2) Bolinas Community Projects (grants that contribute to the well-being of the small coastal community of Bolinas, CA); 3) Commonweal; and 4) Special Projects.
Fields of interest: Environment; Human services, mind/body enrichment; Community/economic development.
Type of support: General/operating support; Continuing support.
Limitations: Applications not accepted. Giving primarily in CA.
Publications: Grants list; Program policy statement.
Application information: Unsolicited requests for funds not accepted.
Board meeting date(s): Fall and spring
Officers and Directors:* Michael Lerner, Ph.D.*, Pres.; Catherine Porter, Secy.; Marni Rosen, Exec. Dir.; John Peterson Myers; Anita Nager; Albert Wells.
Number of staff: 2 full-time professional; 1 part-time professional.
EIN: 943146675

235
Maurice Amado Foundation ✧
3940 Laurel Canyon Blvd., No. 809
Studio City, CA 91604-3709 (818) 980-9190
Contact: Pam Kaizer, Exec. Dir.
FAX: (818) 980-9190;
E-mail: pkaizer@mauriceamadofdn.org; Main URL: http://www.mauriceamadofdn.org
Grants List: http://mauriceamadofdn.org/recent-grants/

Incorporated in 1961 in CA.
Donor: Maurice Amado†.
Foundation type: Independent foundation.
Financial data (yr. ended 11/30/13): Assets, $29,376,220 (M); expenditures, $1,366,394; qualifying distributions, $1,172,919; giving activities include $1,050,000 for 48 grants (high: $346,817; low: $250).
Purpose and activities: Support primarily for activities that promote Sephardic Jewish culture and heritage.
Fields of interest: Arts; Education.
Type of support: Continuing support; Curriculum development; General/operating support; Program development.
Limitations: Applications accepted. Giving in geographical areas of interest to the board. No grants to individuals directly.
Publications: Application guidelines.
Application information: Check foundation web site for guidelines. Letter should be on organizational letterhead. Application form not required.
Initial approach: E-mail
Copies of proposal: 1
Deadline(s): Aug. 15 and Feb. 15
Board meeting date(s): Biannually
Final notification: Late Nov. and late May
Officers and Directors:* Mark E. Tarica,* Pres.; Ellen Amado,* V.P. and Secy.; Samuel Tarica, V.P. and C.F.O.; Richard Amado; Ted Amado; Victor Lavis; Susan Malcom.
Number of staff: 1 part-time professional.
EIN: 956041700
Selected grants: The following grants are a representative sample of this grantmaker's funding activity:
$50,000 to Jewish Free Loan Association, Los Angeles, CA, 2011. For operating expenses.
$10,000 to Israel Cancer Research Fund, Beverly Hills, CA, 2011. For operating expenses.

236
Amar Foundation ✧
c/o McCabe & Totah, LLP
1760 The Almeda, Ste. 300
San Jose, CA 95126-1728
GiveSmart: http://www.givesmart.org/Stories/Donors/Neeru-Khosla
Vinod and Neeru Khosla's Giving Pledge Profile: http://glasspockets.org/philanthropy-in-focus/eye-on-the-giving-pledge/profiles/khosla

Established in 1987 in CA.
Donors: Neeru Khosla; Vinod Khosla.
Foundation type: Independent foundation.
Financial data (yr. ended 12/31/12): Assets, $27,772,692 (M); expenditures, $7,743,354; qualifying distributions, $7,664,552; giving activities include $7,615,000 for 3 grants (high: $6,865,000; low: $250,000), and $28,929 for loans/program-related investments.
Purpose and activities: Giving primarily for education, and to U.S.-based organizations concerning India that support social, economic, and educational programs.

Fields of interest: Education; Human services; International affairs; Microfinance/microlending.
International interests: India.
Limitations: Applications not accepted. Giving primarily in CA. No grants to individuals.
Application information: Contributes only to pre-selected organizations.
Officers and Director:* Neeru Khosla,* Pres.; Vinod Khosla,* Secy.
EIN: 943055731
Selected grants: The following grants are a representative sample of this grantmaker's funding activity:
$5,225,000 to CK12 Foundation, San Jose, CA, 2011. To support development and operations of open educational sources including Web-based materials.
$1,000,000 to Personal Genome Project, Boston, MA, 2011. To encourage development of personal genomics technology.
$900,000 to Stanford University, Stanford, CA, 2011. For professional development, financial aid and for work to improve K-12 education in the United States.
$500,000 to IIT Delhi Excellence Foundation, Scarsdale, NY, 2011. For scientific and technological research activities at Indian Institute of Technology Delhi.
$6,250 to Grameen Foundation USA, Washington, DC, 2011. For program support.

237
American Honda Foundation ✧

1919 Torrance Blvd., M.S. 100-1W-5A
Torrance, CA 90501-2746 (310) 781-4090
FAX: (310) 781-4270; E-mail: ahf@ahm.honda.com; Main URL: http://corporate.honda.com/america/philanthropy.aspx?id=ahf
Grants List: http://corporate.honda.com/america/philanthropy.aspx?id=ahf_fiscal_year_2009

Established in 1984 in CA.
Donor: American Honda Motor Co., Inc.
Foundation type: Company-sponsored foundation.
Financial data (yr. ended 03/31/14): Assets, $32,861,165 (M); expenditures, $2,472,482; qualifying distributions, $2,038,780; giving activities include $1,771,761 for grants.
Purpose and activities: The foundation supports programs designed to promote youth education. Special emphasis is directed toward science, technology, engineering, mathematics, the environment, job training, and literacy.
Fields of interest: Elementary/secondary education; Vocational education; Higher education; Education, reading; Education; Environment; Employment, training; Science, formal/general education; Physical/earth sciences; Mathematics; Engineering/technology; Science; Youth; Minorities.
Type of support: General/operating support; Continuing support; Program development; Seed money; Curriculum development; Scholarship funds; Matching/challenge support.
Limitations: Applications accepted. Giving on a national basis with some emphasis on CA. No support for private foundations, for-profit organizations, churches, religious groups, or sectarian organizations, arts and culture organizations, health and welfare, disaster relief, legislative organizations, political organizations or candidates, advocacy, veterans' or fraternal organizations, or labor groups. No grants to individuals, or for scholarships, operating funds for hospitals, medical or educational research, research papers, fundraising, dinners, parties, receptions, auction charity balls, or 5k walks or runs, sponsorships, advertising, building funds or capital campaigns, endowments, corporate memberships, conferences or seminars, service club activities, youth recreational activities or playground equipment, student foreign exchange programs, trips or tours, or beauty or talent contests; no vehicle or product donations; no loans for small businesses.
Publications: Application guidelines; Grants list; Informational brochure (including application guidelines).
Application information: Grants range from $20,000 to $75,000. No faxed applications are accepted. Support is limited to 1 contribution per organization during any given year. A site visit may be requested. Application form required.
Initial approach: Complete online eligibility quiz and application form
Deadline(s): Feb. 1, May 1, Aug. 1, and Nov. 1
Board meeting date(s): Jan., Apr., July, and Oct.
Final notification: May 1, Aug. 1., Nov. 1. and Feb. 1
Officers and Directors:* Gary Kessler,* Pres.; Naoji Ono, V.P.; Steve Center,* Secy.-Treas.; Oraetta Minor; DeWayne Odom; Michael Rickey; Gail Rodkin; Cicely Salatino; Urvi Sutariya.
Number of staff: 4 full-time professional.
EIN: 953924667
Selected grants: The following grants are a representative sample of this grantmaker's funding activity:
$60,000 to Classroom Central, Charlotte, NC, 2012. For Classroom Central STEM Initiative, which enables low-income students to succeed academically. Classroom Central allows teachers to shop for free school supplies twice a month throughout the school year. Low-income students receive basic Science, Technology, Engineering and Mathematics (STEM) supplies and books necessary to enhance their ability to excel in math and science-related disciplines. These supplies include compasses, protractors, science books and quarterly science magazines, graphing paper and science calculators.
$60,000 to Community Foundation of Northeast Iowa, Waterloo, IA, 2012. For Leader Valley - Leader in Me Program, school-wide transformational model using 7 Habits of Highly Effective People as a common language and integrating the Habits directly into the curriculum, traditions and culture of schools. This result in instilling important leadership principles, improving academic achievement, decreasing discipline issues and raising accountability and engagement among teachers, students and parents.
$60,000 to DC Children and Youth Investment Trust Corporation, Washington, DC, 2012. For DC Inquiry-Based Learning (DCIBL), designed to turn up the volume on Science, Technology, Engineering and Mathematics (STEM) education by providing training to youth workers from selected community-based organizations in hands-on STEM curriculum. Serving as co-explorers, these nontraditional teachers deliver engaging STEM activities to students who typically have little to no exposure to STEM. Students then use what they have learned to address a specific issue occurring in their communities - giving them a real world application of STEM. At the culminating fair, students showcase their findings before peers, family members and community leaders.
$60,000 to Delaware Foundation for Science and Mathematics Education, Wilmington, DE, 2012. For NBC Learn News Archives on Demand, providing middle schools in Delaware with access to NBC Learn Archives on Demand, media tool aligned to state standards in curriculu. The tool is a collection of NBC News videos, primary source documents, photos and images, graphs and charts; designed for use in school classrooms. Teachers and their students can access and download material covering subjects such as science, mathematics, language arts and social studies, from any internet-connected computer.
$60,000 to Freedom School Partners, Charlotte, NC, 2012. For Summer Literacy Program, which targets Title-1 schools serving students in grades K-8. Six-week literacy-based camps are offered free of charge and are led by trained college interns who serve as role models. Daily activities, books and other materials are selected to incorporate culturally relevant themes in effort to make the content engaging and relatable to students. At the end of each week, the children are given a book to take home to ensure that reading continues at home.
$60,000 to Living Arts, Detroit, MI, 2012. For El Arte STEAM/READ (Science, Technology, Engineering, Arts, Math and Literacy Initiative), program which enlists local artists in arts residencies, serving students in grades Pre-Kindergarten through eight Teaching artists partner with classroom teachers in Southwest Detroit to provide innovative arts-based curricula, aligned with academic standards to improve students' science, math, technology and literacy skills. This unique approach integrates the arts into day-to-day education resulting in significant improvement in student performance.
$60,000 to Rainier Scholars, Seattle, WA, 2012. For Academic Enrichment Program, which puts 6th graders on the path to college preparatory success through a 14-month intensive academic boot camp. Students attend rigorous courses focused on science, mathematics, literature and writing, and history. Academic and support services lead to placement into top independent and public schools and continues until the Scholars' final day of college.
$60,000 to San Mateo County Superintendent of Schools, Redwood City, CA, 2012. For Integrated Outdoor Education and the New California Education Environment Initiative State Adopted Curriculum (EEI). 5th and 6th grade teachers receive professional development training and strategies to effectively integrate California's newly adopted EEI curriculum with hands-on outdoor education curriculum taught at week-long residential outdoor science schools. EEI includes 85 instructional units, integrating California science and social studies/history standards.
$50,000 to Young Women's Leadership Charter School of Chicago, Chicago, IL, 2012. For Real Women Do Real Science, program for girls in grades 7-12. They gain a deep understanding of the scientific method through inquiry and experimentation. In addition to year-long science courses, students engage in unique research-based projects and career exploration via extra-curricular activities, internships and Saturday Academies offered through local partnerships. A key component of the curriculum is its annual Science Fair in which all projects are based on the Chicago River, with students analyzing the river based on their grade level's science focus.
$30,400 to Boys and Girls Clubs of Greater Dallas, Dallas, TX, 2012. For CSI-Project Learn which pairs

youth ages 13-18 with seasoned detectives within the Dallas Police Department who will work closely teaching them about the necessary skills and levels of education required to pursue careers in Law Enforcement, Forensic Science, as a Medical Examiner and more. Participants will go beyond the yellow tape and work a mock crime scene from investigation to a mock trial. Students will receive real-world experience and hands-on activities focused on toxicology, chemistry, DNA testing, fingerprinting and courtroom testimony.

238
Amgen Foundation, Inc. ✧
c/o Jewel Smith, Mgr.
1 Amgen Center Dr., M.S. 28-1-B
Thousand Oaks, CA 91320-1799 (805) 447-4056
Contact: Jewel Smith, Mgr., Corp. Contribs.; Eduardo Cetlin, Dir., Corp. Contribs.
FAX: (805) 376-1258;
E-mail: amgenfoundation@amgen.com; Additional e-mail for Eduardo Cetlin: ecetlin@amgen.com; additional e-mail for Jewel Smith: jewels@amgen.com; Main URL: http://www.amgen.com/citizenship/foundation.html
Grants List: http://wwwext.amgen.com/citizenship/foundation_donation_list.html
Twitter: http://twitter.com/AmgenFoundation

Established in 1991 in CA.
Donor: Amgen Inc.
Foundation type: Company-sponsored foundation.
Financial data (yr. ended 12/31/12): Assets, $93,229,705 (M); gifts received, $14,895,000; expenditures, $19,299,061; qualifying distributions, $19,126,188; giving activities include $17,994,001 for grants.
Purpose and activities: The foundation supports programs designed to advance science education; improve quality of care and access for patients; and create sound communities where Amgen staff members live and work.
Fields of interest: Arts; Higher education; Teacher school/education; Education; Health care, reform; Health care, equal rights; Health care, information services; Health care, patient services; Health care; Food banks; Disasters, preparedness/services; Human services; Community/economic development; Science, formal/general education; Engineering/technology; Science.
International interests: Europe.
Type of support: Management development/capacity building; Curriculum development; Continuing support; Employee matching gifts; Employee volunteer services; Equipment; General/operating support; Matching/challenge support; Program development; Program evaluation; Research.
Limitations: Applications accepted. Giving on a national and international basis in areas of company operations, with emphasis on Los Angeles, San Francisco, and Ventura, CA, CO, KY, Greater Boston, Middlesex, and Suffolk counties, MA, Juncos, PR, RI, King and South Snohomish counties, WA, and Europe; giving also to regional and national organizations. No support for religious organizations unless the gift is designated to a program that is secular in nature and benefits a broad range of the community (additionally the program must have a formal mission and separate budget and staff); political organizations or lobbying activity; labor unions; private foundations; organizations not described in sections 501(c)(3) and 509(a)(1), (2), (3) of the Internal Revenue Code; organizations that discriminate on the basis of race, color, religion, sex, age, national origin, sexual orientation, veteran or disability statuses in the delivery of services and in their employment practices. No grants to individuals, or for fundraising or sports-related events, corporate sponsorships, or lobbying activities.
Publications: Application guidelines; Annual report; Grants list.
Application information: A full proposal may be requested at a later date. Support is limited to 1 contribution per organization during any given year. Application form required.
Initial approach: Complete online letter of inquiry; complete online application for AASTE
Deadline(s): None; Feb. for AASTE
Board meeting date(s): Quarterly
Final notification: 1 month for Letter of Inquiry; June for AASTE
Officers and Directors:* Cynthia Patton, Chair.; Jean Lim Terra, Pres.; Richard T. Benson, Secy.; Mary Lehmann, Treas.; Stephen Canepa, C.F.O.; Madhu Balachandran; Laura Hamill; Raymond Jordan; Brian M. McNamee; Joseph P. Miletich; Jonathan M. Peacock; Carsten Thiel.
EIN: 770252898
Selected grants: The following grants are a representative sample of this grantmaker's funding activity:
$373,707 to European Schoolnet, Brussels, Belgium, 2012. For European Amgen Teacher Programme.
$300,000 to Health Leads Boston, Boston, MA, 2012. For Advancing Health Leads Through Operational Excellence, Evaluation Preparation, and Alumni Engagement.
$250,000 to United Network for Organ Sharing, Richmond, VA, 2012. For Automation of the Kidney Paired Donation Program of the Organ Procurement and Transplantation Network/United Network for Organ Sharing.
$229,878 to Education Development Center, Waltham, MA, 2012. For Curriculum Update for the Amgen-Bruce Wallace Biotechnology Lab Program.
$119,062 to University of California, Berkeley, CA, 2012. For San Francisco Bay Area Site: Amgen-Bruce Wallace Biotechnology Laboratory Program.
$54,000 to Casa Pacifica Centers for Children and Families, Casa Pacifica Centers for Children and Families, Camarillo, CA, 2012. For Programs for Abused, Neglected, and At-Risk Children.
$50,000 to Home and Hospice Care of Rhode Island, Providence, RI, 2012. To Continue to Expand and Develop Palliative Care Education, Collaboration and Outreach Program Year Two.
$25,000 to National Math and Science Initiative, Dallas, TX, 2012. For Military Families Program Expansion.
$25,000 to Rhode Island Free Clinic, Providence, RI, 2012. For Healthy Lifestyles for Today and Tomorrow.
$20,000 to Senior Resource Services, Greeley, CO, 2012. For assisting the elderly population to remain independent at home as long as possible.

239
Anaheim Community Foundation ✧ ☆
200 S. Anaheim Blvd., Ste. 433
Anaheim, CA 92805-3820 (714) 765-4419
Contact: Terry D. Lowe, C.E.O.
FAX: (714) 765-4454;
E-mail: AnaheimCommunityFoundation@gmail.com; Grant inquiry e-mail: jbranich@anaheim.net; Grant inquiry tel.: (714) 765-5250; Main URL: http://www.anaheimcommfound.org
Facebook: https://www.facebook.com/AnaheimCF
Twitter: https://twitter.com/anaheimcf

Established in 1984 in CA.
Foundation type: Community foundation.
Financial data (yr. ended 06/30/13): Assets, $1,199,321 (M); gifts received, $899,687; expenditures, $491,641; giving activities include $476,119 for grants to individuals.
Purpose and activities: The foundation seeks to: 1) encourage community participation, partnerships, and collaboration that result in successful responses to community challenges and opportunities; 2) strengthen community-based organizations that effectively address community needs, promote volunteerism, and provide community leadership; 3) promote community-building programs and events that inspire community pride and unity; and 4) provide individuals and business opportunities to make charitable investments that directly benefit the Anaheim community.
Fields of interest: Arts; Libraries/library science; Environment; Medical care, rehabilitation; Public health, obesity; Substance abuse, services; Crime/violence prevention, youth; Athletics/sports, Special Olympics; Youth development, services; Youth development; Human services, emergency aid; Aging, centers/services; Human services; Youth; Aging.
Type of support: General/operating support; Emergency funds; Program development; Scholarships—to individuals.
Limitations: Applications accepted. Giving limited to the Anaheim, CA, area. No support for religious or proselytizing activities. No grants for non program-related salaries or to pay for capital improvements.
Publications: Application guidelines; Annual report; Informational brochure.
Application information: Visit foundation web site for application form and guidelines. Grants will not normally exceed $5,000 but larger amounts may be awarded at the discretion of the foundation's Board. Application form required.
Initial approach: Submit application
Copies of proposal: 6
Deadline(s): Mar. 14
Board meeting date(s): 1st Mon. of each month
Officers and Directors:* William Taormina,* Chair., Emeritus; Steve Sain,* Pres.; David Bostwick,* V.P.; Terry D. Lowe,* C.E.O.; Ed Munson,* Secy.; Jeff Hunter,* Treas.; Orin Abrams; Sarah Alevizon; Steve Faessel; John Guastaferro; Irv Pickler; Michael Rubin; Colleen Smagala-DeVane; Bruce Solari.
EIN: 330033023

240
Kayne Anderson Capital Advisors Foundation ✧
1800 Avenue of the Stars, 3rd Fl.
Los Angeles, CA 90067

Donor: Kayne Anderson Capital Advisors, L.P.
Foundation type: Independent foundation.
Financial data (yr. ended 12/31/12): Assets, $574,579 (M); gifts received, $1,514,580; expenditures, $1,282,565; qualifying distributions,

$1,282,565; giving activities include $1,282,565 for 118 grants (high: $250,000; low: $25).
Fields of interest: Youth development, centers/clubs; Youth development; Human services; Religion.
Limitations: Applications not accepted. Giving primarily in CA and TX.
Application information: Unsolicited requests for funds not accepted.
Officers ad Directors: Howard Zelikow,* Pres.; David Shladovsky,* Secy.; Scott Keys,* Treas.; Richard Kayne; Robert Sinnott.
EIN: 900729378

241
Irene W. & Guy L. Anderson Children's Foundation ✧
1111 E. Tahquitz Canyon Way, Ste. 109
Palm Springs, CA 92262-0113 (760) 778-1777
FAX: (760) 778-1777; Tel./fax: (760) 778-1777; Grant Program contacts: Jane: tel.: (760) 902-7685, e-mail: jmills@andersonchildrensfoundation.org; Bob: tel.: (760) 861-1513, e-mail: bworswick@andersonchildrensfoundation.org; Main URL: http://www.andersonchildrensfoundation.org/
E-Newsletter: http://www.andersongrants.org/sign-up.htm
Facebook: https://www.facebook.com/andersonchildrensfoundation
Grants List: http://www.andersonchildrensfoundation.org/grant-history
Twitter: https://twitter.com/ACFforkids

Established in 1970 in CA.
Foundation type: Independent foundation.
Financial data (yr. ended 11/30/12): Assets, $20,323,387 (M); expenditures, $2,091,073; qualifying distributions, $895,844; giving activities include $734,570 for 68 grants (high: $37,365; low: $675).
Purpose and activities: The foundation makes grant money available to any non-profit group or organization in the Coachella Valley whose purpose is to meet the unmet needs of the youth of the Coachella Valley.
Fields of interest: Education; Youth development; Youth, services; Family services.
Type of support: General/operating support; Continuing support; Program development; Program evaluation.
Limitations: Applications accepted. Giving limited to the Coachella Valley, CA. No grants to individuals.
Publications: Application guidelines; Grants list; Newsletter.
Application information: Application form required.
Initial approach: Use application format on foundation web site, then submit via U.S. mail
Copies of proposal: 8
Deadline(s): June
Final notification: See online application form final notification
Trustee: R. Diane Schlesinger, M.D.
Number of staff: 2 full-time professional; 7 part-time professional.
EIN: 237089096

242
A. Gary Anderson Family Foundation ✧
17772 Cowan
Irvine, CA 92614-6012 (949) 242-5050

Foundation type: Independent foundation.
Financial data (yr. ended 12/31/13): Assets, $71,354,823 (M); expenditures, $4,565,040; qualifying distributions, $3,614,507; giving activities include $2,922,200 for 49 grants (high: $700,000; low: $250).
Fields of interest: Higher education; Education; Hospitals (general); Health care; Human services; Children/youth, services.
Limitations: Applications accepted. Giving primarily in CA.
Application information: Application form required.
Initial approach: Contact foundation for application form
Deadline(s): None
Officers: Erin J. Lastinger, Co-Chair. and C.E.O.; Erik K. Anderson, Co-Chair. and Pres.; Nancy S. Larson, Secy. and C.F.O.
EIN: 271878882

243
Marion & John E. Anderson Foundation ✧
1800 Ave. of the Stars, Ste. 1400
Los Angeles, CA 90067-4216

Established in 1986 in CA.
Donors: John E. Anderson†; Marion Anderson; Topa Insurance Group; Industrial Tools Inc.; Paradise Beverages Inc.; Ace Beverage Co.
Foundation type: Independent foundation.
Financial data (yr. ended 12/31/12): Assets, $50,119,169 (M); gifts received, $14,250,000; expenditures, $12,484,109; qualifying distributions, $12,277,238; giving activities include $12,277,000 for 6 grants (high: $7,000,000; low: $1,000).
Fields of interest: Education; Human services; YM/YWCAs & YM/YWHAs; United Ways and Federated Giving Programs.
Type of support: Scholarship funds.
Limitations: Applications not accepted. Giving primarily in Los Angeles, CA. No grants to individuals.
Application information: Contributes only to pre-selected organizations.
Officers: Marion Anderson, Pres.; Brenda Seuthe, C.F.O.
Directors: John E. Anderson, Jr.; William S. Anderson; Judith Munzig.
EIN: 954074837

244
The Angell Foundation ✧
10880 Wilshire Blvd., Ste. 920
Los Angeles, CA 90024-4110 (310) 446-8700
Contact: Perry Oretzky, Pres.
FAX: (310) 446-8787; Main URL: http://www.angellfoundation.org
Grants Database: http://angellfoundation.org/grants_search.php
Knowledge Center: http://www.angellfoundation.org/content.php?pgID=269

Established in 2003 in CA.
Donors: Paul Jablon; Angell Family Trust; Dorothy Angell Trust.
Foundation type: Independent foundation.
Financial data (yr. ended 06/30/13): Assets, $133,102,031 (M); gifts received, $8,476,992; expenditures, $6,600,804; qualifying distributions, $5,789,173; giving activities include $5,090,592 for 81+ grants (high: $250,000).
Purpose and activities: The foundation pursues its mission by helping people achieve self-sufficiency and well-being by providing them with basic necessities and economic stability in the areas of spirituality, arts, youth, education and social justice.
Fields of interest: Arts; Elementary/secondary education; Higher education; Education; Disasters, Hurricane Katrina; Human services; Children/youth, services; Civil/human rights, advocacy; Catholic agencies & churches; Jewish agencies & synagogues; Spirituality.
Limitations: Applications not accepted. Giving primarily in southern CA, with emphasis on Los Angeles; some funding in CT, MA, RI, and VT. No support for political organizations or campaigns. No grants to individuals, or for fund raising activities, benefit sponsorships, advertisements, or sponsored tables, unrestricted endowments, deficit reduction or capital projects.
Publications: Informational brochure.
Application information: Unsolicited requests for funds not accepted; letters of inquiry are submitted by invitation only.
Officers: Perry Oretzky, Pres.; Angel Roberson Daniels, V.P., Grants; Marian Bukrinsky, Secy.
EIN: 010789717

245
Annenberg Foundation
2000 Ave. of the Stars, Ste. 1000
Los Angeles, CA 90067-4704 (310) 209-4560
Contact: Leonard Aube, Exec. Dir.
FAX: (310) 209-1631;
E-mail: info@annenbergfoundation.org;
Pennsylvania Address: 101 W. Elm St., Ste. 640, Conshohocken, PA 19428; Washington, DC Address: 1301 Pennsylvania Ave., N.W., No. 302, Washington, DC 20004, tel.: (202) 783-0500, fax: (202) 783-0333; Main URL: http://www.annenbergfoundation.org
E-Newsletter: http://www.annenbergfoundation.org/enewsletter-sign-up
Facebook: http://www.facebook.com/pages/The-Annenberg-Foundation/257553628444
GiveSmart: http://www.givesmart.org/Stories/Donors/Wallis-Annenberg-and-Leonard-Aube
Grants Database: http://www.annenbergfoundation.org/grants/grants-database
Twitter: http://twitter.com/Annenberg_FDN

Established in 1989 in PA.
Donor: Hon. Walter H. Annenberg†.
Foundation type: Independent foundation.
Financial data (yr. ended 12/31/13): Assets, $1,690,604,187 (M); gifts received, $62,007; expenditures, $124,531,748; qualifying distributions, $112,646,403; giving activities include $70,025,237 for 542 grants (high: $10,000,000; low: $100), $5,575 for 14 employee matching gifts, and $33,766,254 for 9 foundation-administered programs.
Purpose and activities: The mission of the foundation is to provide funding and support to nonprofit organizations in the United States and globally. The foundation and its Board of Directors are also directly involved in the community with

innovative projects that further its mission to advance the public well-being through improved communication. The foundation encourages the development of effective ways to share ideas and knowledge and it is committed to core values of responsiveness, accessibility, fairness and involvement. Also, the foundation believes in funding organizations that have a deep level of community involvement, are led by effective leaders and tackle challenging and timely problems. Specific organizational attributes valued by the foundation are: visionary leadership, impact, sustainability, innovation, organizational strength, network of partnerships plus the population being served (thus, creating the acronym VISION+).
Fields of interest: Arts; Education; Environment; Animal welfare; Public health; Military/veterans.
Limitations: Applications accepted. Giving on a national and international basis. United States giving has an emphasis on the five-county region of Greater Los Angeles; international giving has an emphasis on countries in Africa, Europe and Asia. No support for political activities. No grants to individuals. Requests for capital campaigns and multi-year commitments are discouraged.
Publications: Application guidelines; Financial statement; Grants list; Newsletter.
Application information: Review the reference copy of the application and the foundation's vision/grantmaking guidelines prior to starting the online application process. Application form required.
Initial approach: Online grant application
Deadline(s): No later than 45 days after the creation of an online grant application account
Board meeting date(s): Varies
Final notification: 90-120 days
Officers and Directors:* Wallis Annenberg,* Chair., C.E.O. and Pres.; Lauren Bon,* V.P.; Charles Annenberg Weingarten,* V.P.; Gregory Annenberg Weingarten,* V.P.
Number of staff: 39 full-time professional.
EIN: 236257083
Selected grants: The following grants are a representative sample of this grantmaker's funding activity:
$10,000,000 to Wallis Annenberg Center for the Performing Arts, Beverly Hills, CA, 2013. For the capital campaign devoted to restoring and building the Wallis Annenberg Center for the Performing Arts, payable over 1.25 years.
$3,000,000 to Rockefeller Philanthropy Advisors, New York, NY, 2013. For City Dock No.1, which will be a world-class marine research center located in the Port of Los Angeles, payable over 2.50 years.
$2,700,000 to Foundation for Craniofacial Surgery, Pacific Palisades, CA, 2013. To improve the lives of children around the world who suffer from craniofacial deformities by supporting advanced health care delivery access, emotional healing, scientific research, education, advocacy and community building, payable over 20.00 years.
$2,500,000 to W E T A-Greater Washington Educational Telecommunications Association, Arlington, VA, 2012. For a discretionary fund for the President at Florentine Films to draw upon to fund special needs, projects and opportunities in order to enhance the educational work of the organization, payable over 6.50 years.
$1,000,000 to Los Angeles Jewish Home for the Aging, Reseda, CA, 2013. For the capital campaign for Building B on the Grancell Village Campus to provide improved facilities for residents, payable over 1.50 years.
$500,000 to Audubon Society, National, New York, NY, 2012. For Seabird Restoration Program activities in Maine to support conservation work on the Seal Island National Wildlife Refuge and Hog Island, payable over 3.00 years.
$500,000 to Childrens Institute, Los Angeles, CA, 2012. For the matching requirement for participation in the True North Fund of the Edna McConnell Clark Foundation, to ensure growth in organizational capacity and number of youth served.
$500,000 to University of California, Department of Atmospheric and Oceanic Sciences, Los Angeles, CA, 2012. For the Climate Change Projections in the Sierra Nevada project of the UCLA Department of Atmospheric and Oceanic Science, which employs dynamical and statistical methods to study climate change in the Sierra Nevada region, payable over 2.25 years.
$500,000 to Youth Policy Institute, Los Angeles, CA, 2013. For the Los Angeles Promise Neighborhood program to transform the communities of Pacoima and Hollywood, California with a continuum of integrated cradle to college and career services, payable over 2.00 years.
$150,000 to Foundation for Pierce College, Woodland Hills, CA, 2012. For labor costs by the Agriculture Department to feed and provide water for the animals; to clean animal facilities, and to irrigate the animal pastures at Pierce College, payable over 3.25 years.
$100,000 to Center for Land Use Interpretation, Culver City, CA, 2012. For a discretionary fund for the Founder and Director to draw upon to fund special needs, projects and opportunities in order to enhance the work of the Center, payable over 2.25 years.
$50,000 to Brigadoon Service Dogs, Bellingham, WA, 2012. For the Canines and Heroes for Independence Program, to provide service dogs to veterans who suffer from Post Traumatic Stress Disorder and Traumatic Brain Injury, payable over 1.25 years.
$50,000 to Prison University Project, San Quentin, CA, 2013. For the College Program at San Quentin to provide rigorous, high-quality college and remedial courses to students in San Quentin State Prison, payable over 1.25 years.
$50,000 to Therapeutic Living Centers for the Blind, Reseda, CA, 2012. For the Early Intervention Program to provide comprehensive services for families with children who are visually impaired with multiple disabilities in the San Fernando Valley region of Southern California, payable over 1.50 years.
$41,060 to Los Angeles County Museum of Natural History Foundation, Los Angeles, CA, 2013. For free museum admission and to create experimental documentary in celebration of the 100th anniversary of the museum and the Los Angeles Aqueduct.
$40,000 to 826LA, Los Angeles, CA, 2012. To support students ages 6 to 18 with their creative and expository writing skills, and to help teachers inspire their students to write, payable over 1.25 years.
$35,000 to Oceanographic Teaching Stations, Manhattan Beach, CA, 2013. For the Free Marine Science and Environmental Education Field Trip Program, which provides students hands-on experiences and education regarding the importance of protecting the oceans, payable over 1.25 years.
$30,000 to Conejo Valley Senior Concerns, Thousand Oaks, CA, 2013. For programs and services for aging seniors, their families, caregivers and the community which support and improve their quality of life, payable over 1.25 years.
$20,000 to Providence Health and Services Foundation, Burbank, CA, 2013. For the Roy and Patricia Disney Family Cancer Center at Providence St. Joseph Medical Center to provide a full range of diagnostics, treatment, care and support services for cancer patients and their families.

246
Carmelo Anthony Foundation, Inc. ✧ ☆
1880 Century Park E., Ste. 1600
Los Angeles, CA 90067-1661
E-mail: carmelocares@gmail.com; Main URL: http://thisismelo.origin.lyn.ag/foundation/about/

Established in 2005 in CA.
Donors: Carmelo K. Anthony; Melo Enterprises, Inc.; Perennial Sports & Entertainment, LLC; Time Warner Cable; Hyde Park.
Foundation type: Independent foundation.
Financial data (yr. ended 12/31/12): Assets, $28,211 (M); gifts received, $958,875; expenditures, $992,210; qualifying distributions, $774,000; giving activities include $774,000 for grants.
Purpose and activities: The foundation's mission is to invest in programs, leaders and community organizations that empower and provide opportunity for underserved children and families.
Fields of interest: Athletics/sports, basketball; Youth, services.
Limitations: Applications not accepted. Giving primarily in Baltimore, MD; some giving nationally.
Application information: Contributes only to pre-selected organizations.
Officers and Directors:* Carmelo K. Anthony,* Pres.; Robert Frazier; Alani Vazquez.
EIN: 203293195

247
The Apatow-Mann Family Foundation, Inc. ✧
9100 Wilshire Blvd., Ste. 400W
Beverly Hills, CA 90212-3415

Established in CA.
Donor: The Apatow Family.
Foundation type: Independent foundation.
Financial data (yr. ended 12/31/12): Assets, $53,772 (M); gifts received, $650,000; expenditures, $735,600; qualifying distributions, $735,510; giving activities include $735,510 for 92 grants (high: $25,000; low: $2,000).
Fields of interest: Health care; Health organizations, association; Human services.
Limitations: Applications not accepted. Giving primarily in CA.
Application information: Unsolicited requests for funds not accepted.
Officers and Directors:* Judd Apatow, Pres.; Leslie Mann,* Secy.
EIN: 261102362

248
Appleton Foundation ✧
P.O. Box 1460
Santa Cruz, CA 95061-1460

Established in 1998 in CA.

Donors: Alexander Gaguine; Jane Yett; John Hellwig; John Gaguine; Benito Gaguine; Gaguine Foundation.
Foundation type: Independent foundation.
Financial data (yr. ended 12/31/13): Assets, $8,964,919 (M); gifts received, $102,291; expenditures, $1,646,245; qualifying distributions, $1,480,900; giving activities include $1,477,750 for 91 grants (high: $290,000; low: $4,000).
Fields of interest: Education; Environment; Health care; Human services; International affairs; Community/economic development.
Type of support: General/operating support.
Limitations: Applications not accepted. Giving primarily in Latin America and Santa Cruz County, CA. No grants to individuals.
Application information: Contributes only to pre-selected organizations. Unsolicited requests for funds not accepted.
Officers: Alexander Gaguine, Pres.; Phil McManus, Secy.; Eileen Balian, Treas.; Don Lane, Fdn. Mgr.
Board Member: Jane Weed Pomerantz.
EIN: 911792407

249
The Applied Materials Foundation
3050 Bowers Ave., MS 0106
Santa Clara, CA 95054-3201
Contact: Claudia Schwiefert, Grant Mgr.; Siobhan Kenney, Exec. Dir.
E-mail: applied_materials_foundation@amat.com; E-mail contact for organizations located outside of the U.S.: community_affairs@amat.com; Main URL: http://www.appliedmaterials.com/company/corporate-responsibility
Corporate Responsibility: http://blog.appliedmaterials.com/corporate-responsibility

Established in 1994.
Donor: Applied Materials, Inc.
Foundation type: Company-sponsored foundation.
Financial data (yr. ended 10/31/13): Assets, $23,279,732 (M); expenditures, $7,569,116; qualifying distributions, $7,473,591; giving activities include $7,401,826 for 239 grants (high: $261,914; low: $1,000).
Purpose and activities: The foundation supports programs designed to promote arts and culture; education; environmental awareness and sustainability; and civic engagement.
Fields of interest: Performing arts, theater; Arts; Elementary/secondary education; Middle schools/education; Charter schools; Adult/continuing education; Education, reading; Education; Environmental education; Environment; Food services; Food banks; Housing/shelter; Disasters, preparedness/services; Youth development, adult & child programs; Youth, services; Homeless, human services; Human services; International relief; Mathematics; Science; Leadership development; Economically disadvantaged.
International interests: China; Europe; India; Israel; Japan; Singapore; South Korea; Taiwan.
Type of support: Continuing support; Annual campaigns; Program development; Curriculum development; Sponsorships.
Limitations: Applications accepted. Giving primarily in areas of company operations, with emphasis on San Jose, CA, Gloucester, MA, Kalispell, MT and Austin, TX. No support for missing children organizations, fraternities, religious or political organizations, commencements, PTAs, or alumni groups. No grants to individuals, or to nonprofits, or for general operating support, capital campaigns, research, sporting events for schools or civic teams, health-related programs or sponsorships, fundraisers such as walk-a-thons, runs, team in training, etc., or bricks/mortar, equipment, home building, or physical structures.
Publications: Application guidelines; Corporate giving report.
Application information:
Initial approach: Complete online application at http://www.appliedmaterials.com/about/cr/community/grants; e-mail community affairs for organizations located outside of the United States
Deadline(s): Jan. 15 and June 15
Board meeting date(s): Semi-annually
Final notification: Mar. 15 to 31 and Aug. 15 to 31
Officers and Directors:* Michael R. Splinter,* Pres.; Yvonne Leyba,* Secy.; Robert M. Friess,* C.F.O.; Siobhan Kenney, Exec. Dir.; Mary E. Humiston; Joseph M. Pon.
EIN: 770386898
Selected grants: The following grants are a representative sample of this grantmaker's funding activity:
$215,556 to Global Impact, Alexandria, VA, 2012. For EMPLOYEE MATCHING - DECEMBER 2011.
$200,000 to Across the Bridge Foundation, Downtown College Preparatory, San Jose, CA, 2012. For EAST SAN JOSE NEW SCHOOL DEVELOPMENT (MULTI YEAR GRANT 2010-2012).
$200,000 to Second Harvest Food Bank of Santa Clara and San Mateo Counties, San Jose, CA, 2012. For FREEDOM FROM HUNGER CAMPAIGN.
$150,000 to Teach for America, Bay Area Chapter, San Francisco, CA, 2012. For BUILDING THE MOVEMENT FOR EDUCATIONAL EQUITY IN SAN JOSE.
$130,000 to Silicon Valley Creates, San Jose, CA, 2012. For EXCELLENCE IN THE ARTS REGRANTING PROGRAM.
$127,301 to Global Impact, Alexandria, VA, 2012. For EMPLOYEE MATCHING - FEBRUARY 2012.
$66,500 to American India Foundation, Santa Clara, CA, 2012. For DIGITAL EQUALIZER PROGRAM AND WILLIAM J. CLINTON FELLOWSHIP PROGRAM.
$32,250 to Partners in School Innovation, San Francisco, CA, 2012. For FRANKLIN-MCKINLEY SCHOOL DISTRICT AND PARTNERS IN SCHOOL INNOVATION PARTNERSHIP.
$15,000 to Meals on Wheels and More, Austin, TX, 2012. For ADOPT-A-ROUTE SPONSORSHIP OF THE MEALS ON WHEELS PROGRAM.
$10,000 to Creative Action, Austin, TX, 2012. For TAP AFTER SCHOOL MANOR.

250
Aratani Foundation ✧
23505 Crenshaw Blvd., No. 230
Torrance, CA 90505-5223 (310) 530-9900
Contact: George T. Aratani, Pres.

Established in 1992 in CA.
Donors: George T. Aratani; Sakaye I. Aratani.
Foundation type: Independent foundation.
Financial data (yr. ended 12/31/12): Assets, $21,679,353 (M); expenditures, $1,698,120; qualifying distributions, $1,089,652; giving activities include $1,089,652 for 54 grants (high: $125,000; low: $125).
Purpose and activities: Giving primarily to Japanese-American cultural organizations.
Fields of interest: Museums; Education; Health care; Recreation; Religion.
Type of support: General/operating support; Continuing support; Income development; Management development/capacity building; Annual campaigns; Capital campaigns; Building/renovation; Endowments; Program development; Conferences/seminars; Seed money; Curriculum development; Fellowships; Scholarship funds; Exchange programs.
Limitations: Giving primarily in Los Angeles, CA. No grants to individuals.
Application information: Application outline is available. Application form not required.
Initial approach: Letter
Copies of proposal: 1
Deadline(s): None
Board meeting date(s): As needed
Officers: George T. Aratani, Pres.; Tetsuo Murata, V.P.; Sakaye I. Aratani, Secy.; Linda Y. Aratani, Treas.
Number of staff: 1 full-time professional; 3 full-time support.
EIN: 954377347

251
The Loreen Arbus Foundation ✧ ☆
8383 Wilshire Blvd., Ste. 240
Beverly Hills, CA 90211-2445

Established in 2004 in CA.
Donors: Loreen Arbus; Goldenson Arbus Foundation.
Foundation type: Independent foundation.
Financial data (yr. ended 12/31/13): Assets, $139,672 (M); gifts received, $632,000; expenditures, $719,773; qualifying distributions, $714,439; giving activities include $528,032 for 52 grants (high: $48,065; low: $100).
Purpose and activities: Giving primarily for medical research and for support for women in the arts, media, and business industries, with an emphasis on equity and workforce preparedness; funding also for the performing arts.
Fields of interest: Media, film/video; Media, television; Museums (specialized); Performing arts; Higher education; Health organizations, association; Medical research, institute; Cerebral palsy research; Cancer research; Human services; Disabilities, people with; Women.
Limitations: Applications not accepted. Giving primarily in Los Angeles, CA, Washington, DC, and New York, NY. No grants to individuals.
Application information: Unsolicited requests for funds not accepted.
Officers: Loreen Arbus, Pres.; Holly Toplitzky, Secy.-Treas.
EIN: 753126107

252
The Archer Family Foundation ✧ ☆
P.O. Box 757
San Jose, CA 95106-0757
Contact: Robert A. Archer, Pres.

Established in 2001 in CA.
Donor: Robert A. Archer.
Foundation type: Independent foundation.
Financial data (yr. ended 12/31/13): Assets, $1,082,859 (M); expenditures, $477,838; qualifying distributions, $468,210; giving activities

include $467,510 for 28 grants (high: $250,000; low: $10).
Purpose and activities: Giving to organizations that improve the quality of life for residents of CA.
Fields of interest: Health organizations; Agriculture/food; Human services.
Type of support: General/operating support.
Limitations: Applications accepted. Giving primarily in CA.
Application information: Application form not required.
Initial approach: Proposal
Deadline(s): None
Officer: Robert A. Archer, Pres.
EIN: 300010211

253
Archstone Foundation ✧
401 E. Ocean Blvd., Ste. 1000
Long Beach, CA 90802-4933 (562) 590-8655
Contact: Tanisha David MAG, Grants Mgr.
FAX: (562) 495-0317;
E-mail: archstone@archstone.org; Main URL: http://www.archstone.org
Grants Database: http://www.archstone.org/grants_info2340/grants_info.htm

Established in 1985 in CA; created as a result of the conversion of the nonprofit FHP health maintenance organization; status changed to a private foundation in 1998.
Foundation type: Independent foundation.
Financial data (yr. ended 06/30/13): Assets, $112,810,258 (M); expenditures, $5,442,180; qualifying distributions, $4,615,285; giving activities include $2,823,278 for 90 grants (high: $450,000; low: $5,000).
Purpose and activities: Giving toward the preparation of society in meeting the needs of an aging population. The majority of the foundation's resources are allocated to programs that address elder abuse prevention, fall prevention among the elderly, end-of-life issues, and emerging needs within the field of aging.
Fields of interest: Palliative care; Geriatrics; Gerontology; Aging.
Type of support: Program development; Conferences/seminars; Curriculum development; Technical assistance; Program evaluation.
Limitations: Applications accepted. Giving primarily in southern CA. No support for biomedical research. No grants to individuals, or for capital expenditures, or bricks and mortar, or building campaigns, endowments or for fundraising.
Publications: Application guidelines; Annual report (including application guidelines); Occasional report.
Application information: Full proposals are by invitation only, upon review of Letter of Inquiry. See foundation web site for specific guidelines and forms. Faxed proposals not accepted. Application form required.
Initial approach: Letter of Inquiry (no more than three pages) for Responsive Grantmaking
Copies of proposal: 1
Deadline(s): None for Responsive Grantmaking
Board meeting date(s): Quarterly
Final notification: Proposals submitted before the 15th of a given month will be reviewed during the following month; Quarterly, the foundation makes funding determinations
Officers and Directors:* Robert C. Maxson, Ed.D.*, Chair.; Joseph F. Prevratil,* C.E.O. and Pres.; Mary Ellen Kullman, V.P.; Diana Bonta; Lynn Daucher; Amye L. Leong; Hon. Renee B. Simon; Mark Douglas Smith, M.D.; Rahamin "Rocky" Suares; Peter C. Szutu.
Number of staff: 5 full-time professional; 2 full-time support.
EIN: 330133359

254
The Argyros Foundation ✧
949 S. Coast Dr., No. 600
Costa Mesa, CA 92626-7734 (714) 481-5000
Contact: Carol Campbell

Established in 1979 in CA.
Donors: George L. Argyros; The Argyros Charitable Trusts; GLA Foundation; HBI Financial Inc.
Foundation type: Independent foundation.
Financial data (yr. ended 07/31/13): Assets, $119,809,370 (M); gifts received, $15,698,556; expenditures, $13,991,580; qualifying distributions, $13,523,134; giving activities include $13,381,692 for 96 grants (high: $3,347,038; low: $250).
Purpose and activities: Giving primarily to arts and cultural programs, education, health care, youth development, and human services.
Fields of interest: Arts; Education; Eye research; Youth development, services; Children/youth, services; Marine science.
Type of support: Program development; Scholarship funds.
Limitations: Applications accepted. Giving primarily in Orange County, CA. No grants to individuals.
Application information: Requests for funding from organizations outside the Orange County, CA, area not considered.
Initial approach: Proposal
Deadline(s): June 1
Officers and Trustees:* George L. Argyros,* C.E.O.; Julie A. Argyros,* Pres.; Brent Law,* Secy.; Daniel Russo,* C.F.O.; Wendy Hales, Exec. Dir.; Chris Dubia; Stephanie Gehl; Lisa Mitchell.
EIN: 953421867
Selected grants: The following grants are a representative sample of this grantmaker's funding activity:
$3,331,081 to Eisenhower Medical Center Foundation, Rancho Mirage, CA, 2012.
$1,055,900 to South Coast Repertory Theater, Costa Mesa, CA, 2012.
$800,000 to University of California at Irvine Foundation, Irvine, CA, 2012.
$744,655 to Childrens Hospital of Orange County Foundation, Orange, CA, 2012.
$500,000 to Saint Andrews Presbyterian Church, Newport Beach, CA, 2012.
$489,802 to City of Hope, Duarte, CA, 2012.
$422,000 to Chapman University, Orange, CA, 2012.
$49,546 to Faith: An Endowment for Orthodoxy and Hellenism, New York, NY, 2012.
$40,000 to Pegasus School, Huntington Beach, CA, 2012.
$20,000 to Film Independent, Los Angeles, CA, 2012.

255
Arkay Foundation ✧
127 University Ave.
Berkeley, CA 94710-1616 (510) 841-4025
Contact: Benita Kline, Fdn. Mgr.
FAX: (510) 841-4093;
E-mail: info@arkayfoundation.org; Main URL: http://www.arkayfoundation.org

Established in 1995 in CA.
Donor: Stephen B. Kahn†.
Foundation type: Independent foundation.
Financial data (yr. ended 12/31/13): Assets, $25,380,906 (M); expenditures, $1,423,503; qualifying distributions, $1,325,493; giving activities include $1,077,000 for 105 grants (high: $100,000; low: $500).
Purpose and activities: Giving primarily to enhance democracy and to reduce the human impact on the environment.
Fields of interest: Environment, alliance/advocacy; Human services; Civil rights, voter education; Civil/human rights; Public affairs, citizen participation.
Type of support: General/operating support; Program development; Seed money; Research; Technical assistance.
Limitations: Applications not accepted. Giving on a national basis. No grants to individuals.
Application information: Contributes only to pre-selected organizations.
Board meeting date(s): Mar., Aug., and Dec.
Officers and Directors:* Marian Penn,* Pres.; Laura Flanagan,* Secy.; Susan Reed Clark,* Treas.; David M. Goldschmidt; Cecelia Hurwich, Ph.D.; Karen M. Kahn; Michael Kieschnick; William H. Soskin, Esq.
EIN: 770404924
Selected grants: The following grants are a representative sample of this grantmaker's funding activity:
$100,000 to Oil Change International, Washington, DC, 2012. For Separation of Oil and State.
$50,000 to Sierra Club Foundation, San Francisco, CA, 2012. For Democracy Initiative.
$37,500 to Rock the Vote, Washington, DC, 2012. For 2012 Civic Engagement and Education Activities.
$37,100 to San Francisco Film Society, San Francisco, CA, 2012. To support Inequality For All.
$30,000 to Proteus Fund, Amherst, MA, 2012. For Piper Fund.
$26,000 to Habitat Media, Portland, OR, 2012. For distribution of PRICELE$$.
$25,000 to Union of Concerned Scientists, Cambridge, MA, 2012. For Center for Science and Democracy.
$25,000 to Voter Participation Center, Washington, DC, 2012. For Voter Registration and Mobilization.
$5,000 to Global Fund for Women, San Francisco, CA, 2012. For granting to organizations working in Morocco.
$5,000 to Sierra Club Foundation, San Francisco, CA, 2012. For Beyond Oil Campaign.

256
The Roland and Dawn Arnall Foundation ✧
c/o Holthouse Carlin and Van Trigt LLP
11444 W. Olympic Blvd., 11th Fl.
Los Angeles, CA 90064-1500

Established in 2005 in CA.
Donors: Roland Arnall†; Dawn Arnall.
Foundation type: Independent foundation.

Financial data (yr. ended 01/31/13): Assets, $30,182 (M); expenditures, $19,710,994; qualifying distributions, $19,673,672; giving activities include $19,659,381 for 34 grants (high: $10,141,949; low: $200).
Purpose and activities: Giving primarily to Jewish organizations, as well as for human services.
Fields of interest: Education; Medical research, institute; Jewish federated giving programs; Jewish agencies & synagogues.
Limitations: Applications not accepted. Giving primarily in Los Angeles, CA and New York, NY. No grants to individuals.
Application information: Contributes only to pre-selected organizations.
Officers and Director:* Dawn Arnall,* Pres.; Lewis Greenblatt, Treas.
EIN: 202144658
Selected grants: The following grants are a representative sample of this grantmaker's funding activity:
$1,000 to California Art Club, Pasadena, CA, 2011.
$1,000 to Greater Los Angeles Zoo Association, Los Angeles, CA, 2011.

257
Red & Nancy Arnold Foundation ✧
7215 N. Dewey Ave.
Fresno, CA 93711-0657

Established in CA.
Donors: Robert Arnold; Nancy Arnold; Robert and Nancy Arnold Trust.
Foundation type: Independent foundation.
Financial data (yr. ended 06/30/13): Assets, $1,134,267 (M); gifts received, $443,805; expenditures, $1,000,633; qualifying distributions, $1,000,000; giving activities include $1,000,000 for 1 grant.
Fields of interest: Hospitals (general).
Limitations: Applications not accepted. Giving primarily in CA. No grants to individuals.
Application information: Contributes only to pre-selected organizations.
Officers: Jean Pennycook, Pres.; Sheila Holmes, Secy.-Treas.
EIN: 205376025

258
John & Hilda Arnold Foundation Inc. ✧ ☆
1888 Century Park E., No. 900
Los Angeles, CA 90025-6912

Established in 2003 in CA.
Donors: Thomas Arnold; John Arnold‡.
Foundation type: Independent foundation.
Financial data (yr. ended 12/31/13): Assets, $9,841,185 (M); expenditures, $717,127; qualifying distributions, $497,195; giving activities include $488,700 for 77 grants (high: $35,000; low: $1,500).
Fields of interest: Higher education; Education; Health care.
Type of support: General/operating support.
Limitations: Applications not accepted. Giving primarily in CA. No grants to individuals.
Application information: Contributes only to pre-selected organizations.
Officers and Directors:* Charles B. Baumer, Esq.,* Pres.; Stanley B. Schneider, C.P.A., C.F.O. and Secy.; Sedda Antekeian.
EIN: 200241446

259
Arntz Family Foundation ✧
(formerly Eugene S. Arntz Foundation)
P.O. Box 66488
Scotts Valley, CA 95067-6488
E-mail: nancy@arntzfamilyfoundation.org; Main URL: http://www.arntzfamilyfoundation.org

Established in 1994 in CA.
Donors: Eugene S. Arntz‡; K. Allan Arntz; Thomas E. Arntz; Donald M. Arntz; Arntz Builders Inc.
Foundation type: Independent foundation.
Financial data (yr. ended 09/30/13): Assets, $14,368,618 (M); expenditures, $707,266; qualifying distributions, $667,539; giving activities include $516,950 for grants.
Purpose and activities: The purpose of the foundation is to support environmental organizations, with an emphasis on those organizations that work toward systematic change and sustainability, particularly where the areas of environment and economic development come together.
Fields of interest: Environment.
International interests: Central America; Mexico.
Type of support: General/operating support; Program development.
Limitations: Applications not accepted. Giving primarily in CA. No grants to individuals.
Publications: Grants list.
Application information: Contributes only to pre-selected organizations. Unsolicited requests for funds not accepted. Proposal submissions are by invitation only.
Board meeting date(s): Feb. and July
Trustees: Donald M. Arntz; K. Allan Arntz; Thomas E. Arntz; Katherine J. Jones.
Number of staff: 1 part-time professional.
EIN: 686109096

260
Aroha Philanthropies ✧
(formerly The Michelson Foundation)
1660 Bush St., Ste. 300
San Francisco, CA 94109-5308 (415) 561-6540
Contact: Hector Melendez, Exec. Dir.
FAX: (415) 561-5477;
E-mail: hmelendez@pfs-llc.net; Main URL: http://www.arohaphilanthropies.org/

Established in 1991 in CA.
Foundation type: Independent foundation.
Financial data (yr. ended 12/31/13): Assets, $3,564,699 (M); expenditures, $1,543,727; qualifying distributions, $1,542,717; giving activities include $1,355,082 for 42 grants (high: $220,000; low: $300).
Purpose and activities: Giving primarily to performing arts education programs, particularly ones which expose children and youth to performing arts and link arts-based education with academic achievement; as well as to adult residential mental health programs that provide services to help clients regain independent living.
Fields of interest: Arts, formal/general education; Education, early childhood education; Education; Mental health/crisis services; Children/youth, services; Infants/toddlers; Children/youth; Adults; Economically disadvantaged.
Limitations: Applications not accepted. Giving limited to San Mateo, Santa Clara, and San Francisco counties, CA, and to the Twin Cities metropolitan area, MN. No support for sectarian religious purposes. No grants to individuals, or for annual appeals, deficit reduction, or conferences and events.
Publications: Grants list.
Application information: Unsolicited requests for funds currently not accepted; however would-be applicants should refer to the foundation web site for updates.
Board meeting date(s): Three times annually; see foundation web site for details
Officers: Ellen A. Michelson, Pres.; Susan P. Schoenthaler, Treas. and C.F.O.
Director: Michael W. Michelson.
EIN: 943131676

261
John Arrillaga Foundation ✧
2450 Watson Ct.
Palo Alto, CA 94303-3216 (650) 618-7000
Contact: John Arrillaga, Pres.

Established around 1978 in CA.
Donors: John Arrillaga; Imperial Promenade Assocs., LLC.
Foundation type: Independent foundation.
Financial data (yr. ended 12/31/13): Assets, $23,700,832 (M); expenditures, $1,219,771; qualifying distributions, $1,067,780; giving activities include $1,067,780 for 26 grants (high: $345,000; low: $72).
Fields of interest: Higher education; Health organizations, association; Human services.
Type of support: Continuing support; Program development.
Limitations: Giving primarily in CA, with emphasis on Menlo Park and Stanford.
Application information: Application form not required.
Initial approach: Letter
Deadline(s): None
Officers and Directors:* John Arrillaga,* Pres.; Laura Arrillaga,* Secy.; John Arrillaga, Jr.,* Treas.
EIN: 942460896

262
The Art of Renewal, Inc. ✧
P.O. Box 776
Point Reyes Station, CA 94956-0776

Established in CA.
Donors: Randy Weil Trust; C. Blitt; Q. Delaney; Sharon Weil.
Foundation type: Independent foundation.
Financial data (yr. ended 12/31/13): Assets, $500,911 (M); gifts received, $16,175; expenditures, $997,276; qualifying distributions, $997,264; giving activities include $794,859 for 52 grants (high: $30,000; low: $5,000).
Fields of interest: Education; Environment; Medical research.
Limitations: Applications not accepted. Giving primarily in CA.
Application information: Unsolicted requests for funds not accepted.

Officers: Sharon Weil Aaron, Pres.; Chela Blitt, V.P.; Eleanore Despina, Secy.; Bing Gong, Treas.
EIN: 264533781
Selected grants: The following grants are a representative sample of this grantmaker's funding activity:
$50,000 to Commonweal, Bolinas, CA, 2012. For Healing Arts Institute.
$20,000 to Earth Island Institute, Berkeley, CA, 2012. For Bay Localize.
$15,000 to Earth Island Institute, Berkeley, CA, 2012. For Project Survival.

263
AS&F Foundation ✧
(formerly Forest Lawn Foundation)
625 Fair Oaks Ave., Ste. 360
South Pasadena, CA 91030-5813 (626) 403-3283
Contact: Julie Lytle Nesbit, V.P. and Exec. Dir., Phil. Svcs., Whitter Trust Co.; Pegine Grayson, V.P., Phil. Svcs., Whitter Trust Co.
FAX: (626) 441-3672;
E-mail: JLytlenesbit@whittiertrust.com; Contact for Pegine Grayson, tel.: (626) 403-3282, fax: (626) 441-3672, e-mail: PGrayson@whittiertrust.com; Main URL: http://www.forestlawnfoundation.org

Incorporated in 1951 in CA.
Donors: Forest Lawn Co.; Hubert Eaton Estate Trust.
Foundation type: Independent foundation.
Financial data (yr. ended 12/31/12): Assets, $56,270,561 (M); expenditures, $3,549,436; qualifying distributions, $3,344,420; giving activities include $3,220,350 for 39 grants (high: $550,000; low: $5,000).
Purpose and activities: The foundation is primarily interested in providing grants to programs dedicated to youth and camping in Los Angeles and Orange Counties in CA. The foundation favors well-established, volunteer-driven organizations that are primarily supported by private donations.
Fields of interest: Recreation, camps; Boys & girls clubs; Boy scouts; Human services; YM/YWCAs & YM/YWHAs; Children/youth, services.
Type of support: General/operating support; Continuing support; Emergency funds; Program development; Matching/challenge support.
Limitations: Applications not accepted. Giving primarily in Los Angeles and Orange counties, CA. No support for federated appeals, political purposes, or projects or programs normally funded by the government, or arts and culture. No grants to individuals, or for endowment funds, or fundraising events.
Application information: Contributes only to pre-selected organizations.
Board meeting date(s): Quarterly
Officers: John Llewellyn, Chair.; Carol Llewellyn, Pres.; Susan Rule Sandler, Secy.; Russell T. Whittenberg, C.F.O.
Director: Darin B. Drabing.
EIN: 956030792

264
Atkinson Family Foundation ✧
6845 La Jolla Scenic Dr. S.
La Jolla, CA 92037-5738

Established in 1993 in CA.
Donors: Richard C. Atkinson; Rita L. Atkinson; Atkinson Family Trust.
Foundation type: Independent foundation.
Financial data (yr. ended 12/31/13): Assets, $18,909,396 (M); expenditures, $1,112,638; qualifying distributions, $952,540; giving activities include $950,075 for 22 grants (high: $323,625; low: $200).
Fields of interest: Arts; Education; Human services; Foundations (private grantmaking).
Limitations: Applications not accepted. Giving primarily in CA; some funding nationally. No grants to individuals.
Application information: Contributes only to pre-selected organizations.
Officers: Richard C. Atkinson, Pres.; Rita L. Atkinson, V.P. and Secy.-Treas.
EIN: 330564842
Selected grants: The following grants are a representative sample of this grantmaker's funding activity:
$184,155 to University of California at San Diego Foundation, La Jolla, CA, 2011. For general support.
$125,000 to Planned Parenthood, Boulder, CO, 2011. For general support.
$101,000 to Navy League of the United States, Doylestown, PA, 2011. For general support.
$100,000 to Athenaeum Music and Arts Library, La Jolla, CA, 2011. For general support.
$100,000 to United States Naval Academy Foundation, Annapolis, MD, 2011. For general support.
$100,000 to University of California at San Diego Foundation, La Jolla, CA, 2011. For general support.

265
Atkinson Foundation ✧
1720 S. Amphlett Blvd., Ste. 100
San Mateo, CA 94402-2710
Contact: Elizabeth H. Curtis, V.P., Admin.
E-mail: atkinfdn@aol.com; Tel./fax: (650) 357-1101; Main URL: http://www.atkinsonfdn.org

Incorporated in 1939 in CA.
Donors: George H. Atkinson†; Mildred M. Atkinson†.
Foundation type: Independent foundation.
Financial data (yr. ended 12/31/13): Assets, $20,203,827 (M); expenditures, $794,230; qualifying distributions, $622,407; giving activities include $503,840 for 96 grants (high: $18,000; low: $580).
Purpose and activities: Primary areas of interest include the disadvantaged and the homeless, child welfare, family planning, and the handicapped. Broad purposes are to help people reach their highest potential and to reach self-sufficiency. Giving for social services, including youth and the aged, education, family planning programs, and international development programs.
Fields of interest: Child development, education; Secondary school/education; Vocational education; Higher education; Adult education—literacy, basic skills & GED; Reproductive health, family planning; Substance abuse, services; Mental health/crisis services; AIDS; Alcoholism; Crime/violence prevention, youth; Food services; Human services; Children/youth, services; Child development, services; Family services; Aging, centers/services; Minorities/immigrants, centers/services; Homeless, human services; International economic development; Infants/toddlers; Children/youth; Youth; Adults; Aging; Disabilities, people with; Physically disabled; Mentally disabled; Minorities; Asians/Pacific Islanders; African Americans/Blacks; Hispanics/Latinos; Women; Offenders/ex-offenders; Substance abusers; Single parents; Crime/abuse victims; Immigrants/refugees; Economically disadvantaged; Homeless; Migrant workers; LGBTQ.
International interests: Central America; Mexico.
Type of support: General/operating support; Continuing support; Income development; Management development/capacity building; Program development; Seed money; Scholarship funds; Technical assistance.
Limitations: Applications accepted. Giving limited for the benefit of San Mateo County, CA, for social welfare, secondary schools, colleges, and church activities. Some international grantmaking (through U.S.-based nonprofit organizations) to benefit Mexico and Central America for technical assistance, population issues, economic development, and water and food resources. No support for sports groups, or national or statewide umbrella organizations. No grants to individuals directly (including scholarships), or for research or doctoral study, annual campaigns, travel to conferences or events, media presentations, or fundraising events; no loans.
Publications: Annual report (including application guidelines); Grants list.
Application information: Applications should include a grant proposal cover sheet, which is available online or from the foundation. Application form required.
Initial approach: Telephone
Copies of proposal: 1
Deadline(s): Feb. 1, May 1, Aug. 1, and Nov. 1
Board meeting date(s): Mar., June, Sept., and Dec.
Final notification: 2 months, maximum
Officers and Directors:* Linda L. Lanier,* Pres.; James R. Avedisian,* V.P., Fin. and Treas.; Elizabeth H. Curtis,* V.P., Admin.; Jean S. Atkinson,* Secy.; Olivia O. Aranda; Susan R. Atkinson; William W. Crandall, Jr.; John E. Herrell.
Number of staff: 1 full-time professional.
EIN: 946075613
Selected grants: The following grants are a representative sample of this grantmaker's funding activity:
$20,000 to Samaritan House, San Mateo, CA, 2012.
$12,500 to Shelter Network of San Mateo County, Burlingame, CA, 2012.
$10,000 to Puente de la Costa Sur, Pescadero, CA, 2012.
$8,000 to Planned Parenthood Mar Monte, San Jose, CA, 2012.
$7,500 to Pacifica School Volunteers, Pacifica, CA, 2012.
$7,500 to Senior Coastsiders, Half Moon Bay, CA, 2012.
$5,000 to Adolescent Counseling Services, Palo Alto, CA, 2012.
$5,000 to Pacific School of Religion, Berkeley, CA, 2012.
$5,000 to Plenty International, Summertown, TN, 2012.
$5,000 to Vida Verde Nature Education, San Gregorio, CA, 2012.
$3,500 to Trees, Water and People, Fort Collins, CO, 2012.
$2,500 to EcoLogic Development Fund, Cambridge, MA, 2012.

266
The Atlas Family Foundation ✧
(formerly Richard & Lezlie Atlas Foundation)
P.O. Box 25338
Los Angeles, CA 90025-0338
Contact: Janis Minton, Exec. Dir.; Casey Rogers, Assoc.
E-mail: Thejmint@janisminton.com; Main URL: http://www.atlasfamilyfoundation.org
GiveSmart: http://www.givesmart.org/Stories/Donors/Richard-Atlas

Established in 1985 in CA.
Donors: Richard S. Atlas; Lezlie Atlas.
Foundation type: Independent foundation.
Financial data (yr. ended 02/28/13): Assets, $1,127,331 (M); expenditures, $1,329,719; qualifying distributions, $1,314,051; giving activities include $1,122,731 for 64 grants (high: $100,000; low: $250).
Purpose and activities: Giving primarily for early childhood education, parenting education, and early child development, pre-natal to age 3, and vulnerable children and families in Los Angeles County, CA.
Fields of interest: Education, early childhood education; Child development, education; Mental health/crisis services; Child development, services.
Type of support: General/operating support; Continuing support; Management development/capacity building; Annual campaigns; Program development; Conferences/seminars; Curriculum development; Technical assistance; Consulting services; Program evaluation; Matching/challenge support.
Limitations: Applications not accepted. Giving primarily in Los Angeles County, CA. No grants to individuals, or for basic research, capital campaigns or legislation.
Application information: Contributes only to pre-selected organizations. Unsolicited requests for funds not considered. Letters of inquiry are by invitation only.
Board meeting date(s): Varies
Officer: Janis Milton, Exec. Dir.
Trustees: Lezlie Atlas; Richard S. Atlas; Michael G. O'Brien; Michelle Atlas O'Brien; Allison Atlas Tannenbaum; David Tannenbaum.
Number of staff: 3 part-time professional.
EIN: 942988629

267
The Elias, Genevieve and Georgianna Atol Charitable Trust ✧
6310 San Vicente Blvd., Ste. 250
Los Angeles, CA 90048-5447

Established in 2008 in CA.
Donor: Genevieve Atol†.
Foundation type: Independent foundation.
Financial data (yr. ended 06/30/13): Assets, $12,693,822 (M); expenditures, $763,825; qualifying distributions, $657,500; giving activities include $657,500 for grants.
Fields of interest: Higher education; Medical research, institute; Human services.
Limitations: Applications not accepted. Giving primarily in CA.
Application information: Contributes only to pre-selected organizations.
Trustees: Frank Lee; Kerri Lee, OD.
EIN: 516590472

Selected grants: The following grants are a representative sample of this grantmaker's funding activity:
$200,000 to Bar-Ilan University in Israel, Beverly Hills, CA, 2011.

268
Attias Family Foundation ✧
10100 Santa Monica Blvd., Ste. 1050
Los Angeles, CA 90067-4143

Established in 2004 in CA.
Foundation type: Independent foundation.
Financial data (yr. ended 12/31/13): Assets, $8,519,749 (M); expenditures, $517,196; qualifying distributions, $470,292; giving activities include $470,292 for 39 grants (high: $120,000; low: $350).
Fields of interest: Arts; Education; Medical research; Human services; Foundations (community).
Limitations: Applications not accepted. Giving primarily in CA, DC, and NY. No grants to individuals.
Application information: Contributes only to pre-selected organizations.
Officers: Elaine Attias, C.E.O.; Jane Attias, V.P.; Daniel R. Attias, C.F.O; Diana Attias, Secy.
EIN: 113737518
Selected grants: The following grants are a representative sample of this grantmaker's funding activity:
$1,000 to Cherish Our Children International, Houston, TX, 2012. To Support Organization's Charitable Purpose.

269
The Auen Foundation ✧ ☆
(formerly The Auen-Bergen Foundation)
P.O. Box 13390
Palm Desert, CA 92255-3390
Main URL: http://www.auenfoundation.org/

Established in 1992 in CA.
Donor: H.N. and Frances C. Berger Foundation.
Foundation type: Independent foundation.
Financial data (yr. ended 12/31/13): Assets, $36,392,922 (M); expenditures, $2,498,520; qualifying distributions, $1,080,825; giving activities include $463,000 for 46 grants (high: $50,000; low: $500).
Purpose and activities: The foundation primarily supports innovative programs that enrich the quality of life for the elderly and aging, with a focus on intergenerational involvement, healthy aging, quality end of life, and care giving issues.
Fields of interest: Arts; Higher education; Education; Health care; Substance abuse, treatment; Health organizations, association; AIDS research; Human services; Aging, centers/services; Aging.
Type of support: General/operating support; Equipment; Program-related investments/loans; Matching/challenge support.
Limitations: Applications not accepted. Giving primarily in CA; eighty percent of the foundation's grantees are located in southern CA; twenty percent may be considered from outside of the foundation's area, only if they are proposals solicited by the foundation trustees. No grants to individuals.
Application information: Unsolicited requests for funds not accepted.
Trustee: Ronald M. Auen.
EIN: 954325051

270
Autry Foundation ✧
4383 Colfax Ave.
Studio City, CA 91604-2837 (818) 752-7770
Contact: Jacqueline Autry, Pres. and Dir.

Established in 1974 in CA.
Donors: Gene Autry†; Jacqueline Autry.
Foundation type: Independent foundation.
Financial data (yr. ended 12/31/13): Assets, $17,682,365 (M); expenditures, $801,691; qualifying distributions, $766,570; giving activities include $766,410 for 18 grants (high: $600,000; low: $810).
Purpose and activities: Giving primarily for a hospital and human services.
Fields of interest: Arts; Hospitals (general); Health organizations; Human services; Homeless, human services.
Limitations: Applications accepted. Giving primarily in the Los Angeles, CA, area, and Riverside and Orange counties. No grants to individuals.
Application information: Application form required.
Initial approach: Letter on organization's letterhead
Copies of proposal: 1
Deadline(s): None
Board meeting date(s): Varies
Officers and Directors:* Jacqueline Autry,* Pres.; Joanne D. Hale,* V.P.; Maxine Hansen, Secy.; Stanley B. Schneider,* Treas.; Karla Buhlman; David W. Cartwright.
EIN: 237433359

271
The Avant! Foundation ✧
4320 Stevens Creek Blvd., Ste. 168
San Jose, CA 95129-1281 (408) 551-0322
FAX: (408) 551-0324;
E-mail: info@avantifoundation.org; Additional tel.: (408) 737-7168

Established in 1998 in CA.
Donor: Avant! Corp.
Foundation type: Company-sponsored foundation.
Financial data (yr. ended 12/31/12): Assets, $2,000,530 (M); expenditures, $661,339; qualifying distributions, $608,567; giving activities include $343,386 for 16 grants (high: $60,000; low: $500), and $102,051 for 22 grants to individuals (high: $10,449; low: $532).
Purpose and activities: The foundation supports programs designed to promote education; improve the lives of disadvantaged individuals; and provide financial assistance for college tuition and expenses.
Fields of interest: Higher education; Education; Economically disadvantaged.
Type of support: General/operating support; Program development; Scholarships—to individuals.
Limitations: Applications not accepted. Giving limited to CA.
Application information: Contributes only to pre-selected organizations and individuals.
Directors: Kamne M. Thomas, Exec. Dir.; Jayne Booker; Charles St. Clair; Reginald Swilley.
EIN: 943290664

272
Avery Dennison Foundation ✧
(formerly Avery International Foundation)
150 N. Orange Grove Blvd.
Pasadena, CA 91103-3534 (626) 304-2000
Contact: Alicia Procello Maddox, Pres. and Exec. Dir.
E-mail: AveryDennison.Foundation@averydennison.com; Main URL: http://www.averydennison.com/avy/en_us/Sustainability/Community

Established in 1977.
Donor: Avery Dennison Corp.
Foundation type: Company-sponsored foundation.
Financial data (yr. ended 12/31/13): Assets, $26,697,523 (M); gifts received, $10,000,000; expenditures, $1,171,569; qualifying distributions, $928,568; giving activities include $849,464 for 31 grants (high: $212,600; low: $1,720).
Purpose and activities: The foundation supports programs designed to promote education and environmental sustainability.
Fields of interest: Visual arts; Visual arts, design; Elementary/secondary education; Vocational education; Higher education; Environment, waste management; Environment, recycling; Environment, natural resources; Environment, water resources; Environment, energy; Environment, forests; Environment; Youth, services; Business/industry; Community/economic development; United Ways and Federated Giving Programs; Mathematics; Engineering/technology; Science; Economically disadvantaged.
Type of support: Continuing support; General/operating support; Program development; Curriculum development; Scholarship funds; Employee volunteer services; Employee matching gifts.
Limitations: Applications accepted. Giving primarily in areas of company operations, with emphasis on CA, Brazil, China, and India. No support for discriminatory organizations, for-profit organizations or ventures, government agencies, service clubs or veterans' or fraternal organizations, churches or religious organizations, private foundations, political organizations or candidates, or United Way-supported organizations (over 30 percent of budget). No grants to individuals, or for conferences, fundraisers, or special events, sponsorships, institutional endowments, beauty or talent contests, political activities, or general operating support for hospitals.
Publications: Application guidelines; Grants list; Occasional report.
Application information: Support is limited to 1 contribution per organization during any given year. Multi-year funding is not automatic. Application form required.
Initial approach: Complete online application
Deadline(s): None
Final notification: 3 to 6 months
Officers: Alicia Procello Maddox, Pres. and Exec. Dir.; Kim Caldwell, V.P.; Judy Abelman, V.P.; David N. Edwards, V.P.; Anne Hill, V.P.; Kim Macaulay, V.P.; Karyn E. Rodriguez, V.P.; Raj Srinivasan, V.P.; Judith K. Gain, Treas.
Number of staff: 1 full-time professional.
EIN: 953251844

273
Avery-Tsui Foundation ✧
5075 Ruffin Rd., Ste. A
San Diego, CA 92123-4684

Established in 2004 in CA.
Donor: The R. Stanton Avery Foundation.
Foundation type: Independent foundation.
Financial data (yr. ended 12/31/13): Assets, $30,234,130 (M); expenditures, $7,598,646; qualifying distributions, $7,278,753; giving activities include $6,934,743 for 16+ grants (high: $6,000,000).
Fields of interest: Higher education; Human services; Foundations (public); Foundations (community).
Limitations: Applications not accepted. Giving primarily in CA; some funding also in OH. No grants to individuals.
Application information: Contributes only to pre-selected organizations.
Officers and Directors:* Sally Tsui Wong-Avery,* C.E.O. and Pres.; Tom Hom,* V.P. and C.F.O.; Natasha Wong,* Secy.
EIN: 656431837
Selected grants: The following grants are a representative sample of this grantmaker's funding activity:
$855,000 to Fidelity Charitable Gift Fund, Boston, MA, 2011.
$20,000 to San Pasqual Academy Foundation, San Diego, CA, 2011. For general support.
$10,000 to University of Arizona Foundation, Tucson, AZ, 2011.

274
The Avis Family Foundation ✧
c/o CTC myCFO, LLC
P.O. Box 10195
Palo Alto, CA 94303-0995

Established in 2000 in CA.
Donors: Anne R. Avis; Gregory M. Avis.
Foundation type: Independent foundation.
Financial data (yr. ended 12/31/13): Assets, $32,230,847 (M); gifts received, $4,073,031; expenditures, $1,748,586; qualifying distributions, $1,604,830; giving activities include $1,584,830 for 5 grants (high: $933,333; low: $697).
Purpose and activities: Giving primarily for a charitable gift fund; funding also for education and a public radio organization.
Fields of interest: Media, radio; Education; Foundations (public).
Limitations: Applications not accepted. Giving in the U.S., with emphasis on Washington, DC, MA, and Cincinnati, OH. No grants to individuals.
Application information: Contributes only to pre-selected organizations.
Officers: Gregory M. Avis, Pres.; Emily R. Avis, C.F.O.; Anne R. Avis, V.P.; Charles D. Avis, Secy.
EIN: 770546893

275
James B. Ax Family Foundation ✧
P.O. Box 1144
La Jolla, CA 92038-1144

Established in 2006 in CA.
Foundation type: Independent foundation.
Financial data (yr. ended 09/30/13): Assets, $4,241,757 (M); expenditures, $606,296; qualifying distributions, $555,495; giving activities include $555,000 for 4 grants (high: $350,000; low: $20,000).
Fields of interest: Higher education; Health care; Medical research.
Limitations: Applications not accepted. Giving primarily in CA.
Application information: Unsolicited requests for funds not accepted.
Officers and Directors:* Brian Keating,* Pres. and C.E.O.; Sarah Beth Price Keating,* C.F.O. and Secy.
EIN: 204977370
Selected grants: The following grants are a representative sample of this grantmaker's funding activity:
$35,000 to Museum of Mathematics, New York, NY, 2013. For funding for the Exhibit Wall of Fire.

276
The Ayrshire Foundation ✧
301 E. Colorado Blvd., No. 802
Pasadena, CA 91101-1917
Contact: Margaret G. Boyer, Pres.
FAX: (626) 795-7689;
E-mail: info@AyrshireFoundation.org; Main URL: http://www.ayrshirefoundation.org

Established in 1998 in CA.
Donor: James N. Gamble†.
Foundation type: Independent foundation.
Financial data (yr. ended 05/31/13): Assets, $19,625,984 (M); expenditures, $1,256,027; qualifying distributions, $1,158,517; giving activities include $1,076,000 for 16 grants (high: $200,000; low: $26,000).
Purpose and activities: Giving primarily for health care, including a hospital, and a cancer center; some giving also for education, the arts, and youth and social services.
Fields of interest: Arts; Education; Environment; Health care; Children/youth, services; Community/economic development; Children/youth; Youth; Aging; Young adults; Disabilities, people with; Mentally disabled; Women.
Type of support: Capital campaigns; Building/renovation; Equipment; Land acquisition; Endowments; Program development; Conferences/seminars; Professorships; Film/video/radio; Seed money; Scholarship funds; Matching/challenge support.
Limitations: Applications accepted. Giving primarily in Pasadena, San Francisco, and Sonoma, CA; giving also in the Petoskey/Harbor Springs, MI, area. No grants to individuals, or for continuing support.
Publications: Annual report; Grants list.
Application information: Following inquiry, an organization may receive a request for proposal from the foundation. Unsolicited requests or proposals are not accepted. Organizations with which Ayrshire board members have some personal involvement are given priority. Application form required.
Initial approach: Inquire through foundation web site before sending an application
Copies of proposal: 1
Deadline(s): Mar. 15 and Sept. 15
Board meeting date(s): May and Oct.
Final notification: One month or less
Officers and Directors:* Margaret G. Boyer,* Pres.; Tracy G. Hirrel,* V.P.; Peter S. Boyer, Secy.; Richard J. Hirrel,* Treas.
Number of staff: 1 full-time professional.
EIN: 954690418

277
J.W. Bagley Foundation ✧
741 Panchita Way
Los Altos, CA 94022-1518

Established in 1994 in TX.
Donors: James W. Bagley; Mark C. Bagley; Teri Bagley; Kimberly Grant.
Foundation type: Independent foundation.
Financial data (yr. ended 12/31/13): Assets, $10,852,600 (M); gifts received, $27,500; expenditures, $608,756; qualifying distributions, $608,756; giving activities include $599,806 for 26 grants (high: $50,000; low: $5,686).
Purpose and activities: Giving primarily for education.
Fields of interest: Education, single organization support; Elementary school/education; Higher education; Health organizations; Human services; United Ways and Federated Giving Programs.
Limitations: Applications not accepted. Giving primarily in CA, MS and TX. No grants to individuals.
Application information: Contributes only to pre-selected organizations.
Officers: Mark C. Bagley, Pres.; Sharon B. Wax, V.P.; Rocky Picasso, Secy.; Susan D. Huurman, Treas.
Trustees: James W. Bagley; Jean A. Bagley.
EIN: 742738464
Selected grants: The following grants are a representative sample of this grantmaker's funding activity:
$15,500 to Harlem Childrens Zone, New York, NY, 2011. For general support.
$15,500 to Joslin Diabetes Center, Boston, MA, 2011. For general support.
$13,500 to Foothill-De Anza Community Colleges Foundation, Los Altos Hills, CA, 2010. For general support.
$13,500 to Samaritan House, San Mateo, CA, 2010. For general support.
$13,500 to Tutwiler Clinic, Tutwiler, MS, 2010. For general support.
$12,500 to Dallas Hearing Foundation, Dallas, TX, 2011. For general support.
$12,500 to Fairhill School, Dallas, TX, 2011. For general support.
$12,000 to Providence Saint Mel School, Chicago, IL, 2011. For general support.
$5,000 to Piney Woods School, Piney Woods, MS, 2011. For general support.

278
Gerson Bakar Foundation ✧
1 Lombard St., Ste. 202
San Francisco, CA 94111-1128

Established in 1984 in CA.
Donor: Gerson Bakar.
Foundation type: Independent foundation.
Financial data (yr. ended 12/31/13): Assets, $83,055,776 (M); gifts received, $16,233,544; expenditures, $3,223,789; qualifying distributions, $2,838,262; giving activities include $2,565,599 for grants.
Fields of interest: Museums (art); Higher education; Education; Animals/wildlife; Health organizations, association; Human services; United Ways and Federated Giving Programs; Science; Jewish agencies & synagogues.
Limitations: Applications not accepted. Giving primarily in the San Francisco Bay Area, CA. No grants to individuals.
Application information: Contributes only to pre-selected organizations.
Officers and Directors:* Barbara Bass Bakar,* Chair. and Pres.; Gerson Baker, Exec. V.P.; Ted Dienstfrey, Secy.; Nalraj Goundar, Treas.; Anne Bakar; Phyllis Cook; Nanci Fredkin; Richard L. Greene; Kathleen McCormick.
EIN: 942949602

279
R. C. Baker Foundation ✧ ☆
c/o ACA Nonprofit Public Benefit Corp.
330 Encinitas Blvd., Ste. 101
Encinitas, CA 92024-3723 (760) 632-3600
Contact: Frank Laurence Scott, Jr.

Foundation type: Independent foundation.
Financial data (yr. ended 12/31/13): Assets, $21,414,388 (M); expenditures, $1,259,306; qualifying distributions, $1,035,931; giving activities include $969,774 for 2+ grants (high: $966,755).
Application information: Application form required.
Initial approach: Letter
Deadline(s): May 1 and Oct. 1
Officers: F. Laurence Scott, Pres.; Ronald Turner, V.P.; Dennis Cronin, Treas.
Directors: James Benedict; Robert Cristiano; James McMillan; Brain Scott.
Trustee: Dickra Semerdjian.
EIN: 453850225

280
The Baker Street Foundation ✧
135 Main St., Ste. 1140
San Francisco, CA 94105-1815

Established in 1993 in CA.
Donor: Mary M. Miner.
Foundation type: Independent foundation.
Financial data (yr. ended 12/31/13): Assets, $86,004,218 (M); gifts received, $6,785,500; expenditures, $6,169,236; qualifying distributions, $5,603,491; giving activities include $5,565,000 for 60 grants (high: $1,100,000; low: $5,000).
Purpose and activities: Giving primarily for the arts and education.
Fields of interest: Performing arts, ballet; Performing arts, theater; Arts; Education; Human services.
Limitations: Applications not accepted. Giving primarily in San Francisco, CA. No grants to individuals.
Application information: Contributes only to pre-selected organizations.
Officers and Directors:* Mary M. Miner,* Pres.; Helen Sedwick,* Secy.; Roy Bukstein,* C.F.O.; Justine Miner; Luke Miner; Nicola Miner.
EIN: 943192365

281
The Bandai Foundation ✧
5551 Katella Ave.
Cypress, CA 90630-5002

Established in 1995 in CA.
Foundation type: Operating foundation.
Financial data (yr. ended 12/31/13): Assets, $8,014,838 (M); expenditures, $473,887; qualifying distributions, $428,507; giving activities include $424,005 for 55 grants (high: $62,500; low: $200).
Purpose and activities: The foundation is focusing their resources on children's issues, particularly for the benefit of children with AIDS.
Fields of interest: AIDS; Children/youth, services.
Limitations: Applications not accepted. Giving primarily in CA, Washington, DC and NY.
Application information: Contributes only to pre-selected organizations.
Officers and Directors:* Akihiro Sato, Co-Chair.; Masayuki Matsuo,* Co-Chair.; Cynthia Nishimoto,* Secy.; Paul Hausback,* Treas.
EIN: 330655933
Selected grants: The following grants are a representative sample of this grantmaker's funding activity:
$13,000 to Global Operations and Development, Buena Park, CA, 2012. For Help in Alleviating Poverty.
$10,000 to American Diabetes Association, Costa Mesa, CA, 2012. To Prevent and Cure Diabetes and Improve Lives of People Affected By Diabetes.
$10,000 to City of Hope, Los Angeles, CA, 2012. To Help Research, Treatment and Education on Cancer.
$8,950 to Boy Scouts of America, Long Beach Area Council, Long Beach, CA, 2012. For a Program for Young People That Trains Them in the Responsibilities of Participating.
$8,550 to American Red Cross, Santa Ana, CA, 2012. For domestic disaster relief.
$6,500 to Children of the Night, Van Nuys, CA, 2012. To Rescue America's Children from Prostitution.
$4,000 to Pediatric Therapy Network, Torrance, CA, 2012. To Enhance Children's Individual Capabilities and Foster Their Independence.
$3,500 to Taking the Reins, Los Angeles, CA, 2012. To Inspires Underserved Girls Facing the Challenges of Adolescence in High Risk Environments.
$2,500 to Hands Extended Loving People, Ludington, MI, 2012. For basic human needs for people in need.

282
The Coeta and Donald Barker Foundation ✧
(formerly The Donald R. Barker Foundation)
P.O. Box 936
Rancho Mirage, CA 92270-0936 (760) 340-1162

Established in 1977 in OR.
Donors: Coeta Barker†; Donald R. Barker†.
Foundation type: Independent foundation.
Financial data (yr. ended 11/30/13): Assets, $22,743,023 (M); expenditures, $1,202,545; qualifying distributions, $928,650; giving activities include $928,650 for 58 grants (high: $212,000; low: $300).
Purpose and activities: Giving primarily for educational, cultural, health care and social services.
Fields of interest: Arts; Secondary school/education; Higher education; Environment, natural resources; Environment; Hospitals (general); Health care; Mental health/crisis services; Health organizations, association; Heart & circulatory diseases; Medical research, institute; Heart & circulatory research; Children/youth, services; Family services; Community/economic development; Disabilities, people with.

Type of support: General/operating support; Continuing support; Equipment; Endowments; Emergency funds; Program development; Scholarship funds.
Limitations: Applications not accepted. Giving limited to CA and OR. No support for sectarian religious purposes, or for agencies that rely on federal or tax dollars for their principal support. No grants to individuals or for conferences, or operational deficits.
Application information: Unsolicited requests for funds not accepted.
Board meeting date(s): May and Oct.
Officer: Nancy G. Harris, Pres.
Trustees: John D. Brennan; Jon V. Buerstatte; Dennis Healey; Dana E. Newquist; James W. Richards.
Number of staff: 1 full-time professional; 1 part-time support.
EIN: 930698411

283
Douglas E. and Nancy J. Barnhart Charitable Foundation ✧ ☆
10805 Thornmint Rd., Ste. 200
San Diego, CA 92127-2429

Established in CA.
Donors: Douglas E. Barnhart; Nancy J. Barnhart.
Foundation type: Independent foundation.
Financial data (yr. ended 12/31/13): Assets, $793,642 (M); gifts received, $500,000; expenditures, $524,407; qualifying distributions, $517,401; giving activities include $515,500 for 6 grants (high: $225,000; low: $500).
Fields of interest: Hospitals (general); Health care.
Limitations: Applications not accepted. Giving primarily in CA and TX.
Application information: Contributes only to pre-selected organizations.
Officers: Douglas E. Barnhart, Pres.; Tamela Reese, Secy.; Nancy J. Barnhart, Treas.
Directors: Fr. Daniel Friedman; West Reese; Eric G. Stenman.
EIN: 262997243
Selected grants: The following grants are a representative sample of this grantmaker's funding activity:
$50,000 to Sharp Healthcare Foundation, San Diego, CA, 2012. For Health Care, Clinical Research, and Education.

284
Richard Allan Barry Charitable Foundation ✧ ☆
11601 Wilshire Blvd.
Los Angeles, CA 90025-0509

Established in 2000 in MA.
Donor: Richard Allen Barry.
Foundation type: Independent foundation.
Financial data (yr. ended 12/31/13): Assets, $10,053,500 (M); expenditures, $521,847; qualifying distributions, $521,847; giving activities include $455,000 for 6 grants (high: $250,000; low: $5,000).
Purpose and activities: Giving primarily for medical research and human services.
Fields of interest: Media, radio; Parkinson's disease; Autism; Medical research, institute; Human services; Foundations (private grantmaking).
Limitations: Applications not accepted. Giving primarily in CA and MA. No grants to individuals.
Application information: Contributes only to pre-selected organizations.
Trustee: Richard Allen Barry.
EIN: 046920279

285
Barth Family Foundation ✧
433 N. Camden Dr., Ste. 1070
Beverly Hills, CA 90210-4434

Established in 2001 in CA.
Donor: Robert Barth.
Foundation type: Independent foundation.
Financial data (yr. ended 12/31/13): Assets, $3,613,460 (M); expenditures, $491,185; qualifying distributions, $492,966; giving activities include $492,966 for 16 grants (high: $200,000; low: $800).
Purpose and activities: Giving primarily for higher education and human services; funding also for a children's hospital.
Fields of interest: Higher education; Hospitals (specialty); Human services; Children/youth, services.
Limitations: Applications not accepted. Giving primarily in MA. No grants to individuals.
Application information: Unsolicited requests for funds not accepted.
Officers: Robert Barth, Pres.; Suzanne Barth, Secy.
EIN: 912171985

286
The Bartman Foundation ✧
11777 San Vicente Blvd., Ste. 600
Los Angeles, CA 90049-5026

Established in 1969 in CA.
Donors: N. Bartman‡; Cecile C. Bartman; John Bartman; David Bartman.
Foundation type: Independent foundation.
Financial data (yr. ended 12/31/13): Assets, $3,978,389 (M); gifts received, $21,787; expenditures, $545,923; qualifying distributions, $500,546; giving activities include $499,050 for 91 grants (high: $50,000; low: $200).
Purpose and activities: Giving primarily for the arts, as well as for higher education and social services.
Fields of interest: Arts; Higher education; Education; Health care; Health organizations, association; Cancer research; Human services; Children/youth, services; Foundations (private grantmaking); Jewish agencies & synagogues; Blind/visually impaired.
Limitations: Applications not accepted. Giving primarily in AZ and CA. No grants to individuals.
Application information: Contributes only to pre-selected organizations.
Trustee: Cecile C. Bartman.
EIN: 237005283
Selected grants: The following grants are a representative sample of this grantmaker's funding activity:
$12,500 to Stanford University, Law School, Stanford, CA, 2012. For general.

287
Evalyn M. Bauer Foundation ✧
(formerly M. R. Bauer Foundation)
1 World Trade Center, No. 1280
Long Beach, CA 90831-1280

Established in 1955 in IL; reorganized in 1995 in CA.
Donors: M.R. Bauer‡; Evalyn M. Bauer‡.
Foundation type: Independent foundation.
Financial data (yr. ended 12/31/13): Assets, $32,271,603 (M); expenditures, $1,757,392; qualifying distributions, $1,583,300; giving activities include $1,386,000 for 79 grants (high: $205,000; low: $500).
Purpose and activities: Giving primarily for the arts, education, children, youth and social services, and to Roman Catholic churches.
Fields of interest: Performing arts; Arts; Higher education; Hospitals (general); Boys & girls clubs; Human services; YM/YWCAs & YM/YWHAs; Children/youth, services; Foundations (community); Catholic agencies & churches.
Type of support: General/operating support; Professorships; Research.
Limitations: Applications not accepted. Giving primarily in CA. No grants to individuals.
Application information: Unsolicited requests for funds not accepted.
Officers and Directors:* Loraine S. Ackerman,* Pres.; Nancy Gains,* C.F.O. and Secy.; Lee Ackerman,* V.P.
EIN: 330669419
Selected grants: The following grants are a representative sample of this grantmaker's funding activity:
$176,000 to California Community Foundation, Los Angeles, CA, 2012. For Donor Advised Fund Discretionary.
$30,000 to Bishop Museum, Honolulu, HI, 2012. For general purposes, discretionary.
$5,000 to Long Beach Bar Foundation, Long Beach, CA, 2012. For Shortstop-Juvenile Crime Diversion Program.
$1,000 to Special Olympics Southern California, Long Beach, CA, 2012. For general purposes discretionary.

288
The Donald E. and Delia B. Baxter Foundation ✧
7915 Via Callendo
Carlsbad, CA 92009-8635

Incorporated in 1959 in CA.
Donor: Delia B. Baxter.
Foundation type: Independent foundation.
Financial data (yr. ended 12/31/13): Assets, $22,341,223 (M); expenditures, $1,276,362; qualifying distributions, $983,132; giving activities include $893,546 for 3 grants (high: $435,546; low: $158,000).
Purpose and activities: Giving primarily to educational and scientific institutions for research and development of medicine, instruments, and fluids for alleviating pain and protecting and prolonging human life.
Fields of interest: Medical school/education; Scholarships/financial aid; Medical research, institute.
Type of support: Building/renovation; Professorships; Fellowships; Scholarship funds; Research.

Limitations: Applications not accepted. Giving primarily in CA and KY. No grants to individuals.
Application information: Grants initiated by the foundation's board. Unsolicited requests for funds not accepted.
Officers: Donald B. Haake, Pres.; Jane Haake Russell, V.P.; James Russell, Secy.; Richard H. Haake, Treas.
Directors: Marla Elliott; Martha Elizabeth Haake; William Haake.
EIN: 956029555

289
BayTree Fund ✧
44 E. Foothill Blvd., Ste. 100
Arcadia, CA 91006-2305

Established in 2004 in CA.
Donor: The R. Stanton Avery Foundation.
Foundation type: Independent foundation.
Financial data (yr. ended 12/31/13): Assets, $37,401,473 (M); gifts received, $694,026; expenditures, $2,951,787; qualifying distributions, $2,618,668; giving activities include $2,465,767 for 22 grants (high: $750,000; low: $2,212).
Fields of interest: Historic preservation/historical societies; Higher education; Education; Environment; Food banks; Foundations (private grantmaking); Social sciences.
Limitations: Applications not accepted. Giving primarily in CA, MA, and Washington, DC. No grants to individuals.
Application information: Contributes only to pre-selected organizations.
Officers and Director:* Judith Avery,* Pres.; John Lewis, Secy.-Treas.
EIN: 260084354
Selected grants: The following grants are a representative sample of this grantmaker's funding activity:
$169,000 to Library Foundation of Los Angeles, Los Angeles, CA, 2012. For Innovation Leadership.
$150,000 to Fidelity Charitable Gift Fund, Boston, MA, 2012. For Dickinson Charitable Gift Fund.
$10,000 to People for the American Way, Washington, DC, 2012. For Yp4/Yeo Network.

290
BCM Foundation ✧
8152 Painter Ave., Ste. 201
Whittier, CA 90602-3757 (562) 696-0338
Contact: James D. Shepard, Tr.; Karen P. Shepard, Managing Tr.
FAX: (562) 698-5508; E-mail: jbcm1897@gmail.com

Established in 2008 in CA.
Foundation type: Independent foundation.
Financial data (yr. ended 12/31/13): Assets, $52,655,514 (M); expenditures, $2,958,739; qualifying distributions, $2,861,531; giving activities include $2,647,521 for 33 grants (high: $400,058; low: $5,000).
Fields of interest: Higher education; Human services; Children/youth, services.
Limitations: Applications accepted. Giving primarily in CA, with emphasis on Whittier.
Application information: Unsolicited grant applications are not accepted prior to initial concept paper.
Initial approach: Concept paper (2 to 3 pages only)
Copies of proposal: 1
Deadline(s): None
Final notification: 2-3 months
Trustees: James D. Shepard; Karen P. Shepard.
EIN: 262667384
Selected grants: The following grants are a representative sample of this grantmaker's funding activity:
$400,000 to Whole Child International, Los Angeles, CA, 2011.
$100,000 to Los Angeles Center for Alcohol and Drug Abuse, Santa Fe Springs, CA, 2011.

291
Beagle Charitable Foundation ✧☆
c/o Brian Kuehnis, CPA
P.O. Box 6978
Redwood City, CA 94063

Established in 1999 in WA.
Donor: Joy D. Covey.
Foundation type: Independent foundation.
Financial data (yr. ended 12/31/13): Assets, $7,314,109 (M); expenditures, $532,616; qualifying distributions, $422,749; giving activities include $420,999 for 4+ grants (high: $415,000).
Purpose and activities: Giving primarily for wildlife and environmental conservation.
Fields of interest: Education; Environment, natural resources; Environment; Animals/wildlife; Foundations (community); Jewish agencies & synagogues.
Limitations: Applications not accepted. Giving on a national basis. No grants to individuals.
Application information: Contributes only to pre-selected organizations.
Officer: Lisa Berglund, Pres.
EIN: 770529181

292
The Beaver Foundation ✧
c/o Knox Ricksen, LLP
1 Kaiser Pl., No. 1101
Oakland, CA 94612-1427

Established in 1969 in CA.
Donor: Wallace W. Knox†.
Foundation type: Independent foundation.
Financial data (yr. ended 12/31/13): Assets, $11,762,485 (M); expenditures, $1,035,970; qualifying distributions, $869,947; giving activities include $805,750 for 9 grants (high: $324,750; low: $6,000).
Fields of interest: Education; Boys & girls clubs; Girls.
Type of support: General/operating support; Continuing support; Building/renovation.
Limitations: Applications not accepted. Giving primarily in CA. No grants to individuals.
Application information: Contributes only to pre-selected organizations.
Officers: Philbrick Bowhay, Pres.; Robert G. Allen, V.P.; John C. Ricksen, V.P.; William C. Robbins III, V.P.
EIN: 941682883

293
Beavers Charitable Trust ✧
2053 Grant Rd.
PMB 370
Los Altos, CA 94024-6913 (650) 694-4834
FAX: (650) 694-4836; E-mail: info@thebeavers.org; Main URL: http://www.thebeavers.org/trust.php

Established in 1977 in CA.
Donors: Homer Olsen; Willis North America, Inc.; Tutor-Saliba; Traylor Brothers, Inc.; S & W Scott Foundation; Livorna Investments; Lamberson Consulting, LLC; Kellogg LLC; Jacob Associates; Granite Construction Co.; FMI - Management Consulting; The Fluor Foundation; The Dutra Group; Diablo Contractors, Inc.; Corey Delta Constructors; Chubb & Son; The Beavers, Inc.; Amoroso Construction; CC Myers, Inc.
Foundation type: Independent foundation.
Financial data (yr. ended 04/30/13): Assets, $11,714,370 (M); gifts received, $840,885; expenditures, $776,168; qualifying distributions, $734,000; giving activities include $734,000 for 8 grants (high: $170,000; low: $6,000).
Purpose and activities: Giving primarily for grants to higher education institutions offering engineering degrees.
Fields of interest: Higher education; Engineering school/education.
Type of support: Endowments; Scholarship funds; Matching/challenge support.
Limitations: Applications not accepted. Giving on a national basis. No grants to individuals.
Application information: Contributes only to pre-selected organizations.
Board meeting date(s): Jan., Apr., Aug., and Oct.
Officer and Trustees:* Lynn E. Barr,* Chair.; Ronald M. Fedrick,* Vice-Chair.; Robert E. Alger,* Pres.; Wilfred W. Clyde,* Sr. V.P.; Paul A. Cocotis,* V.P.; Michael T. Traylor,* Secy.-Treas.; David W. Woods, Exec. Dir.; Michael W. Anderson; John E. Bollier; J.C. Brummond; and 19 additional directors.
Number of staff: 1 full-time professional; 1 part-time support.
EIN: 953605104
Selected grants: The following grants are a representative sample of this grantmaker's funding activity:
$100,000 to Purdue University, West Lafayette, IN, 2013. For Award Scholarships to Schools of Engineering/Construction.

294
Stephen Bechtel Fund ✧
P.O. Box 193809
San Francisco, CA 94119-3809 (415) 284-8675
FAX: (415) 284-8571;
E-mail: information@sdbjrfoundation.org; Main URL: http://www.sdbjrfoundation.org

Established in 2007 in CA and DE.
Donor: Stephen D. Bechtel, Jr.
Foundation type: Independent foundation.
Financial data (yr. ended 12/31/12): Assets, $659,314 (M); gifts received, $40,000,000; expenditures, $39,998,281; qualifying distributions, $40,137,264; giving activities include $37,627,195 for 275 grants (high: $3,000,000; low: $5,000).
Purpose and activities: The foundation invests in preparing California's children and youth to contribute to the state's economy and communities,

and in advancing management of California's water and land resources.
Fields of interest: Education; Environment; Health care; Human services; Children.
Type of support: General/operating support; Management development/capacity building; Annual campaigns; Capital campaigns; Building/renovation; Program development; Curriculum development; Scholarship funds; Employee matching gifts.
Limitations: Applications not accepted. Giving primarily in CA. No grants to individuals.
Publications: Financial statement.
Application information: Applications are by invitation only. Do not send letters of inquiry or proposals by mail or e-mail unless requested to do so by foundation staff.
Board meeting date(s): Quarterly
Officers and Directors:* Stephen D. Bechtel, Jr.,* Chair.; Lauren B. Dachs,* Vice-Chair., Pres. and Exec. Dir.; Patricia Leicher, Secy. and C.F.O.; Barbara Cartier, Cont.; Elizabeth H. Bechtel; Alan B. Dachs; Deborah L. Duncan; Jude P. Laspa; Bob Peck; Nonie B. Ramsay; John W. Weiser.
EIN: 208680679
Selected grants: The following grants are a representative sample of this grantmaker's funding activity:
$3,000,000 to Resources Legacy Fund, Sacramento, CA, 2012.
$1,250,000 to California STEM Learning Network, Sacramento, CA, 2012. For Science, Technology, Engineering, and Mathematics (STEM) program.
$600,000 to Stanford University, Stanford, CA, 2012.
$500,000 to Beta Theta Pi Foundation, Oxford, OH, 2012. For character and citizenship development programs.
$375,000 to East Oakland Youth Development Center, Oakland, CA, 2012. For character and citizenship development programs.
$165,000 to Reasoning Mind, Houston, TX, 2012. For Science, Technology, Engineering, and Mathematics (STEM) program.
$100,000 to United Religions Initiative, San Francisco, CA, 2012. For character and citizenship development programs.
$60,000 to School for Ethics and Global Leadership, Washington, DC, 2012. For character and citizenship development program.
$50,000 to California Business for Education Excellence Foundation, Sacramento, CA, 2012. For general support.
$50,000 to Seven Tepees Youth Program, San Francisco, CA, 2012. For environmental programs.

295
Bechtel Group Foundation ✧

(formerly Bechtel Foundation)
50 Beale St.
San Francisco, CA 94105-1813 (415) 768-1842
Contact: Marthe Patterson, Comms. and Grants Off.
E-mail: becfoun@bechtel.com; Application address: P.O. Box 193965, San Francisco, CA 94119-3965; Main URL: http://www.bechtel.com/foundation.html

Incorporated in 1953 in CA.
Donors: Bechtel Group, Inc.; Bechtel Power Corp.; Bechtel Systems of Infrastructure, Inc.; Bechtel Corp.
Foundation type: Company-sponsored foundation.
Financial data (yr. ended 12/31/12): Assets, $24,994,868 (M); gifts received, $3,534,102; expenditures, $2,324,033; qualifying distributions, $2,232,007; giving activities include $2,083,063 for 17 grants (high: $500,000; low: $5,000), and $148,944 for 453 employee matching gifts.
Purpose and activities: The foundation supports organizations involved with arts and culture, education, human services, science, and civic affairs.
Fields of interest: Arts; Higher education; Business school/education; Engineering school/education; Education; Human services; United Ways and Federated Giving Programs; Mathematics; Engineering; Science; Public affairs.
Type of support: General/operating support; Program development; Scholarship funds; Employee volunteer services; Employee matching gifts; Employee-related scholarships.
Limitations: Applications accepted. Giving on a national and international basis in areas of company operations, with emphasis on CA, Washington, DC, MD, MN, PA, and VA. No support for religious organizations. No grants to individuals (except for employee-related scholarships), or for endowments or special projects.
Application information: Application form not required.
Initial approach: Proposal
Deadline(s): None
Board meeting date(s): Annually
Final notification: Varies
Officers and Directors:* Riley P. Bechtel,* Chair.; Adrian Zaccaria,* Pres.; Michael C. Bailey,* Sr. V.P.; Peter A. Dawson,* Sr. V.P.; M. W. Quazzo, V.P. and Secy.; Annette M. Sparks, V.P. and Cont.; J.K. Deshong, V.P.; Charlene A. Wellness,* V.P.; K. C. Leader, Treas.; William N. Dudley, Jr.
Number of staff: 1 full-time professional; 1 part-time professional; 1 full-time support; 1 part-time support.
EIN: 946078120

296
S.D. Bechtel, Jr. Foundation ✧

(formerly Stephen D. Bechtel, Jr. Charitable Foundation)
P.O. Box 193809
San Francisco, CA 94119-3809 (415) 284-8675
Contact: Kelly Hayashi, Sr. Grants Mgr.
FAX: (415) 284-8571;
E-mail: information@sdbjrfoundation.org; Main URL: http://www.sdbjrfoundation.org

Established in 2005 in CA.
Donors: S.D. Bechtel, Jr.; Elizabeth Hogan Bechtel.
Foundation type: Independent foundation.
Financial data (yr. ended 12/31/12): Assets, $339,549,608 (M); gifts received, $63,317,809; expenditures, $65,137,368; qualifying distributions, $61,878,155; giving activities include $59,422,815 for 326 grants (high: $5,000,000; low: $200).
Purpose and activities: The foundation invests in preparing California's children and youth to contribute to the state's economy and communities, and in advancing management of California's water and land resources.
Fields of interest: Engineering school/education; Education; Environment, natural resources; Environment, beautification programs; Environment; Youth development, scouting agencies (general); Girl scouts; Youth development, services; Youth development; Science; Leadership development; Children/youth.
Type of support: General/operating support; Continuing support; Management development/capacity building; Annual campaigns; Capital campaigns; Building/renovation; Program development; Curriculum development; Scholarship funds; Research; Program evaluation; Employee matching gifts; Matching/challenge support.
Limitations: Applications not accepted. Giving primarily in the San Francisco Bay, CA, area. No grants to individuals or for endowment activities and no international grants.
Publications: Financial statement.
Application information: Applications are by invitation only. Do not send letters of inquiry or proposals by mail or email unless requested to do so by foundation staff.
Officers and Director:* S.D. Bechtel, Jr.,* Chair.; Lauren B. Dachs,* Vice-Chair., Pres. and Exec. Dir.; Patricia W. Leicher, Secy. and C.F.O.; Barbara Cartier, Cont.; Elizabeth Hogan Bechtel; Alan M. Dachs; Deborah L. Duncan; Jude P. Laspa; Bob Peck; Nonie B. Ramsay; John Weiser.
Number of staff: 1 full-time professional; 4 part-time professional; 1 full-time support.
EIN: 203759208
Selected grants: The following grants are a representative sample of this grantmaker's funding activity:
$5,000,000 to Boy Scouts of America National Council, Irving, TX, 2012. For capital.
$4,000,000 to California Waterfowl Association, Sacramento, CA, 2012. For program.
$732,267 to Audubon Society, National, Kensington, CA, 2012. For program.
$212,000 to Delta Waterfowl Foundation, Bismarck, ND, 2012. For program.
$100,000 to East Oakland Youth Development Center, Oakland, CA, 2012. For program.
$75,000 to Oakland Schools Foundation, Oakland, CA, 2012. For program.
$50,000 to Elkhorn Slough Foundation, Moss Landing, CA, 2012. For program.
$50,000 to International Computer Science Institute, Berkeley, CA, 2012. For program.

297
Arnold and Mabel Beckman Foundation ✧

100 Academy
Irvine, CA 92617-3002 (949) 721-2222
Contact: Jacqueline Dorrance, Exec. Dir.
FAX: (949) 721-2225;
E-mail: administration@beckman-foundation.com; Mailing address: P.O. Box 13219, Newport Beach, CA 92658; e-mail (for Kathlene Williams, Exec. Asst.): k.williams@beckman-foundation.com; Main URL: http://www.beckman-foundation.com

Incorporated in 1977 in CA.
Donors: Arnold O. Beckman†; Mabel M. Beckman†; Conexant.
Foundation type: Independent foundation.
Financial data (yr. ended 08/31/13): Assets, $548,425,390 (M); expenditures, $26,561,276; qualifying distributions, $24,034,850; giving activities include $22,625,440 for 97 grants (high: $4,000,000; low: $20).
Purpose and activities: The foundation makes grants to program-related, nonprofit research institutions to promote research in chemistry and life sciences, broadly interpreted, to foster the

invention of methods, instruments, and materials that will open new avenues of research in science.
Fields of interest: Cancer; Eye diseases; Heart & circulatory diseases; Biomedicine; Medical research, institute; Cancer research; Eye research; Heart & circulatory research; AIDS research; Science; Marine science; Physical/earth sciences; Chemistry; Physics; Engineering/technology; Biology/life sciences.
Type of support: Research; Employee matching gifts.
Limitations: Applications accepted. Giving primarily in the U.S. No support for political or religious purposes, or for research that does not fall within the foundation's areas of interest. No grants to individuals (except for Beckman Young Investigator's Program), or for dinners, mass mailings, or fundraising campaigns; no loans.
Publications: Application guidelines; Program policy statement.
Application information: Grant policy and procedure information is available from the foundation. Application form required.
Initial approach: Pre-proposal letter not to exceed 3 pages
Copies of proposal: 1
Deadline(s): Oct. 1
Board meeting date(s): Quarterly
Final notification: Apr. or May
Officers and Directors:* Stephen Ryan,* Co-Chair.; Harry B. Gray, Ph.D.*, Co-Chair.; William H. May,* Secy.; Gary T. Wescombe, Ph.D.*, Treas.; Jacqueline Dorrance, Exec. Dir.; Theodore Shi, Finance Dir.; Gerald E. Gallwas; Jon Fosheim; Peter Simon.
Number of staff: 1 full-time professional; 3 full-time support.
EIN: 953169713
Selected grants: The following grants are a representative sample of this grantmaker's funding activity:
$4,000,000 to University of California at Irvine Foundation, Irvine, CA, 2013. For general support.
$3,508,220 to University of Illinois at Urbana-Champaign, Urbana, IL, 2013. For research.
$3,500,220 to California Institute of Technology, Pasadena, CA, 2013. For general support.
$2,338,880 to Stanford University, Stanford, CA, 2013. For research.
$2,000,000 to Doheny Eye Institute, Los Angeles, CA, 2013. For general support.
$1,754,160 to City of Hope, Duarte, CA, 2013. For research.
$600,000 to New York University School of Medicine Foundation, New York, NY, 2013. For general support.
$50,000 to J. F. Shea Therapeutic Riding Center, San Juan Capistrano, CA, 2013. For general support.
$38,600 to University of Texas, Austin, TX, 2013. For research.
$30,000 to J. F. Shea Therapeutic Riding Center, San Juan Capistrano, CA, 2013. For general support.

298
Beckman Laser Institute & Medical Clinic ✧
1002 Health Sciences Rd. E.
Irvine, CA 92617-3010

Established in 1982 in CA.
Donor: Kratz Foundation.
Foundation type: Independent foundation.
Financial data (yr. ended 06/30/13): Assets, $12,643,451 (M); expenditures, $1,517,017; qualifying distributions, $1,229,110; giving activities include $1,100,000 for 2 grants (high: $835,000; low: $265,000).
Purpose and activities: Giving to universities for research in laser advancement.
Fields of interest: Higher education; Engineering/technology.
Type of support: Research.
Limitations: Applications not accepted. Giving limited to Irvine and La Jolla, CA. No grants to individuals.
Application information: Contributes only to pre-selected organizations.
Officers and Directors:* Michael W. Berns,* Chair. and C.E.O.; Art Fine,* Vice-Chair.; Kenneth Strahs, Secy.; Richard P. Kratz, C.F.O.; Shu Chien; Robert Hanisee; Halina Rubinsztein-Dunlop.
EIN: 953800459
Selected grants: The following grants are a representative sample of this grantmaker's funding activity:
$734,892 to University of California, Irvine, CA, 2011.
$200,000 to University of California at San Diego, La Jolla, CA, 2011.

299
Begin Today for Tomorrow ✧
501 S. Beverly Dr., 3rd Fl.
Beverly Hills, CA 90212-4514

Established in 2001 in CA.
Donor: Cameron Diaz.
Foundation type: Independent foundation.
Financial data (yr. ended 12/31/13): Assets, $1,140,359 (M); gifts received, $750,000; expenditures, $704,224; qualifying distributions, $699,500; giving activities include $699,500 for 19 grants (high: $200,000; low: $1,000).
Fields of interest: Arts; Education, public education; Higher education; Environment, natural resources; Environment; Animals/wildlife, preservation/protection; Children, services; Family services.
Limitations: Applications not accepted. Giving primarily in CA and NY. No grants to individuals.
Application information: Unsolicited requests for funds not accepted.
Officers: Cameron Diaz, Pres. and Secy.; Billie Diaz, V.P.
EIN: 260015211

300
Bell Family Foundation, Inc. ✧
212 E. Rowland St., Ste. 312
Covina, CA 91723-3146

Established in 1990 in IL.
Donors: William J. Bell; Lee Phillip Bell.
Foundation type: Independent foundation.
Financial data (yr. ended 09/30/13): Assets, $3,102,511 (M); expenditures, $1,800,380; qualifying distributions, $1,766,514; giving activities include $1,754,700 for 61 grants (high: $240,000; low: $100).
Purpose and activities: Giving primarily for the arts; funding also for medical research, education, and the environment.
Fields of interest: Performing arts; Arts; Higher education; Environment; Health organizations, association; Human services; Children/youth, services.
Limitations: Applications not accepted. Giving primarily in CA; some funding also in CO.
Application information: Contributes only to pre-selected organizations.
Officers: Lee Phillip Bell, Pres. and Secy.; William James Bell, V.P. and Treas.
Directors: Bradley P. Bell; Lauralee K. Bell.
EIN: 363773191

301
Bella Vista Foundation ✧
1660 Bush St., Ste. 300
San Francisco, CA 94109-5308 (415) 561-6540
Contact: Mary Gregory, Exec. Dir.
FAX: (415) 561-6477; E-mail: mgregory@pfs-llc.net; Main URL: http://www.pfs-llc.net/bellavista/index.html
Grants List: http://www.pfs-llc.net/foundations/bella-vista-foundation/about/grantmaking-history
Knowledge Center: http://www.pfs-llc.net/foundations/bella-vista-foundation/about/theory-of-change-infants-families-connecting-grantmaking-program

Established in 1999 in CA.
Foundation type: Independent foundation.
Financial data (yr. ended 12/31/12): Assets, $51,911,605 (M); gifts received, $395,351; expenditures, $2,728,673; qualifying distributions, $2,550,117; giving activities include $2,278,695 for 60 grants (high: $150,000; low: $1,500).
Purpose and activities: The foundation maintains a two-part grantmaking focus to fund programs that address fundamental causes of societal problems, rather than programs that seek to remedy the effects of those problems. Through its Early Childhood Development Focus Area, the foundation funds programs that help mothers, fathers and caregivers of children (prenatal to age 3) to better cope with the stresses in their lives that might result in depression. Under the Ecosystem Restoration Grants, the foundation focuses on protecting, restoring and revitalizing high priority watershed ecosystems in CA and OR. Within these watersheds, the priorities are promoting the sustainable management of forest and agricultural land, revitalizing streams, and restoring riparian areas, with the goal of enhancing and maintaining self-sustaining watershed ecosystems.
Fields of interest: Environment, natural resources; Children, services; Child development, services; Family services.
Type of support: General/operating support; Program development.
Limitations: Applications accepted. Giving primarily in Marin, San Francisco, San Mateo and Santa Clara counties (in the area of early childhood development) and in California and Oregon (environmental restoration projects). No support for the arts or sectarian religious purposes. No grants to individuals, or for benefit events. Generally, no grants for medical research, health care, publications, or video production (except under special circumstances and only in the early childhood development focus area).
Publications: Application guidelines; Grants list; Program policy statement.

Application information: Please check foundation web site for current grantmaking information and guidelines. Application form not required.
Initial approach: Telephone call or see foundation web site
Copies of proposal: 1
Deadline(s): See foundation web site for application deadlines
Board meeting date(s): Spring and fall
Final notification: 1 month
Officers and Directors:* Robert C. Kirkwood,* Pres.; Susan K. Koe,* V.P.; John H. Kirkwood,* Secy.; Jean K. Casey,* C.F.O.; Mary Gregory, Exec. Dir.; Brooks Kirkwood.
EIN: 943345967
Selected grants: The following grants are a representative sample of this grantmaker's funding activity:
$150,000 to Freshwater Trust, Portland, OR, 2012. For freshwater restoration efforts in the John Day River, including launching a conservation bank, planning a restoration project on Rowe Creek and construction maintenance on the Middle Fork John Day Habitat Restoration project.
$150,000 to Trust for Public Land, San Francisco, CA, 2012. To implement Sierra Checkerboard Initiative: Forests for the Future.
$65,392 to StarVista, San Carlos, CA, 2012. For Early Childhood Mental Health project for children ages 0-3 in child care centers and home visiting services.
$60,000 to Good Samaritan Family Resource Center, San Francisco, CA, 2012. For culturally appropriate support groups, parent classes, workshops, case management, and counseling that help caregivers manage and reduce stress and maternal depression.
$50,000 to Catholic Charities of San Jose, San Jose, CA, 2012. To provide comprehensive services including Raising a Reader for low-income families with children 0-3 at four family centers in San Jose.
$50,000 to Homeless Prenatal Program, San Francisco, CA, 2012. For case management, prenatal and parenting classes, support groups, counseling and alternative support services including yoga, infant massage and doula support.
$50,000 to Sierra Fund, Nevada City, CA, 2012. For additional assessment activities as part of the Humbug Creek Watershed Assessment and Management Plan in the Yuba River watershed.
$40,000 to FamilyWorks, San Rafael, CA, 2012. For Exploring Motherhood Together Program which provides support groups for mothers at risk of depression.
$35,000 to Canal Alliance, San Rafael, CA, 2012. To recruit and train Latina companeras (childbirth coaches) who will provide support and information to women in the Canal District.
$35,000 to Parent Services Project, San Rafael, CA, 2012. For Mentores program which provides home visiting for low-income families with young children (ages 0-3) in Canal District as a way of reducing stress.

302
Shimon ben Joseph Foundation

(also known as Jim Joseph Foundation)
343 Sansome St., Ste. 550
San Francisco, CA 94104-1303 (415) 658-8730
FAX: (415) 658-8736;
E-mail: info@jimjosephfoundation.org; Main URL: http://www.jimjosephfoundation.org
Knowledge Center: http://jimjosephfoundation.org/grants/overview/
Twitter: https://twitter.com/JimJosephFdn

Established in 2003 in CA following the death of Jim Joseph; classified as a private foundation in 2006.
Donor: Jim "Shimon ben Yosef" Joseph‡.
Foundation type: Independent foundation.
Financial data (yr. ended 12/31/13): Assets, $1,041,590,492 (M); expenditures, $35,780,455; qualifying distributions, $40,186,505; giving activities include $31,387,034 for grants.
Purpose and activities: The foundation will take a broad view of education including day schools, camping, youth groups, congregational education and the like. The foundation seeks to identify funding opportunities in support of educational experiences that make an indelible impact on the lives of its Jewish participants.
Fields of interest: Education; Jewish agencies & synagogues; Children/youth; Young adults.
Type of support: Research; Program development; General/operating support.
Limitations: Applications not accepted. Giving in the U.S., initially targeting on the greater metropolitan areas of Los Angeles and San Francisco, CA, Boston, MA and Washington DC. Generally, no support for individual schools, camps, congregations, youth groups, etc. No grants for capital projects, endowments, or to support operating deficits.
Publications: Annual report; Newsletter.
Application information: The foundation accepts grants by invitation only.
Board meeting date(s): Quarterly
Officer and Directors:* Alvin T. Levitt,* Pres.; Mary Seabury, C.F.O.; Charles "Chip" Edelsberg, Ph.D., Exec. Dir.; Phyllis Cook; Susan Folkman, Ph.D.; Dvora Joseph; Joshua Joseph; Alisa Robbins Doctoroff; Dan Safier; Jerome Somers.
Number of staff: 8 full-time professional; 4 full-time support; 2 part-time support.
EIN: 331114104
Selected grants: The following grants are a representative sample of this grantmaker's funding activity:
$3,543,579 to Hebrew Union College-Jewish Institute of Religion, Cincinnati, OH, 2012. For Jim Joseph Foundation (JJF) Education Initiative, effort to increase the number and enhance the quality of Jewish educators working with Jewish youth and young adults.
$3,427,714 to Yeshiva University, New York, NY, 2012. For Jim Joseph Foundation (JJF) Education Initiative, effort to increase the number and enhance the quality of Jewish educators working with Jewish youth and young adults.
$2,500,000 to Birthright Israel Foundation, New York, NY, 2012. For trip participant support.
$1,692,698 to Foundation for Jewish Camp, New York, NY, 2012. For Specialty Camps Incubator 2.
$1,576,278 to Foundation for Jewish Camp, New York, NY, 2012. For New Specialty Camps Incubator.
$1,061,724 to Foundation for Jewish Camp, New York, NY, 2012. For JWest Campership.
$949,605 to Hillel: The Foundation for Jewish Campus Life, Charles and Lynn Schusterman International Center, Washington, DC, 2012. For Senior Jewish Educator-Campus Entrepreneurs Initiative (CEI) Initiative, creating peer networks on campuses and placing mentors with extensive Jewish backgrounds on selected campuses to provide in-depth, meaningful Jewish education.
$198,869 to American Institutes for Research in the Behavioral Sciences, Washington, DC, 2012. To evaluate Jim Joseph Foundation (JJF) Education Initiative. The initiative is an effort to increase the number and enhance the quality of Jewish educators working with Jewish youth and young adults.
$80,000 to American Jewish Joint Distribution Committee, New York, NY, 2012. For JDC Global Learning Networks.
$30,880 to Jewish Community Federation of the Greater East Bay, Oakland, CA, 2012. For PJ Library, Jewish family engagement program implemented on a local level throughout North America. Free, high-quality Jewish children's literature and music is mailed to families on a monthly basis to help engage their children in Jewish life.

303
The Legler Benbough Foundation ✧

2550 5th Ave., Ste. 132
San Diego, CA 92103-6622 (619) 235-8099
Contact: Peter K. Ellsworth, Pres.
FAX: (619) 235-8077;
E-mail: thomas@benboughfoundation.org; Main URL: http://www.benboughfoundation.org

Established in 1985 in CA.
Donor: Legler Benbough‡.
Foundation type: Independent foundation.
Financial data (yr. ended 12/31/13): Assets, $32,252,195 (M); expenditures, $2,494,669; qualifying distributions, $2,199,835; giving activities include $1,980,000 for 32 grants (high: $294,500; low: $500).
Purpose and activities: Giving to: 1) provide economic opportunity through the funding of the research institutions located around the University of California at San Diego and within the university itself; 2) provide cultural opportunity through funding the Institutions located in Balboa Park and; 3) provide opportunity in health, education and welfare through funding of organizations and programs in the Diamond Neighborhoods of San Diego.
Fields of interest: Museums; Education; Health care; Medical research; Youth development; Children/youth, services; Community/economic development.
Type of support: General/operating support; Continuing support; Program development; Scholarship funds; Research; Program-related investments/loans; Matching/challenge support.
Limitations: Applications accepted. Giving limited to within the city of San Diego, CA. No support for religious, political, AIDS, or homeless organizations. No grants to individuals or for capital campaigns, or the performing or modern arts.
Publications: Application guidelines.
Application information: Where the foundation wishes to pursue the request for a grant, it will provide an application form to the applicant. Letters of request made via telephone calls or e-mails are not accepted. Application form required.
Initial approach: Letter to request application via U.S. mail
Copies of proposal: 1

Deadline(s): See foundation web site for specific deadlines
Board meeting date(s): Quarterly
Final notification: Apr. 15 and Oct. 15
Officers and Directors:* Peter K. Ellsworth,* Pres.; John G. Rebelo, Jr.,* Treas.; Frederick P. Crowell; Bob Kelly.
Number of staff: 2 full-time professional.
EIN: 330105049

304
The Bengier Foundation ✧
c/o Seiler & Co., LLP
3 Lagoon Dr., Ste. 400
Redwood City, CA 94065-5157
Contact: Gary F. Bengier, Chair.
E-mail: ideas@bengierfoundation.org; Application address: P.O. Box 590308, San Francisco, CA 94159-0308; Main URL: http://www.bengierfoundation.org/

Established in 2004 in CA.
Donors: Gary F. Bengier; Cynthia S. Bengier.
Foundation type: Independent foundation.
Financial data (yr. ended 12/31/12): Assets, $6,429,862 (M); gifts received, $1,501,113; expenditures, $1,058,081; qualifying distributions, $1,019,611; giving activities include $1,015,000 for 9 grants (high: $550,000; low: $5,000).
Fields of interest: Museums (science/technology); Education; Children/youth, services.
Type of support: General/operating support; Annual campaigns; Research.
Limitations: Applications accepted. Giving primarily in CA. No support for political organizations.
Application information: Application form not required.
Initial approach: Proposal
Copies of proposal: 1
Deadline(s): None
Officers: Gary F. Bengier, Chair.; Cynthia S. Bengier, C.F.O.; Brooke N. Bengier, Secy.
Number of staff: 1 part-time professional; 1 part-time support.
EIN: 113729246

305
The Benificus Foundation ✧
(formerly Vallejo Ventures Private Foundation)
751 Laurel St., Ste. 717
San Carlos, CA 94070-3113
Ann and John Doerr's Giving Pledge Profile: http://glasspockets.org/philanthropy-in-focus/eye-on-the-giving-pledge/profiles/doerr

Established in 1997 in CA.
Donors: Ann Howland Doerr; L. John Doerr.
Foundation type: Independent foundation.
Financial data (yr. ended 09/30/13): Assets, $124,138,217 (M); gifts received, $15,221; expenditures, $9,940,784; qualifying distributions, $9,668,897; giving activities include $9,644,099 for 22 grants (high: $5,022,820; low: $10,000).
Fields of interest: Higher education; Education.
Type of support: Program-related investments/loans.
Limitations: Applications not accepted. Giving primarily in CA; some funding also in DC and MA. No grants to individuals.
Application information: Contributes only to pre-selected organizations.
Officers: Barbara S. Hager, C.E.O. and C.F.O.; L. John Doerr III, Pres.; Ann Howland Doerr, V.P. and Secy.
EIN: 770444504
Selected grants: The following grants are a representative sample of this grantmaker's funding activity:
$5,022,820 to Alliance for Climate Protection, Washington, DC, 2013.
$1,743,222 to Environmental Defense Fund, Washington, DC, 2013.
$1,014,440 to Aspire Public Schools, Oakland, CA, 2013.
$507,220 to New Profit, Boston, MA, 2013.
$501,040 to Aspen Global Change Institute, Basalt, CO, 2013.
$328,137 to Aspen Center for Environmental Studies, Aspen, CO, 2013.
$253,610 to Mayors Fund to Advance New York City, New York, NY, 2013.
$253,610 to SEED Foundation, Washington, DC, 2013.
$10,000 to Mbinga Childrens Organization, San Francisco, CA, 2013.
$10,000 to Raphael House, San Francisco, CA, 2013.

306
The Benjamin Fund, Inc. ✧
17 Peralta Ave.
San Francisco, CA 94110-4828

Established in 2003 in CA.
Donors: Alvin Benjamin; Rose Benjamin†.
Foundation type: Independent foundation.
Financial data (yr. ended 12/31/12): Assets, $11,682,199 (M); expenditures, $744,199; qualifying distributions, $636,283; giving activities include $511,961 for 57 grants (high: $175,000; low: $36).
Fields of interest: Minorities/immigrants, centers/services; International human rights.
Limitations: Applications not accepted. Giving primarily in CA, DC, and NY. No grants to individuals.
Application information: Contributes only to pre-selected organizations.
Officers: Medea Susan Benjamin, Pres.; Kirsten Irgens-Moller, Secy.; Kevin Danaher, Treas.
EIN: 841618483

307
The Bennett Foundation ✧ ☆
c/o William H. Borthwick
1056 Amalfi Dr.
Pacific Palisades, CA 90272-4028

Established in 1999 in CA.
Donors: David Borthwick; Molly Borthwick.
Foundation type: Independent foundation.
Financial data (yr. ended 12/31/13): Assets, $9,753,440 (M); expenditures, $579,364; qualifying distributions, $533,478; giving activities include $533,478 for 18 grants (high: $197,200; low: $1,600).
Fields of interest: Museums; Performing arts, opera; United Ways and Federated Giving Programs.
Limitations: Applications not accepted. No grants to individuals.
Application information: Unsolicited requests for funds not accepted.
Director: William H. Borthwick.
Trustees: David B. Borthwick; Molly Lowell Borthwick.
EIN: 954720080
Selected grants: The following grants are a representative sample of this grantmaker's funding activity:
$12,000 to American Fund for Charities, Wilmington, DE, 2010.
$10,000 to Sir John Soanes Museum Foundation, New York, NY, 2011.

308
Bergen Foundation ✧
c/o Frances Bergen
13701 Riverside Dr., No. 800
Sherman Oaks, CA 91423-2430

Established in 1963 in CA.
Donors: Edgar Bergen†; Frances Bergen†.
Foundation type: Independent foundation.
Financial data (yr. ended 11/30/13): Assets, $17,413,874 (M); expenditures, $1,082,388; qualifying distributions, $839,111; giving activities include $630,000 for 42 grants (high: $100,000; low: $2,500).
Fields of interest: Arts; Health care; Food services, congregate meals; Human services.
Limitations: Applications not accepted. Giving primarily in CA; some giving also in FL. No grants to individuals.
Application information: Contributes only to pre-selected organizations.
Officers: Kris Bergen, Pres.; Candice Bergen, Secy.
Director: John Larkin.
EIN: 956044540

309
H. N. & Frances C. Berger Foundation ✧
P.O. Box 13390
Palm Desert, CA 92255-3390 (760) 341-5293
Contact: Christopher M. McGuire, V.P.
Main URL: http://www.hnberger.org

Established in 1993 in CA, AZ, and TX.
Foundation type: Independent foundation.
Financial data (yr. ended 12/31/12): Assets, $477,907,584 (M); expenditures, $28,781,847; qualifying distributions, $16,167,190; giving activities include $5,214,789 for 145 grants (high: $500,000; low: $500), and $7,841,460 for 3 foundation-administered programs.
Purpose and activities: Emphasis on higher education, cultural programs, public health organizations, and hospitals. Committed to long-term support of present donees.
Fields of interest: Arts; Higher education; Hospitals (general); Health care; Health organizations, association.
Limitations: Applications not accepted. Giving primarily in CA.
Application information: Contributes only to pre-selected organizations.
Board meeting date(s): Semiannually, and as required
Officers and Directors:* Ronald M. Auen,* C.E.O. and Pres.; Darrell Burrage,* V.P.; Christopher M. McGuire,* V.P.; Douglass A. Vance,* V.P.; Joan C. Kalimanis,* Secy.-Treas.; Catharine N. Reed,* Sr. Prog. Off.; Thomas Kalimanis; Mike Rover; Lewis Webb, Jr.; Francis Wong.
EIN: 521757452

Selected grants: The following grants are a representative sample of this grantmaker's funding activity:
$500,000 to Methodist Hospital Foundation, Arcadia, CA, 2012. For acquisition and installation of critical equipment - CT scanner.
$250,000 to Salk Institute for Biological Studies, La Jolla, CA, 2012. For research two year grant.
$190,000 to Philanthropy Roundtable, Washington, DC, 2012. For miscellaneous projects and programs.
$171,200 to City of Hope, Los Angeles, CA, 2012. To support graduate education program.
$125,000 to Huntington Library, Art Collections and Botanical Gardens, San Marino, CA, 2012. For Grant 1 of 3 to support construction/rennovation of the Library Exhibition Hall.
$100,000 to Arnold Palmer Medical Center Foundation, Orlando, FL, 2012. For Pediatric Craniomaxillofacial Surgery Specialty Practice.
$100,000 to Desert Forum, Indian Wells, CA, 2012. For title sponsor of speaker series for Desert Town Hall, and complimentary tickets for Youth Ambasador Program.
$75,000 to Disabled Sports USA Far West, Citrus Heights, CA, 2012. For Matching Grant - for Wounded Warrior Programs.
$30,000 to Make-A-Wish Foundation of Orange County, Tustin, CA, 2012. For Share the Love Charity Event for Coachella Valley children with life threatening illnesses.
$15,000 to I Have A Dream Foundation-Los Angeles, Los Angeles, CA, 2012. For annual brunch and programs.

310
Erik E. and Edith H. Bergstrom Foundation, A Charitable Trust ✧

P.O. Box 520
Palo Alto, CA 94302-0520

Newly formed in 2002 in CA; previously Erik E. and Edith H. Bergstrom Foundation, Inc.
Donors: Edith H. Bergstrom; Erik E. Bergstrom.
Foundation type: Independent foundation.
Financial data (yr. ended 09/30/13): Assets, $80,890,822 (M); gifts received, $30,000; expenditures, $2,071,270; qualifying distributions, $1,226,410; giving activities include $1,098,161 for 15 grants (high: $237,513; low: $3,000).
Purpose and activities: Giving primarily for international affairs.
Fields of interest: Reproductive health, family planning; Health care; International affairs.
Limitations: Applications not accepted. Giving primarily in the U.S., Mexico and Central America. No grants to individuals.
Application information: Contributes only to pre-selected organizations.
Officers: Edith H. Bergstrom, Co-Exec. Dir.; Erik E. Bergstrom, Co-Exec. Dir.
EIN: 912155835
Selected grants: The following grants are a representative sample of this grantmaker's funding activity:
$345,565 to Fundacion Mexicana para la Planeacion Familiar, Mexico City, Mexico, 2011.

311
Philip and Muriel Berman Foundation ✧

P.O. Box 48558
Los Angeles, CA 90048-0558
FAX: (610) 437-1435; E-mail: pmbfound@ptd.net

Established in 1960 in PA.
Donors: Philip I. Berman†; Muriel M. Berman†.
Foundation type: Independent foundation.
Financial data (yr. ended 05/31/13): Assets, $41,772,177 (M); expenditures, $1,622,573; qualifying distributions, $1,247,345; giving activities include $1,247,345 for grants.
Purpose and activities: Giving primarily for arts and culture, education, health and Jewish causes with special focus on eastern PA and Israel.
Fields of interest: Arts, cultural/ethnic awareness; Education; Health care; Jewish agencies & synagogues.
International interests: Israel.
Type of support: Technical assistance; Seed money; Research; Program development; Endowments.
Limitations: Applications not accepted. Giving limited to CA, eastern PA and Israel. No grants to individuals.
Application information: Contributes only to pre-selected organizations.
Board meeting date(s): Biannually
Officers and Directors:* Nancy Berman Bloch,* Pres. and Exec. Dir.; Alan Bloch,* Treas.
Number of staff: 1 full-time professional; 1 part-time professional.
EIN: 236270983
Selected grants: The following grants are a representative sample of this grantmaker's funding activity:
$20,000 to Community Partners, Los Angeles, CA, 2013. For a Muslim - Jewish Partnership for Change.
$20,000 to World Union for Progressive Judaism, New York, NY, 2013. For Israel Religious Action Center Gos.
$15,000 to Camerata Pacifica, Santa Barbara, CA, 2013. For capacity building development.
$15,000 to Fractured Atlas, New York, NY, 2013. For film support.
$15,000 to Southside Community Land Trust, Providence, RI, 2013. For Community Growers' Network - Planning Grant.
$10,000 to Marlborough School, Los Angeles, CA, 2013. For artists' residencies program.
$5,000 to Jewish Museum, New York, NY, 2013. For New York Performances.
$5,000 to LAXART, Los Angeles, CA, 2013. For Made in La Exhibit with Hammer Museum.
$5,000 to Moving Traditions, Jenkintown, PA, 2013. For La Rosh Hodesh Girls Thing Program.
$5,000 to Storm King Art Center, Mountainville, NY, 2013. For Mark Di Suvero Exhibit.

312
The Lowell Berry Foundation ✧

3685 Mt. Diablo Blvd., Ste. 351
Lafayette, CA 94549-6803 (925) 284-4427
Contact: Katherine Sanders, Office Mgr.; For religious grants: Patricia Berry Conklin; For social service grants: Barbara Berry Corneille
FAX: (925) 284-4332;
E-mail: info@lowellberryfoundation.org; Main URL: http://www.lowellberryfoundation.org

Incorporated in 1950 in CA.
Donors: Lowell W. Berry†; Farm Service Co.; The Best Fertilizer Co. of Texas.
Foundation type: Independent foundation.
Financial data (yr. ended 12/31/13): Assets, $27,503,484 (M); expenditures, $1,425,489; qualifying distributions, $1,416,066; giving activities include $1,296,000 for 177 grants (high: $135,000; low: $250).
Purpose and activities: The purpose of the foundation is to support organizations which are dedicated to strengthening the leadership of the local Christian church ministry. The foundation also serves the local community by providing a safety net for those in need while focusing on organizations that shape lives and build leaders.
Fields of interest: Arts; Education; Human services; Children/youth, services; Christian agencies & churches.
Type of support: General/operating support; Continuing support; Program development; Scholarship funds.
Limitations: Applications accepted. Giving limited to Contra Costa and Alameda counties, CA. No support for newly established organizations. No grants to individuals, or for building or capital funds, equipment, seed money, or land acquisition.
Publications: Grants list.
Application information: See foundation web site for updates regarding grant proposal submissions. Application form not required.
Initial approach: Letter, telephone, or visit the foundation web site for application guidelines
Copies of proposal: 1
Deadline(s): None
Board meeting date(s): Quarterly
Final notification: 3 to 4 months for religious grants; 3 to 4 months for social service grants
Officers and Directors:* Larry R. Langdon,* Pres.; Patricia Berry Conklin,* V.P.; Barbara Berry Corneille,* Secy.; Gary L. Depolo,* Treas.; John D. Asher; Jami S. Kane; Jayne S. Mordell; Annette S. Robison.
Number of staff: 1 part-time support.
EIN: 946108391
Selected grants: The following grants are a representative sample of this grantmaker's funding activity:
$115,000 to Fuller Theological Seminary, Pasadena, CA, 2012.
$35,000 to Faith Network of the East Bay, Oakland, CA, 2012.
$20,000 to Bay Area Rescue Mission, Richmond, CA, 2012.
$8,000 to Chabot Space and Science Center, Oakland, CA, 2012.
$5,000 to Regional Parks Foundation, Oakland, CA, 2012.
$4,000 to Monument Crisis Center, Concord, CA, 2012.

313
Bickerstaff Family Foundation ✧

c/o Gursey Schneider
1888 Century Park E.
Century City, CA 90067-1702
Contact: Amy White
E-mail: bickfamilyfound@aol.com; Application address: P.O. Box 41100, Long Beach, CA 90853; Tel./Fax: (562) 433-5661

Established in 2000 in CA.
Donors: Deborah J. Bickerstaff; Glen E. Bickerstaff.
Foundation type: Independent foundation.
Financial data (yr. ended 12/31/13): Assets, $3,924,351 (M); expenditures, $935,993;

qualifying distributions, $910,505; giving activities include $897,017 for 11 grants (high: $413,601; low: $500).
Purpose and activities: Giving primarily for health associations and health care, including a hospital which provides medical treatment for pediatric HIV; funding also for other HIV programs, children, youth and social services, including scholarships for HIV infected teens to go to colleges or vocational schools.
Fields of interest: Higher education; Health care; Health organizations, association; Cancer; Crime/violence prevention, abuse prevention; Housing/shelter, homeless; Human services; Children/youth, services; Family services; Children/youth; Youth; Young adults; Women; Adults, women; AIDS, people with; Crime/abuse victims; Terminal illness, people with.
International interests: Malawi; South Africa.
Type of support: Curriculum development; Endowments; Grants to individuals; Research; Scholarships—to individuals.
Limitations: Applications accepted. Giving primarily in CA; giving limited to residents of Los Angeles and Orange counties in CA for scholarships.
Application information: Application form not required.
Initial approach: Letter
Copies of proposal: 1
Officers: Deborah J. Bickerstaff, Pres.; Glen E. Bickerstaff, Secy.
EIN: 954819633

314
The Bilger Foundation ✧
480 Bel Air Rd.
Los Angeles, CA 90077-3815

Established in 1990 in CA.
Donors: Arthur Bilger; Dahlia Bilger.
Foundation type: Independent foundation.
Financial data (yr. ended 12/31/12): Assets, $2,965,209 (M); gifts received, $1,208; expenditures, $856,071; qualifying distributions, $854,238; giving activities include $846,146 for 35 grants (high: $230,000; low: $250).
Purpose and activities: Giving for Jewish organizations and health associations; some funding also for education, and children, youth, and social services.
Fields of interest: Arts; Elementary/secondary education; Higher education; Education; Health organizations, association; Human services; Children/youth, services; Jewish federated giving programs; Jewish agencies & synagogues.
Limitations: Applications not accepted. Giving primarily in CA. No grants to individuals.
Application information: Contributes only to pre-selected organizations.
Officer: Arthur Bilger, Pres.
EIN: 226524956

315
Bilinski Educational Foundation ✧
P.O. Box 1162
Point Reyes Station, CA 94956-1162

Established in 2008 in CA.
Donor: Bilinski Living Admin. Trust.
Foundation type: Independent foundation.
Financial data (yr. ended 12/31/13): Assets, $17,018,176 (M); expenditures, $1,104,256; qualifying distributions, $926,984; giving activities include $790,000 for 6 grants (high: $250,000; low: $50,000).
Fields of interest: Higher education.
Limitations: Applications not accepted. Giving primarily in CA and HI; some funding also in MN. No grants to individuals.
Application information: Unsolicited requests for funds not accepted.
Officer: Yvonne B. Severietti, Exec. Dir.
Directors: Dwight Allen; Joel Koonce; Fred Springer; Judy Tuttle.
EIN: 263694651
Selected grants: The following grants are a representative sample of this grantmaker's funding activity:
$50,000 to University of Minnesota, Minneapolis, MN, 2012. For Post Graduate Educational Scholarship fund for qualified students.

316
Binder Foundation ✧
225 S. Lake Ave., Ste. 300
Pasadena, CA 91101-3009

Established in 1997 in CA.
Donors: Adele Binder; Gordon M. Binder.
Foundation type: Independent foundation.
Financial data (yr. ended 12/31/13): Assets, $20,165,229 (M); expenditures, $1,171,662; qualifying distributions, $1,103,615; giving activities include $1,102,900 for 36 grants (high: $450,000; low: $50).
Purpose and activities: Giving primarily for hospitals, including children's hospitals, as well as for education, and to an institute for public policy research.
Fields of interest: Higher education; Hospitals (general); Hospitals (specialty); Foundations (private grantmaking); Social sciences, public policy.
Limitations: Applications not accepted. Giving primarily in CA, Washington, DC, and MA. No grants to individuals.
Application information: Contributes only to pre-selected organizations.
Trustees: Adele Binder; Gordon M. Binder.
EIN: 954635806

317
The Stanley and Joyce Black Family Foundation ✧
433 N. Camden Dr., Ste. 1070
Beverly Hills, CA 90210-4434

Established in 1989 in CA.
Donors: Stanley Black; Joyce Black.
Foundation type: Independent foundation.
Financial data (yr. ended 12/31/13): Assets, $38,804,375 (M); gifts received, $4,982,005; expenditures, $1,922,412; qualifying distributions, $1,778,452; giving activities include $1,553,704 for 197 grants (high: $200,000; low: $12).
Fields of interest: Arts; Education; Human services; Aging, centers/services; Jewish federated giving programs; Jewish agencies & synagogues.
Limitations: Applications not accepted. Giving primarily in CA. No grants to individuals.
Application information: Contributes only to pre-selected organizations.
Directors: Jack Black; Joyce Black; Stanley Black; Janis Goldman; Jill Zalben.
EIN: 954259961

318
Bloomfield Family Foundation ✧
P.O. Box 2098
Manhattan Beach, CA 90267

Established in 2004 in CA.
Donors: Margaret Bloomfield†; William E. Bloomfield, Jr.; Joanne B. Hunter.
Foundation type: Independent foundation.
Financial data (yr. ended 12/31/13): Assets, $64,923,308 (M); gifts received, $11,049,621; expenditures, $1,861,712; qualifying distributions, $1,418,966; giving activities include $1,400,000 for 36 grants (high: $263,500; low: $500).
Fields of interest: Higher education; Medical research, institute.
Limitations: Applications not accepted. Giving primarily in Los Angeles, CA. No grants to individuals.
Application information: Contributes only to pre-selected organizations.
Trustees: Bill Bloomfield; Joanne Hunter.
EIN: 206156014

319
Sam & Rie Bloomfield Foundation ✧
1600 Dove St., No. 250
Newport Beach, CA 92660-2405

Established in 1958 in KS.
Donors: Sam Bloomfield†; Rie Bloomfield; Rie Bloomfield Trust fbo Westley Graves.
Foundation type: Independent foundation.
Financial data (yr. ended 11/30/13): Assets, $9,252,769 (M); expenditures, $669,025; qualifying distributions, $532,867; giving activities include $446,130 for 18 grants (high: $200,000; low: $600).
Purpose and activities: Giving primarily for higher education and the arts.
Fields of interest: Museums (art); Performing arts, orchestras; Arts; Higher education; Human services; Jewish agencies & synagogues.
Limitations: Applications not accepted. Giving primarily in Wichita, KS. No grants to individuals.
Application information: Contributes only to pre-selected organizations.
Officers and Trustees:* William L. Lucas,* Co-Secy.; Alan L. McKay,* Co-Secy.; Verlon L. McKay,* Treas.; Debra L. Cathers.
EIN: 956074613

320
Blue Shield of California Foundation ✧
50 Beale St., 14th Fl.
San Francisco, CA 94105-1819
Contact: Gwyneth Tripp, Grants and Contracts Mgr.
FAX: (415) 229-6268;
E-mail: bscf@blueshieldcafoundation.org; E-mail for Gwyneth Tripp:
gwyneth.tripp@blueshieldcafoundation.org;
Additional contact: Jessica Gau, Grants and Contracts Admin,

jessica.gau@blueshieldcafoundation.org; Main URL: http://www.blueshieldcafoundation.org/
Ally for Change - Blue Shield of California Foundation: http://www.blueshieldcafoundation.org/video-and-photo-gallery/ally-change-blue-shield-california-foundation
Blog: http://www.blueshieldcafoundation.org/news/blog
Clinic Leadership Institute on YouTube: http://www.youtube.com/watch?v=D8U77ryTcHM
E-Newsletter: http://www.blueshieldcafoundation.org/news/focus-newsletter-archive
Facebook: http://www.facebook.com/pages/Blue-Shield-of-California-Foundation/222943311073741
Grants Database: http://www.blueshieldcafoundation.org/grants/grantees
Peter Long, Pres. and C.E.O., BSCF: http://twitter.com/PeterLongBSCF
Philanthropy's Promise: http://www.ncrp.org/philanthropys-promise/who
Twitter: http://twitter.com/BSCF
YouTube: http://www.youtube.com/user/BlueShieldCAFdn

Established in 1981 as a grantmaking public charity; status changed to company-sponsored foundation in 2004.
Donor: California Physicians' Service Agency Inc.
Foundation type: Company-sponsored foundation.
Financial data (yr. ended 12/31/12): Assets, $66,284,469 (M); gifts received, $40,114,912; expenditures, $37,220,389; qualifying distributions, $36,980,497; giving activities include $31,167,629 for 449 grants (high: $2,000,000; low: $7,500), and $3,519,033 for foundation-administered programs.
Purpose and activities: The foundation supports programs designed to improve the lives of Californians, particularly underserved populations, by making health care accessible, effective, and affordable for all Californians, and by ending domestic violence.
Fields of interest: Health care, public policy; Health care, reform; Health care, clinics/centers; Health care, insurance; Health care, cost containment; Health care, financing; Health care; Health organizations, reform; Crime/violence prevention, domestic violence; Family services, domestic violence; Leadership development; Economically disadvantaged.
Type of support: General/operating support; Continuing support; Management development/capacity building; Program development; Conferences/seminars; Scholarship funds; Research; Technical assistance; Program evaluation; Employee-related scholarships.
Limitations: Applications accepted. Giving limited to CA. No support for religious organizations not of direct benefit to the entire community or political candidates or organizations. No grants to individuals (except for employee-related scholarships), or for stand-alone sponsorships, award dinners, athletic events, competitions, special events, or tournaments, conferences or seminars, capital construction, television, film, or media production, political causes or campaigns, direct medical, specialty, or social services, subsidies to individuals for insurance coverage, outreach and enrollment activities for public health insurance programs, or case management.
Publications: Application guidelines; Annual report; Financial statement; Grants list; Newsletter; Occasional report; IRS Form 990 or 990-PF printed copy available upon request; Program policy statement (including application guidelines).
Application information: Most BSCF funding is by invitation only, but unsolicited requests for support are welcome for a limited number of funding opportunities. Organizations may be asked to submit a full proposal. Additional information may be requested at a later date. Organizations receiving support are asked to submit final reports, and, potentially, interim reports. Application form required.
Initial approach: Complete online eligibility quiz and letter of inquiry form
Deadline(s): Feb. 7, May 9, July 18, and Oct. 10 for online letter of inquiry form
Board meeting date(s): Quarterly
Final notification: Up to 6 months
Officers and Trustees:* David J. Kears,* Chair.; Peter Long, Ph.D.*, Pres. and C.E.O.; Aden Bliss, C.F.O.; Eliza Daniely-Woolfolk; Thomas W. Epstein; Franklin D. Gilliam, Jr., Ph.D.; William Hauck; Antonia Hernandez; Sandra R. Hernandez, M.D.; N. Marcus Thygeson.
Number of staff: 13 full-time professional; 4 full-time support; 1 part-time support.
EIN: 942822302
Selected grants: The following grants are a representative sample of this grantmaker's funding activity:
$2,000,000 to Community Partners, Los Angeles, CA, 2012. For Catalyzing Innovation in the Healthcare Safety Net.
$1,932,984 to Women's Foundation of California, San Francisco, CA, 2012. For An Intermediary to Implement the Blue Shield Against Violence Strong Field Project Organizational Strengths Grants Program - Cohort I Enhancements and Cohort II Implementation.
$1,057,129 to University of California, San Francisco, CA, 2012. For Clinic Leadership Institute Emerging Leaders Program, Cohort 6, and Chief Executive Program.
$1,049,722 to University of California, San Francisco, CA, 2012. For Clinic Leadership Institute Emerging Leaders, Cobort 5.
$650,000 to CompassPoint Nonprofit Services, Oakland, CA, 2012. For Strong Field Project Leadership Development Cohort III and Alumni Program.
$595,400 to National Family Justice Center Alliance, San Diego, CA, 2012. For California Family Justice Initiative Phase II.
$405,044 to George Washington University, Washington, DC, 2012. For National Health Policy Forum The Role of Community Health Centers in Evolving Health Care System.
$400,000 to CompassPoint Nonprofit Services, Oakland, CA, 2012. For An Intermediary to Implement the Blue Shield Against Violence Strong Field Project Leadership Program - Cohort II.
$30,000 to East Los Angeles Womens Center, Los Angeles, CA, 2012. For Blue Shield Against Violence Core Support Initiative.

321
Blum Family Foundation ✧
909 Montgomery St., Ste. 400
San Francisco, CA 94133-4652 (415) 434-1111

Established in 2002 in CA.
Donor: Richard C. Blum.
Foundation type: Independent foundation.
Financial data (yr. ended 12/31/12): Assets, $2,899,560 (M); gifts received, $3,375,000; expenditures, $9,091,144; qualifying distributions, $7,667,843; giving activities include $7,371,960 for 73 grants (high: $2,405,642; low: $500).
Purpose and activities: Giving primarily for the arts, education, health, human services, and for public policy research.
Fields of interest: Arts; Higher education; Education; Health organizations, association; Human services; Foundations (private grantmaking); Public policy, research; Public affairs; Jewish agencies & synagogues.
Limitations: Applications not accepted. Giving primarily in CA. No grants to individuals.
Application information: Contributes only to pre-selected organizations.
Officers and Directors:* Richard C. Blum, Chair. and Pres.; Erica Stone,* V.P.; Michael Klein; Jim Murray; Marc Scholvinck; Jane Jin Wen Su.
EIN: 954894347
Selected grants: The following grants are a representative sample of this grantmaker's funding activity:
$2,405,642 to American Himalayan Foundation, San Francisco, CA, 2012.
$1,000,000 to University of California at Berkeley Foundation, Blum Center for Developing Economies, Berkeley, CA, 2012.
$1,000,000 to University of California at Berkeley Foundation, Blum Center for Developing Economies, Berkeley, CA, 2012.
$320,171 to Brookings Institution, Washington, DC, 2012.
$250,000 to UCLA Foundation, Los Angeles, CA, 2012.
$250,000 to University of San Francisco, San Francisco, CA, 2012.
$110,000 to Carter Center, Atlanta, GA, 2012.
$100,000 to National Democratic Institute for International Affairs, Washington, DC, 2012.
$25,000 to Synergos Institute, New York, NY, 2012.
$25,000 to University of California, Berkeley, CA, 2012.

322
Blume Foundation ✧
85 El Cerrito Ave.
Hillsborough, CA 94010-6805

Established in 1957 in CA.
Donors: John A. Blume†; Ruth C. Blume.
Foundation type: Independent foundation.
Financial data (yr. ended 11/30/13): Assets, $21,669,230 (M); expenditures, $1,677,140; qualifying distributions, $1,475,000; giving activities include $1,475,000 for 22 grants (high: $980,000; low: $5,000).
Purpose and activities: Giving primarily for higher education; support also for animal welfare and health.
Fields of interest: Higher education; Animal welfare; Health organizations, association; Human services.
Limitations: Applications not accepted. Giving primarily in CA, with emphasis on Stanford and San Francisco. No grants to individuals.
Application information: Contributes only to pre-selected organizations.
Board meeting date(s): Nov.
Officer: Jene F. Blume, Pres.
EIN: 946073163

323
Boeckmann Charitable Foundation ✧ ☆
15505 Roscoe Blvd.
North Hills, CA 91343-6503 (818) 787-3800
Contact: Herbert Boeckmann II, Pres.; Jane F. Boeckmann, C.F.O.

Established in 1982 in CA.
Donors: Herbert F. Boeckmann II; Jane Boeckmann; Todd Rothweiler; Biastre Trust; 8101 Sepulveda LLC; S.M.K.I. PTY LTD.
Foundation type: Independent foundation.
Financial data (yr. ended 11/30/13): Assets, $626,539 (M); gifts received, $326,505; expenditures, $581,829; qualifying distributions, $574,561; giving activities include $574,561 for 107 grants (high: $100,000; low: $500).
Fields of interest: Higher education, university; Children/youth, services; Protestant agencies & churches.
Limitations: Applications accepted. Giving primarily in CA.
Application information: Application form required.
Initial approach: Letter
Deadline(s): None
Officers: Herbert F. Boeckmann II, Pres.; Jane F. Boeckmann, C.F.O.
EIN: 953806976

324
David Bohnett Foundation ✧
245 S. Beverly Dr.
Beverly Hills, CA 90212-3807
Contact: Michael Fleming, Exec. Dir.
FAX: (310) 276-0007;
E-mail: michael@bohnett.com; E-mail for David Bohnett, Chair.: david.bohnett@yahoo.com; Main URL: http://www.bohnettfoundation.org/
Facebook: http://www.facebook.com/pages/David-Bohnett-Foundation/103547889686291

Established in 1999 in CA and DE.
Donor: David C. Bohnett.
Foundation type: Independent foundation.
Financial data (yr. ended 12/31/13): Assets, $15,084,668 (M); expenditures, $4,560,115; qualifying distributions, $4,403,358; giving activities include $3,944,393 for 200 grants (high: $200,000; low: $250).
Purpose and activities: The purpose of the foundation is to improve society through social activism. The foundation supports: 1) Positive portrayals of gays and lesbians in the media; 2) The reduction and elimination of the manufacture and sale of handguns; 3) Eliminating the rare animal trade; 4) Los Angeles organizations that are working to better the civic and cultural life of all who call L.A. home; and 5) Voter registration activities.
Fields of interest: Media/communications; Human services; Civil/human rights, LGBTQ; Civil rights, voter education; LGBTQ.
Type of support: General/operating support; Program development.
Limitations: Giving on a national basis, with emphasis on southern CA. No grants to individuals, or for videos or other film productions.
Publications: Grants list.
Application information: Application information available on web site. Application form required.
Initial approach: New applicants should submit a letter of inquiry (2 pages maximum), through online grant application on foundation web site; Existing applicants may update and submit letters of inquiry in-progress by logging back into their online account from the link on foundation web site
Copies of proposal: 1
Deadline(s): Current deadlines available on foundation web site
Board meeting date(s): Twice a year
Final notification: 4 months
Officers: David C. Bohnett, Chair.; Liz Atherton, Cont.; Michael Fleming, Exec. Dir.
Board of Advisors: Gwendolyn Baba; Christopher Caldwell; Rich Llewellyn; Rob Saltzman.
Number of staff: 1 full-time professional; 1 part-time support.
EIN: 954735846

325
The Bolthouse Foundation ✧
2000 Oak St., Ste. 200
Bakersfield, CA 93301-3058
Contact: Fred Green, Exec. Dir.
Main URL: http://www.thebolthousefoundation.org/

Established in 1988 in CA.
Donors: William Bolthouse Farms, Inc.; Weyerhaeuser Corporation.
Foundation type: Independent foundation.
Financial data (yr. ended 12/31/13): Assets, $35,092,531 (M); expenditures, $2,172,159; qualifying distributions, $2,004,380; giving activities include $1,725,000 for 1 grant.
Purpose and activities: The foundation's purpose is to glorify the Lord Jesus Christ by supporting charitable and religious organizations whose ministry, goals, and operating principles are consistent with evangelical Christianity as described in the foundation's statement of faith.
Fields of interest: Theological school/education; Christian agencies & churches.
Limitations: Applications not accepted. Giving on a national and international basis. No support for private foundations, camping or evangelism with a weak emphasis on discipleship. No grants to individuals, or for debt repayment projects, scholarship funds, environment funds, and research grants, No support for church operating budgets or building projects or for school/ college/university operating budgets or building projects.
Application information: Unsolicited requests for funds are not currently accepted.
Board meeting date(s): Apr.
Officers and Trustees:* William J. Bolthouse,* Pres.; Anthony L. Leggio,* Secy.; Stewart Fleeman,* Treas.; Fred Green, Exec. Dir.
Number of staff: 1 part-time support.
EIN: 770186343
Selected grants: The following grants are a representative sample of this grantmaker's funding activity:
$7,500,000 to National Christian Foundation, Alpharetta, GA, 2012. For unrestricted support.

326
The Otis Booth Foundation ✧
10431 Bellagio Rd.
Los Angeles, CA 90077-3818

Established in 1967 in CA.
Donor: Franklin Otis Booth, Jr.‡.
Foundation type: Independent foundation.
Financial data (yr. ended 11/30/13): Assets, $191,535,469 (M); expenditures, $17,698,502; qualifying distributions, $16,667,344; giving activities include $16,615,633 for 87 grants (high: $5,005,633; low: $1,000).
Purpose and activities: Giving primarily for education, as well as for the arts, hospitals and health organizations, and for children and youth services.
Fields of interest: Arts; Elementary/secondary education; Higher education; Education; Environment; Hospitals (general); Health organizations, association; Children/youth, services.
Limitations: Applications not accepted. Giving in the U.S., primarily in CA. No grants to individuals.
Application information: Contributes only to pre-selected organizations.
Officers and Trustees:* Lynn A. Booth,* Pres.; Loren Booth,* V.P. and Secy.; Palmer N. Murray,* V.P. and Treas.
EIN: 956140019
Selected grants: The following grants are a representative sample of this grantmaker's funding activity:
$3,600,000 to Natural History Museum of Los Angeles County, Los Angeles, CA, 2012.
$2,050,000 to Marlborough School, Los Angeles, CA, 2012.
$666,670 to Ronald Reagan Presidential Foundation, Simi Valley, CA, 2012.
$500,000 to California Agricultural Leadership Foundation, Sacramento, CA, 2012.
$500,000 to House Research Institute, Los Angeles, CA, 2012.
$250,000 to Chapman University, Orange, CA, 2012.
$150,000 to KIPP LA Schools, Los Angeles, CA, 2012.
$50,000 to Polytechnic School, Pasadena, CA, 2012.
$25,000 to Inner-City Arts, Los Angeles, CA, 2012.
$25,000 to New Noise Music Foundation, Santa Barbara, CA, 2012.

327
The Borch Foundation ✧ ☆
14315 Taos Dr.
Saratoga, CA 95070-5567 (408) 395-5585
Contact: Andrea W. Borch, C.E.O.

Established in 2007 in CA.
Donors: Christopher R. Borch; Andrea W. Borch; Sacardia, LLC.
Foundation type: Independent foundation.
Financial data (yr. ended 12/31/13): Assets, $2,554,795 (M); gifts received, $443,433; expenditures, $479,119; qualifying distributions, $475,454; giving activities include $473,675 for 21 grants (high: $390,775; low: $500).
Fields of interest: Higher education, university; Environment, water resources; Housing/shelter, development; Marine science.
Limitations: Applications accepted. Giving primarily in CA and SC. No grants to individuals.
Application information: Application form not required.
Initial approach: Letter
Deadline(s): None
Officers: Andrea W. Borch, C.E.O.; Christopher R. Borch, C.F.O.
EIN: 208777443

328
Albert & Elaine Borchard Foundation, Inc. ✧
22055 Clarendon St., Ste. 210
Woodland Hills, CA 91367-6355 (818) 888-2871
FAX: (818) 888-2872;
E-mail: info@borchardfoundation.org; Main URL: http://www.borchardfoundation.org/

Established in 1978 in CA.
Donors: B. Lawrence Brennan; Robert K. Johnson; Richard E. Kipper; O.W. Moyle III; Alzheimer's Association.
Foundation type: Independent foundation.
Financial data (yr. ended 07/31/13): Assets, $24,116,006 (M); expenditures, $1,858,261; qualifying distributions, $1,215,780; giving activities include $1,003,500 for 74 grants (high: $42,500; low: $2,500).
Purpose and activities: Giving primarily for youth development, health, human services, education, the arts, the environment, and for the elimination of poverty.
Fields of interest: Arts; Higher education; Education; Environment; Health care; Human services; Economically disadvantaged.
Type of support: Scholarship funds.
Limitations: Giving primarily in CA. No grants to individuals.
Publications: Application guidelines.
Application information: Full proposals are by invitation only, upon consideration of initial letter of inquiry. Application guidelines available on foundation web site.
Initial approach: Use online letter of inquiry format on foundation web site. Letter may not exceed 250 words
Copies of proposal: 6
Deadline(s): Feb. 1 and Aug. 1
Officers and Directors:* Edward D. Spurgeon,* Pres.; Janna Beling,* Exec. V.P.; Heidi Gelke,* Secy. and C.F.O.; Kristen Beling; Michael Spurgeon; Stephen Spurgeon, M.D.
EIN: 953294377
Selected grants: The following grants are a representative sample of this grantmaker's funding activity:
$100,000 to University of Southern California, Los Angeles, CA, 2011.
$40,000 to National Senior Citizens Law Center, Washington, DC, 2011.
$25,000 to Southern Center for Human Rights, Atlanta, GA, 2011.
$20,000 to Health Volunteers Overseas, Washington, DC, 2011.
$20,000 to Institute on Aging, San Francisco, CA, 2011.
$15,000 to CARE, San Francisco, CA, 2011.
$15,000 to Midnight Mission, Los Angeles, CA, 2011.
$12,500 to Foodbank of Southern California, Long Beach, CA, 2011.
$10,000 to House Research Institute, Los Angeles, CA, 2011.
$5,000 to Pet Adoption Fund, Canoga Park, CA, 2011.

329
Borina Foundation ✧
P.O. Box 117117
Burlingame, CA 94011

Established in 2003 in CA.
Foundation type: Independent foundation.
Financial data (yr. ended 12/31/13): Assets, $21,811,908 (M); expenditures, $7,281,971; qualifying distributions, $1,770,304; giving activities include $1,678,000 for 46 grants (high: $1,000,000; low: $250).
Purpose and activities: Giving primarily for education, youth and social services, and to a community foundation.
Fields of interest: Elementary/secondary education; Human services; Youth, services; Community/economic development; Foundations (community).
Limitations: Applications not accepted. Giving primarily in CA. No grants to individuals.
Application information: Unsolicited requests for funds not accepted.
Officers: William F. Locke-Paddon, Pres.; Sheila Burke, C.F.O.
Director: Robert H. Allen.
EIN: 680515701
Selected grants: The following grants are a representative sample of this grantmaker's funding activity:
$600,000 to Saint Francis Central Coast Catholic High School, Watsonville, CA, 2010.
$150,000 to YMCA, Watsonville Family, Watsonville, CA, 2011.
$51,500 to Cabrillo College Foundation, Aptos, CA, 2011.
$50,500 to Agricultural History Project, Watsonville, CA, 2011.
$40,000 to MAIA Foundation, Watsonville, CA, 2011.
$25,000 to Jean and Ed Kelly Foundation, Watsonville, CA, 2011.
$5,000 to Learning Ally, Palo Alto, CA, 2011. For general operations.
$1,200 to Aptos High School, Aptos, CA, 2011.
$1,000 to Napili Kai Foundation, Lahaina, HI, 2011.

330
The James G. Boswell Foundation ✧
101 W. Walnut St.
Pasadena, CA 91103-3636

Incorporated in 1947 in CA.
Donor: James G. Boswell†.
Foundation type: Independent foundation.
Financial data (yr. ended 12/31/13): Assets, $121,615,337 (M); expenditures, $2,989,368; qualifying distributions, $2,767,324; giving activities include $2,677,100 for 38 grants (high: $750,000; low: $1,000).
Purpose and activities: Giving primarily for education, health, youth development, agricultural education, and the environment.
Fields of interest: Education; Environment; Health care; Health organizations, association; Medical research, institute; Agriculture; Children/youth, services.
Type of support: General/operating support; Continuing support; Annual campaigns; Scholarship funds.
Limitations: Applications not accepted. Giving primarily in CA.
Application information: Contributes only to pre-selected organizations.
Board meeting date(s): Feb. and as required
Officers and Trustees:* James W. Boswell, Pres.; R. Sherman Railsback,* Secy.; James A. Henry, Exec. Dir.; R. Kenneth Dulin.
EIN: 956047326

331
Bothin Foundation ✧
1660 Bush St., Ste. 300
San Francisco, CA 94109-5308 (415) 561-6540
FAX: (415) 561-6477;
E-mail: skaufmann@pfs-llc.net; Main URL: http://www.pfs-llc.net/foundations/bothin-foundation
Grants List: http://www.pfs-llc.net/userfiles/kcfinder/files/bothin_grants_2013.pdf

Incorporated in 1917 in CA.
Donors: Henry E. Bothin†; Ellen Chabot Bothin†; Genevieve Bothin de Limur†.
Foundation type: Independent foundation.
Financial data (yr. ended 12/31/13): Assets, $40,000,473 (M); expenditures, $2,014,996; qualifying distributions, $1,629,155; giving activities include $1,347,320 for 58 grants (high: $50,000; low: $2,500).
Purpose and activities: Support for organizations providing direct services to low-income, at-risk children, youth and families, the elderly, and disabled. To a limited extent, grants may also be made to environmental agencies and arts organizations that serve youth predominately. The foundation prefers to make grants for capital, building, and equipment needs.
Fields of interest: Environment; Human services; Children/youth, services; Child development, services; Family services; Aging, centers/services; Homeless, human services; Disabilities, people with.
Type of support: Capital campaigns; Building/renovation; Equipment.
Limitations: Applications accepted. Giving primarily in CA, with emphasis on San Francisco, Marin, Sonoma and San Mateo counties. No support for religious organizations, or educational institutions (except those directly aiding the developmentally or learning disabled). No grants to individuals, or for general operating expenses, endowment drives, annual appeals, scholarships, medical research, or videos.
Publications: Application guidelines; Annual report; Grants list.
Application information: The Board prefers that three full years elapse between grants. The foundation has ceased its grant making in Santa Barbara. See foundation web site for application guidelines, procedures, and forms. Do not send audio-visual materials, binders or pamphlets, unless requested to do so. Application form not required.
Initial approach: Use online grants system on foundation web site
Copies of proposal: 1
Deadline(s): See web site for current deadlines
Board meeting date(s): Feb., May, and Oct.
Final notification: 2 to 3 months
Officers and Directors:* Lyman H. Casey,* Pres.; A. Michael Casey,* V.P. and Treas.; Devon Laycox, V.P.; Theodore Griffinger; Katherine Joiner; Pamela McCosker; Christian Miller; Laura King Pfaff; Paul Sussman.
EIN: 941196182
Selected grants: The following grants are a representative sample of this grantmaker's funding activity:

$50,000 to Saint Francis Foundation, San Francisco, CA, 2012. For Upgrades to the Bothin Burn Center.
$40,000 to Marine Science Institute, Redwood City, CA, 2012. To support the Upgrade of the Ship Engines to the Cleanest Marine Engines Possible.
$33,000 to Vida Verde Nature Education, San Gregorio, CA, 2012. For Purchase a Mini-Bus to Transport Participants.
$30,400 to Commonweal, Bolinas, CA, 2012. For Repairs and Ada Upgrades for the Pacific House.
$30,000 to Community Music Center, San Francisco, CA, 2012. For Technology Upgrade to Classrooms and Offices.
$30,000 to Larkin Street Youth Services, San Francisco, CA, 2012. To provide Cabinetry for New Location.
$28,700 to Enterprise for High School Students, San Francisco, CA, 2012. To support the Creation and Implementation of Online Job Bank.
$26,200 to Mateo Lodge, Redwood City, CA, 2012. For Repairs and Updates to a Social Rehabilitation Residential Facility of a Mental Health Agency.
$23,200 to Novato Human Needs Center, Novato, CA, 2012. To upgrade technology.
$20,800 to Bayview Association for Youth, San Francisco, CA, 2012. To support a Technology Upgrade.

332
James G. Bower Foundation ✧
(formerly Bower Foundation)
26 W. Micheltorena St.
Santa Barbara, CA 93101-7169 (805) 564-8814
Contact: Harvey Bottelsen, Chair.
E-mail: info@jsbowerfoundation.org; Main URL: http://www.jsbowerfoundation.org

Established in CA.
Donor: JSB Trusts.
Foundation type: Independent foundation.
Financial data (yr. ended 12/31/12): Assets, $56,194,325 (M); expenditures, $3,262,408; qualifying distributions, $2,994,506; giving activities include $2,395,000 for 24 grants (high: $1,485,000; low: $5,000).
Fields of interest: Performing arts centers; Education; Environment; Hospitals (general); Health organizations, association; Human services; Children/youth, services; Residential/custodial care, hospices.
Type of support: General/operating support.
Limitations: Applications accepted. Giving primarily in Santa Barbara, CA. No grants to individuals.
Publications: Application guidelines; Financial statement; Grants list.
Application information: Full proposals are by invitation only. Application guidelines and form available on foundation web site.
Initial approach: Submit initial proposal online, via foundation web site
Deadline(s): See foundation web site for latest deadlines
Officers: Harvey Bottelsen, Chair.; Jon Clark, Pres.; Christopher A. Jacobs, Secy.; David Alvarado, Treas.
EIN: 770229243

333
Bowes Family Foundation ✧ ☆
1 Maritime Plz., Ste. 1925
San Francisco, CA 94111-3530

Established in CA.
Donors: John G. Bowes; Frances F. Bowes.
Foundation type: Independent foundation.
Financial data (yr. ended 06/30/13): Assets, $1,292,708 (M); gifts received, $2,500,000; expenditures, $1,282,264; qualifying distributions, $1,277,773; giving activities include $1,277,773 for 16 grants (high: $1,148,023; low: $100).
Purpose and activities: Giving primarily for the arts and health care.
Fields of interest: Arts; Education; Health care.
Limitations: Applications not accepted. Giving primarily in San Francisco, CA and NY. No grants to individuals.
Application information: Unsolicited requests for funds not accepted.
Officers and Directors:* Frances F. Bowes,* Chair. and V.P.; Diana Bowes, Secy.; Elena Bowes; Alexandra Bowes Williamson.
EIN: 200489340
Selected grants: The following grants are a representative sample of this grantmaker's funding activity:
$301,230 to University of California San Francisco Foundation, San Francisco, CA, 2011.
$240,000 to Dia Center for the Arts, New York, NY, 2011.
$32,900 to American Patrons of the Tate Gallery Foundation, New York, NY, 2011.
$10,000 to Teach for America, San Francisco, CA, 2011.
$10,000 to United Religions Initiative, San Francisco, CA, 2011.
$5,000 to Fine Arts Museums of San Francisco, San Francisco, CA, 2011.
$2,500 to San Francisco Parks Trust, San Francisco, CA, 2011.
$1,000 to California Pacific Medical Center Foundation, San Francisco, CA, 2011.
$1,000 to Synergy School, San Francisco, CA, 2011.

334
William K. Bowes, Jr. Foundation ✧
c/o Pacific Foundation Services
1660 Bush St., Ste. 300
San Francisco, CA 94109-5308
Contact: Fiona Barrett, Prog. Off.
E-mail for Mary L. Gregory, Sr. Prog. Off.: mgregory@pfs-llc.net;E-mail for Fiona Barrett, Prog. Off., fbarrett@pfs-llc.net; Main URL: http://www.pfs-llc.net/bowes/bowes.html

Established in 1991 in CA.
Donor: William K. Bowes, Jr.
Foundation type: Independent foundation.
Financial data (yr. ended 12/31/13): Assets, $352,588,062 (M); expenditures, $41,309,721; qualifying distributions, $38,207,673; giving activities include $37,724,396 for 109 grants (high: $2,000,000; low: $250).
Purpose and activities: Giving primarily for civic institutions, education and medical research.
Fields of interest: Higher education; Medical research; Civil/human rights.
Type of support: General/operating support; Annual campaigns; Capital campaigns; Building/renovation; Scholarship funds.
Limitations: Applications not accepted. Giving primarily in CA. No grants to individuals.
Application information: Contributes only to pre-selected organizations.
Officers: William K. Bowes, Jr., Pres.; Douglas Tinker, Secy.-Treas.; Ronald J. Henrickson, C.F.O.
EIN: 943148482
Selected grants: The following grants are a representative sample of this grantmaker's funding activity:
$2,000,000 to Environmental Defense Fund, San Francisco Office, San Francisco, CA, 2012. For Corporate Partnerships Program.
$2,000,000 to Exploratorium, San Francisco, CA, 2012. For Capital Campaign.
$2,000,000 to Myelin Repair Foundation, Saratoga, CA, 2012. For Accelerated Research Collaboration.
$1,200,000 to Institute for Systems Biology, Seattle, WA, 2012. For move to new building, faculty recruitment and general support.
$1,000,000 to Sandler Foundation, San Francisco, CA, 2012. For Early Excellence Asthma Initiative.
$700,000 to University of California at Berkeley Foundation, Berkeley, CA, 2012. For Incentive Awards Scholarships Program.
$600,000 to Grace Cathedral, San Francisco, CA, 2012. For Centennial Campaign.
$500,000 to Fogarty Institute for Innovation, Mountain View, CA, 2012. For matching grant for general operating support.
$110,000 to Fine Arts Museums of San Francisco, De Young Museum, San Francisco, CA, 2012. For Youth Education Programs.
$100,000 to Teach for America, New York, NY, 2012. For National Growth Fund.

335
Bowman Family Foundation ✧
c/o Lawrence Bowman
1875 S. Grant St., Ste. 600
San Mateo, CA 94402-7013

Established in 2001 in CA.
Donors: Lawrence Bowman; Mark Hurley.
Foundation type: Independent foundation.
Financial data (yr. ended 05/31/13): Assets, $2,392,332 (M); gifts received, $10,000; expenditures, $527,684; qualifying distributions, $522,360; giving activities include $517,795 for 21 grants (high: $100,000; low: $1,000).
Fields of interest: Performing arts, orchestras; Education; Animals/wildlife; Human services; Marine science.
Limitations: Applications not accepted. Giving primarily in CA, Washington, DC; some funding also in HI. No grants to individuals.
Application information: Contributes only to pre-selected organizations.
Officers: Lawrence Bowman, C.E.O., Pres. and Co-Secy.; Cassandra Trainor, Co-Secy.
EIN: 943380924
Selected grants: The following grants are a representative sample of this grantmaker's funding activity:
$85,000 to San Francisco Symphony, San Francisco, CA, 2011. For general budget.
$85,000 to Wildlife Conservation Network, Los Altos, CA, 2010. For general budget.
$50,000 to Racing for Our Heroes, Dallas, TX, 2011. For general budget.
$50,000 to San Francisco Symphony, San Francisco, CA, 2010. For general budget.

$40,000 to Racing for Our Heroes, Dallas, TX, 2011. For general budget.
$27,000 to Kauai Pacific School, Kilauea, HI, 2011. For general budget.
$20,000 to Snow Leopard Conservancy, Sonoma, CA, 2011. For general budget.
$15,000 to Sierra Club Foundation, San Francisco, CA, 2011. For general budget.
$15,000 to Silicon Valley Community Foundation, Mountain View, CA, 2011. For general budget.
$10,000 to Humane Society, Hawaiian, Honolulu, HI, 2010. For general budget.
$10,000 to Salvation Army of Sioux Falls, Sioux Falls, SD, 2011. For general budget.
$10,000 to YMCA of Silicon Valley, San Jose, CA, 2011. For general budget.
$5,000 to HELPHOPELIVE, Radnor, PA, 2010. For general budget.
$5,000 to Humane Society, Kauai, Lihue, HI, 2011. For general budget.

336
Linda Brandes Foundation ✧

P.O. Box 535
Rancho Santa Fe, CA 92067-0535 (858) 756-9850
FAX: (858) 756-9865;
E-mail: info@lindabrandes.org; Main URL: http://www.lindabrandesfoundation.com

Established in 2005 in CA.
Donors: Brandes Family Foundation; Linda Brandes.
Foundation type: Independent foundation.
Financial data (yr. ended 12/31/12): Assets, $9,341,336 (M); expenditures, $712,077; qualifying distributions, $585,416; giving activities include $585,416 for grants.
Fields of interest: Human services; Family services.
Limitations: Applications not accepted. Giving primarily in CA.
Application information: Unsolicited requests for funds not accepted.
Officer: Linda Brandes, Pres.
Director: Karen Nielson.
EIN: 562511857

337
Saul Brandman Foundation ✧

9595 Wilshire Blvd., No. 511
Beverly Hills, CA 90212-2505

Established in 1993 in CA.
Donor: Saul Brandman.
Foundation type: Independent foundation.
Financial data (yr. ended 12/31/13): Assets, $31,372,435 (M); gifts received, $6,157,498; expenditures, $1,941,568; qualifying distributions, $1,938,835; giving activities include $649,767 for 36 grants (high: $119,354; low: $138).
Purpose and activities: Giving primarily for education and human services.
Fields of interest: Higher education; Education; Medical research, institute; Human services; Jewish federated giving programs; Children; Aging.
Limitations: Applications not accepted. Giving primarily in CA.
Application information: Unsolicited requests for funds not accepted.
Officers: Joyce Christian O'Donnell, Pres.; Lisa Morgan, C.F.O.
EIN: 954456430
Selected grants: The following grants are a representative sample of this grantmaker's funding activity:
$3,220,500 to Los Angeles Jewish Home for the Aging, Reseda, CA, 2011. For medical care for elderly.
$1,250,000 to Chapman University, Orange, CA, 2011.
$842,425 to American Friends of the Hebrew University, Los Angeles, CA, 2011.
$500,300 to Beit TShuvah, Los Angeles, CA, 2011.
$500,000 to UCLA Foundation, Los Angeles, CA, 2011.
$418,400 to Brandman University, Irvine, CA, 2011.
$253,500 to Cedars-Sinai Medical Center, Los Angeles, CA, 2011.
$250,000 to Our House, Los Angeles, CA, 2011.
$76,350 to Jewish Free Loan Association, Los Angeles, CA, 2011. For nursing program.
$10,000 to City of Hope, Los Angeles, CA, 2011.

338
Branson Family Foundation ✧ ☆

701 Los Ninos Way
Los Altos, CA 94022-1508 (650) 917-1737
Contact: Cheryl Branson, Pres.
Main URL: http://bransonfamilyfoundation.bravesites.com

Established in 2006 in CA.
Donors: Ken Branson; Cheryl Branson.
Foundation type: Independent foundation.
Financial data (yr. ended 12/31/13): Assets, $11,805,580 (M); gifts received, $5,743,500; expenditures, $492,119; qualifying distributions, $465,317; giving activities include $460,000 for 30 grants (high: $75,000; low: $1,000).
Purpose and activities: Giving to organizations in the areas of disaster relief, humanitarian aid, economic development, and the environment.
Fields of interest: Education; Health care; Safety/disasters; Human services; Community/economic development.
Publications: IRS Form 990 or 990-PF printed copy available upon request.
Application information: Application form not required.
Initial approach: Contact foundation
Deadline(s): None
Officers and Directors:* Cheryl Branson,* Pres.; Ken Branson,* C.F.O.; Cynthia Lamparter.
EIN: 204963649
Selected grants: The following grants are a representative sample of this grantmaker's funding activity:
$40,000 to Community AIDS Response, South Africa, 2013.
$40,000 to Doctors Without Borders USA, New York, NY, 2013.
$40,000 to International Rescue Committee, New York, NY, 2013.
$20,000 to Heifer Project International, Little Rock, AR, 2013. For economic development.
$19,000 to Environmental Defense Fund, New York, NY, 2013. For environmental protection.
$15,000 to Salvation Army, 2013.
$15,000 to Second Harvest Food Bank, 2013.
$10,000 to Planned Parenthood Federation of America, New York, NY, 2013. For family planning.
$5,000 to Global Fund for Women, San Francisco, CA, 2013. For human rights.
$5,000 to TechnoServe, Washington, DC, 2013. For economic development.

339
The Donald Bren Foundation ✧ ☆

P.O. Box 3090
Newport Beach, CA 92658-3090

Established in 1986 in CA.
Donors: Donald L. Bren; TIC Investment Company.
Foundation type: Independent foundation.
Financial data (yr. ended 11/30/13): Assets, $115,656,424 (M); gifts received, $94,478,429; expenditures, $2,588,711; qualifying distributions, $2,124,694; giving activities include $2,115,000 for 6 grants (high: $1,670,000; low: $20,000).
Fields of interest: Higher education; Medical research, institute; Social sciences, public policy.
Type of support: Endowments; Professorships.
Limitations: Applications not accepted. Giving primarily in CA. No grants to individuals.
Application information: Contributes only to pre-selected organizations.
Officers and Directors:* Donald L. Bren,* Chair. and Pres.; John A. Flynn, Exec. V.P., Secy., and C.F.O.; Gerald Parsky; Frank Quinlan; Stan Ross; Peter Ueberroth; Hon. Pete Wilson.
EIN: 954094426

340
The Mervyn L. Brenner Foundation, Inc. ✧

30 Van Ness Ave., Ste. 3600
San Francisco, CA 94102-6065

Incorporated in 1961 in CA.
Donor: Mervyn L. Brenner†.
Foundation type: Independent foundation.
Financial data (yr. ended 08/31/13): Assets, $10,956,634 (M); expenditures, $1,043,580; qualifying distributions, $1,004,701; giving activities include $1,002,200 for 130 grants (high: $51,500; low: $300).
Fields of interest: Arts; Elementary/secondary education; Higher education; Education; Health care; Human services; Children/youth, services; Jewish agencies & synagogues.
Type of support: General/operating support; Annual campaigns.
Limitations: Applications not accepted. Giving primarily in CA. No grants to individuals.
Application information: Contributes only to pre-selected organizations.
Officers: John R. Gentry, Pres.; Katherine Bukstein, V.P.; Michael Helms, V.P.; Marc H. Monheimer, Secy.; Robert K. Taylor, Treas.
EIN: 946088679
Selected grants: The following grants are a representative sample of this grantmaker's funding activity:
$8,000 to Stanford University, Graduate School, Stanford, CA, 2013. For public/general.
$3,000 to University of Chicago, Law School, Chicago, IL, 2013. For public/general.

341
Breslauer-Soref Foundation ✧

5984 Spinnaker Bay Dr.
Long Beach, CA 90803-6820

Established in 2005 in CA.
Donors: The Investigative Project on Terrorism Foundation; SEE-USA; World Union for Progressive Judaism; Ronald McDonald Charities.
Foundation type: Independent foundation.

Financial data (yr. ended 12/31/13): Assets, $9,566,486 (M); expenditures, $767,296; qualifying distributions, $702,178; giving activities include $695,740 for 23 grants (high: $250,000; low: $600).
Fields of interest: Aquariums; Human services; Foundations (community); Jewish federated giving programs; Jewish agencies & synagogues.
Limitations: Applications not accepted. Giving primarily in CA; some funding also in New York, NY and Washington, DC.
Application information: Contributes only to pre-selected organizations.
Officers: James M. Breslauer, Pres.; Elizabeth H. Breslauer, Secy.; Frank Parlato, Treas.
EIN: 202100908
Selected grants: The following grants are a representative sample of this grantmaker's funding activity:
$115,000 to Aquarium of the Pacific, Long Beach, CA, 2011.
$30,000 to Abraham Geiger College, Potsdam, Germany, 2010. For general support.
$25,000 to Investigative Project on Terrorism Foundation, Washington, DC, 2011.
$15,000 to Jewish Community Foundation, Los Angeles, CA, 2011.
$5,000 to American Islamic Congress, Washington, DC, 2011.
$1,000 to Aquarium of the Pacific, Long Beach, CA, 2011.
$1,000 to Long Beach Day Nursery, Long Beach, CA, 2011.

342
Brewster West Foundation ✧
57 Post St., Ste. 503
San Francisco, CA 94104-5020

Established in 1994 in CA.
Donors: Eric Johnson; Barbara B. Johnson.
Foundation type: Independent foundation.
Financial data (yr. ended 12/31/12): Assets, $4,346,848 (M); expenditures, $480,715; qualifying distributions, $458,125; giving activities include $433,000 for 34 grants (high: $30,000; low: $1,000).
Purpose and activities: Giving primarily for Episcopal churches, education, and human services.
Fields of interest: Museums; Education; Food banks; Human services; Protestant agencies & churches.
Type of support: General/operating support.
Limitations: Applications not accepted. Giving primarily in CA. No grants to individuals.
Application information: Contributes only to pre-selected organizations.
Trustees: Barbara B. Johnson; Eric L. Johnson; Martine B. Larsen; Barbara Loveless; Richard G. Malone.
EIN: 680343603
Selected grants: The following grants are a representative sample of this grantmaker's funding activity:
$25,000 to SF-Marin Food Bank, San Francisco, CA, 2011.
$20,000 to De Marillac Academy, San Francisco, CA, 2011.
$15,000 to Boys Hope Girls Hope of San Francisco, San Francisco, CA, 2011.
$15,000 to Canine Companions for Independence, Santa Rosa, CA, 2011. For general fund.
$15,000 to Capital Research Center, Washington, DC, 2011. For general purposes.
$15,000 to De Marillac Academy, San Francisco, CA, 2011.
$15,000 to Manhattan Institute for Policy Research, New York, NY, 2011.
$15,000 to Stanford University, Stanford, CA, 2011. For general purposes.
$12,500 to Sutter Visiting Nurse Association and Hospice, A Sutter Health Affiliate, Emeryville, CA, 2010.
$10,000 to Henry Ohlhoff House, San Francisco, CA, 2010.
$10,000 to Saint Francis Foundation, San Francisco, CA, 2011.
$10,000 to San Francisco Zoological Society, San Francisco, CA, 2011.
$5,000 to Bay Area Tumor Institute, Oakland, CA, 2010.

343
The Brin Wojcicki Foundation ✧
(formerly The Brin Foundation)
1801 Page Mill Rd.
Palo Alto, CA 94304-1216

Established in 2004 in CA.
Donor: Sergey Brin.
Foundation type: Independent foundation.
Financial data (yr. ended 12/31/13): Assets, $1,033,586,191 (M); gifts received, $186,897,825; expenditures, $26,838,839; qualifying distributions, $25,652,724; giving activities include $25,428,560 for 59 grants (high: $5,000,000; low: $2,500).
Purpose and activities: Giving primarily for private grantmaking foundation, as well as for human services; funding also for a Parkinson's disease organization.
Fields of interest: Parkinson's disease; Human services; Foundations (private grantmaking).
Limitations: Applications not accepted. Giving primarily in CA; some funding also in NY and VA. No grants to individuals.
Application information: Contributes only to pre-selected organizations.
Officers and Directors:* Sergey Brin,* Pres.; Michael Brin, Secy.; Erik Edwards, Gen. Counsel; Anne Wojcicki.
EIN: 201922947
Selected grants: The following grants are a representative sample of this grantmaker's funding activity:
$1,000,000 to Ashoka: Innovators for the Public, Arlington, VA, 2012. For general support.
$1,000,000 to Tipping Point Community, San Francisco, CA, 2012. For general support.
$780,891 to Parkinsons Institute, Sunnyvale, CA, 2012. For general support.
$525,000 to Human Rights Foundation, New York, NY, 2012. For general support.
$500,000 to Electronic Frontier Foundation, San Francisco, CA, 2012. For general support.
$500,000 to Wikimedia Foundation, San Francisco, CA, 2012. For general support.
$375,000 to Stanford University, Stanford, CA, 2012. For general support.
$150,000 to Creative Commons, Mountain View, CA, 2012. For general support.
$35,000 to Los Altos Community Foundation, Los Altos, CA, 2012. For general support.
$25,000 to DonorsChoose.org, New York, NY, 2012. For general support.

344
The Judy and Bernard Briskin Charitable Foundation ✧
c/o Kenneth Goldman
10100 Santa Monica Blvd., Ste. 300
Los Angeles, CA 90067

Established in CA.
Donors: Bernard Briskin; Judy Briskin.
Foundation type: Independent foundation.
Financial data (yr. ended 12/31/13): Assets, $12,858,531 (M); expenditures, $4,496,161; qualifying distributions, $4,559,739; giving activities include $4,489,716 for 5 grants (high: $3,985,216; low: $1,500).
Fields of interest: Education; Philanthropy/voluntarism; Jewish agencies & synagogues.
Limitations: Applications not accepted. Giving primarily in CA. No grants to individuals.
Application information: Contributes only to pre-selected organizations.
Directors: Kenneth A. Goldman; Julie Harelson; Steve Massman.
EIN: 954693445

345
Brittingham Family Foundation ✧
1482 E. Valley Rd., Ste. 703
Santa Barbara, CA 93108-1200
E-mail: info@brittinghamfoundation.org; Main URL: http://www.brittinghamfamilyfoundation.org

Established in 1997 in CA.
Foundation type: Independent foundation.
Financial data (yr. ended 12/31/13): Assets, $47,656,209 (M); expenditures, $4,248,126; qualifying distributions, $3,637,583; giving activities include $3,349,678 for 75 grants (high: $680,000; low: $1,000).
Purpose and activities: Giving primarily for education, art, social services, youth, health, and the environment.
Fields of interest: Arts; Education; Environment; Human services; Children/youth, services.
Limitations: Applications accepted. Giving primarily in CA, with emphasis on Santa Barbara and WI; No giving for institutions outside of the U.S. No grants to individuals.
Application information:
Initial approach: Online application
Deadline(s): None; however applications received by Nov. 1 will most likely be considered for funding in the following calendar year.
Officers and Directors:* Scott Brittingham,* Chair. and Pres.; Ella Brittingham,* Exec. V.P.
EIN: 262992045

346
The Broad Art Foundation ✧
10900 Wilshire Blvd., 12th Fl.
Los Angeles, CA 90024-6532
Contact: Eli Broad, Tr.
Main URL: http://www.broadartfoundation.org
Eli and Edyth Broad's Giving Pledge Profile: http://glasspockets.org/philanthropy-in-focus/eye-on-the-giving-pledge/profiles/broad
GiveSmart: http://www.givesmart.org/Stories/Donors/Eli-Broad

Established in 1984 in CA.
Donors: Eli Broad; Edythe L. Broad.

Foundation type: Operating foundation.
Financial data (yr. ended 12/31/12): Assets, $937,124,622 (M); gifts received, $26,612,646; expenditures, $5,435,084; qualifying distributions, $15,961,340; giving activities include $576,693 for 34 grants (high: $87,000; low: $150), and $14,959,411 for foundation-administered programs.
Purpose and activities: The Broad Art Foundation operates as an educational and lending resource for contemporary art and is dedicated to building a collection that reflects the scope and diversity of the art of our time.
Fields of interest: Museums (art); Arts.
Type of support: General/operating support.
Limitations: Applications not accepted. Giving primarily in CA and NY. No grants to individuals.
Publications: Informational brochure.
Application information: Contributes only to pre-selected organizations.
Manager: Jeannine Guido.
Trustee: Eli Broad.
Number of staff: 6
EIN: 954664939
Selected grants: The following grants are a representative sample of this grantmaker's funding activity:
$87,000 to Museum of Contemporary Art, Los Angeles, CA, 2012. Toward purchase of Vezzoli, Crying Portrait of Patitz'.
$25,000 to Walker Art Center, Minneapolis, MN, 2012. Toward Cindy Sherman retrospective exhibit.
$25,000 to Whitney Museum of American Art, New York, NY, 2012. Toward Exhibition Richard Artschwager.
$5,000 to College Art Association, New York, NY, 2012. For the Student and Emerging Professionals Program.
$5,000 to Museum of the City of New York, New York, NY, 2012. Toward Second Avenue Meets Broadway.
$2,500 to Whitney Museum of American Art, New York, NY, 2012. For the Whitney Fellow Programming.

347
Eli & Edythe Broad Foundation
(also known as The Broad Foundation)
2121 Ave. of the Stars, Ste. 3000
Los Angeles, CA 90067-5058 (310) 954-5000
FAX: (310) 954-5051;
E-mail: info@broadfoundation.org; Main URL: http://www.broadfoundation.org/
Eli and Edythe Broad's Giving Pledge Profile: http://glasspockets.org/philanthropy-in-focus/eye-on-the-giving-pledge/profiles/broad
E-Newsletter: http://broadeducation.org/news/press_releases/index.html
Facebook: http://www.facebook.com/pages/Los-Angeles-CA/The-Broad-Foundation/60623123387
GiveSmart: http://www.givesmart.org/Stories/Donors/Eli-Broad
Twitter: http://www.twitter.com/BroadFoundation

Established in 1999 in CA; As of Jan 1, 2007, the Eli & Edythe L. Broad Foundation merged into the Broad Foundation.
Donors: Eli Broad; U.S. Department of Education.
Foundation type: Independent foundation.
Financial data (yr. ended 12/31/13): Assets, $1,889,617,384 (M); gifts received, $144,090,423; expenditures, $141,758,378; qualifying distributions, $120,086,211; giving activities include $111,692,581 for 289 grants (high: $54,090,973; low: $500), and $1,337,631 for 2 loans/program-related investments (high: $920,000; low: $417,631).
Purpose and activities: The foundation's mission is to dramatically improve K-12 urban public education through better governance, management, labor relations and competition; make significant contributions to advance major scientific and medical research; foster public appreciation of contemporary art by increasing access for audiences world wide and contributing to major civic projects in Los Angeles.
Fields of interest: Arts; Elementary/secondary school reform; Biomedicine; Medical research; Science.
Type of support: Program-related investments/loans.
Limitations: Applications accepted. Giving on a national basis. No grants to individuals.
Publications: Annual report.
Application information: See foundation web site for each program area's policies and guidelines. Application form not required.
Copies of proposal: 1
Deadline(s): Rolling basis
Officers and Directors: Eli Broad,* Chair.; Bruce Reed, Pres.; Gerun Riley, V.P. and Chief of Staff; Cindy Quane, C.F.O.; Marc A. Schwartz, C.I.O.; Edythe L. Broad.
Number of staff: 29 full-time professional; 4 full-time support.
EIN: 954686318
Selected grants: The following grants are a representative sample of this grantmaker's funding activity:
$85,000,000 to Broad Institute, Cambridge, MA, 2012. To support genomic and biomedicine research.
$8,000,000 to Broad Center for the Management of School Systems, Los Angeles, CA, 2012. To identify, train and support successful leaders of public school systems.
$6,450,000 to Michigan State University, East Lansing, MI, 2012. For Eli and Edythe Broad Art Museum at MSU.
$5,357,820 to Michigan Education Excellence Foundation, Lansing, MI, 2012. For start-up support for Education Achievement Authority.
$5,000,000 to University of California, San Francisco, CA, 2012. To create a center to accelerate the development of stem cell research at UCSF and provide funding for the building and the center.
$5,000,000 to University of Southern California, Los Angeles, CA, 2012. For The Eli and Edythe Broad Center for Regenerative Medicine and Stem Cell Research.
$3,000,000 to Museum of Contemporary Art, Los Angeles, CA, 2012. For operations, exhibitions, and endowment support.
$129,000 to University of Washington, Center on Reinventing Public Education, Seattle, WA, 2012. For a study of new models to improve the efficiency and impact of state departments of education.
$110,000 to Stanford University, Stanford, CA, 2012. For Inflammatory bowel disease (IBD) Research Funding.
$5,000 to Studio in a School Association, New York, NY, 2012. For general support.

348
Broad Reach Foundation ✧
2118 Wilshire Blvd., P.O. Box 383
Santa Monica, CA 90403-5704
E-mail: crlal@earthlink.net

Established in 2001 in CA.
Donors: David K. Richards; Carol A. Richards.
Foundation type: Independent foundation.
Financial data (yr. ended 12/31/13): Assets, $102,374,675 (M); gifts received, $22,341,000; expenditures, $4,630,039; qualifying distributions, $4,183,066; giving activities include $4,000,000 for 3 grants (high: $2,000,000; low: $1,000,000).
Purpose and activities: Giving primarily to an organization that is dedicated to providing professional and innovative services to individuals and institutions committed to accelerating positive social change through philanthropy.
Fields of interest: Philanthropy/voluntarism.
Limitations: Applications not accepted. No grants to individuals.
Application information: Contributes only to pre-selected organizations.
Board meeting date(s): As needed
Officers and Directors:* Carol A. Richards,* Pres.; David K. Richards,* Treas.
Number of staff: 1 part-time professional.
EIN: 954861421

349
Broadcom Foundation ✧
5300 California Ave., Ste. 14067
Irvine, CA 92617-3038 (949) 926-9500
FAX: (949) 926-9244;
E-mail: feedback@broadcomfoundation.org; Main URL: http://www.broadcomfoundation.org/

Established in 2009 in CA.
Donor: Broadcom Corp.
Foundation type: Company-sponsored foundation.
Financial data (yr. ended 12/31/12): Assets, $74,498,215 (M); expenditures, $4,191,967; qualifying distributions, $3,845,419; giving activities include $3,526,100 for 96 grants (high: $1,000,000; low: $500).
Purpose and activities: The foundation supports programs designed to advance STEM education; inspire youth to pursue careers in engineering; reduce economic disparity; close the STEM education gap among women, ethnic, and minority populations; improve quality of life in Broadcom communities; create opportunities for volunteerism and civic engagement among Broadcom employees; and strengthen Broadcom Corporation social responsibility and global citizenship.
Fields of interest: Elementary/secondary education; Higher education; Education; Health care; Human services; Economic development; Mathematics; Engineering/technology; Science; Youth; Minorities; Women.
Type of support: Sponsorships; Continuing support; Program development; Research; Employee volunteer services.
Limitations: Applications accepted. Giving primarily in areas of company operations in Tempe, AZ, Irvine, Petaluma, San Diego, San Jose, Santa Clara, and Sunnyvale, CA, Colorado Springs, Fort Collins, and Longmont, CO, Duluth, GA, Andover, Burlington, and Marlborough, MA, Germantown, MD, Edina, MN, Morrisville, NC, Matawan, NJ, Yardley, PA, Austin and Houston, TX, and Federal Way, WA; giving also internationally in select cities in Australia, Belgium,

China, Denmark, France, Greece, India, Israel, Japan, Korea, Netherlands, Singapore, Spain, Taiwan, and United Kingdom. No support for fraternal, labor, political, or social organizations, political candidates, sectarian religious organizations, private K-12 schools, trade or business associations, discriminatory organizations, third party organizations, or agencies normally financed by government sources. No grants to individuals, or for equipment, capital campaigns, advertising journals or booklets, congresses, symposiums, or meetings, scholarships, fellowships, lobbying, technical research in support of Broadcom products, sporting events, tickets, or sponsorships, travel, trips, tours, or cultural exchange programs, university administrative, management, or indirect fees, endowments, ongoing general operating support, debt reduction, memorial tributes, special fundraising event table or ticket purchase, or matching gifts.
Publications: Application guidelines; Annual report; IRS Form 990 or 990-PF printed copy available upon request.
Application information: Most of the foundation funding is by invitation only; however qualified organizations may apply during the open proposal period. Application form required.
Initial approach: Complete online application
Deadline(s): Apr. 30 to June 30
Final notification: 3 months
Officers and Directors:* Scott McGregor,* Pres.; Lauri D. Fischer, Secy.; Gregg S. Morrison, C.F.O.; Maria Wronski, Treas.; Paula Golden, Exec. Dir.; Eric K. Brandt; Arthur Chong; Henry Samueli, Ph.D.; Terri L. Timberman.
EIN: 264754581

350
Dana & Albert R. Broccoli Charitable Foundation ✧
2400 Broadway, Ste. 310
Santa Monica, CA 90404-3096

Established in 1980 in CA.
Donors: Albert R. Broccoli†; Dana Broccoli†; Jane Wilson; Michael G. Wilson; Christina Broccoli; Dana Broccoli Administrative Trust.
Foundation type: Independent foundation.
Financial data (yr. ended 12/31/12): Assets, $0 (M); gifts received, $1,000,000; expenditures, $1,587,642; qualifying distributions, $1,419,290; giving activities include $1,419,290 for 28 grants (high: $400,000; low: $1,000).
Purpose and activities: Giving primarily for the arts, education, health, and human services.
Fields of interest: Museums (science/technology); Arts; Higher education; Education; Hospitals (general); Human services.
Type of support: General/operating support; Scholarship funds.
Limitations: Applications not accepted. Giving primarily in CA; some funding also in London, England. No grants to individuals.
Application information: Contributes only to pre-selected organizations.
Officers: Michael G. Wilson, Pres.; David Pope, Secy.; Deborah Arvesen, Treas.
Director: Burton Forester.
EIN: 953502889

351
The Clarence S. Brooks Foundation ✧
8501 Wilshire Blvd., Ste. 330
Beverly Hills, CA 90211-3128

Established in 2004 in CA.
Donor: Clarence S. Brooks.
Foundation type: Independent foundation.
Financial data (yr. ended 09/30/12): Assets, $14,208,282 (M); gifts received, $396; expenditures, $4,551,333; qualifying distributions, $4,005,000; giving activities include $4,005,000 for grants.
Purpose and activities: Giving primarily for Jewish education.
Fields of interest: Education; Jewish agencies & synagogues.
Limitations: Applications not accepted. Giving primarily in CA and NY. No grants to individuals.
Application information: Contributes only to pre-selected organizations.
Officers: Jeffrey Ratner, Pres.; Irene Gelfen, Secy.
EIN: 201835676

352
Diane and Dorothy Brooks Foundation ✧
(formerly Diane Brooks Charitable Foundation)
10100 Santa Monica Blvd., Ste. 1050
Los Angeles, CA 90067-4143

Established in 2005 in CA.
Donor: James L. Brooks.
Foundation type: Independent foundation.
Financial data (yr. ended 12/31/13): Assets, $25,515,324 (M); gifts received, $15,000,000; expenditures, $567,321; qualifying distributions, $538,200; giving activities include $538,200 for 26 grants (high: $100,000; low: $1,000).
Fields of interest: Higher education, university; Hospitals (general); Mental health/crisis services, association; Medical research.
Limitations: Applications not accepted. Giving primarily in CA. No grants to individuals.
Application information: Contributes only to pre-selected organizations.
Officers: James L. Brooks, Pres.; William Broder, C.F.O. and Secy.; Amy Brooks, V.P.; Chloe Brooks, V.P.; Cooper Brooks, V.P.; Joseph Brooks, V.P.
EIN: 202653929

353
Buchheit Foundation ✧
c/o Frank, Rimerman & Co., LLP
1801 Page Mill Rd.
Palo Alto, CA 94304-1216

Established in 2005 in CA.
Donor: Paul Buchheit.
Foundation type: Independent foundation.
Financial data (yr. ended 06/30/13): Assets, $10,122,948 (M); expenditures, $551,285; qualifying distributions, $525,000; giving activities include $525,000 for 1 grant.
Fields of interest: Philanthropy/voluntarism.
Limitations: Applications not accepted. Giving primarily in Albany, NY. No grants to individuals.
Application information: Contributes only to pre-selected organizations.
Trustee: Paul Buchheit.
EIN: 203830425

354
Vladimir & Araxia Buckhantz Foundation ✧
c/o Crowe Horwath LLP
176 S. Beachwood Dr.
Los Angeles, CA 90004-3826

Foundation type: Independent foundation.
Financial data (yr. ended 02/28/13): Assets, $1 (M); expenditures, $653,665; qualifying distributions, $602,070; giving activities include $602,070 for grants.
Fields of interest: Arts; Hospitals (general); Human services; Youth, services; Jewish federated giving programs; Social sciences.
Limitations: Applications not accepted. Giving primarily in Los Angeles, CA and New York, NY.
Application information: Contributes only to pre-selected organizations.
Trustee: Diana Buckhantz.
EIN: 906109515
Selected grants: The following grants are a representative sample of this grantmaker's funding activity:
$30,000 to Los Angeles Alliance for a New Economy, Los Angeles, CA, 2013. For organization's charitable purpose.

355
Ronald W. Burkle Foundation ✧
c/o Matgaret Brown
9130 W. Sunset Blvd.
Los Angeles, CA 90069-3110 (310) 789-7200
Main URL: http://burklefoundation.com/

Established in 1998 in CA.
Donors: Ronald W. Burkle; OA3, LLC.
Foundation type: Independent foundation.
Financial data (yr. ended 12/31/13): Assets, $13,145 (M); gifts received, $1,775,379; expenditures, $1,804,779; qualifying distributions, $1,791,955; giving activities include $1,778,991 for 47 grants (high: $250,000; low: $1,000).
Fields of interest: Arts education; Higher education; Medical research; Human services.
Limitations: Applications accepted. Giving in the U.S., with emphasis on CA, as well as some emphasis in New York, NY and Canada. No grants to individuals.
Application information: Application form required.
Initial approach: Letter of inquiry
Deadline(s): None
Officers and Director:* Ronald W. Burkle,* Pres. and C.E.O.; Robert P. Bermingham, C.F.O. and Secy.
EIN: 954664750

356
Burnand-Partridge Foundation ✧
c/o H. Scott Partridge Et Al
5699 Country Club Dr.
Rohnert Park, CA 94928-1762

Established in 2001 in CA.
Donor: Kathryn B. Partridge†.
Foundation type: Independent foundation.
Financial data (yr. ended 12/31/12): Assets, $15,892,767 (M); expenditures, $717,551; qualifying distributions, $460,000; giving activities include $460,000 for grants.

Purpose and activities: Scholarship awards to graduating students who will be attending Santa Barbara College.
Fields of interest: Education.
Type of support: Scholarship funds.
Limitations: Applications not accepted. Giving primarily in Santa Barbara, CA.
Application information: Unsolicited requests for funds not accepted.
Trustees: Sherry E. Kimball; Charles Kent Partridge, Sr.; Charles W. Partridge, Jr.; Herbert Scott Partridge; Carolyn B. Welch.
EIN: 776203456

357
The Burnham Foundation ✧
110 W. A St., Ste. 1000
San Diego, CA 92101-3705

Established in 1980 in CA.
Donors: Malin Burnham; Roberta Burnham; Burnham Way.
Foundation type: Independent foundation.
Financial data (yr. ended 12/31/13): Assets, $5,257,058 (M); gifts received, $3,135; expenditures, $1,209,513; qualifying distributions, $1,143,119; giving activities include $1,143,119 for 55 grants (high: $255,000; low: $210).
Purpose and activities: Giving primarily for higher education, as well as for health associations, children, youth and social services, YMCAs, and to the United Way.
Fields of interest: Arts; Secondary school/education; Higher education; Health organizations, association; Cancer research; Human services; YM/YWCAs & YM/YWHAs; Children/youth, services; United Ways and Federated Giving Programs.
Limitations: Applications not accepted. Giving primarily in San Diego, CA. No grants to individuals.
Application information: Contributes only to pre-selected organizations.
Officers and Directors:* Malin Burnham,* Pres.; Roberta Burnham,* V.P.; Kit Sparks, Treas.; George Delafield, Esq.; Robert Lauer; Bruce Merrice.
EIN: 953565278
Selected grants: The following grants are a representative sample of this grantmaker's funding activity:
$135,000 to Campanile Foundation, San Diego, CA, 2012. For Sue Russell scholarship fund.
$75,000 to National Conflict Resolution Center, San Diego, CA, 2012. For Peacemaker honorary committee.
$66,000 to University of San Diego, San Diego, CA, 2012. For Burnham Moores Center for Real Estate.
$50,000 to Mercy Hospital Foundation, San Diego, CA, 2012. To assist with medical care.
$50,000 to Stanford University, Stanford, CA, 2012. For DAPER Coaches' housing fund.
$15,000 to San Diego Education Fund, San Diego, CA, 2012. For Rainforest art project.
$10,000 to Monarch School, San Diego, CA, 2012. For Children's Champion Program.

358
Burns Family Foundation ✧
2055 Woodside Rd., Ste. 250
Redwood City, CA 94061-3379

Established in CA.
Donor: Susan T. Burns‡.
Foundation type: Independent foundation.
Financial data (yr. ended 12/31/12): Assets, $27,432,607 (M); expenditures, $1,206,395; qualifying distributions, $1,170,600; giving activities include $1,170,600 for grants.
Fields of interest: Human services; Foundations (public); Catholic agencies & churches.
Officers: Trina R. Dean, Co-Pres.; Tori A. Burns, Co-Pres.; Kelli Kellerman, Secy.-Treas.
EIN: 261120529

359
Fritz B. Burns Foundation ✧
21800 Oxnard St., No. 490
Woodland Hills, CA 91367-7532 (818) 840-8802
Contact: Rex J. Rawlinson, Pres.

Incorporated in 1955 in CA.
Donor: Fritz B. Burns‡.
Foundation type: Independent foundation.
Financial data (yr. ended 09/30/13): Assets, $165,688,610 (M); expenditures, $9,447,277; qualifying distributions, $7,645,182; giving activities include $7,227,293 for 25 grants (high: $3,207,293; low: $25,000).
Purpose and activities: Grants primarily for education, hospitals and medical research organizations; support also for Roman Catholic religious associations and, social welfare agencies, and church support.
Fields of interest: Higher education; Education; Hospitals (general); Medical research, institute; Human services; Catholic federated giving programs; Catholic agencies & churches.
Type of support: Program-related investments/loans.
Limitations: Applications accepted. Giving primarily in the Los Angeles, CA, area; some giving also in Provo, UT. No support for private foundations. No grants to individuals.
Application information:
Initial approach: Letter
Deadline(s): Sept. 30
Board meeting date(s): Feb., May, Aug., and Nov.
Final notification: Approvals in Nov., payments made in Feb.
Officers and Directors:* Rex J. Rawlinson,* Pres.; Maureen E. Rawlinson,* V.P.; Cheryl R. Robinson,* V.P.; Lorraine F. Perry, Secy.-Treas.
EIN: 943218106
Selected grants: The following grants are a representative sample of this grantmaker's funding activity:
$2,625,000 to Brigham Young University, Provo, UT, 2012.
$1,000,000 to Loyola Law School, Los Angeles, CA, 2012.
$1,000,000 to Loyola Marymount University, Los Angeles, CA, 2012.
$600,000 to Notre Dame High School of Sherman Oaks, Sherman Oaks, CA, 2012.
$300,000 to Saint Genevieve High School, Panorama City, CA, 2012.
$50,000 to Saint Bernard High School, Playa del Rey, CA, 2012.
$50,000 to University of Nevada Reno Foundation, Reno, NV, 2012.

360
Byer Foundation ✧
66 Potrero Ave.
San Francisco, CA 94103-4837 (415) 626-7844
Contact: Allan G. Byer, Tr.

Established in 1995 in CA.
Donor: Allan G. Byer.
Foundation type: Independent foundation.
Financial data (yr. ended 12/31/13): Assets, $4,299,692 (M); gifts received, $1,700,000; expenditures, $800,614; qualifying distributions, $799,650; giving activities include $799,650 for 29 grants (high: $250,000; low: $500).
Purpose and activities: Giving primarily for Jewish organizations and temples, as well as for education, and children, youth and social services.
Fields of interest: Education; Human services; Children/youth, services; Jewish federated giving programs; Jewish agencies & synagogues.
Limitations: Applications accepted. Giving primarily in CA. No grants to individuals.
Application information:
Initial approach: Letter
Deadline(s): None
Trustees: Allan G. Byer; Marian Byer.
EIN: 943216991

361
The C.E.B. Foundation ✧ ☆
1620 N. Carpenter Rd., Bldg. B
Modesto, CA 95351-1153
Contact: Calvin E. Bright, Pres.

Established in 2002 in CA.
Donor: Calvin E. Bright.
Foundation type: Independent foundation.
Financial data (yr. ended 12/31/13): Assets, $441,871 (M); expenditures, $501,628; qualifying distributions, $501,047; giving activities include $500,500 for 2 grants (high: $500,000; low: $500).
Purpose and activities: Giving for local non-profits for education and health related services.
Fields of interest: Higher education.
Limitations: Applications accepted. Giving primarily in Stanislaus County, CA. No grants to individuals.
Application information: Application form required.
Initial approach: Letter on letterhead
Copies of proposal: 1
Deadline(s): None
Board meeting date(s): Nov.
Officers: Calvin E. Bright, Pres.; Carol B. Tougas, V.P., C.F.O. and Secy.
EIN: 460512885

362
CAA Foundation ✧
c/o Bruce E. King
2000 Ave. of the Stars
Los Angeles, CA 90067-4700
Twitter: http://twitter.com/CAAFoundation

Established in 1995 in CA.
Donors: Creative Artists Agency, LLC; Robert Goldman; Bruce King; Richard Lovett; Musictoday, LLC; David O'Connor.
Foundation type: Company-sponsored foundation.
Financial data (yr. ended 11/30/13): Assets, $697,185 (M); gifts received, $627,873; expenditures, $750,395; qualifying distributions,

$561,967; giving activities include $561,967 for 50 grants (high: $123,250; low: $71).
Purpose and activities: The foundation supports organizations involved with arts and culture, education, health, human services, and voluntarism promotion.
Fields of interest: Media, film/video; Performing arts, theater; Arts; Education, public education; Elementary/secondary education; Elementary school/education; Education; Health care; Human services; Voluntarism promotion.
Type of support: General/operating support; Program development; Scholarship funds; Cause-related marketing; Employee volunteer services; In-kind gifts.
Limitations: Applications not accepted. Giving primarily in area of company operations in Los Angeles, CA, New York, NY, and Nashville, TN. No grants to individuals.
Application information: Contributes only to pre-selected organizations.
Officers and Directors:* Richard Lovett,* Pres.; Bruce E. King,* C.F.O.; Michelle Kydd,* Secy.
EIN: 954556189

363
The Caldwell-Fisher Charitable Foundation ✧
c/o John Fisher
3620 Clay St.
San Francisco, CA 94118-1804

Established in 1999 in CA.
Donors: Jennifer Caldwell; John Fisher.
Foundation type: Independent foundation.
Financial data (yr. ended 12/31/12): Assets, $2,992,904 (M); gifts received, $1,815,289; expenditures, $1,794,722; qualifying distributions, $1,746,515; giving activities include $1,746,515 for 57 grants (high: $250,000; low: $50).
Fields of interest: Performing arts, ballet; Education; Environment; Hospitals (general); Children/youth, services.
Limitations: Applications not accepted. Giving primarily in San Francisco, CA and MA. No grants to individuals.
Application information: Contributes only to pre-selected organizations.
Officers: John Fisher, C.E.O. and Secy.; Jennifer Caldwell, Pres. and V.P.
EIN: 770527966

364
Charles G. and Jessie R. Cale Foundation ✧
P.O . Box 688
Pacific Palisades, CA 90272
Application address: Jack G. Charney, P.O. Box 9144, Rancho Santa Fe, CA 92067, tel.: (858) 756-6342

Established in 1995 in CA.
Donor: Charles G. Cale.
Foundation type: Independent foundation.
Financial data (yr. ended 12/31/13): Assets, $2,810,044 (M); gifts received, $319,500; expenditures, $614,240; qualifying distributions, $590,358; giving activities include $568,300 for 10 grants (high: $556,000; low: $500).
Fields of interest: Higher education; Health organizations; Human services; Catholic agencies & churches.
Type of support: General/operating support.
Limitations: Applications accepted. Giving primarily in Los Angeles, CA. No grants to individuals.
Application information: Application form required.
Initial approach: Letter
Deadline(s): None
Officers: Charles G. Cale, Pres.; Jessie R. Cale, V.P.; Jack G. Charney, Secy.-Treas.
Directors: Elizabeth J. Cale; Walter G. Cale; Whitney R. Cale.
EIN: 954509128

365
California Community Foundation ✧
221 S. Figueroa St., Ste. 400
Los Angeles, CA 90012 (213) 413-4130
FAX: (213) 383-2046; E-mail: info@calfund.org; Grants information e-mail: grantsmanager@calfund.org; Main URL: http://www.calfund.org/
Blog: http://givinginla.org/
California Community Foundation's Philanthropy Promise: http://www.ncrp.org/philanthropys-promise/who
CCF Fellowship for Visual Artists: https://www.facebook.com/CCFArtists
E-Newsletter: https://www.calfund.org/page.aspx?pid=736
Facebook: http://www.facebook.com/pages/California-Community-Foundation/62143496512
Flickr: http://www.flickr.com/photos/calfund/
LinkedIn: http://www.linkedin.com/companies/california-community-foundation
YouTube: http://www.youtube.com/calfundtv

Established in 1915 in CA by bank resolution.
Foundation type: Community foundation.
Financial data (yr. ended 06/30/13): Assets, $1,315,930,000 (M); gifts received, $184,700,000; expenditures, $184,177,000; giving activities include $164,428,000 for grants.
Purpose and activities: The mission of the foundation is to strengthen Los Angeles communities through effective philanthropy and civic engagement. The foundation makes multi-year grants (usually two years) in these main areas: arts, education, health care, housing and neighborhoods, transition aged youth and civic engagement.
Fields of interest: Arts; Education, early childhood education; Elementary school/education; Education; Animal welfare; Health care; Housing/shelter, development; Children/youth, services; Aging, centers/services; Human services; Civil rights, race/intergroup relations; Community/economic development; Aging; Disabilities, people with; Asians/Pacific Islanders; African Americans/Blacks; Hispanics/Latinos; Native Americans/American Indians; Women; Immigrants/refugees; Economically disadvantaged; Homeless; LGBTQ.
Type of support: General/operating support; Continuing support; Management development/capacity building; Capital campaigns; Program development; Scholarship funds; Research; Technical assistance; Consulting services; Program evaluation; Program-related investments/loans; Employee matching gifts; Matching/challenge support; Mission-related investments/loans.
Limitations: Applications accepted. Giving limited to Los Angeles County, CA. No support for sectarian purposes. No grants to individuals (except fellowships for artists or scholarships), or for annual campaigns, equipment, endowment funds, debt reduction, operating budgets, re-granting, fellowships, films, conferences, dinners, or special events.
Publications: Application guidelines; Annual report; Financial statement; Informational brochure; Newsletter.
Application information: Based on initial letter of intent submitted, applicants will receive written notification that either invites or discourages the submission of a full grant application. Application form required.
Initial approach: Visit calfund.org for information on general eligibility and specific requirements for each priority area. Interested applicants must submit a letter of intent.
Deadline(s): Varies
Board meeting date(s): Mar., June, Oct., and Dec.
Final notification: Four months
Officers and Board of Governors:* Cynthia Telles, Ph.D.*, Chair.; Antonia Hernandez,* C.E.O. and Pres.; John E. Kobara, Exec. V.P. and C.O.O.; Nichole D. Baker, V.P., Devel. and Donor Rels.; Steve Cobb, V.P. and C.F.O.; Nike Irvin, V.P., Progs.; Carolyn Steffen, Cont.; Sheldon M. Stone,* Chair. Emeritus; Louis Henry Bryson; Patrick Dowling, M.D.; David W. Fleming; Dennis Gertmenian; Meloni M. Hallock; Preston L.C. Johnson; Joanne Corday Kozberg; Hon. Carlos R. Moreno; Quan Phung; Todd Quinn; Paul Schulz; Jean Bixby Smith; Melanie Staggs; Catherine L. Unger; Tom Unterman; Ronald T. Vera; Marie Brooks Washington.
Number of staff: 54 full-time professional.
EIN: 953510055
Selected grants: The following grants are a representative sample of this grantmaker's funding activity:
$615,039 to Cedars-Sinai Medical Center, Los Angeles, CA, 2013.
$320,550 to Community Partners, Los Angeles, CA, 2013.
$300,000 to Boys and Girls Club of Los Angeles, Watts/Willowbrook, Los Angeles, CA, 2012.
$250,000 to YMCA of Greater Long Beach, Long Beach, CA, 2013.
$200,000 to HeArt Project, Los Angeles, CA, 2012.
$180,000 to Alliance for a Better Community, Los Angeles, CA, 2012.
$170,000 to Boys and Girls Club of the Los Angeles Harbor, San Pedro, CA, 2013.
$162,500 to University of Southern California, Los Angeles, CA, 2013.
$150,000 to Los Angeles County Museum of Natural History Foundation, Los Angeles, CA, 2013.
$125,000 to Social Justice Learning Institute, Inglewood, CA, 2013.
$115,000 to Special Service for Groups, Los Angeles, CA, 2012.
$105,000 to Esperanza Community Housing Corporation, Los Angeles, CA, 2013.
$100,000 to Family Health Care Centers of Greater Los Angeles, Bell Gardens, CA, 2013.
$25,000 to Principals Exchange Foundation, Whittier, CA, 2012.
$25,000 to Transcendence Children and Family Services, Pomona, CA, 2013.

366
The California Endowment

1000 N. Alameda St.
Los Angeles, CA 90012-1804 (800) 449-4149
FAX: (213) 928-8800;
E-mail: questions@calendow.org; Main URL: http://www.calendow.org
Bob's BLOG: http://tcenews.calendow.org/pr/tce/blog.aspx
CalConnect: http://www.calendow.org/HealthyCommunities/
E-Newsletter: http://calendow.us2.list-manage.com/subscribe?u=afe755296f10c4ca4f725bb4b&id=3d6712e9bb
Facebook: http://www.facebook.com/Calendow
GiveSmart: http://www.givesmart.org/Stories/Donors/Richard-Atlas
Google Plus: https://plus.google.com/100143257574109327234/videos
Grants Database: http://grantfinder.calendow.org/gf/gf.aspx
Health Happens Here: http://twitter.com/calendow_here
New Health Law Guide for Buiness: http://www.healthlawguideforbusiness.org/
Pinterest: http://pinterest.com/calendow/
Publications and Reports: http://tcenews.calendow.org/releases
The California Endowment's Philanthropy Promise: http://www.ncrp.org/philanthropys-promise/who
Twitter: http://twitter.com/calendow
Youth-focused Californian Health Care Law Education: http://www.getcoveredca.org/
YouTube: https://www.youtube.com/user/HealthHappensHere

Established in 1996 in CA; converted from Blue Cross of California.
Foundation type: Independent foundation.
Financial data (yr. ended 03/31/14): Assets, $3,668,459,217 (M); expenditures, $294,487,859; qualifying distributions, $264,789,192; giving activities include $182,336,918 for 1,475 grants (high: $26,500,000; low: $350), $472,129 for 105 employee matching gifts, $33,988,079 for 4 foundation-administered programs and $3,578,221 for 2 loans/program-related investments (high: $3,500,000; low: $78,221).
Purpose and activities: To expand access to affordable, quality health care for underserved individuals and communities and to promote fundamental improvements in the health status of all Californians.
Fields of interest: Public health; Youth development; Minorities; African Americans/Blacks; Economically disadvantaged.
Type of support: General/operating support; Management development/capacity building; Conferences/seminars; Technical assistance; Program evaluation; Program-related investments/loans; Employee matching gifts; Mission-related investments/loans.
Limitations: Applications accepted. Giving primarily in CA. No support for lobbying, medical or scientific research, or uncompensated care for direct clinical services. No grants to individuals for scholarships, fellowships or grants, or for endowments, operating deficits or retirement of debt, media projects not part of a broader project or strategy, medical supplies, laboratory fees, X-ray services, medications, vaccines or prescriptions; capital funding for purchase, construction or renovation of facilities or other physical infrastructure; indirect costs that exceed 15 percent of the total of requested personnel and operating cost.
Publications: Application guidelines; Annual report; Occasional report.
Application information: See foundation's web site for Innovative Ideas Challenge grant submission requirements. The foundation currently has very limited resources available for proposed grants outside of its Health Happens Here programs and Building Healthy Communities (BHC) 10-year plan. It is highly unlikely a request will be funded unless there is significant alignment with the BHC's 10 Outcomes or 4 Big Results. Thus, an applicant must be able to state clearly how their work aligns with one or more of the 10 BHC Outcomes or 4 Big Results. Application form required.
Initial approach: Complete online application if proposal meets any of the required objectives. See foundation web site: http://www.calendow.org/grants
Deadline(s): Dec, 1, May 1 and Sept. 1
Board meeting date(s): May 16-17, Aug. 20-21, Nov. 19-20, and Feb. 19-20
Final notification: Up to 120 days
Officers and Directors:* C. Dean Germano,* Chair.; Jane Garcia, Vice-Chair.; Robert K. Ross, M.D.*, C.E.O. and Pres.; B. Kathlyn Mead, Exec. V.P. and C.O.O.; Anthony B. Iton, M.D., Sr. V.P., Healthy Communities; Daniel Zingale, Sr. V.P., Healthy California; Dan C. DeLeon, V.P. and C.F.O.; Brytain Ashford, V.P., Human Resources; Jim Keddy, V.P. and Chief Learning Off.; Ruth Wernig, C.I.O.; Stephen Bennett; Susan V. Berresford; Walter L. Buster, Ed.D.; Shan Cretin, Ph.D.; Adrienne Crowe; Hector Flores, M.D.; Shawn A. Ginwright, Ph.D.; Russ Gould; Zac Guevara; Christina Kazhe, Esq.; Kate Kendell, Esq.; Maurice Lim Miller; Steve PonTell; Winston F. Wong, M.D.
Number of staff: 74 full-time professional; 1 part-time professional; 62 full-time support.
EIN: 954523232
Selected grants: The following grants are a representative sample of this grantmaker's funding activity:
$813,600 to Resources Legacy Fund, Sacramento, CA, 2013. For Improving Community Health Through Land Use Planning: Implementation of Sustainable Communities and Climate Protection Act in California.
$400,000 to Oakland Community Organizations, Oakland, CA, 2013. For Organizing for Community Health and Wellness general operating support.
$253,710 to Fresno Street Saints, Fresno, CA, 2013. For Safe and Healthy Neighborhoods: To support stronger alliance between African-American and Lation communities to engage in collective advocacy efforts to prevent and reduce violence in Building Healthy Communities in Fresno.
$250,000 to Equality California Institute, San Francisco, CA, 2013. For Health Coverage Education, Training and Enrollment.
$250,000 to Prevention Institute, Oakland, CA, 2013. For general operating support.
$235,000 to Gifts to Share, Sacramento, CA, 2013. For Youth Leadership for Healthy Schools and Communities.
$200,000 to Bikes Belong Foundation, Boulder, CO, 2013. For Safe Routes to School National Partnership: Promoting Walkable and Bikeable Neighborhoods in California.
$125,000 to Merced County Department of Public Health, Merced, CA, 2013. For Health Improvements Through Local Affordable Care Act Implementation.
$104,263 to Mendota Unified School District, Mendota, CA, 2013. For Positive School Discipline for Improved Social and Emotional Health.
$75,500 to Bay Area Peacekeepers, Richmond, CA, 2013. For Youth Leadership for Community Health and Safety.

367
California HealthCare Foundation ✧

1438 Webster St., Ste. 400
Oakland, CA 94612-3206 (510) 238-1040
Contact: Lisa Kang, Dir., Grants Admin.
FAX: (510) 238-1388; E-mail: info@chcf.org; E-mail for questions regarding Letters of Inquiry: grants@chcf.org; Additional address: 1415 L St., No. 820, Sacramento, CA 95814; tel.: (916) 329-4540; fax: (916) 329-4545; Main URL: http://www.chcf.org
Blog: http://www.chcf.org/innovation-fund/notes-from-the-team
California Healthline: http://www.californiahealthline.org/rss
E-Newsletter: http://www.chcf.org/media
Facebook: http://www.facebook.com/chcfnews
Grants Database: http://www.chcf.org/grants/awarded
iHealthBeat: http://www.ihealthbeat.org/rss
Knowledge Center: http://www.chcf.org/about/assessing-our-impact
Knowledge Center: http://www.chcf.org/almanac
Knowledge Center: http://www.chcf.org/search?type=chcf&se=1&contenttype=publications&sdate=all
Pinterest: http://www.pinterest.com/chcfoundation/the-picture-of-health/
Twitter: https://twitter.com/chcfnews
YouTube: http://www.youtube.com/user/CHCFoundation

Established in 1996 in CA; converted from Blue Cross of California.
Financial data (yr. ended 02/28/13): Assets, $716,354,350 (M); expenditures, $52,443,464; giving activities include $31,775,896 for grants.
Purpose and activities: The foundation's mission is to expand access to affordable, quality health care for underserved individuals and communities, and to promote fundamental improvements in the health status of the people of California. The foundation commissions research and analysis, publishes and disseminates information, convenes stakeholders, and funds the development of programs and models aimed at improving the healthcare delivery and financing systems.
Fields of interest: Health care, HMOs; Health care, insurance; Health care; Health organizations, public policy; Health organizations, public education.
Type of support: Program development; Research; Program evaluation.
Limitations: Applications accepted. Giving primarily in CA. No grants for general operating expenses, capital campaigns, annual campaigns, building, purchases or renovations, direct clinical care costs, or equipment.
Publications: Application guidelines; Informational brochure (including application guidelines); Occasional report; IRS Form 990 or 990-PF printed copy available upon request.
Application information: Projects must have potential to inform or impact healthcare access and health policy issues in California; Application form

required only for RFPs; See web site for latest information including available publications. Application form not required.

Initial approach: Letter of inquiry (1-3 pages)
Copies of proposal: 2
Deadline(s): None
Board meeting date(s): Quarterly
Final notification: 6-8 weeks from receipt

Officers and Directors:* Micheline Chau,* Chair.; Barbara N. Lubash,* Vice-Chair.; Sandra R. Hernandez, M.D.*, C.E.O and Pres.; Craig C. Ziegler, M.B.A., V.P., Fin., Admin. and Investments; Collette Clark, Cont.; Michael V. Drake, M.D.; Maria Echaveste; Daniel L. Gross; Elizabeth G. Hill; Pamela Joyner; Ian Morrison, Ph.D., M.A.; Walter W. "Bill" Noce, Jr.; John D. Welty, Ph.D.
Number of staff: 43 full-time professional; 10 full-time support; 2 part-time support.
EIN: 954523231

368
The California Wellness Foundation ✧

6320 Canoga Ave., Ste. 1700
Woodland Hills, CA 91367-2565 (818) 702-1900
Contact: Amy Scop, Dir., Grants Mgmt.
FAX: (818) 702-1999; E-mail: info@calwellness.org; Branch Office address: 575 Market St., Ste. 1850, San Francisco, CA 94105, tel.: (415) 908-3000, fax: (415) 908-3001. E-mail for grant inquiries: grants@calwellness.org; Main URL: http://www.calwellness.org/
Grants Database: http://www.calwellness.org/grants_database/search.php
Job Resource Center: http://www.healthjobsstarthere.com/resources/welcome
Knowledge Center: http://www.calwellness.org/wellness_library/evaluations.php
Twitter: https://twitter.com/calwellness
YouTube: https://www.youtube.com/user/calwellness

Established in 1992 in CA; converted from Health Net HMO.
Foundation type: Independent foundation.
Financial data (yr. ended 12/31/13): Assets, $939,762,194 (M); expenditures, $58,982,759; qualifying distributions, $52,855,250; giving activities include $42,560,322 for 633 grants (high: $1,000,000; low: $2,500), $150,000 for 6 grants to individuals (high: $25,000; low: $25,000), and $145,001 for 121 employee matching gifts.
Purpose and activities: The foundation's mission is to improve the health of the people of California by making grants for health promotion, wellness education and disease prevention. The foundation pursues the following goals through grantmaking: 1) to address the particular health needs of traditionally underserved populations, including low-income individuals, people of color, youth and residents of rural areas; 2) to support and strengthen nonprofit organizations that seek to improve the health of underserved populations; 3) to recognize and encourage leaders who are working to increase health and wellness within their communities; and 4) to inform policy makers and opinion leaders about important wellness and health care issues.
Fields of interest: Vocational school, secondary; Higher education; Higher education, college (community/junior); Higher education, college; Dental school/education; Medical school/education; Nursing school/education; Public health school/education; Education; Environment, air pollution; Environment, water pollution; Environment, toxics; Environment, waste management; Health care, equal rights; Health care, formal/general education; Medical care, community health systems; Hospitals (general); Health care, clinics/centers; Dental care; Health care, rural areas; Reproductive health; Reproductive health, family planning; Reproductive health, prenatal care; Reproductive health, sexuality education; Public health; Public health, STDs; Public health, communicable diseases; Public health, occupational health; Public health, environmental health; Health care, home services; Health care; Mental health/crisis services, hot-lines; Obstetrics/gynecology; Crime/violence prevention; Offenders/ex-offenders, transitional care; Offenders/ex-offenders, rehabilitation; Offenders/ex-offenders, probation/parole; Offenders/ex-offenders, services; Offenders/ex-offenders, prison alternatives; Food banks; Food distribution, meals on wheels; Nutrition; Housing/shelter, temporary shelter; Housing/shelter, homeless; Youth development, centers/clubs; Boys & girls clubs; Youth development; YM/YWCAs & YM/YWHAs; Youth, pregnancy prevention; Youth, services; Family services; Pregnancy centers; Residential/custodial care, senior continuing care; Aging, centers/services; Women, centers/services; Minorities/immigrants, centers/services; Homeless, human services; Community development, citizen coalitions; Nonprofit management; Military/veterans' organizations; Leadership development; Youth; Aging; Young adults; Minorities; Asians/Pacific Islanders; African Americans/Blacks; Hispanics/Latinos; Native Americans/American Indians; Indigenous peoples; Women; Girls; Adults, women; Men; Boys; Adults, men; Military/veterans; Offenders/ex-offenders; Immigrants/refugees; Economically disadvantaged; Homeless; Migrant workers; LGBTQ.
Type of support: General/operating support; Continuing support; Program development; Conferences/seminars; Publication; Seed money; Scholarship funds; Research; Technical assistance; Program evaluation; Grants to individuals.
Limitations: Applications accepted. Giving limited to CA; national organizations providing programs in CA are also considered. No support for activities that exclusively benefit the members of religious or sectarian organizations. No grants to individuals (except for TCWF awards), or for annual fund drives, building campaigns, major equipment, or for biomedical research.
Publications: Application guidelines; Annual report; Annual report (including application guidelines); Grants list; Informational brochure; Informational brochure (including application guidelines); Newsletter (including application guidelines); Occasional report.
Application information: Review the guidelines and eligibility criteria on the "How To Apply" portal on the foundation's web site, which includes answers to frequently asked questions. All requested information should be included via the online letter of interest and not sent as separate attachments. Application form not required.

Initial approach: Online letter of interest
Deadline(s): None
Board meeting date(s): Quarterly
Final notification: 3 months

Officers and Directors:* Barbara C. Staggers, M.D., M.P.H.*, Chair.; Eugene Washington, M.D., M.Sc.*, Vice-Chair.; Judy Belk, C.E.O. and Pres.; Margaret W. Minnich, V.P., Finance and Admin.; Fatima Angeles, V.P., Programs; Magdalena Beltran-del Olmo, V.P., Comms.; Amy B. Scop, Dir., Grants Mgmt.; David S. Barlow, M.B.A., C.P.A.; M. Isabel Becerra, B.A.; Elizabeth M. Gomez, M.S.W.; Elisabeth Hallman, M.B.A., R.N.; Joseph M. Lumarda; Debra Nakatomi.
Number of staff: 19 full-time professional; 1 part-time professional; 18 full-time support; 2 part-time support.
EIN: 954292101
Selected grants: The following grants are a representative sample of this grantmaker's funding activity:
$1,000,000 to Swords to Plowshares, San Francisco, CA, 2012. For project support for a regranting program focused on the health of women veterans in California, payable over 1.50 years.
$350,000 to California Institute for Nursing and Healthcare, Oakland, CA, 2012. For project support to develop and define the role of registered nurses (RNs) and develop a demonstration of a Transition to Practice Program to prepare RNs for their emerging roles as care coordinators in the era of health care reform.
$330,000 to CompassPoint Nonprofit Services, Oakland, CA, 2012. For project support for the Leadership Development Program for Executives and Managers Serving Transition-Age Youth to train the 2013 and 2014 cohorts and to conduct alumni impact analysis for the previous six cohorts, payable over 2.25 years.
$300,000 to Comite Civico del Valle, Brawley, CA, 2012. For project support for the provision of technical assistance to replicate the Imperial Visions Action Network model in other regions of California, payable over 2.00 years.
$300,000 to Oxfam America, Boston, MA, 2012. For project support for the Equitable Food Initiative to promote the health and safety of California farmworkers, payable over 2.00 years.
$275,000 to Community Partners, Los Angeles, CA, 2012. For project support to develop, implement and evaluate TCWFs 2013 Conference on the Health and Well-Being of Transition-Age Youth, payable over 1.25 years.
$225,000 to Operation Safe House, Riverside, CA, 2012. For core operating support to sustain emergency shelter and transitional housing services in Riverside County for homeless and runaway youth, payable over 3.00 years.
$220,000 to First Place for Youth, Oakland, CA, 2012. For core operating support to sustain safe housing and supportive services for emancipating former foster youth in the San Francisco Bay Area and Los Angeles County, payable over 2.00 years.
$150,000 to Advancement Project, Los Angeles, CA, 2012. For core operating support to sustain the Urban Peace program to continue efforts to inform policymakers about gang violence prevention and juvenile re-entry strategies in Los Angeles County, payable over 2.00 years.
$150,000 to Community Service Programs, Santa Ana, CA, 2012. For core operating support for the Youth Shelter program to sustain emergency shelter-based services in Orange County for homeless and runaway youth, payable over 2.00 years.

369
The Call of Duty Endowment ✧ ☆

3100 Ocean Park Blvd.
Santa Monica, CA 90405-3032 (877) 597-2633
Main URL: http://www.callofdutyendowment.org/

Established in CA.
Donor: Activision Publishing, Inc.
Foundation type: Operating foundation.
Financial data (yr. ended 06/30/13): Assets, $10,010,798 (M); gifts received, $9,032,874; expenditures, $2,114,752; qualifying distributions, $2,114,752; giving activities include $1,169,000 for 8 grants (high: $398,000; low: $1,000).
Fields of interest: Education; Human services; Military/veterans' organizations.
Limitations: Applications accepted. Giving primarily in the Washington, DC, area, including VA.
Application information: Application form required.
Initial approach: Request application form
Deadline(s): None
Officers: Robert Kotick, Co-Chair.; James Jones, Co-Chair.; Collister W. Johnson, Pres.; Daniel Goldenberg, V.P.; Terri Durham, Secy.; Robert Kostich, Traes.
EIN: 371589072

370
Camp Foundation ✧
(formerly Doris & Donald Fisher Foundation)
1 Maritime Plz., Ste. 1400
San Francisco, CA 94111-3504

Established in 1986; the foundation's name changed from the D & DF Foundation to the Doris & Donald Fisher Foundation and is now the Camp Foundation.
Donors: Donald G. Fisher‡; Doris F. Fisher; John J. Fisher; DDF 2005 Charitable Remainder Annuity Trust.
Foundation type: Operating foundation.
Financial data (yr. ended 06/30/13): Assets, $140,335,032 (M); expenditures, $136,253,033; qualifying distributions, $135,642,909; giving activities include $135,600,000 for 1 grant.
Fields of interest: Museums (art).
Limitations: Applications not accepted. Giving primarily in Broomfield, CO; some giving also in San Francisco, CA, Atlanta, GA, and New York, NY. No grants to individuals.
Application information: Contributes only to pre-selected organizations.
Officer: Jane Spray, Treas.
Trustee: Doris F. Fisher.
EIN: 943022002

371
The William V. Campbell Family Foundation ✧
305 Churchill Ave.
Palo Alto, CA 94301-3602

Established in CA.
Donor: William V. Campbell.
Foundation type: Independent foundation.
Financial data (yr. ended 12/31/12): Assets, $17,189,948 (M); gifts received, $202,431; expenditures, $4,195,191; qualifying distributions, $4,000,018; giving activities include $3,991,723 for 53 grants (high: $1,219,239; low: $1,000).
Fields of interest: Education; Recreation; Human services; Children/youth, services.
Limitations: Applications not accepted. Giving primarily in CA, NY, and PA.
Application information: Contributes only to pre-selected organizations.
Officers and Directors:* William V. Campbell,* Pres.; James W. Campbell,* Secy.-Treas.; Tom Baenziger; Margaret R. Campbell.
EIN: 270387300

372
Vera R. Campbell Foundation ✧
c/o Vera R. Campbell
337 S. Anderson St.
Los Angeles, CA 90033-3742

Established in 2006 in CA.
Donor: Vera R. Campbell.
Foundation type: Independent foundation.
Financial data (yr. ended 12/31/12): Assets, $22,187,501 (M); gifts received, $2,500,000; expenditures, $1,145,302; qualifying distributions, $755,595; giving activities include $755,595 for grants.
Fields of interest: Arts; Eye diseases.
Limitations: Applications not accepted. Giving primarily in CA. No grants to individuals.
Application information: Unsolicited requests for funds not accepted.
Officers: Vera R. Campbell, Pres. and C.E.O.; Erika Bsumek-Hannon, Secy.-Treas.
EIN: 421719658

373
The Keith Campbell Foundation for the Environment, Inc. ✧
1450 Sutter St., Ste. 510
San Francisco, CA 94109-5418 (415) 722-4739
Contact: Pacific Region Proposals: Anna Lindgren, Asst. to the Pres.; Chesapeake and Atlantic Proposals: Rebecca Bednarek, Grants Asst.
E-mail: pacificadmin@campbellfoundation.org; Chesapeake Office: 410 Severn Ave., Ste. 210, Annapolis MD 21403, tel: (410) 990-0900, fax: (410) 990-0988; E-mail for Chesapeake and Atlantic Coastal Bay proposals: Rebecca Bednarek (rebednarek@campbellfoundation.org); E-mail for Pacific Region proposals: Anna Lindgren (pacificadmin@campbellfoundation.org); Main URL: http://www.campbellfoundation.org/
Grants Database: http://www.campbellfoundation.org/grantee_search

Established in 1998 in MD.
Donor: Keith Campbell.
Foundation type: Independent foundation.
Financial data (yr. ended 12/31/12): Assets, $143,527,562 (M); gifts received, $9,077,769; expenditures, $12,823,381; qualifying distributions, $12,429,189; giving activities include $9,926,527 for 229 grants (high: $500,000; low: $25), $3,715 for 31 employee matching gifts, and $448,650 for foundation-administered programs.
Purpose and activities: The foundation promotes policy, advocacy, and enforcement to improve water quality, restore ecological balance, and foster an engaged citizenry within the watersheds of the Chesapeake Bay, Atlantic Coastal Bays and the Pacific Coast region.
Fields of interest: Environment, alliance/advocacy; Environment, administration/regulation; Environment, research; Environment, public policy; Environment, single organization support; Environment, public education; Environment, formal/general education; Environment, pollution control; Environment, water pollution; Environment, toxics; Environment, water resources; Environmental education; Environment; Animals/wildlife, fisheries; Animals/wildlife, sanctuaries.
Type of support: General/operating support; Continuing support; Management development/capacity building; Emergency funds; Program development; Employee matching gifts; Matching/challenge support.
Limitations: Applications not accepted. Giving primarily in the Chesapeake Bay area, (MD and VA), the San Francisco Bay Area, CA, OR, and HI. No support for No support generally for on-the-ground restoration or classroom environmental education. No grants to individuals.
Publications: Grants list.
Application information: Unsolicited requests for funds are not currently being accepted. See foundation web site for updates.
Officers: D. Keith Campbell, Chair.; Samantha Campbell, Pres.; Verna Harrison, Exec. Dir.
EIN: 522136842
Selected grants: The following grants are a representative sample of this grantmaker's funding activity:
$834,000 to Nature Conservancy, Bethesda, MD, 2012. For Forever Costa Rica Project.
$500,000 to Chesapeake Bay Foundation, Annapolis, MD, 2012.
$500,000 to Chesapeake Bay Foundation, Annapolis, MD, 2012.
$500,000 to Resources Legacy Fund Foundation, Sacramento, CA, 2012. For the Marine Life Protection Act (MLPA) - Sustaining California's Oceans (SCO).
$237,000 to San Francisco Zoological Society, San Francisco, CA, 2012. For Children's Play Zone.
$200,000 to California Ocean Science Trust, Oakland, CA, 2012. For the Marine Life Protection Act (MLPA) - Convening OceanSpaces.
$175,000 to Environmental Defense Fund, New York, NY, 2012. For Sustainable Fisheries Management Systems.
$140,000 to National Wildlife Federation, Annapolis, MD, 2012. For Mid-Atlantic Office.
$40,000 to Trout Unlimited, Arlington, VA, 2012. For California Water Project.
$30,000 to Conservation Pennsylvania, Philadelphia, PA, 2012. For Marcellus Shale.

374
Frank A. Campini Foundation ✧
220 Sansome St., Ste. 700
San Francisco, CA 94104-2722 (415) 421-4171
Contact: Paul J. Ruby, Dir.

Established in 1960 in CA.
Donor: Frank A. Campini‡.
Foundation type: Independent foundation.
Financial data (yr. ended 12/31/13): Assets, $25,538,611 (M); expenditures, $1,117,986; qualifying distributions, $1,043,000; giving activities include $995,000 for 55 grants (high: $80,000; low: $1,500).
Purpose and activities: Giving primarily for the arts, education, health organizations and medical research, including pediatric oncology, human services, and Jewish organizations.
Fields of interest: Museums; Arts; Education; Health organizations; Pediatrics; Medical research, institute; Human services; Children/youth, services; Jewish federated giving programs.
Type of support: General/operating support; Building/renovation; Endowments; Research.

Limitations: Applications accepted. Giving primarily in the San Francisco Bay Area, CA. No support for religious organizations. No grants to individuals.
Application information: Application form required.
Initial approach: Letter
Copies of proposal: 1
Deadline(s): Oct. 1
Officer: Patricia M. Neys, Secy.-Treas.
Directors: Gysbert Axt; Leigh L. Bills; Hendrika C. Neys; Joshua M. Rubinstein; Paul J. Ruby.
EIN: 946107956

375
The Capital Group Companies Charitable Foundation ✧
333 S. Hope St.
Los Angeles, CA 90071-1406
Main URL: http://thecapitalgroup.com/our-company/company-culture.html

Established in 1997 in CA.
Donors: Capital Management Services, Inc.; Capital Bank & Trust Co.; The Capital Group Cos., Inc.; Capital Research & Management Co.; Capital International, Inc.
Foundation type: Company-sponsored foundation.
Financial data (yr. ended 06/30/13): Assets, $296,517,753 (M); gifts received, $10,615,098; expenditures, $17,538,673; qualifying distributions, $16,900,734; giving activities include $16,863,630 for grants.
Purpose and activities: The foundation supports community foundations and organizations involved with arts and culture, education, the environment, health, youth development, human services, international relief, and leadership development.
Fields of interest: Media, television; Media, radio; Museums; Museums (art); Performing arts; Performing arts, theater; Performing arts, opera; Arts; Middle schools/education; Secondary school/education; Higher education; Libraries (public); Education, reading; Education; Environment; Hospitals (general); Health care; Youth development; Children, services; Family services; Family services, domestic violence; Human services; International relief; Foundations (community); Leadership development.
Type of support: General/operating support; Employee volunteer services; Employee matching gifts.
Limitations: Applications not accepted. Giving on a national and international basis, with emphasis on CA, CT, Washington, DC, NY, and TX. No support for religious, political, fraternal, or professional organizations. No grants to individuals.
Application information: Contributes only to pre-selected organizations.
Officers and Directors:* Thomas J. Condon,* Chair.; Naomi H. Kobayashi, Secy.; Edith H.L. Van Huss, C.F.O.; James B. Lovelace; Bruce E. Meikle; Theodore R. Samuels.
EIN: 954658856
Selected grants: The following grants are a representative sample of this grantmaker's funding activity:
$216,400 to Huntington Library, Art Collections and Botanical Gardens, San Marino, CA, 2013.
$190,800 to Westminster School, Simsbury, CT, 2013.
$168,300 to Salzburg Global Seminar, Washington, DC, 2013.
$162,300 to Westridge School for Girls, Pasadena, CA, 2013.
$90,000 to Los Angeles Opera Company, Los Angeles, CA, 2013.
$60,000 to Westside Childrens Center, Culver City, CA, 2013.
$5,000 to Huntington Library, Art Collections and Botanical Gardens, San Marino, CA, 2013.
$4,500 to Union Station Foundation, Pasadena, CA, 2013.
$3,000 to Han-Schneider International Childrens Foundation, Montebello, CA, 2013.
$3,000 to Saint Marks School, Southborough, MA, 2013.

376
The Truman Capote Literary Trust ✧
9200 Sunset Blvd., Ph. 22
Los Angeles, CA 90069-3306
Contact: Alan U. Schwartz Esq., Tr.
Application address: 1840 Century Park E., Ste. 1900, Los Angeles, CA 90067

Established in 1993 in CA.
Donor: Truman Capote‡.
Foundation type: Independent foundation.
Financial data (yr. ended 12/31/12): Assets, $13,238,621 (M); expenditures, $932,263; qualifying distributions, $750,984; giving activities include $575,383 for 9 grants (high: $151,000; low: $40,000).
Purpose and activities: Giving to institutions of higher education for creative writing and literary criticism fellowships.
Fields of interest: Higher education.
Type of support: Fellowships.
Limitations: Applications accepted. Giving in the U.S., with emphasis on CA and IA. No grants to individuals.
Application information: Application form required.
Initial approach: Letter
Deadline(s): None
Trustee: Alan U. Schwartz, Esq.
EIN: 956957275

377
CareFusion Foundation ✧ ☆
3750 Torrey View Ct.
San Diego, CA 92130-2622
E-mail: carefustion@sdfoundation.org; Main URL: http://www.carefusion.com/company/citizenship/giving/
Community Leadership Grant Awards: http://www.carefusion.com/company/citizenship/giving/grant-programs/awards/

Established in 2009 in CA.
Donor: CareFusion 303, Inc.
Foundation type: Company-sponsored foundation.
Financial data (yr. ended 12/31/13): Assets, $2,844,296 (M); expenditures, $756,535; qualifying distributions, $678,265; giving activities include $678,265 for 3 grants (high: $612,500; low: $2,515).
Purpose and activities: The foundation supports programs designed to improve patient care and enhance community health and wellness.
Fields of interest: Hospitals (general); Health care, clinics/centers; Health care, patient services; Health care.
Type of support: Program development; Employee volunteer services.
Limitations: Giving primarily in areas of company operations in CA. No support for religious organizations, veterans', labor, or political organizations, fraternal, athletic, or social membership groups, member-based organizations including chambers of commerce, rotary clubs, or IRS 501(c)(4) legions or associations, municipalities including fire or police departments, IRS 509(a)(3) supporting organizations, litigious organizations, or sports teams. No grants to individuals, or for advertising or event sponsorships, capital campaigns for health systems, hospitals, or clinics, endowments, general operating support or emergency operating funds, tickets for fundraising events or raffles, athletic competitions, golf outings, or debt retirements; no loans.
Publications: Application guidelines.
Application information: Organizations receiving support are asked to submit a final report.
Initial approach: Visit website for application information
Deadline(s): Varies
Officers: James Mazzola, Pres.; Jean Maschal, C.F.O.; Joan B. Stafslien,* Secy.
EIN: 272071842

378
Cares Foundation ✧ ☆
1500 21st St.
Sacramento, CA 95811-5216 (916) 914-6390
FAX: (916) 914-6266; Main URL: http://www.thecaresfoundation.org/

Donors: Center for Aids Research Education and Services - Sacramento; Cares- Sacramento.
Foundation type: Independent foundation.
Financial data (yr. ended 12/31/12): Assets, $25,943,973 (M); gifts received, $23,934,990; expenditures, $1,322,062; qualifying distributions, $1,131,644; giving activities include $1,095,509 for 2 grants (high: $1,060,509; low: $35,000).
Purpose and activities: Support for a compassionate community for people living with HIV/AIDS, the encouragement of innovative prevention and research programs, raising awareness to eliminate discrimination and stigma, and ensuring access to quality care.
Fields of interest: AIDS.
Limitations: Applications accepted. Giving primarily in the Sacramento, CA, area.
Publications: Annual report.
Application information: Full proposals by invitation only upon review of Letter of Inquiry. Application form required.
Initial approach: Use Letter of Inquiry form on foundation web site
Deadline(s): None
Officers and Directors:* Michael R.O. Martinez,* Pres.; Glennah Trochet,* V.P.; Rosemary Younts,* Secy.; John Kay,* C.F.O.; Mike Evans; Penny Herbert; Luann LaMay, R.N., MPA; Richard Pollard, M.D.; Bary Siegel, M.D.; Richard SooHoo.
EIN: 452544055

379
Carolands Preservation Foundation ✧ ☆
c/o Franklin Resources Inc.
1 Franklin Pkwy., Bldg. 920, 4th Fl.
San Mateo, CA 94403-1906
Contact: Charles B. Johnson, Co-Pres.; Ann L. Johnson, Co-Pres.

Established in CA.
Donors: Charles B. Johnson; Ann J. Johnson.
Foundation type: Independent foundation.
Financial data (yr. ended 11/30/13): Assets, $44,721,543 (M); expenditures, $1,959,118; qualifying distributions, $1,941,723; giving activities include $1,930,000 for 5 grants (high: $950,000; low: $5,000).
Fields of interest: Arts; Environment; Human services.
Limitations: Applications accepted. Giving primarily in CA and NY; some funding nationally.
Application information: Application form not required.
Initial approach: Proposal
Deadline(s): None
Officers and Trustees:* Ann L. Johnson,* Co-Pres.; Charles B. Johnson,* Co-Pres.
EIN: 271545347

380
The Carsey Family Foundation ✧
c/o Capell Rudolph
11601 Wilshire Blvd., Ste. 1840
Los Angeles, CA 90025-1754

Established in 1988 in CA.
Donors: Marcia L. Carsey; John J. Carsey†.
Foundation type: Independent foundation.
Financial data (yr. ended 09/30/13): Assets, $266,971 (M); gifts received, $995,000; expenditures, $1,050,946; qualifying distributions, $1,045,000; giving activities include $1,045,000 for 24 grants (high: $200,000; low: $10,000).
Fields of interest: Media/communications; Arts; Human services.
Type of support: General/operating support; Building/renovation.
Limitations: Applications not accepted. Giving primarily in CA, NC, and NH. No grants to individuals.
Application information: Contributes only to pre-selected organizations.
Officer: Marcia L. Carsey, Pres.
Directors: John Peterson Carsey; Rebecca P. Carsey.
EIN: 954135538
Selected grants: The following grants are a representative sample of this grantmaker's funding activity:
$150,000 to Music Academy of the West, Santa Barbara, CA, 2011.
$100,000 to American Independent News Network, Washington, DC, 2011.
$100,000 to Sojourners, Inc., Washington, DC, 2011.
$50,000 to Sojourners, Inc., Washington, DC, 2011.
$20,000 to L.A. GOAL, Culver City, CA, 2011.
$20,000 to University of New Hampshire Foundation, Durham, NH, 2011.
$12,000 to Center Theatre Group of Los Angeles, Los Angeles, CA, 2011.
$10,000 to Common Cause, Washington, DC, 2011.
$10,000 to Conservation International, Arlington, VA, 2011.
$2,500 to Cotuit Library Association, Cotuit, MA, 2011.

381
The John W. Carson Foundation ✧
16000 Ventura Blvd., Ste. 900
Encino, CA 91436-2760

Established in 2006 in CA and DE as successor foundation to the J.W.C. Foundation, established in 1981 as the John W. Carson Foundation.
Donor: The John W. Carson Trust.
Foundation type: Independent foundation.
Financial data (yr. ended 06/30/13): Assets, $162,569,765 (M); expenditures, $11,991,455; qualifying distributions, $6,744,869; giving activities include $6,232,600 for 155 grants (high: $525,000; low: $1,000).
Fields of interest: Reproductive health, family planning; Youth development; Human services; Children/youth, services; Family services; Aging; Disabilities, people with; Economically disadvantaged.
Type of support: General/operating support.
Limitations: Applications not accepted. Giving primarily in CA. No grants to individuals.
Application information: Contributes only to pre-selected organizations.
Officers and Directors:* Allan L. Alexander,* C.E.O., Pres., and General Counsel; Lawrence L. Witzer,* Secy., C.O.O., and C.F.O.; Lawrence Heller.
EIN: 205885752

382
The Caruso Family Foundation ✧
101 The Grove Dr.
Los Angeles, CA 90036-6221
Contact: Sam Garrison

Established in 1991 in CA.
Donors: Marc A. Caruso; Rick J. Caruso; Christina Stewart; Marvin Rapaport; Henry J. Caruso; GFM, LLC.
Foundation type: Independent foundation.
Financial data (yr. ended 12/31/13): Assets, $1,293,620 (M); gifts received, $1,735,000; expenditures, $1,530,730; qualifying distributions, $1,522,625; giving activities include $1,522,625 for 25 grants (high: $260,146; low: $3,000).
Purpose and activities: Giving primarily for the support of qualified philanthropic endeavors in the areas of education, social welfare, historical and environmental preservation, medical and scientific research, and cultural pursuits.
Fields of interest: Secondary school/education; Higher education; Law school/education; Education; Ear, nose & throat research; Crime/law enforcement; Human services; Children/youth, services; United Ways and Federated Giving Programs; Catholic agencies & churches.
Type of support: General/operating support; Continuing support; Building/renovation; Curriculum development.
Limitations: Applications accepted. Giving primarily in CA. No grants to individuals.
Application information:
Initial approach: 1-page Proposal
Copies of proposal: 1
Deadline(s): None
Board meeting date(s): Dec. 1
Final notification: Jan. 31
Officers and Trustees:* Rick J. Caruso,* Pres.; David J. Liston, C.F.O. and Secy.; Christina J. Caruso,* V.P.; Marc A. Caruso,* V.P.; Gloria G. Caruso; Henry J. Caruso; Tina P. Caruso.
EIN: 954317077
Selected grants: The following grants are a representative sample of this grantmaker's funding activity:
$317,253 to University of Southern California, Los Angeles, CA, 2011. For building fund.

383
Dan and Stacey Case Family Foundation ✧
3324 Washington St.
San Francisco, CA 94118-2034

Established in 2001 in CA.
Donors: Daniel H. Case; Stacey B. Case.
Foundation type: Independent foundation.
Financial data (yr. ended 12/31/12): Assets, $13,633,762 (M); expenditures, $740,447; qualifying distributions, $660,449; giving activities include $651,296 for 34 grants (high: $157,281; low: $1,000).
Purpose and activities: Giving primarily for education, brain cancer, and federated giving programs.
Fields of interest: Elementary/secondary education; Brain research; United Ways and Federated Giving Programs; Philanthropy/voluntarism.
Limitations: Applications not accepted. Giving primarily in CA; some funding also in Washington, DC. No grants to individuals.
Application information: Contributes only to pre-selected organizations.
Officers: Stacey B. Case, Pres.; Karen Morgan, Secy.; John H. Agee, Treas.
Director: Sasha Mardikian.
EIN: 912148156

384
Catalysis Foundation for Health, Inc. ✧
5858 Horton St., Ste. 550
Emeryville, CA 94608-2170 (510) 420-6744
Main URL: http://www.catalysisfoundation.org

Established in 2007 in CA.
Foundation type: Operating foundation.
Financial data (yr. ended 12/31/13): Assets, $1,714,770 (M); gifts received, $1,273,583; expenditures, $1,250,105; qualifying distributions, $687,918; giving activities include $687,918 for 2 grants (high: $551,736; low: $136,182), and $1,250,105 for foundation-administered programs.
Purpose and activities: The foundation's mission is to reduce the impact of life-threatening infectious diseases and chronic conditions in the developing world by engaging global health experts and establishing public-private partnerships to facilitate the development, manufacture and distribution of modern diagnostic solutions.
Fields of interest: Medical research.
International interests: Developing Countries.
Limitations: Applications not accepted.
Application information: Unsolicited requests for funds not accepted.
Officers and Directors:* Mickey Urdea, Ph.D.*, Chair.; Richard M. Thayer,* C.E.O.; Paul Billings, M.D., Ph.D.; Julie L. Gerberding, M.D., M.P.H.; David M. Kelso, Ph.D.; John W. Peabody, M.D., Ph.D.; David H. Persing, M.D., Ph.D.; Louis J. Riceberg, Ph.D.
EIN: 208602047

Selected grants: The following grants are a representative sample of this grantmaker's funding activity:
$248,586 to University of Medicine and Dentistry of New Jersey, Newark, NJ, 2012. For assay development of body fluids on spiked or characterized archival human TB samples.
$201,221 to National Institute of Allergy and Infectious Diseases, Bethesda, MD, 2012. For Initiate and complete Pre-Pilot, Pilot, and Validation clinical sample collection, testing, and shipping in South Korea.
$193,656 to University of Washington, Seattle, WA, 2012. For research study.

385
Cathay Bank Foundation ✧
777 N. Broadway
Los Angeles, CA 90012 (626) 279-3876
Contact: Nancy Morikawa
Application address: c/o Cathay Bank, 9650 Flair Dr., El Monte, CA 91731; Main URL: https://www.cathaybank.com/Cathay-Foundation/Home/

Donors: Ted Stein; Mrs. Ted Stein; Cathay Bank; Diamond Ridge Development, LLC; PrimeVest; Shilo Inn; Highland Capital; Alpha Industries; Pacific BMW; Transcontinental Realty Investors, Inc.; 3 A Holdings, LLC.
Foundation type: Company-sponsored foundation.
Financial data (yr. ended 12/31/13): Assets, $2,215 (M); gifts received, $1,470,148; expenditures, $1,476,545; qualifying distributions, $1,476,545; giving activities include $1,476,365 for 126 grants (high: $80,000; low: $1,500).
Purpose and activities: The foundation supports nonprofit organizations involved with culture and arts, health, and welfare. Special emphasis is directed toward programs designed to address affordable housing, community and economic development, and education.
Fields of interest: Arts; Higher education; Adult/continuing education; Education, ESL programs; Education; Public health, obesity; Public health, physical fitness; Health care; Mental health/crisis services; Diabetes; Employment, services; Employment, training; Food banks; Nutrition; Housing/shelter, owner/renter issues; Housing/shelter; Youth development, adult & child programs; Youth, services; Family services, domestic violence; Human services, financial counseling; Aging, centers/services; Developmentally disabled, centers & services; Human services; Community development, neighborhood development; Community/economic development; Leadership development; Economically disadvantaged.
Type of support: General/operating support; Program development.
Limitations: Applications accepted. Giving primarily in areas of company operations, with emphasis on CA, IL, MA, NJ, NY, NV, TX, and WA. No support for political, religious, fraternal, labor, veterans, or military organizations, or private foundations, or organizations that channel grant funds to third parties. No grants to individuals, or for operating funds for hospitals or other patient care facilities, or travel.
Publications: Application guidelines.
Application information: Unsolicited full proposals are not accepted, applicants must submit a letter of intent. A full proposal may be requested at a later date. Grants range from $1,000 to $10,000. Application form not required.
Initial approach: Letter of intent
Deadline(s): None
Board meeting date(s): Quarterly
Officers and Directors:* Peter Wu, Co-Chair., C.E.O., and Pres.; Deborah Ching, Co-Chair.; Alex Lee,* C.F.O. and Treas.; Esther Wee,* Secy.; Pin Tai; Wilson Tang; Patrick Lee; Irwin Wong; David Lin.
EIN: 743052411
Selected grants: The following grants are a representative sample of this grantmaker's funding activity:
$125,000 to Chinatown Service Center, Los Angeles, CA, 2012. For VITA EITC Program/Youth Center/Financial Education Program for Youth and their Familie/Community Health Center/41st Anniversary Gala Celebration 6 dinner attendees, deduct $600.
$70,000 to Valley Economic Development Center, Van Nuys, CA, 2012. For operational support and sponsorship of the annual Where's the Money Access to Capital Business Events in the San Fernando Valley, Downtown, Los Angeles, and San Francisco General operating support for VEDC's Programs and facilities throughout Los Angeles.
$60,000 to Food Bank for New York City, New York, NY, 2012. For EITC as well as outreach to its low-income customers in New York City's Asian communities to help get free tax services to those in need With a renewed grant the Food Bank will fund our operation in Queens and Chinatown which serve a large Chinese-speaking.
$30,000 to Operation Hope, Los Angeles, CA, 2012. For The HOPE Financial Dignity Centers (HOPE Centers) target adults from low- to moderate income communities, while Banking on Our Future targets youth ages 9-18 from low- to moderate-income communities The four HOPE Centers in Los Angeles County will serve a.
$25,000 to AnewAmerica Community Corporation, Berkeley, CA, 2012. For Business Incubator Program - Provides entrepreneurs with customized business coaching, a certificate course in green Business Planning, financial literacy education, access to markets, industry sector incubation, asset-building support, access to credit.
$25,000 to Asian Pacific Islander Small Business Program, Los Angeles, CA, 2012. For Program operating support API SBP's budget includes over $100,000 in federal SBA funding which requires a non-governmental match Funds will help meet the matching funds requirement, effectively leveraging federal funding Overall, approximately 70% of clie.
$25,000 to Chinese American Service League, Chicago, IL, 2012. For Small Accessible Repairs for Seniors Program, TACIT housing related technical assistance, CEDA's Low Income Home Energy Assistance Program (LIHEAP Program) and the EAN home weatherization and energy assistance to eligible families.
$20,000 to Coalition for Responsible Community Development, Los Angeles, CA, 2012. For Affordable Housing Development in South Los Angeles - funds specifically toward personnel (Director of Real Estate and Economic Development and the Project manager), and operating costs to coordinate the affordable housing development process.
$10,000 to Asian American Civic Association, Boston, MA, 2012. For The Careers in Banking and Finance Program- serve a diverse clientele that includes both immigrants and non-immigrants in the Metropolitan Boston area.
$10,000 to Los Angeles Regional Food Bank, Los Angeles, CA, 2012. For Fund supports the essential functions of the Foodbank that includes purchasing soliciting, collecting, sorting, storing and distributing millions of pounds of food every month to people at risk for hunger.

386
Caufield Family Foundation ✧
4 Embarcadero Ctr., Ste. 1400
San Francisco, CA 94111-4164

Established in 1993 in CA.
Donor: Frank J. Caufield.
Foundation type: Independent foundation.
Financial data (yr. ended 06/30/13): Assets, $3,959,356 (M); gifts received, $194,253; expenditures, $1,215,463; qualifying distributions, $1,138,511; giving activities include $1,117,060 for 47 grants (high: $400,000; low: $250).
Purpose and activities: Giving primarily for the arts, health, children and social services, and to a foreign relations association.
Fields of interest: Museums; Arts; Education; Health care; Health organizations; Human services; Children/youth, services; International affairs, association.
Limitations: Applications not accepted. Giving primarily in San Francisco, CA, and New York, NY. No grants to individuals.
Application information: Contributes only to pre-selected organizations.
Officers: Frank J. Caufield, Pres.; Frank R. Caufield, V.P.; Kirsten N. Caufield, V.P.; Linda Jordan, Secy.-Treas.
EIN: 943187012
Selected grants: The following grants are a representative sample of this grantmaker's funding activity:
$263,281 to Council on Foreign Relations, New York, NY, 2011.
$48,000 to San Francisco Film Society, San Francisco, CA, 2011.
$35,000 to San Francisco Child Abuse Prevention Center, San Francisco, CA, 2011.
$25,000 to Refugees International, Washington, DC, 2011.
$17,970 to San Francisco Symphony, San Francisco, CA, 2011.
$17,000 to San Francisco Museum of Modern Art, San Francisco, CA, 2011.
$5,000 to Human Rights Watch, San Francisco, CA, 2011.
$1,200 to San Francisco Jazz Organization, San Francisco, CA, 2011.
$1,000 to Business Executives for National Security, Washington, DC, 2011.
$1,000 to Child Abuse Listening and Mediation, Santa Barbara, CA, 2011.

387
The George and Dale Cavalletto Charities ✧
111 E. Victoria St., 2nd Fl.
Santa Barbara, CA 93101-2018

Established in 2001 in CA.
Donors: George A. Cavalletto Charitable Lead Annuity Trust; George A. Cavalletto Charitable Lead Unitrust; George and Dale Cavalletto Family Trust; George A. Cavalletto Non Exempt Marital Trust; Dale H. Cavalletto Charitable Lead Annuity Trust.
Foundation type: Independent foundation.

Financial data (yr. ended 12/31/13): Assets, $29,622,771 (M); expenditures, $1,671,320; qualifying distributions, $1,559,114; giving activities include $1,400,000 for 3 grants (high: $875,000; low: $225,000).
Purpose and activities: Support primarily for education through a community foundation and a scholarship foundation; giving also for health care.
Fields of interest: Scholarships/financial aid; Health care; Foundations (community).
Limitations: Applications not accepted. Giving limited to Santa Barbara, CA. No grants to individuals.
Application information: Contributes only to pre-selected organizations.
Trustees: Daniel R. Cavalletto; Valerie J. Fuette; Joseph F. Green, Esq.; David V. Larson, C.P.A.; Dennis W. Reilly, Esq.
EIN: 776192290

388
Hugh Stuart Center Charitable Trust ✧
96 N. 3rd St., No. 500
San Jose, CA 95112-7709 (408) 293-0463
Contact: Arthur K. Lund, Tr.; Shirley Oneal, Tr.

Trust established in 1977 in CA.
Donor: Hugh Stuart Center†.
Foundation type: Independent foundation.
Financial data (yr. ended 12/31/13): Assets, $26,367,677 (M); expenditures, $1,224,748; qualifying distributions, $1,002,612; giving activities include $682,900 for 74 grants (high: $62,500; low: $500).
Purpose and activities: Giving to arts and culture, including radio underwriting and public television, education, health and human services, police activity leagues, and for disasters, conservation, national parks, and sports.
Fields of interest: Media, television; Media, radio; Arts; Elementary/secondary education; Higher education; Environment; Health care; Medical research, institute; Youth development, centers/clubs; Human services; Residential/custodial care, hospices; Residential/custodial care, senior continuing care; Children/youth; Youth; Adults; Aging; Young adults; Disabilities, people with; Physically disabled; Blind/visually impaired; Deaf/hearing impaired; Mentally disabled; Minorities; Native Americans/American Indians; Women; Girls; Boys; Military/veterans; Substance abusers; Single parents; Terminal illness, people with; Economically disadvantaged.
Type of support: Curriculum development; General/operating support; Annual campaigns; Building/renovation; Equipment; Endowments; Emergency funds; Program development; Film/video/radio; Scholarship funds; Research.
Limitations: Applications accepted. Giving primarily in Santa Clara County and San Jose, CA. Occasionally giving out of county and state. No grants to individuals.
Publications: Application guidelines; Annual report; Informational brochure.
Application information: Application form not required.
Initial approach: Preferably, letter requests
Copies of proposal: 1
Deadline(s): None
Board meeting date(s): Varies
Final notification: Positive responses only
Trustees: Arthur K. Lund; Shirley Oneal.
Number of staff: 1 part-time support.
EIN: 942455308
Selected grants: The following grants are a representative sample of this grantmaker's funding activity:
$50,000 to Tower Foundation of San Jose State University, San Jose, CA, 2012.
$25,000 to San Francisco Opera, San Francisco, CA, 2012.
$25,000 to Santa Clara University, Santa Clara, CA, 2012.
$25,000 to Values Advocacy Council, San Jose, CA, 2012.
$25,000 to YMCA, East Valley Family, San Jose, CA, 2012.
$20,000 to Spartan Foundation, San Jose, CA, 2012.
$20,000 to Stroke Awareness Foundation, San Jose, CA, 2012.
$15,000 to History San Jose, San Jose, CA, 2012.
$15,000 to Saint Marys Academy, Inglewood, CA, 2012.
$10,000 to Healthy Heart Foundation, San Diego, CA, 2012.
$10,000 to Red Cloud Indian School, Pine Ridge, SD, 2012.
$10,000 to ReSurge International, Mountain View, CA, 2012.
$10,000 to Salvation Army of Santa Clara County, Golden State Division, San Jose, CA, 2012.
$10,000 to York School, Monterey, CA, 2012.

389
Chamberlin Family Foundation ✧
c/o Stephen W. Chamberlin, Susan Chamberlin
5860 W. Las Positas Blvd., Ste. 21
Pleasanton, CA 94588-8557
Main URL: http://www.cffoundation.net

Donors: Stephen W. Chamberlin; Susan C. Chamberlin; Payette River Foundation.
Foundation type: Independent foundation.
Financial data (yr. ended 12/31/13): Assets, $29,645,059 (M); gifts received, $20,228; expenditures, $3,703,375; qualifying distributions, $3,569,359; giving activities include $3,023,462 for 32 grants (high: $500,000; low: $3,000).
Fields of interest: Arts; Elementary/secondary education; Higher education; Education; Environment; Community/economic development; Foundations (community).
Limitations: Applications not accepted. Giving primarily in CA.
Application information: Giving only to pre-selected organizations.
Trustees: Stephen W. Chamberlin; Susan C. Chamberlin.
EIN: 205794764
Selected grants: The following grants are a representative sample of this grantmaker's funding activity:
$88,000 to East Bay Community Foundation, Oakland, CA, 2012. For Program support - Increasing Literacy in Richmond.
$75,000 to Lighthouse Community Charter School, Oakland, CA, 2012. For replication study.
$50,000 to KIPP Foundation, San Francisco, CA, 2012. For Program support - Investing in Innovation.
$25,000 to University of Hawaii Foundation, Honolulu, HI, 2012. For Lyon Arboretum - Support Ongoing Programs.

390
Chambers Family Foundation ✧
P.O. Box 10195, Dept. 12
Palo Alto, CA 94303-0995

Established in 1997 in CA.
Donors: Constance E. Chambers; John T. Chambers; Suncoast Investment Holdings.
Foundation type: Independent foundation.
Financial data (yr. ended 12/31/13): Assets, $24,976,160 (M); expenditures, $1,068,260; qualifying distributions, $1,047,500; giving activities include $1,047,500 for 13 grants (high: $600,000; low: $2,500).
Purpose and activities: Giving primarily for higher education and to health organizations, including a children's hospital.
Fields of interest: Higher education; Hospitals (specialty); Health organizations; Cancer research.
Limitations: Applications not accepted. Giving primarily in CA; support also in NC. No grants to individuals.
Application information: Contributes only to pre-selected organizations.
Officers: John T. Chambers, C.E.O. and Pres.; Constance E. Chambers, C.F.O. and Secy.-Treas.
EIN: 770443168

391
Chan Soon-Shiong Family Foundation ✧
c/o Steve Hassan
10182 Culver Blvd.
Culver City, CA 90232
Dr. Patrick Soon-Shiong's Twitter Feed: https://twitter.com/solvehealthcare
Michele Chan and Dr. Patrick Soon-Shiong's Giving Pledge Profile: http://glasspockets.org/philanthropy-in-focus/eye-on-the-giving-pledge/profiles/soon-shiong

Established in 2008 in CA.
Donors: Michele Chan; Dr. Patrick Soon-Shiong.
Foundation type: Independent foundation.
Financial data (yr. ended 09/30/13): Assets, $132,546,910 (M); expenditures, $5,104,962; qualifying distributions, $4,969,532; giving activities include $4,944,927 for 21 grants (high: $2,000,000; low: $1,000).
Purpose and activities: The mission of the foundation is to fund research and erase disparities in access to health care and education.
Fields of interest: Education; Health care; Medical research, institute.
Limitations: Applications not accepted. Giving primarily in CA, with emphasis on Los Angeles and San Francisco.
Application information: Unsolicited requests for funds not accepted.
Officers and Directors:* Patrick Soon-Shiong,* Pres.; Michele Soon-Shiong,* Secy. and C.F.O.; Charles Kenworthy, Exec. V.P.
EIN: 264384360
Selected grants: The following grants are a representative sample of this grantmaker's funding activity:
$500,750 to Saint Johns Health Center, Santa Monica, CA, 2011.
$60,000 to Saint Martin of Tours School, Los Angeles, CA, 2011.
$30,000 to Resurrection School, Los Angeles, CA, 2011.
$10,000 to LAs BEST, Los Angeles, CA, 2011.

$5,000 to Marymount High School, Los Angeles, CA, 2011.
$2,500 to Phoenix Community Alliance, Phoenix, AZ, 2011.
$1,200 to Concern Foundation, Los Angeles, CA, 2011.
$1,000 to Autism Speaks, New York, NY, 2011.

392
Camilla Chandler Family Foundation ✧
2029 Century Park E., Ste. 4000
Los Angeles, CA 90067-3036

Established in 1994 in CA.
Donor: Camilla Chandler Frost.
Foundation type: Independent foundation.
Financial data (yr. ended 10/31/13): Assets, $27,112,897 (M); gifts received, $1,905,620; expenditures, $1,959,729; qualifying distributions, $1,810,409; giving activities include $1,750,000 for 2 grants (high: $1,000,000; low: $750,000).
Purpose and activities: Giving primarily to a museum of art; funding also for a hospital.
Fields of interest: Museums (art); Hospitals (general).
Type of support: General/operating support; Capital campaigns; Building/renovation; Equipment.
Limitations: Applications not accepted. Giving primarily in Los Angeles, CA; some funding also in Port Townsend, WA. No grants to individuals.
Application information: Contributes only to pre-selected organizations.
Trustees: Camilla Chandler Frost; Alexander Spear; William Stinehart, Jr.
EIN: 956979804
Selected grants: The following grants are a representative sample of this grantmaker's funding activity:
$500,000 to Museum Associates, Los Angeles County Museum of Art (LACMA), Los Angeles, CA, 2011.
$25,000 to Northwest Maritime Center, Port Townsend, WA, 2011. For capital campaign.

393
Change a Life Foundation ✧
5 Corporate Park, Ste. 210
Irvine, CA 92606-5166 (949) 788-9999
Contact: Lisa C. Fujimoto, Exec. V.P.
FAX: (949) 788-9266; E-mail: info@changealife.org; Main URL: http://www.changealife.org
Facebook: http://www.facebook.com/pages/Change-A-Life-Foundation/132077487018

Established in 2000 in CA.
Donor: SWFF.
Foundation type: Independent foundation.
Financial data (yr. ended 12/31/13): Assets, $233,094 (M); gifts received, $1,903,000; expenditures, $2,074,129; qualifying distributions, $1,433,376; giving activities include $1,433,376 for 117 grants (high: $57,883; low: $298).
Purpose and activities: The Change a Life Foundation's founder has a unique philanthropic vision, which is an altruistic compassion for mankind and a heart-filled desire to help individuals in need. His vision is to help people directly who are in their most desperate hour with little or no resources to help themselves. The ultimate mission of the founder is to inspire and challenge grant recipients to follow his charitable example, and one day repay the favor by helping others in need. The foundation will continue to honor its founder and donor by fulfilling his mission to better society by anonymously helping one person at a time.
Fields of interest: Human services.
Type of support: Equipment; Emergency funds; Scholarship funds; Grants to individuals; Scholarships—to individuals.
Limitations: Giving limited to CA.
Publications: Annual report; Newsletter; Newsletter (including application guidelines).
Application information: Grants to organizations are by invitation only. The foundation awards larger grants, of up to $10,000, to pre-approved partner organizations that impact more individuals needs. To be considered for an organizational grant, a pre-approved nonprofit partner must have submitted at least six individual grant applications, have submitted follow-up reports on time and correctly, and have an organizational grant application that will impact the largest amount of individuals/clients as possible. Grants for individuals must be requested and administered by the foundation's pre-approved nonprofit partner organizations that provide case management services. Individuals may not apply themselves. Nonprofit organizations must be pre-approved and in partnership with the foundation in order to submit grant applications. See foundation web site for further information as well as scholarship application procedures.
Deadline(s): See foundation web site for current deadlines
Board meeting date(s): Feb., Apr., June, Aug., Oct., and Nov.
Officers: Richard E. Tomlin, Jr., Chair. and Pres.; Lisa C. Fujimoto, Exec. V.P. and Exec. Dir.; Andy T. Bui, C.F.O. and Treas.
Number of staff: 5 full-time professional.
EIN: 330935713

394
Ping and Amy Chao Family Foundation ✧
445 S. San Antonio Rd., Ste. 204
Los Altos, CA 94022-3638 (650) 924-1104
Contact: Ping Chao, Chair.
FAX: (650) 434-3770;
E-mail: info@chaofoundation.org; China address: No. 1 Shanyuan St., Rm. 1-307, Haidian District, Beijing, China; Main URL: http://www.chaofoundation.org
Facebook: https://www.facebook.com/chaofoundation
Twitter: https://twitter.com/eastvillagers

Established in 2006 in CA.
Donor: Chao Family Trust.
Foundation type: Independent foundation.
Financial data (yr. ended 11/30/12): Assets, $9,906,161 (M); expenditures, $945,948; qualifying distributions, $920,383; giving activities include $646,150 for 15 grants (high: $200,000; low: $150), and $113,270 for 1 foundation-administered program.
Purpose and activities: Giving primarily to fund and nurture initiatives improving the health and well-being of children and youth in economically disadvantaged regions throughout the world, as well as to promote the spirit of philanthropy and developing awareness of non-profit practices and opportunities for service for the younger generation of China and the greater Chinese Diaspora. Because of these focuses, the foundation seeks to fund grants that either are run by a member of the Asian American community, or that focus on work in Asia or the Asian American community.
Fields of interest: Education; Human services; International affairs, goodwill promotion; Christian agencies & churches.
Limitations: Giving primarily in CA; some giving also NY. No grants to individuals.
Application information:
Initial approach: Use online application on foundation web site
Deadline(s): See foundation web site for current deadlines
Officers and Trustees:* Ping Chao,* Chair.; Amy Chao,* V.P.; Nancy Nguyen, Exec. Dir.
EIN: 206750125

395
Chapman & Associates Foundation
265 N. San Gabriel Blvd.
Pasadena, CA 91107-3423
Contact: Megan Bustamante
E-mail: megan_bustamante@ajg.com; Main URL: http://www.chapmanins.com/about/foundation

Established in 2001 in CA.
Donors: Chapman & Associates; Gil Younger; Philadelphia Insurance Company.
Foundation type: Company-sponsored foundation.
Financial data (yr. ended 12/31/12): Assets, $1,261,537 (M); gifts received, $786,200; expenditures, $904,349; qualifying distributions, $903,388; giving activities include $902,525 for grants.
Purpose and activities: The foundation supports organizations involved with education, forest conservation, health, human services, and religion.
Fields of interest: Education; Environment, forests; Hospitals (general); Health care, clinics/centers; Health care; Children/youth, services; Children, foster care; Human services; Christian agencies & churches; Religion.
Type of support: General/operating support.
Limitations: Applications accepted. Giving primarily in CA. No grants to individuals.
Publications: Application guidelines.
Application information: Letters of inquiry should be no longer than 1 page. Additional information may be requested at a later date. The foundation utilizes a Recommendation Committee to select potential grantees. Application form not required.
Initial approach: E-mail or mail letter of inquiry
Deadline(s): None
Board meeting date(s): Quarterly
Officers and Directors: James Hull, Pres.; Harold Parker, Jr., V.P.; Ryan Dietz, Secy.; Gerald S. Chapman; Gregory S. Chapman.
EIN: 954835227

396
The Ray Charles Foundation, Inc. ✧
(formerly Robinson Foundation for Hearing Disorders, Inc.)
2107 W. Washington Blvd.
Los Angeles, CA 90018-1536
Contact: Joe Adams, Dir.
E-mail: info@theraycharlesfoundation.org; Main URL: http://www.theraycharlesfoundation.org/index.html

Incorporated in 1986 in CA.

Donors: Ray Charles Robinson†; Alexander Andreadis; Los Angeles Chamber of Commerce; Sun Valley Center; Family Celebration; World Events, LLC; American Ocean Campaign; Cass Productions; Bruce Willis Family Trust; Staples Center Foundation; Goldenvoice, LLC.
Foundation type: Independent foundation.
Financial data (yr. ended 12/31/12): Assets, $56,071,107 (M); expenditures, $6,162,273; qualifying distributions, $2,272,740; giving activities include $1,366,045 for 8 grants (high: $1,000,000; low: $25,000).
Fields of interest: Higher education; Education; Human services.
Limitations: Applications accepted. Giving primarily Atlanta, GA; funding also in CA. No grants to individuals.
Publications: Application guidelines.
Application information: See foundation web site for application guidelines.
Initial approach: Letter
Officers: Joseph Adams, Chair.; Valerie Ervin, Pres.; Ronal J. Boyd, Secy.; Rev. Cecil L. Murray, Treas.
Directors: Stuart Ian Alpert; Ramsey Jay, Jr.; Mauri Reese; Diane Treister.
EIN: 954047622
Selected grants: The following grants are a representative sample of this grantmaker's funding activity:
$1,000,000 to Educating Young Minds, Los Angeles, CA, 2012. For Fostering Enriched Environment for Young Children to Learn and Grow.
$25,000 to Providence Speech and Hearing Center, Orange, CA, 2012. For Helping the Speech and Hearing Impaired.
$250,000 to Geffen Playhouse, Los Angeles, CA, 2013.
$200,000 to Free Wheelchair Mission, Irvine, CA, 2013.
$100,000 to Cedars-Sinai Medical Center, Los Angeles, CA, 2013.
$50,000 to Autry National Center of the American West, Los Angeles, CA, 2013.
$50,000 to Communities in Schools National Office, Arlington, VA, 2013.
$50,000 to UCLA Foundation, Center for East-West Medicine Program, Los Angeles, CA, 2013.
$25,000 to MVAT Foundation, Sherman Oaks, CA, 2013.

397
Chartwell Charitable Foundation ✧
1999 Ave. of the Stars, Ste. 3050
Los Angeles, CA 90067-4613 (310) 556-7600

Established in 1998 in CA.
Donor: A. Jerrold Perenchio.
Foundation type: Independent foundation.
Financial data (yr. ended 12/31/13): Assets, $830 (M); gifts received, $6,661,013; expenditures, $6,659,851; qualifying distributions, $6,637,812; giving activities include $6,615,000 for 89 grants (high: $500,000; low: $2,500).
Fields of interest: Arts; Higher education; Education; Environment; Hospitals (general); Human services; Children/youth, services.
Limitations: Applications accepted. Giving primarily in CA and NY.
Application information:
Initial approach: Letter
Deadline(s): None
Officers and Trustee:* A. Jerrold Perenchio,* Chair. and Exec. V.P.; Margaret A. Perenchio, Pres.; Robert V. Cahill, V.P.; Michael A. Enright, Secy.; Kathleen Antion, C.F.O. and Treas.
EIN: 954679659
Selected grants: The following grants are a representative sample of this grantmaker's funding activity:
$500,000 to Archer School for Girls, Los Angeles, CA, 2013.
$500,000 to Arizona State University Foundation for a New American University, Fulton Center, Tempe, AZ, 2013.
$500,000 to California Community Foundation, Los Angeles, CA, 2013.

398
Chintu Gudiya Foundation ✧
453 Lincoln Ave.
Alameda, CA 94501-3235

Established in 1999 in CA.
Donors: Donald Ajit Lobo; Mari Tilos.
Foundation type: Independent foundation.
Financial data (yr. ended 06/30/13): Assets, $12,713,082 (M); expenditures, $781,628; qualifying distributions, $685,000; giving activities include $685,000 for 11 grants (high: $450,000; low: $2,500).
Purpose and activities: Giving primarily for education and human services.
Fields of interest: Education; Human services; Children/youth, services.
Limitations: Applications not accepted. Giving primarily in CA and MN. No grants to individuals.
Application information: Contributes only to pre-selected organizations.
Officers and Directors:* Donald Ajit Lobo,* Pres.; Mari Grace Tilos,* Secy.-Treas.
EIN: 943315265
Selected grants: The following grants are a representative sample of this grantmaker's funding activity:
$110,000 to Free Software Foundation, Boston, MA, 2013. To Provide Free Software to the Public.
$50,000 to Truckee Donner Land Trust, Truckee, CA, 2013. To Preserve and Protect Scenic, Historic and Recreational Lands with High Natural.
$10,000 to East Bay Bicycle Coalition, Oakland, CA, 2013. For Safe, Convenient and Enjoyable Bicycling for All People in the East Bay.

399
The Christensen Fund ✧
260 Townsend St., Ste. 600
San Francisco, CA 94107-1719 (415) 644-1600
Contact: Lourdes Inga, Grants Admin.
FAX: (415) 644-1601;
E-mail: info@christensenfund.org; Main URL: http://www.christensenfund.org
Facebook: http://www.facebook.com/pages/The-Christensen-Fund/170421729636697
Grants Database: http://www.christensenfund.org/funding/grants-search/
Philanthropy's Promise: http://www.ncrp.org/philanthropys-promise/who
The Christensen Fund's Philanthropy Promise: http://www.ncrp.org/philanthropys-promise/who
Twitter: http://twitter.com/christensenfund
YouTube: https://www.youtube.com/user/ChristensenFund?feature=mhee

Incorporated in 1957 in CA.
Donors: Allen D. Christensen†; Carmen M. Christensen†.
Foundation type: Independent foundation.
Financial data (yr. ended 12/31/13): Assets, $244,229,219 (M); gifts received, $245,000; expenditures, $22,741,780; qualifying distributions, $17,615,700; giving activities include $13,187,817 for 216 grants (high: $551,000; low: $2,500), and $17,750 for 13 employee matching gifts.
Purpose and activities: The fund believes in the power of biological and cultural diversity to sustain and enrich a world faced with great change and uncertainty. Focus is on "bio-cultural" - the rich but neglected adaptive interweave of people and place, culture and ecology. The fund's mission is to buttress the efforts of people and institutions who believe in a biodiverse world infused with artistic expression and work to secure ways of life and landscapes that are beautiful, bountiful and resilient. The fund pursues this mission through place-based work in the region chosen for their potential to withstand and recover from the global erosion of diversity. Focus is on backing the efforts of locally-recognized community custodians of this heritage, and their alliances with scholars, artists, advocates and others. International efforts are also funded to help build global understanding of these issues. The fund works primarily through capacity and network building, knowledge generation, collaboration and mission-related investments.
Fields of interest: Arts, cultural/ethnic awareness; Visual arts; Museums; Environment, research; Environment, natural resources; Environment; Biology/life sciences; Native Americans/American Indians; Indigenous peoples.
International interests: Australia; Kyrgyz Republic; Mexico; Papua New Guinea; Tajikistan; Vanuatu.
Type of support: Continuing support; Equipment; Program development; Conferences/seminars; Seed money; Fellowships; Research; Program evaluation; Matching/challenge support.
Limitations: Applications accepted. Giving primarily in the Southwest (Four Corners region), northern Mexico (including the Colorado Plateau and Delta, the Pueblo and Hispanic communities of the Rio Arriba/Rio Grande, the Sonoran Desert on both sides of the Mexican-U.S. border and east of the Colorado River, and the Sierra Tarahumara Montane West), Central Asia (the mountains and associated valleys of northeastern Turkey, the Kyrgyz Republic, and Tajikistan), the Rift Valley (especially southwest Ethiopia and adjacent areas of northern Kenya) Northern Australia (especially Arhem Land, Far Northern Queensland, and the Kimberley and Torres Strait Islands), and Melanesia, (Papua New Guinea and Vanuatu). No grants to individuals, or for capital funds, or building or renovation funding; no loans.
Publications: Financial statement; Grants list; Program policy statement (including application guidelines).
Application information: Please refer to the fund's web site for guidelines and program areas. For events such as conferences and workshops, apply at least six months in advance of their starting date to enable timely review and grant processing. Application form required.
Initial approach: Pre-proposal as outlined on fund's web site
Copies of proposal: 1
Deadline(s): Submit pre-proposal between July 15 and Sept. 15 (for next calendar year)

Board meeting date(s): Quarterly
Final notification: 8 weeks
Officers and Directors:* Atossa Soltani,* Chair.; E. Walter Coward, Jr., Ph.D.*, Vice-Chair.; C. Diane Christensen,* Pres.; Albert Fong, C.F.O. and Dir., Finance and Investment; Peter Liu,* Treas.; Kenneth Wilson, Ph.D., Exec. Dir.; Theresa Fay-Bustillos; Winona LaDuke; Thomas K. Seligman; Richard Williams; Michael Nicoll Yahgulanaas.
Number of staff: 4 full-time professional; 5 full-time support; 1 part-time support.
EIN: 946055879

400
Chrysopolae Foundation ✧
P.O. Box 10174
San Rafael, CA 94912-0174

Established in 1997 in CA.
Donors: Lawrence Charles Ford†; Lawrence Charles Ford, Jr.; Cynthia Carroll.
Foundation type: Independent foundation.
Financial data (yr. ended 12/31/13): Assets, $11,655,411 (M); expenditures, $531,748; qualifying distributions, $456,943; giving activities include $456,617 for 39 grants (high: $47,267; low: $500).
Purpose and activities: Giving primarily for scholarships to former Tamsical High School Team Program students attending an accredited undergraduate college only; funding also for other education, as well as for a charitable endowment fund.
Fields of interest: Elementary/secondary education; Higher education; Education; Medical research, association; Human services; Foundations (public).
Limitations: Applications not accepted. Giving primarily in CA.
Application information: Unsolicited requests for funds not accepted.
Officers: Lawrence Charles Ford, Jr., Pres.; Cynthia Carroll, Secy.-Treas.
EIN: 943265060

401
Arthur & Carlyse Ciocca Charitable Foundation ✧
9 25th Ave. N.
San Francisco, CA 94121-1104

Established in 1997 in CA.
Donors: Arthur Ciocca; Carlyse Ciocca.
Foundation type: Independent foundation.
Financial data (yr. ended 12/31/13): Assets, $3,749,498 (M); gifts received, $1,832,237; expenditures, $1,145,231; giving activities include $1,123,750 for 20 grants (high: $337,500; low: $250).
Purpose and activities: Giving primarily for education, health organizations, and social services.
Fields of interest: Higher education; Education; Health organizations, association; Human services; Foundations (private grantmaking).
Limitations: Applications not accepted. Giving in the U.S., with emphasis on Davis and San Francisco, CA. No grants to individuals.
Application information: Contributes only to pre-selected organizations.
Officers: Carlyse Ciocca, Pres.; Arthur Ciocca, Secy.
EIN: 943279919

402
Cisco Systems Foundation ✧
170 W. Tasman Dr.
San Jose, CA 95134-1706 (408) 527-3040
Contact: Peter Tavernise, Exec. Dir.
Main URL: http://www.cisco.com/go/foundation
Silicon Valley Impact Grant Recipients: http://csr.cisco.com/pages/silicon-valley-impact-grant-recipients—fy2014

Established in 1997 in CA.
Donors: Cisco Systems, Inc.; Scientific-Atlanta Fdn. Inc.
Foundation type: Company-sponsored foundation.
Financial data (yr. ended 07/31/13): Assets, $129,341,993 (M); expenditures, $13,735,307; qualifying distributions, $13,152,479; giving activities include $8,023,084 for 168 grants (high: $445,000; low: $8,334), and $4,901,575 for employee matching gifts.
Purpose and activities: The foundation supports programs designed to improve access to basic human needs, education, and economic opportunity. Special emphasis is directed toward programs designed to address underserved communities; and provide solutions that utilizes the power of the internet and communications technology.
Fields of interest: Elementary/secondary education; Vocational education; Health sciences school/education; Adult/continuing education; Education, reading; Education; Public health, obesity; Public health, clean water supply; Health care; Crime/violence prevention; Employment, training; Employment, retraining; Food services; Housing/shelter, development; Housing/shelter; Disasters, preparedness/services; Children, services; Human services, financial counseling; Human services; Economic development; Social entrepreneurship; Community development, small businesses; Microfinance/microlending; Mathematics; Engineering/technology; Science; Children/youth; Minorities; Women; Girls; Economically disadvantaged; Homeless.
Type of support: General/operating support; Continuing support; Program development; Curriculum development; Employee volunteer services; Employee matching gifts.
Limitations: Applications accepted. Giving primarily within a 50 mile radius of company operations in Lawrenceville, GA, Boxborough, MA, Research Triangle Park, NC, Richardson, TX, Toronto, Canada, Beijing and Shanghai, China, and Bangalore, India, with emphasis on San Jose, CA. No support for discriminatory organizations, religious, political, or sectarian organizations not of direct benefit to the entire community, public schools or school systems, charter schools, school foundations, booster clubs, colleges or universities, pass-through organizations, or grantmaking foundations. No grants to individuals, or for research, start-up needs, scholarships, stipends, loans, athletic events, competitions, tournaments, conferences, seminars, festival or similar one-day events, field trips, fundraising events, sponsorships, capital campaigns, or challenge or matching grants; generally, no equipment funding.
Publications: Application guidelines; Grants list; IRS Form 990 or 990-PF printed copy available upon request.
Application information: A full proposal may be requested at a later date for Global Impact Grants. General Community Impact Cash Grants are by invitation only for eligible organizations that operate programs within a 50 mile radius of Cisco major site community. Application form required.
Initial approach: Complete online eligibility quiz and application form
Deadline(s): None for Global Impact Grants; Varies for Community Impact Cash Grant - Silicon Valley
Board meeting date(s): Fall and spring
Officers and Trustees:* John P. Morgridge,* Pres.; Randy Pond,* Secy.; Roger Biscay, Treas.; Peter Tavernise, Exec. Dir.; Lary Carter; Carlos Dominguez; Patrick Finn; Ehrika Gladden; V C Gopalratnam; Rob Johnson; Michael Vessey; Tae Yoo.
Number of staff: 1 part-time support.
EIN: 770443347
Selected grants: The following grants are a representative sample of this grantmaker's funding activity:
$4,138,695 to JustGive, San Francisco, CA, 2012. For matching employee gifts.
$526,664 to Charities Aid Foundation America, Alexandria, VA, 2012. For matching employee gifts.
$500,000 to Community Voice Mail National Office, Seattle, WA, 2012. For Next Generation of ICT Phase II.
$415,000 to Communities in Schools of North Carolina, Raleigh, NC, 2012. For National Science, Technology, Engineering and Mathematics (STEM) Career Platform Requirements Process and North Carolina Pilot Approach.
$300,000 to Grameen Foundation USA, Washington, DC, 2012. To accelerate a social performance management movement.
$246,000 to American Red Cross National Headquarters, Washington, DC, 2012. For Disaster Relief Fund and Annual Disaster Giving Program.
$100,000 to Georgia Gwinnett College Foundation, Lawrenceville, GA, 2012. For Student Success Programs Project, TIC-TAC-TOE.
$19,500 to Family Violence Prevention Center, Interact, Raleigh, NC, 2012. For Emergency Shelter.
$19,500 to US FIRST, Manchester, NH, 2012. To develop Science, Technology, Engineering and Mathematics (STEM) enrichment after-school activities for underserved students in North Carolina.
$15,000 to Bring Me A Book Foundation, Mountain View, CA, 2012. For San Jose Transitional Kindergarten Classroom Initiative.

403
The Gilbert and Jacki Cisneros Foundation ✧
c/o SSB
10880 Wilshire Blvd., Ste. 2100
Los Angeles, CA 90024-4121 (888) 234-1999
FAX: (877) 746-5889;
E-mail: grantadministration@wellsfargo.com; Main URL: http://cisnerosfoundation.org/

Established in CA.
Donors: Gilbert Cisneros; Jacki Cisneros.
Foundation type: Independent foundation.
Financial data (yr. ended 12/31/12): Assets, $20,130,060 (M); gifts received, $75,000; expenditures, $1,222,529; qualifying distributions, $1,086,696; giving activities include $999,995 for 31 grants (high: $250,000; low: $2,500).

Purpose and activities: Giving primarily to organizations that support Hispanic student education. The foundation is focused on providing assistance to organizations dedicated to making an impact in the areas of college readiness, awareness efforts and individual funding.
Fields of interest: Higher education; Education; Hispanics/Latinos.
Limitations: Giving primarily in Los Angeles and Orange counties in CA. No grants to individuals, or for scholarships.
Publications: Application guidelines.
Application information:
Initial approach: Use online application form via: https://www.wellsfargo.com/privatefoundationgrants/cisneros
Deadline(s): Mar. 31 (for spring meeting) and Aug. 31 (for fall meeting)
Final notification: Generally within 60 days
Officers: Gilbert R. Cisneors, Pres. and Treas.; Jacki Marie Wells Cisneros, V.P. and Secy.
EIN: 273411484
Selected grants: The following grants are a representative sample of this grantmaker's funding activity:
$250,000 to Hispanic Scholarship Fund, Gardena, CA, 2012. For The Frank Terrazas Scholarship Program in Pico Rivera, CA.
$50,000 to Delhi Center, Santa Ana, CA, 2012. For $25,000 for Citizen Leadership Program and $25,000 for The Learning Lounge for elementary education.
$50,000 to Hispanic Scholarship Fund, Gardena, CA, 2012. For The Frank Terrazas Scholarship Endowment.
$15,000 to Hispanic Scholarship Fund, Gardena, CA, 2012. For your general fund.
$10,000 to Los Angeles City College Foundation, Los Angeles, CA, 2012. For Latino(a)/Hispanic Heritage Scholarship.
$10,000 to Our Lady Queen of Angels Church, Newport Beach, CA, 2012. For PSA - Pastoral Service Appeal for the Diocese of Orange.
$4,500 to Navy Supply Corps Foundation, Athens, GA, 2012. To be used for the memorial scholarship fund.
$3,000 to United States Navy Memorial Foundation, Washington, DC, 2012. For grant for their general fund.
$2,500 to Hispanic Scholarship Fund, Gardena, CA, 2012. To be used for the Fidel B. Vargas Memorial Scholarship.

404
Joseph A.W. Clayes, III Charitable Trust ✧

1385 Park Row
La Jolla, CA 92037-3708

Established in 2007 in CA.
Donor: Joseph A.W. Clayes III Living Trust.
Foundation type: Independent foundation.
Financial data (yr. ended 12/31/13): Assets, $40,850,865 (M); expenditures, $2,478,074; qualifying distributions, $1,845,213; giving activities include $1,795,213 for 3 grants (high: $1,000,000; low: $267,453).
Fields of interest: Museums (art); Performing arts centers; Higher education.
Limitations: Applications not accepted. Giving primarily in CA.
Application information: Contributes only to pre-selected organizations.
Trustees: Trulette M. Clayes; Brendan A. Holmes.
EIN: 207515945
Selected grants: The following grants are a representative sample of this grantmaker's funding activity:
$1,352,000 to California State University, Fullerton, CA, 2011.

405
Clif Bar Family Foundation ✧

1451 66th St.
Emeryville, CA 94608-1004 (510) 596-6383
E-mail: familyfoundation@clifbar.com; E-mail for Seed Matters Program: seedmatters@clifbarfamilyfoundation.org; Main URL: http://www.clifbarfamilyfoundation.org
Grants List: http://clifbarfamilyfoundation.org/Grantees/Grantees-Map
Seed Matters Blog: http://www.seedmatters.org/the-seed-commons/
Seed Matters on Facebook: http://www.facebook.com/seedmatters
Seed Matters on Twitter: http://twitter.com/Seed_Matters/

Established in 2006 in CA.
Donor: Clif Bar & Co.
Foundation type: Company-sponsored foundation.
Financial data (yr. ended 12/31/13): Assets, $219,208 (M); gifts received, $3,528,360; expenditures, $3,916,697; qualifying distributions, $3,816,698; giving activities include $3,714,485 for 373 grants (high: $250,000; low: $1,000).
Purpose and activities: The foundation supports programs designed to strengthen the food system and community; enhance public health; and safeguard the environment and natural resources. Special emphasis is directed toward grassroots organizations that have the ability to engage local groups.
Fields of interest: Arts; Education; Environment, pollution control; Environment, air pollution; Environment, waste management; Environment, climate change/global warming; Environment, natural resources; Environment, land resources; Environment, energy; Environment; Employment; Agriculture, community food systems; Agriculture, sustainable programs; Agriculture, farmlands; Food services; Agriculture/food; Housing/shelter; Youth, services; Human services; Community development, small businesses.
Type of support: Donated products; General/operating support; Management development/capacity building; Annual campaigns; Program development; Fellowships; Consulting services.
Limitations: Applications accepted. Giving primarily in CA. No support for religious groups or state agencies. No grants to individuals, or for seminar, media, or fundraising events that are not an integral part of a broader program, capital construction, endowments, or debt reduction.
Publications: Application guidelines; Grants list.
Application information: The average award for Small Grants is $8,000. Capacity-Building Grants, Long-Term Partnerships, and Consulting Grants are by invitation only. Application form required.
Initial approach: Complete online questionnaire and application for Small Grants
Deadline(s): Feb. 15, May 15, Aug. 15, and Nov. 1 for Small Grants
Board meeting date(s): Quarterly
Officers: Kathleen F. Crawford, Pres.; Gary J. Erickson, Secy.-Treas.
EIN: 204345935
Selected grants: The following grants are a representative sample of this grantmaker's funding activity:
$20,000 to WE CARE Solar, Berkeley, CA, 2012. For Programs for Reducing Environment Health Hazards.
$10,000 to World Neighbors, Oklahoma City, OK, 2012. For Programs for Healthy Food Systems.
$8,000 to Worldreader, Seattle, WA, 2012. For Programs for Earths Beauty and Bounty.
$5,000 to Western Lands Project, Seattle, WA, 2012. For Programs for Stronger Communities.
$3,000 to TreePeople, Beverly Hills, CA, 2012. For Programs for Opportunities for Outdoor Activities.
$2,500 to Vashon-Maury Island Land Trust, Vashon, WA, 2012. For Seed Matters.

406
Winifred Johnson Clive Foundation ✧

1660 Bush St., No. 300
San Francisco, CA 94109-5308 (415) 561-6540
Contact: Fatma Abdullahi
Main URL: http://www.pfs-llc.net/foundations/winifred-johnson-clive-foundation
Knowledge Center: http://www.pfs-llc.net/foundations/winifred-johnson-clive-foundation/news

Established in 1986 in FL.
Donors: Winifred Johnson Clive†; Margaret P. Johnson; Thomas P. Johnson; Winifred J. Sharp.
Foundation type: Independent foundation.
Financial data (yr. ended 11/30/13): Assets, $18,176,942 (M); expenditures, $900,735; qualifying distributions, $789,942; giving activities include $680,525 for 31 grants (high: $82,650; low: $500).
Purpose and activities: Giving primarily for the arts, education, animal welfare, youth and social services, and to organizations addressing the problem of aging and the aging and needy.
Fields of interest: Museums (art); Arts; Education; Animal welfare; Human services; Children/youth, services.
Type of support: General/operating support.
Limitations: Applications accepted. Giving primarily in San Francisco, CA, FL, and NY. No grants to individuals.
Application information: Application form required.
Initial approach: Letter
Deadline(s): None
Board meeting date(s): Twice a year
Officers and Trustees:* Winifred J. Sharp, Chair.; Lisa J. Lunday,* Secy.; Jonathan C. Perkins,* Treas.; Steger Johnson; Stephanie J. Kiewlich; Grace J. Perkins; Elizabeth Stewart; Jennifer Thielhelm.
EIN: 256277031
Selected grants: The following grants are a representative sample of this grantmaker's funding activity:
$50,000 to Center for Orangutan and Chimpanzee Conservation, Wauchula, FL, 2011.
$50,000 to Fine Arts Museums of San Francisco, San Francisco, CA, 2011.
$35,000 to Medicine Horse Center, Mancos, CO, 2011.
$35,000 to StreetSquash, New York, NY, 2011.
$30,000 to San Francisco Art Institute, San Francisco, CA, 2011.

$25,000 to Buck Institute for Research on Aging, Novato, CA, 2011.
$25,000 to Institute on Aging, San Francisco, CA, 2011.
$25,000 to Southwest Indian Foundation, Gallup, NM, 2011.
$25,000 to United Religions Initiative, San Francisco, CA, 2011.
$25,000 to Unity Care Group, San Jose, CA, 2011.

407
The Clorox Company Foundation ✧
1221 Broadway
Oakland, CA 94612-1888 (510) 836-3223
E-mail: cloroxfndt@eastbaycf.org; Mailing address: c/o East Bay Community Foundation, De Domenico Bldg., 200 Frank Ogawa Plz., Oakland, CA 94612; Main URL: http://www.thecloroxcompany.com/corporate-responsibility/purpose/clorox-company-foundation/

Incorporated in 1980 in CA.
Donor: The Clorox Co.
Foundation type: Company-sponsored foundation.
Financial data (yr. ended 06/30/13): Assets, $2,147,290 (M); gifts received, $5,705,183; expenditures, $5,996,718; qualifying distributions, $5,793,125; giving activities include $5,793,125 for grants.
Purpose and activities: The foundation supports organizations involved with arts and culture, K-12 education, disaster relief, and youth development. Grants are administered by the East Bay Community Foundation.
Fields of interest: Visual arts; Performing arts; Arts; Elementary/secondary education; Disasters, preparedness/services; Youth development; Voluntarism promotion; Children/youth; Children; Youth; Girls; Boys; Economically disadvantaged.
Type of support: General/operating support; Program development; Scholarship funds; Employee volunteer services; Employee matching gifts; Employee-related scholarships; Donated products.
Limitations: Applications accepted. Giving primarily in areas of company operations, with emphasis on the Oakland, CA, area; giving on a national and international basis for disaster relief. No support for national organizations, religious organizations not of direct benefit to the entire community, political parties, candidates, or organizations, or exclusive membership organizations. No grants for fundraising, athletic events or league sponsorships, travel, advertising or promotional sponsorships, tickets, conferences, conventions, meetings, or similar events, media production, political activities, dues, debt reduction, capital campaigns, or individual school projects.
Publications: Application guidelines; Annual report (including application guidelines).
Application information: Unsolicited requests for scholarship funds are not accepted. East Bay Community Foundation staff receives all applications and reviews them on behalf of The Clorox Company Foundation. Application form required.
Initial approach: Complete online application form
Deadline(s): Jan. 1, Apr. 1, July 1, and Oct. 1
Board meeting date(s): Mar. and Sept.
Final notification: 2 months following deadlines
Officers and Trustees:* Donald R. Knauss,* Chair.; Jacqueline P. Kane,* Pres.; Victoria Jones, V.P. and Secy.; Charles R. Conradi, V.P. and Treas.; Jeffrey R. Brubaker; Benno Dorer; Paola Gonzalez.
EIN: 942674980
Selected grants: The following grants are a representative sample of this grantmaker's funding activity:
$1,676,278 to JK Group, Plainsboro, NJ, 2011. For Gift Campaign Employee Contributions.
$389,441 to JK Group, Plainsboro, NJ, 2011.
$234,050 to JK Group, Plainsboro, NJ, 2011. For Corporate Match.
$133,000 to East Bay Community Foundation, Oakland, CA, 2011. For education/youth program.
$117,211 to JK Group, Plainsboro, NJ, 2011. For One Time Payroll Deduction Match.
$111,500 to East Bay Community Foundation, Oakland, CA, 2011. For cultural/civic program.
$107,000 to East Bay Community Foundation, Oakland, CA, 2011. For culture/civic program.
$98,390 to Scholarship America, Saint Peter, MN, 2011. For scholarship program.
$63,379 to JK Group, Plainsboro, NJ, 2011. For Higher Education Match.
$50,000 to East Bay Community Foundation, Oakland, CA, 2011. For civic/cultural program.
$12,500 to Brothers on the Rise, Oakland, CA, 2012.
$12,500 to Dimensions Dance Theater, Oakland, CA, 2012.
$10,000 to Super Stars Literacy, Oakland, CA, 2012.
$7,500 to Oakland Kids First, Oakland, CA, 2012.
$7,500 to Oakland LEAF Foundation, Oakland, CA, 2012.
$6,300 to Friends of Sausal Creek, Oakland, CA, 2012.
$5,000 to AXIS Dance Company, Oakland, CA, 2012.
$5,000 to Youth Movement Records, Oakland, CA, 2012.

408
Vincent J. Coates Foundation ✧
237 Rigg St.
Santa Cruz, CA 95060-4204

Established in 2000 in CA.
Donor: Vincent J. Coates Trust.
Foundation type: Independent foundation.
Financial data (yr. ended 12/31/13): Assets, $15,671,064 (M); gifts received, $5,546,294; expenditures, $676,069; qualifying distributions, $509,444; giving activities include $500,000 for 1 grant.
Purpose and activities: Giving primarily for higher education and neurological research, including research on Alzheimer's disease.
Fields of interest: Higher education; Alzheimer's disease research; Diabetes research; Neuroscience research.
Limitations: Applications not accepted. Giving primarily in Menlo Park, CA.
Application information: Contributes only to pre-selected organizations.
Officers: Darryl Manning, Pres.; Stella Coates, V.P.; Norman Coates, Secy.; J. Trevor Coates, Treas.
EIN: 770533167
Selected grants: The following grants are a representative sample of this grantmaker's funding activity:
$800,000 to Stanford University Medical Center Auxiliary, Stanford, CA, 2011.

409
Coit Family Foundation ✧ ☆
1655 N. Main St., Ste. 270
Walnut Creek, CA 94596-4688

Established in 1997 CA.
Donors: R. Ken Coit; Donna M. Coit.
Foundation type: Independent foundation.
Financial data (yr. ended 12/31/13): Assets, $14,676,491 (M); gifts received, $932,632; expenditures, $594,193; qualifying distributions, $583,128; giving activities include $576,959 for 32 grants (high: $185,000; low: $500).
Fields of interest: Libraries/library science; Education; Human services; Philanthropy/voluntarism.
Limitations: Applications not accepted. Giving primarily in CA and GA. No grants to individuals.
Application information: Contributes only to pre-selected organizations.
Officers and Directors:* R. Ken Coit,* Pres.; Donna M. Coit,* Secy.-Treas.
EIN: 943289041

410
Colburn Foundation
1000 Wilshire Blvd., Ste. 555
Los Angeles, CA 90017-2462 (213) 452-4300
Contact: Ruth Eliel, Exec. Dir.; Kristin Runnels Goerg, Grants Mgr.
FAX: (213) 452-0502;
E-mail: krgoerg@colburnfoundation.org; Main URL: http://www.colburnfoundation.org
Grants List: http://www.colburnfoundation.org/

Established in 1999 in CA.
Donors: Richard D. Colburn†; Northbrook Properties, Inc.; Richard Colburn Trust.
Foundation type: Independent foundation.
Financial data (yr. ended 12/31/13): Assets, $150,496,792 (M); gifts received, $500; expenditures, $8,080,217; qualifying distributions, $6,814,120; giving activities include $6,172,130 for 67 grants (high: $2,000,000; low: $5).
Purpose and activities: Support for classical music performances, presentations, and education, as well as training of musicians in Southern California.
Fields of interest: Performing arts, music; Performing arts, orchestras; Performing arts, opera; Performing arts, music (choral); Performing arts, music ensembles/groups; Performing arts, education.
Type of support: General/operating support; Scholarship funds; Matching/challenge support.
Limitations: Applications accepted. Giving primarily in southern CA. No support for non 501(c) 3 organizations. No grants to individuals.
Publications: Application guidelines; Grants list.
Application information: See foundation web site for online application process. Application form not required.
Initial approach: Telephone or e-mail
Deadline(s): Varies by year. Usually one month before board meeting
Board meeting date(s): Apr., Jun., Sept. and Dec.
Final notification: 1 to 3 months
Officers and Directors:* Carol Colburn Grigor,* Chair.; Ruth L. Eliel, Secy. and Exec. Dir.; Layne Pinkernell, Treas.; Robert Attiyeh; David Colburn; Richard W. Colburn; Edmund Edelman; Gail Eichenthal.

Number of staff: 2 full-time professional; 1 part-time professional.
EIN: 954693145
Selected grants: The following grants are a representative sample of this grantmaker's funding activity:
$20,000,000 to Colburn School of the Performing Arts, Los Angeles, CA, 2014. For general operating support.
$1,750,000 to Los Angeles Opera Company, Los Angeles, CA, 2013. For Domingo Colburn Stein Young Artists Program.
$750,000 to Los Angeles Philharmonic Association, Los Angeles, CA, 2014. For general operating support.
$400,000 to Los Angeles Master Chorale, Los Angeles, CA, 2014. For general operating support.
$300,000 to Los Angeles Chamber Orchestra Society, Los Angeles, CA, 2014. For general operating support.
$100,000 to University of Southern California, Thornton School of Music, Los Angeles, CA, 2014. For scholarships for Early Music Program.
$20,000 to California State University at Northridge Foundation, Northridge, CA, 2014. For classical music presentation at Valley Performing Arts Center.
$20,000 to Los Angeles Music and Art School, Los Angeles, CA, 2013. For classical music programs.
$15,000 to American Youth Symphony, Los Angeles, CA, 2013. For general operating support.
$15,000 to Monday Evening Concerts, Culver City, CA, 2014. For general operating support.
$5,000 to Music Guild, Los Angeles, CA, 2014. For general operating support.

411
The College Access Foundation of California

(formerly The Education Financing Foundation of California)
1 Front St., Ste. 1325
San Francisco, CA 94111-5325 (415) 287-1800
Contact: Stefanie Charren, Office Admin.; Jessica Eting, Grants. Admin.
FAX: (415) 287-1801;
E-mail: info@collegeaccessfoundation.org; Main URL: http://www.collegeaccessfoundation.org
Facebook: https://www.facebook.com/CollegeAccessCA
LinkedIn: http://www.linkedin.com/company/college-access-foundation-of-california
Twitter: https://twitter.com/CollegeAccessCA

Established in 2005 in CA (created from the sale of Chela Education Financing); foundation status changed to an independent (private) foundation in 2010.
Foundation type: Independent foundation.
Financial data (yr. ended 12/31/13): Assets, $467,326,190 (M); expenditures, $28,063,865; qualifying distributions, $22,580,252; giving activities include $18,763,983 for 304 grants (high: $1,000,000; low: $50), $97,100 for 70 employee matching gifts, and $289,511 for foundation-administered programs.
Purpose and activities: The foundation is committed to increasing the number of low-income students in California who attend and complete college. Foundation staff and leadership believe that improving college achievement is central to California's future, and they work to provide low-income and historically underrepresented students with the knowledge, resources, and tools they need to achieve success.
Fields of interest: Higher education; Scholarships/financial aid.
Type of support: General/operating support; Program development; Scholarship funds; Employee matching gifts.
Limitations: Giving primarily in CA. No grants to individuals directly.
Publications: Application guidelines; Informational brochure; Occasional report.
Application information: The majority of grants are identified by the proactive work of the foundation's program staff.
Initial approach: By invitation
Copies of proposal: 1
Deadline(s): Check web site for inquiry deadlines
Final notification: 60 days after submission of application
Officers and Directors:* Toby Rosenblatt,* Chair.; Russell S. Gould,* Vice-Chair.; Julia I. Lopez,* C.E.O. and Pres.; Jacqueline Khor, V.P., Progs.; Phillipe Wallace, C.F.O. and Treas.; Krysten Curtis, Cont.; Carlene M. Ellis; Donna Lucas; N. Ross Matthews; Gretchen Hartnack Milligan; Eloy Ortiz Oakley; Linda Davis Taylor; Joseph W. Watson, Ph.D.; Richard Whitmore.
EIN: 942618667
Selected grants: The following grants are a representative sample of this grantmaker's funding activity:
$850,000 to Coachella Valley Economic Partnership, Palm Springs, CA, 2012. For Coachella Student Scholarships.
$300,000 to East Bay Consortium of Educational Institutions, Oakland, CA, 2012. For scholarship grant.
$250,000 to Yuba College, Marysville, CA, 2012. For scholarship grant.
$228,000 to California State University Los Angeles Foundation, Los Angeles, CA, 2012. For scholarship grant.
$200,000 to Walking Shield American Indian Society, Lake Forest, CA, 2012. For scholarship grant.
$186,000 to Japanese Community Youth Council, San Francisco, CA, 2012. For scholarship grant.
$70,000 to Orange County Asian and Pacific Islander Community Alliance, Garden Grove, CA, 2012. For scholarship grant.
$70,000 to Orange County Asian and Pacific Islander Community Alliance, Garden Grove, CA, 2012. For scholarship grant.
$45,000 to United Friends of the Children, Los Angeles, CA, 2012. For scholarship grant.
$32,000 to East Bay College Fund, Oakland, CA, 2012. For scholarship grant.

412
The Carol and James Collins Foundation ✧

6101 W. Centinela Ave., Ste. 100
Culver City, CA 90230-6318
Contact: Cathy Hession, Exec. Dir.
E-mail: cathy@jamesacollins.com

Established in 1985 in CA; reincorporated in DE in 2002.
Donors: James A. Collins; Carol L. Collins.
Foundation type: Independent foundation.
Financial data (yr. ended 09/30/13): Assets, $13,105,453 (M); expenditures, $829,651; qualifying distributions, $776,959; giving activities include $693,802 for 91 grants (high: $20,000; low: $500).
Purpose and activities: The foundation's mission is to enrich the lives of children, youth, and families, particularly the underserved, in the southern CA, area. The foundation gives to organizations that give people the tools to become educated, healthy, self-reliant, and contributing members of our society. Also giving to after-school programs.
Fields of interest: Education; Human services; Children/youth, services.
Type of support: General/operating support; Continuing support; Capital campaigns; Building/renovation; Equipment; Program development; Curriculum development; Matching/challenge support.
Limitations: Giving limited to southern CA. No grants to individuals.
Publications: Informational brochure.
Application information: Full grant applications are by invitation only, upon review of letter of inquiry.
Initial approach: Letter of inquiry
Officers: James A. Collins, Chair.; Cathleen Collins Hession, Pres. and Secy.-Treas.
Directors: Carol L. Collins; Melissa Collins Gudim; Kelly L. Collins.
Number of staff: 1 full-time professional.
EIN: 300100019

413
Colombo Charitable Trust ✧

(formerly Elsie T. & Josephine Colombo Charitable Trust)
P.O. Box 60078, SC-MPK-03-M
Los Angeles, CA 90060

Established in 1993.
Donor: Elsie T. Colombo.
Foundation type: Independent foundation.
Financial data (yr. ended 12/31/13): Assets, $3,185,349 (M); expenditures, $837,363; qualifying distributions, $810,262; giving activities include $800,000 for 17 grants (high: $90,000; low: $15,000).
Purpose and activities: Giving primarily for care of the aged, the blind, and cancer patients, and for research into cures for blindness and heart diseases; giving also to Roman Catholic charitable organizations.
Fields of interest: Elementary/secondary education; Hospitals (general); Health care; Cancer; Diabetes; Medical research, institute; Human services; Catholic agencies & churches; Aging; Blind/visually impaired.
Limitations: Applications not accepted. Giving primarily in CA. No grants to individuals.
Application information: Unsolicited requests for funds not accepted.
Trustee: Bank of the West.
EIN: 776098160

414
Community Foundation for Monterey County ✧

2354 Garden Rd.
Monterey, CA 93940-5326 (831) 375-9712
Contact: Dan Baldwin, C.E.O.; For grants: Janet Shing, Sr. Prog. Off.
FAX: (831) 375-4731; E-mail: info@cfmco.org; Additional Address: 945 S. Main St., Ste. 207, Salinas, CA 93901; Additional e-mail:

danb@cfmco.org; Grant inquiry e-mail: julied@cfmco.org; Main URL: http://www.cfmco.org
Facebook: http://www.facebook.com/cfmco
Grants List: http://www.cfmco.org/index.cfm/id/258/Recent-Grants/
RSS Feed: http://www.cfmco.org/modules/news/rss.cfm?type=3&featured=&limit=6
RSS Feed: http://www.cfmco.org/modules/news/rss.cfm?type=2&featured=1&limit=6
YouTube: http://www.youtube.com/user/cfmcmonterey

Incorporated in 1945 in CA.
Foundation type: Community foundation.
Financial data (yr. ended 12/31/13): Assets, $173,143,482 (M); gifts received, $12,034,809; expenditures, $12,297,422; giving activities include $9,929,448 for grants.
Purpose and activities: The foundation seeks to improve the quality of life in Monterey County by raising, managing, and distributing charitable funds to worthy organizations and by creating positive connections between donors and their interests. Primarily supports arts and cultural organizations, libraries, schools and other educational institutions, and human services organizations.
Fields of interest: Historic preservation/historical societies; Arts; Education; Environment; Animal welfare; Health care; Substance abuse, prevention; Employment; Housing/shelter; Human services; Community/economic development; Infants/toddlers; Children/youth; Children; Youth; Adults; Aging; Young adults; Disabilities, people with; Physically disabled; Blind/visually impaired; Asians/Pacific Islanders; African Americans/Blacks; Hispanics/Latinos; Native Americans/American Indians; Indigenous peoples; Offenders/ex-offenders; Substance abusers; AIDS, people with; Single parents; Crime/abuse victims; Terminal illness, people with; Immigrants/refugees; Economically disadvantaged; Homeless; Migrant workers; LGBTQ.
Type of support: General/operating support; Continuing support; Management development/capacity building; Annual campaigns; Capital campaigns; Building/renovation; Equipment; Emergency funds; Program development; Conferences/seminars; Seed money; Technical assistance; Consulting services; Matching/challenge support.
Limitations: Applications accepted. Giving primarily in Monterey County, CA. No support for sectarian religious programs. No grants to individuals (except for scholarships), or for annual campaigns, deficit financing, general endowments, fellowships, travel, fundraising campaigns or events, academic research, or publications.
Publications: Application guidelines; Annual report (including application guidelines); Informational brochure; Newsletter.
Application information: Visit foundation web site for application forms and specific guidelines per grant type. Application form required.
Initial approach: Attend an Information Session
Copies of proposal: 1
Deadline(s): Varies
Board meeting date(s): 4th Tues. of selected months
Final notification: Generally no longer than 2 months
Officers and Directors:* Gail Delorey,* Chair.; Rick Kennifer,* Vice-Chair.; Dan Baldwin,* C.E.O. and Pres.; Julie Kenny Drezner, V.P., Grants and Progs.; Catherine Kobrinsky Evans,* Secy.; Tina Starkey Lopez,* Treas.; Tonya Antle; Ann Brown; Ida Lopez Chan; Greg Chilton; Jim Claypool; Stephen Dart; Alred Diaz-Infante; Patti Hiramoto; Kelly McMillin; Stephen McGowan; Ken Petersen; John M. Phillips; Ana Marie Ponce; Raul C. Rodriguez; Kenneth R. Wright.
Number of staff: 20 full-time professional.
EIN: 941615897

415
Community Foundation for San Benito County ✧
829 San Benito St., Ste. 200
Hollister, CA 95023 (831) 630-1924
Contact: Gary Byrne, C.E.O.
FAX: (831) 630-1934; E-mail: info@cffsbc.org; Mailing address: P.O. Box 2062 Hollister, CA 95024-2062; Additional e-mail: gbyrne@cffsbc.org; Grant application e-mail: grants@cffsbc.org; Main URL: http://www.cffsbc.org/
Facebook: http://www.facebook.com/pages/Community-Foundation-for-San-Benito-County/106418471856

Established in 1992 in CA.
Foundation type: Community foundation.
Financial data (yr. ended 12/31/12): Assets, $5,788,631 (M); gifts received, $1,526,982; expenditures, $1,370,761; giving activities include $839,915 for 47+ grants (high: $165,000), and $25,851 for 13 grants to individuals.
Purpose and activities: The Community Foundation for San Benito County is dedicated to building a stronger community and enhancing the quality of life in San Benito County through support of philanthropic activities.
Fields of interest: Arts; Education; Environment; Medical care, outpatient care; Health care; Human services; Youth.
Limitations: Applications accepted. Giving primarily in San Benito County, CA. No support for private foundations or fundraising organizations, fraternal of service organizations, unless in support of specific programs open to or benefiting the entire community or nonprofit organizations that spend more than 25% of their revenue on management, overhead and/or fundraising costs. No grants to individuals (except for scholarships), or for annual campaigns, walk-a-thons, tournaments, fashion shows, dinners or auctions, or salaries or operating expenses of schools, government departments and agencies or related organizations.
Publications: Application guidelines.
Application information: Visit foundation web site for application forms and guidelines. Grant awards generally will range up to $25,000. Application form required.
Initial approach: E-mail application (if project will be ready to start within three months) or preliminary Intent to Submit Application (if project is expected to start later in the year)
Deadline(s): Oct. 15
Final notification: Applications will be reviewed and approved monthly, with the goal to respond to all applications within 6 to 8 weeks of their acceptance
Officers and Board Members:* Fernando Gonzalez,* Chair.; Phil Fortino,* Vice-Chair.; Gary Byrne,* C.E.O. and Pres.; Kathy Flores,* Secy.; Mike Grace,* C.F.O. and Treas.; Enrique Arreola; Marilyn Ferreira; Kay Filice; Steve Hudner; Susan Schwabacher Modic; Anne Morris; Diane Ortiz; Jim Paxton; Allison Rohnert; Sandy Rose; Ed Stephenson; Bob Tiffany; Rebecca Medeiros Wolf.
EIN: 770312582

416
The Community Foundation of Mendocino County, Inc. ✧
(formerly Mendocino County Community Foundation, Inc.)
204 South Oak St.
Ukiah, CA 95482 (707) 468-9882
Contact: Susanne Norgard, Exec. Dir.
FAX: (707) 468-5529;
E-mail: info@communityfound.org; Main URL: http://www.communityfound.org
Facebook: https://www.facebook.com/pages/The-Community-Foundation-of-Mendocino-County/210963148919337

Established in 1993 in CA.
Foundation type: Community foundation.
Financial data (yr. ended 06/30/13): Assets, $16,161,672 (M); gifts received, $622,622; expenditures, $1,302,284; giving activities include $791,959 for grants (high: $64,757), and $6,049 for grants to individuals.
Purpose and activities: The foundation helps people give back in ways that matter to them and in ways that strengthen local communities.
Fields of interest: Historic preservation/historical societies; Arts; Libraries/library science; Education; Environment; Health care; Recreation, parks/playgrounds; Recreation; Youth development, centers/clubs; Youth development, adult & child programs; Children/youth, services; Economic development; Community/economic development; Economically disadvantaged.
Type of support: Management development/capacity building; General/operating support; Equipment; Endowments; Emergency funds; Program development; Seed money; Scholarship funds; Technical assistance; Matching/challenge support.
Limitations: Applications accepted. Giving limited to Mendocino County, CA, and its service areas. No support for for-profit organizations or religious organizations for religious purposes. No grants to individuals (except for scholarships), or for non-specific requests for large capital projects, normal operating expenses or purchases or activities that occur prior to grant decisions, trips and/or conference attendance; or underwriting/sponsorship of performances or fundraising events.
Publications: Annual report; Informational brochure; Newsletter.
Application information: Visit foundation web site for application form and guidelines. Faxed, e-mailed, or late submissions are not accepted. Application form required.
Initial approach: Letter of inquiry on grant programs and opportunities
Copies of proposal: 1
Deadline(s): Varies by program
Board meeting date(s): 1st Tues. monthly (except for July and Dec.)
Final notification: Varies by program
Officers and Directors:* Jim Mayfield,* Pres.; Judith Bailey,* 1st V.P.; Katie Gibbs,* 2nd V.P.; Francine Selim,* Secy.; Greg Nelson,* Treas.; Susanne Norgard, Exec. Dir.; Guilford Dye; Claire Ellis; Gayle Greene; James King; John Knapp; Rudy Light; Jim Moorehead; Santiago Simental.

Number of staff: 1 full-time professional; 3 part-time professional.
EIN: 680330462
Selected grants: The following grants are a representative sample of this grantmaker's funding activity:
$100,000 to Bainbridge Art Museum, Bainbridge Island, WA, 2014. For general support.
$90,000 to Anderson Valley Community Services District, Boonville, CA, 2013. For re-surfacing of the Anderson Valley tennis courts.
$33,000 to Dollywood Foundation, Pigeon Forge, TN, 2014. For 6-month invoice for First Five Mendocino.
$20,665 to Mendocino Food and Nutrition Program, Fort Bragg, CA, 2014. For annual grant.
$16,000 to Bainbridge Art Museum, Bainbridge Island, WA, 2013. For operational support for event.
$15,000 to Great Old Broads for Wilderness, Durango, CO, 2014. For Proposal Citizen Activists for the Wild: Protecting the Colorado Plateau.
$10,000 to Alliance for Rural Community Health, Ukiah, CA, 2013. For clinic visit vouchers for uninsured children.
$10,000 to Alliance for Rural Community Health, Ukiah, CA, 2014. For clinic visit vouchers for uninsured children.
$10,000 to Arbor Youth Resource Center, Ukiah, CA, 2014. For capital improvements to the new Arbor Youth Resource Center.
$10,000 to Bainbridge Island Land Trust, Bainbridge Island, WA, 2013. For general support.
$10,000 to Bainbridge Island Land Trust, Bainbridge Island, WA, 2013. For West Bainbridge Shoreline Protection Project Acquisition.
$10,000 to Friends of Cedar Mesa, Bluff, UT, 2014. For operations.
$10,000 to Kids Discovery Museum, Bainbridge Island, WA, 2013. For general support.
$10,000 to YWCA of Seattle-King County-Snohomish County, Seattle, WA, 2013. For Women Empowered: A YWCA Community Campaign.
$8,000 to Partnership Scholars Program, Marina Del Rey, CA, 2013. For Mentoring services for Mendocino Coast youth.
$5,331 to Dollywood Foundation, Pigeon Forge, TN, 2013. For cost of mailing books to children.
$5,000 to Redwood Empire Food Bank, Santa Rosa, CA, 2014. For Mendocino County Supplemental Protein and Produce for CSFP Recipients.
$4,000 to Mendocino Family and Youth Services, Ukiah, CA, 2014. For TLP Family Dinner and Assistance Program.
$3,500 to Point Arena Schools, Point Arena, CA, 2014. For Arena Elementary Technology Infusion Project.
$3,000 to Doctors Without Borders USA, New York, NY, 2013. For general support.

417
Community Foundation of San Joaquin ✧ ☆

501 W. Weber Ave., Ste. 200-D
Stockton, CA 95201 (209) 943-2375
Contact: Linda J. Philipp, Pres. and C.E.O.
FAX: (209) 593-2333; E-mail: lphilipp@cfosj.org; Main URL: http://www.cfosj.org
Facebook: https://www.facebook.com/TheCommunityFoundationOfSanJoaquin

Established in 2007 in CA.
Donors: Assistance League of Stockton; Scott Beattie; Scott Beattie; Lorna Boothroyd; Calone Law Group; Child Abuse Prevention Council; Bridget Childs; C. Joseph Crane; Helen Crane; Credit Bureau of San Janquin County Charitable Foundation; Michael P. Duffy; Hospice of San Joaquin; IMPACT; Stefanie Leland; Ted Leland; Sandra Mazzoula; Charles G. Patmon; Dorothy N. Patmon; Irene Perkins; Paul Perkins; Larry Philipp; Linda Philipp; San Joaquin County Office of Education Educational Foundation; United Cerebral Palsy; Francesca Vera; John R. Vera; Women's Center of San Joaquin County; Nishka M. Yudnich.
Foundation type: Community foundation.
Financial data (yr. ended 12/31/12): Assets, $3,787,204 (M); gifts received, $566,022; expenditures, $761,769; giving activities include $463,008 for 28+ grants (high: $16,616).
Purpose and activities: The foundation facilitates and develops philanthropy by providing services to donors and their advisors and by making grants to benefit the local community.
Fields of interest: Children/youth; Children; Youth; Disabilities, people with; Women; Girls; Adults, women; Young adults, female; Boys; Crime/abuse victims; Economically disadvantaged; Homeless.
Type of support: Management development/capacity building; Endowments; Consulting services; Annual campaigns; General/operating support; Continuing support; Capital campaigns; Building/renovation; Equipment; Program development; Conferences/seminars; Scholarship funds.
Limitations: Applications accepted. Giving primarily in San Joaquin County, CA.
Publications: Grants list; Informational brochure; Newsletter; Occasional report.
Application information: Application form not required.
Initial approach: Telephone or e-mail
Copies of proposal: 1
Deadline(s): None
Board meeting date(s): Bi-monthly
Officers and Board Members:* Duane Isetti,* Chair.; Cynthia Souza,* Vice-Chair.; Linda Philipp,* Pres. and C.E.O.; Linda A. Guinn,* V.P.; Ted Leland,* Secy.; David Vaughn,* Treas.; Scott Beattie; Kevin Hawes; Robert Kavanaugh; Teresa Mandella; Charles G. Patmon, III; Colleen Stewart; David Vaccarezza.
Number of staff: 1 full-time professional; 2 part-time professional.
EIN: 261476916

418
Community Foundation Santa Cruz County

(formerly The Community Foundation of Santa Cruz County)
7807 Soquel Dr.
Aptos, CA 95003 (831) 662-2000
Contact: Lance Linares, C.E.O.; For grants: Christina Cuevas, Prog. Dir.
FAX: (831) 662-2001; E-mail: cfhelp@cfscc.org; Additional e-mails: lance@cfscc.org and christina@cfscc.org; Grant application e-mail: grants@cfscc.org; Main URL: http://www.cfscc.org
Blog: http://www.cfscc.org/Philanthropy831Blog.aspx
E-Newsletter: http://www.cfscc.org/Home.aspx
E-Newsletter: http://www.cfscc.org/emailnews
Facebook: http://www.facebook.com/CFSantaCruzCounty
Instagram: http://instagram.com/cfsantacruzco
LinkedIn: http://www.linkedin.com/company/community-foundation-santa-cruz-county
RSS Feed: http://feeds.feedburner.com/AboutNonprofits
Twitter: https://twitter.com/#!/CFSantaCruzCo
YouTube: http://www.youtube.com/user/CFSantaCruzCounty
Scholarship inquiry tel.: (832) 662-2072

Incorporated in 1982 in CA.
Foundation type: Community foundation.
Financial data (yr. ended 12/31/13): Assets, $78,872,547 (M); gifts received, $22,673,685; expenditures, $8,293,230; giving activities include $6,224,519 for 190 grants (high: $687,386).
Purpose and activities: The foundation promotes local philanthropy in Santa Cruz County, CA, through grants and resources for nonprofits, donors and their professional advisors.
Fields of interest: Historic preservation/historical societies; Arts; Education; Environment; Health care; Youth development; Human services; Community/economic development.
Type of support: General/operating support; Continuing support; Management development/capacity building; Program development; Technical assistance; Program evaluation; Scholarships—to individuals.
Limitations: Applications accepted. Giving limited to Santa Cruz County, CA. No support for religious organizations or individual (public or private) schools, as distinct from a school district. No grants to individuals (except for scholarships from designated funds), or for annual fund appeals, deficit financing, building campaigns, land acquisition, fellowships, research, endowments, fundraising events, or celebrations; no student loans.
Publications: Application guidelines; Annual report; Financial statement; Grants list; Informational brochure.
Application information: Application form required.
Initial approach: Attend a Grant Information Session
Deadline(s): Apr. 5 and July 31 for online Letter of Intent, May 20 and Sept. 10 for completed application
Board meeting date(s): Quarterly
Final notification: June 28 and Oct. 17
Officers and Directors:* Lance Linares, C.E.O.; Michael K. O'Farrell,* Pres.; Dina Hoffman,* V.P.; Linda Fawcett,* Secy.; Susan J. Farrar, C.F.O.; Michael Meara,* Treas.; Alexandra Urbick, Cont.; Marilyn Calciano; Martin M. Chemers; Freny Cooper; David Doolin; Cynthia Druley; Julie Haff; Janet Heien; Fred Keeley; Jerry Lopez; Rachel Mayo; Ginny Solari Mazry; Terry Medina; Carlos Palacios; Robert Ridino.
Number of staff: 5 full-time professional; 2 part-time professional; 1 full-time support; 2 part-time support.
EIN: 942808039
Selected grants: The following grants are a representative sample of this grantmaker's funding activity:
$687,386 to Central California Alliance for Health, Scotts Valley, CA, 2013. For Healthy Kids of Santa Cruz County insurance premium costs for kids 6 to 18 years of age.
$250,000 to Sempervirens Fund, Los Altos, CA, 2013. For the Great Park Campaign.
$150,000 to YMCA, Central Coast, Salinas, CA, 2013. For the renovation and reconstruction of the YMCA facilities at 27 Sudden Street, Watsonville, CA.

$80,000 to Pajaro Valley Arts Council, Watsonville, CA, 2013. For CFSCC CLP, payable over 3.00 years.
$75,000 to Rice University, Houston, TX, 2013. For general operating support.
$50,000 to Second Harvest Food Bank Santa Cruz County, Watsonville, CA, 2013. For construction costs of Phase II of the food bank services expansion project.
$5,000 to Childrens Hospital Central California, Madera, CA, 2013. For the Children's Hospital Patient Help Fund support.
$5,000 to Youth for Environmental Sanity, Soquel, CA, 2013. For general operating support.
$4,000 to Peacock Acres, Salinas, CA, 2013. For the Learning Center activities to boost academic achievement.
$2,500 to Tech Museum of Innovation, San Jose, CA, 2013. For general operating support.

419
The Community Foundation Serving Riverside and San Bernardino Counties ✧

(formerly Community Foundation of Riverside County)
3700 6th St., Ste. 200
Riverside, CA 92501 (951) 241-7777
Contact: Celia Cudiamat, Exec. V.P.
FAX: (951) 684-1911;
E-mail: info@thecommunityfoundation.net; Main URL: http://www.thecommunityfoundation.net
Facebook: https://www.facebook.com/tcf1941
Twitter: https://twitter.com/tcf1941

Established as a trust in 1941 in CA.
Foundation type: Community foundation.
Financial data (yr. ended 12/31/13): Assets, $79,584,826 (M); gifts received, $16,052,182; expenditures, $9,971,457; giving activities include $7,468,118 for 462+ grants (high: $1,322,801; low: $100), and $1,010,909 for 141 grants to individuals.
Purpose and activities: The foundation seeks to strengthen the community by meeting the needs and enhancing the lives of individuals in Riverside and San Bernardino counties, CA, in partnership with philanthropic individuals, community leaders, and the nonprofit sector. This is accomplished through building permanent endowments, making prudent grants for charitable causes, being a catalyst to solve community concerns and strengthening nonprofit organizations.
Fields of interest: Arts; Education; Health care; Youth development, adult & child programs; Children/youth, services; Family services; Human services; Public affairs.
Type of support: Equipment; Land acquisition; Emergency funds; Program development; Seed money; Scholarship funds; Program evaluation; Matching/challenge support.
Limitations: Applications accepted. Giving primarily in Riverside and San Bernardino counties, CA. No support for sectarian programs, fraternal organizations, or school or college-based extracurricular activities. No grants to individuals (directly), or for ongoing operating expenses, deficits or existing obligations, endowments, annual fund appeals, capital projects, event sponsorship, regranting purposes, or research.
Publications: Application guidelines; Annual report; Financial statement; Grants list; Informational brochure; Newsletter.
Application information: Visit foundation web site for application form and guidelines; applicants must have been offering programs for at least 3 years. Application form required.
Initial approach: Telephone or e-mail
Copies of proposal: 1
Deadline(s): Feb. 25 for Community Impact grants; varies for others
Board meeting date(s): Feb., Apr., June, Aug., Oct., and Dec.
Final notification: Immediately after board meetings
Officers and Directors:* Jim Cuevas,* Chair.; Philip Savage IV,* Vice-Chair.; Jonathan Lorenzo Yorba, Ph.D., C.E.O. and Pres.; Celia Cudiamat, Exec. V.P. of Grants and Progs.; Paula Myles, V.P., Finance and Admin.; Tom Stephenson, V.P., Philanthropic Svcs.; Sean Varner,* Secy.; Pat Spafford,* C.F.O.; Glenda Bayless; Sergio Bohon; Rabbi Hillel Cohn; Andrea Dutton; Robert Fey; Paul Granillo; Stanley Grube; Kirk Harns; Dr. Al Karnig; Patrick J. O'Reilly; Matt Pim; Rose Salgado; Beverly Stephenson; Hon. Grover Trask.
Number of staff: 5 full-time professional.
EIN: 330748536

420
Community Foundation Sonoma County ✧

(formerly The Sonoma County Community Foundation)
250 D St., Ste. 205
Santa Rosa, CA 95404-4773 (707) 579-4073
Contact: For grants: Robert Judd, V.P., Progs.
FAX: (707) 579-4801; E-mail: info@sonomacf.org; Grant inquiry e-mail: rjudd@sonomacf.org; Main URL: http://www.sonomacf.org
E-Newsletter: http://www.sonomacf.org/about-us/e-newsletter-signup/
Facebook: https://www.facebook.com/sonomacf

Incorporated in 1983 in CA.
Foundation type: Community foundation.
Financial data (yr. ended 12/31/12): Assets, $153,516,532 (M); gifts received, $969,213; expenditures, $13,275,815; giving activities include $9,973,500 for grants.
Purpose and activities: The Community Foundation Sonoma County connects people, ideas and resources to benefit the lives of those who live here. The foundation fulfills this mission by: 1) making grants to respond to important needs in Sonoma County and beyond; 2) encouraging donors to partner with us in fulfilling their financial and charitable goals; 3) ensuring that gifts made to the Community Foundation grow and have lasting impact; 4) convening people to work on relevant community challenges and issues; 5) providing community knowledge about Sonoma County; and 6) catalyzing community involvement and philanthropic commitment to improve the quality of life in Sonoma County.
Fields of interest: Humanities; Arts, artist's services; Arts; Education; Environmental education; Environment; Health care; Housing/shelter, temporary shelter; Housing/shelter; Children/youth, services; Women, centers/services; Homeless, human services; Human services; Community/economic development; Children/youth.
Type of support: General/operating support; Continuing support; Endowments; Emergency funds; Program development; Seed money; Scholarship funds; Technical assistance; Consulting services; Program evaluation; Program-related investments/loans; Scholarships—to individuals; Matching/challenge support.
Limitations: Applications accepted. Giving limited to Sonoma County, CA. No support for religious purposes or advocacy activities, or primary or secondary schools or their academic foundations. No grants to individuals (except for academic scholarships), or for fundraising events, annual fund campaigns, capital campaigns, conferences, or debt retirement; no loans (except program-related investments).
Publications: Application guidelines; Annual report; Financial statement; Informational brochure; Newsletter.
Application information: Visit foundation web site for application forms, guidelines, and specific deadlines. Application form required.
Initial approach: Telephone
Deadline(s): Varies
Board meeting date(s): 1st Tues. of most months
Final notification: Varies
Officers and Directors:* Harriet Derwingson,* Chair.; Elizabeth Brown, C.E.O. and Pres.; Robert Judd, V.P., Progs.; J. Mullineaux, V.P., Philanthropic Planning; Herb Castillo,* Secy.; Kent Wigton, C.F.O.; Linda Kachiu,* Treas.; Lynda Desloges, Cont.; Jean Schulz, Dir. Emeritus; Jay Abbe; Oscar Chavez; Dianne Edwards; Theodore L. Eliot, Jr.; Patrick Emery; Steve Goldberg; Pete Golis; Whitney Hall; Katie Jackson; Deberah B. Kelley; Andrea Learned; Steve Rabinowtish; Lew Reid; Marlene Soiland; David Voss; Barry Weitzenberg; Jody Withee; Joan C. Woodard; Michelle Zygielbaum.
Number of staff: 9 full-time professional; 3 full-time support; 1 part-time support.
EIN: 680003212
Selected grants: The following grants are a representative sample of this grantmaker's funding activity:
$2,600,000 to Charles M. Schulz Museum and Research Center, Santa Rosa, CA, 2012. For general operating support.
$1,431,000 to Sonoma Academy, Santa Rosa, CA, 2012. For general operating support and for Makerspace Tools.
$664,711 to Redwood Empire Food Bank, Santa Rosa, CA, 2012. For general operating support, the capital campaign, and to purchase additional fresh produce.
$533,073 to Pepperwood Foundation, Santa Rosa, CA, 2012. For general operating support and Natural Science Education/Research.
$488,400 to Canine Companions for Independence, Santa Rosa, CA, 2012. For general operating support.
$476,300 to Committee on the Shelterless, Petaluma, CA, 2012. For general operating support to serve the homeless.
$134,000 to Santa Rosa Memorial Hospital Foundation, Santa Rosa, CA, 2012. For a mobile dental van, emergency and trauma center capital campaign, and cardiac department.
$26,600 to Centro Laboral de Graton, Graton, CA, 2012. For general operating support and for the Graton Day Labor Center.
$15,000 to Concord Historical Society, Concord, CA, 2012. For ADA lift at Galindo house.
$12,830 to Sonoma Valley Unified School District, Sonoma, CA, 2012. For the 3rd Grade Reading Program and the Summer School Program of the Youth Initiative.

421
Community Safety Foundation ✧ ☆
3055 Oak Rd.
Walnut Creek, CA 94597-2098

Donor: CSAA Insurance Exchange.
Foundation type: Independent foundation.
Financial data (yr. ended 12/31/13): Assets, $123,668 (M); gifts received, $1,000,000; expenditures, $1,364,770; qualifying distributions, $1,248,986; giving activities include $1,248,986 for 112 grants (high: $178,572; low: $300).
Fields of interest: Safety/disasters; Human services; Youth, services; Community/economic development.
Limitations: Applications not accepted. Giving in the U.S., with some emphasis on CA.
Application information: Unsolicited requests for funds not accepted.
Officers: Rose Guilbault, Pres.; Loren Brown, V.P.; Phyllis Solomon, Secy.; Diane Giampaoli, Treas.
Directors: Marie Andel; Danielle Cagan; Michael Day; Marcus Linden; Steve O'Connor; Debora Tomlin.
EIN: 454171516

422
Compton Foundation, Inc.
101 Montgomery St., Ste. 850
San Francisco, CA 94104-4126 (415) 391-9001
Contact: Ellen Friedman, Exec. Dir.
FAX: (415) 391-9005;
E-mail: info@comptonfoundation.org; Main URL: http://www.comptonfoundation.org
Blog: http://www.comptonfoundation.org/news/updates/
Compton Foundation's Philanthropy Promise: http://www.ncrp.org/philanthropys-promise/who
Grants Database: http://www.comptonfoundation.org/grants-awarded/schedule-of-grants/

Incorporated in 1972 in NY as successor to the Compton Trust; reincorporated in 1992 in CA.
Donor: Members of the Compton family.
Foundation type: Independent foundation.
Financial data (yr. ended 12/31/13): Assets, $63,939,751 (M); expenditures, $5,270,823; qualifying distributions, $4,115,014; giving activities include $3,359,930 for 204 grants (high: $60,000; low: $200).
Purpose and activities: The foundation ignites change. It supports transformative leadership and courageous storytelling, inspiring action toward a peaceful, just, sustainable future. Its new mission highlights a sense of urgency and a willingness to take risks in order to transform the way we live. Bringing forth a positive future requires innovative ways of understanding and naming the problems we face, as well as new methods for collaborating to solve them. To accomplish the foundation's mission it provides financial resources to galvanize the movement for progressive and democratic social change.
Type of support: General/operating support; Continuing support; Land acquisition; Program development; Conferences/seminars; Film/video/radio; Publication; Research; Consulting services; Matching/challenge support; Mission-related investments/loans.
Limitations: Applications accepted. Giving in the U.S. for environmental issues. No support for ocean or marine work, K-12 education, service delivery programs, or on-the-ground restoration projects. No grants to individuals, or for capital or building funds, or for land, water or easement acquisition; no loans.
Application information: Letters of inquiry are accepted online only. LOIs will not be accepted by e-mail or U.S. mail. Full unsolicited proposals are not accepted. Application form required.
Initial approach: Use letter of inquiry form on foundation web site
Deadline(s): None
Board meeting date(s): June and Dec.
Final notification: Varies
Officers and Directors:* Rebecca DiDomenico,* Pres.; Vanessa Compton,* V.P.; W. Danforth Compton,* Secy.; Emilie Cortes,* Treas.; Ellen Friedman, Exec. Dir.; Betty L. Farrell; Stephen Perry; Steven M. Riskin; Terry Tempest Williams.
Number of staff: 4 full-time professional; 1 part-time support.
EIN: 943142932
Selected grants: The following grants are a representative sample of this grantmaker's funding activity:
$50,000 to Capital Initiative, Portland, OR, 2012. For field guide to a regenerative economy.
$50,000 to CERES, Boston, MA, 2012. For ceres aqua gauge: advancing investor and corporate action on water stewardship.
$50,000 to Citizen Engagement Laboratory, Berkeley, CA, 2012. For ultraviolet.
$40,000 to Corporate Accountability International, Boston, MA, 2012. For real food media project.
$30,000 to Center for Diversity and the Environment, Portland, OR, 2012. For 2042 today: young leaders re-imagining conservation, a collaboration with center for whole communities.
$30,000 to Franklin Furnace Archive, Brooklyn, NY, 2012. For inclimate: climate change solutions, awareness and action.
$15,000 to Management Assistance Group, Washington, DC, 2012. For network leaders innovation lab.
$10,000 to Advocates for Youth, Washington, DC, 2012. For 1 in 3 campaign storytelling convening.
$10,000 to Collective Heritage Institute, Santa Fe, NM, 2012. For moonrise: women's leadership - annual bioneers conference.
$10,000 to New Media Advocacy Project, Brooklyn, NY, 2012. For gender justice uncovered awards video.

423
Confidence Foundation ✧
625 Fair Oaks Ave., Ste. 360
South Pasadena, CA 91030-5813 (626) 403-3282

Established in 1980 in CA.
Donors: N. Paul Whittier‡; N. Paul Whittier Charitable Lead Trust.
Foundation type: Independent foundation.
Financial data (yr. ended 12/31/12): Assets, $51,003,888 (M); expenditures, $2,435,339; qualifying distributions, $2,243,958; giving activities include $1,925,500 for 141 grants (high: $150,000; low: $250).
Purpose and activities: Giving primarily for education, social services, youth, children, and families, health and medicine, and communities.
Fields of interest: Education, early childhood education; Secondary school/education; Education; Reproductive health, family planning; Health care; Medical research, institute; Youth development, citizenship; Human services; Family services; Science; Public policy, research; Leadership development; Children; Minorities; Economically disadvantaged.
Type of support: Program development; Matching/challenge support.
Limitations: Applications accepted. Giving primarily in Los Angeles, CA. No grants to individuals; no loans.
Application information: Grants usually initiated by the foundation. Application form not required.
Initial approach: Letter of inquiry
Copies of proposal: 1
Deadline(s): None
Board meeting date(s): As needed
Officers and Directors:* Michael J. Casey,* V.P.; Arlo G. Sorensen,* V.P.; Julie W. Lytle, Secy.; Cheyenna Whittier; Kimberly Whittier; Paul Michael Whittier.
EIN: 953500483
Selected grants: The following grants are a representative sample of this grantmaker's funding activity:
$150,000 to California Science Center Foundation, Los Angeles, CA, 2012. For Endeavor La Campaign.
$150,000 to Homeboy Industries, Los Angeles, CA, 2012. For education and tattoo removal Program.
$100,000 to Los Angeles Regional Food Bank, Los Angeles, CA, 2012. For program operating fund.
$100,000 to Union Rescue Mission, Los Angeles, CA, 2012. For Single Mother and Children's Program.
$50,000 to Midnight Mission, Los Angeles, CA, 2012. For Homeless Family Transitional Housing Program.
$50,000 to Pepperdine University, Malibu, CA, 2012. For Youth Citizenship Seminar Program.
$50,000 to South Central Scholars Foundation, Rancho Palos Verdes, CA, 2012. For College Success Program.
$10,000 to Autry National Center of the American West, Los Angeles, CA, 2012. For $5,000 General Operating and $5,000 Program Support - Gala.
$10,000 to Jewish Child Care Association of New York, New York, NY, 2012. For Ametz Adoption Program.
$5,000 to Escondido Education Foundation, Escondido, CA, 2012. For Amy Foster Scholarship Fund.

424
Michael J. Connell Foundation ✧
776 E. Green St., No. 230
Pasadena, CA 91101-5402 (626) 796-2226
Main URL: http://www.mjcf.org/
Grants List: http://www.mjcf.org/grants.html

Incorporated in 1931 in CA.
Donor: Michael J. Connell.
Foundation type: Independent foundation.
Financial data (yr. ended 06/30/13): Assets, $13,672,901 (M); expenditures, $814,359; qualifying distributions, $668,249; giving activities include $643,900 for 15 grants (high: $200,000; low: $5,000).
Purpose and activities: Giving generally restricted to programs initiated by the foundation in social, cultural, and educational and medical fields.
Fields of interest: Arts; Education; Environment; Health care.
Type of support: Equipment; Program development; Fellowships; Internship funds.

Limitations: Giving limited to Southern CA, South Western MT, and Austin, TX. No support for organizations that limit services to persons of a single religious sect or denomination, that address social or political problems outside the U.S., fraternal organizations, or to for-profit businesses. No grants to individuals, or for building funds, scholarships, fundraising events, dinners, mass mailings, conferences, seminars, workshops or similar events, or program-related investments; no loans.
Application information: Though unsolicited funds are rarely successful, a short proposal letter (2 pages maximum) will be accepted (on applicant's letterhead, and sent via U.S. mail), provided the applicant check foundation web site to see what it does and does not fund. Proposals that are either hand delivered, or sent by messenger, e-mail or fax will not be accepted. Do not include lengthy brochures, tape cassettes, CD ROMs, or videotapes. If the foundation wishes more information, it will request it. See foundation web site for additional information. Application form not required.
Deadline(s): None
Officers: Michael J. Connell, Pres.; Leith O' Leary, V.P. and Treas.; Richard A. Wilson, Secy.
Directors: Christopher Connell; Jennifer Devoll; Paul Grossman.
Number of staff: 1 full-time professional; 1 part-time professional.
EIN: 956000904
Selected grants: The following grants are a representative sample of this grantmaker's funding activity:
$125,000 to Los Angeles Philharmonic Association, Los Angeles, CA, 2011.
$50,000 to Armory Center for the Arts, Pasadena, CA, 2011.
$50,000 to OBA, Inc., Pasadena, CA, 2011.
$50,000 to Rancho Santa Ana Botanic Garden, Claremont, CA, 2011.
$35,000 to Concerned Resource and Environmental Workers, Ojai, CA, 2011.
$35,000 to Montana State University, Bozeman, MT, 2011.
$25,000 to California Science Center, Los Angeles, CA, 2011.
$25,000 to Santa Barbara Zoological Gardens, Santa Barbara, CA, 2011.
$7,000 to American Red Cross, Los Angeles, CA, 2011.
$5,000 to United Way of Greater Los Angeles, Los Angeles, CA, 2011.

425
G. L. Connolly Foundation ✧ ☆
P.O. Box 6657
Rheem Valley, CA 94570-6657
Application address: c/o Thomas A. Connolly, 52 E. 81st St., New York, NY 10028; or c/o Ronald G. Connolly, M.D., P.O. Box 6668, Rheem Valley, CA 94570

Established in 2004 in DE.
Donor: The Laffey-McHugh Foundation.
Foundation type: Independent foundation.
Financial data (yr. ended 12/31/13): Assets, $9,593,886 (M); expenditures, $736,881; qualifying distributions, $627,569; giving activities include $566,000 for 70 grants (high: $40,000; low: $1,000).
Purpose and activities: Giving primarily to Roman Catholic organizations; some funding for education and social services.
Fields of interest: Higher education; Human services; Children/youth, services; Social sciences, public policy; Catholic agencies & churches.
Limitations: Applications accepted. Giving primarily in CA and NJ.
Application information: Application form required.
Initial approach: Letter
Deadline(s): None
Officers: Ronald G. Connolly, M.D., Pres.; Ronald C. Connolly, V.P.
Director: Thomas A. Connolly.
EIN: 200247328
Selected grants: The following grants are a representative sample of this grantmaker's funding activity:
$10,000 to Ethics and Public Policy Center, Washington, DC, 2012. For The G.L. Connolly Foundation.
$10,000 to Thomas Aquinas College, Santa Paula, CA, 2012. For The G.L. Connolly Foundation Education Support.
$10,000 to Urbi et Orbi Communications, New Hope, KY, 2012. For The G.L. Connolly Foundation Charitable Contribution.
$10,000 to Wyoming Catholic College, Lander, WY, 2012. For The G.L. Connolly Foundation Catholic Education.
$5,000 to Catholic Answers, El Cajon, CA, 2012. For The G.L. Connolly Foundation Catholic Apologetics Support.
$5,000 to Intercollegiate Studies Institute, Wilmington, DE, 2012. For the Gal. Connolly Foundation Analysis and Advocacy Concerning Higher Education Support.
$5,000 to Life Legal Defense Foundation, Napa, CA, 2012. For The G.L. Connolly Foundation for Pro Life Defense Support.
$2,000 to A Friendly Manor, Oakland, CA, 2012. For The G.L. Connolly Foundation Funds for Operation of Day Residence-Inner City Women.

426
The Conservation Land Trust ✧
1606 Union St.
San Francisco, CA 94123-4507
E-mail: info@theconservationlandtrust.org; Main URL: http://www.theconservationlandtrust.org
Facebook: http://www.facebook.com/pages/The-Conservation-Land-Trust/188936124452696

Established in 1999 in CA.
Donors: Douglas R. Tompkins; Kristine M. Tompkins; Addison M. Fischer; Charities Aid Foundation.
Foundation type: Operating foundation.
Financial data (yr. ended 03/31/13): Assets, $108,439,607 (M); gifts received, $269,493; expenditures, $3,190,298; qualifying distributions, $6,753,119; giving activities include $2,141,400 for 2+ grants (high: $2,089,000), $632,911 for foundation-administered programs and $3,982,684 for loans/program-related investments (high: $2,803,684; low: $1,179,000).
Purpose and activities: Giving to the conservation of biodiversity and strategically important biota. Important but secondary considerations are good public access, public educational and interpretive programs, appropriate and ecologically sustainable economic activities, and tourist possibilities.
Fields of interest: Environment, natural resources; Environment, water resources; Environment, forests.
International interests: Argentina; Chile.
Type of support: Program-related investments/loans.
Limitations: Applications not accepted. Giving primarily in Argentina and Chile; funding also in Sausalito, CA for a Chile-based cause. No grants to individuals.
Application information: Contributes only to pre-selected organizations.
Officers and Directors:* Douglas R. Tompkins,* Pres.; Quincey T. Imhoff,* V.P.; Esther Li, V.P.; Debra B. Ryker,* Secy.-Treas.; Peter Buckley; Thomas Butler; Kristine M. Tompkins; George Wuerthner.
EIN: 680245471
Selected grants: The following grants are a representative sample of this grantmaker's funding activity:
$2,835,200 to Conservacion Patagonica, Sausalito, CA, 2012. For land preservation in Chile.
$2,089,000 to Conservacion Patagonica, Sausalito, CA, 2013. For land perservation in Chile.
$50,000 to Fideicomiso Fundacion Flora Y Fauna, Buenos Aires, Argentina, 2013. For land conservation in Chile.

427
The Sirpuhe & John Conte Foundation ✧
46650 E. Eldorado Dr.
Indian Wells, CA 92210-8643

Established in 1999 in CA.
Donors: John Conte†; Sirpuhe Conte; The Sirpuhe and John Conte Charitable Lead Annuity Trust.
Foundation type: Operating foundation.
Financial data (yr. ended 12/31/13): Assets, $6,675,486 (M); gifts received, $175,000; expenditures, $539,827; qualifying distributions, $458,142; giving activities include $448,900 for 31 grants (high: $205,000; low: $450).
Fields of interest: Arts; Education; Animal welfare; Health care; Human services.
Limitations: Applications not accepted. Giving in the U.S., with emphasis on CA.
Application information: Contributes only to pre-selected organizations.
Officers: Michael Landes, Pres.; Joyce Stein, Secy.; Stephanie Landes, Treas.
EIN: 330884049

428
David C. Copley Foundation ✧
(formerly James S. Copley Foundation)
2251 San Diego Ave., Ste. A-238
San Diego, CA 92110 (619) 269-8220
Contact: Kimberly Koch, Secy.
Main URL: http://copleyfoundation.org/

Incorporated in 1953 in CA.
Donors: The Copley Press Inc.; San Diego Union Shoe Fund; Helen K. Copley†; David C. Copley Trust.
Foundation type: Company-sponsored foundation.
Financial data (yr. ended 12/31/13): Assets, $46,890,096 (M); gifts received, $42,963,927; expenditures, $2,010,457; qualifying distributions, $1,968,272; giving activities include $1,859,583 for 8 grants (high: $558,333; low: $250).

Purpose and activities: The foundation supports organizations involved with arts and culture, education, animals and wildlife, health, recreation, and human services.
Fields of interest: Arts; Education; Health care.
Type of support: Capital campaigns; Building/renovation; Equipment; Endowments; Scholarship funds; Employee matching gifts.
Limitations: Applications accepted. Giving primarily in areas of company operations in CA, IL, and OH. No support for religious, fraternal, or athletic organizations, government agencies, local chapters of national organizations, public elementary or secondary schools, or public broadcasting systems. No grants to individuals, or for research, publications, conferences, general operating support, or large campaigns; no loans.
Publications: Informational brochure (including application guidelines).
Application information: Application form required.
Initial approach: Letter
Copies of proposal: 1
Deadline(s): Jan. 15 or July 15
Board meeting date(s): Feb.
Final notification: Following board meeting
Officers and Trustees:* Charles F. Patrick,* Chair.; Dean P. Dwyer,* Pres. and C.E.O.; Kimberly Koch, C.O.O.; Eric O. Freeberg,* Secy.; Robert F. Crouch,* Treas.
EIN: 956051770

429
The Copses Family Foundation ✧
2345 Kimridge Rd.
Beverly Hills, CA 90210-1830 (310) 288-2197

Established in 1999 in CA.
Donors: Peter Copses; Judith Mueller.
Foundation type: Independent foundation.
Financial data (yr. ended 12/31/12): Assets, $5,782,852 (M); gifts received, $4,577,500; expenditures, $833,941; qualifying distributions, $763,910; giving activities include $760,000 for 5 grants (high: $500,000; low: $25,000).
Fields of interest: Business school/education; Hospitals (general); Health organizations.
Limitations: Applications not accepted. Giving primarily in CA. No grants to individuals.
Application information: Contributes only to pre-selected organizations.
Officers: Peter Copses, Pres.; Judith Mueller, Secy.
EIN: 954773223

430
The Cortopassi Family Foundation ✧
(formerly The Capecchio Foundation)
11292 N. Alpine Rd.
Stockton, CA 95212-9325

Established in 1990 in CA.
Donors: Dean A. Cortopassi; Joan A. Cortopassi; California Italian-American Cultural Institute, Inc.; UC Davis Foundation; Bank of Stockton.
Foundation type: Independent foundation.
Financial data (yr. ended 12/31/13): Assets, $25,476,521 (M); gifts received, $170,241; expenditures, $3,170,125; qualifying distributions, $1,888,035; giving activities include $1,858,129 for 101 grants (high: $1,000,000; low: $250).
Fields of interest: Arts; Secondary school/education; Education; Environment, natural resources; Health organizations; Human services; Children/youth, services; Family services.
Type of support: Scholarship funds.
Limitations: Applications not accepted. Giving primarily in Stockton, CA.
Application information: Unsolicited requests for funds not accepted.
Officers: Dean A. Cortopassi, Pres.; Donald Lenz, Secy.-Treas.; Ann Bell, Mgr.
Trustees: Rebecca Carlson; Joan A. Cortopassi; Tom Cortopassi; Carla Donaldson; Katherine Whitlow.
EIN: 680232655

431
The Coto Foundation ✧ ☆
625 S. Fair Oaks Ave., Ste. 360
South Pasadena, CA 91030-5813

Established in DE.
Donors: Melanie Coto; Melanie Coto CLAT-Whittier Trust Company.
Foundation type: Independent foundation.
Financial data (yr. ended 12/31/13): Assets, $694,340 (M); gifts received, $300,000; expenditures, $550,798; qualifying distributions, $539,440; giving activities include $524,700 for 22 grants (high: $225,000; low: $3,000).
Fields of interest: Housing/shelter; Youth development; Human services.
Limitations: Applications not accepted. Giving primarily in CA.
Application information: Unsolicited requests for funds not accepted.
Officers and Directors:* Melanie Coto,* Pres.; Chloe Coto, 1st V.P.; Margaret Simpkins,* 2nd V.P. and Treas.; Pegine E. Grayson, Secy.
EIN: 263896152

432
Cotsen Family Foundation ✧
12100 Wilshire Blvd., Ste. 920
Los Angeles, CA 90025-7100 (310) 826-0504
FAX: (310) 826-2667; E-mail: info@cotsen.org; Main URL: http://www.cotsen.org/index.html
E-Newsletter: http://cotsen.org/topic/news/
Knowledge Center: http://cotsen.org/thoughts-on-teaching-excellence/

Established in 1984 in CA.
Donor: Lloyd E. Cotsen.
Foundation type: Independent foundation.
Financial data (yr. ended 06/30/13): Assets, $70,867,396 (M); expenditures, $5,183,350; qualifying distributions, $5,037,345; giving activities include $3,074,960 for 13 grants (high: $608,541; low: $3,972).
Purpose and activities: The foundation provides grants to schools and districts to support the Art of Teaching mentoring program.
Fields of interest: Elementary/secondary education; Higher education; Education.
Limitations: Applications not accepted. Giving limited to CA. No grants to individuals.
Application information: Contributes only to pre-selected organizations.
Officers and Directors:* Lloyd Cotsen,* Chair.; Dr. Barry Munitz,* Pres.; David Hardacre, V.P. and Secy.; Marilyn Payne, C.F.O.; Jerry Harris, Exec. Dir.; Margit Cotsen; Peggy Funkhauser; Gary K. Hart; Dr. Steven Koblik; Lucia Laguarda; Dr. Steven Lavine.
EIN: 953953038

433
Beckman Coulter Foundation ✧
250 S. Kraemer Blvd., M363
Brea, CA 92821-6229
Contact: Catherine Dougherty, Grant Dir.
Main URL: http://www.beckmancoulterfoundation.org/

Established in 2007 in CA.
Donor: Beckman Coulter, Inc.
Foundation type: Company-sponsored foundation.
Financial data (yr. ended 12/31/12): Assets, $2,639,999 (M); expenditures, $2,533,097; qualifying distributions, $2,532,839; giving activities include $2,507,922 for grants.
Purpose and activities: The foundations supports programs designed to promote science; science education; and healthcare-related research that improves patient health and quality of life.
Fields of interest: Higher education; Education; Health care; Medical research; American Red Cross; Science, formal/general education; Mathematics; Engineering/technology; Science.
Type of support: Program development; General/operating support; Employee volunteer services; Sponsorships; Employee matching gifts.
Limitations: Applications not accepted. Giving primarily in areas of company operations in CA. No support for fraternal, labor, or veterans' organizations, for-profit organizations, discriminatory organizations, private foundations, political organizations, or religious organizations or groups. No grants for advertising, beauty or talent contests, capital or building campaigns (including new construction or renovations), fundraisers, galas or dinners, golf tournaments, media productions including radio, TV., film, web-casts, or publications, meetings, conferences, symposia, or workshops unrelated to Beckman Coulter, political campaigns or activities, or sports affiliated activities.
Application information: The foundation is not currently accepting any new requests for support.
Officers and Directors:* G. Russell Bell,* Pres.; Jeffrey Linton,* Secy.; Roger B. Plotkin,* C.F.O.; Sibil Lin, Treas.; Peter Heseltine; James C. Osborne.
EIN: 261126986

434
S. H. Cowell Foundation ✧
595 Market St., Ste. 950
San Francisco, CA 94105-2816 (415) 397-0285
Contact: Lise Maisano, V.P., Grant Progs.
FAX: (415) 986-6786; Main URL: http://www.shcowell.org
Grantee Perception Report: http://www.shcowell.org/docs/Granteeperceptionstudy.pdf
Grants Database: http://www.shcowell.org/sections/grantsinaction/gra_database.php
Grants In Action: http://www.shcowell.org/sections/grantsinaction/gra_results.php
Strategic Plan 2009-2019: http://www.shcowell.org/docs/Strategic%20Plan.pdf

Established in 1956 in CA.
Donor: S.H. Cowell†.
Foundation type: Independent foundation.

Financial data (yr. ended 12/31/13): Assets, $134,166,150 (M); expenditures, $7,858,433; qualifying distributions, $6,917,724; giving activities include $4,925,875 for 100+ grants (high: $215,000), and $189,810 for 104 employee matching gifts.
Purpose and activities: The goal of the foundation is to improve the quality of life of children and families living in Northern and Central California by making grants that directly support and strengthen children, families, and the neighborhoods where they live. Priority is given to communities where Cowell has made, or could make, place-based complementary grants in Northern and Central California towns and neighborhoods where there is widespread and acute poverty and there are strong working relationships among residents and institutional leaders. The foundation funds efforts to increase a town or neighborhood's capacity to engage and serve its low-income families. These guidelines apply across all program areas: Family Resources Centers, K-12 Public Education, Responsive, Youth Development and affordable Housing.
Fields of interest: Education; Housing/shelter; Youth development; Human services; Infants/toddlers; Children/youth; Children; Youth; Minorities; Asians/Pacific Islanders; African Americans/Blacks; Hispanics/Latinos; Native Americans/American Indians; Girls; Boys; Economically disadvantaged.
Type of support: Mission-related investments/loans; General/operating support; Management development/capacity building; Capital campaigns; Building/renovation; Equipment; Land acquisition; Emergency funds; Program development; Seed money; Curriculum development; Technical assistance; Consulting services; Program-related investments/loans; Matching/challenge support.
Limitations: Applications accepted. Giving limited to Northern and Central California. No support for projects restricted to people with specific medical, physical, or health conditions, daycare centers, drug or alcohol abuse programs, environmental or conservation programs, medical service projects, political lobbying, population programs, post-secondary education, projects that are the responsibility of government agencies (except for school districts), or sectarian, politically partisan, or religious projects. No grants to individuals, or for special events conferences, books, films, videos, academic or medical research.
Publications: Application guidelines; Financial statement; Grants list; Occasional report; Program policy statement; Program policy statement (including application guidelines).
Application information: Applicants should submit the following:1. Brief history of organization and description of its mission2. Geographic area and population to be served3. Detailed description of project and amount of funding requested4. Timetable for implementation and evaluation of project5. Results expected from proposed grant6. Copy of most recent annual report/audited financial statement7. Board of Directors Roster8. Budget for proposed workflow9. Copy of IRS 501 (c) (3) Determination Letter. Application form not required.
Initial approach: Visit foundation web site, then telephone inquiry
Copies of proposal: 1
Deadline(s): None
Board meeting date(s): Five times a year
Final notification: 3 to 6 months
Officers and Directors:* Ann Alpers,* Pres.; Don Roberts, Secy. and Genl. Counsel; Dr. Lisa Backus; Charles E. Ellwein; Dr. Mikiko Huang; Scott Mosher; Lydia Tan; Kim Thompson.
Number of staff: 7 full-time professional; 4 part-time professional.
EIN: 941392803
Selected grants: The following grants are a representative sample of this grantmaker's funding activity:
$266,000 to Sanger Unified School District, Sanger, CA, 2012. To sustain collaborative improvement and increase the intellectual rigor of instruction, payable over 1.25 years.
$240,000 to California School-Age Consortium, Oakland, CA, 2012. For California School-Age Consortium to create EL-focused professional development training for after school staff, payable over 1.50 years.
$195,000 to Redwood City School District, Redwood City, CA, 2012. To sustain and expand collaboration among schools serving North Fair Oaks, payable over 1.25 years.
$150,000 to United Way of the Bay Area, San Francisco, CA, 2012. For SparkPoint Centers in East Oakland, Bay Point/East Contra Costa and Solano County.
$115,000 to On The Move, Napa, CA, 2012. For operating support for the McPherson Family Resource Center.
$100,000 to On The Move, Napa, CA, 2012. To continue the Leadership Academy in the McPherson neighborhood.
$75,000 to Businesses United in Investing, Lending and Development, Redwood City, CA, 2012. To strengthen the youth entrepreneurship program.
$75,000 to San Francisco Unified School District, San Francisco, CA, 2012. To accelerate learning for long-term English Learners in Excelsior neighborhood schools.
$60,000 to Asian Womens Shelter Project, San Francisco, CA, 2012. For operating support.
$25,000 to Girls Inc. of Alameda County, San Leandro, CA, 2012. For the purchase and renovation of a new building in downtown Oakland, payable over 1.75 years.

435
The Richard & Jean Coyne Family Foundation ✧
110 Constitution Dr.
Menlo Park, CA 94025-1107 (650) 326-6040
Contact: Jean A. Coyne, Pres.

Established in 1991 in CA.
Donor: Jean A. Coyne.
Foundation type: Independent foundation.
Financial data (yr. ended 12/31/13): Assets, $5,850,205 (M); gifts received, $131,000; expenditures, $592,877; qualifying distributions, $586,000; giving activities include $586,000 for 25 grants (high: $50,000; low: $2,500).
Purpose and activities: Giving primarily to programs whose purpose is to develop high school student portfolios for graphic arts colleges admissions and scholarships.
Fields of interest: Arts; Education.
Type of support: Scholarship funds.
Limitations: Applications accepted. Giving primarily in CA; funding also in NY.
Application information: Application form required.
Initial approach: Letter
Deadline(s): None
Officers: Jean A. Coyne, Pres.; Patrick S. Coyne, V.P.; Martha R. Coyne, Secy.; Eric P. Coyne, Treas.
EIN: 770259860
Selected grants: The following grants are a representative sample of this grantmaker's funding activity:
$50,000 to Art Center College of Design, Pasadena, CA, 2012. For Scholarships-Art Center at Night and Hs Saturday Honor.
$25,000 to Minneapolis College of Art and Design, Minneapolis, MN, 2012. For 10 Portfolio Prep Participants and 4 Scholarships.
$20,000 to California College of the Arts, Oakland, CA, 2012. For Scholarship Fund for Illustration Students.
$20,000 to College for Creative Studies, Detroit, MI, 2012. For Scholarship Fund for Minority and Low Income Students.
$2,500 to Society of Illustrators, New York, NY, 2012. For Drawing Academies for At-Risk Youth Ages 9-13 During Winter/Spring Vacations.

436
Craigslist Charitable Fund ✧
222 Sutter St., 9th Fl.
San Francisco, CA 94108-4460
E-mail: charitable@craigslist.org; Main URL: http://www.craigslist.org/about/charitable

Donor: Craigslist, Inc.
Foundation type: Company-sponsored foundation.
Financial data (yr. ended 12/31/12): Assets, $12,512,514 (M); gifts received, $7,000,000; expenditures, $2,626,341; qualifying distributions, $2,626,341; giving activities include $2,618,669 for 171 grants (high: $206,297).
Purpose and activities: The fund supports programs designed to promote human rights, justice, and education; the environment and transportation; non-violence, world peace, and veteran's issues; and journalism, software, and internet.
Fields of interest: Media, film/video; Media, journalism; Higher education; Education; Environment, energy; Environment; Children/youth, services; Human services; International peace/security; Civil/human rights; Economic development; Computer science; Military/veterans' organizations; Transportation.
Type of support: General/operating support.
Limitations: Applications accepted. Giving primarily in CA and NY.
Publications: Application guidelines.
Application information: Special consideration is given to organizations with annual budgets less than $1 million. Application form required.
Initial approach: E-mail foundation for application inquires
Deadline(s): None
Officers and Directors:* James Buckmaster,* Pres.; Craig Alexander Newmark,* Secy. and C.F.O.
EIN: 263823367
Selected grants: The following grants are a representative sample of this grantmaker's funding activity:
$20,000 to Girls Who Code, New York, NY, 2012. For general grant intented to further charitable purpose.
$150 to San Francisco Museum of Modern Art, San Francisco, CA, 2012. For general grant intented to further charitable purpo purposes.

437
Crail-Johnson Foundation ✧
461 W. 6th St., Ste. 300
San Pedro, CA 90731-2678 (310) 519-7413
Contact: Alan C. Johnson, Pres.
FAX: (310) 519-7221;
E-mail: grantrequest@crail-johnson.org; Additional e-mail: carolyn-johnson@crail-johnson.org; Main URL: http://www.crail-johnson.org

Established in 1987 in CA.
Donors: Jerry L. Johnson†; Robert Johnson†; Robert Johnson Charitable Lead Trust.
Foundation type: Independent foundation.
Financial data (yr. ended 12/31/13): Assets, $22,455,538 (M); expenditures, $2,145,773; qualifying distributions, $1,967,338; giving activities include $1,586,791 for 159 grants (high: $521,406; low: $50), and $245,000 for 1 loan/ program-related investment.
Purpose and activities: The foundation promotes the well-being of children in need through the effective application of human and financial resources.
Fields of interest: Education, early childhood education; Child development, education; Elementary school/education; Education, reading; Health care; Children/youth, services; Child development, services; Family services; Science; Mathematics; Economically disadvantaged.
Type of support: General/operating support; Capital campaigns; Equipment; Emergency funds; Program development; Seed money; Curriculum development; Employee matching gifts; Matching/ challenge support.
Limitations: Giving primarily in Los Angeles County and the greater Los Angeles, CA, area. Generally no support for athletic events, religious programs and causes, political causes, or for university level education. No grants to individuals, or for research.
Publications: Application guidelines; Annual report (including application guidelines); Financial statement; Grants list.
Application information: Please do not send unsolicited proposals with extensive attachments and/or videotapes. Proposals are by invitation only, after review of letter of inquiry. See foundation web site for guidelines. Application form required.
Initial approach: Letter of inquiry (no more than 3 pages)
Copies of proposal: 1
Deadline(s): Oct. through Dec. for letters of inquiry; proposals deadline dates vary
Board meeting date(s): Quarterly
Officers and Directors:* Eric C. Johnson,* Chair.; Alan C. Johnson,* Pres.; Ann L. Johnson,* V.P.; Carolyn E. Johnson,* V.P.; Craig C. Johnson,* V.P.; Jack S. Peterson,* Secy.; Byung Kim,* C.F.O.; Dorothy Courtney; Elizabeth Schindler-Johnson; and 7 additional directors.
Number of staff: 1 full-time professional.
EIN: 330247161

438
Crankstart Foundation ✧
c/o Frank, Rimerman & Co., LLP
1801 Page Mill Rd.
Palo Alto, CA 94304-1216 (650) 845-8100
Michael Moritz and Harriet Heyman's Giving Pledge Profile: http://glasspockets.org/philanthropy-in-focus/eye-on-the-giving-pledge/profiles/moritz

Established in 2000 in CA.
Donors: Michael Moritz; Harriet Heyman.
Foundation type: Independent foundation.
Financial data (yr. ended 12/31/13): Assets, $680,483,501 (M); gifts received, $415,700; expenditures, $21,799,393; qualifying distributions, $8,361,080; giving activities include $8,361,080 for 81 grants (high: $1,686,667; low: $1,000).
Fields of interest: Education; Recreation, parks/ playgrounds; Community/economic development.
Type of support: General/operating support.
Limitations: Applications not accepted. Giving primarily in CA. No grants to individuals.
Application information: Contributes only to pre-selected organizations.
Officer: Michael Moritz, Pres. and C.F.O.
Director: Harriet Heyman.
EIN: 943377099

439
The Crean Foundation ✧
P.O. Box 8449
Newport Beach, CA 92658-8449

Established in 1981 in CA.
Donors: John C. Crean†; Donna S. Crean.
Foundation type: Independent foundation.
Financial data (yr. ended 12/31/13): Assets, $73,214,838 (M); gifts received, $1,001,405; expenditures, $3,910,844; qualifying distributions, $3,188,590; giving activities include $3,188,590 for 86 grants (high: $1,040,000; low: $150).
Purpose and activities: Support primarily for education, health, and children and social services.
Fields of interest: Secondary school/education; Higher education; Education; Hospitals (general); Health organizations; Human services; Children/ youth, services.
Type of support: General/operating support.
Limitations: Applications not accepted. Giving primarily in Orange County, CA. No grants to individuals.
Application information: Contributes only to pre-selected organizations.
Officers: Andrew Crean, Pres.; Marc S. Goldin, C.F.O.; Emily Crean Vogler, V.P.; Susan E. Thomas, Secy.
Number of staff: 1 part-time professional; 1 part-time support.
EIN: 953676334
Selected grants: The following grants are a representative sample of this grantmaker's funding activity:
$2,000,000 to Crean Lutheran South High School, Irvine, CA, 2011. For construction of school building.
$1,000,000 to Webb Schools, Claremont, CA, 2011. For scholarships.
$500,000 to Hoag Hospital Foundation, Newport Beach, CA, 2011. For construction of new hospital facilities.
$240,000 to Childrens Bureau, Anaheim, CA, 2011. For program support.
$200,000 to Pretend City, The Childrens Museum of Orange County, Irvine, CA, 2011. For construction of exhibit.
$110,000 to Childrens Hospital of Orange County Foundation, Orange, CA, 2011.
$60,000 to Pat McCormick and Friends Growing Up Educational Foundation, Seal Beach, CA, 2011. For program support.
$40,000 to New Vista School, Laguna Hills, CA, 2011. For tuition assistance.
$20,000 to RV/MH Heritage Foundation, Elkhart, IN, 2011. For operating support.
$10,000 to El Puente Community Development Corporation, Santa Ana, CA, 2011. For program support.

440
Mary A. Crocker Trust ✧
364 Bush St.
San Francisco, CA 94104-2805 (415) 982-0138
Contact: Abby Wilder, Exec. Dir.
FAX: (415) 982-0141; E-mail: staff@mactrust.org; Main URL: http://www.mactrust.org

Trust established in 1889 in CA.
Donor: Mary A. Crocker†.
Foundation type: Independent foundation.
Financial data (yr. ended 12/31/12): Assets, $11,385,317 (M); expenditures, $692,319; qualifying distributions, $648,969; giving activities include $513,000 for 44 grants (high: $25,000; low: $500).
Fields of interest: Education; Environment; Human services.
Type of support: Program development; Seed money; Matching/challenge support.
Limitations: Applications accepted. Giving primarily in the San Francisco Bay Area, CA. No support for sectarian purposes. No grants to individuals, or for operating budgets, continuing support, annual campaigns, deficit financing, building or endowment funds, capital campaigns, land acquisition, scholarships, fellowships, or conferences; no loans.
Publications: Application guidelines; Grants list; Program policy statement.
Application information: Complete application guidelines available on Trust web site. Application form required.
Initial approach: E-mail 1-page Letter of Interest
Copies of proposal: 1
Board meeting date(s): Spring and fall
Officer: David Whitridge, Chair.
Trustees: Elizabeth Atcheson; Charles Crocker; Tania W. Stepanian; Abigail H. Wilder.
Number of staff: 1 full-time professional.
EIN: 946051917

441
Croul Family Foundation ✧
18101 Von Karman Ave., Ste. 700
Irvine, CA 92612-0145
Contact: Spencer Behr Croul, Secy.
FAX: (949) 833-9584;
E-mail: grants@croulfoundation.org; Toll free tel.: (877) 968-6328; Main URL: http://www.croulfoundation.org

Established in 1997 in CA.
Donors: John V. Croul; Spencer Behr Croul.
Foundation type: Independent foundation.
Financial data (yr. ended 12/31/12): Assets, $20,794,170 (M); gifts received, $1,000,000; expenditures, $1,233,791; qualifying distributions, $1,120,957; giving activities include $1,077,850 for 109 grants (high: $100,000; low: $500).
Purpose and activities: Giving to organizations that are engaged in improving educational outcomes at kindergarten through 12th grade, as well as organizations that assist the homeless and economically disadvantaged in Orange County, CA.

Fields of interest: Education; Food banks; Human services; Economically disadvantaged; Homeless.
Type of support: General/operating support; Endowments.
Limitations: Applications accepted. Giving primarily in Orange County, CA. No support for start-up organizations.
Publications: Application guidelines; Program policy statement.
Application information: Application form required.
Initial approach: Take eligibility quiz on foundation web site
Board meeting date(s): Twice per year
Officers and Trustees:* John V. Croul,* C.E.O.; Spencer Behr Croul,* Secy.; John Bradford Croul,* C.F.O.
Number of staff: 1 part-time support.
EIN: 201222760
Selected grants: The following grants are a representative sample of this grantmaker's funding activity:
$15,000 to Boy Scouts of America, Orange County, Santa Ana, CA, 2012. For program support.

442
CS Fund ✧
469 Bohemian Hwy.
Freestone, CA 95472-9579 (707) 874-2942
Contact: Roxanne Turnage, Exec. Dir.
FAX: (707) 874-1734; E-mail: inquiries@csfund.org; Main URL: http://www.csfund.org

Established in 1981 in CA as "pass through" fund for annual gifts of donors.
Donors: Maryanne Mott; Herman Warsh†.
Foundation type: Independent foundation.
Financial data (yr. ended 10/31/13): Assets, $2,558,987 (M); gifts received, $1,800,000; expenditures, $2,193,670; qualifying distributions, $2,668,965; giving activities include $1,520,241 for 41 grants (high: $270,000; low: $85).
Purpose and activities: A private foundation, giving for programs with national or international impact; specific areas of funding include emerging technology, economic globalizations, food sovereignty, and civil liberties.
Fields of interest: Agriculture/food; Civil/human rights; Economic development.
Type of support: Conferences/seminars; Continuing support; General/operating support; Matching/challenge support; Publication; Research; Technical assistance.
Limitations: Applications accepted. Giving on a national basis. No grants for endowment funds, capital ventures, emergency requests, or video or film production.
Publications: Application guidelines; Grants list.
Application information: The foundation is currently in the process of reducing its grantmaking, and its ability to entertain new proposals is especially limited during this time. A hard copy of the letter of inquiry is preferred over fax or e-mail. If the letter of inquiry describing the project falls within the foundation's area of interest, a full proposal will be invited. Application guidelines and procedures available on foundation web site. Application form not required.
Initial approach: Letter of inquiry, not to exceed 3 pages
Copies of proposal: 1
Deadline(s): None, for letter of inquiry
Board meeting date(s): Apr. and Dec.
Officers and Directors:* Michael Warsh,* Pres.; Marise Meynet Stewart,* V.P.; Corinne Meadows-Efram,* Secy.; Maryanne Mott,* Treas.; Roxanne Turnage, Exec. Dir.; Kau'i Keliipio; Teresa Robinson.
Number of staff: 4 full-time professional; 3 part-time support.
EIN: 953607882

443
John Curci Family Foundation ✧
P.O. Box 1549
Newport Beach, CA 92663-1549
Application address: c/o Patricia Soldano, 151 Kalmus Dr., Ste. J-1, Costa Mesa, CA 92626, tel.: (714) 641-1402

Established in 2004 in CA.
Donor: John Curci Trust.
Foundation type: Independent foundation.
Financial data (yr. ended 12/31/12): Assets, $41,603,963 (M); gifts received, $4,768,482; expenditures, $1,733,494; qualifying distributions, $1,518,606; giving activities include $1,482,500 for 22 grants (high: $815,000; low: $1,000).
Purpose and activities: Giving primarily for health care, including a medical center; support also for education.
Fields of interest: Education; Hospitals (general); Health care; Human services; Children/youth, services; Catholic agencies & churches.
Limitations: Applications accepted. Giving primarily in southern CA.
Application information:
Initial approach: Letter
Deadline(s): None
Directors: John Curci; Robert Curci; Janet Curci Walsh.
EIN: 201477014

444
The Shurl & Kay Curci Foundation ✧
(formerly The TDC Foundation)
2377 Crenshaw Blvd., Ste. 300
Torrance, CA 90501-3330

Established in 2007 in CA.
Donors: Shurl Curci; Kay Curci.
Foundation type: Independent foundation.
Financial data (yr. ended 02/28/14): Assets, $35,895,642 (M); gifts received, $7,500,000; expenditures, $1,185,220; qualifying distributions, $1,134,190; giving activities include $1,134,190 for 7 grants (high: $200,000; low: $50,000).
Fields of interest: Cancer; Health organizations; Medical research.
Limitations: Applications not accepted. Giving primarily in CA and NY. No grants to individuals.
Application information: Unsolicited requests for funds not accepted.
Officers and Directors:* Ronald V. Rosequist,* Pres.; Amy E. Fuermann, Secy.; Roberta P. Irish,* Treas.; Kay Curci; E. Davisson Hardman; John E. Huguenard; Thomas G. Irish; James G. Mitchell.
EIN: 205242604
Selected grants: The following grants are a representative sample of this grantmaker's funding activity:
$100,000 to Human BioMolecular Research Institute, San Diego, CA, 2011.

445
John & Geraldine Cusenza Family Foundation ✧
301 N. Rockingham
Los Angeles, CA 90049 (424) 273-1756

Established in 1995 in CA.
Donors: Geraldine Cusenza; John Cusenza.
Foundation type: Independent foundation.
Financial data (yr. ended 11/30/13): Assets, $8,880,886 (M); expenditures, $526,695; qualifying distributions, $474,702; giving activities include $450,788 for grants.
Purpose and activities: Giving primarily for children and social services.
Fields of interest: Cancer research; Human services; Children/youth, services.
Limitations: Applications accepted. Giving primarily in CA. No grants to individuals.
Application information: Application form required.
Initial approach: Proposal
Deadline(s): None
Officers: Geraldine Cusenza, Pres.; John Cusenza, C.F.O.
EIN: 954556555

446
A.M. Dachs Foundation ✧ ☆
P.O. Box 193809
San Francisco, CA 94119-3809

Established in 1991 in CA.
Donor: Alan M. Dachs.
Foundation type: Independent foundation.
Financial data (yr. ended 12/31/13): Assets, $5,508,882 (M); gifts received, $5,000; expenditures, $961,394; qualifying distributions, $958,936; giving activities include $925,000 for 14 grants (high: $500,000; low: $5,000).
Purpose and activities: Giving primarily for higher and other education, as well as to a public policy research center.
Fields of interest: Higher education; Education; Human services; Social sciences, research.
Type of support: Capital campaigns; Building/renovation; Endowments; Scholarship funds.
Limitations: Applications not accepted. Giving primarily in CA, CT, and DC. No grants to individuals.
Application information: Contributes only to pre-selected organizations.
Officers and Directors:* Alan M. Dachs,* Pres.; Lauren B. Dachs,* V.P.; Shu Huang, Secy.-Treas.; Deborah L. Duncan.
EIN: 943144688
Selected grants: The following grants are a representative sample of this grantmaker's funding activity:
$475,000 to Wesleyan University, Middletown, CT, 2011.
$250,000 to Brookings Institution, Washington, DC, 2010.
$100,000 to Brookings Institution, Washington, DC, 2011.
$100,000 to Brookings Institution, Washington, DC, 2011.
$50,000 to Brookings Institution, Washington, DC, 2011.
$50,000 to Stanford University, Stanford, CA, 2011.
$50,000 to Stanford University, Stanford, CA, 2011.
$25,000 to Head-Royce School, Oakland, CA, 2011.
$25,000 to Stanford University, Stanford, CA, 2011.
$12,500 to Santa Clara University, Santa Clara, CA, 2011.

$5,000 to Thacher School, Ojai, CA, 2011.

447
Robert and Carole Daly Foundation ✧ ☆
(formerly Robert Daly Foundation)
c/o Gelfand Rennert & Feldman LLP
1880 Century Park E., Ste. 1600
Los Angeles, CA 90067

Established in 1987 in CA.
Donors: Robert Daly; Carole Daly.
Foundation type: Independent foundation.
Financial data (yr. ended 12/31/13): Assets, $1,376,403 (M); gifts received, $1,000,000; expenditures, $1,152,570; qualifying distributions, $1,150,667; giving activities include $1,150,667 for 29 grants (high: $200,000; low: $500).
Fields of interest: Arts; Education; Human services.
Type of support: General/operating support; Capital campaigns.
Limitations: Applications not accepted. Giving primarily in CA and CT. No grants to individuals.
Application information: Contributes only to pre-selected organizations.
Trustees: Carole Daly; Robert A. Daly.
EIN: 956875322

448
Danford Foundation ✧
P.O. Box 4609
Foster City, CA 94404-0609 (650) 349-6044
Contact: Katherine F. Fisher, Secy.

Established in CA in 1982.
Donor: Gladys B. Danford†.
Foundation type: Independent foundation.
Financial data (yr. ended 06/30/13): Assets, $18,710,863 (M); expenditures, $942,283; qualifying distributions, $789,445; giving activities include $789,445 for grants.
Purpose and activities: Giving primarily for health associations and medical research, children, youth, and social services, particularly for food, housing, job training, services for the homeless, and substance abuse programs.
Fields of interest: Performing arts; Arts; Elementary/secondary education; Higher education; Libraries/library science; Education; Animal welfare; Hospitals (general); Health organizations, association; Eye diseases; Nerve, muscle & bone diseases; Health organizations; Medical research, association; Medical research, institute; Human services; Children/youth, services; Family services; Homeless, human services; Catholic agencies & churches; Children/youth; Blind/visually impaired; Girls; Boys; Economically disadvantaged.
Type of support: Endowments; Continuing support; Equipment; Scholarship funds; Research.
Limitations: Applications accepted. Giving primarily in the San Francisco Bay Area, CA. No support for political organizations. No grants to individuals.
Publications: Annual report.
Application information: Application form required.
Initial approach: Letter
Copies of proposal: 1
Deadline(s): None
Officers: Frank L. Hannig, Pres.; George A. Fisher, C.F.O. and Treas.; Betty Shehi, V.P.; Katherine F. Fisher, Secy.
Number of staff: 5 part-time professional.
EIN: 942819322
Selected grants: The following grants are a representative sample of this grantmaker's funding activity:
$60,000 to Guide Dogs for the Blind, San Rafael, CA, 2013. For Training for the underprivileged recipients.
$50,000 to Sequoia Hospital Foundation, Redwood City, CA, 2013. For hospital equipment.
$15,000 to Peninsula Conflict Resolution Center, San Mateo, CA, 2013. For parent education.
$5,000 to Notre Dame Elementary School, Belmont, CA, 2013. For scholarship foundation.
$5,000 to Peninsula Volunteers, Menlo Park, CA, 2013. For Development of Programs for seniors.
$5,000 to Trevor Project, West Hollywood, CA, 2013. To provide crisis intervention and suicide prevention funding to lesbian, gay, bisexual, transgender and questioning young people ages 13-24.
$3,000 to Disabled American Veterans, Cold Spring, KY, 2013. For benefits and services for veterans and families.
$2,500 to Larkin Street Youth Services, San Francisco, CA, 2013. For Integrate housing, education, employment and health services to get homeless and at risk kids off the streets.
$2,500 to Pathways Hospice Foundation, Sunnyvale, CA, 2013. For Help low income families with homecare needs.

449
Hugh and Hazel Darling Foundation ✧
500 S. Grand Ave., 19th Fl.
Los Angeles, CA 90071-2668 (213) 683-5200
Contact: Richard L. Stack, Tr.

Established in 1988 in CA.
Donors: Hugh Darling†; Hazel Darling†.
Foundation type: Independent foundation.
Financial data (yr. ended 12/31/13): Assets, $35,009,157 (M); expenditures, $1,859,868; qualifying distributions, $1,710,633; giving activities include $1,550,000 for 42 grants (high: $250,000; low: $1,000).
Purpose and activities: Giving for support of education in California, with emphasis on legal education.
Fields of interest: Law school/education; Education.
Type of support: Capital campaigns; Building/renovation; Equipment; Scholarship funds; Matching/challenge support.
Limitations: Applications accepted. Giving limited to CA. No grants to individuals.
Application information: Application form not required.
Initial approach: Letter
Copies of proposal: 1
Deadline(s): None
Board meeting date(s): Varies
Final notification: Varies
Trustee: Richard L. Stack.
Number of staff: 1 part-time support.
EIN: 956874901
Selected grants: The following grants are a representative sample of this grantmaker's funding activity:
$500,000 to University of San Francisco, San Francisco, CA, 2012. For facilities renovations.
$250,000 to Simpson University, Redding, CA, 2012. For facilities construction.
$100,000 to Loyola Law School, Los Angeles, CA, 2012. For scholarships.
$50,000 to Chapman University, School of Law, Orange, CA, 2012. For faculty.
$50,000 to University of San Diego, San Diego, CA, 2012. For program support.
$30,000 to Independent Scholarship Fund, 2012. For scholarships.
$25,000 to Azusa Pacific University, Azusa, CA, 2012. For scholarships.
$25,000 to Federalist Society for Law and Public Policy Studies, Washington, DC, 2012. For students programs.
$25,000 to Pacific Research Institute for Public Policy, San Francisco, CA, 2012. For educational program.
$25,000 to Pepperdine University, Malibu, CA, 2012. For clinic.
$10,000 to Junior Blind of America, Los Angeles, CA, 2012. For literacy program.

450
Dart-L Foundation ✧
4001 Wilshire Blvd., No. F-165
Los Angeles, CA 90010-3435 (213) 480-3372

Established in 1998 in CA.
Donors: Aaron Friedman; Ira David Friedman; Jacob Friedman; Lea Friedman; Ruchel Friedman Klavan; Libby Friedman Lehmann; Tzippy Friedman Notis.
Foundation type: Independent foundation.
Financial data (yr. ended 12/31/12): Assets, $190,408,323 (M); gifts received, $5,000,000; expenditures, $9,953,688; qualifying distributions, $9,158,813; giving activities include $9,097,580 for 117 grants (high: $6,500,000; low: $180).
Purpose and activities: Giving primarily to Jewish agencies, temples, and schools.
Fields of interest: Education; Human services; Jewish agencies & synagogues.
Limitations: Applications not accepted. Giving primarily in Los Angeles, CA; some funding also in NY, with emphasis on Brooklyn. No grants to individuals.
Application information: Contributes only to pre-selected organizations.
Officers and Directors:* Jacob Friedman, Pres.; Lea Friedman, V.P.; Ira David Friedman,* C.F.O; Aaron Friedman; Ruchel Friedman Klavan; Libby Friedman Lehmann; Tzippy Friedman Notis.
EIN: 954701699
Selected grants: The following grants are a representative sample of this grantmaker's funding activity:
$6,500,000 to Jewish Community Foundation, Los Angeles, CA, 2012.
$540,350 to Mesivta of Greater Los Angeles, Calabasas, CA, 2012.
$500,250 to Keren Lmaan Arad, Brooklyn, NY, 2012.
$250,000 to Bnos Melech of Lakewood, Lakewood, NJ, 2012.
$150,000 to Chasdei David, Brooklyn, NY, 2012.
$150,000 to Congregation Torah V Chesed, Los Angeles, CA, 2012.
$105,000 to Bais Yaakov School for Girls, Los Angeles, CA, 2012.
$100,000 to American Kosher Supervision, Los Angeles, CA, 2012.
$51,000 to Congregation Kollel Yechiel Yehuda, Los Angeles, CA, 2012.
$19,700 to Samuel A. Fryer Yavneh Hebrew Academy, Los Angeles, CA, 2012.

451
The Davidow Charitable Fund ✧
(formerly The Diana and Robert Davidow Foundation)
11601 Wilshire Blvd., Ste. 1925
Los Angeles, CA 90025-1754

Established in 1986 in CA.
Donors: Robert A. Davidow; Diana R. Davidow.
Foundation type: Independent foundation.
Financial data (yr. ended 10/31/13): Assets, $8,965,206 (M); gifts received, $208,932; expenditures, $713,360; qualifying distributions, $688,623; giving activities include $674,975 for 144 grants (high: $75,000; low: $100).
Purpose and activities: Giving primarily for Jewish organizations, as well as for education, health associations, and children, youth and social services.
Fields of interest: Higher education; Education; Hospitals (general); Health organizations, association; Cancer; Cancer research; Human services; Jewish federated giving programs; Jewish agencies & synagogues.
Limitations: Applications not accepted. No grants to individuals.
Application information: Contributes only to pre-selected organizations.
Officers: Robert A. Davidow, Pres. and C.E.O.; Diana R. Davidow, C.F.O. and Secy.
EIN: 330210307
Selected grants: The following grants are a representative sample of this grantmaker's funding activity:
$100,000 to Brooklyn College Foundation, Brooklyn, NY, 2011.
$100,000 to Youth Mentoring Connection, Los Angeles, CA, 2011.
$5,000 to Alfred E. Mann Foundation for Scientific Research, Santa Clarita, CA, 2011.

452
Davidow Family Foundation ✧
85 Robles Dr.
Woodside, CA 94062-2528

Established in 1999 in CA.
Donors: William H. Davidow; Claire Davidow‡; Sonja A. Davidow.
Foundation type: Independent foundation.
Financial data (yr. ended 12/31/13): Assets, $7,493,448 (M); expenditures, $548,874; qualifying distributions, $512,681; giving activities include $511,925 for 45 grants (high: $200,000; low: $75).
Purpose and activities: Giving primarily for education and the arts.
Fields of interest: Arts; Higher education; Human services.
Limitations: Applications not accepted. Giving primarily in CA and NH. No grants to individuals.
Application information: Unsolicited requests for funds not accepted.
Officers: Sonja A. Davidow, Co-Pres.; William H. Davidow, Co-Pres.
Directors: Rebecca Davidow Logan; Carolyn Davidow Putney.
EIN: 770449213

453
The Davidson Family Foundation ✧
255 W. Julian St., Ste. 200
San Jose, CA 95110-2406

Established in 1992 in CA.
Donors: Avex 2009 Charitable Lead Annuity Trust; Anita A. Davidson Charitable Lead Annuity Trust; Anita A. Davidson; Charles W. Davidson.
Foundation type: Independent foundation.
Financial data (yr. ended 10/31/13): Assets, $14,783,721 (M); gifts received, $500,000; expenditures, $631,522; qualifying distributions, $666,946; giving activities include $638,940 for 62 grants (high: $200,000; low: $80).
Purpose and activities: Giving primarily for community services, education, animal welfare, children and youth services, and health organizations; funding also for a YWCA.
Fields of interest: Education; Animal welfare; Health organizations, association; Medical research, institute; Human services; YM/YWCAs & YM/YWHAs; Children/youth, services.
Type of support: Annual campaigns; Scholarship funds; Research.
Limitations: Applications not accepted. Giving primarily in CA. No grants to individuals.
Application information: Contributes only to pre-selected organizations.
Officers: Gloria K. Chiang, Pres.; Sandra Davidson, V.P.; Patricia J. Propolanis, Secy.
EIN: 770325599
Selected grants: The following grants are a representative sample of this grantmaker's funding activity:
$250,000 to YWCA, Mid-Peninsula, San Jose, CA, 2011.
$3,000 to Performing Animal Welfare Society, Galt, CA, 2011.
$2,500 to VMC Foundation, San Jose, CA, 2011.

454
Louise M. Davies Foundation ✧
180 Montgomery St., Ste. 1616
San Francisco, CA 94104-4235

Established in 1974 in CA.
Donor: Louise M. Davies.
Foundation type: Independent foundation.
Financial data (yr. ended 12/31/13): Assets, $33,762,496 (M); expenditures, $1,099,409; qualifying distributions, $931,116; giving activities include $830,000 for 51 grants (high: $101,500; low: $1,000).
Purpose and activities: Giving primarily for Roman Catholic education as well as for the arts, with emphasis on the performing arts.
Fields of interest: Museums (art); Performing arts, orchestras; Performing arts, opera; Elementary/secondary education; Higher education; Education; Human services; Youth, services; Catholic agencies & churches.
Type of support: General/operating support; Capital campaigns; Endowments; Scholarship funds.
Limitations: Applications not accepted. Giving primarily in San Francisco, CA. No grants to individuals.
Application information: Contributes only to pre-selected organizations.
Officers and Director:* Philip Hudner, Jr.,* Pres.; Ann C. Matthews, Secy.-Treas.
EIN: 237359841
Selected grants: The following grants are a representative sample of this grantmaker's funding activity:
$50,000 to San Francisco Opera Association, San Francisco, CA, 2012. For general support for opera.
$20,000 to Keys School, Palo Alto, CA, 2012. For general support for elementary and Junior high school.
$15,000 to Bullis-Purissima Elementary School Foundation, Los Altos, CA, 2012. For general support for elementary school.
$15,000 to Monterey Museum of Art, Monterey, CA, 2012. To support maintenance of Davies Collection of Western Art.
$15,000 to Wyoming Catholic College, Lander, WY, 2012. For general support for college.
$10,000 to Catholic League for Religious and Civil Rights, New York, NY, 2012. For general support for religious and civil rights organization.
$10,000 to Pacific Legal Foundation, Sacramento, CA, 2012. For general support for legal assistance organization.
$5,000 to Archbishop Riordan High School, San Francisco, CA, 2012. For scholarships for school boarding Program.
$5,000 to Woodside Priory School, Portola Valley, CA, 2012. For contribution to John Erkman Scholarship Fund.
$2,500 to Sacred Heart Schools, Atherton, CA, 2012. For general support for preschool through 12th grade schools.

455
The Leonard & Sophie Davis Fund ✧
c/o Alan S. Davis
P.O. Box 590780
San Francisco, CA 94159-0780
Contact: Alan S. Davis, Pres.
E-mail: gerard@lsdfund.org

Established in 2001 in CA.
Donors: Alan S. Davis; Alan Stephen Davis Charitable Lead Annuity Trust.
Foundation type: Independent foundation.
Financial data (yr. ended 11/30/13): Assets, $118,108,797 (M); gifts received, $6,255,338; expenditures, $6,113,095; qualifying distributions, $5,559,750; giving activities include $5,402,000 for 13 grants (high: $2,000,000; low: $3,000).
Fields of interest: Museums (art); Performing arts; Arts; Higher education; Education; Medical research, institute; Human services; Civil/human rights; Jewish federated giving programs; Jewish agencies & synagogues.
International interests: Israel.
Type of support: Scholarship funds; Professorships; Endowments; General/operating support.
Limitations: Applications not accepted. Giving primarily in NY; some giving also in FL and CA. No grants to individuals.
Application information: Contributes only to pre-selected organizations.
Officers: Alan S. Davis, Pres.; Mary Lucille Duray, Secy.; James Hassan, Treas.
EIN: 943402266
Selected grants: The following grants are a representative sample of this grantmaker's funding activity:
$2,000,000 to University of Southern California, School of Gerontology, Los Angeles, CA, 2013.
$1,250,000 to Raymond F. Kravis Center for the Performing Arts, West Palm Beach, FL, 2012.

$1,000,000 to American Friends of the Hebrew University, Walnut Creek, CA, 2011.
$1,000,000 to Beth Israel Medical Center, New York, NY, 2011.
$1,000,000 to United States Holocaust Memorial Museum, Washington, DC, 2013.
$750,000 to Common Cause Education Fund, McGovern Great Government Endowment, Washington, DC, 2012.
$500,000 to City College of the City University of New York, New York, NY, 2012.
$500,000 to Jewish Communal Fund of New York, New York, NY, 2013.
$250,000 to Jewish Federation of Palm Beach County, West Palm Beach, FL, 2012.
$180,000 to Democracy Alliance, New Venture Fund, Washington, DC, 2013.
$125,000 to Proteus Fund, Piper Fund, Amherst, MA, 2013.
$125,000 to Proteus Fund, Piper Fund, Amherst, MA, 2012.
$100,000 to Demos: A Network for Ideas and Action, New York, NY, 2012.
$100,000 to Demos: A Network for Ideas and Action, New York, NY, 2011. For General Support, payable over 2.00 years.
$100,000 to Public Campaign, Washington, DC, 2012.
$100,000 to Public Campaign, Washington, DC, 2011. For General Support, payable over 2.00 years.
$100,000 to United States Holocaust Memorial Museum, Washington, DC, 2013.
$75,000 to American Friends of the Hebrew University, Walnut Creek, CA, 2011.
$75,000 to Demos: A Network for Ideas and Action, New York, NY, 2012. For General Support.
$60,000 to Beth Israel Medical Center, New York, NY, 2011.
$60,000 to City College of the City University of New York, New York, NY, 2011.
$50,000 to Proteus Fund, Piper Fund, Amherst, MA, 2013. For NY State Campaign Public Financing.
$40,000 to Media Matters for America, Washington, DC, 2011. For General Support, payable over 2.00 years.
$30,000 to American Friends of the Israel Philharmonic Orchestra, New York, NY, 2011.
$30,000 to Movement Research, New York, NY, 2012.
$25,000 to Voices for Progress, Washington, DC, 2013.
$20,000 to Art of the Olympians Foundation, Fort Myers, FL, 2012.
$10,000 to United States Holocaust Memorial Museum, Washington, DC, 2011.

456
Robert A. Day Foundation ✧
865 S. Figueroa St., No. 700
Los Angeles, CA 90017-2543 (213) 891-6300

Established in 2008 in DE and CA as a successor trust to the original Robert A. Day Foundation.
Donor: Robert A. Day.
Foundation type: Independent foundation.
Financial data (yr. ended 12/31/12): Assets, $11,889,083 (M); expenditures, $960,979; qualifying distributions, $930,500; giving activities include $930,500 for grants.
Fields of interest: Arts; Higher education; Health organizations; Human services; Children/youth, services; Community/economic development.
Limitations: Applications accepted. Giving primarily in CA.
Application information: Application form not required.
Initial approach: Letter
Deadline(s): None
Officers: Robert A. Day, Jr., Pres.; Joseph Day, V.P.; Jerry W. Carlton, Secy.-Treas.
EIN: 205171559

457
Willametta K. Day Foundation ✧
c/o Oakmont Corp.
865 S. Figueroa St., Ste. 700
Los Angeles, CA 90017-2598 (213) 891-6300
Mailing address: P.O. Box 71289, Los Angeles, CA 90071

Trust established in 1954 in CA.
Donors: Willametta K. Day‡; Robert A. Day; Theodore J. Day; Howard M. Day; Tammis Day; Thomas Joseph Deegan-Day; Dorothy W. Day; Lucinda M. Fournier; Howard M. Day, Jr.
Foundation type: Independent foundation.
Financial data (yr. ended 12/31/12): Assets, $39,060,070 (M); expenditures, $2,268,755; qualifying distributions, $1,754,792; giving activities include $1,707,230 for 114 grants (high: $250,000; low: $250).
Purpose and activities: Giving primarily for education, as well as for arts and cultural organizations, and health and human services.
Fields of interest: Museums; Arts; Secondary school/education; Higher education; Education; Hospitals (general); Health organizations, association; Human services; Jewish federated giving programs; Christian agencies & churches; Jewish agencies & synagogues.
Type of support: General/operating support.
Limitations: Applications accepted. Giving primarily in CA and OR. No grants to individuals.
Publications: Financial statement.
Application information: Application form not required.
Initial approach: Letter
Copies of proposal: 1
Deadline(s): None
Board meeting date(s): Annually
Officers and Trustees:* Robert A. Day, Jr.,* Chair.; Theodore J. Day,* Pres.; Jerry W. Carlton,* V.P.; Howard M. Day,* V.P.; Tammis A. Day,* V.P.; Allison M. Keller,* Secy.-Treas.; Dorothy W. Day; Howard M. Day, Jr.; Thomas Joseph Deegan-Day; Lucinda M. Fournier.
Number of staff: 2 full-time professional; 3 full-time support.
EIN: 956092476

458
Delta Dental Community Care Foundation ✧
100 1st St.
San Francisco, CA 94105

Donors: Delta Dental Insurance Company; Delta Dental of Pennsylvania; Delta Dental of New York Inc.; Delta Dental of Delaware Inc.; Delta Dental of West Virginia Inc.; Delta Dental of the District of Columbia; Delta Dental of California; Gary D. Radine.
Foundation type: Independent foundation.
Financial data (yr. ended 12/31/13): Assets, $1,157,184 (M); gifts received, $1,700,000; expenditures, $1,985,000; qualifying distributions, $1,985,000; giving activities include $1,985,000 for 198 grants (high: $15,000; low: $10,000).
Fields of interest: Health care; Human services.
Limitations: Applications not accepted.
Application information: Unsolicited requests for funds not accepted.
Officers: Gary D. Radine, Pres.; Charles Lamont, Esq., Secy.; Michael J. Castro, Treas.
Directors: Anthony S. Barth; John M. Yamamoto.
EIN: 371570764

459
Cecil B. DeMille Foundation ✧
223 W. Alameda Ave., Ste. 101
Burbank, CA 91502-2575 (818) 566-1801
Contact: Cecilia DeMille Presley, Mgr.
E-mail: entmaninc@aol.com

Established in 1991 in CA.
Foundation type: Independent foundation.
Financial data (yr. ended 12/31/13): Assets, $10,428,498 (M); expenditures, $1,225,545; qualifying distributions, $1,178,598; giving activities include $1,130,152 for 25 grants (high: $205,000; low: $50).
Purpose and activities: Giving primarily for higher education and to film organizations; funding also for children and social services.
Fields of interest: Media, film/video; Higher education; Animal welfare; Human services; Children/youth, services; Foundations (private grantmaking).
Limitations: Applications accepted. Giving primarily in CA. No grants to individuals.
Application information: Application form required.
Initial approach: Proposal
Deadline(s): None
Managers: Travers Boughdadly; Joseph W. Harper, Jr.; Jayne Pasco; Cecilia DeMille Presley.
EIN: 954268286

460
The Corwin D. Denney Foundation ✧
(formerly Denney Foundation)
111 W. Ocean Blvd., Ste. 1900
Long Beach, CA 90802-4648

Established in CA.
Donors: Corwin D. Denney; Nanci Denney Bergin.
Foundation type: Independent foundation.
Financial data (yr. ended 12/31/13): Assets, $7,562,480 (M); expenditures, $963,171; qualifying distributions, $510,763; giving activities include $474,650 for 48 grants (high: $200,000; low: $650).
Fields of interest: Higher education; Education; Hospitals (general).
Limitations: Applications not accepted. No grants to individuals.
Application information: Unsolicited requests for funds not accepted.
Officers: Nanci Denney Bergin, Pres.; L. Andrew Gifford, C.F.O. and Treas.; K. Duane Denney, V.P.; M. Lawrence Lallande, Secy. and Fdn. Mgr.
EIN: 237015087

461
Desert Valley Charitable Foundation ✧
(formerly Dr. Prem Reddy Charitable Foundation)
16850 Bear Valley Rd., Ste. 200
Victorville, CA 92395-5794
Contact: Jana Bullock
Scholarship address: 16716 Bear Valley Rd., Victorville, CA 92395-5797; tel.: (760) 241-8000

Established in CA. Classified as a private operating foundation in 1994.
Donors: Prem N. Reddy, M.D.; Val Armenti; Desert Valley Medical Group; Prime A Investments, LLC.
Foundation type: Operating foundation.
Financial data (yr. ended 12/31/13): Assets, $66,074,025 (M); gifts received, $5,008,560; expenditures, $5,943,359; qualifying distributions, $5,247,279; giving activities include $5,053,042 for 53 grants (high: $3,000,000; low: $100), and $93,167 for 57 grants to individuals (high: $5,000; low: $500).
Purpose and activities: Scholarships to residents of the High Desert, CA communities who are planning to enroll in an accredited program in health care or a medical-related field. Giving also for education, and for human services and youth services.
Fields of interest: Higher education; Education; Health organizations; Human services; Youth, services.
Type of support: Annual campaigns; Emergency funds; Scholarships—to individuals.
Limitations: Giving primarily in CA, with some emphasis on Victorville; giving limited to residents of the High Desert for scholarships.
Publications: Application guidelines; Financial statement; Informational brochure.
Application information: Application form required.
Initial approach: Letter requesting application form
Deadline(s): None for grants; July 15 for scholarships
Officers and Directors:* Prem Reddy, M.D.*, Pres.; Kavitha Reddy Bhatia, M.D.*, Secy. and C.F.O.; Sunitha Reddy.
EIN: 330486173

462
Carl & Roberta Deutsch Foundation ✧
2444 Wilshire Blvd., Ste. 600
Santa Monica, CA 90403-5814 (310) 453-0055
Contact: Janis Minton, Sr. Advisor; Michelle Francois, Prog. Off.

Established in 1997 in CA.
Donors: Carl Deutsch; Roberta Deutsch.
Foundation type: Independent foundation.
Financial data (yr. ended 12/31/12): Assets, $110,820,028 (M); expenditures, $6,187,311; qualifying distributions, $5,595,919; giving activities include $4,961,040 for 91 grants (high: $555,000; low: $900).
Purpose and activities: Giving primarily for human services, including basic needs, homelessness and foster youth; education, including arts education, early childhood education and college access; art programs, women's services, and health, including cancer research and alternative medicine.
Fields of interest: Arts; Higher education; Higher education, college; Education; Cancer research; Boy scouts; Human services; Infants/toddlers; Children/youth; Children; Youth; Women; Homeless.
Limitations: Applications not accepted. Giving primarily in CA. No grants to individuals.
Application information: Unsolicited requests for funds not accepted.
Officers: Carl Deutsch, Pres.; William E. Holler, V.P. and Secy.-Treas.
Number of staff: 2 full-time professional.
EIN: 954610378

463
Dhanam Foundation ✧
2200 Geng Rd., Ste. 100
Palo Alto, CA 94303-3358

Established in 2004 in NV.
Donors: Kavitark R. Shriram; Vidjealatchourny Shriram.
Foundation type: Independent foundation.
Financial data (yr. ended 12/31/12): Assets, $207,837,683 (M); gifts received, $41,749,650; expenditures, $10,254,362; qualifying distributions, $8,538,611; giving activities include $8,505,111 for 9 grants (high: $8,000,000; low: $5).
Purpose and activities: Giving primarily for education.
Fields of interest: Education, fund raising/fund distribution; Secondary school/education; Higher education; Children, services.
Limitations: Applications not accepted. Giving primarily in CA and PA. No grants to individuals.
Application information: Contributes only to pre-selected organizations.
Officers: Kavitark R. Shriram, Pres.; Harvey Armstrong, Secy.; Vidjealatchourny Shriram, Treas.
EIN: 201914298
Selected grants: The following grants are a representative sample of this grantmaker's funding activity:
$8,000,000 to Harris Charitable Fund Program, Jenkintown, PA, 2012. For general support.
$250,000 to Sapling Foundation, New York, NY, 2012. For general support.
$125,000 to Level Playing Field Institute, Oakland, CA, 2012. For general support.
$100,000 to Gooru, Palo Alto, CA, 2012. For general support.
$10,000 to Sacred Heart Community Service, San Jose, CA, 2012. For general support.
$10,000 to Second Harvest Food Bank of Santa Clara and San Mateo Counties, San Jose, CA, 2012. For general support.
$10,000 to SF-Marin Food Bank, San Francisco, CA, 2012. For general support.

464
The Dhont Family Foundation ✧
2700 N. Main St., Ste. 1100
Santa Ana, CA 92705-6680

Established in 1999 in CA.
Donor: Eveline Dhont Irrevocable Trust.
Foundation type: Independent foundation.
Financial data (yr. ended 12/31/13): Assets, $41,629,265 (M); expenditures, $2,381,066; qualifying distributions, $1,924,476; giving activities include $1,802,000 for 41 grants (high: $450,000; low: $1,000).
Fields of interest: Higher education; Education; Hospitals (general); Food banks; Human services; Children/youth, services.
Limitations: Applications not accepted. Giving primarily in CA. No grants to individuals.
Application information: Contributes only to pre-selected organizations.
Officers: Andre G. Dhont, Pres.; Robert E. Topp, C.F.O.; Denis Lesenne, Secy.
EIN: 330846817
Selected grants: The following grants are a representative sample of this grantmaker's funding activity:
$250,000 to Saint Jude Memorial Foundation, Fullerton, CA, 2011.
$200,000 to University of Southern California, Kenneth Norris Jr. Comprehensive Cancer Center, Los Angeles, CA, 2011.
$150,000 to Chapman University, Orange, CA, 2011.
$150,000 to Chapman University, Orange, CA, 2011.
$60,000 to Serve the People, Santa Ana, CA, 2011.
$50,000 to Cal State Fullerton Philanthropic Foundation, Fullerton, CA, 2011.
$50,000 to Fullerton Interfaith Emergency Service, Fullerton, CA, 2011.
$40,000 to Orangewood Childrens Foundation, Santa Ana, CA, 2011.
$40,000 to Orangewood Childrens Foundation, Santa Ana, CA, 2011.
$5,000 to Gary Center, La Habra, CA, 2011. For program services.

465
Chris Dialynas Family Foundation ✧
c/o Edmonds & Edmonds LLP
3300 Irvine Ave., Ste. 235
Newport Beach, CA 92660

Established in 1995 in CA.
Donors: Chris P. Dialynas; Sheri Horne Dialynas.
Foundation type: Independent foundation.
Financial data (yr. ended 10/31/13): Assets, $8,607,268 (M); expenditures, $889,663; qualifying distributions, $876,500; giving activities include $876,500 for 8 grants (high: $750,000; low: $1,000).
Purpose and activities: Giving primarily for higher education.
Fields of interest: Higher education; Hospitals (specialty); Human services.
Limitations: Applications not accepted. Giving primarily in CA and IL. No grants to individuals.
Application information: Contributes only to pre-selected organizations.
Officers: S.P. Dialynas, Pres.; Sheri Horne Dialynas, C.F.O. and Secy.
EIN: 330693259
Selected grants: The following grants are a representative sample of this grantmaker's funding activity:
$60,000 to Duke University, Durham, NC, 2011.
$60,000 to Princeton University, Princeton, NJ, 2011.

466
Donald C. & Elizabeth M. Dickinson Foundation ✧
P.O. Box 7078
Rancho Santa Fe, CA 92067-7078
Contact: Martin C. Dickinson, Pres.

Established in 1995 in CA.

Donor: Elizabeth M. Dickinson.
Foundation type: Independent foundation.
Financial data (yr. ended 12/31/13): Assets, $38,951,152 (M); expenditures, $2,870,708; qualifying distributions, $2,770,780; giving activities include $2,721,600 for 25 grants (high: $1,100,000; low: $12,500).
Purpose and activities: Giving primarily for education, health and human services; some giving also for museums.
Fields of interest: Museums (specialized); Arts; Nursing school/education; Education; Animals/wildlife, special services; Hospitals (specialty); Human services; Children/youth, services.
Limitations: Giving primarily in San Diego, CA, funding also in Oklahoma City, OK and Portland, OR.
Application information: Application form not required.
Initial approach: Letter
Deadline(s): Oct. 31
Officers: Martin C. Dickinson, Pres.; Donald Smoyer, V.P.; Barry C. Fitzpatrick, Secy.; Rebecca Welch, Treas.
Director: Kristopher Dickinson.
Board Member: John Seiber.
EIN: 330653203

467
The Walt Disney Company Foundation ✧
500 S. Buena Vista St.
Burbank, CA 91521-6444
Main URL: http://corporate.disney.go.com/responsibility/index.html

Incorporated in 1951 in CA.
Donor: The Walt Disney Co.
Foundation type: Company-sponsored foundation.
Financial data (yr. ended 09/29/12): Assets, $2,683,614 (M); expenditures, $4,856,807; qualifying distributions, $4,622,475; giving activities include $1,928,500 for 6 grants (high: $985,000; low: $1,098), and $2,693,975 for 1,132 employee matching gifts.
Purpose and activities: The foundation supports organizations involved with arts and culture, education, the environment, and programs involved with the health and well-being of children and youth.
Fields of interest: Media/communications; Media, film/video; Media, television; Arts; Scholarships/financial aid; Education; Environment, land resources; Environment; Health care, clinics/centers; Health care; Children/youth, services.
Type of support: General/operating support; Continuing support; Annual campaigns; Capital campaigns; Program development; Scholarship funds; Employee matching gifts; Employee-related scholarships.
Limitations: Applications not accepted. Giving primarily in CA, DC, FL, NJ, and NY. No support for public agencies or tax-supported organizations.
Application information: Contributes only to pre-selected organizations.
Officers: Robert A. Iger, Pres.; Jay Rasulo, Sr. Exec. V.P.; Leslie Goodman, Sr. V.P.; Kevin Callahan, V.P.; Marsha L. Reed, Secy.; Christine M. McCarthy, Treas.
EIN: 956037079

468
The Walt and Lilly Disney Foundation ✧
(formerly The Lillian B. Disney Foundation)
P.O. Box 2566
San Anselmo, CA 94979-2566

Established in 1974 in CA.
Donor: Lillian B. Disney†.
Foundation type: Independent foundation.
Financial data (yr. ended 12/31/13): Assets, $174,193,063 (M); expenditures, $11,900,659; qualifying distributions, $10,356,926; giving activities include $10,346,571 for 7 grants (high: $8,719,071; low: $10,000).
Purpose and activities: Giving primarily for the arts, education and human services.
Fields of interest: Arts; Education; Human services.
Type of support: General/operating support.
Limitations: Applications not accepted. Giving primarily in CA. No grants to individuals.
Application information: Contributes only to pre-selected organizations.
Board meeting date(s): Annually
Officers: Walter E.D. Miller, Pres.; Christopher D. Miller, V.P.; Ronald W. Miller, Sr., V.P. and Secy.-Treas.
EIN: 237425637
Selected grants: The following grants are a representative sample of this grantmaker's funding activity:
$8,809,871 to Walt Disney Family Museum, San Francisco, CA, 2012. For arts programming.
$1,000,000 to Los Angeles Philharmonic, Los Angeles, CA, 2012. For endowment.
$735,000 to Walt Disney Family Foundation, San Francisco, CA, 2012. For arts education programs.
$250,000 to Los Angeles Philharmonic, Los Angeles, CA, 2012. For program support.
$100,000 to Research to Prevent Blindness, New York, NY, 2012. For research on amblyopia.
$100,000 to Walt Disney Magnet School, Chicago, IL, 2012. For arts education classes.
$16,000 to University Press of Mississippi, Jackson, MS, 2012. For general support.
$10,000 to John Tracy Clinic, Los Angeles, CA, 2012. For program support.
$10,000 to Walt Disney Elementary School, Levittown, PA, 2012. For program support.

469
DJ & T Foundation ✧
200 N. Larchmont Blvd., No. 3
Los Angeles, CA 90004-3707 (323) 465-9955
Contact: William Prappas
FAX: (323) 446-7187; Main URL: http://www.djtfoundation.org

Established in 1995 in CA.
Donors: Robert W. "Bob" Barker; Nanci's Animal Rights Foundation, Inc.
Foundation type: Independent foundation.
Financial data (yr. ended 05/31/14): Assets, $1,429,191 (M); gifts received, $3,504,406; expenditures, $4,785,684; qualifying distributions, $4,785,684; giving activities include $4,638,935 for 1,342 grants (high: $500,000; low: $25).
Purpose and activities: Giving only to free or low cost spay/neuter clinics or spay/neuter voucher programs for companion dogs.
Fields of interest: Animal population control.
Type of support: General/operating support; Continuing support; Capital campaigns; Building/renovation; Equipment.
Limitations: Applications accepted. Giving on a national basis. No grants to individuals.
Application information: Application form required.
Initial approach: Proposal
Deadline(s): None
Board meeting date(s): As needed
Final notification: Within 6 months of receipt of a complete proposal
Officers: Robert W. "Bob" Barker, Pres.; Kent T. Valandra, Secy.; Robert Louis Valandra, C.F.O.
Number of staff: 1 full-time support; 1 part-time support.
EIN: 954499239
Selected grants: The following grants are a representative sample of this grantmaker's funding activity:
$1,000,000 to Chimp Haven, Keithville, LA, 2013.
$500,000 to Association for Parrot C.A.R.E., Frazier Park, CA, 2013.
$250,000 to American Bird Conservancy, The Plains, VA, 2013.
$250,000 to Animal Defenders International US, Los Angeles, CA, 2013.
$250,000 to Jungle Friends Primate Sanctuary, Gainesville, FL, 2013.
$250,000 to Lifesavers, Lancaster, CA, 2013.
$250,000 to Wildlife Rescue and Rehabilitation, Kendalia, TX, 2013.
$210,000 to Association for Parrot C.A.R.E., Frazier Park, CA, 2013.
$178,500 to Feathered Friends Forever Rescue/Refuge, Harlem, GA, 2013.
$2,572 to Humane Society of Putnam County, Cookeville, TN, 2013. For spaying and neutering domestic animals.

470
The DMK Foundation ✧
P.O. Box 24950
Los Angeles, CA 90024-0950

Established in 2002 in CA.
Donors: David E. Kelley; Michelle Kelley.
Foundation type: Independent foundation.
Financial data (yr. ended 12/31/13): Assets, $10,798,565 (M); gifts received, $998,223; expenditures, $2,253,708; qualifying distributions, $2,089,987; giving activities include $2,076,567 for 14 grants (high: $1,666,667; low: $100).
Fields of interest: Education; Human services; Children/youth, services; Foundations (community).
Limitations: Applications not accepted. Giving primarily in CA. No grants to individuals.
Application information: Contributes only to pre-selected organizations.
Trustees: David E. Kelley; Michelle Kelley.
EIN: 611438237
Selected grants: The following grants are a representative sample of this grantmaker's funding activity:
$15,000 to Cedars-Sinai Medical Center, Los Angeles, CA, 2012. For Delivering Quality Healthcare Services.
$10,000 to L.A. GOAL, Culver City, CA, 2012. For Opportunities for Adults with Developmental Disabilities To.
$10,000 to Vista Center for the Blind and Visually Impaired, Palo Alto, CA, 2012. To Enable Individuals Who Are Visually Impaired to Achieve Their Highest Potential.

471
The Doctors Company Foundation ✧
185 Greenwood Rd.
Napa, CA 94558-6270 (707) 226-0373
Contact: Leona Egeland Rice, Exec. Dir.
FAX: (707) 226-0153;
E-mail: apply@tdcfoundation.com; Main URL: http://www.tdcfoundation.com
Grants List: http://www.tdcfoundation.com/Grants/index.htm

Established in 2007 in CA.
Donor: The Doctors Co.
Foundation type: Company-sponsored foundation.
Financial data (yr. ended 12/31/13): Assets, $1,188,167 (M); expenditures, $486,353; qualifying distributions, $484,949; giving activities include $453,332 for 8 grants (high: $148,189; low: $10,000), and $25,000 for 5 grants to individuals (high: $5,000; low: $5,000).
Purpose and activities: The foundation supports programs designed to advance and protect the practice of good medicine. Special emphasis is directed toward patient safety research, forums, and pilot programs; patient safety education; and medical liability research.
Fields of interest: Health care, clinics/centers; Health care, patient services; Health care; Medical research.
Type of support: Continuing support; General/operating support; Program development; Conferences/seminars; Sponsorships; Grants to individuals.
Limitations: Applications accepted. Giving primarily in CA, IL, MA, OH, OR, VA, and WA. No grants for clinical research projects involving clinical or medical support services to patients, construction projects, equipment, or general funding for medical meetings or conferences.
Publications: Application guidelines; Grants list.
Application information: Additional information may be requested at a later date. Organizations receiving support are asked to submit a final report. Application form required.
Initial approach: Download application form and mail to foundation
Deadline(s): Apr. 1 and Nov. 1
Final notification: May and Dec.
Officers and Directors:* David B. Troxel, M.D., Chair.; Robert D. Francis, Vice-Chair.; David G. Preimesberger,* Secy.-Treas.; Leona Egeland Rice, Exec. Dir.; Richard E. Anderson, M.D.; James P. Bagian, M.D.; Robin Diamond; Charles R. Kossman, M.D.; Donald J. Palisano, M.D.; Mary Ann Thode.
EIN: 261636256
Selected grants: The following grants are a representative sample of this grantmaker's funding activity:
$106,032 to Cleveland Clinic Foundation, Cleveland, OH, 2012. For Second of Three Installments for Heart Care at Home.
$99,400 to Washington Hospital Center Foundation, Washington, DC, 2012. For grant for the 2013 Telluride Educational Roundtable.
$50,000 to American College of Physicians, Philadelphia, PA, 2012. For grant Prioritizing Patient Safety - Bringing the Near Miss Registry to Private Practice.
$40,000 to San Diego County Medical Society, San Diego, CA, 2012. For Project Access San Diego - to Deliver Free Healthcare Services to Patients in Need.
$32,326 to Society of Hospital Medicine, Philadelphia, PA, 2012. For Training for Hospitalist Physician Mentors As Part of Their Mentored Implementation Program.
$25,000 to National Patient Safety Foundation, North Adams, MA, 2012. For the Annual Lucian Leape Town Hall Plenary Session at the National Patient Safety Foundation Congress.
$15,072 to University of Hawaii Foundation, Honolulu, HI, 2012. For grant to Support 2nd Cross-Cultural Health Care Conference: Collaborative and Multi-Disciplinary Interventions.
$5,000 to Scripps Health Foundation, San Diego, CA, 2012. For Annual Support of the Quality Summit on Patient-Centered Care.

472
Thelma Doelger Charitable Trust ✧
950 John Daly Blvd., Ste. 300
Daly City, CA 94015-3004 (650) 755-2333
Contact: D. Eugene Richard, Tr.

Established in 1995 in CA.
Foundation type: Independent foundation.
Financial data (yr. ended 06/30/13): Assets, $13,915,125 (M); expenditures, $699,404; qualifying distributions, $500,750; giving activities include $500,750 for grants.
Purpose and activities: Giving primarily for animal welfare, social services, a medical center, and children and youth services.
Fields of interest: Museums; Higher education; Animal welfare; Zoos/zoological societies; Hospitals (general); Boys & girls clubs; Human services; Children/youth, services; Aging, centers/services.
Limitations: Applications accepted. Giving limited to CA. No grants to individuals.
Application information: Application form required.
Initial approach: Letter or telephone requesting application form
Deadline(s): None
Trustees: Howard E. Mason, Jr.; John F. Nicolai; D. Eugene Richard; John R. Violet.
EIN: 943318483
Selected grants: The following grants are a representative sample of this grantmaker's funding activity:
$75,000 to Seton Medical Center, Daly City, CA, 2011.
$50,000 to Humane Society, Marin, Novato, CA, 2011.
$50,000 to Supporters of Doelger Senior Center, Daly City, CA, 2011.
$30,000 to San Francisco Zoological Society, San Francisco, CA, 2011.
$25,000 to CuriOdyssey, San Mateo, CA, 2011.
$10,000 to Boys and Girls Club, Mid-Peninsula, San Mateo, CA, 2011.
$7,500 to Daly City Youth Health Center, Daly City, CA, 2011.
$5,000 to Meals on Wheels of San Francisco, San Francisco, CA, 2011.
$5,000 to San Francisco Suicide Prevention, San Francisco, CA, 2011.
$5,000 to YMCA of San Francisco, San Francisco, CA, 2011.

473
Carrie Estelle Doheny Foundation ✧
707 Wilshire Blvd., Ste. 4960
Los Angeles, CA 90017-9843
Contact: Nina S. Shepherd, Secy.-Treas., C.F.O., and C.A.O.
FAX: (213) 488-1544;
E-mail: doheny@dohenyfoundation.org; Additional e-mail: peggy@dohenyfoundation.org; Main URL: http://www.dohenyfoundation.org
Grants List: http://www.dohenyfoundation.org/grants/current-awards/

Established in 1949 in CA as a Trust; reorganized in 2006 as a non-profit corporation.
Donor: Mrs. Edward L. Doheny†.
Foundation type: Independent foundation.
Financial data (yr. ended 12/31/12): Assets, $168,882,603 (M); expenditures, $10,508,897; qualifying distributions, $8,471,266; giving activities include $7,740,412 for 273 grants (high: $500,000; low: $3,000).
Purpose and activities: The foundation was established for the advancement of education, medicine, religion, science; the improvement of the health and welfare of infants, children, adults, families, and the aged; the help and care of the sick, aged, and incapacitated; and the aid of those in need.
Fields of interest: Elementary/secondary education; Higher education; Hospitals (general); Eye diseases; Eye research; Housing/shelter, temporary shelter; Housing/shelter, homeless; Boys & girls clubs; Children/youth, services; Family services; Aging, centers/services; Voluntarism promotion; Catholic agencies & churches; Religion.
Type of support: General/operating support; Continuing support; Capital campaigns; Building/renovation; Equipment; Program development; Matching/challenge support.
Limitations: Applications accepted. Giving primarily in the Los Angeles, CA, area. No support for tax-supported organizations, radio or television programs, or for political purposes. No grants or scholarships to individuals; no for endowment funds, publications, travel, or advertising.
Publications: Application guidelines; Biennial report; Financial statement; Grants list.
Application information: The foundation considers grant applications in written form and electronically. Application form required.
Initial approach: Review foundation web site for guidelines and application form and then telephone foundation, if necessary
Copies of proposal: 1
Deadline(s): None
Board meeting date(s): Monthly
Final notification: 2 to 3 months
Officers and Directors:* Robert A. Smith III,* Pres.; Austin F. Gavin,* V.P.; Nina S. Shepherd, Secy.-Treas., C.F.O., and C.A.O.; H. Thomas Boyle; Michael S. Feeley; George Gibbs; Joseph Nally; Rev. William Piletic, C.M.; Mrs. Terry Seidler.
Number of staff: 4 full-time professional.
EIN: 956202911

474
Ray and Dagmar Dolby Family Fund ✧
(formerly Dolby Family Foundation)
3340 Jackson St.
San Francisco, CA 94118-2019 (415) 563-7403
Contact: Dagmar Dolby, Secy.-Treas.

Established in 2002 in CA.
Donors: Ray M. Dolby†; Dagmar Dolby.
Foundation type: Independent foundation.
Financial data (yr. ended 12/31/13): Assets, $139,167,419 (M); gifts received, $9,000,000; expenditures, $3,770,977; qualifying distributions, $3,440,785; giving activities include $3,329,160 for 83 grants (high: $1,042,685; low: $250), and $100,000 for 1 loan/program-related investment.
Fields of interest: Museums; Performing arts, orchestras; Performing arts, opera; Higher education; Health organizations; Human services; Civil liberties, reproductive rights.
Type of support: Annual campaigns; Capital campaigns; Building/renovation.
Limitations: Applications not accepted. Giving primarily in San Francisco, CA. No support for religious organizations.
Application information: Unsolicited requests for funds not accepted.
Board meeting date(s): Oct.
Officers: Ray M. Dolby, Pres.; Dagmar Dolby, Secy.-Treas.
EIN: 912159332
Selected grants: The following grants are a representative sample of this grantmaker's funding activity:
$12,237,000 to University of California San Francisco Foundation, San Francisco, CA, 2011. For Regeneration Medicine Building.

475
Dougherty Family Foundation ✧
5380 Arezzo Dr.
San Jose, CA 95138-2201

Established in 2001 in CA.
Donors: Gregory Dougherty; Nancy Dougherty.
Foundation type: Independent foundation.
Financial data (yr. ended 09/30/13): Assets, $10,348,608 (M); expenditures, $623,466; qualifying distributions, $596,840; giving activities include $596,000 for 5 grants (high: $271,000; low: $25,000).
Purpose and activities: Giving primarily for education, and children and youth services, including children's hospitals.
Fields of interest: Higher education; Hospitals (specialty); Children/youth, services.
Limitations: Applications not accepted. Giving primarily in CA. No grants to individuals.
Application information: Contributes only to pre-selected organizations.
Officers: Gregory Dougherty, Chair.; Nancy Dougherty, C.F.O. and Secy.
EIN: 912169485
Selected grants: The following grants are a representative sample of this grantmaker's funding activity:
$205,400 to Lucile Packard Foundation for Childrens Health, Palo Alto, CA, 2011.
$200,000 to University of California San Francisco Foundation, San Francisco, CA, 2011.
$80,000 to Childrens Hospital Los Angeles, Los Angeles, CA, 2011.
$50,000 to Make-A-Wish Foundation, Greater Bay Area, San Francisco, CA, 2011.
$50,000 to Ronald McDonald House at Stanford, Palo Alto, CA, 2011.
$10,000 to Kenyon College, Gambier, OH, 2011.

476
Douglas Foundation ✧
(formerly Douglas Charitable Foundation)
141 El Camino Dr., Ste. 209
Beverly Hills, CA 90212-2718 (310) 274-5294
FAX: (310) 274-2537;
E-mail: info@douglasfoundation.org; Address for Letters of Inquiry: P.O. Box 50709, Santa Barbara, CA 93150, tel.: (805) 565-7700; Main URL: http://douglasfoundation.org/

Established in 1964 in CA.
Donors: Kirk Douglas; Anne Douglas; Pepsico, Inc.; Pacific Vascular Research Foundation; AARP.
Foundation type: Independent foundation.
Financial data (yr. ended 12/31/13): Assets, $22,876,979 (M); gifts received, $500; expenditures, $2,306,471; qualifying distributions, $2,202,750; giving activities include $2,006,590 for 63 grants (high: $500,000; low: $200).
Purpose and activities: Giving primarily for improving the education and health, fostering the well-being, and developing new opportunities for children. Support also to medical research, equipment, and programs within the health system that strive to enhance the quality of care in local communities.
Fields of interest: Performing arts; Performing arts, theater; Arts; Higher education; Education; Hospitals (general); Health care; Medical research, institute; Human services; Women, centers/services; Jewish agencies & synagogues; Children.
Type of support: General/operating support.
Limitations: Giving primarily in CA, with emphasis on the Southern CA counties of: Los Angeles, Santa Barbara and Ventura. No support for political organizations. No grants to individuals, or for emergency funding, conferences, workshops, exhibits, travel, surveys, films or publishing.
Application information: Formal applications are by invitation only, after review of letter of inquiry. Faxed or e-mailed material is not accepted. See foundation web site for application procedure.
Initial approach: Letter of inquiry via U.S. mail only
Deadline(s): None
Officer and Trustees:* Peter Douglas,* Pres.; Anne Douglas; Kirk Douglas; Anita May Rosenstein; Fayez Sarofim.
EIN: 956096827
Selected grants: The following grants are a representative sample of this grantmaker's funding activity:
$200,000 to Saint Lawrence University, Canton, NY, 2010.
$100,000 to Center Theatre Group of Los Angeles, Los Angeles, CA, 2010.
$100,000 to Motion Picture and Television Fund, Woodland Hills, CA, 2010.
$100,000 to Sinai Temple, Champaign, IL, 2010.
$10,000 to University of California, Santa Barbara, CA, 2011.
$1,000 to American Cancer Society, Atlanta, GA, 2011.
$1,000 to American Heart Association, Dallas, TX, 2011.
$1,000 to Elizabeth Glaser Pediatric AIDS Foundation, Washington, DC, 2011.
$1,000 to Special Olympics, Washington, DC, 2011.

477
The James E. Downey Foundation ✧
23 Brookline
Aliso Viejo, CA 92656-1461 (949) 474-0900
Contact: Karl Jonson, Secy. and C.F.O.

Established in 2005 in CA.
Donor: James E. Downey.
Foundation type: Independent foundation.
Financial data (yr. ended 06/30/13): Assets, $4,063,334 (M); gifts received, $84,863; expenditures, $559,774; qualifying distributions, $437,300; giving activities include $437,300 for 275 grants to individuals (high: $2,000; low: $1,500).
Purpose and activities: Giving for scholarship awards to single parents.
Fields of interest: Higher education.
Type of support: Scholarships—to individuals.
Limitations: Applications accepted. Giving primarily in CA.
Application information: Application form required.
Initial approach: Request application form
Deadline(s): Apr. 30 preceding the applicable school year
Officers and Directors: James E. Downey,* Pres.; Keith M. Downey,* V.P.; Karl Jonson,* C.F.O. and Secy.
EIN: 203510627

478
DPR Foundation ✧
1450 Veterans Blvd.
Redwood City, CA 94063-2617
E-mail: info@dprfoundation.org; Main URL: http://www.dprfoundation.org

Established in 2007 in CA.
Donor: DPR Construction, Inc.
Foundation type: Company-sponsored foundation.
Financial data (yr. ended 12/31/13): Assets, $3,543,757 (M); gifts received, $1,021,590; expenditures, $1,216,033; qualifying distributions, $1,211,463; giving activities include $1,125,900 for 21 grants (high: $162,500; low: $3,000).
Fields of interest: Human services; Community/economic development.
Limitations: Applications not accepted.
Application information: Unsolicited requests for funds not accepted.
Officers: Peter Nosier, Pres.; John M. Kramer, Secy.-Treas.
Directors: Gavin R. Keith; Jeff Vertuca.
EIN: 261609927
Selected grants: The following grants are a representative sample of this grantmaker's funding activity:
$120,000 to Seven Tepees Youth Program, San Francisco, CA, 2010.
$65,000 to Peninsula Bridge Program, Palo Alto, CA, 2011.
$65,000 to Peninsula Bridge Program, Palo Alto, CA, 2010.
$60,000 to Boys and Girls Club, John Avery, Durham, NC, 2010.
$60,000 to Latin American Youth Center, Washington, DC, 2010.
$55,000 to Boys and Girls Clubs of Metro Atlanta, Atlanta, GA, 2010.
$45,000 to Future for Kids, Scottsdale, AZ, 2010.
$40,000 to Roberts Family Development Center, Sacramento, CA, 2010.
$40,000 to VMC Foundation, San Jose, CA, 2010.

$35,000 to Milagro Center, Delray Beach, FL, 2010.
$35,000 to New Hope for Kids, Fern Park, FL, 2011.
$35,000 to New Hope for Kids, Fern Park, FL, 2010.

479
Dr. Bronners Family Foundation ✧ ☆
P.O. Box 1958
Vista, CA 92085
Main URL: http://www.drbronner.com/

Established in 2002 in CA.
Donor: All One God Faith, Inc.
Foundation type: Independent foundation.
Financial data (yr. ended 03/31/13): Assets, $106,670 (M); gifts received, $669,200; expenditures, $572,700; qualifying distributions, $572,825; giving activities include $572,700 for 27 grants (high: $100,000; low: $1,000).
Fields of interest: Students, sororities/fraternities; Education; Boys & girls clubs; Human services.
Limitations: Applications not accepted. Giving primarily in CA. No grants to individuals.
Application information: Contributes only to pre-selected organizations.
Officers and Directors:* Ralph Bronner,* Chair.; David Bronner,* Pres.; Michael Bronner,* V.P.; Trudy Bronner,* Secy. and C.F.O.
EIN: 431979565
Selected grants: The following grants are a representative sample of this grantmaker's funding activity:
$2,400 to Urban Ecology Center, Milwaukee, WI, 2011.

480
The Draper Foundation ✧
c/o Draper Fisher Jurvetson
2882 Sand Hill Rd., Ste. 150
Menlo Park, CA 94025-7057 (650) 233-9000
Contact: Tim C. Draper, Pres.
GiveSmart: http://www.givesmart.org/Stories/Donors/Bill-Draper

Established in 1996 in CA.
Donors: William Draper; Phyllis Draper; Tim C. Draper; Melissa Draper; Polly Draper.
Foundation type: Independent foundation.
Financial data (yr. ended 12/31/12): Assets, $27,119,909 (M); expenditures, $4,321,332; qualifying distributions, $4,321,332; giving activities include $4,293,461 for 59 grants (high: $500,000; low: $100).
Purpose and activities: Giving primarily for the arts, education, children and social services, and to Presbyterian churches.
Fields of interest: Arts; Education; Human services; Children, services; Foundations (private grantmaking); Protestant agencies & churches.
Limitations: Applications accepted. Giving primarily in CA.
Application information:
Initial approach: Proposal
Deadline(s): None
Officers: Tim C. Draper, Pres.; Rebecca Draper, Secy.; William Draper, C.F.O.
EIN: 943256415

481
The Draper Richards Kaplan Foundation ✧
(formerly The Draper Richards Foundation)
1600 El Camino Real, Ste. 155
Menlo Park, CA 94111-4779 (650) 319-7808
Contact: Jennifer Shilling Stein, Exec. Dir.; Anne Marie Burgoyne, Dir.; Christy Chin, Dir.; Breanna DiGiammarino, Assoc.
FAX: (650) 323-4060;
E-mail: info@draperrichards.org; MA address: 535 Boylston St., 7th Fl., Boston, MA 02116, tel.: (617) 830-7122; Application e-mail: proposals@draperrichards.org; Main URL: http://www.draperrichards.org/
GiveSmart: http://www.givesmart.org/Stories/Donors/Bill-Draper

Established in 2001 in CA.
Donors: William H. Draper III; Robin R. Donohoe; Robert S. Kaplan.
Foundation type: Operating foundation.
Financial data (yr. ended 12/31/12): Assets, $22,225,614 (M); gifts received, $6,085,792; expenditures, $3,658,984; qualifying distributions, $3,794,933; giving activities include $1,800,000 for 19 grants (high: $150,000; low: $50,000), and $3,544,933 for foundation-administered programs.
Purpose and activities: The foundation awards grants to entrepreneurial leaders at new nonprofits that seek to solve existing social problems in innovative ways at a large scale. The applicant must also be the organization's founder. Grants include seed funding of $100,000 annually for three years, advisory support in the form of a board seat, and access to a network of social entrepreneurs in the Draper Richards Kaplan Foundation portfolio. The foundation only awards six fellowships per year (less than 2 percent of grantees). The foundation selects proposals from a variety of public service areas, including but not limited to, education, youth and families, the environment, health, and community and economic development. The foundation does not fund organizations later in their lifecycle. The foundation does not fund organizations that are unable to scale their impact.
Fields of interest: Education; Environment; Health care; Crime/law enforcement; Employment; Housing/shelter; Youth development, adult & child programs; Youth development; Human services; International affairs, equal rights; International economic development; Civil/human rights; Economic development; Nonprofit management; Community/economic development; Philanthropy/voluntarism; Philanthropy/voluntarism; Public affairs.
Type of support: General/operating support; Management development/capacity building; Program development; Seed money; Fellowships; Technical assistance.
Limitations: Applications accepted. Giving to new high impact nonprofit organizations with headquarters in the U.S., and operations that are domestic or international. No support for faith-based models, single community-based models, lobbying or advocacy. No grants for research or scholarships.
Publications: Application guidelines.
Application information: Please see foundation web site for submission guidelines. Application form not required.
Initial approach: Brief proposal, no more than 3 pages
Deadline(s): None
Final notification: Acknowledgement of receipt within 14 business days
Officers: Robin R. Donohoe, Co-Chair.; William H. Draper III, Co-Chair.; Robert S. Kaplan, Co-Chair.; Cynthia Lam, C.F.O.; Jennifer Shilling Stein, Exec. Dir.
Directors: Anne Marie Burgoyne; Christy Remy Chin.
Number of staff: 4 full-time professional; 1 full-time support; 1 part-time support.
EIN: 912172351

482
Drew Family Foundation ✧
528 Ramona St.
Palo Alto, CA 94301-1709

Established in 2000 in CA.
Donors: John Drew; Ellen Drew.
Foundation type: Independent foundation.
Financial data (yr. ended 06/30/13): Assets, $8,715,977 (M); gifts received, $119,002; expenditures, $733,861; qualifying distributions, $677,000; giving activities include $677,000 for 16 grants (high: $250,000; low: $1,000).
Fields of interest: Elementary/secondary education; Higher education; Human services.
Limitations: Applications not accepted. Giving primarily in CA and VT. No grants to individuals.
Application information: Contributes only to pre-selected organizations.
Officers: Ellen Todd Drew, Pres.; John L. Drew, Secy.-Treas.
EIN: 770552387

483
Drollinger Family Charitable Foundation ✧
8929 S. Sepulveda Blvd., No. 130
Los Angeles, CA 90045-3616

Established in 2005 in CA.
Donor: Howard B. Drollinger†.
Foundation type: Independent foundation.
Financial data (yr. ended 12/31/13): Assets, $26,993,701 (M); expenditures, $1,423,893; qualifying distributions, $1,204,790; giving activities include $1,196,210 for grants.
Fields of interest: Education; Health organizations; Human services.
Limitations: Applications not accepted. Giving primarily in CA. No grants to individuals.
Application information: Contributes only to pre-selected organizations.
Trustees: Karen J. Dial; Kenneth P. Dial; Natalie J. Dial; Terry R. Dial; H. James Drollinger; Andrea Furtivo.
EIN: 206524261
Selected grants: The following grants are a representative sample of this grantmaker's funding activity:
$5,000 to Missoula Urban Demonstration Project, Missoula, MT, 2011.
$1,000 to American Cancer Society, Atlanta, GA, 2011.
$1,000 to American Cancer Society, Atlanta, GA, 2011.

484
Joseph Drown Foundation ✧
1999 Ave. of the Stars, Ste. 2330
Los Angeles, CA 90067-6043 (310) 277-4488
Contact: Wendy Wachtell, Pres.

FAX: (310) 277-4573; E-mail: staff@jdrown.org; Main URL: http://www.jdrown.org

Established in 1953 in CA.
Donor: Joseph W. Drown†.
Foundation type: Independent foundation.
Financial data (yr. ended 03/31/14): Assets, $86,183,728 (M); expenditures, $5,859,707; qualifying distributions, $4,771,381; giving activities include $4,267,260 for 146 grants (high: $100,000; low: $5,000).
Purpose and activities: Education is the primary focus of the foundation, and it supports education programs in K-12, at both public and private schools, that seek to solve the existing problems in Los Angeles, CA, area schools. Grants for education reform can be made directly to the schools or to independent organizations which are closely involved with this issue. In addition, the foundation provides funds to private secondary schools, colleges and universities for student financial assistance, in the form of both scholarships and loan programs. Favor is given to programs directed at talented middle income students who are unable to obtain assistance from sources specifically available to low income students. Committed to improving the quality of life in the local community, the foundation supports programs that encourage all individuals to reach their fullest potential. The foundation believes that the best chance a young person has to reach that goal is to stay in school, inside a functioning family, and outside the juvenile justice system. To that end, the foundation supports programs that deal with issues such as the high drop-out rate, lack of sufficient health care, substance abuse and violence. In addition, the foundation will consider programs that address poverty issues and assist the economically disadvantaged. Programs aimed at solutions to or the prevention of these problems are favored. Although it is not the emphasis of the foundation, grants are made for the arts and humanities and are made primarily for outreach and education programs. The foundation also makes grants for medical and scientific research, but these are initiated by the foundation.
Fields of interest: Humanities; Arts; Education, early childhood education; Elementary school/education; Education; Health care; Substance abuse, services; Medical research, institute; Crime/violence prevention, abuse prevention; Human services; Economically disadvantaged.
Type of support: General/operating support; Program development; Seed money; Scholarship funds; Matching/challenge support.
Limitations: Applications accepted. Giving primarily in Los Angeles County, CA. No support for religious purposes. No grants to individuals, or for endowments, multi-year grants, capital campaigns, building funds, tickets for fundraising events, seminars or conferences.
Publications: Application guidelines; Grants list; Informational brochure (including application guidelines).
Application information: Unsolicited applications are not accepted for medical and scientific research. Please do not send videos or materials that need to be returned. Application form not required.
Initial approach: Proposal and letter
Copies of proposal: 1
Deadline(s): Jan. 15, Apr. 15, July 15, and Oct. 15
Board meeting date(s): Mar., June, Sept., and Dec.
Final notification: Immediately after board meeting
Officers and Directors:* Norman C. Obrow,* Chair.; Wendy Wachtell,* Pres.; Elaine Mahoney,* V.P.; Thomas C. Marshall,* V.P.; Philip S. Magaram,* Secy.-Treas.; Ann T. Miller, C.F.O.
Number of staff: 3 full-time professional; 1 full-time support.
EIN: 956093178
Selected grants: The following grants are a representative sample of this grantmaker's funding activity:
$200,000 to Tower Cancer Research Foundation, Beverly Hills, CA, 2013. For Philomena McAndrew Breast Cancer Research Fund.
$50,000 to Inner-City Arts, Los Angeles, CA, 2013. For Learning and Achieving Through the Arts Program.
$50,000 to Johns Hopkins University, School of Education, Baltimore, MD, 2013. For Neuro-Education Initiative.
$50,000 to Junior Blind of America, Los Angeles, CA, 2013. For Infant and Early Childhood Program.
$50,000 to Los Angeles Leadership Academy, Los Angeles, CA, 2013. For College Counseling Program.
$50,000 to New Visions Foundation, Santa Monica, CA, 2013. For Fostering New Visions Program.
$50,000 to Operation Rainbow, Oakland, CA, 2013. For Medical Missions Program.
$50,000 to Simon Wiesenthal Center, Los Angeles, CA, 2013. For youth education and outreach Programs.
$25,000 to Common Sense Media, San Francisco, CA, 2013. For Digital Literacy and Citizenship Education Program.
$25,000 to Park Century School, Culver City, CA, 2013. For Student Financial Aid.

485
Ducommun & Gross Foundation ✧ ☆
P.O. Box 2172
Healdsburg, CA 95448-2172

Established in 1968 in CA.
Foundation type: Independent foundation.
Financial data (yr. ended 12/31/13): Assets, $7,826,707 (M); expenditures, $459,247; qualifying distributions, $426,493; giving activities include $422,500 for 26 grants (high: $175,000; low: $2,500).
Fields of interest: Media/communications; Arts; Secondary school/education; Higher education; Higher education, university; Education; Environment, land resources; Hospitals (general); Medical research.
Limitations: Applications not accepted. No grants to individuals.
Application information: Unsolicited requests for funds not accepted.
Board meeting date(s): Dec.
Officers: Robert E. Ducommun, Pres.; Electra Ducommun de Peyster, V.P.; Frederick A. Richmand, Secy.
Advisory Directors: Anthony C. Ward; Courtlandt D. Gross.
EIN: 956210834

486
The Duffield Family Foundation ✧
(doing business as Maddie's Fund)
2223 Santa Clara Ave., Ste. B
Alameda, CA 94501-4471 (510) 337-8989
Contact: Richard Avanzino, Pres.
FAX: (510) 337-8988;
E-mail: info@maddiesfund.org; Main URL: http://www.maddiesfund.org
Annual Report: http://www.maddiesfund.org/About_Us/Annual_Report.html
E-Newsletter: http://www.maddiesfund.org/enewsletter-archives.htm
Facebook: http://www.facebook.com/maddiesfund
Twitter: http://twitter.com/MaddiesFund
YouTube: http://www.youtube.com/maddiesfund

Established in 2000 in NV; merged with Maddie's Fund in 2008.
Donors: David A. Duffield; PeopleSoft and Workday.
Foundation type: Independent foundation.
Financial data (yr. ended 06/30/13): Assets, $279,543,666 (M); gifts received, $18,007,835; expenditures, $17,417,210; qualifying distributions, $12,589,895; giving activities include $10,290,419 for 120 grants (high: $2,239,119; low: $1,400).
Purpose and activities: Giving to create a no-kill nation where all healthy and treatable shelter dogs and cats are guaranteed a loving home. To achieve this goal, the foundation is investing its resources in: community collaborations where animal welfare organizations come together to develop successful models of lifesaving; veterinary colleges to help shelter medicine become part of the veterinary curriculum; private practice veterinarians to encourage greater participation in the animal welfare cause; and the implementation of national strategies to collect and report shelter statistics.
Fields of interest: Animals/wildlife, public policy; Animals/wildlife, reform; Animal welfare; Animal population control; Animals/wildlife.
Type of support: General/operating support.
Limitations: Applications accepted. Giving on a national basis. No grants to individuals, for scholarships or for capital building projects, shelter construction, projects for animals other than dogs and cats, land purchases, endowment campaigns, deficit or emergency funding, research, publications, films, videos, or special events.
Publications: Application guidelines; Annual report; Newsletter.
Application information: Applications are available on foundation web site. Do not send any additional materials with initial application unless requested by the fund. One proposal per group per year. Application form required.
Initial approach: Preliminary application for community collaborative project; pre-grant inquiry for starter grants; and letter of inquiry for veterinary school grants
Deadline(s): None
Final notification: 30-90 days
Officers and Directors:* Amy D. Zeifang,* Chair.; Richard Avanzino, Pres.; Mary Ippoliti Smith, V.P., Opers.; Lars Rabbe, C.I.O.; Cheryl D. Duffield; David A. Duffield; Michael D. Duffield.
EIN: 943362163
Selected grants: The following grants are a representative sample of this grantmaker's funding activity:
$2,239,119 to University of Florida, Office of Research and Graduate Programs, Gainesville, FL, 2013. For Shelter Medicine.

$1,086,200 to Erie County Society for the Prevention of Cruelty to Animals, Tonawanda, NY, 2013. For Adoptions.
$672,820 to John Burnam Monument Foundation, Plano, TX, 2013. For Operations.
$499,340 to Purdue University, Sponsored Program Services, West Lafayette, IN, 2013. For Shelter Medicine.
$475,042 to Cornell University, Ithaca, NY, 2013. For Shelter Medicine.
$470,000 to Humane Society, Oregon, Portland, OR, 2013. For Statistics Gathering, Adoptions and Operations.
$310,800 to San Francisco Society for the Prevention of Cruelty to Animals, San Francisco, CA, 2013. For Maddie's Treatable Assistance Program.
$257,689 to Humane Society of the United States, Washington, DC, 2013. For Ad Council Pet Adoption Campaign.
$180,000 to Humane Society for Southwest Washington, Vancouver, WA, 2013. For Statistics Gathering, Adoptions and Operations.
$27,500 to Purrfect Cat Rescue, Fremont, CA, 2013. For Maddie's Adoptathon.

487
The Durfee Foundation ✧
1453 3rd St., Ste. 312
Santa Monica, CA 90401-3430
Contact: Claire Peeps, Exec. Dir.
FAX: (310) 899-5121; E-mail: admin@durfee.org; Main URL: http://www.durfee.org
GiveSmart: http://www.givesmart.org/Stories/Donors/Carrie-Avery

Established in 1969 in CA.
Donor: BayTree Fund.
Foundation type: Independent foundation.
Financial data (yr. ended 12/31/12): Assets, $26,249,676 (M); gifts received, $97,298; expenditures, $2,005,192; qualifying distributions, $1,792,680; giving activities include $1,253,870 for 48 grants (high: $346,405; low: $250), $3,104 for 6 employee matching gifts, and $69,386 for foundation-administered programs.
Purpose and activities: The purpose of the foundation is to support creative individuals and community-based leadership.
Fields of interest: Arts.
Type of support: General/operating support; Grants to individuals.
Limitations: Applications accepted. Giving limited to Los Angeles, CA.
Publications: Application guidelines; Annual report; Financial statement; Informational brochure; IRS Form 990 or 990-PF printed copy available upon request.
Application information: Application form required.
Initial approach: Refer to foundation web site for specific instructions regarding each of the foundation's grant programs
Deadline(s): None
Board meeting date(s): 3 times annually
Final notification: 4 to 6 weeks
Officers and Trustees:* Judith Avery, Chair.; Caroline D. Avery,* Pres.; Michael A. Newkirk,* V.P.; Halina Avery,* Secy.; Jonathan Newkirk,* Treas.; Claire Peeps, Exec. Dir.
Number of staff: 2 full-time professional; 1 part-time professional; 2 part-time support.
EIN: 954856207

Selected grants: The following grants are a representative sample of this grantmaker's funding activity:
$346,405 to Center for Cultural Innovation, Los Angeles, CA, 2012. For artists resource completion.
$38,814 to Los Angeles Conservation Corps, Los Angeles, CA, 2012. For Stanton Fellowship.
$38,318 to Peace Over Violence, Los Angeles, CA, 2012. For Stanton Fellowship.
$25,000 to Food Forward, North Hollywood, CA, 2012. For Sabbatical Program.
$25,000 to GlobalGirl Media, Culver City, CA, 2012. For Springboard Grant.
$25,000 to Pasadena Arts Council, Pasadena, CA, 2012. For Springboard Grant - Libros Schmibros.
$20,000 to United States Artists, Los Angeles, CA, 2012. For artists resource completion Program.
$12,000 to Earthwatch Institute, Boston, MA, 2012. For outreach coordinator support.
$1,000 to Community Coalition, Los Angeles, CA, 2012. For Sabbatical Residency Program.
$1,000 to East Bay Community Law Center, Berkeley, CA, 2012. For matching gift.

488
Roy and Ida Eagle Foundation ✧ ☆
26750 Skyline Dr.
Tehachapi, CA 93561-9690
Contact: Sonya Schroeder, Exec. Dir.
E-mail: royandidaeaglefoundation@gmail.com; Tel./fax: (661) 821-1072; Main URL: http://royandidaeaglefoundation.org/

Established in CA.
Foundation type: Independent foundation.
Financial data (yr. ended 12/31/13): Assets, $16,145,370 (M); expenditures, $1,020,694; qualifying distributions, $787,965; giving activities include $676,725 for 31 grants (high: $80,000; low: $1,000).
Purpose and activities: Support for educational opportunities, abused women and children, violence prevention, health care services, critical needs, and animal protection and welfare.
Fields of interest: Animal welfare; Health organizations; Human services; Family services; Family services, domestic violence; Human services.
Limitations: Applications accepted. Giving primarily in Santa Barbara County, CA, with an emphasis on the North Santa Barbara County region.
Application information: Application form required.
Initial approach: See foundation web site for application form
Deadline(s): Sept. 15
Officer and Trustees:* Sonya Schroeder,* Exec. Dir.; Megan Melero; Mark Schroeder.
EIN: 262505029

489
The Margaret E. Early Medical Research Trust ✧
1055 W. 7th St., 29th Fl.
Los Angeles, CA 90017-2577

Established in 1982 in CA.
Foundation type: Independent foundation.
Financial data (yr. ended 12/31/13): Assets, $15,248,297 (M); expenditures, $1,129,966; qualifying distributions, $1,001,830; giving activities include $900,000 for 12 grants (high: $75,000; low: $75,000).
Purpose and activities: Giving primarily to institutions in the Los Angeles, CA, area, which have substantial research facilities for research into the causes and cures of cancer and related diseases.
Fields of interest: Higher education; Medical school/education; Cancer; Cancer research.
Type of support: Research.
Limitations: Applications not accepted. Giving limited to the greater Los Angeles, CA, area.
Application information: Unsolicited requests for funds not accepted.
Trustee: Eli B. Dubrow.
EIN: 953740506

490
The East Bay Community Foundation ✧
DeDomenico Bldg.
200 Frank H. Ogawa Plz.
Oakland, CA 94612-2005 (510) 836-3223
Contact: John Pachtner, Managing Dir., Comms.
FAX: (510) 836-7418;
E-mail: operations@eastbaycf.org; Main URL: http://www.ebcf.org
Facebook: https://www.facebook.com/Eastbaycf
Knowledge Center: http://www.ebcf.org/?option=com_content&task=view&id=374&Itemid=292
Philanthropy's Promise: http://www.ncrp.org/philanthropys-promise/who
YouTube: https://www.youtube.com/user/2011eastbay?feature=mhee

Established in 1928 in CA as The Alameda County Community Foundation by resolution and declaration of trust; revised in 1972 to include Contra Costa County.
Foundation type: Community foundation.
Financial data (yr. ended 06/30/14): Assets, $398,188,746 (M); gifts received, $138,348,697; expenditures, $43,585,347; giving activities include $38,521,288 for grants.
Purpose and activities: The foundation transforms lives by harnessing financial capital, leadership and philanthropic expertise through the power of many: partnerships with individual donors, business, government, and private foundations. The foundation is especially dedicated to advancing economic opportunity for those in need and the education that leads to it. The foundation manages more than 500 charitable funds and endowments.
Fields of interest: Arts; Education, early childhood education; Environment; Employment, training; Foundations (private grantmaking); Foundations (corporate); Foundations (community); Public policy, research; Public affairs, reform; Children; Minorities; Asians/Pacific Islanders; African Americans/Blacks; Hispanics/Latinos; Economically disadvantaged; LGBTQ.
Type of support: General/operating support; Continuing support; Management development/capacity building; Program development; Seed money; Research; Technical assistance; Program evaluation; Matching/challenge support.
Limitations: Applications accepted. Giving limited to Alameda and Contra Costa counties, CA. The giving of donors (those who hold charitable funds with the foundation) has no geographical limitations. No support for religious organizations for religious purposes. No grants to individuals directly, or for building and endowment funds, capital expenditures, annual fund appeals, existing

obligations, retroactive funding, deficit financing, fundraising events, and celebrations.
Publications: Financial statement; Grants list; Informational brochure; Multi-year report; Newsletter; Occasional report; Program policy statement.
Application information: For more information on the foundation's grantmaking visit the web site: www.ebcf.org.
Board meeting date(s): Board of Directors meet quarterly.
Officers and Trustees:* Sherry M. Hirota,* Chair.; Peter Garcia,* Vice-Chair.; Ingrid Lamirault,* Vice-Chair.; James W. Head, C.E.O. and Pres.; Edward Liebst, C.F.O.; Janet Y. Spears, C.O.O.; Timothy H. Smallsreed,* Secy.; Edward H. Harris, Cont.; Lois DeDomenico, Emeritus; Pamela Calloway, Consultant; Nathan Brostrom; Robert R. Davenport III; Gary Hall; Ken Kawaichi; Robert Kessler; Donald Reinke; Gwen Walden.
Number of staff: 24 full-time professional; 6 part-time professional.
EIN: 946070996
Selected grants: The following grants are a representative sample of this grantmaker's funding activity:
$4,058,642 to Safe Passages, Oakland, CA, 2012. For final disbursement to fund qualified grant expenses for activities required to complete Atlantic Philanthropies' Elev8 grant initiative.
$2,423,129 to Richmond Community Foundation, Richmond, CA, 2012. For general support.
$1,576,688 to Oakland Unified School District, Oakland, CA, 2012. For OUSD'S Health and Wellness Policy and Related Programs and School-Based Health Centers.
$1,400,000 to Doctors Medical Center, Modesto, CA, 2012. For West Contra Costa Health Care District Planning Initiative.
$600,000 to University of California San Francisco Foundation, San Francisco, CA, 2012. For Bridging the Gap Awards.
$400,000 to National Medical Fellowships, New York, NY, 2012. For NMF Alumni Capacity-Building Project.
$74,932 to Coastal Health Alliance, Point Reyes Station, CA, 2012. For Quality Improvement Initiative.
$7,203 to Crockett Community Foundation, Crockett, CA, 2012.
$5,000 to Boise State University Foundation, Boise, ID, 2012. For The Steve Appleton Fund.
$5,000 to Salvation Army of Santa Clara County, San Jose, CA, 2012. For general support.

491
East West Bank Foundation ✧ ☆
135 N. Los Robles Ave., 8th Fl.
Pasadena, CA 91101-1758

Established in CA.
Donor: East West Bank.
Foundation type: Independent foundation.
Financial data (yr. ended 12/31/13): Assets, $3,213,876 (M); gifts received, $4,286,786; expenditures, $1,072,910; qualifying distributions, $1,072,910; giving activities include $1,072,910 for 118 grants (high: $332,428; low: $50).
Fields of interest: Arts; Education; Human services.
Limitations: Applications not accepted.
Application information: Unsolicited requests for funds not accepted.
Officers and Directors:* Emily Wang,* Pres.; Sharon Cheung, C.F.O.; Douglas Krause,* Secy.; Julia Gouw.
EIN: 461648827

492
Easton Sports Development Foundation II ✧
7855 Haskell Ave., Rm. 350
Van Nuys, CA 91406-1936
Contact: Caren Sawyer, Treas.

Established in 2007 in CA.
Donor: James L. Easton.
Foundation type: Independent foundation.
Financial data (yr. ended 06/30/13): Assets, $48,253,170 (M); gifts received, $4,379,079; expenditures, $3,508,620; qualifying distributions, $3,314,701; giving activities include $3,141,263 for 194 grants (high: $388,000; low: $22).
Purpose and activities: Giving primarily to organizations and programs that support archery.
Fields of interest: Athletics/sports, training; Athletics/sports, school programs; Athletics/sports, academies; Recreation.
Limitations: Applications accepted. Giving in the U.S.
Application information: Application form required.
Initial approach: Request grant application
Deadline(s): Mar. 1 and Sept. 1
Officers and Directors:* James L. Easton,* Pres.; Gregory J. Easton,* V.P. and Secy.; Don Rabksa, V.P.; Caren Sawyer,* Treas. and C.F.O.
EIN: 205855118

493
eBay Foundation ✧
c/o Silicon Valley Community Foundation
2440 W. El Camino Real, No. 300
Mountain View, CA 94040-1498 (650) 450-5400
E-mail: ebayfoundation@ebay.com; Additional address: 2065 Hamilton Ave., San Jose, CA 95125; Main URL: http://www.ebayinc.com/profile/ebay_foundation

Established in 1998 in CA; supporting organization of the Community Foundation of Silicon Valley; changed to a private foundation in 2009.
Donor: eBay Inc.
Foundation type: Company-sponsored foundation.
Financial data (yr. ended 12/31/13): Assets, $30,067,443 (M); gifts received, $1,050,000; expenditures, $3,947,391; qualifying distributions, $4,242,878; giving activities include $3,495,103 for 7 grants (high: $3,150,000; low: $3,040).
Purpose and activities: The foundation supports programs designed to improve the economic and social well-being of local communities.
Fields of interest: Employment; Disasters, preparedness/services; Economic development; Business/industry; Social entrepreneurship; Microfinance/microlending; Community/economic development; Foundations (community); Economically disadvantaged.
Type of support: General/operating support; Emergency funds; Program development; Employee volunteer services.
Limitations: Applications not accepted. Giving on a national basis in areas of company operations, with emphasis on CA.
Application information: Unsolicited requests for funds not considered or acknowledged. The foundation awards grants to organizations recommended by employee GIVE Teams. Grants are administered by the Silicon Valley Community Foundation.
Officers and Directors:* Elizabeth Axelrod,* Chair.; Lauren Moore, Pres. and Exec. Dir.; Amyn Thawer, Secy.; Jennifer Ceran, C.F.O.; Bill Barmeier; Alan Marks.
EIN: 020605596

494
The Harold Edelstein Foundation ✧
100 W. Broadway, Ste. 600
Glendale, CA 91210-1211

Donors: Harold Edelstein Charitable Remainder Unitrust No. 2; H. Edelstein Administrative Trust.
Foundation type: Independent foundation.
Financial data (yr. ended 12/31/13): Assets, $15,511,967 (M); expenditures, $1,667,485; qualifying distributions, $1,467,831; giving activities include $1,273,846 for 33 grants (high: $162,081; low: $150).
Purpose and activities: Giving primarily to Jewish organizations, as well as for social services; funding also for children and youth services, particularly a children's hospital.
Fields of interest: Hospitals (specialty); Human services; Children/youth, services; Family services; Aging, centers/services; Jewish federated giving programs; Jewish agencies & synagogues.
Limitations: Applications not accepted. Giving primarily in CA, with emphasis on Los Angeles. No grants to individuals.
Application information: Contributes only to pre-selected organizations.
Directors: Marvin G. Burns; Susan Rothenberg; Frederick L. Simmons.
EIN: 954814292

495
Edgerton Foundation ✧
9454 Wilshire Blvd., 4th Fl.
Beverly Hills, CA 90212-2907

Successor foundation established in 2001 in CA, NV, WA.
Donor: W. Alton Jones Foundation.
Foundation type: Independent foundation.
Financial data (yr. ended 06/30/13): Assets, $101,900,889 (M); expenditures, $7,110,931; qualifying distributions, $5,264,969; giving activities include $4,995,236 for 59 grants (high: $2,659,000; low: $1,000).
Purpose and activities: Giving primarily for the arts, education and human services.
Fields of interest: Performing arts, theater; Arts; Education; Environment; Human services; Foundations (community).
Limitations: Applications not accepted. Giving in the U.S., with emphasis on Los Angeles, CA. No grants to individuals.
Application information: Contributes only to pre-selected organizations.
Officers: Bradford W. Edgerton, M.D., Pres.; Louise D. Edgerton, Secy.-Treas.
EIN: 912160742

496
Egg Foundation ✧
1 Letterman Dr., Bldg. D, Ste. DM700
San Francisco, CA 94129-1494

Established in 2006 in CA.
Donors: Cecily H. Cameron; Derek C. Schrier.
Foundation type: Independent foundation.
Financial data (yr. ended 12/31/12): Assets, $22,002,402 (M); gifts received, $1,005,100; expenditures, $765,222; qualifying distributions, $764,809; giving activities include $657,157 for 21 grants (high: $134,000; low: $2,500).
Fields of interest: International relief; International democracy & civil society development; Leadership development.
International interests: Africa.
Limitations: Applications not accepted. Giving primarily in CA. No grants to individuals.
Application information: Contributes only to pre-selected organizations.
Officers: Derek Schrier, C.E.O.; Cecily Cameron, C.F.O. and Secy.
Board Members: William Maniatis; Andreas Nicholas; Jay Owens.
EIN: 208090285

497
Joseph K. & Inez Eichenbaum Foundation ✧
(formerly J. K. & Inez Eichenbaum Foundation)
20501 Ventura Blvd., Ste. 325
Woodland Hills, CA 91364-6426 (310) 278-5222

Established in 1971.
Donors: J.K. Eichenbaum‡; Inez Eichenbaum.
Foundation type: Independent foundation.
Financial data (yr. ended 11/30/13): Assets, $10,270,075 (M); expenditures, $770,081; qualifying distributions, $511,948; giving activities include $486,372 for 66 grants (high: $101,000; low: $50).
Purpose and activities: Giving primarily for social services and Jewish organizations.
Fields of interest: Arts; Education; Animal welfare; Health organizations, association; Medical research, institute; Youth development, services; Human services; Children/youth, services; Family services; Jewish federated giving programs; Jewish agencies & synagogues.
Limitations: Applications accepted. Giving primarily in CA. No grants to individuals, or for prizes; no loans.
Application information: Application form required.
Initial approach: Letter
Deadline(s): None
Officers: Joann Berry, Pres.; Mark Comer, C.P.A., V.P. and Treas.
Directors: Anthony Boyar; Bram Goldsmith; Vicki Magasinn.
EIN: 956101264
Selected grants: The following grants are a representative sample of this grantmaker's funding activity:
$100,000 to Riverpark Center, Owensboro, KY, 2011.

498
Ben B. and Joyce E. Eisenberg Foundation ✧
12400 Wilshire Blvd., Ste. 1250
Los Angeles, CA 90025-1042

Established in 1986 in CA.
Foundation type: Independent foundation.
Financial data (yr. ended 05/31/13): Assets, $60,078,593 (M); expenditures, $4,212,641; qualifying distributions, $3,019,385; giving activities include $3,019,385 for 52 grants (high: $1,619,400; low: $100).
Fields of interest: Higher education; Hospitals (general); Health care; Health organizations, association; Medical research, institute; Cancer research; Government/public administration; Jewish agencies & synagogues.
International interests: Israel.
Type of support: Continuing support; Annual campaigns; Research.
Limitations: Applications not accepted. Giving primarily in the Los Angeles, CA, area.
Application information: Contributes only to pre-selected organizations.
Officers and Directors:* Joyce Eisenberg-Keefer,* Pres.; Richard A. Bender, Secy.-Treas.; Joyce Green; Richard Stern; Edna Weiss.
Number of staff: 3 full-time support.
EIN: 990246427
Selected grants: The following grants are a representative sample of this grantmaker's funding activity:
$244,200 to Guardians of the Jewish Home for the Aged, Los Angeles, CA, 2011. For program support.
$200,000 to American Committee for the Weizmann Institute of Science, Los Angeles, CA, 2011.
$50,000 to Anti-Defamation League of Bnai Brith, Los Angeles, CA, 2011. For program support.

499
The Eisner Foundation, Inc. ✧
9401 Wilshire Blvd., Ste. 735
Beverly Hills, CA 90212-2947 (310) 228-6808
Contact: Trent Stamp, Exec. Dir.
E-mail: info@eisnerfoundation.org; Main URL: http://www.eisnerfoundation.org
Blog: http://www.eisnerfoundation.org/?page_id=60
E-Newsletter: http://www.eisnerfoundation.org/?page_id=79
Grants List: http://www.eisnerfoundation.org/what_we_do/grantees.htm

Established in 1996 in CA.
Donors: Michael D. Eisner; Jane B. Eisner.
Foundation type: Independent foundation.
Financial data (yr. ended 12/31/12): Assets, $126,869,201 (M); expenditures, $9,476,428; qualifying distributions, $7,994,591; giving activities include $7,369,232 for 174 grants (high: $500,000; low: $150).
Purpose and activities: The foundation exists to provide access and opportunity for disadvantaged children and the aging of Los Angeles County, CA.
Fields of interest: Arts education; Elementary/secondary education; Health care; Crime/violence prevention, abuse prevention; Athletics/sports, school programs; Children/youth; Children; Aging; Young adults; Economically disadvantaged.
Type of support: General/operating support; Continuing support; Management development/capacity building; Capital campaigns; Building/renovation; Equipment; Program development; Seed money; Matching/challenge support.
Limitations: Applications accepted. Giving limited to Los Angeles County CA. No support for sectarian purposes. Generally, no grants to individuals, annual campaigns, existing obligations, re-granting programs, sponsoring conferences or special events.
Application information: Full applications will be accepted by request only following LOI. See foundation's web site for LOI instructions. Applications sent via fax or E-mail not accepted. Application form required.
Initial approach: Letter of inquiry (LOI) not to exceed 2 pages
Copies of proposal: 2
Board meeting date(s): Mar., June, Sept., and Dec.
Final notification: 2 to 4 weeks
Officers and Directors:* Jane B. Eisner,* Pres.; Michael B. Eisner,* V.P.; Anders D. Eisner,* Secy.; Eric D. Eisner,* C.F.O.; Trent Stamp, Exec. Dir.; Breck Eisner; Michael D. Eisner.
Number of staff: 3 full-time professional.
EIN: 954607191
Selected grants: The following grants are a representative sample of this grantmaker's funding activity:
$500,000 to Camino Nuevo Charter Academy, Los Angeles, CA, 2012.
$150,000 to Cedars-Sinai Medical Center, Los Angeles, CA, 2012.
$150,000 to Child Welfare Initiative, Los Angeles, CA, 2012. For General.
$150,000 to City Year Los Angeles, Los Angeles, CA, 2012. For General.
$150,000 to P.S. Arts, Venice, CA, 2012. For General.
$100,000 to GOALS, Anaheim, CA, 2012. For General.
$100,000 to Heart of Los Angeles Youth, Los Angeles, CA, 2012. For General.
$50,000 to Friends Around, Friendship Circle of Los Angeles, Los Angeles, CA, 2012. For General.
$25,000 to Los Angeles Philharmonic Association, Los Angeles, CA, 2012.
$10,000 to University of California at Irvine Foundation, Irvine, CA, 2012.

500
El Dorado Community Foundation ✧
312 Main St., Ste. 201
P.O. Box 1388
Placerville, CA 95667 (530) 622-5621
Contact: William Roby, Dir.; For grants: Marsha Repschlaeger, Acct.
FAX: (888) 404-6855; E-mail: pam@eldoradocf.org; Additional e-mail: megan@eldoradocf.org and bill@eldoradocf.org; For grant inquiries: marsha@eldoradocf.org; Main URL: http://www.eldoradocf.org

Established in 1990 in CA.
Foundation type: Community foundation.
Financial data (yr. ended 12/31/11): Assets, $9,024,270 (M); gifts received, $1,796,101; expenditures, $767,467; giving activities include $568,458 for grants.
Purpose and activities: The foundation is dedicated to strengthening the community both for now and for future generations.

Fields of interest: Humanities; Arts; Education; Environment; Animals/wildlife; Health care; Health organizations; Human services; Community/economic development; Infants/toddlers; Children/youth; Children; Youth; Aging; Young adults; Disabilities, people with; Physically disabled; Hispanics/Latinos; Girls; Adults, women; Adults, men; Immigrants/refugees; Economically disadvantaged; Homeless.
Type of support: General/operating support; Continuing support; Equipment; Endowments; Program development; Conferences/seminars; Publication; Seed money; Scholarship funds; Scholarships—to individuals.
Limitations: Applications accepted. Giving limited to El Dorado County, CA. No support for individuals, or for private charities or foundations, sports sponsorships, performing arts tours, association memberships, or religious activities. No grants for debt reduction, endowments, capital campaigns, or fundraising events.
Publications: Application guidelines; Annual report; Financial statement; Grants list; Informational brochure; Newsletter.
Application information: Visit foundation web site for application guidelines. Application form required.
Initial approach: Telephone
Copies of proposal: 6
Deadline(s): Varies
Board meeting date(s): Last Thurs. of each month
Officers and Directors:* John Black,* Pres.; Paul Zappettini,* V.P.; Charles Stephens,* Secy.; Chris Reeg,* Treas.; Mark Acri; Joyce Amlick; Shelbi Bennett; Ken Burkey; Maureen Carter; Karen Carter-Thomas; Judith Dillon; Charlie Downs; Georgianne Knight; Jeremy Meyers; Lois Patrick; Donald C. Peek.
Number of staff: 3 full-time professional; 1 part-time support.
EIN: 680255556

501
El Roi Foundation ✧
11 Cushing
Irvine, CA 92618-4232

Established in 2006 in CA.
Donors: Tim O'Neil; Sherry O'Neil.
Foundation type: Independent foundation.
Financial data (yr. ended 12/31/13): Assets, $16,442,426 (M); expenditures, $678,075; qualifying distributions, $632,610; giving activities include $627,000 for 6 grants (high: $198,000; low: $44,000).
Fields of interest: Human services; Christian agencies & churches; Protestant agencies & churches.
Limitations: Applications not accepted. Giving primarily in CA and PA; some funding also in NC.
Application information: Unsolicited requests for funds not accepted.
Officer: Sherry O'Neil, Pres.
Director: Tim O'Neil.
EIN: 203762869

502
Elbaz Family Foundation ✧
9663 Santa Monica Blvd., No. 425
Los Angeles, CA 90210-4303

Established in 2005 in CA.
Donors: Gilad Elbaz; Elyssa Elbaz.
Foundation type: Independent foundation.
Financial data (yr. ended 12/31/12): Assets, $26,176,993 (M); gifts received, $2,100,030; expenditures, $1,104,400; qualifying distributions, $1,058,540; giving activities include $1,058,540 for grants.
Fields of interest: Environment, water pollution; Environment, natural resources; Human services; Jewish agencies & synagogues.
Limitations: Applications not accepted. Giving primarily in CA. No grants to individuals.
Application information: Contributes only to pre-selected organizations.
Trustees: Elyssa Elbaz; Gilad Elbaz.
EIN: 206735811

503
Ellis Family Charitable Foundation ✧
5200 E. La Palma Ave.
Anaheim, CA 92807

Established in 2006 in CA.
Donors: Ellis Real Estate Holdings, LLC; Eco Duct, Inc.; Control Air Conditioning Corp.; Air Conditioning Control Systems, Inc; Control Air Services; Insulation Tech.
Foundation type: Company-sponsored foundation.
Financial data (yr. ended 12/31/13): Assets, $3,807,881 (M); gifts received, $953,063; expenditures, $1,100,640; qualifying distributions, $1,077,562; giving activities include $1,070,599 for 38 grants (high: $251,593; low: $100).
Purpose and activities: The foundation supports camps and ranches and organizations involved with substance abuse, youth development, youth, and Christianity.
Fields of interest: Arts; Education; Health care; Substance abuse, services; Recreation, camps; Athletics/sports, equestrianism; Youth development, business; Youth, services; Human services; Christian agencies & churches.
Type of support: General/operating support; Building/renovation; Program development; Publication.
Limitations: Applications accepted. Giving primarily in CA.
Application information: Application form required.
Initial approach: Letter
Deadline(s): None
Officers: Kendrick G. Ellis, C.E.O. and Pres.; Gregory S. Ellis, V.P.; Kenneth M. Ellis, V.P.; Stanley J. Ellis, V.P.; Greg S. Rummler, C.F.O. and Treas.; Jon S. Ellis, Secy.
EIN: 020788743
Selected grants: The following grants are a representative sample of this grantmaker's funding activity:
$60,000 to Calicinto Ranch, San Jacinto, CA, 2012. For funding for Church/Hospital Building Renovations.
$17,900 to Hoag Hospital Foundation, Newport Beach, CA, 2012. To Advance the Mission of Hoag Hospital Through Meaningful and Inspirational.
$3,500 to Autism Speaks, Los Angeles, CA, 2012. For Support/Research to Prevent Autism.
$1,250 to Leukemia & Lymphoma Society, Pittsfield, MA, 2012. For Cancer Centers and Individuals with Cancer.
$1,000 to Royal Family Kids Camp, Costa Mesa, CA, 2012. For a 1-Week Camp Experience for Abused Children.

504
The Lawrence Ellison Foundation
(formerly The Ellison Medical Foundation)
101 Ygnacio Valley Rd., Ste. 310
Walnut Creek, CA 94596-7018 (301) 829-6410
Contact: Kevin Lee Ph.D., Exec. Dir.
E-mail: klee@ellisonfoundation.org; Address for post-award financial reporting: 104 E. Ridgeville Blvd., Mount Airy, MD 21771-5260, tel.: (301) 829-6410, fax: (301) 829-6413; Main URL: http://www.ellisonfoundation.org
Lawrence J. Ellison's Giving Pledge Profile: http://glasspockets.org/philanthropy-in-focus/eye-on-the-giving-pledge/profiles/ellison

Established in 1997 in CA.
Donor: Lawrence J. Ellison.
Foundation type: Operating foundation.
Financial data (yr. ended 12/31/13): Assets, $0 (M); gifts received, $72,200,000; expenditures, $55,324,600; qualifying distributions, $55,869,021; giving activities include $24,511,435 for 33 grants (high: $19,622,190; low: $5,000), $29,326,363 for 180 grants to individuals (high: $292,500; low: $99,304), and $1,005,454 for 3 foundation-administered programs.
Purpose and activities: The foundation supports basic biomedical research on aging relevant to understanding lifespan development processes and age-related diseases and disabilities. The foundation particularly wishes to stimulate new, creative research that might not be funded by traditional sources or that is often under-funded in the U.S.
Fields of interest: Biomedicine; Biomedicine research; Science, research; Biology/life sciences; Gerontology.
Type of support: Conferences/seminars; Research; Grants to individuals.
Limitations: Applications accepted. Giving limited to U.S. institutions only. No support for commercial or for-profit organizations.
Publications: Informational brochure.
Application information: Applications for the Senior Scholar and New Scholar in Aging Awards are currently not being accepted. Any inquiries regarding support for research topics other than aging should be directed to the Exec. Dir. Application form required.
Copies of proposal: 1
Deadline(s): Feb. or early Mar.
Final notification: Late May for letter of intent decision, Aug. for awardees
Officers and Directors:* Lawrence J. Ellison,* Chair. and Pres.; Andrew L. Dudnick, Corp. Secy.; Philip B. Simon, C.F.O.; Kevin Lee, Ph.D., Exec. Dir.; Melanie Craft Ellison.
Scientific Advisory Board: George M. Martin, Chair.; Helen M. Blau, Ph.D.; Eric R. Kandel; Arnold J. Levine; Martin Raff, M.D.; Gary Ruvkun, Ph.D.; Gerald Weissmann.
Number of staff: 2 full-time professional; 3 full-time support; 1 part-time support.
EIN: 943269827
Selected grants: The following grants are a representative sample of this grantmaker's funding activity:
$4,000,000 to Reach to Teach, London, England, 2012. For general support.
$2,000,000 to Massachusetts Institute of Technology, Cambridge, MA, 2012. For research on cognitive neuroscience of autism and dyslexia.

$1,000,000 to Tom Lantos Foundation for Human Rights and Justice, Concord, NH, 2012. For endowment fund.
$951,300 to American Federation for Aging Research, New York, NY, 2012. For American Federation for Aging Research (AFAR) Senior Postdoctoral Research Program.
$907,500 to American Federation for Aging Research, New York, NY, 2012. For American Federation for Aging Research (AFAR)/Ellison Medical Foundation (EMF) Mid-Career Award.
$500,000 to Reach to Teach, London, England, 2012. For general support.
$302,500 to American Federation for Aging Research, New York, NY, 2012. For American Federation for Aging Research (AFAR)/Ellison Medical Foundation (EMF) Mid-Career Award.
$263,697 to Marine Biological Laboratory, Woods Hole, MA, 2012. For Biology of Aging course.
$57,000 to Life Sciences Research Foundation, Baltimore, MD, 2012. For Postdoctoral Fellowship.
$10,000 to International Mammalian Genome Society, Chapel Hill, NC, 2012. For Mouse Genetics Conference.

505
Emerson Family Foundation ✧ ☆
1522 Ensley Ave.
Los Angeles, CA 90024-5325

Established in 2005 in CA.
Donors: J. Steven Emerson; Rita Emerson.
Foundation type: Independent foundation.
Financial data (yr. ended 12/31/12): Assets, $5,272,015 (M); gifts received, $898,010; expenditures, $526,648; qualifying distributions, $514,710; giving activities include $514,710 for grants.
Fields of interest: Jewish federated giving programs.
Limitations: Applications not accepted. Giving primarily in CA. No grants to individuals.
Application information: Unsolicited requests for funds not accepted.
Officers and Directors:* J. Steven Emerson, Pres. and C.E.O.; David Dichner,* C.F.O.; Rita Emerson,* Secy.
EIN: 203997556

506
Engemann Family Foundation ✧
c/o Roger Engemann
1122 E. Green St.
Pasadena, CA 91106-2500

Established in 1998 in CA.
Donors: Roger Engemann; Michele Engemann.
Foundation type: Independent foundation.
Financial data (yr. ended 12/31/13): Assets, $2,268,774 (M); gifts received, $1,500,000; expenditures, $1,319,802; qualifying distributions, $1,314,445; giving activities include $1,314,445 for 24 grants (high: $1,000,000; low: $100).
Purpose and activities: Giving primarily for education, medical research, and human services.
Fields of interest: Arts; Higher education; Libraries (public); Education; Hospitals (general); Health organizations, association; Medical research, institute; Human services.
Limitations: Applications not accepted. Giving primarily in CA. No grants to individuals.
Application information: Contributes only to pre-selected organizations.
Directors: Michele Engemann; Roger Engemann.
EIN: 954677701
Selected grants: The following grants are a representative sample of this grantmaker's funding activity:
$1,500,000 to University of Southern California, Los Angeles, CA, 2011.
$100,000 to Scripps College, Claremont, CA, 2010.
$100,000 to University of Southern California, Los Angeles, CA, 2010.
$100,000 to University of Southern California, Los Angeles, CA, 2011.
$62,000 to Huntington Library, Art Collections and Botanical Gardens, San Marino, CA, 2010.
$55,000 to University of Southern California, Los Angeles, CA, 2010.
$50,000 to University of Southern California, Los Angeles, CA, 2010.
$50,000 to University of Southern California, Los Angeles, CA, 2011.
$42,000 to Scripps College, Claremont, CA, 2011.
$20,000 to University of Southern California, Los Angeles, CA, 2011.
$10,000 to University of Southern California, Los Angeles, CA, 2011.
$5,000 to University of Southern California, Los Angeles, CA, 2011.

507
Enlight Foundation ✧
954 Roble Ridge Rd.
Palo Alto, CA 94306-2609

Established in 2004 in CA.
Donor: Yong Ping Duan.
Foundation type: Independent foundation.
Financial data (yr. ended 12/31/13): Assets, $77,623,312 (M); expenditures, $2,511,699; qualifying distributions, $2,095,695; giving activities include $2,065,177 for 5 grants (high: $610,000; low: $5,000).
Fields of interest: Higher education; Human services.
Limitations: Applications not accepted. Giving in the U.S., with emphasis on CA and FL. No grants to individuals.
Application information: Contributes only to pre-selected organizations.
Officer and Directors:* Xin Liu,* Pres.; Yong Ping Duan.
EIN: 201063909
Selected grants: The following grants are a representative sample of this grantmaker's funding activity:
$610,000 to Robert F. Kennedy Center for Justice and Human Rights, Washington, DC, 2013.
$600,000 to Lucile Packard Foundation for Childrens Health, Palo Alto, CA, 2013.
$250,000 to Stanford University, Stanford, CA, 2013. For fellowships and scholarships.
$200,000 to FeelGood World, San Francisco, CA, 2013.
$151,000 to Creative Center of Los Altos, Pinewood School, Los Altos, CA, 2013.
$100,000 to Palo Alto Partners in Education, Palo Alto, CA, 2013.
$58,377 to University of Cincinnati, Cincinnati, OH, 2013. For fellowships and scholarships.
$10,000 to Give2Asia, San Francisco, CA, 2013.
$10,000 to Morrissey-Compton Educational Center, Palo Alto, CA, 2013.

508
Environment Now Foundation ✧
12400 Wilshire Blvd., Ste. 650
Santa Monica, CA 90025-1055 (310) 829-5568
Contact: Robert G. Wells
FAX: (310) 829-6820;
E-mail: rgwells@environmentnow.org; Main URL: http://www.environmentnow.org

Established in 1989 in CA.
Donors: Frank G. Wells†; Luanne C. Wells.
Foundation type: Independent foundation.
Financial data (yr. ended 12/31/12): Assets, $31,101,368 (M); expenditures, $2,064,269; qualifying distributions, $1,917,308; giving activities include $1,258,915 for 40 grants (high: $537,065; low: $250).
Purpose and activities: The foundation's mission is to be an active leader in creating measurably effective environmental programs to protect and restore California's environment. Focus is on preservation of coasts and forests, and on reduction of air pollution and urban sprawl. The foundation's ultimate goal is to restore the balance and health of California's ecosystems.
Fields of interest: Environment, natural resources.
International interests: Mexico.
Type of support: General/operating support; Program development; Seed money; Program-related investments/loans; Matching/challenge support; Mission-related investments/loans.
Limitations: Applications not accepted. Giving limited to CA, and Baja California, Mexico. No support for projects unrelated to the environment. No grants to individuals.
Publications: Annual report; Informational brochure; Occasional report.
Application information: Unsolicited requests for funds not accepted.
Officer: Robert G. Wells, Interim Exec. Dir.
Directors: Dan Emmett; Paul Heeschen; Mary Nichols; Kevin Wells; Luanne C. Wells; Robert G. Wells.
Number of staff: 2 full-time professional; 1 full-time support; 1 part-time support.
EIN: 954247242
Selected grants: The following grants are a representative sample of this grantmaker's funding activity:
$65,000 to California Coastkeeper Alliance, San Francisco, CA, 2012. For Clean Water, Healthy Seas Initiative.
$60,000 to Center for Biological Diversity, Tucson, AZ, 2012. For Forestry legal program support.
$55,000 to Natural Resources Defense Council, Santa Monica, CA, 2012. For Water use efficiency project.
$50,000 to Natural Resources Defense Council, San Francisco, CA, 2012. For California water project.
$40,000 to Center for Biological Diversity, San Francisco, CA, 2012. For California Water Program Support.
$30,000 to Environmental Defense Center, Santa Barbara, CA, 2012. For Purpose Oil field storm water litigation (30K reimbursed 6/14/2013).
$25,000 to Center for Biological Diversity, Tucson, AZ, 2012. For Biomass Project.
$10,000 to Earth Law Center, Fremont, CA, 2012. For Waterway Rights Campaign.
$10,000 to Ebbetts Pass Forest Watch, Arnold, CA, 2012. For Forest Watch.

$10,000 to Trees Foundation, Redway, CA, 2012. For Sierra Nevada forest protection.

509
Epstein Family Foundation ✧
3990 Ruffin Rd., Ste. 100
San Diego, CA 92123-4805

Established in 2005 in CA.
Donors: Daniel J. Epstein; Phyllis Epstein.
Foundation type: Independent foundation.
Financial data (yr. ended 12/31/13): Assets, $19,662,947 (M); gifts received, $3,309,966; expenditures, $1,103,400; qualifying distributions, $1,103,400; giving activities include $1,056,210 for 74 grants (high: $250,000; low: $100).
Fields of interest: Arts, multipurpose centers/ programs; Education; Health care.
Limitations: Applications not accepted. No grants to individuals.
Application information: Unsolicited requests for funds not accepted.
Officers: Daniel J. Epstein, Pres.; Julie Bronstein, C.F.O.; Phyllis Epstein, Secy.
EIN: 203905090

510
The Eucalyptus Foundation ✧
P.O. Box 29550
San Francisco, CA 94129-0550
E-mail: inbox@eucalyptusassoc.com

Established in 1991 in CA.
Donors: Frances K. Geballe; Theodore H. Geballe; Adam Geballe; Alison F. Geballe.
Foundation type: Independent foundation.
Financial data (yr. ended 06/30/13): Assets, $36,959,545 (M); gifts received, $500,044; expenditures, $3,763,524; qualifying distributions, $3,692,071; giving activities include $3,662,181 for 52 grants (high: $450,000; low: $500).
Purpose and activities: Giving primarily for community development and education.
Fields of interest: Arts; Education; Environment; Human services; Children/youth, services; Community development, neighborhood development; Children/youth; Economically disadvantaged.
Type of support: General/operating support; Continuing support; Annual campaigns; Capital campaigns; Building/renovation; Endowments; Professorships; Curriculum development; Fellowships; Scholarship funds; Research.
Limitations: Applications not accepted. No grants to individuals.
Application information: Contributes only to pre-selected organizations.
Board meeting date(s): Dec. and June
Officers and Directors:* Frances K. Geballe,* Pres.; Theodore H. Geballe,* V.P.; Stephen Schwarz, Secy.; Alison F. Geballe,* C.F.O.; Adam P. Geballe; Gordon T. Geballe.
EIN: 943148772
Selected grants: The following grants are a representative sample of this grantmaker's funding activity:
$300,000 to Exploratorium, San Francisco, CA, 2012. For capital campaign.
$200,000 to San Francisco Symphony, San Francisco, CA, 2012. For capital campaign.
$200,000 to Yale University, New Haven, CT, 2012. For scholarships.
$109,544 to Eastside College Preparatory School, East Palo Alto, CA, 2012. For physics program.
$100,000 to Save San Francisco Bay Association, Oakland, CA, 2012. For education initiatives.
$75,000 to American Jewish World Service, New York, NY, 2012. For general support.
$50,000 to American Physical Society, College Park, MD, 2012. For science education.
$20,000 to San Francisco Free Clinic, San Francisco, CA, 2012. For general support.

511
Eustace-Kwan Family Foundation ✧
205 Hanna Way
Menlo Park, CA 94025-3583

Established in 2005 in CA.
Donors: Robert A. Eustace; Kathy A. Kwan.
Foundation type: Independent foundation.
Financial data (yr. ended 09/30/13): Assets, $25,154,863 (M); gifts received, $2,739,240; expenditures, $2,924,973; qualifying distributions, $2,858,060; giving activities include $2,841,000 for 25 grants (high: $375,000; low: $18,000).
Fields of interest: Elementary/secondary education; Health organizations; Human services; Family services.
Limitations: Applications not accepted. Giving primarily in CA. No grants to individuals.
Application information: Unsolicited requests for funds not accepted.
Officers and Directors:* Kathy A. Kwan,* Pres.; Robert A. Eustace,* C.F.O. and Secy.
EIN: 202865402
Selected grants: The following grants are a representative sample of this grantmaker's funding activity:
$260,000 to University of Central Florida Research Foundation, Orlando, FL, 2011.
$125,000 to University of California at Berkeley Foundation, Berkeley, CA, 2011.
$80,000 to Redwood City School District, Redwood City, CA, 2011.
$75,000 to University of California San Francisco Foundation, San Francisco, CA, 2011.
$60,000 to Donaldina Cameron House, San Francisco, CA, 2011.
$60,000 to Girls Middle School, Palo Alto, CA, 2011. For scholarship fund.
$60,000 to Trust for Hidden Villa, Los Altos Hills, CA, 2011.
$50,000 to JobTrain, Menlo Park, CA, 2011.
$50,000 to Philanthropic Ventures Foundation, Oakland, CA, 2011. For general operating support.
$50,000 to Womens Initiative for Self Employment, San Francisco, CA, 2011.

512
Everlasting Private Foundation ✧
c/o Annie M.H. Chan
19620 Stevens Creek Blvd., Ste. 200
Cupertino, CA 95014-2456

Established in 1996 in CA.
Donor: Annie M.H. Chan.
Foundation type: Operating foundation.
Financial data (yr. ended 12/31/13): Assets, $16,668,200 (M); expenditures, $21,133,991; qualifying distributions, $20,859,576; giving activities include $20,210,405 for 5 grants (high: $20,184,405; low: $1,000), and $202,220 for 1 foundation-administered program.
Purpose and activities: Giving to foster Christian beliefs through the operation of a camp that focuses on religious/biblical education; giving also to a community foundation, a Baptist church and seminary, and for education.
Fields of interest: Education; Human services; Religion.
Limitations: Applications not accepted. Giving primarily in CA and HI. No grants to individuals.
Application information: Contributes only to pre-selected organizations.
Officers: Annie M.H. Chan, Pres.; Myong Shin Woo, Secy. and C.F.O.
Number of staff: 3 full-time professional; 2 part-time professional.
EIN: 770425562

513
Max Factor Family Foundation
6505 Wilshire Blvd., Ste. 1200
Los Angeles, CA 90048-4960 (323) 761-8700

Trust established in 1941 in CA.
Donor: Members of the Factor family.
Foundation type: Independent foundation.
Financial data (yr. ended 12/31/13): Assets, $12,757,925 (M); expenditures, $529,830; qualifying distributions, $521,209; giving activities include $512,500 for 24 grants (high: $225,000; low: $4,000).
Purpose and activities: The foundation primarily provides support to nonprofit organizations in the greater Los Angeles, CA area. The foundation's grant making focuses on programs and services, research and scholarships in the areas of health care, education, and environmental improvement and on their potential to impact youth, seniors and other vulnerable populations.
Fields of interest: Education; Environment; Health care; Human services.
Type of support: Building/renovation; Program development; Scholarship funds; Research.
Limitations: Applications accepted. Giving primarily in the greater Los Angeles, CA, area. No support for religious or political organizations, or for veterans' organizations (unless funds are being sought for the benefit of the whole community), local agencies which are part of national organizations receiving Max Factor Family Foundation contributions, local legal centers affiliated with national legal centers to which the foundation contributes, or municipal employee fraternal groups. In general, no funding for medical research that uses animals. No grants to individuals, or for advertising.
Application information: Organizations that are not previous grant recipients or referred by family members are invited to submit a Letter of Interest (LOI) - a brief, 1- to 2-page letter that describes the organization, proposed program and request. Completed LOIs will be reviewed and applicants are notified if a full application is desired by the foundation. All materials must be sent electronically. Hard copies are no longer accepted. Application form will be provided to screened applicants, if applicable. Telephone foundation for further information.
Initial approach: Telephone
Copies of proposal: 1

Deadline(s): Varies, to be detailed by program officer staff, if applicable
Board meeting date(s): Quarterly
Trustees: David Factor; Dean Factor; Jennifer Factor; Michael Firestein; Jonathan Glaser.
Number of staff: 3 part-time professional.
EIN: 956030779
Selected grants: The following grants are a representative sample of this grantmaker's funding activity:
$225,000 to Jewish Federation Council of Greater Los Angeles, Los Angeles, CA, 2012.
$25,000 to Alliance for Childrens Rights, Los Angeles, CA, 2012.
$20,000 to Advancement Project, Los Angeles, CA, 2012.
$20,000 to Bet Tzedek, Los Angeles, CA, 2012.
$20,000 to Cedars-Sinai Medical Center, Los Angeles, CA, 2012.
$15,000 to Community Partners, Los Angeles, CA, 2012.
$15,000 to Southern California Counseling Center, Los Angeles, CA, 2012.
$15,000 to TreePeople, Beverly Hills, CA, 2012.
$10,000 to Los Angeles Jewish Home for the Aging, Reseda, CA, 2012.
$5,000 to Food Forward, North Hollywood, CA, 2012.

514
Faith, Hope and Love Foundation ✧ ☆
5 Third St., Ste. 430
San Francisco, CA 94103-4509
Application address: c/o Cher Hsiueh Hong Wang, P.O. Box 15272, Warm Spring Station, Fremont, CA 94539, tel.: (415) 421-4343

Established in 2002 in CA.
Donors: Cher Hsiueh Hong Wang; Wen Chi Chen; Via Chip Technologies, Inc.
Foundation type: Independent foundation.
Financial data (yr. ended 12/31/13): Assets, $17,526,668 (M); gifts received, $2,450; expenditures, $4,365,990; qualifying distributions, $4,365,990; giving activities include $4,354,668 for 6 grants (high: $2,100,000; low: $4,668).
Fields of interest: Education; Religion.
Limitations: Applications accepted. Giving primarily in CA and MO. No grants to individuals.
Application information: Application form required.
Initial approach: Request application form
Deadline(s): None
Officers: Cher Hsiueh Hong Wang, C.E.O.; Timothy Chen, Secy.; Amy C. Wan, C.F.O.
EIN: 562302309

515
Falling Leaves Foundation Inc. ✧ ☆
c/o Mar & Associates Inc.
16902 Bolsa Chica Rd., Ste. 203
Huntington Beach, CA 92649-5306

Established in 2006 in CA and DE.
Donors: Adeline Yen Mah; Robert A. Mah.
Foundation type: Independent foundation.
Financial data (yr. ended 12/31/12): Assets, $9,536,797 (M); gifts received, $450,000; expenditures, $1,259,402; qualifying distributions, $611,710; giving activities include $611,710 for grants.
Fields of interest: Museums (art); International human rights; Foundations (community).
Limitations: Applications not accepted. No grants to individuals.
Application information: Contributes only to pre-selected organizations.
Officers: Adeline Yen Mah, Pres.; Robert Mah, V.P.; Shirley Fiewell, Secy.; Larry Mar, Treas.
EIN: 204861119

516
Fansler Foundation ✧
5713 N. West Ave., Ste. 102
Fresno, CA 93711-2366 (559) 432-0544
Contact: Lisa Prudek, Admin. Dir.
FAX: (559) 432-0543; Main URL: http://www.fanslerfoundation.com

Established in 1984 in CA.
Donors: D. Paul Fansler‡; Fansler Living Trust.
Foundation type: Independent foundation.
Financial data (yr. ended 10/31/13): Assets, $32,624,931 (M); expenditures, $2,032,285; qualifying distributions, $1,413,279; giving activities include $1,233,993 for 26 grants (high: $150,486; low: $125).
Purpose and activities: Giving primarily for education and health care, and social services, with emphasis on children and youth; some giving also for a family development center, and handicap accessibility facilities; scholarships to middle school student parishioners are also available.
Fields of interest: Education, early childhood education; Health organizations, association; Cerebral palsy; Crime/violence prevention, child abuse; Children/youth, services; Youth; Disabilities, people with.
Type of support: Scholarships—to individuals.
Limitations: Applications accepted. Giving primarily in the Fresno, Kings, Tulare, Merced, Madera, or Mariposa counties in CA.
Publications: Application guidelines.
Application information: Contact the foundation for specifics to be covered, and required attachments. Application form required.
Initial approach: Letter of intent, no more than 3 typewritten pages, which needs to address the 9 points indicated in the Grant Guidelines on the foundation's web site
Copies of proposal: 7
Deadline(s): Mar. 31 for funding by Oct. 31; Mar. 15 for scholarships
Board meeting date(s): As needed
Final notification: July 31 for letters of intent
Officers and Directors:* Marlene Fansler,* C.E.O. and Pres.; Margie Cooper; Keith Kompsi; Jim Pardini; William B. Saleh; Richard Spencer.
Number of staff: 2 full-time professional.
EIN: 770095125

517
Farallon Foundation ✧
2776 Trailside Cir.
Pleasanton, CA 94588-4756

Established in 1972 in CA.
Donors: Hugh W. Ditzler, Jr.; Nancy M. Ditzler; Marian Zischke; Peter H. Zischke; John R. Shuman‡; Josephine R. Shuman; W. James Lloyd; Pamela Lloyd; Gerald C. Down; William K. Steiner; Frances K. Lloyd‡; Kate Ditzler; Karin Chamberlain; David Chamberlain; Marian Baldauf; Richard Reinhardt; Debra Perry; Mark Perry; Karen Nager; Charles Nager; Susan Wait; Bradford Wait; JoEllen Brean; Park T. Dingwell‡; Joseph Eldridge‡; James G. Siler; Susan Siler; Robert Shuman; Laura Waste; William Waste‡; Hans Baldauf; Barbara Dolliver; Peter Dolliver; Nancy Osborn; James Osborn; Stuart Gasner; Hugh W. Ditzler III.
Foundation type: Independent foundation.
Financial data (yr. ended 12/31/13): Assets, $7,322,739 (M); gifts received, $522,997; expenditures, $709,893; qualifying distributions, $642,995; giving activities include $629,726 for 274 grants (high: $34,500; low: $25).
Purpose and activities: Support only for donor-advised organizations.
Fields of interest: Arts; Education; Health care.
Limitations: Applications not accepted. Giving primarily in the western U.S. No grants to individuals.
Publications: Financial statement.
Application information: Unsolicited requests for funds not accepted. Disbursements only as recommended by donors.
Board meeting date(s): Jan. and July
Officer: Hugh W. Ditzler, Jr., Pres.
Directors: Hugh W. Ditzler III; Kate Ditzler; Nancy M. Ditzler; Karen D. Nager; Debra D. Perry.
Number of staff: None.
EIN: 237216373

518
The Farese Family Foundation ✧
1660 Bush St., Ste. 300
San Francisco, CA 94109-5308 (415) 561-6540
FAX: (415) 561-5477; Main URL: http://www.faresefamilyfoundation.org

Established in 2000 in CA.
Donors: Nancy R. Farese; Robert Farese.
Foundation type: Independent foundation.
Financial data (yr. ended 12/31/13): Assets, $19,227,864 (M); expenditures, $869,382; qualifying distributions, $777,371; giving activities include $682,750 for 53 grants (high: $100,000; low: $500).
Fields of interest: Libraries (public); Education; Human services; Children/youth; Economically disadvantaged.
Type of support: General/operating support.
Limitations: Applications not accepted. Giving primarily in the San Francisco Bay Area, CA. No grants to individuals.
Publications: Grants list; Program policy statement.
Application information: Unsolicited requests for funds not accepted. Proposals are by invitation only.
Board meeting date(s): May and Dec.
Officers: Nancy R. Farese, Pres.; Robert V. Farese, Jr., Secy.-Treas.
Board Members: Conor Farese; Julie Shafer.
Number of staff: 2 part-time professional; 3 part-time support.
EIN: 943376857
Selected grants: The following grants are a representative sample of this grantmaker's funding activity:
$25,000 to Ashesi University Foundation, Seattle, WA, 2012. For Student Financial Support.
$25,000 to Reading Partners, Oakland, CA, 2012. To Expand Program in the Bay Area.
$1,000 to Chicago Public Media, Chicago, IL, 2012. For This American Life.

$1,000 to International Rescue Committee, New York, NY, 2012. For Honorarium for Hosint in Bukavu, Democratic Republic of the Congo.
$1,000 to San Francisco Child Abuse Prevention Center, San Francisco, CA, 2012. For Blue Ribbon Luncheon and Children's Art Auction.
$1,000 to USA Cycling Development Foundation, Colorado Springs, CO, 2012. For The Marin Classic.
$1,000 to Velo Development Foundation, Woodacre, CA, 2012. For Whole Athlete Cycling Team.
$1,000 to Wood River Land Trust, Hailey, ID, 2012. For Hulen Meadows Flood Projects.

519
Farrell Family Foundation ✧
P.O. Box 205
Kentfield, CA 94914-0205
Contact: Kristi Burlingame, Exec. Dir.
E-mail: Kristi@FarrellFamilyFoundation.org; Main URL: http://www.farrellfamilyfoundation.com

Established in 2001 in CA.
Donor: Peter C. Farrell.
Foundation type: Independent foundation.
Financial data (yr. ended 12/31/13): Assets, $8,741,795 (M); gifts received, $3,999,995; expenditures, $1,255,252; qualifying distributions, $1,137,140; giving activities include $1,106,150 for 114 grants (high: $108,046; low: $100).
Purpose and activities: Giving primarily for education, health, human welfare, and the arts. Grants will be given to organizations that demonstrate that they have competent management who have a history of delivering results in an effective and cost efficient manner. Levels of overhead expenses will be taken into consideration.
Fields of interest: Arts; Education; Health care; Human services.
Limitations: Applications accepted. Giving primarily in San Diego County, CA. No grants to individuals, or for operating support, contingencies, deficits or debt reduction.
Publications: Application guidelines; Grants list.
Application information: Application guidelines, cover sheet, and proposal narrative format available on foundation web site. Application form required.
Initial approach: Application cover sheet and proposal narrative
Officers and Directors:* Peter C. Farrell,* Chair.; Kristi Burlingame, Exec. Dir.; Michael J. Farrell; Paul A. Farrell; Catherine A. Sertori.
EIN: 912167530

520
Faucett Catalyst Fund ✧ ☆
(formerly Faucett Family Foundation)
2001 Wilshire Blvd., Ste. 401
Santa Monica, CA 90403-5683

Established in 2001 in CA.
Donors: Russell B. Faucett; Faucett Family Trust.
Foundation type: Independent foundation.
Financial data (yr. ended 06/30/13): Assets, $5,195,982 (M); gifts received, $1,170,000; expenditures, $576,548; qualifying distributions, $482,851; giving activities include $481,000 for 14 grants (high: $60,000; low: $10,000).
Fields of interest: Arts; Education; Health organizations; Human services.
Type of support: General/operating support.
Limitations: Applications not accepted. No grants to individuals.
Application information: Contributes only to pre-selected organizations.
Officers and Directors:* Russell B. Faucett,* Pres.; Carol Ann Faucett,* V.P.; Benjamin Faucett; Robert Faucett; Scott Faucett.
EIN: 954892024
Selected grants: The following grants are a representative sample of this grantmaker's funding activity:
$100,000 to Nature Conservancy, Arlington, VA, 2011.
$40,000 to Point Blue Conservation Science, Petaluma, CA, 2011. For general operating fund.
$30,000 to Princeton University Press, Princeton, NJ, 2011. For general operating fund.
$20,000 to Los Angeles Chamber Orchestra Society, Los Angeles, CA, 2011.

521
The James J. and Sue Femino Foundation ✧
(formerly Femino Foundation)
P.O. Box 70155
Pasadena, CA 91117-7155

Established in 1969 in CA.
Donors: James J. Femino; Sue Femino; Dominic Femino.
Foundation type: Independent foundation.
Financial data (yr. ended 09/30/13): Assets, $18,475,726 (M); gifts received, $500,000; expenditures, $900,363; qualifying distributions, $764,150; giving activities include $764,150 for 39 grants (high: $250,000; low: $500).
Purpose and activities: Support primarily for hospitals, health organizations, and institutions of medical research and education; support also for higher and other educational institutions, as well as for art, music and literature.
Fields of interest: Visual arts; Performing arts, music; Literature; Higher education; Medical school/education; Education; Health organizations, association; Medical research, institute; Engineering/technology; Science.
Type of support: Capital campaigns; Scholarship funds; Research.
Limitations: Applications not accepted. Giving primarily in southern CA. No grants to individuals.
Application information: Contributes only to pre-selected organizations. Unsolicited requests for funds not considered.
Officers: James J. Femino, Pres.; Sue Femino, V.P.; Richard Esbenshade, Secy.
EIN: 237423792
Selected grants: The following grants are a representative sample of this grantmaker's funding activity:
$10,000 to Catholic Education Foundation, Los Angeles, CA, 2013. For Sch.
$6,000 to Homeboy Industries, Los Angeles, CA, 2013. For Ca.

522
Eris & Larry Field Family Foundation ✧
433 N. Camden Dr., Ste. 820
Beverly Hills, CA 90210-4412 (310) 550-1570
Contact: Lawrence N. Field, Pres.

Established in 1983 in CA.
Donors: Lawrence N. Field; Eris M. Field.
Foundation type: Operating foundation.
Financial data (yr. ended 06/30/13): Assets, $180,457 (M); gifts received, $1,600,000; expenditures, $1,535,623; qualifying distributions, $1,498,298; giving activities include $1,498,298 for 39 grants (high: $270,000; low: $1,500).
Purpose and activities: Giving primarily for health, education, and Jewish organizations; funding also for the arts and human services.
Fields of interest: Performing arts; Performing arts, music; Historic preservation/historical societies; Arts; Higher education; Education; Human services; Jewish agencies & synagogues.
Type of support: General/operating support.
Limitations: Giving primarily in the Los Angeles, CA, area.
Application information: Application form not required.
Initial approach: Proposal
Deadline(s): None
Officers and Directors:* Lawrence N. Field,* Pres.; John Harrington, C.F.O.; Lisa S. Field; Robyn L. Field.
EIN: 953905829

523
The Frances K. & Charles D. Field Foundation ✧
155 Montgomery St., Ste. 404
San Francisco, CA 94104-4109

Established in CA.
Donor: The Frances K. Field Private Trust.
Foundation type: Independent foundation.
Financial data (yr. ended 12/31/13): Assets, $15,930,158 (M); expenditures, $924,309; qualifying distributions, $811,375; giving activities include $750,000 for 19 grants (high: $70,000; low: $15,000).
Purpose and activities: Giving primarily to museums, the symphony, and the opera, including music education and opera training programs; funding also for a university's medical student scholarship fund.
Fields of interest: Arts, formal/general education; Museums; Performing arts, orchestras; Performing arts, opera; Child development, education; Higher education; Education; Children/youth; Children; Youth; Hispanics/Latinos.
Type of support: Professorships; Scholarship funds; Scholarships—to individuals; Matching/challenge support.
Limitations: Applications not accepted. Giving primarily in San Francisco, CA. No grants to.
Application information: Unsolicited requests for funds not accepted.
Officers: Yeoryios Apallas, Pres.; John O. Jenkins, 1st V.P. and Secy.; Adrian Sawyer, 2nd V.P. and Treas.
EIN: 680534344
Selected grants: The following grants are a representative sample of this grantmaker's funding activity:
$49,000 to Stanford University, Stanford, CA, 2012. For the purchase of The Confidential Print series on Africa, Field Family Book Fund, Stanford University Library.
$40,000 to San Francisco Symphony, San Francisco, CA, 2012. For the Adventures in Music (AIM) Program.
$30,000 to Marin Shakespeare Company, San Rafael, CA, 2012. For benefiting the educational outreach Programs with classes, Programs in

schools, and free Shakespeare summer camps for low-income youth.
$25,000 to Huckleberry Youth Programs, San Francisco, CA, 2012. For Funding specifically dedicated directly to the Huckleberry House for runaways.

524
The Charles D. and Frances K. Field Fund ✧
180 Montgomery St., Ste. 1616
San Francisco, CA 94104-4235

Established in CA.
Foundation type: Independent foundation.
Financial data (yr. ended 12/31/13): Assets, $19,362,969 (M); expenditures, $977,215; qualifying distributions, $840,614; giving activities include $750,000 for 26 grants (high: $100,000; low: $2,500).
Fields of interest: Performing arts, opera; Education; Hospitals (general); Medical research, institute; Human services; Social sciences, research.
Limitations: Applications not accepted. Giving primarily in San Francisco, CA.
Application information: Contributes only to pre-selected organizations.
Officers and Directors:* Philip Hudner,* Pres.; Michael L. Helms,* Secy.; Guy Annamanthodo,* Treas.
EIN: 460497841
Selected grants: The following grants are a representative sample of this grantmaker's funding activity:
$40,000 to Asian Art Museum Foundation of San Francisco, San Francisco, CA, 2012. To support docent Program.
$25,000 to Keys School, Palo Alto, CA, 2012. To support K to 8th grade school.
$15,000 to Buckelew Programs, San Rafael, CA, 2012. To support mental health and addiction recovery Programs.
$15,000 to California State Parks Foundation, San Francisco, CA, 2012. To support California state parks.
$10,000 to Pacific Legal Foundation, Sacramento, CA, 2012. To support public interest legal organization.
$10,000 to San Domenico School, San Anselmo, CA, 2012. To support K to 12th grade school.
$10,000 to Woodside Priory School, Portola Valley, CA, 2012. To support John Erkman Scholarship Fund.
$5,000 to Redwood Day School, Oakland, CA, 2012. To support financial assistance Program.
$2,500 to Save the Redwoods League, San Francisco, CA, 2012. To support Redwood Land Fund.
$2,500 to Sempervirens Fund, Los Altos, CA, 2012. To support environmental organization.

525
Fineberg Foundation ✧
11812 San Vicente Blvd., Ste. 500
Los Angeles, CA 90049-5081

Donor: Joseph Fineberg 2007 Charitable Trust.
Foundation type: Independent foundation.
Financial data (yr. ended 12/31/13): Assets, $31,984,231 (M); expenditures, $1,886,247; qualifying distributions, $1,668,015; giving activities include $1,339,027 for 14 grants (high: $250,000; low: $3,600).
Fields of interest: Hospitals (general); Medical research; Jewish federated giving programs.
Limitations: Applications not accepted. Giving primarily in CA; some giving also in IL, MI, VA, and in Toronto, Canada.
Application information: Contributes only to pre-selected organizations.
Trustees: Rodney Chase; Sandy L. Chase; Harvey Glasner; Malka Stromer.
EIN: 276816503

526
The Fineshriber Family Foundation
5018 Butterfield Ct.
Culver City, CA 90230-4303
Contact: Marcia Antopol, Secy.-Treas. and Exec. Dir.

Donor: Ruth Moskin Fineshriber.
Foundation type: Independent foundation.
Financial data (yr. ended 12/31/12): Assets, $14,509,018 (M); expenditures, $659,596; qualifying distributions, $635,505; giving activities include $452,070 for 11 grants (high: $200,000; low: $2,778).
Fields of interest: Education; Health care; Children/youth, services.
Limitations: Applications not accepted. Giving primarily in CA. No grants to individuals.
Application information: Contributes only to pre-selected organizations.
Officers: Jeffrey M. Moskin, Pres.; Bernice Silberberg, V.P.; Marcia Antopol, Secy.-Treas. and Exec. Dir.
EIN: 203343226

527
Ernest L. and Ruth W. Finley Foundation ✧
1400 N. Dutton Ave., No. 12
Santa Rosa, CA 95401-4644 (707) 545-3136
Contact: Norma J. Person, Tr.

Established in 1985 in CA.
Donors: Ernest L. Finley†; Ruth W. Finley†; R. Finley Charitable Remainder Unitrust.
Foundation type: Independent foundation.
Financial data (yr. ended 08/31/13): Assets, $32,979,369 (M); expenditures, $6,593,576; qualifying distributions, $6,251,630; giving activities include $6,158,989 for 18 grants (high: $1,500,000; low: $10,000).
Purpose and activities: Giving primarily for the preservation of visual arts, social services, youth activities and support, religious endeavors.
Fields of interest: Arts; Health care; Human services; Children/youth, services.
Type of support: General/operating support; Building/renovation; Endowments; Scholarship funds.
Limitations: Applications accepted. Giving generally limited to Santa Rosa and Sonoma County, CA. No grants to individuals.
Application information: Application form required.
Initial approach: Letter
Copies of proposal: 3
Deadline(s): None
Board meeting date(s): As required
Trustees: Brad Bollinger; William W. Godward; Norma J. Person.
EIN: 941694310

528
Firedoll Foundation ✧
1460 Maria Ln., Ste. 400
Walnut Creek, CA 94596-8802
Contact: Neil Sims, Sr.Prog. Off.
FAX: (925) 937-4530; E-mail: info@firedoll.org; LOI e-mail: LOI@firedoll.org; Main URL: http://www.firedoll.org

Established in 1998 in CA.
Donor: Straus Family Trust.
Foundation type: Independent foundation.
Financial data (yr. ended 05/31/13): Assets, $9,231,624 (M); gifts received, $1,573,514; expenditures, $2,091,476; qualifying distributions, $2,079,502; giving activities include $1,899,825 for 98 grants (high: $40,000; low: $2,500).
Purpose and activities: The foundation offers grants to nonprofits in the areas of environmental conservation, immigrant/human rights, community development, Mid-East peace, and offers support for Bay Area non-profits servicing victims of traumatic brain injury.
Fields of interest: Environment, natural resources; Environment, water resources; Environment, forests; Animals/wildlife, fisheries; Housing/shelter, homeless; International peace/security; Civil/human rights, immigrants; Community development, small businesses.
International interests: Middle East.
Type of support: General/operating support; Continuing support; Capital campaigns; Building/renovation; Equipment; Land acquisition; Emergency funds; Program development; Seed money; Technical assistance; Program evaluation; Matching/challenge support.
Limitations: Applications accepted. Giving limited to Alameda and Contra Costa Counties in CA, for community development. Giving primarily in Alameda and Contra Costa Counties for land acquisition and conservation, HI for Monk seal conservation, and the Eastern Pacific for fish stock preservation. Giving in Alameda and Contra Costa Counties for immigration and human rights, as well as some giving nationally for civil rights work. Giving in Alameda, Contra Costa, Marin, San Mateo, San Francisco and Solano Counties for traumatic brain injury. Giving to U.S.-based or U.S. fiscally sponsored organizations providing relief in Gaza and the West Bank. No support for organizations with budgets less than $150,000, wild animal or pet rescue and rehab, or international support (except for Middle East Peace and an occasional grant in Environmental Conservation). No grants to individuals or for the arts, youth (grades K-12), education, LGBT, general support for first time applicants, climate change, community leadership development, youth development (other than aid for emancipated foster youth), films, videos, documentaries, books, web sites and other media, start-up or seed funding for organizations or projects new to the foundation, or for large-scope, long-term initiatives (the foundation prefers discrete projects with concrete end-of-year deliverables).
Publications: Application guidelines; Grants list; Program policy statement.
Application information: Consult application guidelines on web site before sending proposals.

Proposals not following guidelines will be returned. Application form required.

Initial approach: E-mail or written letter of inquiry or proposal after consulting web site

Copies of proposal: 1

Deadline(s): See foundation web site for current deadlines

Final notification: Within 3 months

Officers: Sandor Straus, Pres. and Treas.; Faye Straus, V.P. and Secy.

Number of staff: 1 full-time professional; 1 part-time professional.

EIN: 943301999

Selected grants: The following grants are a representative sample of this grantmaker's funding activity:

$21,000 to TransForm, Oakland, CA, 2011. For general support.

529
Firelight Endowment ✧ ☆

(formerly Firelight Foundation)
740 Front St., Ste. 380
Santa Cruz, CA 95060 (831) 429-8750
FAX: (831) 429-2036;
E-mail: info@firelightfoundation.org; Main URL: http://www.firelightfoundation.org
Blog: http://blog.firelightfoundation.org/
Facebook: http://www.facebook.com/pages/Firelight-Foundation/186636331584?ref=nf
LinkedIn: http://www.linkedin.com/companies/478035
RSS Feed: http://feeds.feedburner.com/firelightfoundation/KvAb.rss
Twitter: http://twitter.com/peter_laugharn
YouTube: http://www.youtube.com/user/firelighttube

Established in 1999 in CA.

Donors: David M. Katz; Kerry A. Olson.

Foundation type: Independent foundation.

Financial data (yr. ended 06/30/13): Assets, $18,774 (M); gifts received, $3,500; expenditures, $5,088,385; qualifying distributions, $5,062,687; giving activities include $4,977,010 for 1 grant.

Purpose and activities: The mission of the Firelight Foundation is to support and advocate for the needs and rights of children who are orphaned or affected by HIV/AIDS in Sub-Saharan Africa. Firelight strives to increase the resources available to grassroots organizations that are strengthening the capacity of families and communities to care for children made vulnerable by HIV/AIDS.

Fields of interest: Human services.

Type of support: General/operating support; Continuing support; Management development/capacity building; Building/renovation; Program development; Technical assistance.

Limitations: Applications not accepted. Giving primarily in Sub-Saharan Africa; few grants to U.S.-based organizations. No grants to individuals, or for academic or medical research, endowments, or fundraisers.

Application information: Unsolicited requests for funds not accepted.

Officers and Board Members:* Catherine H. Milton,* Chair.; Dick Staufenberger,* Vice-Chair. and Treas.; David Katz,* Secy.; Peter Laugharn, Exec. Dir.; Kerry A. Olson,* Pres. Emeritus; Molly Efrusy; Geoff Foster, M.D.; Rowland P. Hobbs; Gloria Johnston-Cusak; Mark Lorey.

Number of staff: 6 full-time professional; 2 part-time support.

EIN: 770529657

Selected grants: The following grants are a representative sample of this grantmaker's funding activity:

$125,000 to Touch Roots Africa, Metsong Africa, Maseru, Lesotho, 2011.
$75,000 to Rwanda Womens Network, Kigali, Rwanda, 2011.
$75,000 to WEM Integrated Health Services, Thika, Kenya, 2011.
$20,000 to Tsosane Support Group, Maseru, Lesotho, 2011.
$15,000 to Centre for Environment Technology and Rural Development, Kasese, Uganda, 2011.
$15,000 to Kyetume Community Based Health Care Programme, Mukono, Uganda, 2011.
$9,000 to Association des Jeunes Orphelins Rwandais, Kigali, Rwanda, 2011.
$9,000 to Federation of Disability Organizations in Malawi, Blantyre, Malawi, 2011.
$9,000 to Livingstone Anglican Childrens Project, Livingstone, Zambia, 2011.
$9,000 to Masasi Peoples Umbrella Organization, Masasi, Tanzania, 2011.

530
First Fruit, Inc. ✧

14 Corporate Plz., Ste. 200
Newport Beach, CA 92660-7928 (949) 720-3774
Contact: Karen Wallace
FAX: (949) 760-5349; E-mail: info@firstfruit.org; Main URL: http://www.firstfruit.org

Established in 1976 in CA.

Donors: Peter M. Ochs; Gail J. Ochs; Randy Bramel; Susan Bramel; JCBF; Terry and Rosann Douglass Foundation; Cornerstone Trust; The Fourteen Four Group.

Foundation type: Independent foundation.

Financial data (yr. ended 12/31/12): Assets, $51,277,757 (M); expenditures, $2,480,238; qualifying distributions, $1,968,029; giving activities include $1,135,490 for grants.

Purpose and activities: Grants are made only to organizations which engage in advancing the Gospel of Jesus Christ primarily in Third World countries. Preference is given to evangelical ministries, usually with strategic pioneering programs among peoples who have not had repeated contact with the Gospel message.

Fields of interest: Protestant agencies & churches.

International interests: Developing Countries.

Type of support: General/operating support; Building/renovation; Equipment; Program development; Conferences/seminars; Seed money; Curriculum development; Research; Program evaluation; Matching/challenge support.

Limitations: Giving limited to U.S.-based organizations for the benefit of non-developed or developing countries. No grants to individuals.

Application information: See foundation web site for further application information. Application form not required.

Initial approach: Letter of inquiry

Copies of proposal: 1

Deadline(s): None

Board meeting date(s): Three times per year, as determined by the board

Officers and Directors:* Peter M. Ochs,* Pres.; Gail J. Ochs,* V.P.; Dennis W. Thome,* Secy.; Rick Haugen, Treas.; David W. Bennett; Henry Cloud; Victoria Cloud; Kristi Young.

Number of staff: 4 full-time professional; 1 part-time professional; 1 full-time support.

EIN: 953081605

531
Fischmann Family Foundation ✧

4849 Encino Ave.
Encino, CA 91316-3815

Donors: George Fischmann; Susan Weiss-Fischmann.

Foundation type: Independent foundation.

Financial data (yr. ended 12/31/13): Assets, $573 (M); gifts received, $711,000; expenditures, $713,598; qualifying distributions, $713,598; giving activities include $713,513 for 28 grants (high: $325,000; low: $36).

Fields of interest: Education; Human services; Jewish agencies & synagogues.

Limitations: Applications not accepted. Giving primarily in CA.

Application information: Unsolicited requests for funds not accepted.

Officers: George Fischmann, Pres.; Susan Weiss-Fischmann, Secy.

EIN: 273286995

532
Doris & Donald Fisher Fund ✧

(formerly Doris & Donald Fisher Education Fund)
1 Maritime Plz., Ste. 1550
San Francisco, CA 94111-3504

Established in 2008 in CA.

Donors: DDFY2K Family Trust; DFF Article III Trust.

Foundation type: Operating foundation.

Financial data (yr. ended 06/30/13): Assets, $2,667,702 (M); expenditures, $4,593,222; qualifying distributions, $4,580,748; giving activities include $2,517,500 for 4 grants (high: $2,500,000; low: $2,500).

Fields of interest: Charter schools; Higher education; Education.

Limitations: Applications not accepted. Giving primarily in AZ, CA, Washington, DC, and New York, NY. No grants to individuals.

Application information: Contributes only to pre-selected organizations.

Directors: Stephen Mancini; Christopher Nelson.

Trustees: Doris Fisher; Jane Spray.

EIN: 266033047

Selected grants: The following grants are a representative sample of this grantmaker's funding activity:

$2,500,000 to Teach for America, New York, NY, 2012. For general support.
$1,000,000 to National Alliance for Public Charter Schools, Washington, DC, 2012. For general support.
$100,000 to Summit Preparatory High School, Redwood City, CA, 2012. For general support.
$65,000 to EdVoice Institute for Research and Education, Sacramento, CA, 2012. For general support.

533
Five Bridges Foundation
P.O. Box 194405
San Francisco, CA 94119-4405
E-mail: contact@fivebridges.org; Main URL: http://fivebridges.org

Established in 1998 in CA.
Foundation type: Independent foundation.
Financial data (yr. ended 09/30/13): Assets, $12,049,685 (M); expenditures, $809,586; qualifying distributions, $565,121; giving activities include $480,000 for 18 grants (high: $50,000; low: $10,000).
Purpose and activities: The mission of the foundation is to promote and improve the quality of life for the disadvantaged, underserved, and vulnerable residents of the San Francisco Bay Area through the funding of 501(c)(3) public charitable organizations having programs directed toward the achievement of long term, positive change in the communities they serve.
Fields of interest: Youth development; Youth; Young adults; Economically disadvantaged; Homeless.
Type of support: General/operating support; Program development.
Limitations: Giving limited to five Bay Area counties: Alameda, Contra Costa, Marin, San Francisco, and San Mateo, CA. No support for organizations that mainly distribute grants to other organizations. No grants to artistic and aesthetic programs, or for receptions, banquets, displays, shows, or other similar programs.
Publications: Application guidelines; Grants list.
Application information: Unsolicited applications are no longer accepted. The foundation uses an online system for all stages of grantmaking including grant applications, grant agreements, and grant reports. Proposals attached to e-mail messages or paper copies of any of these documents are no longer accepted. Please e-mail all inquiries.
Initial approach: Refer to online application process on foundation web site
Deadline(s): Refer to foundation web site for deadline dates
Board meeting date(s): Varies
Final notification: Sept.
Officers and Directors:* Charles Kallgren,* Pres. and Secy.; Allan Casalou, V.P.; Amy Matthew, V.P. and Treas.
Number of staff: 3 part-time professional; 1 part-time support.
EIN: 940732210
Selected grants: The following grants are a representative sample of this grantmaker's funding activity:
$60,000 to Court Appointed Special Advocates Program, San Francisco, San Francisco, CA, 2014. For staff trains volunteers to be advocates for older youth, create comprehensive plans, make positive adult connections, and develop strategies to achieve positive outcomes both during and after time in foster care.
$50,000 to Abode Services, Fremont, CA, 2014. To help at-risk transition age youth secure and maintain stable housing and access range of services to build self-reliance.
$50,000 to At the Crossroads, San Francisco, CA, 2014. To provide outreach, one-on-one counseling on-the spot counseling and referrals to homeless youth who are disconnected from services and supportive relationships that could make their lives easier.
$50,000 to Community Works/West, Oakland, CA, 2014. For staff works with District Attorney, police, and Juvenile Probation Department to eliminate criminal charges brought against 80 young people/year using Restorative Community Conferences.
$50,000 to New Door Ventures, San Francisco, CA, 2014. For low-income youth pre-employment training, placed in 4-6 month paid internships, working 15-20 hours per week in New Door's social enterprises or in one of over 40 community partner job sites.
$35,000 to Huckleberry Youth Programs, San Francisco, CA, 2014. For general support for four programs.
$30,000 to Acknowledge Alliance, Mountain View, CA, 2014. For Collaborative Counseling Program serves youth offering counseling, intervention, and transition services to at-risk teens, ages 13-18, who are attending San Mateo Court and Community Schools as result of being on probation or due to expulsion at local public schools.
$25,000 to East Bay Community Law Center, Berkeley, CA, 2014. For Youth Justice Program in which addresses school-to-prison pipeline through three projects: Justice in Schools project (prevention), Youth Defense project (legal representation when youth have been detained), and Starting Over Strong project (to help youth with reentry and jobs after detention).
$25,000 to Sunny Hills Childrens Garden, San Anselmo, CA, 2014. For Real Alternatives for Adolescents places transition-age foster youth ages 16 to 21 in two-bedroom apartments in Alameda County.
$15,000 to Court Appointed Special Advocates of Contra Costa County, Walnut Creek, CA, 2014.

534
Fleishhacker Foundation
1016 Lincoln Blvd., Ste. 12
San Francisco, CA 94129 (415) 561-5350
Contact: Christine Elbel, Exec. Dir.
FAX: (415) 561-5345;
E-mail: info@fleishhackerfoundation.org; Main URL: http://www.fleishhackerfoundation.org

Incorporated in 1947 in CA.
Donors: Mortimer Fleishhacker, Sr.‡; Mortimer Fleishhacker, Jr.‡; Janet Fleishhacker Bates‡.
Foundation type: Independent foundation.
Financial data (yr. ended 12/31/13): Assets, $18,206,095 (M); expenditures, $935,770; qualifying distributions, $873,072; giving activities include $530,460 for 110 grants (high: $20,000; low: $1,000), and $150,500 for 9 grants to individuals (high: $25,000; low: $500).
Purpose and activities: Grants to visual and performing arts organizations; support also for precollegiate education.
Fields of interest: Media, film/video; Visual arts; Museums; Performing arts; Performing arts, dance; Performing arts, theater; Performing arts, music; Arts; Elementary school/education; Education; Children/youth; Children; Minorities; Asians/Pacific Islanders; African Americans/Blacks; Hispanics/Latinos; Native Americans/American Indians; Girls; Adults, women; Adults, men; Economically disadvantaged; LGBTQ.
Type of support: General/operating support; Equipment; Program development; Film/video/radio; Curriculum development; Fellowships; Technical assistance; Grants to individuals.
Limitations: Applications accepted. Giving limited to the greater San Francisco Bay Area, CA. No support for religious or political organizations. No grants for annual campaigns, endowments, large capital campaigns, deficit financing, fund raising events, matching gifts or scholarships; no loans.
Publications: Application guidelines; Grants list.
Application information: Fellowships not open to individual application. Application form required.
Initial approach: Full proposal
Copies of proposal: 1
Deadline(s): Usually Jan. 15 and July 15
Board meeting date(s): Biannually
Final notification: 3 to 4 months
Officers and Directors:* David Fleishhacker,* Pres.; John Ehrlich, Jr.,* V.P.; Deborah Sloss,* Secy.; William Fleishhacker,* Treas.; Christine Elbel, Exec. Dir.; Delia Fleishhacker Ehrlich; Jodi Ehrlich; Jeffrey Fleishhacker; Marc Fleishhacker; Edie Fleishhacker Rindal; Laura Sloss; Robin Strawbridge.
Number of staff: 1 full-time professional; 1 part-time support.
EIN: 946051048
Selected grants: The following grants are a representative sample of this grantmaker's funding activity:
$15,000 to 826 Valencia, San Francisco, CA, 2012. For literacy activities at home site and in elementary schools in Mission District.
$15,000 to Reading Partners, Oakland, CA, 2012. For literacy centers at elementary schools in the Bay Area.
$10,000 to Clarity Educational Productions, Berkeley, CA, 2012. For documentary about Palestinian youth in East Jerusalem, visiting American gospel choir, present play about complexity of Israeli-Palestinian conflict and Dr. King's philosophy of non-violent resistance.
$10,000 to CounterPULSE, San Francisco, CA, 2012. For CP Performances, featuring both established dance ensembles and emerging choreographers.
$10,000 to San Francisco Playhouse, San Francisco, CA, 2012. For New Works Program.
$10,000 to Southern Exposure Gallery, San Francisco, CA, 2012. For re-configured exhibitions program featuring project-based commissions in home gallery and out in the community.
$7,500 to Marsh, A Breeding Ground for New Performance, San Francisco, CA, 2012. For The News, about how transition from broadcast to narrowcast media is changing our democracy and world-wide discourse.
$5,000 to Golden Thread Productions, San Francisco, CA, 2012. For ReOrient Festival.
$4,500 to San Francisco Film Society, San Francisco, CA, 2012. For documentary about effects of untested chemicals on Americans' health.
$2,000 to DanceArt, San Francisco, CA, 2012. For SKETCH 2: Women Choreographers.

535
Flextronics Foundation ✧ ☆
847 Gibraltar Dr.
Milpitas, CA 95035-6332 (408) 576-7528
Contact: Lori Kenepp, Community Rels. Mgr.
Regional Contact for Asia Pacific: Tony Khaw, 1 Kallang Pl., 339211 Singapore,
tel.: +65.6854.3737; Regional Contact for Europe: Roy Scott, Unit 10, Keypoint Business Centre, Dublin 11, Lincester, Ireland,
tel.: +52.449.9107125; Main URL: http://

www.flextronics.com/social_resp/Flextronics_Foundation/default.aspx

Established in 2001 in CA.
Donors: Flextronics International U.S.A., Inc.; Richard Sharp; Michael Marks.
Foundation type: Company-sponsored foundation.
Financial data (yr. ended 12/31/13): Assets, $9,393,746 (M); gifts received, $400,000; expenditures, $530,966; qualifying distributions, $493,507; giving activities include $481,733 for 32 grants (high: $83,000; low: $1,415).
Purpose and activities: The foundation supports programs designed to address disaster relief; provide medical relief and health; and promote education. Special emphasis is directed toward programs designed to serve communities where Flextronics employees, suppliers, and customers live and work.
Fields of interest: Education, special; Higher education; Education; Health care; Disasters, preparedness/services; Business/industry; Community/economic development; Mathematics; Engineering/technology; Science; Economically disadvantaged.
Type of support: General/operating support; Continuing support; Emergency funds; Program development; Scholarship funds; Employee volunteer services.
Limitations: Applications accepted. Giving primarily in areas of company operations in CA, and in Asia, Europe, and Mexico. No support for religious, political, discriminatory, or for-profit organizations. No grants to individuals, or for advertising, athletic events or league sponsorships, conventions, conferences, meetings or seminars, clubs, contests, field trips, film and/or video projects, fundraising activities, marketing, sponsorships, or travel or similar activities.
Publications: Application guidelines; IRS Form 990 or 990-PF printed copy available upon request; Program policy statement.
Application information: Multi-year funding is not automatic. Application form required.
Initial approach: Contact a regional representative for application form
Deadline(s): None
Board meeting date(s): Mar., June, Sept., and Dec.
Officers: Paul Humphries, Pres.; Tim Stewart, Secy.; Chris Collier, C.F.O.; Don Standley, Treas.
EIN: 770567788

536
Flora Family Foundation ✧
2121 Sand Hill Rd., Ste. 123
Menlo Park, CA 94025-6909 (650) 233-1335
Contact: Steve Toben, Pres.
FAX: (650) 233-1340; E-mail: info@florafamily.org; Main URL: http://www.florafamily.org
Grants List: http://www.florafamily.org/grantees.html

The Flora Family Foundation was established in 1998 by the family of William R. Hewlett (co-founder of Hewlett-Packard Company) and his late wife, Flora Lamson Hewlett.
Donor: William R. Hewlett Trust.
Foundation type: Independent foundation.
Financial data (yr. ended 12/31/13): Assets, $110,551,130 (M); expenditures, $6,084,819; qualifying distributions, $5,734,901; giving activities include $5,060,750 for grants.
Purpose and activities: The foundation is predicated on the belief that each individual has an obligation to go beyond the narrow confines of his or her personal interests and be mindful of the broader concerns of humanity. The foundation has no constraints on its grantmaking so long as grant candidates fit the philanthropic interests of the Board and Family Council and meet IRS requirements.
Limitations: Applications not accepted.
Publications: Grants list.
Application information: Contributes only to pre-selected organizations.
Board meeting date(s): Mar., July, and Nov.
Officers and Directors:* Susan S. Briggs,* Chair.; Ben Hewlett,* Vice-Chair.; Steve Toben,* Pres.; Patricia Gump, Corp. Secy.; Annette Rado, C.F.O.; Marianne d'Ansembourg; Amir Farman-Farma; Juliette Gimon; David Hewlett; Jeff Zeisler.
Number of staff: 1 full-time professional; 1 part-time professional; 1 part-time support.
EIN: 770500183

537
The Foothills Foundation ✧
P.O. Box 193809
San Francisco, CA 94119-3809

Established in 1977 in CA.
Donors: Gary Hogan Bechtel; Stephen D. Bechtel, Jr.; Mrs. Stephen D. Bechtel, Jr.
Foundation type: Independent foundation.
Financial data (yr. ended 12/31/13): Assets, $5,975,733 (M); gifts received, $2,000,000; expenditures, $845,634; qualifying distributions, $841,556; giving activities include $804,000 for 24 grants (high: $200,000; low: $1,000).
Fields of interest: Secondary school/education; Education; Animal welfare; Human services; Children/youth, services; Foundations (private grantmaking).
Type of support: General/operating support; Annual campaigns; Capital campaigns.
Limitations: Applications not accepted. Giving primarily in CA. No grants to individuals.
Application information: Contributes only to pre-selected organizations.
Officers and Directors:* Gary Hogan Bechtel,* Pres.; Jacquie L. Bechtel, V.P.; George T. Argyris,* Secy.; Shu Huang,* Treas.
EIN: 942412392
Selected grants: The following grants are a representative sample of this grantmaker's funding activity:
$250,000 to Oklahoma State University, Stillwater, OK, 2012. For Pledge-Cowboy Basketball Legends Locker Room Program.
$200,000 to Delta Waterfowl Foundation, Bismarck, ND, 2012. For Legacy Challenge/Fund.
$185,000 to Delta Waterfowl Foundation, Bismarck, ND, 2012. For Discretion of COO and President for 2013.
$150,000 to Delta Waterfowl Foundation, Bismarck, ND, 2012. For Fiscal year End 2/29/12.
$100,000 to Baylor Health Care System Foundation, Dallas, TX, 2012. For Pleade-Pilot Program for Asthma Care in Baylor University's Medical Center.
$100,000 to University of the Pacific, Stockton, CA, 2012. For Pledge-Alex and Jen Vereschagin Alumni House.
$40,000 to National Wildlife Refuge Association, Washington, DC, 2012. For Bear River Watershed Conservation Area Project.
$25,000 to Kids Outdoor Sports Camp, Red Bluff, CA, 2012. For Summer Camp Expense.
$15,000 to Big Hole River Foundation, Butte, MT, 2012. For operations(final challenge grant).

538
Fortisure Foundation ✧
88 Kearny St., Ste. 1650
San Francisco, CA 94108-5564

Established in CA.
Donors: Srinivasan Subramanian; Nita Subramanian.
Foundation type: Independent foundation.
Financial data (yr. ended 12/31/12): Assets, $2,006,870 (M); gifts received, $4,000,000; expenditures, $3,010,921; qualifying distributions, $3,008,769; giving activities include $3,000,000 for 2 grants (high: $2,000,000; low: $1,000,000).
Fields of interest: Higher education; Eye research.
Limitations: Applications not accepted. Giving primarily in San Francisco, CA.
Application information: Unsolicited requests for funds not accepted.
Trustees: Meghna Subramanian; Dr. Nita Subramanian; Priyal Subramanian; Srinivasan Subramanian.
EIN: 456169952

539
The Louis W. Foster and Gladyce L. Foster Family Foundation ✧
10100 Trinity Pkwy., No. 310
Stockton, CA 95219-7238

Established in 1998 in CA.
Donors: Louis Foster†; Gladyce Foster Admin. Trust.
Foundation type: Independent foundation.
Financial data (yr. ended 06/30/13): Assets, $127,150,301 (M); gifts received, $4,626,945; expenditures, $5,092,002; qualifying distributions, $3,769,000; giving activities include $3,769,000 for 18 grants (high: $1,005,000; low: $5,000).
Fields of interest: Higher education; Health organizations; Eye research; Housing/shelter; Human services; Foundations (private grantmaking).
Limitations: Applications not accepted. Giving primarily in CA. No grants to individuals.
Application information: Contributes only to pre-selected organizations.
Officers: R. Scott Foster, M.D., Pres.; Judith Warren, Secy.
Directors: Gregory A. Foster; William L. Foster; Christina M. Kirkpatrick; Judith D. Witt.
EIN: 954712250
Selected grants: The following grants are a representative sample of this grantmaker's funding activity:
$250,000 to Liberty House, Salem, OR, 2011.
$50,000 to Habitat for Humanity International, Americus, GA, 2011.

540
Found Animals Foundation, Inc. ✧
P.O. Box 66370
Los Angeles, CA 90066-0370
E-mail: Info@foundanimals.org; Main URL: http://www.foundanimals.org/
Blog: http://www.foundanimals.org/blog/
E-Newsletter: http://www.foundanimals.org/get-involved/newsletter-signup
Facebook: http://www.facebook.com/foundanimals
Instagram.com: http://instagram.com/foundanimals#
Pinterest: http://www.pinterest.com/foundanimals/
Twitter: http://twitter.com/FoundAnimalsOrg
YouTube: http://www.youtube.com/foundanimals
Application e-mail: michelsonprize@foundanimals.org

Established in 2005 in CA.
Donor: Gary Karlin Michelson, M.D.
Foundation type: Operating foundation.
Financial data (yr. ended 11/30/12): Assets, $796,277 (M); gifts received, $4,306,000; expenditures, $8,971,559; qualifying distributions, $8,516,876; giving activities include $873,447 for 19 grants (high: $200,000; low: $2,500), and $7,234,582 for foundation-administered programs.
Purpose and activities: The foundation is focused on creating innovative, largely self-sustaining programs dedicated to 3 initiatives; spary/neuter; resources for pet owners; and adoption.
Fields of interest: Animal welfare; Hospitals (specialty).
Limitations: Applications not accepted. Giving primarily in CA. No grants to individuals.
Application information: Contributes only to pre-selected organizations.
Officers: Gary Karlin Michelson, M.D., Pres.; Aimee Gilbreath, V.P.; David Cohen, Secy. and C.F.O.; Dennis Phillips, C.O.O.
EIN: 203944602

541
Foundation for Better Education ✧
c/o Bessemer Trust
101 California St., Ste. 2500
San Francisco, CA 94111-5828

Classified as a independent foundation in 2007.
Donor: Jonathan C. Coon.
Foundation type: Independent foundation.
Financial data (yr. ended 12/31/13): Assets, $11,727,380 (M); expenditures, $785,693; qualifying distributions, $764,774; giving activities include $759,000 for 9 grants (high: $200,000; low: $5,000).
Purpose and activities: Giving primarily for children and youth services, including children's hospitals, as well as for education, and to an opera company.
Fields of interest: Performing arts, opera; Elementary/secondary education; Hospitals (specialty); Human services; Children/youth, services.
Limitations: Applications not accepted. Giving primarily in TX; some funding also in UT. No grants to individuals.
Application information: Unsolicited requests for funds not accepted.
Directors: Jonathan C. Coon; Steve Yacktman; Joe Ziedner.
EIN: 870623289

542
Foundation for Deep Ecology ✧
1606 Union St.
San Francisco, CA 94123-4507 (415) 229-9339
Contact: Lizzie Udwin, Prog. Admin.
FAX: (415) 229-9340;
E-mail: info@deepecology.org; Main URL: http://www.deepecology.org

Established in 1989 in CA.
Donors: Douglas R. Tompkins; Clark Family Foundation.
Foundation type: Independent foundation.
Financial data (yr. ended 06/30/13): Assets, $42,091,210 (M); expenditures, $2,407,003; qualifying distributions, $2,136,937; giving activities include $1,111,353 for 24+ grants (high: $121,000), and $179,780 for foundation-administered programs.
Purpose and activities: Focus on fundamental ecological issues: 1) protection of forests, aquatic ecosystems and other habitats, including wildlands philanthropy (buying land to save it), wilderness recovery (supporting the design and implementation of large-scale wilderness recovery networks), funding for activists fighting for full protection of species and ecosystems and funding for efforts to eliminate resource extraction on public lands; 2) support for alternative models of agriculture that support biodiversity, local self-reliance and healthy agrarian communities, support for efforts in the fight against industrial agriculture, and support for efforts to link conservationists with farmers and activists in order to integrate habitat preservation and restoration with diverse farming practices; 3) campaigns for effective analysis, organizing and action in response to the rapid acceleration in macroeconomic trends toward global economic integration and free trade that has shifted real political power away from citizen democracies to global corporate bureaucracies, and the further centralization of global corporate power caused by new technological innovation. Supported projects include educational programs exposing the full consequences of the global economy and new free trade agreements, technological critiques and campaigns, and groups fighting large road-building, infrastructure, and dam projects.
Fields of interest: Environment, natural resources; Environment, land resources; Environment; Animals/wildlife, preservation/protection; Agriculture; International affairs.
International interests: Argentina; Chile; South America.
Type of support: General/operating support; Continuing support; Land acquisition; Program development; Conferences/seminars; Publication; Seed money; Grants to individuals.
Limitations: Applications not accepted. Giving primarily in CA and South America, with emphasis on Chile and Argentina. No support for curriculum development or K-12 educational projects, or for businesses or debt. No grants for television, video, photography (visual arts) or film productions, research, or individual academic pursuits (including graduate work or scholarships).
Publications: Multi-year report.
Application information: Contributes only to pre-selected organizations. Unsolicited requests for funds will not be accepted.
Board meeting date(s): Annually
Officers and Directors:* Douglas R. Tompkins,* Pres.; Quincey Imhoff,* V.P.; Kristine McDivitt Tompkins,* V.P.; Debra B. Ryker,* Secy.-Treas.; Esther Li, Cont.
Number of staff: 3 full-time professional; 2 part-time professional; 3 full-time support.
EIN: 943106115

543
The Foundation for Global Sports Development ✧ ☆
(formerly Justice for Athletes)
333 S. Hope St., 48th Fl.
Los Angeles, CA 90071-1406
Main URL: http://www.globalsportsdevelopment.org/
Blog: http://blog.globalsportsdevelopment.org/
E-Newsletter: http://globalsportsdevelopment.org/join/newsletter/
Facebook: http://www.facebook.com/GlobalSportsDevelopment
Flickr: http://www.flickr.com/photos/106498917@N08/
LinkedIn: http://www.linkedin.com/company/the-foundation-for-global-sports-development
Twitter: http://twitter.com/GlobalSportsD
YouTube: http://www.youtube.com/user/GlobalSportsD

Donor: Dorot Foundation.
Foundation type: Independent foundation.
Financial data (yr. ended 12/31/13): Assets, $37,481,798 (M); gifts received, $53,000; expenditures, $2,585,786; qualifying distributions, $1,959,662; giving activities include $1,029,924 for 43 grants (high: $125,000; low: $2,000), and $2,592,805 for foundation-administered programs.
Purpose and activities: Giving for programs that promote sportsmanship, education, fair play, and ethics among youth.
Fields of interest: Recreation, centers; Athletics/sports, school programs; Athletics/sports, amateur leagues.
Limitations: Applications accepted. Giving primarily in CA; giving internationally in Switzerland. No grants to individuals.
Application information:
Initial approach: Letter (2-3 pages)
Copies of proposal: 1
Board meeting date(s): Biannually
Officers: David C. Ulich, Esq., Pres.; Steven Ungerleider, Ph.D., V.P.; Steven C. Baum, Secy.-Treas.
EIN: 954560243

544
The Sidney E. Frank Foundation ✧
575 Market St., Ste. 3165
San Francisco, CA 94105-2854
Contact: Rae Richman, Philanthropic Advisor
FAX: (415) 543-0753; E-mail for Rae Richman: rrichman@rockpa.org

Established in 2004 in NY.
Donor: Sidney E. Frank†.
Foundation type: Independent foundation.
Financial data (yr. ended 12/31/12): Assets, $293,277,041 (M); gifts received, $1,500,000; expenditures, $9,528,570; qualifying distributions, $9,225,278; giving activities include $6,373,341 for 120 grants (high: $550,000; low: $1,000).
Fields of interest: Arts, multipurpose centers/programs; Elementary/secondary education;

Education; Environment, beautification programs; Environment; Cancer; Medical research.
Limitations: Applications not accepted. Giving primarily in the San Francisco Bay Area and San Diego, CA, HI, and New York City. No grants to individuals.
Application information: Contributes only to pre-selected organizations.
Officer: Amy C. Fisch, C.I.O.
Trustees: Cathy Halstead; Peter Halstead; Anne M. Logan; Harold R. Logan, Jr.
Number of staff: 1 full-time professional.
EIN: 206383779
Selected grants: The following grants are a representative sample of this grantmaker's funding activity:
$550,000 to Brown University, Providence, RI, 2012. For the Ruth Simmons Scholarship Fund.
$250,000 to Connecticut College, New London, CT, 2012. To establish Helen O'Brien Class of 1937 Scholarship.
$250,000 to Israel Science Foundation, Jerusalem, Israel, 2012. For research in the field of renewable and sustainable energies, and in particular the development of novel energy storage systems.
$250,000 to Rockefeller Philanthropy Advisors, New York, NY, 2012. For general operating support for the Skippy Frank Translational Medicine and Life Sciences Fund.
$250,000 to San Francisco, City and County of, Department of the Environment, San Francisco, CA, 2012. For funding to plan and implement projects related to using 100% clean energy.
$115,000 to Musical Arts Association, Cleveland Orchestra, Cleveland, OH, 2012. For the Audio Archive Project.
$100,000 to Natural Resources Defense Council, Santa Monica, CA, 2012. For NRDC's China Energy and Oceans Conservation programs.
$25,000 to Brown University, Providence, RI, 2012. For Lacy Hermann scholarship fund.
$25,000 to Caramoor Center for Music and the Arts, Katonah, NY, 2012. For mentoring programs for young musicians.
$20,000 to Walking Mountains, Avon, CO, 2012. For Science field programs for 4th grade and preschool pilot program.

545
The Don and Lorraine Freeberg Foundation ✧
801 N. Brand Blvd., No. 1010
Glendale, CA 91203-1299 (818) 247-3681
Contact: Daniel Freeberg, Pres. and C.E.O.

Established in 1990 in CA.
Donors: Donald A. Freeberg; Lorraine Freeberg; Donald A. Freeberg 1976 Trusts.
Foundation type: Independent foundation.
Financial data (yr. ended 03/31/13): Assets, $92,470,665 (M); gifts received, $91,080,000; expenditures, $1,660,156; qualifying distributions, $1,660,156; giving activities include $1,638,000 for 17 grants (high: $390,000; low: $2,500).
Fields of interest: Education; Hospitals (specialty); Housing/shelter; Boy scouts; Youth development; Human services.
Type of support: General/operating support; Scholarship funds.
Limitations: Applications accepted. Giving primarily in CA. No grants to individuals.
Application information: Application form not required.
Initial approach: Proposal
Deadline(s): None
Officers: Daniel Freeberg, C.E.O. and Pres.; Shirley Hough, Secy.; James Geary, C.F.O.
Directors: Lorraine Freeberg; Dirk Heim.
EIN: 954307817
Selected grants: The following grants are a representative sample of this grantmaker's funding activity:
$83,500 to Claremont McKenna College, Claremont, CA, 2011. For charitable activities.
$30,000 to University of California, Los Angeles, CA, 2011. For charitable activities.
$20,000 to Greater Los Angeles Zoo Association, Los Angeles, CA, 2011. For charitable activities.
$10,000 to Saint Johns Health Center Foundation, Santa Monica, CA, 2011. For charitable activities.
$10,000 to YMCA of Metropolitan Los Angeles, Los Angeles, CA, 2011. For charitable activities.
$6,000 to Sigma Chi Foundation, Evanston, IL, 2011. For charitable activities.
$5,000 to Pacific Legal Foundation, Sacramento, CA, 2011. For charitable activities.
$5,000 to University of Minnesota Foundation, Minneapolis, MN, 2011. For charitable activities.

546
Bradford M. Freeman Foundation ✧
11100 Santa Monica Blvd., Ste. 1900
Los Angeles, CA 90025-0525

Established in 1985 in CA.
Donors: Bradford M. Freeman; Elizabeth C. Freeman.
Foundation type: Independent foundation.
Financial data (yr. ended 12/31/13): Assets, $21,299,068 (M); expenditures, $2,055,536; qualifying distributions, $1,685,100; giving activities include $1,674,850 for 11 grants (high: $750,050; low: $100).
Fields of interest: Higher education; Education; Foundations (private grantmaking); Public policy, research.
Limitations: Applications not accepted. Giving primarily in CA, GA, IL, and TX. No grants to individuals.
Application information: Contributes only to pre-selected organizations.
Trustees: Bradford M. Freeman; Elizabeth C. Freeman; Ronald P. Spogli.
EIN: 956040946

547
Freidenrich Family Foundation ✧
300 Hamilton Ave., 4th Fl.
Palo Alto, CA 94301-2573 (650) 838-1030
Contact: Austin Wong

Established in CA.
Donors: John Freidenrich; Jill Freidenrich.
Foundation type: Independent foundation.
Financial data (yr. ended 11/30/13): Assets, $489,359 (M); gifts received, $870,914; expenditures, $967,485; qualifying distributions, $969,488; giving activities include $967,485 for 24 grants (high: $324,000; low: $500).
Fields of interest: Cancer research; Youth, services; Public policy, research; Jewish agencies & synagogues.
Type of support: General/operating support.
Limitations: Applications accepted. Giving primarily in CA.
Application information: Application form required.
Initial approach: Letter
Deadline(s): None
Officers: John Freidenrich, Pres.; Jill Freidenrich, V.P.
EIN: 942781744
Selected grants: The following grants are a representative sample of this grantmaker's funding activity:
$200,000 to Breast Cancer Connections, Palo Alto, CA, 2011. For general support.
$100,000 to Center for National Policy, Washington, DC, 2011. For general support.
$88,750 to Stanford University, Stanford, CA, 2011. For general support.
$5,000 to Canary Fund, Palo Alto, CA, 2011. For general support.
$5,000 to Cancer Prevention Institute of California, Fremont, CA, 2011. For general support.
$2,500 to Avenidas, Palo Alto, CA, 2011. For general support.
$2,000 to Ravenswood Family Health Center, East Palo Alto, CA, 2011. For general support.
$1,500 to K Q E D, San Francisco, CA, 2011. For general support.
$1,500 to Planned Parenthood Mar Monte, San Jose, CA, 2011. For general support.
$1,000 to Palo Alto Art Center Foundation, Palo Alto, CA, 2011. For general support.

548
Fremont Bank Foundation ✧
39150 Fremont Blvd.
Fremont, CA 94538-1316
Main URL: https://www.fremontbank.com/about/community-relations/fremont-bank-foundation
Recent Grants: https://www.fremontbank.com/about/community-relations/fremont-bank-foundation/recent-grants

Established as a company-sponsored operating foundation in 1996 in CA.
Donor: Fremont Bank.
Foundation type: Company-sponsored foundation.
Financial data (yr. ended 12/31/12): Assets, $8,310,927 (M); gifts received, $3,721,659; expenditures, $633,577; qualifying distributions, $633,577; giving activities include $627,802 for 78 grants (high: $100,000; low: $250).
Purpose and activities: The Fremont Bank Foundation provides financial assistance to nonprofit organizations for the implementation of series and programs that enhance the quality of life for all people in the communities served by Fremont Bank.
Fields of interest: Performing arts; Arts; Education; Environment; Public health; Health care; Mental health/crisis services; Health organizations; Crime/violence prevention, abuse prevention; Crime/violence prevention, domestic violence; Crime/violence prevention, child abuse; Nutrition; Children/youth, services; Human services, financial counseling; Homeless, human services; Human services.
Type of support: Building/renovation; Capital campaigns; Endowments; Equipment; General/operating support; Program development; Research; Scholarship funds.
Limitations: Applications not accepted. Giving primarily in San Francisco Bay Area, CA in areas of company operations. No support for private

foundations, pass-through organizations, or national or international organizations (except for local chapters addressing the needs of the community). No grants to individuals, or for political or labor activities, debt reduction, or membership fees or dues.
Publications: Grants list.
Application information: Contributes only to pre-selected organizations.
Board meeting date(s): Annually
Officers: Hattie Hyman Hughes, Pres.; Bradford L. Anderson, C.F.O; Howard L. Hyman, V.P.; Chris Chenoweth, Secy.
Directors: Sharon Belshaw-Jones; Brian Hughes; Alan L. Hyman; Michael J. Wallace.
EIN: 943170075
Selected grants: The following grants are a representative sample of this grantmaker's funding activity:
$100,000 to Fremont Unified School District, Fremont, CA, 2012. For professional development center.
$100,000 to Holy Names University, Oakland, CA, 2012. For EverForward Campaign.
$10,000 to Alameda County Library Foundation, Fremont, CA, 2012. For Homework Centers Program.
$10,000 to Holy Names University, Oakland, CA, 2012. For Mission Scholarship Fund.
$7,500 to Fremont Education Foundation, Fremont, CA, 2012. For after-school programs.
$5,000 to Moreau Catholic High School, Hayward, CA, 2012. For Need-Based Tuition Assistance.
$2,500 to Lasallian Educational Opportunities, Oakland, CA, 2012. For Celestial Gala.
$2,500 to Newark Unified School District, Newark, CA, 2012. For Graham Elementary Video/Audio System.
$2,000 to Pleasanton Unified School District, Pleasanton, CA, 2012. For Computer and Internet Access.
$1,000 to New Haven Schools Foundation, Union City, CA, 2012. For Need-Based Scholarships.

549
Fresno Regional Foundation ✧

5250 N. Palm Ave., Ste. 424
Fresno, CA 93704-2210
Contact: For grants: Sandra R. Flores, Sr. Prog. Off.
FAX: (559) 230-2078;
E-mail: info@fresnoregfoundation.org; Grant application e-mail: sandra@fresnoregfoundation.org; Main URL: http://www.fresnoregfoundation.org
E-Newsletter: https://frf.giftlegacy.com/?pageID=42
Facebook: http://www.facebook.com/fresnoregfound
Knowledge Center: http://www.fresnoregfoundation.org/utility/resources/fornonprofits.html
LinkedIn: http://www.linkedin.com/company/1221717?trk=tyah
Twitter: http://twitter.com/fresnoregfound
Vimeo: http://vimeo.com/channels/frf
YouTube: http://www.youtube.com/user/fresnoregfoundation

Established as a trust in 1966 in CA.
Foundation type: Community foundation.
Financial data (yr. ended 12/31/13): Assets, $66,584,252 (M); gifts received, $8,737,868; expenditures, $10,980,615; giving activities include $10,227,475 for grants, and $926,250 for loans/program-related investments.
Purpose and activities: The foundation provides unique opportunities for individual donors, families, businesses, and other foundations to invest in programs that address a wide spectrum of economic, social, educational, cultural and environmental needs.
Fields of interest: Performing arts, music; Arts; Education; Environment; Health care; Recreation, parks/playgrounds; Youth, pregnancy prevention; Human services; Economic development; Government/public administration; Children/youth.
Type of support: Continuing support; Management development/capacity building; Equipment; Seed money; Program-related investments/loans.
Limitations: Applications accepted. Giving primarily in the central San Joaquin Valley, CA, area, especially Fresno, Kings, Madera, Mariposa, Merced, and Tulare counties. No support for sectarian religious purposes. No grants to individuals (except for scholarships), or for previously incurred expenses, endowment funds, or fundraising by one agency on behalf of another.
Publications: Application guidelines; Annual report; Financial statement; Informational brochure; Newsletter; Newsletter (including application guidelines); Quarterly report.
Application information: Visit: www.fresnoregounfation.org/cbo/v2/programs.html for application form and guidelines. Application form required.
Initial approach: Create an online profile
Copies of proposal: 7
Deadline(s): Mar. 7 for Arts and Culture, Mar. 20 for Youth, June 20 for Human Services and Teen Pregnancy Prevention, Sept. 16 for High Impact Grants, and Nov. 7 for Environment
Officers and Governors:* Carole Andersen,* Chair.; Hon. Brad R. Hill,* Vice-Chair.; Hugh J. Ralston,* C.E.O. and Pres.; Lydia Herrera-Mata,* Secy.; Marla Hartman,* Treas.; Susan Abundis; Celia Maldonado Arroyo; Desa C. Belyea; Joe Del Bosque; Carol Chandler; Rich Olsson; Armando Rodriguez; Ray Steele, Jr.; Mariam Stepanian; Allysunn Williams.
Trustee Bank: Wells Fargo Bank, N.A.
Number of staff: 9 full-time professional; 2 full-time support.
EIN: 770478025

550
Friedman Family Foundation ✧

353 Folsom St., 2nd Fl.
San Francisco, CA 94105-2300 (650) 342-8750
FAX: (866) 223-1078;
E-mail: info@friedmanfamilyfoundation.org; Main URL: http://www.friedmanfamilyfoundation.org
Grants List: http://www.friedmanfamilyfoundation.org/grants/

Established in 1964 in CA.
Donors: Phyllis K. Friedman; Howard Friedman†.
Foundation type: Independent foundation.
Financial data (yr. ended 02/28/14): Assets, $9,963,515 (M); expenditures, $660,944; qualifying distributions, $660,797; giving activities include $500,000 for 92 grants (high: $10,000; low: $250).
Purpose and activities: Support for programs which attempt to end the cycle of poverty, especially programs that provide tools, support, asset building, and opportunity to people in need in order to overcome the root causes of their poverty, and in which the people to be helped are part of the design and decision making of the organization or project. Preference is given to new and creative programs, and programs working for systemic change.
Fields of interest: Economic development; Community/economic development; Economically disadvantaged.
Type of support: General/operating support; Program development; Program-related investments/loans.
Limitations: Applications accepted. Giving primarily in the nine counties of the San Francisco Bay Area, CA. No grants to individuals, or for films, videos, conferences, seminars, capital campaigns, scholarships, research, or special or fundraising events.
Publications: Application guidelines; Grants list; Occasional report (including application guidelines).
Application information: Applications are by invitation only, upon review of letter of inquiry. Fax submissions are not accepted. E-mail is preferred. Application form required.
Initial approach: Letter
Copies of proposal: 1
Deadline(s): None, for letters of inquiry; see foundation web site for current application deadlines
Board meeting date(s): Varies, meets 3 times a year
Final notification: Up to 3 months for letters of inquiry
Officers: Phyllis K. Friedman, Pres.; Eleanor Friedman, V.P.; Robert E. Friedman, Secy.; David A. Friedman, Treas.
Number of staff: 1 part-time professional.
EIN: 946109692
Selected grants: The following grants are a representative sample of this grantmaker's funding activity:
$10,000 to Bend the Arc: A Jewish Partnership for Justice, New York, NY, 2012.
$10,000 to Center for Community Change, Washington, DC, 2012.
$10,000 to Center for Responsible Lending, Durham, NC, 2012.
$10,000 to First Nations Development Institute, Longmont, CO, 2012.
$10,000 to Lao Family Community Development, Oakland, CA, 2012.
$10,000 to Mercy Corps, Portland, OR, 2012.
$2,000 to Center for Community Change, Washington, DC, 2012.
$2,000 to New Israel Fund, New York, NY, 2012.
$1,000 to Center for Community Change, Washington, DC, 2012.
$1,000 to Opportunity Fund, San Jose, CA, 2012.

551
Tully and Elise Friedman Fund ✧

65 Raycliff Terr.
San Francisco, CA 94115-1108

Established in 1997 in CA.
Donors: Tully M. Friedman; Elise D. Friedman.
Foundation type: Independent foundation.
Financial data (yr. ended 12/31/13): Assets, $10,229,020 (M); gifts received, $1,524,937; expenditures, $528,681; qualifying distributions, $513,590; giving activities include $500,475 for 31 grants (high: $150,000; low: $225).
Fields of interest: Museums (art); Arts; Elementary/secondary education; Human services; Social sciences, research.

Limitations: Applications not accepted. Giving primarily in the San Francisco Bay Area, CA.
Application information: Unsolicited requests for funds not accepted.
Officers: Tully M. Friedman, Pres.; Elise D. Friedman, V.P.
EIN: 943264446
Selected grants: The following grants are a representative sample of this grantmaker's funding activity:
$655,115 to American Enterprise Institute for Public Policy Research, Washington, DC, 2011. For general support.
$400,000 to Donors Trust, Alexandria, VA, 2011. For general support.
$177,500 to Cathedral School for Boys, San Francisco, CA, 2010. For general support.
$62,500 to Telluride Foundation, Telluride, CO, 2011. For general support.
$25,000 to Eagle Hill Foundation, Greenwich, CT, 2011. For general support.
$25,000 to Katherine Delmar Burke School, San Francisco, CA, 2011. For general support.
$25,000 to New York University, New York, NY, 2011. For general support.
$17,500 to Cathedral School for Boys, San Francisco, CA, 2011. For general support.
$15,000 to Foreign Policy Association, New York, NY, 2010. For general support.
$2,500 to Red Tab Foundation, San Francisco, CA, 2011. For general support.
$1,500 to Yale University, New Haven, CT, 2011. For general support.
$1,000 to Tides Foundation, San Francisco, CA, 2011. For general support.

552
The Friend Family Foundation ✧
(formerly The Eugene Friend Family Foundation)
355 Hayes St.
San Francisco, CA 94102-4420
Contact: Robert B. Friend, Pres.; Additional contact: Donald A. Friend, Secy.
E-mail: bob@friendsf.com

Established in 1967 in CA.
Donors: Donald A. Friend; Eugene L. Friend†; Robert B. Friend.
Foundation type: Independent foundation.
Financial data (yr. ended 06/30/13): Assets, $4,962,747 (M); expenditures, $832,185; qualifying distributions, $812,660; giving activities include $812,500 for 28 grants (high: $250,000; low: $1,000).
Purpose and activities: Grants primarily for Jewish giving, including Jewish welfare funds; support also for cultural programs.
Fields of interest: Arts; Human services; Jewish federated giving programs; Jewish agencies & synagogues.
Limitations: Applications not accepted. Giving primarily in CA, with emphasis on San Rafael and San Francisco. No grants to individuals.
Application information: Contributes only to pre-selected organizations.
Officers and Directors:* Robert Friend,* Pres.; Donald A. Friend,* Secy.
EIN: 946163916
Selected grants: The following grants are a representative sample of this grantmaker's funding activity:
$412,500 to University of California San Francisco Foundation, San Francisco, CA, 2011.
$250,000 to University of California at Berkeley Foundation, Berkeley, CA, 2011.
$80,000 to Taube Foundation for Jewish Life and Culture, San Francisco, CA, 2011.
$50,000 to Congregation Emanu-El, San Francisco, CA, 2011.
$30,000 to Global Citizen Year, Oakland, CA, 2011.
$25,000 to Jewish Family and Childrens Services, San Francisco, CA, 2011.
$25,000 to SF-Marin Food Bank, San Francisco, CA, 2011.
$20,000 to San Francisco Parks Trust, San Francisco, CA, 2011.
$15,000 to Glide Foundation, San Francisco, CA, 2011.
$10,000 to American Himalayan Foundation, San Francisco, CA, 2011.

553
The Alfred & Hanna Fromm Fund ✧
80 E. Sir Francis Drake Blvd., No. 4D
Larkspur, CA 94939-1748

Established in 1965 in CA.
Donors: Alfred Fromm†; Hanna Fromm; Alfred and Hanna Fromm Charitable Lead Annuity Trust.
Foundation type: Independent foundation.
Financial data (yr. ended 09/30/12): Assets, $25,017,406 (M); gifts received, $2,368,967; expenditures, $1,522,307; qualifying distributions, $1,362,500; giving activities include $1,330,000 for 9 grants (high: $790,000; low: $550).
Purpose and activities: Giving primarily to Jewish federated giving funds and to a university's education program for retired persons.
Fields of interest: Higher education; Adult/continuing education; Human services; Jewish federated giving programs; Jewish agencies & synagogues.
International interests: Israel.
Limitations: Applications not accepted. Giving primarily in San Francisco and Larkspur, CA. No grants to individuals.
Application information: Contributes only to pre-selected organizations.
Officers and Directors:* Rabbi Brian L. Lurie, Pres.; Caroline Lurie, V.P.; David George Fromm, Secy.; Peter K. Maier,* Treas.; Barbara Fromm.
Agent: Susan Lechter.
Number of staff: 2 full-time professional; 1 full-time support.
EIN: 946100399

554
The Fruth Family Foundation ✧
2600 Lyon St.
San Francisco, CA 94123

Established in 2003 in CA.
Donor: John Fruth.
Foundation type: Independent foundation.
Financial data (yr. ended 12/31/12): Assets, $10,430,555 (M); expenditures, $633,844; qualifying distributions, $548,193; giving activities include $545,268 for 7 grants (high: $347,050; low: $2,600).
Fields of interest: Education; Health care; Human services; Children/youth, services.
Limitations: Applications not accepted. Giving primarily in CA. No grants to individuals.
Application information: Contributes only to pre-selected organizations.
Officers: John Fruth, Pres.; Jean Fruth, Secy. and C.F.O.
EIN: 710956112

555
Fry Family Foundation ✧
1 Tidecrest
Newport Coast, CA 92657-1801

Established in 2001 in CA.
Donors: Cynthia D. Fry; Stephen T. Fry.
Foundation type: Independent foundation.
Financial data (yr. ended 12/31/13): Assets, $3,008,467 (M); gifts received, $2,046,569; expenditures, $2,813,052; qualifying distributions, $2,789,501; giving activities include $2,765,250 for 22 grants (high: $1,110,000; low: $150).
Fields of interest: Performing arts centers; Higher education; Health organizations; Human services.
Type of support: General/operating support.
Limitations: Applications not accepted. Giving primarily in CA; some funding also in FL. No grants to individuals.
Application information: Contributes only to pre-selected organizations.
Officers: Stephen T. Fry, Pres.; Cynthia D. Fry, Secy. and C.F.O.
EIN: 912146205

556
Fund for Nonviolence ✧
303 Potrero, No. 54
Santa Cruz, CA 95060-2760 (831) 460-9321
Contact: Monica Larenas, Prog. Off.
FAX: (831) 460-9137;
E-mail: mail@fundfornonviolence.org; Toll-free tel.: (866) 454-8006; Main URL: http://www.fundfornonviolence.org
Grants List: http://www.fundfornonviolence.org/grants/grants.html

Established in 1997 in CA.
Foundation type: Independent foundation.
Financial data (yr. ended 12/31/12): Assets, $3,101,996 (M); expenditures, $1,088,550; qualifying distributions, $902,800; giving activities include $585,287 for 29 grants (high: $70,000; low: $500) and $251,750 for set-asides.
Purpose and activities: The fund cultivates and supports efforts to bring about social change that moves humanity towards a more just and compassionate coexistence. Primary interest is placed on proposals from organizations that: 1) pursue structural changes to root causes of race, class, and gender injustice; 2) value the active involvement of members of the communities most impacted by the violence and social injustice being addressed; 3) understand and articulate the impact of their work on women and promote the leadership of women within the organization; 4) work through networks, coalitions and alliances; 5) reflect the spirit of nonviolence in their organizational relations, structure, and process; and 6) demonstrate the capacity to reflect on their experience and adapt to lessons and insights.
Fields of interest: Offenders/ex-offenders, prison alternatives; Civil/human rights, alliance/advocacy; Civil/human rights, advocacy; Civil liberties, death

penalty issues; Offenders/ex-offenders; Crime/abuse victims.
International interests: Colombia; Ecuador; Latin America; Mexico; Peru.
Type of support: Consulting services; General/operating support; Continuing support; Management development/capacity building; Program development; Conferences/seminars; Seed money; Technical assistance; Program evaluation.
Limitations: Giving primarily in CA through the Justice with Dignity Program; giving nationally through the Lifting Voices of Resistance Program. No grants to individuals; no support for one-time events or experiences that are not connected to broader campaigns or movement building or without effective follow up; no support for media production costs.
Publications: Application guidelines; Grants list.
Application information: Unsolicited requests for funding are currently not accepted. Check foundation web site for updates in this area. Application form not required.
Board meeting date(s): Full board: Jan., Apr., and Oct.; grantmaking committees separately
Officers and Directors:* Betsy Fairbanks,* C.E.O. and Pres.; Carolina Martinez, Secy.; Lynda Marin,* Treas.; Kelli Evans; Rebecca Rittgers.
Number of staff: 2 full-time professional; 1 part-time professional.
EIN: 770457185

557
Gaia Fund ✧
235 Montgomery St., Ste. 1011
San Francisco, CA 94104-3003 (415) 391-6943
Contact: Mark L. Schlesinger, C.F.O., Secy. and Dir.
FAX: (415) 391-7155; E-mail: email@gaiaSF.org;
Main URL: http://www.gaiasf.org

Established in 1994 in CA.
Donors: Christine H. Russell; Mark Schlesinger; M.H. Russell 94 Char Lead Trust.
Foundation type: Independent foundation.
Financial data (yr. ended 12/31/12): Assets, $14,066,757 (M); gifts received, $20; expenditures, $916,246; qualifying distributions, $896,943; giving activities include $889,775 for 39 grants (high: $293,100; low: $1,000).
Purpose and activities: Support primarily for organizations involved with environmental programs that promote sustainable practices relative to food production, distribution, and consumption. The fund also makes grants to programs serving the Jewish community of San Francisco, California.
Fields of interest: Environment; Jewish agencies & synagogues.
Type of support: General/operating support; Continuing support; Program development; Conferences/seminars.
Limitations: Applications accepted. Giving primarily in the San Francisco Bay Area, CA. No support for Holocaust related projects, initiatives based in Israel, environmental education programs for children, or social service programs. No grants to individuals.
Application information: Application guidelines and inquiry form available on foundation web site. Applicants should send two sets of the completed inquiry form and optional supporting letter, three-hole punched, to the fund via regular mail. Application form required.
Initial approach: Inquiry form
Copies of proposal: 2
Deadline(s): Feb. 15 and Aug. 15
Board meeting date(s): May and Nov.
Officers and Directors:* Christine H. Russell,* C.E.O.; Mark L. Schlesinger,* Secy. and C.F.O.
EIN: 943215541
Selected grants: The following grants are a representative sample of this grantmaker's funding activity:
$62,500 to Congregation Emanu-El, San Francisco, CA, 2012. For special campaign.
$60,175 to Contemporary Jewish Museum, San Francisco, CA, 2012. For general support and Exhibit Support.
$55,000 to Trust for Conservation Innovation, San Francisco, CA, 2012. For Kitchen Table Advisors and Roots of Change.
$10,000 to Shotgun Players, Berkeley, CA, 2012. For Josh Kornbluth play.
$10,000 to Xerces Society, Portland, OR, 2012. For Restoring Biodiversity Project.
$2,500 to Vassar College, Poughkeepsie, NY, 2012. For Combined Annual/Capital Campaign Contribution.
$1,000 to Golden Gate National Parks Conservancy, San Francisco, CA, 2012. For Golden Gate Bridge Celebration.
$1,000 to Zen Hospice Project, San Francisco, CA, 2012. For One Night, One Heart Gala.

558
The Galen Family Foundation ✧
10253 Century Woods Dr.
Los Angeles, CA 90067-6312

Established in 2004 in CO.
Donors: Louis J. Galen; Helene V. Galen; Louis and Helen Galen Charitable Remainder Trust No. 1; The Museum of Contemporary Art.
Foundation type: Independent foundation.
Financial data (yr. ended 12/31/13): Assets, $6,542,056 (M); gifts received, $32,354; expenditures, $1,011,486; qualifying distributions, $955,135; giving activities include $943,785 for 52 grants (high: $25,000; low: $500).
Fields of interest: Museums (art); Arts; Education; Health organizations, association; Human services; Children/youth, services; Family services; Jewish agencies & synagogues.
Limitations: Applications not accepted. Giving primarily in CA. No grants to individuals.
Application information: Contributes only to pre-selected organizations.
Officers: Helene V. Galen, Pres.; Charles Mostov, Treas.
EIN: 201306111
Selected grants: The following grants are a representative sample of this grantmaker's funding activity:
$393,975 to Palm Springs Art Museum, Palm Springs, CA, 2011.
$5,000 to San Francisco Museum of Modern Art, San Francisco, CA, 2011.
$3,000 to Palm Springs Friends of Philharmonic, Palm Desert, CA, 2011.
$1,500 to Desert Symphony, Palm Desert, CA, 2011.

559
David E. Gallo Foundation ✧ ☆
P.O. Box 1130
Modesto, CA 95353-1130

Established in 1998 in CA.
Donors: Christopher D. Gallo; Mary C. Gallo; Theresa M. Gallo; E. & J. Gallo Winery.
Foundation type: Independent foundation.
Financial data (yr. ended 12/31/13): Assets, $12,878,139 (M); gifts received, $1,000,000; expenditures, $627,963; qualifying distributions, $576,082; giving activities include $576,082 for 54 grants (high: $225,000; low: $250).
Purpose and activities: Giving primarily for education, health, human services, and Roman Catholic agencies and churches.
Fields of interest: Education; Health organizations; Catholic agencies & churches.
Limitations: Applications not accepted. Giving primarily in CA, with emphasis on Modesto. No grants to individuals.
Application information: Unsolicited requests for funds not accepted.
Officers and Directors:* Mary C. Gallo,* Chair.; Theresa M. Gallo,* Secy.; Christopher D. Gallo,* C.F.O.
EIN: 770476093
Selected grants: The following grants are a representative sample of this grantmaker's funding activity:
$5,000 to Modesto Junior College Foundation, Modesto, CA, 2012. For -All Contributions Made During the Year Were for General Use in Carrying Out Charitable, Religious, and Educational Activities. -None of the Recipients Are Individuals Related in Any Way to a Foundation Manager Or Substantial Contributor.

560
The Ernest Gallo Foundation ✧
P.O. Box 1130
Modesto, CA 95353-1130

Incorporated in 1955 in CA.
Donors: Ernest Gallo†; Joseph E. Gallo; E. & J. Gallo Winery; Ernest Gallo Trust.
Foundation type: Independent foundation.
Financial data (yr. ended 10/31/13): Assets, $55,964,458 (M); gifts received, $2,000,000; expenditures, $1,999,816; qualifying distributions, $1,865,000; giving activities include $1,865,000 for 8 grants (high: $1,010,000; low: $20,000).
Fields of interest: Performing arts centers; Higher education; Health care; Foundations (community); Religion.
Limitations: Applications not accepted. Giving primarily in CA; funding also in Notre Dame, IN. No grants to individuals.
Application information: Contributes only to pre-selected organizations.
Officers: Joseph E. Gallo, Pres.; Christopher D. Gallo, V.P.; Ernest J. Gallo, V.P.; Richard M. Beal, Secy.; Mary I. Gallo, Treas.
EIN: 946061537

561
Julio R. Gallo Foundation ✧
P.O. Box 1130
Modesto, CA 95353-1130 (209) 341-3375
Contact: Jessie Nelson

Incorporated in 1955 in CA.
Donors: Julio R. Gallo†; Robert J. Gallo; Aileen Gallo; Aileen Gallo Survivor's Trust; E. & J. Gallo Winery.
Foundation type: Independent foundation.
Financial data (yr. ended 10/31/13): Assets, $22,011,454 (M); gifts received, $2,000,000; expenditures, $1,162,823; qualifying distributions, $986,500; giving activities include $985,500 for 78 grants (high: $461,000; low: $250).
Purpose and activities: Giving primarily for the arts, education, Roman Catholic churches and organizations, and human services.
Fields of interest: Arts; Elementary/secondary education; Higher education; Health organizations; Human services; Children, services; Catholic agencies & churches.
Limitations: Applications accepted. Giving primarily in CA, with emphasis on Modesto. No grants to individuals.
Application information: Application form required.
Initial approach: Letter
Deadline(s): None
Officers: James E. Coleman, Co-Pres.; Robert J. Gallo, Co-Pres.; Matthew I. Friedrich, Secy.; Anthony L. Youga, Treas.
Directors: Gregory J. Coleman; John R. Gallo.
EIN: 946061539
Selected grants: The following grants are a representative sample of this grantmaker's funding activity:
$1,829,850 to Saint Stanislaus Catholic Church, Modesto, CA, 2011.
$63,000 to Diocese of Stockton, Stockton, CA, 2011.
$55,000 to Oregon State University Foundation, Corvallis, OR, 2011.
$20,000 to Eternal Word Television Network, Irondale, AL, 2011.
$15,500 to Education Foundation of Stanislaus County, Modesto, CA, 2011.
$7,500 to Santa Clara University, Santa Clara, CA, 2011.
$5,000 to Archdiocese of Los Angeles, Los Angeles, CA, 2011.
$5,000 to Archdiocese of Philadelphia, Philadelphia, PA, 2011.
$5,000 to Childrens Hospital Central California, Madera, CA, 2010.
$5,000 to Holy Names University, Oakland, CA, 2011.
$5,000 to Naples Children and Education Foundation, Naples, FL, 2010.
$5,000 to Saint Patricks Seminary, Menlo Park, CA, 2011.
$5,000 to United Samaritans Foundation, Turlock, CA, 2010.
$5,000 to United Way of Stanislaus County, Modesto, CA, 2010.

562
The Gamble Foundation ✧ ☆
1660 Bush St., Ste. 300
San Francisco, CA 94109-5308 (415) 561-6540
Contact: Emily Schroeder, Grants Mgr.
FAX: (415) 561-5477; E-mail for Emily Schroeder, Grants Mgr.: eschroeder@pfs-llc.net; tel.: (415) 561-6540, ext. 222; Main URL: http://www.gamblefoundation.org

Established in 1968 in CA.
Donors: Launce E. Gamble; Mary S. Gamble†; George F. Gamble; MSG Charitable Trust; Launce L. Gamble; Mark D. Gamble; Aimee Gamble Price; George T. Gamble; Jim Gamble; Joan L. Gamble.
Foundation type: Independent foundation.
Financial data (yr. ended 12/31/13): Assets, $20,051,653 (M); gifts received, $449,781; expenditures, $801,161; qualifying distributions, $755,696; giving activities include $700,025 for 61 grants (high: $30,000; low: $500).
Purpose and activities: The foundation's primary interest is to support organizations that serve disadvantaged children and youth in San Francisco, Marin and Napa counties. Within the field of youth development, the foundation focuses on educational and personal enrichment programs designed to open doors of opportunity for at risk youth in order to help them succeed in school and become productive, self-sufficient members of society. The foundation is particularly interested in agricultural/environmental education, vocational training, and programs that prevent substance abuse and teen violence. To a lesser degree, the foundation supports environmental organizations that focus on land preservation and sustainability, animal welfare and management, and pollution control. The foundation is interested in promoting green concepts that increase awareness of science-based solutions that help reduce consumption of finite resources.
Fields of interest: Environment, beautification programs; Environment; Youth development.
Type of support: General/operating support; Program development.
Limitations: Applications accepted. Giving primarily in San Francisco, Marin and Napa counties, CA. No support for religious organizations. No grants to individuals, or for medical research, endowment funds, capital improvements, or annual appeals.
Publications: Application guidelines; Annual report; Grants list.
Application information: The foundation accepts proposals for one round of grants each year. Grants range from $10,000 - $25,000 annually over one to four years. The foundation typically funds for no more than four consecutive years. Application guidelines available on foundation web site. Application form required.
Initial approach: Letter
Deadline(s): None
Board meeting date(s): 2nd quarter of each year
Officers and Trustees:* Mark D. Gamble,* Pres.; Aimee Gamble Price,* V.P.; Gregory T. Price,* Secy.; Paul E. Cameron, Treas.; Launce E. Gamble.
EIN: 941680503

563
The Gap Foundation ✧
2 Folsom St., 15th Fl.
San Francisco, CA 94105-1205
E-mail: gap_foundation@gap.com; Main URL: http://www.gapinc.com/content/gapinc/html/csr.html
Be What's Possbile on Twitter: http://twitter.com/bewhatspossible
Be What's Possible on Facebook: https://www.facebook.com/bewhatspossible?sk=wall&filter=1
Be What's Possible on YouTube: http://www.youtube.com/user/bewhatspossible1977?feature=mhee#p/u
Be What's Possible: An Employee and Community Website: http://www.bewhatspossible.com/
GiveSmart: http://www.givesmart.org/Stories/Donors/John-and-Doris-Fisher

Established in 1977 in CA.
Donor: The Gap, Inc.
Foundation type: Company-sponsored foundation.
Financial data (yr. ended 01/31/13): Assets, $14,840,512 (M); gifts received, $3,448,905; expenditures, $3,544,377; qualifying distributions, $3,544,053; giving activities include $2,586,540 for 55 grants (high: $250,000; low: $5,000), and $957,513 for employee matching gifts.
Purpose and activities: The foundation supports programs designed to reach underserved youth in the developed world with an emphasis on job readiness and employment; and advance women in the developing world.
Fields of interest: Secondary school/education; Education; Employment, services; Employment, training; Employment; Boys & girls clubs; Youth development, adult & child programs; Youth development; Human services; International affairs; Youth; Women; Economically disadvantaged.
Type of support: General/operating support; Management development/capacity building; Program development; Scholarship funds; Employee volunteer services; Sponsorships; Employee matching gifts; Donated equipment; Donated products; In-kind gifts.
Limitations: Applications not accepted. Giving primarily in areas of company operations, with emphasis on San Francisco, CA, Chicago, IL, New York, NY. No support for religious, political, or discriminatory organizations. No grants to individuals, or for scholarships, conferences, travel, films, videos, or fundraisers (except for gift card donations).
Application information: The foundation does not accept unsolicited proposals for grants or event sponsorships.
Officers and Trustees:* Glenn Murphy,* Chair.; Bobbi Silten, Pres.; David Jedrezejek, Secy.; Forrest Bryant, Treas.; Doris F. Fisher; Jennifer Gosselin; Dan Henkle; Roy Hunt; Tom Keiser; Liz O'Neill; Art Peck; Sabrina Simmons.
EIN: 942474426

564
Melvin Garb Foundation ✧
5348 Carroll Canyon Rd., Ste. 200
San Diego, CA 92121-1733 (858) 750-4200
Contact: Michael Berlin, Dir.; Stephen J. Cohen, Dir.

Established in 1991 in CA.
Donor: Melvin Garb†.
Foundation type: Independent foundation.
Financial data (yr. ended 12/31/13): Assets, $16,810,846 (M); expenditures, $1,773,242; qualifying distributions, $1,492,083; giving activities include $1,492,083 for 15 grants (high: $885,000; low: $5,000).
Purpose and activities: Giving primarily for social services and Jewish agencies.
Fields of interest: Human services; Jewish federated giving programs; Jewish agencies & synagogues.
Type of support: Continuing support; Annual campaigns; Capital campaigns; Building/renovation; Emergency funds; Professorships.
Limitations: Giving primarily in CA. No grants to individuals.
Application information: Application form required.
Initial approach: Complete application form
Deadline(s): None
Board meeting date(s): Quarterly

Directors: Estee Aaronson; David J. Winkler; Howard Cohen; Michael D. Berlin; Stephen J. Cohen.
EIN: 931067365
Selected grants: The following grants are a representative sample of this grantmaker's funding activity:
$65,000 to Anti-Defamation League of Bnai Brith, Los Angeles, CA, 2011.

565
John Jewett & Helen Chandler Garland Foundation ✧
P.O. Box 550
Pasadena, CA 91102-0550 (626) 440-0052
Contact: Lisa M. Hausler, Mgr.

Trust established in 1959 in CA.
Donors: John Jewett Garland Trust; Members of the Garland family.
Foundation type: Independent foundation.
Financial data (yr. ended 12/31/12): Assets, $6,992,369 (M); gifts received, $206,039; expenditures, $4,181,782; qualifying distributions, $4,142,581; giving activities include $4,009,167 for 86 grants (high: $610,000; low: $1,000).
Purpose and activities: Giving primarily for the arts, education, health care, and children and social services.
Fields of interest: Arts; Education; Hospitals (general); Health care; Human services; Children/youth, services.
Type of support: General/operating support; Continuing support; Annual campaigns; Capital campaigns; Building/renovation; Equipment; Endowments; Debt reduction; Emergency funds; Curriculum development; Scholarship funds; Research; Matching/challenge support.
Limitations: Applications accepted. Giving primarily in CA, with emphasis on southern CA. No grants to individuals, or for seed money.
Publications: Application guidelines.
Application information: Application form not required.
Initial approach: Letter only; no telephone inquiries
Copies of proposal: 1
Deadline(s): None
Board meeting date(s): 2 times per year
Final notification: After each meeting
Officer: Lisa M. Hausler, Exec. Dir.
Trustees: Ann Kelsey Babcock; Gwendolyn Garland Babcock; John Carlile Babcock; Sarah Garland Babcock; Susan Hinman Babcock; Hillary Duque Garland; William M. Garland II.
EIN: 956023587

566
Peter A. & Vernice H. Gasser Foundation ✧
433 Soscol Ave., Ste. A120
Napa, CA 94559-1314 (707) 255-1646
Contact: Joseph G. Peatman, Pres.
FAX: (707) 255-4338;
E-mail: jpeatman@gasserfoundation.org; Main URL: http://www.gasserfoundation.org

Established in 1982 in CA.
Donors: Peter A. Gasser†; Vernice H. Gasser†.
Foundation type: Independent foundation.
Financial data (yr. ended 12/31/13): Assets, $91,910,639 (M); gifts received, $211,129; expenditures, $4,941,863; qualifying distributions, $2,106,061; giving activities include $1,934,367 for 187 grants (high: $250,000; low: $250).
Purpose and activities: The foundation supports programs which enhance quality of life and sustain the environment. Fields of interest include the arts, education, economic development for charitable purposes, health and human services, nutrition and shelter, recreation and the environment. Environmental sustainability guides the foundation's action in all its undertakings. Every year the foundation also gives scholarships to each of the high schools in Napa County as well as Napa Valley College, and the Napa Valley Adult School. Most grants are for $1,000.00 and with a preference given to aging out foster children. In September, the foundation invites elementary and middle school teachers in Napa County (public, private and religious) to apply for grants up to $500.00, which can be used for a variety of purposes (i.e.: new projectors, field trips, musical instruments and planting school gardens). Grants are limited to two per school.
Fields of interest: Arts; Education; Environment; Hospitals (general); Human services; Children/youth, services; Family services.
Type of support: Capital campaigns; Building/renovation; Equipment; Land acquisition; Debt reduction; Program development; Seed money; Curriculum development; Scholarship funds; Matching/challenge support; Mission-related investments/loans.
Limitations: Giving limited to Napa County, CA. No support for political purposes. No grants to individuals or for operating costs.
Publications: Application guidelines.
Application information: Application guidelines available on foundation web site; full grant applications are by invitation only.
Initial approach: Letter of Interest
Deadline(s): See foundation web site
Board meeting date(s): Quarterly
Officers and Directors:* Joseph G. Peatman,* Pres.; Julian N. Stern,* Secy.; Ed Barwick; Henry Gundling; Cathy Roche.
Number of staff: 1 full-time professional; 1 full-time support.
EIN: 942816159

567
The David Geffen Foundation ✧
12011 San Vincente Blvd., Ste. 606
Los Angeles, CA 90049-4926 (310) 581-5955
Contact: Richard Sherman, Tr.; J. Dallas Dishman Ph.D, Exec. Dir.
FAX: (310) 581-5949;
E-mail: ddishman@geffenco.com

Incorporated in 1986 in CA.
Donor: David Geffen.
Foundation type: Independent foundation.
Financial data (yr. ended 12/31/12): Assets, $91,891,773 (M); expenditures, $3,448,556; qualifying distributions, $3,009,902; giving activities include $2,829,733 for 182 grants (high: $333,334; low: $500).
Purpose and activities: The foundation has focused its giving in five major areas: populations affected by HIV/AIDS; civil liberties; the arts; issues of concern to the Jewish community, and health care.
Fields of interest: Arts; Health care; AIDS; Civil/human rights; Jewish agencies & synagogues; Children/youth; Youth; Adults; Aging; Young adults; Minorities; AIDS, people with; Economically disadvantaged; Homeless; LGBTQ.
Type of support: General/operating support; Annual campaigns; Capital campaigns; Program development; Program evaluation.
Limitations: Applications accepted. Giving primarily in Los Angeles, CA, and New York, NY. Some giving in Israel as well. No grants to individuals or for documentaries or other types of audio-visual programming or media projects, including publication of books or magazines.
Publications: Program policy statement (including application guidelines).
Application information: Generally does not fund media-related projects. Application form not required.
Initial approach: Proposal
Copies of proposal: 1
Final notification: 3-4 months
Trustees: David Geffen; Richard Sherman.
EIN: 954085811

568
The Carl Gellert and Celia Berta Gellert Foundation
(formerly The Carl Gellert Foundation)
2171 Junipero Serra Blvd., Ste. 310
Daly City, CA 94014-1995 (650) 985-2080
Contact: Jack Fitzpatrick, Exec. Dir.; Rosa King, Grants Mgr.
E-mail: info@gellertfoundation.org; Main URL: http://www.gellertfoundation.org/

Incorporated in 1958 in CA.
Donors: Carl Gellert†; Gertrude E. Gellert†; Celia Berta Gellert†; Atlas Realty Co.; Pacific Coast Construction Co.
Foundation type: Independent foundation.
Financial data (yr. ended 12/31/13): Assets, $44,254,002 (M); expenditures, $2,294,246; qualifying distributions, $1,802,440; giving activities include $1,574,000 for 176 grants (high: $125,000; low: $1,000).
Purpose and activities: The foundation's policy is to promote exclusively religious, charitable, scientific, literary or educational purposes, restricted to local giving in the nine counties of the greater San Francisco Bay Area (Alameda, Contra Costa, Marin, Napa, San Francisco, San Mateo, Santa Clara, Solano and Sonoma).
Fields of interest: Literature; Elementary school/education; Secondary school/education; Higher education; Engineering school/education; Education; Hospitals (general); Substance abuse, services; Human services; Youth, services; Aging, centers/services; Engineering.
Type of support: General/operating support; Continuing support; Annual campaigns; Capital campaigns; Building/renovation; Equipment; Endowments; Program development; Publication; Scholarship funds; Research; Technical assistance.
Limitations: Applications accepted. Giving limited to the nine counties of the greater San Francisco Bay Area, CA, (Alameda, Contra Costa, Marin, Napa, San Francisco, San Mateo, Santa Clara, Solano and Sonoma). No support for private foundations or for organizations outside the 9 counties of the San Francisco Bay Area. No grants to individuals or fiscal sponsors, or for seed money, emergency funds, land acquisition, matching gifts, conferences, sponsorships, fundraising events sponsorships, dinners, walk-a-thons, tournaments, or fashion shows; no loans.

Publications: Application guidelines; Grants list; Program policy statement.
Application information: Application form available on web site. Application form required.
Initial approach: Proposal with application form and supporting documentation outlined in posted guidelines
Copies of proposal: 1
Deadline(s): Annually, on Aug. 15
Board meeting date(s): Nov.
Final notification: In writing, for all decisions, annually on Dec. 31
Officers and Directors:* Robert J. Grassilli,* Chair.; Andrew A. Cresci,* Vice-Chair.; Jack Fitzpatrick,* Secy. and Exec. Dir.; Lorraine D'Elia; Michael J. King; J. Malcolm Visbal.
Number of staff: 1 full-time professional; 1 full-time support.
EIN: 946062858
Selected grants: The following grants are a representative sample of this grantmaker's funding activity:
$125,000 to Saint Anthony Foundation, San Francisco, CA, 2012. For New Saint Anthony Dining Room.
$100,000 to Bellarmine College Preparatory, San Jose, CA, 2012. For Construction of the Student Life Center and Auxiliary Gym.
$100,000 to Junipero Serra High School, San Mateo, CA, 2012. For Center for the Arts and Sciences and Aquatics Center.
$100,000 to Sequoia Hospital Foundation, Redwood City, CA, 2012. For The New Sequoia Hospital Campaign.
$87,500 to Saint Francis Center of Redwood City, Redwood City, CA, 2012. For On the Courts, Not in the Courts!.
$60,000 to BASIC Fund, San Francisco, CA, 2012. For Scholars Program.
$10,000 to California Pacific Medical Center Foundation, San Francisco, CA, 2012. For Emergency Department Child Life Services at Saint Luke's.
$7,500 to Stanbridge Academy, San Mateo, CA, 2012. For Tuition Assistance Program for 2012-2013 School Year.
$5,000 to Canine Companions for Independence, Santa Rosa, CA, 2012. For Exceptional Dogs for Exceptional Children.
$5,000 to South of Market Health Center, San Francisco, CA, 2012. For LoPrest 551 Minna Project.

569
GenCorp Foundation, Incorporated ✧

P.O. Box 15619
Sacramento, CA 95852-0619
Contact: Juanita Garcia, Exec. Dir.
FAX: (916) 355-2515;
E-mail: gencorp.foundation@gencorp.com; Main URL: http://www.gencorp.com/pages/gcfound.html

Incorporated in 1999 in CA as successor to the GenCorp Foundation Inc., established in 1961 in OH.
Donor: GenCorp Foundation Inc.
Foundation type: Company-sponsored foundation.
Financial data (yr. ended 11/30/13): Assets, $14,879,975 (M); gifts received, $16,372; expenditures, $867,603; qualifying distributions, $706,760; giving activities include $607,888 for 206 grants (high: $52,000; low: $25).
Purpose and activities: The GenCorp Foundation supports the communities where GenCorp has a business presence. The foundation's primary giving focus is education with emphasis on STEM - science, technology, engineering, and mathematics. The foundation may also fund health and social services, arts organizations, and civic and environmental projects.
Fields of interest: Museums; Elementary/secondary education; Higher education; Engineering school/education; Education; American Red Cross; Mathematics; Engineering/technology; Science; Children/youth; Minorities; Girls; Economically disadvantaged.
Type of support: Equipment; Program development; Curriculum development; Scholarship funds; Employee volunteer services; Employee matching gifts; Employee-related scholarships.
Limitations: Applications accepted. Giving primarily in Funds primarily in the communities where the company operates: Huntsville, AL, Camden, AR, Sacramento and Vernon, CA, Washington, DC, Socorro, NM, Jonesborough, TN, Clearfield, UT, Gainesville and Orange, VA, and Redmond, WA. No support for private foundations, religious organizations, or fraternal, athletic, social, political, or disease-specific organizations. No grants to individuals (except for scholarships), or for general operating support, capital campaigns, courtesy advertising, benefits, raffle tickets, golf tournaments, or other fundraising events, research, or conferences; no loans.
Publications: Application guidelines; Annual report; Informational brochure (including application guidelines); Occasional report.
Application information: Letters of inquiry should be no longer than 1 to 2 pages and should be submitted using organization letterhead. A full proposal may be requested at a later date. Funding cycles are Apr., July, and Oct. Application form not required.
Initial approach: Letter of inquiry; contact foundation or participating schools for Aerojet Community Scholarships
Copies of proposal: 1
Deadline(s): None
Board meeting date(s): As required
Final notification: 30 days
Officers and Trustees:* Chris W. Conely,* Pres.; Jennifer Goolis,* Secy.; David Fox,* Treas.; Dave Hatch; Roger M. Myers; Ronald Samborsky; Robert Shenton.
Number of staff: 1 full-time professional; 1 part-time support.
EIN: 680441559
Selected grants: The following grants are a representative sample of this grantmaker's funding activity:
$150,000 to Aviation High School, Seattle, WA, 2012. For science laboratory equipment for new STEM high school.
$50,000 to Southern Arkansas University, Magnolia, AR, 2012. For Engineering Preceptor Program.
$45,000 to Northern Virginia Community College, Annandale, VA, 2012. For SySTEMic Solutions Program, STEM-based K-12 curriculum, developed through public-private partnership.
$25,000 to K V I E Public Television, Sacramento, CA, 2012. To underwrite science program, NOVA.
$20,700 to National Merit Scholarship Corporation, Evanston, IL, 2012. For scholarships.
$20,000 to Powerhouse Science Center, Sacramento, CA, 2012. For scholarships for Challenger Learning Center.
$10,275 to Arkansas School for Mathematics, Sciences and the Arts, Hot Springs, AR, 2012. For science program.
$10,000 to Aerospace Museum of California, McClellan, CA, 2012. For Project Lead the Way.
$10,000 to San Juan Education Foundation, Carmichael, CA, 2012. For elementary school literacy program.
$10,000 to Soil Born Farm Urban Agriculture Project, Sacramento, CA, 2012. For youth environmental education and stewardship program.

570
Genentech Access To Care Foundation ✧

1 DNA Way, M.S. #858A
South San Francisco, CA 94080-4918
FAX: (650) 335-1366;
E-mail: info@genentech-access.com; Main URL: http://www.genentech-access.com/hcp/find-patient-assistance
Genetech Access Solutions: http://www.genentechaccesssolutions.com/portal/site/AS/
Grants List: http://www.genentechfoundation.com/news.html

Established in 2002 as a company-sponsored operating foundation.
Donor: Genentech, Inc.
Foundation type: Operating foundation.
Financial data (yr. ended 12/31/13): Assets, $56,516,388 (M); gifts received, $704,929,465; expenditures, $703,696,268; qualifying distributions, $703,696,268; giving activities include $680,278,040 for grants to individuals.
Purpose and activities: The foundation provides prescription medication to economically disadvantaged patients.
Fields of interest: Health care; Economically disadvantaged.
Type of support: Donated products.
Limitations: Applications accepted. Giving on a national basis.
Publications: Application guidelines.
Application information: The application requires medical information from the patient's physician and financial information from the patient to determine eligibility. Applicants are eligible for free medicine for 1 year then they must reapply annually. Application form required.
Initial approach: Complete online application
Deadline(s): None
Officers and Trustees:* Steve Krognes,* Pres.; Renee Shiota, Secy.; Jane Michan, C.F.O.; Neela Paykel, Genl. Counsel; Alexander Hardy; Sandra Horning; Sean Johnson; Mary Sliwkowski; Geoff Teeter; Carol Zigulis.
EIN: 460500266

571
Genentech Foundation ✧

1 DNA Way, M.S. 24
South San Francisco, CA 94080-4918 (877) 313-5778
E-mail: foundation@gene.com; Main URL: http://www.genentechfoundation.com/index.html

Established in 2002.
Donor: Genentech, Inc.
Foundation type: Company-sponsored foundation.

Financial data (yr. ended 12/31/13): Assets, $35,864,954 (M); gifts received, $9,000,000; expenditures, $2,212,153; qualifying distributions, $2,206,769; giving activities include $2,189,431 for 56 grants (high: $150,000; low: $3,000).
Purpose and activities: The foundation supports programs designed to promote health science education; community-wide civic initiatives; and national patient education and advocacy efforts.
Fields of interest: Higher education; Graduate/professional education; Medical school/education; Libraries (public); Education; Health care, patient services; Health care; Cancer; Pediatrics; Employment, services; Employment, training; Food services; Food banks; Housing/shelter; Community/economic development; Science, formal/general education; Public affairs.
Type of support: General/operating support; Continuing support; Program development; Curriculum development; Fellowships; Research.
Limitations: Applications accepted. Giving primarily in areas of company operations in North San Diego County, Oceanside, South San Francisco, San Francisco County, San Mateo County, Solano County, and Vacaville, CA, Jefferson County, KY, and Washington County, OR; giving also to national organizations. No support for discriminatory organizations, professional sports athletes, religious organizations not of direct benefit to the entire community, or political organizations. No grants to individuals, or for alumni drives, capital campaigns or building funds, infrastructural requests including salary or equipment, memorial funds, professional sports events, sponsorships, or yearbooks.
Publications: Application guidelines; Informational brochure; Program policy statement.
Application information: A site visit may be requested. Application form required.
Initial approach: Complete online application
Copies of proposal: 1
Deadline(s): Jan. 30, Apr. 5, July 5, and Sept. 27
Board meeting date(s): Mar., June, Sept., and Dec.
Officers and Directors:* Richard H. Scheller, Ph.D.*, Chair.; Ashraf Hanna, C.F.O.; Colleen Wilson, Exec. Dir.; Sunil Agarwal, M.D.; Vishva Dixit, M.D.; Markus Gemuend; Nancy Oaks; Michelle Rohrer, Ph.D.; Mary B. Silwkowski, Ph.D.; Denise Smith-Hams; Geoff Teeter.
EIN: 460500264

572
Gensler Family Foundation ✧
2 Harrison St., Ste. 400
San Francisco, CA 94105-1672

Established in 1999 in CA.
Donors: Drucilla C. Gensler; M. Arthur Gensler, Jr.; M. Arthur Gensler Jr. Charitable Lead Annuity Trust.
Foundation type: Independent foundation.
Financial data (yr. ended 12/31/12): Assets, $3,559,325 (M); gifts received, $381,258; expenditures, $578,436; qualifying distributions, $537,615; giving activities include $537,615 for grants.
Fields of interest: Arts; Higher education; Geriatrics research.
Limitations: Applications not accepted. Giving primarily in CA. No grants to individuals.
Application information: Contributes only to pre-selected organizations.
Officers: Drucilla C. Gensler, C.E.O.; M. Arthur Gensler, Jr., Secy.
EIN: 943331601

573
Wallace Alexander Gerbode Foundation ✧
77 Van Ness Ave., Ste. 200
San Francisco, CA 94102-6042 (415) 391-0911
Contact: Molly Barrons, Admin. Mgr.
FAX: (415) 992-4723; E-mail: info@gerbode.org; Main URL: http://www.foundationcenter.org/grantmaker/gerbode/
Grants List: http://foundationcenter.org/grantmaker/gerbode/grcomm.html
Awards inquiry e-mail: olivia@gerbode.org

Incorporated in 1953 in CA.
Donor: Members of the Gerbode family.
Foundation type: Independent foundation.
Financial data (yr. ended 12/31/13): Assets, $66,075,272 (M); gifts received, $525,000; expenditures, $3,747,949; qualifying distributions, $3,205,442; giving activities include $2,439,735 for 103 grants (high: $100,000; low: $1,000).
Purpose and activities: Support for programs and projects offering the potential for significant impact in the areas of arts and culture, the environment, population, reproductive rights, citizen participation/building communities/inclusiveness, strength of the philanthropic process and the nonprofit sector, and foundation-initiated special projects. Grants also to California artists through its Special Awards in the Arts program, to support fresh, dynamic new work in dance, theater and music.
Fields of interest: Arts; Environment; Civil liberties, reproductive rights; Civil/human rights; Community/economic development; Philanthropy/voluntarism; Public affairs; Adults; Aging; Young adults; Minorities; Asians/Pacific Islanders; African Americans/Blacks; Hispanics/Latinos; Indigenous peoples; Women; Girls; Adults, women; Young adults, female; Men; Adults, men; Young adults, male; Immigrants/refugees; LGBTQ.
Type of support: Management development/capacity building; Program development; Technical assistance; Consulting services; Matching/challenge support.
Limitations: Applications accepted. Giving primarily to programs directly affecting residents of Alameda, Contra Costa, Marin, San Francisco, and San Mateo counties in CA, and HI. No support for religious purposes or private schools. No grants to individuals (except for individual artist sections of the foundation's Special Awards in the Arts program), or for direct services, deficit budgets, general operating funds, building or equipment funds, general fundraising campaigns, publications, or scholarships.
Publications: Application guidelines; Annual report; Financial statement; Grants list.
Application information: Application form not required.
Initial approach: Letter; initial contact should not include materials (including DVDs) requiring a return.
Copies of proposal: 1
Board meeting date(s): 4 times per year
Final notification: Generally 2 to 3 months; the foundation's Special Awards in the Arts grants are announced in Jan.
Officers and Trustees:* Maryanna G. Stockholm,* Chair.; Frank A. Gerbode, M.D.*, Vice-Chair. and Secy.; Charles M. Stockholm,* Vice-Chair. and Treas.; Stacie Ma'a, Pres.; Sharon Gerbode, Member; Sarah Shaw, Member.
Number of staff: 2 full-time professional; 2 full-time support; 1 part-time support.
EIN: 946065226
Selected grants: The following grants are a representative sample of this grantmaker's funding activity:
$100,000 to Zellerbach Family Foundation, San Francisco, CA, 2012. For Community Arts program.
$50,000 to American Civil Liberties Union Foundation of Northern California, San Francisco, CA, 2012. For Criminal Justice and Drug Policy project.
$50,000 to La Pena Cultural Center, Berkeley, CA, 2012. For commission and production of a new work by Playwright Ariel Luckey.
$50,000 to Oceanic Preservation Society, Boulder, CO, 2012. For education and outreach initiative to inform the public about species extinction and threats to the ocean ecosystem.
$25,000 to Center for Investigative Reporting, Berkeley, CA, 2012. For work.
$25,000 to Communications Consortium Media Center, Washington, DC, 2012. For Agent Orange/Dioxin Advocacy and Exchange Program.
$25,000 to Equal Justice Society, Oakland, CA, 2012. For California Civil Rights Coalition.
$25,000 to Ibis Reproductive Health, San Francisco Bay Area Office, Oakland, CA, 2012. For reproductive healthcare for women in the US military.
$25,000 to League of Women Voters of California Education Fund, Sacramento, CA, 2012. For Smart Voter 2012 Election project.
$25,000 to San Francisco Foundation, San Francisco, CA, 2012. For its Great Communities Collaborative's communication efforts.

574
The Germanacos Foundation ✧
830 Clayton St.
San Francisco, CA 94117-4424
Main URL: http://thegermanacosfoundation.org/

Established in 2009 in CA.
Donor: Anne H. Germanacos.
Foundation type: Independent foundation.
Financial data (yr. ended 12/31/13): Assets, $7,286,926 (M); gifts received, $495,000; expenditures, $546,407; qualifying distributions, $526,973; giving activities include $513,648 for 21 grants (high: $55,000; low: $5,000).
Fields of interest: Community development, neighborhood development; Nonprofit management; Philanthropy/voluntarism; Leadership development.
Limitations: Applications not accepted. Giving primarily in CA and NY.
Application information: Unsolicited requests for funds not accepted.
Officers: Anne H. Germanacos, Pres.; Elizabeth Billings, C.F.O.; John Esterle, Secy.
EIN: 270965735
Selected grants: The following grants are a representative sample of this grantmaker's funding activity:
$70,000 to Right Question Project, Cambridge, MA, 2011. For unrestricted gift.
$50,000 to New Israel Fund, San Francisco, CA, 2011. For unrestricted gift.

$50,000 to On The Move, Napa, CA, 2011. For unrestricted gift.
$25,000 to Homies Organizing the Mission Empowering Youth, San Francisco, CA, 2011. For unrestricted gift.
$6,250 to YMCA of Greater Seattle, Seattle, WA, 2011. For unrestricted gift.

575
Ronald and Catherine Gershman Foundation ✧
12300 Wilshire Blvd., Ste. 310
Los Angeles, CA 90025-1057

Established in 1995 in CA.
Donors: Harold Gershman Family Survivors/Administrative Trust; Charitable Lead Unitrust under Harold Gershman Survivors Trust; Charitable Lead Annuity Trust under H. Gershman Survivors Trust.
Foundation type: Independent foundation.
Financial data (yr. ended 12/31/11): Assets, $12,593,065 (M); gifts received, $806,303; expenditures, $4,633,951; qualifying distributions, $4,543,892; giving activities include $4,527,000 for 24 grants (high: $4,350,000; low: $500).
Purpose and activities: Giving primarily for animal welfare; support also for human services.
Fields of interest: Animal welfare; Hospitals (general); Mental health/crisis services, rape victim services; Human services.
Limitations: Applications not accepted. Giving primarily in CA and RI. No grants to individuals.
Application information: Contributes only to pre-selected organizations.
Trustees: Catherine Gershman; Ronald A. Gershman.
EIN: 957075530

576
Charles M. Geschke and Nancy A. Geschke Foundation ✧
3 Lagoon Dr., Ste. 400
Redwood City, CA 94065-5157

Established in 1987 in CA.
Donors: Charles M. Geschke; Nancy A. Geschke.
Foundation type: Independent foundation.
Financial data (yr. ended 09/30/13): Assets, $3,042,038 (M); expenditures, $743,147; qualifying distributions, $708,709; giving activities include $703,219 for 4 grants (high: $503,219; low: $50,000).
Fields of interest: Performing arts, orchestras; Secondary school/education; Higher education; Foundations (private grantmaking); Social sciences, public policy.
Type of support: General/operating support; Capital campaigns; Endowments; Program development.
Limitations: Applications not accepted. Giving primarily in CA and OH. No grants to individuals.
Application information: Contributes only to pre-selected organizations.
Officers: Charles M. Geschke, Pres.; Nancy A. Geschke, Secy.-Treas.
Directors: John M. Geschke; Peter C. Geschke; Kathleen A. Orciuoli.
EIN: 943052556

577
The Aileen Getty Foundation ✧ ☆
P.O. Box 866
Los Angeles, CA 90078-0866

Established in CA.
Donor: Aileen Getty.
Foundation type: Independent foundation.
Financial data (yr. ended 12/31/13): Assets, $2,776 (M); gifts received, $2,175,000; expenditures, $2,177,274; qualifying distributions, $2,173,461; giving activities include $2,173,461 for 31 grants (high: $584,000; low: $1,000).
Fields of interest: Education; Human services; Foundations (private grantmaking).
Limitations: Applications not accepted. Giving in the U.S., with some emphasis on CA.
Application information: Unsolicited requests for funds not accepted.
Officers: Aileen Getty, Pres.; John Ladner, Secy.
EIN: 454180922
Selected grants: The following grants are a representative sample of this grantmaker's funding activity:
$100,000 to Trust for Public Land, San Francisco, CA, 2012. For LA Parks.

578
The Ann and Gordon Getty Foundation ✧
1 Embarcadero Ctr., Ste. 1350
San Francisco, CA 94111-3700

Established in 1986 in CA.
Donors: Gordon P. Getty; G.P.G. Foundation.
Foundation type: Independent foundation.
Financial data (yr. ended 12/31/12): Assets, $63,919 (M); gifts received, $9,608,000; expenditures, $9,550,742; qualifying distributions, $9,541,850; giving activities include $9,305,000 for 477 grants (high: $2,000,000; low: $500).
Purpose and activities: Support primarily for symphonies, opera companies, and educational institutions.
Fields of interest: Museums; Performing arts; Performing arts, music; Education; Anthropology/sociology.
Type of support: General/operating support; Continuing support; Annual campaigns; Matching/challenge support.
Limitations: Applications not accepted. Giving primarily in CA, with emphasis on the San Francisco Bay Area. No grants to individuals.
Application information: Contributes only to pre-selected organizations.
Board meeting date(s): Annually
Officer and Directors:* Gordon P. Getty,* Chair. and Pres.; Lisa DeLan; Matthew A. Hall; William A. Newsom.
EIN: 954078340
Selected grants: The following grants are a representative sample of this grantmaker's funding activity:
$2,000,000 to Los Angeles Opera Company, Los Angeles, CA, 2012.
$1,250,000 to San Francisco Opera, War Memorial Opera House, San Francisco, CA, 2012.
$500,000 to American Symphony Orchestra League, New York, NY, 2012.
$500,000 to Opera America, New York, NY, 2012.
$250,000 to Philharmonia Baroque Orchestra, San Francisco, CA, 2012.
$215,000 to Los Angeles Philharmonic Association, Los Angeles, CA, 2012.
$200,000 to Metropolitan Opera, New York, NY, 2012.
$175,000 to San Francisco Opera, San Francisco, CA, 2012.
$5,000 to Chamber Music Northwest, Portland, OR, 2012.

579
J. Paul Getty Trust ✧
1200 Getty Ctr. Dr., Ste. 800
Los Angeles, CA 90049-1679 (310) 440-7320
Contact: The Getty Foundation
FAX: (310) 440-7703;
E-mail: GettyFoundation@getty.edu; Main URL: http://www.getty.edu
Blog: http://blogs.getty.edu/iris/
E-Newsletter: http://www.getty.edu/subscribe/index.html
Facebook: https://www.facebook.com/TheGetty
Flickr: http://www.flickr.com/photos/thegetty/
Grants List: http://www.getty.edu/foundation/grants/
Twitter: http://twitter.com/gettytrust

Operating trust established in 1953 in CA as J. Paul Getty Museum; Grant Program established in 1984.
Donor: J. Paul Getty†.
Foundation type: Operating foundation.
Financial data (yr. ended 06/30/13): Assets, $11,110,918,337 (M); gifts received, $8,958,855; expenditures, $284,453,693; qualifying distributions, $220,207,689; giving activities include $10,065,391 for 123 grants (high: $1,000,000; low: $4,000), $1,894,783 for 156 grants to individuals (high: $67,000; low: $625), $818,134 for 332 employee matching gifts, and $272,380,233 for 4 foundation-administered programs.
Purpose and activities: The grant making arm of the J. Paul Getty Trust, the Getty Foundation, supports individuals and institutions committed to advancing the understanding and preservation of the visual arts locally and throughout the world. The majority of its funding is through initiatives that target a particular issue or region, and that are carried out in collaboration with the other Getty programs-the J. Paul Getty Museum, the Getty Research Institute, and the Getty Conservation Institute. The foundation focuses on the following four broad areas: Access to Museum and Archival Collections, Art History as a Global Discipline, Advancing Conservation Practice, and Leadership and Professional Development.
Fields of interest: Arts, research; Arts, cultural/ethnic awareness; Arts education; Visual arts; Visual arts, architecture; Visual arts, art conservation; Museums; Humanities; Art history; Historic preservation/historical societies; Arts; Minorities.
Type of support: Employee matching gifts; Fellowships; Grants to individuals; Internship funds; Matching/challenge support; Program development; Publication; Research.
Limitations: Applications accepted. Giving on a national and international basis, with emphasis on Los Angeles and Southern CA. No grants for operating or endowment purposes, start-up, construction or maintenance of buildings, or acquisition of works of art.
Publications: Application guidelines; Annual report; Grants list.
Application information: The foundation maintains its commitment to increasing the understanding and

preservation of the visual arts, both in Los Angeles and throughout the world. The foundation's four strategic priorities are: 1) access to museum and archival collections; 2) art history as a global discipline; 3) advancing conservation practice; and 4) leadership and professional development. Within these focus areas, current initiatives range from support for exhibitions about the development of avant-garde art in Southern California to the conservation of mosaics in the Mediterranean. The Getty Foundation also maintains support for long-standing leadership and professional development programs including internships and the Getty Leadership Institute. For additional information, guidelines and updates, or to review current initiatives and programs in detail, please visit the foundation's web site.

Initial approach: See web site for online applications.

Officers and Trustees:* Mark S. Siegel,* Chair.; Neil Rudenstine,* Vice-Chair.; James Cuno,* C.E.O. and Pres.; Patricia Woodworth, V.P., C.O.O. and C.F.O.; Stephen W. Clark, V.P., Secy. and Genl. Counsel; James M. Williams, V.P., Treas. and C.I.O.; J. Timothy Child, V.P., Institutional Advancement; Ron Hartwig, V.P., Comms.; Janet Feldstein McKillop, V.P., Devel.; William Humphries, Cont.; Frances Daly Ferguson; Maria D. Hummer-Tuttle; Joanne Corday Kozberg; Paul LeClerc; David Lee; Thelma Melendez de Santa Ana; Stewart A. Resnick; William E.B. Siart; Ronald P. Spogli; Peter J. Taylor; Jay S. Wintrob.

Number of staff: 1406

EIN: 951790021

Selected grants: The following grants are a representative sample of this grantmaker's funding activity:

$1,950,000 to Claremont Graduate University, Claremont, CA, 2012. For The Getty Leadership Institute at CGU, payable over 3.00 years.

$646,030 to Centre Interdisciplinaire de Conservation et Restauration du Patrimoine, Marseille, France, 2012. For the implementation of a two-year mosaics technician training program in Algeria, payable over 3.25 years.

$385,000 to Museum Associates, Los Angeles County Museum of Art (LACMA), Los Angeles, CA, 2012. For the implementation of online scholarly catalogue of the Southeast Asian art collection, payable over 2.00 years.

$375,000 to San Francisco Museum of Modern Art, San Francisco, CA, 2012. For the implementation of online scholarly catalogue of works by Robert Rauschenberg in the permanent collection, payable over 1.50 years.

$310,000 to State University of Rio de Janeiro, Rio de Janeiro, Brazil, 2012. For a series of research seminars and faculty and student exchanges, as part of the Connecting Art Histories initiative, payable over 1.50 years.

$275,000 to Museum of Contemporary Art, Los Angeles, CA, 2012. For the exhibition and accompanying catalogue A New Sculpturalism: Contemporary Architecture from Southern California, as part of Pacific Standard Time Presents: Modern Architecture in LA, payable over 1.25 years.

$260,000 to Armand Hammer Museum of Art and Cultural Center, Los Angeles, CA, 2012. For the exhibition and accompanying catalogue The Architecture of A. Quincy Jones, as part of Pacific Standard Time Presents: Modern Architecture in LA, payable over 1.25 years.

$246,000 to Los Angeles Conservancy, Los Angeles, CA, 2012. For public programming and activities as part of Pacific Standard Time Presents: Modern Architecture in LA, payable over 1.50 years.

$239,600 to Jan Matejko Academy of Fine Arts in Cracow, Cracow, Poland, 2012. For training and treatment related to six paintings by Hans Suss von Kulmbach from the collection of St. Mary's Church in Cracow, as part of the Panel Paintings Initiative, payable over 2.50 years.

$8,000 to Chinese American Museum, Friends of the, Los Angeles, CA, 2012. For two internships.

580
GGS Foundation ✧

(formerly Georgina G. Stevens Foundation)
1660 Bush St., Ste. 300
San Francisco, CA 94109-5308 (415) 561-6540
Contact: Shawna Hamilton, Grants Mgr.
FAX: (415) 561-5477; E-mail: shamilton@pfs-llc.net; Main URL: http://www.pfs-llc.net/ggs/ggs.html

Established in 1992 in CA.

Donors: Georgiana G. Stevens; The Georgiana G. Stevens 1997 Trust.

Foundation type: Independent foundation.

Financial data (yr. ended 12/31/12): Assets, $19,254,850 (M); expenditures, $1,035,510; qualifying distributions, $922,616; giving activities include $807,010 for 33 grants (high: $50,000; low: $1,510).

Purpose and activities: Giving primarily for: 1) Promoting literacy for children from pre-K through third grade, including access to books, acquisition of reading, writing, and comprehension skills, and application of literacy skills to critical thinking and self-expression; 2) Preventing substance abuse and promoting healthy living for children and youth, with emphasis on programs that enable youth to make healthy decisions and form healthy relationships; and 3) Building vocational and workplace skills for middle and high school-aged youth.

Fields of interest: Substance abuse, prevention; Youth development; Children/youth.

Type of support: Continuing support; Annual campaigns.

Limitations: Applications accepted. Giving primarily in San Francisco, CA. No support for religious organizations, or for medical research. No grants to individuals, or for endowments, events, annual appeals, videos, capital campaigns or conferences.

Publications: Application guidelines; Annual report; Grants list.

Application information: Application form required.

Initial approach: Use online application system on foundation web site

Copies of proposal: 1

Deadline(s): See foundation web site for current deadlines

Board meeting date(s): Spring and Fall

Officers: John H. Kirkwood, Pres.; Amanda H. Kirkwood, V.P.; Jean K. Casey, Secy.-Treas.

Director: A. Michael Casey.

EIN: 943155521

Selected grants: The following grants are a representative sample of this grantmaker's funding activity:

$50,000 to Larkin Street Youth Services, San Francisco, CA, 2012. For Clinical Services for Homeless and Runaway Youth.

$40,000 to 826 Valencia, San Francisco, CA, 2012. For the In-Schools Program, Providing Literacy Tutoring in High Needs San Francisco Elementary Schools.

$40,000 to New Door Ventures, San Francisco, CA, 2012. For youth internship Programs.

$35,000 to Juma Ventures, San Francisco, CA, 2012. For the Pathways to Advancement Program, Providing Employment, Vocational Development, and Access to College Services in San Francisco.

$35,000 to Reading Partners, Oakland, CA, 2012. For the One-On-One Reading Intervention Program.

$25,000 to Bay Area SCORES, San Francisco, CA, 2012. For Words in Action San Francisco, Afterschool Program Combining Soccer and Literary Arts Services.

$25,000 to California Academy of Sciences, San Francisco, CA, 2012. For the Careers in Science Internship Program.

$25,000 to Conservation Corps North Bay, San Rafael, CA, 2012. For the Corps-To-Career Program, Providing Low-Income Youth with the Educational Support, Career Development, and Social Services They Need to Succeed in Education and Gainful Employment.

$25,000 to Larkin Street Youth Services, San Francisco, CA, 2012. For General Operations for the 3rd Street Youth Center and Clinic Serving Youth in Bayview Hunters Point Neighborhood.

$20,000 to Center for Urban Education About Sustainable Agriculture, San Francisco, CA, 2012. For the Schoolyard to Market Program, a Youth Entrepreneurship Pilot at Two San Francisco Public High Schools.

581
A. P. Giannini Foundation ✧

(formerly Giannini Family Foundation)
57 Post St., Ste. 510
San Francisco, CA 94104-5020 (415) 981-2966
Contact: John S. Blum, Admin.; Kenneth J. Blum, Admin.
FAX: (415) 981-5218;
E-mail: info@apgianninifoundation.org; Main URL: http://www.apgianninifoundation.org/

Incorporated in 1945 in CA.

Donor: A.P. Giannini†.

Foundation type: Independent foundation.

Financial data (yr. ended 12/31/13): Assets, $22,852,310 (M); gifts received, $265,685; expenditures, $1,200,940; qualifying distributions, $1,076,787; giving activities include $847,000 for 20 grants (high: $46,000; low: $6,000).

Purpose and activities: Medical research fellowships for applicants sponsored by accredited medical schools.

Fields of interest: Medical research; Adults; Adults, women; Adults, men.

Type of support: Fellowships; Research.

Limitations: Applications accepted. Giving limited to CA.

Publications: Financial statement; Informational brochure (including application guidelines).

Application information: The foundation will not consider applications submitted by e-mail, fax or after the due date and time. Applications accepted for Fellowship Program. See foundation web site for details. Application form required.

Initial approach: Fellowship application available on foundation web site

Copies of proposal: 1

Deadline(s): See foundation web site for current deadline

Board meeting date(s): Feb. and Nov.
Final notification: Mid-Jan.
Officers and Directors:* Donald A. Mullane,* Chair.; V. Hammerness,* Vice-Chair.; Caroline O. Boitano,* Pres. and Secy.; Jerry L. Bowman,* Treas.; Larry McNabb; Anne G. McWilliams; David P. Perry; Tim Ranzetta; Hans Reiser, M.D.; Daniel P. Riley.
Number of staff: None.
EIN: 946089512

582
Claire Giannini Fund ✧
c/o Adler & Colvin
235 Montgomery St., Ste. 1220
San Francisco, CA 94104-3103

Established in 1998 in CA.
Foundation type: Independent foundation.
Financial data (yr. ended 12/31/13): Assets, $28,146,033 (M); expenditures, $3,608,718; qualifying distributions, $3,403,754; giving activities include $3,250,292 for 22 grants (high: $515,000; low: $1,500).
Fields of interest: Education; Health care; Community/economic development.
Limitations: Applications not accepted. Giving primarily in CA, NY, and VA; some funding also in Washington, DC. No grants to individuals.
Application information: Contributes only to pre-selected organizations.
Trustees: Betsy Buchalter Adler; Bruce Hopkins; George Vera.
EIN: 943297004

583
The Gibson, Dunn & Crutcher Foundation ✧
333 S. Grand Ave.
Los Angeles, CA 90071-1504 (213) 229-7252
Contact: Charles E. Woodhouse, C.F.O.

Established in 1990 in CA.
Donor: Gibson, Dunn & Crutcher LLP.
Foundation type: Independent foundation.
Financial data (yr. ended 12/31/13): Assets, $965,776 (M); expenditures, $2,123,470; qualifying distributions, $2,111,483; giving activities include $2,111,483 for 133 grants (high: $160,000; low: $3,500).
Fields of interest: Health organizations, association; Medical research, institute; Legal services; Civil/human rights; United Ways and Federated Giving Programs; Jewish federated giving programs; Public policy, research.
Limitations: Applications accepted. Giving primarily in Los Angeles, CA, Washington, DC, and NY.
Application information: Application form not required.
Initial approach: Letter
Deadline(s): None
Officers: Kenneth M. Doran, Pres.; Dean J. Kitchens, Secy.; Charles E. Woodhouse, C.F.O.
Directors: Theodore J. Boutrous, Jr.; Thomas H. Dupree, Jr.; Randy M. Mastro.
EIN: 954301635

584
The Gifford Foundation, Inc. ✧
3130 Alpine Rd., No. 288-250
Portola Valley, CA 94028-7549

Established in 1998 in CA.
Donors: John F. Gifford‡; Rhodine Gifford.
Foundation type: Independent foundation.
Financial data (yr. ended 05/31/13): Assets, $6,778,052 (M); expenditures, $1,627,419; qualifying distributions, $1,518,164; giving activities include $1,518,164 for 23 grants (high: $1,165,618; low: $100).
Purpose and activities: Giving primarily for university academic scholarships, as well as for baseball and golf programs; funding also for social services.
Fields of interest: Higher education; Education; Athletics/sports, school programs; Human services; Children/youth, services.
Limitations: Applications not accepted. Giving primarily in CA; some giving in HI.
Application information: Unsolicited requests for funds not accepted.
Officers: Tracy Jones, Exec. Dir.; Laural Lynch, Exec. Dir.; Jacquelyn Walsh, Exec. Dir.
EIN: 943303273
Selected grants: The following grants are a representative sample of this grantmaker's funding activity:
$84,488 to University of California, Los Angeles, CA, 2011.
$30,000 to San Jose State University, San Jose, CA, 2011.
$27,000 to Saint Francis High School, Mountain View, CA, 2011.
$15,000 to Carroll College, Helena, MT, 2011. For scholarship.
$10,000 to Santa Clara University, Santa Clara, CA, 2011. For scholarship.
$10,000 to University of the Pacific, Stockton, CA, 2011. For scholarship.
$7,000 to Presentation High School, San Jose, CA, 2011. For scholarship.
$5,090 to Charles Armstrong School, Belmont, CA, 2011.
$1,749 to Ohlone College, Fremont, CA, 2011. For scholarship.
$1,000 to Creative Center of Los Altos, Los Altos, CA, 2011. For general fund.

585
The Rosalinde and Arthur Gilbert Foundation ✧
2730 Wilshire Blvd., Ste. 301
Santa Monica, CA 90403-4749
Main URL: http://www.thegilbertfoundation.org

Established in 2002 in CA; funded in 2003 through a merger with another foundation with the same name.
Donor: A & R Gilbert 1982 Trust.
Foundation type: Independent foundation.
Financial data (yr. ended 12/31/12): Assets, $185,394,359 (M); expenditures, $14,359,804; qualifying distributions, $8,377,333; giving activities include $7,208,244 for 269 grants (high: $250,000; low: $250).
Purpose and activities: Support primarily for access to college, healthcare, Israel, arts education, Jewish organizations and universities in California.
Fields of interest: Higher education; Education; Human services; Jewish agencies & synagogues.
International interests: Israel.
Limitations: Applications accepted. Giving primarily in Los Angeles, CA and Israel. No grants for individuals, capital campaigns or legislation.
Application information: Full proposals accepted by invitation only following a letter of inquiry. After receiving a letter of inquiry, the foundation will send a notice of acknowledgement. If the foundation decides not to proceed, applicants will be notified with an explanation. If the foundation determines from an applicant's letter of inquiry that a request is consistent with the foundation's priorities and interests, the applicant will be asked to submit a full proposal. Only when an organization is invited to submit a proposal, will a full application e-mailed.
Initial approach: Letters of inquiry (1-2 pages). Use the form on the contact page of the foundation's web site
Deadline(s): None for letters of inquiry; If you submit a letter of inquiry and it is declined you must wait 12 months from the date of declination to submit another request
Final notification: Receipt of proposal is acknowledged immediately; Decisions are communicated in a timely manner
Officers and Trustees:* Richard Ziman,* C.E.O.; Martin Blank, Jr.,* Secy.; Melissa Bordy; Rodney Freeman.
EIN: 562305694
Selected grants: The following grants are a representative sample of this grantmaker's funding activity:
$250,000 to University of California, Berkeley, CA, 2012. For The Berkeley Programs on Jewish Law and Israeli Law, Economy and Society.
$175,000 to American Israel Education Foundation, Washington, DC, 2012. For General Activities.
$167,940 to American Federation for Aging Research, New York, NY, 2012. For New Investigator Awards in Alzheimer's Disease.
$150,000 to American Friends of the Hebrew University, Los Angeles, CA, 2012. For Faculty Recruitment and Retention.
$150,000 to Jewish Federation Council of Greater Los Angeles, Los Angeles, CA, 2012. For Camp Scholarships.
$70,000 to MATI-Jerusalem Business Development Center, Jerusalem, Israel, 2012. For Blessing of Business.
$50,000 to Los Angeles County Arts Commission, Los Angeles, CA, 2012. For Arts for All Pooled Fund.
$38,038 to University of California Medical Center, Sacramento, CA, 2012. For UCLA Lewis Center for Regional Policy Studies (parklets).
$25,000 to American Society for Technion-Israel Institute of Technology, Western Region, Los Angeles, CA, 2012. For Second Chance Program.
$20,864 to American Federation for Aging Research, New York, NY, 2012. For AFAR meetings.

586
Gilead Foundation ✧
333 Lakeside Dr.
Foster City, CA 94404-1147
Main URL: http://www.gilead.com/corporate_responsibility
Grants List: http://www.gilead.com/Gilead_Foundation

Established in 2004 in CA.
Donor: Gilead Sciences, Inc.
Foundation type: Company-sponsored foundation.
Financial data (yr. ended 12/31/12): Assets, $4,328,790 (M); gifts received, $5,000,650; expenditures, $3,208,570; qualifying distributions, $3,206,737; giving activities include $3,185,526 for 36 grants (high: $250,000; low: $25,000).

Purpose and activities: The foundation supports organizations involved with improving the health and well-being of underserved communities around the world. Special emphasis is directed toward programs designed to expand access to HIV and hepatitis B education, outreach, prevention, and health services.
Fields of interest: Medical school/education; Health care, formal/general education; Hospitals (general); Health care, clinics/centers; Health care, patient services; Health care; AIDS; AIDS research; Economically disadvantaged.
Type of support: General/operating support; Management development/capacity building; Program development; Conferences/seminars; Curriculum development.
Limitations: Applications not accepted. Giving primarily in CA, CT, Washington, DC, Honolulu, HI, NY, TX, and VA; giving also to international organizations in Africa, Kenya, Mozambique, South Africa, and Zimbabwe. No support for for-profit physician group practices. No grants to individuals, or for standard equipment, or clinical studies.
Publications: Grants list.
Application information: Contributes only to pre-selected organizations.
Officers and Directors:* Howard Jaffe, Chair. and Pres.; Amy Flood, Secy.; Andrew Cheng, Treas.; Gregg H. Alton; Jim Meyers; Coy Stout; Michael Wulfsohn.
EIN: 201042419

587
The William Gillespie Foundation ✧
4910 Campus Dr.
Newport Beach, CA 92660-2119

Established in 1994 in CA.
Donor: William Gillespie.
Foundation type: Independent foundation.
Financial data (yr. ended 12/31/12): Assets, $2,428,249 (M); expenditures, $530,614; qualifying distributions, $472,000; giving activities include $472,000 for grants.
Purpose and activities: Giving primarily for the performing arts, as well as for education and children and youth services.
Fields of interest: Performing arts; Arts; Education; Health organizations; Human services; Children/youth, services.
Limitations: Applications not accepted. Giving primarily in CA. No grants to individuals.
Application information: Contributes only to pre-selected organizations.
Officers: William Gillespie, Pres.; Richard Gadbois III, Secy. and C.F.O.
Director: John M. Gunnin.
EIN: 954480408

588
The William G. Gilmore Foundation ✧
1660 Bush St., Ste. 300
San Francisco, CA 94109-5308
Contact: Eric L. Sloan, Admin.; Maereg Haile, Prog. Coord.
E-mail: esloan@pfs-llc.net; Tel. extension for Maereg Haile: 201; e-mail address for Maereg Haile: mhaile@pfs-llc.org; Main URL: http://www.williamggilmorefoundation.org

Incorporated in 1953 in CA.
Donors: William G. Gilmore†; Mrs. William G. Gilmore†.
Foundation type: Independent foundation.
Financial data (yr. ended 12/31/13): Assets, $23,020,591 (M); expenditures, $2,133,808; qualifying distributions, $2,000,000; giving activities include $2,000,000 for grants.
Purpose and activities: The foundation's mission is to support: the educational opportunities for young people; provide for the health and welfare of the ill and disabled; assist those in need of food, shelter, and counseling; and encourage the arts and other activities generally related to the foregoing.
Fields of interest: Human services; Children/youth, services; Children/youth; Youth; Aging; Disabilities, people with; Terminal illness, people with; Economically disadvantaged; Homeless.
Type of support: General/operating support; Continuing support; Building/renovation; Equipment.
Limitations: Applications accepted. Giving primarily in the Alameda, Contra Costa, Marin, San Francisco, and San Mateo counties in CA, and in OR. No grants to individuals.
Publications: Application guidelines.
Application information: Oregon organizations should not send letters of inquiry or any other materials to the foundation. Board trustees will personally invite eligible organizations from Oregon to apply. Application guidelines available on foundation web site. Audio-visual materials, binders, folders or pamphlets should not be submitted unless requested. Application form not required.
Initial approach: Bay Area organizations may use online application process on foundation web site
Copies of proposal: 1
Deadline(s): See foundation web site for current deadlines
Board meeting date(s): June and Dec.
Final notification: Within 2-3 business days for e-mails
Officers and Trustees:* Mary Lee Boklund,* Pres.; Bob Baton,* V.P.; David Jubb,* Secy.; William Mackay, C.F.O. and Treas.; Emily Schroeder, Mgr., Grants.
EIN: 946079493
Selected grants: The following grants are a representative sample of this grantmaker's funding activity:
$100,000 to Linfield College, McMinnville, OR, 2012. For Linfield-Good Samaritan School of Nursing of Linfield College.
$30,000 to Catlin Gabel School, Portland, OR, 2012. For Lower School Math and Science Technology Equipment.
$20,000 to Options Recovery Services, Berkeley, CA, 2012. For continued support of Client Counseling/Case Management Services.
$15,000 to Edwards Center, Aloha, OR, 2012. For Aloha Project Community Center's Renovation.
$15,000 to Huckleberry Youth Programs, San Francisco, CA, 2012. For Huckleberry Wellness Academy After-School Program.
$10,000 to College Track, Oakland, CA, 2012. For Expansion Program to Bayview Hunters Point Neighborhood.
$10,000 to Each One Reach One, South San Francisco, CA, 2012. For GED Tutoring and Testing Program.
$10,000 to East Oakland Community Project, Oakland, CA, 2012. For Emergency Housing Program - Crossroads.
$10,000 to Friends of the Children-Portland, Portland, OR, 2012. For Newly Enrolled Children to Pair with Professional Mentors.
$10,000 to Hospice By the Bay, Larkspur, CA, 2012. For Art and Grief Support Program.

589
S. L. Gimbel Foundation ✧
P.O. Box 2591
Orange, CA 92859-0591

Established in 2002 in CA.
Donors: Susan L. Gimbel; Florence Neilan Trust.
Foundation type: Independent foundation.
Financial data (yr. ended 12/31/13): Assets, $123,845,456 (M); expenditures, $4,582,135; qualifying distributions, $4,551,589; giving activities include $4,551,589 for 1 grant.
Fields of interest: Environment, natural resources; Human services; Foundations (community).
Limitations: Applications not accepted. Giving primarily in CA. No grants to individuals.
Application information: Contributes only to pre-selected organizations.
Trustees: Denise Ambrosio; M. Lauren Ficaro; Ron Ficaro.
EIN: 036088692
Selected grants: The following grants are a representative sample of this grantmaker's funding activity:
$15,000 to Gabriels Angels, Phoenix, AZ, 2011.

590
Ginn Family Foundation ✧
1111 Bayhill Dr., Ste. 435
San Bruno, CA 94066-3050

Established in 2007 in CA; successor to The Ginn Family Foundation.
Donors: Samuel L. Ginn; Ann Vance Ginn.
Foundation type: Independent foundation.
Financial data (yr. ended 12/31/13): Assets, $16,973,250 (M); expenditures, $905,377; qualifying distributions, $710,500; giving activities include $710,500 for 49 grants (high: $100,000; low: $1,500).
Fields of interest: Elementary school/education; Education; Health care.
Limitations: Applications not accepted. Giving primarily in AZ and CA. No grants to individuals.
Application information: Contributes only to pre-selected organizations.
Officers and Directors:* Samuel L. Ginn, Chair.; Matthew Ginn,* C.F.O.; Samantha Boyd,* Secy.; Michael V. Ginn, Exec. Dir.; Ann Vance Ginn.
EIN: 680636598

591
Girard Foundation ✧
2223 Avenida de la Playa, Ste. 203
La Jolla, CA 92037-3218
Contact: Sarah Setiawan, Admin.
FAX: (858) 551-2723;
E-mail: sarah@girardfoundation.org; Additional e-mail: info@girardfoundation.org; Main URL: http://www.girardfoundation.org

Established in 1986 in CA.
Donor: R.B. Woolley, Jr.
Foundation type: Independent foundation.

Financial data (yr. ended 12/31/13): Assets, $20,491,582 (M); expenditures, $1,400,044; qualifying distributions, $1,377,512; giving activities include $1,328,029 for 41 grants (high: $827,500; low: $500).
Purpose and activities: Giving for systemic K-12 education reform in San Diego County, CA. Priority funding areas include: educational leadership, college/career preparedness, and the charter school movement. The foundation is particularly interested in projects and programs that: 1) demonstrate new, more effective methods of teaching and learning, 2) improve the ways schools operate, 3) are designed around concepts that are transferable and/or scalable, and 4) produce data that can lead to change.
Fields of interest: Education, management/technical assistance; Elementary/secondary education; Education, services.
Type of support: Continuing support; Management development/capacity building; Program development; Conferences/seminars; Seed money; Curriculum development; Scholarship funds; Research; Technical assistance; Consulting services; Program evaluation; Matching/challenge support.
Limitations: Applications accepted. Giving typically limited to San Diego County, CA. No grants to individuals (directly), or for endowments, capital campaigns, or lobbying.
Publications: Application guidelines; Grants list.
Application information: Formal proposals by invitation only, after initial contact. Application form not required.
Initial approach: Please contact foundation before submitting a proposal to determine whether the project fits within current funding priorities
Copies of proposal: 1
Deadline(s): Varies
Board meeting date(s): 3-4 times annually
Final notification: Within 2 weeks following board meeting
Officers and Trustees:* R.B. Woolley, Jr.,* Pres.; Michele Hansen, V.P.; Mary Lindenstein Walshok,* Secy.; Scott Woolley,* Treas.
Number of staff: 1 full-time professional.
EIN: 330202832

592
Gleason Family Foundation ✧
(formerly Gleason Foundation)
1112 Sir Francis Drake Blvd.
Kentfield, CA 94904-1419
Contact: Marcia Smith, C.O.O.

Established in 2006 in DE a as successor to Gleason Family Foundation located in NY.
Foundation type: Independent foundation.
Financial data (yr. ended 12/31/12): Assets, $167,948,066 (M); expenditures, $11,177,933; qualifying distributions, $10,486,837; giving activities include $6,822,471 for 95 grants (high: $1,717,000; low: $50), $1,717,402 for foundation-administered programs and $37,500 for 1 loan/program-related investment.
Fields of interest: Elementary school/education; Secondary school/education.
Limitations: Applications not accepted. Giving primarily in U.S. No grants to individuals.
Application information: Contributes only to pre-selected organizations.
Officers and Directors:* James S. Gleason,* Chair.; Tracy R. Gleason,* C.E.O. and Pres.; Janis F. Gleason,* Secy.-Treas.; Ralph E. Harper; Gary J. Kimmet; Albert W. Moore; Jeffery P. Robinson.
EIN: 205804684
Selected grants: The following grants are a representative sample of this grantmaker's funding activity:
$1,717,000 to Arizona School Choice Trust, Glendale, AZ, 2012. For event.
$1,000,000 to Rochester Institute of Technology, Rochester, NY, 2012. For program support.
$333,333 to Institute for Justice, Arlington, VA, 2012. For program support.
$330,000 to Hope Hall, Rochester, NY, 2012. For program support.
$319,000 to Rundel Library Foundation, Rochester, NY, 2012. For program support.
$150,000 to University of Rochester, Simon School of Business, Rochester, NY, 2012. For program support.
$125,000 to Heritage Foundation, Washington, DC, 2012. For program support.
$100,000 to Pacific Research Institute for Public Policy, San Francisco, CA, 2012. For program support.
$75,000 to Manhattan Institute for Policy Research, New York, NY, 2012. For program support.
$10,000 to Pacific Legal Foundation, Sacramento, CA, 2012. For program support.

593
Josephine Herbert Gleis Foundation ✧ ☆
2532 Dupont Dr.
Irvine, CA 92612

Established in 1999 in CA.
Donor: Josephine D. Gleis.
Foundation type: Independent foundation.
Financial data (yr. ended 12/31/13): Assets, $12,745,402 (M); gifts received, $1,165,340; expenditures, $544,265; qualifying distributions, $459,615; giving activities include $455,000 for 34 grants (high: $50,000; low: $5,000).
Fields of interest: Medical school/education; Hospitals (general); Hospitals (specialty); Health organizations, association; Eye diseases; Diabetes research.
Limitations: Applications not accepted. Giving primarily in CA. No grants to individuals.
Application information: Contributes only to pre-selected organizations.
Trustees: Josephine D. Gleis; Richard Hausman; Gavin Herbert, Jr.
EIN: 330876494
Selected grants: The following grants are a representative sample of this grantmaker's funding activity:
$25,000 to University of California, Department of Ophthalmology - Building Fund, Irvine, CA, 2012. For general use.
$25,000 to University of California, Department of Ophthalmology - Stem Cell, Irvine, CA, 2012. For general use.

594
Glenn Foundation for Medical Research, Inc. ✧
(formerly Paul F. Glenn Foundation for Medical Research, Inc.)
1270 Coast Village Cir., St. 200
Santa Barbara, CA 93108-3724
Contact: Mark R. Collins, Pres.
E-mail: mrc@glennfoundation.org; Main URL: http://www.glennfoundation.org

Established in 1965 in NY; reincorporated in 1992 in AZ.
Donor: Paul F. Glenn.
Foundation type: Independent foundation.
Financial data (yr. ended 09/30/13): Assets, $245,703,267 (M); gifts received, $16,479,609; expenditures, $10,346,058; qualifying distributions, $6,478,696; giving activities include $6,448,409 for 18+ grants (high: $1,455,000).
Purpose and activities: The purpose of the foundation is to extend the healthy, productive years of life, through research into the mechanisms of biological aging.
Fields of interest: Medical research, institute; Geriatrics research; Biology/life sciences; Aging.
Type of support: Conferences/seminars; Fellowships; Research.
Limitations: Applications not accepted. Giving on a national basis. No support for sociological, as opposed to biological, aging projects.
Publications: Grants list; Informational brochure; Program policy statement.
Application information: Unsolicited requests for funds not accepted.
Board meeting date(s): Annually
Officers and Directors:* Paul F. Glenn,* Chair. and Treas.; Mark R. Collins,* Pres.; K. Leonard Judson,* Exec. V.P. and Secy.; A. Ray Copeland; Jack N. Rudel.
Number of staff: None.
EIN: 860710305
Selected grants: The following grants are a representative sample of this grantmaker's funding activity:
$1,455,000 to American Federation for Aging Research, New York, NY, 2013. For research.
$1,190,000 to Mayo Clinic, Rochester, MN, 2012. For medical research.
$1,135,000 to American Federation for Aging Research, New York, NY, 2012. For medical research.
$1,060,000 to Massachusetts Institute of Technology, Cambridge, MA, 2012. For medical research.
$1,060,000 to Salk Institute for Biological Studies, La Jolla, CA, 2013. For research.
$1,000,000 to Albert Einstein College of Medicine of Yeshiva University, Bronx, NY, 2012. For medical research.
$1,000,000 to Harvard University, Cambridge, MA, 2012. For medical research at School of Medicine in Boston, MA.
$1,000,000 to Harvard University, Cambridge, MA, 2013. For medical research at School of Medicine in Boston, MA.
$1,000,000 to Salk Institute for Biological Studies, La Jolla, CA, 2012. For medical research.
$1,000,000 to Stanford University, Stanford, CA, 2013. For research.
$600,000 to Princeton University, Princeton, NJ, 2013. For research.
$570,000 to Buck Institute for Research on Aging, Novato, CA, 2012. For medical research.
$409,006 to University of California, Santa Cruz, CA, 2013. For research.
$218,438 to University of Texas at San Antonio, San Antonio, TX, 2013. For research.
$176,798 to Mayo Clinic, Rochester, MN, 2013. For research.
$60,000 to Albert Einstein College of Medicine of Yeshiva University, Bronx, NY, 2013. For research.

$60,000 to International Healthspan Institute, University Park, PA, 2012. For medical research.
$60,000 to Johns Hopkins University, Baltimore, MD, 2013. For research.
$10,000 to Gerontological Society of America, Washington, DC, 2012. For medical research.
$10,000 to Science Network, La Jolla, CA, 2012. For medical research.

595
Thornton S., Jr. and Katrina D. Glide Foundation ✧

28120 Pierce Ranch Rd.
Davis, CA 95616-9447 (530) 753-3803
FAX: (530) 753-3849;
E-mail: glidefoundation@sprynet.com; Main URL: http://www.glidefoundation.org/

Established in 1997 in CA.
Donors: Katrina D. Glide†; The George and Lena Valente Foundation.
Foundation type: Independent foundation.
Financial data (yr. ended 12/31/13): Assets, $42,858,424 (M); gifts received, $5,700; expenditures, $2,247,809; qualifying distributions, $1,809,028; giving activities include $918,685 for 115 grants (high: $25,000; low: $1,000), and $890,343 for foundation-administered programs.
Purpose and activities: Giving to organizations committed to the preservation of lands in their natural state, including wetlands; organizations committed to agricultural purposes; land and wildlife conservancy groups, and animal protection organizations.
Fields of interest: Arts; Environment, land resources; Animal welfare; Animals/wildlife, preservation/protection; Housing/shelter; Human services; United Ways and Federated Giving Programs.
Limitations: Applications accepted. Giving primarily in CA. Out of state applicants will be considered. No support for programs focused primarily on a sport, general educational institutions, or religious organizations (except for community social service activities). No grants to individuals; no scholarships.
Application information: See foundation web site for downloadable application form. Application form required.
Deadline(s): May 15 to Aug. 15
Trustees: Richard D. Bruga; Yvonne LeMaitre; Russell E. White.
EIN: 943276694
Selected grants: The following grants are a representative sample of this grantmaker's funding activity:
$11,000 to Horses of Tir Na Nog, San Diego, CA, 2012. For Replace Weather Shelters That Were Destroyed During Unusually Heavy Snow Storm in March 2012.
$10,000 to Voice for the Animals, Santa Monica, CA, 2012. For Elderly Companion Animal Rescue Rehabilitation and Adoption Program.
$9,000 to River City Cat Rescue, Sacramento, CA, 2012. To continue Spay/Neuter Program Support Tnr Program Medical Care.
$9,000 to Wildlife Associates, Half Moon Bay, CA, 2012. To support Ongoing Care of Our Retired Non-Releasable Wild Animals at Our Sanctuary.
$7,000 to Feeding Pets of the Homeless, Carson City, NV, 2012. To provide Veterinary Care, Spay/Neuter, Pet Food to Pets of Homeless Across Country.
$7,000 to Helen Woodward Animal Center, Rancho Santa Fe, CA, 2012. For Purchase Five Refurbished Computers and Two Printers for the Adoptions Department.
$7,000 to Muttville, San Francisco, CA, 2012. For New Flooring Treatments and Heating for at Location in Sf Spca.
$7,000 to Pacific Marine Mammal Center, Laguna Beach, CA, 2012. For Purchase Additional Whale Rescue Equipment.
$5,000 to Sacramento Zoological Society, Sacramento, CA, 2012. For Renovation of Small Wonders Exhibit at the Sac Zoo.
$4,500 to Animal Spay and Neuter, Auburn, CA, 2012. For Capstar for All Surgical Patients.

596
Maxwell H. Gluck Foundation, Inc. ✧

P.O. Box 55516
Sherman Oaks, CA 91413-0516
Contact: Camilla Townsend, Exec. Dir.
Main URL: http://www.gluckfoundation.org

Established in 1955 in NY.
Donor: Maxwell H. Gluck†.
Foundation type: Independent foundation.
Financial data (yr. ended 06/30/13): Assets, $104,239,647 (M); expenditures, $5,646,545; qualifying distributions, $4,806,893; giving activities include $4,679,803 for 20 grants (high: $833,291; low: $24,505).
Purpose and activities: Support for higher and other education, and the arts.
Fields of interest: Arts education; Arts; Higher education; Education; Human services.
Limitations: Applications not accepted. Giving limited to southern CA. No grants to individuals.
Application information: Contributes only to pre-selected organizations. Unsolicited requests for funds not accepted.
Officers and Directors:* Jon A. Kaswick, M.D.*, Pres.; Julie Kaswick, Secy.; Camilla Townsend, Exec. Dir.; Jennifer Kaswick; Richard G. Reinis; Betty S. Shelhamer.
Number of staff: 1 part-time support.
EIN: 953979100
Selected grants: The following grants are a representative sample of this grantmaker's funding activity:
$655,651 to University of California, Los Angeles, CA, 2011. For music education and student fellowships.
$626,000 to Natural History Museum of Los Angeles County, Los Angeles, CA, 2011. For science trucks for LAUSD science education.
$600,000 to University of California, Riverside, CA, 2011. For music education and student fellowships.
$559,191 to Museum Associates, Los Angeles County Museum of Art (LACMA), Los Angeles, CA, 2011. For Maya art truck/art education LAUSD.
$342,000 to Colburn School of the Performing Arts, Los Angeles, CA, 2011. For Summer Encounter Arts Education Program.
$250,000 to Juilliard School, New York, NY, 2011. For student fellowship program.
$240,500 to Los Angeles Opera Company, Los Angeles, CA, 2011. For arts education.
$200,000 to Leo Baeck Temple, Los Angeles, CA, 2011. For Arts education.
$113,810 to Los Angeles County High School for the Arts Foundation, Arts High Foundation, Los Angeles, CA, 2011.
$70,000 to Orange County High School of the Arts Foundation, Santa Ana, CA, 2011. For community service arts programs.

597
God's Gift ✧

P.O. Box 890515
Temecula, CA 92589-0515

Established in 1998 in CA.
Donors: Helen Lovaas; Leeland M. Lovaas.
Foundation type: Independent foundation.
Financial data (yr. ended 12/31/13): Assets, $10,698,146 (M); expenditures, $2,913,892; qualifying distributions, $2,802,877; giving activities include $2,788,000 for 78 grants (high: $500,000; low: $5,000).
Fields of interest: Education; Human services; Christian agencies & churches.
Limitations: Applications not accepted. Giving in the U.S., with some emphasis on CA. No grants to individuals.
Application information: Contributes only to pre-selected organizations.
Board meeting date(s): Semiannually
Officers and Directors:* Helen Lovaas,* Pres. and C.F.O.; Leeland M. Lovaas,* V.P. and Secy.
EIN: 330831475

598
John Gogian Family Foundation ✧

(also known as JGFF)
2531 W. 237th St., No. 124
Torrance, CA 90505-5244 (310) 325-0954
Contact: Lindsey Stammerjohn, Exec. Dir.
FAX: (310) 325-0903;
E-mail: jgff@gogianfoundation.org; Main URL: http://www.gogianfoundation.org
Scholarship contact: Kelly Boyle,
e-mail: kboyle@gogianfoundation.org

Established in 1982.
Donors: Rosalia Gogian†; John Gogian.
Foundation type: Independent foundation.
Financial data (yr. ended 12/31/13): Assets, $9,368,101 (M); expenditures, $1,805,313; qualifying distributions, $1,694,566; giving activities include $1,519,125 for 85 grants (high: $50,000; low: $400), and $52,069 for foundation-administered programs.
Purpose and activities: The John Gogian Family Foundation is a private charitable foundation dedicated to supporting community-based organizations that enhance the quality of people's lives in Los Angeles County, California. The foundation supports organizations that provide services and solutions for the developmentally disabled, abused and neglected youth, and for the elderly. Scholarships also for a senior at Lennox Academy, Port of Los Angeles High School, or Verbum Dei, who is a U.S. citizen or legal resident, who has a GPA of 3.0 or higher, is in financial need, and has applied to a university, a 4-year college, a community college, or a state-accredited trade school within the U.S. Scholarships are made directly to the school on behalf of the individual.
Fields of interest: Down syndrome; Autism; Crime/violence prevention, domestic violence; Housing/shelter, temporary shelter; Children, foster care; Residential/custodial care, group home; Residential/custodial care, hospices; Residential/

custodial care, senior continuing care; Aging, centers/services; Developmentally disabled, centers & services; Independent living, disability; Children/youth; Adults; Aging; Mentally disabled; Crime/abuse victims; Terminal illness, people with.
International interests: Armenia.
Type of support: General/operating support; Building/renovation; Equipment; Program development; Scholarships—to individuals; Matching/challenge support.
Limitations: Applications accepted. Giving primarily in Los Angeles County, CA. No support for national organizations or their affiliates, or for care of animals, arts and culture programs, or projects designed to influence legislation. No grants to individuals (directly), or for debt reduction, research, endowments, lending of funds, or for fundraising events.
Publications: Application guidelines; Financial statement; Grants list; Informational brochure.
Application information: Organizations will be notified of their status in six weeks. Those accepted will be e-mailed the full grant application. Grants may be awarded annually for 3 consecutive years, and then the organization must sit-out one year. Grants range from $5,000-20,000. Requests submitted either by fax or e-mail are not accepted. Application form required.
Initial approach: Download letter of inquiry form from web site and send via U.S. mail or commercial carrier
Copies of proposal: 1
Deadline(s): Sept. 10 and Mar. 4 for letters of inquiry; see foundation web site for current scholarship deadline
Board meeting date(s): Quarterly
Final notification: May and Nov.—5 months from receipt of full grant application
Officers and Directors:* Kathleen Crane,* Chair.; Dan Mueller, Pres.; Becky Schroff,* Secy.; Gary Nelson, Treas.; Lindsey Stammerjohn, Exec. Dir.; Tom Cody; John J. Gogian, Jr.; Carole Jouryan.
Number of staff: 1 full-time professional; 1 part-time support.
EIN: 953759369
Selected grants: The following grants are a representative sample of this grantmaker's funding activity:
$25,000 to Court Appointed Special Advocates, Monterey Park, CA, 2012. To increase number of special advocates, working on behalf of foster youth.
$20,000 to A Window Between Worlds, Venice, CA, 2012. For therapeutic art programs for children in domestic violence shelters.
$20,000 to Los Angeles Youth Network, Los Angeles, CA, 2012. For residential services for abused and neglected youth.
$20,000 to OPARC, Montclair, CA, 2012. For speech pathologist salary.
$20,000 to Rainbow Services, San Pedro, CA, 2012. For services.
$20,000 to Richstone Center, Hawthorne, CA, 2012. For therapeutic services for children.
$20,000 to Society To Aid Retarded, Torrance, CA, 2012. For remodel of residential homes.
$15,000 to Carousel Ranch, Santa Clarita, CA, 2012. For scholarships.
$15,000 to Echo Parenting and Education, Los Angeles, CA, 2012. For program services and development of Trauma Informed Care practices.
$15,000 to Grandparents as Parents, Canoga Park, CA, 2012. For services.
$15,000 to L.A. GOAL, Culver City, CA, 2012. For Independent Living Program.
$15,000 to Pediatric Therapy Network, Torrance, CA, 2012. For speech, physical and occupational therapy.

599
Gold Family Foundation ✧
(formerly Gold Family Charitable Foundation)
3500 W. Olive Ave., Ste. 700
Burbank, CA 91505-4054
Contact: Ilene C. Gold, Pres.; Stenley P. Gold, V.P. and Treas.

Established in 1986 in CA.
Donors: Stanley P. Gold; Ilene C. Gold.
Foundation type: Independent foundation.
Financial data (yr. ended 07/31/13): Assets, $1,531 (M); gifts received, $917,955; expenditures, $916,675; qualifying distributions, $913,685; giving activities include $913,685 for 55 grants (high: $200,000; low: $250).
Purpose and activities: Support primarily for Jewish organizations, including education, a welfare fund, and temple support; support also for cultural and educational advancement, and for health and social services.
Fields of interest: Arts; Higher education; Theological school/education; Health care; Health organizations, association; Human services; Jewish federated giving programs; Jewish agencies & synagogues.
Limitations: Applications accepted. Giving primarily in CA and NY. No grants to individuals.
Application information: Application form not required.
Initial approach: Proposal
Deadline(s): None
Officers: Ilene C. Gold, Pres.; Stanley P. Gold, V.P. and Treas.
EIN: 954076113
Selected grants: The following grants are a representative sample of this grantmaker's funding activity:
$1,000 to Memorial Sloan-Kettering Cancer Center, New York, NY, 2013. For Medical Treatment and Research.

600
The David B. Gold Foundation ✧
44 Montgomery St., Ste. 3750
San Francisco, CA 94104-4826 (415) 288-9530
Contact: Elaine Gold, Exec. Dir.
FAX: (415) 288-9549;
E-mail: rose@goldfoundation.org; Main URL: http://www.goldfoundation.org/
Grants List: http://www.goldfoundation.org/grants_awarded/grants_awarded.htm
Knowledge Center: http://www.goldfoundation.org/information_links/information_links.htm

Established in 1992 in CA.
Donor: David B. Gold†.
Foundation type: Independent foundation.
Financial data (yr. ended 12/31/12): Assets, $95,576,376 (M); expenditures, $5,037,232; qualifying distributions, $4,148,267; giving activities include $3,442,500 for 116 grants (high: $150,000; low: $500).
Purpose and activities: Giving primarily for: 1) children, youth and families, particularly to support early childhood development programs, promote enrichment programs for school age youth, reduce domestic violence, improve the welfare of children, and to help prevent teen parenthood; 2) the environment, particularly to reduce toxic emissions, preserve open space, and promote sustainable energy policy; 3) democratic values, 4) and Jewish culture.
Fields of interest: Environment, natural resources; Reproductive health, family planning; Crime/violence prevention, child abuse; Youth development; Jewish agencies & synagogues.
Type of support: General/operating support; Continuing support; Capital campaigns; Building/renovation; Land acquisition; Program development.
Limitations: Applications accepted. Giving primarily to organizations that have an impact on the San Francisco Bay Area, CA, with emphasis on Alameda and San Francisco counties and in the Twin Cities of Minneapolis/St. Paul, MN; some funding to national projects that are particularly relevant to the foundation's mission. No support for sectarian organizations, except for those organizations that fall within the foundation's Jewish Culture program area. No grants to individuals, which includes projects for research, attending conferences, scholarships, musical works, or film.
Publications: Application guidelines.
Application information: See foundation web site for complete application guidelines. Application form required.
Initial approach: On-line proposal via foundation web site
Copies of proposal: 1
Deadline(s): None
Board meeting date(s): Quarterly
Final notification: Within 4 months after the proposal is received
Officers and Directors:* Barbara Gold-Lurie,* Pres.; Diane Gold-Bubier,* Secy.; Steven A. Gold,* Treas. and C.F.O.; Elaine Gold,* Exec. Dir.; Emily Gold.
EIN: 943169439

601
Sheila Gold Foundation ✧
3940 Laurel Canyon Blvd., Ste. 139
Studio City, CA 91604-3709
Contact: Jeff Gold

Established in 1997 in CA.
Donors: Dave Gold; Sherry Gold; Jeff Gold; Howard Gold; Karen Schiffer.
Foundation type: Independent foundation.
Financial data (yr. ended 12/31/12): Assets, $43,834,897 (M); gifts received, $32,676,701; expenditures, $1,904,776; qualifying distributions, $1,897,826; giving activities include $1,897,177 for 89 grants (high: $630,000; low: $250).
Purpose and activities: Giving primarily for health organizations and medical research, as well as for Jewish organizations, education, and children, youth, and social services.
Fields of interest: Higher education; Education; Health organizations, association; Medical research, institute; Human services; Children/youth, services; Jewish agencies & synagogues.
Limitations: Applications not accepted. Giving primarily in Los Angeles, CA. No grants to individuals.
Application information: Contributes only to pre-selected organizations.
Trustees: David Gold; Howard Gold; Jeff Gold; Sherry Gold; Karen Schiffer.
EIN: 954636060

602
Goldhirsh Foundation ✧
6380 Wilshire Blvd., 15th Fl.
Los Angeles, CA 90048-5003
Main URL: http://www.goldhirshfoundation.org/
Facebook: https://www.facebook.com/GoldhirshFoundation

Established in CA.
Donor: Goldirsh Foundation.
Foundation type: Independent foundation.
Financial data (yr. ended 12/31/13): Assets, $63,850,791 (M); expenditures, $3,656,413; qualifying distributions, $2,991,427; giving activities include $2,505,500 for 96 grants (high: $150,000; low: $500).
Fields of interest: Education; Health organizations; Human services.
Limitations: Applications not accepted.
Application information: Unsolicited requests for funds not accepted.
Officers: Benjamin A. Goldhirsh, Pres.; Tara Roth McConaghy, Secy. and Exec. Dir.; Kathleen C. Wallace, Treas.
Director: Claire Denise Hoffman Goldhirsh.
EIN: 272824140

603
Goldhirsh-Yellin Foundation, Inc. ✧
c/o Philpott Bills Stoll & Meeks LLP
16030 Ventura Blvd., Ste. 380
Encino, CA 91436-2778 (310) 838-5131
Contact: Susan Grinel
FAX: (310) 838-5303; Main URL: http://www.goldhirshyellin.org/

Donor: Goldhirsh Foundation.
Foundation type: Independent foundation.
Financial data (yr. ended 12/31/12): Assets, $61,251,581 (M); gifts received, $38,449; expenditures, $3,463,110; qualifying distributions, $2,762,293; giving activities include $2,685,835 for 81 grants (high: $250,000; low: $500).
Fields of interest: History/archaeology; Education; Environment; Cancer research; Children/youth, services; Jewish agencies & synagogues.
Limitations: Applications not accepted.
Application information: Unsolicited requests for funds not accepted.
Officers: Elizabeth A. Goldhrish-Yellin, Pres.; Eric Yellin, V.P.; Kathy Wallace, Treas.; David Beckwith, C.I.O.
EIN: 272968092

604
Goldman Environmental Foundation ✧
160 Pacific Ave., Ste. 200
San Francisco, CA 94111-1976 (415) 249-5800
FAX: (415) 772-9137;
E-mail: info@goldmanprize.org; Main URL: http://www.goldmanprize.org
Blog: http://www.goldmanprize.org/blog
E-Newsletter: http://www.goldmanprize.org/theprize/ouroboros_newsletter_list
Facebook: http://www.facebook.com/goldmanenvironmentalprize
Google Plus: https://plus.google.com/102804815783131510488/posts
Grants Database: http://www.goldmanprize.org/recipients/byname
Twitter: http://twitter.com/goldmanprize
YouTube: http://www.youtube.com/user/goldmanprize

Established in 1989 in CA.
Donors: Richard N. Goldman‡; Rhoda H. Goldman‡.
Foundation type: Independent foundation.
Financial data (yr. ended 12/31/13): Assets, $125,159,565 (M); expenditures, $5,273,741; qualifying distributions, $4,376,684; giving activities include $900,000 for 6 grants to individuals (high: $150,000; low: $150,000).
Purpose and activities: The foundation's purpose is to award one prize annually to an individual in each of the six inhabited continents in recognition of significant achievement in the field of environmental protection. Grants will not be awarded.
Fields of interest: Environment.
Limitations: Applications not accepted. Giving on an international basis, one prize annually is given to each continental region.
Publications: Informational brochure; Newsletter.
Application information: The foundation's grantmaking program has been discontinued. Awards to individuals are by nomination of 30 organizations and a network of environmentalists. No unsolicited nominations or requests for funds will be considered.
Board meeting date(s): Feb., July, and Nov.
Officer and Directors:* Douglas E. Goldman,* Pres.; John D. Goldman,* V.P.; Susan Gelman,* V.P.; David Gordon, Exec. Dir.
Number of staff: 8 full-time professional; 2 part-time professional.
EIN: 943094857

605
John and Marcia Goldman Foundation ✧
(formerly The John and Marcia Goldman Fund)
101 2nd St., Ste. 1625
San Francisco, CA 94105-3672 (415) 744-8787
Contact: Amy Lyons, Exec. Dir.
E-mail: info@gmgoldmanfoundation.org; Main URL: http://www.jmgoldmanfoundation.org

Established in 1997 in CA.
Donors: John D. Goldman; Marcia L. Goldman.
Foundation type: Independent foundation.
Financial data (yr. ended 12/31/12): Assets, $175,967,147 (M); gifts received, $93,049,720; expenditures, $8,055,108; qualifying distributions, $7,504,165; giving activities include $7,151,624 for 51 grants (high: $1,000,000; low: $5,000).
Purpose and activities: Giving primarily to underprivileged children and youth.
Fields of interest: Arts; Education; Health care; Recreation; Human services; Children/youth, services; Family services; Infants/toddlers; Children/youth; Children; Youth; Disabilities, people with; Minorities; Hispanics/Latinos; Girls; Boys; Economically disadvantaged; Homeless.
Type of support: Annual campaigns; Capital campaigns; Building/renovation; Equipment; Emergency funds; Program development; Seed money; Curriculum development; Internship funds; Scholarship funds; Technical assistance; Matching/challenge support.
Limitations: Applications accepted. Giving limited to northern Santa Clara County and southern San Mateo County, CA. No support for sole-denomination religious charities. No grants for salaries, general operating support, films, and Web sites.
Publications: Application guidelines; Grants list.
Application information: Applicants should submit 1 electronic copy and 1 hard copy of their proposal. Application form required.
Initial approach: Proposal/E-mail to Exec. Dir. to request application forms and guidelines
Copies of proposal: 2
Deadline(s): 3 months prior to board meeting dates
Board meeting date(s): Mar., July, and Nov.
Final notification: 2 months
Officers: John D. Goldman, Pres.; Marcia L. Goldman, Secy.-Treas.
Board Members: Alejandro Foung; Jessica Goldman Foung; Aaron D. Goldman.
Number of staff: 4 full-time professional.
EIN: 943274370
Selected grants: The following grants are a representative sample of this grantmaker's funding activity:
$1,850,000 to San Francisco Symphony, San Francisco, CA, 2011. For general support.
$1,510,000 to Jewish Community Federation of San Francisco, the Peninsula, Marin and Sonoma Counties, San Francisco, CA, 2011. For general support.
$1,200,000 to Stanford University, Stanford, CA, 2011. For general support.
$200,563 to American Symphony Orchestra League, New York, NY, 2011. For general support.
$150,000 to American Conservatory Theater, San Francisco, CA, 2011. For general support.
$150,000 to Switchback Films, Berkeley, CA, 2011. For general support.
$100,000 to Swarthmore College, Swarthmore, PA, 2011. For general support.
$100,000 to TheaterWorks, Palo Alto, CA, 2011. For general support.
$50,000 to Eastside College Preparatory School, East Palo Alto, CA, 2011. For general support.
$25,000 to Stanford University, Center on Philanthropy and Civil Society, Stanford, CA, 2011. For general support.

606
Lisa and Douglas Goldman Fund ✧
1 Montgomery St., Ste. 3440
San Francisco, CA 94104-4505 (415) 771-1717
Contact: Nancy S. Kami, Exec. Dir.
FAX: (415) 771-1797; Main URL: http://ldgfund.org

Established in 1992 in CA.
Foundation type: Independent foundation.
Financial data (yr. ended 12/31/12): Assets, $186,570,345 (M); gifts received, $92,710,888; expenditures, $9,834,803; qualifying distributions, $9,426,649; giving activities include $8,088,040 for 323 grants (high: $1,000,000; low: $100).
Purpose and activities: Giving to provide support for charitable organizations that enhance society, primarily those serving the San Francisco, CA, area. Giving primarily for democracy and civil liberties, education and literacy, environment, health and recreation, the Jewish community, and reproductive health and rights.
Fields of interest: Education, reading; Education; Environment; Health care; Recreation; Civil rights, voter education; Civil liberties, reproductive rights; Civil/human rights; Jewish agencies & synagogues.
International interests: Israel.
Type of support: General/operating support; Continuing support; Management development/capacity building; Capital campaigns; Building/renovation; Emergency funds; Program

development; Curriculum development; Technical assistance; Program evaluation; Matching/challenge support.
Limitations: Applications accepted. Giving primarily in the San Francisco Bay Area, CA. No grants to individuals; no support for deficit budgets, endowments, conferences, events, conferences, documentaries, films, books, or research.
Publications: Annual report (including application guidelines); Financial statement; IRS Form 990 or 990-PF printed copy available upon request.
Application information: Unsolicited proposals from educational institutions or arts/cultural organizations not accepted. Application guidelines and procedures are available on foundation web site. Faxes, e-mails, audio/video tapes, not accepted. Applications must also include 3 references familiar with the project. The fund uses an online application system which can be accessed through its website, at http://www.ldgfund.org/grant-seekers/guidelines/. Application form not required.
Initial approach: Brief letter of inquiry (2 pages maximum)
Copies of proposal: 1
Deadline(s): None
Board meeting date(s): 4 times per year
Officers and Directors:* Douglas E. Goldman,* Pres.; Lisa M. Goldman,* Secy.; Derek T. Knudsen,* Treas.; Nancy S. Kami, Exec. Dir.; Jason E. Goldman; Matthew E. Goldman.
Number of staff: 5 full-time professional.
EIN: 943167546
Selected grants: The following grants are a representative sample of this grantmaker's funding activity:
$635,000 to San Francisco Tennis Coalition, San Francisco, CA, 2014. For Phase I of the Golden Gate Park Tennis Center capital project.
$50,000 to Corporate Accountability International, Boston, MA, 2014. To build support for bottled water bans at National Parks throughout the country.
$50,000 to University of California, Haas College of Business, Berkeley, CA, 2014. For Berkeley Board Fellows Program, to help prepare students to become the next generation of non-profit board leaders.
$37,000 to San Francisco Jewish Film Festival, San Francisco, CA, 2014. For New Generation Initiative, to offer film screenings and events for young adults (ages 21 to 35) during the summer festival and throughout the year.
$25,000 to Golden Gate National Parks Conservancy, San Francisco, CA, 2014.

607
The Goldrich Family Foundation ✧
5150 Overland Ave.
Culver City, CA 90230-4914
Contact: Jona Goldrich, Pres.

Established in 1987 in CA.
Donors: Jona Goldrich; Ana Hirth; Emanuel Hirth; Doretta Goldrich; Goldrich & Kest Industries; Goldrich Trust; Hirth Family Foundation; Z Valet Inc.; Phoenix Life Insurance Co.
Foundation type: Independent foundation.
Financial data (yr. ended 11/30/12): Assets, $91,915,690 (M); gifts received, $5,000,000; expenditures, $4,588,325; qualifying distributions, $4,209,544; giving activities include $4,175,021 for 110 grants (high: $1,700,000; low: $100).
Purpose and activities: Support for Jewish education and for other Jewish organizations.
Fields of interest: Education; Community/economic development; Jewish federated giving programs; Jewish agencies & synagogues.
International interests: Israel.
Limitations: Applications not accepted. Giving primarily in Los Angeles, CA, and New York, NY; some funding also in CO. No grants to individuals.
Application information: Contributes only to pre-selected organizations.
Officers: Jona Goldrich, Pres.; Andrea Goldrich Cayton, Secy.; Melinda Goldrich, Treas.; David Rochkind, C.F.O.
Directors: Barry Cayton; Doretta Goldrich.
EIN: 954155986

608
Goldsmith Family Foundation ✧
400 N. Roxbury Dr.
Beverly Hills, CA 90210-5002

Established in 1980 in CA.
Donors: Mrs. Bram Goldsmith; Bram Goldsmith; Karen Goldsmith; Russell Goldsmith; Elm 2006 Charitable Trust; Spruce 2007 Charitable Trust.
Foundation type: Independent foundation.
Financial data (yr. ended 09/30/13): Assets, $16,157,532 (M); gifts received, $207,580; expenditures, $489,389; qualifying distributions, $479,898; giving activities include $473,821 for 77 grants (high: $120,000; low: $100).
Fields of interest: Arts; Education; Hospitals (general); Medical research, institute; Human services; Jewish federated giving programs; Jewish agencies & synagogues.
Type of support: Continuing support; Annual campaigns; Capital campaigns; Building/renovation; Endowments; Professorships; Research; Matching/challenge support.
Limitations: Applications not accepted. Giving primarily in southern CA. No grants to individuals.
Application information: Contributes only to pre-selected organizations.
Board meeting date(s): As needed
Officers: Bram Goldsmith, Pres.; Elaine Goldsmith, V.P. and Treas.
Directors: Bruce L. Goldsmith; Russell Goldsmith.
Number of staff: 1 part-time support.
EIN: 953545880
Selected grants: The following grants are a representative sample of this grantmaker's funding activity:
$25,000 to Alliance for Childrens Rights, Los Angeles, CA, 2011.

609
The Samuel Goldwyn Foundation ✧
9570 W. Pico Blvd., Ste. 400
Los Angeles, CA 90035-1216

Established in 1947 in CA.
Donors: Samuel Goldwyn†; Frances H. Goldwyn†.
Foundation type: Independent foundation.
Financial data (yr. ended 12/31/12): Assets, $23,772,885 (M); expenditures, $2,248,196; qualifying distributions, $1,248,881; giving activities include $1,117,553 for 113 grants (high: $275,000; low: $10).
Purpose and activities: Giving primarily for the arts, particularly a motion picture and television fund; funding also for education, health associations, healthcare services, Jewish organizations, and social services.
Fields of interest: Arts education; Media, film/video; Media, television; Arts; Elementary/secondary education; Higher education; Libraries/library science; Education; Health care; Health organizations, association; Human services; American Red Cross; Children/youth, services; Jewish agencies & synagogues; Women.
Type of support: Annual campaigns; Program development; Seed money; Scholarship funds; Research.
Limitations: Applications not accepted. Giving primarily in CA; some funding nationally. No grants to individuals, or for building funds.
Application information: Contributes only to pre-selected organizations.
Board meeting date(s): Quarterly
Officers and Directors:* Samuel Goldwyn, Jr.,* Pres. and Secy.; John Goldwyn,* V.P.; Meyer Gottlieb, Treas.; Anthony Goldwyn; Catherine Goldwyn; Francis Goldwyn.
Number of staff: 1 full-time professional.
EIN: 956006859

610
Michael & Corlene Gombos Foundation ✧ ☆
(formerly The Gombos Family Charitable Foundation)
11005 Jadestone Dr.
Bakersfield, CA 93311-3539

Established in CA.
Donor: The Gombos Revocable Family Trust.
Foundation type: Independent foundation.
Financial data (yr. ended 12/31/13): Assets, $456,068 (M); gifts received, $500,000; expenditures, $555,336; qualifying distributions, $551,876; giving activities include $551,876 for 5 grants (high: $500,000; low: $5,000).
Fields of interest: Education; Housing/shelter; Community/economic development; Homeless.
Limitations: Applications not accepted. Giving primarily in Bakersfield, CA.
Application information: Unsolicited requests for funds not accepted.
Officer: Michael N. Gombos, Pres.
Directors: Patrice Irene Bussell; Corlene Gombos; John Michael Gombos; Julia Lynn Gombos.
EIN: 273138184

611
Good Hope Medical Foundation ✧
625 Fair Oaks Ave.
South Pasadena, CA 91030
Contact: Julie Lytle Nesbit

Established in 1925 in CA.
Donor: Dorothy May Harris†.
Foundation type: Independent foundation.
Financial data (yr. ended 12/31/13): Assets, $30,975,910 (M); expenditures, $1,287,617; qualifying distributions, $1,076,367; giving activities include $983,074 for 11 grants (high: $200,000; low: $20,000).
Purpose and activities: Giving primarily to hospitals.
Fields of interest: Hospitals (general).
Type of support: General/operating support; Equipment.

Limitations: Applications accepted. Giving limited to CA. No grants to individuals.
Application information: Application form not required.
Initial approach: Proposal
Deadline(s): None
Officers: John Quinn, Pres.; Thomas Hudnut, C.F.O. and Treas.; J. Patrick Whaley, Secy.
Directors: Ernest A. Bryant III; Howard Kahn; Alexander Li; Michael Segal; Philip V. Swan; Robert E. Tranquada, M.D.; Cynthia Tribull; Thomas Wachtell; Lynn Yonekura.
EIN: 950782640

612
The Good Works Foundation ✧
2101 Wilshire Blvd., Ste. 225
Santa Monica, CA 90403-5746 (310) 828-1288
FAX: (310) 829-6090; E-mail: info@goodworks.org; Main URL: http://www.goodworks.org

Established in 1993 in CA.
Donor: Laura Donnelley Family Trust.
Foundation type: Independent foundation.
Financial data (yr. ended 12/31/12): Assets, $2,195,922 (M); gifts received, $992,322; expenditures, $1,048,571; qualifying distributions, $1,009,330; giving activities include $1,009,330 for 81 grants (high: $301,880; low: $500).
Purpose and activities: Giving primarily for the arts, the environment, social action and education, with an emphasis on grassroots organizations and innovative ideas in the Los Angeles, CA, area.
Fields of interest: Museums (art); Performing arts, opera; Arts; Education; Environment.
Type of support: General/operating support; Seed money; Matching/challenge support.
Limitations: Giving primarily in the Los Angeles, CA, area and NY. No support for political causes. No grants to individuals, for fellowships, capital expenditures, construction or endowments.
Publications: Application guidelines.
Application information: Applications are by invitation only, upon review of initial e-mail. Application form not required.
Initial approach: E-mail via contact page on foundation web site
Deadline(s): None
Board meeting date(s): Quarterly
Officer and Trustees:* Laura Donnelley,* Pres.; Philip Yenawine.
Number of staff: 1 part-time support.
EIN: 954471685
Selected grants: The following grants are a representative sample of this grantmaker's funding activity:
$280,000 to Art Matters, New York, NY, 2011.
$121,850 to Santa Monica Museum of Art, Santa Monica, CA, 2011.
$59,000 to Los Angeles Opera Company, Los Angeles, CA, 2011.
$50,000 to New Visions Foundation, Santa Monica, CA, 2011.
$12,000 to T.H.E. Clinic, Los Angeles, CA, 2010.
$10,000 to National Public Radio, Washington, DC, 2011.
$6,000 to UCLA Foundation, Los Angeles, CA, 2011.
$5,000 to Goodman Theater, Chicago, IL, 2011.
$5,000 to Southern California Public Radio, Pasadena, CA, 2011.
$5,000 to University of California at San Diego Foundation, La Jolla, CA, 2011.
$1,000 to University of Santa Monica, Santa Monica, CA, 2011.

613
The Goodman Family Foundation ✧
c/o Sobul, Primes & Schenkel, C.P.A.s
12100 Wilshire Blvd., Ste. 1150
Los Angeles, CA 90025-7117

Established in 1977 in CA.
Donor: Lawrence M. Goodman, Jr.
Foundation type: Independent foundation.
Financial data (yr. ended 06/30/11): Assets, $0 (M); expenditures, $882,356; qualifying distributions, $872,252; giving activities include $872,252 for 6 grants (high: $218,063; low: $3,036).
Purpose and activities: Giving primarily for education and social services.
Fields of interest: Elementary school/education; Higher education; Education; Reproductive health, family planning; Food banks; Human services; Jewish federated giving programs.
Limitations: Applications not accepted. Giving primarily in CA. No grants to individuals.
Application information: Unsolicited requests for funds not accepted.
Trustees: Meyer Luskin; Christopher Morris; David M. Primes.
EIN: 953169740

614
Goodwin Family Memorial Trust ✧ ☆
c/o Wells Fargo Bank, N.A.
P.O. Box. 63954, MAC A0348-012
San Francisco, CA 94163-0001

Foundation type: Independent foundation.
Financial data (yr. ended 02/28/14): Assets, $13,665,186 (M); expenditures, $623,866; qualifying distributions, $499,650; giving activities include $480,000 for 30 grants (high: $40,000; low: $5,000).
Fields of interest: Health care; Health organizations; Human services.
Limitations: Applications not accepted.
Application information: Unsolicited requests for funds not accepted.
Trustee: Wells Fargo Bank, N.A.
EIN: 956674233

615
Google Foundation ✧
1600 Amphitheatre Pkwy.
Mountain View, CA 94043-1351
Main URL: http://www.google.org/foundation.html
RSS Feed: http://feeds.feedburner.com/OfficialGoogleorgBlog
The Official Google.org Blog: http://blog.google.org/
Twitter: https://twitter.com/#!/googlenonprofit
YouTube: http://www.youtube.com/user/Googleorg

Established in 2004 in CA.
Donor: Google Inc.
Foundation type: Company-sponsored foundation.
Financial data (yr. ended 12/31/12): Assets, $72,412,693 (M); gifts received, $39,560,000; expenditures, $39,984,747; qualifying distributions, $39,647,902; giving activities include $39,606,000 for 14 grants (high: $5,000,000; low: $1,200,000).
Purpose and activities: The foundation supports organizations involved with arts and culture, education and computer science, the environment, international development, women and girls, and poverty.
Fields of interest: Media/communications; Museums; Arts; Higher education; Education; Environment, climate change/global warming; Environment, water resources; Animals/wildlife; Disasters, preparedness/services; Children, services; Human services; International development; International human rights; Anti-slavery/human trafficking; Microfinance/microlending; Computer science; Women; Girls; Economically disadvantaged.
Type of support: General/operating support; Program development.
Limitations: Applications not accepted. Giving primarily in CA, Washington, DC, and NY; giving also to international organizations in the United Kingdom.
Publications: Financial statement; IRS Form 990 or 990-PF printed copy available upon request.
Application information: Contributes only to pre-selected organizations. Grants are administered in part by Google.org.
Officers and Directors:* Mathew Stepka,* Pres.; Chris Busselle, Secy.; Kristin Reinke, Treas.; Sergey Brin; Shona Brown; Lawrence Page; Alfred Spector.
EIN: 201548253

616
Steven Gordon Family Foundation ✧
9990 Santa Monica Blvd.
Beverly Hills, CA 90212-1607
Contact: Steven C. Gordon, Pres.

Established in CA.
Donor: Steven C. Gordon.
Foundation type: Independent foundation.
Financial data (yr. ended 12/31/12): Assets, $8,335 (M); gifts received, $563,063; expenditures, $557,391; qualifying distributions, $556,966; giving activities include $556,456 for 25 grants (high: $126,000; low: $100).
Fields of interest: Health care; Health organizations; Religion.
Limitations: Applications accepted. Giving primarily in CA.
Application information: Application form not required.
Initial approach: Proposal
Deadline(s): None
Officer: Steven C. Gordon, Pres.
EIN: 954656330

617
The Betsy Gordon Foundation ✧ ☆
c/o Elizabeth Gordon
1537 4th St.
P.O. Box 15
San Rafael, CA 94901-2737

Established in 2001 in DE and NY.
Donor: Elizabeth Gordon.
Foundation type: Independent foundation.
Financial data (yr. ended 10/31/13): Assets, $127,024 (M); gifts received, $481,454;

expenditures, $446,950; qualifying distributions, $446,950; giving activities include $439,815 for 28 grants (high: $138,134; low: $1,000).
Purpose and activities: Giving primarily for education and spiritual enrichment.
Fields of interest: Education; Human services; Foundations (private grantmaking).
Limitations: Applications not accepted. No grants to individuals.
Application information: Contributes only to pre-selected organizations.
Officers: Elizabeth Gordon, Pres.; Jean Merlin, Secy.; Louis Leeburg, Treas.
Trustees: Angeles Arrien; Ricci Coddington; Frances Vaughan, Ph.D.
EIN: 113634807

618
The Joseph B. Gould Foundation ✧
1801 Century Park E., Ste. 2230
Los Angeles, CA 90067-2324 (323) 557-0008
Contact: Carolyn Dirks, Pres.

Established in 1991 in NV.
Donor: Joseph B. Gould.
Foundation type: Independent foundation.
Financial data (yr. ended 12/31/13): Assets, $5,555,238 (M); expenditures, $1,220,198; qualifying distributions, $1,129,942; giving activities include $1,112,875 for 19 grants (high: $500,000; low: $1,000).
Purpose and activities: Giving primarily for health organizations, the arts, education, and children and social services.
Fields of interest: Arts; Higher education; Health care; Health organizations; Human services; Children/youth, services.
Limitations: Applications accepted. Giving primarily in CA; funding also in CO. No grants to individuals.
Application information: Application form required.
Initial approach: Letter
Deadline(s): None
Officers: Carolyn Dirks, Pres.; David Watts, Secy.; Martin Dirks, Treas.
Director: Steven Spector.
EIN: 880232969
Selected grants: The following grants are a representative sample of this grantmaker's funding activity:
$284,375 to Spine Research Foundation, Santa Monica, CA, 2012. For Medical Equipment and Programs.
$250,000 to USA Swimming Foundation, Colorado Springs, CO, 2012. For Building Fund and Program Services.
$2,500 to Brooklyn Community Foundation, Brooklyn, NY, 2012. For Hurricane Sandy.

619
Richard Grand Foundation ✧
405 Davis Ct., Ste. 2504
San Francisco, CA 94111-2464

Established in 1995 in CA.
Donors: Richard Grand; Marcia Grand; Rena Grand†.
Foundation type: Independent foundation.
Financial data (yr. ended 06/30/13): Assets, $10,730,221 (M); gifts received, $20; expenditures, $977,142; qualifying distributions, $940,000; giving activities include $940,000 for grants.
Purpose and activities: Giving primarily for higher education, the arts, health, and social services.
Fields of interest: Performing arts; Arts; Higher education; Education; Environment, natural resources; Animal welfare; Health organizations; Food services; Human services.
Limitations: Applications not accepted. Giving primarily in Tucson, AZ, San Francisco, CA, and New York, NY. No grants to individuals.
Application information: Contributes only to pre-selected organizations.
Officers: Richard Grand, Chair. and Secy.; Marcia Grand, Pres.; Cindy Grand, V.P. and C.F.O.
EIN: 943221366
Selected grants: The following grants are a representative sample of this grantmaker's funding activity:
$155,000 to Stanford University, Stanford, CA, 2011.
$17,500 to Meals on Wheels of San Francisco, San Francisco, CA, 2011.
$10,000 to Mono Lake Foundation, Lee Vining, CA, 2011.
$10,000 to Pets Unlimited, San Francisco, CA, 2011.
$10,000 to Stanford Hospital and Clinics, Stanford, CA, 2011.
$7,500 to California State Parks Foundation, San Francisco, CA, 2011.
$7,500 to K Q E D, San Francisco, CA, 2011.
$7,500 to San Diego Volunteer Lawyer Program, San Diego, CA, 2011.
$7,500 to San Francisco AIDS Foundation, San Francisco, CA, 2011.
$5,000 to Compass Family Services, San Francisco, CA, 2011.

620
George and Reva Graziadio Foundation ✧ ☆
5501 Keokuk Ave.
Woodland Hills, CA 91367-5521

Established in 1998 in CA.
Donors: George L. Graziadio, Jr.; Reva Graziadio; George & Reva Graziadio Charitable Lead Annuity Trust.
Foundation type: Independent foundation.
Financial data (yr. ended 06/30/13): Assets, $7,878,658 (M); gifts received, $113,130; expenditures, $462,943; qualifying distributions, $425,983; giving activities include $420,350 for 11 grants (high: $260,000; low: $100).
Fields of interest: Higher education; Education; Health care; Prostate cancer research; Human services; Community/economic development; Religion.
Limitations: Applications not accepted. Giving primarily in CA. No grants to individuals.
Application information: Unsolicited requests for funds not accepted.
Officers and Directors:* Mary Lou Area,* Pres.; Phillip M. Bardack,* C.F.O.; Alida Calvillo,* Secy.; G. Louis Graziadio III,* Treas.
EIN: 954697062
Selected grants: The following grants are a representative sample of this grantmaker's funding activity:
$109,000 to Pepperdine University, Malibu, CA, 2011.
$50,000 to California State University Long Beach Foundation, Long Beach, CA, 2011.
$10,000 to University of California San Francisco Foundation, San Francisco, CA, 2011.
$5,000 to Multiple Myeloma Research Foundation, Norwalk, CT, 2011.
$5,000 to National Geographic Society, Washington, DC, 2011.
$5,000 to National Italian American Foundation, Washington, DC, 2011.
$2,500 to Centenary College, Hackettstown, NJ, 2011.
$2,500 to Rancho Palos Verdes, City of, Rancho Palos Verdes, CA, 2011.
$1,000 to George W. Bush Presidential Center, Dallas, TX, 2011.
$1,000 to Swim Across America, Boston, MA, 2011.

621
The Green Foundation ✧
(formerly Leonard I. Green Foundation)
c/o George McCrimlisk
225 S. Lake Ave., Ste. 1410
Pasadena, CA 91101-4855
FAX: (626) 744-0578; Contacts for grant requests and inquiries: Kylie Wright, Sr. Prog. Dir., tel.: (626) 793-6200, ext. 1, e-mail: kylies@ligf.org, Elena Hermanson, Prog. Dir., tel.: (626) 793-6200, ext. 2. or Julianne Green, Fdn. Admin., tel.: (626) 793-6200, ext. 4, e-mail: jgreen@ligf.org; Main URL: http://www.ligf.org
Grants List: http://ligf.org/grantrecipients.php

Established in 1994 in CA.
Donor: Leonard I. Green†.
Foundation type: Independent foundation.
Financial data (yr. ended 11/30/13): Assets, $152,159,847 (M); gifts received, $2,000,000; expenditures, $9,736,467; qualifying distributions, $8,514,600; giving activities include $8,514,600 for 279 grants (high: $250,000; low: $1,000).
Purpose and activities: Giving primarily for the arts, education, and human services, with a secondary focus on special projects. Preferential attention will be given to institutions that exhibit a history of achievement, good management, and a stable financial condition; significant programs with the promise of making a measurable impact; and programs that are self-sustaining and that will not necessitate continued dependence on the foundation. The foundation's mission is to uncover new opportunities, encourage growth, and ultimately effect positive change within those institutions that best reflect the foundation's core focus areas and the communities they serve.
Fields of interest: Arts, multipurpose centers/programs; Arts; Education; Human services; Infants/toddlers; Children/youth; Youth; Adults; Aging; Disabilities, people with; Physically disabled; Deaf/hearing impaired; Mentally disabled; Minorities; Military/veterans; Substance abusers; AIDS, people with; Crime/abuse victims; Terminal illness, people with; Economically disadvantaged; Homeless.
Type of support: General/operating support; Equipment; Emergency funds; Program development; Scholarship funds; Matching/challenge support.
Limitations: Applications accepted. Giving primarily in southern CA, with emphasis on Los Angeles County, Orange County, Riverside County, San Bernardino County, and Ventura County. No support for organizations lacking 501(c)(3) status, private non-operating foundations, religious programs, organizations with net assets or fund balances of

less then $100,000, or for conduit institutions, unified funds, fiscal agents, or institutions using grant funds from donors to support other institutions or individuals. No grants to individuals, or for capital campaigns, annual meetings, conferences, and/or seminars, direct mail campaigns, and multi-year commitments.
Publications: Application guidelines; Financial statement; Grants list; IRS Form 990 or 990-PF printed copy available upon request; Program policy statement; Program policy statement (including application guidelines).
Application information: Unsolicited full grant proposals not accepted. Application information available on foundation web site. Application form required.

Initial approach: Complete initial eligibility questionnaire on foundation web site
Copies of proposal: 1
Deadline(s): Rolling
Final notification: Varies

Officers and Board Members:* George H. McCrimlisk,* Pres. and Secy.; Suzanne Green; Kathleen McCrimlisk; Ronald C. Wilcox.
Number of staff: 1 full-time professional; 2 part-time professional.
EIN: 954509163
Selected grants: The following grants are a representative sample of this grantmaker's funding activity:
$250,000 to Alliance for College-Ready Public Schools, Los Angeles, CA, 2012. For operating support.
$250,000 to Childrens Hospital of Orange County, Orange, CA, 2012. For program support.
$250,000 to Los Angeles Opera Company, Los Angeles, CA, 2012. For program support.
$150,000 to Childrens Bureau of Southern California, Los Angeles, CA, 2012. For program support.
$100,000 to Habitat for Humanity, Powhatan, Powhatan, VA, 2012. For operating support.
$75,000 to Homeboy Industries, Los Angeles, CA, 2012. For program support.
$25,000 to Children, Youth and Family Collaborative, Los Angeles, CA, 2012. For program support.
$25,000 to Environmental Charter Schools, Lawndale, CA, 2012. For program support.
$25,000 to J. F. Shea Therapeutic Riding Center, San Juan Capistrano, CA, 2012. For operating support.
$25,000 to Shakespeare Center of Los Angeles, Los Angeles, CA, 2012. For program support.

622
The Greenbaum Foundation ✧
(formerly The James R. Greenbaum, Jr. Family Foundation)
P.O. Box 9910
Rancho Santa Fe, CA 92067-4910
E-mail: info@GreenbaumFoundation.org; E-mail address for animal welfare inquiries: Info-A@GreenbaumFoundation.org; Main URL: http://www.greenbaumfoundation.org

Established in 1991 in UT.
Donor: James R. Greenbaum, Jr.
Foundation type: Independent foundation.
Financial data (yr. ended 12/31/12): Assets, $28,678,743 (M); gifts received, $24,000; expenditures, $2,141,958; qualifying distributions, $2,024,071; giving activities include $2,024,071 for 45 grants (high: $300,000; low: $2,500).
Purpose and activities: Giving primarily for international innovative human rights projects benefiting children and youth. Giving also for the support of projects aimed at improving world health via promoting whole foods, plant-based diets, and for innovative projects promoting the humane treatment of animals.
Fields of interest: Animal welfare; Human services.
Limitations: Applications not accepted. No grants to individuals.
Application information: Contributes only to pre-selected organizations.
Trustee: James R. Greenbaum, Jr.
EIN: 876217358

623
Mary Jo & Hank Greenberg Animal Welfare Foundation ✧
9903 Santa Monica Blvd., PMB 837
Beverly Hills, CA 90212-1606 (310) 557-8100

Established in 1999 in CA.
Donors: Mary Jo Greenberg; Jeffrey Tarola; Stephen D. Greenberg.
Foundation type: Independent foundation.
Financial data (yr. ended 05/31/13): Assets, $66,875 (M); gifts received, $506,800; expenditures, $610,713; qualifying distributions, $610,600; giving activities include $610,600 for grants.
Purpose and activities: Giving primarily to organizations that rescue, provide care, housing and services for homeless and neglected animals, especially cats and dogs.
Fields of interest: Animals/wildlife, association; Animal welfare; Animals/wildlife.
Limitations: Applications accepted. Giving primarily in Los Angeles (including Los Angeles County), CA.
Application information: Application form required.

Initial approach: Letter
Deadline(s): None

Officers: Mary Jo Greenberg, Pres.; Robert Ferber, V.P.; Marjorie Loeb, V.P.; Shari Lienward, Secy.; Suzie Levin, Treas.
EIN: 954738423
Selected grants: The following grants are a representative sample of this grantmaker's funding activity:
$7,500 to Home at Last Animal Rescue, Berkeley, CA, 2013. For the General Operations of the Organization.

624
The Greenberg Foundation ✧
(formerly The Mayer Greenberg Foundation)
6060 Sepulveda Blvd., No. 300
Van Nuys, CA 91411-2501

Established in 1953 in CA.
Donors: Daniel B. Greenberg; Aaron Masowitz Trust; Electro Rent Corp.
Foundation type: Independent foundation.
Financial data (yr. ended 11/30/13): Assets, $23,109,775 (M); expenditures, $3,784,232; qualifying distributions, $3,763,075; giving activities include $3,757,730 for 159 grants (high: $1,849,225; low: $25).
Purpose and activities: Giving primarily for education, the arts, the environment, and health care.
Fields of interest: Arts education; Media, radio; Museums (art); Museums (specialized); Higher education; Law school/education; Education; Environment; Health organizations, association; Human services; Foundations (public).
Limitations: Applications not accepted. Giving on a national basis, with emphasis on CA, Washington, DC, MA, and New York, NY. No grants to individuals.
Application information: Contributes only to pre-selected organizations.
Officers: Daniel B. Greenberg, Pres.; Ben Greenberg, V.P. and Treas.; Marla Brown, Secy.
EIN: 956037502

625
Greene Van Arsdale Foundation ✧
c/o KKR Accounting Svcs., LLC
2755 Campus Dr., Ste. 240
San Mateo, CA 94403-2515 (650) 653-2406
Contact: James H. Greene, Jr., Pres.

Established in 1997 in CA.
Donors: James H. Greene, Jr.; Charles Van Arsdale, Jr.; Greene 1995 Family Revocable Trust.
Foundation type: Independent foundation.
Financial data (yr. ended 12/31/13): Assets, $16,415,327 (M); expenditures, $1,074,401; qualifying distributions, $1,063,813; giving activities include $1,053,065 for 67 grants (high: $211,000; low: $200).
Purpose and activities: Giving primarily for health and human services.
Fields of interest: Arts; Education; Hospitals (general); Human services.
Limitations: Applications not accepted. Giving primarily in CA. No grants to individuals.
Application information: Unsolicited requests for funds not accepted.
Officers: James H. Greene, Jr., Pres.; Marritje Van Arsdale Greene, Secy.-Treas.
EIN: 943254854

626
Robert A. and Kari L. Grimm Family Foundation ✧
6900 Mountain View Rd.
Bakersfield, CA 93307-9627 (661) 393-3320
Contact: Kellie C. Merriman, Pres.

Established in 2001 in CA.
Donor: Grimmway Enterprises, Inc.
Foundation type: Independent foundation.
Financial data (yr. ended 12/31/12): Assets, $10,550,014 (M); gifts received, $2,750,000; expenditures, $1,710,704; qualifying distributions, $1,687,215; giving activities include $1,658,985 for 13 grants (high: $750,000; low: $10,000).
Purpose and activities: Giving primarily for higher education, as well as to Christian schools and ministries.
Fields of interest: Elementary/secondary education; Higher education; Christian agencies & churches; Protestant agencies & churches.
Limitations: Applications accepted. Giving primarily in CA, with emphasis on Bakersfield.
Application information: Application form required.

Initial approach: Letter
Deadline(s): None

Officers: Kellie C. Merriman, Pres.; Kari L. Anderson, V.P.; Jeffery A. Green, Secy.; Brandon A. Grimm, Treas.
EIN: 770554204

627
The Rodney Grimm Family Foundation ✧
7158 Buena Vista Rd.
Bakersfield, CA 93311-9425 (661) 831-6873
Contact: Barbara M. Grimm

Established in 2001 in CA.
Donor: Grimmway Enterprises, Inc.
Foundation type: Independent foundation.
Financial data (yr. ended 06/30/13): Assets, $4,197,258 (M); gifts received, $1,000,000; expenditures, $1,230,221; qualifying distributions, $1,205,100; giving activities include $1,205,100 for 5 grants (high: $1,150,000; low: $600).
Purpose and activities: Giving primarily for education, including higher education.
Fields of interest: Higher education; Scholarships/financial aid; Education.
Limitations: Giving primarily in CA. No grants to individuals.
Application information:
Initial approach: Letter
Officers: Barbara Grimm-Marshall, Pres.; Catherine E. Card, Secy. and C.F.O.
Directors: Catherine Grimm Gardiner; Bryan Grimm; Melissa Grimm.
EIN: 770572545

628
Richard Grinold Fund ✧
3343 Ondulado Rd.
Pebble Beach, CA 93953

Donor: Richard Grinold.
Foundation type: Independent foundation.
Financial data (yr. ended 12/31/13): Assets, $11,150,172 (M); expenditures, $912,310; qualifying distributions, $900,660; giving activities include $897,775 for 12 grants (high: $267,225; low: $700).
Fields of interest: Education; Human services.
Limitations: Applications not accepted. Giving primarily in NY and VA.
Application information: Unsolicited requests for funds not accepted.
Officers and Directors:* Richard Grinold,* Pres.; Leilani Grinold,* C.F.O. and Secy.
EIN: 900506349
Selected grants: The following grants are a representative sample of this grantmaker's funding activity:
$120,362 to Manhattan Institute for Policy Research, New York, NY, 2011.
$82,605 to Institute for Justice, Arlington, VA, 2011.
$2,500 to Institute for Justice, Arlington, VA, 2011.
$2,000 to YMCA of Greater Boston, Boston, MA, 2011.

629
Stella B. Gross Charitable Trust ✧ ☆
P.O. Box 60078, SC-MPK-03-M
Los Angeles, CA 90060-0078
Application address: c/o Bank of the West, 50 W. Fernando St., Ste. 425, San Jose, CA 95113

Trust established in 1966 in CA.
Donor: Stella B. Gross‡.
Foundation type: Independent foundation.
Financial data (yr. ended 06/30/13): Assets, $6,442,202 (M); expenditures, $562,932; qualifying distributions, $499,543; giving activities include $447,999 for 40 grants (high: $45,000; low: $1,333).
Fields of interest: Visual arts; Museums; Performing arts; Arts; Child development, education; Elementary school/education; Higher education; Education; Hospitals (general); Health care; Health organizations, association; Cancer; Heart & circulatory diseases; Cancer research; Heart & circulatory research; Human services; Children/youth, services; Child development, services; Residential/custodial care, hospices; Aging, centers/services; Catholic federated giving programs; Government/public administration; Aging; Disabilities, people with.
Type of support: General/operating support; Continuing support; Program development; Seed money.
Limitations: Applications accepted. Giving limited to Santa Clara County, CA. No grants to individuals.
Publications: Annual report; Grants list.
Application information: Application form required.
Copies of proposal: 1
Deadline(s): None
Board meeting date(s): June and Dec.
Final notification: 6 months
Directors: Hon. Thomas P. Hansen; Arthur K. Lund; Jeffrey O'Neal.
Trustee: Bank of the West.
EIN: 237142181
Selected grants: The following grants are a representative sample of this grantmaker's funding activity:
$25,000 to Sacred Heart Community Service, San Jose, CA, 2011. For general support.
$20,000 to Boy Scouts of America, San Jose, CA, 2011. For general support.
$12,500 to Bellarmine College Preparatory, San Jose, CA, 2011. For general support.
$10,000 to Cystic Fibrosis Foundation, Bethesda, MD, 2011. For general support.
$10,000 to History San Jose, San Jose, CA, 2011. For general support.
$7,500 to Ascent Employment Program, San Jose, CA, 2011. For general support.
$7,500 to Habitat for Humanity East Bay/Silicon Valley, Milpitas, CA, 2011. For general support.
$7,500 to Second Harvest Food Bank of Santa Clara and San Mateo Counties, San Jose, CA, 2011. For general support.
$7,500 to Villa Siena, Mountain View, CA, 2011. For general support.
$2,500 to Silicon Valley Conference for Community and Justice, San Jose, CA, 2011. For general support.

630
Gardner Grout Foundation ✧
c/o Capital Guardian Trust Co.
333 S. Hope St., 34th Fl.
Los Angeles, CA 90071-3044
Contact: Barbara Brewer, Trust Off., Capital Guardian Trust Co.

Established in 2001 in CA.
Donor: Elizabeth Q. Grout Trust.
Foundation type: Independent foundation.
Financial data (yr. ended 12/31/13): Assets, $44,635,574 (M); gifts received, $2,312,086; expenditures, $2,057,073; qualifying distributions, $1,760,975; giving activities include $1,662,750 for 105 grants (high: $550,000; low: $550).
Purpose and activities: Giving primarily for the arts, education, health organizations and hospitals, and for human services.
Fields of interest: Museums; Performing arts; Arts; Education; Environment, land resources; Hospitals (general); Health care; Medical research, institute; Human services.
Type of support: General/operating support.
Limitations: Applications not accepted. Giving primarily in CA. No grants to individuals.
Application information: Unsolicited requests for funds not accepted.
Trustees: L.G. Brigham; L.B. Hambleton; E.B. Huyck; C.B. Markovich; Capital Guardian Trust Co.
EIN: 957106955

631
The Grove Foundation ✧
P.O. Box 1667
Los Altos, CA 94023-1667

Established in 1986 in CA.
Donors: Andrew S. Grove; Eva K. Grove.
Foundation type: Independent foundation.
Financial data (yr. ended 09/30/13): Assets, $103,476,061 (M); gifts received, $544,078; expenditures, $13,634,539; qualifying distributions, $13,152,793; giving activities include $10,105,287 for 147 grants (high: $1,100,000; low: $500).
Purpose and activities: Giving primarily for family planning and other social services, vocational or professional education, Jewish welfare, international refugee assistance, and the performing arts.
Fields of interest: Performing arts; Higher education; Reproductive health, family planning; Health care; Food banks; Homeless, human services; International relief; Civil/human rights, advocacy; Civil liberties, reproductive rights; Aging; Women; Immigrants/refugees; Economically disadvantaged; Homeless.
Limitations: Applications not accepted. Giving primarily in CA, NJ, and NY. No grants to individuals, or for construction.
Application information: Unsolicited requests not considered; funds are fully committed.
Officers and Directors:* Andrew S. Grove,* Co-Chair.; Karen Grove,* Co-Chair.; Eva K. Grove, Secy.; Leslie Dorsin, C.F.O. and Exec. Dir.; Robie Spector.
EIN: 770108124
Selected grants: The following grants are a representative sample of this grantmaker's funding activity:
$1,000,000 to International Rescue Committee, New York, NY, 2012. For project support.
$350,000 to Silicon Valley Community Foundation, Mountain View, CA, 2012. For project support.
$275,000 to Planned Parenthood Mar Monte, San Jose, CA, 2012. For general support.
$214,000 to University of California, San Francisco, CA, 2012. For project support.
$150,000 to Immigrant Legal Resource Center, San Francisco, CA, 2012. For project support.
$110,000 to Colorado Youth Matter, Denver, CO, 2012. For project support.

$100,000 to International Rescue Committee, New York, NY, 2012. For general support.
$75,000 to Southern Poverty Law Center, Montgomery, AL, 2012. For general support.
$30,000 to University of Southern California, Los Angeles, CA, 2012. For project support.
$25,000 to Planned Parenthood Mar Monte, San Jose, CA, 2012. For general support.

632
Gruber Family Foundation ✧
P.O. Box 214
Ross, CA 94957-0214

Established in 1987 in CA.
Donors: Jon D. Gruber; Linda W. Gruber.
Foundation type: Independent foundation.
Financial data (yr. ended 12/31/13): Assets, $40,283,185 (M); gifts received, $956,986; expenditures, $3,450,775; qualifying distributions, $2,890,326; giving activities include $2,889,000 for 52 grants (high: $510,000; low: $1,000).
Purpose and activities: Giving primarily for education and social services.
Fields of interest: Museums; Arts; Higher education; Education; Environment; Human services.
Type of support: General/operating support; Continuing support; Annual campaigns; Capital campaigns; Building/renovation; Program development; Professorships; Matching/challenge support.
Limitations: Applications not accepted. Giving primarily in CA. No support for religious organizations. No grants to individuals.
Application information: Contributes only to pre-selected organizations.
Officers: Linda W. Gruber, Pres.; Jon D. Gruber, Secy.-Treas.
EIN: 943039716

633
GSF Foundation ✧
18301 Von Karman Ave., Ste. 1100
Irvine, CA 92612-0133 (949) 252-2000
E-mail: helpkids@gsffoundation.org; Additional tel.: (877) 473-5437; Main URL: http://www.gsffoundation.org
E-Newsletter: http://www.gsffoundation.org/newsletter/
Facebook: https://www.facebook.com/goldenstatefoodsfoundation
GSF Foundation Video: http://www.goldenstatefoods.com/foundationvideo.asp

Established in 2002 in CA and OR.
Donors: Mark S. Wetterau; Golden State Foods Corp.; Mike Echolds; Leslie Echolds; Orange Wood Children's Fdn.
Foundation type: Company-sponsored foundation.
Financial data (yr. ended 12/31/13): Assets, $1,158,566 (M); gifts received, $3,640,536; expenditures, $3,859,887; qualifying distributions, $3,806,602; giving activities include $2,199,701 for 117 grants (high: $474,029; low: $160).
Purpose and activities: The foundation supports programs designed to improve the lives of children and families. Special emphasis is directed toward programs designed to serve children with various needs, including food, shelter, clothes, medical treatment, and social activities.
Fields of interest: Arts; Education; Health care, patient services; Health care; Food services; Food banks; Housing/shelter; Big Brothers/Big Sisters; Boy scouts; Children, services; Family services; Developmentally disabled, centers & services.
Type of support: General/operating support; Capital campaigns; Building/renovation; Equipment; Program development; Employee volunteer services; Sponsorships.
Limitations: Applications not accepted. Giving primarily in areas of company operations in AR, CA, GA, IL, MO, NC, NY, OR, SC, VA, WA, and WI. No support for political organizations or candidates, religious, veterans', or fraternal organizations, or sports teams. No grants for individuals, or for sponsorships of fundraising events, tickets or tables, academic or medical research, political causes, sporting events, trips or travel, festivals or parades, or advertising.
Application information: Unsolicited requests for funds not accepted.
Officers and Directors:* Mark S. Wetterau,* Chair. and C.E.O.; Catherine Duffy, Secy.; Lisa Gottlieb,* C.F.O.; Charles Browne,* Exec. Dir.; Steve Becker; Jim Brooks; Neil Cracknell; Shellie Frey; Jim Fusting; Mickey Hamer; Daniel Van Hoozer; Frank Listi; Larry McGill; John Murphy; John Page; Bill Pocilujko; Bill Sanderson; Jeff Steiner; Gregg Tarlton; Scott Thomas; and additional 7 Directors.
EIN: 460501728

634
Henry L. Guenther Foundation ✧
2029 Century Park E., Ste. 4392
Los Angeles, CA 90067-3029 (310) 785-0658
Contact: Sarah Milliken, Pres.

Established in 1956.
Donor: Pearl H. Guenther†.
Foundation type: Independent foundation.
Financial data (yr. ended 12/31/13): Assets, $85,947,074 (M); expenditures, $4,242,768; qualifying distributions, $3,688,211; giving activities include $2,855,000 for 39 grants (high: $1,000,000; low: $5,000).
Purpose and activities: The foundation aims to improve social conditions, promote human welfare, and alleviate pain and suffering.
Fields of interest: Education; Hospitals (general); Medical research, institute; Human services.
Limitations: Applications accepted. Giving primarily in southern CA. Generally no support for government agencies, or religious organizations for religious purposes. No grants to individuals, including scholarships; or for operating deficits.
Application information: Application form required.
Initial approach: Letter (no more than 2 pages)
Copies of proposal: 2
Deadline(s): May 31 and Oct. 31
Board meeting date(s): Jan. and July
Final notification: 3 months
Officers and Directors:* Sarah C. Milliken,* C.E.O. and Pres.; W.D. Milliken,* C.O.O. and Secy.; D.V. Werderman,* C.F.O. and Treas.; Richard Battaglia; Joseph P. Battaglia; Ann Leatherbury; Dennis Sundberg; Susanne Sundberg.
EIN: 956026937

635
Guess? Foundation ✧
1444 S. Alameda St.
Los Angeles, CA 90021-2433

Established in 1994 in CA.
Donor: Guess ?, Inc.
Foundation type: Company-sponsored foundation.
Financial data (yr. ended 12/31/13): Assets, $647,395 (M); gifts received, $1,000,000; expenditures, $1,426,860; qualifying distributions, $1,426,560; giving activities include $1,418,150 for 26 grants (high: $800,000; low: $1,000).
Purpose and activities: The foundation supports organizations involved with education, the environment, health, substance abuse services, heart disease, diabetes, HIV/AIDS research, housing, human services, the fashion industry, and Judaism.
Fields of interest: Education; Environment; Health care; Substance abuse, services; Heart & circulatory diseases; AIDS; Diabetes; AIDS research; Housing/shelter; Recreation, camps; Children/youth, services; Children, foster care; Human services; Business/industry; Jewish agencies & synagogues.
Type of support: Publication; General/operating support; Program development; Scholarship funds; Sponsorships.
Limitations: Applications accepted. Giving primarily in the Greater Los Angeles, CA area. No grants to individuals.
Publications: Application guidelines.
Application information: Application form not required.
Initial approach: Fax proposal to foundation
Deadline(s): 8 weeks prior to need
Officer and Directors: Paul Marciano,* Pres.; Dennis Secor, C.F.O.; Michael Prince, V.P.; Deborah Siegel, Secy.; Maurice Marciano.
EIN: 954500475
Selected grants: The following grants are a representative sample of this grantmaker's funding activity:
$850,000 to New York University, Gallatin School, New York, NY, 2012. For None of the organizations are related All grants are for charitable purposes for general operations or special events.
$8,000 to World of Children, Pleasanton, CA, 2012. For None of the organizations are related All grants are for charitable purposes for general operations or special events.

636
The Josephine S. Gumbiner Foundation ✧
333 W. Broadway, Ste. 312
Long Beach, CA 90802-4438 (562) 437-2882
Contact: Julie Meenan, Secy. and Exec. Dir.
FAX: (562) 437-4212; E-mail: julie@jsgf.org; Main URL: http://www.jsgf.org
Grants List: http://www.jsgf.org/grants-awarded-by-jsgf/

Established in 1989 in CA.
Donor: Josephine S. Gumbiner†.
Foundation type: Independent foundation.
Financial data (yr. ended 12/31/13): Assets, $14,136,305 (M); expenditures, $865,848; qualifying distributions, $783,753; giving activities include $641,000 for 46+ grants.
Purpose and activities: The foundation is dedicated to supporting programs that enrich the women and children in the Long Beach area of southern California. It includes programs focusing on day

care, job training, housing, after school tutoring, and health care, with a special emphasis on intervention, prevention, and direct service. Previously funded projects by the foundation range from prenatal care to women's shelters to programs for at-risk youth, and participatory cultural programs for children and teens. The foundation's goal is to fund projects that protect and enrich the lives of women and children in Long Beach, California.

Fields of interest: Crime/violence prevention, domestic violence; Crime/violence prevention, child abuse; Human services; Children/youth, services; Family services; Women, centers/services; Minorities/immigrants, centers/services; Civil liberties, reproductive rights; Infants/toddlers; Children/youth; Children; Youth; Aging; Young adults; Disabilities, people with; Physically disabled; Deaf/hearing impaired; Mentally disabled; Minorities; African Americans/Blacks; Hispanics/Latinos; Native Americans/American Indians; Women; Infants/toddlers, female; Girls; Adults, women; Young adults, female; Infants/toddlers, male; Boys; Young adults, male; Substance abusers; Single parents; Crime/abuse victims; Economically disadvantaged; Homeless; LGBTQ.

Type of support: General/operating support; Continuing support; Equipment; Emergency funds; Program development; Technical assistance; Matching/challenge support.

Limitations: Applications accepted. Giving limited to Long Beach, CA. No support for political campaigns, pass through organizations, organizations with endowments greater than $5 million, or organizations with Long Beach, CA client bases of less than 75%. No grants to individuals, or for lobbying efforts, or programs that supplant traditional school funding.

Publications: Application guidelines; Grants list; Informational brochure (including application guidelines).

Application information: Grant application packages are by invitation only, upon review of initial Letter of Intent. Application form required.

Initial approach: E-mail to request Letter of Intent Questionnaire
Copies of proposal: 7
Deadline(s): None
Board meeting date(s): Generally in Mar., June, Sept., and Nov.
Final notification: Within 90 days for Letter of Intent

Officers: Lee Gumbiner, Pres.; Alis Gumbiner, C.F.O.; Burke Gumbiner, V.P.; Julie Meenan, Secy. and Exec. Dir.

Directors: Art Gottlieb; Alex Norman; Dennis Rockway.

Number of staff: 1 full-time professional; 1 part-time professional.

EIN: 330345249

Selected grants: The following grants are a representative sample of this grantmaker's funding activity:
$40,000 to PATH Ventures, Los Angeles, CA, 2012. For Transitional Living Center Villages @ Cabrillo.
$22,500 to Comprehensive Child Development, Long Beach, CA, 2012. For HUD Match.
$20,000 to Long Beach Day Nursery, Long Beach, CA, 2012. For Stepping Stones Scholarships.
$17,500 to YMCA of Greater Long Beach, Long Beach, CA, 2012. For youth institute.
$15,000 to Children Today, Long Beach, CA, 2012. For Child and Family Counselor Support.
$15,000 to Grandparents as Parents, Canoga Park, CA, 2012. For Long Beach Support Groups.
$15,000 to Harbor Interfaith Shelter, San Pedro, CA, 2012. For general op support.
$12,500 to Centro CHA, Long Beach, CA, 2012. For Summer Night Lights Youth Squad Support.
$10,000 to Operation Jump Start, Long Beach, CA, 2012. For College Access Mentoring.
$10,000 to Shelter Partnership, Los Angeles, CA, 2012. For LB Agency Support.

637
William Gumpert Foundation ✧

P.O. Box 231549
Encinitas, CA 92023-1549

Established in 2007 in CA.

Donors: William Gumpert Trust; Goldberg Family Trust.

Foundation type: Independent foundation.

Financial data (yr. ended 12/31/13): Assets, $45,589,595 (M); expenditures, $3,075,076; qualifying distributions, $2,495,122; giving activities include $2,135,700 for 21 grants (high: $406,000; low: $1,000).

Fields of interest: Health care; Human services; Children/youth, services; Family services; Residential/custodial care, hospices.

Limitations: Applications not accepted. Giving primarily in CA. No grants to individuals.

Application information: Contributes only to pre-selected organizations; unsolicited requests for funds not accepted; please do not contact foundation.

Directors: David Cornsweet; Patrick Dempsey.

EIN: 266065762

Selected grants: The following grants are a representative sample of this grantmaker's funding activity:
$240,000 to Hospice of the North Coast, Carlsbad, CA, 2012. For Care for Terminally Ill and Their Family.
$220,000 to Venice Family Clinic, Venice, CA, 2012. For Healthcare for People in Need.
$80,000 to Words Alive, San Diego, CA, 2012. For early literacy intervention.
$5,000 to Barrio Station, San Diego, CA, 2012. For Social Services for Individuals and Families.
$1,000 to A Reason to Survive, San Diego, CA, 2012. For Visual, Performing, and Literary Arts Can Transform.

638
The Guthy-Jackson Charitable Foundation ✧

1018 Pamela Dr.
Beverly Hills, CA 90210-2823

Established in 2008 in CA.

Donors: William R. Guthy; Victoria Jackson; Mark Madden; David Fett; Kitchelle Custom Homes.

Foundation type: Independent foundation.

Financial data (yr. ended 12/31/13): Assets, $47,725 (M); gifts received, $5,545,273; expenditures, $5,876,506; qualifying distributions, $5,876,346; giving activities include $5,835,966 for 19 grants (high: $2,502,000; low: $39,960).

Fields of interest: Medical research, institute.

Limitations: Applications not accepted. Giving primarily in CA; some giving also in CO, MA, and London, England.

Application information: Contributes only to pre-selected organizations.

Trustees: William R. Guthy; Victoria Jackson.

EIN: 266461545

Selected grants: The following grants are a representative sample of this grantmaker's funding activity:
$1,680,500 to All Greater Good Foundation, San Diego, CA, 2011. For research.
$558,956 to Mayo Clinic, Rochester, MN, 2011. For Aquaporin Autoimmunity Models and Genetics of NMO.
$486,320 to University of California, San Francisco, CA, 2011. For Role of AQP4 Autoantibody.
$364,022 to University of California, San Francisco, CA, 2011. For T Cell Recognition of Aquaporin-4.
$363,000 to Brigham and Women's Hospital, Boston, MA, 2011. For translating sciencet to patient care.
$247,500 to Mayo Clinic, Rochester, MN, 2011. For synergistic reactions in NMO.
$247,500 to Stanford University, School of Medicine, Stanford, CA, 2011. For Proteomic Studies.
$206,455 to University of Colorado Hospital Foundation, Aurora, CO, 2011. For AQP4 specific immunotherapy.
$81,646 to University of California, San Francisco, CA, 2011. For small molecule blocker therapy.
$78,375 to Accelerated Cure Project, Waltham, MA, 2011. For Samples Repository Project.

639
The Guzik Foundation ✧

2443 Wyandotte St.
Mountain View, CA 94043-2350

Established in 1993 in CA.

Donor: Nahum Guzik.

Foundation type: Independent foundation.

Financial data (yr. ended 12/31/12): Assets, $38,904,934 (M); expenditures, $2,188,290; qualifying distributions, $2,031,042; giving activities include $2,008,000 for 19 grants (high: $1,000,000; low: $2,000).

Purpose and activities: Giving primarily to Jewish organizations, the arts, and for children, youth, and social services; some funding to individuals for their projects.

Fields of interest: Museums; Performing arts; Arts; Higher education; Human services; Children/youth, services; Jewish agencies & synagogues.

Type of support: Grants to individuals.

Limitations: Applications not accepted. Giving primarily in CA.

Application information: Contributes only to pre-selected organizations.

Trustees: Nahum Guzik; Kira Makagon.

EIN: 770360079

640
Gene Haas Foundation ✧

2800 Sturgis Rd.
Oxnard, CA 93030-8901 (805) 988-6979
Contact: Kathy Looman, Admin.
E-mail: info@ghaasfoundation.org; E-mail for Kathy Looman: klooman@ghaasfoundation.org; Main URL: http://ghaasfoundation.org
RSS Feed: http://ghaasfoundation.org/feed/

Established in 1998 in CA.

Donor: Gene Francis Haas.

Foundation type: Independent foundation.

Financial data (yr. ended 12/31/13): Assets, $94,543,061 (M); gifts received, $50,000,000; expenditures, $3,175,636; qualifying distributions, $3,115,477; giving activities include $3,115,477 for 127 grants (high: $500,000; low: $250).
Purpose and activities: Giving primarily to children's charities and organizations that feed the poor, especially within the local community of Ventura County, California; giving also for scholarship funds to high schools, community colleges and special educational programs that help build skills within the machining industry.
Fields of interest: Vocational education; Higher education; Education; Health organizations, association; Medical research, institute; Human services; Children/youth, services; Family services; Foundations (community); Engineering/technology.
Type of support: Scholarship funds; Matching/challenge support.
Limitations: Applications accepted. Giving in the U.S., with emphasis on CA and MI. No grants to individuals.
Publications: Application guidelines; Grants list.
Application information: See foundation web site for complete application guidelines.
Initial approach: Use online contact form on foundation web site
Officers: Gene Francis Haas, Pres.; Kurt Zierhut, Secy.; Robert Murray, C.F.O.
EIN: 954724825
Selected grants: The following grants are a representative sample of this grantmaker's funding activity:
$50,000 to Ventura College Foundation, Ventura, CA, 2012. For Promise Program.
$50,000 to Vincennes University Foundation, Vincennes, IN, 2012. To support new service training Program.
$10,000 to Boys and Girls Club of Santa Clara Valley, Santa Paula, CA, 2012. To support youth Programs.
$10,000 to Chippewa Valley Technical College, Eau Claire, WI, 2012. For Machinist Training Scholarships.
$10,000 to Dunwoody College of Technology, Minneapolis, MN, 2012. For Machine Technology Scholarships.
$10,000 to Los Angeles County Bar Foundation, Los Angeles, CA, 2012. To sponsor 2012 tax practitioners conference.
$10,000 to Los Angeles County Bar Foundation, Los Angeles, CA, 2012. To sponsor 2012 tax practitioners conference-Refund.
$5,000 to Hudson Valley Community College, Troy, NY, 2012. For scholarships or programs.
$4,000 to Los Angeles County Bar Foundation, Los Angeles, CA, 2012. To sponsor 2012 tax practitioners conference.
$750 to Boy Scouts of America, Camarillo, CA, 2012. To sponsor eagle scouts at 2011 2012 recognition meeting.

641
Mimi and Peter Haas Fund ✧
(formerly Miriam and Peter Haas Fund)
201 Filbert St., 5th Fl.
San Francisco, CA 94133-3238 (415) 296-9249
Contact: Lynn Merz, Exec. Dir.

Incorporated in 1982 in CA.
Donors: Peter E. Haas†; Miriam L. Haas; Elise S. Haas†.
Foundation type: Independent foundation.
Financial data (yr. ended 12/31/12): Assets, $192,843,330 (M); expenditures, $10,461,454; qualifying distributions, $7,913,522; giving activities include $6,767,270 for 255 grants (high: $250,000; low: $61), and $2,230 for 1 foundation-administered program.
Purpose and activities: The fund's primary focus is early childhood development. Support is for activities that provide San Francisco's young (ages 2-5), low-income children and their families with access to high-quality early childhood programs that are part of a comprehensive, coordinated system. The fund recognizes the importance of connecting the work of its direct service grants to the ongoing discussions of public policy and will seek specific opportunities to share and collaborate with organizations to improve early childhood settings. The fund will also continue trustee-initiated grantmaking to arts, education, public affairs, and health and human services organizations.
Fields of interest: Education, early childhood education.
Type of support: General/operating support; Continuing support; Annual campaigns; Capital campaigns; Building/renovation; Equipment; Endowments; Program development; Curriculum development; Matching/challenge support.
Limitations: Giving primarily in San Francisco, CA; early childhood, direct service component is limited to San Francisco. No grants to individuals.
Publications: Annual report; Financial statement; Grants list.
Application information: Contributes only to pre-selected organizations.
Board meeting date(s): Approximately 4 times per year
Officers and Trustees:* Miriam L. Haas,* Pres.; Lynn Merz, Exec. Dir.; Ari A. Lurie; Daniel L. Lurie.
Number of staff: 5 full-time professional.
EIN: 946064551
Selected grants: The following grants are a representative sample of this grantmaker's funding activity:
$250,000 to Single Stop USA, New York, NY, 2012. For San Francisco Anti-Poverty Program.
$250,000 to Single Stop USA, New York, NY, 2012. For San Francisco Anti-Poverty Program.
$200,000 to Teach for America, San Francisco, CA, 2012. For general operating support.
$200,000 to Teach for America, San Francisco, CA, 2012. For general operating support.
$125,000 to San Francisco Unified School District, Early Education Department, San Francisco, CA, 2012. For programs for classes in Pre-Kindergarten to 3rd Grade.
$100,000 to San Francisco Museum of Modern Art, San Francisco, CA, 2012. For Modern Ball at Super Benefactor Level.
$50,000 to Bay Area Discovery Museum, Sausalito, CA, 2012. For Connections Program, comprehensive outreach program, that aims to create sustainable relationships between the Museum and the diverse communities of the Bay Area.
$37,475 to Cross Cultural Family Center, San Francisco, CA, 2012. For Model Centers Initiative at Visitacion Valley, Leland Street, enriched early childhood education center with a curriculum tailored to meet the specific needs of children living in extreme poverty and homelessness.
$10,000 to Metropolitan Museum of Art, New York, NY, 2012. For annual membership.
$5,000 to FACES SF, Family and Child Empowerment Services San Francisco, San Francisco, CA, 2012. For program materials and equipment for Bayview/Hunter's Point facility.

642
Walter and Elise Haas Fund ✧
1 Lombard St., Ste. 305
San Francisco, CA 94111-1130 (415) 398-4474
Contact: Pamela H. David, Exec. Dir.
Main URL: http://www.haassr.org
Blog: http://www.haassr.org/blog/
Grants Database: http://www.haassr.org/grants/
Knowledge Center: http://www.haassr.org/resources-links/
Twitter: https://twitter.com/HaasSrFund
Walter and Elise Haas Fund's Philanthropy Promise: http://www.ncrp.org/philanthropys-promise/who
Additional contact: Patricia Mattox, Admin.

Incorporated in 1952 in CA.
Donors: Walter A. Haas†; Elise S. Haas†.
Foundation type: Independent foundation.
Financial data (yr. ended 12/31/12): Assets, $215,734,747 (M); expenditures, $15,685,399; qualifying distributions, $13,666,102; giving activities include $11,414,702 for 387 grants (high: $1,000,000; low: $380), $11,700 for 27 employee matching gifts, and $458 for foundation-administered programs.
Purpose and activities: The mission of the fund is to help build a healthy, just, and vibrant society in which people feel connected to and responsible for their community. The areas of focus are the arts and culture, economic security, Jewish life, and public education. In addition, continuing support is provided to organizations that have long established ties to the fund.
Fields of interest: Arts education; Arts; Education; Economic development; Jewish agencies & synagogues.
Type of support: General/operating support; Continuing support; Management development/capacity building; Capital campaigns; Building/renovation; Equipment; Program development; Seed money; Research; Technical assistance; Program evaluation; Program-related investments/loans; Employee matching gifts; Matching/challenge support.
Limitations: Applications accepted. Giving primarily in San Francisco and Alameda County, CA. No grants to individuals, or for general fundraising, endowment campaigns, scholarships, fellowships, or for video or film production (except through the Creative Work Fund).
Publications: Application guidelines; Annual report; Grants list; Program policy statement.
Application information: Application form not required.
Initial approach: Letter of inquiry, see web site for required format
Copies of proposal: 1
Deadline(s): None
Board meeting date(s): Three times per year
Final notification: 3-4 months
Officers and Trustees:* Jennifer C. Hass,* Pres.; Pamela H. David, Exec. Dir.; Elizabeth H. Eisenhardt; John D. Goldman; William S. Goldman; Peter E. Haas, Jr.; Walter J. Haas.
Number of staff: 6 full-time professional; 4 full-time support.
EIN: 946068564

Selected grants: The following grants are a representative sample of this grantmaker's funding activity:
$1,000,000 to Jewish Community Federation of San Francisco, the Peninsula, Marin and Sonoma Counties, San Francisco, CA, 2013. For general support to the Federation's annual campaign.
$280,000 to Jewish Community Center of San Francisco, San Francisco, CA, 2013. For the Jewish Community Center of San Francisco, which welcomes patrons based on their values, not their heritage. In 2012, more than 25,000 people attended the JCC's arts and cultural programs, 5,000 participated in Jewish programs, and 400 students attended its three preschools. Additionally, the JCC created a series of public programs exploring Judaism as a dynamic system of choices and questions. It launched the city's first non-school-based club for Jewish LGBT teens and it opened the Maurice Kanbar Center for Media and Technology, which helps share JCC content on- and off-line.
$250,000 to Jewish Vocational Service, San Francisco, CA, 2013. For Jewish Vocational Services to offer an array of workforce services to low-income and disabled youth, adults with barriers to employment, incumbent workers seeking career advancement, and unemployed members of the Jewish community. It annually helps more than 2,000 people improve their work-readiness or technical skills, build their professional networks, and secure jobs, payable over 2.00 years.
$130,000 to Bend the Arc: A Jewish Partnership for Justice, New York, NY, 2013. For Bend the Arc: A Jewish Partnership for Justice, the premiere Jewish social justice organization in the United States. In 2013 it will focus its work on immigration reform, striving to galvanize support for worker protections. Goals include codifying minimum-wage protection for employees regardless of their immigration status and creating opportunities for LGBT Americans to sponsor their spouses and partners for citizenship, just as heterosexual couples do, payable over 2.00 years.
$90,000 to Bay Area Organizing Committee, San Francisco, CA, 2013. For faith leaders and their congregations increasingly to use moral suasion to offer policy solutions to community problems. The Bay Area Organizing Committee organizes clusters of synagogues, other faith communities, and nonprofits in the East Bay and San Francisco to develop relationships across lines of faith, race, class, and geography. For example, it recently united 200 faith leaders in support of Proposition 30, which increased tax money for education.
$90,000 to Hillel: The Foundation for Jewish Campus Life, San Francisco, CA, 2013. To support the continuation of bridge-building programs between Jews and other students at 10 local college campuses. Highlights of these programs include a fair highlighting social justice opportunities, Jewish Culture Month, multicultural music concerts, and interfaith Passover Seder, payable over 2.00 years.
$70,000 to Oakland Museum of California, Oakland, CA, 2013. For the Oakland Museum of California, the only museum devoted exclusively to the art, history, and natural environment of California. Year-round, the Museum hosts free Friday evening events, called Friday Nights @ OMCA. These community engagement programs combine live music, dancing, food, and hands-on family art activities. During Friday Nights @ OMCA, visitors can view galleries, lectures, and demonstrations inside the Museum for half-price admission. By lowering participation barriers, OMCA draws 2,000 people each week, with attendance steadily growing.
$30,000 to Mural Music and Arts Project, East Palo Alto, CA, 2013. For artist Edward Scape Martinez's collaboration with five youth artists from Mural Music and Arts Project in East Palo Alto to create Voices of EPA, two murals to be installed at identified crime hot spots for the purpose of promoting community peace and unity. Youth artists will work alongside Mr. Martinez to spread awareness about the project and produce a community design process that invites East Palo Alto residents to contribute ideas for the murals. Scape Martinez is established graffiti artist and writer whose work has been displayed in museums and galleries regionally, nationally, and internationally. He has published several books about graffiti arts. Founded in 2001, the Mural Music and Arts Project is arts-based youth development organization aimed at educating, empowering, and inspiring youth through participation in the arts. For Walter and Elise Haas Fund's portion of the Creative Work Fund 2013.
$30,000 to Shalom Bayit, Oakland, CA, 2013. For Shalom Bayit, the only Northern California agency that provides domestic violence services to the Jewish community. When it was launched over 20 years ago, domestic violence in Jewish homes was barely acknowledged. Shalom Bayit's efforts to educate rabbis, community leaders, and educators have shifted this perception. Its 24-hour emergency phone line, direct financial support, in-person counseling, and community education reached 1,671 adults in 2013. Its teen education program reached additional 1,100 young people, fostering discussions about healthy relationships and helping the community to recognize signs of abuse.
$25,000 to Benevolent, Evanston, IL, 2013. For Benevolent, which manages a new crowd-giving platform that enables individual donors to help people in need directly. Individuals with one-time financial needs of up to $700 make requests related to their economic security. They commonly ask for help paying for things such as computers, eyeglasses, licensing fees, and car repairs. Benevolent trains nonprofit case managers to help these clients prepare written statements and videos about themselves and their needs. Case managers then develop companion materials vouching for clients. Benevolent vets each request and posts them to its website through which the public can make tax-deductible donations. This grant helps establish a Bay Area branch of Benevolent, involving the community in personal philanthropy. Grant made through Technology Innovation Center.

643
Evelyn and Walter Haas, Jr. Fund ✧

114 Sansome St., Ste. 600
San Francisco, CA 94104-3814 (415) 856-1400
Contact: Clayton Juan, Grantmaking and Accounting Assoc.
FAX: (415) 856-1500; E-mail: siteinfo@haasjr.org; Main URL: http://www.haasjr.org
E-Newsletter: http://www.haasjr.org/sign-up
Evelyn and Walter Haas, Jr. Fund's Philanthropy Promise: http://www.ncrp.org/philanthropys-promise/who
Facebook: http://www.facebook.com/haasjrfund
Grants Database: http://www.haasjr.org/grants
Knowledge Center: http://www.haasjr.org/what-were-learning
Twitter: http://twitter.com/HaasJrFund

Incorporated in 1953 in CA.
Donors: Walter A. Haas, Jr.‡; Evelyn D. Haas‡.
Foundation type: Independent foundation.
Financial data (yr. ended 12/31/13): Assets, $557,861,774 (M); expenditures, $37,212,057; qualifying distributions, $35,140,745; giving activities include $29,220,642 for 312 grants (high: $5,000,000; low: $150), $424,860 for employee matching gifts, and $837,795 for foundation-administered programs.
Purpose and activities: The foundation focuses on five primary issue areas: 1) Immigrant Rights and Integration; 2) Gay and Lesbian Rights; 3) Education Equity; 4) Leadership development; 5) Community Partnerships and Initiatives. The foundation works to advance the following beliefs: that immigrants should have equal opportunities to become fully engaged citizens; that gays and lesbians should have equal marriage rights, as well as other protections; and that all people should have equal access to a quality education, to civic and cultural assets, and to programs offering vital services to communities in need.
Fields of interest: Education, early childhood education; Higher education, college (community/junior); Education; Civil/human rights, immigrants; Civil/human rights, LGBTQ; Nonprofit management; Leadership development.
Type of support: General/operating support; Program development; Seed money; Technical assistance; Program evaluation; Employee matching gifts; Matching/challenge support.
Limitations: Applications accepted. Giving primarily in the San Francisco Bay area, CA; some national funding. No support for private foundations, consumer or professional groups, labor or trade associations, research centers, or religious organizations. No grants to individuals, or for deficit or emergency financing, workshops, major equipment, scholarships, direct mail campaigns, fundraising events, annual appeals, conferences, publications, capital or endowment campaigns, films or videos, or basic research.
Publications: Application guidelines; Financial statement; Grants list; Newsletter.
Application information: The fund has limited resources for new grantees and is temporarily accepting grant proposals on an invitation-only basis. Application form not required.
Initial approach: 1- to 2- page letter of inquiry
Copies of proposal: 1
Deadline(s): None
Board meeting date(s): At least 3 times per year
Final notification: Within 4 months of receipt of full proposal

Officers and Trustees:* Walter J. Haas,* Chair.; Ira S. Hirschfield,* Pres.; Michael Blake, V.P., Finance; Jennie Lehua Watson, Comm. and V.P., Special Initiatives; Sylvia Yee, V.P., Progs.; Elizabeth Haas Eisenhardt,* Secy.; Robert D. Haas,* Treas.; Ramona Rey-Murphy, Cont.
Number of staff: 16 full-time professional; 2 part-time professional; 7 full-time support.
EIN: 946068932
Selected grants: The following grants are a representative sample of this grantmaker's funding activity:
$1,500,000 to University of California at Berkeley Foundation, Berkeley, CA, 2012. To endow chair for multidisciplinary Religious Diversity Research Cluster of Haas Diversity Research Center.
$650,000 to National LGBTQ Task Force Foundation, New York, NY, 2012. For Institute for Welcoming Resources, to increase public support

for marriage equality and other civil rights protections.

644
Hager Foundation ✧
8222 Melrose Ave., Ste. 202
Los Angeles, CA 90046-6838

Established in 1997 in CA.
Donors: David J. Hager; Judith Hager; Myriam Wohlgelernter; Bina H. Jacobius; Moshe Hager; Pacific West Management; M.B. Insurance, Inc.; Mila Kornwasser Life Insurance.
Foundation type: Independent foundation.
Financial data (yr. ended 05/31/13): Assets, $20,048,071 (M); gifts received, $2,500,000; expenditures, $959,192; qualifying distributions, $923,700; giving activities include $923,700 for 48 grants (high: $141,000; low: $1,800).
Fields of interest: Jewish agencies & synagogues.
Type of support: General/operating support.
Limitations: Applications not accepted. Giving primarily in CA and NY. No grants to individuals.
Application information: Contributes only to pre-selected organizations.
Officers: David Hager, Pres.; Judy Hager, Secy.
EIN: 954592928
Selected grants: The following grants are a representative sample of this grantmaker's funding activity:
$60,000 to Ohr Eliyahu Academy, Culver City, CA, 2011. For general use.
$25,000 to Yeshivath Torath Emeth Academy, Los Angeles, CA, 2011. For general use.
$15,000 to Ezra Lemarpeh Association, Brooklyn, NY, 2011. For general use.
$12,000 to Minchas Asher Foundation, New York, NY, 2011. For general use.

645
Crescent Porter Hale Foundation ✧
655 Redwood Hwy., Ste. 301
Mill Valley, CA 94941-3028 (415) 388-2333
Contact: Ulla Davis, Exec. Dir.
FAX: (415) 381-4799; Main URL: http://www.crescentporterhale.org

Incorporated in 1961 in CA.
Donors: Elwyn C. Hale†; M. Eugenie Hale†.
Foundation type: Independent foundation.
Financial data (yr. ended 12/31/13): Assets, $86,770,815 (M); expenditures, $4,348,222; qualifying distributions, $4,014,865; giving activities include $3,763,200 for 135 grants (high: $550,000; low: $400).
Purpose and activities: Giving primarily to organizations devoted to education in the fields of art and music, and to Catholic elementary and high schools.
Fields of interest: Arts education; Performing arts, music; Elementary/secondary education; Children/youth, services; Family services; Aging, centers/services.
Type of support: Capital campaigns; General/operating support; Scholarship funds; Matching/challenge support.
Limitations: Applications accepted. Giving limited to the following five Bay Area counties: Alameda, Contra Costa, Marin, San Francisco and San Mateo, CA. No support for non-Catholic public schools. No grants to individuals, or for research, health care or medical projects.
Publications: Application guidelines; Grants list; Program policy statement.
Application information: See foundation web site for LOI information. Application form not required.
Initial approach: Letter of intent (2-3 pages) with budget income and expense projections
Copies of proposal: 1
Deadline(s): None
Board meeting date(s): 3 times a year
Final notification: 2 weeks
Officers: E. William Swanson, Pres.; Sr. Estela Morales, M.S.W., V.P.; Patricia Fata, Secy.-Treas.; Ulla Davis, Exec. Dir.
Directors: A.L. Ballard; Ephraim P. Engleman, M.D.; Hon. Thomas J. Mellon, Jr.
Number of staff: 1 full-time professional; 1 part-time support.
EIN: 946093385
Selected grants: The following grants are a representative sample of this grantmaker's funding activity:
$550,000 to Family Aid Catholic Education, Oakland, CA, 2013.
$440,000 to BASIC Fund, San Francisco, CA, 2013.
$425,000 to Boys and Girls Clubs of San Leandro, San Leandro, CA, 2013.
$50,000 to Food Bank of Contra Costa and Solano, Concord, CA, 2013.
$25,000 to Family House, San Francisco, CA, 2013.
$25,000 to Girls Inc. of Alameda County, San Leandro, CA, 2013.
$15,000 to Project SEED, Berkeley, CA, 2013.
$15,000 to Saint Francis of Assisi Youth Club, East Palo Alto, CA, 2013.

646
Robert and Ruth Halperin Foundation ✧
1 Lombard St., Ste. 305
San Francisco, CA 94111-1130

Established in 1999 in CA.
Donors: Robert Halperin; Ruth Halperin; Philip W. Halperin.
Foundation type: Independent foundation.
Financial data (yr. ended 12/31/12): Assets, $92,325,397 (M); expenditures, $5,287,590; qualifying distributions, $3,960,000; giving activities include $3,960,000 for grants.
Fields of interest: Higher education; Business school/education; Human services.
Limitations: Applications not accepted. Giving primarily in Chicago, IL, Boston, MA and San Francisco and Stanford, CA. No grants to individuals.
Application information: Contributes only to pre-selected organizations.
Officers: Robert Halperin, Pres.; Philip W. Halperin, V.P. and Treas.
Directors: Peggy Dow; Mark Halperin.
EIN: 943334424

647
O. L. Halsell Foundation ✧
3200 Park Center Dr., Ste. 1170
Costa Mesa, CA 92626-7153
Application address: c/o David Stauffer, Pres., P.O. Box 6300, Santa Ana, CA 92707, tel.: (714) 546-0755

Established in 1948 in CA.
Donor: Oliver L. Halsell†.
Foundation type: Independent foundation.
Financial data (yr. ended 12/31/13): Assets, $25,096,098 (M); expenditures, $1,422,910; qualifying distributions, $1,201,482; giving activities include $1,168,500 for 64 grants (high: $70,000; low: $2,500).
Purpose and activities: Giving primarily for youth-related activities, as well as for the arts, social services, and YMCAs.
Fields of interest: Higher education; Boys & girls clubs; Boy scouts; Human services; Salvation Army; YM/YWCAs & YM/YWHAs; Children/youth, services.
Limitations: Giving limited to Orange County, CA. No grants to individuals.
Application information:
Initial approach: Letter on organization letterhead
Deadline(s): 1st Mon. in Nov.
Officers: W. David Stauffer, Pres.; Morgan Roach, Secy.
Trustee: James Schramm.
EIN: 956027266
Selected grants: The following grants are a representative sample of this grantmaker's funding activity:
$50,000 to Saddleback Memorial Foundation, Laguna Hills, CA, 2012. For Atrium Commitment.
$20,000 to Human Options, Irvine, CA, 2012. For Service Programs for Battered Women and Children.
$15,000 to Boys and Girls Club of Laguna Beach, Laguna Beach, CA, 2012. For School Readiness Program.
$10,000 to Habitat for Humanity of Orange County, Santa Ana, CA, 2012. For Santa Ana Vi Development.
$5,000 to Boy Scouts of America, Santa Ana, CA, 2012. For camping scholarship.
$5,000 to THINK Together, Santa Ana, CA, 2012. For Literacy Coach Program, Highland Learning Center.
$5,000 to YMCA of Orange, Orange, CA, 2012. For camping scholarships.

648
The Armand Hammer Foundation ✧
3501 Via Real
Carpinteria, CA 93013-3048 (310) 996-6805
Contact: Michael A. Hammer, Chair., Pres., C.E.O. and Dir.

Established in 1968 in CA.
Donor: Armand Hammer†.
Foundation type: Independent foundation.
Financial data (yr. ended 12/31/13): Assets, $23,036,313 (M); expenditures, $2,493,474; qualifying distributions, $1,534,747; giving activities include $490,931 for 42 grants (high: $105,000; low: $100).
Fields of interest: Arts; Higher education; Education; Medical research, institute; Human services; Christian agencies & churches.
Type of support: General/operating support.
Limitations: Applications accepted. Giving primarily in CA. No grants to individuals.
Application information: Application form not required.
Initial approach: Proposal
Deadline(s): None
Officers and Directors:* Michael A. Hammer,* Chair., C.E.O. and Pres.; Viktor A. Hammer,* V.P.

and Secy.-Treas.; Rex Alexander; Richard Lynch; Peter Sansone.
EIN: 237010813
Selected grants: The following grants are a representative sample of this grantmaker's funding activity:
$82,000 to Santa Barbara Museum of Art, Santa Barbara, CA, 2011.
$25,000 to Dream Center, Los Angeles, CA, 2011. For general funds.
$25,000 to Pepperdine University, School of Law, Malibu, CA, 2011.
$25,000 to Pepperdine University, Malibu, CA, 2011. For general funds.
$20,000 to Stop Cancer, Los Angeles, CA, 2011. For general funds.
$11,000 to Dream Foundation, Santa Barbara, CA, 2011. For general funds.
$10,000 to Partners in Malawi, Santa Monica, CA, 2011. For general funds.
$8,000 to Los Angeles, City of, Los Angeles, CA, 2011.
$1,300 to Petersen Automotive Museum, Los Angeles, CA, 2011. For general funds.
$1,000 to International Foundation for Art Research, New York, NY, 2011.

649
Lynn Handleman Charitable Foundation ✧
(doing business as The Left Tilt Fund)
(formerly Joseph & Sally Handleman Charitable Foundation Trust B)
P.O. Box 3610
Oakland, CA 94609-0610
Contact: Angela Fitzsimons, Fund Coord.
E-mail: info@lefttiltfund.org; Main URL: http://www.lefttiltfund.org/

Established in FL.
Donor: Lynn Handleman.
Foundation type: Independent foundation.
Financial data (yr. ended 12/31/13): Assets, $13,014,064 (M); expenditures, $691,272; qualifying distributions, $656,973; giving activities include $570,500 for 29 grants (high: $50,000; low: $500).
Purpose and activities: The fund's mission is to promote social change, resist oppression, and empower marginalized communities. The fund gives to organizations that address the root causes of economic, political, and social injustice through community-based organizing, education, legal advocacy, and other innovative means. The fund is particularly interested in economic equality, civil liberties, prisoners' rights, labor issues, racial justice, homelessness, the environment, the arts, and international work pertaining to Palestine, the Middle East, and Latin America.
Fields of interest: Education; Human services; International development; Civil/human rights.
International interests: Latin America; Middle East.
Limitations: Applications accepted. Giving primarily in CA and Washington DC. No support for governmental agencies, animal welfare organizations, homeless shelters, housing providers/developers, or for soup kitchens if community organizing is not part of their mission. No grants to individuals, or for conferences.
Publications: Application guidelines; Grants list.
Application information: Applicants should submit the requested information typed in 12 point font, double-spaced, and margins set at a 1-inch minimum. Please limit applications to 7 pages single-sided. Applications that do not comply with the formatting guidelines will be discarded. See foundation web site for specific application instructions which must be followed. Application form required.
Initial approach: Use application form on foundation web site
Deadline(s): See foundation web site for current deadline
Final notification: Within 6 weeks of application deadline
Trustee: Scott Handleman.
EIN: 656263327

650
Bill Hannon Foundation ✧
11611 San Vicente Blvd., Ste. 530
Los Angeles, CA 90049-6509
Contact: Elaine S. Ewen, Chair.
E-mail: elaine@comcast.net

Established in 1999 in NV.
Donor: William H. Hannon†.
Foundation type: Independent foundation.
Financial data (yr. ended 09/30/13): Assets, $44,389,767 (M); expenditures, $2,964,950; qualifying distributions, $2,686,509; giving activities include $2,379,000 for 81 grants (high: $100,000; low: $500).
Purpose and activities: Giving primarily for Roman Catholic secondary and higher education, health care and human services.
Fields of interest: Education; Health care; Human services; Catholic agencies & churches.
Type of support: Capital campaigns; Building/renovation; Equipment; Program development; Conferences/seminars; Scholarship funds.
Limitations: Giving primarily in CA, with emphasis on the Los Angeles area.
Publications: Annual report.
Application information:
Initial approach: Letter
Deadline(s): None
Board meeting date(s): Jan., Apr., July, and Oct.
Officers and Directors:* Elaine S. Ewen,* Pres.; A.N. Mosich, Ph.D.*, Treas.; Hon. Jack E. Goertzen; Sr. Kathleen Kelly; Charlene Laraneta.
Number of staff: 1 full-time professional; 1 full-time support.
EIN: 311663038
Selected grants: The following grants are a representative sample of this grantmaker's funding activity:
$100,000 to Mount Saint Marys College, Los Angeles, CA, 2012.
$75,000 to Dominican University of California, San Rafael, CA, 2012.
$75,000 to Notre Dame de Namur University, Belmont, CA, 2012.
$75,000 to Santa Clara University, Santa Clara, CA, 2012.
$75,000 to University of San Francisco, San Francisco, CA, 2012.
$50,000 to Bishop Amat Memorial High School, La Puente, CA, 2012.
$50,000 to Junipero Serra High School, San Mateo, CA, 2012.
$50,000 to Saint Bernard High School, Playa del Rey, CA, 2012.
$25,000 to Proyecto Pastoral, Los Angeles, CA, 2012.

651
William H. Hannon Foundation ✧
729 Montana Ave., Ste. 5
Santa Monica, CA 90403-1369
Contact: Kathleen Hannon Aikenhead, Pres.
FAX: (310) 260-9740; Main URL: http://www.hannonfoundation.org

Established in 1983 in CA.
Donor: William Herbert Hannon†.
Foundation type: Independent foundation.
Financial data (yr. ended 09/30/13): Assets, $31,493,100 (M); expenditures, $3,543,186; qualifying distributions, $3,199,436; giving activities include $3,003,829 for 321 grants (high: $625,000; low: $35).
Purpose and activities: Giving primarily to enhance the welfare and education of students in both public and private elementary schools, high schools, and universities, primarily within the greater Los Angeles, California area; to aid in the advancement of health care and human services, especially for those who are least able to afford quality care; to address the needs of the disadvantaged, aged, sick, and homeless; and to support and promote the values of the founder's faith through the support of the good works of the Roman Catholic Church.
Fields of interest: Elementary/secondary education; Higher education; Education; Health care; Catholic agencies & churches.
Type of support: General/operating support; Continuing support; Capital campaigns; Building/renovation; Program development; Scholarship funds.
Limitations: Giving primarily in Los Angeles and the southern CA area. No support for private foundations, or for political organizations. No grants to individuals, or for underwriting parties, travel funds, advertisements, or radio or television programming.
Publications: Application guidelines.
Application information: Application information and procedures available on foundation web site. Application form not required.
Initial approach: Letter only
Copies of proposal: 1
Deadline(s): Aug. 1, Nov.1, Feb. 1, and May 1
Board meeting date(s): Sept., Dec., Mar., and June
Final notification: 1 month from receipt
Officers and Directors:* Kathleen Hannon Aikenhead,* Pres.; Nancy B. Cunningham,* V.P. and Secy.; James A. Hannon,* V.P. and C.F.O.; David W. Burcham; David A. Herbst; Robert B. Lawton, S.J.; Rev. Msgr. Royale M. Vadakin.
Number of staff: 1 full-time professional; 1 part-time support.
EIN: 953847664

652
The John and Katie Hansen Family Foundation ✧
P.O. Box 1398
Tiburon, CA 94920-4398

Established in 2005 in CA and DE.
Donors: John Hansen; Katie Hansen; San Leonardo, LLC.
Foundation type: Independent foundation.
Financial data (yr. ended 12/31/13): Assets, $5,943,865 (M); gifts received, $5,075; expenditures, $1,621,693; qualifying distributions,

$1,588,112; giving activities include $1,588,112 for 17 grants.
Fields of interest: Higher education; Education; Health organizations.
Limitations: Applications not accepted. Giving primarily in CA, IL, and MA.
Application information: Unsolicited requests for funds not accepted.
Officers: Katie Vogelheim, Pres.; John Hansen, V.P.
Directors: John Barrett Hansen; Mary Vogelheim.
EIN: 203454511

653
The Stanley E. Hanson Foundation ✧ ☆
2121 E. Via Burton
Anaheim, CA 92806-1220

Established in CA.
Donor: Hanson Family Trust.
Foundation type: Independent foundation.
Financial data (yr. ended 12/31/13): Assets, $42,237,947 (M); expenditures, $3,949,100; qualifying distributions, $3,257,092; giving activities include $3,043,200 for 44 grants (high: $250,000; low: $5,000).
Fields of interest: Education; Hospitals (specialty); Human services; Children/youth, services; Foundations (private grantmaking).
Limitations: Applications not accepted. Giving primarily in CA.
Application information: Unsolicited requests for funds not accepted.
Officers and Directors:* James M. Kilkowski,* Pres.; Larry Kirschenbaum,* C.F.O.
EIN: 271104044

654
Harden Foundation ✧
1636 Ercia St.
Salinas, CA 93906-5200 (831) 442-3005
Contact: Joseph C. Grainger, Exec. Dir.
FAX: (831) 443-1429;
E-mail: maria@hardenfoundation.org; Mailing address: P.O. Box 779 Salinas, CA 93902; Main URL: http://www.hardenfoundation.org
Grants List: http://www.hardenfoundation.org/grants-awarded.html
LinkedIn: http://www.linkedin.com/company/1793824?goback=%2Efcs_MDYS_Harden+Foundation_false

Established in 1963 in CA.
Donors: Eugene E. Harden†; Ercia E. Harden†.
Foundation type: Independent foundation.
Financial data (yr. ended 12/31/13): Assets, $61,520,070 (M); expenditures, $4,088,327; qualifying distributions, $2,996,367; giving activities include $2,357,768 for grants.
Purpose and activities: The foundation supports projects that improve the well-being of young people; strengthen the family; develop individual self-reliance and health; prevent inappropriate institutionalization of individuals; improve the quality of life through cultural activities; encourage more humane treatment of animals; and eliminate duplication and improve coordination of social and community services.
Fields of interest: Arts; Environment; Animal welfare; Health care; Agriculture/food; Human services; Children/youth, services; Family services; Aging, centers/services.
Type of support: General/operating support; Capital campaigns; Seed money; Matching/challenge support.
Limitations: Giving limited to Monterey County, CA, with emphasis on the Salinas Valley, area. No support for sectarian religious programs, nonagricultural related educational programs, operating foundations, or associations established for the benefit of organizations receiving substantial tax support. No grants for endowments, annual campaigns, conferences, academic or medical research, scholarships to individuals, or fundraising events.
Publications: Application guidelines; Annual report (including application guidelines); Grants list.
Application information: Do not submit proposal in a binder or folder. Faxed applications are not accepted. E-mailed applications can be sent either as a Word document or scanned PDF document to: grants@hardenfoundation.org. For applications submitted by e-mail in Word format, a copy of the signed Common Grant Application Form (page 7 of the Monterey County Area Grantmakers Common Grant Application) should be mailed to the foundation. See foundation web site for necessary application requirements including typeface specifications. Application form required.
Initial approach: Use Monterey County Area Grantmakers Common Grant Application (CGA) and include necessary attachments, and send via U.S. mail, e-mail, or by hand delivery
Copies of proposal: 1
Deadline(s): Mar. 1 and Sept. 1
Board meeting date(s): June and Dec.
Officers and Directors:* Patricia Tynan Chapman,* Pres.; C. Bill Elliott,* V.P. and Treas.; Linda Taylor,* Secy.; Joseph C. Grainger, Exec. Dir.; Mike Antle; Bruce C. Taylor.
Number of staff: 1 full-time professional; 2 part-time professional; 2 full-time support.
EIN: 946098887

655
Harman Family Foundation ✧
c/o Oak Investment Partners
525 University Ave., Ste. 1300
Palo Alto, CA 94301-1913

Established in 2003 in CA.
Donors: Frederic Harman; Stephanie Curtis Harman.
Foundation type: Independent foundation.
Financial data (yr. ended 12/31/12): Assets, $2,903,286 (M); gifts received, $6,250; expenditures, $998,567; qualifying distributions, $952,750; giving activities include $933,000 for 19 grants (high: $495,000; low: $1,000).
Fields of interest: Arts; Elementary/secondary education; Higher education; Education; Human services; Foundations (private grantmaking).
Limitations: Applications not accepted. Giving primarily in CA. No grants to individuals.
Application information: Contributes only to pre-selected organizations.
Officers: Stephanie Curtis Harman, Pres.; Frederic Harman, Secy.-Treas.
EIN: 550855839

656
Harman Family Foundation ✧ ☆
(formerly Sidney and Jane Harman Foundation)
10390 Santa Monica Blvd., Ste. 360
Los Angeles, CA 90025-6915
Main URL: http://harman-foundation.org/

Donor: Sidney Harman Administrative Trust.
Foundation type: Independent foundation.
Financial data (yr. ended 12/31/13): Assets, $39,318,763 (M); gifts received, $1,000,000; expenditures, $3,070,656; qualifying distributions, $2,883,467; giving activities include $2,454,344 for 86 grants (high: $522,500; low: $500).
Fields of interest: Arts; Education; Human services.
Limitations: Applications not accepted. Giving primarily in Washington, DC; some funding also in CA and NY.
Application information: Unsolicited requests for funds not accepted.
Trustees: Barbara Harman; Dan Harman; Jane Harman; Lynn Harman; Brian Frank; Megan Quitkin.
EIN: 456495102

657
Mark H. & Blanche M. Harrington Foundation ✧
P.O. Box 2549
Rancho Cucamonga, CA 91729-2549 (626) 405-8335

Established in 1956 in CA.
Donors: Mark S. Harrington; Blanche M. Harrington; Frank Burlingham; Delores C. Harrington; Pamela Harrington Munro; Jerry Harrington.
Foundation type: Independent foundation.
Financial data (yr. ended 12/31/13): Assets, $24,856,682 (M); expenditures, $1,353,361; qualifying distributions, $1,207,894; giving activities include $1,206,500 for 86 grants (high: $208,000; low: $100).
Purpose and activities: Giving primarily for health care, including a children's hospital, as well as for family services, and Christian and Roman Catholic churches and organizations; giving also for the arts, education and social services.
Fields of interest: Arts; Higher education; Education; Hospitals (specialty); Human services; Children/youth, services; Family services; Community/economic development; Christian agencies & churches.
Limitations: Applications accepted. Giving primarily in CA. No grants to individuals.
Application information: Application form required.
Initial approach: Letter
Deadline(s): None
Trustees: Frank Burlingham; Mark S. Harrington; Citizens Business Bank.
Directors: Delores C. Harrington; Jerry Harrington; Pamela Harrington Munro.
EIN: 956025594
Selected grants: The following grants are a representative sample of this grantmaker's funding activity:
$50,000 to Family Research Council, Holland, MI, 2011.
$40,000 to Family Research Council, Holland, MI, 2011.
$40,000 to Family Research Council, Washington, DC, 2011.
$20,000 to Christian Legal Society, Springfield, VA, 2011.

$20,000 to Christian Legal Society, Springfield, VA, 2011.
$20,000 to Christian Legal Society, Springfield, VA, 2011.
$20,000 to Christian Legal Society, Springfield, VA, 2011.
$11,000 to Laguna Playhouse, Laguna Beach, CA, 2011.
$5,000 to Pacific Chorale, Santa Ana, CA, 2011.
$4,000 to Laguna Playhouse, Laguna Beach, CA, 2011.

658
Harris-Johnson Family Foundation ✧ ☆
101 California St., Ste. 2100
San Francisco, CA 94111-5891

Donors: G. Parker Harris III; Hollt L. Jonson.
Foundation type: Independent foundation.
Financial data (yr. ended 12/31/13): Assets, $696,183 (M); gifts received, $1,014,868; expenditures, $492,807; qualifying distributions, $471,099; giving activities include $471,099 for 6 grants (high: $295,000; low: $10,000).
Fields of interest: Arts; Education; Youth development.
Limitations: Applications not accepted. Giving primarily in CA.
Application information: Unsolicited requests for funds not accepted.
Officers: G. Parker Harris III, Pres. and C.F.O.; Holly L. Johnson, Secy.
EIN: 461326243
Selected grants: The following grants are a representative sample of this grantmaker's funding activity:
$250,000 to Katahdin Foundation, Berkeley, CA, 2012. For funding a documentary.

659
Fred L. Hartley Family Foundation ✧
P.O. Box 3474
Palos Verdes Peninsula, CA 90274
Application address: Fred L. Hartley, Jr., 439 Grand Ave., Ste. 325, Bigfork, MT 95511. Tel.: (623) 322-7351. E-mail: fdnflh76@chapter.net

Established in 1997 in CA.
Donor: Margaret A. Hartley.
Foundation type: Independent foundation.
Financial data (yr. ended 09/30/13): Assets, $16,068,883 (M); expenditures, $898,707; qualifying distributions, $898,707; giving activities include $883,751 for 22 grants (high: $200,000; low: $7,500).
Fields of interest: Education; Health organizations; Youth development; Human services; Science.
Limitations: Applications accepted. Giving primarily in CA. No support for religious or political organizations.
Application information: Application form required.
Initial approach: Letter
Deadline(s): None
Trustees: Daniel F. Gruen; Margaret A. Gruen; Fred L. Hartley, Jr.; Therese C. Hartley; J. Steven Hopper.
EIN: 330783531
Selected grants: The following grants are a representative sample of this grantmaker's funding activity:
$123,000 to Purdue University, West Lafayette, IN, 2011.

660
J. Samuel Harwit Z"L and Manya Harwit-Aviv Charitable Trust ✧
6310 San Vincente Blvd., Rm. 250
Los Angeles, CA 90048-5447

Established in 1993 in CA.
Donors: Manya Harwit; Manya Harwit Trust; Manya Harwit Administrative Trust.
Foundation type: Independent foundation.
Financial data (yr. ended 06/30/13): Assets, $9,993,485 (M); expenditures, $670,425; qualifying distributions, $515,000; giving activities include $515,000 for grants.
Purpose and activities: Support for Jewish organizations, temples, and schools.
Fields of interest: Elementary/secondary education; Higher education; Education; Human services; Jewish agencies & synagogues.
Limitations: Applications not accepted. Giving primarily in CA. No grants to individuals.
Application information: Contributes only to pre-selected organizations.
Trustees: E. Nora Harwit Amrani; Steven Harwit; Frank Lee, C.P.A.; Joel A. Levine, Esq.
EIN: 956949206
Selected grants: The following grants are a representative sample of this grantmaker's funding activity:
$95,000 to Jewish National Fund, Rockville Centre, NY, 2011.
$25,000 to Yeshiva University, New York, NY, 2011.

661
Hastings Foundation ✧
530 S. Lake Ave., Ste. 349
Pasadena, CA 91101

Established in CA.
Foundation type: Independent foundation.
Financial data (yr. ended 06/30/13): Assets, $8,193,029 (M); expenditures, $981,575; qualifying distributions, $895,673; giving activities include $859,000 for 1 grant.
Fields of interest: Medical school/education.
Limitations: Applications not accepted.
Application information: Unsolicited requests for funds not accepted.
Officers: Richard H. Zeiss, Pres.; Kevin B. Lake, V.P.; David A. Tirrell, Secy.; John H. Reith, Treas.
Director: Gene E. Gregg.
EIN: 951642370

662
The Hauptman Family Foundation, Inc. ✧
P.O. Box 3337
Beverly Hills, CA 90212-0337

Established in 2006 in CA.
Donors: Andrew Hauptman; Ellen Bronfman Hauptman; The BBH Trust; The Charles Bronfman Trust II.
Foundation type: Independent foundation.
Financial data (yr. ended 12/31/13): Assets, $849,072 (M); gifts received, $1,900,000; expenditures, $1,117,900; qualifying distributions, $1,117,900; giving activities include $1,033,300 for 155 grants (high: $250,000; low: $250).
Fields of interest: Museums (art); Arts; Education, drop-out prevention; Education; Health organizations; Human services; Children/youth, services; Jewish agencies & synagogues.
Limitations: Applications not accepted. Giving primarily in Los Angeles, CA and Boston, MA; some funding also in NY. No grants to individuals.
Application information: Contributes only to pre-selected organizations.
Officers: Kashif Sheikh, Pres.; Dana Rosenkrantz, Secy.; Chris Norton, Co-Treas.; Al Popof, Co-Treas.
Directors: Andrew Hauptman; Ellen Bronfman Hauptman.
EIN: 205618432

663
William R. & Virginia Hayden Foundation ✧
(formerly William R. Hayden Foundation)
110 W. Las Tunas Dr., Ste. A
San Gabriel, CA 91776-1346 (626) 285-9891
Contact: Stanley D. Hayden, Pres. and Dir.

Established in 1960 in CA.
Donors: William R. Hayden†; Mrs. William R. Hayden†; Virginia Hayden Charitable Lead Trust I; Virginia Hayden Charitable Lead Trust II.
Foundation type: Independent foundation.
Financial data (yr. ended 12/31/13): Assets, $5,362,188 (M); gifts received, $114,282; expenditures, $715,368; qualifying distributions, $685,150; giving activities include $675,915 for 30 grants (high: $140,000; low: $1,000).
Purpose and activities: Emphasis on Roman Catholic religious and social service organizations, including support for churches.
Fields of interest: Elementary/secondary education; Human services; Catholic federated giving programs; Catholic agencies & churches.
Type of support: Continuing support; Capital campaigns; Building/renovation.
Limitations: Applications accepted. Giving primarily in CA. No grants to individuals.
Application information: Application form required.
Initial approach: Letter
Copies of proposal: 1
Deadline(s): None
Officers and Directors:* Stanley D. Hayden,* Pres.; William R. Hayden II,* V.P.; Patrick F. Collins,* C.F.O.; David S. Hayden,* Secy.; Catherine H. Marsh; David S. Aikenhead; Marcia M. Hayden; Margaret H. Dietz; Peter J. Vogelsang.
EIN: 956055676

664
The John Randolph Haynes and Dora Haynes Foundation
888 W. 6th St., Ste. 1150
Los Angeles, CA 90017-2737 (213) 623-9151
Contact: William J. Burke, Admin. Dir.
FAX: (213) 623-3951;
E-mail: info@haynesfoundation.org; Main URL: http://www.haynesfoundation.org
Grants Database: http://www.haynesfoundation.org/searcharchive/index.asp

Trust established in 1926 in CA.
Donors: John Randolph Haynes†; Mrs. Dora Fellows Haynes†.
Foundation type: Independent foundation.
Financial data (yr. ended 08/31/13): Assets, $48,435,186 (M); expenditures, $2,476,013;

qualifying distributions, $1,942,746; giving activities include $1,499,500 for grants.
Purpose and activities: The foundation promotes the well-being of mankind by making grants for study and research in the social sciences (economics, history, government, and sociology) with emphasis on education, the environment, immigration and public policy. It also provides doctoral dissertation fellowships, and fellowships for faculty members in the social sciences at colleges and universities in the greater Los Angeles region. Grants made only through local colleges and universities or other nonprofit institutions.
Fields of interest: Social sciences; Public policy, research.
Type of support: Fellowships; Research.
Limitations: Applications accepted. Giving limited to the greater Los Angeles, CA, area. No support for political or religious organizations. No grants to individuals, or for building or endowment funds, operating budgets, or capital improvements.
Publications: Application guidelines; Annual report; Biennial report; Financial statement; Grants list; Informational brochure; Informational brochure (including application guidelines); Newsletter; Program policy statement.
Application information: Application for a faculty fellowship, doctoral dissertation fellowship, or research study grant is made directly to the foundation. See foundation web site for detailed submission guidelines. Application form not required.
Initial approach: Letter or telephone
Copies of proposal: 5
Deadline(s): See foundation web site for deadlines
Board meeting date(s): Quarterly
Final notification: 2 months from receipt
Officer and Trustees:* Jane G. Pisano,* Pres. and Secy.-Treas.; Philip M. Hawley,* V.P.; Gilbert T. Ray,* V.P.; Robert A. Eckert; Gil Garcetti; Enrique Hernandez, Jr.; Daniel A. Mazmanian; Robert Suro; Willis B. Wood, Jr.
Number of staff: 1 full-time professional; 1 full-time support.
EIN: 951644020
Selected grants: The following grants are a representative sample of this grantmaker's funding activity:
$136,421 to University of California, Los Angeles, CA, 2012. Does School Readiness Improve Academic Achievement for Low Income and Immigrant Children in Los Angeles?.
$52,648 to Loyola Marymount University, Los Angeles, CA, 2012. Should I Stay or Should I Go: Exploring the Assignment and Retention of Teach for America Teachers by School and by Neighborhood in the Los Angeles Region.
$50,000 to University of California, Irvine, CA, 2012. For Evaluation of the Effectiveness of Form-Based Codes in Promoting Sustainability.
$25,000 to Library Foundation of Los Angeles, Los Angeles, CA, 2012. For Herman J. Schultheis Collection.
$25,000 to University of California, Los Angeles, CA, 2012. For The Photographic Legacy of Post World War II Mexican American Generation in Los Angeles.

665
Nancy Eccles and Homer M. Hayward Family Foundation ✧
(formerly Hayward Family Foundation)
42 Glen Dr.
Mill Valley, CA 94941-1251

Established in 1993 in UT.
Donors: Nancy Eccles Hayward‡; Hope Eccles Behle‡; Homer M. Hayward; Wendy A. Hayward.
Foundation type: Independent foundation.
Financial data (yr. ended 12/31/13): Assets, $59,110,383 (M); expenditures, $3,109,819; qualifying distributions, $2,716,508; giving activities include $2,666,250 for 30 grants (high: $350,000; low: $1,000).
Fields of interest: Education; Animal welfare; Health care; Human services.
Type of support: General/operating support; Continuing support; Building/renovation; Research; Program evaluation; Matching/challenge support.
Limitations: Applications not accepted. Giving primarily in CA. No grants to individuals.
Application information: Contributes only to pre-selected organizations. Unsolicited requests for funds not accepted.
Board meeting date(s): Varies
Officer: Wendy Hayward, Exec. Dir.
Directors: Bill Hayward; Hope Hayward.
Trustee: Private Trust Co.
EIN: 876227330
Selected grants: The following grants are a representative sample of this grantmaker's funding activity:
$333,000 to Save the Redwoods League, San Francisco, CA, 2012. For capital funding for the purchase of 426 acres of the Noyo River Redwoods.
$100,000 to Hartnell College Foundation, Salinas, CA, 2012. To underwrite the cost of a teaching position in Sustainable design.
$100,000 to Pioneer Montessori School, Ketchum, ID, 2012. For capital funding for the expansion of their school.
$100,000 to Santa Catalina School, Monterey, CA, 2012. For financial aid to provide capital support for the renovation of the Lower School.
$75,000 to Door to Hope, Salinas, CA, 2012. For capital support for a bathroom remodel.
$62,500 to Carmel Mission Foundation, Carmel, CA, 2012. For capital support for the historical renovation.
$25,000 to Trust for Public Land, San Francisco, CA, 2012. For operating support to provide capital support for the Canal Community Garden in Marin County.
$17,500 to League to Save Lake Tahoe, South Lake Tahoe, CA, 2012. For operating support for ongoing preservation.
$5,000 to Tamalpais High School, Mill Valley, CA, 2012. For operating support for families in need during the holiday season.

666
Healing Hearts & Nations ✧ ☆
1650 Oak Tree Terr.
Glendora, CA 91741-3065
Main URL: http://www.healingheartsandnations.org/

Donor: Lynsi Snyder.
Foundation type: Independent foundation.
Financial data (yr. ended 12/31/13): Assets, $19,518 (M); gifts received, $406,679; expenditures, $762,582; qualifying distributions, $731,925; giving activities include $731,925 for 4 grants (high: $575,000; low: $38,016).
Fields of interest: Christian agencies & churches.
Limitations: Applications not accepted.
Application information: Unsolicited requests for funds not accepted.
Officers and Directors:* Richard Martinez,* Pres.; Arnie Wensinger,* Secy.; Jodie Medlock, Fdn. Mgr.
EIN: 542177055

667
The HealthCare Foundation for Orange County ✧
(formerly Westmed Health Foundation)
1450 N. Tustin Ave., Ste. 209
Santa Ana, CA 92705-8667 (714) 245-1650
FAX: (714) 245-1653; Main URL: http://www.hfoc.org

Established in 1994 in CA; converted from the sale of United Western Medical Centers and its affiliates.
Donors: United Western Medical Centers; The California Wellness Foundation; Russell Guy and Ruth Louise Morgan Trust.
Foundation type: Independent foundation.
Financial data (yr. ended 03/31/13): Assets, $16,100,156 (M); expenditures, $725,533; qualifying distributions, $513,407; giving activities include $436,623 for 10 grants (high: $133,356; low: $695).
Purpose and activities: Giving to improve the health of the neediest and most underserved residents of Orange County, CA, by advancing access to health promotion, prevention, and basic health care.
Fields of interest: Hospitals (general); Hospitals (specialty); Health care; Mental health/crisis services; Breast cancer; Asthma; Pediatrics; Obstetrics/gynecology; Human services; Children/youth, services; Family services.
Limitations: Giving primarily in Orange County, CA. No support for biomedical research organizations, disease-specific organizations seeking support for their national programs, or for religious or fraternal organizations. No grants to individuals, or for annual campaigns, social events, telethons, building projects or equipment.
Publications: Annual report; Informational brochure (including application guidelines).
Application information: Application guidelines and procedures available on foundation web site. No faxed proposals. Application form required.
Initial approach: Follow proposal guidelines on web site for Gold Fund for Health and Partners for Health program.
Deadline(s): See web site for current deadlines
Board meeting date(s): Quarterly
Officers and Directors:* Lilia M. Tanakeyowma,* Chair.; J. Fernando Niebla,* Vice-Chair.; Marven E. Howard,* C.F.O.; Zee Mabel Allred; David Dobos; Donald P. Kennedy; Quynh Kieu, M.D.; Anthony M. Magno; Timothy P. Mullins; William B. Stannard; John O. Strong, M.D.
EIN: 330644620
Selected grants: The following grants are a representative sample of this grantmaker's funding activity:
$250,000 to Childrens Hospital of Orange County, Orange, CA, 2011.
$167,937 to Childrens Hospital of Orange County, Orange, CA, 2011.
$100,000 to Saint Joseph Health System, Irvine, CA, 2011.

$75,000 to Hoag Memorial Hospital Presbyterian, Newport Beach, CA, 2011.
$25,000 to YMCA, North Orange County, Fullerton, CA, 2011.
$10,000 to Volunteer Center of Orange County-Central/South, Santa Ana, CA, 2011.

668
Healthy Earthworks Charitable Foundation ✧
65 Carmelita St.
San Francisco, CA 94117-3312

Established in 2004 in CA.
Donor: Dorothy Meyer Trust.
Foundation type: Independent foundation.
Financial data (yr. ended 12/31/13): Assets, $4,949,752 (M); expenditures, $481,266; qualifying distributions, $443,952; giving activities include $443,952 for 38 grants (high: $138,787; low: $75).
Fields of interest: Environment; Food services.
Limitations: Applications not accepted. Giving primarily in CA. No grants to individuals.
Application information: Contributes only to pre-selected organizations.
Officer: Katherine Haas, Pres.
EIN: 200877954

669
David Whitmire Hearst Jr. Foundation ✧
11455 El Camino Real, Ste. 305
San Diego, CA 92130-2088

Established in 2002 in CA.
Donor: David Whitmire Hearst, Jr.
Foundation type: Independent foundation.
Financial data (yr. ended 12/31/13): Assets, $0 (M); gifts received, $5,585,000; expenditures, $1,093,961; qualifying distributions, $973,200; giving activities include $973,200 for grants.
Fields of interest: Visual arts, photography; Heart & circulatory diseases; Military/veterans' organizations.
Limitations: Applications not accepted. Giving primarily in AZ and CA. No grants to individuals.
Application information: Contributes only to pre-selected organizations.
Officers and Directors:* David Whitmire Hearst, Jr.,* Pres.; Ken Nishina,* C.F.O.; Warren Coley,* Secy.; Brigitte J. Coley; Christopher Espineli; Kerstin Richert-Motullo; Cindy Tom.
EIN: 710917959

670
The Heart Foundation ✧
31822 Village Center Rd., Ste. 208
Westlake Village, CA 91361-4330 (818) 865-1100
FAX: (818) 530-7743;
E-mail: info@theheartfoundation.org; Main URL: http://www.theheartfoundation.org
Blog: http://www.theheartfoundation.org/blog/
Facebook: http://www.facebook.com/pages/The-Heart-Foundation-In-Memory-of-Steven-S-Cohen/331339103115?v=wall
Twitter: http://twitter.com/TheHeartFdn/

Established in 1996 in CA; Incorporated in CA in 2002.
Foundation type: Operating foundation.
Financial data (yr. ended 06/30/13): Assets, $3,876,247 (M); gifts received, $1,983,261; expenditures, $1,668,607; qualifying distributions, $1,350,722; giving activities include $1,060,862 for 4 grants (high: $1,050,612; low: $2,000).
Purpose and activities: The Heart Foundation is dedicated to increasing awareness of heart disease, supporting groundbreaking cardiac research at Cedars-Sinai Medical Center and honoring the memory of an incredible husband, father, son, brother and friend. Our goal is to prevent, cure and eradicate this silent killer.
Fields of interest: Heart & circulatory diseases; Heart & circulatory research.
Type of support: Research.
Limitations: Applications not accepted. Giving primarily in Los Angeles, CA, and the surrounding area. No grants to individuals.
Publications: Newsletter.
Application information: Contributes only to pre-selected organizations.
Officers and Directors:* Mark Litman,* Chair.; Dana Kates,* Secy.; Mark Sapiro,* Treas.; Tony Loren, Exec. Dir.; Howard J. Abrams, C.P.A.; Bruce F. Beard, D.D.S.; Jerry Cohen; Thomas Eisenstadt; Marty Fishman, Ph.D.; Lisa Sapiro; Stan Steinberg; Eva Cohen Weingarten; Brian S. Weinhart.
Number of staff: 2 full-time professional; 2 part-time support.
EIN: 450471117
Selected grants: The following grants are a representative sample of this grantmaker's funding activity:
$1,000 to Harold Pump Foundation, Sherman Oaks, CA, 2011.

671
Heavensent Foundation ✧
640 S. San Vicente Blvd.
Los Angeles, CA 90048-4645

Established in 2003 in CA.
Donor: Jose Luis Mazar.
Foundation type: Independent foundation.
Financial data (yr. ended 12/31/13): Assets, $1,293,611 (M); gifts received, $200; expenditures, $904,606; qualifying distributions, $904,415; giving activities include $883,714 for 17 grants (high: $585,714; low: $500).
Fields of interest: United Ways and Federated Giving Programs.
Limitations: Applications not accepted. Giving primarily in Miami, FL; with some giving in CA. No grants to individuals.
Application information: Contributes only to pre-selected organizations.
Trustee: Jose Luis Nazar.
EIN: 200418740

672
Hedco Foundation ✧
P.O. Box 339
Danville, CA 94526-0339
Contact: Mary Goriup, Mgr.

Incorporated in 1972 in CA.
Donors: Herrick Corp.; Catalina Assocs.; Herrick-Pacific Corp.
Foundation type: Independent foundation.
Financial data (yr. ended 12/31/12): Assets, $18,699,375 (M); gifts received, $100,000; expenditures, $2,496,370; qualifying distributions, $2,397,923; giving activities include $2,280,728 for 28 grants (high: $247,670; low: $5,263).
Purpose and activities: Giving predominantly to qualified educational and health institutions; support also for social services.
Fields of interest: Higher education, university; Hospitals (general); Health organizations, association; Human services.
Type of support: Building/renovation; Equipment; Land acquisition; Matching/challenge support.
Limitations: Applications not accepted. Giving primarily in CA. No grants to individuals, or for general support, operating budgets, endowment funds, scholarships, fellowships, special projects, research, publications, or conferences; no loans.
Application information: Contributes only to pre-selected organizations.
Board meeting date(s): Nov.
Officers and Directors:* Dorothy Jernstedt,* Pres.; Rena Brantley,* Secy.; David H. Dornsife,* C.F.O.; Mary A. Goriup, Mgr.; Derek Jernstedt,* Exec. Dir.; James Appleton; Allen L. Dobbins, Ed.D.; Tom Herman; Robert Lowitz, M.D.; Roger Schwab.
EIN: 237259742

673
Heffernan Group Foundation ✧
1350 Carlback Ave., Ste. 350
Walnut Creek, CA 94596-7328
Contact: Michelle Lonaker, Dir.
FAX: (925) 934-8278;
E-mail: michellel@heffernanfoundation.com; Tel. for Michelle Lonaker: (925) 295-2575; Main URL: http://www.heffernanfoundation.com/index.php
Grants List: http://www.heffernanfoundation.com/Who_we_fund.php

Established in 2006 in CA.
Donor: Heffernan Insurance Brokers.
Foundation type: Company-sponsored foundation.
Financial data (yr. ended 12/31/12): Assets, $237,332 (M); gifts received, $849,100; expenditures, $956,913; qualifying distributions, $941,441; giving activities include $941,441 for 326 grants (high: $200,000; low: $200).
Purpose and activities: The foundation supports programs designed to provide shelter, food, and education; and preserve the environment. Special emphasis is directed toward programs designed to serve families or individuals in need.
Fields of interest: Higher education; Education; Environment, natural resources; Environment; Food services; Food banks; Housing/shelter, development; Housing/shelter; Boys & girls clubs; Children/youth, services; Family services; Family services, domestic violence; Residential/custodial care, hospices; Human services.
Type of support: General/operating support; Program development; Scholarship funds; Employee-related scholarships.
Limitations: Applications not accepted. Giving primarily in areas of company operations, with emphasis on CA.
Publications: Grants list.
Application information: Unsolicited applications are not accepted. Grant submissions from local charities are by invitation only. Grants range from $2,500 to $10,000.
Board meeting date(s): Dec.

Officers and Directors:* F. Michael Heffernan,* Chair.; Dan Sebastiani, Treas.; Michelle Lonaker; Kurt Scheidt; Jessica Standiford; Louisa Tallarida.
EIN: 711010693

674
Jason Debus Heigl Foundation ✧
3450 Cahuenga Blvd. W., Unit 905
Los Angeles, CA 90068-1594
Contact: Nancy E. Heigl, Pres.
E-mail: info@jasonheiglfoundation.org; Main URL: http://jasonheiglfoundation.org/
Facebook: https://www.facebook.com/JasonHeiglFoundation
RSS Feed: http://www.jasonheiglfoundation.org/feed
Twitter: https://www.twitter.com/jasonheiglfound
YouTube: http://www.youtube.com/jasonheiglfoundation

Established in 2008.
Donors: Nancy E. Heigl; Katherine Heigl; Paragigm Agency; American Society for the Prevention of Cruelty to Animals; Rachael Ray Foundation; NBC Studio.
Foundation type: Independent foundation.
Financial data (yr. ended 12/31/12): Assets, $203,766 (M); gifts received, $613,340; expenditures, $676,918; qualifying distributions, $500,892; giving activities include $500,892 for 122 grants (high: $138,886; low: $35).
Purpose and activities: The foundation's mission is to eliminate the needless suffering inflicted on animals by human cruelty, indifference, and ignorance.
Fields of interest: Animal welfare.
Application information:
Initial approach: E-mail
Officers: Nancy E. Heigl, Pres.; Katherine M. Heigl, V.P.; Margaret L. Heigl, Secy.; John R. Engelhardt, C.F.O.
EIN: 270187750
Selected grants: The following grants are a representative sample of this grantmaker's funding activity:
$500 to Voice for the Animals, Santa Monica, CA, 2012. For and encourage non-profit animal rescue/ad.

675
The Heising-Simons Foundation ✧
300 2nd St.
Los Altos, CA 94022-3694

Established in 2007 in CA.
Donors: Elizabeth D. Simons; James H. Simons; The Elizabeth Simons DE TR I; The Elizabeth II Trust-Bermuda; The Elizabeth Simons DE Trust II.
Foundation type: Independent foundation.
Financial data (yr. ended 12/31/12): Assets, $234,508,426 (M); gifts received, $56,959,457; expenditures, $20,834,214; qualifying distributions, $18,762,531; giving activities include $17,701,135 for 57 grants (high: $3,575,000; low: $9,000).
Fields of interest: Education; Environment, natural resources; Environment; Social sciences, public policy.
Limitations: Applications not accepted. Giving primarily in CA; funding also in Washington, DC. No grants to individuals.
Application information: Contributes only to pre-selected organizations.
Officers: Elizabeth D. Simons, Pres.; Joanne Reed, V.P., Opers.; Mark W. Heising, Secy.; Deanna Gomby, Exec. Dir.
EIN: 260799587

676
Clarence E. Heller Charitable Foundation ✧
44 Montgomery St., Ste. 1970
San Francisco, CA 94104-4718 (415) 989-9839
FAX: (415) 989-1909; E-mail: info@cehcf.org; Contact for Environment and Health Program: Bruce A. Hirsch, Exec. Dir. Contact for Education and Music Program: Stan Hutton, Sr. Prog. Off.; Main URL: http://cehcf.org

Established in 1982 in CA.
Donor: Clarence E. Heller†.
Foundation type: Independent foundation.
Financial data (yr. ended 12/31/12): Assets, $63,818,931 (M); expenditures, $3,075,305; qualifying distributions, $2,697,311; giving activities include $2,102,550 for 82 grants (high: $150,000; low: $500).
Purpose and activities: The mission of the foundation is to protect and improve the quality of life through support of programs in the environment, human health, education and the arts. Giving to support research, public education, and policy development to reduce health risks from environmental degradation and environmental hazards, innovative educational programs for elementary and secondary students, sustainable natural resource management, and programs that promote the accessibility of symphonic and chamber music.
Fields of interest: Performing arts, music; Performing arts, orchestras; Arts; Higher education; Education; Environment, research; Environment, public policy; Environment, public education; Environment, natural resources; Agriculture.
Type of support: General/operating support; Continuing support; Equipment; Program development; Publication; Seed money; Curriculum development; Scholarship funds; Research; Technical assistance; Consulting services; Program evaluation.
Limitations: Giving primarily in CA. No grants to individuals.
Publications: Application guidelines; Annual report (including application guidelines); Grants list; Program policy statement.
Application information: Applicant should limit the length of the LOI to two pages of narrative and a one-page projected project budget. Full applications are by invitation only, after review of initial letter of inquiry. Application information available on foundation web site. Application form not required.
Initial approach: Letter of inquiry via U.S. mail or e-mail
Copies of proposal: 1
Deadline(s): See foundation web site for current deadline
Board meeting date(s): 3 times a year, usually Mar., June, and Oct.
Officers and Directors:* Anne Heller Andersen,* Pres.; Rolf Lygren, V.P.; Sarah Coade Mandell,* Secy.-Treas.; Bruce A. Hirsch, Exec. Dir.; Janet Harckham; Alfred Heller; Katherine Heller; Ruth Heller.
Number of staff: 1 full-time professional; 1 full-time support.
EIN: 942814266

677
Hellman Family Foundation ✧
1 Maritime Plz., Ste. 2010
San Francisco, CA 94111-3404 (415) 495-5408

Established in 1983 in CA.
Donors: F. Warren Hellman†; Patricia C. Hellman.
Foundation type: Independent foundation.
Financial data (yr. ended 12/31/12): Assets, $9,001,933 (M); gifts received, $350,000; expenditures, $6,871,973; qualifying distributions, $6,796,731; giving activities include $6,642,833 for 34 grants (high: $1,800,000; low: $5,000).
Fields of interest: Performing arts; Arts; Higher education; Education; Human services; Jewish federated giving programs; Jewish agencies & synagogues.
Type of support: General/operating support.
Limitations: Applications not accepted. Giving primarily in CA, with emphasis on San Francisco. No grants to individuals.
Application information: Unsolicited requests for funds not accepted. Funds fully committed for the next few years. No new grantmaking until current commitments have been fulfilled.
Officers and Directors:* Patricia Hellman Gibbs,* V.P.; Joanne Hagopian, Treas.; Susan Hirsch, Corp. Secy.; Patricia C. Hellman,* Chair. Emeritus; Warren Breslau; Richard D. Gibbs; Frances Hellman; Judith Hellman; Marco Hellman*; Sabrina Hellman.
EIN: 942880118

678
Hellman Fellows Fund ✧
c/o Hirsch & Associates
1714 Stockton St., Ste. 400
San Francisco, CA 94133-2930 (415) 837-5408
Contact: Mary Kuehn
FAX: (415) 837-5409;
E-mail: info@hellmanfellows.org; Main URL: http://www.hellmanfellows.org/

Established in 2010 in CA.
Donors: Patricia C. Hellman; F. Warren Hellman†.
Foundation type: Independent foundation.
Financial data (yr. ended 12/31/12): Assets, $61,054,488 (M); expenditures, $116,300; qualifying distributions, $2,349,903; giving activities include $2,247,300 for 7 grants (high: $618,750; low: $100,000).
Purpose and activities: Giving to support early career research.
Fields of interest: Education; Adults.
Type of support: Research; Fellowships.
Limitations: Applications not accepted. Giving primarily in CA.
Publications: IRS Form 990 or 990-PF printed copy available upon request.
Application information: Unsolicited requests for funds not accepted.
Officers and Director:* Frances Hellman,* Pres.; Susan Hirsch, Secy.; Joanne Hagopian, Treas.; Chris Hellman, Chair. Emeritus; Mick Hellman.
Number of staff: 1 part-time professional; 1 part-time support.
EIN: 371606457

Selected grants: The following grants are a representative sample of this grantmaker's funding activity:
$1,500,000 to University of California, Davis, CA, 2012.
$1,250,000 to University of California, Irvine, CA, 2012.

679
John C. Hench Foundation ✧ ☆
556 Sierra Madre Blvd.
San Marino, CA 91108-1435

Established in 1990 in CA.
Donors: John C. Hench†; Lowry Hench†; Hench Family Living Trust A; Hench Family Living Trust B.
Foundation type: Independent foundation.
Financial data (yr. ended 11/30/13): Assets, $21,963,527 (M); expenditures, $688,359; qualifying distributions, $501,648; giving activities include $430,000 for 10 grants (high: $100,000; low: $5,000).
Fields of interest: Arts education; Arts; Higher education; Medical research, institute.
Limitations: Applications not accepted. Giving primarily in CA. No grants to individuals.
Application information: Contributes only to pre-selected organizations.
Board meeting date(s): As required - once a month
Trustees: Jose M. Deetjen; Leonor Deetjen; Sandra L. Huskins.
EIN: 954308746

680
Henley Foundation ✧ ☆
1801-D, Parkcourt Pl., Rm. 102
Santa Ana, CA 92701-5009 (714) 550-0023
Contact: Doy B. Henley, Dir.

Established in 1997 in CA.
Donors: Doy B. Henley; Dolores Henley.
Foundation type: Independent foundation.
Financial data (yr. ended 12/31/12): Assets, $352,904 (M); gifts received, $300,000; expenditures, $669,081; qualifying distributions, $668,850; giving activities include $668,850 for grants.
Fields of interest: Higher education; Libraries/library science; Salvation Army; Protestant agencies & churches.
Type of support: General/operating support.
Limitations: Applications accepted. Giving primarily in CA. No grants to individuals.
Application information: Application form required.
Initial approach: Letter
Deadline(s): None
Director: Doy B. Henley.
EIN: 330783569

681
The Jeanette Bertea Hennings Foundation ✧ ☆
831 Via Lido Soud
Newport Beach, CA 92663-5532
Contact: Ed W. Hennings

Established in 1997 in CA.
Donor: Ed W. Hennings.
Foundation type: Independent foundation.
Financial data (yr. ended 12/31/13): Assets, $13,913,519 (M); gifts received, $8,120,800; expenditures, $470,500; qualifying distributions, $452,000; giving activities include $452,000 for 5 grants (high: $425,000; low: $1,000).
Fields of interest: Education; Animals/wildlife; Community/economic development; Foundations (community).
Limitations: Applications not accepted. Giving primarily in CA. No grants to individuals.
Application information: Unsolicited requests for funds not accepted.
Officers: Ed W. Hennings, C.E.O. and Pres.; Jeffrey J. Pagano, V.P.; Richard Bertea, Secy. and C.F.O.
Director: Baret Bertea Walker.
EIN: 330774466
Selected grants: The following grants are a representative sample of this grantmaker's funding activity:
$10,000 to Seattle Academy of Arts and Sciences, Seattle, WA, 2011.
$5,000 to Escuela de Guadalupe, Denver, CO, 2011.
$5,000 to Hoag Hospital Foundation, Newport Beach, CA, 2011.
$2,500 to Oregon Coast Aquarium, Newport, OR, 2011.

682
The Herbst Foundation, Inc. ✧
30 Van Ness Ave., Ste. 3600
San Francisco, CA 94102-6065

Incorporated in 1961 in CA.
Donors: Herman H. Herbst†; Maurice H. Herbst†.
Foundation type: Independent foundation.
Financial data (yr. ended 07/31/13): Assets, $70,066,530 (M); expenditures, $3,689,956; qualifying distributions, $3,227,647; giving activities include $3,072,222 for 159 grants (high: $678,572; low: $500), and $70,000 for 14 grants to individuals (high: $5,000; low: $5,000).
Purpose and activities: Grants within the city and county of San Francisco for bricks and mortar projects including educational facilities, civic improvement of existing city structures owned by public tax-exempt entities, hospitals, healthcare organizations, and a very small budget per year for broad purposes.
Fields of interest: Elementary school/education; Secondary school/education; Health care; Human services; Community development, neighborhood development.
Type of support: Grants to individuals; General/operating support; Building/renovation.
Limitations: Applications not accepted. Giving limited to the city and county of San Francisco, CA. No grants to individuals (except for Teaching Excellence Awards), or for endowment funds, scholarships, fellowships, research, or matching gifts; no loans.
Application information: Unsolicited requests for funds not accepted.
Board meeting date(s): Usually in Sept., Nov., Feb., and May
Officers and Directors:* Melvyn I. Mark, Pres.; Anthony Cameron,* V.P.; Bruce W. Hart,* V.P.; Jerrol L. Harris,* Secy.; Robert K. Taylor,* Treas.
Number of staff: 1 full-time professional.
EIN: 946061680

683
Hertz Family Foundation, Inc ✧
1880 Century Park E., Ste. 200
Los Angeles, CA 90067-1600

Established in CA.
Donors: Isaac Hertz; Judah Hertz; Sarah Hertz; William Hertz.
Foundation type: Independent foundation.
Financial data (yr. ended 12/31/12): Assets, $73,039 (M); gifts received, $818,500; expenditures, $758,210; qualifying distributions, $712,286; giving activities include $712,286 for grants.
Fields of interest: Education; Medical research; Jewish agencies & synagogues.
Limitations: Applications not accepted. Giving primarily in CA and NY. No grants to individuals.
Application information: Unsolicited requests for funds not accepted.
Officers: Judah Hertz, Pres.; Isaac Hertz, C.F.O.; Sarah Hertz, V.P.; William Hertz, Secy.
EIN: 272536580

684
Herwaldt Foundation ✧ ☆
2615 W. Lake Van Ness Cir.
Fresno, CA 93711-7024

Established in CA.
Donors: Louis Herwaldt; Jo Ann Herwaldt.
Foundation type: Operating foundation.
Financial data (yr. ended 06/30/13): Assets, $523,237 (M); gifts received, $96,808; expenditures, $520,141; qualifying distributions, $508,800; giving activities include $508,800 for 25 grants (high: $311,000; low: $200).
Fields of interest: Higher education; Education; Human services; Youth, services; Christian agencies & churches.
Limitations: Applications not accepted. Giving primarily in CA. No grants to individuals.
Application information: Contributes only to pre-selected organizations.
Officers: Louis Herwaldt, Pres.; Jo Ann Herwaldt, Secy.
EIN: 200507895
Selected grants: The following grants are a representative sample of this grantmaker's funding activity:
$92,000 to Masters College, Santa Clarita, CA, 2011.
$30,000 to Slavic Gospel Association, Loves Park, IL, 2011.
$10,000 to Baptist World Mission, Decatur, AL, 2011.
$6,000 to Youth for Christ, Fresno, CA, 2011.
$4,500 to Hinds Hospice, Fresno, CA, 2011.
$4,000 to Fresno Street Saints, Fresno, CA, 2011.
$2,500 to Break the Barriers, Fresno, CA, 2011.

685
George E. Hewitt Foundation for Medical Research ✧
1048 Irvine Ave., Ste. 742
Newport Beach, CA 92660-4602
Contact: Lois A. Horness, V.P. and Secy.-Treas.

Established in 1982 in CA.
Donors: George E. Hewitt; Hewitt Family Trust; George E. Hewitt Trust; George E. Hewitt Trust No.

1; George E. Hewitt Trust No. 2; George E. Hewitt Trust No. 4; George E. Hewitt Trust No. 5; George E. Hewitt Trust No. 6; Teller Property Inc.; La Mesa Property Inc.
Foundation type: Operating foundation.
Financial data (yr. ended 12/31/13): Assets, $33,993,069 (M); gifts received, $221; expenditures, $1,242,435; qualifying distributions, $1,038,951; giving activities include $739,444 for 23 grants to individuals (high: $51,000; low: $6,000).
Purpose and activities: Funding limited to fellowships for postdoctoral and M.D./Ph.D. programs.
Fields of interest: Medical research, institute.
Type of support: Fellowships.
Limitations: Applications accepted. Giving primarily CA, with emphasis on Irvine, La Jolla, and San Diego.
Application information: Application form required.
Initial approach: Resume
Deadline(s): None
Officers: Dennis D. Cunningham, Ph.D., Pres.; Lois A. Horness, V.P. and Secy.-Treas.
Directors: Kenneth E. Charlton; Walter Eckhart, Ph.D.; Joseph C. Garcia, Jr.; Lawrence D. Piro, M.D.; Robert J. Russo, M.D., Ph.D.; Bruce Tromberg, Ph.D.
EIN: 953711123

686
The William and Flora Hewlett Foundation
2121 Sand Hill Rd.
Menlo Park, CA 94025-6909 (650) 234-4500
Contact: Heath Wickline, Comm. Off.
FAX: (650) 234-4501; E-mail for Heath Wickline: hwickline@hewlett.org; Main URL: http://www.hewlett.org
E-Newsletter: http://www.hewlett.org/newsroom/subscribe
Facebook: http://www.facebook.com/pages/William-and-Flora-Hewlett-Foundation/132972610943?ref=mf
Financials: http://www.hewlett.org/about-us/financials
Grantee Perception Report: http://www.hewlett.org/what-were-learning/grantee-perception-reports
Grants Database: http://www.hewlett.org/grants/search?order=field_date_of_award_value&sort=desc
Library Database: http://www.hewlett.org/library/search
Library Feed: http://www.hewlett.org/rss/library
News Feed: http://www.hewlett.org/rss/newsroom
RSS Grants Feed: http://grantsfeed.hewlett.org/
Twitter: http://www.twitter.com/hewlett_found
Work in Progress: http://www.hewlett.org/blog
YouTube: http://www.youtube.com/hewlettfoundation

Incorporated in 1966 in CA.
Donors: Flora Lamson Hewlett†; William R. Hewlett†.
Foundation type: Independent foundation.
Financial data (yr. ended 12/31/13): Assets, $8,607,073,000 (M); expenditures, $298,400,000; qualifying distributions, $271,100,000; giving activities include $238,700,000 for 634 grants, $1,400,000 for employee matching gifts, and $5,200,000 for foundation-administered programs.
Purpose and activities: The foundation makes grants to help people build measurably better lives. It concentrates its resources on activities in education, the environment, global development, performing arts, philanthropy, and population, and makes grants to support disadvantaged communities in the San Francisco Bay Area. A full list of all the Hewlett Foundation's grants can be found on its website.
Fields of interest: Performing arts; Performing arts, dance; Performing arts, theater; Performing arts, music; Arts; Elementary/secondary education; Higher education; Higher education, college (community/junior); Environment, natural resources; Environment; Reproductive health, family planning; International economic development; Urban/community development; Community/economic development; Philanthropy/voluntarism; Population studies; International studies; Public policy, research; Minorities.
International interests: China; India; Latin America; Southern Asia; Sub-Saharan Africa.
Type of support: General/operating support; Continuing support; Program development; Employee matching gifts; Matching/challenge support.
Limitations: Applications accepted. Giving limited to the San Francisco Bay Area and Central Valley, CA, for family and community development programs; performing arts primarily limited to the Bay Area. No funds for individuals and generally the foundation does not fund scholarships, endowments, capital campaigns, building construction, for-profit organizations, or unincorporated associations or groups. In addition, the foundation's funds can be used only for purposes that are consistent with its status as a charitable organization.
Publications: Application guidelines; Annual report; Grants list; Informational brochure; Newsletter; Program policy statement.
Application information: The Hewlett Foundation prefers to receive letters of inquiry via its online submission form on its web site. The foundation is not currently accepting letters of inquiry for the following programs: Global Development and Population, Philanthropy, and Special Projects. The foundation accepts unsolicited letters of inquiry for various areas of work within its Environment and Performing Arts programs. For detailed application information, visit the foundation's web site page For Grantseekers. Application form not required.
Initial approach: Online letter of inquiry preferred
Copies of proposal: 1
Deadline(s): None
Board meeting date(s): Mar., July, and Nov.
Final notification: 2 to 3 months
Officers and Directors:* Harvey V. Fineberg, M.D.*, Chair.; Larry Kramer, Pres.; Ana Weichers-Marshall, V.P. and C.I.O.; Elizabeth Peters, Corp. Secy. and Genl. Counsel; Susan Ketcham, C.F.O. and Treas.; Mariano-Florentino Cuellar; Alecia A. DeCoudreaux; Eric Gimon; Walter B. Hewlett; Patricia House; Koh Boon Hwee; Mary H. Jaffe; Richard C. Levin; Stephen C. Neal; Rakesh Ranjani; Jean Gleason Stromberg.
Number of staff: 69 full-time professional; 7 part-time professional; 23 full-time support; 2 part-time support.
EIN: 941655673

687
Hewlett-Packard Company Foundation ✧
3000 Hanover St.
Palo Alto, CA 94304-1112 (650) 857-4954
E-mail: philanthropy_ed@hp.com; Main URL: http://www8.hp.com/us/en/hp-information/social-innovation/hp-foundation.html
RSS Feed: http://www8.hp.com/us/en/hp-news/newsroom-rss.jsp
Twitter: https://twitter.com/hpglobalcitizen

Established in 1979 in CA.
Donors: Hewlett-Packard Co.; EDS Foundation.
Foundation type: Company-sponsored foundation.
Financial data (yr. ended 10/13/12): Assets, $100,788,169 (M); gifts received, $40,734,000; expenditures, $4,918,537; qualifying distributions, $4,802,550; giving activities include $1,147,750 for 6 grants (high: $681,291; low: $25,000), and $3,654,800 for employee matching gifts.
Purpose and activities: The foundation supports projects designed to improve education; match employee giving; and provide humanitarian relief to communities hit by disaster.
Fields of interest: Education; Health care; Disasters, preparedness/services; Disasters, floods; Disasters, search/rescue; American Red Cross; Human services; United Ways and Federated Giving Programs; Mathematics; Engineering/technology; Science.
Type of support: General/operating support; Building/renovation; Equipment; Employee matching gifts.
Limitations: Applications not accepted. Giving on a national basis in areas of company operations, with emphasis on Washington, DC; giving also to national organizations. No support for sectarian or denominational groups or discriminatory or political organizations. No grants to individuals or for research.
Application information: Contributes only to pre-selected organizations.
Officers and Directors:* Marcela Perez de Alonso,* Chair.; Martin J. Holston,* Secy.; Catherine A. Lesjak,* C.F.O.; Ashley B. Watson, Exec. Dir.
EIN: 942618409

688
The Hexberg Family Foundation ✧
921 Emerald Bay
Laguna Beach, CA 92651-1260

Established in 2001 in CA.
Donors: Eric Hexberg†; Jane Hexberg†; The Hexberg Charitable Trust.
Foundation type: Independent foundation.
Financial data (yr. ended 12/31/13): Assets, $15,641,794 (M); gifts received, $1,347,935; expenditures, $615,543; qualifying distributions, $540,800; giving activities include $528,800 for 73 grants (high: $75,000; low: $2,000).
Fields of interest: Higher education; Health care; Human services; International relief.
Limitations: Applications not accepted. Giving primarily in CA and IL. No grants to individuals.
Application information: Contributes only to pre-selected organizations.
Trustees: Deborah L. Hexberg; Gregory Hexberg; Jill Hexberg.
EIN: 912172555
Selected grants: The following grants are a representative sample of this grantmaker's funding activity:

$25,000 to Direct Relief International, Santa Barbara, CA, 2012. To provide Medical Assistance and Supplies.
$15,500 to Freedom Alliance, Dulles, VA, 2012. To provide Educational Scholarship to Children.
$12,500 to American Red Cross, Santa Ana, CA, 2012. For General Operating Support of Charitable Organization.
$5,000 to Casa Youth Shelter, Los Alamitos, CA, 2012. To provide Food, Shelter and Crisis Counseling to Youth.
$5,000 to Heal the Bay, Santa Monica, CA, 2012. To protect Our Coastal Waters and Marine Life.
$5,000 to Laguna Beach Animal Shelter, Laguna Beach, CA, 2012. To assist in the Renovation of the Facility.
$5,000 to Orange County Rescue Mission, Tustin, CA, 2012. For the General Operating Support of Charity.
$5,000 to Pacific Marine Mammal Center, Laguna Beach, CA, 2012. To assist in Rescuing and Rehabilitating Marine Mammals.
$5,000 to Surfrider Foundation, San Clemente, CA, 2012. For Programs to Protect Local Beaches, Keep Water Clean.
$3,500 to UNICEF, New York, NY, 2012. To provide Health Care-Emergency Relief for Children.

689
Hidden Leaf Foundation ✧
P.O. Box 1755
Bodega Bay, CA 94923
Main URL: http://hiddenleaf.org/

Donor: David A. Brown.
Foundation type: Independent foundation.
Financial data (yr. ended 12/31/12): Assets, $514,520 (M); gifts received, $600,000; expenditures, $812,243; qualifying distributions, $774,730; giving activities include $665,000 for 23 grants (high: $95,000; low: $10,000).
Purpose and activities: Giving primarily for social justice.
Fields of interest: Civil/human rights.
Limitations: Applications not accepted. Giving primarily in CA.
Application information: Contributes only to pre-selected organizations.
Officers: David A. Brown, Pres.; Tara Brown, V.P.; Karen Brown, Secy.-Treas.
Board Member: Kristen Stinnett-Brown.
EIN: 352338463
Selected grants: The following grants are a representative sample of this grantmaker's funding activity:
$100,000 to Seasons Fund, Santa Fe, NM, 2010. For project support.
$35,000 to Forest Ethics, San Francisco, CA, 2011. For project support.
$35,000 to Movement Strategy Center, Oakland, CA, 2011. For project support.
$30,000 to Bend the Arc: A Jewish Partnership for Justice, New York, NY, 2011. For project support.
$30,000 to Center for Community Change, Washington, DC, 2011. For project support.
$30,000 to Center for Community Change, Washington, DC, 2010. For project support.
$30,000 to Forest Ethics, San Francisco, CA, 2010. For project support.
$30,000 to Movement Strategy Center, Oakland, CA, 2010. For project support.
$30,000 to Social Justice Leadership, New York, NY, 2010. For project support.
$25,000 to Forward Together, Oakland, CA, 2011. For project support.
$25,000 to Forward Together, Oakland, CA, 2010. For project support.
$25,000 to Jobs with Justice Education Fund, Washington, DC, 2010. For project support.
$25,000 to Miami Workers Center, Miami, FL, 2011. For project support.
$25,000 to Miami Workers Center, Miami, FL, 2010. For project support.
$20,000 to Earth Island Institute, Berkeley, CA, 2010. For project support.
$20,000 to Jobs with Justice Education Fund, Washington, DC, 2011. For project support.
$20,000 to Rainforest Action Network, San Francisco, CA, 2010. For project support.
$15,000 to Tides Center, San Francisco, CA, 2011. For project support.
$10,000 to Center for Whole Communities, Fayston, VT, 2011. For project support.
$10,000 to Los Angeles Alliance for a New Economy, Los Angeles, CA, 2011. For project support.

690
The Larry L. Hillblom Foundation, Inc. ✧
755 Baywood Dr., Ste. 180
Petaluma, CA 94954-5509
FAX: (707) 762-6694; E-mail: petaluma@llhf.org; Additional address: 1458 Draper St., Kingsburg, CA 93631, tel.: (559) 897-7050, fax: (559) 897-7590, e-mail: kingsburg@llhf.org; Main URL: http://www.llhf.org
Grants List: http://www.llhf.org/funded-research
RSS Feed: http://www.llhf.org/news-events/all-news-events/RSS

Established in 1996 in CA.
Donor: Larry L. Hillblom†.
Foundation type: Independent foundation.
Financial data (yr. ended 12/31/13): Assets, $138,208,394 (M); expenditures, $4,547,066; qualifying distributions, $2,881,059; giving activities include $2,117,650 for 59 grants (high: $1,075,000; low: $2,000).
Purpose and activities: Giving for research in Diabetes Mellitus and its complications including studies of normal glucose metabolism; and age-related chronic or degenerative disorders of the brain or vision including such studies of the healthy aging processes. Studies should target the prevention, diagnosis, treatment and/or cure of diseases described above. Proposals should employ genetic, molecular, cellular and/or metabolic approaches to one of two categories which are the areas of concern to the foundation.
Fields of interest: Diabetes; Geriatrics; Medical research, institute; Eye research; Brain research.
Type of support: Fellowships; Research.
Limitations: Applications accepted. Giving primarily in CA. No support for cancer, cardiovascular or joint/bone degenerative disease research. No grants to individuals.
Publications: Grants list; Informational brochure; Occasional report; Program policy statement.
Application information: Grant applications need to be formatted as a single Adobe PDF file. See foundation web site for forms and instructions. Hard copies not accepted.
Initial approach: All applications must be submitted via electronic file using the foundation's online grant management system
Deadline(s): See foundation web site for current deadlines
Board meeting date(s): Feb., May, Aug., and Nov.
Officers and Directors:* Peter J. Donnici,* Chair., C.E.O., and Pres.; Terry C. Hillblom,* Vice-Chair., C.O.O., and Exec. V.P.; Grant A. Anderson,* V.P.; Walter Hillblom,* V.P.; Stephen J. Schwartz,* V.P.; David R. Jones, Secy. and C.F.O.; Paul Kimoto; Ida O'Brien; Janice E. Quistad; E. Lewis Reid; William A. Robinson; Joseph W. Waechter.
Number of staff: 6 full-time professional; 3 full-time support.
EIN: 943241600
Selected grants: The following grants are a representative sample of this grantmaker's funding activity:
$1,151,347 to University of California, San Francisco, CA, 2012. For general support.
$836,420 to University of California, Los Angeles, CA, 2012. For general support.
$508,117 to University of California at San Diego, La Jolla, CA, 2012. For general support.
$497,038 to Historical Society of Kingsburg, Kingsburg, CA, 2012. For general support.
$367,566 to University of California, Santa Barbara, CA, 2012. For general support.
$56,899 to Kingsburg Joint Union High School District, Kingsburg, CA, 2012. For general support.
$43,854 to Valley Performing Arts Council, Kingsburg, CA, 2012. For general support.
$40,000 to Oakland School for the Arts, Oakland, CA, 2012. For general support.
$35,575 to E and E Performing Arts Center, Kingsburg, CA, 2012. For general support.
$10,000 to Kings River Union Elementary School, Kingsburg, CA, 2012. For general support.

691
The Edward E. Hills Fund ✧
119 Sheridan Way
Woodside, CA 94062-2345

Incorporated in 1953 in CA.
Donor: Edward E. Hills†.
Foundation type: Operating foundation.
Financial data (yr. ended 12/31/13): Assets, $9,401,808 (M); expenditures, $709,927; qualifying distributions, $504,357; giving activities include $471,457 for 27 grants (high: $150,000; low: $500).
Purpose and activities: Giving primarily for education, the arts, and human services.
Fields of interest: Arts; Education; Environment, natural resources; Hospitals (general); Human services.
Limitations: Applications not accepted. Giving primarily in CA. No grants to individuals.
Application information: Contributes only to pre-selected organizations.
Officers and Directors:* Ingrid von Mangoldt Hills,* Pres.; Joseph M. Breall, Secy.; William S. Breall, M.D.*, Treas.; Ken Monnens.
EIN: 946062537
Selected grants: The following grants are a representative sample of this grantmaker's funding activity:
$100,000 to University of California Medical Center, Sacramento, CA, 2011.

692
Conrad N. Hilton Foundation ✧
30440 Agoura Rd.
Agoura Hills, CA 91301-2145 (818) 851-3700
Contact: Rose M. Arnold, Grants Mgr.
FAX: (818) 851-3791;
E-mail: communications@hiltonfoundation.org;
Main URL: http://www.hiltonfoundation.org
Barron Hilton's Giving Pledge Profile: http://glasspockets.org/philanthropy-in-focus/eye-on-the-giving-pledge/profiles/hilton
Blog: http://www.hiltonfoundation.org/horizons
Conrad N. Hilton Foundation's Philanthropy Promise: http://www.ncrp.org/philanthropys-promise/who
Conrad N. Hilton Humanitarian Prize: http://www.hiltonfoundation.org/prize
Facebook: https://www.facebook.com/hiltonfoundation
Flickr: http://www.flickr.com/photos/hiltonfoundation
GiveSmart: http://www.givesmart.org/Stories/Donors/Steve-Hilton
Knowledge Center: http://www.hiltonfoundation.org/impact-learning
RSS Feed: http://hiltonfoundation.org/rss-feed
Twitter: https://twitter.com/@hiltonfound
Vimeo: http://vimeo.com/hiltonfoundation

Established in 1944 in NV.
Donors: Conrad N. Hilton‡; Barron Hilton.
Foundation type: Independent foundation.
Financial data (yr. ended 12/31/13): Assets, $2,430,703,442 (M); expenditures, $110,155,767; qualifying distributions, $92,000,000; giving activities include $92,000,000 for grants.
Purpose and activities: The Conrad N. Hilton Foundation supports efforts to improve the lives of disadvantaged and vulnerable people throughout the world by focusing on six strategic initiatives and five major program areas. Potential applicants should see Current Programs for more information.
Fields of interest: Education; Environment, water resources; Public health, clean water supply; Public health, hygiene; Public health, sanitation; Mental health/crisis services; Health organizations, association; Multiple sclerosis research; Medical research; Housing/shelter; Safety/disasters; Youth development; Homeless, human services; Human services; Public utilities, water; Public utilities, sewage; Religion; Infants/toddlers; Children/youth; Children; Youth; Young adults; Disabilities, people with; Blind/visually impaired; Substance abusers; AIDS, people with; Economically disadvantaged; Homeless.
International interests: Africa; Asia; Global Programs.
Type of support: General/operating support; Continuing support; Management development/capacity building; Capital campaigns; Building/renovation; Equipment; Endowments; Emergency funds; Program development; Publication; Curriculum development; Fellowships; Scholarship funds; Research; Technical assistance; Program evaluation; Program-related investments/loans; Employee matching gifts; Matching/challenge support.
Limitations: Applications accepted. Giving on a balanced national and international basis. No support for political organizations. No grants to individuals, or for fundraising events.
Publications: Annual report; Financial statement; Grants list; Newsletter; Occasional report.
Application information: The foundation accepts requests for proposals only for the Marilyn Hilton Award for Innovation in MS Research. Full proposals are by invitation only. The foundation accepts applications primarily from its specified beneficiaries; unsolicited proposals generally not considered. If application is invited, information will be requested. Application form required.
Initial approach: Electronic submission for RFP
Board meeting date(s): Quarterly
Officers and Directors:* Steven M. Hilton,* Chair., C.E.O. and Pres.; Randy Kim, V.P. and C.I.O.; Edmund J. Cain, V.P., Grant Progs.; Judy M. Miller, V.P. and Dir., Humanitarian Prize; Patrick J. Modugno, V.P., Admin. and C.F.O.; Monica Emerson, Cont.; Donald H. Hubbs, Dir. Emeritus; William H. Foege, M.D., M.P.H.; James R. Galbraith; Conrad N. Hilton III; Eric M. Hilton; William B. Hilton, Jr.; Hawley Hilton McAuliffe; Joyce Meyer; John L. Notter; William G. Ouchi.
Number of staff: 39 full-time professional; 1 part-time professional; 6 full-time support; 1 part-time support.
EIN: 943100217
Selected grants: The following grants are a representative sample of this grantmaker's funding activity:
$7,775,000 to United Way of Greater Los Angeles, Los Angeles, CA, 2012. Toward a $30 million budget to support the continued implementation of Home for Good Action Plan ($2.275 million for Home For Good implementation and $5.5 million for leveraged grants through the Home For Good Funders Collaborative), payable over 3.00 years.
$5,000,000 to Conrad N. Hilton Fund for Sisters, Los Angeles, CA, 2012. To augment the grant budget of the Fund for Sisters over the next two years, payable over 2.00 years.
$4,600,000 to Catholic Relief Services, Baltimore, MD, 2012. To design and implement a holistic approach to meeting the unique developmental needs of children affected by HIV/AIDS under the age of five in Kenya, Malawi, and Tanzania, payable over 3.00 years.
$1,400,000 to Human Sciences Research Council, Cape Town, South Africa, 2012. To design, conduct, and implement overall monitoring, evaluation, and learning strategy for the Foundation's Children Affected by HIV/AIDS Initiative, payable over 3.00 years.
$300,000 to Housing California, Sacramento, CA, 2012. For community outreach and policy work to build support for affordable housing in California, payable over 2.00 years.
$10,000 to San Diego State University, San Diego, CA, 2012. For general operating support.

693
Hind Foundation ✧
P.O. Box 13259
San Luis Obispo, CA 93406-3259 (805) 544-0914
E-mail: greghind@hindfoundation.org; Main URL: http://www.hindfoundation.org
Grants Database: http://www.hindfoundation.org/Grantees

Established in 2006.
Foundation type: Independent foundation.
Financial data (yr. ended 06/30/13): Assets, $26,751,755 (M); gifts received, $1,000; expenditures, $1,604,291; qualifying distributions, $1,435,106; giving activities include $1,425,888 for 29 grants (high: $150,000; low: $2,500).
Purpose and activities: The foundation's purpose is the preservation of cultural heritage with emphasis in music and visual arts, plant and wildlife preservation, and historical restoration projects. It seeks community based projects that inspire the collective passion of its members to work together and build an enduring legacy for future generations.
Fields of interest: Visual arts; Performing arts, music; Historic preservation/historical societies; Environment, plant conservation; Animals/wildlife, preservation/protection.
Type of support: Land acquisition; Equipment; Capital campaigns; Building/renovation.
Limitations: Applications accepted. Giving primarily in CA, with emphasis on San Luis Obispo County. No support for national or international organizations, educational programs, or community foundations. No grants to individuals, or for endowments, basic research, fellowships, capital campaigns, debt reduction, administrative costs, sustaining funds, multi-year grants, or books, videos, television, or film projects that are not components of a broader strategy.
Publications: Application guidelines.
Application information: Formal applications are by invitation only, upon review of initial letter of inquiry. Application form not required.
Initial approach: Letter of inquiry after creating an account on foundation web site
Deadline(s): None
Directors: Greg Hind; Jane Hind; Kirsten Hind; Meegan Hind.
Number of staff: 2 part-time support.
EIN: 205150383
Selected grants: The following grants are a representative sample of this grantmaker's funding activity:
$173,000 to Santa Barbara Trust for Historic Preservation, Santa Barbara, CA, 2011.
$127,570 to Santa Barbara Botanic Garden, Santa Barbara, CA, 2011.
$100,000 to Music Academy of the West, Santa Barbara, CA, 2011.
$50,000 to Land Trust for Santa Barbara County, Santa Barbara, CA, 2011.
$40,000 to Central Coast Lighthouse Keepers, Carmel, CA, 2011.
$32,000 to Foundation for the Performing Arts Center, San Luis Obispo, CA, 2011.
$5,000 to Studios on the Park, Paso Robles, CA, 2011.
$5,000 to Sustainable Conservation, San Francisco, CA, 2011.
$2,500 to Monterey County Symphony Association, Monterey, CA, 2011.

694
Hitz Foundation ✧
(formerly The XYZZY Foundation)
c/o Frank, Rimerman + Co., LLP
1801 Page Mill Rd.
Palo Alto, CA 94304-1211

Established in 2000 in CA.
Donor: David Hitz.
Foundation type: Independent foundation.
Financial data (yr. ended 12/31/12): Assets, $35,357,958 (M); gifts received, $3,610,010; expenditures, $1,205,534; qualifying distributions, $868,564; giving activities include $860,500 for 6 grants (high: $250,000; low: $2,000).

Fields of interest: Media/communications; Arts; Higher education; Education; Environment, energy; Environment; Human services; International affairs; Civil liberties, advocacy.
Limitations: Applications not accepted. No grants to individuals.
Application information: Contributes only to pre-selected organizations.
Officers: David Hitz, Chair.; Ken Hitz, Pres.; Kevin P. McAuliffe, Secy.; Yen Hitz, Treas.
EIN: 943379521

695
C.K. & Kay Ho Foundation ✧ ☆
6831 Alta Vista Dr.
Rancho Palos Verdes, CA 90275

Established in 2006 in CA.
Donors: C.K. Ho; Kay Ho.
Foundation type: Independent foundation.
Financial data (yr. ended 12/31/13): Assets, $8,656,880 (M); expenditures, $514,260; qualifying distributions, $451,000; giving activities include $451,000 for 25 grants (high: $114,000; low: $2,000).
Fields of interest: Christian agencies & churches.
Limitations: Applications not accepted. No grants to individuals.
Application information: Unsolicited requests for funds not accepted.
Directors: C.K. Ho; Christopher K. Ho; Hing Kay Ho; Vanessa K. Ho.
EIN: 205291583
Selected grants: The following grants are a representative sample of this grantmaker's funding activity:
$11,000 to OC International, Colorado Springs, CO, 2011.
$3,000 to Educational Projects, Farmington, MI, 2011.
$2,000 to Navigators, The, Colorado Springs, CO, 2011.
$2,000 to Wycliffe Bible Translators, Orlando, FL, 2011.
$1,000 to Great Commission Center International, Sunnyvale, CA, 2011.

696
Hoag Family Foundation ✧
221 Park Ln.
Atherton, CA 94027-5410

Established in 2000 in CA and NV.
Donors: Jay C. Hoag; Michaela Hoag.
Foundation type: Independent foundation.
Financial data (yr. ended 12/31/13): Assets, $19,250,231 (M); gifts received, $1,100,236; expenditures, $702,763; qualifying distributions, $600,075; giving activities include $539,500 for 9 grants (high: $250,000; low: $5,000).
Fields of interest: Education; Alzheimer's disease; Human services; Foundations (private grantmaking).
Limitations: Applications not accepted. Giving primarily in CA. No grants to individuals.
Application information: Contributes only to pre-selected organizations.
Officers: Jay Hoag, Pres.; Michaela Hoag, Secy.-Treas.
EIN: 943383126

697
George Hoag Family Foundation ✧
(formerly Hoag Foundation)
2665 Main St., Ste. 220
Santa Monica, CA 90405-4054 (310) 664-1358
Contact: Charles W. Smith, Secy. and Exec. Dir.
FAX: (310) 664-1368;
E-mail: csmith@hoagfoundation.org; E-mail for Sarah Bicknell, Grants Coord.: sbicknell@hoagfoundation.org; Main URL: http://www.hoagfoundation.org/

Incorporated in 1940 in CA.
Donors: George Grant Hoag†; Grace E. Hoag†; George Grant Hoag II†.
Foundation type: Independent foundation.
Financial data (yr. ended 12/31/13): Assets, $68,826,007 (M); expenditures, $3,797,578; qualifying distributions, $3,337,081; giving activities include $3,027,000 for 110 grants (high: $500,000; low: $2,000).
Purpose and activities: Giving to improve social conditions, promote human welfare, and alleviate pain and suffering. Also, giving to improve and expand medical services, and opportunities for youth in CA.
Fields of interest: Arts; Hospitals (general); Medical research, institute; Youth development, services; Children/youth, services; Human services.
Type of support: General/operating support; Capital campaigns; Building/renovation; Equipment; Program development; Scholarship funds; Research.
Limitations: Applications accepted. Giving limited to CA, primarily to southern CA, with emphasis on Los Angeles, and Orange County, as well as parts of the Central Coast of CA. No support for government agencies, tax-supported projects, or sectarian or religious organizations for the benefit of their own members. No grants to individuals, or for deficit financing or normal operating expenses.
Publications: Application guidelines; Program policy statement; Program policy statement (including application guidelines).
Application information: An invitation to apply is required prior to submitting an application. Application form required.
Initial approach: Letter (not exceeding 2 pages)
Copies of proposal: 9
Deadline(s): Mar. 31 and Sept. 30
Board meeting date(s): May and Nov.
Final notification: Following meeting at which proposal is reviewed
Officers and Directors:* Melinda Hoag Smith,* C.E.O. and Pres.; George Grant Hoag III,* V.P. and C.F.O.; Charles W. Smith,* Secy. and Exec. Dir.; Michael B. Sedgwick, Treas.; John L. Curci, Jr.; John G. Ebey; Gwyn P. Parry; Michael D. Stephens.
Number of staff: 1 full-time professional; 1 part-time support.
EIN: 956006885

698
The Roxanna Todd Hodges Foundation ✧
3 La Canada
Irvine, CA 92602

Donor: Roxanna Hodges.
Foundation type: Independent foundation.
Financial data (yr. ended 12/31/13): Assets, $0 (M); gifts received, $866,875; expenditures, $924,413; qualifying distributions, $514,981; giving activities include $514,981 for 4 grants (high: $500,000; low: $1,750).
Fields of interest: Medical school/education; Health organizations.
Type of support: General/operating support.
Limitations: Applications not accepted. Giving primarily in Los Angeles, CA. No grants to individuals.
Application information: Unsolicited requests for funds not accepted.
Officers: Deborah Massaglia, Pres.; Guy Navarro, Exec. Dir.
EIN: 330809745

699
H. Leslie and Elaine S. Hoffman Foundation ✧
225 S. Lake Ave., Ste. 1150
Pasadena, CA 91101-3036
Contact: J. Kristoffer Popovich, Tr.

Established in 1952 in CA.
Donors: H. Leslie Hoffman†; Elaine S. Hoffman†.
Foundation type: Independent foundation.
Financial data (yr. ended 12/31/12): Assets, $30,446,464 (M); expenditures, $1,612,749; qualifying distributions, $1,150,874; giving activities include $770,442 for 45 grants (high: $200,000; low: $1,000).
Purpose and activities: Giving primarily for the arts, education, hospitals and health organizations, children and youth services, including a children's hospital, and social services.
Fields of interest: Museums (children's); Arts; Higher education; Education; Hospitals (general); Hospitals (specialty); Health organizations; Human services; Children/youth, services.
Type of support: General/operating support.
Limitations: Applications accepted. Giving primarily in the Los Angeles, CA, area, with emphasis on Pasadena. No grants to individuals.
Application information: Application form not required.
Initial approach: Proposal
Copies of proposal: 1
Deadline(s): None
Board meeting date(s): As required
Trustees: Jennifer Allen; Patricia Fink; Jane H. Popovich; J. Kristoffer Popovich; Kimberely Shepherd.
EIN: 956048600

700
The Hofmann Family Foundation ✧
(formerly The K.H. Hofmann Foundation)
P.O. Box 907
Concord, CA 94522-0907 (925) 687-1826
Contact: Dennis Costanza, Pres. and Fdn. Mgr.
Application address: 3000 Oak Rd., Ste. 360, Walnut Creek, CA 94595, tel.: (925) 687-1826

Established in 1963 in CA.
Donors: The Hofmann Co.; New Discovery, Inc.; Kenneth H. Hofmann; Martha J. Hofmann; The Hofmann 1987 Revocable Trust.
Foundation type: Company-sponsored foundation.
Financial data (yr. ended 12/31/12): Assets, $42,831,477 (M); expenditures, $4,481,686; qualifying distributions, $4,087,814; giving activities include $3,891,175 for 67 grants (high: $1,000,000; low: $100).

Purpose and activities: The foundation supports organizations involved with secondary and higher education, wildlife protection, health, recreation, human services, and Christianity.
Fields of interest: Secondary school/education; Higher education; Education; Animals/wildlife, preservation/protection; Hospitals (general); Palliative care; Health care; Athletics/sports, baseball; Recreation; Children/youth, services; Human services; Christian agencies & churches.
Type of support: General/operating support; Annual campaigns; Capital campaigns; Sponsorships; Employee matching gifts.
Limitations: Applications accepted. Giving primarily in CA; some giving for national organizations.
Application information: Application form required.
Initial approach: Letter
Copies of proposal: 1
Deadline(s): None
Board meeting date(s): Quarterly
Officers: Kenneth H. Hofmann, Chair.; Dennis Costanza, Pres. and Fdn.Mgr.; Lisa A. Hofmann-Morgan, V.P.; John E. Amaral, Secy.; Dennis M. Drew, Treas.
Direcotrs: Steve Gonsalves; Richard L. Greene; Martha Jean Hofmann; Vita Sechrest.
Number of staff: 4
EIN: 946108897

701
Hollywood Foreign Press Association Charitable Trust ✧ ☆
646 N. Robertson Blvd.
West Hollywood, CA 90069-5022 (310) 657-1731
Main URL: http://www.hfpa.org/grant-general/

Established in CA.
Donor: Hollywood Foreign Press Association.
Foundation type: Independent foundation.
Financial data (yr. ended 06/30/12): Assets, $4,337 (M); gifts received, $1,540,000; expenditures, $1,549,500; qualifying distributions, $1,549,500; giving activities include $1,549,500 for 47 grants (high: $350,000; low: $5,000).
Fields of interest: Arts; Education; Human services.
Limitations: Applications accepted. Giving primarily in CA.
Publications: Application guidelines.
Application information: See foundation web site for specific application instructions and form. Application form required.
Deadline(s): Mar. 30
Trustees: Philip Berk; Elmar Biebi; Jorge Camara; Helen Hoehne; Yoram Kahana; Theo Kingma; Yukiko Nakajima; Yoko Narita; Ruben V. Nepales; Serge Rakhlin; Ali Sar; Frances Schoenberger; Dierk Sindermann; Lorenzo Soria; Dr. Aida Takla-O'Reilly; Meher Tatna.
EIN: 953735188

702
The Bob & Dolores Hope Charitable Foundation ✧
2600 W. Olive Ave., 5th Fl.
Burbank, CA 91505 (818) 333-5067
Contact: Geri Simmons

Established in 1953 in CA.
Donors: Lester T. "Bob" Hope†; Dolores Hope†; Dolores Hope Trust.
Foundation type: Independent foundation.
Financial data (yr. ended 12/31/13): Assets, $30,266,110 (M); gifts received, $10,603,029; expenditures, $2,780,688; qualifying distributions, $2,610,525; giving activities include $2,039,556 for 32 grants (high: $525,000; low: $1,500).
Fields of interest: Museums (sports/hobby); Health organizations; Food services; Human services; Catholic agencies & churches.
Type of support: General/operating support; Building/renovation.
Limitations: Applications accepted. Giving primarily in CA, DC, FL, and NY. No grants to individuals, or for capital construction, fundraising, deficit financing, or for conferences, seminars, research, media events or workshops unless they are an integral part of a broader program; no loans.
Application information: Application form required.
Initial approach: Letter or Proposal
Deadline(s): Dec. 31
Officers: Linda Hope, Pres. and Treas.; Anthony Montalto, C.F.O.; Miranda Hope, V.P.; John McDonnell, Secy.; William Kelly Hope; Zachary Hope; Andrew Lande.
EIN: 956048629

703
The Hoppe Foundation ✧
905 Churrituck Dr.
San Diego, CA 92154-2312

Donors: W.J. Hoppe Charitable Remainder Annuity Trust; Dr. William Hoppe-Sunset Trust; Hoppe Sunset Living Trust.
Foundation type: Independent foundation.
Financial data (yr. ended 06/30/13): Assets, $10,798,882 (M); gifts received, $50,000; expenditures, $665,113; qualifying distributions, $566,000.
Fields of interest: Media, radio; Education; Youth, services; International affairs; Christian agencies & churches.
Limitations: Applications not accepted. No grants to individuals.
Application information: Contributes only to pre-selected organizations.
Officers: William James Hoppe, C.E.O.; Lea Ann Hoppe, Secy.
EIN: 912144087
Selected grants: The following grants are a representative sample of this grantmaker's funding activity:
$25,000 to Wycliffe Bible Translators, Orlando, FL, 2011.
$14,000 to World Aid, Seattle, WA, 2011.
$13,000 to International Students, Colorado Springs, CO, 2011.
$11,000 to Christian Counseling Center, Grand Rapids, MI, 2011.
$11,000 to DESTA, Littleton, CO, 2011.
$10,000 to Barnabas International, Rockford, IL, 2011.
$10,000 to Far East Broadcasting Company, La Mirada, CA, 2011.
$10,000 to Trans World Radio, Cary, NC, 2011.
$10,000 to World Radio Missionary Fellowship, Colorado Springs, CO, 2011.
$8,000 to International Teams, Elgin, IL, 2011.

704
Hopper-Dean Foundation ✧
c/o CTC myCFO, LLC
P.O. Box 10195, Dept. 656
Palo Alto, CA 94303-0995

Established in CA.
Donors: Jeff Dean; Heidi Hopper.
Foundation type: Independent foundation.
Financial data (yr. ended 12/31/13): Assets, $10,585,965 (M); gifts received, $1,745,932; expenditures, $788,577; qualifying distributions, $695,037; giving activities include $695,037 for 26 grants (high: $250,000; low: $500).
Fields of interest: Education; Animals/wildlife, preservation/protection; Children/youth, services.
Limitations: Applications not accepted. Giving primarily in CA; some giving also in GA, NY, and WA.
Application information: Contributes only to pre-selected organizations.
Officers: Heidi Hopper, C.E.O. and Secy.; Jeff Dean, C.F.O.
EIN: 273116560

705
The Horn Foundation ✧
c/o CP Mgmt.
5000 N. Pkwy. Calabasas, Ste. 204
Calabasas, CA 91302-3909

Established in 1989 in CA.
Donors: Alan F. Horn; Cynthia Horn.
Foundation type: Independent foundation.
Financial data (yr. ended 12/31/13): Assets, $18,349,293 (M); gifts received, $2,706,827; expenditures, $1,520,830; qualifying distributions, $1,450,818; giving activities include $1,414,600 for 57 grants (high: $110,000; low: $500).
Fields of interest: Higher education; Education; Environment.
Limitations: Applications not accepted. Giving primarily in CA and NY. No grants to individuals.
Application information: Contributes only to pre-selected organizations.
Officers: Alan F. Horn, Fdn. Mgr.; Cindy Horn, Fdn. Mgr.
EIN: 954247470

706
James and Ada Horwich Family Foundation ✧
630 N. Maple Dr.
Beverly Hills, CA 90210-3410

Established in 1986 in CA.
Donors: Atlas Carpet Mills, Inc.; James Horwich; Ada R. Horwich.
Foundation type: Independent foundation.
Financial data (yr. ended 11/30/13): Assets, $5,601,276 (M); gifts received, $975,567; expenditures, $439,985; qualifying distributions, $439,950; giving activities include $439,950 for 142 grants (high: $250,000; low: $35).
Purpose and activities: Giving primarily for education and Jewish organizations.
Fields of interest: Arts; Elementary/secondary education; Higher education; Human services; Jewish federated giving programs; Jewish agencies & synagogues.
Limitations: Applications not accepted. Giving primarily in CA. No grants to individuals.

Application information: Contributes only to pre-selected organizations.
Officers: James Horwich, Pres.; Ada Horwich, Secy.-Treas.
EIN: 954074377

707
House Family Foundation ✧
(formerly Dave House Family Foundation)
5205 Prospect Rd., Ste. 135-158
San Jose, CA 95129-5000

Established in 1999 in CA.
Donor: David House.
Foundation type: Independent foundation.
Financial data (yr. ended 06/30/13): Assets, $17,606,023 (M); expenditures, $897,476; qualifying distributions, $770,782; giving activities include $671,600 for 23 grants (high: $100,000; low: $500).
Purpose and activities: Giving primarily for higher and other education, children, youth, and social services, and to a museum specializing in computer history.
Fields of interest: Museums; Museums (specialized); Education; Boys & girls clubs; Human services; Children/youth, services.
Limitations: Applications not accepted. Giving primarily in CA; some funding also in MI. No grants to individuals.
Application information: Contributes only to pre-selected organizations.
Officers: David House, C.E.O. and Pres.; Robert Olsen, V.P.; Shelley Cargill, Secy.; Robert House, Treas.; Joyce House, Exec. Dir.
EIN: 522207366
Selected grants: The following grants are a representative sample of this grantmaker's funding activity:
$25,000 to Boys and Girls Clubs of Monterey County, Seaside, CA, 2011. For general support.

708
Melvin and Geraldine Hoven Foundation ✧
96 W. Campbell Ave.
Campbell, CA 95008-1029

Established in CA.
Foundation type: Independent foundation.
Financial data (yr. ended 12/31/13): Assets, $11,092,371 (M); expenditures, $526,528; qualifying distributions, $526,528; giving activities include $486,000 for 16 grants (high: $55,000; low: $10,000).
Fields of interest: Education; Food banks; Human services; Religion.
Limitations: Applications not accepted.
Application information: Unsolicited requests for funds not accepted.
Officers: Barry Elkins, Pres. and C.E.O.; Robert Nigra, Secy.-Treas.
EIN: 272999037

709
HRH Foundation ✧
196 Albion Ave.
Woodside, CA 94062-3657

Established in 2000 in CA.
Donors: Harry R. Hagey; Shirley Hagey.
Foundation type: Independent foundation.
Financial data (yr. ended 12/31/13): Assets, $36,046,592 (M); expenditures, $1,494,860; qualifying distributions, $1,472,000; giving activities include $1,472,000 for 33 grants (high: $545,000; low: $5,000).
Fields of interest: Education; Environment, natural resources; Human services.
Limitations: Applications not accepted. Giving primarily in CA and Hailey, ID. No grants to individuals.
Application information: Contributes only to pre-selected organizations.
Officers and Directors:* Harry R. Hagey,* Pres.; Shirley Hagey,* C.F.O. and Secy.; Casey Crittenden; Paul Crittenden; Hank Hagey; Susannah Johnson; Sandy Manley.
EIN: 943381908
Selected grants: The following grants are a representative sample of this grantmaker's funding activity:
$10,000 to Wood River Land Trust, Hailey, ID, 2012. For general operating purposes.

710
The Hsieh Family Foundation ✧
P.O. Box 3326
South Pasadena, CA 91031-6326

Established in 2005 in CA.
Donors: Ming Hsieh; Fang Zhi Liu Hsieh.
Foundation type: Independent foundation.
Financial data (yr. ended 12/31/12): Assets, $25,662,811 (M); expenditures, $8,380,319; qualifying distributions, $8,197,983; giving activities include $8,180,000 for 8 grants (high: $5,500,000; low: $10,000).
Fields of interest: Museums (art); Higher education; Education; Human services.
Limitations: Applications not accepted. Giving primarily in CA and NY. No grants to individuals.
Application information: Contributes only to pre-selected organizations.
Officers and Directors:* Ming Hsieh,* Chair.; Fang Zhi Liu Hsieh,* Secy. and C.F.O.
EIN: 202790125

711
Alice Wan-Tsen Hsu Foundation ✧
23500 Cristo Rey Dr., No. 203E
Cupertino, CA 95014-6503

Established in CA.
Donors: Laurence Fong; Alice Wan-Tsen Hsu; Steve G.K. Hsu; H.C. Tang; Joseph Tung; Sherif Tung.
Foundation type: Independent foundation.
Financial data (yr. ended 04/30/13): Assets, $3,197,051 (M); gifts received, $4,335,000; expenditures, $1,515,478; qualifying distributions, $1,471,251; giving activities include $1,470,000 for 5 grants (high: $1,300,000; low: $10,000).
Fields of interest: Health organizations; Human services; Religion.
Limitations: Applications not accepted. Giving primarily in CA.
Application information: Contributes only to pre-selected organizations.
Officers: Alice Wan-Tsen Hsu, Pres.; Laurence Fong, Secy. and C.F.O.
Directors: M.S. Chiu; Hsieh-ho Chu; Tony Fu; William Fung.
EIN: 800624504

712
The Jen-Hsun & Lori Huang Foundation ✧
c/o Frank, Rimerman & Co., LLP
1801 Page Mill Rd.
Palo Alto, CA 94304-1216

Established in 2007 in CA.
Donors: Jen-Hsun Huang; Lori L. Huang.
Foundation type: Independent foundation.
Financial data (yr. ended 12/31/13): Assets, $17,782,490 (M); gifts received, $503,896; expenditures, $740,085; qualifying distributions, $740,000; giving activities include $735,000 for 1 grant.
Fields of interest: Higher education, university.
Limitations: Applications not accepted. Giving primarily in Stanford, CA. No grants to individuals.
Application information: Contributes only to pre-selected organizations.
Officers: Lori L. Huang, Pres.; Jen-Hsun Huang, C.F.O. and Secy.
EIN: 261551239
Selected grants: The following grants are a representative sample of this grantmaker's funding activity:
$734,665 to Oregon Health and Science University, Portland, OR, 2011.

713
Mark Hughes Foundation ✧
P.O. Box 9399
Marina Del Rey, CA 90295 (310) 670-7411
Contact: Ann L. Van Dormolen
E-mail: ann@paiservices.com

Established in 1994 in CA.
Foundation type: Independent foundation.
Financial data (yr. ended 12/31/13): Assets, $14,148,620 (M); expenditures, $848,090; qualifying distributions, $783,706; giving activities include $770,000 for 21 grants (high: $80,000; low: $10,000).
Purpose and activities: The foundation contributes to organizations or programs that improve nutrition, support disadvantaged children and families, provide early interventions, and prevent physical and emotional abuse.
Fields of interest: Education; Mental health, treatment; Mental health/crisis services; Nutrition; Youth development; Human services; Children/youth, services; Family services; Economically disadvantaged.
Type of support: General/operating support; Equipment; Emergency funds; Program development; Curriculum development.
Limitations: Applications accepted. Giving primarily in CA, with emphasis on Los Angeles.
Publications: Informational brochure (including application guidelines).
Application information: Application form required.
Initial approach: Letter
Copies of proposal: 1
Deadline(s): None
Officers and Directors:* Conrad Lee Klein,* Pres.; John Reynolds,* V.P.; Carol Hannah,* Secy.-Treas.
EIN: 954487544

714
The Humboldt Area Foundation ✧
373 Indianola Rd.
Bayside, CA 95524-9350 (707) 442-2993
Contact: Kathy VanVleet, Admin. Asst.; Patrick Cleary, Exec. Dir.
FAX: (707) 442-9072;
E-mail: kathyv@hafoundation.org; Additional e-mail: patrickc@hafoundation.org; Main URL: http://www.hafoundation.org
Grants List: http://www.hafoundation.org/haf/grants/grantmaking-summary.html
Philanthropy's Promise: http://www.ncrp.org/philanthropys-promise/who

Established in 1972 in CA by declaration of trust.
Donors: Vera P. Vietor†; Lynn A. Vietor†.
Foundation type: Community foundation.
Financial data (yr. ended 06/30/13): Assets, $90,470,144 (M); gifts received, $8,056,138; expenditures, $6,482,013; giving activities include $2,717,169 for grants.
Purpose and activities: The foundation seeks to serve as an independent staging ground for residents, individually and in concert, to build social, economic and environmental prosperity in the Redwood, Trinity and Wild Rivers Region. Primary areas of interest include youth, health, community development, human services, arts and culture and public safety. The foundation also operates a resource center that hosts public workshops covering a range of nonprofit issues.
Fields of interest: Arts; Health care; Crime/violence prevention; Food services; Housing/shelter; Safety/disasters; Recreation; Children/youth, services; Family services; Human services; Civil rights, race/intergroup relations; Community/economic development; Economically disadvantaged.
Type of support: General/operating support; Management development/capacity building; Capital campaigns; Building/renovation; Equipment; Emergency funds; Program development; Seed money; Scholarship funds; Technical assistance; Consulting services; Grants to individuals; Scholarships—to individuals; Matching/challenge support.
Limitations: Applications accepted. Giving limited to Del Norte, Humboldt, and Trinity counties, CA. No grants to individuals (except from donor-designated funds); generally no grants for endowment funds, unspecified emergency purposes, deficit financing, or operating budgets.
Publications: Application guidelines; Annual report; Financial statement; Grants list.
Application information: Visit foundation web site for application forms and additional guidelines per grant type. Application form required.
Initial approach: Application, telephone, or e-mail
Copies of proposal: 1
Deadline(s): Oct. 1, Jan. 12, Apr. 1, and July 1 for Community Grant Program grants; varies for others
Board meeting date(s): 2nd Wed. of each month
Final notification: Within 10 weeks for Community Grant Program notification; varies for others
Officers and Directors:* Paula Allen,* Chair.; Jon Sapper,* Vice-Chair.; Jim Anderson,* Secy.; Patrick Cleary, Exec. Dir.; Gary Blatnick; Kevin Caldwell; Neal Ewald; Julie Fulkerson; Kathryn Lobato; Greg Nesbitt; Steve O'Meara; Terry Supahan.
Number of staff: 9 full-time professional; 1 part-time professional; 5 full-time support; 2 part-time support.
EIN: 237310660

715
Jaquelin Hume Foundation ✧
600 Montgomery St., Ste. 2800
San Francisco, CA 94111-2803 (415) 705-5115
Contact: Gisele Huff, Exec. Dir.

Established in 1962 in CA.
Donors: Jaquelin H. Hume†; Caroline H. Hume†; William J. Hume.
Foundation type: Independent foundation.
Financial data (yr. ended 12/31/13): Assets, $19,488,692 (M); expenditures, $4,688,343; qualifying distributions, $4,576,970; giving activities include $4,356,250 for 43 grants (high: $500,000; low: $5,000).
Purpose and activities: Giving primarily for K-12 education reform efforts.
Fields of interest: Elementary/secondary school reform; Education; Public policy, research; Children; Youth; Minorities; African Americans/Blacks; Hispanics/Latinos; Girls; Boys; Immigrants/refugees; Economically disadvantaged.
Type of support: General/operating support; Program development; Research; Program evaluation.
Limitations: Applications accepted. Giving on a national basis to organizations with national impact. No support for organizations outside the U.S. No grants to individuals.
Publications: Application guidelines.
Application information: Application form not required.
Initial approach: 1-page letter
Copies of proposal: 1
Deadline(s): Mar. 15 and Sept. 15
Board meeting date(s): Biannually
Officers and Trustees:* William J. Hume,* Pres.; George H. Hume,* V.P.; Gisele Huff,* Exec. Dir. and Secy.; Edward A. Landry,* Treas.
Number of staff: 1 full-time professional.
EIN: 946080099
Selected grants: The following grants are a representative sample of this grantmaker's funding activity:
$500,000 to Learning Accelerator, Cupertino, CA, 2013. For unrestricted support.
$340,000 to Innosight Institute, San Mateo, CA, 2013. For unrestricted support.
$300,000 to Alliance for Excellent Education, Washington, DC, 2013. For unrestricted support.
$275,000 to International Association for K-12 Online Learning, Vienna, VA, 2013. For unrestricted support.
$250,000 to DC Public Education Fund, Washington, DC, 2013. For unrestricted support.
$200,000 to San Francisco Symphony, San Francisco, CA, 2013. For unrestricted support.
$150,000 to Center for Education Reform, Washington, DC, 2013. For unrestricted support.
$150,000 to San Francisco Opera, San Francisco, CA, 2013. For unrestricted support.
$50,000 to American Enterprise Institute for Public Policy Research, Washington, DC, 2013. For unrestricted support.
$40,000 to Independence Institute, Denver, CO, 2013. For unrestricted support.

716
Hurtt Family Foundation ✧ ☆
12571 Western Ave.
Garden Grove, CA 92841-4012

Established in 2004 in CA.
Donors: Robert S. Hurtt, Jr.; Nancy J. Hurtt; Container Supply Co., Inc.
Foundation type: Independent foundation.
Financial data (yr. ended 12/31/13): Assets, $1,058,870 (M); gifts received, $1,000,000; expenditures, $3,794,511; qualifying distributions, $3,792,592; giving activities include $3,792,592 for 4 grants (high: $3,510,000; low: $10,000).
Purpose and activities: Giving primarily to a Christian organization, as well as for human services.
Fields of interest: Education; Human services; Christian agencies & churches.
Type of support: General/operating support.
Limitations: Applications not accepted. Giving primarily in CA. No grants to individuals.
Application information: Contributes only to pre-selected organizations.
Officers: Robert S. Hurtt, Jr., Pres.; Nancy J. Hurtt, Secy.
EIN: 201819513
Selected grants: The following grants are a representative sample of this grantmaker's funding activity:
$3,510,000 to Forest Home, Forest Falls, CA, 2013. For general.
$250,000 to Focus on the Family, Colorado Springs, CO, 2013. For general.
$22,592 to Free Wheelchair Mission, Irvine, CA, 2013. For general.
$10,000 to Red Hill Lutheran School, Tustin, CA, 2013. For general.

717
Hutto Patterson Charitable Foundation ✧
P.O. Box 80880
San Marino, CA 91118-8880

Established in 1988 in CA.
Donor: Clare P. Hutto†.
Foundation type: Independent foundation.
Financial data (yr. ended 09/30/13): Assets, $9,593,252 (M); expenditures, $1,259,261; qualifying distributions, $1,119,919; giving activities include $1,057,500 for 14 grants (high: $200,000; low: $3,000).
Purpose and activities: Giving primarily for education and children's services.
Fields of interest: Education, early childhood education; Higher education; Education; Human services; Children/youth, services; Family services.
Limitations: Applications not accepted.
Application information: Unsolicited requests for funds not accepted.
Officers and Trustees:* Catherine Hutto Gordon,* Pres.; Eileen C. Hutto,* V.P.; Harry L. Hathaway; Douglas Johnson.
EIN: 954181302

718
Hutton Parker Foundation ✧
(doing business as Hutton Parker Foundation)
(formerly Hutton Foundation)
26 W. Anapamu, 4th Fl.
Santa Barbara, CA 93101-3144 (805) 957-4740
Contact: Pamela J. Lewis, Exec. Dir.
FAX: (805) 957-4743;
E-mail: info@huttonfoundation.org; Main URL: http://www.huttonfoundation.org

Established in 1980.
Foundation type: Independent foundation.
Financial data (yr. ended 12/31/13): Assets, $93,497,067 (M); expenditures, $5,260,805; qualifying distributions, $3,257,594; giving activities include $2,656,238 for 116 grants (high: $497,428; low: $500), and $37,370 for 1 loan/program-related investment.
Purpose and activities: Hutton Parker Foundation strives to provide organizational sustainability to community-based nonprofit organizations throughout Santa Barbara County, California and to assist agencies in achieving their highest level of performance and delivery of services resulting in stronger, more efficient communities for all. The foundation specializes in providing quality office space for local area nonprofit organizations through the acquisition and development of commercial real estate properties.
Fields of interest: Arts; Education; Health care; Human services; Children/youth, services; Family services; Community/economic development.
Type of support: General/operating support; Management development/capacity building; Annual campaigns; Capital campaigns; Building/renovation; Equipment; Endowments; Program development; Scholarship funds; Program evaluation; Program-related investments/loans; Matching/challenge support.
Limitations: Giving limited to Santa Barbara County, CA. No support for religious or political organizations. No grants to individuals.
Publications: Application guidelines; Annual report; Annual report (including application guidelines); Financial statement; Grants list; Multi-year report.
Application information: Complete application procedures available on foundation web site.
Board meeting date(s): Annually
Officers and Directors:* Thomas C. Parker,* Pres.; Susan Parker, Exec. V.P.; Arlene R. Craig, V.P. and Secy.-Treas.; Pamela J. Lewis, Exec. Dir.; Charles O. Slosser; Sam Tyler.
Number of staff: 3 full-time professional; 1 part-time professional.
EIN: 330779894

719
Kyupin Philip & Gemma Hwang Foundation ✧
(formerly The Kyupin Philip and C. Gemma Hwang Foundation)
25313 La Loma Dr.
Los Altos Hills, CA 94022-4579

Established in CA.
Donors: K. Phillip Hwang; C. Gemma Hwang.
Foundation type: Independent foundation.
Financial data (yr. ended 12/31/12): Assets, $5,245,091 (M); expenditures, $659,763; qualifying distributions, $625,292; giving activities include $624,955 for 7 grants (high: $500,000; low: $30).
Fields of interest: Education, alumni groups; Education; Human services.
Limitations: Applications not accepted. Giving primarily in Santa Clara County, CA. No grants to individuals.
Application information: Contributes only to pre-selected organizations.
Officers and Directors:* K. Phillip Hwang,* Pres.; C. Gemma Hwang,* V.P.
EIN: 770029903

720
i.am.angel Foundation ✧ ☆
450 Roxbury Dr.
Beverly Hills, CA 90210-4209
Toll-free tel.: (800) 839-1754; Main URL: http://iamangelfoundation.org/
Causes.com URL: http://www.causes.com/causes/434950-i-am-angel
Facebook: http://www.facebook.com/iamangelfoundation
Foundation Blog: http://iamangelfoundation.org/blog/
Google Plus: https://plus.google.com/118314738112858440523/posts
RSS Feed: http://xml.dipdive.com/community/rss/iamhome
Twitter: https://twitter.com/iamangelfdn
Vimeo: http://vimeo.com/34679422
YouTube: http://www.youtube.com/user/iamangelfnd

Established in 2010.
Donors: William James "will.i.am" Adams, Jr.; Sean Parker; Jennifer M. Van Natta; Misael Vasquez; Michael Murphy; Entertainment Industry Foundation; Jeanne and Sanford Roberston Fund; Quantum Realtors Inc.; Silicon Valley Community Foundation; Wells Fargo bank.
Foundation type: Independent foundation.
Financial data (yr. ended 12/31/12): Assets, $116,264 (M); gifts received, $640,460; expenditures, $2,100,055; qualifying distributions, $2,100,050; giving activities include $1,170,000 for 7 grants (high: $785,000; low: $5,000), and $610,827 for 2 foundation-administered programs.
Purpose and activities: The foundation works to make a difference in the lives of individuals and families through education, opportunity, and inspiration.
Fields of interest: Education; Housing/shelter; Economically disadvantaged.
Limitations: Applications not accepted. Giving primarily in CA.
Application information: Unsolicited requests for funds not accepted.
Officers: William James "will.i.am" Adams, Jr., Pres. and Secy.; Justin Paschal, Exec. Dir.
Directors: Ron Conway; Polo Molina.
EIN: 273419857

721
Ing Foundation ✧
c/o WM WAN & Co.
5 3rd St., Ste. 430
San Francisco, CA 94103

Established in 1999 in CA.
Donor: Nita Ing.
Foundation type: Independent foundation.
Financial data (yr. ended 12/31/13): Assets, $456,890 (M); gifts received, $2,403,500; expenditures, $2,447,646; qualifying distributions, $2,447,577; giving activities include $2,444,750 for 8 grants (high: $1,945,500; low: $10,000).
Fields of interest: Language/linguistics; Literature; Historical activities.
Limitations: Applications not accepted. Giving primarily in Canada and India. No grants to individuals.
Application information: Contributes only to pre-selected organizations.
Officers: Nita Ing, Chair. and Pres.; Darwin Tu, Secy. and Exec. Dir.; Yi-Ching Wu, Treas.
Directors: Kendra Ing; Michele W. Ing; Tasha Ing; Christopher D. Yahng; Kacie E. Yhang.
EIN: 943323904
Selected grants: The following grants are a representative sample of this grantmaker's funding activity:
$400,000 to Global Fund for Women, San Francisco, CA, 2012. For India, Mongolia, Tibet, and Nepal. to Enable Global Fund for Women to Partner with Women-Led Organizations Around the World That Are Working to Advance Gender Equality and Women's Empowerment and Leadership in Their Communities.

722
Institute for Healthcare Advancement ✧
501 S. Idaho St., Ste. 300
La Habra, CA 90631-6047 (562) 690-4001
FAX: (562) 690-8988; E-mail: info@iha4health.org; Toll-Free tel.: (800) 434-4633; Main URL: http://iha4health.org
Facebook: http://www.facebook.com/IHAhealthliteracy
Twitter: http://twitter.com/IHAhealthlit

Established in 1999 in CA; converted from Friendly Hills Health Care.
Donors: Bambi Holzer; Jason Buck.
Foundation type: Operating foundation.
Financial data (yr. ended 12/31/12): Assets, $29,093,860 (M); gifts received, $389,891; expenditures, $4,080,853; qualifying distributions, $2,588,464; giving activities include $444,041 for grants (high: $438,291), and $3,348,667 for 4 foundation-administered programs.
Purpose and activities: Giving for the advancement of healthcare. Committed to developing, through a variety of means, programs and projects that will demonstrate innovative healthcare delivery. The Institute will be a conduit for leveraging knowledge, resources and relationships to identify specific needs, understand the constantly changing needs and design educational formats that stimulate and facilitate solutions to the challenges that healthcare will face in the future.
Fields of interest: Health care.
Limitations: Applications not accepted. Giving primarily in CA.
Application information: Contributes only to pre-selected organizations.
Officers: Albert E. Barnett, M.D., Chair.; Michael Villaire, MSLM, C.E.O.; Ronald G. Chow, C.F.O.
Directors: S. Eric Anderson, Ph.D., MBA; Kambiz Arman, M.D.; Juan M. Garcia; George S. Goldstein, Ph.D.; Nancy J. Monk, MPH, MBA; Barbara Price; Duane Saikami, PharmD, MBA.
EIN: 330483197
Selected grants: The following grants are a representative sample of this grantmaker's funding activity:
$438,291 to Friends of Family Health Center, La Habra, CA, 2012. For health center operations.

723
The Intuit Foundation ✧
P.O. Box 7850, MS MTV-07-02
Mountain View, CA 94039-7850
Main URL: http://www.intuit.com/about_intuit/philanthropy/how.jsp#Foundation

Established in 2002 in CA.

Donor: Intuit Inc.
Foundation type: Company-sponsored foundation.
Financial data (yr. ended 03/31/13): Assets, $1,067,191 (M); gifts received, $1,050,000; expenditures, $1,418,366; qualifying distributions, $1,385,200; giving activities include $1,313,481 for 1,192+ grants.
Purpose and activities: The foundation supports organizations involved with education, health, human services, community development, and economically disadvantaged people. Special emphasis is directed toward programs designed to foster economic empowerment.
Fields of interest: Education; Health care; Children/youth, services; Human services, financial counseling; Human services; Economic development; Community development, small businesses; Community/economic development; Economically disadvantaged.
Type of support: General/operating support; Program development; Employee volunteer services; Employee matching gifts.
Limitations: Applications not accepted. Giving primarily in AZ, CA, Washington, DC, GA, MA, NV, NY, TX, and VA. No support for religious organizations, political or labor organizations, private foundations, or discriminatory organizations. No grants to individuals, or for fundraising events or sponsorships, advertising, souvenir journals, or dinner programs, or conferences, exhibits, or academic research.
Application information: Contributes only to pre-selected organizations.
Officers and Directors:* Sherry Whiteley,* C.E.O. and Pres.; Kerry McLean, Secy.; Scott D. Cook; Tayloe Stansbury.
EIN: 470860921
Selected grants: The following grants are a representative sample of this grantmaker's funding activity:
$2,500 to Juvenile Diabetes Research Foundation International, San Diego, CA, 2013. For Intuit Foundation Grant to Health and Human Services Agency.
$1,510 to Sankara Eye Foundation USA, Milpitas, CA, 2013. For matching gift to Health and Human Services Agency.
$1,250 to Santa Cruz Montessori School, Aptos, CA, 2013. For matching gift to Education K-12 Agency.
$525 to Humane Society Silicon Valley, Milpitas, CA, 2013. For matching gift to Civic Agency.
$500 to Denver Dumb Friends League, Denver, CO, 2013. For Intuit Foundation Grant to Civic Agency.
$100 to Nevada Wilderness Project, Reno, NV, 2013. For matching gift to Environment Agency.
$100 to Smith College, Northampton, MA, 2013. For matching gift to Education Higher Agency.
$50 to Monterey Bay Aquarium Foundation, Monterey, CA, 2013. For matching gift to Arts and Culture Agency.

724
The Ray R. Irani Foundation ✧
11100 Santa Monica Blvd., Ste. 600
Los Angeles, CA 90025-3328

Established in 2003 in CA.
Donors: Ray R. Irani; Ray Irani Charitable Trust.
Foundation type: Independent foundation.
Financial data (yr. ended 12/31/12): Assets, $10,581,376 (M); gifts received, $4,113,532; expenditures, $871,506; qualifying distributions, $832,820; giving activities include $832,820 for grants.
Fields of interest: Higher education, university; Education; Islam.
Limitations: Applications not accepted. Giving primarily in CA and NY. No grants to individuals.
Application information: Contributes only to pre-selected organizations.
Trustees: Kenneth J. Anderson; Ray R. Irani.
EIN: 486394885

725
Audrey & Sydney Irmas Charitable Foundation ✧
15910 Ventura Blvd., Ste. 1019
Encino, CA 91436-2822 (818) 382-3313
Contact: Robert J. Irmas
FAX: (818) 382-3315; E-mail: robirm@gmail.com; Additional e-mail: shoshana.kline@gmail.com

Established in 1986 in CA.
Donors: Sydney M. Irmas†; Audrey M. Irmas.
Foundation type: Independent foundation.
Financial data (yr. ended 12/31/12): Assets, $23,619,890 (M); expenditures, $2,366,387; qualifying distributions, $1,266,600; giving activities include $1,227,600 for 117 grants (high: $250,000; low: $100).
Purpose and activities: Giving primarily for education, health and medical research, as well as to a children's hospital, human services, and Jewish organizations; funding also for art museums.
Fields of interest: Museums (art); Elementary/secondary education; Higher education; Law school/education; Hospitals (specialty); Medical research, institute; Housing/shelter, development; Human services; Jewish federated giving programs; Jewish agencies & synagogues.
Type of support: Emergency funds; Professorships; Program-related investments/loans.
Limitations: Giving primarily in Los Angeles, CA.
Application information: Application form not required.
Initial approach: Letter
Copies of proposal: 1
Deadline(s): None
Board meeting date(s): Quarterly
Director: Audrey M. Irmas.
Trustee: Robert J. Irmas.
Number of staff: 1 full-time professional; 1 part-time support.
EIN: 954030813
Selected grants: The following grants are a representative sample of this grantmaker's funding activity:
$5,000 to A Home Within, San Francisco, CA, 2012. To provide General Funds to the Payee Charitable Origination.
$5,000 to Virginia Avenue Project, Santa Monica, CA, 2012. To provide General Funds to the Payee Charitable Organization.
$1,000 to Women Against Gun Violence, Los Angeles, CA, 2012. To provide General Funds to the Payee Charitable Organization.

726
Audrey Irmas Foundation for Social Justice ✧
(formerly Audrey and Sydney Irmas Family Foundation)
15910 Ventura Blvd., Ste. 1019
Encino, CA 91436-2822 (818) 382-3313
Contact: Robert Irmas, Treas.
Additional e-mail: shoshana.kline@gmail.com

Established in 2007 in CA.
Donor: Audrey Irmas.
Foundation type: Independent foundation.
Financial data (yr. ended 11/30/13): Assets, $13,119,929 (M); gifts received, $162,500; expenditures, $582,580; qualifying distributions, $444,500; giving activities include $444,500 for 8 grants (high: $125,000; low: $1,000).
Fields of interest: Law school/education; Education; Health care, clinics/centers; Human services.
Limitations: Giving primarily in CA and WA.
Application information:
Initial approach: Letter
Deadline(s): None
Officers and Directors:* Audrey Irmas,* Pres.; Matthew Irmas,* Secy.; Robert Irmas,* Treas.
EIN: 260821014

727
The James Irvine Foundation ✧
One Bush St., Ste. 800
San Francisco, CA 94104-4425 (415) 777-2244
Contact: Kelly Martin, Dir., Grants Admin.
FAX: (415) 777-0869;
E-mail: grantsadmin@irvine.org; Southern CA office: 865 S. Figueroa St., Ste. 2308, Los Angeles, CA 90017-5430, tel.: (213) 236-0552, fax: (213) 236-0537; Main URL: http://www.irvine.org
Facebook: http://www.facebook.com/pages/The-James-Irvine-Foundation/107030182653162?ref=ts
Grantee Perception Reports: http://www.irvine.org/evaluation/foundation-assessment/2010-grantee-perception-report
Grants Database: http://www.irvine.org/grantmaking/grantsdatabase
James E. Canales on Twitter: http://www.twitter.com/jcanales
Knowledge Center: http://www.irvine.org/evaluation
News & Insights Blog: http://www.irvine.org/news-insights/latest
Twitter: http://twitter.com/IrvineFdn
YouTube: http://www.youtube.com/user/IrvineFoundation

Incorporated in 1937 in CA.
Donor: James Irvine†.
Foundation type: Independent foundation.
Financial data (yr. ended 12/31/13): Assets, $1,953,184,048 (M); expenditures, $78,332,621; qualifying distributions, $69,000,000; giving activities include $69,000,000 for grants.
Purpose and activities: The mission of the foundation is to expand opportunity for the people of CA to participate in a vibrant, successful, and inclusive society.
Fields of interest: Arts, multipurpose centers/programs; Arts, cultural/ethnic awareness; Arts, folk arts; Arts councils; Performing arts; Performing arts centers; Performing arts, dance; Performing

arts, ballet; Performing arts, theater; Performing arts, orchestras; Performing arts, opera; Employment, training; Youth development, services; Civil rights, race/intergroup relations; Community/economic development, management/technical assistance; Community development, neighborhood development; Economic development; Nonprofit management; Philanthropy/voluntarism, association; Philanthropy/voluntarism, administration/regulation; Philanthropy/voluntarism, information services; Foundations (public); Foundations (community); Voluntarism promotion; Philanthropy/voluntarism; Public policy, research; Economically disadvantaged.
Type of support: Research; General/operating support; Program development; Seed money; Technical assistance; Program evaluation; Employee matching gifts; Matching/challenge support.
Limitations: Applications accepted. Giving limited to CA. No support for agencies receiving substantial government support. No grants to individuals.
Publications: Annual report; Informational brochure; Newsletter.
Application information: See foundation web site for additional application information. Application form required.
Initial approach: Online application form
Copies of proposal: 1
Deadline(s): Online letter of inquiry accepted on a rolling basis
Board meeting date(s): Mar., June, Oct., and Dec.
Final notification: 8 to 10 weeks
Officers and Directors:* Greg Avis,* Chair.; Frank H. Cruz,* Vice-Chair.; Don Howard, C.E.O. and Pres.; John R. Jenks, C.I.O. and Treas.; Amy Dominguez-Arms, V.P., Programs; Daniel Olias Silverman, V.P., Strategic Services; Jane Carney; Paula A. Cordeiro; Robert E. Denham; Samuel Hoi; David Mas Masumoto; Regina L. Muehlhauser; Tim Rios; Virgil Roberts; Steven A. Schroeder; Isaac Stein; Lydia M. Villarreal.
Number of staff: 29 full-time professional; 1 part-time professional; 9 full-time support; 2 part-time support.
EIN: 941236937

728
The William G. Irwin Charity Foundation ✧
235 Montgomery St., Ste. 711
San Francisco, CA 94104-2996 (415) 362-6954
Contact: Dianna Deeley, Grants Admin.
E-mail: irwincharity@gmail.com

Trust established in 1919 in CA.
Donors: Fannie M. Irwin‡; Helene Irwin Fagan‡.
Foundation type: Independent foundation.
Financial data (yr. ended 12/31/13): Assets, $109,211,032 (M); expenditures, $5,401,799; qualifying distributions, $4,842,926; giving activities include $4,589,471 for 34 grants (high: $348,000; low: $7,500).
Purpose and activities: Giving primarily for the physical improvement of humanity.
Fields of interest: Elementary/secondary education; Higher education; Education; Human services.
Type of support: Capital campaigns; Building/renovation; Equipment; Land acquisition; Research; Matching/challenge support.
Limitations: Applications accepted. Giving primarily in CA and HI. No grants to individuals, or for scholarships.
Publications: Application guidelines.
Application information: Applicants must wait twelve months between proposal submissions. Application form not required.
Initial approach: Letter or proposal
Copies of proposal: 1
Deadline(s): Approximately 4-6 weeks prior to board meeting
Board meeting date(s): Approximately every 2 months
Officers and Trustees:* William Lee Olds, Jr., Pres.; Jane Olds Bogart,* V.P.; William L. Olds III; Anthony O. Zanze; James F. Zanze.
Number of staff: 2 full-time professional.
EIN: 946069873
Selected grants: The following grants are a representative sample of this grantmaker's funding activity:
$500,000 to Dunn School, Los Olivos, CA, 2012. For new septic system.
$250,000 to Saint Marys Medical Center, San Francisco, CA, 2012. For new vascular suite.
$200,000 to San Francisco Jazz Organization, San Francisco, CA, 2012. For capital campaign.
$150,000 to LifeLong Medical Care, Berkeley, CA, 2012. For clinic construction.
$150,000 to Saint Francis Memorial Hospital, San Francisco, CA, 2012. For Burn Center Expansion.
$100,000 to Arc of San Francisco, San Francisco, CA, 2012. For renovations.
$50,000 to Covenant House California, Oakland, CA, 2012. For campus refurbishment.
$50,000 to Star of the Sea School, San Francisco, CA, 2012. For windows replacement.
$34,000 to Saint Paul of the Shipwreck School, San Francisco, CA, 2012. To retain wall.
$31,000 to Eastside College Preparatory School, East Palo Alto, CA, 2012. For van.

729
The Isambard Kingdom Brunel Society of North America ✧
c/o Peter Norton
225 Arizona Ave., Ste. 350
Santa Monica, CA 90401-1244 (310) 576-7700
Contact: Peter Norton, Tr.

Donor: Peter Norton.
Foundation type: Independent foundation.
Financial data (yr. ended 12/31/13): Assets, $9,422,935 (M); expenditures, $1,122,689; qualifying distributions, $1,004,535; giving activities include $1,000,550 for 27 grants (high: $200,000; low: $150).
Fields of interest: Museums (art); Performing arts; Education; Health care.
Limitations: Applications accepted. Giving primarily in Los Angeles, CA and New York, NY.
Application information: Application form required.
Initial approach: Letter
Deadline(s): None
Trustee: Peter Norton.
EIN: 264312827
Selected grants: The following grants are a representative sample of this grantmaker's funding activity:
$50,000 to Spelman College, Atlanta, GA, 2012. For 2011-2012 board dues.
$50,000 to Visiting Nurse Service of New York, New York, NY, 2012. For unrestricted/fiscal 2012-2013.
$25,000 to Museum of Modern Art, New York, NY, 2012. For annual fund/unrestricted/fiscal 2012-2013.
$20,000 to Museum of Modern Art, New York, NY, 2012. For Media Committee/Fiscal 2012-2013.
$15,000 to California Institute of Technology, Pasadena, CA, 2012. For HSS Committee.
$15,000 to Museum of Modern Art, New York, NY, 2012. For Architecture and Design Committee.
$15,000 to Museum of Modern Art, New York, NY, 2012. For Photography Committee/Fiscal 2012-2013.
$10,000 to Museum of Modern Art, New York, NY, 2012. For Annual Fund/Photo Department/Bill Brandt Project.
$10,000 to World Monuments Fund, New York, NY, 2012. For President's Circle Membership.
$2,500 to Jazz at Lincoln Center, New York, NY, 2012. For Occasion of JLC Gala.

730
The Ishiyama Foundation ✧
465 California St., Ste. 800
San Francisco, CA 94104-1847
Contact: Margaret Raffin, Secy.

Established in 1968 in CA.
Donor: George S. Ishiyama.
Foundation type: Independent foundation.
Financial data (yr. ended 12/31/12): Assets, $82,779,442 (M); expenditures, $4,145,797; qualifying distributions, $3,949,535; giving activities include $3,942,708 for 35 grants (high: $1,333,000; low: $1,000).
Purpose and activities: Giving primarily for the environment, as well as for education, health organizations, social services and the arts.
Fields of interest: Media, radio; Arts; Higher education; Education; Environment; Health organizations; Human services; Foundations (private grantmaking).
Limitations: Applications accepted. Giving primarily in CA; funding also in Arlington, VA; some funding nationally. No support for study programs. No grants to individuals.
Application information: Application form not required.
Deadline(s): None
Officers: Margaret Raffin, Pres.; Patsy Ishiyama, V.P.; Nelson Ishiyama, Secy.
Directors: Alan Arai; Sheryl Lynn Suzuki.
EIN: 941659373

731
The Marcia Israel Foundation, Inc. ✧
(formerly The Marcia and Lawrence Israel Foundation)
9454 Wilshire Blvd., 4th Fl.
Beverly Hills, CA 90212-2907

Established in 1989 in CA.
Donors: Marcia Israel‡; Marcia Israel Trust.
Foundation type: Independent foundation.
Financial data (yr. ended 12/31/13): Assets, $16,787,004 (M); expenditures, $849,339; qualifying distributions, $665,473; giving activities include $608,900 for 28 grants (high: $72,000; low: $1,800).
Fields of interest: Arts; Human services; Jewish federated giving programs; Jewish agencies & synagogues.
Limitations: Applications not accepted. Giving primarily in CA. No grants to individuals.

Application information: Contributes only to pre-selected organizations.
Officers and Directors:* Jack Neinstein,* Pres.; Edward Landry, C.F.O.; Kenneth Miles.
EIN: 954246827

732
Issa Family Foundation ✧
P.O. Box 1388
Vista, CA 92085-1388

Established in 1999 in CA.
Donors: Darrell E. Issa; Katharine S. Issa.
Foundation type: Independent foundation.
Financial data (yr. ended 12/31/13): Assets, $33,064,831 (M); gifts received, $107,644; expenditures, $1,451,097; qualifying distributions, $1,404,441; giving activities include $1,404,441 for 110 grants (high: $150,000; low: $200).
Purpose and activities: Giving primarily for human services.
Fields of interest: Higher education; Higher education, university; Animal welfare; Zoos/zoological societies; Hospitals (specialty); Health organizations, association; Pediatrics; Boys & girls clubs; Human services; Economics; Christian agencies & churches.
Limitations: Applications not accepted. Giving primarily in CA. No grants to individuals.
Application information: Contributes only to pre-selected organizations.
Officers: Darrell E. Issa, C.E.O.; Katharine S. Issa, C.F.O.
EIN: 330834068
Selected grants: The following grants are a representative sample of this grantmaker's funding activity:
$150,000 to North County Solutions for Change, Vista, CA, 2012. For Sponsorship: An Evening to Remember.
$150,000 to North County Solutions for Change, Vista, CA, 2012. For auction donation.
$60,000 to Palomar College Foundation, San Marcos, CA, 2012. For Issa Family Foundation Challenge Grant.
$50,000 to Interfaith Community Services, Escondido, CA, 2012. For Gift to purchase 2195 Oceanside Blvd.
$45,000 to American Task Force for Lebanon, Washington, DC, 2012. For Donation for State Department match.
$27,000 to Armed Forces Foundation, Washington, DC, 2012. For Sponsorship 8th Annual Congressional Gala.
$25,000 to American Task Force for Lebanon, Washington, DC, 2012. For awards gala underwriter.
$25,000 to Vista Community Clinic, Vista, CA, 2012. For Sponsorship 40th Anniversary Gala.
$20,000 to Boys and Girls Club of Vista, Vista, CA, 2012. For College Bound Program.
$2,000 to Interfaith Community Services, Escondido, CA, 2012. For on behalf of Maritsa Lizarraga.

733
It Takes a Family Foundation, Inc. ✧
3912 Calle Ariana
San Clemente, CA 92672-4503

Established in 1997 in CA.
Donors: Kim C. Bengard; Thomas P. Bengard; Tyler T. Bengard; Bengard Foundation; Bengard Charitable Lead Trust.
Foundation type: Independent foundation.
Financial data (yr. ended 12/31/13): Assets, $10,132,348 (M); gifts received, $187,315; expenditures, $1,088,432; qualifying distributions, $987,812; giving activities include $977,077 for 39 grants (high: $250,000; low: $250).
Fields of interest: Human services; Family services; Christian agencies & churches.
Limitations: Applications not accepted. Giving primarily in CA; some funding also in Washington, DC. No grants to individuals.
Application information: Unsolicited requests for funds not accepted.
Officers and Directors:* Thomas P. Bengard,* Pres.; Kim C. Bengard,* Secy.-Treas.; Tyler T. Bengard.
EIN: 582276414

734
J & J Family Foundation ✧
1605 Alisa Ln.
Santa Barbara, CA 93110-2448

Established in 2003 in CA.
Donors: Jeffrey O. Henley; Judy P. Henley.
Foundation type: Independent foundation.
Financial data (yr. ended 12/31/13): Assets, $22,892,970 (M); gifts received, $342,789; expenditures, $2,788,215; qualifying distributions, $2,477,121; giving activities include $2,462,790 for 24 grants (high: $1,500,000; low: $500).
Fields of interest: Higher education; Health care; Boys & girls clubs; Human services.
Limitations: Applications not accepted. Giving primarily in CA. No grants to individuals.
Application information: Contributes only to pre-selected organizations.
Trustees: Jeffrey O. Henley; Judy P. Henley.
EIN: 206077711

735
The J.A.N.S. Foundation ✧
14357 Horizon Ct.
Poway, CA 92064-1459

Established in 2002 in CA.
Donors: Jan E. Nielsen; J&D Family Foundation.
Foundation type: Independent foundation.
Financial data (yr. ended 12/31/13): Assets, $19,572,590 (M); expenditures, $1,143,803; qualifying distributions, $957,542; giving activities include $927,100 for 3 grants (high: $460,000; low: $82,100).
Fields of interest: Secondary school/education; Human services; Catholic agencies & churches.
Limitations: Applications not accepted. Giving primarily in San Diego, CA and ID. No grants to individuals.
Application information: Contributes only to pre-selected organizations.
Trustee: Jan E. Nielsen.
EIN: 306040216
Selected grants: The following grants are a representative sample of this grantmaker's funding activity:
$300,000 to Cathedral Catholic High School, San Diego, CA, 2012. For Funds for Discretionary Use.

736
Jack in the Box Foundation ✧
9330 Balboa Ave.
San Diego, CA 92123-1516 (858) 571-2544
Contact: Kathy Kovacevich, Secy.
E-mail: kathy.kovacevich@jackinthebox.com; Additional contact: Brian Luscomb, Pres., tel.: (858) 571-2291, e-mail: brain.luscomb@jackinthebox.com; Main URL: http://www.jackinthebox.com/corporate/corporate-responsibility/

Established in 1998 in CA.
Donors: Foodmaker, Inc.; Jack in the Box Inc.; VTP Enterprises.
Foundation type: Company-sponsored foundation.
Financial data (yr. ended 09/30/13): Assets, $650,399 (M); gifts received, $1,688,426; expenditures, $1,618,539; qualifying distributions, $1,618,539; giving activities include $1,283,262 for 38 grants (high: $325,000; low: $312), and $2,000 for 4 grants to individuals (high: $500; low: $500).
Purpose and activities: The foundation supports organizations involved with education, health, youth development, human services, and economic development. Special emphasis is directed toward programs designed to help children in need.
Fields of interest: Middle schools/education; Secondary school/education; Education; Hospitals (general); Health care; Youth development, adult & child programs; Big Brothers/Big Sisters; YM/YWCAs & YM/YWHAs; Human services; Economic development; United Ways and Federated Giving Programs; Children.
Type of support: General/operating support; Program development; Sponsorships; Grants to individuals; Matching/challenge support.
Limitations: Applications accepted. Giving on a national basis in areas of company operations, with some emphasis on San Diego, CA.
Application information: Application form not required.
Initial approach: Proposal
Deadline(s): None
Officers and Directors:* Brian Luscomb,* Pres.; Kathy Kovacevich,* Secy.; Mark H. Blankenship, Ph.D.; Keith Guilbault; Elana M. Hobson; Linda A. Lang; Paul D. Melancon; Phillip H. Rudolph; Eric Tunquist.
EIN: 330776076

737
The Ann Jackson Family Foundation ✧
P.O. Box 5580
Santa Barbara, CA 93150-5580 (805) 969-2258
Contact: Palmer G. Jackson, Pres.

Established in 1978.
Donors: Ann G. Jackson; The Ann Jackson Family Charitable Trust.
Foundation type: Independent foundation.
Financial data (yr. ended 05/31/13): Assets, $47,375,070 (M); expenditures, $2,409,490; qualifying distributions, $2,166,560; giving activities include $2,161,600 for 176 grants (high: $70,000; low: $1,000).
Purpose and activities: Giving primarily for the arts, education, health care, children, youth and social services, including services for people who are blind, and to YMCAs.

Fields of interest: Museums; Performing arts centers; Arts; Elementary/secondary education; Higher education; Education; Hospitals (general); Mental health/crisis services, association; Health organizations, association; Boys & girls clubs; Human services; YM/YWCAs & YM/YWHAs; Children/youth, services; Foundations (private grantmaking); Blind/visually impaired.
Type of support: General/operating support; Capital campaigns; Building/renovation.
Limitations: Applications accepted. Giving primarily in CA, with emphasis on Santa Barbara. No grants to individuals.
Application information: Santa Barbara Foundation Roundtable's Common Grant Application Form accepted. Application form required.
Initial approach: Letter
Deadline(s): None
Officers and Directors:* Palmer G. Jackson,* Pres.; Charles A. Jackson,* V.P.; James H. Jackson,* V.P.; William L. Jackson,* C.F.O.; Palmer G. Jackson, Jr.,* Secy.; Debra B. Jones.
EIN: 953367511
Selected grants: The following grants are a representative sample of this grantmaker's funding activity:
$100,000 to Laguna Blanca School, Santa Barbara, CA, 2010. For capital campaign.
$100,000 to Laguna Blanca School, Santa Barbara, CA, 2011. For capital campaign.
$100,000 to Santa Barbara Center for the Performing Arts, Santa Barbara, CA, 2010. For building project.
$100,000 to Santa Barbara Center for the Performing Arts, Santa Barbara, CA, 2011. For capital campaign.
$95,000 to Cate School, Carpinteria, CA, 2011. For capital campaign.
$86,000 to Cate School, Carpinteria, CA, 2010.
$80,000 to Yale Alumni Fund, New Haven, CT, 2010.
$66,500 to Santa Barbara Museum of Natural History, Santa Barbara, CA, 2010. For capital campaign.
$64,000 to Santa Barbara Museum of Natural History, Santa Barbara, CA, 2011. For capital campaign.
$52,000 to YMCA, Santa Ynez Valley, Santa Ynez, CA, 2011. For capital campaign.
$50,000 to Santa Ynez Valley Cottage Hospital Foundation, Solvang, CA, 2011. For capital campaign.
$13,000 to Laguna Blanca School, Santa Barbara, CA, 2010. For general support.
$12,000 to Lobero Theater Foundation, Santa Barbara, CA, 2010. For general support.
$11,000 to Yale Alumni Fund, New Haven, CT, 2011. For general support.
$10,000 to Hillside House, Santa Barbara, CA, 2010.
$10,000 to Santa Barbara Maritime Museum, Santa Barbara, CA, 2011. For general support.
$10,000 to Santa Barbara Rescue Mission, Santa Barbara, CA, 2010. For general support.
$10,000 to Teddy Bear Cancer Foundation, Santa Barbara, CA, 2011. For general support.
$5,000 to Junior Blind of America, Los Angeles, CA, 2010. For general support.
$5,000 to Junior Blind of America, Los Angeles, CA, 2011. For general support.

738
Jacobs Engineering Foundation ✧
c/o Tax Dept.
P.O. Box 7084
Pasadena, CA 91109-7084 (626) 578-3500
Contact: John W. Prosser, Jr., Treas. and Dir.

Established in 1978 in CA.
Donor: Jacobs Engineering Group Inc.
Foundation type: Company-sponsored foundation.
Financial data (yr. ended 12/31/13): Assets, $2,154,407 (M); gifts received, $780,462; expenditures, $988,897; qualifying distributions, $988,897; giving activities include $988,812 for 291 grants (high: $187,100; low: $40).
Purpose and activities: The foundation supports museums and organizations involved with education, health, genetic diseases, cancer, golf, human services, engineering, and civic affairs.
Fields of interest: Education; Human services; Public affairs.
Type of support: General/operating support; Annual campaigns; Scholarship funds; Sponsorships; Employee-related scholarships; Matching/challenge support.
Limitations: Applications accepted. Giving primarily in CA, CO, Washington, DC, IL, MO, NY, TX, and VA.
Application information: Application form required.
Initial approach: Letter
Deadline(s): None
Officers and Directors:* Craig L. Martin,* Pres.; Michael S. Udovic,* Secy.; John W. Prosser, Jr.,* Treas.; Nazim G. Thawerbhoy, Cont.; George A. Kunberger.
EIN: 953195445
Selected grants: The following grants are a representative sample of this grantmaker's funding activity:
$10,000 to After School Matters, Chicago, IL, 2011.
$5,000 to Air Force Villages Charitable Foundation, San Antonio, TX, 2011.

739
Jacobs Family Foundation, Inc. ✧
c/o Joe & Vi Jacobs Ctr.
404 Euclid Ave.
San Diego, CA 92114-2221 (619) 527-6161
Contact: Jennifer Vanica, C.E.O. and Pres.
FAX: (619) 527-6162;
E-mail: info@jacobscenter.org; Toll free tel.: (800) 550-6856; Main URL: http://www.jacobsfamilyfoundation.org/
Multimedia: http://www.jacobsfamilyfoundation.org/news/news_video_frame.htm?newsvar=/jacobs/jacobscenter/jacobsnetwork/news/news_video_content.htm

Established in 1988 in CA.
Donors: Joseph J. Jacobs, Ph.D.†; Violet J. Jacobs; Norman Hapke; Valerie Jacobs Hapke.
Foundation type: Independent foundation.
Financial data (yr. ended 06/30/13): Assets, $22,198,311 (M); expenditures, $2,569,519; qualifying distributions, $2,341,096; giving activities include $2,316,588 for 29 grants (high: $2,145,224; low: $20).
Purpose and activities: The foundation invests in and with communities to seed or strengthen projects and programs that build the capacity of under-invested neighborhoods, through neighborhood-based programs, resident-led initiatives, projects that test new ideas, and activities that build community spirit. This is done through five funds: the Partnership Fund, Community-Building Strategies Fund, Spirit of the Diamond Fund, and the Jabara Scholarship Fund.
Fields of interest: Education; Human services; Children/youth, services; Family services; Community/economic development; Economically disadvantaged.
Type of support: Mission-related investments/loans; General/operating support; Endowments; Program development; Conferences/seminars; Seed money; Scholarship funds; Technical assistance; Consulting services; Program-related investments/loans; Employee matching gifts; Matching/challenge support.
Limitations: Applications accepted. Giving in CA, with primary emphasis in the southeastern San Diego communities of Valencia Park, Lincoln Park, Webster, Emerald Hills, Chollas View, Mountain View, Mount Hope, North Encanto, Oak Park, and South Encanto. No support for medical services, religious purposes, athletics, or the arts. No grants to individuals, or for medical research.
Publications: Annual report (including application guidelines); Financial statement; Grants list; Informational brochure; Newsletter.
Application information: Applicants are encouraged to contact the foundation before applying. See foundation web site for full application guidelines and requirements for each grant fund. Application form not required.
Initial approach: Telephone call
Copies of proposal: 1
Deadline(s): None
Board meeting date(s): Quarterly
Final notification: 30 days
Officer and Directors:* Susan Halliday, C.F.O. and Secy.; Andrew Hapke; Claire Hapke; Norman F. Hapke, Jr.; Valerie Jacobs Hapke; Margaret E. Jacobs; Violet Jabara Jacobs.
Advisors: William Hanna; Kurt Kicklighter; John Landis; Peter Tanous; Christopher Weil.
Number of staff: 4 full-time professional.
EIN: 954187111

740
Paul and Stacy Jacobs Foundation ✧ ☆
7676 Hazard Center Dr., Ste. 700
San Diego, CA 92108

Foundation type: Independent foundation.
Financial data (yr. ended 12/31/12): Assets, $31,872 (M); expenditures, $907,923; qualifying distributions, $898,937; giving activities include $890,100 for 1 grant.
Fields of interest: Higher education.
Limitations: Applications not accepted.
Application information: Contributes only to pre-selected organizations.
Directors: Paul E. Jacobs; Stacy R. Jacobs.
EIN: 455427184

741
The Jaffe Family Foundation ✧ ☆
88 Emerald Bay
Laguna Beach, CA 92651-1232

Established in 2002 in CA.
Donors: Jon Jaffe; Karen Jaffe.
Foundation type: Operating foundation.

Financial data (yr. ended 11/30/13): Assets, $3,351,697 (M); gifts received, $2,802,987; expenditures, $531,202; qualifying distributions, $493,905; giving activities include $493,905 for 27 grants (high: $152,180; low: $75).
Fields of interest: Cancer; Human services; Children/youth, services; Jewish federated giving programs; Jewish agencies & synagogues.
Limitations: Applications accepted. Giving primarily in CA.
Application information: Application form required.
Initial approach: Letter
Deadline(s): None
Officer: Jon Jaffe, Pres.
EIN: 450493621

742
James Family Foundation ✧
(formerly C.M.J. Private Foundation)
3 Lagoon Dr., Ste. 400
Redwood City, CA 94065-5157
Scholarship address: c/o Laura Alford, Pres., 38 Miller Ave., PMB 114, Mill Valley, CA 94941, tel.: (415) 205-9824

Established in 1996 in CA.
Donors: Christopher M. James; Bradley James; Claudine Rosmarino; Daniel Lurie; Crocodile Bay Lodge.
Foundation type: Independent foundation.
Financial data (yr. ended 11/30/13): Assets, $10,619,930 (M); gifts received, $325,000; expenditures, $2,413,212; qualifying distributions, $2,310,775; giving activities include $1,857,927 for 26 grants (high: $300,000; low: $1,000), and $309,564 for 9 grants to individuals (high: $61,093; low: $11,069).
Purpose and activities: Scholarships for attending an out of state university, Tulane University, New York University, University of California at Berkeley, University of California at Los Angeles, Duke University, Rhode Island School of Design, University of Virginia, MIT, or any ivy league school. In addition, scholarships for fields of study within natural resource conservation and/or environmental studies at Colorado State University, Montana State University, Utah State University, University of Wyoming, Michigan State University, Cornell University, Mississippi State University, Oregon State University, Penn State University, Texas A&M University, University of California at Davis, University of Wisconsin/Stevens Point and Dickinson College. For scholarship eligibility, students must attend one of the following 3 high schools for 4 years: Healdsburg High School, Healdsburg, CA; Harrisburg High School, Harrisburg, IL; Pinedale High School, Pinedale, WY. Funding also for youth and social services, art museums, health, and to an organization supporting jazz education.
Fields of interest: Arts, single organization support; Museums (art); Education; Environment, natural resources; Hospitals (specialty); Cancer; Family services; Youth; Economically disadvantaged.
Type of support: Continuing support; Scholarships —to individuals; In-kind gifts.
Limitations: Applications not accepted. Giving primarily in CA, IL, and WY.
Publications: Program policy statement.
Application information: Unsolicited requests for funds not accepted.
Board meeting date(s): Jan.
Officers and Directors:* Christopher M. James,* Chair.; Laura James Alford,* Pres.; Shyla Hendrickson, Secy. and C.F.O.; Bradley G. James; Nathaniel A. Morison.
Number of staff: 1 full-time professional.
EIN: 133864227

743
J. W. and Ida M. Jameson Foundation ✧
115B Sierra Madre Blvd.
P.O. Box 397
Sierra Madre, CA 91024-2478
Contact: Bill B. Betz, Secy.-Treas.

Incorporated in 1956 in CA.
Donor: Ida M. Jameson‡.
Foundation type: Independent foundation.
Financial data (yr. ended 06/30/13): Assets, $13,532,572 (M); expenditures, $953,265; qualifying distributions, $764,047; giving activities include $726,500 for 35 grants (high: $50,000; low: $1,500).
Purpose and activities: Giving primarily for higher education, medical research, cultural programs, human services, and for Protestant and Roman Catholic church support.
Fields of interest: Arts; Higher education; Health care; Medical research, institute; Human services; Catholic agencies & churches.
Type of support: Scholarship funds; Equipment; General/operating support; Research.
Limitations: Applications accepted. Giving primarily in CA. No support for political organizations.
Application information: Application form not required.
Initial approach: Proposal
Copies of proposal: 1
Deadline(s): Mar. 1
Board meeting date(s): Mid-March
Final notification: Apr. 30
Officers: Fred L. Leydorf, Pres.; Jamen Wurm, V.P.; Bill B. Betz, Secy.-Treas.
Number of staff: 1 part-time support.
EIN: 956031465
Selected grants: The following grants are a representative sample of this grantmaker's funding activity:
$50,000 to Cornerstone Bible Church, Glendora, CA, 2013.
$50,000 to La Canada Presbyterian Church, La Canada, CA, 2013.
$50,000 to UCLA Foundation, Los Angeles, CA, 2013.
$50,000 to University of Michigan, Ann Arbor, MI, 2013.
$45,000 to Stepping Stones for Women, Covina, CA, 2013. For unwed mothers and babies.
$40,000 to Union Station Foundation, Pasadena, CA, 2013. For homeless services.
$30,000 to Eisenhower Medical Center, Rancho Mirage, CA, 2013.
$25,000 to Hypoparathyroidism Association, Idaho Falls, ID, 2013.
$25,000 to Reason Foundation, Los Angeles, CA, 2013. For educational purposes.
$20,000 to Pasadena City College, Pasadena, CA, 2013.

744
JAMS Foundation ✧
2 Embarcadero Ctr., Ste. 1500
San Francisco, CA 94111-3906
Main URL: http://www.jamsadr.com/jamsfoundation/xpqGC.aspx?xpST=JAMSFoundation

Established in 2001 in CA.
Donors: Daniel Weinstein; Alex Polsky; Charles Legge; Charles Vogel; Chris Poole; Dickran Tevrizian; Edward Wallin; Ellen James; Fern Smith; Gary Taylor; Gerald Kurland; James Smith; Jay Folberg; Jay Welsh; Jerry Spolter; John Kennedy, Jr.; John Trotter; Linda Singer; Michael McAllister; Michael Young; Read Ambler; Richard Chernick; Richard Neal; Richard Neville; Richard Silver; Robert Davidson; Robert Sabraw; Ross Feinberg; Stephen Crane; Steven Stone; W. Scott Snowden; William Cahill; William Bettinelli; Viggo Boserup; Bruce Edwards; Michael Loeb; James Melinson; Jerry Roscoe; James Warren; Catherine Yanni; Peter Woodin; Carol Wittenberg; Stephen Sundvold; Kathleen Roberts; Brian Parmelee; John Hinchey; William Bettinelli.
Foundation type: Independent foundation.
Financial data (yr. ended 12/31/13): Assets, $799,340 (M); gifts received, $803,227; expenditures, $867,137; qualifying distributions, $696,287; giving activities include $613,331 for 41 grants (high: $170,046; low: $1,000).
Purpose and activities: Giving primarily for financial assistance for conflict resolution initiatives with national or international impact; also shares its dispute resolution experience and judicial expertise for the benefit of the public interest.
Fields of interest: Courts/judicial administration; Dispute resolution; Community/economic development, public policy; Community/economic development, public education; Law/international law.
Limitations: Applications not accepted. Giving primarily in CA, IL, and MA; some giving in Washington, DC. No grants to individuals.
Application information: Unsolicited requests for funds not accepted.
Officers: Bruce Edwards, Co-Chair.; Warren Knight, Co-Chair.; John J. Welsh, Secy.; Julie Sager, Treas.; Jay Folberg, Exec. Dir.
Board Members: Viggo Boserup; Candace Cooper; Bill Hartgering; Michael Lewis; Chris Poole; Daniel Weinstein; Peter Woodin.
EIN: 912147141
Selected grants: The following grants are a representative sample of this grantmaker's funding activity:
$50,000 to National Association for Community Mediation, Washington, DC, 2012. For Mediation training for National Guard and Reservist Troops.
$30,000 to Community Mediation Center, Independence, MO, 2012. For Training and Education Program for at-risk communities.
$25,000 to Partners for Democratic Change, Washington, DC, 2012. For Invitational symposium for government and business leaders.
$20,000 to Kids Turn, San Francisco, CA, 2012. For Workshops for rural families going through family conflict.
$20,000 to University of Colorado Foundation, Boulder, CO, 2012. For Update online conflict resolution information website.
$15,000 to Hamline University, School of Law, Saint Paul, MN, 2012. For Series of international conferences on negotiation.

$15,000 to Search for Common Ground, Washington, DC, 2012. To develop commercial mediation in Morocco.
$10,000 to Suffolk University, Boston, MA, 2012. For Fund creation of a training video demonstrating advocacy.
$7,000 to Central Oregon Mediation, Bend, OR, 2012. To provide Habitat for Humanity families with skills training.
$7,000 to Public Conversations Project, Watertown, MA, 2012. For Bridging Divides Training video.

745
Elizabeth Bixby Janeway Foundation ✧
c/o Shari Leinwand, Esq.
2029 Century Park E., Ste. 4000
Los Angeles, CA 90067-3026

Established in 1966 in CA.
Donor: Elizabeth Bixby Janeway†.
Foundation type: Independent foundation.
Financial data (yr. ended 09/30/13): Assets, $35,208,909 (M); expenditures, $1,884,475; qualifying distributions, $1,688,985; giving activities include $1,687,500 for 50 grants (high: $300,000; low: $5,000).
Purpose and activities: Giving primarily for the arts, education, and private grantmaking foundations.
Fields of interest: Museums (art); Arts; Higher education; Education; Children/youth, services; Foundations (private grantmaking).
Limitations: Applications not accepted. Giving primarily in southern CA. No grants to individuals.
Application information: Contributes only to pre-selected organizations.
Officers and Directors:* Preston B. Hotchkis,* Chair.; John F. Hotchkis,* Pres.; Sarah H. Ketterer,* C.F.O.; Shari Leinwand,* Secy.
EIN: 952466561
Selected grants: The following grants are a representative sample of this grantmaker's funding activity:
$250,000 to Rancho Los Alamitos Foundation, Long Beach, CA, 2011. For operations.
$200,000 to University of California at Berkeley Foundation, Berkeley, CA, 2011.
$125,000 to Hoover Institution on War, Revolution and Peace, Stanford, CA, 2011.

746
JDH Family Foundation ✧ ☆
c/o J. Dale Harvey
1415 Lomita Dr.
Pasadena, CA 91106-4340

Established in 2005 in CA.
Donors: J. Dale Harvey; Stephanie F. Harvey.
Foundation type: Independent foundation.
Financial data (yr. ended 12/31/13): Assets, $1,168,151 (M); expenditures, $1,427,392; qualifying distributions, $1,427,392; giving activities include $1,426,307 for 9 grants (high: $1,112,707; low: $1,000).
Fields of interest: Education; Environment; Protestant agencies & churches.
Limitations: Applications not accepted. No grants to individuals.
Application information: Unsolicited requests for funds not accepted.
Officers: J. Dale Harvey, Pres.; Stephanie F. Harvey, Secy. and C.F.O.
Director: Eddie Newman.
EIN: 203168194
Selected grants: The following grants are a representative sample of this grantmaker's funding activity:
$26,250 to Polytechnic School, Pasadena, CA, 2012. For Unrestricted Donation for the Poly Annual Fund.
$1,000 to University of Colorado, Denver, CO, 2012. For College of Arts and Sciences Unrestricted Donation for the Organization.

747
The Matthew and Roberta Jenkins Family Foundation ✧ ☆
20 13th Pl.
Long Beach, CA 90802-6005

Donors: Johnetta Jenkins; Matthew Jenkins; Roberta Jenkins.
Foundation type: Independent foundation.
Financial data (yr. ended 10/31/13): Assets, $1,071,476 (M); gifts received, $515,150; expenditures, $454,497; qualifying distributions, $445,777; giving activities include $445,777 for 28 grants (high: $230,000; low: $300).
Fields of interest: Higher education.
Type of support: Scholarship funds.
Limitations: Applications not accepted. Giving primarily in CA. No grants to individuals.
Application information: Contributes only to pre-selected organizations.
Officers: Matthew Jenkins, Pres.; Roberta Jenkins, V.P.
EIN: 201259071

748
The Alan K. and Cledith M. Jennings Foundation ✧
P.O. Box 111
Penn Valley, CA 95946-0111

Established in 2000 in CA.
Donors: A.K. Jennings; Cledith Jennings.
Foundation type: Independent foundation.
Financial data (yr. ended 12/31/12): Assets, $7,417,292 (M); expenditures, $873,604; qualifying distributions, $873,604; giving activities include $827,540 for 99 grants (high: $125,000; low: $40).
Fields of interest: Education; Reproductive health, family planning; Health organizations, association; Legal services; Human services; International relief; International human rights; United Ways and Federated Giving Programs.
Limitations: Applications not accepted. Giving primarily in CA. No grants to individuals.
Application information: Unsolicited requests for funds not accepted.
Officers: Tamozelle Jennings, Pres.; C.M. Jennings, V.P.; T.L. Jennings, V.P.
EIN: 943363468

749
Jerome Foundation ✧
541 E. Chapman Ave., Ste. B
Orange, CA 92866-1648 (714) 538-2393
Contact: Sherrie Spray

Incorporated in 1956 in CA.
Donors: James M. Andreoli; Frank Jerome; Baker Commodities, Inc.; members of the Jerome family.
Foundation type: Independent foundation.
Financial data (yr. ended 12/31/13): Assets, $12,667,641 (M); gifts received, $50,000; expenditures, $675,023; qualifying distributions, $640,653; giving activities include $640,653 for 39 grants (high: $218,903; low: $2,500).
Purpose and activities: Giving primarily to an affiliated foundation; giving also for hospitals, youth, and education.
Fields of interest: Education; Hospitals (general); Medical research, institute; Human services; YM/YWCAs & YM/YWHAs; Children/youth, services; Foundations (private grantmaking).
International interests: Philippines.
Limitations: Applications accepted. Giving primarily in southern CA; some giving in Rizal, Philippines. No grants to individuals.
Publications: Annual report.
Application information: Application form not required.
Initial approach: Proposal
Deadline(s): None
Officers: James M. Andreoli, Pres.; Mitchell Ebright, Secy.-Treas.
Directors: Andrew Andreoli; Anthony Andreoli; James A. Andreoli; Richard Jerome; Martha E. Morales.
EIN: 956039063
Selected grants: The following grants are a representative sample of this grantmaker's funding activity:
$25,000 to American Red Cross, Los Angeles, CA, 2011.
$12,000 to House Research Institute, Los Angeles, CA, 2010.
$12,000 to House Research Institute, Los Angeles, CA, 2011.
$10,000 to Boy Scouts of America, Santa Ana, CA, 2011.
$8,000 to University of Southern California Norris Cancer Foundation, Los Angeles, CA, 2011.
$5,000 to Children of the Night, Van Nuys, CA, 2011.
$5,000 to Union Rescue Mission, Los Angeles, CA, 2011.
$5,000 to Whittier College, Whittier, CA, 2011.
$2,500 to Bishop Mora Salesian High School, Los Angeles, CA, 2011.
$2,500 to Resurrection School, Los Angeles, CA, 2011.

750
JG Foundation ✧
9663 Santa Monica Blvd., Ste. 690
Beverly Hills, CA 90210-4303
Contact: James Gipson, Pres.

Established in 1998 in CA.
Donor: James Gipson.
Foundation type: Independent foundation.
Financial data (yr. ended 05/31/13): Assets, $11,635,081 (M); expenditures, $1,112,130; qualifying distributions, $1,100,000; giving activities include $1,100,000 for 2 grants (high: $1,000,000; low: $100,000).
Fields of interest: Elementary/secondary education; Higher education.
Limitations: Applications not accepted. Giving primarily in CA and MA. No grants to individuals.
Application information: Contributes only to pre-selected organizations.

Officers: James Gipson, Pres.; Michael Kromm, Secy. and C.F.O.
EIN: 954693758
Selected grants: The following grants are a representative sample of this grantmaker's funding activity:
$1,000,000 to Boston College, Chestnut Hill, MA, 2012.

751
JL Foundation ✧
c/o J. Arthur Greenfield
10880 Wilshire Blvd., Ste. 800
Los Angeles, CA 90024-4124

Established in 1988 in CA as a public charity; became a private, independent foundation in 2000.
Donors: Jon B. Lovelace; Lillian P. Lovelace; James B. Lovelace; Robert W. Lovelace.
Foundation type: Independent foundation.
Financial data (yr. ended 10/31/13): Assets, $32,418,293 (M); gifts received, $500,000; expenditures, $1,261,923; qualifying distributions, $1,164,645; giving activities include $1,159,525 for 18 grants (high: $200,000; low: $10,000).
Fields of interest: Arts education; Arts; Higher education; Education; Environment, association; Autism research; Human services.
Type of support: General/operating support; Annual campaigns; Capital campaigns; Building/renovation; Program development; Matching/challenge support.
Limitations: Applications not accepted. Giving primarily in states where trustees reside, with emphasis on Los Angeles, CA and CO.
Application information: Contributes only to pre-selected organizations.
Officers: Jeffrey K. Lovelace, Pres.; Robert W. Lovelace, Secy.; James B. Lovelace, Treas.
EIN: 954129163
Selected grants: The following grants are a representative sample of this grantmaker's funding activity:
$200,000 to Nature Conservancy, Boulder, CO, 2011.
$140,000 to Colorado Springs School, Colorado Springs, CO, 2011.
$100,000 to Autism Speaks, Los Angeles, CA, 2011.
$100,000 to California Institute of the Arts, Valencia, CA, 2011.
$100,000 to Idyllwild Arts Foundation, Idyllwild, CA, 2011.
$100,000 to Princeton University, Princeton, NJ, 2011.
$75,000 to Value Schools, Los Angeles, CA, 2011.
$50,000 to Childrens Clinic, Long Beach, CA, 2011.
$40,000 to Vista del Mar Child and Family Services, Los Angeles, CA, 2011.
$25,000 to Pacific Council on International Policy, Los Angeles, CA, 2011.

752
JMM Charitable Foundation Inc. ✧
5200 W. Century Blvd.
Los Angeles, CA 90045-5928

Established in 2006 in NJ.
Donors: J-M Manufacturing Co., Inc.; Walter W. Wang; Shirley W. Wang.
Foundation type: Company-sponsored foundation.
Financial data (yr. ended 12/31/12): Assets, $11,193,441 (M); expenditures, $2,412,886; qualifying distributions, $2,316,100; giving activities include $2,316,100 for 8 grants (high: $1,800,000; low: $10,000).
Purpose and activities: The foundation supports hospitals and organizations involved with legal aid, civil rights, and Christianity.
Fields of interest: Education; Human services; Civil/human rights.
Type of support: General/operating support.
Limitations: Applications not accepted. Giving primarily in Dana Point, Los Angeles, and San Francisco, CA and Plano, TX. No grants to individuals.
Application information: Contributes only to pre-selected organizations.
Officers and Directors:* Walter W. Wang,* Pres.; John Mai, Secy.; Shirley W. Wang.
EIN: 204679694

753
Walter S. Johnson Foundation ✧
505 Montgomery St., Ste. 620
San Francisco, CA 94111-6529 (415) 283-1854
Contact: Grant Inquiries: Yali Lincroft, Prog. Off.; General Inquiries: Christina Thompson, Grants Mgr.; Operational/administrative inquiries: Pegine Grayson, Exec. Dir.
FAX: (415) 283-1840; E-mail: info@wsjf.org; Main URL: http://www.wsjf.org
Grants Database: http://wsjf.org/our-funding-priorities/previous-grant-recipients/

Established in 1968 in CA.
Donor: Walter S. Johnson†.
Foundation type: Independent foundation.
Financial data (yr. ended 12/31/12): Assets, $93,122,341 (M); expenditures, $4,771,002; qualifying distributions, $4,643,344; giving activities include $3,360,695 for 60 grants (high: $400,000; low: $10,000).
Purpose and activities: The foundation provides grants to assist youth to become successful adults by promoting positive change in the policies and systems that serve them and by supporting high impact and promising practices. Grantmaking is limited to organizations providing services in Northern California and Washoe County, Nevada, and policy advocacy organizations effecting change that will impact those areas.
Fields of interest: Education, reform; Elementary/secondary education; Graduate/professional education; Youth development, services; Children/youth, services; Family services; Leadership development; Youth; Young adults; Economically disadvantaged.
Type of support: Research; Program evaluation; General/operating support; Program development; Seed money; Technical assistance.
Limitations: Giving primarily in northern CA and the counties of Alameda, Alpine, Amador, Butte, Calaveras, Colusa, Contra Costa, Del Norte, El Dorado, Fresno, Glenn, Humboldt, Inyo, Kings, Lake, Lassen, Madera, Marin, Mariposa, Mendocino, Merced, Modoc, Mono, Monterey, Napa, Nevada, Placer, Plumas, Sacramento, San Benito, San Francisco, San Joaquin, San Mateo, Santa Clara, Santa Cruz, Shasta, Sierra, Siskiyou, Solano, Sonoma, Stanislaus, Sutter, Tehama, Trinity, Tulare, Tuolumne, Yolo, Yuba; funding also in Washoe County, NV. No support for religious organizations for sectarian purposes or for medical purposes, or for private schools. No grants to individuals, or for annual campaigns, deficit financing, memorial funds, capital or endowment funds, conservation or renovation projects, equipment purchases, awards, prizes, one time events, plays or films, camps or school bands, emergency funding, or scholarships.
Publications: Application guidelines; Financial statement.
Application information: Unsolicited proposals not accepted. Interested applicants should contact foundation Program Officer, Yali Lincroft, at yalilncroft@wsjf.org to discuss their needs and the foundation's current funding priorities. If a proposal is invited, an application form will be required, and it is to be submitted electronically. See foundation web site for further information.
Deadline(s): Varies. Check with Prog. Off.
Board meeting date(s): Feb., May, Aug. and Nov.
Final notification: Shortly after each quarterly Board meeting at which funding decisions are made
Officers and Trustees:* Sandra Bruckner,* Pres.; Samuel Lamont Johnson,* Secy.; Hathily Johnson Winston,* Treas.; Pegine Grayson, Exec. Dir.; Gloria Eddie; Gloria Jeneal Eddie; Peter Lillevand; Scott Shackelton.
Number of staff: 2 part-time professional; 1 full-time support; 1 part-time support.
EIN: 237003595
Selected grants: The following grants are a representative sample of this grantmaker's funding activity:
$200,000 to Foundation for California Community Colleges, Sacramento, CA, 2013. For California College Guidance Initiative, which helps 6-12th grade students prepare for post-secondary success.
$175,000 to California State University, San Francisco, CA, 2013. For data collection and analysis from Give Students a Compass project and to integrate lessons learned from project into broader Associate Degrees for Transfer program.
$80,000 to Beyond Emancipation, Oakland, CA, 2013. For evaluation of Creative and Resourceful and Whole Project.

754
Rupert H. Johnson, Jr. Foundation ✧
c/o Rupert H. Johnson, Jr.
1 Franklin Pkwy., Bldg. 920, 4th Fl.
San Mateo, CA 94403
Contact: Rupert H. Johnson, Jr., Tr.

Established in 1992 in CA.
Donor: Rupert H. Johnson, Jr.
Foundation type: Independent foundation.
Financial data (yr. ended 12/31/13): Assets, $75,951,652 (M); expenditures, $602,950; qualifying distributions, $602,790; giving activities include $595,290 for 34 grants (high: $100,000; low: $300).
Purpose and activities: Giving primarily for higher and other education.
Fields of interest: Higher education; Education; Christian agencies & churches.
Limitations: Applications accepted. Giving primarily in CA and VA. No grants to individuals.
Application information: Application form not required.
Initial approach: Proposal
Deadline(s): None
Trustee: Rupert H. Johnson, Jr.
EIN: 943170047

755
E. Richard Jones Family Foundation ✧
(formerly The Jones Foundation)
c/o E. Richard Jones
P.O. Box 352
Calistoga, CA 94515 (707) 942-0467
Contact: Stephanie Bailey, V.P.
E-mail: erjfoundation@joneswine.com

Established in 1997 in CA and DE.
Donors: Jones Living Trust; Marilyn Jones; ERJ Living Trust.
Foundation type: Independent foundation.
Financial data (yr. ended 06/30/13): Assets, $5,713,219 (M); expenditures, $532,104; qualifying distributions, $462,826; giving activities include $447,200 for 30 grants (high: $200,000; low: $250).
Purpose and activities: Giving to organizations that assist individuals in changing their lives and becoming self-sufficient.
Fields of interest: Elementary/secondary education; Higher education; Education; Health care; Human services; Family services; Foundations (community).
Type of support: Annual campaigns; Seed money.
Limitations: Applications accepted. Giving primarily in the San Francisco Bay Area, CA.
Application information: Application form required.
Initial approach: Letter, no more than 2 pages
Copies of proposal: 1
Deadline(s): None
Officers: Stephanie Bailey, V.P.; Heather Melvin, V.P.
Director: E. Richard Jones.
Number of staff: 1 part-time professional.
EIN: 943288860
Selected grants: The following grants are a representative sample of this grantmaker's funding activity:
$50,000 to Teach for America, San Francisco, CA, 2011. For general support.
$45,000 to Partners in School Innovation, San Francisco, CA, 2011. For general support.
$25,000 to Calistoga Family Center, Calistoga, CA, 2011. For general support.
$25,000 to Community Health Clinic Ole, Napa, CA, 2011. For general support.
$6,000 to Crystal Springs Uplands School, Hillsborough, CA, 2011. For general support.
$5,000 to Denison University, Granville, OH, 2011. For general support.
$5,000 to Princeton University, Princeton, NJ, 2011. For general support.
$1,000 to California Pacific Medical Center Foundation, San Francisco, CA, 2011. For general support.
$1,000 to Children of Shelters, San Francisco, CA, 2011. For general support.
$1,000 to Samaritan House, San Mateo, CA, 2011. For general support.

756
The Fletcher Jones Foundation ✧
(formerly The Jones Foundation)
117 E. Colorado Blvd., Ste. 403
Pasadena, CA 91105-3725 (626) 535-9506
Contact: Christine Sisley, Treas. and Exec. Dir.
FAX: (626) 535-9508; Main URL: http://www.fletcherjonesfdn.org

Established in 1969 in CA.
Donor: Fletcher Jones†.
Foundation type: Independent foundation.
Financial data (yr. ended 12/31/13): Assets, $145,678,944 (M); expenditures, $10,528,762; qualifying distributions, $7,305,746; giving activities include $6,976,557 for 86 grants (high: $1,000,000; low: $150).
Purpose and activities: Support primarily for private colleges and universities, particularly those in CA (over 96 percent of available funds).
Fields of interest: Higher education.
Type of support: Capital campaigns; Building/renovation; Equipment; Endowments; Professorships; Fellowships; Scholarship funds; Matching/challenge support.
Limitations: Applications accepted. Giving primarily in CA. No support for K-12 schools; political campaigns or organizations. No grants to individuals, or for operating funds, deficit financing, conferences, seminars, workshops, travel exhibits, surveys, or projects supported by government agencies; no loans.
Publications: Annual report (including application guidelines); Financial statement; Grants list.
Application information: Submission in any other form will not be accepted. Please visit the foundation's web site for more detailed application procedures. Application form not required.
Initial approach: Online. Prior to online submission call or meet with the Executive Director in order to discuss a tentative proposal and to determine the suitability of the intended request
Copies of proposal: 1
Deadline(s): 6 weeks prior to board meetings
Board meeting date(s): Mar., June, Sept. and Dec.
Final notification: 3 to 6 months
Officers and Trustees:* Peter K. Barker,* Pres.; John D. Pettker, V.P. and Secy.; Samuel P. Bell,* V.P.; Parker S. Kennedy,* V.P.; Robert W. Kummer, Jr.,* V.P.; Daniel E. Lungren,* V.P.; Donald E. Nickelson,* V.P.; Hon. Rockwell Schnabel,* V.P.; Stewart R. Smith,* V.P.; Christine Sisley, Treas. and Exec. Dir.; Patrick C. Haden*.
Number of staff: 1 part-time professional; 1 part-time support.
EIN: 237030155
Selected grants: The following grants are a representative sample of this grantmaker's funding activity:
$1,015,000 to University of Southern California, Institute for Advanced Catholic Studies, Los Angeles, CA, 2012. For renovations and equipment for Organic Chemistry Teaching Lab in Seeley G. Mudd Hall.
$1,000,000 to California Institute of Technology, Kavli Neuroscience Institute, Pasadena, CA, 2012. For Endowed Directorship.
$1,000,000 to John Tracy Clinic, Dickinson C. Ross Center for Education and Innovation, Los Angeles, CA, 2012. For Master's Program for Teachers of the Deaf.
$725,000 to Boy Scouts of America, Los Angeles Area Council, Los Angeles, CA, 2012. For endowment for equipment and maintenance at Camp Pollock.
$500,000 to Harvey Mudd College, Claremont, CA, 2012. For endowment for Summer Undergraduate Research Program.
$500,000 to University of San Francisco, Department of Biology, Fletcher Jones Microscopy Center, San Francisco, CA, 2012. For equipment.
$380,875 to University of the Pacific, Eberhardt School of Business, Stockton, CA, 2012. For merit-based scholarships.
$300,000 to Golden Gate University, San Francisco, CA, 2012. For endowed scholarship fund.
$300,000 to Simpson University, Redding, CA, 2012. For equipment for Nursing Capacity Expansion Project.
$150,000 to Vanguard University, Costa Mesa, CA, 2012. For Endowed Scholarship Fund for veterans of Iraq and Afganistan.

757
The June Foundation ✧
5757 Wilshire Blvd., Ste. 345
Los Angeles, CA 90036-3683

Established in 1999 in CA.
Donors: Michael Kest; Susanne Kest; Sol Kest; Kest 2009 Charitable Lead Trust No 2.
Foundation type: Independent foundation.
Financial data (yr. ended 12/31/12): Assets, $16,744,748 (M); gifts received, $856,391; expenditures, $1,111,681; qualifying distributions, $724,680; giving activities include $724,680 for grants.
Fields of interest: Jewish federated giving programs; Jewish agencies & synagogues.
Limitations: Applications not accepted. Giving primarily in CA and NY. No grants to individuals.
Application information: Contributes only to pre-selected organizations.
Officers: Michael Kest, C.E.O., Pres. and Treas.; Yosef Maneka, Secy.; Matthew Kest, C.F.O.
Director: Rabbi Gershon Bess.
EIN: 954745292

758
JVK Foundation ✧
c/o Savitsky, Satin & Bacon
10880 Wilshire Blvd., Ste. 2100
Los Angeles, CA 90024-4121

Established in 2006 in CA.
Donor: Kevin Knipfing.
Foundation type: Independent foundation.
Financial data (yr. ended 12/31/13): Assets, $3,048,172 (M); expenditures, $742,604; qualifying distributions, $707,431; giving activities include $642,100 for 9 grants (high: $250,000; low: $10,000).
Fields of interest: Education; Hospitals (general); Eye research; Food distribution, meals on wheels; Housing/shelter, homeless; Children/youth, services.
Limitations: Applications not accepted. Giving primarily in CA and NY. No grants to individuals.
Application information: Contributes only to pre-selected organizations.
Trustees: Janet Knipfing; Kevin Knipfing; Leslie Knipfing.
EIN: 207088552

759
Kahle/Austin Foundation ✧
c/o B. Kahle
513B Simonds Loop
San Francisco, CA 94129-1449
Contact: Brewster L. Kahle, Pres.; Mary K. Austin, Secy.

Established in 1997 in WA.
Donors: Mary K. Austin; Brewster L. Kahle.

Foundation type: Independent foundation.
Financial data (yr. ended 12/31/12): Assets, $24,594,626 (M); expenditures, $3,985,089; qualifying distributions, $3,918,081; giving activities include $3,800,735 for 41 grants (high: $3,236,635; low: $500).
Purpose and activities: Giving primarily for human services and an Internet archive.
Fields of interest: Elementary/secondary education; Human services; Electronic communications/Internet.
Limitations: Applications not accepted. Giving primarily in San Francisco, CA. No grants to individuals.
Application information: Contributes only to pre-selected organizations.
Board meeting date(s): Dec.
Officers: Brewster L. Kahle, Pres., V.P. and Treas.; Mary K. Austin, Secy.
EIN: 911816164

760
The Henry J. Kaiser Family Foundation ✧
2400 Sand Hill Rd.
Menlo Park, CA 94025-6941 (650) 854-9400
Contact: Renee Wells, Contracts Mgr.
FAX: (650) 854-4800; E-mail: rwells@kff.org; Washington, DC Office Address: 1330 G St. N.W., Washington, DC 20005, tel.: (202) 347-5270; fax: (202) 347-5274; Main URL: http://www.kff.org
E-Newsletter: http://profile.kff.org/
Facebook: https://www.facebook.com/KaiserFamilyFoundation
Twitter: http://twitter.com/KaiserFamFound
YouTube: http://www.youtube.com/kaiserfoundation

Trust established in 1948 in CA; changed status to operating foundation in 1999.
Donors: Bess F. Kaiser‡; Henry J. Kaiser‡; Henry J. Kaiser, Jr.‡; and others.
Foundation type: Operating foundation.
Financial data (yr. ended 12/31/12): Assets, $573,956,985 (M); gifts received, $1,649,145; expenditures, $59,560,410; qualifying distributions, $46,002,952; giving activities include $665,200 for 50+ grants (high: $75,000), $92,018 for employee matching gifts, and $10,242,558 for 4 foundation-administered programs.
Purpose and activities: The foundation is a nonprofit, private operating foundation that develops and runs its own research and communications programs and does not accept unsolicited funding requests.
Fields of interest: Health care, public policy; Reproductive health; AIDS; Minorities; Women; Economically disadvantaged.
International interests: South Africa.
Limitations: Applications not accepted. Giving in South Africa for the international grants program; other grants nationwide.
Application information: The foundation does not accept unsolicited funding requests.
Officers and Trustees:* Richard T. Scholsberg,* Chair.; Drew E. Altman, Ph.D.*, C.E.O. and Pres.; Susan V. Berresford; James E. Doyle, J.D.; William H. Frist, M.D.; Charles Gibson; Katie B. Kaiser, M.B.A.; Beverly Malone, Ph.D.; Gerald Rosberg, J.D.; Peter Taylor, M.P.P.; Diana Chapman Walsh, M.S., Ph.D.; W. Richard West, Jr., J.D.; Kathy Wehle, CPA.
Number of staff: 82 full-time professional; 36 full-time support.
EIN: 946064808

Selected grants: The following grants are a representative sample of this grantmaker's funding activity:
$65,000 to Barnard College, New York, NY, 2012. To support of the Sally Chapman Fund.
$25,000 to Hope Street Group, Prescott, AZ, 2012. To provide Shelter to Abused Women Throughout Washington Dc.
$25,000 to Massachusetts Institute of Technology, Cambridge, MA, 2012. To support of the Pressman Endowment in the Department of Political Science at MIT.
$25,000 to Morehouse College, Atlanta, GA, 2012. To support of the David Satcher Scholars Scholarship Fund.
$20,000 to Pride Foundation, Seattle, WA, 2012. To support of You Go Girl Scholarship Program and General Operations.
$17,500 to Princeton University, Princeton, NJ, 2012. To support of the Adam Henry Fund and General Operations.
$15,000 to New America Foundation, Washington, DC, 2012. For Report/Book By Jason Deparle on the Causes/Consequences of the Nursing Shortage.
$10,000 to American Cancer Society, Oakland, CA, 2012. To support of a Hope Lodge in Madison to Assist Cancer Patients/Caregivers.
$10,000 to Foundation Fighting Blindness, Columbia, MD, 2012. To support of the Madison, Wisconsin FFB Dining in the Dark Fundraiser.
$7,500 to Orcas Island Community Foundation, Eastsound, WA, 2012. To support of the LGBT Fund.

761
Kalliopeia Foundation ✧
P.O. Box 151020
San Rafael, CA 94915-1020
Contact: Grants Committee
E-mail: info@kalliopeia.org; Main URL: http://www.kalliopeia.org
Facebook: http://www.facebook.com/pages/Kalliopeia-Foundation/249058285108294
Grants List: http://www.kalliopeia.org/alpha_list.html
Podcasts: http://www.kalliopeia.org/podcast/Kalliopeia_Foundation_Podcast.xml
Tumblr: http://kalliopeiafoundation.tumblr.com/
Twitter: https://twitter.com/KalliopeiaF
Vimeo: http://vimeo.com/kalliopeiafoundation
YouTube: https://www.youtube.com/user/KalliopeiaFoundation

Established in 1997 in CA.
Donor: Jubilee Group.
Foundation type: Independent foundation.
Financial data (yr. ended 12/31/12): Assets, $71,774,714 (M); gifts received, $15,002,943; expenditures, $9,006,111; qualifying distributions, $8,689,792; giving activities include $6,774,462 for 165 grants (high: $500,000; low: $1,000), and $876,442 for 1 foundation-administered program.
Purpose and activities: Kalliopeia Foundation works to support programs that honor the underlying unity at the heart of life's rich diversity. The foundation strives to foster ways of living which pay tribute to the innate dignity and creative potential within all people. The foundation supports programs that work to: 1) Foster a global consciousness of oneness; 2) Nurture the inner life through meditation and contemplation, arts and music; 3) Native American youth and culture, and Native American language programs.

Fields of interest: Human services; Children/youth, services; Community/economic development.
Type of support: Curriculum development; General/operating support; Program development; Conferences/seminars; Research.
Limitations: Applications accepted. Giving limited to the U.S. No support for international organizations. No grants to individuals.
Publications: Informational brochure.
Application information: See foundation Web site for application guidelines and procedures. Unsolicited full proposals not accepted, but letters of inquiry (LOI) may be sent anytime. LOIs sent solely by e-mail are not accepted. Nonprofit organizations that align closely with the foundation's mission and meet their evaluation criteria will be sent a request for proposal. Application form not required.
Initial approach: Letter of inquiry sent via mail only
Copies of proposal: 1
Deadline(s): Letters of inquiry accepted anytime
Board meeting date(s): Four times per year
Final notification: Letter of inquiry responded to in 6-8 weeks
Officers and Directors:* Barbara Sargent,* Pres.; D. Thomas Sargent,* Secy.-Treas.; Lisa Kleger; Nancy Hopkin.
Number of staff: 4 full-time professional; 3 full-time support; 2 part-time support.
EIN: 943270387
Selected grants: The following grants are a representative sample of this grantmaker's funding activity:
$500,000 to First Nations Development Institute, Longmont, CO, 2012. For Native Youth and Culture Fund.
$260,000 to Seventh Generation Fund for Indian Development, Arcata, CA, 2012. For Project Support for Re-grants.
$150,000 to Primordial Tradition of AIWP, Asheville, NC, 2012. For General Support.
$130,000 to Center for Contemplative Mind in Society, Northampton, MA, 2012. For General Support.
$100,000 to American Indian College Fund, Denver, CO, 2012. For the Kalliopeia Foundation Tribal College Support Program.
$100,000 to Center for Whole Communities, Fayston, VT, 2012. For General Support.
$85,000 to One Light International, Los Angeles, CA, 2012. For Shade Tree Multicultural Foundation, recommended for general support.
$30,000 to Cultural Conservancy Sacred Land Foundation, San Francisco, CA, 2012. For General Support and Project Support for Tribal Canoe Revitalization Project.
$25,000 to American Indian Institute, Tradition Circle of Indian Elders and Youth, Bozeman, MT, 2012. For Indigenous Leaders Travel Fund.
$25,000 to Sophia Foundation of North America, San Francisco, CA, 2012. For General Support.

762
Kalmanovitz Charitable Foundation ✧
100 Shoreline Hwy., B-395
Mill Valley, CA 94941-6608 (415) 332-0550

Established in 2001 in CA.
Donor: Lydia Kalmanovitz.
Foundation type: Independent foundation.
Financial data (yr. ended 06/30/12): Assets, $159,800,689 (M); expenditures, $6,727,374; qualifying distributions, $6,375,000; giving

activities include $6,375,000 for 9 grants (high: $1,900,000; low: $50,000).
Fields of interest: Higher education; Hospitals (general).
Limitations: Applications not accepted. Giving primarily in CA. No grants to individuals.
Application information: Contributes only to pre-selected organizations.
Officer: Rev. John LoSchiavo, Chair.
Trustees: Dan Giraudo; Lou Girardo; Bernard Orsi; Mark Orsi.
EIN: 946760317
Selected grants: The following grants are a representative sample of this grantmaker's funding activity:
$1,900,000 to University of California, San Francisco, CA, 2012.
$1,250,000 to University of San Francisco, San Francisco, CA, 2012.
$1,000,000 to Georgetown University, Washington, DC, 2012.
$1,000,000 to Saint Marys College of California, Moraga, CA, 2012.
$600,000 to Healthcare Foundation Northern Sonoma County, Healdsburg, CA, 2012.
$250,000 to University of California at Berkeley Foundation, Berkeley, CA, 2012.
$200,000 to Loyola Law School, Los Angeles, CA, 2012.
$125,000 to Franciscan School of Theology, Berkeley, CA, 2012.
$50,000 to University of Southern California, Los Angeles, CA, 2012.

763
The David and Meredith Kaplan Foundation ✧
16130 Ventura Blvd., Ste. 320
Encino, CA 91436-2531

Established in 2007 in CA.
Donors: David Kaplan; Meredith Kaplan; Neil Kaplan; Arlene Kaplan.
Foundation type: Independent foundation.
Financial data (yr. ended 12/31/13): Assets, $11,507,245 (M); gifts received, $1,501,000; expenditures, $856,839; qualifying distributions, $849,559; giving activities include $839,929 for 21 grants (high: $321,429; low: $500).
Fields of interest: Higher education, university; Education; Jewish agencies & synagogues.
Limitations: Applications not accepted. Giving primarily in Los Angeles, CA and in MI. No grants to individuals.
Application information: Contributes only to pre-selected organizations.
Trustees: David Kaplan; Meredith Kaplan.
EIN: 266166619
Selected grants: The following grants are a representative sample of this grantmaker's funding activity:
$75,000 to American Israel Education Foundation, Washington, DC, 2011.
$71,429 to University of Michigan, Ann Arbor, MI, 2011.

764
Kapor Center for Social Impact
(formerly Mitchell Kapor Foundation)
2201 Broadway, Ste. 727
Oakland, CA 94612-3024 (510) 255-4650
Contact: Cedric Brown, C.E.O.
E-mail: info@kaporcenter.org; Tel./Fax: (510) 488-6600; Main URL: http://www.kaporcenter.org
Blog: http://www.kaporcenter.org/blog
Facebook: https://www.facebook.com/KaporCenter
Kapor Center for Social Impact's Philanthropy Promise: http://www.ncrp.org/philanthropys-promise/who
RSS Feed: http://feeds2.feedburner.com/MitchellKaporFoundationWeblog
Twitter: https://twitter.com/KaporCenter
YouTube: https://www.youtube.com/user/KaporCenter

Established in 1997 in MA.
Donor: Mitchell Kapor.
Foundation type: Independent foundation.
Financial data (yr. ended 12/31/12): Assets, $35,589,212 (M); gifts received, $1,175,382; expenditures, $5,545,036; qualifying distributions, $5,013,208; giving activities include $4,201,000 for 95 grants (high: $2,020,000; low: $250).
Purpose and activities: The foundation is based in the San Francisco Bay Area, California, and supports organizations that provoke social change in communities of color en route to equality. It employs three strategies in pursuit of their mission: grantmaking and community partnerships, collaboration with other funders, and technical assistance to organizations. It is particularly interested in working with organizations that have a racial justice analysis and an integrated use of information technology.
Fields of interest: Secondary school/education; Higher education; Education; Environment, administration/regulation; Environment, public policy; Environment, information services; Environment, recycling; Environment, climate change/global warming; Environment; Community/economic development; Public affairs, citizen participation.
Type of support: General/operating support; Continuing support; Management development/capacity building; Program development; Conferences/seminars; Seed money; Curriculum development; Technical assistance; Consulting services; Program evaluation; In-kind gifts; Matching/challenge support; Mission-related investments/loans.
Limitations: Applications accepted. Giving primarily in the San Francisco Bay Area, CA; limited giving in southern CA and nationally. The foundation does not award grants to organizations based or primarily working outside of the U.S. No grants to individuals.
Publications: Application guidelines; Annual report; Financial statement; Grants list; Occasional report.
Application information: Application guidelines available on foundation web site. Application form required.
Initial approach: Apply online only after reviewing guidelines on web site and discussion with staff
Deadline(s): Generally quarterly
Board meeting date(s): Quarterly (some flexibility)
Final notification: Generally within six weeks
Officers and Trustees:* Mitchell Kapor,* Co-Chair.; Freada Kapor Klein, Ph.D.*, Co-Chair.; Cedric Brown, C.E.O.; Stephen DeBerry, Treas.
Number of staff: 3 full-time professional; 1 part-time professional; 1 full-time support.
EIN: 943330604

765
The Bruce Karatz Family Foundation ✧
10960 Wilshire Blvd., 5th Fl.
Los Angeles, CA 90024-3702

Established in 2004 in CA.
Donor: Bruce E. Karatz.
Foundation type: Independent foundation.
Financial data (yr. ended 12/31/12): Assets, $2,452,795 (M); expenditures, $509,849; qualifying distributions, $497,453; giving activities include $497,453 for grants.
Fields of interest: Education; Human services; Jewish federated giving programs; Jewish agencies & synagogues.
Limitations: Applications not accepted. Giving primarily in CA. No grants to individuals.
Application information: Contributes only to pre-selected organizations.
Officers: Bruce E. Karatz, Pres.; Matthew D. Karatz, C.F.O.; Elizabeth D. Karatz, V.P.; Theodore S. Karatz, Secy.
EIN: 201342811

766
Karisma Foundation ✧
2934 1/2 Beverly Glen Cir., Ste. 419
Los Angeles, CA 90077-1724 (818) 342-3022
Contact: Karen Bedrosian Coyne, C.F.O.

Established in 2005 in CA.
Donors: John C. Bedrosian; Judith D. Bedrosian.
Foundation type: Independent foundation.
Financial data (yr. ended 06/30/13): Assets, $8,872,832 (M); expenditures, $739,086; qualifying distributions, $569,000; giving activities include $569,000 for 16 grants (high: $125,000; low: $2,000).
Purpose and activities: Giving for organizations serving people in Armenia; funding for organizations serving children in the Los Angeles area.
Fields of interest: Children/youth, services; Children/youth.
International interests: Armenia.
Type of support: General/operating support; Equipment; Continuing support.
Limitations: Applications accepted. Giving on a national and international basis, primarily in Los Angeles, CA and Armenia. No support for religious organizations.
Application information: Application form required.
Initial approach: Letter
Deadline(s): None
Board meeting date(s): Spring and Fall
Officers and Directors:* John C. Bedrosian,* Pres.; Karen Bedrosian Coyne, C.F.O.; Judith D. Bedrosian,* Secy.
Number of staff: 1 part-time professional.
EIN: 201982120
Selected grants: The following grants are a representative sample of this grantmaker's funding activity:
$2,000 to Nevada Museum of Art, Reno, NV, 2013. For established charity.

767
The Karsh Family Foundation ✧
1201 Tower Grove Dr.
Beverly Hills, CA 90210-2135

Established in 1997 in CA.
Donors: Bruce A. Karsh; Martha L. Karsh.
Foundation type: Independent foundation.
Financial data (yr. ended 06/30/13): Assets, $84,919,151 (M); gifts received, $18,757,502; expenditures, $11,081,712; qualifying distributions, $9,910,663; giving activities include $9,883,974 for 51 grants (high: $1,079,097; low: $1,000).
Fields of interest: Higher education; Human services; Jewish federated giving programs; Jewish agencies & synagogues.
Limitations: Applications not accepted. Giving primarily in CA and NC. No grants to individuals.
Application information: Contributes only to pre-selected organizations.
Trustees: Bruce A. Karsh; Martha L. Karsh.
EIN: 137147287
Selected grants: The following grants are a representative sample of this grantmaker's funding activity:
$9,090,000 to Duke University, Durham, NC, 2012. For Karsh International School, endowment, Jazz Loft Project and general support.
$4,010,000 to Duke University, Karsh International School, Durham, NC, 2013. For endowment, Jazz Loft Project, and general support.
$2,500,000 to Teach for America, New York, NY, 2012. For general support.
$1,079,097 to KIPP LA Schools, Los Angeles, CA, 2013. For general support.
$1,039,304 to KIPP LA Schools, Los Angeles, CA, 2012. For general support.
$1,029,510 to Teach for America, New York, NY, 2013. For general support.
$1,000,000 to University of Virginia Law School Foundation, Charlottesville, VA, 2013. For general support.
$1,000,000 to Wilshire Boulevard Temple, Los Angeles, CA, 2012. For general support.
$618,667 to Brown University, Providence, RI, 2013. To support Kipp Students.
$500,000 to Silicon Schools Fund, Emeryville, CA, 2013. For general support.
$500,000 to University of Pennsylvania, Philadelphia, PA, 2013. For general support.
$400,000 to University of Pennsylvania, Philadelphia, PA, 2012. For general support.
$200,000 to University of Virginia Law School Foundation, Charlottesville, VA, 2012. For general support.
$25,200 to Partnership Scholars Program, Marina Del Rey, CA, 2013. For general support.
$25,000 to Harvard-Westlake School, Office of Advancement, North Hollywood, CA, 2013. For financial aid.
$25,000 to Say Yes to Education, New York, NY, 2013. For general support.
$15,000 to American Friends of the Hebrew University, New York, NY, 2012. For general support.

768
The Katz Family Foundation ✧
9229 Sunset Blvd., Ste. 850
Los Angeles, CA 90069-3413

Established in 2002 in CA.
Donors: Madelyn Katz; Ronald Katz.
Foundation type: Independent foundation.
Financial data (yr. ended 12/31/13): Assets, $19,806,633 (M); expenditures, $905,744; qualifying distributions, $862,273; giving activities include $862,273 for 32 grants (high: $651,700; low: $50).
Fields of interest: Higher education; Jewish federated giving programs; Jewish agencies & synagogues.
Limitations: Applications not accepted. No grants to individuals.
Application information: Unsolicited requests for funds not accepted.
Officer: Ronald Katz, Pres. and C.F.O.
Directors: Randy Katz; Todd Katz.
EIN: 460493067
Selected grants: The following grants are a representative sample of this grantmaker's funding activity:
$3,000 to YMCA of Metropolitan Los Angeles, Los Angeles, CA, 2011.

769
The Marilyn and Jeffrey Katzenberg Foundation ✧
11400 W. Olympic Blvd., Ste. 550
Los Angeles, CA 90064-1551

Established in 1994 in CA.
Donors: Jeffrey Katzenberg; Marilyn Katzenberg; Katzenberg Family Trust.
Foundation type: Independent foundation.
Financial data (yr. ended 12/31/12): Assets, $16,462,723 (M); expenditures, $807,295; qualifying distributions, $621,450; giving activities include $621,450 for 68 grants (high: $40,000; low: $250).
Purpose and activities: Giving primarily for higher education, the arts, particularly for film and television, environmental conservation and protection, and health and human services.
Fields of interest: Media, film/video; Media, television; Arts; Higher education; Environment, natural resources; Hospitals (general); Health care; Health organizations, association; Medical research, institute; Cancer research; Human services; Children/youth, services.
Limitations: Applications not accepted. Giving primarily in CA and VA. No grants to individuals.
Application information: Contributes only to pre-selected organizations.
Officers: Jeffrey Katzenberg, Pres.; Marilyn Katzenberg, V.P. and Secy.; David Geffen, Treas.
EIN: 954513461

770
Glorya Kaufman Dance Foundation ✧ ☆
c/o RBZ, LLP, Attn.: H. Bookstein
11766 Wilshire Blvd., 9th Fl.
Los Angeles, CA 90025-6538
E-mail: info@thegloryakaufmandancefoundation.org ; Main URL: http://www.gloryakaufmandancefoundation.org

Established in CA.
Foundation type: Independent foundation.
Financial data (yr. ended 12/31/12): Assets, $7,615,436 (M); expenditures, $930,182; qualifying distributions, $878,377; giving activities include $878,100 for 10 grants (high: $600,000; low: $500).
Fields of interest: Performing arts, dance; Arts.
Limitations: Applications not accepted. Giving primarily in CA and New York, NY.
Application information: Unsolicited requests for funds not accepted.
Trustee: Glorya Kaufman.
EIN: 806167949
Selected grants: The following grants are a representative sample of this grantmaker's funding activity:
$600,000 to Alvin Ailey Dance Foundation, New York, NY, 2012. For dance performance and education.

771
The Kavli Foundation ✧
1801 Solar Drive, Ste. 250
Oxnard, CA 93030-8297 (805) 683-6000
Contact: Dr. Robert W. Conn, Pres.
FAX: (805) 988-4800; Main URL: http://www.kavlifoundation.org/
E-Newsletter: http://visitor.constantcontact.com/manage/optin/ea?v=001nQUq2GTjwCh2XVyu9nQt_g%3D%3D
E-Newsletter: http://www.kavlifoundation.org/kavli-newsletter
RSS Feed: http://www.kavlifoundation.org/rss.xml
Twitter: http://twitter.com/KavliFoundation
YouTube: http://www.youtube.com/KavliFoundation

Established in 2000 in CA.
Donor: Fred Kavli†.
Foundation type: Independent foundation.
Financial data (yr. ended 12/31/12): Assets, $176,204,117 (M); gifts received, $10,500,000; expenditures, $12,962,806; qualifying distributions, $9,511,150; giving activities include $4,393,555 for 13 grants (high: $1,250,000; low: $30,000).
Purpose and activities: The foundation is dedicated to the goals of advancing science for the benefit of humanity and promoting increased public understanding of and support for scientists and their work. The foundation has selected three areas in which to focus its activities: astrophysics, neuroscience, and nanoscience. An international program of research institutes, prizes, symposia, and endowed professorships is being established to further these goals.
Fields of interest: Education; Science.
Type of support: Professorships; Research.
Limitations: Applications not accepted. Giving primarily on a national basis; some giving internationally. No grants to individuals.
Publications: Informational brochure.
Application information: Participation in the foundation's programs of fellowships, professorships, symposia and prizes is by invitation only; the foundation does not respond to unsolicited proposals.
Officers and Directors:* Rockell N. Hankin,* Chair.; Dr. Robert W. Conn,* C.E.O. and Pres.; Miyoung Chun, Ph.D., Exec. V.P., Science Progs.; Mary Sue Coleman; Thomas E. Everhart; Douglas K. Freeman; Richard A. Meserve; Gunnar K. Nilsen; Henry T. Yang.
Number of staff: 2 full-time professional; 1 part-time professional; 3 full-time support.
EIN: 770560142
Selected grants: The following grants are a representative sample of this grantmaker's funding activity:

$1,250,000 to Cambridge University, Kavli Institute of Cosmology, Cambridge, England, 2011.
$1,250,000 to Science Center in Trondheim, Trondheim, Norway, 2011.
$803,600 to Royal Society, Kavli International Center, London, England, 2011.
$555,000 to Peking University, Beijing, China, 2011.
$525,000 to Chinese Academy of Sciences, Beijing, China, 2011.
$500,000 to National Academy of Sciences, Washington, DC, 2011.
$500,000 to Techniek Educatie Delft, Delft, Netherlands, 2011.
$222,222 to Yale University, New Haven, CT, 2011.
$83,333 to Stanford University, Stanford, CA, 2011.
$80,000 to Society for Neuroscience, Washington, DC, 2011.

772
The Kay Family Foundation ✧
16381 Scientific Way, Ste. 812
Irvine, CA 92618-4354 (949) 379-2300
Contact: Steeve Kay, C.E.O.

Established in 2005 in CA.
Donor: Steeve Kay.
Foundation type: Independent foundation.
Financial data (yr. ended 12/31/12): Assets, $31,633,477 (M); gifts received, $2,000,000; expenditures, $1,488,335; qualifying distributions, $1,294,275; giving activities include $980,987 for 27 grants (high: $624,857; low: $200).
Fields of interest: Higher education; Christian agencies & churches; Protestant agencies & churches.
Limitations: Giving primarily in CA.
Application information:
Initial approach: Contact the foundation
Officers and Directors:* Steeve Kay,* Chair.; Elim Kay,* Pres.; Eleanor Kay,* Secy.; Ethan Kay,* C.F.O.; Timothy Tang.
EIN: 550883567
Selected grants: The following grants are a representative sample of this grantmaker's funding activity:
$1,000 to National Center for Family Philanthropy, Washington, DC, 2012. For charitable giving.

773
Kayne Foundation ✧
1800 Avenue of the Stars, 3rd Fl.
Los Angeles, CA 90067-4201

Established in 1986 in CA.
Donor: Jerry D. Kayne.
Foundation type: Independent foundation.
Financial data (yr. ended 12/31/12): Assets, $28,492,618 (M); gifts received, $9,476,893; expenditures, $3,639,892; qualifying distributions, $3,414,531; giving activities include $3,330,357 for 99 grants (high: $733,336; low: $72).
Fields of interest: Museums (art); Arts; Education; Environment, natural resources; Health organizations, association; Human services; Children/youth, services; Jewish federated giving programs; Jewish agencies & synagogues.
Limitations: Applications not accepted. Giving primarily in CA, with emphasis on the Los Angeles area. No grants to individuals.
Application information: Contributes only to pre-selected organizations.
Officers: Suzanne L. Kayne, Pres.; Janis Minton, Secy.; Howard Zelikow, Treas.; Jerry D. Kayne, C.F.O.
Directors: Maggie Kayne; Richard A. Kayne.
EIN: 954124379

774
W. M. Keck Foundation ✧
550 S. Hope St., Ste. 2500
Los Angeles, CA 90071-2617 (213) 680-3833
Contact: Maria Pellegrini, Exec. Dir., Progs.; Matesha Varma, Sr. Prog. Dir.
FAX: (213) 614-0934; E-mail: info@wmkeck.org;
E-mail for Maria Pellegrini: mpellegrini@wmkeck.org;
Main URL: http://www.wmkeck.org
Grant Abstracts: http://www.wmkeck.org/grant-abstracts-final
Knowledge Center: http://www.wmkeck.org/impact

Established in 1954 and incorporated in 1959 in DE.
Donor: William M. Keck‡.
Foundation type: Independent foundation.
Financial data (yr. ended 12/31/13): Assets, $1,254,540,000 (M); expenditures, $68,999,000; qualifying distributions, $54,992,000; giving activities include $54,992,000 for grants.
Purpose and activities: The foundation continues to adhere to the directions and guidelines established by its founder, using an interdisciplinary/cross-program or thematic funding approach. The foundation has designated the following specific areas of funding: Early Learning Program, Science and Engineering Program, Liberal Arts Program, Medical Research Program, and the Southern CA Program. Concentration is placed on strengthening studies and programs in accredited colleges and universities, medical schools, and major independent medical research institutions in the areas of earth science, engineering, medical research, and to some extent, other sciences, and the liberal arts. Some consideration, limited to southern CA, is given to organizations in the categories of arts and culture, civic and community affairs, health care, precollegiate education, and early learning.
Fields of interest: Arts; Elementary school/education; Secondary school/education; Higher education; Engineering school/education; Health care; Medical research, institute; Children/youth, services; Residential/custodial care, hospices; Marine science; Physical/earth sciences; Chemistry; Mathematics; Engineering/technology; Computer science; Engineering; Biology/life sciences; Science.
Type of support: Capital campaigns; Building/renovation; Equipment; Program development; Curriculum development; Research; Employee matching gifts; Matching/challenge support.
Limitations: Applications accepted. Giving nationally to universities, colleges, and major independent medical research institutions. Arts and culture, civic and community, health care, and precollegiate education and early learning are restricted to southern CA, mainly the greater Los Angeles area. No support for conduit organizations or to organizations that have not received permanent tax-exempt ruling determination from the federal government and state of CA (if state exemption is applicable). No grants to individuals, or for routine expenses, general endowments, deficit reduction, fundraising events, dinners, mass mailings, conferences, seminars, publications, films, theatrical productions, or public policy research.
Publications: Annual report (including application guidelines); Grants list; Informational brochure (including application guidelines); Program policy statement (including application guidelines).
Application information: Unsolicited proposals are not accepted at any time. Proposals received after the deadlines will not be considered. Phase 1: Application available on foundation's web site. Only those organizations invited upon review may submit proposals. Application form required.
Initial approach: Phase 1: Application
Copies of proposal: 1
Deadline(s): Applications due May 1 (for Dec. grant cycle) and Nov. 1 (for June grant cycle); Invited proposals due Aug. 15 (for Dec. board meeting) and Feb. 15 (for June board meeting)
Board meeting date(s): June and Dec.
Final notification: June and Dec.
Officers and Directors:* Robert A. Day,* Chair. and C.E.O.; Matt Day, Sr., Vice-Chair.; James R. Ukropina,* Pres.; Howard B. Keck, Jr.,* V.P.; Allison M. Keller, V.P., C.F.O., and Exec. Dir.; Stephanie L. Garacochea, Secy.; James A. Baker III; Peter K. Barker; William R. Brody; John E. Bryson; Jerry Carlton; Joseph Deegan-Day; James S. Economou; Dr. Thomas E. Everhart; Richard N. Foster; Lucinda Day Fournier; Bradford Freeman; Maria Hummer-Tuttle; Stephen M. Keck; Theodore J. Keck; W.M. Keck III; Kent Kresa; Sherry Lansing; James Paul Lower; Kerry K. Mott; Nelson Rising; Edward C. Stone, Jr.
Number of staff: 10 full-time professional; 6 full-time support; 2 part-time support.
EIN: 956092354
Selected grants: The following grants are a representative sample of this grantmaker's funding activity:
$1,500,000 to California Association for Research in Astronomy, W.M. Keck Observatory, Kamuela, HI, 2012. To procure and install a new laser for the laser guide star Adaptive Optics system at the Keck Observatory, payable over 3.25 years.
$1,000,000 to Purdue University, West Lafayette, IN, 2012. To increase by tenfold the electron mobility in materials for research with two-dimensional electron gases, payable over 3.00 years.
$1,000,000 to University of California, Los Angeles, CA, 2012. To establish the field of imaging science by developing novel approaches based on data sparsity, payable over 2.00 years.
$1,000,000 to University of California at San Diego, La Jolla, CA, 2012. To develop a unique class of small interfering RNA molecules that can self-deliver and thus allow researchers to knockdown gene expression inside cells, payable over 3.00 years.
$1,000,000 to University of North Carolina, Chapel Hill, NC, 2012. To generate new tools to characterize the methylation states of proteins especially those involved in the epigenetic control of gene expression.
$250,000 to Alliance for College-Ready Public Schools, Los Angeles, CA, 2012. To improve student academic performance by supporting a blended learning high school program in Lincoln Heights.
$250,000 to California State University, East Bay, Hayward, CA, 2012. To acquire a confocal microscope for teaching and research, payable over 3.00 years.

$250,000 to California State University, Stanislaus, Turlock, CA, 2012. To implement a new program incorporating research and coursework in visual anthropology, payable over 3.00 years.
$250,000 to P.S. Arts, Venice, CA, 2012. To expand and sustain visual arts education in three Centinela Valley school districts by supporting the Take Part Initiative.
$200,000 to First Place for Youth, Oakland, CA, 2012. To replicate a scattered-site supportive housing program for youth exiting Los Angeles County's foster care system.

775
William M. Keck, Jr. Foundation ✧
12575 Beatrice St.
Los Angeles, CA 90066-7001
Contact: Hilda Avanesian

Incorporated in 1958 in DE.
Donor: William M. Keck, Jr.
Foundation type: Independent foundation.
Financial data (yr. ended 12/31/13): Assets, $13,062,856 (M); expenditures, $593,802; qualifying distributions, $575,000; giving activities include $575,000 for 5 grants (high: $400,000; low: $25,000).
Purpose and activities: Giving primarily to an institute for international economics, as well as for education.
Fields of interest: Higher education; Health care; Homeless, human services; Economics; Christian agencies & churches.
Limitations: Applications accepted. Giving generally limited to southern CA. No grants to individuals.
Application information: Application form not required.
Initial approach: Letter
Copies of proposal: 1
Deadline(s): Nov. 30
Board meeting date(s): Mid-Dec.
Officer and Director:* William M. Keck II,* Pres.
Number of staff: 1 part-time professional; 10 part-time support.
EIN: 136097874
Selected grants: The following grants are a representative sample of this grantmaker's funding activity:
$65,000 to Midnight Mission, Los Angeles, CA, 2012. For Community Improvement homeless Programs.
$35,000 to Church of the Good Shepherd, Beverly Hills, CA, 2012. For Property Education Choir Fund.

776
B. K. Kee Foundation ✧
445 Pullman Rd.
Hillsborough, CA 94010-6749
Contact: Stanley Sze, Pres.
FAX: (650) 490-3153;
E-mail: thekeefoundation@gmail.com

Established in 2005 in CA.
Donor: Dr. Lay K. Kay.
Foundation type: Independent foundation.
Financial data (yr. ended 12/31/13): Assets, $18,904,692 (M); expenditures, $995,652; qualifying distributions, $784,125; giving activities include $655,299 for 9+ grants (high: $211,000).
Purpose and activities: To provide humanitarian aid to the people of Myanmar.
Fields of interest: Education; Health care; Human services.
International interests: Myanmar.
Type of support: Management development/ capacity building; Emergency funds; Seed money; Scholarship funds.
Limitations: Applications not accepted. Giving primarily in CA and Myanmar.
Application information: Unsolicited requests for funds not accepted.
Officers and Directors:* Stanley Sze,* Pres.; Dr. Lay K. Kay,* C.F.O. and Secy.-Treas.
EIN: 562545977
Selected grants: The following grants are a representative sample of this grantmaker's funding activity:
$264,948 to Community Partners International, Berkeley, CA, 2012. To provide Training for Health Workers Offering Maternal Care Rma.
$40,000 to Brackett Foundation, Hamilton, NY, 2012. To provide Access to Education for Burmese Refugees.
$20,000 to Burma Border Projects, Worcester, MA, 2012. For Fund Educational Programs and Orphanage.

777
Keesal, Young & Logan Charitable Foundation ✧ ☆
P.O. Box 1730
Long Beach, CA 90801-1730

Established in 1990 in CA.
Donors: Keesal, Young & Logan, P.C.; William H. Collier, Jr.; Samuel A. Keesal, Jr.; J. Stephen Young; Robert H. Logan; Michael M. Gless; Peter R. Boutin; Scott T. Pratt; Terry Ross; John D. Giffin; Phillip McLeod; Neal S. Robb; Ben Suter; E. Beazley; A. Peacock; C. Stout; R. Stemler; Lisa M. Bertain; R. Bocko; M. Fron; E. Beazley; E. Lindh; G. Young; C. Finan; J. Zinke; J. Walsh; H. Ray; J. Walsh; J. Cohen; P. Lempriere; S. Garrett; J. Taylor.
Foundation type: Independent foundation.
Financial data (yr. ended 12/31/13): Assets, $0 (M); gifts received, $521,465; expenditures, $554,248; qualifying distributions, $554,108; giving activities include $554,108 for 198 grants (high: $84,250; low: $50).
Purpose and activities: The foundation supports aquariums and organizations involved with arts and culture, education, health, youth development, human services, and community development.
Fields of interest: Arts; Education; Aquariums; Health care; Health organizations; AIDS; Medical research; Athletics/sports, Olympics; Boys & girls clubs; Boy scouts; Youth development; Human services; American Red Cross; YM/YWCAs & YM/YWHAs; Children/youth, services; Community/economic development.
Limitations: Applications not accepted. Giving primarily in CA. No grants to individuals.
Application information: Contributes only to pre-selected organizations.
Officers and Directors:* Samuel A. Keesal, Jr.,* Pres.; J. Stephen Young,* V.P. and Secy.; Peter R. Boutin, V.P.; Michael M. Gless, V.P.; Elizabeth Beazley; Lisa M. Bertain; Robert J. Bocko; William H. Collier, Jr.; John D. Giffin; Phillip McLeod; Albert E. Peacock III; Neal S. Robb; Terry Ross; Robert J. Stemler; Cameron G. Stout; Ben Suter.
EIN: 330458127

778
Lora L. and Martin N. Kelley Family Foundation ✧
405 W. 14th St., No. 809
Oakland, CA 94612-2706

Established in 1990 in OR.
Donors: Martin N. Kelley†; Lora L. Kelley†.
Foundation type: Independent foundation.
Financial data (yr. ended 12/31/13): Assets, $22,311,481 (M); expenditures, $995,143; qualifying distributions, $956,394; giving activities include $653,650 for 30 grants (high: $100,000; low: $275), and $200,000 for 1 loan/program-related investment.
Purpose and activities: Giving primarily for the arts, education, human services and community foundations.
Fields of interest: Arts; Higher education; Education; Health care; Food banks; Human services; Foundations (community); Children.
Limitations: Applications not accepted. Giving primarily in MT and OR. No grants to individuals.
Application information: Contributes only to pre-selected organizations.
Officers: Craig C. Kelley, Chair.; Stephen S. Kelley, Secy.; Mark Kelley, Treas.
Trustees: Kent R. Kelley; Karen D. Kelley.
EIN: 476174269

779
The Kenrose Kitchen Table Foundation ✧
2945 Townsgate Rd., Ste. 200
Westlake Village, CA 91361-2987

Established in 2005 in CA.
Donors: The Power Family Limited Partnership; James D. Power III; James D. Power III 2008 Charitable Lead Annuity Trust; James D. Power III 2008 Charitable Lead Unitrust.
Foundation type: Independent foundation.
Financial data (yr. ended 12/31/13): Assets, $19,278,755 (M); gifts received, $1,415,580; expenditures, $1,152,383; qualifying distributions, $998,094; giving activities include $944,406 for 15 grants (high: $270,000; low: $5,000).
Purpose and activities: Giving primarily for health organizations, particularly for multiple sclerosis; funding also for higher education.
Fields of interest: Higher education; Hospitals (specialty); Health care; Health organizations, association; Multiple sclerosis research.
Limitations: Applications not accepted. Giving primarily in CA and MA. No grants to individuals.
Application information: Contributes only to pre-selected organizations.
Officers: James D. Power III, Pres.; Susan Curtin, Secy.; Mary E. Power, C.F.O.
Directors: Michael Curtin; James D. Power IV; Jonathan P. Power; Julie Power.
EIN: 203951665

780
The Kern Community Foundation ✧
(formerly The Kern County Community Foundation)
3300 Truxtun Ave., Ste. 220
Bakersfield, CA 93301 (661) 325-5346
Contact: Jeffrey R. Pickering, C.E.O.
FAX: (661) 325-5358;
E-mail: info@kernfoundation.org; Additional E-mail:

jeff@kernfoundation.org; Main URL: http://www.kernfoundation.org
Facebook: https://www.facebook.com/kernfoundation
RSS Feed: http://www.kernfoundation.org/inc_blog.php?rss
Twitter: https://twitter.com/jeff_pickering
YouTube: http://www.youtube.com/kernfoundationlive

Established in 1999 in CA.
Foundation type: Community foundation.
Financial data (yr. ended 12/31/13): Assets, $17,533,096 (M); gifts received, $2,344,467; expenditures, $2,641,093; giving activities include $1,642,419 for 244+ grants (high: $200,000; low: $10).
Purpose and activities: The foundation seeks to enhance the quality of life for all the people of Kern County, CA by encouraging philanthropy, providing services to the donors, and assisting those who serve to meet the needs of the community.
Fields of interest: Arts; Education; Environment; Animals/wildlife, fisheries; Health care; Human services; Philanthropy/voluntarism.
Type of support: General/operating support; Continuing support; Management development/capacity building; Capital campaigns; Building/renovation; Equipment; Endowments; Program development; Curriculum development; Technical assistance; Consulting services; Program evaluation; Scholarships—to individuals; Matching/challenge support.
Limitations: Applications accepted. Giving primarily in Kern County, CA. No support for single religious sect or denomination services. No grants to individuals (except for scholarships), or for conferences, workshops, exhibits, travel, surveys, films, or publishing activities; no multi-year requests.
Publications: Application guidelines; Annual report; Financial statement; Informational brochure; Newsletter; Occasional report.
Application information: Visit foundation web site for application form, guidelines, and upcoming deadlines. Application form required.
Initial approach: Submit annual Organizational Profile form
Board meeting date(s): Monthly
Officers and Directors:* Stephen H. Boyle,* Chair.; Jeffrey R. Pickering,* C.E.O. and Pres.; Kevin C. Findley,* Secy.; Eugene J. Voiland,* Treas.; John M. Allen; A.J. Antongiovanni; Chandrasekhar Commuri, Ph.D.; Vipul R. Dev, M.D.; Angelo Haddad; Duane Keathley; Byran L. Lynn; Kathy M. Miller; Heather Butler Taylor; Diane L. White.
Number of staff: 2 full-time professional; 2 part-time professional.
EIN: 770555874

781
Kestenbaum Family Foundation ✧
300 N. Swall Dr., Ste. 257
Beverly Hills, CA 90211
Contact: Louis Kestenbaum, Dir.

Established in 1998 in CA.
Donors: Louis Kestenbaum; Gertrude Kestenbaum.
Foundation type: Independent foundation.
Financial data (yr. ended 12/31/12): Assets, $330,648 (M); gifts received, $500,000; expenditures, $546,713; qualifying distributions, $543,114; giving activities include $543,114 for 44 grants (high: $250,000; low: $100).
Purpose and activities: Giving primarily for Jewish organizations.
Fields of interest: Education; Jewish agencies & synagogues.
Limitations: Applications accepted. Giving primarily in CA and NY. No grants to individuals.
Application information: Contact the foundation for application guidelines. Application form required.
Initial approach: Contact the foundation
Deadline(s): Contact the foundation
Directors: Louis Kestenbaum; Lynda Marino; Serena Peters.
EIN: 954705652
Selected grants: The following grants are a representative sample of this grantmaker's funding activity:
$100,000 to Yeshiva University Los Angeles High School, Los Angeles, CA, 2011.

782
The Alicia Keys Family Foundation ✧ ☆
1880 Century Park E., Ste. 1600
Los Angeles, CA 90067-1661

Donors: Alicia Augello-Cook; The Endeavor Agency, LLC; Samsung Telecommunications America; Southern Wine & Spirits of America, Inc.; Cheil Communications America, Inc.; Conde Nast Publications; Cartier Charitable Foundation; Phillips-Van Heusen Foundation, Inc.
Foundation type: Independent foundation.
Financial data (yr. ended 12/31/13): Assets, $120,917 (M); gifts received, $856,290; expenditures, $779,098; qualifying distributions, $773,886; giving activities include $600,000 for 1 grant.
Fields of interest: Human services.
Limitations: Applications not accepted. Giving primarily in NY.
Application information: Unsolicited requests for funds not accepted.
Officer: Alicia Augello-Cook, Pres.
Directors: Terri Augello; Todd Gelfand.
EIN: 141938393

783
The Khachaturian Foundation ✧
360 Post St., Ste. 401
San Francisco, CA 94108-4907 (415) 392-9600
Contact: Rita M. Khachaturian, Secy.-Treas.; Henry Khachaturian, Dir.

Established in 1999 in CA.
Donors: Henry Khachaturian; Rita M. Khachaturian; Chrysler Financial Svcs.; MGM Grand Las Vegas; Toyota Financial Svcs.; Goldman Sachs & Co.; Valli Construction; MJS Advertising; California Superstores.
Foundation type: Independent foundation.
Financial data (yr. ended 12/31/12): Assets, $14,926,192 (M); gifts received, $996,870; expenditures, $774,186; qualifying distributions, $620,000; giving activities include $620,000 for 25 grants (high: $150,000; low: $5,000).
Purpose and activities: Giving primarily for cardiac research and to Armenian causes.
Fields of interest: Health organizations; Heart & circulatory research; Foundations (private grantmaking).
Limitations: Applications accepted. Giving primarily in CA. No grants to individuals, directly.
Application information: Application form required.
Initial approach: Letter
Deadline(s): None
Officers: Rita M. Khachaturian, Secy.-Treas.
Directors: Daphne Kavich; Henry Khachaturian; Natasha Khachaturian.
EIN: 943337684

784
The John B. and Nelly Llanos Kilroy Foundation ✧
12200 W. Olympic Blvd., Ste. 200
Los Angeles, CA 90064-1044

Established in 2005 in CA.
Donors: John B. Kilroy; Nelly Llanos Kilroy.
Foundation type: Independent foundation.
Financial data (yr. ended 12/31/12): Assets, $7,874,092 (M); expenditures, $922,673; qualifying distributions, $1,718,800; giving activities include $1,718,800 for 58 grants (high: $400,000; low: $1,000).
Fields of interest: Elementary/secondary education; Higher education; Education; Human services.
Limitations: Applications not accepted. Giving primarily in CA. No grants to individuals.
Application information: Contributes only to pre-selected organizations.
Officers: John B. Kilroy, Pres.; Beatrice Wallace, V.P.; Chris Krogh, C.F.O.; Nelly Llanos Kilroy, Secy.
Directors: Richard Colyear; Steve Shipman; Mike Wallace.
EIN: 203077473

785
The Steve Y. Kim Foundation ✧ ☆
3530 Wilshire Blvd., Ste. 360
Los Angeles, CA 90010-2344 (213) 738-8608
Contact: Steve Y. Kim, Pres.

Established in 1999 in CA.
Donor: Steve Y. Kim.
Foundation type: Independent foundation.
Financial data (yr. ended 12/31/13): Assets, $17,110,572 (M); expenditures, $1,281,728; qualifying distributions, $1,250,000.
Fields of interest: Foundations (private grantmaking).
Type of support: Continuing support; Building/renovation; Scholarship funds.
Limitations: Applications accepted. Giving primarily in CA, and Seoul, Korea.
Application information: Application form required.
Initial approach: Letter
Deadline(s): None
Officers: Steve Y. Kim, Pres.; Winifrida V. Sison, Secy.
EIN: 954748701

786
The Kimball Foundation ✧
(formerly Sara H. and William R. Kimball Foundation)
1660 Bush St., Ste. 300
San Francisco, CA 94109-5308 (415) 561-6540
FAX: (415) 561-6477; Main URL: http://www.pfs-llc.net/kimball/kimball.html
Grants List: http://www.pfs-llc.net/kimball/kimball_grants_2011.pdf

Established in 1997 in CA.
Donors: Sara H. Kimball‡; William R. Kimball‡.
Foundation type: Independent foundation.
Financial data (yr. ended 12/31/13): Assets, $78,022,013 (M); expenditures, $4,302,801; qualifying distributions, $3,724,408; giving activities include $3,379,445 for 157 grants (high: $150,000; low: $250).
Purpose and activities: Giving primarily to provide opportunities to the disadvantaged and at-risk, including education, youth development, academic enrichment, tutorials, leadership development, vocational training, employment, and sports, recreation and arts activities for low-income youth. High priority is given to organizations which promote college access and encourage community service for low-income youth. Grants in the arts are made to groups that predominately serve youth.
Fields of interest: Historic preservation/historical societies; Environmental education; Children/youth, services.
Type of support: Program development.
Limitations: Applications accepted. Giving to organizations serving the residents in San Francisco, San Mateo, Sonoma, and Marin counties, CA, and to a limited extent, Palo Alto in Santa Clara County. No support for medical research organizations. No grants to individuals or for endowment drives, events, annual appeals, videos, medical research, religious organizations, or the environment.
Publications: Application guidelines; Annual report; Grants list.
Application information: Complete application guidelines and procedures available on foundation website. Application form required.
Initial approach: Use the online Grants Management Portal on foundation website
Deadline(s): See foundation website for specific deadlines
Board meeting date(s): Spring, summer, and fall
Officers and Trustees:* Gretchen B. Kimball,* C.E.O. and Pres.; Stephen C. Kimball,* V.P.; Donald J. McCubbin,* C.F.O. and Treas.; Gerald F. Brush, Jr.; Andrew W. Edwards; Anne C. Kimball; Jeffrey L. Kimball.
EIN: 943263448
Selected grants: The following grants are a representative sample of this grantmaker's funding activity:
$100,000 to Eastside College Preparatory School, East Palo Alto, CA, 2012. For general operating support, payable over 2.00 years.
$50,000 to Businesses United in Investing, Lending and Development, Redwood City, CA, 2012. For Peninsula Youth Entrepreneurship Program, payable over 2.00 years.
$50,000 to Juma Ventures, San Francisco, CA, 2012. For Pathways to Advancement Program, payable over 2.00 years.
$50,000 to San Francisco Symphony, San Francisco, CA, 2012. For 30,000 - unrestricted, 20,000 - Youth Orchestra.
$40,000 to Outward Bound California, San Francisco, CA, 2012. For the Bay Area Center, payable over 2.00 years.
$25,000 to Bay Area Video Coalition, San Francisco, CA, 2012. For Digital Pathways component of Next Generation Programs, providing low-income youth with training and internships in digital media in San Francisco, payable over 2.00 years.
$25,000 to Boys and Girls Clubs of Sonoma Valley, El Verano, CA, 2012. For Teen Services program, payable over 2.00 years.
$25,000 to Collective Impact, Danville, CA, 2012. For Providing academic enrichment, personal skills development, and case management for low-income children and youth in San Francisco.
$25,000 to Student Conservation Association, Arlington, VA, 2012. For Providing vocational development, service learning, and environmental education to low-income southern San Mateo youth, payable over 2.00 years.
$15,000 to TheaterWorks, Palo Alto, CA, 2012. For Write On! San Mateo playwriting initiative, payable over 2.00 years.

787
The Jena & Michael King Foundation ✧
(formerly The Michael King Family Foundation)
c/o P. Jenkins
433 N. Camden Dr., Ste. 600
Los Angeles, CA 90210

Established in 1999 in CA.
Donor: Michael King.
Foundation type: Independent foundation.
Financial data (yr. ended 12/31/13): Assets, $2,651,220 (M); expenditures, $859,381; qualifying distributions, $843,799; giving activities include $843,799 for 59 grants (high: $114,170; low: $400).
Purpose and activities: Giving primarily for education, health, and human services.
Fields of interest: Arts; Higher education; Health care; Health organizations, association; Disasters, Hurricane Katrina; Human services; Children/youth, services.
Type of support: General/operating support.
Limitations: Applications not accepted. Giving primarily in CA, with some emphasis on Los Angeles. No grants to individuals.
Application information: Contributes only to pre-selected organizations.
Officers: Michael King, Pres.; Robert V. Madden, Secy.
Director: Jena Fassett King.
EIN: 954773454

788
The Kingfisher Foundation ✧ ☆
(formerly Timothy Dattels and Kristine Johnson Foundation)
c/o George Argyris & Farella Braun
235 Montgomery St., 17th Fl.
San Francisco, CA 94104-3104

Established in 1998 in NY.
Donors: Dwight Anderson; Timothy D. Dattels; Kristine M. Johnson.
Foundation type: Independent foundation.
Financial data (yr. ended 03/31/13): Assets, $2,884,443 (M); gifts received, $156,798; expenditures, $642,402; qualifying distributions, $603,312; giving activities include $564,965 for 10 grants (high: $100,000; low: $10,000).
Fields of interest: Higher education; Environment, natural resources; Environment; Marine science; Public affairs, research; Public policy, research.
Type of support: General/operating support.
Limitations: Applications not accepted. Giving primarily in CA, Washington, DC; also some giving to Canada. No grants to individuals.
Application information: Contributes only to pre-selected organizations.
Trustees: Timothy D. Dattels; Kristine M. Johnson; Thomas S. Murphy, Jr.
EIN: 133931294
Selected grants: The following grants are a representative sample of this grantmaker's funding activity:
$160,000 to Environmental Defense Fund, Washington, DC, 2011. For general support.
$100,000 to Center for American Progress, Washington, DC, 2011. For general support.
$25,797 to University of British Columbia, Vancouver, Canada, 2011. For general support.
$10,000 to Nature Conservancy, San Francisco, CA, 2011. For general support.

789
Lewis A. Kingsley Foundation ✧
4667 MacArthur Blvd., Ste. 400
Newport Beach, CA 92660-1874

Established in 1963 in CA.
Foundation type: Independent foundation.
Financial data (yr. ended 05/31/13): Assets, $17,835,670 (M); expenditures, $850,943; qualifying distributions, $579,489; giving activities include $558,000 for 63 grants (high: $50,000; low: $250).
Fields of interest: Arts; Secondary school/education; Higher education; Scholarships/financial aid; Hospitals (general); Human services.
Type of support: General/operating support; Scholarship funds.
Limitations: Applications not accepted. Giving primarily in the Los Angeles, CA, area, and in UT. No grants to individuals.
Application information: Contributes only to pre-selected organizations.
Officers: David R. Streiff, V.P.; Frank Cordon, Secy.
Director: Marjorie Camusi.
EIN: 956092364
Selected grants: The following grants are a representative sample of this grantmaker's funding activity:
$35,000 to Brigham Young University, Provo, UT, 2011. For scholarship fund.
$35,000 to University of Utah, Salt Lake City, UT, 2011. For scholarship fund.
$30,000 to Pepperdine University, Malibu, CA, 2011. For scholarship fund.
$30,000 to University of Southern California, Los Angeles, CA, 2011. For scholarship fund.
$25,000 to Loyola Marymount University, Los Angeles, CA, 2011. For scholarship fund.
$25,000 to Mount Saint Marys College, Los Angeles, CA, 2011. For scholarship fund.
$25,000 to Santa Clara University, Santa Clara, CA, 2011. For scholarship fund.
$10,000 to Immaculate Heart High School, Los Angeles, CA, 2011. For scholarship fund.
$9,300 to Santa Clara University, Santa Clara, CA, 2011. For general support.

$5,000 to New York Says Thank You Foundation, New York, NY, 2011. For general support.

790
The Karl Kirchgessner Foundation ✧
c/o Grants Coord.
1525 Aviation Blvd., No. 168
Redondo Beach, CA 90278-2805
Contact: Christine Tuthill, Grants Coord.
FAX: (310) 374-2545;
E-mail: grantscoordinator@kirchgessnerfoundation.org; Main URL: http://www.kirchgessnerfoundation.org

Established in 1979 in CA and reincorporated in NV due to a merger with The Karl Kirchgessner Foundation (CA) in 2003.
Foundation type: Independent foundation.
Financial data (yr. ended 06/30/13): Assets, $17,831,377 (M); expenditures, $1,111,052; qualifying distributions, $837,050; giving activities include $743,720 for 26+ grants (high: $161,530).
Purpose and activities: The foundation's mission is to assist economically disadvantaged persons, especially those among the young, the elderly, and the disabled. While the foundation supports a limited amount of eye research, its emphasis is to support activities in the area of eye care, and in helping those with sight problems to be self-sufficient.
Fields of interest: Health care; Eye diseases; Eye research; Blind/visually impaired.
Type of support: General/operating support; Continuing support; Equipment; Endowments; Program development; Professorships; Seed money; Scholarship funds; Research; Technical assistance; Matching/challenge support.
Limitations: Applications accepted. Giving primarily in CA, with emphasis on southern CA. No support for private foundations, private operating foundations, supporting organizations, or for lobbying organizations or campaigns. No grants to individuals, or for fundraising campaigns, or for dinners.
Publications: Application guidelines; Grants list.
Application information: Letter of intent should not contain any supporting materials. Formal applications will be solicited by the foundation. The foundation strongly encourages applications which incorporate funding through matching grants. Application form required.
Initial approach: Send a brief letter of intent
Copies of proposal: 1
Deadline(s): Nov. 1
Board meeting date(s): May and as required
Officers and Directors:* Robert A. Huber,* Pres.; Karl F. Kramer,* Sr. V.P.; Kathleen McGrath Kramer,* V.P. and Treas.; Darryl W. Cluster, Secy.; Diana Kramer; Michael Kramer; David M. Todd.
Number of staff: None.
EIN: 680530356

791
Kissick Family Foundation ✧
922 Napoli Dr.
Pacific Palisades, CA 90272-4036

Established in 1993 in CA.
Donors: John H. Kissick; Mary Kathleen Kissick.
Foundation type: Independent foundation.
Financial data (yr. ended 12/31/12): Assets, $28,913,483 (M); expenditures, $1,592,680; qualifying distributions, $1,542,900; giving activities include $1,508,780 for 51 grants (high: $472,000; low: $1,000).
Purpose and activities: Giving primarily for education; support also for health organizations.
Fields of interest: Elementary/secondary education; Higher education; Education; Hospitals (general); Health organizations, association.
Limitations: Applications not accepted. Giving primarily in Los Angeles, CA. No grants to individuals.
Application information: Contributes only to pre-selected organizations.
Officers: John H. Kissick, Pres.; Michael S. Warsavsky, V.P.; Mary K. Kissick, Secy.; John R. Kissick, Treas.
EIN: 954443453
Selected grants: The following grants are a representative sample of this grantmaker's funding activity:
$37,500 to CollegeSpring, San Francisco, CA, 2011.
$25,000 to Milken Institute, Santa Monica, CA, 2011.
$25,000 to Painted Turtle, Santa Monica, CA, 2011.
$25,000 to Peer Health Exchange, Boston, MA, 2011.
$10,000 to K C R W Foundation, Santa Monica, CA, 2011.

792
KLA-Tencor Foundation ✧
1 Technology Dr.
Milpitas, CA 95035-7916
E-mail: foundation@kla-tencor.com; Main URL: http://www.kla-tencor.com/foundation/overview.html

Established in 2000 in CA.
Donor: KLA-Tencor Corporation.
Foundation type: Company-sponsored foundation.
Financial data (yr. ended 06/30/13): Assets, $14,999,956 (M); gifts received, $6,000,000; expenditures, $1,177,180; qualifying distributions, $1,192,301; giving activities include $1,147,465 for 85 grants (high: $100,000; low: $30).
Purpose and activities: The foundation supports organizations involved with education, health and wellness, and social services. Special emphasis is directed toward science, technology, engineering, and math education.
Fields of interest: Higher education; Education; Health care; Human services; Community/economic development; Mathematics; Engineering/technology; Science.
Type of support: Donated equipment; General/operating support; Program development; Employee volunteer services; Employee matching gifts; In-kind gifts.
Limitations: Applications accepted. Giving primarily in areas of company operations in CA, FL, MA, NY, and VA, and in Hong Kong and Taiwan. No support for individual schools, school organizations, clubs, radio or television stations, or Boy & Girl Scouts Troops, for-profit entities, discriminatory organizations, political candidates or organizations, professional associations, labor organizations, fraternal organizations, or social clubs, or religious organizations not of direct benefit to the entire community. No grants to individuals, or for scholarships, advertising journals or booklets, congresses, symposiums, or meetings, home-based child care or educational services, athletics, memorials, fundraising events or ticket purchases, travel, trips, tours, or cultural exchange programs, walk-a-thons, ride-a-thons, dance-a-thons, or bowl-a-thons.
Publications: Application guidelines.
Application information: The foundation utilizes an invitation only process for its general grant program. The KLA-Tencor Foundation Committee establishes target organizations for grants and sends a Request for Consideration packet to those organizations. Multi-year funding is not automatic. Support is limited to 1 contribution per organization during any given year. Application form required.
Initial approach: E-mail foundation for application information and for in-kind gifts
Deadline(s): None
Directors: Brian M. Martin; John Van Camp; Rick Wallace.
EIN: 770557004
Selected grants: The following grants are a representative sample of this grantmaker's funding activity:
$100,000 to SEMI Foundation, San Jose, CA, 2011.
$25,000 to Teach for America, San Francisco, CA, 2011.
$20,000 to YMCA of Silicon Valley, San Jose, CA, 2011.
$12,500 to Glow Foundation, San Francisco, CA, 2011.
$10,000 to Family Giving Tree, Milpitas, CA, 2011.
$10,000 to Family Supportive Housing, San Jose, CA, 2011.
$5,000 to American Cancer Society, Oklahoma City, OK, 2011.
$3,000 to Save the Children Federation, Fairfield, CT, 2011.
$2,000 to American Cancer Society, Atlanta, GA, 2011.
$1,000 to UNICEF, New York, NY, 2011.

793
The Lloyd E. & Elisabeth H. Klein Family Foundation ✧
c/o First Foundation Advisors
18101 Von Karman Ave., Ste. 700
Irvine, CA 92612-0145 (877) 968-6328
FAX: (949) 833-9584;
E-mail: grants@kleinfamilyfoundation.org; Main URL: http://www.kleinfamilyfoundation.org

Established in 2002 in CA.
Donors: Elisabeth Klein‡; Lloyd E. Klein‡.
Foundation type: Independent foundation.
Financial data (yr. ended 12/31/13): Assets, $15,222,778 (M); expenditures, $871,186; qualifying distributions, $747,684; giving activities include $700,970 for 31 grants (high: $154,705; low: $150).
Purpose and activities: The mission of the foundation is to empower disadvantaged youth toward improved life achievement through encouragement, education, and emotional support.
Fields of interest: Libraries (public); Education; YM/YWCAs & YM/YWHAs; Children/youth; Youth; Economically disadvantaged.
Limitations: Applications accepted. Giving primarily in CA. No grants to individuals or for endowments.
Application information: Application form required.
Initial approach: Eligibility quiz (available on foundation web site)

Deadline(s): May 15 (Letter of Inquiry); July 25 (Grant Application)
Board meeting date(s): May 1
Officers and Directors:* Catherine A. Sorensen,* Pres.; Kenneth Klein,* V.P.; Christine E. Cross,* Secy.; Nicole Frasz, Co-Treas.; James L. Klein,* Co-Treas.
EIN: 300105588
Selected grants: The following grants are a representative sample of this grantmaker's funding activity:
$85,000 to Rosies Garage, La Habra, CA, 2011.
$50,000 to Assistance League of Anaheim, Anaheim, CA, 2011.
$21,500 to Assistance League of Hemacinto, Hemet, CA, 2011.
$20,000 to Olive Crest Treatment Center, Santa Ana, CA, 2011.
$20,000 to Rose Drive Friends Church, Yorba Linda, CA, 2011.
$15,000 to Boys and Girls Club of San Marcos, San Marcos, CA, 2011.
$10,000 to Childrens Hospital of Orange County Foundation, Orange, CA, 2011.
$10,000 to Concordia University Foundation, Irvine, CA, 2011.
$10,000 to Discovery Science Center of Orange County, Santa Ana, CA, 2011.
$10,000 to Lupus International, Irvine, CA, 2011.

794
The Kling Family Foundation ✧
335 Centennial Way, Ste. 100
Tustin, CA 92780-3756

Established in 1999 in CA.
Donors: Donalyn G. Kling; Griswold Industries, Inc.; Lillian Sherwood Griswold Foundation.
Foundation type: Independent foundation.
Financial data (yr. ended 12/31/12): Assets, $872,651 (M); gifts received, $1,109,000; expenditures, $1,367,905; qualifying distributions, $1,352,000; giving activities include $1,352,000 for 160 grants (high: $50,000; low: $600).
Fields of interest: Human services; United Ways and Federated Giving Programs.
Limitations: Applications not accepted. Giving primarily in CA. No grants to individuals.
Application information: Contributes only to pre-selected organizations.
Officers: Jackie Glass, Pres.; Allen Kling, Secy.
Directors: Vicki Gumm; Daryl Kling; Donalyn G. Kling; Kenneth Kling; Donalyn Mikles; Darryl Sheetz.
EIN: 336272913

795
KLM Foundation ✧
10100 Santa Monica Blvd., Ste. 610
Los Angeles, CA 90067-4110

Established in 1997 in CA.
Donors: Kathleen L. McCarthy; Leavey Trust; Kathleen L. McCarthy Charitable Lead Annuity Trust; Leavey Charitable Lead Annuity Trust.
Foundation type: Independent foundation.
Financial data (yr. ended 12/31/12): Assets, $39,977,322 (M); gifts received, $2,842,425; expenditures, $1,964,355; qualifying distributions, $1,685,728; giving activities include $1,603,175 for 174 grants (high: $500,000; low: $100).
Fields of interest: Arts; Higher education; Education; Health care; Human services; Children/youth, services; Community/economic development; Catholic agencies & churches.
Limitations: Applications not accepted. Giving primarily in CA; some funding nationally. No grants to individuals.
Application information: Contributes only to pre-selected organizations.
Trustee: Kathleen L. McCarthy.
EIN: 954682685

796
Harry Bronson and Edith R. Knapp Foundation ✧
333 S. Hope St., 43rd Fl.
Los Angeles, CA 90071-1422 (213) 617-4175
Contact: Phillip A. Davis, Tr.

Established in 2006 in CA.
Foundation type: Independent foundation.
Financial data (yr. ended 12/31/13): Assets, $15,852,694 (M); expenditures, $826,595; qualifying distributions, $756,802; giving activities include $600,400 for 19 grants (high: $100,000; low: $10,000).
Fields of interest: Arts, services; Education; Children/youth, services.
Limitations: Applications accepted. Giving primarily in CA.
Application information: Application form required.
Initial approach: Letter
Deadline(s): Sept. 30
Trustees: Phillip A. Davis; Sandra Davis.
EIN: 206902511
Selected grants: The following grants are a representative sample of this grantmaker's funding activity:
$65,000 to Shakespeare Center of Los Angeles, Los Angeles, CA, 2011.
$50,000 to Loyola High School of Los Angeles, Los Angeles, CA, 2011.
$50,000 to Verbum Dei High School, Los Angeles, CA, 2011.
$40,000 to San Marino Community Church, San Marino, CA, 2011.
$30,000 to Stanford University, Stanford, CA, 2011.
$25,000 to Pepperdine University, Malibu, CA, 2011.
$25,000 to University of California Hastings College of the Law, San Francisco, CA, 2011.
$15,000 to Thacher School, Ojai, CA, 2011.
$15,000 to Westridge School for Girls, Pasadena, CA, 2011.
$10,000 to Villa Esperanza Services, Pasadena, CA, 2011.

797
Knee Family Foundation ✧ ☆
41-550 Eclectic St.
Palm Desert, CA 92260-1967

Established in 2004 in CA.
Donors: Kevin Knee; Joan Knee.
Foundation type: Independent foundation.
Financial data (yr. ended 12/31/13): Assets, $4,925,478 (M); gifts received, $1,961,681; expenditures, $484,431; qualifying distributions, $454,760; giving activities include $454,760 for 6 grants (high: $300,000; low: $5,000).
Fields of interest: Elementary/secondary education; Hospitals (general).
Limitations: Applications not accepted. Giving primarily in CA. No grants to individuals.
Application information: Contributes only to pre-selected organizations.
Officers: Kevin Knee, Pres.; Joan Knee, Secy.
EIN: 202026185
Selected grants: The following grants are a representative sample of this grantmaker's funding activity:
$50,000 to Martha's Village and Kitchen, Indio, CA, 2011.
$25,000 to Marywood-Palm Valley School, Rancho Mirage, CA, 2011.
$3,000 to American Cancer Society, Palm Desert, CA, 2011.

798
The Knossos Foundation, Inc. ✧
c/o Rothstein, Kass & Co.
101 Montgomery St., 22nd Fl.
San Francisco, CA 94104 (415) 788-6666

Established in 1990 in NY.
Donors: Andrea Wilson†; Fred W. Wilson†.
Foundation type: Independent foundation.
Financial data (yr. ended 12/31/12): Assets, $9,927,182 (M); expenditures, $567,162; qualifying distributions, $498,033; giving activities include $494,116 for 47 grants (high: $40,000; low: $550).
Purpose and activities: Giving primarily for education, and youth and social services.
Fields of interest: Elementary/secondary education; Higher education; Education; Human services; Children/youth, services.
Limitations: Applications accepted. Giving in the U.S., with emphasis on MA, New York, NY, and WA. No grants to individuals.
Application information: Application form not required.
Initial approach: Proposal
Deadline(s): None
Officers and Director:* David Wilson, Pres.; Linda Wilson,* Secy.-Treas.
EIN: 133579596

799
Allen D. Kohl Charitable Foundation, Inc. ✧
11990 San Vicente Blvd., Ste. 200
Los Angeles, CA 90049-6608

Incorporated in 1972 in WI.
Donors: Allen D. Kohl; Max Kohl Charitable Trust No. AK2.
Foundation type: Independent foundation.
Financial data (yr. ended 12/31/12): Assets, $12,309,783 (M); expenditures, $906,133; qualifying distributions, $535,770; giving activities include $535,770 for 47 grants (high: $100,000; low: $5).
Fields of interest: Education; Philanthropy/voluntarism; Religion.
Limitations: Applications not accepted. No grants to individuals.
Application information: Unsolicited requests for funds not accepted.

Officers: Allen D. Kohl, Pres.; David J. Kohl, V.P.; Stephanie S. Cohen, Secy.-Treas.
EIN: 237211587

800
Dean & Gerda Koontz Foundation ✧
P.O. Box 9529
Newport Beach, CA 92658-9529

Established in 1994 in CA.
Donors: Dean R. Koontz; Gerda A. Koontz.
Foundation type: Independent foundation.
Financial data (yr. ended 12/31/13): Assets, $600,550 (M); gifts received, $1,000,000; expenditures, $1,052,761; qualifying distributions, $1,052,761; giving activities include $1,050,000 for 3 grants (high: $750,000; low: $100,000).
Fields of interest: Hospitals (general); Independent living, disability; Catholic agencies & churches.
Limitations: Applications not accepted. Giving primarily in CA. No grants to individuals.
Application information: Contributes only to pre-selected organizations.
Officers: Dean R. Koontz, Pres.; Gerda A. Koontz, C.F.O. and Secy.
EIN: 330622423

801
Koret Foundation
611 Front St.
San Francisco, CA 94111-1963 (415) 882-7740
Contact: Tina Frank, Dir., Grant Opers.
FAX: (415) 882-7775;
E-mail: info@koretfoundation.org; Main URL: http://www.koretfoundation.org
Blog: http://koret.org/news-and-resources/blog/
E-Newsletter: http://koret.org/news-and-resources/
Facebook: http://www.facebook.com/pages/Koret-Foundation/139817769439751
Grants List: http://koret.org/about/grants/
Twitter: https://twitter.com/KoretFoundation
YouTube: https://www.youtube.com/user/KoretFoundation

Grantmaking commenced in 1979.
Donors: Joseph Koret‡; Stephanie Koret‡.
Foundation type: Independent foundation.
Financial data (yr. ended 12/31/13): Assets, $611,652,269 (M); expenditures, $38,266,246; qualifying distributions, $26,867,016; giving activities include $15,931,237 for 395 grants (high: $900,000; low: $250).
Purpose and activities: Koret seeks to address societal challenges and to strengthen Bay Area life. The foundation seeks to invest in strategic, local solutions to help to inspire a multiplier effect-encouraging collaborative funding and developing model initiatives. Koret promotes educational opportunity, the community of Israel, and free market expansion. Areas of focus include arts/culture and civic institutions, K-12 education reform, Israel advocacy (including education and economic development), as well as Jewish community organizations.
Fields of interest: Arts; Elementary/secondary school reform; Higher education; Community/economic development; Jewish federated giving programs; Jewish agencies & synagogues.
International interests: Israel.
Type of support: General/operating support; Continuing support; Management development/capacity building; Annual campaigns; Program development; Conferences/seminars; Fellowships; Scholarship funds; Research; Technical assistance; Program evaluation; Matching/challenge support.
Limitations: Applications not accepted. Giving limited to the Bay Area counties of San Francisco, Alameda, Contra Costa, Marin, Santa Clara, and San Mateo, CA; giving also in Israel and on a national basis for Jewish funding requests. No support for private foundations, or veterans', fraternal, military, religious, or sectarian organizations whose principal activity is for the benefit of their own membership. No grants to individuals, or for endowment funds or deficit financing.
Publications: Biennial report; Financial statement; Grants list; Informational brochure; Newsletter; Occasional report.
Application information: Contributes only to pre-selected organizations.
Board meeting date(s): 4 times per year
Officers and Directors:* Susan Koret,* Chair.; Jeffrey A. Farber, C.E.O.; Michael J. Boskin, Ph.D.*, Co-Pres.; Anita Friedman,* Co-Pres.; Claudia J. Hardin, C.F.O. and C.A.O.; Tad Taube,* Pres. Emeritus; Richard C. Atkinson; Robert Friend; Richard L. Greene; Abraham D. Sofaer.
Number of staff: 9 full-time professional; 5 full-time support; 1 part-time support.
EIN: 941624987
Selected grants: The following grants are a representative sample of this grantmaker's funding activity:
$3,000,000 to Jewish Historical Institute of Poland, Warsaw, Poland, 2012. For Museum of the History of Polish Jews Core Exhibition Support.
$1,500,000 to PEF Israel Endowment Funds, New York, NY, 2012. For General Operating Support and Research Equipment for the Hebrew University Koret School of Veterinary Medicine.
$500,000 to American Friends of Koret Israel Economic Development Fund, San Francisco, CA, 2012. For General Operating Support.
$500,000 to Congregation Kol Shofar, Tiburon, CA, 2012. For Capital Campaign.
$215,000 to Milken Institute, Santa Monica, CA, 2012. For Koret-Milken Institute Fellows Program.
$25,000 to American Enterprise Institute for Public Policy Research, Washington, DC, 2012. For Program on American Citizenship.
$25,000 to Peninsula Jewish Community Center, Foster City, CA, 2012. For Jewish Peoplehood Fellow.
$20,000 to United Nations Watch - USA, Washington, DC, 2012. For General Operating Support.
$15,000 to Menlo School, Atherton, CA, 2012. For Music at Menlo's 10th Anniversary.
$15,000 to University of California, Berkeley, CA, 2012. For General Operating Support.

802
Kornwasser Charitable Foundation ✧
5670 Wilshire Blvd., Ste. 1250
Los Angeles, CA 90036-2166

Established in 1960 in CA.
Donors: Mark Kornwasser; Sonia Kornwasser; Kornland Building Co.; Joseph Kornwasser; Sonia Kornwasser; Kram Construction.
Foundation type: Independent foundation.
Financial data (yr. ended 05/31/13): Assets, $4,753,488 (M); expenditures, $594,386; qualifying distributions, $551,361; giving activities include $549,330 for 48+ grants (high: $62,000).
Purpose and activities: Giving primarily to Jewish agencies and temples, and for Jewish education.
Fields of interest: Elementary/secondary education; Higher education; Jewish agencies & synagogues.
Limitations: Applications not accepted. Giving primarily in CA and NY. No grants to individuals.
Application information: Contributes only to pre-selected organizations.
Officers: Joseph Kornwasser, Pres.; Sonia Kornwasser, V.P.; Judy Moskovits, Secy.
EIN: 956091565
Selected grants: The following grants are a representative sample of this grantmaker's funding activity:
$36,000 to Ohr Eliyahu Academy, Culver City, CA, 2011. For general support.
$35,000 to Samuel A. Fryer Yavneh Hebrew Academy, Los Angeles, CA, 2011. For general support.
$30,300 to Young Israel of Century City, Los Angeles, CA, 2011. For general support.
$28,000 to Chai Lifeline, New York, NY, 2011. For general support.
$19,600 to Yeshiva Gedolah of Los Angeles, Los Angeles, CA, 2011. For general support.
$10,000 to UCLA Foundation, Los Angeles, CA, 2011. For general support.
$6,000 to Yeshiva Beit Rafael, Flushing, NY, 2011. For general support.
$2,800 to Orthodox Union - Union of Orthodox Jewish Congregations of America, New York, NY, 2011. For general support.
$2,600 to Shomrei Emunim Eretz Yisroel, Brooklyn, NY, 2011. For general support.
$1,000 to American Friends of Beit Issie Shapiro, New York, NY, 2011. For general support.

803
Jacob Kornwasser Foundation ✧
336 N. Martel Ave.
Los Angeles, CA 90036-2516

Established in 1991 in CA.
Donors: Jacob Kornwasser; Mila Kornwasser; Kormag Construction Co.
Foundation type: Independent foundation.
Financial data (yr. ended 10/31/13): Assets, $12,599,858 (M); expenditures, $594,358; qualifying distributions, $567,110; giving activities include $565,000 for 12 grants (high: $210,000; low: $1,000).
Purpose and activities: Giving primarily for Jewish organizations.
Fields of interest: Elementary/secondary education; Jewish agencies & synagogues.
Limitations: Applications not accepted. Giving primarily in Los Angeles, CA, and NY. No grants to individuals.
Application information: Contributes only to pre-selected organizations.
Officers: Mila Kornwasser, Pres.; Judith Hager, Secy.
EIN: 954337380
Selected grants: The following grants are a representative sample of this grantmaker's funding activity:
$400,000 to Jewish Community Foundation, Los Angeles, CA, 2011. For general use.

$125,000 to Anshei Chayil, Monsey, NY, 2011. For general use.
$25,000 to Ashreinu Corporation, Los Angeles, CA, 2011. For general use.
$25,000 to Ezer Mizion, Brooklyn, NY, 2011. For general use.

804
The Koshland Foundation ✧
P.O. Box 7310
Menlo Park, CA 94026-7310

Established in 1985 in CA.
Donors: Marian E. Koshland†; James M. Koshland; Daniel E. Koshland, Jr.; Douglas E. Koshland.
Foundation type: Independent foundation.
Financial data (yr. ended 07/31/13): Assets, $31,298,480 (M); expenditures, $1,023,160; qualifying distributions, $851,454; giving activities include $848,500 for 4 grants (high: $650,000; low: $45,000).
Fields of interest: Education; Human services.
Type of support: Endowments; Scholarship funds.
Limitations: Applications not accepted. Giving primarily in CA. No grants to individuals.
Application information: Contributes only to pre-selected organizations.
Officers and Directors:* Gail K. Wachtel,* Pres.; Douglas E. Koshland,* V.P.; Ellen Koshland,* V.P.; James M. Koshland,* V.P.; Phlyssa Koshland,* V.P.; Yvonne Koshland,* V.P.; James E. Esposto, Secy.-Treas. and C.F.O.
EIN: 680069874
Selected grants: The following grants are a representative sample of this grantmaker's funding activity:
$100,000 to Edible Schoolyard Project, Berkeley, CA, 2013. For Operating support for current projects.
$53,500 to Fund for Educational Excellence, Baltimore, MD, 2013. For Public School District Funding Analysis; Grant management fee to the fund as fiscal sponsor.
$45,000 to Tides Center, San Francisco, CA, 2013. For Current support CommunityGrows Project Re: Koshland Community Park Band of Environmentally Educated and Employable Teens (BEETS) Program.

805
The Krause Foundation ✧
25855 Westwind Way
Los Altos Hills, CA 94022-3338

Established in 1994 in CA.
Donors: L. Gay Krause; L. William Krause.
Foundation type: Independent foundation.
Financial data (yr. ended 12/31/13): Assets, $9,320,236 (M); expenditures, $1,592,818; qualifying distributions, $1,544,712; giving activities include $1,538,602 for 16 grants (high: $1,000,000; low: $2).
Fields of interest: Museums; Higher education; Human services.
Limitations: Applications not accepted. Giving primarily in CA and SC. No grants to individuals.
Application information: Contributes only to pre-selected organizations.
Officers: L. Gay Krause, Pres.; L. William Krause, Secy.-Treas.
EIN: 770388463
Selected grants: The following grants are a representative sample of this grantmaker's funding activity:
$70,000 to Foothill-De Anza Community Colleges Foundation, Los Altos Hills, CA, 2010.
$20,000 to Children Now, Oakland, CA, 2011.
$16,700 to Computer History Museum, Mountain View, CA, 2011.
$10,000 to Community Health Awareness Council, Mountain View, CA, 2011.
$10,000 to Tech Museum of Innovation, San Jose, CA, 2011.
$10,000 to YMCA of Silicon Valley, San Jose, CA, 2010.
$10,000 to YMCA of Silicon Valley, San Jose, CA, 2011.
$6,000 to Silicon Valley Community Foundation, Mountain View, CA, 2011.
$5,000 to Los Altos Community Foundation, Los Altos, CA, 2011.
$4,000 to Palo Alto Library Foundation, Palo Alto, CA, 2011.
$3,000 to Fresh Lifelines for Youth, Milpitas, CA, 2011.

806
Kroner Family Foundation ✧
118 Circle Rd.
San Rafael, CA 94903

Established in 2007 in CA.
Donors: Jennifer Kroner; Kenneth Kroner.
Foundation type: Independent foundation.
Financial data (yr. ended 01/31/13): Assets, $12,058,191 (M); gifts received, $1,000,000; expenditures, $1,647,605; qualifying distributions, $1,641,883; giving activities include $1,636,000 for 17 grants (high: $960,000; low: $5,000).
Fields of interest: Education; Human services; Christian agencies & churches.
Limitations: Applications not accepted. Giving primarily in CA, CO and TX. No grants to individuals.
Application information: Contributes only to pre-selected organizations.
Officers and Board Members:* Jennifer G. Kroner,* Chair. and Pres.; Kenneth F. Kroner, C.F.O; Holly Anderson; Jeffrey Anderson; Daryl Kroner; Jennifer J. Kroner.
EIN: 205852031
Selected grants: The following grants are a representative sample of this grantmaker's funding activity:
$200,000 to Marin Covenant Church, San Rafael, CA, 2011. For general funds.
$122,000 to Wycliffe Bible Translators, Orlando, FL, 2011. For general funds.
$100,000 to University of California at San Diego Foundation, La Jolla, CA, 2011.
$50,000 to Young Life, Colorado Springs, CO, 2011. For general funds.
$35,000 to Focus on the Family, Colorado Springs, CO, 2011. For general funds.
$25,000 to Gospel for Asia, Carrollton, TX, 2011. For general funds.
$25,000 to Juvenile Diabetes Research Foundation International, New York, NY, 2011. For general funds.
$15,000 to Gilead House, Novato, CA, 2011. For general funds.
$14,000 to Marin Academy, San Rafael, CA, 2011. For general funds.
$12,000 to Ring Mountain Day School, Mill Valley, CA, 2011. For general funds.

807
The Jean & E. Floyd Kvamme Foundation ✧
P.O. Box 2494
Saratoga, CA 95070-0494
Contact: Jean Kvamme, Tr.

Established in 1993 in CA.
Donors: E. Floyd Kvamme; Jean Kvamme.
Foundation type: Independent foundation.
Financial data (yr. ended 06/30/13): Assets, $10,481,408 (M); gifts received, $55,000; expenditures, $4,465,918; qualifying distributions, $4,346,017; giving activities include $4,334,000 for 18 grants (high: $3,500,000; low: $1,000).
Purpose and activities: Giving primarily to Christian religious organizations, medical grants for Alzheimer's, leukemia, arthritis, and spondylitis research and to the community of northern California for education and the arts.
Fields of interest: Arts; Engineering school/education; Education; Health organizations, association; Medical research, institute; Christian agencies & churches.
Type of support: General/operating support; Continuing support; Building/renovation; Equipment; Research; Matching/challenge support.
Limitations: Applications not accepted. Giving primarily in northern CA. No grants to individuals.
Application information: Contributes only to pre-selected organizations.
Trustees: Damon Kvamme; E. Floyd Kvamme; Jean Kvamme; Todd Kvamme.
Number of staff: 3 part-time support.
EIN: 770359484
Selected grants: The following grants are a representative sample of this grantmaker's funding activity:
$200,000 to George W. Bush Foundation, Dallas, TX, 2011.
$100,000 to International Justice Mission, Arlington, VA, 2011.

808
La Fetra Foundation ✧
1600 Euclid Ave.
Berkeley, CA 94709-1202

Established in 1992 in CA.
Donors: Anthony W. La Fetra; Michael W. La Fetra; Suzanne La Fetra.
Foundation type: Independent foundation.
Financial data (yr. ended 12/31/13): Assets, $17,071,230 (M); gifts received, $500,000; expenditures, $684,412; qualifying distributions, $607,210; giving activities include $600,000 for 16 grants (high: $200,000; low: $8,000).
Fields of interest: Arts; Education; Environment; Human services.
Limitations: Applications not accepted. Giving primarily in CA. No grants to individuals.
Application information: Unsolicited requests for funds not accepted.
Officers: Suzanne La Fetra, Pres.; Anthony W. La Fetra, C.F.O.
Director: Michael W. La Fetra.
EIN: 954380652
Selected grants: The following grants are a representative sample of this grantmaker's funding activity:
$83,000 to Los Angeles Conservancy, Los Angeles, CA, 2011.

$57,008 to Windrush School, El Cerrito, CA, 2011.
$50,000 to Citrus College Foundation, Glendora, CA, 2011.
$50,000 to National Parks Conservation Association, Washington, DC, 2011.
$40,000 to National Trust for Historic Preservation, Washington, DC, 2011.
$35,000 to Heifer Project International, Little Rock, AR, 2011.
$25,000 to K Q E D, San Francisco, CA, 2011.
$25,000 to National Public Radio, Washington, DC, 2011.
$10,000 to Tides Center, San Francisco, CA, 2011.
$5,000 to Inspired Legacies, Ross, CA, 2011.

809
LA84 Foundation ✧
(formerly Amateur Athletic Foundation of Los Angeles)
2141 W. Adams Blvd.
Los Angeles, CA 90018-2040 (323) 730-4600
Contact: F. Patrick Escobar, V.P., Grants and Progs.
FAX: (323) 730-9637;
E-mail: info@LA84Foundation.org; Main URL: http://www.la84foundation.org
Facebook: http://www.facebook.com/pages/LA84-Foundation/135796917696
Grants List: http://www.la84foundation.org/1gm/grantees_frmst.htm
Sportsletter Blog: http://www.sportsletter.org/
Twitter: http://twitter.com/LA84Foundation
weplay: http://www.weplay.com/groups/25069-LA84-Foundation/public
YouTube: http://www.youtube.com/user/LA84Foundation/videos

Established in 1982 in CA.
Donor: Los Angeles Olympic Organizing Comm.
Foundation type: Independent foundation.
Financial data (yr. ended 12/31/12): Assets, $139,555,111 (M); gifts received, $6,902; expenditures, $7,549,701; qualifying distributions, $6,797,305; giving activities include $2,811,935 for 67 grants (high: $500,000; low: $5,000), $2,165 for 5 employee matching gifts, and $1,277,421 for foundation-administered programs.
Purpose and activities: Support for youth sports programs (youth ages 6-17), especially in areas where the risk of delinquency is high. Special attention to sectors of the population underserved by current sports programs: girls, minorities, and the disabled.
Fields of interest: Athletics/sports, training; Athletics/sports, amateur leagues; Youth development; Youth, services; Children/youth; Girls.
Type of support: Capital campaigns; Building/renovation; Equipment; Program development; Matching/challenge support.
Limitations: Applications accepted. Giving limited to eight southern CA counties (Imperial, Los Angeles, Orange, Riverside, San Bernardino, San Diego, Santa Barbara, and Ventura). No support for single, public, or private school facilities or programs not including sports schools. No grants to individuals, endowments, travel outside of southern CA, routine operating expenses, purchase of land, debt recovery (or incurring debt liability), or one or two-day annual events.
Publications: Application guidelines; Biennial report; Biennial report (including application guidelines); Grants list; Occasional report.
Application information: Application form available on foundation web site. Application form required.
Initial approach: Use of online application is the method which the foundation strongly recommends; if submitting an online request is not an option, applicants may contact foundation and request a paper copy of the application
Deadline(s): See foundation web site for current deadlines
Board meeting date(s): 3 times per year
Final notification: 4 weeks
Officers and Directors:* Frank M. Sanchez,* Chair.; Anita L. DeFrantz,* Pres.; F. Patrick Escobar, V.P., Grants and Progs.; Wayne Wilson, V.P., Comm. and Education; Marcia Suzuki, Treas.; Yvonne B. Burke; Jae Min Chang; John F. Chavez; Debra Kay Duncan; James L. Easton; Priscilla Florence; Jonathan Glaser; Robert V. Graziano; Mariann Harris; Rafer Johnson; Stan Kasten; Maureen Kindel; Patrick McClenahan; Peter V. Ueberroth; Walter F. Ulloa; Gilbert R. Vasquez; John Ziffren.
Number of staff: 11 full-time professional; 1 part-time professional.
EIN: 953792725
Selected grants: The following grants are a representative sample of this grantmaker's funding activity:
$500,000 to Los Angeles Unified School District, Los Angeles, CA, 2012. For after-school intramural sports league in basketball, soccer, softball and flag football at middle schools in LAUSD.
$395,000 to Kids In Sports, Los Angeles, CA, 2012. For continued support of baseball/softball/t-ball, basketball, flag football, valleyball and soccer leagues throughout Los Angeles County.
$300,000 to LAs BEST, Los Angeles, CA, 2012. For personnel and athletic expenses in year-round after-school sports program in flag football, softball, basketball and soccer serving boys and girls at elementary schools in Los Angeles Unified School District.
$250,000 to GRYD Foundation, Los Angeles, CA, 2012. For uniforms for basketball and soccer programs offered through parks participating in Summer Night Lights sports program.
$150,000 to Southern California Tennis Association, Los Angeles, CA, 2012. For personnel, athlete expenses and equipment for tennis programs throughout Southern California.
$125,080 to Students Run America, Tarzana, CA, 2012. For personnel and athlete expenses for LA Marathon training program for middle school and high school youth.
$66,042 to THINK Together, Santa Ana, CA, 2012. For personnel, athlete expenses and equipment for middle school sports program.
$60,000 to Friends of Expo Center, Los Angeles, CA, 2012. For personnel for Learn to Swim Program.
$25,000 to Vernon Lee Amateur Gymnastics Academy, Pasadena, CA, 2012. For gymnastics equipment.

810
Lily Lai Foundation ✧ ☆
4227 Mancilla Ct.
San Diego, CA 92130-2203

Established in CA.
Donor: Lily Lai†.
Foundation type: Independent foundation.
Financial data (yr. ended 12/31/13): Assets, $12,244,648 (M); expenditures, $500,119; qualifying distributions, $478,000; giving activities include $478,000 for 8 grants (high: $100,000; low: $2,000).
Purpose and activities: Support public library, school and voice of children.
Fields of interest: Education; Human services.
Limitations: Applications not accepted. Giving primarily in San Diego, CA.
Application information: Unsolicited requests for funds not accepted.
Officers: George Lai, Pres.; Edwin Luwa, Secy.; Doreen Young, Treas.
Directors: Antoinette Haskel; Ching Huang.
EIN: 271159623

811
Alice and Nahum Lainer Family Foundation ✧
16216 Kittridge St.
Van Nuys, CA 91406-5846

Established in 2008 in CA.
Donor: Simha Lainer†.
Foundation type: Independent foundation.
Financial data (yr. ended 12/31/13): Assets, $10,059,636 (M); expenditures, $526,173; qualifying distributions, $496,000; giving activities include $496,000 for 6 grants (high: $190,000; low: $20,000).
Fields of interest: Museums (art); Museums (ethnic/folk arts); Jewish agencies & synagogues.
Limitations: Applications not accepted. Giving primarily in Los Angeles, CA, and New York, NY. No grants to individuals.
Application information: Contributes only to pre-selected organizations.
Trustees: Alice Lainer; Gary Lainer; Leslie Ann Lainer; Nahum Lainer; Nancy Lainer.
EIN: 260576516

812
Ellie and Mark Lainer Family Foundation ✧
16216 Kittridge St.
Van Nuys, CA 91406-5846

Established in 2008 in CA.
Donor: Simha Lainer†.
Foundation type: Independent foundation.
Financial data (yr. ended 12/31/13): Assets, $9,865,931 (M); expenditures, $476,232; qualifying distributions, $450,000; giving activities include $450,000 for 6 grants (high: $110,000; low: $25,000).
Fields of interest: Elementary/secondary education; Jewish federated giving programs; Jewish agencies & synagogues.
Limitations: Applications not accepted. Giving primarily in CA. No grants to individuals.
Application information: Contributes only to pre-selected organizations.
Trustees: Lisa Lainer Fagan; Eleanor Lainer; Jeffrey E. Lainer; Mark Lainer; Steven D. Lainer.
EIN: 260494169

813
Lee And Luis Lainer Family Foundation ✧
16216 Kittridge St.
Van Nuys, CA 91406-5846

Established in 2008 in CA.

Donor: Simha Lainer†.
Foundation type: Independent foundation.
Financial data (yr. ended 12/31/13): Assets, $10,142,814 (M); expenditures, $501,619; qualifying distributions, $465,000; giving activities include $465,000 for 21 grants (high: $100,000; low: $2,500).
Fields of interest: Human services; International peace/security; Jewish federated giving programs; Jewish agencies & synagogues.
Limitations: Applications not accepted. Giving primarily in CA, Washington, DC, and New York, NY. No grants to individuals.
Application information: Contributes only to pre-selected organizations.
Trustees: Anne E. Lainer; Jesse S. Lainer; Lee Lainer; Luis Lainer; Zachary Lainer.
EIN: 260494276

814
Simha and Sara Lainer Family Foundation ✧
16216 Kittridge St.
Van Nuys, CA 91406-5846

Established in 1994 in CA.
Donors: Mark Lavine; Lainer Charitable Lead Trust.
Foundation type: Independent foundation.
Financial data (yr. ended 12/31/13): Assets, $24,744,083 (M); gifts received, $222,000; expenditures, $1,331,161; qualifying distributions, $1,004,000; giving activities include $1,004,000 for 8 grants (high: $700,000; low: $3,000).
Fields of interest: Jewish federated giving programs; Jewish agencies & synagogues.
Limitations: Applications not accepted. Giving primarily in CA. No grants to individuals.
Application information: Unsolicited requests for funds not accepted.
Trustees: Luis Lainer; Mark Lainer; Nahum Lainer.
EIN: 956962300

815
Diane S. Lake Charitable Trust ✧
P.O. Box 1737
Bakersfield, CA 93302-1737

Established in 1999 in CA.
Donors: Western Oilfield Supply Co.; Diane S. Lake.
Foundation type: Company-sponsored foundation.
Financial data (yr. ended 12/31/12): Assets, $652,014 (M); gifts received, $1,000,000; expenditures, $1,094,150; qualifying distributions, $1,094,000; giving activities include $1,094,000 for 64 grants (high: $80,500; low: $2,500).
Purpose and activities: The foundation supports museums and zoos and organizations involved with performing arts, higher education, health, substance abuse, and youth services.
Fields of interest: Education; Health care; Community/economic development.
Type of support: General/operating support.
Limitations: Applications not accepted. Giving limited to Bakersfield, CA. No grants to individuals.
Application information: Contributes only to pre-selected organizations.
Trustees: Christopher Lake; Diane S. Lake.
EIN: 776166455

816
Lakeside Foundation ✧
3697 Mt. Diablo Blvd., Ste. 205
Lafayette, CA 94549-3754
Contact: Laura D. Mateo, Pres.

Incorporated in 1953 in CA.
Foundation type: Independent foundation.
Financial data (yr. ended 12/31/13): Assets, $106,963,193 (M); gifts received, $848,319; expenditures, $5,267,599; qualifying distributions, $4,738,000; giving activities include $4,738,000 for 146 grants (high: $600,000; low: $1,000).
Purpose and activities: Supports the charitable interests of the directors.
Fields of interest: General charitable giving.
Limitations: Applications not accepted. Giving primarily in the San Francisco Bay Area, CA, as well as the Charleston, SC area. No grants to individuals; no loans.
Application information: Contributes only to pre-selected organizations; unsolicited contacts are discouraged.
Board meeting date(s): Annually, usually in the spring
Officers and Directors:* Laura D. Mateo,* Pres.; Paul L. Davies, Jr.,* V.P.; Andrew E. Zeisler, Secy.-Treas.; Paul Lewis Davies III; Pilar H. Davies.
EIN: 946066229

817
Lamond Family Foundation ✧ ☆
167 Isabella Ave.
Atherton, CA 94027-4044 (650) 845-8100
Contact: Pierre Lamond, Pres.; Christine Lamond, V.P. and Treas.

Established in 1994 in CA.
Donors: Pierre Lamond; Christine Lamond.
Foundation type: Independent foundation.
Financial data (yr. ended 12/31/13): Assets, $630,674 (M); gifts received, $802,255; expenditures, $484,895; qualifying distributions, $480,000; giving activities include $480,000 for 10 grants (high: $200,000; low: $5,000).
Fields of interest: Museums (art); Performing arts, orchestras; Arts; Higher education; Law school/education; Hospitals (general); Human services.
Application information: Application form not required.
Initial approach: Proposal
Deadline(s): None
Officers: Pierre Lamond, Pres.; Christine Lamond, V.P. and Treas.
EIN: 943204401

818
Lampert Family Foundation ✧
c/o Mark Lampert
2415 Green St.
San Francisco, CA 94123-4626

Established in 2000 in CA.
Donors: Mark Lampert; Susan Byrd.
Foundation type: Independent foundation.
Financial data (yr. ended 12/31/12): Assets, $24,826,974 (M); expenditures, $1,259,617; qualifying distributions, $1,154,317; giving activities include $1,069,450 for 4 grants (high: $1,000,000; low: $9,450).
Fields of interest: Foundations (community).
Limitations: Applications not accepted. Giving primarily in San Francisco, CA. No grants to individuals.
Application information: Contributes only to pre-selected organizations.
Trustees: Susan Byrd; Mark Lampert.
EIN: 367335154

819
The Stanley S. Langendorf Foundation ✧
P.O. Box 2509
San Francisco, CA 94126-2509 (415) 217-4919
Contact: Jude P. Damasco
FAX: (415) 217-4914;
E-mail: sslfoundation@damasco.com; Main URL: http://www.sslfoundation.org

Established in 1982 in CA.
Donor: Stanley S. Langendorf†.
Foundation type: Independent foundation.
Financial data (yr. ended 12/31/13): Assets, $12,925,339 (M); expenditures, $1,078,845; qualifying distributions, $958,350; giving activities include $958,350 for 89 grants (high: $213,500; low: $500).
Purpose and activities: The foundation funds organizations that benefit community services/social services, youth, primary and secondary education, and the arts.
Fields of interest: Arts; Elementary/secondary education; Youth development; Human services; Children/youth, services.
Type of support: General/operating support; Program development; Scholarship funds.
Limitations: Applications accepted. Giving limited to San Francisco, CA. No grants to individuals.
Publications: Application guidelines.
Application information: The foundation strongly prefers electronic submissions. Full proposals via invitation only. See foundation web site for application guidelines and forms. Application form required.
Initial approach: See foundation web site for letter of intent instructions and guidelines
Copies of proposal: 1
Deadline(s): See foundation web site for current deadlines
Board meeting date(s): Spring and fall
Officers and Trustees:* Richard J. Guggenhime,* Pres. and Treas.; Lisa Guggenhime Hauswirth,* Secy.; Patricia Capbarat; Charles H. Clifford, Jr.; Andrew Guggenhime.
EIN: 942861512
Selected grants: The following grants are a representative sample of this grantmaker's funding activity:
$350 to Tipping Point Community, San Francisco, CA, 2012. For Community and Social Services.

820
The Walter Lantz Foundation ✧
P.O. Box 5150
Lancaster, CA 93539-5150 (818) 842-1616
Contact: Peggy Jackson

Established in 1984 in CA.
Donors: Grace T. Lantz†; Walter Lantz†.
Foundation type: Independent foundation.
Financial data (yr. ended 11/30/13): Assets, $7,261,350 (M); expenditures, $1,214,195;

qualifying distributions, $1,066,222; giving activities include $928,438 for 25 grants.
Purpose and activities: Giving primarily for higher education and the arts, including art education and visual arts; support also for health organizations and social services.
Fields of interest: Arts; Higher education; Botanical gardens; Health care; Health organizations, association; Human services; Children/youth, services.
Limitations: Giving primarily in the Los Angeles, CA, area. No grants to individuals.
Application information: Application form not required.
Initial approach: Letter
Copies of proposal: 1
Deadline(s): None
Trustees: Susan J. Hazard; Margaret Jackson; Edward A. Landry.
Number of staff: 1
EIN: 953994420

821
Las Cumbres Observatory, Inc. ✧
6740 Cortona Dr., Ste. 102
Goleta, CA 93117-5575 (805) 880-1600
FAX: (805) 961-1792; UK address: Unit 2, Hamilton Plz., Duncan St., Birkenhead CH41 5EY UK, tel.: +44 (0) 151 647 8654; Main URL: http://www.lcogt.net
Facebook: https://www.facebook.com/lcogt
RSS Feed: http://lcogt.net/blog/feed
Twitter: http://twitter.com/lcogt

Established in 1995 in CA.
Donors: Wayne E. Rosing; The Tabasgo Foundation.
Foundation type: Operating foundation.
Financial data (yr. ended 12/31/12): Assets, $46,820,975 (M); gifts received, $12,737,540; expenditures, $8,244,244; qualifying distributions, $4,696,922; giving activities include $841,075 for 9 grants (high: $485,031; low: $702), and $3,855,847 for foundation-administered programs.
Fields of interest: Science, public education; Astronomy.
Limitations: Applications not accepted. Giving primarily in CA, HI and TX; some funding internationally, particularly Australia. No grants to individuals.
Application information: Contributes only to pre-selected organizations.
Officers: Wayne E. Rosing, Pres.; Dorothy F. Largay, Secy.-Treas.
Directors: Lars Bildstein; Mike Skrutskie, Ph.D.
EIN: 770361278
Selected grants: The following grants are a representative sample of this grantmaker's funding activity:
$485,031 to University of California, Santa Barbara, CA, 2012. For Education Grants Sedgwick Reserve.
$208,333 to University of Hawaii, Honolulu, HI, 2012. For Pann-Stars Educational.
$1,970 to Astronomical Society of the Pacific, San Francisco, CA, 2012. For outreach and challenge.

822
Cherese Mari Laulhere Foundation ✧
5800 Spinnaker Bay Dr.
Long Beach, CA 90803-6818
E-mail: info@cherese.org; Main URL: http://www.cherese.org
Twitter: https://twitter.com/cheresemari/

Established in 1996 in CA.
Donors: Larry Laulhere; Mrs. Larry Laulhere; Gwen Laulhere; Wakeman Holdings LP.
Foundation type: Independent foundation.
Financial data (yr. ended 06/30/13): Assets, $14,214,990 (M); gifts received, $4,200,025; expenditures, $819,459; qualifying distributions, $817,011; giving activities include $817,000 for 9 grants (high: $600,000; low: $2,000).
Purpose and activities: Giving to organizations that enrich and better the lives of children, adults and/or families through education, cultural or performing arts, or through medical and health-care related causes.
Fields of interest: Arts; Education; Animals/wildlife; Hospitals (general); Health care; Medical research, institute; Boys & girls clubs; Children/youth, services; Family services.
Limitations: Applications not accepted. Giving primarily in CA.
Application information: Contributes only to pre-selected organizations.
Officers and Directors:* Christine Laulhere,* Pres.; Larry Laulhere,* Secy.-Treas.; Teresa Laulhere; Todd Laulhere.
Advisors: Lisa Lungren; Anne-Mare Pedersen; Sophia Pen; Judy Valadez.
EIN: 330735639
Selected grants: The following grants are a representative sample of this grantmaker's funding activity:
$30,000 to Discovery Arts, Orange, CA, 2013. To support Programs for Children with Life Threatening.
$20,000 to Children Today, Long Beach, CA, 2013. For assistance to homeless children.

823
Laural Foundation ✧
c/o Lauren B. Dachs
P.O. Box 193809
San Francisco, CA 94119-3809

Established in 1977 in CA.
Donors: Lauren B. Dachs; Stephen D. Bechtel, Jr.; Elizabeth H. Bechtel.
Foundation type: Independent foundation.
Financial data (yr. ended 12/31/13): Assets, $30,429,772 (M); gifts received, $5,000,000; expenditures, $925,573; qualifying distributions, $908,936; giving activities include $875,000 for 16 grants (high: $300,000; low: $5,000).
Fields of interest: Education; Environment.
Type of support: General/operating support; Continuing support; Annual campaigns; Capital campaigns; Building/renovation; Program development; Scholarship funds; Research; Program evaluation.
Limitations: Applications not accepted. Giving primarily in the San Francisco Bay Area, CA. No grants to individuals.
Application information: Contributes only to pre-selected organizations. Unsolicited requests for funds not considered.
Board meeting date(s): As required
Officers and Directors:* Lauren B. Dachs,* Pres.; Alan M. Dachs,* V.P.; Susan Harvey,* Secy.; Shu Huang, Treas.
EIN: 942417772
Selected grants: The following grants are a representative sample of this grantmaker's funding activity:
$500,000 to Land Trust Alliance, Washington, DC, 2012. For Pledge- Special Initiatives Campaign.
$125,000 to Land Trust Alliance, Washington, DC, 2012. For Pledge- Policy Work and Meet Challenge Grant.
$75,000 to Land Trust Alliance, Washington, DC, 2012. For Pledge- Annual Fund.
$50,000 to Stanford University, Stanford, CA, 2012. For Pledge Woods Institute - Reunion Campaign.
$5,000 to Santa Clara University, Santa Clara, CA, 2012. For annual fund 2012-2013.

824
Lear Family Foundation, Inc. ✧
100 N. Crescent Dr., Ste. 120
Beverly Hills, CA 90210-5427

Established in 1997 in CA.
Donors: Norman Lear; Lyn Lear.
Foundation type: Independent foundation.
Financial data (yr. ended 12/31/12): Assets, $17,003,983 (M); expenditures, $3,327,456; qualifying distributions, $2,980,907; giving activities include $2,322,764 for 105 grants (high: $250,000; low: $10).
Purpose and activities: Giving primarily for the arts, higher education, health and human services.
Fields of interest: Arts; Elementary/secondary education; Higher education; Environment; Animals/wildlife; Health organizations, association; Medical research, institute; Human services; Children/youth, services; Family services; Civil/human rights; Jewish agencies & synagogues.
Type of support: General/operating support.
Limitations: Applications not accepted. Giving primarily in Washington, DC; some giving nationally. No grants to individuals.
Application information: Contributes only to pre-selected organizations.
Officers and Directors:* Norman Lear,* Pres.; Julie Dyer, Treas.; Sherry Simon, Exec. Dir.; Lyn Lear.
EIN: 954661216
Selected grants: The following grants are a representative sample of this grantmaker's funding activity:
$5,000,000 to People for the American Way Foundation, Washington, DC, 2011.
$250,000 to People for the American Way Foundation, Washington, DC, 2011.
$125,000 to Friends of Jazz at UCLA, Los Angeles, CA, 2011.
$125,000 to Friends of Jazz at UCLA, Los Angeles, CA, 2011.
$125,000 to People for the American Way, Washington, DC, 2010.
$125,000 to People for the American Way, Washington, DC, 2010.
$100,000 to University of Southern California, Annenberg School for Communication, Los Angeles, CA, 2011.
$100,000 to University of Southern California, Annenberg School for Communication, Los Angeles, CA, 2011.
$33,333 to University of Southern California, Annenberg School for Communication, Los Angeles, CA, 2011.

$30,000 to Sundance Institute, Park City, UT, 2010.
$25,000 to American Civil Liberties Union Foundation of Southern California, Los Angeles, CA, 2011.
$25,000 to American Civil Liberties Union of Southern California, Los Angeles, CA, 2010.
$25,000 to Children's Defense Fund, Washington, DC, 2011.
$25,000 to Museum Associates, Los Angeles County Museum of Art (LACMA), Los Angeles, CA, 2011.
$25,000 to New York University, New York, NY, 2010.
$25,000 to University of Chicago, Chicago, IL, 2010.
$20,000 to Sundance Institute, Park City, UT, 2010.
$10,000 to Global Green USA, Santa Monica, CA, 2010.
$5,000 to Global Green USA, Santa Monica, CA, 2010.
$5,000 to Human Rights Watch, New York, NY, 2010.

825
Thomas & Dorothy Leavey Foundation ✧

10100 Santa Monica Blvd., Ste. 610
Los Angeles, CA 90067-4110 (310) 551-9936
Contact: Kathleen L. McCarthy, Chair.

Established in 1952 in CA.
Donors: Thomas E. Leavey†; Dorothy E. Leavey†.
Foundation type: Independent foundation.
Financial data (yr. ended 12/31/12): Assets, $249,171,900 (M); expenditures, $14,408,495; qualifying distributions, $11,308,967; giving activities include $10,725,188 for 92 grants (high: $2,000,000; low: $1,200), and $324,000 for grants to individuals.
Purpose and activities: Giving primarily for hospitals, medical research, higher and secondary education, and Catholic church groups; provides scholarships to children of employees of Farmers Group, Inc.
Fields of interest: Education; Health care; Youth, services; Human services; Community/economic development.
Type of support: Scholarships—to individuals.
Limitations: Applications accepted. Giving primarily in southern CA.
Application information:
Initial approach: Letter
Copies of proposal: 1
Deadline(s): None
Board meeting date(s): As required
Officer and Trustees:* Kathleen L. McCarthy,* Chair.; Louis M. Castruccio; Leo E. Denlea, Jr.; Jacqueline Powers Doud; Michael Enright; Karen Hollins; Tom Lemons; John McCarthy; Colleen Pennell.
EIN: 956060162
Selected grants: The following grants are a representative sample of this grantmaker's funding activity:
$2,000,000 to Loyola Marymount University, Los Angeles, CA, 2012.
$1,000,000 to Georgetown University, Washington, DC, 2012.
$1,000,000 to Georgetown University, Washington, DC, 2012.
$1,000,000 to Saint Johns Health Center, Santa Monica, CA, 2012.
$1,000,000 to Saint Paul the Apostle School, Los Angeles, CA, 2012.
$500,000 to Childrens Hospital Los Angeles, Los Angeles, CA, 2012.
$333,333 to California Science Center, Los Angeles, CA, 2012.
$333,333 to California Science Center Foundation, Los Angeles, CA, 2012.
$100,000 to Marycrest Manor, Culver City, CA, 2012.
$25,000 to Thomas Aquinas College, Santa Paula, CA, 2012.

826
The Norman & Sadie Lee Foundation ✧

9454 Wilshire Blvd., 4th Fl.
Beverly Hills, CA 90212-2907

Established in 1978.
Donors: Norman H. Lee; Sadie Lee; The Norman & Sadie Lee Living Trust.
Foundation type: Independent foundation.
Financial data (yr. ended 12/31/12): Assets, $40,237,772 (M); expenditures, $1,934,768; qualifying distributions, $1,793,500; giving activities include $1,793,500 for grants.
Fields of interest: Performing arts, orchestras; Arts; Cancer; Human services.
Type of support: General/operating support.
Limitations: Applications not accepted. Giving primarily in Los Angeles, CA. No grants to individuals.
Application information: Unsolicited requests for funds not accepted.
Officer and Directors:* Paul A. James,* Pres.; Bryan Isaacs.
EIN: 953333368

827
The Lehrer Family Foundation ✧ ☆

c/o Robert A. Morin, C.P.A.
217 E. Alameda Ave., Ste. 305
Burbank, CA 91502-2622

Established in 1996 in CA.
Donors: Seymour Lehrer; Shirley Lehrer.
Foundation type: Independent foundation.
Financial data (yr. ended 06/30/13): Assets, $8,796,133 (M); gifts received, $2,010; expenditures, $481,552; qualifying distributions, $481,552; giving activities include $474,010 for 36 grants (high: $168,000; low: $1,000).
Purpose and activities: Giving primarily for the arts, health organizations and medical research, and human services.
Fields of interest: Museums; Performing arts; Performing arts, education; Arts; Environment; Zoos/zoological societies; Reproductive health, family planning; Health organizations; Medical research, institute; Children/youth, services; Human services; Jewish federated giving programs; Religion.
Limitations: Applications not accepted. No grants to individuals.
Application information: Contributes only to pre-selected organizations.
Officers and Directors:* Seymour Lehrer,* Pres.; Shirley Lehrer,* Secy.; Karen Lehrer; Ellen Lehrer Orlando; Thomas Orlando.
EIN: 770439722
Selected grants: The following grants are a representative sample of this grantmaker's funding activity:
$270,600 to Music Academy of the West, Santa Barbara, CA, 2011.
$52,500 to Santa Barbara Center for the Performing Arts, Santa Barbara, CA, 2011.
$10,000 to Esalen Institute, Big Sur, CA, 2011.
$10,000 to Santa Barbara Symphony, Santa Barbara, CA, 2011.
$9,000 to Santa Barbara Zoological Gardens, Santa Barbara, CA, 2011.
$7,500 to Santa Barbara Bowl Foundation, Santa Barbara, CA, 2011.
$5,500 to State Street Ballet, Santa Barbara, CA, 2011.
$5,000 to Carrillo Counseling Services, Santa Barbara, CA, 2011.
$5,000 to City of Hope, Los Angeles, CA, 2011.
$5,000 to Environmental Defense Center, Santa Barbara, CA, 2011.

828
The Leichtag Foundation ✧

441 Saxony Rd.
Encinitas, CA 92024-2725 (760) 929-1090
E-mail: info@leichtag.org; Main URL: http://jcfsandiego.org/funds-foundations/leichtag-foundation/
Facebook: https://www.facebook.com/LeichtagFoundation?fref=ts

Established in 1991 in CA.
Donors: Max Leichtag; Andre Leichtag; Leichtag Family Trust; Lee and Toni Leichtag Family Trust.
Foundation type: Independent foundation.
Financial data (yr. ended 12/31/13): Assets, $142,622,033 (M); expenditures, $16,402,116; qualifying distributions, $13,808,355; giving activities include $12,230,106 for 172 grants (high: $1,990,000; low: $250), and $12,935,662 for foundation-administered programs.
Purpose and activities: The foundation strives to alleviate human hardship, advance self-sufficiency, and promote tolerance and understanding, reflecting the Leichtags' pride in their Jewish heritage.
Fields of interest: Human services; Foundations (private independent); Jewish federated giving programs.
International interests: Israel.
Limitations: Giving primarily in the North County Coastal Region of San Diego, CA, and in Jerusalem, Israel. No support for political campaigns or lobbying activities. No grants to individuals, or for fundraising events, endowments, medical or scientific research, individual synagogues or churches, and no funding for capital campaigns.
Publications: Financial statement; Grants list; Program policy statement.
Application information: Unsolicited requests for funds not accepted. However, the foundation is interested in hearing about organizations and programs that may fit within its strategic framework and focus areas. Carefully review the strategic framework on the foundation's website. If you feel your organization is a fit, use the letter of introduction form on the foundation's web site.
Board meeting date(s): May and Nov.
Officers and Trustees:* Bernard Reiter,* Chair.; Emily Einhorn,* Vice-Chair.; Jeffrey R. Solomon,* Vice-Chair.; James S. Farley,* C.E.O. and Pres.; Charlene Seidle, Exec. V.P.; Robert Brunst, M.D.*, C.F.O. and Treas.
Number of staff: None.
EIN: 330466189

Selected grants: The following grants are a representative sample of this grantmaker's funding activity:
$1,110,000 to American Jewish Joint Distribution Committee, New York, NY, 2012.
$1,098,775 to Lawrence Family Jewish Community Centers of San Diego County, La Jolla, CA, 2012.
$761,743 to Jewish Community Foundation, San Diego, CA, 2012.
$457,540 to Simon Wiesenthal Center, Los Angeles, CA, 2012.
$259,000 to PresenTense Group, New York, NY, 2012.
$103,409 to New Israel Fund, New York, NY, 2012.
$65,000 to Nonprofit Management Solutions, San Diego, CA, 2012.
$50,000 to San Diego Lesbian, Gay, Bisexual, Transgender Community Center, San Diego, CA, 2012.
$40,000 to Jewish Funders Network, New York, NY, 2012.
$25,466 to American Jewish Committee, New York, NY, 2012.

829
Lauren B. Leichtman and Arthur E. Levine Family Foundation ✧

c/o Teri McClure
335 N. Maple Dr., Ste. 240
Beverly Hills, CA 90210-3859
Main URL: http://foundationcenter.org/grantmaker/leichtmanlevine/

Established in CA.
Donors: Arthur E. Levine; Lauren B. Leichtman.
Foundation type: Independent foundation.
Financial data (yr. ended 05/31/13): Assets, $313,951 (M); gifts received, $732,500; expenditures, $703,928; qualifying distributions, $701,900; giving activities include $701,900 for 21 grants (high: $300,000; low: $500).
Purpose and activities: Giving primarily for higher and other education; funding also for the arts, children services, and Jewish organizations and temples.
Fields of interest: Performing arts, opera; Elementary/secondary education; Higher education; Law school/education; Education; Human services; Children, services; Family services; Jewish agencies & synagogues.
Type of support: General/operating support.
Limitations: Applications not accepted. Giving primarily in Los Angeles, CA.
Application information: Unsolicited requests for funds not accepted.
Trustees: Lauren B. Leichtman; Arthur E. Levine.
EIN: 954051968
Selected grants: The following grants are a representative sample of this grantmaker's funding activity:
$125,000 to UCLA Foundation, Los Angeles, CA, 2011.
$112,500 to Wallis Annenberg Center for the Performing Arts, Beverly Hills, CA, 2011.
$70,000 to UCLA Foundation, Los Angeles, CA, 2011.
$45,000 to Planned Parenthood Federation of America, New York, NY, 2011.
$40,000 to California State University at Northridge Foundation, Northridge, CA, 2011.
$10,250 to Aviva Family and Childrens Services, Los Angeles, CA, 2011. For annual gift.
$10,000 to Windward School, Los Angeles, CA, 2011. For annual gift.
$5,000 to Planned Parenthood Federation of America, New York, NY, 2011. For annual gift.
$5,000 to Wallis Annenberg Center for the Performing Arts, Beverly Hills, CA, 2011. For annual gift.
$3,000 to Union Rescue Mission, Los Angeles, CA, 2011. For annual gift.

830
Leonard & Laila Rose Foundations ✧

600 Spring Rd., Rental Office
Moorpark, CA 93021-1243

Donor: Laila Rose.
Foundation type: Independent foundation.
Financial data (yr. ended 06/30/13): Assets, $92,763 (M); gifts received, $700,000; expenditures, $624,126; qualifying distributions, $620,866; giving activities include $620,866 for 10 grants (high: $192,010; low: $800).
Fields of interest: Human services; Religion.
Limitations: Applications not accepted. Giving primarily in CA and Thailand. No grants to individuals.
Application information: Unsolicited requests for funds not accepted.
Officers and Directors:* Laila Rose,* Chair.; Pablo Pesantez,* Secy.; Chavin Jindarat; Artis Suebpetch.
EIN: 270872803

831
The George & Wilma Leonard Charitable Foundation ✧

c/o Eckhoff Accountancy
145 N. Redwood Dr.
San Rafael, CA 94903-1974

Established in CA.
Donors: Wilma F. Leonard‡; Mark G. Leonard; Candace H. Leonard; Jon Leonard; William Leonard; Jim Leonard.
Foundation type: Independent foundation.
Financial data (yr. ended 03/31/13): Assets, $10,534,803 (M); expenditures, $558,371; qualifying distributions, $541,500; giving activities include $541,500 for grants.
Purpose and activities: Giving primarily for education, Protestant churches, and social services.
Fields of interest: Elementary/secondary education; Higher education; Education; Human services; Foundations (private grantmaking); Protestant agencies & churches.
Limitations: Applications not accepted. Giving primarily in CA and MN. No grants to individuals.
Application information: Contributes only to pre-selected organizations.
Officers: Mark G. Leonard, Pres.; Candace H. Leonard, V.P.; William Leonard, Secy.; Jon Leonard, Treas.
Director: Jim Leonard.
EIN: 942598897
Selected grants: The following grants are a representative sample of this grantmaker's funding activity:
$232,000 to Macalester College, Saint Paul, MN, 2012.
$25,000 to Second Harvest Food Bank of Santa Clara and San Mateo Counties, San Jose, CA, 2012.
$20,000 to Community Services Agency, Mountain View, CA, 2012.
$15,500 to Foothills Congregational Church, Los Altos, CA, 2012.
$10,000 to Habitat for Humanity East Bay/Silicon Valley, Milpitas, CA, 2012.
$10,000 to K Q E D, San Francisco, CA, 2012.
$5,000 to El Camino Hospital Foundation, Mountain View, CA, 2012.
$5,000 to Electronic Frontier Foundation, San Francisco, CA, 2012.
$5,000 to Girl Scouts of the U.S.A., San Jose, CA, 2012.
$5,000 to Pacific School of Religion, Berkeley, CA, 2012.

832
The Leonetti/O'Connell Family Foundation ✧

515 S. Figueroa St., Ste. 1050
Los Angeles, CA 90071-3330 (213) 622-0066
Contact: Alexa Pearl Margalith, Grants Mgr.
FAX: (213) 613-0805; E-mail: amargalith@locff.org; Main URL: http://www.locff.org

Established in 1995 in CA as under The Caroline Leonetti Ahmanson Foundation. In 2004 its name was changed to The Leonetti/O'Connell Foundation. It relocated and merged with its DE foundation in 2006.
Donors: Caroline L. Ahmanson‡; Margo L. O'Connell; Michael F. O'Connell; Michael Kevin O'Connell; Cara Leonetti Esposito; Caolionn Leonetti Esposito; The Leonetti/O'Connell Family Foundation.
Foundation type: Independent foundation.
Financial data (yr. ended 12/31/13): Assets, $43,845,320 (M); expenditures, $2,075,043; qualifying distributions, $1,910,239; giving activities include $1,609,266 for 31 grants (high: $559,530; low: $1,000).
Purpose and activities: The focus of the foundation is education in Los Angeles County, CA.
Fields of interest: Arts; Education; Hospitals (specialty); Health organizations; Human services; Science; Children; Youth; African Americans/Blacks; Hispanics/Latinos; Girls; Single parents; Economically disadvantaged.
Type of support: General/operating support; Program development; Scholarship funds.
Limitations: Applications not accepted. Giving primarily in Los Angeles County, CA. No support for religious or political organizations. No grants to individuals.
Application information: Contributes only to pre-selected organizations.
Board meeting date(s): May
Officers and Directors:* Margo L. O'Connell,* Secy.; Michael F. O'Connell,* C.F.O.; Cara Leonetti Esposito, Exec. Dir.
Number of staff: 1 full-time professional; 1 full-time support.
EIN: 203889415
Selected grants: The following grants are a representative sample of this grantmaker's funding activity:
$287,500 to Loyola Marymount University, Los Angeles, CA, 2013. For Mathematicss Leadership Corps.
$100,000 to Marlborough School, Los Angeles, CA, 2013. For Honors Research in Science and Humanities.

$25,000 to South Central Scholars Foundation, Rancho Palos Verdes, CA, 2013. For Bridge Scholarship Program.

833
Dean & Margaret Lesher Foundation ✧
1333 N. California Blvd., Ste. 330
Walnut Creek, CA 94596-4587 (925) 935-9988
Contact: Kathleen L. Odne, Exec. Dir.
FAX: (925) 935-7459;
E-mail: kodne@lesherfoundation.org; Contact for LOI and grant application questions: Susan Haley, Grants Mgr., e-mail: shaley@lesherfoundation.org; Main URL: http://www.lesherfoundation.org
Application Video Tutorial: http://www.foundant.com/applicant-tutorial.php
Grants Database: http://www.lesherfoundation.org/grants_awarded_arts.html

Established in 1989 in CA.
Donors: Lesher Communications, Inc.; Dean S. Lesher†; Margaret L. Lesher†.
Foundation type: Independent foundation.
Financial data (yr. ended 12/31/13): Assets, $82,468,459 (M); gifts received, $126,556; expenditures, $5,023,176; qualifying distributions, $4,532,094; giving activities include $3,735,525 for 129 grants (high: $450,000; low: $550).
Purpose and activities: The foundation is dedicated to improving the quality of life in Contra Costa County, CA, through educational and cultural endeavors and to support children and strengthen families.
Fields of interest: Arts; Education; Children/youth, services; Family services; Children/youth; Children; Youth; Adults; Aging; Young adults; Disabilities, people with; Physically disabled; Blind/visually impaired; Deaf/hearing impaired; Mentally disabled; Minorities; Asians/Pacific Islanders; African Americans/Blacks; Hispanics/Latinos; Women; Girls; Adults, women; Men; Boys; Adults, men; Military/veterans; Substance abusers; Single parents; Crime/abuse victims; Economically disadvantaged; Homeless; LGBTQ.
Type of support: General/operating support; Continuing support; Management development/capacity building; Capital campaigns; Building/renovation; Equipment; Program development; Scholarship funds; Technical assistance; Matching/challenge support.
Limitations: Applications accepted. Giving limited to Contra Costa County, CA. No support for environmental or open space organizations, health care or for other foundations. No grants to individuals, or for conferences, travel costs, fund drives, annual appeals, endowments or debt retirement; no loans.
Publications: Application guidelines; Annual report; Grants list.
Application information: Applications are by invitation only, upon review of initial Letter of Inquiry. The foundation has transitioned to a web-based grant application system, accessible from the web site on the "How to Apply" page. Applicants should submit 1-copy of their proposal online. Application form required.
Initial approach: Letter of Inquiry required for new organizations (see "How to Apply" page on foundation web site for LOI instructions)
Copies of proposal: 1
Deadline(s): None
Board meeting date(s): Monthly
Final notification: Within 90 days
Officers and Directors:* Cynthia A. Lesher,* Pres.; Steve Lesher,* V.P.; Linda L. Tatum,* Secy.-Treas.; Kathleen L. Odne, Exec. Dir.; David Lesher; Joseph Lesher; Tim Lesher; Jill O'Brien.
Number of staff: 1 full-time professional; 1 full-time support.
EIN: 680208980

834
Leslie Family Foundation ✧
738 Westridge Dr.
Portola Valley, CA 94028-7333

Donors: Leslie Trust; Mark Leslie; Debra A. Leslie.
Foundation type: Independent foundation.
Financial data (yr. ended 12/31/13): Assets, $32,644,764 (M); gifts received, $2,728,108; expenditures, $1,829,449; qualifying distributions, $1,532,068; giving activities include $1,484,000 for 118 grants (high: $545,000; low: $500).
Fields of interest: Arts; Education; Human services; Jewish federated giving programs; Jewish agencies & synagogues.
Limitations: Applications not accepted. Giving primarily in CA; some funding also in NY. No grants to individuals.
Application information: Contributes only to pre-selected organizations.
Officers: Mark Leslie, Chair.; Darrin Martin, Pres.; Seth P. Leslie, Secy.; Joshua M. Leslie, Treas.
Directors: Debra A. Leslie; Sara Leslie; Sharon Leslie.
EIN: 680474709

835
The LeVecke Family Foundation ✧ ☆
18101 Von Karman Ave., No. 750
Irvine, CA 92612-0005

Donor: Reed J. LeVecke†.
Foundation type: Independent foundation.
Financial data (yr. ended 12/31/13): Assets, $22,383,460 (M); gifts received, $718,273; expenditures, $1,253,251; qualifying distributions, $1,128,987; giving activities include $1,104,533 for 32 grants (high: $299,023; low: $1,500).
Fields of interest: Health care; Human services; Religion.
Limitations: Applications not accepted. Giving primarily in CA. No grants to individuals.
Application information: Unsolicited requests for funds not accepted.
Officer: John R. Levecke, Pres.; Mary Joyce LeVecke-Armen, Secy.; Kathryn A. LeVecke-Wilson, Treas.
Directors: Kathryn Hennigan; Marguente Sweeney-LeVecke.
EIN: 330605566

836
Howard and Irene Levine Family Foundation ✧
1660 Bush St., Ste. 300
San Francisco, CA 94109

Established in 1997 in CA.
Donor: Howard Levine.
Foundation type: Independent foundation.
Financial data (yr. ended 12/31/13): Assets, $15,372,427 (M); gifts received, $1,941,472; expenditures, $1,485,255; qualifying distributions, $1,480,006; giving activities include $1,306,563 for 32 grants (high: $562,500; low: $1,000), and $20,000 for 1 employee matching gift.
Fields of interest: Education.
Type of support: General/operating support.
Limitations: Applications not accepted. Giving primarily in Los Angeles, CA. No grants to individuals.
Application information: Contributes only to pre-selected organizations.
Officers: Howard Levine, Pres.; Irene Levine, V.P.; Jay Levine, Treas.; David Levine, Exec. Dir.
Director: Marci Dollinger.
EIN: 954663360

837
Robert and Beverly Lewis Family Foundation ✧ ☆
626 Via Lido Nord
Newport Beach, CA 92663-5521

Established in 1987in CA; Funded in 2005.
Donor: Beverly J. Lewis.
Foundation type: Independent foundation.
Financial data (yr. ended 06/30/13): Assets, $21,488 (M); gifts received, $625,085; expenditures, $615,568; qualifying distributions, $607,223; giving activities include $607,223 for 49 grants (high: $472,948; low: $50).
Fields of interest: Animal welfare; Hospitals (general); Health organizations, association; Medical research, institute; Athletics/sports, equestrianism; Human services.
Limitations: Applications not accepted. Giving primarily in CA. No grants to individuals.
Application information: Contributes only to pre-selected organizations.
Officer and Trustee: Beverly J. Lewis,* C.E.O.
EIN: 330210203
Selected grants: The following grants are a representative sample of this grantmaker's funding activity:
$50,000 to Kentucky Derby Museum Corporation, Louisville, KY, 2011.
$25,000 to California Equine Retirement Foundation, Winchester, CA, 2011.
$1,100 to Kentucky Horse Park Foundation, Lexington, KY, 2011.
$1,000 to Hoag Hospital Foundation, Newport Beach, CA, 2011.
$1,000 to United Pegasus Foundation, Arcadia, CA, 2011.

838
Lilly's Gift Foundation ✧
c/o Lois G. Ericson
8519 Shady Dell Rd.
MacDoel, CA 96058-9758 (530) 398-4373

Established in 2000 in CA.
Donor: Griswold Industries.
Foundation type: Company-sponsored foundation.
Financial data (yr. ended 12/31/13): Assets, $10,916,964 (M); gifts received, $1,161,667; expenditures, $1,191,527; qualifying distributions, $1,118,000; giving activities include $1,118,000 for 41 grants (high: $270,000; low: $1,000).

Purpose and activities: The foundation supports food banks and organizations involved with health, birth defects, ALS, fire prevention and control, and human services.
Fields of interest: Health care; Health organizations; Human services.
Type of support: General/operating support; Equipment; Program development.
Limitations: Applications accepted. Giving primarily in CA.
Application information: Application form required.
Initial approach: Letter
Deadline(s): None
Officer and Directors:* Lois G. Ericson,* Pres.; Steven L. Ericson; Constance D. Shepherd.
EIN: 680445376

839
Marjorie R. Lindsey Charitable Foundation ✧
10202 Dutch Iris Dr.
Bakersfield, CA 93311-3770

Donor: Marjorie R. Lindsey.
Foundation type: Independent foundation.
Financial data (yr. ended 12/31/13): Assets, $30,810,201 (M); expenditures, $2,575,702; qualifying distributions, $2,332,106; giving activities include $2,240,800 for 15 grants (high: $1,000,000; low: $400).
Fields of interest: Christian agencies & churches.
Limitations: Applications not accepted. Giving primarily in Atlanta, GA; some giving also in CA, FL, and IL.
Application information: Contributes only to pre-selected organizations.
Trustees: Marjorie R. Lindsey; Bank of America, N.A.
EIN: 266906657

840
The James and Joan Lindsey Family Foundation ✧
P.O. Box 50309
Santa Barbara, CA 93150-0309

Established in 1994 in CA.
Donors: James B. Lindsey, Jr.; Joan Anne Lindsey.
Foundation type: Independent foundation.
Financial data (yr. ended 12/31/13): Assets, $6,490,899 (M); gifts received, $992,520; expenditures, $986,646; qualifying distributions, $932,681; giving activities include $810,000 for 9 grants (high: $125,000; low: $60,000).
Fields of interest: Family services; Christian agencies & churches.
Limitations: Applications not accepted. Giving primarily in CA. No grants to individuals.
Application information: Unsolicited requests for funds not accepted.
Officers: Joan Anne Lindsey, Pres.; James B. Lindsey, Jr., Secy.
EIN: 770390011
Selected grants: The following grants are a representative sample of this grantmaker's funding activity:
$425,000 to Family Research Council, Washington, DC, 2011.
$110,000 to Pacific Justice Institute, Sacramento, CA, 2011.
$100,000 to Focus on the Family, Colorado Springs, CO, 2011.
$85,000 to Mastermedia International, Redlands, CA, 2011.
$75,000 to Biola University, La Mirada, CA, 2011.
$30,000 to Christian Film and Television Commission, Camarillo, CA, 2011.
$30,000 to Hollywood Prayer Network, Hollywood, CA, 2011.

841
Lingnan Foundation ✧
(formerly Trustees of Lingnan University)
600 Anton Blvd., Ste. 1100
Costa Mesa, CA 92626-7100 (714) 371-4118
Contact: Leslie Stone, Exec. Dir.
E-mail: info@lingnanfoundation.org; Toll free tel.: (866) 438-4999; Main URL: http://www.lingnanfoundation.org

Established in 1893 in NY.
Donors: Anna Luk Liu; Huey Wong; Pausang Wong; Sinclair Louie; May Louie; Jennie Lee Mui Yi-Ching; I.U. Lai.
Foundation type: Independent foundation.
Financial data (yr. ended 06/30/13): Assets, $21,524,386 (M); gifts received, $28,992; expenditures, $980,336; qualifying distributions, $924,784; giving activities include $757,195 for 8 grants (high: $260,000; low: $902).
Purpose and activities: To contribute to the advancement of higher education in South China, and through that process, to promote understanding between Chinese and Americans. The foundation supports scholarly exchange, educational innovation, and service to society.
Fields of interest: Higher education; Social sciences; International studies.
International interests: China; Hong Kong.
Type of support: General/operating support; Continuing support; Management development/capacity building; Building/renovation; Program development; Conferences/seminars; Professorships; Publication; Seed money; Curriculum development; Fellowships; Internship funds; Scholarship funds; Research; Exchange programs.
Limitations: Applications accepted. Giving primarily in Hong Kong and in the People's Republic of China; some funding in the U.S. No grants to individuals, or for annual campaigns or emergency, capital or endowment funds; no loans.
Publications: Application guidelines; Biennial report; Program policy statement.
Application information: See foundation web site for application guidelines and procedures. Application form not required.
Initial approach: Proposal or letter
Copies of proposal: 1
Deadline(s): Inquire with foundation
Board meeting date(s): May and Nov.
Final notification: 1 month after meetings
Officers and Trustees:* Edward Chow,* Chair.; Jane S. Permaul,* Pres.; Bobby Fong,* Secy.; Alex Banker,* Treas.; Jo H. Currie, Exec. Dir.; Shenyu Belsky; Chi-Chao Chan; Kenyon Chan; Albert Chen; Larry Hudspeth; Helena Kolenda; Ralph Lerner; Roy C. Sheldon; Chui L. Tsang; Michael Woo; Yu "Gary" Zeng.
Number of staff: 2 part-time professional.
EIN: 136400470
Selected grants: The following grants are a representative sample of this grantmaker's funding activity:
$902 to Institute of International Education, New York, NY, 2013. For Student Educational Advancement.

842
Linked Foundation ✧ ☆
3749 Santa Claus Ln., Ste. B
Carpinteria, CA 93013-1104 (805) 880-1990
Contact: Nancy Swanson, Exec. Dir.
FAX: (805) 684-5530;
E-mail: dlargay@linkedfoundation.org; Main URL: http://www.linkedfoundation.org
Blog: http://www.linkedfoundation.org/blog

Established in 2006 in CA.
Donors: Dorothy F. Largay; Wayne E. Rosing; Tabasgo Foundation.
Foundation type: Independent foundation.
Financial data (yr. ended 12/31/13): Assets, $7,340,510 (M); expenditures, $772,045; qualifying distributions, $575,788; giving activities include $440,610 for 9 grants (high: $200,000; low: $3,000), and $135,178 for 1 foundation-administered program.
Purpose and activities: Giving primarily to U.S.-based organizations to advance the development of holistic approaches which combine microfinance with health targeted to very poor women in Latin America.
Fields of interest: Human services; International economic development; Civil/human rights, women; Economic development; Women.
International interests: Caribbean; Latin America.
Limitations: Applications not accepted. Giving primarily in CA; funding also in Washington, DC. No grants to individuals.
Application information: Contributes only to pre-selected organizations.
Officers: Dorothy F. Largay, C.E.O.; Wayne E. Rossing, Secy.; Nancy Swanson, Exec. Dir.
EIN: 203880761
Selected grants: The following grants are a representative sample of this grantmaker's funding activity:
$25,000 to Direct Relief International, Santa Barbara, CA, 2012. For Fund Charitable Event for Organization.
$3,000 to Global Fund for Women, San Francisco, CA, 2012. For Projects That Alleviate Poverty.
$1,000 to Santa Barbara Foundation, Santa Barbara, CA, 2012. For Partnership for Excellence.

843
Lippman Family Foundation ✧
c/o J.R.K. Asset Mgmt.
11766 Wilshire Blvd., Ste. 1500
Los Angeles, CA 90025-6552

Established in CA.
Donor: James M. Lippman.
Foundation type: Independent foundation.
Financial data (yr. ended 12/31/13): Assets, $5,326,528 (M); expenditures, $1,578,787; qualifying distributions, $1,523,378; giving activities include $1,523,378 for 20 grants (high: $536,286; low: $100).
Fields of interest: Higher education; Education; Health organizations; Human services.
Limitations: Applications not accepted. Giving primarily in CA and NY. No grants to individuals.

Application information: Contributes only to pre-selected organizations.
Directors: Alexandra Lippman; James M. Lippman; Linda Lippman; Matthew Lippman.
EIN: 274204823

844
Edmund & Jeannik Littlefield Foundation ✧
(formerly Edmund Wattis Littlefield Foundation)
P.O. Box 190577
San Francisco, CA 94119-0577

Established in 1958 in CA.
Donor: Edmund W. Littlefield†.
Foundation type: Independent foundation.
Financial data (yr. ended 12/31/13): Assets, $39,639,717 (M); gifts received, $30,000; expenditures, $2,212,399; qualifying distributions, $2,004,287; giving activities include $1,850,000 for 12 grants (high: $1,000,000; low: $1,500).
Purpose and activities: Giving primarily for higher education.
Fields of interest: Arts; Higher education; Business school/education.
Type of support: General/operating support; Annual campaigns; Capital campaigns; Building/renovation; Equipment; Conferences/seminars; Publication; Research; Consulting services; Matching/challenge support.
Limitations: Applications not accepted. Giving primarily in CA and NY. No support for religious or political organizations. No grants to individuals.
Application information: Contributes only to pre-selected organizations.
Officers: Allison J.D. Littlefield, Co-Pres.; Naomi J. Sobel, Co-Pres.; Edmund W. Littlefield, Jr., V.P.; Scott R. Littlefield, V.P.; Denise R. Sobel, V.P.; George F. Montgomery II, Secy.; James B. Kilgore, Treas.
EIN: 946074780
Selected grants: The following grants are a representative sample of this grantmaker's funding activity:
$2,000 to CuriOdyssey, San Mateo, CA, 2012. For Libraries and Museums.

845
LLWW Foundation ✧
625 S. Fair Oaks Ave., Ste. 360
South Pasadena, CA 91030-2630

Established in 1980 in CA.
Donor: Laura-Lee Whittier Woods.
Foundation type: Independent foundation.
Financial data (yr. ended 12/31/13): Assets, $20,666,196 (M); expenditures, $911,408; qualifying distributions, $821,680; giving activities include $716,598 for 24 grants (high: $250,000; low: $800).
Purpose and activities: Emphasis on the arts, including museums; giving also for education and social services.
Fields of interest: Visual arts; Museums; Performing arts; Arts; Education; Health care; Children/youth, services.
Type of support: Program development.
Limitations: Applications not accepted. Giving primarily in southern CA; funding also nationally. No grants to individuals; no loans.
Application information: Due to funding restrictions, the foundation manager prefers to initiate the grants made by the foundation.
Board meeting date(s): As needed
Officers and Directors:* Laura-Lee Whittier Woods,* Pres.; Greg E. Custer,* C.F.O.; Jim Jeffs,* V.P.; Linda J. Blinkenberg,* Secy.
EIN: 953464689
Selected grants: The following grants are a representative sample of this grantmaker's funding activity:
$50,000 to Good Samaritan Hospital, Los Angeles, CA, 2012. For Cardiology Campaign.
$35,000 to California Heritage Museum, Santa Monica, CA, 2012. For Challenge Grant 2012 Educational and Community Programming.
$10,000 to Santa Barbara Museum of Natural History, Santa Barbara, CA, 2012. For Butterflies Alive and Tadally Frogs Exhibits.
$1,000 to Ganna Walska Lotusland Foundation, Santa Barbara, CA, 2012. For Gifts for the Garden.
$500 to Scholarship Foundation of Santa Barbara, Santa Barbara, CA, 2012. For Casa Dorinda Scholarship Fund.

846
Long Beach Community Foundation ✧
400 Oceangate, Ste. 800
Long Beach, CA 90802 (562) 435-9033
Contact: James A. Worsham, C.E.O.
FAX: (562) 590-0493;
E-mail: marcelle@longbeachcf.org; Main URL: http://www.longbeachcf.org

Established in 1996 in CA.
Foundation type: Community foundation.
Financial data (yr. ended 12/31/13): Assets, $22,585,537 (M); gifts received, $2,950,375; expenditures, $1,511,500; giving activities include $1,151,505 for 36+ grants (high: $201,000).
Purpose and activities: The foundation initiates positive change for Long Beach through charitable giving, stewardship and strategic grant-making.
Fields of interest: Health care.
Application information: Application form required.
Officers and Directors:* Jane Netherton,* Chair.; Blake Christian,* Vice-Chair.; Marcell Epley, C.E.O. and Pres.; Donita Joseph, C.F.O.; Donna Reckseen,* Secy.; William C. Barnes; Gary DeLong; Bob Foster; Robert Stemler; Judy Vander Lans.
EIN: 205054010

847
The Joseph and Vera Long Foundation ✧
P.O. Box 3827
Walnut Creek, CA 94598-0827
Contact: Brenda Kauten, Admin.
Main URL: http://www.jvlf.org/index.html

Established in 1966.
Donors: Joseph M. Long†; Vera M. Long†.
Foundation type: Independent foundation.
Financial data (yr. ended 12/31/13): Assets, $105,516,359 (M); expenditures, $5,453,212; qualifying distributions, $4,454,762; giving activities include $4,221,600 for 49 grants (high: $525,000; low: $3,000).
Purpose and activities: Giving primarily to organizations involved with healthcare, education and conservation in the communities of Northern CA and HI. In addition, the foundation has a special interest in programs which benefit women, families and seniors, or contribute to the conservation of the natural environment. Preference will be given for new, innovative projects which will be completed with the foundation's contribution.
Fields of interest: Education; Environment; Health care; Family services; Community/economic development; Children/youth; Aging; Women.
Type of support: Management development/capacity building; Capital campaigns; Building/renovation; Equipment; Land acquisition; Program development; Matching/challenge support.
Limitations: Giving primarily in northern CA and HI. No support for religious, sacramental or theological functions, foreign organizations, or to organizations which have submitted requests for invitations to the foundation within the same calendar year. No grants to individuals, or for memorializing individuals, debt, or covering operating deficits; no loans.
Publications: Application guidelines.
Application information: Applications are by invitation only, after consideration of RFI. See foundation web site for specific application information and dates. Application form required.
Initial approach: Request for invitation (RFI) using form on foundation web site, only during the open submission period. Dates for the current open period are posted on the foundation's web site
Copies of proposal: 1
Board meeting date(s): May and Nov.
Officers and Trustees:* Robert M. Long,* Pres.; Nan Gefen,* V.P. and Secy.; Milton Long,* V.P., Treas., and Exec. Dir.; Nick Piediscalzi,* V.P.; Ronald Plomgren,* V.P.; Michelle Holstein.
EIN: 941643626

848
Thomas J. Long Foundation
2950 Buskirk Ave., Ste. 160
Walnut Creek, CA 94597-7770 (925) 944-3800
Contact: Aimee S. Eng, Sr. Prog. Off.; Marcia A. Sander, Cont.; Pam Matthews, Admin. Asst.; Nancy J. Shills, Prog. Off.
FAX: (925) 944-3573;
E-mail: info@thomasjlongfdn.org; Main URL: http://www.thomasjlongfdn.org

Established in 1972.
Donor: Thomas J. Long†.
Foundation type: Independent foundation.
Financial data (yr. ended 12/31/13): Assets, $91,036,725 (M); expenditures, $7,417,485; qualifying distributions, $6,692,779; giving activities include $6,076,850 for 225 grants (high: $1,280,000; low: $5,000).
Purpose and activities: Giving primarily for education, the arts, health and human services.
Fields of interest: Arts; Education; Health care; Human services.
Limitations: Applications accepted. Giving primarily in HI and northern CA with preference given to Alameda, Contra Costa, Napa, Solano, and Sonoma counties. No support for supporting organizations. No grants to individuals, or for endowments, loan repayments, research or international grants.
Application information: The foundation does not accept either a Letter of Inquiry or Grant Application in hard copy. Application form required.
Initial approach: Complete online application following instructions posted on foundation website

Deadline(s): None. Applications are accepted throughout the year
Board meeting date(s): Quarterly
Officers and Trustees:* Sidne J. Long,* Chair.; Hank Delevati,* Vice-Chair.; Mark Friedman, C.E.O.; Marcia Sander, Cont.; Catherine M. Fisher,* Secy.; Milton Long,* Treas.; Moira Walsh.
Number of staff: 4 full-time professional; 1 full-time support.
EIN: 237180712

849
Los Altos Community Foundation ✧
183 Hillview Ave.
Los Altos, CA 94022-3742 (650) 949-5908
FAX: (650) 949-0807; E-mail: lacf@losaltoscf.org; Grant inquiry e-mail: CGP@losaltoscf.org; Main URL: http://www.losaltoscf.org
Facebook: https://www.facebook.com/pages/Los-Altos-Community-Foundation/138638339553146
Flickr: http://www.flickr.com/photos/losaltoscf/
Google Plus: https://plus.google.com/+LosaltoscfOrg/posts
RSS Feed: http://feeds.feedburner.com/LosAltosCommunityFoundation
Twitter: https://twitter.com/lacforg
YouTube: http://www.youtube.com/user/LosAltosCF

Established in 1991 in CA.
Foundation type: Community foundation.
Financial data (yr. ended 06/30/13): Assets, $6,035,622 (M); gifts received, $1,123,695; expenditures, $1,123,407; giving activities include $484,064 for 21+ grants.
Purpose and activities: The foundation supports the community by making grants for local programs, building an endowment for the future, and managing philanthropic funding for other organizations. Giving primarily for the arts, conflict resolution, community building, and leadership development.
Fields of interest: Arts; Higher education; Education; Dispute resolution; Disasters, Hurricane Katrina; Community/economic development; Philanthropy/voluntarism, association; Leadership development; Children/youth.
Type of support: Scholarships—to individuals; General/operating support; Capital campaigns; Building/renovation; Program development; Conferences/seminars; Seed money; Technical assistance; Program evaluation; Program-related investments/loans; Matching/challenge support.
Limitations: Applications accepted. Giving primarily in Los Altos and Los Altos Hills, CA, and surrounding unincorporated areas. No support for governmental, religious, or profit-making organizations. No grants to individuals (except for scholarships).
Publications: Application guidelines; Annual report; Financial statement; Grants list; Informational brochure; Newsletter; Occasional report; Program policy statement.
Application information: Visit foundation web site for grant application, guidelines and specific deadlines. Application form required.
Initial approach: Submit application and attachments
Copies of proposal: 1
Deadline(s): 4th Tuesday of June, Sept., and Feb.
Board meeting date(s): 3rd Wed. of each month
Final notification: 4 weeks
Officers and Directors:* Claudia Coleman,* Co-Chair.; Sherie Dodsworth,* Co-Chair.; Henry Roux,* Corp. Secy.; Joe Eyre,* Exec. Dir.; Roy Lave,* Exec. Dir. Emeritus; Cam Chan; Christina Chu; Judy Hanneman; Mike Kasperzak; Crysta Krames; Bob Kresek; George Limbach; Marilyn Manning; Nancy Manning; Scott Riches; Kevin Schick; George Stafford; Brenda Taussig; Emy Thurber; Jim Thurber; Dennis Young.
Number of staff: 1 full-time support.
EIN: 770273721

850
Lowitz Foundation ✧ ☆
520 N. Kenter Ave.
Los Angeles, CA 90049-1949

Established in 1954 in CA.
Donors: Barry Lowitz; Joseph Lowitz.
Foundation type: Independent foundation.
Financial data (yr. ended 12/31/13): Assets, $157,673 (M); expenditures, $1,633,632; qualifying distributions, $1,620,591; giving activities include $1,617,601 for 2 grants (high: $1,607,601; low: $10,000).
Fields of interest: Foundations (community).
Limitations: Applications not accepted. Giving primarily in CA.
Application information: Unsolicited requests for funds not accepted.
Officers: Judy Spiegel, Pres.; David Lehrer, Secy.; Barry Lowitz, Treas.
Directors: Linda Lowitz; John H. Rubel; Joel Shapiro.
EIN: 956048132
Selected grants: The following grants are a representative sample of this grantmaker's funding activity:
$10,000 to American Friends of the Hebrew University, Los Angeles, CA, 2010.
$7,500 to Community Advocates, Los Angeles, CA, 2010. For general support.
$7,500 to Conservation International, Arlington, VA, 2010. For general support.
$7,500 to Hollywood-Sunset Free Clinic, Los Angeles, CA, 2011.
$7,500 to Project Kesher, Evanston, IL, 2010. For general support.
$7,500 to Southern Poverty Law Center, Montgomery, AL, 2010. For general support.
$5,000 to American Friends of the Hebrew University, Los Angeles, CA, 2010.
$5,000 to California State Parks Foundation, San Francisco, CA, 2011. For general support.
$5,000 to Committee for Accuracy in Middle East Reporting in America, Boston, MA, 2010. For general support.
$5,000 to Pacific Legal Foundation, Sacramento, CA, 2010. For general support.
$5,000 to Pacific Legal Foundation, Sacramento, CA, 2011. For general support.
$5,000 to Soldiers Project, North Hollywood, CA, 2011. For general support.
$5,000 to Southern Poverty Law Center, Montgomery, AL, 2011. For general support.
$5,000 to Venice Family Clinic, Venice, CA, 2010. For general support.
$5,000 to Westside Food Bank, Santa Monica, CA, 2011. For general support.
$5,000 to Wheels for Humanity, North Hollywood, CA, 2010. For general support.
$5,000 to Wheels for Humanity, North Hollywood, CA, 2011. For general support.
$2,500 to Long Beach Bar Foundation, Long Beach, CA, 2011. For general support.

851
LS Foundation ✧
555 Byron St., Ste. 105
Palo Alto, CA 94301-2628 (650) 324-1775
Contact: Laurence L. Spitters, Pres.

Established in 1968.
Donor: Laurence L. Spitters.
Foundation type: Independent foundation.
Financial data (yr. ended 12/31/13): Assets, $15,339,341 (M); expenditures, $864,986; qualifying distributions, $742,213; giving activities include $720,900 for 43 grants (high: $50,000; low: $250).
Fields of interest: Arts; Higher education; Medical research, institute.
Limitations: Applications accepted. Giving primarily in CA. No grants to individuals.
Application information: Application form not required.
Initial approach: Proposal
Deadline(s): None
Officers: Laurence L. Spitters, Pres.; Louis Spitters, V.P.
EIN: 941689629

852
Luberski Family Foundation, Inc. ✧
310 N. Harbor Blvd., Ste. 205
Fullerton, CA 92832-1954 (800) 326-3220
Contact: Timothy E. Luberski, Pres. and Secy.

Donor: Timothy E. Luberski.
Foundation type: Independent foundation.
Financial data (yr. ended 06/30/13): Assets, $21,234 (M); gifts received, $1,265,000; expenditures, $1,282,626; qualifying distributions, $1,281,325; giving activities include $1,049,549 for 60 grants (high: $353,210; low: $40), and $172,006 for 10 grants to individuals (high: $105,293; low: $1,184).
Fields of interest: Education; Human services.
Type of support: General/operating support; Grants to individuals.
Application information: Application form not required.
Initial approach: Proposal
Deadline(s): None
Officers and Director:* Timothy E. Luberski,* Pres. and Secy.; Robert Forrest, C.F.O.
EIN: 263187239

853
The Lucas Brothers Foundation ✧
(formerly Richard M. Lucas Foundation)
3000 Sand Hill Rd., Bldg. 3, Ste. 210
Menlo Park, CA 94025-7113

Established in 1982 in CA.
Donors: Jerry Down; Anne Down.
Foundation type: Independent foundation.
Financial data (yr. ended 06/30/13): Assets, $8,803,844 (M); expenditures, $772,095; qualifying distributions, $575,000; giving activities include $575,000 for grants.
Fields of interest: Education; Medical research, institute.
Type of support: Research.
Limitations: Applications not accepted. Giving primarily in CA and WA. No grants to individuals.

Application information: Unsolicited requests for funds not accepted.
Officer: Kurt A. Latta, Secy.
Directors: Mario Bellotti; B.J. Cassin; A. Crawford Cooley; Paul Joas; Christopher B. Lucas; Donald A. Lucas; Donald L. Lucas; John W. Lucas.
Number of staff: 1 part-time support.
EIN: 942781117

854
The George Lucas Educational Foundation ✧
P.O. Box 3494
San Rafael, CA 94912-3494
FAX: (415) 662-1532; E-mail: info@edutopia.org; Main URL: http://www.edutopia.org/
Edutopia.org Blogs: http://www.edutopia.org/spiralnotebook
Eutopia: http://www.edutopia.org/
George Lucas's Giving Pledge Profile: http://glasspockets.org/philanthropy-in-focus/eye-on-the-giving-pledge/profiles/lucas
RSS Feed: http://feeds.feedburner.com/EdutopiaNewContent
YouTube: http://www.youtube.com/edutopia

Established as a company-sponsored operating foundation in 1993 in CA.
Donors: Lucasfilm Ltd.; Lucasfilm Foundation; George W. Lucas, Jr.
Foundation type: Operating foundation.
Financial data (yr. ended 12/31/12): Assets, $1,778,694 (M); gifts received, $3,947,284; expenditures, $4,922,907; qualifying distributions, $4,045,210; giving activities include $683,398 for 3 grants (high: $540,040; low: $44,350), and $3,341,839 for 1 foundation-administered program.
Purpose and activities: The foundation promotes the K-12 learning process through diverse and innovative media to connect and inspire positive change in all areas of education.
Fields of interest: Elementary/secondary education; Elementary/secondary school reform; Education.
Type of support: Program development.
Limitations: Applications not accepted. Giving primarily in AL,AK,AZ,AR,CA,CO,CT,FL,GA,IL,.
Application information: Unsolicited requests for funds not accepted.
Officers: George W. Lucas, Jr., Chair.; Stephen D. Arnold, Vice-Chair. and C.F.O.; Cynthia Johanson Irish, Secy.
Directors: Robert Bradley; Kim Meredith; Kate Nyegaard; Marshall Turner.
EIN: 680065687
Selected grants: The following grants are a representative sample of this grantmaker's funding activity:
$540,040 to University of Washington, Seattle, WA, 2012. For Project Based Learning Research and Development.
$99,000 to Des Moines Public Schools, Des Moines, IA, 2012. For Project Based Learning, Training, and Implementation.

855
George Lucas Family Foundation ✧
(formerly Lucasfilm Foundation)
101 Ygnacio Valley Rd., Rm. 310
Walnut Creek, CA 94596-7018
Application address: Kristine Kolton, P.O. Box 2009, San Rafael, CA 94912; Main URL: http://www.lucasfilm.com/inside/faq/
George Lucas's Giving Pledge Profile: http://glasspockets.org/philanthropy-in-focus/eye-on-the-giving-pledge/profiles/lucas

Established in 2005 in CA.
Donors: George W. Lucas, Jr.; Lucasfilm Ltd.
Foundation type: Company-sponsored foundation.
Financial data (yr. ended 12/31/12): Assets, $1,141,488,469 (M); gifts received, $1,076,191,669; expenditures, $7,715,355; qualifying distributions, $7,584,792; giving activities include $7,527,500 for 147 grants (high: $3,900,000; low: $500).
Purpose and activities: The foundation supports organizations involved with arts and culture, education, and human services. Special emphasis is directed toward programs designed to benefit children.
Fields of interest: Media, film/video; Museums; Arts; Higher education; Education; Environment, land resources; American Red Cross; Children, services; Human services; Children.
Type of support: General/operating support; Continuing support; Annual campaigns; Building/renovation; Endowments; Program development; Scholarship funds.
Limitations: Applications accepted. Giving primarily in the San Francisco Bay Area, CA. No grants to individuals.
Publications: Application guidelines.
Application information: Letters of inquiry should be submitted on organization letterhead. Support is limited to 1 contribution per organization during any given year. Application form not required.
Initial approach: Letter of inquiry
Deadline(s): None
Officers and Directors:* George W. Lucas, Jr.,* C.E.O.; Micheline Chau, V.P. and Secy.; Robert Bradley,* V.P.; Angelo Garcia, V.P.; Natalie Talbott, Secy.; Steve Condioti, Treas. and C.F.O.; Mike Rider, Treas.; Mellody Hobson; Kate Nyegaard.
EIN: 203940983

856
Ludwick Family Foundation ✧
P.O. Box 1796
Glendora, CA 91740-1796 (626) 852-0092
Contact: Trista Campbell, Prog. Off.
FAX: (626) 852-0776;
E-mail: ludwickfndn@ludwick.org; Main URL: http://www.ludwick.org

Established in 1990 in CA.
Donors: Arthur J. Ludwick; Sarah Lynne Ludwick.
Foundation type: Independent foundation.
Financial data (yr. ended 12/31/13): Assets, $31,664,119 (M); expenditures, $1,686,599; qualifying distributions, $1,604,160; giving activities include $1,057,200 for 15 grants (high: $100,000; low: $100), and $237,888 for foundation-administered programs.
Purpose and activities: The purpose of the foundation is to assist a broad array of groups working to make a positive difference.
Fields of interest: Arts; Education; Environment; Animal welfare; Health care; Housing/shelter, services; Children/youth, services; Family services; Community development, neighborhood development; Science; Infants/toddlers; Children/youth; Children; Youth; Aging; Young adults; Disabilities, people with; Blind/visually impaired; Minorities; Women; Economically disadvantaged; Homeless.
Type of support: Building/renovation; Equipment.
Limitations: Applications not accepted. Giving primarily in CA; some giving nationally. No support for voter registration organizations, or for schools, universities, libraries, or hospitals (unless invited), or for daycare centers, fiscal agents, sponsors, or churches. No grants to individuals, or for salaries, general operating expenses, scholarships, endowment funds, fundraising, advertising, or for capital campaigns, travel or research, or for insurance or maintenance contacts.
Publications: Grants list; IRS Form 990 or 990-PF printed copy available upon request.
Application information: Unsolicited requests for funds are not accepted.
Board meeting date(s): Oct.
Officers and Directors:* Sarah Lynne Ludwick,* Chair.; Sharon L. Warner,* Vice-Chair. and Secy.; Arthur J. Ludwick,* Vice-Chair., C.F.O. and Treas.; Daniel Hanson; Heidi Ann Hanson; Eileen Ludwick; Erik Arthur Ludwick; Tom Warner.
Number of staff: 3 full-time professional; 1 part-time professional.
EIN: 954296315
Selected grants: The following grants are a representative sample of this grantmaker's funding activity:
$100,000 to Glendora Unified School District, Glendora, CA, 2012. For grant to purchase various technology equipment and resources to enhance student learning and engagement Glendora Unified School District provides public education to K-12 students in the city of Glendora.
$100,000 to Partnership Scholars Program, Marina Del Rey, CA, 2012. For grant to meet the costs for Scholar Educational/Enrichment Activities throughout the year Grant will allow for a new Fund-development Professional Partnership Scholars Program provides six years of educational and cultural experiences for academic.
$43,200 to Black Hills Area Community Foundation, Rapid City, SD, 2012. For grant to expand the impact of the organization by increasing efficiency, improving communication and strengthening the public presence of BHACF The mission of this organization is to improve the quality of life in the Black Hills area by raising and distribution.
$100 to Academy of Business Leadership, Rosemead, CA, 2012. For general support to this organization, which offers hands on experiential learning that gives students from all communities the opportunity to build bridges of understanding among different youth communities, thus becoming the agents of change needed to ma.
$100 to City of Hope, Los Angeles, CA, 2012. For general support to this organization, which is dedicated to the prevention and cure of cancer and other life-threating illnesses.

857
The Sharon D. Lund Foundation ✧
(formerly The Lund Foundation)
725 Town and Country Rd., Ste. 520
Orange, CA 92868-4737
E-mail: lundfoun@earthlink.net

Established in 1973 in CA.
Donor: Sharon D. Lund†.
Foundation type: Independent foundation.
Financial data (yr. ended 12/31/13): Assets, $125,165,104 (M); expenditures, $6,346,250; qualifying distributions, $5,585,199; giving activities include $5,349,075 for 39 grants (high: $700,000; low: $11,200).
Purpose and activities: Giving primarily for the arts, and children and youth services, including a children's hospital; funding also for education.
Fields of interest: Arts; Higher education; Hospitals (specialty); Human services; Children/youth, services.
Type of support: General/operating support; Capital campaigns; Building/renovation; Equipment; Seed money; Scholarship funds; Grants to individuals; Matching/challenge support.
Limitations: Applications not accepted. Giving primarily in AZ and CA. No grants to individuals directly.
Application information: Contributes only to pre-selected organizations.
Board meeting date(s): Quarterly
Officers: Michelle A. Lund, Pres.; Bradford D. Lund, V.P.; Patricia Patti, V.P.; Robert L. Wilson, Secy.-Treas.
Director: Gloria Wilson.
Number of staff: 1 full-time professional.
EIN: 237306460
Selected grants: The following grants are a representative sample of this grantmaker's funding activity:
$1,050,000 to Learning with a Difference, Westmark School, Encino, CA, 2012. For general support.
$700,000 to Childrens Hospital Los Angeles, Los Angeles, CA, 2012. For general support.
$500,000 to California Institute of the Arts, Valencia, CA, 2012. For general support.
$500,000 to Phoenix Childrens Hospital, Phoenix, AZ, 2012. For general support.
$200,000 to Walt Disney Family Museum, San Francisco, CA, 2012. For general support.
$175,000 to Give Kids the World, Kissimmee, FL, 2012. For general support.
$150,000 to Operation Smile International, Norfolk, VA, 2012. For general support.
$100,000 to Lunds Universitet, Lund, Sweden, 2012. For general support.
$100,000 to Ryman Arts, Los Angeles, CA, 2012. For general support.
$50,000 to International Guiding Eyes, Guide Dogs of America, Sylmar, CA, 2012. For general support.

858
Connie and Bob Lurie Foundation, Inc. ✧
1 Embarcadero Ctr., Ste. 4150
San Francisco, CA 94111-3740

Established in 2006 in DE.
Donors: Connie L. Lurie; Bob A. Lurie; Connie L. Lurie Revocable Trust; Robert A. Lurie Revocable Trust.
Foundation type: Independent foundation.
Financial data (yr. ended 12/31/12): Assets, $17,434,544 (M); expenditures, $994,370; qualifying distributions, $820,242; giving activities include $820,242 for grants.
Purpose and activities: Giving primarily for education; as well as for health and youth and social services.
Fields of interest: Higher education; Education; Environmental education; Hospitals (general); Health care; Youth development; Human services; Family services; Community/economic development.
Limitations: Applications not accepted. Giving primarily in CA. No grants to individuals.
Application information: Contributes only to pre-selected organizations.
Officers and Directors:* Connie L. Lurie,* Pres. and Secy.; Robert A. Lurie,* V.P.
EIN: 208004479

859
Lyons Share Foundation ✧
36 Harbor Island
Newport Beach, CA 92660-7201

Established in 1994 in CA.
Donors: Mary A. Lyons; Phillip N. Lyons.
Foundation type: Independent foundation.
Financial data (yr. ended 12/31/13): Assets, $1,207,809 (M); expenditures, $723,010; qualifying distributions, $718,500; giving activities include $718,500 for 10 grants (high: $310,000; low: $2,500).
Fields of interest: Media, television; Performing arts, orchestras; Performing arts, music (choral); Arts; Human services.
Limitations: Applications not accepted. Giving primarily in CA. No grants to individuals.
Application information: Contributes only to pre-selected organizations.
Officers: Mary A. Lyons, Pres.; Phillip N. Lyons, Secy.
EIN: 330622707

860
Bertha Russ Lytel Foundation ✧
P.O. Box 893
Ferndale, CA 95536-0893 (707) 786-9236

Established in 1974 in CA.
Donors: Bertha Russ Lytel†; L.D. O'Rourke†; Rachel H. Hauge†; Margaret McGovern†.
Foundation type: Independent foundation.
Financial data (yr. ended 09/30/13): Assets, $13,226,375 (M); gifts received, $210,000; expenditures, $970,984; qualifying distributions, $845,526; giving activities include $763,675 for 28 grants (high: $223,725; low: $1,000).
Purpose and activities: Giving primarily to social service agencies for the aged and handicapped, civic and cultural programs, including libraries and museums, elementary and higher education, health associations, including hospitals and hospices, and agricultural funds; also to a scholarship program for Ferndale High School seniors who are planning to attend a four-year university or college in California and major in agriculture. If there are no eligible Ferndale High School students, students from Fortuna High School will be invited to participate.
Fields of interest: Museums; Arts; Elementary school/education; Higher education; Libraries/library science; Education; Hospitals (general); Substance abuse, services; Health organizations, association; Human services; Residential/custodial care, hospices; Aging, centers/services; Government/public administration; Aging; Disabilities, people with.
Type of support: General/operating support; Continuing support; Building/renovation; Equipment; Seed money; Scholarship funds; Matching/challenge support.
Limitations: Applications accepted. Giving limited to Humboldt County, CA. No grants to individuals except for the William Russ Scholarship fund, or for annual campaigns, emergency or endowment funds, deficit financing, land acquisition, renovations, research, demonstration projects, or publications; no loans.
Publications: Application guidelines.
Application information: Application form not required.
Initial approach: Proposal
Copies of proposal: 8
Deadline(s): None
Board meeting date(s): Monthly
Officers: Betty Diehl, Secy.; Donald Hindley, Mgr.
Directors: Charles Lakin; Charles M. Lawrence; James K. Morrison; Tom Renner; Jack Russ; Jack Smith.
Number of staff: 1 part-time professional.
EIN: 942271250
Selected grants: The following grants are a representative sample of this grantmaker's funding activity:
$50,000 to Saint Joseph Hospital Foundation, Eureka, CA, 2011.
$26,000 to Ferndale Museum, Ferndale, CA, 2011. For operating expenses.
$13,000 to Lost Coast Camp, Petrolia, CA, 2011.
$1,170 to Council on Foundations, Arlington, VA, 2011.

861
M & T Foundation ✧
P.O. Box 676370
Rancho Santa Fe, CA 92067-6370 (858) 756-1154
Contact: Frank A. Potenziani, Pres.
E-mail: fpotenziani@mnttrust.com

Established around 1972 in NM.
Donors: Dale J. Bellamah†; A.F. Potenziani; Frank A. Potenziani.
Foundation type: Independent foundation.
Financial data (yr. ended 12/31/12): Assets, $22,700,938 (M); expenditures, $3,433,524; qualifying distributions, $2,852,055; giving activities include $2,340,180 for 26 grants (high: $1,090,000; low: $3,000).
Purpose and activities: Giving for education, health organizations, and social services.
Fields of interest: Secondary school/education; Higher education; Health care; Health organizations, association; Big Brothers/Big Sisters; Children/youth, services.
Type of support: General/operating support; Capital campaigns; Equipment; Program development; Scholarship funds; Research.
Limitations: Applications accepted. Giving in the U.S., with some emphasis on CA. No grants to individuals.
Application information: Application form not required.
Initial approach: Letter

Deadline(s): None
Board meeting date(s): Sept. and Mar.
Officers and Directors:* Frank A. Potenziani,* Chair. and Pres.; Fred G. Botek,* V.P. and Treas.; William Potenziani,* V.P.; Cyrena K. Potenziani, Secy.; James A. Brenneis; Kathleen P. Guggino; Jim Krenn; Michele Pelletier; Jack C. Peterson; Cheryl L. Potenziani; Frederick A. Potenziani; Martha M. Potenziani; Patricia P. Vick.
Number of staff: 4 full-time professional; 1 full-time support.
EIN: 237177691

862
M.Z. Foundation ✧
1330 Broadway, Ste. 1007
Oakland, CA 94612-2528 (510) 465-6000
Contact: Myron Zimmerman, Pres.

Established in 1998 in CA.
Foundation type: Independent foundation.
Financial data (yr. ended 12/31/13): Assets, $19,835,477 (M); gifts received, $2,500,000; expenditures, $1,450,503; qualifying distributions, $1,119,299; giving activities include $1,119,299 for 27+ grants (high: $101,000; low: $99).
Purpose and activities: Giving primarily to Jewish organizations.
Fields of interest: Education; Human services; Jewish agencies & synagogues.
Limitations: Applications accepted. Giving in the U.S., with emphasis on San Francisco, CA. No grants to individuals.
Application information: Application form required.
Initial approach: Letter
Deadline(s): None
Officers: Myron Zimmerman, Pres.; Lance Fong, Secy.; Norman Dress, Treas.
EIN: 943316088
Selected grants: The following grants are a representative sample of this grantmaker's funding activity:
$110,000 to Central Fund of Israel, New York, NY, 2012. For fundraising/fund distributions.
$5,000 to Bureau of Jewish Education, San Francisco, CA, 2012. For Jewish Education.
$1,200 to Jewish Funders Network, New York, NY, 2012. For Philanthropic Network.

863
The William and Inez Mabie Family Foundation ✧
c/o Ron Malone
1 Maritime Plz., 18th Fl.
San Francisco, CA 94111-3508
Contact: Ronald Malone, Dir.

Established in 1987 in CA.
Donors: William J. Mabie†; Inez Mabie†; Inez Mabie Trust.
Foundation type: Independent foundation.
Financial data (yr. ended 12/31/12): Assets, $9,878,039 (M); expenditures, $1,359,701; qualifying distributions, $1,274,000; giving activities include $1,274,000 for 11 grants (high: $508,000; low: $5,000).
Purpose and activities: Giving primarily for education, health care, and human services.
Fields of interest: Higher education; Law school/education; Education; Hospitals (general); Health care; Human services.
Type of support: Management development/capacity building; Capital campaigns; Building/renovation; Endowments; Conferences/seminars; Professorships; Research; Matching/challenge support.
Limitations: Giving primarily in CA. No grants to individuals.
Application information: Application form not required.
Deadline(s): None
Officer: Christine Torres, Secy.-Treas.
Director: Ronald Hayes Malone.
Number of staff: 1 part-time support.
EIN: 943054756
Selected grants: The following grants are a representative sample of this grantmaker's funding activity:
$100,000 to Redwood Empire Food Bank, Santa Rosa, CA, 2012. For feed needy.
$16,000 to Equal Justice America, Midlothian, VA, 2012. For Legal Assistance to the Poor.

864
MacDonald Family Foundation ✧
c/o Dick Patterson
550 S. Hope St., Ste. 550
Los Angeles, CA 90071-2612
E-mail: mltglm@aol.com

Established in 1992 in CA.
Foundation type: Independent foundation.
Financial data (yr. ended 02/28/14): Assets, $49,595,483 (M); gifts received, $50,958; expenditures, $2,759,295; qualifying distributions, $2,012,257; giving activities include $1,955,667 for 28 grants (high: $651,667; low: $5,000).
Purpose and activities: Support for elementary/secondary education, and youth development centers and clubs.
Fields of interest: Elementary/secondary education; Higher education; Youth development, centers/clubs.
Limitations: Applications not accepted. Giving on a national basis. No grants to individuals.
Application information: Contributes only to pre-selected organizations.
Trustees: Roxanne B. Chapman; Peter Hilf; Jane Rodgers; David S. Wang; Grant Winthrop.
EIN: 954396044

865
The Roger I. and Ruth B. Macfarlane Foundation ✧
1909 Via Visalia
Palos Verdes Estates, CA 90274-2046 (310) 418-7414
Contact: Roger I. Macfarlane, Tr.

Donor: The Tambour Foundation.
Foundation type: Independent foundation.
Financial data (yr. ended 12/31/12): Assets, $18,328,484 (M); gifts received, $1,000,000; expenditures, $949,721; qualifying distributions, $800,000; giving activities include $800,000 for grants.
Fields of interest: Food distribution, meals on wheels; Boys & girls clubs; Human services; International affairs; Youth.
Limitations: Applications accepted. Giving primarily in CA.
Application information: Application form required.
Initial approach: Letter
Deadline(s): None
Trustees: Andrew Egyhazi; Alex Macfarlane; Jessica Macfarlane; Katherine Macfarlane; Nicole Macfarlane; Roger I. Macfarlane; Ruth B. Macfarlane; Taryn Macfarlane.
EIN: 266157610

866
MacKenzie Foundation ✧
P.O. Box 60078, SC-MPK-03-M
Los Angeles, CA 90060-0078
Application address: c/o Philip D. Irwin, Tr., 400 Hope St., Los Angeles, CA 90071-2801

Established about 1978 in CA.
Donor: Sophia MacKenzie†.
Foundation type: Independent foundation.
Financial data (yr. ended 12/31/13): Assets, $15,761,197 (M); expenditures, $884,636; qualifying distributions, $759,167; giving activities include $700,000 for 10 grants (high: $80,000; low: $30,000).
Purpose and activities: The purpose of the foundation is to make grants for the benefit of pre-medical or medical students enrolled in schools located in the state of CA.
Fields of interest: Medical school/education.
Type of support: Scholarship funds.
Limitations: Applications accepted. Giving limited to CA. No grants to individuals; no loans.
Application information: Application form required.
Initial approach: Letter
Deadline(s): None
Trustees: Verdi S. Boyer; William G. Corey, M.D.; Philip D. Irwin; Joseph James Pachorek; Bank of the West.
EIN: 956588350
Selected grants: The following grants are a representative sample of this grantmaker's funding activity:
$80,000 to Stanford University, Stanford, CA, 2011. For scholarships.
$80,000 to University of California, Los Angeles, CA, 2011. For scholarships.
$80,000 to University of California, San Francisco, CA, 2011. For scholarships.
$80,000 to University of Southern California, Los Angeles, CA, 2011. For scholarships.

867
The Fred and June MacMurray Foundation ✧ ☆
c/o Al Marsella, C.P.A.
1680 N. Vine St., Ste. 504
Los Angeles, CA 90028

Established in CA.
Foundation type: Independent foundation.
Financial data (yr. ended 12/31/12): Assets, $13,182,227 (M); expenditures, $823,609; qualifying distributions, $705,236; giving activities include $598,963 for 30 grants (high: $100,000; low: $1,000).
Fields of interest: Education; Human services; Catholic agencies & churches.
Limitations: Applications not accepted. Giving primarily in CA. No grants to individuals.
Application information: Unsolicited requests for funds not accepted.

Officers and Board Members: Katherine MacMurray,* Pres.; Al Marsella,* Secy.; Joseph Berberich, Esq.; Msgr. Padraic Loftus.
EIN: 371634786

868
MacNaughton Family Foundation ✧
c/o Genstar Investment Corp.
4115 Blackhawk Plaza Cir., Ste. 100
Danville, CA 94506

Established in 1996 in CA.
Donor: Angus A. MacNaughton.
Foundation type: Independent foundation.
Financial data (yr. ended 12/31/12): Assets, $4,693,696 (M); gifts received, $236,672; expenditures, $544,371; qualifying distributions, $450,091; giving activities include $437,170 for 12 grants (high: $200,000; low: $500).
Fields of interest: Performing arts, opera; Education; Health organizations, association; Boy scouts; Human services.
Limitations: Applications not accepted. No grants to individuals.
Application information: Contributes only to pre-selected organizations.
Officers: Cathy Clement MacNaughton, Exec. V.P.; John W. Ryan, Co-Exec. Dir.; Laura A. Smith, Co-Exec. Dir.
Trustee: Angus A. MacNaughton.
EIN: 946700312

869
The Joe Macpherson Foundation, Inc. ✧
191 E. Main St., Ste. 2A
Santa Ana, CA 92780

Donor: Joe MacPherson Lead Trust.
Foundation type: Independent foundation.
Financial data (yr. ended 12/31/13): Assets, $11,060,044 (M); gifts received, $1,848,912; expenditures, $671,392; qualifying distributions, $650,500; giving activities include $650,500 for 21 grants (high: $418,000; low: $5,000).
Fields of interest: Housing/shelter; Youth development; Human services.
Limitations: Applications not accepted. Giving primarily in CA.
Application information: Unsolicited requests for funds not accepted.
Officers and Directors:* Anne L. MacPherson,* Pres. and C.E.O.; Jeffrey MacPherson,* V.P.; James MacPherson,* C.F.O. and Secy.
EIN: 383779697

870
Manasseh's Children ✧ ☆
1011 Shotwell St.
San Francisco, CA 94110-4015
E-mail: info@manassehschildren.org

Donors: Michael Jacob Sinclair; Homeless Youth Project.
Foundation type: Operating foundation.
Financial data (yr. ended 12/31/13): Assets, $0 (M); gifts received, $817,258; expenditures, $825,664; qualifying distributions, $825,664; giving activities include $778,093 for 3 grants (high: $769,663; low: $1,950).
Purpose and activities: Support for programs helping orphans and widows affected by AIDS.
Fields of interest: Crime/law enforcement; Human services; Community/economic development.
International interests: Africa.
Limitations: Applications not accepted. Giving primarily in Africa. No grants to individuals.
Application information: Unsolicited requests for funds not accepted.
Officers: Michael Jacob Sinclair, Pres.; Lee Paiva, Secy.; Paloma Carbonel, Treas.
Number of staff: None.
EIN: 943226540

871
The Maranatha Charitable Foundation ✧ ☆
100 Sportfisher Dr., Ste. 202
Oceanside, CA 92054 (480) 497-0074
Contact: David W. Kohout, Dir.

Established in 1998 in AZ.
Donors: Thomas J. Kohout; Martha L. Kohout.
Foundation type: Independent foundation.
Financial data (yr. ended 12/31/13): Assets, $4,777,496 (M); gifts received, $2,359,632; expenditures, $492,451; qualifying distributions, $458,806; giving activities include $455,613 for 11 grants (high: $242,720; low: $6,000).
Purpose and activities: Giving exclusively to Christian organizations.
Fields of interest: Christian agencies & churches.
Limitations: Applications accepted. Giving primarily in CO and NC.
Application information: Application form required.
Initial approach: Letter
Deadline(s): Jan. 1 to Dec. 31
Directors: David W. Kohout; Thomas J. Kohout; Anne Vander Haar.
EIN: 860919947
Selected grants: The following grants are a representative sample of this grantmaker's funding activity:
$80,000 to Christian and Missionary Alliance, Colorado Springs, CO, 2012. For Unrestricted gift to be used for general charitable purposes of the organization.

872
The March Foundation ✧ ☆
1016 Lincoln Blvd.
P.O. Box 1
San Francisco, CA 94129-1717

Established in 1994 in CA.
Donor: Laurel M. Samuels.
Foundation type: Independent foundation.
Financial data (yr. ended 12/31/13): Assets, $9,332,339 (M); gifts received, $676,786; expenditures, $657,442; qualifying distributions, $606,716; giving activities include $504,372 for 47 grants (high: $390,000; low: $75).
Fields of interest: Performing arts; Environment; Health care; Jewish agencies & synagogues.
Type of support: General/operating support.
Limitations: Applications not accepted. No grants to individuals.
Application information: Contributes only to pre-selected organizations.
Officers and Directors:* Laurel M. Samuels,* C.E.O.; Sidney P. Samuels,* C.F.O.; Ivan A. Samuels,* V.P. and Secy.
EIN: 680339625
Selected grants: The following grants are a representative sample of this grantmaker's funding activity:
$15,000 to American Bird Conservancy, The Plains, VA, 2011. For general support.
$2,500 to University of Memphis Foundation, Memphis, TN, 2011. For general support.

873
The Maurice Marciano Family Foundation ✧
144 S. Beverly Dr., Ste. 600
Beverly Hills, CA 90212-3024

Established in 2007 in CA.
Donor: Maurice Marciano.
Foundation type: Independent foundation.
Financial data (yr. ended 12/31/12): Assets, $75,327,159 (M); gifts received, $484,746; expenditures, $4,448,616; qualifying distributions, $4,089,800; giving activities include $4,089,800 for grants.
Fields of interest: Arts; Education; Human services; Jewish agencies & synagogues.
Limitations: Applications not accepted. Giving primarily in Los Angeles, CA and New York, NY.
Application information: Unsolicited requests for funds not accepted.
Officer and Director:* Maurice Marciano,* Pres.
EIN: 680661384

874
Paul Marciano Foundation ✧
144 S. Beverly Dr., No. 600
Beverly Hills, CA 90212-3033

Donor: Paul Marciano.
Foundation type: Independent foundation.
Financial data (yr. ended 12/31/13): Assets, $61,655,852 (M); expenditures, $3,346,413; qualifying distributions, $3,096,439; giving activities include $3,073,500 for 11 grants (high: $2,820,000; low: $2,000).
Fields of interest: Elementary/secondary education; Hospitals (general); Jewish agencies & synagogues.
Limitations: Applications not accepted. Giving primarily in CA.
Application information: Contributes only to pre-selected organizations.
Officer and Director:* Paul Marciano,* Pres.
EIN: 421745335

875
The Marcled Foundation ✧
235 Montgomery St., Ste. 1270
San Francisco, CA 94104-2912 (415) 346-5757
FAX: (415) 391-7274; E-mail: marcled@marcled.org; Main URL: http://www.marcled.org
Grants List: http://www.marcled.org/grants.html

Established in 2004 in CA and DE.
Donor: The Virginia and Leonard Marx Foundation.
Foundation type: Independent foundation.
Financial data (yr. ended 12/31/13): Assets, $38,939,338 (M); expenditures, $2,450,493;

qualifying distributions, $2,278,797; giving activities include $1,755,000 for 27 grants (high: $155,000; low: $10,000).
Purpose and activities: The foundation seeks to build the careers and assets of low-income youth, young adults, and families. The foundation provides financial support to organizations, programs, and policies that effectively reduce barriers to economic success for low-income youth and young adults (especially current and former foster youth). The foundation also supports organizations working to assist low-income individuals who are caring for their child or children while struggling to get ahead.
Fields of interest: Higher education; Adult/continuing education; Employment, services; Employment, job counseling; Employment, training; Employment, vocational rehabilitation; Family services; Financial services; Financial services, credit unions; Youth; Adults; Young adults; Single parents; Immigrants/refugees; Economically disadvantaged.
Type of support: General/operating support; Program development; Research; Program evaluation; Matching/challenge support.
Limitations: Applications not accepted. Giving in coastal CA, primarily the San Francisco Bay Area, Los Angeles, and the California Central Coast Region. No support for lobbying efforts. No grants to individuals.
Publications: Grants list.
Application information: Contributes only to pre-selected organizations.
Officers and Trustees:* Edwin Solot,* Chair.; Derek Aspacher, Exec. Dir.; Mary Bianco; Claire Solot.
EIN: 200595609

876
The George and Judy Marcus Family Foundation ✧
777 S. California Ave.
Palo Alto, CA 94304-1102

Established in 1998 in CA.
Donors: George Marcus; Judith Marcus.
Foundation type: Independent foundation.
Financial data (yr. ended 12/31/13): Assets, $5,536,930 (M); gifts received, $3,171,711; expenditures, $1,841,045; qualifying distributions, $1,813,968; giving activities include $1,808,183 for 108 grants (high: $125,000; low: $100).
Fields of interest: Arts; Education; Animal welfare; Medical research; Human services; Children/youth, services; Religion.
Limitations: Applications not accepted. Giving primarily in CA, some giving also in NY. No grants to individuals.
Application information: Contributes only to pre-selected organizations.
Officers and Directors:* George Marcus,* Pres.; Bob Kennis, Secy.; Alex Yarmolinsky, Treas.; Judith Marcus.
EIN: 770500373

877
Marin Community Foundation ✧
5 Hamilton Landing, Ste. 200
Novato, CA 94949-8263 (415) 464-2500
Contact: Vikki Garrod, V.P., Mktg. and Comms.
FAX: (415) 464-2555; E-mail: info@marincf.org;
Main URL: http://www.marincf.org
LinkedIn: http://www.linkedin.com/companies/marin-community-foundation
Philanthropy's Promise: http://www.ncrp.org/philanthropys-promise/who
Twitter: http://twitter.com/MarinCmtyFdn

Incorporated in 1986 in CA.
Foundation type: Community foundation.
Financial data (yr. ended 06/30/13): Assets, $1,300,134,779 (M); gifts received, $91,381,437; expenditures, $141,420,073; giving activities include $59,043,543 for 607+ grants (high: $2,316,921), and $2,776,145 for 1,061 grants to individuals.
Purpose and activities: The Marin Community Foundation was founded with one simple aspiration: to make a difference in the lives of others through thoughtful, effective philanthropy. The foundation's mission is to encourage and apply philanthropic contributions to help improve the human condition, embrace diversity, promote a humane and democratic society, and enhance the community's quality of life, now and for future generations.
Fields of interest: Arts; Adult education—literacy, basic skills & GED; Education; Environment; AIDS; Legal services; Employment; Housing/shelter, development; Human services; Community/economic development; Religion; Aging; Disabilities, people with; Homeless.
Type of support: General/operating support; Continuing support; Capital campaigns; Building/renovation; Equipment; Land acquisition; Debt reduction; Emergency funds; Program development; Conferences/seminars; Seed money; Curriculum development; Scholarship funds; Research; Technical assistance; Consulting services; Program evaluation; Program-related investments/loans; Employee matching gifts; Scholarships—to individuals; Matching/challenge support.
Limitations: Applications accepted. Giving from Buck Trust limited to Marin County, CA; other giving on a national and international basis with emphasis on the San Francisco Bay Area. No grants to individuals (except for scholarships), or for planning initiatives, or capital projects (except those meeting criteria specified in the funding guidelines). Other limitations specific to each program area are outlined in the funding guidelines.
Publications: Application guidelines; Annual report; Informational brochure (including application guidelines); Newsletter.
Application information: Visit foundation web site for grant applications, deadlines and guidelines. Letters of Intent may be completed online or downloaded and submitted by mail; faxed proposals are not accepted. Application form required.
Initial approach: Register with MCF's online Grant Application Center
Deadline(s): Varies
Board meeting date(s): Monthly
Final notification: 3 months minimum
Officers and Trustees:* Thomas Peters, Ph.D.*, C.E.O. and Pres.; Chana Anderson, V.P., Human Resources; Laura Goff, V.P. and C.I.O.; Sandra Nathan, V.P., Grants and Loans; Alexandra Derby Salkin, V.P., Philanthropic Svcs.; Fred Silverman, V.P., Mktg. and Comms.; Aileen Sweeney, V.P., Finance; Sid Hartman, C.F.O. and C.O.O.; Kirk Wong, Cont.; Marilee Eckert; Miguel Gavaldon; Peter Hamilton; Cleveland Justis; Robert J. Reynolds; Curtis Robinson; Fu Schroeder; Steven Schroeder; Julia Sze.
Number of staff: 26 full-time professional; 6 part-time professional; 6 full-time support; 1 part-time support.
EIN: 943007979
Selected grants: The following grants are a representative sample of this grantmaker's funding activity:
$3,871,431 to 10,000 Degrees, San Rafael, CA, 2012.
$3,346,197 to Marin Community Foundation, Novato, CA, 2012.
$1,375,000 to Conservacion Patagonica, Sausalito, CA, 2012.
$1,284,117 to Marin Community Clinic, Novato, CA, 2012.
$914,728 to Canal Alliance, San Rafael, CA, 2012.
$498,500 to Center for Volunteer and Nonprofit Leadership of Marin, San Rafael, CA, 2012.
$10,000 to Lighthouse for the Blind and Visually Impaired, San Francisco, CA, 2012.
$5,000 to Cloverdale Healthcare District Foundation, Cloverdale, CA, 2012.
$5,000 to Holy Names Academy, Seattle, WA, 2012.
$2,500 to Threshold Foundation, San Francisco, CA, 2012.

878
The Marisla Foundation ✧
668 N. Coast Hwy., PMB 1400
Laguna Beach, CA 92651-1513
Contact: Glenda Menges, Admin.
E-mail: glenda@marisla.org; Main URL: http://www.fsrequests.com/marisla

Established in 1986 in CA.
Foundation type: Independent foundation.
Financial data (yr. ended 12/31/13): Assets, $49,580,734 (M); gifts received, $40,000,000; expenditures, $47,008,873; qualifying distributions, $46,903,346; giving activities include $45,946,500 for 324 grants (high: $3,000,000; low: $1,000).
Purpose and activities: Giving primarily through two programs: an Environmental Program, and a Human Services Program.
Fields of interest: Environment, toxics; Women, centers/services; Marine science; Women.
International interests: Chile; Mexico.
Type of support: General/operating support; Program development.
Limitations: Applications accepted. Giving primarily on the West Coast of the U.S. (including Baja, CA), and in HI, Chile, and the Western Pacific for the environment; funding for women limited to Los Angeles and Orange County, CA. No support for political campaigns. No grants to individuals, or for scholarships, fellowships, or film or video projects.
Publications: Application guidelines.
Application information: Applications accepted via foundation web site. All applicants must complete the online application form which can be found on the foundation's web site. The foundation does not accept applications by mail, fax or e-mail. Application form required.
Initial approach: Online
Copies of proposal: 1
Deadline(s): Jan. 15, Apr. 15, Jul. 15, and Oct. 15
Board meeting date(s): Mar., June., Sept., and Dec.
Final notification: Immediate confirmation of receipt; 2-3 months for a decision

Officers and Directors:* Anne G. Earhart, Pres.; Glenda Menges,* Secy. and Prog. Dir., Admin.; Oliver N. Crary, Treas.; Herbert M. Bedolfe,* Exec. Dir.; Sara M. Lowell.
Number of staff: 2 full-time professional.
EIN: 330200133
Selected grants: The following grants are a representative sample of this grantmaker's funding activity:
$3,000,000 to Resources Legacy Fund, Sacramento, CA, 2012. For Northwest Mexico Land Conservation Program.
$2,500,000 to Global Greengrants Fund, Boulder, CO, 2012. For the Marisla Fund.
$2,200,000 to Oceana, Washington, DC, 2012. For general support of International Marine Conservation.
$2,000,000 to Orange County Community Foundation, Newport Beach, CA, 2012. For the Marisla Fund.
$1,900,000 to Orange County Community Foundation, Newport Beach, CA, 2012. For the Marisla Fund.
$1,400,000 to Orange County Community Foundation, Newport Beach, CA, 2012. For the Marisla Fund.
$1,250,000 to Nature Conservancy, Arlington, VA, 2012. For California Central Coast Groundfish and Coastal Resilience.
$250,000 to WildAid, San Francisco, CA, 2012. For Shark Protection.
$50,000 to Resource Media, San Francisco, CA, 2012. For California Marine Protected Areas Communication Campaign.
$40,000 to Ocean Foundation, Washington, DC, 2012. For Iemanya Oceanica.

879
The Markkula Foundation ✧
c/o ACM Investments
P.O. Box 620170
Woodside, CA 94062-0170
Contact: Armas C. Markkula, Jr., C.E.O. and Pres.; Linda K. Markkula, V.P. and Secy.

Established in 1991 in CA.
Donors: Armas C. Markkula, Jr.; Linda K. Markkula.
Foundation type: Independent foundation.
Financial data (yr. ended 06/30/13): Assets, $9,701,523 (M); expenditures, $730,802; qualifying distributions, $687,703; giving activities include $687,703 for grants.
Purpose and activities: Giving primarily for education and human services.
Fields of interest: Arts; Higher education, university; Education; Boys & girls clubs; Human services; Children, services; Protestant agencies & churches.
Limitations: Giving primarily in CA. No grants to individuals.
Application information: Application form not required.
Deadline(s): None
Officers and Directors:* Armas C. Markkula, Jr.,* C.E.O. and Pres.; Linda K. Markkula,* V.P. and Secy.
EIN: 770272230
Selected grants: The following grants are a representative sample of this grantmaker's funding activity:
$104,000 to Santa Clara University, Santa Clara, CA, 2011.
$60,300 to V Foundation for Cancer Research, Cary, NC, 2011.
$50,000 to Boys and Girls Clubs of the Peninsula, Menlo Park, CA, 2011.
$50,000 to El Camino Hospital Foundation, Mountain View, CA, 2011.
$25,000 to Heritage Foundation, Washington, DC, 2011.
$25,000 to Pacific Legal Foundation, Sacramento, CA, 2011.
$10,000 to Habitat for Humanity Greater San Francisco, San Francisco, CA, 2011.
$10,000 to Stanford Jazz Workshop, Stanford, CA, 2011.
$10,000 to Stanford University, Stanford, CA, 2011.
$7,500 to Next Door Solutions to Domestic Violence, San Jose, CA, 2011.

880
Michael E. Marks Family Foundation ✧
c/o Brian Kuehnis, CPA
P.O. Box 6978
Redwood City, CA 94063

Established in 1998 in CA.
Donors: Michael Marks; Carole Marks; W B Investors, LLC; Epping Investments, LLC.
Foundation type: Independent foundation.
Financial data (yr. ended 12/31/13): Assets, $6,591,370 (M); gifts received, $1,212,323; expenditures, $1,138,188; qualifying distributions, $1,125,405; giving activities include $1,125,405 for grants.
Purpose and activities: Giving primarily for health organizations, human services, and community programs.
Fields of interest: Education; Health care; Health organizations, association; Human services; Foundations (private grantmaking); Foundations (community).
Limitations: Applications not accepted. Giving primarily in CA; some funding also in NC. No grants to individuals.
Application information: Unsolicited requests for funds not accepted.
Officers: Michael Marks, Pres.; Carole Marks, C.F.O. and Secy.
EIN: 770500312

881
The Marmor Foundation ✧
(formerly The Cardea Foundation)
c/o Leventhal Kline Mgt.
127 University Ave.
Berkeley, CA 94710-1616

Established in 1968 in CA; classified as a private operating foundation in 1987.
Donors: Judd Marmor†; Katherine Marmor.
Foundation type: Independent foundation.
Financial data (yr. ended 12/31/12): Assets, $13,458,320 (M); expenditures, $592,222; qualifying distributions, $494,996; giving activities include $455,000 for 45 grants (high: $250,000; low: $1,000).
Purpose and activities: Giving primarily for the arts, and to health organizations.
Fields of interest: Visual arts; Museums; Performing arts, theater; Arts; Health organizations; Human services.
Limitations: Applications not accepted. Giving primarily in CA. No grants to individuals.
Application information: Contributes only to pre-selected organizations.
Officers and Directors:* Michael F. Marmor,* Pres.; Harald J. Leventhal, C.F.O.; Jane B. Marmor,* Secy.; Andrea Marmor; David J. Marmor.
EIN: 237005963

882
The Gilbert J. Martin Foundation ✧ ☆
685 Turquoise St.
La Jolla, CA 92037-8131
Contact: Roger Anderson, Tr.

Established in 1983 in CA.
Donor: Gilbert J. Martin.
Foundation type: Independent foundation.
Financial data (yr. ended 12/31/12): Assets, $40,633,298 (M); gifts received, $3,078,091; expenditures, $3,592,309; qualifying distributions, $439,000; giving activities include $439,000 for grants.
Purpose and activities: Giving primarily for education and Christian churches.
Fields of interest: Performing arts, ballet; Elementary school/education; Secondary school/education; Higher education; Boy scouts; Salvation Army; YM/YWCAs & YM/YWHAs; Christian agencies & churches.
Limitations: Applications not accepted. Giving primarily in San Diego County, CA.
Application information: Contributes only to pre-selected organizations.
Trustees: Judy Anderson; Roger Anderson; Paul Berning; Marc Lanci; Susan Lanci.
EIN: 330002513

883
Fairchild Martindale Foundation ✧
P.O. Box 967
Corona, CA 92878-0967

Established in 1969 in CA.
Donors: Elizabeth F. Martindale; Harry T. Martindale.
Foundation type: Independent foundation.
Financial data (yr. ended 12/31/13): Assets, $15,263,685 (M); expenditures, $691,491; qualifying distributions, $487,989; giving activities include $478,000 for 15 grants (high: $100,000; low: $5,000).
Purpose and activities: Giving primarily for education, health and hospitals, the arts, and social services; funding also for Roman Catholic churches.
Fields of interest: Arts; Higher education; Hospitals (general); Health organizations; Human services; Children/youth, services; Catholic agencies & churches.
Limitations: Applications not accepted. Giving primarily in CA and PA. No grants to individuals.
Application information: Contributes only to pre-selected organizations.
Trustees: Sarah Cox; Sarah M. Keller; Stephen F. Keller.
EIN: 237001273

884
The Masimo Foundation for Ethics, Innovation and Competition in Healthcare ✧
(also known as Masimo Foundation)
P.O. Box 9429
Marina del Rey, CA 90295-1829
Contact: Ann L. Van Dormolen, Admin.
E-mail: admin@masimofoundation.org; Main URL: http://www.masimofoundation.org

Donor: Masimo Corp.
Foundation type: Company-sponsored foundation.
Financial data (yr. ended 03/31/13): Assets, $6,588,688 (M); gifts received, $1,100; expenditures, $2,818,855; qualifying distributions, $1,382,670; giving activities include $1,289,892 for 17 grants (high: $265,000; low: $5,000).
Purpose and activities: The foundation's mission is to encourage and promote activities, programs, and research opportunities that improve patient safety and deliver advanced healthcare to people worldwide who may not otherwise have access to lifesaving technologies.
Fields of interest: Health care.
Type of support: Continuing support; General/operating support.
Limitations: Applications accepted. Giving primarily in CA and Washington, D.C.; some support also in Boston, MA and Cincinnati, OH. No support for charity, corporate, or sports events; nor the purchase of tickets or tables to fundraising events. Also, no support for political campaigns or lobbying efforts. No grants for private foundations, donor-advised funds, or individuals.
Publications: Application guidelines; Informational brochure (including application guidelines).
Application information: Letters of inquiry by e-mail or fax not accepted; application guidelines available on foundation web site. Application form not required.
Initial approach: Letter of inquiry, no more than 3 pages by regular mail
Final notification: 30 days
Officers and Directors:* Joe E. Kiani,* Chair.; Mark P. deRaad,* Secy.-Treas.; James R. Bergman; Frederick J. Harris; Sarah Kiani; Michael O'Reilly.
Trustees: Jim Bergman.
EIN: 010956020
Selected grants: The following grants are a representative sample of this grantmaker's funding activity:
$180,000 to Anesthesia Patient Safety Foundation, Indianapolis, IN, 2012.
$135,000 to Childrens Hospital Medical Center, Cincinnati, OH, 2012.
$115,000 to Chapman University, Orange, CA, 2012.
$100,000 to Bill, Hillary and Chelsea Clinton Foundation, New York, NY, 2012.
$100,000 to Childrens Hospital Foundation, Washington, DC, 2012.
$100,000 to Childrens Hospital of Orange County Foundation, Orange, CA, 2012.
$50,000 to Children's Hospital Corporation, Boston, MA, 2012.
$50,000 to Lucile Packard Foundation for Childrens Health, Palo Alto, CA, 2012.
$50,000 to University of California at San Diego, La Jolla, CA, 2012.
$10,000 to Malaria No More, New York, NY, 2012.

885
Matsui Foundation ✧
c/o Teresa Matsui Sanders
1645 Old Stage Rd.
Salinas, CA 93908-9737 (831) 422-6433, Ext. 206
E-mail: teresa@matsuinursery.com; Main URL: http://andymatsuifoundation.org/

Established in 2003 in CA.
Donors: Toshikiyo Andy Matsui; Yasuko Matsui; Michael D. Cling; Matsui Nursery, Inc.
Foundation type: Operating foundation.
Financial data (yr. ended 12/31/13): Assets, $358,893 (M); gifts received, $20,000; expenditures, $642,323; qualifying distributions, $584,816; giving activities include $580,566 for grants, and $637,373 for foundation-administered programs.
Purpose and activities: Giving primarily to improve the quality of life and economic conditions in Monterey County, California; also giving scholarship awards to graduating seniors residing in Monterey County, California.
Fields of interest: Higher education; Community/economic development.
Type of support: General/operating support; Scholarships—to individuals.
Limitations: Applications not accepted. Giving limited to Monterey County, CA.
Application information: Unsolicited requests for funds not accepted.
Officers: Toshikiyo Andy Matsui, Pres.; Yasuko Matsui, Secy. and C.F.O.
EIN: 200483500

886
Mattel Children's Foundation ✧
(formerly Mattel Foundation)
333 Continental Blvd., M.S. M1-0807
El Segundo, CA 90245-5032 (310) 252-6552
Contact: Deidre Lind, Exec. Dir.
E-mail: foundation@mattel.com; Additional e-mail for Deidre Lind: deidre.lind@mattel.com; Additional tel.: (310) 252-3630; Main URL: http://corporate.mattel.com/about-us/philanthropy/
Grants List: http://philanthropy.mattel.com/reports#grants

Established in 1978 in CA.
Donor: Mattel, Inc.
Foundation type: Company-sponsored foundation.
Financial data (yr. ended 12/31/12): Assets, $555,310 (M); gifts received, $5,109,386; expenditures, $4,480,930; qualifying distributions, $4,480,930; giving activities include $4,415,330 for 257 grants (high: $580,910; low: $25).
Purpose and activities: The foundation supports programs designed to enrich the lives of children. Special emphasis is directed toward programs designed to support or enhance the opportunity for children to play.
Fields of interest: Arts; Education, services; Education, reading; Education; Hospitals (general); Health care, clinics/centers; Health care; Disasters, preparedness/services; Athletics/sports, amateur leagues; Athletics/sports, Special Olympics; Youth development; Human services; Children; Girls.
Type of support: General/operating support; Equipment; Program development; Scholarship funds; Technical assistance; Employee volunteer services; Sponsorships; Employee matching gifts; Employee-related scholarships; In-kind gifts.
Limitations: Applications not accepted. Giving primarily in CA, CT, Washington, DC, and NY, and in Argentina, Australia, Brazil, Canada, Chile, China, France, Germany, Hong Kong, Hungary, India, Indonesia, Italy, Japan, Malaysia, Mexico, Poland, Spain, Thailand, and the United Kingdom. No support for political parties, candidates or partisan political organizations, labor or fraternal organizations, athletic or social clubs, sectarian or denominational religious organizations not of direct benefit to the entire community, or schools or school districts. No grants to individuals (except for employee-related scholarships), or for capital campaigns for physical property purchases, renovations, or developments, fundraising events, advertising, sponsorships, or research.
Publications: Annual report; Grants list; IRS Form 990 or 990-PF printed copy available upon request; Program policy statement.
Application information: Unsolicited applications for funding are currently not accepted.
Officers and Directors:* Kevin Farr,* Chair.; Alan Kaye,* Vice-Chair. and Pres.; Lisa Marie Bongiovanni, V.P. and Secy.; Dianne Douglas, V.P. and Treas.; Robert Normile, V.P.; Cary Dickson, C.F.O.; Deidre Lind, Exec. Dir.; David Allmark; Stephanie Cota; Tom Debrowski; Tony Dimichele; Ray Greger; Ricardo Ibarra; Jean Christophe Pean; Tim Kilpin.
Number of staff: 2 full-time professional; 1 full-time support.
EIN: 953263647

887
The Maxfield Foundation ✧
171 Main St., No. 256
Los Altos, CA 94022-2912 (650) 559-1560
Contact: Robert R. Maxfield, Pres. and C.F.O.

Established in 1985 in CA.
Donor: Robert R. Maxfield.
Foundation type: Independent foundation.
Financial data (yr. ended 12/31/13): Assets, $5,918,520 (M); expenditures, $583,579; qualifying distributions, $566,010; giving activities include $566,000 for 9 grants (high: $251,000; low: $10,000).
Purpose and activities: Giving primarily to institutions and individuals doing research in fields related to understanding and treating cancer, with special emphasis on leukemia. Occasionally grants are made to other fields. Grants are generally limited to operational research rather than capital funds, with preference given to short-term (3 years or less) projects rather than general research funds.
Fields of interest: Cancer, leukemia research; Science, research.
Type of support: Annual campaigns; Research.
Limitations: Applications accepted. Giving in the U.S., with some emphasis on CA and TX.
Publications: Annual report; Annual report (including application guidelines).
Application information: Application form required.
Initial approach: Letter
Deadline(s): None
Officers: Robert R. Maxfield, Pres. and C.F.O.; Melinda C. Maxfield, V.P.; Michael P. Groom, Secy.
EIN: 770099366

888
Maya Relief Foundation ✧ ☆
(formerly Reinhart Foundation)
P.O. Box 1707
Rancho Santa Fe, CA 92067-1707
E-mail: Leon@MayaRelief.com; Main URL: http://www.mayarelief.com/

Established in 2002 in CA.
Donors: Leon Reinhart; Randlyn Reinhart; Ken Wooley; Richard Zobrist; Don Mealing; Tom Painter; Robert Allen; Daryl Allen; Lee Daniels; Terry Daniels; Dennis Peters; Kirk Humanitarian; Paul Johnson; Carolyn Johnson; HELPS; Pacifica Real Estate Services; SEC Grandchildren Trust.
Foundation type: Independent foundation.
Financial data (yr. ended 12/31/13): Assets, $85,521 (M); gifts received, $1,902,294; expenditures, $2,287,937; qualifying distributions, $2,173,550; giving activities include $2,173,550 for 4 grants (high: $1,561,893; low: $1,000).
Fields of interest: Human services; Children/youth, services.
Type of support: Technical assistance.
Limitations: Applications not accepted. Giving primarily in CA and Guatemala.
Application information: Unsolicited requests for funds not accepted.
Officer: Leon Reinhart, Chair. and Pres.
Trustee: Randlyn Reinhart.
Number of staff: 1 full-time professional.
EIN: 010726374

889
Maytiv Foundation ✧
5150 Overland Ave.
Culver City, CA 90230-4914

Established in 2000 in CA.
Donors: Sol Kest; KEST 2009 Charitable Trust; Sheval Lev Hatorah; Warren Breslow.
Foundation type: Independent foundation.
Financial data (yr. ended 12/31/12): Assets, $20,037,969 (M); gifts received, $412,891; expenditures, $1,096,554; qualifying distributions, $868,030; giving activities include $868,030 for grants.
Fields of interest: Jewish agencies & synagogues.
Limitations: Applications not accepted. Giving primarily in New York, NY. No grants to individuals.
Application information: Contributes only to pre-selected organizations.
Officers: Ivan Berkowitz, Pres.; Francesca Berkowitz, Secy.
Directors: Adam Berkowitz; Elizabeth Berkowitz; Eric Berkowitz.
EIN: 954788738

890
The Sam Mazza Foundation ✧
P.O. Box 14700
San Francisco, CA 94114-0700 (650) 355-0272
Contact: Jeanette Cool, Pres.
Main URL: http://www.sammazzafoundation.org/

Established in 2005 in CA.
Foundation type: Independent foundation.
Financial data (yr. ended 12/31/12): Assets, $20,475,109 (M); gifts received, $2,590; expenditures, $1,178,759; qualifying distributions, $681,074; giving activities include $529,624 for 28 grants (high: $125,000; low: $3,160).
Fields of interest: Arts; Education; Human services; Children/youth, services.
Limitations: Applications accepted. Giving primarily in the San Francisco Bay Area, CA.
Application information: Application form required.
Initial approach: Proposal
Deadline(s): None
Officers: Robert C. Hood, Treas.; Jeanette Cool, Exec. Dir.
Directors: Dede Estey; David Mazza.
EIN: 203644356
Selected grants: The following grants are a representative sample of this grantmaker's funding activity:
$125,000 to Door Dog Music Productions, San Francisco, CA, 2012. For World Youth Orchestra.
$50,000 to Mission Graduates, San Francisco, CA, 2012. To Help Increase the Number of K-12 Students in San Francisco's Mission District Who Are.
$40,000 to BAYCAT, San Francisco, CA, 2012. To Educate, Empower, and Employ Underserved Youth and Adults.
$30,000 to Oberlin Dance Collective, San Francisco, CA, 2012. To Empower and Develop Innovative Artists.
$17,000 to Rudolf Steiner College, Fair Oaks, CA, 2012. For Education for People of Diverse Ages and Backgrounds.
$5,000 to Homework Central, San Mateo, CA, 2012. For After-School Tutoring Assistance and Family Support to Low Income 3rd, 4th and 5th.
$5,000 to Music at Kohl Mansion, Burlingame, CA, 2012. For Outreach Programs That Provide Access to Interactive Musical Experiences for Diverse.
$5,000 to Pacifica Historical Society, Pacifica, CA, 2012. For the Preservation, Archival and Education of Local History.

891
The Harold McAlister Charitable Foundation ✧
190 N. Canon Dr., Ste. 403
Beverly Hills, CA 90210-5315
Contact: Katrina Browne Bacallao

Incorporated in 1959 in CA.
Donors: Harold McAlister†; Fern Smith McAlister†.
Foundation type: Independent foundation.
Financial data (yr. ended 05/31/13): Assets, $27,737,064 (M); expenditures, $2,324,720; qualifying distributions, $2,159,363; giving activities include $1,890,000 for 33 grants (high: $300,000; low: $2,500).
Purpose and activities: Support primarily for human services, health, education, the arts, religion, and animal welfare.
Fields of interest: Higher education; Environment; Hospitals (general); Health organizations, association; Human services; Children/youth, services.
Limitations: Applications not accepted. Giving primarily in the Los Angeles, CA, area. No grants to individuals.
Application information: Unsolicited requests for funds not accepted.
Board meeting date(s): Monthly
Officer and Trustees:* James P. McAlister,* Pres.; Paul R. Kanin, Jr.; Mari McAlister; Michael H. McAlister; Michelle McAlister.
Number of staff: 1 full-time professional.
EIN: 956050036
Selected grants: The following grants are a representative sample of this grantmaker's funding activity:
$300,000 to University of Southern California, Los Angeles, CA, 2011.
$150,000 to Childrens Hospital Los Angeles, Los Angeles, CA, 2011.
$150,000 to Childrens Institute, Los Angeles, CA, 2011.
$125,000 to John Wayne Cancer Institute, Santa Monica, CA, 2011.
$100,000 to Beverly Hills Education Foundation, Beverly Hills, CA, 2011.
$100,000 to Saint Johns Health Center, Santa Monica, CA, 2011.
$40,000 to Cystic Fibrosis Foundation, Bethesda, MD, 2011.
$40,000 to Heal the Bay, Santa Monica, CA, 2011.
$20,000 to National Disaster Search Dog Foundation, Ojai, CA, 2011.
$20,000 to Pet Adoption Fund, Canoga Park, CA, 2011.

892
Alletta Morris McBean Charitable Trust ✧
1200 Central Blvd., Ste. B
Brentwood, CA 94513-2227 (925) 516-6212
Contact: Charlene Kleiner, Asst. Secy.
FAX: (925) 516-4496;
E-mail: McBeanProperties@att.net

Established in 1986 in CA.
Donor: Alletta Morris McBean†.
Foundation type: Independent foundation.
Financial data (yr. ended 12/31/13): Assets, $53,260,712 (M); expenditures, $2,789,345; qualifying distributions, $2,444,123; giving activities include $2,326,700 for 18 grants (high: $500,000; low: $1,700).
Purpose and activities: Giving to enhance the quality of life in and around Newport and Aquidneck Island, RI.
Fields of interest: Museums; Museums (sports/hobby); Historic preservation/historical societies; Education; Environment, land resources.
Type of support: Capital campaigns; Building/renovation; Land acquisition; Endowments; Matching/challenge support.
Limitations: Applications accepted. Giving primarily in RI. No grants to individuals.
Publications: Application guidelines; Grants list.
Application information: Application form not required.
Initial approach: Letter with specific project identified
Copies of proposal: 6
Deadline(s): Feb. 28 and July 31
Board meeting date(s): 3rd Sat. in May and 1st Sat. in Oct.
Final notification: 30 days from receipt
Officer and Trustees:* Donald Christ,* Chair.; John J. Slocum, Jr.; Gladys V. Szapary; John A. Van Beuren.
Number of staff: 2 part-time support.
EIN: 943019660

893
The Judith McBean Foundation ✧ ☆
(formerly The Judith McBean Cosper Foundation)
26515 Carmel Rancho Blvd., Ste. 100
Carmel, CA 93923 (831) 647-8055
Contact: Judith McBean, Tr.

Established in 1986 in CA.
Donor: Judith McBean Hunt Cosper.
Foundation type: Independent foundation.
Financial data (yr. ended 09/30/13): Assets, $5,052,398 (M); expenditures, $564,795; qualifying distributions, $556,533; giving activities include $551,332 for 18 grants (high: $113,000; low: $1,000).
Fields of interest: Arts; Education; Animals/wildlife, preservation/protection; Human services; Buddhism.
Type of support: General/operating support.
Limitations: Applications accepted. Giving primarily in CA; some giving also in NM and NJ.
Application information: Application form required.
Initial approach: Letter
Deadline(s): Feb. 15
Trustees: Natasha Hunt; Judith McBean.
EIN: 770138294

894
McBeth Foundation ✧
c/o DeKarver and Agle
23101 Lake Center Dr., No. 170
Lake Forest, CA 92630-2801
E-mail: info@mcbethfoundation.com; Application address: c/o Amy Holmes, Wells Fargo Advisors, 19800 MacArthur Blvd., No. 1400, Irvine, CA 92623; Main URL: http://www.mcbethfoundation.com

Established in 1989 in CA.
Donor: Barbara McBeth Woodruff†.
Foundation type: Operating foundation.
Financial data (yr. ended 09/30/13): Assets, $28,647,254 (M); expenditures, $1,806,669; qualifying distributions, $1,451,206; giving activities include $1,355,000 for 33 grants (high: $100,000; low: $5,000).
Fields of interest: Museums; Arts; Higher education; Education; Animal welfare; Veterinary medicine; Zoos/zoological societies; Health organizations, association; Children, services; Blind/visually impaired.
Limitations: Giving primarily in southern CA. No grants to individuals.
Application information: Application form required.
Initial approach: Use application form on foundation web site
Deadline(s): June 1
Final notification: Sept.
Trustee: Martin DeKarver.
Grant Committee Members: Amy Holmes; Tim Metcalf; Norm Timmins; Skye Woods.
EIN: 330399736
Selected grants: The following grants are a representative sample of this grantmaker's funding activity:
$95,000 to Pacific Marine Mammal Center, Laguna Beach, CA, 2011.
$75,000 to New Vista School, Laguna Hills, CA, 2011.
$50,000 to Golden West College Foundation, Huntington Beach, CA, 2011.
$50,000 to Grossmont Hospital Foundation, San Diego, CA, 2011.
$50,000 to Laguna Art Museum, Laguna Beach, CA, 2011.
$50,000 to Saint Mary Medical Center Foundation, Long Beach, CA, 2011.
$45,000 to Guide Dogs for the Blind, San Rafael, CA, 2011.
$45,000 to Guide Dogs of the Desert, White Water, CA, 2011.
$45,000 to South Coast Symphony, Santa Ana, CA, 2011.
$40,000 to Helping Hand Worldwide, Laguna Beach, CA, 2011.

895
McCarthy Family Foundation, Inc. ✧
P.O. Box 27389
San Diego, CA 92198-1389 (858) 485-0129
Contact: Rachel K. McCarthy, Pres.
FAX: (858) 485-0172;
E-mail: mail@mccarthyfamilyfdn.org; Main URL: http://www.mccarthyfamilyfdn.org/
Grants List: http://mccarthyfamilyfdn.org/grants/year/2014/

Established in 1988 in CA.
Donors: James T. McCarthy; Jane D. McCarthy.
Foundation type: Independent foundation.
Financial data (yr. ended 12/31/13): Assets, $11,831,602 (M); gifts received, $236,700; expenditures, $679,778; qualifying distributions, $536,680; giving activities include $495,000 for 38 grants (high: $50,000; low: $500).
Purpose and activities: Primary areas of interest include science education, AIDS, child welfare, and the homeless.
Fields of interest: AIDS; AIDS research; Crime/violence prevention, child abuse; Homeless, human services; Science, formal/general education; Homeless.
Type of support: General/operating support; Capital campaigns; Program development; Publication; Seed money; Research; Matching/challenge support.
Limitations: Applications accepted. Giving limited to San Diego County, CA. No support for religious or political activities. No grants to individuals, or for scholarship funds or fundraising drives.
Publications: Application guidelines; Annual report; Financial statement; Grants list; Informational brochure (including application guidelines).
Application information: Application form required.
Initial approach: Letter
Copies of proposal: 4
Deadline(s): Mar. 15 and Sept. 15
Board meeting date(s): June and Dec.
Officers and Directors:* Rachel K. McCarthy,* Pres.; Kristin L. McCarthy, V.P.; Jane D. McCarthy,* Secy.; James T. McCarthy,* Treas.
Number of staff: 1 part-time support.
EIN: 954182410

896
Patrick M. McCarthy Foundation, Inc. ✧
75483 14th Green Dr.
Indian Wells, CA 92210-8680

Established in 2008 in DE.
Foundation type: Independent foundation.
Financial data (yr. ended 12/31/13): Assets, $10,365,043 (M); expenditures, $679,112; qualifying distributions, $563,019; giving activities include $563,019 for 15 grants (high: $100,000; low: $5,000).
Fields of interest: Performing arts, orchestras; Botanical gardens; Zoos/zoological societies; Physical therapy; Public health; Athletics/sports, equestrianism; Family services.
Limitations: Applications not accepted. No grants to individuals.
Application information: Contributes only to pre-selected organizations.
Trustee: Patrick M. McCarthy.
EIN: 262804772

897
Wendy P. McCaw Foundation ✧
P.O. Box 939
Santa Barbara, CA 93102-0939 (805) 965-8080
Contact: Norman J. Colavincenzo, C.F.O.

Established in 1997 in CA.
Donor: Craig O. McCaw.
Foundation type: Independent foundation.
Financial data (yr. ended 12/31/12): Assets, $30,480,698 (M); expenditures, $1,876,575; qualifying distributions, $1,517,100; giving activities include $1,517,100 for grants.
Purpose and activities: Giving primarily for wildlife conservation and protection as well as for the environment.
Fields of interest: Environment, natural resources; Animals/wildlife, preservation/protection.
Limitations: Applications accepted. Giving primarily in CA and Washington, DC. No grants to individuals.
Application information:
Deadline(s): Oct. 31
Officers: Wendy P. McCaw, Pres.; Norman J. Colavincenzo,* Secy.-Treas. and C.F.O.
EIN: 770469217
Selected grants: The following grants are a representative sample of this grantmaker's funding activity:
$500,000 to Santa Barbara Foundation, Santa Barbara, CA, 2011.
$300,000 to Young Americas Foundation, Santa Barbara, CA, 2011.
$75,000 to Defenders of Wildlife, Washington, DC, 2011.
$50,000 to Hawaii Wildlife Center, Hawi, HI, 2011.
$50,000 to Humane Society of Santa Maria Valley, Santa Maria, CA, 2011.
$50,000 to Humane Society of the United States, Washington, DC, 2011. For general program support.
$30,000 to Ventana Wildlife Society, Salinas, CA, 2011. For program support.
$25,000 to CARE4Paws, Santa Barbara, CA, 2011.
$25,000 to Cheetah Conservation Fund USA, Alexandria, VA, 2010.
$25,000 to Eastern Sierra Wildlife Care, Bishop, CA, 2011. For program support.
$25,000 to Living with Wolves, Sun Valley, ID, 2011. For program support.
$25,000 to Sempervirens Fund, Los Altos, CA, 2010.

898
The McConnell Foundation ✧
800 Shasta View Dr.
Redding, CA 96003-8208 (530) 226-6200
Contact: Lee W. Salter, C.E.O. and Pres.

FAX: (530) 226-6230;
E-mail: info@mcconnellfoundation.org; Main
URL: http://www.mcconnellfoundation.org
E-Newsletter: http://www.mcconnellfoundation.org/contact/
Facebook: https://www.facebook.com/themcconnellfoundation
Knowledge Center: http://www.mcconnellfoundation.org/about/publications

Established in 1964 in CA.
Donors: Carl R. McConnell†; Leah F. McConnell†; National Park Service.
Foundation type: Independent foundation.
Financial data (yr. ended 12/31/12): Assets, $342,881,858 (M); expenditures, $19,489,519; qualifying distributions, $13,316,637; giving activities include $6,077,775 for grants, $706,564 for grants to individuals, $199,335 for 232 employee matching gifts, and $4,467,599 for 4 foundation-administered programs.
Purpose and activities: Primary interests include the children, youth and education, sustainable livable communities, international grantmaking, environment, environmental education, recreation; projects that demonstrate broad based community support, and the promotion of voluntarism and philanthropy.
Fields of interest: Museums; Performing arts; Arts; Secondary school/education; Environment; Health care; Recreation; Aging, centers/services; Community/economic development; Voluntarism promotion.
International interests: Laos; Nepal.
Type of support: Building/renovation; Capital campaigns; Employee matching gifts; Endowments; Equipment; General/operating support; In-kind gifts; Matching/challenge support; Scholarship funds; Technical assistance.
Limitations: Giving limited to Shasta, Trinity, Modoc, Tehama and Siskiyou counties, CA; and Nepal and Laos. No support for sectarian religious purposes or for businesses or non 501(c) (3) organizations. No grants for annual fund drives or budget deficits.
Publications: Annual report; Newsletter.
Application information: Check foundation web site for current active programs.
Board meeting date(s): Feb., Mar., June, Sept., and Dec.
Officers and Directors:* Doreeta J. Domke,* Chair.; Lee W. Salter,* C.E.O. and Pres.; John A. Mancasola,* Exec. V.P. and Secy.; Shannon E. Phillips, V.P., Opers.; William Lox,* Treas.; William B. Nystrom, Dir. Emeritus; Richard J. Stimpel, Dir. Emeritus.
Number of staff: 9 full-time professional; 27 full-time support.
EIN: 946102700
Selected grants: The following grants are a representative sample of this grantmaker's funding activity:
$1,250,000 to Turtle Bay Exploration Park, Redding, CA, 2012. For Operating Support.
$768,279 to University of California, Davis, CA, 2012. For College OPTIONS Partnership, initiative to strengthen college-going culture in Shasta, Siskiyou, Tehama and Trinity Counties by increasing opportunities for students to purse post-secondary education and ensuring that all students can make informed decisions about their education and their future.
$742,500 to Shasta Regional Community Foundation, Redding, CA, 2012. For The McConnell Fund at the Shasta Regional Community Foundation.
$476,719 to YMCA, Shasta County, Redding, CA, 2012. For Healthy Students Initiative.
$357,104 to Women's Power Development Center Nepal, Kathmandu, Nepal, 2012. For Women's Leadership Development Program - Phase III.
$306,000 to Federation of Community Forestry Users, Kathmandu, Nepal, 2012. For Natural Resource Conflict Transformation Project - Phase II.
$102,202 to Donald F. Gallino, Inc, Redding, CA, 2012. For tile work on Sundial Bridge, a cantilever spar cable-stayed bridge for bicycles and pedestrians that spans the Sacramento River in Redding and forms a large sundial.
$69,995 to Shasta Regional Community Foundation, Redding, CA, 2012. For operating support for occupancy.
$18,067 to Trilogy Architecture, Redding, CA, 2012. For Classroom Expansion Schedule Analysis.
$10,000 to San Diego State University, San Diego, CA, 2012. For Vista and McConnell Scholars.

899
The Robert F. McCullough Family Foundation ✧

P.O. Box 655
Tiburon, CA 94920-0655
Contact: Barbara C. McCullough, Dir.
Application address: c/o Barbara C. McCullough, 122 Paradise Dr., Tiburon, CA 94920, tel.: (415) 435-5942

Established in 1994 in CA.
Donors: Robert F. McCullough, Sr.†; Barbara C. McCullough.
Foundation type: Independent foundation.
Financial data (yr. ended 06/30/12): Assets, $0 (M); expenditures, $4,077,396; qualifying distributions, $4,066,778; giving activities include $4,064,278 for 22 grants (high: $3,434,463; low: $1,000).
Fields of interest: Elementary/secondary education; Health care; Catholic agencies & churches.
Type of support: Scholarship funds.
Limitations: Applications accepted. Giving primarily in CA and MA.
Application information: Application form required.
Initial approach: Letter
Deadline(s): None
Directors: Barbara C. McCullough; Brian J. McCullough; Lawrence I. McCullough; Robert F. McCullough, Jr.; Jean McCullough Stiles.
EIN: 943215424
Selected grants: The following grants are a representative sample of this grantmaker's funding activity:
$3,434,463 to Fidelity Charitable Gift Fund, Boston, MA, 2012.
$25,000 to De Marillac Academy, San Francisco, CA, 2012.
$10,000 to Little Sisters of the Poor Home for the Aged, San Francisco, CA, 2010.
$10,000 to Marine Corps League Foundation, Merrifield, VA, 2010.
$5,730 to Saint Hilarys Church, Tiburon, CA, 2012.

900
The McCune Foundation

P.O. Box 24340
Ventura, CA 93002-4340 (805) 223-8373
Contact: Claudia Armann, Exec. Dir.
E-mail: claudia@mccunefoundation.org; Main
URL: http://www.mccunefoundation.org
McCune Foundation's Philanthropy Promise: http://www.ncrp.org/philanthropys-promise/who

Established in 1990 in CA.
Donors: Sara Miller McCune; Sage Publications, Inc.
Foundation type: Independent foundation.
Financial data (yr. ended 02/28/13): Assets, $1,537,821 (M); gifts received, $1,000,000; expenditures, $979,368; qualifying distributions, $892,668; giving activities include $832,743 for 74 grants (high: $79,000; low: $250).
Purpose and activities: The foundation supports grassroots programs which focus on community capacity building and social justice in Santa Barbara and Ventura Counties, California. The foundation also funds efforts that create a social or societal change, rather than individual empowerment or development of leadership skills in individuals, except where such training is directly linked to community action and participants are committed to remaining in the community.
Fields of interest: Civil liberties, advocacy; Civil/human rights; Community/economic development; Economically disadvantaged.
Type of support: Mission-related investments/loans; General/operating support; Management development/capacity building; Program development; Technical assistance.
Limitations: Applications accepted. Giving primarily in Santa Barbara and Ventura counties, CA. No support for religious organizations. No grants to individuals or for budget deficits, construction or renovation of buildings, general funding drives, or events.
Publications: Application guidelines; Grants list.
Application information: Full proposals are by invitation only, upon review of Letter of Inquiry. Additional material must not accompany the initial letter. See foundation web site for specific application procedures which must be followed. Application form required.
Initial approach: Letter of Inquiry (no more than 2-pages, in 12-point font on organization letterhead); New applicants should telephone Exec. Dir. to discuss project prior to submitting a Letter of Inquiry
Copies of proposal: 1
Deadline(s): See foundation web site for current deadlines
Board meeting date(s): May and Nov.
Final notification: May and Nov.
Officers and Directors:* Sara Miller McCune,* Chair. and Pres.; Sandra Ball-Rokeach,* V.P.; Vicki Fisher Magasinn, Secy.; Hilda Zacarias,* Treas.; Claudia Armann, Exec. Dir.; David F. McCune; Melvin Oliver; Susan Rose; Margaret Sirot; Susan McCune Trumble; Marcos Vargas.
EIN: 770242953

901
McDonald Family Foundation ✧

c/o Farmers & Merchants Trust Co.
P.O. Box 891
Long Beach, CA 90801-0891

Established in 2007 in CA.
Donor: Richard A. McDonald.
Foundation type: Independent foundation.
Financial data (yr. ended 12/31/13): Assets, $14,413,337 (M); expenditures, $856,180; qualifying distributions, $664,031; giving activities

include $664,031 for 26 grants (high: $200,000; low: $3,000).
Fields of interest: Higher education; Health care; Human services; Civil liberties, right to life; Catholic agencies & churches.
Limitations: Applications not accepted. Giving primarily in CA.
Application information: Contributes only to pre-selected organizations.
Officers and Directors:* Kevin Tiber,* Pres. and C.F.O.; Edward Corcoran,* V.P.; Loraine Waestman,* Secy.
EIN: 352312036
Selected grants: The following grants are a representative sample of this grantmaker's funding activity:
$8,000 to Xavier Society for the Blind, New York, NY, 2012. To support and Facilitate Charitable Works.

902
The McKay Foundation
455 Market St., Ste. 1270
San Francisco, CA 94105
The McKay Foundation's Philanthropy Promise: http://www.ncrp.org/philanthropys-promise/who

Established in 1992 in CA.
Donors: Robert L. McKay, Sr.; Elaine McKay.
Foundation type: Independent foundation.
Financial data (yr. ended 12/31/12): Assets, $348,164 (M); gifts received, $1,101,842; expenditures, $1,376,371; qualifying distributions, $664,863; giving activities include $664,863 for grants.
Purpose and activities: To strengthen our democracy and promote a more just and equitable American culture, the foundation funds activities that build civil society's energy, leadership, and resources, and utilizes these in the political and policy spheres of civil society. Through grants, capacity building assistance, and other support to allied organizations, the foundation partners with diverse communities in working for long term social, political, and economic progress.
Fields of interest: Environment; Human services; Homeless, human services; Community/economic development; Public policy, research.
Type of support: General/operating support; Income development; Management development/capacity building; Technical assistance.
Limitations: Applications not accepted. Giving primarily in CA.
Publications: Grants list; Occasional report.
Application information: Contributes only to pre-selected organizations. The majority of funding goes to a core set of community organizing groups, located mostly in CA.
Officers: Robert L. McKay, Sr., V.P.; Elaine McKay, Secy.; John P. McKay, Treas.; Robert McKay, Exec. Dir.
Number of staff: 3 full-time professional; 1 part-time support.
EIN: 363946926

903
McKesson Foundation, Inc. ✧
(formerly McKesson HBOC Foundation, Inc.)
1 Post St.
San Francisco, CA 94104-5201 (415) 983-9325
FAX: (415) 983-7590;
E-mail: mckessonfoundation@mckesson.com; Contact for Mobilizing Health: tel.: (415) 983-9478, e-mail: mhealth@mckesson.com; Main URL: http://www.mckesson.com/about-mckesson/corporate-citizenship/mckesson-foundation/
Giving Comfort on Facebook: https://www.facebook.com/GivingComfort
Giving Comfort on Pinterest: http://pinterest.com/givingcomfort/
Giving Comfort on Twitter: https://twitter.com/GivingComfort
Mobilizing for Health Recipients: http://www.mckesson.com/about-mckesson/corporate-citizenship/mckesson-foundation/mobilizing-for-health/research-grant-program/grant-winners/

Incorporated in 1943 in FL.
Donors: McKesson Corp.; McKesson HBOC, Inc.
Foundation type: Company-sponsored foundation.
Financial data (yr. ended 03/31/13): Assets, $13,665,988 (M); gifts received, $903,224; expenditures, $5,507,053; qualifying distributions, $5,389,407; giving activities include $3,995,149 for 2,164 grants (high: $225,000; low: $10), and $526,666 for foundation-administered programs.
Purpose and activities: The foundation supports programs designed to improve the health of patients through access to quality healthcare; personal health management; and lower healthcare costs. Special emphasis is directed toward non-medical direct services to low-income cancer patients.
Fields of interest: Higher education; Medical school/education; Nursing school/education; Education; Health care, equal rights; Health care, clinics/centers; Public health; Health care, patient services; Cancer; Diabetes; United Ways and Federated Giving Programs; Children; Youth; Economically disadvantaged.
Type of support: General/operating support; Continuing support; Equipment; Program development; Scholarship funds; Research; Employee volunteer services; Employee matching gifts; Employee-related scholarships.
Limitations: Applications accepted. Giving on a national basis in areas of company operations. No support for religious organizations not of direct benefit to the entire community or disease-specific organizations. No grants to individuals (except for scholarships), or for endowments, political causes or campaigns, advertising, or research.
Publications: Application guidelines; Corporate giving report.
Application information: Letters of inquiry should be no longer than 1 page. However, unsolicited grant proposals are generally not accepted. Applicants may be invited to submit a full proposal at a later date. Support is limited to 1 contribution per organization during any given year.
Initial approach: E-mail letter of inquiry
Deadline(s): None
Board meeting date(s): Dec.
Officers and Directors:* John H. Hammergren,* Chair.; Carrie J. Varoquiers,* Pres.; Michele Lau, Secy.; Nicholas A. Loiacono,* Treas.; Patrick Blake; Jorge L. Figueredo; Paul C. Julian; Nigel A. Rees.
Number of staff: 1 full-time professional; 1 part-time professional; 1 full-time support.
EIN: 943140036

904
The Joseph R. & Mercedes McMicking Foundation ✧
(formerly McMicking Foundation)
1004B O'Reilly Ave.
San Francisco, CA 94129-2602 (415) 474-1784
Contact: Miriam deQuadros White, Exec. Dir.
FAX: (415) 474-1754;
E-mail: miriam@mcmickingfoundation.org; Main URL: http://www.mcmickingfoundation.org
Grants List: http://www.mcmickingfoundation.org/grants-awarded.shtml

Established in 1958.
Donor: Joseph R. McMicking†.
Foundation type: Independent foundation.
Financial data (yr. ended 12/31/13): Assets, $14,649,049 (M); expenditures, $922,774; qualifying distributions, $807,301; giving activities include $733,580 for 77 grants (high: $20,000; low: $700).
Purpose and activities: Giving primarily for the education of children in the areas of the arts, technology, education, and science.
Fields of interest: Higher education; Education; Science; Children/youth; Children.
Type of support: Scholarship funds.
Limitations: Applications accepted. Giving primarily in the San Francisco Bay Area, CA. No grants to individuals; no loans.
Publications: Application guidelines; Annual report; Grants list.
Application information: Application forms available on foundation web site. Applications sent by fax are not accepted. Telephone calls of inquiry are strongly encouraged. Application form required.
Initial approach: Letter of inquiry and application form
Copies of proposal: 1
Deadline(s): None
Board meeting date(s): Feb., July, and Oct.
Final notification: Generally within 90 days
Officers and Trustees:* Roderick C.M. Hall,* Chair.; Joseph C.M. Hall,* Pres.; Henry C. McMicking,* Secy.-Treas.; Miriam deQuadros White, Exec. Dir.; H. Andrew McMicking Hall; Alaistair C.H. McHugh; Consuelo Hall McHugh; Brent McMicking; Kate Trevelyan-Hall.
Number of staff: 1 part-time professional.
EIN: 946058305

905
McMillen Family Foundation ✧
915 Via Panorama Dr.
Palos Verdes Estates, CA 90274-1635
Application address: c/o Merle Countryman, C.E.O., P.O. Box 3260, Palos Verdes, CA 90274, tel.: (310) 344-7100

Established in 2007 in CA.
Donor: Karl McMillen, Jr.
Foundation type: Independent foundation.
Financial data (yr. ended 12/31/13): Assets, $203,825 (M); gifts received, $1,074,995; expenditures, $1,595,786; qualifying distributions, $1,566,166; giving activities include $1,423,280 for 14 grants (high: $301,000; low: $2,500).

Purpose and activities: Giving to organizations that serve individuals in recovery from drugs and alcohol. Funding also to organizations which provide the education needed by those affected by alcohol, drugs and other unfortunate circumstances to build sound financial, spiritual and physically healthy lives for themselves and their families.
Fields of interest: Mental health/crisis services, formal/general education; Substance abuse, treatment; Adults; Young adults; Physically disabled; Mentally disabled; Minorities; Hispanics/Latinos; Indigenous peoples; Women; Girls; Adults, women; Young adults, female; Men; Boys; Adults, men; Young adults, male; Military/veterans; Substance abusers; Single parents; Immigrants/refugees; Economically disadvantaged; Homeless.
Type of support: Building/renovation; Equipment; Land acquisition; Endowments.
Limitations: Applications accepted. Giving primarily in CA, with emphasis on southern CA. No grants to individuals.
Application information: Application form not required.
Initial approach: Letter
Copies of proposal: 1
Board meeting date(s): Mar. 16, Aug. 25, and Dec. 7
Officers and Directors:* Merle Countryman,* C.E.O.; Karl McMillen, Jr.,* Pres.; Carol McMillen,* Secy. and C.F.O.; David Bishop; Daniel Fiorito; Moe Gelbart; Shannon McMillen; Gary Michel; Dan Patrick.
EIN: 261593449
Selected grants: The following grants are a representative sample of this grantmaker's funding activity:
$395,028 to First Step House of Orange County, Costa Mesa, CA, 2011.
$240,000 to Pathways to Independence, Los Alamitos, CA, 2011.
$36,000 to California Womens Recovery, Laguna Beach, CA, 2011.
$25,000 to Villa Center, Santa Ana, CA, 2011.

906
McMinn Foundation ✧
P.O. Box 93
St. Helena, CA 94574-0093
E-mail: info@mcminnfoundation.org; Main URL: http://www.mcminnfoundation.org

Established in 2000 in CA.
Donors: Anne McMinn; Charles McMinn.
Foundation type: Independent foundation.
Financial data (yr. ended 10/31/13): Assets, $1,303,770 (M); expenditures, $619,416; qualifying distributions, $607,837; giving activities include $606,159 for 42 grants (high: $100,000; low: $25).
Fields of interest: Education; Health care; Medical research, institute; Housing/shelter; Human services; Community/economic development.
Limitations: Applications not accepted. Giving primarily in northern CA. No grants to individuals.
Publications: Grants list.
Application information: Unsolicited requests for funds not accepted.
Officers: Charles J. McMinn, Pres.; Anne W. McMinn, V.P.
EIN: 770529427
Selected grants: The following grants are a representative sample of this grantmaker's funding activity:
$100,000 to Saint Helena Hospital Foundation, Saint Helena, CA, 2011.
$69,000 to Saint Helena Hospital Foundation, Saint Helena, CA, 2011.
$5,000 to Childrens Health Initiative Napa County, Napa, CA, 2011.
$5,000 to Clinic Ole Foundation, Napa, CA, 2011.
$5,000 to Saint Helena Hospital Foundation, Saint Helena, CA, 2011.
$2,000 to Grace Family Vineyards Foundation, Saint Helena, CA, 2011.
$2,000 to Mount Holyoke College, South Hadley, MA, 2011.
$1,250 to PATH, Seattle, WA, 2011.
$1,000 to Humane Society of Charlotte, Charlotte, NC, 2011.
$1,000 to Parkinsons Institute, Sunnyvale, CA, 2011.

907
Giles W. and Elise G. Mead Foundation ✧
P.O. Box 2218
Napa, CA 94558-0221
Contact: Directors
E-mail: meadfoundation@aol.com; Tel./fax: (707) 226-2164; Main URL: http://www.gileswmeadfoundation.org

Incorporated in 1961 in CA.
Donor: Elise G. Mead†.
Foundation type: Independent foundation.
Financial data (yr. ended 10/31/13): Assets, $22,796,028 (M); expenditures, $1,443,546; qualifying distributions, $1,246,660; giving activities include $1,246,660 for 42 grants (high: $155,000; low: $500).
Purpose and activities: The Mead Foundation supports organizations dedicated to preserving and improving the environment, the advancement of medical science, and other important social needs. Environmental organizations supported by the Mead Foundation generally have as their primary emphasis forestry, fisheries, and the sustainable use of natural resources in western North America. Scientific and medical organizations supported by the Mead Foundation generally have as their primary emphasis the endocrine system, and in particular diabetes and its complications.
Fields of interest: Environment, natural resources; Environment, forests; Environment; Animals/wildlife, fisheries; Health care, research; Diabetes.
Type of support: Equipment; Land acquisition; Program development; Seed money; Research; Matching/challenge support.
Limitations: Applications accepted. Giving primarily in the western U.S., with emphasis on AK, northern CA, OR, and WA. No support for local or regional environmental organizations outside the western U.S. No grants to individuals, or for general operating expenses.
Publications: Application guidelines; Annual report (including application guidelines); Biennial report; Grants list.
Application information: Application information available on foundation web site. Proposals are accepted only after a review of letter of inquiry first. If a proposal is requested, submit the proposal and supporting materials in an environmentally sensitive manner. Please use two-sided copying when possible, and do not use binders or plastic packaging. Funding in other program areas except for the environment, medical science, and social needs, are limited to grant proposals initiated by individual board members. A copy of most recent IRS Determination Letter, a copy of most recent annual report/audited financial statement/990, and a listing of board of directors, trustees, officers and other key people and their affiliations, are to be submitted upon request from the foundation only. Additional copies of the proposal will be upon the request of the foundation. Application form not required.
Initial approach: Inquiry by letter
Copies of proposal: 1
Deadline(s): None
Board meeting date(s): Jan., June, and Oct.
Final notification: 2 months
Officers and Directors:* Calder M. Mackay,* C.E.O. and Pres.; Jane W. Mead, V.P.; Parry W. Mead,* V.P.; Richard N. Mackay, Secy.-Treas.; Katherine Cone Keck; Giles W. Mead.
Number of staff: 1 part-time professional.
EIN: 956040921

908
The Meadowview Foundation ✧
(formerly The Wiskemann Family Foundation)
c/o Franklin Resources, Inc.
1 Franklin Pkwy., Bldg. 920/1
San Mateo, CA 94403-1906

Established in 1996 in CA.
Donors: Rico M. Wiskemann; Elizabeth Wiskemann.
Foundation type: Independent foundation.
Financial data (yr. ended 12/31/13): Assets, $153,317,197 (M); gifts received, $89,396,245; expenditures, $2,862,765; qualifying distributions, $2,565,000; giving activities include $2,565,000 for 26 grants (high: $300,000; low: $15,000).
Purpose and activities: Giving primarily for education and health care; some giving for animals and wildlife, and children and social services.
Fields of interest: Elementary/secondary education; Higher education; Education; Animals/wildlife; Hospitals (general); Health organizations, association; Human services; American Red Cross; Children/youth, services.
Limitations: Applications not accepted. Giving primarily in CA; some funding nationally.
Application information: Unsolicited requests for funds not accepted.
Officers and Trustees:* Kim D. Wiskemann Bessolo,* Pres.; Christine Y. Wiskemann, V.P. and Secy.; Esther B. Wiskemann Torres, Treas.; Elizabeth Wiskemann.
EIN: 943256658

909
Melalucca Foundation ✧
2511 Garden Rd., Ste. A180
Monterey, CA 93940

Donors: The Cypress Living Trust; N.E. Jenkins.
Foundation type: Independent foundation.
Financial data (yr. ended 12/31/13): Assets, $37,286,939 (M); gifts received, $12,116,946; expenditures, $978,582; qualifying distributions, $908,828; giving activities include $800,000 for 4 grants (high: $200,000; low: $200,000).
Fields of interest: Education; Mental health/crisis services; Big Brothers/Big Sisters; Human services.
Limitations: Applications not accepted. Giving primarily in AZ, CA, DC, PA, and VA.

Application information: Contributes only to pre-selected organizations.
Officers and Directors:* W. H. Soskin,* Pres.; D. Bauer,* Secy.-Treas.
EIN: 261699444

910
Mellam Family Foundation ✧
P.O. Box 610091
Redwood City, CA 94061-0091
E-mail: info@mellam.org; Main URL: http://www.mellam.org

Established in 1987 in NY.
Donor: Laural D. Mellam†.
Foundation type: Independent foundation.
Financial data (yr. ended 12/31/13): Assets, $15,609,392 (M); expenditures, $923,628; qualifying distributions, $761,150; giving activities include $630,510 for 58 grants (high: $20,000; low: $1,000).
Purpose and activities: Giving for programs in the areas of medical and scientific research, education, the environment and social services.
Fields of interest: Education; Health organizations; Medical research.
Limitations: Applications not accepted. Giving primarily in the San Francisco Bay Area, CA, CO, HI, and NY. No grants to individuals.
Publications: Annual report; Financial statement; Grants list.
Application information: Contributes only to pre-selected organizations. All solicited grant proposals must be submitted in electronic format (Word, Excel, or PDF). Hardcopies are not accepted. See foundation web site for complete information.
Board meeting date(s): Quarterly
Officers and Trustees:* Marilyn Rogers,* Pres.; Tracy Rogers, Exec. Dir.; Clay Rogers; Holly Rogers; Timothy Rogers.
Advisory Board: Barry Waldorf.
Number of staff: 1 full-time professional.
EIN: 136894208
Selected grants: The following grants are a representative sample of this grantmaker's funding activity:
$5,000 to Adler Aphasia Center, Maywood, NJ, 2011.

911
Menard Family Foundation ✧
c/o Lindsay & Brownell, LLP
4225 Executive Sq., Ste. 1150
La Jolla, CA 92037-9153
E-mail: info@menardfoundation.org; Main URL: http://www.menardfoundation.org
Grants List: http://www.menardfoundation.org/grant-organizations

Established in 1998 in CA.
Donors: Bernard Menard†; Mary Menard†; Menard 1979 Family Trust.
Foundation type: Independent foundation.
Financial data (yr. ended 12/31/12): Assets, $15,262,401 (M); expenditures, $841,304; qualifying distributions, $692,012; giving activities include $619,600 for 55 grants (high: $100,000; low: $1,000).
Purpose and activities: The foundation supports organizations which seek to enhance lives through medicine and medical research, education, music and the arts, direct service to the poor and underserved, and by animal conservation and therapeutic programs. The foundation also provides financial assistance to Roman Catholic and other faith-based organizations, including social service organizations, parishes, schools, retreat centers and retired religious.
Fields of interest: Arts; Education; Animals/wildlife, preservation/protection; Hospitals (general); Health care; Human services; Catholic agencies & churches.
Limitations: Applications not accepted. Giving primarily in CA, with emphasis on San Diego. No support for profit-making enterprises of nonprofit groups, private operating foundations, service clubs, fraternal, labor, military, or similar organizations whose principle activity is for the benefit of their own membership. No grants to individuals, or for fundraising, dinners, advertising, or lobbying.
Application information: Contributes only to pre-selected organizations.
Officer: Barbara Menard, Exec. Dir.
Directors: Don Harrington; Marcel Menard; Marlene Miller.
EIN: 330834790
Selected grants: The following grants are a representative sample of this grantmaker's funding activity:
$15,000 to Blessed Sacrament School, Hollywood, CA, 2012. For scholarships and repairs.

912
Littler Mendelson Foundation, Inc. ✧
650 California St., 7th Fl.
San Francisco, CA 94108-2702

Established in 1996 in CA.
Donors: Garry G. Mathiason; Robert Millman; Patrick H. Hicks; Keith C. Hult; Scott A. Forman; A.M. Weber; Mark J. Ogden.
Foundation type: Independent foundation.
Financial data (yr. ended 12/31/12): Assets, $452,392 (M); gifts received, $631,361; expenditures, $572,490; qualifying distributions, $572,490; giving activities include $572,415 for 355 grants (high: $33,123; low: $65).
Fields of interest: Education; Health organizations, association; Medical research, institute; Legal services; Human services; Children/youth, services.
Type of support: General/operating support; Continuing support; Annual campaigns; Emergency funds; Technical assistance.
Limitations: Applications not accepted. Giving in the U.S., with emphasis on CA.
Application information: Contributes only to pre-selected organizations.
Officers: Marko J. Mrkonich, C.E.O. and Pres.; Robert A. Domingues, C.F.O. and C.O.O.; Jennifer Walt, Secy.
EIN: 911814913

913
Menlo Foundation, Inc. ✧
4221 Wilshire Blvd., Ste. 480
Los Angeles, CA 90010-3541

Established in 1978.
Donors: Sam Menlo; Vera Menlo; Irwin Lowi; Yesod Fund.
Foundation type: Independent foundation.
Financial data (yr. ended 11/30/12): Assets, $83,222 (M); gifts received, $4,088,000; expenditures, $4,141,623; qualifying distributions, $4,134,724; giving activities include $4,134,724 for 491 grants (high: $1,000,000; low: $18).
Purpose and activities: Giving primarily for Jewish agencies, temples, and schools.
Fields of interest: Elementary/secondary education; Theological school/education; Jewish federated giving programs; Jewish agencies & synagogues.
Limitations: Applications not accepted. Giving primarily in Los Angeles, CA and in Brooklyn and Monsey, NY.
Application information: Unsolicited requests for funds not accepted.
Directors: Sam Menlo; Vera Menlo.
EIN: 953388159

914
The Mental Insight Foundation ✧
c/o Virginia Hubbell Assocs., Admin.
283 2nd St. E.
Sonoma, CA 95476-5708 (707) 938-8248

Established in 1996 in CA.
Donor: William D. Kimpton†.
Foundation type: Independent foundation.
Financial data (yr. ended 12/31/13): Assets, $19,110,020 (M); expenditures, $1,957,379; qualifying distributions, $1,818,413; giving activities include $1,060,000 for 51 grants (high: $115,000; low: $1,000).
Purpose and activities: Giving to the 7 following areas: 1) Mental health-specifically traditional and alternative forms of healing depression and other mental illnesses; 2) Impoverished youth-programs targeted to reintegrating children in poverty back into society; 3) Cancer support-programs with an emphasis on reducing the sense of isolation experienced by cancer patients and their families; 4) Animal preservation-focused on spay and neuter programs, shelter for domestic and wild animals, and for programs directed to changing laws that increase the protection of domestic and wild animals and humane treatment of farm animals; 5) Arts-experimental theater, experimental emerging visual arts and new media, and programs that bring art back into the classroom; 6) Environment-direct action programs targeted on global warming and the development of renewable energy; and 7) Indigenous people-preservation of indigenous culture and life.
Fields of interest: Arts; Environment, climate change/global warming; Environment; Animals/wildlife, preservation/protection; Mental health, depression.
Type of support: General/operating support; Continuing support; Equipment; Program development; Conferences/seminars; Publication; Seed money; Research.
Limitations: Applications not accepted. Giving primarily in the San Francisco Bay Area, CA, and the metropolitan New York, NY, area; giving in some other areas, by board selection. No support for religious organizations. No grants to individuals, or for endowments, operating deficits, fundraising events, capital campaigns, building renovation, or emergency funds; no loans.
Publications: Grants list.
Application information: Unsolicited requests for funds not accepted.
Board meeting date(s): Dec.

Officers: David Herskovits, Pres.; Graham Lawrence Kimpton, V.P.; Isabelle Kimpton, Secy.; Bob Bunje, Treas.
Trustees: Barry Bunshoft; Len Dell'Amico; Jennifer Catherine Egan; Laura Kimpton.
Number of staff: 1 part-time professional; 1 part-time support.
EIN: 943256579

915
The Paul & Elisabeth Merage Family Foundation ✧
660 Newport Center Dr., Ste. 1300
Newport Beach, CA 92660-2007

Established in 2002 in NV.
Donors: Paul Merage; Elisabeth Merage; Katherine Merage.
Foundation type: Independent foundation.
Financial data (yr. ended 12/31/13): Assets, $34,938,573 (M); expenditures, $1,686,658; qualifying distributions, $1,606,576; giving activities include $1,597,500 for 4 grants (high: $1,525,000; low: $10,000).
Purpose and activities: Giving primarily for education, and human services, particularly for services for immigrants.
Fields of interest: Higher education, university; Human services; Immigrants/refugees.
Limitations: Applications not accepted. Giving primarily in CA. No grants to individuals.
Application information: Contributes only to pre-selected organizations.
Officers and Directors:* Paul Merage,* Pres.; Elisabeth Merage,* Secy.-Treas.
EIN: 680529692

916
Andre & Katherine Merage Foundation of Nevada ✧
660 Newport Center Dr., Ste. 1300
Newport Beach, CA 92660-2007

Established in 2002 in NV.
Donor: Katherine Merage.
Foundation type: Independent foundation.
Financial data (yr. ended 12/31/12): Assets, $34,874,016 (M); expenditures, $1,806,614; qualifying distributions, $1,679,431; giving activities include $1,676,555 for 4 grants (high: $770,000; low: $2,500).
Fields of interest: Health care; Jewish federated giving programs; Jewish agencies & synagogues.
Limitations: Applications not accepted. Giving primarily in CA. No grants to individuals.
Application information: Contributes only to pre-selected organizations.
Officers and Director:* Katherine Merage,* Pres.; Paul Merage, Secy.-Treas.
EIN: 020657534

917
The Johnny Mercer Foundation ✧
c/o Prager & Fenton, LLP
2381 Rosecrans Ave., No. 350
El Segundo, CA 90245-7907
Main URL: http://www.johnnymercerfoundation.org/
Facebook: https://www.facebook.com/pages/The-Johnny-Mercer-Foundation/199566596755138?fref=ts
Twitter: https://twitter.com/johnnymercerorg

Established in 1982 in CA.
Donors: Elizabeth M. Mercer‡; Alan Oppenheimer.
Foundation type: Operating foundation.
Financial data (yr. ended 07/31/13): Assets, $3,151,181 (M); gifts received, $7,500; expenditures, $702,349; qualifying distributions, $479,136; giving activities include $441,354 for 10 grants (high: $80,000; low: $4,500).
Purpose and activities: The mission of the foundation is to distribute funds to preserve and enhance the legacy of Johnny Mercer, to assist children with illness or disability, to provide educational programs for music appreciation, to assist in the development of songwriters, and to enhance the general appreciation of American popular music.
Fields of interest: Performing arts, music; Arts; Education; Health care; Human services.
Type of support: General/operating support.
Limitations: Applications not accepted. Giving on a national basis.
Application information: Unsolicited requests for funds not accepted.
Board meeting date(s): Feb., June, and Oct.
Officers and Directors:* John Marshall,* Chair. and Pres.; Jonathan Brielle,* V.P.; Jeanne Roccon Rohm,* V.P.; Charles S. Tigerman,* Secy.; Neil J. Gillis,* Treas.; Frank P. Scardino, Exec. Dir.; Alan Bergman; Alvin Deutsch; Erin Drake; Bob Fead; Michael A. Kerker; Robert Kimball; Al Kohn; Amanda McBroom; Michael R. Price; Nancy Rishagen; Dianne S. Thurman.
Advisory Board: Tony Bennett; Leslie E. Binder; Michael Feinstein; David Friedman; Barry Manilow; Andre Previn.
Number of staff: 1 full-time professional.
EIN: 953728115
Selected grants: The following grants are a representative sample of this grantmaker's funding activity:
$60,250 to Northwestern University, Evanston, IL, 2013. For Johnny Mercer Songwriters Project.
$50,000 to Goodspeed Musicals, East Haddam, CT, 2013. For Johnny Mercer Writers Colony.

918
The Mericos Foundation ✧
625 S. Fair Oaks Ave., Ste. 360
South Pasadena, CA 91030-2630

Established in 1980 in CA.
Foundation type: Independent foundation.
Financial data (yr. ended 12/31/13): Assets, $38,476,380 (M); expenditures, $1,119,260; qualifying distributions, $986,664; giving activities include $765,000 for 37 grants (high: $50,000; low: $1,000).
Fields of interest: Museums; Arts; Higher education; Education; Human services; Aging.
Type of support: General/operating support; Building/renovation; Equipment; Program development; Fellowships; Matching/challenge support.
Limitations: Applications not accepted. Giving primarily in CA. No grants to individuals, or for capital support; no loans.
Application information: Due to funding restrictions the foundation manager prefers to initiate the grants made by the foundation.
Board meeting date(s): As needed, 3 times per year
Officers and Directors:* Joanne W. Blokker,* Pres.; Michael J. Casey,* C.F.O.; Linda J. Blinkenberg,* V.P.; Julie W. Lytle,* Secy.; Katherine Barnard; Donja Dalquist; Arlo G. Sorensen; Brian Whittier.
EIN: 953500491
Selected grants: The following grants are a representative sample of this grantmaker's funding activity:
$75,000 to International Community Foundation, National City, CA, 2012. For General Operating Support for the Conservation and Environment Program in Baja California.
$51,000 to Santa Barbara Zoological Foundation, Santa Barbara, CA, 2012. To train Renovation Project - New Sound System and Train Renovation.
$40,000 to Foundation for Santa Barbara City College, Santa Barbara, CA, 2012. For Scholarships for Esl Students 30K Kl Textbooks.
$37,500 to Charities Aid Foundation America, Alexandria, VA, 2012. For Horseback UK.
$30,000 to Friends of Independent Schools and Better Education, Tacoma, WA, 2012. For Norfolk School Capital Campaign.
$25,000 to Family Service Agency of Santa Barbara, Santa Barbara, CA, 2012. For Family Service Agency's Information and Referral Services Program.
$25,000 to Institute for Justice, Arlington, VA, 2012. For Law Student Programs.
$25,000 to Jazz at Lincoln Center, New York, NY, 2012. For Essentially Ellington High School Jazz Band Program.
$25,000 to National Outdoor Leadership School, Lander, WY, 2012. For Wyss Wilderness Medicine Campus.
$25,000 to Santa Barbara Neighborhood Clinics, Santa Barbara, CA, 2012. For Diabetes Care, Education and Management Program.

919
Merkin Family Foundation ✧
3115 Ocean Front Walk, No. 301
Marina Del Rey, CA 90292-5142

Established in 2003 in CA and DE.
Donors: Richard Merkin; Brian Reynolds.
Foundation type: Independent foundation.
Financial data (yr. ended 11/30/13): Assets, $89,984,535 (M); gifts received, $35,000,000; expenditures, $6,688,452; qualifying distributions, $6,586,800; giving activities include $6,586,800 for 33 grants (high: $2,000,000; low: $5,000).
Fields of interest: Higher education; Education; Cancer research; Biomedicine research; Children/youth, services; Jewish federated giving programs.
Limitations: Applications not accepted. Giving primarily in CA and MA.
Application information: Contributes only to pre-selected organizations.
Officers: Richard Merkin, Pres.; Anne Wymer, Secy.-Treas.
EIN: 200527223

920
The Steven L. Merrill Family Foundation ✧
1975 Vista Cielo Dr.
Newcastle, CA 95658

Established in 1999 in CA.
Donors: Steven L. Merrill; Merco Ventures II, L.P.
Foundation type: Independent foundation.
Financial data (yr. ended 12/31/13): Assets, $14,848,974 (M); expenditures, $993,464; qualifying distributions, $799,815; giving activities include $799,492 for 45 grants (high: $272,500; low: $500).
Purpose and activities: Giving primarily for education; some funding for the arts, the environment, particularly parks, and social services.
Fields of interest: Arts; Elementary/secondary education; Higher education; Education; Environment; Medical research, institute; Human services.
Limitations: Applications not accepted. Giving primarily in CA. No grants to individuals.
Application information: Contributes only to pre-selected organizations.
Officers: Steven L. Merrill, Pres.; Renate King-O'Neal, Secy.; Dennis Covington, Treas.
EIN: 943333248

921
Metta Fund ✧
(formerly The M Health Foundation)
770 Tamalpais Dr., Ste. 309
Corte Madera, CA 94925-1737 (415) 945-0243
E-mail: info@mettafund.org; Main URL: http://www.mettafund.org

Established around 1986; converted in 1992 from Davies Medical Center.
Donor: Franklin Holding Corp.
Foundation type: Independent foundation.
Financial data (yr. ended 12/31/12): Assets, $75,154,742 (M); expenditures, $7,861,513; qualifying distributions, $6,601,631; giving activities include $4,995,828 for 86 grants (high: $300,000; low: $1,000).
Purpose and activities: Giving primarily for hospitals, health organizations and human services.
Fields of interest: Hospitals (general); Health organizations; Human services; Foundations (private grantmaking).
Limitations: Applications not accepted. Giving primarily in San Francisco, CA. No grants to individuals.
Publications: Annual report; Grants list.
Application information: Contributes only to pre-selected organizations. Grant applications are by invitation only.
Officers and Directors:* Robert Reed,* Chair.; Gregory G. Monardo,* Pres.; Brigitte Garcia, V.P., Admin.; Delia Reid, V.P.; Cherie Mohrfeld, M.D.*, Secy.; Beverly Hayon; James E. Loyce, Jr.; Sandy Ouye Mori; H. Marcia Smolens; J. Edward Tippetts.
EIN: 942992640

922
The Barry and Wendy Meyer Charitable Foundation ✧
10960 Wilshire Blvd., 5th Fl.
Los Angeles, CA 90024

Established in 1999 in CA.
Donors: Wendy Meyer, Ph.D.; Barry Meyer; Lillian H. Meyer Trust.
Foundation type: Independent foundation.
Financial data (yr. ended 12/31/13): Assets, $8,724,902 (M); gifts received, $6,000,000; expenditures, $814,741; qualifying distributions, $811,139; giving activities include $811,139 for 61 grants (high: $203,104; low: $500).
Fields of interest: Education; Human services; Children/youth, services; Civil/human rights; Foundations (private grantmaking).
Limitations: Applications not accepted. Giving primarily in CA and NY.
Application information: Contributes only to pre-selected organizations.
Officers: Wendy Meyer, Ph.D., Pres.; Barry Meyer, Secy. and C.F.O.
EIN: 954754104

923
Michelson Medical Research Foundation, Inc. ✧
(formerly Gary Karlin Michelson, M.D. Charitable Foundation, Inc.)
11755 Wilshire Blvd., Ste. 1400
Los Angeles, CA 90025-1519 (310) 806-9700
Contact: Gary Karlin Michelson M.D., Pres.

Established in 1995 in CA.
Donor: Gary Karlin Michelson, M.D.
Foundation type: Independent foundation.
Financial data (yr. ended 12/31/13): Assets, $113,338,486 (M); expenditures, $8,294,528; qualifying distributions, $7,579,390; giving activities include $7,529,622 for 8 grants (high: $6,200,000; low: $500).
Fields of interest: Animals/wildlife; Medical research.
Limitations: Applications not accepted. Giving primarily in Los Angeles, CA. No grants to individuals.
Application information: Contributes only to pre-selected organizations.
Officers: Gary Karlin Michelson, M.D., Pres.; David Cohen, Secy. and C.F.O.
EIN: 954551615

924
The Middleton Foundation ✧
400 S. El Camino Real, Ste. 1200
San Mateo, CA 94402-1703

Established in 1990 in CA.
Donors: Fred A. Middleton; Carole Middleton.
Foundation type: Independent foundation.
Financial data (yr. ended 12/31/12): Assets, $12,563,994 (M); expenditures, $658,700; qualifying distributions, $489,665; giving activities include $489,665 for grants.
Fields of interest: Arts; Education; Human services.
Limitations: Applications not accepted. Giving primarily in the U.S., with emphasis on CA. No grants to individuals.
Application information: Contributes only to pre-selected organizations.
Officers: Fred A. Middleton, C.E.O.; Carole Middleton, C.F.O.; Lindarae Polaha, Secy.
EIN: 943117882

925
The Milias Foundation ✧
2175 Oak Knoll Ave.
San Marino, CA 91108-1761

Established in 1994 in CA.
Donors: Mitchell J. Milias; Margot A. Milias.
Foundation type: Independent foundation.
Financial data (yr. ended 12/31/13): Assets, $17,091,992 (M); gifts received, $1,029,000; expenditures, $861,637; qualifying distributions, $818,521; giving activities include $806,411 for 59 grants (high: $262,121; low: $100).
Fields of interest: Museums (children's); Arts; Libraries (public); Education; Hospitals (general); Human services; Catholic agencies & churches.
Limitations: Applications not accepted. Giving primarily in CA. No grants to individuals.
Application information: Unsolicited requests for funds not accepted.
Officers: Mitchell J. Milias, Pres.; Margot A. Milias, Secy. and C.F.O.
Directors: Elizabeth A. Milias; Katherine M. Milias; Mitchell C. Milias; Anne M. Ryan.
EIN: 954512936
Selected grants: The following grants are a representative sample of this grantmaker's funding activity:
$2,500,000 to Stanford University, Stanford, CA, 2011. For general purpose.
$113,500 to Huntington Library, Art Collections and Botanical Gardens, San Marino, CA, 2010. For general purpose.
$10,000 to Bellarmine College Preparatory, San Jose, CA, 2010. For general purpose.
$5,000 to Mayfield Junior School of the Holy Child Jesus, Pasadena, CA, 2011. For general purpose.
$2,500 to Saint Lukes Wood River Foundation, Ketchum, ID, 2010. For general purpose.
$1,000 to Community Library, Ketchum, ID, 2011. For general purpose.
$1,000 to San Marino Schools Foundation, San Marino, CA, 2011. For general purpose.

926
Lowell Milken Family Foundation ✧
(formerly L. and S. Milken Foundation)
1250 4th St., 3rd Fl.
Santa Monica, CA 90401-1304
Contact: R. Finerman, C.F.O. and Treas.
E-mail: bsomers@lowellmilken.org; Main URL: http://www.lowellmilken.org/
Multimedia: http://www.lowellmilken.org/news-and-media/videos/

Established in 1986 in CA.
Donors: L. Milken; S. Milken.
Foundation type: Independent foundation.
Financial data (yr. ended 10/31/13): Assets, $77,900,256 (M); gifts received, $14,641,113; expenditures, $5,626,809; qualifying distributions, $5,426,397; giving activities include $5,275,417 for 58 grants (high: $2,928,382; low: $500).
Purpose and activities: Giving to build human resources through programs in four major areas: 1) Education: to reward educational innovators, stimulate creativity among students, involve parents and other citizens in the school system, and offer opportunities to the disadvantaged student; 2) Health Care and Medical Research: to make the benefits of both basic and highly advanced health care available to those who need them; 3) Community Services: to support programs and

facilities that meet the essential needs at the neighborhood level; and 4) Human Welfare: to meet the compelling needs of the disadvantaged.
Fields of interest: Higher education; Education; Health organizations, association; Cancer; Medical research, institute; Cancer research; Human services; Jewish federated giving programs; Jewish agencies & synagogues.
Type of support: General/operating support; Building/renovation; Conferences/seminars; Scholarship funds; Research.
Limitations: Applications not accepted. Giving primarily in the Los Angeles, CA, area. No grants to individuals.
Publications: Annual report.
Application information: Contributes only to pre-selected organizations.
Officers and Directors:* L. Milken,* Pres.; R. Finerman,* Exec. V.P.; S. Fox, Secy.-Treas.; J. Milken,* V.P.; R. Milken,* V.P.; D. Milken; S. Milken.
EIN: 954078354

927
The Milken Family Foundation ✧

1250 4th St.
Santa Monica, CA 90401-1353
Contact: Richard Sandler, Exec. V.P.
FAX: (310) 570-4801; E-mail: admin@mff.org; Main URL: http://www.mff.org
E-Newsletter: http://www.mff.org/connections/connections.taf
Facebook: http://www.facebook.com/pages/Milken-Family-Foundation/22925979701?ref=ts
GiveSmart: http://www.givesmart.org/Stories/Donors/Mike-Milken
Knowledge Center: http://www.mff.org/publications/
Michael and Lori Milken's Giving Pledge Profile: http://glasspockets.org/philanthropy-in-focus/eye-on-the-giving-pledge/profiles/milken
Multimedia: http://www.mff.org/newsroom/news.taf?page=videos
Twitter: http://www.twitter.com/milken
YouTube: http://www.youtube.com/milkenaward

Established in 1982 in CA.
Donors: Lowell Milken; Michael Milken; Lori A. Milken; Sandra Milken; Department of Education.
Foundation type: Independent foundation.
Financial data (yr. ended 11/30/12): Assets, $378,108,280 (M); expenditures, $11,456,371; qualifying distributions, $9,777,930; giving activities include $7,514,862 for 207 grants (high: $2,081,628; low: $272), and $4,372,464 for 6 foundation-administered programs.
Purpose and activities: The purpose of the foundation is to discover and advance inventive and effective ways of helping people help themselves and those around them lead productive and satisfying lives. The foundation advances this mission primarily through its work in education and medical research. In education, the foundation is committed to strengthening the profession by recognizing and rewarding outstanding educators, and by expanding their professional leadership and policy influence; attracting, retaining and motivating the best talent to the teaching profession; stimulating creativity and productivity among educators and students of all ages; fostering the involvement of both family and the community in schools; and helping build vibrant communities, especially by involving young people who have special needs or who live in neighborhoods considered disadvantaged, in school-based programs that contribute to the revitalization of their community and to the well-being of its residents. In medical research, the foundation is committed to advancing and supporting basic and applied medical research, especially in the areas of prostate cancer and epilepsy, and recognizing and rewarding outstanding scientists in these areas; and supporting basic health care programs to assure the well-being of community members of all ages.
Fields of interest: Health care; Medical research, institute; Human services; Jewish federated giving programs; Jewish agencies & synagogues; Children/youth; Economically disadvantaged.
Type of support: General/operating support; Continuing support; Scholarship funds; Research.
Limitations: Applications accepted. Giving primarily in the Los Angeles, CA, area. No loans to individuals.
Application information:
Initial approach: Letter or proposal
Copies of proposal: 1
Deadline(s): None
Officers and Directors:* Lowell Milken,* Chair. and Pres.; Richard Sandler,* Exec. V.P.; Susan M. Fox, Sr. V.P. and C.F.O.; Ralph Finerman,* Sr. V.P. and Treas.; Dr. Jane Foley, Sr. V.P., Educator Awards; Lawrence Lesser, Sr. V.P., Creative Services; Bonnie Somers, Sr. V.P., Comms.; Joni Milken-Noah,* V.P., Mike's Math Club; Gary Panas, V.P., Design; Rosey Grier,* Prog. Dir., Community Affairs; Dr. Thomas C. Boysen,* Ed. Consultant; Mariano Guzman; Katherine Nouri Hughes; Dr. Julius Lesner; Ferne Milken; Gregory A. Milken; Lori A. Milken; Michael Milken; Lynda Resnick; Ellen Sandler.
Number of staff: 41 full-time professional; 1 part-time professional; 5 full-time support; 3 part-time support.
EIN: 954073646
Selected grants: The following grants are a representative sample of this grantmaker's funding activity:
$405,000 to Prostate Cancer Foundation, Santa Monica, CA, 2012.
$312,500 to Sierra Nevada College Foundation, Incline Village, NV, 2012.
$150,000 to Epilepsy Therapy Development Project, Herndon, VA, 2012.
$100,000 to Feinstein Institute for Medical Research, Manhasset, NY, 2012.
$100,000 to Los Angeles Ballet, Los Angeles, CA, 2012.
$100,000 to University of Pennsylvania, Graduate School of Education, Philadelphia, PA, 2012.

928
The Alon and Rosana Miller Foundation ✧

550 S. Hill St., No. 770
Los Angeles, CA 90013-2401 (213) 628-8619

Established in 2003 in CA.
Donors: Alon Miller; Rosana Miller; Milros Co., Inc.
Foundation type: Independent foundation.
Financial data (yr. ended 09/30/13): Assets, $2,977,979 (M); gifts received, $900,000; expenditures, $499,091; qualifying distributions, $498,570; giving activities include $498,570 for grants.
Fields of interest: Scholarships/financial aid; Education; Human services; Jewish agencies & synagogues.
Limitations: Applications accepted. Giving primarily in CA and NY. No grants to individuals.
Application information:
Initial approach: Letter on organization letterhead
Deadline(s): None
Officers: Alon Miller, Pres.; Rosana Miller, Secy.
EIN: 200515170
Selected grants: The following grants are a representative sample of this grantmaker's funding activity:
$5,000 to Bnos Devorah High School, Los Angeles, CA, 2013. For school scholarship fund.
$1,800 to Chai Lifeline, New York, NY, 2013. To support programs for assisting families through both the crises and everyday trials of serious pediatric illness.
$1,800 to Simon Wiesenthal Center, Los Angeles, CA, 2013. For tolerance and Human Rights through education.
$1,800 to Young Israel of Hancock Park, Los Angeles, CA, 2013. To assist families in the community that are in need.
$1,000 to Zion Orphanage, Fresh Meadows, NY, 2013. For Zion Education Scholarship for Orphans and Disadvantaged Children.

929
Earl B. & Loraine H. Miller Foundation ✧

(also known as The Miller Foundation)
192 Marina Dr.
Long Beach, CA 90803-4601 (562) 493-4711
Contact: Walter M. Florie, Jr., C.E.O.
FAX: (562) 493-4719;
E-mail: info@eandlmillerfdn.com; Additional e-mail address: Pam Mello, Exec. Asst., pmello@millerfdn.com; Main URL: http://www.eandlmillerfdn.com/

Established in 1967 in CA.
Foundation type: Independent foundation.
Financial data (yr. ended 06/30/13): Assets, $39,397,414 (M); expenditures, $3,844,774; qualifying distributions, $3,643,040; giving activities include $3,391,530 for 62 grants (high: $704,350; low: $1,000).
Purpose and activities: The foundation only awards grants pertaining to children's issues in 5 categories: 1) Health, 2) Education, 3) Child & Family Development, 4) Moral Citizenship, and 5) The Arts. Included in this is funding for three children's health clinics, child welfare, a hospital and a hospital building fund, and education; support also for arts and cultural activities, including museums, and symphony education of grade school children. The foundation also funds a health education center, dedicated to promoting a healthy city through culturally and linguistically appropriate health education and health promotion programs, training and leadership development, and collaboration with a diverse community.
Fields of interest: Visual arts; Museums; Performing arts; Arts; Education; Health care; Children/youth, services.
Type of support: General/operating support; Continuing support; Capital campaigns; Building/renovation; Equipment; Program development; Seed money; Curriculum development; Scholarship funds; Technical assistance; Consulting services; Program evaluation; Matching/challenge support.
Limitations: Applications not accepted. Giving limited to Long Beach, CA. No support for religious or political organizations. No grants to individuals.
Application information: Contributes only to pre-selected organizations. Unsolicited requests for

funds not accepted. See foundation web site for further information.
Board meeting date(s): Usually Jan., Mar., May, July, Sept. and Nov.
Officers and Trustees:* Walter Florie, Jr.,* Pres.; Warren Schulten,* V.P.; William H. Marmion, Ph.D.*, Secy.; Jeanne Karatsu,* Treas.; Ron R. Arias; Dr. Nancy Kimber; William R. "Randy" Mizer.
Number of staff: 1 part-time professional; 1 part-time support.
EIN: 952500545

930
The Milstein Family Foundation ✧
16027 Ventura Blvd., Ste. 550
Encino, CA 91436-2796
Main URL: http://milsteinff.org/

Established in 2000 in CA.
Donors: Adam Gila Milstein; Guilat Milstein; Lyron Milstein; Merav Milstein; Natalie Milstein; Tuvia Milstein; Wendy Milstein Radparvar; Pacific West Management.
Foundation type: Independent foundation.
Financial data (yr. ended 09/30/13): Assets, $14,659,167 (M); gifts received, $1,010,000; expenditures, $1,523,059; qualifying distributions, $1,432,000; giving activities include $1,432,000 for 78 grants (high: $237,500; low: $250).
Fields of interest: Arts; Education; Hospitals (general); Health care; Jewish agencies & synagogues.
Type of support: General/operating support.
Limitations: Applications not accepted. Giving primarily in Los Angeles, CA. No grants to individuals.
Application information: Contributes only to pre-selected organizations.
Officers: Adam Milstein, Pres.; Gila Milstein, Secy.
EIN: 954824595
Selected grants: The following grants are a representative sample of this grantmaker's funding activity:
$210,000 to American Israel Education Foundation, Washington, DC, 2011. For general use.
$160,000 to Israel Emergency Alliance, Los Angeles, CA, 2011. For general use.
$92,000 to Aish HaTorah, Los Angeles, CA, 2011. For general use.
$32,000 to UCLA Foundation, Los Angeles, CA, 2011. For general use.
$25,000 to Project Interchange, Washington, DC, 2011. For general use.
$20,000 to Israel Project, Washington, DC, 2011. For general use.
$20,000 to Middle East Forum, Philadelphia, PA, 2011. For general use.
$15,000 to Stanford Jewish Center, Palo Alto, CA, 2011. For general use.
$10,000 to Bikur Cholim, Los Angeles, CA, 2011. For general use.
$10,000 to David Horowitz Freedom Center, Sherman Oaks, CA, 2011. For general use.

931
Edward D. and Anna Mitchell Family Foundation ✧
13801 Ventura Blvd.
Sherman Oaks, CA 91423

Established in 1953.
Donors: Anna Mitchell†; Edward D. Mitchell†; and members of the Mitchell family.
Foundation type: Independent foundation.
Financial data (yr. ended 12/31/12): Assets, $12,249,773 (M); expenditures, $1,898,272; qualifying distributions, $1,683,606; giving activities include $1,465,889 for 34 grants (high: $314,286; low: $387).
Purpose and activities: Giving primarily for Jewish welfare funds, higher education, and social services.
Fields of interest: Higher education; Hospitals (general); Human services; United Ways and Federated Giving Programs; Jewish federated giving programs.
Limitations: Applications not accepted. Giving primarily in CA, with emphasis on Los Angeles; some funding also in Washington, DC. No grants to individuals.
Application information: Contributes only to pre-selected organizations.
Officers: Jonathan E. Mitchell, Pres.; Jason H. Mitchell, Secy.-Treas.
Number of staff: 1 part-time professional.
EIN: 954715236

932
The Moca Foundation ✧ ☆
1361 S. Winchester Blvd., Ste. 210
San Jose, CA 95128

Established in 2000 in CA.
Donors: Mary L. Bianco; Claire M. Solot; Edwin L. Solot, Jr.; Merchant's National Properties, Inc.; Dollar Land Syndicate; 17 West Orange Realty Corp.; J.E. Marx. Co. Inc.; The Marcled Foundation.
Foundation type: Independent foundation.
Financial data (yr. ended 12/31/13): Assets, $10,972,185 (M); expenditures, $642,360; qualifying distributions, $600,563; giving activities include $520,000 for 10 grants (high: $225,000; low: $10,000).
Fields of interest: Arts; Education; Human services; Jewish agencies & synagogues.
Type of support: General/operating support.
Limitations: Applications not accepted. Giving primarily in CA and NY. No grants to individuals.
Application information: Contributes only to pre-selected organizations.
Officers: Mary L. Bianco, Pres.; Rob Fletcher, Co-Secy.; May van Scherrenburg, Co-Secy.; Marc Vogl, Treas.
Trustees: Lisa Deutsch; Claudia Looney.
EIN: 943356929
Selected grants: The following grants are a representative sample of this grantmaker's funding activity:
$95,000 to Fidelity Charitable Gift Fund, Boston, MA, 2011. For general support.
$50,000 to Music Conservatory of Westchester, White Plains, NY, 2011. For general support.
$40,000 to Guiding Eyes for the Blind, Yorktown Heights, NY, 2011.
$25,000 to Sarah Lawrence College, Bronxville, NY, 2011. For general support.
$20,000 to Dunn School, Los Olivos, CA, 2011. For general support.
$10,000 to Stagebridge, Oakland, CA, 2011. For general support.

933
The Ken and Julie Moelis Foundation ✧
c/o TMBG & J
10866 Wilshire Blvd., 10th Fl.
Los Angeles, CA 90024-4300

Established in 2005 in CA.
Donors: Kenneth D. Moelis; Julie T. Moelis; The Moelis Family Trust.
Foundation type: Independent foundation.
Financial data (yr. ended 12/31/13): Assets, $2,803,158 (M); expenditures, $889,008; qualifying distributions, $885,659; giving activities include $885,659 for 23 grants (high: $695,000; low: $50).
Purpose and activities: Giving primarily for education, children and social services, and to health organizations, particularly a Tourette Syndrome association.
Fields of interest: Higher education; Education; Health organizations, association; Human services; Children/youth, services.
Limitations: Applications not accepted. Giving primarily in Los Angeles, CA, New York, NY, and Philadelphia PA. No grants to individuals.
Application information: Contributes only to pre-selected organizations.
Trustees: Julie T. Moelis; Kenneth D. Moelis.
EIN: 256872022
Selected grants: The following grants are a representative sample of this grantmaker's funding activity:
$100,000 to Tourette Syndrome Association, Bayside, NY, 2011.
$27,000 to University of Pennsylvania, Philadelphia, PA, 2011.
$25,000 to Simon Wiesenthal Center, New York, NY, 2011.
$10,822 to Temple Emanuel, Beverly Hills, CA, 2011.
$10,000 to Harvard-Westlake School, North Hollywood, CA, 2011.
$10,000 to KIPP LA Schools, Los Angeles, CA, 2011.
$10,000 to Rett Syndrome Research Trust, Trumbull, CT, 2011.
$8,500 to Ayn Rand Institute, Irvine, CA, 2011.
$2,500 to National Dance Institute, New York, NY, 2011.
$1,000 to LAs Promise, Los Angeles, CA, 2011.

934
The Mohn Family Foundation ✧
100 Wilshire Blvd., Ste. 1830
Santa Monica, CA 90401-1184

Established in 2001 in CA.
Donors: Jarl Mohn; Pamela Mohn.
Foundation type: Independent foundation.
Financial data (yr. ended 12/31/13): Assets, $3,647,092 (M); gifts received, $6,000; expenditures, $1,274,493; qualifying distributions, $1,268,635; giving activities include $1,265,067 for 42 grants (high: $525,000; low: $500).
Purpose and activities: Giving primarily for education, human services, and for the arts, particularly to a public radio station.
Fields of interest: Media, radio; Arts; Higher education; Education; Human services; Civil/human rights.
Limitations: Applications not accepted. Giving primarily in CA, with emphasis on Los Angeles. No grants to individuals.

Application information: Contributes only to pre-selected organizations.
Officers: Jarl Mohn, Pres.; Pamela Mohn, Secy.-Treas.
EIN: 954830816

935
Henry E. & Lola Monroe Foundation ✧

1224 Coast Village Cir., No. 16
Santa Barbara, CA 93108-2781
Contact: Frank Miller, Jr., C.E.O.

Established in 1982 in CA.
Donor: Margaret Monroe Brown†.
Foundation type: Independent foundation.
Financial data (yr. ended 06/30/13): Assets, $2,617,920 (M); expenditures, $1,058,722; qualifying distributions, $1,039,710; giving activities include $1,028,500 for 10 grants (high: $1,000,000; low: $1,000).
Purpose and activities: Giving only to benefit youth in America.
Fields of interest: Higher education; Scholarships/financial aid; Children/youth, services; Children/youth; Children; Blind/visually impaired; Minorities; Hispanics/Latinos; Girls; Boys; Crime/abuse victims; Economically disadvantaged.
Type of support: General/operating support; Building/renovation; Equipment; Program development; Seed money; Curriculum development; Internship funds; Scholarship funds.
Limitations: Applications not accepted. Giving primarily in Santa Barbara County, CA. No grants to individuals.
Application information: Unsolicited requests for funds not accepted.
Board meeting date(s): Varies
Trustees: Arthur Miller; F. Robert Miller.
Number of staff: None.
EIN: 953829818
Selected grants: The following grants are a representative sample of this grantmaker's funding activity:
$25,000 to Santa Barbara Cottage Hospital, Santa Barbara, CA, 2011.
$12,500 to Young Americas Foundation, Santa Barbara, CA, 2011.
$10,000 to Emmaus of Santa Barbara, Santa Barbara, CA, 2011.
$10,000 to Music Academy of the West, Santa Barbara, CA, 2011.
$7,000 to Claremont McKenna College, Claremont, CA, 2011.
$5,000 to Bishop Garcia Diego High School, Santa Barbara, CA, 2011. For operating funds.
$5,000 to Kids in Distressed Situations, New York, NY, 2011.
$5,000 to Ventura County Community Foundation, Camarillo, CA, 2011.
$1,250 to Santa Barbara Foundation, Santa Barbara, CA, 2011.

936
Monterey Peninsula Foundation ✧

(formerly Monterey Peninsula Golf Foundation)
1 Lower Ragsdale Dr., Bldg. 3, Ste. 100
Monterey, CA 93940-5769 (831) 649-1533
Contact: Laurel Lee-Alexander, Dir., Philanthropy Prog(s).
FAX: (831) 649-1763;
E-mail: info@montereypeninsulafoundation.org; Additional contact information (for Laurel Lee-Alexander): tel.: (831) 649-1533, ext. 230; e-mail: lla@attpbgolf.com; E-mail to submit electronic applications: grants@montereypeninsulafoundation.org; Main URL: http://www.montereypeninsulafoundation.org
Facebook: https://www.facebook.com/montereypeninsulafoundation

Established in 1978 in CA.
Foundation type: Independent foundation.
Financial data (yr. ended 06/30/13): Assets, $38,929,954 (M); gifts received, $10,598,181; expenditures, $10,591,700; qualifying distributions, $10,287,824; giving activities include $8,514,655 for 231 grants (high: $417,500; low: $1,000), and $500 for 1 employee matching gift.
Purpose and activities: The foundation enhances the quality of life in Monterey County and surrounding areas through strategic disbursements of charitable funds generated by hosting the AT&T Pebble Beach National Pro-Am and the First Tee Open at Pebble Beach. The foundation is guided in grant making by specific areas that include: youth, education, health, human services, arts, community and environmental programs.
Fields of interest: Arts; Education; Environment; Health care; Health organizations, association; Human services; Youth, services; General charitable giving.
Type of support: General/operating support; Management development/capacity building; Capital campaigns; Building/renovation; Equipment; Land acquisition; Program development; Publication; Technical assistance; Program evaluation; Employee matching gifts; In-kind gifts; Matching/challenge support.
Limitations: Applications accepted. Giving primarily in Monterey, Santa Cruz, San Benito counties, CA; limited grants to Northern, CA. No support for labor organizations, fraternal organizations or other organizations with limited constituency, no political parties, candidates or political organizations. No grants to individuals or for emergency operating funds, deficits, research projects, endowments, development of production of books, films or video projects, organization with a limited constituency, annual meetings, advertising, contests, fundraising, ceremonies, conferences, travel, testimonials, or memorials, or for multi-year campaigns, or capital campaigns.
Publications: Application guidelines; Annual report; Grants list; Informational brochure; Occasional report.
Application information: Application form and guidelines are available on foundation web site. Faxed applications and videos are not accepted. Please do not bind application or put it in a presentation folder. The foundation accepts the Monterey County Area Grantmakers Common Grant Application (for grant requests) and the Monterey Peninsula Foundation Youth Fund Grant Application (for the foundation's Youth Fund). Application form required.
Initial approach: Completed application form and grant application checklist
Copies of proposal: 1
Deadline(s): None
Board meeting date(s): June and Dec.
Final notification: 60-90 days from receipt of application (longer if application is incomplete)
Officers and Directors:* Clint Eastwood,* Chair.; Peter Ueberroth, Vice-Chair.; Steve John, C.E.O.; Cindy Zoller Silver, Exec. Dir.; Harris Barton; Dave Clark; Geoff Couch; Greg Jamison; Doug Mackenzie; William L. Perocchi; Ron Spears; Dan Tibbitts; Heidi Ueberroth; Jerry Yang.
Number of staff: 10 full-time professional; 1 part-time professional; 2 full-time support.
EIN: 942541783
Selected grants: The following grants are a representative sample of this grantmaker's funding activity:
$572,500 to University Corporation at Monterey Bay, Seaside, CA, 2013. For Imagine College.
$500,000 to Community Hospital Foundation, Monterey, CA, 2013. For Multi-year support: Kids Eat Right, payable over 3.00 years.
$500,000 to Dominican Santa Cruz Hospital Foundation, Santa Cruz, CA, 2013. For multi-year matching capital support: Acute Rehabilitation Center, payable over 3.00 years.
$500,000 to Northern California Golf Association Foundation, Pebble Beach, CA, 2013. For Multi-year grant: Youth on Course, payable over 3.00 years.
$375,000 to UC Santa Cruz Foundation, Santa Cruz, CA, 2013. For Capital support: Center for Ocean Health facility and K-16 educational programs, payable over 3.00 years.
$325,000 to Homeless Services Center, Santa Cruz, CA, 2013. For operating support and capital support for the Recuperative Care Center, payable over 3.00 years.
$150,000 to Community Foundation for Monterey County, Monterey, CA, 2013. For Monterey Experience Project: consolidated audience building campaign for nine arts nonprofits, payable over 3.00 years.
$20,000 to Future Citizens Foundation, Salinas, CA, 2013. For 2013 3M Celebrity Challenge - Andy Garcia.
$20,000 to Homeless Task Force of San Benito County, Hollister, CA, 2013. For Helping Hands housing program.
$10,000 to Seaside High School, Seaside, CA, 2013. For National Honor Society Scholarship Program.

937
Moore Family Foundation ✧

P.O. Box 3099
Los Altos, CA 94024-0099
Gordon and Betty Moore's Giving Pledge Profile: http://glasspockets.org/philanthropy-in-focus/eye-on-the-giving-pledge/profiles/moore

Established in 1986.
Donors: Betty I. Moore; Gordon E. Moore.
Foundation type: Independent foundation.
Financial data (yr. ended 09/30/13): Assets, $48,480,906 (M); expenditures, $1,406,149; qualifying distributions, $1,120,887; giving activities include $1,001,646 for 25 grants (high: $150,000; low: $5,000).
Purpose and activities: Giving primarily for higher education, conservation, and science; some giving also for local social services.
Fields of interest: Higher education; Environment, natural resources; Human services; Engineering/technology; Science.
Type of support: Research; General/operating support; Annual campaigns; Capital campaigns; Building/renovation; Equipment; Program development.
Limitations: Applications not accepted. Giving primarily in CA. No grants to individuals.

Application information: Contributes only to pre-selected organizations.
Board meeting date(s): As needed
Officer: Steven E. Moore, Exec. Dir.
Trustees: Kathleen E. Justice-Moore; Betty I. Moore; Gordon E. Moore; Kenneth G. Moore; Kristen L. Moore.
Number of staff: 1 full-time professional.
EIN: 943024440
Selected grants: The following grants are a representative sample of this grantmaker's funding activity:
$150,000 to Ecotrust, Portland, OR, 2011. To support Knowledge Systems Program.
$98,845 to University of California at San Diego Foundation, La Jolla, CA, 2011. For Scripps Institution of Oceanography, Center for Marine Biodiversity and Conservation Southern Line Islands Research Expedition.
$75,000 to Ocean Conservancy, Washington, DC, 2011. For Pacific Region Projects.
$50,000 to Exploratorium, San Francisco, CA, 2011. For exhibit maintenance.
$50,000 to Marine Conservation Biology Institute, Seattle, WA, 2011. For program support for Marine Protected Area work and Marine Spatial Planning work.
$50,000 to Point Blue Conservation Science, Petaluma, CA, 2011. For program support to develop on-line data tool in order to make wildlife data accessible to managers, researchers, and educators.
$50,000 to Tech Museum of Innovation, San Jose, CA, 2011. For annual fund for education.
$30,000 to Idea Wild, Fort Collins, CO, 2011. To purchase equipment and supplies for conservation biologists' projects and educators in developing countries around the world.
$25,000 to Seacology, Berkeley, CA, 2011. For Pacific Islands Projects to establish marine and terrestrial reserves.
$15,000 to WildEarth Guardians, Santa Fe, NM, 2011. For Protecting Grey Wolves in Northern Rockies project and Protecting Wild Cats in American West project of Carnivore Conservation Program.

938
Gordon and Betty Moore Foundation

1661 Page Mill Rd.
Palo Alto, CA 94304-1209 (650) 213-3000
Contact: Ginny Biggs, Comm. Manager
FAX: (650) 213-3003; E-mail for Genny Biggs: genny.biggs@moore.org. Additional e-mail: grantprocessing@moore.org; Main URL: http://www.moore.org/
GiveSmart: http://www.givesmart.org/Stories/Donors/Steve-McCormick
Gordon and Betty Moore's Giving Pledge Profile: http://glasspockets.org/philanthropy-in-focus/eye-on-the-giving-pledge/profiles/moore
Grants Database: http://www.moore.org/grants/list
Grants List: http://www.moore.org/about/financials
Twitter: https://twitter.com/MooreFound

Established in 2000 in CA.
Donors: Gordon E. Moore; Betty I. Moore.
Foundation type: Independent foundation.
Financial data (yr. ended 12/31/13): Assets, $6,417,833,620 (M); gifts received, $102,275; expenditures, $303,735,215; qualifying distributions, $272,332,512; giving activities include $272,332,512 for grants.
Purpose and activities: As responsible stewards of the resources entrusted to them, the foundation forms and invests in partnerships to achieve significant, lasting and measurable results in environmental conservation, science and the San Francisco Bay Area. The majority of funding is directed to organizations whose work supports the foundation's initiatives in its three major program areas.
Fields of interest: Environment; Science.
Type of support: Conferences/seminars; Land acquisition; Program development; Research; Program-related investments/loans.
Limitations: Applications not accepted. Giving on a worldwide basis (North Pacific Rim and Andes-Amazon), with some focus on the San Francisco Bay Area, CA, for selected projects. No grants to individuals, or for arts, building/renovation, endowments, capital campaigns, labor issues, or for sports programs.
Publications: Financial statement; Grants list.
Application information: The foundation does not accept unsolicited proposals.
Officers and Trustees:* Gordon E. Moore,* Chair.; Paul Gray, Ph.D., Vice-Chair.; Harvey Fineberg, M.D., Ph.D., Pres.; Nancy J. Koch, Genl. Counsel and Secy.; Denise Strack, C.I.O.; Holly Potter, C.C.O.; Kenneth G. Moore,* Dir., San Francisco Bay Area Prog.; Bruce Alberts, Ph.D.; Rosina Bierbaum, Ph.D.; James C. Gaither; John Hennessy, Ph.D.; Kathleen Justice-Moore; Kristen L. Moore; Steven E. Moore; Kenneth F. Siebel.
Number of staff: 72 full-time professional; 4 part-time professional.
EIN: 943397785
Selected grants: The following grants are a representative sample of this grantmaker's funding activity:
$15,000,000 to World Wildlife Fund, Washington, DC, 2013. To ensure the protection in perpetuity of 15% of the Brazilian Amazon Biome, in the form of 60 million hectares of legally established protected areas that are created, consolidated and maintained through the implementation of the Amazon Region Protected Areas Program (ARPA) in accordance with the conditions established by the ARPA for Life Initiative, payable over 5.00 years.
$10,000,000 to University of Washington, Seattle, WA, 2013. To support data scientists in pursuit of scientific research across the life, physical and social sciences as well as experimentation to identify the best methodologies to improve data science practice within academia, payable over 5.00 years.
$7,113,700 to Coastal First Nations Great Bear Initiative, Vancouver, Canada, 2013. For First Nations leadership and community marine spatial plan development and implementation, payable over 3.00 years.
$5,381,260 to Beth Israel Deaconess Medical Center, Boston, MA, 2013. For efforts to optimize ICU safety through patient engagement, system science and information technology, payable over 2.50 years.
$3,750,000 to Environmental Defense Fund, New York, NY, 2013. To improve the management of U.S. fisheries through the implementation of catch share programs and other science-based tools that protect marine ecosystems and create a sustainable fishing industry, payable over 3.25 years.
$1,667,500 to Derecho Ambiente y Recursos Naturales, Lima, Peru, 2013. To improve the effectiveness of good environmental governance in Loreto by integrating protected areas/ indigenous lands and socio-environmental safeguards into land-use and development planning, payable over 2.00 years.
$1,495,533 to Johns Hopkins University, Department of Computer Science, Baltimore, MD, 2013. For development of a high-fidelity data-driven quality improvement approach that will use 3-dimensional (3D) sensor array and interdisciplinary expertise in the application of machine learning and data-intensive science to measure, analyze, and evaluate patient care processes, payable over 3.00 years.
$634,140 to Nature Conservancy, Arlington, VA, 2013. To enhance the effectiveness and durability of groundfish sector management in New England, through community support, policy engagement, and permit banks; advancing improved monitoring; and exploring financing tools, payable over 2.00 years.
$583,000 to Consumers Union Foundation, Yonkers, NY, 2013. For research quantifying patient and family member responses to, and expectations and perspectives of, care received in hospitals and ICUs, payable over 1.50 years.
$484,188 to National Wildlife Federation, Reston, VA, 2013. For implementing action on Consumers Goods Forum members' commitments to sourcing zero-deforestation beef from the Amazon by 2020, coordinating related affiliate groups, and facilitating the sharing of lessons learned, payable over 2.00 years.

939
The James and Rebecca Morgan Charitable Foundation ✧

P.O. Box 1742
Los Altos, CA 94023-1742

Established in 2004 in CA.
Donors: James C. Morgan; Rebecca Q. Morgan.
Foundation type: Independent foundation.
Financial data (yr. ended 05/31/13): Assets, $2,989,570 (M); expenditures, $420,611; qualifying distributions, $420,500; giving activities include $420,500 for grants.
Fields of interest: Performing arts, theater; Education; Environment; Medical research; Foundations (private grantmaking).
Type of support: Scholarship funds.
Limitations: Applications not accepted. Giving primarily in CA and NY. No grants to individuals.
Application information: Unsolicited requests for funds not accepted.
Officers: James Morgan, Chair. and C.F.O.; Rebecca Morgan, C.E.O. and Pres.; Linda Verhulp, Secy.
EIN: 202029688
Selected grants: The following grants are a representative sample of this grantmaker's funding activity:
$204,000 to Womens Sports Foundation, New York, NY, 2012.

940
James and Rebecca Morgan Family Foundation ✧

P.O. Box 1742
Los Altos, CA 94023-1742
Contact: Linda Verhulp, Exec. Dir.

FAX: (650) 941-1715; Main URL: http://www.morganfamilyfoundation.org
Grants List: http://www.morganfamilyfoundation.org/grants.htm

Established in 1993 in CA.
Donors: James C. Morgan; Rebecca Q. Morgan.
Foundation type: Independent foundation.
Financial data (yr. ended 12/31/12): Assets, $38,797,613 (M); expenditures, $7,783,572; qualifying distributions, $7,306,674; giving activities include $7,033,095 for 69 grants (high: $1,000,000; low: $3,000).
Purpose and activities: The foundation focuses its giving on youth, education, the environment and stewardship. Programs that maximize the potential of an organization and the individuals it serves are of particular interest. The majority of funding is in Santa Clara County and San Mateo County, CA.
Fields of interest: Education; Environment; Youth development; Foundations (community); Leadership development.
Type of support: General/operating support; Continuing support; Management development/capacity building; Annual campaigns; Capital campaigns; Land acquisition; Program development; Seed money; Fellowships; Scholarship funds; Research; Program evaluation; Matching/challenge support.
Limitations: Applications not accepted. Giving primarily in Santa Clara and San Mateo counties, CA. No support for religious organizations. No grants to individuals.
Publications: Grants list.
Application information: Unsolicited applications not accepted. Proposals are by invitation only. See foundation web site for guidelines.
Board meeting date(s): 3 times a year; dates set each year
Officers and Directors:* James C. Morgan,* Chair. and Treas.; Rebecca Q. Morgan,* Pres.; Jeff Morgan,* Secy.; Linda Verhulp, Exec. Dir.
Number of staff: 3 part-time professional; 1 part-time support.
EIN: 943187468
Selected grants: The following grants are a representative sample of this grantmaker's funding activity:
$1,000,000 to Palo Alto Library Foundation, Palo Alto, CA, 2012. For general support.
$500,000 to Nature Conservancy, California Chapter, San Francisco, CA, 2012. For general support.
$500,000 to Teach for America, Bay Area Chapter, San Francisco, CA, 2012. For general support.
$375,000 to Teen Success, CA, 2011. For general support.
$206,000 to Planned Parenthood Mar Monte, San Jose, CA, 2012. For general support.
$204,100 to Teen Success, Milpitas, CA, 2012. For general support.
$184,360 to San Jose State University, San Jose, CA, 2011. For general support.
$180,000 to New Venture Fund, Washington, DC, 2011. For general support.
$159,000 to Environmental Volunteers, Palo Alto, CA, 2011. For general support.
$150,000 to Global Heritage Fund, Palo Alto, CA, 2012. For general support.
$145,000 to Planned Parenthood Mar Monte, San Jose, CA, 2011. For general support.
$105,000 to Planned Parenthood Mar Monte, San Jose, CA, 2012. For general support.
$100,000 to Feather River Land Trust, Quincy, CA, 2011. For general support.
$100,000 to Global Heritage Fund, Palo Alto, CA, 2012. For general support.
$100,000 to Reading Partners, Oakland, CA, 2012. For general support.
$40,000 to Environmental Volunteers, Palo Alto, CA, 2012. For general support.

941
Jay Morris Foundation, Inc. ✧
(formerly Graff Family Foundation)
c/o Squar Milner
11111 Santa Monica Blvd., Ste. 800
Los Angeles, CA 90025-6395

Established in 1999 in IL.
Donors: Jacob Graff; Pnina Graff.
Foundation type: Independent foundation.
Financial data (yr. ended 12/31/12): Assets, $635,073 (M); expenditures, $1,433,304; qualifying distributions, $1,400,338; giving activities include $1,400,338 for 126+ grants (high: $376,692).
Purpose and activities: Giving primarily to Jewish agencies, temples, and schools.
Fields of interest: Education; Jewish agencies & synagogues.
Limitations: Applications not accepted. Giving primarily in CA and NY. No grants to individuals.
Application information: Contributes only to pre-selected organizations.
Officers and Directors:* Jacob Graff,* Pres.; Pnina Graff, Secy.-Treas.
EIN: 364300685

942
The Morris Foundation ✧
c/o Dan J. Hall
4733 Chabot Dr., Ste. 203
Pleasanton, CA 94588-3972

Established in 1993 in CA.
Donors: Kenneth R. Morris; Linda A. Morris.
Foundation type: Independent foundation.
Financial data (yr. ended 12/31/12): Assets, $7,567,185 (M); expenditures, $647,544; qualifying distributions, $575,000; giving activities include $575,000 for 8 grants (high: $200,000; low: $25,000).
Fields of interest: Higher education; Health organizations; Human services; Foundations (private grantmaking).
Limitations: Applications not accepted. Giving primarily in AZ and CA. No grants to individuals.
Application information: Contributes only to pre-selected organizations.
Officers: Kenneth R. Morris, Pres.; Linda A. Morris, V.P.
EIN: 680313709

943
Peter A. Morton Foundation, Inc. ✧
510 N. Robertson Blvd.
Los Angeles, CA 90048-1731

Established in 1999 in DE.
Donor: Peter Morton.
Foundation type: Independent foundation.
Financial data (yr. ended 12/31/11): Assets, $6,303 (M); gifts received, $1,530,600; expenditures, $1,562,200; qualifying distributions, $1,562,200; giving activities include $1,556,000 for 17 grants (high: $1,010,000; low: $1,000).
Purpose and activities: Giving primarily for environmental conservation, education, and medical research.
Fields of interest: Education; Environment, natural resources; Environment; Health organizations, association; Medical research, institute; Cancer research; Human services; Children, services; Civil/human rights; Jewish federated giving programs.
Limitations: Applications not accepted. Giving primarily in Los Angeles, CA. No grants to individuals.
Application information: Contributes only to pre-selected organizations.
Officers: Peter Morton, Pres.; Brian Ogaz, Secy.
EIN: 954687071

944
The Morton Foundation ✧ ☆
100 Pringle Ave., Ste. 410
Walnut Creek, CA 94596-7385 (925) 287-9201
Contact: Paul F. Morton, Pres. and Treas.

Established in 1997 in CA.
Donors: Thomas A. Morton; Helen K. Morton; Helen K. Morton 2013 Charitable Lead Annuity Trust.
Foundation type: Independent foundation.
Financial data (yr. ended 12/31/13): Assets, $14,871,923 (M); gifts received, $40,918; expenditures, $797,816; qualifying distributions, $635,696; giving activities include $618,500 for 43 grants (high: $140,000; low: $500).
Fields of interest: Education; Health organizations, association; Human services; Children/youth, services.
Limitations: Applications accepted. Giving primarily in CA.
Application information: Application form required.
Initial approach: Letter
Deadline(s): None
Board meeting date(s): Varies
Officers and Directors:* Paul F. Morton, Pres. and Treas.; Kevin O. Kleckza,* V.P.; Brian T. Morton,* V.P.
Trustees: Sally Morton; Mary Ann Wolkomir; Margaret Morton Young.
EIN: 911813416
Selected grants: The following grants are a representative sample of this grantmaker's funding activity:
$40,000 to Bridge School, Hillsborough, CA, 2012. To educate Physically Disabled Children.
$25,000 to BASIC Fund, San Francisco, CA, 2012. To support Education of Needy Children W/ Scholarships.
$10,000 to International Guiding Eyes, Sylmar, CA, 2012. For assistance to the blind.
$10,000 to Second Harvest Food Bank of Santa Clara and San Mateo Counties, San Jose, CA, 2012. For Food for the Destitute.
$10,000 to Stanford University, Stanford, CA, 2012. To support of Medical Education Programs.
$7,500 to Northern California Community Loan Fund, San Francisco, CA, 2012. To support Civic Programs and Miscellaneous Charities.
$5,000 to Happy Trails Riding Academy, Visalia, CA, 2012. To support of General Education Programs.

$5,000 to Stanford University, Department of Athletics, Stanford, CA, 2012. For Stanford University Athletic Program.
$2,500 to Charles Armstrong School, Belmont, CA, 2012. To fund education programs.
$2,500 to City of Hope, Los Angeles, CA, 2012. For ongoing research.

945
Samuel B. and Margaret C. Mosher Foundation ✧
(also known as The Mosher Foundation)
(formerly Samuel B. Mosher Foundation)
1114 State St., No. 248
Santa Barbara, CA 93101-2717 (805) 962-1700
Contact: Edward E. Birch, C.E.O. and Pres.
FAX: (805) 962-1792;
E-mail: info@mosher-foundation.org; Application address: 1114 State St., Ste. 252, Santa Barbara, CA 93101; Main URL: http://www.mosher-foundation.org

Incorporated in 1951 in CA.
Donors: Samuel B. Mosher†; Goodwin J. Pelissero†; Deborah S. Pelissero†; Margaret C. Mosher†.
Foundation type: Independent foundation.
Financial data (yr. ended 08/31/13): Assets, $36,024,433 (M); gifts received, $8,907; expenditures, $2,371,602; qualifying distributions, $2,116,170; giving activities include $1,755,864 for 80 grants (high: $882,450; low: $100).
Purpose and activities: Grants mainly for education, health care and the performing arts.
Fields of interest: Arts; Secondary school/education; Higher education; Health care.
Type of support: General/operating support; Equipment; Endowments; Program development; Scholarship funds; Consulting services; Program evaluation; Program-related investments/loans; Employee-related scholarships.
Limitations: Applications accepted. Giving limited to Santa Barbara County, CA. No support for international grants, or for requests from organizations outside of Southern Santa Barbara County, CA. No grants to individuals, or for capital campaigns, endowments, fundraising or gala events, annual funds, or multi-year commitments.
Application information: Full applications by invitation only. Summaries will be kept on file and reviewed when funding is available. See foundation web site for additional information.
Initial approach: 1-page (or less) summary of organization and program
Board meeting date(s): Quarterly
Officer and Trustees:* Edward E. Birch,* C.E.O. and Pres.; Yvette Birch Giller,* V.P., Admin.; Suzanne Birch; Robert J. Emmons, Ph.D.; Jennifer Engmyr; Bruce McFadden, M.D.; David K. Winter, Ph.D.
Number of staff: 1 full-time professional; 1 part-time professional; 1 full-time support.
EIN: 956037266
Selected grants: The following grants are a representative sample of this grantmaker's funding activity:
$22,000 to Westmont College, Santa Barbara, CA, 2013. For General Academic Program Support.

946
Moss Foundation ✧
421 N. Beverly Dr., Ste. 260
Beverly Hills, CA 90210-4625

Established in 1990 in CA.
Donors: Jerome S. Moss; Commemorative Derby Promotions.
Foundation type: Independent foundation.
Financial data (yr. ended 12/31/12): Assets, $12,873,485 (M); gifts received, $913,459; expenditures, $1,917,618; qualifying distributions, $1,828,328; giving activities include $1,828,328 for 106 grants (high: $468,750; low: $500).
Purpose and activities: Giving primarily for education, health organizations, and children, youth, and social services; funding also for the arts.
Fields of interest: Arts; Elementary/secondary education; Higher education; Education; Environment, natural resources; Health organizations, association; Human services; Children/youth, services; Foundations (private grantmaking).
Limitations: Applications not accepted. Giving primarily in the Los Angeles, CA, area. No grants to individuals.
Application information: Contributes only to pre-selected organizations.
Officers: Jerome S. Moss, Pres.; Larry Kartiganer, C.F.O.; Ann Holbrook Moss, V.P.
EIN: 954280605

947
Mosse Foundation ✧
c/o The Roda Group
918 Parker St. Ste. A-14
Berkeley, CA 94710-2429

Foundation type: Independent foundation.
Financial data (yr. ended 09/30/12): Assets, $18,433,151 (M); expenditures, $917,355; qualifying distributions, $808,000; giving activities include $808,000 for 9 grants (high: $210,000; low: $10,000).
Fields of interest: Arts; Higher education; Human services; Jewish agencies & synagogues.
Limitations: Applications not accepted. Giving primarily in CA.
Application information: Contributes only to pre-selected organizations.
Officers: Roger Strauch, Co-Pres.; Hans Strauch, Co-Pres.; Henry H. Muller, Secy.
EIN: 133284747

948
The Mosse Foundation for Education and the Arts ✧
(formerly The Hilde L. Mosse Foundation)
c/o The Roda Group
918 Parker St., Ste. A-14
Berkeley, CA 94710

Established in 1985 in NY.
Foundation type: Independent foundation.
Financial data (yr. ended 09/30/13): Assets, $20,421,642 (M); expenditures, $1,147,689; qualifying distributions, $896,000; giving activities include $896,000 for 8 grants (high: $255,000; low: $8,000).
Purpose and activities: Giving for reading disorders and related problems in children, the effects of violence in mass media on children, and to promote the works of Frederic Wertham.
Fields of interest: Performing arts, theater; Child development, education; Higher education; Child development, services; United Ways and Federated Giving Programs; Jewish agencies & synagogues.
Limitations: Applications not accepted. Giving primarily in CA, MA, and NY. No grants to individuals.
Application information: Unsolicited requests for funds not accepted.
Officers: Hans Strauch, Co-Pres.; Roger Strauch, Co-Pres.; Henry H. Muller, Secy.
EIN: 133284797

949
Mourier Family Foundation ✧
1430 Blue Oaks Blvd., Ste. 190
Roseville, CA 95747-5157

Established in 2000 in CA.
Donors: John Mourier Construction, Inc.; Mourier Land Investment Corporation.
Foundation type: Independent foundation.
Financial data (yr. ended 12/31/13): Assets, $21,609,132 (M); gifts received, $742,000; expenditures, $766,479; qualifying distributions, $754,003; giving activities include $750,200 for 19 grants (high: $100,500; low: $200).
Fields of interest: Human services; Children/youth, services; Christian agencies & churches.
Limitations: Applications not accepted. Giving primarily in CA. No grants to individuals.
Application information: Contributes only to pre-selected organizations.
Officers: John Mourier III, Pres.; Laura Mourier, Secy.
EIN: 680463710
Selected grants: The following grants are a representative sample of this grantmaker's funding activity:
$175,000 to Agape International Missions, Roseville, CA, 2011.
$100,000 to Child Advocates of Placer County, Auburn, CA, 2011.
$50,000 to Boys and Girls Club of Auburn, Auburn, CA, 2011.
$25,000 to Mission Aviation Fellowship, Nampa, ID, 2011.
$20,000 to Christian Veterinary Mission, Seattle, WA, 2011.

950
The Moxie Foundation, Inc. ✧ ☆
9191 Towne Centre Dr., Ste. 380
San Diego, CA 92122-1229 (858) 255-8525
Contact: Irwin Zahn, Pres.
FAX: (858) 255-8521;
E-mail: info@moxiefoundation.org; Main URL: http://moxiefoundation.org/
Facebook: https://www.facebook.com/pages/Moxie-Foundation/253146531447430?ref=ts

Established in 1998 in CA.
Donor: Irwin Zahn.
Foundation type: Independent foundation.
Financial data (yr. ended 12/31/12): Assets, $23,473,092 (M); expenditures, $1,661,525; qualifying distributions, $1,478,123; giving activities include $1,261,100 for 17+ grants (high: $500,000).

Purpose and activities: The foundation is dedicated to enriching and empowering individuals and communities by advancing educational achievement and entrepreneurial success, personal health, and the environment.
Fields of interest: Education, early childhood education; Higher education; Education; Environment; Health care; Human services; Social entrepreneurship; Children; Disabilities, people with.
Limitations: Applications not accepted. Giving primarily in CA, with emphasis on San Diego, and New York, NY. No grants to individuals.
Application information: Unsolicited requests for funds not accepted.
Officers and Directors:* Irwin Zahn,* Chair. and C.E.O.; Peter Zahn,* Pres.; Stephen Karpa; Karen Peterson; Ellen Waddell; Florence Zahn.
EIN: 330803785
Selected grants: The following grants are a representative sample of this grantmaker's funding activity:
$500,000 to University of San Diego, San Diego, CA, 2012. For Education - Incubator support.
$1,000 to International Rescue Committee, New York, NY, 2012. To Provide survival for needy people.
$500 to March of Dimes Foundation, White Plains, NY, 2012. To foster public health.

951
Mildred E. & Harvey S. Mudd Foundation ✧
11726 San Vicente Blvd., Ste. 625
Los Angeles, CA 90049-5078

Established in CA.
Foundation type: Independent foundation.
Financial data (yr. ended 05/31/13): Assets, $22,859,640 (M); expenditures, $1,173,769; qualifying distributions, $1,072,423; giving activities include $1,014,746 for 15 grants (high: $379,200; low: $46).
Purpose and activities: Giving primarily for education, museums, health, and to a children's hospital.
Fields of interest: Museums; Higher education; Hospitals (specialty); Health care.
Type of support: General/operating support.
Limitations: Applications not accepted. Giving primarily in CA; some funding also in OR. No grants to individuals.
Application information: Contributes only to pre-selected organizations.
Trustees: Cynthia Sprague Connolly; Elizabeth S. Day; Caryll S. Mingst; Norman F. Sprague III; William Stinehart, Jr.
EIN: 956021276
Selected grants: The following grants are a representative sample of this grantmaker's funding activity:
$210,000 to Harvey Mudd College, Claremont, CA, 2011.

952
Mulago Foundation ✧
2435 Polk St., Ste. 21
San Francisco, CA 94109-1600
E-mail: info@mulagofoundation.org; Main URL: http://www.mulagofoundation.org

Established around 1968 in CA.
Donors: Rainer Arnhold Trust; Ruth Steiner†.
Foundation type: Independent foundation.
Financial data (yr. ended 12/31/12): Assets, $212,317,909 (M); expenditures, $8,307,950; qualifying distributions, $7,356,582; giving activities include $6,855,638 for 52 grants (high: $600,526).
Purpose and activities: Giving primarily for education, conservation, and health.
Fields of interest: Higher education; Education; Environment; Hospitals (general); Health care; Human services; Children/youth, services.
Limitations: Applications not accepted. Giving primarily in CA, NY and VA. No grants to individuals.
Application information: Contributes only to pre-selected organizations.
Officers: Henry H. Arnhold, Pres.; Christa Dorrego, Secy.; John P. Arnhold, Treas.
EIN: 946182697
Selected grants: The following grants are a representative sample of this grantmaker's funding activity:
$600,526 to Trust for Conservation Innovation, San Francisco, CA, 2012. For general support.
$506,851 to New School, New York, NY, 2012. For general support.
$436,256 to Frick Collection, New York, NY, 2012. For general support.
$300,000 to Island Conservation, Santa Cruz, CA, 2012. For general support.
$300,000 to One Acre Fund, Highland Park, IL, 2012. For general support.
$300,000 to Proximity Designs, South Pasadena, CA, 2012. For general support.
$250,000 to VisionSpring, New York, NY, 2012. For general support.
$150,000 to One Heart World-Wide, San Francisco, CA, 2012. For general support.
$100,000 to Nuru International, Palo Alto, CA, 2012. For general support.
$50,000 to Western Connecticut State University Foundation, Danbury, CT, 2012. For general support.

953
Muller Family Foundation ✧
(formerly Frank Muller, Sr. Foundation)
2003 Bayview Heights Dr., SPC 168
San Diego, CA 92105-5538

Established in 1965 in CA.
Donors: Frank Muller; Shiela Muller.
Foundation type: Independent foundation.
Financial data (yr. ended 07/31/13): Assets, $13,162,192 (M); expenditures, $882,761; qualifying distributions, $618,000; giving activities include $618,000 for grants.
Fields of interest: Arts; Secondary school/education; Higher education; Health care; Health organizations, association; Human services; Children/youth, services; Catholic agencies & churches.
Limitations: Applications not accepted. Giving primarily in CA. No grants to individuals.
Application information: Unsolicited requests for funds not accepted.
Officers: Richard Vilmure, Pres.; John Muller, V.P.; Dolores Muller, V.P.; Mary Thompson, Secy.-Treas.
Director: Melissa Muller.
EIN: 956121774
Selected grants: The following grants are a representative sample of this grantmaker's funding activity:
$22,500 to Los Angeles Master Chorale, Los Angeles, CA, 2010.
$22,400 to University of California, Berkeley, CA, 2011.
$6,400 to University of California, Berkeley, CA, 2010.
$5,400 to University of Wisconsin, Madison, WI, 2011.
$5,350 to Los Angeles Master Chorale, Los Angeles, CA, 2011.
$5,000 to University of Wisconsin, Madison, WI, 2011.
$4,500 to University of Wisconsin, Madison, WI, 2010.
$3,500 to University of Wisconsin, Madison, WI, 2011.
$2,300 to Los Angeles Orphanage Guild, Los Angeles, CA, 2010.
$2,200 to Museum Associates, Los Angeles, CA, 2010.
$1,800 to Catholic Relief Services, Baltimore, MD, 2010.
$1,800 to Catholic Relief Services, Baltimore, MD, 2011.
$1,700 to Pepperdine University, Malibu, CA, 2011.
$1,000 to American Cancer Society, Atlanta, GA, 2010.
$1,000 to Amyotrophic Lateral Sclerosis Association, Calabasas Hills, CA, 2011.
$1,000 to Catholic Charities of Los Angeles, Los Angeles, CA, 2010.
$1,000 to Ocean Conservancy, Washington, DC, 2010.
$1,000 to Ocean Conservancy, Washington, DC, 2011.
$1,000 to Pacific Legal Foundation, Sacramento, CA, 2011.

954
Alfred C. Munger Foundation ✧
c/o R.D. Esbenshade
355 S. Grand Ave., 35th Fl.
Los Angeles, CA 90071-1560

Established in 1965 in CA.
Donors: Charles T. Munger; Nancy B. Munger; Berkshire Hathaway Inc.
Foundation type: Independent foundation.
Financial data (yr. ended 11/30/13): Assets, $18,148,952 (M); expenditures, $1,987,019; qualifying distributions, $1,963,944; giving activities include $1,963,774 for 56 grants (high: $300,000; low: $111).
Purpose and activities: Giving primarily for higher education; some funding also for museums and hospitals.
Fields of interest: Museums; Higher education; Law school/education; Libraries/library science; Education; Hospitals (general); YM/YWCAs & YM/YWHAs.
Limitations: Applications not accepted. Giving primarily in CA. No grants to individuals.
Application information: Contributes only to pre-selected organizations.
Officers and Trustees:* Charles T. Munger,* Pres.; Richard D. Esbenshade,* V.P. and Secy.
EIN: 952462103

955
The Rudolph J. & Daphne A. Munzer Foundation ✧
3450 E. Spring St., Rm. 218
Long Beach, CA 90806-2463

Established in 1995 in CA.
Donors: Rudolph J. Munzer; Daphne A. Munzer.
Foundation type: Independent foundation.
Financial data (yr. ended 12/31/13): Assets, $12,521,200 (M); expenditures, $597,679; qualifying distributions, $523,000; giving activities include $523,000 for 36 grants (high: $50,000; low: $500).
Purpose and activities: Giving primarily for the arts, education, health organizations, and children, youth and social services.
Fields of interest: Museums (art); Arts; Education; Hospitals (general); Health organizations, association; Boys & girls clubs; Human services; Children/youth, services.
Limitations: Applications not accepted. Giving primarily in CA, with emphasis on Long Beach; some funding also in CT. No grants to individuals.
Application information: Contributes only to pre-selected organizations.
Officers and Directors:* Daniel W. Munzer,* Pres.; Daphne A. Munzer,* V.P.; Patcharin Lim, Secy.; Alexandria C. Phillips, Treas.; Anne Bourne Munzer.
EIN: 330686779
Selected grants: The following grants are a representative sample of this grantmaker's funding activity:
$52,500 to Saint Mary Medical Center Foundation, Long Beach, CA, 2011. For general charitable support.
$35,000 to Boys and Girls Clubs of Long Beach, Long Beach, CA, 2011. For general charitable support.
$35,000 to Wooden Floor for Youth Movement, Santa Ana, CA, 2011. For general charitable support.
$30,000 to Long Beach Museum of Art Foundation, Long Beach, CA, 2011. For general charitable support.
$25,000 to Childrens Dental Health Clinic, Long Beach, CA, 2011. For general charitable support.
$25,000 to Long Beach Public Library Foundation, Long Beach, CA, 2011. For general charitable support.
$20,000 to Long Beach Day Nursery, Long Beach, CA, 2011. For general charitable support.
$3,000 to Greenwich Point Conservancy, Old Greenwich, CT, 2011. For general charitable support.
$3,000 to Greenwich Scholarship Association, Greenwich, CT, 2011. For general charitable support.
$3,000 to Port Chester Carver Center, Port Chester, NY, 2011. For general charitable support.

956
Dan Murphy Foundation ✧
800 W. Sixth St., Ste. 1240
Los Angeles, CA 90017-2704
Contact: Debra Kay Duncan, Exec. Dir.; Richard Grant, Pres.

Incorporated in 1957 in CA.
Donor: Bernadine Murphy Donohue†.
Foundation type: Independent foundation.
Financial data (yr. ended 12/31/12): Assets, $207,178,313 (M); expenditures, $12,786,058; qualifying distributions, $11,285,062; giving activities include $10,527,060 for 98 grants (high: $4,879,060; low: $2,000).
Purpose and activities: Giving primarily in support of activities and charities of the Roman Catholic Church in the Archdiocese of Los Angeles, including inner city Catholic high schools, social service agencies, colleges and religious orders.
Fields of interest: Secondary school/education; Higher education; Human services; Catholic agencies & churches.
Type of support: General/operating support; Continuing support; Program development.
Limitations: Applications accepted. Giving primarily in Los Angeles, CA. No support for political organizations. No grants to.
Publications: Informational brochure.
Application information: Grants generally initiated by the trustees.
Initial approach: Letter
Copies of proposal: 1
Deadline(s): None
Board meeting date(s): Quarterly or as needed
Officers and Trustees:* Richard A. Grant, Jr.,* Pres.; Edward A. Landry,* V.P.; Msgr. Jeremiah T. Murphy,* Secy.; Frederick J. Ruopp,* Treas.; Debra Kay Duncan, Exec. Dir.; Jon L. Rewinski; Joseph Sanders; Julia D. Schwartz.
Number of staff: 1
EIN: 956046963
Selected grants: The following grants are a representative sample of this grantmaker's funding activity:
$1,690,000 to Archdiocese of Los Angeles, Department of Catholic Schools, Los Angeles, CA, 2012.
$1,450,000 to Archdiocese of Los Angeles, Los Angeles, CA, 2012.
$1,250,000 to Roman Catholic Archbishop of Los Angeles, Los Angeles, CA, 2012.
$400,000 to Archdiocese of Los Angeles, Department of Catholic Schools, Los Angeles, CA, 2012.
$300,000 to Good Shepherd Center for Homeless Women and Children, Los Angeles, CA, 2012.
$225,000 to Los Angeles Opera Company, Los Angeles, CA, 2012.
$100,000 to American Federation Pueri Cantores, Orange, CA, 2012.
$50,000 to Holy Resurrection Monastery, Newberry Springs, CA, 2012.
$50,000 to Roman Catholic Archbishop of Los Angeles, Theological Institute, Los Angeles, CA, 2012.
$30,000 to Saint Vincent de Paul Society, Los Angeles, CA, 2012.

957
Musk Foundation ✧
11075 Santa Monica Blvd., Ste. 150
Los Angeles, CA 90025-7541
Main URL: http://www.muskfoundation.org
Elon Musk's Giving Pledge Profile: http://glasspockets.org/philanthropy-in-focus/eye-on-the-giving-pledge/profiles/musk

Established in 2001 in CA.
Donor: Elon Musk.
Foundation type: Independent foundation.
Financial data (yr. ended 06/30/13): Assets, $50,317 (M); gifts received, $650,000; expenditures, $804,152; qualifying distributions, $794,547; giving activities include $783,700 for 43 grants (high: $100,000; low: $800).
Purpose and activities: Giving primarily for renewable energy research and advocacy, human space exploration research and advocacy, pediatric research, and science and engineering education.
Fields of interest: Engineering school/education; Environment, alliance/advocacy; Environment, research; Pediatrics research; Science, formal/general education; Space/aviation.
Limitations: Applications not accepted. Giving primarily in CA, some funding also in Washington, DC, MA, NY and WA. No grants to individuals.
Application information: Contributes only to pre-selected organizations.
Officers and Directors:* Elon Musk,* Pres.; Kimbal Musk,* Secy.-Treas.
EIN: 770587507
Selected grants: The following grants are a representative sample of this grantmaker's funding activity:
$183,000 to Kitchen Community, Boulder, CO, 2011.
$75,000 to Fidelity Charitable Gift Fund, Boston, MA, 2011. For general contribution.
$50,000 to Turning Point School, Culver City, CA, 2011.
$50,000 to World Spine Care, Santa Ana, CA, 2011.
$30,000 to Forgotten Harvest, Oak Park, MI, 2011.
$30,000 to Virgin Unite USA, New York, NY, 2011.
$15,000 to California Science Center Foundation, Los Angeles, CA, 2011.
$10,000 to Environmental Volunteers, Palo Alto, CA, 2011.
$10,000 to Space Frontier Foundation, Nyack, NY, 2011.
$5,000 to Charity: Water, New York, NY, 2011.

958
Charles & Gail Muskavitch Foundation ✧ ☆
149 Court St.
Auburn, CA 95603-5003

Established in 2001 in CA.
Donors: Charles Muskavitch; Gail Muskavitch.
Foundation type: Independent foundation.
Financial data (yr. ended 12/31/12): Assets, $267,768 (M); expenditures, $1,019,819; qualifying distributions, $1,004,707; giving activities include $1,000,000 for 1 grant.
Fields of interest: Foundations (community).
Type of support: General/operating support.
Limitations: Applications not accepted. Giving primarily in CA. No grants to individuals.
Application information: Unsolicited requests for funds not accepted.
Officers: Gail Muskavitch, Pres.; Timothy Woodall, Secy.
EIN: 680466474

959
Napa Valley Community Foundation
3299 Claremont Way, Ste. 2
Napa, CA 94558-3382 (707) 254-9565
Contact: Marla B. Tofle, V.P., Philanthropic Svcs.; Julia DeNatale, Mgr., Philanthropic Svcs.

FAX: (707) 254-7955;
E-mail: julia@napavalleycf.org; Main URL: http://www.napavalleycf.org
Facebook: http://www.facebook.com/napavalleycommunityfoundation?filter=2
Twitter: http://twitter.com/NapaValleyGives
YouTube: http://www.youtube.com/TerenceCFNV

Established in 1994 in CA.
Foundation type: Community foundation.
Financial data (yr. ended 06/30/14): Assets, $18,547,283 (M); gifts received, $2,665,428; expenditures, $3,607,195; giving activities include $2,689,857 for 367 grants (high: $500,000; low: $250; average: $500–$100,000), and $531,938 for 1 foundation-administered program.
Purpose and activities: The foundation mobilizes resources, inspires giving, builds knowledge and provides leadership on vital community issues to improve the quality of life for all in Napa County.
Fields of interest: Education; Health organizations; Legal services; Safety/disasters; Youth development; Family services; Children/youth; Youth; Adults; Young adults; Immigrants/refugees.
Type of support: General/operating support; Management development/capacity building; Program development; Seed money; Scholarship funds; Technical assistance; Program-related investments/loans.
Limitations: Applications accepted. Giving primarily in the Napa County, CA. No grants to individuals (except for scholarships), or for events or fundraisers, re-granting programs, fundraising by one agency on behalf of another, travel for conferences, workshops or performing arts events outside of Napa County, or for groups or projects that confer goods and services, or other benefits, to the donor advisor in exchange for a grant.
Publications: Application guidelines; Annual report; Financial statement; Grants list; Newsletter; Program policy statement.
Application information: Visit foundation Web site for application guidelines and due dates of competitive grant programs. Application form not required.
Initial approach: Letter submitted via web site
Copies of proposal: 1
Deadline(s): Varies
Board meeting date(s): Alternate months throughout the year
Final notification: Varies
Officers and Directors:* Patrick Gleeson,* Chair.; Blair Lambert,* Co Vice-Chair.; Carry Thacher,* Co Vice-Chair.; Terence P. Mulligan,* Pres.; Kent Imrie,* Secy.; Iain Silverthorne,* Treas.; Sandra J. Fasold, CPA*, C.F.O.; Jennifer Byram; Mary Ann Cleary; Dell Coats; Elba Gonzalez-Mares; Rick Jones; Richard Meese; Manbin Khaira Monteverdi; Brad Nichinson, M.D.; Melissa Patrino; Loraine Stuart; Marla B. Tofle; Jamie Watson.
Number of staff: 3 full-time professional; 2 part-time professional.
EIN: 680349777
Selected grants: The following grants are a representative sample of this grantmaker's funding activity:
$30,000 to International Institute of the Bay Area, San Francisco, CA, 2014. For Napa Valley DACA Collaborative to provide DACA services.
$30,000 to Up Valley Family Centers, Calistoga, CA, 2014. For general support.
$20,000 to Napa Parent-Child Advocacy Network, Napa, CA, 2014. For general support.
$20,000 to Napa Valley Unified School District, Napa, CA, 2014. For AVID program.
$15,000 to On The Move, Napa, CA, 2014. For Youth Leadership Academies program.
$10,000 to Cope Family Center, Napa, CA, 2014. For Bank on Napa Valley (BONV) program.
$7,000 to Boys and Girls Clubs of Saint Helena and Calistoga, Saint Helena, CA, 2014. For Youth Diversion/Intervention program alternative to juvenile justice system for Calistoga teens.
$7,000 to Family Service of the North Bay, Napa, CA, 2014. For mental health services for students in Calistoga.
$6,000 to Community Health Clinic Ole, Napa, CA, 2014. For Latino Elder Coalition (LEC) program.

960
The Narrow Gate - A Charitable Foundation ✧ ☆
12625 High Bluff Dr., Ste. 315
San Diego, CA 92130-2054

Donors: Tamra Williams; Jon Williams.
Foundation type: Independent foundation.
Financial data (yr. ended 12/31/13): Assets, $24,519 (M); expenditures, $614,552; qualifying distributions, $607,600; giving activities include $607,600 for 9 grants (high: $550,000; low: $100).
Fields of interest: Human services; Christian agencies & churches.
Limitations: Applications not accepted.
Application information: Unsolicited requests for funds not accepted.
Officers: Jon Williams, Pres. and C.E.O.; Tamra Williams, V.P.; Jeffrey D. Strong, Secy.-Treas.
EIN: 263934475

961
Native American Preparatory Scholarships ✧
P.O. Box 5297
Fullerton, CA 92838-0297

Established in NM.
Foundation type: Independent foundation.
Financial data (yr. ended 06/30/12): Assets, $104,338 (M); expenditures, $1,118,345; qualifying distributions, $1,110,051; giving activities include $1,110,051 for 1 grant.
Fields of interest: Foundations (community).
Limitations: Applications not accepted. Giving primarily in NM.
Application information: Unsolicited requests for funds not accepted.
Officers: Frances Knott, Pres.; Norbert S. Hill, Jr., V.P.; Peter Thorp, Secy.; Richard Boyle, Treas.
Director: Bruce Sunrise.
EIN: 850389606

962
Y. & S. Nazarian Family Foundation ✧
1801 Century Park W., 5th Fl.
Los Angeles, CA 90067-6408

Established in 1999 in CA.
Donors: Younes Nazarian; Soraya J. Nazarian.
Foundation type: Independent foundation.
Financial data (yr. ended 12/31/12): Assets, $39,653,878 (M); gifts received, $11,987,508; expenditures, $1,943,501; qualifying distributions, $1,521,505; giving activities include $1,521,505 for 51 grants (high: $699,400; low: $9).
Purpose and activities: Giving primarily for Jewish organizations, temples, and federated giving programs; funding also for the arts, and health organizations.
Fields of interest: Arts; Education; Health organizations, association; Human services; Jewish federated giving programs; Jewish agencies & synagogues.
Limitations: Applications not accepted. Giving primarily in CA, with some emphasis on Los Angeles; some funding also in Tel Aviv, Israel. No grants to individuals.
Application information: Contributes only to pre-selected organizations.
Officers: Sharon Baradaran, Pres.; David Nazarian, C.F.O.
Trustees: Shulamit Nazarian; Soraya J. Nazarian; Younes Nazarian.
EIN: 954774321

963
Lucille and Ronald Neeley Foundation ✧ ☆
P.O. Box 371347
San Diego, CA 92137-1347

Established in 1989 in CA.
Donors: Lucille A. Neeley; Ronald Neeley.
Foundation type: Independent foundation.
Financial data (yr. ended 12/31/13): Assets, $5,293,669 (M); gifts received, $159,153; expenditures, $924,758; qualifying distributions, $849,450; giving activities include $849,165 for 10 grants (high: $545,100; low: $1,000).
Fields of interest: Museums (art); Arts; Cancer; International relief; Foundations (community).
Type of support: General/operating support.
Limitations: Applications not accepted. Giving primarily in San Diego, CA; some funding in New York, NY. No grants to individuals.
Application information: Contributes only to pre-selected organizations.
Officers: Lucille Neeley, Chair. and Pres.; Ronald Neeley, C.F.O. and V.P.; Alison Neeley, Secy.
EIN: 330386127
Selected grants: The following grants are a representative sample of this grantmaker's funding activity:
$144,667 to Project Concern International, San Diego, CA, 2012. For Installment of Grow Funding.
$25,000 to American Red Cross, San Diego, CA, 2012. For Superstorm Sandy Relief.
$5,000 to San Diego Museum of Man, San Diego, CA, 2012. For Give Or Get Donation.
$3,900 to Museum of Contemporary Art San Diego, La Jolla, CA, 2012. For Art Pods Project.

964
Craig H. Neilsen Foundation ✧
16830 Ventura Blvd., Ste. 352
Encino, CA 91436-1707 (818) 925-1245
E-mail: contact@chnfoundation.org; Main URL: http://www.chnfoundation.org

Established in 2002 in ID and NV.
Donors: Craig H. Neilsen‡; Gordon Kanofsky; Marcia Kanofsky; John Boushy; Lisa Boushy; Bally Gaming; Wells Fargo Bank Nevada, N.A.
Foundation type: Independent foundation.

Financial data (yr. ended 12/31/12): Assets, $452,380,544 (M); expenditures, $9,741,245; qualifying distributions, $8,620,899; giving activities include $7,448,323 for 135 grants (high: $200,000; low: $13).
Purpose and activities: The primary mission of the foundation is to find a cure for spinal cord injury (SCI). In an effort to reach this goal, the foundation supports: 1) Cutting edge research that seeks to understand the biological basis for recovery of function after SCI, and to translate these findings to a clinical setting; 2) Clinical research that will develop new treatments for people living with SCI, and; 3) Innovative rehabilitation programs for people living with spinal cord injuries throughout the U.S.
Fields of interest: Medical research, institute; Disabilities, people with.
International interests: Canada.
Type of support: Research.
Limitations: Applications accepted. Giving in the U.S. and Canada. No support for religious or political organizations. No grants to individuals.
Publications: Grants list.
Application information: Application information (search by foundation name) available at Proposal Central web site: https://proposalcentral.altum.com/.
Initial approach: Letter of Intent (online only)
Final notification: 3 months
Officer and Directors:* Beth Goldsmith, Exec. Dir.; Robert D. Brown, Jr., M.D., M.P.H.; Gordon R. Kanofsky; Daniel P. Lammertse, M.D.; Lorne M. Mendell, Ph.D.; Ray H. Neilsen.
Number of staff: 1 full-time professional.
EIN: 061695275
Selected grants: The following grants are a representative sample of this grantmaker's funding activity:
$177,354 to Temple University, Philadelphia, PA, 2012. For grant to support spinal cord injury research.
$150,000 to Drexel University, Philadelphia, PA, 2012. For grant to support spinal cord injury research.
$150,000 to Drexel University, Philadelphia, PA, 2012. For grant to support spinal cord injury research.
$150,000 to Drexel University, Philadelphia, PA, 2012. For grant to support spinal cord injury research.
$138,371 to University of California, Los Angeles, CA, 2012. For grant to support spinal cord injury research.
$75,000 to Courage Center, Minneapolis, MN, 2012. For grant to support programs/services for persons living with a spinal cord injury.
$75,000 to Craig Hospital Foundation, Englewood, CO, 2012. For contribution to support spinal cord injury rehabilitation services.
$75,000 to Neurological Recovery House, Rochester, MN, 2012. For grant to support programs/ services for persons living with a spinal cord injury.
$70,000 to Copperview Community Center Advisory Board, Midvale, UT, 2012. For grant to support programs/services for persons living with a spinal cord injury.
$25,200 to Spaulding Rehabilitation Hospital, Boston, MA, 2012. For grant to support programs/ services for persons living with a spinal cord injury.

965
Nestle USA Foundation ✧
(formerly Carnation Company Foundation)
800 N. Brand Blvd.
Glendale, CA 91203-1289 (818) 549-6000

Incorporated in 1952 in CA.
Donors: Nestle USA, Inc.; Nestle Dreyer's Grand Ice Cream Company.
Foundation type: Company-sponsored foundation.
Financial data (yr. ended 12/31/13): Assets, $25,613,417 (M); expenditures, $1,668,713; qualifying distributions, $1,506,250; giving activities include $1,506,250 for 130 grants (high: $225,773; low: $100).
Purpose and activities: The foundation supports programs designed to address the health and wellness of children and youth; and promote education and literacy.
Fields of interest: Museums; Elementary/secondary education; Higher education; Libraries (public); Education, reading; Education; Hospitals (general); Health care, patient services; Health care; Food services; Boys & girls clubs; American Red Cross; Human services; United Ways and Federated Giving Programs; Children; Youth.
Type of support: General/operating support; Program development.
Limitations: Applications accepted. Giving primarily in CA, Washington, DC, FL, and OH. No grants to individuals.
Application information: Application form required.
Initial approach: Proposal
Deadline(s): None
Officers: Paul Grimwood, Pres.; Judy Cascepara, V.P.; Jonathan Jackman, Secy.; Don W. Gosline, Treas.
Director: Steven Presley.
EIN: 956027479
Selected grants: The following grants are a representative sample of this grantmaker's funding activity:
$25,000 to Miami University Foundation, Farmer School of Business, Oxford, OH, 2012.

966
The Henry Mayo Newhall Foundation ✧
57 Post St., Ste. 510
San Francisco, CA 94104-5020 (415) 981-2966
Contact: Kenneth Blum, Admin. Dir.; John S. Blum, Admin. Dir.
FAX: (415) 981-5218;
E-mail: info@newhallfoundation.org; Additional e-mail: administrator@newhallfoundation.org; Main URL: http://www.newhallfoundation.org

Incorporated in 1963 in CA.
Donors: Alice O'Meara†; Leila G. Newhall†; The Newhall Land and Farming Co.
Foundation type: Independent foundation.
Financial data (yr. ended 12/31/13): Assets, $40,807,034 (M); gifts received, $911; expenditures, $2,385,973; qualifying distributions, $2,140,303; giving activities include $1,964,500 for 76 grants (high: $149,000; low: $1,000).
Purpose and activities: Giving limited to agriculture and conservation, human services and education in San Francisco, Santa Clarita Valley and Santa Maria Valley, CA.
Fields of interest: Arts; Education; Environment; Agriculture; Human services; Children/youth, services; Family services; Children/youth; Adults; Disabilities, people with.
Type of support: Program development; General/operating support; Capital campaigns; Seed money; Scholarship funds; Matching/challenge support.
Limitations: Applications accepted. Giving limited to San Francisco, and the Santa Clarita and Santa Maria Valleys, CA. No grants to individuals, or for scholarships; no loans.
Publications: Application guidelines; Grants list.
Application information: See foundation web site for application guidelines and procedures. The foundation encourages telephone calls to inquire as to whether or not a proposed program is eligible. If so, a full proposal can be submitted. Application form not required.
Initial approach: Letter or telephone
Copies of proposal: 1
Deadline(s): Mar. 15 and Sept. 15
Board meeting date(s): Spring and fall
Final notification: 1 week after board meeting
Officers and Directors:* David Newhall,* Pres.; Angelica C. Simmons, V.P.; Scott Dunham, Secy.; Roger Newhall,* Treas.; Donna Chesebrough; Robert N. Chesebrough III; Caroline Conroy; Marion Hill; Natasha Hunt; Anthony Newhall; George A. Newhall; Prudence J. Noon; Francine Woods.
Consultants: John S. Blum, Admin. Dir.; Kenneth Blum, Admin. Dir.
EIN: 946073084
Selected grants: The following grants are a representative sample of this grantmaker's funding activity:
$100,000 to College of the Canyons, Santa Clarita, CA, 2011.
$75,000 to Exploratorium, San Francisco, CA, 2011.
$50,000 to Boys and Girls Club of Santa Clarita Valley, Santa Clarita, CA, 2011.
$50,000 to Huntington Library, Art Collections and Botanical Gardens, San Marino, CA, 2011.
$20,000 to Transitions - Mental Health Association, San Luis Obispo, CA, 2011.
$15,000 to Education Outside, San Francisco, CA, 2011.
$10,000 to Creativity Explored, San Francisco, CA, 2011.

967
C. & R. Newman Family Foundation ✧ ☆
2024 La Mesa Dr.
Santa Monica, CA 90402-2325

Established in 2007 in CA.
Donors: R. & C. Newman Trust; Christine H. Newman; Richard G. Newman.
Foundation type: Independent foundation.
Financial data (yr. ended 12/31/13): Assets, $7,478,229 (M); expenditures, $513,708; qualifying distributions, $493,258; giving activities include $484,350 for 59 grants (high: $250,000; low: $50).
Fields of interest: Education; Health care; Human services; Children.
Limitations: Applications not accepted. No grants to individuals.
Application information: Unsolicited requests for funds not accepted.
Officers and Directors:* Christine H. Newman,* Pres.; Richard G. Newman,* Secy.-Treas.
EIN: 680661680

968
Nicholas Endowment ✧
1505 E. 17th St., Ste.101
Santa Ana, CA 92705-3831 (714) 647-0900
FAX: (714) 647-0901;
E-mail: info@nicholas-endowment.org; Main URL: http://www.nicholas-endowment.org/

Established in 2002 in CA; supporting organization of The Bowers Museum in Santa Ana, CHOC Foundation, Harris myCFO Foundation, Justice for Homicide Victims, Mission San Juan Capistrano, The Ocean Institute, Orange County Community Foundation, Pacific Symphony Association, South Coast Repertory, St. Margaret's of Scotland Episcopal School, UCI Foundation, UCLA Foundation, and University of California.
Foundation type: Independent foundation.
Financial data (yr. ended 12/31/12): Assets, $34,923,016 (M); expenditures, $1,905,423; qualifying distributions, $1,680,260; giving activities include $1,680,260 for 21 grants (high: $150,000; low: $3,760).
Purpose and activities: The organization aims to enrich the community of Santa Ana and the world by supporting the performing and visual arts, assisting the advancement of science and education, and engaging other charities to make a difference in people lives.
Fields of interest: Arts; Education; Community/economic development; Science.
Limitations: Applications accepted. Giving primarily in CA. No support for salaries or for capacity building. No grants to individuals.
Publications: Financial statement.
Application information: See foundation web site for latest application procedures.
Officers and Trustees:* Claudia Sangster,* Chair.; Daniel T. Stetson,* Treas.; Robert Feller; Paula Tomei.
EIN: 466117991
Selected grants: The following grants are a representative sample of this grantmaker's funding activity:
$150,000 to Pacific Symphony, Santa Ana, CA, 2012. For grant award: Classical Series.
$140,000 to Ocean Institute, Dana Point, CA, 2012. For grant award: Core Operating/Capacity Building (2 of 2 Year).
$80,000 to Orange County Community Foundation, Newport Beach, CA, 2012. For Trustee Directed Grants.
$75,000 to Orange County Community Foundation, Newport Beach, CA, 2012. For grant award: Community Leadership Initiative.
$73,000 to Mission San Juan Capistrano, San Juan Capistrano, CA, 2012. For grant award: It Manager.
$40,000 to Mission San Juan Capistrano, San Juan Capistrano, CA, 2012. For grant award: Adopt-A-Class.

969
Henry T. Nicholas, III Foundation ✧
15 Enterprise, Ste. 550
Aliso Viejo, CA 92656-2656 (949) 448-4480
E-mail: info@htnfoundation.org; Main URL: http://www.htnfoundation.org
Articles of Interest: http://feeds.feedburner.com/htnfoundation/articlesofinterest
News and Events: http://feeds.feedburner.com/htnfoundation/newsandevents

Established in 2006 in CA.
Donor: Henry T. Nicholas III.
Foundation type: Independent foundation.
Financial data (yr. ended 12/31/12): Assets, $4,714,143 (M); expenditures, $1,558,715; qualifying distributions, $1,537,276; giving activities include $1,533,266 for 2 grants (high: $1,483,266; low: $50,000).
Purpose and activities: Giving primarily for improving communities and individual lives through education, youth sports, technology, science, medical research, victim's rights and national defense.
Fields of interest: Education; Employment, services; Human services.
Limitations: Applications accepted. Giving primarily in CA, with emphasis on Santa Ana. No grants to individuals.
Publications: Application guidelines.
Application information: See foundation web site for application procedure and form. Application form required.
Deadline(s): None
Director: Jay Noonan.
Trustee: Henry T. Nicholas III.
EIN: 207201390

970
Noll Foundation, Inc. ✧
100 Bayview Cir., Ste. 3500
Newport Beach, CA 92660 (949) 725-6504
Contact: Frederick McIntosh
E-mail: fmcintosh86@gmail.com

Established in CA.
Donor: Patricia R. Noll.
Foundation type: Independent foundation.
Financial data (yr. ended 12/31/13): Assets, $13,311,445 (M); expenditures, $936,766; qualifying distributions, $669,919; giving activities include $592,800 for 18 grants (high: $235,000; low: $5,000).
Purpose and activities: Giving primarily for children's organizations, as well as for human services and health. Although the existence of faith-based programs is not a criterion, the existence of faith-based programs by a grantee organization will be a favorable factor.
Fields of interest: Education; Health care; Down syndrome; Human services; Children/youth, services; Christian agencies & churches; Children.
Limitations: Applications accepted. Giving primarily in CA and IL. No grants to individuals.
Application information: Applicants who receive a favorable response to their initial letter of inquiry will be invited to submit a formal proposal with supporting materials. Application form required.
Initial approach: Letter of inquiry
Deadline(s): None
Officers: Thomas J. McIntosh, Pres.; Bruce A. McIntosh, Secy.; Frederick J. McIntosh, C.F.O.
Directors: Jon McIntosh; Katie McIntosh; Calvin Sodestrom; Julie Sodestrom.
EIN: 990209620
Selected grants: The following grants are a representative sample of this grantmaker's funding activity:
$4,000 to Foundation for His Ministry, San Clemente, CA, 2012. For program activities.

971
The Kenneth T. and Eileen L. Norris Foundation ✧
11 Golden Shore, Ste. 450
Long Beach, CA 90802-4274
Contact: Walter J. Zanino, Exec. Dir.
FAX: (562) 436-0584; E-mail: grants@ktn.org; Main URL: http://www.norrisfoundation.org

Trust established in 1963 in CA.
Donors: Kenneth T. Norris†; Eileen L. Norris†.
Foundation type: Independent foundation.
Financial data (yr. ended 11/30/13): Assets, $180,658,108 (M); expenditures, $8,464,630; qualifying distributions, $7,761,340; giving activities include $7,189,690 for 286 grants (high: $1,500,000; low: $1,500).
Purpose and activities: The foundation supports programs that advance better health and intellectual enlightenment through education, cultivation of the arts, individual responsibility, freedom and dignity. Funding areas are: Community, Cultural, Youth, Medicine, and Education/Science.
Fields of interest: Performing arts; Arts; Secondary school/education; Higher education; Education; Hospitals (general); Nursing care; Health care; Substance abuse, services; Mental health/crisis services; Cancer; AIDS; Alcoholism; Medical research, institute; Cancer research; AIDS research; Crime/law enforcement; Food services; Housing/shelter, development; Human services; Children/youth, services; Family services; Women, centers/services; Homeless, human services; Engineering/technology; Science; Disabilities, people with; Women; Economically disadvantaged.
Type of support: General/operating support; Continuing support; Annual campaigns; Building/renovation; Equipment; Endowments; Program development; Professorships; Scholarship funds; Research; Matching/challenge support.
Limitations: Applications accepted. Giving primarily in southern CA. No support for political organizations or campaigns. No grants to individuals, or for film or video projects; no loans.
Publications: Application guidelines; Annual report; Financial statement.
Application information: Application form is available on foundation web site. Qualifying organizations may submit a request once a year and receive no more than one grant per year. Application form required.
Initial approach: Full proposal
Copies of proposal: 1
Deadline(s): Medicine: May 1 - June 30; Education/Science: May 1 - June 30; Youth: Feb. 15 - Mar. 31; Community/Cultural: Dec. 1 - Jan. 31
Board meeting date(s): Mar., May, Aug., and Oct.
Final notification: Within 5 months
Officers and Trustees:* Lisa D. Hansen,* Chair.; Walter J. Zanino,* Exec. Dir.; Ronald R. Barnes; James R. Martin; Bradley K. Norris; Harlyne J. Norris; Kimberley Presley.
Number of staff: None.
EIN: 956080374
Selected grants: The following grants are a representative sample of this grantmaker's funding activity:
$1,500,000 to University of Southern California Norris Cancer Foundation, Norris HealthCare Consultation Center, Los Angeles, CA, 2013.
$340,000 to Torrance Memorial Medical Center Health Care Foundation, Torrance, CA, 2013. For Heart Lung Machine.

$200,000 to Huntington Library, Art Collections and Botanical Gardens, San Marino, CA, 2013. For Norris Foundation Desert Garden Plant Conservation Program.
$200,000 to Norris Center for the Performing Arts, Rolling Hills Estates, CA, 2013. For 30th Anniversary Season (2012-2013) operating support.
$175,000 to Little Company of Mary Community Health Foundation, Torrance, CA, 2013. To enhance and Expand Cardiovascular Services and Technology.
$135,000 to Accelerated School, Los Angeles, CA, 2013. For The Accelerated Charter Elementary School (ACES) New School Construction Project.
$25,000 to Five Acres, Altadena, CA, 2013. For Five Acres residential programs.
$20,000 to Angel Flight West, Santa Monica, CA, 2013. For Southern California programs.
$15,000 to BookEnds, Los Angeles, CA, 2013. For BookEnds BookDrives Literacy for All.
$10,000 to Los Angeles Chamber Orchestra Society, Los Angeles, CA, 2013. For Meet the Music.

972
North Valley Community Foundation ✧
(formerly Chico Community Foundation)
240 Main St., Ste. 260
Chico, CA 95928 (530) 891-1150
Contact: Alexa Benson-Valavanis, C.E.O.
FAX: (530) 891-1502; E-mail: nvcf@nvcf.org; Mailing address: P.O. Box 6581, Chico, CA 95927; Additional e-mail: avalavanis@nvcf.org; Main URL: http://www.nvcf.org
Facebook: http://www.facebook.com/northvalleycf
LinkedIn: http://www.linkedin.com/companies/north-valley-community-foundation
Twitter: http://twitter.com/NVCF
YouTube: http://www.youtube.com/user/northvalleycf

Established in 1989 in CA.
Foundation type: Community foundation.
Financial data (yr. ended 06/30/13): Assets, $10,902,403 (M); gifts received, $3,221,195; expenditures, $3,454,371; giving activities include $2,651,505 for 72+ grants (high: $987,463; low: $7), and $78,963 for 103 grants to individuals.
Purpose and activities: The mission of the foundation is to facilitate philanthropy in Butte, Colusa, Glenn, and Tehama counties and support community efforts to improve the quality of life in the North Valley.
Fields of interest: Elementary/secondary education; Children/youth, services; Human services; Community development, neighborhood development; Economic development; Christian agencies & churches.
Type of support: General/operating support; Management development/capacity building; Endowments; Program development; Conferences/seminars; Scholarship funds; Research; Technical assistance; Consulting services; In-kind gifts; Matching/challenge support.
Limitations: Applications not accepted. Giving limited to the North Valley area, Butte, Colusa, Glenn, and Tehama counties, CA.
Publications: Annual report; Financial statement; Grants list; Informational brochure; Occasional report.
Application information:
Board meeting date(s): 4th Thurs. monthly
Officers and Directors:* Joan Stoner,* Co-Chair.; Carolyn Nava,* Co-Chair.; Alexa Benson-Valavanis,* Pres. and C.E.O.; Vanessa Sundin,* Secy.; Lori Parris,* Treas.; Karen White,* C.F.O.; Lisa Furr; Sherry Holbrook; Marc Nemanic; Diane Ruby; Deborah Rossi.
Number of staff: 1 full-time professional; 1 part-time support.
EIN: 680161455

973
The Northern California Scholarship Foundation ✧
(formerly The Northern California Scholarship Foundation and the Scaife Scholarship Foundation)
1547 Lakeside Dr.
Oakland, CA 94612-4520
Contact: Clyde Minar, Secy.-Treas.
E-mail: ncsf@pacbell.net; Main URL: http://www.ncsfscholarships.org

Incorporated in 1927 in CA.
Donors: Irene Jones†; Walter B. Scaife†; S. Sidney Morton; Lois Irene Sweeney†; Mrs. John Gifford; Eleanor Monroe DiPietro†; E. & J. West Trusts; Alumni Association Foundation.
Foundation type: Independent foundation.
Financial data (yr. ended 05/31/13): Assets, $19,166,941 (M); gifts received, $1,173,326; expenditures, $915,498; qualifying distributions, $896,681; giving activities include $776,000 for grants to individuals.
Purpose and activities: Scholarships for high school seniors who are attending a Northern or Central California public school.
Fields of interest: Education.
Type of support: Scholarships—to individuals.
Limitations: Giving limited to Kern, San Luis Obispo and Inyo counties, CA, to the Oregon border. Refer to county map on foundation web site for geographic areas served.
Publications: Application guidelines; Informational brochure; Program policy statement.
Application information: Applications sent only to those students recommended by northern and central CA public high school administrations. Only one nomination per high school is accepted. Students are required to maintain a 3.0 accumulative GPA. Applications must be submitted with transcripts of high school records, college entrance exam scores, and statement of financial need. Application form required.
Initial approach: Letter
Copies of proposal: 1
Deadline(s): Mar. 15
Board meeting date(s): Jan., Feb., May, and Aug.
Final notification: Final selections made by May 10
Officers: Bryon Flanders, Pres.; Dave Arp, Vice-Pres.; Cal Gilbert, Secy.-Treas.
Trustees: Wade Bingham; Hans Bissinger; Dallas G. Cason; Robert Crow; Don Emig; Thomas D. Eychner; Bill K'Burg; Julius "Sandy" Kahn III; George Klopping; James F. McClung, Jr.; Dan Miller; Clyde D. Minar; Norman Owen; James Sloneker; Hon. Zook Sutton; George Vukasin.
Number of staff: 1 part-time professional; 1 part-time support.
EIN: 941540333

974
The Noyce Foundation ✧
419 S. San Antonio Rd., Ste. 213
Los Altos, CA 94022-3640 (650) 856-2600
Contact: Ann S. Bowers, Chair.
FAX: (650) 856-2601; E-mail: info@noycefdn.org; Main URL: http://www.noycefdn.org
Grants Database: http://www.noycefdn.org/annualReport.php

Established in 1990 in CA.
Donor: Robert N. Noyce Residual Trust.
Foundation type: Independent foundation.
Financial data (yr. ended 12/31/12): Assets, $126,369,989 (M); expenditures, $15,319,290; qualifying distributions, $13,853,845; giving activities include $12,903,294 for 61 grants, and $832,190 for foundation-administered programs.
Purpose and activities: The foundation is dedicated to stimulating ideas and supporting initiatives designed to produce significant improvement in teaching and learning in mathematics and science in grades K-12.
Fields of interest: Education, public education; Elementary/secondary education; Mathematics; Science.
Type of support: General/operating support; Continuing support; Management development/capacity building; Program development; Film/video/radio; Publication; Curriculum development; Research; Technical assistance; Program evaluation; Program-related investments/loans; Matching/challenge support.
Limitations: Applications not accepted. Giving primarily in Silicon Valley, CA and MA. No grants to individuals.
Publications: Annual report; Financial statement; Grants list.
Application information: Contributes only to pre-selected organizations.
Board meeting date(s): Monthly
Officers and Trustees:* Ann S. Bowers,* Chair.; Ronald Ottinger, Exec. Dir.; Phil Daro; Alan J. Friedman; Paul Goren; Pendred Noyce, M.D.; Robert Schwartz; Lester Strong.
Number of staff: 2 full-time professional; 1 full-time support.
EIN: 770257009
Selected grants: The following grants are a representative sample of this grantmaker's funding activity:
$1,375,000 to New Teacher Project, Brooklyn, NY, 2012. To produce the most effective and dedicated teachers in the country, at reasonable cost; prove that strategically managing teacher effectiveness improves student outcomes; and become the nation's most authoritative voice on effective teachers.
$805,563 to Four-H Council, National, Chevy Chase, MD, 2012. To implement the evaluation plan for the 4-H SET program and build capacity of 4-H state leaders, local leaders, and national infrastructure.
$800,000 to Four-H Council, National, Chevy Chase, MD, 2012. To implement the evaluation plan for the 4-H SET program and build capacity of 4-H state leaders, local leaders, and national infrastructure.
$742,900 to Education Resource Strategies, Watertown, MA, 2012. To implement Tough Times campaign, increase organizational capacity to scale more quickly, and fill in gaps in product and tool offerings.
$660,583 to Techbridge Girls, Oakland, CA, 2012. To scale up Girls Go Techbridge to provide science, engineering, and career exploration resources for

12,000 Girl Scouts in 12 Girl Scout councils across the U.S.
$500,000 to New Leaders for New Schools, National Office, New York, NY, 2012. For New Leaders for New Schools to develop the capacity, tools, and knowledge to help districts change their approach to recruiting, training, and supporting principals.
$400,000 to Association of Science-Technology Centers, Washington, DC, 2012. For the continued development of the Noyce Leadership Institute to provide executive leadership programs for new and aspiring chief executives, primarily in the science center field. Program evaluation and assessment of greater impact will be ongoing.
$400,000 to Association of Science-Technology Centers, Washington, DC, 2012. For the continued development of the Noyce Leadership Institute to provide executive leadership programs for new and aspiring chief executives, primarily in the science center field. Program evaluation and assessment of greater impact will be ongoing.
$200,000 to Baltimore City Public School System, Baltimore, MD, 2012. For Baltimore City Public Schools Leadership Pipeline and Development Project.
$75,000 to Nebraska Community Learning Center Network, Lincoln, NE, 2012. To develop and implement statewide systems for informal STEM education.

975
NuVasive Spine Foundation ✧
7475 Lusk Blvd.
San Diego, CA 92121-5707 (858) 909-1902
Contact: Kay Sirianni, Secy.
E-mail: info@nuvasivespinefoundation.org; Toll free tel.: (1-800) 455-1476; Main URL: http://www.nuvasivespinefoundation.org

Donors: Allosource; James Blair; Larry Butler; Andrew Cappuccino; Helen Cappuccino; Adam Donovan; FedEx; Stephen Gould Corporation; Jeff Greengrass; Craig Hampson; Dave Harvey; KPMG, LLP; David Lane; Bob Leone; Alex Lukianov; Kathy Lukianov; MacKay Manufacturing; Madsen Medical, Inc.; Midnite Express; NuVasive, Inc.; Joe Orlich; Seabrook International, Inc.; Stephan Siemers; Structure; Gary Teuton.
Foundation type: Company-sponsored foundation.
Financial data (yr. ended 12/31/12): Assets, $1,271,767 (M); gifts received, $2,306,992; expenditures, $2,111,700; qualifying distributions, $2,109,995; giving activities include $1,890,043 for 9 grants (high: $1,392,246; low: $3,210).
Purpose and activities: The foundation provides life-changing spine surgery to individuals around the world who have limited access to medical treatment. Additionally, it focuses on developing sustainable spine care programs and advancing spine surgery technology by training and educating surgeons in disadvantaged communities. The foundation also is committed to providing innovative spine surgery products to individuals living in disadvantaged communities in the U.S. who suffer from debilitating back or neck pain.
Fields of interest: Health care; Human services.
Application information: Application form required.
Initial approach: Fill out a request for funding form on foundation web site
Deadline(s): Ongoing
Officers and Directors:* Kay Sirianni,* Secy.; Christian Zaal, Exec. Dir.; Daveed Frazier, M.D.; Craig Hunsaker; Alex Lukianov; David Schwartz, M.D.; Keith Valentine; Bill Walton.
EIN: 264835245

976
Oak Meadow Foundation ✧
(formerly Royal Barney Hogan Foundation)
P.O. Box 193809
San Francisco, CA 94119-3809

Established in 1977 in CA.
Donors: Riley P. Bechtel; Stephen D Bechtel, Jr.; Elizabeth H. Bechtel.
Foundation type: Independent foundation.
Financial data (yr. ended 12/31/13): Assets, $30,673,471 (M); gifts received, $2,000,000; expenditures, $681,869; qualifying distributions, $663,256; giving activities include $629,320 for 6 grants (high: $375,000; low: $4,320).
Fields of interest: Higher education; Medical research, institute; Food banks; Human services; Marine science; Women.
Type of support: General/operating support; Equipment.
Limitations: Applications not accepted. Giving primarily in CA, with some giving in Washington, DC. No grants to individuals.
Application information: Contributes only to pre-selected organizations.
Officers and Directors:* Susan P. Bechtel,* Pres.; Riley P. Bechtel,* V.P.; Shu Huang, Secy.-Treas.; Brendan P. Bechtel; Darren H. Bechtel; Katherine E. Bechtel.
EIN: 942416417

977
The Oakland Athletics Community Fund ✧
(also known as The Oakland A's Community Fund)
McAfee Coliseum
7000 Coliseum Way
Oakland, CA 94621-1917 (510) 563-2261
Contact: Kendall R. Pries, Dir.; Detra Page, Dir.
E-mail: community@oaklandathletics.com.; Main URL: http://oakland.athletics.mlb.com/NASApp/mlb/oak/community/index.jsp

Established in 1981 in CA.
Donors: Athletics Investment Group, LLC; Hofmann Foundation; Citation Homes Central; Teammates for Kids Foundation; The Gifford Foundation; Ross Stores, Inc.; BD & A.
Foundation type: Company-sponsored foundation.
Financial data (yr. ended 12/31/13): Assets, $749,896 (M); gifts received, $993,640; expenditures, $890,902; qualifying distributions, $890,562; giving activities include $495,085 for 147 grants (high: $32,000; low: $16).
Purpose and activities: The foundation supports programs designed to improve education; aid the underprivileged; promote crime and drug prevention; promote health awareness; and champion children and senior welfare.
Fields of interest: Media, radio; Media, journalism; Secondary school/education; Education; Hospitals (general); Public health, physical fitness; Health care; Substance abuse, prevention; Cancer; Breast cancer; Diabetes research; Crime/violence prevention; Athletics/sports, amateur leagues; Athletics/sports, baseball; Children; Aging; Disabilities, people with; Economically disadvantaged.
Type of support: General/operating support; Equipment; Program development; Sponsorships; Scholarships—to individuals; Donated products; In-kind gifts; Matching/challenge support.
Limitations: Applications accepted. Giving limited to northern CA, with emphasis on the Bay Area counties.
Publications: Application guidelines.
Application information:
Initial approach: Proposal
Deadline(s): None
Directors: Ken Hofmann; Detra G. Paige; Kendall R. Pries; Jane Spray; Kari Wolff.
Officer: Michael Crowley, Pres.
EIN: 942826655
Selected grants: The following grants are a representative sample of this grantmaker's funding activity:
$24,750 to Good Tidings Foundation, San Francisco, CA, 2012. For Athletics Grant Skyline High School Baseball Field repair.
$16,200 to American Cancer Society, San Francisco, CA, 2012. For Donation Breast Cancer Awareness Day.
$9,046 to Humane Society of the Pikes Peak Region, Colorado Springs, CO, 2012. For Brandon McCarthy Colorado Fire Relief donations and online auction.
$8,200 to Feed the Children, Oklahoma City, OK, 2012. For Sponsorship for Feed the Children Event 6/5/12.
$6,795 to American Tinnitus Association, Portland, OR, 2012. For Donation S A P 9/30/12.
$5,000 to Silicon Valley Jewish Film Festival, Cupertino, CA, 2012. For Donation Silicon Valley Jewish Film Festival 2012.
$4,200 to Professional Baseball Scouts Foundation, Calabasas, CA, 2012. For 10th Annual In the Spirit of the Game.
$3,000 to Good Tidings Foundation, San Francisco, CA, 2012. For Event Vida Blue Field. Item Contribution for Storage Container.
$2,500 to Autism Speaks, New York, NY, 2012. For Sponsorship - Half Page Ad 4/12/2012.
$2,500 to Community Youth Center, Concord, CA, 2012. For CYC Golf Challenge Silverado Sponsor 9/10/2012.

978
The Mary Oakley Foundation, Inc. ✧
494 Twin Oaks Ct.
Thousand Oaks, CA 91362-3166 (805) 494-5137
Contact: William C. Stivelman M.D., C.E.O. and Medical Dir.
FAX: (805) 379-4157;
E-mail: maryoakleyfndtn@aol.com; Application address: c/o Deborah Dunn, M.F.T., Liaison, 1056 Debra Dr., Santa Barbara, CA 93110, tel.: (805) 448-3461, e-mail: deborahdunn@cox.net; Main URL: http://www.maryoakleyfoundation.org

Established in 1995 in AZ and CA.
Donor: Oakley Family Trust.
Foundation type: Independent foundation.
Financial data (yr. ended 12/31/13): Assets, $11,495,664 (M); expenditures, $584,542; qualifying distributions, $533,877.
Purpose and activities: The foundation provides funding for indigent individuals diagnosed with dementia, Alzheimer's Disease, or a related disorder, to stay at residential care facilities.

Applicants must also be qualified for and be issued a Medi-Cal number.
Fields of interest: Alzheimer's disease.
Type of support: Grants to individuals.
Limitations: Applications accepted. Giving limited to long-term residents of the tri-counties of Santa Barbara, San Luis Obispo, and Ventura, CA only.
Application information: Application information available on foundation web site.
Initial approach: Long-term residents of the tri-counties of Santa Barbara, San Luis Obispo, and Ventura, CA, may contact Admissions Liaison, Deborah Dunn for application
Deadline(s): None
Officer: William Stivelman, C.E.O. and Medical Dir.
EIN: 770391113
Selected grants: The following grants are a representative sample of this grantmaker's funding activity:
$45,000 to Estelle Doheny Eye Foundation, Los Angeles, CA, 2012. For Research Regarding the Optic Nerve of Persons with Alzheimer's.

979
Oarsmen Foundation ✧
25550 Hawthorne Blvd., Ste. 310
Torrance, CA 90505-6832

Established in 1998 in CA.
Donors: George Schuler; Rosalie Schuler.
Foundation type: Independent foundation.
Financial data (yr. ended 12/31/13): Assets, $16,517,153 (M); gifts received, $2,717,670; expenditures, $845,703; qualifying distributions, $743,050; giving activities include $743,050 for 65 grants (high: $180,200; low: $125).
Fields of interest: Human services; Christian agencies & churches.
Limitations: Applications not accepted. Giving primarily in CA. No grants to individuals.
Application information: Unsolicited requests for funds not accepted.
Officers: Kimberly S. Whitcombe, Pres.; G.L. Schuler, V.P.; Hunt Schuler, V.P.; Scott D. Schuler, V.P.; Rosalie T. Schuler, Secy.
EIN: 330754362

980
Marvin "Buzz" Oates Charitable Foundation ✧
8615 Elder Creek Rd.
Sacramento, CA 95828-1800

Established in 2007 in CA.
Donor: Marvin Buzz L. Oates.
Foundation type: Independent foundation.
Financial data (yr. ended 12/31/13): Assets, $16,112,989 (M); gifts received, $679,675; expenditures, $1,025,532; qualifying distributions, $957,894; giving activities include $952,500 for 25 grants (high: $575,000; low: $2,500).
Fields of interest: Education; Christian agencies & churches.
Limitations: Applications not accepted. Giving primarily in CA. No grants to individuals.
Application information: Contributes only to pre-selected organizations.
Officers and Directors:* Marvin Buzz L. Oates, Chair.; Phillip D. Oates,* Pres.; Larry Allbaugh,* V.P. and Secy.; Michael Stodden,* Treas.; Kathryn Fairrington.
EIN: 261481981
Selected grants: The following grants are a representative sample of this grantmaker's funding activity:
$25,000 to Capital Christian School, Sacramento, CA, 2011. For general support.
$25,000 to Cristo Rey High School Sacramento, Sacramento, CA, 2011. For general support.
$20,000 to Save the Children Federation, Fairfield, CT, 2011. For general support.
$10,000 to Faith Medical Missions, Chickasha, OK, 2011. For general support.
$10,000 to Jenna and Patricks Foundation of Hope, Sacramento, CA, 2011. For general support.
$10,000 to Pacific Legal Foundation, Sacramento, CA, 2011. For general support.
$5,000 to Africa Inland Mission International, Pearl River, NY, 2011. For general support.
$5,000 to Compassion International, Colorado Springs, CO, 2011. For general support.

981
Bill and Susan Oberndorf Foundation ✧
(formerly Oberndorf Foundation)
505 Sansome St., Ste. 1950
San Francisco, CA 94111-3173

Established in 1993 in CA.
Donors: William E. Oberndorf; Susan C. Oberndorf.
Foundation type: Independent foundation.
Financial data (yr. ended 12/31/12): Assets, $44,335,728 (M); gifts received, $16,971,963; expenditures, $8,520,242; qualifying distributions, $8,250,504; giving activities include $8,243,213 for 63 grants (high: $4,246,436; low: $500).
Fields of interest: Secondary school/education; Higher education; Education; Health organizations, association; Human services.
Limitations: Applications not accepted. Giving primarily in the San Francisco Bay Area, CA. No grants to individuals.
Application information: Contributes only to pre-selected organizations.
Officers: Susan C. Oberndorf, Pres.; William E. Oberndorf, Secy.
EIN: 680299542
Selected grants: The following grants are a representative sample of this grantmaker's funding activity:
$4,246,436 to University of California San Francisco Foundation, San Francisco, CA, 2012.
$1,750,000 to California Academy of Sciences, San Francisco, CA, 2012.
$701,000 to Thacher School, Ojai, CA, 2012.
$195,927 to Alliance for School Choice, Washington, DC, 2012.
$150,000 to University School, Hunting Valley, OH, 2012.
$100,000 to Foundation for Excellence in Education, Tallahassee, FL, 2012.
$100,000 to Stanford University, Graduate School of Business, Stanford, CA, 2012.
$57,600 to University of California San Francisco Foundation, San Francisco, CA, 2012.
$50,000 to Williams College, Williamstown, MA, 2012.
$25,000 to San Francisco Education Fund, San Francisco, CA, 2012.

982
O'Connell Family Foundation Trust ✧
30882 Steeplechase Dr.
San Juan Capistrano, CA 92675-1926

Established in 2004 in CA.
Donor: George O'Connell.
Foundation type: Independent foundation.
Financial data (yr. ended 12/31/13): Assets, $345,316 (M); gifts received, $400,000; expenditures, $498,347; qualifying distributions, $497,445; giving activities include $496,675 for 18 grants (high: $108,000; low: $1,000).
Purpose and activities: Giving primarily for health organizations, particularly for cancer; funding also for children, youth and social services.
Fields of interest: Hospitals (general); Health care; Cancer; Health organizations; Human services; Children/youth, services; Family services; Residential/custodial care, hospices.
Limitations: Applications not accepted. Giving primarily in CA, with some emphasis on San Juan Capistrano. No grants to individuals.
Application information: Contributes only to pre-selected organizations.
Officer: George O'Connell, Pres.
EIN: 476265357

983
Thomas Ohana Foundation ✧ ☆
515 Amphitheatre Dr.
Del Mar, CA 92014-2611

Established in CA.
Donors: Frank Thomas; Joan C. Thomas.
Foundation type: Independent foundation.
Financial data (yr. ended 12/31/13): Assets, $3,310,468 (M); gifts received, $750,000; expenditures, $427,343; qualifying distributions, $424,657; giving activities include $197,110 for 4 grants (high: $131,200; low: $15,000), and $227,547 for 7 grants to individuals (high: $65,618; low: $1,380).
Fields of interest: Education.
Type of support: Scholarships—to individuals.
Limitations: Applications not accepted.
Application information: Unsolicited requests for funds not accepted.
Officers: Joan C. Thomas, Pres.; Jillian G. Thomas, Secy.; Jeffrey K. Thomas, Treas.
Director: Megan A. Thomas.
EIN: 271538278
Selected grants: The following grants are a representative sample of this grantmaker's funding activity:
$88,000 to Monarch School, San Diego, CA, 2012. For Cash Donations to Assist Students Impacted By Homelessness.
$5,000 to Mira Costa College Foundation, Oceanside, CA, 2012. For Cash Donations to Assist Students with Resources and Funding toward a Higher Education.

984
Omidyar Network Fund, Inc. ✧
1991 Broadway St., Ste. 200
Redwood City, CA 94063-1958
E-mail: info@omidyar.net; Main URL: http://www.omidyar.com/
Blog: http://www.omidyar.com/blog
E-Newsletter: http://www.omidyar.com/news

Facebook: http://www.facebook.com/OmidyarNetwork
GiveSmart: http://www.givesmart.org/Stories/Donors/Pierre-Omidyar
Grants Database: http://www.omidyar.com/investees
Pierre and Pam Omidyar's Giving Pledge Profile: http://glasspockets.org/philanthropy-in-focus/eye-on-the-giving-pledge/profiles/omidyar
The Omidyar Group: http://www.omidyargroup.com/
Twitter: http://twitter.com/OmidyarNetwork

Established in 2004 in CA from the transfer of funds from the Omidyar Foundation.
Donors: Pierre Omidyar; Omidyar Network, LLC.
Foundation type: Independent foundation.
Financial data (yr. ended 12/31/13): Assets, $319,941,051 (M); gifts received, $78,654,020; expenditures, $58,141,301; qualifying distributions, $44,881,834; giving activities include $44,881,834 for grants.
Purpose and activities: The fund makes both investments and grants, identifying likeminded organizations to support, help scale, and collaborate with to help realize their full potential. The fund's efforts are organized around two investment initiatives: 1) Access to Capital - The fund works to create economic opportunity for people in emerging markets. The focus of this initiative is on microfinance, small/medium enterprises, emerging market ventures, and property rights; 2) Media, Markets and Transparency- The fund emphasizes technology that promotes transparency, accountability, and trust across media, markets, and government. The focus of this initiative is on social media, marketplaces, government transparency, and trust/reputation and identity.
Fields of interest: International economic development; Economic development; Social entrepreneurship; Community development, small businesses; Engineering/technology; Computer science; Public affairs, information services; Public affairs; Economically disadvantaged.
Type of support: General/operating support; Program-related investments/loans; Employee matching gifts.
Limitations: Applications not accepted. Giving primarily on a national and international basis. No grants to individuals.
Application information: Contributes only to pre-selected organizations.
Officers: Pierre Omidyar, Chair.; Matthew Bannick, Pres.; Mike Kubzansky, V.P., Intellectual Capital; Will Fitzpatrick, Secy.
Trustees: Matt Halprin; Michael Mohr; Pam Omidyar; Iqbal Paroo.
Number of staff: 30
EIN: 201173866
Selected grants: The following grants are a representative sample of this grantmaker's funding activity:
$5,500,000 to Endeavor Global, New York, NY, 2012. For general operating support and to support the Endeavor Catalyst Donor Fund.
$2,000,000 to Kiva Microfunds, San Francisco, CA, 2012. For General operating support.
$1,100,000 to Common Sense Media, San Francisco, CA, 2012. For General operating support.
$300,000 to International Bank for Reconstruction and Development, Washington, DC, 2012. For the Consultative Group to Assist the Poor project to help build inclusive financial systems for the poor in developing countries.
$250,000 to Social Finance, London, England, 2012. For the international expansion of the Grantee's work in developing social impact bonds as a potential financing solution for social problems and social enterprises.
$225,000 to Open Knowledge, Cambridge, England, 2012. To develop open knowledge in order to deliver better governance, transparency, understanding of culture and research.
$200,000 to Ushahidi, Orlando, FL, 2012. For General Operating Support.

985
OneWest Foundation ✧
888 E. Walnut St.
Pasadena, CA 91101-1802

Established in 2009 in CA.
Donor: OneWest Bank Group, LLC.
Foundation type: Independent foundation.
Financial data (yr. ended 12/31/13): Assets, $6,445,094 (M); expenditures, $854,309; qualifying distributions, $854,309; giving activities include $854,000 for 15 grants (high: $100,000; low: $10,000).
Fields of interest: Elementary/secondary education; Higher education; Hospitals (general); Boys & girls clubs; Human services; Children/youth, services.
Limitations: Applications not accepted. Giving primarily in Los Angeles, CA. No grants to individuals.
Application information: Contributes only to pre-selected organizations.
Officers and Directors:* Steven T. Mnuchin,* Chair. and C.E.O.; Alesia J. Haas,* Secy. and C.F.O.; S. Kenneth Leech.
EIN: 271487168
Selected grants: The following grants are a representative sample of this grantmaker's funding activity:
$250,000 to Partnership for Los Angeles Schools, Los Angeles, CA, 2012. For The Purpose of This Grant Is Financial Support of Laptops for Teachers Participating in the Blended Learning Initiative to Help Them Better Track Student Performance.
$100,000 to City Year Los Angeles, Los Angeles, CA, 2012. For The Purpose of This Grant Is Financial Support of Corps Members at Markham Middle School. Corps Members Provide Students with Remediation and Afterschool Homework Help. Eighty-One Percent of Students at Markham Middle School Qualify for the Free and Reduce.
$100,000 to Geffen Playhouse, Los Angeles, CA, 2012. For The general purposes of Onewest Foundation's Grants to the Geffen Playhouse, a Non-Profit Performing Arts Theater, Is to Promote Performing Arts and Build Stronger Communities Within the Los Angeles Area.
$100,000 to Los Angeles Police Foundation, Los Angeles, CA, 2012. For The Purpose of This Grant Is to Support the Juvenile Impact Program, a Police Program That Works with At-Risk Youth Between the Ages of 9 and 15, Immersing Them in a Boot Style Program That Helps Them Resist Gangs While Improving Their School Attendance a.
$100,000 to Saban Free Clinic, Los Angeles, CA, 2012. For The general purposes of Onewest Foundation's Grant to the Saban Free Clinic, Is to Partner with This Medical Home to Provide Comprehensive, Dependable and Affordable Health Care to Those in Need.
$100,000 to UCLA Foundation, Los Angeles, CA, 2012. For The Purpose of This Grant Is to Support Low- to Moderate-Income Patients Who Lack Private Insurance and Do Not Qualify for Medical-Cal Or Medicare Coverage By Making a Gift Pledge Through the UCLA Foundation.
$75,000 to Junior Achievement of Southern California, Los Angeles, CA, 2012. For The Purpose of This Grant Is to Fund Junior Achievement of Southern California (Ja), a Nonprofit Leader in Youth Personal Finance Education, with Their New Initiative Aimed at Delivering Jab's Cutting Edge Suite of Personal Economics Curricula to the Student.
$70,000 to Greater Los Angeles Zoo Association, Los Angeles, CA, 2012. For The Purpose of This Grant Is Financial Support of the Zoomobile Outreach Program to Bring the Zoo to Thousands of School Children and Institutionalized Children and Adults Throughout the Greater Los Angeles Area. Fifty-Five Percent of the Schools That Par.
$50,000 to P.S. Arts, Venice, CA, 2012. For The general purposes of Onewest Foundation's Grants to the P.S. Arts Is to Help Restore Art Programs in Public Education.
$44,000 to Segerstrom Center for the Arts, Costa Mesa, CA, 2012. For The Purpose of This Grant Is Financial Support of the Artsconnect Program at Sonora Elementary School in Costa Mesa. the Program Uses Art As a Medium in Which Help Students Better Grasp Core Material in School By Strengthening Their Cognitive, Social.

986
Open Doors International, Inc.
2953 S. Pullman St.
Santa Ana, CA 92705-5840
E-mail for United States Office: opendoorsusa.org;
Main URL: http://www.od.org

Established in 1993 in CA.
Foundation type: Operating foundation.
Financial data (yr. ended 12/31/13): Assets, $21,199,498 (M); expenditures, $26,942,614; qualifying distributions, $27,326,639; giving activities include $22,089,814 for grants, and $23,707,134 for 4 foundation-administered programs.
Purpose and activities: The purpose of the foundation is to "strengthen and equip the Body of Christ living under or facing restriction and persecution because of their faith in Jesus Christ, and to encourage their involvement in world evangelism" by providing bibles and literature, media, leadership training, socio-economic development, as well as mobilizing the free world to identify with threatened and persecuted Christians and be actively involved in assisting them.
Fields of interest: Christian agencies & churches.
International interests: Africa; Asia; Latin America; Middle East; Southeastern Asia.
Limitations: Applications not accepted. Giving on an international basis. No grants to individuals.
Application information: Contributes only to pre-selected organizations.
Officers and Directors:* Brian McFarlane,* Chair.; Gunnhild Oftedal, Vice-Chair.; Jeff Taylor, C.E.O.; Jill Garrett, Secy.; Kelley Valdez, C.F.O.; Evert Schut, C.O.O.; Robert Dalton; Maarton Dees; Ken Pridmore; Roger Spoelman; Zaldeus Steenkamp; David Stone.

Number of staff: 21 full-time professional; 6 full-time support.
EIN: 330523832
Selected grants: The following grants are a representative sample of this grantmaker's funding activity:
$8,221,206 to Open Doors Holland, Ermelo, Netherlands, 2012.
$3,394,181 to Open Doors Sub-Saharan Africa, Johannesburg, South Africa, 2012.
$2,963,526 to Open Doors Southeast Asia, Quezon City, Philippines, 2012.
$2,859,111 to Open Doors Gulf, Santa Ana, CA, 2012.
$2,240,770 to Open Doors Egypt, Ermelo, Netherlands, 2012.
$1,134,438 to Open Doors Latin America, Santa Ana, CA, 2012.
$1,089,483 to Open Doors India, Noida, India, 2012.
$827,008 to Open Doors Asia, Quezon City, Philippines, 2012.
$764,593 to Open Doors Central Asia, Ermelo, Netherlands, 2012.
$305,138 to Open Doors Salt NL, Harderwijk, Netherlands, 2012.

987
Gerald Oppenheimer Family Foundation ✧
(formerly Gerald and Virginia Oppenheimer Family Foundation)
P.O. Box 30
Beverly Hills, CA 90213-0030

Established in 1987 in CA.
Donors: Gerald H. Oppenheimer; Doris Jones Stein Charitable Lead Trust No. 2; Doris Jones Stein Charitable Lead Trust No. 4.
Foundation type: Independent foundation.
Financial data (yr. ended 12/31/13): Assets, $16,908,781 (M); expenditures, $1,300,683; qualifying distributions, $1,033,216; giving activities include $954,500 for 89 grants (high: $400,000; low: $450).
Purpose and activities: Giving primarily for health care, education, and the arts.
Fields of interest: Arts; Higher education; Health care; Human services.
Type of support: Program-related investments/loans; General/operating support.
Limitations: Applications not accepted. Giving primarily in Los Angeles, CA. No grants to individuals.
Application information: Contributes only to pre-selected organizations.
Officers: Gail Oppenheimer, Chair.; Gerald H. Oppenheimer, Pres.; Patricia Burns, V.P.; Bill Oppenheimer, V.P.; Mark Oppenheimer, V.P.; Tracey Boldemann-Tatkin, Secy.; Stephen P. Petty, Treas.
EIN: 953957582
Selected grants: The following grants are a representative sample of this grantmaker's funding activity:
$5,000 to Pittsburgh Foundation, Pittsburgh, PA, 2012. For Gene Kelly Charitable Fund support.
$2,500 to Colonial Williamsburg Foundation, Williamsburg, VA, 2012. For Summer teacher institute support.
$1,500 to Loyola High School of Los Angeles, Los Angeles, CA, 2012. For robotics Program support.
$1,000 to Synergy Services, Parkville, MO, 2012. For women and girl's home facilities.
$250 to William Holden Wildlife Foundation, Beverly Hills, CA, 2012. To support in honor of Stephanie's birthday.

988
The Dwight D. Opperman Foundation ✧
c/o Maginnis Knechtel & McIntyre LLP
300 W. Colorado Blvd.
Pasadena, CA 91105-1824

Established in 1996 in MN.
Donor: Dwight D. Opperman.
Foundation type: Independent foundation.
Financial data (yr. ended 12/31/11): Assets, $14,536,812 (M); expenditures, $729,516; qualifying distributions, $724,739; giving activities include $711,614 for 22 grants (high: $134,000; low: $1,000).
Fields of interest: Performing arts; Higher education; Education; Medical research, institute; Courts/judicial administration; Human services; Foundations (private grantmaking).
Limitations: Applications not accepted. Giving primarily in MN, with emphasis on Minneapolis and St. Paul. No grants to individuals.
Application information: Contributes only to pre-selected organizations.
Officer: Dwight D. Opperman, Pres.
Directors: Julie Chrystyn-Opperman; Cathy Farrell; Fane W. Opperman; Vance K. Opperman.
EIN: 411856258

989
Opus Community Foundation ✧ ☆
19900 MacArthur Blvd., 12th Fl.
Irvine, CA 92612-2445 (949) 251-8129
Contact: Katie Steele

Established in CA.
Foundation type: Independent foundation.
Financial data (yr. ended 12/31/13): Assets, $3,035,265 (M); gifts received, $188,566; expenditures, $720,230; qualifying distributions, $519,161; giving activities include $519,161 for 146 grants (high: $15,053; low: $30).
Purpose and activities: Giving primarily in the areas of affordable housing, community development, education, financial literacy, critical health issues, and the arts.
Fields of interest: Arts; Education; Human services; YM/YWCAs & YM/YWHAs; Children/youth, services.
Limitations: Applications accepted. Giving primarily in CA and WA, and mainly to applicants living in and around Opus Bank's service area.
Application information: Application form required.
Initial approach: Request application form
Deadline(s): None
Officers: Stephen Gordon, Pres.; Thea Stuedli, C.F.O.; Richard Sanchez, Secy.; Katherine Steele, Exec. Dir.
EIN: 272413705
Selected grants: The following grants are a representative sample of this grantmaker's funding activity:
$5,000 to Junior Achievement of Orange County, Costa Mesa, CA, 2012. For non-profit organization.
$2,548 to Center for Human Services, Shoreline, WA, 2012. For non-profit organization.

990
Opus Foundation ✧
c/o CBIZ MHM LLC
10474 Santa Monica Blvd., Ste. 200
Los Angeles, CA 90025-6930

Established in 2006 in CA.
Donor: Stacey Nicholas.
Foundation type: Independent foundation.
Financial data (yr. ended 12/31/12): Assets, $13,303,762 (M); gifts received, $30,658; expenditures, $804,258; qualifying distributions, $614,225; giving activities include $614,225 for 8 grants (high: $250,000; low: $5,725).
Fields of interest: Education.
Limitations: Applications not accepted. Giving primarily in CA. No grants to individuals.
Application information: Contributes only to pre-selected organizations.
Officers and Directors:* Stacey Nicholas,* Pres.; Robert D. Feller,* Secy.-Treas.; James R. Parks.
EIN: 204927621

991
Oracle Education Foundation ✧ ☆
(formerly Oracle Help Us Help Foundation)
500 Oracle Pkwy.
P.O. Box 50P-8
Redwood Shores, CA 94065-1677
Main URL: http://www.oraclefoundation.org
YouTube: http://www.youtube.com/oraclefoundation

Established in 1997; supporting organization of Eastside College Preparatory School, University of Washington Trio Training, and Educators for Social Responsibility.
Donors: Oracle USA, Inc.; Adobe.
Foundation type: Company-sponsored foundation.
Financial data (yr. ended 05/31/13): Assets, $107,348 (M); gifts received, $1,377,585; expenditures, $2,267,540; qualifying distributions, $2,141,817; giving activities include $631,472 for 225 grants to individuals (high: $5,560; low: $899).
Purpose and activities: The foundation assists K-12 public schools and youth organizations in economically challenged communities by providing resources, training, and technical support to integrate technology into the learning environment. As part of its mission, the foundation operates two programs, ThinkQuest and Think.com, as free services to the global primary and secondary school community.
Fields of interest: Elementary/secondary education; Education, services; Education, computer literacy/technology training; Education, e-learning; Education; Youth development, community service clubs; Youth development.
Type of support: Curriculum development; Program development.
Limitations: Applications not accepted. Giving on a national and international basis.
Publications: Annual report.
Application information: Grant proposals are accepted by invitation only. No unsolicited proposals will be considered.
Board meeting date(s): Quarterly
Officers: Safra A. Catz, Chair.; Colleen Cassity, Secy. and Exec. Dir.
Directors: John Baugh; Matthew Mayerson; Barbara Means; Sally Osberg; Ray Pecheone; Kevin Walsh.
Number of staff: 29 full-time professional.
EIN: 943382118

992
Orange County Community Foundation ✧
4041 MacArthur Blvd., Ste. 510
Newport Beach, CA 92660-0000 (949) 553-4202
Contact: Todd Hanson, V.P., Donor Rels. and Progs.
FAX: (949) 553-4211; E-mail: thanson@oc-cf.org;
Main URL: http://www.oc-cf.org
Facebook: http://www.facebook.com/OCCommunityFdn
Twitter: http://twitter.com/OCCommunityFdn
YouTube: http://www.youtube.com/user/OCCF2009

Incorporated in 1989 in CA.
Foundation type: Community foundation.
Financial data (yr. ended 06/30/14): Assets, $228,719,000 (M); gifts received, $55,834,000; expenditures, $51,315,000; giving activities include $46,816,000 for grants.
Purpose and activities: The foundation seeks to encourage, support and facilitate philanthropy in Orange County.
Fields of interest: Arts; Education, early childhood education; Education; Environment; Health care; Children/youth, services; Family services; Minorities/immigrants, centers/services; Human services; Civil rights, race/intergroup relations; Aging.
Type of support: General/operating support; Continuing support; Management development/capacity building; Equipment; Program development; Conferences/seminars; Scholarship funds; Technical assistance; Program evaluation; Scholarships—to individuals.
Limitations: Applications accepted. Giving limited to Orange County, CA for discretionary grants; donor-advised grants are national in scope.
Publications: Application guidelines; Annual report; Financial statement; Informational brochure; Newsletter; Occasional report.
Application information: Visit foundation web site for application information. Application form required.
Initial approach: Telephone
Deadline(s): Varies
Board meeting date(s): 5 times per year
Final notification: 4 to 8 weeks after deadline
Officers and Governors:* Vicki U. Booth,* Chair.; Doug Holte,* Vice-Chair.; Keith Swayne, Secy. and Asst. Treas.; Shelley Hoss, Pres.; Tracy Branson, V.P., Finance and Admin.; Todd Hanson, V.P., Donor Rels. and Progs.; Cynthia Ragland, V.P., Mktg. and Comms.; Jeff Swanson, V.P., Philanthropic Svcs.; Michael Berchtold; DeAnna Colglazier; Manuel Gomez; Paul C. Heeschen; Alberto Manetta; Anoosheh M. Oskouian; Greg Palmer; Kelly Smith; Susanna Vakili.
Number of staff: 14 full-time professional; 4 part-time support.
EIN: 330378778
Selected grants: The following grants are a representative sample of this grantmaker's funding activity:
$1,650,349 to Pomona College, Claremont, CA, 2012.
$368,079 to First Place for Youth, Oakland, CA, 2012.
$277,500 to Cape Eleuthera Foundation, Lawrenceville, NJ, 2012.
$271,700 to Childrens Hospital of Orange County Foundation, Orange, CA, 2012.
$206,000 to Saint Michaels Abbey Foundation, Laguna Woods, CA, 2012.
$175,146 to Balboa Performing Arts Theater Foundation, Newport Beach, CA, 2012.
$30,000 to Grand Theater Foundation, Salt Lake City, UT, 2012.
$25,000 to Equinox Center, Encinitas, CA, 2012.
$25,000 to Jewish Family Service of Los Angeles, Los Angeles, CA, 2012.
$17,600 to Huntington Beach School District, Huntington Beach, CA, 2012.

993
Oreggia Family Foundation ✧
955 Blanco Cir., Ste. B
Salinas, CA 93901-4454

Established in 2006 in CA.
Donors: Arden Oreggia Living Trust; Sabina Oreggia Living Trust.
Foundation type: Independent foundation.
Financial data (yr. ended 12/31/13): Assets, $9,325,312 (M); expenditures, $967,687; qualifying distributions, $690,000; giving activities include $650,000 for 2 grants (high: $620,000; low: $30,000).
Fields of interest: Higher education, university; Education.
Limitations: Applications not accepted. Giving primarily in CA. No grants to individuals.
Application information: Unsolicited requests for funds not accepted.
Trustees: Arlene Bertelsman; Robert C. Taylor, Jr.
EIN: 010854918
Selected grants: The following grants are a representative sample of this grantmaker's funding activity:
$30,000 to Monterey County Agricultural and Historic Land Conservancy, Salinas, CA, 2011.

994
The Orfalea Family Foundation ✧
1283 Coast Village Cir., Ste. A
Santa Barbara, CA 93108-3753 (805) 565-7550
Contact: Solveig Chandler, Grants Dir.
FAX: (805) 565-7554;
E-mail: Schandler@orfalea.org; Main URL: http://www.orfaleafoundations.org/go/our-foundations/orfalea-family-foundation/
Giving Pledge Participant: http://www.glasspockets.org/philanthropy-in-focus/eye-on-the-giving-pledge/profiles/orfalea

Established in 2000 in CA.
Donors: Paul J. Orfalea; Paul Vit; Kinko's Corporation.
Foundation type: Independent foundation.
Financial data (yr. ended 12/31/12): Assets, $28,499,684 (M); gifts received, $17,086; expenditures, $1,665,706; qualifying distributions, $3,975,138; giving activities include $962,471 for 21 grants (high: $285,000; low: $200).
Purpose and activities: Giving for the improvement of life for children and families through learning opportunities, and to support sustainable systemic change in the community, and around the world.
Fields of interest: Education, early childhood education; Higher education; Youth development; Human services.
Type of support: General/operating support; Program development; Scholarship funds; Employee matching gifts; In-kind gifts; Matching/challenge support.
Limitations: Applications accepted. Giving primarily in San Luis Obispo, Santa Barbara, and Ventura County, CA. No grants to individuals.
Application information: See foundation web site for application guidelines and procedures. If letter of inquiry is approved, then the foundation will request the submission of a detailed proposal and other documented materials. A detailed proposal is by invitation only.
Initial approach: Letter of inquiry (1-2 pages) via e-mail
Officers: Natalie Fleet Orfalea, Chair. and Secy.; Lois Mitchell, Pres.; Catherine Brozowski, V.P.; Paul J. Orfalea, Treas.
Directors: Keenan J. Orfalea; Mason J. Orfalea.
Number of staff: 2 full-time professional; 1 part-time professional.
EIN: 770541226
Selected grants: The following grants are a representative sample of this grantmaker's funding activity:
$195,000 to University of Southern California, Los Angeles, CA, 2012. For Clinton-Orfalea Fellowship.
$50,000 to National Public Radio, Washington, DC, 2012. For On-air and website recognition.
$16,000 to Trinity School, Oklahoma City, OK, 2012. For Trinity School's Life Learning Garden.
$5,000 to Sundance Institute, Park City, UT, 2012. For Benefactor level Sponsorship 2013 Fi.
$2,630 to Council on Foundations, Arlington, VA, 2012. For Council on Foundations.
$250 to Leukemia & Lymphoma Society, Pittsfield, MA, 2012. For Donation of Elizabeth Warren for Tea.

995
Orthodox Vision Foundation ✧ ☆
4412 Oakwood Ave.
La Canada Flintridge, CA 91011-3414

Established in 2000 in CA.
Donors: Charles R. Ajalat; Marilee N. Ajalat.
Foundation type: Independent foundation.
Financial data (yr. ended 01/31/14): Assets, $9,517,572 (M); gifts received, $11,958; expenditures, $430,849; qualifying distributions, $423,841; giving activities include $423,841 for 16 grants (high: $262,226; low: $100).
Fields of interest: Education; Christian agencies & churches; Orthodox agencies & churches.
Limitations: Applications not accepted. No grants to individuals.
Application information: Contributes only to pre-selected organizations.
Trustees: Charles R. Ajalat; Marilee N. Ajalat.
EIN: 954834517
Selected grants: The following grants are a representative sample of this grantmaker's funding activity:
$159,956 to FOCUS North America, Kansas City, MO, 2012.
$86,820 to Antiochian Orthodox Christian Archdiocese, Englewood, NJ, 2012.
$15,000 to International Orthodox Christian Charities, Baltimore, MD, 2012.
$5,000 to Orthodox Christian Fellowship, Fishers, IN, 2012.
$5,000 to Orthodox Christian Mission Center, Saint Augustine, FL, 2012.
$1,000 to Saint Marys College of California, Moraga, CA, 2012.

996
Mr. & Mrs. Samuel Oschin Family Foundation ✧
503 W. Palm Dr.
Placentia, CA 92870-2421

Established in 2004 in Delaware; established as successor foundation as a result of a merger with foundation of the same name.
Donor: Samuel Oschin Trust.
Foundation type: Independent foundation.
Financial data (yr. ended 09/30/13): Assets, $107,358,710 (M); gifts received, $37; expenditures, $5,012,710; qualifying distributions, $5,359,351; giving activities include $5,003,600 for 5 grants (high: $5,000,000; low: $100).
Fields of interest: Family services; Foundations (community); Jewish federated giving programs; Science, single organization support.
Limitations: Applications not accepted. Giving primarily in CA, with emphasis on Los Angeles. No grants to individuals.
Application information: Contributes only to pre-selected organizations. Unsolicited requests for funds not accepted.
Officers and Trustees:* Lynda Oschin,* Chair. and Secy.; Michael Oschin, Pres. and C.F.O.; Daniel Oschin, V.P.
EIN: 200533204
Selected grants: The following grants are a representative sample of this grantmaker's funding activity:
$5,001,000 to California Science Center Foundation, Los Angeles, CA, 2011. For Endeavour La Campaign.
$10,000 to Jewish Federation Council of Greater Los Angeles, Los Angeles, CA, 2011. For operating support.

997
Bernard Osher Foundation ✧
1 Ferry Bldg., Ste. 255
San Francisco, CA 94111-4243 (415) 861-5587
Contact: Jeanie Hirokane, Corp. Secy.
FAX: (415) 677-5868; E-mail for Jeanie Hirokane: jhirokane@osherfoundation.org; Main URL: http://www.osherfoundation.org
Bernard and Barbro Osher's Giving Pledge Profile: http://glasspockets.org/philanthropy-in-focus/eye-on-the-giving-pledge/profiles/osher

Established in 1977 in CA.
Donor: Bernard Osher.
Foundation type: Independent foundation.
Financial data (yr. ended 12/31/13): Assets, $32,273,468 (M); gifts received, $3,701,000; expenditures, $12,088,324; qualifying distributions, $11,660,528; giving activities include $10,715,600 for 175 grants (high: $2,000,000; low: $1,000).
Purpose and activities: The foundation seeks to improve the quality of life for residents of the San Francisco Bay Area and the state of Maine through post-secondary student scholarships and arts and humanities grants. It also supports selected programs in integrative medicine, as well as a national network of lifelong learning institutes for older adults.
Fields of interest: Visual arts; Museums; Performing arts; Performing arts, dance; Performing arts, theater; Performing arts, music; Humanities; Arts; Higher education; Scholarships/financial aid; Education; Environment; Health care.
Type of support: General/operating support; Capital campaigns; Program development.
Limitations: Applications accepted. Giving primarily in Alameda and San Francisco counties, CA, and ME. No grants to individuals.
Publications: Application guidelines; Informational brochure.
Application information: Unsolicited proposals are accepted for the local Arts, cultural, and Educational Program. All other program areas are governed by a Request for Proposals (RFP) process. Nonetheless, colleges and universities interested in the four areas of support in the field of higher education may submit letters of inquiry to the foundation along with a concise description of their plans and activities relevant to the given program area. Application form not required.
Initial approach: Letter
Copies of proposal: 1
Deadline(s): None
Board meeting date(s): 6 times per year
Final notification: Within 90 days
Officers and Directors:* Barbro Osher,* Chair.; Mary G.F. Bitterman,* Pres.; Thomas Moffett, C.F.O. & C.I.O.; Bernard Osher,* Treas.; David Agger; Phyllis Cook; Robert Friend; John Gallo; Laura Lauder; John Pritzker.
Number of staff: 1 full-time professional; 1 part-time professional.
EIN: 942506257
Selected grants: The following grants are a representative sample of this grantmaker's funding activity:
$2,000,000 to University of North Carolina, Asheville, NC, 2012. For OLLI Conference.
$1,150,000 to University of Arizona, Tucson, AZ, 2012. For OLLI Conference.
$1,150,000 to University of Rhode Island, Kingston, RI, 2012. For OLLI Conference.
$1,100,000 to Coastal Carolina University, Conway, SC, 2012. For OLLI Conference.
$200,000 to San Francisco Museum of Modern Art, San Francisco, CA, 2012.
$100,000 to Commonwealth Club of California, Good Lit, San Francisco, CA, 2012.
$100,000 to Fine Arts Museums of San Francisco, San Francisco, CA, 2012.
$100,000 to K Q E D, San Francisco, CA, 2012.
$100,000 to North Carolina State University, Raleigh, NC, 2012. For OLLI Conference.
$8,000 to Marin Symphony Association, San Rafael, CA, 2012. For Arts and Humanities.

998
The Barbro Osher Pro Suecia Foundation ✧
1 Ferry Bldg., Rm. 255
San Francisco, CA 94111-4243 (415) 677-2886
Contact: Ulla W. Reilly, Exec. Admin.
E-mail: ulla.reilly@prosuecia.org
Bernard and Barbro Osher's Giving Pledge Profile: http://glasspockets.org/philanthropy-in-focus/eye-on-the-giving-pledge/profiles/osher

Established in 1996 in CA.
Donor: Bernard Osher.
Foundation type: Independent foundation.
Financial data (yr. ended 12/31/12): Assets, $7,158,934 (M); expenditures, $5,584,580; qualifying distributions, $5,545,717; giving activities include $5,505,956 for 184 grants (high: $130,000; low: $1,700).
Purpose and activities: The foundation's intent is to provide support to nonprofit organizations that benefit Swedish education, culture and arts.
Fields of interest: Museums (art); Higher education; Education.
Limitations: Applications accepted. Giving on a national basis. No grants to individuals.
Application information: Applicants must benefit Swedish culture, education or arts. Application form not required.
Initial approach: Letter or e-mail
Copies of proposal: 1
Deadline(s): None
Officers and Directors:* Barbro Osher,* Pres.; Bernard Osher,* V.P.; Ulla Reilly, Secy.; Thomas Moffett,* C.F.O.
EIN: 943241225

999
Otter Cove Foundation ✧
316 Mid Valley Ctr., Ste. 123
Carmel, CA 93923-8516

Established in 1997 in CA.
Donor: James P. Read, Jr.
Foundation type: Independent foundation.
Financial data (yr. ended 12/31/13): Assets, $6,279,996 (M); gifts received, $250,000; expenditures, $1,033,614; qualifying distributions, $1,017,672; giving activities include $966,000 for 11 grants (high: $400,000; low: $10,000).
Purpose and activities: Giving to provide a more secure future for the well-being of humans and animals.
Fields of interest: Museums (specialized); Education; Animal welfare.
Limitations: Applications not accepted. Giving primarily in CA. No grants to individuals.
Application information: Unsolicited requests for funds not accepted.
Officers and Directors:* James P. Read, Jr., Pres.; Gilan M. Read,* C.F.O.; Mark Plumley, Secy.; Megan G. Lindberg.
EIN: 943287969

1000
June G. Outhwaite Charitable Trust ✧
26 W. Anapamu St., Ste. 103
Santa Barbara, CA 93101-3144 (805) 560-0841
Contact: Jean Volmar
FAX: (805) 560-0811;
E-mail: jean@outhwaitefoundation.org; Main URL: http://www.outhwaitefoundation.org/

Established in 1998 in CA.
Donor: The 1994 June G. Outhwaite Revocable Trust.
Foundation type: Independent foundation.
Financial data (yr. ended 12/31/13): Assets, $20,683,123 (M); expenditures, $1,333,963; qualifying distributions, $962,150; giving activities include $889,500 for 65 grants (high: $100,000; low: $500).
Purpose and activities: Giving primarily for medical care support and research, general assistance to the disabled, elderly and children, support for abused women and children, the prevention of cruelty to animals, for the preservation of wildlife

and natural resources, historic preservation, and for educational institutions.
Fields of interest: Museums (marine/maritime); Education; Zoos/zoological societies; Cancer; Medical research; Family services; Children; Youth; Aging; Physically disabled.
Type of support: General/operating support; Annual campaigns; Capital campaigns; Building/renovation; Equipment; Program development; Matching/challenge support.
Limitations: Applications accepted. Giving primarily in South Santa Barbara County, CA.
Publications: Application guidelines.
Application information: Santa Barbara Foundation Roundtable's Common Grant Application Form accepted or Outhwaite Foundation Application form accepted; application guidelines and forms available on foundation web site. Application form required.
Initial approach: Submit application preferably by e-mail
Copies of proposal: 1
Deadline(s): July 31
Trustees: C. Michael Cooney; Kent L. Englert; John S. Poucher.
Number of staff: 1 part-time support.
EIN: 776154307
Selected grants: The following grants are a representative sample of this grantmaker's funding activity:
$35,000 to Carpinteria Education Foundation, Carpinteria, CA, 2012. For Carpinteria Summer Academy.
$25,000 to Santa Barbara Zoological Foundation, Santa Barbara, CA, 2012. For Discovery Pavilion Campaign.
$20,000 to Cancer Center of Santa Barbara, Santa Barbara, CA, 2012. For Arthur J. Merovick Patient Assistance Fund.
$20,000 to Casa Esperanza Homeless Center, Santa Barbara, CA, 2012. For Medical Clinic, Respite Care and Wellness Project.
$20,000 to Council on Alcoholism and Drug Abuse, Santa Barbara, CA, 2012. For Daniel Bryant Youth and Family Treatment Center.
$20,000 to Santa Barbara Maritime Museum, Santa Barbara, CA, 2012. For lease buyout.
$17,000 to Santa Barbara Foundation, Santa Barbara, CA, 2012. For Cornerstone Family Fund.
$17,000 to Unity Shoppe, Santa Barbara, CA, 2012. For Fixed Asset Debt Reduction.
$15,000 to Foodbank of Santa Barbara County, Santa Barbara, CA, 2012. To produce Initiative in South County.
$15,000 to Santa Barbara Neighborhood Clinics, Santa Barbara, CA, 2012. For Care for Every Child Program.

1001
Oxnard Foundation ✧ ☆

5 Royal St. George Rd.
Newport Beach, CA 92660-5218 (949) 475-0890
Contact: Christopher O. Veitch, Dir.

Established in 1973.
Donor: Thomas Thornton Oxnard‡.
Foundation type: Independent foundation.
Financial data (yr. ended 12/31/13): Assets, $10,031,400 (M); expenditures, $571,728; qualifying distributions, $517,246; giving activities include $478,241 for 9 grants (high: $100,000; low: $25,000).
Purpose and activities: Giving for medical research.
Fields of interest: Higher education, university; Medical research, institute; Cancer research; Parkinson's disease research.
Type of support: Research; Matching/challenge support.
Limitations: Applications accepted. Giving primarily in CA; some funding also in NM and TN. No grants to individuals, or for general support, capital funds, endowments, scholarships, fellowships, special projects, publications, or conferences; no loans.
Application information: Application form required.
Initial approach: Letter
Copies of proposal: 1
Deadline(s): None
Board meeting date(s): Quarterly
Directors: Caroline O. Meade; Christopher O. Veitch; Gary J. Meade; Thomas Meade; Julie Veitch.
Number of staff: 1 part-time support.
EIN: 237323007
Selected grants: The following grants are a representative sample of this grantmaker's funding activity:
$50,000 to University of New Mexico, Albuquerque, NM, 2012. For drug repurposing study.
$20,000 to University of California, Irvine, CA, 2012. For spinal chord research.

1002
Pacific Forest & Watershed Lands Stewardship Council ✧

155 Bovet Road, Suite 405
San Mateo, CA 94402 (650) 372-9047
FAX: (650) 372-9303;
E-mail: info@stewardshipcouncil.org; Contact for Foundation for Youth Investment: PaHoua Lee, Sr. Prog. Assoc. and Grants Mgr., 436 14th St., Ste. 1209, Oakland, CA 94612, tel.: (510) 839-0731; e-mail: plee@fyifoundation.org;; Main URL: http://www.stewardshipcouncil.org
Foundation for Youth Investment on Facebook: http://www.facebook.com/FYIorg?ref=ts
Foundation for Youth Investment on Twitter: http://twitter.com/FYIorg
Youth Investment Grants: http://www.fyifoundation.org/grantmaking/awards/C62/2014-grant-fund1

Established in 2004 in CA.
Donor: Pacific Gas and Electric Co.
Foundation type: Company-sponsored foundation.
Financial data (yr. ended 12/31/13): Assets, $56,633,494 (M); gifts received, $37,360; expenditures, $16,286,566; qualifying distributions, $16,217,666; giving activities include $13,633,093 for 48 grants (high: $9,437,000; low: $15,000).
Purpose and activities: The foundation supports watershed land conservation and invests in programs designed to improve the lives of Californian youth through connections with the outdoors.
Fields of interest: Environment, public education; Environment, land resources; Environmental education; Environment; Recreation, parks/playgrounds; Recreation; Boys & girls clubs; Youth development; Children/youth, services; Youth; Economically disadvantaged.
Type of support: General/operating support; Continuing support; Management development/capacity building; Capital campaigns; Program development.
Limitations: Applications accepted. Giving primarily in CA, with emphasis on the metropolitan Bay Area, urban areas of the Central Valley, and rural areas with high rates of poverty. No grants to individuals; no multi-year grants.
Publications: Application guidelines; Program policy statement.
Application information: The Youth Investment Program is administered by the Foundation for Youth Investment. A full proposal for the Youth Investment Program may be requested at a later date.
Initial approach: E-mail letter of inquiry for Youth Investment Program; contact foundation for Enhancement Program
Deadline(s): Dec. 5 for Youth Investment Program; None for Enhancement Program
Officers and Directors:* Art Baggett,* Pres.; Truman Burns,* V.P.; David Muraki,* V.P.; Soapy Mulholland,* V.P.; Randy Livingston,* Secy.; Mike Schonherr, Treas.; Allene Zanger, Exec. Dir.; Lee Adams; Art Bagget, Jr.; Truman Burns; Paul Clanon; DeeDee D'Adamo; Nina Kapoor; John Laird; Karen Mills; Sandra Morey; Larry Myers; Chris Nota; Tim Quinn; Richard Roos-Collins; David Sutton.
EIN: 201358125

1003
Pacific Life Foundation ✧

(formerly Pacific Mutual Charitable Foundation)
700 Newport Center Dr.
Newport Beach, CA 92660-6397 (949) 219-3214
Contact: Tennyson S. Oyler, Pres.
FAX: (949) 719-7614;
E-mail: PLFoundation@PacificLife.com; Main URL: http://www.pacificlife.com/content/content_corp/crp/foundation/overview.html
Grants List: http://www.pacificlife.com/content/dam/paclife_corp/crp/public/about_pacific_life/foundation_community/grant_recipients/PLFFundingasof03312014.pdf

Established in 1984 in CA.
Donors: Pacific Life Insurance Co.; Pacific Mutual Holding Co.
Foundation type: Company-sponsored foundation.
Financial data (yr. ended 12/31/12): Assets, $77,116,278 (M); gifts received, $5,214,270; expenditures, $5,713,258; qualifying distributions, $5,548,637; giving activities include $5,542,000 for 747 grants (high: $1,000,000; low: $50).
Purpose and activities: The foundation supports programs designed to address health and human services; education; arts and culture; and civic, community, and the environment.
Fields of interest: Museums; Performing arts centers; Arts; Elementary/secondary education; Adult education—literacy, basic skills & GED; Education; Environment, natural resources; Environment, water resources; Environmental education; Environment; Dental care; Health care; Mental health/crisis services; Food services; Youth development, adult & child programs; American Red Cross; Children, services; Family services; Homeless, human services; Human services; Civil/human rights, equal rights; Biology/life sciences; Science; Leadership development; Public affairs; Youth; Aging; Economically disadvantaged.
Type of support: General/operating support; Continuing support; Management development/capacity building; Capital campaigns; Equipment;

Program development; Conferences/seminars; Research; Employee matching gifts.
Limitations: Applications accepted. Giving primarily in areas of company operations in the greater Orange County, CA, area and Omaha, NE; giving also to statewide and national organizations. No support for political parties or candidates or partisan political organizations, labor or fraternal organizations, athletic or social clubs, K-12 schools, school districts, or school foundations (except for 3T's of Education), sectarian or denominational religious organizations not of direct benefit to the entire community, or sports leagues or teams. No grants to individuals, or for fundraising events or advertising sponsorships; no in-kind donations.
Publications: Application guidelines; Annual report (including application guidelines); Grants list.
Application information: Capital grants range from $10,0000 to $100,000 and are given to an agency with an organized campaign already under way. Support is limited to 1 contribution per organization during any given year for three years. Organizations must reapply each year. Multi-year funding is not automatic. Audio and video submissions are not accepted. Unsolicited applications for Focus Program Funding and 3T's of Education Program are not accepted. Application form required.
Initial approach: Download application form and mail proposal and application form to foundation
Copies of proposal: 1
Deadline(s): July 15 to Aug. 15
Board meeting date(s): Oct. or Nov.
Final notification: Nov.
Officers and Directors:* James T. Morris,* Chair.; Carol R. Sudbeck,* Vice-Chair.; Tennyson S. Oyler,* Pres.; Michele A. Townsend,* V.P.; Jane M. Guon, Secy.; Joseph L. Tortorelli, Genl. Counsel; Edward R. Byrd, C.F.O.; Thomas D. Billard; David R. Finear; Luther N. Martin, Sr.; Chris van Mierlo; Dawn M. Trautman; Madhu Vijay; Rebecca Warwar.
Number of staff: 2 full-time professional; 1 part-time professional; 1 full-time support.
EIN: 953433806

1004
Pacific Theatres Foundation ✧
120 N. Robertson Blvd., 3rd Fl.
Los Angeles, CA 90048-3102

Established around 1995 in CA.
Donors: Michael R. Forman; Christopher S. Forman; The Decurion Corp.; HI 120 Properties Inc.; Cinerama Inc.
Foundation type: Independent foundation.
Financial data (yr. ended 12/31/13): Assets, $623,500 (M); gifts received, $2,084,151; expenditures, $1,684,076; qualifying distributions, $1,660,695; giving activities include $1,660,535 for 11 grants (high: $1,175,535; low: $10,000).
Fields of interest: Media, film/video; Arts; Secondary school/education; Higher education; Medical school/education; Hospitals (general); Health care; Boys & girls clubs; Jewish agencies & synagogues.
Limitations: Applications not accepted. Giving primarily in CA. No grants to individuals.
Application information: Contributes only to pre-selected organizations.
Officers and Directors:* Christopher S. Forman,* Pres.; Jeff Koblentz, C.F.O. and V.P.; Nora Dashwood, V.P.; Bradley Dreyfus, V.P.; Stephen Green, V.P.; John Manavian, V.P.; Bryan Ungard, V.P.; James D. Vandever, V.P.; Mark Weinstock, V.P.; Jill Saperstein, Secy.; Pascal Coustar, Treas.; Michael R. Forman.
EIN: 954509765

1005
Pacific Youth Foundation ✧
1640 5th St., Ste. 110
Santa Monica, CA 90401-3325 (310) 774-0057
Contact: Allan C. Young, Dir.
E-mail: info@pyfoundation.org; Main URL: http://www.pyfoundation.org

Established in 2008 in CA.
Donor: Wells Fargo Bank.
Foundation type: Independent foundation.
Financial data (yr. ended 12/31/13): Assets, $48,107,853 (M); expenditures, $4,594,580; qualifying distributions, $4,495,982; giving activities include $3,688,569 for 81 grants (high: $300,000; low: $450).
Fields of interest: Boys & girls clubs.
Limitations: Giving in the U.S., with emphasis on CA and GA. No support for programs that do not directly involve youth, staff or board members of a Boys & Girls' Club; Boys & Girls' Clubs that offer fee based programming (any club that charges more than a nominal membership fee), or Boys & Girls' Clubs that receive more than 50 percent of their funding from government support. No grants for multi-year funds.
Publications: Application guidelines.
Application information: Unsolicited grant applications are not accepted. It is requested that only Executive Directors/CPOs contact the foundation. The amount requested from the foundation should appear in the first paragraph of the concept paper in bold and underlined font. The first page of the concept paper should be on organization's letterhead, and proceeding pages should be footnoted with the page number, organization's name, address and the date of submission. Ensure all addendums are labeled with the organization's name. Follow specific concept paper guidelines on foundation web site.
Initial approach: Concept paper (2 pages maximum)
Deadline(s): See foundation web site for current deadline
Directors: Evan McElroy; James D. Shepard; Allan C. Young.
Advising Trustees: Michelle Arellano; Corey Dantzler; Aaron Young.
EIN: 800162835
Selected grants: The following grants are a representative sample of this grantmaker's funding activity:
$300,000 to Boys and Girls Clubs of America, Atlanta, GA, 2011.
$250,000 to Boys and Girls Club of Santa Monica, Santa Monica, CA, 2011.
$150,000 to Boys and Girls Clubs of America, Atlanta, GA, 2011.
$136,000 to Boys and Girls Club of Santa Monica, Santa Monica, CA, 2011.
$97,000 to Boys and Girls Club of Santa Monica, Santa Monica, CA, 2011.
$95,000 to Boys and Girls Club of Fontana, Fontana, CA, 2011.
$88,000 to Boys and Girls Club, Challengers, Los Angeles, CA, 2011.
$62,500 to Boys and Girls Clubs of America, Atlanta, GA, 2011.
$50,000 to Boys and Girls Club of the San Fernando Valley, Pacoima, CA, 2011.
$38,000 to Boys and Girls Club of Santa Clarita Valley, Santa Clarita, CA, 2011.

1006
The David and Lucile Packard Foundation ✧
343 Second St.
Los Altos, CA 94022-3632 (650) 948-7658
Contact: Communications Dept.
E-mail: communications@packard.org; Main URL: http://www.packard.org
Grantee Perception Report: http://www.packard.org/about-the-foundation/how-we-operate-2/grantee-experience/about-grantee-perception-report-content/
Grants Database: http://www.packard.org/what-we-fund/grants-database/
Knowledge Center: http://www.packard.org/about-the-foundation/news/

Incorporated in 1964 in CA.
Donors: David Packard†; Lucile Packard†.
Foundation type: Independent foundation.
Financial data (yr. ended 12/31/13): Assets, $6,902,501,278 (M); expenditures, $360,070,053; qualifying distributions, $339,184,829; giving activities include $293,438,407 for 987 grants (high: $66,100,000; low: $5,000), $1,576,860 for employee matching gifts, $3,506,376 for foundation-administered programs and $17,915,951 for 11 loans/program-related investments (high: $4,951,020; low: $64,931).
Purpose and activities: The David and Lucile Packard Foundation is a family foundation. The foundation works on the issues its founders cared about most: improving the lives of children, enabling the creative pursuit of science, advancing reproductive health, and conserving and restoring the earth's natural systems. The foundation invests in effective organizations and leaders, collaborates with them to identify strategic solutions, and supports them over time to reach its common goals.
Fields of interest: Arts, cultural/ethnic awareness; Museums; Performing arts; Arts; Education, early childhood education; Education; Environment, public education; Environment, natural resources; Environment, energy; Environment, beautification programs; Environment; Animals/wildlife, fisheries; Reproductive health; Reproductive health, family planning; Health care, insurance; Food services; Agriculture/food; Housing/shelter; Youth development; Child development, services; Family services; Civil liberties, reproductive rights; Philanthropy/voluntarism, management/technical assistance; Foundations (private operating); Philanthropy/voluntarism; Marine science; Engineering; Science; Population studies.
International interests: Global Programs; Oceania; Southern Asia; Sub-Saharan Africa.
Type of support: General/operating support; Continuing support; Management development/capacity building; Land acquisition; Program development; Fellowships; Research; Consulting services; Program evaluation; Program-related investments/loans; Employee matching gifts; Matching/challenge support.
Limitations: Applications accepted. Giving for national and international grants, with a special focus on the Northern CA counties of San Mateo, Santa Clara, Santa Cruz, Monterey, and San Benito;

giving also in Pueblo, Colorado. No support for religious or political organizations. No grants to individuals.
Publications: Application guidelines; Annual report; Financial statement; Grants list; Newsletter; Occasional report; Program policy statement; Program policy statement (including application guidelines).
Application information: Review program guidelines online; foundation does not accept proposals for all of their areas of interest. Application form not required.
Initial approach: Proposal or 2- to 3-page letter of inquiry
Copies of proposal: 1
Deadline(s): None
Board meeting date(s): Mar., June, Sept., and Dec.
Final notification: Varies
Officers and Trustees:* Susan Packard Orr,* Chair.; Nancy Packard Burnett,* Vice-Chair.; Julie E. Packard,* Vice-Chair.; Carol S. Larson,* C.E.O. and Pres.; Chris DeCardy, V.P. and Dir., Progs.; Craig Neyman, V.P. and C.F.O.; John H. Moehling, C.I.O.; Mary Anne Rodgers, Secy. and Genl. Counsel; Edward W. Barnholt; Ipek S. Burnett; Jason K. Burnett; Linda Griego; Michael J. Klag; Jane Lubchenco; Linda A. Mason; David Orr; Louise Stephens; Ward W. Woods.
Number of staff: 56 full-time professional; 3 part-time professional; 36 full-time support; 5 part-time support.
EIN: 942278431
Selected grants: The following grants are a representative sample of this grantmaker's funding activity:
$66,100,000 to ClimateWorks Foundation, San Francisco, CA, 2013. For general support of the ClimateWorks Foundation's work to help reduce global greenhouse gas emissions and avert climate change.
$38,209,855 to Monterey Bay Aquarium Research Institute, Moss Landing, CA, 2013. For operating support, research projects, and ordinary capital support.
$10,000,000 to Monterey Bay Aquarium Foundation, Monterey, CA, 2013. For general support, payable over 5.00 years.
$2,100,000 to Institute of International Education, New York, NY, 2013. For the Technical Assistance Program in South Asia and Sub-Saharan Africa.
$2,100,000 to Resources Legacy Fund, Sacramento, CA, 2013. For the sixth and final year of grantmaking activities under the Northwest Mexico Land Conservation Program of Resources Legacy Fund.
$1,000,000 to Tides Center, San Francisco, CA, 2013. For Communications Partnership for Science and the Sea (COMPASS).
$875,000 to University of California, Berkeley, CA, 2013. For 2013 Packard Fellowship for Felix Fischer, Department of Chemistry, payable over 5.00 years.
$170,000 to Planned Parenthood Education Fund, California, Sacramento, CA, 2013. For general support.
$110,220 to BirdLife International, Cambridge, England, 2013. For Indian Ocean Tuna Commission seabird bycatch workshop and a study of gillnet bycatch mitigation methods.
$100,000 to ONeill Sea Odyssey, Santa Cruz, CA, 2013. For environmental education classes over two years through 5/31/15, payable over 2.00 years.

1007
The Packard Humanities Institute ✧
300 2nd St.
Los Altos, CA 94022-3694
Main URL: http://www.packhum.org

Established in 1987 in CA.
Donor: The David and Lucile Packard Foundation.
Foundation type: Operating foundation.
Financial data (yr. ended 12/31/13): Assets, $783,387,957 (M); expenditures, $19,532,394; qualifying distributions, $85,785,135; giving activities include $8,113,260 for 26 grants (high: $1,300,000; low: $20,000), and $76,437,008 for 4 foundation-administered programs.
Purpose and activities: Giving primarily for archeology, music, film preservation, historic conservation, and early education.
Fields of interest: Media, film/video; Performing arts, music; History/archaeology; Historic preservation/historical societies; Arts; Education, early childhood education; Education; Human services.
Limitations: Applications not accepted. Giving primarily in CA. No grants to individuals.
Application information: Contributes only to pre-selected organizations.
Officers and Directors:* David W. Packard,* Chair. and Pres.; Susan Packard Orr,* V.P.; Barbara P. Wright, Secy.; Alberta Astras, C.F.O. and Treas.; G. Gervaise Davis III; Walter B. Hewlett; Richard Hodges; William A. Johnson; Arianna Packard Martell; Pamela M. Packard; Woodley Packard; Christoph J. Wolff.
EIN: 943038401
Selected grants: The following grants are a representative sample of this grantmaker's funding activity:
$1,250,000 to Internationale Stiftung Mozarteum, Mozart Institute, Salzburg, Austria, 2012. For staff salaries and general expenses of Digital Mozart Edition.
$1,014,900 to British School at Rome, Rome, Italy, 2012. For conservation of ancient Roman town of Herculaneum.
$1,000,000 to British School at Rome, Rome, Italy, 2012. For conservation of ancient Roman town of Herculaneum.
$720,000 to Internationale Stiftung Mozarteum, Salzburg, Austria, 2012. For staff salaries and general expenses of Digital Mozart Edition.
$560,000 to British School at Rome, Rome, Italy, 2012. For Herculaneum Conservation Project work at basilica area near Via Mare.
$556,300 to University of Texas, Austin, TX, 2012. For archaeological research at Metaponto and Croton, Italy and Chersonesos, Ukraine.
$550,000 to Butrint Foundation, London, England, 2012. For activities of Albanian Heritage Foundation and Gjirokastra Conservation and Development Organization.
$394,000 to University of Western Australia, Perth, Australia, 2012. For Aerial Photographic Archive for Archaeology in the Middle East.
$317,500 to American School of Classical Studies at Athens, Princeton, NJ, 2012. For excavations in the ancient Agora (marketplace) of Athens.
$225,000 to Stanford Theater Foundation, Los Altos, CA, 2012. For general operating support.

1008
Beatrix Finston Padway Charitable Trust for the Arts and Education ✧
1529 Gilcrest Dr.
Beverly Hills, CA 90210-2515

Established in 2002 in CA.
Donors: Beatrix Finston Padway; Padway Survivor's Trust.
Foundation type: Independent foundation.
Financial data (yr. ended 12/31/12): Assets, $10,733,325 (M); expenditures, $643,137; qualifying distributions, $464,700; giving activities include $464,700 for grants.
Fields of interest: Arts; Secondary school/education; Higher education; Health organizations; Human services; Christian agencies & churches.
Limitations: Applications not accepted. Giving primarily in CA. No grants to individuals.
Application information: Contributes only to pre-selected organizations.
Trustee: Roberta L. Weintraub.
EIN: 316018432

1009
The Carl Victor Page Memorial Foundation ✧
2200 Geng Rd., Ste. 100
Palo Alto, CA 94303-3358 (650) 210-5000

Established in 2004 in CA.
Donor: Lawrence Page.
Foundation type: Independent foundation.
Financial data (yr. ended 12/31/13): Assets, $1,119,754,597 (M); gifts received, $308,121,875; expenditures, $41,460,524; qualifying distributions, $40,391,393; giving activities include $40,355,326 for 4 grants (high: $20,254,320; low: $6).
Fields of interest: Environment; Human services.
Limitations: Applications not accepted. Giving primarily in Boston, MA. No grants to individuals.
Application information: Contributes only to pre-selected organizations.
Officers and Directors:* Lawrence Page,* Chair. and Pres.; Lucinda Southworth Page, Secy. and C.F.O.; Gloria Page.
EIN: 201922957
Selected grants: The following grants are a representative sample of this grantmaker's funding activity:
$29,010,080 to Vanguard Charitable Endowment Program, Boston, MA, 2012. For general operating support.

1010
The Panda Charitable Foundation ✧
1683 Walnut Grove Ave.
Rosemead, CA 91770-3711 (626) 372-9898
Contact: Winnie Chan, Mgr.

Changed status to a company-sponsored operating foundation in 1999.
Donors: Panda Management Co., Inc.; Panda Restaurant Group, Inc.
Foundation type: Operating foundation.
Financial data (yr. ended 12/31/12): Assets, $3,484,787 (M); gifts received, $6,697,360; expenditures, $6,280,829; qualifying distributions, $6,149,447; giving activities include $6,149,447 for 29 grants (high: $3,250,000; low: $1,000).

Purpose and activities: The foundation supports museums and organizations involved with Asian culture, disaster relief, leadership development, and Buddhism. Special emphasis is directed toward the educational and medical assistance of children.
Fields of interest: Arts, cultural/ethnic awareness; Museums; Higher education; Education; Hospitals (general); Health care; Disasters, preparedness/services; American Red Cross; Children, services; Leadership development; Buddhism; Children; Asians/Pacific Islanders.
Type of support: General/operating support; Program development.
Limitations: Applications accepted. Giving primarily in CA.
Application information: Application form not required.
Initial approach: Letter of inquiry
Deadline(s): None
Trustee: Andrew Cherng.
EIN: 954142346

1011
Paramitas Foundation ✧
P.O. Box 2699
Saratoga, CA 95070-0699

Established in 1992 in CA.
Donor: Winston H. Chen.
Foundation type: Operating foundation.
Financial data (yr. ended 12/31/13): Assets, $33,479,416 (M); expenditures, $1,107,520; qualifying distributions, $1,107,520; giving activities include $1,038,000 for 22 grants (high: $350,000; low: $2,500).
Purpose and activities: Giving primarily for higher education, and to Buddhist temples and societies, as well as to organizations that aid Taiwanese-Americans.
Fields of interest: Education; Buddhism.
Limitations: Applications not accepted. Giving primarily in CA. No grants to individuals.
Application information: Contributes only to pre-selected organizations.
Officers: Winston H. Chen, Chair.; Phyllis Huang, C.F.O.; Alex Chen, Secy.
EIN: 770295773

1012
The Parker Foundation ✧
2604-B El Camino Real, Ste. 244
Carlsbad, CA 92008-1214 (760) 720-0630
Contact: Robbin C. Powell, C.A.O.
FAX: (760) 720-1239; Main URL: http://www.TheParkerFoundation.org

Trust established in 1971 in CA; incorporated in 1975.
Donors: Gerald T. Parker†; Inez Grant Parker†.
Foundation type: Independent foundation.
Financial data (yr. ended 09/30/13): Assets, $41,231,583 (M); expenditures, $2,306,579; qualifying distributions, $2,086,595; giving activities include $1,937,824 for 84 grants (high: $65,000; low: $1,000).
Purpose and activities: Equal emphasis on cultural programs, health and welfare, including medical support and research, adult services, and youth agencies; grants also for education and community activities. Giving largely in the form of partial seed money and matching or challenge grants; generally no support that would make an organization dependent on the foundation.
Fields of interest: Visual arts; Museums; Performing arts; Arts; Education; Environment; Health care; Children/youth, services; Community/economic development.
Type of support: General/operating support; Continuing support; Annual campaigns; Building/renovation; Equipment; Land acquisition; Emergency funds; Program development; Publication; Seed money; Research; Matching/challenge support.
Limitations: Giving limited to San Diego County, CA. No support for sectarian religious purposes. No grants to individuals, or for endowment funds, conferences, symposia, scholarships, or fellowships; no loans.
Publications: Application guidelines; Annual report; Financial statement; Grants list.
Application information: Application guidelines available on foundation web site: http://www.theparkerfoundation.org. Application form not required.
Initial approach: See web site
Copies of proposal: 1
Deadline(s): See web site for current deadlines
Board meeting date(s): Varies, see web site
Final notification: 2 months
Officers: Judy McDonald, Pres.; William E. Beamer, V.P.; Mark C. Trotter, Secy.; Ann Davies, Treas.
Directors: Ernest Borunda; Raymond Ellis; Mary Herron; Gordon Swanson.
Directors Emeritus: V. DeWitt Shuck; Paul Mosher.
EIN: 510141231
Selected grants: The following grants are a representative sample of this grantmaker's funding activity:
$125,000 to Zoological Society of San Diego, San Diego, CA, 2011.
$75,000 to San Diego Museum of Art, San Diego, CA, 2011.
$60,000 to Corporation for Supportive Housing, New York, NY, 2011.
$50,000 to San Diego State University Foundation, San Diego, CA, 2011.
$30,000 to San Diego Blood Bank Foundation, San Diego, CA, 2011.
$30,000 to Social Advocates for Youth, Santa Rosa, CA, 2011.
$25,000 to San Diego Center for Children Foundation, San Diego, CA, 2011.
$25,000 to San Diego Workforce Partnership, San Diego, CA, 2011.
$15,000 to San Diego Adaptive Sports Foundation, San Diego, CA, 2011.
$10,000 to San Diego Human Dignity Foundation, San Diego, CA, 2011.

1013
The Ralph M. Parsons Foundation ✧
888 W. 6th St., Ste. 700
Los Angeles, CA 90017-2733 (213) 362-7600
Contact: Wendy Garen, C.E.O. and Pres.
Main URL: http://www.parsonsfoundation.org
Grants Database: http://www.rmpf.org/GrantDatabase.html

Incorporated in 1961 in CA.
Donor: Ralph M. Parsons†.
Foundation type: Independent foundation.
Financial data (yr. ended 12/31/13): Assets, $409,333,132 (M); expenditures, $27,385,260; qualifying distributions, $21,252,723; giving activities include $19,297,919 for 324 grants (high: $500,000; low: $2,500).
Purpose and activities: Since 1978, the foundation's grantmaking has helped Southern California nonprofit organizations improve the broad fabric of the entire community. This approach recognizes that museums and arts programs are as important to our collective well-being as after school services, community clinics and food banks. Accordingly, the foundation invests in excellence in social services, health care, the arts and higher education in Los Angeles County. The foundation is a responsive grantmaker. It has always invited local organizations to come to it for what they need to do their best work. This includes core operating support, which is a powerful way to help nonprofits struggling to fulfill their missions in hard economic times.It's not that the foundation does not fund capital campaigns, equipment purchases, and staff positions, because it does. It simply encourage carefully considered requests for top organizational priorities.
Fields of interest: Arts, alliance/advocacy; Arts education; Museums; Performing arts; Arts, services; Education, early childhood education; Secondary school/education; Higher education; Education; Health care; Legal services; Housing/shelter, development; Youth development, centers/clubs; Human services; Children/youth, services; Family services; Aging, centers/services; Homeless, human services; Community/economic development; Science; Children/youth; Youth; Economically disadvantaged; Homeless.
Type of support: General/operating support; Capital campaigns; Building/renovation; Equipment; Program development; Seed money; Fellowships; Internship funds; Scholarship funds; Research; Technical assistance; Matching/challenge support.
Limitations: Applications accepted. Giving limited to organizations providing services in Los Angeles County, CA. No support for sectarian, religious, or fraternal purposes, or for political organizations. No grants to individuals, or for annual campaigns, fundraising events, dinners, mass mailings, workshops, federated fundraising appeals, seminars, conferences; no loans.
Publications: Biennial report; Grants list; Informational brochure.
Application information: If review of the LOI results in a decision to explore specifics of the grant request in more detail, applicant will be asked to submit a full proposal. Guidance on how to prepare a complete request will be provided in writing. As part of the subsequent review, applicant will probably be contacted by a program officer. Application form not required.
Initial approach: Letter of inquiry, no more than three pages
Copies of proposal: 1
Deadline(s): None. Applications considered in order of receipt
Board meeting date(s): Five times a year
Final notification: 3 months for full proposal and six weeks for letter of intent
Officers and Directors:* Franklin E. Ulf,* Chair.; James A. Thomas,* Vice-Chair.; Wendy Garen, C.E.O. and Pres.; Astra Anderson Galang, C.F.O.; Angelica K. Clark, C.I.O.; William Bamattre; Linda M. Griego; Karen Hill-Scott; Elizabeth Lowe; Walter B. Rose*; Robert E. Tranquada, M.D.; Gayle Wilson.
Number of staff: 5 full-time professional; 3 full-time support.
EIN: 956085895

Selected grants: The following grants are a representative sample of this grantmaker's funding activity:
$1,500,000 to Los Angeles County Museum of Natural History Foundation, Los Angeles, CA, 2012. For a capital campaign, payable over 3.00 years.
$1,000,000 to Art Center College of Design, Pasadena, CA, 2012. Toward the acquisition of property to enable the expansion of the South Campus, payable over 3.00 years.
$750,000 to Martin Luther King Jr Community Health Foundation, Los Angeles, CA, 2013. For over two years toward construction of the expanded Maternity Center at the new Martin Luther King, Jr. Hospital, payable over 2.00 years.
$500,000 to Otis College of Art and Design, Los Angeles, CA, 2013. For over two years for campus expansion, payable over 2.00 years.
$500,000 to Volunteers of America of Los Angeles, Los Angeles, CA, 2013. For over two years for capital support, payable over 2.00 years.
$400,000 to Occidental College, Los Angeles, CA, 2013. For the restoration and expansion of Johnson Hall.
$300,000 to Pomona College, Claremont Colleges, Claremont, CA, 2013. For over three years toward construction of a new Studio Art Center, payable over 3.00 years.
$250,000 to Child Welfare Initiative, Los Angeles, CA, 2012. For general support of this project serving children and families in the child welfare system, payable over 2.00 years.
$250,000 to Saint Annes Maternity Home, Los Angeles, CA, 2013. For over two years for general support, payable over 2.00 years.
$200,000 to Beit TShuvah, Los Angeles, CA, 2012. For capital campaign, payable over 2.00 years.
$140,000 to Program for Torture Victims, Los Angeles, CA, 2012. For general support, payable over 2.00 years.
$50,000 to Alliance for Housing and Healing, Los Angeles, CA, 2012. For general support.
$50,000 to Amanecer Community Counseling Services, Los Angeles, CA, 2012. For postpartum depression and domestic violence counseling services.
$50,000 to Boys and Girls Club of the West Valley, Canoga Park, CA, 2012. For Project Learn, after-school academic advancement program.
$50,000 to Direct Relief International, Santa Barbara, CA, 2013. For Safety-Net Support Program.
$50,000 to Harbor Free Clinic, San Pedro, CA, 2012. For general support.
$50,000 to Madison Project, Santa Monica, CA, 2013. For general support.
$50,000 to MUSE/IQUE, Pasadena, CA, 2012. For general support, payable over 2.00 years.
$50,000 to Santa Anita Family Service, Monrovia, CA, 2013. For over two years for a development staff position, payable over 2.00 years.
$50,000 to Synergy Academies, Los Angeles, CA, 2013. For general support.

1014
Partners for Developing Futures, Inc. ✧
850 Colorado Blvd., Ste. 203
Los Angeles, CA 90041-1733 (877) 516-8076
FAX: (323) 739-3697;
E-mail: partners@partnersdevelopingfutures.org; Main URL: http://www.partnersdevelopingfutures.org/

Established in 2008 in DE.
Foundation type: Operating foundation.
Financial data (yr. ended 12/31/12): Assets, $2,166,474 (M); gifts received, $1,497,500; expenditures, $1,973,849; qualifying distributions, $1,919,986; giving activities include $1,300,000 for 13 grants (high: $200,000; low: $5,000).
Fields of interest: Charter schools.
Limitations: Giving in the U.S., with some emphasis on CA.
Application information: The foundation is not accepting investment applications at this time. Please check foundation web site for news regarding the application process.
Initial approach: Letter of interest
Deadline(s): Varies
Officer and Directors:* Ref Rodriguez, Ed.D.*, C.E.O. and Pres.; Angela Bass, Ed.D., V.P.; Howard Fuller, Ph.D.; Peter Groff; Delia Pompa.
Advisory Board: Mashea Ashton; Michelle Bullock; Mike Feinberg; Diane Robinson; Johnathan Williams; Ursula Wright; Andrea Zayas.
EIN: 262045125

1015
Pasadena Community Foundation ✧
(formerly Pasadena Foundation)
301 E. Colorado Blvd., Ste. 810
Pasadena, CA 91101 (626) 796-2097
Contact: Jennifer Fleming DeVoll, Exec. Dir.
FAX: (626) 583-4738;
E-mail: pcfstaff@pasadenacf.org; Additional E-mail: jdevoll@pasadenacf.org; Main URL: http://www.pasadenacf.org
Facebook: https://www.facebook.com/pages/Pasadena-Community-Foundation/349231191832761

Established in 1953 in CA by resolution and declaration of trust; in 2003, reorganized as a nonprofit public benefit corporation.
Donors: Louis A. Webb†; Marion L. Webb†; Helen B. Lockett†; Dorothy I. Stewart†; Rebecca R. Anthony†; Lucille Crumb†; Cornelia Eaton†; Ralph Norrington†; Margaret Norrington†; Ella C. Price†; Orrin K. Earl†; Jean Hubbard†.
Foundation type: Community foundation.
Financial data (yr. ended 12/31/13): Assets, $45,450,358 (M); gifts received, $9,023,417; expenditures, $5,841,658; giving activities include $5,098,252 for 132+ grants (high: $750,000).
Purpose and activities: The foundation serves as a leader, catalyst, and resource for philanthropy in order to improve the lives of people in the greater Pasadena area, now and for future generations. To fulfill this mission, the foundation: 1) fosters, builds and preserves permanently endowed charitable funds; 2) provides grants and assistance to nurture and strengthen community organizations; 3) promotes and participates in community partnerships; 4) serves donors to meet their philanthropic goals.
Fields of interest: Humanities; Arts; Education; Environment; Health care; Children/youth, services; Family services; Human services; Community/economic development; Youth; Aging; Disabilities, people with.
Type of support: Capital campaigns; Building/renovation; Equipment.
Limitations: Applications accepted. Giving limited to the Altadena, Pasadena, and Sierra Madre, CA, areas. No support for private foundations, or for educational institutions or sectarian organizations (except for social service programs sponsored by educational institutions or sectarian organizations). No grants to individuals (except for scholarships), or for continuing support, debt retirement, general or operating support, expenses incurred in performance of program services, or elections.
Publications: Application guidelines; Annual report; Financial statement; Informational brochure; Newsletter.
Application information: Visit foundation web site for application forms and guidelines. Eligible organizations must be at least 2 years old. Application form required.
Initial approach: Submit grant application and attachments
Copies of proposal: 16
Deadline(s): Feb. 6
Board meeting date(s): Quarterly
Final notification: Late Apr.
Officers and Directors:* David Davis,* Chair.; Judy Gain,* Vice-Chair.; Jennifer Fleming DeVoll, Exec. Dir.; Ann Dobson Barrett; Rita Diaz; Lois Matthews; Peter McAniff; Margaret Mgrublian; Wendy Munger; Eddie Newman; Corene L. Pindroh; Michael D. Schneickert; Fran Scoble; Les Stocker; Philip V. Swan; Michelle Tyson, M.D.
Number of staff: 2 full-time professional; 1 full-time support.
EIN: 200253310

1016
Passport Foundation ✧
1 Market St., Ste. 2200
Steuart Tower
San Francisco, CA 94105-1420

Established in 2007 in NC.
Foundation type: Independent foundation.
Financial data (yr. ended 12/31/12): Assets, $27,020,330 (M); gifts received, $518,821; expenditures, $2,214,924; qualifying distributions, $1,843,131; giving activities include $1,580,830 for 68 grants (high: $200,000; low: $100).
Fields of interest: Education; Environment; Health care; Foundations (private grantmaking).
Limitations: Applications not accepted. Giving primarily in CA, Washington, DC and VA.
Application information: Contributes only to pre-selected organizations.
Officers and Directors:* John H. Burbank III,* Pres.; Michele Clifford, Secy.; Joanne Cormican,* Treas.; Jim Cunningham; Walther Lovato.
EIN: 261580196
Selected grants: The following grants are a representative sample of this grantmaker's funding activity:
$200,000 to Natural Resources Defense Council, New York, NY, 2011. For Chemical Policy Reform.
$150,000 to Breast Cancer Fund, San Francisco, CA, 2011. For general support.
$150,000 to Environmental Defense Fund, Washington, DC, 2011. To educate decision makers and citizens about chemicals policy reform.
$100,000 to TechnoServe, Norwalk, CT, 2011. To increase incomes of Women Shea Butter Producers in Ghana.
$75,000 to Environmental Defense Fund, Washington, DC, 2010.
$75,000 to Natural Resources Defense Council, New York, NY, 2010.
$75,000 to Tides Center, San Francisco, CA, 2010.
$75,000 to University of California, San Francisco, CA, 2010.

$50,000 to Breast Cancer Fund, San Francisco, CA, 2010.
$50,000 to Commonweal, Bolinas, CA, 2010.
$50,000 to Environmental Working Group, Washington, DC, 2011. To educate consumers about chemicals and health.
$50,000 to Health Care Without Harm, Reston, VA, 2011. For Healthy Hospitals Initiative.
$50,000 to Icahn School of Medicine at Mount Sinai, New York, NY, 2011. For environmental chemical exposure in neonatal intensive care unit.
$45,000 to University of Missouri, Columbia, MO, 2010.
$40,840 to University of California, San Francisco, CA, 2011. For phthalate mixtures in early pregnancy and effects on placental-fetal interactions.
$40,000 to Western States Center, Portland, OR, 2011. For MomsRising to Expand Environmental Health Program.
$30,000 to Commonweal, Bolinas, CA, 2011. For Collaborative on Health and the Environment (CHE).
$25,000 to Tufts University, Medford, MA, 2010.
$21,700 to Breast Cancer Fund, San Francisco, CA, 2010.
$15,000 to Hedge Funds Care, New York, NY, 2010.

1017
Patagonia.org ✧
c/o Moss Adams LLP
P.O. Box 24950
Los Angeles, CA 90024-0950
Contact for World Trout Initiative: Bill Klyn, bill_klyn@patagonia.com; Main URL: http://www.patagonia.com/us/patagonia.go?assetid=2927
Grants List: http://www.patagonia.com/us/patagonia.go?assetid=80551

Established in 2008 in CA.
Donor: Patagonia, Inc.
Foundation type: Company-sponsored foundation.
Financial data (yr. ended 04/30/13): Assets, $6,023,191 (M); gifts received, $6,000,000; expenditures, $5,987,569; qualifying distributions, $5,974,666; giving activities include $5,969,904 for 570 grants (high: $1,170,000; low: $150).
Purpose and activities: The foundation supports programs designed to preserve and promote the environment. Special emphasis is directed toward protecting and restoring native fish populations and the habitat on which they depend.
Fields of interest: Environment, natural resources; Environment, water resources; Environment; Animals/wildlife, fisheries; Public affairs, citizen participation.
Type of support: General/operating support.
Limitations: Applications accepted. Giving primarily in CA, CO, MT, NY, and WY. No grants for general environmental education efforts, land acquisition, land trusts, or conservation easements, research (unless it's in direct support of a developed pan to alleviate an environmental problem), environmental conferences, endowments, political campaigns, or green building projects.
Publications: Application guidelines.
Application information: Applications are reviewed by local store employees or the Grants Council at Patagonia headquarters. Grants of up to $12,000 are awarded. Support is limited to 1 contribution per organization during any given year.
Initial approach: Complete online application
Deadline(s): Apr. 30 and Aug. 31
Final notification: Aug. and Jan.

Officers and Directors: Casey Sheahan, Pres.; Rose Marcario, C.F.O.; Hilary Dessouky, Secy.; Malinda P. Chouinard; Yvon Chouinard.
EIN: 142004175

1018
Ravi and Naina Patel Foundation ✧
(formerly Shree Krishna Karuna Foundation)
6501 Truxtun Ave.
Bakersfield, CA 93309-0633 (661) 322-2206
Contact: Pradip Shah

Established in 1998 in CA.
Donors: Ravi Patel, M.D., Inc.; Arun Keni, M.D.; Susan Dillbeck; Michael Dillbeck; Levin Foundation.
Foundation type: Independent foundation.
Financial data (yr. ended 12/31/12): Assets, $10,939,261 (M); gifts received, $86,531; expenditures, $712,883; qualifying distributions, $611,580; giving activities include $611,500 for 8 grants (high: $493,880; low: $500).
Purpose and activities: Giving to raise cancer awareness, including early detection, and to fund cancer research, in India.
Fields of interest: Cancer; Cancer research; Economically disadvantaged.
International interests: India.
Limitations: Applications accepted. Giving primarily in CA, IA and in India. No grants to individuals.
Application information: Application form required.
Initial approach: Letter
Deadline(s): None
Officers: Ravi Patel, Pres.; Naina Patel, V.P.
EIN: 770490360

1019
Pathways in Education, Inc. ✧ ☆
320 N. Halstead St., Ste. 210
Pasadena, CA 91107-3147
Main URL: http://pathwaysedu.org/

Donor: Opportunities for Learning Charters.
Foundation type: Independent foundation.
Financial data (yr. ended 06/30/13): Assets, $5,777,607 (M); gifts received, $462,015; expenditures, $9,042,937; qualifying distributions, $10,449,290; giving activities include $7,870,000 for 2 grants (high: $7,370,000; low: $500,000), $87,586 for grants to individuals, and $8,963,296 for foundation-administered programs.
Fields of interest: Scholarships/financial aid; Education; Human services.
Limitations: Applications not accepted. Giving primarily in Pasadena and San Marco, CA.
Application information: Unsolicited requests for funds not accepted.
Officers: Jamie Hall, Pres. and Exec.Dir.; Joan Hall, V.P.; John Hall, V.P.; Jodi Hall, Secy.; John Hall, Jr., Treas.
Directors: Phil Jordan; Pete Lakey; Bobbi Newman.
EIN: 020541020
Selected grants: The following grants are a representative sample of this grantmaker's funding activity:
$87,586 to California State University, San Marcos, CA, 2013. For financial assistance for university level courses.

1020
The Patron Saints Foundation ✧
260 S. Los Robles Ave., Ste. 201
Pasadena, CA 91101-3614
Contact: Kathleen T. Shannon, Exec. Dir.
E-mail: patronsaintsfdn@sbcglobal.net; Tel./fax: (626) 564-0444; Main URL: http://www.patronsaintsfoundation.org

Established in 1986 in CA.
Donors: Rose Trust; St. Luke Medical Staff; Friends of St. Luke.
Foundation type: Independent foundation.
Financial data (yr. ended 06/30/13): Assets, $10,985,461 (M); expenditures, $659,255; qualifying distributions, $584,786; giving activities include $450,856 for 29 grants (high: $36,356; low: $5,000).
Purpose and activities: The foundation provides grants to public charities that improve the health of individuals residing in the West San Gabriel Valley through healthcare programs that are consistent with the moral and religious teachings of the Roman Catholic Church.
Fields of interest: Medicine/medical care, public education; Health care, government agencies; Health care, formal/general education; Medical care, community health systems; Hospitals (general); Hospitals (specialty); Medical care, outpatient care; Health care, clinics/centers; Health care, infants; Dental care; Medical care, rehabilitation; Speech/hearing centers; Health care, support services; Pharmacy/prescriptions; Public health; Health care; Health care, patient services; Nursing care; Health care; Substance abuse, services; Mental health/crisis services; Medical research; Infants/toddlers; Children/youth; Children; Youth; Adults; Aging; Young adults; Disabilities, people with; Physically disabled; Blind/visually impaired; Deaf/hearing impaired; Mentally disabled; Minorities; Women; Infants/toddlers, female; Girls; Adults, women; Young adults, female; Men; Infants/toddlers, male; Boys; Adults, men; Young adults, male; Substance abusers; AIDS, people with; Single parents; Economically disadvantaged; Homeless.
Type of support: General/operating support; Continuing support; Capital campaigns; Building/renovation; Equipment; Research.
Limitations: Applications accepted. Giving limited to Alhambra, Arcadia, Duarte, El Monte, La Canada Flintridge, Monrovia, Monterey Park, Pasadena, Rosemead, San Gabriel, San Marino, Sierra Madre, South El Monte, South Pasadena, Temple City, and unincorporated areas of Los Angeles, known as Altadena and South San Gabriel, CA, along with the unincorporated portions of Los Angeles County bounded by these areas. No support for political or fundraising activities, or for programs unrelated to health care. No grants to individuals, or for endowment funds, travel, or surveys.
Publications: Application guidelines; Grants list; Informational brochure.
Application information: Application forms and guidelines available on foundation web site. A completed H.R. 4 Self-Certification form and a signed accountability statement are required with proposal submission. Application form required.
Initial approach: 3-page proposal
Copies of proposal: 2
Deadline(s): 1st Fri. in Mar. and 1st Fri. in Oct.
Board meeting date(s): Mid-May and early Dec.
Final notification: May and mid-Dec.

Officers and Directors:* Margaret Landry,* Pres.; Britt McConnell, Pres.-Elect.; Kathryn Meagher,* Secy.; Charles Carroll,* Treas.; Kathleen T. Shannon, Exec. Dir.; Thomas Collins; James Gamb; James Graunke; Bryan Herrmann; Susan Kane, Ph.D.; Margaret Landry; Nathan Lewis, M.D.; Nan Okum; Sarah Orth; Comm. John Perez; Joseph W. Skeehan; Debra Spiegel.
Number of staff: 1 part-time professional.
EIN: 953484257

1021
L. Robert & Patricia L. Payne Family Foundation Inc. ✧
1011 Camino del Rio S., Ste. 210
San Diego, CA 92108-3533

Established in 2000 in CA.
Donors: L. Robert Payne; Patricia L. Payne; Sharon L. Payne.
Foundation type: Independent foundation.
Financial data (yr. ended 12/31/13): Assets, $4,033,439 (M); gifts received, $2,209,281; expenditures, $801,032; qualifying distributions, $783,377; giving activities include $783,377 for 31 grants (high: $400,000; low: $55).
Fields of interest: Arts; Education; Health care; Medical research, institute; Children/youth, services; Children/youth; Children; Adults.
Type of support: Capital campaigns; Endowments; Program development; Curriculum development.
Limitations: Applications not accepted. Giving primarily in San Diego County, CA.
Application information: Contributes only to pre-selected organizations.
Officers: L. Robert Payne, Pres.; Sharon L. Payne, C.F.O. and Treas.; Susan M. Payne, Secy.
Number of staff: None.
EIN: 330923365
Selected grants: The following grants are a representative sample of this grantmaker's funding activity:
$365 to YMCA of San Diego County, San Diego, CA, 2012. For public television.
$100 to Sharp Healthcare Foundation, San Diego, CA, 2012. For Medical Care and Research.
$75 to Disabled American Veterans, Cold Spring, KY, 2012. For veterans Programs.

1022
Peery Foundation ✧
2450 Watson Ct.
Palo Alto, CA 94303-3216 (650) 644-4660
Contact: David Peery, V.P.
FAX: (650) 618-7810;
E-mail: dave@peeryfoundation.org; Main URL: http://www.peeryfoundation.org
Blog: http://www.peeryfoundation.org/pfwhiteboard
Facebook: https://www.facebook.com/peeryfoundation
Flickr: http://www.flickr.com/photos/peeryfoundation
Pinterest: http://www.pinterest.com/peeryfoundation/
Twitter: http://twitter.com/peeryfoundation
YouTube: http://www.youtube.com/user/peeryfoundation

Established in 1978.
Donor: Richard T. Peery.
Foundation type: Independent foundation.
Financial data (yr. ended 12/31/13): Assets, $47,953,215 (M); expenditures, $2,854,979; qualifying distributions, $2,503,321; giving activities include $2,503,321 for 41 grants (high: $250,000; low: $500).
Purpose and activities: The mission of the Peery Foundation is to strengthen youth and families to build lives of dignity and self-reliance. The foundation does this by investing in social entrepreneurs in the San Francisco Bay Area and around the world. The foundation has three portfolios of grantees: local, regional, and global. Local: focusing on building the capacity of at-risk youth in East Palo Alto. Regional: funding early to mid-stage entrepreneurs as they scale their programs throughout the bay and beyond. Also providing expansion funds for proven programs from around the country which are growing into the Bay Area. Global: investing in market-based approaches to poverty which create opportunities for youth and families around the world.
Fields of interest: Youth development; Social entrepreneurship; Community/economic development; Science; Children/youth; Youth; Women; Girls; Economically disadvantaged.
Type of support: General/operating support; Income development; Management development/capacity building; Program development; Film/video/radio; Seed money; Technical assistance; Program evaluation; Program-related investments/loans.
Limitations: Applications not accepted. Giving primarily in the San Francisco Bay Area, CA some international giving. No grants to individuals.
Application information: Contributes only to pre-selected organizations; unsolicited proposals not accepted.
Directors: David Peery; Dennis T. Peery; Jason Peery; Jennifer Peery; Mimi Peery; Richard T. Peery.
EIN: 942460894

1023
Pell Family Foundation ✧
100 Smith Ranch Rd., Ste. 325
San Rafael, CA 94903-1994
Contact: Eda Pell, Pres.

Established in 1991 in CA.
Donors: Joseph Pell; Eda Pell.
Foundation type: Independent foundation.
Financial data (yr. ended 12/31/13): Assets, $20,406,633 (M); gifts received, $1,000,000; expenditures, $847,622; qualifying distributions, $832,200; giving activities include $832,200 for 55 grants (high: $107,500; low: $100).
Purpose and activities: Funding primarily for education and Jewish agencies.
Fields of interest: Arts, cultural/ethnic awareness; Arts; Education; Jewish agencies & synagogues.
Type of support: General/operating support.
Limitations: Applications accepted. Giving primarily in CA.
Application information: Application form required.
Initial approach: Letter on official letterhead
Deadline(s): None
Officers: Eda Pell, Pres.; Joseph Pell, V.P.
EIN: 680262734
Selected grants: The following grants are a representative sample of this grantmaker's funding activity:
$50,000 to Jewish Community Federation, 2010.
$50,000 to University of California, Berkeley, CA, 2011.
$25,000 to Jewish Family and Childrens Services, 2010.
$25,000 to Lehrhaus Judaica, Berkeley, CA, 2010.
$15,600 to Congregation Rodef Shalom, Denver, CO, 2010.
$15,000 to Hampshire College, Amherst, MA, 2010.
$10,000 to San Jose State University, San Jose, CA, 2011.
$5,000 to Chronicle Season of Sharing Fund, San Francisco, CA, 2011.
$1,000 to California Academy of Sciences, San Francisco, CA, 2011.

1024
The Ann Peppers Foundation ✧
625 S. Fair Oaks Ave., Ste. 360
South Pasadena, CA 91030-5813
E-mail for Mary Tran: mtran@whittiertrust.com

Established in 1959 in CA.
Donor: Ann Peppers†.
Foundation type: Independent foundation.
Financial data (yr. ended 12/31/13): Assets, $23,500,726 (M); expenditures, $1,251,575; qualifying distributions, $1,130,127; giving activities include $905,000 for 39 grants (high: $250,000; low: $5,000).
Purpose and activities: Giving primarily for small private colleges and community organizations with limited resources for fundraising; support also for activities that benefit young people and enhance their moral, educational and social well-being; support also for activities for senior citizens.
Fields of interest: Arts; Education; Health care; Human services.
Type of support: General/operating support; Continuing support; Endowments; Program development; Scholarship funds.
Limitations: Giving limited to the metropolitan Los Angeles area and southern CA. No support for government-financed projects. No grants to individuals.
Application information: Grantseekers may not re-apply for 15 months, except for scholarships. Application form required.
Initial approach: E-mail for submission guidelines
Board meeting date(s): Quarterly
Officers and Directors:* Philip V. Swan,* Pres.; H. Ross MacMichael,* V.P.; Philip A. Swan,* Treas.; Pegine Grayson,* Secy.; Jennifer F. Devoll; Howard O. Wilson.
EIN: 952114455
Selected grants: The following grants are a representative sample of this grantmaker's funding activity:
$250,000 to University of Redlands, Redlands, CA, 2012. For Ann Peppers Art Education Center.
$15,000 to Institute for Educational Advancement, South Pasadena, CA, 2012. For academy program.
$15,000 to Marianne Frostig Center of Educational Therapy, Pasadena, CA, 2012. For assistive technology for high school students with disabilities.
$15,000 to Pacific Oaks College, Pasadena, CA, 2012. To support Children's School Library.
$15,000 to Villa Esperanza Services, Pasadena, CA, 2012. For Purchase Smart Board and 3 IPad Computers.
$10,000 to Armory Center for the Arts, Pasadena, CA, 2012. For Armory Artists in the Community Program.
$10,000 to Pasadena Child Development Associates, Pasadena, CA, 2012. For Underwriting

Equipment Purchases Associated with the Establishment of New Physical Therapy Department.
$10,000 to Pasadena Conservatory of Music, Pasadena, CA, 2012. For Music Education Outreach Program.
$8,500 to Loyola Marymount University, Los Angeles, CA, 2012. For Financial Support for Students.
$8,500 to Pepperdine University, Malibu, CA, 2012. For capital campaign support.

1025
The Perfect Moment Foundation ✧
31755 S. Coast Hwy., Ste. 202
Laguna Beach, CA 92651-7004
E-mail: info@theperfectmomentfoundation.org; Main URL: http://theperfectmomentfoundation.org/

Established in 2007 in CA.
Foundation type: Independent foundation.
Financial data (yr. ended 12/31/12): Assets, $3,774,482 (M); expenditures, $486,210; qualifying distributions, $460,799; giving activities include $460,799 for 4 grants (high: $425,000; low: $1,080).
Fields of interest: Education; Human services; Economically disadvantaged.
Limitations: Applications not accepted.
Application information: Unsolicited requests for funds not accepted.
Trustee: Steve Samuelian.
EIN: 261608596

1026
Perforce Foundation ✧ ☆
2320 Blanding Ave.
Alameda, CA 94501-1403
Main URL: http://www.perforce.com/company/perforce-foundation

Established in 1999 in CA.
Donor: Perforce Software, Inc.
Foundation type: Company-sponsored foundation.
Financial data (yr. ended 03/31/14): Assets, $6,369,840 (M); expenditures, $585,472; qualifying distributions, $565,850; giving activities include $466,587 for 321 grants (high: $50,000; low: $100).
Purpose and activities: The foundation supports food banks and organizations involved with arts and culture, education, animal welfare, health, breast cancer, soccer, human services, and science.
Fields of interest: Arts; Secondary school/education; Higher education; Education; Animal welfare; Health care, volunteer services; Hospitals (general); Health care; Breast cancer; Food banks; Athletics/sports, soccer; Boys & girls clubs; American Red Cross; Homeless, human services; Human services; Science.
Type of support: General/operating support; Building/renovation; Matching/challenge support.
Limitations: Applications not accepted. Giving primarily in CA; giving also to national organizations. No grants to individuals.
Application information: Unsolicited requests for funds not accepted. The foundation awards grants to nonprofit organizations recommended by Perforce employees.
Officers and Directors:* Christopher Seiwald,* Pres.; Trudi Seiwald,* Secy.-Treas.
EIN: 943327346

Selected grants: The following grants are a representative sample of this grantmaker's funding activity:
$250,000 to University of San Francisco, San Francisco, CA, 2012.
$10,000 to Saint Joseph Notre Dame High School, Alameda, CA, 2012.
$5,000 to Berkeley Public Education Foundation, Berkeley, CA, 2012.
$2,000 to Alameda High School, Alameda, CA, 2012.
$1,500 to De La Salle High School, Concord, CA, 2012.
$1,500 to University of Pittsburgh, Pittsburgh, PA, 2012.
$1,500 to University of Pittsburgh, Pittsburgh, PA, 2012.
$1,100 to New School of Monmouth County, Holmdel, NJ, 2012.
$1,000 to Christian Brothers High School, Sacramento, CA, 2012.

1027
Jean Perkins Foundation ✧
c/o James J. Carroll, III
10880 Wilshire Blvd., Rm. 800
Los Angeles, CA 90024-4124 (310) 208-7733

Established in CA.
Foundation type: Independent foundation.
Financial data (yr. ended 12/31/13): Assets, $113,975,984 (M); expenditures, $6,375,256; qualifying distributions, $5,445,292; giving activities include $4,715,434 for 21+ grants (high: $1,210,000).
Fields of interest: Higher education; Education; Hospitals (general); Hospitals (specialty); Children.
Limitations: Applications not accepted. Giving primarily in CA.
Application information: Unsolicited requests for funds not accepted.
Officers: James Carroll III, C.E.O. and Pres.; J. Joe Connolly, Fin. Off.
Directors: Caitlin Bell Carroll; Cynthia Sprague Connolly; R. Joseph Hull.
EIN: 330436485

1028
Leon S. Peters Foundation ✧
6424 E. Butler Ave.
Fresno, CA 93727-5708 (559) 251-3002
Contact: Samuel K. Peters, Pres. and C.E.O.

Established in 1959 in CA.
Donor: Leon S. Peters†.
Foundation type: Independent foundation.
Financial data (yr. ended 11/30/13): Assets, $21,810,038 (M); expenditures, $1,194,391; qualifying distributions, $1,177,444; giving activities include $1,160,500 for 48 grants (high: $340,000; low: $1,000).
Purpose and activities: Giving primarily for education and human services; funding also for Armenian churches.
Fields of interest: Higher education; Health care, burn centers; Health care; Human services; Christian agencies & churches.
Type of support: General/operating support; Building/renovation; Scholarship funds.
Limitations: Applications accepted. Giving primarily in Fresno, CA. No grants to individuals.
Application information: Application form required.
Initial approach: Letter
Deadline(s): None
Officers: Samuel K. Peters, Pres. and C.E.O.; Ron Peters, C.F.O.; Mark Ruof, V.P.; Janice Chitjian, Secy.
Directors: Craig Apregan; Edward J. Hashim; David Peters.
EIN: 946064669
Selected grants: The following grants are a representative sample of this grantmaker's funding activity:
$340,000 to Community Medical Foundation, Fresno, CA, 2013. For Funds for Operation, Administration and Scholarships.
$5,000 to American Cancer Society, Fresno, CA, 2013. For Funds for Operation and Administration.

1029
Margie & Robert E. Petersen Foundation ✧
c/o Petersen Enterprises
6420 Wilshire Blvd., No. 840
Los Angeles, CA 90048-5502
Contact: Gigi Carleton, Pres.

Established in 1997 in CA.
Donors: Margaret M. Petersen; Robert E. Petersen†; Robert E. and Margaret M. Petersen Living Trust.
Foundation type: Independent foundation.
Financial data (yr. ended 12/31/13): Assets, $0 (M); gifts received, $118,816,795; expenditures, $51,008,937; qualifying distributions, $50,745,595; giving activities include $50,745,595 for 11 grants (high: $29,844,047; low: $1,500).
Fields of interest: Museums (specialized); Medical research, institute; Cancer research; Human services; Community/economic development.
Limitations: Giving primarily in CA. No grants to individuals.
Application information:
Initial approach: Letter
Deadline(s): None
Officers: Gigi Carleton, Pres.; Theodore Calleton, Esq., Treas.
Director: Kevin Strauch.
Number of staff: 2 full-time support.
EIN: 954608757

1030
Pfaffinger Foundation ✧
316 W. 2nd St., Ste. PH-C
Los Angeles, CA 90012-3504
Contact: Roberto F. Valdez, Business Mgr.
FAX: (213) 680-7474;
E-mail: rvaldez@pfoundation.org

Incorporated in 1936 in CA.
Donor: Frank X. Pfaffinger†.
Foundation type: Independent foundation.
Financial data (yr. ended 12/31/13): Assets, $84,432,234 (M); expenditures, $5,244,411; qualifying distributions, $4,339,096; giving activities include $3,710,611 for grants.
Purpose and activities: Giving to assist former employees and retirees of the former Times Mirror Co.; employees and retirees of the Los Angeles Times; and working poor families in downtown Los Angeles, CA on the recommendation of partner agencies. Limited assistance to social service

agencies in Los Angeles and Orange counties in some years.
Fields of interest: Human services; Economically disadvantaged.
Type of support: General/operating support.
Limitations: Applications accepted. Giving limited to Los Angeles and Orange counties, CA, for charitable institutions. No grants to individuals (except company employees); no scholarships.
Application information: Application form required for grants to individuals. Application form required.
Initial approach: Letter
Copies of proposal: 1
Board meeting date(s): May, Sept., and Dec.
Final notification: Sept. and Dec.
Officers and Directors:* Steve Meier,* Chair. and C.E.O.; William A. Niese,* Secy.; William R. Isinger,* C.F.O. and Treas.
Number of staff: 6 full-time professional; 2 part-time professional.
EIN: 951661675

1031
George T. Pfleger Foundation ✧
c/o Optivest, Inc.
24901 Dana Point Harbor Dr., Ste. 230
Dana Point, CA 92629-2930

Established in 1968 in CA.
Donors: George T. Pfleger; U.S. Motors Foundation.
Foundation type: Independent foundation.
Financial data (yr. ended 12/31/12): Assets, $15,022,698 (M); expenditures, $1,755,627; qualifying distributions, $1,448,250; giving activities include $890,750 for 13 grants (high: $601,600; low: $1,000), and $58,711 for 2 foundation-administered programs.
Fields of interest: Environment, research; Environment, natural resources; Animal welfare; Human services.
Limitations: Applications not accepted. Giving primarily in CA. No grants to individuals.
Application information: Contributes only to pre-selected organizations.
Officers and Trustees:* Thomas G. Pfleger,* Pres.; Victoria L. Wintrode, Secy.-Treas.; Scott R. Baugh; John P. King, Jr.; Layne Marceau; Sandra B. Pfleger.
EIN: 952561117

1032
The Harriet E. Pfleger Foundation ✧
7676 Hazard Center Dr., Ste. 700
San Diego, CA 92108-4510

Established in 1999 in CA.
Foundation type: Independent foundation.
Financial data (yr. ended 03/31/13): Assets, $26,428,916 (M); expenditures, $1,400,503; qualifying distributions, $1,268,587; giving activities include $1,198,965 for 22 grants (high: $150,000; low: $10,000).
Purpose and activities: Giving primarily to health organizations, including a center for equine health, as well as for children, youth and social services.
Fields of interest: Animal welfare; Health organizations; Athletics/sports, equestrianism; Human services; Children/youth, services; Family services; Foundations (private grantmaking).
Limitations: Applications not accepted. Giving primarily in CA; with some funding also in NJ. No grants to individuals.
Application information: Contributes only to pre-selected organizations.
Officers: Linda Pfleger Edwards, Pres.; W. Richard Mills, Treas.
Trustee: Marc Edwards.
EIN: 330817673
Selected grants: The following grants are a representative sample of this grantmaker's funding activity:
$100,000 to Casa de Amparo, San Marcos, CA, 2011.
$100,000 to Rancho Santa Fe Community Center, Rancho Santa Fe, CA, 2011. For general fund.
$100,000 to TERI, Oceanside, CA, 2011.
$50,000 to Helen Woodward Animal Center, Rancho Santa Fe, CA, 2011.
$50,000 to SCI Special Fund, Rancho Santa Margarita, CA, 2011. For general fund.
$40,000 to Oceana, Washington, DC, 2011. For fundraiser.
$35,000 to Acirfa, San Diego, CA, 2011. For general fund.
$27,000 to Bishops School, La Jolla, CA, 2011. For general fund.
$25,000 to House Research Institute, Los Angeles, CA, 2011. For general fund.
$25,000 to Pro Kids Golf Academy, San Diego, CA, 2011. For general fund.

1033
The PG&E Corporation Foundation ✧
77 Beale St.
San Francisco, CA 94105-1814
E-mail: communityrelations@exchange.pge.com; Additional e-mail: CharitableContributions@pge.com; Main URL: http://www.pge.com/en/about/community/foundation/index.page
Grants List: http://pgecorporationfoundation.org/resources/docs/2012%20Charitable%20Contributions_Foundation_Website.pdf

Established in 2000 in CA.
Donors: PG&E Corporation; Pacific Gas and Electric Company; PG&E Gas Transmission, Texas Corp.
Foundation type: Company-sponsored foundation.
Financial data (yr. ended 12/31/12): Assets, $42,864,166 (M); gifts received, $39,565,368; expenditures, $17,551,303; qualifying distributions, $16,941,936; giving activities include $16,941,936 for 930 grants (high: $1,017,000; low: $165).
Purpose and activities: The foundation supports programs designed to promote education, environmental stewardship, and economic and community vitality. Special emphasis is directed toward underserved communities and populations.
Fields of interest: Secondary school/education; Education; Environment, natural resources; Environment, land resources; Environment, energy; Environment, plant conservation; Environmental education; Environment; Employment, services; Disasters, preparedness/services; Recreation, parks/playgrounds; American Red Cross; Family services; Human services; Utilities; Disabilities, people with; Minorities; Women; Girls; Economically disadvantaged; LGBTQ.
Type of support: General/operating support; Continuing support; Building/renovation; Program development; Scholarship funds; Employee matching gifts.
Limitations: Applications accepted. Giving primarily in areas of company operations in CA. No support for religious organizations not of direct benefit to the entire community, political or partisan organizations, or discriminatory organizations. No grants to individuals, or for tickets for contests, raffles, or other activities with prizes; endowments, filmmaking, debt-reduction campaigns, or political or partisan events.
Publications: Application guidelines; Grants list; Program policy statement.
Application information: Applications from organizations that do not make preliminary contact with PG&E Public Affairs staff are rarely funded. Grants range from $1,000 to $25,000. Multi-year funding is not automatic. Application form required.
Initial approach: Contact local PG&E Public Affairs representative to discuss grant proposal; complete online application
Deadline(s): Feb. to Sept.
Final notification: 3 months
Officers and Directors:* Greg S. Pruett,* Chair.; Linda Y.H. Cheng, Secy.; Christopher P. Johns,* C.F.O.; Ezra Garrett, Exec. Dir.; Tim Fitzpatrick; Hyun Park; Dinyar B. Mistry.
EIN: 943358729
Selected grants: The following grants are a representative sample of this grantmaker's funding activity:
$1,017,000 to Habitat for Humanity International, Operational Headquarters, Americus, GA, 2012. For PG and E/Habitat Program.
$775,000 to Exploratorium, San Francisco, CA, 2012. For Field Trip Program.
$683,250 to American Red Cross National Headquarters, Washington, DC, 2012. For Bay Area Ready Neighborhoods program.
$627,733 to JK Group, Plainsboro, NJ, 2012. For funding of Q3 Matching of Employee Campaign donations and Prefunding.
$545,215 to National Energy Education Development Project, Manassas, VA, 2012. For PG and E Bright Ideas Grants and Solar Schools Program.
$500,000 to Salvation Army, Golden State Division, San Francisco, CA, 2012. For the REACH Program.
$500,000 to United Way of the Bay Area, San Francisco, CA, 2012. For SF Summer Jobs+ and Collective Impact Strategy to Cut Bay Area Poverty in Half.
$312,000 to San Francisco Reviving Baseball for Inner-City Youth, San Francisco, CA, 2012. For Literacy Program.
$226,500 to KaBOOM, Washington, DC, 2012. For KaBOOM-led Community Playground Builds.
$122,000 to Bay Area Council Foundation, San Francisco, CA, 2012. For general operating and Outlook Conference.

1034
Phelps Family Foundation ✧
16720 Huerta Rd.
Encino, CA 91436-3544

Established in 2005 in CA.
Donors: Michael E. Phelps; Patricia E. Phelps.
Foundation type: Independent foundation.
Financial data (yr. ended 03/31/13): Assets, $4,529,949 (M); gifts received, $1,603; expenditures, $1,525,844; qualifying distributions, $1,507,291; giving activities include $1,507,291 for 4 grants (high: $826,203; low: $12,450).
Fields of interest: Higher education.
Limitations: Applications not accepted. Giving primarily in CA. No grants to organizations lacking

501(c)(3) which are not private foundations and/or governmental entities.
Application information: Contributes only to pre-selected organizations.
Officers: Michael E. Phelps, Pres.; Patricia E. Phelps, V.P. and Secy.; Randy Rich, Treas.
EIN: 201974643
Selected grants: The following grants are a representative sample of this grantmaker's funding activity:
$826,203 to UCLA Foundation, Los Angeles, CA, 2013. To Help Fund General Charitable Operations.

1035
Philanthropy International ✧
333 N. Indian Hill Blvd.
Claremont, CA 91711-4612 (909) 625-4511
Contact: Duke Draeger
E-mail: info@picharity.org; Main URL: http://www.picharity.org/

Donors: David Marvin; Tim Triplett; Deborah Triplett; Patrick Leicester; Anna Visser; Doug Faber; Marilyn Faber; Rick Todd; Mary Todd; Kurtwood Smith; Joan Smith; Mitch Allen; Michael Connor; Merlene Connor; Joyce Davis Guine; Mickey McKenzie; Barbara Mckenzie; Conrad Stout; Bruncati Charitable Lead Remainder Trust; Lewis Family Trust; Meisinger Trust; Aidikoff, Uhl & Bakhtiari; David Davis; Tammy Davis; Crystal Heft; Apex Settlement; Langham; Robert & Pamela Smith Investment LP; James Yee; Mckenzie 2008.
Foundation type: Independent foundation.
Financial data (yr. ended 12/31/12): Assets, $11,295,800 (M); gifts received, $1,280,989; expenditures, $1,638,510; qualifying distributions, $1,442,870; giving activities include $1,442,870 for 168 grants (high: $200,000; low: $50).
Purpose and activities: The foundation's mission is to build stronger communities and secure lasting family legacies.
Fields of interest: Education; Animal welfare; Hospitals (general); Health organizations, association; Medical research, institute; Human services; Christian agencies & churches; Protestant agencies & churches; Catholic agencies & churches.
Limitations: Applications accepted. Giving primarily in CA.
Application information:
Initial approach: Letter
Deadline(s): None
Trustee: Tracy Haraksin.
EIN: 870643877
Selected grants: The following grants are a representative sample of this grantmaker's funding activity:
$10,000 to Austin Lyric Opera, Austin, TX, 2012. To support the enjoyment of opera and musical theater.
$3,000 to Union Rescue Mission, Los Angeles, CA, 2012. To support Programs feeding the homeless and hungry.
$2,500 to City of Hope, Duarte, CA, 2012. For research on cancer treatment and cures.

1036
The Stephen Philibosian Foundation ✧
46-930 W. El Dorado Dr.
Indian Wells, CA 92210-8649

Established in 1969 in PA.
Donor: Armenian Missionary Association of America.
Foundation type: Independent foundation.
Financial data (yr. ended 12/31/13): Assets, $8,454,349 (M); expenditures, $720,272; qualifying distributions, $680,185; giving activities include $656,057 for 114 grants (high: $81,440; low: $50).
Purpose and activities: Giving primarily for Armenian-American churches and organizations, as well as for other Christian organizations, education, arts and culture, and health and human services.
Fields of interest: Arts; Education; Health care; Human services; Children/youth, services; Christian agencies & churches.
International interests: Middle East.
Type of support: Continuing support; Annual campaigns; Endowments; Scholarship funds.
Limitations: Applications not accepted. Giving primarily in CA. No grants to individuals, or for operating budgets, seed money, emergency funds, deficit financing, building funds, matching gifts, research, special projects, publications, or conferences; no loans.
Application information: Contributes only to pre-selected organizations.
Board meeting date(s): Spring and fall
Trustees: Richard Danelian; Stephanie Landes; Albert Momjian; George Phillips; Joyce Stein.
EIN: 237029751

1037
The PIMCO Foundation ✧
840 Newport Center Dr., Ste. 100
Newport Beach, CA 92660-6398 (949) 723-4483
Contact: Sarah Middleton, Exec. Dir.
E-mail: sarah.middleton@pimco.com; Additional tel.: (949) 720-7690; Main URL: http://www.pimco.com/EN/OurFirm/Pages/PIMCO-Foundation.aspx
Twitter: https://twitter.com/pimcofoundation

Established in 1999 in CA.
Donors: Bill Benz; Wes Burns; Chris Dialynas; Mohamed El-Erian; Bill Gross; John Hague; Pasi Hamlainen; Brent Harris; Brent Holden; Margaret Isberg; Ray Kennedy; John Loftus; Mark McCray; Paul McCulley; Dean Meiling; Jim Muzzy; Bill Podlich; Bill Powers; Ernie Schmider; Lee Thomas; Bill Thompson; Ben Trosky; David Hattum; PIMCO.
Foundation type: Company-sponsored foundation.
Financial data (yr. ended 12/31/12): Assets, $64,312,265 (M); gifts received, $9,881,908; expenditures, $2,898,667; qualifying distributions, $2,698,498; giving activities include $2,613,923 for 1,143 grants (high: $250,000; low: $25).
Purpose and activities: Giving to empower people globally to reach their full potential. The foundation's charter: To engage with its communities, donating its time and resources; to empower through education, with a focus on financial literacy and college readiness; to invest in people through partnerships fostering economic development.
Type of support: Scholarship funds; Program development; Pro bono services; Management development/capacity building; In-kind gifts; Employee matching gifts; Emergency funds.
Limitations: Applications accepted. Giving primarily in Orange County, CA and New York City, NY. No support for political organizations, veterans and labor organizations, fraternal organizations, athletic or social clubs, or sectarian religious organizations. No grants to individuals, or for fundraising events (e.g. membership drives, dinners, tournaments, and benefits), or advertising sponsorships, capital campaigns, and golf tournaments.
Application information: The foundation does not accept faxed or e-mailed applications nor does it accept videos. Application form required.
Initial approach: Proposal
Deadline(s): Between June 15 and July 15
Final notification: Nov.
Officers and Directors:* William H. Gross,* Chair.; Mohamed El-Erian,* Pres.; Mark J. Porterfield, Secy.; Wendy Cupps, Treas.; Sarah Middleton, Exec. Dir.; Sabrina Callin; Curtis Mewbourne; Arthur Ong; Candice Stack.
EIN: 330891470

1038
Pisces Foundation ✧
1 Maritime Plz., Ste. 1545
San Francisco, CA 94111-3504
E-mail: admin@piscesfoundation.org; Main URL: http://piscesfoundation.org
Blog: http://piscesfoundation.org/blog/
Twitter: https://twitter.com/PiscesFnd

Established in 2006 in CA.
Donors: Robert J. Fisher; Elizabeth S. Fischer.
Foundation type: Independent foundation.
Financial data (yr. ended 06/30/13): Assets, $49,674,385 (M); gifts received, $43,796,500; expenditures, $9,644,842; qualifying distributions, $9,090,440; giving activities include $8,557,247 for 48 grants (high: $3,500,000; low: $1,000).
Purpose and activities: The foundation works to advance strategic solutions to natural resource challenges and prepare the next generation by supporting environmental education.
Fields of interest: Environment, formal/general education; Environment, climate change/global warming; Environment, water resources; Environment.
Limitations: Applications not accepted. Giving primarily in CA, NY, and VA.
Application information: Contributes only to pre-selected organizations.
Officer: David Beckman, Exec. Dir.
Trustees: Elizabeth S. Fisher; Robert J. Fisher; David Beckman.
EIN: 207415160
Selected grants: The following grants are a representative sample of this grantmaker's funding activity:
$3,500,000 to Resources Legacy Fund, Sacramento, CA, 2012. For work to conserve and restore native landscapes and marine systems.
$3,500,000 to Resources Legacy Fund, Sacramento, CA, 2013. To support a program to enhance and protect California's water resources.
$2,000,000 to California Academy of Sciences, San Francisco, CA, 2013. To explore, explain, and protect the natural world.
$1,675,683 to California Academy of Sciences, San Francisco, CA, 2012. For general support.
$1,002,066 to Natural Resources Defense Council, New York, NY, 2012. For program support.
$1,001,000 to Conservation International, Arlington, VA, 2012. For operating support.
$1,001,000 to Conservation International, Arlington, VA, 2013. To benefit the conservation of nature and biodiversity in the world.
$750,000 to Energy Foundation, San Francisco, CA, 2012. To advance energy efficiency and renewable energy.

$750,000 to Natural Resources Defense Council, New York, NY, 2013. To protect the planet's wildlife, wild places, and water resources.
$500,000 to Energy Foundation, San Francisco, CA, 2013. To advance energy efficiency and renewable energy.
$225,000 to Friends of Environmental Education, San Francisco, CA, 2012. For education programs.
$211,238 to NatureBridge, San Francisco, CA, 2013. For education on science and the environment.
$200,000 to Education Outside, San Francisco, CA, 2013. To support environmental education for elementary school children in San Francisco.
$170,000 to NatureBridge, San Francisco, CA, 2012. For education programs on science and the environment.
$100,000 to League of Conservation Voters Education Fund, Washington, DC, 2012. To educate citizens about the environmental movement.
$39,759 to North American Association for Environmental Education, Washington, DC, 2013. To support environmental education.
$25,000 to Climate Central, Princeton, NJ, 2012. To promote education on climate change.
$20,000 to Education Outside, San Francisco, CA, 2013. To redesign website and develop The Toolshed.
$12,500 to Monterey Bay Aquarium, Monterey, CA, 2012. For ocean conservation work.
$12,500 to Monterey Bay Aquarium, Monterey, CA, 2013. For conservation of oceans.

1039
Placer Community Foundation ✧
219 Maple St.
Auburn, CA 95603 (530) 885-4920
Contact: Veronica Blake, C.E.O.; Jessica Hubbard, Philanthropic Svcs. Mgr.
FAX: (530) 885-4989; E-mail: info@placercf.org; Mailing address: P.O. 9207, Auburn, CA 95604-9207; Main URL: http://www.placercf.org
Facebook: https://www.facebook.com/placercommunityfoundation
LinkedIn: http://www.linkedin.com/in/placercommunityfoundation
Twitter: https://twitter.com/placercf
YouTube: http://www.youtube.com/user/PlacerCommunityFound

Established in 2004 in CA.
Foundation type: Community foundation.
Financial data (yr. ended 12/31/13): Assets, $11,764,041 (M); gifts received, $1,291,441; expenditures, $1,268,723; giving activities include $1,132,400 for grants.
Purpose and activities: The foundation distributes grants to nonprofit organizations who, through direct services, build sustainable communities and enhance the quality of life for residents of Placer County, CA. The foundation's values are to: 1) be open to learning and listening; 2) act with integrity; 3) value the community and respond to its needs; and 4) lead by example.
Fields of interest: Visual arts; Performing arts; Historic preservation/historical societies; Animals/wildlife; Health care; Youth development; Human services; Children/youth, services; Aging, centers/services; Nonprofit management; Community/economic development; Leadership development.
Type of support: Continuing support; Income development; Management development/capacity building; Conferences/seminars; Scholarship funds; Technical assistance; Consulting services; Program evaluation; Matching/challenge support.
Limitations: Applications accepted. Giving primarily in the western slope of Placer County, CA. No support for for-profit entities. No grants to individuals, or for debt reduction or fundraisers.
Publications: Application guidelines; Annual report; Financial statement; Grants list; Informational brochure; Newsletter.
Application information: Visit foundation web site for application forms and guidelines per grant type.
Initial approach: Submit application
Deadline(s): Varies
Board meeting date(s): Jan., Mar., May, July, Sept. and Nov.
Final notification: Varies
Officers and Directors:* Pamela Constantino,* Chair.; Janice L. Forbes,* Founding Chair.; Hon. Justice Keith F. Sparks,* 1st Vice-Chair.; Todd Jensen,* 2nd Vice-Chair.; Veronica Blake,* C.E.O.; Elizabeth Jansen,* Secy.; Larry Welch,* Treas.; Jeff Birkholz; Ruth Burgess; Guy R. Gibson; Ken Larson; Nadder Mirsepassi; Kelly C. Richardson; Tim Sands; Curt Sproul; Jim Williams.
Number of staff: 1 full-time professional; 3 full-time support.
EIN: 201485011

1040
Plaza De Panama Committee ✧ ☆
5451 Avenida Encinas, Ste. A
San Diego, CA 92008

Donors: Irwin Jacobs; Jewish Community Fdn. of San Diego; Jay Kovtun; Lael Kovtun; The Legler Benbough Foundation.
Foundation type: Operating foundation.
Financial data (yr. ended 05/31/13): Assets, $4,137 (M); gifts received, $6,040,000; expenditures, $5,025,891; qualifying distributions, $5,025,891; giving activities include $4,448,969 for 1 grant.
Fields of interest: Recreation, parks/playgrounds; Human services.
Limitations: Applications not accepted. Giving primarily in San Diego, CA.
Application information: Unsolicited requests for funds not accepted.
Officers: Irwin Jacobs, Chair.; Iris Lynn Strauss, Secy.; Tom Gildred, Treas.
Directors: David Cohn; Donald Cohn; Peter Ellsworth; Alan Kidd; Jessie Knight, Jr.; Mike McDowell; Dene Oliver; Betty Peabody; Darlene Shiley.
EIN: 273007658

1041
The Sandra and Lawrence Post Family Foundation ✧
1160 Tower Rd.
Beverly Hills, CA 90210-2131

Established in 1993 in CA.
Donors: Lawrence Post; Sandra Post; Larsand Corp.
Foundation type: Independent foundation.
Financial data (yr. ended 12/31/13): Assets, $16,465,357 (M); gifts received, $715,000; expenditures, $1,189,062; qualifying distributions, $1,128,228; giving activities include $1,115,253 for 53 grants (high: $184,300; low: $300).
Purpose and activities: Giving primarily for Jewish organizations, medical research and social services.
Fields of interest: Health organizations, association; Medical research, institute; Human services; Jewish federated giving programs; Jewish agencies & synagogues.
Type of support: General/operating support.
Limitations: Applications not accepted. Giving primarily in CA; funding also in Washington, DC. No grants to individuals.
Application information: Contributes only to pre-selected organizations.
Officers: Lawrence A. Post, Pres.; Sandra Post, Secy.
Trustees: Susan P. Rizzo; Bryan L. Sanders.
EIN: 954442473
Selected grants: The following grants are a representative sample of this grantmaker's funding activity:
$57,820 to Center for Independent Thought, Philadelphia, PA, 2011.
$35,000 to Wheels for Humanity, North Hollywood, CA, 2011.
$20,000 to Milken Institute, Santa Monica, CA, 2011.
$15,000 to FasterCures, Washington, DC, 2011.
$15,000 to Prostate Cancer Foundation, Santa Monica, CA, 2011.
$14,830 to Israel Emergency Alliance, Los Angeles, CA, 2011.
$9,533 to Childrens Burn Foundation, Sherman Oaks, CA, 2011.
$2,500 to Investigative Project on Terrorism, Washington, DC, 2011.
$1,000 to Jewish Free Loan Association, Los Angeles, CA, 2011.
$1,000 to Middle East Forum, Philadelphia, PA, 2011.

1042
Hughes and Sheila Potiker Family Foundation ✧
(formerly Potiker Family Foundation)
875 Prospect St., Ste. 220
La Jolla, CA 92037-4264 (858) 657-9400
Contact: Lowell Potiker, Pres.

Established in 1992 in MI.
Donors: Sheila Potiker; Lowell Potiker; Members of the Potiker family.
Foundation type: Independent foundation.
Financial data (yr. ended 12/31/13): Assets, $3,208,862 (M); expenditures, $470,658; qualifying distributions, $447,428; giving activities include $422,025 for 2 grants (high: $372,025; low: $50,000).
Purpose and activities: Giving primarily for a Jewish community foundation; funding also for the arts.
Fields of interest: Performing arts; Performing arts, theater; Arts; Health organizations; Jewish federated giving programs.
Application information: Application form not required.
Initial approach: Proposal
Deadline(s): None
Officers: Lowell Potiker, Pres.; Brian Potiker, Secy.; Jori Potiker, Treas.
EIN: 383066992

1043
The Price Family Charitable Fund ✧
(formerly The Sol & Helen Price Foundation)
7979 Ivanhoe Ave., Ste. 520
La Jolla, CA 92037-4513 (858) 551-2321
Contact: Terry Malavenda
E-mail: tmalavenda@pricefamilyfund.org; Main URL: http://www.pricefamilyfund.org

Established in 1983 in CA.
Donors: Pollyanna Keating; Sol Price; Helen Price.
Foundation type: Independent foundation.
Financial data (yr. ended 12/31/13): Assets, $579,314,058 (M); gifts received, $1,049,912; expenditures, $29,501,961; qualifying distributions, $28,093,976; giving activities include $23,787,340 for 537 grants (high: $6,678,000; low: $1,000), and $3,034,768 for foundation-administered programs.
Purpose and activities: Giving primarily for education and philanthropy.
Fields of interest: Elementary/secondary education; Urban/community development; Economically disadvantaged.
Type of support: Scholarships—to individuals; Annual campaigns; Fellowships; Scholarship funds; Program evaluation.
Limitations: Applications accepted. Giving limited to San Diego, CA.
Application information:
Initial approach: Online
Deadline(s): None
Officers and Directors:* Robert Price,* Chair. and Pres.; Sherry Barhrambeygui, Vice-Chair., V.P., and Secy.; Allison Price,* Vice-Chair and V.P.; Ted Parzen, Exec. V.P.; Jeff Fisher, C.F.O.; William Gorham; Don Levi; Maggie Meyer; M. Edward Spring.
Number of staff: 2 full-time professional; 1 part-time professional; 1 full-time support; 1 part-time support.
EIN: 953842468
Selected grants: The following grants are a representative sample of this grantmaker's funding activity:
$10,556,800 to University of Southern California, Los Angeles, CA, 2012. For general support.
$3,184,935 to San Diego State University Research Foundation, San Diego, CA, 2012. For general support.
$785,874 to San Diego Unified School District, San Diego, CA, 2012. For general support.
$605,000 to Scripps Health Foundation, San Diego, CA, 2012. For general support.
$229,305 to Lucile Packard Foundation for Childrens Health, Palo Alto, CA, 2012. For general support.
$107,836 to San Diego Futures Foundation, San Diego, CA, 2012. For general support.
$29,481 to Rady Childrens Hospital and Health Center, San Diego, CA, 2012. For general support.
$10,000 to Vietnam Veterans of San Diego, San Diego, CA, 2012. For general support.
$3,250 to KnowledgeWorks Foundation, Cincinnati, OH, 2012. For general support.

1044
M. B. Price Foundation, Inc. ✧
P.O. Box 5100
Visalia, CA 93278-5100

Established in 2002 in CA.
Donor: Mary Barbara Price.
Foundation type: Independent foundation.
Financial data (yr. ended 10/31/12): Assets, $1,193,182 (M); expenditures, $995,207; qualifying distributions, $947,212; giving activities include $503,325 for 56 grants (high: $26,386; low: $500), and $443,887 for grants to individuals.
Fields of interest: Higher education; Education; Human services; Children/youth, services.
Type of support: Scholarships—to individuals.
Limitations: Applications not accepted. Giving primarily in CA.
Application information: Unsolicited requests for funds not accepted.
Officers: Mary B. Price, Pres.; William D. Pine, Treas.
EIN: 300121911
Selected grants: The following grants are a representative sample of this grantmaker's funding activity:
$13,920 to University of Phoenix, Phoenix, AZ, 2011.
$10,000 to American Cancer Society, Atlanta, GA, 2011.
$8,000 to Texas A & M University, College Station, TX, 2011.
$1,000 to Guide Dogs for the Blind, San Rafael, CA, 2011.
$1,000 to Young Life, Colorado Springs, CO, 2011.

1045
The Priem Family Foundation ✧
c/o Dan Moreno
180 Park Rd.
Burlingame, CA 94010-4317 (650) 342-5915
Main URL: http://www.priem.org

Established in 1999 in CA.
Donors: Curtis Priem; Veronica Priem.
Foundation type: Operating foundation.
Financial data (yr. ended 06/30/13): Assets, $202,108,696 (M); expenditures, $15,512,089; qualifying distributions, $13,444,115; giving activities include $13,427,957 for 7 grants (high: $10,000,000; low: $5,183).
Purpose and activities: The purpose of the foundation is the reduction of non-human induced suffering. The foundation's activities are currently in the area of nature conservancy, education, and the performing arts.
Fields of interest: Performing arts; Education; Environment, natural resources; Environment, land resources.
Limitations: Applications not accepted. Giving primarily in NY; some giving also in CA. No grants to individuals.
Application information: Contributes only to pre-selected organizations.
Officers and Directors:* Curtis Priem,* C.E.O. and Pres.; Edward Miles,* V.P.; Veronica Priem,* C.F.O.
EIN: 943340371
Selected grants: The following grants are a representative sample of this grantmaker's funding activity:
$10,000,000 to Rensselaer Polytechnic Institute, Troy, NY, 2012.
$10,000,000 to Rensselaer Polytechnic Institute, Troy, NY, 2013.
$3,058,083 to Rensselaer Polytechnic Institute, Troy, NY, 2013.
$3,010,083 to Rensselaer Polytechnic Institute, Troy, NY, 2012.
$250,000 to Alameda County Library, Fremont, CA, 2013.
$250,000 to Alameda County Library Foundation, Fremont, CA, 2012.
$84,500 to Amateur Athletic Union of the United States, Amateur Athletic Union of the Bay Area Supriem, Union City, CA, 2013.
$45,000 to Amateur Athletic Union of the United States, Amateur Athletic Union of the Bay Area Supriem, Union City, CA, 2012.
$20,000 to Indo-Americans for Better Community, Fremont, CA, 2012. For Indo-American Charity Ball.
$20,000 to Indo-Americans for Better Community, Fremont, CA, 2013. For Charity Ball.
$10,000 to Washington Hospital Healthcare Foundation, Fremont, CA, 2013.
$5,183 to Palomares Parent Teacher Club, Castro Valley, CA, 2013.

1046
The John and Lisa Pritzker Family Fund ✧
c/o Seiler LLP
3 Lagoon Dr., Ste. 400
Redwood City, CA 94065-5157 (650) 365-4646

Established in 2002 in CA and IL.
Donor: John A. Pritzker.
Foundation type: Independent foundation.
Financial data (yr. ended 12/31/12): Assets, $57,799,886 (M); gifts received, $15,882,892; expenditures, $17,766,024; qualifying distributions, $17,199,036; giving activities include $16,683,946 for 212 grants (high: $3,000,000; low: $200).
Purpose and activities: Giving primarily for education, health associations, children, youth, and social services, and Jewish organizations; some funding also for the arts.
Fields of interest: Museums (art); Performing arts, theater; Arts; Elementary/secondary education; Higher education; Education; Hospitals (general); Hospitals (specialty); Health care; Health organizations, association; Human services; Children/youth, services; Jewish federated giving programs; Jewish agencies & synagogues.
Limitations: Applications not accepted. Giving primarily in San Francisco, CA. No grants to individuals.
Application information: Contributes only to pre-selected organizations.
Officers and Directors:* John A. Pritzker,* Chair. and Co-Pres.; Lisa Pritzker,* Co-Pres.; Beverly Symonik, Secy.; Michael Mayer, C.F.O. and Treas.; Cheryl Polk, Exec. Dir.; Adam Nicholas Pritzker; Noah Stone Pritzker.
EIN: 300039815
Selected grants: The following grants are a representative sample of this grantmaker's funding activity:
$3,500,000 to Zero1: The Art and Technology Network, San Jose, CA, 2012. For Bay Lights Project.
$3,000,000 to University of California San Francisco Foundation, San Francisco, CA, 2012. For Benioff Children's Hospital in Support of Construction on the UCSF Mission Bay Campus.
$400,000 to Columbia University, New York, NY, 2012. For Pritzker Family Internship Fund, Internship Program for Financially Needy Students.
$382,165 to Jewish Community Federation of San Francisco, the Peninsula, Marin and Sonoma Counties, San Francisco, CA, 2012. For Annual Campaign Teen Foundation.
$375,000 to Tipping Point Community, San Francisco, CA, 2012. For Benefit.
$250,000 to Tipping Point Community, San Francisco, CA, 2012. For Tipping Point Benefit.

$15,000 to Jewish Family and Childrens Services, San Francisco, CA, 2012. For Annual Family Awards Gala.
$15,000 to Museum of Modern Art, New York, NY, 2012. For Dues for the Committee on Photography.
$10,000 to San Francisco Day School, San Francisco, CA, 2012. For Collectors Forum Accessions.
$10,000 to University of California at Berkeley Foundation, Berkeley, CA, 2012. For Public Health Heroes 03/12/12.

1047
The David & Julianna Pyott Foundation ✧
P.O. Box 50520
Irvine, CA 92619

Established in 2005 in CA.
Donor: David I. Pyott.
Foundation type: Operating foundation.
Financial data (yr. ended 12/31/13): Assets, $1,877,641 (M); expenditures, $794,404; qualifying distributions, $746,930; giving activities include $746,930 for 29 grants (high: $550,000; low: $100).
Fields of interest: Higher education, university; Business school/education.
Limitations: Applications not accepted. Giving primarily in CA and the United Kingdom. No grants to individuals.
Application information: Contributes only to pre-selected organizations.
Officers: David E.I. Pyott, Pres.; Julianna Pyott, Secy.
EIN: 205622633
Selected grants: The following grants are a representative sample of this grantmaker's funding activity:
$255,000 to Fountain Valley School of Colorado, Colorado Springs, CO, 2011.
$25,000 to Chapman University, Orange, CA, 2011.
$10,000 to United Way, Orange County, Irvine, CA, 2011.
$5,000 to American Heart Association, Irvine, CA, 2011.
$2,000 to Direct Relief International, Santa Barbara, CA, 2011.

1048
Qualcomm Charitable Foundation ✧
5775 Morehouse Dr.
San Diego, CA 92121-1714
Main URL: http://www.qualcomm.com/about/citizenship/community/philanthropy

Established in CA.
Donor: Qualcomm Incorporated.
Foundation type: Independent foundation.
Financial data (yr. ended 09/30/13): Assets, $19,682,507 (M); gifts received, $10,000,000; expenditures, $12,173,914; qualifying distributions, $12,170,226; giving activities include $11,213,787 for 2,628 grants (high: $1,000,000; low: $50).
Purpose and activities: The mission of the foundation is to create educated, healthy, sustainable and culturally vibrant communities.
Fields of interest: Arts; Education; Health care; Medical research, institute; Human services; Children/youth, services.
Limitations: Giving on a national basis and in regions of business operation. No support for sporting events without a charitable beneficiary, sectarian or denominational religious groups, strict faith-based schools, primary and secondary schools. No grants to individuals and no political contributions.
Application information: Grant proposals are by invitation only. Unsolicited proposals will not be considered.
Initial approach: Online letter of inquiry
Deadline(s): June 1 to June 30
Final notification: Oct. 1
Officers and Directors: Paul E. Jacobs, Chair.; Daniel L. Sullivan,* Pres.; William Sailer,* Secy.; Akash Palkhiwala,* Treas.; William Bold; Warren Kneeshaw; Susan Laun; Michelle Sterling.
EIN: 274621444
Selected grants: The following grants are a representative sample of this grantmaker's funding activity:
$15,941,747 to X PRIZE Foundation, Playa Vista, CA, 2012.
$3,750,000 to X PRIZE Foundation, Playa Vista, CA, 2012.
$3,737,223 to Scripps Health, San Diego, CA, 2012.
$2,078,923 to San Diego Public Library Foundation, San Diego, CA, 2012.
$1,650,000 to University of California, Berkeley, CA, 2012.
$1,123,800 to University of California at San Diego Foundation, La Jolla, CA, 2012.
$100,000 to Corporation for National Research Initiatives, Reston, VA, 2012. For matching grant.
$50,000 to Rady Childrens Hospital Foundation, San Diego, CA, 2012. For matching grant.
$5,690 to Movember, Venice, CA, 2012. For matching grant.
$5,000 to University of California at San Diego Foundation, La Jolla, CA, 2012. For matching grant.

1049
Frank and Denise Quattrone Foundation ✧
P.O. Box 1707
Los Altos, CA 94023-1707

Established in 2002 in CA.
Donors: Denise A. Foderaro; Frank P. Quattrone.
Foundation type: Independent foundation.
Financial data (yr. ended 12/31/12): Assets, $41,043,678 (M); gifts received, $14,861,222; expenditures, $2,691,733; qualifying distributions, $2,379,921; giving activities include $2,379,921 for 24 grants (high: $511,500; low: $12).
Fields of interest: Arts; Education; Health organizations, association.
Limitations: Applications not accepted. Giving primarily in CA. No grants to individuals.
Application information: Contributes only to pre-selected organizations.
Trustees: Denise A. Foderaro; Frank P. Quattrone.
EIN: 776220832

1050
Quest Foundation ✧
P.O. Box 339
Danville, CA 94526-0339 (925) 743-1925

Established in 2005 in CA.
Donors: Herrick-Pacific Corporation; Dorothy Jernstedt Trust.
Foundation type: Company-sponsored foundation.
Financial data (yr. ended 12/31/12): Assets, $87,514,485 (M); expenditures, $4,791,895; qualifying distributions, $4,524,014; giving activities include $4,200,820 for 90 grants (high: $1,504,000; low: $4,620).
Purpose and activities: The foundation supports youth development clubs and community foundations and organizations involved with education and human services.
Fields of interest: Secondary school/education; Charter schools; Higher education; Education, services; Education, reading; Education; Youth development, centers/clubs; Boys & girls clubs; Children/youth, services; Family services; Human services; Foundations (community).
Type of support: General/operating support; Continuing support.
Limitations: Applications not accepted. Giving primarily in CA.
Application information: Contributes only to pre-selected organizations.
Officers and Directors:* Dorothy Jernstedt,* Pres.; Derek Jernstedt, Exec. Dir.; Richard Becher,* C.F.O.; Jennifer Jernstedt, Secy.; Jaci Jernstedt.
EIN: 201844715

1051
Kenneth Rainin Foundation ✧
c/o Rainin Group, Inc.
155 Grand Ave., Ste. 1000
Oakland, CA 94612
E-mail: info@krfoundation.org
E-Newsletter: http://krfoundation.org/contact-us/
Grants Database: http://krfoundation.org/grants/grants-awarded-2011/
Knowledge Center: http://krfoundation.org/resources/
RSS Feed: http://krfoundation.org/feed/

Established in 1998 in CA.
Donors: Kenneth Rainin; Kenneth Rainin Charitable Lead Annuity Trust 1; Kenneth Rainin Charitable Lead Annuity Trust 2; Kenneth Rainin Charitable Lead Annuity Trust 3.
Foundation type: Independent foundation.
Financial data (yr. ended 12/31/12): Assets, $143,219,966 (M); gifts received, $56,103,146; expenditures, $5,103,720; qualifying distributions, $4,521,573; giving activities include $2,843,543 for 55 grants (high: $963,000; low: $1,000).
Purpose and activities: The foundation focuses on health, education and the arts and childhood literacy. Medical research focus is on Inflammatory Bowel Disease.
Fields of interest: Performing arts, dance; Performing arts, theater; Arts; Education; Health care; Medical research.
Limitations: Applications not accepted. Giving primarily in the San Francisco Bay Area, CA for literacy, dance and theater. Giving for medical research is global in scope. No support for organizations located outside of the United States (except for medical research), or projects of organizations that discriminate based on religion, race, sexual orientation or gender. No grants to individuals, start-up organizations or fraternal organizations, no support for sponsorships, deficits or retroactive funding.
Application information: Unsolicited requests for funds not accepted.
Officers and Directors:* Jennifer Anne Rainin,* Pres.; Pat Curcio, C.O.O.; Edward Weinsoff, C.F.O.;

Brian Igoe, C.I.O.; Rivkah Beth Medow; Eric Rodenbeck.
Number of staff: 1 full-time professional; 1 part-time professional.
EIN: 943289283
Selected grants: The following grants are a representative sample of this grantmaker's funding activity:
$963,000 to San Francisco Film Society, San Francisco, CA, 2012. For the Film Society's New Filmmaker Services Program - to Make Grants to Independent Filmmakers.
$170,000 to ODC Theater, San Francisco, CA, 2012. For the Renovation of the ODC Theater and the Opportunity Fund.
$100,000 to East Bay Community Foundation, Oakland, CA, 2012. For the Oakland Literacy Coalition to Support the Pilot Program with the Brookfield Elementary.
$100,000 to Emory University, School of Medicine, Atlanta, GA, 2012. For 2011 and 2012 Breakthrough Awards for IBD Research.
$66,833 to Intersection for the Arts, San Francisco, CA, 2012. For Sponsorship: The Central Market Arts Alliance for What on Stage? Performing; the Mugwumpin.
$50,000 to American Conservatory Theater, San Francisco, CA, 2012. For the Costume Shop Theater.
$50,000 to University of Washington, Seattle, WA, 2012. For Innovator Award for IDB Research.
$30,000 to Reading Partners, Oakland, CA, 2012. For Reading Partners - Oakland.
$23,099 to Northern California Grantmakers, San Francisco, CA, 2012. For the Arts Loan Fund and General Contribution.
$20,000 to Z Space Studio, San Francisco, CA, 2012. For the Technical Development Residency Program.

1052
Raintree Foundation ✧
(formerly Harold & Diana Frank Family Foundation)
1255 Franklin Ranch Rd.
Goleta, CA 93117-1784 (805) 967-7964
Contact: James A. Frank, Pres. and C.F.O.

Established in 1994 in CA.
Donors: Diana D. Frank; Harold R. Frank; H.R. Frank Family Trust.
Foundation type: Independent foundation.
Financial data (yr. ended 12/31/13): Assets, $16,819,721; gifts received, $230,160; expenditures, $1,489,058; qualifying distributions, $1,357,552; giving activities include $1,354,346 for 22 grants (high: $600,000; low: $200).
Purpose and activities: Giving primarily for education, health care, and youth activities.
Fields of interest: Higher education; Education; Health care; Human services; Youth, services; Protestant agencies & churches.
Limitations: Applications accepted. Giving primarily in Santa Barbara County, CA. No grants to individuals.
Application information: Application form required.
Initial approach: Letter
Deadline(s): None
Officers: James A. Frank, Pres. and C.F.O.; Jessica Frank, V.P.; Ellicott Million, Secy.
EIN: 770359291
Selected grants: The following grants are a representative sample of this grantmaker's funding activity:
$600,000 to University of California, Santa Barbara, CA, 2011.
$200,000 to First Presbyterian Church of Santa Barbara, Santa Barbara, CA, 2010. For capital campaign.
$100,000 to Cottage Rehabilitation Hospital Foundation, Santa Barbara, CA, 2010. For capital campaign.
$100,000 to Saint Johns Health Center Foundation, Santa Monica, CA, 2011.
$2,500 to Santa Barbara Foundation, Santa Barbara, CA, 2011.
$2,500 to Santa Barbara Zoological Gardens, Santa Barbara, CA, 2011.
$2,500 to Scholarship Foundation of Santa Barbara, Santa Barbara, CA, 2011.
$2,500 to Wilderness Youth Project, Santa Barbara, CA, 2011.
$2,000 to Santa Barbara Historical Museum, Santa Barbara, CA, 2011.
$1,000 to Santa Barbara Museum of Art, Santa Barbara, CA, 2011.

1053
Rancho Santa Fe Foundation ✧
(formerly Rancho Santa Fe Community Foundation)
162 S. Rancho Santa Fe Rd., Ste. B-30
Encinitas, CA 92024 (858) 756-6557
Contact: Christina Wilson, Exec. Dir.; For grants: Debbie Anderson, Progs. Mgr.
FAX: (858) 756-6561;
E-mail: info@rsffoundation.org; Mailing address: P.O. Box 811, Rancho Santa Fe, CA 92067; Main URL: http://www.rsffoundation.org
E-Newsletter: http://visitor.r20.constantcontact.com/manage/optin/ea?v=001D5M72sEPb7qboQ3MvxTAIA%3D%3D
Facebook: https://www.facebook.com/RSFFoundation
LinkedIn: http://www.linkedin.com/company/rancho-santa-fe-foundation
Twitter: https://twitter.com/rsffoundation
Application e-mail: christy@rsffoundation.org

Established in 1981 in CA.
Foundation type: Community foundation.
Financial data (yr. ended 12/31/13): Assets, $82,134,300 (M); gifts received, $16,116,400; expenditures, $4,225,300; giving activities include $3,507,800 for grants.
Purpose and activities: The foundation seeks to connect donors with regional and global needs through visionary community leadership, personalized service and effective grantmaking.
Fields of interest: Arts; Education; Health care; Human services; Community/economic development.
Type of support: General/operating support; Continuing support; Management development/capacity building; Building/renovation; Equipment; Land acquisition; Emergency funds; Program development; Publication; Seed money; Curriculum development; Scholarship funds; Technical assistance; Grants to individuals.
Limitations: Applications accepted. Giving primarily in San Diego County, CA. No support for religious organizations (from discretionary funds). No grants for capital campaigns, annual campaigns, or endowments (from discretionary funds).
Publications: Annual report; Financial statement; Informational brochure; Newsletter.
Application information: Visit foundation website for application timeline and information. Application form required.
Initial approach: Contact foundation
Board meeting date(s): Bimonthly
Officers and Directors:* William J. Ruh,* Chair.; Franci Free,* Secy.; Robert Vanosky,* Treas.; Christina P. Wilson, Exec. Dir.; Mark Holmlund, Chair.-Elect; Alyce Ashcraft; Terry Atkinson; Ed Blodgett; Richard Collato; Kevin Crawford; Craig Dado; William Davidson; David Down; Gigi Fenley; Victoria Hanlon; Neil C. Hokanson; Kimberly Davis King; Constance Levi; Dr. Michael Lobatz; John Major; Glenn Oratz; Daniel Platt; Paula Powers; Richard Sapp; Steve Simpson; Robert Stine; Gordon Swanson; paul Thiel; Donna Walker; Kate Williams.
Number of staff: 1 full-time professional; 3 part-time professional.
EIN: 953709639

1054
The Randall Family Foundation ✧ ☆
15200 Don Julian Rd.
City of Industry, CA 91745-1001

Established in 1997 in CA.
Donors: James H. Randall; Eleanor Randall.
Foundation type: Independent foundation.
Financial data (yr. ended 09/30/13): Assets, $7,881,396 (M); gifts received, $2,385,050; expenditures, $685,492; qualifying distributions, $680,000; giving activities include $680,000 for 5 grants (high: $500,000; low: $5,000).
Fields of interest: Performing arts centers; Arts; Higher education; Education; Hospitals (specialty); Health care.
Limitations: Applications not accepted. Giving primarily in CA. No grants to individuals.
Application information: Unsolicited requests for funds not accepted.
Officer: James H. Randall, Pres.
EIN: 954663969
Selected grants: The following grants are a representative sample of this grantmaker's funding activity:
$200,000 to Pepperdine University, Malibu, CA, 2011.
$20,000 to Childrens Hospital Los Angeles, Los Angeles, CA, 2011.
$20,000 to Exceptional Childrens Foundation, Culver City, CA, 2010.

1055
Nancy Buck Ransom Foundation ✧
P.O. Box 749
Monterey, CA 93942-0749
Main URL: http://www.nbrfoundation.org

Established in 1979 in CA.
Foundation type: Independent foundation.
Financial data (yr. ended 12/31/12): Assets, $40,786,124 (M); expenditures, $4,297,146; qualifying distributions, $3,962,902; giving activities include $3,855,265 for 60 grants (high: $2,725,000; low: $1,000).
Purpose and activities: Support for projects that provide positive enrichment opportunities for mainstream youths.
Fields of interest: Arts; Youth development, centers/clubs; Human services.
Type of support: General/operating support.

Limitations: Applications accepted. Giving primarily in Monterey County, CA; some funding also in WI. No support for governmental or religious programs. No grants to individuals or for endowments, regranting, capital projects or campaigns or capacity building; no multi-year grants.
Application information: Application guidelines and form available on foundation web site.
Initial approach: Proposal
Deadline(s): Feb. 15
Board meeting date(s): Apr.
Officers and Directors:* Lucinda B. Ewing, Pres.; C. Lee Cox, V.P.; Katherine M. Coopman,* Secy. and Exec. Dir.; Sandra Stutzman,* Treas.; Richard Arentz.
EIN: 942601172

1056
The Erwin Rautenberg Foundation ✧ ☆
2811 Wilshire Blvd., Ste. 570
Santa Monica, CA 90403-4806
Contact: Thomas B. Corby, Pres.

Donor: Erwin Rautenberg Trust.
Foundation type: Independent foundation.
Financial data (yr. ended 11/30/13): Assets, $58,440,914 (M); gifts received, $50,691,012; expenditures, $2,891,582; qualifying distributions, $1,893,436; giving activities include $1,749,040 for 43 grants (high: $500,000; low: $1,000).
Fields of interest: Human services; Jewish agencies & synagogues.
Limitations: Applications accepted. Giving primarily in Los Angeles, CA.
Application information: Application form required.
Initial approach: Proposal
Deadline(s): None
Officer: Thomas B. Corby, Pres.
EIN: 455514206

1057
The Rav-Noy Family Foundation, Inc. ✧
c/o KETW
15303 Ventura Blvd., Ste. 1040
Sherman Oaks, CA 91403-5805

Donors: Zeev Rav-Noy; Varda Rav-Noy; Abraham Bernstein.
Foundation type: Independent foundation.
Financial data (yr. ended 09/30/13): Assets, $1,901,977 (M); gifts received, $676,271; expenditures, $635,841; qualifying distributions, $608,817; giving activities include $608,817 for 137 grants (high: $140,330; low: $18).
Purpose and activities: Giving primarily to Jewish agencies, temples, and schools.
Fields of interest: Education; Jewish agencies & synagogues.
Limitations: Applications not accepted. Giving primarily in CA and NY. No grants to individuals.
Application information: Contributes only to pre-selected organizations.
Officers and Directors:* Zeev Rav-Noy,* Pres.; Varda Rav-Noy,* Secy. and C.F.O.
EIN: 954663319
Selected grants: The following grants are a representative sample of this grantmaker's funding activity:
$105,588 to Friends Around, Los Angeles, CA, 2011.
$39,629 to Ezrat Israel, Brooklyn, NY, 2011.
$10,000 to Cheder Menachem, Los Angeles, CA, 2011.
$2,160 to Chabad Israel Center, Los Angeles, CA, 2011.
$1,500 to Chabad of Burbank, Burbank, CA, 2011.
$1,000 to Chabad of Brandeis, Waltham, MA, 2011.

1058
Ray of Light Foundation ✧
10960 Wilshire Blvd., 5th Fl.
Los Angeles, CA 90024-3702 (310) 277-4657
Contact: Richard Feldstein

Established in 1998 in CA.
Donor: Madonna Ciccone.
Foundation type: Independent foundation.
Financial data (yr. ended 12/31/12): Assets, $8,924,558 (M); expenditures, $1,098,963; qualifying distributions, $1,025,000; giving activities include $1,025,000 for 4 grants (high: $1,000,000; low: $5,000).
Fields of interest: Human services; American Red Cross; Children, services; International relief.
Limitations: Applications accepted. Giving primarily in CA, with emphasis on Los Angeles; some funding also in NY.
Application information: Application form required.
Initial approach: Proposal
Deadline(s): None
Trustee: Melanie Ciccone.
EIN: 954716881

1059
Red Husky Foundation ✧
720 University Ave., Ste. 200
Los Gatos, CA 95032-7651

Established in 1997 in NV and CA.
Donors: Jerry Yang; Akiko Yamazaki; Jerry Yang Living Trust.
Foundation type: Independent foundation.
Financial data (yr. ended 06/30/13): Assets, $33,663,038 (M); expenditures, $917,696; qualifying distributions, $649,059; giving activities include $649,059 for 5 grants (high: $333,804; low: $5,000).
Fields of interest: Museums (art); Arts; Foundations (community).
Limitations: Applications not accepted. Giving in the U.S., with emphasis on CA. No grants to individuals.
Application information: Funds fully committed. Contributes only to pre-selected organizations. Unsolicited requests for funds not accepted.
Officers and Director:* Akiko Yamazaki,* Pres.; Jerry Yang, Secy.; Gregory R. Hardester, Treas.
EIN: 770472127
Selected grants: The following grants are a representative sample of this grantmaker's funding activity:
$47,350 to Committee of 100, New York, NY, 2012. To address important issues concerning the Chinese-American community, as well as issues affecting U.S.-China relations.
$15,000 to Digital Divide Data, New York, NY, 2012. To work to create better futures for disadvantaged youth through employment in sustainable businesses.

1060
Will J. Reid Foundation ✧
c/o E.M. Westbrook
2801 E. Ocean Blvd.
Long Beach, CA 90803-2521

Established in 1955 in CA.
Donors: Will J. Reid†; Virginia Reid Moore†; Ella Hancock Reid; Charles Reid Gaylord; Elizabeth Moore Westbrook.
Foundation type: Independent foundation.
Financial data (yr. ended 12/31/13): Assets, $15,949,652 (M); expenditures, $750,867; qualifying distributions, $743,395; giving activities include $729,681 for 38 grants (high: $100,000; low: $1,000).
Purpose and activities: Giving primarily for education, human services, community foundations, as well as to a marine research institute.
Fields of interest: Higher education; Education; Camp Fire; Human services; Foundations (private grantmaking); Foundations (community); Marine science.
Type of support: General/operating support; Continuing support; Annual campaigns; Land acquisition; Program evaluation; Program-related investments/loans.
Limitations: Applications not accepted. Giving primarily in southern CA; some funding also in HI. No grants to individuals.
Application information: Contributes only to pre-selected organizations.
Board meeting date(s): Annual meeting and distribution, usually in May
Officers and Directors:* E.M. Westbrook,* Pres. and Treas.; Charlotte G. Burgess, V.P.; W.J. Hancock, V.P.; C.R. Moore,* Secy.; W.R. Moore.
Number of staff: 1 part-time support.
EIN: 956041915
Selected grants: The following grants are a representative sample of this grantmaker's funding activity:
$25,000 to Hawaii Preparatory Academy, Kamuela, HI, 2012. For iPads and Speaker Series.
$5,000 to Thacher School, Ojai, CA, 2012. For Math workshop and computers.

1061
The Myra Reinhard Family Foundation ✧
15729 Los Gatos Blvd., Ste. 201
Los Gatos, CA 95032-2539 (408) 358-3907
Contact: Myra Reinhard, Pres.

Established in 1999 in CA.
Donor: Myra Reinhard.
Foundation type: Independent foundation.
Financial data (yr. ended 12/31/13): Assets, $1,147,680 (M); gifts received, $1,300,000; expenditures, $1,322,771; qualifying distributions, $1,285,992; giving activities include $1,272,000 for 41 grants (high: $137,500; low: $1,500).
Fields of interest: Media, film/video; Arts; Education; Hospitals (general); Health organizations, association; Medical research; Children/youth, services; Family services; Jewish federated giving programs; Jewish agencies & synagogues.
International interests: Israel.
Type of support: Continuing support; Program development; Curriculum development.

Limitations: Applications accepted. Giving primarily in CA and Washington, DC. No grants for building funds.
Application information: Application form required.
Initial approach: Completed application form
Deadline(s): None
Board meeting date(s): Mar.
Officers and Directors:* Myra Reinhard,* Pres.; Neil Reinhard,* C.F.O. and Treas.; Ian Reinhard,* V.P.; Erica Krauss,* Secy.
Number of staff: 1 part-time professional.
EIN: 770514955

1062
The Reis Foundation, Inc. ✧
1 Wagon Ln.
Rolling Hills, CA 90274-5021

Established in 1996 in FL.
Donors: Barbara Reis Johnson; Curtis S. Reis; L. Sanford Reis; Pamela Petre Reis; Reis & Chandler, Inc.
Foundation type: Independent foundation.
Financial data (yr. ended 06/30/13): Assets, $14,046,013 (M); gifts received, $208,792; expenditures, $1,948,347; qualifying distributions, $1,887,193; giving activities include $1,886,000 for 30 grants (high: $1,750,000; low: $1,000).
Fields of interest: Higher education; Education; Environment; Human services.
Type of support: Scholarship funds.
Limitations: Applications not accepted. Giving primarily in CA and PA.
Application information: Contributes only to pre-selected organizations.
Officers: Curtis S. Reis, C.E.O. and Pres.; Pamela P. Reis, V.P.; Kyle C. Reis, Treas.
EIN: 311486993
Selected grants: The following grants are a representative sample of this grantmaker's funding activity:
$20,000 to University of California, Oakland, CA, 2011.
$10,000 to Rockefeller Philanthropy Advisors, New York, NY, 2011. For general contribution.
$5,000 to Harlem Childrens Zone, New York, NY, 2011. For general contribution.
$5,000 to Mid Klamath Watershed Council, Orleans, CA, 2011.
$5,000 to Teen Talk Sexuality Education, Redwood City, CA, 2011.
$5,000 to University of Southern California, Los Angeles, CA, 2011. For general contribution.
$2,500 to California Council on Economic Education, San Bernardino, CA, 2011. For general contribution.
$1,000 to Global Fund for Women, San Francisco, CA, 2011. For general contribution.

1063
ResMed Foundation ✧
(also known as ResMed Sleep Disordered Breathing Foundation)
7514 Girard Ave., Ste. 1-343
La Jolla, CA 92037-5149 (858) 775-1616
Contact: Fiona Tudor, Exec. Dir.
FAX: (858) 459-6557;
E-mail: fiona.tudor@resmedfoundation.org;
Additional e-mail:
resmedsdbfoundation@resmed.com; Main
URL: http://www.resmedfoundation.org/
Grants List: http://www.resmedfoundation.org/grant-recipients.php

Established in 2002 in CA.
Donor: ResMed Inc.
Foundation type: Company-sponsored foundation.
Financial data (yr. ended 12/31/13): Assets, $5,020,396 (M); gifts received, $450,000; expenditures, $1,566,677; qualifying distributions, $1,368,478; giving activities include $1,368,478 for 34 grants (high: $333,334; low: $5,000).
Purpose and activities: The foundation supports programs designed to promote research and public and physician awareness about the importance of sleep and respiratory health.
Fields of interest: Arts; Secondary school/education; Education; Hospitals (general); Public health; Health care; Health organizations; Medical research; Mathematics; Engineering/technology; Science.
Type of support: Continuing support; Annual campaigns; Publication; Research.
Limitations: Applications accepted. Giving primarily in La Jolla and San Diego, CA, Boston, MA, Australia, Canada, France, Norway, and Sweden. No support for political organizations. No grants to individuals, or for general operating or continuing support, contingencies, deficits, or debt reduction; no loans.
Publications: Application guidelines; Grants list; Program policy statement.
Application information: Additional information may be requested at a later date. Proposals should be no longer than 5 pages. Organizations receiving support may be asked to provide periodic progress reports and a final report.
Initial approach: Complete online application or download cover sheet and mail cover sheet and proposal to foundation
Copies of proposal: 1
Deadline(s): Mar. 15 and Sept. 15 for Clinical Research; June 15 and Dec. 15 for Physician and Public Awareness; and May 15 for Community Philanthropy
Final notification: Apr. 30 and Oct. 31 for Clinical Research; July 31 and Jan. 31 for Physician and Pubic Awareness; and July 31 for Community Philanthropy
Officers and Trustees:* Edward Blair,* Chair.; Peter C. Farrell, Ph.D., Secy.; Edward A. Dennis, Ph.D., Treas.; Fiona Tudor, Exec. Dir.; Peter Cistulli, MD, Ph.D.; Charles G. Cochrane, M.D.; Michael P. Coppola, M.D.; Terrence M. Davidson, M.D.; Klaus Schindhelm, BE, Ph.D.
EIN: 020622126

1064
Resnick Foundation ✧
(formerly Resnick Family Foundation)
11444 W. Olympic Blvd., 10th Fl.
Los Angeles, CA 90064-1557

Established in 1997 in CA.
Donors: Lynda R. Resnick; Stewart A. Resnick; Resnick Family Foundation, Inc.
Foundation type: Independent foundation.
Financial data (yr. ended 09/30/13): Assets, $38,029,917 (M); gifts received, $43,534,100; expenditures, $11,648,325; qualifying distributions, $11,641,825; giving activities include $11,640,900 for 18+ grants (high: $5,100,000; low: $500).
Purpose and activities: The foundation gives to specific organizations and causes each year, and is not expanding its giving outside of these areas.
Limitations: Applications not accepted. Giving primarily in areas of company operations, including the Central Valley, CA. No grants to individuals.
Application information: Unsolicited requests for funds not accepted. Grants are initiated by the foundation. Do not send letters and/or e-mails of introduction and do not telephone.
Officers and Directors:* Lynda R. Resnick,* Chair.; Stewart A. Resnick,* Pres.; Marc Washington, Sr. V.P. and C.F.O.; Jeremiah L. Kalan, V.P. and Treas.; Jessica Aronoff, V.P., Philanthropy; Craig B. Cooper, Secy.; Robert Bryant, C.F.O.; Jordan P. Weiss.
Number of staff: None.
EIN: 954658095
Selected grants: The following grants are a representative sample of this grantmaker's funding activity:
$5,050,000 to California Institute of Technology, Pasadena, CA, 2012.
$4,100,000 to Museum Associates, Los Angeles County Museum of Art, Los Angeles, CA, 2012.
$1,000,000 to Aspen Valley Medical Foundation, Aspen, CO, 2012.
$75,000 to DonorsChoose.org, New York, NY, 2012.
$75,000 to New Schools Fund, NewSchools Venture Fund, Oakland, CA, 2012.
$50,000 to University of California, Los Angeles, CA, 2012.
$30,000 to Bard Graduate Center for Studies in the Decorative Arts, Design and Culture, New York, NY, 2012.
$25,000 to KIPP LA Schools, Los Angeles, CA, 2012.
$25,000 to San Joaquin Community Hospital Corporation, Bakersfield, CA, 2012.
$25,000 to Water for People, Denver, CO, 2012.

1065
The Ressler Family Foundation ✧ ☆
6922 Hollywood Blvd., Ste. 900
Los Angeles, CA 90028-6129

Established in 1994 in CA.
Donors: Alison Ressler; Richard Ressler.
Foundation type: Independent foundation.
Financial data (yr. ended 12/31/13): Assets, $33,666,286 (M); gifts received, $526,925; expenditures, $4,821,622; qualifying distributions, $4,634,111; giving activities include $4,634,111 for 21 grants (high: $3,113,250; low: $1,000).
Purpose and activities: Giving primarily for higher and other education, including a law school; some funding for medical research and human services.
Fields of interest: Higher education; Law school/education; Education; Medical research, institute; Human services.
Limitations: Applications not accepted. Giving primarily in Los Angeles, CA; funding also in New York, NY and Providence, RI. No grants to individuals.
Application information: Contributes only to pre-selected organizations.
Trustees: Alison Ressler; Richard Ressler.
EIN: 956979496

1066
The Ressler/Gertz Foundation ✧
16130 Ventura Blvd., Ste. 320
Encino, CA 91436-2531

Established in 1997 in CA.
Donors: Jami Gertz; Antony Ressler.
Foundation type: Independent foundation.
Financial data (yr. ended 12/31/13): Assets, $58,502,443 (M); expenditures, $3,451,875; qualifying distributions, $3,154,689; giving activities include $3,135,944 for 45 grants (high: $600,000; low: $500).
Purpose and activities: Giving primarily for an arts museum, education, Jewish organizations and temples, and health and human services.
Fields of interest: Museums (art); Education, management/technical assistance; Education; Health organizations, association; Medical research, institute; Children/youth, services; Jewish agencies & synagogues.
Limitations: Applications not accepted. Giving primarily in Los Angeles, CA. No grants to individuals.
Application information: Contributes only to pre-selected organizations.
Trustees: Jami Gertz; Antony Ressler.
EIN: 311533199

1067
The Rey-Vaden Family Foundation ✧
c/o Harris myCFO, Inc.
P.O. Box 10195, Dept. 39
Palo Alto, CA 94303-0995

Established in 1999 in CA.
Donors: Val E. Vaden; Lilli J. Rey.
Foundation type: Independent foundation.
Financial data (yr. ended 02/28/13): Assets, $1,080,890 (M); expenditures, $1,818,208; qualifying distributions, $1,756,000; giving activities include $1,756,000 for grants.
Fields of interest: Higher education, university; Education; Health organizations, association; Human services.
Limitations: Applications not accepted. Giving primarily in CA. No grants to individuals.
Application information: Contributes only to pre-selected organizations.
Officers: Val E. Vaden, Pres.; Lilli J. Rey, Secy.
EIN: 943346004
Selected grants: The following grants are a representative sample of this grantmaker's funding activity:
$400,000 to Stanford University, Stanford, CA, 2011.
$100,000 to Crystal Springs Uplands School, Hillsborough, CA, 2011.
$60,000 to Sacred Heart Schools, Atherton, CA, 2011.
$15,000 to Crystal Springs Uplands School, Hillsborough, CA, 2011.
$15,000 to Crystal Springs Uplands School, Hillsborough, CA, 2011.
$15,000 to Hillsborough Schools Foundation, Hillsborough, CA, 2011.
$15,000 to Sacred Heart Schools, Atherton, CA, 2011.
$5,000 to Family Service Agency of San Francisco, San Francisco, CA, 2011.
$2,500 to Community Gatepath, Burlingame, CA, 2011.
$1,500 to PARCA, Burlingame, CA, 2011.

1068
The Mabel Wilson Richards Scholarship Fund ✧ ☆
4712 Admiralty Way, Ste. 227
Marina del Rey, CA 90292 (310) 577-7984
Contact: Joanie C. Freckman, Tr.

Trust established in 1951 in CA.
Donor: Mabel Wilson Richards†.
Foundation type: Independent foundation.
Financial data (yr. ended 06/30/13): Assets, $8,977,232 (M); expenditures, $792,542; qualifying distributions, $644,260; giving activities include $570,000 for 25 grants (high: $100,000; low: $5,000).
Fields of interest: Education.
Type of support: Scholarship funds.
Publications: Application guidelines; Program policy statement.
Application information: Application form required.
Initial approach: Proposal
Copies of proposal: 1
Deadline(s): None
Board meeting date(s): Jan., Apr., July, and Oct.
Trustees: Joanie C. Freckman; Barbara Sandler.
EIN: 956021322

1069
Richmond Community Foundation ✧ ☆
(formerly Richmond Children's Foundation)
1014 Florida Ave., Ste. 200
Richmond, CA 94804-2420 (510) 234-1200
Contact: Jim Becker, C.E.O.; For grants: Erwin Reeves, Chief Community Investment Off.
FAX: (510) 234-3399; E-mail: info@richmondcf.org; Additional e-mail: jbecker@richmondcf.org; Grant inquiry e-mail: ereeves@richmondcf.org; Main URL: http://www.richmondcf.org
Facebook: http://www.facebook.com/RichmondCF
Twitter: https://twitter.com/RichmondCF

Established in 1990 in CA; supporting organization of the East Bay Community Foundation.
Foundation type: Community foundation.
Financial data (yr. ended 06/30/13): Assets, $2,918,795 (M); gifts received, $616,376; expenditures, $2,253,060; giving activities include $970,670 for 21+ grants (high: $267,500), and $4,950 for grants to individuals.
Purpose and activities: The organization aims to build a strong, healthy Richmond community.
Fields of interest: Education, early childhood education; Adult education—literacy, basic skills & GED; Public health; Crime/violence prevention; Agriculture, community food systems; Housing/shelter, development.
Limitations: Applications accepted. Giving primarily in Richmond, CA and West Contra Costa County.
Publications: Application guidelines; Annual report; Financial statement; Grants list; Informational brochure; Newsletter; Occasional report.
Application information: Application form required.
Copies of proposal: 1
Deadline(s): Varies
Final notification: Four to six weeks
Officers and Directors:* Josh Genser,* Chair.; Jim Goins,* Vice-Chair.; Jim Becker, Pres.; Roxanne Cruz,* Secy.; Bielle Moore,* Treas.; Leonard Berry; E.M. Downer III; Stephanie Forbes; Dr. Erica Goode; Laura Johnson; Cynthia LeBlanc; Ken Maxey; Becky Ross.
EIN: 943337754

1070
Dave Rickey & Daughters Foundation ✧
15629 Boulder Mountain Rd.
Poway, CA 92064-2145

Established in CA.
Donor: J&D Family Foundation.
Foundation type: Independent foundation.
Financial data (yr. ended 12/31/12): Assets, $11,352,979 (M); expenditures, $964,365; qualifying distributions, $831,145; giving activities include $775,000 for 2 grants (high: $675,000; low: $100,000).
Fields of interest: Higher education; Foundations (private grantmaking); Catholic agencies & churches.
Limitations: Applications not accepted. Giving primarily in CA and NY. No grants to individuals.
Application information: Contributes only to pre-selected organizations.
Officer and Directors:* David M. Rickey,* Pres.; Brenda Sjodin Rickey.
EIN: 116574096

1071
Brenda and Dave Rickey Foundation ✧
15629 Boulder Mountain Rd.
Poway, CA 92064-2145

Established in 2004 in CA.
Donor: Dave Rickey and Daughters Foundation.
Foundation type: Independent foundation.
Financial data (yr. ended 12/31/12): Assets, $138,614 (M); gifts received, $675,000; expenditures, $594,631; qualifying distributions, $573,625; giving activities include $573,625 for 35 grants (high: $210,000; low: $100).
Fields of interest: Arts; Secondary school/education; Higher education; Health organizations, association; Boys & girls clubs; Human services.
Limitations: Applications not accepted. Giving primarily in CA, Geneva, NY, and Marietta, OH. No grants to individuals.
Application information: Unsolicited requests for funds not accepted.
Directors: Brenda Rickey; David M. Rickey.
EIN: 306089207

1072
Right Fork Foundation ✧
P.O. Box 38
Sierraville, CA 96126-0038

Established in CA.
Donors: Albert John Roen; Betty Joyce Roen.
Foundation type: Operating foundation.
Financial data (yr. ended 12/31/12): Assets, $3,916,386 (M); gifts received, $400; expenditures, $644,888; qualifying distributions, $2,674,888; giving activities include $597,219 for grants.
Trustees: Albert John Roen; Betty Joyce Roen.
EIN: 454037351

1073
Righteous Persons Foundation ✧
2800 28th St., Ste. 105
Santa Monica, CA 90405-6204 (310) 314-8393
Contact: Rachel Levin, Assoc. Dir.

FAX: (310) 314-8396;
E-mail: grants@righteouspersons.org; Main URL: http://www.righteouspersons.org/
Grants Database: http://www.righteouspersons.org/index.php/grants-awarded/core-rpf-grants-archive

Established in 1994 in CA.
Donors: Steven A. Spielberg; Spielberg Family Living Trust; The Wunderkinder Foundation.
Foundation type: Independent foundation.
Financial data (yr. ended 12/31/12): Assets, $66,201 (M); gifts received, $2,800,000; expenditures, $2,968,665; qualifying distributions, $2,466,000; giving activities include $2,466,000 for 37 grants (high: $225,000; low: $5,000).
Purpose and activities: Giving primarily for Jewish arts and culture, Jewish youth, synagogue revitalization, intergroup relations and social justice.
Fields of interest: Civil/human rights, advocacy; Jewish agencies & synagogues.
International interests: Middle East.
Type of support: Management development/capacity building; Film/video/radio; General/operating support; Continuing support; Program development; Seed money; Curriculum development; Fellowships; Technical assistance; Program evaluation; Matching/challenge support.
Limitations: Applications accepted. Giving on a national basis and in Israel. No support for individual schools or synagogues. No grants to individuals or for research or publications.
Publications: Application guidelines; Grants list.
Application information: Application guidelines available on foundation web site. Application form required.
Initial approach: Letter of inquiry
Deadline(s): See foundation web site for application deadline
Board meeting date(s): Twice a year
Officers and Directors:* Steven A. Spielberg,* Chair.; Gerald Breslauer,* Pres.; Margery Tabankin, Exec. Dir.; Tammy Anderson.
Number of staff: 1 full-time professional; 1 part-time professional; 1 full-time support; 1 part-time support.
EIN: 954497916
Selected grants: The following grants are a representative sample of this grantmaker's funding activity:
$250,000 to National Museum of American Jewish History, Philadelphia, PA, 2011.
$150,000 to Anti-Defamation League of Bnai Brith, Los Angeles, CA, 2011.
$150,000 to Layalina Productions, Washington, DC, 2011.
$125,000 to Foundation for Jewish Culture, New York, NY, 2011.
$100,000 to Bend the Arc: A Jewish Partnership for Justice, New York, NY, 2011.
$100,000 to New Israel Fund, Washington, DC, 2011.
$100,000 to PeaceWorks Foundation, New York, NY, 2011.
$50,000 to Museum of Jewish Heritage, New York, NY, 2011.
$50,000 to Shine Global, Montclair, NJ, 2011.
$25,000 to Gerda and Kurt Klein Foundation, Narberth, PA, 2011.

1074
Lloyd Rigler Lawrence E. Deutsch Foundation ✧
(formerly The Ledler Foundation)
7250 Franklin Ave., Ste. 1401
Los Angeles, CA 90046-3047

Established in 1966 in CA.
Donors: Lawrence E. Deutsch‡; Lloyd E. Rigler.
Foundation type: Independent foundation.
Financial data (yr. ended 12/31/12): Assets, $73,746,339 (M); expenditures, $6,777,596; qualifying distributions, $4,949,537; giving activities include $4,528,928 for 28 grants (high: $2,141,741; low: $2,500), and $2,141,741 for 1 foundation-administered program.
Purpose and activities: Grants mainly for cultural programs and the performing arts.
Fields of interest: Performing arts; Performing arts, opera; Arts.
Limitations: Applications not accepted. Giving primarily in CA and NY. No grants to individuals.
Application information: Contributes only to pre-selected organizations.
Board meeting date(s): As necessary
Officers and Trustees:* James Rigler,* Pres.; Vyacheslav Klevansky, Cont.; Joan Copeland; Melanie Robinson.
EIN: 956155653

1075
Ring Foundation ✧ ☆
12301 Wilshire Blvd., No. 203
Los Angeles, CA 90025-1024

Established in 1994 in CA.
Donor: Norma Ring‡.
Foundation type: Independent foundation.
Financial data (yr. ended 07/31/13): Assets, $13,085,127 (M); gifts received, $500,000; expenditures, $749,296; qualifying distributions, $705,000; giving activities include $705,000 for 31 grants (high: $150,000; low: $2,000).
Fields of interest: Higher education; Education.
Type of support: Scholarship funds.
Limitations: Applications not accepted. Giving primarily in CA. No grants to individuals.
Application information: Unsolicited requests for funds not accepted.
Officers and Directors:* Cynthia Ann Miscikowski,* Pres.; Fred Cowan,* V.P.; Eileen La Russo.
EIN: 954500900

1076
Herb Ritts Foundation ✧
9100 Wilshire Blvd., Ste. 1000W
Beverly Hills, CA 90212-3413

Established in 2003 in CA.
Donors: Ellen Francisco; The Herb Ritts Trust of 1998.
Foundation type: Independent foundation.
Financial data (yr. ended 12/31/12): Assets, $37,484,269 (M); expenditures, $1,655,022; qualifying distributions, $1,287,452; giving activities include $1,034,000 for 19 grants (high: $448,500; low: $4,000).
Fields of interest: Museums (art); Arts; Human services; AIDS, people with.
Limitations: Applications not accepted. Giving primarily in CA, MA, and NY. No grants to individuals.
Application information: Contributes only to pre-selected organizations.
Officer: Mark McKenna, Exec. Dir.
Directors: Steve Fink; Richard Gere; Warren Grant; Manfred Heiting; Erik Hyman; Ingrid Sischy; Michael Whalen.
EIN: 810593759

1077
Rivendell Stewards' Trust ✧
P.O. Box 6009
Santa Barbara, CA 93160-6009 (805) 964-9999
Contact: Amity Wicks, Admin.
FAX: (805) 823-4594; E-mail: info@rstrust.org; Main URL: http://www.rstrust.org

Established in 1985 in CA.
Donors: K.N. Hansen, Sr.; K.N. Hansen, Jr.; G.W. Hansen; Vince Nelson; Walter Hansen.
Foundation type: Independent foundation.
Financial data (yr. ended 12/31/13): Assets, $15,385,435 (M); expenditures, $7,345,727; qualifying distributions, $7,199,435; giving activities include $7,111,927 for grants.
Purpose and activities: Giving for Christian institutions and missionary efforts in the two-thirds world.
Fields of interest: Theological school/education; Religion.
International interests: Developing Countries.
Type of support: General/operating support; Management development/capacity building; Program development; Seed money; Curriculum development; Scholarship funds; Matching/challenge support.
Limitations: Giving limited to developing countries. No support for Western ministries. No grants to individuals (except for program for retired missionaries).
Application information: The foundation does not accept unsolicited proposals for support, but it offers organizations new to the foundation the opportunity to introduce their programs through a Letter of Inquiry, using the foundation's easy online submission process. Application form not required.
Initial approach: Online letter of inquiry
Copies of proposal: 1
Deadline(s): See foundation web site for current deadlines
Officers: Walter Hansen, Pres.; Darlene Hansen, Secy.; Vince Nelson, Treas.
Trustees: Steve Hoke; Jean Johnson; Cathy Nelson; Doug Spurlock; Joyce Spurlock.
Number of staff: 1 part-time support.
EIN: 776016389

1078
RJM Foundation ✧
350 2nd St., Ste. 7
Los Altos, CA 94022-3645

Established in CA.
Donor: Roberta Campbell.
Foundation type: Independent foundation.
Financial data (yr. ended 12/31/12): Assets, $24,819,772 (M); gifts received, $115,645; expenditures, $4,851,191; qualifying distributions, $4,680,468; giving activities include $4,675,000 for 12 grants (high: $2,250,000; low: $10,000).

Fields of interest: Higher education; Education; Human services; Children/youth, services.
Limitations: Applications not accepted. Giving primarily in New York, NY. No grants to individuals.
Application information: Unsolicited requests for funds not accepted.
Officers: Roberta Campbell, Pres.; James W. Campbell, V.P.; Margaret R. Campbell, Secy.-Treas. and C.F.O.
Director: Tom Baenziger.
EIN: 270429976

1079
Rmlow Foundation ✧
125 Edgewood Ave.
San Francisco, CA 94117-3712

Donor: Roger M. Low.
Foundation type: Independent foundation.
Financial data (yr. ended 12/31/13): Assets, $2,436,454 (M); gifts received, $810; expenditures, $676,562; qualifying distributions, $666,462; giving activities include $637,168 for 39 grants (high: $135,500; low: $360).
Fields of interest: Education; Youth development; Human services; Jewish agencies & synagogues; Religion.
Limitations: Applications not accepted. Giving primarily in CA.
Application information: Unsolicited requests for funds not accepted.
Officer and Director:* Roger M. Low,* C.E.O.
EIN: 275255976
Selected grants: The following grants are a representative sample of this grantmaker's funding activity:
$130,400 to Congregation Emanu-El, San Francisco, CA, 2012. For religion.

1080
The Eric Roberts Foundation ✧
c/o KKR Accounting Srvcs., LLC
2755 Campus Dr., Ste. 240
San Mateo, CA 94403-2515

Established in 2007 in CA.
Donors: Eric B. Roberts; George Roberts; Roberts Children 1987 Trust f/b/o Eric.
Foundation type: Independent foundation.
Financial data (yr. ended 12/31/13): Assets, $2,006,640 (M); gifts received, $2,009,198; expenditures, $563,550; qualifying distributions, $563,514; giving activities include $563,514 for 15 grants (high: $168,506; low: $6,712).
Fields of interest: Education; Animal welfare; Human services; Economically disadvantaged.
Limitations: Applications not accepted. Giving primarily in CA. No grants to individuals.
Application information: Contributes only to pre-selected organizations.
Trustee: Eric B. Roberts.
EIN: 260271567
Selected grants: The following grants are a representative sample of this grantmaker's funding activity:
$148,375 to Tipping Point Community, San Francisco, CA, 2011. For general operations.
$100,000 to Tipping Point Community, San Francisco, CA, 2011. For general operations.
$50,000 to Environmental Defense Fund, San Francisco, CA, 2011. For general operations.
$20,000 to Eastern Horizons, Palo Alto, CA, 2011. For general operations.
$20,000 to Marine Mammal Center, Sausalito, CA, 2011. For general operations.
$15,000 to San Francisco Film Society, San Francisco, CA, 2011. For general operations.
$10,000 to Council for Responsible Genetics, Cambridge, MA, 2011. For general operations.
$10,000 to San Francisco Zoological Society, San Francisco, CA, 2011. For general operations.
$10,000 to Wildlife Associates, Half Moon Bay, CA, 2011. For general operations.

1081
The Roberts Foundation ✧
c/o KKR Accounting Svcs.
2800 Sand Hill Rd., No. 200
Menlo Park, CA 94025-7080

Established in 1985 in CA.
Donors: George R. Roberts; Leanne B. Roberts†; Hewlett Foundation.
Foundation type: Independent foundation.
Financial data (yr. ended 12/31/12): Assets, $72,325,926 (M); gifts received, $55,019,842; expenditures, $17,778,341; qualifying distributions, $17,533,614; giving activities include $17,473,785 for 61 grants (high: $5,000,000; low: $200).
Purpose and activities: Support for the Roberts Enterprise Development Fund (REDF) which creates opportunities for homeless and low-income individuals to move out of poverty. REDF partners with a portfolio of Bay Area nonprofit organizations to create jobs and training opportunities in social purpose enterprises.
Fields of interest: Education, special; Vocational education; Animal welfare; Animals/wildlife, preservation/protection; Health care; Employment; Children/youth, services; Family services; Homeless, human services; Economic development; Economically disadvantaged; Homeless.
Type of support: General/operating support; Continuing support; Program development.
Limitations: Applications not accepted. Giving limited to northern CA, with emphasis on San Francisco, San Mateo, Sonoma, Santa Clara, and San Benito counties. No support for religious organizations. No grants to individuals, or for medical research, endowment funds, or annual or year-end appeals.
Publications: Annual report.
Application information: Currently, the foundation has suspended all grantmaking except for that associated with the Roberts Enterprise Development Fund, URL: http://www.redf.org. No proposals are being accepted.
Board meeting date(s): Approximately Jan. and June
Officers: George R. Roberts, Pres.; Courtney A. Roberts, V.P.; Eric B. Roberts, V.P.; Mark B. Roberts, V.P.; Sue Schoenthaler, Secy.-Treas.
Number of staff: None.
EIN: 942967074
Selected grants: The following grants are a representative sample of this grantmaker's funding activity:
$5,000,000 to San Francisco Museum of Modern Art, San Francisco, CA, 2012. For unrestricted support of the expansion campaign.
$3,023,031 to Claremont McKenna College, Claremont, CA, 2012. For Roberts Challenge.
$2,000,000 to Culver Academies, Culver, IN, 2012. For Roberts Leadership Scholarship Endowment.
$1,500,000 to REDF, San Francisco, CA, 2012. For unrestricted support.
$1,000,000 to American Enterprise Institute for Public Policy Research, Washington, DC, 2012. For Road to Freedom Project.
$1,000,000 to REDF, San Francisco, CA, 2012. For unrestricted support.
$584,960 to Culver Educational Foundation, Culver, IN, 2012. For facilities endowment.
$125,000 to San Francisco Symphony, San Francisco, CA, 2012. For unrestricted support.
$100,000 to San Francisco Museum of Modern Art, San Francisco, CA, 2012. For unrestricted support.
$35,000 to Oakland Schools Foundation, Oakland, CA, 2012. For unrestricted support for Greenleaf Elementary School.

1082
Jeanne and Sanford Robertson Fund ✧
825 Francisco St.
San Francisco, CA 94109-1322

Established in 1993 in CA.
Donors: Sanford R. Robertson; Jeanne Robertson.
Foundation type: Independent foundation.
Financial data (yr. ended 03/31/13): Assets, $3,907,720 (M); gifts received, $4,986,456; expenditures, $1,095,217; qualifying distributions, $1,081,390; giving activities include $1,081,390 for grants.
Purpose and activities: Giving primarily higher education, hospitals, human services, and museums.
Fields of interest: Museums; Higher education; Education; Hospitals (general); Human services; Foundations (private grantmaking).
Limitations: Applications not accepted. Giving primarily in CA, with emphasis on San Francisco; some funding in Washington, DC and HI. No grants to individuals.
Application information: Unsolicited requests for funds not accepted.
Officers: Sanford R. Robertson, C.E.O. and Pres.; Jeanne Robertson, Secy.-Treas. and C.F.O.
EIN: 943181457
Selected grants: The following grants are a representative sample of this grantmaker's funding activity:
$10,000 to Stanford Jazz Workshop, Stanford, CA, 2013. For cultural.

1083
The Roche Foundation ✧
(formerly The Hoffmann-La Roche Foundation)
1 DNA Way, MS #24
South San Francisco, CA 94080-4918
Application address: P.O. Box 278, Nutley, NJ 07110-0278; Main URL: http://www.rocheusa.com/portal/usa/the_roche_foundation

Trust established in 1945 in NJ.
Donors: Hoffmann-La Roche Inc.; Roche Laboratories Inc.
Foundation type: Company-sponsored foundation.
Financial data (yr. ended 12/31/13): Assets, $3,605,635 (M); expenditures, $456,143; qualifying distributions, $456,143; giving activities

include $450,000 for 5 grants (high: $100,000; low: $50,000).
Purpose and activities: The foundation supports organizations involved with arts and culture, education, health, the environment, human services, and science.
Fields of interest: Museums; Arts; Elementary/secondary education; Higher education; Teacher school/education; Education; Environment; Health care; Health organizations; Food banks; Human services; Science, formal/general education; Science.
Type of support: General/operating support; Program development; Curriculum development.
Limitations: Applications accepted. Giving primarily in areas of company operations, with emphasis on NJ. No support for political organizations, candidates, or office holders, sectarian groups (except for education or health programs which serve the general public), or labor or veterans' organizations not of direct benefit to the entire community. No grants to individuals, or for endowments, scholarship funds, purchasing or renovating facilities, equipment, capital campaigns, sponsorships of athletic teams or events, or goodwill advertising.
Publications: Application guidelines.
Application information: Application form required.
Initial approach: Complete online application
Copies of proposal: 1
Deadline(s): 60 days prior to need
Board meeting date(s): As required
Officers and Trustees:* Frederick C. Kentz III,* Secy.; Patricia Hughes, Exec. Dir.; Jean-Jacques Garaud; David P. McDede.
EIN: 226063790
Selected grants: The following grants are a representative sample of this grantmaker's funding activity:
$150,000 to Teach for America, Newark, NJ, 2012. For Math and Science Partnership.
$142,500 to Montclair State University, Montclair, NJ, 2012. For Science Honors Innovation Program.
$75,000 to Paterson Education Foundation, Paterson, NJ, 2012. For Development of Science Curriculum; Life Advisory Program.
$50,000 to Bloomfield College, Bloomfield, NJ, 2012. For STEM Careers Pilot Program.
$50,000 to Liberty Science Center, Jersey City, NJ, 2012. For Teacher Professional Development, Curriculum Connection Project.

1084
The Rock Foundation ✧
1 Maritime Plz., Ste. 1220
San Francisco, CA 94111-3502

Established in 1969.
Donors: Arthur Rock; Arthur Rock S Corp.
Foundation type: Independent foundation.
Financial data (yr. ended 12/31/13): Assets, $43,250,438 (M); expenditures, $2,039,501; qualifying distributions, $2,025,920; giving activities include $1,995,040 for 149 grants (high: $250,000; low: $100).
Fields of interest: Museums; Performing arts; Arts; Education; Human services; Foundations (private grantmaking).
Limitations: Applications not accepted. Giving primarily in CA, with emphasis on the San Francisco Bay Area. No grants to individuals.
Application information: Contributes only to pre-selected organizations.
Officers and Directors:* Arthur Rock,* Pres.; Toni Rembe Rock,* C.F.O. and Secy.
EIN: 941671318

1085
Rock, Paper, Scissors Foundation, Inc. ✧
13769 Wildflower Ln.
Los Altos Hills, CA 94022-6205

Established in 2005 in CA.
Donors: Keith H. Randall; Kay Marie Boissicat Randall; Kay Marie Boissicat Charitable Remainder Trust; Keith H. Randall Charitable Remainder Trust.
Foundation type: Independent foundation.
Financial data (yr. ended 12/31/13): Assets, $14,114,504 (M); expenditures, $534,153; qualifying distributions, $523,680; giving activities include $521,000 for 14 grants (high: $100,000; low: $2,000).
Purpose and activities: Giving primarily for international development, health care, and human services.
Fields of interest: Elementary/secondary education; Health care; Human services; International development.
Limitations: Applications not accepted. Giving primarily in CA, Washington, DC, GA, IL, and NY. No grants to individuals.
Application information: Contributes only to pre-selected organizations.
Officers and Director:* Keith H. Randall,* Pres. and Treas.; Kay Marie Boissicat Randall, Secy.
EIN: 202427803
Selected grants: The following grants are a representative sample of this grantmaker's funding activity:
$2,000 to Humane Society, Palo Alto, Menlo Park, CA, 2011.

1086
The Roddenberry Foundation ✧
(formerly Gene Roddenberry Animal Sanctuary)
17835 Ventura Blvd., No. 102
Encino, CA 91316-3634
E-mail: info@roddenberryfoundation.org; Tel. and fax: (855) 855-4342; Main URL: http://roddenberryfoundation.org

Established in CA.
Donors: Majel Barrett Roddenberry†; Eugene Roddenberry; Gene Roddenberry†; Majel Roddenberry Trust.
Foundation type: Independent foundation.
Financial data (yr. ended 12/31/12): Assets, $85,422,274 (M); gifts received, $5,065,883; expenditures, $3,318,427; qualifying distributions, $2,975,395; giving activities include $2,160,200 for 41 grants (high: $1,215,000; low: $200).
Purpose and activities: The foundation supports and inspires efforts that create and expand new frontiers for the benefit of humanity. It funds innovative solutions to critical global issues in the areas of science and technology, the environment, education, and humanitarian advances.
Fields of interest: Arts; Animals/wildlife; Health organizations.
Limitations: Applications not accepted.
Application information: Unsolicited requests for funds not accepted.
Directors: Andrew Garb; Mort Kessler; Eugene Roddenberry; Heidi Roddenberry.
Advisory Board: Sheila Garb; Cheryl Kessler.
EIN: 954755672

1087
Mary Stuart Rogers Foundation ✧
1025 16th St.
Modesto, CA 95354-1105
Contact: John Stuart Rogers, Pres.

Established in 1985 in CA.
Donors: Mary Stuart Rogers†; John Stuart Rogers.
Foundation type: Independent foundation.
Financial data (yr. ended 12/31/13): Assets, $10,020,918 (M); gifts received, $400,000; expenditures, $1,105,398; qualifying distributions, $990,108; giving activities include $968,100 for 44 grants (high: $200,000; low: $100).
Purpose and activities: Giving primarily for higher education.
Fields of interest: Higher education; Human services; Children/youth, services; Christian agencies & churches; Children/youth; Children; Adults; Physically disabled; Blind/visually impaired; Women; Adults, women; Adults, men; Single parents; Economically disadvantaged.
Type of support: General/operating support; Continuing support; Endowments; Program development; Scholarship funds; Matching/challenge support.
Limitations: Applications accepted. Giving primarily in CA. No grants to individuals.
Application information: Application form not required.
Initial approach: Proposal
Deadline(s): None
Officers: John Stuart Rogers, Pres.; June Rogers, Secy.
Number of staff: 1 full-time professional.
EIN: 770099519
Selected grants: The following grants are a representative sample of this grantmaker's funding activity:
$2,500 to Memorial Hospital Foundation, Modesto, CA, 2012. For A - Relationship -None B - Status of Recipient-Public Charity C - Purpose of Contribution-General Charitable Purposes.

1088
Rosenberg Foundation
131 Steuart St., Ste. 650
San Francisco, CA 94105-1244
Contact: Linda Moll, Business and Grants Mgr.; Tammy Tanner, Exec. Asst. and Office Mgr.
FAX: (415) 357-5016;
E-mail: linda@rosenfound.org; Main URL: http://www.rosenbergfound.org
Facebook: https://www.facebook.com/Rosenbergfound
Rosenberg Foundation's Philanthropy Promise: http://www.ncrp.org/philanthropys-promise/who
Twitter: https://twitter.com/Rosenbergfound

Incorporated in 1935 in CA.
Donors: Max L. Rosenberg†; Charlotte S. Mack†.
Foundation type: Independent foundation.
Financial data (yr. ended 12/31/12): Assets, $56,214,745 (M); expenditures, $3,051,143; qualifying distributions, $3,051,143; giving activities include $2,080,930 for grants.

Purpose and activities: In the more than seven decades since making its first grant, the Rosenberg Foundation has distinguished itself as an ally of the state's most vulnerable residents. From its early work supporting efforts on behalf of Japanese American families returning from internment camps to more recent work to reduce the incarceration rates for women in California, the foundation's aim has remained consistent: to achieve significant and lasting improvements in the life of Californians.
Fields of interest: Legal services; Employment, labor unions/organizations; Human services, reform; Civil/human rights, immigrants; Economics; Poverty studies; Public policy, research; Public affairs, reform; Minorities; Offenders/ex-offenders; Immigrants/refugees; Economically disadvantaged.
Type of support: General/operating support; Continuing support; Management development/capacity building; Program development.
Limitations: Applications accepted. Giving limited to CA, except for national grants. No grants to individuals, or for endowment, building, or capital funds, scholarships, fellowships, continuing support, annual campaigns, emergency funds, deficit financing, matching funds, land acquisition, renovation projects, or conferences and seminars; generally no grants for equipment, films, or publications (except when a necessary part of larger project).
Publications: Application guidelines; Grants list; Multi-year report; Occasional report.
Application information: See foundation web site for application guidelines. The foundation will request additional and specific information if desired after receipt of letter of inquiry. Application form not required.
Initial approach: Letter of Inquiry (1-2 pages)
Deadline(s): None, for letter of inquiry
Final notification: Varies
Officers and Directors:* Hon. Bill Lann Lee,* Chair.; Clara J. Shin,* Vice-Chair. and Secy.; Sarah Stein, 2nd Vice-Chair.; Timothy P. Silard,* Pres.; Robert E. Friedman,* Treas.; Phyllis Cook; Daniel Grossman; Mick Hellman; Benjamin Todd Jealous; Herma Hill Kay; Kate Kendell; Shauna I. Marshall; Hugo Morales; Albert F. Moreno; Hon. Henry Ramsey, Jr.
Number of staff: 3 full-time professional; 1 full-time support.
EIN: 941186182
Selected grants: The following grants are a representative sample of this grantmaker's funding activity:
$250,000 to Farmworker Justice Fund, Washington, DC, 2013. For general support.
$150,000 to National Employment Law Project, New York, NY, 2013. To expand employment opportunities for people with criminal records in California.
$50,000 to National Center for Lesbian Rights, San Francisco, CA, 2013. To increase access to no-cost legal assistance for low-income LGBT farm workers and other LGBT individuals living in California's rural communities.
$35,000 to Alliance for Justice, Washington, DC, 2013. To strength advocacy capacity of Southern California nonprofit organizations working at intersection of immigrants rights and workers rights.
$35,000 to South San Francisco Unified School District, South San Francisco, CA, 2013. For Informant, online news site focusing on criminal justice beat, policing, courts and communities.
$30,000 to Clergy and Laity United for Economic Justice, Los Angeles, CA, 2013. To mobilize Los Angeles faith-based and community support to protect rights of carwash workers to decent work conditions and fair wages.
$9,700 to California Children and Families Foundation, Alameda, CA, 2013. To expand revenue streams for children's funding.
$4,000 to Foundation Center San Francisco, San Francisco, CA, 2013. For national and Bay Area programs for publications and library services to assist grantseekers.
$2,500 to National Committee for Responsive Philanthropy, Washington, DC, 2013.
$2,000 to Council on Foundations, Arlington, VA, 2013.

1089
Rosenthal Family Foundation ✧
16255 Ventura Blvd., Ste. 625
Encino, CA 91436-2307

Donors: Philip Rosenthal; Monica Rosenthal; Margery Tabankin and Assocs.; Summit Business Mgmt.
Foundation type: Independent foundation.
Financial data (yr. ended 12/31/12): Assets, $9,901,527 (M); gifts received, $4,013,550; expenditures, $2,655,504; qualifying distributions, $2,018,785; giving activities include $1,862,518 for 78 grants (high: $121,000; low: $250).
Fields of interest: Arts; Human services; Children/youth, services.
Limitations: Applications not accepted. Giving primarily in CA and NY.
Application information: Contributes only to pre-selected organizations.
Officers: Philip Rosenthal, Pres.; Monica Rosenthal, C.F.O.; Patti Felker, Secy.
EIN: 262982710

1090
Barbara Ross Charitable Trust ✧
c/o Wallace V. Mills
265 Claiborne Pl.
Long Beach, CA 90807-2612

Established in 2005 in CA.
Donors: Joseph W. Aidlin; Barbara M. Ross Trust.
Foundation type: Independent foundation.
Financial data (yr. ended 12/31/13): Assets, $6,911,586 (M); expenditures, $518,842; qualifying distributions, $465,000; giving activities include $465,000 for 35 grants (high: $25,000; low: $2,500).
Fields of interest: Performing arts, music; Medical research; Human services; American Red Cross; Salvation Army; Aging, centers/services; Jewish agencies & synagogues; Homeless.
Type of support: Advocacy.
Limitations: Applications not accepted. Giving primarily in CA. No grants to individuals.
Application information: Contributes only to pre-selected organizations.
Trustees: Gary J. Herman; Wallace V. Mills.
EIN: 367435624
Selected grants: The following grants are a representative sample of this grantmaker's funding activity:
$25,000 to City of Hope, Los Angeles, CA, 2012. For Providing cancer research and help for cancer patients.
$25,000 to Homeboy Industries, Los Angeles, CA, 2012. For Jobs for former gang members.
$25,000 to Hospitaller Foundation of California, Los Angeles, CA, 2012. For Providing funds to care for elderly and Alzheimer patients.
$25,000 to Memorial Medical Center Foundation, Long Beach, CA, 2012. For Memorial Hospital of Long Beach.
$10,000 to Good Shepherd Center for Homeless Women and Children, Los Angeles, CA, 2012. For Care and training of women living facility.
$10,000 to Los Angeles Mission, Los Angeles, CA, 2012. For Providing help for needy.
$10,000 to Midnight Mission, Los Angeles, CA, 2012. For meals and services for needy in Los Angeles.
$10,000 to Union Rescue Mission, Los Angeles, CA, 2012. For Providing help for people in need.
$5,000 to Children of the Night, Van Nuys, CA, 2012. For Help for sexuality exploited children.
$5,000 to Long Beach Rescue Mission, Long Beach, CA, 2012. For meals and services for needy in L.B.

1091
Bob A. Ross Foundation Inc. ✧
950 Rockdale Dr.
San Francisco, CA 94127-1725

Established in 1998 in CA.
Donors: Robert A. Ross Revocable Trust; Thomas E. Horn.
Foundation type: Independent foundation.
Financial data (yr. ended 12/31/13): Assets, $5,117,002 (M); expenditures, $559,141; qualifying distributions, $491,000; giving activities include $491,000 for 33 grants (high: $100,000; low: $1,000).
Fields of interest: Performing arts, ballet; Arts; Human services; Youth, services; Human services.
Limitations: Applications not accepted. Giving primarily in CA. No grants to individuals.
Application information: Contributes only to pre-selected organizations.
Officers: Thomas E. Horn, Pres.; Mitchell Richstone, C.F.O.; Edward T. Peter, Secy.
EIN: 943254090

1092
Rotasa Foundation ✧
(formerly Webb Roven Foundation)
775 E. Blithedale Ave., Ste. 309
Mill Valley, CA 94941-1554

Established in 2001 in CA.
Donors: Max Webb; Rose Webb Roven; Max Webb Charitable Lead Trust.
Foundation type: Independent foundation.
Financial data (yr. ended 06/30/13): Assets, $233,430 (M); gifts received, $552,319; expenditures, $445,448; qualifying distributions, $440,048; giving activities include $436,348 for 38 grants (high: $100,000; low: $250).
Purpose and activities: Giving primarily to increase the knowledge of art jewelry and related metalsmithing.
Fields of interest: Media/communications; Visual arts; Performing arts, theater; Education, early childhood education; Environment, natural resources; Health care; Diabetes; Housing/shelter.
Limitations: Applications not accepted. Giving on a national basis, with an emphasis on CA. No grants to individuals.

Application information: Contributes only to pre-selected organizations.
Officers: Rose Webb Roven, Pres.; Susan Cummins, Secy.
EIN: 943412390

1093
Roth Family Foundation ✧
12021 Wilshire Blvd., Ste. 505
Los Angeles, CA 90025-1206 (213) 383-9207
Contact: Sandy Chiang, Grants Mgr.
FAX: (213) 383-9222; E-mail: sandy@roth-la.org;
Main URL: http://www.rothfamilyfoundation.org

Established in 1966 in CA.
Donors: Louis Roth and Co.; Louis Roth‡; Fannie Roth‡; Harry Roth‡.
Foundation type: Independent foundation.
Financial data (yr. ended 12/31/13): Assets, $13,054,709 (M); expenditures, $644,299; qualifying distributions, $631,210; giving activities include $569,420 for 86 grants (high: $25,000; low: $500).
Purpose and activities: The foundation seeks to improve lives through a variety of focus areas, primarily in the Los Angeles area. Specifically, it provides general operating support and new and/or on-going program/project support to organizations that fall into the following focus areas: 1) Arts and Culture; 2) Youth; 3) Environment; 4) Economic Development; 5) International Development; 6) Reproductive Health and Rights/Sex Education.
Fields of interest: Media/communications; Media, radio; Performing arts, music; Performing arts, education; Environment, formal/general education; Environment, beautification programs; Environment; Reproductive health; Youth development; International development; Economic development; Children/youth; Youth; Women; Girls; Economically disadvantaged.
International interests: Africa.
Type of support: General/operating support; Program development; Matching/challenge support.
Limitations: Giving primarily in Los Angeles County, CA. No support for fraternal organizations, or for religious or political organizations. No grants to individuals; generally no grants to fund dinners, special events or fundraising events.
Publications: Application guidelines; Annual report; Grants list.
Application information:
Initial approach: Use Grant Request form on foundation web site for all program areas except for Global Programs
Copies of proposal: 1
Board meeting date(s): Semiannually
Final notification: 3-6 months for grant request
Officers and Directors:* Michael P. Roth,* Pres.; Gil Garcetti,* V.P.; Sukey Garcetti,* Secy.-Treas.; Rachel Roth,* Exec. Dir.; Dana Boldt; Eric Garcetti; Sarah Roth; Andrea Roth-Fedida.
Number of staff: 1 full-time professional.
EIN: 880352682
Selected grants: The following grants are a representative sample of this grantmaker's funding activity:
$30,000 to National Public Radio, Washington, DC, 2012. For Veterans Affairs Initiative/NPR Internships.
$15,000 to Medical Students for Choice, Philadelphia, PA, 2012. For Reproductive Health Externship Program.
$10,000 to Communities for a Better Environment, Huntington Park, CA, 2012. For General Operating Support for LA Programs.
$10,000 to Liberty Hill Foundation, Los Angeles, CA, 2012. For Wakeland/Garcetti Human Rights and Economic Justice Donor Advised Fund.
$10,000 to Spark, San Francisco, CA, 2012. For Expansion for LA Programs.
$7,500 to Westside Family Health Center, Santa Monica, CA, 2012. For Teen Reproductive Health Services on WFHC's Mobile Medical Unit.
$5,000 to Liberty Hill Foundation, Los Angeles, CA, 2012. For KMG DA Fund: Discretionary Funds for Professional Development.
$5,000 to Pasadena Arts Council, Pasadena, CA, 2012. For Libros Schmibros Lendy Library and Used Bookshop.
$2,750 to UCLA Foundation, Los Angeles, CA, 2012. For Fowler Museum: Director's Discretionary Fund.
$2,500 to UCLA Foundation, Los Angeles, CA, 2012. For Chancellor's Associates.

1094
The Florence and Bernard B. Roth Family Foundation ✧ ☆
9302 S. Garfield Ave.
South Gate, CA 90280-3805

Established in 1999 in CA.
Donors: Bernard B. Roth; Florence Roth.
Foundation type: Independent foundation.
Financial data (yr. ended 11/30/13): Assets, $1,646,995 (M); expenditures, $1,260,596; qualifying distributions, $1,253,970; giving activities include $1,252,935 for 3 grants (high: $1,175,435; low: $12,500).
Fields of interest: Jewish agencies & synagogues.
Type of support: General/operating support.
Limitations: Applications not accepted. Giving primarily in Los Angeles, CA. No grants to individuals.
Application information: Unsolicited requests for funds not accepted.
Trustees: Paul Frimmer; Richard Roth; Robert S. Roth; Steven F. Roth.
EIN: 957087755
Selected grants: The following grants are a representative sample of this grantmaker's funding activity:
$6,400 to Wilshire Boulevard Temple, Los Angeles, CA, 2011.

1095
Ruby Family Foundation ✧
11845 W. Olympic Blvd., Ste. 1200
Los Angeles, CA 90064-5071

Established in 2007 in CA.
Donors: Kenneth A. Ruby; Wendy Ruby.
Foundation type: Independent foundation.
Financial data (yr. ended 12/31/13): Assets, $8,396,106 (M); gifts received, $500,000; expenditures, $1,428,443; qualifying distributions, $1,363,000; giving activities include $1,363,000 for 41 grants (high: $300,000; low: $1,000).
Fields of interest: Arts; Higher education; Jewish agencies & synagogues.
Limitations: Applications not accepted.
Application information: Contributes only to pre-selected organizations.
Officers: Kenneth A. Ruby, Co-Pres.; Wendy L. Ruby, Co-Pres.
EIN: 261509899
Selected grants: The following grants are a representative sample of this grantmaker's funding activity:
$300,000 to Skirball Cultural Center, Los Angeles, CA, 2011.
$160,000 to Stephen S. Wise Temple, Los Angeles, CA, 2011.
$100,000 to UCLA Foundation, Los Angeles, CA, 2011.

1096
Rudd Family Foundation ✧ ☆
2175 N. California Blvd., Ste. 400
Walnut Creek, CA 94596-7103

Established in 1998 in CA.
Donors: Andrew T. Rudd; Virginia A. Rudd.
Foundation type: Independent foundation.
Financial data (yr. ended 08/31/13): Assets, $12,972,884 (M); expenditures, $778,905; qualifying distributions, $768,584; giving activities include $768,584 for 12 grants (high: $483,000; low: $100).
Purpose and activities: Giving primarily for higher education and human services.
Fields of interest: Higher education; Education; Human services.
Type of support: General/operating support; Equipment; Endowments; Research.
Limitations: Applications not accepted. Giving primarily in CA, DE, MA, and NY. No grants to individuals.
Application information: Contributes only to pre-selected organizations.
Trustees: Alexandra H. Rudd; Andrew T. Rudd; Christopher A. Rudd; Natalie A. Rudd; Nicholas S. Rudd; Virginia A. Rudd.
EIN: 946715800
Selected grants: The following grants are a representative sample of this grantmaker's funding activity:
$600,000 to University of California at Berkeley Foundation, Berkeley, CA, 2011.
$3,500 to American Himalayan Foundation, San Francisco, CA, 2011.

1097
Arthur N. Rupe Foundation ✧
(formerly Rupe Foundation)
c/o Susan C. Van Aacken
3887 State St., Ste. 22
Santa Barbara, CA 93105-6111 (805) 687-8586
Contact: Jeffrey J. Cain, Pres. and Exec. Dir.
FAX: (805) 682-5955; E-mail: christine@anrf.net;
Main URL: http://www.rupefoundation.org

Established in 1991 in CA.
Donors: Arthur N. Rupe; Arloma Corp.
Foundation type: Independent foundation.
Financial data (yr. ended 06/30/13): Assets, $53,455,405 (M); expenditures, $3,289,180; qualifying distributions, $2,817,064; giving activities include $2,501,528 for 15 grants (high: $1,894,118; low: $12,500).
Purpose and activities: Giving to organizations that promote and/or provide aid, research, and services in the furtherance of select educational, medical,

and social studies programs. Areas of focus include the support of qualified organizations that: 1) conduct public debates; 2) provide training to vocational nursing students; and 3) perform research affecting public policy and achieving widespread dissemination.
Fields of interest: Philosophy/ethics; Education, public policy; Education, reform; Education, ethics; Employment, labor unions/organizations; Foundations (public); Social sciences, ethics; Public policy, research.
Type of support: Program development; Professorships; Seed money; Curriculum development; Fellowships; Internship funds; Scholarship funds; Research.
Limitations: Giving on a national basis. No support for organizations lacking 501(c)(3) status. No grants to individuals, or for fundraising events, conferences, endowments, or capital campaigns.
Application information: Unsolicited proposals are not accepted. Full proposals are by invitation only, upon review of initial Letter of Inquiry.
Initial approach: Letter of Inquiry through foundation web site
Board meeting date(s): Spring and Fall
Officers and Directors:* Arthur N. Rupe,* Chair.; Jeffrey J. Cain, Ph.D.*, Pres. and Exec. Dir.; Susan C. Van Aacken, Secy.; Richard L. Hunt, C.P.A.*, Treas.; Kimberly O. Dennis; Lanny Eberstein, Ph.D.; Richard L. Hunt, C.P.A.; Evan Coyne Maloney; Beverly Rupe Schwarz, J.D.
EIN: 770278838
Selected grants: The following grants are a representative sample of this grantmaker's funding activity:
$2,400,000 to Fidelity Charitable Gift Fund, Boston, MA, 2011.
$100,000 to Foundation for Santa Barbara City College, Santa Barbara, CA, 2011.

1098
Ryan Family Charitable Foundation ✧
(formerly David Claude Ryan Foundation)
P.O. Box 6409
San Diego, CA 92166-0409 (619) 223-0411
Contact: Jerome D. Ryan, Pres.

Established in 1959 in CA.
Donors: Jerome D. Ryan; Gladys B. Ryan; Anne E. Ryan; Amy Ryan; Ryco Assocs.; Gladys B. Ryan Trust; Now Trust; Ryan Family Partnership, LP; Thomas F. Ryan.
Foundation type: Independent foundation.
Financial data (yr. ended 12/31/13): Assets, $10,018,423 (M); gifts received, $175,229; expenditures, $577,321; qualifying distributions, $556,937; giving activities include $552,955 for 96 grants (high: $98,520; low: $300).
Purpose and activities: Giving primarily to religious institutions; funding also for YMCAs.
Fields of interest: Human services; YM/YWCAs & YM/YWHAs; Children/youth, services; Christian agencies & churches; Religion.
Type of support: General/operating support; Continuing support.
Limitations: Applications accepted. Giving primarily in CA, with emphasis on San Diego. No grants to individuals.
Application information: Application form required.
Initial approach: Letter
Deadline(s): None
Officers: Jerome D. Ryan, Pres.; David C. Ryan, V.P. and Secy.-Treas.; Michael F. Ryan, V.P.
EIN: 956051140

1099
Ryzman Foundation, Inc. ✧
c/o Barak
5967 W. 3rd St., Ste. 102
Los Angeles, CA 90036-2835

Established in 1980 in CA.
Donors: Betty Ryzman; Zvi Ryzman; Mickey Fenig; Elie Ryzman; Sol Majer; Rafael Ryzman; Abraham Ryzman; David Wolf; Mila Kornwasser Life Insurance; SRYZ Corp.; ARYZ Corp.
Foundation type: Independent foundation.
Financial data (yr. ended 11/30/11): Assets, $25,732,345 (M); gifts received, $8,032,000; expenditures, $2,553,400; qualifying distributions, $2,526,800; giving activities include $2,526,800 for 29 grants (high: $1,180,000; low: $1,800).
Purpose and activities: Giving primarily to Jewish agencies, temples, and schools.
Fields of interest: Education; Jewish agencies & synagogues.
Limitations: Applications not accepted. Giving primarily in New York, NY. No grants to individuals.
Application information: Contributes only to pre-selected organizations.
Officers: Zvi Ryzman, Pres.; Betty Ryzman, Secy.
EIN: 953653055

1100
S.G. Foundation ✧
P.O. Box 444
Buellton, CA 93427-0444 (805) 688-0088
Contact: Pamela Grattan, Exec. Dir.; Dee Reed, Progs. Analyst
FAX: (805) 686-1250; E-mail: sgfound@utech.net; E-mail address for Dee Reed, Progs. Analyst, for questions regarding proposals: dpreed@verizon.net; Main URL: http://www.sgfoundation.org

Established in 1984 in CA.
Foundation type: Independent foundation.
Financial data (yr. ended 12/31/12): Assets, $11,746,537 (M); expenditures, $945,990; qualifying distributions, $774,550; giving activities include $774,550 for 44 grants (high: $160,000; average: $5,000–$25,000).
Purpose and activities: The foundation's purpose is to encourage and enable individuals and communities to partner together to help people to help themselves. The foundation supports projects that are self-help in nature, affirm individual dignity, and create incentives for people to participate in their own self-development. The foundation accepts proposals for program expenses for national and international human service relief and development projects. Projects must demonstrate a specific and focused community-based strategy for economic development in the areas of food security, jobs, and small business start-up. The foundation also accepts proposals for senior care, and educational/leadership development programs for youth, child abuse and neglect prevention, and strengthening family values.
Fields of interest: Vocational education, post-secondary; Education; Health care; Agriculture; Family services; Rural development; Community/economic development; Economically disadvantaged.
International interests: Central America; Dominican Republic; Haiti; Mexico.
Type of support: General/operating support; Continuing support; Equipment; Program development; Matching/challenge support.
Limitations: Applications accepted. Giving primarily for Central America, Dominican Republic, Mexico, and Haiti with a small budget for Fresno, Kings, Kern and northern Santa Barbara Counties in CA. No support for athletics, politics, the arts, music, or museums. No grants for building projects, capital improvement, endowments, research, books, films, or media.
Publications: Application guidelines.
Application information: Applications are accepted for projects located in the posted geographic area of interest for the coming yea. See foundation web site for application guidelines. Application form not required.
Initial approach: Proposal in accordance with guidelines posted on foundation web site
Copies of proposal: 1
Deadline(s): None
Board meeting date(s): Monthly
Final notification: 60-90 days
Officers and Trustees:* Lynn R. Gildred,* Pres.; William Sauer,* V.P.; Duane Serritslev, Secy.; Stuart Gildred, Jr.,* Treas.; Pamela Grattan, Exec. Dir.
Directors: John Crowell; John Donati; Joseph Lambert.
Number of staff: 2 part-time professional.
EIN: 330048410
Selected grants: The following grants are a representative sample of this grantmaker's funding activity:
$22,600 to Food for the Poor, Coconut Creek, FL, 2012. For Clean Water in Cavaillon, Haiti.
$20,000 to Cooperative for Education, Cincinnati, OH, 2012. For School book and literacy Program in Guatemala.
$20,000 to Medical Teams International, Redmond, WA, 2012. For Prosthetics and Rehabilitation Program in Les Cayes, Haiti.
$15,000 to Partners Worldwide, Grand Rapids, MI, 2012. For Cap Haitien Job Initiative.
$15,000 to PathPoint, Santa Barbara, CA, 2012. For North County Employment Program for Disabled Adults.
$15,000 to Sisters of Notre Dame, Ipswich, MA, 2012. For Women's Employment Program for the Disabled in Matagalpa, Nicaragua.
$12,500 to All Hands Volunteers, Mattapoisett, MA, 2012. For Haiti Clean Water Project.
$12,500 to Lambi Fund of Haiti, Washington, DC, 2012. For Community Credit Project in Artibonite, Haiti.
$12,500 to Project Concern International, San Diego, CA, 2012. For Clean Water Program in Mozonte, Nicaragua.
$12,000 to Santa Ynez Valley Foundation, Solvang, CA, 2012. For Computer Education Program.

1101
The Saban Family Foundation ✧
10100 Santa Monica Blvd., Ste. 2600
Los Angeles, CA 90067-4003 (310) 557-5100
Contact: Alex De Campo

Established in 1999 in CA.
Donors: Haim Saban; Cheryl Saban.
Foundation type: Independent foundation.

Financial data (yr. ended 12/31/12): Assets, $1,242,106 (M); expenditures, $11,421,238; qualifying distributions, $11,407,269; giving activities include $10,977,507 for 11 grants (high: $4,000,000; low: $2,500).
Purpose and activities: Support for children's health research and social welfare in Los Angeles, CA, and in Israel.
Fields of interest: Hospitals (specialty); Medical research, institute; Nutrition; Children, services; International affairs; Jewish agencies & synagogues.
International interests: Israel.
Type of support: General/operating support; Continuing support; Annual campaigns; Building/renovation; Program development; Conferences/seminars; Seed money; Curriculum development; Scholarship funds; Research; Matching/challenge support.
Limitations: Applications accepted. Giving primarily in CA and Washington, DC; some giving in New York, NY and Israel. No grants to individuals.
Publications: Application guidelines.
Application information: Application form required.
Initial approach: Letter on organization letterhead
Copies of proposal: 1
Deadline(s): None
Final notification: Within 6 months
Officers: Cheryl Saban, Pres.; Adam Chesnoff, V.P.; Haim Saban, V.P.; Niveen Tadros, Secy.; Fred Gluckman, Treas.; Judy Friedman.
Number of staff: 1 full-time professional; 1 full-time support.
EIN: 954769273
Selected grants: The following grants are a representative sample of this grantmaker's funding activity:
$4,000,000 to Childrens Hospital Los Angeles, Los Angeles, CA, 2012. For pediatric research institute.
$2,000,000 to Brookings Institution, Washington, DC, 2012. For research and policy institute.
$2,000,000 to Childrens Hospital Los Angeles, Los Angeles, CA, 2012. For infrastructure.
$1,000,000 to American Israel Education Foundation, Washington, DC, 2012.
$940,500 to Friends of the Israel Defense Forces, National/New York Tri-State Region, New York, NY, 2012. To support social, educational, and recreational programs and facilities for Israeli soldiers including services to widows and families of fallen soldiers.
$500,000 to Saban Free Clinic, Los Angeles, CA, 2012.
$426,174 to Temple of the Air, Beverly Hills, CA, 2012.
$83,333 to Cedars-Sinai Medical Center, Women's Heart Center, Los Angeles, CA, 2012. For research for female patients heart disease and develop new diagnostic tools and specialized care for women.
$20,000 to Childrens Hospital Los Angeles, Los Angeles, CA, 2012. For pediatric surgical research.

1102
The Albert and Bettie Sacchi Foundation ✧

(formerly The Sacchi Foundation)
c/o IFF Advisors, LLC
18101 Von Karman Ave., Ste. 700
Irvine, CA 92612-0145 (877) 968-6328
FAX: (310) 622-1547;
E-mail: grants@sacchifoundation.org; Main URL: http://www.sacchifoundation.org

Established in 2004 in CA and DE.
Donors: Albert Sacchi; Bettie Sacchi.
Foundation type: Operating foundation.
Financial data (yr. ended 12/31/13): Assets, $236,315 (M); gifts received, $555,000; expenditures, $555,074; qualifying distributions, $552,347; giving activities include $511,000 for 32 grants (high: $45,000; low: $1,000).
Purpose and activities: The foundation's mission is to create opportunity for disadvantaged youth and young adults, and to enhance the quality of life in the communities in which the Sacchi family members live, work, and take an interest. The focus of the foundation includes: assisting non-profits engaged in child and protective services; and educational opportunities for financially or mentally disadvantaged youth or young adults.
Fields of interest: Education; Human services; Youth.
Type of support: General/operating support.
Limitations: Giving primarily in Montebello, Pico Rivera, Whittier, La Verne, Downey, Monterrey Park, Norwalk, Santa Fe Springs, Pasadena, and Long Beach, CA.
Publications: Application guidelines.
Application information: Select organizations are invited to submit a full Grant Application after review of the Letter of Inquiry. These organizations are given instructions on how to access the Grant Application. See foundation web site for complete application guidelines.
Initial approach: Letter of Inquiry system on foundation web site
Deadline(s): Mar. 1 for Letter of Inquiry
Officers: Albert Sacchi, Pres.; Bettie Sacchi, Secy.-Treas.
Directors: Tracy Gardner Fish; Douglas Freeman; Andrea Stein O'Neal.
EIN: 201886561
Selected grants: The following grants are a representative sample of this grantmaker's funding activity:
$45,000 to MIND Research Institute, Irvine, CA, 2011.
$31,300 to Literacy Project Foundation, Corona del Mar, CA, 2011.
$25,000 to Boys and Girls Club of Whittier, Whittier, CA, 2011.
$25,000 to Helpline Youth Counseling, Norwalk, CA, 2011.
$25,000 to Interval House, Long Beach, CA, 2011.
$25,000 to LAs BEST, Los Angeles, CA, 2011.
$25,000 to Rosemary Childrens Services, Pasadena, CA, 2011.
$20,000 to Friends of Child Advocates, Monterey Park, CA, 2011.
$7,000 to Humane Farming Association, San Rafael, CA, 2011.
$5,000 to Camp Ocean Pines, Cambria, CA, 2011.

1103
Sacramento Region Community Foundation ✧

(formerly Sacramento Regional Foundation)
955 University Ave., Ste. A
Sacramento, CA 95825 (916) 921-7723
Contact: Linda Beech Cutler, C.E.O.
FAX: (916) 921-7725; E-mail: info@sacregcf.org;
Application e-mail: applications@sacregcf.org; Main URL: http://www.sacregcf.org
Blog: http://www.sacregcf.org/index.cfm/learn/foundation-blog/
E-Newsletter: http://www.sacregcf.org/index.cfm/learn/e-news/
Facebook: http://www.facebook.com/sacregcf
Google Plus: https://plus.google.com/105391282457155881466/posts
LinkedIn: http://www.linkedin.com/company/sacramento-region-community-foundation
RSS Feed: http://sacregcf.org/tasks/feed/?feedID=BADCE22E-155D-0204-75B83AD94C7622CC
Twitter: http://twitter.com/sacregcf
YouTube: http://youtube.com/sacregcf
Scholarship contact e-mail: scholarships@sacregcf.org

Incorporated in 1983 in CA.
Foundation type: Community foundation.
Financial data (yr. ended 12/31/12): Assets, $106,540,710 (M); gifts received, $7,758,742; expenditures, $6,357,805; giving activities include $3,354,218 for 117+ grants (high: $218,000; low: $1,000), and $819,894 for 259 grants to individuals.
Purpose and activities: The mission of the foundation is to serve as a leader and trusted partner in expanding philanthropic activity and enhancing its impact for the betterment of the Sacramento region community.
Fields of interest: Visual arts; Museums; Performing arts; Performing arts, theater; Humanities; Historic preservation/historical societies; Arts; Child development, education; Elementary school/education; Vocational education; Higher education; Adult education—literacy, basic skills & GED; Education, reading; Education; Environment, natural resources; Environmental education; Environment; Health care; Mental health/crisis services; Health organizations, association; AIDS; Alcoholism; Legal services; Food services; Housing/shelter, development; Youth development, services; Children/youth, services; Child development, services; Family services; Residential/custodial care, hospices; Aging, centers/services; Minorities/immigrants, centers/services; Homeless, human services; Human services; Urban/community development; Community/economic development; Voluntarism promotion; Social sciences; Public policy, research; Government/public administration; Leadership development; Aging; Disabilities, people with; Minorities; Economically disadvantaged; Homeless.
Type of support: General/operating support; Management development/capacity building; Building/renovation; Emergency funds; Program development; Publication; Seed money; Scholarship funds; Technical assistance; Program evaluation; Employee-related scholarships; Scholarships—to individuals; Matching/challenge support.
Limitations: Applications accepted. Giving primarily focused on organizations within or those offering services to El Dorado, Placer, Sacramento, and Yolo counties, CA. No support for sectarian purposes or private foundations. No grants to individuals (except designated fund scholarships and through the Artists in Crisis Fund), or for annual campaigns, operating funds, capital campaigns, endowments, building funds, continuing support, deficit financing, foundation-managed projects, research, or land acquisition; no loans.
Publications: Annual report; Financial statement; Informational brochure; Newsletter.
Application information: Visit foundation web site for application forms and guidelines. Applications

may be submitted via U.S. mail, e-mail, or fax. Application form required.

Initial approach: Submit application form and attachments
Copies of proposal: 10
Deadline(s): Varies
Board meeting date(s): Jan., Mar., May, July, Sept., and Nov.

Officers and Directors:* Henry Wirz,* Chair.; Dennis Mangers,* Vice-Chair.; Linda Beech Cutler, C.E.O.; Jim McCallum, C.F.O.; Carlin Naify, Secy.; Donna L. Courville,* Treas.; Winston Hom, Cont.; Margie Campbell; Jane Einhorn; Cassandra Jennings; Linda Merksamer; Diane Mizell; Darren Morris; William Niemi; Meg Stallard; Martin Steiner; Gary Strong; Stephen Tse; Clarence Williams.
Number of staff: 7 full-time professional; 2 full-time support.
EIN: 942891517

1104
The Saje Foundation ✧
P.O. Box 809
Tustin, CA 92781-0809 (714) 734-7808
FAX: (714) 734-7834;
E-mail: info@sajefoundation.org; Main URL: http://www.sajefoundation.org

Established in 1998 in IL.
Donors: Elaine McKay; Robert L. McKay.
Foundation type: Independent foundation.
Financial data (yr. ended 12/31/13): Assets, $33,678 (M); gifts received, $995,176; expenditures, $1,037,143; qualifying distributions, $900,750; giving activities include $900,750 for 16 grants (high: $175,000; low: $5,000).
Purpose and activities: The mission of the foundation is to support Christian organizations in the United States and in the developing world. Focus areas include: 1) HIV/Aids in Africa; 2) Christian Community Development; 3) Spread of Evangelism; 4) Emergency crisis relief and 5) Christian Micro-Enterprise Development.
Fields of interest: Education; AIDS; Youth development; Human services; International economic development; International relief; International affairs; Christian agencies & churches.
International interests: Developing Countries.
Limitations: Applications not accepted. Giving primarily in CA and IL. No grants to individuals.
Application information: Contributes only to pre-selected organizations.
Officers and Trustees:* John McKay,* Pres.; Elaine McKay,* Secy.; Robert L. McKay, Jr.,* Treas.; Christine McKay.
EIN: 364309903

1105
Mike and Jan Salta Foundation ✧ ☆
20 Executive Cir., Ste. 150
Irvine, CA 92614-4732

Established in 2004 in CA.
Donors: Salta Charitable Lead Trust; Mike Salta; Jan Salta.
Foundation type: Independent foundation.
Financial data (yr. ended 12/31/13): Assets, $108,686 (M); gifts received, $844,552; expenditures, $805,365; qualifying distributions, $794,875; giving activities include $793,535 for 22 grants (high: $608,000; low: $100).
Fields of interest: Arts; Education; Health organizations; Christian agencies & churches; Religion.
Limitations: Applications not accepted. Giving primarily in CA. No grants to individuals.
Application information: Contributes only to pre-selected organizations.
Officers and Directors:* Janet Lyn Salta,* Pres.; Gabriel Farao Salta,* Secy.-Treas.; Louis A. Basile; Judy Harrington; Steven J. Salta.
EIN: 201885144

1106
The Samueli Foundation ✧
(formerly The Samueli Family Foundation)
2101 E. Coast Hwy., Ste. 300
Corona del Mar, CA 92625-1941
FAX: (949) 759-5707; E-mail: info@samueli.org; E-mail for questions pertaining to the Building Communities in Orange County Grant Program: grants@samueli.org; Main URL: http://www.samueli.org
Henry and Susan Samueli's Giving Pledge Profile: http://glasspockets.org/philanthropy-in-focus/eye-on-the-giving-pledge/profiles/samueli

Established in 1998 in CA.
Donors: Henry Samueli; Susan Samueli; HS Management, LP; The Samueli 1995 Family Trust; Samueli Charitable Trust No. 00-1.
Foundation type: Independent foundation.
Financial data (yr. ended 12/31/13): Assets, $179,956 (M); gifts received, $1,320,170; expenditures, $1,540,044; qualifying distributions, $1,389,897; giving activities include $882,004 for 69 grants (high: $81,000; low: $150).
Purpose and activities: Giving primarily to promote scholastic, technical and creative exploration and achievement; build a community of sharing, acceptance and altruism; increase awareness, knowledge and opportunities; and to enhance the quality of life of the underserved.
Fields of interest: Performing arts centers; Education, research; Education; Human services; Christian agencies & churches; Jewish agencies & synagogues.
Limitations: Applications not accepted. Giving primarily in Orange County, CA; some funding also in Israel. No support for umbrella fundraising organizations, political parties, candidates, partisan political organizations, labor organizations, faith-based organizations when the proposed program will exclusively benefit the organization or its members, or fraternal organizations or social clubs. No grants to individuals, or for gala or event sponsorship, research, endowments, capital campaigns, physical improvements (bricks and mortar), association or chamber memberships, or scholarships.
Publications: Financial statement; Grants list.
Application information: Unsolicited requests for funds are no longer accepted. See foundation web site for any updates in this matter.
Officers: Susan Samueli, Pres.; Henry Samueli, Secy.; Gerald R. Solomon, Exec. Dir.
Director: Michael Schulman.
EIN: 330758237

1107
Harriet H. Samuelsson Foundation ✧
P.O. Box 5244
Oxnard, CA 93031-5244 (877) 968-6328
FAX: (949) 833-9584;
E-mail: grants@samuelssonfoundation.org; Additional tel.: (805) 487-5350; Main URL: http://www.samuelssonfoundation.org

Established in 2005 in CA.
Foundation type: Independent foundation.
Financial data (yr. ended 09/30/13): Assets, $27,125,638 (M); expenditures, $1,434,382; qualifying distributions, $1,207,309; giving activities include $1,009,600 for 46 grants (high: $100,000; low: $500).
Purpose and activities: Giving to support organizations that further the health, education, guidance or welfare of youth who reside in Ventura County, CA; organizations that are engaged in cancer research and for the St. John's Regional Medical Center in Oxnard, CA, exclusively for the purchase and maintenance of fetal monitors.
Fields of interest: Cancer research; Boys clubs; Girls clubs; Boys & girls clubs; Human services; Children/youth, services; Children/youth.
Type of support: General/operating support; Capital campaigns; Building/renovation; Equipment; Program development; Conferences/seminars; Research.
Limitations: Giving primarily in Ventura County, CA. No support for non 501(c)(3) organizations. No grants to individuals.
Publications: Application guidelines.
Application information: Letters of inquiry are by invitation only, upon results of eligibility quiz. See foundation web site for information.

Initial approach: Take eligibility quiz on foundation web site
Deadline(s): Mar. 31 and Sept. 30
Board meeting date(s): First Wed. of the month

Trustees: Robert Compton; Thomas Petrovich; Rick B. Smith; Irene Yabu.
Number of staff: None.
EIN: 201687782

1108
The San Diego Foundation ✧
(formerly San Diego Community Foundation)
2508 Historic Decatur Rd., Ste. 200
San Diego, CA 92106-6138 (619) 402-1827
Contact: Robert A. Kelly, C.E.O.
FAX: (619) 239-1710;
E-mail: info@sdfoundation.org; Main URL: http://www.sdfoundation.org
E-Newsletter: http://www.sdfoundation.org/Newsroom/Publications/ENewsletters/Subscribe.aspx
Facebook: http://www.facebook.com/TSDF1?v=wall&ref=search
Knowledge Center: http://www.sdfoundation.org/AboutUs/StudiesResearchReports.aspx
Twitter: http://twitter.com/sd_fdn
YouTube: http://www.youtube.com/user/tsdf01
Scholarship inquiry e-mail: scholarships@sdfoundation.org; Scholarship inquiry tel.: (619) 814-1343

Established in 1975 in CA.
Foundation type: Community foundation.
Financial data (yr. ended 06/30/14): Assets, $674,294,000 (M); gifts received, $37,294,000;

expenditures, $60,260,000; giving activities include $50,669,000 for grants.
Purpose and activities: The mission of The San Diego Foundation is to improve the quality of life in local communities by providing leadership for effective philanthropy that builds enduring assets and by promoting community solutions through research, convenings and actions that advance the common good.
Fields of interest: Arts; Elementary school/education; Secondary school/education; Vocational education; Higher education; Adult education—literacy, basic skills & GED; Education, reading; Education; Environment, research; Environment, public policy; Environment, pollution control; Environment, water resources; Environment, land resources; Environment; Health care; Medical research, institute; Child development, services; Human services; Science, research; Engineering/technology; Science; Aging; Disabilities, people with; Minorities; Women; Economically disadvantaged; Homeless.
International interests: Mexico.
Type of support: General/operating support; Equipment; Land acquisition; Program development; Research; Program evaluation; Employee matching gifts; Scholarships—to individuals; Matching/challenge support.
Limitations: Applications accepted. Giving primarily in the greater San Diego, CA, region. No support for religious organizations. No grants to individuals (except for scholarships), or for annual or capital fund campaigns, endowment funds, conferences, travel, or to underwrite fundraising events and performances.
Publications: Annual report; Financial statement; Grants list; Informational brochure; Newsletter.
Application information: Visit foundation web site for grant application and guidelines. Application form required.
Initial approach: Submit online application and proposal
Deadline(s): Varies
Board meeting date(s): Bimonthly beginning July through May
Final notification: 3 to 5 months
Officers and Board Members:* Steve Smith,* Chair.; Connie L. Matsui,* Vice-Chair. and Secy.; William K. Geppert,* Vice-Chair., Center for Civic Engagement; Benjamin Haddad,* Vice-Chair., Charitable Giving and External Rels.; John Cambon, Ph.D.*, Vice-Chair., Finance; B. Kathryn Mead, C.E.O. and Pres.; Matt Fettig, V.P. and C.I.O.; Theresa Nakata, V.P., Chief Comms. Off.; Emily Young, Ph.D., V.P., Community Impact; Adrienne Vargas, Chief Giving Off.; Daniel Brown, Cont.; Yamila M. Ayad; Darcy C. Bingham; Constance M. Carroll, Ph.D.; Ted Chan, M.D.; Kay Chandler; Richard A. Collato; Roger Cornell, M.D.; Audie de Castro; Robert Dynes, Ph.D.; Ileana Ovalle Engel; Elisabeth Eisner Forbes; Bill Geppert; Kevin Harris; Jacob James; Jennifer LeSar; Bob McNeely; Hollyce J. Phillips; Derek J. Quackenbush; Donna Marie Robinson; Barbara A. Sawrey, Ph.D.; Nancy Spector; Horacio A. Valeiras; Yolanda Selene Walther-Meade.
Number of staff: 26 full-time professional; 8 part-time professional; 11 full-time support; 1 part-time support.
EIN: 952942582
Selected grants: The following grants are a representative sample of this grantmaker's funding activity:
$500,000 to San Diego Unified Port District, San Diego, CA, 2012. For development of Ruocco Park, due for beginning of construction.
$490,927 to Marine Corps Scholarship Foundation, Alexandria, VA, 2012. To create a scholarship fund that will provide annual scholarships in perpetuity to children of Marines from Southern California to go to college.
$300,000 to National Gallery of Victoria, Melbourne, Australia, 2012. For general charitable support.
$200,000 to Interfaith Community Services, Escondido, CA, 2012. To be divided equally between housing and general support.
$131,000 to San Dieguito River Valley Land Conservancy, San Diego, CA, 2012. For general support.
$100,000 to International Community Foundation, National City, CA, 2012. For general support for Olivewood Gardens.
$20,000 to Young Life, Colorado Springs, CO, 2012. For general purpose.
$10,000 to Ocean Discovery Institute, San Diego, CA, 2012. For a Cox Conserves Heroes grant.
$9,250 to Mingei International Museum, San Diego, CA, 2012. For Founder's Circle Membership.
$5,000 to Nativity Prep Academy, San Diego, CA, 2012. For general support.

1109
The San Francisco Foundation ✧
1 Embarcadero Ctr., Ste. 1400
San Francisco, CA 94111 (415) 733-8500
Contact: Dee Dee Brantley, Interim C.E.O.
FAX: (415) 477-2783; E-mail: info@sff.org; Intent to Apply e-mail: apps@sff.org; Main URL: http://www.sff.org
Blog: http://www.sff.org/a-seat-at-the-table/
E-Newsletter: http://www.sff.org/e-newsletter/
Facebook: http://www.facebook.com/TheSanFranciscoFoundation
Flickr: http://www.flickr.com/photos/thesanfranciscofoundation/
LinkedIn: http://www.linkedin.com/company/the-san-francisco-foundation
The San Francisco Foundation's Philanthropy Promise: http://www.ncrp.org/philanthropys-promise/who
Twitter: https://twitter.com/TSFF
YouTube: https://www.youtube.com/tsffvideo

Established in 1948 in CA by resolution and declaration of trust.
Foundation type: Community foundation.
Financial data (yr. ended 06/30/13): Assets, $1,183,262,000 (M); gifts received, $68,749,000; expenditures, $99,928,000; giving activities include $86,830,000 for grants.
Purpose and activities: The foundation mobilizes resources and acts as a catalyst for change to build strong communities, foster civic leadership, and promote philanthropy. Grants principally in six categories: the arts and culture, community health, education, environment, neighborhood and community development, and social justice.
Fields of interest: Arts, cultural/ethnic awareness; Media/communications; Performing arts; Performing arts, dance; Humanities; Arts, artist's services; Arts; Education, early childhood education; Child development, education; Elementary school/education; Higher education; Adult education—literacy, basic skills & GED; Education, reading; Education; Environment, natural resources; Environment; Reproductive health, family planning; Health care; Substance abuse, services; Mental health/crisis services; Health organizations, association; Cancer; AIDS; Alcoholism; Crime/violence prevention, youth; Legal services; Employment; Housing/shelter, development; Youth development, services; Children/youth, services; Child development, services; Family services; Aging, centers/services; Homeless, human services; Human services; International human rights; Civil/human rights; Urban/community development; Community/economic development; Voluntarism promotion; Public policy, research; Government/public administration; Leadership development; Public affairs; Aging; Disabilities, people with; Minorities; Immigrants/refugees; Economically disadvantaged; Homeless.
Type of support: General/operating support; Program development; Fellowships; Technical assistance; Program-related investments/loans; Employee matching gifts; Scholarships—to individuals.
Limitations: Applications accepted. Giving limited to the San Francisco Bay Area, CA, counties of Alameda, Contra Costa, Marin, San Francisco, and San Mateo. No support for religious purposes, or medical, academic, or scientific research. No grants to individuals (except scholarships and fellowships designated by a donor) or for conferences or one-time events.
Publications: Annual report; Financial statement; Grants list; Newsletter; Program policy statement.
Application information: Visit foundation web site for Grantee Center online application, application guidelines and specific deadlines. Application form required.
Initial approach: Complete online grant application
Deadline(s): Mar. 13
Board meeting date(s): Monthly except Jan., Apr., and Aug.; applications are reviewed two times each year
Final notification: Approx. 16 weeks after deadline
Officers and Trustees:* Andy Ballard,* Chair.; Dee Dee Brantley, V.P., Human Resources and C.O.O.; Ruben Orduna, V.P., Devel. and Donor Svcs.; Jane Sullivan, V.P., Mktg. and Strategic Comms.; Myra Chow, Interim V.P., Progs.; Monica Pressley, C.F.O.; Susan Frohlich, Cont.; Ophelia B. Basgal; Fred Blackwell; David Friedman; Edward H. McDermott; John Murray; Kurt C. Organista, Ph.D.; Duncan Robertson; Peggy Saika; Sarah Stein; Sheyl Wong.
Number of staff: 35 full-time professional; 2 part-time professional; 13 full-time support; 3 part-time support.
EIN: 010679337

1110
San Luis Obispo County Community Foundation ✧
550 Dana St.
San Luis Obispo, CA 93401 (805) 543-2323
Contact: For grants: Janice Fong Wolf, Dir., Grants & Progs.
FAX: (805) 543-2346; E-mail: info@sloccf.org; Additional e-mail: jwolf@sloccf.org; Main URL: http://www.sloccf.org
Facebook: http://www.facebook.com/pages/San-Luis-Obispo-County-Community-Foundation/359118103540

Established in 1998 in CA.
Foundation type: Community foundation.

Financial data (yr. ended 12/31/13): Assets, $40,753,353 (M); gifts received, $2,778,049; expenditures, $2,225,269; giving activities include $1,453,638 for grants.
Purpose and activities: The foundation is a public trust established to assist donors in building an enduring source of charitable funds to meet the changing needs and interests of the community. The foundation offers grants for area nonprofits aimed at helping them increase their organizational capacity.
Fields of interest: Historic preservation/historical societies; Arts; Education; Environment; Health care; Recreation; Human services; Nonprofit management; Community/economic development; Children/youth; Youth; Aging; Young adults; Disabilities, people with; Physically disabled; Hispanics/Latinos; Women; Girls; Economically disadvantaged; Homeless; Migrant workers; LGBTQ.
Type of support: General/operating support; Continuing support; Management development/ capacity building; Building/renovation; Equipment; Program development; Technical assistance; Consulting services; Scholarships—to individuals; Matching/challenge support.
Limitations: Applications accepted. Giving primarily in San Luis Obispo County, CA. No support for religious programs (unless open to the public regardless of religious affiliation), governmental organizations, or fraternal organizations (unless in support of a specific program open to or benefiting the entire community). No grants to individuals (except for scholarships), or for endowments, debt reduction, fundraising events, fellowships, travel, or technical or specialized research.
Publications: Application guidelines; Annual report; Grants list; Informational brochure; Newsletter; Occasional report.
Application information: Visit foundation web site for application cover sheet and guidelines. Faxed or e-mailed applications are not accepted. Application form required.
Initial approach: Submit application cover sheet, narrative, and attachments
Copies of proposal: 6
Deadline(s): Varies
Board meeting date(s): Monthly
Final notification: Within 3 months
Officers and Directors:* Ann Robinson,* Pres.; Heidi McPherson,* C.E.O.; Steve McCarty,* V.P.; Nick Thille, Secy.; Bill Raver,* C.F.O. and Treas.; Jim Brabeck; Jim Glinn; Lee Hollister; Steven B. Jobst, M.D.; Steve McCarty; Mike Miner; Barbara Leigh Partridge; Mike Patrick; Ann Robinson; Johnnie Talley; Mary Verdin.
Number of staff: 1 full-time professional; 5 part-time professional.
EIN: 770496500
Selected grants: The following grants are a representative sample of this grantmaker's funding activity:
$504,448 to California Polytechnic State University, San Luis Obispo, CA, 2012. For music department capital improvements.
$232,836 to French Hospital Medical Center Foundation, San Luis Obispo, CA, 2012. For heart disease care and treatment.
$129,000 to Five Cities Homeless Coalition, Grover Beach, CA, 2012. For organizational capacity building.
$41,075 to Womens Shelter Program of San Luis Obispo County, San Luis Obispo, CA, 2012. For program support.
$38,000 to Community Action Partnership of San Luis Obispo County, San Luis Obispo, CA, 2012. For business management training for childcare providers.
$19,403 to Community Counseling Center of San Luis Obispo County, San Luis Obispo, CA, 2012. For program support.
$13,500 to San Luis Obispo County Office of Education, San Luis Obispo, CA, 2012. For Raising a Reader Program.
$4,000 to Transitional Food and Shelter, Paso Robles, CA, 2012. For temporary emergency shelter for homeless children.

1111
The San Simeon Fund, Inc. ✧
c/o William R. Hearst III
765 Market St., No. 34D
San Francisco, CA 94103-2040

Established in 2004 in CA.
Donors: William R. Hearst III; Margaret C. Hearst.
Foundation type: Independent foundation.
Financial data (yr. ended 12/31/13): Assets, $55,837,224 (M); gifts received, $3,471,706; expenditures, $2,441,935; qualifying distributions, $1,912,849; giving activities include $1,899,912 for 4 grants (high: $999,912; low: $100,000).
Fields of interest: Museums (natural history); Performing arts centers; Performing arts, ballet; Higher education; Science, single organization support.
Limitations: Applications not accepted. Giving primarily in San Francisco, CA and New York, NY. No grants to individuals.
Application information: Contributes only to pre-selected organizations.
Officers: William R. Hearst III, Pres.; Margaret C. Hearst, V.P. and C.F.O.; Cynthia D. Lund, Secy.
EIN: 201986583

1112
Sand Hill Foundation ✧
3000 Sand Hill Rd., 1-120
Menlo Park, CA 94025-7122 (650) 854-9310
Contact: Susan Ford Dorsey, Pres.
FAX: (650) 854-8031;
E-mail: ash@sandhillfoundation.org; Main URL: http://www.sandhillfoundation.org

Established in 1995 in CA.
Donor: Thomas W. Ford.
Foundation type: Independent foundation.
Financial data (yr. ended 12/31/12): Assets, $57,074,208 (M); expenditures, $4,063,989; qualifying distributions, $3,592,792; giving activities include $3,072,679 for 81 grants (high: $750,000; low: $90).
Purpose and activities: The foundation provides funding for promising and proven nonprofit organizations working to strengthen families and preserve the natural environment, with a primary focus in San Mateo and northern Santa Clara Counties. The foundation seeks to invest in organizations that demonstrate effective, inspiring leadership in their areas of service and are managed for long-term sustainability. The foundation strongly favors approaches to strengthening families and preserving the environment that work at pivotal inflection points when the greatest opportunity for transformational change exists.
Fields of interest: Vocational education; Adult/ continuing education; Education; Environment; Health care; Mental health/crisis services; Employment, retraining; Youth development, adult & child programs; Human services; Children/youth, services; Family services; Financial services.
Limitations: Applications accepted. Giving primarily in San Mateo and northern Santa Clara counties, CA. No support for medical research. No grants to individuals, or for deficit financing; no loans.
Publications: Application guidelines.
Application information: Unsolicited proposals for Preserving and Protecting Environment grants will not be accepted. Inquires and proposals sent by U.S. Mail or e-mail are not accepted. Application form not required.
Initial approach: Use online grant system on foundation web site only.
Copies of proposal: 1
Deadline(s): Rolling deadlines
Final notification: Within 4 to 6 weeks
Officers and Directors:* Susan Ford Dorsey,* Pres.; Susan Lockwood,* V.P.; Laura Arrillaga-Andreessen,* Treas.; Ash McNeely, Exec. Dir.
Number of staff: 1 part-time professional.
EIN: 943219107

1113
George H. Sandy Foundation ✧
P.O. Box 591717
San Francisco, CA 94159-1717
Contact: Trey MacPhee, Tr.

Trust established in 1960 in CA.
Donor: George H. Sandy†.
Foundation type: Independent foundation.
Financial data (yr. ended 12/31/13): Assets, $39,542,610 (M); expenditures, $3,209,395; qualifying distributions, $1,856,506; giving activities include $1,790,000 for 88 grants (high: $60,000; low: $5,000).
Purpose and activities: Giving for charitable purposes, and educational purposes, with emphasis on aid to the handicapped and underprivileged.
Fields of interest: Human services; Disabilities, people with; Physically disabled; Blind/visually impaired; Economically disadvantaged.
Type of support: General/operating support; Continuing support; Scholarship funds.
Limitations: Applications accepted. Giving limited to the San Francisco Bay Area, CA. No support for other private non-operating foundations, or for any particular religious order. No grants to individuals, or for annual campaigns, seed money, emergency funds, deficit financing, capital campaigns, endowment or building funds, matching gifts, scholarships, fellowships, special projects, research, publications, or conferences; no loans.
Publications: Annual report; Annual report (including application guidelines); Financial statement; Informational brochure.
Application information: Application form not required.
Initial approach: Letter
Copies of proposal: 1
Deadline(s): Aug. 31
Board meeting date(s): Quarterly, and as needed
Final notification: Varies
Trustees: Thomas J. Feeney; Trey MacPhee; Union Bank of California, N.A.
EIN: 946054473

Selected grants: The following grants are a representative sample of this grantmaker's funding activity:
$60,000 to Larkin Street Youth Services, San Francisco, CA, 2012. For their Housing and Support services.
$40,000 to Homeless Prenatal Program, San Francisco, CA, 2012. For services for low-income and homeless families.
$35,000 to Janet Pomeroy Center, San Francisco, CA, 2012. For their after-school Programs for children and teens.
$35,000 to Okizu Foundation, Novato, CA, 2012. For their general operation and core Programs.
$35,000 to SF-Marin Food Bank, San Francisco, CA, 2012. To open new weekly Neighborhood Grocery Networks and to support and expand the Healthy Children Pantry Program.
$35,000 to Stanbridge Academy, San Mateo, CA, 2012. For their tuition assistance Program.
$20,000 to Eastside College Preparatory School, East Palo Alto, CA, 2012. For their Programs for college preparation for low income students.
$20,000 to Halleck Creek Ranch, Nicasio, CA, 2012. For their therapeutic horseback riding Programs for children with disabilities.
$20,000 to Marin Center for Independent Living, San Rafael, CA, 2012. For their Attendant Referral Registry.
$15,000 to Redwood Empire Food Bank, Santa Rosa, CA, 2012. For their Food Pantry Program.

1114
Sangham Foundation ✧ ☆

1114 State St., Ste. 310
Santa Barbara, CA 93101-2739 (805) 845-0253
Contact: Christiane Santoro, Treas.
FAX: (858) 712-8935;
E-mail: contact@sanghamfoundation.org; Main URL: http://www.sanghamfoundation.org/
Grants List: http://www.sanghamfoundation.org/grant-portfolio.php

Established in 2003 in HI.
Donors: The Hecht Family, LLC; Margaret Hecht; 2008 Hecht Trust.
Foundation type: Independent foundation.
Financial data (yr. ended 12/31/13): Assets, $5,747,059 (M); expenditures, $485,112; qualifying distributions, $465,133; giving activities include $458,239 for 34 grants (high: $89,000; low: $1,000).
Purpose and activities: Giving for non-profit organizations committed to protecting water resources, improving water quality, and improving the lives of children.
Fields of interest: Environment, water resources; Environment, forests; Food services; Family services; Infants/toddlers; Children/youth; Children; Youth; Young adults; Infants/toddlers, female; Girls; Young adults, female; Infants/toddlers, male; Young adults, male.
International interests: Africa; India.
Type of support: General/operating support; Continuing support; Income development; Management development/capacity building; Capital campaigns; Program development; Publication; Consulting services; Matching/challenge support.
Limitations: Applications not accepted. Giving primarily in CA, ID and OR.
Publications: Grants list.
Application information: Unsolicited requests for funds not accepted.
Officers and Directors:* Sean Hecht,* Pres.; Dayvin Turchiano,* V.P.; Nicoya Hecht,* Secy.; Christiane Santoro,* Treas.; Amara Hecht; James Christopher Hecht; James Grey Hecht; Jennifer Hecht; Margaret Hecht; Marya Hecht.
Number of staff: 1 part-time professional; 1 full-time support; 1 part-time support.
EIN: 731681596
Selected grants: The following grants are a representative sample of this grantmaker's funding activity:
$3,000 to Maui Food Bank, Wailuku, HI, 2012. For general.

1115
Yvonne and Angelo Sangiacomo Family Foundation ✧

1145 Market St., 12th Fl.
San Francisco, CA 94103-1545

Established in 2001 in CA.
Donors: Maryanne Iacomini; Ann Marie Kane; Angelo Sangiacomo; James Sangiacomo; Mark Sangiacomo; Mia Sangiacomo; Sandro Sangiacomo; Susan Sangiacomo; Yvonne Sangiacomo.
Foundation type: Operating foundation.
Financial data (yr. ended 12/31/13): Assets, $16,862,861 (M); expenditures, $823,362; qualifying distributions, $726,679; giving activities include $724,580 for grants.
Fields of interest: Higher education, university; Education; Human services; Children/youth, services; Catholic agencies & churches; Economically disadvantaged.
Limitations: Applications not accepted. Giving primarily in CA. No grants to individuals.
Application information: Contributes only to pre-selected organizations.
Officers and Directors:* Angelo Sangiacomo,* C.E.O.; Yvonne Sangiacomo,* Pres.; Maria Sangiacomo,* Secy.; Susan Sangiacomo,* Treas. and C.F.O.; Anne Sangiacomo Kane; James Sangiacomo; Mark Sangiacomo; Sandro Sangiacomo; Maryanne Sangiacomo-Iacomini.
EIN: 943412371
Selected grants: The following grants are a representative sample of this grantmaker's funding activity:
$3,500 to City of Hope, Duarte, CA, 2011.

1116
Santa Barbara Foundation ✧

1111 Chapala St., Ste. 200
Santa Barbara, CA 93101 (805) 963-1873
Contact: Ronald V. Gallo, C.E.O.
FAX: (805) 966-2345;
E-mail: info@sbfoundation.org; Grant application e-mail: grants@sbfoundation.org; Main URL: http://www.sbfoundation.org
Blog: http://www.sbfoundation.org/feed.rss?id=3
E-Newsletter: http://www.sbfoundation.org/Page.aspx?pid=452
Facebook: https://www.facebook.com/sbfoundation
Flickr: http://www.flickr.com/photos/68044616@N08/sets/
Grants Database: https://www.sbfoundation.org/page.aspx?pid=435
Twitter: http://twitter.com/sbfoundation
YouTube: http://www.youtube.com/user/SBFoundationImpact

Incorporated Oct. 16, 1928 in CA.
Foundation type: Community foundation.
Financial data (yr. ended 12/31/13): Assets, $320,130,872 (M); gifts received, $19,689,768; expenditures, $30,211,233; giving activities include $22,686,386 for grants.
Purpose and activities: The foundation's mission is to enrich the lives of the people of Santa Barbara County through philanthropy. To achieve this mission, the foundation will: 1) serve as a leader, catalyst, and resource for philanthropy; 2) strive for measurable community improvement through strategic funding in such fields as community enhancement, culture, education, environment, health, human services, personal development, and recreation; 3) promote partnerships to address important community issues and leverage resources to meet community needs; 4) build and prudently manage a growing endowment for the community's present and future needs; and 5) provide secure, flexible, and effective opportunities for donors to improve their community.
Fields of interest: Arts; Education; Environment; Animal welfare; Public health; Health care; Substance abuse, services; Housing/shelter; Recreation; Children/youth, services; Children, day care; Human services, personal services; Residential/custodial care, hospices; Aging, centers/services; Human services; Community/economic development; Public affairs, citizen participation.
Type of support: Capital campaigns; Building/renovation; Equipment; Land acquisition; Emergency funds; Program development; Scholarship funds; Scholarships—to individuals; Matching/challenge support; Student loans—to individuals.
Limitations: Applications accepted. Giving limited to Santa Barbara County, CA. No support for religious organizations for religious purposes. No grants to individuals (except for scholarships), or for deficit financing, endowment funds, capital needs, fundraising drives, fellowships, or for research.
Publications: Application guidelines; Annual report; Financial statement; Informational brochure; Newsletter; Occasional report.
Application information: Visit foundation web site for application forms and guidelines. Application form required.
Initial approach: Application
Deadline(s): Varies
Board meeting date(s): Jan., Mar., May, June, Sept., Oct., and Dec.
Final notification: Varies
Officers and Trustees:* Eileen F. Sheridan,* Chair.; James Morouse,* Vice-Chair.; Ronald V. Gallo, C.E.O. and Pres.; Jan Campbell, Sr. V.P., Philanthropic Svcs.; Dee Jennings, Sr. V.P., Finance and Admin./C.F.O.; Al Rodriguez, V.P., Community Investments; Diane Adam,* Secy.; Gretchen Milligan,* Treas.; Peter MacDougall,* Chair. Emeritus; Cheri Savage, Asst. Treas.; Laurie Ashton; Hugh M. Boss; Frederick W. Gluck; Stephen Hicks; Ralph Iannelli; Michael G. Mayfield; Jennifer Murray; Cathy Pepe; Michelle Lee Pickett; Niki Sandoval; Robert Skinner; Chris Slaughter; Luis Villegas; Polly Firestone Walker; Michael D. Young.
Fund Managers: Alternative Investment Manager; Capital Research & Management Co.; Hammond

and Associates; Luther King Capital Management; Straleu and Co.; Wells Fargo Bank, N.A.
Number of staff: 17 full-time professional; 4 full-time support.
EIN: 951866094
Selected grants: The following grants are a representative sample of this grantmaker's funding activity:
$90,000 to University of California, Santa Barbara, CA, 2012. For the Postdoctoral Fellowship Program in the scientific research area of blood banking.
$75,000 to 2nd Story, Santa Barbara, CA, 2012. For the collective impact project to address homelessness and prioritize services for those living on the streets who are most vulnerable.
$75,000 to Good Samaritan Shelter, Santa Maria, CA, 2012. For core operating support to address shelter, food and healthcare needs in Santa Barbara County.
$75,000 to Just Communities Central Coast, Santa Barbara, CA, 2012. To increase parent involvement in their children's education, schools and community and large to improve academic outcomes for all students.
$50,000 to Santa Barbara Museum of Natural History, Santa Barbara, CA, 2012. To produce four civic engagement Town Hall meetings in partnership with Santa Barbara Foundation on topics relevant to community needs and priorities.
$50,000 to Santa Barbara Rape Crisis Center, Santa Barbara, CA, 2012. For core operating support to address mental health care and education needs in Santa Barbara County.
$31,000 to PCPA Foundation, Santa Maria, CA, 2012. To develop a costume and properties rental inventory management system to increase revenue and create organizational efficiencies.
$12,000 to Foundation for Santa Barbara City College, Santa Barbara, CA, 2012. To support existing ESL program and student support services.
$5,940 to Blood Systems, San Luis Obispo, CA, 2012. For the EldonCard program and the utilization of pheresis technology.
$5,000 to YMCA, Santa Maria Valley, Santa Maria, CA, 2012. To increase the understanding of the factors that contribute to bullying and violence among students and provide incentives to correct such behavior.

1117
Bernard G. Sarnat and Rhoda G. Sarnat Family Foundation-Joan Sarnat Family ✧
123 Mission St., Ste. 1800
San Francisco, CA 94105-1551

Established in 2003 in CA and DE.
Donors: Bernard G. Sarnat†; Rhoda G. Sarnat; Sarnat Charitable Lead Trust II.
Foundation type: Independent foundation.
Financial data (yr. ended 06/30/13): Assets, $14,454,103 (M); gifts received, $257,608; expenditures, $636,204; qualifying distributions, $528,998; giving activities include $528,998 for grants.
Fields of interest: Jewish federated giving programs.
Limitations: Applications not accepted. Giving primarily in San Francisco, CA. No grants to individuals.
Application information: Contributes only to pre-selected organizations.
Officers: Joan E. Sarnat, Pres.; David A. Hoffman, V.P.; Jascha S. Hoffman, Secy.; Michael S. Hoffman, Treas.
EIN: 201004445
Selected grants: The following grants are a representative sample of this grantmaker's funding activity:
$399,932 to Jewish Community Endowment Fund, San Francisco, CA, 2011.

1118
Saunders Family Charitable Fund ✧
765 Market St., No. 24D
San Francisco, CA 94103-2037
Application address: c/o Joseph Clare, 135 Main St., 9th Fl., San Francisco, CA 94105 tel.: (415) 655-6365

Established in 2005 in CA.
Donors: Joseph W. Saunders; Sharon P. Saunders.
Foundation type: Operating foundation.
Financial data (yr. ended 12/31/13): Assets, $4,743,206 (M); gifts received, $891,171; expenditures, $1,743,069; qualifying distributions, $1,683,335; giving activities include $1,647,925 for 13 grants (high: $1,000,000; low: $154).
Fields of interest: Higher education; Medical school/education; Education.
Limitations: Applications accepted. Giving primarily in CA, CT and RI.
Application information: Application form required.
Initial approach: Contact application address
Deadline(s): Contact application address
Trustees: Christine Saunders; Joseph W. Saunders; Sharon P. Saunders; Thomas J. Saunders; John N. Staples III.
EIN: 680616611
Selected grants: The following grants are a representative sample of this grantmaker's funding activity:
$250,000 to Stanford University, Stanford, CA, 2011.
$97,566 to Salisbury School, Salisbury, CT, 2011.
$50,000 to Teach for All, New York, NY, 2011.

1119
Saw Island Foundation Inc. ✧
(formerly Emil Mosbacher, Jr. Foundation, Inc.)
524 Moore Rd., Ste. A
Woodside, CA 94062-1109 (650) 851-9990
Contact: R. Bruce Mosbacher, Pres.
Main URL: http://sawisland.org/

Incorporated in 1974 in NY.
Donors: Emil Mosbacher, Jr.†; R. Bruce Mosbacher; The Emil Mosbacher Jr. Charitable Annuity Trust.
Foundation type: Independent foundation.
Financial data (yr. ended 11/30/13): Assets, $14,292,846 (M); gifts received, $640,713; expenditures, $936,982; qualifying distributions, $900,885; giving activities include $900,000 for 35 grants (high: $353,900; low: $100).
Purpose and activities: The foundation seeks to empower innovative and high-impact institutions to improve existing programs and pioneer new approaches to solving problems and inefficiencies in health, education and delivery of social services.
Fields of interest: Higher education; Education; Medical research, institute; Cancer research; Human services; Children/youth, services; Philanthropy/voluntarism.
Type of support: Scholarship funds; Research.
Limitations: Applications accepted. Giving primarily in the San Francisco Bay Area, CA. No support for political organizations. No grants to individuals, or for lobbying.
Application information: Formal applications or requests for more information will be based on review of initial online submission.
Initial approach: Use application format on foundation web site
Deadline(s): None
Officers and Director:* R. Bruce Mosbacher, Pres.; Nancy J. Ditz, Secy.; Jack Ryan Mosbacher,* Treas.
EIN: 237454106
Selected grants: The following grants are a representative sample of this grantmaker's funding activity:
$100,000 to Lucile Packard Foundation for Childrens Health, Palo Alto, CA, 2011.
$100,000 to Stanford University, Stanford, CA, 2011.
$100,000 to University of California, Oakland, CA, 2011.
$20,000 to Dartmouth College, Hanover, NH, 2011.
$20,000 to Hospital for Special Surgery Fund, New York, NY, 2011.
$15,000 to Herreshoff Marine Museum, Bristol, RI, 2011.
$15,000 to Palo Alto Medical Foundation for Health Care, Research and Education, Mountain View, CA, 2011.
$10,000 to Memorial Sloan-Kettering Cancer Center, New York, NY, 2011.
$10,000 to University of California, Oakland, CA, 2011.
$1,000 to San Francisco Girls Chorus, San Francisco, CA, 2011.

1120
Scaife Scholarship Foundation ✧ ☆
1547 Lakeside Dr.
Oakland, CA 94612-4520 (510) 451-1906
Contact: Cal Gilbert, Secy.-Treas.

Established in fiscal 1992 pursuant to an IRS ruling ending the combined filing of the foundation and the Northern California Scholarship Foundation.
Donors: Clarence Benjamin†; Rogert Ervin Schulze†; RBC Dain Rauscher Inc.
Foundation type: Independent foundation.
Financial data (yr. ended 05/31/13): Assets, $12,761,843 (M); expenditures, $601,427; qualifying distributions, $585,006; giving activities include $500,500 for grants to individuals.
Purpose and activities: Scholarship awards to graduates of northern California public high schools whose parents were born in the United States.
Fields of interest: Higher education.
Type of support: Scholarships—to individuals.
Limitations: Giving limited to northern CA residents.
Application information: Written application on pre-printed forms, including transcripts of high school records, college entrance exam scores, and statement of financial need. Application form required.
Initial approach: Letter requesting application form
Deadline(s): Mar. 15
Officers: Byron Flanders, Pres.; Dave Arp, V.P.; Cal Gilbert, Secy.-Treas.
Trustees: Wade Bingham; Hans Bissinger; Dallas G. Cason; Robert Crow; Don Emig; Thomas D. Eychner; Bill K'Burg; Julius "Sandy" Khan III; George

Klopping; James F. McClung, Jr.; Dan Miller; Clyde Minar; Norman Owen; James Sloenaker; Zook Sutton; George Vukasin.
EIN: 943161402

1121
George W. Schaeffer Foundation ✧
716 N. Maple Dr.
Beverly Hills, CA 90210-3411

Donors: George Schaeffer; Schaeffer Family Foundation.
Foundation type: Independent foundation.
Financial data (yr. ended 12/31/12): Assets, $709,585 (M); gifts received, $5,000,000; expenditures, $5,066,748; qualifying distributions, $5,062,987; giving activities include $3,875,729 for 68 grants (high: $1,570,000; low: $20).
Purpose and activities: Giving primarily to Orthodox Jewish agencies, temples, and schools.
Fields of interest: Education; Hospitals (general); Human services; Jewish agencies & synagogues.
Limitations: Applications not accepted. Giving primarily in CA, CO, and NY.
Application information: Contributes only to pre-selected organizations.
Officer: George Schaeffer, Pres. and C.E.O.
Directors: Fred Fenster; Vinesh Nathu; Eric Varady.
EIN: 262261640

1122
The Stephen Harold Schimmel Foundation, Inc. ✧ ☆
8 Archipelago Dr.
Newport Coast, CA 92657-2106

Established in 1995 in DE.
Donors: Stephen Harold Schimmel; Rosalba Schimmel.
Foundation type: Independent foundation.
Financial data (yr. ended 09/30/13): Assets, $5,817,987 (M); expenditures, $575,053; qualifying distributions, $521,570; giving activities include $500,000 for 1 grant.
Purpose and activities: Giving primarily for Christian organizations.
Fields of interest: Botanical gardens; Christian agencies & churches.
Type of support: General/operating support.
Limitations: Applications not accepted. Giving primarily in VA. No grants to individuals.
Application information: Unsolicited requests for funds not accepted.
Officers: Stephen Harold Schimmel, Pres. and Secy.; Rosalba Schimmel, V.P. and Treas.
EIN: 223386066
Selected grants: The following grants are a representative sample of this grantmaker's funding activity:
$275,000 to Christian Broadcasting Network, Virginia Beach, VA, 2011. For general support.

1123
Schlinger Family Foundation ✧
1250 N. Lakeview Ave., Apt. B
Anaheim, CA 92807-1801

Established in 2003 in CA.
Donors: Michael Stewart Schlinger; Michael S. Schlinger Trust; Warren & Katherine Schlinger Foundation.
Foundation type: Independent foundation.
Financial data (yr. ended 12/31/12): Assets, $2,055,674 (M); gifts received, $656,830; expenditures, $629,127; qualifying distributions, $605,225; giving activities include $592,090 for 54 grants (high: $400,000; low: $100).
Fields of interest: Performing arts centers; Arts; Animal welfare; Health organizations; Human services; Children/youth, services; Protestant agencies & churches.
Limitations: Applications not accepted. Giving primarily in AZ and CA. No grants to individuals.
Application information: Contributes only to pre-selected organizations.
Officers and Director:* Michael Stewart Schlinger,* Pres.; Stacy Schlinger, V.P., Secy.-Treas., and C.F.O.; Greg S. Schlinger, V.P.; Leanne M. Schlinger, V.P.
EIN: 522390970

1124
Warren & Katherine Schlinger Foundation ✧
1250 N. Lakeview Ave., Ste. B
Anaheim, CA 92807-1801

Established in 1994 in CA.
Donor: Warren G. Schlinger.
Foundation type: Independent foundation.
Financial data (yr. ended 12/31/12): Assets, $51,476,980 (M); expenditures, $2,945,931; qualifying distributions, $2,716,860; giving activities include $2,700,000 for 60 grants (high: $500,000; low: $1,000).
Purpose and activities: Giving primarily for higher education, with emphasis on engineering schools; giving also for arts and cultural programs, human services and Congregational churches.
Fields of interest: Arts; Higher education; Engineering school/education; Human services; Engineering/technology; Christian agencies & churches.
Type of support: Capital campaigns; Professorships; Seed money; Fellowships; Scholarship funds.
Limitations: Applications not accepted. Giving primarily in CA. No grants to individuals.
Application information: Contributes only to pre-selected organizations.
Board meeting date(s): Nov.
Officers and Directors:* Warren G. Schlinger,* Pres.; Michael S. Schlinger,* V.P.; Norman W. Schlinger,* Secy.; Sarah L. Chrisman,* C.F.O.
EIN: 954494669

1125
The Schmidt Family Foundation ✧
555 Bryant St., No. 370
Palo Alto, CA 94301-1704
Contact: Sarah Bell, Prog. Mgr., 11th Hour Project
FAX: (650) 454-8993; E-mail: staff@theschmidt.org; Main URL: http://theschmidt.org/

Established in 2006 in CA.
Donors: Eric Schmidt; Wendy Schmidt.
Foundation type: Independent foundation.
Financial data (yr. ended 12/31/12): Assets, $312,189,881 (M); gifts received, $143,260,276; expenditures, $22,518,322; qualifying distributions, $21,840,872; giving activities include $17,502,100 for 115 grants (high: $1,500,000; low: $500), $3,746,395 for 3 foundation-administered programs and $608,609 for 3 loans/program-related investments.
Purpose and activities: The foundation supports efforts, using best expert information, to help transform the world's environmental and energy practices in the 21st century. The foundation's mission, at its broadest, is to advance the creation of an increasingly intelligent relationship between human activity and the use of the world's natural resources. The foundation works strategically, and often in collaboration, to create successful models of their vision. This includes the restoration and protection of vulnerable historic places while improving their environmental profile, using new technologies, and the growing knowledge about the impact of the built environment on the Earth's climate system. The foundation supports efforts around the world to improve health, education, transportation and communications through investing in a pattern of economic development that includes green, sustainable environmental practices and design. In addition, the foundation supports public education around issues of energy and the environment and promote public understanding of the science of climate change.
Fields of interest: Environment.
Limitations: Applications not accepted. Giving primarily in CA.
Publications: Annual report; Financial statement; Grants list; IRS Form 990 or 990-PF printed copy available upon request.
Application information: Unsolicited requests for funds not accepted. Grantmaking is by invitation only.
Officers and Directors:* Wendy Schmidt,* Pres., Schmidt Family Foundation; Eric Schmidt,* V.P.; Sophie Schmidt,* V.P.; William J. Arthur, Secy.; Jeanne W. Huey, C.F.O.; Joe Sciortino, Exec. Dir., Schmidt Family Foundation; Amy Rao, Pres., 11th Hour Project.
EIN: 204170342

1126
The Schow Foundation ✧
201 Mission St., Ste. 1825
San Francisco, CA 94105-8121

Established in 2000 in CA.
Donors: Howard Schow; Nan Schow.
Foundation type: Independent foundation.
Financial data (yr. ended 12/31/13): Assets, $37,358,699 (M); expenditures, $7,067,189; qualifying distributions, $6,729,253; giving activities include $6,686,026 for 46 grants (high: $1,070,647; low: $1,000).
Purpose and activities: Giving primarily for a hospital, as well as for health care and education.
Fields of interest: Arts; Higher education; Education; Hospitals (general); Health care; Human services.
Limitations: Applications not accepted. Giving primarily in CA; with some emphasis on Pasadena. No grants to individuals.
Application information: Contributes only to pre-selected organizations.
Officers: Nan Schow, Pres.; Steven Schow, C.F.O.; Melanie J. Schow, Secy. and Exec. Dir.; Roger Schow, Treas.
EIN: 954791558

Selected grants: The following grants are a representative sample of this grantmaker's funding activity:
$515,000 to Marin Agricultural Land Trust, Point Reyes Station, CA, 2012. For Farmland Forever Campaign.

1127
Charles Schwab Foundation ✧
211 Main St.
SF211 MN-16-205
San Francisco, CA 94105-1905 (877) 408-5438
Contact: Elinore Robey, Dir. of Progs.; Roger K. Wong, Progs. Mgr.
FAX: (415) 636-3262;
E-mail: charlesschwabfoundation@schwab.com; Main URL: http://www.aboutschwab.com/community

Established in 1993 in CA.
Donors: The Charles Schwab Corp.; Charles Schwab & Co., Inc.
Foundation type: Company-sponsored foundation.
Financial data (yr. ended 12/31/12): Assets, $1,275,247 (M); gifts received, $2,835,645; expenditures, $5,020,241; qualifying distributions, $5,018,097; giving activities include $4,573,852 for 2,282 grants (high: $500,000; low: $25).
Purpose and activities: Charles Schwab Foundation provides direct grants to select nonprofit organizations that support Schwab's commitment to financial literacy and respond to local cultural and social needs.
Fields of interest: Arts; Disasters, preparedness/services; Boys & girls clubs; Human services, financial counseling; Human services; Community/economic development; Philanthropy/voluntarism; Financial services; Children/youth; Adults; Aging; Young adults; Military/veterans; Economically disadvantaged.
Type of support: Sponsorships; Matching/challenge support; Management development/capacity building; Conferences/seminars; Continuing support; Employee matching gifts; Employee volunteer services; General/operating support; In-kind gifts; Scholarship funds.
Limitations: Applications not accepted. Giving on a national basis with emphasis on San Francisco Bay Area, CA, Denver, CO, Orlando, FL, Indianapolis, IN, Richfield, OH, and Austin, TX. No support for religious, political, or athletic organizations, disease-specific organizations, member-based organizations, discriminatory organizations, organizations with litigious or divisive public agendas, or private foundations; generally, no support for institutions of higher education or hospitals. No grants to individuals (except for Money Matters scholarships), or for advertising or cause-related marketing projects, business development activities, group travel, sponsorships, promotional events, video productions, capital campaigns, or challenge or seed funding; generally, no medical research.
Application information: The foundation currently has an invitation only process for giving.
Board meeting date(s): Bi-annual
Officers and Directors:* Charles R. Schwab,* Chair.; Carrie Schwab-Pomerantz, Pres.; Charmel Huffman,* Secy.; Jordan Oliver,* Treas.; Jay L. Allen; Steve Anderson; John Clendening; Patricia Cox; Sherri Kroonenberg; Scott Rhoades; Paul Woolway.
Number of staff: 3 full-time professional; 2 part-time professional.
EIN: 943192615

1128
Charles and Helen Schwab Foundation ✧
201 Mission St., Ste. 1960
San Francisco, CA 94105-1880 (415) 795-4920
Contact: Ana A. Thompson, Managing Dir. Finance and Admin.
FAX: (415) 795-4921;
E-mail: info@schwabfoundation.org; Main URL: http://www.schwabfoundation.org

Established in 2001 in DE and CA as a result of the merger of the Schwab Foundation for Learning and The Charles and Helen Schwab Family Foundation.
Donor: Charles R. Schwab.
Foundation type: Independent foundation.
Financial data (yr. ended 12/31/12): Assets, $160,866,620 (M); expenditures, $10,270,202; qualifying distributions, $9,685,850; giving activities include $9,100,775 for grants.
Purpose and activities: The foundation aspires to help kids with learning and attention problems lead satisfying and productive lives in an environment that recognizes, values, and supports the unique attributes of every child.
Fields of interest: Learning disorders; Housing/shelter, development; Housing/shelter, services; Human services.
Type of support: General/operating support; Continuing support; Management development/capacity building; Capital campaigns; Program development; Employee matching gifts.
Limitations: Applications not accepted. Giving primarily in Bay Area, CA.
Application information: Contributes only to pre-selected organizations.
Board meeting date(s): Varies
Officers and Directors:* Charles R. Schwab,* Chair.; Helen O. Schwab,* Pres.; Kristi Kimball, Exec. Dir.; Nancy Bechtle; Katie Schwab.
Number of staff: 26 full-time professional; 4 full-time support.
EIN: 943374170
Selected grants: The following grants are a representative sample of this grantmaker's funding activity:
$1,000,000 to Tipping Point Community, San Francisco, CA, 2012. For general operating support.
$1,000,000 to Tipping Point Community, San Francisco, CA, 2013. For gift renewal.
$500,000 to California Charter Schools Association, Los Angeles, CA, 2012. For general operating support.
$500,000 to California Charter Schools Association, Los Angeles, CA, 2013. For general operating support.
$500,000 to Foundation for Excellence in Education, Tallahassee, FL, 2012. For general operating support.
$500,000 to Foundation for Excellence in Education, Tallahassee, FL, 2013. For general operating support.
$500,000 to Innovate Public Schools, Mountain View, CA, 2013. For general operating support.
$500,000 to KIPP Bay Area Schools, Oakland, CA, 2012. For general operating support.
$500,000 to KIPP Bay Area Schools, Oakland, CA, 2013. For general operating support.
$500,000 to New Teacher Project, Brooklyn, NY, 2012. For general operating support.
$500,000 to Silicon Schools Fund, Emeryville, CA, 2013. For general operating support.
$500,000 to StudentsFirst Institute, Sacramento, CA, 2013. For general operating support.
$500,000 to Teach for America, Bay Area Chapter, San Francisco, CA, 2012. For general operating support.
$500,000 to Teach for America, Bay Area Chapter, San Francisco, CA, 2013. For general operating support.
$250,000 to Iraq and Afghanistan Veterans of America, New York, NY, 2012. For general operating support.
$250,000 to New Teacher Center, Santa Cruz, CA, 2013. For general operating support.
$145,000 to Project HIRED, San Jose, CA, 2012. For Wounded Warrior Workforce Program.
$125,000 to Hire America's Heroes, Tacoma, WA, 2012. For general operating support.
$125,000 to Philanthropy Roundtable, Washington, DC, 2012. For general operating support.
$100,000 to Tipping Point Community, San Francisco, CA, 2013. For Trustee Grant.

1129
The Ellen Browning Scripps Foundation ✧
c/o E. Douglas Dawson
6121 Terryhill Dr.
La Jolla, CA 92037-6837
E-mail: dougdawson46@yahoo.com

Established in 1935 in CA.
Donors: Ellen Browning Scripps†; Robert Paine Scripps†.
Foundation type: Independent foundation.
Financial data (yr. ended 06/30/13): Assets, $18,912,049 (M); expenditures, $1,347,957; qualifying distributions, $1,209,348; giving activities include $1,163,144 for 51 grants (high: $100,000; low: $5,000).
Fields of interest: Arts; Education; Animals/wildlife; Hospitals (general); Human services; Children/youth, services; Residential/custodial care, hospices.
Type of support: Equipment; Program development; Scholarship funds; Research; Program-related investments/loans.
Limitations: Giving primarily in San Diego and La Jolla, CA, and Rushville, IL. No grants to individuals.
Application information: Unsolicited requests for funds not accepted.
Initial approach: Letter of intent
Copies of proposal: 4
Deadline(s): May 1
Board meeting date(s): June
Final notification: July
Officer: E. Douglas Dawson, Exec. Dir.
Trustees: Deborah M. Goddard; Roxanne Davis Greene; Paul K. Scripps.
EIN: 951644633
Selected grants: The following grants are a representative sample of this grantmaker's funding activity:
$100,000 to Scripps Foundation for Medicine and Science, San Diego, CA, 2012. For Mobetron mammography equipment.
$100,000 to Zoological Society of San Diego, San Diego, CA, 2012. For disease prevention.
$94,000 to Scripps Foundation for Medicine and Science, San Diego, CA, 2012. To remodel hospital.
$30,000 to Bishops School, La Jolla, CA, 2012. For library audio visual equipment.

$30,000 to Francis Parker School, San Diego, CA, 2012. For progressive education through journalism.
$30,000 to Knox College, Galesburg, IL, 2012. For biology and biochemistry laboratory.
$20,000 to Humane Society of Escondido, Escondido, CA, 2012. For database management software.
$20,000 to La Jolla Recreation Council, La Jolla, CA, 2012.
$20,000 to Scripps College, Claremont, CA, 2012. For science equipment.

1130
Irene S. Scully Family Foundation ✧
100 Drakes Landing Rd., Ste. 105
Greenbrae, CA 94904-3119
Contact: Mayuko Lee, Grants Mgr.
Contact information for Mayuko Lee: tel.: (415) 925-4340, fax: (415) 925-4334;
e-mail: mayukolee@irenescullyfoundation.org; Main URL: http://www.irenescullyfoundation.org

Established in 2004 in CA.
Donors: Irene S. Scully; Phoebe Snow Foundation.
Foundation type: Independent foundation.
Financial data (yr. ended 12/31/12): Assets, $41,772,837 (M); expenditures, $1,800,337; qualifying distributions, $1,522,864; giving activities include $1,251,099 for 59 grants (high: $150,000; low: $149).
Purpose and activities: Giving primarily to support improvements in educational outcomes for economically disadvantaged students living in West Contra Costa County and Alameda County, California.
Fields of interest: Arts; Elementary school/education; Education; Youth development; Human services; Children/youth, services; Foundations (private grantmaking).
Limitations: Applications accepted. Giving primarily in West Contra Costa County and Alameda County, CA. No support for any one program 100 percent, nor will the foundation fund more than 25 percent of an organization's total budget; no support also for colleges or universities. No grants to individuals, or for capital campaigns, lobbying, building projects or endowments.
Application information: Full proposals are accepted by invitation only. If invited to submit a full proposal, follow application guidelines available on foundation web site. Organizations requesting renewal funding are advised to contact a program officer prior to submitting proposals. Application form required.
Initial approach: Submit 1-page letter of inquiry and Applicant Information Form (available on foundation web site)
Deadline(s): See foundation web site for current deadlines
Final notification: Following review of letter of inquiry
Officers and Directors:* Irene S. Scully,* Pres.; Katie Peterson,* V.P. and Secy-Treas.; Elizabeth Scully; John Scully.
EIN: 200414306

1131
Sea Change Foundation ✧
1 Embarcadero Ctr., 8th Fl.
San Francisco, CA 94111-3629 (415) 830-9330
Main URL: http://www.seachange.org
Facebook: http://www.facebook.com/pages/Sea-Change-Foundation/150728151621277

Established in 2006 in CA.
Donors: Nathaniel Simons Trust; Nathaniel Simons; Laura Simons.
Foundation type: Independent foundation.
Financial data (yr. ended 07/31/13): Assets, $134,481,603 (M); gifts received, $25,149,000; expenditures, $44,493,797; qualifying distributions, $44,112,986; giving activities include $40,824,699 for 60 grants (high: $2,393,867; low: $150,000).
Purpose and activities: Giving to address the serious threats posed by global warming.
Fields of interest: Education; Environment, research.
Limitations: Applications not accepted. Giving primarily in CA; Washington, DC., and NY, with some giving in AK and FL.
Application information: Contributes only to pre-selected organizations.
Officers: Nathaniel Simons, Pres.; Shawn Reifsteck, C.O.O.; Laura Baxter-Simons, Secy.; Stephen Colwell, Exec. Dir.
EIN: 204952986
Selected grants: The following grants are a representative sample of this grantmaker's funding activity:
$2,393,867 to University of California at Berkeley Foundation, Berkeley, CA, 2013. To mitigate climate change.
$2,000,000 to Partnership Project, Washington, DC, 2013. To mitigate climate change.
$2,000,000 to Partnership Project, Washington, DC, 2013. To mitigate climate change.
$2,000,000 to Partnership Project, Washington, DC, 2013. To mitigate climate change.
$1,500,000 to League of Conservation Voters Education Fund, Washington, DC, 2013. To mitigate climate change.
$1,500,000 to League of Conservation Voters Education Fund, Washington, DC, 2013. To mitigate climate change.
$1,500,000 to Sierra Club Foundation, San Francisco, CA, 2013. To mitigate climate change.
$1,500,000 to Sierra Club Foundation, San Francisco, CA, 2013. To mitigate climate change.
$1,050,000 to Alaska Conservation Foundation, Anchorage, AK, 2013. To mitigate climate change.
$480,000 to Southwest Energy Efficiency Project, Boulder, CO, 2013. To mitigate climate change.

1132
Richard C. Seaver Charitable Trust ✧ ☆
12400 Wilshire Blvd., Ste. 1240
Los Angeles, CA 90025-1058

Established in 1978 in CA.
Donors: Catalina Island Conservancy; Jonsson Cancer Center Foundation; Good Samaritan Hospital; St. John's Health Center Foundation; Los Angeles Philharmonic Assn.
Foundation type: Independent foundation.
Financial data (yr. ended 12/31/13): Assets, $24,263,246 (M); expenditures, $1,018,850; qualifying distributions, $833,705; giving activities include $810,000 for 13 grants (high: $170,000; low: $10,000).
Purpose and activities: Giving primarily for the arts and education.
Fields of interest: Performing arts, opera; Arts; Education; Environment.
Limitations: Applications not accepted. Giving primarily in CA; funding also in Calgary, Alberta, Canada. No grants to individuals.
Application information: Contributes only to pre-selected organizations.
Trustee: Victoria S. Dean.
EIN: 953311102
Selected grants: The following grants are a representative sample of this grantmaker's funding activity:
$100,000 to Long Beach Opera, Long Beach, CA, 2011.
$100,000 to Pomona College, Claremont, CA, 2011.
$100,000 to Santa Catalina Island Conservancy, Avalon, CA, 2011.
$55,000 to Jonsson Cancer Center Foundation, Los Angeles, CA, 2011.
$50,000 to Long Marine Laboratory, Friends of, Santa Cruz, CA, 2011.
$30,000 to TheaterWorks, Palo Alto, CA, 2011.
$25,000 to Tannery Arts Center, Santa Cruz, CA, 2011.
$20,000 to Calgary Board of Education, Calgary, Canada, 2011.
$15,000 to Los Angeles Philharmonic Association, Los Angeles, CA, 2011.
$10,000 to Castilleja School, Palo Alto, CA, 2011.

1133
The Seaver Institute
12400 Wilshire Blvd, Ste. 1240
Los Angeles, CA 90025-1058 (310) 979-0298
Contact: Victoria Seaver Dean, Pres.
FAX: (310) 979-0297;
E-mail: vsd@theseaverinstitute.org

Incorporated in 1955 in CA.
Foundation type: Independent foundation.
Financial data (yr. ended 06/30/13): Assets, $33,413,880 (M); expenditures, $2,799,296; qualifying distributions, $2,424,809; giving activities include $2,058,750 for 88 grants (high: $346,000; low: $100).
Purpose and activities: The Seaver Institute provides seed money to highly regarded organizations for particular projects which offer the potential for significant advancement in their fields.
Fields of interest: Arts; Science.
Type of support: Seed money; Research.
Limitations: Applications accepted. Giving on a national basis. No grants to individuals, or for operating budgets, continuing support, annual campaigns, emergency or endowment funds, scholarships, fellowships, deficit financing, capital or building funds, equipment, land acquisition, publications, disease-specific research or conferences; no loans.
Publications: Application guidelines; Informational brochure (including application guidelines).
Application information: Application form not required.
Initial approach: Letter addressed to the president, requesting guidelines
Copies of proposal: 1
Deadline(s): Early Apr. and early Nov.
Board meeting date(s): May

Officers and Directors:* Victoria Seaver Dean,* Pres.; Martha Seaver,* Vice-Chair.; Robert Flick,* Secy.; Christopher Seaver,* Treas.; Nancy Bekavac; Margaret Keene; Marie Knowles; Thomas Pfister; Carlton Seaver; Patrick Seaver; Roxanne Wilson.
Number of staff: 2 part-time professional.
EIN: 956054764

1134
J. W. Sefton Foundation ✧
2550 5th Ave., Ste. 808
San Diego, CA 92103-6624

Incorporated in 1945 in CA.
Donor: J.W. Sefton, Jr.‡.
Foundation type: Independent foundation.
Financial data (yr. ended 12/31/13): Assets, $24,471,955 (M); gifts received, $321; expenditures, $1,366,897; qualifying distributions, $1,254,861; giving activities include $1,200,000 for 8 grants (high: $1,000,000; low: $20,000).
Purpose and activities: Giving primarily to foster the fields of natural science and natural history in the areas of education, research, and preservation.
Fields of interest: Education; Environment; Science; Children/youth; Children; Adults.
Type of support: General/operating support; Capital campaigns; Equipment; Program development; Fellowships; Research.
Limitations: Applications not accepted. Giving primarily in San Diego, CA. No support for religious or political organizations. No grants to individuals, or for special events or conferences.
Application information: Contributes only to pre-selected organizations.
Board meeting date(s): Quarterly
Officers: Harley Sefton, Pres.; Peter R. Ladow, V.P. and Treas.; Robert Scott, Secy.
Directors: William E. Beamer, Esq.; Donna K. Sefton.
Number of staff: 1 part-time professional; 1 part-time support.
EIN: 951513384
Selected grants: The following grants are a representative sample of this grantmaker's funding activity:
$11,000 to Project Wildlife, San Diego, CA, 2012. For operating expense grant.

1135
Hal and Jeanette Segerstrom Family Foundation ✧
818 W. Bay Ave.
Newport Beach, CA 92661-1110 (949) 675-3490
Contact: Sally Eileen Segerstrom, V.P.

Established in 2000 in CA.
Donors: Jeanette E. Segerstrom; Susan Perry; Sally Segerstrom.
Foundation type: Independent foundation.
Financial data (yr. ended 12/31/13): Assets, $5,998,349 (M); gifts received, $330,020; expenditures, $1,029,096; qualifying distributions, $1,007,610; giving activities include $1,000,000 for 1 grant.
Purpose and activities: Giving primarily to performing arts institutions engaged in providing music and music training.
Fields of interest: Arts.
Limitations: Applications accepted. Giving primarily in CA, with emphasis on Santa Ana.
Application information: Application form required.
Initial approach: Letter of inquiry
Deadline(s): None
Officers: Theodore Walter Segerstrom, Pres.; Sandra Segerstrom Daniels, C.F.O.; Sally Eileen Segerstrom, V.P.; Susan Jeanette Segerstrom Perry, Secy.
EIN: 330925151
Selected grants: The following grants are a representative sample of this grantmaker's funding activity:
$10,000 to Orange County High School of the Arts Foundation, Santa Ana, CA, 2011.
$2,500 to De Angelis Vocal Ensemble, Santa Ana, CA, 2011.

1136
The Segerstrom Foundation ✧
3315 Fairview Rd.
Costa Mesa, CA 92626-1610
Application address: The Segerstrom Foundation, c/o Nancy West, 3333 Bristol St., Costa Mesa, CA 92626

Established in 1987 in CA.
Donors: Henry T. Segerstrom; Jeanette Segerstrom; C. J. Segerstrom & Sons; Nellie R. Segerstrom Trust; Harold T. Segerstrom Residuary Trust.
Foundation type: Independent foundation.
Financial data (yr. ended 12/31/13): Assets, $13,271,609 (M); expenditures, $698,192; qualifying distributions, $587,510; giving activities include $587,500 for 22 grants (high: $150,000; low: $2,500).
Purpose and activities: Giving primarily to performing and other cultural arts organizations in Orange County, CA.
Fields of interest: Museums; Performing arts; Arts.
Limitations: Applications accepted. Giving primarily in the Orange County, CA, area. No grants to individuals.
Application information: Application form required.
Initial approach: Letter of inquiry
Deadline(s): None
Officers: Mark Heim, Pres. and C.F.O.; Susan Adams, V.P.; Nancy West, V.P.; Mary Westbrook, Secy.
Directors: Sandra Segerstrom Daniels; Anton Segerstrom; Henry T. Segerstrom; Ted Segerstrom.
EIN: 330269599
Selected grants: The following grants are a representative sample of this grantmaker's funding activity:
$5,000 to Smile Train, Washington, DC, 2011.

1137
The Seiger Family Foundation ✧ ☆
27087 Old Trace Ln.
Los Altos Hills, CA 94022-1926

Established in 1996 in CA.
Donor: Joseph R. Seiger.
Foundation type: Independent foundation.
Financial data (yr. ended 11/30/13): Assets, $3,736,003 (M); gifts received, $667,000; expenditures, $728,860; qualifying distributions, $698,669; giving activities include $697,000 for 39 grants (high: $100,000; low: $1,000).
Fields of interest: Museums; Education; Human services; Children/youth, services; Community/economic development; Jewish federated giving programs; Jewish agencies & synagogues.
Limitations: Applications not accepted. Giving primarily in CA. No grants to individuals.
Application information: Contributes only to pre-selected organizations.
Officer: Randee Seiger, Pres.
EIN: 770469511

1138
The Semel Charitable Foundation ✧
9460 Wilshire Blvd., Ste. 600
Beverly Hills, CA 90212-2712
Contact: Terry Semel, Co-Chair. and Pres.

Established in 1998 in CA.
Donors: Terry Semel; Jane Semel.
Foundation type: Independent foundation.
Financial data (yr. ended 12/31/12): Assets, $15,069,760 (M); gifts received, $2,000,000; expenditures, $4,211,849; qualifying distributions, $4,077,025; giving activities include $4,077,025 for 25 grants (high: $2,015,000; low: $25).
Fields of interest: Arts; Higher education; Hospitals (specialty); Health organizations, association; Human services; Children, services; Jewish federated giving programs.
Limitations: Applications accepted. Giving primarily in CA, Washington, DC and NY. No grants to individuals.
Application information: Application form required.
Initial approach: Proposal
Deadline(s): None
Officers: Jane Semel, Co-Chair. and C.E.O.; Terry Semel, Co-Chair. and Pres.; Bernard J. Beiser, Secy. and C.F.O.
EIN: 954691748
Selected grants: The following grants are a representative sample of this grantmaker's funding activity:
$40,000 to Prostate Cancer Foundation, Santa Monica, CA, 2012. For prostate cancer research.
$25,000 to Long Island University, Brookville, NY, 2012. For Superior and Affordable Education.
$1,000 to United Friends of the Children, Los Angeles, CA, 2012. To foster youth.

1139
Semloh Foundation ✧
c/o Whittier Trust
625 Fair Oaks Ave., Ste. 360
South Pasadena, CA 91030-5813

Donors: Lisa Edwards; Paul Hancock; Barbara Holmes; Fred Holmes.
Foundation type: Independent foundation.
Financial data (yr. ended 12/31/13): Assets, $17,208,391 (M); gifts received, $3,908,520; expenditures, $611,934; qualifying distributions, $552,100; giving activities include $422,338 for 9 grants (high: $192,000; low: $2,000).
Fields of interest: Education; Christian agencies & churches; Protestant agencies & churches.
Limitations: Applications not accepted. Giving primarily in CA.
Application information: Unsolicited requests for funds not accepted.

Officers and Trustees:* Barbara Holmes,* Pres.; Lisa Delgado,* C.F.O.; Julie W. Lytle, Secy.-Treas.; Paul Hancock; Kelly Lopez; Haley Tobin.
EIN: 800319514
Selected grants: The following grants are a representative sample of this grantmaker's funding activity:
$26,250 to Court Appointed Special Advocates of Kern County, Bakersfield, CA, 2012. To support Case Management for Volunteers Program.

1140
Sempra Energy Foundation ✧
101 Ash St., HQ-07
San Diego, CA 92101-3017 (619) 696-2012
E-mail: SempraEnergyFoundation@sempra.com; Additional tel.: (866) 262-4842; Main URL: http://www.sempraenergyfoundation.org
Environmental Champion Awards Grant Recipients: http://www.sempraenergyfoundation.org/pages/areas-of-giving/rfp.shtml
Twitter: http://twitter.com/SempraFdn

Established in 2007 in CA.
Donors: Donald E. Felsinger; Sempra Energy; American Gas Assn.
Foundation type: Company-sponsored foundation.
Financial data (yr. ended 12/31/13): Assets, $5,684,340 (M); gifts received, $2,000,000; expenditures, $1,583,631; qualifying distributions, $1,583,606; giving activities include $1,583,606 for 1,478 grants (high: $50,000; low: $25).
Purpose and activities: The foundation supports programs designed to promote environmental stewardship; advance education; and support communities in need.
Fields of interest: Arts; Education; Environment, natural resources; Environment, water resources; Environment, land resources; Environment, energy; Environmental education; Environment; Health care; Disasters, preparedness/services; Safety/disasters; American Red Cross; Children/youth, services; Family services; Human services; Community/economic development; United Ways and Federated Giving Programs; Mathematics; Engineering/technology; Science.
Type of support: General/operating support; Program development; Employee volunteer services; Employee matching gifts; Grants to individuals; Matching/challenge support.
Limitations: Applications not accepted. Giving primarily in CA; giving also to national organizations. No support for religious organizations not of direct benefit to the entire community, political or discriminatory organizations, or other private non-operating foundations. No grants to individuals (except for disaster response/relief or company-sponsored scholarship programs), or for capital campaigns, travel expenses, loans or loan guarantees, debt reduction or past operating deficits, or liquidation of an organization.
Publications: Financial statement; Grants list; IRS Form 990 or 990-PF printed copy available upon request.
Application information: Unsolicited applications are currently not accepted. The foundation periodically initiates Request for Proposals (RFP) for grants in specific funding areas.
Officers and Directors:* Joseph A. Householder,* Chair.; G. Joyce Rowland,* Vice-Chair. and Pres.; Paul Young, V.P. and Treas.; Diana L. Day, Secy.; Beatriz Palomino Young, Exec. Dir.; Steven D. Davis; Jessie Knight, Jr.; George S. Liparidis; Anne Shen Smith.
EIN: 261325469

1141
Sence Foundation ✧ ☆
1020 E. Mineral King Ave.
Visalia, CA 93291 (559) 625-1588
Contact: Kim A. Oviatt, Pres.

Established in 1958 in CA.
Foundation type: Independent foundation.
Financial data (yr. ended 12/31/13): Assets, $7,435,419 (M); expenditures, $596,535; qualifying distributions, $441,000; giving activities include $441,000 for 70 grants (high: $25,000; low: $1,000).
Purpose and activities: Giving primarily for education, general health, and children's health.
Fields of interest: Higher education; Education; Hospitals (general); Health care; Human services; Children/youth, services; Community/economic development.
Limitations: Applications accepted. Giving primarily in southern CA.
Application information: Application form not required.
Initial approach: Proposal
Deadline(s): None
Officers: Kim A. Oviatt, Pres.; Gary A. Artis, C.F.O.; David G. Hyde, V.P.; Terry Shaw, Secy.
EIN: 956052236
Selected grants: The following grants are a representative sample of this grantmaker's funding activity:
$50,000 to Happy Trails Riding Academy, Visalia, CA, 2010.
$25,000 to University of California, San Francisco, CA, 2011.
$10,000 to Community Medical Foundation, Fresno, CA, 2010.
$10,000 to Dream Street Foundation, Beverly Hills, CA, 2010.
$10,000 to Ronald McDonald House Charities, Oak Brook, IL, 2011.
$7,000 to Smile Train, New York, NY, 2011.

1142
M. B. Seretean Foundation ✧
214 Giardino Way
Pacific Palisades, CA 90272
Application Address: c/o Robert Benham, 1850 Overton Park Ave., Memphis, TN 38112. Tel: (901) 274-0052

Established in 1964 in GA.
Donor: M.B. Seretean.
Foundation type: Independent foundation.
Financial data (yr. ended 06/30/13): Assets, $118,820 (M); gifts received, $33,673; expenditures, $502,295; qualifying distributions, $495,151; giving activities include $492,351 for 14 grants (high: $350,351; low: $1,000).
Purpose and activities: Giving primarily for the arts, education, family services, and Jewish programs.
Fields of interest: Crime/law enforcement; Human services; Community/economic development.
Limitations: Applications accepted. Giving primarily in FL, GA, NY, OK, and TN. No grants to individuals.
Application information: Application form not required.
Initial approach: Proposal
Deadline(s): None
Officers: Tracy Seretean, Pres.; Robert Benham, Treas.
Trustee: David Holt.
EIN: 620725600
Selected grants: The following grants are a representative sample of this grantmaker's funding activity:
$60,000 to CASI Foundation for Children, Boise, ID, 2011. For general operations.
$50,000 to Smith College, Northampton, MA, 2011. For general operations.
$25,000 to Bet Tzedek, Los Angeles, CA, 2011. For general operations.
$12,500 to Girls Preparatory School, Chattanooga, TN, 2011. For general operations.
$10,000 to Court Appointed Special Advocates, Monterey Park, CA, 2011. For general operations.
$10,000 to North Carolina Textile Foundation, Raleigh, NC, 2011. For general operations.
$10,000 to One Voice, Santa Monica, CA, 2011. For general operations.
$10,000 to Siskin Childrens Institute, Chattanooga, TN, 2011. For general operations.
$6,000 to Puppies Behind Bars, New York, NY, 2011. For general operations.

1143
Severns Family Foundation ✧
P.O. Box 460762
San Francisco, CA 94146-0762
FAX: (408) 730-9627;
E-mail: info@severnsfoundation.org; Main URL: http://www.severnsfoundation.org

Established in 1989 in CA.
Donors: Robert L. Severns†; Helen A. Severns.
Foundation type: Independent foundation.
Financial data (yr. ended 09/30/13): Assets, $10,673,226 (M); gifts received, $632,197; expenditures, $561,662; qualifying distributions, $553,730; giving activities include $551,167 for 17 grants (high: $100,000; low: $3,167).
Purpose and activities: The foundation's current focus is on early literacy and environmental awareness, specifically the reduction of dependence on non-renewable resources.
Fields of interest: Education, public policy; Education.
Type of support: Building/renovation; Equipment; Program development; Curriculum development; Research; Matching/challenge support.
Limitations: Applications not accepted. Giving primarily in Northern CA. No grants to individuals.
Application information: Unsolicited requests for funds not accepted.
Officers: Nancy E. Stevens, C.E.O. and Pres.; Sharon L. Severns, Treas.
EIN: 770235139
Selected grants: The following grants are a representative sample of this grantmaker's funding activity:
$133,255 to Second Harvest Food Bank of Santa Clara and San Mateo Counties, San Jose, CA, 2011.
$60,000 to Teach for America, San Francisco, CA, 2011.
$50,000 to University of Illinois at Urbana-Champaign, College of Engineering, Urbana, IL, 2011.
$30,000 to Computer History Museum, Mountain View, CA, 2011.
$30,000 to Reading Partners, Milpitas, CA, 2011.

$20,000 to ACE Public School Network, San Jose, CA, 2011.
$10,000 to California State University Long Beach Foundation, Long Beach, CA, 2011.
$10,000 to Fremont High School, Sunnyvale, CA, 2011.

1144
The Gwendolyn Sexton Foundation ✧
260 Maple Ct., Ste. 230
Ventura, CA 93003-3569

Established in 1982 in CA.
Donor: Gwendolyn W. Sexton.
Foundation type: Independent foundation.
Financial data (yr. ended 03/31/14): Assets, $13,182,729 (M); expenditures, $644,400; qualifying distributions, $584,465; giving activities include $534,000 for 10 grants (high: $210,000; low: $5,000).
Purpose and activities: Giving primarily for education and YMCAs.
Fields of interest: Elementary/secondary education; Education, early childhood education; Education; YM/YWCAs & YM/YWHAs.
Limitations: Applications not accepted. Giving primarily in CA, with emphasis on Ventura. No grants to individuals.
Application information: Contributes only to pre-selected organizations.
Trustees: David G. Phinney; Michael J. Regan.
EIN: 953783371
Selected grants: The following grants are a representative sample of this grantmaker's funding activity:
$5,000 to Glendale College Foundation, Glendale, CA, 2013. For Student Success Fund.

1145
Shaffer Family Foundation ✧ ☆
c/o Lawrence M. Schwartz, CPA
2211 Encinitas Blvd., Ste. 200
Encinitas, CA 92024-4361

Established in CA.
Donors: James D. Shaffer; Tanya L. Sterling-Shaffer; Tanya L. Shaffer.
Foundation type: Independent foundation.
Financial data (yr. ended 12/31/13): Assets, $31,059,487 (M); gifts received, $615,271; expenditures, $1,544,053; qualifying distributions, $1,406,924; giving activities include $1,344,300 for 4 grants (high: $960,000; low: $2,000).
Fields of interest: Elementary/secondary education; Health care.
Limitations: Applications not accepted. Giving primarily in CA.
Application information: Unsolicited requests for funds not accepted.
Trustees: James D. Shaffer; Tanya L. Sterling-Shaffer.
EIN: 456314648

1146
The Shanahan Family Charitable Foundation ✧
c/o Greg Stanislawski
301 N. Lake Ave., Ste. 900
Pasadena, CA 91101-4132

Established in 2007 in CA.
Donor: Robert Michael Shanahan.
Foundation type: Independent foundation.
Financial data (yr. ended 12/31/13): Assets, $19,436,677 (M); expenditures, $9,962,888; qualifying distributions, $9,857,506; giving activities include $9,847,381 for 17 grants (high: $8,647,381; low: $5,000).
Purpose and activities: Giving primarily for education and for children's hospitals.
Fields of interest: Higher education; Education; Hospitals (specialty); Human services.
Limitations: Applications not accepted. Giving in the U.S., with some emphasis on CA and PA.
Application information: Contributes only to pre-selected organizations.
Trustees: Robert Michael Shanahan; Capital Guardian Trust Co.
EIN: 207267377

1147
The Shanbrom Family Foundation ✧
603 W. Ojai Ave., Ste. B
Ojai, CA 93023-3732 (805) 646-6864
Contact: William J. Shanbrom, Pres.

Established in 1999 in CA.
Donors: Edward Shanbrom; Helen Shanbrom.
Foundation type: Independent foundation.
Financial data (yr. ended 12/31/13): Assets, $13,286,572 (M); expenditures, $532,473; qualifying distributions, $523,520; giving activities include $519,125 for 35 grants (high: $65,000; low: $5,000).
Fields of interest: Performing arts centers; Performing arts, orchestras; Higher education.
Limitations: Applications accepted. Giving primarily in CA.
Application information:
Initial approach: Letter
Deadline(s): None
Officers: William J. Shanbrom, Pres.; Susan F. Krabbe, Secy.
EIN: 770518326
Selected grants: The following grants are a representative sample of this grantmaker's funding activity:
$56,000 to Pacific Symphony, Santa Ana, CA, 2012. For funding of Mozart Concerts.
$55,000 to Philharmonic Society of Orange County, Irvine, CA, 2012. For Honorary Sponsorship of 2012 - 2013 Season.
$50,000 to Allegheny College, Meadville, PA, 2012. For funding of Research Grants.
$25,000 to Philharmonic Society of Orange County, Irvine, CA, 2012. For Honorary Sponsorship of the 2013-2013 Season.
$20,000 to Pacific Chorale, Santa Ana, CA, 2012. For funding of 2012 Choral Festival.
$5,000 to Anaheim Ballet, Anaheim, CA, 2012. For education and outreach.
$5,000 to Anaheim Ballet, Anaheim, CA, 2012. For Anaheim International Dance Festival Sponsorship.
$5,000 to Anaheim Ballet, Anaheim, CA, 2012. For funding of Ballet Performances.

1148
David and Fela Shapell Family Foundation ✧
(formerly David and Fela Shapell Foundation)
9401 Wilshire Blvd., Ste. 1200
Beverly Hills, CA 90212-2926

Established in 1967.
Donors: David Shapell; Fela Shapell; David Shapell 2009 Charitable Lead Trust; Fela Shapell 2009 Charitable Lead Trust.
Foundation type: Independent foundation.
Financial data (yr. ended 12/31/13): Assets, $3,093,821 (M); gifts received, $3,274,200; expenditures, $2,888,044; qualifying distributions, $2,738,526; giving activities include $2,663,990 for 69 grants (high: $400,000; low: $50).
Purpose and activities: Giving primarily for higher education and Jewish agencies and temples.
Fields of interest: Higher education; Hospitals (general); Health organizations, association; Foundations (community); Jewish agencies & synagogues.
International interests: Israel.
Limitations: Applications not accepted. Giving primarily in CA; some giving also in NY. No grants to individuals.
Application information: Contributes only to pre-selected organizations.
Officers: Rochelle Shapell, C.E.O.; David Shapell, V.P.; Benjamin Shapell, Secy.; Irvin N. Shapell, C.F.O.
EIN: 956187271
Selected grants: The following grants are a representative sample of this grantmaker's funding activity:
$400,000 to American Friends of Darche Noam, David Shapell College, Woodmere, NY, 2013.
$255,000 to United States Holocaust Memorial Museum, Washington, DC, 2013.
$200,000 to American Friends of Beit Issie Shapiro, New York, NY, 2013.
$200,000 to Simon Wiesenthal Center, Los Angeles, CA, 2013.
$150,000 to PEF Israel Endowment Funds, New York, NY, 2013.
$120,000 to Orthodox Union - Union of Orthodox Jewish Congregations of America, New York, NY, 2013.
$100,000 to California Community Foundation, Los Angeles, CA, 2013.
$40,300 to Beth Jacob Congregation, Beverly Hills, CA, 2013.
$33,000 to Oakland Hebrew Day School, Oakland, CA, 2013.
$25,000 to Jewish Family and Childrens Services of the East Bay, Berkeley, CA, 2013.

1149
Shapell Family Manuscript Foundation ✧
(formerly Benjamin Shapell Family Manuscript Foundation)
9401 Wilshire Blvd., Ste. 1200
Beverly Hills, CA 90212-2902

Established in 2005 in CA.
Donors: Benjamin Shapell; The David & Fela Shapell Lead Unitrust; David Shapell 2009 Trust.
Foundation type: Independent foundation.
Financial data (yr. ended 12/31/12): Assets, $1,449,991 (M); gifts received, $1,508,061; expenditures, $1,727,808; qualifying distributions,

$1,050,000; giving activities include $1,050,000 for grants.
Fields of interest: Historical activities.
Limitations: Applications not accepted. Giving primarily in Israel.
Application information: Contributes only to pre-selected organizations.
Officers: Benjamin Shapell, Pres.; Robert Enders, Secy.; Joe Maddalena, C.F.O.
EIN: 202159043

1150
Nathan & Lilly Shapell Foundation ✧
8383 Wilshire Blvd., Ste. 724
Beverly Hills, CA 90211-2406

Established in 1959 in CA.
Donors: Nathan Shapell; Shapell Industries; The Nathan Shapell Lead Unitrust.
Foundation type: Independent foundation.
Financial data (yr. ended 12/31/12): Assets, $75,941,802 (M); gifts received, $2,082,937; expenditures, $3,670,125; qualifying distributions, $3,435,250; giving activities include $3,435,250 for grants.
Fields of interest: Higher education; Medical school/education; Medical research, institute; Jewish federated giving programs; Jewish agencies & synagogues.
Type of support: General/operating support.
Limitations: Applications not accepted. Giving primarily in Los Angeles, CA; funding also in New York, NY. No grants to individuals.
Application information: Contributes only to pre-selected organizations.
Officers and Directors:* Vera Guerin,* C.E.O. and Pres.; Paul Guerin,* V.P.; Gregory Scott,* Secy.-Treas. and C.F.O.; Jeffrey L. Glassman; Dana Guerin; Lisa Guerin; Michael Guerin.
EIN: 956047847
Selected grants: The following grants are a representative sample of this grantmaker's funding activity:
$1,275,000 to Cedars-Sinai Medical Center, Los Angeles, CA, 2011. For general support.
$1,000,000 to Skirball Cultural Center, Los Angeles, CA, 2011. For general support.
$30,000 to Tower Cancer Research Foundation, Beverly Hills, CA, 2011. For general support.
$25,000 to Cedars-Sinai Medical Center, Los Angeles, CA, 2011. For general support.
$10,200 to Beit TShuvah, Los Angeles, CA, 2011. For general support.
$10,000 to DEA Educational Foundation, Washington, DC, 2011. For general support.
$10,000 to Los Angeles Police Foundation, Los Angeles, CA, 2011. For general support.
$5,000 to California International Theater Festival, Sherman Oaks, CA, 2011. For general support.
$2,500 to American Committee for the Weizmann Institute of Science, New York, NY, 2011. For general support.

1151
Shapiro Family Charitable Foundation ✧
(formerly The Hanover Foundation)
9401 Wilshire Blvd., No. 1201
Beverly Hills, CA 90212-2945

Established in 1983 in CA.
Donors: Ralph J. Shapiro; Shirley Shapiro; Flavia J. Kavanau; Earl W. Kavanau; Alison Shapiro; Peter W. Shapiro; Kihi Foundation; Knoll International Holdings, Inc.; Raps Industries, LLP; SDI Industries, Inc.; B.D. Fischer; F.K. Fischer; Ira Klein; Jeffrey Merriam; Rachel Rehwald; CNA Property Co.; Kameron 2006 Charitable Remainder Trust; Pete Kameron Trust.
Foundation type: Independent foundation.
Financial data (yr. ended 01/31/14): Assets, $353,771 (M); gifts received, $1,072,484; expenditures, $1,200,594; qualifying distributions, $1,203,185; giving activities include $1,202,380 for 141 grants (high: $155,575; low: $100).
Purpose and activities: Giving primarily for the United Way, as well as for health organizations, human services, and education.
Fields of interest: Higher education; Education; Health organizations; Human services; Children/youth, services; United Ways and Federated Giving Programs.
Type of support: General/operating support.
Limitations: Applications accepted. Giving primarily in southern CA. No grants to individuals.
Application information: Application form not required.
Deadline(s): None
Officers: Ralph J. Shapiro, Chair.; Peter W. Shapiro, Pres.; Alison D. Shapiro, V.P.; Ava Coyne, Secy.; Floyd P. Cook, Jr., C.F.O.
EIN: 953887151
Selected grants: The following grants are a representative sample of this grantmaker's funding activity:
$2,000,000 to United Way of Greater Los Angeles, Los Angeles, CA, 2012. For general use.
$722,075 to UCLA Foundation, Los Angeles, CA, 2012. For general use.
$100,000 to California Community Foundation, Los Angeles, CA, 2012. For general use.
$50,000 to Jewish Federation Council of Greater Los Angeles, Los Angeles, CA, 2012. For general use.
$50,000 to YMCA, Westside Family, Los Angeles, CA, 2012. For general use.
$11,000 to Uncommon Good, Claremont, CA, 2012. For general use.
$5,000 to University of California at Berkeley Foundation, Berkeley, CA, 2012. For general use.
$2,000 to Hospice of the Wood River Valley, Ketchum, ID, 2012. For general use.
$2,000 to Network for Good, Washington, DC, 2012. For general use.
$1,000 to University of California, Los Angeles, CA, 2012. For general use.

1152
The Shapiro Foundation ✧
c/o Esmond & Assocs., Inc.
23901 Calabasas Rd., Ste. 1010
Calabasas, CA 91302-3308

Established in 2000 in MA.
Donors: Barbara J. Shapiro; Edward L. Shapiro.
Foundation type: Independent foundation.
Financial data (yr. ended 12/31/13): Assets, $59,450,547 (M); gifts received, $678,920; expenditures, $3,567,378; qualifying distributions, $2,822,301; giving activities include $2,822,301 for 42 grants (high: $825,100; low: $31).
Purpose and activities: Giving primarily for health care, including a children's hospital, and human services.
Fields of interest: Education; Hospitals (specialty); Health organizations, association; Cancer; Human services; Children/youth, services.
Limitations: Applications not accepted. Giving primarily in MA. No grants to individuals.
Application information: Contributes only to pre-selected organizations.
Trustees: Barbara J. Shapiro; Edward L. Shapiro.
EIN: 043541595

1153
The Sharks Foundation ✧ ☆
525 W. Santa Clara St.
San Jose, CA 95113-1520
Main URL: http://www.thesharksfoundation.com/
Facebook: http://www.facebook.com/SharksFoundation
Grants List: http://www.thesharksfoundation.com/communityassistance/CurrentBeneficiaries.asp

Established in 1997 in CA.
Donors: Compton Family Trust; SONY Playstation; SAP Global Marketing, Inc.; Cadence Design Systems, Inc.; Seagate Technology LLC; Ticketmaster Group, Inc.; WorldCom, Inc.; Brocade; Citrix.
Foundation type: Company-sponsored foundation.
Financial data (yr. ended 07/31/13): Assets, $1,391,097 (M); gifts received, $155,437; expenditures, $1,132,880; qualifying distributions, $495,630; giving activities include $495,630 for 27 grants (high: $25,000; low: $2,500).
Purpose and activities: The foundation supports programs designed to benefit youth and their families, with emphasis is directed towards underserved populations and at-risk youth. The foundation also supports programs designed to promote health and safety; education; and character development.
Fields of interest: Education, reading; Education; Health care; Safety/disasters; Athletics/sports, winter sports; Boys & girls clubs; Youth development; Children/youth, services; Family services; Youth; Economically disadvantaged.
Type of support: Program development.
Limitations: Applications accepted. Giving limited to Santa Clara and Santa Cruz County, CA. No support for athletic teams, schools, or school-associated 501(c)(3) organizations like PTA's or booster clubs. No grants to individuals, or for general operating deficits, staff salaries, sponsorships or fundraisers, recreational group outings or trips, capital campaigns or building improvement projects, endowments, or reserve funds.
Publications: Application guidelines; Grants list.
Application information: Application form required.
Initial approach: Letter
Copies of proposal: 6
Deadline(s): Sept. 30
Officers: Jim Sparaco, Chair. and Pres.; Ken Caveney, C.F.O.; Jeff Cafuir, Mgr.
Board Members: Amber Boyle; Monte Chavez; Fionna Ow Giuffre; Jim Goddard; Mary Grace Miller; Marjorie Taylor; Jeannine Turner.
EIN: 770374062
Selected grants: The following grants are a representative sample of this grantmaker's funding activity:
$31,873 to Triple Negative Breast Cancer Foundation, Norwood, NJ, 2011. For general charitable purpose.
$25,000 to Across the Bridge Foundation, San Jose, CA, 2011. For general charitable purpose.

$25,000 to Boys and Girls Clubs of Silicon Valley, Milpitas, CA, 2011. For general charitable purpose.
$25,000 to Child Advocates of Silicon Valley, Milpitas, CA, 2011. For general charitable purpose.
$25,000 to City Year San Jose/Silicon Valley, San Jose, CA, 2011. For general charitable purpose.
$25,000 to Pathways Hospice Foundation, Sunnyvale, CA, 2011. For general charitable purpose.
$25,000 to Role Model Program, San Jose, CA, 2011. For general charitable purpose.
$22,140 to Sacred Heart Community Service, San Jose, CA, 2011. For general charitable purpose.
$5,000 to Bill Wilson Center, Santa Clara, CA, 2011. For general charitable purpose.

1154
Shasta Regional Community Foundation ✧

1335 Arboretum Dr., Ste. B
Redding, CA 96003-3627 (530) 244-1219
Contact: Kerri Caranci, C.E.O.; For grants: Amanda Hutchings, Prog. Off.
FAX: (530) 244-0905; E-mail: info@shastarcf.org; Grant inquiry e-mail: amanda@shastarcf.org; Main URL: http://www.shastarcf.org
E-Newsletter: http://visitor.constantcontact.com/manage/optin/ea?v=001Qo1SzxA2oRTI6dK0BeIH4w%3D%3D
Facebook: http://www.facebook.com/pages/Shasta-Regional-Community-Foundation/138119199544511

Established in 2000 in CA.
Foundation type: Community foundation.
Financial data (yr. ended 06/30/13): Assets, $21,285,013 (M); gifts received, $3,466,522; expenditures, $3,129,928; giving activities include $1,250,520 for 156+ grants (high: $60,620; low: $100), and $135,308 for 62 grants to individuals (high: $58,508; low: $500).
Purpose and activities: The mission of the foundation is to build resources to meet needs in Shasta and Siskiyou communities through philanthropy, education, and information.
Fields of interest: Arts; Higher education; Education; Environment; Animals/wildlife; Health care; Safety/disasters; Recreation; Youth development; Human services; Nonprofit management; Community/economic development; Leadership development.
Type of support: Student loans—to individuals; General/operating support; Building/renovation; Equipment; Scholarship funds; Scholarships—to individuals.
Limitations: Applications accepted. Giving primarily to Shasta and Siskiyou counties, CA, with limited grantmaking in Modoc, Tehama and Trinity counties, CA.
Publications: Application guidelines; Annual report; Grants list; Informational brochure.
Application information: The foundation currently makes grants from individual Scholarship funds and Donor-Advised funds; visit foundation web site for application forms and guidelines. Application form required.
Initial approach: Telephone
Deadline(s): Varies
Board meeting date(s): Monthly
Final notification: 2-3 months
Officers and Directors:* Joe Tallerico,* Chair.; DeAnne Parker,* Vice-Chair.; Kerry Caranci,* C.E.O.; Mary Rickert,* Secy.; Raiann Wilson,* C.F.O.; Dorian Aiello; Barbara Cross; Joan Favero; Dan Ghidinelli; Leo Graham; Bill Haedrich; Jon Halfhide; Evelyn Jacobs; Bill Kohn; Brian Meek; Jim Zauher.
Number of staff: 2 full-time professional; 2 part-time professional; 1 part-time support.
EIN: 680242276

1155
J.F. Shea Company Foundation ✧ ☆

655 Brea Canyon Rd.
Walnut, CA 91789-3078

Established in 1967 in CA.
Donor: J.F. Shea Co., Inc.
Foundation type: Company-sponsored foundation.
Financial data (yr. ended 12/31/13): Assets, $5,714,923 (M); expenditures, $725,482; qualifying distributions, $706,597; giving activities include $706,597 for 55 grants (high: $394,441; low: $100).
Purpose and activities: The foundation supports health centers and organizations involved with education, human services, and Catholicism.
Fields of interest: Secondary school/education; Education; Health care, clinics/centers; Children/youth, services; Family services, domestic violence; Human services; United Ways and Federated Giving Programs; Catholic agencies & churches.
Type of support: Program development; General/operating support.
Limitations: Applications not accepted. Giving primarily in CA. No grants to individuals.
Application information: Contributes only to pre-selected organizations.
Officers: John F. Shea, Pres.; Ronald L. Lakey, V.P.; Peter O. Shea, Treas.
EIN: 952554052

1156
Edmund and Mary Shea Family Foundation ✧

655 Brea Canyon Rd.
Walnut, CA 91789-3010

Established in 1987 in CA.
Donors: Edmund H. Shea, Jr.†; J.F. Shea Co., Inc.; 1996 Mary Shea Trust.
Foundation type: Independent foundation.
Financial data (yr. ended 12/31/12): Assets, $12,791,154 (M); gifts received, $4,501,319; expenditures, $854,062; qualifying distributions, $711,950; giving activities include $711,950 for grants.
Purpose and activities: Giving primarily for education, health organizations, children, youth and social services, and Roman Catholic organizations and schools.
Fields of interest: Elementary/secondary education; Higher education; Theological school/education; Health organizations, association; Human services; Children/youth, services; Foundations (private grantmaking); Catholic agencies & churches.
Limitations: Applications not accepted. Giving primarily in CA, with some emphasis on Pasadena. No grants to individuals.
Application information: Unsolicited requests for funds not accepted.
Officers: Mary S. Shea, Pres.; Colleen Shea Morrissey, Treas.
EIN: 954107214

1157
The Shiley Foundation ✧ ☆

P.O. Box 207
Pauma Valley, CA 92061-0207

Established in CA.
Donor: Donald P. Shiley.
Foundation type: Independent foundation.
Financial data (yr. ended 12/31/13): Assets, $12,827,896 (M); expenditures, $5,072,669; qualifying distributions, $5,059,518; giving activities include $5,052,764 for 10 grants (high: $5,000,764; low: $1,000).
Purpose and activities: Giving primarily for education and health organizations.
Fields of interest: Performing arts, theater; Higher education; Health care; Alzheimer's disease.
Limitations: Applications not accepted. Giving primarily in CA, with emphasis on San Diego. No grants to individuals.
Application information: Contributes only to pre-selected organizations.
Officer: Darlene V. Shiley, Pres. and Secy.
EIN: 953466851
Selected grants: The following grants are a representative sample of this grantmaker's funding activity:
$5,000 to San Diego Center for Children, San Diego, CA, 2012. To promote the well-being of children, youth, families, and communities.

1158
The Shillman Foundation ✧

P.O. Box 676267
Rancho Santa Fe, CA 92067-6267

Established in 2000 in MA.
Donors: Robert J. Shillman; Destination Concepts.
Foundation type: Independent foundation.
Financial data (yr. ended 12/31/12): Assets, $19,575,883 (M); gifts received, $9,537,500; expenditures, $3,792,365; qualifying distributions, $3,742,821; giving activities include $3,717,821 for 10 grants (high: $2,725,000; low: $500).
Fields of interest: Human services; Foundations (public); Jewish federated giving programs; Jewish agencies & synagogues.
Limitations: Applications not accepted. Giving primarily in Cincinnati, OH, as well as in CA and NY. No grants to individuals.
Application information: Contributes only to pre-selected organizations.
Trustees: Dianne Parrotte; Robert J. Shillman.
EIN: 043511089

1159
Shoresh Foundation ✧

(formerly Wirshup Family Foundation)
132 Hillside Ave.
Piedmont, CA 94611-3905

Established in 1986 in CA.
Donors: David Wirshup; Rochelle Shapell Wirshup; The David and Fela Shapell Lead Unitrust; Lorne M. Buchman.
Foundation type: Independent foundation.
Financial data (yr. ended 12/31/12): Assets, $8,921,654 (M); gifts received, $1,620,061; expenditures, $796,436; qualifying distributions, $754,714; giving activities include $754,714 for 58 grants (high: $298,589; low: $100).

Purpose and activities: Giving primarily to Jewish organizations; some funding also for human services.
Fields of interest: Museums (ethnic/folk arts); Education; Human services; Jewish federated giving programs; Jewish agencies & synagogues.
Limitations: Applications not accepted. Giving primarily in CA. No grants to individuals.
Application information: Contributes only to pre-selected organizations.
Officers: Rochelle Shapell, Pres.; Lorne M. Buchman, Secy. and C.F.O.
EIN: 943044121

1160
The Leo M. Shortino Family Foundation ✧
(also known as The Shortino Foundation)
1760 The Alameda, Ste. 200
San Jose, CA 95126-1728 (408) 275-6306
Contact: Elaine Curran, Exec. Dir.; Grants Inquiries: Tara Sumanaseni, Grants Mgr.
FAX: (408) 294-1856;
E-mail: ecurran@leomshortino.org; Main URL: http://www.leomshortino.org

Established in 1992 in CA.
Donor: Leo M. Shortino†.
Foundation type: Independent foundation.
Financial data (yr. ended 12/31/13): Assets, $49,369,288 (M); gifts received, $5,000; expenditures, $2,909,896; qualifying distributions, $2,403,241; giving activities include $2,240,939 for 75 grants (high: $107,000; low: $1,000).
Purpose and activities: The foundation's mission is to act as a catalyst to enhance the quality of life in Santa Clara County by supporting at-risk youth and their families through education, healthy lifestyles and the arts. Areas of focus are: K-12 education: 1. Systemic education reform/improvement focused on closing the achievement gap; 2. academic remediation for underachieving students;.
Fields of interest: Arts; Elementary/secondary education; Elementary/secondary school reform; Vocational education; Higher education; Public health; Human services; Youth.
Type of support: Scholarship funds; Program evaluation; Program development; Capital campaigns.
Limitations: Applications accepted. Giving primarily in Santa Clara County, CA. No support for the United Way or other regranting agencies. No grants to individuals, or for fundraisers, or endowments.
Publications: Annual report.
Application information: Full proposals accepted by invitation only following approval of letter of intent. Application form required.
Initial approach: Online letter of inquiry
Deadline(s): See foundation web site for current deadlines
Board meeting date(s): Mar., June, and Oct.
Final notification: Applications are considered at the end of the month following the submittal of the application (e.g., an application submitted in Feb. will be considered at the end of Mar.)
Officers and Directors:* Gary T. Shara,* Chair.; Christine Burroughs, Vice-Chair.; Linda Murray,* Secy.; Frank L. Boitano, Treas.; Elaine Curran, Exec. Dir.; Martin Baccaglio*; David Heiman; Gerald T. Wade, SJ.
EIN: 680237238

1161
Sidell-Kagan Foundation ✧
(formerly Sidell-Kagan Scientific & Medical Research Foundation)
c/o Jerilee Nickerson, C.P.A.
513 Beirut Ave.
Pacific Palisades, CA 90272-4357

Foundation type: Independent foundation.
Financial data (yr. ended 05/31/13): Assets, $6,448,600 (M); expenditures, $854,043; qualifying distributions, $794,400; giving activities include $794,400 for 2 grants (high: $534,400; low: $260,000).
Fields of interest: Medical school/education; Medical research.
Limitations: Applications not accepted. Giving primarily in Los Angeles, CA.
Application information: Contributes only to pre-selected organizations.
Officer and Directors:* Jeannette Hahm, Esq.*, Chair. and Secy.; Noelle Gervais; Josh Grill, Ph.D.; Jerilee Nickerson.
EIN: 952501843

1162
The Thomas and Stacey Siebel Foundation ✧
1300 Seaport Blvd., Ste. 400
Redwood City, CA 94063-5591 (650) 299-5200
Contact: Thomas M. Siebel, Pres.
FAX: (650) 299-5250; E-mail: info@fvgroup.com; Main URL: http://www.fvgroup.com/philanthropy.htm

Established in 1996 in CA.
Donors: Stacey Siebel; Thomas M. Siebel.
Foundation type: Independent foundation.
Financial data (yr. ended 12/31/12): Assets, $223,325,978 (M); expenditures, $8,976,432; qualifying distributions, $7,177,922; giving activities include $6,801,500 for 39 grants (high: $1,000,000; low: $500).
Purpose and activities: Giving primarily to the Salvation Arm as well as for land conservation and children's scholarships and services.
Fields of interest: Education, single organization support; Elementary/secondary education; Higher education, university; Environment, land resources; Salvation Army; Children, services; Homeless, human services.
Limitations: Applications not accepted. Giving primarily in CA, with some giving in MA, MD and NY.
Application information: Contributes only to pre-selected organizations.
Officers: Thomas M. Siebel, Pres.; Stacey Siebel, Secy.; Bill Dougherty, C.F.O.; Nitsa Zuppas, Exec. Dir.
EIN: 943256331
Selected grants: The following grants are a representative sample of this grantmaker's funding activity:
$1,000,000 to Salvation Army of Santa Clara County, San Jose, CA, 2012. To provide food and shelter to homeless families and individuals in San Jose area.
$1,000,000 to Salvation Army, Golden State Division, San Francisco, CA, 2012. To provide food and shelter to homeless families and individuals in San Francisco area.
$800,000 to Siebel Scholars Foundation, Palo Alto, CA, 2012.
$500,000 to Salvation Army of Great Falls, Northwest Division, Great Falls, MT, 2012. To provide food and shelter to homeless families and individuals in Great Falls area.
$500,000 to Salvation Army of Helena, Northwest Division, Helena, MT, 2012. To provide food and shelter to homeless.
$500,000 to Stanford University, Stanford, CA, 2012. For operations of Stanford Athletics.
$250,000 to American Enterprise Institute for Public Policy Research, Washington, DC, 2012. For general operating support.
$250,000 to Eastside College Preparatory School, East Palo Alto, CA, 2012. For program support.
$50,000 to Menlo School, Atherton, CA, 2012. For annual fund.
$15,000 to United States Equestrian Team Foundation, Gladstone, NJ, 2012. For international competitions.

1163
Sierra Health Foundation ✧
1321 Garden Hwy.
Sacramento, CA 95833-9754
Contact: Chet P. Hewitt, C.E.O. and Pres.
E-mail: info@sierrahealth.org; Additional e-mail: grants@sierrahealth.org; Main URL: http://www.sierrahealth.org
Health Leadership Program: http://www.facebook.com/shfhlp
Knowledge Center: http://www.sierrahealth.org/doc.aspx?9

Established in 1984 in CA; converted from Foundation Health Plan of Sacramento.
Donor: Foundation Health Plan of Sacramento.
Foundation type: Independent foundation.
Financial data (yr. ended 12/31/13): Assets, $104,447,124 (M); gifts received, $599,841; expenditures, $11,669,582; qualifying distributions, $9,576,337; giving activities include $3,616,800 for grants, $429,523 for employee matching gifts, and $9,976,439 for foundation-administered programs.
Purpose and activities: To invest in and serve as a catalyst for ideas, partnerships and programs to improve health and quality of life in Northern California through convening educating and strategic grantmaking.
Fields of interest: Child development, education; Medical care, rehabilitation; Health care; Substance abuse, services; Mental health/crisis services; Health organizations, association; AIDS; Alcoholism; Biomedicine; Crime/violence prevention, youth; Nutrition; Youth development; Human services; Children/youth, services; Child development, services; Family services; Community/economic development; Leadership development; Youth.
Type of support: Program development; Technical assistance; Program evaluation; Employee matching gifts; In-kind gifts.
Limitations: Applications not accepted. Giving limited to all or a portion of 26 Northern California counties depending on grant program: Alpine, Amador, Butte, Calaveras, Colusa, El Dorado, Glenn, Lassen, Modoc, Mono, Nevada, Placer, Plumas, Sacramento, San Joaquin, Shasta, Sierra, Siskiyou, Solano (eastern), Stanislaus, Sutter, Tehama, Trinity, Tuolumne, Yolo and Yuba. No support for programs, activities, or organizations that are not health-related. No support for activities that exclusively benefit members of sectarian or

religious organizations or for support organizations. No grants to individuals or for endowments.
Publications: Biennial report; Informational brochure; Occasional report.
Application information: Newsletter and funding opportunities are available on foundation web site. Application instructions vary by program. See foundation web site for instructions.
Board meeting date(s): Quarterly
Officers and Directors:* Jose Hermocillo,* Chair.; David W. Gordon,* Vice-Chair.; Chet P. Hewitt,* C.E.O and Pres.; Gilbert Alvarado, V.P., Admin. and C.F.O.; Nancy Lee; Robert Petersen, C.P.A.; Dr. Claire Pomeroy; Dr. Earl Washburn; Carol Whiteside.
Number of staff: 8 full-time professional; 11 full-time support.
EIN: 680050036
Selected grants: The following grants are a representative sample of this grantmaker's funding activity:
$200,000 to Sierra Health Foundation Center for Health Program Management, Sacramento, CA, 2012. To initiate health disparity, equity and well-being grantmaking in the San Joaquin Valley.
$130,000 to Center on Juvenile and Criminal Justice, San Francisco, CA, 2012. To strengthen the operational capacity of Positive Youth Justice sites through training and technical assistance focused on Wraparound service delivery and leveraging the EPSDT as well as support the coordination of Technical Assistance.
$100,000 to ZeroDivide, San Francisco, CA, 2012. To help build a community of practice amongst the six PYJI partners, Technical Assistance partners and Sierra Health Foundation by developing online resource/engagement and providing appropriate training.
$90,000 to W. Haywood Burns Institute, Oakland, CA, 2012. To build capacity in youth development principles through training and technical assistance in six Positive Youth Justice sites.
$75,000 to Sacramento Area Council of Governments, Sacramento, CA, 2012. To integrate a health and equity perspective into Sacramento Area Council of Government (SACOG) approaches to its development and transportation planning efforts.
$75,000 to San Joaquin County Probation Department, French Camp, CA, 2012. To improve the social, educational, workforce and health outcomes for crossover youth by promoting juvenile justice system redesigns at the county level through technical assistance, training and awarding for a 12-month planning grant.
$65,000 to Center for Youth Wellness, San Francisco, CA, 2012. To build local knowledge and capacity in trauma-informed care through training and technical assistance in six Positive Youth Justice sites.
$25,000 to Prevent Child Abuse California, Sacramento, CA, 2012. For FRC regional networks in launching ACA Access and Advocacy Coalitions and to educate statewide policymakers about the role of FRC's for ACA implementation.
$25,000 to Sacramento Region Community Foundation, Sacramento, CA, 2012. For nonprofit sustainability in the Sacramento Region through the implementation of DonorEdge, online, Web-based nonprofit database.
$24,178 to Del Oro Caregiver Resource Center, Citrus Heights, CA, 2012. To improve outcomes for chronically ill seniors and reduce hospital readmissions through a Community-based Care Transition pilot creating integrated follow-up care and support model.

1164
Sierra Pacific Foundation ✧

c/o Jon D. Gartman
P.O. Box 496028
Redding, CA 96049-6028 (530) 378-8000
E-mail: foundation@spi-ind.com; Main URL: http://www.spi-ind.com/spf_home.aspx
Grants List: http://www.spi-ind.com/html/pdf_foundation/spf_contribution11.pdf

Established in 1979 in CA.
Donor: Sierra Pacific Industries.
Foundation type: Company-sponsored foundation.
Financial data (yr. ended 06/30/13): Assets, $22,599 (M); gifts received, $800,500; expenditures, $801,780; qualifying distributions, $776,662; giving activities include $433,690 for 240 grants (high: $100,000), and $342,972 for 311 grants to individuals (high: $2,500; low: $375).
Purpose and activities: The foundation supports organizations involved with arts and culture, education, forest conservation, animals and wildlife, health, agriculture, recreation, human services, and youth.
Fields of interest: Performing arts, theater; Arts; Secondary school/education; Education; Environment, forests; Animals/wildlife; Health care, clinics/centers; Health care; Agriculture; Athletics/sports, school programs; Recreation, fairs/festivals; Recreation; Human services; Youth.
Type of support: Sponsorships; General/operating support; Program development; Employee-related scholarships.
Limitations: Applications accepted. Giving primarily in areas of company operations in CA and WA. No support for religious organizations or foundations. No grants to individuals (except for employee-related scholarships), or for salaries, general operating support for schools or public agencies, or religious activities.
Publications: Grants list.
Application information: Application form required.
Initial approach: Request application form
Copies of proposal: 1
Deadline(s): Feb. 28
Officers: Carolyn Emmerson Dietz, Pres.; George Emmerson, V.P.; M.D. Emmerson, Secy.
EIN: 942574178
Selected grants: The following grants are a representative sample of this grantmaker's funding activity:
$1,404 to Aberdeen Fire Department, Aberdeen, WA, 2011.

1165
The Stephen M. Silberstein Foundation ✧

c/o Stephen M. Silberstein
29 Eucalyptus Rd.
Belvedere, CA 94920-2435 (415) 435-1692

Established in 1997 in CA.
Donor: Stephen M. Silberstein.
Foundation type: Independent foundation.
Financial data (yr. ended 12/31/12): Assets, $96,681,363 (M); gifts received, $681,886; expenditures, $5,148,523; qualifying distributions, $4,877,175; giving activities include $4,877,175 for 55 grants (high: $700,000; low: $1,000).
Fields of interest: Education; Civil/human rights; Public affairs, equal rights.
Type of support: General/operating support.
Limitations: Applications not accepted. Giving primarily in CA, some funding also in Washington, DC and NY. No grants to individuals.
Application information: Contributes only to pre-selected organizations.
Officers: Stephen M. Silberstein, Pres. and Treas.; Paul Silberstein, Secy.
EIN: 911852739

1166
Silicon Valley Community Foundation

2440 West El Camino Real, Ste. 300
Mountain View, CA 94040-1498 (650) 450-5400
Contact: Vera Bennett, C.O.O. and C.F.O.; Katarina Koster, Exec. Asst. to C.O.O./C.F.O.
FAX: (650) 450-5401;
E-mail: info@siliconvalleycf.org; Additional e-mail: vlbennett@siliconvalleycf.org; Grant inquiry e-mail: grants@siliconvalleycf.org; Grant application e-mail: grantproposals@siliconvalleycf.org; Main URL: http://www.siliconvalleycf.org/
E-Newsletter: http://www.siliconvalleycf.org/content/enewsletters
Facebook: http://www.facebook.com/siliconvalleycf
GiveSmart: http://www.givesmart.org/Stories/Donors/Emmett-Carson
LinkedIn: http://www.linkedin.com/companies/silicon-valley-community-foundation
Silicon Valley Community Foundation's Philanthropy Promise: http://www.ncrp.org/philanthropys-promise/who
Twitter: http://twitter.com/siliconvalleycf
Vimeo: http://vimeo.com/9174091
YouTube: http://www.youtube.com/TheSVCF
Scholarship e-mail: scholarships@siliconvalleycf.org.

Established in 2007 in CA.
Foundation type: Community foundation.
Financial data (yr. ended 12/31/13): Assets, $4,723,897,000 (M); gifts received, $1,388,154,000; expenditures, $398,485,000; giving activities include $362,390,000 for grants.
Purpose and activities: The mission of the foundation is to strengthen the common good, improve quality of life and address the most challenging problems of the community. The foundation's endowment grantmaking strategies are focused on five key areas: Economic Security, Education, Immigrant Integration, Regional Planning, and Community Opportunity Fund.
Fields of interest: Education; Human services; Economic development; Community/economic development; Public affairs; Children/youth; Youth; Adults; Immigrants/refugees; Economically disadvantaged; Homeless.
Type of support: Mission-related investments/loans; General/operating support; Continuing support; Management development/capacity building; Program development; Conferences/seminars; Seed money; Scholarship funds; Scholarships—to individuals.
Limitations: Applications accepted. Giving of endowment grants are restricted to programs, services, and efforts that benefit the San Mateo and Santa Clara counties in CA. No support for religious purposes or private non-operating foundations.
Publications: Application guidelines; Annual report; Financial statement; Grants list; Informational brochure; Newsletter; Occasional report.

Application information: Visit foundation web site for request for proposal forms (which includes application), guidelines, and deadlines per grant type. Application form required.
Initial approach: Attend an information session, request for proposal
Deadline(s): Varies, see web site for requests for proposals specific deadline dates
Board meeting date(s): Mar., June, Oct., and Dec.
Final notification: Within 6 to 12 weeks
Officers and Directors:* Thomas J. Friel,* Chair.; C.S. Park,* Vice-Chair.; Emmett D. Carson, Ph.D., C.E.O. and Pres.; Don Aguilar, V.P., Human Resources; Bert Feuss, V.P., Investments; Patrick O'Sullivan, V.P., Inf. Tech.; Sidney G. Griffin, Jr., V.P., Mktg. and Comms.; Maeve Miccio, V.P., Corporate Responsibility; D. Lea Rauscher, V.P., Grants, Gifts and Compliance; Manuel Santamaria, V.P., Strategic Initiatives and Grantmaking; Sarah Valencia, V.P., Finance; Marie Young, Interim V.P., Donor Experience and Engagement; Erica Wood, Chief Community Impact Off.; Vera Bennett, C.O.O.; Paul Velaski, C.F.O.; Nancy H. Handel,* Secy.-Treas.; David Haugen, Cont.; Mari Ellen Reynolds Loijens, Chief Business, Devel and Brand Off.; Jane Battey; Rose Jacobs Gibson; Samuel Johnson, Jr.; Robert A. Keller; Dan'l Lewin; David P. Lopez; Anne F. Macdonald; Lynn A. McGovern; Catherine Molnar; Eduardo Rallo; Tom Stocky; Sanjay Vaswani; Thurman V. White, Jr.; Gordon Yamate.
Number of staff: 80 full-time professional; 6 part-time professional; 10 full-time support.
EIN: 205205488
Selected grants: The following grants are a representative sample of this grantmaker's funding activity:
$26,300,428 to Foundation for Newarks Future, Newark, NJ, 2012.
$18,000,000 to Lucile Packard Foundation for Childrens Health, Palo Alto, CA, 2012.
$5,000,000 to Root Capital, Cambridge, MA, 2012.
$4,558,273 to Bank of America Charitable Gift Fund, Providence, RI, 2012.
$2,500,000 to Smithsonian Institution, Washington, DC, 2012.
$2,000,000 to Mercy Corps, Portland, OR, 2012.
$9,000 to Los Altos Community Foundation, Los Altos, CA, 2012.
$5,000 to Menlo School, Atherton, CA, 2012.
$5,000 to Music in the Schools Foundation, Palo Alto, CA, 2012.
$5,000 to Veterans Administration Health Care System, Palo Alto, CA, 2012.

1167
The Silk Family Foundation ✧ ☆
1613 Chelsea Rd., Ste. 267
San Marino, CA 91108-2419

Established in 2005 in CA.
Donor: Stephen Silk.
Foundation type: Independent foundation.
Financial data (yr. ended 12/31/13): Assets, $4,759,413 (L); gifts received, $753,266; expenditures, $490,708; qualifying distributions, $456,171; giving activities include $456,171 for 21 grants (high: $200,000; low: $500).
Fields of interest: Higher education, university; Eye research; YM/YWCAs & YM/YWHAs; Christian agencies & churches.
Limitations: Applications not accepted. Giving primarily in CA; some giving to TX and IL. No grants to individuals.
Application information: Contributes only to pre-selected organizations.
Officer and Trustees:* Stephen Silk,* Pres.; Susan Silk.
EIN: 203997071

1168
The Silver Giving Foundation ✧
(formerly The Silver Lining Foundation)
1 Lombard St., Ste. 305
San Francisco, CA 94111-1130 (415) 834-9934
FAX: (415) 834-9935; E-mail: info@silvergiving.org; Main URL: http://www.silvergiving.org

Established in 1997 in CA.
Foundation type: Independent foundation.
Financial data (yr. ended 12/31/13): Assets, $43,596,663 (M); expenditures, $2,250,965; qualifying distributions, $2,070,261; giving activities include $1,788,937 for 29 grants (high: $385,000; low: $1,000).
Purpose and activities: The foundation hopes to improve the lives and prospects of low-income children in the San Francisco Bay Area, CA, by affording them increased and more accessible educational opportunities. To that end, it aims to identify and contribute to organizations whose work promotes success in school or other academically-oriented enrichment activities, with a special focus on literacy.
Fields of interest: Elementary/secondary education; Education; Children/youth, services; Community development, neighborhood development.
Limitations: Giving primarily in the San Francisco Bay Area, CA. No grants to individuals, or for scholarships or multi-year grants.
Application information:
Initial approach: See foundation web site for proposal guidelines
Board meeting date(s): Twice yearly
Officers and Directors:* Philip W. Halperin,* Pres.; Peggy Ann Dow,* Secy.; Maurine S. Halperin, Mgr.
EIN: 943285094
Selected grants: The following grants are a representative sample of this grantmaker's funding activity:
$25,000 to Youth Speaks, San Francisco, CA, 2012. To further charitable programs.
$15,000 to Occidental College, Los Angeles, CA, 2012. To further school programs.

1169
The Simms/Mann Family Foundation ✧
(formerly The Ted Mann Family Foundation)
9320 Wilshire Blvd., Ste. 300
Beverly Hills, CA 90212-3218

Established in 2002 in DE.
Donors: Ronald A. Simms; Victoria Mann Simms; Ted Mann‡; The U.S. Life Fund for Julie Simms Liebman; The U.S. Life Fund for Josh Simms.
Foundation type: Independent foundation.
Financial data (yr. ended 12/31/13): Assets, $83,851,183 (M); gifts received, $2,425,000; expenditures, $4,338,541; qualifying distributions, $3,293,505; giving activities include $2,793,769 for 64 grants (high: $507,500; low: $200).
Purpose and activities: Giving primarily for health care, including a children's hospital.
Fields of interest: Higher education; Hospitals (specialty); Health care; Jewish federated giving programs.
Limitations: Applications not accepted. Giving primarily in CA, with some emphasis on Los Angeles. No grants to individuals.
Application information: Contributes only to pre-selected organizations.
Officers and Directors:* Victoria Mann Simms,* Pres.; Ronald A. Simms, V.P. and Treas.; Josh Simms,* Secy.; Julie Simms Liebman.
EIN: 311812498

1170
Lucille Ellis Simon Foundation ✧ ☆
c/o Avery & Greig, LLP
2811 Wilshire Blvd., Ste. 700
Santa Monica, CA 90403-4804

Established in 1960 in CA.
Donors: Donald Ellis Simon; Lucille Ellis Simon; Douglas Simon Charitable Trust; Pamela Simon-Jensen Charitable Trust; Eric Simon Charitable Trust.
Foundation type: Independent foundation.
Financial data (yr. ended 12/31/13): Assets, $9,849,026 (M); expenditures, $550,959; qualifying distributions, $456,111; giving activities include $422,600 for 57 grants (high: $50,000; low: $1,000).
Purpose and activities: Giving for Jewish organizations, education, health services, the environment, and art organizations.
Fields of interest: Arts; Medical research; Community/economic development.
Limitations: Applications not accepted. No grants to individuals.
Application information: Contributes only to pre-selected organizations.
Officers: Donald Simon, Pres.; Pamela Simon Jensen, V.P.; Douglas Simon, V.P.; Eric Simon, V.P.; Jerome H. Craig, Esq., Secy.-Treas.
EIN: 956035906

1171
Simon Foundation for Education and Housing ✧
(formerly Ronald M. Simon Family Foundation)
620 Newport Center Dr., 12th Fl.
Newport Beach, CA 92660-8012 (949) 270-3644
FAX: (949) 729-8072; E-mail: info@sfeh.org; Main URL: http://www.sfeh.org
Facebook: http://www.facebook.com/pages/Simon-Family-Foundation/128337287226682?v=wall

Established in 2003.
Donors: Gilbert E. Levasseur, Jr.; Ronald M. Simon.
Foundation type: Independent foundation.
Financial data (yr. ended 06/30/13): Assets, $857,920 (M); gifts received, $800,000; expenditures, $1,429,816; qualifying distributions, $1,423,153; giving activities include $316,500 for 14 grants (high: $100,000; low: $1,000), and $236,336 for 117 grants to individuals (high: $6,000; low: $168).

Purpose and activities: Giving primarily for enabling deserving individuals to achieve the American dream of higher education and home ownership.
Fields of interest: Education; Health care; Human services.
Type of support: General/operating support; Scholarships—to individuals.
Limitations: Giving primarily to organizations in CA, Washington, DC, and Santa Fe, NM; scholarship giving primarily in CA, GA and NM.
Application information: Unsolicited requests for funds not accepted. See foundation web site for scholarship guidelines and procedures.
Officer and Directors:* Ronald M. Simon,* Chair.; Kathy Simon Abels; Byron Allumbaugh; Alex Calabrese; James L. Doti, Ph.D.; David R. Dukes; James B. Freedman; Gilbert E. LeVasseur, Jr.; Ronald M. Simon; Steven H. Simon; Gary Singer, Esq.
EIN: 680524905
Selected grants: The following grants are a representative sample of this grantmaker's funding activity:
$50,000 to Eisenhower Medical Center Foundation, Rancho Mirage, CA, 2011.
$10,000 to Marist Brothers of the Schools, Bayonne, NJ, 2011.
$10,000 to Santa Fe Community College Foundation, Santa Fe, NM, 2011.
$10,000 to South Valley Academy, Albuquerque, NM, 2011.
$8,224 to California State University, Fullerton, CA, 2011.
$5,000 to Centennial Farm Foundation, Costa Mesa, CA, 2011.
$5,000 to Humboldt State University, Arcata, CA, 2011.
$5,000 to Mercy House Transitional Living Center, Santa Ana, CA, 2011.
$2,500 to Santa Fe International Folk Art Market, Santa Fe, NM, 2011.
$2,000 to Southern Polytechnic State University, Marietta, GA, 2011.

1172
Simon-Strauss Foundation ✧ ☆
c/o William Simon
1433 Allenford Ave.
Los Angeles, CA 90049-3613

Established in 2007 in CA.
Foundation type: Independent foundation.
Financial data (yr. ended 12/31/13): Assets, $10,002,519 (M); expenditures, $611,041; qualifying distributions, $583,672; giving activities include $516,100 for 94 grants (high: $20,000; low: $1,000).
Fields of interest: Arts; Education; Health organizations, association; Medical research, institute.
Limitations: Applications not accepted. Giving primarily in CA.
Application information: Contributes only to pre-selected organizations.
Officers and Directors:* Paul Simon,* Pres.; Michelle Simon Fromme,* V.P.; John Simon,* V.P.; Michael Simon,* V.P.; Ralph Simon, V.P.; Steven Simon,* V.P.; William Simon,* Secy.-Treas.
EIN: 260604831
Selected grants: The following grants are a representative sample of this grantmaker's funding activity:
$20,000 to City of Hope, Duarte, CA, 2011.
$6,000 to Los Angeles Conservancy, Los Angeles, CA, 2011.
$5,000 to Arthritis Foundation, Atlanta, GA, 2011. For general funds.
$5,000 to Los Angeles Mission, Los Angeles, CA, 2011.
$3,000 to Juvenile Diabetes Research Foundation International, New York, NY, 2011.
$3,000 to Young Life, Colorado Springs, CO, 2011.
$2,500 to Electronic Frontier Foundation, San Francisco, CA, 2011.
$2,500 to SPCA LA, Los Angeles, CA, 2011.

1173
Simpson PSB Fund ✧
(formerly Simpson Foundation)
21 Orinda Way, Ste. C, #358
Orinda, CA 94563-2534
Contact: Barclay Simpson, Chair.; Sharon Simpson

Established in 1988 in CA.
Donors: Simpson Manufacturing Co., Inc.; Barclay Simpson.
Foundation type: Company-sponsored foundation.
Financial data (yr. ended 12/31/12): Assets, $34,616,409 (M); gifts received, $506,789; expenditures, $16,299,225; qualifying distributions, $15,579,090; giving activities include $15,570,090 for 35 grants (high: $7,015,000; low: $1,000).
Purpose and activities: The foundation supports organizations involved with arts and culture, education, rainforests, and domestic violence.
Fields of interest: Museums (art); Performing arts; Performing arts, orchestras; Arts; Elementary school/education; Libraries (public); Education; Environment, forests; Girls clubs; Family services, domestic violence; Children; Youth; Minorities; Hispanics/Latinos; Girls; Young adults, female; Boys; Crime/abuse victims.
Type of support: Annual campaigns; General/operating support; Scholarship funds.
Limitations: Applications accepted. Giving primarily in CA. No grants to individuals.
Application information: Proposal should be submitted on organization letterhead. Application form not required.
Initial approach: Proposal
Copies of proposal: 1
Deadline(s): None
Officer: Barclay Simpson,* Chair.
EIN: 680168017

1174
The Robert M. Sinskey Foundation ✧
c/o Gordon, Fishburn & Schlossmann, LLP
11812 San Vicente Blvd., Ste. 200
Los Angeles, CA 90049-6622
Application address: c/o Robert M. Sinskey, 2232 Santa Monica Blvd., Santa Monica, CA 90404-2312, tel.: (310) 453-8911

Established in 1997 in CA.
Donors: Robert M. Sinskey, M.D.; Sinskey Vineyard.
Foundation type: Independent foundation.
Financial data (yr. ended 12/31/13): Assets, $6,626,483 (M); gifts received, $760,034; expenditures, $624,945; qualifying distributions, $564,857; giving activities include $564,857 for 18 grants (high: $300,000; low: $15).
Fields of interest: Higher education; Environment, natural resources; Eye research; Human services; United Ways and Federated Giving Programs.
Type of support: General/operating support.
Limitations: Applications accepted. Giving primarily in CA, NC, and VA. No grants to individuals.
Application information: Application form required.
Initial approach: Letter
Deadline(s): June 1 and Dec. 1
Officers: Robert M. Sinskey, M.D., Pres.; Jeffery C. Lapin, Esq., Secy.
EIN: 954628223

1175
The Skoll Foundation ✧
250 University Ave., Ste. 200
Palo Alto, CA 94301-1738 (650) 331-1031
FAX: (650) 331-1033;
E-mail: info@skollfoundation.org; Main URL: http://www.skollfoundation.org/
Flickr: http://www.flickr.com/photos/44608864@N08/with/5576999744/
iTunes: http://itunes.apple.com/us/podcast/skoll-world-forum-on-social/id348258086
Jeff Skoll's Giving Pledge Profile: http://glasspockets.org/philanthropy-in-focus/eye-on-the-giving-pledge/profiles/skoll
Twitter: http://www.twitter.com/skollfoundation
YouTube: http://www.youtube.com/user/skollfoundation

Established in 2002 in CA. In 2004, the foundation incorporated the Skoll Community Fund, a supporting organization associated with the Silicon Valley Community Foundation of San Jose, CA, into its operations.
Donor: Jeffrey S. Skoll.
Foundation type: Independent foundation.
Financial data (yr. ended 12/31/12): Assets, $521,009,795 (M); gifts received, $42,139,184; expenditures, $32,767,782; qualifying distributions, $29,346,349; giving activities include $18,473,267 for 23 grants (high: $11,000,000; low: $5,000), $4,927,826 for foundation-administered programs and $673,905 for 3 loans/program-related investments (high: $343,510; low: $75,000).
Purpose and activities: The Skoll Foundation drives large-scale change by investing in, connecting, and celebrating social entrepreneurs and other innovators dedicated to solving the world's most pressing problems.
Fields of interest: Social entrepreneurship.
Type of support: Mission-related investments/loans; General/operating support; Program-related investments/loans.
Limitations: Applications accepted. No support for organizations new or early-stage business plans or ideas, schools and school districts, or programs promoting religious doctrine. No grants to individuals, or for scholarships, endowments, deficit reduction or land acquisition.
Publications: Application guidelines; Annual report; Financial statement; Newsletter.
Application information: New SASE award winners celebrated once each year at the annual Skoll World Forum on Social Entrepreneurship. Application form required.
Initial approach: Online eligibility quiz and application
Deadline(s): Online applications are accepted between Jan. 4 and the deadline of Mar. 1

Board meeting date(s): Annually
Final notification: Application status: July. Award decisions: Nov.
Officers and Directors:* Jeffrey S. Skoll,* Chair.; Sally Osberg, C.E.O. and Pres.; Ben Binswanger, C.A.O.; Richard Fahey, C.O.O.; Renee Kaplan, Chief Strategy Off.; Larry Brilliant; James G.B. DeMartini III; Debra L. Dunn; Kirk O. Hanson; Peter Hero; Roger L. Martin.
Number of staff: 33
EIN: 113659133
Selected grants: The following grants are a representative sample of this grantmaker's funding activity:
$15,000,000 to Skoll Global Threats Fund, Palo Alto, CA, 2012. For general operating support, payable over 1.50 years.
$5,000,000 to Root Capital, Cambridge, MA, 2012. For building the smallholder lending market in sustainable agriculture, payable over 4.50 years.
$4,717,471 to Oxford University, Oxford, England, 2012. For Skoll Centre for Social Entrepreneurship, payable over 3.00 years.
$2,600,000 to Imazon - Instituto do Homem e Meio Ambiente da Amazonia, Belem, Brazil, 2012. For Net Zero Deforestation in Para, Brazil, payable over 3.00 years.
$1,601,140 to Oxford University, Oxford, England, 2012. For Said Business School West Wing capital campaign.
$150,000 to Public Radio International, Minneapolis, MN, 2012. For social entrepreneurship broadcast coverage, payable over 1.50 years.
$95,000 to New Teacher Center, Santa Cruz, CA, 2012. For Launching the Next Generation of Effective Educators in Florida, Illinois, and Iowa.
$75,000 to Dalberg, Washington, DC, 2012. For sustainable finance market assessment.
$25,000 to Silicon Valley Community Foundation, Mountain View, CA, 2012. For 2012 Regional Meeting sponsorship.

1176
Skoll Global Threats Fund ✧
250 University Ave., Ste. 200
Palo Alto, CA 94301-1738
Main URL: http://www.skollglobalthreats.org/
Blog: http://www.skollglobalthreats.org/blog/
Facebook: http://www.facebook.com/pages/Skoll-Global-Threats-Fund/225493127502399
Twitter: http://twitter.com/SkollGlobal

Established in 2010 in CA.
Foundation type: Independent foundation.
Financial data (yr. ended 12/31/12): Assets, $4,435,867 (M); gifts received, $15,000,000; expenditures, $16,952,099; qualifying distributions, $16,510,478; giving activities include $12,291,110 for 49 grants (high: $5,000,000; low: $3,840).
Purpose and activities: The fund's mission is to confront global threats imperiling humanity by seeking solutions, strengthening alliances, and spurring actions needed to safeguard the future.
Fields of interest: Human services; International affairs; Civil/human rights.
Limitations: Applications not accepted. Giving primarily in CA and Washington, DC.
Application information: Unsolicited requests for funds not accepted.
Officers and Directors:* Jeffrey S. Skoll,* Chair.; Annie Maxwell, Pres.; James G.B. Demartini III; Sally Osberg.
EIN: 270198398

1177
Skywords Family Foundation ✧
c/o Cynthia Rowland
235 Montgomery St., 17th Fl.
San Francisco, CA 94104-2902

Established in 2005 in CA.
Donor: M. Davis Charitable Lead Trust.
Foundation type: Independent foundation.
Financial data (yr. ended 12/31/13): Assets, $76,577,343 (M); gifts received, $6,113,260; expenditures, $2,076,912; qualifying distributions, $1,773,380; giving activities include $1,466,850 for 6 grants (high: $600,000; low: $250).
Fields of interest: Media, film/video; Education, fund raising/fund distribution; Human services; Foundations (private grantmaking).
Limitations: Applications not accepted. Giving primarily in San Francisco, CA.
Application information: Contributes only to pre-selected organizations.
Officers: Michael Davis, Pres.; Janet Jyll Johnstone, Secy.-Treas.
EIN: 201247525

1178
Donald M. Slager Sunset Foundation ✧
P.O. Box 51
Bishop, CA 93515-0051
Application address: 250 Sneden St., Bishop, CA 93514; tel.: (760) 873-7360

Established in 2004 in CA.
Donor: Donald M. Slager Trust.
Foundation type: Independent foundation.
Financial data (yr. ended 12/31/13): Assets, $10,017,743 (M); expenditures, $575,354; qualifying distributions, $473,960; giving activities include $460,700 for 71 grants (high: $28,730; low: $1,000).
Fields of interest: Higher education; Disasters, search/rescue.
Type of support: Scholarship funds; General/operating support.
Limitations: Applications accepted. Giving primarily in CA.
Application information: Application form required.
Initial approach: Request application form
Deadline(s): 1st week of Mar., Varies annually
Officers: Tom Hardy, Pres.; Phil McDowell, Secy.; M.C. Hubbard, Treas.
Directors: Pat Canfield; John Helm.
EIN: 912150933
Selected grants: The following grants are a representative sample of this grantmaker's funding activity:
$35,000 to Kern Community College District, Bakersfield, CA, 2010.
$35,000 to University of California, Davis, CA, 2010. For scholarship.
$25,000 to Eastern Sierra Institute for Collaborative Education, Bishop, CA, 2010.
$7,000 to Chamber Music Unbound, Mammoth Lakes, CA, 2011.
$5,000 to Inyo Council for the Arts, Bishop, CA, 2011.
$5,000 to Inyo Mono Advocates for Community Action, Bishop, CA, 2011.
$5,000 to Sierra Business Council, Truckee, CA, 2010.
$3,500 to Inyo Council for the Arts, Bishop, CA, 2010.
$2,000 to Bishop Museum and Historical Society, Bishop, CA, 2011.

1179
The Harry and Florence Sloan Foundation ✧
c/o Meloni Hribal Tratner, LLP
21255 Burbank Blvd., Ste. 250
Woodland Hills, CA 91367-6682

Established in CA.
Donors: Harry E. Sloan; Florence Sloan.
Foundation type: Independent foundation.
Financial data (yr. ended 12/31/12): Assets, $3,433,792 (M); gifts received, $10,219; expenditures, $577,763; qualifying distributions, $503,341; giving activities include $503,341 for 41 grants (high: $100,000; low: $15).
Fields of interest: Museums (art); Performing arts, ballet; Arts; Education; Health care.
Limitations: Applications not accepted. Giving primarily in CA and New York, NY. No grants to individuals.
Application information: Unsolicited requests for funds not accepted.
Officers: Harry E. Sloan, Pres. and C.F.O.; Florence Sloan, Secy.
EIN: 954256339

1180
The Small Change Foundation ✧ ☆
19 Sutter St.
San Francisco, CA 94104-4901
Contact: Raymond L. Mulliner, V.P. and Secy.

Established in 1996 in CA.
Donor: James C. Hormel.
Foundation type: Independent foundation.
Financial data (yr. ended 10/31/13): Assets, $5,618,315 (M); expenditures, $481,233; qualifying distributions, $435,015; giving activities include $435,000 for 29 grants (high: $50,000; low: $5,000).
Purpose and activities: Giving primarily for gay and lesbian issues, as well as for human services.
Fields of interest: Media/communications; Museums (art); Performing arts; Education; Environmental education; Human services; Civil/human rights, LGBTQ; Asians/Pacific Islanders; Military/veterans; AIDS, people with; LGBTQ.
Type of support: Advocacy.
Limitations: Applications accepted. Giving primarily in San Francisco, CA; funding also in Washington, DC, and New York, NY.
Application information: Application form required.
Initial approach: Letter
Deadline(s): None
Officers: James C. Hormel, Pres.; Raymond L. Mulliner, V.P. and Secy.; Paul Grippardi, Treas.
EIN: 943271247
Selected grants: The following grants are a representative sample of this grantmaker's funding activity:
$50,000 to Freedom to Marry, New York, NY, 2011.

$25,000 to Media Matters for America, Washington, DC, 2011.
$25,000 to Trevor Project, West Hollywood, CA, 2011.
$15,000 to Equality Federation Institute, San Francisco, CA, 2011.
$15,000 to New Conservatory Theater Center, San Francisco, CA, 2011.
$10,000 to Equal Justice Society, Oakland, CA, 2011.
$10,000 to Legal Services for Children, San Francisco, CA, 2011.
$10,000 to Presbyterian Welcome, New York, NY, 2011.
$10,000 to Tectonic Theater Project, New York, NY, 2011.
$5,000 to California Institute of Integral Studies, San Francisco, CA, 2011.

1181
The John H. & Cynthia Lee Smet Foundation ✧

2810 Tennyson Pl.
Hermosa Beach, CA 90254-2258

Established in CA.
Donors: John H. Smet; Cynthia Lee Smet.
Foundation type: Independent foundation.
Financial data (yr. ended 12/31/13): Assets, $37,805,563 (M); gifts received, $4,177,278; expenditures, $1,742,238; qualifying distributions, $1,547,579; giving activities include $1,033,539 for 24 grants (high: $496,514; low: $250).
Purpose and activities: Giving primarily for education.
Fields of interest: Higher education; Scholarships/financial aid; Education; Human services; Catholic federated giving programs.
Type of support: General/operating support; Scholarship funds.
Limitations: Applications not accepted. Giving primarily in CA. No grants to individuals.
Application information: Unsolicited requests for funds not accepted.
Officers: John H. Smet, Pres.; Cynthia Lee Smet, Secy.
EIN: 954399946

1182
Joan Irvine Smith & Athalie R. Clarke Foundation ✧

18881 Von Karman Ave., No. 1275
Irvine, CA 92612-1500
Contact: James I. Swinden, V.P.

Established in 1991 in CA.
Donors: Athalie R. Clarke‡; Joan Irvine Smith.
Foundation type: Independent foundation.
Financial data (yr. ended 04/30/13): Assets, $6,232,607 (M); expenditures, $1,230,143; qualifying distributions, $1,230,143; giving activities include $1,077,000 for 7 grants (high: $952,000; low: $1,000).
Purpose and activities: Giving for environmental protection, medical research, and California Impressionist art.
Fields of interest: Museums; Higher education; Environment.
Type of support: Endowments; Research; Matching/challenge support.
Limitations: Applications not accepted. Giving primarily in southern CA. No grants to individuals.
Application information: Contributes only to pre-selected organizations.
Officers and Directors:* Joan Irvine Smith,* Pres.; James I. Swinden,* V.P. and Treas.; Russell S. Penniman IV,* V.P.; Brett J. Williamson,* Secy.; Mark S. Ashworth; Sheri Grady; Paul Mosley.
EIN: 330461971
Selected grants: The following grants are a representative sample of this grantmaker's funding activity:
$1,153,000 to Irvine Museum, Irvine, CA, 2011.
$1,011,000 to Irvine Museum, Irvine, CA, 2012.
$225,000 to National Water Research Institute, Fountain Valley, CA, 2012.
$200,000 to University of California, Irvine, CA, 2011.
$200,000 to University of California at Irvine Foundation, Irvine, CA, 2012.
$150,000 to National Water Research Institute, Fountain Valley, CA, 2011.
$12,000 to Mission San Juan Capistrano, San Juan Capistrano, CA, 2012.
$10,000 to Audubon Society, National, New York, NY, 2012.
$5,000 to Crystal Cove Alliance, Newport Coast, CA, 2012.
$1,000 to Crystal Cove Conservancy, Irvine, CA, 2012.
$1,000 to Pacific Marine Mammal Center, Laguna Beach, CA, 2012.
$1,000 to University of California, Department of Chemistry, Irvine, CA, 2012.
$1,000 to Zoological Society of San Diego, San Diego, CA, 2011.
$1,000 to Zoological Society of San Diego, San Diego, CA, 2012.

1183
May and Stanley Smith Charitable Trust

2320 Marinship Way, Ste. 150
Sausalito, CA 94965-2830 (415) 332-0166
Contact: Admini Trust LLC
E-mail: grantsmanager@adminitrustllc.com; Main URL: http://www.adminitrustllc.com/may-and-stanley-smith-charitable-trust/

Established in 1989.
Donor: May Smith‡.
Foundation type: Independent foundation.
Financial data (yr. ended 12/31/13): Assets, $437,234,593 (M); expenditures, $18,631,417; qualifying distributions, $13,813,536; giving activities include $12,500,876 for 375 grants (high: $200,000; low: $1,500).
Purpose and activities: The Trust supports organizations that offer opportunities to children and youth; adults and families; elders; and people with disabilities that enrich the quality of life, promote self-sufficiency, and assist individuals in achieving their highest potential.
Fields of interest: Education; Art & music therapy; Nursing home/convalescent facility; Health care, home services; Mental health, counseling/support groups; Employment, job counseling; Employment, training; Employment, retraining; Employment, vocational rehabilitation; Employment, sheltered workshops; Housing/shelter, services; Youth development; Human services; Neighborhood centers; Family resources and services, disability; Human services, transportation; Self-advocacy services, disability; Supported living; Personal assistance services (PAS); Transition planning; Human services, mind/body enrichment; Residential/custodial care; Developmentally disabled, centers & services; Independent living, disability; Military/veterans' organizations; Children/youth; Aging; Young adults; Disabilities, people with; Physically disabled; Blind/visually impaired; Deaf/hearing impaired; Mentally disabled; Minorities; Economically disadvantaged.
International interests: Canada.
Type of support: General/operating support; Continuing support; Management development/capacity building; Equipment; Program development.
Limitations: Applications accepted. Giving to organizations meeting the trust's program area priorities and serving individuals living in British Columbia Canada, and in AK, AZ, CA, CO HI, ID, MT, NV, NM, OR, TX, UT, WA, and WY. No support for start-up or emerging organizations or new programs; scientific or medical research programs; the promotion of religion; projects that carry on propaganda or otherwise attempt to influence legislation; activities that participate or intervene in any political campaign on behalf of or in opposition to any candidate for public office; or conduct, directly or indirectly, voter registration. Organizations that pass through funding to an organization or project that would not be eligible for direct funding are not eligible for funding consideration. No grants to individuals or for endowment funds, or for building/capital projects or for capital equipment; no funding for general fundraising appeals, debt reduction, conferences, benefit events or one-time events.
Application information: Unsolicited Letters of Inquiry are accepted through the online process only. Full proposals are by invitation only, after review of the Letter of Inquiry. The foundation provides a step-by-step guide to the grant application process on its web site. It is highly recommended that grantseekers review these steps in the order presented before beginning the application process.
Initial approach: Submit online Letter of Inquiry
Copies of proposal: 1
Deadline(s): None
Board meeting date(s): Quarterly
Final notification: Six weeks for Letters of Inquiry. Four to six months for full proposals.
Trustees: Ruth M. Collins; Daniel F. Piombo, Jr.
Number of staff: 7 full-time professional.
EIN: 946622075
Selected grants: The following grants are a representative sample of this grantmaker's funding activity:
$400,000 to Arc of the United States, Washington, DC, 2013. For School to Community Transition Project (SCTP).
$200,000 to OASIS Institute, Saint Louis, MO, 2013. To assist vulnerable elders in five cities.
$120,000 to Marriott Foundation for People with Disabilities, Bethesda, MD, 2013. For Bridges from School to Work.
$80,000 to Peace 4 Kids, Compton, CA, 2013. For recreational and supportive programs for foster children and youth.
$76,000 to Center for a New American Security, Washington, DC, 2013. To conduct assessment of veterans and military families in the Western Region of the United States.
$70,000 to Grandparents as Parents, Canoga Park, CA, 2013. For grandparents and other relatives raising children and youth.

$70,000 to Wilderness Inquiry, Minneapolis, MN, 2013. For Share the Adventure Program.
$50,000 to National Dance Institute New Mexico, Santa Fe, NM, 2013. For in-school and community programs.
$35,000 to Farmer Veteran Coalition, Davis, CA, 2013. To link veterans to supportive services and financial assistance to pursue careers in the agricultural industry.
$30,000 to A Home Within, San Francisco, CA, 2013. For pro bono mental health services to current and former foster youth.
$10,000 to Communities in Schools of Seattle, Seattle, WA, 2013. For program support.
$10,000 to Eldergivers, San Francisco, CA, 2013. For Arts With Elders (AWE) program.

1184
Will and Jada Smith Family Foundation ✧ ☆

(formerly Will Smith Foundation)
c/o Gelfand Rennert & Feldman
1880 Century Park E., Ste. 1600
Los Angeles, CA 90067-1661

Established in 1996 in CA.
Donors: Howard J. Saks; Willard Smith II; Sony Pictures Entertainment; Treyball, Inc.; WJS Trust.
Foundation type: Independent foundation.
Financial data (yr. ended 12/31/13): Assets, $17,878 (M); gifts received, $560,000; expenditures, $564,027; qualifying distributions, $435,160; giving activities include $435,160 for 48 grants (high: $50,000; low: $340).
Purpose and activities: Giving primarily for social services, health organizations, including an organization determined to end malaria deaths, as well as for arts education, and to Christian and Baptist churches and organizations.
Fields of interest: Arts education; Health organizations, association; Tropical diseases; Human services; Children/youth, services; Foundations (private grantmaking); Christian agencies & churches; Protestant agencies & churches.
Limitations: Applications not accepted. Giving primarily in Los Angeles, CA, Baltimore, MD, New York, NY, and Philadelphia, PA. No grants to individuals.
Application information: Contributes only to pre-selected organizations.
Officers: Willard Smith II, Pres.; Harry Smith, C.F.O.; Jada P. Smith, V.P.
Directors: Karen Evans; James Lassiter.
EIN: 954607014

1185
The H. Russell Smith Foundation ✧

4675 MacArthur Ct., Ste. 540
Newport Beach, CA 92660-8813

Established in 2002 in CA and DE.
Donors: H. Russell Smith; Jeanne R. Smith; Douglas H. Smith.
Foundation type: Independent foundation.
Financial data (yr. ended 12/31/13): Assets, $12,831,208 (M); gifts received, $26,215; expenditures, $1,326,780; qualifying distributions, $1,059,609; giving activities include $977,682 for 12 grants (high: $450,000; low: $1,000).
Fields of interest: Arts; Higher education; Education; Hospitals (general); United Ways and Federated Giving Programs.
Limitations: Applications not accepted. Giving primarily in CA. No grants to individuals.
Application information: Contributes only to pre-selected organizations.
Officers and Directors:* H. Russell Smith,* Chair.; Stewart R. Smith,* Pres.; Kate Parker, Secy.-Treas.
EIN: 562283549

1186
Lon V. Smith Foundation ✧

9440 Santa Monica Blvd., Ste. 300
Beverly Hills, CA 90210-4614

Established in 1952 in CA.
Foundation type: Independent foundation.
Financial data (yr. ended 12/31/13): Assets, $27,659,800 (M); expenditures, $1,955,876; qualifying distributions, $1,765,777; giving activities include $1,618,000 for 147 grants (high: $40,000; low: $1,000).
Purpose and activities: Giving primarily for health organizations and medical research, children, youth and social services, and for family services.
Fields of interest: Health care; Health organizations, association; Medical research, institute; Boy scouts; Human services; Children/youth, services; Family services; United Ways and Federated Giving Programs; Blind/visually impaired.
Type of support: General/operating support.
Limitations: Applications not accepted. Giving primarily in southern CA. No grants to individuals.
Application information: Contributes only to pre-selected organizations.
Officers: Stefan A. Kantardjieff, Pres.; Lawrence S. Clark, V.P.; John L. Lahn, V.P.; Michael Lahn, V.P.; Stephan A. Rados, V.P.; Matthew Whelan, V.P.; Louise Offit, Secy.-Treas.
EIN: 956045384

1187
Morris S. Smith Foundation ✧

8457 Colbath Ave.
Van Nuys, CA 91402-3703
Application address: c/o Sterling Franklin, Tr., Ying & Associates, 700 S. Flower St., Ste. 1205, Los Angeles, CA 90017, tel.: (213) 430-4730

Established in 1993 in NE.
Foundation type: Independent foundation.
Financial data (yr. ended 09/30/13): Assets, $14,563,315 (M); expenditures, $753,050; qualifying distributions, $646,000; giving activities include $550,000 for 1 grant.
Purpose and activities: Giving primarily for higher education.
Fields of interest: Higher education; Education; Health organizations, association; Human services.
Type of support: Annual campaigns; Endowments; Scholarship funds.
Limitations: Applications accepted. Giving primarily in the greater Los Angeles, CA, area. No grants to individuals.
Application information: Application form required.
Initial approach: Letter
Deadline(s): None
Trustees: Larry Franklin; Sterling C. Franklin; Wei-Ching K. Franklin.
EIN: 954452450

1188
Barbara Smith Fund ✧

c/o Shorey Myers
P.O. Box 29209
San Francisco, CA 94129-0209
FAX: (415) 561-6480; E-mail: info@jaf.org; Main URL: http://www.barbarasmithfund.org

Established in 2003 in DE.
Donor: Barbara Smith†.
Foundation type: Independent foundation.
Financial data (yr. ended 12/31/12): Assets, $9,882,609 (M); gifts received, $825,895; expenditures, $738,117; qualifying distributions, $634,079; giving activities include $562,500 for 3 grants (high: $550,000; low: $2,500).
Purpose and activities: Giving primarily for health, the healing arts, and environmental health, with emphasis on prevention for future generations.
Fields of interest: Environment; Art & music therapy; Health care; Mental health, counseling/support groups; Human services, mind/body enrichment.
Type of support: General/operating support; Continuing support.
Limitations: Applications not accepted. Giving primarily in CA and Washington, DC. No grants to individuals.
Publications: Grants list.
Application information: Unsolicited requests for funds not accepted.
Board meeting date(s): Spring and fall
Officers: Michael Lerner, Pres.; Kathy Sessions, Secy.; Norton Smith, Treas.; Marni Rosen, Exec. Dir.
Director: Sharyle Patton.
Number of staff: None.
EIN: 680531308

1189
The Stanley Smith Horticultural Trust ✧

2320 Marinship Way, Ste. 150
Sausalito, CA 94965-2830 (415) 332-0166
E-mail: tdaniel@calacademy.org; Main URL: http://www.adminitrustllc.com/stanley-smith-horticultural-trust/

Established in 1970 in CA.
Donor: May Smith†.
Foundation type: Independent foundation.
Financial data (yr. ended 12/31/13): Assets, $17,280,527 (M); expenditures, $851,213; qualifying distributions, $708,503; giving activities include $605,000 for 44 grants (high: $20,000; low: $5,000).
Purpose and activities: Grants to organizations for education and research in ornamental horticulture, particularly in North and South America. Specific interest is in funding organizations that pursue the following activities: 1) the advancement of research in ornamental horticulture and the publication of the results of such research; 2) assisting in the creation, development, preservation, and maintenance of gardens accessible to the public for educational purposes; 3) promotion of the environmentally responsible introduction, cultivation, and distribution of plants which have ornamental horticultural value; 4) assisting in the publication of books or other works relating to the science of horticulture; and 5) informal and/or formal educational activities which further ornamental horticulture.
Fields of interest: Environment, research; Botanical gardens.

Type of support: General/operating support; Equipment; Program development; Publication; Research.
Limitations: Applications accepted. Giving primarily in North and South America. No support for environmental issues, science education, or horticultural therapy. No grants to individuals, or for endowment funds or for indirect costs.
Publications: Application guidelines.
Application information: Application form not required.
Initial approach: Take eligibility quiz on foundation web site, then proceed with Project Description Form (which can be downloaded from foundation web site) if eligible
Deadline(s): Jan. 1 to Aug. 15
Board meeting date(s): As required
Final notification: Early Dec.
Trustees: John P. Collins, Jr.; Ruth M. Collins; Thomas F. Daniel; James R. Gibbs; Bruce J. Raabe.
EIN: 946209165

1190
Patricia D. and William B. Smullin Foundation ✧

2930 Domingo Ave., No. 163
Berkeley, CA 94705-2454 (510) 704-0194
Contact: Carol Anne Smullin Brown, Pres.
FAX: (510) 704-0295;
E-mail: smullin.foundation@gmail.com; Main URL: http://foundationcenter.org/grantmaker/smullin/

Established in 1990 in OR.
Donors: Patricia D. Smullin†; William B. Smullin†.
Foundation type: Independent foundation.
Financial data (yr. ended 12/31/13): Assets, $14,378,548 (M); expenditures, $644,618; qualifying distributions, $435,030; giving activities include $435,030 for 28 grants (high: $80,000; low: $530).
Purpose and activities: The mission of the foundation is to help educate the citizens of Northern California and Oregon through gifts to higher education, health education, and the Episcopal Church.
Fields of interest: Higher education; Health care, formal/general education; Alzheimer's disease; Pregnancy centers; Residential/custodial care, hospices; Foundations (community); Protestant agencies & churches.
Type of support: General/operating support; Capital campaigns; Endowments; Program development; Scholarship funds.
Limitations: Applications not accepted. Giving limited to northern CA and OR.
Publications: Financial statement; Program policy statement.
Application information: Unsolicited requests for funds not accepted.
Board meeting date(s): Nov.
Officers and Directors:* Carol Anne Smullin Brown,* Pres. and Exec. Dir.; Nikki C. Hatton,* Secy.; Kevin Smullin Brown; Meredith A. Brown; Patricia C. Smullin.
Number of staff: 1 full-time professional.
EIN: 931055546
Selected grants: The following grants are a representative sample of this grantmaker's funding activity:
$80,000 to Hospice of Humboldt, Eureka, CA, 2012. For Chapel and Operational Costs.
$60,000 to Humboldt Senior Resource Center, Eureka, CA, 2012. For Alzheimer Day Care and Resource Center.
$24,000 to Humboldt Area Foundation, Bayside, CA, 2012. For Oral Health Partnership - Circle of Smiles.
$15,779 to Redwood Community Action Agency, Eureka, CA, 2012. For Volunteer Income Tax Assistance Program.
$10,000 to Humboldt Area Foundation, Bayside, CA, 2012. For Food for People's Backpacks for Kids.
$10,000 to Humboldt Area Foundation, Bayside, CA, 2012. For Humboldt Senior Resource Center.
$8,163 to Humboldt Area Foundation, Bayside, CA, 2012. For Holiday Funding.
$7,000 to Humboldt Area Foundation, Bayside, CA, 2012. For Boys and Girls Club of the Redwoods.
$7,000 to Humboldt Area Foundation, Bayside, CA, 2012. For Safety Net Program - Volunteer Center of Redwoods Senior Transport.
$5,000 to Humboldt Area Foundation, Bayside, CA, 2012. For car seats.

1191
Phoebe Snow Foundation ✧

591 Redwood Hwy., Ste. 3215
Mill Valley, CA 94941-6006

Established in 1993 in CA.
Donors: John H. Scully; Irene S. Scully; Scully 1994 Family Trust No. 2; The Tyrell Foundation.
Foundation type: Independent foundation.
Financial data (yr. ended 12/31/12): Assets, $86,551,271 (M); gifts received, $3,418,428; expenditures, $14,787,959; qualifying distributions, $14,243,577; giving activities include $14,197,381 for 63 grants (high: $10,000,000; low: $500).
Fields of interest: Higher education; Education; Health organizations; Human services.
Limitations: Applications not accepted. Giving primarily in CA. No grants to individuals.
Application information: Contributes only to pre-selected organizations.
Officers and Director:* John H. Scully,* Pres. and Treas.; Regina K. Scully,* V.P.; Kim Silva, Secy.
EIN: 680315880
Selected grants: The following grants are a representative sample of this grantmaker's funding activity:
$10,000,000 to Success Charter Network, New York, NY, 2012.
$895,000 to Artemis, Mill Valley, CA, 2012.
$275,000 to Salt Lake City Film Center and Artists Collaborative, Salt Lake City, UT, 2012.
$270,000 to Georgetown University, Washington, DC, 2012.
$250,000 to Force Film Foundation, New York, NY, 2012.
$225,000 to International Documentary Association, Los Angeles, CA, 2012.
$200,000 to Stanford University, Stanford, CA, 2012.
$100,000 to Womens Media Center, New York, NY, 2012.
$40,125 to Horace Mann School, Riverdale, NY, 2012.
$12,456 to NARAL Pro-Choice America Foundation, Washington, DC, 2012.

1192
The Snyder Family Foundation ✧

16030 Ventura Blvd., Ste. 320
Encino, CA 91436-2769

Established in 2006 in CA.
Donor: The Snyder Family Living Trust.
Foundation type: Independent foundation.
Financial data (yr. ended 12/31/13): Assets, $73,048,622 (M); expenditures, $1,679,788; qualifying distributions, $1,678,823; giving activities include $1,570,250 for 26 grants (high: $1,167,500; low: $500).
Fields of interest: Arts; Children/youth, services; Family services; Jewish federated giving programs; Jewish agencies & synagogues.
Limitations: Applications not accepted. Giving primarily in CA, with emphasis on Los Angeles and Tarzana.
Application information: Unsolicited requests for funds not accepted.
Officer: Joel Goodman, Mgr.
Trustees: Lisa Kabaker Hess; Randy Snyder; Susan Snyder.
EIN: 207159050

1193
Sobrato Family Foundation ✧

10600 N. De Anza Blvd., Ste. 200
Cupertino, CA 95014-2059 (408) 446-0700
Contact: Diane Ford, Exec. Dir.
E-mail: grants@sobrato.org; Main URL: http://www.sobrato.org
John A. and Susan Sobrato, and John Michael Sobrato's Giving Pledge Profile: http://glasspockets.org/philanthropy-in-focus/eye-on-the-giving-pledge/profiles/sobrato

Established in 1996 in CA.
Donors: Sobrato Charitable Capital Trust; John A. Sobrato; Lisa Sobrato; Ann Sobrato Trust Estate; Sobrato Charitable Lead Trust I; Sobrato Charitable Lead Trust II; Sobrato Charitable Lead Trust III; Sobrato Charitable Lead Trust IV.
Foundation type: Independent foundation.
Financial data (yr. ended 12/31/12): Assets, $177,670,777 (M); gifts received, $1,140,680; expenditures, $15,454,165; qualifying distributions, $13,363,056; giving activities include $10,730,276 for 116 grants, and $1,830,309 for 2 foundation-administered programs.
Purpose and activities: The foundation is dedicated to helping to create and sustain a strong and vibrant community where all Silicon Valley residents have an equal opportunity to live, work, and be enriched. To accomplish its purpose, the foundation invests in strong community-based organizations that promote self-reliance and economic independence, and positively contribute to the quality of life for economically, physically, and emotionally challenged individuals.
Fields of interest: Education; Health care; Youth development; Human services; Economic development; Community/economic development; Foundations (community).
Type of support: General/operating support; Continuing support; Capital campaigns; Building/renovation; Emergency funds; Program development; Seed money; Technical assistance; Program evaluation; Matching/challenge support.
Limitations: Giving primarily in San Mateo, Santa Clara, and southern Alameda counties, CA. No support for religious organizations for sectarian

purposes, or political or fraternal organizations, environmental and arts causes, mental health agencies (due to Proposition 63), or for fiscally-sponsored programs or organizations, individual schools, school-managed clubs, or for public libraries or their foundations. No grants to individuals (except through specific scholarship programs), endowment campaigns or annual fund drives, or for fundraising events, medical research or specific diseases.
Publications: Application guidelines; Annual report (including application guidelines); Financial statement.
Application information: See foundation web site for application guidelines and procedures. After taking the eligibility quiz, and if the foundation decides you are eligible, a pre-application form available on foundation web site will be available for downloading. Full proposal will be requested from successful pre-applicants only. Application form required.
Initial approach: Eligibility quiz available on foundation web site
Copies of proposal: 1
Deadline(s): The foundation will notify as grant cycles rotate every 24 months
Board meeting date(s): Quarterly
Final notification: Approximately 2 to 3 months after deadline
Officers and Trustees:* John A. Sobrato,* Chair.; Lisa Sobrato Sonsini,* Pres.; Matt Sonsini,* Secy.; John M. Sobrato,* C.F.O.; Bryan C. Polster; Sheri J. Sobrato; Susan Sobrato.
Number of staff: 1 full-time professional; 1 full-time support.
EIN: 770348912

1194
Y & H Soda Foundation ✧
1635 School St.
Moraga, CA 94556-1150 (925) 631-1133
Contact: Kappy Dye, C.F.O. and Grants Mgr.
FAX: (925) 631-0248; Information for grant inquiries:
Program-Assistant@yhsodafoundation.org; Main URL: http://www.yhsodafoundation.org

Established in 1964.
Donors: Y. Charles Soda Trust; Y. Charles Soda†; Helen C. Soda†.
Foundation type: Independent foundation.
Financial data (yr. ended 12/31/13): Assets, $129,936,003 (M); expenditures, $9,475,265; qualifying distributions, $6,381,394; giving activities include $5,256,500 for 178 grants (high: $375,000; low: $350).
Purpose and activities: The foundation focuses grantmaking on four program areas: 1) Family Economic Success; 2) Community Organizing; 3) Immigration Legal Services; and 4) Urban Catholic Education.
Fields of interest: Employment, training; Community/economic development, public policy; Economic development; Community/economic development; Financial services; Catholic agencies & churches; Immigrants/refugees; Economically disadvantaged.
Type of support: Management development/ capacity building; General/operating support; Continuing support; Program development; Technical assistance; Program evaluation.
Limitations: Giving limited to Alameda and Contra Costa Counties, CA. No support for private foundations, or for partisan political activities. No grants to individuals, or for annual fundraising campaigns, production of film/video or other media, faculty chairs, or for general fundraisers, benefits or events.
Application information: Program Asst. will steer potential applicants to appropriate Program Officer for application guidance.
Initial approach: After ascertaining that program/ organization is a geographic and programmatic fit, contact Prog. Asst. by e-mail or telephone to initiate a discussion regarding potential funding.
Board meeting date(s): 2nd Weds. of each month
Officers and Directors:* Rosemary Soda,* Chair.; Robert Uyeki, C.E.O.; Alfred Dossa,* V.P. and Secy.; Alan Holloway,* V.P.; Judith Murphy,* V.P.; Kappy Dye, C.F.O. and Grants Mgr.; James Dye,* Treas.; Bob Uyeki, Exec. Dir.
Number of staff: 4 full-time professional; 1 part-time support.
EIN: 941611668
Selected grants: The following grants are a representative sample of this grantmaker's funding activity:
$300,000 to Mujeres Unidas y Activas, San Francisco, CA, 2012. For East Bay Organizing Program.
$200,000 to Inner City Advisors, Oakland, CA, 2012. For general operating support.
$160,000 to Contra Costa Interfaith Sponsoring Committee, Richmond, CA, 2012. For general operating support.
$150,000 to Rubicon Programs, Richmond, CA, 2012. For general operating support.
$100,000 to Earned Assets Resource Network, San Francisco, CA, 2012. For East Bay Asset Building.
$98,500 to International Institute of the Bay Area, San Francisco, CA, 2012. For Immigration Legal Services for Oakland and Antioch.
$80,000 to Cypress Mandela Training Center, Oakland, CA, 2012. For general operating support.
$60,000 to Immigrant Legal Resource Center, San Francisco, CA, 2012. For East Bay Naturalization Collaboration.

1195
The Harry and Estelle Soicher Foundation ✧
1925 Century Park E., No. 620
Los Angeles, CA 90067-2730

Established in 2007 in CA.
Donor: The Estelle Soicher Trust.
Foundation type: Independent foundation.
Financial data (yr. ended 12/31/13): Assets, $8,095,751 (M); gifts received, $7,910; expenditures, $460,467; qualifying distributions, $442,311; giving activities include $442,311 for 9 grants (high: $70,000; low: $1,000).
Fields of interest: Hospitals (specialty).
Limitations: Applications not accepted. Giving primarily in CA. No grants to individuals.
Application information: Contributes only to pre-selected organizations.
Officers: Stanley B. Gitlin, Pres.; Joni Gitlin, Secy.; Sheri Rosen, Treas.
EIN: 208477430
Selected grants: The following grants are a representative sample of this grantmaker's funding activity:
$75,000 to Childrens Hospital of Philadelphia, Philadelphia, PA, 2011.
$50,000 to Saint Jude Childrens Research Hospital, Memphis, TN, 2011.
$50,000 to University of Texas M.D. Anderson Cancer Center, Houston, TX, 2011.
$25,000 to Childrens Hospital Los Angeles, Los Angeles, CA, 2011.
$25,000 to City of Hope, Los Angeles, CA, 2011.
$25,000 to University of California at San Diego Foundation, La Jolla, CA, 2011.

1196
Richard & Mary Solari Charitable Trust ✧
15 Florido Ave.
La Selva Beach, CA 95076-1794

Established in 1984 in CA.
Donors: Richard C. Solari; Mary C. Solari.
Foundation type: Independent foundation.
Financial data (yr. ended 09/30/13): Assets, $5,971,487 (M); expenditures, $1,917,614; qualifying distributions, $1,801,918; giving activities include $1,726,350 for 35 grants (high: $1,030,000; low: $150).
Purpose and activities: Giving primarily for higher education, health care including medical research, and youth and social services.
Fields of interest: Higher education; Education; Hospitals (general); Medical research, institute; Human services; Children/youth, services; Foundations (community).
Limitations: Applications not accepted. Giving primarily in CA. No grants to individuals.
Application information: Contributes only to pre-selected organizations.
Trustee: Mary C. Solari.
EIN: 770069120
Selected grants: The following grants are a representative sample of this grantmaker's funding activity:
$1,030,000 to University of Oregon Foundation, Eugene, OR, 2011. For general operating support.
$300,000 to Monterey Bay Aquarium, Monterey, CA, 2011.
$50,000 to Fanconi Anemia Research Fund, Eugene, OR, 2011. For research.
$15,000 to Elkhorn Slough Foundation, Moss Landing, CA, 2011. For general operating support.
$15,000 to Pajaro Valley Shelter Services, Watsonville, CA, 2011.
$10,000 to Hospice of Santa Cruz County, Scotts Valley, CA, 2011. For general operating support.
$5,000 to Salvation Army of Santa Cruz, Santa Cruz, CA, 2011. For general operating support.
$1,500 to California Grey Bears, Santa Cruz, CA, 2011. For general operating support.
$1,500 to Easter Seals Central California, Aptos, CA, 2011. For general operating support.
$1,000 to Tannery Arts Center, Santa Cruz, CA, 2011. For general operating support.

1197
Solid Rock Foundation ✧
2182 Parkside Ave.
Hillsborough, CA 94010-6453
Contact: Jennifer W. Budge, Pres.

Established in 1992 in CA.
Donor: William W. Budge.
Foundation type: Independent foundation.
Financial data (yr. ended 12/31/13): Assets, $19,793,011 (M); gifts received, $519;

expenditures, $980,834; qualifying distributions, $967,189; giving activities include $900,000 for 14 grants (high: $100,000; low: $25,000).
Purpose and activities: Giving to programs that primarily support the education and advancement of disadvantaged youth.
Fields of interest: Elementary/secondary education; Children/youth, services; Children/youth; Economically disadvantaged.
Type of support: General/operating support; Scholarship funds.
Limitations: Applications not accepted. Giving primarily in CA and MD. No grants to individuals.
Application information: Contributes only to pre-selected organizations.
Officers: Jennifer W. Budge, Pres.; William W. Budge, V.P.; Elizabeth Budge D'Hemery, V.P.; Mayo A. Shattuck IV, V.P.; George Tarleton, V.P.; Willa Kathleen Budge, Secy.; Joseph H. Budge, Treas.
EIN: 943155938
Selected grants: The following grants are a representative sample of this grantmaker's funding activity:
$100,000 to Habitat for Humanity Greater San Francisco, San Francisco, CA, 2012.
$100,000 to Saint Anns Center for Children Youth and Families, Hyattsville, MD, 2012.
$100,000 to Saint Martin de Porres Regional School, Oakland, CA, 2012.
$95,000 to Mother Seton Academy, Baltimore, MD, 2012.
$60,235 to Shelter Network of San Mateo County, Burlingame, CA, 2012.
$50,000 to Living Classrooms Foundation, Baltimore, MD, 2012.
$45,000 to Samaritan House, San Mateo, CA, 2012.
$30,000 to Foundation for Students Rising Above, San Francisco, CA, 2012.
$30,000 to Homework Central, San Mateo, CA, 2012.
$30,000 to SEED School of Maryland, Baltimore, MD, 2012.

1198
Sonora Area Foundation ✧
362 S. Stewart St.
Sonora, CA 95370 (209) 533-2596
Contact: Lin Freer, Prog. Mgr.; Ed Wyllie, Exec. Dir.
FAX: (209) 533-2412;
E-mail: edwyllie@sonora-area.org; Grant application e-mail: leaf@sonara-area.org; Main URL: http://www.sonora-area.org
E-Newsletter: http://www.sonora-area.org/newsletters.html

Established in 1989 in CA.
Foundation type: Community foundation.
Financial data (yr. ended 12/31/12): Assets, $44,076,675 (M); gifts received, $1,872,152; expenditures, $2,640,275; giving activities include $1,829,528 for 51+ grants (high: $487,797), and $178,603 for 162 grants to individuals.
Purpose and activities: The foundation assists donors, makes grants, and provides community leadership. Primary areas of interest include human services, education, arts, culture and humanities, health, public and society benefit, and environment and animals.
Fields of interest: Visual arts; Performing arts; Performing arts, music; Humanities; Arts; Education, early childhood education; Child development, education; Elementary school/education; Libraries/library science; Education; Environment; Animal welfare; Hospitals (general); Health care; Substance abuse, services; Mental health/crisis services; Health organizations, association; Alcoholism; Food services; Recreation; Children/youth, services; Child development, services; Family services; Residential/custodial care, hospices; Aging, centers/services; Women, centers/services; Human services; Community/economic development; Voluntarism promotion; Children/youth; Aging; Disabilities, people with; Women; Economically disadvantaged; Homeless.
Type of support: General/operating support; Continuing support; Management development/capacity building; Capital campaigns; Building/renovation; Equipment; Emergency funds; Program development; Conferences/seminars; Publication; Seed money; Curriculum development; Scholarship funds; Technical assistance; Consulting services; Program evaluation; Grants to individuals; Scholarships—to individuals; Matching/challenge support.
Limitations: Applications accepted. Giving limited to Tuolumne County, CA. No support for sectarian purposes or private foundations. No grants for annual campaigns, endowment funds, or debt retirement.
Publications: Application guidelines; Annual report; Biennial report; Financial statement; Grants list; Informational brochure; Informational brochure (including application guidelines); Newsletter; Occasional report.
Application information: Visit foundation web site for application guidelines. Application form not required.
Initial approach: Mail, e-mail, or fax letter of inquiry (2-page maximum)
Copies of proposal: 1
Deadline(s): Late Jan., Mar., May, July, Sept. and Nov.
Board meeting date(s): 4th Tues. of Feb., Apr., June, Aug., Oct. and Dec.
Final notification: 2 months
Officers and Directors:* Jim Johnson,* Pres.; Roger Francis,* V.P.; Clark Segerstrom,* Secy.; Bob Ozbirn,* Treas.; Ed Wyllie, Exec. Dir.; Gary Dambacher; Carey Haughy; Pete Kerns; William Polley; Tracy A. Russell.
Number of staff: 3 full-time professional.
EIN: 931023051
Selected grants: The following grants are a representative sample of this grantmaker's funding activity:
$50,000 to ATCAA Food Bank, Jamestown, CA, 2011. For operating support.
$40,824 to Center for a Non Violent Community, Sonora, CA, 2011. For Suicide Prevention Task Force.
$37,137 to ATCAA Head Start, CA, 2011. For equity match for building.
$34,216 to Mother Lode Fair, Sonora, CA, 2011. To improve livestock area.
$32,966 to Sonora High School, Sonora, CA, 2011. For ROP Wildland Fire Fighting Program.
$30,000 to Sierra Repertory Theater, Sonora, CA, 2011. For community and student programs.
$25,000 to Smile Keepers Program, Sacramento, CA, 2011. For matching support to child dental progam.
$20,000 to Christian Heights Church, Sonora, CA, 2011. For community meals.
$20,000 to Habitat for Humanity of Tuolumne County, Sonora, CA, 2011. For construction of units.
$10,000 to Sonora Sunrise Rotary, Sonora, CA, 2011. For community park project.

1199
Samuel and Helene Soref Foundation ✧
(formerly Samuel M. Soref & Helene K. Soref Foundation)
11530 Dona Dorotea Dr.
Studio City, CA 91604-4249

Established in 1983 in FL.
Foundation type: Independent foundation.
Financial data (yr. ended 12/31/13): Assets, $15,309,885 (M); expenditures, $953,445; qualifying distributions, $913,253; giving activities include $903,550 for 70 grants (high: $150,000; low: $500).
Purpose and activities: Giving primarily to Jewish agencies and for education.
Fields of interest: Higher education; Human services; Children/youth, services; Family services; Jewish federated giving programs.
Type of support: General/operating support.
Limitations: Applications not accepted. Giving primarily in CA and Washington, DC. No grants to individuals.
Application information: Contributes only to pre-selected organizations.
Trustees: Jeffrey I. Abrams; Alan D. Breslauer; Benjamin F. Breslauer; Irma G. Breslauer; Michele Breslauer; Richard Demak.
EIN: 592246963
Selected grants: The following grants are a representative sample of this grantmaker's funding activity:
$170,000 to Washington Institute for Near East Policy, Washington, DC, 2011.
$12,500 to L.A. Family Housing Corporation, North Hollywood, CA, 2011.

1200
Harvey L. & Maud C. Sorensen Foundation ✧
80 E. Sir Francis Drake Blvd., Ste. 2G
Larkspur, CA 94939-1709

Incorporated in 1960 in CA.
Donors: Harvey L. Sorensen†; Maud C. Sorensen†.
Foundation type: Independent foundation.
Financial data (yr. ended 09/30/13): Assets, $30,179,067 (M); expenditures, $1,346,361; qualifying distributions, $1,234,617; giving activities include $1,200,000 for 28 grants (high: $300,000; low: $2,500).
Fields of interest: Environment, natural resources; Animals/wildlife, preservation/protection; Hospitals (general); Human services.
Type of support: Annual campaigns; Building/renovation; Program development; Matching/challenge support.
Limitations: Applications not accepted. Giving primarily in CA, particularly the San Francisco Bay Area. No grants to individuals; no loans.
Application information: Contributes only to pre-selected organizations.
Officers and Directors:* James R. Bancroft,* Pres.; Paul M. Bancroft,* C.F.O.; Duncan McCormack III,* V.P.; Leslie Tuel,* V.P.; Dean Witter III,* V.P.; George R. Dirkes,* Secy.
EIN: 941542559

Selected grants: The following grants are a representative sample of this grantmaker's funding activity:
$300,000 to California Pacific Medical Center Foundation, San Francisco, CA, 2011.
$300,000 to Childrens Hospital and Research Center Foundation, Oakland, CA, 2011.
$300,000 to Saint Lukes Hospital, San Francisco, CA, 2011.
$45,000 to Ducks Unlimited, Memphis, TN, 2011.
$30,000 to Boy Scouts of America, San Leandro, CA, 2011.
$30,000 to University of California, San Francisco, CA, 2011. For general purpose.
$25,000 to Ducks Unlimited, Rancho Cordova, CA, 2011.
$25,000 to Vascular Cures, Redwood City, CA, 2011.
$15,000 to California Polytechnic State University, College of Agriculture, San Luis Obispo, CA, 2011.
$10,000 to University of California, San Francisco, CA, 2011.

1201
The Grace Helen Spearman Foundation ✧ ☆
3511 Dixie Canyon Pl.
Sherman Oaks, CA 91423-4820

Donor: Grace H. Spearman†.
Foundation type: Independent foundation.
Financial data (yr. ended 11/30/13): Assets, $14,759,139 (M); gifts received, $228,646; expenditures, $1,465,999; qualifying distributions, $739,625; giving activities include $722,500 for 65 grants (high: $30,000; low: $500).
Fields of interest: Health organizations; Human services; Religion.
Limitations: Applications not accepted. Giving primarily in CA. No grants to individuals.
Application information: Contributes only to pre-selected organizations.
Officer and Directors: Steven Tobin,* Pres.; Alma Banuelos; Dirk Etchison; John Ostler; Ken Randmand.
EIN: 760721677

1202
The Special Hope Foundation ✧
2225 E. Bayshore Rd., Ste. 200
Palo Alto, CA 94303-3220 (650) 320-1715
Contact: E. Lynne O'Hara, Pres.
FAX: (650) 320-1716;
E-mail: proposals@specialhope.org; Additional e-mail: info@specialhope.org; Main URL: http://www.specialhope.org
Facebook: https://www.facebook.com/pages/The-Special-Hope-Foundation/146990365339829?v=wall
Twitter: https://twitter.com/specialhope

Established in 2002 in CA.
Donor: Elena Lynne O'Hara.
Foundation type: Independent foundation.
Financial data (yr. ended 06/30/13): Assets, $14,152,435 (M); expenditures, $780,663; qualifying distributions, $737,688; giving activities include $643,290 for 14 grants (high: $100,000; low: $350).
Purpose and activities: The foundation supports the causes of the physically, emotionally, and developmentally disabled. It welcomes the opportunity to fund innovative projects that challenge the prevailing attitudes towards these special people.
Fields of interest: Health care; Developmentally disabled, centers & services; Adults; Disabilities, people with.
Type of support: General/operating support; Continuing support; Income development; Management development/capacity building; Equipment; Program development; Conferences/seminars; Film/video/radio; Seed money; Curriculum development; Scholarship funds; Research; Program evaluation; Matching/challenge support.
Limitations: Applications accepted. Giving on a national basis. No support for political campaigns, specific therapies that are provided outside of a formal healthcare setting, i.e. physical fitness and/or nutritional programs ("healthy lifestyle programs"), projects that do not address healthcare delivery, or for organizations or programs that are based and/or provide services to populations outside the U.S. No grants to individuals and/or equipment for individuals, or for endowments, debt reduction, administrative expenses exceeding 20% of the total funding request, or for occupational, physical, and speech therapies, or equestrian therapy.
Publications: Application guidelines; Program policy statement (including application guidelines).
Application information: Formal grant proposals are by invitation only. The foundation considers international interests only if there is a U.S.-based 501(c)(3) affiliation. Application form required.
Initial approach: Complete pre-application questionnaire on foundation web site
Deadline(s): 4 months prior to quarterly board meeting
Final notification: Per invitation
Officers and Directors:* E. Lynne O'Hara,* Pres.; John W. O'Hara,* V.P.; Margaret Motamed,* Secy.; Jackie Donaho,* Treas.; Lucy Crain; Carrie Jones.
Number of staff: 1 part-time professional.
EIN: 731644863
Selected grants: The following grants are a representative sample of this grantmaker's funding activity:
$150,000 to American Academy of Developmental Medicine and Dentistry, Prospect, KY, 2013.
$100,000 to Arc of San Francisco, San Francisco, CA, 2013.
$50,000 to Autism Self Advocacy Network, Washington, DC, 2013.
$40,000 to Achievable Foundation, Culver City, CA, 2013.
$35,000 to Coalition for Compassionate Care of California, Sacramento, CA, 2013.
$35,000 to Disability Rights Education and Defense Fund, Berkeley, CA, 2013.
$16,000 to Connecticut Institute for the Blind, Hartford, CT, 2013.

1203
Specialty Foundation ✧
501 Santa Monica Blvd., Ste. 703
Santa Monica, CA 90401-2443 (310) 899-9700
E-mail: info@specialtyfamilyfoundation.org; Main URL: http://www.specialtyfamilyfoundation.org

Established in 2006 in CA.
Foundation type: Independent foundation.
Financial data (yr. ended 12/31/12): Assets, $69,564,226 (M); gifts received, $13,365,000; expenditures, $4,789,845; qualifying distributions, $4,486,654; giving activities include $3,387,208 for 76 grants (high: $525,000; low: $556).
Purpose and activities: The foundation seeks to alleviate the conditions that lead to persistent poverty. Primary program areas include expanding educational opportunities in low-income communities, and supporting long-term residential treatment for people struggling with substance abuse and alcoholism. More specifically, the foundation supports inner-city Catholic education, and long-term residential treatment for women with children.
Fields of interest: Elementary/secondary education; Higher education; Education; Catholic agencies & churches.
Type of support: Program-related investments/loans.
Limitations: Applications not accepted. Giving primarily in the Los Angeles metro area, CA. No grants to individuals.
Application information: Contributes only to pre-selected organizations.
Officers and Directors:* Deborah Ann Estes,* Chair.; Joan C. Peter,* V.P.; James B. Peter, Jr.,* Secy.; Arthur L. Peter,* Treas.; Joe Womac, Exec. Dir.; Karen Marie Cane; Christine Mary Gard; Joan Carol Noneman.
EIN: 204896662

1204
The W. L. S. Spencer Foundation ✧
1660 Bush St., Ste. 300
San Francisco, CA 94109-5308 (415) 561-6540
Contact: Emily Schroeder, Grants Mgr.
FAX: (415) 561-5477;
E-mail: eschroeder@pfs-llc.net; Main URL: http://www.pfs-llc.net/spencer/spencer.html

Established in 1994 in DE.
Foundation type: Independent foundation.
Financial data (yr. ended 12/31/13): Assets, $12,439,300 (M); gifts received, $2,164,805; expenditures, $976,178; qualifying distributions, $926,966; giving activities include $846,150 for 39 grants (high: $100,000; low: $500).
Purpose and activities: The foundation funds educational activities, publications, and outreach associated with innovative art and/or contemporary art exhibitions, especially those focusing on contemporary Asian Art. The foundation has a particular interest in projects that encourage knowledge about art and culture, foster international understanding, and are supported by academic scholarship. Funding also for programs that are innovative and that motivate children to stay in school, do well academically, and continue their education beyond high school (to college or other higher education opportunities). In this area, the foundation may continue to fund programs that it believes in, and may fund replication of a successful program in a new site. The foundation tends to fund programs that are national or regional in nature, but which have a chapter in San Francisco, CA. The foundation prefers specific initiatives that conform with this mission, and enjoys the leverage that arises from seed grants, challenge grants, and matching grants.
Fields of interest: Arts; Education.
International interests: Asia.

Type of support: Program development; Seed money; Matching/challenge support.
Limitations: Applications accepted. Giving on a worldwide basis through intermediaries based in the United States. No support for individual schools. No grants to individuals, or for films, events, endowments or ongoing operational expenses.
Publications: Application guidelines; Annual report (including application guidelines); Grants list; Program policy statement.
Application information: The foundation will ONLY consider grant requests for compelling needs within previously funded organizations. Unsolicited full proposals are accepted by invitation only. Application form not required.
Initial approach: Letter of Intent via foundation web site (for new applicants); renewing applicants should visit the Renewal Procedures page on the foundation's web site
Copies of proposal: 2
Deadline(s): None
Board meeting date(s): Varies
Final notification: Up to 1 month from receipt of application
EIN: 133799186

1205
The Burt and Charlene Sperber Foundation ✧
23858 Malibu Rd.
Malibu, CA 90265-4604

Established in 2006 in CA.
Foundation type: Independent foundation.
Financial data (yr. ended 12/31/11): Assets, $0 (M); expenditures, $2,517,036; qualifying distributions, $2,516,366; giving activities include $2,516,366 for 1 grant.
Fields of interest: Education; Human services; Jewish agencies & synagogues.
Limitations: Applications not accepted. Giving primarily in CA. No grants to individuals.
Application information: Contributes only to pre-selected organizations.
Officers: Burton S. Sperber, Pres.; Charlene M. Sperber, Secy. and C.F.O.
EIN: 205433879
Selected grants: The following grants are a representative sample of this grantmaker's funding activity:
$2,516,366 to weSPARK, Sherman Oaks, CA, 2011. For general contribution.

1206
Arthur Spitzer Foundation ✧
P.O. Box 30
Beverly Hills, CA 90213-0030

Established in 1984 in CA.
Donor: Arthur Spitzer‡.
Foundation type: Independent foundation.
Financial data (yr. ended 11/30/13): Assets, $12,362,786 (M); expenditures, $769,028; qualifying distributions, $635,006; giving activities include $616,000 for 23 grants (high: $120,000; low: $1,000).
Fields of interest: Performing arts; Higher education; Education; Health organizations, association; Human services.
Limitations: Applications not accepted. Giving primarily in Los Angeles, CA; some funding also in CO. No grants to individuals.
Application information: Contributes only to pre-selected organizations.
Trustees: Ann Violet Lucas; Jerry Oppenheimer; A. Travis Spitzer.
EIN: 953950529
Selected grants: The following grants are a representative sample of this grantmaker's funding activity:
$5,000 to Telluride Foundation, Telluride, CO, 2013. For scholarship fund support.

1207
Norman F. Sprague, Jr. Foundation ✧
11726 San Vicente Blvd., No. 625
Los Angeles, CA 90049-5078

Established in 1997 in CA.
Foundation type: Independent foundation.
Financial data (yr. ended 02/28/14): Assets, $13,555,323 (M); expenditures, $774,895; qualifying distributions, $615,087; giving activities include $587,700 for 52 grants (high: $55,000; low: $1,000).
Purpose and activities: Giving primarily for education, health care, and museums.
Fields of interest: Museums; Museums (art); Higher education; Education; Environment, natural resources; Hospitals (general); Health care.
Limitations: Giving primarily in CA. No grants to individuals.
Trustees: Cynthia Sprague Connolly; Elizabeth Sprague Day; Caryll Sprague Mingst; Norman F. Sprague III, M.D.
EIN: 954621772
Selected grants: The following grants are a representative sample of this grantmaker's funding activity:
$40,000 to Santa Barbara Museum of Natural History, Santa Barbara, CA, 2012.
$25,000 to Childrens Hospital Los Angeles, Los Angeles, CA, 2012.
$12,000 to Santa Barbara Museum of Art, Santa Barbara, CA, 2012.

1208
The Springcreek Foundation ✧
c/o Leventhal Kline Management Inc.
127 University Ave.
Berkeley, CA 94710-1616
Main URL: http://www.thespringcreekfoundation.org/

Established in 1994 in CA.
Donors: T. Dixon Long; Henry H. Corning; Maud-Alison C. Long; Springcreek Advisors.
Foundation type: Independent foundation.
Financial data (yr. ended 12/31/13): Assets, $14,568,655 (M); expenditures, $833,565; qualifying distributions, $645,157; giving activities include $532,987 for 112 grants (high: $70,000; low: $200).
Purpose and activities: The foundation aspires to strengthen its community through individual and collaborative grants and investments; its collaborative investments foster the transition to a conservation economy.
Fields of interest: Museums; Performing arts; Performing arts, theater; Performing arts, orchestras; Literature; Arts; Higher education; Environment, land resources; Environment; Reproductive health, family planning; Human services; Children/youth, services; Community/economic development; Philanthropy/voluntarism.
Type of support: General/operating support; Capital campaigns; Building/renovation; Equipment; Professorships; Program-related investments/loans; Mission-related investments/loans.
Limitations: Applications not accepted. Giving primarily in CA. No grants to individuals.
Application information: Contributes only to pre-selected organizations. Unsolicited requests for funds not accepted.
Board meeting date(s): Jan., June, and Sept.
Officers and Directors:* Maud-Alison Long,* Pres.; Harald Leventhal, C.F.O.; Marlis Corning Jansen,* V.P. and Secy.-Treas.
Number of staff: 3 full-time professional.
EIN: 680344778

1209
Emil J. Stache Charitable Trust ✧ ☆
1351 Upland Hills Dr. N.
Upland, CA 91784-9168

Established in 2003 in CA.
Donor: Emil Stache Trust.
Foundation type: Independent foundation.
Financial data (yr. ended 12/31/13): Assets, $48,967 (M); expenditures, $795,808; qualifying distributions, $783,983; giving activities include $780,000 for 2 grants (high: $755,000; low: $25,000).
Fields of interest: Higher education.
Limitations: Applications not accepted. Giving primarily in CA. No grants to individuals.
Application information: Unsolicited requests for funds not accepted.
Trustee: Irene Guth.
EIN: 562356544
Selected grants: The following grants are a representative sample of this grantmaker's funding activity:
$235,643 to University of California, Los Angeles, CA, 2010.
$213,156 to University of California, School of Law, Los Angeles, CA, 2011. For scholarship.

1210
James L. Stamps Foundation, Inc. ✧
600 N. Tustin Ave., No. 260
Santa Ana, CA 92705-3782
Contact: Richard D. Salyer, Pres.

Incorporated in 1963 in CA.
Donors: James L. Stamps‡; Stephen Lewis.
Foundation type: Independent foundation.
Financial data (yr. ended 12/31/13): Assets, $30,891,101 (M); expenditures, $2,010,812; qualifying distributions, $1,671,461; giving activities include $1,470,502 for 172 grants (high: $50,000; low: $500).
Purpose and activities: Emphasis on Protestant evangelical churches, seminaries, associations, and programs. Capital fund grants and new equipment grants restricted to Christian organizations; camping grants restricted to Christian camps.
Fields of interest: Education; Christian agencies & churches.

Type of support: Equipment; Program development; Matching/challenge support.
Limitations: Giving primarily in southern CA and selected foreign countries in Africa, South and Southeast Asia. No grants for general and administrative costs, endowments, debt payments or fund raising costs.
Publications: Application guidelines.
Application information: Organizations may be invited to submit further information upon review of letter. Application form required.
Initial approach: Letter
Copies of proposal: 1
Deadline(s): None
Board meeting date(s): Bimonthly beginning in Feb., on the 2nd Tuesday of the month
Officers and Trustees:* Thomas Lynch,* Chair.; Richard Salyer, Pres.; Richard Kredel, Secy.-Treas.
Number of staff: 2 full-time support; 1 part-time support.
EIN: 956086125
Selected grants: The following grants are a representative sample of this grantmaker's funding activity:
$15,000 to Pocket Testament League, Lititz, PA, 2012. For program materials.
$10,500 to World Impact, Los Angeles, CA, 2012. For infrastructure.
$5,000 to Union Rescue Mission, Los Angeles, CA, 2012. For Relief.
$4,000 to First Baptist Church of Downey, Downey, CA, 2012. For church interns.
$2,030 to Boy Scouts of America, OC Council, Santa Ana, CA, 2012. For equipment.
$1,000 to Every Generation Ministries, Temecula, CA, 2012. For tournament sponsorship.

1211
Stanislaus Community Foundation ✧
1029 16th St.
Modesto, CA 95354 (209) 576-1608
Contact: Marion Kaanon, C.E.O.; For grants: Amanda Hughes, Prog. Off.
FAX: (209) 576-1609;
E-mail: mkaanon@stanislauscf.org; Grant inquiry e-mail: ahughes@stanislauscf.org; Main URL: http://www.StanislausCF.org

Established in 2001 in CA.
Foundation type: Community foundation.
Financial data (yr. ended 12/31/13): Assets, $15,718,102 (M); gifts received, $2,124,768; expenditures, $1,329,553; giving activities include $1,007,931 for 36+ grants (high: $151,700), and $2,250 for grants to individuals.
Purpose and activities: The foundation seeks to mobilize resources and guide their use to promote a vibrant and sustainable community. In service to the people of the local community, the foundation partners with organizations and donors to create new opportunities while acting as a catalyst for improvement and involvement.
Fields of interest: Arts; Education; Environment; Health care; Human services; Children/youth; Children; Youth.
Type of support: Endowments; Program development; Seed money; Scholarships—to individuals.
Limitations: Applications accepted. Giving primarily in Stanislaus County, CA. No support for religious activities. No grants for individuals (except for scholarships), debt reduction, fundraising events.
Publications: Annual report; Informational brochure; Newsletter.
Application information: Visit foundation web site for application form. Application form required.
Initial approach: Contact foundation
Deadline(s): Aug. 2
Officers and Board Members:* Jeff Grover, Chair.; Craig C. Lewis,* Vice-Chair.; Marian Kaanon,* C.E.O. and Pres.; Jeff Grover,* V.P.; Melanie Chiesa,* Secy.; Doris Daniel-Brima, Cont.; Jeff Coleman,* Treas.; John Bellizzi; Jeffrey P. Burda; Randy Clark; Lynn Dickerson; Joe Duran; John Evans; Mike Gianelli; Judy Sly Herrero; Bill Jackson; Daryn Kumar; Marian Martino; Evan Porges.
Number of staff: 3 full-time professional.
EIN: 680483054

1212
Stanley And Erika Tobin Foundation ✧
c/o Thomas F. Reed
300 S. Grand Ave., 37th Fl.
Los Angeles, CA 90071

Foundation type: Independent foundation.
Financial data (yr. ended 12/31/11): Assets, $38,313 (M); gifts received, $1,475,816; expenditures, $1,437,620; qualifying distributions, $1,437,620; giving activities include $1,430,000 for 1 grant.
Fields of interest: Higher education.
Limitations: Applications not accepted. Giving primarily in AZ.
Application information: Unsolicited requests for funds not accepted.
Trustees: Katherine Driesen; Ursula Eastman-Cook; David Kekst; Mark Tobin.
EIN: 261730779

1213
The Fran & Ray Stark Foundation ✧
(formerly The Stark Foundation)
1990 S. Bundy Dr., Ste. 420
Los Angeles, CA 90025-1578

Established in 1982 in CA.
Donors: Ray Stark†; Ray & Frances Stark Revocable Trust; Allison Gorsuch Charitable Lead Unitrust No. 1; Allison Gorsuch Charitable Lead Unitrust No. 2; Ray Stark Revocable Trust.
Foundation type: Independent foundation.
Financial data (yr. ended 12/31/13): Assets, $50,583,828 (M); gifts received, $528,657; expenditures, $3,088,338; qualifying distributions, $2,814,967; giving activities include $2,598,333 for 43 grants (high: $850,000; low: $1,000).
Purpose and activities: Giving primarily for education, health organizations, and human services.
Fields of interest: Museums (art); Arts; Higher education; Education; Reproductive health, family planning; Health organizations; Crime/law enforcement, police agencies; Human services; Children/youth, services.
Limitations: Applications not accepted. Giving primarily in Los Angeles, CA. No grants to individuals.
Application information: Contributes only to pre-selected organizations.
Directors: Herbert A. Allen; David Geffen; Allison Gorsuch; Bonnie Grey; Wendy Stark Morrissey; Anita Rosenstein; Franklin Wallis.
EIN: 953767859
Selected grants: The following grants are a representative sample of this grantmaker's funding activity:
$100,000 to Homeboy Industries, Los Angeles, CA, 2012. For Programs and Resources for Formerly Gang Involved and Recently Incarcerated Men and Women.
$17,500 to Music Center Foundation, Los Angeles, CA, 2012. For Preservation and Promotion of Theatrical and Performing Arts in the Community.
$10,000 to Whitney Museum of American Art, New York, NY, 2012. For Preservation and Promotion of Art in the Community.
$5,000 to Angels at Risk, Los Angeles, CA, 2012. For awareness, prevention, and treatment of drug and alcohol abuse.
$5,000 to Teach for America, Los Angeles, CA, 2012. For Educational Institutions and Programs.
$2,500 to Women for Women International, Washington, DC, 2012. For Programs Supporting Women Survivors of War, Civil Strife and Other Conflicts.

1214
John Stauffer Charitable Trust ✧
301 N. Lake Ave., 10th Fl.
Pasadena, CA 91101-4108 (626) 793-9400
Contact: H. Jess Senecal, Tr.
FAX: (626) 793-5900;
E-mail: tgosney@lagerlof.com.

Trust established in 1974 in CA.
Donor: John Stauffer†.
Foundation type: Independent foundation.
Financial data (yr. ended 05/31/13): Assets, $49,596,607 (M); expenditures, $2,014,496; qualifying distributions, $1,511,538; giving activities include $1,260,700 for 14 grants (high: $1,000,000; low: $80,000).
Purpose and activities: Grants restricted to hospitals, colleges, and universities in California.
Fields of interest: Higher education; Hospitals (general); Chemistry; Biology/life sciences.
Type of support: Building/renovation; Equipment; Endowments; Professorships; Fellowships; Scholarship funds; Matching/challenge support.
Limitations: Applications accepted. Giving limited to CA. No grants to individuals, no loans.
Publications: Application guidelines.
Application information: Application form not required.
Initial approach: Letter
Copies of proposal: 3
Deadline(s): None
Board meeting date(s): Quarterly beginning in Jan.
Final notification: 6 to 9 months
Trustees: John F. Bradley; Timothy J. Gosney; Michael S. Whalen.
Number of staff: None.
EIN: 237434707
Selected grants: The following grants are a representative sample of this grantmaker's funding activity:
$500,000 to California Institute of Technology, Pasadena, CA, 2012.
$500,000 to Westmont College, Santa Barbara, CA, 2012.
$210,170 to Occidental College, Los Angeles, CA, 2012.

$150,000 to Harvey Mudd College, Claremont, CA, 2012.
$100,000 to Good Samaritan Hospital, Los Angeles, CA, 2012.

1215
Eugene and Marilyn Stein Family Foundation ✧
333 S. Hope St., 34th Fl.
Los Angeles, CA 90071-1406

Established in 1997 in CA.
Donors: Eugene P. Stein; Marilyn L. Stein.
Foundation type: Independent foundation.
Financial data (yr. ended 12/31/13): Assets, $44,009,716 (M); expenditures, $2,132,859; qualifying distributions, $2,071,577; giving activities include $2,070,600 for 30 grants (high: $1,400,000; low: $250).
Purpose and activities: Giving for higher education, the arts, and to a community foundation.
Fields of interest: Arts; Higher education; Education; Children/youth, services; Foundations (community).
Limitations: Applications not accepted. Giving primarily in CA. No grants to individuals.
Application information: Contributes only to pre-selected organizations.
Officers: Marilyn L. Stein,* Chair. and Secy.; Eugene P. Stein, Pres.
EIN: 954659838

1216
Steinmetz Foundation ✧
c/o BCWS
3424 Carson St., Ste. 600
Torrance, CA 90503-5725

Established in 1997 in CA.
Donor: William Steinmetz.
Foundation type: Independent foundation.
Financial data (yr. ended 12/31/13): Assets, $6,626,576 (M); expenditures, $540,589; qualifying distributions, $480,000; giving activities include $480,000 for 18 grants (high: $110,000; low: $5,000).
Purpose and activities: Giving primarily for education and educational programs, (including a Catholic education foundation), and children and youth services.
Fields of interest: Higher education; Libraries (academic/research); Education, reading; Education; Environmental education; Human services; Children/youth, services; Catholic agencies & churches.
Limitations: Applications not accepted. Giving primarily in CA. No grants to individuals.
Application information: Contributes only to pre-selected organizations.
Officers and Directors:* Charles William Steinmetz,* Pres.; Terry Kay, C.F.O.; Jean S. Kay, V.P., Admin. and Secy.; Ann Marie Steinmetz; Mary L. Steinmetz.
EIN: 954649432

1217
Stephenson Foundation ✧
3000 Sand Hill Rd., Bldg. 4, Ste. 250
Menlo Park, CA 94025-7113 (650) 854-3927
Contact: Barbara Stephenson, Pres.

Established in 1999 in CA.
Donors: Barbara Stephenson; Thomas F. Stephenson.
Foundation type: Independent foundation.
Financial data (yr. ended 12/31/12): Assets, $21,387,837 (M); expenditures, $1,104,350; qualifying distributions, $1,015,346; giving activities include $974,620 for 35 grants (high: $400,000; low: $500).
Purpose and activities: Giving primarily for education and the environment.
Fields of interest: Higher education; Education; Environment; Health organizations, association; Children/youth, services; International affairs, goodwill promotion.
Limitations: Applications accepted. Giving primarily in CA. No grants to individuals.
Application information: Application form required.
Initial approach: Letter
Deadline(s): None
Officers: Barbara Stephenson, Pres.; Thomas F. Stephenson, V.P.
EIN: 943320092

1218
The Donald T. Sterling Charitable Foundation ✧ ☆
9441 Wilshire Blvd.
Beverly Hills, CA 90212-2808 (310) 278-8010

Established in 2007 in CA.
Donor: Donald T. Sterling.
Foundation type: Independent foundation.
Financial data (yr. ended 12/31/13): Assets, $51,912 (M); gifts received, $600,000; expenditures, $607,617; qualifying distributions, $605,085; giving activities include $605,000 for 52 grants (high: $125,000; low: $5,000).
Purpose and activities: The foundation supports nonprofit organizations and events involved with issues of poverty, homelessness, education and literacy. Special emphasis is directed to programs benefiting at-risk children and families located in greater Los Angeles and southern California.
Fields of interest: Education; Health care; Homeless, human services.
Type of support: General/operating support.
Limitations: Applications accepted. Giving primarily in Los Angeles, CA.
Application information: Organizations are limited to one request per calendar year. Application form required.
Initial approach: Letter
Deadline(s): Varies
Officers: Donald T. Sterling, Pres.; Rochelle H. Sterling, V.P.; Douglas L. Walton, Secy.; Darren Schield, C.F.O.
EIN: 208731101
Selected grants: The following grants are a representative sample of this grantmaker's funding activity:
$10,000 to A Place Called Home, Los Angeles, CA, 2011.
$10,000 to Beit TShuvah, Los Angeles, CA, 2011.
$10,000 to Childrens Hospital Los Angeles, Los Angeles, CA, 2011.
$10,000 to Guardians of the Jewish Home for the Aged, Los Angeles, CA, 2011.
$10,000 to Jewish Vocational Service, Los Angeles, CA, 2011.
$10,000 to Para Los Ninos, Los Angeles, CA, 2011.
$10,000 to Simon Wiesenthal Center, Los Angeles, CA, 2011.
$10,000 to Step Up On Second Street, Santa Monica, CA, 2011.
$10,000 to Union Rescue Mission, Los Angeles, CA, 2011.
$10,000 to United Negro College Fund, Los Angeles, CA, 2011.

1219
The Marc and Eva Stern Foundation ✧
(formerly The Stern Family Foundation)
865 S. Figueroa St., Ste. 1800
Los Angeles, CA 90017-2593 (213) 244-0744
Contact: Marc I. Stern, Pres.

Established in 1986 in CA.
Donors: Marc I. Stern; Robert A. Day; Eva Stern; Adam Stern; Erika Stern; Henley Manufacturing, Inc.; The Henley Group, Inc.; W.K. Day Foundation; The Penates Foundation.
Foundation type: Independent foundation.
Financial data (yr. ended 12/31/12): Assets, $2,512,623 (M); gifts received, $2,277,385; expenditures, $1,391,229; qualifying distributions, $1,366,065; giving activities include $1,350,755 for 61 grants (high: $110,000; low: $250), and $15,000 for 6 grants to individuals (high: $2,500; low: $2,500).
Purpose and activities: Giving primarily for the arts, particularly the opera, as well as for health and medical research, and education. The Albert B. Stern Scholarship Awards are limited to graduating seniors at Vineland High School in Vineland, NJ, who plan to continue their education by studying agriculture in college. Preference will be given to a student in agricultural sciences or business and agronomy, but students interested in environmental studies or life sciences may also apply.
Fields of interest: Museums; Performing arts; Performing arts, theater; Performing arts, opera; Arts; Higher education; Education; Medical research, institute; Human services; Jewish federated giving programs; Jewish agencies & synagogues.
Limitations: Giving primarily in CA, for non-scholarship grants; some funding also in New York, NY. Giving limited to Vineland, NJ, for scholarships.
Application information: Albert B. Stern Scholarship Award applicants must complete the Vineland High School local scholarship application, as well as submit a transcript, a letter of recommendation from a teacher or counselor, and a 50-word or fewer statement concerning their interests and career goals, and how their goals relate to agriculture. Scholarship amount is $2,500 per year for up to 4 years.
Initial approach: Letter
Deadline(s): None
Officers: Marc I. Stern, Pres.; Eva S. Stern, V.P.; Patricia A. Curtis, Secy.
EIN: 330220467
Selected grants: The following grants are a representative sample of this grantmaker's funding activity:
$25,000 to Columbia University, School of Law, New York, NY, 2012. For education.
$10,000 to Layalina Productions, Washington, DC, 2012. For cultural awareness.
$7,500 to Ironman Foundation, Tampa, FL, 2012. To promote Sporting events.

$7,500 to SLE Lupus Foundation, New York, NY, 2012. For Health and Medical Research.
$5,000 to American Cancer Society, Pasadena, CA, 2012. For health/medical research.
$5,000 to Homeboy Industries, Los Angeles, CA, 2012. For education and youth services.
$1,000 to CoachArt, Los Angeles, CA, 2012. For art therapy.

1220
Stewardship Foundation ✧
1508 W. Mission Rd.
Escondido, CA 92029-1105

Established in 1987 in CA.
Donors: Doreen Broek; Chris Brouwer; Garrett Brouwer; Jack Brouwer; Jacob Brouwer; Jane Brouwer; Richard Brouwer; Joanne Cooper; Brouwer Family L.P.; Jeanette Brouwer; Theresa Veld Kamp; Escondido Ready Mix Concrete, Inc.; JJB Land Company, LP; Superior Ready Mix Concrete, LP.
Foundation type: Independent foundation.
Financial data (yr. ended 11/30/13): Assets, $70,604,453 (M); gifts received, $5,221,007; expenditures, $2,749,604; qualifying distributions, $1,518,925; giving activities include $1,516,500 for 58 grants (high: $600,000; low: $1,000).
Purpose and activities: Giving primarily to Christian schools, churches and organizations.
Fields of interest: Theological school/education; Youth, services; Christian agencies & churches.
Limitations: Applications not accepted. Giving primarily in the Escondido, CA area. No grants to individuals.
Application information: Unsolicited requests for funds not accepted.
Officers: Jacob Brouwer, Pres.; Jeanette Brouwer, C.F.O.; Arnold Veldkamp, Secy.
EIN: 330273191
Selected grants: The following grants are a representative sample of this grantmaker's funding activity:
$35,200 to Dordt College, Sioux Center, IA, 2011.
$20,100 to Christian Reformed World Missions, Grand Rapids, MI, 2011.
$15,000 to Barnabas Foundation, Tinley Park, IL, 2011.
$15,000 to Calvin Theological Seminary, Grand Rapids, MI, 2011.
$9,100 to San Diego Rescue Mission, San Diego, CA, 2011.
$7,300 to Interfaith Community Services, Escondido, CA, 2011.
$5,600 to Trinity Christian College, Palos Heights, IL, 2011.
$4,200 to Talking Bibles International, Escondido, CA, 2011.
$3,750 to Mission India, Grand Rapids, MI, 2011.
$3,000 to Kuyper College, Grand Rapids, MI, 2011.

1221
The Stotsenberg Foundation ✧
(formerly Edward G. and Dorothy D. Stotsenberg Foundation)
40836 Calle Bandido
Murrieta, CA 92562-9235 (800) 331-8128
Contact: Henry Stotsenberg, Pres.

Established in 1990 in CA.
Donor: Dorothy Stotsenberg Trust.
Foundation type: Independent foundation.
Financial data (yr. ended 12/31/13): Assets, $2,307,741 (M); gifts received, $981; expenditures, $575,938; qualifying distributions, $538,597; giving activities include $474,400 for 1 grant.
Fields of interest: Arts education; Performing arts, music; Education; Human services.
Type of support: General/operating support; Scholarship funds.
Limitations: Applications accepted. Giving limited to CA. No grants to individuals.
Application information: Application form required.
Initial approach: Letter
Deadline(s): None
Officers and Directors:* Henry Stotsenberg, Jr.,* Pres.; Pauline Stotsenberg,* Secy.
EIN: 954265406

1222
The Stover Foundation ✧
1981 N. Broadway, Ste. 362
Walnut Creek, CA 94596-8213

Established in 1994 in CA.
Donors: Joan C. Stover; W. Robert Stover.
Foundation type: Independent foundation.
Financial data (yr. ended 12/31/13): Assets, $13,815,053 (M); expenditures, $730,457; qualifying distributions, $599,326; giving activities include $560,450 for 23 grants (high: $175,000; low: $450).
Purpose and activities: Giving only to Christian organizations.
Fields of interest: Human services; Youth, services; Christian agencies & churches.
Limitations: Applications not accepted. Giving in the U.S., with some emphasis on CO and PA. No grants to individuals.
Application information: Unsolicited requests for funds not accepted.
Officers: Joan C. Stover, Pres.; W. Robert Stover, V.P.; Wenche M. Rae, Secy.
Directors: David Carlson; Ted Johnson; Amy Newton; Gary Nickerson; Susan J. Stover; Parker Williamson.
EIN: 680392330
Selected grants: The following grants are a representative sample of this grantmaker's funding activity:
$125,000 to Young Life, Colorado Springs, CO, 2012. For Several Programs; Support Senior Vice President Work; First Time Kids for Week of Camp; Evangelical Outreach; Camping Support for Under Privileged Children.
$10,000 to Caldwell Memorial Hospital Foundation, Lenoir, NC, 2012. For Chapel in New Cancer Center.
$10,000 to Darren Patterson Christian Academy, Buena Vista, CO, 2012. For Christian Education and Field Trips.
$10,000 to Horizon Christian School, Hood River, OR, 2012. For Host Constitutional Conferences W/ Christian Values.
$10,000 to Presbyterian Lay Committee, Lenoir, NC, 2012. For God Equips Resource Ministry.
$10,000 to Seattle Urban Academy, Seattle, WA, 2012. For Academic Service and Operational Costs for At-Risk Teens.

1223
Levi Strauss Foundation ✧
1155 Battery St.
Levi Plaza
San Francisco, CA 94111-1203 (415) 501-3577
Contact: Daniel Jae-Won Lee, Exec. Dir.
FAX: (415) 501-6575; Main URL: http://www.levistrauss.com/levi-strauss-foundation/
Grants List: http://www.levistrauss.com/about/foundations/levi-strauss-foundation/grant-list
Philanthropy's Promise: http://www.ncrp.org/philanthropys-promise/who
Twitter: https://twitter.com/LeviStraussFdn
Unzipped: http://www.levistrauss.com/unzipped-blog/category/archive/community/
YouTube: https://www.youtube.com/watch?v=U7NYg5pPJP8#t=100

Incorporated in 1952 in CA.
Donors: Levi Strauss & Co.; Peter E. Haas, Jr.; F. Warren Hellman.
Foundation type: Company-sponsored foundation.
Financial data (yr. ended 11/30/13): Assets, $65,917,837 (M); gifts received, $5,220,000; expenditures, $7,863,189; qualifying distributions, $7,817,014; giving activities include $6,426,775 for 157 grants (high: $168,000; low: $100).
Purpose and activities: The foundation supports programs designed to address HIV/AIDS; asset building; worker rights and well-being; human rights and social justice; and employee engagement. Special emphasis is directed toward programs designed to advance the human rights and well-being of underserved people.
Fields of interest: Education; Reproductive health; Public health; Public health, hygiene; Health care; AIDS; AIDS research; Legal services; Employment, equal rights; Employment; Disasters, preparedness/services; American Red Cross; Human services, financial counseling; Human services; Civil/human rights, equal rights; Civil/human rights, advocacy; Civil/human rights; Business/industry; Community development, small businesses; Community/economic development; Public policy, research; Financial services; Public affairs; Women; Economically disadvantaged.
International interests: Africa; Asia; Canada; China; Europe; Haiti; Latin America.
Type of support: General/operating support; Continuing support; Management development/capacity building; Capital campaigns; Equipment; Program development; Publication; Scholarship funds; Research; Technical assistance; Employee volunteer services; Sponsorships; Employee matching gifts.
Limitations: Applications not accepted. Giving on a national and international basis in areas of company operations, with emphasis on CA, NY, Africa, Asia, Canada, China, Europe, Latin America, and Mexico. No support for political, sectarian, religious, or discriminatory organizations, or athletic associations. No grants to individuals, or for capital, endowment, or building funds, sporting events, or advertising.
Publications: Grants list; Program policy statement.
Application information: Unsolicited applications are not accepted. The foundation supports a network of partners across the sector.
Officers and Directors:* Robert D. Haas,* Pres.; Jennifer Haas, V.P.; Seth Jaffe, V.P.; Daniel Jae-Won Lee, Secy. and Exec. Dir.; Johan Nystedt, Treas.; Haluk Aksoy; Chip Bergh; Dan Geballe; Elise Haas; Peter E. Haas, Jr.; Michael Kobori; Margaret Lourenco; Daniel Lurie; Sanjay Purohit.

Number of staff: 14
EIN: 946064702
Selected grants: The following grants are a representative sample of this grantmaker's funding activity:
$242,500 to Tides Center New York, International Treatment Preparedness Coalition (ITPC), New York, NY, 2012. To strengthen community responses and advocacy strategies to improve HIV/AIDS treatment and services in Russia, Latin America, China and South Asia.
$168,000 to CARE USA, Atlanta, GA, 2013. For renewal support of the Sewing for a Brighter Future program for women garment workers in Cambodia, as well as its pilot role in the Improving Worker Well-being initiative.
$160,000 to Tides Center New York, International Treatment Preparedness Coalition (ITPC), New York, NY, 2013. For regional advocacy on access to treatment and a small grants program to build capacity among community-based organizations in Eastern European and Central Asia, payable over 2.00 years.
$150,000 to Canadian HIV/AIDS Legal Network, Toronto, Canada, 2012. For general support to build domestic capacity for legal advocacy on HIV/AIDS-related human rights issues in Canada.
$140,000 to International Bridges to Justice, Geneva, Switzerland, 2012. To safeguard legal rights for people living with or vulnerable to HIV/AIDS through sponsorship of the 2012 JusticeMakers Competition, payable over 1.50 years.
$130,000 to ZeroDivide, San Francisco, CA, 2012. To advance the use of social media and technology among nonprofits participating in the Pioneers in Justice initiative and build the field of social justice philanthropy, payable over 1.25 years.
$120,000 to Better Work, Geneva, Switzerland, 2013. For the Better Work program to implement HERproject in Haiti and expand training to improve the rights and well-being of apparel workers in Cambodia, Vietnam, Jordan, Nicaragua, Lesotho and Indonesia.
$110,000 to Center for Promotion of Quality of Life, Life Center, Ho Chi Minh City, Vietnam, 2013. To scale and expand a factory-based approach to improve the well-being of apparel workers in Vietnam, payable over 2.00 years.
$100,000 to Chinese For Affirmative Action, San Francisco, CA, 2012. For a second year of support to a leading social justice organization in San Francisco to build strategic alliances for positive social change through participation in the Pioneers in Justice initiative.
$100,000 to Earned Assets Resource Network, San Francisco, CA, 2013. For general support to drive asset-based program innovations to scale and advance policies to promote savings, access to fair financial products and asset protection among low-income working people, payable over 2.00 years.
$70,000 to Asociacion de Mujeres Meretrices de la Argentina, Buenos Aires, Argentina, 2012. For advocacy to address HIV/AIDS stigma and discrimination and advance the human rights of sex workers in Argentina, payable over 2.00 years.
$70,000 to Mercado Global, Brooklyn, NY, 2013. To strengthen Mercado Global's asset-building model for indigenous women artisans in Guatemala through expansion to new communities, development of training curricula and improved evaluation.
$70,000 to Tides Center New York, Hive Young Leaders Fund, New York, NY, 2013. For youth-led initiatives that address the impact of HIV/AIDS on young women in Southern Africa through the HIV Young Leaders Fund.
$50,000 to Arbitration Council Foundation, Phnom Penh, Cambodia, 2012. To promote stable industrial relations among employers and trade unions in Cambodia's apparel sector, payable over 2.00 years.
$50,000 to Global Fund for Women, San Francisco, CA, 2013. For general support for human rights leadership, payable over 2.00 years.
$50,000 to Insight Center for Community Economic Development, Oakland, CA, 2013. To continue support to the Closing the Racial Wealth Gap Initiative by developing new messaging for new audiences to support a public policy agenda that builds economic health and opportunity in vulnerable communities.
$50,000 to Philanthropy New York, New York, NY, 2012. For general support to the Asset Funder Network to promote wealth-building for low-income people as effective strategy for philanthropy, payable over 2.00 years.
$25,000 to Corporation for Enterprise Development, Washington, DC, 2013. For the 1:1 Fund, online platform providing matching funds for special bank accounts helping students in the 2013 kindergarten class in San Francisco public schools save for college.
$19,000 to International Association for Community Development, Falkland, Scotland, 2012. To continue facilitation of the Indigo Asset Building Network.
$10,000 to Seven Sisters, Bangkok, Thailand, 2012. To participate in the biannual International AIDS Conference (IAC) and the AIDS 'Advocacy 2.0' Summit organized by LSF in Washington, DC.

1224
The Streisand Foundation ✧

1327 Ocean Ave., Ste. H
Santa Monica, CA 90401-1008
Contact: Margery Tabankin, Exec. Dir.
FAX: (310) 314-8396; Main URL: http://www.barbrastreisand.com/us/streisand-foundation

Established in 1986 in NY.
Donors: Barbra Streisand; The Lincy Foundation.
Foundation type: Independent foundation.
Financial data (yr. ended 12/31/12): Assets, $7,525,059 (M); gifts received, $258,525; expenditures, $888,576; qualifying distributions, $676,606; giving activities include $666,400 for 88 grants (high: $62,500; low: $500).
Purpose and activities: Giving primarily for environmental issues, women's issues, including reproductive choice and health-related concerns, civil liberties and democratic values, civil rights and race relations, AIDS research, advocacy, service and litigation, and in Los Angeles, CA only: children and youth-related issues with a focus on the economically disadvantaged.
Fields of interest: Arts; Education; Environment; Medical research; Children/youth, services; Civil rights, voter education; Civil liberties, advocacy; Civil/human rights; Women.
Type of support: General/operating support; Continuing support; Program development.
Limitations: Applications not accepted. Giving to nationally-based groups; some local giving in Los Angeles, CA for disadvantaged children and youth. No support for start-up organizations or international organizations. No grants to individuals, or for capital campaigns, endowments, documentaries or audio-visual programming, or publication of books or magazines.
Application information: Unsolicited requests for funds not accepted.
Board meeting date(s): Varies
Officer and Trustees:* Margery Tabankin,* Exec. Dir.; Richard Baskin; Marilyn Bergman; Jason Gould; Barry Hirsh; Lester Knispel; Barbra Streisand.
Number of staff: 1 part-time professional; 1 full-time support.
EIN: 132620702
Selected grants: The following grants are a representative sample of this grantmaker's funding activity:
$15,000 to Movement Strategy Center, Oakland, CA, 2012. For Programs That Help the Progressive Social Justice Movement.
$15,000 to Rock the Vote, Washington, DC, 2012. For Promotion of Youth Political Power.
$15,000 to Urban Zen Foundation, New York, NY, 2012. For culture and empowering children.
$15,000 to Working America Education Fund, Washington, DC, 2012. For Issues Relating to Working Americans.
$10,000 to Advancement Project, Washington, DC, 2012. For Legal Advocacy for Racial Justice.
$10,000 to Common Cause Education Fund, Washington, DC, 2012. For Programs for Accountability in Elected Leaders and Political Process.
$10,000 to Consumer Watchdog, Santa Monica, CA, 2012. For consumer protection.
$10,000 to Environmental Media Association, Los Angeles, CA, 2012. For Environmental Education and Protection.
$10,000 to Media Matters for America, Washington, DC, 2012. To Help Analyze and Correct Conservative Misinformation in the U S Media.
$10,000 to Natural Resources Defense Council, New York, NY, 2012. To support conservation.

1225
Stuart Foundation ✧

(also known as Elbridge Stuart Foundation)
500 Washington St., 8th Fl.
San Francisco, CA 94111-4735 (415) 393-1551
Contact: Carol Ting, C.O.O.; Brad Sink, Cont.
FAX: (415) 393-1552;
E-mail: rsotelo@stuartfoundation.org; Main URL: http://www.stuartfoundation.org
Grantee Perception Report: http://www.stuartfoundation.org/Files/Stuart%20Foundation%20GPR%20-%20Spring%202006%20-%20For%20Web.pdf
Grants Database: http://www.stuartfoundation.org/GrantSearch
Knowledge Center: http://www.stuartfoundation.org/NewsAndReports
Report on Stuart Foundation Child Welfare Program: http://www.stuartfoundation.org/Files/CEP_Stuart_CaseStudy.pdf

Elbridge Stuart Foundation created in 1937 in CA, Elbridge and Mary Stuart Foundation in 1941 in CA, and Mary Horner Stuart Foundation in 1941 in WA; in 1995 and 1996, the two smaller foundations were merged into the Elbridge Stuart Foundation, DBA Stuart Foundation.
Donors: Elbridge A. Stuart†; Elbridge H. Stuart†; Mary H. Stuart†.
Foundation type: Independent foundation.

Financial data (yr. ended 12/31/12): Assets, $461,733,374 (M); gifts received, $149,713; expenditures, $32,070,974; qualifying distributions, $25,127,370; giving activities include $20,096,321 for 442 grants (high: $425,000; low: $100), and $360,200 for 4 foundation-administered programs.

Purpose and activities: The foundation is dedicated to supporting the education and development of children and youth in California and Washington with a goal of them becoming become self-sustaining, responsible, and contributing members of their communities. The foundation serves as a partner and convener that helps gather the resources, thought, and energy needed to create and sustain change. It is committed to creating powerful partnerships with those who work toward sustainable, scalable, and system-wide change for all young people, especially those who are most in need The foundation looks for partners who share the same mission and values. Many of the foundation's relationships are long-term, with some spanning over a decade of successful collaboration. Its partners share the following characteristics: They support and engage in continuous learning and improvement. Demonstrate, succeed, spread, and engage in practice that informs policy. Recognize the needs of vulnerable youth, and a possess commitment to bolster their education and development. Find, work with, and support the expert implementers and change agents. Build a culture of collaboration; work with others to create a movement. Invest in irresistible information to drive evidence-based decision making. Work on public policy with an incisive role in contributing to statewide system improvement.

Fields of interest: Education, research; Education, public policy; Education, reform; Education, public education; Elementary/secondary school reform; Education; Children/youth, services; Public policy, research; Children/youth.

Type of support: Conferences/seminars; Continuing support; Employee matching gifts; General/operating support; Management development/capacity building; Program development; Program evaluation; Publication; Research; Technical assistance.

Limitations: Applications accepted. Giving primarily in CA and WA. No support for political activities. No grants to individuals, for capital campaigns, or generally for endowments, building funds, or annual campaigns, capital or operating support to sustain existing service capacity.

Application information: Following review of letter of inquiry, program staff will contact you if your request aligns with the foundation's strategy and additional information and/or a full proposal will be invited. At this point, staff will share specific proposal guidelines, provide a list of required documents, and assign a due date for submittal. Please note that it can take an additional four to eight months to conduct the necessary due diligence (which may include but is not limited to a site visit, follow-up meetings, reference checks and program and financial assessment) to bring funding recommendations to the board of directors. During the review process, staff will be in touch to keep you informed of the status of your submittal. Application form required.

Initial approach: Letter of inquiry (can be downloaded from web site and e-mailed)
Copies of proposal: 1
Deadline(s): None
Board meeting date(s): Spring, Summer and Fall
Final notification: Within 60 days for letters of inquiry

Officers and Directors:* Dwight L. Stuart, Jr.,* Chair.; Elbridge H. Stuart III,* Vice.-Chair. and Treas.; Stuart E. Lucas,* Vice-Chair.; Carol Ting, C.O.O.; Jonathan Raymond, Pres.; David S. Barlow, C.F.O.; Brad S. Sink, Cont.; Davis Campbell.

Number of staff: 21 full-time professional.

EIN: 200882784

Selected grants: The following grants are a representative sample of this grantmaker's funding activity:

$850,000 to California Education Partners, San Francisco, CA, 2012. For the California Office to Reform Education (CORE) to enhance and expand innovative district efforts and a unique collaboration among eight unified school districts: Clovis, Fresno, Los Angeles, Long Beach, Oakland, Sacramento, San Francisco and Sanger. CORE identifies shared goals for systemic reform and jointly develops and implements strategies to achieve those goals.

$750,000 to University of Chicago, Chicago, IL, 2012. For the evaluation of the impact of extended foster care on outcomes for transition-age foster youth, age 17-21, in California. This evaluation will follow 800 foster youth over five years and will involve in-person interviews of the youth and their child welfare workers, analysis of data on outcomes related to education, employment and criminal justice, and qualitative research on the living arrangements of youth who choose to remain in care. The evaluation will produce a mid-course data run at age 19 which will generate several issue briefs that will provide early indication of whether the array of housing options, employment and higher education supports offered through extended foster care are making a significant difference and should be replicated, or need to be redesigned to be more effective, payable over 5.00 years.

$500,000 to University of Washington, School of Social Work, Seattle, WA, 2012. To expand the publicly accessible child welfare database to promote transparency, accountability and effective service delivery to vulnerable children and families in Washington. In 2012, Partners for Our Children (POC) launched the Washington State Child Well-Being Data Portal, a longitudinal database to analyze child welfare outcomes. Over the next three years, POC will expand the existing web platform to integrate additional data sets across a variety of health, education and human service systems. The build out will include enhancements to the site by adding array of interactive tools and online user support functions. At the conclusion of this project, Washington State will have a comprehensive data portal to drive system improvement that is unmatched anywhere the country, payable over 3.25 years.

$375,000 to University of California, School of Education, Davis, CA, 2012. To implement Michael Fullan's whole system reform strategy in a cohort of five Northern California districts with a total of 90 schools*. The whole system reform project at UC Davis Center for Applied Policy in Education (CAP-Ed) is based on the change model developed in Ontario. The model develops district and school level structures and systems that allow districts to focus resources on teaching and learning; build social capital and a professional culture; and ensure that district and site leaders have the commitment and skill to sustain the transformation. Michael Fullan, with a group of experienced education leaders, will help build interconnected district leadership teams and school site leadership teams comprised of principals and teachers. Working inside all 90 schools and across school and district boundaries, the project will create the momentum and skills for change. CAP-Ed will document and evaluate the project to capture lessons learned as a basis for potential replication in other districts.

$350,000 to Los Angeles Education Partnership, Los Angeles, CA, 2012. To transform education leadership and teaching, and establish a college success culture at John C. Fremont High School and its feeder middle schools, Bethune and Edison, in South Los Angeles. The Fremont Family of Schools initiative implements small learning communities, the Humanitas team teaching model, instructional coaching, parent engagement, coordination of community support services, and GEAR UP college pathway centers. The Los Angeles Education Partnership (LAEP) has successfully become the District's lead school transformation partner for this family of schools in the Florence-Firestone community, establishing a memorandum of understanding to deliver teacher professional development and community school strategies. Over the past year, LAEP's work has gained traction, with academic performance showing impressive increases at both middle schools as measured by the California Academic Performance Index (API). Bethune's API increased 47 points from 620 to 667 and Edison increased 60 points from 600 to 660. Gains at Fremont were more modest, with API increasing 22 points from 550 to 572.

$350,000 to Pivot Learning Partners, San Francisco, CA, 2012. For Pivot Learning Partners to expand the Strategic School Funding for Results (SSFR) model. The SSFR model is a new approach to school finance that builds the capacity of principals to develop school budgets that align instructional goals with resources. Expansion of SSFR will include developing a financial readiness assessment and new online planning and budgeting tools to be piloted in the Sacramento City Unified School District. Pivot will continue working with more than 250 schools in Twin Rivers and Los Angeles Unified School Districts to deepen implementation of SSFR. Using these on-the-ground examples, Pivot will release a series of policy briefs to inform state and district leaders on how best to transition to a new school finance model, specifically addressing local implementation issues. The goal of SSFR is to create a transparent school finance system where school leaders focus budget decisions on student needs and learning outcomes, rather than compliance issues.

$225,000 to Foundation for California Community Colleges, Sacramento, CA, 2012. To improve community college participation, persistence and graduation rates for foster youth by providing intensive coaching and direct support to six community colleges in California. Career Ladders Project (CLP) will grow each college's capacity to reach more youth, accelerate learning, facilitate transitions to four year campuses and provide comprehensive support for foster youth on campus. In addition, CLP will expand learning communities by partnering the six new and eleven mature Community College Pathways sites with successful existing two-and four-year campuses in California and Washington.

$215,000 to Institute for the Study of Family, Work and Community, Berkeley, CA, 2012. To develop evaluation design for the installation and implementation phases of the Education Equals Partnership. The evaluation, designed in partnership

with the Foundation and key Education Equals partners, will report on progress made on lag and lead indicators and provide a foundation for ongoing practice and systems improvements that will improve the educational trajectory for foster youth.
$100,000 to Community Schools Collaboration, Burien, WA, 2012. For the West Coast Collaborative for Community Schools (WCC), a formal partnership of three veteran community schools initiatives: Community Schools Collaboration serving South King County, WA; Los Angeles Education Partnership serving greater Los Angeles, CA; and, Schools Uniting Neighborhoods serving Multnomah County/ Portland, Oregon. Working together, these exemplar practice sites are contributing knowledge and tools to benefit the broader community schools movement. WCC developed a white paper on aligning community schools with other place-based initiatives, a critical issue because these initiatives are increasing in number and gaining public and private attention. Addressing this important thought leadership issue was met with enthusiasm by the community schools field and is resulting in significant demand for related tools and presentations. WCC has provided technical assistance and showcased the elements of their models for a growing audience in California and Washington.
$75,000 to University of California, School of Education, Davis, CA, 2012. To establish the infrastructure for a Guardian Professions Program at University of California, Davis - a structured program designed to provide former foster youth with graduate and professional degrees to encourage them to enter a broad range of professions. UC Davis will conduct strategic planning, formalize relationships with key external partners, establish program infrastructure and design a plan for financial sustainability. In addition, UC Davis will recruit intensively throughout California to identify and support a minimum of eight Guardian Profession Scholars to enroll in graduate programs including the Schools of Education, Medicine, Law and Engineering for the Fall semester in 2014. The emerging Guardian Professions pilot program is inspired by the Guardian Teacher program which began in 2010 and is currently serving two students, payable over 1.50 years.

1226
The Morris Stulsaft Foundation ✧

1660 Bush St., Ste. 300
San Francisco, CA 94109-5308 (415) 561-6540
Contact: Emily Schroeder, Grants Mgr.
FAX: (415) 561-6477;
E-mail: eschroeder@pfs-llc.net; Main URL: http://www.stulsaft.org
Grants List: http://stulsaft.org/grants2011-2012.php

Incorporated in 1953 in CA; sole beneficiary of feeder trust created in 1965.
Donor: The Morris Stulsaft Testamentary Trust.
Foundation type: Independent foundation.
Financial data (yr. ended 06/30/13): Assets, $633,599 (M); gifts received, $1,502,500; expenditures, $1,361,321; qualifying distributions, $1,306,989; giving activities include $1,133,369 for 66 grants (high: $100,000; low: $1,000).
Purpose and activities: The foundation is dedicated to the well-being of children and youth (ages 0-22) through financial support of nonprofit organizations serving foster and homeless youth, and youth with disabilities; providing child care to low-income families and training to childcare providers; and educational enrichment and mentoring to disadvantaged youth. More strategically, the foundation makes grants in four particular areas: 1) Support Services for Vulnerable Children and Youth - funds for services that are provided to children and youth in shelters or transitional housing, or in foster care, that will help them to obtain a good education and to develop healthy relationships with others. The foundation looks for programs that provide safe, supportive and tolerant physical and emotional environments; 2) Preparing Youth for Independent Futures - funds to programs that seek to develop the individual potential in young people ages 13-22, by exposing them to meaningful experiences in the workplace, whether as an intern, a volunteer, or by shadowing someone in a particular job. The foundation funds programs that help participants to determine what work they enjoy doing, are best suited for, and how to pursue it. Programs should also seek to teach soft skills behaviors that help youth to get and keep a job, thereby helping them to ensure independent futures; 3) Setting the Stage for Education - support for pre-schools that predominately service children from low-income backgrounds and that demonstrate their commitment to quality early childhood development through thoughtful curriculum, excellent facilities, and qualified staff who are supported with professional development opportunities. Grants may be made for general support, scholarships, professional development, and occasionally for upgrading facilities; and 4) Inspiring Youth through Participation in the Arts - support for programs that go beyond the normal classroom curriculum and that offer opportunities for young people to actively participate in the arts (drawing, painting, sculpting, acting, singing, dancing), and that may also expose students to art at museums, theaters, etc. The foundation is most interested in programs that cooperate closely with public schools and are aligned with the California State Board of Education Standards for Visual and Performing Arts.
Fields of interest: Arts; Education; Employment; Human services; Children/youth, services; Children, foster care; Children, day care; Children/youth; Children.
Type of support: General/operating support; Continuing support; Program development; Matching/challenge support.
Limitations: Applications accepted. Giving limited to the San Francisco Bay Area, CA: Alameda, west Contra Costa, Marin, San Francisco, and northern San Mateo (extending south to Redwood City). No support for sectarian religious projects or ongoing support for private schools. No grants to individuals, or for emergency funding, endowments, annual campaigns, workshops, conferences, or deficit funding.
Publications: Application guidelines; Financial statement; Grants list; Occasional report.
Application information: Application form not required.
Initial approach: Use online application process on foundation web site
Board meeting date(s): Jan., Mar., May, July, and Sept.
Officers and Directors:* Adele K. Corvin,* Pres.; Isadore Pivnick,* V.P.; Dana A. Corvin, Secy.; Mary Gregory, Exec. Dir.; Stuart Corvin; William D. Glenn; Pat Loomes.
Number of staff: None.
EIN: 946064379

1227
The David and Diana Sun Foundation ✧

P.O. Box 8566
Fountain Valley, CA 92728-8566 (714) 435-2640
Contact: Albert Kong

Established in 1999 in CA.
Donors: David Sun; Diana Sun.
Foundation type: Independent foundation.
Financial data (yr. ended 12/31/12): Assets, $656,257 (M); gifts received, $1,500,000; expenditures, $1,744,335; qualifying distributions, $1,733,112; giving activities include $1,733,112 for grants.
Fields of interest: Education; Asians/Pacific Islanders.
Limitations: Giving primarily in Taiwan; some funding also in Irvine, CA. No grants to individuals.
Application information: Application form not required.
Initial approach: Letter
Deadline(s): None
Officers: David Sun, Pres.; Diana Sun, V.P.; Diana Kong, Secy.; Yvonne Curry, C.F.O.
EIN: 330868088

1228
The Swanson Foundation ✧

330 Primrose Rd., Ste. 404
Burlingame, CA 94010-4029

Established in 1994 in CA.
Donors: Judy C. Swanson; Swanson Charitable Remainder Unitrust; Zip-A-Dee-Doo-Dah Charitable Lead Annuity Trust; Tweedle Dee Dee Charitable Lead Annuity Trust.
Foundation type: Independent foundation.
Financial data (yr. ended 12/31/13): Assets, $17,776,217 (M); gifts received, $193,575; expenditures, $1,246,790; qualifying distributions, $1,108,550; giving activities include $1,100,000 for 1 grant.
Fields of interest: Education; Cancer research.
Limitations: Applications not accepted. Giving primarily in Cambridge, MA. No grants to individuals.
Application information: Contributes only to pre-selected organizations.
Officers: Judy C. Swanson, Pres. and C.E.O.; Christine Sherry, C.F.O. and Treas.; Mary Lynn Bell, Secy.
Director: Erica Swanson.
EIN: 943211277

1229
Swenson Family Foundation ✧

34372 Cove Lantern
Dana Point, CA 92629-2870
Contact: James I. Swenson, Pres.

Established in 1994 in CA.
Donors: James I. Swenson; Susan G. Swenson.
Foundation type: Independent foundation.
Financial data (yr. ended 12/31/13): Assets, $55,596,783 (M); expenditures, $3,353,463; qualifying distributions, $3,259,447; giving

activities include $3,241,767 for 26 grants (high: $500,000; low: $5,000).
Purpose and activities: Giving primarily for secular and Lutheran higher education.
Fields of interest: Higher education.
Type of support: Scholarship funds.
Limitations: Applications not accepted. Giving primarily in CA, Minneapolis, MN, and Superior, WI. No grants to individuals.
Application information: Contributes only to pre-selected organizations.
Officers: James I. Swenson, Pres.; Susan G. Swenson, Secy.
EIN: 330603766

1230
The Swift Foundation ✧
c/o Manchester Capital Mgmt., LLC
1157 Coast Village Rd., Ste. A
Montecito, CA 93108-2723
Contact: Morgan Roberts, Manchester Capital

Established in 2000 in CA.
Donors: John Swift; MST 2000 Charitable Lead Annuity Trust; MSST Foundation.
Foundation type: Independent foundation.
Financial data (yr. ended 09/30/13): Assets, $58,156,067 (M); gifts received, $539,407; expenditures, $2,685,973; qualifying distributions, $2,282,199; giving activities include $2,097,240 for 37 grants (high: $550,000; low: $2,500).
Fields of interest: Education; Environment; Community/economic development.
Limitations: Applications accepted. Giving primarily in CA, CO, and MA.
Application information: Application form not required.
Initial approach: Proposal
Deadline(s): None
Officers and Directors:* John Swift,* Pres.; Sonja Swift, Secy.; Karen Swift, Treas.; Jeannette Armstrong.
EIN: 770559600

1231
Swig Foundation ✧
220 Montgomery St.
San Francisco, CA 94104-3526 (415) 291-1100
Contact: Carolyn Zecca Ferris, Tr.

Established in 1957 in CA.
Donors: Benjamin H. Swig†; members of the Swig family.
Foundation type: Independent foundation.
Financial data (yr. ended 12/31/13): Assets, $15,695,677 (M); expenditures, $923,766; qualifying distributions, $890,175; giving activities include $890,175 for 268 grants (high: $35,000; low: $200).
Purpose and activities: Giving primarily for arts and culture, education, community welfare, and medical care.
Fields of interest: Arts; Higher education; Education; Health care; Health organizations, association; Human services; Children/youth, services; Jewish federated giving programs.
Limitations: Applications accepted. Giving primarily in the San Francisco Bay Area, CA. No grants to individuals, or for conferences, seminars, or workshops.
Application information: Application form required.
Initial approach: Letter
Deadline(s): None
Trustees: Carolyn Zecca Ferris; Steven Swig; Susan Watkins.
EIN: 946065205

1232
The Synopsys Foundation ✧
(formerly Synopsys Technology Education Opportunity Foundation)
700 E. Middlefield Rd.
Mountain View, CA 94043-4024
Main URL: http://www.synopsys.com/home.aspx

Established in 1998 in CA.
Donor: Synopsys Inc.
Foundation type: Company-sponsored foundation.
Financial data (yr. ended 12/31/13): Assets, $1,967,494 (M); gifts received, $1,900,000; expenditures, $1,882,240; qualifying distributions, $1,870,000; giving activities include $1,870,000 for 2 grants (high: $950,000; low: $920,000).
Purpose and activities: The foundation supports programs designed to promote K-12 science and math education.
Fields of interest: Elementary/secondary education; Education; American Red Cross; Science, formal/general education; Mathematics; Science.
Type of support: Annual campaigns; Program development; Fellowships; Scholarship funds; Sponsorships; Employee matching gifts.
Limitations: Applications not accepted. Giving primarily in CA.
Application information: Unsolicited applications are not accepted.
Officers: Aart de Geus, Chair.; Erin Brennock, Pres. and C.E.O.; Karen Brochier, C.F.O. and Treas.; Ericka Varga McEnroe, Secy.
Board Members: Brian Beattie; Deirdre Hanford.
EIN: 770488629

1233
Talbert Family Foundation, Inc. ✧
25003 Jim Bridger Rd.
Hidden Hills, CA 91302-1128 (818) 715-0428
Contact: Julie A. Talbert, Exec. Dir.
FAX: (818) 715-0456;
E-mail: Julie@TalbertFamilyFoundation.org; Main URL: http://www.talbertfamilyfoundation.org
Facebook: https://www.facebook.com/pages/The-Talbert-Family-Foundation/140761320074
Instagram: http://instagram.com/talbertfamilyfoundation#
Twitter: https://twitter.com/TFFKids

Established in 2003 in CA.
Donors: Julie A. Talbert; Lloyd W. Talbert; Mona Duncan; Ryan Duncan; Stephen Gen; Gudrun Mason; Albert Kudisizaden; Sean Russell; Julie Russell; Brenda Rueffert; Mark Gordon; Richard Husky; Michael Kerouac; Ann Kerouac; Aerospace Service and Controls; The Joyce Smith Family Foundation; Thrive Community Church; Wells Fargo Commercial Banking Office.
Foundation type: Operating foundation.
Financial data (yr. ended 12/31/12): Assets, $25,432 (M); gifts received, $587,891; expenditures, $677,892; qualifying distributions, $578,840; giving activities include $578,840 for 63 + grants (high: $59,078), and $63,418 for 1 foundation-administered program.
Purpose and activities: The grantmaker is dedicated to providing financial assistance to local families with members suffering from catastrophic illnesses, primarily cancer.
Fields of interest: Cancer; Family services.
Limitations: Applications accepted. Giving primarily in CA. No grants to individuals.
Application information: Application form not required.
Initial approach: Use form on foundation web site
Deadline(s): None
Officers: Lloyd W. Talbert, Pres.; Julie A. Talbert, Exec. Dir.
EIN: 200330559
Selected grants: The following grants are a representative sample of this grantmaker's funding activity:
$59,078 to Oaks Christian School, Westlake Village, CA, 2012. For TFF Kid Program.
$500 to Leukemia & Lymphoma Society, Los Angeles, CA, 2012. For general pledge.

1234
Linda Tallen & David Paul Kane Educational and Research Foundation ✧
433 N. Camden Dr., Ste. 1070
Beverly Hills, CA 90210-4434

Established in 1994 in CA.
Donor: David Paul Kane†.
Foundation type: Independent foundation.
Financial data (yr. ended 12/31/12): Assets, $10,256,710 (M); expenditures, $695,982; qualifying distributions, $520,000; giving activities include $520,000 for grants.
Purpose and activities: Giving primarily for medical research, and to hospitals, particularly for cancer, as well as to a children's hospital.
Fields of interest: Hospitals (general); Hospitals (specialty); Health organizations; Cancer research.
Limitations: Applications not accepted. No grants to individuals.
Application information: Contributes only to pre-selected organizations.
Directors: Stanley Black; Andrew S. Garb; Alan Wolf.
EIN: 954477151

1235
The Haeyoung and Kevin Tang Foundation, Inc. ✧
4747 Executive Dr., Ste. 510
San Diego, CA 92121-3100

Established in 2006 in CA.
Donors: Haeyoung K. Tang; Kevin C. Tang.
Foundation type: Independent foundation.
Financial data (yr. ended 12/31/12): Assets, $25,283,285 (M); gifts received, $3,045,759; expenditures, $1,313,118; qualifying distributions, $1,236,250; giving activities include $1,236,250 for grants.
Fields of interest: Higher education; Environment; Hospitals (specialty); AIDS research.
Limitations: Applications not accepted. Giving primarily in CA and NY. No grants to individuals.
Application information: Unsolicited requests for funds not accepted.

Officers: Haeyoung K. Tang, Chair. and Secy.; Kevin C. Tang, Pres. and Treas.
EIN: 205932781

1236
The Tanimura Family Foundation ✧ ☆
P.O. Box 4070
Salinas, CA 93912-4070

Established in 1997 in CA.
Donors: Robert T. Tanimura; Tom T. Tanimura; George T. Tanimura; George M. Tanimura.
Foundation type: Independent foundation.
Financial data (yr. ended 09/30/13): Assets, $10,259,509 (M); gifts received, $5,789; expenditures, $621,328; qualifying distributions, $533,061; giving activities include $525,070 for 27 grants (high: $100,000; low: $2,100).
Fields of interest: Libraries (public); Education; Health organizations, association; Boy scouts; American Red Cross; YM/YWCAs & YM/YWHAs; Buddhism.
Limitations: Applications not accepted. Giving primarily in CA. No grants to individuals.
Application information: Contributes only to pre-selected organizations.
Officers: Katsuyoski Murano, Pres.; Ken Morishita, C.F.O. and Treas.; Sheila C. Tanimura, V.P.; Ronald Yokota, V.P.; Bonita A.T. Yokota, Secy.; Kerry Varney, Exec. Dir.
Directors: Gary K. Tanimura; George M. Tanimura; Tom T. Tanimura.
EIN: 770456779

1237
S. Mark Taper Foundation ✧
Comerica Bank Bldg.
12011 San Vicente Blvd., Ste. 400
Los Angeles, CA 90049-4946 (310) 476-5413
Contact: Adrienne Wittenberg, Grants Dir.
FAX: (310) 471-4993;
E-mail: questions@smtfoundation.org; Main URL: http://www.smtfoundation.org/

Incorporated in 1989 in CA.
Donor: S. Mark Taper‡.
Foundation type: Independent foundation.
Financial data (yr. ended 12/31/13): Assets, $126,012,292 (M); expenditures, $6,069,124; qualifying distributions, $5,119,217; giving activities include $4,437,550 for 87+ grants.
Purpose and activities: Giving primarily to children and youth, health care, social services, employment, education, and the environment.
Fields of interest: Arts; Education; Environment; Health care; Crime/violence prevention; Employment; Housing/shelter, development; Human services; Children/youth, services; Family services; Civil liberties, reproductive rights; Government/public administration; Children/youth; Youth; Adults; Aging; Young adults; Disabilities, people with; Blind/visually impaired; Deaf/hearing impaired; Mentally disabled; Asians/Pacific Islanders; Women; Offenders/ex-offenders; AIDS, people with; Economically disadvantaged; Homeless.
Type of support: General/operating support; Annual campaigns; Capital campaigns; Building/renovation; Equipment; Emergency funds; Program development; Conferences/seminars; Publication; Seed money; Curriculum development; Scholarship funds; Research; Program-related investments/loans; Matching/challenge support.
Limitations: Applications accepted. Giving primarily in Los Angeles County, CA. No support for religious organizations or specific diseases. No grants to individuals.
Publications: Application guidelines.
Application information: See foundation web site for specific LOI instructions for general operating support and program/project support. Do not include brochures, annual reports, audited financial statements, Forms 990, and DVDs with LOIs. Application form required.
Initial approach: Letter of inquiry (3 pages maximum, not including attachments)
Copies of proposal: 1
Deadline(s): Dec. 1 through the end of Feb.
Board meeting date(s): As required
Final notification: 6-9 months
Officers and Director:* Janice Taper Lazarof,* Pres.; Cynthia Taper Bolker, V.P.; Amelia Taper Stabler, Secy.; Deborah Taper Ringel, Treas.; Roy Weitz, C.F.O.
Number of staff: 3 full-time professional; 2 full-time support.
EIN: 954245076

1238
Tarble Foundation ✧
(formerly Louise A. Tarble Foundation)
11075 Santa Monica Blvd., No. 150
Los Angeles, CA 90025-7541 (310) 473-7575

Established in 2006 in CA.
Foundation type: Independent foundation.
Financial data (yr. ended 06/30/13): Assets, $85,246,710 (M); expenditures, $2,415,154; qualifying distributions, $2,100,000; giving activities include $2,100,000 for grants.
Fields of interest: Museums (art); Health care.
Limitations: Applications not accepted. Giving primarily in CA and NV. No grants to individuals.
Application information: Contributes only to pre-selected organizations.
Trustee: Jan Tarble.
EIN: 203510478
Selected grants: The following grants are a representative sample of this grantmaker's funding activity:
$3,000,000 to Eastern Illinois University, Charleston, IL, 2012. For general support.
$1,500,000 to Saint Johns Health Center Foundation, Santa Monica, CA, 2013. For general support.
$1,000,000 to Saint Johns Health Center Foundation, Santa Monica, CA, 2012. For general support.
$500,000 to Nevada Museum of Art, Reno, NV, 2013. For general support.
$150,000 to Nevada Museum of Art, Reno, NV, 2012. For general support.
$100,000 to Louisville High School, Woodland Hills, CA, 2013. For general support.

1239
Tarsadia Foundation ✧
(formerly Singgod Foundation)
620 Newport Center Dr., 14th Fl.
Newport Beach, CA 92660-6420

Established in 1999 in CA.
Donors: B.U. Patel; Tushar Patel; T-Twelve Legacy Trust; Krishan Tarsadia Trust.
Foundation type: Independent foundation.
Financial data (yr. ended 12/31/12): Assets, $39,870,272 (M); gifts received, $4,700,000; expenditures, $2,076,683; qualifying distributions, $2,022,012; giving activities include $1,690,320 for 75 grants (high: $100,000; low: $500).
Fields of interest: Higher education; Education; Human services.
International interests: India.
Limitations: Applications not accepted. Giving primarily in CA and India. No grants to individuals.
Application information: Contributes only to pre-selected organizations.
Officers: B.U. Patel, C.E.O.; Tushar Patel, Secy.
Director: Shirish Dayal.
EIN: 330879062

1240
The Buddy Taub Foundation ✧
9200 Sunset Blvd., Ste. 525
Los Angeles, CA 90069-3507

Established in 1998 in CA.
Foundation type: Independent foundation.
Financial data (yr. ended 05/31/13): Assets, $10,131,848 (M); expenditures, $795,100; qualifying distributions, $695,439; giving activities include $640,779 for 35 grants (high: $170,000; low: $725).
Fields of interest: Museums (art); Human services.
Limitations: Applications not accepted. Giving primarily in CA. No grants to individuals.
Application information: Contributes only to pre-selected organizations.
Officers: Dennis A. Roach, Pres.; Jill J. Roach, Secy. and C.F.O.
Directors: Alexis Roach; Stephanie Roach.
EIN: 954588448
Selected grants: The following grants are a representative sample of this grantmaker's funding activity:
$152,000 to Metropolitan Museum of Art, New York, NY, 2011. For general purpose.
$91,274 to Dallas Museum of Art, Dallas, TX, 2011. For general purpose.
$55,340 to University of California, Oakland, CA, 2011. For general purpose.
$48,761 to Washington and Lee University, Lexington, VA, 2011. For general purpose.
$45,844 to Museum of Contemporary Art, Chicago, IL, 2011. For general purpose.
$28,480 to Seattle Art Museum, Seattle, WA, 2011. For general purpose.
$22,500 to Birmingham Museum of Art, Birmingham, AL, 2011. For general purpose.
$14,955 to Colonial Williamsburg Foundation, Williamsburg, VA, 2011. For general purpose.
$13,500 to Museum Associates, Los Angeles County Museum of Art (LACMA), Los Angeles, CA, 2011. For general purpose.
$8,363 to Columbia Museum of Art, Columbia, SC, 2011. For general purpose.

1241
Taube Family Foundation ✧
1050 Ralston Ave.
Belmont, CA 94002-2243 (650) 592-3960

Established in 1980 in CA.

Donor: Members of the Taube family.
Foundation type: Independent foundation.
Financial data (yr. ended 12/31/13): Assets, $35,857,960 (M); gifts received, $562,100; expenditures, $1,806,313; qualifying distributions, $1,719,480; giving activities include $1,719,480 for 88 grants (high: $400,000; low: $50).
Purpose and activities: Giving primarily for higher education and human services.
Fields of interest: Arts; Higher education; Education; Health organizations, association; Human services; Foundations (private grantmaking); United Ways and Federated Giving Programs.
Type of support: General/operating support; Continuing support; Building/renovation; Fellowships.
Limitations: Applications accepted. Giving primarily in the San Francisco Bay Area, CA. No grants to individuals.
Application information: Application form required.
Initial approach: Letter
Copies of proposal: 1
Deadline(s): None
Officers and Directors:* Thaddeus N. Taube,* Pres. and C.E.O.; Kenneth L. Marciano, C.F.O. and Secy.-Treas.; Dianne M. Taube,* V.P.; Jeff Farber.
EIN: 942702180

1242
Teach A Man To Fish Foundation ✧ ☆
2560 E. Chapman Ave., Ste. 173
Orange, CA 92869-3205

Established in CA.
Foundation type: Independent foundation.
Financial data (yr. ended 12/31/12): Assets, $38,521,568 (M); gifts received, $34,937,500; expenditures, $1,957,278; qualifying distributions, $1,918,446; giving activities include $1,918,446 for 19 grants (high: $575,418; low: $1,000).
Fields of interest: Health organizations; Human services; Foundations (private grantmaking); Foundations (community).
Limitations: Applications not accepted. Giving primarily in CA.
Application information: Unsolicited requests for funds not accepted.
Officers: Vincent Smith, Pres.; Victoria Flaherty, Secy.-Treas.
EIN: 274213183

1243
Jim & Joyce Teel Family Foundation ✧
P.O. Box 15618
Sacramento, CA 95852-0618

Established in 2002 in CA.
Donors: Jim Teel; Joyce Teel.
Foundation type: Independent foundation.
Financial data (yr. ended 12/31/13): Assets, $5,467,421 (M); expenditures, $553,130; qualifying distributions, $500,010; giving activities include $500,000 for 1 grant.
Purpose and activities: Giving primarily to an art museum.
Fields of interest: Museums (art).
Limitations: Applications not accepted. Giving in Sacramento, CA.
Application information: Contributes only to pre-selected organizations.
Officers: Joyce Teel, Pres.; Jim Teel, V.P.; Neil Doerhoff, Secy.-Treas.
Directors: Lisa Davidson; Claudia Doerhoff; Diane Perry; Laurie Struck; Mike Teel.
EIN: 680521463

1244
Teichert Foundation ✧
c/o Fred Teichert
3500 American River Dr.
Sacramento, CA 95864-5802 (916) 484-3255
Contact: Emily Begay
Additional address: P.O. Box 15002, Sacramento, CA 95851-1002 tel.: (916) 484-3255
Grants List: http://www.teichert.com/grant-recipients.cfm

Established in 1990 in CA.
Donors: A. Teichert & Son, Inc.; Teichert, Inc.; Ruth Tucker.
Foundation type: Company-sponsored foundation.
Financial data (yr. ended 03/31/14): Assets, $10,288,286 (M); gifts received, $1,385; expenditures, $868,702; qualifying distributions, $782,132; giving activities include $516,370 for 100 grants (high: $100,000; low: $25).
Purpose and activities: The foundation supports organizations involved with arts and culture, education, environmental planning and preservation, health, youth development, human services, community development, transportation and planning, civic affairs, and senior citizens. Special emphasis is directed toward programs designed to focus on children and youth.
Fields of interest: Historic preservation/historical societies; Arts; Education; Environment; Medical care, rehabilitation; Health care; Boys & girls clubs; Youth development; Children/youth, services; Human services; Community/economic development; Transportation; Public affairs; Children; Youth; Aging.
Type of support: Employee matching gifts; Capital campaigns; Continuing support; General/operating support.
Limitations: Applications accepted. Giving primarily in areas of company operations in Amador, Calaveras, Colusa, El Dorado, Mariposa, Merced, Nevada, North Solano, Placer, Sacramento, San Joaquin, Stanislaus, Sutter, Tuolumne, Yolo, and Yuba counties, CA. No support for religious organizations not of direct benefit to the entire community, political organizations, or fraternal organizations, societies, or orders. No grants to individuals, or for political campaigns, courtesy advertising or tickets for benefits, telephone solicitations, or national fundraising campaigns.
Publications: Application guidelines; Grants list.
Application information: Application form not required.
Initial approach: Complete online application
Deadline(s): Feb. 28 and Aug. 29
Board meeting date(s): Biannually
Officers: Norman Eilert, C.F.O.; Anne S. Haslam, Secy.; Frederick A. Teichert, Exec. Dir.
Directors: Judson T. Riggs; Melita M. Teichert.
Number of staff: 1 full-time professional; 1 full-time support.
EIN: 680212355
Selected grants: The following grants are a representative sample of this grantmaker's funding activity:
$7,500 to Boy Scouts of America, Greater Yosemite Council, Modesto, CA, 2013. To support public charity Programs.
$7,500 to Yolo Basin Foundation, Davis, CA, 2013. To support public charity Programs.

1245
William and Anna Tenenblatt Foundation ✧
3750 S. Broadway Pl.
Los Angeles, CA 90007-4481

Established in 1999 in CA.
Donors: Anna Tenenblatt; William Tenenblatt.
Foundation type: Independent foundation.
Financial data (yr. ended 12/31/13): Assets, $3,512,499 (M); gifts received, $250,000; expenditures, $736,539; qualifying distributions, $696,165; giving activities include $696,165 for 61 grants (high: $146,300; low: $65).
Purpose and activities: Giving primarily for Jewish agencies, temples, and schools.
Fields of interest: Education; Jewish federated giving programs; Jewish agencies & synagogues.
Limitations: Applications not accepted. Giving primarily in Los Angeles, CA. No grants to individuals.
Application information: Unsolicited requests for funds not accepted.
Officers and Directors: Anna Tenenblatt,* Pres.; William Tenenblatt,* Secy. and C.F.O.
EIN: 954774270
Selected grants: The following grants are a representative sample of this grantmaker's funding activity:
$100,000 to One Israel Fund, Hewlett, NY, 2011.
$63,624 to Sinai Akiba Academy, Los Angeles, CA, 2011.
$59,755 to Sinai Temple, Los Angeles, CA, 2011.
$8,000 to Shalhevet High School, Los Angeles, CA, 2011.
$6,000 to Chabad of California, Los Angeles, CA, 2011.
$4,300 to Jewish National Fund, Rockville Centre, NY, 2011.
$4,250 to UCLA Foundation, Los Angeles, CA, 2011.
$1,000 to American Jewish University, Los Angeles, CA, 2011.
$1,000 to Camp Ramah in California, Encino, CA, 2011.
$1,000 to Washington Institute for Near East Policy, Washington, DC, 2011.

1246
The Tesuque Foundation, Inc. ✧
c/o Shea Labagh Dobberstein, CPA's
1700 S. El Camino Real, Ste. 500
San Mateo, CA 94402 (650) 579-7200

Established in 1990 in NY.
Donors: Andrea Wilson†; Fred W. Wilson†.
Foundation type: Independent foundation.
Financial data (yr. ended 12/31/12): Assets, $4,930,849 (M); expenditures, $569,683; qualifying distributions, $444,572; giving activities include $440,000 for 16 grants (high: $120,000; low: $5,000).
Purpose and activities: Giving primarily for the arts, libraries, and general charitable giving, with an

emphasis on homelessness, and prison rehabilitation programs.
Fields of interest: Arts; Libraries/library science.
Type of support: General/operating support; Capital campaigns; Endowments; Program development.
Limitations: Applications accepted. Giving primarily in CA.
Application information: Application form not required.
Initial approach: Proposal
Deadline(s): None
Officer: Pamela Wilson, Pres.
Number of staff: 1 part-time professional.
EIN: 133579598

1247
TF Educational Foundation ✧
580 Silver Spur Rd.
Rancho Palos Verdes, CA 90275-3614

Established in 2006 in CA.
Donors: Gerald H. Turpanjian; Patricia Turpanjian.
Foundation type: Independent foundation.
Financial data (yr. ended 12/31/13): Assets, $50,230,597 (M); expenditures, $3,933,681; qualifying distributions, $3,623,361; giving activities include $3,565,306 for 26 grants (high: $1,191,000; low: $1,000), and $25,475 for 1 foundation-administered program.
Purpose and activities: Giving primarily for Armenian organizations and churches.
Fields of interest: Higher education; Human services; Christian agencies & churches.
Limitations: Applications not accepted. Giving primarily in CA. No grants to individuals.
Application information: Contributes only to pre-selected organizations.
Officers and Directors:* Gerald H. Turpanjian,* Pres.; Patricia Turpanjian,* V.P.; Lori Muncherian,* Secy.; Gary Turpanjian,* C.F.O.; Deann Nazarian; Paul Turpanjian.
EIN: 611504200

1248
Thatcher Foundation ✧ ☆
c/o Phillip M. Bardack, C.P.A.
5501 Keokuk Ave.
Woodland Hills, CA 91367-5521

Established in 1998 in CA.
Donors: George A. Thatcher‡; Georgia R. Thatcher.
Foundation type: Operating foundation.
Financial data (yr. ended 06/30/13): Assets, $14,081,233 (M); expenditures, $873,074; qualifying distributions, $826,760; giving activities include $810,000 for 39 grants (high: $50,000; low: $5,000).
Fields of interest: Education; Hospitals (general); Health organizations; Human services.
Limitations: Applications not accepted. Giving primarily in CA. No grants to individuals.
Application information: Unsolicited requests for funds not accepted.
Officers and Directors:* Diane Thatcher,* V.P.; Nancy J. Thatcher,* Secy.; Phillip M. Bardack,* C.F.O.; William Herzog.
EIN: 954697063

1249
The Thiel Foundation ✧
(formerly Shire Philanthropic Foundation)
1 Letterman Dr., Bldg. C, Ste. 400
San Francisco, CA 94129-1495
Main URL: http://www.thielfoundation.org

Established in 2005 in CA.
Donor: Peter Thiel.
Foundation type: Independent foundation.
Financial data (yr. ended 12/31/12): Assets, $24,783,613 (M); gifts received, $35,106,000; expenditures, $12,316,484; qualifying distributions, $11,012,416; giving activities include $7,012,549 for 41 grants (high: $760,000; low: $400), and $1,890,861 for 51 grants to individuals (high: $200,000; low: $4,167).
Purpose and activities: The foundation defends and promotes freedom in all its dimensions by supporting innovative scientific research and new technologies that empower people to improve their lives, by championing organizations and individuals who expose human rights abuses and authoritarianism, and by encouraging the exploration of new ideas and new spaces where freedom can flourish.
Fields of interest: Education; Medical research; Human services.
Limitations: Applications not accepted. Giving primarily in the U.S., with some emphasis on CA; some giving internationally, with some emphasis on France. No grants to individuals, except for fellowships.
Application information: Unsolicited requests for funds not accepted. Refer to foundation web site for fellowship application information.
Officers: Robert Hamerton-Kelly, Chair.; Jonathan Cain, Pres.; Amber Fowler, Secy.; James O'Neill, Treas.
Directors: Lynne Fishburne, Exec. Dir.; Peter Thiel.
EIN: 203846597

1250
The William S. and Nancy E. Thompson Foundation ✧
610 Newport Ctr. Dr., Ste. 1220
Newport Beach, CA 92660-6447

Established in 2004 in CA.
Donors: William S. Thompson; Nancy E. Thompson; The Thompson Family Trust.
Foundation type: Independent foundation.
Financial data (yr. ended 12/31/12): Assets, $44,772,749 (M); gifts received, $4,435,841; expenditures, $3,147,833; qualifying distributions, $2,895,160; giving activities include $2,695,000 for 33 grants (high: $2,000,000; low: $250).
Fields of interest: Higher education; Education; Health care; Human services.
Limitations: Applications not accepted. Giving primarily in CA. No grants to individuals.
Application information: Contributes only to pre-selected organizations.
Officer: Jennifer T. Lavenson, C.F.O.
Director: Donald C. Thompson.
Trustees: Nancy E. Thompson; William S. Thompson.
EIN: 206371108

1251
Thornton Foundation ✧
(formerly Charles Thornton Foundation)
1220 Virginia Rd.
San Marino, CA 91108-1054 (626) 795-8604
Contact: C.B. Thornton, Pres.

Established in 2004 in CA.
Donor: Charles B. Thornton.
Foundation type: Independent foundation.
Financial data (yr. ended 12/31/13): Assets, $45,084,137 (M); gifts received, $8,288,424; expenditures, $1,725,004; qualifying distributions, $1,559,616; giving activities include $1,545,200 for 30 grants (high: $1,035,000; low: $1,000).
Purpose and activities: Giving primarily to libraries, as well as for education.
Fields of interest: Arts; Higher education; Libraries (public).
Limitations: Applications accepted. Giving primarily in CA. No grants for None.
Application information: Application form required.
Initial approach: Letter
Deadline(s): None
Officers: Charles B. Thornton, Pres.; Terry D. Chapin, Secy.
EIN: 201660366
Selected grants: The following grants are a representative sample of this grantmaker's funding activity:
$150,000 to Harvard-Westlake School, North Hollywood, CA, 2011.

1252
Flora L. Thornton Foundation ✧
419 Larchmont Blvd., Ste. 278
Los Angeles, CA 90004-3013

Established in 1983 in CA.
Donors: Flora L. Thornton‡; Flora L. Thornton Charitable Remainder Trust.
Foundation type: Independent foundation.
Financial data (yr. ended 11/30/11): Assets, $39,450,537 (M); gifts received, $13,030,131; expenditures, $2,052,155; qualifying distributions, $1,599,098; giving activities include $1,599,098 for 53 grants (high: $991,098; low: $500).
Purpose and activities: Giving primarily for elementary and higher education, arts and cultural organizations, nutrition education and preventive medicine education.
Fields of interest: Performing arts, music; Performing arts, orchestras; Performing arts, opera; Arts; Elementary school/education; Higher education; Public health; Health organizations, association; Nutrition.
Type of support: General/operating support; Continuing support; Endowments; Conferences/seminars; Professorships; Scholarship funds; Matching/challenge support.
Limitations: Applications not accepted. Giving primarily in Los Angeles, CA. No support for religious or political causes. No grants to individuals.
Application information: Unsolicited requests for funds not accepted.
Board meeting date(s): Quarterly
Officer: Kay Tornborg, Exec. Dir.
Trustees: Edward A. Landry; Eric L. Small; Anne C. Thornton; Charles Thornton III; Laney Thornton; Elizabeth Thornton Troy; Jennifer Thornton Wieland.
Number of staff: 1 part-time professional.
EIN: 953855595

1253
The Laney Thornton Foundation ✧
633 Battery St., Ste. 100
San Francisco, CA 94111-1812

Established in 2004 in CA.
Foundation type: Independent foundation.
Financial data (yr. ended 12/31/13): Assets, $9,673,150 (M); expenditures, $676,874; qualifying distributions, $596,817; giving activities include $590,817 for 69 grants (high: $120,000; low: $235).
Purpose and activities: Giving primarily for the arts, higher education, and the environment.
Fields of interest: Performing arts; Arts; Higher education; Education; Environment.
Limitations: Applications not accepted. Giving primarily in CA, with emphasis on San Francisco.
Application information: Unsolicited requests for funds not accepted.
Officers and Director:* W. Laney Thornton,* Pres.; Pasha D. Thornton, Secy.-Treas.
EIN: 201660400

1254
Three Guineas Fund ✧ ☆
153 Upper Terr.
San Francisco, CA 94117-4513
E-mail: info@3gf.org; Main URL: http://www.3gf.org

Established in 1994 in CA.
Foundation type: Independent foundation.
Financial data (yr. ended 12/31/12): Assets, $3,463,641 (M); expenditures, $1,078,396; qualifying distributions, $1,046,431; giving activities include $988,674 for 4 grants (high: $948,424; low: $250).
Purpose and activities: The foundation seeks to promote social justice for women and girls by expanding access to economic opportunity.
Fields of interest: Human services.
Type of support: General/operating support.
Limitations: Applications not accepted. Giving in the U.S., with emphasis on CA. No grants to individuals.
Application information: Unsolicited requests for funds not accepted.
Officer: Catherine S. Muther, Pres.
Number of staff: 2 part-time professional.
EIN: 943215954

1255
Thrive Foundation for Youth ✧
c/o Carol W. Gray, Exec. Dir.
1010 El Camino Real, Ste. 250
Menlo Park, CA 94025-4349
E-mail: info@thrivefoundation.org; Main URL: http://www.thrivefoundation.org

Established in 2000 in CA.
Donors: Dorothy J. King; Robert E. King; Jennifer C. King; Timothy C. Fredel; Cynthia King Guffey; Alan Guffey; Thrive Charitable Remainder Trust.
Foundation type: Independent foundation.
Financial data (yr. ended 12/31/12): Assets, $32,772,432 (M); expenditures, $5,141,149; qualifying distributions, $4,561,148; giving activities include $2,211,373 for 35 grants (high: $468,877; low: $2).
Purpose and activities: Giving to organizations which enable young people to thrive.
Fields of interest: Youth development; Children/youth; Youth.
Type of support: General/operating support; Continuing support; Program development; Curriculum development; Fellowships; Research; Consulting services; Program evaluation.
Limitations: Applications not accepted. Giving primarily in the U.S.
Application information: Contributes only to pre-selected organizations. Unsolicited requests for funds not accepted.
Officers and Trustees:* Robert E. King,* Chair.; Carol Welsh Gray,* Exec. Dir.; Raquel Burgos, M.D., MPH; Dottie King; Duncan Campbell; Dana MacLaurin Nunn; Ulrico "Rico" Rosales.
Number of staff: 4 full-time professional; 1 full-time support; 2 part-time support.
EIN: 943382864

1256
Tomkat Charitable Trust
1 Maritime Plz., 11th Fl.
San Francisco, CA 94111-3519 (415) 956-9588
E-mail: info@tomkattrust.org; Main URL: http://tomkattrust.org/
GiveSmart: http://www.givesmart.org/Stories/Donors/Tom-Steyer
Tom Steyer and Kathryn Taylor's Giving Pledge Profile: http://www.glasspockets.org/philanthropy-in-focus/eye-on-the-giving-pledge/profiles/steyer

Established in 2008 in CA.
Donors: Thomas Steyer; Kathryn Taylor.
Foundation type: Independent foundation.
Financial data (yr. ended 12/31/12): Assets, $177,849,515 (M); expenditures, $28,130,054; qualifying distributions, $27,986,020; giving activities include $27,225,520 for 85 grants (high: $10,000,000; low: $2,000).
Purpose and activities: Giving primary for education, energy and environmental issues.
Fields of interest: Education; Environment, climate change/global warming; Environment, energy; Environment; Agriculture, sustainable programs.
Limitations: Applications not accepted.
Application information: Contributes only to pre-selected organizations.
Trustee: Kathryn Hall.
EIN: 386866542

1257
TomKat Foundation ✧ ☆
1 Maritime Plz., Ste. 1102
San Francisco, CA 94111-3404
GiveSmart: http://www.givesmart.org/Stories/Donors/Tom-Steyer
Tom Steyer and Kathryn Taylor's Giving Pledge Profile: http://glasspockets.org/philanthropy-in-focus/eye-on-the-giving-pledge/profiles/steyer

Established in 2006 in CA.
Donors: Thomas F. Steyer; Kathryn A. Taylor.
Foundation type: Independent foundation.
Financial data (yr. ended 12/31/13): Assets, $28,458 (M); gifts received, $1,775,000; expenditures, $1,804,765; qualifying distributions, $1,797,522; giving activities include $1,779,620 for 1 grant.
Fields of interest: Environment; Human services.
Limitations: Applications not accepted. Giving primarily in CA.
Application information: Unsolicited requests for funds not accepted.
Officers: Thomas F. Steyer, Pres.; Kathryn A. Taylor, Secy.-Treas.; Brooks Shumway, Exec. Dir.
EIN: 205730828

1258
Torrey Foundation ✧
2568 Del Mar Heights Rd., No. 424
Del Mar, CA 92014-3100

Established in 1990 in NV.
Donors: L. Legallet; Kent R. Wilson; Lana L. Wilson.
Foundation type: Independent foundation.
Financial data (yr. ended 12/31/13): Assets, $19,235,265 (M); expenditures, $998,985; qualifying distributions, $737,885; giving activities include $722,367 for 1 grant.
Fields of interest: Human services; Foundations (public).
Type of support: Research.
Limitations: Applications not accepted. Giving primarily in NY. No grants to individuals.
Publications: Annual report.
Application information: Contributes only to pre-selected organizations.
Officers: L. Legallet, Pres.; T. Wilson, Secy.; M. Wilson, Treas.
Director: M. Chakko.
EIN: 880268986

1259
Tosa Foundation ✧
(formerly Morgridge Family Foundation)
c/o Tashia F. Morgridge
3130 Alpine Road, PMB 705, Ste. 288
Portola Valley, CA 94028-8005
Contact: Tashia F. Morgridge, Pres.
GiveSmart: http://www.givesmart.org/Stories/Donors/Tashia-and-John-Morgridge
Tashia and John Morgridge's Giving Pledge Profile: http://glasspockets.org/philanthropy-in-focus/eye-on-the-giving-pledge/profiles/morgridge

Established in 1992 in CA.
Donors: Tashia F. Morgridge; John P. Morgridge.
Foundation type: Independent foundation.
Financial data (yr. ended 12/31/12): Assets, $727,037,004 (M); gifts received, $242,962,780; expenditures, $53,625,112; qualifying distributions, $52,753,715; giving activities include $52,528,340 for 298 grants (high: $10,110,000; low: $15), and $1,962,210 for 1 foundation-administered program.
Purpose and activities: Giving support to education, the environment, medical research, the arts, and human services.
Fields of interest: Arts; Higher education; Education; Environment; Animal welfare; Youth development, services; Human services; International development; International affairs.
Limitations: Applications not accepted. Giving primarily in CA and MA. No grants to individuals.
Application information: Contributes only to pre-selected organizations.

Officers and Directors:* Tashia F. Morgridge,* Pres.; Kate M. Greswold,* Secy.; John P. Morgridge,* C.F.O.; John D. Morgridge.
EIN: 943165171
Selected grants: The following grants are a representative sample of this grantmaker's funding activity:
$14,857,500 to Wisconsin Alumni Research Foundation, Madison, WI, 2012. For education grant made in form of stock.
$10,000,000 to Morgridge Family Foundation, Denver, CO, 2012. For education programs and to provide 21st Century technology in classrooms for teachers and to support education content development.
$5,055,000 to CARE USA, Atlanta, GA, 2012. For international education grant made in form of stock.
$5,055,000 to Nature Conservancy, Arlington, VA, 2012. For conservation education grant made in form of stock.
$5,000,000 to Fidelity Charitable Gift Fund, Boston, MA, 2012. For general support for TAUPO.
$5,000,000 to Fidelity Charitable Gift Fund, Boston, MA, 2012. For general support for TAUPO.
$1,097,081 to Ravenswood City School District, East Palo Alto, CA, 2012. For general support for education.
$250,000 to Squam Lakes Natural Science Center, Holderness, NH, 2012. For general support for education.
$25,000 to Monticello School District, Monticello, WI, 2012. For general support for education.
$5,000 to Squam Lakes Natural Science Center, Holderness, NH, 2012. For general support for education.

1260
The Towbes Foundation ✧
21 E. Victoria St., Ste. 200
Santa Barbara, CA 93101-2605 (805) 962-2121
Contact: Barbara Ross, Secy.
FAX: (805) 568-1411;
E-mail: towbesfoundation@towbes.com; Additional address: P.O. Box 20130, Santa Barbara, CA 93120-0130; e-mail for Barbara Ross: bross@towbes.com

Established in 1980 in CA.
Donors: Michael Towbes; Gail Towbes†.
Foundation type: Independent foundation.
Financial data (yr. ended 06/30/13): Assets, $1,558,416 (M); gifts received, $1,251,131; expenditures, $1,027,061; qualifying distributions, $933,900; giving activities include $932,900 for 140 grants (high: $40,000; low: $250).
Purpose and activities: Primary areas of interest include: education, including scholarships; medical research, especially in the area of neurological disease; promotion of the performing arts; and promotion and preservation of the free enterprise system.
Fields of interest: Performing arts; Arts; Higher education; Education; Medical research, institute; Economics.
Type of support: General/operating support; Capital campaigns; Program development; Conferences/seminars; Fellowships; Scholarship funds; Research; Matching/challenge support.
Limitations: Applications accepted. Giving primarily in Santa Barbara, CA, and immediate environs. No grants to individuals.
Publications: Application guidelines.
Application information: Santa Barbara Foundation Roundtable's Common Grant Application Form accepted. Application form required.
Initial approach: E-mail, telephone, or letter
Copies of proposal: 6
Deadline(s): Aug. 31, Dec. 31, and Apr. 30
Board meeting date(s): Feb., June, and Oct.
Final notification: Approximately 2 months
Officers: Sheridah Gerard, Pres.; Barbara Ross, Secy.; Michael Towbes, C.F.O.
Directors: Robert Skinner; Lynn C. Towbes; Craig Zimmerman.
Number of staff: 1 part-time support.
EIN: 953519577
Selected grants: The following grants are a representative sample of this grantmaker's funding activity:
$7,500 to AIDS Housing of Santa Barbara, Santa Barbara, CA, 2011.

1261
The Travers Family Foundation ✧
2950 Merced St., Ste. 109
San Leandro, CA 94577-5636 (510) 483-1288
Contact: Charles N. Travers, Dir.

Established in 1993 in CA.
Foundation type: Independent foundation.
Financial data (yr. ended 12/31/13): Assets, $44,919,267 (M); expenditures, $1,944,292; qualifying distributions, $1,469,668; giving activities include $1,469,668 for 2 grants (high: $1,420,393; low: $49,275).
Fields of interest: Higher education; Animal welfare; Public affairs, public education.
Limitations: Applications accepted. Giving primarily in CA.
Application information: Application form required.
Initial approach: Letter
Deadline(s): None
Directors: Larry Lucas; Nancy Lucas; Tarn Sublett; Charles N. Travers; Elizabeth Travers; Gayle Travers; Todd Travers.
EIN: 686095780
Selected grants: The following grants are a representative sample of this grantmaker's funding activity:
$775,088 to University of California, Berkeley, CA, 2011. For general purpose.
$99,456 to Commonwealth Club of California, San Francisco, CA, 2011. For general purpose.

1262
The Nora Eccles Treadwell Foundation ✧
1004 B. O'Reilly Ave
San Francisco, CA 94129-2602

Established in 1962 in UT.
Donors: Nora Eccles Treadwell Harrison†; Nora Eccles Treadwell Charitable Trust.
Foundation type: Independent foundation.
Financial data (yr. ended 12/31/12): Assets, $5,457,827 (M); gifts received, $3,746,378; expenditures, $3,645,621; qualifying distributions, $3,605,369; giving activities include $3,269,575 for 44 grants (high: $391,800; low: $500).
Purpose and activities: Grants primarily for health and cardiovascular, diabetes, and arthritis research.
Fields of interest: Health care; Health organizations, association; Heart & circulatory diseases; Medical research, institute; Heart & circulatory research; Arthritis research; Diabetes research.
Type of support: General/operating support; Equipment; Professorships; Research.
Limitations: Applications not accepted. Giving primarily in CA. No grants to individuals, or for research in areas not related to the cardiovascular system, diabetes, or arthritis.
Application information: Contributes only to pre-selected organizations.
Officers and Directors:* Patricia Canepa,* Chair.; Lawrence M. Harrison,* Secy.; Katie A. Eccles; Spencer F. Eccles; Kathryn C. Econome, M.D.; Robert M. Graham.
Number of staff: 3
EIN: 237425351

1263
Truckee Tahoe Community Foundation ✧
11071 Donner Pass Rd.
Truckee, CA 96161 (530) 587-1776
Contact: Stacy Caldwell, C.E.O.
FAX: (530) 550-7985; E-mail: phebe@ttcf.net; Mailing address: P.O. Box 366, Truckee, CA 96160; Additional e-mail: kelly@ttcf.net; Main URL: http://www.ttcf.net
Facebook: https://www.facebook.com/pages/Tahoe-Truckee-Community-Foundation/188729387821765
Twitter: http://twitter.com/ttcfoundation

Established in 1998 in CA.
Foundation type: Community foundation.
Financial data (yr. ended 06/30/13): Assets, $22,643,377 (M); gifts received, $2,162,702; expenditures, $2,594,196; giving activities include $1,577,233 for 61+ grants (high: $100,000).
Purpose and activities: The foundation seeks to enhance the quality of life in the Truckee/Tahoe, CA area by seeking, accepting, managing, and disbursing funds for the benefit of the community.
Fields of interest: Arts; Education; Environment; Animals/wildlife, preservation/protection; Health care; Mental health/crisis services; Recreation; Youth development; Human services; Children/youth, services; Human services; Community/economic development.
Type of support: General/operating support; Continuing support; Income development; Management development/capacity building; Equipment; Program development; Publication; Seed money; Technical assistance; Consulting services.
Limitations: Applications accepted. Giving limited to the Truckee/North Tahoe, CA, area. No support for direct religious activities. No grants for field trips and participation in activities by parental choice, capital campaigns, activities that have already occurred, or school-based activities (unless they impact students district wide or impact the broader community).
Publications: Application guidelines; Grants list; Newsletter.
Application information: Visit foundation web site for application forms and guidelines per grant type. Application form required.
Initial approach: Telephone
Deadline(s): Varies
Board meeting date(s): 2nd Thurs. of every month
Final notification: 90 days
Officers and Directors:* Craig Lundin,* Chair.; Stacy Caldwell,* C.E.O.; Kathryn Rohlf,* Secy.; Michael Sabarese,* Treas.; Paquita Bath; Douglas

Dale; Marilyn Disbrow; Geoff Edelstein; Steve Gross; David Hansen; Brad Koch; Lauren O'Brien; Bob Richards.
Number of staff: 1 full-time support; 3 part-time support.
EIN: 680416404

1264
True North Foundation ✧
P.O. Box 1177
Grass Valley, CA 95945-1177 (530) 274-1620
Contact: Ms. Kerry Anderson, Pres.
E-mail: kka1119@aol.com

Established in 1986 in CO.
Foundation type: Independent foundation.
Financial data (yr. ended 12/31/13): Assets, $7,255,554 (M); expenditures, $3,404,446; qualifying distributions, $3,288,157; giving activities include $3,045,000 for 56 grants (high: $500,000; low: $7,000).
Purpose and activities: Giving primarily for environmental programs such as environmental work in AK, mining reform in the West, and sustainable agriculture in northern CA; also giving to independent living programs for the frail elderly/disabled in the northern CA region.
Fields of interest: Environment, natural resources; Environment; Aging; Disabilities, people with.
Type of support: General/operating support; Equipment; Program development; Conferences/seminars; Seed money; Technical assistance; Consulting services; Matching/challenge support.
Limitations: Applications accepted. Giving primarily in AK, and northern CA, with emphasis on the San Francisco Bay Area. No support for religious purposes. No grants to individuals.
Publications: Informational brochure (including application guidelines).
Application information: Application form required.
Initial approach: Letter
Copies of proposal: 1
Deadline(s): None
Board meeting date(s): Generally bimonthly
Final notification: 6-8 weeks
Officer and Directors:* Kerry Anderson,* Pres.; Susan O'Hara; Kathy Fong Stephens.
Number of staff: 1 full-time professional; 1 part-time professional.
EIN: 742421528

1265
John and Mary Tu Foundation ✧ ☆
P. O. Box 8505
Fountain Valley, CA 92728-8505
Application address: c/o Albert Kong, 17600 Newhope St., Fountain Valley, CA 92708

Donors: John Tu; Mary Tu.
Foundation type: Independent foundation.
Financial data (yr. ended 12/31/12): Assets, $3,163,669 (M); gifts received, $2,075,824; expenditures, $2,317,450; qualifying distributions, $2,298,774; giving activities include $2,287,146 for 11 grants (high: $500,000; low: $2,000).
Fields of interest: Museums; Performing arts; Arts; Higher education; Education; Human services.
Limitations: Applications accepted. Giving primarily in CA.
Application information: Application form required.
Initial approach: Letter
Deadline(s): None
Officers: John Tu, Pres.; Mary Tu, Secy.; Albert Kong, C.F.O.
EIN: 271598417

1266
The Tuffli Family Foundation ✧ ☆
1412 Lower Paseo La Cresta
Palos Verdes Estates, CA 90274-2075

Established in 1996 in CA.
Donor: Don L. Tuffli.
Foundation type: Independent foundation.
Financial data (yr. ended 12/31/13): Assets, $13,476,363 (M); gifts received, $4,715,413; expenditures, $826,721; qualifying distributions, $566,250; giving activities include $566,250 for 15 grants (high: $222,500; low: $500).
Fields of interest: Higher education; Higher education, university; Business school/education; Environment, land resources; Multiple sclerosis; Health organizations; American Red Cross; Community/economic development; Foundations (community).
Limitations: Applications not accepted. Giving primarily in CA. No grants to individuals.
Application information: Unsolicited requests for funds not accepted.
Officers: Don L. Tuffli, Pres.; Martha T. Tuffli, V.P.; Laura T. Carruth, Secy.; Carol T. Cutting, Treas.
EIN: 330658864
Selected grants: The following grants are a representative sample of this grantmaker's funding activity:
$10,000 to Long Beach Rescue Mission, Long Beach, CA, 2012. For homeless program.
$6,000 to Palos Verdes Peninsula Land Conservancy, Rolling Hills Estates, CA, 2012. For the Legacy Circle Program.

1267
Alice Tweed Tuohy Foundation ✧
205 E. Carrillo St., Rm. 219
Santa Barbara, CA 93101-7186
FAX: (805) 962-7135; E-mail: atuohyfdn@aol.com; Mailing address: c/o Jeanne McKay, P.O. Box 1328, Santa Barbara, CA 93102-1328

Incorporated in 1956 in CA.
Donors: Alice Tweed Tuohy†; Kenneth Millar†; Margaret Millar†.
Foundation type: Independent foundation.
Financial data (yr. ended 06/30/13): Assets, $19,521,170 (M); expenditures, $1,214,480; qualifying distributions, $1,061,857; giving activities include $806,354 for 30 grants (high: $142,000; low: $1,000).
Purpose and activities: Grants to nonprofit organizations within the south coast area of Santa Barbara County, CA, serving young people, educational institutions, selected healthcare and medical organizations, and community projects; substantial support also for the art program at the Duluth Campus of the University of Minnesota.
Fields of interest: Scholarships/financial aid; Human services; Children/youth, services; Children/youth; Youth; Adults; Aging; Physically disabled; Mentally disabled.
Type of support: Capital campaigns; Building/renovation; Equipment; Land acquisition; Endowments; Scholarship funds; Program-related investments/loans; Matching/challenge support.
Limitations: Applications accepted. Giving limited to the Santa Barbara, CA area (except for very limited funding in Duluth, MN for a university art program). No support for private foundations, national campaigns, or private and public grade schools. No grants to individuals, or for operating budgets, research, or unrestricted purposes.
Publications: Biennial report (including application guidelines); Occasional report (including application guidelines).
Application information: Application form not required.
Initial approach: Letter
Copies of proposal: 7
Deadline(s): Submit proposal between July 1 and Sept. 15
Board meeting date(s): Apr. or May, and Nov. or Dec.
Final notification: 3 to 4 months
Officers and Directors:* John R. Mackall,* C.E.O. and Pres.; Joseph L. Cole,* V.P.; Jeanne McKay, Secy.-Treas.; Paul W. Hartloff; Harris W. Seed; Eleanor Van Cott.
Number of staff: 2 full-time professional.
EIN: 956036471

1268
Ueberroth Family Foundation ✧
P.O. Box 37
Corona del Mar, CA 92625-0037
Contact: Vicki U. Booth
E-mail: info@ueberroth.org; Main URL: http://www.ueberroth.org

Established in 1984 in CA.
Donors: Peter Ueberroth; Virginia Ueberroth; Kathy Clark; Teri Hoops; Alan Hoops; Washington Speakers Bureau; Deutsche Bank AG; Autry Foundation; William Thompson; Healthcare CEO Summit; KPMG; Redpoint Management LLP; Venture Strategy Group; Ueberroth Family Trust; Building Owners & Mgrs. of O.C.; Premier Resource Group.
Foundation type: Independent foundation.
Financial data (yr. ended 12/31/13): Assets, $41,198,295 (M); gifts received, $200,000; expenditures, $2,792,982; qualifying distributions, $2,527,450; giving activities include $2,527,450 for 128 grants (high: $102,000; low: $1,000).
Purpose and activities: Giving primarily to assist local community-based groups and programs that promote social change. The foundation favors projects that: 1) Promote education, self-sufficiency, and volunteerism in communities, 2) Research cancer and increase awareness of the importance of early detection, and 3) Support agencies that assist people who are underserved.
Fields of interest: Elementary/secondary education; Education; Hospitals (general); Health organizations, association; Medical research; Boys & girls clubs; Human services; Children/youth, services; Foundations (private grantmaking); Children.
Type of support: General/operating support; Annual campaigns; Capital campaigns; Building/renovation; Equipment; Endowments; Program development; Conferences/seminars; Curriculum development; Research.
Limitations: Applications accepted. Giving primarily in Orange County, CA. No support for religious

organizations. No grants for scholarships, debt or budget deficits.
Publications: Application guidelines.
Application information: Contributes mainly to groups with donor involvement or connection. E-mailed applications, certified or registered letters, DVDs or videos will not be accepted. Application guidelines available on foundation web site. Application form required.
Initial approach: Letter via U.S. mail only
Deadline(s): Mar. 1 and Sept. 1
Officers: Virginia Ueberroth, Chair.; Vicki Booth, Pres.
Directors: Heidi Ueberroth; Keri Ueberroth; Peter Ueberroth.
EIN: 330078919
Selected grants: The following grants are a representative sample of this grantmaker's funding activity:
$100,000 to MIND Research Institute, Irvine, CA, 2011.

1269
Ullman Foundation ✧
28212 Kelly Johnson Pkwy., Ste. 165
Valencia, CA 91355-5084

Established in 2005 in CA.
Donors: George Ullman, Jr.; Steven Ullman; Shari Ullman.
Foundation type: Independent foundation.
Financial data (yr. ended 12/31/13): Assets, $3,777,939 (M); expenditures, $449,975; qualifying distributions, $448,250; giving activities include $448,250 for 8 grants (high: $400,000; low: $1,500).
Fields of interest: Higher education, university; YM/YWCAs & YM/YWHAs; Protestant agencies & churches; Blind/visually impaired.
Limitations: Applications not accepted. Giving primarily in CA. No grants to individuals.
Application information: Unsolicited requests for funds not accepted.
Officers: Steven Ullman, Pres.; George Ullman, Jr., V.P.
EIN: 202791727

1270
UniHealth Foundation ✧
800 Wilshire Blvd., Ste. 1300
Los Angeles, CA 90017-2665 (213) 630-6500
Contact: Mary Odell, Pres.
FAX: (213) 630-6509;
E-mail: webadmin@unihealthfoundation.org; Main URL: http://www.unihealthfoundation.org/
E-Newsletter: http://visitor.constantcontact.com/manage/optin/ea?v=001VGGvr8xQIKg86pN3Wzq9Uw%3D%3D
Grants Database: http://www.unihealthfoundation.org/Grantee-Database
Grants Database: http://www.unihealthfoundation.org/Grantee-Database
Grants List: http://www.unihealthfoundation.org/Grantee-Highlights

Established in 1998 in CA.
Foundation type: Independent foundation.
Financial data (yr. ended 09/30/13): Assets, $289,569,228 (M); gifts received, $63,107; expenditures, $18,791,660; qualifying distributions, $14,625,316; giving activities include $13,870,985 for 114 grants (high: $500,000; low: $25).
Purpose and activities: To support and facilitate activities that significantly improve the health and well being of individuals and communities within its service area. The majority of funding will be to hospitals in Los Angeles and northern Orange Counties, CA.
Fields of interest: Hospitals (general); Hospitals (specialty); Public health; Palliative care; Health care.
Type of support: Program-related investments/loans; Management development/capacity building; Program development; Curriculum development; Scholarship funds; Technical assistance; Program evaluation; Employee matching gifts.
Limitations: Giving primarily in CA in the following areas: San Fernando and Santa Clarita Valley, Westside and Downtown Los Angeles, San Gabriel Valley, and Long Beach and Orange County. No support for propagandizing and/or influencing legislation, political campaigns, programs that promote religious doctrine, or biomedical/non-applied research. No grants to individuals, or for endowments, annual drives, or retirement of debt.
Publications: Application guidelines; Financial statement; Grants list; Informational brochure (including application guidelines); Newsletter; Occasional report; Program policy statement; Program policy statement (including application guidelines).
Application information: The foundation does not accept unsolicited applications. Grantseekers must send a preliminary letter and those qualified to submit a proposal will be contacted by foundation program staff. One hard copy and electronic copy of the proposal is required.
Initial approach: Letter of inquiry. If invited, a grant proposal outline will be provided.
Deadline(s): Determined annually
Board meeting date(s): 4 times per year
Final notification: Within 3 months
Officers and Directors:* David R. Carpenter,* Chair. and C.E.O.; Bradley C. Call,* Vice-Chair.; Mary Odell, Pres.; Lydia H. Kennard,* Secy.; Kathleen H. Salazar, C.F.O. and Treas.; David M. Cannom, M.D.; Patrick C. Haden; Charles C. Reed; Keith W. Renken; Frank M. Sanchez, Ph.D.; Robert Splawn, M.D.
Number of staff: 7 full-time professional; 1 full-time support; 1 part-time support.
EIN: 955004033
Selected grants: The following grants are a representative sample of this grantmaker's funding activity:
$500,000 to Los Angeles County Department of Health Services, Los Angeles, CA, 2013. For housing for health primary care clinic and supportive housing laboratory.
$440,189 to Pomona Valley Hospital Medical Center, Pomona, CA, 2013. For medical respite program for PVHMC discharged homeless patients.
$384,086 to University of California, San Francisco, CA, 2013. For Palliative Care Quality Network (PCQN).
$333,333 to White Memorial Medical Center, Los Angeles, CA, 2013. For From Theory to Practice in Diabetes Care Planning for Health Care Delivery System Transformation.
$293,155 to Providence Little Company of Mary Medical Center Torrance, Torrance, CA, 2013. To improve clinical outcomes through interdisciplinary clinical simulation.
$228,422 to California Hospital Medical Center, Los Angeles, CA, 2013. For Healthy Homes Approach to Reducing Severe Asthma Attacks and ER Utilization.
$209,345 to Casa Colina Centers for Rehabilitation, Pomona, CA, 2013. To bring Open-Source Electronic Health Record to Rehabilitation Hospital and Human Factor in Implementation.
$200,000 to University of Southern California, Keck School of Medicine, Los Angeles, CA, 2013. For restructuring graduate medical education.
$150,700 to Beverly Hospital, Montebello, CA, 2013. For Emergency Department Approved for Pediatrics (EDAP).
$50,000 to University of Southern California, Keck School of Medicine, Los Angeles, CA, 2013. For medical student scholarship.

1271
Union Bank Foundation ✧
P.O. Box 45174
San Francisco, CA 94145-0174 (619) 230-3105
Contact: J.R. Raines, Asst. V.P.
E-mail: charitablegiving@unionbank.com; Contact for J.R. Raines: Union Bank, N.A., 530 B Street, M.C. S-1450, San Diego, CA 92101, e-mail: jr.raines@unionbank.com; Contact for Northern CA, Central CA, and Pacific Northwest: Karen Murakami, Asst. V.P., Union Bank, N.A., 400 California Street, Mail Code 1-001-08, San Francisco, CA 94104, tel.: (415) 765-3890; Main URL: https://www.unionbank.com/global/about/corporate-social-responsibility/foundation/foundation-grants.jsp

Established in 1953.
Donors: Union Bank of California, N.A.; Union Bank.
Foundation type: Company-sponsored foundation.
Financial data (yr. ended 12/31/12): Assets, $1,145,690 (M); gifts received, $3,950,332; expenditures, $4,805,226; qualifying distributions, $4,758,652; giving activities include $4,740,392 for 411 grants (high: $100,000; low: $750).
Purpose and activities: The foundation supports nonprofit organizations involved with affordable housing, community economic development, education, and the environment. Special emphasis is directed toward programs designed to benefit low-to-moderate income populations.
Fields of interest: Museums; Business school/education; Adult education—literacy, basic skills & GED; Education, ESL programs; Scholarships/financial aid; Education, services; Education, reading; Education, computer literacy/technology training; Education; Environment, waste management; Environment, recycling; Environment, natural resources; Environment, energy; Botanical gardens; Environmental education; Environment; Aquariums; Substance abuse, treatment; Crime/violence prevention; Crime/violence prevention, youth; Dispute resolution; Employment, services; Employment, training; Agriculture; Housing/shelter, aging; Independent housing for people with disabilities; Housing/shelter, temporary shelter; Housing/shelter, homeless; Housing/shelter; Children, day care; Youth, services; Human services, financial counseling; Community development, small businesses; Microfinance/microlending; Community/economic development; Economically disadvantaged.
Type of support: General/operating support; Continuing support; Management development/capacity building; Program development; Scholarship funds.

Limitations: Applications accepted. Giving primarily in areas of company operations in CA. No support for political, religious, veterans, military, fraternal, or professional organizations, service clubs, individual elementary or secondary level schools, or intermediary foundations. No grants to individuals, or for capital campaigns, or educational institution operating funds.
Publications: Application guidelines; Corporate giving report.
Application information: Grant requests exceeding $10,000 must include performance measurement criteria and the requester must submit a report of achievement annually. Multi-year funding is not automatic. Application form required.
Initial approach: Complete online application
Deadline(s): None
Board meeting date(s): Bi-Monthly
Officers: Carl A. Ballton, Pres.; Gabriela Martinez, Secy.
EIN: 542178792

1272
United Plankton Charitable Trust ✧ ☆
11400 W. Olympic Blvd., Ste.590
Los Angeles, CA 90064

Established in 2005 in CA.
Donors: Hillenburg Family Trust; Stephen Hillenburg; Karen Hillenburg.
Foundation type: Independent foundation.
Financial data (yr. ended 12/31/13): Assets, $6,637,925 (M); expenditures, $476,766; qualifying distributions, $427,587; giving activities include $427,587 for 14 grants (high: $163,500; low: $1,000).
Fields of interest: Arts education; Elementary/secondary education; Higher education, university; Hospitals (general); Women.
Limitations: Applications not accepted. Giving primarily in CA. No grants to individuals.
Application information: Contributes only to pre-selected organizations.
Trustees: Karen Hillenburg; Stephen Hillenburg.
EIN: 206582607
Selected grants: The following grants are a representative sample of this grantmaker's funding activity:
$6,500 to Southern California Public Radio, Pasadena, CA, 2012. To further organization's charitable purpose.

1273
United World of the Universe Foundation ✧
P.O. Box 24950
Los Angeles, CA 90024-0950

Classified as a private operating foundation in 1981.
Donors: Frederick M. Segal; Ronald W. Burkle; Michael Segal; Leanne Segal.
Foundation type: Independent foundation.
Financial data (yr. ended 11/30/13): Assets, $19,063,645 (M); expenditures, $1,483,608; qualifying distributions, $722,653; giving activities include $505,500 for 28 grants (high: $50,000; low: $1,000).
Fields of interest: Human services; Children/youth, services; Human services, mind/body enrichment.
Limitations: Applications not accepted. Giving primarily in CA. No grants to individuals.
Application information: Contributes only to pre-selected organizations.
Officer: Michael Segal, Secy.
Trustees: Marvin Prudholme; Frederick M. Segal; Tina Segal; George Sisino.
EIN: 953185105

1274
Ute City Charitable Trust ✧
5484 Shannon Ridge Ln.
San Diego, CA 92130-2757

Established in 1999 in CA.
Donors: Gary B. Davis; Elissa R. Davis; Davis Charitable Lead Trust.
Foundation type: Independent foundation.
Financial data (yr. ended 12/31/12): Assets, $4,967,312 (M); expenditures, $884,540; qualifying distributions, $884,505; giving activities include $884,505 for grants.
Fields of interest: Arts; Education; Jewish agencies & synagogues.
Limitations: Applications not accepted. Giving primarily in CA, with emphasis on San Diego, and New York, NY. No grants to individuals.
Application information: Contributes only to pre-selected organizations.
Trustees: Dawn M. Berson; Elissa R. Davis; Gary B. Davis.
EIN: 330833915

1275
The Vadasz Family Foundation ✧
P.O. Box 1347
Sonoma, CA 95476-1347 (707) 938-3014
Contact: Pamela Winston; Meghan Beynon
FAX: (707) 938-3015;
E-mail: pam@vadaszfoundation.org; Additional e-mail: meghan@vadaszfoundation.org (for Meghan Beynon)

Established in 1997 in CA.
Donors: Judy K. Vadasz; Les L. Vadasz.
Foundation type: Independent foundation.
Financial data (yr. ended 11/30/13): Assets, $17,859,268 (M); expenditures, $2,535,893; qualifying distributions, $2,418,425; giving activities include $2,324,292 for 42 grants (high: $1,009,306; low: $300).
Purpose and activities: Giving primarily for higher education, as well as for educational foundations; funding also for health care, including a medical center, and for the support of social and cultural community needs.
Fields of interest: Museums; Elementary/secondary education; Higher education; Education; Environment; Hospitals (general); Health organizations, association; Human services; Aging, centers/services; Foundations (private grantmaking); Children/youth; Adults; Economically disadvantaged; Migrant workers.
Type of support: General/operating support; Continuing support; Annual campaigns; Endowments; Emergency funds; Fellowships; Matching/challenge support.
Limitations: Applications not accepted. Giving primarily in CA and in Montreal, Canada. No support for religious or political organizations. No grants to individuals.
Application information: Contributes only to pre-selected organizations.
Board meeting date(s): Quarterly
Officers and Directors:* Les L. Vadasz,* Pres.; Jeffrey E. Vadasz,* Secy.; Judy K. Vadasz,* Treas.; David Vadasz.
Number of staff: 1 part-time professional; 1 part-time support.
EIN: 770469457

1276
The George and Lena Valente Foundation ✧
44465 N. El Macero Dr.
El Macero, CA 95618-1062
Main URL: http://www.valentefoundation.org/

Established in 1995 in CA.
Donor: George Valente.
Foundation type: Independent foundation.
Financial data (yr. ended 09/30/13): Assets, $13,291,548 (M); expenditures, $854,907; qualifying distributions, $653,000; giving activities include $653,000 for 13 grants (high: $100,000; low: $3,000).
Purpose and activities: Giving to health organizations, senior citizens' services, and education, and medical research.
Fields of interest: Higher education; Health organizations, association; Medical research, institute; Human services; Aging.
Limitations: Applications not accepted. Giving primarily in CA.
Application information: Unsolicited requests for funds not accepted.
Officers: Keith Volkerts, Pres.; Linda L. Volkerts, Secy.
Board Members: Jerry Dye; Gene Hume; Jared Monez; Gerald Valente; Drake Volkerts.
EIN: 680370358
Selected grants: The following grants are a representative sample of this grantmaker's funding activity:
$10,000 to WarmLine Family Resource Center, Sacramento, CA, 2013. For Services to Parents of Children with Disabilities.

1277
The Valentine Family Foundation ✧
(formerly Donald T. and Rachel C. Valentine Foundation)
c/o Frank, Rimerman & Co. LLP
1801 Page Mill Rd.
Palo Alto, CA 94304-1211 (650) 845-8100
Contact: Donald T. Valentine; Rachel C. Valentine

Established in 1992 in CA.
Donors: Rachel C. Valentine; Donald T. Valentine; Christian Valentine.
Foundation type: Independent foundation.
Financial data (yr. ended 10/31/13): Assets, $18,933,125 (M); gifts received, $60; expenditures, $2,473,437; qualifying distributions, $2,406,752; giving activities include $2,406,752 for 14 grants (high: $792,229; low: $7,469).
Fields of interest: Performing arts, orchestras; Education; Environment, natural resources; Animals/wildlife; Reproductive health; Health care; Breast cancer; Family services, parent education; Community/economic development; Foundations (community).

Limitations: Applications accepted. Giving primarily in CA, MT and NY.
Application information: Application form not required.
Initial approach: Proposal
Deadline(s): None
Officers: Christian Valentine, Pres.; Mark Valentine, Secy.-Treas.
Trustee: Hilary Valentine.
EIN: 943169134

1278
The Valhalla Charitable Foundation ✧
(formerly The Scott Cook and Signe Ostby Charitable Foundation)
2995 Woodside Rd., Ste. 400-400
Woodside, CA 94062-2446

Established in 2003 in CA.
Donors: Scott D. Cook; H. Signe Ostby.
Foundation type: Independent foundation.
Financial data (yr. ended 12/31/13): Assets, $127,854,664 (M); gifts received, $702,685; expenditures, $4,823,721; qualifying distributions, $4,533,944; giving activities include $4,511,500 for 18 grants (high: $2,500,000; low: $500).
Fields of interest: Education; Environment; Youth development; Human services; Philanthropy/voluntarism; Protestant agencies & churches.
Limitations: Applications not accepted. Giving primarily in CA, NY, and WI. No grants to individuals.
Application information: Unsolicited requests for funds not accepted.
Officers and Directors:* H. Signe Ostby,* Pres.; Scott D. Cook,* C.F.O.; Sharon Cook Farney,* Secy.
EIN: 200478828
Selected grants: The following grants are a representative sample of this grantmaker's funding activity:
$2,500,000 to University of California San Francisco Foundation, San Francisco, CA, 2013.
$1,000,000 to Ridges Sanctuary, Baileys Harbor, WI, 2013.
$500,000 to African Leadership Foundation, San Francisco, CA, 2013.
$200,000 to United States Equestrian Team Foundation, Gladstone, NJ, 2013.
$100,000 to Intuit Scholarship Foundation, Palo Alto, CA, 2013.
$50,000 to Boys Hope Girls Hope, Bridgeton, MO, 2013.
$50,000 to Bridges to Prosperity, Yorktown, VA, 2013.
$50,000 to New Door Ventures, San Francisco, CA, 2013.
$25,000 to Yale University, New Haven, CT, 2013.
$10,000 to Japan Society of Northern California, San Francisco, CA, 2013.

1279
The Valley Foundation ✧ ☆
16450 Los Gatos Blvd., Ste. 210
Los Gatos, CA 95032-5594
Main URL: http://valley.org
Facebook: http://www.facebook.com/pages/The-Valley-Foundation/121159584579187

Established in 1984 in CA.
Foundation type: Independent foundation.
Financial data (yr. ended 09/30/13): Assets, $61,414,106 (M); expenditures, $626,991; qualifying distributions, $1,058,599; giving activities include $1,000,000 for 1 grant.
Purpose and activities: The primary goal of the foundation is to improve health care and medical services for lower income households within Santa Clara County, CA. More than 50 percent of all grants are authorized for this purpose. The foundation's core competency and interest is providing grants to the medical field, dealing with research, education, health awareness, direct services and critical diseases. The foundation will also consider social services requests that relate to the health of its community.
Fields of interest: Education.
Type of support: General/operating support; Continuing support; Capital campaigns; Equipment; Program development; Seed money; Research; Technical assistance; Matching/challenge support.
Limitations: Applications not accepted. Giving limited to Santa Clara County, CA. No support for political or religious organizations. No grants to individuals.
Publications: Annual report; Grants list; Informational brochure.
Application information: Unsolicited requests for funds not accepted.
Board meeting date(s): Quarterly
Officers: Phillip R. Boyce,* Chair.; Richard Sieve, M.D.*, Vice-Chair.; Herbert Kain, M.D., Secy.; Daniel P. Doore, Treas.
Trustees: Arthur A. Basham; Joseph Parisi.
Number of staff: 1 part-time professional; 1 part-time support.
EIN: 941584547

1280
Wayne & Gladys Valley Foundation ✧
1939 Harrison St., Ste. 510
Oakland, CA 94612-3532 (510) 466-6060
Contact: Michael D. Desler, Exec. Dir.
FAX: (510) 466-6067; E-mail: info@wgvalley.org;
Main URL: http://fdnweb.org/wgvalley

Established in 1977 in CA.
Donors: F. Wayne Valley†; Gladys Valley†.
Foundation type: Independent foundation.
Financial data (yr. ended 09/30/13): Assets, $454,116,970 (M); expenditures, $29,988,413; qualifying distributions, $27,936,670; giving activities include $27,143,695 for 59 grants (high: $10,000,000; low: $7,500).
Purpose and activities: Primary areas of interest include higher, secondary, and other education, medical research, health care, youth, local parks and recreational facilities and local Catholic organizations. The foundation seeks to make grants to organizations having broad based funding support; specifically defined goals and purposes; demonstrated effectiveness in its programs; expectations for continued success in its activities without future dependence on support from the foundation; and committed, enthusiastic and diligent leadership.
Fields of interest: Elementary/secondary education; Higher education; Health care; Medical research; Recreation, parks/playgrounds; Human services; Children/youth, services; Catholic agencies & churches.
Type of support: General/operating support; Capital campaigns; Building/renovation; Program development; Scholarship funds; Research; Matching/challenge support.
Limitations: Applications accepted. Giving primarily in Alameda and Contra Costa counties, CA. No support for veterans, fraternal, labor, service club, military, or similar organizations. No grants to individuals, or for fundraising events, dinners, advertising, private operating foundations, or generally for endowments.
Publications: Application guidelines; Annual report.
Application information: More detailed application guidelines may be obtained by contacting the foundation. Application form not required.
Initial approach: Letter
Copies of proposal: 1
Deadline(s): None
Board meeting date(s): Mar., June, Sept., and Dec.
Final notification: 3-6 months
Officers and Directors:* Tamara A. Valley,* Pres.; Richard M. Kingsland,* V.P. and C.F.O.; Carolyn A. Worth, Corp. Secy.; Michael D. Desler, Exec. Dir.; Stephen M. Chandler; Barbara B. LaSalle; John P. Stock.
Number of staff: 4 full-time professional; 1 full-time support.
EIN: 953203014
Selected grants: The following grants are a representative sample of this grantmaker's funding activity:
$10,000,000 to University of California at Berkeley Foundation, Berkeley, CA, 2013. To establish John P. Stock Faculty Fellows Fund for research in biomedical science, in memory of John P. Stock.
$4,600,000 to University of Massachusetts Medical School, Worcester, MA, 2013. For construction of Dr. Lou Messina's lab in new Advanced BioTherapeutics Center at Albert Sherman Center.
$3,571,428 to University of California, Berkeley, CA, 2013. For construction of Li Ka Shing Center for Biomedical and Health Sciences.
$3,571,428 to University of California, Berkeley, CA, 2012. For The construction of Li Ka Shing Center for Biomedical and Health Sciences (old Warren Hall).
$3,333,334 to Oregon State University Foundation, Corvallis, OR, 2012. For construction of a science facility at Oregon State University (the Linus Pauling Science Center).
$3,333,334 to Oregon State University Foundation, Corvallis, OR, 2012. For construction of a science facility at Oregon State University (the Linus Pauling Science Center).
$2,500,000 to Bellarmine College Preparatory, San Jose, CA, 2012. For Construction of the Student Life Center and the Auxiliary Gym.
$2,500,000 to Bellarmine College Preparatory, San Jose, CA, 2012. For Construction of the Student Life Center and the Auxiliary Gym.
$2,500,000 to East Bay Zoological Society, Oakland, CA, 2012. For Construction of the new Veterinary Medical Hospital.
$2,000,000 to John Muir Health Foundation, Walnut Creek, CA, 2013. For equipment for new facilities.
$2,000,000 to John Muir Health Foundation, Walnut Creek, CA, 2012. For Equipment costs for new facilities at the John Muir Medical Center (the new Patient Care Tower).
$1,666,667 to University of California, School of Veterinary Medicine, Davis, CA, 2013. For construction of Veterinary Medicine III B (VM3B) for interdisciplinary research.
$1,666,667 to University of California, School of Veterinary Medicine, Davis, CA, 2012. For

construction of Veterinary Medicine III B (VM3B) for interdisciplinary research.
$500,000 to Oakland Unified School District, Oakland, CA, 2013. For Quality Community School Development Department (QCSD) and Secondary Literacy Program.
$450,000 to Teach for America, San Francisco, CA, 2013. For East Bay Area Operations.
$200,000 to LifeLong Medical Care, Berkeley, CA, 2013. For renovations and expansion of West Berkeley Family Practice clinic.
$150,000 to Diocese of Oakland, Oakland, CA, 2012. For budget support for the Department of Catholic Schools for the needs of five urban schools, and for the FACE tuition assistance program.
$150,000 to Family Aid Catholic Education, Oakland, CA, 2013. For FACE tuition assistance program.
$125,000 to Tri-City Health Center, Fremont, CA, 2012. For construction coast for the renovation of Mowry Clinic in Fremont.
$40,000 to Down Syndrome Connection of the Bay Area, Danville, CA, 2013. For general operating support.

1281
Mike and Linda Van Daele Family Foundation ✧

2900 Adams St., Ste. C-25
Riverside, CA 92504-8312

Established in 1998 in CA.
Donors: Mike Van Daele; Linda Van Daele; Mike and Linda Van Daele Family Trust.
Foundation type: Independent foundation.
Financial data (yr. ended 12/31/13): Assets, $3,761,174 (M); gifts received, $3,300,000; expenditures, $1,576,555; qualifying distributions, $1,576,454; giving activities include $1,516,962 for 24 grants (high: $250,000; low: $500).
Purpose and activities: Giving primarily to Christian organizations.
Fields of interest: Human services; Christian agencies & churches.
Limitations: Applications not accepted. Giving primarily in CA, with emphasis on Riverside. No grants to individuals.
Application information: Contributes only to pre-selected organizations.
Officers: Linda Van Daele, Secy.; Mike Van Daele, Mgr.
EIN: 330833774

1282
Van Konynenburg Foundation ✧

13681 W. Sunset Blvd.
Pacific Palisades, CA 90272-4019

Established in CA.
Donors: Claire Van Konynenburg; D. Michael Van Konynenburg.
Foundation type: Independent foundation.
Financial data (yr. ended 12/31/13): Assets, $5,906,925 (M); gifts received, $1,312,910; expenditures, $548,612; qualifying distributions, $524,500; giving activities include $524,500 for 20 grants (high: $100,000; low: $1,000).
Fields of interest: Elementary/secondary education; Human services; Christian agencies & churches.
Type of support: General/operating support.
Limitations: Applications not accepted. Giving primarily in CA and WA. No grants to individuals.
Application information: Contributes only to pre-selected organizations.
Trustees: Claire Van Konynenburg; D. Michael Van Konynenburg.
EIN: 954505575

1283
van Loben Sels/RembeRock Foundation

(formerly van Loben Sels Foundation)
131 Steuart St., Ste. 301
San Francisco, CA 94105-1241 (415) 512-0500
Contact: Gail Shuster, Grants Mgr.; Dan Corsello, Interim Exec. Dir.; Nancy Wiltsek, Exec. Dir.
FAX: (415) 371-0227; E-mail: gshuster@vlsrr.org; Tel. for application information: Gail Shuster, Grants Mgr. Mail applications to Ms. Toni Rembe. Additional tel. for Dan Corsello, Interim Exec. Dir.: (415) 512-0572, e-mail: dcorsello@vlsrr.org; Main URL: http://www.vlsrr.org

Incorporated in 1964 in CA.
Donors: Ernst D. van Loben Sels†; Arthur Rock.
Foundation type: Independent foundation.
Financial data (yr. ended 12/31/13): Assets, $29,055,465 (M); expenditures, $2,431,691; qualifying distributions, $2,306,205; giving activities include $1,995,000 for 168 grants (high: $41,000; low: $2,000).
Purpose and activities: The van Loben Sels/RembeRock Foundation's mission is to promote social justice in Northern California by means of legal services and advocacy.
Fields of interest: Legal services; Legal services, public interest law; Civil/human rights, immigrants; Civil/human rights, minorities; Civil/human rights, women; Civil/human rights, LGBTQ; Civil liberties, due process; Civil/human rights.
Type of support: General/operating support; Continuing support.
Limitations: Applications accepted. Giving limited to Northern CA. The foundation defines northern CA as including Santa Cruz, Santa Clara, Stanislaus, Tuolumne, and Mono Counties and all counties north of these five counties. No support for national organizations unless for a specific local project, or to projects requiring medical, scientific, or other technical knowledge for evaluation. No grants to individuals, or for deficit financing, capital or endowment funds, scholarships, stipends, or fellowships or for capital campaigns, fund raisers, annual dinners, galas or award banquets.
Publications: Grants list; Program policy statement.
Application information: See foundation web site for application requirements, guidelines, and application and year-end report templates. Application form and year-end reports are downloaded as a Word documents from the web site, www.vlsrr.org. Videotapes, audiotapes, CDs, etc., are not accepted unless requested. Certified or signature-required mail is not accepted. Application form required.
Initial approach: Proposal
Copies of proposal: 1
Deadline(s): Rolling
Board meeting date(s): Every 8-10 weeks
Final notification: In writing
Officers: Toni Rembe, Pres.; Richard Odgers, Secy.; Dan Corsello, Treas.; Nancy Wiltsek, Exec. Dir.
Trustees: Julie Divola; Tom Layton.
Number of staff: 1 full-time professional.
EIN: 946109309
Selected grants: The following grants are a representative sample of this grantmaker's funding activity:
$50,000 to Napa County Probation Department, Napa, CA, 2012. For Evening Reporting Center.
$41,000 to Legal Services of Northern California, Sacramento, CA, 2012. For core support.
$40,500 to Legal Aid Society-Employment Law Center, San Francisco, CA, 2012. For core support.
$30,000 to American Civil Liberties Union of Northern California, San Francisco, CA, 2012. For core support.
$27,500 to Lawyers Committee for Civil Rights of the San Francisco Bay Area, San Francisco, CA, 2012. For core support.
$20,000 to At the Crossroads, San Francisco, CA, 2012. For general operating support.
$15,000 to Positive Resource Center, San Francisco, CA, 2012. For Benefits Counseling Program.
$12,500 to Family Resource Center of Truckee, Truckee, CA, 2012. For Community Legal Program.
$11,500 to Disability Rights Education and Defense Fund, Berkeley, CA, 2012. For general operating support.
$10,000 to International Rescue Committee, Oakland, CA, 2012. For its Immigration Program.

1284
J. B. & Emily Van Nuys Charities ✧

P.O. Box 2946
Palos Verdes Peninsula, CA 90274-8946

Incorporated in 1957 in CA.
Donors: Emily Van Nuys Trust; J. Benton Van Nuys Trust; Emily Van Nuys†; J. Benton Van Nuys†.
Foundation type: Independent foundation.
Financial data (yr. ended 12/31/13): Assets, $725,249 (M); gifts received, $1,122,213; expenditures, $995,508; qualifying distributions, $993,257; giving activities include $890,000 for 1 grant.
Purpose and activities: Preference is given to organizations whose activities are directed toward aid for the needy, providing food and shelter to the poor, disaster relief, child welfare and youth programs for the disadvantaged. Primary areas of interest include health agencies, child welfare, the disadvantaged, and issues of homelessness and hunger.
Fields of interest: Hospitals (general); Health care; Health organizations, association; Crime/violence prevention, domestic violence; Crime/violence prevention, child abuse; Human services; Children/youth, services; Aging, centers/services; Children/youth; Youth; Aging; Disabilities, people with; Mentally disabled; Economically disadvantaged; Homeless.
Type of support: General/operating support; Continuing support; Capital campaigns; Building/renovation; Equipment; Emergency funds; Program development; Curriculum development; Internship funds; Scholarship funds; Technical assistance.
Limitations: Applications not accepted. Giving primarily in the Los Angeles, CA, area. No support for religious organizations. No grants to individuals, or for research, fundraising events, or special events.
Application information: Contributes only to pre-selected organizations.
Officers: Terrence D. Dibble, Pres.; Robert K. Maloney, M.D., V.P.; Lawrence Chaffin, Jr., Secy.; Morgan W. St. John, Treas.

Number of staff: 1 part-time professional.
EIN: 956096134
Selected grants: The following grants are a representative sample of this grantmaker's funding activity:
$20,000 to Stone Soup Child Care Programs, Encino, CA, 2011. For scholarship program.
$15,000 to A Place Called Home, Los Angeles, CA, 2011.
$15,000 to Barlow Respiratory Hospital, Los Angeles, CA, 2011.
$15,000 to Chrysalis Center, Los Angeles, CA, 2011.
$15,000 to Court Appointed Special Advocates, Monterey Park, CA, 2011.
$15,000 to Foodbank of Southern California, Long Beach, CA, 2011.
$15,000 to Neighborhood Homework House, Azusa, CA, 2011.
$12,500 to Epilepsy Foundation of Greater Los Angeles, Los Angeles, CA, 2011. For scholarship program.
$10,000 to Pasadena Mental Health Association, Pasadena, CA, 2011.
$10,000 to TreePeople, Beverly Hills, CA, 2011.

1285
I. N. & Susanna H. Van Nuys Foundation ✧
400 N. Roxbury Dr., Ste. 600
Beverly Hills, CA 90210-5021

Established in 1950 in CA.
Foundation type: Independent foundation.
Financial data (yr. ended 05/31/13): Assets, $21,279,989 (M); expenditures, $1,003,638; qualifying distributions, $914,462; giving activities include $914,462 for grants.
Purpose and activities: Support primarily in those fields favored by the original grantor, including a private hospital, secondary schools and colleges, and generally related activities.
Fields of interest: Arts; Elementary/secondary education; Higher education; Education; Hospitals (general); Human services.
Limitations: Applications not accepted. Giving primarily in CA, with emphasis on Los Angeles; some funding also in MA. No grants to individuals.
Application information: Contributes only to pre-selected organizations.
Trustees: George A. Bender; Maribeth A. Borthwick; Stuart M. Ketchum.
EIN: 956006019
Selected grants: The following grants are a representative sample of this grantmaker's funding activity:
$410,788 to Good Samaritan Hospital, Los Angeles, CA, 2011. For general support.
$78,157 to Wellesley College, Wellesley, MA, 2011. For general support.
$46,896 to Childrens Hospital Los Angeles, Los Angeles, CA, 2011. For general support.
$39,081 to California Institute of Technology, Pasadena, CA, 2011. For general support.
$20,000 to Buckley School, Sherman Oaks, CA, 2011. For general support.
$20,000 to Center Theatre Group of Los Angeles, Los Angeles, CA, 2011. For general support.
$20,000 to Marlborough School, Los Angeles, CA, 2011. For general support.
$10,000 to Braille Institute of America, Los Angeles, CA, 2011. For general support.
$10,000 to Hillsides, Pasadena, CA, 2011. For general support.
$7,815 to Museum Associates, Los Angeles, CA, 2011. For general support.

1286
The Raju Vegesna Foundation ✧
5808 Trowbridge Way
San Jose, CA 95138-2362

Donors: Anatakoti Raju Vegesna; Bala Vegesna.
Foundation type: Independent foundation.
Financial data (yr. ended 12/31/13): Assets, $6,579,013 (M); expenditures, $1,040,477; qualifying distributions, $974,555; giving activities include $971,002 for 6 grants (high: $400,000; low: $1,000).
Fields of interest: Hinduism.
Limitations: Applications not accepted. Giving primarily in CA and India. No grants to individuals.
Application information: Contributes only to pre-selected organizations.
Director: Richard T. McCoy.
EIN: 061694446

1287
Ventura County Community Foundation ✧
4001 Mission Oaks Blvd.
Camarillo, CA 93010-8364 (805) 988-0196
Contact: For grants: LaToya Ford, Prog. Assoc. and Grants Mgr.
FAX: (805) 485-2700; E-mail: vccf@vccf.org; Grant inquiry e-mail: lford@vccf.org; Main URL: http://www.vccf.org
E-Newsletter: http://visitor.constantcontact.com/manage/optin/ea?v=001P1yAzTPelCySJ0jwzZ6XZQ%3D%3D
Grants List: http://www.vccf.org/grantmaking.shtml
Scholarships Facebook Page: http://www.facebook.com/VCCFScholarships

Incorporated in 1987 in CA.
Foundation type: Community foundation.
Financial data (yr. ended 09/30/13): Assets, $127,159,983 (M); gifts received, $3,333,241; expenditures, $6,058,472; giving activities include $4,233,958 for grants.
Purpose and activities: The foundation seeks to enrich and enhance the quality of life in Ventura County and to provide leadership to residents and nonprofit organizations in building an enduring source of funds and strengthening community participation to meet the changing needs and challenges of the community.
Fields of interest: Arts; Education; Health organizations, association; Housing/shelter; Youth, services; Family services; Human services; Civil/human rights; Hispanics/Latinos; Women; Girls; Economically disadvantaged.
Type of support: General/operating support; Management development/capacity building; Equipment; Emergency funds; Program development; Conferences/seminars; Seed money; Scholarship funds; Technical assistance; Program evaluation; Scholarships—to individuals; Matching/challenge support.
Limitations: Applications accepted. Giving primarily in Ventura County, CA. No support for religious purposes. No grants to individuals (except for scholarships), or for endowments, annual campaigns, budget deficits, or land acquisition; no program-related investments.
Publications: Application guidelines; Annual report (including application guidelines); Financial statement; Informational brochure; Newsletter.
Application information: Number of requested proposal copies may vary from 1 to 12. Visit foundation web site for application forms and specific guidelines per grant type. Application form required.
Initial approach: Complete applications in response to RFP
Deadline(s): Varies (as designated by RFP)
Board meeting date(s): Bimonthly
Final notification: June for scholarships; for all other applications, as designated by RFP
Officers and Directors:* Gary E. Erickson,* Chair.; Henry L. "Hank" Lacayo,* Vice-Chair.; Terri E. Lisagor,* Vice-Chair.; Stacy A. Roscoe,* Vice-Chair.; Mike Silacci,* Vice-Chair. and Treas.; Stacy Roscoe, Interim C.E.O. and Pres.; Linda Garcia, V.P., Prog. and Grants; Bonnie Gilles, V.P., Finance; Dena C. Jenson, V.P. and Dir., Center for Nonprofit Leadership; Roz McGrath, Secy.; Tim Gallagher; Scott Hansen; Robert J. Katch; Stan Mantooth; Charles Maxey, Ph.D.; M. Carmen Ramirez; Mary L. Schwabauer; Pierre Y. Tada; Bonnie Weigel.
Number of staff: 5 full-time professional; 8 full-time support; 5 part-time support.
EIN: 770165029
Selected grants: The following grants are a representative sample of this grantmaker's funding activity:
$100,000 to California State University Channel Islands Foundation, Camarillo, CA, 2011. For Ventura Nursing Legacy Grants Fund.
$50,922 to Ventura College Foundation, Ventura, CA, 2011. For James V. and Idah W. Iiff Scholarship Fund.
$19,500 to Childrens Burn Foundation, Sherman Oaks, CA, 2011. For Douglas Roy III We Care Trust Fund.
$15,000 to Saint Jude the Apostle Catholic Church, Atlanta, GA, 2011. For RED Family Fund.
$10,000 to Ventura County Community AIDS Partnership, Camarillo, CA, 2011. For Ruth Daily Livingston Fund.
$9,190 to Ventura County Behavioral Health Department, Oxnard, CA, 2011. For Greenblatt Family Fund.
$8,463 to Casa Pacifica Centers for Children and Families, Casa Pacifica Centers for Children and Families, Camarillo, CA, 2011. For James C. Basile Fund.
$5,000 to Ventura County Housing Trust Fund, CA, 2011. For VCCF Community Response Fund.
$3,000 to Future Leaders of America, Oxnard, CA, 2011. For Reiter Brothers Inc Foundation Fund.
$500 to Rain Communities, Camarillo, CA, 2011. For Bobbie Steindler Beatty Academic Opportunity Fund in honor of Howie and Ann Steindler.

1288
Versacare, Inc. ✧
c/o The Versafund
4097 Trail Creek Rd., Ste. B
Riverside, CA 92505-5869
FAX: (951) 343-5855; E-mail: versacare@aol.com; Main URL: http://www.versacare.org

Established in 1996 in CA and FL.
Foundation type: Independent foundation.
Financial data (yr. ended 09/30/13): Assets, $23,518,994 (M); expenditures, $1,737,874; qualifying distributions, $1,590,238; giving

activities include $1,343,950 for 59 grants (high: $100,000; low: $1,000).

Purpose and activities: Giving to projects consistent with the principles and mission of the Seventh-day Adventist Church. Priority is given to proposals which advance education and science, promote healthcare activities, assist the distressed and under privileged, and provide general community benefit. Applying organizations should be in operation for two or more years, and provide matching or supporting funds.

Fields of interest: Higher education, university; Health care, association; Hospitals (general); Protestant agencies & churches.

Type of support: Equipment; Program development; Curriculum development; Scholarship funds; Matching/challenge support.

Limitations: Applications accepted. Giving in the U.S., with some emphasis on CA and WA; Versacare provides a limited number of Non-SDA-related grants that are consistent with its mission, with preference given to organizations located within the Inland Empire of Southern California, or in proximity to a facility or entity that Versacare either operates or is closely affiliated with. No grants for debt reduction, or for salaries or general operations; no grants to individuals.

Publications: Application guidelines; Grants list; Informational brochure.

Application information: Application guidelines and form available on foundation web site. Application form required.

Initial approach: Submit application online via foundation web site
Copies of proposal: 1
Deadline(s): Dec. 31
Final notification: Mar. 31

Officers: Charles C. Sandefur, Chair.; Robert E. Coy, J.D., Vice-Chair. and Pres.; Ron Wisbey, V.P.; Calvin J. Hanson, C.P.C.U., Secy.; Ellen H. Brodersen, C.P.A., Treas.

Trustees: George W. Brown; Debra Brill; Myrna Costa; Roscoe Howard; Tom Macomber; Richard Pershing.

EIN: 330052434

1289
The David Vickter Foundation ✧

865 Via Abajo
Santa Barbara, CA 93110-2034

Established in 1983 in CA.

Donors: David Vickter; David Vickter Trust.

Foundation type: Independent foundation.

Financial data (yr. ended 10/31/13): Assets, $10,834,101 (M); expenditures, $737,214; qualifying distributions, $572,100; giving activities include $542,100 for 25 grants (high: $65,000; low: $1,000).

Fields of interest: ALS; Health organizations; ALS research; Human services; Foundations (private grantmaking); Jewish agencies & synagogues.

Limitations: Applications not accepted. Giving primarily in CA. No grants to individuals.

Application information: Unsolicited requests for funds not accepted.

Officers: Lenore Jacoby, Pres.; Frances Feinman, Secy.

EIN: 953883733

Selected grants: The following grants are a representative sample of this grantmaker's funding activity:

$65,000 to United Friends of the Children, Los Angeles, CA, 2011.
$50,000 to Amyotrophic Lateral Sclerosis Association, Calabasas Hills, CA, 2011.
$33,000 to VIP Community Mental Health Center, Los Angeles, CA, 2011.
$20,000 to Direct Relief International, Santa Barbara, CA, 2011.
$20,000 to Lowell Alumni Association, San Francisco, CA, 2011.
$20,000 to University of California, Los Angeles, CA, 2011.
$7,500 to American Printing House for the Blind, Louisville, KY, 2011.
$5,000 to Doctors Without Borders USA, New York, NY, 2011.
$4,000 to Crossroads, Claremont, CA, 2011.

1290
Vidalakis Family Foundation ✧ ☆

c/o Nick S. Vidalakis
405 El Camino Real, No. 153
Menlo Park, CA 94025-5240

Established in 1999 in WA.

Donors: Nick S. Vidalakis; Nancy G. Vidalakis.

Foundation type: Independent foundation.

Financial data (yr. ended 12/31/12): Assets, $294,332 (M); gifts received, $601,468; expenditures, $475,788; qualifying distributions, $471,445; giving activities include $471,445 for grants.

Fields of interest: Education; Health care; Religion.

Limitations: Applications not accepted. Giving primarily in CA. No grants to individuals.

Application information: Contributes only to pre-selected organizations.

Officers: Nick S. Vidalakis, Pres.; Perry N. Vidalakis, Exec. V.P. and Secy.; John N. Vidalakis, Exec. V.P. and Treas.; Nancy G. Vidalakis, Sr. Exec. V.P.; George N. Vidalakis, V.P.; Nicole N. Vidalakis, V.P.

EIN: 911997816

1291
Volentine Family Foundation ✧

(formerly Myatt W. Volentine Foundation)
19 W. Carrillo St.
Santa Barbara, CA 93101-3212
Contact: Diane K. Hayes, Pres.

Established in 1988 in CA.

Donors: Myatt W. Volentine; Mary G. Volentine; Mary G. Volentine Admin. Trust.

Foundation type: Independent foundation.

Financial data (yr. ended 12/31/13): Assets, $30,402,177 (M); gifts received, $25,000; expenditures, $1,637,306; qualifying distributions, $1,186,353; giving activities include $1,061,175 for 81 grants (high: $89,500; low: $200).

Purpose and activities: Giving for community health services, youth and social services, and education.

Fields of interest: Education; Health organizations, association; Human services; YM/YWCAs & YM/YWHAs; Children/youth, services; Residential/custodial care, hospices; United Ways and Federated Giving Programs.

Limitations: Applications accepted. Giving limited to Santa Barbara, CA, Loveland, CO, and McCook, NE. No grants to individuals.

Application information: Application form required.

Initial approach: Letter
Deadline(s): Mar. 31

Officers: Diane K. Hayes, Pres.; Richard A. Nightingale, C.F.O.; John Mackall, V.P.; Claudette Sabiron, Secy.

Director: Nancy K. Popenhagen.

EIN: 770203235

1292
The Omer G. Voss Family Foundation ✧ ☆

(formerly The Omer G. & Annabelle K. Voss Charitable Trust)
136 Stanyan St.
San Francisco, CA 94118-4220

Established in IL.

Donors: Omer G. Voss†; Annabelle K. Voss.

Foundation type: Independent foundation.

Financial data (yr. ended 12/31/13): Assets, $1,077,670 (M); gifts received, $1,950,000; expenditures, $942,750; qualifying distributions, $942,746; giving activities include $935,100 for 17 grants (high: $200,000; low: $100).

Fields of interest: Higher education; Health organizations; Protestant agencies & churches.

Limitations: Applications not accepted. Giving on a national basis, with emphasis on IL. No grants to individuals.

Application information: Unsolicited requests for funds not accepted.

Officer and Trustees:* Omer G. Voss, Jr.,* Mgr.; Jerrol A. Pohl.

EIN: 363467637

1293
Wade Family Charitable Foundation ✧

1716 Catalina Ave.
Seal Beach, CA 90740-5711 (562) 431-9593
Contact: Chris Wade, Pres. and C.E.O.
E-mail: chris.wade@wfcf.org

Established in 2008 in CA.

Donors: Charles Wade; Diana Wade; Chris Wade; Tuko Pamoja Mkyashi.

Foundation type: Independent foundation.

Financial data (yr. ended 12/31/13): Assets, $3,431,328 (M); expenditures, $492,523; qualifying distributions, $452,910; giving activities include $425,950 for 12 grants (high: $189,800; low: $1,000), and $16,463 for 3 loans/program-related investments (high: $7,656; low: $3,200).

Fields of interest: Education; Christian agencies & churches.

International interests: Philippines; Tanzania.

Limitations: Applications accepted. Giving primarily in CA, Philippines and Tanzania.

Application information: Application form required.

Initial approach: E-mail
Deadline(s): None

Officers: Chris Wade, Pres. and C.E.O.; Diana Wade, Secy.

Director: Angela Wade.

EIN: 263664913

1294
Wadhwani Foundation ✧
(formerly Tekchand Foundation)
2475 Hanover St.
Palo Alto, CA 94304-1114
U.S. contacts: Gayatri Agnew, Prog. Dir., and Rishi Chopra, Prog. Coord.
e-mail: rishi@chopra@wadhwani-foundation.org; India contact: Atul Raja, Exec. V.P., Marketing, e-mail: marketing@wadhwani-foundation.org; Bangalore address: 113/1B, Benaka Tech Park, Block II, 3rd Fl., ITPL Main Rd., Kundalahalli, Bangalore - 560037; New Delhi address: B-315, Basement, Chittaranjan Park, New Delhi - 110 019; Main URL: http://wadhwani-foundation.org/
Dr. Romesh and Kathleen Wadhwani's Giving Pledge Profile: http://glasspockets.org/philanthropy-in-focus/eye-on-the-giving-pledge/profiles/wadhwani

Established in 1997 in CA.
Donors: Kathleen E. Wadhwani; Romesh T. Wadhwani.
Foundation type: Independent foundation.
Financial data (yr. ended 12/31/12): Assets, $62,412,877 (M); gifts received, $54,000,000; expenditures, $4,948,697; qualifying distributions, $2,721,389; giving activities include $1,662,552 for 30 grants (high: $414,882; low: $767).
Purpose and activities: Giving primarily for international affairs, particularly concerning India; funding also for the arts, education, and social services.
Fields of interest: Arts education; Performing arts, music; Arts; Secondary school/education; Disasters, floods; Safety/disasters; Human services; International affairs; Philanthropy/voluntarism.
International interests: India.
Limitations: Giving primarily in CA and India. No grants to individuals.
Application information: Applicants must be a legally registered (under 80G and FCRA) NGO in India. Application information available on foundation web site.
Officers: Dr. Romesh T. Wadhwani, Chair.; Dr. Ajay Kela, C.E.O. and Pres.; Atul Raja, Exec. V.P., Marketing.
EIN: 770450893
Selected grants: The following grants are a representative sample of this grantmaker's funding activity:
$250,000 to Center for Strategic and International Studies, Washington, DC, 2011.

1295
Waitt Foundation ✧
(formerly Waitt Family Foundation)
P.O. Box 1948
La Jolla, CA 92038-1948 (858) 551-4437
Contact: Cherie Prothro, Dir., Opers.
FAX: (858) 551-6871; E-mail for Cherie Prothro: cherie@waittfoundation.org; Main URL: http://www.waittfoundation.org/
Grants List: http://waittfoundation.org/ngswaitt-grants

Established in 1993 in SD.
Donor: Theodore "Ted" W. Waitt.
Foundation type: Independent foundation.
Financial data (yr. ended 12/31/12): Assets, $139,187,620 (M); expenditures, $7,233,068; qualifying distributions, $6,877,214; giving activities include $6,256,228 for 48 grants (high: $500,000; low: $25).
Purpose and activities: The primary mission is to protect the ocean from the impacts of overfishing by facilitating the creation of marine protected areas, engaging stakeholders to improve management of fisheries, fostering sustainable solutions, and raising public awareness as to the problem via a network of collaborative NGO's and foundations.
Fields of interest: Animals/wildlife, fisheries; Animals/wildlife, sanctuaries; Foundations (private grantmaking); Foundations (private independent); Science, research; Science; Marine science.
Type of support: Program development; Research; Program-related investments/loans; Employee matching gifts.
Limitations: Applications accepted. Giving on a national and international basis. No support for for-profit organizations, or for arts or religious organizations, public education institutions or healthcare organizations/hospitals. No grants for individuals, capital campaigns, endowments, debt reduction or lobbying.
Publications: Application guidelines.
Application information: If the grant request is a fit within the foundation's current giving guidelines, you will be prompted to complete stage two of the application. Only applications submitted via the online application system will be accepted. Faxes, e-mails, or applications sent through the mail will not be considered. There is a $100,000 minimum for all grant requests. Multi-year proposals will be considered. For the ROC Grants Program, the typical funding amount is $1,000 - $10,000 and not to exceed a request of $20,000. Application form required.
Initial approach: Fill out preliminary online application form
Board meeting date(s): Varies
Officer and Directors:* Theodore "Ted" W. Waitt,* Chair. and Pres.; Dave Russell,* Vice-Chair.; Jacob James,* Managing Dir.; Shane Hartnett; Cindy Waitt; Hailey Waitt.
Number of staff: 4
EIN: 460428166
Selected grants: The following grants are a representative sample of this grantmaker's funding activity:
$500,000 to Environmental Defense Fund, New York, NY, 2012. For ocean conservation work.
$500,000 to Pew Charitable Trusts, Philadelphia, PA, 2012. For ocean conservation work.
$500,000 to RARE, Arlington, VA, 2012. For ocean conservation work.
$500,000 to University of California, Bren School of Environmental Science and Management, Santa Barbara, CA, 2012. For ocean conservation work.
$391,352 to Scripps Institution of Oceanography, La Jolla, CA, 2012. For ocean conservation work.
$362,500 to Oceans 5, New York, NY, 2012. For ocean conservation work.
$330,075 to Nature Conservancy, Arlington, VA, 2012. For ocean conservation work.
$260,635 to Natural Resources Defense Council, New York, NY, 2012. For ocean conservation work.
$260,000 to Oceans 5, New York, NY, 2012. For ocean conservation work.
$150,000 to Conservation Law Foundation, Boston, MA, 2012. For ocean conservation.

1296
Wallis Foundation ✧
1880 Century Park E., Ste. 950
Los Angeles, CA 90067-1612 (310) 286-9777

Established in 1957 in CA.
Donor: Hal B. Wallis†.
Foundation type: Independent foundation.
Financial data (yr. ended 06/30/13): Assets, $17,769,480 (M); expenditures, $4,310,321; qualifying distributions, $4,025,878; giving activities include $3,894,000 for 164 grants (high: $300,000; low: $1,000).
Purpose and activities: Giving primarily for the arts, education, the environment, health care and human services.
Fields of interest: Performing arts; Arts; Higher education; Education; Environment, natural resources; Health care; Health organizations; Human services; Foundations (community).
Limitations: Applications not accepted. Giving primarily in CA, with emphasis on Los Angeles, San Francisco, and Santa Barbara. No grants to individuals.
Application information: Contributes only to pre-selected organizations.
Officers and Directors:* Beth Wallis,* Pres.; Jeffrey Glassman,* Secy.; Michael Sack,* C.F.O.
EIN: 956027469

1297
The Warnack Foundation ✧ ☆
P.O. Box 1409
Lancaster, CA 93584-1409

Established in 2003.
Donor: A.C. Warnack.
Foundation type: Operating foundation.
Financial data (yr. ended 12/31/13): Assets, $0 (M); expenditures, $555,575; qualifying distributions, $551,007; giving activities include $551,007 for 25 grants (high: $245,000; low: $100).
Fields of interest: Education; Health care; Boys & girls clubs; Human services; Foundations (community).
Limitations: Applications not accepted. Giving primarily in CA.
Application information: Unsolicited requests for funds not accepted.
Officers: A.C. Warnack, C.E.O.; Shaughne Warnack, Secy.; Robert J. Pluss, Treas.
Directors: Kathy Smith; William Walsh.
EIN: 412113946
Selected grants: The following grants are a representative sample of this grantmaker's funding activity:
$62,500 to Eisenhower Medical Center, Rancho Mirage, CA, 2012. To support the Research for Finding a Cure for AL's.
$6,000 to Guide Dogs of the Desert, White Water, CA, 2012. To support the Training and Supplying of Guide Dogs to the Visually Handicapped.
$2,000 to Boy Scouts of America, Van Nuys, CA, 2012. For children's support.
$1,000 to Autism Society Of America, Palm Desert, CA, 2012. For Research to Find a Cure for Autism.
$1,000 to Coachella Valley Rescue Mission, Indio, CA, 2012. To provide Support for the Homeless.
$1,000 to Los Angeles Mission, Los Angeles, CA, 2012. For the homeless.

1298
The Diane Warren Foundation ✧
1880 Century Park E., Ste. 1600
Los Angeles, CA 90067-4114

Established in 1999 in CA.
Donor: Diane Warren.
Foundation type: Independent foundation.
Financial data (yr. ended 12/31/13): Assets, $3,395,901 (M); gifts received, $1,088,922; expenditures, $1,014,166; qualifying distributions, $922,450; giving activities include $922,450 for 47 grants (high: $75,000; low: $2,500).
Purpose and activities: Giving primarily to animal rescue, animal rights and endangered animal organizations; funding also for the needs of the elderly.
Fields of interest: Animals/wildlife; Human services; Aging.
Limitations: Applications not accepted. Giving primarily in CA. No support for organizations that perform tests on animals. No grants to individuals.
Application information: Contributes only to pre-selected organizations.
Officer and Director:* Diane Warren,* Pres. and C.F.O.
EIN: 954742413
Selected grants: The following grants are a representative sample of this grantmaker's funding activity:
$100,000 to Dream Foundation, Santa Barbara, CA, 2011.
$90,000 to Lange Foundation, Los Angeles, CA, 2011.
$80,000 to In Defense of Animals, San Rafael, CA, 2011.
$60,000 to People for the Ethical Treatment of Animals, Norfolk, VA, 2011.
$48,000 to Los Angeles Jewish Home for the Aging, Reseda, CA, 2011.
$45,000 to Happy Tails Pet Sanctuary, Sacramento, CA, 2011.
$40,000 to Save the Manatee Club, Maitland, FL, 2011.
$37,000 to Haven-Friends for Life, Raeford, NC, 2011.
$35,000 to Pet Adoption Fund, Canoga Park, CA, 2011.
$20,000 to ONEgeneration, Van Nuys, CA, 2011.

1299
Warsh-Mott Legacy ✧
469 Bohemian Hwy.
Freestone, CA 95472-9579 (707) 874-2942
Contact: Roxanne Turnage, Exec. Dir.
FAX: (707) 874-1734; E-mail: inquiries@csfund.org;
Main URL: http://www.csfund.org
Grants List: http://www.csfund.org/grants2013-1rg.html

Established in 1985 in CA.
Donors: Maryanne Mott; Herman E. Warsh‡.
Foundation type: Independent foundation.
Financial data (yr. ended 09/30/13): Assets, $27,447,458 (M); expenditures, $1,532,392; qualifying distributions, $1,409,464; giving activities include $1,059,078 for 24 grants (high: $125,000; low: $2,000).
Purpose and activities: Funding in the areas of economic globalization, food sovereignty (seed saving, soil building, and protecting pollinators), civil liberties, and emerging technology.
Fields of interest: Agriculture/food, research; Agriculture/food; Civil liberties, advocacy.
Type of support: General/operating support; Continuing support; Conferences/seminars; Publication; Research; Technical assistance; Matching/challenge support.
Limitations: Applications accepted. Giving on a national basis. No grants to individuals, or for endowments, capital funds, video or film production, books, or emergency requests.
Publications: Application guidelines; Grants list; IRS Form 990 or 990-PF printed copy available upon request.
Application information: The foundation is currently in the process of reducing its grantmaking, and its ability to entertain new proposals is especially limited during this time. Please do not include brochures, reports, news clippings, CDs, DVDs, or other materials with letters of inquiry. Plastic folders, binders or other presentation materials are not necessary. Application form not required.
Initial approach: Letter of inquiry (no more than 3 pages) preferred over fax or e-mail
Copies of proposal: 1
Deadline(s): None
Board meeting date(s): Apr. and Dec.
Officers and Board Members:* Michael Warsh,* Pres.; Marise Meynet Stewart,* V.P.; Maryanne Mott,* C.F.O.; Corinne Meadows-Efram,* Secy.; Roxanne Turnage, Exec. Dir.; Kau'i Keliipio; Teresa Robinson.
EIN: 680049658

1300
Wasserman Foundation ✧
10960 Wilshire Blvd., 5th Fl.
Los Angeles, CA 90024-3708 (310) 407-0200
FAX: (310) 882-4601;
E-mail: feedback@wassermanfoundation.org; Main URL: http://www.wassermanfoundation.org
E-Newsletter: http://www.wassermanfoundation.org/news/
Facebook: http://www.facebook.com/pages/Wasserman-Foundation/182428898469669?sk=info
Flickr: http://www.flickr.com/photos/wassermanfdn/
Tumblr: http://wassermanfdn.tumblr.com/
Twitter: http://twitter.com/wassermanfdn

Incorporated in 1952 in CA.
Donors: Lew R. Wasserman‡; Edith B. Wasserman‡.
Foundation type: Independent foundation.
Financial data (yr. ended 12/31/12): Assets, $188,476,343 (M); expenditures, $13,748,666; qualifying distributions, $12,552,798; giving activities include $12,272,298 for 135 grants (high: $1,500,000; low: $1,000).
Purpose and activities: Giving primarily to organizations focused on advancing and promoting education, environmental responsibility, health and welfare, and the arts. With a diversified list of recipients, the foundation continually strives to partner with groups that are committed to assisting those less fortunate, and bettering the community at large.
Fields of interest: Performing arts; Higher education; Environment; Hospitals (general); Medical research, institute; Human services; Jewish federated giving programs; Public policy, research.
Type of support: Capital campaigns; Endowments; Scholarship funds; Research.
Limitations: Applications not accepted. Giving primarily in CA. No grants to individuals.
Application information: Unsolicited requests for funds not accepted.
Officers and Directors:* Casey Wasserman,* C.E.O. and Pres.; Carol A. Leif, V.P.; Lynne Wasserman, V.P.; Rica Rodman, Exec. Dir.
EIN: 956038762
Selected grants: The following grants are a representative sample of this grantmaker's funding activity:
$1,500,000 to DonorsChoose.org, New York, NY, 2012.
$1,000,000 to Los Angeles Unified School District, Los Angeles, CA, 2012.
$500,000 to ONE Campaign, Washington, DC, 2012.
$500,000 to University of California, Athletics, Los Angeles, CA, 2012.
$300,000 to Bill, Hillary and Chelsea Clinton Foundation, New York, NY, 2012.
$300,000 to Grammy Museum Foundation, Los Angeles, CA, 2012.
$250,000 to IDEO.Org, San Francisco, CA, 2012.
$228,500 to Tony Blair Faith Foundation-US, Washington, DC, 2012.
$100,000 to University of Houston-University Park, Houston, TX, 2012.
$15,000 to Womens Sports Foundation, New York, NY, 2012.

1301
Waterford Foundation ✧
1396 W. Herndon Ave., Ste. 101
Fresno, CA 93711-7126 (559) 436-0900
Contact: Darius Assemi, C.E.O.

Established in 1997 in CA.
Donors: Darius Assemi; Farshid Assemi; Farid Assemi; Granville Homes, Inc.; Assemi Brothers, LLC; Grantland Avenue, LLC; Afshar Hospital.
Foundation type: Operating foundation.
Financial data (yr. ended 12/31/11): Assets, $10,842,553 (M); gifts received, $48,090; expenditures, $2,004,004; qualifying distributions, $1,822,958; giving activities include $1,689,697 for 10 grants (high: $387,483).
Purpose and activities: Giving primarily to Islamic organizations and mosques; some funding also for social services.
Fields of interest: Human services; Islam.
Limitations: Giving primarily in CA.
Application information:
Initial approach: Letter
Deadline(s): None
Officers: Darius Assemi, C.E.O.; Farshid Assemi, V.P.; Farid Assemi, V.P.; Steven G. Rau, Secy.
EIN: 770437521
Selected grants: The following grants are a representative sample of this grantmaker's funding activity:
$318,153 to Islamic Cultural Center of Fresno, Fresno, CA, 2012. For general support.
$312,000 to Development and Relief Foundation, Fresno, CA, 2012. For general support.
$100,000 to American Near East Refugee Aid, Washington, DC, 2012. For general support.
$100,000 to Medical Foundation of North Carolina, Chapel Hill, NC, 2012. For general support.
$84,000 to Friends of the University of Surrey, Wilmington, DE, 2012. For general support.
$82,184 to California State University, Fresno, CA, 2012. For general support.

$66,616 to Community Food Bank, Fresno, CA, 2012. For general support.
$60,560 to Poverello House, Fresno, CA, 2012. For general support.
$30,280 to Assistance League of Fresno, Fresno, CA, 2012. For general support.
$27,252 to Foundation for Sanger Schools, Sanger, CA, 2012. For general support.

1302
Phyllis C. Wattis Foundation
720 York St., Ste. 103
San Francisco, CA 94110 (415) 986-1571
FAX: (415) 986-1547;
E-mail: info@wattisfoundation.org; Main URL: http://www.wattisfoundation.org
Grants List: http://www.wattisfoundation.org/grantees.php

Donors: Carol Casey; Paul L. Wattis Foundation.
Foundation type: Independent foundation.
Financial data (yr. ended 12/31/12): Assets, $9,510,762 (M); gifts received, $75,000; expenditures, $677,617; qualifying distributions, $470,000; giving activities include $470,000 for grants.
Purpose and activities: Giving for the support of the fine arts, including the exhibition of painting and sculpture, and the performing arts, including opera, symphony, and dance.
Fields of interest: Visual arts; Performing arts; Arts.
Limitations: Giving primarily in San Francisco, Berkeley, and Oakland, as well as in Marin County, California. No grants for general support, operating expenses, capital expansion, endowment funds, seed grants, scholarships, awards, or research and planning.
Publications: Application guidelines.
Application information:
Initial approach: Letter of inquiry of no more than 2 pages
Deadline(s): See foundation web site for current deadlines
Board meeting date(s): Spring and fall
Directors: Carol Casey; Carlie Wilmans.
EIN: 900653262

1303
Webb Family Foundation ✧ ☆
(formerly The Maynard and Irene Webb Family Charitable Foundation)
P.O. Box 1060
Los Gatos, CA 95031-1060
Application address: c/o GW & Wade, Inc., Attn.: Maynard G. Webb or Irene C. Webb, 93 Worcester St., Wellesley, MA 02481, tel.: (781) 239-1188

Established in 2004 in CA.
Donors: Maynard G. Webb, Jr.; Irene C. Webb.
Foundation type: Independent foundation.
Financial data (yr. ended 12/31/13): Assets, $10,364,528 (M); gifts received, $100; expenditures, $833,278; qualifying distributions, $752,500; giving activities include $752,500 for 25 grants (high: $160,000; low: $500).
Purpose and activities: Giving primarily for higher education, a children's hospital, and human services.
Fields of interest: Education; Human services; Religion.
Type of support: General/operating support.
Limitations: Applications accepted. Giving primarily in CA.
Application information: Application form not required.
Initial approach: Proposal
Deadline(s): None
Officers and Directors:* Maynard G. Webb, Jr.,* Chair. and C.F.O.; Irene C. Webb,* Pres. and Secy.; Kevin Webb.
EIN: 200864199
Selected grants: The following grants are a representative sample of this grantmaker's funding activity:
$90,000 to Summer Search, San Jose, CA, 2013. For general.
$55,000 to Year Up, Boston, MA, 2013. For general.
$50,000 to Spark, San Francisco, CA, 2013. For general.
$22,500 to La Clinica de la Raza, Oakland, CA, 2013. For general.
$20,000 to Breakthrough Collaborative, San Francisco, CA, 2013. For general.
$20,000 to College Track, Oakland, CA, 2013. For general.
$20,000 to Tony La Russas Animal Rescue Foundation, Walnut Creek, CA, 2013. For general.
$13,750 to Albert B. Sabin Vaccine Institute, Washington, DC, 2013. For general.
$5,000 to East Bay Society for the Prevention of Cruelty to Animals, Oakland, CA, 2013. For general.
$5,000 to Edgewood Childrens Ranch, Orlando, FL, 2013. For general.

1304
Max Webb Foundation ✧
8383 Wilshire Blvd., Ste. 740
Beverly Hills, CA 90211-2406

Incorporated in 1961 in CA.
Donor: Max Webb.
Foundation type: Independent foundation.
Financial data (yr. ended 11/30/13): Assets, $19,688,175 (M); expenditures, $907,505; qualifying distributions, $842,259; giving activities include $842,259 for 47 grants (high: $150,000; low: $68).
Purpose and activities: Giving primarily to Jewish organizations and education.
Fields of interest: Higher education; Education; Human services; Jewish federated giving programs; Jewish agencies & synagogues.
Limitations: Applications not accepted. Giving primarily in Los Angeles, CA. No grants to individuals.
Application information: Contributes only to pre-selected organizations.
Officers: Max Webb, Chair.; Rose Webb Roven, Pres.; Chara Schreyer, V.P.; Justine Podell, Secy.; Talia Roven, Treas.
EIN: 956052391
Selected grants: The following grants are a representative sample of this grantmaker's funding activity:
$250 to Young Israel of North Beverly Hills, Beverly Hills, CA, 2013. To Aid and Promote Literacy, Educational and Scientific Research.

1305
Helen and Will Webster Foundation ✧
1388 Crest Dr.
Altadena, CA 91001-1835

Established in 1997 in CA.
Donors: Helen E. Webster; Wilton W. Webster, Jr.
Foundation type: Independent foundation.
Financial data (yr. ended 12/31/12): Assets, $5,725,791 (M); gifts received, $1,595,261; expenditures, $5,149,467; qualifying distributions, $4,809,350; giving activities include $4,809,350 for grants.
Fields of interest: Education; Food services; Human services.
Limitations: Applications not accepted. Giving primarily in CA. No grants to individuals.
Application information: Contributes only to pre-selected organizations.
Officers and Directors:* Wilton Webster, Jr.,* C.E.O. and Pres.; Helen E. Webster,* V.P.; Alec J. Webster,* Secy.-Treas.; Richard B. Webster,* Treas.
EIN: 954624483

1306
Joe Weider Foundation ✧
20750 Ventura Blvd., Ste. 310
Woodland Hills, CA 91364-6236

Established in 1993 in CA.
Donor: Weider Health and Fitness.
Foundation type: Independent foundation.
Financial data (yr. ended 11/30/13): Assets, $4,771,200 (M); gifts received, $5,000,000; expenditures, $744,474; qualifying distributions, $709,885; giving activities include $707,500 for 10 grants (high: $250,000; low: $2,000).
Purpose and activities: Giving primarily for education and to Jewish organizations.
Fields of interest: Education; Human services; Jewish agencies & synagogues.
International interests: Canada.
Limitations: Applications not accepted. Giving primarily in CA and NY; some giving also in Montreal, Canada. No grants to individuals.
Application information: Contributes only to pre-selected organizations.
Officers: Joe Weider, C.E.O.; Eric Weider, C.F.O.; Sidney Machtinger, Secy.
EIN: 954349698

1307
Weingart Foundation ✧
1055 W. 7th St., Ste. 3200
Los Angeles, CA 90017-2305 (213) 688-7799
Contact: Fred J. Ali, C.E.O. and Pres.
FAX: (213) 688-1515; E-mail: info@weingartfnd.org; Main URL: http://www.weingartfnd.org
Grants Database: http://www.weingartfnd.org/grants-database
Knowledge Center: http://www.weingartfnd.org/Leading-with-Core-Support

Incorporated in 1951 in CA.
Donors: Ben Weingart†; Stella Weingart†.
Foundation type: Independent foundation.
Financial data (yr. ended 06/30/14): Assets, $798,922,695 (M); expenditures, $45,480,869; qualifying distributions, $35,872,057; giving activities include $32,320,067 for 542 grants (high:

$1,000,000; low: $200), and $345,511 for 116 employee matching gifts.
Purpose and activities: The foundation seeks to build a better America by offering constructive assistance to people in need, thereby helping them to lead more rewarding, responsible lives.
Fields of interest: Education, early childhood education; Child development, education; Elementary school/education; Secondary school/education; Higher education; Adult education—literacy, basic skills & GED; Education, reading; Education; Hospitals (general); Medical care, rehabilitation; Nursing care; Health care; Substance abuse, services; AIDS; Crime/violence prevention, youth; Legal services; Employment, services; Food services; Housing/shelter; Recreation; Youth development, services; Human services; Children/youth, services; Child development, services; Family services; Residential/custodial care, hospices; Minorities/immigrants, centers/services; Homeless, human services; Community/economic development, formal/general education; Community/economic development; Leadership development; Infants/toddlers; Children/youth; Children; Youth; Adults; Aging; Young adults; Disabilities, people with; Physically disabled; Blind/visually impaired; Deaf/hearing impaired; Mentally disabled; Minorities; Asians/Pacific Islanders; African Americans/Blacks; Hispanics/Latinos; Native Americans/American Indians; Indigenous peoples; Women; Infants/toddlers, female; Girls; Adults, women; Young adults, female; Men; Infants/toddlers, male; Boys; Adults, men; Young adults, male; Military/veterans; Offenders/ex-offenders; Substance abusers; AIDS, people with; Single parents; Crime/abuse victims; Terminal illness, people with; Sex workers; Immigrants/refugees; Economically disadvantaged; Homeless; Migrant workers; LGBTQ; Lesbians; Gay men; Bisexual; Transgender and gender nonconforming; Intersex.
Type of support: General/operating support; Management development/capacity building; Capital campaigns; Building/renovation; Equipment; Program development; Program-related investments/loans; Employee matching gifts; Matching/challenge support.
Limitations: Applications accepted. Giving for the regular grant program limited to 7 southern CA counties: Los Angeles, Orange, Santa Barbara, Riverside, San Bernardino, Ventura counties, and for the small grant program all the aforementioned and limited grantmaking in San Diego County. No support for religious programs, consumer interest or environmental advocacy, projects or programs exclusively or predominately financed by government sources, social or political issues outside the United States of America, or national organizations that do not have chapters operating in Southern California, or for propagandizing, influencing legislation and/or elections, promoting voter registration; for political candidates, political campaigns; or for litigation. No grants to individuals, or for endowment funds, annual campaigns, emergency funds, deficit financing, fellowships, seminars, conferences, publications, workshops, travel, surveys, films, medical research, or publishing activities.
Publications: Application guidelines; Annual report (including application guidelines); Grants list; Newsletter.
Application information: Applications for the "Small Grant Program" are now being accepted. See foundation web site for application criteria. Application form required.

Initial approach: Regular Grant Program (requests over $25,000): Online letter of inquiry; Small Grant Program (requests $25,000 and under): Online application
Deadline(s): See foundation web site for current deadlines
Board meeting date(s): Sept., Dec., Feb., Apr. and June
Final notification: 3 to 4 months

Officers and Directors:* Monica Lozano,* Chair.; Fred J. Ali, C.E.O. and Pres.; Deborah M. Ives, V.P. and Treas.; Belen Vargas, V.P., Grant Operations; Aileen Adams; William C. Allen; Andrew E. Bogen; Steven D. Broidy; John W. Mack; Miriam Muscarolas; Steven L. Soboroff.
Number of staff: 10 full-time professional; 1 part-time professional; 5 full-time support.
EIN: 956054814
Selected grants: The following grants are a representative sample of this grantmaker's funding activity:
$1,500,000 to United Way of Greater Los Angeles, Los Angeles, CA, 2014. For program support for Home for Good Funders Collaborative, partnership of public and private funders, led by United Way of Greater Los Angeles, who have come together to align funds for permanent supportive housing for chronically homeless people, payable over 2.00 years.
$1,050,000 to White Memorial Medical Center Charitable Foundation, Los Angeles, CA, 2014. To enhance the Diabetes Management Program, payable over 3.00 years.
$750,000 to Martin Luther King Jr Community Health Foundation, Los Angeles, CA, 2014. For capital support for Martin Luther King Jr. Community Hospital's Healthy Babies, Healthy Beginnings campaign.
$500,000 to Rape Foundation, Santa Monica, CA, 2014. For capital support for construction of a new facility for the Stuart House program, payable over 1.75 years.
$500,000 to Youth Policy Institute, Los Angeles, CA, 2014. To strengthen YPI's capacity by enhancing financial and payroll systems, and by hiring staff and consultants for private fundraising, payable over 2.00 years.
$360,000 to AbilityFirst, Pasadena, CA, 2014. For capital support for the construction of a new building to replace agency's community center in Inglewood.
$175,000 to Boys and Girls Club of Santa Ana, Santa Ana, CA, 2014. For Core support, payable over 2.00 years.
$125,000 to Enterprise Community Partners, Columbia, MD, 2014. For Core support, payable over 2.00 years.
$100,000 to Gay and Lesbian Community Services Center of Orange County, Santa Ana, CA, 2014. For Core support, payable over 2.00 years.
$99,000 to Verbum Dei High School, Los Angeles, CA, 2014. For capital support for campus renovation.

1308
The Weisman Family Foundation ✧
14001 Ventura Blvd.
Sherman Oaks, CA 91423-3511

Established in 2004 in CA.
Donors: Joel Aaronson; Platinum Properties.
Foundation type: Independent foundation.
Financial data (yr. ended 12/31/12): Assets, $8,461,133 (M); expenditures, $785,735; qualifying distributions, $645,682; giving activities include $645,682 for 81 grants (high: $200,000; low: $36).
Purpose and activities: Giving primarily to Jewish agencies, temples, and schools.
Fields of interest: Education; Jewish federated giving programs; Jewish agencies & synagogues.
Limitations: Applications not accepted. No grants to individuals.
Application information: Contributes only to pre-selected organizations.
Director: Aaron Weisman; Lyle Weisman.
EIN: 201187960

1309
Frederick R. Weisman Philanthropic Foundation ✧
265 N. Carolwood Dr.
Los Angeles, CA 90077-3535

Established in 1993 in CA and DE.
Donors: Frederick R. Weisman Trust of 1991; Nancy Weisman Trust.
Foundation type: Independent foundation.
Financial data (yr. ended 12/31/13): Assets, $17,242,057 (M); gifts received, $8,168; expenditures, $1,035,385; qualifying distributions, $812,104; giving activities include $629,000 for 116 grants (high: $46,000; low: $1,000).
Purpose and activities: Giving primarily for the arts, education, children, youth services, and social services, as well as services and art programs for adults and children with developmental or other disabilities.
Fields of interest: Museums (art); Arts; Education; Health care, clinics/centers; Health care; Human services; Children/youth, services; Disabilities, people with; Economically disadvantaged.
Limitations: Applications not accepted. Giving primarily in Los Angeles, CA. No grants to individuals.
Application information: Unsolicited requests for funds not accepted.
Officers and Directors:* Billie Milam Weisman,* Pres.; Steven L. Arnold, C.F.O.; Frederick M. Nicholas,* Treas.; Sidney J. Machtinger.
EIN: 954442308

1310
The David and Heidi Welch Foundation ✧
217 Camino Al Lago
Atherton, CA 94027-5424

Established in 1999 in CA.
Donors: David F. Welch; Heidi A. Welch; LRFA LLC; Gary Morgenthaler; Jesse Rogers; Mindy Rogers.
Foundation type: Independent foundation.
Financial data (yr. ended 12/31/13): Assets, $1,533,326 (M); gifts received, $1,152,972; expenditures, $460,924; qualifying distributions, $457,100; giving activities include $441,000 for 8 grants (high: $250,000; low: $1,000).
Fields of interest: Higher education; Education; Environment.
Type of support: General/operating support.
Limitations: Applications not accepted. Giving primarily in CA. No grants to individuals.
Application information: Unsolicited requests for funds not accepted.

Officers and Directors:* David F. Welch,* Pres.; Heidi A. Welch,* V.P., C.F.O. and Secy.
EIN: 943332166
Selected grants: The following grants are a representative sample of this grantmaker's funding activity:
$200,000 to New Schools Fund, Oakland, CA, 2011.

1311
The John and Marilyn Wells Family Foundation ✧

c/o Singer Burke & Co.
6345 Balboa Blvd., Ste. 375
Encino, CA 91316-5238

Established in 2002 in CA.
Donors: John Wells; Marilyn Wells.
Foundation type: Independent foundation.
Financial data (yr. ended 12/31/12): Assets, $11,817,259 (M); gifts received, $993,896; expenditures, $1,579,416; qualifying distributions, $1,567,435; giving activities include $1,562,382 for 35 grants (high: $500,000; low: $50).
Fields of interest: Arts; Health organizations, association; Human services; Children/youth, services.
Limitations: Applications not accepted. Giving primarily in CA. No grants to individuals.
Application information: Contributes only to pre-selected organizations.
Officers: John Wells, Chair. and Pres.; Marilyn Wells, Secy.-Treas. and C.F.O.
EIN: 680526427

1312
Wells Fargo Foundation ✧

333 S. Grant Ave., 12th Fl.
Los Angeles, CA 90071
Contact: Timothy G. Hanlon, Pres.
FAX: (310) 789-8989;
E-mail: thanlon@wellsfargo.com; Main URL: http://www.wellsfargo.com/donations
Wells Fargo Housing Foundation: https://www.wellsfargo.com/about/wfhf_oview.jhtml

Established in 1979 in MN.
Donors: Norwest Corp.; Wells Fargo & Co.; Norwest Ltd.
Foundation type: Company-sponsored foundation.
Financial data (yr. ended 12/31/13): Assets, $488,707,083 (M); gifts received, $1,153,010; expenditures, $188,060,170; qualifying distributions, $188,060,170; giving activities include $166,326,302 for 15,407 grants (high: $9,000,000; low: $50), and $20,449,573 for employee matching gifts.
Purpose and activities: The foundation supports organizations involved with education, job creation and job training, housing, financial literacy, human services, and community economic development.
Fields of interest: Elementary/secondary education; Education; Employment, services; Employment, training; Housing/shelter, development; Housing/shelter, home owners; Housing/shelter, services; Housing/shelter; Human services, financial counseling; Human services; Economic development; Community/economic development; Economically disadvantaged.
Type of support: General/operating support; Continuing support; Management development/capacity building; Annual campaigns; Program development; Employee volunteer services; Employee matching gifts.
Limitations: Applications accepted. Giving primarily in areas of company operations. No support for religious organizations not of direct benefit to the entire community, lobbying organizations, or fraternal organizations. No grants to individuals, or for political campaigns, advertising purchases including booths and tickets, fundraising dinners, video or film productions, club memberships, or endowments.
Publications: Application guidelines; Corporate giving report.
Application information: Application form not required.
Initial approach: Varies by state. Visit website for details
Copies of proposal: 1
Deadline(s): Varies
Final notification: 90 to 120 days
Officers and Directors:* Timothy G. Hanlon,* Pres.; Richard D. Levy, Exec. V.P.; Dean L. Thorp, Sr. V.P.; Timothy R. Chinn, V.P.; James A. Horton, V.P.; Cynthia E. Ishigaki,* V.P.; Carolyn H. Roby, V.P.; Mary E. Schaffner, Secy.; Juan Austin; John R. Campbell; Deborah Alicia Smith.
Number of staff: None.
EIN: 411367441
Selected grants: The following grants are a representative sample of this grantmaker's funding activity:
$12,860,000 to Neighborhood Reinvestment Corporation, Washington, DC, 2012.
$9,000,000 to Neighborhood Reinvestment Corporation, Washington, DC, 2012.
$1,614,300 to Scholarship America, Saint Peter, MN, 2012.
$1,152,080 to United Way of Central Iowa, Des Moines, IA, 2012.
$500,000 to Wake Forest University, Winston-Salem, NC, 2012.
$400,000 to Camillus House, Miami, FL, 2012.
$25,000 to United Way of the Midlands, Omaha, NE, 2012.
$15,000 to California State University Bakersfield Foundation, Bakersfield, CA, 2012.
$15,000 to Rebuilding Together Valley of the Sun, Tempe, AZ, 2012.
$15,000 to Salvation Army, 2012.

1313
The Werner Family Foundation ✧

11601 Wilshire Blvd., Ste. 1840
Los Angeles, CA 90025-1754

Established in 1987 in CA.
Donors: Thomas Werner; Jill Troy Werner.
Foundation type: Independent foundation.
Financial data (yr. ended 09/30/13): Assets, $19,617,386 (M); gifts received, $1,031,893; expenditures, $1,051,760; qualifying distributions, $764,985; giving activities include $764,985 for 28 grants (high: $250,000; low: $1,500).
Fields of interest: Education; Human services; YM/YWCAs & YM/YWHAs; Foundations (private grantmaking).
Type of support: General/operating support.
Limitations: Applications not accepted. Giving primarily in CA and WI; some funding also in MA. No grants to individuals.
Application information: Contributes only to pre-selected organizations.
Officers and Directors: Thomas Werner,* Pres.; Jill Werner,* V.P.; Edward Werner,* Secy.-Treas.; Amanda Werner; Carolyn Werner.
EIN: 954139253
Selected grants: The following grants are a representative sample of this grantmaker's funding activity:
$137,500 to Red Sox Foundation, Boston, MA, 2011.
$125,000 to YMCA of Metropolitan Milwaukee, Milwaukee, WI, 2011.
$100,000 to Wilshire Boulevard Temple, Los Angeles, CA, 2011.
$100,000 to Wilshire Boulevard Temple, Los Angeles, CA, 2011.
$75,000 to Clare Foundation, Santa Monica, CA, 2011.
$60,000 to After-School All-Stars, Los Angeles, CA, 2011.
$50,000 to Clare Foundation, Santa Monica, CA, 2011.
$10,000 to Ploughshares Fund, Washington, DC, 2011.
$10,000 to University School of Milwaukee, Milwaukee, WI, 2011.
$5,000 to Breast Cancer Research Foundation, New York, NY, 2011.

1314
Gary and Mary West Foundation ✧

(formerly Sunset Foundation)
5796 Armada Dr., Ste. 300
Carlsbad, CA 92008-4693
E-mail: info@gmwf.org; Main URL: http://www.gmwf.org/

Donors: Gary L. West; Mary L. West.
Foundation type: Independent foundation.
Financial data (yr. ended 12/31/13): Assets, $158,077,911 (M); expenditures, $21,047,870; qualifying distributions, $19,946,345; giving activities include $18,764,136 for 40 grants (high: $9,986,489; low: $500).
Fields of interest: Health care; Health organizations, association; Medical research, institute; Human services; Military/veterans' organizations.
Limitations: Applications not accepted. Giving primarily in San Diego County CA, and Omaha, NE. No grants to individuals.
Application information: Unsolicited requests for funds not accepted.
Officers: Gary L. West, Co-Chair.; Mary E. West, Co-Chair.; Shelley M. Lyford, Pres.; Ginny Merrifield, Exec. Dir.; Roland J. Santoni, Mgr. Dir.
EIN: 470793015

1315
Western Asset Management Company Charitable Foundation ✧

385 E. Colorado Blvd.
Pasadena, CA 91101

Established in 2005 in CA.
Donors: Western Asset Management Co.; Legg Mason, Inc.
Foundation type: Company-sponsored foundation.
Financial data (yr. ended 03/31/14): Assets, $4,103,129 (M); gifts received, $25,799; expenditures, $1,202,621; qualifying distributions,

$1,202,161; giving activities include $1,187,101 for 411 grants (high: $50,000; low: $11).
Purpose and activities: The foundation supports organizations involved with arts and culture, education, health, water sports, and human services.
Fields of interest: Media, radio; Performing arts, orchestras; Arts; Higher education; Education; Hospitals (general); Health care, clinics/centers; Health care; Athletics/sports, water sports; American Red Cross; Children/youth, services; Children, foster care; Human services; Community/economic development; Religion.
Type of support: General/operating support.
Limitations: Applications not accepted. Giving primarily in CA. No grants to individuals.
Application information: Contributes only to pre-selected organizations.
Officers: James W. Hirschmann, Pres.; Bruce D. Alberts, C.F.O.
Directors: Tracy A. Hutson; Paul White.
EIN: 202589546
Selected grants: The following grants are a representative sample of this grantmaker's funding activity:
$30,000 to Pasadena Community Foundation, Pasadena, CA, 2011.
$30,000 to Pasadena Community Foundation, Pasadena, CA, 2011.
$25,000 to Los Angeles Chamber Orchestra Society, Los Angeles, CA, 2011.
$25,000 to UCLA Foundation, Los Angeles, CA, 2011.
$20,000 to AAF Rose Bowl Aquatics Center, Pasadena, CA, 2011.
$15,000 to Pasadena Hospital Association, Pasadena, CA, 2011.
$10,000 to Hillsides, Pasadena, CA, 2011.
$7,000 to Los Angeles Philharmonic Association, Los Angeles, CA, 2011.
$1,000 to Saint Mary Medical Center Foundation, Langhorne, PA, 2011.
$1,000 to San Marino Schools Foundation, San Marino, CA, 2011.

1316
Western Digital Foundation ✧
3355 Michelson Dr., Ste. 100
Irvine, CA 92612-5964
Contact: Rosemary Krupp, Dir.; Milissa Bedell, Mgr., Community Rels.
FAX: (949) 672-9676;
E-mail: Rosemary.Krupp@wdc.com; E-mail for Milissa Bedell: Milissa.bedell@wdc.com; Main URL: http://www.wdc.com/en/company/communityrelations/
Grants List: http://www.wdc.com/en/company/charitablegrantawards.asp

Established in 1997 in CA.
Donors: Western Digital Corp.; Texas Instruments Inc.; Western Digital Technologies, Inc.
Foundation type: Company-sponsored foundation.
Financial data (yr. ended 06/28/13): Assets, $264,927 (M); gifts received, $2,639,310; expenditures, $2,575,795; qualifying distributions, $2,575,795; giving activities include $2,568,905 for 151 grants (high: $300,000; low: $100).
Purpose and activities: The foundation supports organizations involved with education, the environment, disaster relief, human services, community development, science, civic affairs, economically disadvantaged people and veterans.
Fields of interest: Education, computer literacy/technology training; Education; Environment, natural resources; Environment; Disasters, preparedness/services; Family services; Community/economic development; United Ways and Federated Giving Programs; Mathematics; Engineering/technology; Computer science; Science; Military/veterans' organizations; Military/veterans; Economically disadvantaged.
Type of support: Employee volunteer services; Employee matching gifts; Donated products; In-kind gifts.
Limitations: Applications accepted. Giving limited to areas of company operations, with emphasis on Alameda, Orange, and Santa Clara, CA, Boulder County, CO, and Olmsted County, MN. No support for religious organization not of direct benefit to the entire community, sports teams, discriminatory organizations, grantmaking foundations, political organizations, hospitals, or museums. No grants to individuals, or for capital campaigns, athletic events, fundraising, conferences or seminars, research, scholarships or stipends, or start-up funds; no multi-year grants.
Publications: Application guidelines; Program policy statement.
Application information: Proposals should be submitted using organization letterhead. Requests for multi-year funding are not accepted. Support is limited to 1 contribution per organization during any given year. Video and audio submissions are not accepted. Application form required.
Initial approach: Complete online application
Copies of proposal: 1
Deadline(s): Jan. 15 and July 15
Board meeting date(s): Semi-annual
Final notification: 3 months
Officers: Michael D. Cordano; Jacqueline M. DeMana; Timothy M. Leyden; Stephen D. Miligan; Wolfgang Nickl.
Number of staff: 1 full-time professional; 1 part-time professional.
EIN: 330769372

1317
The Westreich Foundation ✧
c/o Stanley I. Westreich
P.O. Box 3601
Rancho Santa Fe, CA 92067-3601 (858) 735-0811
E-mail: ruthwestreich@cox.net; Main URL: http://www.thewestreichfoundation.org

Established in 2005 in DE.
Donor: Stanley I. Westreich.
Foundation type: Independent foundation.
Financial data (yr. ended 12/31/12): Assets, $10,551,186 (M); expenditures, $470,461; qualifying distributions, $469,940; giving activities include $469,940 for grants.
Purpose and activities: The focus of the foundation is education and literacy, women and children at risk, and optimum health wellness.
Fields of interest: Higher education; Health organizations; Human services.
Limitations: Applications not accepted. Giving primarily in La Jolla and San Diego, CA. No grants to individuals.
Application information: Contributes only to pre-selected organizations.
Officers: Ruth Westreich, Pres.; Lauren Westriech, 1st V.P.; Dana Westreich Hirt, 2nd V.P.; Anthony Westreich, Secy.; Stanley I. Westreich, Treas.
EIN: 203598096

1318
Barbara Wetzel Charitable Foundation ✧
P.O. Box 503825
San Diego, CA 92150-3825
Main URL: http://www.bwcft.org

Established in 2004 in CA.
Donor: Barbara A. Wetzel.
Foundation type: Independent foundation.
Financial data (yr. ended 12/31/13): Assets, $3,727,993 (M); expenditures, $732,416; qualifying distributions, $730,484; giving activities include $712,654 for 4 grants (high: $300,000; low: $29,470).
Purpose and activities: Giving to improve the lives of homeless or battered women and children.
Fields of interest: Food banks; Human services; Family services, domestic violence; Homeless, human services; Children/youth; Women; Crime/abuse victims; Homeless.
Limitations: Applications not accepted. Giving in the U.S., with emphasis on CA. No grants to individuals.
Application information: Contributes only to pre-selected organizations.
Trustees: Deborah Ng; Dan Sola; Richard Sola; Tamara Sola.
EIN: 766201712
Selected grants: The following grants are a representative sample of this grantmaker's funding activity:
$100,000 to Mercy Hospice, Philadelphia, PA, 2011.
$100,000 to Saint Annes Maternity Home, Los Angeles, CA, 2011.
$90,335 to Saint Marthas Hall, Saint Louis, MO, 2011.

1319
The Wheeler Foundation ✧
21031 Manessa Cir.
Huntington Beach, CA 92646-7414

Established in CA.
Donors: Park Water Co.; Henry H. Wheeler, Jr.
Foundation type: Independent foundation.
Financial data (yr. ended 12/31/13): Assets, $5,250,733 (M); expenditures, $640,480; qualifying distributions, $608,767; giving activities include $600,000 for 2 grants (high: $350,000; low: $250,000).
Fields of interest: Higher education.
Limitations: Applications not accepted. Giving primarily in CA.
Application information: Unsolicited requests for funds not accepted.
Trustees: David A. Ebershoff; Howard Fields, M.D., Ph.D.; Paul Licht, Ph.D.; Henry Hugh Wheeler III; Henry H. Wheeler, Jr.; Nyri Antia Wheeler.
EIN: 957106465

1320
WHH Foundation ✧
333 S. Hope St., 54th Fl.
Los Angeles, CA 90071-1406
Main URL: http://www.whh-foundation.org

Established in 2004 in CA.
Donors: William H. Hurt; Sarah S. Hurt.
Foundation type: Independent foundation.
Financial data (yr. ended 12/31/13): Assets, $16,952,092 (M); gifts received, $1,267,405; expenditures, $1,258,070; qualifying distributions, $1,106,487; giving activities include $1,000,266 for 125 grants (high: $84,375; low: $60).
Purpose and activities: Giving primarily for education, health, the arts, and community-building.
Fields of interest: Museums; Performing arts; Arts; Libraries (public); Education; Medical research; Human services; Children/youth, services.
Type of support: Matching/challenge support.
Limitations: Applications not accepted. Giving in the U.S., with emphasis on CA. No support for religious organizations. No grants to individuals.
Application information: Unsolicited requests for funds not accepted.
Officers and Directors:* Mark L. Purnell,* Chair.; Bernadette Glenn,* Pres.; William H. Hurt,* V.P.; Molly Purnell, Secy.; Kelley H. Purnell,* Treas.; Andrew F. Barth; J. Dale Harvey; Otis M. Healey; Kathleen C. Hurt; Sarah S. Hurt; Michael T. Kerr; Courtney D. MacMillan; Terrence A. MacMillan; Douglas S. Murray; Elizabeth Murray; Eve-Lynne G. Murray; James R. Murray; Katharine J. Purnell; Mary L. Purnell.
EIN: 200775264
Selected grants: The following grants are a representative sample of this grantmaker's funding activity:
$5,000 to Project POOCH, Lake Oswego, OR, 2012. For community/education/health.
$2,791 to Los Angeles Philharmonic, Los Angeles, CA, 2012. For arts/community.

1321
The Howard & Betty White Foundation ✧

131 Durazno
Portola Valley, CA 94028-7408

Established in 1990 in CA.
Donors: Betty D. White; Betty D. White Living Trust.
Foundation type: Independent foundation.
Financial data (yr. ended 06/30/13): Assets, $16,535,580 (M); gifts received, $245,000; expenditures, $1,102,808; qualifying distributions, $754,460; giving activities include $752,550 for 31 grants (high: $105,000; low: $4,000).
Purpose and activities: Giving primarily for youth and social services.
Fields of interest: Cancer; Human services; Youth, services; Christian agencies & churches.
Limitations: Applications not accepted. Giving primarily in CA. No grants to individuals.
Application information: Unsolicited requests for funds not accepted.
Officers: Eddie Dove, Pres.; Carolee White, Secy.; Mary M. McDowell, Treas.
EIN: 770250057
Selected grants: The following grants are a representative sample of this grantmaker's funding activity:
$25,000 to Charles Armstrong School, Belmont, CA, 2011. For general support.
$20,000 to CityTeam Ministries, San Jose, CA, 2011. For general support.
$15,000 to Mercy Ships, Garden Valley, TX, 2011. For general support.
$10,000 to Foundation for the Future, Atherton, CA, 2011. For general support.
$10,000 to Prison Fellowship Ministries, Lansdowne, VA, 2011. For general support.
$5,000 to Doctors Without Borders USA, New York, NY, 2011. For general support.

1322
The Whitman Institute

405 Davis Ct., Ste. 301
San Francisco, CA 94111-2405
The Whitman Institute's Philanthropy Promise: http://www.ncrp.org/philanthropys-promise/who

Established in CA; Classified as a private operating foundation in 1985.
Donor: Frederick C. Whitman.
Foundation type: Operating foundation.
Financial data (yr. ended 06/30/13): Assets, $12,546,314 (M); expenditures, $1,716,986; qualifying distributions, $1,605,590; giving activities include $1,279,000 for grants.
Fields of interest: Education; Human services; Leadership development.
Limitations: Applications not accepted. Giving primarily in CA. No grants to individuals.
Application information: Contributes only to pre-selected organizations.
Officers: John Esterle, Secy. and Exec. Dir.; C.J. Callen, Treas.
Directors: Dr. Les K. Adler; Jill Blair; Sue Ellen McCann.
EIN: 942984079
Selected grants: The following grants are a representative sample of this grantmaker's funding activity:
$75,000 to Active Voice, San Francisco, CA, 2011.
$55,000 to Tides Center, San Francisco, CA, 2011.
$50,000 to Mediators Foundation, Boulder, CO, 2011.
$50,000 to On The Move, Napa, CA, 2011.
$50,000 to Pacific News Service, San Francisco, CA, 2011.
$50,000 to Right Question Project, Cambridge, MA, 2011.
$50,000 to University of California, School of Law, Berkeley, CA, 2011.
$25,000 to Community Housing Partnership, San Francisco, CA, 2011.
$25,000 to PassageWorks Institute, Boulder, CO, 2011.
$25,000 to Western Justice Center Foundation, Pasadena, CA, 2011.

1323
L. K. Whittier Foundation ✧

(formerly Whittier Foundation)
625 S. Fair Oaks Ave., Ste. 360
South Pasadena, CA 91030-5813
Contact: Linda J. Blinkenberg, Secy.

Incorporated in 1955 in CA.
Donors: Leland K. Whittier†; and members of the Whittier family.
Foundation type: Independent foundation.
Financial data (yr. ended 04/30/13): Assets, $101,055,462 (M); expenditures, $9,599,398; qualifying distributions, $9,205,619; giving activities include $8,734,634 for 13 grants (high: $2,000,000; low: $5,000).
Purpose and activities: Emphasis on medical research; support also for youth agencies.
Fields of interest: Higher education; Education; Medical research, institute; Youth, services.
Type of support: Program development; Seed money; Research; Matching/challenge support.
Limitations: Applications not accepted. Giving primarily in southern CA, with emphasis on Los Angeles. No grants to individuals; no loans.
Application information: Contributes only to pre-selected organizations.
Board meeting date(s): Annually and as necessary
Officers and Directors:* Laura-Lee Whittier Woods, Pres.; James A. Jeffs,* V.P.; Linda J. Blinkenberg,* Secy.; Greg E. Custer,* C.F.O.; Laure W. Kastanis.
EIN: 956027493
Selected grants: The following grants are a representative sample of this grantmaker's funding activity:
$2,000,000 to Bennington College, Bennington, VT, 2013. For Peter Drucker Fund for Excellence and Innovation.
$2,000,000 to J. David Gladstone Institutes, San Francisco, CA, 2013. For stem cell research.
$1,019,634 to Childrens Hospital Los Angeles, Los Angeles, CA, 2013. For Whittier VPICU 2.0 Program (Virtual Pediatric Intensive Care Unit).
$1,000,000 to University of Southern California, Keck School of Medicine, Los Angeles, CA, 2013. For Nano-Biotechnology Research Initiative.
$1,000,000 to University of Southern California, Keck School of Medicine, Los Angeles, CA, 2013. To establish Whittier Health Sciences Innovatie Tailored Therapies Initiative in collaboration with Norris Comprehensive Cancer Center.
$1,000,000 to University of Southern California, Keck School of Medicine, Los Angeles, CA, 2013. For Whittier Health Sciences Innovatice Tailored Therapies Initiative in collaboration with Norris Comprehensive Cancer Center.
$200,000 to ICEF Public Schools, Los Angeles, CA, 2013. For challenge grant.
$100,000 to California State University, School of Nursing, Los Angeles, CA, 2013. For Bachelor of Science in Nursing (BSN) Program.
$50,000 to Stanford University, Stanford, CA, 2013. For research on links between Alzheimer and Lyme Diseases.

1324
Wilcox Family Foundation ✧

480 St. Francis Dr.
Danville, CA 94526-5410

Donors: Stephen Wilcox; Margaret Wilcox.
Foundation type: Independent foundation.
Financial data (yr. ended 12/31/13): Assets, $4,302,852 (M); expenditures, $497,581; qualifying distributions, $470,291; giving activities include $443,000 for 15 grants (high: $125,000; low: $10,000).
Fields of interest: Education; Housing/shelter; Human services.
Limitations: Applications not accepted.
Application information: Unsolicited requests for funds not accepted.
Officers: Stephen Wilcox, Pres.; Margaret Wilcox, Secy.; Daniel Wilcox, Treas.
Directors: Joseph Wilcox; Thomas Wilcox.
EIN: 800342340

1325
Ronald & Ann Williams Charitable Foundation ✧
1000 Fremont Ave., Ste. 210
Los Altos, CA 94024-6055

Established in 2001.
Donors: The Williams Family Trust; Palo Alto Town & Country Village, Inc.
Foundation type: Independent foundation.
Financial data (yr. ended 12/31/12): Assets, $43,834,472 (M); gifts received, $300,000; expenditures, $2,089,984; qualifying distributions, $1,854,320; giving activities include $1,808,711 for 18 grants (high: $250,000; low: $1,000).
Fields of interest: Hospitals (general); Health care; Health organizations; Human services.
Limitations: Applications not accepted. Giving primarily in CA. No grants to individuals.
Application information: Contributes only to pre-selected organizations.
Officers: Julian N. Stern, Pres. and C.E.O.; Richard Newton, V.P. and C.F.O.
Trustee: Roberto Rosenkranz.
EIN: 912154616

1326
Sara & Evan Williams Foundation ✧ ☆
2000 University Ave., Ste. 201
East Palo Alto, CA 94303

Donors: Sara Williams; Evan Williams.
Foundation type: Independent foundation.
Financial data (yr. ended 12/31/12): Assets, $19,078,339 (M); expenditures, $2,473,854; qualifying distributions, $2,047,934; giving activities include $2,047,934 for 30 grants (high: $500,000; low: $2,000).
Fields of interest: Higher education; Education; Human services.
Limitations: Applications not accepted. Giving primarily in CA.
Application information: Unsolicited requests for funds not accepted.
Officers and Director:* Sara Williams,* Pres.; Evan Williams, V.P. and Secy.-Treas.
EIN: 453437376

1327
Williams-Corbett Foundation ✧
c/o Northern Trust
P.O. Box 22107
Santa Barbara, CA 93121-2107

Established in 1997 in CA.
Donors: Annette W. Corbett; George Corbett; Corbett Charitable Lead Trust.
Foundation type: Independent foundation.
Financial data (yr. ended 12/31/13): Assets, $17,959,808 (M); gifts received, $848,314; expenditures, $1,150,798; qualifying distributions, $1,009,971; giving activities include $1,009,971 for 56 grants (high: $50,000; low: $4,000).
Fields of interest: Education; Health care; Human services; Children/youth, services.
Limitations: Applications not accepted. Giving primarily in Santa Barbara, CA.
Application information: Contributes only to pre-selected organizations.
Trustees: A. Carneros; A.J. Carneros.
EIN: 776150330

1328
Wilson Thornhill Foundation ✧
c/o Dreyer, Edmonds & Robbins
355 S. Grand Ave., No. 1710
Los Angeles, CA 90071-1532

Established in 1992 in CA.
Donor: Gary L. Wilson.
Foundation type: Independent foundation.
Financial data (yr. ended 12/31/12): Assets, $12,219,060 (M); expenditures, $534,856; qualifying distributions, $457,374; giving activities include $448,599 for 19 grants (high: $150,000; low: $441).
Purpose and activities: Giving primarily to an international affairs organization dedicated to the Millennium Development Goals; funding also for higher and other education, and for social services.
Fields of interest: Arts; Higher education; Education; Human services; Children/youth, services; International affairs, U.N..
Limitations: Applications not accepted. Giving in the U.S., with emphasis on NY, as well as CA and NC. No grants to individuals.
Application information: Contributes only to pre-selected organizations.
Trustees: Derek Wilson; Gary L. Wilson.
EIN: 954400754

1329
Windsong Trust ✧
838 Manhattan Beach Blvd.
Manhattan Beach, CA 90266-4933

Established in 2004 in CA.
Donor: Martin Crowley†.
Foundation type: Independent foundation.
Financial data (yr. ended 12/31/12): Assets, $514,287,015 (M); expenditures, $27,401,704; qualifying distributions, $25,127,401; giving activities include $23,625,990 for 66 grants (high: $2,000,000; low: $10,710).
Purpose and activities: Giving to support education of underprivileged children across the globe.
Fields of interest: Education; Children/youth.
Limitations: Applications not accepted. Giving in CA and NV.
Application information: Unsolicited requests for funds not accepted.
Trustees: Gigi Osco-Bingeman; Vadim Fridman.
EIN: 562461733

1330
The Jan and Mitsuko Wine and Art Educational Foundation ✧ ☆
c/o Educational Foundation
1060 Dunaweal Ln.
Calistoga, CA 94515-9798

Donor: Jan Shrem.
Foundation type: Independent foundation.
Financial data (yr. ended 12/31/13): Assets, $145,396 (M); expenditures, $509,693; qualifying distributions, $500,000; giving activities include $500,000 for 2 grants (high: $250,000; low: $250,000).
Fields of interest: Museums (art); Arts; Higher education; Education.
Limitations: Applications not accepted. Giving primarily in CA and NY.
Application information: Unsolicited requests for funds not accepted.
Officers: Jan Shrem, Pres.; Maria Shrem, C.F.O. and Secy.
EIN: 263119986

1331
Wings of Freedom Foundation ✧
c/o B. Higgins, Janet Joyce
5000 Birch St., Ste. 600
Newport Beach, CA 92660-2183

Donor: Betty Higgins.
Foundation type: Independent foundation.
Financial data (yr. ended 09/30/12): Assets, $19,411,883 (M); gifts received, $807,995; expenditures, $756,578; qualifying distributions, $610,840; giving activities include $580,000 for 5 grants (high: $200,000; low: $5,000).
Fields of interest: Arts; Education; Human services; Aging; Military/veterans.
Limitations: Applications not accepted. Giving primarily in CA.
Application information: Unsolicited requests for funds not accepted.
Trustees: Betty Higgins.
EIN: 271064974

1332
Winiarski Family Foundation ✧
P.O. Box 3327
Yountville, CA 94599-3327

Established in 2007 in CA.
Donors: Warren Winiarski; Barbara Winiarski.
Foundation type: Independent foundation.
Financial data (yr. ended 12/31/12): Assets, $18,224,922 (M); expenditures, $2,727,734; qualifying distributions, $2,571,900; giving activities include $2,571,900 for grants.
Fields of interest: Environment, land resources.
Limitations: Applications not accepted. Giving primarily in CA. No grants to individuals.
Application information: Contributes only to pre-selected organizations.
Officers: Warren Winiarski, Pres.; Barbara Winiarski, Secy. and Treas.
EIN: 260474242

1333
The Winnick Family Foundation ✧
(formerly The Gary and Karen Winnick Foundation)
9355 Wilshire Blvd., 4th Floor
Beverly Hills, CA 90210-5421 (310) 499-5330
Contact: Jay Rakow

Established in 1983 in MD.
Donors: Gary Winnick; Karen Winnick; Pacific Capital Group; GKW Unified Holdings, LLC.
Foundation type: Independent foundation.
Financial data (yr. ended 12/31/13): Assets, $141,052 (M); gifts received, $970,000; expenditures, $1,600,742; qualifying distributions, $838,637; giving activities include $828,418 for 135 grants (high: $200,000; low: $100).
Purpose and activities: Giving primarily for education, health organizations, Jewish organizations, and to a museum of modern art.
Fields of interest: Museums (art); Arts; Higher education; Education; Zoos/zoological societies;

Animals/wildlife; Health organizations, association; Jewish federated giving programs.
International interests: Israel.
Limitations: Applications accepted. Giving primarily in CA and NY. No support for political organizations. No grants to individuals.
Publications: Application guidelines.
Application information: Application form required.
Initial approach: 3-page proposal
Copies of proposal: 1
Deadline(s): None
Officers: Gary Winnick, Chair.; Karen Winnick, Pres.; Gregg W. Ritchie, C.F.O. and Secy.; Alex Winnick, V.P.
Board Member: Adam Winnick.
Number of staff: 1 part-time professional; 1 part-time support.
EIN: 953855792

1334
Witherbee Foundation ✧
528 Arizona Ave., Ste. 220
Santa Monica, CA 90401-1442

Established in 1996 in CA.
Donor: Victoria Witherbee.
Foundation type: Independent foundation.
Financial data (yr. ended 12/31/13): Assets, $13,180,968 (M); expenditures, $889,210; qualifying distributions, $870,199; giving activities include $833,460 for 26 grants (high: $100,000; low: $1,100).
Purpose and activities: Giving primarily for the arts, education, health care, and children, youth, and social services.
Fields of interest: Performing arts; Arts; Elementary/secondary education; Higher education; Education; Health care; Boys & girls clubs; Human services; Children/youth, services.
Limitations: Applications not accepted. Giving primarily in CA. No grants to individuals.
Application information: Contributes only to pre-selected organizations.
Officers and Director:* Robert Falls,* Pres.; Florita Ruskin, Secy.-Treas.
EIN: 954583560

1335
Dean Witter Foundation ✧
57 Post St., Ste. 510
San Francisco, CA 94104-5020 (415) 981-2966
Contact: Kenneth J. Blum, Administrative Dir.
FAX: (415) 981-5218;
E-mail: admin@deanwitterfoundation.org; Main URL: http://www.deanwitterfoundation.org

Incorporated in 1952 in CA.
Donors: Dean Witter†; Mrs. Dean Witter; Dean Witter & Co.
Foundation type: Independent foundation.
Financial data (yr. ended 06/30/13): Assets, $19,117,353 (M); expenditures, $1,110,496; qualifying distributions, $947,696; giving activities include $822,000 for 40 grants (high: $50,000; low: $5,000).
Purpose and activities: Giving primarily to support specific wildlife conservation projects in Northern California, and seminal opportunities to improve and extend environmental education and to stimulate learning. Funding also to launch and expand innovative K-12 public education initiatives.
Fields of interest: Elementary/secondary education; Environment, natural resources; Animals/wildlife.
Type of support: Equipment; Program development; Publication; Seed money; Research.
Limitations: Applications accepted. Giving for conservation projects limited to northern CA. No support for religious organizations. No grants to individuals, or for endowment funds, scholarships, capital campaigns, opportunity deficits, and fundraising events; no loans.
Publications: Application guidelines; Grants list.
Application information: Application guidelines available on foundation web site. Application form not required.
Initial approach: Applicants are encouraged to telephone or write to the foundation's consultant to determine whether their proposed program falls within the foundation's areas of interest and grantmaking priorities
Copies of proposal: 1
Deadline(s): None
Board meeting date(s): Jan., Apr., July, and Oct.
Officers and Trustees:* Dean Witter III,* Pres.; Stephen Nessier,* V.P. and C.F.O.; Roland Tognazzini, Jr., Secy.; Deanne Gillette Violich; Malcolm G. Witter; William P. Witter.
EIN: 946065150
Selected grants: The following grants are a representative sample of this grantmaker's funding activity:
$40,000 to Environmental Traveling Companions, San Francisco, CA, 2013. For the salary of the Associate Director and the Make a Ripple Fundraiser (Matching grant).
$25,000 to IslandWood, Bainbridge Island, WA, 2013. For the Graduate Program in Education, Environment, and Community (Matching grant).
$25,000 to Pie Ranch, Pescadero, CA, 2013. For the Community-Supported Agriculture Program (Matching grant).
$25,000 to Rising Sun Energy Center, Berkeley, CA, 2013. For the California Youth Energy Services Program.
$25,000 to Sempervirens Fund, Los Altos, CA, 2013. For the Major Gifts Program (Matching grant).
$25,000 to Stanford University, School of Education, Stanford, CA, 2013. For the Principal Fellows Program.
$20,000 to Community Alliance for Learning, Albany, CA, 2013. For the WriterCoach Connection at El Cerrito High School.
$20,000 to Earned Assets Resource Network, San Francisco, CA, 2013. For discretionary use by the President.
$20,000 to KIDS for the BAY, Berkeley, CA, 2013. For the Urban Wilderness Program and Anniversary Campaign (Matching grant).
$15,000 to Community Resources for Science, Berkeley, CA, 2013. For science and environmental education resources (Matching grant).

1336
Mary Wohlford Foundation ✧
c/o Margaretta Kildebeck and Jude Damasco
700 Monte Vista Ln.
Half Moon Bay, CA 94019-2179

Established in 1999 in CA.
Donor: Mary M. Wohlford†.
Foundation type: Independent foundation.
Financial data (yr. ended 06/30/13): Assets, $20,599,129 (M); expenditures, $1,739,090; qualifying distributions, $1,589,512; giving activities include $1,589,512 for 68 grants (high: $105,000; low: $500).
Purpose and activities: Giving primarily to support reproductive health, education, and rights.
Fields of interest: Education; Reproductive health; Reproductive health, family planning; Health organizations, association; Human services; Civil liberties, reproductive rights; Foundations (private grantmaking); Women.
Type of support: General/operating support; Management development/capacity building; Building/renovation; Emergency funds; Program development; Conferences/seminars; Professorships; Film/video/radio; Seed money; Curriculum development; Internship funds; Research; Technical assistance; Consulting services; Program evaluation.
Limitations: Applications not accepted. Giving primarily in CA. No grants to individuals.
Application information: Contributes only to pre-selected organizations.
Trustees: Jude Damasco; Margaretta Kildebeck.
EIN: 943318493

1337
Randall A. Wolf Family Foundation ✧
41450 Boscell Rd.
Fremont, CA 94538-3103
Contact: Randall A. Wolf, Dir.

Established in 1997 in CA.
Donor: Randall A. Wolf.
Foundation type: Independent foundation.
Financial data (yr. ended 12/31/13): Assets, $15,612,022 (M); gifts received, $3,000,000; expenditures, $618,107; qualifying distributions, $581,350; giving activities include $581,350 for 33 grants (high: $225,000; low: $350).
Fields of interest: Higher education; Education; Food services; Children/youth, services; Human services; Community/economic development; Foundations (community).
Limitations: Applications accepted. Giving primarily in CA. No grants to individuals.
Application information: Generally contributes to pre-selected organizations. Application form not required.
Initial approach: Proposal
Deadline(s): None
Officers: Annetta Calhoun, Secy.; Christopher Wolf, Treas.
Director: Randall A. Wolf.
EIN: 946719570
Selected grants: The following grants are a representative sample of this grantmaker's funding activity:
$245,000 to Community Foundation for San Benito County, Hollister, CA, 2012. For Donation to fund which makes grants to various community charitable organizations.
$90,000 to Eastside College Preparatory School, East Palo Alto, CA, 2012. For Donation to Private school dedicated to improving education of children in impoverished area.
$50,000 to Community Food Bank of San Benito County, Hollister, CA, 2012. For Donation to fund for Programs providing food to people in need.
$25,000 to Bellarmine College Preparatory, San Jose, CA, 2012. For Donation to general Programs of the school.

$5,000 to Reading Partners, Oakland, CA, 2012. For Donation to reading tutoring Program in low income school areas.

1338
Wolfen Family Foundation ✧
c/o Irell & Manella, LLP
1800 Ave. of the Stars, Ste. 900
Los Angeles, CA 90067-4276

Established in 1999 in CA.
Donors: Werner F. Wolfen; Mary G. Wolfen.
Foundation type: Independent foundation.
Financial data (yr. ended 12/31/13): Assets, $1,395,420 (M); gifts received, $192,935; expenditures, $720,008; qualifying distributions, $699,614; giving activities include $699,614 for 65 grants (high: $200,000; low: $75).
Purpose and activities: Giving primarily for health care, particularly to a cancer center that provides research and patient care activities, including clinical trials and new cancer therapies; funding also for higher education, the arts, Jewish organizations, and children, youth, and social services.
Fields of interest: Arts; Higher education; Health care; Cancer; Human services; Children/youth, services; Jewish federated giving programs; Jewish agencies & synagogues.
Limitations: Applications not accepted. Giving primarily in CA. No grants to individuals.
Application information: Unsolicited requests for funds not accepted.
Trustees: Mary G. Wolfen; Werner F. Wolfen.
EIN: 954745065

1339
Wollenberg Foundation ✧
800 El Camino Real, Ste. 210
Menlo Park, CA 94025-4875

Trust established in 1952 in CA.
Donor: H.L. Wollenberg†.
Foundation type: Independent foundation.
Financial data (yr. ended 12/31/12): Assets, $44,582,320 (M); gifts received, $407,682; expenditures, $2,723,015; qualifying distributions, $2,339,620; giving activities include $2,330,620 for 74 grants (high: $500,000; low: $1,000).
Purpose and activities: Giving primarily for higher education; funding also for the arts.
Fields of interest: Arts; Higher education; Medical school/education.
Type of support: General/operating support; Endowments; Program development.
Limitations: Applications not accepted. Giving primarily in CA, the Washington, DC metropolitan area, OR, and WA. No support for sectarian or political purposes. No grants to individuals; no loans.
Application information: Contributes only to pre-selected organizations.
Trustees: Christopher Wollenberg; David A. Wollenberg; Richard H. Wollenberg.
EIN: 946072264

1340
Womens Self Worth Foundation ✧
10100 Santa Monica Blvd., Ste. 2600
Los Angeles, CA 90067-4000 (310) 557-5100
Contact: Alex De Ocampo
E-mail: selfworthcs@gmail.com; Main URL: http://www.whatisyourselfworth.com/foundation/

Established in CA.
Donors: Cheryl Saban; Haim Saban.
Foundation type: Independent foundation.
Financial data (yr. ended 12/31/12): Assets, $12,586 (M); gifts received, $500,000; expenditures, $580,282; qualifying distributions, $579,852; giving activities include $556,833 for 4 grants (high: $250,000; low: $48,500).
Purpose and activities: Giving primarily to organizations that work towards the empowerment and advancement of women.
Fields of interest: Education; Human services; Women.
Limitations: Applications accepted. Giving in the U.S., with emphasis on CA and NY. No grants to individuals, or for lobbying, start-up costs, seed money, fundraising drives, or capital costs, including equipment or real estate purchases and renovations.
Publications: Application guidelines.
Application information: Organizations must have been in existence for 3 years at the time of application. Application form required.
Initial approach: Proposal via e-mail
Deadline(s): None
Officers: Cheryl Saban, Pres.; Adam Chesnoff, V.P.; Haim Saban, V.P.; Niveen Tadros, Secy.; Fred Gluckman, Treas.
EIN: 264200302
Selected grants: The following grants are a representative sample of this grantmaker's funding activity:
$175,000 to Girls Incorporated, New York, NY, 2012. To Fund 240 Girls Over Four Years in the Eureka! Mentorship Program.
$83,333 to Cedars-Sinai Medical Center, Los Angeles, CA, 2012. For funding for Researching Female-Pattern Heart Disease and Developing New Diagnostic Tools and Specialized Care for Women.

1341
Dsea Wong Foundation ✧
88 Kearny St., Ste. 1818
San Francisco, CA 94108-5523

Established in 2007 in CA.
Foundation type: Independent foundation.
Financial data (yr. ended 09/30/13): Assets, $3,206,663 (M); expenditures, $2,048,016; qualifying distributions, $2,010,174; giving activities include $2,010,174 for 24 grants (high: $500,000; low: $1,000).
Fields of interest: Elementary/secondary education; Higher education; Human services.
Limitations: Applications not accepted. Giving primarily in CA and MA.
Application information: Unsolicited requests for funds not accepted.
Officers: Dennis Jason Wong, Pres. and Treas.; Shannon Elizabeth Wong, V.P. and Secy.
EIN: 260387265
Selected grants: The following grants are a representative sample of this grantmaker's funding activity:
$50,000 to Nueva School, Hillsborough, CA, 2011.
$35,000 to Nueva School, Hillsborough, CA, 2011.
$33,950 to Nueva School, Hillsborough, CA, 2011.
$32,500 to Nueva School, Hillsborough, CA, 2011.
$24,475 to San Francisco Museum of Modern Art, San Francisco, CA, 2011.
$10,000 to SYDA Foundation, South Fallsburg, NY, 2011.
$6,750 to San Francisco Museum of Modern Art, San Francisco, CA, 2011.
$5,250 to All Stars Helping Kids, Redwood City, CA, 2011.
$5,000 to Homeless Prenatal Program, San Francisco, CA, 2011.
$5,000 to Tenderloin Neighborhood Development Corporation, San Francisco, CA, 2011.

1342
I. S. Wong Foundation ✧
P.O. Box 80121
San Marino, CA 91118-8121

Established in 1989 in CA.
Donors: Ellen H. Sam; Wah-Pui Sam; Dr. Hing-Lan Ho.
Foundation type: Independent foundation.
Financial data (yr. ended 12/31/13): Assets, $12,857,556 (M); expenditures, $1,000,734; qualifying distributions, $912,266; giving activities include $906,740 for 22 grants (high: $250,000; low: $3,000).
Fields of interest: Disasters, preparedness/services; Human services; International affairs; Christian agencies & churches.
Type of support: General/operating support.
Limitations: Applications not accepted. Giving in the U.S., with some emphasis on CA and Washington, DC; some funding also in Singapore. No grants to individuals.
Application information: Contributes only to pre-selected organizations.
Officers: Wah-Pui Sam, Pres.; Ellen H. Sam, Secy.
EIN: 954194427
Selected grants: The following grants are a representative sample of this grantmaker's funding activity:
$30,000 to World Concern, Seattle, WA, 2012. For Famine Relief - Africa.
$5,000 to Give2Asia, San Francisco, CA, 2012. For Center for Prison Children.

1343
The William Brown & Paul Wonner Foundation ✧
250 Oak Grove, Ste. A
Menlo PArk, CA 94025-2251

Foundation type: Independent foundation.
Financial data (yr. ended 12/31/12): Assets, $0 (M); gifts received, $108,009; expenditures, $968,493; qualifying distributions, $964,493; giving activities include $919,512 for 2 grants (high: $798,932; low: $120,580).
Fields of interest: Arts; Foundations (community).
Limitations: Applications not accepted. Giving primarily in CA.
Application information: Unsolicited requests for funds not accepted.
Trustee: Robert Levenson.
EIN: 264010221

1344
Wood-Claeyssens Foundation ✧
P.O. Box 30586
Santa Barbara, CA 93130-0586
Contact: Noelle Claeyssens Burkey, Pres.

FAX: (805) 966-1415; E-mail: wcf0543@gmail.com; Main URL: http://www.woodclaeyssensfoundation.com/

Established in 1980 in CA.
Donors: Ailene B. Claeyssens†; Pierre P. Claeyssens†; Cynthia Wood†; Claeyssens Charitable Trust.
Foundation type: Independent foundation.
Financial data (yr. ended 03/31/12): Assets, $130,422,272 (M); gifts received, $223,000; expenditures, $33,949,914; qualifying distributions, $23,602,480; giving activities include $22,684,379 for 342 grants (high: $1,750,000; low: $1,000; average: $10,000–$100,000).
Purpose and activities: Grant support primarily for education, housing, and youth; support also for health care and the arts.
Fields of interest: Performing arts, theater; Performing arts, music; Health care; Mental health/crisis services; Health organizations, association; Human services; Children/youth, services; Family services; Aging; Disabilities, people with.
Type of support: Annual campaigns; Building/renovation; Capital campaigns; Continuing support; Equipment; General/operating support.
Limitations: Applications accepted. Giving limited to Santa Barbara and Ventura counties, CA. No support for tax-supported educational institutions, government-funded organizations, religious or political organizations, or for medical research. No grants to individuals.
Application information: New applicants must create a new account to submit an online letter of intent. Returning applicants must use their login information to apply online. For more information see foundation web site. Application form required.
Initial approach: Online
Deadline(s): June 30
Board meeting date(s): As needed
Officers and Directors:* Noelle Claeyssens Burkey,* Pres. and Genl. Mgr.; Brett L. Burkey,* Vice-Pres.; Jenna M. Burkey, 2nd V.P.; Shelby Hughes, Secy.; Charles C. Gray, Treas.; J. Brad Burkey; James Burkey; Jared P. Burkey.
Number of staff: 1 full-time professional; 2 full-time support.
EIN: 953514017
Selected grants: The following grants are a representative sample of this grantmaker's funding activity:
$1,750,000 to Saint Johns Healthcare Foundation, Oxnard, CA, 2012. For program support.
$1,000,000 to Santa Barbara Bowl Foundation, Santa Barbara, CA, 2012. For program support.
$764,301 to Santa Maria Fairpark, Santa Maria, CA, 2012. For program support.
$500,000 to Casa Pacifica Centers for Children and Families, Casa Pacifica Centers for Children and Families, Camarillo, CA, 2012. For program support.
$350,000 to Project: Rescue Flight, Santa Barbara, CA, 2012. For program support.
$300,000 to Santa Barbara Foundation, Santa Barbara, CA, 2012. For program support for Thrive Santa Barbara County, public-private collaboration focused on funding to prepare students in Santa Barbara County to be productive and responsible adults by improving school readiness, college readiness and college completion.
$200,000 to Painted Cave Volunteer Fire Department, Santa Barbara, CA, 2012. For program support.
$50,000 to Adventures in Caring Foundation, Santa Barbara, CA, 2012. For program support.
$25,000 to Community Arts Music Association of Santa Barbara, Santa Barbara, CA, 2012. For program support.
$25,000 to YMCA, Miller Family, Newbury Park, CA, 2012. For program support.

1345
The Paul and Betty Woolls Foundation ✧
(formerly O'Shaughnessy Foundation)
P.O. Box 923
Angwin, CA 94508-6023 (707) 944-2235
Contact: Betty O'Shaughnessy Woolls, Pres.

Established in 1997 in MN.
Donor: Betty L. O'Shaughnessy.
Foundation type: Independent foundation.
Financial data (yr. ended 10/31/13): Assets, $1,620,862 (M); expenditures, $462,014; qualifying distributions, $449,431; giving activities include $449,431 for 4 grants (high: $125,000; low: $100,000).
Fields of interest: Education; Health care; Philanthropy/voluntarism.
Limitations: Applications accepted. Giving primarily in CA; some giving also in IN and MN. No grants to individuals.
Publications: Application guidelines; Annual report; Financial statement; Grants list.
Application information: Application form required.
Initial approach: Written proposal
Copies of proposal: 1
Deadline(s): June 1
Board meeting date(s): Sept.
Final notification: Nov. 1
Officer: Betty O'Shaughnessy Woolls, Pres.
Directors: Linda Bagaason; Susan O'Shaughnessy; Dr. Dan Peters; Jack Thomas.
Number of staff: None.
EIN: 411859964
Selected grants: The following grants are a representative sample of this grantmaker's funding activity:
$75,000 to Wabash College, Crawfordsville, IN, 2011.
$10,000 to Community Health Clinic Ole, Napa, CA, 2011.

1346
World Children's Fund ✧
5442 Thornwood Dr., Ste. 250
San Jose, CA 95123-1207 (408) 363-8100
Contact: Ruth Kendrick
FAX: (408) 629-4846; E-mail: info@wcf-intl.org; Main URL: http://www.worldchildrensfund.org

Established in 1984 in CA.
Donors: Universal Aide Society; World Childrens Fund-Europe (CH); World Harvest Church; Window to Asia.
Foundation type: Operating foundation.
Financial data (yr. ended 03/31/13): Assets, $511,365 (M); gifts received, $4,821,224; expenditures, $4,769,616; qualifying distributions, $3,662,163; giving activities include $3,208,030 for 23 grants (high: $3,000,042; low: $50), and $3,735,052 for foundation-administered programs.
Purpose and activities: Giving for aid to needy, suffering children in crisis situations worldwide.
Fields of interest: Children/youth, services; International relief.
Type of support: In-kind gifts.
Limitations: Applications accepted. Giving on an international basis. No grants to individuals.
Publications: Annual report; Financial statement.
Application information:
Initial approach: Proposal
Deadline(s): None
Officers and Directors:* Joseph Lam,* C.E.O. and Pres.; Ruth Kendrick,* V.P.; Paul Chiar, Secy.; Stanley Chen,* Treas.; Douglas Kendrick, C.F.O.; Anne Chiang, Cont.; Bruce Barnes.
EIN: 770210616
Selected grants: The following grants are a representative sample of this grantmaker's funding activity:
$3,000,042 to Nyumbani Children of God Relief Fund, Nyumbani House, Children of God Relief Institute, Nairobi, Kenya, 2013. For program support.
$1,359,543 to Saint Michaels Mission Hospital, Mhondoro, Zimbabwe, 2012. For general support.
$94,333 to Nora Lam Chinese Ministries International, San Jose, CA, 2013. For program support.
$38,249 to Missao Medica Internacional, Sao Paulo, Brazil, 2013. For program support.
$22,422 to Gandhi World Hunger Fund, Hempstead, England, 2013. For program support.
$18,763 to Gandhi Welthungerhilfswerk, Berlin, Germany, 2012. For general support.
$18,014 to Gandhi Welthungerhilfswerk, Berlin, Germany, 2013. For program support.
$17,907 to Nora Lam Chinese Ministries International, San Jose, CA, 2012. For general support.
$17,564 to Medical Mission International USA, San Jose, CA, 2013. For program support.
$15,854 to Gandhi World Hunger Fund, Hempstead, England, 2012. For general support.
$15,500 to Community Network, Tuscaloosa, AL, 2012. For general support.
$14,061 to Slovak-Czech Women's Fund, Bratislava, Slovakia, 2012. For general support.
$13,000 to Stichting Gandhi World Hunger Fund, Amsterdam, Netherlands, 2012. For general support.

1347
Susan & Bruce Worster Foundation ✧ ☆
11271 Magdalena Rd.
Los Altos Hills, CA 94024

Established in 2000 in CA.
Donors: Bruce Worster; Susan Worster.
Foundation type: Independent foundation.
Financial data (yr. ended 12/31/13): Assets, $6,183,177 (M); expenditures, $490,639; qualifying distributions, $429,993; giving activities include $425,000 for 4 grants (high: $275,000; low: $25,000).
Fields of interest: Higher education; United Ways and Federated Giving Programs.
Limitations: Applications not accepted. Giving primarily in CA. No grants to individuals.
Application information: Contributes only to pre-selected organizations.
Officers: Bruce Worster, Pres.; Susan Worster, Secy.
EIN: 770549392
Selected grants: The following grants are a representative sample of this grantmaker's funding activity:
$185,000 to Harvey Mudd College, Claremont, CA, 2011. For general use.

$75,000 to University of California, Oakland, CA, 2010. For general use.
$75,000 to University of California, Oakland, CA, 2011. For general use.
$25,000 to University of California at Santa Barbara Foundation, Santa Barbara, CA, 2011. For general use.
$5,000 to Direct Relief International, Santa Barbara, CA, 2011. For general use.
$2,500 to Math for America, New York, NY, 2011. For general use.
$1,000 to Occidental College, Los Angeles, CA, 2011. For general use.
$1,000 to Santa Clara University, Santa Clara, CA, 2011. For general use.
$1,000 to United Way Silicon Valley, San Jose, CA, 2011. For general use.
$1,000 to Wellesley College, Wellesley, MA, 2011. For general use.

1348
The Wunderkinder Foundation ✧
(formerly Max Charitable Foundation)
c/o Breslauer, Rutman & Anderson, LLC
11400 W. Olympic Blvd., Ste. 550
Los Angeles, CA 90064-1551 (310) 481-3513

Established in 1985 in CA.
Donors: Steven A. Spielberg; Amblin Entertainment, Inc.
Foundation type: Independent foundation.
Financial data (yr. ended 11/30/13): Assets, $4,285,881 (M); gifts received, $271,258; expenditures, $8,042,707; qualifying distributions, $7,527,834; giving activities include $7,527,834 for 93 grants (high: $1,900,000; low: $1,000).
Purpose and activities: Giving primarily to the arts, education, war memorials and veterans' organizations, and Jewish organizations; giving also for human services, with an emphasis on children and medical research.
Fields of interest: Historical activities, war memorials; Arts; Education; Environment, natural resources; Health organizations, association; Youth development; Children/youth, services; Military/veterans' organizations; Jewish agencies & synagogues; Native Americans/American Indians; LGBTQ.
Limitations: Applications not accepted. Giving primarily in CA and NY. No grants to individuals.
Application information: Contributes only to pre-selected organizations.
Officers and Directors:* Gerald Breslauer,* Pres.; Tammy Anderson, Secy.; Michael Rutman,* C.F.O.; Kristie Macosko Krieger.
EIN: 954016320
Selected grants: The following grants are a representative sample of this grantmaker's funding activity:
$2,010,000 to Cedars-Sinai Medical Center, Los Angeles, CA, 2012. For medical research.
$1,900,000 to Righteous Persons Foundation, Santa Monica, CA, 2012.
$1,000,000 to Campbell Hall, North Hollywood, CA, 2012.
$400,000 to Yale University, School of Medicine, New Haven, CT, 2012.
$250,000 to Pomona College, Claremont, CA, 2012.
$150,000 to Los Angeles Museum of the Holocaust Martyrs Memorial, Los Angeles, CA, 2012. For Holocaust Studies Program.
$100,000 to Planned Parenthood Los Angeles, Los Angeles, CA, 2012.
$50,000 to UCLA Foundation, Los Angeles, CA, 2012.
$25,000 to International Medical Corps, Los Angeles, CA, 2012.
$25,000 to Museum of Jewish Heritage, New York, NY, 2012.

1349
WWW Foundation ✧
625 S. Fair Oaks Ave., Ste. 360
South Pasadena, CA 91030-2630

Established in 1983 in CA.
Donors: Helen W. Woodward†; Winifred W. Rhodes; Helen Woodward Charitable Lead Trust.
Foundation type: Independent foundation.
Financial data (yr. ended 12/31/13): Assets, $67,932,642 (M); expenditures, $2,867,430; qualifying distributions, $2,500,669; giving activities include $2,325,830 for 130 grants (high: $450,000; low: $500).
Purpose and activities: Giving primarily for an animal care center; support also for boys and girls clubs, hospitals, civic affairs, and the arts.
Fields of interest: Education; Animal welfare; Hospitals (general); Medical research, institute; Boys & girls clubs; Human services; Children/youth, services.
Type of support: General/operating support; Equipment; Program development; Research; Matching/challenge support.
Limitations: Applications not accepted. Giving primarily in southern CA. No grants to individuals; no loans.
Application information: Unsolicited requests for funds are not accepted. The foundation prefers to initiate grants.
Board meeting date(s): As needed, 2 times a year
Officers: Sharon H. Bradford, Pres.; David A. Dahl, C.F.O.; Bryce W. Rhodes, V.P.; Winifred W. Rhodes, V.P.; Pegine E. Grayson, Secy.
Directors: Linda J. Blinkenberg; Michael J. Casey; Marcia W. Constance; Brett E. Hodges; Brian M. Hodges; Adam J. Rhodes; Emery W. Rhodes; Arlo G. Sorensen.
EIN: 953694741

1350
Carl E. Wynn Foundation ✧
444 S. Flower St., Ste. 1700
Los Angeles, CA 90071-2901 (877) 686-9215
Contact: William R. Christian, Pres.

Established in 1966.
Donors: Bee Wynn†; Carl Wynn†.
Foundation type: Independent foundation.
Financial data (yr. ended 12/31/13): Assets, $27,832,564 (M); expenditures, $1,499,799; qualifying distributions, $1,265,710; giving activities include $1,108,878 for 170 grants (high: $121,128; low: $1,000).
Purpose and activities: Giving primarily for the welfare of children, families, and the disabled.
Fields of interest: Elementary/secondary education; Higher education; Education; Environmental education; Hospitals (general); Medical research, institute; Human services; Children/youth, services; Family services; Disabilities, people with; Economically disadvantaged; Homeless.
Limitations: Applications accepted. Giving primarily in Los Angeles County, San Gabriel Valley, and Orange County, CA.
Application information: Application form required.
Initial approach: Proposal
Copies of proposal: 1
Deadline(s): Between May 1-15
Officers and Trustees:* William R. Christian,* Pres.; Billie A. Fischer,* V.P.; Jaki Fischer,* V.P.; Mel Masuda, V.P.; Dorothy L. Frey,* Secy.-Treas.
EIN: 956136231
Selected grants: The following grants are a representative sample of this grantmaker's funding activity:
$80,000 to Peppermint Ridge, Corona, CA, 2012. For Residential Programs for developmentally disabled and support for Wynn Home.
$15,000 to Children of the Night, Van Nuys, CA, 2012. For help for child prostitution.
$7,000 to International Guiding Eyes, Sylmar, CA, 2012. To Provide guide dogs to blind individuals 16 yrs. of age and older free of charge.
$5,000 to Angels Charity, Newport Beach, CA, 2012. To enhance the physical, emotional and social development of children with special needs.
$5,000 to Foothill Unity Center, Monrovia, CA, 2012. For food distribution to the needy and hungry.
$3,000 to Glendale Association for the Retarded, Glendale, CA, 2012. For Programs for developmentally disabled adults.
$3,000 to Safe Alternatives for Everyone, Temecula, CA, 2012. For Services for individuals who have experiences or are at risk of abuse.
$2,000 to Laurel House, Tustin, CA, 2012. To support teens in crisis.
$2,000 to Operation Safe House, Riverside, CA, 2012. For programs for abused children.
$1,000 to Valley Village, Winnetka, CA, 2012. To protect foster and advance the rights and interests of people with developmental disabilities.

1351
Xie Foundation ✧
325 Sharon Park Dr., Ste. 802
Menlo Park, CA 94025-1003

Donors: Xie Children's Irrevocable Trust; Xie Ken; Michael Xie; Danke Wu; Ken Xie; Bing Xie; Yuyi Wu.
Foundation type: Independent foundation.
Financial data (yr. ended 12/31/13): Assets, $16,299,570 (M); gifts received, $1,261,500; expenditures, $1,055,284; qualifying distributions, $992,060; giving activities include $992,060 for 9 grants (high: $330,000; low: $2,000).
Fields of interest: Education; Youth development; Human services.
Limitations: Applications not accepted. Giving primarily in CA.
Application information: Unsolicited requests for funds not accepted.
Officers and Directors:* Ken Xie,* Co-Pres. and Secy.; Michael Xie,* Co-Pres.; Yuyi Wu,* V.P.; Bing Xie,* V.P.
EIN: 271208110

1352
J. Yang & Family Foundation ✧
19401 S. Harborgate Way
Torrance, CA 90501-1322

Established in 2006.
Foundation type: Independent foundation.
Financial data (yr. ended 12/31/13): Assets, $20,597,403 (M); gifts received, $2,000,000; expenditures, $777,142; qualifying distributions, $764,041; giving activities include $583,950 for 25 grants (high: $100,000; low: $500).
Fields of interest: Health organizations; Buddhism.
Limitations: Applications not accepted. Giving primarily in CA. No grants to individuals.
Application information: Unsolicited requests for funds not accepted.
Officers: Jennifer Yang, Chair.; Jackson Yang, Pres. and C.E.O.; Julie Yang, V.P.; Peter Yang, Treas.
Directors: Frank Yang; Jimmy Yang; Linda Yang.
EIN: 562628813
Selected grants: The following grants are a representative sample of this grantmaker's funding activity:
$50,000 to Formosa Foundation, Los Angeles, CA, 2012. For Student Ambassador Program.
$2,000 to Los Angeles Mission, Los Angeles, CA, 2012. To help homeless people.

1353
Yang Family Foundation ✧
3000 Sand Hill Rd., Bldg. 2, Ste. 290
Menlo Park, CA 94025

Donors: Geoffrey Yang; Amy Yang.
Foundation type: Independent foundation.
Financial data (yr. ended 12/31/12): Assets, $1,785,708 (M); gifts received, $290,675; expenditures, $592,730; qualifying distributions, $570,000; giving activities include $570,000 for 6 grants (high: $202,500; low: $5,000).
Fields of interest: Education; Health organizations; Recreation.
Limitations: Applications not accepted.
Application information: Unsolicited requests for funds not accepted.
Trustees: Amy Yang; Geoffrey Yang.
EIN: 274068845
Selected grants: The following grants are a representative sample of this grantmaker's funding activity:
$202,500 to Menlo School, Atherton, CA, 2012. For The Help Fund New Facilities and Support Education.
$100,000 to Masters Tournament Foundation, Augusta, GA, 2012. To Help Identify, Invest In, and Promote Development of Golf.

1354
Yellow Chair Foundation ✧
c/o Pacific Foundation Services, LLC
1660 Bush St., Ste. 300
San Francisco, CA 94109-5308 (415) 561-6540
Contact: Charles Casey; Katarina Merotti
FAX: (415) 561-6477; E-mail: CCasey@pfs-llc.net

Established in 2000 in CA.
Donor: David Filo.
Foundation type: Independent foundation.
Financial data (yr. ended 12/31/13): Assets, $227,554,208 (M); gifts received, $9,745,500; expenditures, $11,076,343; qualifying distributions, $9,352,311; giving activities include $9,128,530 for 44 grants (high: $1,330,000; low: $1,000).
Purpose and activities: Giving primarily for higher education.
Fields of interest: Higher education, college; Civil/human rights; Philanthropy/voluntarism; Children/youth; Youth; Young adults; Economically disadvantaged.
Type of support: General/operating support.
Limitations: Applications not accepted. No grants to individuals.
Application information: Contributes only to pre-selected organizations.
Officers and Director:* David Filo,* Pres.; Angela Filo, Secy.-Treas.
EIN: 943380194
Selected grants: The following grants are a representative sample of this grantmaker's funding activity:
$5,387,000 to Stanford University, Stanford, CA, 2012. For Interdisciplinary Graduate Fellowship Fund.
$1,250,000 to American Civil Liberties Union Foundation of Northern California, San Francisco, CA, 2012. For general support.
$650,000 to Environmental Defense Fund, New York, NY, 2012. For general support.
$150,000 to New Teacher Center, Santa Cruz, CA, 2012. For general support.
$125,000 to University of California at Berkeley Foundation, School of Journalism, Berkeley, CA, 2012. For general support.
$40,000 to Stanford Schools Corporation, Stanford New Schools, Menlo Park, CA, 2012. For general support.
$35,000 to DonorsChoose.org, New York, NY, 2012. For high school newspapers.
$25,000 to 826 National, San Francisco, CA, 2012. For general support.
$25,000 to Eastside College Preparatory School, East Palo Alto, CA, 2012. For general operating support.
$10,000 to Canopy, Palo Alto, CA, 2012. For general support.

1355
Walter J. & Betty C. Zable Foundation ✧
1660 Hotel Cir. N., Ste. 710
San Diego, CA 92108-2807
Contact: Warren Magill, Pres. and Dir.

Established in 2007 in CA.
Donors: Walter J. Zable†; Zable Qtip Marital Trust.
Foundation type: Independent foundation.
Financial data (yr. ended 09/30/13): Assets, $101,022,903 (M); gifts received, $45,390,608; expenditures, $2,211,611; qualifying distributions, $1,961,578; giving activities include $1,552,210 for 43 grants (high: $300,000; low: $2,500).
Fields of interest: Higher education; Education; Athletics/sports, school programs; Human services; United Ways and Federated Giving Programs.
Type of support: General/operating support; Scholarship funds.
Limitations: Applications accepted. Giving primarily in CA; some funding also in VA.
Application information: Application form required.
Initial approach: Letter
Deadline(s): None
Officers and Directors:* Warren Magill,* Pres.; Kathryn M. Starr,* Secy.; John D. Thomas,* Treas.; William W. Boyle.
EIN: 311540383
Selected grants: The following grants are a representative sample of this grantmaker's funding activity:
$273,000 to College of William and Mary Foundation, Williamsburg, VA, 2011.
$50,000 to San Diego Blood Bank, San Diego, CA, 2011. For general assistance.
$35,000 to Saint Vincent de Paul Village, San Diego, CA, 2011. For general assistance.
$32,000 to YMCA of San Diego County, San Diego, CA, 2011. For general assistance.
$30,000 to Vietnam Veterans of San Diego, Veterans Village of San Diego, San Diego, CA, 2011. For general support.
$25,000 to San Diego Center for Children, San Diego, CA, 2011.
$15,000 to Campanile Foundation, San Diego, CA, 2011.
$10,000 to Childrens Initiative, San Diego, CA, 2011.
$10,000 to Promises2Kids, San Diego, CA, 2011.
$7,000 to San Diego Carrier Museum, San Diego, CA, 2011.

1356
The Mona & Edward Zander Family Foundation ✧ ☆
9 Vasquez Trail
Carmel, CA 93923-7731

Established in 1999 in CA.
Donors: Edward Zander; Mona Zander.
Foundation type: Independent foundation.
Financial data (yr. ended 06/30/13): Assets, $2,508,634 (M); expenditures, $553,872; qualifying distributions, $539,672; giving activities include $539,657 for 39 grants (high: $250,000; low: $250).
Purpose and activities: Giving primarily for education, health, and social services.
Fields of interest: Museums (art); Secondary school/education; Higher education; Education; Hospitals (general); Health care; Health organizations, association; Cancer; Alzheimer's disease research; Human services.
Limitations: Applications not accepted. Giving primarily in CA, GA, IL and NY. No grants to individuals.
Application information: Unsolicited requests for funds not accepted.
Officers: Edward Zander, Pres.; Mona Zander, C.F.O. and Secy.
EIN: 770528781
Selected grants: The following grants are a representative sample of this grantmaker's funding activity:
$1,500 to TEAM Academy, Friends of, Newark, NJ, 2011. For general fund.

1357
Zee Foundation ✧
4001 Via Oro, Ste. 210
Long Beach, CA 90810-1400

Established in 1993 in CA.
Donor: Tien P. Zee.
Foundation type: Independent foundation.
Financial data (yr. ended 12/31/13): Assets, $9,439,297 (M); expenditures, $531,099; qualifying distributions, $458,805; giving activities

include $458,805 for 19 grants (high: $116,405; low: $1,000).
Purpose and activities: Giving primarily for education and health.
Fields of interest: Higher education; Education; Hospitals (general); Medical research; Buddhism.
Type of support: General/operating support; Program development; Scholarship funds; Research.
Limitations: Applications not accepted. Giving primarily in CA, and in China and Hong Kong.
Application information: Unsolicited requests for funds not accepted.
Officers and Director:* Tien P. Zee, Chair. and Pres.; William G. Smith,* Secy.; Jinly Zee; Jinsen Zee.
EIN: 330592374
Selected grants: The following grants are a representative sample of this grantmaker's funding activity:
$35,000 to Whittier College, Whittier, CA, 2011.
$10,000 to Childrens Health Fund, New York, NY, 2011.
$5,000 to We Care of Los Alamitos, Los Alamitos, CA, 2011.
$1,000 to American Cancer Society, Oakland, CA, 2011.
$1,000 to Asian Improv Arts, San Francisco, CA, 2011.
$1,000 to Chinese Christian Herald Crusades, San Gabriel, CA, 2011.

1358
The Zellerbach Family Foundation

(formerly The Zellerbach Family Fund)
575 Market St., Ste. 2950
San Francisco, CA 94105-2854 (415) 421-2629
Contact: Allison Magee, Exec. Dir.
FAX: (415) 421-6713;
E-mail: info@zellerbachfamilyfoundation.org; Main URL: http://www.zellerbachfamilyfoundation.org
Knowledge Center: http://www.zellerbachfamilyfoundation.org/publications.html

Incorporated in 1956 in CA.
Donor: Jennie B. Zellerbach‡.
Foundation type: Independent foundation.
Financial data (yr. ended 12/31/13): Assets, $134,123,431 (M); gifts received, $200,000; expenditures, $8,417,788; qualifying distributions, $6,409,666; giving activities include $5,023,583 for 326 grants (high: $250,000; low: $750).
Purpose and activities: The foundation focuses its giving in the San Francisco Bay Area, CA and concentrates on the following program areas: Strengthening communities; Improving the management, practice and accountability of public systems with a focus on child welfare, mental health and education; Improving the quality of life for refugees and immigrants and supporting their participation in society; Youth development through the arts; Major community institutions; and Community Arts.
Fields of interest: Arts, single organization support; Performing arts; Youth development; Human services; Minorities/immigrants, centers/services; Immigrants/refugees; Economically disadvantaged.
Type of support: General/operating support; Continuing support; Program development; Technical assistance; Program evaluation.
Limitations: Giving primarily in the San Francisco Bay Area, CA. No grants to individuals, or for capital or endowment funds, research, scholarships, or fellowships; no loans.
Publications: Annual report.
Application information: The foundation accepts proposals only for its Community Arts program. All other program grants are initiated by the foundation. See foundation's web site for Community Arts application information. Application form required.
Initial approach: Community Arts application with application on foundation web site
Deadline(s): See foundation web site for current deadlines
Board meeting date(s): Quarterly
Final notification: Quarterly
Officers and Trustees:* William J. Zellerbach,* Chair.; Thomas H. Zellerbach,* Pres.; Nancy Zellerbach Boschwitz,* V.P. and Secy.; Charles R. Zellerbach,* V.P. and Treas.; Raymond H. Williams,* V.P.; Allison Magee, Exec. Dir.; Jeanette M. Dunckel; Philip S. Ehrlich, Jr.; Mary Ann Milias; Stephen R. Shapiro; Suchi Somasekar; Mildred Thompson.
Number of staff: 5 full-time professional; 1 part-time professional; 1 full-time support; 1 part-time support.
EIN: 946069482
Selected grants: The following grants are a representative sample of this grantmaker's funding activity:
$100,000 to New America Media, San Francisco, CA, 2012. For California Council on Youth Relations, speakers bureau of youth who have been involved in the mental health, foster care, and other public systems, to provide shared learning and support for Zellerbach Family Foundation grantees focused on youth leadership.
$55,000 to La Cocina, San Francisco, CA, 2012. For full-service, shared-use commercial kitchen, technical assistance, and business incubator project that assists low-income Latina women to develop and manage successful food-related businesses.

1359
The Anita and Julius L. Zelman Foundation ✧

10580 Wilshire Blvd., Ste. 59
Los Angeles, CA 90024-4500

Established in 2002 in CA.
Donors: Julius L. Zelman; Anita Zelman.
Foundation type: Independent foundation.
Financial data (yr. ended 03/31/13): Assets, $829,217 (M); gifts received, $25,000; expenditures, $1,027,671; qualifying distributions, $1,024,456; giving activities include $1,021,990 for 6 grants (high: $1,000,000; low: $250).
Fields of interest: Arts; Higher education; Food services; Human services.
Type of support: General/operating support.
Limitations: Applications not accepted. Giving primarily in Los Angeles, CA.
Application information: Unsolicited requests for funds not accepted.
Officers and Directors:* Julius L. Zelman,* Pres.; Anita Zelman,* Secy.-Treas.
EIN: 020588453
Selected grants: The following grants are a representative sample of this grantmaker's funding activity:
$25,000 to UCLA Foundation, Los Angeles, CA, 2012.
$10,000 to Museum Associates, Los Angeles, CA, 2012.
$2,000 to Yiddishkayt Los Angeles, Los Angeles, CA, 2012.

1360
Ruth/Allen Ziegler Foundation ✧

c/o Gumbiner Savett
1723 Cloverfield Blvd.
Santa Monica, CA 90404-4007

Established in 1986 in CA.
Donors: Allen S. Ziegler; Ruth B. Ziegler.
Foundation type: Independent foundation.
Financial data (yr. ended 11/30/13): Assets, $7,143,928 (M); expenditures, $488,120; qualifying distributions, $478,000; giving activities include $478,000 for 41 grants (high: $30,000; low: $1,500).
Purpose and activities: Funding primarily for Jewish organizations, as well as children, youth, and social services, including services for people who are blind.
Fields of interest: Human services; Children/youth, services; Jewish federated giving programs; Jewish agencies & synagogues.
Limitations: Applications not accepted. Giving primarily in CA. No grants to individuals.
Application information: Contributes only to pre-selected organizations.
Trustees: Richard Corleto, Esq.; David Rose; Ronald Ziegler; Ruth B. Ziegler.
EIN: 954113690

1361
Max & Pauline Zimmer Family Foundation ✧

1880 Century Park E., Ste. 613
Los Angeles, CA 90067-1622

Established in 1951 in CA.
Donor: Max Zimmer.
Foundation type: Independent foundation.
Financial data (yr. ended 05/31/13): Assets, $4,890,888 (M); expenditures, $554,740; qualifying distributions, $424,000; giving activities include $424,000 for 24 grants (high: $100,000; low: $500).
Purpose and activities: Giving primarily for higher education and Jewish agencies and temples.
Fields of interest: Museums; Performing arts, orchestras; Higher education; Jewish agencies & synagogues.
Limitations: Applications not accepted. Giving primarily in CA and NY. No grants to individuals.
Application information: Contributes only to pre-selected organizations.
Officers: Nathan S. Krems, Pres.; Jonathan Flier, V.P.; Edith Flier, Secy.; Ruth Lieberman, Treas.
Directors: David Z. Krems; Charles Lieberman.
EIN: 956097374
Selected grants: The following grants are a representative sample of this grantmaker's funding activity:
$15,000 to Southern California Counseling Center, Los Angeles, CA, 2013. For Trauma Resource Training.
$10,000 to American Jewish University, Los Angeles, CA, 2013. For Platt Gallery.
$500 to Cleveland High School Booster Club, Reseda, CA, 2013. For Humanities Magnet Program.

COLORADO

1362
6/S Foundation ✧ ☆
1755 Shy Cir.
Westcliffe, CO 81252-1348

Established in 1998 in NE.
Donors: Audrey M. Stermer; Richard A. Stermer.
Foundation type: Independent foundation.
Financial data (yr. ended 06/30/13): Assets, $2,226,925 (M); expenditures, $458,905; qualifying distributions, $443,724; giving activities include $439,000 for 8 grants (high: $306,000; low: $3,000).
Fields of interest: Environment, natural resources; Human services; Children/youth, services; Family services.
Limitations: Applications not accepted. Giving primarily in CO and Baltimore, MD. No grants to individuals.
Application information: Unsolicited requests for funds not accepted.
Officers and Directors:* Richard A. Stermer,* Pres.; Audrey M. Stermer,* V.P.; Patricia M. Dunn,* Secy.-Treas.; Lisa A. Freeseman; Katherine E. Schulze; Richard C. Stermer.
EIN: 841457491
Selected grants: The following grants are a representative sample of this grantmaker's funding activity:
$115,000 to Colorado Conservation Trust, Denver, CO, 2011.
$100,000 to Grace Place for Children and Families, Naples, FL, 2011.

1363
Animal Assistance Foundation ✧
405 Urban St., Ste. 340
Lakewood, CO 80228-1236 (303) 744-8396
Contact: David L. Gies
FAX: (303) 744-7065; E-mail: info@aaf-fd.org; Contact for questions: Katie Parker, Prog. Dir., tel.: (303) 744-8396, ext. 302, e-mail: KParker@aaf-fd.org; Main URL: http://www.aaf-fd.org

Established in 1975 in CO.
Donor: Louise C. Harrison‡.
Foundation type: Independent foundation.
Financial data (yr. ended 07/31/13): Assets, $27,668,355 (M); gifts received, $11,750; expenditures, $1,289,254; qualifying distributions, $1,197,239; giving activities include $770,278 for 58 grants (high: $234,950; low: $500).
Purpose and activities: The foundation's mission is to provide leadership for the enhancement of animal welfare through charitable, scientific, and educational means. Its vision is to transform the relationship between human beings and all animals, for the betterment of both. Giving for animal welfare, especially to prevent cruelty to cats and dogs; also to promote pet population control, provide for humane treatment education, and expand scientific inquiry.
Fields of interest: Animal welfare; Animal population control.
Type of support: General/operating support; Building/renovation; Emergency funds; Program development; Conferences/seminars; Seed money; Curriculum development; Technical assistance.
Limitations: Applications accepted. Giving limited to CO. No grants to individuals, or for endowment funds, debt retirement, or long-term funding.
Publications: Application guidelines; Annual report; Financial statement; Multi-year report.
Application information: Application form required.
Initial approach: Use online application system on foundation web site
Copies of proposal: 8
Deadline(s): Generally, last Fri. in Mar. and Sept.
Board meeting date(s): Bimonthly
Final notification: Within two weeks
Officers and Directors:* Mark Lacy,* Pres.; Todd Towell, V.P.; Dan Figliola, Secy.; Ted J. Cohn, DVM*, Treas.; Roger Haston, Exec. Dir.; Tory Bond; and 8 additional directors.
Number of staff: 4 full-time professional; 1 part-time professional; 1 part-time support.
EIN: 840715412

1364
Anschutz Family Foundation ✧
555 17th St., Ste. 2400
Denver, CO 80202-3941
Contact: Sue Anschutz-Rodgers, Chair. and Pres.
FAX: (303) 299-1235;
E-mail: info@anschutzfamilyfoundation.org; Main URL: http://www.anschutzfamilyfoundation.org/

Established in 1982 in CO.
Donors: Fred B. Anschutz‡; Sue Anschutz-Rodgers.
Foundation type: Independent foundation.
Financial data (yr. ended 11/30/13): Assets, $56,474,743 (M); expenditures, $3,149,682; qualifying distributions, $2,800,408; giving activities include $2,362,476 for 346 grants (high: $31,500; low: $500).
Purpose and activities: Giving primarily for civic, community and capacity building, economic development, neighborhoods, crisis intervention, disabled people, food, shelter and the homeless, low income housing, self-sufficiency, families, literacy, senior programs, and youth development and children.
Fields of interest: Adult education—literacy, basic skills & GED; Mental health/crisis services; Crime/violence prevention; Crime/violence prevention, domestic violence; Food services; Nutrition; Housing/shelter; Human services; Children/youth, services; Family services; Homeless, human services; Economic development; Community/economic development; Philanthropy/voluntarism; Aging; Disabilities, people with; Economically disadvantaged.
Type of support: General/operating support; Program development; Technical assistance.
Limitations: Applications accepted. Giving limited to CO. No support for religious organizations for religious purposes, or for organizations with an annual budget exceeding $5 million, organizations with an Interim Exec. Dir./C.E.O., start-up organizations, or health care, specific disease and mental health agencies. No grants to individuals, or for capital or building funds, deficit financing, endowment funds, special events or promotions, conferences, graduate or post-graduate research, multi-year grants, education, policy, advocacy or research, or arts and culture.
Publications: Application guidelines; Annual report (including application guidelines); Grants list.
Application information: Complete the Colorado Common Grant Application available at http://www.coloradocommongrantforms.org or via foundation web site. Faxed or e-mailed proposals are not accepted. Organizations receiving successive support for 2 years are required to take one year off before reapplying. Only 1 proposal per organization per 12-month funding cycle will be considered. See foundation web site for application guidelines and procedures. Application form required.
Initial approach: Letter of inquiry or telephone to see if a proposal fits the foundation's guidelines, or submit full proposal using only the Colorado Common Grant Application
Copies of proposal: 1
Deadline(s): See foundation web site for current deadline
Board meeting date(s): Apr. and Nov.
Final notification: Late Apr. and Nov.
Officers and Directors:* Sue Anschutz-Rodgers,* Chair. and Pres.; Robert S. Rich,* V.P. and Secy.; Susan A. Spindler, Treas.; Debbie Jessup, Exec. Dir.; Henry Porter Couzens; John Manning Couzens, Jr.; Melinda Rodgers Couzens; Susan Rodgers Drumm; Sarah Anschutz Hunt; Melissa Rodgers Padgett.
Number of staff: 2 full-time professional.
EIN: 742132676

1365
The Anschutz Foundation
1727 Tremont Pl.
Denver, CO 80202-4006 (303) 308-8220
Contact: Ted Harms, Exec. Dir.

Established in 1984 in CO.
Donors: Philip F. Anschutz; The Anschutz Corp.
Foundation type: Independent foundation.
Financial data (yr. ended 11/30/13): Assets, $1,126,706,872 (M); expenditures, $53,893,099; qualifying distributions, $50,842,001; giving activities include $50,069,897 for 700 grants (high: $1,000,000; low: $250).
Purpose and activities: Giving nationwide with emphasis on social and cultural organizations which work in areas larger than local communities; support for media projects, projects that support the underprivileged, public policy and traditional family values.
Fields of interest: Arts; Public affairs; Economically disadvantaged.
Type of support: General/operating support.
Limitations: Applications accepted. Giving on a national basis. No grants to individuals, or for continuing support.
Publications: Application guidelines.
Application information: Application form not required.
Initial approach: Letter (no more than 2-3 pages)
Copies of proposal: 1
Deadline(s): Jan. 15, Apr. 15, July 15, and Sept. 30
Board meeting date(s): Nov.
Final notification: Dec.
Officers and Directors:* Philip F. Anschutz,* Chair.; Cannon Y. Harvey,* V.P.; Sarah Anschutz Hunt,* V.P.; Craig D. Slater,* Secy.-Treas.; Ted E. Harms, Exec. Dir.; Nancy P. Anschutz; Christopher Hunt; M. LaVoy Robison.
Number of staff: 1 full-time support; 1 part-time support.
EIN: 742316617

Selected grants: The following grants are a representative sample of this grantmaker's funding activity:
$10,660,000 to University of Colorado Foundation, Denver, CO, 2012. For general support.
$3,575,000 to Boys and Girls Clubs of Metro Denver, Program Support Center, Denver, CO, 2012. For general support.
$3,302,082 to Foundation for a Better Life, Denver, CO, 2012. For general support.
$1,000,000 to Colorado Coalition for the Homeless, Denver, CO, 2012. For general support.
$505,000 to Random Acts of Kindness Foundation, Denver, CO, 2012. For general support.
$50,000 to Hunt Family Foundation, Denver, CO, 2012. For general support.
$25,000 to Cultural Office of the Pikes Peak Region, Colorado Springs, CO, 2012. For general support.
$25,000 to Florence Crittenton Services of Colorado, Denver, CO, 2012. For general support.
$25,000 to University Preparatory School, Denver, CO, 2012. For general support.
$22,000 to Young Philanthropists Foundation, Denver, CO, 2012. For general support.

1366
The Armstrong Foundation ✧
1421 Blake St.
Denver, CO 80202-1325

Established in 2002 in CO.
Donors: William Armstrong; Elisabeth Armstrong; Armstrong Ventures.
Foundation type: Independent foundation.
Financial data (yr. ended 12/31/13): Assets, $19,374,013 (M); gifts received, $1,538,191; expenditures, $1,373,793; qualifying distributions, $1,369,950; giving activities include $1,369,950 for 22 grants (high: $1,167,500; low: $100).
Fields of interest: Arts; Higher education; Education; Protestant agencies & churches.
Limitations: Applications not accepted. Giving in the U.S., with emphasis on TX. No grants to individuals.
Application information: Contributes only to pre-selected organizations.
Directors: Elisabeth Armstrong; William Armstrong.
EIN: 841612524

1367
Aspen Business Center Foundation ✧
(formerly Airport Business Center Foundation)
303 AABC, Ste. E
Aspen, CO 81611-3540

Established in 1986 in CO.
Donors: John P. McBride; John P. McBride, Jr.; Katherine H. McBride; Peter McBride; Lester D. Pedicord; Katherine M. Puckett; Sopris Foundation.
Foundation type: Independent foundation.
Financial data (yr. ended 12/31/13): Assets, $3,796,915 (M); expenditures, $812,524; qualifying distributions, $772,524; giving activities include $734,608 for 92 grants (high: $250,000; low: $150).
Purpose and activities: Giving to promote the preservation of natural resources, conduct research and educational programs on world over-population and family planning, promote amateur sports, and provide education or medical services for distressed or underprivileged communities.
Fields of interest: Education; Environment; Animal welfare; Health organizations; Athletics/sports, amateur competition; Human services.
Limitations: Applications not accepted. Giving in the U.S., with emphasis on CO. No grants to individuals.
Application information: Contributes only to pre-selected organizations.
Trustees: John P. McBride; John P. McBride, Jr.; Laurie M. McBride; Peter M. McBride; Lester D. Pedicord; Kate Puckett.
EIN: 841042661
Selected grants: The following grants are a representative sample of this grantmaker's funding activity:
$10,000 to National Public Radio, Washington, DC, 2012. For communications.
$5,000 to Wilderness Society, Washington, DC, 2012. For land protection.
$1,000 to Population Media Center, Shelburne, VT, 2012. For population issues.

1368
Aspen Community Foundation ✧
(formerly Aspen Valley Community Foundation)
110 E. Hallam St., Ste. 126
Aspen, CO 81611-1460 (970) 925-9300
Contact: Tamara Tormohlen, Exec. Dir.
FAX: (970) 920-2892;
E-mail: info@aspencommunityfoundation.org;
Additional e-mail:
tamara@aspencommunityfoundation.org; Main
URL: http://www.aspencommunityfoundation.org
Facebook: http://www.facebook.com/pages/Aspen-Community-Foundation/113705925321857?ref=ts
LinkedIn: http://www.linkedin.com/companies/aspen-community-foundation
Twitter: http://twitter.com/AspenCommFound
YouTube: http://www.youtube.com/user/aspenCF

Established in 1980 in CO.
Foundation type: Community foundation.
Financial data (yr. ended 12/31/13): Assets, $42,591,421 (M); gifts received, $12,053,633; expenditures, $14,361,140; giving activities include $12,627,877 for 153+ grants (high: $4,515,867).
Purpose and activities: The foundation builds philanthropy and supports nonprofit organizations by connecting donors with community needs, building permanent charitable funds, and bringing people together to solve community problems.
Fields of interest: Education; Health care; Human services; Community/economic development; Infants/toddlers; Children/youth; Youth; Aging; Hispanics/Latinos; Immigrants/refugees; Economically disadvantaged.
Type of support: General/operating support; Continuing support; Management development/capacity building; Building/renovation; Equipment; Emergency funds; Program development; Seed money; Curriculum development; Technical assistance; Program evaluation; Program-related investments/loans; Matching/challenge support.
Limitations: Applications accepted. Giving primarily to Pitkin and Garfield counties and portions of Eagle County in the Roaring Fork Valley, CO. No support for religious purposes, conduit organizations, or organizations primarily supported by tax-derived funding. No grants to individuals, or for debt retirement, endowments, medical research or hospital equipment, scholarships, conferences, seminars, trips, or speaker series.
Publications: Application guidelines; Annual report; Grants list; Newsletter.
Application information: Visit foundation web site for online Qualifying Application and additional guidelines.
Initial approach: Complete online Qualifying Application
Deadline(s): Apr. 1
Board meeting date(s): Varies
Final notification: Within 4 weeks for invitation to submit full application (based on Qualifying Application); 3 months for grant determination
Officers and Directors:* Barbara Gold,* Chair.; Carrie Wells,* Secy.; Michael D. Kaplan,* Treas.; Tamara Tormohlen, Exec. Dir.; Pamela Alexander; Lawrence Altman; Kimbo Brown-Schirato; Susan Crown; Tony DiLucia; Sally Hansen; Jeanie Humble; Soledad Hurst; Adam Lewis; Mike Murray; Marcie Musser; Mary Scanlan; Gail Schwartz; Judith Zee Steinberg; Tom van Straaten.
Number of staff: 5 full-time professional; 1 part-time professional; 1 part-time support.
EIN: 840829226

1369
Avenir Foundation, Inc. ✧
215 Union Blvd., Ste. 300
Lakewood, CO 80228-1841 (303) 232-2262

Established in 1993 in CO.
Donors: Alice Dodge Wallace; William Dodge Wallace; Margaret Boynton Wallace; Berkshire Hathaway Inc.; Varki Investments, Inc.; Beaumont Investments, Ltd.
Foundation type: Independent foundation.
Financial data (yr. ended 06/30/13): Assets, $228,479 (M); gifts received, $12,684,500; expenditures, $12,803,578; qualifying distributions, $12,684,500; giving activities include $12,684,500 for 21 grants.
Purpose and activities: Giving primarily for education, and the arts, particularly museums; funding also for a public research center for music theory in Vienna, Austria, which focuses on the methods of Arnold Schoenberg.
Fields of interest: Museums (specialized); Performing arts, opera; Arts; Education; Reproductive health, family planning.
International interests: Austria.
Limitations: Applications not accepted. Giving primarily in CO, MD, NM, NY, as well as in Vienna, Austria. No grants to individuals.
Application information: Contributes only to pre-selected organizations.
Officers and Directors:* Alice Dodge Wallace,* Pres.; William Dodge Wallace,* V.P.; Margaret Boynton Wallace,* Secy.; Norman L. Wilson,* Treas.
EIN: 841245939
Selected grants: The following grants are a representative sample of this grantmaker's funding activity:
$3,000,000 to American Institute of Physics, College Park, MD, 2013. For Endowment of R Joseph Anderson Director of the Niels Bohr Library and Archives.
$2,500,000 to Antique Boat Museum, Clayton, NY, 2013. For funding educational endowment.
$1,500,000 to Colorado State University, Fort Collins, CO, 2013. For Endowment for the Director of the Avenir Museum of Design and Merchandising.
$650,000 to Santa Fe Opera, Santa Fe, NM, 2013. To produce opera Arabella.

$250,000 to Santa Fe Opera, Santa Fe, NM, 2013. To fund engineering study.
$9,500 to Hofstra University, Hempstead, NY, 2013. For Funding the Smith/Wallace Papers.

1370
Bacon Family Foundation ✧
P.O. Box 4570
Grand Junction, CO 81502-4570 (970) 243-3767

Established in CO.
Foundation type: Independent foundation.
Financial data (yr. ended 06/30/13): Assets, $10,641,894 (M); expenditures, $764,720; qualifying distributions, $696,929; giving activities include $681,875 for 54 grants (high: $50,000; low: $1,000).
Purpose and activities: Giving primarily for health care and hospitals, as well as for children, youth, and social services.
Fields of interest: Education; Hospitals (general); Health care; Health organizations, association; Human services; Children/youth, services; Residential/custodial care, hospices.
Limitations: Applications accepted. Giving primarily in western CO, with emphasis on Grand Junction.
Application information: Application form not required.
Initial approach: Proposal
Deadline(s): None
Officers: Stephen Bacon, Pres.; Andrew Bacon, V.P.; Linda Bacon Reid, Secy.-Treas.
Directors: Herbert Bacon; Laura May Bacon; Pat Gormley; Amy Bacon Hill.
EIN: 841269589
Selected grants: The following grants are a representative sample of this grantmaker's funding activity:
$25,000 to Bird City Century II Development Foundation, Bird City, KS, 2013. For Capital Campaign for Security State Bank Building Renovation.
$25,000 to Iliff School of Theology, Denver, CO, 2013. To establish Endowment to Support Faculty Development.
$25,000 to University of Colorado Foundation, Boulder, CO, 2013. To establish Scholarship Endowment for Economics Department.
$5,000 to Boy Scouts of America, Western Colorado Council, Grand Junction, CO, 2013. For general support.

1371
The Ball Foundation ✧ ☆
P.O. Box 9005
Broomfield, CO 80021-0905
E-mail: ballfoundation@easymatch.com

Established in CO.
Donor: Ball Corp.
Foundation type: Independent foundation.
Financial data (yr. ended 12/31/13): Assets, $12,531,602 (M); gifts received, $55,252; expenditures, $2,411,495; qualifying distributions, $2,401,403; giving activities include $2,401,403 for 31 grants (high: $1,047,216; low: $75).
Purpose and activities: Giving primarily for education, community engagement, and to programs that increase recycling rates, improve collection processes, and provide education about the benefits of recycling.
Fields of interest: Education; Environment, natural resources; Youth development; Human services; Community/economic development.
Limitations: Applications accepted. No support for religious groups for religious purposes, programs targeted for people with specific physical, medical or psychological conditions, non-501(c)(3) organizations, unaccredited public/private schools, or for programs or organizations for which the foundation is asked to serve as the sole funding source. No grants to individuals, or for audio, film, video, medical research, or travel.
Application information: Visit https://www.easymatch.com/BALLFOUNDATION/APPLICATIONS/AGENCY for complete application guidelines. Application form required.
Initial approach: Complete online application form
Deadline(s): None
Officers and Directors:* John A. Hayes,* Pres.; Scott C. Morrison,* V.P.; James N. Peterson,* V.P.; Jeffrey A. Knobel,* Secy.-Treas.
EIN: 274099620

1372
Paula & William Bernstein Foundation ✧
16 Polo Club Dr.
Denver, CO 80209-3310

Established in 1984.
Donors: Paula Bernstein, Ph.D.; William Bernstein, M.D.
Foundation type: Independent foundation.
Financial data (yr. ended 09/30/13): Assets, $8,434,289 (M); expenditures, $565,879; qualifying distributions, $511,563; giving activities include $506,250 for 26 grants (high: $176,000; low: $250).
Purpose and activities: Giving primarily for arts, health and human services.
Fields of interest: Performing arts, music; Health care; Human services; Family services; Jewish federated giving programs; Jewish agencies & synagogues.
Type of support: General/operating support.
Limitations: Applications not accepted. Giving limited to CO, with emphasis on Denver. No grants to individuals.
Application information: Contributes only to pre-selected organizations. Unsolicited requests for funds not accepted.
Officers: Paula Bernstein, Ph.D., Pres.; William Bernstein, M.D., Secy.
EIN: 742351575

1373
The Boedecker Foundation ✧
(formerly Anthony H. Kruse Foundation)
2120 13th St.
Boulder, CO 80302-4802
Main URL: http://www.boefoundation.org/site/

Established in 2006 in CO.
Donors: George Boedecker, Jr; Anthony H. Kruse†.
Foundation type: Independent foundation.
Financial data (yr. ended 12/31/12): Assets, $55,778,621 (M); expenditures, $4,907,263; qualifying distributions, $3,313,029; giving activities include $2,654,556 for 48 grants (high: $621,168; low: $1,000).
Purpose and activities: Giving to assist in empowering young people to transform themselves and their community. The foundation provides funding and support to nonprofit organizations that provide critical youth development skills training in the areas of education, health and wellness, and family and community development.
Fields of interest: Arts; Higher education; Education; Health organizations; Human services; Children/youth, services; Community/economic development.
Limitations: Applications not accepted. Giving primarily in CO; some funding nationally. No grants to individuals.
Application information: Unsolicited requests for funds not accepted.
Officers and Directors:* George Boedecker,* Pres. and C.E.O.; Jeffrey Humphrey, C.O.O.; Joel Davis, C.F.O.; Shelley Diede, Cont.; Brad Stoffer.
EIN: 208495254
Selected grants: The following grants are a representative sample of this grantmaker's funding activity:
$113,000 to University of Colorado Foundation, Boulder, CO, 2012. For sports programs.
$100,000 to University of Colorado Foundation, Boulder, CO, 2012. For Cardio Rehab Gym.
$50,000 to Special Olympics Colorado, Englewood, CO, 2012. For Project Unify.
$35,000 to There With Care, Boulder, CO, 2012. For program needs.
$17,500 to Nashville Rescue Mission, Nashville, TN, 2012. For turkeys.
$10,000 to Niwot Cultural Arts Association, Niwot, CO, 2012. For Jazz on 2nd Street.
$10,000 to YMCA Foundation of Middle Tennessee, Nashville, TN, 2012. For Holiday Game.
$3,000 to Black Rock Arts Foundation, San Francisco, CA, 2012. For Restoration Historical Landmark.

1374
Boettcher Foundation ✧
600 17th St., Ste. 2210 S.
Denver, CO 80202-5422
Contact: Timothy W. Schultz, Pres. and Exec. Dir.; Julie Lerudis, Dir., Grants Prog.
E-mail: grants@boettcherfoundation.org; Main URL: http://www.boettcherfoundation.org/

Incorporated in 1937 in CO.
Donors: C.K. Boettcher†; Mrs. C.K. Boettcher†; Charles Boettcher†; Fannie Boettcher†; Ruth Boettcher Humphreys†; Mrs. Charles Boettcher II†; Mae B. Boettcher†; Webb-Waring Foundation.
Foundation type: Independent foundation.
Financial data (yr. ended 12/31/13): Assets, $304,648,905 (M); gifts received, $1,600; expenditures, $14,706,081; qualifying distributions, $13,823,419; giving activities include $10,265,309 for 133 grants (high: $1,796,130; low: $500), and $54,757 for employee matching gifts.
Purpose and activities: Since 1937, the foundation's mission has been to invest in the minds and mortar of Colorado. It does this by awarding full 4-year in-state scholarships to the state's top high school seniors , awarding grants to early-career Colorado scientists through its Webb-Waring Biomedical Research Program, investing in the Boettcher Teachers Program and providing capital grants to Colorado nonprofit organizations.

Fields of interest: Visual arts; Museums; Performing arts; Performing arts, music; Arts; Education, early childhood education; Higher education; Scholarships/financial aid; Education; Reproductive health, family planning; Medical care, rehabilitation; Health care; Health organizations, association; Human services; Children/youth, services; Residential/custodial care, hospices; Women, centers/services; Homeless, human services; Rural development; Community/economic development; Women; Economically disadvantaged; Homeless.
Type of support: Building/renovation; Capital campaigns; Land acquisition; Matching/challenge support; Scholarship funds.
Limitations: Applications accepted. Giving limited to CO. No support for housing, open spaces/parks, organizations that primarily serve animals, large urban hospitals, gymnasiums, athletic fields, or religious groups or organizations for religious purposes. No grants to individuals, or for endowment funds, pilot programs, operations, purchase of tables or tickets for dinners/events, media presentations, small business start-ups, conferences, seminars, workshops, debt reduction, or travel.
Publications: Application guidelines; Annual report (including application guidelines).
Application information: Once invited to apply, the Colorado Common Grant Application is required. Application form not required.
Initial approach: Complete a prequalification form before being invited to apply for a competitive capital grant
Copies of proposal: 1
Deadline(s): Quarterly deadlines indicated on web site and based on giving category for capital grants; Feb. 15 for Webb-Waring Biomedical Research Awards; Nov. 1 for Boettcher Scholarship Program
Board meeting date(s): Monthly
Final notification: Seven working days for prequalification form; 3 months for applications
Officers and Trustees:* Theodore F. Schlegel, M.D.*, Chair.; Russell George,* Vice.-Chair.; Timothy W. Schultz, Pres. and Exec. Dir.; Katie S. Kramer, V.P.; Sharon H. Linhart,* Secy.; Donald McG. Woods,* Treas.; Larry A. Allen, M.D.; Paul H. Chan; Cile Chavez, Ed.D.; Kenzo Kawanabe; Christine Marquez-Hudson; M. Ann Penny; Judith B. Wagner; Thomas Williams.
Number of staff: 8 full-time professional; 2 full-time support.
EIN: 840404274
Selected grants: The following grants are a representative sample of this grantmaker's funding activity:
$1,671,713 to University of Denver, College of Education, Denver, CO, 2011. For scholarships.
$1,000,000 to Public Education and Business Coalition, Denver, CO, 2011. For program support.
$855,099 to Colorado College, Colorado Springs, CO, 2011. For scholarships.
$800,000 to University of Colorado Foundation, Denver, CO, 2011. For program support.
$500,000 to History Colorado Center, Denver, CO, 2011. Toward construction of History Colorado Center.
$250,000 to Biennial of the Americas, Denver, CO, 2011. For program support.
$250,000 to Biennial of the Americas, Denver, CO, 2011. For capital support.
$200,000 to Denver Museum of Nature and Science, Denver, CO, 2011. For capital support.
$175,000 to Clyfford Still Museum, Denver, CO, 2011. For capital support.
$150,000 to Colorado State University, Fort Collins, CO, 2011. Toward construction of College of Engineering Building.
$75,000 to Colorado School of Mines, Golden, CO, 2011. For program support.
$75,000 to Opera Colorado, Denver, CO, 2011. For program support.
$50,000 to Axis Healthcare, Cortez, CO, 2011. Toward construction of new integrated healthcare facility.
$35,000 to Rialto Theater Guild, Loveland, CO, 2011. Toward construction of addition to historic theater.
$25,000 to Mesa Developmental Services, Grand Junction, CO, 2011. Toward purchase of group homes for the disabled.
$25,000 to Sister Carmen Community Center, Lafayette, CO, 2011. Toward purchase and renovation of second service facility.

1375
Bohemian Foundation ✧
(formerly The Stryker-Short Foundation)
262 E. Mountain Ave.
Fort Collins, CO 80524-2835 (970) 221-2636
Contact: Tana Atwood, Grants Admin.; Hannah Bustos, Community Programs Asst.
E-mail: info@bohemianfoundation.org; Main URL: http://www.bohemianfoundation.org

Established in CO in 2001.
Donors: Patricia A. Short; Pat Stryker.
Foundation type: Independent foundation.
Financial data (yr. ended 12/31/13): Assets, $47,384,149 (M); gifts received, $502; expenditures, $11,245,662; qualifying distributions, $10,147,549; giving activities include $9,235,630 for 284 grants (high: $750,000; low: $500).
Purpose and activities: The mission of the foundation is to involve fellow citizens in the care and improvement of the community.
Fields of interest: Children/youth, services.
Type of support: General/operating support; Continuing support; Capital campaigns; Building/renovation; Equipment; Program development; Publication; Seed money; Research; Technical assistance; Consulting services; Program evaluation; Matching/challenge support.
Limitations: Applications accepted. Giving limited to the Fort Collins, CO, area. No support for specific religious programs, tuition-based private schools, private foundations, individual team requests or discriminatory programs. No grants to individuals, or for scholarships, debt reduction, multi-year requests, multi-program requests, fundraising events, or for program-related investments.
Publications: Application guidelines.
Application information: Please visit the foundation Web site for more information as well as grant guidelines and application form. Application form required.
Initial approach: Website
Copies of proposal: 1
Deadline(s): Feb. and Sept.; specific dates available on foundation web site
Final notification: May for Feb. deadline; Dec. for Sept. deadline; specific dates available on foundation web site
Officers and Director:* Pat Stryker, Pres.; Joe Zimlich,* Secy.-Treas; Cheryl Zimlich.
Number of staff: 2 full-time professional; 1 part-time professional; 2 full-time support.
EIN: 841605993

1376
Bonfils-Stanton Foundation ✧
Daniels and Fisher Twr.
1601 Arapahoe St., Ste. 500
Denver, CO 80202-2015 (303) 825-3774
Contact: Gary P. Steuer, C.E.O. and Pres.
FAX: (303) 825-0802;
E-mail: webinfo@bonfils-stanton.org; Main URL: http://www.bonfils-stantonfoundation.org

Established in 1962 in CO.
Donors: Charles E. Stanton†; Robert E. Stanton†.
Foundation type: Independent foundation.
Financial data (yr. ended 06/30/13): Assets, $77,475,043 (M); expenditures, $4,382,372; qualifying distributions, $4,116,927; giving activities include $3,293,560 for 65 grants (high: $500,000; low: $500), and $35,000 for 1 grant to an individual.
Purpose and activities: The foundation was created to enhance the quality of life for residents of Colorado. Its mission is to advance excellence in the areas of arts and culture, community service, and science and medicine through strategic investments resulting in significant and unique contributions in these fields. In addition to grantmaking, the foundation annually provides 3 awards to Coloradans who have made significant contributions in the fields of arts and humanities, community service, and science and medicine.
Fields of interest: Museums (art); Humanities; Arts; Human services; Economically disadvantaged.
Type of support: Management development/capacity building; Building/renovation; Equipment; Program development; Research; Technical assistance.
Limitations: Applications accepted. Giving limited to CO. No support for activities or initiatives that have a religious purpose or objective, or for organizations that are not for the benefit of CO citizens. Generally no grants to individuals (except for award programs), or for scholarships, loans, fellowships, endowments, seminars, conferences, media productions, fundraising, travel expenses, or to retire debt.
Publications: Application guidelines; Annual report (including application guidelines); Grants list.
Application information: Colorado Common Grant Application form accepted. Application information available on foundation web site. Application form not required.
Initial approach: Telephone call
Copies of proposal: 1
Deadline(s): Last business day of Jan., Apr., Jul., Oct.
Board meeting date(s): Jan., Apr., July, and Oct.
Final notification: Generally 4 months following application deadline
Officers and Trustees:* J. Landis Martin,* Chair.; Gary P. Steuer, C.E.O and Pres.; Ann M. Hovland, C.F.O. and Treas.; Louis J. Duman, M.D., Tr. Emeritus; W. Eileen Greenawalt, Tr. Emeritus; Mark G. Falcone; Julanna V. Gilbert, Ph.D.; Harold R. Logan, Jr.; Denise M. O'Leary; John E. Repine, M.D.
Number of staff: 2 full-time professional; 1 part-time professional; 1 full-time support.
EIN: 846029014

Selected grants: The following grants are a representative sample of this grantmaker's funding activity:
$300,000 to Clyfford Still Museum, Denver, CO, 2012. For activities related to the establishment of the museum.
$300,000 to Denver Botanic Gardens, Denver, CO, 2012. For the Flourish Campaign.
$200,000 to Museum of Contemporary Art Denver, Denver, CO, 2012. For the Director's Vision Campaign.
$125,000 to Arts and Venues Denver, Denver, CO, 2012. To renovate the McNichols Building.
$125,000 to University of Colorado Foundation, Boulder, CO, 2012. For the Fulginiti Pavilion for Bioethics and Humanities.
$90,000 to Central City Opera House Association, Denver, CO, 2012. For the Opera Festival and innovation experiments.
$50,000 to Denver Botanic Gardens, Denver, CO, 2012. For the Bonfils-Stanton Lecture Series.
$50,000 to Warren Village, Denver, CO, 2012. For general operating support.
$20,000 to Denver Young Artists Orchestra Association, Denver, CO, 2012. For general operating support.
$10,000 to Volunteers of America, Denver, CO, 2012. For programs at Brandon Center/Theodora House.

1377
Bowana Foundation ✧

831 Pearl St.
Boulder, CO 80302-5007

Donor: Scott A. Beck.
Foundation type: Independent foundation.
Financial data (yr. ended 11/30/13): Assets, $36,911,759 (M); expenditures, $6,645,267; qualifying distributions, $6,456,963; giving activities include $3,801,536 for 58 grants (high: $500,000; low: $25).
Purpose and activities: Giving primarily for education, children and social services, and to Christian and Protestant churches, ministries and organizations.
Fields of interest: Higher education; Human services; Children/youth, services; Christian agencies & churches; Protestant agencies & churches.
Limitations: Applications not accepted. Giving primarily in CO and FL.
Application information: Contributes only to pre-selected organizations.
Officers and Director:* Thomas Beck,* Pres.; Scott Beck, V.P. and Secy.-Treas.
EIN: 363799613
Selected grants: The following grants are a representative sample of this grantmaker's funding activity:
$694,783 to National Christian Charitable Foundation, Alpharetta, GA, 2011.
$18,300 to University of Colorado Foundation, Boulder, CO, 2011.
$10,000 to A Glimmer of Hope Foundation, Austin, TX, 2011.
$10,000 to Hampton University, Hampton, VA, 2011.
$5,000 to Colorado UpLIFT, Denver, CO, 2011.
$2,962 to Adventures in Missions, Gainesville, GA, 2011.
$1,500 to Save Our Youth, Denver, CO, 2011.
$1,000 to There With Care, Boulder, CO, 2011.

1378
Brett Family Foundation ✧

1123 Spruce St.
Boulder, CO 80302-4001 (303) 442-1200
Contact: Michael Brewer, Exec. Dir.; Claire Hamilton, Grants Admin.
FAX: (303) 442-1221;
E-mail: claire@brettfoundation.org; Main URL: http://www.brettfoundation.org
Grants List: http://www.brettfoundation.org/2009

Established in 1999 in CO.
Donors: Stephen M. Brett; Linda J. Shoemaker.
Foundation type: Independent foundation.
Financial data (yr. ended 12/31/13): Assets, $9,246,444 (M); expenditures, $602,285; qualifying distributions, $544,410; giving activities include $495,000 for 74 grants (high: $60,000; low: $1,000).
Purpose and activities: The foundation's mission is to promote caring communities by investing in organizations throughout Colorado working for social justice, developing nonprofit media, and Boulder County nonprofits addressing the needs of at-risk teens.
Fields of interest: Education; Health care; Youth, services; Community/economic development; Public policy, research.
Type of support: General/operating support; Continuing support; Program development; Seed money; Technical assistance.
Limitations: Applications accepted. Giving primarily in CO. No support for religious organizations, or for individual public or private schools (K-12, graduate or post graduate), or for large public charities. No grants to individuals.
Publications: Application guidelines; Annual report; Financial statement; Grants list; IRS Form 990 or 990-PF printed copy available upon request.
Application information: Application guidelines and forms available on foundation web site. Application form required.
Copies of proposal: 1
Deadline(s): See foundation web site for current deadlines
Final notification: 2-3 months
Officers and Trustees:* Stephen M. Brett,* Chair.; Linda J. Shoemaker,* Pres.; Emily P. Shoemaker Brett; Matthew S. Brett; Claudia Brett Goldin.
Number of staff: 1 part-time professional.
EIN: 841525821

1379
L.P. Brown Foundation ✧

505 Mountain View Rd.
Boulder, CO 80302-5013

Established in 1956 in TN.
Donors: L.P. Brown III; Axson B. Morgan.
Foundation type: Independent foundation.
Financial data (yr. ended 12/31/13): Assets, $29,042,461 (M); expenditures, $1,349,395; qualifying distributions, $1,203,000; giving activities include $1,203,000 for 46 grants (high: $125,000; low: $1,000).
Purpose and activities: Giving primarily for the environment, health care, and human services.
Fields of interest: Environment, natural resources; Health care; Health organizations, association; Human services.
Type of support: General/operating support.
Limitations: Applications not accepted. Giving primarily in CO. No grants to individuals.
Application information: Contributes only to pre-selected organizations.
Officers: Axson B. Morgan, Pres.; G. Bryan Morgan, V.P.; Octavia E. Morgan, Secy.
Directors: Kathryn M. Bauer; Darcia B. Morgan; William P. Morgan.
EIN: 626036338
Selected grants: The following grants are a representative sample of this grantmaker's funding activity:
$100,000 to Colorado Conservation Trust, Denver, CO, 2011.
$100,000 to Multiple Sclerosis Society, National, New York, NY, 2011.

1380
Jerome V. Bruni Foundation ✧ ☆

1528 N. Tejon St.
Colorado Springs, CO 80907-7439

Established in 1993 in CO.
Donor: Jerome V. Bruni.
Foundation type: Independent foundation.
Financial data (yr. ended 09/30/13): Assets, $10,969,605 (M); gifts received, $310,180; expenditures, $493,244; qualifying distributions, $475,400; giving activities include $475,400 for 49 grants (high: $51,000; low: $1,000).
Fields of interest: Human services; Community/economic development; Economics; Christian agencies & churches; Religion.
Type of support: General/operating support; Research.
Limitations: Applications not accepted. Giving primarily in CO. No grants to individuals.
Application information: Contributes only to pre-selected organizations.
Officer: John R. Brock, Exec. Dir.
Directors: Jerome V. Bruni; Pamela S. Bruni.
EIN: 841246148
Selected grants: The following grants are a representative sample of this grantmaker's funding activity:
$25,000 to Acton Institute for the Study of Religion and Liberty, Grand Rapids, MI, 2011.
$20,000 to Council for Economic Education, New York, NY, 2011.
$15,000 to United Way, Pikes Peak, Colorado Springs, CO, 2011.
$7,875 to Care and Share, Colorado Springs, CO, 2011.
$5,000 to Hope and Home, Colorado Springs, CO, 2011.
$5,000 to Philanthropy Roundtable, Washington, DC, 2011.
$3,000 to CASA of the Pikes Peak Region, Colorado Springs, CO, 2011.
$3,000 to Dreampower Animal Rescue, Colorado Springs, CO, 2011.
$1,400 to Partners in Housing, Colorado Springs, CO, 2011.
$1,000 to Nature Conservancy, Boulder, CO, 2011.

1381
Temple Hoyne Buell Foundation ✧

1666 S. University Blvd., Ste. B
Denver, CO 80210-2834 (303) 744-1688
Contact: Susan J. Steele, Exec. Dir.
FAX: (303) 744-1601;
E-mail: info@buellfoundation.org; E-mail for Susan J.

Steele: ssteele@buellfoundation.org; Main URL: http://www.buellfoundation.org

Incorporated in 1962 in CO.
Donor: Temple Hoyne Buell†.
Foundation type: Independent foundation.
Financial data (yr. ended 06/30/13): Assets, $267,460,996 (M); expenditures, $13,058,856; qualifying distributions, $9,281,393; giving activities include $8,611,460 for 369 grants (high: $396,000; low: $500).
Purpose and activities: The foundation is a professional philanthropic organization supporting the positive development of children through grants and partnerships with other sectors of the community.
Fields of interest: Education, early childhood education; Children/youth, services; Children, day care; Youth, pregnancy prevention; Infants/toddlers; Children/youth; Children; Youth.
Type of support: General/operating support; Continuing support; Capital campaigns; Building/renovation; Equipment; Technical assistance; Program evaluation.
Limitations: Applications accepted. Giving only in CO. No support for political organizations. Generally, no support for medical programs. No grants to individuals, or for past operating deficit, or retirement of debt. Generally, no grants for testimonial dinners, multi-year awards, events, annual campaigns, membership drives, emergency needs, conferences, or endowments; no loans.
Publications: Application guidelines; Financial statement; Grants list; Informational brochure.
Application information: Colorado Common Grant Application form accepted. Proposals sent by fax not considered. Application forms and guidelines are available on the foundation web site. Organizations are limited to one grant request in any twelve month period. Application form required.
Initial approach: Proposal or telephone for guidelines or go to website
Copies of proposal: 1
Deadline(s): Jan. 15 and the first business day of May and Sept.
Board meeting date(s): 6 times per year
Final notification: 4 months after deadline
Officers and Trustees:* Daniel L. Ritchie,* Pres.; Reginald L. Washington, M.D.,* V.P.; Arthur H. Bosworth II,* Secy.; Thomas J. Curnes,* Treas.; Stephen ErkenBrack; Noelle Hagan; Priscilla Lucero.
Number of staff: 4 full-time professional; 1 part-time professional; 1 part-time support.
EIN: 846037604
Selected grants: The following grants are a representative sample of this grantmaker's funding activity:
$396,000 to University of Colorado Foundation, School of Education and Human Development, Denver, CO, 2013. For Buell Early Childhood Leadership Program for 2013/2014.
$325,000 to Qualistar Early Learning, Denver, CO, 2013. For $250,000 for general operating support and $75,000 for TEACH scholarships outside the seven-county metro area.
$145,000 to Clayton Early Learning, Denver, CO, 2013. For $135,000 in general operating support and $10,000 to support early childhood policy and systems work at Clayton Early Learning Institute.
$100,000 to Riverhouse Childrens Center, Durango, CO, 2013. For construction of the new Riverhouse Children's Center.
$99,280 to Clayton Early Learning, Denver, CO, 2013. For Buell Early Childhood Leaders Network for 2013-2014.
$95,000 to Joint Initiatives for Youth and Families, Colorado Springs, CO, 2013. For The Alliance Office of Professional Development.
$80,000 to Early Childhood Council of Larimer County, Fort Collins, CO, 2013. For the professional development project.
$75,000 to Clayton Early Learning, Denver, CO, 2013. For the Environment Rating System project.
$20,000 to Rural Communities Resource Center, Yuma, CO, 2013. For professional development and quality improvement program of the Early Childhood Council of Yuma, Washington, and Kit Carson Counties.
$15,000 to Sprouts Christian Learning Center, Aurora, CO, 2013. To support the sliding scale.

1382
Carson Foundation ✧
(formerly The Leila Carroll Foundation)
450 9th Ave.
Denver, CO 80203

Established in 1994 in CO.
Donor: Lelia Carroll.
Foundation type: Independent foundation.
Financial data (yr. ended 12/31/12): Assets, $11,523,078 (M); expenditures, $837,714; qualifying distributions, $681,310; giving activities include $587,231 for 82 grants (high: $67,100; low: $1).
Purpose and activities: Giving primarily for education, children, youth and social services, and federated giving programs.
Fields of interest: Higher education; Education; Boys & girls clubs; Human services; Children/youth, services; United Ways and Federated Giving Programs.
Limitations: Applications not accepted. No grants to individuals.
Application information: Contributes only to pre-selected organizations.
Officers: Brooke Johnson Brown, Pres.; Lelia Carroll, V.P.; Brandon Johnson, Secy.-Treas.
EIN: 846277774
Selected grants: The following grants are a representative sample of this grantmaker's funding activity:
$67,100 to Colorado Academy, Denver, CO, 2012. For Capital campaign; general operating.
$37,371 to Denver Public Schools Foundation, Denver, CO, 2012. For Program support, general operating.

1383
Catto Charitable Foundation ✧
c/o Woody Creek Mgmt. Grp.
250 Steele St., Ste. 375
Denver, CO 80206-5200

Established in 1967.
Donors: Jessica Cato; Henry Catto; Hobby Family Foundation.
Foundation type: Independent foundation.
Financial data (yr. ended 12/31/12): Assets, $47,176,277 (M); expenditures, $1,581,784; qualifying distributions, $782,500; giving activities include $782,500 for 102 grants (high: $100,000; low: $125).
Purpose and activities: Giving primarily for the arts, the environment, and human services.
Fields of interest: Media, radio; Arts; Environment, research; Environment, natural resources; Human services; Social sciences, public policy.
Limitations: Applications not accepted. Giving primarily in CO, Washington, DC, and TX. No grants to individuals.
Application information: Contributes only to pre-selected organizations.
Officers and Directors:* Heather Catto Kohout,* Pres.; Elizabeth Pettus Catto,* V.P.; William Halsell Catto,* V.P.; Jennifer A. Crossett, Secy.-Treas.
EIN: 742773632

1384
CH2M Hill Foundation ✧
9191 S. Jamaica St.
Englewood, CO 80112
Main URL: http://www.ch2m.com

Established in 1992.
Donors: James W. Poirot; CH2M Hill, Inc.; CH2M Hill Companies, Ltd.
Foundation type: Company-sponsored foundation.
Financial data (yr. ended 12/31/13): Assets, $436,782 (M); gifts received, $1,003,940; expenditures, $931,894; qualifying distributions, $930,165; giving activities include $880,766 for 264 grants (high: $50,000; low: $500).
Purpose and activities: The foundation supports undergraduate and graduate engineering and science programs, and technology initiatives designed to promote sustainable communities, clean water, a healthy environment, safe transportation systems, renewable energy, and efficient industry.
Fields of interest: Education; Environment; Human services.
Limitations: Applications not accepted. Giving primarily in CA, CO, Washington, DC, OR, and WA. No grants to individuals.
Application information: Contributes only to pre-selected organizations.
Board meeting date(s): Varies
Officers: Elisa M. Speranza, Pres.; Cynthia Jones, Secy.; Steven C. Mathews, Treas.
Directors: William D. Bellamy; Judith Ibarra Bianchetta; Marina Arana Biscaldi; Didier Menard; Margaret B. McLean; Patrick O'Keefe; Rachel White.
EIN: 841227384
Selected grants: The following grants are a representative sample of this grantmaker's funding activity:
$12,500 to University of Washington, Seattle, WA, 2012. For Academic Steering Committee Grants.
$1,000 to Woodford Cedar Run Wildlife Refuge, Medford, NJ, 2012. For Dollars for Doers - Gen. Op. Grant.

1385
Chambers Family Fund
(formerly Axem Foundation)
44 Cook St., Ste. 240
Denver, CO 80206-5813 (303) 839-4620
Contact: Letty Bass, Exec. Dir.
FAX: (303) 839-4619;
E-mail: info@chambersfund.org; Main URL: http://www.chambersfund.org

Established in 1983 in CO.

Donors: Evelyn H. Chambers†; Merle C. Chambers.
Foundation type: Independent foundation.
Financial data (yr. ended 11/30/13): Assets, $61,227,832 (M); gifts received, $989; expenditures, $3,357,013; qualifying distributions, $3,213,196; giving activities include $2,729,106 for 90 grants (high: $736,000; low: $100), $2,935 for 27 employee matching gifts, and $193,547 for foundation-administered programs.
Purpose and activities: The fund supports regional and national nonprofit organizations that create systems change, improve the quality and circumstances of life and reflect its values and interests. The fund invests time, expertise and funding in organizations that help women become economically self-sufficient, enhance the early care and education of children, strengthen justice, equality and opportunity, and enrich the arts and culture. The fund also publishes "Creating a Women's Fund Within a Community Foundation".
Fields of interest: Humanities; Arts; Education, early childhood education; Child development, education; Civil/human rights, advocacy; Economic development; Philanthropy/voluntarism; Children; Women.
Type of support: General/operating support; Continuing support; Management development/capacity building; Capital campaigns; Endowments; Program development; Research; Technical assistance; Program evaluation; Employee matching gifts; Matching/challenge support.
Limitations: Applications not accepted. Giving primarily in CO and the Rocky Mountain region. No grants to individuals.
Publications: Annual report.
Application information: All grants are researched and initiated by the foundation. Unsolicited requests for funds are not accepted.
Officers and Directors:* Merle C. Chambers,* Pres.; Letty Bass, Exec. Dir.; Joy Hall, Treas.; Hugh A. Grant; Donald J. Hopkins; Sally W. Liebbrandt; Marla J. Williams.
Number of staff: 1 full-time professional; 1 part-time professional; 1 full-time support; 1 part-time support.
EIN: 840929410
Selected grants: The following grants are a representative sample of this grantmaker's funding activity:
$736,000 to Kirkland Museum, Denver, CO, 2013.
$500,000 to Ascend, Washington, DC, 2013.
$150,000 to Bell Policy Center, Denver, CO, 2013.
$75,000 to Clyfford Still Museum, Denver, CO, 2013.
$60,000 to Planned Parenthood of the Rocky Mountains, Denver, CO, 2013.
$30,000 to NARAL Pro-Choice Colorado Foundation, Denver, CO, 2013.
$25,000 to Colorado Children's Campaign, Denver, CO, 2013.
$20,000 to Colorado Center on Law and Policy, Denver, CO, 2013.
$15,000 to 9 to 5 National Association of Working Women, Denver, CO, 2013.

1386
Change Happens Foundation ✧
P.O. Box 600
Erie, CO 80516-0600
Contact: Michael D. Troxel, C.F.O.
E-mail: Admin@ChangeHappens.us; Main URL: http://www.changehappens.us/

Established in 2006 in DE and HI.
Foundation type: Independent foundation.
Financial data (yr. ended 12/31/12): Assets, $15,738,885 (M); expenditures, $1,681,005; qualifying distributions, $1,579,036; giving activities include $1,439,735 for 22 grants (high: $1,191,903; low: $3,000).
Purpose and activities: Giving for the development and implementation of innovative technology and progressive ideas to generate a positive force for change in the world.
Fields of interest: Arts; Higher education; Human services; Children/youth, services; Science.
Limitations: Giving primarily in IA; funding also in CA and HI. No support for faith-based organizations or religious activities. No grants to individuals, or for scholarships, land purchases, third-party sponsorships, or special events.
Application information: Formal grant proposals are by invitation only, after review of initial letter of inquiry. Unsolicited grant proposals will not be considered. Application form required.
Initial approach: Use online letter of inquiry on foundation web site
Deadline(s): None
Officers: Douglas D. Troxel, C.E.O. and Pres.; Michael Douglas Troxel, V.P., Admin. and C.F.O.; Sergei George Troxel, Secy.
Directors: Kristin D. Nong; Kenneth D. Troxel.
EIN: 205222620
Selected grants: The following grants are a representative sample of this grantmaker's funding activity:
$1,191,903 to Iowa State University Foundation, Ames, IA, 2012. For Capital Grant for 400 Seat Lecture Hall Facility.
$6,000 to Project Dignity, Garden Grove, CA, 2012. For Eldorado Inn Children's Library.
$5,000 to American Bird Conservancy, The Plains, VA, 2012. For Saving Hawaii Endangered Native Bird Species.
$5,000 to Shelter Partnership, Los Angeles, CA, 2012. For Food Bank Warehouse for 225 Non-Profit Agencies.

1387
Charter School Growth Fund ✧
(also known as Charter Fund, Inc.)
350 Interlocken Blvd., Ste. 390
Broomfield, CO 80021-3485 (303) 217-8090
E-mail: info@chartergrowthfund.org; Main URL: http://www.chartergrowthfund.org/
Twitter: https://twitter.com/CharterGrowth

Established in 2005 in CA and CO.
Donors: Don and Doris Fisher Foundation; School Futures Research Foundation; Bill & Melinda Gates Foundation; Walton Family Foundation; Woolley Fund.
Foundation type: Operating foundation.
Financial data (yr. ended 12/31/13): Assets, $200,323,615 (M); gifts received, $51,934,089; expenditures, $39,192,431; qualifying distributions, $60,694,239; giving activities include $33,560,746 for 80 grants (high: $2,500,000; low: $1,000), $244,028 for 8 grants to individuals, $38,996,382 for 1 foundation-administered program and $22,965,000 for 26 loans/program-related investments.
Purpose and activities: The grantmaker primarily provides grants and loans to charter school management organizations that manage networks of schools. It only supports organizations that can demonstrate an impact on underserved student populations and outstanding value added academic gains.
Fields of interest: Elementary/secondary education; Charter schools.
Type of support: General/operating support; Program-related investments/loans.
Limitations: Applications accepted. Giving primarily in CA, IL, and TX. Generally, no support for individual charter schools.
Application information: See web site for complete online application process. Application form not required.
Initial approach: Online
Deadline(s): Varies
Officers and Directors:* John Fisher,* Chair.; Kevin Hall,* C.E.O. and Pres.; Rich Billings, C.O.O. and C.F.O.; Darryl Cobb, V.P.; Alex Hernandez, V.P.; Julie Maier, V.P., Finance and Investor Relations; Tawnya Ramirez, Cont.; Allan C. Golston; Michael Grebe; Mason Hawkins; Carrie Walton Penner; James C. Rahn; Stacy Schusterman.
EIN: 050620063
Selected grants: The following grants are a representative sample of this grantmaker's funding activity:
$1,250,000 to Lead Public Schools, Nashville, TN, 2012.
$1,050,000 to Touchstone Education, Newark, NJ, 2012.
$1,000,000 to Gestalt Community Schools, Memphis, TN, 2012.
$1,000,000 to KIPP Memphis, Memphis, TN, 2012.
$1,000,000 to Rocketship Education, Redwood City, CA, 2012.
$800,000 to KIPP New Orleans, New Orleans, LA, 2012.
$775,000 to LEARN Charter School, Chicago, IL, 2012.
$750,000 to LEARN Charter School, Chicago, IL, 2012. For startup support.
$616,667 to Tennessee Charter School Incubator, Nashville, TN, 2012.
$250,000 to Youth Co-Op, Miami, FL, 2012. For Next School.

1388
Chipotle Cultivate Foundation ✧ ☆
1401 Wynkoop St., Ste. 500
Denver, CO 80202-1729
Main URL: http://www.cultivatefoundation.org

Donors: Chipotle Mexican Grill, Inc.; Kellogg's; Event Brite; Burleigh Point, Ltd.
Foundation type: Independent foundation.
Financial data (yr. ended 12/31/13): Assets, $1,990,431 (M); gifts received, $1,019,354; expenditures, $661,984; qualifying distributions, $654,590; giving activities include $600,000 for 3 grants (high: $250,000; low: $150,000).
Fields of interest: Agriculture, farmlands.
Limitations: Applications not accepted. Giving in the U.S.
Application information: Unsolicited requests for funds not accepted.
Officers and Board Members:* Steve Ells,* Chair.; Mark Crumpacker,* Pres.; Chris Arnold, Secy.; Ryan Murrin, Treas.; Mike McGawn; Jason Von Rohr.
EIN: 452606186
Selected grants: The following grants are a representative sample of this grantmaker's funding activity:

$55,000 to La Semilla Food Center, Anthony, NM, 2012. For La Semilla Food Center's Youth Farm which teaches youth and families about the connections between the environment, local economies, and public health while creating a vibrant regional food system that supports diversified small farms in the Pa.
$50,000 to Pennsylvania Horticultural Society, Philadelphia, PA, 2012. For the PHS City Harvest Program, creating a robust infrastructure of organic agricultural supply and education centers, while encouraging a healthier future for thousands of Philadelphians.
$40,000 to PCC Farmland Trust, Seattle, WA, 2012. For PCC Farmland Trust's Puyallup Valley Farm Corridor Project to conserve and steward threatened farmland and environmental quality in Washington State, in a way that Promotes the long-term economic viability of sustainable family farms and farming.

1389
Colorado Masons Benevolent Fund Association ✧

2400 Consistory Ct.
Grand Junction, CO 81501-2009
E-mail: tomcox@cmbfa.org; Main URL: http://www.cmbfa.org/
Scholarship address: c/o Scholarship Admin.: 1130 Panorama Dr., Colorado Springs, CO 80904, tel.: (800) 482-4441

Established in 1899; incorporated in 1912 in CO.
Donors: Irene Houle; Ella Rose†; William D. Hewitt; William Blackwell; A.F. and A.M Grand Lodge of Colorado; Tenet Healtcare Foundation.
Foundation type: Operating foundation.
Financial data (yr. ended 10/31/13): Assets, $9,217,811 (M); gifts received, $33,500; expenditures, $780,682; qualifying distributions, $1,567,845; giving activities include $610,706 for 84 grants (high: $70,000; low: $200), and $617,187 for foundation-administered programs.
Purpose and activities: A private operating foundation; awards assistance grants to needy, distressed CO Masons and their families through local lodges, and scholarships to CO public high school seniors who are planning to attend college in CO. Masonic affiliation not required for scholarships.
Fields of interest: Higher education; Economically disadvantaged.
Type of support: Grants to individuals; Scholarships—to individuals; Matching/challenge support; Student loans—to individuals.
Limitations: Applications accepted. Giving limited to CO.
Application information: Scholarship application forms available on foundation web site. Application form required.
Initial approach: Letter
Deadline(s): Mar. 7
Officers: Richard W. Schmidt, Pres.; Ben H. Bell, Jr., V.P.; Thomas J. Cox, Exec. Secy.; Charles G. Johnson, Secy.; Robert W. Gregory, Jr., Treas.
Trustee: Roy Snyder.
Number of staff: 1 full-time professional; 1 part-time support.
EIN: 840406813

1390
The Colorado Trust ✧

1600 Sherman St.
Denver, CO 80203-1604 (303) 837-1200
FAX: (303) 839-9034;
E-mail: questions@coloradotrust.org; Toll free tel.: (888) 847-9140; Additional e-mail: (for Christie McElhinney): christie@coloradotrust.org; e-mail: (for Maggie Frasure): maggie@coloradotrust.org; Main URL: http://www.coloradotrust.org
Blog: http://www.coloradotrust.org/news/blog
Colorado Trust's Instagram: http://instagram.com/thecoloradotrust
Facebook: http://www.facebook.com/pages/The-Colorado-Trust/89447823595
Grants Database: http://www.coloradotrust.org/grants/search-grants
LinkedIn: http://www.linkedin.com/companies/the-colorado-trust
Twitter: http://twitter.com/coloradotrust

Established in 1985 in CO; with the proceeds from the sale of the PSL Health Care corporation.
Donor: PSL Health Care Corporation.
Foundation type: Independent foundation.
Financial data (yr. ended 12/31/13): Assets, $454,609,911 (M); expenditures, $15,477,630; qualifying distributions, $13,855,883; giving activities include $6,511,740 for 198 grants (high: $726,334; low: $1,000), and $117,000 for 136 employee matching gifts.
Purpose and activities: The Colorado Trust is dedicated to achieving access to health for all Coloradans, with an emphasis on advancing health equity, working together with communities to provide opportunities for the most vulnerable individuals and families to make healthy choices.
Fields of interest: Health care; Mental health/crisis services; Health organizations, association; Family services; Community development, citizen coalitions; Urban/community development; Children/youth; Children; Youth; Adults; Aging; Young adults; Minorities; African Americans/Blacks; Hispanics/Latinos; Immigrants/refugees; Economically disadvantaged; Homeless.
Type of support: Technical assistance; Seed money; Research; Publication; Program evaluation; Program development; Matching/challenge support; General/operating support; Employee matching gifts; Continuing support.
Limitations: Giving limited to CO. No support for religious organizations for religious purposes, political organizations, or private foundations. No grants to individuals, or for endowments, deficit financing or debt retirement, building funds, or real estate acquisition.
Publications: Annual report; Occasional report.
Application information: Unsolicited requests for funds not accepted. Application form not required.
Initial approach: Applications are invited or accepted following the release of requests for proposals (RFP) issued by the foundation; you can print the RFP directly from the foundation web site
Deadline(s): Governed by individual requests for proposals invitations
Board meeting date(s): Quarterly
Final notification: Varies
Officers and Trustees:* Rev. R. J. Ross,* Chair.; Gail S. Schoettler, Vice-Chair.; Reginald L. Washington, M.D.*, Vice-Chair.; Ned Calonge, M.D.,* C.E.O. and Pres.; Deb DeMuth, V.P. and C.F.O.; Gay Cook, V.P., Strategy and Philanthropic Relations; Christie McElhinney, V.P., Comm. and Public Affairs; Jennifer Paquette,* Secy.; Colleen Schwarz, Treas.; Deborah McCluiston, Cont.; Cara B. Lawrence, Genl. Counsel; John P. Hopkins; Warren T. Johnson; Donald J. Mares; Alan Synn, M.D.; William Wright, M.D.
Number of staff: 15 full-time professional; 8 full-time support.
EIN: 840994055
Selected grants: The following grants are a representative sample of this grantmaker's funding activity:
$9,600,000 to Project Health Colorado, Denver, CO, 2011. To increase awareness, understanding and support for making health care and health coverage work better for every Coloradan.
$4,500,000 to Colorado Health Access Survey, Denver, CO, 2011. To provide information to help policymakers, and healthcare, business and community leaders fully understand health challenges and advance shared solutions to improve health coverage and care for Coloradans, Colorado Health Institute manages data collection and analysis.
$2,049,977 to Colorado Health Institute, Denver, CO, 2011. For partnership with The Colorado Trust, Rose Community Foundation and Caring for Colorado serving as reliable and impartial clearinghouse for data and data resources related to Colorado's health care issues and systems, communicates these data to policymakers, funding organizations, health planners, business and nonprofit community, consumer groups, health care providers and the media.
$2,000,000 to Center for Improving Value in Health Care, Denver, CO, 2012. For partnership with Colorado Health Foundation, Colorado Trust support CIVHC in developing Colorado all-payer claims database to better understand cost and utilize health care services and develop payment solutions to lower health care costs.
$1,012,500 to Health Care Advocacy, Denver, CO, 2011. For Bell Policy Center, Colorado Center on Law and Policy, and Colorado Children's Campaign to advocate on behalf of improve system of health coverage and care in Colorado.
$942,956 to Colorado Episcopal Foundation, Denver, CO, 2011. For general operating support, Church Distribution.
$942,956 to Presbytery of Denver, Denver, CO, 2011. For general operating support, Church Distribution.
$682,486 to Colorado Health Institute, Denver, CO, 2011. For Access to Health program.
$535,436 to Colorado Health Institute, Denver, CO, 2011. To advance accessible and affordable health care.
$500,000 to Colorado Trust, Convening for Colorado, Denver, CO, 2012. For Convening for Colorado, program provides support to bring people together to discuss issues central to advancing health and well-being of Coloradans, to share information and learn from experts, personally engage and actively deliberate with the goal of tackling tough challenge or taking advantage of a timely opportunity.
$363,166 to Colorado Health Institute, Denver, CO, 2011. For Access to Health program.
$320,703 to Colorado Center for Nursing Excellence, Denver, CO, 2011. For Access to Health program.
$320,703 to Colorado Center for Nursing Excellence, Denver, CO, 2011. For Access to Health program.

$50,050 to ACS Community LIFT, Denver, CO, 2011. For Access to Health program.
$2,000 to Centro San Juan Diego, Denver, CO, 2011. For general operating support.

1391
The Community Foundation - Boulder County ✧
(formerly Boulder Area Communities Foundation)
1123 Spruce St.
Boulder, CO 80302-5281 (303) 442-0436
Contact: Josie Heath, Pres.; Elvira Ramos, Prog. Dir.
FAX: (303) 442-1221; E-mail: info@commfound.org; Toll-free telephone: (877) 744-7239; Additional e-mail: elvira@commfound.org; Grant application e-mail: application@commfound.org; Main URL: http://www.commfound.org
Blog: http://www.commfound.org/blogs/tcfblogger
Facebook: http://www.facebook.com/pages/Community-Foundation-Serving-Boulder-County/130803350161
Twitter: http://twitter.com/CommFound

Established in 1991 in CO.
Foundation type: Community foundation.
Financial data (yr. ended 12/31/12): Assets, $37,340,483 (M); gifts received, $5,968,893; expenditures, $5,265,465; giving activities include $3,987,069 for grants.
Purpose and activities: The foundation seeks to improve the quality of life in Boulder County, now and forever, build a culture of giving. The foundation provides support for arts and culture, education, the environment, health care, human services, and civic organizations.
Fields of interest: Arts; Education; Environment; Health care; Safety/disasters; Human services; Public affairs; Children/youth; Youth; Adults; Aging; Young adults; Disabilities, people with; Minorities; African Americans/Blacks; Hispanics/Latinos; Women; Adults, women; Young adults, female; Men; Adults, men; Young adults, male; LGBTQ.
Type of support: General/operating support; Continuing support; Annual campaigns; Capital campaigns; Building/renovation; Equipment; Endowments; Emergency funds; Program development; Conferences/seminars; Seed money; Scholarship funds; Technical assistance; Consulting services; Program-related investments/loans; Employee matching gifts; Scholarships—to individuals; In-kind gifts; Student loans—to individuals.
Limitations: Applications accepted. Giving primarily in the Boulder County, CO, area. No support for religious purposes from unrestricted funds.
Publications: Application guidelines; Annual report; Financial statement; Grants list; Informational brochure; Informational brochure (including application guidelines); Newsletter.
Application information: Visit foundation web site for application form and guidelines. The foundation strongly encourages applicants to submit application via e-mail; faxed applications are not accepted. Colorado Common Grant Application form accepted. Application form required.
Initial approach: Submit application form, concept letter, and attachments
Copies of proposal: 1
Deadline(s): Sep. 30 for community trust fund grants; varies for others
Board meeting date(s): Monthly
Final notification: Jan.
Officers and Trustees:* Rhonda Wallen,* Chair.; Chris Hazlitt,* Vice-Chair.; Josie Heath,* Pres.; David Brantz,* Secy.; Rick Doty,* Treas.; Leslie Allen; Linda Bachrach; Alexander E. Bracken; John Creighton; Richard Garcia; Helen Gemmill; James Graham; Randi Grassgreen; Philip N. Hernandez; Kathy Leonard; Richard Lopez; Jane McConnell; Jann Oldham; Rogelio Pena; Amanda Prentiss; Diane Soucheray.
Number of staff: 8 full-time professional; 3 part-time professional.
EIN: 841171836

1392
Community Foundation of Gunnison Valley ✧
805 W. Tomichi Ave., W. Door
P.O. Box 7057
Gunnison, CO 81230 (970) 641-8837
Contact: Pam Montgomery, Exec. Dir.
FAX: (970) 641-0443; E-mail: info@cfgv.org; Grant inquiry e-mail: pam@cfgv.org; Additional Tel.: (970)-349-5966; Main URL: http://www.cfgv.org
Facebook: https://www.facebook.com/myCFGV?ref=ts&fref=ts

Established in 2007 in CO.
Foundation type: Community foundation.
Financial data (yr. ended 12/31/13): Assets, $6,951,601 (M); gifts received, $1,223,372; expenditures, $1,092,120; giving activities include $855,488 for grants (high: $73,744), and $4,655 for grants to individuals.
Purpose and activities: The foundation strengthens and enriches the community through engaged philanthropy, thoughtful grantmaking, strategic education, and collaborative leadership.
Fields of interest: Historic preservation/historical societies; Arts; Education; Environment; Animals/wildlife; Health care; Recreation; Human services; Community/economic development.
Limitations: Applications accepted. Giving primarily in Crested Butte, Gunnison, and Upper Gunnison Watershed, CO. No support for religious activities that serve, or appear to serve, a specific group or denomination. No grants to individuals (except for scholarships), or for national, state or local fundraising, website development, PR/marketing, capital building projects, or to establish or enhance endowments, debt retirement, deficit financing, reduction of an operating deficit or to liquidate debt or replenish resources used to pay for such purposes.
Publications: Application guidelines; Annual report; Financial statement; Newsletter.
Application information: Visit foundation web site for application form and guidelines. Application form required.
Initial approach: Submit application
Deadline(s): May 15
Officers and Board Members:* Noelle Hagan,* Pres.; Anne Lamkin Kinder,* V.P.; Don Haver,* Secy.; Pam Montgomery, Exec. Dir.; Tina Brudzinski; Ashley Burt; Gail Digate; Roger Dorf; Laura Egedy; Gary Hartman; Jonathan Houck; Jim MacAllister; Diane Mueller; Steve Ogden; Boyd Pederson; Robert Pickering; Lyndsey Ruehle; Doug Tredway; Jacob With.
EIN: 311650658

1393
Community Foundation of Northern Colorado ✧
(formerly Fort Collins Area Community Foundation)
4745 Wheaton Dr., Ste. 100
Fort Collins, CO 80525-9403 (970) 224-3462
Contact: Ray Caraway, Pres.
FAX: (970) 488-1990;
E-mail: info@nocofoundation.org; Additional e-mail: ray@communityfoundationnc.org; Grant inquiry e-mail: applications@communityfoundationnc.org; Main URL: http://www.nocofoundation.org/
E-Newsletter: http://nocofoundation.org/66/Receive%20Our%20E-Newsletter/
Facebook: http://www.facebook.com/pages/Community-Foundation-of-Northern-Colorado/45884021375
Twitter: http://twitter.com/NoCoFoundation
YouTube: http://www.youtube.com/user/cfNorthernColorado
Scholarship inquiry e-mail: scholarships@nocofoundation.org

Incorporated in 1975 in CO.
Foundation type: Community foundation.
Financial data (yr. ended 06/30/13): Assets, $72,473,461 (M); gifts received, $8,168,952; expenditures, $4,320,271; giving activities include $3,965,933 for grants.
Purpose and activities: The foundation builds a better community by promoting philanthropy through creative donor services.
Fields of interest: Humanities; Arts; Education; Health care; Human services; Community/economic development.
Type of support: General/operating support; Endowments; Program development; Scholarship funds; Matching/challenge support.
Limitations: Applications accepted. Giving limited to Larimer County, CO.
Publications: Annual report; Newsletter.
Application information: Visit foundation web site for application guidelines. Application form required.
Initial approach: Submit grant application
Deadline(s): July
Board meeting date(s): Every other month
Final notification: Late Nov.
Officers and Trustees:* Chris Otto,* Chair.; Ray Caraway,* Pres.; Stephanie Cashman, C.F.O.; Roxanne Fry, C.O.O.; Greg Anderson; Rhys Christensen; Constance Dohn; Doug Hutchinson; Polly Juneau; Robert Kearney; Lisa Larsen; Chuck Levine; Krishna Murthy; Spiro Palmer; Suzanne Peterson; Kathay Rennels; Cathy Schott; Earl Sethre.
Number of staff: 5 full-time professional; 1 part-time support.
EIN: 840699243

1394
Community Foundation Serving Greeley and Weld County ✧
2425 35th Ave., Ste.201
Greeley, CO 80634 (970) 304-9970
Contact: Judy Knapp, Pres.
FAX: (970) 352-1271; E-mail: info@cfsgwc.org; Main URL: http://www.cfsgwc.org
Facebook: http://www.facebook.com/pages/The-Community-Foundation-Serving-Greeley-and-Weld-County/135338119125

LinkedIn: https://www.linkedin.com/company/community-foundation-serving-greeley-and-weld-county
Twitter: https://twitter.com/CommFoundGWC
YouTube: http://www.youtube.com/channel/UC2929I3rlZntGfl-bGvvn2Q

Established in 1972; merged in 1997 in CO.
Donors: Cameron DeCamp; Annette Fulton; Lucile J. Gray†; Alpine Gardens; H + H Excavation; BMC West; Siegrist Construction; Monfort Family Foundation; Platte Valley Medical Center; Lawrence Hertzke; Rick Jenkins; Barbara Jenkins; Betty Whitson; Bill McDonald; Richard Bond; Reva Bond; Martin Lind; Richard Boettcher; Irene Boettcher; Gerald Shadwick; Jeannine Shadwick; Philip Hood; Robert Kron; Judy Kron; Robert Oshsner†; Lena Ochsner; Poudre Valley Healthcare Inc.; Greeley Rotary Club; Gay and Lesbian Fund for Colorado; Bond Family Foundation; El Pomar; Banner Health and NCMC.
Foundation type: Community foundation.
Financial data (yr. ended 12/31/13): Assets, $16,599,616 (M); gifts received, $2,952,601; expenditures, $2,041,346; giving activities include $1,002,823 for 21 grants (high: $406,683).
Purpose and activities: The Community Foundation Serving Greeley and Weld County promotes philanthropy to build resources, develops partnerships, and provides leadership that will be of lasting benefit to the local communities.
Fields of interest: Arts; Education; Health care; Housing/shelter; Recreation; Youth development; Youth, services; Human services; Community/economic development; General charitable giving; Children/youth; Women; Girls.
Type of support: Equipment; Curriculum development; Emergency funds; General/operating support; Matching/challenge support; Program development; Scholarship funds; Seed money.
Limitations: Applications accepted. Giving primarily to residents of Greeley and Weld County, CO. No support for sectarian religious purposes or for-profit organizations. No grants for capital fund drives, endowments, debt reduction or event sponsorships.
Publications: Application guidelines; Annual report; Financial statement; Informational brochure; Newsletter.
Application information: Visit foundation web site for application forms and guidelines. Application form required.
Initial approach: Submit application form and attachments
Deadline(s): Varies
Board meeting date(s): Feb., May, Aug., and Nov.
Final notification: Within 6 weeks
Officers and Directors:* Rob Waldo,* Chair.; John Adams,* Vice-Chair.; Judy Knapp,* Pres.; Rochelle Mitchell-Miller,* V.P., Devel.; Christine Richardson,* Secy.; Heidi Klepper,* Treas.; Matt Anderson; Beth Bashor; Karen Burd; Nora Garza; Christine Larsen; Bill Meier; Allen McConnell; Stephanie McCune; Tim Ulrich; Lucie Wisehart.
Number of staff: 4 full-time professional.
EIN: 841315296

1395
Community Foundation Serving Southwest Colorado ✧

1309 E. 3rd Ave.
Smiley Bldg., St. 20A
Durango, CO 81301 (970) 375-5807
Contact: Briggen Wrinkle, Exec. Dir.
FAX: (970) 375-5806;
E-mail: director@swcommunityfoundation.org; Mailing address: P.O. Box 1673, Durango, CO 81302-1673; Main URL: http://www.swcommunityfoundation.org

Established in 1999 in CO.
Foundation type: Community foundation.
Financial data (yr. ended 12/31/12): Assets, $3,200,382 (M); gifts received, $1,961,140; expenditures, $1,117,966; giving activities include $267,853 for 3+ grants (high: $150,000), and $258,497 for 71 grants to individuals.
Purpose and activities: Giving for the development of endowed funds that serve the southwest CO area.
Fields of interest: Arts; Education; Health care; Recreation; Children/youth, services; Human services; Children/youth; Disabilities, people with.
Type of support: General/operating support; Continuing support; Annual campaigns; Building/renovation; Equipment; Endowments; Conferences/seminars; Scholarship funds.
Limitations: Applications accepted. Giving limited to CO.
Publications: Financial statement; Informational brochure; Occasional report.
Application information: Visit foundation web site for application form and guidelines. Colorado Common Grant Application form accepted. Application form required.
Initial approach: Submit application form and attachments
Copies of proposal: 1
Deadline(s): None
Board meeting date(s): 2nd Thurs. in Feb., Apr., June, Aug., and Oct.
Final notification: Generally within 1 month
Officers and Directors:* Mike Hudson,* Pres.; John Anderson,* V.P.; June Russell,* Secy.; Herb Brodsky,* Treas.; Briggen Wrinkle, Exec. Dir.; Richard Ballantine; Chuck Fredrick; o Dir. Lopez; Molly Martin; Allison Morrissey; Mike Smedley; Todd Starr; Michael Whiting.
Number of staff: 1 part-time professional.
EIN: 841474900

1396
Adolph Coors Foundation ✧

4100 E. Mississippi Ave., Ste. 1850
Denver, CO 80246-3074 (303) 388-1636
Contact: John Jackson, Exec. Dir.
FAX: (303) 388-1684;
E-mail: generalinfo@acoorsfnd.org; Main URL: http://www.coorsfoundation.org

Incorporated in 1975 in CO.
Donors: Adolph Coors, Jr.†; Gertrude S. Coors†; Janet Coors†; William K. Coors; Rita Bass Coors.
Foundation type: Independent foundation.
Financial data (yr. ended 11/30/13): Assets, $168,409,463 (M); expenditures, $6,340,372; qualifying distributions, $6,497,553; giving activities include $4,302,170 for 122 grants (high: $448,015; low: $3,655).
Purpose and activities: The primary areas of foundation interest are: 1) Health, with emphasis on programs that are preventive in nature, promote wellness and/or can demonstrate a reduction in health-care costs; 2) Education, focusing on institutions and programs that foster excellence in the knowledge of free enterprise, science, technology and ethics; 3) Youth Mentoring—agencies that assist the disadvantaged in their efforts to be self-sufficient and productive and that nurture the development of integrity and leadership; and 4) Self-sufficiency—agencies that assist people in becoming independent and productive.
Fields of interest: Education; Health care; Youth, services; Youth; Economically disadvantaged.
Type of support: Building/renovation; General/operating support; Program development.
Limitations: Applications accepted. Giving primarily in CO. No support for preschools, day care centers, nursing homes or other extended care facilities, museums or museum projects, churches or church projects, animals or animal-related programs, national health organizations, historic renovation, tax-supported organizations, public or private K-12 schools or programs for senior citizens. Generally, no grants to individuals, or for endowment funds, research, production of films or other media-related projects, conduit funding, deficits, debt retirement, computer equipment, start-up funding, special events, meetings, or seminars.
Publications: Annual report (including application guidelines).
Application information: Applications must be submitted online via foundation web site. The foundation does not accept proposals sent by fax or e-mail. Only one request is considered for an organization during any 12-month period. Application form required.
Initial approach: Use online application system
Copies of proposal: 1
Deadline(s): Mar. 1, July 1 and Nov. 1
Board meeting date(s): 3 times per year
Final notification: 3 months
Officers and Trustees:* Peter H. Coors,* Chair.; Rev. Robert G. Windsor,* Vice-Chair.; Jeffrey H. Coors,* Treas.; John W. Jackson, Exec. Dir.; William K. Coors; Cecily Coors Garnsey; Melissa Coors Osborn.
Number of staff: 4 full-time professional; 1 full-time support.
EIN: 510172279
Selected grants: The following grants are a representative sample of this grantmaker's funding activity:
$195,500 to Save Our Youth, Denver, CO, 2011. For general operating support.
$150,000 to Heritage Foundation, Washington, DC, 2011. For general operating support.
$140,000 to Thomas Jefferson University Hospitals, Philadelphia, PA, 2011. For Myrna Brind Center for Integrative Medicine.
$125,000 to Teach for America, Denver, CO, 2011. For general operating support.
$75,000 to Discovery Science Center, Fort Collins, CO, 2011. For capital needs.
$50,000 to Colorado Center for the Blind, Littleton, CO, 2011. For renovations.
$25,000 to Work Options for Women, Denver, CO, 2011. For general operating support.
$20,000 to Project Self-Sufficiency of Loveland-Fort Collins, Loveland, CO, 2011. For general operating support.
$15,000 to Big Brothers Big Sisters of Southwest Colorado, Durango, CO, 2011. For general operating support.
$10,000 to San Miguel Mentoring Program, Telluride, CO, 2011. For general operating support.

1397
COPIC Medical Foundation ✧ ☆
7351 E. Lowry Blvd.
Denver, CO 80230-6082 (720) 858-6000
Contact: Kathy Brown
E-mail: lsidener@copic.com; Main URL: https://www.callcopic.com/who-we-are/copic-medical/Pages/default.aspx

Established in 1992 in CO.
Donor: COPIC Insurance Company.
Foundation type: Company-sponsored foundation.
Financial data (yr. ended 12/31/13): Assets, $13,824,325 (M); gifts received, $501,210; expenditures, $596,547; qualifying distributions, $576,021; giving activities include $537,073 for 50 grants (high: $126,035; low: $535).
Purpose and activities: The foundation supports programs designed to improve patient safety, quality of care, disease management, and transitions in care and to reduce medical errors. Special emphasis is directed toward educating and training health care professionals; system changes and improvements; pilot programs designed to improve medicine; and the development and implementation of checklists and other tools.
Fields of interest: Medical school/education; Education; Health care, clinics/centers; Dental care; Health care, blood supply; Public health; Health care, patient services; Health care; Cerebral palsy; Medical research; Human services.
Type of support: Equipment; Program development; Conferences/seminars; Scholarship funds; Employee volunteer services.
Limitations: Applications accepted. Giving primarily in CO and NE. No support for political organizations, religious organizations, societies, or fraternal organizations. No grants to individuals, or for political campaigns or lobbying, endowments, telephone solicitations, ongoing general operating support, construction or repair of facilities, or capital campaigns.
Publications: Application guidelines; Informational brochure.
Application information: Application form required.
Initial approach: Completed application form
Deadline(s): None
Directors: Ray Blum; Linda A. Clark; James Dreisbach, M.D.; Ray J. Groves; Brian C. Harrington, M.D.; Steven Hoffenberg, M.D.; Roberto Masferrer, M.D.; Matthew J. Fleishman; Richard K. Parker, M.D.; Kathryn Paul; Jennifer A. Roller, M.D.; Walter K. Rush III; Peter Whittied, M.D.; John F. Wolz, M.D.; Gerald V. Zarlengo, M.D.
Officers: Theodore J. Clarke, M.D., C.E.O.; Steven A. Rubin, C.O.O.
EIN: 841197083
Selected grants: The following grants are a representative sample of this grantmaker's funding activity:
$40,000 to University of Colorado, Denver, CO, 2011. For general program support.
$15,000 to Cerebral Palsy of Colorado, Denver, CO, 2011. For general program support.
$15,000 to Colorado Nonprofit Development Center, Denver, CO, 2011. For general program support.
$10,000 to Bonfils Blood Center Foundation, Denver, CO, 2011. For general program support.
$10,000 to Colorado Mission of Mercy, Pueblo, CO, 2011. For general program support.
$10,000 to Regis University, Denver, CO, 2011. For general program support.
$10,000 to Stapleton 2040, Denver, CO, 2011. For general program support.
$5,000 to MDS Counseling Center, Denver, CO, 2011. For general program support.
$3,000 to Childrens Museum of Denver, Denver, CO, 2011. For general program support.
$1,750 to Alzheimers Association, Denver, CO, 2011. For general program support.

1398
The Crowell Trust ✧
(also known as Henry P. and Susan C. Crowell Trust)
102 N. Cascade Ave., Ste. 300
Colorado Springs, CO 80903-1418 (719) 645-8119
Contact: Candace "Candy" Sparks, Exec. Dir.
FAX: (719) 418-2695; E-mail: info@crowelltrust.org; Main URL: http://www.crowelltrust.org

Trust established in 1927 in IL.
Donors: Henry P. Crowell†; Henry P. Crowell Benevolence and Education Trust; Henry P. and Susan C. Crowell Trust.
Foundation type: Independent foundation.
Financial data (yr. ended 12/31/12): Assets, $99,963,779 (M); expenditures, $5,466,454; qualifying distributions, $4,766,054; giving activities include $4,225,000 for 113 grants (high: $215,000; low: $500).
Purpose and activities: Created to aid evangelical Christianity by support to organizations having for their purposes its teaching, advancement, and active extension at home and abroad.
Fields of interest: Theological school/education; Christian agencies & churches; Religion.
Type of support: General/operating support; Management development/capacity building; Equipment; Program development; Publication; Curriculum development; Scholarship funds; Technical assistance.
Limitations: Applications accepted. Giving on a national basis. No support for churches or schooling from kindergarten through 12th grade. No grants to individuals, or for endowment funds; no loans.
Application information: Applications accepted online. Application form required.
Initial approach: Preliminary proposal, see foundation web site for full details
Copies of proposal: 1
Deadline(s): See web site for current deadlines
Board meeting date(s): Spring and fall
Final notification: 1 to 2 months
Officers and Trustees:* John T. Lewis,* Chair.; John T. Bass,* Vice-Chair. and Treas.; Dr. Jane Overstreet,* Secy.; Candace "Candy" Sparks, Exec. Dir.; Paul Borthwick; Jack Robinson.
Corporate Trustee: The Northern Trust Company.
Number of staff: 1 full-time professional; 2 part-time support.
EIN: 366038028

1399
Daniels Fund
101 Monroe St.
Denver, CO 80206-4467 (303) 393-7220
Contact: Bill Fowler, Sr. V.P., Grants Prog.
FAX: (720) 941-4110; E-mail: info@danielsfund.org; Toll free tel.: (877) 791- 4726; Additional e-mail for general contact: grantsinfo@danielsfund.org; Main URL: http://www.danielsfund.org
E-Newsletter: http://www.danielsfund.org/contact/newsletter.asp
Twitter: https://twitter.com/Daniels_Fund

Established in 1997 in CO.
Donor: Bill Daniels†.
Foundation type: Independent foundation.
Financial data (yr. ended 12/31/13): Assets, $1,388,360,517 (M); expenditures, $55,677,151; qualifying distributions, $52,881,939; giving activities include $32,994,514 for 531 grants (high: $1,000,000; low: $750), $13,400,844 for 1,157 grants to individuals, and $10,933 for 22 employee matching gifts.
Purpose and activities: Giving primarily for child care education reform and early childhood education, higher education, youth development, the elderly, homelessness and self-sufficiency, alcoholism, and substance abuse, amateur athletics, and for people with physical disabilities.
Fields of interest: Education, reform; Education, ethics; Education, early childhood education; Education; Substance abuse, services; Alcoholism; Geriatrics; Housing/shelter, homeless; Athletics/sports, amateur leagues; Youth development; Developmentally disabled, centers & services; Homeless, human services; Aging; Disabilities, people with; Economically disadvantaged; Homeless.
Type of support: General/operating support; Annual campaigns; Capital campaigns; Building/renovation; Equipment; Program development; Program evaluation; Scholarships—to individuals; Matching/challenge support.
Limitations: Applications accepted. Giving primarily in CO, NM (primarily on education-related initiatives), UT and WY. No support for arts and cultural programs. No grants to individuals (except for Daniels Fund Scholarship Program) or for academic, medical, or scientific research or symposia, or for endowments or debt elimination.
Publications: Annual report; Financial statement; Grants list; Informational brochure; Newsletter; IRS Form 990 or 990-PF printed copy available upon request.
Application information: Generally only one active grant is allowed per organization. Please contact the fund prior to submitting an application if you are applying for a program or project that is part of a larger institution such as a university. Apply for additional funding once all reporting requirements from a previous grant have been fulfilled. The Daniels Fund has revised its grantmaking strategy for New Mexico to focus primarily on education-related initiatives. Application form required.
Initial approach: Submit online full proposal. Letter or telephone for other inquiries
Copies of proposal: 1
Deadline(s): None
Board meeting date(s): Quarterly
Final notification: Within 120 days
Officers and Directors:* June Travis,* Chair.; Linda Childears,* C.E.O. and Pres.; Jeb Dickey, Exec. V.P. and C.F.O.; Bill Fowler, Sr. V.P., Grants; Kristin Todd, Sr. V.P., Scholarships Prog.; David Brown, V.P., Inf. Tech. and Business Applications; Gretchen Lenamond, V.P., Financial Accounting; Bo Peretto, Sr. V.P., Comm. and Opers.; Debbie Pierce, V.P., Media and Community Relations; Tony Acone; Brian Deevy; Hank Brown; Francisco Garcia; Gayle Greer; Jim Griesmer; Tom Marinkovich; Jim Nicholson.

Number of staff: 38 full-time professional; 1 full-time support; 2 part-time support.
EIN: 841393308
Selected grants: The following grants are a representative sample of this grantmaker's funding activity:
$1,975,694 to University of Denver, Denver, CO, 2013. For Scholarships.
$1,405,187 to Young Americans Education Foundation, Denver, CO, 2013. For 2013 Operating Support.
$1,136,491 to Colorado State University, Fort Collins, CO, 2013. For Scholarships.
$1,000,000 to American Enterprise Institute for Public Policy Research, Washington, DC, 2013. For Free Enterprise on College Campuses.
$968,711 to University of Colorado, Boulder, CO, 2013. For Scholarships.
$500,000 to Volunteers of America Northern Rockies, Sheridan, WY, 2013. For Capital Campaign.
$485,000 to Metro CareRing, Denver, CO, 2013. For Hunger Relief Center Capital Campaign.
$30,000 to Boy Scouts of America, Rocky Mountain Council, Pueblo, CO, 2013. For Learning For Life Program.
$30,000 to Hilltop Health Services Corporation, Grand Junction, CO, 2013. For Emergency Shelter Services.
$19,996 to Seattle University, Seattle, WA, 2013. For Scholarships.

1400
The Courtenay C. and Lucy Patten Davis Foundation ✧
(formerly The Courtenay C. Davis Foundation)
2595 E. Cedar Ave.
Denver, CO 80209-3204

Established in 1992 in WY.
Donors: Alfred P. Davis; Courtenay C. Davis‡; Lucy Davis‡.
Foundation type: Independent foundation.
Financial data (yr. ended 12/31/13): Assets, $27,462,259 (M); expenditures, $2,994,260; qualifying distributions, $2,866,394; giving activities include $2,729,510 for 21 grants (high: $1,599,455; low: $5,278).
Fields of interest: Historic preservation/historical societies; Higher education; Hospitals (general); Health care; Human services.
Limitations: Applications not accepted. Giving primarily in CO, Washington, DC, NY and WY. No grants to individuals.
Application information: Contributes only to pre-selected organizations.
Officers and Directors:* Amy Davis,* Pres.; Joan Bell,* Secy.; Tyson Dines III,* Treas.
EIN: 830300897
Selected grants: The following grants are a representative sample of this grantmaker's funding activity:
$908,814 to Hospice of Metro Denver, Denver, CO, 2011.
$350,000 to National Trust for Historic Preservation, Washington, DC, 2011.
$25,000 to Denver Parks and Recreation Foundation, Denver, CO, 2011.
$20,000 to Colorado Council on Economic Education, Denver, CO, 2011.
$20,000 to Food Bank of the Rockies, Denver, CO, 2011.
$15,000 to Smile Train, New York, NY, 2011.

1401
The Denver Foundation ✧
55 Madison St., 8th Fl.
Denver, CO 80206 (303) 300-1790
Contact: David J. Miller, C.E.O.; Bill Inama, Grants Mgr.
FAX: (303) 300-6547;
E-mail: information@denverfoundation.org; Grant application e-mail: binama@denverfoundation.org; Main URL: http://www.denverfoundation.org
Facebook: http://www.facebook.com/pages/The-Denver-Foundation/280105511218?ref=nf
RSS Feed: http://denverfoundation.org/rss/announcements
Twitter: http://twitter.com/TDFcommunity
YouTube: http://www.youtube.com/TheDenverFoundation

Established in 1925 in CO by resolution and declaration of trust.
Foundation type: Community foundation.
Financial data (yr. ended 12/31/12): Assets, $606,066,260 (M); gifts received, $51,061,679; expenditures, $74,999,756; giving activities include $61,829,537 for 4,558 grants, $2,477,000 for 1,000 grants to individuals, and $215,000 for 3 loans/program-related investments.
Purpose and activities: The foundation seeks to improve life in Metro Denver through philanthropy, leadership, and strengthening the community. Grants primarily for education, basic human needs, economic opportunity, and community leadership programs and strengthening neighborhoods with Small Grants Program.
Fields of interest: Education; Health care; Human services; Community/economic development; Immigrants/refugees; Economically disadvantaged; Homeless.
Type of support: Building/renovation; Consulting services; General/operating support; Matching/challenge support; Program development; Program-related investments/loans; Seed money; Technical assistance.
Limitations: Applications accepted. Giving limited to Adams, Arapahoe, Boulder, Broomfield, Denver, Douglas, and Jefferson counties, CO. No support for government agencies, parochial or religious schools, or organizations that further religious doctrine. No grants to individuals (except for scholarships), or for sponsorships, debt liquidation, debt retirement, endowments or other reserve funds, membership or affiliation campaigns, dinners, or special events, research, publications, films, travel, or conferences, symposiums, workshops, or individual medical procedures, medical, scientific, or academic research, creation or installation of art objects, capital campaigns, grants for re-granting purposes or multi-year funding requests.
Publications: Application guidelines; Annual report; Annual report (including application guidelines); Financial statement; Grants list; Informational brochure; Informational brochure (including application guidelines); Newsletter; Occasional report; Program policy statement (including application guidelines).
Application information: Visit foundation web site for application guidelines. The foundation offers free grant proposal workshops that help organizations learn how to prepare a complete grant proposal. Colorado Common Grant Application form accepted. Application form not required.
Initial approach: Submit proposal
Copies of proposal: 1
Deadline(s): Feb. 1 and Aug. 1
Board meeting date(s): Jan., Apr., July, and Oct.
Final notification: Within 4 months
Officers and Trustees:* Bill Ryan,* Chair.; Sandra Shreve,* Vice-Chair.; David J. Miller, C.E.O. and Pres.; Rebecca Arno, V.P., Comms.; Barbara Berv, V.P., Philanthropic Svcs. and Sr. Philanthropic Planner; Lauren Y. Casteel, V.P., Philanthropic Partnerships; Jeff Hirota, V.P., Progs.; Daniel Lee, V.P., Finance and Admin.; Sarah Harrison, Deputy V.P., Philanthropic Svcs. and Sr. Philanthropic Planner; Rico Munn,* Secy.; Jim Kelley,* Treas.; Jennifer Corzine, Cont.; Jandell Allen-Davis; Pamela Kenney Basey; Sarah Bock; Ginny Bayless; Denise Burgess; Linda Campbell; Linda Campbell; Daniel Escalente; Cole Finegan; K.C. Gallagher; Maria Guajardo; Kenzo Kawanabe; Joyce Nakamura; Denise O'Leary; Bruce Schroffel; Stephen Seifert; George Sparks; Chris Urbina, M.D.; Maria Zubia.
Number of staff: 34 full-time professional; 1 part-time professional; 7 full-time support.
EIN: 846048381
Selected grants: The following grants are a representative sample of this grantmaker's funding activity:
$7,500,000 to Alliance for Sustainable Colorado, Denver, CO, 2013.
$1,574,863 to Colorado Community Health Network, Denver, CO, 2013. For support of preparing the Safety Net for the Future of Health Care.
$1,500,000 to Colorado Community College System Foundation, Denver, CO, 2013. For support of the Campaign for Colorado's Community Colleges.
$1,150,000 to Wildlife Experience, Parker, CO, 2013. For general operating support.
$500,000 to Learning Ally, National Headquarters, Princeton, NJ, 2013. To support the Parent Engagement Program.
$5,000 to North Colorado Medical Center Foundation, Greeley, CO, 2013. For support of the Rothman Chaplaincy Program.
$4,000 to Safehouse Denver, Denver, CO, 2013. For general operating support.
$4,000 to University of Colorado, Financial Aid Office, Colorado Springs, CO, 2013. For scholarship.
$2,500 to Art Students League of Denver, Denver, CO, 2013. To support strategic planning.
$2,000 to Greenway Foundation, Greenwood Village, CO, 2013. To support the upkeep of and dog waste bags in Commons Park.

1402
The Doolin Family Foundation ✧ ☆
c/o Reese Henry
400 E. Main St., Ste. 2
Aspen, CO 81611-2919

Established in 1998 in TX.
Donors: Earl L. Doolin; Kaleta Doolin; Charles W. Doolin; Mary Kathryn Dooley Charitable Lead Unity Trust Foundation.
Foundation type: Independent foundation.
Financial data (yr. ended 12/31/13): Assets, $877,399 (M); gifts received, $332,767; expenditures, $549,436; qualifying distributions, $545,000; giving activities include $545,000 for 4 grants (high: $500,000; low: $5,000).
Fields of interest: Medical research; Human services.

Type of support: General/operating support.
Limitations: Applications not accepted. Giving primarily in Dallas, TX. No grants to individuals.
Application information: Unsolicited requests for funds not accepted.
Officer: Willadean Doolin, Pres.
Directors: Krista Eddy; Brett Malcolm.
EIN: 752780279

1403
Dornick Foundation Inc. ✧
(formerly Cross Creek Foundation, Inc.)
P.O. Box 219
Woody Creek, CO 81656-0219

Established in 1997 in NC.
Donor: William Idema.
Foundation type: Independent foundation.
Financial data (yr. ended 12/31/13): Assets, $6,425,523 (M); gifts received, $2,500,000; expenditures, $1,630,582; qualifying distributions, $1,573,238; giving activities include $1,556,466 for 20 grants (high: $606,500; low: $4,500).
Fields of interest: Higher education; Environment, natural resources; Animal welfare; Human services; Community/economic development; Science, formal/general education.
Limitations: Applications not accepted. Giving primarily in CO and NC. No grants to individuals.
Application information: Contributes only to pre-selected organizations.
Officers: Robert C. Pew III, Pres. and Treas.; Susan H. Taylor, Secy.
Board Member: Kate Wolters.
EIN: 562057825

1404
ECA Foundation, Inc. ✧
4643 S. Ulster St., Ste. 1100
Denver, CO 80237-2867 (303) 694-2667
Contact: Julie M. Mork, Dir.

Established in 1996 in CO.
Donors: Eastern American Energy Corp.; Mountaineer Gas Co.; Energy Corp. of America; Julie M. Mork.
Foundation type: Company-sponsored foundation.
Financial data (yr. ended 06/30/14): Assets, $1,318,061 (M); gifts received, $1,209,306; expenditures, $1,314,458; qualifying distributions, $1,302,251; giving activities include $1,302,251 for 60 grants (high: $350,000; low: $100).
Purpose and activities: The foundation supports programs designed to maximize the development and potential of youth academically, physically, and spiritually.
Fields of interest: Arts; Elementary/secondary education; Education; Health care; Children/youth, services; Children/youth; Children; Youth.
Type of support: Management development/capacity building; Program development; Curriculum development; Scholarship funds; Employee matching gifts; Matching/challenge support.
Limitations: Applications accepted. Giving primarily in areas of company operations in the metropolitan Denver, CO, area, metropolitan Houston, TX, area, PA and WV. No support for political organizations or discriminatory organizations. No grants to individuals, or for publications, films, media projects, seminars, conferences, events, or meetings travel, start-up needs, research, general operating support, capital campaigns or acquisitions, construction or renovation, debt reduction, endowments, or recruiting or training.
Publications: Application guidelines; Grants list; Informational brochure (including application guidelines).
Application information: Application form not required.
Initial approach: Proposal
Copies of proposal: 1
Deadline(s): Quarterly deadline
Board meeting date(s): Mar., June, Sept., and Dec.
Officers: Sara E. Dimanna, Secy.; J. Michael Forbes, Treas.
Directors: Joseph E. Casabona; Frank H. McCullough III; John F. Mork; Julie M. Mork; Kyle M. Mork; Don C. Supcoe.
Number of staff: 2 part-time professional.
EIN: 841349588

1405
The Joseph Henry Edmondson Foundation ✧
10 Lake Cir.
Colorado Springs, CO 80906-4201 (719) 471-1241
Contact: Heather L. Carroll, Exec. Dir.

Established in 1987 in CO.
Foundation type: Independent foundation.
Financial data (yr. ended 07/31/13): Assets, $20,091,151 (M); expenditures, $854,767; qualifying distributions, $566,770; giving activities include $566,770 for grants.
Purpose and activities: Giving primarily for the welfare of children, the ill, and the elderly, the preservation and improvement of the environment, historic and folk art museums, medical research, and the United Church of Christ outreach programs.
Fields of interest: Museums (ethnic/folk arts); Museums (history); Arts; Environment; Health care; Medical research, institute; Children/youth, services; Family services; Homeless, human services; Protestant agencies & churches.
Type of support: General/operating support; Continuing support; Capital campaigns; Building/renovation; Equipment; Land acquisition; Emergency funds; Program development; Technical assistance; Matching/challenge support.
Limitations: Applications accepted. Giving primarily in the Colorado Springs, CO, area. No support for evangelical organizations or political organizations. No grants to individuals or for sponsorships or for debt reduction or event funding.
Publications: Application guidelines; Grants list; Informational brochure (including application guidelines).
Application information: Application form required.
Initial approach: Proposal
Copies of proposal: 2
Deadline(s): None
Board meeting date(s): Jan., Apr., July, and Oct.
Officers: Bruce T. Buell, Chair.; Sharie Higgins, Secy.; Ben Sparks, Treas.; Heather Carroll, Exec. Dir.
Board Members: Christopher Bruce Duff; Sean Duff; Mary Kanas; Susan Ramsay.
Number of staff: 1 full-time professional.
EIN: 841090456
Selected grants: The following grants are a representative sample of this grantmaker's funding activity:
$25,000 to Homeward Pikes Peak, Colorado Springs, CO, 2013. For Housing First Pikes Peak Program.
$15,000 to Pikes Peak Community Foundation, Colorado Springs, CO, 2013. For Meadows Park Community Center Fund.
$15,000 to Westside CARES, Colorado Springs, CO, 2013. For emergency human services.
$13,000 to Kids in Need of Dentistry, Denver, CO, 2013. For KIND Colorado Springs Clinic.
$10,000 to Coalition for the Upper South Platte, Lake George, CO, 2013. For Fire-Recovery Project.
$10,000 to Colorado College, Colorado Springs, CO, 2013. For Masters of Arts in Teaching.
$10,000 to Colorado Open Lands, Lakewood, CO, 2013. For Peak to Prairie Conservation Initiative.
$4,000 to Pikes Peak Community Foundation, Colorado Springs, CO, 2013. For Voice of Grief Fund.
$3,000 to Pikes Peak Community Foundation, Colorado Springs, CO, 2013. For IndyGiveI Fund.
$2,000 to Pikes Peak Community Foundation, Colorado Springs, CO, 2013. For Venetucci Farm Barn.

1406
El Pomar Foundation ✧
10 Lake Cir.
Colorado Springs, CO 80906-4201 (719) 633-7733
Contact: William J. Hybl, Chair.
FAX: (719) 577-5702; Additional tel.: (800) 554-7711; Main URL: http://www.elpomar.org
Blog: http://blog.elpomar.org/
Facebook: https://www.facebook.com/elpomarfoundation?v=wall&ref=ts
Grants Database: http://www.elpomar.org/grants
Twitter: http://twitter.com/elpomarfdtn

Incorporated in 1937 in CO.
Donors: Spencer Penrose†; Mrs. Spencer Penrose†.
Foundation type: Independent foundation.
Financial data (yr. ended 12/31/13): Assets, $552,170,661 (M); gifts received, $1,981,050; expenditures, $20,713,894; qualifying distributions, $22,018,826; giving activities include $11,788,502 for 917 grants (high: $1,500,000; low: $272), $169,417 for 49 employee matching gifts, and $256,751 for 56 in-kind gifts.
Purpose and activities: Grants only to nonprofit organizations for public, educational, arts and humanities, health, and welfare purposes, including child welfare, the disadvantaged, and housing; municipalities may request funds for specific projects.
Fields of interest: Visual arts; Museums; Performing arts; Performing arts, theater; Performing arts, music; Humanities; Historic preservation/historical societies; Arts; Child development, education; Vocational education; Higher education; Adult/continuing education; Adult education—literacy, basic skills & GED; Libraries/library science; Education, reading; Education; Environment, natural resources; Environment; Hospitals (general); Pharmacy/prescriptions; Health care; Substance abuse, services; Health organizations, association; Employment; Food services; Nutrition; Housing/shelter, development; Recreation; Human services; Children/youth, services; Child development, services; Family services; Residential/custodial

care, hospices; Aging, centers/services; Homeless, human services; Community/economic development; Voluntarism promotion; Transportation; Aging; Disabilities, people with; Minorities; Economically disadvantaged; Homeless.
Type of support: General/operating support; Continuing support; Capital campaigns; Building/renovation; Equipment; Land acquisition; Emergency funds; Program development; Scholarship funds; Employee matching gifts; In-kind gifts.
Limitations: Applications accepted. Giving limited to CO. No support for organizations that distribute funds to other grantees, religious or political organizations, primary or secondary education, or for camps or seasonal facilities. No grants to individuals, or for travel, film or other media projects, conferences, seminars, deficit financing, endowment funds, research.
Publications: Application guidelines; Annual report (including application guidelines); Financial statement; Grants list; Informational brochure.
Application information: Colorado Common Grant Application form accepted. Application form not required.
Initial approach: Proposal
Copies of proposal: 1
Deadline(s): One month before board meeting
Board meeting date(s): 6 to 8 times a year
Final notification: 90 days
Officers and Trustees:* William J. Hybl,* Chair. and C.E.O.; William R. Ward,* Vice-Chair.; Kyle Hybl,* C.O.O. and Gen. Counsel; R. Thayer Tutt, Jr.,* Pres. and C.I.O.; Gary Butterworth, Sr. V.P. ,Dir., El Pomar Fellowship and Dir., Penrose House; Matt Carpenter, Sr. V.P., Grants; George Guerrero, Sr. V.P., Facilities; Theophilus Gregory, Sr. V.P.; Cathy Robbins, Sr. V.P. and Dir., Regional Partnerships; Terrence McWilliams, V.P., Military and Veteran Affairs; Peter Maiurro, V.P.; Robert J. Hilbert, C.F.O. and Trustee Emeritus; Brenda J. Smith, Trustee Emeritus; Andrea Aragon; Judith M. Bell; Hon. Dennis Maes; Bob Manning; Christina McGrath; David J. Palenchar; Genl. Victor Eugene Renuart, Jr.
Number of staff: 33 full-time professional; 20 full-time support; 7 part-time support.
EIN: 846002373
Selected grants: The following grants are a representative sample of this grantmaker's funding activity:
$310,000 to Peak Vista Community Health Centers Foundation, Colorado Springs, CO, 2012. For General operating support.
$250,000 to Atlas Preparatory School, Colorado Springs, CO, 2012. For classroom expansion and renovation.
$200,000 to United Way, Pikes Peak, Colorado Springs, CO, 2012. For annual campaign.
$150,000 to Pikes Peak Hospice Foundation, Colorado Springs, CO, 2012. For Capital campaign.
$140,000 to Colorado Springs Sports Corporation, Colorado Springs, CO, 2012. For General operating support.
$104,120 to Colorado Springs Pioneers Museum, Colorado Springs, CO, 2012. For Gifts in Kind - Donation of Artwork.
$40,000 to Vail Valley Foundation, Avon, CO, 2012. For Youth Foundation programs.
$7,500 to Peak Vista Community Health Centers Foundation, Colorado Springs, CO, 2012. For Healthcare and direct services.
$5,000 to Roundup Fellowship, Denver, CO, 2012. For General operating support in Colorado Springs area.
$5,000 to USAFA Endowment, USAF Academy, CO, 2012. For Support of the Air Force Athletic Corporation.

1407
EnCana Cares (USA) Foundation ✧
370 17th St., Ste. 1700
Denver, CO 80202-5632
Main URL: http://www.encana.com/

Established in 2006 in CO.
Donors: Galen Archer; Clark L. Vickers; Julia Gwaltney; Lisa Mallin; David Smith II; John Holmberg; Encana Oil & Gas (USA), Inc.
Foundation type: Company-sponsored foundation.
Financial data (yr. ended 12/31/13): Assets, $0 (M); gifts received, $1,925,138; expenditures, $1,925,138; qualifying distributions, $1,925,138; giving activities include $1,925,138 for 771 grants (high: $46,350; low: $50).
Purpose and activities: The foundation matches contributions made by employees of EnCana to nonprofit organizations.
Fields of interest: Education; Health care; Human services.
Type of support: Employee matching gifts.
Limitations: Applications not accepted. Giving primarily in CO and TX.
Application information: Contributes only through employee matching gifts.
Officers and Directors:* Renee E. Zemljak,* Pres.; Don McClure,* V.P. and Treas.; Doug Hock,* Secy.
EIN: 205064193

1408
Erion Foundation ✧
P.O. Box 732
Loveland, CO 80539-0732 (970) 667-4549
Contact: Kristin M. Harmon, Admin., Comm.
FAX: (970) 663-6187;
E-mail: contact@erionfoundation.org; General inquiries should be directed to Summer Scott, Admin., Comms. at the foundation's main e-mail address; E-mail for applications: GrantRequest@erionfoundation.org; Applications sent via U.S. mail should be to the attention of the Board of Directors; Main URL: http://www.erionfoundation.org

Established in 1997 in CO.
Donors: Ken Erion†; Helen Erion†.
Foundation type: Independent foundation.
Financial data (yr. ended 12/31/12): Assets, $9,789,647 (M); gifts received, $105,785; expenditures, $701,432; qualifying distributions, $1,222,760; giving activities include $565,449 for 37 grants (high: $311,249; low: $116), and $641,895 for 1 foundation-administered program.
Purpose and activities: The foundation balances its grantmaking between 5 general areas of interest: 1) Major Project Advocacy; 2) Health and Welfare; 3) Basic Needs; 4) Education; and 5) Culture and Community. The foundation prefers grants for capital projects, specific programs, and joint ventures with other funder.
Fields of interest: Arts; Education; Health care; Human services.
Limitations: Applications accepted. Giving primarily in Northern CO, particularly in the Loveland Planning Area, the Thomson and Poudre School Districts, and in Larimer County. No support for private foundations, organizations that don't have fiscal responsibility for the proposed project, private schools, or religious or political programs. No grants to individuals, or for debt reduction.
Application information: The foundation prefers that grant requests be sent via e-mail. Application form required.
Initial approach: Letter requesting application form or download form from foundation web site
Copies of proposal: 1
Deadline(s): Last day of Jan., Apr., July, and Oct.
Board meeting date(s): Quarterly
Final notification: Last day of Mar., June, Sept., and Dec.
Officers and Directors:* Douglas J. Erion,* Pres.; Roger E. Clark,* V.P.; Eli Scott,* Treas.; Janice Pierce Atnip; Justin Erion; Travis Erion; Christine Erion Klein.
Trustee: First National Bank.
EIN: 841358074
Selected grants: The following grants are a representative sample of this grantmaker's funding activity:
$311,249 to Thompson School District, Loveland, CO, 2012. For Education-Lisa Program Education-Bill Reed Theater.
$26,987 to House of Neighborly Service, Loveland, CO, 2012. To assist Local Individuals to Become Self-Sustaining Through Emergency Services Funds to Match Volunteer Hours Contributed By Foundation Family Members.
$6,000 to Community Kitchen, Loveland, CO, 2012. For operating funds to feed the homeless.
$3,000 to Ensight Skills Center, Fort Collins, CO, 2012. For education and training for the low vision and blind.
$2,500 to Northern Colorado AIDS Project, Fort Collins, CO, 2012. For basic needs, health and welfare.
$2,131 to Ridges Sanctuary, Baileys Harbor, WI, 2012. For Funds to Match Volunteer Hours Contributed By Foundation Family Members.
$2,000 to Beet Street, Fort Collins, CO, 2012. For culture and community.

1409
Find Us Faithful Foundation ✧
5994 S. Holly St., Ste. 254
Greenwood Village, CO 80111-4221
Main URL: http://www.findusfaithful.org/

Established in 2006 in DE.
Donors: David Clouse; Elizabeth L. Clouse; Solid Rock Trust.
Foundation type: Independent foundation.
Financial data (yr. ended 12/31/12): Assets, $91,056,027 (M); gifts received, $205,590; expenditures, $4,319,079; qualifying distributions, $3,840,908; giving activities include $3,739,700 for 35 grants (high: $1,700,000; low: $1,600).
Fields of interest: Education; Human services.
Limitations: Applications not accepted. Giving primarily in CO, some funding also in PA. No grants to individuals.
Application information: Contributes only to pre-selected organizations.
Officers and Directors:* David Clouse,* Chair.; Matthew Clouse, Pres.; Elizabeth Lynn Clouse,* V.P.; Patricia Friesen,* V.P.; Steve Laird, Secy.; Jeffrey Kahler, Treas.; McKenzie Clouse; Michael Clouse; Monty Friesen; Jenna Morrow-Clouse.
EIN: 205632085

Selected grants: The following grants are a representative sample of this grantmaker's funding activity:
$200,000 to LifeNet International, Orlando, FL, 2012. For Burundi Clinic.
$165,000 to Hope International, Lancaster, PA, 2012. For Congo Relief Fund.
$165,000 to Hope International, Lancaster, PA, 2012. For Rwanda Relief Fund.
$140,000 to Hope International, Lancaster, PA, 2012. For Democratic Rep of Congo Relief Fund.
$90,000 to Floresta USA, San Diego, CA, 2012. For Oaxaca Mexico Project.
$90,000 to Floresta USA, San Diego, CA, 2012. For World Areas Fund.
$60,000 to Edify, San Diego, CA, 2012. For Loan Capital Fund.
$45,000 to Edify, San Diego, CA, 2012. For Christian Curriculum and Training.
$40,000 to Hope International, Lancaster, PA, 2012. For New Donor Match Fund.
$35,000 to Edify, San Diego, CA, 2012. For Teacher Technology Training.

1410
Harmes C. Fishback Foundation Trust ✧
8 Village Rd.
Englewood, CO 80110-4908 (303) 789-1753
Contact: Katharine H. Stapleton, Tr.
E-mail: kties@aol.com

Trust established in 1972 in CO.
Donor: Harmes C. Fishback‡.
Foundation type: Independent foundation.
Financial data (yr. ended 12/31/13): Assets, $12,471,320 (M); expenditures, $512,174; qualifying distributions, $476,300; giving activities include $421,300 for 83 grants (high: $29,000; low: $100).
Purpose and activities: Giving primarily for education, health and human services, and the arts.
Fields of interest: Museums; Historical activities; Arts; Higher education; Hospitals (general); Health organizations, association; Medical research, institute; Children/youth, services; Adults; Young adults; Physically disabled.
International interests: France.
Type of support: Continuing support; General/operating support; Scholarship funds.
Limitations: Applications accepted. Giving primarily in the metropolitan Denver, CO, area. No support for health organizations or hospitals, with few exceptions. No grants to individuals.
Application information: Application form not required.
Initial approach: Proposal
Copies of proposal: 1
Deadline(s): None
Trustees: Benjamin F. Stepleton III; Craig R. Stapleton; Jenna Stapleton; Katharine H. Stapleton.
Number of staff: None.
EIN: 846094542
Selected grants: The following grants are a representative sample of this grantmaker's funding activity:
$5,000 to Boy Scouts of America, Dnvr Area, Denver, CO, 2012. For educational.
$5,000 to Phoenix Multisport, Boulder, CO, 2012. For health and hospitals.

1411
Foundation for Educational Excellence ✧
4908 Tower Rd., Ste. 108
Denver, CO 80249-6684 (303) 486-8500
Contact: Eric Montoya, Secy.-Treas.

Established in 1997 in CO.
Donors: Oakwood Homes, LLC; Richmond Homes; The Boeing Co.; Orchard Crossing III; Alpert Companies; Aurora Chamber of Conference.
Foundation type: Independent foundation.
Financial data (yr. ended 12/31/12): Assets, $533,656 (M); gifts received, $5,141,987; expenditures, $4,948,689; qualifying distributions, $4,780,512; giving activities include $4,780,512 for 10 grants (high: $3,530,157; low: $636).
Purpose and activities: The foundation is focused on new school development, school reform, and community engagement on educational issues.
Fields of interest: Education, public policy; Education, reform; Education.
Type of support: Seed money; Program development; Equipment; Consulting services; Conferences/seminars; Building/renovation; General/operating support.
Limitations: Applications accepted. Giving primarily in northeastern Denver, CO. No support for religious or political organizations.
Publications: Informational brochure; Occasional report.
Application information: Application form not required.
Initial approach: Letter
Copies of proposal: 1
Deadline(s): Quarterly
Board meeting date(s): Quarterly (usually the final week of the quarter)
Final notification: 30 days
Officers: Hap Legg, Chair.; Kelly Leid, Vice-Chair.; Eric Montoya, Secy.-Treas.; Amy Schwartz, Exec. Dir.
Directors: Gail Busby; Jeff Carlson; Scott Gilmore; Stacie Gilmore; William T. Golson; Patrick Hamill; Tim Sheahan.
Number of staff: 1 full-time professional.
EIN: 841396597

1412
Fox Family Foundation ✧ ☆
3003 E. 1st Ave., Ste. 400
Denver, CO 80206-5611

Established in 2007 in CO.
Donors: John M. Fox; Marcella F. Fox; John F. Fox, Jr.; Anne E. Fox Mounsey; Kelley P. Fox; Peter Mounsey; Becca Selvidge Fox.
Foundation type: Independent foundation.
Financial data (yr. ended 06/30/13): Assets, $21,497,763 (M); gifts received, $3,351,769; expenditures, $670,022; qualifying distributions, $655,568; giving activities include $621,000 for 42 grants (high: $50,000; low: $2,000).
Fields of interest: Education; Hospitals (specialty); Housing/shelter; Youth, services; Human services; Catholic agencies & churches.
Limitations: Applications not accepted. Giving primarily in CO and LA. No grants to individuals.
Application information: Contributes only to pre-selected organizations.
Officers: John M. Fox, Pres. and Treas.; Marcella F. Fox, V.P.; John M. Fox, Jr., Secy.
Directors: Kelley P. Fox; Anne Mounsey; Rick Simms.
EIN: 205854615
Selected grants: The following grants are a representative sample of this grantmaker's funding activity:
$26,000 to Isidore Newman School, New Orleans, LA, 2011.
$15,000 to Denver Childrens Home, Denver, CO, 2011.
$15,000 to Denver Kids, Denver, CO, 2011.
$15,000 to Denver Urban Scholars, Denver, CO, 2011.
$15,000 to Nurse-Family Partnership, Denver, CO, 2011.
$15,000 to Womens Bean Project, Denver, CO, 2011.
$10,000 to Libertys Kitchen, New Orleans, LA, 2011.
$6,000 to YouthBiz, Denver, CO, 2011.
$5,000 to Challenged Athletes Foundation, San Diego, CA, 2011.
$5,000 to CityWILD, Denver, CO, 2011.

1413
Fries Family Foundation ✧
c/o Liberty Global
12300 Liberty Blvd.
Englewood, CO 80112

Donors: Amber L. Fries; Michael T. Fries.
Foundation type: Independent foundation.
Financial data (yr. ended 12/31/12): Assets, $3,866,463 (M); gifts received, $2,995,117; expenditures, $1,919,055; qualifying distributions, $1,887,116; giving activities include $1,870,603 for 44 grants (high: $475,000; low: $500).
Fields of interest: Arts; Education; Human services.
Limitations: Applications not accepted. Giving primarily in CO.
Application information: Unsolicited requests for funds not accepted.
Officers and Directors:* Michael T. Fries,* Pres. and Treas.; Amber L. Fries,* V.P. and Secy.
EIN: 272436308

1414
Fulcrum Foundation ✧ ☆
1685 S. Colorado Blvd., Unit S
P.O. Box 358
Denver, CO 80222-4011

Established in 2001 in PA.
Donors: Ralph J. Roberts, Jr.; Kimberley I. Roberts.
Foundation type: Independent foundation.
Financial data (yr. ended 12/31/12): Assets, $11,209,282 (M); expenditures, $649,337; qualifying distributions, $571,250; giving activities include $563,500 for 32 grants (high: $50,000; low: $1,000).
Fields of interest: Environment; Food services; Human services.
Limitations: Applications not accepted. Giving primarily in CO. No grants to individuals.
Application information: Contributes only to pre-selected organizations.
Trustees: Kimberley I. Roberts; Ralph J. Roberts, Jr.
EIN: 233081735

1415
The Fullerton Family Charitable Trust ✧
306 W. Francis St.
Aspen, CO 81611-1955

Established in 1991 in CA.
Donors: Jessica Fullerton; John B. Fullerton; Baxter Fullerton.
Foundation type: Independent foundation.
Financial data (yr. ended 06/30/13): Assets, $21,830,719 (M); gifts received, $4,175,770; expenditures, $2,114,569; qualifying distributions, $2,104,131; giving activities include $2,101,850 for 20 grants (high: $866,550; low: $1,000).
Purpose and activities: Giving primarily to an education organization supporting students in low-income communities; funding also for the performing arts.
Fields of interest: Performing arts; Elementary/secondary education; Education.
Limitations: Applications not accepted. Giving primarily in CA and CO. No grants to individuals.
Application information: Contributes only to pre-selected organizations.
Trustees: Jessica Fullerton; John B. Fullerton.
EIN: 680262543
Selected grants: The following grants are a representative sample of this grantmaker's funding activity:
$1,375,000 to World Security Institute, Washington, DC, 2011. For general budget.
$105,000 to Theater Aspen, Aspen, CO, 2011. For general budget.
$47,000 to Aspen Institute, Aspen, CO, 2011. For general budget.
$35,000 to Aspen Music Festival and School, Aspen, CO, 2011. For general budget.
$22,000 to Jewish Community Center of San Francisco, San Francisco, CA, 2011. For general budget.
$15,700 to York Country Day School, York, PA, 2011. For general budget.
$10,000 to Childrens Museum of Houston, Houston, TX, 2011. For general budget.
$10,000 to Ross School Foundation, Ross, CA, 2011. For general budget.

1416
Furlotti Family Foundation ✧
P.O. Box 1187
Aspen, CO 81612

Foundation type: Independent foundation.
Financial data (yr. ended 12/31/13): Assets, $0 (M); expenditures, $1,740,137; qualifying distributions, $1,671,129; giving activities include $1,661,933 for 24 grants (high: $250,000; low: $5,000).
Fields of interest: Arts; Education.
Limitations: Applications not accepted.
Application information: Unsolicited requests for funds not accepted.
Officers: Nancy Furlotti, Pres.; Allison Furlotti, Secy.; Michael Furlotti, Treas.
Directors: Alex Furlotti; Patrick Furlotti.
EIN: 208043553

1417
The Galena Foundation ✧
4725 S. Monaco St., Ste. 215
Denver, CO 80237-3445 (303) 761-5213
Contact: Abigail S. Mooney, Pres.; F. Steven Mooney, Tr.

Established in 1996 in CO.
Donors: Abigail S. Mooney; F. Steven Mooney.
Foundation type: Independent foundation.
Financial data (yr. ended 12/31/13): Assets, $43,082,516 (M); gifts received, $500,000; expenditures, $2,172,386; qualifying distributions, $2,029,761; giving activities include $2,026,976 for 24 grants (high: $600,000; low: $5,000).
Fields of interest: Education; Children/youth, services; Christian agencies & churches.
Limitations: Applications accepted. Giving primarily in CO.
Application information: Application form required.
Initial approach: Proposal
Deadline(s): None
Officer: Abigail S. Mooney, Pres.
Trustees: Alice G. Harwood; F. Steven Mooney.
EIN: 841326379

1418
Gates Family Foundation ✧
(formerly Gates Foundation)
3575 Cherry Creek N. Dr., Ste. 100
Denver, CO 80209-3601
Contact: Thomas A. Gougeon, Pres.
FAX: (303) 316-3038;
E-mail: info@gatesfamilyfoundation.org; Main URL: http://www.gatesfamilyfoundation.org

Incorporated in 1946 in CO.
Donors: Charles C. Gates†; Charles C. Gates, Sr.†; Hazel Gates†; John Gates†; June S. Gates†; Berenice Hopper; Robert Hopper.
Foundation type: Independent foundation.
Financial data (yr. ended 12/31/13): Assets, $450,683,702 (M); gifts received, $11,628,931; expenditures, $22,976,485; qualifying distributions, $23,979,448; giving activities include $19,873,375 for 215 grants (high: $2,000,000; low: $2,000), and $200,000 for 1 loan/program-related investment.
Purpose and activities: The mission of the Gates Family Foundation is to invest in projects and organizations which have meaningful impact in Colorado primarily through capital grants and Foundation initiatives that enhance the quality of life for those living in, working in and visiting the state. The foundation seeks to promote excellence, innovation and self-sufficiency in education, healthy lifestyles, community enrichment, connection to nature and stewardship of the state's natural inheritance. The foundation's actions will remain consistent with the founders' intentions and the principles of citizenship, entrepreneurship and free enterprise.
Fields of interest: Arts, multipurpose centers/programs; Visual arts; Museums; Performing arts; Performing arts, dance; Performing arts, theater; Performing arts, music; Humanities; Historic preservation/historical societies; Arts; Libraries/library science; Education; Environment, natural resources; Recreation; Youth development, services; Youth development; Human services; Youth, services; Aging, centers/services.
Type of support: Program-related investments/loans; Capital campaigns; Building/renovation; Land acquisition; Matching/challenge support.
Limitations: Applications accepted. Giving limited to CO. No support for private foundations, medical facilities, or individual public schools or public school districts. No grants to individuals, or for operating budgets, medical research, annual campaigns, emergency funds, deficit financing, purchase of tickets for fundraising dinners, parties, balls, or other social fundraising events, purchase of vehicles or office equipment, conferences, meetings, research, or scholarships; no loans (except for program-related investments).
Publications: Annual report (including application guidelines); Grants list.
Application information: If the summary proposal seems to dovetail with the current interests of the foundation additional information will be required. The foundation accepts the Colorado Common Grant Application for capital campaigns that is provided on the foundation's web site. Application form required.
Initial approach: Telephone call or short summary proposal
Copies of proposal: 1
Deadline(s): Jan. 15, Apr. 1, July 1, and Oct. 1
Board meeting date(s): Quarterly
Final notification: 2 weeks following board decisions and generally less than 3-4 months
Officers and Trustees:* Richard G. Kiely,* Chair.; Valerie Gates,* Vice-Chair.; Thomas A. Gougeon, Pres. and Secy.; Diane Gates Wallach,* Treas.; Christina H. Turissini, Compt.; Doris J. Biester; Richard Celeste; Donald M. Elliman, Jr.; Walter Obermeyer.
Number of staff: 5 full-time professional; 1 full-time support.
EIN: 840474837
Selected grants: The following grants are a representative sample of this grantmaker's funding activity:
$2,000,000 to California Institute of Technology, Pasadena, CA, 2013.
$250,000 to Lucile Packard Foundation for Childrens Health, Palo Alto, CA, 2013.
$250,000 to Peninsula Open Space Trust, Palo Alto, CA, 2013.
$250,000 to Salvation Army of Santa Clara County, San Jose, CA, 2013.
$200,000 to State Historical Society of Colorado, Denver, CO, 2013.
$100,000 to Pathways Home Health and Hospice, Sunnyvale, CA, 2013.
$50,375 to Teens4Oceans, Boulder, CO, 2013.
$50,000 to Colorado State University, Fort Collins, CO, 2013.
$35,000 to Magic Circle Players, Montrose, CO, 2013.
$35,000 to Tu Casa, Alamosa, CO, 2013.

1419
General Service Foundation
557 N. Mill St., Ste. 201
Aspen, CO 81611-1513 (970) 920-6834
FAX: (970) 920-4578;
E-mail: info@generalservice.org; E-mail for Letters of Inquiry (if applicant cannot apply online): grantmanager@generalservice.org; Additional tel. (for William M. Repplinger, Cont.): (970) 920-6834, ext. 5; Main URL: http://www.generalservice.org
General Service Foundation's Philanthropy Promise: http://www.ncrp.org/philanthropys-promise/who

Incorporated in 1946 in IL.
Donors: Clifton R. Musser†; Margaret K. Musser†.
Foundation type: Independent foundation.
Financial data (yr. ended 12/31/12): Assets, $59,037,431 (M); expenditures, $3,639,462; qualifying distributions, $2,886,840; giving activities include $2,117,180 for 91 grants (high: $80,900; low: $500).
Purpose and activities: The foundation believes it can make its best contribution at this point in time

by addressing some of the world's basic long-term problems in three areas: Human Rights and Economic Justice, Reproductive Justice and the Colorado Program.
Fields of interest: Environment, natural resources; Reproductive health; Reproductive health, family planning; Youth, pregnancy prevention; International peace/security; International human rights; Civil liberties, reproductive rights.
International interests: Caribbean; Central America; Mexico.
Type of support: Mission-related investments/loans; General/operating support; Emergency funds; Program development; Conferences/seminars; Seed money; Technical assistance.
Limitations: Applications accepted. Giving limited to the U.S., Mexico, Central America, and the Caribbean.
Publications: Application guidelines; Financial statement; Grants list; Informational brochure (including application guidelines).
Application information: Applicants are strongly encouraged to submit letters of inquiry via e-mail or using the online submission form on the foundation web site. Applicants who are unable to apply online may submit their letters of inquiry via e-mail or U.S. mail, but this only if applying online is not an option. The foundation encourages applicants to who apply via U.S. mail to use non-chlorine bleached recycled paper, and not to use plastic binders. Application form required.
Initial approach: Online letter of inquiry (4 pages)
Copies of proposal: 1
Deadline(s): Feb. 1 and Sept. 1 for letter of inquiry; Mar. 1 and Oct. 1 for invited proposals
Board meeting date(s): Apr. and Nov.
Final notification: 6 months
Officers and Directors:* Robin Snidow,* Chair.; Zoe Estrin,* Vice-Chair.; Marcie J. Musser,* Secy.; Will Halby,* Treas.; William M. Repplinger, CPA, C.F.O.; Lani A. Shaw, Exec. Dir.; Mary Lloyd Estrin; Robert L. Estrin; Zoe L. Foxley; Peter C. Halby; Cleo Hill; Marcie J. Musser; Robert W. Musser; Crystal Plati; Arturo Sandoval; Bill Vandenberg.
Number of staff: 4 full-time professional; 1 full-time support.
EIN: 366018535

1420
Ephraim F. Gildor Foundation ✧
1280 Ute Ave., Ste. 13
Aspen, CO 81611

Established in 1997 in CT.
Donor: Ephraim F. Gildor.
Foundation type: Independent foundation.
Financial data (yr. ended 12/31/13): Assets, $2,017,576 (M); expenditures, $845,937; qualifying distributions, $842,100; giving activities include $842,100 for 10 grants (high: $200,000; low: $100).
Purpose and activities: Giving primarily for the arts, education, Jewish organizations, and to an orthopedic research center.
Fields of interest: Arts; Higher education; Orthopedics research; Jewish agencies & synagogues.
Limitations: Applications not accepted. Giving in the U.S., with emphasis on CO and MN. No grants to individuals.
Application information: Unsolicited requests for funds not accepted.
Trustee: Ephraim F. Gildor.
EIN: 367184924

1421
The Gill Foundation ✧
2215 Market St.
Denver, CO 80205-2026 (303) 292-4455
Contact: Tim Sweeney, C.E.O. and Pres.
FAX: (303) 292-2155;
E-mail: info@gillfoundation.org; Toll free tel.: (888) 530-4455; Main URL: http://www.gillfoundation.org
A program of the Gill Foundation: http://www.facebook.com/gayandlesbianfund
A program of the Gill Foundation: http://www.gayandlesbianfund.org
A program of the Gill Foundation: http://twitter.com/gaylesbianfund
Facebook: http://www.facebook.com/pages/Gill-Foundation/132968166459
Grants Database: http://www.gillfoundation.org/annual-reports/year-2010/grants
Twitter: http://twitter.com/gillfoundation#

Established in 1994 in CO.
Donors: Tim Gill; The Ford Foundation.
Foundation type: Independent foundation.
Financial data (yr. ended 12/31/12): Assets, $222,817,729 (M); gifts received, $1,073,100; expenditures, $21,880,823; qualifying distributions, $19,998,905; giving activities include $14,168,560 for 608 grants (high: $500,000; low: $10), and $1,988,683 for 2 foundation-administered programs.
Purpose and activities: The mission of the foundation is to secure equal opportunity for all people, regardless of sexual orientation or gender expression. The mission is accomplished by: providing grants to nonprofit organizations, strengthening the leadership and managerial skills of nonprofit leaders, increasing financial resources to nonprofit organizations, strengthening democratic institutions, and building awareness of the contributions people of diverse sexual orientations and gender expressions make to American society.
Fields of interest: AIDS; Civil/human rights, LGBTQ; Philanthropy/voluntarism; LGBTQ.
Type of support: General/operating support; Continuing support; Annual campaigns; Emergency funds; Program development; Conferences/seminars; Consulting services; Employee matching gifts; Matching/challenge support.
Limitations: Applications not accepted. Giving on a national basis to national and state-wide organizations. No support for clinical HIV/AIDS research, prevention or direct client services to community based HIV/AIDS organizations outside CO, or art programs for or about HIV. No support to individuals, endowments, scholarships, capital projects, direct care services, pride events, film or media production.
Publications: Annual report; Grants list.
Application information: Unsolicited requests for funds not accepted at this time. Grants to organizations are by invitation only.
Board meeting date(s): Quarterly
Officers and Board Members:* Tim Gill,* Chair.; Courtney Cuff, C.E.O. and Pres.; Robin Hubbard, C.O.O.; Katherine Peck, Sr. V.P., National Progs.; Lance King, V.P., Donor Resources; Bobby Clark, V.P., Marketing and Comms.; Lauren Arnold, Chief of Staff; Urvashi Vaid,* Secy.; Laurie Meili, C.F.O.; John Barabino,* Treas.
Number of staff: 19 full-time professional; 7 full-time support; 2 part-time support.
EIN: 841264186
Selected grants: The following grants are a representative sample of this grantmaker's funding activity:
$600,000 to Tides Foundation, San Francisco, CA, 2012. For program support for State Equality Fund.
$500,000 to Public Interest Projects, New York, NY, 2012. For project support for Federal Agencies Project.
$200,000 to Public Interest Projects, New York, NY, 2012. For program support for Four Freedoms Fund.
$150,000 to American Independent News Network, Washington, DC, 2012. For program support for Colorado Independent.
$115,000 to Gay, Lesbian, Bisexual and Transgendered Community Services Center of Colorado, Denver, CO, 2012. For general operating support for Denver location ($100,000), for general operating support for the Fort Collins location ($30,000) and for Leadership Through Pride program ($35,000).
$30,000 to Coloradans for Fairness and Equality, Denver, CO, 2012. For program support for American Values Project.
$20,000 to Common Cause Education Fund, Washington, DC, 2012. For program support for Colorado Common Cause Education Fund.
$5,000 to Colorado Public Television, Denver, CO, 2012. For general operating support.
$5,000 to Public Interest Projects, New York, NY, 2012. For travel support for LGBT immigrant leaders to attend Creating Change.
$5,000 to Riverhouse Childrens Center, Durango, CO, 2012. For general operating support.

1422
Richard C. Goldstein Private Foundation ✧
c/o Jeffrey Goldstein
1025 S. Race St.
Denver, CO 80209-1003

Established in 1992 in CO.
Donor: Richard C. Goldstein‡.
Foundation type: Independent foundation.
Financial data (yr. ended 12/31/13): Assets, $57,841,972 (M); expenditures, $1,156,224; qualifying distributions, $600,000; giving activities include $600,000 for 1 grant.
Purpose and activities: Giving primarily to a community foundation; some giving also to a Pre-K-secondary independent school.
Fields of interest: Elementary/secondary education; Foundations (community).
Limitations: Applications not accepted. Giving primarily in CO. No grants to individuals.
Application information: Unsolicited requests for funds not accepted.
Officers: Jeffrey Goldstein, Pres.; Julie Ann Goldstein, Secy.; Leslie Karen Goldstein, Treas.
EIN: 841204808
Selected grants: The following grants are a representative sample of this grantmaker's funding activity:
$400,000 to Rose Community Foundation, Denver, CO, 2012. For general, to the donor advised fund.
$25,000 to Colorado Academy, Denver, CO, 2012. For general, non-restrictive use.

1423
Grand Foundation ✧
(formerly Columbine Foundation for the Grand Foundation)
P.O. Box 1342
Winter Park, CO 80482-1342 (970) 887-3111
Contact: Megan Ledin, Exec. Dir.; For grants: Stacy Starr, Grants and Mktg. Coord.
FAX: (970) 887-3176;
E-mail: info@grandfoundation.com; Grant inquiry e-mail: stacy@grandfoundation.com; Main URL: http://www.grandfoundation.com
Facebook: http://www.facebook.com/pages/Grand-Foundation/128508847201033
Twitter: http://twitter.com/GrandFoundation
YouTube: http://www.youtube.com/TheGrandFoundation

Established in 1996 in CO.
Foundation type: Community foundation.
Financial data (yr. ended 12/31/13): Assets, $2,413,688 (M); gifts received, $785,859; expenditures, $728,889; giving activities include $493,417 for 7+ grants.
Purpose and activities: The Grand Foundation is a philanthropic organization serving all of Grand County, Colorado. The foundation seeks to improve the quality of life in Grand County by proactively addressing current and future needs in the areas of Health & Human Services, Arts & Culture, Education, Amateur Sports and Environment.
Fields of interest: Arts; Education; Environment; Health care; Recreation; Human services; Community/economic development.
Limitations: Applications accepted. Giving primarily in Grant County, CO.
Application information: Visit foundation web site for application cover page and guidelines. The standard application is recommended for grant requests of $2,501 or more. Application form required.
Initial approach: Submit cover page and proposal
Copies of proposal: 11
Deadline(s): May 1
Final notification: June
Officers and Board Members:* Ben Watson,* Chair.; Megan Ledin, Exec. Dir.; Barbara Ahrens; Jennifer Colley; Sean Damery; Jerry Groswold; Kyle Harris; Jancie Hughes; David Kafer; Dr. Jim Kennedy; C.A. Lane; Dick Lacouture; Sheri Lock; Shelly Neibauer; Greg Norwick; Jynnifer Pierro; Mike Ritschard; Catherine Ross; Dennis Saffell; Cheryl Shaul; Trinna Tressler; Julie Watkins.
EIN: 841374928

1424
Green Fund ✧
c/o Kathryn A. Porter
4155 W. 105th Pl.
Westminster, CO 80031-1905

Established in 1993 in CO.
Donors: Frances Green‡; Alice K. Green.
Foundation type: Independent foundation.
Financial data (yr. ended 12/31/13): Assets, $9,739,751 (M); expenditures, $554,316; qualifying distributions, $509,123; giving activities include $480,000 for 32 grants (high: $100,000; low: $1,000).
Fields of interest: Higher education; Environment, natural resources; Human services; United Ways and Federated Giving Programs.
Limitations: Applications not accepted. Giving primarily in CO, with emphasis on Boulder and Denver, and in MD. No grants to individuals.
Application information: Contributes only to pre-selected organizations.
Officers: Ann C. Wylie, Pres.; Kathryn A. Porter, V.P. and Secy.
Director: Maggie Fox.
EIN: 841155083
Selected grants: The following grants are a representative sample of this grantmaker's funding activity:
$50,000 to George Washington University, Law School, Washington, DC, 2012. For scholarship.

1425
The Griffin Foundation, Inc. ✧
303 W. Prospect Rd.
Fort Collins, CO 80526-2003 (970) 482-3030
Contact: David L. Wood, Chair. and Treas.
FAX: (970) 484-6648;
E-mail: carol.wood@thegriffinfoundation.org; Main URL: http://www.thegriffinfoundation.org
Grants List: http://www.thegriffinfoundation.org/about.shtml

Established in 1991 in CO.
Donor: Pat Griffin.
Foundation type: Independent foundation.
Financial data (yr. ended 12/31/13): Assets, $2,255,330 (M); expenditures, $832,379; qualifying distributions, $551,358; giving activities include $416,358 for grants, and $135,000 for 20 grants to individuals (high: $10,000; low: $5,000).
Purpose and activities: Giving primarily for health care, higher education and performing arts organizations. Scholarships also to students who have an associate degree or at least sixty academic hours from a junior or community college and are seeking to complete a baccalaureate degree and are attending Colorado State University (Fort Collins campus), the University of Northern Colorado or the University of Wyoming (Laramie campus).
Fields of interest: Performing arts, orchestras; Arts; Higher education; Health care.
Type of support: Building/renovation; Scholarships —to individuals.
Limitations: Applications accepted. Giving primarily in Fort Collins, CO; some giving in Laramie, WY.
Publications: Application guidelines.
Application information: Complete scholarship application guidelines available on foundation web site. Application form required.
Initial approach: E-mail; Scholarship application available to download on foundation web site
Deadline(s): None
Officers and Directors:* David L. Wood,* Chair. and Pres.; Beatrice C. Griffin,* V.P. and Secy.; Jerry W. Rizley,* V.P.
EIN: 841171483
Selected grants: The following grants are a representative sample of this grantmaker's funding activity:
$76,000 to Colorado State University, Fort Collins, CO, 2011.
$50,000 to Lincoln Center Support League, Fort Collins, CO, 2010.
$50,000 to Lincoln Center Support League, Fort Collins, CO, 2011.
$15,000 to Fort Collins Symphony Association, Fort Collins, CO, 2010.
$10,000 to Respite Care, Fort Collins, CO, 2011.
$5,000 to Colorado State University Foundation, Fort Collins, CO, 2011.
$5,000 to Greeley Philharmonic Orchestra, Greeley, CO, 2011.
$2,400 to Colorado State University Foundation, Fort Collins, CO, 2011.
$1,000 to Colorado State University Foundation, Fort Collins, CO, 2011.

1426
D. F. Halton Foundation, Inc. ✧
(formerly Pepsi-Cola of Charlotte Foundation, Inc.)
P.O. Box 834
Ophir, CO 81426-0834
Contact: Dale F. Halton, Pres.

Established in 1987 in NC.
Donor: Dale F. Halton.
Foundation type: Independent foundation.
Financial data (yr. ended 12/31/13): Assets, $1,127,910 (M); gifts received, $1,000,000; expenditures, $913,021; qualifying distributions, $913,021; giving activities include $913,021 for 55 grants (high: $330,071; low: $25).
Purpose and activities: The foundation supports organizations involved with arts and culture, education, substance abuse, health, medical research, housing, human services, community development, and homeless people.
Fields of interest: Museums; Performing arts; Performing arts, dance; Performing arts, music; Historic preservation/historical societies; Arts; Education, association; Vocational education; Business school/education; Education; Substance abuse, services; Cancer; Heart & circulatory diseases; Cancer research; Heart & circulatory research; Housing/shelter; Family services; Residential/custodial care, hospices; Homeless, human services; Human services; Community/economic development; Children/youth; Children; Youth; Young adults; Disabilities, people with; Physically disabled; Women; Girls; Adults, women; Young adults, female; Young adults, male; Crime/abuse victims; Economically disadvantaged; Homeless.
Type of support: General/operating support; Annual campaigns; Capital campaigns; Endowments; Emergency funds; Scholarship funds; Matching/challenge support.
Limitations: Applications accepted. Giving limited to Cabarrus, Cleveland, Gaston, Lincoln, Mecklenburg, Stanly, and Union counties, NC, and San Miguel County, CO. No support for political organizations. No grants to individuals.
Application information: Application form not required.
Initial approach: Proposal
Copies of proposal: 1
Deadline(s): None
Board meeting date(s): Annually
Final notification: Varies
Officers: Dale F. Halton, Pres. and Treas.; Fred A. Wagner, V.P.; Darrell Holland, Secy.
EIN: 561591985

1427
Zenon C. R. Hansen Foundation ✧
6501 E. Belleview Ave., Ste. 400
Englewood, CO 80111-6020

Established in 1994.

Foundation type: Independent foundation.
Financial data (yr. ended 04/30/13): Assets, $3,915,171 (M); expenditures, $722,713; qualifying distributions, $650,048; giving activities include $614,102 for 14 grants (high: $125,000; low: $1,000).
Fields of interest: Education; Youth development; Human services.
Limitations: Applications not accepted. Giving primarily in CO and NC. No grants to individuals.
Application information: Contributes only to pre-selected organizations.
Officers: Thomas S. Haggai, Pres.; Earl L. Wright, Treas.
EIN: 650428044

1428
The Hugh & Michelle Harvey Family Foundation ✧
1600 Stout St., No. 1800
Denver, CO 80202-3561
Application address: c/o Peter Konrad, 2965 Akron Ct., Denver, CO 80238; tel.: (303) 993-5385

Donors: Hugh E. Harvey, Jr.; Michelle M. Harvey.
Foundation type: Independent foundation.
Financial data (yr. ended 12/31/13): Assets, $28,898,180 (M); expenditures, $1,375,414; qualifying distributions, $1,170,780; giving activities include $1,170,780 for 26 grants (high: $220,000; low: $3,500).
Fields of interest: Education; Physical/earth sciences.
Limitations: Applications accepted. Giving primarily in CO.
Application information: Application form required.
Initial approach: Letter
Deadline(s): None
Officers and Directors:* Michelle M. Harvey,* Pres.; Hugh E. Harvey, Jr.,* Secy.-Treas.
EIN: 263640406

1429
Hawley Family Foundation ✧
(formerly RHW Foundation, Inc.)
2810 N. Speer Blvd.
Denver, CO 80211 (303) 674-5111
Contact: MacDonald Hawley, Pres. and Treas.

Established in 1994.
Foundation type: Independent foundation.
Financial data (yr. ended 12/31/12): Assets, $5,440,607 (M); expenditures, $719,792; qualifying distributions, $444,481; giving activities include $444,481 for grants.
Purpose and activities: Giving primarily for the environment and animal welfare; funding also for the arts.
Fields of interest: Arts; Education; Environment, natural resources; Animals/wildlife, preservation/protection.
Limitations: Applications accepted. Giving primarily in CO. No grants to individuals.
Application information: Application form not required.
Initial approach: Proposal
Deadline(s): None
Officers and Directors:* MacDonald Hawley,* Pres. and Treas.; James M. Hawley,* V.P. and Secy.
EIN: 841224613

1430
Eleanor and Henry Hitchcock Charitable Foundation ✧
P.O. Box 4389
Aspen, CO 81612-4389

Established in 2002 in MO.
Donor: Eleanor H. Hitchcock Trust.
Foundation type: Independent foundation.
Financial data (yr. ended 12/31/13): Assets, $13,105,465 (M); expenditures, $718,749; qualifying distributions, $579,290; giving activities include $567,167 for 12 grants (high: $125,000; low: $12,373).
Purpose and activities: The foundation will also make grants for up to 4 years for the benefit of individuals who are full-time students enrolled in colleges, universities and secondary schools, and for up to two years for students who are full-time and enrolled in trade or technical schools in the U.S. Funding also for the arts.
Fields of interest: Museums; Performing arts, theater; Arts; Higher education; Environment.
Limitations: Applications not accepted. Giving in the U.S., with emphasis on CO. No grants to individuals.
Application information: Unsolicited requests for funds not accepted.
Trustee: Harrison H. Augur.
EIN: 316672533

1431
A. V. Hunter Trust, Inc. ✧
650 S. Cherry St., Ste. 535
Glendale, CO 80246-1897 (303) 399-5450
Contact: Barbara Howie, Exec. Dir
FAX: (303) 399-5499;
E-mail: barbarahowie@avhuntertrust.org; Main URL: http://www.avhuntertrust.org

Trust established in 1924 in CO.
Donor: A.V. Hunter‡.
Foundation type: Independent foundation.
Financial data (yr. ended 12/31/13): Assets, $67,749,603 (M); expenditures, $3,219,935; qualifying distributions, $2,741,087; giving activities include $1,753,125 for 196 grants (high: $30,000; low: $2,500), and $452,729 for grants to individuals.
Purpose and activities: Distributions to organizations giving aid, comfort, support, or assistance to children, aged persons, indigent adults or the disabled.
Fields of interest: Human services; Children/youth, services; Children/youth; Children; Youth; Aging; Disabilities, people with; Physically disabled; Blind/visually impaired; Deaf/hearing impaired; Mentally disabled; Crime/abuse victims; Economically disadvantaged; Homeless.
Type of support: General/operating support.
Limitations: Applications accepted. Giving limited to CO. No support for tax-supported institutions, political organizations, disease-specific programs, or organizations using a fiscal agent or fiscal sponsor. No grants to individuals (directly), or for scholarships, capital improvements, acquisitions, staff recruitment and training, endowments, publications, films, media projects, tickets, fundraising benefits, special events, sponsorships, pass-through or start-up funds, research or debt reduction; no loans.
Publications: Application guidelines; Grants list.
Application information: Colorado Common Grant Application form accepted. Organizations applying for funding must have been operating as a 501(c)(3) for at least 3 years. Faxed or e-mailed applications are not accepted. Application form required.
Initial approach: Telephone or 1-page letter
Copies of proposal: 1
Deadline(s): Varies, telephone office before submitting application
Board meeting date(s): Mar., May, Aug., and Nov.
Final notification: Within 20 days after Board meeting
Officers and Trustees:* Allan B. Adams,* Pres.; Mary K. Anstine,* V.P.; Barbara L. Howie, Secy. and Exec. Dir.; George C. Gibson, Treas.; Janet Willson, Cont.; Bruce K. Alexander; W. Robert Alexander.
Number of staff: 3 full-time professional; 1 part-time professional; 1 part-time support.
EIN: 840461332
Selected grants: The following grants are a representative sample of this grantmaker's funding activity:
$30,000 to Urban Peak Denver, Denver, CO, 2012. For operations.
$25,000 to Brothers Redevelopment, Denver, CO, 2012. For operations.
$20,000 to Boys and Girls Clubs of the San Luis Valley, Alamosa, CO, 2012. For operations.
$20,000 to Project Angel Heart, Denver, CO, 2012. For operations.
$15,000 to Center for Hearing, Speech and Language, Denver, CO, 2012. For operations.
$15,000 to Project PAVE, Denver, CO, 2012. For program support.
$12,500 to Meals on Wheels, Longmont, Longmont, CO, 2012. For operations.
$10,000 to Colorado Therapeutic Riding Center, Longmont, CO, 2012. For operations.
$10,000 to Regional Home Visitation Program, Baby Bear Hugs, Yuma, CO, 2012. For operations.
$10,000 to Safe Shelter of Saint Vrain Valley, Longmont, CO, 2012. For operations.
$7,500 to Boys and Girls Club, Black Canyon, Montrose, CO, 2012. For for operations.

1432
The Janus Foundation ✧
151 Detroit St.
Denver, CO 80206-4805 (303) 333-3863
FAX: (303) 394-7797;
E-mail: janusfoundation@janus.com; Main URL: https://www.janus.com/community
Janus Charity Challenge: http://www.januscharitychallenge.com/

Established in 1994 in CO.
Donors: Janus Capital Corp.; Janus Capital Management LLC.
Foundation type: Company-sponsored foundation.
Financial data (yr. ended 12/31/13): Assets, $202,783 (M); gifts received, $800,095; expenditures, $1,135,484; qualifying distributions, $1,121,213; giving activities include $896,472 for 62 grants (high: $350,000; low: $210), and $224,741 for 731 employee matching gifts.
Purpose and activities: The foundation supports organizations involved with education.
Fields of interest: Elementary/secondary education; Libraries (public); Education; Children/youth, services; Economically disadvantaged.
Type of support: Continuing support; Program development; Curriculum development; Scholarship funds; Employee matching gifts.

Limitations: Applications not accepted. Giving primarily in areas of company operations in Denver, CO. No grants to individuals, or for sponsorship events or tables, field trips or tours, recreational activities, conferences, seminars, workshops, annual membership or affiliation campaigns, publication or distribution of books, articles, newsletters, videos, or electronic media, religious or political purposes, health-related programs, or environmental projects.
Application information: Contributes only to pre-selected organizations.
Board meeting date(s): 1st week of each month
Officers: Brennan Hughes, Treas.; Casey Cotese, Pres.; Karlene Lacy, Sr. V.P., Taxation.
Director: Tiphani Krueger.
Number of staff: 2 part-time professional.
EIN: 841271105

1433
The JFM Foundation ✧
P.O. Box 17965
Denver, CO 80217-0965 (303) 864-2316
Contact: Joanie Wimberg Pacheco, Fdn. Admin.
FAX: (303) 894-9088;
E-mail: info@jfmfoundation.org

Established in 1980 in CO.
Donors: Frederick R. Mayer†; Jan Perry Mayer.
Foundation type: Independent foundation.
Financial data (yr. ended 11/30/13): Assets, $1,177,467 (M); gifts received, $1,700,000; expenditures, $3,800,051; qualifying distributions, $3,738,258; giving activities include $3,735,000 for 8 grants (high: $2,474,114; low: $10,000).
Purpose and activities: Support for innovative and cooperative projects in the areas of art, education, child development, women's issues and economic development that achieve long lasting and tangible impact.
Fields of interest: Arts; Education; Children/youth, services; Community/economic development; Women.
International interests: Mexico.
Type of support: Program development; Seed money; Matching/challenge support.
Limitations: Applications not accepted. Giving limited to CO for community projects and social issues; cultural programs having national or international significance are considered. No support for medical or health-related fields or religious organizations for religious purposes. No grants to individuals, or for endowments, deficit financing, fundraising, testimonials, or basic research.
Publications: Annual report.
Application information: Unsolicited requests for funds are not accepted.
Board meeting date(s): Varies
Officers and Trustees:* Jan Perry Mayer,* Pres.; Frederick M. Mayer,* V.P. and Secy.; Anthony R. Mayer,* V.P. and Treas.; Ann Daley; Gloria J. Higgins; Harold R. Logan, Jr.
Number of staff: 1 part-time professional.
EIN: 840833163

1434
Jumping Mouse Foundation ✧
c/o Graham & Co.
1295 S. Broadway
Boulder, CO 80305

Established in 2008.
Donors: Brian Boone; Theresa Boone; Farzin Lalezari; Shirley Lalezari.
Foundation type: Independent foundation.
Financial data (yr. ended 12/31/13): Assets, $12,800,931 (M); expenditures, $593,658; qualifying distributions, $530,000; giving activities include $530,000 for 9 grants (high: $200,000; low: $5,000).
Fields of interest: Food services; YM/YWCAs & YM/YWHAs; Military/veterans' organizations.
Type of support: General/operating support.
Limitations: Applications not accepted. Giving primarily in CO, FL and TX.
Application information: Unsolicited requests for funds not accepted.
Officers: Theresa Boone, Pres.; Brian Boone, V.P.
EIN: 263889003

1435
Kane Family Foundation, Inc. ✧ ☆
6510-A S. Academy Blvd.
P.O. Box. 285
Colorado Springs, CO 80906-8691 (719) 381-5629
Main URL: http://kanefamilyfoundation.org/

Foundation type: Independent foundation.
Financial data (yr. ended 10/31/13): Assets, $27,957,316 (M); expenditures, $1,474,103; qualifying distributions, $1,280,802; giving activities include $1,254,643 for 8 grants (high: $754,905; low: $13,098).
Purpose and activities: The foundation is a merit-based scholarship program that provides financial assistance to students who attend the University of Colorado at Colorado Springs, Lamar Community College, Otero Junior College, Pikes Peak Community College, Pueblo Community College, Colorado State University- Pueblo, and Trinidad State Junior College.
Fields of interest: Higher education; Scholarships/financial aid.
Limitations: Applications accepted. Giving primarily in CO.
Application information: Application form required.
Initial approach: Contact foundation for details of scholarship forms and requirements
Deadline(s): None
Trustees: William S. Corrigan; Tad A. Goodenbour; Gregory L. Johnson; Ryan W. Styre.
EIN: 900689673

1436
Marion Esser Kaufmann Foundation ✧
1153 Bergen Pkwy., Ste. I-434
Evergreen, CO 80439-9406
Contact: Julia Keough Esser, Tr.

Established in 1986 in NY.
Donor: Marion Esser Kaufmann†.
Foundation type: Independent foundation.
Financial data (yr. ended 12/31/13): Assets, $13,848,917 (M); expenditures, $694,874; qualifying distributions, $515,000; giving activities include $515,000 for 16 grants (high: $100,000; low: $5,000).
Purpose and activities: Giving for higher education, health care, including research in cancer, the fields of sudden infant death syndrome (SIDS) and Alzheimer's disease.
Fields of interest: Child development, education; Elementary school/education; Higher education; Hospitals (general); Health care, infants; Health care; Medical research, institute; Cancer research; Alzheimer's disease research; SIDS (Sudden Infant Death Syndrome) research; Pediatrics research; Child development, services; Aging.
Type of support: Program development; Scholarship funds; Research.
Limitations: Applications accepted. Giving primarily in CO, Washington, DC, and NY. No grants to individuals.
Application information: Application form required.
Initial approach: Letter
Deadline(s): None
Final notification: Within 3 months
Trustees: Julia Keough Esser; Richard B. Esser.
EIN: 133339941

1437
The KBK Foundation ✧
(formerly The Kavadas Foundation)
1700 Lincoln St., Ste. 4100
Denver, CO 80203-4541

Established in 1991 in CO.
Donor: Kathryn B. Kavadas.
Foundation type: Independent foundation.
Financial data (yr. ended 12/31/13): Assets, $705,099 (M); gifts received, $165,269; expenditures, $786,055; qualifying distributions, $771,933; giving activities include $771,933 for 15 grants (high: $291,933; low: $10,000).
Purpose and activities: Giving primarily for arts and culture, the environment, education, health care, and human services.
Fields of interest: Media, television; Museums; Elementary/secondary education; Higher education; Environment; Reproductive health, family planning; American Red Cross; Residential/custodial care, senior continuing care; Aging.
Type of support: General/operating support; Continuing support; Matching/challenge support.
Limitations: Applications not accepted. Giving primarily in the greater Boston, MA, area. No grants to individuals.
Application information: Contributes only to pre-selected organizations.
Officers: Lynn P. Hendrix, Pres. and Treas.; Charles A. Ramunno, V.P. and Secy.; Kathryn B. Kavadas, Mgr.
EIN: 841186316
Selected grants: The following grants are a representative sample of this grantmaker's funding activity:
$15,000 to New England Aquarium, Boston, MA, 2012. For Navigators Society.

1438
Kern Family Foundation ✧ ☆
1133 14th St., Ste. 4300
Denver, CO 80202-2282

Established in 1999 in CO.
Donors: Jerome Kern; Mary Kern.
Foundation type: Independent foundation.
Financial data (yr. ended 12/31/13): Assets, $488,096 (M); expenditures, $671,838; qualifying distributions, $671,700; giving activities include $671,700 for 8 grants (high: $500,000; low: $200).
Fields of interest: Arts; Human services.

Limitations: Applications not accepted. Giving primarily in Denver, CO.
Application information: Unsolicited requests for funds not accepted.
Officer: Jerome Kern, Pres.
EIN: 841522247

1439
Kinder Morgan Foundation ✧
370 Van Gordon St.
Lakewood, CO 80228-1519 (303) 914-7655
Contact: Maureen Bulkley, Mgr.
FAX: (303) 984-3306;
E-mail: km_foundation@kindermorgan.com; Main URL: http://www.kindermorgan.com/community/km_foundation.cfm

Established in 1990 in CO.
Donors: Knight Inc.; K N Energy, Inc.; Kinder Morgan, Inc.
Foundation type: Company-sponsored foundation.
Financial data (yr. ended 12/31/13): Assets, $13,836,614 (M); expenditures, $2,074,864; qualifying distributions, $2,064,075; giving activities include $2,064,075 for 708 grants (high: $100,000).
Purpose and activities: The foundation supports programs designed to promote the academic and artistic interests of youth. Special emphasis is directed toward academic programs including tutoring; arts education; and environmental education initiatives designed to work with local schools and meet curriculum standards.
Fields of interest: Arts education; Arts; Elementary/secondary education; Higher education; Libraries (public); Education, services; Education; Environmental education; Youth.
Type of support: Continuing support; Program development; Curriculum development; Employee matching gifts.
Limitations: Applications accepted. Giving primarily in areas of company operations in the U.S. and in Canada. No support for political candidates or lobbying organizations, service clubs, fraternal organizations, or organizations located outside the U.S. and Canada. No grants to individuals, or for scholarships, political causes, general operating support, capital projects (excluding libraries), religious projects, advertising, sponsorships, travel, conventions, conferences, or seminars, mentoring, leadership, or social development initiatives.
Publications: Application guidelines; Informational brochure (including application guidelines).
Application information: Grants range between $1,000 and $5,000. Proposals should be no longer than 3 pages. CDs, DVDs, annual reports, and brochures are not accepted. Support is limited to 1 contribution per organization during any given year. Application form not required.
Initial approach: E-mail or mail cover letter and proposal
Copies of proposal: 1
Deadline(s): Jan. 10, Mar. 10, May 10, July 10, Sept. 10, and Nov. 10
Final notification: 60 to 90 days
Directors: Jeffrey R. Armstrong; Larry S. Pierce; C. Park Shaper; James E. Street.
Number of staff: None.
EIN: 841148161
Selected grants: The following grants are a representative sample of this grantmaker's funding activity:
$5,000 to Chicago Childrens Museum, Chicago, IL, 2011.
$5,000 to Chicago Symphony Orchestra, Chicago, IL, 2011.
$5,000 to Genesys Works, Houston, TX, 2011.
$4,000 to Junior Achievement of Chicago, Chicago, IL, 2011.
$3,500 to Catalyst Schools, Chicago, IL, 2011.
$3,500 to Keystone Center, Keystone, CO, 2011.
$3,500 to Texas State University, San Marcos, TX, 2011.
$2,500 to Boys Hope Girls Hope, Bridgeton, MO, 2011.
$2,500 to Chicago Lights, Chicago, IL, 2011.
$2,000 to University of Oklahoma Foundation, Norman, OK, 2011.

1440
The Kenneth King Foundation ✧
(formerly Kenneth Kendal King Foundation)
100 Fillmore St., 5th Fl.
Denver, CO 80206 (303) 832-3200
Contact: Janice Fritsch, Pres.
FAX: (303) 832-4176;
E-mail: info@kennethkingfoundation.org; Main URL: http://www.kennethkingfoundation.org

Established in 1990 in CO.
Donor: Kenneth Kendal King‡.
Foundation type: Independent foundation.
Financial data (yr. ended 12/31/13): Assets, $43,250,847 (M); gifts received, $250; expenditures, $2,207,523; qualifying distributions, $1,718,034; giving activities include $865,252 for 141 grants (high: $100,000; low: $144).
Purpose and activities: Giving primarily for job creation and entrepreneurship.
Fields of interest: Higher education; Employment; Food banks; Human services; Christian agencies & churches; Infants/toddlers; Children/youth; Children; Youth; Adults; Aging; Young adults; Disabilities, people with; Physically disabled; Blind/visually impaired; Deaf/hearing impaired; Mentally disabled; Minorities; African Americans/Blacks; Hispanics/Latinos; Native Americans/American Indians; Indigenous peoples; Women; Infants/toddlers, female; Girls; Adults, women; Young adults, female; Men; Infants/toddlers, male; Boys; Adults, men; Young adults, male; Military/veterans; Substance abusers; Single parents; Terminal illness, people with; Immigrants/refugees; Economically disadvantaged; Homeless; Migrant workers.
Type of support: General/operating support; Building/renovation; Equipment; Emergency funds; Program development; Scholarship funds; Matching/challenge support.
Limitations: Giving primarily in CO. No support for political organizations, or for government agencies or public or private schools. No grants to individuals.
Publications: Annual report; Financial statement; Grants list.
Application information: See foundation web site for application information and guidelines.
Board meeting date(s): Quarterly
Officers and Directors:* T.E. "Tim" Welker,* Chair.; Janice Fritsch,* Pres.; John Love,* Treas.; Matthew R. "Pete" Banner III.
Number of staff: 3 full-time professional; 2 full-time support.
EIN: 841148157
Selected grants: The following grants are a representative sample of this grantmaker's funding activity:
$200,000 to Rocky Mountain Multiple Sclerosis Center, Westminster, CO, 2012. To help with their mortgage payback.
$100,000 to Auraria Library, Denver, CO, 2012. To advance Programmatic mission of Center for Colorado and the West History, media, education student stipends to advance 4th grade Colorado history initiative, ensuring statewide impact.
$58,000 to Sigma Chi Foundation, Evanston, IL, 2012. For Annual gift including $50,000 Programs $5,000 board fee $3,000 White Cross memberships.
$35,000 to Goodwill Industries of Denver, Denver, CO, 2012. For Youth Career Development Programs that help at-risk students graduate from high school and prepare for work or college. The Program supports 28 area high schools.
$25,000 to Rocky Mountain Multiple Sclerosis Center, Westminster, CO, 2012. For the King Adult Day Enrichment Program.
$12,000 to Regis University, Denver, CO, 2012. To help Arrupe Jesuit High School students attend Regis University.
$10,000 to Iliff School of Theology, Denver, CO, 2012. To renovate their elevator in the main building.
$9,000 to Cancer League of Colorado, Englewood, CO, 2012. For Research grant awards, $5,000; Fundraising dinner: $5,000.
$2,860 to Regis University, Denver, CO, 2012. For Laptops for students.
$2,500 to Goodwill Industries of Denver, Denver, CO, 2012. For Matching funds from luncheon on April 25, 2012.

1441
Kitzmiller-Bales Trust ✧
P.O. Box 96
Wray, CO 80758-0096 (970) 332-4824
Contact: Robert U. Hansen, Tr.

Established in 1984 in CO.
Donor: Edna B. Kitzmiller‡.
Foundation type: Independent foundation.
Financial data (yr. ended 12/31/13): Assets, $12,437,774 (M); expenditures, $616,654; qualifying distributions, $601,154; giving activities include $600,000 for 11 grants (high: $141,000; low: $2,000).
Purpose and activities: Giving primarily for community development; funding also for education and human services.
Fields of interest: Education; Human services; Community/economic development; Government/public administration.
Type of support: Continuing support; Capital campaigns; Building/renovation; Equipment; Program development; Matching/challenge support.
Limitations: Applications accepted. Giving limited to projects benefiting the inhabitants of Wray, Colorado and its vicinity. No support for religious or political organizations. No grants for scholarships, or endowments.
Publications: Application guidelines.
Application information: Application form required.
Initial approach: Letter
Copies of proposal: 1
Deadline(s): None
Board meeting date(s): 3rd Mon. of month

Trustees: Robert U. Hansen; L. Karen Loyd; Robert Loyd; Farmers State Bank.
EIN: 846178085

1442
Kroh Charitable Trust ✧ ☆
c/o Home State Bank
300 E. 29th St.
Loveland, CO 80538-2762
E-mail: lahlawyer@aol.com; Application address: c/o Lynn A. Hammond, 200 E. 7th St., Ste. 418, Loveland, CO 80537-4871, tel.: (970) 667-1023

Established in CO.
Donor: Lois L. Kroh Marital Trust.
Foundation type: Independent foundation.
Financial data (yr. ended 12/31/13): Assets, $246,444 (M); expenditures, $844,127; qualifying distributions, $836,584; giving activities include $834,671 for 11 grants (high: $250,000; low: $4,000).
Fields of interest: Arts; Education; Health care.
Limitations: Applications accepted. Giving primarily in the Loveland, CO, area.
Application information: Application form required.
Initial approach: Letter
Deadline(s): None
Trustee: Home State Bank.
EIN: 846214217
Selected grants: The following grants are a representative sample of this grantmaker's funding activity:
$150,000 to Thompson Education Foundation, Loveland, CO, 2011. For general purposes.
$100,000 to Community Foundation of Northern Colorado, Fort Collins, CO, 2011. For general purposes.
$50,000 to Alternatives to Violence, Loveland, CO, 2011. For general purposes.
$50,000 to Hearts and Horses, Loveland, CO, 2011. For general purposes.
$40,000 to Colorado Youth Outdoors, Loveland, CO, 2011. For general purposes.
$21,476 to Respite Care, Fort Collins, CO, 2011. For general purposes.
$9,000 to Respite Care, Fort Collins, CO, 2010. For general purposes.
$5,000 to Loveland, City of, Loveland, CO, 2010.
$5,000 to Project Self-Sufficiency of Loveland-Fort Collins, Loveland, CO, 2011. For general purposes.
$2,760 to McKee Medical Center Foundation, Loveland, CO, 2010. For general purposes.

1443
The John E. and Margaret L. Lane Foundation ✧
102 N. Cascade Ave., Ste. 610
Colorado Springs, CO 80903-1427

Established in 1997 in CO.
Donors: John E. Lane; Margaret L. Lane; Margaret L. Lane Charitable Lead Unitrust II.
Foundation type: Independent foundation.
Financial data (yr. ended 12/31/13): Assets, $11,424,290 (M); gifts received, $224,407; expenditures, $1,877,375; qualifying distributions, $1,796,993; giving activities include $1,790,000 for 7 grants (high: $500,000; low: $40,000).
Purpose and activities: Giving primarily for religious and educational purposes.
Fields of interest: Education; Zoos/zoological societies; Christian agencies & churches; Protestant agencies & churches; Religion.
Limitations: Applications not accepted. Giving primarily in Colorado Springs, CO. No grants to individuals.
Application information: Contributes only to pre-selected organizations.
Officers: Margaret L. Lane, Pres.; Philip R. Lane, Secy.-Treas.
EIN: 311531619

1444
Larrk Foundation ✧
707 17th St., Ste. 4100
Denver, CO 80202-3404
Contact: Wendell Fleming, Exec. Dir.

Established in 2008 in CO.
Donor: Intrepid Production Corp.
Foundation type: Company-sponsored foundation.
Financial data (yr. ended 12/31/13): Assets, $17,930,063 (M); expenditures, $1,213,058; qualifying distributions, $973,595; giving activities include $973,595 for 27 grants (high: $110,000; low: $3,000).
Fields of interest: Education; Health care; Human services.
Limitations: Applications accepted. Giving primarily in CO.
Application information: Application form not required.
Initial approach: Proposal
Deadline(s): None
Officers and Directors:* Robert Jornayvaz,* Pres.; Louisa Craft Jornayvaz,* Secy.; Wendell Fleming, Exec. Dir.
EIN: 263818473

1445
Left Hand Foundation ✧ ☆
c/o Matthew McConnell
2350 Linden Ave.
Boulder, CO 80304-1619

Established in 2000 in CO.
Donor: Matthew McConnell.
Foundation type: Independent foundation.
Financial data (yr. ended 12/31/13): Assets, $12,784,054 (M); expenditures, $744,907; qualifying distributions, $663,349; giving activities include $661,500 for 2 grants (high: $646,500; low: $15,000).
Fields of interest: Multiple sclerosis; Foundations (community).
Limitations: Applications not accepted. Giving primarily in CO and NY. No grants to individuals.
Application information: Contributes only to pre-selected organizations.
Officer: Matthew McConnell, Pres.
EIN: 841550837
Selected grants: The following grants are a representative sample of this grantmaker's funding activity:
$653,538 to Denver Foundation, Denver, CO, 2011. For general operations.
$15,000 to Multiple Sclerosis Society, National, New York, NY, 2011. For general operations.

1446
Leptas Foundation Trust ✧
(formerly Kevin E. & Colleen K. McVaney Family Foundation Trust)
1520 W. Canal Ct., Ste. 220
Littleton, CO 80120-5651

Established in 2000 in CO.
Donors: Kevin E. McVaney; Colleen K. McVaney.
Foundation type: Independent foundation.
Financial data (yr. ended 12/31/12): Assets, $52,608,420 (M); gifts received, $1,199,781; expenditures, $2,025,481; qualifying distributions, $1,915,371; giving activities include $1,904,200 for 35 grants (high: $871,500; low: $3,000).
Purpose and activities: Giving primarily for education for religious organizations.
Fields of interest: Education; Christian agencies & churches.
Limitations: Applications not accepted. Giving primarily in CO, with some emphasis on Colorado Springs and Denver.
Application information: Contributes only to pre-selected organizations.
Trustee: Kevin E. McVaney.
EIN: 470833530

1447
Richard H. Lewis Family Foundation ✧ ☆
7117 S. Locust Cir.
Englewood, CO 80112-1576

Established in 2000 in CO.
Donor: Richard H. Lewis.
Foundation type: Independent foundation.
Financial data (yr. ended 12/31/12): Assets, $7,963,806 (M); gifts received, $410,789; expenditures, $544,090; qualifying distributions, $437,179; giving activities include $437,179 for grants.
Purpose and activities: Giving primarily for education, youth and social services, and Christian churches and organizations.
Fields of interest: Higher education; Human services; Children/youth, services; United Ways and Federated Giving Programs; Christian agencies & churches.
Type of support: General/operating support.
Limitations: Applications not accepted. Giving primarily in CO. No grants to individuals.
Application information: Contributes only to pre-selected organizations.
Directors: Bradford H. Lewis; Carol A. Lewis; Richard H. Lewis.
EIN: 841568116

1448
Libertygives Foundation ✧
12300 Liberty Blvd.
Englewood, CO 80112-7009 (720) 875-5400
E-mail: LibertyGives@libertymedia.com; Main URL: http://www.libertymedia.com/liberty-gives.aspx

Established in 2007 in CO.
Donor: Liberty Media Corporation.
Foundation type: Company-sponsored foundation.
Financial data (yr. ended 12/31/13): Assets, $0 (M); gifts received, $562,794; expenditures, $554,544; qualifying distributions, $554,544;

giving activities include $549,038 for 147 grants (high: $75,000; low: $10).
Purpose and activities: The foundation supports programs designed to serve underprivileged and at-risk youth, with a focus on proactive and preventative services.
Fields of interest: Higher education; Education; Girls clubs; Boys & girls clubs; Big Brothers/Big Sisters; Children/youth, services; Family services; Human services; Youth; Economically disadvantaged.
Type of support: General/operating support; Program development.
Limitations: Applications accepted. Giving primarily in CO.
Publications: Application guidelines.
Application information: Grants range from $1,000 to $150,000. Application form required.
Initial approach: Complete online application
Deadline(s): Varies
Officers and Directors:* Gregory B. Maffei,* Pres.; Charles Y. Tanabe,* Secy.; Christopher W. Shean,* Treas.
EIN: 208004437

1449
Lipscomb Family Foundation ✧
P.O. Box 102943
Denver, CO 80250-2943 (803) 765-4567
Contact: Margaret Foster
E-mail: margaret@lipscombfoundation.org

Established in 1995 in SC.
Foundation type: Independent foundation.
Financial data (yr. ended 12/31/13): Assets, $15,369,677 (M); expenditures, $879,889; qualifying distributions, $749,608; giving activities include $675,930 for 73 grants (high: $45,000; low: $930).
Purpose and activities: Giving primarily for programs designed to encourage positive development of youth.
Fields of interest: Youth development; Infants/toddlers; Children/youth; Children; Youth; Infants/toddlers, female; Girls; Infants/toddlers, male; Boys.
Type of support: Annual campaigns; Building/renovation; Capital campaigns; Continuing support; Endowments; General/operating support; Internship funds; Management development/capacity building; Matching/challenge support; Program development; Scholarship funds.
Limitations: Applications accepted. Giving primarily in the midlands of SC, or in areas in which board members reside (Atlanta, GA, the Black Mountain-Asheville, NC, area, and Chattanooga, TN). No support for political organizations.
Publications: Application guidelines.
Application information: Application form required.
Initial approach: Letter or e-mail
Copies of proposal: 1
Deadline(s): Feb. 15 and Sept. 15
Board meeting date(s): Mar., July, and Oct.
Final notification: Approx. 8 weeks
Trustees: Georgia L. Cheek; George C. Fant; Marshall L. Foster; Louise L. Howell; Elizabeth L. Tracy.
Number of staff: 1 part-time professional.
EIN: 581368915
Selected grants: The following grants are a representative sample of this grantmaker's funding activity:
$10,000 to Columbia College, Columbia, SC, 2012. For Leadership Camp.

1450
M.D.C./Richmond American Homes Foundation ✧
(formerly M.D.C. Holdings, Inc. Charitable Foundation)
4350 S. Monaco St.
Denver, CO 80237-3400 (303) 804-7716
Contact: Michael Touff, V.P.
Main URL: http://www.mdcrahfoundation.org/

Established in 1999 in CO.
Donor: M.D.C. Holdings, Inc.
Foundation type: Company-sponsored foundation.
Financial data (yr. ended 12/31/13): Assets, $30,446,813 (M); gifts received, $1,000,000; expenditures, $1,433,275; qualifying distributions, $1,316,300; giving activities include $1,316,300 for 118 grants (high: $200,000; low: $500).
Purpose and activities: The foundation supports organizations involved with performing arts, education, health, Down syndrome, cancer, child welfare, disaster relief, sports, human services, philanthropy, and Judaism.
Fields of interest: Performing arts; Higher education; Education; Health care; Down syndrome; Cancer; Cancer, leukemia; Crime/violence prevention, child abuse; Disasters, preparedness/services; Athletics/sports, amateur leagues; Children, services; Homeless, human services; Human services; Philanthropy/voluntarism; Jewish agencies & synagogues.
Type of support: General/operating support; Endowments; Emergency funds; Program development; Scholarship funds.
Limitations: Applications accepted. Giving primarily in Denver, CO.
Application information: Application form not required.
Initial approach: Proposal
Deadline(s): None
Officers and Trustees:* Larry A. Mizel,* Chair. and C.E.O; David D. Mandanch,* Pres.; John J. Heaney, V.P. and Treas.; Michael Touff, V.P.; Joseph H. Fretz, Secy.; Steven J. Borick; Gilbert Godstein.
EIN: 841561013
Selected grants: The following grants are a representative sample of this grantmaker's funding activity:
$440,000 to Fidelity Charitable Gift Fund, Boston, MA, 2011.
$15,000 to Boys and Girls Clubs of Metro Denver, Denver, CO, 2011.

1451
Maffei Foundation ✧ ☆
c/o EKS&H LLP
7979 E. Tufts Ave., Ste. 400
Denver, CO 80237-2521

Established in CO.
Donor: Gregory B. Maffei.
Foundation type: Independent foundation.
Financial data (yr. ended 12/31/12): Assets, $6,486,717 (M); gifts received, $2,392,707; expenditures, $1,481,711; qualifying distributions, $1,481,711; giving activities include $1,481,711 for 8 grants (high: $1,094,485; low: $24,841).
Fields of interest: Higher education; Human services.
Limitations: Applications not accepted. Giving in the U.S., with emphasis on Hanover, NH. No grants to individuals.
Application information: Unsolicited requests for funds not accepted.
Officers and Directors:* Gregory B. Maffei,* Pres. and Treas.; Jeffrey C. Kirwood,* V.P. and Secy.
EIN: 454040790

1452
The Maggiegeorge Foundation ✧
3033 E. 1st Ave., Ste. 400
Denver, CO 80206-5619

Established in 1998 in CO.
Donors: Anne E. Mounsey Fox; Kelley P. Fox; John Macgregor Fox, Jr.; Becca Selvidge Fox.
Foundation type: Independent foundation.
Financial data (yr. ended 05/31/13): Assets, $13,390,136 (M); expenditures, $692,125; qualifying distributions, $626,432; giving activities include $626,432 for grants.
Fields of interest: Arts; Children/youth, services; Family services; Human services; Disabilities, people with.
Limitations: Applications not accepted. Giving primarily in CO and LA. No grants to individuals.
Application information: Contributes only to pre-selected organizations.
Officers and Directors:* Kelley P. Fox,* Pres.; Anne E. Fox Mounsey,* Secy.; John Macgregor Fox, Jr., Treas.; Pete Mounsey; Becca A. Selvidge.
EIN: 841465773
Selected grants: The following grants are a representative sample of this grantmaker's funding activity:
$50,000 to Roots of Music, New Orleans, LA, 2011.
$35,500 to Denver Inner City Parish, Denver, CO, 2011.
$25,000 to Ogden Museum of Southern Art, New Orleans, LA, 2011.
$13,000 to CityWILD, Denver, CO, 2011.
$12,500 to YouthBiz, Denver, CO, 2011.
$12,000 to Colorado UpLIFT, Denver, CO, 2011.
$8,500 to Whiz Kids Tutoring, Denver, CO, 2011.
$5,000 to Challenged Athletes Foundation, San Diego, CA, 2011.

1453
The Malone Family Foundation ✧
12300 Liberty Blvd.
Englewood, CO 80112-7009 (720) 875-5201
Contact: Cathie Wlaschin, Exec. Dir.; Tracy Amonette, Prog. Dir.
E-mail: fdtn@malonefamilyfoundation.org; E-mail: cathie@malonefamilyfoundation.org. E-mail for Tracy Amonette: tracy.malonefdn@gmail.com; Main URL: http://www.malonefamilyfoundation.org

Established in 1997 in CO.
Donor: John C. Malone.
Foundation type: Independent foundation.
Financial data (yr. ended 12/31/13): Assets, $158,987,921 (M); expenditures, $14,276,656; qualifying distributions, $12,581,962; giving activities include $12,576,293 for 7 grants (high: $6,046,414; low: $50,000).
Purpose and activities: The foundation primarily funds endowments to independent secondary

schools for scholarships for underfunded, highly capable students. Also, a small discretionary fund supports gifted research.
Fields of interest: Education, gifted students.
Type of support: Endowments; Research.
Limitations: Applications not accepted. Giving on a national basis. No grants to individuals.
Publications: IRS Form 990 or 990-PF printed copy available upon request.
Application information: Contributes only to pre-selected organizations.
Board meeting date(s): May
Officers and Directors:* John C. Malone,* Pres. and Treas.; Leslie A. Malone,* Secy.; Evan D. Malone; Tracy L. Amonette.
Number of staff: 1 part-time professional.
EIN: 841408520
Selected grants: The following grants are a representative sample of this grantmaker's funding activity:
$2,000,000 to Derryfield School, Manchester, NH, 2012. For general support.
$2,000,000 to Linsly School, Wheeling, WV, 2012. For general support.
$2,000,000 to Mounds Park Academy, Saint Paul, MN, 2012. For general support.
$2,000,000 to Norfolk Academy, Norfolk, VA, 2012. For general support.
$2,000,000 to Park School of Baltimore, Baltimore, MD, 2012. For general support.
$2,000,000 to Saint Paul Academy and Summit School, Saint Paul, MN, 2012. For general support.
$2,000,000 to Santa Fe Preparatory School, Santa Fe, NM, 2012. For general support.
$2,000,000 to Seabury Hall, Makawao, HI, 2012. For general support.
$2,000,000 to Severn School, Severna Park, MD, 2012. For general support.
$2,000,000 to Teton Science Schools, Journeys School, Jackson, WY, 2012. For general support.

1454
Timothy & Bernadette Marquez Foundation ✧

(formerly Marquez Foundation)
P.O. Box 44354
Denver, CO 80201-4354 (303) 583-1609
Contact: Lisa Roy, Exec. Dir.
E-mail: lisa@tbmfoundation.org; Main URL: http://www.tbmfoundation.org

Established in 2005 in CO.
Foundation type: Independent foundation.
Financial data (yr. ended 12/31/12): Assets, $20,568,653; expenditures, $4,625,939; qualifying distributions, $4,428,599; giving activities include $4,428,599 for 54 grants (high: $2,000,000; low: $10).
Purpose and activities: The foundation currently awards Innovative Planning and Implementation grants in the areas of education, health and human services. Both Planning and Implementation grants will support organizations that are creative in offering innovative solutions to complex problems that promote systems change in one of the foundation's funding areas. The foundation's objective in education is to support student achievement and success within public schools as well as in higher education. The foundation's objective in health is to expand access to and options for quality health care resources to low-income, high-risk individuals and families. The objective in human services is to assist low-income, high-risk individuals and families to improve their life circumstances by promoting self-sufficiency.
Fields of interest: Higher education; Education; Health care; Human services; Family services; Economically disadvantaged.
Type of support: General/operating support; Continuing support; Capital campaigns; Building/renovation; Program development; Matching/challenge support.
Limitations: Applications accepted. Giving primarily in the metropolitan Denver, CO area.
Publications: Application guidelines.
Application information: Application form and guidelines which must be used are available on foundation web site. Application form not required.
Initial approach: E-mail, letter or telephone
Copies of proposal: 1
Board meeting date(s): Monthly
Final notification: 30-60 days
Officer and Directors: Lisa Roy, Exec. Dir.; Bernadette Marquez; Timothy Marquez; David Mokros.
EIN: 203507025

1455
Cydney and Tom Marsico Family Foundation ✧

(formerly CTM Foundation)
101 University Blvd., Ste. 220
Denver, CO 80206-4664

Established in 1997 in CO.
Donors: Tom Marsico; Cydney Marsico.
Foundation type: Independent foundation.
Financial data (yr. ended 11/30/13): Assets, $279,882 (M); gifts received, $734,557; expenditures, $1,000,602; qualifying distributions, $995,277; giving activities include $662,500 for 6 grants (high: $250,000; low: $10,000).
Fields of interest: Museums (children's); Higher education; Recreation, parks/playgrounds; Human services.
Limitations: Applications not accepted. Giving primarily in Denver, CO. No grants to individuals.
Application information: Contributes only to pre-selected organizations.
Officers: Cydney Marsico, C.E.O. and Pres.; Tom Marsico, V.P.; Cindy Schulz, Secy.-Treas. and Exec. Dir.
Trustees: James Marisco; Peter Marsico.
EIN: 841475920
Selected grants: The following grants are a representative sample of this grantmaker's funding activity:
$200,000 to University of Denver, Denver, CO, 2012. For Marsico Institute for Early Learning.
$80,000 to Denver Foundation, Denver, CO, 2012. For State Education Initiative.

1456
J. Landis and Sharon Martin Family Foundation ✧

150 Vine St.
Denver, CO 80206-4627

Established in 1998 in CO.
Donors: J. Landis Martin; Sharon Martin.
Foundation type: Independent foundation.
Financial data (yr. ended 12/31/13): Assets, $3,588,504 (M); gifts received, $1,997,750; expenditures, $3,548,258; qualifying distributions, $3,518,946; giving activities include $3,503,250 for 13 grants (high: $1,590,000; low: $500).
Fields of interest: Museums (specialized); Arts; Education.
Type of support: General/operating support.
Limitations: Applications not accepted. Giving primarily in AZ, CO, and IL. No grants to individuals.
Application information: Contributes only to pre-selected organizations.
Directors: Mary F. Henderson; Emily P. Martin; J. Landis Martin; Sarah L. Martin; Sharon S. Martin.
EIN: 841466263
Selected grants: The following grants are a representative sample of this grantmaker's funding activity:
$710,000 to Clyfford Still Museum, Denver, CO, 2011. To further program services.
$150,000 to Colorado Historical Foundation, Denver, CO, 2011. To further program services.
$106,796 to Central City Opera House Association, Denver, CO, 2011. To further program services.
$100,000 to Wickenburg Foundation for the Performing Arts, Wickenburg, AZ, 2011. To further program services.

1457
Anthony and Delisa Mayer Foundation ✧

8001 S. Interport Blvd., Ste 360
Englewood, CO 80112-5908

Established in 2008 in CO.
Donors: JFM Foundation; Anthony R. Mayer; Delisa A. Mayer.
Foundation type: Independent foundation.
Financial data (yr. ended 11/30/13): Assets, $1,277,830 (M); gifts received, $25,500; expenditures, $736,766; qualifying distributions, $674,475; giving activities include $672,493 for 12 grants (high: $513,555; low: $1,000).
Fields of interest: Museums (art); Education.
Limitations: Applications not accepted. Giving primarily in Denver, CO. No grants to individuals.
Application information: Unsolicited requests for funds not accepted.
Officers: Anthony R. Mayer, Pres.; Delisa A. Mayer, V.P.; Mary J. Wimberg, Secy.
EIN: 263801020
Selected grants: The following grants are a representative sample of this grantmaker's funding activity:
$25,000 to Biennial of the Americas, Denver, CO, 2013. To support organization's charitable purpose.

1458
McDonnell Family Foundation ✧

609 Cliffgate Ln.
Castle Rock, CO 80108-8395 (303) 881-9747
E-mail: mcdonnellfamilyfoundation@gmail.com; Main URL: http://www.mcdonnellfoundation.org/

Established in 1999 in CO.
Donors: John F. McDonnell; Patricia L. McDonnell; Matthew J. McDonnell.
Foundation type: Independent foundation.
Financial data (yr. ended 12/31/12): Assets, $9,715,953 (M); expenditures, $712,441; qualifying distributions, $614,489; giving activities include $566,336 for 16 grants (high: $156,448; low: $1,000).

Fields of interest: Education; Health organizations; Human services; Children/youth, services; Christian agencies & churches.
Limitations: Applications not accepted. Giving primarily in CA and CO. No grants to individuals.
Application information: Contributes only to pre-selected organizations, which the foundation's individual board members seek out.
Officers: John F. McDonnell, Pres.; Patricia L. McDonnell, V.P.; Matthew J. McDonnell, Secy.-Treas.
EIN: 841498562
Selected grants: The following grants are a representative sample of this grantmaker's funding activity:
$12,900 to Voices for Children, San Diego, CA, 2012. For Jlc - 04/21/09 10:55Am Worksheet Private Foundation.

1459
Andre & Katherine Merage Foundation ✧
18 Inverness Pl. E.
Englewood, CO 80112-5622 (303) 789-2664
FAX: (303) 789-2696; E-mail: info@merage.org;
Main URL: http://www.merage.org
Facebook: https://www.facebook.com/pages/Early-Learning-Ventures/147565111396
Google Plus: https://plus.google.com/103345660533511436759/posts
LinkedIn: http://www.linkedin.com/company/merage-foundation?trk=top_nav_home
YouTube: http://www.youtube.com/user/MerageFoundation

Established in 2002 in CO.
Donor: Katherine Merage.
Foundation type: Independent foundation.
Financial data (yr. ended 11/30/13): Assets, $37,576,859 (M); gifts received, $491,334; expenditures, $2,222,480; qualifying distributions, $2,063,882; giving activities include $1,036,750 for 2+ grants.
Purpose and activities: Giving primarily to a donor-advised fund and to Jewish federated giving programs.
Fields of interest: Jewish federated giving programs; Philanthropy/voluntarism.
Limitations: Applications not accepted. Giving primarily in CO, DE and NY. No grants to individuals.
Application information: Contributes only to pre-selected organizations.
Officer: Sue Renner, Exec. Dir.
Directors: David Merage; Katherine Merage.
EIN: 450493929
Selected grants: The following grants are a representative sample of this grantmaker's funding activity:
$735,000 to JPMorgan Chase Foundation, New York, NY, 2011.
$212,500 to Allied Jewish Federation of Colorado, Denver, CO, 2011. For general operations.

1460
David and Laura Merage Foundation ✧
18 Inverness Pl. E.
Englewood, CO 80112-5622 (303) 789-2664
FAX: (303) 789-2696; Main URL: http://www.merage.org
Facebook: https://www.facebook.com/pages/Early-Learning-Ventures/147565111396
Google Plus: https://plus.google.com/103345660533511436759/posts
LinkedIn: http://www.linkedin.com/company/merage-foundation?trk=top_nav_home
YouTube: http://www.youtube.com/user/MerageFoundation

Established in 2002 in CO.
Donors: David Merage; Laura Merage; Katherine Merage.
Foundation type: Independent foundation.
Financial data (yr. ended 11/30/13): Assets, $47,263,832 (M); gifts received, $457,870; expenditures, $2,290,177; qualifying distributions, $2,091,065; giving activities include $1,703,721 for 26 grants (high: $803,000; low: $250).
Fields of interest: Arts; Education, early childhood education; Education; Foundations (private grantmaking); Jewish federated giving programs; Philanthropy/voluntarism; Jewish agencies & synagogues.
Limitations: Applications not accepted. Giving primarily in CO; funding also in CA, DE and Israel. No grants to individuals.
Application information: Contributes only to pre-selected organizations.
Officer: Sue Renner, Exec. Dir.
Directors: David Merage; Laura Merage.
EIN: 450493925
Selected grants: The following grants are a representative sample of this grantmaker's funding activity:
$940,000 to Early Connections Learning Centers, Colorado Springs, CO, 2010. For general operations.
$453,374 to National Philanthropic Trust, Jenkintown, PA, 2010.
$100,000 to RedLine, Denver, CO, 2011. For operations.
$35,000 to American Friends of the Tel Aviv University, New York, NY, 2011. For general operations.
$6,000 to Colorado Conservatory of Dance, Broomfield, CO, 2011. For general operations.
$5,000 to Colorado Children's Campaign, Denver, CO, 2011. For programs.
$5,000 to Colorado Succeeds, Denver, CO, 2011.
$2,500 to University of Colorado, Denver, CO, 2011.

1461
Flora and Morris Mizel Foundation I ✧ ☆
4350 S. Monaco St., 5th Fl.
Denver, CO 80237-3400

Established in 1997 in CO.
Donor: Mizel Resources Trust.
Foundation type: Independent foundation.
Financial data (yr. ended 12/31/12): Assets, $9,536,149 (M); gifts received, $325,000; expenditures, $497,374; qualifying distributions, $459,987; giving activities include $459,987 for grants.
Fields of interest: Philanthropy/voluntarism, management/technical assistance; Philanthropy/voluntarism, fund raising/fund distribution.
Limitations: Applications not accepted. Giving primarily in CA and MA. No grants to individuals.
Application information: Contributes only to pre-selected organizations.
Officers: Larry A. Mizel, Pres.; Charles G. Hauber, V.P. and Secy.; Carol Mizel, V.P. and Treas.
EIN: 841383695

1462
Flora and Morris Mizel Foundation II ✧ ☆
4350 S. Monaco St., 5th Fl.
Denver, CO 80237-3400

Established in 1997 in CO.
Donor: Mizel Resources Trust.
Foundation type: Independent foundation.
Financial data (yr. ended 12/31/12): Assets, $6,516,732 (M); gifts received, $325,000; expenditures, $524,983; qualifying distributions, $496,190; giving activities include $496,190 for grants.
Fields of interest: Jewish federated giving programs; Jewish agencies & synagogues.
Limitations: Applications not accepted. Giving primarily in CA, CO and OK; some giving also in Washington, D.C. No grants to individuals.
Application information: Contributes only to pre-selected organizations.
Officers: Larry A. Mizel, Pres.; Charles G. Hauber, V.P. and Secy.; Carol Mizel, V.P. and Treas.
EIN: 841383692

1463
Mol Family Foundation ✧
P.O. Box 631024
Highlands Ranch, CO 80163-1024

Established in 1993 in MI.
Donor: Edward K. Mol‡.
Foundation type: Independent foundation.
Financial data (yr. ended 12/31/11): Assets, $218,687 (M); expenditures, $3,749,806; qualifying distributions, $3,720,203; giving activities include $3,708,088 for 18 grants (high: $3,571,588; low: $1,000).
Fields of interest: Theological school/education; Christian agencies & churches.
Limitations: Applications not accepted. Giving primarily in CO, MI, PA, and VA. No grants to individuals.
Application information: Unsolicited requests for funds not accepted.
Board meeting date(s): June and Dec.
Officers: Ronald M. Mol, Pres.; Edward T. Mol, V.P.; Jeffrey Batchelder, Secy.; Brant Cuthbert, Treas.
EIN: 383152069

1464
Kenneth and Myra Monfort Charitable Foundation Inc. ✧
4376 Woody Creek Ln.
Fort Collins, CO 80524-9555

Established in 1998 in FL.
Donors: Kenneth Monfort; Myra Monfort.
Foundation type: Independent foundation.
Financial data (yr. ended 12/31/13): Assets, $18,939,453 (M); expenditures, $646,448; qualifying distributions, $522,500; giving activities include $495,000 for 38 grants (high: $170,000; low: $500).
Purpose and activities: Giving primarily for the arts, higher education, and youth and social services.
Fields of interest: Arts; Higher education; Law school/education; Education; Animal welfare; Boys & girls clubs; Human services.
Limitations: Applications not accepted. Giving primarily in CO. No grants to individuals.

Application information: Contributes only to pre-selected organizations.
Officers: Brad Ellins, V.P.; Rachel Iozzia, Secy.
Trustee: Myra Monfort.
EIN: 650881056

1465
Monfort Family Foundation ✧
(formerly Monfort Charitable Foundation)
134 Oak Ave.
Eaton, CO 80615-3491 (970) 454-2192
Contact: Patty Penfold

Established in 1970 in CO.
Donor: Kenneth W. Monfort‡.
Foundation type: Independent foundation.
Financial data (yr. ended 12/31/13): Assets, $26,154,925 (M); expenditures, $2,377,201; qualifying distributions, $2,109,736; giving activities include $1,858,272 for 28 grants (high: $770,000; low: $1,000).
Purpose and activities: Giving primarily for education, developing the arts and humanities, conducting scientific research into the causes, treatment and prevention of life-threatening diseases, and providing aid to the disadvantaged.
Fields of interest: Arts; Education, fund raising/fund distribution; Education; Health care, fund raising/fund distribution; Health organizations, association; United Ways and Federated Giving Programs.
Type of support: General/operating support.
Limitations: Applications accepted. Giving primarily in Weld County, CO. No support for political or religious organizations, or for environmental organizations, charter schools or lobbying. No grants to individuals.
Application information: Funding for single-year grants will need to be approved each year for continued support; funding for multi-year grants will be limited to a 3-year time frame. Application form required.
Initial approach: Proposal
Copies of proposal: 1
Deadline(s): None
Board meeting date(s): Varies as necessary
Officers: Kaye C. Montford, Pres.; Kyle Monfort Futo, V.P.; Charlie Monfort, V.P.; Myra Monfort, Secy.; Dick Monfort, Treas.
EIN: 237068253

1466
Morgridge Family Foundation ✧
4242 E. Amherst Ave.
Denver, CO 80222-6702
Contact: Renee Joyce, Prog. Off.
GiveSmart: http://www.givesmart.org/Stories/Donors/Tashia-and-John-Morgridge
John and Tashia Morgridge's Giving Pledge Profile: http://glasspockets.org/philanthropy-in-focus/eye-on-the-giving-pledge/profiles/morgridge

Established in 2008 in CO.
Donors: John P. Morgridge; Tashia Morgridge.
Foundation type: Independent foundation.
Financial data (yr. ended 12/31/12): Assets, $50,985,234 (M); gifts received, $19,502,500; expenditures, $11,642,877; qualifying distributions, $10,191,483; giving activities include $10,000,000 for 135 grants (high: $1,250,000; low: $500), and $13,389 for 1 foundation-administered program.
Purpose and activities: The foundation's mission is to serve the neediest of the needy, with emphasis on support for educational programs. Support also for arts and culture, strengthening the community, health and wellness, and early childhood literacy.
Fields of interest: Arts; Education, reading; Education; Health care; Community/economic development; Economically disadvantaged.
Limitations: Applications not accepted. Giving in the U.S., with emphasis in CO.
Application information: Applications not accepted.
Officers: John D. Morgridge, Pres.; Carrie Morgridge, V.P.
Directors: John P. Morgridge; Tashia Morgridge.
Number of staff: 1 full-time professional.
EIN: 262336633
Selected grants: The following grants are a representative sample of this grantmaker's funding activity:
$1,250,000 to Denver Museum of Nature and Science, Denver, CO, 2012. For Science in Action Building Campaign.
$1,000,000 to Nature Conservancy, Arlington, VA, 2012. For Development and Digital Distribution of Educational Content on the Natural World and Conservation Science.
$750,000 to Denver Museum of Nature and Science, Denver, CO, 2012. For Restricted Grant to Science Engagement Center Campaign.
$750,000 to Denver Museum of Nature and Science, Denver, CO, 2012. For Science in Action Building Campaign.
$400,000 to United Way, Mile High, Denver, CO, 2012. For Literacy - Reading Plus for all Colorado Students.
$400,000 to United Way, Mile High, Denver, CO, 2012. For foster care pilot program to create a new system in CO.
$50,000 to Denver Museum of Nature and Science, Denver, CO, 2012. For 21st CCC Project.
$31,000 to Five Star Education Foundation, Thornton, CO, 2012. For STEM Laser Engraver for District.
$25,000 to United Way, Mile High, Denver, CO, 2012. For Professional Development - 21st Century Classroom Training.
$13,493 to Raft, Inc., Los Angeles, CA, 2012. For SMART Board, Projector, Floor Stand and Installation Costs.

1467
Munger Family Foundation ✧
c/o Reuban S. & Melinda S. Munger
707 Kalmia Ave.
Colorado, CO 80304-1737

Established in 2006 in MA.
Donors: Reuban S. Munger; Melinda Sick Munger.
Foundation type: Independent foundation.
Financial data (yr. ended 12/31/12): Assets, $954,049 (M); expenditures, $953,999; qualifying distributions, $951,027; giving activities include $950,000 for 5 grants (high: $250,000; low: $100,000).
Fields of interest: Education; Children.
Limitations: Applications not accepted. Giving primarily in Washington, DC, and MA. No grants to individuals.
Application information: Contributes only to pre-selected organizations.
Trustees: Melinda Sick Munger; Reuban S. Munger.
EIN: 208064396

1468
Nagel Foundation ✧
1225 17th St., Ste. 2440
Denver, CO 80202-5524 (303) 376-1400
Contact: Ralph J. Nagel, Pres.

Established in 1994 in CO.
Donors: Ralph J. Nagel; Steven A. Denning; Ciga, LLP; General Atlantic Service Corp.
Foundation type: Independent foundation.
Financial data (yr. ended 12/31/13): Assets, $25,810,337 (M); gifts received, $600,000; expenditures, $1,494,731; qualifying distributions, $1,358,750; giving activities include $1,358,750 for 37 grants (high: $250,000; low: $2,500).
Purpose and activities: Giving primarily for higher education.
Fields of interest: Higher education; Education; Human services.
Limitations: Applications accepted. Giving primarily in Denver, CO. No grants to individuals.
Application information: Application form required.
Initial approach: Proposal
Deadline(s): Nov. 15
Officer: Ralph J. Nagel, Pres.
EIN: 841285137

1469
National Endowment for Financial Education ✧ ☆
(also known as NEFE)
1331 17th St., Ste. 1200
Denver, CO 80202-1595
Contact: Londell Jackson, Asst. Dir., Grants & Research
FAX: (303) 220-0838; E-mail: ldj@nefe.org; Main URL: http://www.nefe.org
E-Newsletter: http://www.nefe.org/NEFENews/PressRoom/Subscribe/tabid/230/Default.aspx
Twitter: http://twitter.com/NEFE_ORG
YouTube: http://www.youtube.com/user/NonprofitNEFE

Established in 1972 in CO.
Foundation type: Operating foundation.
Financial data (yr. ended 12/31/13): Assets, $166,169,812 (M); gifts received, $443,833; expenditures, $6,789,404; qualifying distributions, $5,603,497; giving activities include $440,907 for 8 grants (high: $131,997; low: $27,571), and $4,485,947 for 4 foundation-administered programs.
Purpose and activities: The National Endowment for Financial Education (NEFE) is the only private, nonprofit, national foundation wholly dedicated to improving the financial well-being of all Americans. The mission of the National Endowment for Financial Education is to help individual Americans acquire the knowledge and skills necessary to take control of their financial destiny. NEFE's mission is grounded in the belief that regardless of background or income level, financially informed individuals are better able to 1) take control of their circumstances, 2) improve their quality of life, and 3) ensure a stable future for themselves and their families. NEFE's guiding principles are stated in eight initiatives. These initiatives describe how NEFE achieves its mission, and outlines the goals and standards that

guide the foundation's activities. Every project or program undertaken by NEFE must fit within the scope of at least one initiative. NEFE accomplishes its mission primarily by partnering with other organizations to: 1) provide practical, reliable, and unbiased financial education to members of the public, 2) accomplish research in the field of financial literacy education, and 3) create demand for financial education. NEFE's activities place special emphasis on those who face financial challenges that are not being addressed by others. Among the target audiences are: youth, low-income individuals and families, and people in difficult or unusual life circumstances. NEFE's partnerships and the foundation's own efforts result in a wide range of free and low-cost activities and materials, including: resources for consumers, materials for educators and facilitators, the NEFE High School Financial Planning Program, which includes joint efforts with numerous nonprofit, for-profit, and government entities to develop financial literacy resources for specific audiences, research, conferences, and think tanks on a variety of financial literacy topics, and grant awards to organizations and academic institutions whose work can contribute to the field of financial literacy.
Fields of interest: Education, research; Education, public education; Education; Foundations (private grantmaking).
Type of support: Program development; Research; Program evaluation.
Limitations: Applications accepted. Giving on a national basis. No support for organizations lacking 501(c)(3) IRS status, or foreign organizations. No grants to individuals, or for general operating support, deficits, salaries, capital costs, computer equipment, pass-through funding, conferences, seminars, fundraisers, sponsorships, endowments, challenge grants, matching funds, scholarships, or for registration fees.
Publications: Application guidelines; Informational brochure; Newsletter.
Application information: Full proposals will be accepted by invitation only following submission of inquiry. See foundation web site for application information. Application form required.
Initial approach: Complete the Concept Inquiry form after checking guidelines and eligibility
Copies of proposal: 1
Deadline(s): June and Dec.
Board meeting date(s): Apr. and Nov.
Final notification: 5 business days following board meetings
Officers and Directors:* Alexander Gonzalez, Ph.D*, Chair.; Karen Vahouny,* Vice-Chair.; Ted Beck,* C.E.O. and Pres.; Patrick Bannigan; Michael A. Bedke; Dorothy J. Bridges; Pip Coburn; Denise V. Crawford; John R. Woerner; and 5 additional directors.
Number of staff: 10 full-time professional; 5 full-time support; 2 part-time support.
EIN: 840632115
Selected grants: The following grants are a representative sample of this grantmaker's funding activity:
$71,671 to Ohio State University, Columbus, OH, 2012. For Financial Behavior, Debt and Early -Life Transitions.

1470
Neuman Family Foundation ✧
819 10th St.
Boulder, CO 80302-7551

Established in 1998 in IL.
Donor: Werner Neuman.
Foundation type: Independent foundation.
Financial data (yr. ended 12/31/13): Assets, $2,699,365 (M); expenditures, $627,811; qualifying distributions, $626,000; giving activities include $625,500 for 8 grants (high: $300,000; low: $1,000).
Purpose and activities: Giving primarily for education, the environment, and human services.
Fields of interest: Arts; Education; Environment; Human services.
Limitations: Applications not accepted. Giving primarily in Chicago, IL; some giving also in CA, CO, MN and NY. No grants to individuals.
Application information: Unsolicited requests for funds not accepted.
Trustees: Judith Neuman; Suzanne Neuman; Werner Neuman; William Neuman.
EIN: 367234939

1471
The Norwood Foundation ✧
P.O. Box 792
Manitou Springs, CO 80829-0792 (719) 593-2600
Contact: Christopher S. Jenkins, Secy.-Treas.

Established in 2002 in CO.
Donors: Carolyn S. Jenkins; David D. Jenkins; Development Mgmt., Inc.; First and Main, LLC.
Foundation type: Independent foundation.
Financial data (yr. ended 02/28/13): Assets, $20,346 (M); gifts received, $1,425,000; expenditures, $1,412,597; qualifying distributions, $1,412,221; giving activities include $1,412,221 for 49+ grants (high: $560,100).
Purpose and activities: Giving primarily for education, Christian organizations, and to a Presbyterian church.
Fields of interest: Health organizations, association; Human services; Child development, services; Christian agencies & churches; Protestant agencies & churches.
Type of support: General/operating support; Scholarships—to individuals.
Limitations: Giving primarily in CO; with some emphasis on Colorado Springs.
Application information: Application form required.
Initial approach: Letter
Deadline(s): None
Officers: David D. Jenkins, Pres.; Carolyn S. Jenkins, V.P.; Christopher S. Jenkins, Secy.-Treas.
EIN: 010705471
Selected grants: The following grants are a representative sample of this grantmaker's funding activity:
$101,368 to Compassion International, Colorado Springs, CO, 2011. For general purpose.
$25,000 to University of Colorado Foundation, Boulder, CO, 2011. For general purpose.
$10,000 to ULI Foundation, Washington, DC, 2011. For general purpose.
$10,000 to University of Colorado Foundation, Boulder, CO, 2011. For general purpose.
$7,500 to Empty Stocking Fund, Colorado Springs, CO, 2011. For general purpose.
$7,500 to Young Life, Colorado Springs, CO, 2011. For general purpose.
$4,000 to Boy Scouts of America, Colorado Springs, CO, 2011. For general purpose.
$2,500 to Cheyenne Village, Colorado Springs, CO, 2011. For general purpose.
$2,500 to Silver Key Senior Services, Colorado Springs, CO, 2011. For general purpose.
$1,000 to Pikes Peak Hospice Foundation, Colorado Springs, CO, 2011. For general purpose.

1472
The John and Sophie Ottens Foundation ✧
P.O. Box 429
Ridgway, CO 81432-0429 (970) 626-5310
Contact: Henry O. Hooper, Pres.
E-mail: h2o@ouraynet.com

Established in 1998 in AZ.
Donors: John Ottens†; Sophie Ottens†.
Foundation type: Independent foundation.
Financial data (yr. ended 01/31/13): Assets, $18,490,974 (M); expenditures, $1,807,918; qualifying distributions, $1,557,480; giving activities include $1,557,480 for 30+ grants (high: $258,522).
Purpose and activities: Giving for the physical or mental rehabilitation of Native Americans; giving also for education, health professions, and social work for Native Americans.
Fields of interest: Higher education, college; Hospitals (general); Medical research; Native Americans/American Indians.
Type of support: Building/renovation; General/operating support; Continuing support; Management development/capacity building; Equipment; Program development; Curriculum development; Internship funds; Scholarship funds; Technical assistance; Matching/challenge support.
Limitations: Applications accepted. Giving limited to AZ, CO, NM, and UT.
Publications: Application guidelines; Newsletter.
Application information: Application form not required.
Initial approach: E-mail, letter, or telephone
Copies of proposal: 1
Deadline(s): None
Board meeting date(s): June or Sept.
Final notification: within 30 days
Officers and Directors:* Henry O. Hooper,* Pres.; Steven K. Aronoff,* Secy.-Treas.; Cynthia Aronoff; Jeanne R. Hooper.
Number of staff: 2 part-time professional; 1 part-time support.
EIN: 860911121
Selected grants: The following grants are a representative sample of this grantmaker's funding activity:
$677,000 to Northern Arizona University Foundation, Flagstaff, AZ, 2012.
$210,000 to Fort Lewis College Foundation, Durango, CO, 2012.
$118,000 to Hopi Foundation, Kykotsmovi, AZ, 2012.
$75,000 to Institute of American Indian Arts, Santa Fe, NM, 2012.
$58,750 to Colorado State University, Native American Center, Fort Collins, CO, 2012.
$55,000 to Hopi Senior Center, Moenkopi, AZ, 2012.
$50,000 to Boys and Girls Clubs of Greater Scottsdale, Scottsdale, AZ, 2012.
$45,000 to Albuquerque Indian Center, Albuquerque, NM, 2012.
$43,000 to Flagstaff Medical Center, Flagstaff, AZ, 2012.
$36,000 to Brigham and Women's Hospital, Boston, MA, 2012.

1473
Otter Cares Foundation ✧
(doing business as OtterCares Foundation)
401 W. Oak St.
Fort Collins, CO 80521
Main URL: http://www.ottercares.org/

Established in CO.
Donors: OtterBox Products; Otter Products, LLC.
Foundation type: Independent foundation.
Financial data (yr. ended 12/31/12): Assets, $30,692 (M); expenditures, $890,498; qualifying distributions, $890,498; giving activities include $799,104 for 413 grants (high: $50,000; low: $75).
Fields of interest: Education; Youth development.
Application information: Application form required.
Initial approach: See website for application form
Deadline(s): Quarterly
Officers and Directors:* Nancy A. Richardson,* Pres.; Curtis R. Richardson,* Secy.-Treas.; Susie Gunstream; Pete Richardson; Cheryl Thomas.
EIN: 271649019
Selected grants: The following grants are a representative sample of this grantmaker's funding activity:
$20,000 to Plymouth State University, Plymouth, NH, 2011.
$20,000 to Plymouth State University, Plymouth, NH, 2011.
$16,500 to Plymouth State University, Plymouth, NH, 2010.
$14,012 to Partners Mentoring Youth of Larimer County, Fort Collins, CO, 2010.
$10,000 to Boys and Girls Clubs of Larimer County, Fort Collins, CO, 2011.
$10,000 to OK Corral Camp, Avon, CO, 2011.
$7,910 to Poudre Valley Health System Foundation, Fort Collins, CO, 2010.
$7,800 to Respite Care, Fort Collins, CO, 2011.
$7,000 to Timberline Church, Fort Collins, CO, 2010.
$5,000 to Poudre Valley Health System Foundation, Fort Collins, CO, 2011.
$3,565 to Partners Mentoring Youth of Larimer County, Fort Collins, CO, 2011.
$2,750 to Colorado State University Foundation, Fort Collins, CO, 2010.
$2,500 to Hearts and Horses, Loveland, CO, 2011.
$2,500 to Poudre School District, Fort Collins, CO, 2011.
$1,500 to Live the Victory, Fort Collins, CO, 2011.
$1,000 to Colorado State University Foundation, Fort Collins, CO, 2010.
$1,000 to Denver Active 20-30 Childrens Foundation, Denver, CO, 2010.
$1,000 to Family Center/La Familia, Fort Collins, CO, 2010.
$1,000 to Pathways Hospice, Community Care for Northern Colorado, Fort Collins, CO, 2010.
$1,000 to Young Life, Colorado Springs, CO, 2010.

1474
PB&K Family Foundation ✧ ☆
c/o Baker Hostetler LLP
303 E. 17th Ave., Ste. 1100
Denver, CO 80203-1264

Established in CO.
Donors: Jeffrey V. Baldwin; Debra J. Perry.
Foundation type: Independent foundation.
Financial data (yr. ended 12/31/13): Assets, $18,059,624 (M); gifts received, $1,000,000; expenditures, $754,662; qualifying distributions, $675,504; giving activities include $672,004 for 18 grants (high: $200,000; low: $1,000).
Fields of interest: Performing arts, ballet; Arts; Health care; Human services.
Limitations: Applications not accepted. Giving in the U.S., with emphasis on CO.
Application information: Unsolicited request for funds not accepted.
Officers: Jeffrey V. Baldwin, Pres. and Treas.; Debra J. Perry, V.P. and Secy.
EIN: 453982905

1475
Peierls Foundation ✧
73 S. Holman Way
Golden, CO 80401-5108
Contact: E. Jeffrey Peierls, Pres.

Incorporated in 1956 in NY.
Donors: Brian E. Peierls; Edgar S. Peierls†; Ethel F. Peierls; E. Jeffrey Peierls; Ethel F. Peierls Charitable Lead Trust; and sons.
Foundation type: Independent foundation.
Financial data (yr. ended 10/31/13): Assets, $109,844,753 (M); gifts received, $1,370,007; expenditures, $6,010,991; qualifying distributions, $5,668,000; giving activities include $5,668,000 for 54 grants (high: $1,041,300; low: $7,600).
Purpose and activities: Primary areas of interest include higher education, international relief, and programs benefiting minorities.
Fields of interest: Higher education; Reproductive health, family planning; Health organizations, association; Medical research, institute; Children/youth, services; Minorities/immigrants, centers/services; International relief; Civil rights, race/intergroup relations; Minorities.
Type of support: Annual campaigns; Endowments; Scholarship funds.
Limitations: Applications accepted. Giving primarily in CA, CO, Washington, DC, NJ, NY and TX. No grants to individuals.
Application information: Application form not required.
Initial approach: Letter
Deadline(s): None
Final notification: Only positive responses will be sent
Officers: E. Jeffrey Peierls, Pres.; Brian Eliot Peierls, V.P.; Malcolm A. Moore, Secy.
EIN: 136082503
Selected grants: The following grants are a representative sample of this grantmaker's funding activity:
$680,500 to American Red Cross National Headquarters, Washington, DC, 2012.
$607,500 to Nature Conservancy, Colorado Field Office, Boulder, CO, 2012.
$520,500 to International Rescue Committee, New York, NY, 2012.
$500,500 to CARE, San Francisco, CA, 2012.
$211,500 to Planned Parenthood Federation of America, New York, NY, 2012.
$122,200 to I Have A Dream Foundation, Denver, CO, 2012.
$113,500 to Colorado UpLIFT, Denver, CO, 2012.
$75,700 to Planned Parenthood of the Texas Capital Region, Austin, TX, 2012.
$53,600 to Meharry Medical College, Nashville, TN, 2012.
$51,500 to Hope Center, Denver, CO, 2012.

1476
Pema Foundation, Inc. ✧ ☆
15205 W. 32nd Ave.
Golden, CO 80401-1217

Established in DE.
Donors: Peter H. Coors; Holland H. Coors Charitable Trust.
Foundation type: Independent foundation.
Financial data (yr. ended 12/31/12): Assets, $4,686,606 (M); gifts received, $730,963; expenditures, $1,020,712; qualifying distributions, $996,500; giving activities include $996,500 for grants.
Fields of interest: Medical care, bioethics; Catholic agencies & churches.
Limitations: Applications not accepted. Giving primarily in CO.
Application information: Unsolicited requests for funds not accepted.
Directors: Marilyn E. Coors; Peter H. Coors.
EIN: 300202608

1477
Jack Petteys Memorial Foundation ✧
P.O. Box 324
Brush, CO 80723-0324 (970) 842-5101
Contact: Judith A. Gunnon

Established about 1943 in CO.
Foundation type: Independent foundation.
Financial data (yr. ended 12/31/13): Assets, $13,344,319 (M); expenditures, $710,043; qualifying distributions, $671,176; giving activities include $669,398 for 21 grants (high: $525,665; low: $600).
Purpose and activities: Giving primarily to undergraduate scholarship funds; support also for hospitals and civic projects.
Fields of interest: Higher education; Education; Hospitals (general); Community/economic development; Government/public administration.
Type of support: Equipment; Scholarship funds.
Limitations: Applications accepted. Giving primarily in the northeastern CO area.
Application information: Application form required.
Initial approach: Letter
Copies of proposal: 1
Deadline(s): Dec. 1
Director: Robert Hansen.
Trustee: The Farmers State Bank.
EIN: 846036239

1478
Pikes Peak Community Foundation ✧
730 N. Nevada Ave.
Colorado Springs, CO 80903-5014 (719) 389-1251
Contact: For grants: Michael R. Hannigan, Exec. Dir.; Jamie Brown, Dir., Community Svcs.
FAX: (719) 389-1252; E-mail: info@ppcf.org; Additional E-mails: jbrown@ppcf.org and mhannigan@ppcf.org; Main URL: http://www.ppcf.org
E-Newsletter: http://www.ppcf.org/connect/enews
Facebook: https://www.facebook.com/pikespeakcommunityfoundation
Twitter: https://twitter.com/PPCommFdn

Established in 1996 in CO.
Foundation type: Community foundation.

Financial data (yr. ended 12/31/13): Assets, $50,451,636 (M); gifts received, $7,176,156; expenditures, $7,165,858; giving activities include $3,984,454 for 122+ grants (high: $250,000), and $65,983 for 32 grants to individuals.
Purpose and activities: PPCF will boldly commit to dramatically improve the quality of life in the Pikes Peak region. Through education and actions, the foundation will improve the understanding of, appreciation for, and the practice of philanthropy.
Fields of interest: Arts; Education; Environment; Health care; Housing/shelter; Children/youth, services; Human services; Community development, neighborhood development; Economic development; Community/economic development; Public affairs.
Type of support: General/operating support; Continuing support; Income development; Management development/capacity building; Seed money; Matching/challenge support.
Limitations: Applications accepted. Giving primarily in El Paso and Teller counties in CO. No support for religious purposes. No grants to individuals (except for scholarships), or for debt retirement, endowment funds, medical, scientific, or academic research, sponsorships or camperships, travel, publications, fees for conferences, symposiums, or workshops, creation or installation of art objects, or annual memberships of affiliation campaigns, dinners, or special events; no loans.
Publications: Annual report (including application guidelines).
Application information: Visit foundation web site for application guidelines. Application form not required.
Initial approach: E-mail letter of intent (1 page)
Copies of proposal: 1
Deadline(s): None
Board meeting date(s): Varies
Final notification: None
Officers and Directors:* Paula D. Pollet,* Chair.; Trudy Strewler Hodges, C.E.O.; Michael R. Hannigan, Exec. Dir.; Deborah Adams; Michael Berniger; Suzanne Connaughton; Cari Davis; Susan Foerster; Larry R. Gaddis; Greg Gandy; Alicia McConnell; Kae Rader; Jannie Richardson; Pam Shipp; Wendel P. Torres; Rob Wrubel.
EIN: 841339670

1479
The Pioneer Fund ✧
1228 15th St., Ste. 309
Denver, CO 80202-1642 (303) 260-6914

Established in 1960 in IL.
Donors: Helen M. McLoraine†; Bird Oil Corp.
Foundation type: Independent foundation.
Financial data (yr. ended 12/31/13): Assets, $11,829,473 (M); expenditures, $2,033,772; qualifying distributions, $1,751,151; giving activities include $1,751,151 for 28 grants (high: $280,307; low: $200).
Purpose and activities: Giving primarily for medical research and to a children's hospital, as well as for education, and children, youth and social services.
Fields of interest: Education; Hospitals (specialty); Medical research, institute; Human services; Children/youth, services.
Type of support: Endowments.
Limitations: Applications not accepted. Giving primarily in Denver, CO; some giving also in Memphis, TN and on a national basis. No grants to individuals.
Application information: Contributes only to pre-selected organizations.
Officers: Robert Anderson, Pres. and Treas.; Scott Hamilton, V.P.; Lark Birdsong, Secy.
EIN: 366108943
Selected grants: The following grants are a representative sample of this grantmaker's funding activity:
$1,000,000 to Vanderbilt University, Nashville, TN, 2012. For Medical Student Scholarship Endowment Fund.
$500,000 to Multiple Myeloma Research Foundation, Norwalk, CT, 2012. For genomics research and operating support.
$479,200 to Denver Foundation, Helen M. McLoraine Opportunity Fund, Denver, CO, 2012. For Scholarship Endowment Fund.
$235,444 to LiveBeyond, Nashville, TN, 2012. For Overseas Medical Clinic Projects.
$210,000 to Community Child Health Foundation, Denver, CO, 2012. For medical assistance.
$200,000 to Colorado Skating Club, Centennial, CO, 2012. For Amateur Figure Skater Assistance Fund.
$125,000 to Friends of the Family, Van Nuys, CA, 2012. For cash reserve matching fund.
$100,000 to Helmar Skating Fund, Denver, CO, 2012. For Amateur Figure Skating Assistance Fund.
$100,000 to House Research Institute, Los Angeles, CA, 2012. For medical research.
$20,000 to Margaret Hallauer Scholarship Fund, Breckenridge, TX, 2012. For general operating support.

1480
The Piton Foundation ✧
1705 17th St., Ste. 200
Denver, CO 80202-1293 (303) 825-6246
Contact: Carol Bush, Cont.
FAX: (303) 628-3839; E-mail: info@piton.org; Main URL: http://www.piton.org

Incorporated in 1976 in CO.
Donors: Samuel Gary; Gary Williams Energy Corp.; The Gary Williams Co.
Foundation type: Operating foundation.
Financial data (yr. ended 11/30/12): Assets, $5,971,171 (M); gifts received, $15,186,803; expenditures, $10,730,645; qualifying distributions, $11,750,507; giving activities include $7,630,491 for 172 grants (high: $1,535,182; low: $250), $57,212 for 116 employee matching gifts, $35,100 for 7 in-kind gifts, $968,607 for foundation-administered programs and $1,076,866 for 1 loan/program-related investment.
Purpose and activities: Highly limited funds to support activities of the foundation in 4 areas: Improving Public Education; Revitalizing Neighborhoods; Promoting Economic Opportunities; and Strengthening Families.
Fields of interest: Education; Employment; Youth development; Family services; Community/economic development; Leadership development; Children.
Type of support: General/operating support; Capital campaigns; Program development; Conferences/seminars; Seed money; Curriculum development; Technical assistance; Program evaluation; Employee matching gifts.
Limitations: Applications not accepted. Giving limited to Denver, CO.
Publications: Biennial report; Informational brochure; Occasional report; Program policy statement.
Application information: Unsolicited requests for funds not considered.
Board meeting date(s): As required
Officers and Directors:* Samuel Gary,* Chair.; Dave Younggren,* Pres.; Carol Bush, C.F.O.; Nancy Gary; Rob Gary; Tim Howard.
Number of staff: 14 full-time professional; 5 full-time support.
EIN: 840719486

1481
The Piton Investment Fund ✧
(formerly The Gary-Williams Foundation)
370 17th St., Ste. 5300
Denver, CO 80202-5653

Established in 2002 in CO.
Donors: Samuel Gary; Ronald W. Williams; The Gary-Williams Company.
Foundation type: Independent foundation.
Financial data (yr. ended 11/30/12): Assets, $194,762,597 (M); gifts received, $120,000,000; expenditures, $12,002,959; qualifying distributions, $11,125,837; giving activities include $10,907,460 for 117 grants (high: $10,076,866; low: $1).
Purpose and activities: Giving primarily for land conservation.
Fields of interest: Environment, land resources; Foundations (private operating).
Limitations: Applications not accepted. Giving primarily in CO. No grants to individuals.
Application information: Contributes only to pre-selected organizations.
Officers and Directors:* Samuel Gary,* Chair.; Terry Minger,* C.E.O. and Pres.; David J. Younggren,* Secy.-Treas.; Nancy Gary; Rob Gary; Tim Howard.
EIN: 810587194

1482
The Ponzio Family Foundation ✧
(formerly The June and Craig Ponzio Foundation)
34350 Stagecoach Blvd.
Evergreen, CO 80439-7913

Established in CO.
Donors: Craig Ponzio; June Ponzio.
Foundation type: Independent foundation.
Financial data (yr. ended 12/31/13): Assets, $5,127,825 (M); expenditures, $3,030,540; qualifying distributions, $2,857,941; giving activities include $2,857,941 for 8 grants (high: $2,510,000; low: $241).
Purpose and activities: Giving primarily for a children's hospital; support also for higher education.
Fields of interest: Arts; Higher education; Hospitals (specialty).
Type of support: General/operating support.
Limitations: Applications not accepted. Giving primarily in WI; some giving also in CO. No grants to individuals.
Application information: Contributes only to pre-selected organizations.
Officer: Craig Ponzio, Pres.
EIN: 841603731

1483
The Precourt Foundation ✧
887 Lake Creek Rd.
Edwards, CO 81632

Established in 1994 in TX and CO.
Donors: Jay A. Precourt; Amanda J. Precourt; Jay Anthony Precourt, Jr.; Pepi Gramshammer; Sheika Gramshammer.
Foundation type: Independent foundation.
Financial data (yr. ended 12/31/13): Assets, $37,714,797 (M); gifts received, $25,000; expenditures, $1,200,143; qualifying distributions, $1,094,009; giving activities include $1,094,009 for 62 grants (high: $282,067; low: $50).
Purpose and activities: Giving primarily for education, children, youth and social services, and for the arts, particularly art museums.
Fields of interest: Museums (art); Arts; Elementary/secondary education; Higher education; Human services; Children/youth, services; Foundations (private grantmaking).
Limitations: Applications not accepted. Giving primarily in CA and CO;. No grants to individuals.
Application information: Contributes only to pre-selected organizations.
Trustees: Amanda J. Precourt; Jay A. Precourt; Jay Anthony Precourt, Jr.
Number of staff: 2 part-time professional; 2 part-time support.
EIN: 760430659

1484
The Louis and Harold Price Foundation, Inc. ✧
1371 Hecla Dr., Ste. B-1
Louisville, CO 80027-2318 (303) 665-9201
Contact: Kishawn Leuthauser, V.P.
FAX: (303) 665-1027;
E-mail: grantinquiry@pricefoundation.org; Main URL: http://www.pricefoundation.org

Incorporated in 1951 in NY.
Donors: Louis Price†; Harold Price†.
Foundation type: Independent foundation.
Financial data (yr. ended 12/31/12): Assets, $77,311,310 (M); expenditures, $3,801,622; qualifying distributions, $3,581,903; giving activities include $3,250,884 for 136 grants (high: $350,000; low: $250).
Purpose and activities: Giving primarily for arts and culture (with an emphasis on education), children and youth, education, entrepreneurship, the environment, health, human services, medical research, and civic and community and Jewish related causes.
Fields of interest: Arts; Education; Health care; Medical research; Human services; Children/youth, services; Community/economic development.
Type of support: General/operating support; Continuing support; Annual campaigns; Program development; Matching/challenge support.
Limitations: Applications accepted. Giving primarily in southern CA; some funding nationally. No support for religious or political organizations. No grants to individuals, or for building funds, capital campaigns, or endowments.
Publications: Application guidelines; Grants list.
Application information: Applicants are encouraged to submit letters on inquiry online through foundation web site. Letters submitted via U.S. mail are also accepted. Smaller organizations are advised to apply for general operating support. On an annual basis, only a small portion of the foundation's resources are directed toward unsolicited proposals. Unsolicited funds are rarely made to arts and culture and medical research proposals. See foundation web site for guidelines. Application form not required.
Initial approach: Submit Letter of Inquiry through foundation web site (not more than 2 pages, on organization letterhead)
Copies of proposal: 1
Deadline(s): None
Board meeting date(s): 3 or 4 times per year
Final notification: Within 30 days
Officers and Trustees:* Linda Vitti Herbst,* Chair.; Bonnie Vitti,* Pres.; Kishawn Leuthauser, V.P.; George Asch; Alfred E. Osborne, Jr., Ph.D.
Number of staff: 1 full-time professional; 1 part-time support.
EIN: 136121358

1485
ProLogis Foundation ✧
4545 Airport Way
Denver, CO 80239-5716 (303) 567-5000
Contact: Edward S. Nekritz, Sr. V.P. and Secy.-Treas.
Main URL: http://www.prologis.com/en/aboutus/CommunityInvolvement.aspx

Established in 2001 in CO.
Donors: Catellus Land & Development Corporation and Subsidiaries; Development Services Trust; ProLogis.
Foundation type: Company-sponsored foundation.
Financial data (yr. ended 12/31/12): Assets, $12,175,235 (M); gifts received, $1,000,000; expenditures, $661,325; qualifying distributions, $647,260; giving activities include $647,260 for 120 grants (high: $125,000; low: $50).
Purpose and activities: The foundation supports museums and organizations involved with education, health, spine injuries, human services, and international relief.
Fields of interest: Museums; Elementary school/education; Higher education; Scholarships/financial aid; Education; Hospitals (general); Health care, patient services; Spine disorders; Boys & girls clubs; Youth development, adult & child programs; Boy scouts; Youth development, business; Children/youth, services; Human services; International relief.
Type of support: General/operating support; Program development; Scholarship funds; Employee matching gifts.
Limitations: Applications accepted. Giving primarily in areas of company operations, with emphasis on CO; giving also to national organizations.
Application information: Application form not required.
Initial approach: Proposal
Deadline(s): None
Officers and Directors:* Walter C. Rakowich,* Pres.; Edward S. Nekritz,* Sr. V.P. and Secy.-Treas.; Lori Palazzolo, V.P.
EIN: 364439409
Selected grants: The following grants are a representative sample of this grantmaker's funding activity:
$142,982 to Mercy Corps, Portland, OR, 2011.
$5,000 to Posse Foundation, New York, NY, 2011.
$1,000 to Colorado Academy, Denver, CO, 2011.

1486
Ricketts Conservation Fund ✧ ☆
1395 S. Platte River Dr.
Denver, CO 80223-3467

Established in IA.
Donor: John J. Ricketts.
Foundation type: Independent foundation.
Financial data (yr. ended 12/31/13): Assets, $3,047,593 (M); gifts received, $3,099,682; expenditures, $1,102,689; qualifying distributions, $1,096,562; giving activities include $1,077,418 for 9 grants (high: $1,011,822; low: $5,085).
Fields of interest: Education; Environment, research; Environment.
Limitations: Applications not accepted. Giving in the U.S., with some emphasis on Omaha, NE, and WY.
Application information: Unsolicited requests for funds not accepted.
Officer: John J. Ricketts, Pres. and Secy.-Treas.
EIN: 462927195

1487
Rose Community Foundation ✧
600 S. Cherry St., Ste. 1200
Denver, CO 80246-1712 (303) 398-7400
Contact: For grants: Cheryl McDonald, Grants Mgr.
FAX: (303) 398-7430; E-mail: info@rcfdenver.org; Grant inquiry e-mail: cmcdonald@RCFdenver.org; Grant inquiry tel.: 303-398-7446; Main URL: http://www.rcfdenver.org

Established in 1995 in CO.
Donors: Rose Foundation; DPS Foundation.
Foundation type: Community foundation.
Financial data (yr. ended 12/31/12): Assets, $271,775,000 (M); gifts received, $9,133,000; expenditures, $15,932,000; giving activities include $11,957,000 for grants.
Purpose and activities: The foundation seeks to enhance the quality of life in the greater Denver community through its leadership, resources, tradition, and values.
Fields of interest: Education; Health care; Children, services; Child development, services; Family services; Human services; Jewish agencies & synagogues; Children/youth; Adults; Aging; Minorities; Hispanics/Latinos; Economically disadvantaged; Homeless.
Type of support: Technical assistance; Research; Publication; Program evaluation; Program development; Matching/challenge support; Management development/capacity building; General/operating support; Equipment; Curriculum development; Consulting services; Capital campaigns; Building/renovation.
Limitations: Applications accepted. Giving limited to the greater Denver, CO, area. No support for political candidates or pass-through organizations. Generally, no grants to individuals, or for endowments, annual appeals, membership drives, or fundraising events.
Publications: Application guidelines; Annual report; Financial statement; Newsletter.
Application information: Visit foundation web site for application guidelines. The foundation encourages prospective applicants to contact the foundation's program staff before submitting a grant request. Application form required.
Initial approach: Telephone
Deadline(s): None

Board meeting date(s): Feb. 5, May 6, July 1, Sept. 2, and Dec. 2
Final notification: Within 4 months
Officers and Trustees:* Jennifer Atler Fischer,* Chair.; Sheila Budganowitz, C.E.O. and Pres.; Anne Garcia, C.F.O. and C.O.O.; Mark Huckenberg, Cont.; Milroy A. Alexander; Judy Altenberg; Steven A. Cohen; Lisa Reckler Cohn; Jerrold L. Glick; Katherine Gold; Douglas L. Jones; Helayne B. Jones; Rob Klugman; William N. Lindsay III; Evan Makovsky; Ronald E. Montoya; Monte Moses, Ph.D.; Neil Oberfeld; Dean Prina, M.D.; Irit Waldbaum.
Number of staff: 15 full-time professional; 1 part-time professional; 5 full-time support; 1 part-time support.
EIN: 840920862
Selected grants: The following grants are a representative sample of this grantmaker's funding activity:
$400,000 to Clayton Early Learning, Denver, CO, 2012. For the expansion of the Early Childhood Resource Institute, payable over 2.00 years.
$310,000 to Colorado Health Institute, Denver, CO, 2012. For the Legislator Health Policy Services program and Hot Issues in Health Care, payable over 2.00 years.
$200,000 to Colorado Department of Human Services, Denver, CO, 2012. To continue support for 9NEWS Senior Source, a multimedia information and education campaign for older adults and their caregivers.
$200,000 to Wexner Foundation, New Albany, OH, 2012. For grant over two years to bring the Wexner Heritage Program, a leadership development program for Jewish leaders ages 30 to 45, to Denver in 2014, payable over 2.00 years.
$50,000 to Bell Policy Center, Denver, CO, 2012. Toward a grant totaling $150,000 to build support for fiscal reform efforts in the state. The grant was jointly funded by the Foundation's Child and Family Development, Health, and Opportunities and Innovation program areas.
$50,000 to Doctors Care, Littleton, CO, 2012. For the purchase and renovation of a new clinic in Littleton.
$23,000 to National Council on Aging, Washington, DC, 2012. For a pilot project to conduct outreach and public benefits application assistance to low-income older adults in four Denver-area grocery stores.
$20,000 to Great Education Colorado Fund, Denver, CO, 2012. For education advocacy efforts.
$3,500 to Grantmakers in Aging, Arlington, VA, 2012. For the activities of this national association that focuses on aging issues.

1488
Saccomanno Higher Education Foundation ✧

P.O. Box 3788
Grand Junction, CO 81502-3788
Address for inquiries or changes: c/o Alpine Trust and Asset Mgmt., Attn: Joanne Cornell or Marsha Harbert, 225 N. 5th St., Grand Junction, CO 81501; Toll free tel.: (877) 808-7878; Main URL: http://www.saccomannoed.org

Established in 1991 in CO.
Donors: Geno Saccomanno‡; Virginia Saccomanno.
Foundation type: Independent foundation.
Financial data (yr. ended 06/30/13): Assets, $17,873,323 (M); gifts received, $36,703; expenditures, $1,123,792; qualifying distributions, $1,000,649; giving activities include $116,960 for 1 grant, and $812,300 for grants to individuals.
Purpose and activities: Awards to educational institutions for academic expenses of Mesa County, CO, and Carbon County, UT residents. Scholarships are granted for accredited colleges, universities and vocational schools.
Fields of interest: Higher education.
Type of support: Scholarship funds; Research; Scholarships—to individuals.
Limitations: Giving limited to Mesa County, CO, and Carbon County, UT residents. No grants to individuals directly.
Publications: Annual report; Financial statement; Program policy statement.
Application information: Application forms may be obtained from local Carbon County, UT and Mesa County high schools, as well as Mesa State College, Western Colorado Community College, Intellitec Colleges, St. Mary's Hospital Foundation, Colorado Christian University, the Immaculate Heart of Mary Church, St. Mary's Hospital Education Dept., or Alpine Trust & Asset Management. Application forms also available on foundation web site. Scholarship awards are paid directly to the institution. Application form required.
Copies of proposal: 1
Deadline(s): Apr. 2
Board meeting date(s): Varies
Final notification: July 1
Officers: Virginia Saccomanno, Pres.; Terrance Farina, V.P.; Carol Murphy, Secy.-Treas.
Directors: Gena Cooper; Tim Foster; Michael McBride; Dr. William Patterson; Steven D. Schultz; Jay D. Seaton; Linda Siedow; Lenna Watson.
EIN: 841164982

1489
Sachs Foundation ✧

90 S. Cascade Ave., Ste. 1410
Colorado Springs, CO 80903-1680 (719) 633-2353
Contact: Morris A. Esmiol, Jr., Pres.
FAX: (719) 633-3663; Main URL: http://www.sachsfoundation.org
Facebook: https://www.facebook.com/SachsFoundation?fref=ts
Twitter: https://twitter.com/SachsScholars

Incorporated in 1931 in CO.
Donors: Henry Sachs‡; Henry Sachs Trust.
Foundation type: Independent foundation.
Financial data (yr. ended 12/31/12): Assets, $35,910,854 (M); gifts received, $1,397,000; expenditures, $1,592,703; qualifying distributions, $1,304,031; giving activities include $1,122,789 for grants to individuals.
Purpose and activities: Provides undergraduate scholarships to African-American high school seniors who have a 3.5 GPA or better, and who have been CO residents for five or more years; also, limited graduate scholarships only to African-Americans who have participated in the undergraduate scholarship program and who have been residents of CO five or more years.
Fields of interest: African Americans/Blacks.
Type of support: Grants to individuals; Scholarships—to individuals.
Limitations: Giving limited to residents of CO.
Publications: Application guidelines; Financial statement.
Application information: Applications are accepted only from Jan. 1-Mar. 1. Application form, complete application guidelines, and required financial statement are available on foundation web site. Application form required.
Initial approach: Use online application process on foundation web site
Copies of proposal: 2
Deadline(s): Applications accepted from Jan. 1 to Mar. 17 annually
Board meeting date(s): May
Final notification: 45 days
Officer: Craig Ralston, Pres.; Lisa Harris, Secy.-Treas.; Stewart P. Dodge, 1st V.P.; Wilton W. Cogswell III, 2nd V.P.
Directors: Morris A. Esmiol, Jr.; Thomas M. James.
Number of staff: 2 full-time professional.
EIN: 840500835

1490
Saeman Family Foundation, a Charitable Trust ✧

299 Milwaukee St., Ste. 300
Denver, CO 80206-5133

Established in 1994 in CO.
Donors: Carolyn Ann Saeman; John V. Saeman.
Foundation type: Independent foundation.
Financial data (yr. ended 12/31/12): Assets, $207,255 (M); gifts received, $1,960,000; expenditures, $1,946,635; qualifying distributions, $1,946,608; giving activities include $1,698,691 for 43 grants (high: $543,272; low: $600).
Purpose and activities: Giving primarily to philanthropic endeavors in support of the Roman Catholic Church; funding also for education, health associations, children, youth, family services, and human services.
Fields of interest: Secondary school/education; Health organizations, association; Human services; Children/youth, services; Family services; Catholic federated giving programs; Catholic agencies & churches.
Type of support: General/operating support; Annual campaigns; Program development; In-kind gifts.
Limitations: Applications accepted. Giving primarily in Denver, CO. No grants to individuals.
Publications: Application guidelines.
Application information: Application form required.
Initial approach: Propsoal
Deadline(s): None
Officers: Catherine Bortle, V.P., Religious Education; Craig Saeman, V.P., Evangelization; John V. Saeman III, V.P., Capital Projects; Nick J. Zieser, Secy.-Treas.
Director: Richard O. Campbell.
Trustees: Carolyn Ann Saeman; John V. Saeman.
Number of staff: 1 part-time professional.
EIN: 841442064
Selected grants: The following grants are a representative sample of this grantmaker's funding activity:
$260,000 to Loras College, Dubuque, IA, 2012. For Center for Catholic Studies $30,000 John Paul II Scholarship $60,000 Chair for Catholic Thought $60,000 Focus Campus Ministry $50,000 Marriage Prep $30,000 Center for Catholic Studies $30,000.
$28,150 to Ave Maria University, Ave Maria, FL, 2012. For Fran and Suann Maier Magnificat Scholarship.
$15,000 to Arrupe Jesuit High School, Denver, CO, 2012. For Capital Campaign Fund $5,000 Senior Class Sponsorship $10,000.

$10,000 to Boy Scouts of America, Denver, CO, 2012. For Family Apostolate's Mission in Nigeria.
$10,000 to Dominican Campus, Nashville, TN, 2012. For Aquinas College Fund.
$5,000 to Archdiocese of Denver, Denver, CO, 2012. For Campus Ministry Scholarship.
$5,000 to Centro San Juan Diego, Denver, CO, 2012. For Seventh Annual Archbishop Jose Gomez Gala Fund.

1491
The Salvador Foundation ✧
5423 Lions Gate Ln.
Colorado Springs, CO 80919-3248
E-mail address for applications:
grants@salvadorfoundation.org; Main URL: http://www.salvadorfoundation.org/

Established in 2005 in CO.
Donor: Salvador Imaging, Inc.
Foundation type: Company-sponsored foundation.
Financial data (yr. ended 12/31/13): Assets, $22,235,914 (M); gifts received, $2,617; expenditures, $1,165,707; qualifying distributions, $970,241; giving activities include $846,103 for 24 grants (high: $248,829; low: $250).
Purpose and activities: The foundation supports programs designed empower individuals, organizations, and communities through Christianity. Special emphasis is directed toward helping people who are truly in need.
Fields of interest: Education; Environment, water resources; Health care; Agriculture; Human services; Economic development; Microfinance/microlending; Christian agencies & churches; Economically disadvantaged.
International interests: Latin America.
Type of support: General/operating support.
Limitations: Applications not accepted. Giving primarily in Miami, FL, and in Latin America. No support for organizations that advocate abortion or the taking of human life. No grants to individuals, or for sports activities (unless participants are mentally or physically handicapped), general operating support of K-12 schools or colleges, or mission trips.
Application information: Unsolicited requests for funds not accepted.
Officers: H. William Mahaffey, Chair.; David W. Gardner, Pres.; Mary Gardner, Secy.-Treas.
Director: Nick Gonzales.
EIN: 202760889

1492
The Adler Schermer Foundation ✧
(formerly The Betty A. & Lloyd G. Schermer Foundation)
c/o Lloyd G. Schermer
210 Lake Ave.
Aspen, CO 81611-1347

Established in 1992 in CO.
Donors: Betty A. Schermer; Lloyd G. Schermer.
Foundation type: Independent foundation.
Financial data (yr. ended 12/31/13): Assets, $5,799,520 (M); expenditures, $734,287; qualifying distributions, $504,205; giving activities include $502,700 for 37 grants (high: $200,000; low: $50).
Fields of interest: Arts; Higher education; Human services; Jewish federated giving programs.
Limitations: Applications not accepted. Giving primarily in Aspen, CO, Davenport, IA, and Philadelphia, PA. No grants to individuals.
Application information: Contributes only to pre-selected organizations.
Directors: Betty A. Schermer; Lloyd G. Schermer.
EIN: 841210699

1493
Schmitz Family Foundation ✧ ☆
c/o Annie McBournie
6500 E. Hampden Ave., Ste. 203
Denver, CO 80224

Established in 2001 in CO.
Donors: Vincent N. Schmitz‡; Marilyn J. Schmitz‡; Martin J. Schmitz; Jeff J. Schmitz; Richard V. Schmitz; Ann E. McBournie; Patricia J. Job; Julie Bunsness; Citywide Banks; Trinity GST Exempt Trust.
Foundation type: Independent foundation.
Financial data (yr. ended 12/31/13): Assets, $20,365,680 (M); gifts received, $8,482; expenditures, $955,669; qualifying distributions, $682,475; giving activities include $682,475 for 25 grants (high: $160,375; low: $500).
Purpose and activities: Giving primarily for education, particularly to Roman Catholic schools.
Fields of interest: Education; Catholic agencies & churches.
Limitations: Applications not accepted. Giving primarily in CO. No grants to individuals.
Application information: Contributes only to pre-selected organizations.
Officers: Ann McBournie, Pres.; Julie Bunsness, V.P.; Richard Schmitz, V.P.; Pat Job, Secy.
EIN: 841548781

1494
The John S. Scurci Foundation ✧
c/o Jeff Watkins
7979 E. Tufts Ave., Ste. 400
Denver, CO 80237-2843

Established in 2000 in NJ.
Donors: Tamara A. Ogorzaly; John S. Scurci.
Foundation type: Independent foundation.
Financial data (yr. ended 12/31/11): Assets, $10,695,128 (M); expenditures, $631,784; qualifying distributions, $584,209; giving activities include $527,000 for 26 grants (high: $250,000; low: $2,500).
Fields of interest: Museums; Arts; Higher education; Education; Human services.
Limitations: Applications not accepted. Giving primarily in CO and NJ. No grants to individuals.
Application information: Contributes only to pre-selected organizations.
Trustees: Tamara A. Ogorzaly; John S. Scurci.
EIN: 137267581

1495
Seay Foundation ✧
c/o American National Bank & Trust Co., Trust Div.
P.O. Box 9250
Colorado Springs, CO 80932-0250
Application address: c/o American National Bank, 102 N. Cascade Ave., Colorado Springs, CO 80903-1455, tel.: (719) 381-5623

Foundation type: Independent foundation.
Financial data (yr. ended 12/31/13): Assets, $21,026,258 (M); expenditures, $1,208,153; qualifying distributions, $958,702; giving activities include $953,992 for 2+ grants (high: $704,492).
Fields of interest: Higher education; Youth development; Human services; Christian agencies & churches.
Type of support: General/operating support; Building/renovation; Scholarships—to individuals.
Limitations: Applications accepted. Giving primarily in CO.
Application information: Candidates must be nominated by a member of the foundation's Advisory Committee; application forms available upon request by the nominator. Application form required.
Initial approach: Proposal
Deadline(s): May 1
Director: Carolyn S. Kopper.
Trustee: American National Bank & Trust Co.
EIN: 436055549
Selected grants: The following grants are a representative sample of this grantmaker's funding activity:
$91,250 to First Presbyterian Church of Colorado Springs, Colorado Springs, CO, 2011.
$42,000 to First Presbyterian Church of Colorado Springs, Colorado Springs, CO, 2011.
$40,000 to Colorado Springs Philharmonic Orchestra, Colorado Springs, CO, 2011.
$5,000 to Smile Train, Washington, DC, 2011.

1496
Serimus Foundation ✧
148 Remington St.
Fort Collins, CO 80524-2834

Established in 1999 in WY and CO.
Donors: Jill M. Schatz; Douglas S. Schatz.
Foundation type: Independent foundation.
Financial data (yr. ended 12/31/13): Assets, $2,274,363 (M); expenditures, $966,930; qualifying distributions, $962,660; giving activities include $825,970 for 13 grants (high: $173,970; low: $500).
Fields of interest: Education, early childhood education.
Type of support: General/operating support; Program development; Program evaluation; Matching/challenge support.
Limitations: Applications not accepted. Giving primarily in CO. No grants to individuals.
Application information: Contributes only to pre-selected organizations.
Board meeting date(s): Twice per year
Officers: Jill E. Schatz, Pres.; Douglas S. Schatz, V.P. and Treas.; Kirsten Bump, Secy.
Directors: Adrienne Schatz; David Schatz.
EIN: 830328155
Selected grants: The following grants are a representative sample of this grantmaker's funding activity:
$686,859 to Book Trust, Fort Collins, CO, 2012. For General Operations - Provides books for children from low-income families.
$57,785 to Serimus Operating Foundation, Fort Collins, CO, 2012. For General operations - Provide music, art and books to children.
$15,000 to Golden Willow Retreat, Arroyo Hondo, NM, 2012. For General Operations - Support and educate individuals, families and communities experiencing grief.

1497
The Servant Leadership Foundation ✧ ☆
950 E. Westglow Ln.
Littleton, CO 80121-1375

Donors: Larry LaKamp; Martha LaKamp; TYL Foundation; McVaney Family Foundation; Lepitas Foundation; Pete Morgan Foundation; Jon Sittko; Kitsy Gregory; Valencia Foundation; Leverage Discovery LLC; Mark Wolfe; Peggy Wolfe.
Foundation type: Independent foundation.
Financial data (yr. ended 12/31/13): Assets, $13,844 (M); gifts received, $421,700; expenditures, $432,554; qualifying distributions, $430,850; giving activities include $21,500 for 2 grants (high: $11,500; low: $10,000), and $409,350 for 21 grants to individuals (high: $28,000; low: $500).
Purpose and activities: Provides scholarships for people in full-time ministry who must raise their own financial support to do so. Funding also to grant men and women who have been in full-time ministry for ten consecutive years or more, and who, due to salary limitations of their ministry, have acquired financial debt. The scholarships will be used strictly for the purpose of paying off, or down, their debt.
Fields of interest: Education; Human services.
Limitations: Applications not accepted. Giving primarily in CO.
Application information: Unsolicited requests for funds not accepted.
Directors: Dan Jessup; Jeff Newman; Steven G. Sittko.
EIN: 841400820

1498
The Shamos Family Foundation ✧
766 Monaco Pkwy.
Denver, CO 80220-6061

Established in 1993 in CO.
Donors: Jeremy Shamos; Susan Shamos.
Foundation type: Independent foundation.
Financial data (yr. ended 11/30/13): Assets, $3,664,788 (M); expenditures, $650,859; qualifying distributions, $575,338; giving activities include $574,000 for 32 grants (high: $221,000; low: $500).
Purpose and activities: Giving primarily for education and the arts.
Fields of interest: Performing arts, opera; Arts; Elementary/secondary education; Higher education.
Type of support: Annual campaigns; Capital campaigns.
Limitations: Applications not accepted. Giving primarily in Denver, CO; some funding also in Santa Fe, NM. No grants to individuals.
Application information: Unsolicited requests for funds not accepted.
Officers and Directors:* Susan Shamos,* Pres.; Jeremy Shamos,* V.P. and Secy.-Treas.
EIN: 841251784
Selected grants: The following grants are a representative sample of this grantmaker's funding activity:
$375,000 to Curious Theater Company, Denver, CO, 2011. For general support.
$150,000 to Saint Johns College, Santa Fe, NM, 2011.
$55,000 to Opera Colorado, Denver, CO, 2011. For general support.
$35,000 to Group I Acting Company, New York, NY, 2011. For general support.
$5,000 to Theater for a New Audience, New York, NY, 2011.
$3,000 to Saint Martins Chamber Choir, Denver, CO, 2011. For general support.
$2,500 to Colorado Academy, Denver, CO, 2011. For general support.
$2,000 to Colorado Symphony Association, Denver, CO, 2011. For general support.
$2,000 to Summer Scholars, Denver, CO, 2011. For general support.
$1,000 to New England Conservatory of Music, Boston, MA, 2011. For general support.

1499
The Harold W. & Mary Louise Shaw Foundation ✧
c/o Stockman Kast Ryan & Co.
1 S. Nevada Ave., Ste. 200
Colorado Springs, CO 80903-1809

Established in 1997 in OH.
Donors: Harold Shaw; Louise Shaw; Mary L. Shaw Charitable Lead Annuity Trust.
Foundation type: Independent foundation.
Financial data (yr. ended 11/30/13): Assets, $38,169,589 (M); gifts received, $2,402,003; expenditures, $1,711,528; qualifying distributions, $1,261,100; giving activities include $1,261,100 for 17 grants (high: $207,500; low: $10,000).
Fields of interest: Arts; Higher education; Zoos/zoological societies; Hospitals (general); Human services; Children/youth, services; Community/economic development.
Limitations: Applications not accepted. Giving primarily in CO and ME; some funding also in GA. No grants to individuals.
Application information: Unsolicited requests for funds not accepted.
Officers: Robert D. Veitch, Pres.; Sally Louise Veitch, V.P. and Treas.; Frederick A. Veitch III, Secy.
Trustees: John Christopher; Heather K. Veitch; Kelly A. Veitch.
EIN: 311577890
Selected grants: The following grants are a representative sample of this grantmaker's funding activity:
$400,000 to Cheyenne Mountain Zoological Society, Colorado Springs, CO, 2010. For general support.
$125,000 to Snowboard Outreach Society, Avon, CO, 2010. For general support.
$75,000 to Vail Valley Medical Center, Vail, CO, 2011.
$60,000 to Dayton Art Institute, Dayton, OH, 2011.
$40,000 to Teton Valley Hospital, Driggs, ID, 2011.
$25,000 to OK Corral Camp, Avon, CO, 2011.
$20,000 to University of Colorado, Colorado Springs, CO, 2011.
$10,000 to Vail Valley Charitable Fund, Edwards, CO, 2010. For general support.

1500
The Anna and John J. Sie Foundation ✧
3300 E. 1st Ave., No. 390
Denver, CO 80206-5806

Established in 2003 in CO.
Donors: John J. Sie; Anna M. Sie.
Foundation type: Independent foundation.
Financial data (yr. ended 12/31/12): Assets, $82,631,359 (M); expenditures, $7,488,409; qualifying distributions, $7,352,987; giving activities include $7,098,737 for 127 grants (high: $1,500,000; low: $200).
Purpose and activities: Giving primarily for the arts, particularly an art museum, as well as for health organizations, particularly for people with Down syndrome, as well as for a children's hospital.
Fields of interest: Museums (art); Arts; Higher education; Hospitals (specialty); Down syndrome research; Children/youth, services.
Limitations: Applications not accepted. Giving primarily in CO.
Application information: Contributes only to pre-selected organizations.
Officer: Michelle S. Whitten, Exec. Dir.
Trustees: Anna M. Sie; John J. Sie.
EIN: 836058353
Selected grants: The following grants are a representative sample of this grantmaker's funding activity:
$1,500,000 to Denver Film Society, Denver, CO, 2012. For grant for a building for DFS as they cultivate the art of film.
$1,100,000 to University of Denver, Josef Korbel School of International Studies, Denver, CO, 2012. For Sie Cheou-Kang Center Chair Fund Pmt.
$1,000,000 to University of Colorado Hospital Foundation, Linda Crinic Institute for Down Syndrome, Aurora, CO, 2012. For Anna and John J Sie Quasi Endowment for CIMB to support research for down syndrome.
$480,000 to University of Colorado Foundation, Denver, CO, 2012. For proving consultation support for search for Executive Director for Linda Crinic Institute which focused on improving the lives of individuals with Down syndrome through basic research, clinical research and clinical care.
$476,333 to Global Down Syndrome Foundation, Denver, CO, 2012. For supporting Groupon Matching Challenge Grant to improve the lives of people with Down Syndrome by supporting basic research, clinical research and clinical care.
$250,000 to Denver School of Science and Technology, Denver, CO, 2012. To support the Malone Matching Grant event benefitting the education for students with special needs.
$25,000 to Global Down Syndrome Foundation, Denver, CO, 2012. For supporting the BBBY 2012 Haute Couture to improve the lives of people with Down Syndrome by supporting basic research, clinical research and clinical care.
$10,000 to Denver Art Museum, Denver, CO, 2012. To help enrich the Denver community through dynamic cultural exhibitions, exceptional adult and family programs and renowned collections.
$10,000 to Iowa State University Foundation, Ames, IA, 2012. For using education and research to help others, paying it forward so others can benefit from a world-class educational experience.

1501
Singer Family Foundation ✧
(formerly Joseph Singer & Ann Singer Family Foundation)
P.O. Box 22066
Denver, CO 80222-0066 (303) 321-0606
Contact: Andrea S. Pollack, Pres.

Established in 1995 in CO.
Donor: Andrea S. Pollack.
Foundation type: Independent foundation.
Financial data (yr. ended 12/31/13): Assets, $15,469,138 (M); gifts received, $4,500,000;

expenditures, $784,814; qualifying distributions, $774,625; giving activities include $774,625 for 51 grants (high: $339,000; low: $500).
Fields of interest: Arts; Education; Family services; Jewish federated giving programs; Jewish agencies & synagogues.
Limitations: Applications accepted. Giving primarily in CO.
Application information:
Initial approach: Contact foundation for application form
Deadline(s): None
Officers: Andrea S. Pollack, Pres.; Cintra Pollack, Secy.-Treas.
EIN: 841327455
Selected grants: The following grants are a representative sample of this grantmaker's funding activity:
$305,000 to Allied Jewish Federation of Colorado, Denver, CO, 2011. For general support.

1502
The Slater Foundation ✧ ☆
1800 Glenarm Pl.
Denver, CO 80202-1386 (720) 226-0581
Contact: Colleen M. Slater, Pres.; Craig D. Slater, V.P.

Established in CO.
Donors: Craig D. Slater; Colleen M. Slater.
Foundation type: Independent foundation.
Financial data (yr. ended 12/31/13): Assets, $2,680,098 (M); expenditures, $1,070,767; qualifying distributions, $1,068,575; giving activities include $1,065,167 for 6 grants (high: $1,000,000; low: $3,500).
Fields of interest: Arts; Elementary/secondary education; Medical research; Human services.
Type of support: General/operating support.
Limitations: Applications accepted. Giving primarily in CO and RI.
Application information: Application form not required.
Initial approach: Proposal
Deadline(s): None
Officers: Colleen M. Slater, Pres.; Craig D. Slater, V.P.
EIN: 412073119
Selected grants: The following grants are a representative sample of this grantmaker's funding activity:
$210,000 to Brown University, Providence, RI, 2012. For Sports Foundation Support.
$16,667 to Colorado Academy, Denver, CO, 2012. For General operating support for secondary school.
$5,000 to Chris Klug Foundation, Aspen, CO, 2012. For Supporting the promotion of organ and tissue donation through action sports.

1503
Society of Economic Geologists Foundation, Inc. ✧
7811 Shaffer Pkwy.
Littleton, CO 80127-3732 (720) 981-7882
FAX: (720) 981-7874; E-mail: seg@segweb.org;
Main URL: http://www.segweb.org/SEG/Foundation/SEG/Foundation.aspx?hkey=18dc5157-3cbd-4cc3-b8bc-7dca63166e04
Facebook: https://www.facebook.com/segweb
LinkedIn: http://www.linkedin.com/company/society-of-economic-geologists-inc-
Twitter: https://twitter.com/societyecongeol
Application e-mail: studentprograms@segweb.org

Established in 1966.
Foundation type: Operating foundation.
Financial data (yr. ended 12/31/12): Assets, $4,553,607 (M); gifts received, $184,729; expenditures, $632,506; qualifying distributions, $1,141,383; giving activities include $519,820 for 9+ grants (high: $192,975).
Purpose and activities: Giving to fund education, research, publications, student support, public outreach and other geoscientific programs endorsed by the Society of Economic Geologists, Inc. (SEG), or other programs considered for funding by the trustees of the corporation. Support is limited to programs, projects, and research in economic geology as they relate to metallic mineral deposits.
Fields of interest: Geology.
International interests: Global Programs.
Type of support: Publication; Seed money; Grants to individuals.
Limitations: Applications not accepted.
Publications: Informational brochure; Newsletter.
Application information: Unsolicited requests for funds not accepted.
Officers and Trustees:* Andrew T. Swarthout,* Pres.; John E. Black, V.P.; Ruth A. Carraher,* Secy.
Number of staff: 1 part-time support.
EIN: 516020487

1504
Southern Colorado Community Foundation ✧
121 W. First St., Ste. 240
P.O. Box 1432
Pueblo, CO 81002 (719) 546-6677
Contact: Doris Kester, Exec.Dir.
FAX: (719) 566-7842; E-mail: kester@ddmktg.com;
Main URL: http://www.southerncoloradocommunityfoundation.org

Established in 1998 in CO.
Foundation type: Community foundation.
Financial data (yr. ended 12/31/13): Assets, $10,845,738 (M); gifts received, $390,239; expenditures, $735,571; giving activities include $583,193 for 19+ grants (high: $168,638).
Purpose and activities: The foundation accepts donations and makes grants in accordance with the donor's wishes covering all of southern Colorado.
Fields of interest: Health care; Human services; Community/economic development.
Type of support: Program development.
Limitations: Applications accepted. Giving limited to southern CO.
Application information: Application form required.
Initial approach: Submit application
Deadline(s): Mar. 1 and Sept. 1
Officers and Directors:* Dan Derose,* Pres.; Jane L. Rawlings,* V.P.; Mark Swanson,* Secy.; Dan Lere,* Treas.; Doris Kester, Exec. Dir.; Joe Bower; Midori Clark; Barbara Duff; Barbara Fortino; Priscilla Lucero; Donna Maes; Kevin McCarthy; Rosemary Reilly; Jeff Shaw; Paulette Stuart; Ken West.
Number of staff: 1 full-time professional.
EIN: 841449305

1505
Sprout Foundation ✧
(formerly Fanch Family Foundation, Inc.)
1601 Arapahoe St., Ste. 800
Denver, CO 80202-2064

Established in 2004 in CO.
Donor: Robert C. Fanch.
Foundation type: Independent foundation.
Financial data (yr. ended 12/31/12): Assets, $33,111,775 (M); expenditures, $1,326,010; qualifying distributions, $1,161,783; giving activities include $1,161,783 for grants.
Fields of interest: Education; Human services; Foundations (community).
Type of support: General/operating support.
Limitations: Applications not accepted. Giving primarily in Denver and Winter Park, CO. No grants to individuals.
Application information: Contributes only to pre-selected organizations.
Officer and Director:* Robert C. Fanch,* Pres. and Treas.
EIN: 200378579

1506
SSB Charitable Foundation ✧
c/o Susan Smith Burghart
1330 Timber Valley Rd.
Colorado Springs, CO 80919-2812

Established in 2007 in CO.
Donor: Susan Smith Burghart.
Foundation type: Independent foundation.
Financial data (yr. ended 12/31/13): Assets, $5,643,197 (M); expenditures, $632,109; qualifying distributions, $627,450; giving activities include $625,000 for 4 grants (high: $250,000; low: $25,000).
Fields of interest: Arts; Higher education; Zoos/zoological societies.
Limitations: Applications not accepted. Giving primarily in CO, with emphasis on Colorado Springs.
Application information: Contributes only to pre-selected organizations.
Trustee: Susan Smith Burghart.
EIN: 208671537

1507
Staley Family Foundation ✧
P.O. Box 19000
Avon, CO 81620

Donors: Warren Staley; Mary Lynn Staley.
Foundation type: Independent foundation.
Financial data (yr. ended 12/31/13): Assets, $40,684,923 (M); gifts received, $1,329,284; expenditures, $1,853,256; qualifying distributions, $1,533,025; giving activities include $1,524,500 for 25 grants (high: $250,000; low: $1,000).
Fields of interest: Education; Housing/shelter, single organization support; Children/youth, services; United Ways and Federated Giving Programs; Catholic agencies & churches.
Limitations: Applications not accepted. Giving primarily in MN.
Application information: Unsolicited requests for funds not accepted.
Trustees: Mary Lynn Staley; Warren Staley.
EIN: 263442296

Selected grants: The following grants are a representative sample of this grantmaker's funding activity:
$25,000 to Cornell University, Johnson School of Business, Ithaca, NY, 2012. For general support.

1508
The Strear Family Foundation, Inc. ✧ ☆
6825 E. Tennessee Ave., Ste. 235
Denver, CO 80224-1630

Established in 1987 in CO.
Donors: Leonard Strear; Pluss Poultry; Strear Farms Co., Inc.
Foundation type: Independent foundation.
Financial data (yr. ended 09/30/13): Assets, $10,353,570 (M); expenditures, $493,325; qualifying distributions, $429,063; giving activities include $429,063 for grants.
Purpose and activities: Giving primarily to Jewish causes.
Fields of interest: Education; Health organizations, association; Human services; Jewish federated giving programs; Jewish agencies & synagogues.
Limitations: Applications not accepted. Giving primarily in Denver, CO. No grants to individuals.
Application information: Contributes only to pre-selected organizations.
Officers: Leonard Strear, Pres.; Irma Strear, V.P. and Secy.
EIN: 841078190
Selected grants: The following grants are a representative sample of this grantmaker's funding activity:
$104,000 to Beth Israel Foundation, New York, NY, 2011.
$99,400 to Allied Jewish Federation of Colorado, Denver, CO, 2011.

1509
Hadley and Marion Stuart Foundation ✧
11732 Crystal View Ln.
Longmont, CO 80504-8453

Established in 1988 in CA.
Donor: Marion Butler Stuart.
Foundation type: Independent foundation.
Financial data (yr. ended 10/31/13): Assets, $156,080,965 (M); expenditures, $8,107,289; qualifying distributions, $7,381,780; giving activities include $7,381,780 for 26 grants (high: $2,100,000; low: $10,000).
Purpose and activities: Giving primarily for education and animal welfare.
Fields of interest: Elementary/secondary education; Environment, natural resources; Animal welfare; Veterinary medicine; Animals/wildlife, special services.
Limitations: Applications not accepted. Giving in the U.S., primarily in CT, CO, and VA. No grants to individuals.
Application information: Contributes only to pre-selected organizations.
Trustees: Brett Fullerton Stuart; Nan M. Stuart.
EIN: 946607854
Selected grants: The following grants are a representative sample of this grantmaker's funding activity:
$1,500,000 to Colorado State University Foundation, Fort Collins, CO, 2011.
$625,000 to Foxcroft School, Middleburg, VA, 2011.
$250,000 to Humane Society, Dubuque, Dubuque, IA, 2011.
$150,000 to Saint Aloysius School, New York, NY, 2011.
$100,000 to Nature Conservancy, Arlington, VA, 2011.
$75,000 to Childrens Hospital of Illinois, Peoria, IL, 2011.
$50,000 to PetAid Colorado Foundation, Denver, CO, 2011.

1510
Sturm Family Foundation ✧
3033 E. 1st Ave., Ste. 300
Denver, CO 80206-5619

Donors: Donald L. Sturm; Susan M. Sturm.
Foundation type: Independent foundation.
Financial data (yr. ended 12/31/13): Assets, $58,492,529 (M); gifts received, $5,050,691; expenditures, $2,625,829; qualifying distributions, $2,294,748; giving activities include $2,293,557 for 20 grants (high: $1,750,000; low: $100).
Fields of interest: Higher education; Education; Children/youth, services; Jewish federated giving programs.
Limitations: Applications not accepted. Giving primarily in CO, with emphasis on Denver. No grants to individuals.
Application information: Contributes only to pre-selected organizations.
Officers: Donald L. Sturm, Chair., Pres. and Treas.; Susan M. Sturm, Vice-Chair., V.P. and Secy.
EIN: 841483429
Selected grants: The following grants are a representative sample of this grantmaker's funding activity:
$1,150,000 to Denver Foundation, Denver, CO, 2011.
$255,350 to Judaism Your Way, Denver, CO, 2011.
$50,000 to Denver School of Science and Technology, Denver, CO, 2011.
$50,000 to Teach for America, Denver, CO, 2011.
$10,000 to Colorado Oral-Deaf Preschool, Greenwood Village, CO, 2011.
$10,000 to Mesa State College, Grand Junction, CO, 2011.
$5,000 to Temple Shalom, Colorado Springs, CO, 2011.
$1,333 to Monument Academy, Monument, CO, 2011.
$1,000 to University of Colorado Foundation, Aurora, CO, 2011.
$1,000 to University of Puget Sound, Tacoma, WA, 2011.

1511
The Summit Foundation ✧
103 S. Harris St.
P.O. Box 4000
Breckenridge, CO 80424-4000 (970) 453-5970
Contact: Lee Zimmerman, Exec. Dir.
FAX: (970) 453-1423;
E-mail: sumfound@summitfoundation.org;
Additional e-mail:
TSFADmin@summitfoundation.org; Grant application e-mail:
tsfdirector@summitfoundation.org; Main URL: http://www.summitfoundation.org
Facebook: https://www.facebook.com/TheSummitFoundation
LinkedIn: http://www.linkedin.com/company/the-summit-foundation
Twitter: https://twitter.com/TheSummitFdtn

Established in 1984 in CO.
Foundation type: Community foundation.
Financial data (yr. ended 09/30/13): Assets, $8,188,927 (M); gifts received, $3,003,357; expenditures, $3,000,842; giving activities include $2,131,981 for 73 grants (high: $503,100), and $207,749 for 120 grants to individuals.
Purpose and activities: The foundation seeks to improve the quality of life for residents and guests of Summit County and neighboring communities. Giving primarily for arts and culture, health and human services, education, environment, sports and recreation, scholarships, and all projects with measurable results.
Fields of interest: Media, film/video; Visual arts; Museums; Performing arts; Performing arts, theater; Performing arts, music; Historic preservation/historical societies; Arts; Elementary/secondary education; Education, early childhood education; Elementary school/education; Secondary school/education; Education; Environment, natural resources; Environment; Health care; Mental health/crisis services; Health organizations, association; Recreation; Children/youth, services; Family services; Residential/custodial care, hospices; Aging, centers/services; Human services; Infants/toddlers; Children/youth; Youth; Adults; Aging; Young adults; Disabilities, people with; Physically disabled; Mentally disabled; Hispanics/Latinos; Women; Girls; Adults, women; Adults, men; Substance abusers; Single parents; Terminal illness, people with; Immigrants/refugees; Economically disadvantaged; Homeless.
Type of support: General/operating support; Continuing support; Management development/capacity building; Annual campaigns; Capital campaigns; Building/renovation; Equipment; Land acquisition; Endowments; Program development; Conferences/seminars; Seed money; Curriculum development; Scholarship funds; Technical assistance; Program evaluation; Exchange programs; In-kind gifts; Matching/challenge support.
Limitations: Applications accepted. Giving limited to Summit County, and the communities of Alma, Fairplay, Kremmling, and Leadville, CO. No support for religious organizations. No grants to individuals (except for designated scholarship programs).
Publications: Application guidelines; Annual report; Grants list; Informational brochure; Newsletter; Program policy statement.
Application information: Visit the foundation's web site for online application and additional guidelines. Application form required.
Initial approach: Telephone
Copies of proposal: 2
Deadline(s): Apr. 11 and Oct. 3
Board meeting date(s): 3rd Wed. of Mar., May, July, Aug., Sept., Oct., and Nov.; 2nd Wed. of Feb., June, and Dec.
Final notification: June and Dec.
Officers and Trustees:* Kevin McDonald,* Pres.; Mike Schilling,* V.P.; Lucy Kay,* Secy.; Lee E. Zimmerman, Exec. Dir.; Gini Bradley; John Buhler; Pat Campbell; Ed Casias; Cary Cooper; Deb Crook; Thomas Davidson; Nicky DeFord; Wally Ducayet;

Greg Finch; Tim Gagen; Kathy Grotemeyer; Millie Hamner; Alan Henceroth; Katha Jenkins; Tom Keltner; Jeff Leigh; Andy Lewis; Phyllis Martinez; Rob Millisor; Rick Oshlo; Susan Propper; Kelly Renoux; Gary Rodgers; Steven Smith; Mark Spiers; Carre Warner; Maureen Westerland; Wendy Wolfe; Hans Wurster.
Number of staff: 3 full-time professional; 2 part-time support.
EIN: 742341399
Selected grants: The following grants are a representative sample of this grantmaker's funding activity:
$82,000 to Summit County Family and Intercultural Resource Center, Dillon, CO, 2012.
$52,000 to Summit School District RE-1, Frisco, CO, 2012. For preschool scholarships.
$50,600 to Youth Services Center, Dillon, CO, 2012. For primary health for children at schools.
$50,500 to Summit Community Care Clinic, Frisco, CO, 2012. For low-income health wage.
$36,500 to Advocates for Victims of Assault, Frisco, CO, 2012. For support groups.
$30,000 to Team Summit, Frisco, CO, 2012. For scholarships.
$17,500 to Keystone Center, Keystone, CO, 2012. For science camp for kids.
$7,500 to Boys and Girls Club of South Park, Fairplay, CO, 2012. For youth program.
$7,500 to Lake County School District, Leadville, CO, 2012. For Even Start program.

1512
Telluride Foundation
220 E. Colorado Ave., Ste. 106
P.O. Box 4222
Telluride, CO 81435 (970) 728-8717
Contact: For grants: April Montgomery, Progs. Dir.
FAX: (970) 728-9007;
E-mail: info@telluridefoundation.org; Additional e-mail: april@telluridefoundation.org; Main URL: http://www.telluridefoundation.org
Facebook: http://www.facebook.com/pages/Telluride-Foundation/110163245072
RSS Feed: http://www.telluridefoundation.org/index.php?mact=News,cntnt01,rss,0&cntnt01makerssbutton=true&cntnt01showtemplate=false&cntnt01returnid=15

Established in 2000 in Telluride, CO.
Foundation type: Community foundation.
Financial data (yr. ended 12/31/13): Assets, $10,695,174 (M); gifts received, $3,582,234; expenditures, $3,583,907; giving activities include $2,967,713 for grants.
Purpose and activities: The foundation is committed to preserving and enriching the quality of life of the residents, visitors and workforce of the Telluride, CO, region. It provides year-round support for donors and local community-based organizations by facilitating the charitable intent of donors and grantmaking, technical assistance and education for community groups.
Fields of interest: Arts; Higher education; Education; Environment; Children/youth, services; Children, day care; Child development, services; Human services.
Type of support: Capital campaigns; General/operating support; Annual campaigns; Equipment; Program development; Seed money; Scholarship funds; Technical assistance; Consulting services; Scholarships—to individuals; Matching/challenge support.
Limitations: Applications accepted. Giving primarily in Ouray, San Miguel, and West Montrose counties, CO, as well as some portions of Dolores County. No support for religious organizations for religious purposes. No grants to individuals (except for designated scholarships), debt reduction, non-educational publications, graduate or post-graduate research, economic development, or endowments; no loans.
Publications: Application guidelines; Annual report (including application guidelines); Financial statement; Grants list; Newsletter; Program policy statement.
Application information: Visit foundation web site for application form and guidelines per grant type. The foundation holds a pre-applications Q&A session; visit web site for details. Application form required.
Initial approach: Submit application form and attachments
Deadline(s): Oct. 28 for community grants; varies for others
Board meeting date(s): Dec. and July
Final notification: Dec. 31 for community grants; varies for others
Officers and Directors:* Bridgitt Evans,* Chair.; Davis Fansler,* Vice-Chair.; Paul Major,* C.E.O. and Pres.; Ron Allred; Anne Andrew; Carol Armstrong; Mike Armstrong; Ed Barlow; Lynne Beck; Richard Betts; Harmon Brown; Joanne Brown; Mark Dalton; Stu Fraser; Tully Friedman; Bunny Freidus; Allan Gerstle; J. Tomilson Hill; Kevin Holbrook; Chuck Horning; Dan Jansen; Jesse Johnson; Andrew Karow; Joan May; Megan McManemin; Melanie Montoya; Brian O'Neill; Michael Plank; Susan Saint James; Kyle Schumacher; Edward Sheridan; Dan Tishman.
Number of staff: 2 full-time professional; 3 part-time professional.
EIN: 841530768
Selected grants: The following grants are a representative sample of this grantmaker's funding activity:
$50,000 to Region Ten Economics Assistance Planning, Telluride, CO, 2013.
$40,000 to San Miguel Mentoring Program, One to One, Telluride, CO, 2013.
$40,000 to Wright Stuff Community Foundation, Norwood, CO, 2013.
$30,000 to Rainbow School and Day Care Center, Telluride, CO, 2013.
$28,500 to Telluride Academy, Telluride, CO, 2013.
$18,500 to Ah Haa School for the Arts, Telluride, CO, 2013.
$9,000 to Animal Humane Society of Ouray County, Ridgway, CO, 2013.
$8,000 to Hilltop Health Services Corporation, Grand Junction, CO, 2013.
$6,500 to Ridgway School District, Ridgway, CO, 2013.
$6,500 to Telluride AIDS Benefit, Telluride, CO, 2013.
$6,000 to Telluride Lizard Heads, Telluride, CO, 2013.
$5,000 to Colorado Fourteeners Initiative, Golden, CO, 2013.
$5,000 to Telluride Choral Society, Telluride, CO, 2013.
$5,000 to Telluride R1 School District, Telluride, CO, 2013.

1513
The Tointon Family Foundation ✧ ☆
P.O. Box 9
Greeley, CO 80632-0009 (970) 353-7000
Contact: Travis W. Gillmore

Established in 1989 in CO.
Donors: Robert G. Tointon; Phelps-Tointon, Inc.
Foundation type: Independent foundation.
Financial data (yr. ended 12/31/13): Assets, $46,894 (M); gifts received, $750,000; expenditures, $723,150; qualifying distributions, $723,150; giving activities include $723,150 for 21 grants (high: $511,000; low: $500).
Fields of interest: Higher education; Human services.
Limitations: Applications accepted. Giving primarily in Greeley, CO and Manhattan, KS. No grants to individuals.
Application information: CGA Colorado Common Grant Application accepted. Application form not required.
Initial approach: Letter
Copies of proposal: 1
Deadline(s): None
Final notification: 1-3 weeks
Directors: Travis W. Gillmore; Betty L. Tointon; Bryan E. Tointon; Robert G. Tointon; William I. Tointon.
EIN: 841113542
Selected grants: The following grants are a representative sample of this grantmaker's funding activity:
$251,000 to Kansas State University Foundation, Manhattan, KS, 2011.
$21,000 to Colorado State University Foundation, Fort Collins, CO, 2011.
$3,000 to Alliance for Choice in Education, Denver, CO, 2011.
$2,000 to Book Trust, Fort Collins, CO, 2011.
$2,000 to Greeley Dream Team, Greeley, CO, 2011.

1514
Tuchman Family Foundation ✧
c/o Mantucket Capital Mgmt. Corp.
5251 DTC Pkwy., Ste. 995
Englewood, CO 80111-2738

Established in 1996 in CO.
Donors: Kenneth D. Tuchman; Debra Mautner Tuchman; Leizor Rosen†.
Foundation type: Independent foundation.
Financial data (yr. ended 12/31/12): Assets, $8,562,279 (M); expenditures, $660,033; qualifying distributions, $642,494; giving activities include $626,795 for 44 grants (high: $20,000; low: $150).
Purpose and activities: Giving primarily for education, health, social services, and Jewish organizations.
Fields of interest: Education; Hospitals (general); Medical research, institute; Human services; Family services, domestic violence; Jewish federated giving programs; Jewish agencies & synagogues.
Limitations: Applications not accepted. Giving primarily in CO; some funding also in NY. No grants to individuals.
Application information: Contributes only to pre-selected organizations.
Officers and Directors:* Kenneth D. Tuchman,* Pres. and Treas.; Debra Mautner Tuchman,* Secy.
EIN: 841366236

Selected grants: The following grants are a representative sample of this grantmaker's funding activity:
$200,000 to National Jewish Health, Denver, CO, 2012. For Beaux Arts Ball.
$100,000 to Boulder Jewish Community Center, Boulder, CO, 2012. For Construction of New Jewish Community Center in Boulder, Colorado.
$25,000 to Regis University, Denver, CO, 2012. For general - education.
$2,500 to Mizel Museum, Denver, CO, 2012. For Multicultural Institution Teaching Cultural Appreciation Confronting Prejudice and Embracing Diversity.
$1,000 to Global Down Syndrome Foundation, Denver, CO, 2012. For fashion show.

1515
Twelve Labors Foundation, Inc. ✧
218 E. Valley Rd., Ste. 104-335
Carbondale, CO 81623-7735 (970) 927-4206
Contact: J. Alston Gardner, Pres. and Treas.

Established in 2005 in CO.
Donors: Barbara K. Lee; J. Alston Gardner.
Foundation type: Independent foundation.
Financial data (yr. ended 12/31/13): Assets, $800,164 (M); gifts received, $1,245,689; expenditures, $477,956; qualifying distributions, $475,997; giving activities include $475,400 for 12 grants (high: $250,000; low: $2,500).
Fields of interest: Higher education; Education; Housing/shelter, development.
Limitations: Applications accepted. Giving primarily in NC, some emphasis on Raleigh, Durham and Chapel Hill; some giving also in NY.
Application information: Application form required.
Initial approach: Letter
Deadline(s): None
Officers and Board Members:* J. Alston Gardner, Pres. and Treas.; Barbara K. Lee,* V.P. and Secy.; Emma Gardner; Lucy Stokes.
EIN: 010733593
Selected grants: The following grants are a representative sample of this grantmaker's funding activity:
$25,000 to KidZNotes, Durham, NC, 2012. To provide Operating Funds for the Organization.

1516
TYL Foundation ✧
(formerly McVaney Family Foundation)
1520 W. Canal Ct., No. 220
Littleton, CO 80120-5651

Established in 1993 in CO.
Donors: Charles McVaney; Carole McVaney; Kylee McVaney Fernalld Trust; Kevin Edward McVaney Trust.
Foundation type: Independent foundation.
Financial data (yr. ended 11/30/13): Assets, $20,912,945 (M); gifts received, $1,775,137; expenditures, $1,347,360; qualifying distributions, $1,236,826; giving activities include $1,222,530 for 19 grants (high: $472,130; low: $400).
Purpose and activities: Funding primarily for Christian agencies and churches, human services, and education.
Fields of interest: Education; Health care; Human services; Christian agencies & churches; Protestant agencies & churches.
Limitations: Applications not accepted. Giving primarily in CO. No grants to individuals.
Application information: Unsolicited requests for funds not accepted.
Officers and Directors:* Carole McVaney,* Pres. and Mgr.; Kevin E. McVaney,* V.P.; Kylee Lourie,* Secy.-Treas.
EIN: 841256356

1517
Mazel U'Brocha Foundation ✧
1888 Sherman St., Ste. 600
Denver, CO 80203-1160

Established in 2006 in CO.
Donor: Miriam Beren.
Foundation type: Independent foundation.
Financial data (yr. ended 12/31/13): Assets, $2,695,720 (M); expenditures, $519,101; qualifying distributions, $512,551; giving activities include $512,551 for 49 grants (high: $108,300; low: $200).
Fields of interest: Education; Jewish agencies & synagogues.
Limitations: Applications not accepted. Giving primarily in NY. No grants to individuals.
Application information: Unsolicited requests for funds not accepted.
Officer: Miriam Beren, Pres.
Directors: Joshua Beren; Dena Grossman.
EIN: 161780620

1518
Vail Valley Foundation, Inc. ✧
90 Benchmark Rd., Ste. 300
Avon, CO 81620 (970) 777-2015
FAX: (970) 949-9265; E-mail: info@vvf.org; Mailing Address: P.O. Box 309, Vail, CO 81658; Main URL: http://www.vvf.org
Blog: http://www.vailvalleyfoundation.blogspot.com/
Facebook: http://www.facebook.com/pages/Vail-Valley-Foundation/169530086401875
Flickr: http://www.flickr.com/photos/vailvalleyfoundation/
Twitter: http://twitter.com/VVFoundation
YouTube: http://www.youtube.com/vailvalleyfoundation
Tel. for scholarships: (970) 949-1999; Karri Casner Scholarship: c/o Cheryl Lindstrom, P.O. Box 2088, Edwards, CO 81632, tel.: (970) 926-5290, fax: (970) 926-5293

Established in 1981 in CO.
Foundation type: Community foundation.
Financial data (yr. ended 09/30/13): Assets, $32,320,965 (M); gifts received, $14,010,443; expenditures, $20,931,038; giving activities include $527,471 for 8+ grants (high: $169,135), and $32,205 for 25 grants to individuals.
Purpose and activities: The foundation seeks to provide leadership in athletic, cultural, and educational endeavors to enhance the quality of life in the Vail Valley, CO, area.
Fields of interest: Performing arts, dance; Performing arts, music; Arts; Education; Environment; Athletics/sports, winter sports; Human services.
Limitations: Applications accepted. Giving primarily in Eagle County, CO. No grants to individuals (except for scholarships).
Publications: Annual report; Grants list; Newsletter.
Application information: Application form required.
Initial approach: Proposal
Copies of proposal: 1
Deadline(s): Ongoing
Board meeting date(s): Aug. and Dec.
Final notification: Within 12 months
Officers and Directors:* Harry Frampton III,* Chair.; Cecilia Folz,* C.E.O. and Pres.; Katrina Ammer,* V.P., Opers.; John Dakin,* V.P., Comms.; Duncan Horner,* V.P., Mktg.; Mike Imhof,* Sr. V.P., Opers. and Sales; Rob Gaffney,* C.F.O.; Dillon DeMore, Cont.; Andy Arnold; Judy Berkowitz; Marlene Boll; Bjorn Erik Borgen; Steve Coyer; Jack Crosby; Andrew Daly; Ron Davis; Jack Eck; William Esrey; Tim Finchem; Peter Frechette; Steve Friedman; John Garnsey; Margie Gart; Bob Gary; George Gillett, Jr.; Donna Giordano; Sheika Gramshammer; Martha Head; Mike Herman; Robert Hernreich; Al Hubbard; William Hybl; Yvonne Jacobs; Chris Jarnot; Robert Katz; Kent Logan; Peter May; Brian Nolan; Michael Price; Don Remey; Eric Resnick; Doug Rippeto; Dick Rothkopf; Ken Schanzer; Michael Shannon; Stanley Shuman; Rodney Slifer; Ann Smead; Oscar Tang; Stewart Turley; Steve Virostek; Betsy Wiegers.
EIN: 742215035

1519
Vodafone Americas Foundation ✧
(formerly Vodafone-US Foundation)
999 18th St., Ste. 1750
Denver, CO 80202-2404
Contact: June Sugiyama, Dir.
E-mail: americasfoundation@vodafone.com; Application address: 275 Shoreline Dr., Ste. 400, Redwood City, CA 94065, tel.: (925) 210-3870, fax: (925) 210-3852; e-mail for Julie Sugiyama, Dir.: June.Sugiyama@vodafone.com; e-mail for Genevieve Sublette, Assoc.: genevieve.sublette@vodafone.com; e-mail for Wireless Innovation Project: project@vodafone.com; Main URL: http://www.vodafone-us.com/
Grants List: http://www.vodafone-us.com/about/community-support/grants-2011/
Vofafone Americas Foundation Blog: http://vodafoneamericasfoundation.blog.com/
Wireless Innovation Progrect Video of Winners: http://vimeo.com/40438301
Wireless Innovation Project: http://project.vodafone-us.com/
Wireless Innovation Project on Facebook: http://www.facebook.com/VodafoneProject
Wireless Innovation Project on Twitter: http://twitter.com/VodafoneProject

Established in 1993 as a spin-off of Pacific Telesis Foundation; current name adopted in Jan. 2000.
Donors: AirTouch Communications, Inc.; Vodafone Americas Inc.
Foundation type: Company-sponsored foundation.
Financial data (yr. ended 12/31/12): Assets, $20,832,241 (M); gifts received, $24,115; expenditures, $1,553,542; qualifying distributions, $1,452,893; giving activities include $1,036,923 for 84 grants (high: $100,000; low: $100).
Purpose and activities: The foundation supports programs designed to strengthen families; serve children and youth; foster leadership development; address civic participation and urban issues; promote the arts; and promote technology.
Fields of interest: Performing arts; Arts; Higher education; Teacher school/education; Education; Environment; Health care; Substance abuse,

prevention; Housing/shelter; Youth development, adult & child programs; Youth development; Children/youth, services; Youth, pregnancy prevention; Family services; Human services; Community/economic development; Engineering/technology; Public policy, research; Public affairs, citizen participation; Leadership development; Public affairs.

Type of support: General/operating support; Continuing support; Program development; Scholarship funds; Employee matching gifts.

Limitations: Applications accepted. Giving primarily in areas of company operations in CA, with emphasis on the San Francisco Bay Area and Denver, CO metro area; giving in the U.S. for the Wireless Innovation Project. No support for political organizations or religious organizations not of direct benefit to the entire community, fraternal, veterans', or labor groups, individual K-12 schools or school districts, or discriminatory organizations. No grants to individuals, or for capital campaigns, endowments, sports programs, fundraising events, goodwill advertising, cause-related marketing, health-related programs, memberships, administrative services, emergency appeals, or large national projects; no product or service donations.

Publications: Application guidelines; Grants list.

Application information: Unsolicited applications for general funding are not accepted, but the foundation will keep all inquiries on file and contact applying organizations if opportunities arise within the grantmaking cycle. Organizations receiving Vodafone Wireless Innovation Project funds are asked to submit a progress report twice a year. Application form not required.

Initial approach: Complete online eligibility quiz and application for Vodafone Wireless Innovation Project

Deadline(s): Oct. to Dec. 31 for Vodafone Wireless Innovation Project

Final notification: Feb. 3 for Vodafone Wireless Innovation Project

Officers and Directors:* Megan Doberneck,* Secy.; Fay Arjomandi; William Keever; Arun Sarin; Peters Suh; Paul Martin.

Number of staff: 1 part-time professional; 1 full-time support.

EIN: 205900761

1520
Western Colorado Community Foundation, Inc. ✧

225 North 5th, Ste. 505
P.O. Box 4334
Grand Junction, CO 81502-4334 (970) 243-3767
Contact: Anne Wenzel, Pres.
FAX: (970) 243-9767; E-mail: awenzel@wc-cf.org; Main URL: http://www.wc-cf.org

Established in 1996 in CO.

Foundation type: Community foundation.

Financial data (yr. ended 12/31/12): Assets, $35,765,311 (M); gifts received, $4,274,575; expenditures, $3,124,974; giving activities include $1,525,483 for 39+ grants (high: $108,125).

Purpose and activities: The foundation seeks to promote philanthropy and to build and manage permanent charitable assets to benefit the residents of western CO.

Fields of interest: Arts; Education; Environment; Health care; Human services; Community/economic development.

Type of support: General/operating support; Seed money; Scholarships—to individuals; Matching/challenge support.

Limitations: Applications accepted. Giving limited to Delta, Eagle, Garfield, Gunnison, Mesa, Montrose, Ouray and Rio Blanco counties, CO. No grants to individuals (except for scholarships), or for fundraising events.

Publications: Application guidelines; Annual report; Informational brochure; Newsletter.

Application information: Visit foundation web site for application guidelines. Application form not required.

Initial approach: Letter of inquiry or telephone

Deadline(s): Varies

Board meeting date(s): Jan., Apr., July, and Oct.

Officers and Directors:* Tom Stuver,* Chair.; Ann Brach,* Vice-Chair.; Anne Wenzel,* Pres. and Exec. Dir.; Rob Bleiberg,* Secy.; Jim Grisier,* Treas.; Lee Ambrose; Elaine Brett; Morgan Bridge; Aaron Clay; Susan Diaz; Martie Edwards; Sue Hillhouse; Robert Hutchins; Dick McKinley; Amy Nuernberg; Tony Prinster; Jane Quimby; Ken Stein.

Number of staff: 1 full-time professional; 2 part-time professional; 1 part-time support.

EIN: 841354894

1521
Western Union Foundation ✧

12500 E. Belford Ave., Ste. M1-I
Englewood, CO 80112-5939 (720) 332-6606
FAX: (720) 332-4772;
E-mail: wufoundation@westernunion.com; Contact information for Family Scholarship Program: Institute of International Education, 1400 K St. NY, Ste. 700, Washington, DC 20005, tel.: (202) 326-7742, fax: (202) 326-7841, e-mail: wufoundation@iie.org; Main URL: http://foundation.westernunion.com/
Grants List: http://foundation.westernunion.com/giving_map.html
LifeWires Newsletter: http://foundation.westernunion.com/lifewires.html
RSS Feed: http://foundationblog.westernunion.com/western-union-foundation/atom.xml
Twitter: https://twitter.com/TheWUFoundation
Western Union Foundation Blog: http://foundationblog.westernunion.com/

Established as a company-sponsored operating foundation in 2000 in CO.

Donors: First Data Corp.; Western Union Co.

Foundation type: Operating foundation.

Financial data (yr. ended 12/31/13): Assets, $4,434,447 (M); gifts received, $11,513,514; expenditures, $11,318,846; qualifying distributions, $11,310,372; giving activities include $9,237,402 for 222 grants (high: $300,000; low: $10), and $537,674 for employee matching gifts.

Purpose and activities: The foundation supports programs designed to provide individuals with better access to educational opportunities, promote economic development, and provide basic human services to communities in developing countries. Special emphasis is directed toward programs designed to address economic opportunity through job training, life-skills development, small-business development, and financial literacy.

Fields of interest: Secondary school/education; Vocational education; Education, ESL programs; Education; Employment, services; Employment, training; Disasters, preparedness/services; American Red Cross; Human services, financial counseling; Human services; International affairs, U.N.; Economic development; Business/industry; Social entrepreneurship; Community development, small businesses; Community/economic development; Engineering/technology; Public affairs; Children; Adults; Minorities; Immigrants/refugees; Economically disadvantaged; Migrant workers.

International interests: Brazil; China; Global Programs; India; Mexico; Philippines.

Type of support: Continuing support; Building/renovation; Equipment; Program development; Scholarship funds; Employee volunteer services; Employee matching gifts; Scholarships—to individuals; Matching/challenge support.

Limitations: Applications not accepted. Giving on a national and international basis, with emphasis on Phoenix, AZ, Los Angeles and San Francisco, CA, Denver, CO, Washington, DC, Miami, FL, Chicago, IL, New York, NY, Argentina, Australia, Austria, Brazil, Canada, China, Costa Rica, Egypt, Ghana, Guatemala, Haiti, India, Indonesia, Kenya, Lithuania, Mexico, Morocco, New Zealand, Nigeria, Pakistan, Peru, Philippines, Romania, Russia, South Africa, Uganda, and United Arab Emirates. No support for pass-through organizations, health organizations, arts, media, or humanities organizations, or religious or political organizations. No grants for general operating support, endowments, special events, capital campaigns, post-secondary scholarship programs, early childhood education, debt reduction, disease research, environmental causes, sports, or athletics.

Publications: Annual report; Financial statement; Grants list; Informational brochure; Newsletter.

Application information: Unsolicited requests for general grants are not accepted at this time. The foundation is working with its current NGO partners and will solicit proposals from NGOs that align with its giving platform.

Board meeting date(s): Quarterly

Officers and Directors:* John Dye,* Chair.; Patrick Gaston, Pres.; Jo-Anne Scharmann, Treas.; Jean Claude Farah; Davida Fedeli; Anne-Marie Fortier; Paul Foster; Diane Scott; Ignacio Videla; Drina Yue.

Number of staff: 3 full-time professional; 2 full-time support.

EIN: 311738614

Selected grants: The following grants are a representative sample of this grantmaker's funding activity:

$300,000 to Illinois Currency Exchange Charitable Foundation, Des Plaines, IL, 2012. For restricted support.
$300,000 to Small Enterprise Assistance Funds, Washington, DC, 2012. For restricted support.
$300,000 to Small Enterprise Assistance Funds, Washington, DC, 2012. For unrestricted support.
$200,000 to BI-LO Charities, Mauldin, SC, 2012. For restricted support.
$144,000 to BI-LO Charities, Mauldin, SC, 2012. For unrestricted support.
$112,438 to American Red Cross National Headquarters, Washington, DC, 2012. For restricted support.
$25,000 to New York Community Trust, New York, NY, 2012.

$20,000 to AWECA Foundation, San Fernando, Philippines, 2012. For unrestricted support.
$20,000 to University of Miami, Coral Gables, FL, 2012. For restricted support.
$11,400 to Save the Children Federation, Fairfield, CT, 2012. For restricted support.

1522
Whispering Fox Foundation ✧ ☆
c/o Maffei & Assocs., CPAs, LLC
3225 Templeton Gap Rd., Ste. 105
Colorado Springs, CO 80907-8729

Established in 2005 in CO.
Donors: Betty M. Higgins; Douglas S. Higgins.
Foundation type: Independent foundation.
Financial data (yr. ended 12/31/13): Assets, $12,150,533 (M); expenditures, $530,785; qualifying distributions, $477,834; giving activities include $450,100 for 15 grants (high: $47,000; low: $6,000).
Fields of interest: Education; Animal welfare; Health care; Safety/disasters, volunteer services; Human services; Catholic federated giving programs; Protestant agencies & churches.
Limitations: Applications not accepted. Giving primarily in CO.
Application information: Contributes only to pre-selected organizations.
Officers: Douglas S. Higgins, Pres.; Margaret M. Higgins, Secy.-Treas.
EIN: 364579715
Selected grants: The following grants are a representative sample of this grantmaker's funding activity:
$66,000 to National Forest Foundation, Missoula, MT, 2012. To support forest restoration in Waldo Canyon burn areas.
$50,000 to Archdiocese of Chicago, Chicago, IL, 2012. To support Cardinal's student scholarship fund.
$50,000 to Faith in Practice, Houston, TX, 2012. For Support for medical services in Guatemala.
$40,000 to Silver Key Senior Services, Colorado Springs, CO, 2012. To provide support for the elderly.
$27,000 to Catholic Charities USA, Alexandria, VA, 2012. For disaster relief and health services.
$25,000 to Special Operations Warrior Foundation, Tampa, FL, 2012. For families of fallen and wounded warriors.

1523
Harry L. Willett Foundation ✧
c/o Boyd Ryan Willett Jr., Carol Cox
518 17th St.
Denver, CO 80202

Established in CO.
Donor: Harry L. Willett†.
Foundation type: Independent foundation.
Financial data (yr. ended 04/30/13): Assets, $889,566 (M); gifts received, $1,694,814; expenditures, $1,517,385; qualifying distributions, $1,473,334; giving activities include $1,473,334 for grants.
Fields of interest: Medical research, institute; Human services; Christian agencies & churches.
Limitations: Applications not accepted. Giving in the U.S., with emphasis on TX.
Application information: Unsolicited requests for funds not accepted.
Officers: Boyd Ryan Willett, Jr., Pres.; Boyd Willett Curtis, V.P.; Louise Willett Curtis, Secy.-Treas.
EIN: 271868389
Selected grants: The following grants are a representative sample of this grantmaker's funding activity:
$160,000 to Campus Crusade for Christ International, Orlando, FL, 2012.
$70,000 to Denver Zoological Foundation, Denver, CO, 2012.
$60,000 to Medical Teams International, Tigard, OR, 2012.
$50,000 to Bridges to Life, Houston, TX, 2012.
$49,000 to Childrens Association for Maximum Potential, San Antonio, TX, 2012.
$35,000 to Audubon Society, Montana, Helena, MT, 2012.
$25,000 to Texas State University, San Marcos, TX, 2012.
$6,000 to Achievement Rewards for College Scientists Foundation, Denver, CO, 2012.

1524
The Williams Family Foundation ✧
626 E. Platte Ave.
Fort Morgan, CO 80701-3339
Contact: Edward L. Zorn, Tr.

Trust established about 1958 in CO.
Donors: A.F. Williams, M.D.†; Mrs. A.F. Williams†.
Foundation type: Independent foundation.
Financial data (yr. ended 12/31/13): Assets, $16,275,181 (M); expenditures, $905,080; qualifying distributions, $878,785; giving activities include $872,785 for 25 grants (high: $649,461; low: $1,000).
Purpose and activities: Giving for higher and secondary education; scholarships limited to graduates of Morgan County, CO, high schools for medical-oriented study, hospitals, and civic affairs.
Fields of interest: Secondary school/education; Medical school/education; Hospitals (general); Government/public administration.
Type of support: Scholarship funds; Research.
Limitations: Applications accepted. Giving primarily in CO; scholarships limited to Morgan County, CO, high school graduates.
Application information: Scholarship applicants must be graduates of, and be nominated by, Morgan County, CO, high schools; CGA Colorado Common Grant Application accepted. Application form not required.
Initial approach: Letter
Copies of proposal: 1
Deadline(s): None
Board meeting date(s): 4th Wed. of each month
Final notification: 3-6 months
Trustees: Kathleen Thompson; Patrick Thompson; Shawn Thompson; Edward L. Zorn.
Number of staff: None.
EIN: 846023379
Selected grants: The following grants are a representative sample of this grantmaker's funding activity:
$5,000 to Scottish Rite Foundation, Denver, CO, 2012. For therapy for Providing children.
$1,000 to Muscular Dystrophy Association, Denver, CO, 2012. For medical research.

1525
The Winslow Foundation
(formerly Windie Foundation)
1430 Front St.
Louisville, CO 80027-1422 (720) 428-2341
Contact: Ellen Marshall, Exec. Dir.

Established in 1987 in NJ.
Donor: Julia D. Winslow†.
Foundation type: Independent foundation.
Financial data (yr. ended 12/31/13): Assets, $33,159,302 (M); expenditures, $1,765,345; qualifying distributions, $1,448,581; giving activities include $1,268,000 for 29 grants (high: $125,000; low: $1,000).
Purpose and activities: Giving primarily for the environment and population studies.
Fields of interest: Environment, natural resources; Population studies.
Type of support: General/operating support; Continuing support; Program development; Conferences/seminars; Seed money; Research; Matching/challenge support.
Limitations: Applications accepted. Giving on a national basis. No grants to individuals.
Application information: Unsolicited full proposals are generally not accepted. Proposals will be invited. Application guidelines available upon request. Application form not required.
Initial approach: 2-page letter of inquiry
Copies of proposal: 1
Deadline(s): None
Board meeting date(s): Varies
Officers and Directors:* Wren Winslow Wirth,* Pres.; Christopher Wirth,* V.P.; Kelsey Wirth,* V.P.; Betty Ann Ottinger,* Secy.; Samuel W. Lambert III,* Treas.; Ellen Marshall, Exec. Dir.
Number of staff: 1 part-time professional; 1 part-time support.
EIN: 222778703

1526
Melvin and Elaine Wolf Foundation Inc. ✧
6825 E. Tennessee Ave., Ste. 235
Denver, CO 80224-1630 (303) 398-0275

Established in 1978 in CO.
Donors: Melvin Wolf; Elaine Wolf.
Foundation type: Independent foundation.
Financial data (yr. ended 06/30/13): Assets, $9,699,163 (M); expenditures, $570,940; qualifying distributions, $457,251; giving activities include $457,251 for grants.
Purpose and activities: Giving primarily for the arts, health, including a children's hospital foundation, and for human services.
Fields of interest: Arts; Hospitals (specialty); Health organizations, association; Human services; Children/youth, services; Foundations (private grantmaking); Jewish agencies & synagogues.
Type of support: General/operating support; Equipment; Program development.
Limitations: Applications not accepted. Giving primarily in Denver, CO. No grants to individuals.
Application information: Contributes only to pre-selected organizations.
Officers and Directors:* Elaine Wolf,* Pres.; Ian D. Gardenswartz, V.P. and Treas.; Sandra Wolf,* V.P.
EIN: 840797937
Selected grants: The following grants are a representative sample of this grantmaker's funding activity:

$30,000 to University of Colorado Foundation, Boulder, CO, 2013. For Wolf Foundation Fund for Children's Advocacy.
$25,755 to American Red Cross, Denver, CO, 2013. For Comfort Kits and Clean-Up Kits.
$20,000 to Food Bank of the Rockies, Denver, CO, 2013. To support Well-Fed Program at Maddox Early Learning Center.
$17,396 to Jewish Family Service of Colorado, Denver, CO, 2013. To assist JFS to Purchase a 2012 Isuzu Truck for Shalom Denver.
$10,000 to Cancer League of Colorado, Englewood, CO, 2013. For cancer research projects.
$1,500 to Planned Parenthood of the Rocky Mountains, Denver, CO, 2013. For Clients in Need Fund.

1527
Wolf Mountain Foundation ✧
1333 Charles Dr., Ste. 14
Longmont, CO 80503

Established in 1999 in CO.
Donors: Pierce Mangurian; North Fork Investment Co.
Foundation type: Independent foundation.
Financial data (yr. ended 12/31/13): Assets, $25,174,069 (M); expenditures, $871,209; qualifying distributions, $797,522; giving activities include $765,000 for 17 grants (high: $45,000; low: $45,000).
Fields of interest: Children/youth, services.
Limitations: Applications not accepted. Giving primarily in NY and TX. No grants to individuals.
Application information: Contributes only to pre-selected organizations.
Officers: Pierce Mangurian, Chair. and Treas.; Charles D. Walton, Pres.; Warren Lloyd, Exec. V.P.; Norma Shutts, Secy.
Directors: Marcia Lloyd; Renee Wright.
EIN: 841524399
Selected grants: The following grants are a representative sample of this grantmaker's funding activity:
$37,000 to Boysville, Converse, TX, 2012. To Carry Out the Exempt Purposes.
$37,000 to West Texas Boys Ranch, San Angelo, TX, 2012. To Carry Out the Exempt Purposes.

1528
Yampa Valley Community Foundation ✧
385 Anglers Dr., Ste. B
Sundance Office Plaza
Steamboat Springs, CO 80487 (970) 879-8632
Contact: Mark Andersen, Exec. Dir.
FAX: (970) 871-0431; E-mail: info@yvcf.org; Mailing address: P.O. Box 881869, Steamboat Springs, CO 80488; Main URL: http://www.yvcf.org
E-Newsletter: http://www.yvcf.org/newsletter.php
Facebook: https://www.facebook.com/yvcf.org
LinkedIn: http://www.linkedin.com/company/yampa-valley-community-foundation?trk=cp_followed_name_yampa-valley-community-foundation
Pinterest: http://www.pinterest.com/yvcf/
Twitter: https://twitter.com/yvcf

Established in 1979 in CO.
Foundation type: Community foundation.
Financial data (yr. ended 12/31/13): Assets, $10,427,453 (M); gifts received, $962,024; expenditures, $1,341,001; giving activities include $656,406 for 167+ grants (high: $50,000; low: $100), and $89,110 for 81 grants to individuals.
Purpose and activities: The foundation provides leadership in raising funds, in partnership with community members, to support innovative programs benefiting the Yampa Valley community. Giving primarily to arts and culture, education, environment, health organizations, recreation and human services.
Fields of interest: Arts; Education; Environment; Health care; Health organizations, association; Recreation; Human services.
Type of support: General/operating support; Continuing support; Annual campaigns; Capital campaigns; Building/renovation; Equipment; Endowments; Emergency funds; Program development; Conferences/seminars; Seed money; Curriculum development; Scholarships—to individuals; Exchange programs.
Limitations: Applications accepted. Giving primarily in Yampa Valley, specifically Moffat and Routt counties, CO. No support for religious purposes. No grants for debt reduction or endowments; generally no grants for team or travel expenses.
Publications: Application guidelines; Annual report; Financial statement; Grants list; Informational brochure; Newsletter.
Application information: Visit foundation web site for the Colorado Common Grant Form and application guidelines. Application form required.
Initial approach: Submit Letter of Intent
Copies of proposal: 1
Deadline(s): Aug. 1
Board meeting date(s): Semi-monthly
Final notification: Late Sept.
Officers and Trustees:* Adonna Allen,* Chair.; Jim Bronner,* Vice-Chair.; Laura Cusenbary,* Vice-Chair.; Dana Tredway,* Secy.-Treas.; Mark Andersen, Exec. Dir.; Paula Cooper Black,* Emeritus; Tammy Delaney; Chris Diamond; Jay Fetcher; Rod Hanna; Ron Krall; Gary Neale; Kathryn Pedersen; Tom Sharp; Pam Vanatta.
Number of staff: 2 full-time professional; 2 part-time professional.
EIN: 840794536
Selected grants: The following grants are a representative sample of this grantmaker's funding activity:
$12,000 to Yampa Valley Sustainability Council, Steamboat Springs, CO, 2012. For Multiple Recycling, Zero-Waste and educational initiatives.
$10,000 to Born Free Animal Rehabilitation, Steamboat Springs, CO, 2012. For repair of fences, pens, and barns for sanctuary.
$10,000 to Yampatika Outdoor Awareness Association, Steamboat Springs, CO, 2012. For environmental education.
$9,000 to Rocky Mountain Youth Corps, Steamboat Springs, CO, 2012. For Service Learning Institute.
$5,000 to Boys & Girls Club of Northwest Colorado, Craig, CO, 2012. For Club Operating Support.
$5,000 to Healthcare Foundation for the Yampa Valley, Steamboat Springs, CO, 2012. For Cancer Services Administration.
$5,000 to Integrated Community, Steamboat Springs, CO, 2012. For Resource and Referral program.
$5,000 to South Routt School District, Oak Creek, CO, 2012. For Hands-In Community Involvement Project.
$5,000 to Strings Music Festival, Steamboat Springs, CO, 2012. For Strings School Days Outreach.
$3,500 to Hayden School District RE-1, Hayden, CO, 2012. For Theatre Curtain for auditorium/theatre space.

1529
YPI Charitable Trust ✧
c/o J. Harvey
P.O. Box 2132
Crested Butte, CO 81224-2132

Established in 1991.
Donors: John T. Dorrance III; Charles A. Dorrance.
Foundation type: Independent foundation.
Financial data (yr. ended 05/31/12): Assets, $0 (M); expenditures, $1,106,732; qualifying distributions, $1,106,326; giving activities include $1,106,326 for 20 grants (high: $700,526; low: $10,000).
Fields of interest: Arts; Education; Environment, natural resources; Human services; Foundations (private grantmaking).
Limitations: Applications not accepted. Giving primarily in FL, NY, TN, and TX; some giving also in WY. No grants to individuals.
Application information: Contributes only to pre-selected organizations.
Trustees: Charles A. Dorrance; Gunda S. Dorrance; John T. Dorrance III; John T. Dorrance IV.
EIN: 237675355
Selected grants: The following grants are a representative sample of this grantmaker's funding activity:
$75,000 to Versailles Foundation, New York, NY, 2012.
$50,000 to Brandywine Conservancy, Chadds Ford, PA, 2012.
$20,000 to Advocacy for Visual Arts, Gillette, WY, 2012.
$20,000 to Winterthur Museum, Garden and Library, Winterthur, DE, 2012.
$15,800 to Charities Aid Foundation America, Alexandria, VA, 2012.
$15,000 to Wyoming Womens Foundation, Laramie, WY, 2012.

CONNECTICUT

1530
1772 Foundation, Inc. ✧
P.O. Box 112
Pomfret Center, CT 06259-0112 (860) 928-1772
Contact: Mary Anthony
E-mail: maryanthony@1772foundation.org; Main URL: http://www.1772foundation.org

Established in 1985 in NJ.
Donors: Stewart B. Kean‡; Stewart B. Kean Residuary Trust.
Foundation type: Independent foundation.
Financial data (yr. ended 12/31/12): Assets, $75,861,121 (M); gifts received, $2,000,000; expenditures, $3,901,351; qualifying distributions, $3,553,620; giving activities include $3,221,857 for 140 grants (high: $190,000; low: $500).
Purpose and activities: Giving for the preservation and enhancement of American historical entities and projects. Key areas of interest are: 1) Revolving funds for endangered properties, 2) New Jersey inner-city revitalization, 3) Preservation trades and crafts schools and programs, 4) Agricultural endeavors, 5) Historic site sustainability training and conferences, and 6) African American historic site development.
Fields of interest: Historic preservation/historical societies.
Type of support: Building/renovation.
Limitations: Applications accepted. Giving primarily on the East Coast, with emphasis on CT, MA, ME, NJ, NY, and RI. No support for schools and universities, or for non-501(c)(3) organizations, privately owned structures, relocation or purchase of historic structures, hospitals, or religious organizations. No grants to individuals, or for general operating support, scholarships, professional fees, studies and reports, books, strategic planning, endowments, or sabbaticals.
Publications: Annual report.
Application information: Application form required.
Initial approach: Use application on foundation web site
Officers and Trustees:* G. Stanton Geary,* Pres.; B. Danforth Ely,* V.P.; Mary Anthony,* Exec. Dir.; Nancy E. Davis; Dr. Robert Raynolds; Dr. Gretchen Sullivan Sorin.
EIN: 222578377
Selected grants: The following grants are a representative sample of this grantmaker's funding activity:
$100,000 to Hamilton Partnership for Paterson, Paterson, NJ, 2012. For historic property preservation.
$95,000 to Historic Macon Foundation, Macon, GA, 2012. For historic properties redevelopment program.
$75,000 to Palmetto Trust for Historic Preservation, Columbia, SC, 2012. For historic properties redevelopment program.
$50,000 to City Green, Clifton, NJ, 2012. For urban agricultural programming.
$50,000 to Island Institute, Rockland, ME, 2012. For sustainable food systems work.
$50,000 to New York Harbor Foundation, New York, NY, 2012. For oyster restoration and educational programming.
$50,000 to North Bennet Street School, Boston, MA, 2012. For preservation trades and crafts education.
$25,000 to Southside Community Land Trust, Providence, RI, 2012. For farmland protection.
$20,000 to Old Sturbridge Village, Sturbridge, MA, 2012. For charter school study.
$15,000 to Museum of African American History, Boston, MA, 2012. For African American historic site preservation.

1531
Aetna Foundation, Inc. ✧
(formerly Aetna Life & Casualty Foundation, Inc.)
151 Farmington Ave., RE2R
Hartford, CT 06156-3180
FAX: (860) 273-7764;
E-mail: aetnafoundation@aetna.com; Main URL: http://www.aetna.com/foundation
AcademyHealth/Aetna Foundation Minority Scholars Recipients: http://www.aetnafoundationscholars.org/2010-scholars.php
Grants List: http://www.aetna.com/about-aetna-insurance/aetna-foundation/aetna-grants/annual-reports-grant-listings.html
Minority Scholars Program Video: http://www.aetnafoundationscholars.org/includes/video_overview
National Medical Fellowships Healthcare Leadership Recipients: http://www.aetna-foundation.org/foundation/aetna-foundation-programs/scholars/nmf-healthcare-leadership-program.html
RSS Feed: http://news.aetnafoundation.org/feeds/press_release/all/rss.xml
The Aetna Foundation: http://news.aetnafoundation.org/multimedia

Incorporated in 1972 in CT.
Donors: Aetna Inc.; Aetna Life Insurance Company; Aetna Health Inc.
Foundation type: Company-sponsored foundation.
Financial data (yr. ended 12/31/12): Assets, $54,426,641 (M); expenditures, $9,580,326; qualifying distributions, $7,864,411; giving activities include $7,864,411 for 205 grants (high: $595,156; low: $92).
Purpose and activities: The foundation supports programs designed to promote wellness, health, and access to high-quality care. Special emphasis is directed toward obesity; racial and ethnic health care equity; and integrated health care.
Fields of interest: Medical school/education; Health care, public policy; Health care, equal rights; Hospitals (general); Health care, clinics/centers; Health care, infants; Public health; Public health, obesity; Public health, physical fitness; Health care, cost containment; Health care, patient services; Health care; Food services; Food banks; Nutrition; Engineering/technology; Children; Minorities; Women; Economically disadvantaged.
Type of support: Program development; Conferences/seminars; Scholarship funds; Research; Employee volunteer services; Sponsorships; Employee matching gifts; Matching/challenge support.
Limitations: Applications not accepted. Giving primarily in areas of company operations in Phoenix, AZ, Los Angeles, Fresno, San Diego, and San Francisco, CA, CT, Washington, DC, Miami and Tampa, FL, Atlanta, GA, Chicago, IL, Baltimore, MD, ME, Charlotte, NC, NJ, New York, NY, Cleveland and Columbus, OH, Philadelphia and Pittsburgh, PA, Austin, Dallas, Houston, and San Antonio, TX, and WA; giving also to national and regional organizations. No support for religious organizations not of direct benefit to the entire community. No grants to individuals, or for scholarships, endowments, capital campaigns, construction, renovation, or equipment, direct delivery of reimbursable healthcare services, biomedical research, advertising, golf tournaments, advocacy, political causes, or events, or general operating support or deficits.
Publications: Annual report; Grants list; Newsletter; Program policy statement.
Application information: Unsolicited requests for national grants are currently not accepted. Sponsorship applications are by invitation only. Visit website for periodic Request for Proposals.
Board meeting date(s): Apr. and Dec.
Officers and Directors:* Mark T. Bertolini,* Chair.; Garth Graham, M.D., M.P.H., Pres.; Gilian R. Barclay, D.D.S., DrPH, V.P.; Sharon C. Dalton,* V.P.; Judith Jones, Secy.; Elaine R. Confranceso, Treas.; Sheryl A. Burke; Molly J. Coye, M.D.; Jeffrey E. Garten; Jerald B. Gooden; Steven B. Kelmar; Susan M. Krosman, RN; Andrew J. Lee; Kristi A. Matus; Margaret M. McCarthy; Kay D. Mooney; Joseph P. Newhouse; Sandip Patel; Lonny Reisman, M.D.
Number of staff: 14 full-time professional.
EIN: 237241940

1532
The Josef and Anni Albers Foundation, Inc. ✧
(formerly Josef Albers Foundation, Inc.)
88 Beacon Rd.
Bethany, CT 06524-3074 (203) 393-4089
Contact: Nicholas Fox Weber, Exec. Dir.
FAX: (203) 393-4094;
E-mail: info@albersfoundation.org; Main URL: http://www.albersfoundation.org

Incorporated in 1971 in NY.
Donors: Josef Albers‡; Anni Albers‡; John Richardson; Margot Wilkie.
Foundation type: Operating foundation.
Financial data (yr. ended 12/31/12): Assets, $14,997,222 (M); gifts received, $197,344; expenditures, $3,241,504; qualifying distributions, $3,565,726; giving activities include $600,839 for 23 grants (high: $249,798), and $1,545,163 for foundation-administered programs.
Purpose and activities: Giving primarily for the preparation and organization of various exhibitions of art by Josef Albers and Anni Albers.
Fields of interest: Arts, management/technical assistance; Arts, administration/regulation; Arts, research; Arts, single organization support; Arts, information services; Arts, public education; Visual arts; Visual arts, painting; Museums; Performing arts; Arts, services; Arts, artist's services; Arts; Higher education; Children/youth, services.
Type of support: Program development; Publication; Seed money.
Limitations: Applications not accepted. Giving primarily in the U.S., with emphasis on CT and NY; funding also in France.
Application information: Unsolicited requests for funds not accepted.
Officer and Directors:* Nicholas Fox Weber,* Exec. Dir.; John Eastman; Charles Kingsley; Emma Lewis.

Number of staff: 4 full-time professional; 2 full-time support.
EIN: 237104223

1533
Alexion Complement Foundation ✧
352 Knotter Dr.
Cheshire, CT 06410-1138 (888) 765-4747

Established in 2007 in CT.
Donor: Alexion Pharmaceuticals, Inc.
Foundation type: Operating foundation.
Financial data (yr. ended 12/31/12): Assets, $491,454 (M); gifts received, $1,764,780; expenditures, $1,295,710; qualifying distributions, $1,275,287; giving activities include $1,275,287 for 2 grants (high: $786,741; low: $488,546).
Purpose and activities: The foundation provides prescription drug Soliris to uninsured ill patients for treatment of paroxysmal nocturnal hemoglobinura (PNH) and atypical hemolytic uremic syndrome (aHUS).
Fields of interest: Pharmacy/prescriptions; Health care; Economically disadvantaged.
Type of support: Donated products; In-kind gifts.
Application information:
Initial approach: Telephone foundation for application information
Officers: Irving Adler, Pres.; John C. Markow, Secy.; Scott Phillips, Treas.
EIN: 208963321

1534
The ALFA Foundation ✧
240 Greenwich Ave., 3rd Fl.
Greenwich, CT 06830-6507

Established in 2000 in CT.
Donor: Ali Fayed.
Foundation type: Independent foundation.
Financial data (yr. ended 12/31/13): Assets, $36,952,656 (M); gifts received, $20,000,000; expenditures, $1,798,714; qualifying distributions, $1,769,533; giving activities include $1,758,333 for 9 grants (high: $1,000,000; low: $5,000).
Purpose and activities: Giving primarily for education; funding also for hospitals and medical research.
Fields of interest: Higher education; Education; Hospitals (specialty); Medical research, institute.
Limitations: Applications not accepted. Giving primarily in CT, ID, and NY. No grants to individuals.
Application information: Contributes only to pre-selected organizations.
Trustees: Ali Fayed; Lee A. Kuntz.
EIN: 137228276

1535
Allison Foundation Inc. ✧
(formerly The Allison Family Foundation, Inc.)
P.O. Box 122
Greens Farms, CT 06838-0122

Established in 1998 in NY.
Donor: Herbert M. Allison, Jr.
Foundation type: Independent foundation.
Financial data (yr. ended 05/31/13): Assets, $7,362,437 (M); gifts received, $5,625; expenditures, $1,227,312; qualifying distributions, $1,203,350; giving activities include $1,200,000 for 2 grants (high: $1,000,000; low: $200,000).
Fields of interest: Performing arts, dance; Business school/education; Human services; International affairs.
Type of support: General/operating support.
Limitations: Applications not accepted. Giving primarily in New York, NY; some funding also in Stanford, CA. No grants to individuals.
Application information: Contributes only to pre-selected organizations.
Officers: Simin N. Allison, Pres.; John R. Allison, V.P. and Secy.; Andrew G. Allison, V.P. and Treas.
EIN: 134011223
Selected grants: The following grants are a representative sample of this grantmaker's funding activity:
$250,000 to International Rescue Committee, New York, NY, 2011.

1536
The Allwin Family Foundation ✧ ☆
c/o Maria Allwin
116 Clapboard Ridge Rd.
Greenwich, CT 06830-3433

Established in 1997 in NY.
Donors: James M. Allwin‡; Maria Allwin.
Foundation type: Independent foundation.
Financial data (yr. ended 12/31/13): Assets, $289,052 (M); gifts received, $10,225; expenditures, $445,127; qualifying distributions, $442,125; giving activities include $432,000 for 8 grants (high: $250,000; low: $500).
Purpose and activities: Giving primarily for education and the arts.
Fields of interest: Museums; Higher education; Education; Hospitals (general); Children/youth, services.
Limitations: Applications not accepted. Giving primarily in CT, NH, and NY.
Application information: Contributes only to pre-selected organizations.
Trustee: Maria Allwin.
EIN: 137088461

1537
American Savings Foundation ✧
(formerly American Savings Foundation of Connecticut, Inc.)
185 Main St.
New Britain, CT 06051-2296 (860) 827-2556
Contact: David Davison, Pres. and C.E.O.
FAX: (860) 832-4582; E-mail: info@asfdn.org; Contact for Capital Grants: Maria Sanchez, Sr. Prog. Off., e-mail: msanchez@asfdn.org; Main URL: http://www.asfdn.org
Grants List: http://www.asfdn.org/2011_Grants.cfm

Established in 1995 in CT.
Donor: American Financial Holdings, Inc.
Foundation type: Independent foundation.
Financial data (yr. ended 12/31/13): Assets, $87,111,382 (M); expenditures, $4,373,763; qualifying distributions, $3,888,595; giving activities include $2,566,978 for grants, $630,531 for grants to individuals, and $87,314 for foundation-administered programs.
Purpose and activities: The foundation is dedicated to strengthening the community by supporting education, human services, and the arts, with a special emphasis on the needs of children, youth, and families, through grants to community organizations and college scholarships.
Fields of interest: Arts; Education; Health care; Mental health/crisis services; Crime/violence prevention; Employment; Housing/shelter; Youth development; Human services; Children/youth; Youth.
Type of support: Matching/challenge support; Film/video/radio; Equipment; Continuing support; Consulting services; Management development/capacity building; Capital campaigns; Building/renovation; Program development; Seed money; Technical assistance; Scholarships—to individuals.
Limitations: Applications accepted. Giving only within 64-town service area in CT, with a primary focus on New Britain, and a secondary focus on Waterbury. No support for religious institutions unless the program benefits the community at large or for political advocacy or lobbying, environmental issues, primary or secondary schools—public, private, independent or parochial, or colleges and universities. No support for endowments, annual campaigns, and general and operating support.
Application information: See foundation web site for guidelines for scholarships, program grants and capital grants.
Initial approach: Proposals for Program Grants, Letter of Intent for Capital Grants, visit web site for scholarships
Copies of proposal: 1
Deadline(s): See foundation web site for current deadlines
Board meeting date(s): Quarterly
Officers and Directors:* Harry N. Mazadoorian,* Chair.; Charles J. Boulier III, Vice-Chair.; David Davison,* C.E.O. and Pres.; Maria A. Falvo, C.O.O.; Sheri C. Pasqualoni,* Secy.; Gregory B. Howey,* Treas.; Carl R. Cicchetti; Marie S. Gustin; Helen E. Kenney; James McNair; James O'Rourke; John J. Patrick, Jr.; Pamela Reynolds; Laurence A. Tanner.
Number of staff: 5 full-time professional; 1 full-time support.
EIN: 300308972

1538
The Aronson Family Foundation ✧ ☆
15 Westfair Dr.
Westport, CT 06880-4161

Established in 1992 in NY.
Foundation type: Independent foundation.
Financial data (yr. ended 12/31/13): Assets, $5,870,749 (M); expenditures, $1,204,967; qualifying distributions, $1,189,567; giving activities include $1,175,287 for 10 grants (high: $714,286; low: $1).
Fields of interest: Education; Hospitals (general); Hospitals (specialty); Health organizations, association; Human services; Jewish agencies & synagogues.
Limitations: Applications not accepted. Giving primarily in NY. No grants to individuals.
Application information: Contributes only to pre-selected organizations.
Trustees: Henry W. Berinstein; Roger A. Goldman, Esq.; Dennis B. Poster.
EIN: 133693381
Selected grants: The following grants are a representative sample of this grantmaker's funding activity:

$10,000 to Cystic Fibrosis Foundation, New York, NY, 2012. For Research, Education and Providing Cures for Cystic Fibrosis.
$4,000 to Save the Chimps, Fort Pierce, FL, 2012. For animal rescue, care and veterinary services.

1539
Ramani and Louise D. Ayer Family Foundation ✧ ☆
c/o Cummings & Lockwood
P.O. Box 271820
West Hartford, CT 06127 (860) 313-4930
Contact: Paul L. Bourdeau

Established in 2001 in CT.
Donors: Ramani Ayer; Louise D. Ayer.
Foundation type: Independent foundation.
Financial data (yr. ended 11/30/13): Assets, $3,066,900 (M); expenditures, $527,987; qualifying distributions, $505,000; giving activities include $505,000 for 5 grants (high: $375,000; low: $5,000).
Fields of interest: Higher education, university; Hospitals (general); Human services, mind/body enrichment.
Limitations: Applications not accepted. Giving primarily in CT and IA.
Application information: Contributes only to pre-selected organizations.
Trustees: Louise D. Ayer; Ramani Ayer.
EIN: 066504470

1540
The Elinor Patterson Baker Foundation ✧
c/o Cummings & Lockwood LLC
P.O. Box 2505
Greenwich, CT 06836-2505
Application address: c/o Ann Panoli, BNY Mellon, N.A., 10 Mason St., Greenwich, CT 06830

Established in 1984 in CT.
Donor: Elinor Patterson Baker†.
Foundation type: Independent foundation.
Financial data (yr. ended 05/31/13): Assets, $43,963,294 (M); expenditures, $2,388,796; qualifying distributions, $1,870,000; giving activities include $1,870,000 for grants.
Purpose and activities: Giving primarily to organizations that help to care for dogs, cats, and other animals.
Fields of interest: Animal welfare; Animals/wildlife, preservation/protection.
Application information: Application form required.
Initial approach: Letter requesting application form
Deadline(s): None
Trustee: BNY Mellon, N.A.
EIN: 066276403

1541
The Baldwin Foundation ✧ ☆
c/o D. Brandrup
57 Old Post Rd., No. 2
Greenwich, CT 06830-6241

Established in 1980 in DE and NY.
Donor: Winifred B. Baldwin†.
Foundation type: Independent foundation.
Financial data (yr. ended 12/31/13): Assets, $11,758,699 (M); expenditures, $608,164; qualifying distributions, $560,370; giving activities include $430,000 for 14 grants (high: $100,000; low: $5,000).
Purpose and activities: Giving primarily for health care and education; some support also for environmental conservation and animal welfare.
Fields of interest: Elementary/secondary education; Environment, natural resources; Animals/wildlife, preservation/protection; Hospitals (general); Health care.
Type of support: General/operating support; Annual campaigns; Capital campaigns; Building/renovation; Land acquisition; Emergency funds; Matching/challenge support.
Limitations: Applications not accepted. Giving primarily in southern ME. No grants to individuals, or for scholarships.
Publications: Annual report.
Application information: Contributes only to pre-selected organizations.
Board meeting date(s): July and Aug.
Officers and Directors:* Diana B. Dunnan,* Pres.; Rev. D. Stuart Dunnan,* V.P.; Douglas M. Dunnan,* V.P.; Winifred D. Faust,* V.P.; Joan W. Trimble,* V.P.; Douglas W. Brandrup, Secy.-Treas.; Bruce B. Dunnan; John M. Dunnan; Brian W. Gregg.
Number of staff: None.
EIN: 133039728
Selected grants: The following grants are a representative sample of this grantmaker's funding activity:
$50,000 to Porter-Gaud School, Charleston, SC, 2012. For general historical society.
$40,000 to York Land Trust, York Harbor, ME, 2012. For general hospital.
$10,000 to Laudholm Trust, Wells, ME, 2012. For general animal welfare.
$10,000 to Old York Historical Society, York, ME, 2012. For general land preservation.

1542
Barnes Group Foundation Inc. ✧
123 Main St.
Bristol, CT 06010-0489 (603) 627-3870
Main URL: http://www.barnesgroupinc.com/about_foundation.php

Incorporated in 1973 in CT.
Donors: Barnes Group Inc.; Edmund Carpenter.
Foundation type: Company-sponsored foundation.
Financial data (yr. ended 12/31/13): Assets, $1,508,038 (M); gifts received, $1,100,000; expenditures, $1,216,127; qualifying distributions, $1,210,440; giving activities include $1,210,440 for 452 grants (high: $183,500; low: $50).
Purpose and activities: The foundation supports organizations involved with arts and culture, education, the environment, health, cancer, youth services, and civic affairs.
Fields of interest: Arts; Higher education; Education; Environment, natural resources; Environment, land resources; Environment; Health care; Cancer; American Red Cross; Youth, services; United Ways and Federated Giving Programs; Public affairs.
Type of support: General/operating support; Annual campaigns; Building/renovation; Employee volunteer services; Employee matching gifts; Employee-related scholarships.
Limitations: Applications accepted. Giving primarily in areas of company operations, with emphasis on CT. No grants to individuals (except for employee-related scholarships).
Application information: Application form required.
Initial approach: Proposal
Deadline(s): Mar. 1
Officers: Gregory F. Milzcik, Pres.; Thomas O. Barnes, Secy.
Directors: Dawn N. Edwards; Christopher J. Stephens, Jr.; Claudia S. Toussaint.
EIN: 237339727
Selected grants: The following grants are a representative sample of this grantmaker's funding activity:
$118,250 to Scholarship America, Saint Peter, MN, 2011.
$118,250 to Scholarship America, Saint Peter, MN, 2011.
$5,000 to National Conference for Community and Justice, Willowbrook, IL, 2011.
$2,500 to Special Olympics Connecticut, Hamden, CT, 2011.
$2,500 to United Negro College Fund, Fairfax, VA, 2011.
$2,000 to Cystic Fibrosis Foundation, Bethesda, MD, 2011.
$1,000 to University of Vermont, Burlington, VT, 2011.

1543
The Bauer Foundation ✧
206 Dudley Rd.
Wilton, CT 06897-3513

Established in 1989 in CT and GA.
Donor: George P. Bauer.
Foundation type: Independent foundation.
Financial data (yr. ended 12/31/13): Assets, $24,610,065 (M); expenditures, $4,727,216; qualifying distributions, $4,684,237; giving activities include $4,682,500 for 18 grants (high: $2,600,000; low: $5,000).
Fields of interest: Higher education; Education; Health care; Cancer; Children/youth, services; Foundations (private grantmaking).
Limitations: Applications not accepted. Giving primarily in Norwalk, CT and St. Louis, MO. No grants to individuals.
Application information: Contributes only to pre-selected organizations.
Officers: George P. Bauer, Pres.; Carol Bauer, Secy.
Board Members: Diane M. Allison; Brad Bauer; Jocelyn Bauer; Jennifer Bauer Toll.
EIN: 581861919

1544
The Beagary Charitable Trust ✧
49 Westview Dr.
Brooklyn, CT 06234-3338 (860) 779-0429
Contact: Patricia A. Morgan, Tr.

Established in 1995 in CT.
Foundation type: Independent foundation.
Financial data (yr. ended 12/31/13): Assets, $9,653,252 (M); expenditures, $839,768; qualifying distributions, $744,293; giving activities include $648,465 for 25 grants (high: $100,000; low: $1,000).
Fields of interest: Arts; Education; YM/YWCAs & YM/YWHAs.
Type of support: General/operating support.
Limitations: Applications accepted. Giving primarily in CT and MA. No grants to individuals.
Application information: Application form required.

Initial approach: Letter
Deadline(s): None
Trustee: Patricia A. Morgan.
EIN: 066419011

1545
Walter J. and Lille A. Berbecker Scholarship Fund ✧

(formerly Walter J. Berbecker and Lille A. Webb Scholarship Fund)
30 Maltbie Rd.
Newtown, CT 06470-2508
Contact: Robert A. Beer, Tr.

Established in 1988 in NY.
Foundation type: Independent foundation.
Financial data (yr. ended 02/28/13): Assets, $77,913 (M); expenditures, $443,196; qualifying distributions, $440,597; giving activities include $440,000 for 4 grants (high: $150,000; low: $95,000).
Fields of interest: Higher education; Medical research, institute; Autism research.
Limitations: Applications accepted. Giving in the U.S., with some emphasis on CT and NC. No grants to individuals.
Application information: Application form required.
Initial approach: Letter
Deadline(s): None
Trustees: Robert A. Beer; F. Brower Moffitt.
EIN: 222801843

1546
James R. and Frances H. Berger Foundation ✧ ☆

21 Marlow Ct.
Riverside, CT 06878-2614

Established in 2010 in CT.
Donors: James R. Berger; Frances H. Berger.
Foundation type: Independent foundation.
Financial data (yr. ended 12/31/13): Assets, $17,298,260 (M); expenditures, $2,328,264; qualifying distributions, $2,164,256; giving activities include $2,159,006 for 25 grants (high: $1,000,000; low: $3).
Fields of interest: Media/communications; Education; Health care.
Limitations: Applications not accepted. Giving primarily in CT and NY.
Application information: Unsolicited requests for funds not accepted.
Officers: James R. Berger, Pres.; Frances H. Berger, V.P.; James W. Berger, Secy.-Treas.
EIN: 274238729

1547
J. Walton Bissell Foundation, Inc. ✧

P.O. Box 370067
West Hartford, CT 06137-0067 (860) 586-8201
Contact: Sarah D. Anthony, Pres. and C.E.O.

Established in 1989 in CT as successor to J. Walton Bissell Foundation.
Donor: J. Walton Bissell†.
Foundation type: Independent foundation.
Financial data (yr. ended 12/31/13): Assets, $24,210,431 (M); expenditures, $1,156,137; qualifying distributions, $1,075,011; giving activities include $895,300 for 58 grants (high: $90,000; low: $3,000).
Purpose and activities: Special consideration is given by the foundation to grants relating to the abuse of children and others, the nurture of children and families, the aid of those with visual or other physical or mental disability, and the encouragement of the arts.
Fields of interest: Performing arts; Arts; Elementary/secondary education; Education; Offenders/ex-offenders, rehabilitation; Crime/violence prevention, abuse prevention; Crime/violence prevention, domestic violence; Housing/shelter, homeless; Youth development, centers/clubs; Human services; Children/youth, services; Family services; Children/youth; Youth; Disabilities, people with; Blind/visually impaired; Economically disadvantaged.
Type of support: General/operating support; Program development; Seed money.
Limitations: Applications accepted. Giving primarily in the Connecticut River Valley area, with emphasis on the greater Hartford, CT, area. Preference is given to organizations serving persons living in the city of Hartford. No grants to individuals, or for endowments or capital campaigns.
Publications: Application guidelines.
Application information: Application form required.
Initial approach: Application
Copies of proposal: 1
Deadline(s): Feb. 1, May 1, Aug. 1, and Nov. 1
Officers and Directors:* J. Danforth Anthony, Co-Pres. and Co-C.E.O.; Sarah D. Anthony, Co-Pres. and Exec. Dir.; Philip R. Reynolds,* Secy.-Treas.; Hyacinth Douglas-Bailey; Lyn G. Walker.
EIN: 061245402

1548
Bob's Discount Furniture Charitable Foundation, Inc. ✧

428 Tolland Tpke.
Manchester, CT 06042-1765
Contact: Kathryn Pianta, Charity Coord.
E-mail: info@bobscares.com; Additional tel.: (860) 233-6200; Main URL: http://bobscares.org/

Established in 1997 in CT.
Donors: Stan Adelstein; John Espinosa; Julieus Feinblum; Joseph Goodman; Lee Goodman; Rick Guyan; Roy Hester; Michael Hoffman; Burt Homonoff; Randy Jaffee; Robert Kaufman; Alan Parvizian; Gene Rosenberg; W.R. Allen Company; BH Associates; Bob's Discount Furniture of Mass., LLC; Bob's Discount Furniture, Inc.; Bob's Discount Furniture, LLC; Furniture Auctions of America; Gene Rosenberg Associates; Great American Group; Powell Company.
Foundation type: Company-sponsored foundation.
Financial data (yr. ended 12/31/12): Assets, $414,969 (M); gifts received, $624,521; expenditures, $566,245; qualifying distributions, $495,817; giving activities include $495,817 for 241 grants (high: $90,500; low: $50).
Purpose and activities: The foundation supports organizations involved with education, health, cancer, human services, and children.
Fields of interest: Elementary/secondary education; Education; Health care, clinics/centers; Health care, patient services; Health care; Cancer; Big Brothers/Big Sisters; American Red Cross; Children/youth, services; Family services; Human services; Children.
Type of support: General/operating support; Sponsorships.
Limitations: Applications accepted. Giving primarily in areas of company operations. No grants to individuals.
Publications: Application guidelines.
Application information: Letter of inquiry should be submitted on organization letterhead. Application form not required.
Initial approach: Letter of inquiry
Deadline(s): 60 days prior to need
Officers and Directors:* Robert Kaufman,* Pres.; Ilene Kaufman,* Secy.; Eugene Rosenberg.
EIN: 061475682

1549
Boehringer Ingelheim Cares Foundation, Inc. ✧

900 Ridgebury Rd.
P.O. Box 368
Ridgefield, CT 06877-0358
Contact: Frank A. Pomer Esq., V.P. and Treas.
E-mail: bicaresfoundation.rdg@boehringer-ingelheim.com; Contact for Patient Assistance Prog.: P.O. Box 66745, St. Louis, MO 63166-674555, tel.: (800) 556-8317, fax: (866) 851-2827; Main URL: http://us.boehringer-ingelheim.com/our_responsibility/grants-and-funding/charitable_donations.html

Established as a company-sponsored operating foundation in 2001 in CT.
Donors: Boehringer Ingelheim Pharmaceuticals, Inc.; Boehringer Ingelheim USA Corp.; Roxane Laboratories, Inc.
Foundation type: Operating foundation.
Financial data (yr. ended 12/31/13): Assets, $30,640,335 (M); gifts received, $178,846,508; expenditures, $183,754,391; qualifying distributions, $183,715,525; giving activities include $3,394,821 for 64 grants (high: $2,447,670; low: $25), and $176,582,189 for grants to individuals.
Purpose and activities: The foundation supports programs designed to improve access to healthcare for underserved patients, and enhance math and science education for teachers and students in underserved communities; and provides Boehringer Ingelheim pharmaceuticals to uninsured patients in need.
Fields of interest: Higher education; Education; Health care, equal rights; Health care, clinics/centers; Health care; Disasters, preparedness/services; Youth, services; Human services; United Ways and Federated Giving Programs; Science, formal/general education; Mathematics; Science; Economically disadvantaged.
Type of support: General/operating support; Equipment; Program development; Research; Employee volunteer services; Grants to individuals; Donated products; In-kind gifts.
Limitations: Applications accepted. Giving primarily in northern Fairfield County, CT; giving also to national organizations for Patient Assistance and Product Donation Program. No support for political or religious organizations. No grants for event sponsorships.
Publications: Application guidelines; Program policy statement.
Application information: Application form required.
Initial approach: Complete online eligibility quiz and application; download application form and fax or mail completed application for Patient Assistance Program

Deadline(s): None
Board meeting date(s): May and Nov.
Officers and Directors:* Paul Fonteyne,* Chair.; Lilly Ackley, Pres.; Frank A. Pomer, Esq., V.P.; Tina Clark Beamon, Esq., Secy.; Michelle Potpan, Treas.; Stefan Rinn.
EIN: 311810072

1550
The Bok Family Foundation ✧
c/o Seth L. Starr
P.O. Box 966
Canaan, CT 06018-0966

Established in 2005 in CT.
Donors: Scott L. Bok; Roxanne Bok.
Foundation type: Independent foundation.
Financial data (yr. ended 12/31/13): Assets, $54,439,101 (M); expenditures, $2,860,445; qualifying distributions, $2,680,203; giving activities include $2,677,500 for 25 grants (high: $610,000; low: $5,000).
Fields of interest: Elementary/secondary education; Higher education, university; Education; Environment, natural resources.
Limitations: Applications not accepted. Giving in the U.S., with emphasis on NY and PA. No grants to individuals.
Application information: Contributes only to pre-selected organizations.
Trustees: Elliot P. Bok; Roxanne Bok; Scott L. Bok.
EIN: 256872863

1551
The Lawrence A. Bossidy Foundation ✧ ☆
452 W. Mountain Rd.
Ridgefield, CT 06877-2926

Established in 1986 in CT.
Donors: Lawrence A. Bossidy; Larry Bossidy.
Foundation type: Independent foundation.
Financial data (yr. ended 12/31/13): Assets, $4,781,641 (M); gifts received, $2,375,320; expenditures, $2,473,211; qualifying distributions, $2,465,716; giving activities include $2,465,716 for 18 grants (high: $1,057,200; low: $1,000).
Fields of interest: Education; Cancer research; Human services; Children/youth, services.
Type of support: General/operating support.
Limitations: Applications not accepted. Giving primarily in CT and NY. No grants to individuals.
Application information: Unsolicited requests for funds not accepted.
Trustee: Lawrence A. Bossidy.
EIN: 061188527

1552
The Brightwater Fund ✧
c/o Vogel & Co.
685 Post Rd.
Darien, CT 06820-4718

Established in 2009 in NY.
Donor: The Brightwater Trust.
Foundation type: Independent foundation.
Financial data (yr. ended 06/30/13): Assets, $15,234,881 (M); expenditures, $6,010,332; qualifying distributions, $5,900,787; giving activities include $5,900,787 for 83 grants (high: $500,000; low: $1,000).
Fields of interest: Human services.
Limitations: Applications not accepted. Giving primarily in NY.
Application information: Contributes only to pre-selected organizations.
Officers and Directors:* Gloria Jarecki,* Pres.; AnnChristine Gormley, Secy.-Treas. and Admin.; Ellen B. Chandler; Donna M. C. Jarecki; Nancy Jarecki.
EIN: 271041109

1553
Bullfrogs & Butterflies Foundation ✧ ☆
30 Lost District Dr.
New Canaan, CT 06840-2004

Established in 1997 in CT.
Donor: Bruce Bottomley.
Foundation type: Independent foundation.
Financial data (yr. ended 12/31/13): Assets, $13,199,961 (M); gifts received, $1,009,775; expenditures, $464,033; qualifying distributions, $438,110; giving activities include $435,000 for 5 grants (high: $125,000; low: $25,000).
Fields of interest: Human services; Christian agencies & churches.
Type of support: General/operating support.
Limitations: Applications not accepted. Giving primarily in FL, NC, New York, NY and TN. No grants to individuals.
Application information: Contributes only to pre-selected organizations.
Officer and Director:* Bruce Bottomley,* Pres.
EIN: 066454919
Selected grants: The following grants are a representative sample of this grantmaker's funding activity:
$90,000 to Wears Valley Ranch, Sevierville, TN, 2011.
$75,000 to Samaritans Purse, Boone, NC, 2011.
$30,000 to International Justice Mission, Arlington, VA, 2011.
$25,000 to Covenant House, New York, NY, 2011.

1554
The Louis Calder Foundation
125 Elm St., Ste. 1
New Canaan, CT 06840-5420 (203) 966-8925
Contact: Holly Nuechterlein, Grant Prog. Dir.; Kayla Bettenhauser, Prog. Assoc.
FAX: (203) 966-5330;
E-mail: proposals@calderfdn.org; Main URL: http://www.louiscalderfdn.org

Trust established in 1951 in NY.
Donor: Louis Calder†.
Foundation type: Independent foundation.
Financial data (yr. ended 10/31/13): Assets, $166,483,274 (M); expenditures, $9,302,449; qualifying distributions, $8,049,011; giving activities include $7,126,367 for 65 grants (high: $375,000; low: $2,000).
Purpose and activities: To promote the scholastic development of children and youth by improving elementary and secondary education through its support of charter and parochial schools.
Fields of interest: Elementary/secondary education.
Type of support: Capital campaigns; Building/renovation; Program development; Curriculum development; Matching/challenge support.
Limitations: Giving on a national basis. No support for political organizations, private foundations, or governmental organizations. No grants to individuals; generally no support for annual funds or special events.
Publications: Application guidelines; Financial statement; Grants list; IRS Form 990 or 990-PF printed copy available upon request.
Application information: Full proposals may only be submitted if requested by the foundation. The foundation accepts the New York/ New Jersey Area Common Application Form and the New York/ New Jersey Common Report Form. The foundation has issued a RFP seeking background letters from charter and parochial schools, charter management organizations and community based organizations for initiatives to develop comprehensive content based core curriculum education programs. Please see the foundation's web site for additional information. Application form required.
Initial approach: Submit letter of inquiry on web site at www.louiscalderfdn.org
Deadline(s): None
Board meeting date(s): Monthly
Final notification: Process can take several months
Trustees: Peter D. Calder; Frank E. Shanley; JPMorgan Chase Bank, N.A.
Number of staff: 2 full-time professional; 2 full-time support.
EIN: 136015562
Selected grants: The following grants are a representative sample of this grantmaker's funding activity:
$250,000 to Core Knowledge Foundation, Charlottesville, VA, 2011. For CKLA (Core Knowledge Language Arts) Grade 3 materials development.
$250,000 to New Schools for New Orleans, New Orleans, LA, 2011. For Human Capital Investment Fund.
$250,000 to Uncommon Schools, New York, NY, 2011. For capital support for Troy Prep Charter School and Rochester Preparatory Charter School.
$200,000 to Common Core, Washington, DC, 2011. For programs, projects, and research initiatives.
$200,000 to Hope Christian Schools, Hope Lutheran School, Milwaukee, WI, 2011. For alignment of K-12 school model.
$200,000 to New Leaders for New Schools, National Office, New York, NY, 2011. For Aspiring Principals Program.
$200,000 to Seton Education Partners, San Francisco, CA, 2011. For Phaedrus and New School Initiatives.
$100,000 to Connecticut Coalition for Achievement Now, New Haven, CT, 2011. For programming support.
$100,000 to Cristo Rey Boston High School, Boston, MA, 2011. For academic program support.
$65,000 to KIPP Delta Public Schools, Helena, AR, 2011. For KIPP Delta Elementary Literacy Academy.
$60,000 to Read Alliance, New York, NY, 2011. For Summer Reading Program pilot.

1555
Cheryl Chase & Stuart Bear Family Foundation Inc. ✧ ☆
c/o Chase Enterpgoodwin Sq.
225 Asylum St., 29th Fl.
Hartford, CT 06103-1534 (860) 549-1674
Contact: John P. Redding, Secy.

Established in 2000 in CT.
Donors: Cheryl Anne Chase; Fordham Renaissance Management; The Rhoda David Chase Family Foundation; The Sandra Arnold Chase Family Foundation; David T. Chase.
Foundation type: Independent foundation.
Financial data (yr. ended 09/30/13): Assets, $2,045,065 (M); gifts received, $467,024; expenditures, $552,059; qualifying distributions, $534,464; giving activities include $533,629 for 90 grants (high: $83,333; low: $45).
Purpose and activities: Giving primarily for the arts, higher education, social services, and to Jewish organizations; funding also for health care.
Fields of interest: Museums; Museums (art); Performing arts; Performing arts centers; Arts; Higher education; Education; Health care; Human services; United Ways and Federated Giving Programs; Jewish federated giving programs; Jewish agencies & synagogues.
Limitations: Applications accepted. Giving primarily in CT, with some emphasis on Hartford. No grants to individuals.
Application information: Application form not required.
Initial approach: Proposal
Deadline(s): None
Officers and Directors:* Cheryl A. Chase, Chair. and Pres.; John P. Redding,* Secy.; David T. Chase.
EIN: 061562154
Selected grants: The following grants are a representative sample of this grantmaker's funding activity:
$50,000 to Connecticut Childrens Medical Center, Hartford, CT, 2011.
$50,000 to Connecticut Science Center, Hartford, CT, 2011.
$20,000 to University of Connecticut Foundation, Storrs, CT, 2011.
$17,000 to Jewish Federation of Greater Hartford, West Hartford, CT, 2011.
$15,000 to Foodshare, Bloomfield, CT, 2011.
$10,100 to Kingswood-Oxford School, West Hartford, CT, 2011.
$10,000 to Connecticut Public Broadcasting, Hartford, CT, 2011.
$10,000 to National Conference for Community and Justice, Windsor, CT, 2011.
$7,500 to University of Connecticut Foundation, Storrs, CT, 2011.
$5,000 to New Britain Museum of American Art, New Britain, CT, 2011.

1556
Rhoda & David Chase Family Foundation Inc. ✧
(formerly The Chase Family Foundation, Inc.)
c/o Chase Enterprises, Inc
Goodwin Sq., 225 Asylum St., 29th Fl.
Hartford, CT 06103-1534 (203) 549-1674
Contact: John P. Redding, V.P. and Dir.

Established in 1997 in CT.
Donors: Rhoda L. Chase; David T. Chase Enterprises Inc.; Chase Enterprises Holdings LLC; One Fordham Plz. LLC; Fordham Renaissance Mgmt.; RLC Investments LLC; David T. Chase.
Foundation type: Independent foundation.
Financial data (yr. ended 09/30/13): Assets, $1,784,233 (M); gifts received, $552,900; expenditures, $790,439; qualifying distributions, $782,529; giving activities include $781,739 for 110 grants (high: $140,562; low: $25).
Fields of interest: Health care; Health organizations, association; Foundations (community); Jewish agencies & synagogues.
Limitations: Applications accepted. Giving in the U.S., with emphasis on West Hartford, CT.
Application information: Application form not required.
Initial approach: Proposal
Deadline(s): None
Officers and Directors:* David T. Chase,* Pres.; Rhoda L. Chase,* V.P.; John P. Redding,* V.P.; Theresa A. Kasuga-Laliberte, Secy.
EIN: 061499922

1557
The Children's Investment Fund Foundation ✧
(formerly Cooper-Hohn Family Foundation)
c/o Day Pitney LLP
Blue Back Sq.
75 Isham Rd., Ste. 300
West Hartford, CT 06107-2237
UK address: 7 Clifford St., London, W1S 2FT, England, tel.: +44 (0) 20 3740 6100; Main URL: http://www.ciff.org

Established in 2002 in NY.
Donors: Perry Capital Corp.; The Children's Investment Fund, Ltd.; The Children's Investment Fund, LP; TCIF Fund; TCIFM UK LLP.
Foundation type: Independent foundation.
Financial data (yr. ended 12/31/12): Assets, $123,356,829 (M); expenditures, $5,704,754; qualifying distributions, $5,207,316; giving activities include $5,186,472 for 4 grants (high: $4,956,747; low: $29,725).
Purpose and activities: Support for organizations benefiting children in developing countries.
Fields of interest: Education; Environment, climate change/global warming; AIDS; Food services; Nutrition; Youth development; International development; International economic development.
International interests: Developing Countries.
Limitations: Applications not accepted. Giving on a national and international basis for the benefit of developing countries. No grants to individuals.
Application information: Contributes only to pre-selected organizations.
Officers and Trustees:* Jamie Cooper-Hohn,* Chair.; Michael Anderson, C.E.O.; Mark Dybul; Peter McDermott; Joy Phumaphi.
EIN: 043632641

1558
The Jane Coffin Childs Memorial Fund for Medical Research ✧
333 Cedar St., SHM, L300
New Haven, CT 06510 (203) 785-4612
Contact: Kim Roberts, Admin. Dir.
FAX: (203) 785-3301; E-mail: jccfund@yale.edu; E-mail for referees and sponsors with regard to the Fellowship Program: letters@jccfund.org; Main URL: http://www.jccfund.org

Established in 1937 in CT.
Donors: Alice S. Coffin†; Starling W. Childs†; John W. Childs; Merck & Co., Inc.; Agouron Institution; Torrington Area Foundation; Heiman/Fidelity Foundation; Genentech; Howard Hughes Medical Institute; Anna Fuller Fund.
Foundation type: Independent foundation.
Financial data (yr. ended 06/30/13): Assets, $53,070,898 (M); gifts received, $1,789,710; expenditures, $4,505,998; qualifying distributions, $4,217,982; giving activities include $213,682 for 1 grant, and $3,536,980 for 76 grants to individuals (high: $54,508; low: $4,000).
Purpose and activities: Giving primarily for medical research into the causes, origins and treatment of cancer. Grants to institutions only for support of cancer research fellowships.
Fields of interest: Medical research, institute; Cancer research.
Type of support: Fellowships; Research.
Limitations: Giving primarily in CA, CT, and MA; foreign nationals are funded provided they are working in a U.S. lab. No grants to individuals (except for fellowships), or for building or endowment funds, matching gifts, or general purposes; no loans.
Publications: Application guidelines; Annual report; Newsletter; Program policy statement.
Application information: Application form and requirements available on foundation web site. Application form required.
Copies of proposal: 5
Deadline(s): See foundation web site for current deadline
Board meeting date(s): Oct. or Nov. and Apr. or May
Officers and Managers:* Dr. James E. Childs,* Chair.; John W. Childs, Secy.; Hendon C. Pingeon,* Treas.; Alice Childs Anderson; Elizabeth Borden; Bronwen A. Childs; John D. Childs; Dr. Richard S. Childs, Jr.; Elisabeth Childs Gill; Brett D. Hellerman; Dr. Richard C. Levin; Gardner Mundy; Dr. Joan A. Steitz.
Number of staff: 1 full-time professional; 1 full-time support.
EIN: 066034840

1559
Rona and Jeffrey Citrin Charitable Foundation ✧ ☆
7 Dewart Rd.
Greenwich, CT 06830-3418

Established in CT.
Donor: Jeffrey Citrin.
Foundation type: Independent foundation.
Financial data (yr. ended 06/30/13): Assets, $2,288,853 (M); gifts received, $900,000; expenditures, $504,062; qualifying distributions, $487,500; giving activities include $487,500 for 6 grants (high: $300,000; low: $10,000).
Fields of interest: Higher education.
Limitations: Applications not accepted. Giving primarily in Hanover, NH; some funding also in MA and NY.
Application information: Unsolicited requests for funds not accepted.
Trustees: Jeffrey Citrin; Rona Hollander Citrin.
EIN: 203144815

Selected grants: The following grants are a representative sample of this grantmaker's funding activity:
$350,000 to Dartmouth College, Hanover, NH, 2011. For general support.
$55,000 to Cornell University, Ithaca, NY, 2011. For general support.

1560
Steven A. and Alexandra M. Cohen Foundation ✧

c/o Stephen Canna, SAC Capital Advisors
P.O. Box 142
Greenwich, CT 06832-0142 (203) 890-2302

Established in 2001 in CT.
Donors: Stephen Canna; Alexandra M. Cohen; Steven A. Cohen; Sac Capital Advisors, LLC.
Foundation type: Independent foundation.
Financial data (yr. ended 12/31/13): Assets, $283,079,949 (M); gifts received, $245,400,000; expenditures, $43,641,239; qualifying distributions, $43,575,218; giving activities include $43,548,162 for 181 grants (high: $7,651,266; low: $168).
Purpose and activities: Giving primarily to a foundation concerned with people who are economically disadvantaged; funding also for health as well as to a hospital, youth services, and social services, including a YWCA.
Fields of interest: Higher education, university; Education; Hospitals (general); Autism; Medical research; Human services; YM/YWCAs & YM/YWHAs; Youth, services; Philanthropy/voluntarism; Economically disadvantaged.
Limitations: Applications not accepted. Giving primarily in CT, NY, and RI.
Application information: Contributes only to pre-selected organizations.
Officers: Alexandra M. Cohen, Pres. and Secy.; Steven A. Cohen, V.P. and Treas.
EIN: 061627638
Selected grants: The following grants are a representative sample of this grantmaker's funding activity:
$13,350,000 to Robin Hood Foundation, New York, NY, 2012. For work to fight poverty.
$5,720,000 to Brown University, Providence, RI, 2012.
$5,639,378 to North Shore-Long Island Jewish Health System Foundation, Great Neck, NY, 2012.
$5,020,000 to New York-Presbyterian Fund, New York, NY, 2012.
$1,280,000 to Museum of Contemporary Art, Los Angeles, CA, 2012.
$50,000 to Fairfield County Community Foundation, Norwalk, CT, 2012.
$25,000 to Calvary Fund, Bronx, NY, 2012.
$25,000 to Excel Bridgeport, Bridgeport, CT, 2012.
$12,000 to School of American Ballet, New York, NY, 2012.
$5,000 to Celebrity Fight Night Foundation, Phoenix, AZ, 2012.

1561
The Common Sense Fund Inc. ✧

c/o Eric Schwartz
10 Glenville St., 1st Fl.
Greenwich, CT 06831-3680
E-mail: info@commonsensefund.org; Main URL: http://www.commonsensefund.org
Grants List: http://www.commonsensefund.org/current-grants

Established in 1983.
Donor: Seymour Schwartz.
Foundation type: Independent foundation.
Financial data (yr. ended 12/31/12): Assets, $4,565,640 (M); gifts received, $2,944,022; expenditures, $900,897; qualifying distributions, $813,000; giving activities include $813,000 for grants.
Purpose and activities: Giving primarily for the environment and for the arts.
Fields of interest: Arts; Elementary/secondary education; Environment, climate change/global warming; Environment, water resources; Environment, energy; Environment; Human services; United Ways and Federated Giving Programs; Jewish agencies & synagogues.
Limitations: Applications not accepted. No grants to individuals.
Application information: Unsolicited requests for funds not accepted.
Officers: Adlyn S. Loewenthal, Pres.; Eric Schwartz, V.P. and Treas.; Ted Loewenthal, Secy.
Trustees: Carolyn Schwartz; David Schwartz; Debra Fram.
EIN: 133157570

1562
The Community Foundation for Greater New Haven ✧

(formerly The New Haven Foundation)
70 Audubon St.
New Haven, CT 06510-9755 (203) 777-2386
Contact: William W. Ginsberg, C.E.O.
FAX: (203) 787-6584; E-mail: contactus@cfgnh.org; Main URL: http://www.cfgnh.org/
Facebook: http://www.facebook.com/pages/New-Haven-CT/The-Community-Foundation-for-Greater-New-Haven/41991835517
LinkedIn: http://www.linkedin.com/companies/community-foundation-for-greater-new-haven
RSS Feed: http://www.cfgnh.org/DesktopModules/DNNArticle/DNNArticleRSS.aspx?moduleid=895&tabid=311&categoryid=1
Twitter: http://twitter.com/CFGNH

Established in 1928 in CT by resolution and declaration of trust.
Foundation type: Community foundation.
Financial data (yr. ended 12/31/13): Assets, $434,050,752 (M); gifts received, $24,365,190; expenditures, $26,864,163; giving activities include $23,670,346 for grants.
Purpose and activities: The foundation seeks to create positive and sustainable change in Greater New Haven, CT by increasing the amount of and enhancing the impact of community philanthropy.
Fields of interest: Arts, multipurpose centers/programs; Arts, cultural/ethnic awareness; Arts; Education; Environment, beautification programs; Environment; Health care; Housing/shelter, development; Housing/shelter; Disasters, preparedness/services; Youth development; Community development, neighborhood development; Economic development; Community/economic development; Infants/toddlers; Children/youth; Children; Youth; Adults; Aging; Young adults; Disabilities, people with; Physically disabled; Blind/visually impaired; Deaf/hearing impaired; Mentally disabled; Minorities; Asians/Pacific Islanders; African Americans/Blacks; Hispanics/Latinos; Native Americans/American Indians; Women; Infants/toddlers, female; Girls; Adults, women; Young adults, female; Men; Infants/toddlers, male; Boys; Adults, men; Young adults, male; Military/veterans; Offenders/ex-offenders; Substance abusers; AIDS, people with; Single parents; Crime/abuse victims; Terminal illness, people with; Immigrants/refugees; Economically disadvantaged; Homeless; LGBTQ.
Type of support: Curriculum development; General/operating support; Continuing support; Management development/capacity building; Annual campaigns; Capital campaigns; Building/renovation; Equipment; Endowments; Emergency funds; Program development; Conferences/seminars; Film/video/radio; Publication; Seed money; Fellowships; Scholarship funds; Research; Technical assistance; Consulting services; Program evaluation; Program-related investments/loans; Matching/challenge support.
Limitations: Applications accepted. Giving primarily in greater New Haven, CT, and the lower Naugatuck River Valley. No support for religious activities. No grants to individuals (including direct scholarships), or for endowment campaigns, lobbying, previously incurred debt, deficit financing or travel.
Publications: Application guidelines; Annual report; Annual report (including application guidelines); Financial statement; Grants list; Informational brochure; Informational brochure (including application guidelines); Newsletter; Occasional report.
Application information: Visit foundation web site for application forms, guidelines, and specific deadlines. Application form required.
Initial approach: Telephone
Deadline(s): Varies
Board meeting date(s): Varies
Final notification: Within 10 days of board meeting
Officers and Directors:* William S. Colwell,* Chair.; Kica Matos,* Vice-Chair.; William W. Ginsberg, C.E.O. and Pres.; A.F. Drew Alden, Sr. V.P. and C.F.O.; Leon Bailey, Sr. V.P., Organizational Effectiveness; Christina M. Ciociola, Sr. V.P., Grantmaking and Strategy; Sarah J.H. Fabish, V.P., Grants and Scholarships; Angela Powers, Sr. V.P., Devel., Stewardship, and Donor Svcs.; Dotty Weston-Murphy, V.P., Donor and Professional Svcs.; Kalilah Brown-Dean; Emily Byrne; Alicia Caraballo; Kellyann Day; Carlton Highsmith; Howard K. Hill; Charles H. Long; James E. Ryan; Shelley Saczynski.
Trustees: Bank of America, N.A.; New Alliance Bank; The Peoples Bank; Wachovia Bank, N.A.
Number of staff: 22 full-time professional; 4 full-time support.
EIN: 066032106
Selected grants: The following grants are a representative sample of this grantmaker's funding activity:
$900,000 to Healthy Start, New Haven, New Haven, CT, 2012. For HRSA12: Eliminating Disparities in Perinatal Health.
$778,823 to Valley Community Foundation, Derby, CT, 2012. For Affiliation Agreement Appropriation.

$613,800 to New Haven Public Schools, New Haven, CT, 2012. For Accelerating Leadership Development Program.
$75,000 to Connecticut Players Foundation, Long Wharf Theatre, New Haven, CT, 2012. For general operating support.
$75,000 to Life Haven, New Haven, CT, 2012. For general operating support.
$21,858 to Bank of America Charitable Gift Fund, Providence, RI, 2012. For The Glotzbach Family Gift Fund.
$3,000 to Doctors Without Borders USA, New York, NY, 2012. For general support.
$3,000 to Operation Fuel, Hartford, CT, 2012. For infrastructure needs.
$2,000 to Saint Bernadette School, New Haven, CT, 2012. For Christina Ruggiero Forever In The Light Scholarship Fund.

1563
Community Foundation of Eastern Connecticut ✧

(formerly The Community Foundation of Southeastern Connecticut, Inc.)
68 Federal St.
P.O. Box 769
New London, CT 06320-6302 (860) 442-3572
FAX: (860) 442-0584; E-mail: bmorgan@cfect.org; Main URL: http://www.cfect.org
Facebook: https://www.facebook.com/pages/Community-Foundation-of-Eastern-Connecticut/196829230501210
Twitter: https://twitter.com/cfectnews
Scholarship inquiry e-mail: jennob@cfect.org

Established in 1982 in CT.
Donors: J. Martin Leatherman†; Beatrice G. McEwen†; Dorothy Morgan†; Jim Smith; Linda Korolkiewicz†; Priscilla Hodges†; Marjorie Stanton†; Smith Memorial Fund; Edmund O'Brien†; Eleanor Norman; members of the White Family.
Foundation type: Community foundation.
Financial data (yr. ended 12/31/13): Assets, $51,695,447 (M); gifts received, $4,921,054; expenditures, $4,611,601; giving activities include $3,132,969 for 146+ grants, and $357,130 for 224 grants to individuals.
Purpose and activities: The foundation seeks to transform our region into a more vital, caring community, through a number of strategies in pursuit of this goal. Among them are those that focus on grants, scholarships and other resources that serve our partners, the nonprofit agencies and organizations that enrich the local community.
Fields of interest: Arts; Libraries/library science; Education; Environment, natural resources; Environment; Animal welfare; Health care; Substance abuse, services; Mental health/crisis services; Children/youth, services; Family services; Aging, centers/services; Women, centers/services; Human services; Community/economic development; Voluntarism promotion; Children/youth; Children; Youth; Adults; Aging; Disabilities, people with; Mentally disabled; Minorities; Women; Substance abusers; AIDS, people with; Economically disadvantaged; Homeless.
Type of support: General/operating support; Management development/capacity building; Building/renovation; Equipment; Emergency funds; Program development; Scholarship funds; Technical assistance; Consulting services; Scholarships—to individuals.
Limitations: Applications accepted. Giving limited to Eastern CT: Ashford, Bozrah, Brooklyn, Canterbury, Chaplin, Colchester, Columbia, Coventry, Eastford, East Lyme, Franklin, Griswold, Groton, Hampton, Killingly, Lebanon, Ledyard, Lisbon, Lyme, Mansfield, Montville, New London, North Stonington, Norwich, Old Lyme, Plainfield, Pomfret, Preston, Putnam, Salem, Scotland, Sprague, Stafford, Sterling, Stonington, Thompson, Union, Voluntown, Waterford, Willington, Windham, and Woodstock. No support for sectarian or religious programs. No grants to individuals (except for scholarships), or for fundraising events, or endowment, memorial, or building funds, deficit financing, annual campaigns, or debt retirement; no loans.
Publications: Application guidelines; Annual report; Annual report (including application guidelines); Financial statement; Grants list; Informational brochure; Newsletter; Occasional report; IRS Form 990 or 990-PF printed copy available upon request.
Application information: Visit foundation web site for application form and guidelines. The Connecticut Common Grant Application Form may be submitted in lieu of the foundation's application form. Application form required.
Initial approach: Telephone or e-mail
Copies of proposal: 2
Deadline(s): Nov. 15 for general grants; varies for others
Board meeting date(s): Jan., Mar., Apr., May, June, Sept., and Nov.
Final notification: General grants are distributed in Mar.
Officers and Trustees:* Paul Nunes,* Chair.; Susan Pochal,* Vice-Chair.; Maryam Elahi,* C.E.O. and Pres.; Alison Woods,* V.P. and C.O.O.; Valerie Grimm,* Secy.; Ruth Crocker,* Treas.; Frederic Anderson; Thomas Borner; Theresa Broach; Brian Carey; Sam Childs; John Duggan; Elizabeth Kuszaj; John LaMattina; Stephen Larcen; Marcia Marien; Dyanne Rafal; Mary Seidner; Lee Ellen Terry; Claire Warren, M.D.; Dianne E. Williams.
Number of staff: 6 full-time professional; 2 part-time support.
EIN: 061080097

1564
Community Foundation of Greater New Britain ✧

(formerly New Britain Foundation for Public Giving)
74A Vine St.
New Britain, CT 06052-1431 (860) 229-6018
Contact: James G. Williamson, Pres.; For grants: Joeline Wruck, Dir., Progs.
FAX: (860) 225-2666; E-mail: info@cfgnb.org; Grant inquiry e-mail: jwruck@cfgnb.org; Main URL: http://www.cfgnb.org
E-Newsletter: http://www.cfgnb.org/EmailSignup/tabid/77/Default.aspx

Established in 1941 in CT.
Foundation type: Community foundation.
Financial data (yr. ended 12/31/13): Assets, $44,652,863 (M); gifts received, $2,881,243; expenditures, $2,155,030; giving activities include $734,323 for grants, and $173,057 for grants to individuals.
Purpose and activities: The foundation seeks to meet the needs of the greater New Britain, CT, community through support of programs dedicated to health and human services, education, community and economic development, the environment, arts and humanities, and civic affairs.
Fields of interest: Humanities; Arts; Child development, education; Secondary school/education; Libraries/library science; Education; Environment; Hospitals (general); Reproductive health, family planning; Health care; Substance abuse, services; Mental health/crisis services; Health organizations, association; Crime/violence prevention, domestic violence; Youth development, services; Children/youth, services; Child development, services; Family services; Aging, centers/services; Homeless, human services; Human services; Economic development; Community/economic development; Leadership development; General charitable giving; Infants/toddlers; Children/youth; Youth; Adults; Aging; Disabilities, people with; Economically disadvantaged.
Type of support: General/operating support; Continuing support; Capital campaigns; Building/renovation; Equipment; Emergency funds; Program development; Seed money; Curriculum development; Research; Technical assistance; Consulting services; Program evaluation; Scholarships—to individuals; Matching/challenge support.
Limitations: Applications accepted. Giving limited to Berlin, New Britain, Plainville, and Southington, CT. No support for sectarian or religious activities. No grants to individuals (except for scholarships), or for annual or endowment campaigns, previously incurred expenses, sponsorships or fundraisers, performances or one-time events, conferences, advertising, or school-sponsored field trips or student trips for cultural, academic, enrichment or competitive purposes.
Publications: Application guidelines; Annual report; Financial statement; Grants list; Informational brochure; Newsletter.
Application information: Visit foundation web site for application guidelines per grant type. Submitted Letters of Intent will be reviewed by staff and selected applicants will be contacted directly to submit a complete, formal application. Application form not required.
Initial approach: Letter of Intent
Copies of proposal: 15
Deadline(s): Feb. 15, June 15, and Oct. 15
Board meeting date(s): Feb., Mar., June, Sept., and Dec.
Officers and Directors:* J. Leo Gagne,* Chair.; Laurence A. Tanner,* Vice-Chair. and Chair.-Elect; James G. Williamson,* Pres.; Robert S. Trojanowski,* V.P. Opers.; James G. Williamson,* Secy.; Mark Bernacki; Cori Humes; Rebecca Karabim-Ahern; Dr. John Miller; Marc S. Pelletier; Paul G. Salina; The Rev. Victoria Triano; Patricia M. Walden; Paul Zagorsky, Esq.; and 6 additional directors.
Number of staff: 4 full-time professional; 1 part-time professional; 2 part-time support.
EIN: 066036461

1565
The Community Foundation of Northwest Connecticut, Inc. ☆
(formerly Northwest Connecticut Community Foundation, Inc.)
32 City Hall Ave.
P.O. Box 1144
Torrington, CT 06790 (860) 626-1245
FAX: (860) 489-7517; E-mail: info@cfnwct.org; Main URL: http://www.cfnwct.org
Facebook: http://www.facebook.com/pages/The-Community-Foundation-of-Northwest-Connecticut/475663995816447?fref=ts/
RSS Feed: https://cfnwct.org/rss-feed-instructions

Established in 1970 in CT; Incorporated in 1999 in CT under Northwest Connecticut Community Foundation, Inc.
Donors: Carlton D. Fyler†; Jenny R. Fyler†; Robert Venn Carr; John H. Brooks†; Margaret C. Tupper†; Eva Coty†; Vincent Stanulis†; BankBoston, N.A. Fund; B.O.A.T. Fund; Brooks Bank Fund; First National Bank of Litchfield Fund; Torrington Savings Bank; Marion Wm. Edwards†; Alice Edwards†.
Foundation type: Community foundation.
Financial data (yr. ended 12/31/13): Assets, $80,715,242 (M); gifts received, $1,336,492; expenditures, $3,401,463; giving activities include $2,858,397 for grants.
Purpose and activities: The foundation seeks to enhance the quality of life for the citizens of its service area by: 1) identifying community needs and opportunities with a focus on the arts, education, the environment, health and social services; 2) responding to those needs and opportunities with grants to nonprofit 501(c)(3) organizations in an informed and responsible way; 3) providing financial assistance for higher education in the form of scholarships; 4) providing donors with a permanent endowment for philanthropic giving; and 5) prudently investing those funds entrusted to it.
Fields of interest: Museums; Performing arts; Historic preservation/historical societies; Arts; Higher education; Libraries/library science; Education; Environment; Animal welfare; Hospitals (general); Health care; Mental health/crisis services; Housing/shelter; Recreation, parks/playgrounds; Recreation; Children/youth, services; Human services, emergency aid; Aging, centers/services; Human services; Community/economic development.
Type of support: Consulting services; Capital campaigns; Building/renovation; General/operating support; Continuing support; Equipment; Endowments; Emergency funds; Program development; Publication; Seed money; Scholarship funds; Technical assistance; Scholarships—to individuals; Matching/challenge support.
Limitations: Applications accepted. Giving limited to the Barkhamsted, Bethlehem, Colebrook, Cornwall, Falls Village, Goshen, Hartland, Harwinton, Kent, Litchfield, Morris, New Hartford, Norfolk, North Canaan, Salisbury, Sharon, Torrington, Warren, Washington, and Winsted, CT, areas. No support for parochial, religious, or public schools for programs that should be part of their operating budget, or for religious doctrine. No grants for individuals (except for scholarships), or for membership or affiliation campaigns, debt retirement, endowments, re-granting programs, retroactive funding, or event sponsorships.
Publications: Application guidelines; Annual report; Financial statement; Informational brochure; Informational brochure (including application guidelines); Newsletter; Occasional report.
Application information: Visit foundation web site for application form and guidelines. Faxed applications are not accepted. Application form required.
Initial approach: Submit application
Copies of proposal: 19
Deadline(s): Jan. 30, Apr. 30, and Sept. 30 for competitive cycle grants; Apr. 1 for scholarships
Board meeting date(s): Monthly (except July and December)
Final notification: End of Mar., June, and Nov.
Officers and Directors:* Tom Bechtle,* Chair.; Douglas K. O'Connell,* Vice-Chair.; Gayle Moraski,* 2nd Vice-Chair.; Guy Rovezzi,* Pres. and C.E.O.; Brad Hoar,* V.P., Philanthropic Svcs.; Alyson Thomson,* Secy.; Roberta Lee August,* Recording Secy.; Victoria Patrick,* Treas.; Anita Baxter; Jim Blackketter; Miki Duisterhof; Dan Dwyer; William Giles Harding; Jeffrey Lalonde; F. Robert Petricone; Norman E. Rogers; Ronald S. Rosenstein; Christopher G. Wall.
Trustee Banks: First National Bank of Litchfield; Bank of America, N.A.; Torrington Savings Bank.
Number of staff: 3 full-time professional; 3 part-time professional; 1 part-time support.
EIN: 061565733

1566
The Connecticut Community Foundation ✧
(formerly The Waterbury Foundation)
43 Field St.
Waterbury, CT 06702-1906 (203) 753-1315
Contact: For grants and scholarships: Josh Carey, Dir., Grants Mgmt.
FAX: (203) 756-3054; E-mail: info@conncf.org; Grant inquiry e-mail: grants@conncf.org; Main URL: http://conncf.org
Facebook: https://www.facebook.com/conncf.org
Grants List: http://www.conncf.org/nonprofits/our-grants/
LinkedIn: http://www.linkedin.com/companies/ct-community-foundation
Twitter: https://twitter.com/CCF1923
YouTube: http://www.youtube.com/user/conncf
Scholarship inquiry e-mail: scholarships@conncf.org

Incorporated in 1923 by special Act of the CT Legislature.
Donors: Katherine Pomeroy†; Edith Chase†.
Foundation type: Community foundation.
Financial data (yr. ended 12/31/13): Assets, $92,717,899 (M); gifts received, $4,119,294; expenditures, $5,077,852; giving activities include $2,758,027 for 120+ grants (high: $157,993), and $690,757 for 142 grants to individuals.
Purpose and activities: The foundation serves the people of Central Naugatuck Valley and Litchfield Hills to improve the quality of life by: 1) giving grants, scholarships, and organizational support to address the changing needs of the community; 2) helping donors create a legacy for the future through a permanent endowment fund; 3) promoting informed philanthropy and volunteerism to increase charitable resources for the region; and 4) providing leadership and building partnerships to identify and solve community concerns.
Fields of interest: Humanities; Historic preservation/historical societies; Arts; Education, early childhood education; Child development, education; Secondary school/education; Vocational education; Higher education; Adult/continuing education; Education; Health care; Substance abuse, services; Mental health/crisis services; Health organizations, association; Heart & circulatory diseases; AIDS; Employment; Housing/shelter, development; Recreation; Children/youth, services; Child development, services; Family services; Residential/custodial care, hospices; Aging, centers/services; Homeless, human services; Human services; Economic development; Community/economic development; Children/youth; Youth; Aging; Young adults; Disabilities, people with; Mentally disabled; Minorities; Hispanics/Latinos; Women; Economically disadvantaged; Homeless.
Type of support: Program evaluation; Management development/capacity building; Capital campaigns; Building/renovation; Equipment; Program development; Conferences/seminars; Publication; Seed money; Curriculum development; Scholarship funds; Research; Technical assistance; Consulting services; Scholarships—to individuals; Matching/challenge support.
Limitations: Applications accepted. Giving limited to Beacon Falls, Bethlehem, Bridgewater, Cheshire, Goshen, Litchfield, Middlebury, Morris, Naugatuck, New Milford, Oxford, Prospect, Roxbury, Southbury, Thomaston, Warren, Washington, Waterbury, Watertown, Wolcott, or Woodbury, CT. No support for sectarian or religious purposes. No grants to individuals (except for college scholarships), or for general operating support, capital campaigns for endowments, previously incurred expenses, capital/equipment for public agencies, schools or churches, or fundraising by one agency on behalf of another; no loans.
Publications: Application guidelines; Annual report; Informational brochure; Newsletter; Occasional report.
Application information: Visit foundation web site for application guidelines. Application form required.
Initial approach: E-mail application
Copies of proposal: 1
Deadline(s): Feb. 1 and Oct. 1 for General Grant Program; varies for others
Board meeting date(s): Mar. and Nov.; grants committee meets prior to each board meeting
Final notification: Within 10 weeks for full grant application
Officers and Trustees:* Jack Baker,* Chair.; Margaret W. Field,* Vice-Chair.; Paula Van Ness,* C.E.O. and Pres.; Ann Merriam Feiberg,* V.P.; Wayne P. McCormack,* Secy.; Charles J. Boulier, III*, Treas.; Robert Bailey; Daniel L. Bedard, C.P.A.; Martha Bernstein; Daniel Caron; Craig Carragan; Anne Delo; Michelle Fica; Brian Henebry; Richard E. Lau; John T. McCarthy; John Michaels; Elner Morrell; David Pelletier, C.P.A.; Antonio Paulo Pinto; Edith Reynolds; Carolyn E. Setlow; Anne Slattery.
Number of staff: 9 full-time professional; 2 part-time professional; 9 full-time support.
EIN: 066038074

1567
Connecticut Health Foundation, Inc.
100 Pearl St.
Hartford, CT 06103-4506 (860) 724-1580
Contact: Rochel Lantz, Cont.
FAX: (860) 724-1589; E-mail: info@cthealth.org; E-mail for Carol Pollack: carol@cthealth.org; e-mail for Patricia Baker: Pat@cthealth.org; e-mail for Lina

Paredes: lina@cthealth.org; Main URL: http://www.cthealth.org
Connecticut Health Foundation's Philanthropy Promise: http://www.ncrp.org/philanthropys-promise/who
E-Newsletter: http://visitor.r20.constantcontact.com/manage/optin?v=001-COKnEtb87dgcSfrJ_d2S8q2MgdJz9o_
Facebook: http://www.facebook.com/CTHealth
Twitter: http://twitter.com/cthealth

Established in 2000 in CT; converted in 1999 from Connecticare Health Plan.
Foundation type: Independent foundation.
Financial data (yr. ended 12/31/13): Assets, $112,680,825 (M); expenditures, $6,554,262; qualifying distributions, $5,985,834; giving activities include $2,776,817 for grants.
Purpose and activities: The foundation focuses on helping more people of color gain better access to quality health care through grant making and policy development. The foundation's approach to expanding health equity involves leveraging its resources and relationships to: 1) Help people get enrolled in affordable health insurance; 2) help them to navigate the health system; 3) transform delivery systems to provide more care that is more comprehensive, affordable and accountable.
Fields of interest: Health care, equal rights; Dental care; Health care; Mental health, treatment; Children/youth, services; Infants/toddlers; Children/youth; Children; Youth; Adults; Mentally disabled; Minorities; African Americans/Blacks; Hispanics/Latinos; Native Americans/American Indians; Economically disadvantaged.
Type of support: General/operating support; Management development/capacity building; Program development; Conferences/seminars; Research; Technical assistance; Consulting services; Program evaluation.
Limitations: Applications accepted. Giving limited to CT. No grants to individuals, or for construction, alteration or maintenance of buildings, capital projects, endowments, or chairs associated with universities and medical schools, billable services or lobbying.
Publications: Annual report (including application guidelines); Financial statement; Grants list; Informational brochure; Newsletter.
Application information: Application guidelines and forms available on foundation web site. The foundation will announce requests for proposals (RFP). Application form for unsolicited grant proposals available on foundation web site. Application form required.
Initial approach: Concept paper
Deadline(s): As announced/quarterly on web-site
Board meeting date(s): Quarterly
Final notification: Within 2 weeks following the board meeting
Officers and Directors:* Sanford Cloud, Jr.*, Chair.; Patricia Baker, Chair., Progs.; Gregory B. Butler, J.D., Chair., Governance; Martin "Marty" Gavin, Vice-Chair., Finance; Harold Rives III, Vice-Chair., Finance; Lina Paredes, V.P., Progs.; Carol Pollack, V.P., Finance and Opers.; Marilyn Alverio,* Secy.; Rochel Lantz, Cont.; Tina Brown-Stevenson; J.C. David Hadden; Steven J. Huleatt; Robert Krzys; David I. Newton; Elaine O'Keefe; Robert M. Schreibman, DMD; Todd D. Shepard; Margarita V. Torres; Victor Villagra, M.D.
Number of staff: 9 full-time professional; 1 part-time professional; 1 full-time support; 1 part-time support.
EIN: 061057387
Selected grants: The following grants are a representative sample of this grantmaker's funding activity:
$200,000 to Connecticut Voices for Children, New Haven, CT, 2012. For general operating support.
$150,000 to Connecticut Juvenile Justice Alliance, Bridgeport, CT, 2012. To increase early identification and intervention for children ages 6 thru 14 with mental health needs in Connecticut.
$100,000 to Connecticut Association of School-Based Health Centers, East Hartford, CT, 2012. For general operating support.
$85,151 to Saint Francis Hospital and Medical Center, Hartford, CT, 2012. For education component for providers and pregnant women and integrated system of dental screening and referral based oral health care for pregnant patients at hospital.
$75,000 to Connecticut State Medical Society, New Haven, CT, 2012. To increase leadership, strategic partnerships and physician engagement and educations to reduce racial and ethnic health disparities in Connecticut.
$50,000 to Connecticut, State of, Office of Health Reform and Innovation, Hartford, CT, 2012. For Health Equity Learning Collaborative include research and planning of All-Payer Claims Database.
$50,000 to National Alliance on Mental Illness Connecticut, Hartford, CT, 2012. For Keep the Promise Children's Coalition to advocate policies and support early identification and intervention for children 6 thru 14 with mental health needs including addressing racial and ethnic health disparities.

1568
The Daphne Seybolt Culpeper Memorial Foundation, Inc. ✧
129 Musket Ridge Rd.
Norwalk, CT 06850-1315 (203) 762-3984
Application address: c/o Amy Bloom, Secy.-Treas., P.O. Box 206, Norwalk, CT 06852-0206

Established in 1983 in DE.
Donor: Daphne Seybolt Culpeper‡.
Foundation type: Independent foundation.
Financial data (yr. ended 12/31/13): Assets, $18,203,261 (M); expenditures, $1,394,045; qualifying distributions, $1,352,830; giving activities include $1,122,670 for 125 grants (high: $75,000; low: $400).
Purpose and activities: Giving primarily for education, health care and human services.
Fields of interest: Higher education; Medical school/education; Nursing school/education; Education; Hospitals (general); Health care; Health organizations, association; Crime/violence prevention, domestic violence; Food services; Human services; Children/youth, services; Residential/custodial care, hospices; Disabilities, people with; Minorities; Native Americans/American Indians; Women; Economically disadvantaged; Homeless.
Type of support: General/operating support; Continuing support; Annual campaigns; Capital campaigns; Building/renovation; Equipment; Program development; Scholarship funds; Matching/challenge support.
Limitations: Applications accepted. Giving limited to Fairfield County, CT and Palm Beach County, FL. No support for political organizations. No grants to individuals, or for endowments, forums, conferences, seminars, gratuities, honorariums, travel, meals or lodging; no loans.
Publications: Application guidelines.
Application information: Application form not required.
Initial approach: Letter
Copies of proposal: 1
Deadline(s): None
Board meeting date(s): Varies
Officers and Trustees:* Rodney S. Eielson,* Pres.; Amy Bloom,* Secy.-Treas.; Lori G. Brayton,* Secy.-Treas.
Number of staff: 1 full-time professional; 1 full-time support.
EIN: 222478755

1569
Dalio Foundation, Inc. ✧
(formerly Dalio Family Foundation, Inc.)
1 Glendinning Pl.
Westport, CT 06880-1242 (203) 291-5130
Raymond and Barbara Dalio's Giving Pledge Profile: http://glasspockets.org/philanthropy-in-focus/eye-on-the-giving-pledge/profiles/dalio

Established in 2003 in CT.
Donor: Raymond T. Dalio.
Foundation type: Independent foundation.
Financial data (yr. ended 12/31/12): Assets, $590,509,728 (M); gifts received, $223,059,351; expenditures, $30,725,270; qualifying distributions, $30,133,495; giving activities include $29,029,942 for 346 grants (high: $2,832,500; low: $470), $106,544 for foundation-administered programs and $80,723 for 1 loan/program-related investment.
Fields of interest: Elementary/secondary education; Higher education; Health organizations, association; Human services.
Type of support: Program-related investments/loans.
Limitations: Applications not accepted. Giving primarily in CT, MA, NY, and Washington DC, with some giving in FL and NC. No grants to individuals.
Application information: Contributes only to pre-selected organizations.
Officers and Directors:* Raymond T. Dalio,* Pres.; Devon Dalio,* V.P.; Matthew Dalio,* V.P.; Barbara Dalio.
EIN: 431965846
Selected grants: The following grants are a representative sample of this grantmaker's funding activity:
$2,832,500 to David Lynch Foundation, Fairfield, IA, 2012. For general operations.
$1,500,000 to Johns Hopkins University, Baltimore, MD, 2012. To support the Whole Genome Associate for Bipolar Disorders.
$1,200,000 to Marymount College, Rancho Palos Verdes, CA, 2012. To fund the Utilities Upgrade portion of Phase I of the Campus Master Plan.
$1,110,000 to Grameen Research, Woburn, MA, 2012. For general operations.
$1,010,000 to National Philanthropic Trust, Jenkintown, PA, 2012. For general operations.
$1,000,000 to American Red Cross National Headquarters, Washington, DC, 2012. For the Hurricane Sandy Relief Fund.

$1,000,000 to New York-Presbyterian Fund, New York, NY, 2012. For support of the highest clinical priorities at the discretion of James Bussell, MD.
$1,000,000 to W E T A-Greater Washington Educational Telecommunications Association, Arlington, VA, 2012. For the Better Angels Society in support of the work of Ken Burns.
$10,000 to New York Public Library, New York, NY, 2012. For general operations.
$10,000 to Opportunity, Inc., West Palm Beach, FL, 2012. For general operations.

1570
The Daniell Family Foundation Inc. ✧
c/o Claudia Jacques-Soto, Capital Strategies
2 Barnard Ln.
Bloomfield, CT 06002-2410

Established in 1992 in CT.
Donors: Barbara E. Daniell; Robert F. Daniell.
Foundation type: Independent foundation.
Financial data (yr. ended 12/31/13): Assets, $23,935,711 (M); gifts received, $10,276; expenditures, $903,276; qualifying distributions, $893,000; giving activities include $893,000 for 52 grants (high: $550,000; low: $500).
Fields of interest: Performing arts, music; Higher education; Education; Hospitals (general); Health organizations; Human services; Children/youth, services; Christian agencies & churches.
Limitations: Applications not accepted. Giving primarily in CT and NH. No grants to individuals.
Application information: Contributes only to pre-selected organizations.
Officers and Directors:* Barbara E. Daniell,* Pres.; Robert F. Daniell,* Secy.; Holly D. Miller.
EIN: 061356015
Selected grants: The following grants are a representative sample of this grantmaker's funding activity:
$1,000 to American Cancer Society, Atlanta, GA, 2011.
$1,000 to Scleroderma Foundation, Danvers, MA, 2011.

1571
The Ellen and Gary Davis Foundation ✧
45 Pecksland Rd.
Greenwich, CT 06831-3711

Established in 1992 in CT.
Donors: Gary S. Davis; Ellen Davis; Bradford Klein; Chester Square Partners LP.
Foundation type: Independent foundation.
Financial data (yr. ended 12/31/12): Assets, $4,717,103 (M); gifts received, $519,915; expenditures, $772,949; qualifying distributions, $737,974; giving activities include $737,974 for grants.
Purpose and activities: Giving primarily for education; funding also for health organizations, the arts, social services, and Jewish organizations.
Fields of interest: Arts; Elementary/secondary education; Higher education; Education; Hospitals (general); Health organizations, association; Human services; Jewish federated giving programs.
Limitations: Applications not accepted. Giving primarily in NY, some funding also in PA. No grants to individuals.
Application information: Unsolicited requests for funds not accepted.
Trustees: Richard J. Bronstein; Ellen Davis; Gary Davis.
EIN: 061357318

1572
Deloitte Foundation ✧
(formerly Deloitte & Touche Foundation)
10 Westport Rd.
P.O. Box 820
Wilton, CT 06897-0820
Contact for Doctoral Fellowship Program: Peg Levine, tel.: (203) 761-3413, e-mail: plevine@deloitte.com; Main URL: http://www.deloitte.com/us/df
AAA/Deloitte Wildman Medal Recipients: http://aaahq.org/awards/wildmanhistory.htm#Winners
Doctoral Fellowships Recipients: http://www.deloitte.com/view/en_US/us/press/Press-Releases/bb5b649227024410VgnVCM2000003356f70aRCRD.htm

Incorporated in 1928 in NY.
Donors: Deloitte LLP; Deloitte Haskins & Sells; Deloitte & Touche LLP; Charles Stewart Ludlam†; Charles C. Croggon†; Weldon Powell†; Deloitte & Touche USA LLP; Wayne Williamson.
Foundation type: Company-sponsored foundation.
Financial data (yr. ended 06/01/13): Assets, $15,245,101 (M); gifts received, $7,388,553; expenditures, $7,604,007; qualifying distributions, $7,597,770; giving activities include $2,486,948 for 24 grants (high: $400,000; low: $1,037), and $5,037,373 for 391 employee matching gifts.
Purpose and activities: The foundation supports educational programs designed to promote excellence in teaching, research, and curriculum innovation; and awards fellowships to doctoral accounting students.
Fields of interest: Higher education; Business school/education; Education.
Type of support: Conferences/seminars; Professorships; Curriculum development; Fellowships; Scholarship funds; Research; Sponsorships; Employee matching gifts.
Limitations: Applications accepted. Giving primarily in Washington, DC, FL, IL, KS, TX, and VA; giving on a national basis for fellowships. No grants for general operating support, capital campaigns, special programs, or publications; no loans; no matching support.
Publications: Application guidelines; Grants list; Informational brochure.
Application information: An application form is required for Doctoral Fellowships.
Initial approach: Contact foundation or accounting department head at educational institution for application form for Doctoral Fellowships
Copies of proposal: 1
Deadline(s): Oct. 15 for Doctoral Fellowships
Board meeting date(s): 3 times per year
Final notification: Jan. for Doctoral Fellowships
Officers and Directors:* Punit Renjen, Chair.; Carol Lindstrom, Pres.; Jennifer Steinmann, Secy.-Treas.; Nathan Andrews; Philip Brunson; Amy Chronis; Leslie Knowlton; Adi Padha; Sandra Shirai; John Sizer; Sylvia Smyth.
EIN: 136400341

1573
The Frederick A. DeLuca Foundation, Inc. ✧ ☆
300 Bic Dr.
Milford, CT 06461-3055 (203) 877-4281
Contact: Janice Szabo
E-mail: delucafoundation@subway.com

Established in 1997.
Donor: Frederick A. DeLuca.
Foundation type: Independent foundation.
Financial data (yr. ended 12/31/13): Assets, $1,838,804 (M); gifts received, $759,305; expenditures, $431,856; qualifying distributions, $424,448; giving activities include $423,000 for 2 grants (high: $273,000; low: $150,000).
Fields of interest: Arts; Elementary/secondary education; Athletics/sports, school programs; Youth.
Type of support: General/operating support.
Limitations: Applications accepted. Giving primarily in CT, OH and OK.
Application information: For an application form email: delucafoundation@subway.com. Application form required.
Initial approach: Letter and Email.
Deadline(s): Oct. 8
Officers and Driectors:* Elizabeth DeLuca,* Pres.; Jonathan DeLuca,* Secy.-Treas.; Frederick A. DeLuca.
EIN: 650755554

1574
The Diebold Foundation, Inc. ✧
102 Painter Hill Rd.
Roxbury, CT 06783-1102

Established in 2000 in CT.
Foundation type: Independent foundation.
Financial data (yr. ended 12/31/13): Assets, $31,417,587 (M); expenditures, $1,632,754; qualifying distributions, $1,456,533; giving activities include $962,260 for 20 grants (high: $250,000; low: $2,750).
Purpose and activities: Giving primarily for education, human services, including the Boy Scouts, hospitals, and to farm organizations.
Fields of interest: Arts; Higher education; Education; Hospitals (general); Agriculture, farm bureaus/granges; Boy scouts; Human services.
Limitations: Applications not accepted. Giving primarily in CT; some giving in New York, NY. Generally, no support for Christian organizations. No grants to individuals.
Application information: Contributes only to pre-selected organizations.
Directors: Caitlin Diebold; Dudley Diebold; Honoria Diebold; Daphne Stoughton.
EIN: 311681649

1575
The Donaghue Foundation ✧
(also known as The Patrick and Catherine Weldon Donaghue Medical Research Foundation)
18 N. Main St.
West Hartford, CT 06107-1919 (860) 521-9011
Contact: Lynne Garner, Pres. and Tr.

FAX: (860) 521-9018; E-mail: office@donaghue.org; E-mail for letters of intent: r3@donaghue.org; Main URL: http://www.donaghue.org
Facebook: https://www.facebook.com/TheDonaghueFoundation
RSS Feed: http://donaghue.org/feed/
Twitter: https://twitter.com/DonaghueFnd
YouTube: http://www.youtube.com/user/donaghue18?feature=guide

Established in 1991 in CT.
Donor: Ethel F. Donaghue†.
Foundation type: Independent foundation.
Financial data (yr. ended 12/31/13): Assets, $69,209,336 (M); expenditures, $3,156,352; qualifying distributions, $2,834,890; giving activities include $2,051,989 for 26 grants (high: $220,000; low: $1,000), and $57,080 for 4 foundation-administered programs.
Purpose and activities: Support for medical and health-related research including epidemiological, community health, and health services research academic, and other health-related institutions. The foundation is particularly interested in understanding the process by which knowledge from research is adopted in to practice or policy.
Fields of interest: Education; Medical research, institute.
Type of support: Research.
Limitations: Applications accepted. Giving primarily in CT.
Publications: Application guidelines; Annual report; Financial statement; Newsletter.
Application information: Only the foundation's R3 Making Research Relevant & Ready program is currently open to new submissions from past foundation grantees. Specific letter of intent guidelines available on foundation web site. Currently, the foundation is not accepting applications for the clinical and community Health Issues program. Check web site for updates in this area. Application form required.
Initial approach: Letter of intent (on applicant's letterhead, and not exceeding 2 pages) via e-mail
Deadline(s): See foundation web site for current deadlines
Officers and Trustees:* Lynne Garner, Ph.D.*, Pres.; Nancy Yedlin, V.P.; Bank of America, N.A.
Number of staff: 4 full-time professional.
EIN: 066348275
Selected grants: The following grants are a representative sample of this grantmaker's funding activity:
$100,000 to Myelin Repair Foundation, Saratoga, CA, 2012. For Myelin Repair Foundation.
$50,000 to Swarthmore College, Swarthmore, PA, 2012. For Behavioral Economics to Perplexing Problems in Health and Health Care Initiative.
$50,000 to University of Pennsylvania, Philadelphia, PA, 2012. For Using Behavioral Economics to Promote Medication Adherence and Habit for Formation.
$17,000 to Connecticut Council for Philanthropy, Hartford, CT, 2012. For Ct Health Care Survey.

1576
Richard Davoud Donchian Foundation, Inc. ✧
(formerly Richard D. Donchian Charitable Foundation, Inc.)
c/o Foundation Services, LLP
640 W. Putnam Ave., 3rd Fl.
Greenwich, CT 06830-6008
E-mail: rdd@fsllc.net; Main URL: http://www.rddonchian.org

Established in 1991 in CT; reincorporated in 1998.
Donor: Richard D. Donchian†.
Foundation type: Independent foundation.
Financial data (yr. ended 12/31/13): Assets, $9,841,305 (M); expenditures, $616,158; qualifying distributions, $515,940; giving activities include $423,500 for 59 grants (high: $50,000; low: $500).
Purpose and activities: The foundation focuses its grantmaking in four key areas: 1) Literacy & Education; 2) Humanitarian Efforts; 3) Health; and 4) Ethics and Personal Development.
Fields of interest: Adult/continuing education; Education; Health care; Employment, ethics; Employment; Housing/shelter, homeless; Housing/shelter; Disasters, search/rescue; Youth development; Human services; Homeless, human services; International economic development; Business/industry; Leadership development.
Limitations: Applications accepted. Giving primarily in the northeastern U.S. No grants to individuals, or for endowments.
Publications: Application guidelines.
Application information: Application form available on foundation web site. Application form required.
Initial approach: See foundation web site for guidelines
Deadline(s): None
Board meeting date(s): Quarterly
Officers and Directors:* Geoffrey M. Parkinson,* Pres.; Leland C. Selby,* Secy.-Treas.; Geoffrey M. Parkinson, Jr.
EIN: 061514402
Selected grants: The following grants are a representative sample of this grantmaker's funding activity:
$50,000 to ProLiteracy Worldwide, Syracuse, NY, 2012. For National Book Fund (2 of 3).
$20,000 to Medical Missions for Children, Paterson, NJ, 2012. For Armenia Pad Telemedicine and Continuing Medical Education Project (1 of 3).
$15,000 to Medical Missions for Children, Paterson, NJ, 2012. For Armenia Pediatric Telemedicine and Continuing Medical Education (2 of 3).
$10,000 to AmeriCares, Stamford, CT, 2012. For Hurricane Sandy Relief Efforts.
$10,000 to Episcopal Relief and Development, New York, NY, 2012. For Hurricane Sandy Response Fund.
$10,000 to School for Ethical Education, Milford, CT, 2012. For Achieving with Integrity Program.
$10,000 to University of Virginia, School of Law, Charlottesville, VA, 2012. For general purposes.
$8,000 to Davidson College, Davidson, NC, 2012. For Lectures On Ethics In Professional Life.
$5,000 to School for Ethical Education, Milford, CT, 2012. For Agency Bridge Grant.
$2,000 to University of Virginia, Charlottesville, VA, 2012. For Annual Fund - College of Arts and Sciences.

1577
Yvette & Arthur Eder Charitable Foundation Trust ✧
105 Court St., 3rd Fl.
New Haven, CT 06511-6957

Established in 2002 in CT.
Donors: Mauro Motors; Yvette Eder Trust; Jill P. Eder; Arthur Eder.
Foundation type: Independent foundation.
Financial data (yr. ended 12/31/13): Assets, $19,013,550 (M); gifts received, $189,395; expenditures, $631,234; qualifying distributions, $535,500; giving activities include $535,500 for 8 grants (high: $140,000; low: $8,500).
Fields of interest: Hospitals (specialty); Human services; Catholic agencies & churches; Jewish agencies & synagogues; Children.
Limitations: Applications not accepted. Giving primarily in CT. No grants to individuals.
Application information: Unsolicited requests for funds not accepted.
Trustee: Raymond Bershtein.
EIN: 756642619
Selected grants: The following grants are a representative sample of this grantmaker's funding activity:
$6,000 to Jewish Federation of Greater New Haven, Woodbridge, CT, 2012. For contribution to Support 501(C) 3 Purpose.

1578
The Educational Foundation of America ✧
c/o Foundation Source
55 Walls Dr.
Fairfield, CT 06824-5163
E-mail: info@theefa.org; Main URL: http://www.efaw.org

Trust established in 1959 in NY.
Donors: Richard P. Ettinger†; Elsie Ettinger†; Richard P. Ettinger, Jr.†; Elaine P. Hapgood; Paul R. Andrews†; Virgil P. Ettinger†.
Foundation type: Independent foundation.
Financial data (yr. ended 12/31/13): Assets, $174,755,412 (M); expenditures, $8,148,353; qualifying distributions, $6,233,576; giving activities include $5,363,354 for 143 grants (high: $350,000; low: $500).
Purpose and activities: Giving primarily for arts and education, the environment and for sustainable population.
Fields of interest: Arts; Education; Environment; Reproductive health, family planning; Civil liberties, reproductive rights.
Limitations: Applications not accepted. Giving limited to the U.S. No support for political and religious organizations. No grants to individuals, annual fundraising campaigns, or for capital or endowment funds; no loans.
Publications: Annual report.
Application information: Unsolicited requests for funds not accepted at this time.
Board meeting date(s): Varies
Officers and Directors:* Sven Huseby,* Pres.; Barbara Hapgood,* V.P.; Christian P. Ettinger,* Secy.; Jerry Babicka,* Treas.; Melissa Beck, Exec. Dir.; Lynn P. Babicka; James Bohart, Jr.; Barbara P. Ettinger; Heidi P. Ettinger; Wendy W.P. Ettinger; Matthew Hapgood; North Landesman; John Powers; Trevor Renner; Lauren Zuskin.

Adjunct Committee Members: Morey Zuskin, Chair.; Jonathan Babicka, Secy.; Clarice Annegers; Missy Babicka; Holly Bohart; Mackenzie Dawson; Matthew P. Ettinger; Dodge Landesman; Holly Marsh; Jacob Marsh; Cooper McLane; Christopher Renner; Jill Renner; Todd Renner; Jonathan Reynolds; Britton Rollins.
Number of staff: 3 full-time professional; 2 part-time professional; 1 full-time support.
EIN: 133424750
Selected grants: The following grants are a representative sample of this grantmaker's funding activity:
$318,000 to Southern Environmental Law Center, Charlottesville, VA, 2012. To address climate change through coal waste in the Southeast.
$275,000 to iQuilt Partnership, Hartford, CT, 2012. For architectural and urban planning for Bushnell Park North, pilot project design and Gold Street construction documents.
$222,500 to Planned Parenthood of South Florida and the Treasure Coast, West Palm Beach, FL, 2012. To implement and expand Electronic Medical Records (EMR).
$154,000 to Hudson Opera House, Hudson, NY, 2012. For historic preservation and acoustic design costs associated with restoration of the Main Theater.
$125,000 to NARAL Pro-Choice America Foundation, Washington, DC, 2012. For The Path Forward: Fighting Anti-Choice Attacks.
$60,000 to Environmental Defense Fund, New York, NY, 2012. For work in Raleigh, North Carolina Office.
$60,000 to iQuilt Partnership, Hartford, CT, 2012. For Phase III Quilt planning and design work, Quilt pilot projects and EnvionFest.
$60,000 to Planned Parenthood of Greater Texas, Dallas, TX, 2012. For Patient Assistance Fund.
$50,000 to NARAL Pro-Choice Colorado Foundation, Denver, CO, 2012. For capacity building.
$25,000 to Music Unites, Old Tappan, NJ, 2012. For general unrestricted support.

1579
The Ellis Fund ✧
55 Highland St.
New Haven, CT 06511-1329
Contact: Charles D. Ellis, Tr.

Established in 1983 in CT.
Donor: Charles D. Ellis.
Foundation type: Independent foundation.
Financial data (yr. ended 12/31/13): Assets, $11,562,905 (M); expenditures, $741,493; qualifying distributions, $670,296; giving activities include $668,986 for 52 grants (high: $333,000; low: $50).
Purpose and activities: Support primarily for higher and other education.
Fields of interest: Higher education; Education; Human services; United Ways and Federated Giving Programs.
Limitations: Applications accepted. Giving primarily in CT and MA. No grants to individuals.
Application information: Application form not required.
Initial approach: Proposal
Deadline(s): None
Trustees: Charles D. Ellis; Linda Koch Lorimer.
EIN: 222505228

1580
Ensworth Charitable Foundation ✧
c/o US Trust, Philanthropic Solutions
200 Glastonbury Blvd., Ste. 200
Glastonbury, CT 06033-4458 (860) 657-7015
Contact: Amy Lynch, Market Philanthropy Dir., U.S. Trust
E-mail: amy.r.lynch@ustrust.com; Main URL: https://www.bankofamerica.com/philanthropic/grantmaking.go

Trust established in 1948 in CT.
Donor: Antoinette L. Ensworth†.
Foundation type: Independent foundation.
Financial data (yr. ended 05/31/13): Assets, $21,787,410 (M); expenditures, $1,111,597; qualifying distributions, $1,020,291; giving activities include $912,800 for 90 grants (high: $25,000; low: $1,000).
Purpose and activities: Primary areas of interest include health and welfare programs, youth activities, enjoyment of the natural environment, relief of human suffering, education, religion, and the arts, particularly music.
Fields of interest: Arts; Education; Environment; Health care; Health organizations, association; AIDS research; Housing/shelter, development; Human services; Youth, services; Family services; Homeless, human services; Community/economic development.
Type of support: Program development; Seed money; Technical assistance; Matching/challenge support.
Limitations: Applications accepted. Giving limited to Hartford, CT, and its surrounding communities. No grants to individuals, or for operating budgets, annual campaigns, deficit financing, building or endowment funds, equipment and materials, land acquisition, scholarships, fellowships, research, or publications; no loans.
Publications: Program policy statement.
Application information: Online proposal available on foundation web site.
Initial approach: Letter
Copies of proposal: 4
Deadline(s): Jan. 15
Board meeting date(s): Mar.
Final notification: Within 3-4 months
Trustee: Bank of America, N.A.
Number of staff: 1 full-time professional.
EIN: 066026018
Selected grants: The following grants are a representative sample of this grantmaker's funding activity:
$50,000 to Connecticut Childrens Medical Center Foundation, Hartford, CT, 2011. To help meet the $5 million goal to create a state-of-the-art Clinical Care Center for Cancer and Blood Disorders.
$25,000 to Teach for America, New Haven, CT, 2011. For general operations of the organization.
$20,000 to Immaculate Conception Shelter and Housing Corporation, Hartford, CT, 2011. For general operations of the organization.
$15,000 to Artists Collective, Hartford, CT, 2011. For Transforming the Lives of High Risk Youth: Training in the Arts and Culture of the African Diaspora.
$15,000 to Our Piece of the Pie, Hartford, CT, 2011. For general operations of the organization.
$15,000 to Planned Parenthood of Southern New England, Rhode Island Administrative Office, Providence, RI, 2011. For Fund for Access - Hartford.
$10,000 to HandsOn Hartford, Hartford, CT, 2011. For MANNA Basic Needs Program.
$10,000 to Organized Parents Make a Difference, Hartford, CT, 2011. For general operations for the organization.
$5,000 to Connecticut Aeronautical Historical Association, Windsor Locks, CT, 2011. For SOAR for Science - Windsor Elementary Schools.
$5,000 to Covenant to Care for Children, Bloomfield, CT, 2011. For Hartford area operations of the organization.

1581
Fairfield County's Community Foundation, Inc. ✧
(also known as FCCF)
(formerly Fairfield County Community Foundation, Inc.)
383 Main Ave.
Norwalk, CT 06851-1543 (203) 750-3200
Contact: For grants: Sharon Jones, Prog. Admin. Asst.
FAX: (203) 750-3232;
E-mail: info@fccfoundation.org; Main URL: http://www.fccfoundation.org
E-Newsletter: http://visitor.constantcontact.com/manage/optin/ea?v=001PhdQ1BjzXNSMd6qefAsB2A%3D%3D
Facebook: https://www.facebook.com/FCCFoundation?ref=bookmarks
Fairfield County Community Foundation's Philanthropy Promise: http://www.youtube.com/user/FCCFoundation?feature=mhum
Philanthropy's Promise: http://www.ncrp.org/philanthropys-promise/who
Twitter: http://twitter.com/fccfoundation

Established in 1992 in CT as a result of the merger of the Five Town Foundation, Danbury Community Endowment, Fairfield County Cooperative Foundation, Greenwich Foundation for Public Giving, and Stamford Foundation; merged with The Greater Bridgeport Area Foundation in 2008.
Foundation type: Community foundation.
Financial data (yr. ended 06/30/13): Assets, $159,971,017 (M); gifts received, $11,909,531; expenditures, $22,507,299; giving activities include $18,104,849 for 835+ grants (high: $400,000; low: $157), and $482,944 for 240 grants to individuals.
Purpose and activities: The foundation promotes the growth of philanthropy by helping donors achieve their philanthropic goals. The foundation: 1) serves as a leader, catalyst and resource for philanthropy; 2) creates and manages charitable funds; and 3) identifies and addresses community needs through initiatives, partnerships and strategic grantmaking.
Fields of interest: Arts; Education, early childhood education; Higher education; Education; Environment; Health care; Employment; Housing/shelter; Youth development; Children/youth, services; Women, centers/services; Human services; Economic development; Urban/community development; Nonprofit management; Economically disadvantaged.
Type of support: General/operating support; Management development/capacity building; Equipment; Program development; Scholarship funds; Technical assistance; Scholarships—to individuals; Matching/challenge support.
Limitations: Applications accepted. Giving limited to the Fairfield County, CT, area from discretionary funds; giving throughout the U.S. from grants made from Donor-Advised funds. No support for religious purposes, or for start-up or new nonprofit

organizations, or for parochial, charter, or private schools. No grants for endowments, building campaigns, deficit financing, fellowships, annual campaigns, or fundraising events.
Publications: Application guidelines; Annual report; Financial statement; Grants list; Informational brochure; Newsletter; Occasional report.
Application information: Visit foundation web site for application guidelines. The foundation's staff will respond to a letter of inquiry with a preliminary assessment of the project's fit. Application form required.
Initial approach: Submit online letter of inquiry
Deadline(s): Mar. 1 and Aug. 15 for letter of inquiry
Board meeting date(s): Quarterly
Officers and Directors:* Vicki Craver,* Chair.; Lizanne G. Megrue,* Vice-Chair.; Juanita T. James, C.E.O. and Pres.; Joseph R. Baker, V.P., Finance and Admin.; Karen Brown, V.P., Progs.; Fiona K. Hodgson, V.P., Devel. and Mktg.; Suzanne Brown Peters, V.P., Fund for Women and Girls; Hon. John P. Chiota,* Secy.; Ronald B. Noren,* Treas.; John Bailey; Maxwell Bonnie; Annie Burleigh; Brandon Cardwell; Abelardo S. Curdumi; Amy C. Downer; Bob Eydt; John Freeman; Steven Goldstein; Greg Hartch; Gary A. Kraut; Janet L. Lebovitz; David Levinson; Jackie Millan; Jonathan Moffly; Elisabeth Morten; Martha Olson; M. Suzette Recinos; James Schmotter; Eileen L. Swerdlick; Katharine H. Welling; Steven A. Wolff.
Number of staff: 16 full-time professional; 1 part-time professional; 3 full-time support; 1 part-time support.
EIN: 061083893
Selected grants: The following grants are a representative sample of this grantmaker's funding activity:
$440,700 to Connecticut Association for Human Services, Hartford, CT, 2012. For a K-3 reading assessment pilot study.
$350,000 to Child Health and Development Institute of Connecticut, Farmington, CT, 2012. To replicate the Child First Model in four Connecticut communities.
$315,250 to Bridgeport Public Schools, Bridgeport, CT, 2012. For salary expenses and HR, organizational and curriculum assessments.
$250,000 to Norwalk Community College Foundation, Norwalk, CT, 2012. For Family Economic Security Program-Year 4 Renewal Grant.
$187,900 to Domus Kids, Stamford, CT, 2012. For expansion of the Family Advocate Program.
$100,000 to International Documentary Association, Los Angeles, CA, 2012. For Untitled Film.
$7,500 to Neighborhood Studios of Fairfield County, Bridgeport, CT, 2012. For Ailey Camp.
$5,000 to Darien Emergency Medical Services, Darien, CT, 2012. For general support.
$5,000 to Middlebury College, Middlebury, VT, 2012. For general support.
$5,000 to Southwestern Connecticut Agency on Aging, Bridgeport, CT, 2012. For general support.

1582
Farid Foundation ✧
95 Barnes Rd.
Wallingford, CT 06492-1800 (203) 774-8000
Contact: Tariq Farid, Tr.

Established in 2005 in CT.
Donors: Edible Arrangements Franchise Group, Inc.; Kamran Farid; Netsolace, Inc.; Edible Brands, LLC; Tariq Farid.
Foundation type: Company-sponsored foundation.
Financial data (yr. ended 12/31/12): Assets, $689,554 (M); gifts received, $670,000; expenditures, $756,929; qualifying distributions, $724,515; giving activities include $724,515 for 44 grants (high: $211,000; low: $150).
Purpose and activities: The foundation supports organizations involved with education and Islam.
Fields of interest: Education; Human services; Community/economic development.
Type of support: General/operating support.
Limitations: Applications accepted. Giving primarily in CT.
Application information: Application form not required.
Initial approach: Proposal
Deadline(s): None
Trustees: Kamran Farid; Tariq Farid.
EIN: 203096696
Selected grants: The following grants are a representative sample of this grantmaker's funding activity:
$12,000 to Columbus House, New Haven, CT, 2011.
$12,000 to Downtown Evening Soup Kitchen, New Haven, CT, 2011.

1583
Betsy and Jesse Fink Foundation ✧
20 Marshall St., Ste. 300
Norwalk, CT 06854-2204

Established in 1999 in CT.
Donors: Jesse Fink; Betsy Fink.
Foundation type: Independent foundation.
Financial data (yr. ended 12/31/12): Assets, $18,552,184 (M); expenditures, $1,383,378; qualifying distributions, $1,440,489; giving activities include $1,284,525 for 47 grants (high: $200,000; low: $2,000).
Purpose and activities: Giving primarily for environmental conservation and farm land trusts; funding also for education.
Fields of interest: Education; Environment; Agriculture, farmlands; Foundations (community).
Type of support: Mission-related investments/loans; General/operating support; Program-related investments/loans.
Limitations: Applications not accepted. Giving in the U.S., with emphasis on CT; some giving in MA and NY. No grants to individuals.
Application information: Contributes only to pre-selected organizations.
Trustees: Betsy Fink; Jesse Fink.
EIN: 137219308

1584
First County Bank Foundation, Inc. ✧
c/o Ron Holbert
117 Prospect St., 4th Fl.
Stamford, CT 06901-1201 (203) 462-4858
Contact: Katherine A. Harris, V.P.
E-mail: foundation@firstcountybank.com; Main URL: https://www.firstcountybank.com/first-county-bank-foundation-inc

Established in 2000 in CT.
Donor: First County Bank.
Foundation type: Company-sponsored foundation.
Financial data (yr. ended 12/31/13): Assets, $3,151,174 (M); expenditures, $607,929; qualifying distributions, $577,569; giving activities include $577,569 for 128 grants (high: $20,000; low: $500).
Purpose and activities: The foundation supports programs designed to address community economic development and children and families. Special emphasis is directed toward programs designed to serve low-to-moderate income populations.
Fields of interest: Higher education; Education; Health care; Food services; Housing/shelter; Boys & girls clubs; Salvation Army; Children/youth, services; Family services; Homeless, human services; Human services; Community/economic development; United Ways and Federated Giving Programs; Economically disadvantaged.
Type of support: General/operating support; Continuing support; Equipment; Program development; Scholarship funds; Scholarships—to individuals.
Limitations: Applications accepted. Giving limited to areas of company operations in Darien, Greenwich, New Canaan, Norwalk, Stamford, and Westport, CT. No support for religious organizations not of direct benefit to the entire community, private or parochial schools, discriminatory organizations, or organizations not open to the public. No grants to individuals (except for the Richard E. Taber Citizenship Award), or for capital or endowment campaigns, fundraising events, trips, tours, or conferences, debt spending or liquidation, or political causes.
Publications: Application guidelines.
Application information: Application form required.
Initial approach: Letter
Deadline(s): Jan. 1 to Mar. 31
Officers and Directors:* Richard Taber, Jr.,* Pres.; Katherine Harris, V.P.; Ronald Holbert, Treas.; Thomas L. Bartram; Robert A. Beer; Dr. Marcia Bull; Francis DeLuca; Nicholas Dubiago; Robert Emslie; Mark Lapine; James McArdle, Jr.; Alphonse Palmer.
EIN: 061604469
Selected grants: The following grants are a representative sample of this grantmaker's funding activity:
$15,000 to Kids in Crisis, Cos Cob, CT, 2012. For Safe Haven for Kids Shelter Program-provides emergency residential shall or for children aged birth to 17 yrs.
$10,000 to Senior Services of Stamford, Stamford, CT, 2012. For Medical Transportation Program KK on BOD.
$10,000 to Shelter for the Homeless, Stamford, CT, 2012. For assistance with safe costs associated with a housing development initiative to create 50 units of Permanent Supported Housing (PSH) Peter Rugen on BOD.
$10,000 to SoundWaters, Stamford, CT, 2012. For Camp SoundWaters.
$9,794 to Stamford Emergency Medical Services, Stamford, CT, 2012. For Stryker Power Pro Stratchers (3).
$7,500 to Norwalk Hospital Foundation, Norwalk, CT, 2012. For Project LEAN (learning with energy from activity and nutrition) obesity Program for underserved 2nd and 3rd grades at Jefferson Elementary School.
$5,000 to AmeriCares Free Clinics, Stamford, CT, 2012. For AmeriCares Free Clinic of Norwalk Individualized Home Supports/Emergency Fund Program - assists Individuals residing in our

supported fiving Program with food clothing and shelter Also locking to expend Program Dick Taber?.
$5,000 to Domestic Violence Crisis Center, Stamford, CT, 2012. For DVCC is the largest provider of emergency shelter to victims of domestic violence in the state of CT.
$5,000 to Stepping Stones Museum for Children, Norwalk, CT, 2012. For Gat Into III FREE - over the costs of one evening.
$1,500 to New Canaan Group Home, New Canaan, CT, 2012. For Reptaca ongoing refingenior (2000) Nick on the BOD.

1585
Fisher Foundation, Inc. ✧ ☆
36 Brookside Blvd.
West Hartford, CT 06107-1107 (860) 570-0221
Contact: Hinda Fisher, Pres.
FAX: (860) 570-0225; E-mail: bboyle@fisherfdn.org; Contact for information regarding application form or the foundation's requirements: Beverly Boyle, Exec. Dir.; Main URL: http://www.fisherfdn.org
Grants List: http://www.fisherfdn.org/grants/2011/2011-grants.pdf

Established in 1959.
Donors: Stanley D. Fisher Trust; FIP Corp.
Foundation type: Independent foundation.
Financial data (yr. ended 12/31/13): Assets, $11,212,677 (M); gifts received, $40,692; expenditures, $561,993; qualifying distributions, $440,368; giving activities include $431,500 for 81 grants (high: $25,000; low: $500).
Purpose and activities: Giving primarily for education, arts and culture, health, human services, housing and community needs.
Fields of interest: Performing arts; Arts; Higher education; Education; Health care; Housing/shelter; Human services.
Type of support: General/operating support; Program development.
Limitations: Giving primarily in the greater Hartford, CT, area, (Andover, Avon, Bloomfield, Bolton, Canton, East Hartford, East Granby, East Windsor, Ellington, Enfield, Farmington, Glastonbury, Granby, Hartford, Hebron, Manchester, Marlborough, Newington, Rocky Hill, Simsbury, Somers, South Windsor, Suffield, Tolland, Vernon, West Hartford, Wethersfield, Windsor, and Windsor Locks). No grants to individuals, or for conferences, retreats, performances or events, or for capital campaigns.
Publications: Application guidelines; Annual report (including application guidelines); Grants list; Informational brochure.
Application information: Application information and form available on foundation web site. Audio or videotapes are not accepted, nor are applications submitted via fax or e-mail. Application form required.
Initial approach: Letter or telephone
Copies of proposal: 2
Deadline(s): Jan. 15, Apr. 15, and Sept. 15
Board meeting date(s): Mar., June, and Nov.
Officers and Directors:* Hinda N. Fisher,* Pres. and Treas.; Diane Fisher Bell,* V.P.; Lois Fisher Dietzel,* V.P.; Beverly Boyle, Secy. and Exec. Dir.; Michael Finklestein.
Number of staff: 1 part-time professional.
EIN: 066039415
Selected grants: The following grants are a representative sample of this grantmaker's funding activity:
$5,000 to South Park Inn, Hartford, CT, 2012. For housing and community.

1586
Renee B. Fisher Foundation Inc. ✧
P.O. Box 366
Green Farms, CT 06838-0366 (203) 255-0707
Contact: Carol P. Fisher, Dir.

Foundation type: Independent foundation.
Financial data (yr. ended 12/31/12): Assets, $13,824,994 (M); expenditures, $776,812; qualifying distributions, $643,054; giving activities include $643,054 for grants.
Fields of interest: Performing arts, music; Education; Human services; Foundations (community).
Application information: Application form required.
Initial approach: Letter
Deadline(s): None
Officer and Directors:* Shelley Fishkin,* Pres.; C.P. Fisher; James Fishkin.
EIN: 060952015

1587
Lawrence & Megan Foley Family Foundation Inc. ✧
P.O. Box 824
Southport, CT 06890-0824

Established in 2001 in CT.
Donors: Lawrence G. Foley; Megan M. Foley; Andrew Schwartz.
Foundation type: Independent foundation.
Financial data (yr. ended 11/30/12): Assets, $2,698,727 (M); gifts received, $1,512,000; expenditures, $551,671; qualifying distributions, $522,696; giving activities include $521,676 for 39 grants (high: $110,000; low: $90).
Fields of interest: Elementary/secondary education; Higher education; Health organizations, association; Human services; Children/youth, services; Catholic agencies & churches.
Limitations: Applications not accepted. No grants to individuals.
Application information: Contributes only to pre-selected organizations.
Directors: Lawrence G. Foley; Megan M. Foley; David J. McCabe.
EIN: 421528874

1588
Foster-Davis Foundation, Inc. ✧
P.O. Box 1669
Greenwich, CT 06836-1669

Established about 1966 in CT.
Donor: Alma F. Davis Charitable Lead Trust.
Foundation type: Independent foundation.
Financial data (yr. ended 12/31/13): Assets, $10,354,116 (M); expenditures, $672,459; qualifying distributions, $599,300; giving activities include $599,300 for 47 grants (high: $283,000; low: $500).
Purpose and activities: Giving primarily to higher education; grants also for research in mental health and biology, recreational facilities, fisheries and wildlife preservation, and health associations.
Fields of interest: Higher education; Animals/wildlife, preservation/protection; Hospitals (general); Mental health/crisis services; Health organizations, association; Recreation; Biology/life sciences.
Limitations: Applications not accepted. Giving primarily in CT. No grants to individuals.
Application information: Contributes only to pre-selected organizations.
Board meeting date(s): 3rd week in July
Officers and Directors:* Foster Bam, Pres.; Edward F. Rodenbach,* V.P. and Secy.; Patricia S. Bam, Treas.; Howard S. Tuthill.
EIN: 060811599

1589
The Fund for Greater Hartford
(formerly The Hartford Courant Foundation, Inc.)
75 Charter Oak Ave., Ste. 2-200
Hartford, CT 06106-1903 (860) 232-3113
Contact: Kate Miller, Exec. Dir.
E-mail: info@fundforgreaterhartford.org; Main URL: http://www.fundforgreaterhartford.org/

Established in 1950 in CT as a corporate foundation; restructured in 1980 as a private, independent foundation.
Donor: The Hartford Courant Co.
Foundation type: Independent foundation.
Financial data (yr. ended 12/31/13): Assets, $17,415,043 (M); expenditures, $915,453; qualifying distributions, $807,550; giving activities include $591,629 for 81 grants (high: $50,000; low: $213).
Purpose and activities: Giving primarily for arts and cultural programs, education, health, social services, and community development, with a strong focus on programs that benefit youth, children, and families.
Fields of interest: Arts; Education, early childhood education; Child development, education; Education; Health care; Crime/violence prevention, domestic violence; Housing/shelter, development; Human services; Children/youth, services; Child development, services; Family services; Homeless, human services; Community/economic development; Infants/toddlers; Children/youth; Children; Minorities; Economically disadvantaged; Homeless.
Type of support: General/operating support; Management development/capacity building; Capital campaigns; Building/renovation; Equipment; Land acquisition; Program development; Seed money; Matching/challenge support.
Limitations: Applications accepted. Giving limited to New Britain, Middletown and the capital region of CT. No support for religious organizations for sectarian purposes, veterans', fraternal, professional, or business associations, or private schools. No grants to individuals, or for continuing support, endowment or emergency funds, conferences, performances, or other short-term, one-time events; no loans.
Publications: Application guidelines; Annual report; Financial statement; Grants list; Informational brochure; Program policy statement (including application guidelines).
Application information: Application form required.
Initial approach: Proposal
Copies of proposal: 1
Deadline(s): Mar. 15, June 15, Sept. 15, and Dec. 15
Board meeting date(s): Feb., May, Sept., and Nov.
Final notification: 8-10 weeks

Officers: Jan-Gee McCollam, Pres.; Estela Lopez, V.P.; Kate Miller, Secy. and Exec. Dir.; David E.A. Carson, Treas.
Trustees: Raymond S. Andrews, Jr.; Chris Aroh; Christel Ford Berry; Sanford Cloud, Jr.; Justice Nina Elgo; Heidi Hadsell; Christopher C. Morrill; Justice Richard N. Palmer; Anita Ford Saunders; Toni Smith-Rosario.
Number of staff: 1 full-time professional.
EIN: 060759107
Selected grants: The following grants are a representative sample of this grantmaker's funding activity:
$15,000 to Watkinson School, Hartford, CT, 2012. For Hispanic Program.
$10,000 to American School for the Deaf, West Hartford, CT, 2012. For Health and Social Services.
$7,500 to Families in Crisis, Hartford, CT, 2012. For Health and Social Services.
$221 to Camp Courant, Hartford, CT, 2012. For Spellacy Fund.

1590
Garden Homes Fund ✧
29 Knapp St.
P.O. Box 4401
Stamford, CT 06907-1799
Contact: Joel E. Freedman, Tr.

Established in 1981 in CT.
Donor: Members of the Joel Freedman family.
Foundation type: Independent foundation.
Financial data (yr. ended 12/31/13): Assets, $24,335,032 (M); gifts received, $540,098; expenditures, $1,858,151; qualifying distributions, $781,663; giving activities include $781,663 for 98 grants (high: $100,000; low: $250).
Purpose and activities: Giving primarily for conservation, education, social services, and the performing arts.
Fields of interest: Performing arts; Education; Environment, natural resources; Human services.
Type of support: Annual campaigns; Capital campaigns; Building/renovation; Endowments; Scholarship funds; Employee-related scholarships; Scholarships—to individuals.
Limitations: Applications not accepted. Giving primarily in CT, NJ, and NY. No support for religious organizations.
Application information: Contributes only to pre-selected organizations. Unsolicited requests for funds not accepted.
Trustees: Deborah Freedman; Jane Freedman; Joel E. Freedman; Naomi K. Freedman; Richard Freedman.
Number of staff: None.
EIN: 061043730

1591
GE Foundation ✧
(formerly GE Fund)
3135 Easton Tpke.
Fairfield, CT 06828-0001 (203) 373-3216
Contact: Robert L. Corcoran, Chair.
FAX: (203) 373-3029;
E-mail: gefoundation@ge.com; E-mail for Corporate Citizenship Team: citizenship@ge.com; e-mail for Developing Health: developing.health@ge.com; e-mail for David Barash: David.Barash@ge.com; e-mail for Kim Hessler: kim.hessler@ge.com; Main URL: http://www.gefoundation.com
Twitter: https://twitter.com/GE_Foundation

Trust established in 1952 in NY.
Donor: General Electric Co.
Foundation type: Company-sponsored foundation.
Financial data (yr. ended 12/31/13): Assets, $24,057,981 (M); gifts received, $133,426,087; expenditures, $128,661,671; qualifying distributions, $128,808,934; giving activities include $85,403,514 for 888 grants (high: $2,500,000; low: $25), and $39,108,551 for 22,673 employee matching gifts.
Purpose and activities: The foundation supports organizations involved with education, health, disaster relief, human services, international affairs, human rights, community development, science, public policy, and leadership development.
Fields of interest: Education, reform; Elementary/secondary education; Middle schools/education; Higher education; Business school/education; Scholarships/financial aid; Education; Health care, clinics/centers; Health care, infants; Reproductive health; Public health; Public health, clean water supply; Public health, sanitation; Health care, patient services; Health care; Heart & circulatory diseases; Asthma; Diabetes; Tropical diseases; Disasters, preparedness/services; Youth development, business; Human services; International affairs, U.N.; International economics/trade policy; International affairs; Community/economic development; United Ways and Federated Giving Programs; Mathematics; Engineering/technology; Science; Public policy, research; Leadership development; Girls; Economically disadvantaged.
International interests: Africa; China; Europe; India; Latin America; Middle East; Southeastern Asia; Sub-Saharan Africa.
Type of support: Continuing support; Management development/capacity building; Program development; Faculty/staff development; Publication; Curriculum development; Scholarship funds; Research; Employee matching gifts; Employee-related scholarships.
Limitations: Applications not accepted. Giving on a national and international basis, with emphasis on Los Angeles, CA, Stamford, CT, Washington, DC, Chicago, IL, Atlanta, GA, Jefferson County and Louisville, KY, New Orleans, LA, Baltimore, MD, New York and Schenectady, NY, Cincinnati, OH, Erie, PA, Houston, TX, VA, Milwaukee, WI, Africa, Canada, China, Europe, India, Latin America, the Middle East, and Southeast Asia. No support for religious or political organizations. No grants to individuals (except for employee-related scholarships), or for capital campaigns, endowments, or other special purpose campaigns; no loans; no equipment donations.
Publications: Program policy statement.
Application information: The foundation practices an invitation only process for giving. The foundation does not encourage unsolicited proposals.
Board meeting date(s): Quarterly
Officers and Directors:* Susan P. Peters, Chair.; Deborah A. Elam, Pres.; Janine Rouson, Secy.; Michael J. Cosgrove, Treas.; Donna Granfors, Cont.; E. W. Fraser, Genl. Counsel; Alfredo Arguello; Nani Beccalli-Falco; Jeffrey S. Bornstein; Brackett B. Denniston II; Nancy Dorn; John G. Rice; Gary Sheffer; Dmitri Stockton.
Number of staff: 6 full-time professional; 1 part-time professional; 4 full-time support.
EIN: 222621967
Selected grants: The following grants are a representative sample of this grantmaker's funding activity:
$4,000,000 to Robin Hood Foundation, New York, NY, 2012.
$2,000,000 to Assist International, Scotts Valley, CA, 2012.
$2,000,000 to Fund for Public Schools, New York, NY, 2012.
$1,099,000 to Engineering World Health, Durham, NC, 2012.
$7,176 to Savannah Jewish Federation, Savannah, GA, 2012.
$5,011 to Lake Area Free Clinic, Oconomowoc, WI, 2012.
$5,000 to School Year Abroad, North Andover, MA, 2012.
$3,700 to University of Michigan, Ann Arbor, MI, 2012.

1592
The Meredith and Whitney George Family Foundation, Inc. ✧
24 Three Wells Rd.
Darien, CT 06820-2606

Established in 2005 in CT.
Donors: W. Whitney George; Meredith M. George.
Foundation type: Independent foundation.
Financial data (yr. ended 10/31/13): Assets, $38,591,767 (M); gifts received, $5,026,564; expenditures, $1,919,879; qualifying distributions, $1,831,341; giving activities include $1,826,000 for 29 grants (high: $550,000; low: $1,000).
Fields of interest: Higher education; Education; Human services; YM/YWCAs & YM/YWHAs.
Limitations: Applications not accepted. Giving primarily in CT. No grants to individuals.
Application information: Contributes only to pre-selected organizations.
Officers: W. Whitney George, Chair. and Secy.; Meredith M. George, Pres. and Treas.
EIN: 830414025
Selected grants: The following grants are a representative sample of this grantmaker's funding activity:
$1,000,000 to Trinity College, Hartford, CT, 2011. For capital campaign.
$150,000 to Stepping Stones Museum for Children, Norwalk, CT, 2010. For capital campaign.
$100,000 to Tony Blair Faith Foundation-US, Washington, DC, 2010. For capital campaign.
$50,000 to Choate Rosemary Hall, Wallingford, CT, 2011.
$15,000 to Saint Lukes Church, Darien, CT, 2011.
$10,000 to Saint Lukes Church, Darien, CT, 2011.
$5,000 to AmeriCares, Stamford, CT, 2011.
$5,000 to Darien Nature Center, Darien, CT, 2011.
$5,000 to Westerly Hospital Foundation, Westerly, RI, 2011.
$1,500 to City of Hope, Duarte, CA, 2011.
$1,000 to YMCA, Ocean Community, Westerly, RI, 2011.

1593
The Georgescu Family Foundation ✧
P.O. Box 2630
Westport, CT 06880-0630
Contact: Barbara Georgescu, Secy.-Treas.; Peter Georgescu, Pres.
Application address: 435 E. 52nd St., New York, NY 10022, tel.: (203) 226-8997

Donors: Barbara Georgescu; Peter Georgescu.
Foundation type: Independent foundation.
Financial data (yr. ended 12/31/13): Assets, $446,333 (M); gifts received, $70,700; expenditures, $518,100; qualifying distributions, $515,750; giving activities include $515,750 for 79 grants (high: $68,300; low: $100).
Fields of interest: Performing arts, theater; Performing arts, orchestras; Arts; Education; Hospitals (general); Health care; Athletics/sports, racquet sports; Human services; Protestant agencies & churches.
Limitations: Applications accepted. Giving primarily in NY; some giving in CA, CT, FL, and RI.
Application information: Application form not required.
Initial approach: Proposal
Deadline(s): None
Officers: Peter Georgescu, Pres.; Andrew Georgescu, V.P.; Barbara Georgescu, Secy.-Treas.
Trustee: Elwood B. Davis.
EIN: 134111095

1594
Glover-Crask Charitable Trust ✧
100 Pearl St., 13th Fl.
Hartford, CT 06103
Application address: c/o Gina Dimonda, First Niagara Bank, 777 Canal View Blvd., Rochester, NY 14623; tel.: (585) 770-1621

Established in 1998 in NY.
Donor: Ethel M. Glover.
Foundation type: Independent foundation.
Financial data (yr. ended 12/31/13): Assets, $15,291,349 (M); expenditures, $904,479; qualifying distributions, $842,840; giving activities include $793,160 for 69 grants (high: $100,000; low: $750).
Fields of interest: Higher education; Food services; Human services; Children/youth, services; Protestant agencies & churches.
Limitations: Applications accepted. Giving primarily in Rochester, NY. No grants to individuals.
Application information: Application form required.
Initial approach: Letter
Deadline(s): None
Trustees: John T. Harris, Esq.; First Niagara Bank; JPMorgan Chase Bank, N.A.
EIN: 166478709
Selected grants: The following grants are a representative sample of this grantmaker's funding activity:
$40,000 to University of Rochester, Rochester, NY, 2012. For grant: Eye Institute.
$35,000 to University of Rochester, Rochester, NY, 2012. For grant: School of Medicine.
$25,000 to Center for Youth Services, Rochester, NY, 2012. For grant: Crisis Nursery Gala.
$20,000 to Bivona Child Advocacy Center, Rochester, NY, 2012. For grant: Stop Abuse Program.
$15,000 to Rochester Area Community Foundation, Rochester, NY, 2012. For grant: Quad a for Kids After School.
$2,500 to Diocese of Rochester, Rochester, NY, 2012. For grant: St Andrews Church Food Cupboard.
$2,500 to Third Presbyterian Church, Rochester, NY, 2012. For grant: Food Cupboard.
$2,500 to United Church of Christ, Cleveland, OH, 2012. For grant: Salem Church Rochester.

1595
The Goergen Foundation, Inc. ✧
c/o Marcum LLP
35 Mason St.
Greenwich, CT 06830-5433

Established in 1986 in CT.
Donors: Robert B. Goergen; Robert B. Goergen, Jr.; Todd A. Goergen, Jr.
Foundation type: Independent foundation.
Financial data (yr. ended 12/31/13): Assets, $22,234,799 (M); expenditures, $1,330,887; qualifying distributions, $856,671; giving activities include $758,835 for 62 grants (high: $60,000; low: $100).
Purpose and activities: Giving primarily for the arts, particularly museums, as well as for human services, education, animals and wildlife, and YM/YWCAs.
Fields of interest: Museums (art); Arts; Higher education; Animals/wildlife; Hospitals (general); Health organizations, association; Human services; YM/YWCAs & YM/YWHAs.
Type of support: General/operating support.
Limitations: Applications not accepted. Giving primarily in CT, NY, and PA. No grants to individuals.
Application information: Contributes only to pre-selected organizations.
Officers and Trustees:* Robert B. Goergen,* Pres.; Robert B. Goergen, Jr.,* V.P.; Todd A. Goergen,* V.P.; Pamela M. Goergen,* Secy.-Treas.
EIN: 061180035

1596
The Goldring Family Foundation, Inc. ✧
48 Mill Pond Rd.
Sherman, CT 06784-2102

Established in 1995.
Donors: Gary F. Goldring; Education for Youth Society.
Foundation type: Independent foundation.
Financial data (yr. ended 12/31/13): Assets, $22,550,568 (M); gifts received, $1,829,625; expenditures, $935,400; qualifying distributions, $932,150; giving activities include $928,850 for 57 grants (high: $206,000; low: $100).
Purpose and activities: Giving primarily for the arts, education, health and human service organizations.
Fields of interest: Arts; Higher education; Education; Hospitals (general); Health organizations, association; Human services; Foundations (public).
Limitations: Applications not accepted. Giving primarily in MA, NJ, NY, and PA. No grants to individuals.
Application information: Contributes only to pre-selected organizations.
Officers and Directors:* Gary F. Goldring,* Pres. and Treas.; Paul Wolanksy, V.P. and Secy.; Gregory Goldring; Rebecca Goldring.
EIN: 223407792
Selected grants: The following grants are a representative sample of this grantmaker's funding activity:
$100,000 to Columbia University, Law School, New York, NY, 2012. To Aid the Donee Organization in Carrying Out Its Exempt Function.

1597
The Goldstone Family Foundation ✧
445 Main St.
Ridgefield, CT 06877-4513

Established in 2000.
Donors: Steven F. Goldstone; Elizabeth Goldstone.
Foundation type: Independent foundation.
Financial data (yr. ended 12/31/12): Assets, $24,298,481 (M); expenditures, $1,524,932; qualifying distributions, $1,152,821; giving activities include $952,425 for 63 grants (high: $360,000; low: $100).
Purpose and activities: Giving primarily for the arts, education, and human services.
Fields of interest: Museums; Arts; Education; Health organizations, association; Housing/shelter, development; Human services.
Limitations: Applications not accepted. Giving primarily in CT and NY. No grants to individuals.
Application information: Contributes only to pre-selected organizations.
Officers and Directors:* Steven F. Goldstone,* Pres. and Treas.; Elizabeth Goldstone,* V.P. and Secy.; Kerri Glass, Mgr.
EIN: 061596255

1598
The Goodnow Fund ✧
9 Old King's Hwy. S.
Darien, CT 06820-4523 (203) 655-6272
Contact: Edward B. Goodnow, Tr.

Established in 1993 in CT.
Donors: Edward B. Goodnow; Dianne T. Goodnow, Revocable Trust.
Foundation type: Independent foundation.
Financial data (yr. ended 12/31/12): Assets, $24,220,890 (M); gifts received, $3,000,000; expenditures, $1,315,394; qualifying distributions, $1,257,372; giving activities include $1,257,372 for 78 grants (high: $200,000; low: $100).
Purpose and activities: Giving primarily for education and human services.
Fields of interest: Education; Health care; Human services; Children/youth, services; Catholic agencies & churches.
Limitations: Applications accepted. Giving primarily in CT. No grants to individuals.
Application information: Application form not required.
Initial approach: Proposal
Deadline(s): None
Trustee: Edward B. Goodnow.
EIN: 066395384

1599
Eugene A. & Suzanne H. Gorab Foundation ✧ ☆
c/o Greenfield Partners LLC
2 Post Rd. W.
Westport, CT 06880-4203

Established in 2000 in CT.
Donors: Eugene A. Gorab; Suzanne H. Gorab.
Foundation type: Independent foundation.
Financial data (yr. ended 12/31/13): Assets, $71,043 (L); gifts received, $475,000; expenditures, $440,361; qualifying distributions, $440,361; giving activities include $435,350 for 15 grants (high: $200,000; low: $200).
Fields of interest: Higher education, university; Environment, water resources; Cancer; Residential/custodial care, hospices.
Limitations: Applications not accepted. Giving primarily in CT and PA. No grants to individuals.
Application information: Contributes only to pre-selected organizations.
Trustees: Eugene A. Gorab; Suzanne H. Gorab.
EIN: 061603317

1600
William Caspar Graustein Memorial Fund ✧
1 Hamden Ctr.
2319 Whitney Ave., Ste. 2B
Hamden, CT 06518-3509 (203) 230-3330
FAX: (203) 230-3331; E-mail: contact@wcgmf.org;
Main URL: http://www.wcgmf.org
Discovery initiative: http://www.discovery.wcgmf.org/
Knowledge Center: http://www.wcgmf.org/publications.php

Established in 1964 in NY.
Donors: Archibald R. Graustein†; Hallie H. Graustein†; William C. Graustein; D.W. Rich & Co., Inc.; Jean Graustein; Thelma Ewig†.
Foundation type: Independent foundation.
Financial data (yr. ended 12/31/13): Assets, $113,687,201 (M); gifts received, $400,130; expenditures, $7,732,006; qualifying distributions, $6,433,662; giving activities include $3,393,127 for 210 grants (high: $350,000; low: $500), and $75,000 for 1 loan/program-related investment.
Purpose and activities: The mission of the fund is to improve the effectiveness of education in fostering both personal development and leadership. To accomplish this mission, the fund has set three goals: 1) to engage young children more deeply in their own education; 2) to support Connecticut communities in improving education for their elementary and pre-school children; and 3) to develop both statewide and local leadership dedicated to improving and advocating for education.
Fields of interest: Education, early childhood education; Elementary school/education; Infants/toddlers; Children; Minorities; Economically disadvantaged.
Type of support: General/operating support; Management development/capacity building; Program development; Conferences/seminars; Film/video/radio; Seed money; Research; Technical assistance; Consulting services; Program evaluation; Program-related investments/loans; Matching/challenge support; Mission-related investments/loans.
Limitations: Applications accepted. Giving primarily in CT. No support for religious organizations for sectarian purposes or political causes and activities. No grants to individuals or for capital campaigns or scholarships.
Publications: Application guidelines; Financial statement; Grants list; Multi-year report; Occasional report; Program policy statement.
Application information: Contact foundation or see foundation web set for additional program information. Application guidelines dependent on specific type of grant sought. Application form required.
Initial approach: Letter of Inquiry
Copies of proposal: 4
Deadline(s): 6 weeks prior to board meetings
Board meeting date(s): Apr., June, and Dec.
Final notification: 6 weeks
Officer: R. David Addams, Exec. Dir.
Trustees: Laura Berry; Lisa Graustein; William C. Graustein; Kica Matos; David C. Oxman; Jessica Sager; Benjamin R. Shute, Jr.; Barbara Tinney.
Number of staff: 6 full-time professional; 3 full-time support; 3 part-time support.
EIN: 046037391
Selected grants: The following grants are a representative sample of this grantmaker's funding activity:
$100,000 to Connecticut Voices for Children, New Haven, CT, 2012. For Early Care and Education Year XII 2012.
$75,000 to All Our Kin, New Haven, CT, 2012. For Expanding High-Quality Infant-Toddler Care in CT: Sharing the All Our Kin Model.
$65,000 to Connecticut Center for School Change, Hartford, CT, 2012. For early literacy partnership grant.
$50,000 to Connecticut Association for Human Services, Hartford, CT, 2012. For early childhood communication and outreach project.
$25,000 to Connecticut Council for Philanthropy, Hartford, CT, 2012. For State's Planning Process.
$16,393 to Community Foundation of Greater New Britain, New Britain, CT, 2012. For New Britain Discovery.
$16,393 to Education Connection, Litchfield, CT, 2012. For Torrington Discovery.
$16,393 to United Way of Greater New Haven, New Haven, CT, 2012. For New Haven Discovery.
$6,579 to EASTCONN, Hampton, CT, 2012. For Chaplin Discovery.
$6,579 to United Way of Greater New Haven, New Haven, CT, 2012. For Hamden Discovery.

1601
Sanford J. Grossman Charitable Trust ✧
c/o Quantitative Financial Strategies
10 Glenville St.
Greenwich, CT 06831-3680

Established in 2002 in CT.
Donor: Sanford J. Grossman.
Foundation type: Independent foundation.
Financial data (yr. ended 12/31/12): Assets, $2,816,137 (M); expenditures, $1,133,903; qualifying distributions, $1,103,904; giving activities include $1,102,521 for 15 grants (high: $1,000,000; low: $75).
Purpose and activities: Giving primarily for education, the arts, and health associations.
Fields of interest: Arts; Higher education; Health organizations, association; Medical research, institute; Human services; International terrorism.
Limitations: Applications not accepted. Giving primarily in CA, Washington, DC, IL, and New York, NY. No grants to individuals.
Application information: Contributes only to pre-selected organizations.
Trustee: Sanford J. Grossman.
EIN: 336316059

1602
The Grossman Family Foundation ✧
133 River Rd.
Cos Cob, CT 06807-2539

Established in 2008 in CT.
Donor: Steven Grossman.
Foundation type: Independent foundation.
Financial data (yr. ended 12/31/12): Assets, $168,457,935 (M); expenditures, $8,305,159; qualifying distributions, $7,513,173; giving activities include $7,169,549 for 6 grants (high: $7,135,088; low: $7).
Fields of interest: Education; Human services.
Type of support: General/operating support.
Limitations: Applications not accepted. Giving primarily in Jenkintown, PA; some giving also in Minneapolis, MN.
Application information: Contributes only to pre-selected organizations.
Officer and Trustees:* Linda Franciscovich,* Exec. Dir.; Carole Greenberg; Steven Grossman; Morton E. Marvin; Judith C. Meyers; Paul Napoli.
EIN: 263919092
Selected grants: The following grants are a representative sample of this grantmaker's funding activity:
$7,135,088 to National Philanthropic Trust, Jenkintown, PA, 2012. For general support.
$33,925 to Scholarship America, Minneapolis, MN, 2012. For general support.

1603
The Aryn and Matthew Grossman Foundation ✧
707 Lake Ave.
Greenwich, CT 06830-3333

Established in 2004 in NY.
Donor: Matthew Grossman.
Foundation type: Independent foundation.
Financial data (yr. ended 12/31/13): Assets, $18,796 (M); gifts received, $240,600; expenditures, $470,733; qualifying distributions, $470,548; giving activities include $470,548 for 35 grants (high: $150,000; low: $100).
Fields of interest: Secondary school/education; Higher education, university; Health organizations; United Ways and Federated Giving Programs.
Type of support: General/operating support.
Limitations: Applications not accepted. No grants to individuals.
Application information: Contributes only to pre-selected organizations.
Trustees: Aryn Grossman; Matthew Grossman.
EIN: 137437176
Selected grants: The following grants are a representative sample of this grantmaker's funding activity:
$5,000 to George Washington University, Washington, DC, 2011.

1604
Randall and Mary Hack Foundation ✧
c/o Taxpayer
238 Byram Shore Rd
Greenwich, CT 06830-6932

Established in 2007 in NJ.
Donors: Randall A. Hack; Mary Hack.
Foundation type: Independent foundation.
Financial data (yr. ended 12/31/13): Assets, $235,126 (M); gifts received, $635,916; expenditures, $732,001; qualifying distributions, $729,350; giving activities include $729,350 for 36 grants (high: $425,000; low: $50).
Fields of interest: Arts; Education; Human services; Christian agencies & churches.
Limitations: Applications not accepted. No grants to individuals.
Application information: Contributes only to pre-selected organizations.
Trustees: Mary A. Hack; Randall A. Hack; Randall A. Hack, Jr.; Tobin Ayres Hack; David Stoll.
EIN: 061810820

1605
R. Hahn Foundation ✧
24 Partridge Ln.
Weston, CT 06883-2440

Established in 1998 in CT.
Foundation type: Independent foundation.
Financial data (yr. ended 12/31/12): Assets, $9,334,650 (M); gifts received, $9,195,594; expenditures, $542,696; qualifying distributions, $512,550; giving activities include $512,550 for grants.
Fields of interest: Performing arts, orchestras; Education.
Limitations: Applications not accepted. No grants to individuals.
Application information: Contributes only to pre-selected organizations.
Trustee: Robert Hahn.
EIN: 066459415

1606
Halvorsen Family Foundation ✧
c/o Ole Andreas Halvorsen
55 Railroad Ave.
Greenwich, CT 06830

Established in 2000 in CT.
Donors: Ole Andreas Halvorsen; Diane K. Halvorsen.
Foundation type: Independent foundation.
Financial data (yr. ended 11/30/13): Assets, $38,150,429 (M); gifts received, $10,009,173; expenditures, $5,823,743; qualifying distributions, $5,819,092; giving activities include $5,814,570 for 4 grants (high: $4,100,000; low: $14,570).
Fields of interest: Higher education; Education.
Limitations: Applications not accepted. Giving primarily in CA and MA; some giving also in Oslo, Norway. No grants to individuals.
Application information: Contributes only to pre-selected organizations.
Trustees: Diane K. Halvorsen; Ole Andreas Halvorsen.
EIN: 061603158
Selected grants: The following grants are a representative sample of this grantmaker's funding activity:
$5,246,156 to Williams College, Williamstown, MA, 2011.
$636,937 to Williams College, Williamstown, MA, 2010.
$300,000 to Stanford University, Graduate School of Business, Stanford, CA, 2011.
$90,000 to New Canaan Country School, New Canaan, CT, 2010.
$90,000 to New Canaan Country School, New Canaan, CT, 2011.
$75,000 to Green Mountain Valley School, Waitsfield, VT, 2010.
$42,250 to Green Mountain Valley School, Waitsfield, VT, 2011.

1607
Hamm Family Foundation Inc. ✧
6 Cove Hill Rd.
Mystic, CT 06355-3219

Established in 2005 in CT.
Donor: Charles J. Hamm.
Foundation type: Independent foundation.
Financial data (yr. ended 12/31/13): Assets, $3,064,237 (M); expenditures, $2,160,646; qualifying distributions, $2,143,507; giving activities include $2,141,637 for 9 grants (high: $1,000,000; low: $1,000).
Purpose and activities: Giving primarily for the arts and education.
Fields of interest: Arts education; Arts; Higher education; Education.
Limitations: Applications not accepted. Giving primarily in CT. No grants to individuals.
Application information: Contributes only to pre-selected organizations.
Officers and Directors:* Charles J. Hamm,* Pres. and Treas.; Irene F. Hamm,* V.P. and Secy.; Liza H. Hamm.
EIN: 203963109

1608
The Hampshire Foundation ✧
151 New Park Ave., Ste. 7
Hartford, CT 06106 (860) 236-5751
Contact: Sabina E. Shelby, Tr.
FAX: (860) 586-7035;
E-mail: info@hampshirefoundation.org; Main URL: http://www.hampshirefoundation.org

Established in 2000 in CT.
Donor: The Hadley Trust.
Foundation type: Independent foundation.
Financial data (yr. ended 12/31/12): Assets, $22,928,294 (M); gifts received, $5,283,344; expenditures, $1,603,800; qualifying distributions, $1,539,647; giving activities include $1,032,010 for 24 grants (high: $158,000; low: $400).
Purpose and activities: The purpose of the foundation is to achieve sustainable growth for rural Peruvians.
Fields of interest: Education; Human services; International economic development.
International interests: Peru.
Limitations: Applications not accepted. Giving primarily in Peru. No grants to individuals.
Application information: Primary funding is through Peru Opportunity Fund. See web site for additional information.
Trustees: Nicholas N. Cournoyer; Sabina G. Cournoyer; Sabina E. Shelby.
EIN: 061584535
Selected grants: The following grants are a representative sample of this grantmaker's funding activity:
$113,400 to GreenWood, South Berwick, ME, 2012. For Sustainable Wood Artisanry in the Peruvian Amazon.
$69,500 to Rainforest Alliance, New York, NY, 2012. For Enhanced Livelihoods Through Sustainable Coffee and Cocoa.

1609
Hartford Foundation for Public Giving
10 Columbus Blvd., 8th Fl.
Hartford, CT 06106-1976 (860) 548-1888
Contact: Virgil Blondet, Jr., V.P., Finance and Admin.
FAX: (860) 524-8346;
E-mail: hartfordfoundation@hfpg.org; Additional e-mail: vblondet@hfpg.org; Main URL: http://www.hfpg.org
E-Newsletter: http://www.hfpg.org/conversations
Facebook: https://www.facebook.com/HartfordFoundation
Grants List: http://www.hfpg.org/grants
RSS Feed: http://www.hfpg.org/tabid/549/Default.aspx
Twitter: http://twitter.com/hartfordfdn
YouTube: http://www.youtube.com/user/HartfordFoundation
Foundation Scholarship URL: http://www.hfpgscholarships.org/Scholarships/Home/tabid/305/Default.aspx

Established in 1925 in CT by resolution and declaration of trust.
Foundation type: Community foundation.
Financial data (yr. ended 12/31/12): Assets, $810,709,993 (M); gifts received, $18,821,029; expenditures, $39,667,565; giving activities include $28,217,996 for 1,847 grants, and $4,818,515 for 5 foundation-administered programs.
Purpose and activities: As greater Hartford's community-wide charitable endowment, the foundation is permanently committed to improving the quality of life for residents throughout the region.
Fields of interest: Arts; Education; Health care; Children/youth, services; Aging, centers/services; Human services; Community/economic development.
Type of support: General/operating support; Continuing support; Management development/capacity building; Capital campaigns; Building/renovation; Equipment; Land acquisition; Emergency funds; Program development; Publication; Seed money; Curriculum development; Scholarship funds; Research; Technical assistance; Consulting services; Program evaluation; Program-related investments/loans; Scholarships—to individuals; Matching/challenge support.
Limitations: Applications accepted. Giving limited to the greater Hartford, CT area. No support for sectarian or religious activities, private foundations, tax-supported agencies, or activities primarily national or international in perspective. No grants to individuals (except for scholarships), or for recurring operating expenses, deficit financing, endowment funds, research, conferences, or support for one-time events.
Publications: Application guidelines; Annual report; Financial statement; Grants list; Informational

brochure; Newsletter; Occasional report; Program policy statement.
Application information: Visit foundation web site for application information. Once an applicant has confirmed with a Prog. Off. that the agency is eligible for a foundation grant, a complete grant application packet will be sent. Application form required.
Initial approach: Telephone
Copies of proposal: 3
Deadline(s): None, except for Summer Program Grants (telephone foundation for specific deadline)
Board meeting date(s): Monthly except Jan., May, Aug., and Oct.
Final notification: 60 to 90 days
Officers and Directors:* Yvette Melendez,* Chair.; Bonnie J. Malley,* Vice-Chair.; Linda J. Kelly, Pres.; Nancy Benben, V.P., Mktg. and Comms.; Virgil Blondet, Jr., V.P., Finance and Admin.; Cyrus Driver,* V.P., Strategy; Lori Rabb, V.P., Philanthropic Svcs.; Judy Rozie-Battle, V.P., Prog.; Robert B. Goldfarb,* Treas.; Alison Granger, C.I.O.; LouAnn Campanello, Cont.; Nancy Bernstein; David M. Borden; Thea Montanez; Rodney O. Powell; JoAnn H. Price; Theodore S. Sergi.
Trustee Banks: Bank of America, N.A.; Trust Co. of Connecticut.
Number of staff: 40 full-time professional; 13 full-time support; 2 part-time support.
EIN: 060699252
Selected grants: The following grants are a representative sample of this grantmaker's funding activity:
$724,939 to Jumoke Academy, Hartford, CT, 2013.
$500,000 to Greater Hartford Arts Council, Hartford, CT, 2013.
$475,000 to Local Initiatives Support Corporation, Hartford, CT, 2013.
$375,000 to Bridge Family Center, West Hartford, CT, 2013.
$300,000 to Compass Youth Collaborative, Hartford, CT, 2013.
$300,000 to Planned Parenthood of Southern New England, Connecticut Administrative Office, New Haven, CT, 2013.
$265,000 to Connecticut Fair Housing Center, Hartford, CT, 2013.
$9,500 to Mercy Housing and Shelter Corporation, Hartford, CT, 2013.
$5,000 to Amistad Center for Art and Culture, Hartford, CT, 2013.
$3,000 to Temple University, Philadelphia, PA, 2013. For scholarship.

1610
...n and Kelly Hartman Foundation ✧
...Cummings & Lockwood LLC
...Box 271820
...Hartford, CT 06127-1820 (860) 313-4930
...*ct:* Paul L. Bourdeau Esq., Tr.

...ished in 1992 in FL.
...: John W. Hartman‡; Esther Kelly B. ...n; John W. Hartman Charitable Lead Annuity ...Mercik, Kuczarski & Bolduc LLC.
...tion type: Independent foundation.
...l data (yr. ended 03/31/13): Assets, ...,524 (M); gifts received, $84,682; ...ures, $637,785; qualifying distributions, ...5; giving activities include $519,975 for

...nterest: Performing arts, theater; Arts; ...special); Human services.

Limitations: Applications accepted. Giving primarily in the U.S., with emphasis on CT. No grants to individuals.
Application information: Application form required.
Initial approach: Letter
Deadline(s): None
Trustees: Larry Biehl; Paul L. Bourdeau.
EIN: 223139258
Selected grants: The following grants are a representative sample of this grantmaker's funding activity:
$100,000 to Duke University, Durham, NC, 2011.
$6,000 to Lyme Public Library, Lyme, CT, 2011.
$5,000 to Middlesex Hospital, Middletown, CT, 2011.

1611
The Per and Astrid Heidenreich Family Foundation ✧
1010 Washington Blvd., 9th Fl.
Stamford, CT 06901-2202

Established in 2004 in CT.
Donors: Per Heidenreich; Astrid Heidenreich; Fritz Heidenreich; Cecilie H. Jedlicka.
Foundation type: Independent foundation.
Financial data (yr. ended 12/31/13): Assets, $10,896,028 (M); gifts received, $1,500; expenditures, $1,746,685; qualifying distributions, $1,710,225; giving activities include $1,689,750 for 81 grants (high: $898,500; low: $250).
Fields of interest: Higher education; Environment; Human services; Children/youth, services.
Limitations: Applications not accepted. Giving primarily in CT. No grants to individuals.
Application information: Contributes only to pre-selected organizations.
Officer and Trustees:* Cecilie H. Jedlicka,* Exec. Dir.; Astrid Heidenreich; Fritz Heidenreich; Per Heidenreich.
EIN: 206382658
Selected grants: The following grants are a representative sample of this grantmaker's funding activity:
$145,178 to Maritime Aquarium at Norwalk, Norwalk, CT, 2011. For general support.
$36,200 to Teach for America, New York, NY, 2011. For general support.
$33,500 to Boys and Girls Club of Martin County, Hobe Sound, FL, 2011. For general support.
$25,000 to Fisher House Foundation, Rockville, MD, 2011. For general support.
$20,000 to Environmental Defense Fund, Washington, DC, 2011. For general support.
$20,000 to Greenwich Adult Day Care, Cos Cob, CT, 2011. For general support.
$10,000 to AmeriCares, Stamford, CT, 2011. For general support.
$10,000 to Connecticut Food Bank, East Haven, CT, 2011. For general support.
$10,000 to Memorial Sloan-Kettering Cancer Center, New York, NY, 2011. For general support.
$5,000 to Camp AmeriKids, Stamford, CT, 2011. For general support.

1612
Heimbold Foundation, Inc. ✧
c/o HHG
23 Old Kings Hwy. S.
Darien, CT 06820-4541

Established in 1986 in CT.
Donors: Charles A. Heimbold, Jr.; Monika A. Heimbold.
Foundation type: Independent foundation.
Financial data (yr. ended 12/31/13): Assets, $2,952,201 (M); expenditures, $879,366; qualifying distributions, $862,815; giving activities include $722,694 for 88 grants (high: $100,000; low: $100).
Fields of interest: Arts; Higher education; Medical care, in-patient care; Health care; Children/youth, services; Foundations (private grantmaking); United Ways and Federated Giving Programs.
Limitations: Applications not accepted. Giving primarily in CT and NY. No grants to individuals.
Application information: Contributes only to pre-selected organizations.
Directors: Eric C. Heimbold; Joanna M. Heimbold; Leif C. Heimbold; Monika A. Heimbold; Peter Heimbold.
EIN: 061188361
Selected grants: The following grants are a representative sample of this grantmaker's funding activity:
$2,500 to Columbia University, School of Social Work, New York, NY, 2012. For education.
$1,000 to Greenwich Adult Day Care, Cos Cob, CT, 2012. For geriatric care.

1613
The Maximilian E. & Marion O. Hoffman Foundation, Inc. ✧
970 Farmington Ave., Ste. 203
West Hartford, CT 06107-2134 (860) 521-2949
Contact: Marion L. Barrak, Pres.

Established in 1986 in CT as a successor foundation of the Maximilian E. & Marion O. Hoffman Foundation.
Foundation type: Independent foundation.
Financial data (yr. ended 06/30/14): Assets, $65,203,294 (M); expenditures, $3,722,009; qualifying distributions, $3,077,423; giving activities include $2,859,950 for 59 grants (high: $375,000; low: $2,000).
Fields of interest: Arts; Higher education; Education; Hospitals (general); Human services; Catholic agencies & churches; Orthodox agencies & churches.
Type of support: General/operating support; Program development.
Limitations: Giving primarily in CT. No grants to individuals.
Application information: Application form required.
Initial approach: Letter of inquiry
Copies of proposal: 1
Deadline(s): 2 months prior to board meeting
Board meeting date(s): Mid-Oct., Jan., Apr., and June
Final notification: Few weeks after board meeting
Officers and Directors:* Marion L. Barrak,* Pres.; Joseph B. Chaho, V.P. and Secy.; Michael B. Chaho, M.D., Treas.; Anne Marie Fauliso; Marie Gustin, Ph.D.; Robert M. Jeresaty, M.D.
Number of staff: 3 full-time professional.
EIN: 222648036

1614
Harvey Hubbell Foundation ✧
40 Waterview Dr.
Shelton, CT 06484-2228

Trust established in 1959 in CT.
Donor: Hubbell Inc.
Foundation type: Company-sponsored foundation.
Financial data (yr. ended 12/31/13): Assets, $13,678,233 (M); gifts received, $222,000; expenditures, $479,649; qualifying distributions, $470,455; giving activities include $405,624 for 194 grants (high: $33,683; low: $100), and $64,831 for 4 employee matching gifts.
Purpose and activities: The foundation supports health centers and organizations involved with performing arts, education, breast cancer, diabetes, safety, youth development, and children services.
Fields of interest: Education; Safety/disasters; Human services.
Type of support: General/operating support; Annual campaigns; Capital campaigns; Building/renovation; Employee matching gifts.
Limitations: Applications not accepted. Giving primarily in areas of company operations in CT. No grants to individuals.
Application information: Contributes only to pre-selected organizations.
Trustees: A. Digennaro; Stephen M. Mais; Megan Preneta; J. van Hoof.
EIN: 066078177
Selected grants: The following grants are a representative sample of this grantmaker's funding activity:
$4,000 to University of Alabama, Tuscaloosa, AL, 2011.
$1,000 to Alliance for Quality Education, Albany, NY, 2011.
$1,000 to American Cancer Society, Atlanta, GA, 2011.
$1,000 to Leukemia & Lymphoma Society, White Plains, NY, 2011.

1615
The Huisking Foundation, Inc. ✧
291 Peddlers Rd.
Guilford, CT 06437-2324
Contact: Frank R. Huisking, Secy.-Treas.
E-mail: wwh@huiskingfoundation.org; Main URL: http://www.huiskingfoundation.org

Incorporated in 1946 in NY as the Frank R. Huisking Foundation, Inc. In Sept., 1971 the name was officially amended to The Huisking Foundation, Inc.
Donors: Claire F. Hanavan; Richard V. Huisking; Jean M. Steinschneider; and members of the Huisking family and family-related corps.
Foundation type: Independent foundation.
Financial data (yr. ended 12/31/12): Assets, $31,418,013 (M); expenditures, $1,636,123; qualifying distributions, $1,540,624; giving activities include $1,518,500 for 298 grants (high: $50,000; low: $1,000).
Purpose and activities: Giving primarily for arts and culture, education, the environment, animal protection, health and hospitals, human services, federated giving programs, and religious purposes. Projects are reviewed and recommended by specific directors of the foundation who have knowledge of the project or program, and thus, support its goals.
Fields of interest: Media/communications; Museums; Performing arts; Historic preservation/historical societies; Higher education; Education; Environment, natural resources; Animal welfare; Hospitals (general); Health organizations, association; Medical research, institute; Human services; United Ways and Federated Giving Programs; Catholic agencies & churches.
Type of support: General/operating support; Continuing support; Building/renovation; Endowments; Program development; Scholarship funds; Research.
Limitations: Giving primarily in CA, CT, DE, FL, IN, NJ, NY and UT. No grants to individuals.
Application information: Application form not required.
Initial approach: Letter
Copies of proposal: 1
Deadline(s): Submit proposal in Feb. and Aug.
Board meeting date(s): Apr. and Nov.
Officers and Directors:* William W. Huisking,* Pres.; Claire-Marie Field,* V.P.; Frank R. Huisking,* Secy.-Treas.; Helen H. Crawford; Claire F. Hanavan; Charles L. Huisking III; Paul Huisking; Margaret McCrary; Anne Roome; Jean M. Steinschneider.
EIN: 136117501
Selected grants: The following grants are a representative sample of this grantmaker's funding activity:
$45,000 to United Way of Western Connecticut, Danbury, CT, 2012. For Sandy Hook School Fund.
$10,000 to Delaware Center for Horticulture, Wilmington, DE, 2012. For Erosion/garden maintenance.
$10,000 to Delaware Center for Horticulture, Wilmington, DE, 2012. For Services and Site Space.
$10,000 to Ministry of Caring, Wilmington, DE, 2012. For food/shelter - homeless.
$10,000 to University of Connecticut, Medical School, Storrs, CT, 2012. For research/support.
$7,500 to University of Notre Dame, Notre Dame, IN, 2012. For Steven Todd Sullivan School.
$5,000 to New Jersey Performing Arts Center, Newark, NJ, 2012. For underprivileged programs.
$3,500 to Key Chorale, Sarasota, FL, 2012. For Proa and Education Outreach.
$3,500 to University of Notre Dame, Notre Dame, IN, 2012. For Steven Todd Sullivan School.
$2,000 to Mercy High School, Middletown, CT, 2012. For operations support/community program.

1616
Ion Bank Foundation, Inc. ✧
(formerly Naugatuck Savings Bank Foundation, Inc.)
251 Church St.
P.O. Box 370
Naugatuck, CT 06770
Contact: June M. Jarvis
E-mail: jjarvis@ionbank.com; Main URL: http://www.ionbank.com

Donors: Naugatuck Savings Bank; Ion Bank, N.A.
Foundation type: Company-sponsored foundation.
Financial data (yr. ended 12/31/13): Assets, $8,610,674 (M); gifts received, $144,502; expenditures, $621,271; qualifying distributions, $533,546; giving activities include $496,360 for 165 grants (high: $50,000; low: $200).
Purpose and activities: The foundation supports organizations involved with arts and culture, education, health, human services, and community economic development. Special emphasis is directed toward programs designed to promote education and homeownership.
Fields of interest: Health care; Human services; Religion.
Limitations: Applications accepted. Giving primarily in areas of company operations in Ansonia, Cheshire, Meridan, Middlebury, Naugatuck, Oxford, Prospect, Southbury, Waterbury, Watertown, and Woodbury, CT. No support for political or lobbying organizations, or religious organizations not of direct benefit to the entire community. No grants to individuals.
Publications: Application guidelines.
Application information: Application form not required.
Initial approach: Proposal
Copies of proposal: 2
Deadline(s): None
Officer and Directors:* Charles J. Boulier III, Pres.; David J. Rotatori, Secy. and Treas.; Ann Merriam Feinberg; Richard H. Gesseck; Lucille Janatka; David Nurnberger; Francis R. Powell; John H. Tobin; Stephen Widman; Mark C. Yanarella.
EIN: 061513293
Selected grants: The following grants are a representative sample of this grantmaker's funding activity:
$10,000 to Brass City Harvest, Waterbury, CT, 2012. For Matching Food Stamp Program.
$10,000 to Greater Waterbury Interfaith Ministries, Waterbury, CT, 2012. For USDA Food Stamp Outreach.
$5,000 to Griffin Hospital, Derby, CT, 2012. For partner sponsor.
$5,000 to Hidden Acres Therapeutic Riding Center, Naugatuck, CT, 2012. For Covered Round-Pen-Arena.
$3,150 to Literacy Volunteers of Greater Waterbury, Waterbury, CT, 2012. For continuing education program.
$2,500 to Special Olympics Connecticut, Southbury, CT, 2012. For 2013 SOCT Basketball Invitational.
$1,250 to Literacy Volunteers of Greater Waterbury, Waterbury, CT, 2012. For Scrabble Challenge Sponsor.
$1,250 to Waterbury Hospital, Waterbury, CT, 2012. For 13th Annual Gala-Outside Back Cover.
$1,038 to Howard Whittemore Memorial Library, Naugatuck, CT, 2012. For Community Award Program.
$1,000 to American Cancer Society, Meriden, CT, 2012. For Relay for Life of Waterbury.

1617
The Robert A. & Elizabeth R. Jeffe Foundation ✧
19 Hawkwood Ln.
Greenwich, CT 06830-3924

Established in 1997 in CT.
Donors: Robert A. Jeffe; Elizabeth R. Jeffe.
Foundation type: Independent foundation.
Financial data (yr. ended 12/31/12): Assets, $12,269,441 (M); expenditures, $641,997; qualifying distributions, $636,437; giving activities include $554,483 for 13 grants (high: $200,000; low: $33).
Fields of interest: Historic preservation/historical societies; Business school/education; Foundations (private grantmaking).
Limitations: Applications not accepted. Giving primarily in Stanford, CA, Washington, DC, and NY. No grants to individuals.
Application information: Contributes only to pre-selected organizations.
Trustees: Elizabeth R. Jeffe; Robert A. Jeffe.
EIN: 066455294

1618
JJJ Charitable Foundation ✧
201 Tresser Blvd., Ste. 300
Stamford, CT 06901

Established in 1997 in CT.
Donors: Hillside Capital, Inc.; John N. Irwin III.
Foundation type: Company-sponsored foundation.
Financial data (yr. ended 12/31/12): Assets, $13,503,381 (M); expenditures, $881,404; qualifying distributions, $721,761; giving activities include $712,000 for 17 grants (high: $410,000; low: $1,000).
Purpose and activities: The foundation supports camps and organizations involved with arts and culture, education, wildlife conservation, and health.
Fields of interest: Arts; Education; Animals/wildlife.
Type of support: General/operating support; Annual campaigns.
Limitations: Applications not accepted. Giving primarily in CT and NY. No grants to individuals.
Application information: Contributes only to pre-selected organizations.
Officers and Directors:* John N. Irwin III,* Pres. and Treas.; Raymond F. Weldon, Secy.; Jane W.I. Droppa; Anna M. Irwin; Genevieve T. Irwin; Jeanet H. Irwin.
EIN: 133932002

1619
Keefe Family Foundation ✧ ☆
21 Aiken Rd.
Greenwich, CT 06831-2707

Established in 1989 in NY.
Donor: Harry V. Keefe, Jr.
Foundation type: Independent foundation.
Financial data (yr. ended 12/31/13): Assets, $8,667,411 (M); expenditures, $454,555; qualifying distributions, $434,151; giving activities include $428,450 for 14 grants (high: $100,000; low: $6,280).
Purpose and activities: Giving primarily for education and children and family services.
Fields of interest: Higher education; Education; Animals/wildlife; Human services; Children/youth, services; Family services.
Type of support: General/operating support; Capital campaigns; Program development.
Limitations: Applications not accepted. Giving primarily in MA. No support for private foundations. No grants to individuals.
Application information: Contributes only to pre-selected organizations.
Officers and Directors:* Anita L. Keefe,* Pres.; Harry V. Keefe III,* V.P.; Kathleen Keefe Raffel,* Secy.-Treas.; Carol A. Keefe; Corey Raffel.
EIN: 133520397

1620
Kelly Family Foundation ✧ ☆
c/o Knox & Co.
830 Post Rd. E., Ste. 205
Westport, CT 06880-5222 (203) 226-6288
Contact: Paul K. Kelly, Pres. and Dir.

Established in 1997 in CT.
Donors: Paul K. Kelly; Knox Enterprises.
Foundation type: Independent foundation.
Financial data (yr. ended 12/31/13): Assets, $224,884 (M); gifts received, $775,000; expenditures, $574,838; qualifying distributions, $572,000; giving activities include $572,000 for 6 grants (high: $490,000; low: $1,000).
Fields of interest: Elementary/secondary education; Higher education, university; Cancer.
Limitations: Applications accepted. Giving primarily in PA. No grants to individuals.
Application information: Application form not required.
Initial approach: Proposal
Deadline(s): None
Officer and Director:* Paul K. Kelly,* Pres.
EIN: 522068796
Selected grants: The following grants are a representative sample of this grantmaker's funding activity:
$435,000 to University of Pennsylvania, Philadelphia, PA, 2011.
$15,000 to Choate Rosemary Hall, Wallingford, CT, 2011.
$2,500 to Hathaway Brown School, Shaker Heights, OH, 2011.
$2,500 to Lauri Strauss Leukemia Foundation, New York, NY, 2011.
$1,000 to Gesu School, Philadelphia, PA, 2011.

1621
The Chester Kitchings Family Foundation ✧
(formerly The Chester W. Kitchings Foundation)
P.O. Box 309
Essex, CT 06426-0309

Established in 1961 in CT.
Donors: Chester W. Kitchings, Sr.; Margaret Howe Kitchings.
Foundation type: Independent foundation.
Financial data (yr. ended 12/31/13): Assets, $57,890,643 (M); expenditures, $2,857,903; qualifying distributions, $2,657,128; giving activities include $2,506,000 for 112 grants (high: $260,000; low: $5,000).
Purpose and activities: Giving primarily for cultural programs, human service agencies and youth groups; support also for education and health.
Fields of interest: Arts; Education; Health care; Health organizations, association; Human services; Children/youth, services; Foundations (community); United Ways and Federated Giving Programs.
Limitations: Applications not accepted. Giving limited to southeastern CT. No grants to individuals.
Application information: Contributes only to pre-selected organizations. Unsolicited requests for funds not accepted.
Trustee: Chester W. Kitchings, Jr.
EIN: 066044228

1622
Kohn-Joseloff Foundation, Inc. ✧
(formerly Morris Joseloff Foundation, Inc.)
20 Loeffler Rd., Apt. T309
Bloomfield, CT 06002-1534 (860) 243-0684
Contact: Bernard L. Kohn, Jr., Pres.

Incorporated in 1936 in CT.
Donors: Lillian L. Joseloff†; Morris Joseloff†; Morris Joseloff Foundation Trust.
Foundation type: Independent foundation.
Financial data (yr. ended 12/31/13): Assets, $8,123,762 (M); expenditures, $1,141,869; qualifying distributions, $1,067,710; giving activities include $993,195 for 58 grants (high: $250,000; low: $50).
Fields of interest: Arts education; Museums; Performing arts; Performing arts centers; Arts; Education; Health organizations, association; Human services; Jewish federated giving programs.
Limitations: Applications accepted. Giving primarily in CT. No grants to individuals; no loans.
Application information: Application form not required.
Initial approach: Proposal
Deadline(s): None
Officers: Bernard L. Kohn, Jr., Pres.; Kathryn K. Rieger, V.P.; Joan J. Kohn, Secy.
Number of staff: 2
EIN: 136062846
Selected grants: The following grants are a representative sample of this grantmaker's funding activity:
$500,000 to Westminster School, Simsbury, CT, 2011.
$30,000 to Kingswood-Oxford School, West Hartford, CT, 2011.
$15,000 to Loomis Chaffee School, Windsor, CT, 2011.
$15,000 to Wadsworth Atheneum Museum of Art, Hartford, CT, 2011.
$2,875 to Art Institute of Chicago, Chicago, IL, 2011.
$2,500 to Hartford Symphony Orchestra, Hartford, CT, 2011.
$2,500 to Philharmonic Center for the Arts, Naples, FL, 2011.
$2,500 to Wadsworth Atheneum Museum of Art, Hartford, CT, 2011.
$2,500 to Westminster School, Simsbury, CT, 2011.
$2,000 to University of Hartford, West Hartford, CT, 2011.

1623
John & Evelyn Kossak Foundation Inc. ✧ ☆
68 Cross Hwy.
Westport, CT 06880-2147

Established in 1969 in CT.
Donors: Evelyn K. Kossak; Jeffrey Kossak; Steven M. Kossak.
Foundation type: Independent foundation.
Financial data (yr. ended 12/31/12): Assets, $9,603,886 (M); gifts received, $350,000; expenditures, $1,003,978; qualifying distributions, $968,000; giving activities include $968,000 for grants.
Purpose and activities: Support primarily for higher education, health organizations, music, and the fine arts.
Fields of interest: Visual arts; Museums; Performing arts; Performing arts, music; Historic preservation/historical societies; Arts; Higher education; Health care; Health organizations, association.
Limitations: Applications not accepted. Giving primarily in CT and NY. No grants to individuals.
Application information: Contributes only to pre-selected organizations.
Officers: Evelyn K. Kossak, Pres.; Jeffrey M. Kossak, V.P.; Steven M. Kossak, Secy.
EIN: 237045906

1624
Larsen Fund ✧
P.O. Box 271677
West Hartford, CT 06127-1677
Contact: Kathryn Allen, Grant Admin.

Incorporated in 1941 in NY.
Donors: Roy E. Larsen‡; Margaret Zerbe Larsen.
Foundation type: Independent foundation.
Financial data (yr. ended 12/31/13): Assets, $15,790,189 (M); expenditures, $1,171,025; qualifying distributions, $812,100; giving activities include $785,000 for 119 grants (high: $100,000; low: $200).
Purpose and activities: Support for: 1) education, including medical and secondary schools, educational research, computer sciences, and social sciences; 2) human services, including youth, family services, and family planning; 3) hospitals; 4) population studies; 5) law, justice and urban affairs; 6) intercultural relations; 7) conservation, ecology, and wildlife preservation; and 8) the arts.
Fields of interest: Museums; Education, research; Secondary school/education; Higher education; Medical school/education; Libraries/library science; Environment, natural resources; Environment; Animals/wildlife, preservation/ protection; Hospitals (general); Children/youth, services; Family services; Civil rights, race/ intergroup relations; Community/economic development; Computer science; Social sciences; Public affairs.
Type of support: Annual campaigns; Capital campaigns; Land acquisition; Program development; Professorships; Curriculum development; Fellowships; Internship funds; Scholarship funds; Research.
Limitations: Applications accepted. Giving primarily in CT, MA, the Minneapolis, MN, area, and the New York, NY, area, and VT. No grants to individuals.
Publications: Annual report.
Application information: Application form required.
Initial approach: Proposal
Deadline(s): None
Board meeting date(s): Beginning of Nov.
Officers and Directors:* Todd H. Larsen,* Pres.; Susan Z. Ritz,* V.P.; Chad M. Larsen,* Secy.; Gordon H. Ritz, Jr.,* Treas.; Christopher Larsen; Jonathan Z. Larsen; Mark C. Larsen; Robert R. Larsen; Timothy Larsen; Margot L. Ritz; Ann Larsen Simonson.
Number of staff: 1 part-time support.
EIN: 136104430

1625
The Laverack Family Foundation ✧ ☆
(formerly The William and Cordelia Laverack Foundation)
c/o WTAS LLC
1700 E. Putnam Ave., No. 206
Old Greenwich, CT 06870-1370 (203) 987-3660
Contact: William Laverack, Tr.

Established in 2002 in CT.
Donors: Cordelia Laverack; William Laverack, Jr.; William Laverack.
Foundation type: Independent foundation.
Financial data (yr. ended 11/30/13): Assets, $5,773,201 (M); expenditures, $470,119; qualifying distributions, $433,756; giving activities include $431,000 for 9 grants (high: $220,000; low: $1,000).
Purpose and activities: Giving primarily for higher education.
Fields of interest: Elementary/secondary education; Higher education; Christian agencies & churches.
Limitations: Applications accepted. Giving primarily in CT and MA; some funding also in NC and NH.
Application information: Application form required.
Initial approach: Letter or telephone
Deadline(s): None
Trustees: Cordelia Laverack; William Laverack.
EIN: 562307477
Selected grants: The following grants are a representative sample of this grantmaker's funding activity:
$166,667 to New Canaan Country School, New Canaan, CT, 2011.
$50,000 to Harvard University, Cambridge, MA, 2011.
$10,000 to Choate Rosemary Hall, Wallingford, CT, 2011.
$1,000 to Multiple Sclerosis Society, National, Hartford, CT, 2011.
$1,000 to Saint Pauls School, Concord, NH, 2011.

1626
The Lee Family Foundation, Inc. ✧ ☆
c/o Day Pitney LLP
1 Canterbury Green
Stamford, CT 06901-2032

Established in 1999 in CT.
Donor: Charles R. Lee.
Foundation type: Independent foundation.
Financial data (yr. ended 10/31/13): Assets, $5,043,930 (M); expenditures, $441,823; qualifying distributions, $435,000; giving activities include $435,000 for 22 grants (high: $100,000; low: $1,000).
Purpose and activities: Giving primarily for education, health and medical research, and to a Congregational and Unitarian-Universalist church.
Fields of interest: Performing arts, dance; Higher education; Medical school/education; Education; Health care; Breast cancer; Medical research, institute; Protestant agencies & churches.
Limitations: Applications not accepted. Giving primarily in CT, NY, and TX. No grants to individuals.
Application information: Contributes only to pre-selected organizations.
Officers and Directors:* Charles R. Lee,* Pres.; Ilda G. Lee,* V.P.; Robert J. Miller,* Secy.; Bruce Carswell,* Treas.
EIN: 061563501
Selected grants: The following grants are a representative sample of this grantmaker's funding activity:
$50,000 to Heart Care International, Greenwich, CT, 2011.
$30,000 to United Way of Greenwich, Greenwich, CT, 2011.
$25,000 to Breast Cancer Alliance, Greenwich, CT, 2011.
$15,000 to Columbia University, New York, NY, 2011.
$10,000 to Boys Club of New York, New York, NY, 2011.
$10,000 to Pathways, Greenwich, CT, 2011.
$10,000 to Philharmonic-Symphony Society of New York, New York, NY, 2011.
$10,000 to University of California, Berkeley, CA, 2011.
$10,000 to University of California at Berkeley Foundation, Berkeley, CA, 2011.
$2,500 to Association for the Advancement of Blind and Retarded, College Point, NY, 2011.

1627
Lego Children's Fund, Inc. ✧
555 Taylor Rd.
Enfield, CT 06082-2372 (860) 763-6670
E-mail: legochildrensfund@lego.com; Application address: c/o Grant Administrator, P.O. Box 916 Enfield, CT 06083-0916; Main URL: http://www.legochildrensfund.org/
Grants List: http://www.legochildrensfund.org/Awarded.html

Established in 2006 in CT.
Donor: Lego Systems, Inc.
Foundation type: Company-sponsored foundation.
Financial data (yr. ended 12/31/13): Assets, $6,616,337 (M); gifts received, $3,000,075; expenditures, $859,343; qualifying distributions, $859,343; giving activities include $859,228 for 66 grants (high: $250,000; low: $25).
Purpose and activities: The foundation supports programs designed to help children develop their creativity and learning skills through constructive play. Special emphasis is directed toward programs designed to promote early childhood education and development that is directly related to creativity; and technology and communication projects that advance learning opportunities.
Fields of interest: Child development, education; Engineering/technology; Children; Economically disadvantaged.
Type of support: Employee volunteer services; Employee matching gifts; Matching/challenge support; Program development.
Limitations: Applications accepted. Giving primarily in areas of company operations, with emphasis on CT and western MA. No support for political or religious organizations. No grants to individuals, or for capital campaigns, direct humanitarian or disaster relief, debt retirement, ongoing operating costs, general or annual fundraising drives, institutional benefits, honorary functions, endowments, annual appeals, or similar appeals, overhead costs, operating budgets, staff salaries, capital projects including buildings, furniture, or renovation projects, deficit financing, operating budgets, efforts routinely supported by government agencies or the general public, or expansion or continuation funding of existing programs.
Publications: Application guidelines; Grants list.
Application information: Preference is given to organizations and groups that support disadvantaged children and are supported by LEGO employee volunteers. Grants range from $500 to $5,000. Support is limited to 1 contribution per organization during any given year. Application form required.
Initial approach: Complete online eligibility quiz and application
Deadline(s): Dec. 28, Mar. 28, July 12, and Sept. 28 for eligibility quiz; Jan. 15, Apr. 15, July 29, and Oct. 15 for application
Board meeting date(s): Quarterly
Final notification: Mar., June, Sept., and Dec.
Officers and Directors:* Soren Torp Laursen,* Pres. and Treas.; Brian Specht,* V.P.; Peter Arakas; Michael McNally; Mary Sutton.
EIN: 205960904

1628
The Lehrman Institute ✧
1 Fawcett Pl., Ste. 130
Greenwich, CT 06830-6553

Established in CT.
Donors: Lewis E. Lehrman; Five Way Partners, LLP; F.P. Trotta.
Foundation type: Operating foundation.
Financial data (yr. ended 07/31/13): Assets, $7,390,266 (M); expenditures, $2,389,500; qualifying distributions, $2,206,472; giving activities include $1,739,500 for 30 grants.
Fields of interest: Historical activities; Higher education; Education; Human services; Social sciences, public policy.
Type of support: General/operating support; Fellowships; Research.
Limitations: Applications not accepted. Giving primarily in CT, DE, NY and Washington, DC.
Application information: Unsolicited requests for funds not accepted. Unsolicited requests for funds will not be accepted or acknowledged under any circumstances.
Officers and Directors:* Lewis E. Lehrman,* Chair.; Frank Trotta,* Pres.; Susan Tang, Secy.; Stephen Szymanski, Treas.; Richard J. Behn; Louise Lehrman.
EIN: 237218534

1629
The Tammy and Jay Levine Foundation Inc. ✧
157 Church St., 19th Fl.
New Haven, CT 06510-2100 (203) 789-1320
Contact: Louis R. Piscatelli

Established in 2006 in CT.
Donors: Tammy Levine; Jay N. Levine.
Foundation type: Independent foundation.
Financial data (yr. ended 12/31/12): Assets, $10,972,703 (M); expenditures, $540,196; qualifying distributions, $471,629; giving activities include $471,629 for 57 grants (high: $126,976; low: $25).
Fields of interest: Education; Children, services; Jewish agencies & synagogues.
Application information: Application form not required.
Initial approach: Proposal
Deadline(s): None
Officers: Tammy Levine, Pres.; Jay N. Levine, V.P.
EIN: 204398295

1630
Liberty Bank Foundation, Inc. ✧
55 High St.
P.O. Box 1212
Middletown, CT 06457-1212 (860) 638-2961
Contact: Susan Murphy, V.P., Secy., and Exec. Dir.
E-mail: smurphy@liberty-bank.com; Tel. for Susan Murphy: (860) 638-2959; Additional contacts: Betty Sugerman Weintraub, Assoc. Dir. for Grantmaking and Community Initiatives, tel.: (860) 704-2181, e-mail: bweintraub@liberty-bank.com; Toral Maher, Grants Coord., e-mail: tmaher@liberty-bank.com; Main URL: https://www.liberty-bank.com/your-community/liberty-foundation
Grants List: https://www.liberty-bank.com/files/2011Grants.pdf
Liberty Bank Foundation Website on WTNH: http://www.wtnh.com/generic/online_guides/liberty-bank-foundation
Application e-mail: Toral Maher, Grants Coord., tmaher@liberty-bank.com

Established in 1997 in CT.
Donor: Liberty Bank.
Foundation type: Company-sponsored foundation.
Financial data (yr. ended 12/31/13): Assets, $11,033,930 (M); gifts received, $1,697,457; expenditures, $1,258,842; qualifying distributions, $1,159,094; giving activities include $815,373 for 155 grants (high: $62,500; low: $500).
Purpose and activities: The foundation supports preventative programs for children and families; affordable housing; building the capacity of nonprofits to address community needs; and basic human services for those most in need; and awards scholarships to high school seniors in areas of Liberty Bank operations.
Fields of interest: Education, early childhood education; Higher education; Higher education, college (community/junior); Adult/continuing education; Education, services; Education; Health care, infants; Public health; Health care; Employment, training; Employment; Food services; Food banks; Housing/shelter, development; Housing/shelter, temporary shelter; Housing/shelter, home owners; Housing/shelter; Youth development, adult & child programs; Children/youth, services; Children, day care; Family services; Family services, parent education; Family services, domestic violence; Human services, financial counseling; Homeless, human services; Human services; Community/economic development; United Ways and Federated Giving Programs; Engineering/technology; Utilities; Economically disadvantaged.
Type of support: General/operating support; Management development/capacity building; Capital campaigns; Building/renovation; Equipment; Program development; Scholarship funds; Technical assistance; Scholarships—to individuals; Matching/challenge support.
Limitations: Applications accepted. Giving limited to areas of company operations in towns of Berlin, Cheshire, Clinton, Colchester, Cromwell, Deep River, Durham, East Haddam, East Hampton, East Lyme, Essex, Glastonbury, Groton, Haddam, Madison, Mansfield, Marlborough, Meriden, Middlefield, Montville, Mystic, North Haven, Norwich, Old Saybrook, Plainville, Portland, Stonington, Wallingford, Waterford, West Hartford, Wethersfield, and Windham, and Middlesex and New London counties, CT. No support for political, religious, or fraternal organizations not of direct benefit to the entire community, or other grantmaking foundations. No grants to individuals (except for scholarships), or for multi-year capital campaigns, annual fund drives or campaigns (other than United Way), trips, tours, or conferences, sponsorships of events, scientific or medical research, single-disease research, deficit spending or debt liquidation, or endowments.
Publications: Application guidelines; Grants list; Program policy statement.
Application information: Grants range from $2,000 to $5,000. Applications are not accepted via fax or e-mail. The Connecticut Council for Philanthropy Common Application Form is accepted. Support is limited to 1 contribution per organization during any given year. After three consecutive years of funding, an organization must refrain from re-applying until a waiting period of one calendar year has elapsed. Application form required.
Initial approach: Telephone for preliminary discussion; download application form and mail for Academic Grant Program and Donald B. Wilbur Scholarships; download nomination form and mail for William M. McCrae Community Diversity Award; contact participating schools for nomination forms for Liberty Bank Foundation Scholarships
Copies of proposal: 1
Deadline(s): Mar. 31, June 30, Sept. 30, and Dec. 31; Late Feb. for Academic Grant Program; Mar. 29 for Liberty Bank Foundation Scholarships; Early May for Donald B. Wilbur Scholarships; Aug. 20 for William M. McCrae Community Diversity Award
Board meeting date(s): Mar., June, Sept., and Dec.
Final notification: Within 3 months; June 3 for Liberty Foundation Scholarships
Officers and Trustees:* Michael Helfgott,* Chair.; Chandler J. Howard,* Pres. and C.E.O.; Susan Murphy,* V.P, Secy., and Exec. Dir.; Kathleen Doucette, Treas.; Catalina Caban-Owen; Mark R. Gingras; Willard McRae; Mary G. Murphy; Wilfredo Nieves; Thomas J. Pastorello; Calvin K. Price; Richard W. Tomc.
Number of staff: 1 full-time professional; 1 part-time professional.
EIN: 061479957

1631
The George Link, Jr. Charitable Trust ✧
4 Guardhouse Dr.
Redding, CT 06896 (203) 664-1083
Contact: Colleen Joyce, Treas.

Established in 1999 in NJ.
Donor: Eleanor I. Link.
Foundation type: Independent foundation.
Financial data (yr. ended 12/31/13): Assets, $30,509,668 (M); expenditures, $1,666,182; qualifying distributions, $1,276,664; giving activities include $1,101,660 for 86 grants (high: $75,000; low: $600).
Purpose and activities: Giving primarily for education, hospitals and health organizations, Roman Catholic churches and agencies, social services, and community programs.
Fields of interest: Elementary/secondary education; Higher education; Education; Hospitals (general); Health organizations; Human services; Catholic agencies & churches.
Limitations: Applications accepted. Giving primarily in NY, with emphasis on the metropolitan New York, NY, area, and NJ.
Application information: Application form required.
Initial approach: Letter
Deadline(s): None
Trustees: Michael J. Catanzaro; Nora M. Link.
Officers: Debra Ann Wayne, Secy.; Colleen T. Joyce, Treas.
EIN: 226799699
Selected grants: The following grants are a representative sample of this grantmaker's funding activity:
$100,000 to Saint Francis Hospital Foundation, Roslyn, NY, 2011.
$60,000 to Catholic Relief Services, Baltimore, MD, 2011.
$20,000 to Columbia University, New York, NY, 2011.

$20,000 to RENEW International, Plainfield, NJ, 2011.
$15,000 to Abbott House, Irvington, NY, 2011.
$15,000 to Alfred E. Smith Memorial Foundation, New York, NY, 2011.
$15,000 to Elizabeth Seton Pediatric Center, New York, NY, 2011.
$10,000 to Alzheimers Association, Denville, NJ, 2011.
$10,000 to Diocese of Bridgeport, Bridgeport, CT, 2011.
$10,000 to Nuci Phillips Memorial Foundation, Athens, GA, 2011.

1632
Lone Pine Foundation, Inc.

2 Greenwich Plz., 2nd Fl.
Greenwich, CT 06830-6353
Contact: Lucy Ball, Exec. Dir.
E-mail: info@lonepinefoundation.org; Main URL: http://www.lonepinefoundation.org

Established in 2001 in CT.
Donors: Stephen F. Mandel, Jr.; Kerry Tyler; Brian Doherty; David Craver; Luke Walsh; Leslie Dahl; David Kralwasser; Lone Pine Capital, LLC.
Foundation type: Independent foundation.
Financial data (yr. ended 12/31/13): Assets, $40,469,764 (M); gifts received, $5,691,744; expenditures, $6,236,890; qualifying distributions, $5,634,130; giving activities include $5,555,113 for 500 grants (high: $200,000; low: $93).
Purpose and activities: Giving primarily for programs that serve low-income families and children in the areas of education and youth development. Through the foundation's Fairfield County Academic Gain Award, public elementary schools (and their employees) in Fairfield County, CT, are eligible to be awarded for providing quality education. Each full time employee in the prior academic year at the winning school receives $500, and the school receives $1,000 to be used at its discretion. The foundation's mission is to break the cycle of poverty through education.
Fields of interest: Education; Youth development.
Type of support: General/operating support; Program development.
Limitations: Applications not accepted. Giving limited to New York, NY, Westchester County, NY, Fairfield County, CT, London, England, and Hong Kong, China. No support for political campaigns, or for non-operating private foundations. No grants to individuals directly, or for capital campaigns, endowments and fundraising events.
Application information: Unsolicited requests for funds not accepted.
Officers and Directors:* Stephen F. Mandel, Jr.,* Chair. and Pres.; Kerry A. Tyler,* V.P. and Treas.; Christeen Bernard Dur,* Secy.; Lucy Ball,* Exec. Dir.; Dave Craver; Marco Tablada.
Number of staff: 2 full-time professional; 1 part-time professional.
EIN: 061637040
Selected grants: The following grants are a representative sample of this grantmaker's funding activity:
$350,000 to Teach for America, New York, NY, 2012. For NYC and CT programs.
$200,000 to Achievement First, Connecticut Office, New Haven, CT, 2012. For Achievement First Bridgeport Academies.
$200,000 to Childrens Village, Dobbs Ferry, NY, 2012. For Work Appreciation for Youth Program.
$200,000 to Domus Kids, Stamford, CT, 2012. For Trailblazers Academy and Lion's Den Afterschool Program.
$200,000 to Good Shepherd Services, New York, NY, 2012. For Transfer High Schools.
$200,000 to Harlem Childrens Zone, New York, NY, 2012. For early childhood programs.
$200,000 to Year Up New York, New York, NY, 2012. For NYC Program.
$190,000 to Port Chester Carver Center, Port Chester, NY, 2012. For playground and building renovations.
$150,000 to Building Educated Leaders for Life Foundation, New York, NY, 2012. For New York City Program.
$150,000 to Childrens Village, Dobbs Ferry, NY, 2012. For technology equipment upgrades.

1633
The Michael & Carol Lowenstein Foundation Inc. ✧

55 Railroad Ave., 2nd Fl.
Greenwich, CT 06830-6378

Established in 2007 in NY.
Donors: Michael B. Lowenstein; Carol Lowenstein; Lake Road Holding Co.; Lowenstein Holding Company Inc.
Foundation type: Independent foundation.
Financial data (yr. ended 10/31/13): Assets, $32,487,566 (M); gifts received, $4,627,333; expenditures, $618,644; qualifying distributions, $562,640; giving activities include $558,507 for 25 grants (high: $150,000; low: $200).
Fields of interest: Human services; Jewish federated giving programs; Jewish agencies & synagogues; Homeless.
Type of support: General/operating support.
Limitations: Applications not accepted. Giving primarily in Washington, D.C. and NY. No grants to individuals.
Application information: Contributes only to pre-selected organizations.
Directors: Thomas Coleman; Carol Lowenstein; Michael B. Lowenstein.
EIN: 205953051
Selected grants: The following grants are a representative sample of this grantmaker's funding activity:
$100,000 to Israel Project, Washington, DC, 2011.
$56,000 to Birthright Israel Foundation, New York, NY, 2011.
$30,000 to Say Yes to Education, New York, NY, 2011.
$14,000 to Facing History and Ourselves National Foundation, New York, NY, 2011.
$5,000 to Byram Hills Education Foundation, Armonk, NY, 2011.
$5,000 to Columbia University, New York, NY, 2011.
$5,000 to Jewish Institute for National Security Affairs, Washington, DC, 2011.
$1,000 to From the Top, Boston, MA, 2011.

1634
Main Street Community Foundation ✧ ☆

200 Main St.
P.O. Box 2702
Bristol, CT 06011-2702 (860) 583-6363
Contact: Susan Sadecki, Pres. and C.E.O.
FAX: (860) 589-1252;
E-mail: office@mainstreetfoundation.org; Grant inquiry e-mail: jarre@mainstreetfoundation.org; Main URL: http://www.mainstreetfoundation.org
Facebook: http://www.facebook.com/MainStreetCommunityFoundation
YouTube: http://www.youtube.com/TheMSCF

Established in 1995 in CT.
Foundation type: Community foundation.
Financial data (yr. ended 12/31/13): Assets, $14,548,767 (M); gifts received, $1,767,419; expenditures, $928,297; giving activities include $366,067 for 15+ grants (high: $50,000), and $121,898 for 139 grants to individuals.
Purpose and activities: The foundation is committed to assisting donors who wish to build charitable endowments to support the communities of Bristol, Burlington, Plainville, Plymouth, Southington, and Wolcott, CT, helping to make each town a better community in which to live and work.
Fields of interest: Arts; Education, early childhood education; Higher education; Education; Environment; Animals/wildlife; Health care; Youth development; Human services; Community/economic development.
Type of support: General/operating support; Management development/capacity building; Building/renovation; Equipment; Emergency funds; Program development; Conferences/seminars; Seed money; Curriculum development; Scholarship funds; Technical assistance; Grants to individuals; Scholarships—to individuals; Matching/challenge support.
Limitations: Applications accepted. Giving primarily in Bristol, Burlington, Plainville, Plymouth, Southington, and Wolcott, CT. No support for governmental agencies unless it is determined that overriding special circumstances exist, or religious activities. No grants to individuals (except through the scholarship program, immediate response funds), or for operating or budget deficits, previously incurred obligations, fundraising events, endowments, research, property repairs and maintenance, or memorials; no loans.
Publications: Application guidelines; Annual report; Financial statement; Informational brochure; Newsletter.
Application information: Visit foundation web site for application forms and guidelines. Interested organizations are asked to contact Jarre Betts, Director of Programs & Community Relations, before applying to discuss the proposal and process. Application form required.
Initial approach: Telephone
Copies of proposal: 5
Deadline(s): Mar. 31
Board meeting date(s): 2nd Fri. of each month
Final notification: Mid-June
Officers and Directors:* Janis L. Neri,* Chair.; John A. Letizia,* Vice-Chair.; Susan Sadecki,* Pres. and C.E.O.; Jarre B. Betts, V.P., Progs.; Robert M. Caiaze,* Secy.; John D. Scarritt,* Treas.; David J. Aldieri; Michael Brault; Todd Burton; Kristine J. Dargenio; Valerie A. DePaolo; Val Dumais; Patricia B. Dunn; David C. England; Marguerite P. Fletcher; Barbara Fontaine; Arthur P. Funk, Jr.; Anita Hamzy; Daniel J. LaPorte; Mark Peterson; Jeffrey Sonenstein.
Number of staff: 1 full-time professional; 2 part-time professional; 1 part-time support.
EIN: 061433299

1635
Andrew J. & Joyce D. Mandell Family Foundation, Inc. ✧
(formerly The Mandell Family Foundation, Inc.)
240 Hartford Ave.
Newington, CT 06111-2077

Established in 1984 in CT.
Donors: Andrew J. Mandell; Joyce D. Mandell; Bruce A. Mandell; Mark N. Mandell; Meryl L. Mandell Braunstein.
Foundation type: Independent foundation.
Financial data (yr. ended 04/30/13): Assets, $15,855,363 (M); gifts received, $3,099,600; expenditures, $738,788; qualifying distributions, $689,124; giving activities include $689,124 for 45 grants (high: $115,100; low: $500).
Purpose and activities: Giving primarily for health and Jewish organizations; funding also for a film and video association.
Fields of interest: Media, film/video; Health organizations, association; Jewish agencies & synagogues.
Limitations: Applications not accepted. Giving primarily in CT, with emphasis on West Hartford; some funding also in Los Angeles, CA. No grants to individuals.
Application information: Contributes only to pre-selected organizations.
Officers: Joyce D. Mandell, Pres.; Andrew J. Mandell, V.P.; Bruce A. Mandell, Secy.
Director: Mark N. Mandell.
EIN: 222536600

1636
Maranatha Foundation, Inc. ✧
c/o William G. Beattie
13 Rose St.
Danbury, CT 06810-3006

Established in CT.
Donors: William G. Beattie; Zambezi Foundation.
Foundation type: Operating foundation.
Financial data (yr. ended 12/31/12): Assets, $17,218,041 (M); gifts received, $769,707; expenditures, $2,843,896; qualifying distributions, $2,491,185; giving activities include $2,255,735 for 5 grants (high: $2,176,660; low: $1,575).
Fields of interest: Education; Human services; Youth, services; Community/economic development.
Limitations: Applications not accepted. Giving primarily in Danbury, CT.
Application information: Contributes only to pre-selected organizations.
Officers and Directors:* William G. Beattie,* Chair.; Katherine L. Beattie,* Secy.; Michael G. Beattie; Elizabeth A. Wylie.
EIN: 061531327

1637
The Martino Family Foundation ✧ ☆
c/o Michael E. Martino
329 Mariomi Rd.
New Canaan, CT 06840

Donor: Michael E. Martino.
Foundation type: Independent foundation.
Financial data (yr. ended 12/31/13): Assets, $21,008,973 (M); gifts received, $9,988,050; expenditures, $540,012; qualifying distributions, $540,000; giving activities include $540,000 for 20 grants (high: $150,000; low: $500).
Fields of interest: Education; Catholic agencies & churches.
Limitations: Applications not accepted. Giving in the U.S., with emphasis on CT.
Application information: Unsolicited requests for funds not accepted.
Director: Michael E. Martino.
EIN: 456635594

1638
S&L Marx Foundation, Inc. ✧
(formerly The Marx-Better Foundation, Inc.)
15 E. Putnam Ave., No. 270
Greenwich, CT 06830-5424

Established in 2004 in CT.
Donors: The Virginia & Leanoard Marx Fund; Merchants National Properties, Inc.
Foundation type: Independent foundation.
Financial data (yr. ended 12/31/13): Assets, $86,243,940 (M); expenditures, $4,323,018; qualifying distributions, $4,278,984; giving activities include $4,139,300 for 96 grants (high: $1,025,000; low: $300).
Purpose and activities: Giving primarily for the arts, education, medical research, and human services.
Fields of interest: Arts; Education; Medical research, institute; Human services; Jewish agencies & synagogues.
Limitations: Applications not accepted. Giving primarily in CT, MA, MD, and NY. No grants to individuals.
Application information: Contributes only to pre-selected organizations.
Officers: Sylvia Marx, Pres.; Leonard Marx, Treas.; Nancy Marx Better, Exec. Dir.
Director: James Better.
EIN: 200677535

1639
Katharine Matthies Foundation ✧
c/o US Trust
200 Glastonbury Blvd., Ste. 200
Glastonbury, CT 06033-4056
Contact: Amy R. Lynch, .
E-mail: amy.r.lynch@ustrust.com; E-mail to discuss application process or for questions about the foundation: ct.grantmaking@ustrust.com (Foundation name should appear in subject line); Main URL: http://www.bankofamerica.com/grantmaking

Established in 1987 in CT.
Donor: Katharine Matthies†.
Foundation type: Independent foundation.
Financial data (yr. ended 12/31/13): Assets, $19,268,574 (M); expenditures, $975,603; qualifying distributions, $850,276; giving activities include $787,389 for 52 grants (high: $125,000; low: $1,590).
Purpose and activities: Giving primarily to support and promote quality educational, human services, and health care programming for underserved populations. Special consideration is given to organizations that work to prevent cruelty to children and animals.
Fields of interest: Arts; Animals/wildlife; Recreation; Human services; Youth, services; Family services; Community/economic development.
Type of support: General/operating support; Capital campaigns; Building/renovation; Equipment; Program development; Publication; Seed money; Matching/challenge support.
Limitations: Giving limited to the Lower Naugatuck Valley of CT, particularly the towns of Ansonia, Derby, Oxford, Shelton and Beacon Falls, with special consideration to organizations that serve the people of Seymour.
Publications: Application guidelines; Grants list.
Application information:
Initial approach: Online
Copies of proposal: 6
Deadline(s): May 1
Trustee: Bank of America, N.A.
EIN: 066261860
Selected grants: The following grants are a representative sample of this grantmaker's funding activity:
$44,825 to Derby Historical Society, Derby, CT, 2013. For Restoration work to the exterior of the David Humphreys House.
$35,000 to Area Congregations Together, Shelton, CT, 2013. For General operations of the organization.
$35,000 to Area Congregations Together, Shelton, CT, 2013. For General operations of the organization.
$35,000 to Boys and Girls Club of the Lower Naugatuck Valley, Shelton, CT, 2013. For General Operations of the Organization.
$25,000 to TEAM, Derby Discovery Collaborative, Derby, CT, 2013. For 2nd year commitment to support Derby Comprehensive Plan.
$19,300 to Seymour, Town of, Seymour, CT, 2013. For Smart Board and Recording System for Seymour Town Hall.
$15,000 to Boy Scouts of America, Derby, CT, 2013. For new Marketing and Development Director position.
$11,000 to Shakesperience Productions, Waterbury, CT, 2013. For Curricular Enhancement for Students in Seymour, Ansonia, Beacon Falls, Derby, Oxford, and Shelton Schools.
$10,000 to Junior Achievement of Western Connecticut, Bridgeport, CT, 2013. For existing and new JA economic education initiative in Ansonia, Derby and Seymour.
$7,500 to Maritime Aquarium at Norwalk, Norwalk, CT, 2013. For Transportation Fund for Lower Naugatuck Valley Schools.

1640
The Harold W. McGraw, Jr. Family Foundation, Inc. ✧
c/o Cummings & Lockwood
6 Landmark Sq. (HST III), 9th Fl.
Stamford, CT 06901

Donor: Harold W. McGraw, Jr.
Foundation type: Independent foundation.
Financial data (yr. ended 12/31/13): Assets, $55,872,719 (M); expenditures, $1,977,861; qualifying distributions, $1,832,711; giving activities include $1,820,488 for 2 grants (high: $1,815,488; low: $5,000).
Fields of interest: Education.
Limitations: Applications not accepted. Giving primarily in CT.
Application information: Unsolicited requests for funds not accepted.

Officers and Directors:* Suzanne McGraw,* Pres.; Robert P. McGraw,* Secy.; Harold W. McGraw III,* Treas.
EIN: 273418504

1641
McLeod Blue Skye Charitable Foundation, Inc. ✧ ☆

86 Seaview Ave.
Branford, CT 06405-5444

Established in 1992 in CT.
Donor: Christopher K. McLeod.
Foundation type: Independent foundation.
Financial data (yr. ended 12/31/13): Assets, $7,419,763 (M); gifts received, $535,575; expenditures, $536,259; qualifying distributions, $473,988; giving activities include $473,910 for 8 grants (high: $150,000; low: $2,000).
Purpose and activities: Giving primarily for educational purposes.
Fields of interest: Secondary school/education; Higher education; United Ways and Federated Giving Programs.
Type of support: Scholarship funds; Capital campaigns.
Limitations: Applications not accepted. Giving primarily in CT and MA. No grants to individuals.
Application information: Contributes only to pre-selected organizations.
Officers and Directors:* Christopher K. McLeod,* Pres. and Treas.; Elaine M. McLeod,* Secy.; Scott McLeod.
EIN: 223216389
Selected grants: The following grants are a representative sample of this grantmaker's funding activity:
$50,000 to Lehigh University, Bethlehem, PA, 2011. For capital campaign.
$30,000 to Sacred Heart University, Fairfield, CT, 2011. For annual support.
$25,000 to Right Question Project, Cambridge, MA, 2011. For annual support.
$5,000 to Fairfield College Preparatory School, Fairfield, CT, 2011. For annual support.

1642
Vince & Linda McMahon Family Foundation, Inc. ✧

1241 E. Main St.
Stamford, CT 06902-3520 (203) 352-8612
Contact: Linda E. McMahon, Secy.-Treas.

Established in 2006 in CT.
Donors: Vincent K. McMahon; Linda E. McMahon.
Foundation type: Independent foundation.
Financial data (yr. ended 12/31/13): Assets, $4,429,634 (M); gifts received, $3,838,500; expenditures, $2,006,917; qualifying distributions, $1,804,155; giving activities include $1,804,155 for 32 grants (high: $500,000; low: $1,000).
Fields of interest: Higher education; Breast cancer; Boys & girls clubs; YM/YWCAs & YM/YWHAs; Children/youth, services.
Limitations: Applications accepted. Giving primarily in CT; some funding also in Dallas, TX. No grants to individuals.
Application information:
Initial approach: Written request with detailed proposal for use of funds
Copies of proposal: 1
Deadline(s): None
Officers and Directors:* Vincent K. McMahon,* Pres.; Linda E. McMahon,* Secy.-Treas.; Jerry S. McDevitt.
EIN: 204717289
Selected grants: The following grants are a representative sample of this grantmaker's funding activity:
$1,000,000 to Sacred Heart University, Fairfield, CT, 2011.
$333,000 to East Carolina University, Greenville, NC, 2011.
$150,000 to Ability Beyond Disability, Bethel, CT, 2011.
$150,000 to Achievement First, New Haven, CT, 2011. For general use.
$100,000 to Boys and Girls Club of Stamford, Stamford, CT, 2011. For general operations.
$100,000 to Mill River Collaborative, Stamford, CT, 2011. For capital campaign.
$75,000 to Connecticut Public Broadcasting, Hartford, CT, 2011.
$50,000 to Inspirica, Stamford, CT, 2011.
$25,000 to Stamford Hospital, Stamford, CT, 2011.
$25,000 to Yerwood Center, Stamford, CT, 2011.

1643
The Meriden Foundation ✧

c/o Webster Bank, N.A.
123 Bank St.
Waterbury, CT 06702-2205 (860) 692-1751
Contact: Paul M. McAfee

Established in 1983.
Donors: A. Leo Ricci†; I. Margaret Mesite; Rose Mesite; Jessie Wilcox Clark†; Warren Gardner†; Charles Hasburg†; F. Marino D'Amato†; Shirley Samaris†.
Foundation type: Independent foundation.
Financial data (yr. ended 12/31/12): Assets, $20,927,788 (M); gifts received, $19,159; expenditures, $1,434,124; qualifying distributions, $1,229,757; giving activities include $1,043,594 for 89+ grants (high: $57,200), and $146,185 for 62 grants to individuals (high: $5,000; low: $500).
Purpose and activities: Giving primarily for education, health organizations and hospitals, children and youth services, including children's hospitals, social services, YMCAs, and Protestant and Roman Catholic churches.
Fields of interest: Law school/education; Education; Hospitals (general); Hospitals (specialty); Health organizations, association; Boys & girls clubs; Human services; Salvation Army; YM/YWCAs & YM/YWHAs; Children/youth, services; United Ways and Federated Giving Programs; Protestant agencies & churches; Catholic agencies & churches.
Type of support: General/operating support; Annual campaigns; Scholarships—to individuals.
Limitations: Giving limited to the greater Meriden, CT, area.
Application information: Application form required.
Initial approach: Letter, on organizational letterhead, for grants; application form for scholarship requests
Deadline(s): None
Trustee: Webster Bank, N.A.
Ditribution Committee: Thomas Griglun, Chair.; Walter G. Alwang, Vice-Chair.; Elsa Bradford; Maureen Kane; Peter Vouras, Jr.
EIN: 066037849
Selected grants: The following grants are a representative sample of this grantmaker's funding activity:
$16,630 to Gaylord Hospital, Wallingford, CT, 2012. For general use.

1644
Middlesex County Community Foundation, Inc. ✧

211 S. Main St.
Middletown, CT 06457 (860) 347-0025
Contact: Cynthia H. Clegg, Pres. and C.E.O.; Ms. Thayer Talbott, Dir., Progs. and Opers.
FAX: (860) 347-0029;
E-mail: info@middlesexcountycf.org; Additional e-mail: cynthia@middlesexcountycf.org and thayer@middlesexcountycf.org; Main URL: http://www.middlesexcountycf.org
E-Newsletter: http://middlesexcountycf.org/news-events/newsletters-annual-reports/
Facebook: https://www.facebook.com/CommunityFoundationMC?rf=126312434089559

Established in 1997 in CT.
Foundation type: Community foundation.
Financial data (yr. ended 12/31/13): Assets, $11,739,436 (M); gifts received, $1,695,998; expenditures, $1,061,635; giving activities include $582,109 for 18+ grants (high: $77,000).
Purpose and activities: The foundation is dedicated to improving the quality of life in Middlesex County, CT. The foundation's grantmaking areas of interest include the arts, the environment, women and girls issues, heritage enhancement, education, neighborhood enhancement, safer communities, and services to help the less fortunate.
Fields of interest: Historic preservation/historical societies; Arts; Education; Environment; Animals/wildlife; Human services; Community development, neighborhood development; Community/economic development.
Type of support: General/operating support; Management development/capacity building; Equipment; Program development; Conferences/seminars; Technical assistance; Program evaluation; Matching/challenge support.
Limitations: Applications accepted. Giving primarily in Middlesex County, CT. No grants to individuals, or for endowment, capital campaigns, building programs, or debt reduction.
Publications: Application guidelines; Annual report; Financial statement; Grants list; Newsletter.
Application information: Visit foundation web site for application forms and guidelines. The foundation's Grants Committee requests full grant proposals from most viable Letters of Intent. Application form required.
Initial approach: Letter of Intent (no more than 2 pages)
Copies of proposal: 16
Deadline(s): Sept. 17
Board meeting date(s): Quarterly
Final notification: Dec. 31
Officers and Directors:* John S. Biddiscombe,* Chair.; Moira B. Martin,* Vice-Chair.; Cynthia H. Clegg,* Pres. and C.E.O.; Nancy Fischbach,* Secy.; Richard W. Tomc,* Asst. Secy.; David Director,* Treas.; John L. Boccalatte; Vincent G. Capece, Jr.; Sharon Griffin; Wallace C. Jones; Jean C. LaTorre; Marc V. Levin; Deborah L. Moore; Gregory P. Rainey; Gary P. Salva; Judith D. Schoonmaker; Eric W. Thornburg; Anna M. Wasescha; Frantz Williams, Jr.

Number of staff: 2 full-time professional; 1 part-time professional; 1 part-time support.
EIN: 061477711

1645
MJPM Foundation ✧
c/o Vail & Vail LLP
7 Academy St.
P.O. Box 572
Salisbury, CT 06068
E-mail: hheld@Mclaughlinstern.com

Established in 1999 in NY.
Donor: Mary J.P. Moore†.
Foundation type: Independent foundation.
Financial data (yr. ended 12/31/13): Assets, $16,366,517 (M); expenditures, $747,201; qualifying distributions, $663,925; giving activities include $630,300 for 10 grants (high: $300,000; low: $2,500).
Purpose and activities: Giving primarily to a community foundation, and for land and other natural resource conservation; funding also for human services.
Fields of interest: Historic preservation/historical societies; Environment, natural resources; Environment, land resources; Food services; Human services; Foundations (community).
Limitations: Applications not accepted. Giving primarily in the northwest corner of CT. No grants to individuals, or for research or professional fellowships.
Application information: Contributes only to pre-selected organizations.
Officers: Samuel F. Posey, Pres.; Nicholas J. Moore, Secy.; David W. Moore, Treas.
Number of staff: 1 part-time support.
EIN: 134043598

1646
The William T. Morris Foundation, Inc. ✧
49 Richmondville Ave., Ste. 306
Westport, CT 06880-2054
Contact: Bruce A. August, Pres.
FAX: (203) 557-9103; Main URL: http://www.wtmf.org

Trust established in 1937; incorporated in 1941 in DE.
Donor: William T. Morris†.
Foundation type: Independent foundation.
Financial data (yr. ended 06/30/13): Assets, $52,380,352 (M); expenditures, $3,194,375; qualifying distributions, $2,628,659; giving activities include $2,100,500 for 50 grants (high: $238,000; low: $2,500).
Purpose and activities: Giving primarily to charitable, scientific, and/or educational institutions.
Fields of interest: Arts; Higher education; Hospitals (general); Health care; Children/youth, services.
Type of support: Research; General/operating support; Continuing support; Scholarship funds.
Limitations: Applications not accepted. Giving primarily in the northeastern states, especially NY, CT, RI, NH, NJ, and NC. No support for religious or political organizations. No grants to individuals.
Publications: IRS Form 990 or 990-PF printed copy available upon request.
Application information: Unsolicited requests for funds not accepted.
Board meeting date(s): As required
Officers and Directors:* Bruce A. August,* C.E.O. and Pres.; Jeffrey Johnson,* Exec. V.P. and Treas.; Robert Patti, V.P. and Secy.; Steven April, V.P.; Paul Barret, V.P.
Number of staff: 2 full-time professional.
EIN: 131600908
Selected grants: The following grants are a representative sample of this grantmaker's funding activity:
$125,000 to Boston College, Chestnut Hill, MA, 2011. For program and project support.
$125,000 to Dartmouth College, Hanover, NH, 2011. For program and project support.
$100,000 to Arthritis Foundation, Atlanta, GA, 2011. For program and project support.
$75,000 to Appalachian Mountain Club, Boston, MA, 2011. For program and project support.
$75,000 to Multiple Sclerosis Society, National, New York, NY, 2011. For program and project support.
$55,000 to University of Pittsburgh, Pittsburgh, PA, 2011. For program and project support.
$50,000 to Alzheimers Association, Chicago, IL, 2011. For program and project support.
$35,000 to Foundation Center, New York, NY, 2011. For program and project support.

1647
The William & Alice Mortensen Foundation ✧
85 Memorial Rd., Unit 410
West Hartford, CT 06107-4212 (860) 461-7927
Contact: Robert S. Carter, Jr., Pres.
E-mail: bob58car@comcast.net

Established in 1982 in DE.
Donors: William Mortensen†; Trice Mortensen†; Alice Mortensen†.
Foundation type: Independent foundation.
Financial data (yr. ended 12/31/12): Assets, $14,804,023 (M); expenditures, $831,438; qualifying distributions, $788,864; giving activities include $745,769 for 62 grants (high: $94,500; low: $1,500).
Fields of interest: Historic preservation/historical societies; Arts; Elementary/secondary education; Higher education; Education; Hospitals (general); Human services; Religion; Children; Youth; Physically disabled; Women; Adults, men; Single parents; Homeless.
Type of support: Equipment; Program development; Seed money; Research; Technical assistance.
Limitations: Applications accepted. Giving primarily in CT, with emphasis on Hartford.
Publications: Application guidelines; Program policy statement (including application guidelines).
Application information: Applicants should submit one original plus 3 copies of the proposal. Application form required.
Initial approach: Letter or telephone
Copies of proposal: 4
Deadline(s): May 15 and Nov. 15
Board meeting date(s): June 1 and Dec. 1
Officer: Robert S. Carter, Jr., Pres. and Treas.
Directors: Hon. Alfred V. Covello; Robert M. Hadley, C.P.A.; Ellen Coote Solek, Ph.D.
EIN: 061064150

1648
Ner Tzion Foundation ✧
c/o DKR Capital, Attn.: Helaine Uliano
1281 E. Main St.
Stamford, CT 06902-3544

Established in 2002 in DE.
Donors: Barry Klein; Seth Fischer; Robert Rubin.
Foundation type: Independent foundation.
Financial data (yr. ended 12/31/12): Assets, $20,937,497 (M); gifts received, $100,000; expenditures, $1,211,042; qualifying distributions, $813,850; giving activities include $813,850 for 9 grants (high: $537,000; low: $250).
Fields of interest: Jewish federated giving programs; Jewish agencies & synagogues.
Limitations: Applications not accepted. Giving primarily in New York, NY. No grants to individuals.
Application information: Contributes only to pre-selected organizations.
Officer: Amy Saleeby, Secy.
Directors: Barry Klein; Elaine S. Klein; Keren Klein Vavyad.
EIN: 020613293

1649
Roy R. and Marie S. Neuberger Foundation, Inc. ✧
55 Walls Dr., 3rd Fl.
Fairfield, CT 06824-5163
Contact: Gloria Silverman

Incorporated in 1954 in NY.
Donors: Roy R. Neuberger; Marie S. Neuberger†; Ann N. Aceves; James A. Neuberger; Roy S. Neuberger.
Foundation type: Independent foundation.
Financial data (yr. ended 12/31/12): Assets, $4,501,027 (M); expenditures, $4,923,833; qualifying distributions, $4,868,388; giving activities include $4,810,212 for 57 grants (high: $4,500,737; low: $60).
Purpose and activities: Giving primarily for education, as well as to arts and culture organizations, and Jewish agencies and temples.
Fields of interest: Visual arts; Performing arts; Arts; Higher education; Jewish agencies & synagogues.
Type of support: General/operating support; Continuing support; Annual campaigns.
Limitations: Applications not accepted. Giving primarily in NY. No support for political organizations. No grants to individuals.
Application information: Contributes only to pre-selected organizations.
Board meeting date(s): Varies
Officers and Directors:* Roy R. Neuberger,* Pres.; Roy S. Neuberger,* V.P. and Treas.; Ann N. Aceves,* V.P.; James A. Neuberger,* V.P.
Number of staff: None.
EIN: 136066102

1650
New Canaan Community Foundation, Inc. ✧
111 Cherry St.
New Canaan, CT 06840 (203) 966-0231
Contact: Cynthia Gorey, Exec. Dir.
FAX: (203) 966-0831;
E-mail: info@newcanaancf.org; Additional E-mail: cgorey@newcanaancf.org; Main URL: http://www.newcanaancf.org

Established in 1977 in CT.
Donors: Alex G. Nason Foundation; Theodore and Veda Stanley Foundation; Bruce Calvert; Joseph Dionne; Joan Dionne; Marjorie Calvert; Martha Sweeters‡; Anne Sapienza‡; William Walbert; Laura Walbert; Wendy Hilboldt; James Hilboldt; Harry Rein; Susan Rein; Chase Carey; Wendy Carey; Edwin Brooks; Louise Brooks; John Burns; Barbara Burns; Stuart Lovejoy; Susan Lovejoy; Timothy Pettee; Sheila Pettee; John Rice; Pat Rice; William Mahoney; Alice Mahoney; Anne Cotton; Leonard Cotton; Mark Mitchell; Janet Mitchell; Debbie Perkins; Maurice Perkins; Trish Worden; Richard Worden.
Foundation type: Community foundation.
Financial data (yr. ended 12/31/13): Assets, $16,423,088 (M); gifts received, $1,428,961; expenditures, $1,446,232; giving activities include $837,521 for 94+ grants (high: $27,000; low: $100), and $203,170 for grants to individuals.
Purpose and activities: The foundation's mission is to promote community philanthropy and help donors achieve their charitable goals.
Fields of interest: Museums; Historical activities; Arts; Libraries (public); Education; Environment; Health care; Recreation, parks/playgrounds; Recreation; Youth development, adult & child programs; YM/YWCAs & YM/YWHAs; Children/youth, services; Family services; Human services; Community/economic development.
Type of support: General/operating support; Management development/capacity building; Capital campaigns; Building/renovation; Equipment; Emergency funds; Program development; Conferences/seminars; Seed money; Scholarship funds; Technical assistance; Grants to individuals; Scholarships—to individuals; Matching/challenge support.
Limitations: Applications accepted. Giving limited to New Canaan, CT and the surrounding towns for NCCF discretionary fund grants. No grants for expenses already incurred or to build endowment.
Publications: Application guidelines; Annual report; Annual report (including application guidelines); Financial statement; Grants list; Informational brochure.
Application information: Visit foundation web site for grant proposal cover sheet and application guidelines. Applicants should call the foundation's office before submitting proposal. Application form required.
Initial approach: Telephone
Copies of proposal: 1
Deadline(s): Sept. 8 for Young Philanthropist Fund grants; Feb. 13 for main discretionary grant cycle
Board meeting date(s): Monthly from Sept. to July
Final notification: May
Officers and Directors:* Dave Hunt,* Pres.; Rich Townsend,* Treas.; Cynthia Gorey, Exec. Dir.; Barb Achenbaum; Susan Boston; Kathleen Corbet; Tom Cronin; Majorie Furman; Alan Haas; Diane Hanauer; Janet Lanaway; Kevin Moynihan; John Murphy; Ed O'Neil; Kathy Schulte; Don Smith; Tom Stadler; Karen Stevenson; Sharon Stevenson; Amy Wilkinson.
Number of staff: 3 part-time professional.
EIN: 060970466
Selected grants: The following grants are a representative sample of this grantmaker's funding activity:
$30,000 to Waveny Care Center Network, New Canaan, CT, 2013. For second generator for skilled nursing facility.
$29,000 to STAR, Lighting the Way, Norwalk, CT, 2013. For general operating support.
$25,000 to Getabout, New Canaan, CT, 2013. For general operating support for transportation for elderly and special needs residents.
$20,000 to Domestic Violence Crisis Center, Norwalk, CT, 2013. For Family Justice Project staff/counseling project and public policy and advocacy platform.
$20,000 to George Washington Carver Community Center, Norwalk, CT, 2013. For general operating support for youth program.
$20,000 to Inspiria Science Center, Gralum, Norway, 2013. For general operating support for homeless services.
$17,000 to Family Centers, Greenwich, CT, 2013. For general operating support for behavioral health services.
$15,000 to Northern Connecticut Land Trust, Somers, CT, 2013. For increase awareness, re-survey top 10 land holdings and mark boundaries.
$14,000 to New Canaan Cares, New Canaan, CT, 2013. For preschool program and general operating support for health educational programs.
$13,200 to Town Players of New Canaan, New Canaan, CT, 2013. To replace stage lighting and sound systems.

1651
NewAlliance Foundation, Inc. ✧

195 Church St., 7th Fl.
New Haven, CT 06510-2009
Contact: Kim A. Healey, Exec. Dir.
E-mail: khealey@newalliancefoundation.org; Additional contacts: Maryann Ott, Assoc. Dir., tel.: (203) 859-6555, e-mail: mott@newalliancefoundation.org; Bobbi Griffith, Admin. Asst., tel.: (203) 859-6543, e-mail: bgriffith@newalliancefoundation.org; Main URL: http://newalliancefoundation.org/

Established in 2004 in CT.
Donor: NewAlliance Bancshares, Inc.
Foundation type: Independent foundation.
Financial data (yr. ended 12/31/13): Assets, $31,592,866 (M); expenditures, $1,991,724; qualifying distributions, $1,658,781; giving activities include $1,190,000 for 180 grants (high: $35,000; low: $1,000).
Purpose and activities: The foundation supports nonprofit and charitable organizations that promote the arts; community development; health and human services; and youth and education.
Fields of interest: Museums; Performing arts; Arts; Elementary/secondary education; Education, services; Education, reading; Education; Environment; Health care; Employment, services; Employment, training; Food services; Food banks; Housing/shelter; Youth development; Children/youth, services; Developmentally disabled, centers & services; Homeless, human services; Human services; Economic development; Community/economic development; Mathematics; Engineering/technology; Science; Children/youth; Aging; Economically disadvantaged.
Type of support: General/operating support; Continuing support; Management development/capacity building; Capital campaigns; Building/renovation; Equipment; Endowments; Program development; Seed money; Sponsorships; Employee matching gifts; Matching/challenge support.
Limitations: Applications accepted. Giving limited to Branford, Centerbrook, Cheshire, Chester, Clinton, Columbia, Coventry, Danielson, Dayville, East Hartford, East Haven, Ellington, Enfield, Essex, Glastonbury, Guilford, Hamden, Hartford, Hebron, Madison, Manchester, Milford, New Haven, North Branford, North Haven, Old Saybrook, Orange, Putnam, Seymour, South Windsor, Stafford Springs, Storrs, Tolland, Vernon, Wallingford, West Hartford, West Haven, Westbrook, Wethersfield, Willington, Willimantic, Windsor, Woodbridge, and Woodstock, CT. No support for religious organizations not of direct benefit to the entire community, service clubs, fraternal organizations, or third party fundraising organizations, Parent Teacher Organizations, state agencies, departments, or organizations raising money for specific diseases. No grants to individuals, or for political or lobbying activities, interest expenses on loans or debt reduction, feasibility studies, trips, tours, transportation, or conference attendance, golf tournaments, animal causes, team sponsorships, "a-thon" fundraising events, pageants, or start-up needs for programs initiated by organizations not located in areas of company operations.
Publications: Application guidelines; Annual report.
Application information: Support is limited to 1 contribution per organization during any given year. Organizations receiving support are asked to provide a final report. Proposal narratives should be no longer than 2 pages. Application form required.
Initial approach: Complete the on-line Application Coversheet on foundation web site
Copies of proposal: 1
Deadline(s): See foundation web site for current deadline
Board meeting date(s): Mar. and Sept.
Final notification: Within a week of board meeting
Officers and Directors:* Robert Lyons, Jr.,* Chair.; Paul A. McCraven,* Secy.-Treas.; Kim A. Healey, Exec. Dir.; William W. Bouton III; Shiela B. Flanagan; Marjorie Bussmann Gillis, Ed.D.; D. Anthony Guglielmo; Dr. Dorsey L. Kendrick; Dr. Julia M. McNamara; Joseph H. Rossi; Donald E. Waggaman, Jr.; Diane Wishnafski.
Number of staff: 2 full-time professional; 1 full-time support.
EIN: 562453619
Selected grants: The following grants are a representative sample of this grantmaker's funding activity:
$35,000 to Killingly Public Library, Danielson, CT, 2012. For READy for the Grade, K-3 summer reading initiative where the library partners with Killingly Central School to develop a program to stem summer reading loss and maintain grade level reading in children from low-income families.
$35,000 to New Haven Free Public Library, New Haven, CT, 2012. For READy for the Grade, K-3 summer reading initiative where the library partners with Clinton Avenue School to develop a program to stem summer reading loss and maintain grade level reading in children from low-income families.
$35,000 to Rockville Public Library, Vernon, CT, 2012. For READy for the Grade, K-3 summer reading initiative where the library partners with Maple Street School to develop a program to stem summer reading loss and maintain grade level reading in children from low-income families.
$20,000 to Boys and Girls Club of New Haven, New Haven, CT, 2012. For general operating support.
$20,000 to Connecticut Players Foundation, Long Wharf Theater, New Haven, CT, 2012. For

production support and campaign to renovate the facility.
$20,000 to New Haven Reads Community Book Bank, New Haven, CT, 2012. For general operating support for one-on-one after school tutoring program.
$15,000 to Columbus House, New Haven, CT, 2012. For general operating and maintenance support.
$15,000 to Yale-New Haven Childrens Hospital, Children's Psychiatric Inpatient Service Unit, New Haven, CT, 2012. For Silver Lining Expansion Project, to meet the needs of children and adolescents.
$12,500 to New Haven International Festival of Arts and Ideas, New Haven, CT, 2012. For free performances and community programs.
$12,500 to Yale Child Study Center, New Haven, CT, 2012. For clinical coordinator and community advocacy work to provide acute and follow-up services to children exposed to violence and other trauma throughout New Haven. Additional support granted after the Dec 14, 2012 Newtown tragedy..

1652
Newman's Own Foundation ✧
790 Farmington Ave., No. 4B
Farmington, CT 06032-2300
E-mail: info@newmansownfoundation.org; Main URL: http://www.newmansownfoundation.org/
Facebook: https://www.facebook.com/NewmansOwnFoundation
Pinterest: http://www.pinterest.com/newmansownfdn
Twitter: https://twitter.com/newmansownfdn
YouTube: http://www.youtube.com/newmansownfoundatn

Established in 2004 in DE and CT.
Donors: Paul L. Newman‡; Newman's Own.
Foundation type: Company-sponsored foundation.
Financial data (yr. ended 12/31/12): Assets, $226,069,474 (M); expenditures, $33,765,504; qualifying distributions, $33,329,009; giving activities include $30,000,000 for 773 grants (high: $2,500,000; low: $1,000).
Purpose and activities: Newman's Own Foundation funds a broad geographic range of 501(c) 3 nonprofits that fit within its focus areas (listed under Program Areas). In addition, the Foundation supports grantees that: Demonstrate potential for significant impact or growth; Present innovative and effective model programs with potential for replication; Encourage philanthropy by leveraging Foundation resources to stimulate giving from other sources; Possess existing or potential for strong organizational leadership/governance; Demonstrate fiscal responsibility.
Fields of interest: Agriculture/food, alliance/advocacy; Nutrition; Disasters, preparedness/services; Children/youth, services; Civil/human rights; Community/economic development; Voluntarism promotion; Philanthropy/voluntarism; Public affairs, equal rights; Military/veterans' organizations; Leadership development; Children; Military/veterans; Economically disadvantaged.
Type of support: General/operating support; Management development/capacity building; Program development; Fellowships; Matching/challenge support.
Limitations: Applications not accepted. Giving on a national and international basis. No support for No funding goes to: organizations that discriminate on any basis; private foundations, Type III supporting organizations, or other organizations that require expenditure responsibility by the Foundation; direct grants to individuals. No funding goes to: specific religious activities or beliefs; lobbying or political activities; major research projects; any commercial business purpose; any litigation that is underway, contemplated, or completed; endowments, building campaigns, special events, or annual funds.
Application information: Grant process is by invitation only.
Officers and Directors:* Joanne Woodward Newman,* Chair.; Robert H. Forrester,* C.E.O. and Pres.; Brian J. Murphy,* V.P. and Treas.; Clea Newman Soderlund,* V.P.; Jamie K. Gerard, Esq.*, Secy.; Robert E. Patricelli.
EIN: 061606588
Selected grants: The following grants are a representative sample of this grantmaker's funding activity:
$2,500,000 to Association of Hole in the Wall Camps, Westport, CT, 2012. For CAPACITY BUILDING.
$1,551,470 to Rockefeller Philanthropy Advisors, Philanthropic Collaborative, New York, NY, 2012. For Donor-Advised Fund.
$825,000 to Safe Water Network, New York, NY, 2012. For CAPACITY BUILDING AND LAKE VOLTA INITIATIVE.
$250,000 to Discovery Center, Farmington, CT, 2012. For CAPACITY BUILDING.
$250,000 to Food Research and Action Center, Washington, DC, 2012. For BREAKFAST IN THE CLASSROOM INITIATIVE.
$250,000 to Four Freedoms Park Conservancy, New York, NY, 2012. For TRANSITIONAL LANDSCAPE and COMMEMORATIVE BOOK.
$250,000 to Shining Hope for Communities, New York, NY, 2012. For SUSTAINABLE GROWTH AND EXPANSION.
$25,000 to Committee to Encourage Corporate Philanthropy, New York, NY, 2012. For 2013 CECP SUMMIT.
$10,000 to Double H Hole in the Woods Ranch, Lake Luzerne, NY, 2012. For GENERAL OPERATIONS.
$10,000 to W F U V Radio, Bronx, NY, 2012.

1653
The Niblack Foundation ✧ ☆
c/o Day Pitney LLP
1 Canterbury Green
Stamford, CT 06901-2032

Established in 2003 in CT.
Donors: John F. Niblack; Heidi G. Niblack.
Foundation type: Independent foundation.
Financial data (yr. ended 12/31/13): Assets, $908,808 (M); expenditures, $456,032; qualifying distributions, $452,397; giving activities include $452,397 for 15 grants (high: $280,000; low: $1,000).
Fields of interest: Museums; Higher education; Education; Human services; Science, association.
Limitations: Applications not accepted. Giving primarily in CT, FL, NH and NY. No grants to individuals.
Application information: Contributes only to pre-selected organizations.
Trustees: Elwood B. Davis; Robert J. Miller; Heidi G. Niblack; John F. Niblack.
EIN: 527323778

1654
Henry E. Niles Foundation
c/o Fogarty, Cohen, Selby, & Nemiroff LLC
1700 E. Putnam Ave., Ste. 406
Old Greenwich, CT 06870-1370
Contact: Ashley C. Lantz, Admin.
FAX: (203) 629-7300; E-mail: agaran@fcsn.com; Main URL: http://www.heniles.org

Established in 1990 in CT.
Foundation type: Independent foundation.
Financial data (yr. ended 12/31/13): Assets, $30,716,372 (M); expenditures, $1,873,765; qualifying distributions, $1,666,549; giving activities include $1,472,000 for 133 grants (high: $100,000; low: $2,000).
Purpose and activities: The foundation strives to support humanitarian efforts, including faith-based endeavors, that: 1) strengthen education, including special education, literacy, and others; 2) fight economic hardships through self-help opportunities; and 3) enhance public health and sanitation on a global basis. The foundation also has particular interest in organizations that promote partnerships and collaborative efforts among multiple groups and organizations, and it encourages pilot initiatives that test new program models.
Fields of interest: Higher education; Education; Health care; Human services.
Limitations: Applications accepted. Giving primarily in the Northeast, with emphasis on CT and NY. No support for government agencies or for organizations that subsist mainly on third-party funding, and that have demonstrated no ability or have exerted little effort to attract public funding, or for organizations based outside the U.S. No grants to individuals or for general fundraising drives.
Publications: Application guidelines.
Application information: Application form required.
Initial approach: Use application form on foundation web site
Copies of proposal: 1
Deadline(s): Rolling
Board meeting date(s): 10 times per year
Final notification: 1 week after board meeting
Officers and Directors:* Geoffrey M. Parkinson,* Pres.; Leland C. Selby,* V.P. and Secy.; James R. Lamb,* Treas.
EIN: 061252486
Selected grants: The following grants are a representative sample of this grantmaker's funding activity:
$100,000 to Bowery Mission, New York, NY, 2012. For a New Beginning for Women in Crisis (1 of 3).
$50,000 to Episcopal Relief and Development, New York, NY, 2012. For Child Survival, Angola.
$50,000 to Innovations for Poverty Action, New Haven, CT, 2012. For general purposes (1 of 3).
$40,000 to Network for Teaching Entrepreneurship, White Plains, NY, 2012. For youth entrepreneurship education Program.
$40,000 to Water for People, Denver, CO, 2012. For Sanitation Education and Capacity Building (2 of 2).
$37,500 to East Meets West Foundation, Oakland, CA, 2012. For Breath of Life in the Philippines (2 of 2).
$25,000 to Feeding America, Chicago, IL, 2012. For National Produce Program.
$20,000 to Classroom, Inc., New York, NY, 2012. For Middle School Adolescent Library and Health Education Program.
$7,500 to University of Michigan, Law School, Ann Arbor, MI, 2012. For Law School Fund.

$5,000 to Family Service, Lawrence, MA, 2012. For Stand and Deliver.

1655
Laura J. Niles Foundation
c/o Fogerty, Cohen, Selby, & Nemiroff LLC
1700 E. Putnam Ave., Ste. 406
Old Greenwich, CT 06870-1370 (203) 629-7314
Contact: Ashley C. Garan, Admin.
FAX: (203) 629-7300; E-mail: agaran@fcsn.com; Main URL: http://www.ljniles.org

Established in 1997 in CT.
Donors: Laura Janet Niles‡; Laura J. Niles Revocable Trust.
Foundation type: Independent foundation.
Financial data (yr. ended 12/31/13): Assets, $24,463,572 (M); expenditures, $1,472,140; qualifying distributions, $1,303,456; giving activities include $1,120,500 for 113 grants (high: $90,000; low: $1,500).
Purpose and activities: The foundation encourages and supports efforts to improve the lives of both people and animals. The foundation seeks to benefit animals, primarily dogs, through research, training, and adoption, especially where people and animals benefit simultaneously. Additionally, the foundation strives to nurture and assist individuals in leading responsible and productive lives by enabling them to help themselves.
Fields of interest: Education; Animals/wildlife; Employment; Children/youth, services; Economically disadvantaged.
Limitations: Applications accepted. Giving in the U.S., but priority is given to organizations in the Northeast. No support for any non-U.S. 501(c)(3)s, or for spay or neuter projects. No grants to individuals.
Publications: Application guidelines.
Application information: Application form required.
Initial approach: Use application form on foundation web site
Copies of proposal: 1
Deadline(s): Rolling
Board meeting date(s): 10 times per year
Final notification: 1 week after board meeting
Officers and Directors:* Geoffrey M. Parkinson,* Pres.; Leland C. Selby,* V.P. and Secy.; James R. Lamb,* Treas.
EIN: 223188304

1656
Northeast Utilities Foundation, Inc. ✧
P.O. Box 270
Hartford, CT 06141-0270 (860) 665-3306
Contact: Lindsay Parke, Community Rels.
FAX: (860) 728-4594;
E-mail: lindsay.parke@nu.com; Additional tel.: (888) 682-4639; Contact in Western MA: Edgar Alejandro, Economic and Community Devel., Western Massachusetts Electric Co., P.O. Box 2010, West Springfield, MA 01090-2010, tel.: (413) 785-5871, fax: (413) 787-9289, ext. 2289, e-mail: alejae@nu.com; Contact in NH: Paulette Faggiano, Comms. and Public Affairs, Public Service Co. of New Hampshire, P.O. Box 330, Manchester, NH 03105, tel.: (603) 634-3386, fax: (603) 634-2367, e-mail: faggips@nu.com; Main URL: http://www.northeastutilitiesfoundation.org
Additional URL: http://www.cl-p.com/community/partners/grants/nufoundation.asp
Grants List: http://www.northeastutilitiesfoundation.org/what/partners.html

Established in 1998 in CT.
Donors: The Connecticut Light and Power Co.; Northeast Nuclear Energy Co.; Northeast Utilities; Public Service Co. of New Hampshire; Western Massachusetts Electric Co.; Select Energy, Inc.; Yankee Gas Services Company.
Foundation type: Company-sponsored foundation.
Financial data (yr. ended 12/31/12): Assets, $22,964,884 (M); expenditures, $1,020,711; qualifying distributions, $983,641; giving activities include $983,641 for 24 grants (high: $125,000; low: $7,217).
Purpose and activities: The foundation supports programs designed to promote economic and community development, workforce development, and environmental stewardship.
Fields of interest: Museums (science/technology); Education; Environment, water resources; Environment, land resources; Environment, energy; Environment; Employment, training; Employment; Salvation Army; Economic development; Community development, small businesses; Community/economic development.
Type of support: General/operating support; Continuing support; Program development; Sponsorships; Employee matching gifts; Employee-related scholarships.
Limitations: Applications accepted. Giving primarily in areas of company operations, with emphasis on CT, western MA, and NH. No support for private foundations, religious, political, or fraternal organizations, or organizations not of direct benefit to the entire community. No grants to individuals (except for employee-related scholarships), or for endowments, debt reduction, or athletic trips.
Publications: Application guidelines; Grants list.
Application information: The foundation supports large regional projects through select partners and through requests for proposals that address a specific issue or focus areas. Inquiries and proposals for small grant requests should be directed toward local state representatives. Application form not required.
Initial approach: Proposal to local state representative in Connecticut, Massachusetts, and New Hampshire
Deadline(s): None
Board meeting date(s): Feb., May, Aug., and Nov.
Officers and Directors:* Thomas J. May,* Chair. and Pres.; Richard J. Morrison, Secy.; James J. Judge,* Treas.; Joseph R. Nolan, Jr.,* Exec. Dir.; Gregory B. Butler; Christine M. Carmody; David R. McHale; Leon J. Oliver.
EIN: 061527290

1657
The Oaklawn Foundation, Inc. ✧
P.O. Box 272
Old Greenwich, CT 06870-2227 (203) 637-3784
Contact: William S. Kies III, Pres. and Dir.

Incorporated in 1948 in NY.
Donors: Mabel B. Kies‡; W.S. Kies‡; Margaret K. Gibb‡; William S. Kies III.
Foundation type: Independent foundation.
Financial data (yr. ended 12/31/13): Assets, $16,897,437 (M); expenditures, $796,687; qualifying distributions, $697,095; giving activities include $626,000 for 50 grants (high: $30,000; low: $1,000).
Purpose and activities: Giving primarily for education, with emphasis on higher and private secondary education scholarships.
Fields of interest: Secondary school/education; Higher education.
Type of support: Endowments; Scholarship funds.
Limitations: Applications accepted. Giving primarily in CT. No support for religious or political organizations. No grants to individuals, or for operating budgets, deficit financing, emergency funds, capital funds, research, special projects, publications, conferences or bricks and mortar; no loans.
Publications: Annual report.
Application information: Application form required.
Initial approach: Proposal
Copies of proposal: 1
Deadline(s): None
Board meeting date(s): Mar., June, and Oct.
Officers and Directors:* William S. Kies III,* Pres.; Betsy K. Raftery,* Treas.; Stephen K. Grimm; Cameron F. Hopper, Esq.; Audrey S. Paight.
Number of staff: 2 part-time professional; 2 part-time support.
EIN: 136127896

1658
O'Connell Family Foundation, Inc. ✧
c/o Daniel S. O'Connell
16 Rock Ridge Ave.
Greenwich, CT 06831-4401

Established in 1993.
Donors: Daniel S. O'Connell; Gloria P. O'Connell.
Foundation type: Independent foundation.
Financial data (yr. ended 11/30/13): Assets, $42,624; gifts received, $776,517; expenditures, $792,888; qualifying distributions, $792,888; giving activities include $791,761 for 25 grants (high: $600,000; low: $20).
Fields of interest: Elementary/secondary education; Higher education; Health organizations.
Limitations: Applications not accepted. Giving primarily in CT, NY, and RI. No grants to individuals.
Application information: Contributes only to pre-selected organizations.
Officers: Daniel S. O'Connell, Pres.; Gloria P. O'Connell, V.P.
Director: Christine Pomar.
EIN: 133745912
Selected grants: The following grants are a representative sample of this grantmaker's funding activity:
$550,000 to Brown University, Providence, RI, 2011.
$25,000 to Cardinal Spellman High School, Bronx, NY, 2011.
$25,000 to Partnership for Inner-City Education, New York, NY, 2011.
$10,000 to University of Colorado Foundation, Denver, CO, 2011.
$2,500 to Boston Preparatory Charter School, Hyde Park, MA, 2011.
$2,500 to Preparatory Foundation, Hyde Park, MA, 2011.
$2,500 to Waterside School, Stamford, CT, 2011.

1659
The October Hill Foundation ✧
17 Taunton Ridge Rd.
Newtown, CT 06470-1419

Established in 1994 in DE.
Donor: Gretchen A. Bauta.
Foundation type: Independent foundation.
Financial data (yr. ended 12/31/13): Assets, $3,573,307 (M); expenditures, $1,089,482; qualifying distributions, $1,080,831; giving activities include $1,078,228 for 16 grants (high: $300,000; low: $1,000).
Purpose and activities: Giving primarily for animal welfare and environmental conservation.
Fields of interest: Environment, natural resources; Animal welfare; Human services; United Ways and Federated Giving Programs.
Type of support: General/operating support.
Limitations: Applications not accepted. Giving primarily in CA, CT, and VA, funding also in MA, Washington, DC, TX, and in Canada. No grants to individuals.
Application information: Contributes only to pre-selected organizations.
Officers: Gretchen A. Bauta, Pres.; Christian Bauta, V.P. and Secy.; Humberto P. Bauta, M.D., V.P. and Treas.; Nicholas Bauta, V.P.; Pilar Bauta, V.P.
EIN: 137049883
Selected grants: The following grants are a representative sample of this grantmaker's funding activity:
$250,000 to American Ireland Fund, Boston, MA, 2012. For Native Woodland Trust.
$20,000 to World Wildlife Fund, Washington, DC, 2012. For Habitat Conservation.
$10,000 to Dorothy Day Hospitality House, Danbury, CT, 2012. For Housing of the Homeless.

1660
The O'Herron Family Foundation ✧
(formerly Jonathan & Shirley O'Herron Foundation)
P.O. Box 4816
Stamford, CT 06907-0816
Contact: Anne O'Herron Burleigh, Pres.

Established in 1984 in NY.
Donors: Jonathan O'Herron; Shirley O'Herron†.
Foundation type: Independent foundation.
Financial data (yr. ended 06/30/13): Assets, $290,716 (M); gifts received, $575,600; expenditures, $444,380; qualifying distributions, $439,380; giving activities include $439,200 for 60 grants (high: $32,500; low: $500).
Fields of interest: Elementary/secondary education; Higher education; Business school/education; Medical school/education; Health organizations, association; Human services; American Red Cross; Catholic federated giving programs; Catholic agencies & churches.
Type of support: General/operating support; Capital campaigns.
Limitations: Giving primarily in CT, MA, NH, NY, and VT. No grants to individuals.
Application information: Application form not required.
Initial approach: Letter
Deadline(s): None
Officers and Directors:* Anne O'Herron Burleigh,* Pres. and Exec. Dir.; Sarah O'Herron Casey; Jonathan O'Herron, Jr.
EIN: 133244207

Selected grants: The following grants are a representative sample of this grantmaker's funding activity:
$50,000 to New Canaan Country School, New Canaan, CT, 2011.
$30,500 to Middlebury College, Middlebury, VT, 2011.
$25,000 to Saint Pauls School, Concord, NH, 2011.
$20,000 to Middlebury College, Middlebury, VT, 2011.
$15,000 to Diocese of Bridgeport, Bridgeport, CT, 2011.
$13,750 to New Canaan Country School, New Canaan, CT, 2011.
$7,500 to Saint Marys School, Middlebury, VT, 2011.
$6,500 to Saint Johns Church, Darien, CT, 2011.
$5,000 to Christ the King Church, Trumbull, CT, 2011.
$3,000 to National Leadership Roundtable on Church Management, Washington, DC, 2011.

1661
The Ohnell Family Foundation ✧
75 Khakum Wood Rd.
Greenwich, CT 06831-3729

Established in 1992 in CT.
Donors: Ernst Ohnell; Ernst Ohnell III.
Foundation type: Independent foundation.
Financial data (yr. ended 12/31/13): Assets, $10,485,650 (M); gifts received, $601,380; expenditures, $460,436; qualifying distributions, $449,000; giving activities include $449,000 for 43 grants (high: $80,000; low: $1,000).
Fields of interest: Education; Human services; Public policy, research; Christian agencies & churches.
Type of support: Annual campaigns; Capital campaigns; Building/renovation; Endowments; Emergency funds; Seed money; Scholarships—to individuals.
Limitations: Applications not accepted. Giving primarily in CT and NY.
Application information: Unsolicited requests for funds not accepted.
Officers: Ernst Ohnell, Pres.; Patricia Ohnell, Secy.
Number of staff: None.
EIN: 223219022
Selected grants: The following grants are a representative sample of this grantmaker's funding activity:
$500 to Pegasus Therapeutic Riding, Brewster, NY, 2012. For care.

1662
The Olson Foundation ✧
c/o Cummings & Lockwood (BCD)
P.O. Box 2505
Greenwich, CT 06836-2505

Established in CT.
Donors: Brian T. Olson; Jill J. Olson; Kokino LLC.
Foundation type: Independent foundation.
Financial data (yr. ended 12/31/13): Assets, $4,033,054 (M); gifts received, $61,658; expenditures, $985,650; qualifying distributions, $976,913; giving activities include $973,500 for 16 grants (high: $280,000; low: $1,000).
Fields of interest: Education; Health care; Human services.

Limitations: Applications not accepted. Giving primarily in CT and NY; some giving in MN.
Application information: Contributes only to pre-selected organizations.
Trustees: Brian T. Olson; Jill J. Olson.
EIN: 203863006
Selected grants: The following grants are a representative sample of this grantmaker's funding activity:
$112,500 to Sapling Foundation, New York, NY, 2012. For the TED Conference and/or other TED Programs.
$100,500 to Greenwich Country Day School, Greenwich, CT, 2012. For Waterside Scholarship.

1663
The Orchard Farm Foundation ✧
c/o Graham Capital Mgmt. L.P.
40 Highland Ave.
Norwalk, CT 06853-1510

Established in 1998 in CT.
Donors: Kenneth G. Tropin; Paul Jones; Nicholas Maounis.
Foundation type: Independent foundation.
Financial data (yr. ended 12/31/12): Assets, $10,589 (M); gifts received, $1,360,000; expenditures, $1,353,310; qualifying distributions, $1,353,310; giving activities include $1,353,310 for 55 grants (high: $455,930; low: $480).
Purpose and activities: Giving primarily for children and youth services, the arts, health associations, and human services.
Fields of interest: Arts; Education; Animals/wildlife, preservation/protection; Health organizations, association; Food banks; Housing/shelter, homeless; Human services; Children/youth, services; Homeless, human services; Foundations (public); Economically disadvantaged.
Limitations: Applications not accepted. Giving primarily in CT and NY. No grants to individuals.
Application information: Contributes only to pre-selected organizations.
Officer: Kenneth G. Tropin, Pres.
Trustee: Kathleen O. Tropin.
EIN: 223626152

1664
Jeffrey P. Ossen Family Foundation ✧ ☆
c/o Cummings & Lockwood, LLC
P.O. Box 271820
West Hartford, CT 06127-1820

Established in 2008 in CT.
Donors: Jeffrey P. Ossen Revocable Trust; Samuel J. Gordon.
Foundation type: Independent foundation.
Financial data (yr. ended 07/31/13): Assets, $17,152,933 (M); gifts received, $50,000; expenditures, $969,539; qualifying distributions, $780,286; giving activities include $780,286 for 20 grants (high: $200,000; low: $5,000).
Fields of interest: Hospitals (general); Health care; Legal services; Food banks; Human services.
Limitations: Applications not accepted. Giving primarily in CT. No grants to individuals.
Application information: Unsolicited requests for funds not accepted.
Trustees: Richard Brvenik; Eileen M. Ossen.
EIN: 261243178

1665
The Owenoke Foundation ✧
c/o Avery Rockefeller, III
22 Squirrel Hill Rd.
West Hartford, CT 06107-1003

Established in 1999 in DE.
Donors: Underhill Charitable Trust; A.M. Rockefeller Trust; Rockefeller Charitable Trust.
Foundation type: Independent foundation.
Financial data (yr. ended 11/30/13): Assets, $10,545,256 (M); expenditures, $517,772; qualifying distributions, $486,300; giving activities include $480,000 for 28 grants (high: $50,000; low: $2,000).
Purpose and activities: Giving primarily for education, human services and health care.
Fields of interest: Elementary/secondary education; Higher education; Education; Health organizations; Food banks; Human services.
Limitations: Applications not accepted. Giving in the U.S., with emphasis on CT. No grants to individuals.
Application information: Contributes only to pre-selected organizations.
Officers and Directors:* Avery Rockefeller III,* Pres.; Mary Runestad,* Secy.; Monica Rockefeller; Rodney Runestad.
EIN: 223483048
Selected grants: The following grants are a representative sample of this grantmaker's funding activity:
$50,000 to Kingswood-Oxford School, West Hartford, CT, 2011. For general support.
$35,000 to AmeriCares, Stamford, CT, 2011. For general support.
$30,000 to Adirondack Council, Elizabethtown, NY, 2011. For general support.
$25,000 to Literacy Volunteers of Greater Hartford, Hartford, CT, 2011. For general support.
$23,000 to Team Tobati, New Britain, CT, 2011. For general support.
$20,000 to Foodshare, Bloomfield, CT, 2011. For general support.
$20,000 to V Foundation for Cancer Research, Cary, NC, 2011. For general support.
$17,000 to Food Bank of Lower Fairfield County, Stamford, CT, 2011. For general support.
$15,000 to Inspirica, Stamford, CT, 2011. For general support.
$10,000 to Lutheran Social Services of New England, Wellesley, MA, 2011. For general support.

1666
Frank Loomis Palmer Fund ✧
c/o Bank of America, N.A.
200 Glastonbury Blvd., Ste. 200
Glastonbury, CT 06033-4458 (860) 657-7015
E-mail: ct.grantmaking@ustrust.com; Main URL: https://www.bankofamerica.com/philanthropic/grantmaking.go

Trust established in 1936 in CT.
Donor: Virginia Palmer‡.
Foundation type: Independent foundation.
Financial data (yr. ended 07/31/13): Assets, $33,463,416 (M); expenditures, $1,711,955; qualifying distributions, $1,562,930; giving activities include $1,418,046 for 83 grants (high: $100,000; low: $1,250).
Purpose and activities: Grants to encourage new projects and to provide seed money, with emphasis on child welfare and family services and youth agencies; support also for civic groups, cultural programs, social services, and educational programs.
Fields of interest: Performing arts; Arts; Elementary school/education; Secondary school/education; Higher education; Adult/continuing education; Libraries/library science; Education; Environment, natural resources; Environment; Hospitals (general); Reproductive health, family planning; Health care; Health organizations, association; AIDS; Alcoholism; AIDS research; Legal services; Safety/disasters; Children/youth, services; Family services; Residential/custodial care, hospices; Aging, centers/services; Minorities/immigrants, centers/services; Community/economic development; Engineering/technology; Science; Government/public administration; Transportation; Religion; Aging; Minorities.
Type of support: Equipment; Program development; Conferences/seminars; Publication; Seed money; Scholarship funds; Research; Consulting services; Matching/challenge support.
Limitations: Applications accepted. Giving limited to New London, CT. No grants to individuals, or for endowment funds.
Publications: Informational brochure (including application guidelines).
Application information: Application information available at http://www.bankofamerica.com/grantmaking. Application form required.
Initial approach: Telephone
Copies of proposal: 1
Deadline(s): Nov. 15
Board meeting date(s): Jan. and July
Final notification: Feb. 1 and Aug. 1
Trustee: Bank of America, N.A.
EIN: 066026043
Selected grants: The following grants are a representative sample of this grantmaker's funding activity:
$100,000 to New London Homeless Hospitality Center, New London, CT, 2012. For capital support for the shelter at the New State Pier Road Site.
$41,756 to Community Health Center, Middletown, CT, 2012. For addressing obesity and its sequellae of hypertension and diabetes: nutritional intervention in the primary care settings of CHC of New London.
$40,000 to Center: A Drop-In Community Learning and Resource Center, New London, CT, 2012. For Out of School Care and Enrichment Programs.
$40,000 to New London, City of, New London, CT, 2012. For Hygienic Art Park Phase II Renovations.
$40,000 to United Way of Southeastern Connecticut, Gales Ferry, CT, 2012. For Emergency Food and Emergency Heating Assistance Project.
$30,000 to Flock Theater, New London, CT, 2012. For a complete season of full-length productions.
$30,000 to Habitat for Humanity of Southeastern Connecticut, New London, CT, 2012. For New London Home Construction and Rehabilitation.
$10,000 to Child and Family Agency of Southeastern Connecticut, New London, CT, 2012. For children literacy after-school program that emphasizes pro-social behavior, and theatre arts during school days and during the summer.
$9,864 to Connecticut College, New London, CT, 2012. For Connecticut College Children's Program - Family Literacy Project.
$7,630 to New London County Historical Society, New London, CT, 2012. For Shaw Mansion Chimney Restoration.

1667
Panoram Foundation Inc. ✧ ☆
(formerly The Copp Foundation, Inc.)
19 Smith Neck Rd.
Old Lyme, CT 06371-2618

Established in 1984 in CT.
Donor: Joseph A. Copp‡.
Foundation type: Independent foundation.
Financial data (yr. ended 12/31/13): Assets, $5,379,257 (M); gifts received, $5,000; expenditures, $471,286; qualifying distributions, $441,431; giving activities include $438,636 for 7 grants (high: $200,000; low: $4,000).
Fields of interest: Museums; Historic preservation/historical societies.
Type of support: General/operating support.
Limitations: Applications not accepted. Giving primarily in CT. No grants to individuals.
Application information: Unsolicited requests for funds not accepted.
Officers: B. Allyn Copp, Pres.; Betsey A. Copp, Secy.; Eugenie C.T. Copp, Treas.
Director: Lucy A. Copp.
EIN: 222647132
Selected grants: The following grants are a representative sample of this grantmaker's funding activity:
$3,100 to Saint Andrews School, Barrington, RI, 2011. For scholarship.

1668
The Pasculano Foundation ✧
12 Loch Ln.
Greenwich, CT 06830-3024

Established in DE.
Donors: Lynne Pasculano; Mark Pasculano; Richard Pasculano; Suzanne McGinn.
Foundation type: Independent foundation.
Financial data (yr. ended 12/31/12): Assets, $16,125,607 (M); gifts received, $21,270; expenditures, $577,482; qualifying distributions, $505,000; giving activities include $505,000 for 8 grants (high: $200,000; low: $10,000).
Fields of interest: Performing arts centers; Environment, water pollution; International affairs.
Limitations: Applications not accepted. Giving primarily in CA, CO, ME and NY.
Application information: Contributes only to pre-selected organizations.
Officers and Directors:* Lynne Pasculano,* Co-Pres. and Secy.; Richard Pasculano,* Co-Pres.; Suzanne McGinn,* V.P.; Mark Pasculano,* V.P.
EIN: 208037834

1669
Robert E. Leet & Clara Guthrie Patterson Trust ✧
c/o U.S. Trust, Bank of America, N.A.
200 Glastonbury Blvd., Ste. 200
Glastonbury, CT 06033-4458
Contact: Carmen Britt, V.P.
E-mail: carmen.britt@ustrust.com; Main URL: https://www.bankofamerica.com/philanthropic/grantmaking.go

Established in 1981 in CT.
Donors: Robert Leet Patterson‡; Clara Guthrie Patterson‡; Robert Patterson Trust No. 2.
Foundation type: Independent foundation.

Financial data (yr. ended 01/31/14): Assets, $20,456,217 (M); expenditures, $1,138,562; qualifying distributions, $973,155; giving activities include $891,000 for 5 grants (high: $116,000; low: $75,000).
Fields of interest: Health care.
Type of support: Research.
Limitations: Applications not accepted. Giving limited to CA, CT, and NY. No grants to individuals, or for operating budgets, continuing support, annual campaigns, emergency funds, deficit financing, endowment funds, consulting services, technical assistance, demonstration projects, publications, conferences and seminars, or for medical equipment; no loans.
Application information: Unsolicited requests for funds are currently not accepted.
Board meeting date(s): Dec.
Trustee: Bank of America Merrill Lynch.
EIN: 066236358
Selected grants: The following grants are a representative sample of this grantmaker's funding activity:
$100,000 to Multiple Myeloma Research Foundation, Norwalk, CT, 2011. To fund a senior researcher. Research involves the increased activation of a key signaling pathway called IRE1-XBP1.

1670
The Pay it Forward Foundation ✧ ☆
c/o Walter, Berlingo and Co.
P.O. Box 4080
Darien, CT 06820-1480

Established in 2008 in CT.
Donor: D. Gregory Horrigan.
Foundation type: Independent foundation.
Financial data (yr. ended 06/30/13): Assets, $16,453,288 (M); expenditures, $641,031; qualifying distributions, $604,465; giving activities include $600,000 for 1 grant.
Fields of interest: Human services; Foundations (private grantmaking).
Limitations: Applications not accepted. Giving primarily in CT and FL.
Application information: Unsolicited requests for funds not accepted.
Trustees: D. Gregory Horrigan; Judith Anne Horrigan.
EIN: 261466660

1671
The People's United Community Foundation, Inc. ✧
850 Main St.
Bridgeport, CT 06604-4917
Contact: Tammy L. Torres, Admin. and Agency Liaison Dir.
FAX: (203) 338-6116; E-mail: foundation@pucf.org; Tel. and e-mail for Tammy L. Torres: (203) 338-6112, tammy.torres@peoples.com; Additional contacts: Vincent E. Santilli, tel.: (203) 338-5157, e-mail: Vincent.Santilli@peoples.com, Karen Galbo, Mktg., Public & Community Rels. Dir., tel.: (203) 338-6113, e-mail: Karen.Galbo@peoples.com;
Main URL: https://www.pucf.org/
Grants List: https://www.pucf.org/Grant_Recipients.html

stablished in 2007 in CT.
nor: People's United Bank.
Foundation type: Company-sponsored foundation.
Financial data (yr. ended 12/31/12): Assets, $42,426,528 (M); gifts received, $351,267; expenditures, $2,803,758; qualifying distributions, $2,720,702; giving activities include $2,288,131 for 348 grants (high: $177,111; low: $2,500).
Purpose and activities: The foundation supports programs designed to promote affordable housing, youth development, and community development. Special emphasis is directed toward programs and services designed to advance economic self-sufficiency, education, and improved quality of life for low-income individuals and families, at-risk children and youth, and individuals with special needs.
Fields of interest: Education, early childhood education; Education, special; Charter schools; Vocational education; Higher education; Teacher school/education; Adult education—literacy, basic skills & GED; Education, ESL programs; Education, reading; Education; Employment, services; Employment, training; Employment, retraining; Employment; Food banks; Food distribution, meals on wheels; Housing/shelter, development; Housing/shelter, rehabilitation; Housing/shelter, home owners; Housing/shelter, services; Youth development, intergenerational programs; Youth development, business; Youth development; Human services, financial counseling; Developmentally disabled, centers & services; Community/economic development, management/technical assistance; Community development, neighborhood development; Economic development; Urban/community development; Business/industry; Community development, business promotion; Community development, small businesses; Microfinance/microlending; Community/economic development; Mathematics; Engineering/technology; Science; Children/youth; Youth; Disabilities, people with; Minorities; Women; Economically disadvantaged.
Type of support: Program development.
Limitations: Applications accepted. Giving primarily in areas of company operations in CT, MA, ME, NH, Long Island and Westchester County, NY, and VT. No support for arts and culture organizations, childcare or daycare agencies, discriminatory organizations, disease-specific organizations, health organizations, historic preservation, organizations serving a limited constituency, municipal or government entities, nursery schools, political action committees (PAC's), political, labor, or fraternal, or health care organizations, private foundations, private schools or colleges, private pre-college schools, public school districts and their individual schools, religious organizations not of direct benefit to the entire community, assisted living for seniors, or pass-through organizations. No grants to individuals, or for activism, advertising, advocacy, animal causes, annual appeals or operational fundraising campaigns, beauty contests, capital campaigns, conferences, seminars, panel discussions, or trips, conservation or environmental causes, consultants, debt reduction, endowments, event sponsorships, fundraising activities or events, media including television, radio, film, video, or books, medical equipment or patient treatment funds, pilot programs or start-ups, research or feasibility studies, sports, athletic events, or recreational programs, sponsorships or projects where the Bank or its employees receive benefits, student trips or tours, substance abuse programs, or theater, dance, or music programs.
Publications: Application guidelines; Annual report; Grants list; Newsletter; Program policy statement.
Application information: The minimum grant request is $2,500. The average grant range is between $2,500 and $5,000. Support is limited to 1 contribution per organization during any 12-month period. Multi-year funding is not automatic. Telephone calls during the application process are not encouraged. Organizations receiving support are required to submit a final report. Application form required.
Initial approach: Complete online eligibility quiz and application
Copies of proposal: 1
Deadline(s): Feb. 1, June 1, and Oct. 1
Board meeting date(s): Trimester funding cycle
Final notification: Within 2 weeks of board meeting
Officers and Directors:* Jack P. Barnes, Chair.; Robert R. D'Amore,* Exec. V.P.; Michael J. Casparino, V.P.; Timothy P. Crimmins, Jr., V.P.; Armando F. Goncalves, V.P.; Kathleen E. Jones, V.P.; Samuel A. Ladd III, V.P.; William P. Lucy, V.P.; Dianne Mercer, V.P.; Michael L. Seaver, V.P.; Susan D. Stanley, Secy.; Jeremy Araujo, Treas.; Vincent E. Santilli, Exec. Dir.; George P. Carter; Arthur F. Casavant; Robert B. Dannies, Jr.; Eunice S. Groark.
Number of staff: 2 full-time professional; 1 part-time professional.
EIN: 208675365
Selected grants: The following grants are a representative sample of this grantmaker's funding activity:
$20,000 to Vermont Foodbank, Barre, VT, 2012. For food purchase project.
$15,000 to Corporation for Supportive Housing, New York, NY, 2012. For Building the Capacity of Connecticut's Supportive Housing Industry.
$15,000 to Gulf of Maine Research Institute, Portland, ME, 2012. For Free Access to Hands-on Learning.
$12,000 to ITNAmerica, Westbrook, ME, 2012. For Parent Agency - Building Capacity Through Volunteers and Business Partners.
$12,000 to Local Initiatives Support Corporation, New York, NY, 2012. For Connecticut Statewide and Hartford LISC Project.
$10,000 to Bay Path College, Longmeadow, MA, 2012. For Supporting the Academic Success of Adult Undergraduate Women.
$7,000 to Genesis Fund, Damariscotta, ME, 2012. For Genesis Community Loan Fund Technical Assistance.
$5,000 to Junior Achievement of Southwest New England, Hartford, CT, 2012. For Junior Achievement.
$5,000 to Twin Cities Community Development Corporation, Fitchburg, MA, 2012. For Strong Neighborhoods Campaign in Leominster.
$3,000 to Kennebec Valley Community Action Program, Waterville, ME, 2012. For South End Teen Center.

1672
Arthur W. Perdue Foundation, Inc. ✧
c/o Foundation Source
55 Walls Dr.
Fairfield, CT 06824
Application address: c/o Kim Nechay, P.O. Box 1537, Salisbury, MD 21802, tel.: (410) 543-3289

Donors: Franklin P. Perdue†; Perdue Incorporated.
Foundation type: Independent foundation.

Financial data (yr. ended 12/31/13): Assets, $25,842,754 (M); expenditures, $1,167,148; qualifying distributions, $1,118,259; giving activities include $964,839 for 106 grants (high: $100,000; low: $241), and $80,000 for 16 grants to individuals (high: $5,000; low: $5,000).
Purpose and activities: The foundation strives to strengthen the communities where Perdue Farms associates live and work by focusing its efforts on education, agriculture, the environment, health and social services, and fighting hunger and poverty.
Fields of interest: Education; Environment; Agriculture/food; Human services.
Limitations: Giving limited to communities where Purdue associates employees live and work. No support for individual churches or religious denominations, fraternal, service or veterans organizations, political action or lobbying groups or for teams. No grants to individuals or families.
Application information:
Initial approach: Letter
Deadline(s): Quarterly
Officers and Directors:* James A. Perdue,* Pres.; Mark Garth, Secy.-Treas.; Kim Nechay, Exec. Dir.; Mary H. Perdue; Sandra Spedden; Whitney M. Van Der Hyde.
EIN: 526054332
Selected grants: The following grants are a representative sample of this grantmaker's funding activity:
$28,000 to Wicomico County Board of Education, Salisbury, MD, 2012. For The Wicomico Mentoring Project.
$25,000 to University of Puerto Rico, Mayaguez, PR, 2012. For CITAI Program.
$20,000 to One Economy Corporation, Washington, DC, 2012. For Family Resource Center.
$13,500 to American Red Cross, Salisbury, MD, 2012. For Disaster Relief Trailers Project.
$13,000 to Foodbank of Southeastern Virginia, Norfolk, VA, 2012. For E Shore Branch Cooler Replacement Project.
$10,000 to Hampton University, Hampton, VA, 2012. For Perdue Scholarship Program.
$10,000 to Junior Achievement of the Eastern Shore, Salisbury, MD, 2012. For Our Regions Program.
$2,500 to Preble Street, Portland, ME, 2012. For Teen Center.
$1,000 to Boy Scouts of America, Wilmington, DE, 2012. For Del-Mar-VA Council - Boy Scouts of America.

1673
The Perrin Family Foundation ✧
4 Prospect St.
Ridgefield, CT 06877-4510 (203) 438-7349
Contact: Kelly Weldon, Grants Mgr.
E-mail: info@perrinfamilyfoundation.org; Additional address: The Grove, 760 Chapel St., New Haven, CT 06533; Laura McCargar e-mail: lmccargar@perrinfamilyfoundation.org.; Main URL: http://www.perrinfamilyfoundation.org
Blog: http://perrinfamilyfoundation.blogspot.com/
Facebook: https://www.facebook.com/pages/Perrin-Family-Foundation/407486896010548
Pinterest: http://www.pinterest.com/perrinfamilyfdn/
Twitter: http://twitter.com/Perrinfamilyfdn

Established in 1994 in CT.
Donors: Charles Perrin; Sheila Perrin.
Foundation type: Independent foundation.
Financial data (yr. ended 12/31/13): Assets, $17,946,305 (M); gifts received, $768,651; expenditures, $877,603; qualifying distributions, $753,664; giving activities include $539,250 for 37 grants (high: $25,000; low: $6,250).
Purpose and activities: The foundation's mission is to provide equal opportunities for children and young adults to lead safe, productive, and creative lives. Giving for education, health and cultural services for children, including after-school programs.
Fields of interest: Arts; Education; Health care; Children, services; Youth, services; Children/youth; Youth; Economically disadvantaged.
Type of support: General/operating support; Continuing support; Program development.
Limitations: Giving in Fairfield County, CT for social services, and in CT for youth engagement. No support for public or private schools. No grants to individuals.
Publications: Application guidelines; Grants list.
Application information: Applications are by invitation only, upon review of letter of inquiry. Complete application guidelines available on foundation web site.
Initial approach: Letter of inquiry via e-mail to Laura McCarger, or U.S. mail
Deadline(s): See foundation web site for current deadlines
Board meeting date(s): Three times a year
Officer and Trustees:* Sheila A. Perrin,* Pres.; Anne Kenan; Charles R. Perrin; David B. Perrin; Jeffrey L. Perrin.
Number of staff: 2 part-time professional.
EIN: 223309886

1674
The Pitney Bowes Foundation ✧
(formerly The Pitney Bowes Employees Involvement Fund, Inc.)
1 Elmcroft Rd., MSC 6101
Stamford, CT 06926-0700
Contact: Kathleen Ryan Mufson, Pres.
FAX: (203) 460-5336;
E-mail: Kathleen.RyanMufson@pb.com; Main URL: http://www.pitneybowes.com/us/our-company/corporate-responsibility/community.html
Pitney Bowes Corporate Social Responsibility Video: http://embed.vidyard.com/share/naBRrxwYAcL—x69Pponvw

Donor: Pitney Bowes Inc.
Foundation type: Company-sponsored foundation.
Financial data (yr. ended 12/31/12): Assets, $8,801,042 (M); expenditures, $3,598,240; qualifying distributions, $3,584,089; giving activities include $3,545,994 for 148 grants (high: $1,586,200; low: $300).
Purpose and activities: The foundation supports programs designed to promote literacy and education.
Fields of interest: Education, early childhood education; Higher education; Adult/continuing education; Adult education—literacy, basic skills & GED; Education, continuing education; Education, services; Education, reading; Education; Employment, services; Employment, training; Employment; Youth development, adult & child programs; Engineering; Disabilities, people with; Minorities; Women.
Type of support: Sponsorships; General/operating support; Program development; Curriculum development; Employee volunteer services; Employee matching gifts.
Limitations: Applications accepted. Giving primarily in areas of company operations in Bridgeport, Danbury, Hartford, Shelton, and Stamford, CT, Washington, DC, Atlanta, GA, Waltham, MA, Detroit and Grand Rapids, MI, Troy, NY, Chesapeake, VA, Dallas, TX, Spokane, WA, and Appleton, WI; giving also to national organizations. No support for religious organizations not of direct benefit to the entire community, political candidates or lobbying organizations, organizations with limited constituency including fraternal, labor, veterans' groups, or business associations, anti-business groups, discriminatory organizations, or single disease health organizations. No grants to individuals, or for conferences, sporting events, auctions, trade shows, or other one-time short term events, sponsorships, advertising or television programming, team sponsorships or athletic scholarships, fundraising, or indirect costs that exceeds 20% of program budget.
Publications: Application guidelines.
Application information: Support is limited to 1 contribution per organization during any given year. Application form required.
Initial approach: Complete online application
Deadline(s): Jan. 15 and June 1 for Literacy and Education; Feb. 15 and Aug. 31 for Local Community Grants
Board meeting date(s): Quarterly
Final notification: 4 to 6 months for Literacy and Education
Officers and Directors:* Johnna G. Torsone,* Chair.; Kathleen Ryan Mufson,* Pres.; Polly O'Brien Morrow, V.P.; Juanita James; Murray D. Martin; Michael Monahan; Helen Shan.
Number of staff: 1 full-time professional; 1 part-time professional.
EIN: 200523317

1675
The William H. Pitt Foundation, Inc. ✧
(formerly The William H. Pitt III Foundation, Inc.)
383 Main Ave.
Norwalk, CT 06851 (203) 750-3241
FAX: (203) 750-3251;
E-mail: dhertz@williampitt.com

Established in 1984 in CT.
Donors: William H. Pitt†; The Jean Keller Carros and Robert Carros Foundation.
Foundation type: Independent foundation.
Financial data (yr. ended 09/30/13): Assets, $84,175,785 (L); expenditures, $5,139,211; qualifying distributions, $3,809,881; giving activities include $3,114,210 for 105 grants (high: $322,500; low: $100).
Fields of interest: Elementary/secondary education; Higher education; Boys & girls clubs; Human services; Children/youth; Youth; Young adults; Economically disadvantaged.
Type of support: General/operating support; Scholarship funds.
Limitations: Applications not accepted. Giving primarily in Fairfield County, CT and Palm Beach County, FL. No grants to individuals.
Application information: Contributes only to pre-selected organizations.
Officers and Directors:* Robert Scinto,* Chair. and C.E.O.; Robert G. Simses, Esq.*, C.O.O. and Pres.; Charles Mallory, Secy.; Debra Hertz, Ph.D., Exec.

Dir.; Warner DePuy; Pauline Baker Pitt; Hon. Lesley Stockard Smith.
Number of staff: 1 full-time professional.
EIN: 222570737

1676
Praxair Foundation, Inc. ✧
39 Old Ridgebury Rd.-K2
Danbury, CT 06810-5113
Contact: Susan M. Neuman, Pres.
FAX: (203) 837-2454;
E-mail: Praxair_GlobalGiving@praxair.com; Main URL: http://www.praxair.com/our-company/our-people/praxair-foundation

Established in 1994.
Donor: Praxair, Inc.
Foundation type: Company-sponsored foundation.
Financial data (yr. ended 11/30/12): Assets, $760,543 (M); gifts received, $4,099,993; expenditures, $3,842,325; qualifying distributions, $3,842,325; giving activities include $3,842,325 for 221 grants (high: $519,063; low: $250).
Purpose and activities: The foundation supports public libraries and organizations involved with higher education, the environment, health, disaster relief, diversity, and community development.
Fields of interest: Higher education; Libraries (public); Environment; Hospitals (general); Health care; Disasters, preparedness/services; Civil rights, race/intergroup relations; Community/economic development; United Ways and Federated Giving Programs.
Type of support: General/operating support; Building/renovation; Equipment; Program development; Scholarship funds; Employee volunteer services; Employee matching gifts.
Limitations: Applications accepted. Giving on a national and international basis in areas of company operations, with emphasis on CT, Asia, Brazil, India, and South America. No support for religious organizations, fraternal or labor organizations, or discriminatory organizations. No grants to individuals or for sports programs.
Publications: Application guidelines.
Application information: Organizations receiving support of $25,000 or more are required to submit a final report. Application form required.
Initial approach: Complete online application form
Deadline(s): None
Officers: Susan M. Neumann, Pres.; Anthony M. Pepper, Secy.; Timothy S. Heenan, Treas.
EIN: 061413665
Selected grants: The following grants are a representative sample of this grantmaker's funding activity:
$37,388 to Community Health Charities, Arlington, VA, 2011.
$35,000 to Urban League, National, New York, NY, 2011.
$25,000 to American Indian Science and Engineering Society, Albuquerque, NM, 2011.
$25,000 to Guiding Eyes for the Blind, Yorktown Heights, NY, 2011.
$20,000 to Nature Conservancy, Arlington, VA, 2011.
$17,500 to American Association of University Women, Washington, DC, 2011.
$15,000 to American Institute of Chemical Engineers, New York, NY, 2011.
$15,000 to Jackie Robinson Foundation, New York, NY, 2011.
$13,200 to Society of Hispanic Professional Engineers, City of Industry, CA, 2011.
$7,500 to Ivy Tech Foundation, Indianapolis, IN, 2011.

1677
Provident Foundation ✧
c/o Daniel M. Rosen
67 Mason St.
Greenwich, CT 06830-3104

Established in 1999 in DE.
Donors: C.V. Safith; Phoenix Charitable Trust.
Foundation type: Independent foundation.
Financial data (yr. ended 12/31/12): Assets, $91,824 (M); gifts received, $515,000; expenditures, $560,635; qualifying distributions, $559,148; giving activities include $557,660 for 30 grants (high: $100,000; low: $100).
Fields of interest: Museums (children's); Performing arts, dance; Medical research, institute; Athletics/sports, school programs; Human services; Children, services; Jewish federated giving programs.
Limitations: Applications not accepted. Giving primarily in NY. No grants to individuals.
Application information: Contributes only to pre-selected organizations.
Officers: Leonard Blavatnik, Pres.; Emily Blavatnik, V.P.
EIN: 134067635

1678
William H. Prusoff Foundation ✧
880 Old Post Rd.
Fairfield, CT 06824-8403

Established in 2000 in CT.
Donor: William H. Prusoff Charitable Lead Annuity Trust.
Foundation type: Independent foundation.
Financial data (yr. ended 12/31/13): Assets, $2,314,447 (M); expenditures, $533,699; qualifying distributions, $528,000; giving activities include $528,000 for 29 grants (high: $220,000; low: $1,000).
Fields of interest: Medical school/education; Medical research, institute; Human services.
Limitations: Applications not accepted. Giving primarily in CT. No grants to individuals.
Application information: Contributes only to pre-selected organizations.
Trustees: Alvin Prusoff; Laura Prusoff.
EIN: 061601597

1679
Smith Richardson Foundation, Inc. ✧
60 Jesup Rd.
Westport, CT 06880-4311 (203) 222-6222
Contact: Marin J. Strmecki, Sr. V.P. and Dir., Progs.
FAX: (203) 222-6282; E-mail: jhollings@srf.org;
Main URL: https://www.srf.org
Wiki: http://en.wikipedia.org/wiki/Smith_Richardson_Foundation

Incorporated in 1935 in NC.
Donors: H.S. Richardson, Sr.‡; Grace Jones Richardson‡.
Foundation type: Independent foundation.
Financial data (yr. ended 12/31/13): Assets, $521,570,780 (M); gifts received, $2,292,000; expenditures, $27,688,500; qualifying distributions, $25,231,755; giving activities include $20,695,903 for 411 grants (high: $424,036; low: $500).
Purpose and activities: The mission of the foundation is to contribute to important public debates and to help address serious public policy challenges facing the United States. The foundation seeks to help ensure the vitality of social, economic, and governmental institutions. It also seeks to assist with the development of effective policies to compete internationally and advance U.S. interests and values abroad. This mission is embodied in their domestic and international grant programs.
Fields of interest: Education; International affairs, foreign policy; International affairs; Social sciences; Economics; Political science; International studies; Public policy, research; Government/public administration.
International interests: Asia; Europe; Middle East; Soviet Union.
Type of support: Fellowships; Conferences/seminars; Publication; Research.
Limitations: Applications accepted. Giving limited to U.S.-based organizations only. No support for programs in the arts and humanities, direct service programs, or historic restoration projects. No grants to individuals, or for deficit financing, building or construction projects, or research in the physical sciences; no loans.
Publications: Annual report (including application guidelines).
Application information: If the staff determines that a project warrants further consideration, an applicant will be asked to submit a full proposal. Requests for grants greater than $50,000 and for multi-year grant support are made at one of the foundation's regular board meetings. Requests for grants of $50,000 or less are reviewed on an ongoing basis and are handled as promptly as possible. Application form not required.
Initial approach: Concept paper (no longer than 5 pages)
Copies of proposal: 1
Deadline(s): None
Final notification: 45 to 60 days
Officers and Trustees:* Peter L. Richardson,* Chair., Pres. and Gov.; Stuart S. Richardson, Vice-Chair.; Marin J. Strmecki, Sr. V.P. and Dir., Progs.; Ross F. Hemphill, V.P. and C.F.O.; Arvid R. Nelson,* Secy. and Gov.; Michael Blair; W. Winburne King III; Adele Richardson Ray; Lunsford Richardson, Jr.; Tyler Richardson; E. William Stetson III.
Board of Governors: Hon. Zbigniew Brzezinski; Dr. Paula J. Dobriansky; Dr. Martin Feldstein; Jack Keane; Robert E. Litan; Arvid R. Nelson; Adele Rirchardson Ray; Dr. Carmen Reinhart; Lunsford Richardson, Jr.; Peter L. Richardson; E. William Stetson III; Dr. Ashley Tellis; Dr. Grover J. Whitehurst; R. James Woolsey.
Number of staff: 5 full-time professional; 6 full-time support.
EIN: 560611550
Selected grants: The following grants are a representative sample of this grantmaker's funding activity:
$500,000 to Urban Institute, Washington, DC, 2012.
$437,637 to Stanford University, Stanford, CA, 2012.
$419,448 to Johns Hopkins University, Baltimore, MD, 2012.

$300,000 to Jamestown Foundation, Washington, DC, 2012.
$275,000 to Institute for the Study of War, Washington, DC, 2012.
$268,824 to National Bureau of Economic Research, Cambridge, MA, 2012.
$120,000 to Hoover Institution on War, Revolution and Peace, Stanford, CA, 2012.
$115,000 to Pacific Forum CSIS, Honolulu, HI, 2012.
$100,000 to National Strategy Information Center, Washington, DC, 2012.
$25,000 to Massachusetts Institute of Technology, Cambridge, MA, 2012.

1680
Richard and Ellen Richman Private Family Foundation ✧
340 Pemberwick Rd.
Greenwich, CT 06831-4240

Established in 2007 in CT.
Donors: Richard P. Richman; Ellen S. Richman.
Foundation type: Independent foundation.
Financial data (yr. ended 12/31/13): Assets, $1,051,442 (M); gifts received, $1,000,000; expenditures, $1,781,129; qualifying distributions, $1,773,243; giving activities include $1,771,093 for 31 grants (high: $350,000; low: $500).
Fields of interest: Business school/education; Law school/education; Education; Health care; Human services.
Limitations: Applications not accepted. Giving primarily in New York, NY. No grants to individuals.
Application information: Contributes only to pre-selected organizations.
Trustees: Ellen S. Richman; Richard P. Richman.
EIN: 266161542
Selected grants: The following grants are a representative sample of this grantmaker's funding activity:
$2,825,000 to Columbia University, New York, NY, 2011.
$102,500 to Facing History and Ourselves National Foundation, New York, NY, 2011. To support operations.
$100,000 to Columbia University, New York, NY, 2011. To support operations.
$100,000 to New York University School of Medicine Foundation, New York, NY, 2011. To support operations.

1681
The Robbins Family Foundation ✧ ☆
(formerly Robbins Foundation, Inc.)
32 Calhoun Dr.
Greenwich, CT 06831-4437

Established in 1993 in NY.
Donors: Clifton S. Robbins; Edwin Robbins; Beverly Robbins; Edward Milstein; Gabe Kaplan; Tobey Maguire; General Atlantic Service Corp.; Larry Robbins.
Foundation type: Independent foundation.
Financial data (yr. ended 12/31/13): Assets, $53,498 (M); gifts received, $940,120; expenditures, $1,288,686; qualifying distributions, $1,283,365; giving activities include $1,283,365 for 117 grants (high: $400,000; low: $15).
Purpose and activities: Giving primarily for Jewish organizations, as well as for health organizations and hospitals, particularly a cancer center; funding also for higher education.
Fields of interest: Higher education; Education; Hospitals (specialty); Health care; Health organizations, association; Cancer; Human services; Children/youth, services; Jewish federated giving programs; Jewish agencies & synagogues.
Limitations: Applications not accepted. Giving primarily in CT and NY; some funding also in MA. No grants to individuals.
Application information: Contributes only to pre-selected organizations.
Officers: Clifton S. Robbins, Pres.; Edwin Robbins, V.P.
EIN: 133745914

1682
Rockville Bank Foundation, Inc. ✧
(formerly Rockville Bank Community Foundation, Inc.)
1645 Ellington Rd.
South Windsor, CT 06074-2764 (860) 291-3652
Contact: Judy Keppner, Secy.
Application address: 25 Park St., P.O. Box 660, Rockville, CT 06066; Main URL: http://www.rockvillebank.com/category/6522/rockville-bank-foundation.htm

Established in 2005.
Donor: Rockville Bank.
Foundation type: Company-sponsored foundation.
Financial data (yr. ended 12/31/13): Assets, $11,370,675 (M); expenditures, $653,167; qualifying distributions, $620,703; giving activities include $620,703 for 365 grants (high: $57,500; low: $25).
Purpose and activities: The foundation supports organizations involved with education, health, sports, human services, and community development and awards scholarships, vocational, and agricultural awards to high school seniors.
Fields of interest: Secondary school/education; Vocational education; Higher education; Libraries (public); Education, reading; Education; Health care; Agriculture; Athletics/sports, amateur leagues; YM/YWCAs & YM/YWHAs; Children, services; Developmentally disabled, centers & services; Human services; Community/economic development.
Type of support: General/operating support; Continuing support; Annual campaigns; Equipment; Program development; Employee volunteer services; Sponsorships; Scholarships—to individuals; Matching/challenge support.
Limitations: Applications accepted. Giving primarily in areas of bank operations in Colchester, Coventry, East Windsor, Ellington, Enfield, Glastonbury, Manchester, Rockville, Somers, South Glastonbury, South Windsor, Suffield, Tolland, and Vernon, CT. No grants for past deficits or lobbying.
Publications: Application guidelines.
Application information: Multi-year funding is not automatic. Application form required.
Initial approach: Download application form and mail to foundation; contact foundation for application information for scholarships and awards
Deadline(s): None; varies for scholarships and awards
Final notification: 45 to 60 days
Officers: William H.W. Crawford IV, Chair.; Richard J. Trachimowicz, Pres.; Scott C. Bechtle, Sr. V.P.; Marino J. Santarelli, Sr. V.P.; John T. Lund, V.P., C.F.O., and Treas.; Judy L. Keppner, Secy.
EIN: 203000295

1683
The Rogow Greenberg Foundation, Inc. ✧
(formerly The Rogow Birken Foundation, Inc.)
c/o Birken Manufacturing Co.
3 Old Windsor Rd.
Bloomfield, CT 06002-1397 (860) 242-2211
Contact: Gary Greenberg, Pres.

Established in 1981 in CT.
Donors: Louis B. Rogow†; Glen Greenberg; Sidney Greenberg; Helen Rogow†; Bruce Rogow.
Foundation type: Independent foundation.
Financial data (yr. ended 12/31/13): Assets, $4,306,733 (M); expenditures, $643,712; qualifying distributions, $544,040; giving activities include $423,000 for 39 grants (high: $101,000; low: $50), and $66,700 for 26 grants to individuals (high: $6,000; low: $400).
Purpose and activities: Giving primarily for higher education and Jewish organizations.
Fields of interest: Higher education; Education; Health organizations; Human services; Children/youth, services; United Ways and Federated Giving Programs; Jewish federated giving programs; Jewish agencies & synagogues.
Type of support: General/operating support; Annual campaigns; Capital campaigns; Scholarship funds; Scholarships—to individuals.
Limitations: Applications accepted. Giving primarily in CT, FL, MA, and NY.
Application information: Application form required.
Initial approach: Letter
Deadline(s): None
Officers: Gary Greenberg, Pres.; Bruce Rogow, V.P.
EIN: 061051591

1684
Rosenthal Family Foundation ✧
(formerly The Richard and Hinda Rosenthal Foundation)
2777 Summer St., Ste. 208 B
Stamford, CT 06905-4843
Contact: Nancy Stephens Rosenthal, Pres.
E-mail: rosefdn@sbcglobal.net

Established in 1946 in NY.
Donors: The Richard L. Rosenthal family; and associated interests.
Foundation type: Independent foundation.
Financial data (yr. ended 12/31/13): Assets, $27,540,761 (M); gifts received, $1,061,150; expenditures, $2,521,287; qualifying distributions, $2,335,112; giving activities include $2,060,373 for 214 grants (high: $500,633; low: $75), and $61,910 for loans/program-related investments.
Purpose and activities: Giving to encourage achievement and excellence in the arts, social sciences, medical and scientific research, and clinical medicine. The foundation conceived and annually sponsors the Rosenthal Awards for Fiction and for Painting through the American Academy and National Institute of Arts and Letters; also conceived and sponsors five national awards in clinical medicine through the American College of Physicians, American Heart Association, American

Association for Cancer Research, and others. It has sponsored similar "discovery" awards for film.
Fields of interest: Media/communications; Media, film/video; Media, print publishing; Museums; Performing arts, theater; Language/linguistics; Literature; Child development, education; Higher education; Business school/education; Education; Biomedicine; Medical research, institute; Human services; Child development, services; Residential/custodial care, hospices; Jewish federated giving programs; Social sciences; Economics; Public affairs.
Type of support: General/operating support; Continuing support; Annual campaigns; Building/renovation; Program development; Conferences/seminars; Film/video/radio; Fellowships; Research; Matching/challenge support.
Limitations: Applications accepted. Giving primarily in CA, CT and NY. No grants to individuals.
Publications: Annual report.
Application information: Application form not required.
Initial approach: Letter
Copies of proposal: 1
Deadline(s): None
Board meeting date(s): As required
Final notification: 30 days
Officers and Trustees:* Nancy Stephens Rosenthal,* Pres.; Jamie R. Wolf,* Secy.; Rick Rosenthal,* Treas.; Arnold Paperno, Cont.; Noah Rosenthal; David M. Wolf; Kate Wolf.
Number of staff: 2 part-time professional; 2 part-time support.
EIN: 136104817
Selected grants: The following grants are a representative sample of this grantmaker's funding activity:
$40,000 to Americans for the Arts, Washington, DC, 2011.
$40,000 to Insight LA, Santa Monica, CA, 2011.
$35,000 to American Film Institute, Los Angeles, CA, 2011.
$22,000 to American Academy of Arts and Letters, New York, NY, 2011.
$17,096 to American Association for Cancer Research, Philadelphia, PA, 2011.
$15,000 to University of California Press Foundation, Berkeley, CA, 2011.
$10,000 to Barnard College, New York, NY, 2011.
$7,500 to Shelter Partnership, Los Angeles, CA, 2011.
$6,000 to Manhattan Theater Club, New York, NY, 2011.

1685
Royce Family Fund, Inc. ✧
c/o Royce & Assocs.
8 Sound Shore Dr., Ste. 140
Greenwich, CT 06830-7259

Established in 1985 in DE.
Donor: Charles M. Royce.
Foundation type: Independent foundation.
Financial data (yr. ended 12/31/12): Assets, $98,559,849 (M); gifts received, $16,500,000; expenditures, $6,431,613; qualifying distributions, $9,982,953; giving activities include $5,845,827 for 210 grants (high: $1,022,163; low: $1,000), $68,912 for 1 foundation-administered program and $3,981,485 for 3 loans/program-related investments (high: $2,036,458; low: $621,868).
Purpose and activities: Giving primarily for higher education and the arts, and to Episcopal agencies and churches.
Fields of interest: Museums; Historic preservation/historical societies; Arts; Education; Protestant agencies & churches.
Type of support: Program-related investments/loans.
Limitations: Applications not accepted. Giving primarily in CT and NY. No grants to individuals.
Application information: Contributes only to pre-selected organizations.
Officers and Directors:* Charles M. Royce,* Pres. and Treas.; Nicholas Moore,* Secy.
EIN: 133318620
Selected grants: The following grants are a representative sample of this grantmaker's funding activity:
$677,833 to Christ Church, Greenwich, CT, 2011.
$567,000 to Bruce Museum, Greenwich, CT, 2011.
$507,000 to Brown University, Providence, RI, 2011.
$268,500 to Trinity Church, Greenwich, CT, 2011.
$250,000 to Kings College, Wilkes Barre, PA, 2011.
$167,500 to YMCA, Ocean Community, Westerly, RI, 2011.
$114,700 to YWCA of Greenwich, Greenwich, CT, 2011.
$106,250 to Lake Erie College, Painesville, OH, 2011.
$50,000 to Episcopal Church of Bethesda-by-the-Sea, Palm Beach, FL, 2011.
$16,000 to Society of the Four Arts, Palm Beach, FL, 2011.

1686
The Rubin-Ladd Foundation ✧
P.O. Box 63
Georgetown, CT 06829-0063 (203) 938-0903
Contact: Robert S. Walzer, Pres.

Established in NY.
Foundation type: Independent foundation.
Financial data (yr. ended 06/30/13): Assets, $7,715,409 (M); expenditures, $697,597; qualifying distributions, $614,223; giving activities include $458,929 for 27 grants (high: $231,000; low: $75).
Purpose and activities: The foundation supports fine arts, education, cultural events and health facilities.
Fields of interest: Arts; Higher education; Education.
Type of support: General/operating support.
Limitations: Applications accepted. Giving primarily in CT, Miami, FL, and NY. No grants to individuals.
Application information: Application form required.
Initial approach: Letter
Deadline(s): None
Officers: Robert S. Walzer, Pres.; Ann Walzer, V.P.; Steven Walzer, V.P.
Directors: Francis Coughlin; Eric Walzer; Shelley Weiner.
EIN: 061556098
Selected grants: The following grants are a representative sample of this grantmaker's funding activity:
$45,000 to Yale University, New Haven, CT, 2011. For general purpose.
$35,000 to Yale University, New Haven, CT, 2011. For general purpose.
$25,000 to Yale University, New Haven, CT, 2011. For general purpose.
$15,000 to Yale University, New Haven, CT, 2011. For general purpose.
$8,500 to Yale University, New Haven, CT, 2011. For general purpose.
$8,500 to Yale University, New Haven, CT, 2011. For general purpose.
$8,000 to Yale University, New Haven, CT, 2011. For general purpose.
$4,000 to Yale University, New Haven, CT, 2011. For general purpose.
$3,500 to Yale University, New Haven, CT, 2011. For general purpose.
$3,500 to Yale University, New Haven, CT, 2011. For general purpose.

1687
The Sage Foundation, Inc. ✧
c/o Steven A. Denning
16 Khakum Dr.
Greenwich, CT 06831-3727

Established in 1997 in CT.
Donor: Steven A. Denning.
Foundation type: Independent foundation.
Financial data (yr. ended 12/31/12): Assets, $101,953,261 (M); gifts received, $616,717; expenditures, $5,894,444; qualifying distributions, $5,696,970; giving activities include $5,696,970 for 167 grants (high: $918,750; low: $500).
Purpose and activities: Giving primarily for the arts and education.
Fields of interest: Museums; Museums (natural history); Higher education; Education; Environment; Human services.
Limitations: Applications not accepted. Giving primarily in CA, CT, NY, and WY. No grants to individuals.
Application information: Contributes only to pre-selected organizations.
Officers and Director:* Roberta B. Denning,* Chair.; Steven A. Denning, Secy.; Alan H. Rappaport.
EIN: 061478711

1688
The Sassafras Foundation ✧
P.O. Box 3004
Branford, CT 06405-1604

Established in 2006 in CT.
Donors: G.T. Geballe 1996 Trust B; Gordon T. Geballe.
Foundation type: Independent foundation.
Financial data (yr. ended 12/31/13): Assets, $12,330,270 (M); gifts received, $23; expenditures, $580,546; qualifying distributions, $542,423; giving activities include $540,400 for 18 grants (high: $105,000; low: $2,000).
Fields of interest: Arts; Higher education; Environment, natural resources.
Limitations: Applications not accepted. Giving primarily in New Haven, CT.
Application information: Contributes only to pre-selected organizations.
Officers and Directors:* Gordon T. Geballe,* Pres.; Shelley D. Geballe,* Secy.-Treas.; Benjamin D. Geballe; Daniel W. Geballe; Joshua G. Geballe.
EIN: 203082522
Selected grants: The following grants are a representative sample of this grantmaker's funding activity:

$90,000 to Connecticut News Project, Hartford, CT, 2011.
$75,000 to Leadership, Education and Athletics in Partnership, New Haven, CT, 2011.
$60,000 to Christian Community Action, New Haven, CT, 2011.
$50,000 to Connecticut Fund for the Environment, New Haven, CT, 2011.
$40,000 to New Haven International Festival of Arts and Ideas, New Haven, CT, 2011.
$20,000 to Dwight Hall at Yale, New Haven, CT, 2011.
$11,000 to Online Journalism Project, New Haven, CT, 2011.
$10,000 to Connecticut Players Foundation, New Haven, CT, 2011.
$10,000 to United Way of Greater New Haven, New Haven, CT, 2011.
$5,000 to Jewish Federation of Greater New Haven, Woodbridge, CT, 2011.

1689
Say Yes To Education Foundation ✧

c/o George Weiss Assocs., Inc.
1 State St., 20th Fl.
Hartford, CT 06103-3113 (860) 240-8900

Established in 2007 in CT.
Donors: George A. Weiss; George A. Weiss Assocs., Inc.; Execution LLC Charitable Foundation.
Foundation type: Independent foundation.
Financial data (yr. ended 12/31/12): Assets, $28,051,318 (M); gifts received, $900,914; expenditures, $8,371,911; qualifying distributions, $8,237,608; giving activities include $8,235,000 for 14 grants (high: $7,000,000; low: $15,000).
Fields of interest: Higher education; Human services; Children/youth, services; Aging, centers/services; Jewish federated giving programs.
Limitations: Applications not accepted. Giving primarily in CT, NJ, NY, and PA.
Application information: Contributes only to pre-selected organizations.
Trustee: George A. Weiss.
EIN: 208916545
Selected grants: The following grants are a representative sample of this grantmaker's funding activity:
$7,000,000 to University of Pennsylvania, Philadelphia, PA, 2012. For Professorships.
$733,000 to University of Pennsylvania, Philadelphia, PA, 2012. For Penn Center for Orphan, disease research and therapy.
$175,000 to Woodrow Wilson National Fellowship Foundation, Princeton, NJ, 2012. For program support.
$50,000 to Antigua International Education Foundation, Baltimore, MD, 2012. For program support.
$25,000 to Johns Hopkins University, Baltimore, MD, 2012. For neurology research.
$25,000 to Village Academies Network, Harlem Village Academies, New York, NY, 2012. For program support.
$20,000 to Institute for Educational Leadership, Washington, DC, 2012. To support programs that prepare all children for post-secondary education.
$15,000 to Say Yes to Education, Hartford, CT, 2012. To support programs that promote post-secondary education for at-risk children and youth.

1690
SBM Charitable Foundation, Inc. ✧

935 Main St., Level C, Unit B-101
Manchester, CT 06040-6050 (860) 533-0355
Contact: Doreen Downham, Exec. Dir.
FAX: (860) 533-0241; Main URL: http://www.sbmfoundation.org
Scholarship contact/inquiry: Kelley Gunther, Foundation and Scholarship Dir., tel.: (860) 533-1067, e-mail: kgunther@sbmfoundation.org

Established as a company-sponsored foundation in 2000 in CT; status changed to independent foundation in 2004.
Donor: Savings Bank of Manchester Foundation, Inc.
Foundation type: Independent foundation.
Financial data (yr. ended 12/31/12): Assets, $37,843,533 (M); expenditures, $2,486,078; qualifying distributions, $2,318,858; giving activities include $2,051,987 for 139 grants (high: $175,000; low: $100).
Purpose and activities: The foundation supports organizations involved with arts and culture, education, health, housing, human services, and children and youth. College scholarships of up to $5,000 each are awarded annually to students who are permanent residents of the CT counties which the foundation serves, are in the top 40 percent of their high school class or maintain a 2.5 GPA or higher in college, and who plan on attending an accredited institution of higher learning in CT.
Fields of interest: Arts; Education; Hospitals (general); Health care; Housing/shelter; Children/youth, services; Human services; United Ways and Federated Giving Programs.
Type of support: Scholarships—to individuals; In-kind gifts.
Limitations: Applications accepted. Giving primarily in Hartford, Tolland and Windham counties in CT. No support for public or private schools (both primary and secondary), or for religious institutions, unless the program benefits the community at large. No grants to individuals, (except for scholarships).
Application information: Application forms available on foundation web site. Application form required.
Initial approach: First-time applicants use Pre-Application form; past recipients may use the Request for Grant form; scholarship applicants use scholarship application form
Copies of proposal: 1
Deadline(s): See foundation web site for current deadlines
Officers and Directors:* Laurence P. Rubinow,* Chair.; Richard P. Meduski,* Pres.; Douglas K. Anderson,* V.P.; Charles L. Pike,* V.P.; Brian A. Orenstein,* Treas.; Doreen Downham, Exec. Dir.; Timothy J. Devanney; Sheila B. Flanagan; Harry S. Gaucher; Michael J. Hartl; Linda S. Klein; John D. LaBelle, Jr.; Eric A. Marziali; Timothy J. Moynihan; Jon L. Norris; William D. O'Neill; Richard Suski; Gregory S. Wolff.
Number of staff: 2 full-time support; 1 part-time support.
EIN: 061574365

1691
Seedlings Foundation ✧

984 Main St.
Branford, CT 06405-3730 (203) 481-5740
Main URL: http://seedlingsct.org/

Established in 2002 in IL.
Donors: Pritzker Foundation; Pritzker Cousins Foundation; Karen Pritzker.
Foundation type: Independent foundation.
Financial data (yr. ended 12/31/13): Assets, $73,172,449 (M); gifts received, $24,567,005; expenditures, $27,385,056; qualifying distributions, $27,083,688; giving activities include $26,105,163 for 107 grants (high: $4,000,000; low: $1,000), and $978,525 for 2 foundation-administered programs.
Purpose and activities: Giving to support programs that nourish the physical and mental health of children and families, and that foster an educated and engaged citizenship.
Fields of interest: Performing arts, theater; Arts; Secondary school/education; Higher education; Education, reading; Education; Human services; Foundations (community).
Type of support: General/operating support.
Limitations: Applications not accepted. Giving primarily in CT. No grants to individuals.
Application information: Contributes only to pre-selected organizations.
Officers and Directors:* Karen Pritzker,* Pres.; Michael Vlock,* Secy.-Treas.; Linda Pritzker; Audrey Ratner.
EIN: 043600502
Selected grants: The following grants are a representative sample of this grantmaker's funding activity:
$9,154,700 to Yale University, School of Medicine, New Haven, CT, 2012.
$1,000,000 to George W. Bush Foundation, Dallas, TX, 2012.
$1,000,000 to Illinois Institute of Technology, Chicago, IL, 2012.
$1,000,000 to Teach for America, New York, NY, 2012.
$566,109 to My Hero Project, Laguna Beach, CA, 2012.
$520,000 to Network for Teaching Entrepreneurship, New York, NY, 2012.
$347,500 to Connecticut Players Foundation, Long Wharf Theatre, New Haven, CT, 2012.
$221,666 to Jazz at Lincoln Center, New York, NY, 2012.
$50,000 to New Haven Reads Community Book Bank, New Haven, CT, 2012.
$25,000 to Hartford Stage Company, Hartford, CT, 2012.

1692
The Seidenberg Family Foundation, Inc. ✧

(formerly The Ivan Seidenberg Foundation)
c/o HHG
23 Old Kings Hwy. S.
Darien, CT 06820-4541

Established in 1993 in CT.
Donors: Ivan Seidenberg; Phyllis Seidenberg.
Foundation type: Independent foundation.
Financial data (yr. ended 12/31/13): Assets, $14,405,092 (M); gifts received, $6,003,005; expenditures, $6,824,705; qualifying distributions, $6,802,085; giving activities include $6,801,315 for 35 grants (high: $6,000,000; low: $50).
Purpose and activities: Giving for higher and other education, Jewish organizations, federated giving programs and for health services.
Fields of interest: Higher education; Hospitals (general); Jewish agencies & synagogues.

Limitations: Applications not accepted. Giving primarily in the New York, NY, area. No grants to individuals.
Application information: Contributes only to pre-selected organizations.
Directors: Lisa Agdern; Douglas Seidenberg; Ivan Seidenberg; Phyllis Seidenberg.
EIN: 061386525

1693
The Selander Foundation ✧ ☆
15 E. Putnam Ave., Ste. 244
Greenwich, CT 06830-7020

Established in 2004 in CT.
Donor: Robert W. Selander.
Foundation type: Independent foundation.
Financial data (yr. ended 11/30/13): Assets, $12,739,663 (M); gifts received, $234,000; expenditures, $514,541; qualifying distributions, $453,250; giving activities include $453,250 for 14 grants (high: $250,000; low: $250).
Fields of interest: Brain research; Medical research; Boys & girls clubs; Human services, victim aid; Crime/abuse victims.
Type of support: General/operating support.
Limitations: Applications not accepted. Giving primarily in CT; some giving in OH, MA, and NY. No grants to individuals.
Application information: Contributes only to pre-selected organizations.
Officers: Robert W. Selander, Chair.; Nancy Cross Selander, Pres.
Trustees: Jessica Anne Lundgren; Tracey Kay Lundgren; Crosby Selander; Russell Selander.
EIN: 202024998
Selected grants: The following grants are a representative sample of this grantmaker's funding activity:
$105,000 to Boys and Girls Club of Greenwich, Greenwich, CT, 2011.
$10,000 to Summer on the Hill, Riverdale, NY, 2011.
$5,000 to Danas Angels Research Trust, Greenwich, CT, 2011.
$3,000 to Breast Cancer Alliance, Greenwich, CT, 2011.
$1,000 to Community Health Center of Cape Cod, Mashpee, MA, 2011.
$1,000 to Cook Childrens Medical Center, Fort Worth, TX, 2011.
$1,000 to Wounded Warrior Project, Jacksonville, FL, 2011.

1694
Selkowitz Family Foundation ✧
262 Ocean Dr. E.
Stamford, CT 06902-8238

Established in 2000 in CT.
Donors: Arthur Selkowitz; Betsey Selkowitz.
Foundation type: Independent foundation.
Financial data (yr. ended 12/31/13): Assets, $1,186,223 (M); gifts received, $391,965; expenditures, $508,307; qualifying distributions, $484,046; giving activities include $477,550 for 35 grants (high: $255,000; low: $500).
Fields of interest: Lupus; Recreation, parks/playgrounds; Children/youth, services; Jewish agencies & synagogues.
Limitations: Applications not accepted. Giving primarily in CA, CT, and NY. No grants to individuals.
Application information: Contributes only to pre-selected organizations.
Trustees: Adam Selkowitz; Arthur Selkowitz; Betsey Selkowitz; Jed Selkowitz.
EIN: 061599301
Selected grants: The following grants are a representative sample of this grantmaker's funding activity:
$241,000 to Mill River Collaborative, Stamford, CT, 2012. For Creating and Sustaining a World Class Park Along the Mill River.
$39,300 to Jewish Community Center of Stamford, Stamford, CT, 2012. For Jewish Community Center.
$17,100 to Lupus Research Institute, New York, NY, 2012. For Research for Lupus Treatments and a Cure.

1695
Eric P. Sheinberg Foundation ✧
c/o R&R
51 Locust Ave., Ste. 303
New Canaan, CT 06840-4739

Established in 1971.
Donor: Eric P. Sheinberg.
Foundation type: Independent foundation.
Financial data (yr. ended 06/30/13): Assets, $14,132,286 (M); expenditures, $616,903; qualifying distributions, $595,350; giving activities include $595,350 for grants.
Fields of interest: Museums (art); Arts; Libraries (public); Education; Hospitals (general); Health care; Human services.
Type of support: General/operating support.
Limitations: Applications not accepted. Giving primarily in New Canaan, CT, and New York, NY. No grants to individuals.
Application information: Contributes only to pre-selected organizations.
Trustees: Eric P. Sheinberg; Michael Steinhardt.
EIN: 137004291
Selected grants: The following grants are a representative sample of this grantmaker's funding activity:
$120,000 to Mount Sinai Medical Center, New York, NY, 2011. For general purposes.
$25,000 to New York Public Library, New York, NY, 2011. For general purposes.
$13,000 to Central Park Conservancy, New York, NY, 2011. For general purposes.
$10,000 to New Canaan Community Foundation, New Canaan, CT, 2011. For general purposes.
$9,000 to Metropolitan Museum of Art, New York, NY, 2011. For general purposes.
$5,000 to Asia Society, New York, NY, 2011. For general purposes.
$5,000 to Cancer Research Institute, New York, NY, 2011. For general purposes.
$5,000 to New Canaan Nature Center Association, New Canaan, CT, 2011. For general purposes.
$5,000 to Wildlife Conservation Society, Bronx, NY, 2011. For general purposes.
$2,000 to Boy Scouts of America, Derby, CT, 2011. For general purposes.

1696
Silver Family Foundation ✧
(formerly Barbara Silver Foundation)
c/o Walter, Berlingo and Co.
P.O. Box 4080
Darien, CT 06820-1480

Established in 1998 in CT.
Donors: Barbara Silver; R. Philip Silver.
Foundation type: Independent foundation.
Financial data (yr. ended 06/30/13): Assets, $19,213,061 (M); expenditures, $1,904,596; qualifying distributions, $1,824,602; giving activities include $1,762,696 for 43 grants (high: $400,725; low: $5,000).
Fields of interest: Education; Human services; Children/youth, services.
Limitations: Applications not accepted. Giving primarily in OR and WA. No grants to individuals.
Application information: Contributes only to pre-selected organizations.
Trustees: Barbara Silver; Peter Milo Silver; Philip Silver; Philip Tyler Silver.
EIN: 061532898
Selected grants: The following grants are a representative sample of this grantmaker's funding activity:
$100,175 to De La Salle North Catholic High School, Portland, OR, 2013. For College Prep Education.
$50,000 to Community Schools Collaboration, Burien, WA, 2013. To provide students with the Support and Opportunities to Succeed Academically.
$50,000 to French American International School, Portland, OR, 2013. To provide Bilingual Education.
$50,000 to Rainier Scholars, Seattle, WA, 2013. For Youth Academic Enrichment/College Prep/Leadership Development.
$50,000 to Washington Initiative for Supported Employment, Seattle, WA, 2013. For Promoting Equitable Employment for People with Developmental Disabilities Through Innovation, Training and Technical Assistance.
$40,000 to Team Read, Seattle, WA, 2013. For Tutoring Center for Children.
$35,130 to Marathon Education Partners, Portland, OR, 2013. For scholarship opportunity for children with financial need.
$35,000 to Summer Search Seattle, Seattle, WA, 2013. For mentoring program for low income students.
$32,500 to New Futures, Burien, WA, 2013. For Human Service Organization for Children and Families.
$30,000 to Technology Access Foundation, Seattle, WA, 2013. To equip students of color for success in college and life.

1697
The Smart Family Foundation, Inc. ✧
74 Pin Oak Ln.
Wilton, CT 06897-1329 (914) 632-2762

Trust established in 1951 in IL.
Donors: David A. Smart†; A.D. Elden†; Vera Elden†; John Smart†; Edgar G. Richards†; Florence Richards†.
Foundation type: Independent foundation.
Financial data (yr. ended 12/31/13): Assets, $200,592,245 (M); expenditures, $8,913,370; qualifying distributions, $7,212,203; giving

activities include $6,663,076 for 107 grants (high: $895,000; low: $2,000).
Purpose and activities: The foundation is primarily interested in education projects and has, in particular, been focusing on projects that affect primary and secondary school children.
Fields of interest: Elementary school/education; Secondary school/education; Higher education, university; Education; Hospitals (general).
Type of support: General/operating support; Seed money; Research; Program-related investments/loans.
Limitations: Applications not accepted. Giving primarily in CT, IL, NJ and NY. No grants to individuals.
Application information: Unsolicited requests for funds not accepted.
Board meeting date(s): Fall and spring
Officers and Directors:* Robert Feitler,* Chair. and Secy.; Mary Smart,* Pres.; William Oswald,* Treas.; Raymond L. Smart,* Pres. Emeritus; Chris Hoehn-Saric; Ellen Smart Oswald; David Stone.
Number of staff: 1 full-time professional; 1 part-time support.
EIN: 061232323

1698
Joel E. Smilow Charitable Trust ✧
830 Post Rd. E., Ste. 105
Westport, CT 06880-5222

Established in 1987 in CT.
Donor: Joel E. Smilow.
Foundation type: Independent foundation.
Financial data (yr. ended 12/31/12): Assets, $9,769,437 (M); expenditures, $17,643,805; qualifying distributions, $17,622,520; giving activities include $17,622,520 for 62 grants (high: $9,567,603; low: $100).
Purpose and activities: Giving primarily for the arts, higher education, and health care.
Fields of interest: Museums; Performing arts, theater; Arts; Higher education; Education; Hospitals (general); Health care; Health organizations, association; Human services; Children/youth, services.
Limitations: Applications not accepted. Giving primarily in CT, NY, and PA. No grants to individuals.
Application information: Contributes only to pre-selected organizations.
Officer: Joel E. Smilow, Mgr.
Trustee: Deborah Berger.
EIN: 066299809

1699
The John and Polly Sparks Foundation ☆
c/o Bank of America, U.S. Trust
99 Founders Plz., CT2-547-05-19, 5th Fl.
East Hartford, CT 06108-3208 (860) 244-4870
Contact: Amy R. Lynch, Senior V.P., Bank of America, U.S. Trust
E-mail: amy.r.lynch@ustrust.com; Main URL: http://fdnweb.org/sparks

Donor: Pauline Sparks†.
Foundation type: Independent foundation.
Financial data (yr. ended 11/30/13): Assets, $55,906,315 (M); gifts received, $16,737,930; expenditures, $2,061,846; qualifying distributions, $1,772,333; giving activities include $1,569,638 for 25 grants (high: $1,000,000; low: $10,000).
Purpose and activities: Giving primarily for mental illness, chemical imbalance and depression in infancy, housing for children and adults, and assistance with health and aging.
Fields of interest: Health care; Medical research; Recreation.
Limitations: Applications accepted. Giving primarily in FL, GA and the Southeast. No grants for endowments, annual giving campaigns, debt reduction or financing, conferences and seminars, travel or advertising.
Publications: Application guidelines.
Application information: Application form required.
Initial approach: Use online application on foundation web site
Deadline(s): July 1
Trustees: Robert Morgan; Bank of America, N.A.
EIN: 272992779

1700
Stanley Family Foundation ✧
(formerly Theodore & Vada Stanley Foundation)
47 Richards Ave.
Norwalk, CT 06857-1915
Contact: Theodore R. Stanley, Tr.
Ted and Vada Stanley's Giving Pledge Profile: http://glasspockets.org/philanthropy-in-focus/eye-on-the-giving-pledge/profiles/stanley

Established in 1985 in CT.
Donor: Theodore R. Stanley.
Foundation type: Independent foundation.
Financial data (yr. ended 12/31/13): Assets, $297,125,778 (M); gifts received, $132,716,963; expenditures, $5,318,695; qualifying distributions, $5,151,825; giving activities include $5,140,000 for 25 grants (high: $4,250,000; low: $1,500).
Purpose and activities: Support primarily to a mental health organization, as well as for education and human services; funding also for the arts.
Fields of interest: Arts; Education; Mental health/crisis services; Human services.
Limitations: Applications not accepted. Giving primarily in Cambridge, MA, NY, the Washington, DC area, and Austin, TX. No grants to individuals.
Application information: Contributes only to pre-selected organizations.
Trustees: Julius F. Friese; Jonathan A. Stanley; Theodore R. Stanley.
EIN: 061157888

1701
William & Lynda Steere Foundation ✧
P.O. Box 2630
Westport, CT 06880-0630

Established in 1999.
Donors: William Steere, Jr.; Lynda Steere; William C. Steere.
Foundation type: Independent foundation.
Financial data (yr. ended 12/31/13): Assets, $6,978,980 (M); gifts received, $1,548,888; expenditures, $1,365,655; qualifying distributions, $1,240,650; giving activities include $1,240,650 for 31 grants (high: $500,000; low: $500).
Purpose and activities: Giving primarily for the arts, education, health care and hospitals, and human services.
Fields of interest: Performing arts, orchestras; Arts; Elementary/secondary education; Higher education; Medical school/education; Education; Botanical gardens; Hospitals (specialty); Health care; Human services.
Limitations: Applications not accepted. Giving primarily in NY. No grants to individuals.
Application information: Contributes only to pre-selected organizations.
Trustees: Elwood B. Davis; Lynda Steere; William C. Steere.
EIN: 656286705

1702
Martha Washington Straus & Harry H. Straus Foundation, Inc. ✧
10 Skyline Ln.
Stamford, CT 06903-2916

Incorporated in 1949 in NC.
Donors: Harry H. Straus, Sr.†; Louise Straus King.
Foundation type: Independent foundation.
Financial data (yr. ended 12/31/13): Assets, $12,197,017 (M); expenditures, $580,715; qualifying distributions, $565,000; giving activities include $565,000 for 80 grants (high: $20,000; low: $1,000).
Purpose and activities: Giving primarily for health, including medical research and education, hospitals, and health associations; some support also for Roman Catholic and Jewish religious institutions and federated giving programs, persons with disabilities, and social services.
Fields of interest: Arts; Higher education; Hospitals (general); Health care; Health organizations, association; Medical research, institute; Human services; Catholic federated giving programs; Jewish federated giving programs; Catholic agencies & churches; Jewish agencies & synagogues.
Limitations: Applications not accepted. Giving primarily in the metropolitan Washington, DC, area, including MD, and New York, NY. No grants to individuals.
Application information: Contributes only to pre-selected organizations.
Board meeting date(s): As required
Officers: David Straus, V.P.; Thomas King, Treas. and Mgr.
EIN: 560645526
Selected grants: The following grants are a representative sample of this grantmaker's funding activity:
$50,000 to Boston College, Chestnut Hill, MA, 2011.
$15,000 to Connelly School of the Holy Child, Potomac, MD, 2011.
$15,000 to Georgetown University Medical Center, Washington, DC, 2011.
$10,000 to Autism Research Institute, San Diego, CA, 2011.
$10,000 to Guiding Eyes for the Blind, Yorktown Heights, NY, 2011.
$10,000 to UJA-Federation of New York, New York, NY, 2010.
$7,000 to Muscular Dystrophy Association, New York, NY, 2011.
$7,000 to Operation Smile International, Norfolk, VA, 2011.
$6,000 to Catholic Relief Services, Baltimore, MD, 2010.
$6,000 to John F. Kennedy Center for the Performing Arts, Washington, DC, 2011.
$6,000 to So Others Might Eat, Washington, DC, 2010.

$5,000 to Visions Services for the Blind and Visually Impaired, New York, NY, 2011.
$5,000 to Washington Middle School for Girls, Washington, DC, 2011.
$3,000 to Washington Middle School for Girls, Washington, DC, 2010.

1703
Ray & Pauline Sullivan Foundation ✧

c/o Bank of America, N.A.
200 Glastonbury Blvd., 2nd Fl.
Glastonbury, CT 06033-4458
Contact: Amy R. Lynch, V.P.

Established in 1972 in CT.
Donor: Ray H. Sullivan‡.
Foundation type: Independent foundation.
Financial data (yr. ended 01/31/14): Assets, $14,905,447 (M); expenditures, $799,830; qualifying distributions, $696,574; giving activities include $653,500 for grants.
Purpose and activities: Giving primarily to Roman Catholic charities and educational institutions located in the Diocese of Norwich, CT only; also awards scholarships and student loans to graduates of St. Bernard's High School in Uncasville, CT.
Fields of interest: Elementary/secondary education; Human services; Catholic agencies & churches.
Type of support: Scholarship funds; Scholarships—to individuals; Student loans—to individuals.
Limitations: Giving limited to the Diocese of Norwich, CT.
Application information: Application form required.
Initial approach: Letter
Deadline(s): May 1 for scholarships and loans
Final notification: 8 weeks
Trustees: Maureen Fraser; Jeremiah J. Lowney, Jr.; James C. McGuire; Rev. Mark D. O'Donnell; Bank of America, N.A.
EIN: 066141242
Selected grants: The following grants are a representative sample of this grantmaker's funding activity:
$2,000 to Columbia University, New York, NY, 2011. For scholarships.
$2,000 to George Washington University, Washington, DC, 2011.
$2,000 to George Washington University, Washington, DC, 2011.
$2,000 to Northeastern University, Boston, MA, 2011.
$2,000 to University of Connecticut, Storrs, CT, 2011. For scholarships.
$2,000 to University of Connecticut, Storrs, CT, 2011.
$2,000 to University of Connecticut, Storrs, CT, 2011.
$2,000 to University of Notre Dame, Notre Dame, IN, 2011. For scholarships.
$2,000 to Vanderbilt University, Nashville, TN, 2011.
$1,500 to University of Connecticut, Storrs, CT, 2011. For scholarships.

1704
The Summer Hill Foundation ✧

888 Summer Hill Rd.
Madison, CT 06443-1604 (203) 421-3669
Contact: Michael Johnson, Tr.

Established in 2007 in CT.
Donors: Michael D. Johnson; Teresa H. Johnson Family Trust.
Foundation type: Independent foundation.
Financial data (yr. ended 12/31/13): Assets, $14,948,454 (M); expenditures, $574,759; qualifying distributions, $483,605; giving activities include $480,000 for 5 grants (high: $250,000; low: $10,000).
Purpose and activities: Giving primarily to land trusts and other organizations that are dedicated to protecting the environment, especially in ecologically sensitive areas. The foundation will support charitable organizations that help to preserve land in its natural state, re-introduce native plants to areas where they have been removed, and preserve historically significant buildings that are associated with open space. It also will support charitable and educational institutions that provide environmentally-related education. The foundation may also make distributions to local governments or government agencies for the preservation of historically significant buildings.
Fields of interest: Environment, natural resources; Philanthropy/voluntarism.
Limitations: Applications accepted. Giving primarily in CA; some giving also in CT and VA.
Application information: Application form required.
Initial approach: Proposal
Deadline(s): None
Trustee: Michael D. Johnson.
EIN: 261344446
Selected grants: The following grants are a representative sample of this grantmaker's funding activity:
$400,000 to Trust for Public Land, San Francisco, CA, 2011.
$50,000 to Nature Conservancy, Arlington, VA, 2011.

1705
Swordspoint Foundation, Inc. ✧

134 Main St.
New Canaan, CT 06840-5512

Donors: Robert J. Bishop; Impala Asset Management LLC.
Foundation type: Independent foundation.
Financial data (yr. ended 06/30/13): Assets, $8,486,057 (M); gifts received, $1,000,000; expenditures, $910,911; qualifying distributions, $804,502; giving activities include $785,000 for 43 grants (high: $100,000; low: $1,000).
Purpose and activities: Giving primarily for the environment, including an oceanography institution and education; some giving also for landmark and animal preservation.
Fields of interest: Historic preservation/historical societies; Higher education; Education; Environment, water resources; Animals/wildlife, preservation/protection.
Limitations: Applications not accepted. Giving primarily in CT, IL, and MA. No grants to individuals.
Application information: Contributes only to pre-selected organizations.
Officers: Robert J. Bishop, Pres. and Treas.; Susan Bishop, V.P. and Secy.
EIN: 593814672
Selected grants: The following grants are a representative sample of this grantmaker's funding activity:
$100,000 to New Canaan Historical Society, New Canaan, CT, 2013. For landmark preservation.
$5,000 to International Crane Foundation, Baraboo, WI, 2013. For Dedicated to conservation of cranes in the wild through research.
$2,500 to Fisher House Foundation, Rockville, MD, 2013. For Housing for Families of Soldiers Being Treated in Military Hospitals.

1706
Tauck Family Foundation, Inc. ✧ ☆

(formerly The Tauck Foundation, Inc.)
P.O. Box 5020
10 Norden Pl.
Norwalk, CT 06856 (203) 899-6824
Contact: Eden Werring, Exec. Dir.; Mirellise Vazquez, Prog. Off.
FAX: (203) 286-1340; Main URL: http://www.tauckfamilyfoundation.org/
Twitter: https://twitter.com/TauckFamilyFdn

Donors: Elizabeth T. Walters; Arthur C. Tauck III.
Foundation type: Independent foundation.
Financial data (yr. ended 12/31/13): Assets, $21,346,803 (M); gifts received, $60,369; expenditures, $832,172; qualifying distributions, $803,149; giving activities include $474,368 for 56 grants (high: $100,000; low: $100), and $36,756 for 2 foundation-administered programs.
Purpose and activities: The foundation's mission is to invest in the development of essential life skills that lead to better prospects for children from low-income families in Bridgeport, Connecticut. Its vision is that Bridgeport children will cultivate the skills they need to take control of their future, succeed in their education, break the cycle of poverty, and reach their full potential.
Fields of interest: Education; Youth development; Children/youth; Economically disadvantaged.
Limitations: Applications accepted. Giving primarily in Bridgeport, CT.
Application information: Complete application guidelines available on foundation web site. Application form required.
Officers and Directors:* Arthur C. Tauck, Jr.,* Chair. and Secy.-Treas.; Elizabeth T. Walters,* Pres.; Eden Werring, Exec. Dir.; Christopher Duermmeier; Christen Romano Lert; Colleen Ritzau Leth; Arthur C. Tauck III; Chuck Tauck; Peter Tauck; Robin Tauck; Tyler Tauck.
EIN: 270729341
Selected grants: The following grants are a representative sample of this grantmaker's funding activity:
$20,000 to Solar Youth, New Haven, CT, 2012. For Citycology Program.
$20,000 to Summer Search Seattle, Seattle, WA, 2012. For High School Mentorship Program.
$20,000 to Treehouse, Seattle, WA, 2012. For Summer Academy Program.
$2,500 to Columbia University, New York, NY, 2012. For rowing endowment.
$750 to Adirondack Mountain Club, Lake George, NY, 2012. For Public Lands Campaign.
$500 to Barnard College, New York, NY, 2012. For annual fund faculty support.
$250 to Neighbors Link Stamford, Stamford, CT, 2012. For Hiring Site Program.
$100 to Bowdoin College, Brunswick, ME, 2012. For Scholarship and Financial Aid Fund.

1707
The Tombros Foundation ✧
c/o Reynolds & Rowella LLP
90 Grove St.
Ridgefield, CT 06877-4114

Established in 2000 in DE.
Donor: Peter G. Tombros.
Foundation type: Independent foundation.
Financial data (yr. ended 12/31/12): Assets, $11,465,250 (M); expenditures, $1,058,364; qualifying distributions, $906,850; giving activities include $906,850 for grants.
Purpose and activities: Giving primarily for a land preservation organization and higher and other education; some funding also medical research.
Fields of interest: Elementary/secondary education; Higher education; Environment, land resources; Medical research, institute; Human services.
Limitations: Applications not accepted. Giving primarily in CT, NY and PA. No grants to individuals.
Application information: Contributes only to pre-selected organizations.
Officers: Peter G. Tombros, Pres.; Ann C. Tombros, V.P.
EIN: 522284151

1708
The Tow Foundation, Inc. ✧
(formerly The Leonard & Claire Tow Charitable Trust, Inc.)
50 Locust Ave., 2nd Fl.
New Canaan, CT 06840-4737 (203) 761-6604
FAX: (203) 761-6605;
E-mail: info@towfoundation.org; Main URL: http://towfoundation.org/
Claire and Leonard Tow's Giving Pledge Profile: http://glasspockets.org/philanthropy-in-focus/eye-on-the-giving-pledge/profiles/tow
Facebook: https://www.facebook.com/TowFdn
Twitter: https://twitter.com/TowFdn

Established in 1988 in CT.
Donors: Claire Tow‡; Leonard Tow.
Foundation type: Independent foundation.
Financial data (yr. ended 12/31/13): Assets, $215,396,249 (M); gifts received, $3,768,645; expenditures, $14,945,896; qualifying distributions, $13,470,272; giving activities include $12,349,166 for 105 grants (high: $2,000,000; low: $100).
Purpose and activities: The foundation will fund projects and create collaborative ventures where it see opportunities for reform and benefits for underserved populations. It strives to provide leverage to make possible far greater things than it could achieve alone.
Fields of interest: Performing arts centers; Higher education; Public health; Cancer research; ALS research; Crime/violence prevention, youth.
Type of support: Research; Program development; General/operating support.
Limitations: Applications not accepted. Giving primarily in CT and New York, NY. No support for political causes, candidates or campaigns. No grants to individuals or for capital campaigns.
Publications: Grants list; Informational brochure.
Application information: Contributes only to pre-selected organizations. Invited applicants will receive a link to an application form.
Officers and Trustees:* Leonard Tow,* Chair.; Emily Tow Jackson,* Pres. and Exec. Dir.; Frank Tow,* V.P.; David Rosensweig,* Secy.; Scott N. Schneider,* Treas.; Pamela Castori, Ph. D.; Amy Lefkof; Maureen Strafford, M.D.; David Tobias; Andrew Tow.
EIN: 066484045
Selected grants: The following grants are a representative sample of this grantmaker's funding activity:
$2,000,000 to Brooklyn College Foundation, Brooklyn, NY, 2012. For Creation of The Leonard and Claire Tow Performing Arts Center.
$2,000,000 to Columbia University Medical Center, Center for Motor Neuron Biology and Disease, New York, NY, 2012. For College of Physicians and Surgeons, Center for Motor Neuron Biology and Disease.
$1,600,000 to Memorial Sloan-Kettering Cancer Center, New York, NY, 2012. For Michael G. Harris Cell Therapy and Cell Engineering Facility.
$1,600,000 to Memorial Sloan-Kettering Cancer Center, New York, NY, 2012. For Michael G. Harris Cell Therapy and Cell Engineering Facility.
$1,500,000 to Lincoln Center Theater, New York, NY, 2012. For $7.5 million to Lincoln Center Theater solely for the construction of the Claire Tow Theater.
$1,000,000 to Columbia University, Graduate School of Journalism, New York, NY, 2012. To create The Tow Center for Digital Journalism.
$1,000,000 to Memorial Sloan-Kettering Cancer Center, New York, NY, 2012. For Lucille Castori Center for Microbes, Inflammation and Cancer.
$110,000 to Barnard College, New York, NY, 2012. For The Tow Family Award for Innovative and Outstanding Pedagogy and Tow Family Professorships for Distinguished Scholars and Practitioners.
$50,000 to THIRTEEN, New York, NY, 2012. For the 50th Anniversary of PBS.
$25,000 to Amyotrophic Lateral Sclerosis Association, Greater New York Chapter, New York, NY, 2012. For The 18th Annual Lou Gehrig Benefit.

1709
Ernest and Joan Trefz Foundation ✧
10 Middle St.
Bridgeport, CT 06604-4223

Established in 1997 in CT.
Donors: Ernest C. Trefz; Joan M. Trefz.
Foundation type: Independent foundation.
Financial data (yr. ended 04/30/13): Assets, $14,075,211 (M); gifts received, $995,073; expenditures, $571,875; qualifying distributions, $570,400; giving activities include $570,400 for grants.
Fields of interest: Arts; Higher education, university; Education, services; Health organizations, association; Medical research; Youth development, services; Human services; United Ways and Federated Giving Programs.
Limitations: Applications not accepted. Giving primarily in CT and NY. No grants to individuals.
Application information: Unsolicited requests for funds not accepted.
Trustees: Christian C. Trefz; Ernest C. Trefz; Joan M. Trefz; Linda M. Trefz; Paul D. Trefz.
EIN: 061485833
Selected grants: The following grants are a representative sample of this grantmaker's funding activity:
$2,500 to Tiny Miracles Foundation, Darien, CT, 2013. For In Furtherance of Stated Objectives of the Foundation.

1710
Emily Hall Tremaine Foundation, Inc. ✧
171 Orange St.
New Haven, CT 06510-3111
Main URL: http://www.tremainefoundation.org

Established in 1987 in CT.
Donors: Emily Hall Tremaine‡; Burton G. Tremaine, Sr.‡; Burton G. Tremaine, Jr.‡.
Foundation type: Independent foundation.
Financial data (yr. ended 12/31/13): Assets, $86,804,932 (M); expenditures, $4,781,266; qualifying distributions, $4,542,627; giving activities include $3,369,269 for 257 grants (high: $514,000; low: $300).
Purpose and activities: The foundation seeks to fund innovative projects that advance practical solutions to basic problems in our society. With an overall emphasis on education principally in the United States, it takes an active role in the arts, the environment, and in learning disabilities.
Fields of interest: Arts; Education; Environment.
Limitations: Applications not accepted. Giving on a national basis. No grants to individuals or for building funds, research projects, or experimental demonstrations.
Application information: Unsolicited requests for funds not accepted; however the foundation does accept 1-page letters of inquiry.
Board meeting date(s): Rolling
Officers and Directors:* Amanda G. Stanley,* Chair.; Michelle Knapik, Pres.; Wyndsor DePetro,* Secy.; Atwood Collins III,* Treas.; Lauren Collins; Jordan Nodelman; William O'Brien; Janet T. Stanley; Philip T. Stanley; Burton G. Tremaine III; John M. Tremaine; John M. Tremaine, Jr.; Sarah C. Tremaine; Susan C. Tremaine; Emily R. Wick.
Number of staff: 2 full-time professional; 2 part-time professional; 1 part-time support.
EIN: 222533743

1711
The Tudor Foundation, Inc. ✧
1275 King St.
Greenwich, CT 06831-2936
GiveSmart: http://www.givesmart.org/Stories/Donors/Paul-Tudor-Jones

Established in 1997 in CT.
Donors: Tudor Arbitrage Partners; Tudor Group Holdings, LLC; Tudor Proprietary Trading, LLC; Tudor Investment Corp.
Foundation type: Independent foundation.
Financial data (yr. ended 12/31/13): Assets, $726,505 (M); gifts received, $4,557,000; expenditures, $4,687,799; qualifying distributions, $4,660,589; giving activities include $4,641,518 for 108 grants (high: $145,000; low: $2,000).
Purpose and activities: Giving primarily for education and human services, with emphasis on children and youth services.
Fields of interest: Education; Human services; Children/youth, services; Disabilities, people with.
International interests: Australia; England.
Limitations: Applications not accepted. Giving primarily in CT, MA, NY and England; some funding also in Australia. No grants to individuals.

Application information: Contributes only to pre-selected organizations.
Officers and Directors:* Andrew S. Paul,* Pres. and Secy.-Treas.; Paul T. Jones II; Michael Riccardi.
EIN: 061502288

1712
Twenty-Seven Foundation ✧
c/o Bank of America, N.A., US Trust
200 Glastonbury Blvd., Ste. 200
Glastonbury, CT 06033-6715

Established in 2007 in CT.
Donor: D. Travis Engen.
Foundation type: Independent foundation.
Financial data (yr. ended 12/31/13): Assets, $50,401,692 (M); expenditures, $2,209,099; qualifying distributions, $2,127,000; giving activities include $2,127,000 for 31 grants (high: $250,000; low: $2,000).
Fields of interest: Education; Veterinary medicine; Animals/wildlife; Protestant agencies & churches.
Limitations: Applications not accepted. Giving primarily in CT, IN, and MA. No grants to individuals.
Application information: Contributes only to pre-selected organizations.
Trustees: Anne E. Engen; D. Travis Engen; Leigh E. Engen.
EIN: 266147397

1713
Lawson Valentine Foundation ✧
1000 Farmington Ave.
West Hartford, CT 06107-2138 (860) 570-0728
Contact: Valentine Doyle, Tr.
E-mail: valentinedoyle@sbcglobal.net

Established in 1989 in CT.
Donor: Alice P. Doyle†.
Foundation type: Independent foundation.
Financial data (yr. ended 12/31/13): Assets, $13,334,670 (M); expenditures, $809,115; qualifying distributions, $659,718; giving activities include $507,001 for 53 grants (high: $31,667; low: $1,000).
Purpose and activities: Primary areas of interest include human rights, environmental and economic justice, and food systems, including sustainable agriculture.
Fields of interest: Environment, legal rights; Agriculture, sustainable programs; Agriculture/food; International human rights; Civil/human rights, advocacy.
Type of support: General/operating support; Continuing support; Program development; Seed money; Technical assistance.
Limitations: Applications accepted. Giving primarily in CT, NJ and NY; some giving in CA. No support for religious activities, schools, or land trusts. No grants to individuals.
Publications: Annual report (including application guidelines).
Application information: Application form required.
Initial approach: Letter
Deadline(s): None
Trustees: Allen Doyle; Valentine Doyle; Mark Lindeman; Lucy Miller; Paul E. Vawter.
Number of staff: 2 part-time professional.
EIN: 136920044

1714
Valley Community Foundation ✧ ☆
253-A Elizabeth St.
Derby, CT 06418 (203) 751-9162
Contact: For grants: Beth Colette, Admin Asst.
E-mail: contactus@valleyfoundation.org; Grant inquiry e-mail: bcolette@valleyfoundation.org; Main URL: http://www.valleyfoundation.org
Facebook: https://www.facebook.com/vcfct

Established in 2004 in CT; a geographic affiliate of the Community Foundation for Greater New Haven.
Foundation type: Community foundation.
Financial data (yr. ended 12/31/13): Assets, $17,755,188 (M); gifts received, $1,832,370; expenditures, $1,931,264; giving activities include $1,375,388 for grants.
Purpose and activities: The foundation seeks to promote increased philanthropy and serve the charitable needs of the Lower Naugatuck Valley.
Fields of interest: Community/economic development; Voluntarism promotion; Philanthropy/voluntarism.
Type of support: Management development/capacity building; Program development; General/operating support.
Limitations: Applications accepted. Giving to organizations in or those serving the communities of Ansonia, Derby, Oxford, Seymour, and Shelton, CT.
Publications: Annual report; Financial statement; Newsletter.
Application information: Visit web site for more information. Application form required.
Initial approach: Submit application electronically
Copies of proposal: 1
Deadline(s): Varies
Board meeting date(s): 2nd Mon. of each month
Final notification: Decisions made at Sept. meeting
Officers and Directors:* John Zaprzalka, C.P.A.*, Chair.; Alan J. Tyma, Esq.*, Vice-Chair.; Sharon R. Closius, C.E.O. and Pres.; Tim Dillon, Esq.*, Secy.; William C. Nimons,* Treas.; A.F. Drew Alden, C.F.O.; Sue Coyle; Rick Dunne; William W. Ginsberg; M. Elizabeth Kennard; Joseph A. Pagliaro, Jr.; Lynne Bassett Perry; James Ryan; Karen Stanek; Diane Stroman; Leon Sylvester.
Number of staff: 1 full-time professional; 1 part-time professional.
EIN: 841637102

1715
Pieter and Yvette Eenkema van Dijk Foundation ✧ ☆
P.O. Box 808
Westport, CT 06880

Donors: Pieter Eenkema van Dijk; Yvette Francois; Yvette Eenkema Van Dijk-Francois.
Foundation type: Independent foundation.
Financial data (yr. ended 12/31/13): Assets, $190,151 (M); expenditures, $530,880; qualifying distributions, $530,880; giving activities include $530,880 for 14 grants (high: $500,060; low: $100).
Fields of interest: Higher education.
Limitations: Applications not accepted. Giving primarily in CT and MA.
Application information: Unsolicited requests for funds not accepted.
Trustees: Yvette Francois; Pieter Eenkema van Dijk.
EIN: 461529829

1716
Vervane, Inc. ✧
P.O. Box 371
Cos Cob, CT 06807-0371

Established in 1993 in CT.
Donor: Josephine Merck.
Foundation type: Independent foundation.
Financial data (yr. ended 12/31/13): Assets, $9,070,439 (M); expenditures, $598,158; qualifying distributions, $551,503; giving activities include $510,000 for 26 grants (high: $50,000; low: $5,000).
Fields of interest: Environment, natural resources; Environment.
Type of support: General/operating support; Land acquisition.
Limitations: Applications not accepted. Giving in the U.S., with emphasis on CT and NY. No grants to individuals.
Application information: Unsolicited requests for funds not accepted.
Officers: Josephine Merck, Pres.; Tom Passios, Secy.-Treas.
Director: Oona Coy.
EIN: 223256829
Selected grants: The following grants are a representative sample of this grantmaker's funding activity:
$25,000 to Connecticut Fund for the Environment, New Haven, CT, 2012. For Designated for Western Long Island Sound Project.
$25,000 to Connecticut Fund for the Environment, New Haven, CT, 2012. For Designated for new intern.
$15,000 to Natural Resources Defense Council, New York, NY, 2012. For On-Earth Publication.

1717
Viking Global Foundation Inc. ✧ ☆
c/o Viking Global Investors LP
55 Railroad Ave.
Greenwich, CT 06830

Donor: Viking Global Investors LP.
Foundation type: Company-sponsored foundation.
Financial data (yr. ended 12/31/13): Assets, $4,827,414 (M); gifts received, $114,722; expenditures, $1,856,517; qualifying distributions, $1,829,307; giving activities include $1,724,085 for 149 grants (high: $200,000; low: $100).
Purpose and activities: Giving primarily support to hurricane sandy disaster relief fund. Advancement in cancer research and cancer treatment.
Fields of interest: Education; Health care; Human services.
Limitations: Applications not accepted.
Application information: Unsolicited requests for funds not accepted.
Officers: Carolyn O'Brien,* Pres. and Exec. Dir.; Eric R. Komitee, Secy.; Barrett C. Brown, Treas.
Directors: O. Andreas Halvorsen; Thomas W. Purcell, Jr.; Rose Shabet.
EIN: 900512778

1718
The Vranos Family Foundation ✧
c/o Ellington Mgmt. Group
53 Forest Ave., 2nd Fl.
Old Greenwich, CT 06870-1526

Established in 1997 in DE.
Donor: Michael Vranos.
Foundation type: Independent foundation.
Financial data (yr. ended 12/31/13): Assets, $1,872,131 (M); gifts received, $1,885,388; expenditures, $2,108,165; qualifying distributions, $2,089,480; giving activities include $2,089,480 for 101 grants (high: $1,000,000; low: $50).
Purpose and activities: Giving primarily for health care, education, human services, children's services, and international relief.
Fields of interest: Education; Health care; Cancer research; Human services; Children, services; International development; International relief.
Limitations: Applications not accepted. Giving primarily in CT and NY. No grants to individuals.
Application information: Contributes only to pre-selected organizations.
Trustees: James Ledley; Michael Vranos.
EIN: 133948273

1719
The Werth Family Foundation, Inc. ✧
c/o Peter J. Werth, Jr.
85 Rimmon Rd.
Woodbridge, CT 06525-2003

Established in 2001 in CT.
Donor: Peter J. Werth, Jr.
Foundation type: Independent foundation.
Financial data (yr. ended 06/30/13): Assets, $9,179,219 (M); gifts received, $1,005,750; expenditures, $912,300; qualifying distributions, $871,853; giving activities include $871,853 for 53 + grants (high: $100,000).
Fields of interest: Arts; Higher education; Environment, natural resources; Human services; Children/youth, services.
Limitations: Applications not accepted. Giving primarily in CT. No grants to individuals.
Application information: Contributes only to pre-selected organizations.
Officers: Peter J. Werth, Jr., Pres.; Pamela Werth, V.P.; Deborah K. Bachard, Secy.
Directors: Robert Bachard; David Moore; Jaqueline A. Moore; Peter J. Werth III; Suzanne Werth.
EIN: 800024133
Selected grants: The following grants are a representative sample of this grantmaker's funding activity:
$15,000 to Arts Council of Greater New Haven, New Haven, CT, 2011.
$10,000 to New Reach, New Haven, CT, 2011.
$10,000 to Smile Train, New York, NY, 2011.
$1,200 to Housatonic Valley Association, Cornwall Bridge, CT, 2011.

1720
The Whittingham Family Foundation Inc. ✧
1200 High Ridge Rd., 2nd Fl.
Stamford, CT 06905-1223

Established in 1997 in CT.
Donors: Cecil A. Whittingham; C. Anthony Whittingham; Andrew Whittingham; Jean Whittingham‡.
Foundation type: Independent foundation.
Financial data (yr. ended 12/31/13): Assets, $579,664 (M); gifts received, $933,142; expenditures, $554,521; qualifying distributions, $551,500; giving activities include $551,500 for 9 grants (high: $500,000; low: $1,000).
Fields of interest: Health care; Cancer research.
Type of support: General/operating support.
Limitations: Applications not accepted. Giving primarily in CT. No grants to individuals.
Application information: Contributes only to pre-selected organizations.
Officer: Andrew Whittingham, Pres.
EIN: 061476873
Selected grants: The following grants are a representative sample of this grantmaker's funding activity:
$500,000 to Norwalk Hospital Foundation, Norwalk, CT, 2011. For general support.
$8,000 to Boys Town of Italy, New York, NY, 2011. For general support.
$4,100 to American Cancer Society, Wilton, CT, 2011. For general support.

1721
John T. and Jane A. Wiederhold Foundation ✧
32 City Hall Ave.
P.O. Box 1144
Torrington, CT 06790-2246 (860) 626-1245

Donor: Jane A. Wiederhold‡.
Foundation type: Independent foundation.
Financial data (yr. ended 06/30/13): Assets, $18,584,465 (M); expenditures, $816,311; qualifying distributions, $605,234; giving activities include $556,262 for 9 grants (high: $129,433; low: $10,000).
Fields of interest: Animal welfare.
Application information: Application form not required.
Initial approach: Proposal
Deadline(s): None
Officer: Marsha Sterling, Chair.
Trustees: Roberta Lee August; Marnie Fitzmaurice Cryer; Susan B. Linker; Sandy Monterose.
EIN: 061830842

1722
The Wiggins Foundation Inc. ✧
c/o Foundation Source
12 North Rd.
Darien, CT 06820-6216

Established in 1994 in CT.
Donor: Stephen F. Wiggins.
Foundation type: Independent foundation.
Financial data (yr. ended 12/31/13): Assets, $10,503,249 (M); expenditures, $514,659; qualifying distributions, $511,620; giving activities include $469,000 for 36 grants (high: $75,000; low: $1,000).
Purpose and activities: Funding provided for education, community needs, and healthcare services; some funding also for Christian organizations and for children.
Fields of interest: Arts; Elementary/secondary education; Higher education; Business school/education; Libraries/library science; Education; Hospitals (general); Health organizations, association; Medical research, association; Human services; Family services; Christian agencies & churches.
Limitations: Applications not accepted. Giving primarily in CT; some giving nationally. No grants to individuals.
Application information: Contributes only to pre-selected organizations.
Officer and Directors:* Stephen F. Wiggins,* Pres.; Anthony A. Wiggins; Matthew Maxwell Wiggins.
EIN: 061415108
Selected grants: The following grants are a representative sample of this grantmaker's funding activity:
$80,000 to University of Bridgeport, Bridgeport, CT, 2012. For Health Sciences New Center for Naturopathic Medicine.
$25,000 to Macalester College, Saint Paul, MN, 2012. For Step Forward Campaign.
$1,000 to Make-A-Wish Foundation of America, Phoenix, AZ, 2012. For Connecticut Chapter of the Make-A-Wish Foundation.
$1,000 to University of Bridgeport, Bridgeport, CT, 2012. For New Center for Naturopathic Medicine Campaign.

1723
The Windmill Foundation, Inc. ✧
c/o Cummings & Lockwood (JRM)
P.O. Box 120
Stamford, CT 06904-0120

Established in 1987 in CT.
Donors: Anna B. Steiner; Ernest F. Steiner.
Foundation type: Independent foundation.
Financial data (yr. ended 02/28/14): Assets, $10,902,908 (M); gifts received, $10,000; expenditures, $533,762; qualifying distributions, $469,194; giving activities include $450,000 for grants.
Purpose and activities: Giving primarily to human services and community development organizations.
Fields of interest: Education; Human services; Women, centers/services; Community/economic development; Foundations (public).
Limitations: Applications not accepted. Giving primarily in CT, MT, New York, NY. No grants to individuals.
Application information: Unsolicited requests for funds not accepted.
Officers and Directors:* Anna B. Steiner,* Pres.; Ernest F. Steiner,* V.P. and Treas.; John R. Musicaro, Jr.,* Secy.; Richard Beilock; Brian Bellamy; Walter Simon.
EIN: 133411161
Selected grants: The following grants are a representative sample of this grantmaker's funding activity:
$10,000 to Habitat for Humanity International, Americus, GA, 2012. For general support.

1724
Windreich Family Foundation Inc. ✧
1 Rock Ridge Ave.
Greenwich, CT 06831-4413

Established in CT.
Donors: David Windreich; Christine Hikawa.
Foundation type: Independent foundation.
Financial data (yr. ended 12/31/12): Assets, $13,834,364 (M); expenditures, $814,473; qualifying distributions, $780,000; giving activities

include $780,000 for 5 grants (high: $500,000; low: $10,000).
Fields of interest: Hospitals (general); Medical research, institute; Human services; Family services; Jewish federated giving programs; Economically disadvantaged.
Limitations: Applications not accepted. Giving primarily in New York, NY.
Application information: Unsolicited requests for funds not accepted.
Officers and Directors:* Christine Hikawa,* Chair.; David Windreich,* Pres.
EIN: 263814543

1725
Charles R. Wood Foundation ✧
c/o Foundation Source
55 Walls Dr., Ste. 302
Fairfield, CT 06824-5163 (203) 319-3718
Contact: Georgia Beckos-Wood, Chair.; Shirley Myott
FAX: (800) 839-1764;
E-mail: lfaria@foundationsource.com; Main URL: http://www.charlesrwoodfoundation.com
Facebook: https://www.facebook.com/pages/Charles-R-Wood-Foundation/328326557266429
Grants List: http://charlesrwoodfoundation.com/?page_id=12
Twitter: https://twitter.com/CWFoundationNY

Established in 1978.
Donor: Charles R. Wood†.
Foundation type: Independent foundation.
Financial data (yr. ended 12/31/12): Assets, $32,686,635 (M); gifts received, $815; expenditures, $1,863,526; qualifying distributions, $1,576,551; giving activities include $1,462,914 for 76 grants (high: $250,000; low: $500).
Purpose and activities: Giving primarily to support programs for children, health care, and the arts.
Fields of interest: Arts; Hospitals (general); Health care; Children, services.
Type of support: General/operating support.
Limitations: Applications accepted. Giving primarily in the Lake George, NY, region and its surrounding areas. No support for colleges or universities. No grants to individuals, or for salaries.
Publications: Financial statement; Grants list; Informational brochure.
Application information:
Initial approach: Use application form on foundation web site
Deadline(s): Apr. 1 (for spring meeting), and Sept. 1 (for fall meeting)
Board meeting date(s): May and in the fall
Officers and Trustees:* Georgia Beckos-Wood,* Chair.; Barbara Wages,* Pres.; Barbara J. Beckos,* V.P.; Page Wages,* Secy.; Charlene W. Courtney,* Treas.; Dean J. Beckos; Michael Della Bella; Shirley Myott; Dennis J. Phillips; Chelsea Hoopes Silver; Heather Ward.
Number of staff: None.
EIN: 222237193
Selected grants: The following grants are a representative sample of this grantmaker's funding activity:
$114,000 to North Country Cultural Center for the Arts, Plattsburgh, NY, 2012. For Strand Theater Orchestra Pit.
$50,000 to Hudson Headwaters Health Network, Queensbury, NY, 2012. For Warrensburg Health Center.
$25,000 to Dollywood Foundation, Pigeon Forge, TN, 2012. For Imagination Library Program in the New York Counties of Essex, Clinton, Franklin and Hamilton.
$10,000 to Vermont Foodbank, Barre, VT, 2012. For Rutland Distribution Center.
$4,850 to Keene Valley Library Association, Keene Valley, NY, 2012. For Technology Related Components of the Construction Project.
$2,500 to Lake Placid Public Library, Lake Placid, NY, 2012. For archival space renovation project.
$2,000 to Rutland Area Foodshelf, Rutland, VT, 2012. For Holiday Food Pantry Meals.
$500 to Lake Placid North Elba Historical Society, Lake Placid, NY, 2012. For History Camp.

1726
WorldQuant Foundation Corp. ✧ ☆
1700 E. Putnam Ave.
Old Greenwich, CT 06870-1366
E-mail: info@worldquant.org; Main URL: http://worldquant.org/

Donor: Igor Tulchinsky.
Foundation type: Independent foundation.
Financial data (yr. ended 12/31/12): Assets, $3,841,944 (M); gifts received, $100; expenditures, $495,978; qualifying distributions, $432,000; giving activities include $432,000 for grants.
Fields of interest: Education; Human services.
Limitations: Applications not accepted.
Application information: Unsolicited requests for funds not accepted.
Officers: Mina Joy Tulchinsky, Chair. and Secy.; Igor Tulchinsky, Pres.
EIN: 263576736

1727
The Wright Foundation Inc. ✧
c/o P.A.W. Partners
4 Greenwich Office Park
Greenwich, CT 06831-5153

Established in 2000 in CT.
Donors: Peter A. Wright; Wendy Wright.
Foundation type: Independent foundation.
Financial data (yr. ended 12/31/13): Assets, $14,769,321 (M); expenditures, $742,200; qualifying distributions, $620,000; giving activities include $620,000 for 4 grants (high: $370,000; low: $50,000).
Fields of interest: Higher education; Education; Jewish federated giving programs.
Type of support: General/operating support.
Limitations: Applications not accepted. No grants to individuals.
Application information: Contributes only to pre-selected organizations.
Officers and Directors:* Peter A. Wright,* Pres.; Jonathan K. Golden, Esq.*, V.P.; Wendy Wright,* Secy.
EIN: 134141287

1728
Xerox Foundation ✧
45 Glover Ave.
P.O. Box 4505
Norwalk, CT 06856-4505
Contact: Mark J. Conlin, Pres.
E-mail: mark.conlin@xerox.com; Main URL: http://www.xerox.com/foundation

Incorporated in 1979 in DE as successor to the Xerox Fund.
Donor: Xerox Corp.
Foundation type: Company-sponsored foundation.
Financial data (yr. ended 12/31/12): Assets, $344 (M); gifts received, $558,200; expenditures, $558,200; qualifying distributions, $558,200; giving activities include $392,700 for 40 grants (high: $50,000; low: $25), and $165,500 for 131 grants to individuals (high: $10,000; low: $1,000).
Purpose and activities: The foundation supports organizations involved with arts and culture, education, including the application of information technology, the environment, workforce preparedness, human services, science and technology, national public policy issues, civic affairs, minorities, women, and economically disadvantaged people.
Fields of interest: Education; Human services.
Type of support: General/operating support; Continuing support; Emergency funds; Program development; Professorships; Seed money; Curriculum development; Scholarship funds; Research; Technical assistance; Employee volunteer services; Sponsorships; Employee matching gifts; Employee-related scholarships.
Limitations: Applications accepted. Giving on a national basis primarily in areas of company operations. No support for political organizations or candidates, religious or sectarian organizations, or municipal, county, state, federal, or quasi-government agencies. No grants to individuals (Except for Technical Minority Scholarships), or for endowments or endowed chairs; no product donations.
Publications: Application guidelines; Annual report; Corporate report; Corporate giving report (including application guidelines); Informational brochure (including application guidelines); Program policy statement (including application guidelines).
Application information: Application form not required.
Initial approach: Letter
Copies of proposal: 1
Deadline(s): None
Board meeting date(s): Monthly contributions meetings; quarterly board meetings
Officer: Joseph M. Cahalan, Pres.
Trustees: Ursula Burns; Bank of America.
Number of staff: 3 full-time professional; 2 part-time professional; 2 full-time support.
EIN: 060996443

1729
Yale Scripps Trust-Cust ✧
c/o Yale University
P.O. Box 208214
New Haven, CT 06520-8214

Established in 1978; supporting organization of Brigham Young University, Northern Arizona University, Northern Illinois University, Thomas Jefferson Memorial Foundation, University of Virginia Medical School Foundation, and Yale University.
Foundation type: Independent foundation.
Financial data (yr. ended 12/31/13): Assets, $11,997,886 (M); expenditures, $477,709; qualifying distributions, $447,015; giving activities include $445,565 for 6 grants (high: $74,261; low: $74,261).
Fields of interest: Higher education, university; Medical school/education.

Limitations: Applications not accepted.
Application information: Contributes only to pre-selected organizations.
Trustee: Yale University.
EIN: 060983815
Selected grants: The following grants are a representative sample of this grantmaker's funding activity:
$75,227 to Yale University, New Haven, CT, 2012. For educational.

1730
The Zachs Family Foundation Inc. ✧ ☆

(formerly The Henry M. Zachs & Judith M. Zachs Foundation, Inc.)
40 Woodland St.
Hartford, CT 06105-2327
E-mail: HZachs@mcmgmt.com

Established in 1985 in CT.
Donors: Henry M. Zachs; William Zachs; Eric Zachs; Judith M. Zachs; Jessica P. Zachs; Louise Zachs.
Foundation type: Independent foundation.
Financial data (yr. ended 06/30/13): Assets, $15,560,215 (M); expenditures, $509,345; qualifying distributions, $495,028; giving activities include $494,908 for 48 grants (high: $100,000; low: $100).
Purpose and activities: Funding primarily for Jewish agencies and temples and higher education; also some general charitable giving.
Fields of interest: Education, fund raising/fund distribution; Secondary school/education; Higher education; Education; Hospitals (general); United Ways and Federated Giving Programs; Jewish agencies & synagogues.
Type of support: Annual campaigns; Capital campaigns; Building/renovation; Endowments; Scholarship funds.
Limitations: Applications not accepted. Giving primarily in CT. No grants to individuals.
Publications: Financial statement.
Application information: Contributes only to pre-selected organizations.
Board meeting date(s): Annually
Officers: Henry M. Zachs, Pres.; Judith M. Zachs, V.P. and Secy.
Directors: Eric Zachs; William Zachs.
Number of staff: None.
EIN: 061157320
Selected grants: The following grants are a representative sample of this grantmaker's funding activity:
$100,000 to Connecticut College, New London, CT, 2013. For Hillel House.

1731
The E. Matilda Ziegler Foundation for the Blind, Inc. ✧

c/o Swisher Intl.
20 Thorndal Cir.
Darien, CT 06820-5421
Contact: Cynthia Z. Brighton, Pres.; Marcia C. Cleary
FAX: (203) 656-1494; E-mail: mcleary@swisher.com

Incorporated in 1928 in NY.
Donors: Mrs. William Ziegler‡; William Ziegler III.
Foundation type: Independent foundation.
Financial data (yr. ended 12/31/12): Assets, $18,866,525 (M); expenditures, $650,711; qualifying distributions, $571,000; giving activities include $571,000 for grants.
Purpose and activities: Giving for charitable and educational work to ameliorate the condition of the blind; support largely for the monthly publication and free distribution of the Matilda Ziegler Magazine for the Blind.
Fields of interest: Eye diseases; Eye research; Blind/visually impaired.
Type of support: Publication; General/operating support; Continuing support; Annual campaigns; Research.
Limitations: Applications accepted. Giving primarily in the U.S. No grants to individuals, or for endowment funds, scholarships, or matching gifts; no loans.
Application information: Application form not required.
Initial approach: Letter only; no telephone
Copies of proposal: 1
Deadline(s): Sept. 30
Board meeting date(s): Dec.
Final notification: Dec. 31
Officers and Directors:* Cynthia Z. Brighton,* Pres.; Eric M. Steinkraus,* V.P. and Treas.; Karl Ziegler,* Secy.; C. Michael Mellor; Dr. Marvin L. Sears; Helen Z. Steinkraus; Philip C. Steinkraus.
Number of staff: 2 full-time professional; 1 part-time professional; 1 part-time support.
EIN: 136086195

1732
The ZOOM Foundation ✧

1210 Post Rd. E.
Fairfield, CT 06824-6008

Established in 2000 in CT.
Donors: Stephen F. Mandel, Jr.; Susan Z. Mandel.
Foundation type: Independent foundation.
Financial data (yr. ended 06/30/13): Assets, $738,246,659 (M); gifts received, $61,000,000; expenditures, $35,853,986; qualifying distributions, $35,694,488; giving activities include $35,000,000 for 1 grant, and $408,136 for foundation-administered programs.
Purpose and activities: Giving primarily for education.
Fields of interest: Elementary/secondary education; Higher education; Education; Philanthropy/voluntarism.
Limitations: Applications not accepted. Giving primarily in Cincinnati, OH; some giving also in Greenwich, CT. No grants to individuals.
Application information: Contributes only to pre-selected organizations.
Officer: Meghan Lowney, Exec. Dir.
Trustees: Stephen F. Mandel, Jr.; Susan Z. Mandel.
EIN: 061600601
Selected grants: The following grants are a representative sample of this grantmaker's funding activity:
$35,000,000 to Fidelity Charitable Gift Fund, Boston, MA, 2013. For general support.
$30,000,000 to Fidelity Charitable Gift Fund, Boston, MA, 2012. For general support.
$500 to Bridgeport Board of Education, Bridgeport, CT, 2012. For Parent Advisory Council.

DELAWARE

1733
The 9:7 Fund ✧
c/o Foundation Source
501 Silverside Rd., Ste. 123
Wilmington, DE 19809-1377

Established in 2007 in WA.
Donors: Leslie M. Strong; Peter D. Strong.
Foundation type: Independent foundation.
Financial data (yr. ended 12/31/13): Assets, $1,172,958 (M); expenditures, $753,519; qualifying distributions, $751,823; giving activities include $719,270 for 63 grants (high: $50,000; low: $50).
Purpose and activities: Giving primarily for human services, particularly to Christian human service organizations and programs.
Fields of interest: Human services; Christian agencies & churches.
Limitations: Applications not accepted. Giving in the U.S., with emphasis on GA and WA. No grants to individuals.
Application information: Unsolicited requests for funds not accepted.
Officers and Directors:* Peter D. Strong,* Pres.; Linnea Gallo, V.P.; Alicia Strong, V.P.; Daniel Strong, V.P.; Elliot Strong, V.P.; Leslie M. Strong.
EIN: 261464326
Selected grants: The following grants are a representative sample of this grantmaker's funding activity:
$100,000 to Operation Mobilization USA, Tyrone, GA, 2011.
$10,000 to Breakthrough Partners, Edmonds, WA, 2011.

1734
Adobe Foundation ✧
c/o Foundation Source
501 Silverside Rd., Ste. 123
Wilmington, DE 19809-1377
Main URL: http://www.adobe.com/corporate-responsibility/community.html
Adobe Youth Voices on Facebook: http://www.facebook.com/adobeyouthvoices
Adobe Youth Voices on Twitter: https://twitter.com/#!/adobeyv
Adobe Youth Voices on YouTube: http://www.youtube.com/user/adobeyouthvoices
Corporate Social Responsibility Blog: http://blogs.adobe.com/conversations/category/corporate-social-responsibilit
Facebook: http://www.facebook.com/AdobeCSR
Grants List: http://www.adobe.com/corporate-responsibility/community/grants-recipients.html

Established in 2007.
Donor: Adobe Systems Incorporated.
Foundation type: Company-sponsored foundation.
Financial data (yr. ended 11/30/13): Assets, $25,125,359 (M); gifts received, $16,500,000; expenditures, $8,804,779; qualifying distributions, $8,736,377; giving activities include $4,258,270 for 119 grants (high: $225,000; low: $1,000), $11,250 for grants to individuals, and $3,775,394 for 1 foundation-administered program.
Purpose and activities: The foundation supports organizations involved with arts and culture, education, hunger, housing, safety, human services, and community development. Special emphasis is directed toward programs designed to promote access to underserved communities, giving them the opportunity to develop 21st century skills.
Fields of interest: Media/communications; Visual arts; Museums; Arts; Education, computer literacy/technology training; Education; Food services; Food banks; Housing/shelter, development; Housing/shelter; Safety/disasters; Children/youth, services; Homeless, human services; Human services; Community/economic development; Computer science.
Type of support: General/operating support; Continuing support; Annual campaigns; Program development; Scholarship funds; Grants to individuals.
Limitations: Applications not accepted. Giving primarily in areas of company operations, with emphasis on San Francisco and San Jose, CA, Boston, MA, New York, NY, Orem, UT, Seattle, WA, Ottawa, Canada, Beijing, China, London, England, Bangalore and Noida, India, Tokyo, Japan, and Bucharest, Romania.
Publications: Corporate giving report.
Application information: Contributes only to pre-selected organizations and individuals. The foundation utilizes an invitation only process for Community Grants.
Officers and Directors:* Shantanu Narayen,* Pres.; Ann Lewnes, Secy.; Mark Garrett, Treas.; Michelle Crozier Yates, Exec. Dir.; Mike Dillon; Donna Morris.
EIN: 260233808
Selected grants: The following grants are a representative sample of this grantmaker's funding activity:
$225,000 to iEARN, International Education and Resource Network, New York, NY, 2013. For Execution of Adobe Youth Voices Program through the iEARN Network.
$100,000 to Common Ground Foundation, Chicago, IL, 2013. For summer youth camp in San Francisco.
$75,000 to Second Harvest Food Bank of Santa Clara and San Mateo Counties, San Jose, CA, 2013. For Providing Meals Through CalFresh Outreach Program.
$50,000 to Bill Wilson Center, Santa Clara, CA, 2013. For YouthWorks Academy.
$50,000 to Khan Academy, Mountain View, CA, 2013. For general and unrestricted.
$49,926 to Urban Arts Partnership, New York, NY, 2013. For Implementation of Adobe Youth Voices Program.
$30,000 to Friends for Youth, Redwood City, CA, 2013. For educational enhancement.
$25,000 to Sunday Friends Foundation, San Jose, CA, 2013. For Preparing Children in Need for School Success.
$18,000 to Saint Anthony Foundation, San Francisco, CA, 2013. For St Anthony's Dining Room.
$15,000 to Good Karma Bikes, San Jose, CA, 2013. For Bicycle Repair Clinic (BRC).

1735
The AEC Trust ✧
c/o Foundation Source
501 Silverside Rd., Ste. 123
Wilmington, DE 19809-1377
Contact for technical questions regarding the online submission process: tel.: (800) 839-1821, e-mail: requests@foundationsource.com; Main URL: http://www.fsrequests.com/aec

Established in 1980 in IL.
Donor: Members of the Cofrin family.
Foundation type: Independent foundation.
Financial data (yr. ended 12/31/12): Assets, $27,350,956 (M); expenditures, $4,451,316; qualifying distributions, $4,239,584; giving activities include $4,239,584 for 48 grants (high: $2,942,103; low: $5,000).
Purpose and activities: Giving primarily for the arts, educational support for pre-selected schools, the environment, women's issues, and AIDS-related services.
Fields of interest: Museums; Arts; Education; Environment; Women; AIDS, people with.
Type of support: General/operating support; Capital campaigns; Building/renovation; Equipment; Land acquisition; Debt reduction; Conferences/seminars; Professorships; Publication; Research; Technical assistance; Matching/challenge support.
Limitations: Applications accepted. Giving primarily in Boulder, CO, Gainesville, FL, Atlanta or Decatur, GA (within Fulton or Dekalb Counties), and Western MA. No support for religious organizations, government agencies, affiliates of large public charities, or for organizations with budgets over $1 million. No grants to individuals, or for special events, annual campaigns, or sponsorships; endowments generally not funded.
Application information: All proposals must be submitted electronically via foundation web site. Paper documents will not be reviewed or accepted. Grant requests should be made within the $10,000 to $50,000 range and should not exceed 50% of total budget. Application form required.
Initial approach: Take eligibility quiz on foundation web site
Deadline(s): Apr. 1 and Sept. 1
Board meeting date(s): May and Oct.
Final notification: On a rolling basis
Advisory Committee: Edith Dee Cofrin, Chair.; David H. Cofrin; Gladys G. Cofrin; Mary Ann H. Cofrin; Mary Ann P. Cofrin; Paige W. Cofrin.
Corporate Trustee: Atlantic Trust Co., N.A.
EIN: 366725987

1736
The Miner Anderson Family Foundation ✧
c/o Foundation Source
501 Silverside Rd., Ste. 123
Wilmington, DE 19809-1377

Established in 2007 in DE.
Donors: Nicola Miner; Robert Mailer Anderson; Miner Anderson 2009 Charitable Lead Annuity Trust.
Foundation type: Independent foundation.
Financial data (yr. ended 06/30/13): Assets, $5,557,424 (M); gifts received, $155,556; expenditures, $1,762,753; qualifying distributions, $1,731,215; giving activities include $1,697,940 for 19 grants (high: $400,000; low: $5,000).
Purpose and activities: Giving primarily for the arts and education.
Fields of interest: Performing arts, theater; Arts; Elementary/secondary education.
Limitations: Applications not accepted. Giving primarily in San Francisco, CA. No grants to individuals.
Application information: Contributes only to pre-selected organizations.

Officers and Directors:* Nicola Miner,* Pres.; Robert Mailer Anderson,* Secy.
EIN: 261119005
Selected grants: The following grants are a representative sample of this grantmaker's funding activity:
$400,000 to San Francisco Day School, San Francisco, CA, 2013. For Endowment for Financial Aid Program.
$200,000 to San Francisco University High School, San Francisco, CA, 2013. For Gift to Financial Aid Endowment.
$150,000 to San Francisco Jazz Organization, San Francisco, CA, 2013. For Underwriting SFJAZZ Historic Grand Opening Concert.
$75,000 to San Francisco Jazz Organization, San Francisco, CA, 2013. For Underwriting the Stevie Wonder Album Program.
$60,000 to Brown University, Providence, RI, 2013. For Batishwa Miner Fund and Annual Fund.
$50,000 to San Francisco Jazz Organization, San Francisco, CA, 2013. To underwrite Sandow Birk Mural.
$5,000 to California Shakespeare Theater, Berkeley, CA, 2013. For Make a Difference Campaign.

1737
Richard F. Aster, Jr. Foundation ✧
c/o First Republic Trust Co.
1201 N. Market St., Ste. 1002
Wilmington, DE 19801-1807
Contact: John F. McCabe IV, Tr.

Established in 2005 in CA.
Donors: Richard F. Aster, Jr.; Richard Aster Administrative Trust.
Foundation type: Independent foundation.
Financial data (yr. ended 12/31/13): Assets, $67,066 (M); expenditures, $15,763,789; qualifying distributions, $15,740,219; giving activities include $15,669,517 for 8 grants.
Purpose and activities: Giving primarily to a charitable gift fund.
Fields of interest: Foundations (public).
Limitations: Applications not accepted. Giving primarily in Cincinnati, OH. No grants to individuals.
Application information: Contributes only to pre-selected organizations.
Trustee: John F. McCabe IV.
EIN: 141934614

1738
AstraZeneca HealthCare Foundation ✧
(formerly Zeneca HealthCare Foundation)
1800 Concord Pike
P.O. Box 15437
Wilmington, DE 19850-5437 (302) 886-3000
E-mail: ConnectionsforCardiovascularHealth@astrazeneca.com; Additional tel.: (800) 236-9933; Main URL: http://www.astrazeneca-us.com/foundation/

Established as a company-sponsored operating foundation in 1993 in DE.
Donors: Zeneca Inc.; AstraZeneca Pharmaceuticals LP.
Foundation type: Operating foundation.
Financial data (yr. ended 12/31/13): Assets, $10,380,179 (M); gifts received, $14,783; expenditures, $4,455,652; qualifying distributions, $4,411,574; giving activities include $3,722,921 for 20 grants (high: $250,000; low: $45,000).
Purpose and activities: The foundation promotes public awareness of healthcare issues and provides public education of medical knowledge.
Fields of interest: Education; Health care, clinics/centers; Health care, patient services; Nursing care; Health care; Cancer; Breast cancer; Heart & circulatory diseases; Health organizations; Disasters, preparedness/services.
Type of support: General/operating support; Continuing support; Annual campaigns; Program development; Grants to individuals.
Limitations: Applications accepted. Giving on a national basis. No support for religious or faith-based programs not of direct benefit to the entire community, for-profit organizations, lobbying, fraternal, or social organizations, or discriminatory organizations. No grants to individuals (except for employee-related disaster relief grants), or for capital investments, unsolicited capital campaigns, media or awareness campaigns, enhancements of existing hospital services or hospital software systems, professional education, training for healthcare professionals, research or clinical trials, healthcare providers or cardiologist salaries, endowments, journals, or advertising.
Publications: Application guidelines; Annual report; Grants list.
Application information: Grants range from $150,000 to $250,000. Multi-year funding is not automatic. Organizations receiving support are asked to provide a mid-year report and final report. Application form required.
Initial approach: Complete online application for Connections for Cardiovascular Health
Deadline(s): Feb. 3 to Feb. 15 for Connections for Cardiovascular Health grants
Final notification: Nov.
Officers and Directors:* James W. Blasetto,* Chair.; David P. Nicoli, Esq.*, Pres.; Emily Denney,* V.P.; Ann V. Booth-Barbarin,* Secy.; David E. White, Treas.; Joyce Jacobson, Exec. Dir.; Cindy Bertrando; John B. Buse; Timothy J. Gardner; Howard G. Hutchinson; Michael Miller; L. Kristin Newby.
EIN: 510349682

1739
C. E. Bennett Foundation ✧
Little Falls Two
2751 Centerville Rd., Ste. 300
Wilmington, DE 19808-1632

Established in 1964 in DE.
Donor: C. Eugene Bennett†.
Foundation type: Independent foundation.
Financial data (yr. ended 12/31/12): Assets, $8,716,432 (M); expenditures, $495,249; qualifying distributions, $426,875; giving activities include $425,000 for 5 grants (high: $100,000; low: $25,000).
Fields of interest: Performing arts; Education; Human services; Christian agencies & churches.
Type of support: Annual campaigns; Professorships; Scholarship funds.
Limitations: Applications not accepted. Giving primarily in DE and NY. No grants to individuals.
Application information: Contributes only to pre-selected organizations. Telephone calls will not be accepted.
Board meeting date(s): Nov.
Officers: Edna B. Pierce, Pres.; Karl E. Bennett, V.P.
Number of staff: None.
EIN: 510102289

1740
David and Karen Bere Foundation ✧
c/o Foundation Source
501 Silverside Rd., Ste. 123
Wilmington, DE 19809-1377

Donors: David L. Bere; Karen Bere.
Foundation type: Independent foundation.
Financial data (yr. ended 12/31/13): Assets, $3,310,646 (M); gifts received, $493,664; expenditures, $747,336; qualifying distributions, $728,865; giving activities include $712,350 for 40 grants (high: $160,000; low: $100).
Fields of interest: Education; Human services; Religion.
Limitations: Applications not accepted.
Application information: Unsolicited requests for funds not accepted.
Officers and Directors:* David L. Bere,* Pres.; J. Daniel Bere, V.P.; J. David Bere, V.P.; Anne Ber Carson, V.P.; Karen Bere,* Secy.
EIN: 273335437

1741
W.R. Berkley Corporation Charitable Foundation ✧ ☆
c/o Foundation Source
501 Silverside Rd., Ste. 123
Wilmington, DE 19809-1377

Established in 2002 in DE.
Donors: W.R. Berkley Corp.; Acadia Insurance Company; Berkley Aviation LLC; Berkley Risk Administrators Company, LLC; Carolina Casualty Insurance Company; Continental Western Insurance Company; Monitor Liability Managers, Inc.; Nautilus Insurance Company; Union Insurance Company.
Foundation type: Company-sponsored foundation.
Financial data (yr. ended 12/31/13): Assets, $309,795 (M); gifts received, $606,988; expenditures, $463,931; qualifying distributions, $463,930; giving activities include $460,905 for 164 grants (high: $28,932; low: $25).
Purpose and activities: The foundation supports food banks and organizations involved with arts and culture, education, diabetes, legal aid, human services, and public policy.
Fields of interest: Performing arts; Performing arts, orchestras; Arts; Higher education; Education; Diabetes; Legal services; Food banks; Boys & girls clubs; Children/youth, services; Human services; Public policy, research.
Type of support: General/operating support; Program development.
Limitations: Applications not accepted. Giving primarily in CT, Washington, DC, IA, MA, ME, NY, and PA. No grants to individuals.
Application information: Contributes only to pre-selected organizations.
Officers and Directors:* William R. Berkley,* Pres.; Josephine A. Raimondi,* V.P. and Secy.; William R. Berkley, Jr.,* V.P. and Treas.
EIN: 364516560
Selected grants: The following grants are a representative sample of this grantmaker's funding activity:

$25,000 to Saint Johns University, School of Risk Management, New York, NY, 2012. For general unrestricted.
$20,000 to New York University, Leonard N Stern School of Business Division, New York, NY, 2012. For urbanization project.
$2,300 to New Hampshire Food Bank, Manchester, NH, 2012. For Operation Front Line.
$2,000 to Visiting Nurse Association of Chittenden and Grand Isle Counties, Colchester, VT, 2012. For Family Support Services.
$1,500 to New York University, School of Medicine, New York, NY, 2012. For Urology Research Program.
$1,000 to New Hampshire Food Bank, Manchester, NH, 2012. For Recipe for Success Culinary Job Training.
$750 to Junior Achievement of Northern New England, Waltham, MA, 2012. For Framingham Elementary School Program.

1742
Berkshire Charitable Foundation ✧

c/o Foundation Source
501 Silverside Rd., Ste. 123
Wilmington, DE 19809-1377

Foundation type: Independent foundation.
Financial data (yr. ended 12/31/13): Assets, $10,864,763 (M); expenditures, $552,955; qualifying distributions, $495,951; giving activities include $449,500 for 38 grants (high: $50,000; low: $1,000).
Purpose and activities: Giving primarily for health services, the arts and higher education; some funding also for social services.
Fields of interest: Education; Civil/human rights; Community/economic development.
Limitations: Applications not accepted. Giving primarily in Reading and Wernersville, PA.
Application information: Contributes only to pre-selected organizations.
Officers and Trustees:* Elizabeth B. Rothermel,* Pres.; Jeffrey W. Bowman,* V.P.; Helen B. Shumate,* V.P.; Jonathan Shumate,* Secy.; Andrew J. Rothermel,* Treas.
EIN: 201812559
Selected grants: The following grants are a representative sample of this grantmaker's funding activity:
$5,000 to Wells College, Aurora, NY, 2012. For Advancing Athletics at Wells.
$1,000 to Billy Graham Evangelistic Association, Charlotte, NC, 2012. For Rapid Response Team Ministry.

1743
Berlin Family Foundation ✧ ☆

c/o Foundation Source
501 Silverside Rd.
Wilimington, DE 19809-1377

Established in 2001 in NY.
Donors: Daniel Berlin; David Berlin.
Foundation type: Independent foundation.
Financial data (yr. ended 12/31/12): Assets, $14,415,946 (M); gifts received, $6,000,000; expenditures, $971,560; qualifying distributions, $864,654; giving activities include $788,000 for 28 grants (high: $125,000; low: $500).
Fields of interest: Museums (specialized); Youth development; Human services; Community/economic development; Engineering.
Type of support: General/operating support.
Limitations: Applications not accepted. Giving primarily in FL and NY. No grants to individuals.
Application information: Contributes only to pre-selected organizations.
Officers and Directors:* Michelle Grande, C.O.O. and Exec. V.P.; William Maglio,* Pres.; Nicole Maglio Bessette,* V.P.; Stefan Bodstrom, V.P. of Finance; Danielle Jenkins, V.P. of Operations; Marc Sabatino, V.P. of Operations.
Board Members: Vicki Bodstrom; Madeline Maglio; Barbara Sabatino.
EIN: 113635864

1744
Stephen and Mary Birch Foundation, Inc. ✧

103 Foulk Rd., Ste. 200
Wilmington, DE 19803-3742 (888) 372-6303
Contact: Rose B. Patek, Pres.

Incorporated in 1938 in DE.
Donor: Stephen Birch†.
Foundation type: Independent foundation.
Financial data (yr. ended 12/31/12): Assets, $176,172,707 (M); expenditures, $9,451,193; qualifying distributions, $7,104,806; giving activities include $5,473,900 for 112 grants (high: $2,000,000; low: $1,000).
Purpose and activities: The foundation provides funding in support of other nonprofit institutions, communities, and organizations that are or that have been instrumental in strengthening and heightening both culturally and educationally, the impact of research, medical, health, educational, sports, social service, and artistic programs in communities across the nation, from coast to coast.
Fields of interest: Arts education; Museums (sports/hobby); Arts; Education; Health care; Human services; Youth, services; International relief; Government/public administration; Catholic agencies & churches.
Limitations: Applications accepted. Giving on a national basis. No support for political organizations.
Application information: Application form not required.
Initial approach: Letter only
Copies of proposal: 1
Deadline(s): None
Board meeting date(s): Quarterly
Officers: Rose B. Patek, Pres. and Treas.; Debra D. Durkin, V.P. and Secy.; Christopher Patek, V.P.
EIN: 221713022
Selected grants: The following grants are a representative sample of this grantmaker's funding activity:
$2,000,000 to Sharp Healthcare Foundation, San Diego, CA, 2012. For Capital Improvements.
$400,000 to Marys House, Tickfaw, LA, 2012. For Retreat Center.
$350,000 to Circle in the Square Theater School, New York, NY, 2012. For General Support.
$300,000 to Mission of Divine Mercy, New Braunfels, TX, 2012. For General Operating Support.
$300,000 to Valley Hospital Foundation, Ridgewood, NJ, 2012. For General Operating Support.
$40,000 to San Diego Natural History Museum, San Diego, CA, 2012. For Education and Exhibits.
$25,000 to Saint Joseph Abbey, Saint Benedict, LA, 2012. For General Support.
$20,000 to Agape Therapeutic Riding Resources, Cicero, IN, 2012. For equine assisted living program.
$15,000 to New Jersey Performing Arts Center, Newark, NJ, 2012. For General Operating Support.
$12,500 to Christian Health Care Center, Wyckoff, NJ, 2012. For General Support.

1745
Edward E. and Lillian H. Bishop Foundation ✧

c/o Wilmington Trust Co.
1100 N. Market St.
Wilmington, DE 19890-0001
Contact: Carlo Lombardi

Trust established in 1953 in DE.
Donor: Lillian H. Bishop.
Foundation type: Independent foundation.
Financial data (yr. ended 12/31/13): Assets, $10,525,218 (M); expenditures, $493,995; qualifying distributions, $467,469; giving activities include $449,284 for 68 grants (high: $101,477; low: $1,000).
Purpose and activities: Giving primarily to a museum, as well as for health organizations, and children, youth, and social services.
Fields of interest: Museums; Health organizations, association; Human services; Children/youth, services; United Ways and Federated Giving Programs.
Type of support: General/operating support.
Limitations: Applications accepted. Giving primarily in Manatee County, FL.
Publications: Informational brochure (including application guidelines).
Application information: Application form required.
Initial approach: Letter
Deadline(s): Apr. 30
Board meeting date(s): Dec.
Final notification: Positive responses only
Trustees: Robert G. Blalock; Burdette R. Parent; Beverly J. Parker; Mary E. Parker; Richard W. Pratt; Wilmington Trust Co.
EIN: 516017762

1746
Lillian H. Bishop Trust A for the SPCA of Manatee County, Florida ✧

c/o Wilmington Trust Co.
1100 N. Market St.
Wilmington, DE 19890-0900

Established in 1973 in DE.
Foundation type: Independent foundation.
Financial data (yr. ended 12/31/13): Assets, $16,691,843 (M); expenditures, $753,694; qualifying distributions, $696,825; giving activities include $669,067 for 1 grant.
Fields of interest: Animal welfare.
Limitations: Applications not accepted. Giving primarily in Manatee County, FL. No grants to individuals.
Application information: Contributes only to pre-selected organizations.
Trustee: Wilmington Trust Co.
EIN: 237334266

1747
Ron and Lisa Brill Charitable Trust ✧ ☆
c/o Foundation Source
501 Silverside Rd.
Wilmington, DE 19809-1377

Established in 1992 in GA.
Donors: Ronald M. Brill; Lisa F. Brill.
Foundation type: Independent foundation.
Financial data (yr. ended 06/30/13): Assets, $6,746,522 (M); expenditures, $541,346; qualifying distributions, $505,178; giving activities include $480,425 for 69 grants (high: $100,000; low: $25).
Purpose and activities: Giving primarily for Jewish organizations; funding also for the arts, education, health organizations, and human services.
Fields of interest: Arts; Education; Health organizations, association; Human services; Jewish federated giving programs; Jewish agencies & synagogues.
Limitations: Applications not accepted. Giving primarily in Atlanta, GA. No grants to individuals.
Application information: Contributes only to pre-selected organizations.
Trustees: Ronald M. Brill; Jonathan Brill; Lisa F. Brill; Matt Brill.
EIN: 586275452
Selected grants: The following grants are a representative sample of this grantmaker's funding activity:
$150,000 to Jewish Federation of Greater Atlanta, Atlanta, GA, 2010. For annual campaign.
$60,000 to Marcus Jewish Community Center of Atlanta, Dunwoody, GA, 2010.
$25,000 to Jenkins Clinic, Atlanta, GA, 2010.
$15,000 to Vail Valley Foundation, Avon, CO, 2010.
$15,000 to Vail Valley Foundation, Avon, CO, 2011.
$10,000 to American Friends of Brothers Aid, Monsey, NY, 2011.
$10,000 to Childrens Healthcare of Atlanta, Atlanta, GA, 2011. For Annual Fund.
$5,290 to Atlanta Community Food Bank, Atlanta, GA, 2011.
$5,000 to Robert W. Woodruff Arts Center, Atlanta, GA, 2011.
$5,000 to Teach for America, Atlanta, GA, 2011.
$5,000 to Vail Valley Foundation, Avon, CO, 2011.
$2,408 to Congregation Bnai Torah, Atlanta, GA, 2011.
$1,000 to University of Vermont, Burlington, VT, 2011.
$1,000 to William Breman Jewish Home, Atlanta, GA, 2011. For charitable event.

1748
Bucks Creek Foundation ✧ ☆
c/o Foundation Source
501 Silverside Rd.
Wilmington, DE 19809-1377

Donors: Christopher LaCroix; Kathleen LaCroix.
Foundation type: Independent foundation.
Financial data (yr. ended 12/31/13): Assets, $3,846,134 (M); gifts received, $500,000; expenditures, $890,383; qualifying distributions, $890,230; giving activities include $871,883 for 50 grants (high: $150,500; low: $250).
Fields of interest: Higher education; Education; Housing/shelter; Human services.
Limitations: Applications not accepted. Giving primarily in CT and NY; some funding also in VA.
Application information: Unsolicited requests for funds not accepted.
Trustees: Caitlin E. LaCroix; Christopher LaCroix; Kathleen LaCroix.
EIN: 207131734

1749
The Campbell Family Foundation ✧
c/o Foundation Source
501 Silverside Rd., Ste. 123
Wilmington, DE 19809-1377

Established in 2000 in NY and DE.
Donors: William I. Campbell; Christine Wachter-Campbell.
Foundation type: Independent foundation.
Financial data (yr. ended 12/31/13): Assets, $8,047,535 (M); expenditures, $675,235; qualifying distributions, $649,563; giving activities include $612,270 for 34 grants (high: $210,000; low: $250).
Purpose and activities: Giving primarily for the arts; some funding for education and social services.
Fields of interest: Arts; Education; Health care.
Limitations: Applications not accepted. No grants to individuals.
Application information: Contributes only to pre-selected organizations.
Officers and Directors:* William I. Campbell,* Pres; Christine Wachter-Campbell,* V.P.; Sarah Campbell, Secy.; Nora Wood, Treas.
EIN: 134149591

1750
CenturyLink-Clarke M. Williams Foundation ✧
(formerly Qwest Foundation)
c/o Foundation Source
501 Silverside Rd., Ste. 123
Wilmington, DE 19809-1377
Main URL: http://www.centurylink.com/Pages/AboutUs/Community/Foundation/
Facebook: http://www.facebook.com/Qwest#!/Qwest?v=app_354459035481

Established in 1985 in CO.
Donors: U S WEST, Inc.; Qwest Communications International Inc.
Foundation type: Company-sponsored foundation.
Financial data (yr. ended 12/31/12): Assets, $16,474,473 (M); gifts received, $2,099,424; expenditures, $4,090,884; qualifying distributions, $3,921,662; giving activities include $3,822,512 for 1,378 grants (high: $261,334).
Purpose and activities: The foundation supports programs designed to improve the well-being and overall quality of life for people throughout CenturyLink's communities.
Fields of interest: Elementary/secondary education; Education; Food services; Food banks; Children/youth, services; Homeless, human services; Human services; United Ways and Federated Giving Programs; Engineering/technology; Science.
Type of support: General/operating support; Continuing support; Annual campaigns; Program development; Employee volunteer services; Employee matching gifts; Grants to individuals.
Limitations: Applications accepted. Giving on a national basis in areas of company operations in AR, IA, ID, CO, MN, MO, ND, NE, NM, OR, SD, UT, WA, and WY. No support for political organizations, private foundations, pass-through organizations, or organizations that receive 3 percent or more funding from the United Way. No grants to individuals (except for Qwest Teacher Grants), or for scholarships, sectarian religious activities, capital campaigns, chairs, endowments, general operating support for single-disease health groups, or goodwill advertising.
Publications: Application guidelines.
Application information: Applications for general funding are currently not accepted. Applicants for the Teachers and Technology Program should email local coordinators for more information.
Initial approach: Download application form and mail to application address for Teachers and Technology Program
Deadline(s): Oct. 1 to Jan. 10 for Teachers and Technology Program
Final notification: Apr. 1 for Teachers and Technology
Officers and Directors:* Stacey Goff,* Pres.; Christine Searls, Secy.; Jonathan Robinson, Treas.; Steven Davis; Tony Davis; Odell Riley.
Number of staff: 2 full-time professional.
EIN: 840978668
Selected grants: The following grants are a representative sample of this grantmaker's funding activity:
$100,000 to National Center for Missing and Exploited Children, Alexandria, VA, 2012. For NetSmartz 411 Program.
$50,000 to Utah State Office of Education, Salt Lake City, UT, 2012. For 2011-2012 Teachers and Technology Program.
$35,000 to Applied Information Management Institute, Omaha, NE, 2012. For AIM Youth Business Seminar Program.
$20,000 to Albuquerque Hispano Chamber of Commerce, Albuquerque, NM, 2012. For Rio Grande Tech.
$15,000 to Arizona State University Foundation for a New American University, Tempe, AZ, 2012. For Asset Digital Learning Library.
$15,000 to Young Americans Center for Financial Education, Denver, CO, 2012. For Young AmeriTowne.
$11,450 to Be a Leader Foundation, Phoenix, AZ, 2012. For Pipeline College.
$10,000 to Achieve Minneapolis, Minneapolis, MN, 2012. For parent coaches.
$7,500 to Arizona State University Foundation for a New American University, Tempe, AZ, 2012. For Story Makers.
$500 to Boy Scouts of America, Denver Area Council, Denver, CO, 2012. For recognition of volunteer time.

1751
CGLC Charitable Trust ✧
c/o Foundation Source
501 Silverside Rd.
Wilmington, DE 19809-1377 (310) 553-0373
Contact: Dale C. Rosenbloom, Tr.
Main URL: http://www.cglctrust.org

Donors: Georgia Frontiere; Georgia Frontiere Revocable Trust.
Foundation type: Independent foundation.
Financial data (yr. ended 12/31/13): Assets, $8,309,862 (M); expenditures, $1,215,548; qualifying distributions, $1,152,085; giving

activities include $1,125,000 for 25 grants (high: $200,000; low: $5,000).
Fields of interest: Education; Government/public administration.
Limitations: Applications not accepted. Giving primarily in Los Angeles, CA.
Application information: Contributes only to pre-selected organizations.
Officer and Trustee:* Dale C. Rosenbloom,* Pres.
EIN: 276565175

1752
Chapman Hanson Foundation ✧
c/o Advisory Trust Co. of DE
1100 N. Market St., DE3-C070
Wilmington, DE 19890-0001

Foundation type: Independent foundation.
Financial data (yr. ended 12/31/13): Assets, $16,470,400 (M); expenditures, $922,494; qualifying distributions, $658,777; giving activities include $640,557 for 8 grants (high: $170,279; low: $29,056).
Fields of interest: Arts; Human services.
Limitations: Applications not accepted.
Application information: Unsolicited requests for funds not accepted.
Trustee: Advisory Trust Co. of Delaware.
EIN: 386872202
Selected grants: The following grants are a representative sample of this grantmaker's funding activity:
$125,000 to Save the Redwoods League, San Francisco, CA, 2011. For general charitable purposes.

1753
Chase Family Foundation ✧
c/o Foundation Source
501 Silverside Rd., Ste. 123
Wilmington, DE 19809-1377

Established in OH.
Donors: W. Rowell Chase; Alison Mason Chase; W. Rowell Chase Charitable Lead Annuity Trust.
Foundation type: Independent foundation.
Financial data (yr. ended 12/31/13): Assets, $19,169,310 (M); expenditures, $921,562; qualifying distributions, $833,989; giving activities include $770,000 for 103 grants (high: $100,000; low: $100).
Fields of interest: Arts; Higher education; Environment, natural resources; Environment, land resources; Animals/wildlife; Human services; United Ways and Federated Giving Programs; Christian agencies & churches; Protestant agencies & churches.
Limitations: Applications not accepted. Generally no grants to individuals.
Application information: Contributes only to pre-selected organizations.
Officers: Dave Chase, Pres.; Alison Mason Chase, V.P.; Lee Molen Chase, Secy.
Trustees: Barbara K. Chase; Dawn K. Chase; Michael Clooney; Joseph C. Hill.
EIN: 316038352

1754
Chichester duPont Foundation, Inc. ✧
5720 Kennett Pike
P.O. Box 3598
Wilmington, DE 19807-1326 (302) 658-5244
Contact: Gregory F. Fields, Secy.
FAX: (302) 658-5091;
E-mail: gfields@chichesterdupont.org; Main URL: http://www.chichesterdupont.org

Incorporated in 1946 in DE.
Donors: Lydia Chichester duPont†; Mary Chichester duPont Clark†; A. Felix duPont, Jr.; Alice duPont Mills.
Foundation type: Independent foundation.
Financial data (yr. ended 12/31/12): Assets, $38,917,686 (M); expenditures, $2,269,014; qualifying distributions, $2,050,200; giving activities include $2,050,200 for 55 grants (high: $645,000; low: $5,000).
Purpose and activities: The trustees of the foundation devote particular emphasis to programs concerned with the environment, education, health care, and those to which the foundation's giving will play a pivotal role.
Fields of interest: Arts; Elementary/secondary education; Education; Environment, natural resources; Health care; Human services; Children/youth, services.
Type of support: General/operating support; Building/renovation.
Limitations: Giving on a national basis. No grants to individuals.
Publications: Application guidelines; Grants list.
Application information: Applicants are encouraged to discuss their proposal with the foundation's staff or board members either by telephone or in person. Application form not required.
Initial approach: Cover letter containing brief project description and specific amount requested, and a proposal (not exceeding 5 pages)
Deadline(s): Sept. 1
Board meeting date(s): Dec.
Final notification: 2 weeks after meeting
Officers and Trustees:* Christopher T. duPont,* Pres.; Lynn L. Dorsey,* V.P.; Caroline D. Prickett,* V.P.; Gregory F. Fields, Secy.; Katharine Gahagan,* Treas.; Mary Mills Abel-Smith; Sophie M. Derrickson; Alexis D. Gahagan; Phyllis M. Wyeth.
EIN: 516011641

1755
Common Wealth Trust ✧
c/o PNC Bank, N.A.-Delaware
222 Delaware Ave.
Wilmington, DE 19899-1621

Established in 1978.
Donor: Ralph W. Hayes†.
Foundation type: Independent foundation.
Financial data (yr. ended 12/31/13): Assets, $8,080,605 (M); expenditures, $587,360; qualifying distributions, $454,000; giving activities include $454,000 for 5 grants (high: $220,000; low: $1,000).
Purpose and activities: Support for a historical society and for educational purposes; also gives distinguished service awards to prominent individuals in the fields of literature, science and invention, public service, sociology, government and mass communication.
Fields of interest: Performing arts; Literature; Historic preservation/historical societies; Higher education, university; Human services; Community/economic development; Science.
Type of support: General/operating support; Grants to individuals.
Limitations: Applications not accepted. Giving on a national basis, with emphasis on Cleveland, OH.
Application information: Recipients must be nominated by specific professional associations.
Officers: Nicholas Marsini, Pres.; Richard E. Meinkiewicz, Secy. and Treas.
Directors: Mary Liz Biddle; Jacqueline B. Lessman; Linda R. Manfredonia; Thomas Melcher; Connie Bond Stuart.
Trustee: PNC Bank, N.A.
EIN: 510232187
Selected grants: The following grants are a representative sample of this grantmaker's funding activity:
$220,000 to Western Reserve Historical Society, Cleveland, OH, 2012. For Allocation Per Trust Document.

1756
Corkins Family Foundation ✧
c/o Foundation Source
501 Silverside Rd., Ste. 123
Wilmington, DE 19809-1377

Established in DE.
Donor: David Corkins.
Foundation type: Independent foundation.
Financial data (yr. ended 12/31/12): Assets, $6,048,679 (M); gifts received, $251,250; expenditures, $574,977; qualifying distributions, $546,421; giving activities include $518,000 for 3 grants (high: $250,000; low: $18,000).
Fields of interest: Education; Recreation, camps.
Limitations: Applications not accepted.
Application information: Unsolicited requests for funds not accepted.
Officer and Director:* David Corkins,* Pres. and Secy.
EIN: 270858631

1757
Crestlea Foundation, Inc. ✧
100 W. 10th St., Ste. 1109
Wilmington, DE 19801-1694 (302) 654-2477
Contact: Stephen A. Martinenza, Pres.

Incorporated in 1955 in DE.
Donor: Henry B. duPont†.
Foundation type: Independent foundation.
Financial data (yr. ended 12/31/13): Assets, $18,238,975 (M); expenditures, $583,710; qualifying distributions, $531,466; giving activities include $512,745 for 32 grants (high: $100,000; low: $4,000).
Fields of interest: Museums; Human services.
Type of support: Annual campaigns; Capital campaigns; Building/renovation; Equipment.
Limitations: Applications accepted. Giving primarily in DE and PA. No grants to individuals.
Application information: Application form required.
Initial approach: 2-page letter
Copies of proposal: 1
Deadline(s): Nov. 1
Board meeting date(s): As required

Officers: Stephen A. Martinenza, Pres.; Sandra S. Drew, V.P. and Treas.; Joanne S. Reilly, Secy.
Number of staff: 1
EIN: 516015638
Selected grants: The following grants are a representative sample of this grantmaker's funding activity:
$25,000 to University of Delaware, Newark, DE, 2011.
$15,000 to United Way of Delaware, Wilmington, DE, 2011.
$10,000 to YMCA of Delaware, Wilmington, DE, 2011.
$5,000 to Operation Warm, Chadds Ford, PA, 2011.

1758
Crystal Trust ✧
P.O. Box 39
Montchanin, DE 19710-0039 (302) 651-0533
Contact: Stephen C. Doberstein, Dir.

Trust established in 1947 in DE.
Donor: Irenee duPont†.
Foundation type: Independent foundation.
Financial data (yr. ended 12/31/13): Assets, $182,376,080 (M); gifts received, $2,850,591; expenditures, $6,784,228; qualifying distributions, $4,689,773; giving activities include $4,634,600 for 85 grants (high: $250,000; low: $2,800).
Purpose and activities: Giving mainly for higher and secondary education and social and family services, including youth and child welfare agencies, family planning, and programs for the aged, the disadvantaged, and the homeless; support also for the arts and cultural programs, health and hospitals, conservation programs, and historical preservation. Needs of the State of Delaware have priority.
Fields of interest: Museums; Performing arts, music; Arts; Secondary school/education; Higher education; Libraries/library science; Education; Environment, natural resources; Hospitals (general); Reproductive health, family planning; Health care; Health organizations, association; Food services; Housing/shelter, development; Human services; Children/youth, services; Family services; Residential/custodial care, hospices; Aging, centers/services; Homeless, human services; Aging; Economically disadvantaged; Homeless.
Type of support: Capital campaigns; Building/renovation; Equipment; Land acquisition.
Limitations: Applications accepted. Giving primarily in DE, with emphasis on Wilmington; some funding also in PA. No grants to individuals, or for endowment funds, research, scholarships, fellowships, or matching gifts.
Publications: Informational brochure (including application guidelines).
Application information: Application form not required.
Initial approach: Proposal
Copies of proposal: 1
Deadline(s): Sept. 30
Board meeting date(s): Nov.
Final notification: Dec. 15
Director: Stephen C. Doberstein.
Trustees: Eleanor S. Maroney, Advisory Tr.; Ernest N. May, Jr., Advisory Tr.; Irenee duPont, Jr.
Number of staff: 1 part-time professional; 1 part-time support.
EIN: 516015063
Selected grants: The following grants are a representative sample of this grantmaker's funding activity:
$3,000,000 to Nemours Foundation, Wilmington, DE, 2012. For capital campaign.
$2,500,000 to Chester County Hospital Foundation, West Chester, PA, 2012. For emergency room.
$2,500,000 to Massachusetts Institute of Technology, Cambridge, MA, 2012. For Independent Residence Fund.
$1,000,000 to Wilmington Friends School, Wilmington, DE, 2012. For reconstruction.
$481,000 to Historical Society of Delaware, Wilmington, DE, 2012. For Read House maintenance.
$200,000 to Christiana Care Health System, Wilmington, DE, 2012. For medical equipment.
$50,000 to Centreville School, Wilmington, DE, 2012. For scholarships.
$50,000 to Chesapeake Bay Maritime Museum, Saint Michaels, MD, 2012. For capital improvements.
$41,000 to Saint Annes Episcopal School, Middletown, DE, 2012. For technology upgrades.
$25,000 to Havre de Grace Maritime Museum, Havre de Grace, MD, 2012. For capital improvements.

1759
CTW Foundation, Inc. ✧
(formerly Beneficial Foundation, Inc.)
P.O. Box 911
Wilmington, DE 19899-0911 (302) 429-9427
Contact: Robert A. Tucker, Pres. and Dir.
Application address: C/o Hodson Services, LLC, 200 Bellevue Pkwy., Ste. 100, Wilmington, DE 19809

Incorporated in 1951 in DE.
Donors: Beneficial Corp.; Beneficial New Jersey.
Foundation type: Company-sponsored foundation.
Financial data (yr. ended 12/31/12): Assets, $12,938,432 (M); expenditures, $749,870; qualifying distributions, $724,933; giving activities include $697,500 for 26 grants (high: $250,000; low: $5,000).
Purpose and activities: The foundation supports hospices and hospitals and organizations involved with arts and culture, secondary, higher, and law education, conservation, and nursing.
Fields of interest: Arts; Education; Health care.
Limitations: Applications accepted. Giving primarily in MA, NJ, NY, and RI. No grants for endowments; no loans.
Application information: Application form not required.
Initial approach: Proposal
Deadline(s): None
Board meeting date(s): Usually in May and Dec.
Officers and Directors:* Robert A. Tucker,* Pres.; Eileen D. Dickey, Secy.; Finn M.W. Caspersen, Jr.; Bruce R. Tucker.
Number of staff: 2 part-time support.
EIN: 516011637

1760
The David Minkin Foundation ✧
c/o JP Morgan Services
P.O. Box 6089
Newark, DE 19714-6089

Established in FL.
Foundation type: Independent foundation.
Financial data (yr. ended 12/31/11): Assets, $19,569,726 (M); expenditures, $1,056,951; qualifying distributions, $1,029,418; giving activities include $965,000 for 23 grants (high: $260,000; low: $2,500).
Fields of interest: Arts; Education; Health care.
Limitations: Applications not accepted. Giving primarily in FL; some funding also in MN. No grants to individuals.
Application information: Unsolicited requests for funds not accepted.
Trustees: Paul Briger; Howard Lester; Patricia Lester.
EIN: 550874960

1761
Shelby Cullom Davis Charitable Fund ✧
c/o Foundation Source
501 Silverside Rd., No. 123
Wilmington, DE 19809-1377

Donor: Kathryn W. Davis.
Foundation type: Independent foundation.
Financial data (yr. ended 12/31/12): Assets, $67,937,323 (M); expenditures, $2,891,071; qualifying distributions, $3,031,714; giving activities include $2,399,532 for 29 grants (high: $297,532; low: $2,000), and $325,000 for 1 loan/program-related investment.
Fields of interest: Museums; Libraries (special); Education; Environment, water resources; Environment; Human services.
Limitations: Applications not accepted. Giving primarily in NY and IL.
Application information: Unsolicited requests for funds not accepted.
Officers and Directors:* Kathryn W. Davis,* Chair.; Shelby M.C. Davis,* Vice-Chair.; Christopher C. Davis,* Secy.; Andrew A. Davis,* Treas.; Philip O. Geier, Ph.D., Exec. Dir.; Alida Davis; Cullom Davis; Lansing Davis; Victoria Davis Nosler.
EIN: 203734688

1762
The Happy Davis Foundation, Inc. ✧
c/o Foundation Source
501 Silverside Rd., Ste. 123
Wilmington, DE 19809-1377

Established in 2005 in DE.
Donor: Ray C. Davis.
Foundation type: Independent foundation.
Financial data (yr. ended 12/31/13): Assets, $2,314,127 (M); gifts received, $6,000,000; expenditures, $6,322,801; qualifying distributions, $6,321,676; giving activities include $6,285,000 for 15 grants (high: $2,000,000; low: $10,000).
Fields of interest: Higher education; Health care; Cancer; Human services; Children, services; Foundations (private grantmaking).
Limitations: Applications not accepted. Giving primarily in TX. No grants to individuals.
Application information: Contributes only to pre-selected organizations.
Officers and Directors:* Ray C. Davis,* Pres. and Secy.; Kris Davis,* V.P.
EIN: 203246052

1763
Nancy Sayles Day Foundation ✧
c/o WFO
1100 N. Market St., No. 1010
Wilmington, DE 19801-1289

Trust established in 1964 in CT.
Donors: Nancy Sayles Day‡; Mrs. Lee Day Gillespie.
Foundation type: Independent foundation.
Financial data (yr. ended 09/30/13): Assets, $14,206,830 (M); expenditures, $801,793; qualifying distributions, $682,122; giving activities include $649,000 for 21 grants (high: $250,000; low: $2,500).
Fields of interest: Environment, natural resources; Health organizations; Human services.
Type of support: General/operating support; Continuing support.
Limitations: Applications not accepted. Giving primarily in Nantucket, MA. No grants to individuals, or for building or endowment funds, research, or matching gifts; no loans.
Application information: Contributes only to pre-selected organizations.
Trustees: Mary G. West; Wilmington Trust Co.
EIN: 066071254
Selected grants: The following grants are a representative sample of this grantmaker's funding activity:
$250,000 to Nantucket Community Sailing, Nantucket, MA, 2011.
$100,000 to Nantucket Conservation Foundation, Nantucket, MA, 2011.
$75,000 to Nantucket Maria Mitchell Association, Nantucket, MA, 2011.
$25,000 to Boys and Girls Club of Nantucket, Nantucket, MA, 2011.
$10,000 to Haiti Projects, Hanover, MA, 2011.
$10,000 to Nantucket Community Sailing, Nantucket, MA, 2011.
$10,000 to Nantucket Cottage Hospital, Nantucket, MA, 2011.
$5,000 to A Safe Place, Nantucket, MA, 2011.
$5,000 to Artists Association of Nantucket, Nantucket, MA, 2011.

1764
M. M. and P. A. Day Memorial Fund ✧
c/o Wilmington Trust Co.
1100 N. Market St.
Wilmington, DE 19890-0900 (302) 855-2257
Contact: Susan Nickel

Established in DE.
Donor: Margaret Day Interim Trust.
Foundation type: Independent foundation.
Financial data (yr. ended 12/31/13): Assets, $7,755,316 (M); expenditures, $543,897; qualifying distributions, $488,852; giving activities include $438,233 for 6 grants (high: $249,793; low: $17,529).
Purpose and activities: Giving primarily for Episcopal and United Methodist churches and organizations.
Fields of interest: Human services; Protestant agencies & churches.
Limitations: Applications not accepted. Giving primarily in DE.
Application information: Generally contributes to pre-selected organizations.
Trustees: Patricia G. Zaharko; Wilmington Trust Co.
EIN: 207053268
Selected grants: The following grants are a representative sample of this grantmaker's funding activity:
$61,353 to Trinity Episcopal Church, Wilmington, DE, 2012. For operations and/or education.

1765
Delaware Community Foundation ✧
100 W. 10th Street, Ste. 115
P.O. Box 1636
Wilmington, DE 19899 (302) 571-8004
Contact: Elizabeth M. Bouchelle, Dir., Grants
FAX: (302) 571-1553; E-mail: info@delcf.org; Tel. for grant application inquiries: (302) 504-5239; E-mail for grant application inquiries: bbouchelle@delcf.org; Main URL: http://www.delcf.org
Twitter: https://twitter.com/@DelCommunity

Incorporated in 1986 in DE.
Foundation type: Community foundation.
Financial data (yr. ended 06/30/13): Assets, $219,684,923 (M); gifts received, $14,026,726; expenditures, $33,371,595; giving activities include $28,100,711 for grants.
Purpose and activities: The foundation is a nonprofit, philanthropic community organization created by and for the people of Delaware to build community. The DCF is dedicated to inspiring and helping people of all backgrounds and means create lasting legacies to benefit the people of Delaware. It enables people with philanthropic interests to easily and effectively support the issues they care about by establishing a charitable fund at the foundation and recommending grants to nonprofit groups they want to support. The foundation offers personalized service, local expertise and community leadership. The foundation itself awards grants to qualified nonprofit organizations that serve Delawareans for selected programs and capital projects.
Fields of interest: Arts; Education; Environment; Animals/wildlife; Health care; Substance abuse, prevention; Health organizations, association; Crime/violence prevention, child abuse; Nutrition; Housing/shelter, development; Children/youth, services; Human services; Community/economic development; Aging.
Type of support: Continuing support; Capital campaigns; Building/renovation; Equipment; Program development; Seed money; Technical assistance.
Limitations: Applications accepted. Giving limited to DE. No support for religious organizations for sectarian purposes or educational institutions for capital projects. No grants to individuals (except for scholarships), or for annual fundraising campaigns, special events, operating costs, endowments, debt reduction, or sports clubs or leagues.
Publications: Application guidelines; Annual report; Financial statement; Informational brochure; Newsletter.
Application information: Visit foundation web site for application form and guidelines. Handwritten or faxed application forms are not accepted. Application form required.
Initial approach: Submit application form and attachments
Copies of proposal: 1
Deadline(s): Varies
Board meeting date(s): Quarterly
Final notification: Varies
Officers and Directors:* Marilyn Rushworth Hayward,* Chair.; Thomas L. Sager,* Vice-Chair.; Fred C. Sears II, C.E.O. and Pres.; Richard A. Gentsch, Exec. V.P.; David Fleming, Sr. V.P., Devel.; William R. Allan, Sr. V.P., Southern Delaware; Becky Cahill Garofalo, C.F.O.; Stephen P. Lamb, Secy.; Stephen A. Fowle,* Treas.; Doneen Keemer Damon; Bill Dugdale; Martha S. Gilman; Daryl A. Graham; Jennings Hastings; John C. Hawkins; Nancy Karibjanian; Rob MacGovern; Kathleen McDonough; Janice E. Nevin, M.D.; Donald W. Nicholson, Jr.; John W. Noble; Laurisa S. Schutt; Joan L. Sharp; Valerie J. Sill; David Singleton; Gary Stockbridge; Cindy L. Szabo; Michelle A. Taylor; Michelle Whetzel.
Number of staff: 10 full-time professional; 2 part-time professional.
EIN: 222804785
Selected grants: The following grants are a representative sample of this grantmaker's funding activity:
$260,084 to YWCA Delaware, Wilmington, DE, 2012.
$252,496 to Saint Edmonds Academy, Wilmington, DE, 2012.
$223,000 to Grand Opera House, Wilmington, DE, 2012.
$220,061 to Delaware Futures, Wilmington, DE, 2012. For Annual Distribution.
$202,430 to Latin American Community Center, Wilmington, DE, 2012.
$140,000 to Nemours Partnership for Children's Health, Wilmington, DE, 2012. For Dental Program.
$35,100 to Beebe Medical Foundation, Lewes, DE, 2012.
$22,500 to National Building Museum, Washington, DC, 2012.
$17,700 to Friendship House, Wilmington, DE, 2012.
$10,883 to Cape Henlopen Educational Foundation, Milton, DE, 2012.

1766
Richard Desich Foundation ✧ ☆
c/o Foundation Source
501 Silverside Rd.
Wilmington, DE 19809-1377

Donor: Richard Desich.
Foundation type: Independent foundation.
Financial data (yr. ended 12/31/12): Assets, $1,364,754 (M); gifts received, $1,207,800; expenditures, $930,828; qualifying distributions, $506,678; giving activities include $500,000 for 1 grant.
Fields of interest: Higher education.
Limitations: Applications not accepted. Giving primarily in Elyria, OH.
Application information: Unsolicited requests for funds not accepted.
Officer and Director:* Richard Desich,* Pres. and Secy.
EIN: 264308958

1767
The Peter and Michelle Detkin Family Foundation ✧ ☆
c/o Foundation Source
501 Silverside Rd.
Wilmington, DE 19809-1377

Established in CA.

Donors: Michelle Detkin; Peter Detkin.
Foundation type: Independent foundation.
Financial data (yr. ended 12/31/13): Assets, $1,710,818 (M); expenditures, $630,608; qualifying distributions, $621,560; giving activities include $608,055 for 6 grants (high: $386,994; low: $1,000).
Fields of interest: Health organizations; Recreation; Human services.
Limitations: Applications not accepted.
Application information: Unsolicited requests for funds not accepted.
Officers: Michelle Detkin, Pres.; Peter Detkin, Secy.-Treas.
EIN: 263411122
Selected grants: The following grants are a representative sample of this grantmaker's funding activity:
$72,105 to Law Foundation of Silicon Valley, San Jose, CA, 2011.
$51,303 to University of Pennsylvania, Philadelphia, PA, 2011.

1768
Devonwood Foundation ✧
c/o Wilmington Trust Co.
1100 N. Market St., DE3-C070
Wilmington, DE 19890-0001

Established in 1968 in DE.
Donors: E.H. Brodie; L.S. Brodie.
Foundation type: Independent foundation.
Financial data (yr. ended 12/31/13): Assets, $18,803,785 (M); expenditures, $803,053; qualifying distributions, $776,003; giving activities include $772,000 for 55 grants (high: $190,000; low: $1,000).
Purpose and activities: Giving primarily for higher education and the arts, and sustainability programs.
Fields of interest: Media, film/video; Arts; Higher education; Education; Agriculture, sustainable programs; Human services.
Type of support: General/operating support; Endowments.
Limitations: Applications not accepted. Giving primarily in New York, NY and Durham, NC, with some giving in MA and ME. No grants to individuals.
Application information: Contributes only to pre-selected organizations.
Trustees: Brenda B. Brodie; Bryson B. Brodie; Cameron K. Brodie; H. Keith H. Brodie; Tyler H. Brodie; Melissa B. Hanenberger; Wilmington Trust Co.
EIN: 516024607
Selected grants: The following grants are a representative sample of this grantmaker's funding activity:
$182,000 to Duke University, Durham, NC, 2011.
$170,000 to Southeastern Efforts Developing Sustainable Spaces, Durham, NC, 2011.
$128,000 to Southeastern Efforts Developing Sustainable Spaces, Durham, NC, 2010.
$100,000 to Cinereach, New York, NY, 2010.
$21,000 to Columbia University, School of Nursing, New York, NY, 2011.
$20,000 to Bowdoin College, Brunswick, ME, 2011.
$20,000 to Northern Rockies Conservation Cooperative, Jackson, WY, 2011. For operations.
$10,000 to Actors Studio, New York, NY, 2011. For operations.
$10,000 to Milton Academy, Milton, MA, 2011.
$10,000 to North Alabama Conference of the United Methodist Church, Birmingham, AL, 2010.
$5,000 to American Dance Festival, Durham, NC, 2011.
$5,000 to Carolina Farm Stewardship Association, Pittsboro, NC, 2010.
$5,000 to Museum of Modern Art, New York, NY, 2010.
$5,000 to Museum of Modern Art, New York, NY, 2011.
$5,000 to Nature Conservancy, Arlington, VA, 2011. For operations.
$1,000 to Nature Conservancy, Arlington, VA, 2010.

1769
Doctorbird Foundation ✧
c/o Foundation Source
501 Silverside Rd., Ste. 123
Wilmington, DE 19809-1377

Established in DE.
Donors: E Porter; L. Robins Revocable Trust.
Foundation type: Independent foundation.
Financial data (yr. ended 12/31/13): Assets, $35,827,134 (M); expenditures, $1,623,503; qualifying distributions, $1,535,462; giving activities include $1,462,400 for 27 grants (high: $125,000; low: $7,000).
Fields of interest: Arts; Education.
Limitations: Applications not accepted.
Application information: Unsolicited requests for funds not accepted.
Officer and Director:* E. Porter,* Pres. and Secy.
EIN: 273900238

1770
Nancy-Carroll Draper Charitable Foundation ✧ ☆
c/o Wilmington Trust Co
1100 N. Market St.
Wilmington, DE 19890-0900
Application address: Bingham McCutchen LLP, Attn.: Thomas Peckham, 1 Federal St., Boston, MA 02110, tel.: (617) 951-8576

Established in 1997 in MA.
Donor: N. C. Draper.
Foundation type: Independent foundation.
Financial data (yr. ended 12/31/13): Assets, $16,167,201 (M); gifts received, $72,325; expenditures, $1,332,942; qualifying distributions, $1,078,970; giving activities include $1,013,517 for 7 grants (high: $500,000; low: $5,000).
Purpose and activities: Giving primarily to organizations concerned with environmental and conservation causes, or the welfare and preservation of animals, including disease research.
Fields of interest: Museums (natural history); Environment; Animals/wildlife.
Type of support: General/operating support.
Limitations: Applications accepted. Giving primarily in Washington, DC and WY. No grants to individuals.
Application information: Application form required.
Initial approach: Letter
Deadline(s): None
Trustees: Louisa K. Blodgett; Colin S. Marshall; Thomas Peckham.
EIN: 046726873
Selected grants: The following grants are a representative sample of this grantmaker's funding activity:
$100,000 to African Wildlife Foundation, Washington, DC, 2012. For Elephant and Leopard Projects.

1771
Duane Reade Charitable Foundation ✧ ☆
c/o Foundation Source
501 Silverside Rd., Ste. 123
Wilmington, DE 19809-1377 (212) 356-5241
Contact: Yadira Velasquez
E-mail: Drcharity@duanereade.com; Application address: 40 Wall St., New York, NY 10005; Additional e-mail: DRCFcares@gmail.com; Main URL: http://www.duanereade.com/CharitableFoundation.aspx
Facebook: https://www.facebook.com/drcfcares

Established in 2007 in DE and NJ.
Donors: Beyer Farms, Inc.; Proctor and Gamble; Coca Cola Bottling Company NY; Graphics Atlanta Inc; Interactive Communications Intl Inc.; Johnson & Johnson; Kimberly-Clark; Kiss Products; L'Oreal Paris Division; Maybelline; Nature's Bounty Inc.; Novartis Consumer Health; Oak Hill Capital Management LLC; Paul, Weiss, Rifkind, Wharton & Garrison LLP; Steiner Foods Inc.; The American Bottling Company; The Michael Alan Group; The Walking Man Inc.; Tropical Foods; UTZ Quality Foods, Inc; Winick Realty Group, LLC; Wrigley.
Foundation type: Company-sponsored foundation.
Financial data (yr. ended 12/31/13): Assets, $684,802 (M); gifts received, $655,808; expenditures, $697,241; qualifying distributions, $692,318; giving activities include $615,455 for 55 grants (high: $75,000; low: $7).
Purpose and activities: The foundation supports programs designed to promote health and wellness; address local community needs; and promote growth and development of communities in the New York Metro area.
Fields of interest: Health care, clinics/centers; Health care, patient services; Health care; Breast cancer; ALS; AIDS; Diabetes; Food services; Children/youth, services; Human services.
Type of support: General/operating support; Annual campaigns; Program development; Scholarship funds; Sponsorships; Donated products.
Limitations: Applications accepted. Giving primarily in areas of store operations in NY. No grants to individuals.
Publications: Application guidelines.
Application information: Application form not required.
Initial approach: E-mail letter of inquiry to foundation
Deadline(s): 1 month prior to need
Board meeting date(s): Monthly
Officers and Directors:* Aileen Rodriguez,* Pres. and Secy.; Fran Baruch, V.P.; Gregory Calvano, V.P.; Dan Gralton, V.P.; Adrienne Johnson, V.P.; Jeffrey Koziel,* V.P.; Scorr McCulloch, V.P.; Anthony Riso, V.P.; Kenneth Wistreich, V.P.; Deidre Zaccone, V.P.
EIN: 208607795
Selected grants: The following grants are a representative sample of this grantmaker's funding activity:
$132,010 to Susan G. Komen for the Cure, New York, NY, 2011.
$40,000 to Gay Mens Health Crisis, New York, NY, 2011.
$25,000 to American Diabetes Association, New York, NY, 2011.
$15,000 to Family Center, New York, NY, 2011.

$10,000 to Ronald McDonald House of New York, New York, NY, 2011.
$10,000 to Susan G. Komen for the Cure, New York, NY, 2011.
$5,000 to Dress for Success Worldwide, New York, NY, 2011.
$5,000 to Hope for the Warriors, Jacksonville, NC, 2011.
$2,000 to Dress for Success Worldwide, New York, NY, 2011.
$1,000 to Dress for Success Worldwide, New York, NY, 2011.

1772
The Dwoskin Family Foundation ✧
c/o Foundation Source
501 Silverside Rd., Ste. 123
Wilmington, DE 19809-1377

Established in 2001 in VA; funded in 2005.
Donors: Albert James Dwoskin; Lisa Claire Dwoskin; Focus Autism; Mario M. Morino Trust.
Foundation type: Independent foundation.
Financial data (yr. ended 12/31/13): Assets, $2,403,964 (M); expenditures, $695,635; qualifying distributions, $693,594; giving activities include $655,745 for 17 grants (high: $367,010; low: $738).
Fields of interest: Media, film/video; Media, television; Salvation Army; Philanthropy/voluntarism.
Type of support: General/operating support.
Limitations: Applications not accepted. Giving primarily in Arlington, VA, and Washington, DC. No grants to individuals.
Application information: Contributes only to pre-selected organizations.
Officers and Directors:* Albert James Dwoskin,* Pres.; Lisa Claire Dwoskin,* Secy.-Treas.
EIN: 542060115
Selected grants: The following grants are a representative sample of this grantmaker's funding activity:
$125,000 to American Foundation for the University of British Columbia, Washington, DC, 2011.
$120,218 to National Vaccine Information Center, Vienna, VA, 2011.
$62,500 to American Foundation for the University of British Columbia, Washington, DC, 2011.
$62,500 to University of British Columbia, Vancouver, Canada, 2011.
$32,000 to National Vaccine Information Center, Vienna, VA, 2011.
$25,000 to National Vaccine Information Center, Vienna, VA, 2011.
$25,000 to Women Make Movies, New York, NY, 2011.
$17,500 to National Vaccine Information Center, Vienna, VA, 2011.
$13,475 to National Vaccine Information Center, Vienna, VA, 2011.
$10,000 to Miller Center Foundation, Charlottesville, VA, 2011.

1773
Joan C. Edwards Charitable Foundation ✧
c/o NY Private Bank & Trust Co.
200 Bellevue Pkwy., Ste. 150
Wilmington, DE 19809-3725

Established in 2006 in IL.
Donors: Susan Drake Trust; Joan C. Edwards Trust.
Foundation type: Independent foundation.
Financial data (yr. ended 12/31/13): Assets, $36,642,935 (M); expenditures, $2,275,602; qualifying distributions, $1,608,417; giving activities include $1,475,015 for 3 grants (high: $850,724; low: $150,000).
Fields of interest: Higher education; Hospitals (general); Foundations (public).
Limitations: Applications not accepted. Giving primarily in OH, with emphasis on Cleveland; some giving also in Huntington, WV.
Application information: Contributes only to pre-selected organizations.
Directors: Thomas M. McDonald; Dr. Charles H. McKown, Jr.; Marshall T. Reynolds.
Trustee: NY Private Bank & Trust Co.
EIN: 208374445
Selected grants: The following grants are a representative sample of this grantmaker's funding activity:
$798,549 to Case Western Reserve University, Cleveland, OH, 2012. To Fund Edwards Scholars Endowment.
$473,250 to Marshall University, School of Medicine, Huntington, WV, 2012. For Endowment for J C Edwards School of Medicine.

1774
Edwards Mother Earth Foundation ✧
c/o Foundation Source
501 Silverside Rd., Ste. 123
Wilmington, DE 19809-1377
E-mail: ruth@tjedwards.com; Main URL: http://www.fsrequests.com/EMEF

Established in 1997 in WA.
Donors: Bob Edwards†; Jane Edwards†.
Foundation type: Independent foundation.
Financial data (yr. ended 12/31/13): Assets, $35,018,366 (M); expenditures, $1,586,625; qualifying distributions, $1,469,173; giving activities include $1,321,460 for 67 grants (high: $142,000; low: $75).
Purpose and activities: The foundation is currently responding to global climate disruption (global warming) by working with utilities to develop energy efficient models and policies within AR, AZ, CO, ID, IL, MO, and OH.
Fields of interest: Environment, climate change/global warming.
Type of support: General/operating support; Continuing support; Management development/capacity building; Equipment; Program development; Technical assistance; Matching/challenge support.
Limitations: Applications not accepted. Giving is currently limited to AR, AZ, CO, ID, IL, MO and OH. See foundation web site for updates on state giving. No support for organizations that are not nationally-based. No grants to individuals.
Application information: Contributes only to pre-selected organizations.
Board meeting date(s): Last Fri/Sat. in April and the 3rd weekend in Oct.
Officers and Directors:* Tara Reinertson, Secy.; Paul Cunningham,* Treas.; Eileen Bell; Garrett Bell; Robbin Finch; Kristina Rayl; Sutter Wehmeier.
Number of staff: 1 part-time professional; 1 part-time support.
EIN: 911789783

1775
The Enoch Foundation ✧
(formerly Enoch Foundation Charitable Trust)
c/o Foundation Source
501 Silverside Rd., Ste. 123
Wilmington, DE 19809-1377

Established in 2003 in NY.
Donor: Margaret Enoch†.
Foundation type: Independent foundation.
Financial data (yr. ended 12/31/13): Assets, $32,557,612 (M); expenditures, $1,630,968; qualifying distributions, $1,388,734; giving activities include $1,320,500 for 28 grants (high: $175,000; low: $7,500).
Fields of interest: Arts; Education.
Limitations: Applications not accepted. Giving primarily in New York, NY. No grants to individuals.
Application information: Contributes only to pre-selected organizations.
Trustee: Robert B. Ferguson.
EIN: 136989587

1776
The Eshelman Foundation ✧ ☆
c/o Foundation Source
501 Silverside Rd., Ste. 123
Wilmington, DE 19809-1377

Established in 2007 in NC.
Donors: Fred Eshelman; Walker Taylor IV; Steve Diab.
Foundation type: Independent foundation.
Financial data (yr. ended 12/31/13): Assets, $262,368 (M); expenditures, $617,448; qualifying distributions, $616,677; giving activities include $526,346 for 22 grants (high: $72,936; low: $3,500).
Fields of interest: Education; Hospitals (general); Boys clubs; Residential/custodial care.
Limitations: Applications not accepted. Giving primarily in Wilmington, NC.
Application information: Unsolicited requests for funds not accepted.
Officers and Director:* Fred Eshelman, Chair.; Kimberly Batten,* Pres.; Steve Diab, Secy.; Walker Taylor IV, Treas.
Board Member: Laura Bonifacio.
EIN: 261751826

1777
The Esperance Family Foundation ✧
c/o Foundation Source
501 Silverside Rd., Ste. 123
Wilmington, DE 19809-1377

Established in DE.
Donors: Roger S. Newton; Coco Newton.
Foundation type: Independent foundation.
Financial data (yr. ended 12/31/12): Assets, $2,697,315 (M); gifts received, $402,011; expenditures, $1,200,819; qualifying distributions, $1,140,698; giving activities include $1,119,008 for 26 grants (high: $300,000; low: $500).
Purpose and activities: Giving primarily for education, including arts education, health associations, youth services, and a YMCA.
Fields of interest: Performing arts, education; Higher education; Environment; Health organizations, association; YM/YWCAs & YM/

YWHAs; Youth, services; Community/economic development.
Type of support: General/operating support; Capital campaigns; Building/renovation; Program development.
Limitations: Applications not accepted. Giving primarily in MI. No grants to individuals.
Application information: Contributes only to pre-selected organizations.
Officers and Directors:* Roger S. Newton,* Pres. and Secy.; Alex Newton,* V.P.; Coco Newton,* V.P.; Keri Newton, V.P.; Russell Newton,* V.P.
EIN: 200494459

1778
Oliver Etnier Charitable Trust ✧
c/o Wilmington Trust Co.
1100 N. Market St., Drop 1050
Wilmington, DE 19801-1243
Contact: Michela Rossi

Established in 1989 in DE.
Donor: Oliver L. Etnier.
Foundation type: Independent foundation.
Financial data (yr. ended 04/30/13): Assets, $15,684,782 (M); expenditures, $860,674; qualifying distributions, $725,143; giving activities include $658,688 for 4 grants (high: $468,820; low: $24,553).
Purpose and activities: Scholarships awarded to local area high school graduates majoring in engineering, physics, or computer science at one of six qualifying universities.
Fields of interest: Higher education; Scholarships/financial aid.
Type of support: Scholarships—to individuals; Scholarship funds.
Limitations: Applications not accepted. Giving primarily in NJ, NY, and PA.
Application information: Grants selected by trustees. Unsolicited requests for funds not accepted.
Trustee: Wilmington Trust Co.
EIN: 516170516

1779
The Ettinger Foundation, Inc. ✧
501 Silverside Rd.
Wilmington, DE 19809-3515

Incorporated in 1949 in DE.
Donors: Ronene E. Anderson; Elaine P. Hapgood; Lynn P. Babicka; John P. Powers; Heidi Ettinger; Barbara P. Ettinger; Wendy P. Ettinger; and members of the Ettinger family.
Foundation type: Independent foundation.
Financial data (yr. ended 12/31/12): Assets, $17,043,005 (M); expenditures, $1,627,914; qualifying distributions, $1,361,832; giving activities include $1,292,600 for 201 grants (high: $52,500; low: $250).
Purpose and activities: Giving primarily for education, the arts, health care, and for children, youth and social services.
Fields of interest: Arts; Higher education; Education; Reproductive health, family planning; Health care; Health organizations, association; Human services; Children/youth, services; Family services; Civil liberties, reproductive rights; Community/economic development; Foundations (private grantmaking); Foundations (community); Women.
Type of support: General/operating support; Program development; Seed money; Matching/challenge support.
Limitations: Applications not accepted. Giving primarily in NY; giving also in CO, and Washington, DC. No grants to individuals, or for building or endowment funds; no loans.
Application information: Contributes only to pre-selected organizations.
Board meeting date(s): Varies
Officers and Directors:* Elaine P. Hapgood,* Pres.; Barbara P. Ettinger,* V.P.; John P. Powers,* V.P.; Diane M. Allison, Secy.; Christian Ettinger, Treas.; Lynn P. Babicka; Heidi P. Ettinger; Wendy P. Ettinger.
EIN: 066038938

1780
Fair Play Foundation ✧
100 W. 10th St., Ste. 1010
Wilmington, DE 19801-6606 (302) 777-4711
Contact: Blaine T. Phillips, Jr., Exec. Dir.

Established about 1961 in DE.
Foundation type: Independent foundation.
Financial data (yr. ended 12/31/13): Assets, $13,080,133 (M); expenditures, $808,458; qualifying distributions, $599,172; giving activities include $547,500 for 44 grants (high: $50,000; low: $2,500).
Fields of interest: Museums; Arts; Higher education; Environment, water resources; Animals/wildlife, preservation/protection.
Type of support: Building/renovation; Equipment; Land acquisition.
Limitations: Giving primarily in DE, MD and VA; funding also in Washington, DC. No support for business-oriented organizations.
Application information: Application form required.
Initial approach: 1-page letter
Copies of proposal: 1
Deadline(s): None
Board meeting date(s): Dec.
Final notification: Positive responses only
Officers and Trustees:* W. Halsey Spruance, Jr.,* V.P.; Gregory A. Inskip,* Secy.; Richard L. Laird, Jr.,* Treas.; Blaine T. Philips, Jr., Exec. Dir.; James F. Burnett; Thomas H. Fooks V; Milbrey R. Jacobs; Blaine T. Phillips.
Number of staff: 1 full-time professional.
EIN: 516017779
Selected grants: The following grants are a representative sample of this grantmaker's funding activity:
$50,000 to Conservation Fund, Arlington, VA, 2012. For Mid-Atlantic land protection efforts.
$45,000 to Fauna and Flora International, Washington, DC, 2012. For Protection of endangered mountain gorillas and threatened sea turtles Environmental projects and research.
$35,000 to Delaware Wild Lands, Odessa, DE, 2012. For Continued efforts to protect and restore the natural resources of the Sharp Farm.
$25,000 to University of Virginia, Law School, Charlottesville, VA, 2012. For Environmental Law Program.
$20,000 to Chesapeake Bay Foundation, Annapolis, MD, 2012. For Preservation and maintenance of Fox Island education and research center.
$20,000 to Delaware Museum of Natural History, Wilmington, DE, 2012. For Program support and new roof.
$20,000 to Trout Unlimited, Arlington, VA, 2012. For Coldwater Conservation Fund projects to protect wild trout and the streams they inhabit.
$15,000 to Southern Environmental Law Center, Charlottesville, VA, 2012. For Environmental Law Fellow Program.
$10,000 to Midshore Riverkeeper Conservancy, Easton, MD, 2012. For publication of Tom Horton and David Harp's Choptank Odyssey.
$7,500 to Brandywine Conservancy, Chadds Ford, PA, 2012. To upgrade membership card system.

1781
First Eagle Investment Management Foundation ✧
c/o Foundation Source
501 Silverside Rd., Ste. 123
Wilmington, DE 19809-1377

Established in DE.
Donor: First Eagle Investment Management LLC.
Foundation type: Independent foundation.
Financial data (yr. ended 12/31/13): Assets, $1,731,060 (M); gifts received, $1,000,000; expenditures, $692,150; qualifying distributions, $691,300; giving activities include $678,711 for 141 grants (high: $50,000; low: $25).
Fields of interest: Arts; Health organizations; Human services.
Limitations: Applications not accepted. Giving primarily in the U.S., with emphasis on NY.
Application information: Unsolicited requests for funds not accepted.
Officers and Directors:* Bridget Macaskill,* Pres. and Secy.; John Arnhold,* V.P.; Melanie Dow,* V.P.; Robert Hackney; Matt McLennan.
EIN: 454165305
Selected grants: The following grants are a representative sample of this grantmaker's funding activity:
$23,510 to American Cancer Society, Oklahoma City, OK, 2012. For Lee National Denim Day Campaign.

1782
G.D.S Legacy Foundation, Inc. ✧
1201 Market St., Ste. 1202
Wilmington, DE 19801-1163

Donors: Peter Swift; MST 2000 Charitable Lead Trust.
Foundation type: Independent foundation.
Financial data (yr. ended 12/31/13): Assets, $48,522,510 (M); gifts received, $539,219; expenditures, $1,854,182; qualifying distributions, $1,468,696; giving activities include $1,453,500 for 17 grants (high: $325,000; low: $3,500).
Fields of interest: Arts; Environment; Animals/wildlife.
Limitations: Applications not accepted. Giving primarily in DC, NY, and VT.
Application information: Contributes only to pre-selected organizations.
Trustee: P. Swift.
EIN: 271463916

1783
Ganatra Family Foundation ✧ ☆
500 Delaware Ave., Ste.900
Wilmington, DE 19801-7409

Established in 2000 in NC.
Donors: Tansukh V. Ganatra; Sarlaben T. Ganatra.
Foundation type: Independent foundation.
Financial data (yr. ended 12/31/13): Assets, $294,588 (M); expenditures, $779,200; qualifying distributions, $776,005; giving activities include $774,035 for 11 grants (high: $500,000; low: $180).
Fields of interest: Arts; Environment; Health care.
Limitations: Applications not accepted. Giving primarily in Charlotte, NC. No grants to individuals.
Application information: Unsolicited requests for funds not accepted.
Officers: Tansukh V. Ganatra, Pres.; Sharlaben T. Ganatra, V.P.
Director: Rajesh T. Ganatra.
EIN: 562195283

1784
Gloria Dei Foundation ✧
c/o Foundation Source
501 Silverside Rd., Ste. 123
Wilmington, DE 19809-1377
E-mail: info@thegloriadeifoundation.org; Main URL: http://www.gloriadeifoundation.org/

Established in 2005 in FL.
Donor: Mary Cade.
Foundation type: Independent foundation.
Financial data (yr. ended 12/31/12): Assets, $3,235,174 (M); expenditures, $499,191; qualifying distributions, $490,591; giving activities include $472,800 for 15 grants (high: $60,000; low: $3,750).
Purpose and activities: Giving primarily for causes dealing with the arts, the community, education, evangelism, discipleship and outreach, justice and public policy, and the sanctity of life.
Fields of interest: Arts; Education; Public health; Civil liberties, right to life; Public affairs; Christian agencies & churches; Economically disadvantaged.
Limitations: Giving on a worldwide basis. No grants to individuals.
Application information: See foundation web site for current application information.
Officers and Directors:* Emily Cade Morrison,* Pres.; Phoebe C. Miles,* V.P.; Robert L. Morrison,* Secy.-Treas.; Martha Cade; Mary Cade.
EIN: 203723933
Selected grants: The following grants are a representative sample of this grantmaker's funding activity:
$48,000 to Desire Street Ministries, Atlanta, GA, 2012. For Goal South Atlanta Project.
$30,000 to American Bible Society, New York, NY, 2012. For Resilience For Trauma Survivors in DR Congo.
$30,000 to Coalition of Children in Need Association, Columbus, OH, 2012. For Expanding Vocational Education Programs.
$3,750 to Timothy Leadership Training Institute, Grand Rapids, MI, 2012. For Translation of Teaching Manuals into Portuguese.

1785
Good Samaritan, Inc. ✧
600 Center Mill Rd.
Wilmington, DE 19807-1502
Contact: Mrs. Carroll M. Carpenter

Incorporated in 1938 in DE.
Donor: Elias Ahuja†.
Foundation type: Independent foundation.
Financial data (yr. ended 12/31/13): Assets, $20,715,610 (M); expenditures, $1,813,208; qualifying distributions, $1,683,553; giving activities include $1,666,500 for 24 grants (high: $200,000; low: $5,000).
Fields of interest: Elementary/secondary education; Higher education; Education; Hospitals (general); Human services.
Type of support: General/operating support; Endowments; Program development; Professorships; Seed money.
Limitations: Applications accepted. Giving primarily in the northeastern U.S. No grants to individuals, or for building funds, capital assets or conferences.
Publications: Application guidelines.
Application information: Application form not required.
Initial approach: Letter
Copies of proposal: 1
Deadline(s): Apr. 1 for May meeting, Oct. 1 for Nov. meeting
Board meeting date(s): May and Nov.
Officers: Carroll M. Carpenter, Pres.; Lea Carpenter Brokaw, V.P.; Jeffrey M. Nielsen, Secy.-Treas.
Directors: Elizabeth A. Du P. Nielsen; Edmund K. Sherrill II; H. Sinclair Sherrill.
Number of staff: 1 part-time support.
EIN: 516000401

1786
Gospel Growth Fund ✧
1901 Millers Rd.
Wilmington, DE 19810-4031

Established in 2005 in DE.
Donors: John W. Scheflen; Marcia W. Scheflen.
Foundation type: Independent foundation.
Financial data (yr. ended 12/31/13): Assets, $17,603,574 (M); expenditures, $948,314; qualifying distributions, $875,875; giving activities include $875,850 for 33 grants (high: $83,000; low: $6,000).
Purpose and activities: Giving primarily to Presbyterian and other Christian churches and organizations, particularly for international humanitarian and religious purposes.
Fields of interest: Human services; Christian agencies & churches; Protestant agencies & churches.
Limitations: Applications not accepted. Giving primarily in DE and GA. No grants to individuals.
Application information: Contributes only to pre-selected organizations.
Officers and Trustees:* John W. Scheflen,* Pres. and Treas.; Marcia W. Scheflen,* V.P.; Janna E. Scheflen,* Secy.; Rev. James O. Brown, Jr.; Gregg Noll; Neil Roosma; Elizabeth Wilkins.
EIN: 841696604
Selected grants: The following grants are a representative sample of this grantmaker's funding activity:
$25,000 to International Health Services, Southeastern, PA, 2012. For Translation and training.

1787
John C. Griswold Foundation ✧
c/o Foundation Source
501 Silverside Rd., Ste. 123
Wilmington, DE 19809-1377

Established in 1978 in NY.
Donor: John C. Griswold†.
Foundation type: Independent foundation.
Financial data (yr. ended 11/30/13): Assets, $14,610,304 (M); expenditures, $923,576; qualifying distributions, $772,356; giving activities include $660,239 for 58 grants (high: $60,000; low: $500).
Purpose and activities: Giving only to organizations in which family and outside trustees have a direct interest.
Type of support: General/operating support; Continuing support; Annual campaigns; Building/renovation.
Limitations: Applications not accepted. Giving in the U.S. No grants to individuals.
Application information: Support limited to charities which are already known to the trustees.
Board meeting date(s): Varies
Officers and Trustees:* Mark Griswold,* Pres.; David Earls,* V.P. and Co-Secy.; Jeffrey W. Earls,* Co-Secy.; John G. Earls,* Treas.; Allyson Griswold Dayak; Christopher B. Earls; Michael G. Earls; D. Ross Griswold, Jr.
Number of staff: 1 part-time support.
EIN: 132978937
Selected grants: The following grants are a representative sample of this grantmaker's funding activity:
$60,000 to Millikin University, Decatur, IL, 2013. For Exercise Science and Sport Pavilion.
$25,000 to Bolsa Chica Conservancy, Huntington Beach, CA, 2013. For Fencing for Nest Sites at the Bolsa Chica Site.
$2,800 to Heart of America Shakespeare Festival, Kansas City, MO, 2013. To support Romeo and Juliet to Go Performances.
$2,000 to Chabad of California, Los Angeles, CA, 2013. For Save the Drew Fund of Chabad RTC.
$1,000 to Greater Kansas City Community Foundation, Kansas City, MO, 2013. For WaterfireKC Fund.

1788
Gynesis Women's International Foundation ✧
(formerly Des Femmes International Foundation)
c/o Wilmington Trust Co.
1100 N. Market St., DE3-C070
Wilmington, DE 19890-0001

Established in 2002 in DE.
Donors: Sylvinia Boissonnas; Scaler Foundation, Inc.
Foundation type: Independent foundation.
Financial data (yr. ended 07/31/13): Assets, $2,115,846 (M); gifts received, $772,025; expenditures, $1,178,310; qualifying distributions, $1,094,050; giving activities include $1,016,181 for 2 grants (high: $831,763; low: $184,418).
Fields of interest: Education; Women; Young adults, female.
Limitations: Applications not accepted. Giving primarily in Paris, France. No grants to individuals.
Application information: Contributes only to pre-selected organizations.

Members: Sylvinia Boissonnas; Michele Idels; Elisabeth Nicoli; Florence Prudhomme.
EIN: 510412529

1789
Robert & Ardis James Foundation ✧
c/o Foundation Source
501 Silverside Rd., Ste. 123
Wilmington, DE 19809-1377

Established in 1986 in NY.
Donor: Robert James.
Foundation type: Independent foundation.
Financial data (yr. ended 12/31/13): Assets, $123,035,528 (M); gifts received, $578,275; expenditures, $4,272,393; qualifying distributions, $3,508,975; giving activities include $3,270,047 for 90 grants (high: $2,161,358; low: $10).
Purpose and activities: Giving primarily for higher education, international affairs, and to Presbyterian churches.
Fields of interest: Higher education; International affairs, arms control; International affairs, foreign policy; International human rights; Public policy, research; Protestant agencies & churches.
Limitations: Applications not accepted. Giving primarily in MA, MN, NE and NY; some funding also in Washington, DC. No grants to individuals.
Application information: Unsolicited requests for funds not accepted.
Trustees: Ralph M. James; Robert James; Catherine James Paglia.
Number of staff: 1 part-time support.
EIN: 136880057

1790
The Joseph and Catherine Johnson Family Foundation ✧
c/o Foundation Source
501 Silverside Rd., Ste. 123
Wilmington, DE 19809-1377

Established in 1998 in IL.
Donors: Winifred M. Johnson; Catherine Richter; Wendy Johnson; Catherine M. Johnson Charitable Lead Unitrust.
Foundation type: Independent foundation.
Financial data (yr. ended 12/31/13): Assets, $7,993,618 (M); gifts received, $149,884; expenditures, $553,322; qualifying distributions, $488,143; giving activities include $454,000 for 84 grants (high: $60,000; low: $500).
Fields of interest: Animals/wildlife; Food banks; Children/youth, services; Catholic agencies & churches; Fraternal societies.
Type of support: General/operating support.
Limitations: Applications not accepted. Giving primarily in GA, IL, and LA. No grants to individuals.
Application information: Contributes only to pre-selected organizations.
Officers and Directors:* Karen E. Gillespie,* Pres.; Theodore E. Richter,* V.P.; Rebecca A. Steiner,* Secy.; Linda A. Johnson,* Treas.; Ruth A. Pivar.
EIN: 367228534
Selected grants: The following grants are a representative sample of this grantmaker's funding activity:
$17,500 to Fraternite Notre Dame, Chicago, IL, 2011.
$8,500 to Franciscan Outreach Association, Chicago, IL, 2011.
$6,000 to Doctors Without Borders USA, New York, NY, 2011.
$6,000 to Northern Illinois Food Bank, Geneva, IL, 2011.
$5,000 to Lake County Haven, Libertyville, IL, 2011.
$5,000 to Lambs Farm, Libertyville, IL, 2011.
$5,000 to Mailisita Foundation, Green Oaks, IL, 2011.
$5,000 to Yellowstone Park Foundation, Bozeman, MT, 2011.
$4,000 to Saint Jude Childrens Research Hospital, Memphis, TN, 2011.
$3,500 to Best Friends Animal Society, Kanab, UT, 2011.

1791
Jolie-Pitt Foundation ✧
c/o Foundation Source
501 Silverside Rd., Ste. 123
Wilmington, DE 19809-1377

Established in 2006.
Donors: Brad Pitt; Angelina Jolie; Robert Offer; Potter Inc.; Weintraub Family Trust; Chivan; Australian Center for International Ag Research; The Elementary Teachers' Foundation of Ontario; Asprey Holdings Ltd.; Saic General Motors Sales Co.; The Robert and Daryl Offer Family Trust; Robert Procop; Robert Wang; National Health Services.
Foundation type: Independent foundation.
Financial data (yr. ended 12/31/13): Assets, $1,768,881 (M); gifts received, $1,652,406; expenditures, $2,262,407; qualifying distributions, $2,246,054; giving activities include $1,000,130 for 10 grants (high: $283,465; low: $10,000).
Fields of interest: Children, services; International affairs, volunteer services; International relief; International human rights.
Limitations: Applications not accepted. Giving primarily in Washington, DC, and MO; some funding internationally. No grants to individuals.
Application information: Contributes only to pre-selected organizations.
Officers and Directors:* Brad Pitt,* Co-Pres. and Secy.; Angelina Jolie,* Co-Pres.; Terry Bird, V.P.; Warren Grant, V.P.
EIN: 205176706
Selected grants: The following grants are a representative sample of this grantmaker's funding activity:
$566,000 to Global Health Committee, Boston, MA, 2012. For Zahara Center in Addis, Ethiopia.
$200,000 to Drury University, Springfield, MO, 2012. For O'Reilly Family Event Center.
$117,000 to Global Health Committee, Boston, MA, 2012. For the Zahara Center in Addis, Ethiopia.
$2,500 to Mount Sinai Hospital, New York, NY, 2012. For Tisch Cancer Institute.

1792
Oluv C. Joynor Foundation Inc. ✧ ☆
601 Delaware Ave.
Wilmington, DE 19801 (302) 778-5412
Contact: Kathleen Kinne

Foundation type: Independent foundation.
Financial data (yr. ended 11/30/13): Assets, $13,365,814 (M); expenditures, $724,344; qualifying distributions, $673,027; giving activities include $588,340 for 22 grants (high: $200,000; low: $1,000).
Fields of interest: Education; Recreation; Religion.
Limitations: Applications not accepted.
Application information: Unsolicited requests for funds not accepted.
Trustees: Deborah D. Evensen; Walter S. Evensen.
Board Members: Andrew Evensen; Daniel C. Evensen; Danielle M. Evensen; Jessica Evensen; Joan C. Evensen; Randolph E. Evensen; Katherine Kelly; Neil Kelly.
EIN: 453987964

1793
JP's Peace Love & Happiness Foundation ✧
c/o Foundation Source
501 Silverside Rd., Ste. 123
Wilmington, DE 19809-1377

Donors: John Paul Dejoria Family Trust; John Paul Dejoria; Making Good LLC.
Foundation type: Independent foundation.
Financial data (yr. ended 12/31/13): Assets, $10,986,706 (M); gifts received, $13,402,825; expenditures, $3,506,551; qualifying distributions, $3,494,655; giving activities include $3,397,228 for 89 grants (high: $1,500,000; low: $30).
Fields of interest: Higher education; Animal welfare; Health care; Human services.
Limitations: Applications not accepted. Giving primarily in CA, KY, and TX.
Application information: Contributes only to pre-selected organizations.
Officers and Director:* John Paul DeJoria,* Pres.; Eloise Dejoria, V.P.; Constance Dykhuizen, Secy.-Treas. and Exec. Dir.
EIN: 274449810

1794
The Kendeda Fund ✧
c/o Foundation Source
501 Silverside Rd., Ste. 123
Wilmington, DE 19809-1377 (800) 839-1754

Donor: The March 23, 2006 Trust.
Foundation type: Independent foundation.
Financial data (yr. ended 12/31/13): Assets, $72,352,430 (M); gifts received, $40,987,000; expenditures, $29,058,737; qualifying distributions, $27,927,511; giving activities include $27,418,311 for 113 grants (high: $1,500,000; low: $5,000), and $2,374 for foundation-administered programs.
Fields of interest: Higher education; Environment, climate change/global warming; Environment; Animals/wildlife; Housing/shelter, development.
Limitations: Applications not accepted. Giving primarily in CA, Washington, DC, MA, MT, NY and VA.
Application information: Unsolicited requests for funds not accepted.
Trustee: Atlantic Trust Co., N.A.
EIN: 206881642
Selected grants: The following grants are a representative sample of this grantmaker's funding activity:
$5,000,000 to National Parks Conservation Association, Washington, DC, 2012. For general unrestricted support.
$1,450,000 to W G B H Educational Foundation, Boston, MA, 2012. For Green Media Discretionary Fund.

$1,410,000 to Blessed Earth, Lexington, KY, 2012. For General Unrestricted Support.
$1,000,000 to Earth Island Institute, Berkeley, CA, 2012. For Energy Action Coalition.
$1,000,000 to Green for All, Oakland, CA, 2012. For General Unrestricted Support.
$500,000 to Emerald Cities Collaborative, Washington, DC, 2012. For General Unrestricted Support.
$500,000 to Local Initiatives Support Corporation, New York, NY, 2012. For LISCs Green Development Center.
$400,000 to Pulitzer Center on Crisis Reporting, Washington, DC, 2012. For General Unrestricted Support.
$300,000 to Democracy Collaborative Foundation, Cleveland, OH, 2012. For General Unrestricted Support.
$125,000 to American Rivers, Washington, DC, 2012. For general operating support and Montana's Headwaters Campaign.

1795
The Khan Foundation, Inc. ✧
c/o Foundation Source
501 Silverside Rd., Ste. 123
Wilmington, DE 19809-1377

Established in DE.
Donors: Shahid Rafiq Khan; Ann Margaret Khan.
Foundation type: Independent foundation.
Financial data (yr. ended 12/31/13): Assets, $2,005,967 (M); gifts received, $500,000; expenditures, $1,168,635; qualifying distributions, $1,150,601; giving activities include $1,135,000 for 3 grants (high: $600,000; low: $35,000).
Fields of interest: Higher education; YM/YWCAs & YM/YWHAs.
Limitations: Applications not accepted. Giving primarily in IL. No grants to individuals.
Application information: Contributes only to pre-selected organizations.
Officers and Directors:* Ann Margaret Khan,* Pres. and Secy.; Anthony Rafiq Khan,* V.P.; Samina Khan, V.P.; Shahid Rafiq Khan,* V.P.; Shanna Noelle Khan, V.P.; Zakia Khan, V.P.
EIN: 200461026

1796
The Kirby Foundation ✧
c/o T. Pulsifer
1201 N. Market St., 18th Fl.
Wilmington, DE 19801-1147

Established in 2006 in CA.
Donors: Kirby Foundation; Robert G. Kirby†.
Foundation type: Independent foundation.
Financial data (yr. ended 12/31/13): Assets, $11,030,558 (M); expenditures, $620,551; qualifying distributions, $580,006; giving activities include $500,000 for 5 grants (high: $100,000; low: $100,000).
Fields of interest: Foundations (private grantmaking); Foundations (community).
Limitations: Applications not accepted. Giving primarily in CA, MA, MO, and OR. No grants to individuals.
Application information: Contributes only to pre-selected organizations.
Officers and Directors:* Lisa K. Gibbs, C.E.O.; Laurel Francis, Pres.; Kristin E. Kirby,* C.F.O.; Robin S. Kirby, Secy.; Scott D. Kirby.
EIN: 205146083

1797
David L. Klein, Jr. Foundation ✧
(formerly David L. Klein, Jr. Memorial Foundation, Inc.)
c/o Foundation Source
501 Silverside Rd., Ste. 123
Wilmington, DE 19809-1377
Contact: Janet E. Traub, Pres.; Stephanie Gillis, Fdn. Admin.
E-mail: kleinjr@blueprintrd.com

Incorporated in 1959 in NY.
Donors: David L. Klein†; Miriam Klein†; Saretta Barnet; Marjorie Traub; Barry Traub; Endo Laboratories, Inc.
Foundation type: Independent foundation.
Financial data (yr. ended 12/31/12): Assets, $6,702,240 (M); expenditures, $6,998,598; qualifying distributions, $6,964,753; giving activities include $6,903,488 for 35 grants (high: $6,513,988; low: $1,000).
Purpose and activities: Giving primarily for education and human services.
Fields of interest: Arts; Education; Health organizations, association; Human services; Foundations (community); Jewish agencies & synagogues.
Limitations: Applications not accepted. Giving primarily in the San Francisco Bay Area, CA, and New York, NY. No grants to individuals.
Application information: Contributes only to pre-selected organizations. Grants initiated by trustees.
Board meeting date(s): Annually in Nov.
Officers and Trustees:* Jane Barnet,* Pres.; Peter Barnet, Secy.; Howard Barnet, Jr.,* Treas.; Geoff Barnet; Saretta Barnet.
Number of staff: 1 part-time professional.
EIN: 136085432

1798
Jerry and Terri Kohl Family Foundation ✧
c/o Foundation Source
501 Silverside Rd., Ste. 123
Wilmington, DE 19809-1377

Established in 2007 in CA and DE.
Donors: Jerry Kohl; Terri Marilyn Kohl.
Foundation type: Independent foundation.
Financial data (yr. ended 12/31/12): Assets, $6,767,177 (M); expenditures, $1,108,845; qualifying distributions, $1,036,050; giving activities include $1,036,050 for grants.
Fields of interest: Arts; Education; Health care; Human services; Jewish agencies & synagogues.
Limitations: Applications not accepted. Giving primarily in CA; some emphasis on Los Angeles. No grants to individuals.
Application information: Contributes only to pre-selected organizations.
Officers and Directors:* Jerry Kohl,* Pres. and Secy.; Karyn Kohl, V.P.; Matthew Kohl, V.P.; Terri Marilyn Kohl,* Secy.-Treas.
EIN: 204757707

1799
La Vida Feliz Foundation ✧
c/o Foundation Source
501 Silverside Rd., Ste. 123
Wilmington, DE 19809-1377

Established in 2007 in NY.
Donor: Aaron Sosnick.
Foundation type: Independent foundation.
Financial data (yr. ended 12/31/12): Assets, $392,050,614 (M); gifts received, $30,000,000; expenditures, $16,873,342; qualifying distributions, $16,859,242; giving activities include $16,717,250 for 61 grants (high: $9,000,000; low: $250).
Fields of interest: Arts; Education; Philanthropy/voluntarism.
Limitations: Applications not accepted. Giving primarily in NY; some giving also in CA and MA. No grants to individuals.
Application information: Contributes only to pre-selected organizations.
Trustee: Aaron Sosnick.
EIN: 261622021
Selected grants: The following grants are a representative sample of this grantmaker's funding activity:
$9,190,000 to Fidelity Charitable Gift Fund, Boston, MA, 2011. For La Vida Feliz Fund.
$1,000,000 to Girls Club of New York, Lower East Side, New York, NY, 2010.
$1,000,000 to New York Landmarks Conservancy, New York, NY, 2011. For general support.
$1,000,000 to University of Southern California, Los Angeles, CA, 2011. For Math for America Los Angeles Program.
$900,000 to Coney Island, USA, Brooklyn, NY, 2011. For building purchase.
$500,000 to Electronic Frontier Foundation, San Francisco, CA, 2010.
$500,000 to Neighborhood Trust Financial Partners, New York, NY, 2010. For capital campaign.
$500,000 to Transportation Alternatives, New York, NY, 2010.
$500,000 to University of Southern California, Los Angeles, CA, 2010.
$250,000 to Greenwich Village Society for Historic Preservation, New York, NY, 2010.
$250,000 to Greenwich Village Society for Historic Preservation, New York, NY, 2011. For general support.
$200,000 to Historic Districts Council, New York, NY, 2011. For general support.
$200,000 to Math for America, New York, NY, 2011. For general support.
$200,000 to Robin Hood Foundation, New York, NY, 2010.
$200,000 to Robin Hood Foundation, New York, NY, 2011. For general support.
$150,000 to Fresh Youth Initiatives, New York, NY, 2010.
$150,000 to Los Angeles Conservancy, Los Angeles, CA, 2011. For general support.
$100,000 to Math for America, New York, NY, 2010.
$50,000 to Los Angeles County Bicycle Coalition, Los Angeles, CA, 2010.
$25,000 to Figment Project, New York, NY, 2011.

1800
Laffey-McHugh Foundation ✧
P.O. Box 2286
Wilmington, DE 19899-2286 (302) 654-1680
Contact: David Sysko
FAX: (302) 654-1681;
E-mail: laffeymchugh@gmail.com; E-mail for application requests: laffeymchugh@gmail.com; Fax: (302) 654-1681

Incorporated in 1959 in DE.
Donors: Alice L. McHugh†; Frank A. McHugh, Jr.†; Marie L. McHugh†.
Foundation type: Independent foundation.
Financial data (yr. ended 12/31/12): Assets, $59,981,791 (M); gifts received, $20,373; expenditures, $3,586,814; qualifying distributions, $2,991,088; giving activities include $2,811,600 for 124 grants (high: $175,000; low: $5,000).
Purpose and activities: Grants for Roman Catholic church support and church-related institutions, including schools, welfare agencies, religious associations, child welfare agencies, and a school for the handicapped; support also for a community fund, higher education, and hospitals.
Fields of interest: Elementary/secondary education; Secondary school/education; Higher education; Hospitals (general); Human services; Children/youth, services; United Ways and Federated Giving Programs; Catholic agencies & churches; Religion; Disabilities, people with.
Type of support: Annual campaigns; Building/renovation; Equipment; Land acquisition; Emergency funds; Seed money; Matching/challenge support.
Limitations: Giving primarily in DE. No grants to individuals, or for operating budgets, endowment funds, research, demonstration projects, publications, conferences, professorships, internships, consulting services, technical assistance, scholarships, or fellowships; no loans or program-related investments.
Application information: Application form required.
Initial approach: Letter or e-mail requesting application
Copies of proposal: 1
Deadline(s): Apr. and Oct.
Board meeting date(s): May and Nov.
Final notification: Shortly after board meeting
Officers and Directors:* Arthur G. Connolly, Jr.,* Pres.; Mary C. Braun,* V.P. and Secy.; Arthur G. Connolly III,* V.P. and Co-Treas.; Colins J. Seitz, Jr.,* V.P. and Co-Treas.; Dr. Christopher Connolly,* V.P.; Dr. Antoine Allen, Sr., V.P.; David Sysko, Exec. Dir.
EIN: 516015095

1801
Margaret Q. Landenberger Research Foundation ✧
919 N. Market St., Ste. 420
Wilmington, DE 19801-3014

Established around 1992 in FL.
Donor: Margaret Landenberger Trust.
Foundation type: Independent foundation.
Financial data (yr. ended 12/31/13): Assets, $19,467,368 (M); expenditures, $950,137; qualifying distributions, $785,517; giving activities include $733,583 for 6 grants (high: $200,000; low: $35,000).
Fields of interest: Higher education, university; Medical research, institute.
Type of support: Research.
Limitations: Applications not accepted. Giving primarily in CA, FL, MD, and PA. No grants to individuals.
Application information: Contributes only to pre-selected organizations.
Trustee: Brown Brothers Harriman Trust Co., N.A.
EIN: 650350358
Selected grants: The following grants are a representative sample of this grantmaker's funding activity:
$125,000 to University of Florida, Gainesville, FL, 2011.

1802
Richard S. and Karen Lefrak Charitable Foundation, Inc. ✧
c/o Lefrak Trust Co.
1007 N. Orange St., Ste. 210
Wilmington, DE 19801-1255

Established in 1989 in DE.
Donor: Richard S. Lefrak.
Foundation type: Independent foundation.
Financial data (yr. ended 11/30/12): Assets, $1,606,027 (M); gifts received, $3,000,000; expenditures, $3,630,115; qualifying distributions, $3,604,220; giving activities include $3,578,300 for 51 grants (high: $1,000,000; low: $100).
Purpose and activities: Giving primarily for the arts, education, health and human services.
Fields of interest: Performing arts, orchestras; Arts; Higher education; Hospitals (general); Health organizations, association; Human services.
Limitations: Applications not accepted. Giving primarily in New York, NY. No grants to individuals.
Application information: Contributes only to pre-selected organizations.
Officer: Deborah A. Dolan, Pres.
Director: Richard S. Lefrak.
EIN: 112994678
Selected grants: The following grants are a representative sample of this grantmaker's funding activity:
$150,000 to Prostate Cancer Foundation, Santa Monica, CA, 2011.
$20,000 to Prostate Cancer Foundation, Santa Monica, CA, 2011.

1803
The Samuel J. & Ethel LeFrak Charitable Foundation, Inc. ✧
1007 N. Orange St., Ste. 210
Wilmington, DE 19801-1255

Established in 1989 in DE.
Donor: Samuel J. LeFrak.
Foundation type: Independent foundation.
Financial data (yr. ended 11/30/13): Assets, $8,798,003 (M); expenditures, $2,629,446; qualifying distributions, $2,310,272; giving activities include $2,240,712 for 30 grants (high: $2,000,000; low: $150).
Fields of interest: Arts; Education; Hospitals (general); Human services.
Limitations: Applications not accepted. Giving primarily in NY. No grants to individuals.
Application information: Contributes only to pre-selected organizations.
Officer: Harrison T. Lefrak, Pres.
EIN: 112994768
Selected grants: The following grants are a representative sample of this grantmaker's funding activity:
$5,000 to Jewish National Fund, Rockville Centre, NY, 2011.

1804
Samuel J. and Ethel Lefrak Charitable Trust ✧
1007 N. Orange St., Ste. 210
Wilmington, DE 19801-1255

Established in DE.
Donors: Samuel J. Lefrak; Ethel Lefrak.
Foundation type: Independent foundation.
Financial data (yr. ended 12/31/12): Assets, $8,094,905 (M); expenditures, $1,064,630; qualifying distributions, $989,329; giving activities include $922,450 for 164 grants (high: $312,500; low: $60).
Fields of interest: Museums; Museums (art); Higher education; Education; Foundations (private grantmaking); Jewish agencies & synagogues.
Limitations: Applications not accepted. No grants to individuals.
Application information: Contributes only to pre-selected organizations.
Trustee: Harrison Lefrak.
EIN: 133378881
Selected grants: The following grants are a representative sample of this grantmaker's funding activity:
$10,000 to National Osteoporosis Foundation, Washington, DC, 2011.
$5,000 to New York City Police Museum, New York, NY, 2011.
$5,000 to United Cerebral Palsy of New York City, New York, NY, 2011.
$2,500 to National Osteoporosis Foundation, Washington, DC, 2011.
$1,500 to American Cancer Society, Atlanta, GA, 2011.
$1,500 to Epilepsy Foundation, Landover, MD, 2011.
$1,000 to Leukemia & Lymphoma Society, White Plains, NY, 2011.
$1,000 to National Osteoporosis Foundation, Washington, DC, 2011.
$1,000 to New York City Police Foundation, New York, NY, 2011.
$1,000 to Women for Women International, Washington, DC, 2011.

1805
Lennox Foundation ✧
c/o Foundation Source
501 Silverside Rd., Ste 123
Wilmington, DE 19809-1377
Mailing address: c/o David H. Anderson, Treas., 1114 State St., Ste. 200, Santa Barbara, CA 93101-2767, tel.: (805) 963-6503

Incorporated in 1951 in IA.
Donor: Lennox Industries, Inc.
Foundation type: Independent foundation.
Financial data (yr. ended 12/31/12): Assets, $36,425,518 (M); expenditures, $1,827,132; qualifying distributions, $1,729,439; giving

activities include $1,619,675 for 26 grants (high: $100,000; low: $7,000).
Purpose and activities: Grants primarily for land conservation, human services, education and health, within geographic areas of the family's involvement.
Fields of interest: Higher education; Education; Environment, land resources; Health care; Human services.
Type of support: General/operating support; Continuing support; Annual campaigns; Capital campaigns; Building/renovation; Equipment; Land acquisition; Program development; Matching/challenge support.
Limitations: Applications not accepted. Giving in the U.S., with some emphasis on MA and ME. No grants to individuals.
Application information: Unsolicited requests for funds not accepted.
Board meeting date(s): Mar. and Sept.
Officers and Trustees:* Jeff Norris,* Co-Chair.; Stefan Norris,* Co-Chair.; Karen Waeschle,* Co-Vice-Chair.; Frank Zink,* Co-Vice-Chair.; Beth A. Booth,* Co-Secy.; Amy Rattner,* Co-Secy.; Eron Malone,* Co-Treas.; Andrew Rattner,* Co-Treas.; Lyn Anderson; Sarah W. Carlan; Cathy Houlihan; Eileen Murphy.
EIN: 426053380
Selected grants: The following grants are a representative sample of this grantmaker's funding activity:
$100,000 to Preble Street, Portland, ME, 2012. For Lighthouse Shelter Replacement Project.
$81,500 to Clackamas Heritage Partners, Oregon City, OR, 2012. For End of the Oregon Trail Project and Site Revitalization Project.
$25,000 to Hospice of Southern Maine, Scarborough, ME, 2012. For Mobile Computer Technology Project.
$25,000 to Maine Association of Nonprofits, Portland, ME, 2012. For Maine Network Partners Fellowship Program for Practitioners.
$25,000 to Nature Conservancy, Arlington, VA, 2012. For Central U S Division - Staff Enrichment VI Project.
$25,000 to Santa Barbara Museum of Natural History, Santa Barbara, CA, 2012. For Quasars to Sea Stars Project.

1806
Longwood Foundation, Inc.

c/o Eleuthere I. du Pont
100 W. 10th St., Ste. 1109
Wilmington, DE 19801-1653 (302) 654-2477
Contact: Eleuthere I. du Pont, Pres.
E-mail: contactus@longwood.org; Main URL: http://www.longwoodfoundation.org

Incorporated in 1937 in DE.
Donor: Pierre S. du Pont†.
Foundation type: Independent foundation.
Financial data (yr. ended 09/30/13): Assets, $625,762,845 (M); expenditures, $34,801,218; qualifying distributions, $32,780,688; giving activities include $32,386,913 for 94 grants (high: $15,000,000; low: $2,500).
Purpose and activities: The mission is to be thoughtful stewards of Pierre S. dePont's legacy by being creative philanthropic leaders and by providing support to Longwood Gardens.
Fields of interest: Arts; Education; Environment; Health care; Housing/shelter; Human services.
Type of support: Seed money; General/operating support; Management development/capacity building; Capital campaigns; Building/renovation; Equipment; Land acquisition; Program development; Matching/challenge support.
Limitations: Applications accepted. Giving primarily in DE and southern Chester County, PA. No support for religious or political programs. No grants to individuals, or for special projects or events. Generally no grants for endowments and limited operating support.
Application information: The foundation accepts online applications only. Application form required.
Initial approach: Online
Copies of proposal: 1
Deadline(s): Mar. 15 and Sept. 15
Board meeting date(s): May and Nov.
Final notification: The following board meeting (approximately 60 days)
Officers and Trustees:* Charles T.L. Copeland,* Chair.; Eleuthere I. du Pont II,* Pres.; Dr. M. Lynn du Pont,* V.P.; C. Roderick Maroney,* Secy.; Eli R. Sharp,* Treas.; Gerret van S. Copeland; David L. Craven; Edward B. du Pont; Pierre S. du Pont IV.
Number of staff: 4 full-time professional; 1 part-time professional.
EIN: 510066734
Selected grants: The following grants are a representative sample of this grantmaker's funding activity:
$15,000,000 to Longwood Gardens, Kennett Square, PA, 2013.
$7,000,000 to Longwood Gardens, Kennett Square, PA, 2012.
$1,500,000 to Sussex Prepartory Academy, Lewes, DE, 2013.
$1,500,000 to Wilmington Friends School, Wilmington, DE, 2013.
$1,000,000 to Boy Scouts of America, Del-Mar-Va Council, Wilmington, DE, 2012.
$1,000,000 to Community Education Building, Wilmington, DE, 2013.
$1,000,000 to Community Education Building, Wilmington, DE, 2012.
$785,000 to Padua Academy, Wilmington, DE, 2012.
$750,000 to Ministry of Caring, Wilmington, DE, 2013.
$700,000 to Connections Community Support Programs, Wilmington, DE, 2012.
$500,000 to Light up the Queen Foundation, Wilmington, DE, 2013.
$250,000 to Kuumba Academy Charter School, Wilmington, DE, 2012.
$200,000 to Chester County Historical Society, West Chester, PA, 2013.
$200,000 to Conservation Fund, Mid-Atlantic Regional Office, Wilmington, DE, 2013.
$150,000 to Saint Elizabeth High School, Wilmington, DE, 2013.
$100,000 to Jewish Family Services of Delaware, Wilmington, DE, 2013.
$100,000 to Junior Achievement of Delaware, Wilmington, DE, 2012.
$100,000 to Kennett Township Land Trust, Kennett Square, PA, 2012.
$100,000 to West Rehoboth Community Land Trust, Rehoboth Beach, DE, 2012.
$92,250 to Modern Maturity Center, Dover, DE, 2012.

1807
The Lourie Foundation Inc. ✧

c/o Foundation Source
501 Silverside Rd., Ste. 123
Wilmington, DE 19809-1377

Established in 2006 in DE.
Donor: Robert Lourie.
Foundation type: Independent foundation.
Financial data (yr. ended 12/31/13): Assets, $7,479,037 (M); expenditures, $1,224,143; qualifying distributions, $1,070,607; giving activities include $1,038,000 for 8 grants (high: $500,000; low: $1,000).
Fields of interest: Higher education; Education; Medical research, institute.
Limitations: Applications not accepted. Giving primarily in CA and NY. No grants to individuals.
Application information: Contributes only to pre-selected organizations.
Officer and Director:* Robert Lourie,* Pres. and Secy.
EIN: 204000015

1808
Donald Lee and Sally Steadman Lucas Foundation ✧ ☆

c/o Foundation Source
501 Silverside Rd., Ste. 123
Wilmington, DE 19809-1377

Established in 2009 in DE.
Donors: Donald Lee Lucas; Sally Steadman Lucas.
Foundation type: Independent foundation.
Financial data (yr. ended 12/31/12): Assets, $8,202,687 (M); gifts received, $1,000,000; expenditures, $5,677,328; qualifying distributions, $5,673,677; giving activities include $5,629,500 for 11 grants (high: $5,000,000; low: $500).
Fields of interest: Arts; Higher education; Hospitals (general).
Limitations: Applications not accepted. Giving primarily in CA. No grants to individuals.
Application information: Contributes only to pre-selected organizations.
Officers and Directors:* Donald Lee Lucas,* Co-Pres. and Secy.; Sally Steadman Lucas,* Co-Pres.
EIN: 270167162

1809
Mackenzie Family Foundation ✧

c/o Foundation Source
501 Silverside Rd., Ste. 123
Wilmington, DE 19809-1377

Established in 2006 in CA.
Donors: Douglas Mackenzie; Shawn Mackenzie; Mackenzie Trust.
Foundation type: Independent foundation.
Financial data (yr. ended 12/31/13): Assets, $33,865,424 (M); gifts received, $4,388,362; expenditures, $1,364,112; qualifying distributions, $732,013; giving activities include $670,000 for 5 grants (high: $500,000; low: $20,000).
Fields of interest: Higher education; Human services.
Limitations: Applications not accepted. Giving primarily in CA and NC. No grants to individuals.
Application information: Contributes only to pre-selected organizations.

Officers and Directors:* Douglas Mackenzie,* Pres.; Shawn Mackenzie,* Secy.
EIN: 205700615

1810
The Thomas & Sarah MacMahon Family Charitable Foundation ✧
c/o Foundation Source
501 Silverside Rd., Ste. 123
Wilmington, DE 19809-1377

Established in 2003 in NJ.
Donors: Thomas P. MacMahon; Sarah MacMahon.
Foundation type: Independent foundation.
Financial data (yr. ended 12/31/13): Assets, $6,960,771 (M); gifts received, $755,114; expenditures, $612,118; qualifying distributions, $552,588; giving activities include $523,000 for 15 grants (high: $444,500; low: $500).
Fields of interest: Secondary school/education; Higher education, college; Higher education, university.
Limitations: Applications not accepted. Giving primarily in NC and NJ. No grants to individuals.
Application information: Contributes only to pre-selected organizations.
Trustees: Kelly MacMahon Ewing; Lauren Colleen Hand; Sarah MacMahon; Thomas P. MacMahon.
EIN: 056141146
Selected grants: The following grants are a representative sample of this grantmaker's funding activity:
$1,000 to American Cancer Society, Cedar Knolls, NJ, 2012. For Making Strides Program.

1811
The Mancheski Foundation Inc. ✧
c/o Foundation Source
501 Silverside Rd., Ste. 123
Wilmington, DE 19809-1377

Established in 2006 in DE and NV.
Donors: Fred Mancheski; Judith Mancheski; GAMCO Investors.
Foundation type: Independent foundation.
Financial data (yr. ended 11/30/13): Assets, $30,094,592 (M); gifts received, $2,546,809; expenditures, $749,924; qualifying distributions, $746,080; giving activities include $685,000 for 13 grants (high: $10,000; low: $10,000).
Fields of interest: Higher education; United Ways and Federated Giving Programs.
Limitations: Applications not accepted. Giving primarily in CT. No grants to individuals.
Application information: Unsolicited requests for funds not accepted.
Officers and Directors:* Fred Mancheski,* Chair.; Philip M. Halpern,* Pres.; Judith Mancheski,* Secy. and Treas.
EIN: 205810736

1812
Robert and Lisa Margolis Family Foundation ✧
Orange St. 1414, The Nemours Bldg.-1007 N
Wilmington, DE 19810-1242

Established in 2005 in CA.
Donors: Robert J. Margolis, M.D.; Lisa Margolis; The Robert Margolis Trust; The Lisa Margolis Trust.
Foundation type: Independent foundation.
Financial data (yr. ended 12/31/12): Assets, $66,912,337 (M); gifts received, $50,000,000; expenditures, $643,069; qualifying distributions, $640,500; giving activities include $640,500 for 5 grants (high: $615,000; low: $500).
Fields of interest: Education; Health care; Religion.
Limitations: Applications not accepted. Giving primarily in Los Angeles, CA. No grants to individuals.
Application information: Unsolicited requests for funds not accepted.
Officer: Robert J. Margolis, M.D., C.E.O. and Pres.
EIN: 203951826

1813
Carl Marks Foundation, Inc. ✧
c/o Foundation Source
501 Silverside Rd., Ste. 123
Wilmington, DE 19809-1377

Established in 1986 in NY.
Donors: Mark Claster; Susan Claster; Andrew M. Boas; and members of the Boas family.
Foundation type: Independent foundation.
Financial data (yr. ended 06/30/13): Assets, $23,549,208 (M); gifts received, $251; expenditures, $3,061,336; qualifying distributions, $3,048,793; giving activities include $2,839,139 for 169 grants (high: $250,000; low: $90).
Fields of interest: Higher education; Health organizations; Human services; Jewish federated giving programs; Jewish agencies & synagogues.
Type of support: General/operating support.
Limitations: Applications not accepted. Giving primarily in New York, NY; some funding also in CT and South Korea.
Application information: Unsolicited requests for funds not accepted.
Officers and Directors:* Marjorie Boas-Levins,* Chair.; Andrew M. Boas,* Co-Pres.; Mark Claster,* Co-Pres.; Rick Boas,* V.P.; Susan B. Claster,* V.P.; Carol L. Boas, Secy.; Carol A. Boas, Treas.
EIN: 136169215
Selected grants: The following grants are a representative sample of this grantmaker's funding activity:
$342,036 to Korean National Council of Women, Seoul, South Korea, 2011.
$50,000 to Fiver Children's Foundation, New York, NY, 2011.

1814
The Marmot Foundation ✧
c/o Wilmington Trust Co.
1100 N. Market St., DE3-C070
Wilmington, DE 19890-0900
Contact: Willis H. duPont, Chair. (for FL Organizations)

Established in 1968 in DE.
Donor: Margaret F. duPont Trust.
Foundation type: Independent foundation.
Financial data (yr. ended 12/31/13): Assets, $28,345,701 (M); expenditures, $1,516,377; qualifying distributions, $1,290,000; giving activities include $1,290,000 for 82 grants (high: $75,000; low: $2,000).
Purpose and activities: Support for hospitals, health, higher and secondary education, (including libraries), community funds, cultural programs, (including museums), youth agencies, social services, literacy programs, and environmental and ecological organizations.
Fields of interest: Museums; Arts; Secondary school/education; Higher education; Adult education—literacy, basic skills & GED; Libraries/library science; Education, reading; Environment, natural resources; Environment; Hospitals (general); Reproductive health, family planning; Health care; Health organizations, association; Housing/shelter, development; Human services; Children/youth, services; Residential/custodial care, hospices; Homeless.
Type of support: Capital campaigns; Building/renovation; Equipment; Land acquisition; Research; Matching/challenge support.
Limitations: Giving primarily in DE and FL. No support for political or religious organizations. No grants to individuals, or for operating budgets, endowments or scholarships; no loans.
Publications: Application guidelines.
Application information: Application form not required.
Initial approach: Letter
Copies of proposal: 1
Deadline(s): Apr. 30 and Oct. 31 for DE, and Oct. 31 for FL
Board meeting date(s): Late May and late Nov. in DE and late Nov. in FL.
Final notification: 2 weeks after board meeting
Officers: Willis H. duPont,* Chair.; Charles F. Gummey, Jr., Secy.
Trustees: Lammot J. duPont; Miren Dea duPont; Miren duPont Sanchez.
Number of staff: 1 part-time professional; 1 part-time support.
EIN: 516022487
Selected grants: The following grants are a representative sample of this grantmaker's funding activity:
$20,000 to Mayo Foundation, Rochester, MN, 2011.
$20,000 to University of Delaware, Newark, DE, 2011.
$5,000 to 1000 Friends of Florida, Tallahassee, FL, 2011.
$5,000 to 1103 Market Street Foundation, Wilmington, DE, 2011.
$5,000 to United Negro College Fund, Fairfax, VA, 2011.
$3,000 to Foundation Center, New York, NY, 2011.

1815
Charles A. Mastronardi Foundation ✧
(formerly The Charles A. Mastronardi Charitable Foundation)
c/o Wilmington Trust Co.
1100 N. Market St., Ste. 612230
Wilmington, DE 19890-0900
Contact: Frazier Rice
Contact telephone: (212) 415-0557

Established in 1964 in NY.
Donor: Charles A. Mastronardi†.
Foundation type: Independent foundation.
Financial data (yr. ended 12/31/13): Assets, $20,068,065 (M); expenditures, $1,247,441; qualifying distributions, $1,131,412; giving activities include $1,065,000 for 76 grants (high: $144,500; low: $1,000).
Purpose and activities: Giving primarily for hospitals and children's services; funding also for higher education and human services.

Fields of interest: Secondary school/education; Higher education; Hospitals (general); Health organizations, association; Human services; Children, services; Child development, services; Catholic agencies & churches.
Type of support: General/operating support; Continuing support; Capital campaigns; Equipment; Seed money; Research.
Limitations: Applications accepted. Giving primarily in NY. No grants to individuals.
Application information: Application form not required.
Initial approach: Proposal
Deadline(s): None
Officers: Margaret Mastronardi, V.P.; Nicholas D. Mastronardi, V.P.; Val Mastronardi, V.P.; Ronald L. Nurnberg, Esq., V.P.; Bernadette Traub, V.P.; Mary Turino, V.P.; William Turino, V.P.
EIN: 136167916

1816
The Edward E. & Marie L. Matthews Foundation ✧

c/o Foundation Source
501 Silverside Rd., Ste. 123
Wilmington, DE 19809-1377

Established in 2003 in NY and DE.
Donors: Edward E. Matthews; Marie L. Matthews.
Foundation type: Independent foundation.
Financial data (yr. ended 12/31/13): Assets, $16,458,909 (M); expenditures, $1,007,634; qualifying distributions, $872,954; giving activities include $800,000 for 51 grants (high: $400,000; low: $250).
Fields of interest: Elementary/secondary education; Higher education; Education; Health care; Human services.
Type of support: General/operating support; Capital campaigns; Building/renovation; Program development; Scholarship funds; Research.
Limitations: Applications not accepted. Giving primarily in NJ and NY; funding also in CA and IL. No grants to individuals.
Application information: Contributes only to pre-selected organizations.
Officers and Directors:* Edward E. Matthews,* Pres.; Douglas L. Matthews,* Secy.; Louise M. Flickinger; Gregory E. Matthews; Russell E. Matthews.
EIN: 020656117

1817
J. M. McDonald Foundation Inc. ✧

c/o Foundation Source
501 Silverside Rd., Ste. 123
Wilmington, DE 19809-1377 (800) 839-1754

Incorporated in 1952 in NE.
Donor: James M. McDonald, Sr.†.
Foundation type: Independent foundation.
Financial data (yr. ended 12/31/13): Assets, $25,214,014 (M); expenditures, $1,284,241; qualifying distributions, $1,145,412; giving activities include $1,095,000 for 91 grants (high: $80,000; low: $2,000).
Purpose and activities: Grants for the aged, orphans, and children who are sick, infirm, blind, or crippled; support for youth and child care in an effort to combat juvenile delinquency and to aid underprivileged, mentally or physically handicapped children. Other interests include health and hospitals and education, especially higher education. The foundation prefers to fund capital projects.
Fields of interest: Higher education; Education; Hospitals (general); Health care; Crime/law enforcement; Human services; Children/youth, services; Aging, centers/services; Aging; Disabilities, people with.
Type of support: General/operating support; Continuing support; Annual campaigns; Capital campaigns; Building/renovation; Equipment.
Limitations: Applications not accepted. Giving primarily in upstate NY. No grants to individuals, or for seminars, workshops, endowment funds, fellowships, travel, exhibits, or conferences; no loans.
Application information: Contributes only to pre-selected organizations.
Board meeting date(s): May and Oct.
Officers and Trustees:* Donald R. McJunkin,* Pres.; Janet E. Stanton,* V.P. and Secy.; Nancy J. Palmer,* V.P.; Donald C. Berry, Jr.,* Treas.; Dana Amundson; Pamela Criswell; Scott Michael Palmer.
EIN: 471431059
Selected grants: The following grants are a representative sample of this grantmaker's funding activity:
$150,000 to Northwood School, Lake Placid, NY, 2011.
$50,000 to Cazenovia College, Cazenovia, NY, 2011.
$36,000 to Cortland Repertory Theater, Cortland, NY, 2011.
$25,000 to Natural History Museum of the Adirondacks, Tupper Lake, NY, 2011.
$15,000 to Olmsted Center for Sight, Buffalo, NY, 2011.
$15,000 to Rosamond Gifford Zoo at Burnet Park, Friends of the, Syracuse, NY, 2010.
$10,000 to Stepping Stones Learning Center, Rochester, NY, 2011.
$5,000 to Columbia-Greene Hospital Foundation, Hudson, NY, 2011.
$5,000 to Hospice and Palliative Care of Saint Lawrence Valley, Potsdam, NY, 2011.
$5,000 to Mercy Flight Central, Canandaigua, NY, 2011.
$5,000 to Musical Theater Festival, Auburn, NY, 2011.

1818
Frank McHugh-O'Donovan Foundation, Inc. ✧

c/o Foundation Source
501 Silverside Rd., Ste. 123
Wilmington, DE 19809-1377

Established in 2004 in CT.
Donor: Christine O'Donovan Trust A '86.
Foundation type: Independent foundation.
Financial data (yr. ended 12/31/12): Assets, $53,614,553 (M); gifts received, $3,185,449; expenditures, $2,235,302; qualifying distributions, $2,015,709; giving activities include $1,724,456 for 15 grants (high: $1,000,000; low: $10,000).
Fields of interest: Higher education; Education.
Limitations: Applications not accepted. Giving primarily in CA, with emphasis on Los Angeles. No grants to individuals.
Application information: Contributes only to pre-selected organizations.
Officers and Directors:* Frank McHugh,* C.E.O.; Richard Riordan,* V.P.; Theresa McHugh,* Secy. and C.F.O.; Katherine Cadiente; Loree A. Vincent; Oscar Zaldana.
EIN: 200842449

1819
The Memton Fund, Inc. ✧ ☆

c/o Foundation Source
501 Silverside Rd., Ste. 123
Wilmington, DE 19809-1377
Contact: Barrie White, Pres.

Incorporated in 1936 in NY.
Donors: Albert G. Milbank†; Charles M. Cauldwell†.
Foundation type: Independent foundation.
Financial data (yr. ended 12/31/13): Assets, $13,058,122 (M); expenditures, $673,085; qualifying distributions, $565,937; giving activities include $486,850 for 11 grants (high: $125,000; low: $500).
Fields of interest: Museums; Performing arts; Historic preservation/historical societies; Arts; Adult education—literacy, basic skills & GED; Libraries/library science; Education; Environment, natural resources; Environment; Animal welfare; Animals/wildlife; Health care; AIDS; Youth development, citizenship; Human services; Children/youth, services; Family services; Science; Public affairs, citizen participation.
Type of support: General/operating support; Continuing support; Annual campaigns; Capital campaigns; Building/renovation; Endowments; Program development; Curriculum development; Internship funds; Scholarship funds.
Limitations: Applications not accepted. Giving limited to the U.S. and U.S. Pacific Islands. No support for religious or political organizations. No grants to individuals.
Application information: Unsolicited requests for funds not accepted.
Board meeting date(s): Apr. and the fall
Officers and Directors:* Barrie M. White,* Pres.; Elenita M. Drumwright,* V.P.; Lillian I. Daniels,* Secy. and Exec. Dir.; Elizabeth Shepard Farrar,* Treas.; Elizabeth R.M. Drumwright; Robert V. Edgar; Alexandra Giordano; Ellen White Levy; Michelle Milbank; Samuel L. Milbank; Thomas L. Milbank; Debbie Piccone; Barrie M. White; Pamela White.
Number of staff: 1 full-time professional; 1 part-time support.
EIN: 136096608
Selected grants: The following grants are a representative sample of this grantmaker's funding activity:
$10,000 to Kingsborough Community College Foundation, Brooklyn, NY, 2012. For Physical Therapy Assistant Scholarship Fund.
$4,000 to Barnard College, New York, NY, 2012. For Student Courses at ICP.
$3,000 to Nature Conservancy, Arlington, VA, 2012. For Palau Conservation Society.
$2,500 to Natural History Museum of the Adirondacks, Tupper Lake, NY, 2012. For educational outreach program.
$2,000 to Pacific Islanders in Communications, Honolulu, HI, 2012. For Outreach Program to Guam, Saipan, Tinian and Rota.
$1,500 to Colorado College, Colorado Springs, CO, 2012. For Low Income Scholarship Fund.
$1,250 to Brearley School, New York, NY, 2012. For Class of '55 Annual Fund.

$1,000 to Stanford University, Stanford, CA, 2012. For School of Humanities.
$1,000 to Vassar College, Poughkeepsie, NY, 2012. For Alumnae Fund.
$500 to Brooks School, North Andover, MA, 2012. For Alumni Class of 1959 Fund.

1820
Daniel and Janet Mordecai Foundation ✧
c/o Foundation Source
501 Silverside Rd., Ste. 123
Wilmington, DE 19809-1377

Established in 2003 in CO.
Donor: Janet Mordecai.
Foundation type: Independent foundation.
Financial data (yr. ended 12/31/13): Assets, $7,813,129 (M); expenditures, $738,865; qualifying distributions, $666,688; giving activities include $642,500 for 29 grants (high: $125,000; low: $500).
Purpose and activities: Giving primarily for the arts, education, and youth organizations, including a children's garden project.
Fields of interest: Arts; Higher education; Education; Botanical gardens; Boys & girls clubs; Human services.
Limitations: Applications not accepted. Giving primarily in CO. No grants to individuals.
Application information: Contributes only to pre-selected organizations.
Officer and Director:* Janet Mordecai,* Pres. and Secy.-Treas.
EIN: 200185059
Selected grants: The following grants are a representative sample of this grantmaker's funding activity:
$120,000 to Denver Scholarship Foundation, Denver, CO, 2012. For Mordecai Transfer and Completion Grant.
$100,000 to National Alopecia Areata Foundation, San Rafael, CA, 2012. For Alopecia Ariata Treatment Development.
$5,000 to Anti-Defamation League of Bnai Brith, Denver, CO, 2012. For No Place for Hate Program.

1821
Mount Cuba Center, Inc. ✧
3120 Barley Mill Rd.
Hockessin, DE 19707-9579 (302) 239-4244
FAX: (302) 239-5366;
E-mail: info@mtcubacenter.org; Main URL: http://www.mtcubacenter.org
Facebook: http://www.facebook.com/MtCubaCenter
YouTube: http://www.youtube.com/user/MtCubaCenter

Incorporated in 1953 in DE.
Donor: Lammot duPont Copeland.
Foundation type: Independent foundation.
Financial data (yr. ended 12/31/12): Assets, $309,651,485 (M); gifts received, $50; expenditures, $17,137,491; qualifying distributions, $16,623,004; giving activities include $10,906,335 for 8 grants (high: $10,000,000; low: $600).
Purpose and activities: Giving primarily to foster an appreciation for plants of the Appalachian Piedmont and the conservation of their environment through garden display, education, and research.
Fields of interest: Environment, public education; Environment, plant conservation.
Limitations: Applications not accepted. Giving limited to Wilmington, DE, and its 50-mile radius. No grants to individuals.
Application information: Contributes only to pre-selected organizations.
Officers: Ann C. Rose, Pres.; Rick J. Lewandowski, Exec. Dir.
Directors: Mrs. James C. Biddle; Charles L. Copeland; Gerret van S. Copeland; Lammot duPont Copeland; Louisa C. Duemling; Marilyn Hayward; Blaine T. Phillips; Mrs. William M.W. Sharp; David D. Shields.
EIN: 516001265
Selected grants: The following grants are a representative sample of this grantmaker's funding activity:
$10,000,000 to Conservation Fund, Arlington, VA, 2012. To purchase land.
$672,235 to Brandywine Conservancy, Chadds Ford, PA, 2012. To purchase land.
$200,000 to Flora of North America Association, Point Arena, CA, 2012.
$24,000 to Delaware Nature Society, Hockessin, DE, 2012.

1822
Natembea Foundation ✧ ☆
c/o Foundation Source
501 Silverside Rd., Ste. 123
Wilmington, DE 19809-1377

Established in 2005 in DE.
Donors: Devon Wiel Cohn; David A. Cohn; David A. & Devon W. Cohn Living Trust.
Foundation type: Independent foundation.
Financial data (yr. ended 12/31/13): Assets, $6,154,200 (M); gifts received, $116,340; expenditures, $1,198,733; qualifying distributions, $1,144,167; giving activities include $1,082,750 for 17 grants (high: $1,000,000; low: $500).
Fields of interest: Higher education, university; Environment, forests; Medical research; United Ways and Federated Giving Programs; Jewish federated giving programs; Jewish agencies & synagogues.
Limitations: Applications not accepted. Giving primarily in CA. No grants to individuals.
Application information: Unsolicited requests for funds not accepted.
Officers and Director:* Devon Wiel Cohn,* Pres. and Secy.; David A. Cohn, V.P.
EIN: 203448030

1823
Neda Nobari Foundation ✧ ☆
(formerly The Neda Foundation)
c/o Foundation Source
501 Silverside Rd., Ste. 123
Wilmington, DE 19809-1377

Established in 2007 in CA and DE.
Donors: Neda Mashouf; Neda Nobari.
Foundation type: Independent foundation.
Financial data (yr. ended 12/31/13): Assets, $13,022,879 (M); expenditures, $708,960; qualifying distributions, $670,194; giving activities include $628,000 for 44 grants (high: $50,000; low: $5,000).
Fields of interest: Arts; Education; Human services.
Limitations: Applications not accepted. Giving primarily in CA; funding also in MA, NH, NY and VT. No grants to individuals.
Application information: Unsolicited requests for funds not accepted.
Officer and Director:* Neda Nobari,* Pres. and Secy.
EIN: 208104037

1824
Nor'Easter Foundation ✧
P.O. Box 3568
Greenville, DE 19807-0568

Established in 1993 in DE.
Donor: Henry B. du Pont IV.
Foundation type: Independent foundation.
Financial data (yr. ended 12/31/13): Assets, $12,702,418 (M); expenditures, $531,834; qualifying distributions, $529,188; giving activities include $522,500 for 33 grants (high: $100,000; low: $1,000).
Fields of interest: Museums (specialized); Libraries (special); Environment.
Limitations: Applications not accepted. Giving primarily in DE. No grants to individuals.
Application information: Contributes only to pre-selected organizations.
Trustee: Henry B. duPont IV.
EIN: 510350173
Selected grants: The following grants are a representative sample of this grantmaker's funding activity:
$25,000 to University of Delaware, Newark, DE, 2012. For Men's Crew Shell Fund.
$10,000 to Delaware Nature Society, Hockessin, DE, 2012. For Red Clay Scenic ByWay.
$5,000 to Delaware Nature Society, Hockessin, DE, 2012. For Michael E. Riska Endowment.
$5,000 to Discovery Museum, Bridgeport, CT, 2012. For Bickmeier Fund.
$5,000 to Light up the Queen Foundation, Wilmington, DE, 2012. To build Community through Music.
$5,000 to University of Delaware, Newark, DE, 2012. For Men's Rowing Club.
$1,000 to Delaware Wild Lands, Odessa, DE, 2012. For land management/restoration.
$1,000 to Historic Red Clay Valley, Wilmington, DE, 2012. For Wilmington Western RR.

1825
Oak Tree Foundation of Colorado ✧
(doing business as Oak Tree Foundation)
c/o Foundation Source
501 Silverside Rd., Ste. 123
Wilmington, DE 19809-1377

Established in 2006 in DE.
Donors: Margaret Sue Allon; Harvey Allon; Jewish Community Fdn. of CO.
Foundation type: Independent foundation.
Financial data (yr. ended 12/31/13): Assets, $176,691 (M); gifts received, $483,050; expenditures, $536,061; qualifying distributions, $534,225; giving activities include $486,800 for 35 grants (high: $170,000; low: $150).
Fields of interest: Education; Jewish agencies & synagogues.
Limitations: Applications not accepted. Giving primarily in CO. No grants to individuals.

Application information: Contributes only to pre-selected organizations.
Officers and Directors:* Margaret Sue Allon,* Pres. and Secy.; Harvey Allon,* V.P.
EIN: 205429063

1826
William C. & Joyce C. O'Neil Charitable Trust ✧
200 Bellevue Parkway., Ste. 525
Wilmington, DE 19809
Application address: Hollis F. Russell C/o Ackermann, Levine, Cullen, Brickman & Limmer, LLP, 1010 Northern Blvd., Great Neck, NY 11021

Established in 1993.
Donors: Joyce C. O'Neil; Joyce C. O'neil 1994 Trust.
Foundation type: Independent foundation.
Financial data (yr. ended 12/31/13): Assets, $15,407,252 (M); expenditures, $747,284; qualifying distributions, $660,376; giving activities include $543,686 for 57 grants (high: $121,686; low: $1,000).
Fields of interest: Higher education, university; Medical school/education; Education; Hospitals (general); Human services; Catholic agencies & churches.
Type of support: Scholarship funds.
Limitations: Applications accepted. Giving primarily in NY. No grants to individuals.
Application information: Application form not required.
Initial approach: Proposal
Deadline(s): None
Trustees: John Crabill, Esq.; Hollis Russell, Esq.; JPMorgan Chase Bank, N.A.
EIN: 656110806
Selected grants: The following grants are a representative sample of this grantmaker's funding activity:
$1,000 to Cornell University, Law School, Ithaca, NY, 2012. For program support.

1827
Orr Family Foundation ✧ ☆
c/o Foundation Source
501 Silverside Rd., Ste. 123
Wilmington, DE 19809-1377

Donor: Dominic P. Orr.
Foundation type: Independent foundation.
Financial data (yr. ended 12/31/13): Assets, $1,525,430 (M); expenditures, $849,584; qualifying distributions, $848,884; giving activities include $837,494 for 18 grants (high: $300,000; low: $500).
Fields of interest: Environment; Housing/shelter; Community/economic development.
Limitations: Applications not accepted. Giving primarily in CA, Washington, DC and New York, NY.
Application information: Unsolicited requests for funds not accepted.
Officers and Director:* Dominic P. Orr,* Pres. and Secy.; Adria Cee-Wing Orr, V.P.; Alvin Cee-Yeong Orr, V.P.
EIN: 261622217

1828
Ortega Charitable Foundation ✧
c/o Foundation Source
501 Silverside Rd., Ste. 123
Wilmington, DE 19809-1377

Established in 1988 in FL.
Donors: Jose A. Ortega†; Maria Elena Wollberg.
Foundation type: Independent foundation.
Financial data (yr. ended 12/31/12): Assets, $39,809,973 (M); gifts received, $8,431,622; expenditures, $1,046,927; qualifying distributions, $763,523; giving activities include $725,750 for 23 grants (high: $200,000; low: $250).
Fields of interest: Education; Hospitals (general); Cancer; United Ways and Federated Giving Programs; Minorities.
Type of support: General/operating support; Scholarship funds; Scholarships—to individuals.
Limitations: Applications not accepted. Giving primarily in FL; some giving in PR.
Application information: Unsolicited requests for funds not accepted.
Trustee: Maria Elena Wollberg.
EIN: 650014714
Selected grants: The following grants are a representative sample of this grantmaker's funding activity:
$180,000 to Liga Contra El Cancer, Miami, FL, 2011.
$5,000 to Camillus House, Miami, FL, 2011.
$5,000 to Epiphany Church, Miami, FL, 2011.
$5,000 to Handi-Crafters, Thorndale, PA, 2011.
$5,000 to Regis House, Miami, FL, 2011.
$5,000 to Saint Jude Childrens Research Hospital, Memphis, TN, 2011.
$5,000 to Smile Train, New York, NY, 2011.

1829
The Mary E. Parker Foundation ✧
c/o Wilmington Trust Co.
1100 N. Market St.
Wilmington, DE 19890-0900
Application address: Budd Parent, c/o CPA Associates, 1301 6th Ave. W., Ste. 600, Bradenton, FL 34205

Established in 1986 in FL.
Donor: Mary E. Parker.
Foundation type: Independent foundation.
Financial data (yr. ended 12/31/13): Assets, $19,372,559 (M); expenditures, $865,362; qualifying distributions, $815,852; giving activities include $776,909 for 80 grants (high: $200,000; low: $1,000).
Purpose and activities: Giving for the arts, higher education, youth and social services, community funds, and animal welfare.
Fields of interest: Museums; Arts; Higher education; Animal welfare; Human services; Children/youth, services; United Ways and Federated Giving Programs.
Type of support: General/operating support; Endowments.
Limitations: Applications accepted. Giving primarily in FL.
Publications: Informational brochure (including application guidelines).
Application information: Application form required.
Initial approach: Letter
Deadline(s): Nov. 15
Board meeting date(s): Dec.
Trustee: Mary E. Parker.
Adviser: Robert G. Blalock.
EIN: 592708325
Selected grants: The following grants are a representative sample of this grantmaker's funding activity:
$160,000 to South Florida Museum and Bishop Planetarium, Bradenton, FL, 2011.
$111,845 to South Florida Museum and Bishop Planetarium, Bradenton, FL, 2011.

1830
Steve and Diane Parrish Foundation ✧
c/o Foundation Source
501 Silverside Rd., Ste. 123
Wilmington, DE 19809-1377

Established in 2007 in CT.
Donors: Steven C. Parrish; Diane S. Parrish.
Foundation type: Independent foundation.
Financial data (yr. ended 12/31/13): Assets, $2,827,652 (M); expenditures, $580,935; qualifying distributions, $548,020; giving activities include $525,500 for 12 grants (high: $215,000; low: $500).
Purpose and activities: Giving primarily for human services, particularly to an organization which offers support to victims of crime and abuse; funding also for the arts.
Fields of interest: Arts; Human services.
Limitations: Applications not accepted. Giving primarily in CT and NY.
Application information: Unsolicited requests for funds not accepted.
Officers and Trustees:* Diane S. Parrish,* Pres.; Steven C. Parrish,* V.P.; Amanda Parrish Morgan,* Recording Secy.; Clay Parrish,* Treas.; UBS Trust Co.
EIN: 261116145

1831
Patterson Family Foundation ✧
c/o Brandywine Trust Co.
7234 Lancaster Pike, Ste. 300-A
Hockessin, DE 19707-8743

Established in 1997 in CA.
Donor: Arthur C. Patterson.
Foundation type: Independent foundation.
Financial data (yr. ended 12/31/13): Assets, $11,727,296 (M); expenditures, $722,864; qualifying distributions, $583,130; giving activities include $541,000 for 30 grants (high: $100,000; low: $500).
Fields of interest: Elementary/secondary education; Higher education; Education; Human services.
Limitations: Applications not accepted. Giving primarily in CA; funding also in MA and ME.
Application information: Contributes only to pre-selected organizations.
Officers and Directors:* Arthur C. Patterson,* Chair. and Treas.; Louise M. Patterson,* Pres.; Hume R Steyer, Secy.
EIN: 943268717
Selected grants: The following grants are a representative sample of this grantmaker's funding activity:
$100,000 to Aspire Public Schools, Oakland, CA, 2012. For California Annual Fund.

$50,000 to Urban School of San Francisco, San Francisco, CA, 2012. For the Mark Salkind Scholarship Fund.
$25,000 to Katherine Branson School, Ross, CA, 2012. For Fund-A-Need Campaign.
$6,000 to Meritus College Fund, San Francisco, CA, 2012. For Meritus College Scholarship Fund.
$5,000 to San Francisco Film Society, San Francisco, CA, 2012. For general unrestricted.

1832
Jean T. and Heyward G. Pelham Foundation ✧
c/o Foundation Source
501 Silverside Rd., Ste. 123
Wilmington, DE 19809-1377

Established in 2006 in SC.
Donors: Heyward Gibbes Pelham Testamentary Charitable Lead Annuity Trust; Heyward Gibbes Pelham Testamentary.
Foundation type: Independent foundation.
Financial data (yr. ended 12/31/13): Assets, $15,258,701 (M); gifts received, $2,134,590; expenditures, $960,742; qualifying distributions, $930,613; giving activities include $883,500 for 34 grants (high: $100,000; low: $1,000).
Fields of interest: Higher education; Protestant agencies & churches.
Limitations: Applications not accepted. Giving primarily in NC and SC. No grants to individuals.
Application information: Contributes only to pre-selected organizations.
Officer: William H. Pelham, Chair.
Trustees: Ann P. Cullen; Richard T. Pelham.
EIN: 203291660

1833
The Kors Le Pere Foundation ✧ ☆
c/o The Rockefeller Trust Co.
1201 N. Market St., Ste. 1401
Wilmington, DE 19801-1163

Established in DE.
Donor: Michael Kors.
Foundation type: Independent foundation.
Financial data (yr. ended 12/31/12): Assets, $25,328,864 (M); gifts received, $5,063,025; expenditures, $890,350; qualifying distributions, $850,922; giving activities include $812,300 for 24 grants (high: $100,000; low: $5,000).
Fields of interest: Arts; Hospitals (general); Hospitals (specialty); Health care; Medical research, institute; Cancer research; Human services.
Limitations: Applications not accepted. Giving primarily in NY; funding also in Washington, DC.
Application information: Unsolicited requests for funds not accepted.
Officers: Michael Kors, Pres.; Lance Le Pere, Secy.-Treas.
EIN: 454035400

1834
The Pfeil Foundation Inc. ✧
c/o Foundation Source
501 Silverside Rd.
Wilmington, DE 19809-1377

Established in 2003 in DE.
Donors: David Pefil; Mindy K. Pfeil.
Foundation type: Independent foundation.
Financial data (yr. ended 12/31/12): Assets, $7,707,514 (M); gifts received, $680,000; expenditures, $860,144; qualifying distributions, $837,365; giving activities include $800,000 for 2 grants (high: $500,000; low: $300,000).
Fields of interest: Health care; Human services; Religion.
Limitations: Applications not accepted. Giving primarily in TX. No grants to individuals.
Application information: Contributes only to pre-selected organizations.
Officers and Directors:* Mindy K. Pfeil,* Pres. and Secy.; David Pfeil,* V.P.
EIN: 200495820

1835
The L. E. Phillips Family Foundation, Inc. ✧
1011 Centre Rd., Ste. 310
Wilmington, DE 19805-1266
Application address: c/o Maryjo Cohen, Pres., 3925 N. Hastings Way, Eau Claire, WI 54703, tel.: (715) 839-2139

Incorporated in 1943 in WI.
Donor: Members of the Phillips family and a family-related company.
Foundation type: Independent foundation.
Financial data (yr. ended 02/28/14): Assets, $112,422,014 (M); expenditures, $5,673,698; qualifying distributions, $5,573,829; giving activities include $5,558,125 for 108 grants (high: $3,538,000; low: $50).
Purpose and activities: Support primarily for a Jewish welfare fund; giving also for higher education, and human services.
Fields of interest: Arts; Higher education; Education; Health organizations, association; Human services; Jewish federated giving programs; Jewish agencies & synagogues.
Type of support: General/operating support; Building/renovation; Endowments; Program development; Scholarship funds; Research.
Limitations: Giving primarily in northwestern WI, with emphasis on Eau Claire and Chippewa County. No grants to individuals.
Application information:
Initial approach: Letter requesting application guidelines
Deadline(s): Jan. 1
Board meeting date(s): As required
Final notification: 1 month
Officers and Directors:* Maryjo Cohen,* Pres.; Randy F. Lieble,* V.P. and Treas.; Eileen Cohen,* V.P.; Vernon B. Haas,* Secy.; Amy Alpine.
Number of staff: 1 full-time professional; 2 part-time support.
EIN: 396046126
Selected grants: The following grants are a representative sample of this grantmaker's funding activity:
$2,000 to University of Minnesota Foundation, Minneapolis, MN, 2013. For Bee Fund.
$1,250 to University of Michigan, Ann Arbor, MI, 2013. For Martha Cook Building.
$500 to University of Michigan, Ann Arbor, MI, 2013. For business school.

1836
The Pincus Family Foundation ✧
c/o Foundation Source
501 Silverside Rd., Ste. 123
Wilmington, DE 19809-1377

Established in 2005.
Donors: David N. Pincus; Ellen Sargent Revocable Trust.
Foundation type: Independent foundation.
Financial data (yr. ended 12/31/12): Assets, $15,198,444 (M); gifts received, $7,600; expenditures, $1,183,986; qualifying distributions, $1,118,236; giving activities include $1,118,236 for 78 grants (high: $250,000; low: $250).
Fields of interest: Arts; Higher education; Education; Hospitals (general); Hospitals (specialty); Health organizations; Human services; Jewish agencies & synagogues.
Limitations: Applications not accepted. Giving primarily in NY and PA.
Application information: Contributes only to pre-selected organizations.
Trustees: Leslie Pincus Elliott; Andrew Epstein; Eric Epstein; George Hirschhorn; Stephen Nicholas; Geraldine Pincus.
EIN: 256874818
Selected grants: The following grants are a representative sample of this grantmaker's funding activity:
$50,000 to Pennsylvania State University, University Park, PA, 2012. For Penn State Hillel.
$4,500 to Association for Public Art, Philadelphia, PA, 2012. For Open Air Project.
$4,000 to Rhode Island School of Design, Providence, RI, 2012. For Museum of Art.
$1,000 to Moore College of Art and Design, Philadelphia, PA, 2012. For The Galleries at Moore.

1837
Planet Heritage Foundation, Inc. ✧
c/o Foundation Source
501 Silverside Rd., Ste. 123
Wilmington, DE 19809-1377

Established in 2008 in DE.
Donor: A. Fischer.
Foundation type: Independent foundation.
Financial data (yr. ended 12/31/13): Assets, $49,715,368 (M); expenditures, $2,542,947; qualifying distributions, $2,538,239; giving activities include $2,023,318 for 12 grants (high: $1,000,000; low: $2,500).
Fields of interest: Environment, natural resources; Human services.
Limitations: Applications not accepted. Giving primarily in CA, NY and VA. No grants to individuals.
Application information: Contributes only to pre-selected organizations.
Officers and Director:* A. Fischer,* Pres.; C. K. Mercer, V.P.
EIN: 263878866

1838
Prairie Creek Partners Charitable Foundation ✧ ☆
c/o Foundation Source
501 Silverside Rd., Ste. 123
Wilmington, DE 19809-1377

Established in 2007 in DE.

Donors: Alan K. Engstrom; Randall Robert Engstrom.
Foundation type: Independent foundation.
Financial data (yr. ended 12/31/12): Assets, $18,923,965 (M); gifts received, $20,834; expenditures, $1,044,939; qualifying distributions, $934,114; giving activities include $854,700 for 32 grants (high: $100,000; low: $1,000).
Fields of interest: Christian agencies & churches.
Limitations: Applications not accepted. Giving primarily in TX. No grants to individuals.
Application information: Unsolicited requests for funds not accepted.
Officers and Directors:* Randall Robert Engstrom,* Pres. and Secy.; Alan K. Engstrom,* V.P.; Alyson T. Engstrom,* V.P.; Randall Robert Engstrom, Jr., V.P.; Ellen Porter,* V.P.; Reid Porter,* V.P.
EIN: 260639084
Selected grants: The following grants are a representative sample of this grantmaker's funding activity:
$100,000 to Gladney Center for Adoption, Fort Worth, TX, 2012. For Brave Love Campaign.
$25,000 to Gladney Center for Adoption, Fort Worth, TX, 2012. For Brave Love Initiative.
$20,000 to Dallas Leadership Foundation, Dallas, TX, 2012. For Van Purchase for Ring of Hope Program.
$10,000 to Downtown Pregnancy Center, Dallas, TX, 2012. For Dallas Stork Bus Initiative.
$10,000 to Downtown Pregnancy Center, Dallas, TX, 2012. For Sonograms on Site.

1839
The Prentice Foundation, Inc. ✧
c/o Foundation Source
501 Silverside Rd., Ste. 123
Wilmington, DE 19809-1377

Established in 1994 in CT.
Donors: Elaine P. Hapgood; Jerry Babicka; Lynn P. Babicka; John P. Powers; Barbara Bohart Trust; James Bohart Trust.
Foundation type: Independent foundation.
Financial data (yr. ended 12/31/12): Assets, $16,732,865 (M); expenditures, $1,551,966; qualifying distributions, $1,313,478; giving activities include $1,226,775 for 149 grants (high: $52,500; low: $500).
Purpose and activities: Giving primarily for the environment, education, and social services.
Fields of interest: Education; Environment; Health care; Human services; Government/public administration.
Type of support: Program development; Seed money; Matching/challenge support.
Limitations: Applications not accepted. Giving primarily in CO, Washington, DC, NC, NJ, and NY. No grants to individuals, or for capital campaigns or endowments; no loans.
Application information: Contributes only to pre-selected organizations.
Board meeting date(s): Varies
Officers and Directors:* John Powers,* Pres.; Jerry Babicka,* V.P. and Secy.-Co-Treas.; Lynn P. Babicka,* V.P.; David L. Godfrey, Co-Treas.
EIN: 061386173

1840
The Presto Foundation ✧
1011 Centre Rd., Ste. 310
Wilmington, DE 19805-1267 (715) 839-2119
Contact: Joan Gehler
Application address: 3925 N. Hastings Way, Eau Claire, WI 54703, tel.: (715) 839-2119

Incorporated in 1952 in WI.
Donor: National Presto Industries, Inc.
Foundation type: Company-sponsored foundation.
Financial data (yr. ended 05/31/13): Assets, $20,614,108 (M); expenditures, $1,822,491; qualifying distributions, $1,627,600; giving activities include $1,287,580 for 83 grants (high: $264,000; low: $50), and $335,245 for 28 grants to individuals (high: $13,000; low: $2,897).
Purpose and activities: The foundation supports organizations involved with arts and culture, education, conservation, animals and wildlife, health, employment, recreation, human services, and religion.
Fields of interest: Arts; Higher education; Libraries (public); Education; Environment, natural resources; Animals/wildlife, preservation/protection; Hospitals (general); Health care, clinics/centers; Health care; Employment; Recreation; Boys & girls clubs; YM/YWCAs & YM/YWHAs; Youth, services; Human services; United Ways and Federated Giving Programs; Religion.
Type of support: General/operating support; Employee-related scholarships.
Limitations: Applications accepted. Giving primarily in northwestern WI, with emphasis on Chippewa Falls and Eau Claire counties.
Application information: Application form required.
Initial approach: Letter
Deadline(s): None
Officers and Trustees:* Maryjo R. Cohen,* Pres.; Lawrence J. Tienor,* V.P. and Treas.; Arthur Petzold,* V.P.; Libby Stupak,* Secy.; Eileen Phillips Cohen; Vernon B. Haas; Richard Myhers.
EIN: 396045769
Selected grants: The following grants are a representative sample of this grantmaker's funding activity:
$215,000 to Mayo Foundation, Rochester, MN, 2011.
$102,000 to University of Wisconsin, Eau Claire, WI, 2011.
$15,100 to United Way of the Greater Chippewa Valley, Eau Claire, WI, 2011.
$11,000 to Saint Johns University, Collegeville, MN, 2011.
$11,000 to Tulane University, New Orleans, LA, 2011.
$11,000 to University of Phoenix, Phoenix, AZ, 2011.
$11,000 to Vanderbilt University, Nashville, TN, 2011.
$10,450 to YMCA of Eau Claire, Eau Claire, WI, 2011.
$5,000 to Boys and Girls Club of Langlade County, Antigo, WI, 2011.
$3,500 to Long Island Head Injury Association, Hauppauge, NY, 2011.

1841
Julian Price Family Foundation ✧ ☆
500 Delaware Ave., Ste. 730
Wilmington, DE 19801-7407

Established in 1996 in NC.
Foundation type: Independent foundation.
Financial data (yr. ended 12/31/12): Assets, $8,474,856 (M); expenditures, $554,904; qualifying distributions, $465,000; giving activities include $465,000 for grants.
Purpose and activities: Giving primarily for environmental conservation programs, as well as for education, the arts, community development, and health and human services.
Fields of interest: Arts; Education; Human services.
Limitations: Applications not accepted. Giving primarily in NC. No grants to individuals.
Application information: Unsolicited requests for funds not accepted.
Trustees: Laura Deboisfeuillet Edwards; Melaine Ann Taylor; Mary Price Taylor Harrison; Charles Schwab Bank, N.A.; Charles Schwab Bank; Wells Fargo Bank, N.A.
EIN: 311665269

1842
Progress Charitable Foundation Delaware ✧
874 Walker Rd., Ste. C
Dover, DE 19904-2778

Established in DE.
Donor: Alvin Dworman.
Foundation type: Independent foundation.
Financial data (yr. ended 11/30/13): Assets, $2,252 (M); gifts received, $510,000; expenditures, $520,150; qualifying distributions, $520,000; giving activities include $520,000 for 3 grants (high: $500,000; low: $10,000).
Purpose and activities: Giving primarily for a medical center in Israel; some funding for education.
Fields of interest: Higher education; Hospitals (general).
Limitations: Applications not accepted. Giving primarily in Tel Hashomer, Israel; some funding in the U.S. No grants to individuals.
Application information: Unsolicited requests for funds not accepted.
Directors: Alan Hoffman; Martin Kimelman; Mitchell Waxman.
EIN: 203987489
Selected grants: The following grants are a representative sample of this grantmaker's funding activity:
$18,610 to Chapman University, Orange, CA, 2011.
$10,000 to Foundation for the Defense of Democracies, Washington, DC, 2011.

1843
The Paul & Anne-Marie Queally Family Foundation ✧
c/o Foundation Source
501 Silverside Rd., Ste. 123
Wilmington, DE 19809-1377

Established in 2004 in DE.
Donors: Paul Queally; Anne-Marie Queally; Queally Family Foundation.
Foundation type: Independent foundation.
Financial data (yr. ended 12/31/13): Assets, $3,271,527 (M); gifts received, $2,775,554; expenditures, $2,106,513; qualifying distributions, $2,079,875; giving activities include $2,065,786 for 12 grants (high: $1,714,286; low: $2,500).
Fields of interest: Higher education; Children/youth, services; Catholic agencies & churches.

Limitations: Applications not accepted. Giving primarily in VA; some funding also in CT. No grants to individuals.
Application information: Contributes only to pre-selected organizations.
Officers and Directors:* Paul B. Queally,* Pres. and Secy.; Anne-Marie Queally,* V.P.
EIN: 770607990

1844
Quitiplas Foundation ✧
c/o Foundation Source
501 Silverside Rd., Ste. 123
Wilmington, DE 19809-1377

Donor: Thomas M. Scruggs, Jr.
Foundation type: Independent foundation.
Financial data (yr. ended 12/31/13): Assets, $9,568,395 (M); gifts received, $500,000; expenditures, $3,676,169; qualifying distributions, $3,584,915; giving activities include $3,436,030 for 41 grants (high: $2,100,000; low: $100).
Fields of interest: Human services; Public affairs.
Limitations: Applications not accepted. Giving in the U.S., with emphasis on Washington, DC, and MD.
Application information: Unsolicited requests for funds not accepted.
Officer and Director:* Thomas M. Scruggs, Jr.,* Pres. and Secy.
EIN: 261622017

1845
Raskob Foundation for Catholic Activities, Inc. ✧
P.O. Box 4019
Wilmington, DE 19807-0019 (302) 655-4440
Contact: Paul A. Zambernardi, Exec. V.P.
FAX: (302) 655-3223; E-mail: info@rfca.org; Additional address for overnight delivery: 10 Montchanin Rd., Wilmington, DE 19807-2166; Main URL: http://www.rfca.org

Incorporated in 1945 in DE.
Donors: John J. Raskob‡; Helena Raskob‡.
Foundation type: Independent foundation.
Financial data (yr. ended 12/31/13): Assets, $165,728,768 (M); expenditures, $8,228,895; qualifying distributions, $6,743,823; giving activities include $5,125,882 for 446 grants (high: $150,000; low: $250).
Purpose and activities: Giving to support Roman Catholic church organizations and activities worldwide by providing funds to official Catholic organizations for education, training, social services, health, emergency relief, as well as a wide variety of charitable needs.
Fields of interest: Education; Environment, water resources; Health care; Agriculture, sustainable programs; Human services; Children/youth, services; International relief; Catholic federated giving programs; Catholic agencies & churches; Religion; Infants/toddlers; Children/youth; Children; Youth; Adults; Aging; Young adults; Disabilities, people with; Physically disabled; Blind/visually impaired; Deaf/hearing impaired; Mentally disabled; Minorities; Asians/Pacific Islanders; African Americans/Blacks; Hispanics/Latinos; Native Americans/American Indians; Indigenous peoples; Women; Infants/toddlers, female; Girls; Adults, women; Young adults, female; Men; Infants/toddlers, male; Boys; Adults, men; Young adults, male; Military/veterans; Offenders/ex-offenders; Substance abusers; AIDS, people with; Single parents; Crime/abuse victims; Terminal illness, people with; Immigrants/refugees; Economically disadvantaged; Homeless; Migrant workers; LGBTQ.
International interests: Global Programs.
Type of support: General/operating support; Management development/capacity building; Building/renovation; Equipment; Land acquisition; Emergency funds; Program development; Conferences/seminars; Film/video/radio; Publication; Seed money; Curriculum development; Technical assistance; Consulting services; Program evaluation; Program-related investments/loans; Matching/challenge support.
Limitations: Applications accepted. Giving to domestic and international programs affiliated with the Roman Catholic church. No grants to individuals, or for continuing support, annual campaigns, deficit financing (except missions), endowment funds, tuition, scholarships, fellowships, individual research, capital campaigns, building projects prior to the start or after the completion of construction, continuing subsidies, or requests that are after-the-fact by the time of the spring and fall trustee meetings.
Publications: Application guidelines; Grants list; IRS Form 990 or 990-PF printed copy available upon request.
Application information: The foundation is currently not accepting applications for projects located within the continent of Africa. Applications sent via e-mail will not be accepted. Application form required.
Initial approach: Applications can be completed and submitted online or request application package via mail or fax on organization letter head, or request downloadable application from foundation web site
Copies of proposal: 1
Deadline(s): Applications accepted for spring meeting from Dec. 8 to Jan. 15, for fall meeting from June 8 to July 15
Board meeting date(s): May and mid-Nov.
Final notification: 4 months
Officers and Trustees:* Patrick W. McGrory III,* Chair.; Edward H. Robinson,* Pres.; Theresa G. Robinson, Exec. V.P., Finance and Opers.; L. Charles Rotunno, Jr., Exec. V.P., Grants and External Affairs; Noelle M. Fracyon,* 1st V.P.; Kathleen D. Smith, 2nd V.P.; Timothy T. Raskob,* Secy.; Christopher R. Raskob,* Treas.; Jonathan K. Goff, Cont.; Adam J. Borden; Theodore H. Bremekamp III; Gregory B. Brown; Sr. Patricia Geuting; Erin E. Henderson; J. Max Raskob; Richard G. Raskob; T. Mark Raskob; Maria R. Robinson; Elizabeth M. Woodward.
Number of staff: 3 full-time professional; 4 full-time support; 1 part-time support.
EIN: 510070060

1846
The Horowitz Ratner Family Foundation ✧ ☆
c/o Foundation Source
501 Silverside Rd., Ste. 123
Wilmington, DE 19809-1377

Established in 2006 in DE.
Donors: Chuck Ratner; Charles A. Ratner; Ilana Horowitz Ratner.
Foundation type: Independent foundation.
Financial data (yr. ended 12/31/13): Assets, $194,341 (M); gifts received, $188,100; expenditures, $519,541; qualifying distributions, $511,883; giving activities include $505,822 for 23 grants (high: $150,000; low: $250).
Fields of interest: Education; United Ways and Federated Giving Programs; Jewish federated giving programs.
Limitations: Applications not accepted. Giving primarily in OH.
Application information: Unsolicited requests for funds not accepted.
Officers and Directors:* Ilana Horowitz Ratner,* Pres. and Secy.; Robert Gephart, V.P.; Charles A. Ratner,* V.P.
EIN: 208004682

1847
Ronald and Deborah Ratner Family Foundation ✧
c/o Foundation Source
501 Silverside Rd., Ste. 123
Wilmington, DE 19809-1377

Established in 2006 in DE.
Donors: Co RMS MGMT Company 50 Public Squar; Mathew Ratner; Sarah Ratner.
Foundation type: Independent foundation.
Financial data (yr. ended 12/31/13): Assets, $702,348 (M); gifts received, $517,590; expenditures, $862,629; qualifying distributions, $860,290; giving activities include $850,573 for 36 grants (high: $200,000; low: $1,000).
Fields of interest: Arts; Education; Religion.
Limitations: Applications not accepted. Giving primarily in MA.
Application information: Unsolicited requests for funds not accepted.
Officers and Directors:* Mathew Ratner,* Co-Pres. and Co-Secy.; Sarah Ratner,* Co-Pres.
EIN: 208038060

1848
Reynolds Family Foundation ✧
c/o Foundation Source
501 Silverside Rd., Ste. 123
Wilmington, DE 19809-1377

Established in 2006 in FL.
Donor: Robert J. Reynolds Trust.
Foundation type: Independent foundation.
Financial data (yr. ended 12/31/12): Assets, $52,812,721 (M); expenditures, $2,801,758; qualifying distributions, $2,595,017; giving activities include $2,515,850 for 109 grants (high: $600,500; low: $500).
Fields of interest: Education; Health organizations; Human services; Family services; United Ways and Federated Giving Programs.
Limitations: Applications not accepted. Giving primarily in CA, FL and IL.
Application information: Contributes only to pre-selected organizations.
Trustees: Alison L. Baird; Timothy D. Friedman; Donald F. Mintmire; Patricia R. Mintmire.
EIN: 383739715

1849
Marshall Reynolds Foundation ✧
c/o Wilmington Trust Co.
1100 N. Market St., DE3-C070
Wilmington, DE 19890-0001

Established in DE.
Foundation type: Independent foundation.
Financial data (yr. ended 06/30/13): Assets, $26,970,242 (M); expenditures, $1,372,820; qualifying distributions, $1,259,482; giving activities include $1,180,036 for 57 grants (high: $50,000; low: $600).
Purpose and activities: Giving primarily for environmental conservation, the arts, health care, including hospitals, and to Quaker and Lutheran ministries and organizations; some giving also for education, and social services.
Fields of interest: Museums (natural history); Arts; Higher education; Libraries/library science; Education; Environment, natural resources; Animals/wildlife, bird preserves; Hospitals (general); Health care; Human services; YM/YWCAs & YM/YWHAs; Aging, centers/services; Community development, neighborhood development; Protestant agencies & churches; Economically disadvantaged.
Limitations: Applications not accepted. Giving primarily in DE and PA, with emphasis on Philadelphia. No grants to individuals.
Application information: Contributes only to pre-selected organizations.
Trustees: Richard A. Newman, M.D.; Jacklen E. Powell; Minturn T. Wright III, Esq.
EIN: 233053828

1850
Mariano Rivera Foundation ✧ ☆
321 Chattahoochee Dr.
Bear, DE 19701-4809 (847) 291-0603
Contact: Naomi Gandia, Secy.-Treas.
Main URL: http://www.marianoriverafoundation.org/

Established in NY.
Donors: Mariano Rivera; Steiner Sports; Charity Buzz; Frozen Ropes of Morris County NJ, LLC; Neuro Rays Imaging; Ridgefield High School Student Activity Account; VF Services; Yes Network; BTIG, LLC; Major League Baseball; Topps Us; Wish You Were Here Productions; OLILVY; Chardan Capital; David R. Tarella; Joseph Nicolla; Racing Rest of America II Inc.; Colorado Rockies Baseball Club Foundation; Mariners Care; Minnesota Twins; Royals Charities Inc.; Michael Weinberger; Arianne Weinberger; KCH Group; Curmark.
Foundation type: Independent foundation.
Financial data (yr. ended 06/30/13): Assets, $4,374,884 (M); gifts received, $402,963; expenditures, $864,975; qualifying distributions, $853,770; giving activities include $773,000 for 2 grants (high: $500,000; low: $273,000).
Fields of interest: Christian agencies & churches.
Limitations: Applications accepted. Giving in the U.S., with some emphasis on NY and TN.
Application information: Application form required.
Initial approach: Letter
Deadline(s): None
Officers: Mariano Rivera, Pres.; Clara Rivera, V.P.; Naomi Gandia, Secy.-Treas.
EIN: 134076067

1851
Romill Foundation ✧
c/o Wilmington Trust Co.
1100 N. Market St., DE3-C070
Wilmington, DE 19890-0900

Trust established in 1960 in SC.
Donors: Roger Milliken†; Gerrish H. Milliken, Sr.; Justine V. Milliken.
Foundation type: Independent foundation.
Financial data (yr. ended 12/31/13): Assets, $9,582,515 (M); expenditures, $564,977; qualifying distributions, $561,075; giving activities include $559,500 for 18 grants (high: $416,000; low: $1,000).
Purpose and activities: Giving primarily for the arts and education.
Fields of interest: Arts councils; Historic preservation/historical societies; Arts; Elementary/secondary education; Education; United Ways and Federated Giving Programs; Public affairs.
Type of support: General/operating support.
Limitations: Applications not accepted. Giving primarily in Spartanburg County, SC. No grants to individuals.
Application information: Contributes only to pre-selected organizations.
Board meeting date(s): As required
Officers: Thomas J. Hamilton, Co-Treas.; James F. Zahrn, Co-Treas.
Trustees: Gerrish H. Milliken; Nancy Milliken; Justine V.R. Russell; Wilmington Trust Co.
EIN: 136102069
Selected grants: The following grants are a representative sample of this grantmaker's funding activity:
$208,386 to Spartanburg Day School, Spartanburg, SC, 2011.
$55,000 to Arts Partnership of Greater Spartanburg, Spartanburg, SC, 2011.
$25,000 to Maine TREE Foundation, Augusta, ME, 2011.
$10,000 to Saint Timothys School, Stevenson, MD, 2011.
$5,000 to Hub Culture, Spartanburg, SC, 2011.
$2,500 to College of the Atlantic, Bar Harbor, ME, 2011.
$2,500 to Groton School, Groton, MA, 2011.
$2,500 to LaGrange Academy, LaGrange, GA, 2011.
$2,500 to LaGrange College, LaGrange, GA, 2011.
$2,500 to Philadelphia University, Philadelphia, PA, 2011.

1852
Clare Rose Foundation ✧
c/o Foundation Source
501 Silverside Rd., Ste. 123
Wilmington, DE 19809-1377

Established in 1997 in CT.
Donor: Valerie Vincent†.
Foundation type: Independent foundation.
Financial data (yr. ended 12/31/13): Assets, $11,992,042 (M); expenditures, $582,409; qualifying distributions, $527,705; giving activities include $480,532 for 16 grants (high: $100,000; low: $5,000).
Purpose and activities: Giving primarily for education, and children and youth services.
Fields of interest: Elementary/secondary education; Higher education; Education; Human services; Children/youth, services; Catholic agencies & churches.
Limitations: Applications not accepted. Giving primarily in CT and SC. No grants to individuals.
Application information: Contributes only to pre-selected organizations.
Officers and Directors:* Anne B. Vincent, Pres.; Elise Furer,* Secy.; Edward Vincent; William Vincent.
EIN: 061480029

1853
Ellen & Douglas Rosenberg Foundation ✧
c/o Foundation Source
501 Silverside Rd., Ste. 123
Wilmington, DE 19809-1377

Donors: Douglas C. Rosenberg; Ellen A. Rosenberg; Louise & Claude Rosenberg Jr. Family Foundation.
Foundation type: Independent foundation.
Financial data (yr. ended 12/31/12): Assets, $3,740,984 (M); gifts received, $6,128; expenditures, $1,709,405; qualifying distributions, $1,708,304; giving activities include $1,355,000 for 7 grants (high: $1,000,000; low: $10,000).
Fields of interest: Education; Alzheimer's disease research.
Limitations: Applications not accepted.
Application information: Unsolicited requests for funds not accepted.
Officers and Directors:* Douglas C. Rosenberg,* Pres.; Ellen A. Rosenberg,* Secy.-Treas.
EIN: 263347594

1854
Cornolia Cogswell Rossi Foundation Inc. ✧
c/o Foundation Source
501 Silver Rd., Ste. 123
Wilmington, DE 19809-1377

Foundation type: Independent foundation.
Financial data (yr. ended 12/31/13): Assets, $18,097,076 (M); expenditures, $1,234,101; qualifying distributions, $1,153,213; giving activities include $1,040,000 for 63 grants (high: $500,000; low: $500).
Fields of interest: Higher education; Animal welfare; Health care; Human services.
Limitations: Applications not accepted. Giving primarily in CT and NY.
Application information: Contributes only to pre-selected organizations.
Officers: Charles B. Kaufmann III, Pres.; Laurie A. Warren, V.P. and Secy.; John R. Raben, Jr., V.P. and Treas.
EIN: 201420345
Selected grants: The following grants are a representative sample of this grantmaker's funding activity:
$1,000,000 to Yale University, New Haven, CT, 2012. For Hendrie Hall Renovation.
$300,000 to Jackson Laboratory, Bar Harbor, ME, 2012. For Connie Ross! Biosafety Facility Project.
$50,000 to Friends of Acadia, Bar Harbor, ME, 2012. For Acadia Youth Technology Team.
$20,000 to Yale University, Law School, New Haven, CT, 2012. For Audio Visual Equipment in the Law School Faculty Lounge.
$10,000 to Widener University, Chester, PA, 2012. For Oskin Leadership Institute.
$5,000 to Yale University, New Haven, CT, 2012. For Dwight A. Miller '67 Scholarship Fund.
$2,500 to Yale University, New Haven, CT, 2012. For Brewster Papers.

1855
James H. Salah Foundation ✧
919 N. Market St., Ste. 420
Wilmington, DE 19801-3014

Donor: James M. Salah†.
Foundation type: Independent foundation.
Financial data (yr. ended 12/31/12): Assets, $120,801,363 (M); gifts received, $12,500,000; expenditures, $5,602,817; qualifying distributions, $4,999,727; giving activities include $4,447,689 for 44 grants (high: $100,000; low: $5,000).
Fields of interest: Arts; Law school/education; Education; Housing/shelter; Boys & girls clubs; Human services; Children/youth, services; Children.
Type of support: General/operating support.
Limitations: Applications accepted. Giving primarily in CA, CO, FL, MA, NC and OH.
Application information: Application form required.
Initial approach: Proposal
Deadline(s): None
Officer: Noreen S. Burpee, Exec. Dir.
Trustees: Brown Brothers Harriman.
EIN: 546882525

1856
Micol Schejola Foundation ✧
c/o Foundation Source
501 Silverside Rd., Ste. 123
Wilmington, DE 19809-1377

Established in 2000 in NY.
Donor: Linda Schejola.
Foundation type: Independent foundation.
Financial data (yr. ended 12/31/13): Assets, $9,628,036 (M); expenditures, $718,179; qualifying distributions, $705,963; giving activities include $671,040 for 22 grants (high: $260,000; low: $1,000).
Fields of interest: Museums (art); Hospitals (general); Health care; Boys & girls clubs; International relief.
Limitations: Applications not accepted. Giving primarily in GA and NY. No grants to individuals.
Application information: Contributes only to pre-selected organizations.
Trustees: Jeff Akin; Linda Schejola; Lisa Schejola.
EIN: 137257959

1857
Bernard Lee Schwartz Foundation, Inc. ✧
c/o Wilmington Trust SP Svcs., Inc.
1105 N. Market St., Ste. 1300
Wilmington, DE 19801-1241

Incorporated in 1951 in NY.
Donors: Tilda R. Orr; Bernard L. Schwartz†; Eric A. Schwartz; Michael L. Schwartz; Rosalyn R. Schwartz; Donald N. Ravitich; Henry Friedricks Foundation.
Foundation type: Independent foundation.
Financial data (yr. ended 09/30/13): Assets, $22,014,244 (M); expenditures, $1,022,851; qualifying distributions, $857,662; giving activities include $829,977 for 33 grants (high: $150,000; low: $25).
Purpose and activities: Giving primarily for education, medical research, and human services.
Fields of interest: Elementary/secondary education; Higher education; Health organizations, association; Medical research, institute; Cancer research; Human services.
Type of support: General/operating support; Continuing support; Annual campaigns; Capital campaigns; Building/renovation; Equipment; Endowments; Fellowships; Internship funds; Research.
Limitations: Applications not accepted. Giving primarily in CA; funding also in NY and Washington, DC. No grants to individuals, or for annual campaigns, seed money, emergency funds, deficit financing, land acquisition, demonstration projects, publications, or conferences; no loans.
Application information: Contributes only to pre-selected organizations.
Officers: Michael L. Schwartz, Pres.; Eric A. Schwartz, V.P. and Treas.; Tilda R. Orr, Secy.
Directors: Fred W. Conklin; Rosalyn R. Schwartz.
EIN: 136096198
Selected grants: The following grants are a representative sample of this grantmaker's funding activity:
$125,000 to BASIC Fund, San Francisco, CA, 2011. For general purposes.
$110,000 to Stanford University, Stanford, CA, 2011.
$100,000 to Alliance for School Choice, Washington, DC, 2011. For general purposes.
$25,000 to Bryn Mawr College, Bryn Mawr, PA, 2011. For general purposes.
$25,000 to Pancreatic Cancer Action Network, Manhattan Beach, CA, 2011. For general purposes.
$20,000 to International Center of Photography, New York, NY, 2011.
$20,000 to Pomfret School, Pomfret, CT, 2011. For general purposes.
$10,000 to Museum of Photographic Arts, San Diego, CA, 2011. For general purposes.
$10,000 to National Dance Institute, New York, NY, 2011. For general purposes.
$5,000 to Jerusalem Foundation, New York, NY, 2011.

1858
Lydia and Doug Shorenstein Foundation Inc. ✧
c/o Foundation Source
501 Silverside Rd., Ste. 123
Wilmington, DE 19809-1377

Established in 2005 in DE.
Donors: Lydia Shorenstein; Douglas W. Shorenstein.
Foundation type: Independent foundation.
Financial data (yr. ended 12/31/12): Assets, $6,743,664 (M); gifts received, $646,621; expenditures, $691,692; qualifying distributions, $664,293; giving activities include $633,333 for grants (high: $250,000; low: $25,000).
Fields of interest: Education; Environment.
Limitations: Applications not accepted. Giving primarily in CA, IN, PA and TN. No grants to individuals.
Application information: Contributes only to pre-selected organizations.
Officers and Directors:* Douglas Shorenstein,* Co-Pres. and Secy.; Lydia Shorenstein,* Co-Pres.
EIN: 203131229

1859
The Paul Singer Family Foundation ✧
(formerly The Paul & Linda Singer Foundation)
1105 N. Market St., Ste. 1300
Wilmington, DE 19801-1241

Established in 1986 in DE.
Donors: Linda Singer; Paul E. Singer.
Foundation type: Independent foundation.
Financial data (yr. ended 11/30/13): Assets, $13,725,502 (M); expenditures, $634,329; qualifying distributions, $630,483; giving activities include $628,500 for 5 grants (high: $275,000; low: $3,500).
Fields of interest: Higher education; Athletics/sports, basketball; Recreation; Children, services.
Limitations: Applications not accepted. Giving primarily in Williamstown, MA; some giving also in Washington, DC and New York, NY. No grants to individuals.
Application information: Contributes only to pre-selected organizations.
Officers and Directors:* Paul E. Singer,* Pres.; Andrew Morris-Singer,* V.P.; Gordon Singer,* V.P.
EIN: 222664654

1860
Herbert & Nell Singer Foundation, Inc. ✧
c/o Foundation Source
501 Silverside Rd., Ste. 123
Wilmington, DE 19809-1377

Established in DE.
Donors: Herbert M. Singer†; Nell Singer†; The Peter Singer Trust; The Steven Singer Trust; Herbert Singer Trust; Jay H. Sandak; Singer Family Char. Remainder Unitrust.
Foundation type: Independent foundation.
Financial data (yr. ended 12/31/13): Assets, $74,048,655 (M); gifts received, $10,970; expenditures, $4,215,101; qualifying distributions, $3,822,816; giving activities include $3,671,900 for 61 grants (high: $500,000; low: $2,500).
Purpose and activities: Giving primarily for higher education, family services, and Jewish agencies and temples.
Fields of interest: Arts; Higher education; Hospitals (general); Family services; Jewish agencies & synagogues.
Limitations: Applications not accepted. Giving primarily in CT and New York, NY. No grants to individuals.
Application information: Unsolicited requests for funds not accepted.
Officers and Directors:* Jay H. Sandak,* Pres.; Ernest N. Abate,* V.P. and Treas.; Mary E. Sandak,* Secy.
EIN: 133151548

1861
The Sternlicht Family Foundation Inc. ✧
c/o Foundation Source
501 Silverside Rd., Ste. 123
Wilmington, DE 19809-1377

Established in DE.
Donors: Barry Sternlicht; Miriam Klein Sternlicht.
Foundation type: Independent foundation.
Financial data (yr. ended 12/31/12): Assets, $69,555,039 (M); gifts received, $13,878,550; expenditures, $1,064,027; qualifying distributions,

$1,002,327; giving activities include $917,618 for 52 grants (high: $166,666; low: $126).
Purpose and activities: Giving primarily for education, health, youth and social services, and to Jewish organizations.
Fields of interest: Higher education; Education; Health care; Human services; Children/youth, services; Foundations (private grantmaking); Jewish federated giving programs; Jewish agencies & synagogues; Religion, interfaith issues.
Limitations: Applications not accepted. Giving primarily in CT, MA and NY. No grants to individuals.
Application information: Contributes only to pre-selected organizations.
Officers and Directors:* Barry Sternlicht,* Pres. and Secy.; David Lewis Dubrow,* V.P.; Miriam Klein Sternlicht,* V.P.; David A. Stern.
EIN: 260039094

1862
The Sam & Diane Stewart Family Foundation ✧ ☆
501 Silverside Rd., Ste. 123
Wilmington, DE 19809-1377

Established in 2003 in UT.
Donors: Samuel S. Stewart, Jr.; Diane P. Stewart.
Foundation type: Independent foundation.
Financial data (yr. ended 12/31/13): Assets, $5,621,789 (M); expenditures, $824,769; qualifying distributions, $724,793; giving activities include $694,428 for 35 grants (high: $125,000; low: $2,500).
Fields of interest: Museums (art); Arts; Education; Health care.
Limitations: Applications not accepted. Giving primarily in UT. No grants to individuals.
Application information: Unsolicited requests for funds not accepted.
Trustees: Diane P. Stewart; Samuel S. Stewart, Jr.
EIN: 206090860
Selected grants: The following grants are a representative sample of this grantmaker's funding activity:
$50,000 to Utah Museum of Fine Arts, Salt Lake City, UT, 2012. For Indian Portrait Show - Bierstadt to Warhol.
$30,000 to Springville Museum of Art, Springville, UT, 2012. For Stewart Fellowship Program.
$25,000 to Friends of Historic Spring City, Spring City, UT, 2012. For Old School Project.
$15,000 to Northwestern University, Evanston, IL, 2012. For Campaign for Alpha-Iota Zeta Fund.
$10,000 to University of Utah, School of Pharmacy, Salt Lake City, UT, 2012. For charitable event.
$10,000 to Utah Museum of Natural History, Salt Lake City, UT, 2012. For Indian Basketry Exhibition.
$5,000 to Salt Lake Art Center, Salt Lake City, UT, 2012. To support UMOCA and the New Frontier.
$5,000 to Utah Museum of Fine Arts, Salt Lake City, UT, 2012. For Sponsorship of Friends of Utah and Western Art.

1863
The Michael and Karen Stone Family Foundation, Inc. ✧ ☆
c/o Foundation Source
501 Silverside Rd., Ste. 123
Wilmington, DE 19809-1377

Established in 2002 in DE.
Donors: Michael R. Stone; Karen Stone.
Foundation type: Independent foundation.
Financial data (yr. ended 12/31/12): Assets, $9,586,158 (M); gifts received, $1,150,554; expenditures, $1,185,539; qualifying distributions, $1,027,100; giving activities include $1,027,100 for grants.
Fields of interest: Museums (art); Higher education; Education; Big Brothers/Big Sisters; Children, services.
International interests: Kenya.
Limitations: Applications not accepted. Giving primarily in CA, CT, and VT. No grants to individuals.
Application information: Unsolicited requests for funds not accepted.
Officer and Director:* Michael R. Stone,* Pres. and Secy.
EIN: 050544633

1864
Stratus Foundation ✧ ☆
(formerly The Regis de Ramel Family Charitable Trust)
2207 Old Kennett Rd.
Wilmington, DE 19807

Established in 2007 in DE.
Foundation type: Independent foundation.
Financial data (yr. ended 12/31/12): Assets, $12,131,374 (M); expenditures, $730,548; qualifying distributions, $592,000; giving activities include $592,000 for grants.
Fields of interest: Museums (marine/maritime); Arts; Education; Human services.
Limitations: Applications not accepted. Giving primarily in DE, ME, and RI.
Application information: Unsolicited request for funds not accepted.
Officer: Regis A. de Ramel, Pres.
EIN: 266190250

1865
The Struthers Family Foundation ✧
c/o Richard K. Struthers
900 Old Kennett Rd.
Greenville, DE 19807-1520

Established in 1999 in DE.
Donors: Richard K. Struthers; Sharon M. Struthers.
Foundation type: Independent foundation.
Financial data (yr. ended 12/31/13): Assets, $2,152,650 (M); expenditures, $949,155; qualifying distributions, $936,748; giving activities include $936,748 for 25 grants (high: $673,523; low: $150).
Purpose and activities: Giving primarily for higher and other education, and to a federated giving program; funding also for human services.
Fields of interest: Higher education; Education; Human services; United Ways and Federated Giving Programs; Christian agencies & churches.
Type of support: General/operating support.
Limitations: Applications not accepted. Giving primarily in DE and PA. No grants to individuals.
Application information: Unsolicited requests for funds not accepted.
Officers: Richard K. Struthers, Pres. and Treas.; Sharon M. Struthers, V.P. and Secy.
EIN: 510392526

1866
The Howard W., Alma K. and Richard Kemper Swank Foundation ✧
1925 Lovering Ave.
Wilmington, DE 19806-2157

Established in 2006 in DE.
Donor: Alma K. Swank†.
Foundation type: Independent foundation.
Financial data (yr. ended 03/31/13): Assets, $15,011,523 (M); expenditures, $806,067; qualifying distributions, $750,333; giving activities include $750,333 for grants.
Fields of interest: Health care; Medical research, institute.
Limitations: Applications not accepted. Giving primarily in DE. No grants to individuals.
Application information: Contributes only to pre-selected organizations.
Officers and Directors:* Edward M. Goldenberg,* Pres. and Treas.; Donald D. Franceschini,* 1st V.P.; Stephen T. Brumi,* V.P.; Nancy N. Gale,* V.P.; Denise D. Schwartz,* V.P.
EIN: 205145157
Selected grants: The following grants are a representative sample of this grantmaker's funding activity:
$333,333 to Nemours Foundation, Wilmington, DE, 2012.

1867
Sylvan/Laureate Foundation, Inc. ✧
(formerly The Sylvan Learning Foundation, Inc.)
c/o Foundation Source
501 Silverside Rd., Ste. 123
Wilmington, DE 19809-1377
Contact: Carol Maivelett, Admin.
E-mail: Carol.Maivelett@laureate.net; Main URL: http://www.laureate.net/HereforGood/TheSylvanLaureateFoundation

Established in 1997 in MD.
Donors: Sylvan Learning Systems, Inc.; Laureate Education, Inc.; Leadform Est. LTD.
Foundation type: Company-sponsored foundation.
Financial data (yr. ended 12/31/12): Assets, $11,643,008 (M); gifts received, $4,000,000; expenditures, $2,994,286; qualifying distributions, $2,926,139; giving activities include $2,578,785 for 60 grants (high: $689,812; low: $1,500), and $279,625 for 4 foundation-administered programs.
Purpose and activities: The foundation supports organizations involved with arts and culture, health, children and youth, youth development, international development, public policy research. Special emphasis is directed toward programs designed to promote best practices in education.
Fields of interest: Museums; Performing arts, theater; Performing arts, orchestras; Arts; Elementary/secondary education; Higher education; Teacher school/education; Education; Health care; Youth development, citizenship; Youth development; Children/youth, services; International development; Business/industry; United Ways and Federated Giving Programs; Public policy, research; Leadership development.
Type of support: General/operating support; Annual campaigns; Capital campaigns; Program development; Sponsorships.
Limitations: Applications not accepted. Giving primarily in Baltimore, MD. No support for religious organizations or political or lobbying organizations. No grants to individuals.

Application information: Contributes only to pre-selected organizations.
Board meeting date(s): Apr., July, Oct., and Jan.
Officers and Trustees:* Douglas L. Becker,* Pres.; R. Christopher Hoehn-Saric,* 1st V.P.; Robert W. Zentz, 2nd V.P. and Secy.; Eilif Serck-Hanssen, Treas.; B. Lee McGee.
EIN: 522044008
Selected grants: The following grants are a representative sample of this grantmaker's funding activity:
$689,812 to International Youth Foundation, Baltimore, MD, 2012. For YouthActionNet Program.
$609,796 to International Youth Foundation, Baltimore, MD, 2012. For YouthActionNet 50 Program.
$151,435 to International Youth Foundation, Baltimore, MD, 2012. For 2011 YouthActionNet Program.
$100,000 to International Youth Foundation, Baltimore, MD, 2012. For youth work program expansion.
$100,000 to International Youth Foundation, Baltimore, MD, 2012. For 2011 annual fund.
$25,000 to Johns Hopkins University, Baltimore, MD, 2012. For School of Education.

1868
The Tapeats Fund ✧
c/o Foundation Source
501 Silverside Rd., Ste. 123
Wilmington, DE 19809-1377

Established in 1993 in TX.
Donors: Robert H. Graham; Laurel A.W. Graham.
Foundation type: Independent foundation.
Financial data (yr. ended 12/31/13): Assets, $15,394,841 (M); gifts received, $750,000; expenditures, $827,026; qualifying distributions, $715,341; giving activities include $603,161 for 62 grants (high: $82,500; low: $448).
Fields of interest: Environment; Animals/wildlife; Human services; Children/youth, services.
Type of support: General/operating support; Continuing support; Annual campaigns; Capital campaigns; Building/renovation; Equipment.
Limitations: Applications not accepted. Giving primarily in TX, with emphasis on Houston.
Application information: Unsolicited requests for funds not accepted.
Officers and Trustees:* Robert H. Graham,* Pres. and Treas.; Laurel A. Graham,* Exec. V.P.; Margaret Worden, Exec. Dir. and Secy.; David R. Graham; Spencer R. Graham; Whitney G. Mixon.
Number of staff: 6 full-time support.
EIN: 760412011

1869
Jeffrey Tarrant Family Foundation ✧
P.O. Box 158
St. Georges, DE 19733-0158

Established in DE.
Donor: Jeffrey Tarrant.
Foundation type: Independent foundation.
Financial data (yr. ended 06/30/13): Assets, $309,687 (M); gifts received, $100,000; expenditures, $429,215; qualifying distributions, $427,150; giving activities include $427,150 for grants.
Purpose and activities: Giving primarily to a film company that seeks to finance the development of films intended to raise public awareness of important social issues.
Fields of interest: Media, film/video.
Limitations: Applications not accepted. Giving primarily in New York, NY.
Application information: Unsolicited requests for funds not accepted.
Officers and Directors;:* Jeffrey Tarrant,* C.E.O. and Pres.; Terri Meeks,* Secy.-Treas.; Cornelia Tarrant.
EIN: 271311573

1870
Victory Foundation ✧
c/o Wilmington Trust Company
1100 N. Market St.
Wilmington, DE 19890-0900

Established in 1997 in PA.
Donors: Robert L. McNeil, Jr.; Victoria McNeil Le Vine.
Foundation type: Independent foundation.
Financial data (yr. ended 12/31/13): Assets, $13,655,846 (M); expenditures, $592,155; qualifying distributions, $552,610; giving activities include $549,650 for 21 grants (high: $162,500; low: $2,500).
Fields of interest: Museums; Museums (art); Higher education, university; Children, services; Children/youth.
Type of support: General/operating support.
Limitations: Applications not accepted. Giving primarily in GA and PA. No grants to individuals.
Application information: Unsolicited requests for funds not accepted.
Trustee: Victoria McNeil Le Vine.
EIN: 526854620
Selected grants: The following grants are a representative sample of this grantmaker's funding activity:
$66,500 to Carnegie Mellon University, Pittsburgh, PA, 2010. For general operating support.
$25,000 to Philadelphia Museum of Art, Philadelphia, PA, 2011. For general operating support.
$15,000 to Philadelphia Theater Company, Philadelphia, PA, 2011. For general operating support.
$7,500 to Camp Dreamcatcher, Kennett Square, PA, 2011. For general operating support.
$7,100 to Kimmel Center for the Performing Arts, Philadelphia, PA, 2011. For general operating support.
$6,000 to Agnes Irwin School, Rosemont, PA, 2011. For general operating support.
$5,000 to Gesu School, Philadelphia, PA, 2011. For general operating support.
$5,000 to Please Touch Museum, Philadelphia, PA, 2011. For general operating support.
$2,500 to Arden Theater Company, Philadelphia, PA, 2011. For general operating support.
$2,500 to Theater Horizon, Norristown, PA, 2011. For general operating support.
$2,000 to Episcopal Academy, Newtown Square, PA, 2011. For general operating support.

1871
The Wasily Family Foundation, Inc. ✧
2711 Centerville Rd.
P.O. Box 1041
Wilmington, DE 19808-1660 (631) 979-2142
Contact: Patrick N. Moloney, Pres.

Established in 1988 in NY.
Donors: Anne V. Wasily‡; H. Vira Kolisch‡; Anne V. Wasily Irrevocable Trust.
Foundation type: Independent foundation.
Financial data (yr. ended 06/30/13): Assets, $102,954,890 (M); gifts received, $41,505,824; expenditures, $3,260,021; qualifying distributions, $2,582,756; giving activities include $2,420,000 for 76 grants (high: $50,000; low: $10,000).
Purpose and activities: Giving primarily for health and human services.
Fields of interest: Arts education; Arts; Hospitals (general); Health organizations; Cancer research; Human services; Children/youth, services; Family services; United Ways and Federated Giving Programs; Catholic agencies & churches.
Type of support: General/operating support; Research.
Limitations: Applications accepted. Giving primarily in New York, NY.
Application information: Application form not required.
Initial approach: E-mail
Deadline(s): None
Board meeting date(s): June
Officers: Patrick Moloney, Pres.; Margaret Moloney, V.P.; Frank Suchomel, Jr., Treas.
Trustee: Kenneth Gheno.
EIN: 133503227
Selected grants: The following grants are a representative sample of this grantmaker's funding activity:
$50,000 to Behre Piano Associates, Adamant, VT, 2011.
$50,000 to Doctors Without Borders USA, New York, NY, 2011.
$50,000 to Franciscan Friars of the Atonement, Garrison, NY, 2011.
$50,000 to International Rescue Committee, New York, NY, 2011.
$50,000 to Intrepid Fallen Heroes Fund, New York, NY, 2011.
$40,000 to Alzheimers Association, Chicago, IL, 2011.
$40,000 to Parkinsons Disease Foundation, New York, NY, 2011.
$30,000 to Camp Heartland, Milwaukee, WI, 2011.
$30,000 to City Harvest, New York, NY, 2011.
$20,000 to Fisher House Foundation, Rockville, MD, 2011.

1872
Welfare Foundation, Inc. ✧
100 W. 10th St., Ste. 1109
Wilmington, DE 19801-1653 (302) 654-2477
Contact: Peter C. Morrow, Pres.

Incorporated in 1930 in DE.
Donors: Pierre S. du Pont‡; University of Delaware.
Foundation type: Independent foundation.
Financial data (yr. ended 12/31/13): Assets, $114,074,679 (M); expenditures, $6,023,177; qualifying distributions, $5,130,007; giving activities include $4,879,495 for 76 grants (high: $400,000; low: $300).

Purpose and activities: Emphasis on education, hospitals, and social service agencies.
Fields of interest: Humanities; Arts; Education; Environment; Hospitals (general); Human services; Government/public administration.
Type of support: Capital campaigns; Building/renovation; Equipment; Matching/challenge support.
Limitations: Applications accepted. Giving limited to DE and Chester County, PA. No grants to individuals, endowments, or for operating support.
Application information: Application form not required.
Initial approach: Letter (2 pages) and proposal
Copies of proposal: 1
Deadline(s): Apr. 15 and Oct. 15
Board meeting date(s): May and Dec.
Final notification: 60 days
Officers and Trustees:* Edward B. du Pont,* Chair.; Peter C. Morrow,* Pres.; Margaretta K. Stabler, Jr.,* V.P.; Leatrice D. Elliman,* Secy.; W. Laird Stabler III,* Treas.; Robert H. Bolling III; E. Bradford du Pont, Jr.; William L. Kitchel III.
Number of staff: 4 part-time professional.
EIN: 516015916
Selected grants: The following grants are a representative sample of this grantmaker's funding activity:
$250,000 to Newark Charter School, Newark, DE, 2012. For new high school building.
$165,000 to United Way of Delaware, Wilmington, DE, 2012. For annual support.
$125,000 to Practice Without Pressure, Newark, DE, 2012. For building expansion.
$100,000 to Easter Seals Delaware and Marylands Eastern Shore, New Castle, DE, 2012. For expansion of Georgetown building.
$100,000 to Innovative Schools Development Corporation, Wilmington, DE, 2012. For Revolving Charter App Fund.
$100,000 to Kalmar Nyckel Foundation, Wilmington, DE, 2012. For building expansion.
$100,000 to Ministry of Caring, Wilmington, DE, 2012. To restore Saint Patrick's House.
$50,000 to Delaware Association of Nonprofit Agencies, Wilmington, DE, 2012. For operating support.
$37,500 to Friends of Woodburn, Dover, DE, 2012. To make facility improvements to comply with Americans with Disability Act (ADA).
$35,000 to Wilmington Senior Center, Wilmington, DE, 2012. To install insulation to HVAC equipment.

1873
The Steve and Anita Westly Foundation ✧
c/o Foundation Source
501 Silverside Rd., Ste. 123
Wilmington, DE 19809-1377
E-mail: contact@westly.org; Mailing address: c/o Fidelity Private Foundation Services, P.O. Box 55158, Boston, MA 02205-5158; Main URL: http://www.westly.org
Blog: http://westly.org/westly-blog/
Twitter: https://twitter.com/WestlyFound

Established in 2000 in CA.
Donors: Steve Westly; Anita Westly.
Foundation type: Independent foundation.
Financial data (yr. ended 12/31/12): Assets, $10,289,575 (M); gifts received, $187,850; expenditures, $1,077,208; qualifying distributions, $925,061; giving activities include $699,576 for 37 grants (high: $50,000; low: $1,000), and $92,500 for 9 grants to individuals (high: $20,000; low: $2,500).
Purpose and activities: Giving primarily for areas of education, youth, health, immigration, and global security.
Fields of interest: Arts; Elementary/secondary education; Higher education; Education; Health organizations, association; Human services; Children/youth, services.
Type of support: General/operating support; Capital campaigns.
Limitations: Applications not accepted. Giving primarily in CA, with emphasis on the San Francisco Bay Area. No grants to individuals (except for the Westly Prize).
Publications: Grants list.
Application information: Unsolicited requests for funds not accepted.
Officers: Steven P. Westly,* Chair.; Anita W. Yu,* Secy.-Treas.; Dave Viotti, Exec. Dir.
EIN: 943368338
Selected grants: The following grants are a representative sample of this grantmaker's funding activity:
$40,000 to Philanthropic Ventures Foundation, Oakland, CA, 2012. For Teacher Mini Grants for The Arts Program.
$25,000 to Equal Opportunity Schools, Seattle, WA, 2012. For Equal Opp Schools' Program at Lincoln Unified Schools.
$25,000 to Summit Institute, Redwood City, CA, 2012. For Optimized Learning School Curriculum Initiative.
$22,000 to Sequoia High School Education Foundation, Redwood City, CA, 2012. For AVID Program at Sequoia High School.
$20,000 to Aspire Public Schools, Oakland, CA, 2012. For Family and College Resource Center at East Palo Alto Phoenix Acad.
$20,000 to Stanford University, Stanford, CA, 2012. For Undergraduate Scholarships and Lee Jackson Fund at Stanford Grad School of Business.
$14,076 to ALearn, Santa Clara, CA, 2012. For A-Learn Summer Program in Redwood City for Sequoia HS.
$10,000 to Silicon Valley Education Foundation, San Jose, CA, 2012. For Participation in Stepping Up To Science Summer Biology Program.
$5,000 to Oakland Schools Foundation, Oakland, CA, 2012. For Five Scholarships to Think College Now.
$5,000 to Stanford University, Stanford, CA, 2012. For matching grant of Gift to Stanford University.

1874
Whitton-Spector Foundation ✧
c/o Foundation Source
501 Silverside Rd., Ste. 123
Wilmington, DE 19809-1377

Established in 2005 in DE.
Donors: Warren J. Spector; Margaret Whitton.
Foundation type: Independent foundation.
Financial data (yr. ended 12/31/13): Assets, $22,396,134 (M); expenditures, $1,062,680; qualifying distributions, $977,941; giving activities include $876,234 for 32 grants (high: $325,000; low: $200).
Fields of interest: Performing arts; Performing arts, theater; Hospitals (general); Health organizations; Human services; Jewish federated giving programs.
Limitations: Applications not accepted. Giving in the U.S., with emphasis on FL, MA, and NY. No grants to individuals.
Application information: Contributes only pre-selected organizations.
Officer and Director:* Warren J. Spector,* Pres. and Secy.
EIN: 203926141

1875
The Wilke Family Foundation ✧
c/o Foundation Source
501 Silverside Rd., Ste. 123
Wilmington, DE 19809-1377

Established in 2007 in DE.
Donors: Jeffrey Allan Wilke; Liesl D. Wilke.
Foundation type: Independent foundation.
Financial data (yr. ended 12/31/13): Assets, $12,661,174 (M); gifts received, $3,928,395; expenditures, $651,850; qualifying distributions, $603,878; giving activities include $569,243 for 19 grants (high: $333,333; low: $500).
Fields of interest: Higher education; Education; United Ways and Federated Giving Programs.
Limitations: Applications not accepted. Giving primarily in CO, CA, MA, NJ and WA. No grants to individuals.
Application information: Unsolicited requests for funds not accepted.
Officers and Directors:* Liesl D. Wilke,* Pres. and Secy.; Jeffrey Allan Wilke,* V.P.
EIN: 261207948

1876
Yavanna Foundation ✧ ☆
c/o Foundation Source
501 Silverside Rd.
Wilmington, DE 19809-1377

Donor: Philip H. Jensen.
Foundation type: Independent foundation.
Financial data (yr. ended 12/31/13): Assets, $10,072,954 (M); expenditures, $549,962; qualifying distributions, $493,134; giving activities include $447,600 for 17 grants (high: $100,000; low: $500).
Fields of interest: Education; Environment; Economics.
Limitations: Applications not accepted. Giving primarily in CA; funding also in OH and WI.
Application information: Unsolicited requests for funds not accepted.
Officer and Director:* Philip H. Jensen,* Pres. and Secy.
EIN: 261865668
Selected grants: The following grants are a representative sample of this grantmaker's funding activity:
$25,000 to Global Village Institute, Summertown, TN, 2012. For culture change Program.

DISTRICT OF COLUMBIA

1877
The Anne and Ronald Abramson Family Foundation ✧
c/o Ronald Abramson
1700 K St. N.W., Ste. 300
Washington, DC 20006-3807

Donors: Ronald D. Abramson; The Albert Abramson Revocable Trust; Albert Abramson‡.
Foundation type: Independent foundation.
Financial data (yr. ended 12/31/12): Assets, $33,543,064 (M); gifts received, $34,287,291; expenditures, $1,772,515; qualifying distributions, $1,771,390; giving activities include $1,771,390 for 71 grants (high: $553,700; low: $500).
Fields of interest: Jewish federated giving programs; Jewish agencies & synagogues.
Limitations: Applications not accepted. Giving primarily in Washington, D.C., and Silver Spring, MD.
Application information: Unsolicited requests for funds not accepted.
Trustees: Anne E. Abramson; Ronald D. Abramson.
EIN: 616356354
Selected grants: The following grants are a representative sample of this grantmaker's funding activity:
$237,500 to Yeshiva of Greater Washington, Silver Spring, MD, 2011. For unrestricted funds.
$104,344 to Sixth and I Historic Synagogue, Washington, DC, 2011. For unrestricted funds.
$25,000 to Northern Virginia Transportation Alliance, McLean, VA, 2011. For unrestricted funds.
$20,000 to 2030 Group, Gaithersburg, MD, 2011. For unrestricted funds.
$15,000 to District of Columbia College Access Program, Washington, DC, 2011. For unrestricted funds.
$15,000 to International Arts and Artists, Washington, DC, 2011. For unrestricted funds.
$15,000 to Spoleto Festival USA, Charleston, SC, 2011. For unrestricted funds.
$10,000 to Pyramid Atlantic, Silver Spring, MD, 2011. For unrestricted funds.
$7,500 to Hand Print Workshop, Alexandria, VA, 2011. For unrestricted funds.
$7,500 to SEED Foundation, Washington, DC, 2011. For unrestricted funds.

1878
Agua Fund, Inc. ✧
1010 Wisconsin Ave. N.W., Ste. 550
Washington, DC 20007-3678 (202) 944-9622
FAX: (202) 944-9623; E-mail: info@aguafund.org; Main URL: http://www.aguafund.org/
Grants List: http://www.aguafund.org/?page_id=635

Established in 2002 in DC.
Donor: Catherine M. Conover.
Foundation type: Independent foundation.
Financial data (yr. ended 12/31/12): Assets, $9,642,459 (M); gifts received, $9,244,173; expenditures, $2,449,872; qualifying distributions, $2,346,323; giving activities include $1,977,488 for 106 grants (high: $250,000; low: $1,000).
Purpose and activities: The fund's mission is to improve the quality of life through support of work to protect the natural environment and to help the poor, disadvantaged, and underserved.
Environmental grants focus on protecting the watershed of the Shenandoah River in VA by addressing issues of land, water, and food. Grants support organizations that advocate for resource protection, sustainable agriculture, and locally-produced food. Environmental grants for FL emphasize protection of the Gulf Coast. Social service grants primarily address the vulnerable elderly in southwest FL and Washington, DC.
Board-directed grants support arts and culture, disaster relief, women's rights in the Middle East, mental health care for returning veterans, and solar cooking. Board-directed grants and grants to organizations in FL are made through the fund's donor-advised fund at the Community Foundation of Collier County.
Fields of interest: Arts; Environment, natural resources; Health care; Disasters, preparedness/services; Human services; Aging; Women; Military/veterans; Economically disadvantaged.
Limitations: Applications not accepted. Giving primarily in the U.S., with emphasis on Washington, DC, FL, and VA. No grants to individuals.
Publications: Grants list.
Application information: The foundation considers invited proposals only.
Board meeting date(s): 4 times annually
Officers and Directors:* Catherine M. Conover,* Pres.; Richard J. Cicero,* V.P.; Cecily Kihn, Secy.; Nanci Aydelotte, Treas.; Ann K. Batlle, Esq.
EIN: 113659697

1879
Aid Association for the Blind of the District of Columbia ✧
5008 44th St. N.W.
Washington, DC 20016-4037
E-mail: bpoc@starpower.net

Established in 1989 in DC.
Foundation type: Independent foundation.
Financial data (yr. ended 06/30/13): Assets, $5,604,778 (M); expenditures, $530,531; qualifying distributions, $479,640; giving activities include $479,640 for grants.
Purpose and activities: Giving to hospitals, clinics, social service agencies, and issue-oriented projects serving the blind/visually impaired people in the Washington, DC, metropolitan area.
Fields of interest: Medical school/education; Hospitals (general); Optometry/vision screening; Eye diseases; Eye research; Disabilities, people with; Blind/visually impaired.
Type of support: General/operating support; Annual campaigns; Capital campaigns; Building/renovation; Equipment; Emergency funds; Program development; Publication; Seed money; Fellowships; Internship funds; Research.
Limitations: Applications not accepted. Giving limited to the Washington, DC metropolitan area. No grants to individuals.
Application information: Unsolicited requests for funds not accepted.
Officers and Directors:* Betsy Paull O'Connell,* Pres.; William B. Glew,* Treas.; Patricia Beattie; James Dickson; Betsy Feinberg; Wendy Gasch; Beth Ourisman Glassman; Anne Norman; John F. O'Neill; Stephen Pappas; Courtney Clark Pastrick; Carolyn Post; Deacon Ulysses Rice; Denise Rozell.
EIN: 530196564
Selected grants: The following grants are a representative sample of this grantmaker's funding activity:
$30,000 to American Council of the Blind, Arlington, VA, 2013. For Federal Workforce Program for Blind/Low Vision workers and Audio Description Program.
$25,000 to American Association of People with Disabilities, Washington, DC, 2013. For Voting Education Project for Blind/low Vision Residents of Washington, DC Metropolitan Area.
$10,000 to Iona Senior Services, Washington, DC, 2013. For Program for Seniors who have Visual Disabilities.

1880
The Arca Foundation
1308 19th St. N.W.
Washington, DC 20036-1602
Contact: Anna Lefer Kuhn, Exec. Dir.
FAX: (202) 785-1446;
E-mail: proposals@arcafoundation.org; Main URL: http://www.arcafoundation.org
Grants List: http://www.arcafoundation.org/current_grantees.htm
The Arca Foundation's Philanthropy Promise: http://www.ncrp.org/philanthropys-promise/who

Incorporated in 1952 in NY.
Donor: Nancy R. Reynolds‡.
Foundation type: Independent foundation.
Financial data (yr. ended 12/31/13): Assets, $55,727,462 (M); gifts received, $25,000; expenditures, $3,324,480; qualifying distributions, $3,009,676; giving activities include $2,457,075 for 75 grants (high: $110,000; low: $500).
Purpose and activities: The foundation is dedicated to advancing social equity and justice. It believes that a vibrant democracy requires an organized and informed citizenry that has access to information and free expression. In pursuit of these principles, the foundation supports innovative and strategic efforts that work to advance equity, accountability, social justice, and participatory democracy in the U.S. and abroad. While its areas of focus evolve over time, it achieves its fundamental purpose by supporting efforts that affect public policy.
Fields of interest: International affairs, national security; International affairs, foreign policy; International human rights; Civil/human rights, advocacy; Civil/human rights; Public policy, research; Public affairs.
Type of support: General/operating support; Continuing support; Management development/capacity building; Program development; Conferences/seminars; Film/video/radio; Publication; Seed money; Research; Program evaluation; Matching/challenge support.
Limitations: Applications accepted. Giving on a national basis. No support for direct social services, government programs, or groups outside the U.S. No grants to individuals, or for annual campaigns, emergency funds, capital or endowment funds, scholarly research, deficit financing, scholarships, or fellowships; no loans.
Publications: Application guidelines; Financial statement; Grants list.
Application information: Applications guidelines and form available on foundation web site. Preliminary letters of inquiry are not considered;

proposals received outside the biennial deadlines will not be considered. Application form required.

Initial approach: Proposal via online application process on foundation web site only
Copies of proposal: 1
Deadline(s): Feb. 1 and Aug. 1
Board meeting date(s): June and Dec.
Final notification: June and Dec.

Officers and Directors:* Nancy R. Bagley,* Pres.; Nicole Bagley,* V.P.; Mary E. King,* Secy.; Anna Lefer Kuhn, Exec. Dir.; The Rev. Joseph Eldrige; Michael Lux; Janet Shenk; Margery A. Tabankin.
Number of staff: 2 full-time professional.
EIN: 132751798
Selected grants: The following grants are a representative sample of this grantmaker's funding activity:
$100,000 to J Street Education Fund, Washington, DC, 2012. For general support.
$100,000 to Leadership Center for the Common Good, Washington, DC, 2012. For bank accountability work.
$75,000 to ACCE Institute, Los Angeles, CA, 2012. For general support.
$75,000 to Alliance for a Just Society, Seattle, WA, 2012. For the New Bottom Line's work on the Home Defenders' League.
$75,000 to Leadership Conference Education Fund, Washington, DC, 2012. For Americans for Financial Reform.
$75,000 to National Security Archive Fund, Washington, DC, 2012. For general support.
$75,000 to New Organizing Institute Education Fund, Washington, DC, 2012. For the economic justice program.
$50,000 to Alliance for a Just Society, Seattle, WA, 2012. For general Support.
$50,000 to National Security Initiative, Washington, DC, 2012. For general support.
$50,000 to Womens Action for New Directions, Arlington, MA, 2012. For media and message training on budget issues.

1881
Banyan Tree Foundation ✧
1775 Pennsylvania Ave., Ste. 1200
Washington, DC 20006-4671
Contact: Carolyn Stremlau, Exec. Dir.

Established in 1986 in CA.
Donors: Peter Ackerman; Joanne Leedom Ackerman.
Foundation type: Independent foundation.
Financial data (yr. ended 12/31/12): Assets, $140,158 (M); gifts received, $3,750,000; expenditures, $3,834,692; qualifying distributions, $3,833,835; giving activities include $3,112,246 for 34 grants (high: $546,970; low: $2,500).
Purpose and activities: Giving primarily to international education in selected countries; support also for education programs in Washington, DC.
Fields of interest: Education; Children/youth; Children; Economically disadvantaged.
International interests: Africa; Southeastern Asia.
Type of support: General/operating support; Continuing support; Program development; Matching/challenge support.
Limitations: Applications not accepted. Giving on an international basis to select countries in Africa and Southeast Asia and on a limited basis in Washington, DC. No support for organizations with religious affiliations and/or medical or environmental focus or for individual schools; no grants outside listed geographic focus. No grants to individuals.
Application information: Unsolicited requests for funds not accepted.
Officers: Joanne Leedom-Ackerman, Pres.; Peter Ackerman, Secy.-Treas.; Carolyn Stremlau, Exec. Dir.
Number of staff: 3 full-time professional.
EIN: 954088915

1882
The Bauman Foundation
(formerly Bauman Family Foundation, Inc.)
c/o Jewett House
2040 S St. N.W.
Washington, DC 20009-1110 (202) 328-2040
Contact: Patricia Bauman, Pres.; John L. Bryant, Jr., V.P.
FAX: (202) 328-2003;
E-mail: baumanfoundation@baumanfoundation.org;
Main URL: http://www.baumanfoundation.org

Established in 1982 in NY.
Donor: Lionel R. Bauman†.
Foundation type: Independent foundation.
Financial data (yr. ended 06/30/14): Assets, $95,105,002 (M); expenditures, $8,225,164; qualifying distributions, $6,845,063; giving activities include $6,059,100 for 78 grants (high: $500,000; low: $1,000).
Purpose and activities: The foundation is dedicated to achieving the values of a true democratic society — the common good and general welfare, as articulated in the Constitution.
Fields of interest: Arts; Education; Environment; Public health; Employment; Economic development; Public policy, research.
Type of support: General/operating support; Continuing support; Program development; Conferences/seminars; Publication; Seed money; Curriculum development; Research; Technical assistance; Matching/challenge support.
Limitations: Applications not accepted. Giving primarily in Washington, DC, and New York, NY. No grants to individuals.
Application information: Unsolicited requests for funds not accepted.

Board meeting date(s): Quarterly

Officers and Directors:* Patricia Bauman,* Pres.; John Landrum Bryant, Jr.,* V.P. and Treas.; Gary D. Bass, Exec. Dir.; Marcia Avner; Anne Bartley; Amy Bauman; Jessica Bauman; Deepak Bhargava; David Brock; Anne H. Hess; Rev. Msgr. Kevin W. Irwin; Rev. Walter G. Lewis; Gerald Torres.
Number of staff: 2 full-time professional; 1 full-time support.
EIN: 133119290
Selected grants: The following grants are a representative sample of this grantmaker's funding activity:
$735,000 to Public Interest Projects, New York, NY, 2013. For civic engagement.
$600,000 to Rockefeller Philanthropy Advisors, Philanthropic Collaborative, New York, NY, 2012. For general support.
$500,000 to Tides Foundation, San Francisco, CA, 2012. For Voter Action Fund.
$500,000 to Tides Foundation, San Francisco, CA, 2013. For Voter Action Fund.
$450,000 to Rockefeller Philanthropy Advisors, New York, NY, 2013. For general support.
$400,000 to Natural Resources Defense Council, New York, NY, 2012. For general support.
$400,000 to Natural Resources Defense Council, Washington, DC, 2013. For general support.
$400,000 to Rockefeller Family Fund, New York, NY, 2013. For civic engagement.
$350,000 to Public Interest Projects, New York, NY, 2013. For state infrastructure fund.
$275,000 to Center for Effective Government, OMB Watch, Washington, DC, 2013. For general support.
$250,000 to Center for Effective Government, Washington, DC, 2012. For general support.
$250,000 to Montefiore Medical Center, Bronx, NY, 2012. For education project.
$250,000 to New Venture Fund, Washington, DC, 2013. For Americans for Tax Fairness.
$150,000 to Labor/Community Strategy Center, Los Angeles, CA, 2012. For general support.
$125,000 to National Council of La Raza, Washington, DC, 2012. For civic engagement.
$100,000 to Tides Foundation, San Francisco, CA, 2012. For New Strategies Fund.
$50,000 to Environmental Defense Fund, Washington, DC, 2012. For Chemical Policy Project.
$50,000 to Fund for Constitutional Government, Washington, DC, 2012. For Openthegovernment.org.
$40,000 to Blue Green Alliance Foundation, Minneapolis, MN, 2013. For Regulatory Protections Project.
$25,000 to Federation of American Scientists, Washington, DC, 2013. For general support.

1883
Bedford Falls Foundation ✧
1001 Pennsylvania Ave. N.W., Ste. 220S
Washington, DC 20004-2525

Established in 1997 in VA.
Donors: William E. Conway; Joanne Conway; William E. Conway, Jr.
Foundation type: Independent foundation.
Financial data (yr. ended 12/31/13): Assets, $23,359,215 (M); gifts received, $4,212,000; expenditures, $9,522,190; qualifying distributions, $9,519,240; giving activities include $9,514,114 for 16 grants (high: $1,000,000; low: $10,000).
Purpose and activities: Giving primarily for social services and Roman Catholic churches; funding also for health organizations and animal welfare.
Fields of interest: Animal welfare; Hospitals (general); Health organizations; Human services; Catholic agencies & churches.
Limitations: Applications not accepted. Giving primarily in Washington, DC, and Nashua, NH. No grants to individuals.
Application information: Contributes only to pre-selected organizations.
Trustees: Joanne Conway; William E. Conway, Jr.
EIN: 526834462

1884
Beech Street Foundation ✧
2409 49th St., N.W.
Washington, DC 20007-1004 (202) 966-9159
Contact: Jeffrey Bauman, Tr.

Established in 1987 in DC.
Donors: Jeffrey Bauman; Linda Fienberg.
Foundation type: Independent foundation.

Financial data (yr. ended 12/31/12): Assets, $2,489,180 (M); gifts received, $290,555; expenditures, $444,711; qualifying distributions, $430,550; giving activities include $430,550 for 32 grants (high: $71,500; low: $1,000).
Purpose and activities: Giving primarily for the performing arts; funding also for higher education, and human services.
Fields of interest: Performing arts, theater; Arts; Higher education; Education; Legal services; Human services.
Limitations: Applications accepted. Giving primarily in Washington, DC. No grants to individuals.
Application information: Application form required.
Initial approach: Letter
Deadline(s): None
Trustees: Jeffrey Bauman; Linda Fienberg.
EIN: 521781489

1885
Bender Foundation, Inc. ✧
1120 Connecticut Ave., N.W.
Washington, DC 20036-3932 (202) 828-9000
E-mail: benderfoundation@blakereal.com

Incorporated in 1958 in DC.
Donors: Jack I. Bender‡; Howard M. Bender; Julie B. Silver; Stanley S. Bender‡; Sondra Bender; The Stanley S. Bender 2002 Trust.
Foundation type: Independent foundation.
Financial data (yr. ended 12/31/12): Assets, $53,843,657 (M); gifts received, $6,119,657; expenditures, $2,637,928; qualifying distributions, $2,400,928; giving activities include $2,124,600 for 108 grants (high: $200,000; low: $500).
Fields of interest: Performing arts; Higher education; Health care; Health organizations, association; Human services; Jewish federated giving programs; Jewish agencies & synagogues.
Type of support: General/operating support; Annual campaigns; Capital campaigns; Building/renovation; Endowments; Program development; Seed money; Curriculum development; Scholarship funds; Research; Matching/challenge support.
Limitations: Applications not accepted. Giving primarily in Washington, DC, and MD. No grants to individuals.
Publications: Annual report.
Application information: Contributes only to pre-selected organizations.
Board meeting date(s): Quarterly
Officers: Julie Bender Silver, Pres.; Howard M. Bender, Exec. V.P.; David S. Bender, V.P.; Barbara A. Bender, V.P.; Eileen Bender Greenberg, V.P.
Directors: Jason Belinkie; Nanette Bender; Richard Greenberg; David Silver.
Number of staff: 1 full-time professional.
EIN: 526054193
Selected grants: The following grants are a representative sample of this grantmaker's funding activity:
$100,000 to American Heart Association, Glen Allen, VA, 2012. For Heart Ball/Gala.
$57,750 to KaBOOM, Washington, DC, 2012. For Community Build Playground Project.
$50,000 to Jewish Women International, Washington, DC, 2012. For Women to Watch Luncheon and $45,000 earmarked for the Sondra D. Bender Leadership Institute.
$25,000 to Hope and a Home, Washington, DC, 2012. For Higher Education for All Programs.
$25,000 to Suburban Hospital, Bethesda, MD, 2012. For Earmarked as Seed Money for the Naming of the Emergency Room.
$25,000 to Washington Hospital Center, Washington, DC, 2012. For donation only.
$18,000 to American University, Washington, DC, 2012. For Operations Center for Israel Studies and Sponsorships.
$15,000 to Suburban Hospital, Bethesda, MD, 2012. Toward Showcase 2012 at the Bolger Center as a Diamond Level to Benefit Cardiovascular Care Programs and NIH Heart Center.
$10,000 to Jewish Foundation for Group Homes, Rockville, MD, 2012. For annual scholarship gala.
$5,000 to Cystic Fibrosis Foundation, Denver, CO, 2012. For Helping People with Disabilities.

1886
Bernstein Family Foundation ✧ ☆
(formerly Leo M. Bernstein Family Foundation)
c/o The Bernstein Companies, Attn.: Ami Becker Aronson
3299 K St. N.W., Ste. 700
Washington, DC 20007-4438 (202) 255-4477
FAX: (202) 333-3323;
E-mail: info@bernsteinfamilyfoundationdc.org; Main URL: http://bernsteinfamilyfoundationdc.org/
Grants List: http://bernsteinfamilyfoundationdc.org/downloads/bff_grants.pdf

Established in 1952 in DC and VA.
Donors: Leo M. Bernstein‡; Wayside of Virginia Inc.
Foundation type: Independent foundation.
Financial data (yr. ended 12/31/13): Assets, $11,572,085 (M); expenditures, $1,098,936; qualifying distributions, $594,516; giving activities include $503,250 for 49 grants (high: $50,000; low: $500).
Purpose and activities: Giving primarily for: 1) Jewish causes which strengthen the Jewish community of Washington, DC, through support of spiritual leaders, synagogues and community programs that educate Jewish children and adults, and support the development of Jewish identity. Priority will be given to leaders, institutions and projects that: a) use innovative tools to examine the current state of Jewish identity; b) foster dialogue and bridge cultural divides; and c) expand Jewish culture in a modern way; 2) Programs that advance and promote public understanding and appreciation for the United States of America and American democracy; 3) Arts and Culture programs, including support for museum activities, performing arts, visual arts, film, media and art education programs. Priority will be given to projects that: a) use art as a tool for public dialogue and education; b) use public celebrations of art as a way to bring the community together; c) share community-building models developed by community-based arts institutions; and d) integrate different segments of society and awaken civic engagement; and 4) Special projects as defined by the foundation's Board of Directors.
Fields of interest: Arts education; Arts; Education; Community/economic development; Jewish agencies & synagogues.
Type of support: General/operating support; Capital campaigns; Program development; Conferences/seminars.
Limitations: Applications not accepted. Giving limited to charitable organizations located in or serving areas within a 100-mile radius of Washington, DC, and have a strong interest in focusing on needs within the district itself. No support for private foundations. No grants to individuals, or for general operating support; no loans.
Publications: Grants list.
Application information: Contributes only to pre-selected organizations.
Board meeting date(s): Mar. and Sept.
Officers and Directors:* Amb. Stuart Bernstein,* Pres.; Richard Bernstein,* V.P.; Mauree Jane Perry,* Secy.; Adam K. Bernstein,* Treas.; Ami Becker Aronson, Exec. Dir.; Shawn Becker, M.D.; Baron John Bernstein; Rabbi Boruch Bernstein; Tara Bernstein; Alison Bernstein Shulman.
Number of staff: 1 part-time professional.
EIN: 526041822

1887
Diane & Norman Bernstein Foundation, Inc. ✧
1156 15th St. N.W., Ste. 601
Washington, DC 20005-4802 (202) 223-2002

Established in 1965 in DC.
Donors: Diane Bernstein; Norman Bernstein.
Foundation type: Independent foundation.
Financial data (yr. ended 12/31/12): Assets, $17,037,315 (M); gifts received, $1,000,000; expenditures, $1,350,200; qualifying distributions, $896,011; giving activities include $790,055 for 23 grants (high: $250,000; low: $55).
Purpose and activities: Primary areas of interest include the arts, health, social services, Jewish welfare, and Israel. Support for those institutions and organizations, identified by the foundation's donors and their family members, which perpetuate and nurture the educational, religious, humanitarian, health, cultural and social aspects of society, including support for the Jewish community.
Fields of interest: Performing arts; Performing arts, music; Arts; Elementary/secondary education; Health care; Health organizations, association; AIDS; AIDS research; Human services; Child development, services; Jewish federated giving programs; Biology/life sciences; Religion; Children/youth; Children; Youth; Women; Economically disadvantaged.
International interests: Israel.
Type of support: General/operating support; Continuing support; Annual campaigns; Capital campaigns; Program development.
Limitations: Applications not accepted. Giving primarily in Washington, DC; support for the Jewish community on a local, national, and international basis. No grants to individuals.
Publications: Annual report.
Application information: Contributes only to pre-selected organizations.
Board meeting date(s): Oct. and Aug.
Officers and Directors:* Norman Bernstein,* Chair.; Diane Bernstein,* Pres.; Elizabeth B. Norton,* Secy.; Joshua Benjamin Bernstein,* Treas.; Celia Ellen Bernstein; Lisa Bernstein; Susan Amy Bernstein; Marianne Bernstein Kalb; Robert Kalb; Robert Norton; Nancy Bernstein Schoen; Robert Schoen.
Number of staff: 1 full-time professional.
EIN: 526047356

1888
Herb Block Foundation ✧
1730 M St. N.W., Ste. 901
Washington, DC 20036-4509 (202) 223-8801
Contact: Sarah Armstrong Alex, C.O.O. and Exec. Dir.
FAX: (202) 223-8804; E-mail: info@herbblock.org; Main URL: http://www.herbblockfoundation.org; Facebook: https://www.facebook.com/pages/The-Herb-Block-Foundation/194650137248067
Scholarship address: The Herb Block Scholarship, ISTS, 1321 Murfreesboro Rd., Ste. 800, Nashville, TN 37217, tel.: (855) 670-4787, e-mail: contactus@applyists.com

Established in 2001 in DC and VA.
Donor: Herbert L. Block†.
Foundation type: Independent foundation.
Financial data (yr. ended 09/30/13): Assets, $53,421,175 (M); expenditures, $2,875,910; qualifying distributions, $3,479,807; giving activities include $1,554,500 for 150 grants (high: $25,000; low: $500).
Purpose and activities: The foundation is committed to defending the basic freedoms guaranteed to all Americans, combating all forms of discrimination and prejudice, and improving the conditions of the poor and underprivileged through the creation or support of charitable and educational programs with the same goals. It is also committed to providing educational opportunity to deserving students through post-secondary education scholarships, and to promoting editorial cartooning through continued research.
Fields of interest: Adult education—literacy, basic skills & GED; Scholarships/financial aid; Education; Employment, services; Youth development; Civil liberties, advocacy; Civil liberties, first amendment; Civil/human rights; Public affairs, citizen participation; Economically disadvantaged.
Type of support: General/operating support; Emergency funds; Program development; Curriculum development; Program evaluation; Matching/challenge support.
Limitations: Applications accepted. Giving limited for the benefit of the greater metropolitan Washington, DC, region, including Montgomery and Prince George's counties, MD, and the counties of Arlington, Fairfax, and the city of Alexandria, VA. Applicants for the Defending Basic Freedoms Program and the Encouraging Citizen Involvement Program may be located in or provide services in areas outside the District of Columbia region. No support for sectarian religious purposes. No grants for capital or endowment programs.
Publications: Application guidelines; Grants list; Informational brochure; Program policy statement; Program policy statement (including application guidelines).
Application information: Washington Regional Association of Grantmakers' Common Grant Application Format accepted. See foundation web site for full application information, including grant program cycles, application timelines, and eligibility requirements. Application form required.
Initial approach: Letter of inquiry; submit full proposals upon foundation invitation only
Copies of proposal: 1
Deadline(s): Check foundation web site for application deadlines
Board meeting date(s): Jan., May, and late Sept.
Final notification: Approximately 4 weeks
Officers and Executive Committee:* Athelia Knight,* Chair.; Marcela Brane,* Pres.; Jean J. Rickard,* V.P. and Exec. Dir. Emerita; Sarah Armstrong Alex,* C.O.O. and Exec. Dir.; Robin Meszoly,* Treas.
Directors: Jane Asher; Robert Asher; Raymond Bonieskie; Laura Hutchison; Donna McNulty; Clarence Page; Jill Hammer Stanley; Laurie Strayer; Roger Wilkins.
Number of staff: 3 full-time professional; 1 part-time professional.
EIN: 260008276

1889
The Butler Family Fund ✧
1634 I St. N.W., Ste. 1000
Washington, DC 20006-4015 (202) 463-8288
Contact: Martha A. Toll, Exec. Dir.; Anne H. Morin, Prog. Assoc.
FAX: (202) 783-8499;
E-mail: info@butlerfamilyfund.org; Main URL: http://www.butlerfamilyfund.org
Grants Database: http://www.butlerfamilyfund.org/grantees.php

Established in 1992 in DC.
Donor: J.E. and Z.B. Butler Foundation.
Foundation type: Independent foundation.
Financial data (yr. ended 12/31/13): Assets, $11,543,504 (M); gifts received, $67,000; expenditures, $750,173; qualifying distributions, $666,938; giving activities include $441,680 for 32 grants (high: $40,000; low: $500).
Purpose and activities: Support for homeless families and criminal justice reform (death penalty and juvenile justice).
Fields of interest: Environment, climate change/global warming; Crime/law enforcement, reform; Housing/shelter; Civil liberties, death penalty issues; Homeless.
International interests: United Kingdom.
Type of support: General/operating support; Program development; Seed money.
Limitations: Applications not accepted. Giving primarily in Los Angeles, San Diego and the San Francisco Bay Area, CA, Washington, DC, Chicago, IL, NY, Philadelphia, PA, WI, and London, England. No grants to individuals.
Publications: Grants list; Multi-year report; Program policy statement.
Application information: Unsolicited proposals or letters of inquiry are not accepted. No grants for more than 3 consecutive years.
Board meeting date(s): Biannually
Officers and Directors:* Eve B. Wildrick,* Pres.; Martha A. Toll, Exec. Dir.; Jennifer Gravin; Dina Hirsch; Eleanor Leyden-Dunbar; Nina Morrison; Rebecca Morrison; Jody Snider.
Number of staff: 1 part-time professional; 1 part-time support.
EIN: 521786778

1890
The Morris and Gwendolyn Cafritz Foundation ✧
1825 K St. N.W., Ste. 1400
Washington, DC 20006-1202 (202) 223-3100
Contact: Rose Ann Cleveland, Exec. Dir.
FAX: (202) 296-7567;
E-mail: info@cafritzfoundation.org; Main URL: http://www.cafritzfoundation.org
Grants Database: http://www.cafritzfoundation.org/grantees/recent_grantees.asp

Incorporated in 1948 in DC.
Donors: Morris Cafritz†; Gwendolyn D. Cafritz†.
Foundation type: Independent foundation.
Financial data (yr. ended 04/30/14): Assets, $725,140,070 (M); expenditures, $42,706,185; qualifying distributions, $25,091,503; giving activities include $16,513,952 for 589 grants (high: $316,667; low: $2,500), and $37,225 for 56 employee matching gifts.
Purpose and activities: The foundation is committed to building a stronger community for residents of the Washington, D.C. area through support of programs in arts and humanities, community services, education, and health and the environment.
Fields of interest: Museums; Performing arts; Performing arts, dance; Performing arts, theater; Performing arts, music; Arts; Education, early childhood education; Child development, education; Elementary school/education; Secondary school/education; Higher education; Adult/continuing education; Adult education—literacy, basic skills & GED; Environment, formal/general education; Environment, natural resources; Environment; Reproductive health, family planning; Medical care, rehabilitation; Health care; Substance abuse, services; Mental health/crisis services; AIDS; Health organizations; Food services; Housing/shelter, development; Housing/shelter; Human services; Children/youth, services; Child development, services; Family services; Residential/custodial care, hospices; Aging, centers/services; Women, centers/services; Homeless, human services; Civil/human rights, immigrants; Civil/human rights, minorities; Civil/human rights, women; Civil/human rights, aging; Civil liberties, reproductive rights; Civil/human rights; Community/economic development; Voluntarism promotion; Infants/toddlers; Children/youth; Youth; Aging; Young adults; Disabilities, people with; Physically disabled; Blind/visually impaired; Deaf/hearing impaired; Mentally disabled; Minorities; Asians/Pacific Islanders; African Americans/Blacks; Hispanics/Latinos; Women; Infants/toddlers, female; Girls; Military/veterans; Offenders/ex-offenders; Substance abusers; AIDS, people with; Single parents; Crime/abuse victims; Immigrants/refugees; Economically disadvantaged; Homeless; LGBTQ.
Type of support: General/operating support; Management development/capacity building; Program development; Scholarship funds; Technical assistance; Program evaluation; Matching/challenge support.
Limitations: Applications accepted. Giving limited to the Washington, DC, area and the immediate surrounding counties in MD and VA, specifically Prince George's and Montgomery counties, MD, and Arlington and Fairfax counties, and the cities of Alexandria and Falls Church, VA. No grants to individuals, or for emergency funds, deficit financing, endowments, demonstration projects and no loans.
Publications: Application guidelines; Annual report; Grants list.
Application information: Washington Regional Association of Grantmakers' Common Grant Application Format accepted. Proposals may not be submitted via fax or e-mail. Proposals may be submitted online. Application form required.
Initial approach: Telephone e-mail or full proposal
Copies of proposal: 1
Deadline(s): Mar. 1, July 1, and Nov. 1

Board meeting date(s): Generally 3 to 9 months after deadline dates
Final notification: 4 to 6 months
Officers and Directors:* Calvin Cafritz,* Chair., C.E.O. and Pres.; John E. Chapoton,* Vice-Chair.; Ed McGeogh, V.P., Asset Mgmt.; Rohan Rodrigo, V.P., Finance; Rose Ann Cleveland, Exec. Dir.; Michael F. Brewer; LaSalle D. Leffall, Jr., M.D.; Patricia McGuire; Robert Peck; Earl A. Powell III; Alice M. Rivlin; Norman O. Scribner.
Advisory Board: Anthony W. Cafritz; Elliot S. Cafritz; Jane Lipton Cafritz; Carolyn J. Deaver; Hon. Constance A. Morella; Elizabeth M. Peltekian; Julia Sparkman Shepard.
Number of staff: 12 full-time professional; 2 part-time professional; 5 full-time support.
EIN: 526036989
Selected grants: The following grants are a representative sample of this grantmaker's funding activity:
$135,000 to Iona Senior Services, Washington, DC, 2014. For $80,000 for Iona Senior Services, $25,000 for the DC Long Term Care Coalition, 20,000 for the DC Senior Advisory Coalition, and $10,000 for the Take Charge, Live Well project.
$125,000 to New Leaders for New Schools, Washington, DC, 2014. For General support.
$40,000 to Folger Shakespeare Library, Washington, DC, 2014. For General support.
$40,000 to Home Care Partners, Washington, DC, 2014. For $35,000 outright and $5,000 as a 1:1 match for general support.
$30,000 to Fillmore Arts Center, Washington, DC, 2014. For $25,000 outright and $5,000 as a 1:1 match for general support.
$30,000 to For Love of Children, Washington, DC, 2014. For the Neighborhood Tutoring program.

1891
The Case Foundation ✧
(formerly The Stephen Case Foundation)
1717 Rhode Island Ave. N.W., 7th Fl.
Washington, DC 20036-3023 (202) 467-5788
Contact: Brian Sasscer, Sr. V.P., Strategic Opers.
FAX: (202) 775-8513;
E-mail: contactus@casefoundation.org; Main URL: http://www.casefoundation.org
Case Foundation Blog: http://www.casefoundation.org/blog
Case Foundation Video Library: http://www.casefoundation.org/videos
Case Soup: http://www.casefoundation.org/videos/case-soup
Facebook: http://www.facebook.com/casefoundation
Foundation's Instagram Profile: http://instagram.com/casefoundation
GiveSmart: http://www.givesmart.org/Stories/Donors/Jean-and-Steve-Case
Google Plus: https://plus.google.com/+casefoundation/posts
Jean and Steve Case's Giving Pledge Profile: http://glasspockets.org/philanthropy-in-focus/eye-on-the-giving-pledge/profiles/case
LinkedIn: http://www.linkedin.com/company/the-case-foundation
Pinterest: http://www.pinterest.com/casefoundation/
RSS Feed: http://feed.casefoundation.org/casefoundation
Twitter: http://www.twitter.com/CaseFoundation
YouTube: http://www.youtube.com/casefoundation

Established in 1997 in VA.
Donors: Stephen M. Case; Jean N. Case; Goldhirsh Foundation.
Foundation type: Independent foundation.
Financial data (yr. ended 12/31/13): Assets, $647,333 (M); gifts received, $4,000,000; expenditures, $3,850,400; qualifying distributions, $3,834,444; giving activities include $1,217,073 for 36 grants (high: $275,000; low: $110).
Purpose and activities: Giving to achieve sustainable solutions to complex social problems by investing in collaboration, leadership, and entrepreneurship. Supports individuals and organizations that have the strategy, leadership, and commitment to make positive, widespread social change. The foundation seeks to meet the needs of families and children in poverty; create thriving and sustainable economic development for communities; bridge cultural and religious divides; expand civic engagement and volunteerism; and accelerate innovative approaches to health care.
Fields of interest: Education; Health care; Youth development, services; Community/economic development; Engineering/technology.
International interests: Global Programs.
Type of support: Program-related investments/loans.
Limitations: Applications not accepted. Giving in the U.S. and abroad. No grants to individuals.
Application information: Unsolicited requests for funds not considered.
Officers and Directors:* Stephen M. Case,* Chair.; Jean N. Case,* C.E.O. and Pres.; Erich Brokas, Sr. V.P., Strategy and International Investment; Allyson Burns, Sr. V.P., Comms. and Marketing; Sheila Herrling, Sr. V.P., Social Innovation; Brian Sasscer, Sr., V.P., Strategic Operations; Kate Ahern, V.P., Social Innovation; Emily Yu, V.P., Marketing and Partnerships; John Sabin, Secy.-Treas. and C.F.O.
Number of staff: 2 full-time professional; 1 part-time professional; 3 full-time support; 1 part-time support.
EIN: 541848791
Selected grants: The following grants are a representative sample of this grantmaker's funding activity:
$60,000 to Water for People, Denver, CO, 2012. For international development.
$10,000 to New World Foundation, New York, NY, 2012. For Community and International Development.
$2,500 to Independent Sector, Washington, DC, 2012. For Community Development.
$936 to Buxton Initiative, Washington, DC, 2012. For in-kind support.

1892
The CityBridge Foundation, Inc. ✧
(formerly The Advisory Board Foundation, Inc.)
600 New Hampshire Ave. N.W., Ste. 800
Washington, DC 20037-2403 (202) 266-7990
E-mail: info@citybridgefoundation.org; Main URL: http://www.citybridgefoundation.org

Established in 1993 in DC.
Donors: David G. Bradley; Katherine B. Bradley; Atlantic Media; Capital Source Finance LLC; Acumen Solutions; Glover Park Group LLC.
Foundation type: Independent foundation.
Financial data (yr. ended 12/31/12): Assets, $6,196,104 (M); gifts received, $3,008,590; expenditures, $4,289,333; qualifying distributions, $4,028,670; giving activities include $2,988,808 for 111 grants (high: $365,405; low: $50), and $3,974,764 for 2 foundation-administered programs.
Purpose and activities: Giving primarily for youth, voluntarism promotion, and international development and relief.
Fields of interest: Education; Public health; Health care; Employment; Youth development; Children/youth, services; International development; International relief; Voluntarism promotion; Infants/toddlers; Children/youth; Children; Youth; Adults; Young adults; Asians/Pacific Islanders; Crime/abuse victims; Economically disadvantaged.
International interests: Philippines; South Africa.
Type of support: Program development; Research; Program evaluation.
Limitations: Applications not accepted. Giving in the U.S. (primarily in the greater metropolitan Washington, DC, area) and internationally, with emphasis on South Africa and the Philippines. No grants to individuals.
Application information: Contributes only to pre-selected organizations.
Officers and Directors:* Katherine Brittain Bradley,* Pres.; David G. Bradley,* V.P. and Secy.-Treas.; Steven LaFemina, C.O.O.; Mieka Wick, Exec. Dir.; Spencer Bradley.
Number of staff: 6 full-time professional.
EIN: 521870074

1893
The Community Foundation for the National Capital Region ✧
(formerly The Foundation for the National Capital Region)
1201 15th St. N.W., Ste. 420
Washington, DC 20005-2842 (202) 955-5890
Contact: Terri Lee Freeman, Pres.
FAX: (202) 955-8084; E-mail: tfreeman@cfncr.org; Main URL: http://www.thecommunityfoundation.org
E-Newsletter: http://www.cfncr.org/site/c.ihLSJ5PLKuG/b.4475731/k.A0E9/Publications.htm
Facebook: http://www.facebook.com/CFNCR
RSS Feed: http://www.cfncr.org/site/apps/nl/rss2.asp?c=ihLSJ5PLKuG&b=5298963
Twitter: http://twitter.com/CommunityFndn
Twitter: http://twitter.com/terrileefreeman

Incorporated in 1973 in DC.
Foundation type: Community foundation.
Financial data (yr. ended 03/31/13): Assets, $334,979,789 (M); gifts received, $54,376,795; expenditures, $101,071,503; giving activities include $95,397,756 for grants.
Purpose and activities: The mission of the foundation is to strengthen the metropolitan Washington region by encouraging and supporting effective charitable giving and by taking leadership on critical issues in the community and retain jobs that provide good wages, benefits and opportunities for advancement. Competitive grant opportunities are available and include the following areas: arts, individual and organizational capacity-building, children and families, education and youth development, employment and workforce development, environment, emergency services, family literacy and libraries and violence prevention.
Fields of interest: Arts; Elementary/secondary education; Education; Environment; Health care; Health organizations, association; Housing/shelter; Youth development, services; Children/youth,

services; Human services; Civil/human rights, advocacy; Nonprofit management; Community/economic development; Aging.
Type of support: General/operating support; Management development/capacity building; Program development; Research; Technical assistance; Program evaluation; Matching/challenge support.
Limitations: Applications accepted. Giving limited to the Washington, DC, Prince George's and Montgomery counties, MD, and northern VA. No grants to individuals (except for scholarships), or from discretionary funds for annual campaigns, endowment funds, land acquisition or renovation projects.
Publications: Application guidelines; Annual report; Financial statement; Informational brochure; Newsletter; Program policy statement.
Application information: Visit foundation web site for application forms, deadlines, and guidelines. Application form required.
Initial approach: Contact foundation
Copies of proposal: 1
Deadline(s): Varies
Board meeting date(s): Quarterly
Officers and Trustees:* Martin Weinstein,* Chair.; Gene Sachs,* Vice-Chair.; Terri Lee Freeman,* Pres.; Daniel Studnicky, V.P., Donor Engagement and Professional Svcs.; Angela Jones Hackley, V.P., Philanthropic Svcs.; Verdia Haywood,* Secy.; Mark Hansen, C.F.O.; Richard J. Dumais,* Treas.; Juliana Mitrojorgji, Cont.; Victoria P. Sant, Emeritus; Eric Adler; Mary Pat Alcus; Fernando Barrueta; John Terry Beaty; Virginia Cheung; Wendy Goldberg; Nancy Kfoury, Ph.D.; Natalie Ludaway; Wendy Thompson Marquez; Daniel K. Mayers; Patricia McGuire; Michael O'Neill; William "Bill" Shipp.
Number of staff: 27 full-time professional; 41 part-time professional.
EIN: 237343119
Selected grants: The following grants are a representative sample of this grantmaker's funding activity:
$2,700,000 to Maranatha Volunteers International, Roseville, CA, 2012. For general support.
$1,695,893 to Barbara Bush Texas Fund for Family Literacy, Houston, TX, 2012. For general support.
$1,200,000 to Alliance for Global Good, Greensboro, NC, 2012. For general support.
$1,155,000 to City First Enterprises, Washington, DC, 2012. For general support.
$750,000 to Habitat for Humanity, DC, Washington, DC, 2012. For general support.
$314,295 to Shakespeare Theater, Washington, DC, 2012. For general support.
$50,000 to Housing Options and Planning Enterprises, Oxon Hill, MD, 2012. For general support.
$25,000 to Shaw Community Ministry, Washington, DC, 2012. For general support.
$24,000 to Columbia University, New York, NY, 2012. For general support.
$20,000 to Georgetown Visitation Monastery, Washington, DC, 2012. For general support.

1894
Consumer Health Foundation

1400 16th St. N.W., Ste. 710
Washington, DC 20036-2224 (202) 939-3390
Contact: Yanique Redwood, C.E.O. and Pres.
FAX: (202) 939-3391;
E-mail: chf@consumerhealthfdn.org; Main URL: http://www.consumerhealthfdn.org
Consumer Health Foundation's Philanthropy Promise: http://www.ncrp.org/philanthropys-promise/who
E-Newsletter: http://www.consumerhealthfdn.org/index.php/site/newsletter_signup/
Facebook: http://www.facebook.com/chf365
Twitter: http://twitter.com/chf_news

Established in 1994 in DC; converted from the proceeds of the sale of Group Health Association to Humana, Inc.
Donor: Group Health Assn., Inc.
Foundation type: Independent foundation.
Financial data (yr. ended 12/31/13): Assets, $28,127,264 (M); gifts received, $93,989; expenditures, $3,246,433; qualifying distributions, $3,018,640; giving activities include $1,549,177 for 56 grants (high: $91,000; low: $1,000).
Purpose and activities: The mission of the Consumer Health Foundation is to achieve health justice in the Washington, DC region through activities that advance the health and well being of historically underserved communities. It supports initiatives that empower consumers to make decisions and take actions that improve personal, family and community health.
Fields of interest: Health care, equal rights; Public health; Health care, financing; Health care; Offenders/ex-offenders, transitional care; Children/youth, services; Aging, centers/services; Children/youth; Youth; Adults; Disabilities, people with; Minorities; AIDS, people with; Immigrants/refugees; Economically disadvantaged.
Type of support: Continuing support; Management development/capacity building; Program development; Seed money; Technical assistance; Program evaluation; Program-related investments/loans; Mission-related investments/loans.
Limitations: Applications accepted. Giving limited to organizations within the metropolitan Washington, DC, area, including Prince George's and Montgomery counties, MD, and northern VA. National, regional or statewide organizations providing services in metropolitan Washington, DC, and working in full partnership with local, community-based organizations will also be considered. No support for organizations lacking 501(c)(3) status. No grants to individuals, or for general operating support, capital campaigns, or for building/renovation activities.
Publications: Application guidelines; Annual report; Financial statement; Grants list; Newsletter.
Application information: The foundation generally does not accept unsolicited requests for funds. See foundation web site for guidelines and updates in this area. Application form required.
Initial approach: Brief e-mail
Copies of proposal: 1
Board meeting date(s): Quarterly; committees meet in the interim
Officers and Trustees:* Jacquelyn L. Lendsey,* Chair.; Roberta Milman,* Vice-Chair.; Yanique Redwood,* C.E.O. and Pres.; Deborah Smith,* Secy.-Treas.; Christopher J. King; Ed Lazere; Naomi Mezey; Jeanette Noltenius; Chan Park; David C. Rose; Joseph Wright.
Number of staff: 3 full-time professional; 1 full-time support; 1 part-time support.
EIN: 530078064
Selected grants: The following grants are a representative sample of this grantmaker's funding activity:
$75,000 to District of Columbia Primary Care Association, Washington, DC, 2013. To advocate for health reforms that will expand access to care for low-income, uninsured residents and to implement the Medical Homes D.C. Initiative.
$75,000 to Primary Care Coalition of Montgomery County, Silver Spring, MD, 2013. To develop a comprehensive and integrated system of care for low-income, uninsured and ethnically diverse Montgomery County residents.
$50,000 to CASA de Maryland, Hyattsville, MD, 2012. To educate, train and mobilize low-income, uninsured residets in Langley Park around fair development campaign designed to preserve affordable housing and small businesses, and to establish community health clinic.
$50,000 to CASA de Maryland, Hyattsville, MD, 2013. To educate, train and mobilize low-income, uninsured residents in Langley Park around fair development campaign designed to preserve affordable housing and small businesses, and to establish community health clinic.
$50,000 to Greater Baden Medical Services, Brandywine, MD, 2013. For Primary care association.
$40,000 to DC Appleseed Center for Law and Justice, Washington, DC, 2012. To advocate and monitor implementation key reforms related to following projects: CareFirst Blue Cross Blue Shield reform, HIV/AIDS, lead in drinking water, and end of life care system reform.
$40,000 to IMPACT Silver Spring, Neighbors Campaign, Silver Spring, MD, 2012. To organize residents in six communities in Montgomery County to gain better access to public health and social services and to transform their neighborhoods into supportive, healthful environments.
$35,000 to DC Hunger Solutions, D.C. Food Justice Project, Washington, DC, 2012. To advocate policies to expand participation and benefts in federal nutrition programs and increase access to healthy food in low-income communities.
$35,000 to Latin American Youth Center, Washington, DC, 2013. To engage young people and nonprofit leaders in advocacy campaign focused on increasing access to linguistically and culturally competent mental health services for immigrant youth in Prince George's County.
$30,000 to Community Foundation for the National Capital Region, Metropolitan Washington Regional Community Wealth Building Feasibility Assessment (Evergreen), Washington, DC, 2013. To develop a community wealth building strategy for the Metropolitan Washington, DC region, drawing on the experience of Evergreen Cooperatives in Cleveland, OH.
$30,000 to DC Coalition on Long Term Care, Washington, DC, 2012. To advocate for a continuum of affordable, quality long-term care services for low and moderate-income Washington, D.C. residents.
$30,000 to DC Prisoners Legal Services Project, Washington, DC, 2012. To advocate for access to appropriate healthcare services for D.C. Code offenders held in the Central Detention Facility/D.C. Jail facilities, federal prisons and halfway houses.
$30,000 to Foster and Adoptive Parent Advocacy Center, Birth Parent and Kinship Caregivers Advocacy Project, Washington, DC, 2012. To engage foster and birth parents and kinship caregivers in a joint advocacy campaign focused on improving

access to continuous, high-quality health and mental health services for children in DC.
$30,000 to University Legal Services, DC Jail Advocacy Project, Washington, DC, 2013. To advocate for policies that will reduce the over-incarceration of people with psychiatric disabilities and remove barriers to services and supports as they transition back into the community.
$30,000 to Virginia Interfaith Center for Public Policy, Richmond, VA, 2013. For Health Reform Advocacy. To advocate for health care reform implementation in Virginia by organizing and engaging patients, community organizations, labor, small businesses, and other advocacy groups.
$25,000 to Community Foundation for the National Capital Region, Washington, DC, 2013. To support Greater Washington Workforce Development Collaborative, funding partnership that will work to strengthen regional education and skills training systems in health care and construction trades, with goal of moving low-income adults into sustainable employment.
$25,000 to District of Columbia Behavioral Health Association, Mental Health Policy and System Reform Project, Washington, DC, 2012. To advocate for changes in policy and practice that will support integrated and seamless mental health services for children and adults enrolled in D.C.'s public healthcare programs.
$25,000 to McClendon Center, Consumer Advisory Board (CAB), Washington, DC, 2013. For patient engagement work that will ensure the participation of patients in improving their mental health, quality of life, and the Center's services and programs.
$21,000 to DIRECT Action, Disability-Rights Advocacy for Home and Community-Based Care Project, Washington, DC, 2012. To educate consumers who are disabled, under the age of 65, and living in nursing homes about the option of home and community-based long-term care and to advocate for policies and funding that will expand access to these services.
$15,000 to Childrens National Medical Center, Preventive Oral Health Care Integration Project, Washington, DC, 2012. To advocate for changes in policy and clinical practice that will support integration of preventive oral health care into pediatric primary care medical homes in DC.

1895
Dallas Morse Coors Foundation for the Performing Arts ✧

c/o Covington & Burling
850 Tenth St. NW, Ste. 778S
Washington, DC 20001-4956
E-mail: dmcfoundation@cov.com

Established in 1990 in DC.
Donor: Dallas M. Coors‡.
Foundation type: Independent foundation.
Financial data (yr. ended 12/31/13): Assets, $12,964,050 (M); expenditures, $724,908; qualifying distributions, $540,994; giving activities include $483,920 for 47 grants (high: $75,000; low: $2,000).
Purpose and activities: Awards given to general organizations or entities involved in the performing arts in the metropolitan District of Columbia area.
Fields of interest: Performing arts.
Type of support: General/operating support; Continuing support.
Limitations: Applications not accepted. Giving limited to the greater metropolitan Washington, DC, area, including portions of MD and VA. No support for organizations which are not directly involved in the performing arts.
Application information: Unsolicited requests for funds not accepted.
Trustee: Doris D. Blazek-White.
Number of staff: 1 part-time support.
EIN: 526436554
Selected grants: The following grants are a representative sample of this grantmaker's funding activity:
$75,000 to Washington National Opera, Washington, DC, 2012. For Production of Bellini's Norma.
$60,000 to Washington Performing Arts Society, Washington, DC, 2012. For Presentation of Youth Orchestra of Venezuela, Royal Concertgebouw Orchestra and San Francisco Symphony.
$35,000 to National Symphony Orchestra, Washington, DC, 2012. For Labor Day and Season Open Concerts.
$30,000 to Cornell University, Ithaca, NY, 2012. For Main stage theatre curtains.
$15,000 to Levine School of Music, Washington, DC, 2012. For 2012-2013 Performance Series (Levine) Presents).
$7,000 to Wolf Trap Foundation for the Performing Arts, Vienna, VA, 2012. For Wolf Trap Opera Company 2013 Season.
$2,000 to Cantate Chamber Singers, Bethesda, MD, 2012. For 2012-2013 concert season.

1896
Marshall B. Coyne Foundation, Inc. ✧

2000 L St. N.W.
Washington, DC 20036-4907

Established in 1952.
Donor: Marshall B. Coyne‡.
Foundation type: Independent foundation.
Financial data (yr. ended 08/31/13): Assets, $19,661,355 (M); expenditures, $1,070,222; qualifying distributions, $919,612; giving activities include $911,950 for 92 grants (high: $300,000; low: $500).
Purpose and activities: Giving primarily for education, health organizations, including a children's hospital, human services, including services for people who are blind, the arts, and Jewish organizations.
Fields of interest: Arts, cultural/ethnic awareness; Museums (art); Performing arts, theater; Higher education; Education; Hospitals (specialty); Health organizations; Human services; Jewish agencies & synagogues.
Type of support: General/operating support; Conferences/seminars; Research; Employee matching gifts.
Limitations: Applications accepted. Giving primarily in Washington, DC.
Application information: Application form not required.
Initial approach: Proposal
Deadline(s): None
Trustees: C. Richard Beyda; Sheldon Cohen; Amelia McCarthy; Bennett Stichman.
EIN: 526054965
Selected grants: The following grants are a representative sample of this grantmaker's funding activity:
$250,000 to Concord Academy, Concord, MA, 2011.
$100,000 to National Gallery of Art, Washington, DC, 2011.

1897
CrossCurrents Foundation, Inc. ✧

3220 N St. N.W., No. 162
Washington, DC 20007-2829

Established in 2006 in DC.
Donors: Micheline Klagsburn; Celerina Holdings.
Foundation type: Independent foundation.
Financial data (yr. ended 12/31/13): Assets, $288,506 (M); expenditures, $518,138; qualifying distributions, $511,050; giving activities include $443,821 for 60 grants (high: $30,621; low: $500).
Fields of interest: Human services; Social sciences, public policy.
Limitations: Applications not accepted. Giving primarily in Washington, DC; some funding also in NY. No grants to individuals.
Application information: Contributes only to pre-selected organizations.
Officers: Micheline Klagsbrun, Pres.; Ken Grossinger, C.O.O.
Director: Diane J. Fuchs.
EIN: 205557338
Selected grants: The following grants are a representative sample of this grantmaker's funding activity:
$40,000 to State Voices, Detroit, MI, 2011.
$30,000 to Alliance for Justice, Washington, DC, 2011.
$20,000 to Open Arms Housing, Washington, DC, 2011.
$20,000 to Working Films, Wilmington, NC, 2011.
$13,000 to Transformer, Washington, DC, 2011.
$12,000 to Washington District of Columbia Jewish Community Center, Washington, DC, 2011.
$10,000 to DC Vote, Washington, DC, 2011.
$10,000 to HeadCount, New York, NY, 2011.
$10,000 to Media Matters for America, Washington, DC, 2011.
$5,000 to Studio Theater, Washington, DC, 2011.

1898
The Evelyn Y. Davis Foundation ✧ ☆

1120 20th St. N.W., 3rd Fl.
Washington, DC 20036-3437
Application address: c/o Evelyn Y. Davis, 1330 Massachusetts Ave., Washington, DC 20005, (202) 737-7755

Established in 1989 in DC.
Donor: Evelyn Y. Davis.
Foundation type: Independent foundation.
Financial data (yr. ended 12/31/13): Assets, $3,005,515 (M); expenditures, $650,141; qualifying distributions, $650,000; giving activities include $650,000 for 1 grant.
Fields of interest: Arts; Education; Human services.
Type of support: Endowments.
Limitations: Applications accepted. Giving on a national basis. No grants to individuals.
Application information:
Initial approach: Letter
Deadline(s): None
Trustee: Evelyn Y. Davis.
Number of staff: None.
EIN: 521632305

1899
The DeLaski Family Foundation ✧
(formerly The Donald and Nancy L. DeLaski Foundation)
c/o Arabella
1201 Connecticut Ave. N.W., Ste. 300
Washington, DC 20036

Established in 1998 in VA.
Donors: Donald DeLaski; Nancy L. DeLaski; Kenneth E. DeLaski.
Foundation type: Independent foundation.
Financial data (yr. ended 12/31/12): Assets, $34,401,114 (M); gifts received, $3,852,380; expenditures, $3,140,240; qualifying distributions, $3,196,021; giving activities include $3,168,000 for 13 grants (high: $800,000; low: $10,000).
Fields of interest: Museums (art); Performing arts; Health organizations, association.
Limitations: Applications not accepted. Giving primarily in Washington, DC and VA. No grants to individuals.
Application information: Contributes only to pre-selected organizations.
Officers and Directors:* Kathleen DeLaski,* Pres.; David DeLaski,* Secy.; Kenneth DeLaski,* Treas.
EIN: 541902570

1900
The Elizabeth Dole Charitable Foundation ✧ ☆
700 New Hampshire Ave., N.W., Ste. 112
Washington, DC 20037-2407

Established in 1997 in VA.
Donors: Elizabeth H. Dole; The Starr Foundation; Wayne Berman; Thomas Clancy; Alexandra Clancy; J. Ronald Terwilliger; Senator Elizabeth H. Dole.
Foundation type: Independent foundation.
Financial data (yr. ended 12/31/13): Assets, $582,245 (M); gifts received, $14,300; expenditures, $785,670; qualifying distributions, $775,059; giving activities include $775,059 for 2 grants (high: $765,059; low: $10,000).
Fields of interest: Human services; Public affairs.
Type of support: General/operating support.
Limitations: Applications not accepted. Giving primarily in NC. No grants to individuals.
Application information: Contributes only to pre-selected organizations.
Officers: Elizabeth H. Dole, Pres.; Robert P. Davis, Secy.
Director: John Heubusch.
EIN: 522071982

1901
The Max and Victoria Dreyfus Foundation, Inc. ✧
2233 Wisconsin Ave., N.W., Ste. 414
Washington, DC 20007-4122 (202) 337-3300
Contact: Mary P. Surrey, Pres.
FAX: (202) 337-3302;
E-mail: info@mvdreyfusfoundation.org; Main URL: http://mvdreyfusfoundation.org

Incorporated in 1965 in NY.
Donors: Victoria Dreyfus†; Max Dreyfus†.
Foundation type: Independent foundation.
Financial data (yr. ended 12/31/13): Assets, $58,098,200 (M); expenditures, $3,162,199; qualifying distributions, $2,206,002; giving activities include $1,625,576 for 206 grants (high: $50,000; low: $1,040).
Purpose and activities: Support for museums, cultural, performing, and visual arts programs, schools, hospitals, educational and skills training projects, programs for youth, seniors, and people who are handicapped, environmental and wildlife protection activities, and other community-based organizations and their programs.
Fields of interest: Performing arts; Arts; Education; Environment; Animals/wildlife; Hospitals (general); Health care; Medical research, institute; Human services.
Type of support: General/operating support.
Limitations: Applications accepted. Giving on a national basis. No support for foreign charitable organizations. No grants to individuals.
Publications: Application guidelines.
Application information: Do not submit financial statements or copies of audit reports with letter and proposal. E-mailed submissions are not accepted. Application form not required.
Initial approach: Letter of request, not exceeding 3 pages, as well as a 200-word synopsis of the proposal (via U.S. mail)
Copies of proposal: 1
Deadline(s): Post marked by May 10 and Nov. 10
Board meeting date(s): Mar., June, and Oct.
Final notification: Notification made by mail, approximately 8-10 weeks after respective deadlines dates
Officers and Directors:* Mary P. Surrey,* Pres.; Winifred Riggs Portenoy,* Chair.; Elizabeth Brown,* V.P.; Nancy E. Oddo,* V.P.; Sara R. Surrey,* Secy.-Treas.
Number of staff: 1 full-time support; 2 part-time support.
EIN: 131687573

1902
Ralph S. and Frances R. Dweck Family Foundation, Inc. ✧
1730 M St. N.W., Ste. 408
Washington, DC 20036-4569

Established in 2005 in MD.
Donors: Ralph S. Dweck; Frances Dweck.
Foundation type: Independent foundation.
Financial data (yr. ended 12/31/13): Assets, $222,896 (M); gifts received, $100,000; expenditures, $680,901; qualifying distributions, $678,264; giving activities include $673,265 for 50 grants (high: $126,873; low: $250).
Fields of interest: Education; Jewish federated giving programs; Jewish agencies & synagogues.
Limitations: Giving primarily in Washington, DC and MD.
Application information: Application form not required.
Deadline(s): None
Directors: Frances R. Dweck; Ralph S. Dweck.
EIN: 020762730
Selected grants: The following grants are a representative sample of this grantmaker's funding activity:
$125,000 to Bread for the City, Washington, DC, 2011.
$74,475 to Washington Humane Society, Washington, DC, 2011.
$60,000 to University of Pennsylvania, Philadelphia, PA, 2011.
$40,750 to Washington District of Columbia Jewish Community Center, Washington, DC, 2011.
$35,000 to Jewish Federation of Greater Washington, Rockville, MD, 2011.
$20,000 to Yeshiva of Greater Washington, Silver Spring, MD, 2011.
$2,500 to American Friends of the Hebrew University, New York, NY, 2011.
$2,500 to Jewish Social Service Agency, Rockville, MD, 2011.
$2,500 to University of Rochester, Rochester, NY, 2011.
$1,500 to N Street Village, Washington, DC, 2011.

1903
El-Hibri Foundation ✧
(formerly El-Hibri Charitable Foundation)
Ibrahim El-Hibri Bldg.
1420 16th St. N.W.
Washington, DC 20036-2202 (202) 387-9500
FAX: (202) 387-9050;
E-mail: info@elhibrifoundation.org; Application address: c/o Zen Hunter-Ishikawa, 12001 Glen Rd., Potomac, MD 20854, tel.: (301) 983-1133; Main URL: http://www.elhibrifoundation.org/
Facebook: https://www.facebook.com/elhibrifoundation
Google Plus: https://plus.google.com/105636087442972680528/about#105636087442972680528/about
LinkedIn: http://www.linkedin.com/company/el-hibri-charitable-foundation
Twitter: https://twitter.com/ElHibriFdn

Established in 2001 in DC.
Donors: Fuad El-Hibri; Ibrahim Y. El-Hibri†.
Foundation type: Independent foundation.
Financial data (yr. ended 12/31/13): Assets, $43,406,517 (M); gifts received, $70,455; expenditures, $1,818,556; qualifying distributions, $1,431,438; giving activities include $458,600 for 12 grants (high: $100,000; low: $8,100), and $439,486 for 4 foundation-administered programs.
Purpose and activities: Giving primarily to: 1) Promote the fields of peace studies and conflict resolution through education, training, media production and related activities; 2) Encourage respect for religious diversity through research, education, interfaith collaboration and dialogue, and related activities; 3) Enable disadvantaged youth, primarily in Lebanon, to become productive members of society by supporting education, training and related activities; and 4) Advance human rights for women in the Middle East by fostering knowledge about Islam and building skills to empower women.
Fields of interest: Education; International relief; International democracy & civil society development; International peace/security; International conflict resolution; International human rights; Islam; Religion, interfaith issues.
International interests: Lebanon; Middle East.
Type of support: General/operating support; Management development/capacity building; Capital campaigns; Seed money.
Limitations: Applications accepted. Giving primarily in the Washington, DC area, and Lebanon.
Publications: Application guidelines.
Application information: Full proposals are by invitation only, upon review of Letter of Intent.
Initial approach: Letter of Intent via online portal on foundation web site

Officers and Directors:* Fuad El-Hibri, Chair.; Judy Barsalou, Pres.; Marcia Thayer Nass, V.P. and Genl. Counsel; Greg Siegrist, V.P., Fin. and Admin. and Treas.; Zen Hunter-Ishikawa, V.P., Opers. and Devel.; Karim El-Hibri,* Dir., Opers.; Nancy El-Hibri; Mary Goudie; Nadia Roumani; Abdo Sabban; Abdul Aziz Said; Allen Shofe.
EIN: 522306995

1904
Flamboyan Foundation, Inc. ✧
1730 Massachusetts Ave. N.W.
Washington, DC 20036-1903
E-mail: info@flamboyanfoundation.org; Puerto Rico address: P.O. Box 16699, San Juan, PR 00908-6699, tel.: (787) 977-5522; Main URL: http://www.flamboyanfoundation.org

Established in 2007 in DC.
Donors: Fundacion Flamboyan; Coqui Development Co.
Foundation type: Independent foundation.
Financial data (yr. ended 12/31/13): Assets, $3,915,109 (M); gifts received, $119,500; expenditures, $3,511,247; qualifying distributions, $3,426,579; giving activities include $1,364,613 for 28 grants (high: $325,000; low: $1,500), and $35,000 for 26 grants to individuals (high: $1,600; low: $1,000).
Purpose and activities: Giving primarily for the improvement of educational outcomes for children in public schools in Washington, DC, and San Juan, PR.
Fields of interest: Education.
Limitations: Applications accepted. Giving primarily in Washington, DC, and San Juan, PR.
Application information: See foundation website for complete application guidelines. Application form required.
Officers and Directors:* Kristin Ehrgood,* Chair. and Pres.; Vadim Nikitine, Treas.; Rea Carey, Exec. Dir.; Guiomar Garcia Guerra, Exec. Dir.; Susan K. Stevenson, Exec. Dir.
EIN: 208924675

1905
The Forster Family Foundation ✧
c/o Peter C. Forster
5291 Partridge Ln., N.W.
Washington, DC 20016-5338

Established in 2004 in DC.
Donors: Elizabeth D. Forster; Peter C. Forster.
Foundation type: Independent foundation.
Financial data (yr. ended 12/31/13): Assets, $30,564,158 (M); gifts received, $4,056,111; expenditures, $2,780,029; qualifying distributions, $2,547,800; giving activities include $2,547,800 for 22 grants (high: $500,000; low: $9,250).
Fields of interest: Higher education; Boy scouts.
Limitations: Applications not accepted. Giving primarily in MD and TX.
Application information: Contributes only to pre-selected organizations.
Officers: Peter C. Forster, Pres. and Treas.; Elizabeth D. Forster, V.P. and Secy.
EIN: 201512250

1906
Forsythia Foundation ✧
1201 Connecticut Ave. N.W., Ste. 300
Washington, DC 20036-2656

Donor: Alison Carlson.
Foundation type: Independent foundation.
Financial data (yr. ended 12/31/12): Assets, $22,709,291 (M); gifts received, $150,000; expenditures, $992,853; qualifying distributions, $489,000; giving activities include $489,000 for 16 grants (high: $100,000; low: $5,000).
Fields of interest: Environment; Health organizations; Human services.
Type of support: General/operating support.
Limitations: Applications not accepted. Giving primarily in CA.
Application information: Unsolicited requests for funds not accepted.
Officers: Alison Carlson, Pres.; Janet Maughan, Secy.-Treas.
EIN: 800609967

1907
The Freedom Forum, Inc.
555 Pennsylvania Ave. N.W.
Washington, DC 20001-2114 (202) 292-6100
Contact: James Duff, Pres. and C.E.O.
E-mail: news@freedomforum.org; Main URL: http://www.freedomforum.org

Incorporated in 1991 in VA.
Foundation type: Operating foundation.
Financial data (yr. ended 12/31/13): Assets, $774,590,324 (M); expenditures, $49,512,418; qualifying distributions, $36,180,945; giving activities include $28,674,556 for 43 grants (high: $22,904,093; low: $1,000), $500 for 1 grant to an individual, and $204,282 for 1 foundation-administered program.
Purpose and activities: The Freedom Forum, based in Washington, D.C., is a nonpartisan foundation that champions the First Amendment as a cornerstone of democracy.
Fields of interest: Civil liberties, first amendment; Civil liberties, freedom of information.
Type of support: Scholarships—to individuals.
Limitations: Applications not accepted. Giving on a national and international basis.
Publications: Annual report; Occasional report.
Application information: Unsolicited requests for funds not accepted.
Board meeting date(s): Quarterly
Officers and Trustees:* Jan Neuharth,* Chair.; James C. Duff,* Pres. and C.E.O., Freedom Forum and C.E.O., Newseum and Pres. and C.E.O., Newseum Institute; James W. Abbott,* Chair., Newseum Institute; Peter S. Prichard,* Chair., Newseum; Shelby Coffey III, Vice-Chair., Newseum; Gene Policinski, C.O.O., Newseum Institute; Ken Paulson,* Pres. and C.E.O., First Amendment Center; Jack Marsh, Pres., Al Neuharth Media Ctr.; Pamela Y. Galloway-Tabb, Sr. V.P., Conferences and Special Svcs.; Nicole F. Mandeville, Sr. V.P., Finance, and Treas.; Cathy Trost, Sr. V.P., Exhibits and Prog(s); Paul Sparrow, Sr. V.P., Broadcasting; Courtney L. Surls, Sr. V.P., Devel.; James Thompson, Sr. V.P., Operations; Jim Updike, Sr. V.P., Technology; Scott Williams, Sr. V.P, Marketing; Howard H. Baker, Jr.,* Secy.; Michael Coleman; Malcolm R. Kirschenbaum; H. Wilbert Norton, Jr.; Orage Quarles III; Judy C. Woodruff.
Number of staff: 111 full-time professional; 6 part-time professional; 45 full-time support; 5 part-time support.
EIN: 541604427

1908
Friedman-French Foundation Inc. ✧
2330 California St. N.W.
Washington, DC 20008-1637

Established in 1993.
Donors: Emanuel Friedman; Kindy French; Millicent Roth.
Foundation type: Independent foundation.
Financial data (yr. ended 06/30/13): Assets, $14,545,554 (M); gifts received, $3,695,000; expenditures, $917,916; qualifying distributions, $814,380; giving activities include $808,880 for 44 grants (high: $105,000; low: $250).
Purpose and activities: Giving primarily to Jewish organizations; some funding also for the arts and education.
Fields of interest: Arts; Education; Jewish federated giving programs; Jewish agencies & synagogues.
Limitations: Applications not accepted. Giving in the U.S., with some emphasis on MD and Washington, D.C. No grants to individuals.
Application information: Contributes only to pre-selected organizations.
Directors: Kindy French; Emanuel Friedman; Millicent Roth.
EIN: 521853718
Selected grants: The following grants are a representative sample of this grantmaker's funding activity:
$125,000 to Jewish Federation of Greater Washington, Rockville, MD, 2011.
$25,000 to Jewish Enrichment Center, New York, NY, 2011.
$25,000 to Sixth and I Historic Synagogue, Washington, DC, 2011.
$25,000 to Washington Humane Society, Washington, DC, 2011.
$10,000 to Metropolitan Center for the Visual Arts, Rockville, MD, 2011.
$10,000 to North Shore Hebrew Academy, Great Neck, NY, 2011.
$10,000 to We Are Family Foundation, New York, NY, 2011.
$5,000 to New York Institute of Technology, Old Westbury, NY, 2011.
$5,000 to Shoresh, Baltimore, MD, 2011.
$5,000 to We Are Family Foundation, New York, NY, 2011.

1909
Bernard & Sarah Gewirz Foundation, Inc. ✧
1666 K St. N.W., Ste. 430
Washington, DC 20006-1223
Contact: Bernard S. Gewirz, Pres.

Established in 1984 in DC.
Donors: Bernard S. Gewirz; Sarah M. Gewirz.
Foundation type: Independent foundation.
Financial data (yr. ended 11/30/13): Assets, $4,459,522 (M); gifts received, $100,000; expenditures, $556,129; qualifying distributions, $543,269; giving activities include $543,269 for 95 grants (high: $50,000; low: $100).

Purpose and activities: Support primarily for education and Jewish giving.
Fields of interest: Arts; Education; Human services; Jewish federated giving programs; Jewish agencies & synagogues.
Type of support: Research; Endowments; Capital campaigns; Building/renovation; Annual campaigns.
Limitations: Applications accepted. Giving primarily in the metropolitan Washington, DC, area.
Application information: Application form not required.
Initial approach: Proposal
Deadline(s): None
Officers and Directors:* Bernard S. Gewirz, Pres.; Michael K. Gewirz,* V.P.; Sarah M. Gewirz,* Secy.; Jonathan K. Gewirz; Steven B. Gewirz.
EIN: 521381689
Selected grants: The following grants are a representative sample of this grantmaker's funding activity:
$135,000 to Georgetown Memorial Hospital, Georgetown, SC, 2011.
$10,000 to Adas Israel Hebrew Congregation, Washington, DC, 2011.

1910
Richard W. Goldman Family Foundation ✧ ☆
c/o Arabella Advisors
1201 Connecticut ave., N.W., Ste. 300
Washington, DC 20036
Contact: Alice R. Goldman, Pres.

Established in DE.
Donors: Richard N. Goldman†; Richard N. Goldman Administrative Trust.
Foundation type: Independent foundation.
Financial data (yr. ended 12/31/13): Assets, $74,564,599 (M); gifts received, $2,688,000; expenditures, $3,310,702; qualifying distributions, $2,948,711; giving activities include $2,863,000 for 3 grants (high: $1,242,000; low: $621,000).
Fields of interest: Higher education; Human services.
Limitations: Applications accepted. Giving in the U.S., with emphasis on CA, CT, and NY.
Application information: Application form required.
Initial approach: Letter
Deadline(s): None
Officers: Alice R. Goldman, Pres.; Daniel S. Goldman, Secy.; William S. Goldman, Treas.
EIN: 451261400

1911
The Gottesman Fund ✧
1818 N St. N.W., Ste. 400
Washington, DC 20036-2477
Contact: Diane Bennett Eidman, Dir.; Elaine Randall, Asst. Secy.
E-mail: deidman@firstmanhattan.com; NYC Address: c/o First Manhattan Co., 399 Park Ave., 27th Fl., New York, NY 10022

Established in 1965 in DC.
Donor: Gottesman family members.
Foundation type: Independent foundation.
Financial data (yr. ended 08/31/13): Assets, $323,969,755 (M); gifts received, $5,044,224; expenditures, $20,708,424; qualifying distributions, $20,237,260; giving activities include $19,834,865 for 147 grants (high: $6,008,290; low: $500).
Purpose and activities: The Gottesman Fund is managed by members of the Gottesman family and is dedicated to: 1) Enhancing and perpetuating Jewish life in the United States; 2) Supporting cultural, medical, scientific and educational institutions in the United States; and 3) Improving the quality of life for Israel's inhabitants.
Fields of interest: Museums; Arts; Higher education; Hospitals (general); Human services; Jewish federated giving programs; Jewish agencies & synagogues.
Type of support: Building/renovation; Capital campaigns; Emergency funds; General/operating support; Program development; Scholarship funds.
Limitations: Applications not accepted. Giving primarily in the New York, NY, metropolitan area. No grants to individuals.
Application information: Unsolicited requests for funds not accepted.
Board meeting date(s): Sept.
Officers: David S. Gottesman, Pres.; Alice R. Gottesman, V.P.; Ruth L. Gottesman, V.P.; William L. Gottesman, V.P.; Diane Bennett Eidman, Secy.; Robert W. Gottesman, Treas.
Number of staff: 1 full-time professional; 2 part-time professional.
EIN: 526061469

1912
The Isadore and Bertha Gudelsky Family Foundation, Inc. ✧
c/o Margolius Firm LLC
4201 Connecticut Ave. N.W., Ste. 600
Washington, DC 20008-1128
FAX: (202) 332-1800;
E-mail: jennifer@themargoliusfirm.com

Incorporated in 1955 in MD.
Donor: Members of the Gudelsky family.
Foundation type: Independent foundation.
Financial data (yr. ended 04/30/13): Assets, $12,477,157 (M); expenditures, $740,303; qualifying distributions, $608,000; giving activities include $608,000 for grants.
Purpose and activities: Giving primarily to Jewish organizations, education, and for the arts.
Fields of interest: Performing arts centers; Arts; Education; Human services; Jewish federated giving programs; Jewish agencies & synagogues.
International interests: Israel.
Type of support: Endowments; General/operating support; Continuing support; Capital campaigns; Building/renovation; Emergency funds; Program development; Conferences/seminars; Professorships; Fellowships; Scholarship funds.
Limitations: Applications not accepted. Giving primarily in the metropolitan Washington, DC, and surrounding areas, including MD; funding also in New York, NY. No grants to individuals.
Application information: Unsolicited requests for funds not accepted.
Board meeting date(s): May or June
Officers: Arlene G. Kaufman, Pres.; Shelley G. Mulitz, V.P.; Philip Margolius, Secy.-Treas.
Board Members: Paul S. Berger; Michael Friedman; Laura Bryna Gudelsky Mulitz.
Number of staff: 1 part-time professional.
EIN: 526036621

Selected grants: The following grants are a representative sample of this grantmaker's funding activity:
$150,000 to Jewish Federation of Greater Washington, Rockville, MD, 2013. For 2012 annual campaign.
$60,000 to Autism Speaks, New York, NY, 2013. For autism research.
$40,000 to American Jewish Committee, New York, NY, 2013. For University Campus Editors Seminar.
$25,000 to Jewish Social Service Agency, Rockville, MD, 2013. To be used for funding for continued professional services to the elderly including costs of increased weekly baths and additional meal support.
$10,000 to Israel Guide Dog Center for the Blind, Warrington, PA, 2013. To help with the costs of breeding, caring for, training and matching one dog with one blind/visually impaired client.
$5,000 to Columbia Center for Theatrical Arts, Columbia, MD, 2013. For Costs of outreach and youth at risk Programs for students who have few opportunities to participate in those Programs due to financial limitations.
$5,000 to National Guard Youth Foundation, Alexandria, VA, 2013. For Costs of Aberdeen, MD Program.

1913
The Mark and Anne Hansen Foundation ✧
1615 M St. N.W., Ste. 400
Washington, DC 20036-3215 (877) 829-5500

Established in 2007 in DC.
Donors: Reid Figel; Anne Hansen; Mark Hansen; Michael Kellog; Chris Todd.
Foundation type: Independent foundation.
Financial data (yr. ended 09/30/13): Assets, $6,576,828 (M); gifts received, $1,000,000; expenditures, $1,310,867; qualifying distributions, $1,228,985; giving activities include $1,226,984 for 35 grants (high: $1,012,579; low: $150).
Fields of interest: Elementary/secondary education; Higher education; Human services.
Limitations: Applications accepted. Giving primarily in Washington, DC; some funding also in Hanover, NH.
Application information: Application form required.
Initial approach: Proposal
Deadline(s): None
Trustees: Anne Hansen; Elisabeth Hansen; Mark Hansen.
EIN: 205794944
Selected grants: The following grants are a representative sample of this grantmaker's funding activity:
$1,000 to Alternative House, Vienna, VA, 2013. For donation.

1914
The Hillside Foundation, Inc. ✧
1001 Pennsylvania Ave. N.W., Ste. 220S
Washington, DC 20004-2525

Established in 2005 in MD.
Donors: Allan M. Holt; Shelley L. Holt.
Foundation type: Independent foundation.
Financial data (yr. ended 12/31/13): Assets, $1,611,943 (M); gifts received, $3,205,800; expenditures, $4,398,191; qualifying distributions,

$4,388,785; giving activities include $4,385,885 for 15 grants (high: $1,000,000; low: $100,000).
Fields of interest: Museums (children's); Museums (specialized); Hospitals (general); Foundations (private grantmaking); Jewish agencies & synagogues.
Limitations: Applications not accepted. Giving primarily in Washington, DC, MD, and Mt. Pleasant, SC. No grants to individuals.
Application information: Contributes only to pre-selected organizations.
Officers and Directors:* Allan M. Holt,* Pres. and Treas.; Shelly L. Holt,* V.P. and Secy.; David H. Holt.
EIN: 202787879

1915
Hill-Snowdon Foundation

1201 Connecticut Ave. N.W., 3rd Fl.
Washington, DC 20036-2605
FAX: (202) 833-8606; E-mail: info@hillsnowdon.org;
Main URL: http://www.hillsnowdon.org/
Grants Database: http://www.hillsnowdon.org/grantlistings.asp
Hill-Snowden Foundation's Philanthropy Promise: http://www.ncrp.org/philanthropys-promise/who
RSS Feed: http://www.hillsnowdon.org/newsresources.asp

Established in 1959 in NJ.
Donors: Arthur B. Hill†; Edward Snowdon Charitable Lead Unitrust.
Foundation type: Independent foundation.
Financial data (yr. ended 12/31/12): Assets, $28,138,443 (M); gifts received, $367,358; expenditures, $2,155,413; qualifying distributions, $1,770,369; giving activities include $1,232,540 for 84 grants (high: $35,000; low: $1,000).
Purpose and activities: Giving primarily for organization working with low-income families and communities to create a fair and just society by helping them develop the capacity and leadership skills necessary to influence the decisions that shape their lives. HSF seeks to accomplish this mission by providing grants to organizations that work directly to build the power of low-income families; leveraging our and others' resources; and promoting opportunities for learning and growth.
Fields of interest: Employment, services; Youth development; Human services; Children/youth, services; Family services; Civil/human rights, advocacy; Economic development; Community/economic development; Leadership development; Youth; Minorities; Women; Economically disadvantaged; Homeless.
Type of support: General/operating support.
Limitations: Applications not accepted. Giving in Washington, DC, for the Fund for DC program; 60-70% of the Youth Organizations and Economic Justice Organizing program areas will be directed toward the U.S. South; and strategic investments made nationally to help promote the goals of Youth Organizing and Economic Organizing program areas. No grants to individuals.
Publications: Grants list; Program policy statement.
Application information: While unsolicited proposals are not considered, the foundation will accept initial inquiry contacts from nonprofits whose work intersects with its areas of interest. Refer to foundation web site for guidelines.
Board meeting date(s): Nov.
Officers and Trustees:* Elizabeth Snowdon Bonner,* Pres.; Ashley Snowdon Blanchard,* V.P.; Richard Snowdon III,* Secy.-Treas.; Nat Chioke Williams, Ph.D., Exec. Dir.; Andrew L. Snowdon; Ariana Snowdon; Edward W. Snowdon, Jr.; Marguerite Snowdon.
Number of staff: 3 full-time professional; 1 part-time professional.
EIN: 226081122

1916
The Hitachi Foundation ✧

1215 17th St., N.W., 3rd Fl.
Washington, DC 20036-3019 (202) 457-0588
Contact: Barbara Dyer, C.E.O. and Pres.; Mark Popovich, Sr. Prog. Off.
FAX: (202) 298-1098;
E-mail: info@hitachifoundation.org; Main URL: http://www.hitachifoundation.org
Facebook: https://www.facebook.com/pages/The-Hitachi-Foundation/542427755792314?ref=br_rs
Flickr: https://www.flickr.com/photos/75775267@N03/
LinkedIn: http://www.linkedin.com/company/the-hitachi-foundation
Twitter: http://twitter.com/HitachiFdn#
YouTube: http://www.youtube.com/user/TheHitachiFoundation

Established in 1985 in DC.
Donor: Hitachi, Ltd.
Foundation type: Independent foundation.
Financial data (yr. ended 12/31/13): Assets, $25,548,825 (M); gifts received, $3,165,063; expenditures, $3,599,052; qualifying distributions, $3,459,342; giving activities include $1,649,780 for 317 grants (high: $190,000; low: $250).
Purpose and activities: The foundation supports organizations involved with education, employment, and economically disadvantaged people and awards grants to high school seniors.
Fields of interest: Employment; Economically disadvantaged.
Type of support: Mission-related investments/loans; Program development; Employee volunteer services; Matching/challenge support.
Limitations: Applications accepted. Giving on a national basis. No grants to individuals (except for Yoshiyama Awards), or for capital campaigns or fundraising.
Publications: Application guidelines; Annual report; Financial statement; Grants list; Informational brochure; Occasional report.
Application information: Application forms are available online. Application form required.
Initial approach: Complete online letter of inquiry form for Business and Communities Grants; complete online narration form for Yoshiyama Awards
Copies of proposal: 1
Deadline(s): Apr. 1 for Yoshiyama Awards
Board meeting date(s): Spring, summer, and fall
Final notification: Aug. or Sept. for Yoshiyama Awards
Officers and Directors:* Patrick W. Gross,* Chair.; Barbara Dyer,* C.E.O. and Pres.; Takashi Kawamura, Honorary Chair.; Jason Baron; Sherry Salway Black; Albert D. Fuller; David Langstaff; Bruce MacLaury, Ph.D.; Jennifer Pryce; Kelly Ryan.
Number of staff: 4 full-time professional; 3 full-time support.
EIN: 521429292

1917
HRH Foundation ✧

3100 R St. N.W.
Washington, DC 20007-2937
Contact: Helen Lee Henderson, Exec. Dir.
E-mail: hlh.hrh@verizon.net

Established in 1997 in PA.
Donors: Helen Ruth Henderson†; Helen Lee Henderson; Benson G. Henderson†.
Foundation type: Independent foundation.
Financial data (yr. ended 12/31/13): Assets, $11,000,574 (M); gifts received, $100,000; expenditures, $1,624,826; qualifying distributions, $1,602,640; giving activities include $1,450,000 for 5 grants (high: $500,000; low: $100,000).
Purpose and activities: Giving primarily for the visual and performing arts.
Fields of interest: Museums (art); Performing arts centers; Performing arts, theater.
Limitations: Applications not accepted. Giving primarily in Washington, DC, NY and VA. No grants to individuals.
Application information: Unsolicited requests for funds not accepted.
Officer: Helen Lee Henderson, Exec. Dir.
EIN: 522048784
Selected grants: The following grants are a representative sample of this grantmaker's funding activity:
$350,000 to National Gallery of Art, Washington, DC, 2012. For As Donee Sees Fit.

1918
The Joseph E. & Marjorie B. Jones Foundation ✧

1666 Connecticut Ave. N.W., Ste. 200
Washington, DC 20009-1039 (202) 797-6720
Contact: Joyce Havard, Pres.
FAX: (202) 797-6723;
E-mail: info@thejonesfoundation.com; Main URL: http://www.thejonesfoundation.com

Established in 1989 in DC.
Donors: Marjorie B. Jones; Joseph E. Jones Trust; Marjorie B. Jones Trust.
Foundation type: Independent foundation.
Financial data (yr. ended 12/31/13): Assets, $29,041,137 (M); expenditures, $3,717,691; qualifying distributions, $1,168,198; giving activities include $959,100 for 18 grants (high: $300,000; low: $250).
Purpose and activities: Support for human services, including youth groups, family programs, and the homeless; health organizations, including pediatrics, eye research, mental health, and medical research; and conservation education.
Fields of interest: Child development, education; Adult education—literacy, basic skills & GED; Education; Crime/violence prevention, domestic violence; Aging, centers/services; Children/youth; Children; Youth; Minorities; Military/veterans; Economically disadvantaged; Homeless.
Type of support: General/operating support.
Limitations: Applications accepted. Giving primarily in the Washington, DC, area. No grants for basic research, scholarships, endowment funds, publications, films, events, construction or the acquisition of buildings.
Publications: Annual report; Informational brochure.
Application information: Do not send additional information/brochures unless requested.

Applications are to be sent via U.S. mail. Faxed or e-mailed applications not accepted. Application form required.

Initial approach: Apply via application form on foundation web site; or telephone requesting application

Copies of proposal: 1

Deadline(s): May 31 (postmarked)

Board meeting date(s): Nov.

Final notification: Following Nov. board meeting

Officers and Directors:* Harris W. Havard,* Chair.; Joyce Havard,* Pres.; Stephanie Havard,* Secy.; John Marvin Jones,* Treas.; Donald P. Havard.

Number of staff: 1 full-time professional.

EIN: 521628951

Selected grants: The following grants are a representative sample of this grantmaker's funding activity:

$100,000 to Levine School of Music, Washington, DC, 2012. For Levine at Thearc Music Education Program 1901 Mississippi Avenue, Se, No. 201 Washington, Dc 20020.

$80,000 to Chesapeake Bay Foundation, Annapolis, MD, 2012. For Maryland Schools Education Project.

$80,000 to Downtown Cluster of Congregations, Washington, DC, 2012. For Homeless Services Unit.

$75,000 to Bread for the City, Washington, DC, 2012. For medical clinic.

$65,000 to Academy of Hope, Washington, DC, 2012. For Adult Education and Job Training.

$40,000 to Byte Back, Washington, DC, 2012. For Computer and Job Readiness Training.

$10,000 to Alexandria Seaport Foundation, Alexandria, VA, 2012. For Boatbuilding Apprenticeship Program.

1919
The Charles I. & Mary Kaplan Family Foundation ✧

1919 M St. N.W., Ste. 320
Washington, DC 20036

Established in 1956 in DE.

Donors: Joan L. Gindes; Edward H. Kaplan; Jerome A. Kaplan; EHK Securities LP.

Foundation type: Independent foundation.

Financial data (yr. ended 12/31/12): Assets, $1,482,495 (M); gifts received, $150,000; expenditures, $3,632,499; qualifying distributions, $3,629,000; giving activities include $3,629,000 for 2 grants (high: $3,604,000; low: $25,000).

Purpose and activities: Giving primarily to a Jewish historical society.

Fields of interest: Historic preservation/historical societies; Jewish federated giving programs; Jewish agencies & synagogues.

Limitations: Applications not accepted. Giving primarily in Washington, DC and New York, NY. No grants to individuals.

Application information: Contributes only to pre-selected organizations.

Officers: Irene R. Kaplan, Pres.; Martine Kaplan, V.P.; Edward H. Kaplan, Secy.-Treas.

EIN: 526043928

1920
Danny and Sylvia Fine Kaye Foundation ✧

c/o Weidenfeld Law Firm
888 17th St. N.W., Ste. 1250
Washington, DC 20006-3328

Established in 1995 in CO.

Donors: Danny Kaye†; Sylvia Fine Kaye†.

Foundation type: Independent foundation.

Financial data (yr. ended 12/31/12): Assets, $11,639,614 (M); expenditures, $1,307,634; qualifying distributions, $989,841; giving activities include $989,841 for grants.

Purpose and activities: Giving primarily for the arts, health, human services, and international affairs.

Fields of interest: Media, film/video; Performing arts; Arts; Biomedicine research; Medical research; Human services; International affairs, goodwill promotion; International relief; Civil liberties, reproductive rights; Social sciences.

Type of support: Program development; General/operating support.

Limitations: Applications not accepted. Giving in the U.S., with emphasis on CA, Aspen, CO, New York, NY, and VA. No grants to individuals.

Application information: Contributes only to pre-selected organizations.

Directors: Richard Fallin; Dena Kaye; Edward L. Weidenfeld.

EIN: 841283914

1921
Kimsey Foundation ✧

1700 Pennsylvania Ave. N.W., Ste. 900
Washington, DC 20006-4722

Established in 1997 in VA.

Donor: James V. Kimsey.

Foundation type: Independent foundation.

Financial data (yr. ended 12/31/13): Assets, $16,285,955 (M); gifts received, $113,526; expenditures, $1,323,027; qualifying distributions, $1,257,991; giving activities include $610,100 for 28 grants (high: $100,000; low: $500).

Purpose and activities: The foundation focuses on educational and cultural initiatives; supporting thriving communities that offer hope and opportunity to youth. The foundation gives preference to organizations using a proactive collaborative approach. The foundation participates in funding partnerships. It also serves the international community through policy research and humanitarian outreach. The foundation has narrowed its focus to include a few specific projects that leverage systemic change in public education and community development. The majority of new grants will be related to existing partnerships and initiatives.

Fields of interest: Arts; Education; Children/youth, services; International affairs, public policy; International human rights; Community/economic development; Public affairs, political organizations; Immigrants/refugees.

Type of support: General/operating support; Program development; Technical assistance; Matching/challenge support.

Limitations: Applications not accepted. Giving primarily in Washington, DC. No grants to individuals, or for building or renovations, endowments, capital campaigns, conferences, or for competition expenses.

Application information: Unsolicited requests for funds not accepted.

Officers: James V. Kimsey, Chair.; Michael P. Kimsey, Exec. Dir.

Directors: Mark J. Kimsey; Raymond C. Kimsey.

Number of staff: 2 full-time professional; 1 part-time professional.

EIN: 522007895

1922
The Kiplinger Foundation ✧

1100 13th St. N.W., Ste. 750
Washington, DC 20005-4051
Contact: Andrea B. Wilkes, Secy.
FAX: (202) 778-8976;
E-mail: foundation@kiplinger.com

Incorporated in 1948 in MD.

Donor: Willard M. Kiplinger†.

Foundation type: Independent foundation.

Financial data (yr. ended 12/31/13): Assets, $10,347,352 (M); expenditures, $924,334; qualifying distributions, $913,187; giving activities include $838,316 for 84 grants (high: $275,000; low: $50), and $49,874 for 48 employee matching gifts.

Purpose and activities: Support primarily for educational, health, welfare, civic, and cultural organizations.

Fields of interest: Arts; Education; Human services.

Type of support: General/operating support; Continuing support; Annual campaigns; Capital campaigns; Building/renovation; Endowments; Employee matching gifts.

Limitations: Applications accepted. Giving primarily in the greater Washington, DC, area. No support for political organizations. No grants to individuals, or for seed money, emergency funds, deficit financing, equipment and materials, medical research, land acquisition, or scholarship funds; general no support for capital campaigns.

Publications: Application guidelines.

Application information: Washington Regional Association of Grantmakers applications are acceptable. Application form not required.

Initial approach: Letter

Copies of proposal: 1

Deadline(s): None

Board meeting date(s): 4 times per year

Final notification: 3 to 6 months

Officers and Trustees:* Austin H. Kiplinger,* Pres.; Andrea B. Wilkes,* Secy.; David M. Daugherty, Treas.; Knight A. Kiplinger; Janet Bodnar Linnehan.

Number of staff: 1 part-time professional.

EIN: 520792570

Selected grants: The following grants are a representative sample of this grantmaker's funding activity:

$7,500 to Washington Middle School for Girls, Washington, DC, 2012. For other education.

1923
The Lavin Family Foundation, Inc. ✧ ☆

3030 K. St. N.W., Ste. 107
Washington, DC 20007-5156

Established in 2000 in MD.

Donors: Francis P. Lavin; Joanne G. Lavin.

Foundation type: Independent foundation.

Financial data (yr. ended 12/31/13): Assets, $2,270,262 (M); gifts received, $303,470; expenditures, $512,566; qualifying distributions, $496,421; giving activities include $496,421 for 14 grants (high: $150,000; low: $100).

Fields of interest: Education; Health care; Mental health/crisis services.

Limitations: Applications not accepted. Giving primarily in MA and PA. No grants to individuals.

Application information: Unsolicited requests for funds not accepted.

Trustees: Francis P. Lavin; Joanne G. Lavin.

EIN: 522284964

Selected grants: The following grants are a representative sample of this grantmaker's funding activity:
$25,000 to Wounded Warrior Project, Jacksonville, FL, 2012. For direct support.
$5,000 to Phillips Collection, Washington, DC, 2011. For general operations.
$5,000 to Washington Hebrew Congregation, Washington, DC, 2011.

1925
Mary and Daniel Loughran Foundation Inc. ✧
4910 Mass Ave. N.W., Ste. 215
Washington, DC 20016-4300 (202) 362-7986
Contact: F. William Burke, Exec. Dir.

Incorporated in 1967 in DC.
Donor: John Loughran‡.
Foundation type: Independent foundation.
Financial data (yr. ended 07/31/13): Assets, $14,066,184 (M); gifts received, $1,000; expenditures, $956,312; qualifying distributions, $702,500; giving activities include $702,500 for 110 grants (high: $25,000; low: $5,000).
Purpose and activities: Giving for education, arts and culture, and human services.
Fields of interest: Performing arts, theater; Arts; Higher education; Human services; Children/youth, services; Disabilities, people with.
Type of support: General/operating support; Continuing support; Annual campaigns; Scholarship funds; Matching/challenge support.
Limitations: Applications accepted. Giving limited to Washington, DC, MD, and VA. No grants to individuals, or for capital or endowment funds; no loans.
Publications: IRS Form 990 or 990-PF printed copy available upon request.
Application information: Letter up to two pages. Application form required.
Initial approach: Letter
Copies of proposal: 1
Deadline(s): May 1
Board meeting date(s): July
Final notification: Aug.
Officer and Directors:* William Couper,* Pres.; Richard J.M. Poulson,* V.P.; Walter R. Fatzinger, Jr.,* V.P.; Stephen D. Harlan,* Treas.; F. William Burke, Mgr. and Exec. Dir.; George P. Clancy, Jr.; Thomas T. Firth; Carl L. Gell; John T. Hazel; A. Linwood Holton, Jr.; John P. McDaniel; John Whitmore; Howard M . Weiss.
Trustee: Bank of America, N.A.
Number of staff: 1 full-time professional; 1 part-time support.
EIN: 521095883
Selected grants: The following grants are a representative sample of this grantmaker's funding activity:
$20,000 to Catholic Charities Foundation, Washington, DC, 2013. For 2012: Request for unspecified amount to support this organization which contributes to numerous charitable operations in the Metropolitan area.
$15,000 to Washington and Lee University, Lexington, VA, 2013. For 2012: Request for $45,000 over 3 years so that the Mary and Daniel Loughran Law scholarship fund may continue to grow.
$10,000 to Boy Scouts of America, National Capital Area Council, Bethesda, MD, 2013. For 2012: Request for unspecified amount to support inner city scouting.
$10,000 to George Washington University Medical Center, Washington, DC, 2013. For 2012: Request for $10,000 to fund the Hirsh Medicine and Policy Scholars Program that permits medical residents to gain understanding of the US healthcare system and the evolution and development of health policy.
$10,000 to National Presbyterian Church, Washington, DC, 2013. For Request for $50,000 to support the Church and National Cathedral with rebuilding and construction due to earthquake uninsured damage of $1.5 million.
$10,000 to Washington DC Police Foundation, Washington, DC, 2013. For 2012: Request for unspecified amount over 2 years for general operating support. The funds will assist the DC Police Foundation in its mission to bring together the business and civic communities to promote public safety in DC.
$5,000 to Fairfax Symphony Orchestra, Fairfax, VA, 2013. For 2012: Request for $5,000 to support Programs that integrate academic subjects under a music banner through a multimedia presentation combined with live performances by FSO musicians.
$5,000 to Northern Neck Free Health Clinic, Kilmarnock, VA, 2013. For 2012: Request for $15,000 to support the clinic which provides health care to uninsured residents, most of them working, who are not able to afford it.
$5,000 to Virginia College Fund, Richmond, VA, 2013. For 2012: Request for $5,000 to provide continued financial support to five small Virginia colleges on behalf of underserved student population in Virginia.
$5,000 to YMCA of Metropolitan Washington, Washington, DC, 2013. For 2012: Request for an unspecified amount for support for YMCA Capital View, a Program center for low-income and at-risk children in Southeast DC, providing a safe haven for children ages 5-14 when parents and caregivers are at work.

1924
Jacob and Charlotte Lehrman Foundation, Inc. ✧
1836 Columbia Rd. N.W.
Washington, DC 20009-2002 (202) 328-8400
FAX: (202) 328-8405;
E-mail: info@lehrmanfoundation.org; Main URL: http://www.lehrmanfoundation.org
Grants List: http://www.lehrmanfoundation.org/grants.html

Incorporated in 1953 in DC.
Donors: Jacob J. Lehrman‡; Charlotte F. Lehrman‡.
Foundation type: Independent foundation.
Financial data (yr. ended 10/31/13): Assets, $13,523,809 (M); expenditures, $769,642; qualifying distributions, $694,471; giving activities include $674,000 for 24 grants (high: $250,000; low: $2,500).
Purpose and activities: The foundation supports and seeks to enrich Jewish life in Washington, DC, Israel, and around the world. It is committed to making Washington a better place for all people and it supports the arts, education and underserved children, the environment, and health care.
Fields of interest: Museums; Arts; Vocational education; Education; Health care; Health organizations, association; Medical research, institute; Human services; Aging, centers/services; Community/economic development; Jewish federated giving programs; Jewish agencies & synagogues; Aging.
Type of support: General/operating support; Scholarship funds; Research.
Limitations: Applications not accepted. Giving primarily in metropolitan Washington, DC. No grants to individuals; no loans.
Publications: Grants list.
Application information: Unsolicited requests for funds not accepted; however an organization may be asked to submit a grant/request for proposal (RFP) by a Trustee of the Board and/or staff member. See foundation web site for details.
Board meeting date(s): Apr. and Oct.
Officers and Trustees:* Robert Lehrman,* Pres.; Marc Dubick,* V.P. and Admin.; Elizabeth Berry,* Secy.; Samuel Lehrman,* Treas.
EIN: 526035666
Selected grants: The following grants are a representative sample of this grantmaker's funding activity:
$75,000 to Jewish Federation of Greater Washington, Rockville, MD, 2011.
$75,000 to Jewish Federation of Greater Washington, Rockville, MD, 2011.
$17,500 to Washington District of Columbia Jewish Community Center, Washington, DC, 2011.
$10,000 to American Committee for the Weizmann Institute of Science, Bethesda, MD, 2011.
$10,000 to Childrens National Medical Center, Washington, DC, 2011.
$10,000 to Student Conservation Association, Arlington, VA, 2011.
$5,000 to Food and Friends, Washington, DC, 2011.
$5,000 to Partnership for Jewish Life and Learning, Rockville, MD, 2011.

1926
Richard Lounsbery Foundation, Inc. ✧
1020 19th St. N.W., Ste. LL60
Washington, DC 20036-6100 (202) 872-8080
Contact: Maxmillian Angerholzer III, Secy.
FAX: (202) 872-9292;
E-mail: foundation@rlounsbery.org; Main URL: http://www.rlounsbery.org/

Incorporated in 1959 in NY.
Donors: Richard Lounsbery‡; Richard Lounsbery Foundation Trust, Inc.
Foundation type: Independent foundation.
Financial data (yr. ended 12/31/13): Assets, $23,726,788 (M); gifts received, $1,827,241; expenditures, $3,193,303; qualifying distributions, $2,970,657; giving activities include $2,387,578 for 66 grants (high: $150,000; low: $1,000).
Purpose and activities: The foundation aims to enhance national strengths in science and technology through support of programs in the following areas: science and technology components of key U.S. policy issues; elementary and secondary science and math education; historical studies and contemporary assessments of key trends in the physical and biomedical sciences; and start-up assistance for establishing the infrastructure of research projects.
Fields of interest: Elementary/secondary education; Health care; Biomedicine research; Science, public policy; Science.
Type of support: Seed money; Matching/challenge support.
Limitations: Giving primarily in Washington, DC and NY; giving internationally including in France and the

United Kingdom. No grants to individuals, or for endowments, capital or building funds; no loans.
Application information: Funds mainly committed to projects developed by the director. The foundation does not print any material and has no mailing list. Application form not required.
Initial approach: Letter
Deadline(s): Six weeks prior to Jan. 1, Apr. 1, July 1, and Oct. 1
Board meeting date(s): Jan., Apr., July and Oct.
Officers and Directors:* David M. Abshire, Ph.D.*, Pres.; William Happer,* V.P.; Maxmillian Angerholzer III, Secy. and Exec. Dir.; Glenn Strehle,* Treas.; Jesse H. Ausubel; R. Nicholas Burns; Richard J. McHenry; Homer A. Neal; David D. Sabatini.
Number of staff: 2 full-time professional; 1 part-time professional; 1 full-time support.
EIN: 136081860

1927
The Ludwig Family Foundation, Inc. ✧
c/o Eugene A. Ludwig
801 17th St., NW, No. 1100
Washington, DC 20006-3922

Established in 2002 in DC.
Donor: Eugene A. Ludwig.
Foundation type: Independent foundation.
Financial data (yr. ended 12/31/11): Assets, $128,310 (M); gifts received, $1,850,495; expenditures, $2,068,241; qualifying distributions, $2,062,174; giving activities include $2,062,174 for 102 grants (high: $400,000; low: $500).
Purpose and activities: The foundation will make grants to organizations that emphasize fostering education and improving the living conditions of the poor. In performing this mission, the foundation generally will adhere to the following priorities when it comes to choosing which organizations will receive grants: 1) organizations that assist in improving education, especially in the greater Washington, DC area; 2) organizations that assist in improving the living conditions of low and moderate income families and that seek to fulfill the needs of the homeless and indigents; 3) organizations that provide funding and services to medical facilities, as well as to organizations that provide funding for research into cures for life-threatening diseases; and 4) to a lesser extent, to organizations that seek to improve the mental and emotional well-being of the community by fostering an interest in the arts.
Fields of interest: Higher education; Health care; Human services; Economically disadvantaged; Homeless.
Limitations: Giving primarily in Washington, DC. No grants to individuals.
Application information:
Initial approach: Letter
Deadline(s): None
Officers: Eugene A. Ludwig, Pres. and Treas.; Carol Ludwig, Secy.
Director: Robert B. Barnett, Esq.
EIN: 562305290

1928
The McIntosh Foundation ✧
1200 18th St. N.W., Ste. 801
Washington, DC 20036-2542 (202) 338-8055

Incorporated in 1949 in NY.
Donors: Josephine H. McIntosh‡; Karen McIntosh‡; Peter McIntosh‡; Marie Joy McIntosh‡.
Foundation type: Independent foundation.
Financial data (yr. ended 12/31/13): Assets, $42,396,195 (M); expenditures, $2,230,239; qualifying distributions, $1,700,260; giving activities include $1,480,050 for 58 grants (high: $240,000; low: $1,000).
Purpose and activities: Giving primarily for environmental conservation.
Fields of interest: Environment, natural resources; Women.
Type of support: Continuing support; General/operating support.
Limitations: Applications not accepted.
Application information: Due to the number of ongoing and/or permanent projects, the foundation is accepting grant applications by invitation only.
Board meeting date(s): Every 4 months
Officers and Directors:* Michael A. McIntosh,* Pres. and C.I.O.; Joan H. McIntosh,* V.P.; Winsome D. McIntosh,* V.P.; Frederick A. Terry, Jr.,* Secy.; Colin H. McIntosh; Hunter H. McIntosh; Michael A. McIntosh, Jr.
Number of staff: 1 full-time professional; 1 part-time professional; 1 full-time support.
EIN: 136096459

1929
Merck Childhood Asthma Network, Inc. ✧
1400 K St. N.W., Ste. 750
Washington, DC 20005-2424 (202) 326-5200
FAX: (202) 326-5201; Main URL: http://www.mcanonline.org

Established in 2005 in NJ.
Donor: The Merck Company Foundation.
Foundation type: Independent foundation.
Financial data (yr. ended 12/31/13): Assets, $763,786 (M); gifts received, $4,104,160; expenditures, $4,040,587; qualifying distributions, $4,053,587; giving activities include $2,037,057 for 7 grants (high: $683,186; low: $90,340).
Purpose and activities: Giving to support and advance evidence-based programs that improve the quality of life for children with asthma and their families and to reduce through the dissemination of effective interventions the burden of the disease on them and society.
Fields of interest: Hospitals (general); Health care; Lung diseases; Asthma.
Limitations: Applications not accepted. Giving on a national basis.
Publications: Grants list.
Application information: Currently not accepting unsolicited requests for funds.
Officers and Trustees:* Geralyn S. Ritter,* Pres.; Floyd J. Malveaux, Exec. V.P. and Exec. Dir.; Celia A. Colbert, Secy.; Mark E. McDonough, Treas.; Evalyn N. Grant, M.D.; Bruce N. Kuhlik; Leona E. Markson, ScD; Richard K. Murray, M.D.; Nancy C. Santanello, M.D.
EIN: 251923556

1930
Merriman Foundation ✧
c/o Linda Sonnenmoser
1747 Pennsylvania Ave.
Washington, DC 20006-4604

Established in MO.
Donors: Trading Partners I; Trading Partners II; Joe Jack Merriman‡.
Foundation type: Independent foundation.
Financial data (yr. ended 12/31/12): Assets, $8,234,917 (M); expenditures, $451,983; qualifying distributions, $428,276; giving activities include $428,276 for grants.
Fields of interest: Arts; Education; Medical research, institute; Boys & girls clubs; Boy scouts; Human services; United Ways and Federated Giving Programs; Religion.
International interests: Bahamas.
Limitations: Applications not accepted. No grants to individuals.
Application information: Unsolicited requests for funds not accepted.
Officers: Michael A. Merriman, Pres. and Treas.; Elaine A. Merriman, V.P.; Marybeth M. Sotos, Secy.
EIN: 237113720

1931
Eugene and Agnes E. Meyer Foundation
1250 Connecticut Ave. N.W., Ste. 800
Washington, DC 20036-2620 (202) 483-8294
FAX: (202) 328-6850; E-mail: info@meyerfdn.org; Main URL: http://www.meyerfoundation.org
E-Newsletter: https://app.e2ma.net/app/view:Join/signupId:1357652/acctId:1356193
Eugene and Agnes E. Meyer Foundation's Philanthropy's Promise: http://www.ncrp.org/philanthropys-promise/who
Facebook: http://www.facebook.com/meyerfoundation
Flickr: https://www.flickr.com/photos/97762193@N03/
Grants Database: http://meyerfoundation.org/impact/our-grantees/grantee-search
Twitter: http://twitter.com/meyerfoundation
Vimeo: http://vimeo.com/meyerfoundation
YouTube: http://www.youtube.com/user/TheMeyerFoundation

Incorporated in 1944 in NY.
Donors: Eugene Meyer‡; Agnes E. Meyer‡; Marpat Foundation.
Foundation type: Independent foundation.
Financial data (yr. ended 12/31/13): Assets, $222,808,736 (M); gifts received, $4,935; expenditures, $11,603,788; qualifying distributions, $8,972,001; giving activities include $6,309,195 for 229 grants (high: $100,000; low: $1,500), and $20,839 for 4 foundation-administered programs.
Purpose and activities: The mission of the foundation is to identify and invest in visionary leaders and effective community-based nonprofit organizations that are working to create lasting improvements in the lives of low-income people in the Washington, D.C. metropolitan region, and to work to strengthen the region's nonprofit sector as a vital and respected partner in meeting community needs.
Fields of interest: Education, early childhood education; Child development, education; Elementary school/education; Secondary school/education; Vocational education; Adult education—literacy, basic skills & GED; Education; Health care; Substance abuse, services; Mental health/crisis services; Health organizations; Legal services; Employment; Youth development, services; Human services; Children/youth, services; Child development, services; Family services; Women, centers/services; Minorities/immigrants, centers/

services; Homeless, human services; Civil rights, race/intergroup relations; Civil/human rights; Urban/community development; Community/economic development; Leadership development; Economically disadvantaged.
Type of support: General/operating support; Management development/capacity building; Program development; Technical assistance; Consulting services; Matching/challenge support.
Limitations: Applications accepted. Giving limited to the Washington, DC, metropolitan area, including, Montgomery and Prince George's counties in MD; Arlington County, City of Alexandria, City of Falls Church, City of Manassas Park, City of Manassas, Fairfax County, and Prince William County in VA. No support for sectarian purposes, or for programs that are national or international in scope. No grants to individuals, or for annual campaigns, deficit financing, endowment funds, equipment, scholarships, fellowships, scientific or medical research, publications, special events or conferences.
Publications: Application guidelines; Grants list; Newsletter.
Application information: Applicants should read the foundation's guidelines thoroughly at www.meyerfoundation.org. Letters of inquiry should be submitted online via a link on the foundation's web site. The foundation will acknowledge receipt of all applications within two weeks. If further information is needed, the applicant will be contacted by a foundation staff member. The foundation may or may not invite a full proposal. Application form required.
Initial approach: Online application required
Deadline(s): See foundation web site for current deadline
Board meeting date(s): May and Oct.
Final notification: Within 2 weeks after board meetings
Officers and Directors:* Joshua B. Bernstein,* Chair.; Deborah Ratner Salzberg, Vice-Chair.; Nicky Goren, C.E.O. and Pres.; Janice A. Thomas, V.P., Finance and Opers.; Richard L. Moyers, V.P. Progs. and Comm.; Barbara Lang, Secy.-Treas; William Dunbar; Newman T. Halvorson, Jr.; James Sandman; Lidia Soto-Harmon; Robert G. Templin, Jr., Ph.D.; Kerrie B. Wilson.
Number of staff: 5 full-time professional; 2 part-time professional; 4 full-time support.
EIN: 530241716
Selected grants: The following grants are a representative sample of this grantmaker's funding activity:
$500,000 to NewSchools Venture Fund, Washington, DC, 2012. For general operations of the DC Schools Fund over five years, payable over 5.00 years.
$175,000 to Community of Hope, Washington, DC, 2012. To support the capital campaign ($50,000 in 2012 and $75,000 in 2013), health programs ($35,000), and housing programs ($15,000), payable over 2.00 years.
$150,000 to District of Columbia College Access Program, Washington, DC, 2012. For general operations over three years, payable over 3.00 years.
$50,000 to Center on Budget and Policy Priorities, Washington, DC, 2012. For fiscal and policy analysis of public education in DC by the DC Fiscal Policy Institute.
$50,000 to College Summit, Washington, DC, 2012. For general operations in the National Capital region.
$50,000 to Urban Alliance Foundation, Washington, DC, 2012. For general operations.
$35,000 to Arlington Free Clinic, Arlington, VA, 2012. For general operations.
$30,000 to Washington Legal Clinic for the Homeless, Washington, DC, 2012. For general operations.
$25,000 to Interfaith Works, Rockville, MD, 2012. For a Vocational Counselor.
$20,000 to Ayuda, Washington, DC, 2012. For general operations.

1932
Moriah Fund ✧

1 Farragut Sq. S.
1634 I St. N.W., Ste. 1000
Washington, DC 20006-4015 (202) 783-8488
Contact: Mary Ann Stein, Pres.
FAX: (202) 783-8499; E-mail: info@moriahfund.org; Israel office e-mail: MoriahF@actcom.net.il; Requests in Israel: Don Futterman, 18 Weizman St., Kfar Saba, Israel 44247; Main URL: http://www.moriahfund.org
Grants List: http://www.moriahfund.org/grants/index.htm

Established in 1985 in IN.
Donors: Clarence W. Efroymson†; Robert A. Efroymson†; Ben-Ephraim Gershon Fund; Gustave Aaron Efroymson Fund.
Foundation type: Independent foundation.
Financial data (yr. ended 12/31/12): Assets, $99,283,417 (M); expenditures, $13,207,071; qualifying distributions, $12,996,138; giving activities include $11,570,650 for 205 grants (high: $1,419,000; low: $500), and $100,000 for 1 loan/program-related investment.
Purpose and activities: Promote human rights and democracy, help disadvantaged people gain self-sufficiency and control over their lives, and promote women's rights and reproductive health. The fund supports programs that strengthen local involvement, leadership and institutional development. The fund focuses on areas where private funding can make a difference, that is, areas that receive inadequate government funds, or that leverage public and private support through advocacy and the modeling of innovative programs.
Fields of interest: Reproductive health; Reproductive health, family planning; Family services, single parents; International human rights; Civil/human rights; Community/economic development; Leadership development.
International interests: Israel.
Type of support: General/operating support; Continuing support; Income development; Management development/capacity building; Endowments; Emergency funds; Program development; Conferences/seminars; Seed money; Technical assistance; Program evaluation; Program-related investments/loans; In-kind gifts; Matching/challenge support.
Limitations: Applications accepted. Giving nationally and internationally in the United States and Israel. Giving for the Economic Justice Program focuses on Washington, DC, MD and VA. No support for lobbying or political campaigns, private foundations, or arts organizations. No grants to individuals, or for medical research.
Publications: Application guidelines; Financial statement; Grants list; Program policy statement.
Application information: The Moriah Fund will no longer accept or review unsolicited proposals. This new policy, a result of the current economic situation and decline in Moriah's assets, is intended to save organizations the work of preparing proposals that cannot be funded. As Moriah determines new strategies, policies and plans, the foundation will keep you updated on the web site. In the meantime, grantmaking will continue on an invitation-only basis. See web site for specific policies regarding the proposal process after a letter of inquiry is reviewed.
Initial approach: Letter of inquiry. Proposals only by invitation.
Deadline(s): Mar. 1 and Sept. 1
Board meeting date(s): May and Nov.
Officers, Program Board and Directors:* Mary Ann Stein,* Pres. and Prog. Board; Barbara Schrirfer, C.F.O.; Craig Cramer, Prog. Board; Debra Delee, Prog. Board; Jane Fox Johnson, Prog. Board; Kim Jones, Prog. Board; Judith Lichtman,* Prog. Board; Norman Rosenberg, Prog. Board; Gideon Stein,* Prog. Board; Noah Stein, Prog. Board; Dorothy Swamy, Prog. Board.
Number of staff: 8 full-time professional; 2 part-time professional; 5 full-time support.
EIN: 311129589
Selected grants: The following grants are a representative sample of this grantmaker's funding activity:
$1,419,000 to New Israel Fund, Washington, DC, 2012. For the operations, grants and programs.
$650,000 to Fund for Global Human Rights, Washington, DC, 2012. For the Centro Mujeres.
$200,000 to Future Is Now Schools, Los Angeles, CA, 2012. For general support.
$100,000 to Center on Budget and Policy Priorities, Washington, DC, 2012. For public education among key stakeholders on fiscal issues, provide analysis of education fiscal polices.
$100,000 to National Network of Abortion Funds, Boston, MA, 2012. For general support.
$50,000 to New America Foundation, Washington, DC, 2012. For its Open Zion project.
$40,000 to National Family Planning and Reproductive Health Association, Washington, DC, 2012. For general support.
$30,000 to Jews United for Justice, Washington, DC, 2012. For general support.
$30,000 to Urgent Action Fund for Womens Human Rights, San Francisco, CA, 2012. For general support.
$20,000 to Dc Special Education Co-Operative, Washington, DC, 2012. For general support.

1933
Curtis & Edith Munson Foundation ✧

1990 M St. N.W., Ste. 250
Washington, DC 20036-3430 (202) 887-8992
Contact: Angel Braestrup, Exec. Dir.
FAX: (202) 887-8987; E-mail: info@munsonfdn.org; Main URL: http://www.munsonfdn.org

Incorporated in 1982 in FL.
Foundation type: Independent foundation.
Financial data (yr. ended 12/31/13): Assets, $30,875,387 (M); expenditures, $2,083,468; qualifying distributions, $1,952,158; giving activities include $1,695,609 for 137 grants (high: $152,499; low: $250).
Purpose and activities: Support for conservation of marine wildlife and natural resources in North America. In descending order by expenditure, the foundation gives primarily for marine/fisheries conservation, the south Florida environment, the

Alabama environment, the Chesapeake Bay watershed, and community need.
Fields of interest: Environment, natural resources; Environment, water resources; Environment; Animals/wildlife, fisheries.
Type of support: Internship funds; General/operating support; Program development; Conferences/seminars; Seed money; Matching/challenge support.
Limitations: Giving primarily in AL and FL; some giving also in the Chesapeake Bay watershed. No grants to individuals, or for endowment funds, capital campaigns, or for building or renovation; no loans.
Publications: Application guidelines; Grants list.
Application information: Contributes primarily to pre-selected organizations. Full proposals will not be accepted unless invited by the foundation. Washington Grantmakers Common Letter of Inquiry format accepted. Application form required.
Initial approach: 1-2 page letter of inquiry, along with separate project summary whose form must follow guidelines on foundation web site. E-mail inquires are encouraged.
Copies of proposal: 1
Deadline(s): Apr. 6 and Aug. 31 for letters of inquiry and project summary
Board meeting date(s): July, Nov., and as required
Final notification: 3 weeks after meetings
Officers and Directors:* C. Wolcott Henry III,* Pres.; Bruce Reid, Secy.; H. Alexander Henry, Treas.; Angel Braestrup, Exec. Dir.; Truman M. Hobbs, Jr.
Number of staff: None.
EIN: 592235907
Selected grants: The following grants are a representative sample of this grantmaker's funding activity:
$40,000 to Ocean Project, Providence, RI, 2012.
$30,000 to Ocean Foundation, Washington, DC, 2012.
$30,000 to Potomac Riverkeeper, Washington, DC, 2012.
$30,000 to Southern Environmental Law Center, Atlanta, GA, 2012.
$25,000 to Student Conservation Association, Charlestown, NH, 2012.
$25,000 to Surfrider Foundation, San Clemente, CA, 2012.
$22,000 to University of Alabama, Tuscaloosa, AL, 2012.
$20,000 to Alabama Rivers Alliance, Birmingham, AL, 2012.
$10,000 to Anacostia Watershed Society, Bladensburg, MD, 2012.

1934
The National Academy of Education ✧
500 5th St. N.W., No. 307
Washington, DC 20001-2736 (202) 334-2093
Contact: Gregory White, Exec. Dir.; Philip Perrin, Sr. Prog. Off., Professional Devel. Progs.; Jack Busbee
FAX: (202) 334-2350; E-mail: info@naeducation.org; Main URL: http://www.naeducation.org/

Established in 1965 in NY; classified as a private operating foundation in 1973.
Donors: Carnegie Corporation of New York; Spencer Foundation.
Foundation type: Operating foundation.
Financial data (yr. ended 12/31/12): Assets, $6,769,453 (M); gifts received, $266,447; expenditures, $2,736,370; qualifying distributions, $2,630,550; giving activities include $1,583,750 for 61 grants (high: $55,000; low: $12,500).
Purpose and activities: Awards fellowships to dissertation completion and to recent recipients of Ph.D., Ed.D., or equivalent degrees planning to study matters relevant to the improvement of education.
Fields of interest: Education, research; Education.
Type of support: Fellowships.
Limitations: Applications accepted. Giving on an international basis. No support for organizations.
Publications: Application guidelines; Informational brochure.
Application information: Applications must be in English. Application guidelines are available on The Academy's web site. Application form required.
Initial approach: Letter, telephone, e-mail, or download application from web site
Deadline(s): See web site for details
Board meeting date(s): Spring and fall
Final notification: Mid-May
Officers and Directors:* Michael Feuer,* Pres.; James Pellegrino,* V.P.; Catherine Snow,* Secy.-Treas.; Gregory White, Exec. Dir.; Greg Duncan; Margaret Eisenhart; Susan H. Fuhrman; Pamela Grossman; Kenji Hakuta; Margaret Beale Spencer; Claude Steele.
Number of staff: 4 full-time professional; 2 part-time professional.
EIN: 770415802

1935
NDPI Foundation, Inc. ✧
1401 I St. N.W., 7th Fl.
Washington, DC 20005-2225
Main URL: http://ndpifoundation.org/

Donor: Chevron Corporation.
Foundation type: Independent foundation.
Financial data (yr. ended 12/31/12): Assets, $33,112,494 (M); gifts received, $681,595; expenditures, $8,515,132; qualifying distributions, $8,515,132; giving activities include $8,062,742 for 1 grant.
Purpose and activities: Giving to establish and encourage innovative multi-stakeholder partnerships that support programs and activities, which empower communities to achieve a peaceful and enabling environment for equitable economic growth in the Niger Delta.
Fields of interest: Human services; International economic development; Economic development.
International interests: Nigeria.
Limitations: Applications not accepted. Giving primarily in the Niger Delta region of Nigeria.
Application information: Contributes only to pre-selected organizations.
Officers: Alireza Moshiri, Chair. and Pres.; Walter Maguire, Treas.
Directors: Pauline Baker; Dennis Flemming; Princeton Lyman; Jane Nelson; Linda Padon; Laurie Regelbrugge.
EIN: 272924204

1936
New Mighty Foundation ✧
c/o Stephen K. Vetter
1666 K St., N.W., Ste. 400
Washington, DC 20006-1219 (202) 457-7200
Contact: George Harris

Established in 2007 in DC.
Donors: New Mighty US Trust; Goldman Sachs.
Foundation type: Operating foundation.
Financial data (yr. ended 12/31/13): Assets, $70,066,053 (M); expenditures, $15,251,808; qualifying distributions, $15,226,364; giving activities include $15,226,364 for 68 grants (high: $1,203,626; low: $200).
Fields of interest: Education.
Limitations: Giving primarily in China.
Application information:
Initial approach: Letter of pre-grant inquiry
Deadline(s): None
Officer and Directors:* Wen-Hsiung Hung,* Chair.; Sandy R.Y. Wang; Susan R.H. Wang; Wilfred Wang; William H. Wong.
EIN: 204282979
Selected grants: The following grants are a representative sample of this grantmaker's funding activity:
$1,175,500 to Sichuan Province Education Foundation, Chengdu City, China, 2012. For support of school.
$1,031,000 to Provincial Education Department of Gansu, Lanshou City, China, 2012. For support of school.
$780,000 to Education Department of Henan Province, Zhengzhou, China, 2012. For support of school.
$747,500 to Provincial Education Department of Gansu, Lanshou City, China, 2012. For support of school.
$692,000 to Provincial Education Department of Gansu, Lanshou City, China, 2012. For support of school.
$644,500 to Shandong Provincial Education Department, Jinan, China, 2012. For support of school.
$623,000 to Yunnan Provincial Department of Education, Kunming, China, 2012. For support of school.
$608,000 to Provincial Education Department of Gansu, Lanshou City, China, 2012. For support of school.
$598,500 to Education Department of Inner Mongolia Autonomous Region, Hohhot, China, 2012. For support of school.
$250,500 to Education Bureau of Qinghai Province, Xining, China, 2012. For support of school.

1937
The Palmer Foundation ✧
1201 Connecticut Ave. N.W., Ste. 300
Washington, DC 20036-2656
FAX: (202) 833-5540;
E-mail: admin@thepalmerfoundation.org; Main URL: http://www.thepalmerfoundation.org

Established in 1990 in IL.
Donors: Rogers Palmer†; Mary Palmer†; Mary P. Enroth.
Foundation type: Independent foundation.
Financial data (yr. ended 12/31/12): Assets, $14,380,061 (M); gifts received, $200,000; expenditures, $697,275; qualifying distributions, $652,906; giving activities include $498,000 for 27 grants (high: $60,000; low: $1,000).
Purpose and activities: Giving primarily for youth, the environment and public health.
Fields of interest: Environment; Public health; Human services; Children/youth; Youth.
International interests: Guatemala; Mexico.

Type of support: Program development; Matching/challenge support.
Limitations: Applications not accepted. Giving limited to the Midwest states of: IL and WI, and the Mid Atlantic states of: MD, NC, VA, and in Washington, DC, unless one of the foundation's directors has a personal interest elsewhere. No support for lobbying, sectarian religious purposes, individual medical purposes, or for scientific research. No grants to individuals, or for multi-year grants, endowment drives, operational support, annual campaigns, or salaries.
Publications: Annual report; Grants list; Program policy statement.
Application information: Unsolicited requests for funds not accepted.
Board meeting date(s): Apr. and Oct.
Officers: Mary P. Enroth, Chair.; Karen E. Lischick, Pres.; Susan Le Mieux Enroth, V.P.; Jay L. Owen, Secy.; Peter Lischick, Treas.
Director: Charlly Enroth.
Number of staff: 1 part-time support.
EIN: 363700897

1938
The James & Theodore Pedas Family Foundation, Inc. ✧
4018 Brandywine St. N.W.
Washington, DC 20016-1844

Established in 1999 in MD and DC.
Donors: James Pedas; Theodore Pedas.
Foundation type: Independent foundation.
Financial data (yr. ended 12/31/13): Assets, $8,238,627 (M); gifts received, $200,000; expenditures, $451,459; qualifying distributions, $449,225; giving activities include $449,225 for 74 grants (high: $40,000; low: $500).
Fields of interest: Education; Human services; Religion.
Limitations: Applications not accepted. Giving primarily in Washington, DC. No grants to individuals.
Application information: Unsolicited requests for funds not accepted.
Officers: James Pedas, Pres.; Theodore Pedas, V.P.
EIN: 911979866

1939
Professional Athletes Foundation ✧
1133 20th St. N.W.
Washington, DC 20036-3408

Established around 1981 in Washington, DC.
Donors: The National Football League; The National Football League Players Association; Player's Grievance Trust.
Foundation type: Independent foundation.
Financial data (yr. ended 12/31/13): Assets, $27,104,314 (M); gifts received, $2,859,172; expenditures, $2,268,860; qualifying distributions, $1,887,916; giving activities include $292,080 for 23 grants (high: $25,000; low: $2,000), and $1,595,836 for 292 grants to individuals (high: $95,565; low: $66).
Purpose and activities: Giving primarily to support former professional and amateur athletes and their families in times of financial crisis.
Fields of interest: Economically disadvantaged.
Type of support: Grants to individuals.
Limitations: Applications not accepted.
Application information: Unsolicited requests for funds not accepted.
Officer and Directors:* Demaurice Smith,* Chair.; Maxine Baker; Andre Collins; Ned Ehrlich; Ken Jolly; Peter Kirsch; Dewey McClain; Emery Moorehead; Brig Owens; Charles Swisher.
EIN: 521205920

1940
Public Welfare Foundation, Inc. ✧
1200 U St. N.W.
Washington, DC 20009-4443 (202) 965-1800
Contact: Grants Mgnt.
FAX: (202) 265-8851;
E-mail: info@publicwelfare.org; Main URL: http://www.publicwelfare.org
CEP Study: http://www.publicwelfare.org/about-us/governance-and-policies/center-for-effective-philanthropy-survey/
E-Newsletter: http://www.publicwelfare.org/news/
Facebook: http://www.facebook.com/pages/Washington-DC/Public-Welfare-Foundation/371167644067?ref=ts
Grants Database: http://www.publicwelfare.org/grants-process/our-grants/
Public Welfare Foundation's Philanthropy Promise: http://www.ncrp.org/philanthropys-promise/who
Twitter: http://twitter.com/PublicWelfare

Incorporated in 1947 in TX; reincorporated in 1951 in DE.
Donor: Charles Edward Marsh‡.
Foundation type: Independent foundation.
Financial data (yr. ended 09/30/13): Assets, $488,153,146 (M); expenditures, $25,029,585; qualifying distributions, $23,514,779; giving activities include $20,192,300 for 224 grants (high: $700,000; low: $100).
Purpose and activities: The Public Welfare Foundation supports efforts to ensure fundamental rights and opportunities for people in need. It looks for carefully defined points where our funds can make a difference in bringing about systemic changes that can improve lives. The Public Welfare Foundation focuses on three program areas: 1) Criminal Justice, 2) Juvenile Justice and 3) Workers' Rights. A small number of grants will also be made under the Special Opportunities and President's Discretionary categories.
Fields of interest: Crime/law enforcement, reform; Offenders/ex-offenders, bail issues; Offenders/ex-offenders, prison alternatives; Employment, labor unions/organizations; Minorities/immigrants, centers/services.
Type of support: Research; Publication; Seed money; Program development; General/operating support; Employee matching gifts; Continuing support.
Limitations: Applications accepted. Giving is limited to the U.S. No support for international funding. No funding for individuals, scholarships, direct services, international projects or endowment campaigns.
Publications: Application guidelines; Financial statement; Grants list; Newsletter.
Application information: There is a two-step application process, lasting four to six months: 1) The applicant creates an account and submits an online letter of inquiry, up to five pages. Please read letter of inquiry content guide on the foundation web site. Once a letter of inquiry arrives at the foundation, the staff determines whether the proposed project fits the foundation's funding guidelines. Please read the program guidelines carefully before applying. The foundation staff will let applicants know if they are invited to submit a full proposal; and 2) Only full proposals that have been invited will be considered. Applicants will be invited by e-mail to submit full proposals and will be sent an online link to the same account login page used to submit the letter of inquiry. There, they will be able to access an online form for submitting a full proposal. Application form required.
Initial approach: Online letter of inquiry (all applicants, new and those renewing grants, must complete this step); Please see the foundation web site: http://www.publicwelfare.org/ApplyGrant.aspx
Copies of proposal: 1
Deadline(s): Letters of inquiry are accepted throughout the year but it is recommended to submit a LOI 4 to 6 weeks before proposal deadlines. See the foundation's web site for full and invited proposals deadlines
Board meeting date(s): Board (or a committee of the board) meets 3 times annually
Final notification: For LOI: 30 working days; for full and invited proposals, successful applicants receive an award letter by e-mail, and generally funds are disbursed within 45 days of approval. Entire application process generally takes 4 to 6 months
Officers and Directors:* Lydia Micheaux Marshall,* Chair.; Myrtis H. Powell,* Vice-Chair.; Mary E. McClymont, Pres.; Phillipa P. Taylor, C.F.O. and C.A.O. and Secy.-Treas.; Ellen Gordon, Cont.; Craig Aase; Stephanie Bell-Rose; Jackie M. Clegg; David Dodson; Juliet Villarreal Garcia; Yolanda Orozco; Maria Otero; Shirley Sagawa; Cliff Sloan; Landis Zimmerman.
Number of staff: 9 full-time professional; 4 full-time support.
EIN: 540597601
Selected grants: The following grants are a representative sample of this grantmaker's funding activity:
$600,000 to Campaign for Youth Justice, Washington, DC, 2011. For general support, payable over 2.00 years.
$350,000 to Pretrial Justice Institute, Washington, DC, 2011. For efforts to protect pretrial services programs, which allow non-violent defendants pending trial to be released under treatment and supervision, against challenges by the bail bonding industry seeking to increase its profits.
$300,000 to Center for Public Integrity, Washington, DC, 2012. To produce original investigative journalism that holds policymakers accountable to the public, for a workers' rights reporting beat, payable over 2.00 years.
$250,000 to Leadership Conference Education Fund, Washington, DC, 2011. For the Americans for Financial Reform project to support its research and advocacy for policy reforms at the Commodity Futures Trading Commission and the new Consumer Financial Protection Bureau, payable over 1.50 years.
$200,000 to Colorado Criminal Justice Reform Coalition, Denver, CO, 2011. For general support, payable over 2.00 years.
$200,000 to National Council for Occupational Safety and Health, Chapel Hill, NC, 2012. For general support.
$200,000 to W. Haywood Burns Institute, Oakland, CA, 2010. For general support, payable over 2.00 years.

$150,000 to Northern Kentucky Childrens Law Center, Covington, KY, 2011. For litigation, advocacy, public education, and research to reduce detention and incarceration rates in Ohio's juvenile justice system, as well as to conduct research about youth tried in Ohio's adult criminal justice system.
$100,000 to Crime and Justice Institute, Boston, MA, 2012. To conduct a needs assessment, provide technical assistance and build capacity for a broad range of corrections stakeholders responsible for implementing California's criminal justice realignment legislation.

1941
The Quetzal Trust ✧
(formerly Peter Brown and Margaret Hamburg Charitable Trust)
P.O. Box 39337
Washington, DC 20016-3147

Established in 2000 in DC.
Donors: Peter F. Brown; Margaret A. Hamburg.
Foundation type: Independent foundation.
Financial data (yr. ended 12/31/12): Assets, $90,397,478 (M); gifts received, $36,000,000; expenditures, $3,646,393; qualifying distributions, $3,644,800; giving activities include $3,644,800 for 16 grants (high: $3,500,000; low: $250).
Fields of interest: Media/communications; Elementary/secondary education; Higher education.
Limitations: Applications not accepted. Giving primarily in Washington, DC, and New York, NY. No grants to individuals.
Application information: Contributes only to pre-selected organizations.
Trustees: Peter F. Brown; Rachel Brown; Margaret A. Hamburg.
EIN: 527140888

1942
The Norman R. Rales and Ruth Rales Foundation ✧
2200 Pennsylvania Ave. N.W., Ste. 800W
Washington, DC 20037-1731

Established in 1986 in FL.
Donors: Norman R. Rales†; Paul Pearl; Richard Siemens; Desmond Roberts; Gulfstream Park.
Foundation type: Independent foundation.
Financial data (yr. ended 11/30/13): Assets, $100,777,468 (M); gifts received, $81,080,071; expenditures, $893,330; qualifying distributions, $830,539; giving activities include $776,000 for grants.
Purpose and activities: Giving primarily for education, health organizations, children, youth, and social services, Roman Catholic churches, and to Jewish agencies and temples.
Fields of interest: Education; Hospitals (general); Health organizations, association; Human services; Children/youth, services; Jewish federated giving programs; Catholic agencies & churches; Jewish agencies & synagogues.
Limitations: Applications not accepted. Giving primarily in FL.
Application information: Unsolicited requests for funds not accepted.
Trustees: Joshua B. Rales; Mitchell P. Rales; Steven M. Rales; Morris E. Sampson.
EIN: 596874589

Selected grants: The following grants are a representative sample of this grantmaker's funding activity:
$350,000 to Ruth Rales Jewish Family Service, Boca Raton, FL, 2011.

1943
Rumsfeld Foundation ✧
1718 M St. N.W., No. 366
Washington, DC 20036-4504
E-mail: contact@rumsfeldfoundation.org; Main URL: http://rumsfeldfoundation.org/
Facebook: https://www.facebook.com/rumsfeldfoundation
LinkedIn: http://www.linkedin.com/company/rumsfeld-foundation
Twitter: https://twitter.com/RumsfeldOffice

Established in 2007 in DC.
Donors: Donald H. Rumsfeld; Joyce P. Rumsfeld; Ralph Eberhart; Joyce and Donald Rumsfeld Foundation; DHR Holdings, LLC; Charity Buzz; Infosoft Group, Inc.; Morgan Stanley; Forrest Fenn; Data Tresary Charitable Foundation.
Foundation type: Independent foundation.
Financial data (yr. ended 12/31/12): Assets, $11,482,329 (M); gifts received, $827,560; expenditures, $1,832,727; qualifying distributions, $1,588,931; giving activities include $1,588,931 for 79 grants (high: $281,912; low: $40).
Fields of interest: Higher education; Human services; International affairs, research; Military/veterans' organizations.
Limitations: Applications not accepted. Giving in the U.S., with emphasis on Washington, DC.
Application information: Unsolicited requests for funds not accepted.
Officers and Directors:* Donald H. Rumsfeld,* Pres. and Secy.; Joyce P. Rumsfeld,* V.P. and Treas.; Edward G. Biester, Jr.; Dr. Steve Cambone; Lawrence Di Rita.
EIN: 260580915

1944
Thomas Rutherfoord Foundation ✧
3333 P St. N.W.
Washington, DC 20007-2702

Established in 2004 in VA.
Donor: Thomas D. Rutherfoord.
Foundation type: Independent foundation.
Financial data (yr. ended 12/31/12): Assets, $19,010,219 (M); expenditures, $1,047,751; qualifying distributions, $949,325; giving activities include $949,325 for 66 grants (high: $191,895; low: $200).
Fields of interest: Higher education; Human services; Christian agencies & churches; General charitable giving.
Type of support: General/operating support.
Limitations: Applications not accepted. Giving primarily in Washington, DC. No grants to individuals.
Application information: Unsolicited requests for funds not accepted.
Trustee: Thomas D. Rutherfoord.
EIN: 202057953

1945
San Giacomo Charitable Foundation ✧
2801 New Mexico Ave., N.W., Ste. 209
Washington, DC 20007-3907 (202) 338-5728
Contact: Luigi R. Einaudi, Tr.

Established in DC.
Foundation type: Independent foundation.
Financial data (yr. ended 12/31/12): Assets, $8,765,551 (M); expenditures, $1,433,294; qualifying distributions, $1,404,062; giving activities include $1,375,080 for 7 grants (high: $1,200,080; low: $3,500).
Purpose and activities: The foundation's goals are to foster international, cultural and educational exchange; to support institutional development and research, primarily in the economic and social sciences; and to support medical research, particularly towards cures for various forms of cancer.
Fields of interest: Medical research, institute; Cancer research; International exchange, arts; International exchange; Social sciences; Economics.
International interests: Italy.
Limitations: Applications accepted. Giving limited to Italy. No grants to individuals.
Application information: Application form required.
Initial approach: Proposal
Deadline(s): None
Trustees: Luigi R. Einaudi; Roberta Einaudi.
EIN: 521963583

1946
Searle Freedom Trust ✧
(formerly D & D Foundation)
1055 Thomas Jefferson St. N.W., Ste. L26
Washington, DC 20007-5259 (202) 375-7820
Contact: Kimberly O. Dennis, C.E.O. and Pres.
FAX: (202) 375-7821; Kim Berly O. Dennis, C.E.O. and Pres. Phone: (202) 375-7822, and E-mail: Kdennis@searlefreedomtrust.org; Main URL: http://www.searlefreedomtrust.org

Established in 1998 in IL.
Donor: Daniel C. Searle†.
Foundation type: Independent foundation.
Financial data (yr. ended 12/31/12): Assets, $111,578,641 (M); gifts received, $13,817; expenditures, $18,747,813; qualifying distributions, $14,912,835; giving activities include $14,001,422 for 102 grants (high: $1,500,000; low: $9,218).
Purpose and activities: The trust aims to foster research and encourage public policies that promote individual freedom and economic liberty while at the same time advancing a commitment to personal responsibility and a respect for traditional American values. One of the foundation's chief objectives is to help develop policies that advance liberty without encouraging license, and that demand personal responsibility without compromising freedom. Issues the foundation supports include: Tax and budget issues, cost-benefit analysis of regulatory practices, welfare policy, K-12 reform, environmental policy, and legal reform.
Fields of interest: Elementary/secondary education; Higher education; Environment, public policy; Social sciences; Welfare policy/reform; Public affairs.
Type of support: Conferences/seminars; Publication; Fellowships; Research.

Limitations: Applications accepted. Giving on a national basis. No support for for-profit organizations. No grants to individuals, or for endowments, operating support capital campaigns, or building projects.
Application information:
Initial approach: Online grant proposal
Board meeting date(s): Apr., July and Nov.
Officer and Trustees:* Kimberly O. Dennis,* C.E.O. and Pres.; D. Gideon Searle; Kinship Trust Co.
EIN: 367244615
Selected grants: The following grants are a representative sample of this grantmaker's funding activity:
$1,500,000 to American Enterprise Institute for Public Policy Research, Washington, DC, 2012. For Research on Economics and Regulation.
$1,000,000 to Art Institute of Chicago, Chicago, IL, 2012. For Bridge Project.
$688,000 to Reason Foundation, Los Angeles, CA, 2012. For Reason TV.
$330,000 to Donors Trust, Alexandria, VA, 2012. For Center for College Affordability and Productivity (CCAP).
$250,000 to Donors Trust, Alexandria, VA, 2012. For Project on Fair Representation.
$100,000 to Fraser Institute, Vancouver, Canada, 2012. For Economic Freedom of the World Index.
$100,000 to Philanthropy Roundtable, Washington, DC, 2012. For Donor Recruitment and Policy Conference.
$75,000 to Barry Goldwater Institute for Public Policy Research, Phoenix, AZ, 2012. For Center for Constitutional Litigation.
$75,000 to Institute for Justice, Arlington, VA, 2012. For Social Media.
$75,000 to University of California, Berkeley, CA, 2012. For School of Law: Moot Court.

1947
The Nathan Seter Foundation ✧
(formerly The Heller Foundation)
c/o Milbank, Tweed, Hadley & McCloy LLP
1850 K St. N.W.
Washington, DC 20006-2236

Established in 2001 in NY.
Donors: Benjamin Heller; Fanny Heller; Jacqueline Heller; Fanya Heller; Educational Health Alliance LLC.
Foundation type: Independent foundation.
Financial data (yr. ended 12/31/12): Assets, $6,866,598 (M); gifts received, $775,000; expenditures, $1,336,794; qualifying distributions, $1,319,925; giving activities include $1,319,675 for 81 grants (high: $150,000; low: $1,000).
Purpose and activities: Giving primarily to Jewish organizations, temples, and schools.
Fields of interest: Arts; Elementary/secondary education; Higher education; Education; Human services; Jewish federated giving programs; Jewish agencies & synagogues.
Limitations: Applications not accepted. Giving primarily in the metropolitan New York, NY, area. No grants to individuals.
Application information: Contributes only to pre-selected organizations.
Officers: Arnold Simon, Pres.; Robert Moss, V.P.; Jonathan Blattmachr, Secy.
EIN: 134150736
Selected grants: The following grants are a representative sample of this grantmaker's funding activity:
$88,500 to Museum of Jewish Heritage, New York, NY, 2011.
$85,000 to American Society for Yad Vashem, New York, NY, 2011.
$36,000 to Jewish Museum, New York, NY, 2011.
$35,000 to Aleph Society, New York, NY, 2011.
$25,000 to Foundation for the Defense of Democracies, Washington, DC, 2011.
$20,000 to Paideia School, Atlanta, GA, 2011.
$18,000 to Open University Foundation, New York, NY, 2011.
$16,000 to Congregation Kehilath Jeshurun, New York, NY, 2011.
$15,000 to Columbia University, New York, NY, 2011.
$3,600 to Fifth Avenue Synagogue, New York, NY, 2011.

1948
Spectemur Agendo, Inc. ✧
122 Maryland Ave. N.E.
Washington, DC 20002-5610 (202) 546-3732
Contact: Conrad Martin, Tr.

Established in 2007 in DC.
Donor: 122 Maryland Corp.
Foundation type: Independent foundation.
Financial data (yr. ended 12/31/13): Assets, $11,417,236 (M); gifts received, $5,100,000; expenditures, $1,329,556; qualifying distributions, $1,272,778; giving activities include $849,537 for 125 grants (high: $115,000; low: $100).
Fields of interest: Education; Human services; Social sciences, public policy; Public affairs, ethics.
Limitations: Applications accepted. Giving primarily in Washington, DC; some funding also in New York, NY.
Application information: Application form not required.
Initial approach: Proposal
Deadline(s): None
Trsutees: Julie Burton; Russell Hemenway; Conrad Martin; Jolene Smith; Anne Zill.
EIN: 010751046

1949
Alexander and Margaret Stewart Trust ✧
888 17th St. N.W., Ste. 610
Washington, DC 20006-3321 (202) 785-9892
Contact: Lori A. Jackson, Exec. Mgr.
FAX: (202) 785-0918;
E-mail: ljackson@stewart-trust.org; Main URL: http://www.stewart-trust.org
RSS Feed: http://www.stewart-trust.org/?feed=rss2

Trust established in 1947 in DC; in 1997 combined with the Helen S. Devore Trust that was established in 1960.
Donors: Helen S. Devore†; Mary E. Stewart†.
Foundation type: Independent foundation.
Financial data (yr. ended 12/31/12): Assets, $96,846,721 (M); expenditures, $4,806,174; qualifying distributions, $4,661,304; giving activities include $4,366,074 for 49+ grants (high: $400,000).
Purpose and activities: Giving for the care, prevention, and treatment of cancer, and for the care of children who are physically or mentally ill or handicapped; and research, education, or prevention of diseases common to childhood, including societal behavioral patterns having a negative impact on the welfare of children.
Fields of interest: Health care, infants; Health care; Cancer; Children/youth, services; Economically disadvantaged.
Type of support: General/operating support; Continuing support; Equipment; Program development; Research.
Limitations: Applications accepted. Giving primarily in the Washington, DC, area. No grants to individuals, or for endowment funds, annual campaigns, building funds, land acquisition, renovation projects, scholarships, or fellowships.
Publications: Application guidelines; Grants list.
Application information: Applications by invitation only, upon review of initial Letter of Inquiry. Applicants who have received a grant from the trust within the past three years already pre-quality, and may submit an application through foundation web site. Application form required.
Initial approach: Online Letter of Inquiry form on foundation web site
Copies of proposal: 1
Deadline(s): See foundation web site for current deadline
Board meeting date(s): Monthly
Final notification: Usually by late Dec.
Officer: Lori A. Jackson, Exec. Mgr.
Trustees: William J. Bierbower; George Hamilton; Rockefeller Trust Co., N.A.
Number of staff: 1 full-time professional.
EIN: 526020260

1950
The Summit Foundation
(also known as The Summit Charitable Foundation, Inc.)
2100 Pennsylvania Ave., N.W., Ste. 525
Washington, DC 20037-3223
Contact: Carlos Saavedra, Exec. Dir.
FAX: (202) 912-2901; Main URL: http://www.summitfdn.org/foundation/about/
Roger and Victoria Sant's Giving Pledge Profile: http://glasspockets.org/philanthropy-in-focus/eye-on-the-giving-pledge/profiles/sant

Established in 1991 in DE.
Donors: Roger Sant; Victoria P. Sant; AES Corp.; Aspen Charitable Remainder Unitrust No. 3.
Foundation type: Independent foundation.
Financial data (yr. ended 12/31/12): Assets, $65,788,608 (M); expenditures, $8,543,028; qualifying distributions, $8,306,805; giving activities include $6,866,336 for 90 grants (high: $457,375; low: $1,000).
Purpose and activities: The mission of the foundation is to promote the health and well-being of the planet - its people and its natural environment - by achieving a sustainable global population, protecting the earth's biodiversity and making cities livable. To achieve this, the foundation focuses on empowering girls, conserving the Mesoamerican Reef and promoting sustainable cities.
Fields of interest: Environment, natural resources; Environment; Reproductive health; Reproductive health, family planning; Reproductive health, sexuality education; Health care; Youth development; Youth, pregnancy prevention; International human rights; Girls.
International interests: Belize; Guatemala; Honduras; Mexico.

Type of support: General/operating support; Continuing support; Program development; Seed money; Technical assistance; Program evaluation; Matching/challenge support.
Limitations: Applications not accepted. Giving through the Biodiversity and Empowering Youth Programs focuses on international Mesoamerican Reef countries only; Sustainable Cities Program focuses generally on the United States. No grants to individuals, or for freestanding conferences, film and video projects or basic research.
Publications: Grants list.
Application information: Unsolicited requests for funds not considered.
Board meeting date(s): 2 times a year
Officers and Trustees:* Roger Sant,* Chair.; Victoria P. Sant,* Pres.; Shari Sant Plummer,* Secy.; Lex Sant,* Treas.; Carlos Saavedra, Exec. Dir.; Kathryn S. Fuller; Dan Plummer; Ali Sant-Johnson; Chrissie Sant; Kristin Sant; Michael Sant; Shira Saperstein.
Number of staff: 4 full-time professional; 2 part-time professional; 2 part-time support.
EIN: 521743817
Selected grants: The following grants are a representative sample of this grantmaker's funding activity:
$370,000 to Comunidad y Biodiversidad, Guaymas, Mexico, 2013. To create Network of Fish Refuges in Quintana Roo, Mexico.
$285,000 to Mexican Nature Conservation Fund, Mexico City, Mexico, 2013. For MAR Leadership Program.
$205,217 to Coral Reef Alliance, Oakland, CA, 2013. For Mesoamerican Reef Tourism Initiative.
$200,000 to Global Philanthropy Partnership, Chicago, IL, 2013. For Urban Sustainability Directors Network.
$170,000 to Environmental Defense Fund, New York, NY, 2013. For Mesoamerican Reef Sustainable Fisheries Initiative in Belize: Toward Managed Access.
$150,000 to Population Services International, Washington, DC, 2013. For Regional Adolescent Reproductive Health and HIV/STI Prevention Program in Central America and Mexico.
$100,000 to Global Philanthropy Partnership, Chicago, IL, 2013. To Engage Cities in STAR Communities Rating System.
$48,000 to Mesoamerican Reef Fund, Guatemala, Guatemala, 2013. For Maintaining Enforcement Presence in Southern Belize Reef Complex.
$40,000 to Center for Reproductive Rights, New York, NY, 2013. To Secure Adolescents' Access to Emergency Contraception in Honduras.
$25,000 to Starfish One by One, Evergreen, CO, 2013. For Permanent Pioneers: Creating Lasting Female Leadership in Guatemala.

1951
Alice and Russell True Foundation ✧
4100 Cathedral Ave. N.W., Ste. 510
Washington, DC 20016-3513

Established in 1997 in Washington, DC.
Donor: Alice True Gasch.
Foundation type: Independent foundation.
Financial data (yr. ended 12/31/13): Assets, $16,499,109 (M); expenditures, $776,167; qualifying distributions, $709,560; giving activities include $708,810 for 18 grants (high: $100,000; low: $5,000).
Fields of interest: Higher education; Health organizations; Human services.
Type of support: Equipment; Program development; Research.
Limitations: Applications not accepted. Giving primarily in Washington, DC; some giving also in VT. No grants to individuals.
Application information: Contributes only to pre-selected organizations.
Board meeting date(s): Varies
Officers and Directors:* Alice True Gasch,* Pres. and Treas.; Linda Brown,* Secy.; Lawrence True.
EIN: 522048715
Selected grants: The following grants are a representative sample of this grantmaker's funding activity:
$100,000 to Family Matters of Greater Washington, Washington, DC, 2012. For Camp Moss Hollow.
$100,000 to Georgetown University, Washington, DC, 2012. For Alice and Russell True Endowed Scholarship Fund.

1952
U. S. Justice Charitable Foundation, Inc. ✧
2009 Massachusetts Ave. N.W.
Washington, DC 20036-1011

Established in DE.
Donors: American Legal Foundation; Washington Legal Foundation.
Foundation type: Independent foundation.
Financial data (yr. ended 12/31/13): Assets, $26,402,486 (M); expenditures, $1,379,155; qualifying distributions, $1,340,000; giving activities include $1,340,000 for 3 grants (high: $1,300,000; low: $15,000).
Fields of interest: Public affairs.
Limitations: Applications not accepted. Giving primarily in Washington, DC.
Application information: Contributes only to pre-selected organizations.
Officers: Constance C. Larcher, Chair. and Pres.; John W. Popeo, V.P. and Secy.; Helen B. Popeo, Treas.
EIN: 262588270

1953
Union Plus Education Foundation ✧ ☆
1100 1st St. N.E., Ste. 850
Washington, DC 20002-4894
FAX: (202) 293-5311;
E-mail: shiggins@unionprivilege.org

Established in 1993 in DC.
Donors: Household Bank; AT&T; HSBC Card Retail Services.
Foundation type: Independent foundation.
Financial data (yr. ended 12/31/13): Assets, $400,814 (M); gifts received, $616,500; expenditures, $476,976; qualifying distributions, $463,395; giving activities include $463,395 for 178 grants to individuals (high: $5,000; low: $500).
Purpose and activities: Provides scholarships to members of unions participating in any Union Plus program, their spouses, and their dependent children (foster children, step-children, and any other child for whom the individual member provides greater than 50 percent of their support). Participating members from Canada and U.S. territories of Guam, Puerto Rico, and the Virgin Islands are also eligible. The individual must be accepted into an accredited college or university, community college or recognized technical or trade school at the time the award is issued.
Fields of interest: Scholarships/financial aid; Human services; Military/veterans' organizations; Children; Adults; Young adults; Disabilities, people with; Physically disabled; Blind/visually impaired; Deaf/hearing impaired; Minorities; Asians/Pacific Islanders; African Americans/Blacks; Hispanics/Latinos; Native Americans/American Indians; Women; Girls; Adults, women; Young adults, female; Men; Boys; Adults, men; Young adults, male; Single parents; Economically disadvantaged; LGBTQ.
International interests: Canada.
Type of support: Scholarship funds; Scholarships—to individuals.
Limitations: Applications not accepted. Giving in the U.S., Guam, Puerto Rico, the Virgin Islands, and Canada.
Application information: Unsolicited requests for funds not accepted.
Trustees: Stephen Goldsmith; Leslie A. Tolf.
Number of staff: None.
EIN: 383647522

1954
Vradenburg Foundation ✧
1101 K St. N.W., Ste. 400
Washington, DC 20005-7032

Established in 1999 in DE and DC.
Donors: George A. Vradenburg III; Trish Vradenburg; Patricia L. Vradenburg.
Foundation type: Independent foundation.
Financial data (yr. ended 12/31/13): Assets, $6,018,560 (M); gifts received, $928,007; expenditures, $1,572,541; qualifying distributions, $1,560,269; giving activities include $1,342,834 for 74 grants (high: $300,000; low: $75).
Fields of interest: Museums (art); Arts; Heart & circulatory diseases; Health organizations; Alzheimer's disease; Community/economic development; Foundations (community).
Type of support: General/operating support; Income development; Management development/capacity building; Program development.
Limitations: Applications not accepted. Giving primarily in the greater Washington, DC, region; some funding also in CA. No grants to individuals.
Application information: Contributes only to pre-selected organizations.
Officers: George A. Vradenburg III, Pres.; Patricia L. Vradenburg, Secy.-Treas.
Directors: Alissa Vradenburg; Tyler Vradenburg.
EIN: 770529620

1955
Wallace Genetic Foundation, Inc. ✧
4910 Massachusetts Ave., NW, Ste. 221
Washington, DC 20016-4368 (202) 966-2932
Contact: Patricia Lee, Co-Exec. Dir.; Carolyn Sand, Co-Exec. Dir.
FAX: (202) 966-3370;
E-mail: info@wallacegenetic.org; Additional e-mail: president@wallacegenetic.org; Main URL: http://www.wallacegenetic.org

Incorporated in 1959 in NY.
Donors: Henry A. Wallace†; Jean Douglas.

Foundation type: Independent foundation.
Financial data (yr. ended 12/31/13): Assets, $188,972,465 (M); expenditures, $9,756,525; qualifying distributions, $8,933,255; giving activities include $8,525,000 for 128 grants (high: $500,000; low: $5,000).
Purpose and activities: Areas of interest are sustainable agriculture, protection of farmland near cities, plant genetic research, biodiversity protection, and environmental education.
Fields of interest: Environment, natural resources; Environmental education; Public health, clean water supply; Agriculture; Public policy, research.
International interests: Latin America; Soviet Union.
Type of support: General/operating support; Continuing support; Land acquisition; Program development; Seed money; Research; Matching/challenge support.
Limitations: Applications accepted. Giving on a national basis. No grants to individuals, or for scholarships, endowments, multi-year commitments, or university overhead expenses; no loans.
Publications: Grants list.
Application information: Faxed or e-mailed proposals will not be accepted; application guidelines available on foundation web site. Application form not required.
Initial approach: 1- or 2-page letter and proposal
Copies of proposal: 1
Deadline(s): None
Board meeting date(s): Six times a year
Final notification: None
Officers and Directors:* Joan D. Murray,* Pres.; Ann D. Cornell,* V.P. and Secy.; David W. Douglas,* V.P. and Treas.; Patricia Lee, Co-Exec. Dir.; Carolyn H. Sand, Co-Exec. Dir.
Number of staff: 2 part-time professional.
EIN: 136162575
Selected grants: The following grants are a representative sample of this grantmaker's funding activity:
$300,000 to Chesapeake Conservancy, Annapolis, MD, 2012. For Jean W. Douglas Special Places Fund and to implement a conservation vision for the Chesapeake Bay.
$300,000 to New Venture Fund, Washington, DC, 2012. For general support and salary for Director for WASH in Schools, initiative to ensure a healthy physical learning environment in schools.
$200,000 to New Venture Fund, Washington, DC, 2012. For supplemental support for Advocates for Development Assistance project.
$130,000 to Environmental Film Festival, Washington, DC, 2012. For general support.
$100,000 to Capital Area Food Bank, Washington, DC, 2012. For general support.
$100,000 to Doctors Without Borders USA, New York, NY, 2012. For general support.
$50,000 to H2O for Life, White Bear Lake, MN, 2012. For general support.
$40,000 to Louisiana Bucket Brigade, New Orleans, LA, 2012. For general support.
$40,000 to Tropics Foundation, Centro Agronomico Tropical de Investigacion y Ensenanza (CATIE), Atlanta, GA, 2012. For general support for work in Turrialba, Costa Rica.
$30,000 to Sustainable Harvest International, Ellsworth, ME, 2012. For Tropical Agroforestry Education and Biodiversity Conservation in Central America.

1956
Wallace Global Fund II ✧

1990 M. St., NW, Ste. 250
Washington, DC 20036-3430 (202) 452-1530
FAX: (202) 452-0922; E-mail: tkroll@wgf.org; Main URL: http://www.wgf.org
Wallace Global Fund II's Philanthropy's Promise: http://www.ncrp.org/philanthropys-promise/who

Foundation type: Independent foundation.
Financial data (yr. ended 12/31/12): Assets, $155,471,213 (M); expenditures, $10,122,114; qualifying distributions, $8,875,955; giving activities include $7,413,625 for 146 grants (high: $150,000; low: $500).
Purpose and activities: The fund's mission is to promote an informed and engaged citizenry to fight injustice, and to protect the diversity of native and the natural systems upon which all life depends.
Fields of interest: Environment; Public affairs.
Type of support: General/operating support; Management development/capacity building; Program development; Program evaluation; Matching/challenge support.
Publications: Grants list; Occasional report.
Application information: No e-mail or mailed proposals accepted; application guidelines available on foundation web site. Application form required.
Initial approach: Letter of inquiry, no more than 2 pages, submitted via foundation web site.
Deadline(s): Quarterly, in Mar., June, Sept., and Dec.
Board meeting date(s): Quarterly
Officer: Ellen Dorsey, Exec. Dir.
Directors: Scott Fitzmorris; Annie Leonard; Christy Wallace; Scott Wallace.
Number of staff: 3 full-time professional; 2 part-time professional.
EIN: 800424607
Selected grants: The following grants are a representative sample of this grantmaker's funding activity:
$150,000 to Earth Island Institute, Berkeley, CA, 2012. For general support for the Women's Earth Alliance Africa program.
$150,000 to Public Citizen Foundation, Washington, DC, 2012. For Global Trade Watch program.
$140,000 to Center for Constitutional Rights, New York, NY, 2012. For General Support.
$100,000 to Movement Strategy Center, Oakland, CA, 2012. For general support for the Rebuild the Dream Innovation Fund.
$100,000 to Sundance Institute, Los Angeles, CA, 2012. For general support for Documentary Film Program and Fund.
$75,000 to Constitution Project, Washington, DC, 2012. For General Support.
$75,000 to Population Action International, Washington, DC, 2012. For Advancing Population, Family Planning, and Reproductive Health as Critical to Environmental Sustainability and International Development.
$75,000 to SumOfUs, Washington, DC, 2012. For their Corporate Accountability, Human Rights and Environment Program.
$60,000 to Forest Ethics, San Francisco, CA, 2012. For General operating support.
$50,000 to Orchid Project, London, England, 2012. For work to end female genital mutilation/cutting around the world.

1957
George Wolf Memorial Trust ✧

1220 North St. N.W.
Washington, DC 20005-5114

Established in 2003 in IL.
Donor: Daniel Wolf.
Foundation type: Independent foundation.
Financial data (yr. ended 06/30/13): Assets, $8,501,233 (M); gifts received, $901,222; expenditures, $1,539,025; qualifying distributions, $953,050; giving activities include $953,050 for 3 grants (high: $950,000; low: $50).
Fields of interest: Human services; International relief; Foundations (private operating).
International interests: Uganda.
Limitations: Applications not accepted. Giving primarily in CA, Washington, DC, Chicago, IL, and New York, NY.
Application information: Unsolicited requests for funds not accepted.
Trustee: Daniel Wolf.
EIN: 367412819
Selected grants: The following grants are a representative sample of this grantmaker's funding activity:
$2,500 to Refugees International, Washington, DC, 2011. For general support.

1958
The Wyss Foundation ✧

1601 Connecticut Ave., N.W., Ste. 802
Washington, DC 20009-1055
Contact: Francesca DiSilvio
FAX: (202) 232-4419;
E-mail: email@wyssfoundation.org; Main URL: http://www.wyssfoundation.org
Hansjorg Wyss' Giving Pledge Profile: http://glasspockets.org/philanthropy-in-focus/eye-on-the-giving-pledge/profiles#w

Established in 1990 in PA.
Donor: Hansjoerg Wyss.
Foundation type: Independent foundation.
Financial data (yr. ended 12/31/13): Assets, $2,115,965,902 (M); gifts received, $174,993,273; expenditures, $22,971,090; qualifying distributions, $59,044,582; giving activities include $19,014,335 for 55 grants (high: $2,940,000; low: $32).
Purpose and activities: The purpose of the foundation is to preserve, protect, and restore public lands, waters, and open spaces of the American west to achieve ecological health across the landscape.
Fields of interest: Environment, natural resources.
Type of support: General/operating support; Program development; Seed money; Research.
Limitations: Applications not accepted. Giving primarily in the western U.S. (AZ, CO, ID, MT, NV, NM, UT, WY). No grants to individuals.
Application information: Unsolicited requests for funds not accepted. Proposals by requests only.
Board meeting date(s): Varies
Officers and Trustees: Hansjoerg Wyss,* Chair.; John Leshy,* Vice-Chair.; Molly McUsic, Pres.; Mary Killingsworth, V.P.; Joseph M. Fisher, Treas.; Jacquelyn Bennet, C.A.O.
Number of staff: 5 full-time professional; 1 part-time professional.
EIN: 251823874

1959
The Wyss Medical Foundation, Inc. ✧
(formerly The Wyss Peace Foundation, Inc.)
1601 Connecticut Ave., N.W., Ste. 802
Washington, DC 20009-1055 (202) 232-4418
Hansjorg Wyss' Giving Pledge Profile: http://glasspockets.org/philanthropy-in-focus/eye-on-the-giving-pledge/profiles#w

Donor: Hansjoerg Wyss.
Foundation type: Independent foundation.
Financial data (yr. ended 12/31/13): Assets, $86,444,416 (M); expenditures, $3,413,559; qualifying distributions, $3,407,074; giving activities include $3,336,600 for 6 grants (high: $1,000,000; low: $100,000).
Fields of interest: Higher education; Education; Health care; Orthopedics; Spine disorders research; International peace/security; Civil/human rights.
Limitations: Applications not accepted. Giving primarily in Switzerland; some giving also in Washington, DC, Philadelphia, PA, Layton, UT, and Richland, WA.
Application information: Contributes only to pre-selected organizations.
Officers: Patricia Davis, Secy.; Joseph Fisher, Treas.
Directors: David Helfet; Steve Schwartz; Hansjoerg Wyss.
EIN: 263962795

1960
The Zients Family Foundation, Inc. ✧
4500 Garfield St., N.W.
Washington, DC 20007-1131

Established in 2003 in DC.
Donor: Jeffery D. Zients.
Foundation type: Independent foundation.
Financial data (yr. ended 12/31/13): Assets, $5,683,305 (M); expenditures, $1,157,796; qualifying distributions, $1,070,598; giving activities include $1,060,298 for 75 grants (high: $166,667; low: $500).
Purpose and activities: Giving primarily for education, health organizations, children, youth and social services, and to an organization supporting women of conflict.
Fields of interest: Education; Health organizations; Human services; Children/youth, services; Women, centers/services; International conflict resolution.
Type of support: Annual campaigns; Program development.
Limitations: Applications not accepted. Giving primarily in Washington, DC.
Application information: Unsolicited requests for funds not accepted.
Trustees: Steven Farina; Jennifer Nance; Mary Zients.
EIN: 546520936

FLORIDA

1961
100 Times Foundation Corporation ✧
534 Ponte Vedra Blvd.
Ponte Vedra Beach, FL 32082-2316

Established in 2007 in FL as successor to 100 Times Foundation.
Donor: Keith E. Lindner.
Foundation type: Independent foundation.
Financial data (yr. ended 12/31/13): Assets, $22,594,324 (M); expenditures, $2,808,985; qualifying distributions, $2,774,749; giving activities include $2,765,806 for 28 grants (high: $500,000; low: $150).
Fields of interest: Education; Human services; Christian agencies & churches.
Limitations: Applications not accepted. Giving primarily in FL and OH; some funding also in CO. No grants to individuals.
Application information: Contributes only to pre-selected organizations.
Officers and Director:* Keith E. Lindner,* Pres.; Courtney O'Neil Lindner, Secy.; Brendon Hansford, Treas.
EIN: 261211203

1962
Anthony R. Abraham Foundation, Inc. ✧
1320 S. Dixie Hwy., Ste. 241
Coral Gables, FL 33146-2937 (305) 665-2222
Contact: Anthony R. Abraham, Chair.

Established in 1978 in FL.
Donor: Anthony R. Abraham.
Foundation type: Independent foundation.
Financial data (yr. ended 12/31/12): Assets, $34,978,203 (M); gifts received, $100; expenditures, $1,985,830; qualifying distributions, $1,713,632; giving activities include $1,713,632 for grants.
Purpose and activities: Giving primarily for health, children, youth and social services, education, and Christian churches and organizations.
Fields of interest: Education; Health organizations, association; Medical research, institute; Human services; Children/youth, services; International relief; Foundations (private grantmaking); Christian agencies & churches.
Limitations: Giving primarily in Miami, FL. No grants to individuals.
Application information: Application form not required.
Initial approach: Letter
Copies of proposal: 1
Deadline(s): None
Board meeting date(s): Various
Officers and Directors:* Thomas G. Abraham,* Chair.; Thomas H. Malouf,* V.P.; Norma Jean Abraham,* Secy.-Treas.; Nancy Bailey; Judith Baker; Nicholas Daniels; Marion Jones.
EIN: 591837290

1963
The Abramson Family Foundation ✧
376 Regatta Dr.
Jupiter, FL 33477-4076 (215) 542-1222
Contact: Judith Abramson Felgoise, Tr.

Established in 1996 in FL.
Donor: Judith Abramson Felgoise.
Foundation type: Independent foundation.
Financial data (yr. ended 06/30/13): Assets, $49,049,439 (M); gifts received, $4,528,363; expenditures, $8,923,389; qualifying distributions, $8,605,022; giving activities include $8,266,606 for 51 grants (high: $3,189,020; low: $350).
Purpose and activities: Giving primarily to Jewish organizations, educational institutions, and health associations.
Fields of interest: Arts; Higher education; Education; Hospitals (general); Human services; Jewish federated giving programs; Jewish agencies & synagogues.
International interests: Israel.
Type of support: Scholarships—to individuals.
Limitations: Applications accepted. Giving primarily in PA.
Application information: Contact foundation for scholarship application guidelines. Application form required.
Initial approach: Proposal
Deadline(s): None
Trustees: Leonard Abramson; Madlyn Abramson; Judith Abramson Felgoise; Jerome S. Goodman; Marcy Abramson Shoemaker; Nancy Abramson Wolfson; Joseph M. Yohlin.
EIN: 311482888
Selected grants: The following grants are a representative sample of this grantmaker's funding activity:
$2,746,033 to Leonard and Madlyn Abramson Family Cancer Research Institute, Blue Bell, PA, 2012. For general support.
$1,921,675 to Leonard and Madlyn Abramson Family Cancer Research Institute, Blue Bell, PA, 2012. For general support.
$500,000 to Madlyn and Leonard Abramson Center for Jewish Life, North Wales, PA, 2012. For general support.
$500,000 to Temple University, Philadelphia, PA, 2012. For general support.
$200,000 to Public School of Germantown, Germantown Academy, Fort Washington, PA, 2012. For general support.
$200,000 to Temple University, Kornberg School of Dentistry, Philadelphia, PA, 2012. For general support.
$100,000 to Childrens Hospital of Philadelphia, Philadelphia, PA, 2012. For general support.
$100,000 to Jupiter Medical Center, Jupiter, FL, 2012. For general support.
$34,000 to Cheder Chabad of Philadelphia, Wynnewood, PA, 2012. For general support.
$32,634 to Leonard and Madlyn Abramson Family Cancer Research Institute, Blue Bell, PA, 2012. For general support.

1964
Anne & Leo N. Albert Charitable Trust ✧
1020 Crosspointe Dr.
Naples, FL 34110-0918 (239) 593-8364
Contact: Gene Pranzo, Tr.

Donor: Leo Albert‡.
Foundation type: Independent foundation.
Financial data (yr. ended 12/31/13): Assets, $15,493,884 (M); expenditures, $1,352,027; qualifying distributions, $1,281,388; giving activities include $1,219,663 for 13 grants (high: $340,000; low: $50,000).
Fields of interest: Health care; Cancer; Alzheimer's disease; Housing/shelter; Christian agencies & churches.
Limitations: Applications accepted. Giving primarily in FL; some giving also in CA and CT.
Application information: Application form not required.
Initial approach: Proposal
Deadline(s): None
Trustee: Gene Pranzo.
EIN: 656473109

1965
Leslie L. Alexander Foundation, Inc. ✧
1200 N. Federal Hwy., Ste. 411
Boca Raton, FL 33432-2846

Established in 2003 in FL.
Donors: Leslie L. Alexander; Alexander Foundation, Inc.; Telecom Capital Partners II LP.
Foundation type: Operating foundation.
Financial data (yr. ended 12/31/13): Assets, $6,920,680 (M); gifts received, $2,670,000; expenditures, $493,973; qualifying distributions, $493,455; giving activities include $493,000 for 26 grants (high: $175,000; low: $3,500).
Fields of interest: Animals/wildlife; Human services.
Limitations: Applications not accepted. Giving primarily in FL, NY, and TX. No grants to individuals.
Application information: Unsolicited requests for funds not accepted.
Directors: Leslie L. Alexander; Jodi Alexander Smith; Logan Smith.
EIN: 753126055
Selected grants: The following grants are a representative sample of this grantmaker's funding activity:
$42,500 to Dorot, New York, NY, 2012. For Keep isolated seniors connected to a caring co with food, housing, comp.
$10,000 to Big Cat Rescue, Tampa, FL, 2012. To provide better home for these animals.
$10,000 to Green Beret Foundation, Fort Bragg, NC, 2012. For Caring for our Brave Professionals.
$10,000 to International Rescue Committee, New York, NY, 2012. For Humanitarianism in over 40 countries.
$10,000 to Save the Chimps, Fort Pierce, FL, 2012. For Chimp Sanctuary meals, vet care, captivity.
$5,000 to Jewish Federation of Palm Beach County, West Palm Beach, FL, 2012. For Meet Human needs locally and Globally.

1966
The Amaturo Family Foundation, Inc. ✧
3101 N. Federal Hwy., Ste. 601
Fort Lauderdale, FL 33306-1018
Contact: Jeanette E. Nickel, Dir.
FAX: (954) 565-1311;
E-mail: jan@amaturogroups.com

Established in 1986 in FL.
Donors: Joseph C. Amaturo; Winifred J. Amaturo; Lawrence V. Amaturo.
Foundation type: Independent foundation.

Financial data (yr. ended 06/30/13): Assets, $24,664,548 (M); gifts received, $120,023; expenditures, $1,608,955; qualifying distributions, $1,597,347; giving activities include $1,597,347 for grants.
Purpose and activities: Giving primarily for education, child welfare, and medical research, with emphasis on Roman Catholic organizations.
Fields of interest: Arts; Elementary/secondary education; Higher education; Education; Cancer research; Heart & circulatory research; Human services; Children/youth, services; Catholic federated giving programs; Catholic agencies & churches.
Type of support: Curriculum development; Emergency funds; Continuing support; Building/renovation; Scholarship funds; Research; Matching/challenge support.
Limitations: Applications accepted. Giving primarily in, but not limited to, FL. No grants to individuals, or for fellowships.
Publications: Application guidelines.
Application information: Application form not required.
Initial approach: Letter
Copies of proposal: 1
Deadline(s): None
Officers and Directors:* Winifred J. Amaturo,* Pres.; Joseph C. Amaturo,* V.P.; Cara Ebert Cameron, Secy.; Cynthia M. Whitney, Treas.; Douglas Q. Amaturo; Lawrence V. Amaturo; Winifred L. Amaturo; Lorna Amaturo Walsh.
EIN: 592718130
Selected grants: The following grants are a representative sample of this grantmaker's funding activity:
$50,000 to Ave Maria University, Ave Maria, FL, 2013. For classroom dedication.
$50,000 to Urban League of Broward County, Fort Lauderdale, FL, 2013. For Digital Classroom World of Possibilities.
$40,000 to Broward Performing Arts Foundation, Fort Lauderdale, FL, 2013. For Winjo Room Additional (2nd Payment).
$25,000 to National Leadership Roundtable on Church Management, Washington, DC, 2013. For Catholic Temporal Needs Support.
$20,000 to Center for Science in the Public Interest, Washington, DC, 2013. For National Nutrition Studies.
$20,000 to Salvation Army of Santa Rosa, Santa Rosa, CA, 2013. For Literacy Coalition, Health Services.
$6,000 to University of the South, Sewanee, TN, 2013. For Golf Course Project - $5,000 Sswanee Annual Fund - $1,000.
$5,000 to Alliance for the Arts, Thousand Oaks, CA, 2013. For Cultural Support $2,500 Playlist and $2,600 Muvico.
$5,000 to American Red Cross, Plantation, FL, 2013. For Returning Vets Ajd.
$100 to State Policy Network, Arlington, VA, 2013. For Limit Government/Advance State Think Tanks.

1967
W. L. Amos, Sr. Foundation, Inc. ✧
c/o William L. Amos, Jr., M.D.
38 Ocean Club Dr.
Amelia Island, FL 32034-6629
Scholarship application address: c/o Cecil Cheves, P.O. Box 1199, Columbus, GA 31902-1199, tel.: (706) 324-0251

Established in 1998 in GA.
Donors: Olivia D. Amos‡; Olivia D. Amos IRA; William L. Amos Charitable Lead Annuity Trust.
Foundation type: Independent foundation.
Financial data (yr. ended 12/31/13): Assets, $24,171,503 (M); gifts received, $561,866; expenditures, $908,620; qualifying distributions, $842,790; giving activities include $842,790 for 58 grants (high: $128,500; low: $100).
Purpose and activities: Scholarship awards for college expenses benefiting children whose parent or grandparent worked for AFLAC.
Fields of interest: Higher education; Children, services.
Type of support: General/operating support; Scholarship funds.
Limitations: Applications not accepted. Giving primarily in FL and GA.
Application information: Unsolicited requests for funds not accepted.
Officers: William L Amos, Jr., M.D., Pres. and Secy.-Treas.; William L. Amos III, V.P.; Ashley Copelan, V.P.
EIN: 582399470
Selected grants: The following grants are a representative sample of this grantmaker's funding activity:
$5,000 to Methodist Home for Children, Raleigh, NC, 2012. For humanitarian purposes.
$500 to Adventures in Missions, Gainesville, GA, 2012. For Religious and Humanitarian Purposes.
$500 to Columbus Museum, Columbus, GA, 2012. For History Preservation and Educational Purposes.
$240 to Columbus Regional Medical Foundation, Columbus, GA, 2012. For medical purposes.

1968
Martin Andersen-Gracia Andersen Foundation ✧
P.O. Box 547918
Orlando, FL 32854-7918 (407) 647-5654
Contact: Thomas P. Warlow III, Pres.

Established in 1953 in FL.
Donors: Gracia B. Andersen‡; L. Graham Barr, Jr., Trust.
Foundation type: Independent foundation.
Financial data (yr. ended 10/31/13): Assets, $53,234,384 (M); expenditures, $3,191,239; qualifying distributions, $2,033,867; giving activities include $1,215,450 for 1 grant.
Purpose and activities: Giving primarily to a hospital foundation.
Fields of interest: Hospitals (general).
Limitations: Applications accepted. Giving primarily in Orlando, FL. No grants to individuals.
Application information:
Initial approach: Letter
Deadline(s): None
Officers: Thomas P. Warlow III, Pres.; T. Picton Warlow IV, V.P.; Jeffry B. Fuqua, Secy.; Marina C. Nice, Treas.
Director: Megan O. Warlow.
EIN: 596166589

1969
Ansin Foundation ✧
P.O. Box 610727
N. Miami, FL 33261-0727

Established in 1957.
Donors: Sunbeam Television Corp.; WHDH-TV, Inc.; Sunbeam Development Corp.; Sunbeam Properties, Inc.; Edmund N. Ansin.
Foundation type: Company-sponsored foundation.
Financial data (yr. ended 12/31/13): Assets, $55,850,601 (M); gifts received, $1,000,000; expenditures, $1,703,567; qualifying distributions, $1,667,432; giving activities include $1,667,432 for 45 grants (high: $530,000; low: $100).
Purpose and activities: The foundation supports hospitals and organizations involved with arts and culture, education, youth development, and community development.
Fields of interest: Museums (art); Performing arts, ballet; Performing arts, theater; Arts; Secondary school/education; Higher education; Education, services; Education; Hospitals (general); Boys & girls clubs; Community/economic development; United Ways and Federated Giving Programs.
Type of support: General/operating support; Scholarship funds.
Limitations: Applications not accepted. Giving primarily in FL and Boston, MA. No grants to individuals.
Application information: Contributes only to pre-selected organizations.
Trustee: Edmund N. Ansin.
EIN: 046046113

1970
The Applebaum Foundation, Inc. ✧
11111 Biscayne Blvd., Twr. 3, Apt. 853
North Miami, FL 33181-3404

Incorporated in 1949 in NY.
Donors: Joseph Applebaum‡; Leila Applebaum.
Foundation type: Independent foundation.
Financial data (yr. ended 02/28/13): Assets, $46,420,683 (M); gifts received, $522,900; expenditures, $2,432,255; qualifying distributions, $2,306,500; giving activities include $2,301,000 for 66 grants (high: $600,000; low: $500).
Purpose and activities: Giving primarily for higher education, hospitals and medical research, and to Jewish organizations, including welfare agencies, schools, and temple support; some funding for children, youth, and social services.
Fields of interest: Elementary/secondary education; Higher education; Medical school/education; Hospitals (general); Health organizations, association; Pediatrics; Medical research, institute; Cancer research; Human services; Children/youth, services; Jewish federated giving programs; Jewish agencies & synagogues.
Limitations: Applications not accepted. Giving primarily in Miami, FL and in the metropolitan New York, NY area. No grants to individuals.
Application information: Contributes only to pre-selected organizations.
Officers and Directors:* Leila Applebaum,* C.E.O. and Treas.; Warren Weiss, Esq.*, Pres.; Alan T. Applebaum,* V.P. and Secy.; Judy Borger,* V.P.; Jane Weiss.
EIN: 591002714
Selected grants: The following grants are a representative sample of this grantmaker's funding activity:
$390,000 to Rabbi Jacob Joseph School, Edison, NJ, 2011.
$130,000 to Ohr Torah Institutions of Israel, New York, NY, 2011.

1971
Micky and Madeleine Arison Family Foundation ✧
c/o Richard Kohan, AFO LLC
2 Alhambra Plz., Ste. 1040
Coral Gables, FL 33134-5249

Established in 2006 in FL.
Donors: Micky Arison; Madeleine Arison; The Ted Arison Family Foundation USA Inc.
Foundation type: Independent foundation.
Financial data (yr. ended 12/31/13): Assets, $47,215,314 (M); expenditures, $3,067,865; qualifying distributions, $2,845,000; giving activities include $2,845,000 for 28 grants (high: $500,000; low: $5,000).
Purpose and activities: Giving primarily for medical research, as well as to a children's hospital; funding also for a community foundation.
Fields of interest: Hospitals (specialty); Medical research, institute; Foundations (community).
Limitations: Applications not accepted. Giving primarily in FL.
Application information: Unsolicited requests for funds not accepted.
Trustees: James M. Dubin; John J. O'Neil.
EIN: 204822537

1972
Ted Arison Family Foundation USA, Inc. ✧
(formerly Arison Foundation, Inc.)
c/o Safo, LLC
20900 N. E. 30th Ave., Ste. 1015
Aventura, FL 33180-2166 (305) 891-0017
E-mail: hanna@SAFOUSA.com; Main URL: http://www.shariarison.com/en/content/ted-arison-family-foundation

Incorporated in 1981 in FL.
Donors: Carnival Cruise Lines, Inc.; Festivale Maritime, Inc.; Intercon Overseas, Inc.; Ted Arison Charitable Trust.
Foundation type: Independent foundation.
Financial data (yr. ended 12/31/12): Assets, $471,347,559 (M); gifts received, $345,175; expenditures, $22,185,780; qualifying distributions, $21,744,763; giving activities include $15,569,705 for 59 grants (high: $3,638,922; low: $5,000).
Purpose and activities: Emphasis on arts and cultural programs; support also for Jewish welfare funds.
Fields of interest: Arts; Education; Health care; Human services; Children/youth, services; Jewish federated giving programs; Disabilities, people with.
Limitations: Applications accepted. Giving primarily in NY and Israel.
Publications: Grants list.
Application information:
Initial approach: Letter
Deadline(s): None
Officers and Trustees:* Jason Arison,* Chair.; Shlomit de Vries, C.E.O.; Rachel Cohen, Deputy C.E.O. and C.F.O.; Kaynan Rabino, V.P., Vision Ventures; Cassie Arison; David Arison; Marilyn Arison; Shari Arison Glazer.
EIN: 592128429
Selected grants: The following grants are a representative sample of this grantmaker's funding activity:
$3,638,922 to Ruach Tova, Tel Aviv, Israel, 2012. For Vision Ventures-general operating support.
$2,206,737 to Essence of Life, Tel Aviv, Israel, 2012. For Vision Ventures - general operating support.
$1,250,491 to PEF Israel Endowment Funds, New York, NY, 2012.
$1,006,741 to Center for Young Art, Tel Aviv, Israel, 2012. For Vision Ventures-general operating support.
$750,000 to Interdisciplinary Center Herzliya, Herzliya, Israel, 2012. For GMBA Program Awareness Concept.
$155,000 to MATAN - Your Way to Give, Tel Aviv, Israel, 2012. For membership fee and special grant.
$100,000 to American Friends of the Alliance Israelite Universelle, New York, NY, 2012. For Cracking the Glass Ceiling.
$100,000 to Yad Vashem - The Holocaust Martyrs and Heroes Remembrance Authority, Jerusalem, Israel, 2012.
$75,000 to American Friends of the Technoda, Warren, NJ, 2012. For equipment for medical simulation unit.
$37,973 to Tikva Childrens Home, New York, NY, 2012. For Big Brother Project.

1973
Asofsky Family Foundation Inc. ✧
10247 El Caballo Ct.
Delray Beach, FL 33446-2711 (561) 703-4930
Contact: Mark Asofsky, Pres.

Established in 2007 in FL.
Donor: Mark Asofsky.
Foundation type: Independent foundation.
Financial data (yr. ended 12/31/13): Assets, $10,020,975 (M); gifts received, $1,722; expenditures, $575,930; qualifying distributions, $534,000; giving activities include $534,000 for 13 grants (high: $250,000; low: $1,000).
Fields of interest: Human services; Children/youth, services.
Limitations: Applications accepted. Giving primarily in FL and NY.
Application information: Application form required.
Initial approach: Letter
Deadline(s): None
Officers: Mark Asofsky, Pres.; Madeline Asofsky, V.P.; Marilyn Asofsky, Secy.; Howard Asofsky, Treas.
Directors: David Asofsky; Ethan Asofsky; Karen Asofsky; Seth Asofsky.
EIN: 261446613

1974
The Aurora Foundation ✧ ☆
(also known as The Aurora Ministries)
P.O. Box 1848
Bradenton, FL 34206-1848
Contact: Joseph A. Aleppo, Exec. Dir.
FAX: (941) 748-2625;
E-mail: aurora@auroraministries.org; Main URL: http://www.auroraministries.org

Established in 1969.
Donor: Anthony T. Rossi.
Foundation type: Independent foundation.
Financial data (yr. ended 12/31/12): Assets, $1,397,853 (M); expenditures, $3,067,718; qualifying distributions, $3,067,718; giving activities include $2,838,801 for 2 grants (high: $2,837,701; low: $1,100).
Purpose and activities: Support largely for missionary work; grants also for Christian church support, religious associations, education, and social services; also administers and operates the Bradenton Missionary Village, a rent-free housing complex for retired missionaries.
Fields of interest: Christian agencies & churches.
Type of support: General/operating support; Continuing support.
Limitations: Applications not accepted. Giving primarily in FL. No grants for professorships or building funds of schools and colleges.
Application information: Unsolicited requests for funds not considered.
Board meeting date(s): Usually mid-Oct.
Officers and Directors:* Ezio Aleppo, C.O.O.; Mark Stingley, Sr. Cont.; Joseph A. Aleppo, Exec. Dir.; Georgia Aleppo; Mike Hamrick.
Number of staff: 38 full-time support; 2 part-time support.
EIN: 237044641

1975
The Azeez Foundation ✧
(formerly The Michael and Kathleen Azeez Foundation)
2187 Marseille Dr.
Palm Beach Gardens, FL 33410-1279

Established in 1998 in NJ.
Donors: Michael Azeez; Kathleen Azeez; Anne Azeez.
Foundation type: Independent foundation.
Financial data (yr. ended 12/31/12): Assets, $12,179,737 (M); expenditures, $952,617; qualifying distributions, $764,339; giving activities include $764,333 for 49 grants (high: $214,990; low: $485).
Purpose and activities: Giving primarily to Jewish organizations, including a Jewish history museum.
Fields of interest: Museums (ethnic/folk arts); Health care; Human services; Jewish federated giving programs; Jewish agencies & synagogues.
Limitations: Applications not accepted. Giving primarily in NJ; funding also in CA, CO, Washington, DC, and FL. No grants to individuals.
Application information: Contributes only to pre-selected organizations.
Directors and Officers:* Michael Azeez,* Chair. and Pres.; Kathleen Azeez, Secy.; Anne Azeez, Treas.
EIN: 232967146
Selected grants: The following grants are a representative sample of this grantmaker's funding activity:
$5,000 to Columbus Foundation, Columbus, OH, 2012. For organization's exempt purpose.

1976
The Bailey Family Foundation, Inc. ✧
912 W. Platt St., Ste. 200
Tampa, FL 33606-2114 (813) 549-6140
Contact: Ron K. Bailey, Pres.; Kimberly M. Czabaj, Admin.
FAX: (813) 549-6141;
E-mail: contact@bailey-family.org; Main URL: http://www.bailey-family.org/
Scholarship Admin.: tel.: (813) 549-6139

Established in 1997 in VA.

Donors: Beverly W. Bailey; Ron K. Bailey; Greg Manocherian; Florida Coastal School of Law; Strayer University Educational Foundation.
Foundation type: Operating foundation.
Financial data (yr. ended 12/31/13): Assets, $52,479,740 (M); expenditures, $3,469,007; qualifying distributions, $3,918,037; giving activities include $252,333 for 85 grants (high: $40,000; low: $100), and $2,121,631 for grants to individuals.
Purpose and activities: The primary mission of the foundation is to expand the availability and enhance the quality of post secondary education by providing financial assistance to students based on their academic record, financial need and level of community involvement. The foundation also conducts research directed toward improving the state of higher education.
Fields of interest: Education.
Type of support: Research; Scholarships—to individuals.
Limitations: Applications not accepted. Giving primarily to students attending educational institutions in FL and VA.
Publications: Informational brochure; Newsletter; Program policy statement.
Application information: Unsolicited requests for funds not accepted for grants. See foundation web site for scholarship application information.
Board meeting date(s): Mar., July, Sept., and Dec.
Officer and Directors:* Ron K. Bailey,* Pres.; Beverly W. Bailey; Ronnie Kyle Bailey; Ryan Kent Bailey.
Number of staff: 2 full-time professional; 2 part-time professional.
EIN: 541850780

1977
Bobbie Bailey Foundation, Inc. ✧ ☆
c/o Bank of America, N.A.
P.O. Box 40200, FL9-100-10-19
Jacksonville, FL 32203-0200
Contact: Bobbie Bailey, Tr.
Application address: Attn.: Kim Sexton, 3414 Peachtree Rd. N.E., Atlanta, GA 30326-1113

Established in 1994 in GA.
Donor: Bobbie Bailey.
Foundation type: Independent foundation.
Financial data (yr. ended 12/31/13): Assets, $317,926 (M); expenditures, $1,085,260; qualifying distributions, $1,076,954; giving activities include $1,075,217 for 6 grants (high: $549,137; low: $20,000).
Fields of interest: Higher education; Health organizations; Foundations (private grantmaking).
Limitations: Applications accepted. Giving primarily in GA.
Application information: Application form required.
Initial approach: Letter
Deadline(s): None
Trustee: Bobbie Bailey.
EIN: 582085849

1978
George M. Baldwin Foundation ✧
200 W. Forsyth St., Ste. 1300
Jacksonville, FL 32202-3607

Established in 2004 in FL.
Donor: George M. Baldwin†.
Foundation type: Independent foundation.
Financial data (yr. ended 12/31/13): Assets, $17,096,090 (M); expenditures, $831,613; qualifying distributions, $786,503; giving activities include $770,000 for 13 grants (high: $360,000; low: $5,000).
Fields of interest: Housing/shelter; Youth development; Human services; United Ways and Federated Giving Programs; Homeless.
Limitations: Applications not accepted. Giving primarily in Jacksonville, FL. No grants to individuals.
Application information: Unsolicited requests for funds not accepted.
Trustee: John G. Grimsley.
EIN: 201377117
Selected grants: The following grants are a representative sample of this grantmaker's funding activity:
$110,000 to Bridge of Northeast Florida, Jacksonville, FL, 2012. For Scholarships, Staff Training, Camps.
$10,000 to Cathedral Arts Project, Jacksonville, FL, 2012. To support Classes and General Programs for Indigent Children.
$10,000 to Community Hospice Foundation, Jacksonville, FL, 2012. For Children's Bereavement Camp.

1979
Bank of America Client Foundation ✧
(also known as BOA Client Foundation)
50 Central Ave., Ste. 750, MC FL4-234-07-01
Sarasota, FL 34236-5743 (941) 951-4103
Contact: Maryann L. Smith, V.P.
E-mail: maryann.l.smith@ustrust.com; Main URL: http://fdnweb.org/boacf
Grants List: http://fdnweb.org/boacf/grants/category/annual-grants/

Established in 1961 in FL as the Sarasota Bank and Trust Company Community Foundation.
Donors: Eileen Kroeger; Julius Brandenburg†; Leona Hughes†.
Foundation type: Independent foundation.
Financial data (yr. ended 12/31/13): Assets, $17,564,625 (M); expenditures, $807,014; qualifying distributions, $680,707; giving activities include $582,848 for 38 grants (high: $50,000; low: $1,257).
Purpose and activities: Giving primarily for the arts, education, human services, natural science, youth and family organizations, and historic preservation.
Fields of interest: Media, film/video; Visual arts; Museums; Performing arts; Performing arts, dance; Performing arts, theater; Humanities; Historic preservation/historical societies; Arts; Education, early childhood education; Child development, education; Elementary school/education; Secondary school/education; Vocational education; Higher education; Adult education—literacy, basic skills & GED; Education, reading; Education; Environment, natural resources; Environment; Reproductive health, family planning; Health care; Mental health/crisis services; Health organizations, association; AIDS; Crime/violence prevention, youth; Recreation; Human services; Children/youth, services; Child development, services; Family services; Residential/custodial care, hospices; Aging, centers/services; Women, centers/services; Minorities/immigrants, centers/services; Homeless, human services; Urban/community development; Community/economic development; Marine science; Protestant agencies & churches; Aging; Disabilities, people with; Minorities; Women; Economically disadvantaged; Homeless.
Type of support: Building/renovation; Equipment; Program development; Matching/challenge support.
Limitations: Applications accepted. Giving limited to organizations operating in or providing services to residents of Sarasota County, FL and DE. No support for individual schools or child care facilities. No grants to individuals, or for general operating expenses, endowment or annual giving campaigns, debt reduction or financing, conferences, seminars, workshops, travel, surveys or advertising.
Publications: Application guidelines.
Application information: Electronic transmittals are not acceptable. Applications must have arrived by deadline. See web site for full application guidelines. Application form required.
Initial approach: Proposal
Copies of proposal: 10
Deadline(s): Apr. 15 and Sept. 15
Board meeting date(s): End of June and Nov.
Final notification: Within 3 to 4 months after the deadline
Trustee: Bank of America, N.A.
EIN: 596142753

1980
Bernice Barbour Foundation, Inc. ✧
12230 Forest Hill Blvd., Ste. 110-RR
Wellington, FL 33414-5700 (561) 791-0861
Contact: Eve Lloyd Thompson, Pres.
Main URL: http://bernicebarbour.org/

Established in 1987 in NJ; funded in 1990.
Donor: Bernice Barbour†.
Foundation type: Independent foundation.
Financial data (yr. ended 12/31/13): Assets, $21,676,329 (M); expenditures, $1,506,539; qualifying distributions, $1,025,965; giving activities include $888,906 for 144 grants (high: $51,700; low: $1,000).
Purpose and activities: Giving to organizations which provide programs to protect, preserve, and nurture animals, including marine animals and wildlife, in the U.S. Hands-on care, animal health/welfare, and veterinary medical research are priorities.
Fields of interest: Animals/wildlife.
Type of support: General/operating support; Continuing support; Building/renovation; Equipment; Program development; Fellowships; Research; Technical assistance; Matching/challenge support.
Limitations: Applications accepted. Giving only on a national basis. No support for organizations that do not spay/neuter animals before adopting them out. No grants to individuals, or for indirect costs, litigation, or for costs relating to animals which are not indigenous to the United States, or land acquisition.
Publications: Application guidelines; Informational brochure; Program policy statement (including application guidelines).
Application information: Application form required.
Initial approach: Completed application form
Copies of proposal: 2
Deadline(s): July 31
Officers: Eve Lloyd Thompson, Pres.; Gregory Little, V.P.; Jacqueline Little, Secy.; Kristina Lloyd Sample, Treas.
Trustees: Kathryn L. Champ; Judith Little; Karen Lloyd; Heather Sherman; Henry Turmon.

Number of staff: 2 full-time professional.
EIN: 222779967

1981
J. H. Baroco Foundation, Inc. ✧ ☆
P.O. Box 9727
Pensacola, FL 32513-2441
Application address: c/o Vicki Ann Baroco, Pres., 1182 E. Lakeview Ave., Pensacola, FL 32503, tel.: (850) 380-2530

Established in 1988 in FL.
Donor: James H. Baroco, Sr.†.
Foundation type: Independent foundation.
Financial data (yr. ended 12/31/13): Assets, $854,930 (M); expenditures, $439,488; qualifying distributions, $435,245; giving activities include $435,245 for 53 grants (high: $25,000; low: $1,000).
Fields of interest: Health care; Food services; Human services; Salvation Army; Homeless, human services; Catholic agencies & churches.
Type of support: General/operating support; Capital campaigns; Building/renovation.
Limitations: Applications accepted. Giving primarily in Pensacola, FL. No grants to individuals.
Application information: Application form required.
Initial approach: Proposal
Deadline(s): None
Officers and Directors:* Vicki Ann Baroco,* Pres.; Ronald Anthony Baroco,* V.P.; Mary Antonia Noonan, Secy.- Treas.; J. H. Baroco III; Julie M. Baroco.
EIN: 592912852
Selected grants: The following grants are a representative sample of this grantmaker's funding activity:
$15,000 to Hazelden Foundation, Minneapolis, MN, 2012. For patient aid.
$5,000 to Catholic Charities of Northwest Florida, Pensacola, FL, 2012. For Bridges to Circles Project Operating Income.
$5,000 to Covenant Hospice, Pensacola, FL, 2012. For Butterfly Bag Program.
$2,500 to Baptist Health Care Foundation, Pensacola, FL, 2012. For Life Flight Fund.
$1,500 to United Ministries, Pensacola, FL, 2012. For operating income.

1982
Danker Basham Foundation, Inc. ✧ ☆
c/o Robert Basham
4343 Anchor Plz. Pkwy., Ste. 1
Tampa, FL 33634

Established in 1994 in FL.
Donor: Robert D. Basham.
Foundation type: Independent foundation.
Financial data (yr. ended 12/31/13): Assets, $9,728,045 (M); expenditures, $470,938; qualifying distributions, $433,058; giving activities include $433,058 for 23 grants (high: $71,358; low: $100).
Purpose and activities: Giving primarily for Christian ministries, and children, youth, and human services.
Fields of interest: Education; Youth development, centers/clubs; Boys & girls clubs; Human services; Children/youth, services; International relief, 2004 tsunami; United Ways and Federated Giving Programs; Christian agencies & churches.
Limitations: Applications not accepted. Giving primarily in FL. No grants to individuals.
Application information: Contributes only to pre-selected organizations.
Officer: Robert D. Basham, Pres.
Director: Richard Danker.
EIN: 593284079

1983
The Batchelor Foundation, Inc. ✧
1680 Michigan Ave., No. PH 1
Miami Beach, FL 33139-2538 (305) 534-5004
Contact: Anne O. Batchelor-Robjohns, Co-C.E.O.

Established in 1990 in FL.
Donors: International Air Leases, Inc.; Batchelor Enterprises; George E. Batchelor†.
Foundation type: Company-sponsored foundation.
Financial data (yr. ended 06/30/13): Assets, $352,753,085 (M); gifts received, $40,125,144; expenditures, $23,057,999; qualifying distributions, $20,281,144; giving activities include $19,674,515 for 192 grants (high: $3,520,000; low: $800).
Purpose and activities: The foundation supports organizations involved with arts and culture, education, animals and wildlife, health, agriculture and food, housing, recreation, human services, and economically disadvantaged people. Special emphasis is directed toward programs designed to engage in medical research and provide care for childhood diseases; and promote study, preservation, and public awareness of the natural environment.
Fields of interest: Museums; Arts; Higher education; Education; Environment, research; Environment, public education; Environment, natural resources; Botanical gardens; Environment; Animals/wildlife, preservation/protection; Zoos/zoological societies; Animals/wildlife; Hospitals (general); Health care; Diabetes research; Medical research; Food services; Agriculture/food; Housing/shelter, development; Recreation; Boy scouts; YM/YWCAs & YM/YWHAs; Children/youth, services; Homeless, human services; Human services; United Ways and Federated Giving Programs; Economically disadvantaged.
Type of support: General/operating support; Continuing support; Capital campaigns; Endowments; Program development; Matching/challenge support.
Limitations: Applications accepted. Giving primarily in Miami, FL. No grants to individuals.
Application information: Application form not required.
Initial approach: Letter of inquiry
Deadline(s): None
Officers and Trustees:* Anne O. Batchelor-Robjohns,* Co-C.E.O.; Daniel J. Ferraresi,* Co-C.E.O.; Jon Batchelor, Exec. V.P.; Nancy Ansley, C.F.O.; Caridad Velasco, Cont.; Jack Falk.
EIN: 650188171
Selected grants: The following grants are a representative sample of this grantmaker's funding activity:
$3,520,000 to Florida International University Foundation, University Park/Hls, Miami, FL, 2013. For general operations and endowment.
$1,050,000 to University of Miami, Rosenstiel School of Marine and Atmospheric Science, Miami, FL, 2013. For general operations.
$570,000 to Community Television Foundation of South Florida, North Miami, FL, 2013. For general operations.
$510,000 to Audubon Society, Florida, Miami, FL, 2013. For general operations.
$508,122 to Easter Seals South Florida, Miami, FL, 2013. For general operations.
$402,500 to Chapman Partnership, Miami, FL, 2013. For general operations.
$236,667 to McCarthys Wildlife Sanctuary, West Palm Beach, FL, 2013. For general operations and endowment.
$100,000 to SunSystem Development Corporation, Orlando, FL, 2013. For general operations.
$30,000 to Gateway Community Outreach, Deerfield Beach, FL, 2013. For general operations.
$25,000 to United Negro College Fund, Fort Lauderdale, FL, 2013. For general operations.

1984
The Robert & Patricia Bauman Family Foundation, Inc. ✧
6720 S.E. Harbor Cir.
Stuart, FL 34996-1963 (772) 225-4118
Contact: Robert P. Bauman, Dir.

Established in 1997 in FL.
Donors: Patricia Bauman; Robert Bauman; Patricia McVey.
Foundation type: Independent foundation.
Financial data (yr. ended 12/31/13): Assets, $15,349,147 (M); expenditures, $987,704; qualifying distributions, $720,700; giving activities include $720,700 for 96 grants (high: $150,000; low: $500).
Purpose and activities: Giving primarily for health organizations and medical research, as well as for the arts, education, and human services.
Fields of interest: Arts; Higher education; Education; Hospitals (general); Health organizations, association; Medical research, institute; Human services; United Ways and Federated Giving Programs.
Limitations: Applications accepted. Giving primarily in CT, ME, FL and NY; some funding also in NH and OH. No grants to individuals.
Application information: Application form not required.
Initial approach: Proposal
Deadline(s): None
Directors: Elizabeth H. Bauman; John Bauman; Robert Bauman.
EIN: 311535223
Selected grants: The following grants are a representative sample of this grantmaker's funding activity:
$110,000 to Ohio Wesleyan University, Delaware, OH, 2011.
$25,000 to Friends of Karen, North Salem, NY, 2011.
$15,000 to Massachusetts Eye and Ear Infirmary, Boston, MA, 2011.
$5,000 to Exeter Hospital, Exeter, NH, 2011.
$5,000 to Maine Medical Center, Portland, ME, 2011.
$5,000 to Martin Memorial Foundation, Stuart, FL, 2011.
$3,300 to Library Foundation of Martin County, Stuart, FL, 2011.
$1,500 to Mollys House, Stuart, FL, 2011.
$1,000 to Sailfish Point Foundation, Stuart, FL, 2011.

$1,000 to University School, Hunting Valley, OH, 2011.

1985
The Bay Branch Foundation ✧
1515 S. Federal Hwy., Ste. 201
Boca Raton, FL 33432-7404

Trust established in 1963 in NJ.
Donors: Keith C. Wold, Jr.; Mary Lea Johnson Richards Charitable Trust.
Foundation type: Independent foundation.
Financial data (yr. ended 12/31/13): Assets, $13,407,742 (M); expenditures, $582,277; qualifying distributions, $573,727; giving activities include $560,277 for 58 grants (high: $100,527; low: $500).
Purpose and activities: Giving primarily for education, the arts, medical care, Christian organizations and churches, and children, youth, and social services.
Fields of interest: Historic preservation/historical societies; Arts; Higher education; Education; Animals/wildlife, association; Hospitals (general); Reproductive health, family planning; Health organizations, association; Human services; Children/youth, services; Christian agencies & churches; Economically disadvantaged.
Limitations: Applications not accepted. Giving in the U.S., with emphasis on DE and FL. No grants to individuals.
Application information: Contributes only to pre-selected organizations.
Directors: Diana E. Marszalek Bekmyrza; Diana J. Wold; Elaine J. Wold; Keith C. Wold, Jr.
Trustees: Andrea P. Westergom; Donald E. Baker.
EIN: 226054888
Selected grants: The following grants are a representative sample of this grantmaker's funding activity:
$150,000 to Hospital for Special Surgery, New York, NY, 2012. To finance research.
$76,000 to Boca Raton Regional Hospital Foundation, Boca Raton, FL, 2012. To finance operations of donee organization and fundraising events.
$63,000 to Lynn University, Boca Raton, FL, 2012. To finance scholarship fund and other operations of the donee organization.
$20,000 to Alliance for Lupus Research, New York, NY, 2012. To benefit research Programs.
$1,000 to George Washington University, Washington, DC, 2012. To contribute to the Mount Vernon Annual Giving Fund.

1986
Beaver Street Foundation, Inc. ✧
P.O. Box 41430
Jacksonville, FL 32203-1430

Established in 1986 in FL.
Donors: Beaver Street Fisheries, Inc.; Hans Frisch; Benjamin Frisch; Mark Frisch; Adam Frisch.
Foundation type: Company-sponsored foundation.
Financial data (yr. ended 12/31/13): Assets, $12,914,364 (M); gifts received, $601,587; expenditures, $635,560; qualifying distributions, $634,694; giving activities include $634,694 for 88 grants (high: $100,000; low: $25).
Purpose and activities: The foundation supports organizations involved with higher education, animal welfare, health, cancer, human services, and Judaism.
Fields of interest: Higher education; Animal welfare; Hospitals (general); Health care, clinics/centers; Health care; Cancer; Cancer, leukemia; Youth development, business; Children, services; Human services; United Ways and Federated Giving Programs; Jewish federated giving programs; Jewish agencies & synagogues.
Type of support: Sponsorships; Continuing support; Annual campaigns; General/operating support.
Limitations: Applications not accepted. Giving primarily in Jacksonville, FL. No grants to individuals.
Application information: Contributes only to pre-selected organizations.
Directors: Adam Frisch; Benjamin Frisch; Hans Frisch; Mark Frisch.
EIN: 592714980
Selected grants: The following grants are a representative sample of this grantmaker's funding activity:
$20,000 to Edward Waters College, Jacksonville, FL, 2012. For 1st of 5 Year $100K Pledge.
$20,000 to Edward Waters College, Jacksonville, FL, 2012. For 2013 2nd of 5 Year $100K Pledge.
$20,000 to Jacksonville Jewish Center, Jacksonville, FL, 2012. For 50th Anniversary HF 2010 IRA Contribution.
$12,000 to United Way of Northeast Florida, Jacksonville, FL, 2012. For 2012-2013 campaign.
$2,500 to HandsOn Jacksonville, Jacksonville, FL, 2012. For Visit From Saint Nick 2012 (Formerly Volunteer Jax).
$1,000 to American Cancer Society, Jacksonville, FL, 2012. For Cowford Ball 2013.
$500 to United States Holocaust Memorial Museum, Washington, DC, 2012. For annual.

1987
The Henry E. Becker and Pauline S. Becker Charitable Foundation ✧
4700 Bay Shore Rd.
Sarasota, FL 34234-4528

Established in 2004 in FL.
Donor: Pauline S. Becker.
Foundation type: Independent foundation.
Financial data (yr. ended 12/31/13): Assets, $11,887,682 (M); gifts received, $2,000,000; expenditures, $1,097,926; qualifying distributions, $1,097,091; giving activities include $1,093,000 for 20 grants (high: $601,000; low: $6,000).
Fields of interest: Arts education; Education; Health organizations; Boys & girls clubs; Human services; Marine science.
Limitations: Applications not accepted. Giving primarily in FL, with emphasis on Sarasota.
Application information: Contributes only to pre-selected organizations.
Trustee: Pauline S. Becker.
EIN: 206297485
Selected grants: The following grants are a representative sample of this grantmaker's funding activity:
$601,000 to Ringling School of Art and Design, Sarasota, FL, 2012. For Heb Scholarship, Trustee Scholarship, Smoa, Health Care Center; Listtotal 1101000.
$307,000 to Mote Marine Laboratory, Sarasota, FL, 2012. For Flood/Library/Scholars.

1988
Edward T. Bedford Foundation ✧
c/o Bessemer Trust Company of Florida
222 Royal Palm Way
Palm Beach, FL 33480-4303
Contact: Alfred J. Stashis, Jr.
Application address: Edward T. Bedford Foundation, c/o Dunwody White & Landon, PA, 4001 Tamiami Trail N., Ste. 200, Naples, FL 34103; Main URL: http://edwardtbedfordfoundation.org/

Established in 1995 in FL.
Donors: E.T. Bedford Davie‡; Diana W. Davie; Bedford Davie Trust; D. Davie Mar Trust.
Foundation type: Independent foundation.
Financial data (yr. ended 12/31/12): Assets, $17,540,037 (M); expenditures, $1,247,871; qualifying distributions, $1,000,016; giving activities include $940,668 for 41 grants (high: $100,000; low: $3,500).
Fields of interest: Animals/wildlife; Human services; American Red Cross; YM/YWCAs & YM/YWHAs; Residential/custodial care, hospices; United Ways and Federated Giving Programs.
Limitations: Applications accepted. Giving primarily in FL. No grants to individuals.
Application information: Application form required.
Initial approach: see foundation website
Deadline(s): None
Trustees: Ronald L. Fick, Esq.; Bessemer Trust Company of Florida.
EIN: 656164872

1989
The Believers Foundation, Inc. ✧
P.O. Box 428
Mango, FL 33550-0428
Contact: Kenneth Fuller, V.P. and Exec. Dir.

Established in 1987 in GA.
Donors: Robert Jaeb‡; Lorena Jaeb; Stephen Jaeb; Sandra D. Jaeb; Maria Geer; Richard Nelson; Pat Nelson.
Foundation type: Independent foundation.
Financial data (yr. ended 08/31/13): Assets, $19,536,973 (M); gifts received, $15,000; expenditures, $2,676,627; qualifying distributions, $2,315,924; giving activities include $2,245,557 for 34 grants (high: $474,000; low: $3,000), and $34,531 for foundation-administered programs.
Purpose and activities: Giving to religious organizations to proclaim the Gospel of Christ, and for training of pastors and disciples to accurately teach the Scriptures.
Fields of interest: Christian agencies & churches; Protestant agencies & churches.
Type of support: General/operating support; Continuing support; Annual campaigns; Program development; Conferences/seminars; Publication; Curriculum development; Technical assistance; Grants to individuals.
Limitations: Applications accepted. Giving on a national and international basis. No support for political organizations.
Publications: Annual report.
Application information: Application form not required.
Initial approach: Letter
Copies of proposal: 1
Deadline(s): None
Board meeting date(s): Varies

Officers and Directors:* Stephen L. Jaeb,* Pres.; Sandra D. Jaeb,* Secy.-Treas.; Kenneth G. Fuller,* V.P. and Exec. Dir.
Number of staff: 2 full-time professional.
EIN: 592851282

1990
Helen W. Bell Charitable Foundation ✧
800 Laurel Oak Dr., Ste. 600
Naples, FL 34108-2705

Donor: Helen W. Bell Revocable Trust.
Foundation type: Independent foundation.
Financial data (yr. ended 12/31/13): Assets, $18,444,499 (M); expenditures, $1,338,596; qualifying distributions, $955,040; giving activities include $955,040 for 54 grants (high: $100,000; low: $40).
Fields of interest: Education; Human services; Catholic agencies & churches.
Limitations: Applications not accepted. Giving primarily in DC, FL, GA, and TN.
Application information: Contributes only to pre-selected organizations.
Trustees: Andrew J. Krause; Madonna Lintzenich.
EIN: 616384143

1991
Bell Family Foundation ✧
457 Leucadendra Dr.
Coral Gables, FL 33156-2367

Established in 1987 in FL.
Donors: Daniel M. Bell; Patricia B. Bell.
Foundation type: Independent foundation.
Financial data (yr. ended 12/31/13): Assets, $7,880,259 (M); expenditures, $800,101; qualifying distributions, $779,196; giving activities include $774,131 for 1 grant.
Purpose and activities: Giving primarily to United Methodist churches and ministries; some funding also to an organization for the homeless.
Fields of interest: Human services; Protestant agencies & churches.
Limitations: Applications not accepted. Giving primarily in Miami, FL. No grants to individuals.
Application information: Contributes only to pre-selected organizations.
Officers and Directors:* Patricia B. Bell,* Chair.; Daniel M. Bell,* Pres. and Treas.; Rodney H. Bell,* V.P. and Secy.; Daniel M. Bell, Jr.,* V.P.
EIN: 650016516

1992
Gertrude Josephine Bennett Family Foundation ✧
660 U.S. Hwy. 1, 3rd Fl.
North Palm Beach, FL 33408-4629

Established in 2007 in FL.
Foundation type: Independent foundation.
Financial data (yr. ended 12/31/12): Assets, $8,091,798 (M); expenditures, $578,379; qualifying distributions, $500,000; giving activities include $500,000 for grants.
Fields of interest: Education; Medical research, institute; Human services; Jewish agencies & synagogues.
Limitations: Applications not accepted. Giving in the U.S., with emphasis on CA and NY. No grants to individuals.
Application information: Unsolicited requests for funds not accepted.
Officers: Joel I. Bennett, Pres.; Pamela H. Bennett, V.P.; Wendy M. Bennett, V.P.; Gerald Principe, Secy.
Director: David Henry Frankel.
EIN: 205716045

1993
Berg Family Charitable Foundation ✧
4306 Pablo Oaks Ct.
Jacksonville, FL 32224-9631

Established in 1986 in FL.
Donors: Gilchrist B. Berg; Berkshire Hathaway Inc.; Water Street Capital.
Foundation type: Independent foundation.
Financial data (yr. ended 12/31/13): Assets, $3,379,671 (M); gifts received, $540,000; expenditures, $762,977; qualifying distributions, $752,422; giving activities include $750,287 for 23 grants (high: $60,000; low: $60).
Purpose and activities: Giving primarily for higher and secondary education, health associations, children, youth, and social services, the symphony, and to Episcopal churches and organizations.
Fields of interest: Performing arts, orchestras; Secondary school/education; Higher education; Health organizations, association; Human services; Children/youth, services; Protestant agencies & churches.
Limitations: Applications not accepted. Giving primarily in Jacksonville, FL. No grants to individuals.
Application information: Contributes only to pre-selected organizations.
Trustee: Gilchrist B. Berg.
EIN: 592803980

1994
Sam Berman Charitable Foundation ✧ ☆
c/o Sheryl Greenwald
1920 E. Hallandale Beach Blvd., Ste. 606
Hallandale Beach, FL 33009

Foundation type: Independent foundation.
Financial data (yr. ended 12/31/12): Assets, $15,522,172 (M); expenditures, $1,427,559; qualifying distributions, $582,188; giving activities include $493,919 for 24 grants (high: $104,106; low: $1,000).
Fields of interest: Education; Youth development; Human services; Jewish federated giving programs; Jewish agencies & synagogues.
Limitations: Applications not accepted. Giving primarily in FL.
Application information: Contributes only to pre-selected organizations.
Officer and Directors:* Sheryl Greenwald,* Pres.; Carole Berman.
EIN: 592812513

1995
The Steven E. Bernstein Family Foundation Inc. ✧ ☆
P.O. Box 810664
Boca Raton, FL 33481-0664

Established in FL.
Foundation type: Independent foundation.
Financial data (yr. ended 06/30/13): Assets, $2,654,239 (M); expenditures, $459,465; qualifying distributions, $450,999; giving activities include $450,999 for 13 grants (high: $275,000; low: $1,000).
Fields of interest: Higher education, university; Human services; Religion.
Type of support: General/operating support.
Limitations: Applications not accepted. Giving primarily in FL.
Application information: Unsolicited requests for funds not accepted.
Officer: Steven E. Bernstein, Pres.
Directors: Abby Bernstein; Herman Moskowitz.
EIN: 205120272

1996
Bi-Lo Holdings Foundation, Inc.
(formerly Winn-Dixie Foundation, Inc.)
5050 Edgewood Ct.
Jacksonville, FL 32254-3601 (904) 783-5000
Contact: Melissa Adams, Mgr., Charitable Giving
Main URL: https://www.winndixie.com/CO/Community%20Events/Default.aspx
Grants List: https://www.winndixie.com/Community/BiLoFoundation/FoundationGrants.aspx

Incorporated in 1943 in FL.
Donors: PGA Tour Charities, Inc.; Winn-Dixie Stores, Inc.
Foundation type: Company-sponsored foundation.
Financial data (yr. ended 12/31/13): Assets, $843,762 (M); gifts received, $3,641,027; expenditures, $4,235,809; qualifying distributions, $4,228,228; giving activities include $4,228,228 for 367 grants (high: $76,500; low: $115).
Purpose and activities: The foundation supports programs designed to alleviate hunger directly or enhance hunger-related education or health initiatives.
Fields of interest: Elementary school/education; Higher education; Education; Hospitals (general); Cancer; Food services; Food banks; Food distribution, meals on wheels; Housing/shelter, development; Disasters, preparedness/services; Boys & girls clubs; American Red Cross; Salvation Army; Youth, services; Developmentally disabled, centers & services; Human services; United Ways and Federated Giving Programs; Jewish federated giving programs.
Type of support: Continuing support; Annual campaigns; Building/renovation; Equipment; Program development; Conferences/seminars; Scholarship funds; Research; Employee matching gifts; Matching/challenge support.
Limitations: Applications accepted. Giving primarily in areas of company operations in AL, FL, GA, LA, MS, NC, SC, and TN. No support for religious or political organizations or schools. No grants to individuals, or for capital campaigns, general operating support, multi-year commitments, capital campaigns, fundraising, or sponsorships.
Publications: Application guidelines; Grants list.
Application information: Application form required.
Initial approach: Complete online application
Deadline(s): Apr. 15 to June 30
Board meeting date(s): As required
Officers and Directors: Mary Kellmanson, Pres.; M. Sandlin Grimm, Secy.; D. Michael Byrum, Treas.; Anthea Jones.
EIN: 590995428

1997
The Blank Family Foundation, Inc. ✧
(formerly The New Blank Family Foundation, Inc.)
3455 N.W. 54th St.
Miami, FL 33142-3309
Contact: Robin Reiter
Main URL: http://www.blankfamily.org

Established in 2002 in FL.
Donor: Rose Blank Kramer Revocable Living Trust.
Foundation type: Independent foundation.
Financial data (yr. ended 12/31/12): Assets, $19,623,305 (M); gifts received, $320,000; expenditures, $1,066,592; qualifying distributions, $998,500; giving activities include $998,500 for grants.
Purpose and activities: Giving primarily for Jewish causes, including federated giving programs; support also for human services, and the environment.
Fields of interest: Environment; Health organizations; Human services; Jewish federated giving programs; Jewish agencies & synagogues.
International interests: Israel.
Type of support: General/operating support.
Limitations: Applications not accepted. Giving primarily in FL, MT, and UT. No support for political or social organizations. No grants to individuals.
Application information: Contributes only to pre-selected organizations. Unsolicited requests for funds not accepted.
Board meeting date(s): Quarterly
Officers and Directors:* Jerome Blank,* Chair.; Andrew S. Blank,* Pres.; Kathleen Blank,* Secy.; Robert Frehling; Kathy Martin.
Number of staff: 1 part-time professional.
EIN: 920185953
Selected grants: The following grants are a representative sample of this grantmaker's funding activity:
$735,000 to Jewish Federation, Greater Miami, Miami, FL, 2012.
$50,000 to Anti-Defamation League of Bnai Brith, New York, NY, 2012.
$20,000 to Natural Resources Defense Council, New York, NY, 2012.
$10,000 to Feeding South Florida, Pembroke Park, FL, 2012.
$10,000 to Goodwill Industries of South Florida, Miami, FL, 2012.
$10,000 to Miami Jewish Health Systems, Miami, FL, 2012.
$5,000 to Ballet West, Salt Lake City, UT, 2012.
$5,000 to National Ability Center, Park City, UT, 2012.
$1,000 to Deep Listening Institute, Kingston, NY, 2012.
$1,000 to Wood River Jewish Community, Ketchum, ID, 2012.

1998
Ellen & Ronald Block Family Foundation Inc. ✧ ☆
(formerly Lamis Crown Foundation, Inc.)
2 N. Breakers Row, Apt. S24
Palm Beach, FL 33480-3811

Established in 2005 in FL.
Donor: Ellen H. Block.
Foundation type: Independent foundation.
Financial data (yr. ended 12/31/13): Assets, $6,214,066 (M); gifts received, $255,170; expenditures, $856,461; qualifying distributions, $808,740; giving activities include $694,699 for 43 grants (high: $200,903; low: $250).
Fields of interest: Higher education, university; Hospitals (general); Jewish federated giving programs; Jewish agencies & synagogues.
Limitations: Applications not accepted. Giving primarily in FL, IL, MA, and NY. No grants to individuals.
Application information: Contributes only to pre-selected organizations.
Directors: Ellen H. Block; Laurie A. Block; Michael H. Block; Susan S. Block Casdin.
Trustee: Jane S. Englebardt.
EIN: 202067790

1999
Walter & Adi Blum Foundation, Inc. ✧
P.O. Box 33598
Palm Beach Gardens, FL 33420-3598
Main URL: http://www.thewalterandadiblumfoundation.org/

Established in 1987 in FL.
Donor: Adi Blum Revocable Trust.
Foundation type: Independent foundation.
Financial data (yr. ended 12/31/13): Assets, $13,045,569 (M); expenditures, $763,574; qualifying distributions, $586,610; giving activities include $512,200 for 44 grants (high: $50,000; low: $1,000).
Purpose and activities: Giving primarily for health organizations, and children and social services.
Fields of interest: Health organizations, association; Human services; Children/youth, services; Community/economic development; Foundations (community).
Limitations: Applications not accepted. Giving primarily in FL; with emphasis on Palm Beach. No grants to individuals.
Application information: Contributes only to pre-selected organizations.
Officers and Directors:* Norman Shaw, Esq.*, Pres.; Eugene W. Murphy, Jr., Esq.*, V.P. and Secy.; Sandra E. Gambill,* Treas.
EIN: 650008826
Selected grants: The following grants are a representative sample of this grantmaker's funding activity:
$37,500 to Jane Voorhees Zimmerli Art Museum, New Brunswick, NJ, 2011.
$30,000 to Center for Group Counseling, Boca Raton, FL, 2011.
$30,000 to Paws 4 Liberty, Lake Worth, FL, 2011.
$25,000 to Ferd and Gladys Alpert Jewish Family and Childrens Service of Palm Beach County, West Palm Beach, FL, 2010.
$25,000 to Florida Atlantic University Foundation, Boca Raton, FL, 2010.
$22,500 to Gateway Community Outreach, Deerfield Beach, FL, 2011.
$22,500 to Seagull Industries for the Disabled, Riviera Beach, FL, 2011.
$20,000 to Arc of Palm Beach County, Riviera Beach, FL, 2011.
$20,000 to Doctors Without Borders USA, New York, NY, 2010.
$20,000 to Hospice by the Sea, Boca Raton, FL, 2010.
$20,000 to Israel Childrens Centers, New York, NY, 2010.
$20,000 to Jay Ministries, Riviera Beach, FL, 2010.
$20,000 to Memorial Sloan-Kettering Cancer Center, New York, NY, 2011.
$17,500 to Saint Jude Childrens Research Hospital, Memphis, TN, 2011.
$15,000 to Alzheimers Community Care, West Palm Beach, FL, 2010.
$15,000 to My Choice Community Development, Riviera Beach, FL, 2011.
$12,500 to Jane Voorhees Zimmerli Art Museum, New Brunswick, NJ, 2010.
$10,000 to Habitat for Humanity of Palm Beach County, West Palm Beach, FL, 2010.
$2,500 to Preservation Foundation of Palm Beach, Palm Beach, FL, 2011.

2000
Booth Foundation, Inc. ✧
2001 Sailfish Point Blvd., No. 316
Stuart, FL 34996-1971

Established in 2004 in FL.
Donors: Alex E. Booth, Jr.; HTOOB, Inc.
Foundation type: Independent foundation.
Financial data (yr. ended 12/31/12): Assets, $23,368,076 (M); expenditures, $1,530,995; qualifying distributions, $1,430,924; giving activities include $1,430,000 for 2 grants (high: $1,400,000; low: $30,000).
Purpose and activities: Giving primarily for Presbyterian churches.
Fields of interest: Protestant agencies & churches.
Limitations: Applications not accepted. Giving primarily in TN and WV. No grants to individuals.
Application information: Contributes only to pre-selected organizations.
Officers and Directors:* Alex E. Booth, Jr.,* Pres. and Treas.; Katherine Booth,* V.P.; Beth Terdo Prinz,* Secy.; William Bryant; Susan Machamer.
EIN: 200667161

2001
Harry L. Bradley, Jr. Charitable Fund ✧
777 S. Flagler Dr., 8th Fl., West Tower
West Palm Beach, FL 33401-6161
E-mail: info@hlbjr.org; Main URL: http://www.hlbjrfund.org/

Established in 1981 in MA.
Donor: Mark S. Bradley Trust.
Foundation type: Independent foundation.
Financial data (yr. ended 06/30/13): Assets, $159,063,775 (M); gifts received, $750,000; expenditures, $4,411,704; qualifying distributions, $3,148,230; giving activities include $3,148,230 for 39 grants (high: $2,260,000; low: $500).
Purpose and activities: Giving primarily for education, human services, and Catholic organizations.
Fields of interest: Museums; Higher education; Law school/education; Education; Health organizations; Human services; Catholic agencies & churches.
Type of support: General/operating support.
Limitations: Applications not accepted. Giving primarily in MA, with emphasis on the Boston area. No grants to individuals.
Publications: IRS Form 990 or 990-PF printed copy available upon request.
Application information: Contributes only to pre-selected organizations. Unsolicited requests for funds not accepted.
Officer: Robert F. Morrissey, Exec. Dir.
Trustee: Robert J. Morrissey.
EIN: 042747025

Selected grants: The following grants are a representative sample of this grantmaker's funding activity:
$2,000,000 to Boston College, Chestnut Hill, MA, 2011.
$10,000 to Catholic Relief Services, Baltimore, MD, 2011.

2002
The Shepard Broad Foundation, Inc. ✧
1 Brickell Sq.
801 Brickell Ave., Ste. 2350
Miami, FL 33131-4944

Incorporated in 1956 in FL.
Donors: Shepard Broad; Ruth K. Broad; Morris N. Broad; Shepard Broad Trust.
Foundation type: Independent foundation.
Financial data (yr. ended 12/31/12): Assets, $13,941,407 (M); gifts received, $1,344,571; expenditures, $1,466,862; qualifying distributions, $1,390,898; giving activities include $1,315,473 for 127 grants (high: $216,600; low: $150).
Fields of interest: Elementary/secondary education; Higher education; Education; Hospitals (general); Health care; Human services; Children/youth, services; Jewish agencies & synagogues.
Type of support: Program-related investments/loans.
Limitations: Applications not accepted. Giving primarily in FL. No grants to individuals.
Application information: Contributes only to pre-selected organizations.
Officers and Directors:* Morris N. Broad,* Chair.; John M. Bussel,* Pres.; Ann B. Bussel,* V.P.; Deborah Bussel,* Secy.-Treas.; Karen A.B. Berman; Daniel J. Bussel.
EIN: 590998866

2003
Ann L. Bronfman Foundation ✧
c/o Marilyn Silver, CPA
7700 Wexford Way
Port St. Lucie, FL 34986-3007

Established in 1958.
Donor: Ann L. Bronfman†.
Foundation type: Independent foundation.
Financial data (yr. ended 07/31/13): Assets, $5,604,504 (M); expenditures, $5,983,038; qualifying distributions, $5,935,872; giving activities include $5,932,167 for 10 grants (high: $1,000,000; low: $3,000).
Purpose and activities: Giving primarily for education, human services, and Jewish organizations.
Fields of interest: Higher education; Human services; Children/youth, services; Foundations (private grantmaking); Jewish federated giving programs; Jewish agencies & synagogues.
Type of support: General/operating support.
Limitations: Applications not accepted. Giving primarily in Washington, DC, and New York, NY. No grants to individuals.
Application information: Contributes only to pre-selected organizations.
Officers: Matthew Bronfman, Pres.; Edgar Miles Bronfman, Jr., V.P.; Adam Bronfman, Secy.-Treas.
EIN: 136085595

Selected grants: The following grants are a representative sample of this grantmaker's funding activity:
$125,000 to Planned Parenthood Federation, International, New York, NY, 2011. For general purpose.
$105,000 to Washington District of Columbia Jewish Community Center, Washington, DC, 2011. For general purpose.
$100,000 to Teamwork Foundation, Bronx, NY, 2011. For general purpose.
$100,000 to UJA-Federation of New York, New York, NY, 2011. For general purpose.
$70,000 to Endeavor Global, New York, NY, 2011. For general purpose.
$62,200 to Watkinson School, Hartford, CT, 2011. For general purpose.
$60,000 to Exponents, New York, NY, 2011. For general purpose.
$45,000 to Positively Sports, Miami, FL, 2011. For general purpose.
$25,000 to Carnegie Hall Society, New York, NY, 2011. For general purpose.
$10,000 to Corporate Accountability International, Boston, MA, 2011. For general purpose.

2004
Brown Shoe Co., Charitable Trust ✧
(formerly Brown Group, Inc. Charitable Trust)
P.O. Box 1908
Orlando, FL 32802-1908 (314) 854-4000
E-mail: charitablegiving@brownshoe.com; Additional address: 8400 Maryland Ave., St. Louis, MO 36166; Main URL: http://brownshoe.com/brown-shoe-company/community/charitable-trust/

Trust established in 1951 in MO.
Donors: Brown Group Inc., Charitable Trust, Inc.; Brown Shoe Co., Inc.
Foundation type: Company-sponsored foundation.
Financial data (yr. ended 12/31/13): Assets, $5,468,919 (M); gifts received, $3,000,000; expenditures, $3,069,066; qualifying distributions, $3,057,483; giving activities include $3,043,752 for 113 grants (high: $2,000,000; low: $50).
Purpose and activities: The foundation supports programs designed to develop strong families through opportunity enrichment; encourage individuals to live better lives through health and wellness efforts; and provide occasions for families and individuals to step feet first into the arts and cultural opportunities in the community.
Fields of interest: Arts councils; Media, television; Museums (art); Performing arts, theater; Performing arts, orchestras; Arts; Higher education; Education; Hospitals (general); Health care, clinics/centers; Health care; Boy scouts; Youth development, business; YM/YWCAs & YM/YWHAs; Family services; Human services; Foundations (community); United Ways and Federated Giving Programs; Jewish federated giving programs.
Type of support: General/operating support; Continuing support; Annual campaigns; Capital campaigns; Program development.
Limitations: Applications accepted. Giving limited to areas of major company operations, with emphasis on St. Louis, MO. No support for private foundations, organizations primarily funded by state or federal taxes, fraternal organizations, political or advocacy groups, organizations located outside of the U.S. operating primarily in the U.S., international charities, religious organizations not of direct benefit to the entire community, pass-through organizations, or United Way-supported organizations. No grants to individuals, or for endowments, special projects, research, publications, or conferences; no loans.
Publications: Application guidelines.
Application information: Application form not required.
Initial approach: Complete online application
Copies of proposal: 1
Deadline(s): Mar. 31, June 30, Sept. 30, and Dec. 31
Board meeting date(s): Quarterly
Officer: Ronald A. Fromm, Chair.
Board Members: Bill Berberich; Ann Joos; Michael Oberlander.
Trustee: SunTrust Banks, Inc.
EIN: 237443082
Selected grants: The following grants are a representative sample of this grantmaker's funding activity:
$16,500 to American Heart Association, Dallas, TX, 2011. For general charitable purpose.
$2,500 to American Liver Foundation, New York, NY, 2011. For general charitable purpose.
$2,500 to Boys Hope Girls Hope, Bridgeton, MO, 2011. For general charitable purpose.
$2,500 to University of Chicago, Chicago, IL, 2011. For general charitable purpose.

2005
Bryce L. West Foundation, Inc. ✧ ☆
8815 Conroy Windermere Rd., Ste. 418
Orlando, FL 32835-3129

Donor: Bryce L. West.
Foundation type: Independent foundation.
Financial data (yr. ended 12/31/13): Assets, $2,508,706 (M); expenditures, $1,152,441; qualifying distributions, $1,011,557; giving activities include $989,250 for 22 grants (high: $525,000; low: $1,000).
Fields of interest: Performing arts, orchestras; Arts; Education; Human services.
Limitations: Applications not accepted. Giving primarily in FL and New York, NY.
Application information: Unsolicited requests for funds not accepted.
Officer: Bryce L. West, Pres. and Secy.-Treas.
Directors: Julia L. Frey; Michael Norton.
EIN: 453787163

2006
Donald A. Burns Foundation Inc. ✧ ☆
450 Royal Palm Way, Ste. 450
Palm Beach, FL 33480-4100 (561) 655-7855
Contact: Ginger Gibas

Established in 1998 in FL.
Donor: Donald A. Burns.
Foundation type: Independent foundation.
Financial data (yr. ended 12/31/12): Assets, $10,190,885 (M); expenditures, $1,267,582; qualifying distributions, $480,994; giving activities include $461,690 for 18 grants (high: $322,790; low: $100).
Fields of interest: Arts, formal/general education; Museums; Elementary/secondary education; Reproductive health, prenatal care; Human services; Children/youth, services; Family services; Christian agencies & churches; LGBTQ.

Type of support: Annual campaigns; Equipment; Program development; Curriculum development; Technical assistance.
Application information: Application form required.
Initial approach: Contact foundation for the application form
Copies of proposal: 1
Deadline(s): None
Officer: Donald A. Burns, Pres.
Number of staff: 2 full-time professional.
EIN: 650870379

2007
Burton Foundation, Inc. ✧
1899 Sycamore Ln.
Fernandina Beach, FL 32034-7857

Established in 2001 in FL.
Donors: Dr. Barry A. Gray; Mrs. Barry A. Gray; David Gray.
Foundation type: Independent foundation.
Financial data (yr. ended 12/31/12): Assets, $26,418,884 (M); gifts received, $15,039; expenditures, $2,294,774; qualifying distributions, $2,058,483; giving activities include $1,884,500 for 50 grants (high: $1,500,000; low: $500).
Fields of interest: Higher education; Education; Environment, natural resources; Human services; Foundations (community); Catholic agencies & churches.
Limitations: Applications not accepted. Giving in the U.S., with emphasis on OK. No grants to individuals.
Application information: Contributes only to pre-selected organizations.
Officers and Trustees:* David Gray,* Pres.; Gretchen Gray,* Secy.; Sherrie Schroeder, Treas.; Joseph Gray; Robert Gray; Lisa Wall.
EIN: 731584983

2008
Edyth Bush Charitable Foundation, Inc. ✧
199 E. Welbourne Ave.
P.O. Box 1967
Winter Park, FL 32790-1967 (407) 647-4322
Contact: David A. Odahowski, C.E.O. and Pres.; Deborah Hessler, Corp. Secy. and Prog.Off.
FAX: (407) 647-7716;
E-mail: dhessler@edythbush.org; Deborah Hessler direct tel.: (407) 647-4322 x17; additional tel.: (888) 647-4322; Main URL: http://www.edythbush.org
Facebook: https://www.facebook.com/EdythBushCharitableFoundation
Google Plus: https://plus.google.com/+EdythbushOrg/about
YouTube: http://www.youtube.com/channel/UCkToIOhE9pRdpobW8hd7FGw

Originally incorporated in 1966 in MN; reincorporated in 1973 in FL.
Donors: Edyth Bassler Bush†; H. Clifford Lee†; Richard Conlee†.
Foundation type: Independent foundation.
Financial data (yr. ended 08/31/13): Assets, $75,414,999 (M); gifts received, $35,000; expenditures, $4,761,188; qualifying distributions, $3,837,012; giving activities include $2,350,890 for 42+ grants (high: $600,000), and $70,200 for employee matching gifts.
Purpose and activities: Support for charitable, educational, and health service organizations, with emphasis on human services, the elderly, youth services, the handicapped, and nationally recognized quality arts or cultural programs. Provides limited number of program-related investment loans for construction, land purchase, emergency or similar purposes to organizations otherwise qualified to receive grants. Active programs directly managed and/or financed for management/volunteer development of nonprofits.
Fields of interest: Arts education; Arts; Education; Health care; Crime/violence prevention, domestic violence; Employment; Housing/shelter; Human services; Children/youth, services; Nonprofit management; Children/youth; Aging; Young adults; Disabilities, people with; Women; Military/veterans; Crime/abuse victims; Economically disadvantaged; Homeless.
Type of support: Management development/capacity building; Capital campaigns; Building/renovation; Equipment; Land acquisition; Emergency funds; Program development; Technical assistance; Consulting services; Program-related investments/loans; Employee matching gifts; Matching/challenge support.
Limitations: Giving limited to organizations that are headquartered within Orange, Seminole, Lake, and Osceola counties, FL. No support for alcohol or drug abuse prevention/treatment projects or organizations, religious facilities or functions, primarily (50 percent or more) tax-supported institutions, advocacy organizations, foreign organizations, or, generally, for cultural programs. No grants to individuals, or for scholarships or individual research projects, endowments, fellowships, travel, routine operating expenses, annual campaigns, or deficit financing.
Publications: Application guidelines; Financial statement; Grants list; Informational brochure; Program policy statement.
Application information: Application guidelines and form available on foundation web site. The foundation is open to discussing your funding needs. If we determine there is significant interest, the foundation may invite you to submit an online application. With the many needs facing the people of Central Florida in this challenging economic environment, the foundation receives far more requests than it can possibly fund. Due to this increased demand on the foundation's limited resources, we are unable to fund every new request. Check foundation web site periodically for further updates. Application form required.
Initial approach: Telephone, e-mail, personal visit, or stated interest by foundation.
Deadline(s): None
Board meeting date(s): May and Nov.
Final notification: Varies depending on scope of request
Officers and Directors:* Gerald F. Hilbrich,* Chair.; Herbert W. Holm, Vice-Chair.; David A. Odahowski,* C.E.O. and Pres.; Mary Ellen Hutcheson, V.P., Treas. and C.F.O.; Deborah J. Hessler, Corp. Secy. and Prog. Off.; Elizabeth Dvorak; Deborah C. German, M.D.; Harvey L. Massey; Glenn "Doc" Rivers; Richard J. Walsh.
Number of staff: 3 full-time professional; 2 full-time support.
EIN: 237318041
Selected grants: The following grants are a representative sample of this grantmaker's funding activity:
$1,000,000 to Rollins College, Winter Park, FL, 2011. To expand and renovate Rollins College's Archibald Granville Bush Science Center into modern facility to support collaborative, interdisciplinary learning and research.
$500,000 to Nemours Foundation, Jacksonville, FL, 2011. For challenge grant to promote philanthropy for Nemours Children's Hospital at Lake Nona.
$400,000 to Lifestream Behavioral Center, Leesburg, FL, 2012. To reopen Anthony House providing transitional housing and services for homeless families and individuals.
$95,493 to Harvest Time International, Sanford, FL, 2012. For equipment, dental supplies, computers and software for free dental clinic serving homeless and uninsured families.
$77,000 to Bread of Life Fellowship, Winter Garden, FL, 2012. For phase two of building expansion program consisting of purchase and installation of commodity storage-agricultural building.
$50,000 to Conductive Education Center of Orlando, Winter Park, FL, 2012. For program support.
$50,000 to Idignity, Orlando, FL, 2012. For fundraising initiatives.
$13,965 to Orlando VA Medical Center, Orlando, FL, 2011. To provide OrbiTouch keyboards, along with orientation and training to disabled veterans.
$10,000 to Celebration Foundation, Celebration, FL, 2012. For partnership with Celebration Cares provide food for homeless Osceola students and their families during Spring Break.

2009
The Trust for Fuller E. Callaway Professorial Chairs ✧
P.O. Box 40200, FL9-100-10-19
Jacksonville, FL 32203-0200

Trust established in 1968 in GA; supporting organization of Agnes Scott College, Clark Atlanta University, Georgia Institute of Technology, Georgia Southern University, Georgia State University, Interdenominational Theological School, LaGrange College, Mercer University, Morehouse College, Paine College, Piedmont College, Shorter College, and Wesleyan College.
Donor: Callaway Foundation, Inc.
Foundation type: Independent foundation.
Financial data (yr. ended 06/30/13): Assets, $27,309,064 (M); expenditures, $1,027,735; qualifying distributions, $902,528; giving activities include $841,216 for 19 grants (high: $157,405; low: $1,142).
Fields of interest: Higher education.
Type of support: Professorships.
Limitations: Applications not accepted. Giving limited to GA.
Application information: Unsolicited requests for funds not acknowledged or considered.
Board meeting date(s): Annually
Trustees: Marilyn Jackson; Geri Thomas; James Wagner; Robb Watts; Bank of America, N.A.
Number of staff: 1 full-time professional.
EIN: 586075259

2010
Cammarata Family Foundation ✧
3680 Carlton Pl.
Boca Raton, FL 33496-4005

Established in 1997 in MA.
Donor: Bernard Cammarata.
Foundation type: Independent foundation.

Financial data (yr. ended 12/31/13): Assets, $14,080,943 (M); gifts received, $300,000; expenditures, $1,087,674; qualifying distributions, $1,071,000; giving activities include $1,071,000 for 6 grants (high: $500,000; low: $1,000).
Fields of interest: Education; Health care.
Limitations: Applications not accepted. Giving primarily in MA; some giving also in NH. No grants to individuals.
Application information: Contributes only to pre-selected organizations.
Trustee: Bernard Cammarata.
EIN: 043374858

2011
Cecilia & Dan Carmichael Family Foundation Inc. ✧
(formerly CF2 Foundation, Inc.)
605 Ocean Club Villas S.
Fernandina Beach, FL 32034-6564 (904) 261-6624
Contact: Danny R. Carmichael, Dir.

Established in 2007 in FL.
Donor: Danny R. Carmichael.
Foundation type: Independent foundation.
Financial data (yr. ended 12/31/13): Assets, $6,004,029 (M); gifts received, $665,646; expenditures, $1,119,844; qualifying distributions, $1,102,530; giving activities include $1,100,000 for 3 grants (high: $1,000,000; low: $50,000).
Fields of interest: Health care; Athletics/sports, equestrianism.
Limitations: Applications accepted. Giving primarily in MN and OH.
Application information: Application form not required.
Initial approach: Proposal
Deadline(s): None
Directors: Deena M. Bowers; Danny R. Carmichael; David R. Carmichael; E. Cecilia Carmichael.
EIN: 260614106
Selected grants: The following grants are a representative sample of this grantmaker's funding activity:
$40,000 to Ohio State University, Columbus, OH, 2012. For Comprehensive Cancer Center.

2012
The Jean Keller and Robert Carros Foundation ✧
400 Royal Palm Way, Ste. 304
Palm Beach, FL 33480

Donors: Jean Carros‡; Jean Carros Revocable Trust.
Foundation type: Independent foundation.
Financial data (yr. ended 12/31/11): Assets, $4,318,445 (M); gifts received, $468,934; expenditures, $566,187; qualifying distributions, $475,000; giving activities include $475,000 for 1 grant.
Fields of interest: Recreation; Youth development, services.
Limitations: Applications not accepted.
Application information: Unsolicited requests for funds not accepted.
Trustee: Robert G. Simses.
EIN: 260902413

2013
The Michael, Jr. and Elizabeth Belyea Cascone Family Foundation ✧
(also known as The Cascone Family Foundation)
8022 James Island Trail
Jacksonville, FL 32256

Established in 2004 in FL.
Donors: Elizabeth B. Cascone; Michael Cascone, Jr.
Foundation type: Independent foundation.
Financial data (yr. ended 12/31/13): Assets, $9,808,720 (M); gifts received, $300,000; expenditures, $657,409; qualifying distributions, $577,200; giving activities include $576,000 for 36 grants (high: $102,500; low: $1,000).
Limitations: Applications not accepted. Giving primarily in Jacksonville, FL. No grants to individuals.
Application information: Unsolicited requests for funds not accepted.
Directors: Brian J. Cascone; Elizabeth B. Cascone; Michael J. Cascone; Michael Cascone, Jr.; Steven D. Cascone; Juliette C. Gredenhag; Elizabeth C. Higgs; Kathleen C. Kilbane.
EIN: 597246237
Selected grants: The following grants are a representative sample of this grantmaker's funding activity:
$2,500 to Boy Scouts of America, North Fl Council, Jacksonville, FL, 2012. For general fund.

2014
Catholic Integrity Foundation ✧
901 N.W. 4th Ct.
Boca Raton, FL 33432-2505

Established in 2007 in PA.
Donors: Edward J. Constantine; Anne-Marie Constantine.
Foundation type: Independent foundation.
Financial data (yr. ended 12/31/12): Assets, $4,005 (M); gifts received, $1,500; expenditures, $600,970; qualifying distributions, $595,000; giving activities include $595,000 for grants.
Fields of interest: Human services; Catholic agencies & churches.
Limitations: Applications not accepted. Giving primarily in DC, IL, and PA; some giving also in India.
Application information: Contributes only to pre-selected organizations.
Officers and Directors:* Edward J. Constantine,* Pres.; Anne-Marie Constantine,* Secy.-Treas.; Alex W. Thomson.
EIN: 261611406

2015
Central Florida Foundation, Inc. ✧
(formerly Community Foundation of Central Florida, Inc.)
1411 Edgewater Dr., Ste. 203
Orlando, FL 32804-6361 (407) 872-3050
Contact: Mark Brewer, C.E.O.
FAX: (407) 425-2990; E-mail: info@cfcflorida.org; Additional Address: P.O. Box 2071, Orlando, FL 32802; Main URL: http://www.cfcflorida.org
RSS Feed: http://mycfcf.wordpress.com/
Twitter: https://twitter.com/cffound

Established in 1993 in FL.
Foundation type: Community foundation.
Financial data (yr. ended 04/30/14): Assets, $60,894,679 (M); gifts received, $3,355,595; expenditures, $5,181,118; giving activities include $3,921,298 for grants.
Purpose and activities: The mission of the foundation is "Building Community by Building Philanthropy." The foundation works to fulfill this mission by managing and investing donor funds, connecting people with charitable causes they feel passionate about and empowering donors to make informed decisions through research and evaluation.
Fields of interest: Arts; Elementary/secondary education; Higher education; Health care; Children/youth, services; Youth, services; Human services; Community/economic development; Aging.
Type of support: Management development/capacity building; Program development; Seed money; Scholarship funds; Scholarships—to individuals.
Limitations: Applications accepted. Giving limited to central FL, with emphasis on Orange, Osceola, and Seminole counties. No grants to individuals (except for scholarships).
Publications: Application guidelines; Annual report; Financial statement; Grants list; Informational brochure; Informational brochure (including application guidelines); Newsletter.
Application information: Visit foundation web site for application guidelines. Application form required.
Initial approach: Create an online Nonprofit Portrait
Copies of proposal: 1
Deadline(s): Spring and Fall
Board meeting date(s): Monthly
Officers and Board Members:* Martin A. Rubin,* Chair.; Robert Panepinto,* Vice-Chair.; Mark Brewer,* C.E.O. and Pres.; Michelle Chapin,* V.P., Community Strategies and Initiatives; Meghan Warrick,* Exec. V.P. and C.F.O.; Robert F. Thomson II,* Secy.; Kaki Rawls,* Treas.; Elizabeth Gordon, Cont.; Waymon Armstrong; Eugene Campbell; Thomas V. Durkee; Aaron Gorovitz; Tony Jenkins; Robert Newland; Stacey Prince-Troutman; Thomasa Sanchez; James Scrivener.
Number of staff: 4 full-time professional; 2 full-time support.
EIN: 593182886

2016
Nicholas and Eleanor Chabraja Foundation ✧
5100 N. Tamiami Trail, Ste. 103
Naples, FL 34103-2810

Established in 2004 in VA.
Donors: Nicholas Chabraja; Eleanor Chabraja.
Foundation type: Independent foundation.
Financial data (yr. ended 12/31/13): Assets, $7,159,222 (M); gifts received, $296,148; expenditures, $519,440; qualifying distributions, $493,093; giving activities include $479,500 for 6 grants (high: $250,000; low: $17,000).
Fields of interest: Botanical gardens; Christian agencies & churches.
Limitations: Applications not accepted. Giving in the U.S., with emphasis on IL. No grants to individuals.
Application information: Unsolicited requests for funds not accepted.
Officers: Nicholas Chabraja, Pres. and Treas.; Eleanor Chabraja, V.P. and Secy.
EIN: 202020571
Selected grants: The following grants are a representative sample of this grantmaker's funding activity:

$25,000 to Lambda Chi Alpha Educational Foundation, Indianapolis, IN, 2012. For Investing in Future Leaders Campaign.

2017
Paul & Karen Chaplin Family Foundation ✧ ☆
(formerly Chaplin Family Foundation Inc.)
c/o Robert M. Hersh
1600 N.W. 163rd St.
Miami, FL 33169-5641

Established in 1998 in FL.
Donors: Arlene Chaplin†; Harvey R. Chaplin; Paul B. Chaplin; Monica Chaplin; Wayne Chaplin; Karen Chaplin.
Foundation type: Independent foundation.
Financial data (yr. ended 12/31/13): Assets, $370,782 (M); gifts received, $13,700; expenditures, $932,484; qualifying distributions, $929,900; giving activities include $929,900 for 14 grants (high: $250,000; low: $200).
Fields of interest: Elementary/secondary education; Jewish agencies & synagogues.
Limitations: Applications not accepted. Giving primarily in NY, some giving in FL. No grants to individuals.
Application information: Contributes only to pre-selected organizations.
Trustees: Karen Chaplin; Monica Chaplin; Paul Chaplin.
EIN: 650732508
Selected grants: The following grants are a representative sample of this grantmaker's funding activity:
$1,505,000 to Mount Sinai Medical Center, 2010.
$146,931 to Miami Country Day School, Miami, FL, 2010.
$54,000 to Temple Beth Shalom, 2010.
$25,000 to Jewish Museum of Florida, Miami Beach, FL, 2010.
$10,000 to Helping Hands Foundation, Brentwood, TN, 2010.
$10,000 to University of Miami, Miami, FL, 2010.
$5,867 to Smile Train, New York, NY, 2011.
$5,000 to Simon Wiesenthal Center, Los Angeles, CA, 2011.

2018
The Chartrand Foundation, Inc. ✧
2038 Gilmore St.
Jacksonville, FL 32204-3210
E-mail: info@thechartrandfoundation.org; Main URL: http://www.thechartrandfoundation.org/

Established in 2006 in FL.
Donor: Gary R. Chartrand.
Foundation type: Independent foundation.
Financial data (yr. ended 12/31/13): Assets, $6,957,108 (M); expenditures, $1,008,587; qualifying distributions, $885,500; giving activities include $885,500 for 3 grants (high: $880,000; low: $1,000).
Fields of interest: Elementary/secondary education; Education.
Limitations: Applications not accepted. Giving primarily in Jacksonville, FL; some giving in New York, NY. No grants to individuals.
Application information: The foundation is currently redesigning its grantmaking strategy, systems and timeline. Check foundation web site for updates in this matter.
Officers: Nancy J. Chartrand, Chair.; Sandy Ramsey, V.P.; Ashley Smith Juarez, Exec. Dir.
Directors: Gary R. Chartrand; Jeffrey Chartrand; Meredith Chartrand.
EIN: 205440166

2019
The Chatlos Foundation, Inc. ✧
P.O. Box 915048
Longwood, FL 32791-5048 (407) 862-5077
Contact: William J. Chatlos, C.E.O. and Pres.
E-mail: info@chatlos.org; Main URL: http://www.chatlos.org
Grants Database: http://chatlos.org/grants.html

Incorporated in 1953 in NY.
Donors: Bristol Door and Lumber Co., Inc.; William F. Chatlos†.
Foundation type: Independent foundation.
Financial data (yr. ended 12/31/13): Assets, $65,726,173 (M); expenditures, $3,935,533; qualifying distributions, $3,054,410; giving activities include $1,972,976 for 293 grants (high: $85,000; low: $200).
Purpose and activities: Grants for higher education and religious causes; giving also for hospitals, health agencies, social services, and child welfare.
Fields of interest: Higher education; Nursing school/education; Theological school/education; Education; Hospitals (general); Health care; Health organizations, association; Human services; Children/youth, services.
Type of support: General/operating support; Equipment; Debt reduction; Program development; Publication; Curriculum development; Scholarship funds; Technical assistance; Matching/challenge support.
Limitations: Applications accepted. Giving on a national basis. No support for individual church congregations, primary or secondary schools, the arts, or for organizations in existence for less than two years as indicated by the date of their tax exempt letter from the IRS. No grants to individuals, or for seed money, deficit financing, endowment funds, medical research, conferences, bricks and mortar, or multi-year grants; no loans.
Publications: Application guidelines; Informational brochure (including application guidelines).
Application information: See foundation web site for proposal instructions. Application form may be requested in writing or printed from the foundation web site. Only 1 grant to an organization within a 12-month period. Application form required.
Initial approach: Submit proposal (no more than 5 pages)
Copies of proposal: 1
Deadline(s): None
Board meeting date(s): Quarterly
Final notification: Immediately
Officers and Trustees:* Kathryn A. Randle,* Chair.; William J. Chatlos,* C.E.O. and Pres.; Michele C. Roach, Sr. V.P.; William J. Chatlos III, V.P.; Cindee L. Random, Treas.; Janet Chatlos; Cherlyn Dannhaeuser; Kimberly C. Grimm; Charles O. Morgan; Brianne Ortt.
Number of staff: 4 full-time professional; 1 part-time professional.
EIN: 136161425
Selected grants: The following grants are a representative sample of this grantmaker's funding activity:
$85,901 to University of Pennsylvania, Department of Ophthalmology, Philadelphia, PA, 2012. For further progress toward treatment of X-linked retinitis pigmentosa caused by RPGR mutations.
$75,000 to Florida Southern College, Lakeland, FL, 2012. To correct the unexpected water intrusion, of the William F. Chatlos Communication Building, before further problems, such as mold and air-quality issues develop.
$55,000 to Davis College, Johnson City, NY, 2012. To restore project to help maintain many campus buildings.
$20,000 to Christian Service Center for Central Florida, Orlando, FL, 2012. To continue to build upon the success of the Fresh Start Program.
$20,000 to Trans World Radio, Cary, NC, 2012. To cover airtime costs of the Mandarin Seminary on the Air broadcasts and broadcasts to the Uyghurs.
$15,000 to Christian Research Institute, Charlotte, NC, 2012. For four specific initiatives to help make the Christian Research Journal more accessible.
$10,000 to Bowery Mission, New York, NY, 2012. For continued support of the Chapel ministry under the direction of Jason Storbakken, Chapel Director.
$10,000 to Cedarville University, Cedarville, OH, 2012. For faculty and staff leaders of short-term student missions teams.
$7,000 to National Foundation for Facial Reconstruction, New York, NY, 2012. For creation of a Parent Guide on Nutrition and Feeding for Parents of Children with Facial Difference.
$5,000 to Kids House of Seminole, Sanford, FL, 2012. For the Medically Neglected Children's Initiative and specifically the Medical Neglect Advocate Position and necessary equipment.

2020
Jack Chester Foundation ✧
333 S.E. 2nd Ave., Ste. 4400
Miami, FL 33131-2184 (305) 579-0503
Contact: Norman H. Lipoff, Chair.
FAX: (305) 961-5503; E-mail: lipoffn@gtlaw.com; Address for applications and grant-related inquiries: c/o SunTrust Bank Foundations & Endowments, 200 S. Orange Ave., S.O.A.B. 10, Orlando, FL 32801-3410; Main URL: http://jackchesterfoundation.org

Established in 2001 in FL.
Donor: Jack Chester†.
Foundation type: Independent foundation.
Financial data (yr. ended 12/31/13): Assets, $9,973,225 (M); expenditures, $746,966; qualifying distributions, $664,098; giving activities include $538,100 for 76 grants (high: $135,000; low: $1,000).
Purpose and activities: giving primarily for: 1) Jewish education (formal and informal) and Jewish identity, in Miami and Israel; 2) Social services for vulnerable segments of the Jewish communities of Miami and Israel (including people with disabilities and children at risk); 3) Israel Experience programs; 4) Higher education in Israel; 5) Holocaust education; 6) Israel education and Zionist initiatives; and 7) Health care in Israel or serving the Jewish community in Miami.
Fields of interest: Education, formal/general education; Higher education; Human services; Jewish federated giving programs; Jewish agencies & synagogues.
International interests: Israel.
Type of support: General/operating support; Annual campaigns; Capital campaigns; Scholarship funds.

Limitations: Applications accepted. Giving on a national and international basis, particularly in Miami, FL and Israel.
Publications: Application guidelines.
Application information: Application form required.
Initial approach: The foundation recommends the use of its online application procedure on its web site. Applications sent by U.S. mail are also accepted, and the grant proposal format for mailing is also located on the foundation's web site
Deadline(s): Dec. 31
Board meeting date(s): Feb.
Final notification: Mar.
Officer and Trustees:* Norman H. Lipoff,* Chair.; Jorge Lerman; Bernardo Pedro Szwarc.
EIN: 316660664

2021
Chia Family Foundation, Inc. ✧
7801 Blue Heron Way
West Palm Beach, FL 33412-3149

Established in 1996 in NY.
Donors: Pei-Yuan Chia; Frances T.C. Chia; Kitty S.H. Chia.
Foundation type: Independent foundation.
Financial data (yr. ended 03/31/13): Assets, $17,569,059 (M); gifts received, $286,551; expenditures, $1,104,119; qualifying distributions, $1,004,732; giving activities include $989,429 for 10 grants (high: $312,000; low: $1,500).
Purpose and activities: Giving primarily for higher education, and to Asian cultural organizations.
Fields of interest: Higher education; Human services; Asians/Pacific Islanders.
Limitations: Applications not accepted. Giving in the U.S., with some emphasis on NY and MA. No grants to individuals.
Application information: Contributes only to pre-selected organizations.
Directors: Candice Chia; Douglas K. Chia; Katherine Chia; Pei-Yuan Chia; Pei-Loh Lo; Katherine Shen.
EIN: 133904882
Selected grants: The following grants are a representative sample of this grantmaker's funding activity:
$311,100 to Tunghai University, Taichung, Taiwan, 2011.
$200,000 to Dartmouth College, Hanover, NH, 2011.
$137,055 to Yale-China Association, New Haven, CT, 2011.
$127,898 to Amherst College, Amherst, MA, 2011.
$75,000 to Half the Sky Foundation, Berkeley, CA, 2011.
$25,305 to Scholarship America, Minneapolis, MN, 2011.

2022
James H. Clark Charitable Foundation ✧
505 S. Flagler Dr., Ste. 900
West Palm Beach, FL 33401-5948

Established in 1999 in NV.
Donors: James H. Clark; James K. Clark; Monaco Partners, LP.
Foundation type: Independent foundation.
Financial data (yr. ended 03/31/13): Assets, $39,328,983 (M); expenditures, $2,391,964; qualifying distributions, $2,194,573; giving activities include $2,188,631 for 8 grants (high: $1,522,691; low: $7,400).
Fields of interest: Performing arts, music; Environment, water resources; Animals/wildlife; Youth, services.
Limitations: Applications not accepted. Giving primarily in CT, CO, Washington, DC, and NY. No grants to individuals.
Application information: Contributes only to pre-selected organizations.
Directors: James H. Clark; Louis M. Cohen; Thomas A. Jermoluk.
EIN: 943346273

2023
Clermont Charitable Trust ✧
P.O. Box 43250
Jacksonville, FL 32202-3250

Established in 1994 in MA.
Donor: Howard E. Cox, Jr.
Foundation type: Independent foundation.
Financial data (yr. ended 12/31/13): Assets, $3,900,572 (M); gifts received, $4,077,350; expenditures, $1,546,869; qualifying distributions, $1,439,250; giving activities include $1,438,200 for 87 grants (high: $200,000; low: $100).
Purpose and activities: Giving primarily for higher education, Christian churches, and the arts.
Fields of interest: Museums; Arts; Higher education; Hospitals (general); Cancer; Christian agencies & churches.
Limitations: Applications not accepted. Giving primarily in MA. No grants to individuals.
Application information: Contributes only to pre-selected organizations.
Trustee: Howard E. Cox.
EIN: 046772761
Selected grants: The following grants are a representative sample of this grantmaker's funding activity:
$275,000 to HBS Professional Services, Monsey, NY, 2010. For general support.
$250,000 to Harvard University, Cambridge, MA, 2010. For general support.
$200,000 to Dana-Farber Cancer Institute, Boston, MA, 2010. For general support.
$200,000 to Princeton University, Princeton, NJ, 2010. For general support.
$150,000 to Council on Foreign Relations, New York, NY, 2011.
$100,000 to Princeton University, Princeton, NJ, 2010. For general support.
$100,000 to Sears House Association, Boston, MA, 2010. For general support.
$50,000 to Aspen Institute, Washington, DC, 2011.
$50,000 to Business Executives for National Security, Washington, DC, 2011.
$15,000 to Council on Foreign Relations, New York, NY, 2011.
$10,000 to National Tropical Botanical Garden, Kalaheo, HI, 2011.
$5,000 to Population Council, New York, NY, 2011.
$3,000 to Aspen Institute, Washington, DC, 2011.
$2,500 to Aspen Institute, Washington, DC, 2011.
$1,500 to Aspen Institute, Washington, DC, 2011.

2024
The Cline Family Foundation, Inc. ✧
3801 PGA Blvd.
Palm Beach Gardens, FL 33410-2758 (561) 626-4999

Donor: Christopher Cline.
Foundation type: Independent foundation.
Financial data (yr. ended 12/31/12): Assets, $7,843,453 (M); gifts received, $7,000,000; expenditures, $2,214,941; qualifying distributions, $2,059,060; giving activities include $2,059,060 for grants.
Fields of interest: Higher education.
Limitations: Applications accepted. Giving primarily in WV; some funding nationally.
Application information: Application form not required.
Officer: Candice Cline Keenan, Exec. Dir.
EIN: 262866189

2025
CNL Charitable Foundation, Inc. ✧
P.O. Box 4920
Orlando, FL 32802-4920
Contact: Luder G. Whitlock, Jr.

Established in 2000 in FL.
Donor: CNL Financial Group, Inc.
Foundation type: Independent foundation.
Financial data (yr. ended 12/31/13): Assets, $459,849 (M); gifts received, $675,000; expenditures, $1,129,172; qualifying distributions, $1,127,061; giving activities include $1,125,950 for 16 grants (high: $425,000; low: $5,000).
Purpose and activities: Giving primarily for the arts, education, youth, and cancer research.
Fields of interest: Arts, association; Elementary/secondary education; Higher education; Education; Health care; Medical research, institute; Boy scouts; Christian agencies & churches.
Limitations: Giving primarily in central FL.
Application information: Application form required.
Initial approach: Letter
Deadline(s): None
Officers: James M. Seneff, Jr., Chair.; Robert A. Bourne, Vice-Chair.; Timothy J. Seneff, Pres.; Tracy G. Schmidt, Treas.
EIN: 593613312
Selected grants: The following grants are a representative sample of this grantmaker's funding activity:
$25,000 to American Enterprise Institute for Public Policy Research, Washington, DC, 2012. To support Their Programs- Social Science Research.
$10,000 to Frontline Outreach, Orlando, FL, 2012. To support Their Programs.
$5,000 to Lifework Leadership, Orlando, FL, 2012. To support and Enhance Lives of People with Disabilities.

2026
Cobb Family Foundation, Inc. ✧
P.O. Box 14-4200
Coral Gables, FL 33114-4200 (305) 441-1700

Established in 1984 in FL.
Donor: Charles E. Cobb, Jr.
Foundation type: Independent foundation.
Financial data (yr. ended 09/30/13): Assets, $21,712,186 (M); gifts received, $1,300,000;

expenditures, $889,758; qualifying distributions, $872,176; giving activities include $860,176 for 191 grants (high: $62,500; low: $25).
Purpose and activities: Support primarily for higher and other education, health organizations, human services, and community development, including a sports facility; funding also for a Protestant church.
Fields of interest: Higher education; Education; Health organizations, association; Human services; Community/economic development; Protestant agencies & churches.
Type of support: General/operating support.
Limitations: Applications accepted. Giving primarily in the Dade County, FL, area.
Application information: Application form required.
Initial approach: Letter
Deadline(s): None
Board meeting date(s): Aug.
Officers: Charles E. Cobb, Jr., Pres.; Christian M. Cobb, V.P.; Sue M. Cobb, V.P.; Tobin T. Cobb, V.P.
Directors: Kolleen O. Cobb; Luisa S. Cobb.
EIN: 592477459
Selected grants: The following grants are a representative sample of this grantmaker's funding activity:
$60,000 to University of Miami, Coral Gables, FL, 2011.
$25,000 to Eisenhower Exchange Fellowships, Philadelphia, PA, 2011.
$5,000 to That Man May See, San Francisco, CA, 2011.
$5,000 to University of Miami, Coral Gables, FL, 2011.
$3,000 to South Florida Golf Foundation, Miami, FL, 2011.
$2,500 to Alpha-1 Foundation, Miami, FL, 2011.
$2,000 to American-Scandinavian Foundation, New York, NY, 2011.
$2,000 to Chapman Partnership, Miami, FL, 2011.
$1,500 to American Heart Association, Miami, FL, 2011.
$1,000 to Coral Gables Museum, Coral Gables, FL, 2011.

2027
Cobb Foundation ✧
336 Coconut Palm Rd.
Boca Raton, FL 33432-7916 (561) 832-9292
Contact: Rhoda Cobb, Pres. and Dir.

Established in 1996 in FL.
Donor: Northern Trust Company.
Foundation type: Independent foundation.
Financial data (yr. ended 12/31/13): Assets, $18,342,614 (M); expenditures, $1,222,326; qualifying distributions, $856,039; giving activities include $795,000 for 30 grants (high: $167,500; low: $2,500).
Purpose and activities: Giving primarily for education, human services, and to cancer and other health organizations.
Fields of interest: Higher education; Education; Cancer; Health organizations; Human services.
Limitations: Applications accepted. Giving primarily in FL, KY and NC.
Application information: Telephone inquiries are not accepted. Application form required.
Initial approach: Letter
Deadline(s): None
Officer and Directors:* Rhoda W. Cobb,* Pres.; Bradley Cobb; Nancy Cox; Rhoda Juckett; Jennifer Little.
EIN: 650593216
Selected grants: The following grants are a representative sample of this grantmaker's funding activity:
$265,000 to Wake Forest University, Winston-Salem, NC, 2011. For general support.
$69,414 to Boca Helping Hands, Boca Raton, FL, 2011. For general support.
$50,000 to Salem College, Winston-Salem, NC, 2011. For general support.
$25,000 to Mission Healthcare Foundation, Asheville, NC, 2011. For general support.
$25,000 to Susan G. Komen for the Cure, Dallas, TX, 2011. For general support.
$20,000 to Myers Park Presbyterian Church, Charlotte, NC, 2011. For general support.
$15,000 to Chrysalis House, Lexington, KY, 2011. For general support.
$12,500 to Charlotte Latin School, Charlotte, NC, 2011. For general support.
$5,000 to Junior League of Charlotte, Charlotte, NC, 2011. For general support.
$5,000 to Leukemia & Lymphoma Society, Palm Beach Gardens, FL, 2011. For general support.

2028
John and Golda Cohen Trust ✧
P.O. Box 607772
Orlando, FL 32860-7772

Established in 2002 in FL.
Donor: The John S. Cohen Foundation.
Foundation type: Independent foundation.
Financial data (yr. ended 12/31/12): Assets, $10,601,984 (M); expenditures, $766,398; qualifying distributions, $548,000; giving activities include $548,000 for 74 grants (high: $71,500; low: $250).
Fields of interest: Media/communications; Education; Human services; Homeless, human services; Jewish agencies & synagogues.
Limitations: Applications not accepted. Giving primarily in FL and MA. No grants to individuals.
Application information: Contributes only to pre-selected organizations.
Trustees: Elizabeth Ann Cohen; Jenny Cohen; Richard S. Cohen; Jolyon Ellis Cowan.
EIN: 597222346

2029
The Colen Foundation, Inc. ✧
(formerly The On Top of the World Foundation, Inc.)
8447 S.W. 99th St.
Ocala, FL 34481-4547

Established in 1984 in FL.
Donors: Kenneth D. Colen; Sidney Colen†.
Foundation type: Independent foundation.
Financial data (yr. ended 11/30/13): Assets, $9,066,987 (M); expenditures, $558,467; qualifying distributions, $546,849; giving activities include $504,020 for 42 grants (high: $150,000; low: $1,000), $793 for 1 grant to an individual, and $3,492 for loans/program-related investments.
Purpose and activities: The foundation makes grants to qualified charities and provides assistance to the charitable class of the aged to enable members of the class to maintain a modest standard of living in their communities during their declining years.
Fields of interest: Museums (history); Performing arts, music; Elementary school/education; Higher education; Education; Horticulture/garden clubs; Developmentally disabled, centers & services; Jewish agencies & synagogues.
Type of support: General/operating support; Program-related investments/loans.
Limitations: Applications accepted. Giving primarily in FL.
Application information: Application form required.
Initial approach: Letter
Copies of proposal: 2
Deadline(s): None
Board meeting date(s): 2 times annually
Final notification: Up to 6 months
Officers and Directors:* Ina A. Colen,* Pres.; Kenneth D. Colen,* V.P.; Gerald R. Colen,* Secy.-Treas.; Barbara Ortiz, Compt.; Leslee R. Colen; Robert Colen.
Number of staff: None.
EIN: 592474711
Selected grants: The following grants are a representative sample of this grantmaker's funding activity:
$175,000 to Horticultural Arts and Park Institute, Ocala, FL, 2010.
$150,000 to Horticultural Arts and Park Institute, Ocala, FL, 2011.
$100,000 to Horticultural Arts and Park Institute, Ocala, FL, 2011.
$24,288 to Ruth Eckerd Hall, Clearwater, FL, 2010.
$20,000 to Hillel: The Foundation for Jewish Campus Life, Gainesville, FL, 2010.
$20,000 to New Israel Fund, New York, NY, 2011.
$10,000 to Community Foundation of Tampa Bay, Tampa, FL, 2011.
$10,000 to Florida Orchestra, Saint Petersburg, FL, 2011.
$10,000 to Perlman Music Program Suncoast, Sarasota, FL, 2011.
$5,000 to Diocese of Saint Augustine, Jacksonville, FL, 2011.
$2,500 to National Disaster Search Dog Foundation, Ojai, CA, 2011.
$1,000 to Canine Companions for Independence, Orlando, FL, 2011.
$1,000 to UPARC Foundation, Clearwater, FL, 2011.

2030
The Columbus Phipps Foundation ✧
P.O. Box 40200, FL9-100-10-19
Jacksonville, FL 32203-0200
Application address: c/o Paul D. Buchanan, Tr., P.O. Box 1145, Clintwood, VA 24228-1145

Established in 1993 in VA.
Donors: Beulah G. Phipps†; Carol Phipps Buchanan†.
Foundation type: Independent foundation.
Financial data (yr. ended 03/31/13): Assets, $17,544,856 (M); gifts received, $11,000; expenditures, $856,301; qualifying distributions, $748,305; giving activities include $662,572 for 62 grants (high: $198,250; low: $497).
Purpose and activities: Support for local cultural and educational activities, including scholarships to high school graduates of Dickenson County.
Fields of interest: Arts, multipurpose centers/programs; Performing arts; Higher education; Education.
Type of support: General/operating support; Building/renovation; Scholarships—to individuals.
Limitations: Applications accepted. Giving primarily in Dickenson County, VA.
Application information: Application form required.

Initial approach: Proposal
Deadline(s): May 15; June 15 for renewal applications

Trustees: Jerry Artrip; Dr. Jewell Askins; Paul D. Buchanan; Clarence Phillips; Michael A. Strough.
Advisory Committee: Betty Jo Dodson; Rita F. Justice; Rick Mullins.
Number of staff: 1 part-time professional.
EIN: 546338751

2031
The Community Foundation, Inc. ✧

(doing business as The Community Foundation of Northeast Florida, Inc.)
(also known as The Community Foundation in Jacksonville)
(formerly The Community Foundation in Jacksonville)
245 Riverside Ave., Ste. 310
Jacksonville, FL 32202 (904) 356-4483
FAX: (904) 356-7910; E-mail: info@jaxcf.org; Grant application e-mail: applications@jaxcf.org; Main URL: http://www.jaxcf.org
Facebook: http://www.facebook.com/cfjacksonville
Twitter: http://twitter.com/CFJacksonville
YouTube: http://www.youtube.com/user/TCFJacksonville

Established in 1964 in FL.
Foundation type: Community foundation.
Financial data (yr. ended 12/31/12): Assets, $257,249,260 (M); gifts received, $99,162,430; expenditures, $33,308,777; giving activities include $30,588,464 for 532+ grants (high: $6,092,644), and $58,888 for 47 grants to individuals.
Purpose and activities: The foundation's mission is to stimulate philanthropy to build a better community.
Fields of interest: Performing arts, theater; Arts; Children/youth, services; Aging, centers/services; Infants/toddlers; Children/youth; Aging.
Type of support: Endowments; Emergency funds; Program development; Seed money; Internship funds; Scholarship funds; Technical assistance; Consulting services; Program-related investments/loans; Grants to individuals; Matching/challenge support.
Limitations: Applications accepted. Giving primarily in northeastern FL, including Baker, Clay, Duval, Nassau and St. Johns counties. No support for religious programming. No grants for general operating support of existing programs, construction or renovation, equipment, or tickets for fundraising activities.
Publications: Application guidelines; Annual report; Informational brochure; Newsletter.
Application information: Visit foundation web site for preliminary application form and guidelines. If preliminary application is selected for further consideration, the foundation will provide a full grant application and related information to the organization's contact person (full applications are available only to organizations which are invited to apply based on preliminary applications). Application form required.
Initial approach: Submit preliminary application
Copies of proposal: 1
Deadline(s): Varies
Board meeting date(s): Mar., June, Sept., and Nov.
Final notification: Varies

Officers and Trustees:* Paul Perez,* Chair.; William D. Brinton,* Vice-Chair.; Nina M. Waters, Pres.; Grace Sacerdote, Exec. V.P. and C.F.O.; Joanne Cohen, V.P., Philanthropic Svcs.; Susan Datz Edelman, V.P., Strategic Comms.; Kathleen Shaw, V.P., Progs.; John Zell, V.P., Devel.; Yan Cumper, Cont.; Martha Baker; Peggy Bryan; Hon. Brian J. Davis; Michael DuBow; Cindy Edelman; Charles D. "Chuck" Hyman; Deborah S. Pass-Durham; Hon. Harvey E. Schlesinger; Ryan Schwartz; James Van Vleck; Dori Walton; Tracey Westbrook; Jim Winston.
Number of staff: 8 full-time professional; 4 full-time support.
EIN: 596150746
Selected grants: The following grants are a representative sample of this grantmaker's funding activity:
$6,092,644 to Delores Barr Weaver Policy Center, Jacksonville, FL, 2012.
$3,000,000 to Jacksonville Zoological Society, Jacksonville, FL, 2012.
$1,000,000 to Habitat for Humanity of Jacksonville, Jacksonville, FL, 2012.
$1,000,000 to Jacksonville Public Education Fund, Jacksonville, FL, 2012.
$750,000 to Cummer Museum of Art and Gardens, Jacksonville, FL, 2012.
$500,000 to Jacksonville Jewish Center, Jacksonville, FL, 2012.
$7,500 to Humane Society, Jacksonville, Jacksonville, FL, 2012.
$6,969 to Jacksonville University, Jacksonville, FL, 2012.
$5,000 to Jacksonville Symphony Association, Jacksonville, FL, 2012.
$5,000 to Seamark Ranch, Jacksonville, FL, 2012.

2032
Community Foundation for Palm Beach and Martin Counties, Inc. ✧

(formerly Palm Beach County Community Foundation)
700 S. Dixie Hwy., Ste. 200
West Palm Beach, FL 33401-5854 (561) 659-6800
FAX: (561) 832-6542; E-mail: info@cfpbmc.org; Additional tel.: (888) 853-4438; Grant application e-mail: grants@cfpbmc.org; Main URL: http://www.yourcommunityfoundation.org
Additional URL: http://www.cfpbmc.org
E-Newsletter: http://www.yourcommunityfoundation.org/email-signup
Facebook: http://www.facebook.com/cfpbmc
Flickr: http://www.flickr.com/photos/cfpbmc
Picture Philanthropy Blog: http://picturephilanthropy.wordpress.com/
Twitter: http://twitter.com/cfpbmc
YouTube: http://www.youtube.com/palmbeachmartincf

Incorporated in 1972 in FL.
Foundation type: Community foundation.
Financial data (yr. ended 06/30/14): Assets, $169,947,758 (M); gifts received, $5,199,017; expenditures, $11,761,421; giving activities include $8,801,662 for grants.
Purpose and activities: The foundation devotes its resources to building and sustaining vital, prosperous communities region wide through the power of charitable giving. The foundation fulfills this mission in three principal ways: 1) working in partnership with donors and other funders to achieve high-impact philanthropy; 2) making grants to effective nonprofit organizations and designing special funding initiatives to address this community's critical challenges; and 3) serving as a catalyst, convener, leader and center of community knowledge where ideas and data are shared, opportunities for positive change are identified, and common agendas for the future are developed in partnership with others.
Fields of interest: Historic preservation/historical societies; Arts; Education, early childhood education; Elementary school/education; Adult education—literacy, basic skills & GED; Education, reading; Education; Environment, natural resources; Environment; Health care; Health organizations, association; AIDS; Housing/shelter; Youth development, intergenerational programs; Children/youth, services; Human services; Civil rights, race/intergroup relations; Economic development; Community/economic development; Children/youth; Aging; Immigrants/refugees; Economically disadvantaged; Migrant workers.
Type of support: Management development/capacity building; Equipment; Program development; Conferences/seminars; Seed money; Scholarship funds; Research; Technical assistance; Consulting services; Program evaluation; Employee-related scholarships; Scholarships—to individuals; Matching/challenge support.
Limitations: Applications accepted. Giving primarily in Palm Beach and Martin counties, FL. No support for religious organizations for religious purposes. No grants to individuals (except for scholarships and the Dwight Allison Fellows Program), or for operating funds, building campaigns, computers, endowments, annual campaigns, fundraising events, fundraising feasibility studies, celebration functions, or deficit financing.
Publications: Application guidelines; Annual report (including application guidelines); Grants list; Informational brochure; Newsletter.
Application information: Visit foundation web site for Letter of Inquiry forms and guidelines. Faxed or e-mailed proposals are not accepted. Grant Seekers Orientations are offered periodically to introduce new grant seekers to the application process; visit web site for further information. Application form required.
Initial approach: Complete online organization profile
Copies of proposal: 1
Deadline(s): Varies
Board meeting date(s): Feb., Apr., May, Sept., Oct., and Dec.
Final notification: Within 3 months

Officers and Directors:* J.B. Murray,* Vice-Chair.; Lawrence J. Miller,* Vice-Chair.; Douglas A. Stockham,* Vice-Chair.; Bradley Hurlburt, C.E.O. and Pres.; Peter Matwiczyk,* Secy.; Danielle Blangy Cameron, V.P., Personal and Family Philanthropy; Gloria Ortega Rex, V.P., Finance and Admin.; Jillian C. Vukusich, V.P., Community Investment; Steven A. Templeton,* Treas.; Sue Sharra, Cont.; Anson Beard; Sherry S. Barrat; Ray S. Celedinas; Lore Moran Dodge; George T. Elmore; Kathleen B. Emmett; Paulette Koch; Hon. Kathleen J. Kroll; Andrew Kushner; Christina M. Macfarland; Elizabeth "Libby" Marshall; Lisa M. Morgan; David G. Ober; Deborah Dale Pucillo; Virginia Smith; Christopher W. Storkerson; Roy Zuckerberg.
Number of staff: 9 full-time professional; 5 full-time support.
EIN: 237181875

2033
Community Foundation of Brevard ✧
(formerly Community Foundation of Brevard County, Inc.)
1361 Bedford Dr., Ste. 102
Melbourne, FL 32940 (321) 752-5505
Contact: Sandi Scannelli, C.E.O.
E-mail: info@cfbrevard.org; Main URL: http://www.cfbrevard.org
Facebook: https://www.facebook.com/communityfoundationforbrevard
Scholarship submission e-mail: lisad@cfbrevard.org

Established as a community foundation in 1981 in FL.
Foundation type: Community foundation.
Financial data (yr. ended 12/31/13): Assets, $12,535,393 (M); gifts received, $207,010; expenditures, $1,613,383; giving activities include $1,243,082 for 24+ grants (high: $600,000).
Purpose and activities: The foundation seeks to provide a cost-effective bridge for all donors to the community's changing needs, serve as a leader, catalyst, and resource for philanthropy, produce an expanding pool of permanent endowment funds for now and all time, improve the quality of life with grants and technical assistance to local charities and partner with and be an advocate for the endowment of local charities.
Fields of interest: Arts; Education; Environment; Animal welfare; Health care; Food services; Housing/shelter; Recreation; Family services; Human services; Community/economic development; Youth; Aging.
Type of support: Program development; Management development/capacity building.
Limitations: Applications accepted. Giving limited to Brevard County, FL. No support for sectarian religious activities. No grants to individuals (except for scholarships), or for endowment campaigns, event sponsorships or advertising, debt retirement or budget deficits, sustaining operating support, or group trips.
Publications: Application guidelines; Grants list; Informational brochure.
Application information: Visit foundation web site for application Cover Page and guidelines. Application form required.
Initial approach: Create online profile
Copies of proposal: 6
Deadline(s): Feb. 14
Board meeting date(s): Monthly
Final notification: 90 days after deadline
Officers and Directors:* Brian Fisher,* Chair.; Ronald E. Bray,* Vice-Chair.; Sandi Scannelli,* C.E.O. and Pres.; Matthew Kucera,* Secy.; Michael S. Cerow,* Treas.; Dale Dettmer, Esq., Emeritus; William Harris, Emeritus; I. Wayne Cooper; Bill Fillmore; Juliana Kreul; Linda J. May; Gina H. Rall; Todd Russell; Erik Shuman, Esq.; Lynne Strynchuk; Bob Sukolsky; Kurt C. Weiss, Esq.; Mick Welch; Holly Woolsey.
Number of staff: 1 full-time professional.
EIN: 592114988

2034
Community Foundation of Broward ✧
(formerly Broward Community Foundation, Inc.)
910 E. Las Olas Blvd., Ste. 200
Fort Lauderdale, FL 33301 (954) 761-9503
Contact: Linda B. Carter, C.E.O.; For grant applications: Sheri Brown, V.P., Grants and Initiatives
FAX: (954) 761-7102;
E-mail: lcarter@cfbroward.org; Tel. for Sheri Brown: (954) 761-9503, ext. 103; Grant application E-mail: sbrown@cfbroward.org; Main URL: http://www.cfbroward.org

Incorporated in 1984 in FL.
Foundation type: Community foundation.
Financial data (yr. ended 06/30/13): Assets, $153,811,064 (M); gifts received, $48,637,190; expenditures, $7,884,540; giving activities include $5,235,331 for 302+ grants (high: $165,297; low: $111).
Purpose and activities: The foundation seeks to provide leadership on community solutions, and foster philanthropy that connects people who care with causes that matter.
Fields of interest: Arts; Education; Environment; Animal welfare; Health care; Cancer; Arthritis; AIDS; Children/youth, services; Children, foster care; Youth, services; Family services; Human services; Engineering/technology; Public affairs; Young adults.
Type of support: Management development/capacity building; Program development; Seed money; Research; Technical assistance; Scholarships—to individuals; Matching/challenge support.
Limitations: Applications accepted. Giving limited to Broward County, FL. No support for religious purposes. No grants to individuals (except for designated scholarship funds), or for capital campaigns, annual campaigns, fundraising events, building funds, deficit financing, endowment funds, or operating budgets; no loans.
Publications: Application guidelines; Annual report; Financial statement; Informational brochure (including application guidelines); Newsletter.
Application information: The foundation is currently refining new priority areas. Until these are finalized, the foundation is only accepting applications in response to RFPs and/or for posting online for fundholders' review. Updates will be posted online as this ongoing process develops. Application form required.
Board meeting date(s): Various, 6-7 times per year
Officers and Directors:* James B. Labate,* Chair.; Joan K. Crain,* Vice-Chair.; Linda B. Carter,* C.E.O. and Pres.; Thor Barraclough,* V.P., Mktg and Comm.; Sheri Brown,* V.P., Grants and Initiatives; William A. Snyder,* Secy.; Karen Mitchell Curran,* Treas.; Carol Dorko,* C.F.O.; Bill Linehan, Cont.; Bob Avian; Margarita T. Castellon; Louise F. Dill; Steven W. Hudson; Bacardi L. Jackson; Janet C. Jordan; Michael G. Landry; Jarret S. Levan; Alan Levy; Cori Flam Meltzer; Jim W. Monroe; Ramon A. Rodriguez; Tony Segreto; Kim Sweers.
Number of staff: 9 full-time professional.
EIN: 592477112

2035
Community Foundation of Collier County ✧
2400 Tamiami Trail N., Ste. 300
Naples, FL 34103-4435 (239) 649-5000
Contact: Eileen Connolly-Keesler, C.E.O.
FAX: (239) 649-5337;
E-mail: ekeesler@cfcollier.org; Main URL: http://www.cfcollier.org
Facebook: https://www.facebook.com/communityfoundationcolliercounty
Flickr: http://www.flickr.com/photos/communityfoundationcolliercounty
Google+: https://plus.google.com/105975789018047994123/posts
Twitter: https://twitter.com/CFCCFL
YouTube: http://www.youtube.com/cfcolliercounty
Scholarship inquiry e-mail: sbayata@cfcollier.org

Incorporated in 1983 in FL.
Foundation type: Community foundation.
Financial data (yr. ended 06/30/13): Assets, $64,157,718 (M); gifts received, $6,963,448; expenditures, $11,309,520; giving activities include $9,055,474 for 173+ grants (high: $1,200,521), and $236,150 for 114 grants to individuals.
Purpose and activities: The foundation provides donors with philanthropic knowledge and financial stewardship to strengthen the community.
Fields of interest: Arts, cultural/ethnic awareness; Arts; Education, early childhood education; Adult education—literacy, basic skills & GED; Education, services; Education; Environment, natural resources; Environment; Health care; Mental health/crisis services; Food services; Housing/shelter, homeless; Children/youth, services; Family services, domestic violence; Women, centers/services; Human services; Nonprofit management; Community/economic development; Philanthropy/voluntarism; Disabilities, people with.
Type of support: Building/renovation; Equipment; Emergency funds; Program development; Seed money; Internship funds; Scholarship funds; Technical assistance; Program evaluation; Matching/challenge support.
Limitations: Applications accepted. Giving limited to Collier County, FL. No support for religious purposes or private schools. No grants to individuals (except for scholarships), or for operating budgets, deficit financing, scholarly research, school-day activities, curriculum, and materials, annual campaigns, capital campaigns, conferences, or endowment funds.
Publications: Application guidelines; Annual report (including application guidelines); Newsletter.
Application information: Visit foundation web site for application form, guidelines, and specific deadlines. Application form required.
Initial approach: Register online with The Resource Guide to Collier Nonprofits
Deadline(s): Varies
Board meeting date(s): Monthly from Oct. to May
Final notification: Within 3 weeks
Officers and Trustees:* Dennis C. Brown,* Chair.; Eileen Connolly-Keesler,* C.E.O. and Pres.; Mary George, V.P., Community Grantmaking; Jennifer B. Walker,* Secy.; Lisette Holmes,* C.F.O.; William D. Lange,* Treas.; Mana Holtz, Emeritus; Thomas D. McCann, Emeritus; J. Richard Munro, Emeritus; Patricia Aiken-O'Neil; T. Robert Bulloch; Christine Flynn; John D. Fumagalli; Laird Grant Goody; Alan M. Horton; Patricia A. Jilk; Mary Beth Johns; Kathleen Kapnick; Kim Ciccarelli Kantor; Kathleen

Kircher; Suzanne Lount; Brian V. McAvoy; Marsha Murphy; Mary Lynn Myers; Deborah L. Russell; John F. Sorey III; Mario Valle; Harold L. Zink.
Number of staff: 5 full-time professional; 5 full-time support; 1 part-time support.
EIN: 592396243
Selected grants: The following grants are a representative sample of this grantmaker's funding activity:
$498,341 to Columbus Foundation, Columbus, OH, 2012. To establish Donor Advised Fund.
$458,537 to NARAL Pro-Choice America Foundation, Washington, DC, 2012. For unrestricted use.
$400,000 to ESF College Foundation, Syracuse, NY, 2012. To support Center For Native Peoples and unrestricted use.
$115,414 to Shelter for Abused Women of Collier County, Naples, FL, 2012. To support various programs to fulfill their charitable purpose.
$88,392 to Philharmonic Center for the Arts, Naples, FL, 2012. To support various programs to fulfill their charitable purpose.
$70,000 to United Way of Lee, Hendry and Glades, Fort Myers, FL, 2012. For unrestricted use.
$47,053 to Miami Childrens Hospital Foundation, Miami, FL, 2012. For unrestricted use.
$20,000 to Feminist Majority Foundation, Beverly Hills, CA, 2012. To support Campaign For Afghan Women And Girls.
$16,000 to Center for Family Connections, Cambridge, MA, 2012. For unrestricted use.
$10,000 to Kneads, a Fresh Vision for Special Education, Englewood, FL, 2012. To support Social Programs.

2036
Community Foundation of North Central Florida, Inc. ✧
(formerly Gainesville Community Foundation)
3919 W. Newberry Rd., Ste. 3
Gainesville, FL 32607 (352) 367-0060
FAX: (352) 378-1718; E-mail: office@gnvcf.org;
Main URL: http://www.gnvcf.org
Facebook: https://www.facebook.com/pages/Community-Foundation-of-North-Central-Florida/132775353446284
RSS Feed: http://cfncf.org/feed/

Established in 1998 in FL.
Foundation type: Community foundation.
Financial data (yr. ended 12/31/12): Assets, $11,276,761 (M); gifts received, $543,496; expenditures, $1,063,610; giving activities include $714,163 for 22+ grants (high: $200,000).
Purpose and activities: The foundation seeks to promote and sustain philanthropy among the communities of North Central Florida.
Fields of interest: Arts; Higher education; Libraries/library science; Education; Environment; Animal welfare; Hospitals (general); Health care; Substance abuse, prevention; Medical research; Housing/shelter; Athletics/sports, water sports; Recreation; Family services; Human services; Philanthropy/voluntarism; Religion; Children/youth; Aging; Women; Girls; Economically disadvantaged; Homeless.
International interests: Costa Rica.
Type of support: General/operating support; Program development; Scholarship funds.
Limitations: Giving limited to Gainesville and the surrounding areas in north central FL.
Publications: Application guidelines; Annual report; Financial statement.
Application information:
Board meeting date(s): 3rd Thurs of Jan., Mar. May, Sept. and Nov.
Officers and Directors:* Eric Godet,* Chair.; Mitch Gleaser,* Vice-Chair.; Barzella Papa,* C.E.O. and Pres.; Tony Kendzior,* Secy.; WJ Rossi,* Treas.; Mark Avera; Phil Emmer; Stan Given; Dink Henderson; Clark Hodge; Cathy Jenkins; Linda Kallman; Carrie Lee; Peter Maren; Wes Marston; Howard Patrick; Susannah Peddie; Mike Ryals; Melanie Shore; Ester Tibbs; Marilyn Tubb; Terry Van Nortwick; Richard White; and 6 additional Directors.
Number of staff: 1 full-time professional; 1 full-time support.
EIN: 593532330

2037
The Community Foundation of North Florida, Inc. ✧
1621 Metropolitan Blvd., Ste. A
Tallahassee, FL 32308-3792 (850) 222-2899
Contact: Joy R. Watkins, Pres.
FAX: (850) 222-3624; E-mail: info@cfnf.org;
Additional e-mail: jwatkins@cfnf.org; Main URL: http://www.cfnf.org/
: http://www.firstfd.com

Established in 1997 in FL.
Foundation type: Community foundation.
Financial data (yr. ended 12/31/13): Assets, $35,314,829 (M); gifts received, $7,666,335; expenditures, $2,879,606; giving activities include $2,328,178 for 32 grants (high: $1,100,000).
Purpose and activities: The foundation's primary purpose is to receive and raise charitable giving from third parties and to distribute property and extend financial aid and support through grants, gifts, and assistance to qualified charitable organizations.
Fields of interest: Arts; Education; Environment; Housing/shelter; Youth, services; Family services; Human services; Economic development; Community/economic development.
Limitations: Applications accepted. Giving limited to the North Florida counties of Franklin, Gadsden, Gulf, Jackson, Jefferson, Leon, Liberty, Madison, Taylor and Wakulla. No grants to individuals (except for scholarships).
Publications: Application guidelines; Annual report; Financial statement; Grants list; Informational brochure.
Application information: Visit foundation web site for application guidelines. Faxed or e-mailed proposals are not accepted. Application form not required.
Initial approach: Telephone or e-mail
Copies of proposal: 1
Board meeting date(s): 2nd Thurs. of Jan., Mar., May, July, Sept., and Nov.
Officers and Directors:* Everitt Drew,* Chair.; Joy R. Watkins, J.D.*, Pres. and C.E.O.; Rick Shapley,* Secy.-Treas.; Todd Abernethy,* C.F.O.; Carrol Dadisman, Emeritus; Louise Humphrey, Emeritus; Brooks Pettit, Emeritus; Mildred Dadisman; Kathy Dahl; Erin Ennis; Alex Hinson, Esq.; Winston Howell; Rob Langford; Julie Moreno; Martin Proctor; Katrina Rolle.
Number of staff: 2 full-time professional; 1 part-time support.
EIN: 593473384

2038
The Community Foundation of Sarasota County, Inc.
(formerly The Sarasota County Community Foundation, Inc.)
2635 Fruitville Rd.
Sarasota, FL 34237-5222 (941) 955-3000
Contact: For grants: Patricia Martin, Mgr., Grants and Community Initiatives
FAX: (941) 952-1951; E-mail: info@cfsarasota.org;
Email for grant inquiries: patricia@cfsarasopta.org;
Main URL: http://www.cfsarasota.org
E-Newsletter: https://www.cfsarasota.org/AboutUs/GoodNewsENewsletterSignup/tabid/510/Default.aspx
Facebook: http://www.facebook.com/pages/Sarasota-FL/Community-Foundation-of-Sarasota-County/74962141153
Google Plus: https://plus.google.com/+CfsarasotaOrg
LinkedIn: http://www.linkedin.com/company/community-foundation-of-sarasota-county
Twitter: https://twitter.com/#!/CFSarasota
YouTube: http://www.youtube.com/user/CFSC34237
Scholarship inquiries: tel. (941) 556-7114 or e-mail eyoung@cfsarasota.org

Incorporated in 1979 in FL.
Foundation type: Community foundation.
Financial data (yr. ended 05/31/13): Assets, $239,462,234 (M); gifts received, $36,098,583; expenditures, $20,627,031; giving activities include $15,831,757 for grants.
Purpose and activities: The foundation brings together citizens and organizations who care deeply about their community and who believe that people can act locally to improve quality of life. The foundation supports organizations involved with the arts, education, environment, animal protection, health care, human services, and community development.
Fields of interest: Humanities; Arts; Child development, education; Higher education; Education; Environment; Animals/wildlife; Health care; Mental health/crisis services; Health organizations, association; Youth development, centers/clubs; Children/youth, services; Family services; Residential/custodial care, hospices; Human services; Community/economic development; Youth; Aging; Disabilities, people with; Economically disadvantaged.
Type of support: Equipment; Emergency funds; Program development; Seed money; Scholarship funds; Scholarships—to individuals.
Limitations: Applications accepted. Giving primarily in Sarasota County, FL, and surrounding communities. No support for fraternal organizations, societies or orders, or religious organizations for sectarian purposes. No grants to individuals (except for selected scholarships), or for annual campaigns, building campaigns, endowment funds, deficit financing, debt retirement, publications, operating expenses, travel, fundraising events, scientific research, or conferences.
Publications: Application guidelines; Annual report; Grants list; Informational brochure; Newsletter; Occasional report; Program policy statement.
Application information: The foundation is currently not accepting competitive grant requests for EdExplore Exploration, Immediate Impact, discretionary or unrestricted grants. Visit the foundation's web site donor-advised grant

guidelines and scholarship information. Application form required.

Board meeting date(s): Jan., Mar., May, July, Sept., and Nov.

Officers and Directors:* Philip A. Delaney, Jr.,* Chair.; Orion Marx,* Vice-Chair.; Kathleen Roberts, Vice-Chair., Governance Committee; Roxanne Jerde, C.E.O. and Pres.; John Annis, V.P., Community Investment; Janet K. Ginn, Sr. V.P., Devel. and Donor Rels.; Laura Spencer, C.F.O.; Patricia Courtois,* Secy.; Vicente Medina,* Treas.; Erin Jones, Cont.; Audrey Coleman; Dr. Duncan Finlay; C.J. Fishman; Barbara Freeman; Richard Gans, Esq.; Victoria Leopold; Rodney Linford; Michael P. Martella; Jeffrey McCurdy; Vincente Medina; Austin Nadwondny; Michael R. Pender, Jr.; William M. Seider; Richard Smith; Terri Vitale.

Number of staff: 7 full-time professional; 1 part-time professional; 9 full-time support; 2 part-time support.

EIN: 591956886

Selected grants: The following grants are a representative sample of this grantmaker's funding activity:

$320,105 to Tidewell Hospice and Palliative Care, Sarasota, FL, 2012. For general support.

$283,227 to Catholic Charities Diocese of Venice, Venice, FL, 2012. For general support/various programs support.

$209,106 to Manatee Players, Bradenton, FL, 2012. For general support.

$117,339 to Planned Parenthood of Southwest and Central Florida, Sarasota, FL, 2012. For general support/various programs support.

$46,122 to Unidosnow Inc., Sarasota, FL, 2012. For general support/various programs support.

$26,000 to Beloit College, Beloit, WI, 2012. For general support/various programs support.

$25,218 to ArtCenter Manatee, Bradenton, FL, 2012. For general support.

$15,152 to University of Minnesota Foundation, Minneapolis, MN, 2012. For the Richard J McCauley Graduate Fellowship in Occupational Therapy Program.

2039
Community Foundation of South Lake County, Inc. ✧ ☆

(formerly South Lake County Community Foundation, Inc.)

2150 Oakley Seaver Dr.

Clermont, FL 34711-1964 (352) 394-3818

Contact: For grants: Jessica Whitehouse, Prog. Mgr.

FAX: (352) 394-7739;

E-mail: foundationinfo@cfslc.org; Additional e-mail: jessica@cfslc.org; Main URL: http://www.cfslc.org

Facebook: http://www.facebook.com/pages/Community-Foundation-of-South-Lake/186236661407797

YouTube: http://www.youtube.com/user/CFSLC?feature=watch

Established in 1995 in FL; converted from endowment resulting from the joint partnership between South Lake Hospital and Orlando Regional Healthcare System.

Foundation type: Community foundation.

Financial data (yr. ended 09/30/13): Assets, $10,742,875 (M); gifts received, $260,716; expenditures, $872,948; giving activities include $513,608 for grants.

Purpose and activities: The mission of the foundation is to provide leadership to enhance the quality of life in South Lake County by identifying community needs and seeking philanthropic support as permanent funding to meet those needs.

Fields of interest: Arts; Higher education; Education; Health care; Food services; Youth, services; Family services; Community/economic development, association; Community/economic development.

Type of support: General/operating support; Building/renovation; Equipment; Endowments; Program development; Conferences/seminars; Scholarship funds; Scholarships—to individuals; Matching/challenge support.

Limitations: Applications accepted. Giving primarily in South Lake County, FL. No support for lobbying, activism, litigation, or religious organizations for religious purposes. No grants to individuals (except for scholarships), or for endowments, capital campaigns, fundraising expenses, sponsorships, infrastructure improvements when the land/building is not owned by the organization, indirect costs or overhead expenses, or salaries.

Publications: Application guidelines; Annual report; Financial statement; Grants list; Informational brochure; Newsletter.

Application information: Visit foundation web site for application form and guidelines. Grants awards range from $1,000 to $10,000 with the average grant award of $3,000-$5,000. Application form required.

Initial approach: Telephone

Copies of proposal: 2

Deadline(s): Mar. 29

Board meeting date(s): Last Thurs. of every other month

Final notification: July 30

Officers and Directors:* Rocky DeStefano,* Pres.; Gary Clark,* V.P.; Anita Geraci-Carver,* Secy.; Paul Rountree,* Treas.; Bruce Greer, Exec. Dir.; Tom English; Ray Goodgame; Sally Hessburg; Wayne King; John Moore; Merideth Negal; Jeffery Rice; Timothee Sallin.

Number of staff: 1 full-time professional; 1 full-time support; 1 part-time support.

EIN: 593343026

2040
Community Foundation of Tampa Bay, Inc. ✧

(formerly The Community Foundation of Greater Tampa, Inc.)

550 N. Reo St., Ste. 301

Tampa, FL 33609-1037 (813) 282-1975

FAX: (813) 282-3119;

E-mail: ghardy@cftampabay.org; Grant application e-mail: grantapps@cftampabay.org; Main URL: http://www.cftampabay.org

E-Newsletter: http://visitor.constantcontact.com/manage/optin?v=001f-KEXzn5t02G39Ylz0y99dcwfMn_d0wW

Facebook: https://www.facebook.com/CFTampaBay

Grants List: http://www.cftampabay.org/about-us,community-impact-initiatives,recent-competitive-grants#.UtRRkdAw98E

Twitter: https://twitter.com/cftampabay

YouTube: http://www.youtube.com/cftampabay

Established in 1990 in FL.

Foundation type: Community foundation.

Financial data (yr. ended 06/30/13): Assets, $161,912,058 (M); gifts received, $8,613,620; expenditures, $10,409,753; giving activities include $8,272,869 for 241+ grants (high: $316,405), and $325,975 for 157 grants to individuals.

Purpose and activities: The mission of the foundation and its Board is to encourage the residents and nonprofits of the Tampa Bay area to take advantage of the foundation's flexibility in developing and implementing their charitable giving through programs that will make the Tampa Bay area a better place for all its citizens.

Fields of interest: Visual arts; Performing arts; Historic preservation/historical societies; Arts; Elementary school/education; Higher education; Education; Environment; Animals/wildlife; Health care; Medical research, institute; Housing/shelter, development; Children/youth, services; Family services; Aging, centers/services; Human services; Community development, neighborhood development; Community/economic development; Government/public administration; Public affairs; Aging; Homeless.

Type of support: Equipment; Emergency funds; Program development; Seed money; Curriculum development; Scholarship funds; Technical assistance; Consulting services; Matching/challenge support.

Limitations: Applications accepted. Giving generally limited to Hillsborough, Pasco, and Pinellas counties, FL. No support for religious or sectarian purposes. No grants to individuals (except for scholarships), or for funding of ongoing operating costs, capital campaigns or expenditures, medical research or tickets for any fundraising event, conference, or membership contributions.

Publications: Application guidelines; Annual report; Annual report (including application guidelines); Financial statement; Informational brochure; Newsletter.

Application information: Visit foundation web site for application form and guidelines. Application form required.

Initial approach: Submit letter of intent

Copies of proposal: 1

Deadline(s): None

Board meeting date(s): Jan., Mar., May, Sept., and Nov.

Officers and Trustees:* Gregory A. Rosica,* Chair.; Patricia L. Douglas,* Vice-Chair.; Marlene Spalten,* C.E.O. and Pres.; Beverley McLain, V.P., Philanthropic Svcs.; Robert H. Mohr,* Secy.; George Hardy, C.F.O. and V.P.; Donna L. Longhouse,* Treas.; Diana Baker; Anesta P. Boice; Phillip Casey; Betty Castor; Tony Coleman; Gail Eggeman; Wayne "Skipp" Fraser; Susanna F. Grady; Ben T. Guzzle; Linda Hanna; Linda Hartley; Alan D. Harvill; Gerald F. Hogan; George B. Howell III; Adam H. Palmer; Mary Ann Reilly; Richard Rios; Linda Saul-Sena; Geoffrey A. Simon; James Themides; Jennifer Williams; William Zewadski.

Number of staff: 4 full-time professional; 1 part-time professional; 3 full-time support; 1 part-time support.

EIN: 593001853

Selected grants: The following grants are a representative sample of this grantmaker's funding activity:

$1,000,000 to Police Athletic League of Tampa, Tampa, FL, 2012. To support mission.

$273,877 to Eckerd College, Saint Petersburg, FL, 2012. For project support.

$268,301 to Tampa Bay Performing Arts Center Foundation, Tampa, FL, 2012. For project support.

$117,850 to Christ the King Catholic Church, Tampa, FL, 2012. For project support.
$92,378 to Alpha House of Tampa, Tampa, FL, 2012. To support mission.
$84,335 to Saint Josephs Hospital of Tampa Foundation, Tampa, FL, 2012. For project support.
$30,000 to Powerstories Theater of Tampa Bay, Tampa, FL, 2012. To support mission.
$20,682 to Young Life, Colorado Springs, CO, 2012. To support mission.
$13,500 to Community Action Stops Abuse, Saint Petersburg, FL, 2012. To support mission.
$12,500 to Gibsonton Elementary School, Gibsonton, FL, 2012. For project support.

2041
Community Foundation of the Florida Keys, Inc. ✧

300 Southard St., Ste. 201
Key West, FL 33040 (305) 292-1502
Contact: Dianna Sutton, C.E.O.
FAX: (305) 292-1598; E-mail: cffk@cffk.org; Main URL: http://www.cffk.org
Facebook: https://www.facebook.com/cffkkw
Twitter: https://twitter.com/cffkflakeys

Established in 1996 in FL.
Foundation type: Community foundation.
Financial data (yr. ended 12/31/13): Assets, $10,207,880 (M); gifts received, $2,066,946; expenditures, $1,772,707; giving activities include $838,267 for 17+ grants (high: $230,000), and $162,931 for grants to individuals.
Purpose and activities: The foundation seeks to help support quality of life in the community by providing a way for donors to give financial support to charitable organizations that meet the community's varied needs.
Fields of interest: Historic preservation/historical societies; Arts; Education; Environment; Health care; Recreation; Human services; Public affairs.
Type of support: Equipment; General/operating support; Continuing support; Management development/capacity building; Annual campaigns; Capital campaigns; Building/renovation; Emergency funds; Program development; Conferences/seminars; Curriculum development; Scholarship funds; Scholarships—to individuals; Matching/challenge support.
Limitations: Applications not accepted. Giving primarily in Monroe County, FL. No support for religious purposes.
Publications: Financial statement; Grants list; Informational brochure; Newsletter; Occasional report.
Application information: The foundation does not accept unsolicited applications.
Board meeting date(s): 3rd Tues. monthly
Officers and Board Members:* Robert Spottswood,* Chair.; Brian Wruble,* Vice-Chair.; Todd German,* Vice-Chair., Devel.; Roger Heinen,* Vice-Chair., Mktg.; W. Ann Reynolds, Vice-Chair., Grants; Karen Sharp, Vice-Chair., Finance and Treas.; Dianna Sutton, C.E.O. and Pres.; Susanne Woods,* Secy.; Susan Cardenas; Bobby Highsmith; Michael Ingram; Rita A. Linder; Doug Mayberry; Sandra McMannis; Greg Oropeza; William Porter; Allan Wimer.
Number of staff: 1 full-time professional; 1 full-time support.
EIN: 650648968

Selected grants: The following grants are a representative sample of this grantmaker's funding activity:
$5,000 to Florida Keys Educational Foundation, Key West, FL, 2012. For scholarships.
$3,000 to Key West Film Society, Key West, FL, 2012. For general operating support.
$2,500 to Equality Florida, Saint Petersburg, FL, 2012. For general operating support.
$2,000 to Key West Literary Seminar, Key West, FL, 2012. For general operating support.
$2,000 to Star of the Sea Foundation, Key West, FL, 2012. For general operating support.
$1,500 to Studios of Key West, Key West, FL, 2012. For general operating support.
$1,000 to Boys and Girls Clubs of the Keys Area, Key West, FL, 2012. For general operating support.
$600 to Women in Military Service for America Memorial Foundation, Arlington, VA, 2012. For memorial.
$500 to Community Television Foundation of South Florida, North Miami, FL, 2012. For general operating support.
$500 to Monroe Council of the Arts, Key West, FL, 2012. For Artists in Schools Initiative.

2042
Conn Memorial Foundation ✧

3410 Henderson Blvd., Ste. 200
Tampa, FL 33609-3975 (813) 554-1210
Contact: Beth Doyle, Grant Dir.
tel./fax: (813) 554-1210;
e-mail: Beth@connfoundation.org; Main URL: http://www.connfoundation.org

Incorporated in 1954 in FL.
Donors: Fred K. Conn‡; Edith F. Conn‡.
Foundation type: Independent foundation.
Financial data (yr. ended 07/31/13): Assets, $22,982,249 (M); expenditures, $1,495,902; qualifying distributions, $1,275,207; giving activities include $1,024,000 for 50 grants (high: $75,000; low: $1,000).
Purpose and activities: Giving primarily for programs that support at-risk children and families in Hillsborough County, Florida; funding also for inner-city youth outreach, college scholarships, and capacity grants.
Fields of interest: Education; Human services; Family services; Children; Economically disadvantaged.
Type of support: General/operating support; Continuing support; Management development/capacity building; Capital campaigns; Building/renovation; Equipment; Emergency funds; Program development; Conferences/seminars; Seed money; Scholarship funds; Technical assistance; Consulting services; Program evaluation; Matching/challenge support.
Limitations: Applications accepted. Giving limited to Hillsborough County, FL. No grants for individual scholarships, no loans.
Publications: Application guidelines; Informational brochure (including application guidelines); Multi-year report.
Application information: Applications are by invitation only upon review of letter of intent. Application form required.
Initial approach: 1-page letter of intent using form on foundation web site
Copies of proposal: 1
Deadline(s): Jan. 1 (for spring cycle), and June 1 (for fall cycle)
Board meeting date(s): Monthly
Final notification: Following board meetings
Officers: Ron Peterson, Chair.; Dr. Mario Hernandez, Vice-Chair.; Sheff Crowder, Pres.; Sonja Garcia, Secy.; Peter J. Gardner, Treas.
Directors: Nuri Delacruz Ayres; Dave Kennedy; Scott Pieper.
Number of staff: 2 part-time professional; 1 part-time support.
EIN: 590978713
Selected grants: The following grants are a representative sample of this grantmaker's funding activity:
$45,000 to Academy Prep Foundation, Saint Petersburg, FL, 2011.

2043
The Connors Foundation, Inc. ✧ ☆

102 Banyan Rd.
Palm Beach, FL 33480

Established in 1999 in DE.
Donors: Michael M. Connors; Julia B. Connors.
Foundation type: Independent foundation.
Financial data (yr. ended 12/31/13): Assets, $13,324,267 (M); gifts received, $10,150; expenditures, $482,777; qualifying distributions, $475,402; giving activities include $468,771 for 38 grants (high: $59,669; low: $350).
Purpose and activities: Giving primarily for the fine and performing arts.
Fields of interest: Museums (art); Performing arts; Hospitals (general); Human services.
Limitations: Applications not accepted. Giving primarily in Washington, DC. No grants to individuals.
Application information: Contributes only to pre-selected organizations.
Board meeting date(s): 4 times per year
Officers: Michael M. Connors, Pres.; Julia B. Connors, V.P.
Directors: Gregory Connors; Patrick E. Connors; Kathleen C. Mueller.
EIN: 522204597

2044
The Copham Family Foundation ✧

c/o Karen Gill, Capital Wealth Advisors
787 5th Ave. S.
Naples, FL 34102-6603

Established in 2007 in FL.
Donors: Cheryl K. Copham; David L. Copham; Copham LP.
Foundation type: Independent foundation.
Financial data (yr. ended 12/31/13): Assets, $220,038 (M); gifts received, $700,000; expenditures, $719,981; qualifying distributions, $716,965; giving activities include $714,740 for 25 grants (high: $200,000; low: $4,000).
Fields of interest: Higher education; Health organizations; Food services; Housing/shelter; Athletics/sports, baseball; Salvation Army; Youth, services; Human services, emergency aid.
Type of support: Equipment.
Limitations: Applications not accepted. Giving primarily in FL, MN and PA. No grants to individuals.
Application information: Contributes only to pre-selected organizations.

Officers: Cheryl K. Copham, Mgr.; David L. Copham, Mgr.
EIN: 656466097
Selected grants: The following grants are a representative sample of this grantmaker's funding activity:
$200,000 to Lee Memorial Health System Foundation, Fort Myers, FL, 2012. For Help Meet Health Care Needs of Southwest Florida.
$50,000 to Mayo Foundation, Rochester, MN, 2012. To provide Health Care, Medical Education and Research.
$37,500 to Pitch in for Baseball, Harleysville, PA, 2012. To provide Baseball Equipment for the Needy.
$30,000 to Edison State College Foundation, Fort Myers, FL, 2012. To support College's Academic and Instructional Departments.
$5,000 to Central Park Conservancy, New York, NY, 2012. To restore and Enhance Central Park for Present and Future Generations.
$5,000 to Mohonk Preserve, New Paltz, NY, 2012. To manage and Preserve Land in the Shawangunk Mountains.
$2,500 to Veterans of Foreign Wars Foundation, Kansas City, MO, 2012. To improve Lives of Veterans and Service Personnel.
$2,500 to YMCA of Lee County, Fort Myers, FL, 2012. To provide Programs That Build Health Spirit, Mind and Body.

2045
The Corbett Family Charitable Foundation Inc. ✧
509 Guisandro de Avila Dr., Ste. 201
Tampa, FL 33613

Established in 1999 in FL.
Donors: Richard A. Corbett; Cornelia Gerry Corbett; Rothman Foundation.
Foundation type: Independent foundation.
Financial data (yr. ended 12/31/13): Assets, $12,137,989 (M); gifts received, $508,703; expenditures, $1,180,560; qualifying distributions, $1,169,195; giving activities include $1,169,195 for 20 grants (high: $304,195; low: $5,000).
Fields of interest: Elementary school/education; Environment; Animal welfare; Children, services.
Limitations: Applications not accepted. Giving primarily in CA, FL and MA. No grants to individuals.
Application information: Contributes only to pre-selected organizations.
Officer: Richard A. Corbett, Mgr.
EIN: 593548652

2046
The Joseph and Robert Cornell Memorial Foundation ✧
550 S.E. Mizner Blvd.
Boca Raton, FL 33432-6078

Donor: Joseph Cornell†.
Foundation type: Independent foundation.
Financial data (yr. ended 12/31/13): Assets, $81,265,521 (M); expenditures, $2,515,161; qualifying distributions, $2,181,940; giving activities include $1,935,000 for 13 grants (high: $350,000; low: $10,000).
Purpose and activities: Giving primarily for a hospital and higher education.
Fields of interest: Historic preservation/historical societies; Higher education; Hospitals (general).
Type of support: Program development.
Limitations: Applications not accepted. Giving on national basis, with some emphasis on Washington, DC, MD, and VA. No grants to individuals.
Application information: Contributes only to pre-selected organizations.
Trustees: Richard M. Ader; Joseph Erdman.
EIN: 133097502
Selected grants: The following grants are a representative sample of this grantmaker's funding activity:
$300,000 to Martha Jefferson Hospital Foundation, Charlottesville, VA, 2012. For grant for Donee's Exempt Purpose.

2047
Wallace H. Coulter Foundation ✧
790 N.W. 107th Ave., Ste. 215
Miami, FL 33172-3158 (305) 559-2991
Contact: Wayne A. Barlin, V.P. and Genl. Counsel
FAX: (305) 559-5490; Main URL: http://www.whcf.org
Grants List: http://www.whcf.org/coulter-translational-research-award-recipients

Established in 2000 in DE and FL.
Donors: Wallace H. Coulter Charitable Remainder Unitrust; Wallace H. Coulter Trust.
Foundation type: Independent foundation.
Financial data (yr. ended 09/30/13): Assets, $244,057,784 (M); expenditures, $34,465,086; qualifying distributions, $32,012,323; giving activities include $26,431,062 for 65 grants, $133,000 for 23 employee matching gifts, and $27,540 for 1 loan/program-related investment.
Purpose and activities: The foundation is dedicated to improving human health care by supporting translational research in biomedical engineering-research directed at the transfer of promising technologies within the university research laboratory that are progressing towards commercial development and clinical practice.
Fields of interest: Health care; Biomedicine; Medical research, institute; United Ways and Federated Giving Programs; Science.
Type of support: Research.
Limitations: Applications accepted. Giving primarily in FL, GA, MO and NY. No support for religious organizations. No grants to individuals.
Application information: See foundation web site for more application information. Application forms are available on the foundation web site. Application form required.
Initial approach: Preliminary application
Officers: Sue Van, C.E.O. and Pres.; Susan Racher, V.P. and C.F.O.; Wayne A. Barlin, V.P. and Genl. Counsel; Elias Caro, V.P., Tech. Devel.; Greg Thornton, Cont.
EIN: 311546126
Selected grants: The following grants are a representative sample of this grantmaker's funding activity:
$7,625,000 to Case Western Reserve University, Cleveland, OH, 2012. For endowment directed at supporting technologies within the university research laboratory that are progressing toward clinical practice.
$1,000,000 to Asian Americans Advancing Justice, Washington, DC, 2012. To support a broad agenda including capacity building and civic engagement.
$1,000,000 to Asian Americans Advancing Justice, Washington, DC, 2012. To support a broad agenda including capacity building and civic engagement.
$1,000,000 to Asian Americans Advancing Justice - Los Angeles, Los Angeles, CA, 2012. To support a broad agenda including capacity building and civic engagement.
$867,000 to Columbia University, New York, NY, 2012. To enhance and support research directed at promising technologies within the University research laboratory that are progressing toward clinical practice.
$750,000 to Asian Pacific Fund, San Francisco, CA, 2012. For re-grant to Asian American community-based organizations in the greater San Francisco Bay area.
$667,000 to University of Pittsburgh, Pittsburgh, PA, 2012. To enhance and support research directed at promising technologies within the University research laboratory that are progressing toward clinical practice.
$666,600 to University of Louisville Research Foundation, Louisville, KY, 2012. To enhance and support research directed at promising technologies within the University research laboratory that are progressing toward clinical practice.
$600,000 to Asian American Federation of New York, New York, NY, 2012. For demographic profiles, National Issue Reports and capacity building for community-based organizations in the New York area.
$229,930 to European Hematology Association, The Hague, Netherlands, 2012. To plan and conduct annual course in medical translational research in hematology and oncology.

2048
Wallace H. Coulter Trust ✧
790 N.W. 107th Ave., Ste. 215
Miami, FL 33172-3158 (305) 559-2991
Contact: Wayne A. Barlin, Genl. Counsel

Established in 1999 in FL.
Donors: Wallace H. Coulter; Wallace H. Coulter Irrevocable Trust.
Foundation type: Independent foundation.
Financial data (yr. ended 09/30/13): Assets, $53,335,721 (M); expenditures, $4,725,432; qualifying distributions, $3,881,146; giving activities include $3,795,000 for 12 grants (high: $500,000; low: $100,000).
Fields of interest: Higher education; Medical school/education; Medical research; Foundations (private grantmaking).
Limitations: Applications not accepted. Giving primarily in CA, FL, IL, and DC. No support for religious organizations. No grants to individuals.
Application information: Contributes to pre-selected organizations.
Officers: Susan Racher, C.F.O. and V.P.; Wayne Barlin, V.P. and Genl. Counsel.
Trustee: Sue Van.
EIN: 656310670
Selected grants: The following grants are a representative sample of this grantmaker's funding activity:
$1,000,000 to Shanghai Jiao Tong University Foundation of America, Tustin, CA, 2011. For matching grant and fundraising campaigns.
$600,000 to Asian American Federation of New York, New York, NY, 2011. For National Issue Reports and capacity building for community organizations in New York area.
$500,000 to American Nicaraguan Foundation, Miami, FL, 2011. For humanitarian relief to improve education and healthcare in Nicaragua.

$500,000 to Asian Americans Advancing Justice - Chicago, Chicago, IL, 2011. For capacity building and civic engagement.
$500,000 to Asian Law Caucus, San Francisco, CA, 2011. For capacity building and civic engagment.
$500,000 to Georgia Tech Foundation, Atlanta, GA, 2011. For GA Tech/Emory joint venture with Peking University.
$400,000 to University of Miami, Miami, FL, 2011. For Wallace H. Coulter Research Fund for translational research in blood platelet induced disorders presenting in vascular and neurological dysfunction.
$200,000 to Florida Institute of Certified Public Accountants Educational Foundation, Tallahassee, FL, 2011. For matching grant for minority summer residency program and scholarships for underrepresented high school students interested in becoming CPAs and for scholarships for African-American students majoring in accounting.
$150,000 to American Nicaraguan Foundation, Miami, FL, 2011. For humanitarian relief to improve education and healthcare in Nicaragua.
$150,000 to Biomedical Engineering Career Alliance, Phoenix, AZ, 2011. For annual regional conference and fundraising.

2049
The Joanne & John Dallepezze Foundation ✧

81 Seagate Dr., Apt. 1701
Naples, FL 34103-2486

Established in 2000 in FL.
Donors: Joanne M. Dallepezze; John R. Dallepezze.
Foundation type: Independent foundation.
Financial data (yr. ended 12/31/13): Assets, $4,028,501 (M); expenditures, $615,135; qualifying distributions, $607,634; giving activities include $603,455 for 31 grants (high: $250,000; low: $1,000).
Fields of interest: Education; Environment, natural resources; Health organizations; Human services; Family services, domestic violence; Residential/custodial care, hospices; United Ways and Federated Giving Programs; Protestant agencies & churches.
Type of support: General/operating support.
Limitations: Applications not accepted. Giving primarily in FL and NY. No grants to individuals.
Application information: Unsolicited requests for funds not accepted.
Officer: John R. Dallepezze, Pres. and Secy.-Treas.
Directors: Georgia D. Dallepezze; Peter A. Dallepezze.
EIN: 593650218
Selected grants: The following grants are a representative sample of this grantmaker's funding activity:
$10,000 to American Red Cross, Fort Myers, FL, 2012. For Health, Human Services and Public Welfare Program.
$10,000 to Princeton University, Princeton, NJ, 2012. For higher education programs.
$10,000 to United Way of Collier County, Naples, FL, 2012. For Health Human Services and Public Welfare Program.
$5,000 to Guadalupe Center, Immokalee, FL, 2012. For Human Services and Education.
$5,000 to Prep for Prep, New York, NY, 2012. For Human Service and Welfare Programs.
$4,630 to Houston Zoo, Houston, TX, 2012. For Human Services and Education Programs.
$1,000 to Columbus Museum of Art, Columbus, OH, 2012. For Public Art Programs.

2050
Danial Family Foundation, Inc. ✧ ☆

5151 Collins Ave., Ste. 1727
Miami Beach, FL 33140-2717 (305) 867-8484
Contact: Robert Danial, Pres.

Established in 2000 in FL.
Donors: Robert Danial; Mojdeh Khaghan; Ariel Holdings, LLC; Ariel Funding, LLC; KPK Holdings, LLC; Eleanor Cohen; Menachem Cohen.
Foundation type: Independent foundation.
Financial data (yr. ended 12/31/13): Assets, $1,900,762 (M); gifts received, $569,525; expenditures, $566,212; qualifying distributions, $563,007; giving activities include $561,756 for 38 grants (high: $366,440; low: $65).
Fields of interest: Education; Human services; Jewish agencies & synagogues.
Application information: Application form required.
Initial approach: Proposal
Deadline(s): None
Officers: Robert Danial, Pres.; Mojdeh Khaghan, Secy.; Terrence Danial, Treas.
EIN: 651062781

2051
Darden Restaurants, Inc. Foundation ✧

P.O. Box 695011
Orlando, FL 32869-5011 (407) 245-5366
FAX: (407) 245-4462;
E-mail: communityaffairs@darden.com; Additional address: 1000 Darden Center Dr., Orlando, FL 32837; e-mail: dardeninthecommunity@darden.com; Main URL: http://www.dardenfoundation.com/cms/index.php
Darden Digest Blog: http://www.darden.com/sustainability/default.aspx?lang=en&page=sustainability§ion=blog
Facebook: https://www.facebook.com/DardenCitizen
Twitter: https://twitter.com/DardenCitizen
YouTube: http://www.youtube.com/DardenTV

Established in 1995 in FL.
Donor: Darden Restaurants, Inc.
Foundation type: Company-sponsored foundation.
Financial data (yr. ended 06/26/13): Assets, $277,076 (M); gifts received, $5,842,661; expenditures, $6,478,006; qualifying distributions, $6,478,006; giving activities include $6,478,006 for 648 grants (high: $700,000; low: $100).
Purpose and activities: The foundation supports organizations involved with arts and culture, education, the environment, animal welfare, hunger, and human services.
Fields of interest: Arts; Middle schools/education; Secondary school/education; Higher education; Education, services; Education; Environment, natural resources; Environment, water resources; Environment, land resources; Environmental education; Environment; Animal welfare; Food services; Food banks; Recreation, parks/playgrounds; Boys & girls clubs; American Red Cross; Children/youth, services; Human services; United Ways and Federated Giving Programs.
Type of support: General/operating support; Program development; Conferences/seminars; Scholarship funds; Employee volunteer services; Employee matching gifts; In-kind gifts; Matching/challenge support.
Limitations: Applications accepted. Giving primarily in areas of company operations, with some emphasis on central FL; giving also to national organizations. No support for discriminatory organizations, religious organizations not of direct benefit to the entire community, or political, lobbying, anti-business, international, or disease-specific organizations, fraternities, or sororities. No grants to individuals, or for event sponsorships, health-related funding, national conferences, capital campaigns, travel, athletic team sponsorships or scholarships, fundraising, galas, benefits, dinners, or sporting events, goodwill advertising, souvenir journals, or dinner programs.
Publications: Application guidelines; Corporate giving report.
Application information: National or regional grants are by invitation only. Organizations receiving support of $5,000 or more are asked to submit a grant report. Application form required.
Initial approach: Complete online application form
Copies of proposal: 1
Deadline(s): Nov. 15 to Dec. 10
Board meeting date(s): Feb., May, Sept., and Nov.
Final notification: March
Officers and Trustees:* Clarence Otis, Jr.,* Chair. and Pres.; Robert S. McAdam,* V.P.; Teresa Sebastian,* Secy.; Bradford C. Richmond, Treas.; Laurie Burns; Mary Darden; Tom Gathers; Valerie L. Insignares.
Number of staff: 1 full-time professional.
EIN: 593332929
Selected grants: The following grants are a representative sample of this grantmaker's funding activity:
$693,000 to College Summit, Washington, DC, 2012. For Recipe for Success.
$544,267 to Boys and Girls Clubs of America, Atlanta, GA, 2012. For Recipe for Success.
$500,000 to Dr. Phillips Center for the Performing Arts, Orlando, FL, 2012. For Good Neighbor.
$359,948 to United Way, Heart of Florida, Orlando, FL, 2012. For Good Neighbor.
$349,000 to Feeding America, Chicago, IL, 2012. For Restaurant Community Grants Program.
$231,504 to National Recreation and Park Association, Ashburn, VA, 2012. For Sustainability.
$207,206 to American Red Cross National Headquarters, Washington, DC, 2012. For Good Neighbor.
$50,000 to Orlando Philharmonic Orchestra, Orlando, FL, 2012. For Good Neighbor.
$10,000 to University of Michigan, Ann Arbor, MI, 2012. For Education.
$4,000 to Big Brothers Big Sisters of El Paso, El Paso, TX, 2012. For Restaurant Community Grants Program.

2052
Isaac Davenport Trust ✧

P.O. Box 40200, FL9-100-10-19
Jacksonville, FL 32203-0200

Donor: Isaac Davenport Annuity Trust.
Foundation type: Independent foundation.
Financial data (yr. ended 12/31/13): Assets, $26,381,578 (M); gifts received, $5,000; expenditures, $1,582,737; qualifying distributions, $1,454,079; giving activities include $1,388,598 for 5 grants (high: $721,934; low: $166,666).

Fields of interest: Health care; Community/economic development.
Limitations: Applications not accepted.
Application information: Unsolicited requests for funds not accepted.
Trustee: Bank of America, N.A.
EIN: 546034453

2053
The Marvin H. Davidson Foundation, Inc. ✧
220 Sunrise Ave., Ste. 218
Palm Beach, FL 33480-3803

Established in 1967 in NY.
Donors: Marvin H. Davidson; Scott Davidson; Davidson Kempner Advisors, Inc.
Foundation type: Independent foundation.
Financial data (yr. ended 12/31/12): Assets, $21,342,859 (M); gifts received, $550,000; expenditures, $1,064,302; qualifying distributions, $1,019,394; giving activities include $1,015,694 for 70 grants (high: $100,000; low: $430).
Purpose and activities: Giving primarily for the arts, education, health organizations, and social services.
Fields of interest: Arts; Medical research; Recreation.
Limitations: Applications not accepted. Giving primarily in NY; funding also in FL. No grants to individuals.
Application information: Contributes only to pre-selected organizations.
Officers and Directors:* Marvin H. Davidson,* Pres. and Treas.; Scott Davidson,* V.P. and Secy.; Mary McDonnell Davidson; Robert Friedman.
EIN: 136217756

2054
Tine W. Davis Family - W.D. Charities, Inc. ✧
1910 San Marco Blvd.
Jacksonville, FL 32207-3204 (904) 398-3986
Contact: T. Wayne Davis, Pres. and Secy.-Treas.

Incorporated in 1950 in FL.
Donor: Tine W. Davis.
Foundation type: Independent foundation.
Financial data (yr. ended 12/31/13): Assets, $10,638,125 (M); expenditures, $2,421,046; qualifying distributions, $1,111,039; giving activities include $585,171 for 37 grants (high: $100,000; low: $1).
Purpose and activities: Giving primarily for children's services; funding also for education, health organizations and human services.
Fields of interest: Higher education; Health care; Health organizations; Human services; Children/youth, services.
Limitations: Applications accepted. Giving limited to the southeastern U.S., with emphasis on FL. No grants to individuals.
Publications: Application guidelines.
Application information: Application form required.
Initial approach: Request application form
Copies of proposal: 1
Deadline(s): Apr. and Oct.
Board meeting date(s): 2nd Tues. in Apr.
Officer: T. Wayne Davis, Pres. and Secy.-Treas.
Directors: Margaret M. Riley; Paul K. Saffell.
Number of staff: 3
EIN: 590995388
Selected grants: The following grants are a representative sample of this grantmaker's funding activity:
$15,000 to Ducks Unlimited, Memphis, TN, 2011.
$10,000 to American Heart Association, Dallas, TX, 2011.
$5,000 to American Cancer Society, Atlanta, GA, 2011.

2055
M. Austin Davis Foundation Inc. ✧
(formerly Austin Davis Family - W.D. Charities, Inc.)
4310 Pablo Oaks Ct.
Jacksonville, FL 32224-9631

Incorporated in 1950 in FL.
Donor: Milton Austin Davis.
Foundation type: Independent foundation.
Financial data (yr. ended 12/31/13): Assets, $15,566,534 (M); expenditures, $907,665; qualifying distributions, $831,164; giving activities include $764,168 for 54 grants (high: $60,000; low: $1,000).
Fields of interest: Elementary/secondary education; Higher education; Health care; Human services; Children/youth, services.
Type of support: General/operating support.
Limitations: Applications not accepted. Giving primarily in the southeastern U.S. No grants to individuals.
Application information: Contributes only to pre-selected organizations.
Officers: Charles P. Stephens, Pres.; C. Austin Stephens, V.P. and Treas.; H.D. Francis, V.P.; Scott A. Oko, V.P.; Sandra D. Stephens, V.P.; Scott R. Stephens, V.P.; E. Ellis Zahra, Jr., V.P.; Judy B. Morgan, Secy.
Number of staff: None.
EIN: 596128871
Selected grants: The following grants are a representative sample of this grantmaker's funding activity:
$10,000 to University of Georgia, Athens, GA, 2012. For unspecified.

2056
The Arthur Vining Davis Foundations ✧
225 Water St., Ste. 1510
Jacksonville, FL 32202-5185 (904) 359-0670
Contact: Dr. Nancy J. Cable, Pres.
FAX: (904) 359-0675; E-mail: office@avdf.org; Main URL: http://www.avdf.org/

The Foundations are comprised of three separate foundations established in 1952 and 1965 in PA; and in 1965 in FL. In early 2001, Foundation No. 1 merged with Foundation No. 2.
Donor: Arthur Vining Davis†.
Foundation type: Independent foundation.
Financial data (yr. ended 12/31/12): Assets, $220,896,499 (M); expenditures, $11,510,952; qualifying distributions, $10,858,765; giving activities include $9,486,289 for 45 grants (high: $5,000,000; low: $100,000), and $4,540 for 17 employee matching gifts.
Purpose and activities: Support largely for private higher education; teacher professional development in health care with emphasis on caring attitudes, public television, and graduate theological education and private higher education.
Fields of interest: Media, film/video; Secondary school/education; Higher education; Medical school/education; Theological school/education.
Type of support: Seed money; Film/video/radio; General/operating support; Continuing support; Capital campaigns; Building/renovation; Equipment; Endowments; Program development; Professorships; Publication; Curriculum development; Fellowships; Internship funds; Scholarship funds; Research; Technical assistance; Consulting services; Program evaluation; Employee matching gifts; Matching/challenge support.
Limitations: Applications accepted. Giving limited to the U.S., including possessions and territories. No support for community chests, publicly governed colleges and universities, and institutions primarily supported by government funds (except in secondary education and health care programs), voter education, voter registration drives, or projects incurring obligations extending over many years. No grants to individuals; no loans.
Publications: Application guidelines; Annual report; Grants list; Informational brochure; IRS Form 990 or 990-PF printed copy available upon request.
Application information: All proposals must come from the president or other primary executive of an institution. Applicants for higher education and religion program grants should complete the Institutional Information form on foundation web site. Application form required.
Initial approach: Letter
Copies of proposal: 1
Deadline(s): None
Board meeting date(s): Spring, fall, and winter
Final notification: 10 to 15 months for approvals
Officer and Trustees:* J.H. Dow Davis,* Chair.; Joel P. Davis, Emeritus; W.R. Wright, Emeritus; Holbrook R. Davis; Jonathan P. Davis; Maynard K. Davis; Serena Davis Hall; Dorothy Davis Kee; Dorothy Given Kee; Hilary Kirk Rosenthal; BNY Mellon; SunTrust Bank.
Number of staff: 5 full-time professional; 1 full-time support.
Selected grants: The following grants are a representative sample of this grantmaker's funding activity:
$285,000 to W E T A-Greater Washington Educational Telecommunications Association, Arlington, VA, 2011. To complete production of PBS series, The Latino Americans.
$250,000 to Claremont McKenna College, Claremont, CA, 2011. For endowment for programming at the Center for Writing and Public Discourse.
$250,000 to Hampden-Sydney College, Hampden Sydney, VA, 2011. For classroom improvements.
$200,000 to Brite Divinity School, Fort Worth, TX, 2011. For scholarship enhancement for highly qualified Master of Divinity degree students.
$200,000 to Catholic Theological Union at Chicago, Chicago, IL, 2011. For scholarships for lay students.
$200,000 to Salk Institute for Biological Studies, La Jolla, CA, 2011. For purchase of Environmental Scanning Electron Microscope.
$191,532 to Brown University, Providence, RI, 2011. For professional development and literacy instruction for high school teachers.
$190,000 to Duke University, Durham, NC, 2011. For Civic Engagement Program.
$100,000 to New York University, School of Medicine, New York, NY, 2011. For dissemination of

a curriculum for instilling caring attitudes in surgical residents.

2057
The Jon Holden DeHaan Foundation ✧
975 6th Ave. S., Ste. 103
Naples, FL 34102-6753
Contact: Jon Holden DeHaan, Tr.

Established in 1990 in IN.
Donor: Jon Holden DeHaan.
Foundation type: Independent foundation.
Financial data (yr. ended 12/31/12): Assets, $7,770,941 (M); expenditures, $1,208,595; qualifying distributions, $1,000,500; giving activities include $1,000,500 for grants.
Purpose and activities: Giving primarily for health organizations, including a heart association and a private foundation, as well as a research center.
Fields of interest: Higher education; Health organizations, association; Foundations (private grantmaking).
Limitations: Giving primarily in Naples, FL and Minneapolis, MN. No grants to individuals.
Application information:
Initial approach: Letter
Deadline(s): None
Officer: Thomas H. DeHaan, Mgr.
Trustee: Jon Holden DeHaan.
EIN: 346924212

2058
Jack C. & Betty A. Demetree Family Foundation ✧
(formerly Demetree Family Foundation)
1551 Atlantic Blvd., Ste. 300
Jacksonville, FL 32207-3368

Established in 1996 in FL.
Donors: Elisa A. Demetree; Jack C. Demetree.
Foundation type: Independent foundation.
Financial data (yr. ended 12/31/13): Assets, $12,031,594 (M); expenditures, $665,829; qualifying distributions, $566,375; giving activities include $566,375 for 44 grants (high: $201,000; low: $375).
Purpose and activities: Giving primarily to Christian and Roman Catholic agencies and churches. Support also for children, youth, and social services, and health care.
Fields of interest: Education; Hospitals (general); Hospitals (specialty); Health care; Human services; Children/youth, services; Christian agencies & churches; Catholic agencies & churches.
Limitations: Applications not accepted. Giving primarily in FL, with emphasis on Jacksonville. No grants to individuals.
Application information: Contributes only to pre-selected organizations.
Officers and Directors:* Jack C. Demetree,* Pres.; Jack C. Demetree, Jr.,* V.P.; Elisa A. Demetree,* Secy.-Treas.; Betty A. Demetree; Christopher C. Demetree; Leslie A. Demetree-Doherty; Mark C. Demetree.
EIN: 593407379

2059
Arthur S. DeMoss Foundation ✧
777 S. Flagler Dr., Ste. 215E
West Palm Beach, FL 33401-6165
Contact: Nancy S. DeMoss, Chair.

Incorporated in PA in 1955 as the National Liberty Foundation of Valley Forge, Inc.
Donor: Arthur S. DeMoss†.
Foundation type: Independent foundation.
Financial data (yr. ended 12/31/13): Assets, $122,928,161 (M); gifts received, $27,863; expenditures, $30,141,073; qualifying distributions, $28,055,017; giving activities include $25,766,179 for 32+ grants (high: $5,592,000), and $2,684,309 for 1 foundation-administered program.
Purpose and activities: Support primarily for operating programs initiated and managed by the foundation itself that are evangelistic and disciplined in nature in the U.S. and other countries, primarily the Third World. To a limited extent, a few grants are made to organizations both in the U.S. and overseas that have these same goals.
Fields of interest: Christian agencies & churches.
International interests: Kenya; Tanzania; Uganda.
Type of support: Program development.
Limitations: Applications not accepted. Giving on an international basis. No support for local churches, denominational agencies and/or schools or colleges. No grants to individuals, or for scholarships or endowments; no loans.
Publications: Informational brochure.
Application information: Unsolicited requests for funds not accepted.
Board meeting date(s): Quarterly
Officers and Directors:* Nancy S. DeMoss,* Chair., C.E.O., and Treas.; Robert G. DeMoss,* Pres.; Charlotte DeMoss,* Secy.; Larry R. Nelson, C.F.O.; Elizabeth J. DeMoss.
Number of staff: 9 full-time professional; 8 full-time support.
EIN: 236404136
Selected grants: The following grants are a representative sample of this grantmaker's funding activity:
$10,356,724 to Africa Ministries, Tuscaloosa, AL, 2012.
$5,384,000 to Evangelism Explosion International, Fort Lauderdale, FL, 2012.
$3,399,746 to Eastern Europe Ministries, 2012.
$3,250,000 to Compassion International, Colorado Springs, CO, 2012.
$1,044,000 to Life Action Ministries, Buchanan, MI, 2012.
$700,000 to Billy Graham Evangelistic Association, Charlotte, NC, 2012.
$350,000 to Thru the Bible Radio Network, Pasadena, CA, 2012.
$93,730 to Child Evangelism Fellowship, Warrenton, MO, 2012.
$31,500 to Logan Hope, Philadelphia, PA, 2012.
$20,000 to Crossroads Community Center, Philadelphia, PA, 2012.

2060
Franklin A. Denison, Sr. Trust ✧
500 E. Broward Blvd., Ste. 850
Fort Lauderdale, FL 33394-3008

Established in FL.
Foundation type: Independent foundation.
Financial data (yr. ended 12/31/11): Assets, $3,430,570 (M); expenditures, $1,017,573; qualifying distributions, $1,000,000; giving activities include $1,000,000 for 8 grants (high: $250,000; low: $50,000).
Fields of interest: Health organizations, association; Salvation Army; Human services.
Limitations: Giving primarily in Fort Lauderdale, FL and MI.
Trustee: Dennis Delong.
EIN: 656445297

2061
Wayne M. Densch Charitable Trust ✧
1603 E. Marks St.
Orlando, FL 32803-4135 (407) 896-3884
Contact: Leonard E. Williams, Pres.

Established in 1997 in FL.
Foundation type: Independent foundation.
Financial data (yr. ended 12/31/13): Assets, $30,293,587 (M); expenditures, $1,715,017; qualifying distributions, $1,540,675; giving activities include $1,524,873 for 41 grants (high: $328,000; low: $500).
Purpose and activities: Giving primarily for disadvantaged populations; support also for education.
Fields of interest: Education; Human services; YM/YWCAs & YM/YWHAs.
Limitations: Applications accepted. Giving primarily in FL and NC. No grants to individuals.
Application information: Application form required.
Initial approach: Proposal
Deadline(s): None
Officers: Leonard E. Williams, Pres. and Secy.-Treas.; John A. Williams, V.P.
EIN: 597033503
Selected grants: The following grants are a representative sample of this grantmaker's funding activity:
$200,000 to University of Central Florida Foundation, Orlando, FL, 2012. For Construction of new facilities.
$10,000 to Boy Scouts of America, Central FL Council, Apopka, FL, 2012. For auction.
$6,000 to American Cancer Society, Orlando, FL, 2012. For golf tournament.
$3,000 to Boy Scouts of America, Central FL Council, Apopka, FL, 2012. For general operating expenses.
$2,500 to Boy Scouts of America, Central FL Council, Apopka, FL, 2012. For golf tournament fundraiser.

2062
Ann and Ari Deshe Foundation ✧ ☆
20801 Biscayne Blvd., No. 431
Aventura, FL 33180

Established in 1997 in OH.
Donors: Ann Deshe; Ari Deshe; Elie Deshe; Daniel Deshe; Dara Deshe; David Deshe.
Foundation type: Independent foundation.
Financial data (yr. ended 12/31/13): Assets, $4,991,537 (M); gifts received, $1,050,000; expenditures, $727,391; qualifying distributions, $711,170; giving activities include $711,170 for 56 grants (high: $100,000; low: $40).
Fields of interest: Education; Philanthropy/voluntarism; Jewish agencies & synagogues.

Limitations: Applications not accepted. Giving primarily in CO, NY, and OH. No grants to individuals.
Application information: Contributes only to pre-selected organizations.
Officers: Ann Deshe, Pres.; Ari Deshe, V.P.
EIN: 311499050

2063
Diermeier Family Foundation ✧
2113 Canna Way
Naples, FL 34105-3069 (630) 655-8845
Contact: Julie Diermeier, Tr.
FAX: (630) 789-6249;
E-mail: diermeier1@comcast.net; Main URL: http://www.diermeierff.org/
Grants List: http://www.diermeierff.org/past-grants.html

Established in 2003 in IL.
Donors: Jeffrey J. Diermeier; Julia M. Diermeier.
Foundation type: Independent foundation.
Financial data (yr. ended 12/31/13): Assets, $9,416,371 (M); expenditures, $506,781; qualifying distributions, $443,615; giving activities include $438,000 for 15 grants (high: $100,000; low: $1,000).
Fields of interest: Elementary/secondary education; Higher education; Health care; Mental health, treatment; Cancer research; Human services.
Type of support: General/operating support.
Limitations: Giving primarily in FL, GA, IL, and WI. No grants to individuals.
Application information: Application form available on foundation web site. Application form required.
Initial approach: Download application form from foundation web site. Applications may be submitted via fax or e-mail.
Trustees: Jeffrey J. Diermeier; Julie M. Diermeier.
EIN: 364545339

2064
The Paul J. DiMare Foundation ✧
P.O. Box 900460
Homestead, FL 33090-0460

Established in 1995 in FL.
Donors: Paul J. DiMare; DiMare Management, Inc.; DiMare Johns Island Inc.
Foundation type: Independent foundation.
Financial data (yr. ended 12/31/13): Assets, $36,799,931 (L); gifts received, $150,000; expenditures, $1,347,908; qualifying distributions, $1,259,635; giving activities include $1,259,635 for 35 grants (high: $595,000; low: $100).
Purpose and activities: Giving primarily for education, children and youth services, health organizations and medical research, including a children's hospital, and social services.
Fields of interest: Arts; Higher education; Botanical gardens; Hospitals (specialty); Health organizations, association; Medical research, institute; Human services; Children/youth, services; Christian agencies & churches.
Limitations: Applications not accepted. Giving primarily in FL. No grants to individuals.
Application information: Contributes only to pre-selected organizations.
Officer: Anthony DiMare, V.P.
Trustee: Paul J. DiMare.
EIN: 650537843

2065
Do Unto Others Trust, Inc. ✧
2746 S.W. 11th St.
Miami, FL 33135-4702

Established in 1999 in FL.
Donor: Justino Celorio.
Foundation type: Independent foundation.
Financial data (yr. ended 12/31/13): Assets, $3,261,985 (M); gifts received, $49,998; expenditures, $97,721; qualifying distributions, $458,075; giving activities include $458,075 for 24 grants (high: $101,000; low: $100).
Fields of interest: Animal welfare; American Red Cross; Protestant agencies & churches; Catholic agencies & churches.
Limitations: Applications not accepted. Giving primarily in Washington, DC and Miami, FL. No grants to individuals.
Application information: Contributes only to pre-selected organizations.
Officer: Alicia Celorio, Pres.
EIN: 650517915

2066
Oliver S. and Jennie R. Donaldson Charitable Trust ✧
P.O. Box 1908
Orlando, FL 32802-1908

Established in 1969 in NY.
Donor: Oliver S. Donaldson†.
Foundation type: Independent foundation.
Financial data (yr. ended 12/31/13): Assets, $34,471,249 (M); expenditures, $1,750,290; qualifying distributions, $1,572,523; giving activities include $1,494,605 for 58 grants (high: $182,760; low: $879).
Purpose and activities: Interests include cancer research and treatment, child welfare and youth agencies, hospitals and health agencies, elementary, secondary, and higher education; support also for wildlife preservation, and the town of Pawling, NY; 11 named institutions are given first consideration.
Fields of interest: Cancer research.
Limitations: Applications not accepted. Giving primarily in MA and NY. No grants to individuals.
Application information: Unsolicited requests for funds not accepted.
Board meeting date(s): Semiannually
Trustees: Pamela A. Curtis; Helen R. Flynn; Mark A. Lawrence; Priscilla A. Lawrence; Robert P. Lawrence; Christopher Lirakis; Stephen Lirakis; Susan Lirakis; Hilton C. Smith, Jr.; SunTrust Bank, N.A.
EIN: 046229044

2067
The DS Foundation ✧
7274 Fisher Island Dr.
Miami Beach, FL 33109-0772

Donor: Bharat Desai.
Foundation type: Independent foundation.
Financial data (yr. ended 12/31/13): Assets, $199,834,650 (M); gifts received, $35,094,500; expenditures, $3,992,085; qualifying distributions, $3,858,352; giving activities include $3,858,352 for 14 grants (high: $1,250,000; low: $352).
Fields of interest: Higher education; Education.
Limitations: Applications not accepted. Giving in the U.S., with some emphasis on Cambridge, MA; funding also in Cupertino, CA.
Application information: Contributes only to pre-selected organizations.
Directors: Bharat Desai; Pia Desai; Saahill Desai; Neerja Sethi.
EIN: 412115627

2068
DuBow Family Foundation, Inc. ✧
P.O. Box 57759
Jacksonville, FL 32241-7759

Established in 1989.
Donors: Lawrence J. DuBow; Michael I. DuBow; Susan Dubow.
Foundation type: Independent foundation.
Financial data (yr. ended 08/31/13): Assets, $23,992,804 (M); expenditures, $1,320,417; qualifying distributions, $1,172,704; giving activities include $1,170,456 for 77 grants (high: $202,940; low: $50).
Purpose and activities: Giving primarily for Jewish organizations, education, the arts, and children, youth, and social services.
Fields of interest: Arts; Education; Human services; Children/youth, services; Residential/custodial care, hospices; United Ways and Federated Giving Programs; Jewish agencies & synagogues.
Limitations: Applications not accepted. Giving primarily in Jacksonville, FL. No grants to individuals.
Application information: Unsolicited requests for funds not accepted.
Officers and Trustees:* Lawrence J. DuBow,* Pres.; Helen A. DuBow, V.P. and Admin.; Michael I. DuBow,* V.P.; Susan E. DuBow,* V.P.; Linda J. DuBow,* Treas.
EIN: 592981682
Selected grants: The following grants are a representative sample of this grantmaker's funding activity:
$72,290 to Jacksonville Jewish Center, Jacksonville, FL, 2011.
$46,000 to University of North Florida, Jacksonville, FL, 2011.
$41,000 to Jewish Community Foundation of Northeast Florida, Jacksonville, FL, 2011.
$13,900 to River Garden Foundation, Jacksonville, FL, 2011.
$12,000 to Camp Ramah Darom, Atlanta, GA, 2011.
$11,666 to Jacksonville Community Council, Jacksonville, FL, 2011.
$10,000 to Habitat for Humanity of Jacksonville, Jacksonville, FL, 2011.
$5,000 to Jewish Community Alliance, Jacksonville, FL, 2011.
$3,500 to American Cancer Society, Jacksonville, FL, 2011.
$3,000 to Theaterworks, Jacksonville, FL, 2011.

2069
Frank E. Duckwall Foundation ✧ ☆
P.O. Box 3351
Tampa, FL 33601-3351 (813) 634-4172
Contact: Sandra E. Tolle

Established in 1983 in FL.
Donor: Frank E. Duckwall†.
Foundation type: Independent foundation.

Financial data (yr. ended 12/31/13): Assets, $8,381,017 (M); expenditures, $541,713; qualifying distributions, $472,145; giving activities include $440,628 for 40 grants (high: $85,000; low: $1,500).
Purpose and activities: Giving primarily for scientific, educational and charitable purposes, with primary focus on the Tampa Bay, FL, area.
Fields of interest: Arts; Higher education; Education; Health care; Cancer; Human services; Foundations (community).
Type of support: Capital campaigns; Building/renovation; Equipment; Endowments; Professorships; Scholarship funds; Research; Matching/challenge support.
Limitations: Applications accepted. Giving limited to the Tampa Bay, FL, area.
Publications: Application guidelines; Financial statement; Informational brochure (including application guidelines); Occasional report.
Application information: Application form required.
Initial approach: Proposal
Copies of proposal: 3
Deadline(s): None
Trustees: G. Lowe Morrison; Frank J. Rief III.
EIN: 596773462

2070
The Ferdinand & Anna Duda Foundation, Inc. ✧ ☆
P.O. Box 620257
Oviedo, FL 32762-0257

Established in 1991 in FL as partial successor to the Duda Foundation.
Donors: Ferdinand S. Duda; A. Duda & Sons Inc.
Foundation type: Independent foundation.
Financial data (yr. ended 12/31/13): Assets, $4,142,779 (M); gifts received, $376,925; expenditures, $592,341; qualifying distributions, $549,160; giving activities include $548,000 for 19 grants (high: $100,000; low: $1,000).
Purpose and activities: Giving primarily for Christian education.
Fields of interest: Elementary/secondary education; Christian agencies & churches; Protestant agencies & churches.
Type of support: Research.
Limitations: Applications not accepted. Giving primarily in FL. No grants to individuals.
Application information: Contributes only to pre-selected organizations.
Officers: Eleanor Hrncir, Pres.; Wendy Clark, V.P.; Susan D. Hanas, Secy.; Valerie Miller, Treas.
EIN: 593041353
Selected grants: The following grants are a representative sample of this grantmaker's funding activity:
$5,000 to Devereux Foundation, Orlando, FL, 2012. For youth mission.

2071
The Lowell S. and Betty L. Dunn Family Foundation Inc. ✧
8083 N.W. 103rd St.
Hialeah Gardens, FL 33016-2201

Donor: Betty L. Dunn.
Foundation type: Independent foundation.
Financial data (yr. ended 12/31/13): Assets, $16,053,478 (M); gifts received, $4,500,000; expenditures, $686,175; qualifying distributions, $684,150; giving activities include $683,100 for 16 grants (high: $150,000; low: $500).
Fields of interest: Diabetes research.
Limitations: Applications not accepted. Giving primarily in FL.
Application information: Unsolicited requests for funds not accepted.
Officers: Betty L. Dunn, Pres.; Loretta S. Dunn, V.P.; Lowell Dunn II, Secy.; Lizbeth Dunn Arencibia, Treas.
EIN: 271237743

2072
Dunn's Foundation for the Advancement of Right Thinking ✧
309 S.E. Osceola St., Ste. 350
Stuart, FL 34994-2250
Contact: William A. Dunn, Tr.

Established in 1993 in FL.
Donors: William A. Dunn; William A. Dunn Trust.
Foundation type: Independent foundation.
Financial data (yr. ended 03/31/14): Assets, $84,005,771 (M); expenditures, $7,553,633; qualifying distributions, $7,539,750; giving activities include $7,539,750 for grants.
Purpose and activities: Giving primarily to organizations that are concerned with public affairs issues.
Fields of interest: Higher education, university; Public affairs, research; Public policy, research; Public affairs.
Limitations: Applications not accepted. Giving primarily in CA, Washington, DC, and VA, with some giving in MT. No grants to individuals.
Application information: Contributes only to pre-selected organizations.
Trustees: David Dreyer; Rebecca Water Dunn; William A. Dunn.
EIN: 650415977
Selected grants: The following grants are a representative sample of this grantmaker's funding activity:
$1,100,000 to Reason Foundation, Los Angeles, CA, 2012.
$1,000,000 to George Mason University, Institute for Humane Studies, Fairfax, VA, 2012.
$500,000 to Chapman University, Orange, CA, 2012.
$500,000 to Chapman University, Orange, CA, 2013. For general support.
$500,000 to Greater Houston Community Foundation, Houston, TX, 2013. For general support.
$300,000 to Marijuana Policy Project Foundation, Washington, DC, 2013. For general support.
$300,000 to Marijuana Policy Project Foundation, Washington, DC, 2013. For general support.
$300,000 to Property and Environment Research Center, Bozeman, MT, 2012.
$250,000 to Foundation for Government Accountability, Naples, FL, 2013. For general support.
$250,000 to Institute for Humane Studies, Arlington, VA, 2013. For general support.
$200,000 to Institute for Justice, Arlington, VA, 2012.
$200,000 to Institute for Justice, Arlington, VA, 2012.
$100,000 to Institute for Humane Studies, Arlington, VA, 2013. For general support.
$100,000 to Marijuana Policy Project Foundation, Washington, DC, 2012.
$100,000 to Pacific Legal Foundation, Sacramento, CA, 2013. For general support.
$100,000 to Property and Environment Research Center, Bozeman, MT, 2012.
$75,000 to George Mason University Foundation, Fairfax, VA, 2013. For general support.
$50,000 to Foundation for Economic Education, Irvington, NY, 2012.
$50,000 to Foundation for Government Accountability, Naples, FL, 2012.
$50,000 to Heartland Institute, Chicago, IL, 2013. For general support.

2073
Dunspaugh-Dalton Foundation Inc. ✧
1500 San Remo Ave., Ste. 103
Coral Gables, FL 33146-3054 (305) 668-4192
FAX: (305) 668-4247;
E-mail: ddf@dunspaughdalton.org; Main
URL: http://www.dunspaughdalton.org
Grants List: http://www.dunspaughdalton.org/giving-grantees.html

Incorporated in 1963 in FL.
Donor: Ann V. Dalton†.
Foundation type: Independent foundation.
Financial data (yr. ended 12/31/12): Assets, $34,313,822 (M); expenditures, $2,264,727; qualifying distributions, $1,892,752; giving activities include $1,404,789 for 51 grants (high: $225,000; low: $695).
Purpose and activities: Giving primarily for the arts, education, social services, and for health care.
Fields of interest: Performing arts; Performing arts, theater; Elementary/secondary education; Higher education; Education; Hospitals (general); Health care; Human services.
Type of support: General/operating support; Continuing support; Capital campaigns; Endowments; Program development; Professorships; Matching/challenge support.
Limitations: Applications accepted. Giving primarily in Monterey, CA, and Miami, FL, and NC. No grants to individuals; no loans.
Application information: See foundation website for complete application guidelines. Application form required.
Deadline(s): None
Officers: Sarah L. Bonner, Pres.; Alexina Lane, V.P.; Leslie Buchanan, Secy.-Treas.
Number of staff: 3 full-time professional; 1 full-time support.
EIN: 591055300

2074
Alfred I. duPont Foundation, Inc. ✧
10140 Centurion Pkwy. N.
Jacksonville, FL 32256-0532 (904) 697-4123
Contact: Rosemary C. Wills, Secy.

Incorporated in 1936 in FL.
Donors: Jessie Ball duPont†; Jessie Ball DuPont Ditchley Trust.
Foundation type: Independent foundation.
Financial data (yr. ended 12/31/13): Assets, $42,560,535 (M); expenditures, $2,090,370; qualifying distributions, $2,006,119; giving activities include $1,433,480 for 108 grants (high: $101,500; low: $1,000), and $348,150 for 142 grants to individuals (high: $6,000; low: $125).

Purpose and activities: Giving primarily to elderly persons residing in the southeastern U.S., who are in distressed situations requiring health, economic, or educational assistance; support also for higher education and medical research.
Fields of interest: Higher education; Medical research, institute; Aging, centers/services; Christian agencies & churches; Protestant agencies & churches; Catholic agencies & churches; Aging; Economically disadvantaged.
Type of support: General/operating support; Grants to individuals.
Limitations: Giving primarily in the southeastern U.S., with emphasis on FL.
Application information: Application forms are mailed upon request. Application form required.
Initial approach: Letter
Copies of proposal: 1
Deadline(s): None
Board meeting date(s): 2nd Tues. in Feb.
Officers and Directors:* R.E. Nedley,* Pres. and Treas.; E.C. Brownlie,* V.P.; W.W. Carlson,* V.P.; Rosemary C. Wills,* Secy.; Braden Ball, Jr.; Fred Kent, Jr.; Rush Loving; Clay Smallwood; John Vaughn.
EIN: 591297267
Selected grants: The following grants are a representative sample of this grantmaker's funding activity:
$5,000 to Alice Lloyd College, Pippa Passes, KY, 2011.
$1,200 to Florida State College, Jacksonville, FL, 2011.

2075
Jessie Ball duPont Fund
(formerly Jessie Ball duPont Religious, Charitable and Educational Fund)
1 Independent Dr., Ste. 1400
Jacksonville, FL 32202-5011 (800) 252-3452
Contact: Sherry Magill, Pres.
FAX: (904) 353-3870;
E-mail: contactus@dupontfund.org; E-mail for Davena Sawyer, Exec. Asst. to the President: dsawyer@dupontfund.org; Main URL: http://www.dupontfund.org/
Grants Database: http://www.dupontfund.org/grantmaking/grants-database/
Knowledge Center: http://www.dupontfund.org/library/

Trust established in 1976 in FL.
Donor: Jessie Ball duPont†.
Foundation type: Independent foundation.
Financial data (yr. ended 12/31/13): Assets, $291,555,138 (M); gifts received, $105,321; expenditures, $18,687,543; qualifying distributions, $17,644,228; giving activities include $13,774,600 for 382 grants (high: $2,735,544; low: $627), $817,302 for 12 foundation-administered programs and $500,000 for 1 loan/program-related investment.
Purpose and activities: The fund's three focus areas are: 1) helping eligible organizations to be financially healthy, organizationally sound and strategically responsive to the changing needs of their communities and constituents; 2) helping communities gain access to the essentials of healthy, productive living: financial assets, health care, quality education and job preparation, affordable housing and strong and safe communities; and 3) helping to strengthen the nonprofit sector by supporting research, community education, and infrastructure development and advocacy.
Fields of interest: Historic preservation/historical societies; Arts; Secondary school/education; Higher education; Education; Health care; Crime/violence prevention; Human services; Children, day care; Youth, services; Economic development; Community/economic development; Religion; AIDS, people with; Economically disadvantaged; Homeless.
Type of support: Mission-related investments/loans; General/operating support; Management development/capacity building; Equipment; Program development; Conferences/seminars; Professorships; Publication; Seed money; Curriculum development; Research; Technical assistance; Consulting services; Program evaluation; Program-related investments/loans; Matching/challenge support.
Limitations: Applications accepted. Giving primarily in the South, especially DE, FL, and VA. No support for organizations other than those awarded gifts by the donor from 1960-1964. No grants to individuals, or generally for capital campaigns or endowments.
Publications: Annual report (including application guidelines); Financial statement; Grants list; Informational brochure; Occasional report.
Application information: Applications are accepted only from organizations that received a contribution from Mrs. duPont during the years 1960-1964. Applicants must submit proof with application that a contribution was received from the donor between 1960 and 1964. Application form required.
Initial approach: Brief proposal or telephone call to program staff
Copies of proposal: 1
Deadline(s): None
Board meeting date(s): Quarterly, beginning in Feb.
Final notification: Approximately 1 month
Officers and Trustees:* Eddie E. Jones, Jr.,* Chair.; Leroy Davis, Vice-Chair.; Sherry P. Magill, Ph.D., Pres.; Mark Constantine, Sr. V.P.; Mary Lynn Huntley; Thomas Jeavons; Marty Lanahan; David Llewellyn; Mary K. Phillips.
Corporate Trustee: Northern Trust Bank of Florida, N.A.
Number of staff: 7 full-time professional; 4 full-time support; 1 part-time support.
EIN: 596368632
Selected grants: The following grants are a representative sample of this grantmaker's funding activity:
$600,000 to Community Foundation, Jacksonville, FL, 2012. For Round 4 grants for Jessie Ball duPont Safety Net Fund.
$500,000 to Community Foundation, Jacksonville, FL, 2012. For Jessie Ball duPont Port Saint Joe Capacity Building Fund.
$250,000 to Alfred I. duPont Awards Foundation, Orlando, FL, 2012. For Alfred I. duPont - Columbia University Awards in Broadcast Journalism.
$200,000 to Edward Waters College, Jacksonville, FL, 2012. To re-launch summer school and provide student-focused retention services during the summer months, and to hire a construction site manager to oversee construction associated with a one million dollar challenge grant.
$150,000 to Sheltering Arms Hospital, Glen Allen, VA, 2012. To establish development office and institute annual and planning giving programs, payable over 3.00 years.
$150,000 to Washington National Cathedral, Washington, DC, 2012. For matching support needed to leverage a $700,000 grant from the National Park Service to help repair catastrophic damage to the cathedral caused by the 2011 5.8 earthquake that struck the East Coast.
$10,000 to Kilmarnock Baptist Church, Kilmarnock, VA, 2012. For People in Need Funds.
$10,000 to San Jose Episcopal Day School, Jacksonville, FL, 2012. For Independent School Discretionary Fund.
$10,000 to Temple Beth El, Newark, DE, 2012. For People in Need Funds.
$5,000 to Alliance for Christian Media, Atlanta, GA, 2012. To transition to API-based content distribution framework for internet-based devices. This will allow them to use multiple types of devices to access their website, including tablets and mobile phones.

2076
The Jess & Brewster J. Durkee Foundation ✧
4495-304 Roosevelt Blvd., Ste. 114
Jacksonville, FL 32210-3381 (904) 388-9979
Contact: Edward McCarthy, Jr., Tr.

Established in FL.
Donors: Brewster J. Durkee†; Julie McCarthy; Edward McCarthy, Jr.
Foundation type: Independent foundation.
Financial data (yr. ended 12/31/13): Assets, $12,672,836 (M); expenditures, $675,653; qualifying distributions, $663,750; giving activities include $630,750 for 83 grants (high: $40,000; low: $250).
Fields of interest: Christian agencies & churches.
Limitations: Applications accepted. Giving primarily in FL. No grants to individuals.
Application information: Application form required.
Initial approach: Letter
Deadline(s): None
Trustees: Beville Anderson; Kendall G. Durkee; Edward McCarthy, Jr.; Edward McCarthy III.
EIN: 593293247
Selected grants: The following grants are a representative sample of this grantmaker's funding activity:
$10,000 to City Rescue Mission, Jacksonville, FL, 2012. For unrestricted.

2077
The E. J. N. R. A. Foundation ✧
2200 Biscayne Blvd.
Miami, FL 33137-5016

Established in 2006 in DE and FL.
Donors: Sonny Kahn; Suzanne Kahn; Ala Moana Property Developer, LLC; SK Financial, LLC; 1301 N. Troy, LLC; City Front Chicago, LLC; Casey Klein; Russell Ronalee Galbut Family Foundation Inc.; Bruce and Julie Menin Charitable Foundation Inc.
Foundation type: Independent foundation.
Financial data (yr. ended 12/31/13): Assets, $1,402,161 (M); gifts received, $3,599,275; expenditures, $2,603,883; qualifying distributions, $2,603,408; giving activities include $2,603,408 for 47 grants (high: $1,660,284; low: $180).
Fields of interest: Education; Human services; Jewish agencies & synagogues.
Limitations: Applications not accepted. Giving primarily in FL and NY. No grants to individuals.
Application information: Contributes only to pre-selected organizations.

Officers and Directors:* Erica Kahn,* Pres.; Elliot Kahn,* Secy.; Sonny Kahn,* Treas.
EIN: 205990090

2078
Eagle Foundation, Inc. ✧
2022 Hendricks Ave.
Jacksonville, FL 32207

Established in 1995 in FL.
Donors: Education & Research Foundation of Florida, Inc.; Raymond K. Mason.
Foundation type: Independent foundation.
Financial data (yr. ended 12/31/11): Assets, $1,382,847 (M); expenditures, $548,429; qualifying distributions, $547,169; giving activities include $547,169 for 63 grants (high: $500,000; low: $1).
Purpose and activities: Giving for higher education, international relief programs, federated giving programs, and religious organizations.
Fields of interest: Museums (art); Arts; Education; Health organizations, association; United Ways and Federated Giving Programs; Christian agencies & churches; Protestant agencies & churches.
Limitations: Applications not accepted. Giving primarily in FL. No grants to individuals.
Application information: Unsolicited requests for funds not accepted.
Officers: Minerva R. Mason, Pres.; Marcy M. Moody, V.P. and Secy.; Varina M. Steuert, V.P. and Treas.
EIN: 593310956

2079
Horatio B. Ebert Charitable Foundation ✧
1240 Wellington Ter.
Maitland, FL 32751-3448

Established in 1985 in FL.
Donors: Lyda G. Ebert†; Robert O. Ebert†.
Foundation type: Independent foundation.
Financial data (yr. ended 12/31/13): Assets, $318,526 (M); expenditures, $810,556; qualifying distributions, $796,692; giving activities include $794,900 for 59 grants (high: $79,500; low: $100).
Purpose and activities: Giving primarily for higher education.
Fields of interest: Museums (sports/hobby); Higher education; Human services; Children/youth, services; Christian agencies & churches.
Type of support: General/operating support; Building/renovation.
Limitations: Applications not accepted. Giving primarily in FL, KY, MD, NC, and TN. No grants to individuals.
Application information: Unsolicited requests for funds not accepted.
Board meeting date(s): Aug. 1
Directors: Catherine G. Ebert; Cecile G. Ebert; Michael L. Ebert; Adrienne E. Miller.
Number of staff: 1 full-time professional.
EIN: 592602801

2080
The Cynthia G. Edelman Family Foundation ✧
6622 Southpoint Dr. S., Ste. 495
Jacksonville, FL 32216-6188

Established in FL.
Donors: Cynthia G. Edelman; Daniel M. Edelman.
Foundation type: Independent foundation.
Financial data (yr. ended 06/30/13): Assets, $16,301,911 (M); expenditures, $1,192,604; qualifying distributions, $1,063,149; giving activities include $1,063,149 for grants.
Purpose and activities: Giving primarily to Jewish organizations and cultural educational organizations.
Fields of interest: Museums (art); Higher education; Theological school/education; Jewish federated giving programs; Jewish agencies & synagogues.
Limitations: Applications not accepted. Giving primarily in FL and TN. No grants to individuals.
Application information: Contributes only to pre-selected organizations.
Officer: Daniel M. Edelman, Mgr.
Trustee: Cynthia G. Edelman.
EIN: 597109743
Selected grants: The following grants are a representative sample of this grantmaker's funding activity:
$166,291 to Community Foundation for the National Capital Region, Washington, DC, 2011.
$150,000 to Community Foundation, Jacksonville, FL, 2011.
$100,000 to KIPP Foundation, San Francisco, CA, 2011.

2081
The Edgemer Foundation, Inc. ✧
401 E. Las Olas Blvd., Ste. 2200
Fort Lauderdale, FL 33301-2244

Established in 2000 in FL.
Donors: Linda Roth; WLD Trust; DL Trust.
Foundation type: Independent foundation.
Financial data (yr. ended 12/31/13): Assets, $13,496,590 (M); gifts received, $2,500,000; expenditures, $2,139,200; qualifying distributions, $2,076,000; giving activities include $2,076,000 for 16 grants (high: $1,050,000; low: $5,000).
Purpose and activities: Giving primarily for the arts, higher and other education, hospitals, including a children's hospital, and Jewish organizations.
Fields of interest: Museums (art); Performing arts; Higher education; Education; Hospitals (general); Hospitals (specialty); Jewish federated giving programs; Jewish agencies & synagogues.
Limitations: Applications not accepted. Giving primarily in CT. No grants to individuals.
Application information: Contributes only to pre-selected organizations.
Directors: David W. Horvitz; David M. Roth; Linda H. Roth.
EIN: 650976539

2082
The Bernard A. Egan Foundation Inc. ✧
1900 Old Dixie Hwy.
Fort Pierce, FL 34946-1423

Established in 1994 in FL.
Donor: Egan Family Charitable Trust.
Foundation type: Independent foundation.
Financial data (yr. ended 05/31/13): Assets, $50,564,986 (M); gifts received, $7,603,491; expenditures, $1,817,427; qualifying distributions, $1,588,600; giving activities include $1,588,600 for 128 grants (high: $250,000; low: $250).
Fields of interest: Education; Cancer research; Ear, nose & throat research; Diabetes research; Housing/shelter, homeless; Religion.
Type of support: Scholarship funds.
Limitations: Applications not accepted. Giving primarily in FL. No grants to individuals.
Application information: Contributes only to pre-selected organizations.
Officers and Trustees:* Bernadette Emerick,* Pres.; J.B. Egan III,* V.P.; Gregory P. Nelson,* Secy.; J.J. Gilet,* Treas.; Catherine Rohm.
EIN: 650501660
Selected grants: The following grants are a representative sample of this grantmaker's funding activity:
$45,000 to Samaritan Center, Vero Beach, FL, 2011.
$40,281 to Indian River Medical Center Foundation, Vero Beach, FL, 2011.
$35,000 to Samaritan Center, Vero Beach, FL, 2010.
$20,000 to Boys and Girls Clubs of Indian River County, Vero Beach, FL, 2010.
$10,000 to American Cancer Society, Vero Beach, FL, 2011.
$10,000 to Bureau of Catholic Indian Missions, Washington, DC, 2011.
$10,000 to Paulist Fathers, Washington, DC, 2011.
$10,000 to Saint Anastasia Catholic Church, Fort Pierce, FL, 2011.
$10,000 to Saint Helen Catholic Church, Vero Beach, FL, 2011.
$9,000 to Samaritan Center, Vero Beach, FL, 2011.
$7,000 to Saint Francis Manor of Vero Beach, Vero Beach, FL, 2011.
$2,000 to Catholic Relief Services, Baltimore, MD, 2010.
$2,000 to Saint Helen Catholic Church, Vero Beach, FL, 2011.

2083
Egleston Support Fund Trust ✧
(formerly Children's Healthcare Support Fund)
P.O. Box 1908
Orlando, FL 32802-1908

Established in 1945; supporting organization of the American Lung Association, the AG Rhodes Home Inc., Family First, Children's Healthcare of Atlanta, Westview Cemetry, Inc., and the Henrietta Egleston Hospital.
Foundation type: Independent foundation.
Financial data (yr. ended 12/31/13): Assets, $20,722,163 (M); expenditures, $895,767; qualifying distributions, $862,916; giving activities include $835,108 for 4 grants (high: $834,508; low: $100).
Purpose and activities: Giving primarily to a children's health organization.
Fields of interest: Health care; Children, services.
Limitations: Applications not accepted. Giving limited to GA. No grants to individuals.
Application information: Contributes only to pre-selected organizations; unsolicited requests for funds not considered or acknowledged.
Trustee: SunTrust Banks, Inc.
EIN: 586026009
Selected grants: The following grants are a representative sample of this grantmaker's funding activity:
$660,441 to Childrens Healthcare of Atlanta, Atlanta, GA, 2011. For general charitable purpose.

2084
Albert E. & Birdie W. Einstein Fund ✧ ☆
P.O. Box 310
Melbourne, FL 32902-0310 (864) 241-8562
Contact: Michael S. Lee, Pres.

Established about 1967 in FL.
Donors: Albert E. Einstein†; Birdie W. Einstein†.
Foundation type: Independent foundation.
Financial data (yr. ended 06/30/13): Assets, $10,143,734 (M); expenditures, $636,621; qualifying distributions, $528,000; giving activities include $528,000 for 28 grants (high: $75,000; low: $2,500).
Fields of interest: Human services; Children/youth, services; Jewish federated giving programs; Christian agencies & churches; Jewish agencies & synagogues; Economically disadvantaged.
Limitations: Applications accepted. Giving generally limited to FL. No grants to individuals.
Application information: Application form required.
Initial approach: Letter or telephone
Deadline(s): None
Officers: Michael S. Lee, Pres.; J. Michael Smith, V.P.; Debi Malone, Secy.-Treas.
EIN: 596127412
Selected grants: The following grants are a representative sample of this grantmaker's funding activity:
$25,000 to Broward Childrens Center, Pompano Beach, FL, 2011. For challenge grant.
$25,000 to Place of Hope, Palm Beach Gardens, FL, 2011. For challenge grant.
$25,000 to Quantum House, West Palm Beach, FL, 2011.
$15,000 to Avenue D Boys Choir, Fort Pierce, FL, 2011.
$14,700 to Maltz Jupiter Theater, Jupiter, FL, 2011.
$10,000 to Health and Palliative Services of the Treasure Coast, Stuart, FL, 2011.
$10,000 to Island Dolphin Care, Key Largo, FL, 2011.
$9,000 to Canine Companions for Independence, Orlando, FL, 2011.
$7,364 to Broward Childrens Center, Pompano Beach, FL, 2011.
$2,000 to Haven Ranch, Saint Augustine, FL, 2011.

2085
Ellmar Foundation, Inc. ✧
(formerly Marell Foundation, Inc.)
P.O. Box 1291
Tarpon Springs, FL 34688-1291
Application address: c/o Peter J. Ristorcelli, C.F.O. and Dir., P.O. Box 1879, Tarpon Springs, FL 34688-1879, tel.: (727) 938-0160

Established in 1997 in FL.
Donor: Carol E. Martin.
Foundation type: Operating foundation.
Financial data (yr. ended 04/30/13): Assets, $16,366,169 (M); expenditures, $1,215,311; qualifying distributions, $1,099,171; giving activities include $1,087,545 for 14 grants (high: $280,000; low: $650).
Purpose and activities: Giving primarily to educational and social assistance programs and charities.
Fields of interest: Education; Hospitals (general); Human services.
Limitations: Applications accepted. Giving primarily in Tarpon Springs, FL. No grants to individuals.
Application information:
Initial approach: Letter on organization's letterhead
Deadline(s): None
Officers and Directors:* Carol E. Martin,* Pres.; Stanley G. Gibson, Jr.,* V.P.; Peter J. Ristorcelli, C.F.O.; Stella Himenetos, Secy.-Treas.; Helen J. Cahalin; Christine L. Gagnon; Donald R. Hall; Lynn Ann Sharpe.
EIN: 593451317
Selected grants: The following grants are a representative sample of this grantmaker's funding activity:
$28,000 to Georgetown University, Washington, DC, 2013. For All Grants Are to Further the Charitable Activities of the Recipient.

2086
The Engelberg Foundation ✧
1050 N. Lake Way
Palm Beach, FL 33480-3252
Contact: Alfred B. Engelberg, Tr.
E-mail: aengelberg@nglbrg.com

Established in 1990 in CT.
Donor: Alfred Engelberg.
Foundation type: Independent foundation.
Financial data (yr. ended 01/31/13): Assets, $13,582,874 (M); gifts received, $137,227; expenditures, $891,822; qualifying distributions, $791,706; giving activities include $787,170 for 49 grants (high: $100,000; low: $250).
Purpose and activities: Giving primarily for the arts, human services, Jewish organizations, and to a law school, as well as to a public policy organization.
Fields of interest: Arts; Law school/education; Human services; Public policy, research; Jewish agencies & synagogues.
International interests: Israel.
Type of support: General/operating support; Continuing support; Annual campaigns; Capital campaigns; Building/renovation; Emergency funds; Program development; Conferences/seminars; Professorships; Seed money; Curriculum development; Fellowships; Program evaluation.
Limitations: Applications not accepted. Giving primarily in FL and NY. No grants to individuals.
Application information: Unsolicited requests for funds are not accepted or reviewed.
Board meeting date(s): None
Trustee: Alfred Engelberg.
Number of staff: None.
EIN: 061309603

2087
The Ephraim Project, Inc. ✧ ☆
P.O. Box 720902
Orlando, FL 32872-0902 (407) 451-0242
Contact: Rachelle Hood, Pres.
FAX: (888) 384-5087;
E-mail: info@theephraimproject.org; Main URL: http://www.theephraimproject.org

Established in 2006 in FL.
Donors: Life International; Global Aid Network; Rachelle Hood; Samaritan's Purse; Denny's, Inc.; Ronald Blue & Co., LLC; Margaret Jenkins; Henry Nasella; Christian Business Network.
Foundation type: Independent foundation.
Financial data (yr. ended 12/31/13): Assets, $0 (M); gifts received, $523,785; expenditures, $522,955; qualifying distributions, $503,388; giving activities include $503,388 for grants.
Fields of interest: Homeless, human services.
Limitations: Applications not accepted. Giving primarily in FL, the South Atlantic and Ethiopia. No grants to individuals.
Application information: Contributes only to pre-selected organizations.
Officers and Directors:* Rachelle Hood,* Pres.; Tara Concelman,* Secy.; Scott Concelman,* Treas.; John-Paul Conners; John Hamatie; Paulette Lawson; J.R. Ross; Anne van den Berg.
EIN: 204149806

2088
The Saul and Theresa Esman Foundation, Inc. ✧
2101 N.W. Corporate Blvd., Ste. 206
Boca Raton, FL 33431

Foundation type: Independent foundation.
Financial data (yr. ended 12/31/13): Assets, $8,904,806 (M); expenditures, $774,550; qualifying distributions, $774,500; giving activities include $705,000 for 14 grants (high: $95,000; low: $5,000).
Fields of interest: Higher education, university; Education; Health care; Alzheimer's disease; Health organizations.
Limitations: Applications not accepted. Giving primarily in FL.
Application information: Unsolicited requests for funds not accepted.
Officers: Theresa Esman, Pres.; Steven Levin, Secy.; Vinessa Morgan, Treas.; Murray Levin, Exec. Dir.
EIN: 331215642
Selected grants: The following grants are a representative sample of this grantmaker's funding activity:
$90,000 to Scripps Research Institute, Jupiter, FL, 2010.
$80,000 to Scripps Research Institute, Jupiter, FL, 2011.
$40,000 to American Heart Association, West Palm Beach, FL, 2011.
$25,000 to Boca Raton Regional Hospital, Boca Raton, FL, 2011.

2089
Faigen Family Foundation, Inc. ✧
231 Bradley Pl., Ste. 200
Palm Beach, FL 33480-3725

Established in 1997 in FL.
Donors: George Faigen; Greta Faigen; Warren Miller; Andrew Faigen; Amanda Faigen.
Foundation type: Independent foundation.
Financial data (yr. ended 12/31/13): Assets, $13,748,666 (M); gifts received, $85,788; expenditures, $1,218,708; qualifying distributions, $1,133,296; giving activities include $1,132,179 for 3 grants (high: $531,000; low: $180,000).
Fields of interest: Education; Health organizations; Catholic agencies & churches.
Limitations: Applications not accepted. Giving primarily in Washington, DC, Pahokee, FL, and Baltimore, MD. No grants to individuals.
Application information: Contributes only to pre-selected organizations.

Officers: Greta Faigen, Pres.; Lisa Seigel, V.P.; Brenda McGowan, Secy.; Andrew Faigen, Treas.
Directors: Amanda Faigen; Warren Miller.
EIN: 311509512
Selected grants: The following grants are a representative sample of this grantmaker's funding activity:
$100,000 to Sheppard Pratt Health System, Baltimore, MD, 2011.

2090
The Fairholme Foundation ✧
(formerly Bruce and Tracey Berkowitz Foundation)
c/o Bruce Berkowitz
14 Tahiti Beach Island Rd.
Coral Gables, FL 33143-6540

Established in 2002 in NJ.
Donors: Bruce Berkowitz; Tracey Berkowitz; Daniel Berkowitz; Fairholme Capital Mgmt. LLC; East Lane LLC.
Foundation type: Independent foundation.
Financial data (yr. ended 12/31/12): Assets, $155,280,997 (M); gifts received, $20,768,950; expenditures, $5,076,583; qualifying distributions, $5,052,873; giving activities include $5,046,360 for 53 grants (high: $3,301,250; low: $100), and $6,513 for 1 foundation-administered program.
Fields of interest: Arts; Higher education; Education; Health care; Jewish federated giving programs; Jewish agencies & synagogues.
Limitations: Applications not accepted. Giving primarily in FL, with some emphasis on Miami. No grants to individuals.
Application information: Contributes only to pre-selected organizations.
Trustees: Bruce Berkowitz; Tracey Berkowitz.
EIN: 010718240

2091
The Falic Family Foundation ✧
6100 Hollywood Blvd., 7th Fl.
Hollywood, FL 33024-7900

Established in 2005 in FL and TX.
Donors: Duty Free Americas, Inc.; G-5 Trading Inc.; Central-Med Distribution Inc.; Dir Trading Inc.; Hard Candy LLC; UETA Tzedukah Inc.
Foundation type: Operating foundation.
Financial data (yr. ended 12/31/11): Assets, $151,700 (M); gifts received, $1,704,000; expenditures, $1,603,672; qualifying distributions, $1,703,672; giving activities include $1,603,462 for grants.
Purpose and activities: Giving primarily to Jewish agencies, temples, and schools.
Fields of interest: Education; Human services; Jewish federated giving programs; Jewish agencies & synagogues.
Limitations: Applications not accepted.
Application information: Unsolicited requests for funds not accepted.
Officers and Directors:* Jerome Falic,* Pres.; Leon Falic,* V.P. and Secy.; Simon Falic,* V.P. and Treas.; Fima Falic; Nily Falic.
EIN: 202734770

2092
Fancelli Foundation, Inc. ✧
c/o L J Mgmt. Svcs., Inc.
2000 E. Edgewood Dr., Ste 102
Lakeland, FL 33803-3600

Established in 2001 in FL.
Donors: Julia J. Fancelli; Julia J. Fancelli 2006 Charitable Lead; The 2002 Charitable Lead Annuity Trust; Julia J. Fancelli 2002 Charitable Lead Annuity Trust.
Foundation type: Independent foundation.
Financial data (yr. ended 12/31/13): Assets, $20,696,059 (M); gifts received, $746,248; expenditures, $1,065,599; qualifying distributions, $1,009,828; giving activities include $1,000,000 for 7 grants (high: $600,000; low: $5,000).
Fields of interest: Education; Human services.
Limitations: Applications not accepted. Giving primarily in FL. No grants to individuals.
Application information: Contributes only to pre-selected organizations.
Officers: Julia J. Fancelli, Pres.; Brenda Craft, V.P.; Marianne Parsons, Secy.-Treas.
Directors: Fran Munson; Leslie Fancelli Sonatori.
EIN: 593753198
Selected grants: The following grants are a representative sample of this grantmaker's funding activity:
$280,000 to Lake Wales Care Center, Lake Wales, FL, 2012. For Transitional Housing for 2 Apartments, Stay at Home Work Camp for 2 Projects, Meals on Wheels for One Route, Basic Needs for Families, 2011 Shortfall, and Rebuilding of the Donaldson Family Home in Babson Park.
$100,000 to Alliance for Independence, Lakeland, FL, 2012. For operating expenses, student scholarships and culinary training Program.
$100,000 to Lakeland Christian School, Lakeland, FL, 2012. For Tuition Assistance for Children Attending the Discovery Program.
$73,701 to Polk Museum of Art, Lakeland, FL, 2012. For Community Outreach - Changing Lives Through Art Program.

2093
Dan C. Ferguson Charitable Trust ✧
3033 Riviera Dr., No. 202
Naples, FL 34103-2750
Application address: Daniel C. Ferguson, 1300 3rd St. S., Ste. 300, Naples, FL 34102, tel.: (239) 262-0203

Established in 1986 in FL.
Donor: Daniel C. Ferguson.
Foundation type: Independent foundation.
Financial data (yr. ended 12/31/13): Assets, $2,931,969 (M); expenditures, $464,408; qualifying distributions, $438,700; giving activities include $438,700 for 9 grants (high: $100,000; low: $2,000).
Fields of interest: Education; Health care; Human services.
Type of support: General/operating support.
Application information: Application form required.
Initial approach: Letter
Deadline(s): None
Trustee: Daniel C. Ferguson.
EIN: 366848627

2094
Ferraro Family Foundation Inc. ✧
600 Brickell Ave., Ste. 3800
Miami, FL 33131

Established in 1999 in FL.
Donor: James L. Ferraro.
Foundation type: Independent foundation.
Financial data (yr. ended 06/30/13): Assets, $3,945,877 (M); gifts received, $2,548,500; expenditures, $777,679; qualifying distributions, $715,908; giving activities include $715,908 for 20 grants (high: $174,500; low: $500).
Fields of interest: Health care; Human services; Community/economic development.
Limitations: Applications not accepted. Giving primarily in Ft. Lauderdale and Miami, FL. No grants to individuals.
Application information: Contributes only to pre-selected organizations.
Officer and Directors:* James L. Ferraro,* Pres.; James L. Ferraro, Jr.; Luella S. Ferraro.
EIN: 650953780
Selected grants: The following grants are a representative sample of this grantmaker's funding activity:
$244,575 to Make-A-Wish Foundation of Southern Florida, Fort Lauderdale, FL, 2011. For general operations.
$150,000 to Elton John AIDS Foundation, New York, NY, 2011. For general operations.
$35,000 to Buoniconti Fund to Cure Paralysis, Miami, FL, 2011. For general operations.
$25,000 to Bill, Hillary and Chelsea Clinton Foundation, Little Rock, AR, 2011. For general operations.
$25,000 to Catholic Charities Legal Services, Miami, FL, 2011. For general operations.
$25,000 to Jackson Memorial Foundation, Miami, FL, 2011. For general operations.
$12,000 to Desert Classic Charities, Rancho Mirage, CA, 2011. For general operations.
$2,500 to Multiple Sclerosis Society, National, Washington, DC, 2011. For general operations.

2095
The Fine & Greenwald Foundation, Inc. ✧ ☆
c/o Marsha Soffer
19501 Biscayne Blvd., Ste. 400
Aventura, FL 33180-2337

Established in NY.
Donor: Martin Fine†.
Foundation type: Independent foundation.
Financial data (yr. ended 12/31/13): Assets, $17,013,274 (M); expenditures, $767,996; qualifying distributions, $685,000; giving activities include $685,000 for 32 grants (high: $100,000; low: $2,000).
Fields of interest: Education; Health organizations; Jewish agencies & synagogues.
Limitations: Applications not accepted. Giving primarily in FL and NY.
Application information: Unsolicited requests for funds not accepted.
Officer: Marsha Soffer, Pres.
Director: Jack Karson.
EIN: 241697726
Selected grants: The following grants are a representative sample of this grantmaker's funding activity:

$25,000 to American Jewish World Service, New York, NY, 2012. For Relief Foundation.
$20,000 to Peconic BayKeeper, Quogue, NY, 2012. For Environmental Protection and Restoration.
$15,000 to Southern Poverty Law Center, Montgomery, AL, 2012. For Legal Aid and Education.
$6,250 to Slow Food USA, Brooklyn, NY, 2012. For cultural/educational.
$5,000 to Dartmouth Medical School, Hanover, NH, 2012. For educational advancement.
$5,000 to Natural Resources Defense Council, New York, NY, 2012. For environ protection.
$3,600 to Jewish Museum, New York, NY, 2012. For cultural advancement.

2096
The Simon C. Fireman Charitable Foundation ✧ ☆
c/o Shutts and Bowen LLP
525 Okeechobee Blvd., Ste. 1100
Cityplace Twr.
West Palm Beach, FL 33401-6351 (508) 587-5400
Contact: Simon C. Fireman, Tr.

Established in 1995 in MA.
Donor: Simon C. Fireman.
Foundation type: Operating foundation.
Financial data (yr. ended 12/31/13): Assets, $1,488,407 (M); expenditures, $528,408; qualifying distributions, $500,000; giving activities include $500,000 for 1 grant.
Purpose and activities: Giving primarily for health care and to services for the elderly and children; some funding also for the arts.
Fields of interest: Arts; Health care; Health organizations, association; Cancer; Diabetes research; Children/youth, services; Aging, centers/services; Jewish agencies & synagogues.
Limitations: Giving primarily in FL and MA. No grants to individuals.
Application information:
Initial approach: Letter
Deadline(s): None
Trustees: Eric Christu; Kenneth Meewes.
EIN: 046774656

2097
FIS Foundation, Inc. ✧
(formerly Metavante Technologies Foundation, Inc.)
c/o Corp. Tax Dept.
601 Riverside Ave.
Jacksonville, FL 32204-2901

Established in 2007 in WI.
Donors: Metavante Technologies, Inc.; Fidelity National Information Services, Inc.
Foundation type: Company-sponsored foundation.
Financial data (yr. ended 12/31/12): Assets, $1,670,053 (M); gifts received, $1,500,000; expenditures, $718,537; qualifying distributions, $718,525; giving activities include $718,525 for 188 grants (high: $25,000; low: $100).
Purpose and activities: The foundation supports organizations involved with arts and culture, education, health, cancer, cancer research, and children services.
Fields of interest: Arts; Education; Human services.
Type of support: General/operating support; Program development.
Limitations: Applications not accepted. Giving primarily in FL.
Application information: Contributes only to pre-selected organizations.
Officers: Frank R. Martire, Pres.; Michael D. Hayford, V.P. and Treas.; Michael Oates, Secy.
EIN: 261628191

2098
Fites Family Charitable Trust ✧ ☆
9943 Brassie Bend
Naples, FL 34108-1923

Established in 1999 in IL.
Donors: Donald V. Fites; Sylvia D. Fites.
Foundation type: Independent foundation.
Financial data (yr. ended 12/31/13): Assets, $15,426,376 (M); expenditures, $785,010; qualifying distributions, $721,315; giving activities include $718,550 for 28 grants (high: $425,000; low: $200).
Purpose and activities: Giving primarily for higher education as well as for the arts, and human services.
Fields of interest: Education; Health care; Human services.
Limitations: Applications not accepted. No grants to individuals.
Application information: Contributes only to pre-selected organizations.
Trustees: Donald V. Fites; Joyce S. Hagen; Linda F. Reed.
EIN: 371375732

2099
Flight Attendant Medical Research Institute, Inc. ✧
(also known as FAMRI)
201 S. Biscayne Blvd., Ste. 1310
Miami, FL 33131-4333 (305) 379-7007
Contact: Elizabeth A. Kress, Exec. Dir.
FAX: (305) 577-0005; E-mail: ekress@famri.org;
Main URL: http://www.famri.org
E-Newsletter: http://www.famri.org/researchers/famri_research_funding_mailing.html

Established in 2000 in FL.
Foundation type: Independent foundation.
Financial data (yr. ended 09/30/12): Assets, $125,441,065 (M); expenditures, $20,069,451; qualifying distributions, $19,479,987; giving activities include $16,884,463 for 148 grants.
Purpose and activities: FAMRI's mission is to sponsor scientific and medical research for the early diagnosis, and cure of diseases and medical conditions caused from exposure to tobacco smoke.
Fields of interest: Lung diseases; Medical research, institute; Lung research; Medical research; Science.
Limitations: Applications accepted. Giving on a national and international basis. No grants to individuals who are currently receiving money from tobacco companies.
Publications: Multi-year report.
Application information: Each proposal must be accompanied by an institutional Tobacco Disclosure statement and Individual Disclosure statements for everyone involved with the project. Application form required.
Initial approach: A letter of intent is required. Once approved, applicant can download application forms provided on foundation web site
Deadline(s): Mid-Sept.
Final notification: 6 months
Officers and Trustees:* Stanley M. Rosenblatt,* Chair. and C.E.O.; Elizabeth A. Kress, Exec. Dir.; Patricia L. Young,* Secy.; Lani Blissard,* Treas.; Kathleen S. Cheney; John B. Ostrow; Susan Rosenblatt; Leisa Sudderth.
Number of staff: 1 full-time professional; 2 full-time support.
EIN: 651057724
Selected grants: The following grants are a representative sample of this grantmaker's funding activity:
$1,751,824 to Mount Sinai Medical Center, Department of Radiology, New York, NY, 2012. For research project at Flight Attendant Medical Research Institute, Inc. (FAMRI)-International Early Lung Cancer Action Programme (IELCAP) Center for Early Detection of Second Hand Tobacco Smoke Diseases.
$1,700,000 to American Committee for the Weizmann Institute of Science, New York, NY, 2012. For research projects at Center for Advanced Research on Lung Cancer (CARE).
$1,627,500 to American Academy of Pediatrics, Elk Grove Village, IL, 2012. For research projects at Julius B. Richmond, MD Center of Excellence for Children.
$1,627,500 to Johns Hopkins University, School of Medicine, Baltimore, MD, 2012. For research projects at Johns Hopkins Flight Attendant Medical Research Institute, Inc. (FAMRI) Center of Excellence.
$271,250 to Lunds Universitet, Lund, Sweden, 2012. For research projects at Flight Attendant Medical Research Institute, Inc. (FAMRI) Scandinavian Center of Excellence on Treatment of Second Hand Smoke Effects.
$108,500 to Boston Medical Center, Boston, MA, 2012. For research project, Smoking and Intrauterine Growth Restriction (IUGR), poor growth of a baby while in the mother's womb during pregnancy.
$108,500 to Johns Hopkins University, Baltimore, MD, 2012. For research project, Cigarette Smoke Induces XOR Mediated Apoptosis.
$108,500 to National Jewish Health, Denver, CO, 2012. For research project, Human Alveolar Type II Cell Injury by Cigarette Smoke.
$108,500 to University of Texas Health Science Center, Tyler, TX, 2012. For research project, Second Hand Smoke and Atherosclerosis.
$108,500 to Yale University, New Haven, CT, 2012. For research project, The Mechanisms of Synergy Between Cigarette Smoke and Respiratory Syncytial Vvirus (RSV).

2100
Florescue Family Foundation, Inc. ✧
50 E. Sample Rd., Ste. 400
Pompano Beach, FL 33064-3552

Established in 1993 in FL.
Donors: Barry Florescue; Renate Florescue; Geremy Florescue; Bryan Florescue; Gretchen Florescue.
Foundation type: Independent foundation.
Financial data (yr. ended 12/31/13): Assets, $11,171,007 (M); gifts received, $313,750; expenditures, $806,533; qualifying distributions, $590,827; giving activities include $590,827 for 11 grants (high: $472,500; low: $300).

Purpose and activities: Giving primarily for higher education.
Fields of interest: Higher education; Higher education, university; Health organizations, association; United Ways and Federated Giving Programs; Jewish agencies & synagogues; Children/youth; Children; Economically disadvantaged.
Type of support: In-kind gifts; Capital campaigns; Continuing support.
Limitations: Applications not accepted. Giving primarily in Rochester, NY and in south FL. No grants to individuals.
Application information: Contributes only to pre-selected organizations.
Board meeting date(s): Quarterly
Officer and Directors:* Barry Florescue,* Pres.; Gretchen Florescue; Renate Florescue; Sharon Gustafson; Mark Myers; Dana Scheer.
EIN: 650375751

2101
Florida Blue Foundation ✧
(formerly Blue Cross and Blue Shield of Florida Foundation)
4800 Deerwood Campus Pkwy., DC 3-4
Jacksonville, FL 32246-6498 (800) 477-3736 ext. 63215
Contact: Susan B. Towler, V.P.; Susan F. Wildes, Sr. Prog. Mgr.
FAX: (904) 357-8367;
E-mail: thebluefoundationfl@bcbsfl.com; E-mail for Susan B. Towler: susan.towler@bcbsfl.com; E-mail for Sapphire Award: TheSapphireAward@bcbsfl.com; E-mail for Embrace a Healthy Florida: embrace@bcbsfl.com; E-mail for Improve Quality of Life Grants: communityrelations@floridablue.com; Main URL: http://www3.bcbsfl.com/wps/portal/bcbsfl/bluefoundation

Established in 2001 in FL.
Donors: Blue Cross and Blue Shield of Florida, Inc.; Health Options, Inc.; Tracy Leinbach.
Foundation type: Company-sponsored foundation.
Financial data (yr. ended 12/31/13): Assets, $156,519,933 (M); gifts received, $19,163,253; expenditures, $11,779,694; qualifying distributions, $11,655,052; giving activities include $9,864,078 for 472 grants (high: $1,000,000; low: $244), and $496,118 for 4 foundation-administered programs.
Purpose and activities: The foundation supports programs designed to improve the health of Floridians and their communities. Special emphasis is directed toward programs designed to improve access to health care; consumer health; the quality and safety of patient care; quality of life; and the healthcare system.
Fields of interest: Arts; Elementary/secondary education; Higher education; Nursing school/education; Education, reading; Education; Health care, alliance/advocacy; Health care, public policy; Health care, equal rights; Health care, clinics/centers; Dental care; Optometry/vision screening; Public health; Public health, obesity; Public health, physical fitness; Health care, financing; Health care, patient services; Health care; Mental health, counseling/support groups; Mental health/crisis services; Nutrition; Family services; Human services; Civil/human rights, equal rights; Community/economic development; Leadership development; Children; Minorities; Economically disadvantaged.
Type of support: General/operating support; Continuing support; Management development/capacity building; Capital campaigns; Equipment; Program development; Scholarship funds; Technical assistance.
Limitations: Applications accepted. Giving limited to areas of company operations in FL. No support for political or lobbying organizations, fraternal, athletic, or social organizations, or religious organizations not of direct benefit to the entire community, private foundations, or Type III supporting organizations. No grants to individuals (except for the Sapphire Award) or for fundraising.
Publications: Application guidelines; Corporate giving report; Grants list; Newsletter.
Application information: Organizations may apply for support only once during a 12-moth period. Unsolicited applications for Embrace a Healthy Florida are not accepted. An interview may be requested for the Sapphire Award. Organizations receiving support are asked to submit a final report. Application form required.
Initial approach: Complete online nomination form for Sapphire Award; complete online application for Build Healthy, Strong Communities
Deadline(s): Varies for Sapphire Award; None for Build Healthy, Strong Communities
Board meeting date(s): Feb., Apr., June, Aug., Oct., and Dec.
Final notification: Varies for Sapphire Award
Officers and Directors:* Charles S. Joseph,* Chair.; Jason Altmire, Vice-Chair.; Susan B. Towler, V.P.; Mark S. McGowan,* Secy.; Gary M. Healy, Treas.; Chuck Divita; Renee Finley; Camille Harrison; Joyce A. Kramzer; Robert Lufrano; Maria Moutinho; Penelope S. Shaffer; Darnell Smith.
Number of staff: 4 full-time professional.
EIN: 593707820
Selected grants: The following grants are a representative sample of this grantmaker's funding activity:
$1,600,001 to University of Florida Foundation, Gainesville, FL, 2011. To sponsor Chair in Health Disparities and Health Disparities Support.
$250,000 to Florida Association of Food Banks, Fort Myers, FL, 2011. For food for the entire State of Florida.
$150,000 to University of Central Florida, Orlando, FL, 2011. For Center for Nursing and Nursing Education.
$125,000 to Americas Health Insurance Plans Foundation, Washington, DC, 2011. For ChildObesity180 Initiative.
$122,500 to Susan B. Anthony Center, Pembroke Pines, FL, 2011. For medical care for homeless and recovering women by offering substance abuse treatment services and quality physical and mental health care programs.
$104,000 to War on Poverty - Florida, Jacksonville, FL, 2011. For coordination of local efforts, Lead Agency for Opa-Locka Embrace Initiative.
$76,500 to Hebni Nutrition Consultants, Orlando, FL, 2011. For programs providing nutrition education and intervention strategies to prevent diet-related diseases.
$49,242 to Institute for Child and Family Health, Miami, FL, 2011. For Pediatric Capacity.
$18,000 to Good Samaritan Health Centers, Saint Augustine, FL, 2011. For Wildflower Clinic Dental Program Manager.
$9,000 to Hialeah Public Libraries, Hialeah, FL, 2011. For Healthy Lifestyle at your Library.

2102
The Florman Family Foundation Inc. ✧ ☆
c/o WLD Enterprises, Robert Puck
401 E. Las Olas Blvd., Ste. 2200
Fort Lauderdale, FL 33301-2244

Established in 1996 in FL.
Donor: Betty E. Florman‡.
Foundation type: Independent foundation.
Financial data (yr. ended 12/31/13): Assets, $7,464,882 (M); gifts received, $29,333; expenditures, $640,964; qualifying distributions, $547,500; giving activities include $517,500 for 17 grants (high: $120,000; low: $2,500).
Purpose and activities: Giving primarily for higher education, and human services.
Fields of interest: Higher education; Education; Health organizations, association; Youth development, adult & child programs; Human services; Children/youth, services; Aging, centers/services; Jewish federated giving programs.
Limitations: Applications not accepted.
Application information: Contributes only to pre-selected organizations.
Officers: Robert J. Puck, Pres.; Shelley Marciano, Secy.-Treas.
Directors: Mark Blank; Neil Florman.
EIN: 650662182

2103
Flournoy Georgia Portsmouth Trust ✧ ☆
P.O. Box 1908
Orlando, FL 32802-1908

Established in VA.
Donors: Georgia Flournoy; Flournoy Threadcraft Port Tes Trust.
Foundation type: Independent foundation.
Financial data (yr. ended 11/30/13): Assets, $540,623 (M); gifts received, $71,541; expenditures, $1,605,373; qualifying distributions, $1,574,794; giving activities include $1,529,809 for 8 grants (high: $663,298; low: $9,209).
Fields of interest: Human services; Children/youth, services; Community/economic development.
Limitations: Applications not accepted. Giving primarily in VA.
Application information: Unsolicited requests for funds not accepted.
Trustee: Suntrust Banks, Inc.
EIN: 546191990

2104
The Foley Family Charitable Foundation ✧ ☆
601 Riverside Ave., 12th Fl.
Jacksonville, FL 32204-2950

Established in 1997 in CA.
Donors: William P. Foley II; Carol J. Foley.
Foundation type: Independent foundation.
Financial data (yr. ended 12/31/12): Assets, $42,025,678 (M); expenditures, $1,506,360; qualifying distributions, $1,264,700; giving activities include $1,264,700 for grants.
Purpose and activities: Giving primarily for education; some funding also for a theater.

Fields of interest: Performing arts, theater; Higher education; Education.
Limitations: Applications not accepted. Giving primarily in MT and NY. No grants to individuals.
Application information: Contributes only to pre-selected organizations.
Officers: Lindsay E. Foley, Pres.; Carol J. Foley, Secy.
Directors: Ed Dewey; William P. Foley II; Peter Sadowski; Alan L. Stinson.
EIN: 770472642

2105
The Mary Alice Fortin Foundation ✧
201 Chilean Ave.
Palm Beach, FL 33480-6118

Established in 1993 in FL.
Donors: Mary Alice Fortin†; Fortin Foundation of Florida; Mary Alice Fortine Irrevocable Trust.
Foundation type: Independent foundation.
Financial data (yr. ended 12/31/12): Assets, $136,355,236 (M); gifts received, $57,900,425; expenditures, $4,972,513; qualifying distributions, $3,019,601; giving activities include $2,335,618 for 114 grants (high: $500,000; low: $1).
Fields of interest: Education; Health care; Boys & girls clubs; Human services; Children/youth, services; Community/economic development; Foundations (private grantmaking).
Limitations: Applications not accepted. Giving primarily in FL. No grants to individuals.
Application information: Contributes only to pre-selected organizations.
Officers: Danielle Hickox Moore, Pres. and Treas.; Carol McCracken, Secy.
Directors: Larry Alexander; Susan Stockard Channing; Nick R. Cladis; Mary Alice Plisco; Lesly S. Smith.
EIN: 592469696

2106
The Fortin Foundation of Florida, Inc. ✧
201 Chilean Ave.
Palm Beach, FL 33480-4629
Contact: Lesly Stockard Smith, Pres.

Established in 1986 in FL.
Donor: Mary Alice Fortin†.
Foundation type: Independent foundation.
Financial data (yr. ended 12/31/12): Assets, $50,537,748 (M); expenditures, $3,818,181; qualifying distributions, $3,138,699; giving activities include $2,766,320 for 100 grants (high: $500,000; low: $550).
Purpose and activities: Giving primarily for children's and other healthcare associations, a day care center, children, youth and social services, federated giving programs, and Roman Catholic churches.
Fields of interest: Higher education; Education; Health care; Health organizations; Disasters, preparedness/services; Human services; Children/youth, services; Children, day care; United Ways and Federated Giving Programs; Catholic agencies & churches; Infants/toddlers; Children/youth; Children; Youth; Boys; AIDS, people with.
Limitations: Applications not accepted. Giving primarily in FL and MT. No grants to individuals.
Application information: Unsolicited requests for funds not accepted.
Officers and Directors:* Lesly Stockard Smith,* Pres.; Danielle Moore, V.P. and Secy.; Susan Stockard Channing,* V.P.
Number of staff: 1 full-time professional.
EIN: 592707197

2107
Julie and Martin Franklin Charitable Foundation, Inc. ✧
c/o Jarden
5200 Blue Lagoon Dr., 8th Fl.
Miami, FL 33126

Established in 1994 in NY.
Donors: Julie Franklin; Martin E. Franklin.
Foundation type: Independent foundation.
Financial data (yr. ended 10/31/13): Assets, $3,871,524 (M); expenditures, $1,143,679; qualifying distributions, $1,109,023; giving activities include $1,085,689 for 48 grants (high: $250,000; low: $500).
Fields of interest: Higher education; Education; Human services; Jewish federated giving programs; Jewish agencies & synagogues.
Limitations: Applications not accepted. Giving primarily in NY; some funding also in Philadelphia, PA. No grants to individuals.
Application information: Contributes only to pre-selected organizations.
Officers: Martin E. Franklin, Pres. and Treas.; Julie Franklin, V.P. and Secy.
EIN: 133800643

2108
Fredman Family Foundation Inc. ✧
7301 S.W. 57th Ct., Ste. 410
Miami, FL 33143-5324

Donors: Andreww Fredman; Kerin Fredman.
Foundation type: Independent foundation.
Financial data (yr. ended 12/31/12): Assets, $26,251,784 (M); gifts received, $9,999,995; expenditures, $1,180,550; qualifying distributions, $807,998; giving activities include $793,065 for 27 grants (high: $300,000; low: $12).
Fields of interest: Education; Health care; Health organizations; Cancer research.
Limitations: Applications not accepted. Giving primarily in CA.
Application information: Unsolicited requests for funds not accepted.
Board Members: Andrew Fredman; Kerin McCarthy Fredman; Lauren Huot.
EIN: 271430745

2109
Free Family Foundation Corp. ✧ ☆
614 W. Bay St., Ste. B
Tampa, FL 33606-2758 (813) 435-5600

Established in 1999 in FL.
Donors: Harry J. Free; Carole J. Free; Douglas Free; Tabitha Free; Diane E. Hanlon; Charles G. Hanlon; Thomas E. Free.
Foundation type: Independent foundation.
Financial data (yr. ended 12/31/13): Assets, $4,263,482 (M); gifts received, $1,910,868; expenditures, $1,031,245; qualifying distributions, $1,010,371; giving activities include $983,713 for 1 grant, and $1,010,371 for foundation-administered programs.
Purpose and activities: Giving primarily to Christian organizations.
Fields of interest: Religious federated giving programs; Christian agencies & churches.
Limitations: Applications not accepted. Giving primarily in Tampa, FL. No grants to individuals.
Application information: Contributes only to pre-selected organizations.
Officers: Harry J. Free, Pres.; Carole J. Free, V.P.; Diane E. Hanlon, Secy.; Douglas J. Free, Treas.
Director: Thomas E. Free.
EIN: 593611945

2110
Ralph S. French Charitable Foundation Trust ✧
3201 26th St. W.
Bradenton, FL 34205

Foundation type: Independent foundation.
Financial data (yr. ended 12/31/13): Assets, $29,357,829 (M); expenditures, $1,711,346; qualifying distributions, $1,330,547; giving activities include $1,330,547 for 19 grants (high: $332,637; low: $13,305).
Fields of interest: Education; Medical research, institute; Human services.
Limitations: Applications not accepted. Giving in the U.S., with some emphasis on FL, NJ, and NY.
Application information: Unsolicited requests for funds not accepted.
Trustees: James F. Alderman; Virginia Heinrich; John Seibert; Gordon Straka; Georgeanne Williams.
EIN: 273542831

2111
The Fred O. Funkhouser Charitable Foundation ✧
7508 Hawks Landing Dr.
West Palm Beach, FL 33412-3108

Established in 1997 in FL.
Foundation type: Independent foundation.
Financial data (yr. ended 08/31/13): Assets, $10,318,273 (M); expenditures, $723,818; qualifying distributions, $508,659; giving activities include $466,854 for 12 grants (high: $25,000; low: $1,854).
Fields of interest: Higher education; Hospitals (general); Human services; Children/youth, services.
Limitations: Applications not accepted. Giving primarily in VA. No grants to individuals.
Application information: Unsolicited requests for funds not accepted.
Trustee: Janice F. Scaglione.
EIN: 656243936
Selected grants: The following grants are a representative sample of this grantmaker's funding activity:
$250,000 to Rockingham Memorial Hospital, Harrisonburg, VA, 2013. For medical building.
$150,000 to Bridgewater College, Bridgewater, VA, 2013. For Educational general purposes.
$5,000 to Harrisonburg Rockingham Free Clinic, Harrisonburg, VA, 2013. For Medical Care to the Needy.

2112
The Galloway Foundation ✧
P.O. Box 2695
Winter Park, FL 32790-2695 (407) 246-8684
Contact: Jere Daniels, Tr.

Donor: Sarah B. Galloway Trust.
Foundation type: Independent foundation.
Financial data (yr. ended 12/31/13): Assets, $23,507,015 (M); expenditures, $1,244,485; qualifying distributions, $1,034,944; giving activities include $991,744 for 43 grants (high: $100,000; low: $900).
Fields of interest: Museums (history); Secondary school/education; Education; Human services; YM/YWCAs & YM/YWHAs; Family services; United Ways and Federated Giving Programs; Christian agencies & churches.
Limitations: Applications accepted. Giving primarily in FL. No grants to individuals.
Application information: Application form required.
Initial approach: Proposal
Deadline(s): None
Trustees: Jere F. Daniels; Jere F. Daniels, Jr.; Robert C. Klettner.
EIN: 596147133
Selected grants: The following grants are a representative sample of this grantmaker's funding activity:
$120,000 to University of Central Florida Foundation, Orlando, FL, 2011.

2113
Joseph and Rae Gann Charitable Foundation ✧
10185 Collins Ave., Ste. 317
Bal Harbour, FL 33154

Established in 1990 in FL.
Donors: Joseph Gann†; Rae Gann†.
Foundation type: Independent foundation.
Financial data (yr. ended 12/31/13): Assets, $41,883,137 (M); expenditures, $1,694,587; qualifying distributions, $1,657,450; giving activities include $1,657,450 for 130+ grants (high: $211,500).
Purpose and activities: Giving primarily to Jewish agencies, schools, and temples.
Fields of interest: Elementary/secondary education; Jewish federated giving programs; Jewish agencies & synagogues.
Limitations: Applications not accepted. Giving primarily in the Boston, MA, area. No grants to individuals.
Application information: Contributes only to pre-selected organizations.
Trustees: Beverly G. Bavly; Herbert M. Gann; Shirley R. Saunders.
EIN: 656043241
Selected grants: The following grants are a representative sample of this grantmaker's funding activity:
$200,000 to Hebrew Academy, 2010.
$124,000 to Combined Jewish Philanthropies of Greater Boston, Boston, MA, 2010.
$50,423 to Temple Emanu-El, 2010.
$50,000 to Chelsea Jewish Nursing Home Foundation, Chelsea, MA, 2010.
$50,000 to Rashi School, Dedham, MA, 2010.
$15,000 to Boston Jewish Film Festival, West Newton, MA, 2010.
$12,300 to Kollel of Greater Boston, Brighton, MA, 2010.
$10,000 to American Friends of Magen David Adom, New York, NY, 2011.
$5,000 to American Committee for Shaare Zedek Hospital in Jerusalem, New York, NY, 2011.
$1,800 to American Red Magen David for Israel, New York, NY, 2011.
$1,500 to Jewish National Fund, Rockville Centre, NY, 2011.
$1,000 to Friends of Israel Disabled Veterans, New York, NY, 2011.
$1,000 to Hillel: The Foundation for Jewish Campus Life, Washington, DC, 2011.

2114
The Gardener Foundation, Inc. ✧
44 S. Washington Dr.
Sarasota, FL 34236-5731

Established in 2008 in NJ.
Donor: Priscilla Knapp.
Foundation type: Independent foundation.
Financial data (yr. ended 06/30/13): Assets, $31,250,947 (M); expenditures, $2,228,540; qualifying distributions, $1,673,443; giving activities include $1,673,443 for 22 grants (high: $550,000; low: $50).
Fields of interest: Museums (marine/maritime); Education; Environment; Housing/shelter; Human services; Foundations (community).
Limitations: Applications not accepted. No grants to individuals.
Application information: Contributes only to pre-selected organizations.
Officers: William Knapp, Pres.; Jane Knapp, Secy.
Director: George Mazzarantani.
EIN: 260615969
Selected grants: The following grants are a representative sample of this grantmaker's funding activity:
$210,000 to Rocky Mountain Institute, Snowmass, CO, 2011.
$125,000 to Stony Brook Foundation, Stony Brook, NY, 2011.
$20,000 to Literacy Council of Sarasota, Sarasota, FL, 2011.
$15,000 to Greater Patchogue Foundation, Patchogue, NY, 2011.

2115
Joseph & Sherrie Garfield Charitable Foundation Inc. ✧
c/o Michael Katz
2699 S. Bayshore Dr.
Miami, FL 33133-5408

Established in FL.
Donor: Sherrie S. Garfield Trust.
Foundation type: Independent foundation.
Financial data (yr. ended 12/31/13): Assets, $7,842,148 (M); gifts received, $1,069,941; expenditures, $718,383; qualifying distributions, $468,250; giving activities include $468,250 for 29 grants (high: $45,000; low: $250).
Fields of interest: Arts; Education; Boys & girls clubs; Salvation Army; Children, services; Human services; Jewish agencies & synagogues; Blind/visually impaired; Deaf/hearing impaired.
Limitations: Applications not accepted. Giving primarily in FL. No grants to individuals.
Application information: Contributes only to pre-selected organizations.
Officer and Directors:* Walter E. Lieber,* Pres.; Sherrie S. Garfield; Michael D. Katz.
EIN: 061669075

2116
Thomas M. Garrott Foundation ✧ ☆
P.O. Box 1908
Orlando, FL 32802-1908
Contact: Arthur Oliver

Established in 1995 in TN.
Donor: Thomas M. Garrott.
Foundation type: Independent foundation.
Financial data (yr. ended 12/31/13): Assets, $11,474,345 (M); expenditures, $583,329; qualifying distributions, $575,904; giving activities include $569,600 for 50 grants (high: $170,000; low: $100).
Fields of interest: Museums (art); Arts; Elementary/secondary education; Higher education; Education; Health organizations; Human services; Foundations (private grantmaking); Foundations (community); United Ways and Federated Giving Programs; Christian agencies & churches.
Limitations: Applications accepted. Giving primarily in FL, TN and VA.
Application information: Application form required.
Initial approach: Letter
Deadline(s): None
Trustee: SunTrust Banks, Inc.
EIN: 626289645
Selected grants: The following grants are a representative sample of this grantmaker's funding activity:
$25,000 to Independent Presbyterian Church, Birmingham, AL, 2010. For general charitable purposes.
$15,000 to Brigham and Women's Hospital, Boston, MA, 2010. For general charitable purposes.
$10,000 to Saint Marys Episcopal School, Memphis, TN, 2011. For general charitable purposes.
$10,000 to Second Presbyterian Church, 2010. For general charitable purposes.
$10,000 to University of Memphis, Memphis, TN, 2010. For general charitable purposes.
$5,000 to Exceptional Foundation of West Tennessee, Memphis, TN, 2011. For general charitable purposes.
$5,000 to Saint Marys Episcopal School, Memphis, TN, 2011. For general charitable purposes.
$5,000 to Teach for America, New York, NY, 2011. For general charitable purposes.
$5,000 to Young Life, Colorado Springs, CO, 2011. For general charitable purposes.
$4,400 to Memphis University School, Memphis, TN, 2011. For general charitable purposes.
$3,000 to Saint Marys Episcopal School, Memphis, TN, 2011. For general charitable purposes.
$1,000 to Boys and Girls Clubs of Indian River County, Vero Beach, FL, 2011. For general charitable purposes.
$1,000 to Streets Ministries, Memphis, TN, 2011. For general charitable purposes.
$1,000 to Womens Refuge of Vero Beach, Vero Beach, FL, 2011. For general charitable purposes.

2117
W. W. and Eloise D. Gay Foundation ✧
524 Stockton St.
Jacksonville, FL 32204-2535 (904) 280-2053
Contact: W.W. Gay, Tr.

Established in 2000 in FL.
Donors: W.W. Gay; Eloise D. Gay; Alpha Equipment Sales & Rental Co.; Florida Mechanical Systems; W.W. Gay Mechanical Contractors of Orlando, Inc.; FMS Maintenance Inc.; NFC Construction & Rental Co.
Foundation type: Independent foundation.
Financial data (yr. ended 12/31/13): Assets, $2,778,467 (M); gifts received, $308,000; expenditures, $452,403; qualifying distributions, $447,750; giving activities include $447,750 for 62 grants (high: $90,000; low: $500).
Fields of interest: Higher education; Education; Hospitals (general); Health organizations, association; Human services; Children/youth, services; Christian agencies & churches; Protestant agencies & churches.
Limitations: Applications accepted. Giving primarily in Jacksonville, FL. No support for the United Way. No grants for fundraising campaigns.
Application information: Application form required.
Initial approach: Proposal
Deadline(s): None
Trustees: Kathleen Holbrook Cold; Eloise D. Gay; W.W. Gay.
EIN: 311724609
Selected grants: The following grants are a representative sample of this grantmaker's funding activity:
$50,000 to University of Florida, College of Engineering, Gainesville, FL, 2011.
$20,000 to Southern Baptist Hospital of Florida, Jacksonville, FL, 2011.
$10,000 to Bob Tebow Evangelistic Association, Jacksonville, FL, 2011.
$10,000 to Boy Scouts of America, Jacksonville, FL, 2011.
$10,000 to Cathedral Arts Project, Jacksonville, FL, 2011.
$10,000 to Daniel Foundation, Jacksonville, FL, 2011.
$10,000 to University of North Florida, Jacksonville, FL, 2011.
$5,000 to Baptist Association for Special Children and Adults, Orange Park, FL, 2011.
$5,000 to LArche Harbor House, Jacksonville, FL, 2011.
$3,000 to Community Foundation, Jacksonville, FL, 2011.

2118
Gemcon Family Foundation ✧
P.O. Box 2689
Palm Beach, FL 33480-2689

Established in 2004 in FL.
Donors: CMM Children Charitable Lead Annuity Trust; CM Miesel Charitable Lead Annuity Trust.
Foundation type: Independent foundation.
Financial data (yr. ended 12/31/13): Assets, $17,493,883 (M); gifts received, $836,400; expenditures, $969,085; qualifying distributions, $885,977; giving activities include $767,175 for 14 grants (high: $150,000; low: $1,000).
Fields of interest: Education; Autism; Medical research, institute; Human services.
Limitations: Applications not accepted. Giving primarily in FL. No grants to individuals.
Application information: Unsolicited requests for funds not accepted.
Trustees: Norma J. Bach; Timothy J. Bach; Judith Ann Jokiel; Constance M. Liphardt.
EIN: 576199853

2119
Joel F. Gemunder Foundation ✧ ☆
35 Canvasback Dr.
Amelia Island, FL 32034-6623 (513) 579-5310
Contact: Joel F. Gemunder, Tr.

Established in 1997 in OH.
Foundation type: Independent foundation.
Financial data (yr. ended 12/31/12): Assets, $30,162,272 (M); expenditures, $503,234; qualifying distributions, $458,415; giving activities include $441,995 for 6 grants (high: $377,895; low: $2,500).
Fields of interest: Education; Jewish agencies & synagogues.
Limitations: Applications accepted. Giving primarily in Washington, DC, IL, NY, and OH. No grants to individuals.
Application information: Application form required.
Initial approach: Letter
Deadline(s): None
Trustee: Joel F. Gemunder.
EIN: 311534042

2120
The Geo Group Foundation, Inc. ✧
621 N.W. 53rd St., Ste. 700
Boca Raton, FL 33487-8242 (561) 999-7455
FAX: (561) 443-6045; Main URL: http://www.geogroupfoundation.com

Established in FL.
Foundation type: Independent foundation.
Financial data (yr. ended 12/31/13): Assets, $38,302 (M); gifts received, $1,567,471; expenditures, $1,607,673; qualifying distributions, $1,607,673; giving activities include $1,607,242 for 527 grants (high: $200,000; low: $10).
Purpose and activities: Giving primarily to local charitable nonprofit organizations, schools, and public entities. The foundation also grants scholarships to help children pursue educational opportunities that may otherwise be unavailable to them.
Fields of interest: Higher education; Scholarships/financial aid; Education; Children.
Limitations: Applications accepted. Giving in areas where The GRO Group, Inc., its subsidiaries or affiliated companies operate.
Application information: Application form required.
Initial approach: Letter requesting application form
Deadline(s): None
Officers and Directors:* George C. Zoley,* Chair. and Pres.; Brian R. Evans,* V.P.; John J. Bulfin, Secy.; Marcel Maier, Treas.; Pablo E. Paez,* Exec. Dir.; John M. Hurley.
EIN: 274034030

2121
The Gerstner Family Foundation ✧
c/o Bessemer Trust Co. of Florida
222 Royal Palm Way
Palm Beach, FL 33480-4303

Established in 2006 in FL.
Donors: Louis V. Gerstner, Jr.; Louis V. Gerstner, Jr. Trust.
Foundation type: Independent foundation.
Financial data (yr. ended 12/31/13): Assets, $154,032,919 (M); gifts received, $21,362,836; expenditures, $4,066,935; qualifying distributions, $3,596,347; giving activities include $3,296,595 for 48+ grants (high: $621,222).
Fields of interest: Museums (natural history); Higher education; Education; Hospitals (specialty); Cancer; Catholic agencies & churches.
Limitations: Applications not accepted. Giving primarily in New York, NY; some giving also in Cambridge, PA.
Application information: Contributes only to pre-selected organizations.
Trustees: Lea Carpenter-Brokaw; Elizabeth R. Gerstner; Louis V. Gerstner, Jr.; Louis V. Gerstner III; Kara Klein; Preston Koster; Stan Litow; Bessemer Trust Company of Florida.
EIN: 208559135

2122
Charlotte Geyer Foundation ✧
c/o Nancy Falletta
471 Meadow Lark Dr.
Sarasota, FL 34236-1901
E-mail: nefalletta@roadrunner.com; Tel. for inquiries: (716) 632-6448; fax: (716) 632-6098

Established in 1991 in FL.
Donor: Paul F. Eckel.
Foundation type: Independent foundation.
Financial data (yr. ended 12/31/13): Assets, $4,305 (M); gifts received, $2,232,200; expenditures, $2,231,670; qualifying distributions, $2,229,379; giving activities include $2,138,200 for 5 grants (high: $1,100,000; low: $20,000).
Fields of interest: Medical research, institute.
Type of support: Research.
Limitations: Applications not accepted. Giving on a national basis. No grants to individuals.
Application information: Contributes only to pre-selected organizations.
Board meeting date(s): 30 days following deadline
Officer and Trustees:* Nancy E. Falletta,* Exec. Dir.; Charlotte E. Blaney; Joyce A. Eckel.
Number of staff: 1 full-time professional.
EIN: 650281614
Selected grants: The following grants are a representative sample of this grantmaker's funding activity:
$25,000 to Community Foundation for Greater Buffalo, Buffalo, NY, 2012. For community/education.

2123
The GiveWell Community Foundation, Inc. ✧
(also known as CFGL)
(formerly The Community Foundation of Greater Lakeland, Inc.)
1501 S. Florida Ave.
Lakeland, FL 33803-2258 (863) 683-3131
Contact: Terry Simmers, C.E.O.; For Communications and Operations: Lori Martini, C.O.O.; For Finance/Investments: Amy Royal, C.F.O.; For grants: Johnna Martinez, Grants Mgr.
FAX: (863) 683-3131; E-mail: info@givecf.org; Additional e-mails: tsimmers@givecf.org, lmartini@givecf.org, and aroyal@givecf.org; Grant inquiry e-mail: jmartinez@GiveCF.org; Main URL: http://www.givecf.org/
Facebook: http://www.facebook.com/pages/Community-Foundation-of-Greater-Lakeland/62619659572

Established in 1997 in FL.
Foundation type: Community foundation.
Financial data (yr. ended 06/30/14): Assets, $129,506,437 (M); gifts received, $18,912,680; expenditures, $10,557,338; giving activities include $9,896,861 for 30+ grants (high: $1,432,500).
Purpose and activities: The foundation seeks to improve the quality of life in all areas of greater Lakeland, FL. It does this by serving donors, local nonprofit charities, and the community at large.
Fields of interest: Historic preservation/historical societies; Arts; Education; Environment; Health care; Housing/shelter; Family services; Aging, centers/services; Human services; Community/economic development; Youth.
Type of support: Capital campaigns; Equipment; Seed money; Matching/challenge support.
Limitations: Applications accepted. Giving primarily in the greater Lakeland, FL, area. No support for sectarian religious projects that are not open to all. No grants for to individuals (except for scholarships and emergency grants), or for tickets, annual or building campaigns, endowments, operating expense, galas, membership dues, medical or scientific research, debt reduction or bridge funding, or fundraising events or celebrations.
Application information: Visit foundation web site for application form and guidelines. The foundation offers one grant orientation each fiscal year; attendance is mandatory. Application form required.
Initial approach: Attend grant orientation
Copies of proposal: 1
Deadline(s): Changes annually -check web site for most current information
Final notification: Oct. for initial qualification determination
Officers and Board Members:* Clayton Hollis,* Chair.; Suzie Moraco,* Vice-Chair.; Terry Simmers, C.E.O. and Pres.; Amy Royal, C.F.O.; Lori Martini, Chief Philanthropic Off.; Laura Hawley,* Secy.; Walker Wilkerson,* Treas.; Bruce Abels; Barney Barnett; Brenda Craft; Jim Chaffin; Jeff Cox; Patrick Fagan; Bill Dorman; Ed Grossman; Sarah McKay; Bonnie Parker; Lyle Philpson; R. Gary Price; Tim Putnam; Linda Rich; Carol Shira; Rick Stephens; John Vreeland.
EIN: 593649871
Selected grants: The following grants are a representative sample of this grantmaker's funding activity:
$666,030 to United Way of Central Florida, Highland City, FL, 2012.
$502,550 to First United Methodist Church, Lakeland, FL, 2012. For operations.
$495,375 to Parker Street Ministries, Lakeland, FL, 2012. For general operations.
$432,500 to Talbot House Ministries of Lakeland, Lakeland, FL, 2012. For general operations.
$419,300 to All Saints Academy, Winter Haven, FL, 2012. For tuition assistance and operations.
$396,975 to Florida Southern College, Lakeland, FL, 2012. For tuition assistance and operations.
$330,000 to United Way Worldwide, Alexandria, VA, 2012.
$244,500 to Polk Theater, Lakeland, FL, 2012. For general support.
$210,927 to VISTE, Lakeland, FL, 2012. For annual campaign.
$151,000 to Florida Air Museum, Lakeland, FL, 2012. For programs.

2124
Glazer Family Foundation, Inc. ✧
c/o Coord.
1 Buccaneer Pl.
Tampa, FL 33607-5701 (813) 870-2700
E-mail: GlazerFamilyFoundation@buccaneers.nfl.com; Main URL: http://www.glazerfamilyfoundation.com/
Facebook: http://www.facebook.com/glazerfamilyfoundation
Grants List: http://www.glazerfamilyfoundation.org/our-programs/grant-program/who-has-received-grants

Established in 1999 in FL.
Donors: Buccaneer L.P.; Florida Sports Foundation.
Foundation type: Company-sponsored foundation.
Financial data (yr. ended 12/31/12): Assets, $1,014,825 (M); gifts received, $3,591,204; expenditures, $2,588,441; qualifying distributions, $2,561,236; giving activities include $2,561,236 for 55 grants (high: $1,010,000; low: $875).
Purpose and activities: The foundation supports programs designed to serve disadvantaged youth and families.
Fields of interest: Museums; Libraries (public); Education, reading; Education; Hospitals (general); Health care, clinics/centers; Optometry/vision screening; Health care, patient services; Health care; Food services; Safety/disasters; Athletics/sports, amateur leagues; Athletics/sports, football; Recreation; Children/youth, services; Human services; Community/economic development; Youth; Economically disadvantaged.
Type of support: Equipment; Program development; Donated products; In-kind gifts.
Limitations: Applications not accepted. Giving primarily in Tampa Bay and central FL, with emphasis on Charlotte, Citrus, De Soto, Hardee, Hernando, Highlands, Hillsborough, Lake, Manatee, Marion, Orange, Osceola, Pasco, Pinellas, Polk, Sarasota, Seminole, Sumter counties. No support for political organizations. No grants to individuals, or for fundraising, celebrations, administrative/training costs, capital campaigns, sponsorships, scholarships, basic research/conferences, or political campaigns.
Publications: Program policy statement.
Application information: The foundation currently practices an invitation only process for giving.
Officers and Directors: Darcie Glazer Kassewitz, Co-Pres.; Edward Glazer, Co-Pres.; Avie Glazer; Bryan Glazer; Joel Glazer; Kevin Glazer.
EIN: 593578188

2125
Jack and Anne Glenn Charitable Foundation ✧
P.O. Box 1908
Orlando, FL 32802-1908
Application address: c/o SunTrust Bank, Attn.: Allen Mast, P.O. Box 4655, MC 221, Atlanta, GA 30302, tel.: (404) 588-7347

Foundation type: Independent foundation.
Financial data (yr. ended 12/31/12): Assets, $9,952,168 (M); expenditures, $521,261; qualifying distributions, $498,454; giving activities include $477,000 for 26 grants (high: $75,000; low: $2,000).
Fields of interest: Education; Environment; Human services.
Application information: Application form required.
Initial approach: Proposal
Deadline(s): Feb 15 and July 15
Trustee: SunTrust Bank.
Directors: Alston Glenn; Jack Glenn; Lewis Glenn; Robert Glenn.
EIN: 200543515

2126
Global Village Charitable Trust ✧
4000 Ponce de Leon Blvd., Ste. 510
Coral Gables, FL 33146-1431

Established in 1993 in OH.
Donors: Daniel R. Lewis; Marley B. Lewis.
Foundation type: Independent foundation.
Financial data (yr. ended 12/31/12): Assets, $8,147,272 (M); gifts received, $4,264,302; expenditures, $3,483,757; qualifying distributions, $3,476,145; giving activities include $3,468,260 for 97 grants (high: $526,676; low: $180).
Fields of interest: Performing arts, music; Arts; Health organizations; Human services; Jewish federated giving programs.
Limitations: Applications not accepted. Giving primarily in CA, FL, and NY. No grants to individuals.
Application information: Contributes only to pre-selected organizations.
Manager: Marley B. Lewis.
Trustee: Daniel R. Lewis.
EIN: 341757652

2127
Goel Family Foundation Inc. ✧
6710 Old Wolf Bay Rd.
Palatka, FL 32177-6830

Established in 2006 in FL.
Donor: Mukesh Goel.
Foundation type: Independent foundation.
Financial data (yr. ended 12/31/12): Assets, $283,504 (M); gifts received, $150,000; expenditures, $456,343; qualifying distributions, $450,301; giving activities include $450,301 for grants.
Fields of interest: Arts, cultural/ethnic awareness; Education; Hinduism.
Limitations: Applications not accepted. Giving primarily in FL. No grants to individuals.
Application information: Contributes only to pre-selected organizations.
Officers: Mukesh Goel, Pres.; Ramesh Gupta, V.P.; Manju Goel, Secy.-Treas.
EIN: 205307211

2128
Alfred & Ann Goldstein Foundation, Inc. ✧
682 Mourning Dove Dr.
Sarasota, FL 34236-1926

Established in 1955 in NY.
Donors: Alfred R. Goldstein; Ann L. Goldstein; Joseph I. Lubin†.
Foundation type: Independent foundation.
Financial data (yr. ended 12/31/13): Assets, $14,457,275 (M); expenditures, $1,067,503; qualifying distributions, $1,042,420; giving activities include $1,037,320 for 77 grants (high: $600,000; low: $100).
Purpose and activities: Grants primarily for the arts and education; support also for health associations, Jewish organizations, and social services.
Fields of interest: Performing arts; Arts; Education; Health organizations, association; Human services; Foundations (community); Jewish federated giving programs; Jewish agencies & synagogues.
Limitations: Applications not accepted. Giving primarily in FL and NY. No grants to individuals.
Application information: Contributes only to pre-selected organizations.
Officer: Alfred R. Goldstein, Pres.
Directors: Wendy H. Cohen; Cynthia Goldstein; Richard Goldstein; Steven R. Goldstein; Dana Yaphe.
EIN: 136033997
Selected grants: The following grants are a representative sample of this grantmaker's funding activity:
$25,000 to Institute for the Ages, Sarasota, FL, 2011.
$5,000 to Westcoast Black Theater Troupe of Florida, Sarasota, FL, 2011.

2129
Melvin R. Goodes Family Foundation, Inc. ✧
640 Ocean Rd.
Vero Beach, FL 32963-3516
Contact: Melvin R. Goodes, Pres.

Established in 1997 in NJ.
Donors: Melvin R. Goodes; Nancy Goodes.
Foundation type: Independent foundation.
Financial data (yr. ended 12/31/13): Assets, $3,341,784 (M); expenditures, $1,819,068; qualifying distributions, $1,798,637; giving activities include $1,798,637 for 32 grants (high: $1,000,000; low: $1,000).
Fields of interest: Higher education, university; Alzheimer's disease research; Housing/shelter, development; Boys & girls clubs; Human services; Children/youth, services.
Type of support: Building/renovation.
Limitations: Applications accepted. No support for private foundations. No grants to individuals.
Application information:
Initial approach: Letter
Deadline(s): None
Officers: Melvin R. Goodes, Pres.; Melanie G. Caceres, V.P.; Michelle R. Goodes, Co-Secy.; Nancy Goodes, Co-Secy.; David R. Goodes, Treas.
EIN: 223513671

2130
The Lucy Gooding Charitable Foundation Trust ✧
P.O. Box 37349
Jacksonville, FL 32236-7349
Contact: Bonnie H. Smith, Tr.
E-mail: bhsmith@bellsouth.net; Tel./fax: (904) 786-4796

Established in 1988 in FL.
Donor: Lucy B. Gooding†.
Foundation type: Independent foundation.
Financial data (yr. ended 12/31/13): Assets, $104,250,100 (M); expenditures, $5,099,705; qualifying distributions, $4,091,986; giving activities include $3,892,184 for 49 grants (high: $500,000; low: $2,500).
Purpose and activities: Funding preference is for organizations in the five county area surrounding Jacksonville, Florida, with projects helping children.
Fields of interest: Education; Health care; Human services; Children/youth, services; Children; Disabilities, people with; Economically disadvantaged.
Type of support: General/operating support; Continuing support; Annual campaigns; Capital campaigns; Building/renovation; Equipment; Land acquisition; Endowments; Program development.
Limitations: Applications accepted. Giving limited to Duval, Clay, Baker, Nassau, and St. Johns, counties, FL. No support for private foundations, religious organizations, or for adults-only services. No grants to individuals.
Publications: Informational brochure (including application guidelines).
Application information: Application form required.
Initial approach: Request application form
Copies of proposal: 1
Deadline(s): Sept. 30
Final notification: By Dec. 1
Trustees: Bonnie H. Smith, Managing Tr.; Wilford C. Lyon, Jr.; Robert A. Mills; David H. Peek.
Number of staff: 1 full-time professional.
EIN: 592891582

2131
Leo Goodwin Foundation, Inc. ✧
800 Corporate Dr., Ste. 500
Fort Lauderdale, FL 33334-3621 (954) 772-6863
Contact: Helen M. Furia, Pres.

Established in 1977 in FL.
Donors: Leo Goodwin, Jr.†; Emerald Asset Advisors, Inc.
Foundation type: Independent foundation.
Financial data (yr. ended 10/31/13): Assets, $14,946,337 (M); gifts received, $25,000; expenditures, $1,350,893; qualifying distributions, $823,560; giving activities include $484,400 for 41 grants (high: $102,000; low: $1,000).
Purpose and activities: Giving primarily for children, youth and health organizations; some funding also for the arts and education.
Fields of interest: Arts; Education; Health organizations; Boys & girls clubs; Children/youth, services.
Type of support: General/operating support; Scholarship funds.
Limitations: Giving primarily in FL, with emphasis on Broward County. No grants to individuals.
Application information: Application form not required.
Initial approach: Letter
Deadline(s): None
Officers: Helen M. Furia, Pres.; Elliot P. Borkson, V.P.; Alan J. Goldberg, Treas.
EIN: 526054098
Selected grants: The following grants are a representative sample of this grantmaker's funding activity:
$100,000 to Henderson Behavioral Health, Lauderdale Lakes, FL, 2011.
$100,000 to Junior Achievement of South Florida, Coconut Creek, FL, 2011.
$15,000 to Achievement and Rehabilitation Centers, Sunrise, FL, 2011.

2132
GPD Charitable Trust ✧ ☆
9110 Strada Pl., Ste. 6200
Naples, FL 34108-2396

Established in FL.
Foundation type: Independent foundation.
Financial data (yr. ended 06/30/13): Assets, $14,026,164 (M); expenditures, $1,489,325; qualifying distributions, $1,357,392; giving activities include $1,224,678 for 20 grants (high: $511,765; low: $300), and $132,714 for foundation-administered programs.
Purpose and activities: Giving primarily for higher education, a YMCA, and for youth services, particularly at-risk youth.
Fields of interest: Higher education; Human services; YM/YWCAs & YM/YWHAs; Children/youth, services.
Limitations: Applications not accepted. Giving in the U.S., with some emphasis on NY.
Application information: Unsolicited requests for funds not accepted.
Trustees: John DeBlasio; Pasquale DeBlasio.
EIN: 277008643

2133
George H. Graff Irrevocable Trust ✧ ☆
311 S. 2nd St., Ste. 200
Fort Pierce, FL 34950-1515

Established in FL.
Foundation type: Independent foundation.
Financial data (yr. ended 12/31/13): Assets, $11,892,178 (M); expenditures, $645,079; qualifying distributions, $505,264; giving activities include $505,264 for 8 grants (high: $63,158; low: $63,158).
Fields of interest: Media, television; Media, radio; Animal welfare; Alzheimer's disease; AIDS research; Children/youth, services.
Limitations: Applications not accepted. Giving primarily in Darien, CT, Washington, DC, Chicago, IL, Boston, MA, Durham, NH, New York, NY, and Seattle, WA.
Application information: Contributes only to pre-selected organizations.
Trustee: Chester B. Griffin.
EIN: 656463779

2134
Green Family Foundation, Inc. ✧
2601 S. Bayshore Dr., 9th Fl.
Coconut Grove, FL 33133-5417 (305) 858-4225
E-mail: info@greenff.org; Miami Beach address: 1820 Bay Rd., Miami Beach, FL 33139, tel.: (305) 538-4848, ext. 14; fax: (305) 538-4890; e-mail for information about current grant opportunities or to be added to the foundation's RFP contact list: grants@greenff.org; Main URL: http://www.greenff.org
Facebook: http://www.facebook.com/greenff
Twitter: https://twitter.com/GreenFamilyFdn
YouTube: http://www.youtube.com/greenfamilymiami

Established in 1991 in FL.
Donor: Steven J. Green.
Foundation type: Independent foundation.
Financial data (yr. ended 12/31/12): Assets, $25,098,656 (M); gifts received, $12,511,316; expenditures, $1,999,265; qualifying distributions, $1,523,749; giving activities include $1,512,186 for 37 grants (high: $1,200,000; low: $100), and $11,563 for foundation-administered programs.
Purpose and activities: The foundation provides seed grants to support holistic programs that empower entire communities. The end goal is to enable underserved communities to achieve sustainability and self-reliance by alleviating the cycle of poverty and disease. The foundation lends resources to programs that focus on, 1) global health and development, 2) community empowerment, 3) youth arts, and 4) education.
Fields of interest: Arts; Education; Human services; Children/youth, services; International development; Foundations (private grantmaking); Immigrants/refugees; Economically disadvantaged.
Limitations: Applications not accepted. Giving primarily in Miami, FL. No grants to individuals, or for emergency funding to cover ongoing program or operational deficits.
Publications: Grants list.
Application information: Contributes only to pre-selected organizations. See foundation web site for current RFP information.
Officers: Kimberly Green, Pres.; Kevin Coster, V.P.
EIN: 650284913
Selected grants: The following grants are a representative sample of this grantmaker's funding activity:
$7,000 to United Through Reading, San Diego, CA, 2012. For Cultural and Educational Purpose.
$2,500 to Unity on the Bay, Miami, FL, 2012. For religious purpose.
$2,000 to Kristi House, Miami, FL, 2012. To Assist Those in Need.
$100 to University of Colorado Foundation, Denver, CO, 2012. For educational purpose.

2135
Green Family Foundation, Inc. ✧
9726 53rd Dr. E.
Bradenton, FL 34211-3760 (315) 218-8286
Contact: Jeffrey B. Scheer Esq., Tr.
Application address: 1 Lincoln Ctr., Syracuse, NY 13202-1355, tel.: (315) 218-8286

Established in 2006 in NJ.
Donor: Howard L. Green†.
Foundation type: Independent foundation.
Financial data (yr. ended 12/31/12): Assets, $16,638,607 (M); expenditures, $1,085,866; qualifying distributions, $923,083; giving activities include $828,000 for 44 grants (high: $100,000; low: $2,000).
Purpose and activities: Funding for new or remodeled facilities, scholarship funding for colleges and universities, medical institutions, start-up funding for educational, cultural, artistic and other social service initiatives, and start-up or scholarship funding for after-school, weekend or summer program for youth.
Fields of interest: Arts; Higher education; Human services; Salvation Army.
Limitations: Applications accepted. Giving primarily in FL, NY and SC. No grants to individuals.
Application information: Application form required.
Initial approach: Grant application form
Deadline(s): Aug. 31
Final notification: Dec. 31
Trustees: Calvin Green; Donald J. Green; Eric Green; Ivor Rich; Jeffrey Scheer; Richard S. Scolaro.
EIN: 204256553

2136
Green Park Foundation ✧ ☆
9611 N. US Hwy. 1, Ste. 340
Sebastian, FL 32958-6363

Established in 1999 in DC.
Donors: Melissa Baron Murdoch; Stephen Murdoch.
Foundation type: Independent foundation.
Financial data (yr. ended 12/31/13): Assets, $4,295,299 (M); gifts received, $500,000; expenditures, $609,642; qualifying distributions, $600,811; giving activities include $599,503 for 7 grants (high: $425,503; low: $10,000).
Fields of interest: Libraries (public); Education, reading; Education; Environment, natural resources; Public health; Human services; International relief; Women.
Limitations: Applications not accepted. Giving primarily in CA, Washington, DC, MA and OH. No grants to individuals.
Application information: Contributes only to pre-selected organizations.
Directors: Nancy C. Baron; Melissa Baron Murdoch; Stephen I. Murdoch.
EIN: 522178078

2137
Greenburg May Foundation, Inc. ✧
9999 Collins Ave., Apt. 15A
Bal Harbour, FL 33154-1834

Incorporated in 1947 in DE.
Donors: Harry Greenburg†; Samuel D. May†.
Foundation type: Independent foundation.
Financial data (yr. ended 12/31/13): Assets, $12,431,094 (M); expenditures, $820,608; qualifying distributions, $668,296; giving activities include $668,296 for 33 grants (high: $500,000; low: $100).
Purpose and activities: Grants almost entirely for medical research, primarily cancer, heart, diabetes, Parkinson's, and neurological research; support also for the aged, hospitals, Jewish welfare funds, and temples.
Fields of interest: Hospitals (general); Cancer; Heart & circulatory diseases; Neuroscience; Medical research, institute; Cancer research; Human services; Aging, centers/services; Jewish federated giving programs; Jewish agencies & synagogues; Children; Aging; Blind/visually impaired.
International interests: Israel.
Type of support: General/operating support; Continuing support; Annual campaigns; Endowments; Emergency funds; Program development; Internship funds; Scholarship funds; Research; Consulting services.
Limitations: Applications accepted. Giving primarily in southern FL and Long Island, NY. No grants to individuals, or for conferences; generally no grants for scholarships or fellowships; no loans.
Application information: Application form required.
Initial approach: Letter
Copies of proposal: 1
Deadline(s): None
Board meeting date(s): Jan., Apr., July, and Oct.
Final notification: 1 to 2 months
Officer: Isabel May, Pres.
Directors: Peter May; Linda Sklar.
Number of staff: 2 part-time support.
EIN: 136162935
Selected grants: The following grants are a representative sample of this grantmaker's funding activity:
$5,000 to Simon Wiesenthal Center, Los Angeles, CA, 2012. For aid donees in carrying out exempt purpose.

2138
The Griffin Foundation, Inc. ✧
c/o D. Clay Lovett
1601 Gulf Shore Blvd. N., Ste. 16
Naples, FL 34102-4995

Established in 2000 in FL.
Donor: John F. Griffin.
Foundation type: Independent foundation.
Financial data (yr. ended 12/31/13): Assets, $8,120,643 (M); expenditures, $748,736; qualifying distributions, $738,875; giving activities include $735,139 for 11 grants (high: $200,000; low: $8,245).
Fields of interest: Secondary school/education; Health organizations; Human services; Catholic federated giving programs; Catholic agencies & churches.
Limitations: Applications not accepted. Giving primarily in the U.S., with emphasis on Washington, DC; some funding also in Aguadilla, Puerto Rico, and in London, England. No grants to individuals.
Application information: Contributes only to pre-selected organizations.
Officers and Directors:* John F. Griffin,* Pres.; Daniel Clay Lovett,* Secy.-Treas.; Beth Ann Griffin Adler; Martin P. Griffin; Nancy M. Griffin; Sean P. Griffin.
EIN: 311730661
Selected grants: The following grants are a representative sample of this grantmaker's funding activity:
$25,000 to Friends of Choice in Urban Schools, Washington, DC, 2012. For Education Support/Promote Public Charter Schools.
$20,000 to Hereditary Disease Foundation, New York, NY, 2012. For medical care.
$15,000 to Archbishop Carroll High School, Washington, DC, 2012. For education employee recognition.
$10,000 to So Others Might Eat, Washington, DC, 2012. For employee recognition.

2139
Alice Busch Gronewaldt Foundation Inc. ✧
c/o Caldwell Pacetti
250 S. Australian Ave.
West Palm Beach, FL 33401-5018
Contact: Andrew Regan, Secy.

Established in 1990 in FL.
Donor: Alice Busch Gronewaldt‡.
Foundation type: Independent foundation.
Financial data (yr. ended 12/31/12): Assets, $9,283,627 (M); expenditures, $552,036; qualifying distributions, $459,544; giving activities include $459,544 for grants.
Purpose and activities: Support primarily for education, the arts, historic preservation, health care, and human services; some funding also for Christian organizations and churches.
Fields of interest: Historic preservation/historical societies; Arts; Elementary/secondary education; Higher education; Education; Hospitals (general); Health care; Human services; Children/youth, services; Christian agencies & churches.
Type of support: Matching/challenge support; General/operating support.
Limitations: Applications accepted. Giving primarily in FL and NY. No grants to individuals.
Application information: Application form not required.
Initial approach: Proposal
Deadline(s): None
Officers and Directors:* Louis Busch Hager, Jr., Pres.; Andrew W. Regan,* Secy.; Alice Hager Holbrook; Mary Hager Thomas.
EIN: 650212289

2140
Grundy Family Foundation Inc ✧
11811 Hope Ln.
Tampa, FL 33618-3752

Donors: Laurence S. Grundy; Terrill S. Grundy.
Foundation type: Independent foundation.
Financial data (yr. ended 08/31/13): Assets, $805,172 (M); gifts received, $332,917; expenditures, $1,955,841; qualifying distributions, $1,951,650; giving activities include $1,951,650 for 23 grants (high: $710,000; low: $50).
Fields of interest: Education; Agriculture/food; Religion.
Limitations: Applications not accepted.
Application information: Unsolicited requests for funds not accepted.
Directors: James P. Gills; Laurence S. Grundy; Terrill S. Grundy.
EIN: 263925489

2141
Audrey and Martin Gruss Foundation ✧
c/o Gruss & Co., Inc.
777 S. Flagler Dr., Ste. 801-E
West Palm Beach, FL 33401-6134

Established in 2009 in FL.
Donors: Martin D. Gruss; Joseph S. Gruss Settlor Trust; Joseph S. Gruss Trust.
Foundation type: Independent foundation.
Financial data (yr. ended 08/31/13): Assets, $102,220,548 (M); gifts received, $2,593,661; expenditures, $8,484,291; qualifying distributions, $6,573,074; giving activities include $6,560,982 for grants.
Fields of interest: Medical research; Human services.
Limitations: Applications not accepted. Giving primarily in San Francisco, CA and New York, NY.
Application information: Unsolicited requests for funds not accepted.
Officers: Audrey B. Gruss, Co-Pres.; Martin D. Gruss, Co-Pres.; Brash Lalta, V.P.
EIN: 900445575
Selected grants: The following grants are a representative sample of this grantmaker's funding activity:
$1,500,000 to Schwab Charitable Fund, San Francisco, CA, 2011. For general support.
$850,000 to Schwab Charitable Fund, San Francisco, CA, 2011. For general support.
$785,000 to Schwab Charitable Fund, San Francisco, CA, 2011. For general support.
$715,000 to Hope for Depression Research Foundation, New York, NY, 2011. For medical research.
$275,000 to Hope for Depression Research Foundation, New York, NY, 2011. For medical research.
$250,000 to Boston Medical Center, Boston, MA, 2011. For medical research.
$150,000 to Center for Initiatives in Jewish Education, New York, NY, 2011. For general support.
$35,000 to Tufts University, Medford, MA, 2011. For general support.
$25,000 to Teach for America, New York, NY, 2011. For general support.
$20,000 to Melanoma Research Alliance Foundation, Washington, DC, 2011. For general support.

2142
Gulf Coast Community Foundation, Inc. ✧
(doing business as Gulf Coast Community Foundation)
(formerly Gulf Coast Community Foundation of Venice)
601 Tamiami Trail South
Venice, FL 34285-3237 (941) 486-4600
Contact: Wendy Deming, Chief of Staff and Corp. Secy.; Teri A. Hansen, C.E.O./Pres.
FAX: (941) 486-4699; E-mail: info@gulfcoastcf.org; Additional e-mail: thansen@gulfcoastcf.org; Main URL: http://www.gulfcoastcf.org/
Facebook: https://www.facebook.com/GulfCoastCommFnd
LinkedIn: http://www.linkedin.com/companies/gulf-coast-community-foundation-of-venice
Twitter: http://www.twitter.com/gulfcoastcf
YouTube: http://www.youtube.com/user/GulfCoastCF

Established in 1995 in FL.
Foundation type: Community foundation.
Financial data (yr. ended 06/30/13): Assets, $232,647,057 (M); gifts received, $19,904,665; expenditures, $22,670,492; giving activities include $16,432,516 for grants.
Purpose and activities: Together with donors, the Gulf Coast Community Foundation transforms the local region through bold and proactive philanthropy. Gulf Coast is a public charity that was created in 1995 through the sale of the Venice Hospital. Since then, the foundation has welcomed more than 500 charitable funds established by generous donors and invested $148 million in grants in the areas of health and human services, civic and economic development, education, arts and culture, and the environment.
Fields of interest: Media, film/video; Arts; Higher education; Education; Environmental education; Environment; Health care; Mental health/crisis services; Disasters, preparedness/services; Youth development; Youth, services; Aging, centers/services; Human services; Community development, neighborhood development; Community development, citizen coalitions; Public affairs, citizen participation; Public affairs.
Type of support: Emergency funds; Program development; Scholarship funds; Consulting services.
Limitations: Applications accepted. Giving limited to Charlotte, DeSoto, Lee, Manatee, Sarasota counties in FL. No support for religious purposes. No grants to individuals (except for scholarships), or for endowments, debt reduction, basic scientific research, events, or travel.
Publications: Application guidelines; Annual report; Grants list; Informational brochure (including application guidelines); Occasional report.
Application information: Each year, the foundation's grantmaking evolves to stay ahead of emerging issues and to make the greatest positive impact throughout the region. The foundation invites nonprofit organizations to partner with them as they transform the region through bold ideas, creative projects, and proactive philanthropy. This year, Gulf Coast will fund Leveraged grants and Transformative grants greater than $10,000, and Community grants of $10,000 and under. Application form required.
Initial approach: Visit grant page on website: http://www.gulfcoastcf.org/resources.php
Deadline(s): Varies
Board meeting date(s): Bimonthly
Final notification: Varies
Officers and Directors:* Tommy Taylor,* Chair.; Jay McHarque,* Vice-Chair.; Teri A. Hansen,* C.E.O. and Pres.; Veronica Brady, Sr. V.P., Philanthropy; Mark Pritchett, Sr. V.P., Community Investment; Rich Jones, V.P., Finance; Wendy Deming, Chief of Staff and Corp. Secy.; Judy Cahn; Lisa Carlton; Scott Collins; Norbert Donelly; Janis Fawn; Jim Gallogly; Benjamin Hanan; Phil Humann; Michael Saunders; Bayne Stevenson; R. Elton White.
Number of staff: 15 full-time professional.
EIN: 591052433
Selected grants: The following grants are a representative sample of this grantmaker's funding activity:
$250,000 to Florida West Coast Public Broadcasting, WEDU-TV, Tampa, FL, 2011.
$30,000 to Big Brothers Big Sisters of the Sun Coast, Venice, FL, 2011.
$30,000 to Boca Grande Fire Control District, Boca Grande, FL, 2011.
$30,000 to Forty Carrots of Sarasota, Sarasota, FL, 2011.
$30,000 to Venice Area Mobile Meals, Venice, FL, 2011.
$24,890 to Catholic Charities Diocese of Venice, Venice, FL, 2011.
$20,000 to Ringling School of Art and Design, Sarasota, FL, 2011.
$10,000 to Military Spouse Corporate Career Network, Lake Saint Louis, MO, 2011.
$5,000 to North Port, City of, North Port, FL, 2011.
$1,500 to Chamber of Commerce Foundation of Greater Sarasota, Sarasota, FL, 2011.

2143
Irving and Barbara C. Gutin Charitable Foundation ✧ ☆
2150 E. Maya Palm Way
Boca Raton, FL 33432-7992

Established in 2000 in FL.
Donors: Irving Gutin; Barbara Gutin.
Foundation type: Operating foundation.
Financial data (yr. ended 11/30/13): Assets, $6,809,186 (M); expenditures, $513,580; qualifying distributions, $475,100; giving activities include $460,000 for 1 grant.
Fields of interest: Elementary/secondary education; Health care; Human services; Homeless, human services.
Limitations: Applications not accepted. Giving primarily in FL and NY. No grants to individuals.
Application information: Contributes only to pre-selected organizations.
Trustees: Barbara C. Gutin; Irving Gutin.
EIN: 656358038
Selected grants: The following grants are a representative sample of this grantmaker's funding activity:
$350,000 to Boca Raton Regional Hospital Foundation, Boca Raton, FL, 2011.
$50,000 to Family Promise of South Palm Beach County, Delray Beach, FL, 2011.
$25,000 to American Friends of Bet El Yeshiva Center, Hempstead, NY, 2011.

2144
The Hahn Family Foundation ✧
9204 Sloane St.
Orlando, FL 32827-7026

Established in 2006 in NV.
Donors: Paul Hahn; David J. Hahn; Sang Hoon Hahn; Hai Joung Hahn; Hahn Waianae Land, LLC; Mauna Kea Villages, LLC.
Foundation type: Independent foundation.
Financial data (yr. ended 12/31/13): Assets, $13,843,642 (M); gifts received, $121,255; expenditures, $538,169; qualifying distributions, $520,324; giving activities include $462,500 for 7 grants (high: $250,000; low: $1,000).
Fields of interest: Christian agencies & churches; Protestant agencies & churches.
Type of support: General/operating support.
Limitations: Applications not accepted. Giving primarily in NJ; some funding also in CA, HI and MA. No grants to individuals.
Application information: Unsolicited requests for funds not accepted.
Trustees: Hai Joung Yoon Hahn; Sang Hoon Hahn.
EIN: 207055857

2145
The Andrew J. and Christine C. Hall Foundation, Inc. ✧
300 S. Ocean Blvd.
Palm Beach, FL 33480

Established in 1995 in CT.
Donor: Andrew J. Hall.
Foundation type: Independent foundation.
Financial data (yr. ended 06/30/13): Assets, $14,485,401 (M); gifts received, $150,000; expenditures, $541,256; qualifying distributions, $512,647; giving activities include $510,000 for 3 grants (high: $400,000; low: $10,000).
Fields of interest: Museums; Education.
Limitations: Applications not accepted. Giving primarily in CT, MA and NY. No grants to individuals.
Application information: Contributes only to pre-selected organizations.
Officers: Andrew J. Hall, Pres.; Christine C. Hall, Secy.-Treas.
Directors: Emma Hall; Mark Hall; David Tobey; Michael D. Young.
EIN: 061442498
Selected grants: The following grants are a representative sample of this grantmaker's funding activity:
$20,000 to Westport Arts Center, Westport, CT, 2011.
$15,000 to American Patrons of the Tate Gallery Foundation, New York, NY, 2011.

2146
Henry E. Haller, Jr. Foundation ✧ ☆
2100 S. Ocean Ln., No. 1101
Ft. Laudrdale, FL 33316-0757 (954) 764-6260
Contact: Linda L. Boyce Haller, Exec. Dir. and Tr.

Established in 2000 in PA.
Donor: Henry E. Haller, Jr.‡.
Foundation type: Independent foundation.
Financial data (yr. ended 12/31/13): Assets, $43,924,195 (M); gifts received, $32,063,907; expenditures, $1,758,982; qualifying distributions, $1,665,881; giving activities include $1,610,309 for 31 grants (high: $1,000,000; low: $50).
Fields of interest: Arts; Higher education; Education; Hospitals (general); Human services.
Type of support: Annual campaigns; Capital campaigns; Fellowships; Internship funds; Research; Employee matching gifts.
Limitations: Applications accepted. Giving primarily in Pittsburgh, PA.
Publications: Annual report.
Application information: Application form required.
Initial approach: Proposal
Deadline(s): None
Officer and Trustees:* Linda L. Boyce Haller,* Exec. Dir.; Kevin D. Boyce, Esq.; Joseph S. Scherle, C.P.A.
Number of staff: 1 full-time professional; 1 part-time support.
EIN: 522250015

2147
Hard Rock Cafe Foundation, Inc. ✧
6100 Old Park Ln.
Orlando, FL 32835-2466

Established in 2000 in FL.
Donors: Hard Rock Cafe International (USA) Inc.; WDI Corporation.
Foundation type: Company-sponsored foundation.
Financial data (yr. ended 12/31/12): Assets, $962 (M); gifts received, $2,268,478; expenditures, $2,267,758; qualifying distributions, $2,267,184; giving activities include $2,211,389 for 15 grants (high: $630,976; low: $14), and $55,795 for 91 grants to individuals (high: $3,000; low: $200).
Purpose and activities: The foundation supports organizations involved with music, substance abuse services, cancer research, hunger, agriculture, human services, civil and human rights, and economically disadvantaged people.
Fields of interest: Health organizations; Agriculture/food; Recreation.
Type of support: General/operating support; Program development; Research; Grants to individuals.
Limitations: Applications not accepted. Giving limited to Washington, DC and New York, NY.
Application information: Contributes only to pre-selected organizations and individuals.
Officers and Directors:* Hamish Dodds,* Pres.; Jay Wolszczak,* Secy.; Thomas Gispanski,* Treas.
EIN: 593686985
Selected grants: The following grants are a representative sample of this grantmaker's funding activity:
$492,132 to Breast Cancer Research Foundation, New York, NY, 2012. To achieve prevention and a cure for breast cancer by providing critical funding for innovative medical research and increasing public awareness about good breast health.
$105,155 to City of Hope, Duarte, CA, 2012. For Innovative biomedical research, treatment and educational institution dedicated to the prevention and cure of cancer and other life-threatening diseases.
$37 to Musicians on Call, New York, NY, 2012. For music and entertainment to promote and complement the healing process for patients in the interest of improving their quality of life and creating a better living and healing environment. Additionally seeks to raise awareness of the beneficial effect.

2148
The Harrington Family Foundation ✧
(formerly The Harrington-McLaughlin Family Foundation)
c/o Ronald G. Harrington
13 Sail Point Rd.
Key Largo, FL 33037-3769

Established in 2002 in OH.
Donors: Ronald G. Harrington; Ronald M. Harrington; Jill A. McLaughlin; Stephen M. McLaughlin; Nancy A. Harrington.
Foundation type: Independent foundation.
Financial data (yr. ended 12/31/12): Assets, $26,521,317 (M); expenditures, $4,974,879; qualifying distributions, $4,825,584; giving activities include $4,825,584 for 24 grants (high: $3,106,100; low: $200).
Purpose and activities: Giving primarily for education, human services, and health, including therapeutic riding services.
Fields of interest: Education; Hospitals (general); Health organizations, association; Human services; Foundations (private grantmaking).
Limitations: Applications not accepted. Giving primarily in OH, with some emphasis on Cleveland and Bath. No grants to individuals.
Application information: Contributes only to pre-selected organizations.
Trustees: Nancy A. Harrington; Ronald G. Harrington; Ronald M. Harrington; Jill A. McLaughlin; Stephen M. McLaughlin.
EIN: 830343509

2149
Harris Foundation ✧
1025 W. NASA Blvd., M.S. A-11P
Melbourne, FL 32919-0002 (321) 724-3167
E-mail: harris.foundation@harris.com; Main URL: http://harris.com/corporate_responsibility/foundation.aspx

Incorporated in 1958 in OH.
Donor: Harris Corp.
Foundation type: Company-sponsored foundation.
Financial data (yr. ended 06/30/12): Assets, $1,369,075 (M); gifts received, $890,728; expenditures, $1,374,934; qualifying distributions, $1,374,834; giving activities include $1,229,123 for 31 grants (high: $530,000; low: $100), and $131,577 for employee matching gifts.
Purpose and activities: The foundation supports organizations involved with arts and culture, education, health, human services, and civic affairs. Special emphasis is directed toward science, math, engineering, and technology (STEM).
Fields of interest: Arts; Higher education; Education; Health care; Children/youth, services; Human services; United Ways and Federated Giving Programs; Mathematics; Engineering/technology; Science; Public affairs.
Type of support: General/operating support; Capital campaigns; Employee matching gifts.
Limitations: Applications accepted. Giving limited to areas of company operations, with emphasis on FL. No support for discriminatory organizations, school organizations or clubs, radio/TV stations, or Boy & Girl Scout Troops, religious organizations not of direct benefit to the entire community, professional associations, labor organizations, fraternal organizations, or social clubs. No grants to individuals, or for school sponsored events, athletics, home-based child care/educational services, walk-a-thons, ride-a-thons, dance-a-thons, or bowl-a-thons, salaries, travel, accounting, license fees, maintenance or repairs, office expenses, utilities, insurance, or property management or taxes.
Publications: Application guidelines.
Application information: Support is limited to 1 contribution per organization during any given year. Support for capital campaigns (bricks and mortar) are given priority. Application form not required.
Initial approach: E-mail proposal to foundation
Deadline(s): Feb. 1 to 28
Officers and Trustees:* Jeffrey S. Shuman, Pres.; William M. Brown,* V.P.; Scott T. Mikuen, Secy.; Gary L. McArthur, Treas.; Cindy Kane; D. Mehnert.
EIN: 346520425

2150
John T. and Winifred Hayward Foundation ✧
P.O. Box 2918
Clearwater, FL 33757-2918

Trust established in 1973 in FL.
Donors: John T. Hayward‡; Winifred M. Hayward‡.
Foundation type: Independent foundation.
Financial data (yr. ended 12/31/13): Assets, $9,343,882 (M); expenditures, $645,972; qualifying distributions, $606,978; giving activities include $490,000 for 4 grants (high: $200,000; low: $55,000).
Purpose and activities: Support for medical research organizations and schools involved in the field of genetics, with emphasis on birth defects and inheritable diseases.
Fields of interest: Medical research, institute.
Type of support: Research.
Limitations: Applications not accepted. Giving primarily in FL, IN and LA. No grants to individuals, or for building or endowment funds or operating budgets.
Application information: Contributes only to pre-selected organizations.
Trustees: William R. LaRosa; Browder Rives; Regions Bank Trust Dept.
EIN: 237363201
Selected grants: The following grants are a representative sample of this grantmaker's funding activity:
$150,000 to Tulane University, Medical School, New Orleans, LA, 2011.

2151
Heartbeat International Worldwide, Inc. ✧
(formerly Heartbeat International of West Central Florida)
4302 Henderson Blvd., Ste. 102
Tampa, FL 33629-5693 (813) 259-1213
FAX: (813) 259-1215;
E-mail: connect@HeartbeatSavesLives.org; Main URL: http://www.heartbeatsaveslives.org
E-Newsletter: https://www.heartbeatsaveslives.org/?nav=6&pos=0&sub=0
Facebook: https://www.facebook.com/pages/Heartbeat-Saves-Lives-Heartbeat-International-Foundation/281723716762
Flickr: http://www.flickr.com/photos/65420182@N06
Google Plus: https://plus.google.com/114014326670221637661/posts
Twitter: https://twitter.com/HeartbeatSaves
YouTube: http://www.youtube.com/user/HeartbeatSavesLives

Established in 1984.
Donors: Medtronic, Inc.; Pacesetter Systems, Inc.; Intermedics, Inc.; St. Joseph's Hospital; Watson Clinic Foundation; St. Jude Medical, CRM Div.; George Lorton; Biotronik SE & Co. KG; Boston Scientific.
Foundation type: Independent foundation.
Financial data (yr. ended 12/31/12): Assets, $7,818,506 (M); gifts received, $4,015,066; expenditures, $3,100,527; qualifying distributions, $3,100,527; giving activities include $3,032,722 for 12 grants (high: $1,252,722; low: $8,000).
Purpose and activities: Heartbeat International provides free cardiac pacemakers, implantable defibrillators and medical care to needy patients around the world.
Fields of interest: Health care.
Limitations: Applications not accepted. Giving worldwide.
Application information: Unsolicited requests for funds not accepted.
Officers and Directors:* Benedict Maniscalco, M.D.*, Chair. and C.E.O.; Albert Salem, Jr.,* Chair.; Laura DeLise, Exec. V.P.; Jorge Bahena, M.D.; Sandra Kreul; Basha G. Mohammed; Arthur Noriega IV.
Number of staff: 1 full-time professional; 2 full-time support; 1 part-time support.
EIN: 593236060

2152
The A. D. Henderson Foundation, Inc. ✧
P.O. Box 14096
Fort Lauderdale, FL 33302-4096 (954) 764-2819
Contact: Karen Pfeiffer, Sr. Admin.
E-mail: karen@hendersonfdn.org; Additional FL office contact: Monica Menahem, Admin, Asst. and Prog. Assoc., tel.: (954) 764-2819, ext. 2, e-mail: monica@hendersonfdn.org; VT. office contact: Eddie Gale, Prog. Dir., tel.: (902) 888-1188, e-mail: egale@hendersonfdn.org; Main URL: http://www.hendersonfdn.org

Established in 1969.
Foundation type: Independent foundation.
Financial data (yr. ended 09/30/13): Assets, $56,763,509 (M); expenditures, $2,788,448; qualifying distributions, $2,378,377; giving activities include $1,806,017 for 36 grants (high: $400,000; low: $2,500).
Purpose and activities: In FL, the foundation supports high quality early care and education for children ages 0-5. In VT, the foundation supports high quality early care and education for children ages 0-5, and capacity building for the non-profit sector, with a focus on mentoring and early learning.
Fields of interest: Education, early childhood education; Child development, education; Education; Children/youth, services.
Type of support: Continuing support; Management development/capacity building; Program development; Seed money; Curriculum development; Technical assistance; Matching/challenge support.
Limitations: Applications accepted. Giving primarily in Broward and Marion counties, FL, and VT. No support for private foundations or organizations lacking 501(c)(3) status, or for sectarian purposes. No grants to individuals, or for scholarships, annual campaigns or fundraising events, operating budgets, endowments, building or renovation, equipment (unless it is an integral part of an eligible project), capital campaigns, debt reduction, general operating support, or medical or clinical research; no loans.
Publications: Application guidelines; Grants list; Program policy statement; Program policy statement (including application guidelines).
Application information: Applications are by invitation, based on initial telephone call. Application guidelines available on foundation web site.
Initial approach: Telephone a foundation Program Dir. prior to formal submission to discuss project idea
Deadline(s): Quarterly
Board meeting date(s): Quarterly
Officers and Trustees:* Allen Douglas Henderson,* Pres.; Lucia Henderson,* 1st V.P.; Anne Rider, 2nd V.P.; Barbara K. Henderson,* 3rd V.P.; Karen M. Pfeiffer,* Secy. and Sr. Admin.; Maureen C. Tompkins,* Treas.; A. Holly Fouladi; James Hasson, Jr.; Robert S. Hinrichs.
Number of staff: 1 full-time professional; 1 part-time professional; 1 full-time support; 1 part-time support.
EIN: 237047045
Selected grants: The following grants are a representative sample of this grantmaker's funding activity:
$86,250 to Stern Center for Language and Learning, Williston, VT, 2011.

$86,250 to Vermont Center for the Book, Chester, VT, 2011.
$86,250 to Vermont Humanities Council, Montpelier, VT, 2011.
$75,000 to Vermont Community Foundation, Middlebury, VT, 2011.
$40,000 to Susan B. Anthony Center, Pembroke Pines, FL, 2011.
$34,605 to Jack and Jill Childrens Center, Fort Lauderdale, FL, 2011.
$34,525 to Volunteer Action Center of Broward County, Lauderhill, FL, 2011.
$27,000 to Hispanic Unity of Florida, Hollywood, FL, 2011.
$26,150 to Shelburne Farms, Shelburne, VT, 2011.
$25,000 to King Street Center, Burlington, VT, 2011.

2153
The Henriksen Charitable Trust ✧

9218 Cypress Green Dr., Ste. 2
Jacksonville, FL 32256-5510

Established in 2000 in CT.
Foundation type: Independent foundation.
Financial data (yr. ended 12/31/12): Assets, $14,881,750 (M); expenditures, $1,144,974; qualifying distributions, $609,627; giving activities include $609,627 for grants.
Fields of interest: Education; Health care; Human services.
Limitations: Applications not accepted. Giving primarily in CT and FL. No grants to individuals.
Application information: Contributes only to pre-selected organizations.
Trustee: Bradley S. Anderson.
EIN: 066460490

2154
John W. Henry Family Foundation, Inc. ✧

301 Yamato Rd., Ste. 2200
Boca Raton, FL 33431-4931 (617) 686-0973
Contact: Charlotte Vena, Dir.

Established in 2004 in DE.
Donor: John W. Henry.
Foundation type: Independent foundation.
Financial data (yr. ended 12/31/13): Assets, $3,440,940 (M); expenditures, $1,692,911; qualifying distributions, $1,675,555; giving activities include $1,664,600 for 42 grants (high: $1,000,000; low: $100).
Fields of interest: Arts; Education; Hospitals (general); Boys & girls clubs; Youth development; Human services.
Type of support: General/operating support.
Limitations: Applications accepted. Giving primarily in Boston, MA. No grants to individuals.
Application information: Application form not required.
Initial approach: Proposal
Deadline(s): None
Officers and Directors:* John W. Henry,* Pres.; Edwin Twist,* Secy.; A. David Carrillo; David Ginsberg; Linda Pizzuti; Charlotte Vena.
EIN: 201555835
Selected grants: The following grants are a representative sample of this grantmaker's funding activity:
$10,000 to CEOs for Cities, Chicago, IL, 2012. To fund operations.

2155
Herr Family Foundation ✧

775 119th Ave.
Treasure Island, FL 33706-1027

Established in 2001 in FL.
Donors: Lawrence W. Herr; Nancy R. Herr.
Foundation type: Independent foundation.
Financial data (yr. ended 09/30/13): Assets, $3,430,002 (M); expenditures, $528,692; qualifying distributions, $525,500; giving activities include $525,500 for 24 grants (high: $200,000; low: $1,000).
Fields of interest: Christian agencies & churches; Protestant agencies & churches.
Limitations: Applications not accepted. Giving primarily in PA; with some giving in FL. No grants to individuals.
Application information: Unsolicited requests for funds not accepted.
Trustee: Nancy R. Herr.
EIN: 226913883
Selected grants: The following grants are a representative sample of this grantmaker's funding activity:
$10,000 to Answers in Genesis of Kentucky, Petersburg, KY, 2011.
$10,000 to Clearwater Christian College, Clearwater, FL, 2011.
$10,000 to Word of Life Fellowship, Schroon Lake, NY, 2011.
$6,000 to Liberty University, Lynchburg, VA, 2011.
$5,000 to Brookwood Florida-Central, Saint Petersburg, FL, 2011.

2156
Dorothy B. Hersh Foundation, Inc. ✧

1299 N. Tamiami Trail, Ste. 423
Sarasota, FL 34236-2466 (941) 951-0531
Contact: Robert W. Donnelly, Sr., Recording Secy. and Grant Admin.; Harriet L. Donnelly, Corp. Secy.
FAX: (941) 951-0532;
E-mail: rwdonnelly@comcast.net; Additional tel.: (908) 901-9280; additional fax: (908) 901-9281; additional e-mail: tmi@ix.netcom.com

Established in 1982 in NJ.
Donor: Dorothy B. Hersh‡.
Foundation type: Independent foundation.
Financial data (yr. ended 05/31/12): Assets, $11,681,675 (M); expenditures, $595,492; qualifying distributions, $552,462; giving activities include $500,734 for 9 grants (high: $125,000; low: $10,000).
Purpose and activities: Giving limited to agencies that represent handicapped children.
Fields of interest: Hospitals (general); Health organizations, association; Human services; Children/youth, services.
Type of support: Capital campaigns; Building/renovation; Equipment; Land acquisition; Matching/challenge support.
Limitations: Applications accepted. Giving limited to NJ. No grants to individuals, or for programs, or operating budgets.
Publications: Application guidelines; Annual report.
Application information: Grant requests must be for capital purposes for handicapped children only. Application form required.
Initial approach: Letter requesting application requirements
Copies of proposal: 6
Deadline(s): None
Board meeting date(s): Varies
Final notification: After board meetings
Officers and Directors:* Robert Donnelly, Jr.,* Pres.; Robert W. Donnelly, Sr., Recording Secy. and Grant Admin.; Harriet L. Donnelly, Corp. Secy.; Stanley Bernard; Paul Schack.
Number of staff: 1 part-time professional.
EIN: 222280011
Selected grants: The following grants are a representative sample of this grantmaker's funding activity:
$125,000 to Cerebral Palsy Association of Middlesex County, Edison, NJ, 2012.
$100,000 to Cerebral Palsy Center of Bergen County, Fair Lawn, NJ, 2011.
$100,000 to Learning Center for Exceptional Children, Clifton, NJ, 2012.
$60,000 to Arc of Somerset County, Manville, NJ, 2011.
$50,000 to Search Day Program, Ocean, NJ, 2012.
$30,000 to Phoenix Center, Nutley, NJ, 2012.
$25,000 to Delbarton School, Morristown, NJ, 2011.
$25,000 to Occupational Center of Union County, Roselle, NJ, 2011.
$22,400 to Trinitas Health Foundation, Elizabeth, NJ, 2011.
$22,000 to Phoenix Center, Nutley, NJ, 2011.
$20,000 to Dysautonomia Foundation, New York, NY, 2011.
$18,294 to Childrens Aid and Family Services, Paramus, NJ, 2012.
$10,000 to Girl Scouts of the U.S.A., Montclair, NJ, 2012.
$8,000 to Summit Speech School, New Providence, NJ, 2011.

2157
Hertog Foundation, Inc. ✧

c/o Rampell and Rampell, P.A.
223 Sunset Ave., Ste. 200
Palm Beach, FL 33480-3855
GiveSmart: http://www.givesmart.org/Stories/Donors/Roger-Hertog

Donors: Roger Hertog; Susan Hertog.
Foundation type: Independent foundation.
Financial data (yr. ended 02/28/14): Assets, $31,147,333 (M); gifts received, $10,000,000; expenditures, $12,704,825; qualifying distributions, $12,254,751; giving activities include $10,712,604 for 114 grants (high: $1,400,000; low: $1,800).
Fields of interest: Historic preservation/historical societies; Higher education; Libraries (public); Medical research, institute; Jewish federated giving programs; Public affairs; Jewish agencies & synagogues.
Limitations: Applications not accepted. Giving primarily in Washington, DC and New York, NY.
Application information: Contributes only to pre-selected organizations.
Officers and Directors:* Roger Hertog,* Pres. and Treas.; Susan Hertog,* Secy.
EIN: 262002295
Selected grants: The following grants are a representative sample of this grantmaker's funding activity:
$2,000,000 to American Enterprise Institute for Public Policy Research, Washington, DC, 2012. For program support.
$1,338,950 to New-York Historical Society, New York, NY, 2012. For program support.

$1,162,500 to Hudson Institute, New York, NY, 2012. For research.
$1,000,000 to New York Public Library, New York, NY, 2012. For program support.
$660,000 to Relay Graduate School of Education, New York, NY, 2012. For program support.
$550,000 to Council on Foreign Relations, New York, NY, 2012. For providing an understanding of foreign policies.
$517,500 to Brookings Institution, Washington, DC, 2012. For research.
$100,000 to Success Charter Network, New York, NY, 2012. For program support.
$50,000 to Institute for the Study of War, Washington, DC, 2012. For program support.
$35,000 to Philharmonic-Symphony Society of New York, New York, NY, 2012. For program support.

2158
Howard E. Hill Foundation Inc. ✧
1324 S. Main St.
Belle Glade, FL 33430-4914 (561) 996-4524
Contact: Jennifer Earnest
Main URL: http://www.hehill.org/
Grants List: http://www.hehill.org/#/charities/4584658452

Established in FL.
Donors: Howard E. Hill†; The Big Lake Trust.
Foundation type: Operating foundation.
Financial data (yr. ended 12/31/13): Assets, $28,121,257 (M); expenditures, $5,497,627; qualifying distributions, $1,973,154; giving activities include $1,019,014 for 80 grants (high: $92,864; low: $1,000).
Purpose and activities: Giving to support residents of Western Palm Beach, Hendry, and Glades counties, Florida to obtain affordable housing, as well as for education and human services.
Fields of interest: Education; Health care; Housing/shelter, rehabilitation; Human services.
Type of support: General/operating support; Loans—to individuals.
Limitations: Applications accepted. Giving primarily in Hendry, Glades, Okeechobee, and western Palm Beach, FL.
Application information: Application form required.
Initial approach: Use application form on foundation web site
Deadline(s): None
Officers: Barbara Alston, Pres.; Jennifer R. Earnest, V.P.
Director: Robert D. Hoppmann.
EIN: 311513075
Selected grants: The following grants are a representative sample of this grantmaker's funding activity:
$117,000 to Glades Day School, Belle Glade, FL, 2012. For replace roof/academic programs.
$2,500 to American Red Cross, West Palm Beach, FL, 2012. For Emergencies in the Lake Region.
$1,000 to Clewiston Museum, Clewiston, FL, 2012. For Historical outreach Programs - Glade.

2159
The Hillenbrand Family Foundation ✧
(formerly Roch & Carol Hillenbrand Foundation)
c/o Michael R. Hillenbrand
3150 Fort Charles Dr.
Naples, FL 34102

Established in 1999 in NJ.
Donors: Michael R. Hillenbrand; Roch Hillenbrand.
Foundation type: Independent foundation.
Financial data (yr. ended 09/30/13): Assets, $1,640,531 (M); expenditures, $572,451; qualifying distributions, $544,791; giving activities include $518,291 for 25 grants (high: $110,000; low: $32).
Purpose and activities: Giving primarily for education and human services, including a YMCA.
Fields of interest: Higher education; Education; Human services; YM/YWCAs & YM/YWHAs.
Limitations: Applications not accepted. Giving in the U.S., with some emphasis on FL, and Washington, DC. No grants to individuals.
Application information: Contributes only to pre-selected organizations.
Trustees: Carol Hillenbrand; Justin Hillenbrand; Michael R. Hillenbrand; Molly Vernon.
EIN: 134050660

2160
Hoehl Family Foundation ✧
1560 Gulf Blvd., Ste. PH4
Clearwater, FL 33767
Application address: c/o Laura Latka, P.O. Box 4589, Burlington, VT 05406 tel.: (802) 448-0629; Main URL: http://www.hoehlfamilyfoundation.org/

Established in 1996 in VT.
Donors: Cynthia K. Hoehl; Robert H. Hoehl Family Trust.
Foundation type: Independent foundation.
Financial data (yr. ended 12/31/13): Assets, $42,790,778 (M); gifts received, $241,464; expenditures, $2,769,291; qualifying distributions, $2,082,899; giving activities include $2,016,000 for 52 grants (high: $215,000; low: $5,000).
Fields of interest: Education; Human services; Children/youth, services.
Type of support: General/operating support.
Limitations: Applications accepted. Giving primarily in VT, with emphasis on Burlington and Williston; giving also in FL. No grants to individuals.
Application information:
Initial approach: Letter
Deadline(s): None
Officer and Trustees:* Ronald L. Roberts,* Treas.; Krystin B. Downes; John M. Hoehl; Robert F. Hoehl.
EIN: 030354374

2161
David & Francie Horvitz Family Foundation, Inc. ✧
401 E. Las Olas Blvd., Ste. 2200
Fort Lauderdale, FL 33301-2244

Established in 2000 in FL.
Donors: DL Trust; Amber Trust; Moreland Management Co.
Foundation type: Independent foundation.
Financial data (yr. ended 12/31/12): Assets, $133,570 (M); gifts received, $2,535,000; expenditures, $2,402,326; qualifying distributions, $2,402,265; giving activities include $2,402,265 for 50 grants (high: $1,050,000; low: $100).
Purpose and activities: Giving primarily for the arts, education, and children and youth services.
Fields of interest: Arts; Higher education; Hospitals (specialty); Children/youth, services; Jewish agencies & synagogues.
Limitations: Applications not accepted. Giving primarily in FL. No grants to individuals.
Application information: Contributes only to pre-selected organizations.
Officers: David W. Horvitz, Pres.; Francie Horvitz, Secy.; Robert J. Puck, Treas.
EIN: 650974291
Selected grants: The following grants are a representative sample of this grantmaker's funding activity:
$500,000 to Hole in the Wall Camps Foundation, New Haven, CT, 2011. For general contribution.
$250,250 to Nova Southeastern University, Davie, FL, 2011. For general contribution.
$165,000 to Jewish Federation of Broward County, Fort Lauderdale, FL, 2011. For general contribution.

2162
The Hough Family Foundation, Inc. ✧
200 2nd Ave. S., No. 330
St. Petersburg, FL 33701-4313
Contact: Dr. Henry
E-mail: HFFHenry@gmail.com

Established in 1996 in FL.
Donor: William R. Hough.
Foundation type: Independent foundation.
Financial data (yr. ended 12/31/13): Assets, $10,759,682 (M); expenditures, $551,596; qualifying distributions, $505,000; giving activities include $505,000 for 7 grants (high: $350,000; low: $5,000).
Purpose and activities: The foundation funds charities that improve St. Petersburg, Florida, and that enhance all aspects of the community. It tends to focus on the arts and education, but provides funding in other areas too.
Fields of interest: Performing arts, theater; Arts; Higher education; Education; Children; Adults.
Type of support: General/operating support; Continuing support; Capital campaigns; Building/renovation; Equipment.
Limitations: Applications not accepted. Giving primarily in St. Petersburg, FL. No grants to individuals or for endowments.
Application information: Unsolicited requests for funds not accepted.
Board meeting date(s): Feb. 1
Officers and Directors:* Susan Hough Henry, Ph.D.*, Pres.; Hazel C. Hough,* V.P.; William R. Hough,* V.P.; W. Robb Hough,* Secy.; Helen H. Feinberg,* Treas.
EIN: 593395491
Selected grants: The following grants are a representative sample of this grantmaker's funding activity:
$50,000 to American Stage Company, Saint Petersburg, FL, 2012. For season support.
$50,000 to Salvador Dali Museum, Saint Petersburg, FL, 2012. For capital campaign.
$40,000 to Saint Petersburg Historical Society, Saint Petersburg, FL, 2012. For operating support.
$30,000 to University of South Florida, Tampa, FL, 2012. For computer lab.
$25,000 to Palladium Theater, Saint Petersburg, FL, 2012. For season support.
$7,500 to Arts Center Association, Saint Petersburg, FL, 2012. For education.
$5,000 to First Night Saint Petersburg, Saint Petersburg, FL, 2012.
$5,000 to Junior Achievement of Pinellas, Saint Petersburg, FL, 2012.

2163
O. C. Hubert Charitable Trust ✧
c/o Bank of America, N.A.
P.O. Box 40200, FL9-100-10-19
Jacksonville, FL 32203-0200

Established in 1997 in GA.
Foundation type: Independent foundation.
Financial data (yr. ended 05/31/13): Assets, $8,366,566 (M); expenditures, $579,387; qualifying distributions, $505,000; giving activities include $505,000 for grants.
Purpose and activities: Giving primarily for public health education.
Fields of interest: Higher education, university; Public health school/education.
Limitations: Applications not accepted. Giving primarily in Atlanta, GA, and NC. No grants to individuals.
Application information: Contributes only to pre-selected organizations.
Trustees: Richard N. Hubert; William Foege; Bank of America, N.A.
EIN: 586316941
Selected grants: The following grants are a representative sample of this grantmaker's funding activity:
$250,000 to Duke University, Durham, NC, 2013. For Hubert-Yeargan Center.
$250,000 to Emory University, Atlanta, GA, 2013. For Hubert Department of Global Health.

2164
Hudson Family Foundation, Inc. ✧
1535 S.E. 17th St., Ste. 107
Fort Lauderdale, FL 33316-1737

Established in 1997 in FL.
Donors: Harris W. Hudson; Jean Huizenga Charitable Lead Annuity Trust; Jean Huizenga Restated Living Trust.
Foundation type: Independent foundation.
Financial data (yr. ended 04/30/13): Assets, $13,205,907 (M); expenditures, $939,732; qualifying distributions, $580,565; giving activities include $580,565 for 25 grants (high: $209,000; low: $500).
Purpose and activities: Giving primarily for the arts, health care, education, and for children and youth services.
Fields of interest: Museums (art); Museums (children's); Arts; Elementary school/education; Education; Hospitals (specialty); Health organizations, association; Human services; Children/youth, services.
Limitations: Applications not accepted. Giving primarily in FL. No grants to individuals.
Application information: Contributes only to pre-selected organizations.
Board meeting date(s): Varies
Officers: Holly J. Bodenweber, Pres. and Treas.; Steven W. Hudson, V.P. and Secy.
EIN: 650753612
Selected grants: The following grants are a representative sample of this grantmaker's funding activity:
$300,000 to Habitat for Humanity in Atlanta, Atlanta, GA, 2011. For general contribution.

2165
Huizenga Family Foundation ✧
450 E. Las Olas Blvd., Ste. 1500
Fort Lauderdale, FL 33301-2291 (954) 627-5000
Contact: H. Wayne Huizenga, Jr., Pres.

Established in 1987 in FL.
Donor: H. Wayne Huizenga.
Foundation type: Independent foundation.
Financial data (yr. ended 12/31/12): Assets, $236,292 (M); gifts received, $3,768,352; expenditures, $8,149,752; qualifying distributions, $8,009,695; giving activities include $8,006,684 for 134 grants (high: $1,666,665; low: $150).
Purpose and activities: Giving primarily for social services.
Fields of interest: Education; Animal welfare; Hospitals (general); Health care; Cancer; Recreation; Boys & girls clubs; Human services; Philanthropy/voluntarism.
Limitations: Applications not accepted. Giving primarily in FL.
Application information: Contributes only to pre-selected organizations.
Officers and Directors:* H. Wayne Huizenga, Jr.,* Pres.; Martha Jean Huizenga,* V.P.; Cris V. Branden,* Treas.; Harris W. Hudson; H. Wayne Huizenga.
EIN: 650018158
Selected grants: The following grants are a representative sample of this grantmaker's funding activity:
$2,000,000 to Nova Southeastern University, Davie, FL, 2012.
$1,666,665 to Broward Performing Arts Foundation, Fort Lauderdale, FL, 2012.
$1,000,000 to Saint Simons Land Trust, Saint Simons Island, GA, 2012.
$800,000 to Nova Southeastern University, Davie, FL, 2012.
$250,000 to Nova Southeastern University, Davie, FL, 2012.
$250,000 to Palm City Presbyterian Church, Palm City, FL, 2012.
$200,000 to Nova Southeastern University, Davie, FL, 2012.
$100,000 to Boy Scouts of America, South Florida Council, Miami Lakes, FL, 2012.
$50,000 to Junior Achievement of South Florida, Coconut Creek, FL, 2012.
$15,000 to Christian Leaders, Homer Glen, IL, 2012.

2166
Indian River Community Foundation ✧
3055 Cardinal Dr., Ste. 106
Vero Beach, FL 32963 (772) 492-1407
Contact: Kerry Bartlett, Exec. Dir.
FAX: (772) 492-1408;
E-mail: kerry@ircommunityfoundation.com; Mailing address: P.O. Box 643968, Vero Beach, FL 32964-3968; Main URL: http://www.ircommunityfoundation.com/
E-Newsletter: http://www.ircommunityfoundation.com/eNewsletter.cfm

Established in 2005 in FL.
Foundation type: Community foundation.
Financial data (yr. ended 06/30/13): Assets, $18,927,245 (M); gifts received, $13,093,378; expenditures, $7,225,736; giving activities include $6,643,016 for 68+ grants (high: $1,840,500).
Purpose and activities: The mission of the foundation is to build a stronger community through donor-driven philanthropy.
Fields of interest: Arts; Education, reading; Education; Environment; Health care; Substance abuse, services; Mental health, treatment; Food services; Family services; Human services; Substance abusers; Homeless.
Type of support: General/operating support; Management development/capacity building; Annual campaigns; Capital campaigns; Building/renovation; Equipment; Endowments; Program development; Scholarship funds; Program evaluation; Matching/challenge support.
Limitations: Applications accepted. Giving limited to Indian River County, FL for unrestricted funds.
Publications: Annual report; Informational brochure.
Application information: Visit foundation web site for application guidelines.
Initial approach: Submit application
Copies of proposal: 9
Deadline(s): Mar. 22
Board meeting date(s): Monthly
Officers and Directors:* Robert C. Puff,* Chair.; Scott Alexander,* Vice-Chair.; Lois W. Appleby,* Secy.; Ted Michael,* Treas.; Kerry A. Bartlett, Exec. Dir.; Andrew P. Barton, Jr.; Paul A. Becker; Robert B. Burr, Jr.; Rebecca F. Emmons; William L. Frick; Kevin J. Given; Alma Lee Loy; Richard G. McDermott, Jr.; Robert S. Morrison; Ray Oglethorpe; Andrea B. Thurn; Sue Tompkins; Henry "Buzz" Wurzer.
Number of staff: 1 full-time professional; 1 part-time professional.
EIN: 201729243

2167
Jacksonville Jaguars Foundation ✧
1 EverBank Field Dr.
Jacksonville, FL 32202-1920 (904) 633-5437
Contact: Peter M. Racine, Pres.
FAX: (904) 633-5683;
E-mail: sahil@nfl.jaguars.com; E-mail for Peter Racine: racinep@jaguars.nfl.com; Contact for Honor Rows: T-Neisha Tate, tel.: (904) 633-6516, e-mail: tatet@nfl.jaguars.com; Community Scholars: Heather Burk, University of North Florida, Service Learning Coord., tel.: (904) 620-3922, E-mail: hburk@unf.edu; Main URL: http://www.jaguars.com/foundation-community/index.html
Facebook: https://www.facebook.com/JaguarsFoundation

Established in 1994 in FL.
Donor: Jacksonville Jaguars, Ltd.
Foundation type: Company-sponsored foundation.
Financial data (yr. ended 12/31/12): Assets, $4,976,349 (M); gifts received, $1,943,596; expenditures, $2,296,353; qualifying distributions, $2,233,072; giving activities include $1,244,316 for 99 grants (high: $78,500; low: $500).
Purpose and activities: The foundation supports programs designed to serve economically and socially disadvantaged youth and families.
Fields of interest: Media/communications; Arts; Education, reading; Education; Public health, physical fitness; Nutrition; Recreation; YM/YWCAs & YM/YWHAs; Family services; Human services; Youth; Economically disadvantaged.
Type of support: General/operating support; Continuing support; Capital campaigns; Program development; Scholarship funds; In-kind gifts; Matching/challenge support.

Limitations: Applications accepted. Giving limited to the greater Jacksonville, FL, area, including Baker, Clay, Duval, Nassau, and St. Johns counties. No support for schools, religious organizations not of direct benefit to the entire community, or disease-specific organizations. No grants to individuals or for fundraising or sponsorships.
Publications: Application guidelines.
Application information: A full proposal may be requested at a later date for new applicants. Multi-year funding is limited to a maximum of 2 to 3 consecutive years. Requests for general operating support and capital campaigns must include a long-term (3-5 year) strategic plan. Organizations receiving support are asked to submit a progress report and a final report.
Initial approach: Complete online eligibility quiz and letter of inquiry for new applicants; complete online application for returning grantees and for Honor Rows
Deadline(s): None for new applicants; Feb. 15 for Cycle 1 and July 15 for Cycle 2 for returning grantees; Mar. 24 for Honor Rows deadline
Board meeting date(s): Generally, summer and winter
Final notification: 30 days; June 1 for Honor Rows
Officer: Peter M. Racine, Pres.
Number of staff: 3 full-time professional; 1 full-time support; 1 part-time support.
EIN: 593249687
Selected grants: The following grants are a representative sample of this grantmaker's funding activity:
$80,000 to Boys and Girls Clubs of Northeast Florida, Jacksonville, FL, 2011.
$73,000 to Bridge of Northeast Florida, Jacksonville, FL, 2011.
$44,000 to Metro Kids Konnection, Jacksonville, FL, 2010.
$42,000 to Metro Kids Konnection, Jacksonville, FL, 2011.
$42,000 to PACE Center for Girls of Jacksonville, Jacksonville, FL, 2011.
$30,000 to Habitat for Humanity of the Jacksonville Beaches, Atlantic Beach, FL, 2011.
$25,000 to Junior Achievement of North Florida, Jacksonville, FL, 2011.
$25,000 to Limelight Theater, Saint Augustine, FL, 2011.
$22,000 to Stage Aurora Theatrical Company, Jacksonville, FL, 2011.
$17,500 to Jacksonville Area Sexual Minority Youth Network, Jacksonville, FL, 2011.
$12,500 to APEL Health Services Center, Jacksonville, FL, 2010.
$7,500 to University of North Florida Foundation, Jacksonville, FL, 2011.

2168
Mohsin & Fauzia Jaffer Foundation ✧
3410 Stallion Ln.
Weston, FL 33331-3035

Established in 2005 in FL.
Donors: Mohsin Jaffer; Fauzia Jaffer; Family Doctors of Broward; Medina Properties, Inc.; Sam Weston Properties, Inc.; Mayfair Medical Mgmt.
Foundation type: Independent foundation.
Financial data (yr. ended 12/31/12): Assets, $5,031,903 (M); gifts received, $5,684,000; expenditures, $1,044,800; qualifying distributions, $1,044,800; giving activities include $1,044,800 for 35 grants (high: $101,000; low: $200).
Fields of interest: Education; Human services; Islam; Religion.
Type of support: General/operating support.
Limitations: Applications not accepted. Giving primarily in FL, and on an international basis. No grants to individuals.
Application information: Contributes only to pre-selected organizations.
Directors: Fauzia Jaffer; Mohsin Jaffer.
EIN: 202965144

2169
Thomas A. and Mary S. James Foundation, Inc. ✧ ☆
880 Carillon Pkwy.
Saint Petersburg, FL 33716-1102

Established in 1994 in FL.
Donor: Thomas A. James.
Foundation type: Independent foundation.
Financial data (yr. ended 12/31/13): Assets, $12,348,774 (M); gifts received, $1,953,800; expenditures, $577,944; qualifying distributions, $520,750; giving activities include $520,750 for 68 grants (high: $107,750; low: $1,000).
Purpose and activities: Giving primarily for arts and culture, education, and social services.
Fields of interest: Arts, multipurpose centers/programs; Museums (art); Museums (science/technology); Performing arts; Higher education; Law school/education; Education; Disasters, Hurricane Katrina; Recreation, social clubs; American Red Cross; United Ways and Federated Giving Programs.
Limitations: Applications not accepted. Giving primarily in FL. No grants to individuals.
Application information: Contributes only to pre-selected organizations.
Officers: Thomas A. James, Pres.; Mary S. James, Secy.
Trustees: Court James; Hunt James.
EIN: 593288143

2170
The William James Foundation, Inc. ✧ ☆
1762 Hawthrone St., Ste. 5
Sarasota, FL 34239

Established in 2000 in FL.
Donors: Barry Silverstein; JM Silverstein 2003 Charitable Lead Annuity Trust; Mark S. Silverstein 2003 Charitable Lead Annuity Trust; Susan S. Potter 2003 Charitable Lead Annuity Trust.
Foundation type: Independent foundation.
Financial data (yr. ended 12/31/13): Assets, $2,145,540 (M); gifts received, $649,837; expenditures, $776,804; qualifying distributions, $700,000; giving activities include $700,000 for 4 grants (high: $250,000; low: $100,000).
Fields of interest: Arts; Education; Community/economic development; Public affairs, citizen participation.
Limitations: Applications not accepted. Giving primarily in CA, with some giving in FL. No grants to individuals.
Application information: Contributes only to pre-selected organizations.
Officer and Directors:* Trudy Silverstein, Pres.; Randall T. Arnaud; Randall A. Meeks; Jacob Silverstein; Molly Silverstein.
EIN: 141782873

2171
Victoria Jenkins Charitable Foundation ✧
P.O. Box 40200, FL9-100-10-19
Jacksonville, FL 32203-0200

Established in 1993 in GA.
Donor: Victoria Jenkins†.
Foundation type: Independent foundation.
Financial data (yr. ended 12/31/13): Assets, $21,243,785 (M); expenditures, $1,507,671; qualifying distributions, $1,328,017; giving activities include $1,273,132 for 7 grants (high: $381,940; low: $127,313).
Purpose and activities: Giving primarily to a Presbyterian church, as well as for education.
Fields of interest: Elementary/secondary education; Boys clubs; Christian agencies & churches; Protestant agencies & churches.
Limitations: Applications not accepted. Giving primarily in Savannah, GA. No grants to individuals.
Application information: Contributes only to pre-selected organizations.
Trustee: Bank of America, N.A.
EIN: 586281550

2172
Charles and Ann Johnson Foundation ✧
703 Island Dr.
Palm Beach, FL 33480-4742
Contact: Charles B. Johnson, Tr.

Established in 1986 in CA.
Donors: Ann L. Johnson; Charles B. Johnson.
Foundation type: Independent foundation.
Financial data (yr. ended 12/31/13): Assets, $205,530,918 (M); expenditures, $13,272,755; qualifying distributions, $13,150,796; giving activities include $13,147,046 for 153 grants (high: $2,001,090; low: $100).
Purpose and activities: Giving primarily for arts and culture, higher education, health associations, and human services.
Fields of interest: Museums; Historic preservation/historical societies; Higher education; Education; Botanical gardens; Health organizations, association; Diabetes research; Boys & girls clubs; Human services; American Red Cross.
Limitations: Giving primarily in CA. No grants to individuals.
Application information: Application form not required.
Initial approach: Letter
Deadline(s): None
Trustees: Ann L. Johnson; Charles B. Johnson.
EIN: 943026398

2173
The Manuel H. & Mary Johnson Foundation ✧
(formerly Manuel H. Johnson Foundation)
10045 Renfrew Ave.
Vero Beach, FL 32963-4917
Contact: Manuel Johnson, Pres.

Established in 1994 in VA.
Donor: Manuel Johnson.
Foundation type: Independent foundation.
Financial data (yr. ended 12/31/12): Assets, $6,067,759 (M); gifts received, $100,000; expenditures, $595,240; qualifying distributions,

$595,240; giving activities include $595,240 for 10 grants (high: $240,000; low: $2,100).
Purpose and activities: Giving primarily for higher education, as well as for health organizations, an arts center, and to sporting libraries.
Fields of interest: Arts, multipurpose centers/programs; Higher education; Libraries (special); Health organizations, association; Athletics/sports, equestrianism.
Limitations: Applications accepted. Giving primarily in Troy, AL, FL, and Middleburg and Upperville, VA.
Application information: Application form required.
Initial approach: Letter
Deadline(s): None
Officer: Manuel Johnson, Pres.
EIN: 541737123

2174
Theodore R. & Vivian M. Johnson Scholarship Foundation, Inc. ✧

505 S. Flagler Dr., Ste. 1460
West Palm Beach, FL 33401-5923 (561) 659-2005
Contact: Sharon Wood, Prog. Off.
FAX: (561) 659-1054; E-mail: wood@jsf.bz; Additional tel.: (888) 523-7797; Main URL: http://www.jsf.bz

Established in 1991 in FL.
Donors: Theodore R. Johnson†; Vivian M. Johnson†.
Foundation type: Independent foundation.
Financial data (yr. ended 12/31/13): Assets, $168,082,324 (M); expenditures, $9,808,320; qualifying distributions, $7,608,298; giving activities include $6,555,841 for 60 grants (high: $1,148,125; low: $100).
Purpose and activities: Scholarship grants are made to a variety of institutions and programs specified by the founders and the Board of Directors. The foundation seeks to enable qualified individuals, who might not be able to otherwise do so, to acquire skills and develop strengths which enable them to realize their potential. The foundation believes that by doing so, they can became positive contributing members of their community and its economy.
Fields of interest: Higher education; Health care, administration/regulation; Disabilities, people with; Economically disadvantaged.
Type of support: Endowments; Curriculum development; Scholarship funds; Employee matching gifts; Matching/challenge support.
Limitations: Giving on a national basis. No grants to individuals directly.
Publications: Annual report; Financial statement.
Application information: See foundation's Web site for more information. Applicants must apply directly to one of the following organizations: 1) Palm Beach Atlantic University, 2) Scholarship America (for UPS scholarships), 3) State University System of Florida, 4) American Indian Tribal Colleges, 5) Gallaudet University, and 6) Gonzaga University.
Deadline(s): None
Board meeting date(s): Spring and fall
Officers and Directors:* R. Malcolm Macleod, Q.C.*, C.E.O. and Pres.; I. King Jordan,* V.P.; Hugh M. Brown, C.F.A.*, Secy.; Richard A. Krause,* C.F.O. and Treas.; Bea Awoniyi; Sherry Salway Black; David L. Blaikie, LLM; Bobby Krause; Marjorie O'Malley; David B. Rinker.
Number of staff: 1 full-time professional; 2 part-time professional.
EIN: 311613890
Selected grants: The following grants are a representative sample of this grantmaker's funding activity:
$1,817,500 to Palm Beach Atlantic University, West Palm Beach, FL, 2012.
$1,040,000 to Scholarship America, Edina, MN, 2012.
$550,000 to State University System of Florida, Tallahassee, FL, 2012.
$475,000 to Florida School for the Deaf and Blind, Saint Augustine, FL, 2012.
$475,000 to Gallaudet University, Washington, DC, 2012.
$217,083 to Northern Arizona University Foundation, Flagstaff, AZ, 2012.
$210,001 to University of Florida Foundation, Gainesville, FL, 2012.
$150,000 to Dalhousie University, Halifax, Canada, 2012.
$50,000 to Gonzaga University, Spokane, WA, 2012.

2175
The Lillian Jean Kaplan Foundation, Inc. ✧

3551 Estepona Ave.
Doral, FL 33178-2953 (786) 385-6525
Contact: Luis Aguiar, Dir.

Established in FL.
Donors: Thomas Kaplan; Guma Aguiar; Dafna Recanati Kaplan; Consolidated Commodities Ltd.
Foundation type: Independent foundation.
Financial data (yr. ended 12/31/13): Assets, $2,402,827 (M); expenditures, $18,301,877; qualifying distributions, $17,987,602; giving activities include $17,892,000 for 14 grants (high: $6,500,000; low: $50,000).
Fields of interest: Health organizations; Jewish federated giving programs; Jewish agencies & synagogues.
Limitations: Applications accepted. Giving primarily in FL and NY.
Application information: Application form required.
Initial approach: Letter
Deadline(s): None
Directors: Ellen Aguiar; Luis Aguiar; Angelika Drew; Justin Corey Drew.
EIN: 300127083
Selected grants: The following grants are a representative sample of this grantmaker's funding activity:
$15,000 to ALS Worldwide, Madison, WI, 2012. To ALS Patients.
$15,000 to Broward College, Fort Lauderdale, FL, 2012. For higher education support.
$5,000 to Smile Train, New York, NY, 2012. To provide Support Children with Clefts.
$2,500 to Lighthouse International, New York, NY, 2012. For Fight Against Vision Loss.

2176
The Katcher Family Foundation, Inc. ✧

4197 S. Douglas Rd.
Miami, FL 33133-6832
Contact: Gerald Katcher, Dir.

Established in 1996 in DE and FL.
Donors: Gerald Katcher; Dorothy Katcher†.
Foundation type: Independent foundation.
Financial data (yr. ended 11/30/13): Assets, $3,201,232 (M); gifts received, $1,100,000; expenditures, $1,960,778; qualifying distributions, $1,954,637; giving activities include $1,952,564 for 64 grants (high: $378,891; low: $50).
Purpose and activities: Giving primarily for the arts, particularly to museums, as well as for higher education, and Jewish organizations.
Fields of interest: Museums (art); Museums (ethnic/folk arts); Performing arts, music; Arts; Higher education; Education; Environment, research; Children/youth, services; United Ways and Federated Giving Programs; Jewish federated giving programs; Jewish agencies & synagogues.
Limitations: Applications not accepted. Giving primarily in CO, FL and NY.
Application information: Unsolicited requests for funds not accepted.
Directors: Lesley Heller; Gerald Katcher; Jane Katcher.
EIN: 650715498
Selected grants: The following grants are a representative sample of this grantmaker's funding activity:
$528,050 to Museum for African Art, Long Island City, NY, 2011.
$350,541 to New World Symphony, Miami Beach, FL, 2011.
$350,000 to United Way of Miami-Dade, Miami, FL, 2010.
$275,000 to Early Childhood Foundation, Miami, FL, 2010.
$250,000 to Early Childhood Initiative, Miami, FL, 2011.
$140,000 to Yale University, New Haven, CT, 2010.
$50,000 to National Public Radio, Washington, DC, 2011.
$17,500 to Aspen Music Festival and School, Aspen, CO, 2011.
$10,000 to Concert Artists Guild, New York, NY, 2011.
$2,950 to K A J X Aspen Public Radio, Aspen, CO, 2011.
$1,000 to Cleveland Orchestra, Cleveland, OH, 2011.

2177
The Eleanor M. and Herbert D. Katz Family Foundation, Inc. ✧

c/o Thomas O. Katz, Secy.-Treas.
21218 St. Andrews Blvd., No. 404
Boca Raton, FL 33433-2449

Established in 1983 in FL.
Donors: Eleanor M. Katz; Herbert D. Katz.
Foundation type: Independent foundation.
Financial data (yr. ended 12/31/13): Assets, $10,671,752 (M); expenditures, $1,140,536; qualifying distributions, $1,048,906; giving activities include $1,047,606 for 33 grants (high: $750,000; low: $6).
Purpose and activities: Primary areas of interest include higher education, and Jewish organizations.
Fields of interest: Higher education; Education; Health organizations, association; Human services; Jewish federated giving programs; Leadership development; Jewish agencies & synagogues.
International interests: Israel.
Type of support: Continuing support; Annual campaigns; Capital campaigns; Program development.

Limitations: Applications not accepted. Giving on a national and international basis. No grants to individuals.
Application information: Contributes only to pre-selected organizations.
Board meeting date(s): Quarterly
Officers and Directors:* Eleanor M. Katz,* Pres.; Thomas O. Katz,* Secy.-Treas.; Laura Katz Cutler; Daniel Katz; Sally Katz; Walter Katz.
Number of staff: 1 part-time support.
EIN: 592320940

2178
Katzman Family Foundation, Inc. ✧
1696 N.E. Miami Gardens Dr.
North Miami Beach, FL 33179-4902 (305) 947-8800
Contact: Chaim Katzman, Mgr.

Established in 2003 in FL.
Donor: Chaim Katzman.
Foundation type: Independent foundation.
Financial data (yr. ended 12/31/13): Assets, $28,875,873 (M); gifts received, $3,466,667; expenditures, $1,110,569; qualifying distributions, $1,107,619; giving activities include $1,107,619 for 75 grants (high: $221,500; low: $180).
Fields of interest: Arts; Higher education; Higher education, university; Education; Human services; Jewish federated giving programs; Jewish agencies & synagogues.
Limitations: Applications accepted. Giving primarily in Washington, DC, FL, and NY.
Application information: Application form not required.
Initial approach: Proposal
Deadline(s): Dec. 31
Officer: Chaim Katzman, Mgr.
EIN: 200255604

2179
Kazma Family Foundation ✧
1 N. Federal Hwy., Ste. 400
Boca Raton, FL 33432-3930
Contact: Leigh-Anne Kazma, Pres.

Established in 1997 in IL.
Donors: Gerald Kazma; Amzak Corp.
Foundation type: Independent foundation.
Financial data (yr. ended 04/30/13): Assets, $276,748 (M); gifts received, $793,408; expenditures, $1,635,866; qualifying distributions, $1,525,854; giving activities include $1,525,854 for grants.
Purpose and activities: Giving primarily to Roman Catholic schools and organizations, and for social services.
Fields of interest: Elementary/secondary education; Higher education; Education; Human services; Children, services; Catholic federated giving programs; Catholic agencies & churches.
Limitations: Giving primarily in Chicago, IL; some funding also in El Salvador.
Officers: Leigh-Anne Kazma, Pres.; Gerald Kazma, Treas.
Directors: Margaret Kazma; Michael Kazma.
EIN: 364206371
Selected grants: The following grants are a representative sample of this grantmaker's funding activity:
$312,100 to Big Shoulders Fund, Chicago, IL, 2011.

2180
Kazma Family Foundation ✧ ☆
c/o Leigh-Anne Kazma
1 N. Federal Hwy., Ste. 400
Boca Raton, FL 33432-3930

Donor: Amzak Capital Management.
Foundation type: Independent foundation.
Financial data (yr. ended 12/31/13): Assets, $3,055,220 (M); gifts received, $3,600,000; expenditures, $709,142; qualifying distributions, $687,845; giving activities include $687,845 for 5 grants (high: $250,000; low: $50,000).
Fields of interest: Education; Catholic agencies & churches.
Limitations: Applications not accepted. Giving primarily in FL and IL.
Application information: Unsolicited requests for funds not accepted.
Officers: Leigh-Anne Kazma, Pres.; Gerald Kazma, Treas.
Directors: Margaret Kazma; Michael Kazma.
EIN: 462160108

2181
Kelly Foundation, Inc. ✧
17225 S.W. 77th Ct.
Miami, FL 33157-4859 (800) 232-2282
Contact: Janis Isom, Secy.-Treas.

Established in 1956 in FL.
Donor: Marjorie Kelly Trust.
Foundation type: Company-sponsored foundation.
Financial data (yr. ended 12/31/13): Assets, $20,188,470 (M); gifts received, $1,200; expenditures, $858,031; qualifying distributions, $779,500; giving activities include $779,500 for grants.
Purpose and activities: The foundation supports botanical gardens and organizations involved with education, health, housing development, human services, and other areas and awards college scholarships to undergraduate students.
Fields of interest: Education; Environment; Human services.
Type of support: General/operating support; Scholarship funds; Employee-related scholarships; Scholarships—to individuals.
Limitations: Applications accepted. Giving primarily in areas of company operations in FL.
Application information: Application form required.
Initial approach: Request application form
Deadline(s): None
Officers: L. Patrick Kelly, Chair. and Pres.; Nicholas D. Kelly, Vice-Chair. and V.P.; Janis Isom, Secy.-Treas.
Directors: Barbara Kelly; Eileen Kelly; Luisa Kelly; Robert W. Kelly, Jr.; Christabel Vartanian.
EIN: 596153269
Selected grants: The following grants are a representative sample of this grantmaker's funding activity:
$50,000 to Immokalee Foundation, Naples, FL, 2011.
$25,000 to Clewiston Christian School, Clewiston, FL, 2011.
$10,000 to Habitat for Humanity of Greater Miami, Miami, FL, 2011.
$5,000 to New Hope Charities, West Palm Beach, FL, 2011.
$2,500 to Gulliver Schools, Coral Gables, FL, 2011.
$1,000 to Emory University, Atlanta, GA, 2011.
$1,000 to Northwest Missouri State University, Maryville, MO, 2011.

2182
The Ethel & W. George Kennedy Family Foundation, Inc. ✧
1550 Madruga Ave., Ste. 225
Coral Gables, FL 33146-3051 (305) 666-6226
Contact: Kathleen Kennedy-Olsen, Managing Dir.
FAX: (305) 666-2441;
E-mail: admin@kennedyfamilyfdn.org; Main URL: http://www.kennedyfamilyfdn.org

Established in 1968 in FL.
Donor: W. George Kennedy†.
Foundation type: Independent foundation.
Financial data (yr. ended 12/31/12): Assets, $26,155,045 (M); expenditures, $1,480,915; qualifying distributions, $1,215,761; giving activities include $1,038,150 for 97 grants (high: $80,000; low: $250).
Purpose and activities: Giving primarily to organizations that directly support children and families by means of education, health care, technological assistance, rehabilitation and welfare.
Fields of interest: Education; Human services; Children/youth, services; Child development, services; Family services; Infants/toddlers; Children/youth; Children; Youth; Economically disadvantaged.
Type of support: General/operating support; Capital campaigns; Building/renovation; Equipment; Endowments; Program development; Seed money; Scholarship funds; Technical assistance; Matching/challenge support.
Limitations: Applications not accepted. Giving limited to Miami-Dade County, FL. No grants to individuals.
Application information: Unsolicited requests for funds not accepted. The foundation now receives and reviews all grant proposals by Board invitation only.
Board meeting date(s): Mar. and Oct.
Officers and Directors:* Karyn Kennedy Herterich,* Pres.; Kendel Kennedy,* V.P.; Kimberly Kennedy,* V.P.; Kathleen Kennedy-Olsen,* Secy.-Treas. and Managing Dir.; Morgan Herterich; Forrest Mulcahy; Martin Nash; Guy Rizzo.
Number of staff: 2 full-time professional.
EIN: 596204880
Selected grants: The following grants are a representative sample of this grantmaker's funding activity:
$30,000 to Peaceful Acres Horses, Pattersonville, NY, 2012. For Retreats and Capital Campaign.
$25,000 to Americans for Immigrant Justice, Miami, FL, 2012. For Protecting Our Children Initiative.
$20,000 to Community Smiles, Miami, FL, 2012. For Improving Smiles Project.
$20,000 to Franklin Community Center, Saratoga Springs, NY, 2012. For Project Lift.
$20,000 to Kristi House, Miami, FL, 2012. For Project Gold Safe House.
$16,500 to Museum of Contemporary Art, North Miami, FL, 2012. For art educational programs.
$15,000 to Seraphic Fire, Miami, FL, 2012. For Miami Choral Academy.

$14,000 to National Symphony Orchestra, Washington, DC, 2012. For Contribution in Support of the Arts.
$13,450 to Camp Happy Days, Charleston, SC, 2012. For Cancer Camp.
$11,000 to University of Mississippi Foundation, Oxford, MS, 2012. For Memorial Scholarships - Education.

2183
Ethel Kennedy Foundation ✧ ☆
c/o Ethel K. Marran
271 Johns Island Dr.
Vero Beach, FL 32963-3238

Established in 1986 in DE and NY.
Donors: Ethel Marran; 271 Johns Island Dr.; Vero Beach Florida 32963.
Foundation type: Independent foundation.
Financial data (yr. ended 12/31/13): Assets, $9,803,724 (M); gifts received, $9,286; expenditures, $504,184; qualifying distributions, $473,371; giving activities include $460,691 for 83 grants (high: $50,000; low: $16).
Purpose and activities: Giving primarily to religious, educational, medical, or welfare organizations.
Fields of interest: Arts; Secondary school/education; Higher education; Environment; Reproductive health, family planning; Health organizations, association; Medical research, institute; Eye research; Human services; Family services; Residential/custodial care, hospices; Women.
Limitations: Applications not accepted. Giving primarily in NY. No grants to individuals.
Application information: Unsolicited Requests for funds not accepted.
Officers: Ethel K. Marran, Pres. and Treas.; Elizabeth Marran, V.P.; Laura Marran, Secy.
EIN: 112768682

2184
Eloise Kimmelman Foundation ✧
c/o Jan Yemen
1104 Ponce de Leon Blvd.
Coral Gables, FL 33134-3322

Established in 2005 in FL.
Donors: David Kimmelman†; David Kimmelman Charitable Remainder Annuity Trust.
Foundation type: Independent foundation.
Financial data (yr. ended 04/30/13): Assets, $14,507,133 (M); expenditures, $1,610,423; qualifying distributions, $1,400,000; giving activities include $1,400,000 for 6 grants (high: $500,000; low: $100,000).
Fields of interest: Higher education; Medical school/education; Hospitals (general).
Limitations: Applications not accepted. Giving in the U.S., with emphasis on FL. No grants to individuals.
Application information: Contributes only to pre-selected organizations.
Trustee: Jan Yelen.
EIN: 203270603
Selected grants: The following grants are a representative sample of this grantmaker's funding activity:
$500,000 to University of Miami, Miami, FL, 2011.
$400,000 to University of Miami, Miami, FL, 2011.
$300,000 to Bethesda Hospital Foundation, Boynton Beach, FL, 2011.
$200,000 to University of Miami, School of Business, Coral Gables, FL, 2011.
$100,000 to Indiana University, Bloomington, IN, 2011.
$100,000 to University of Memphis, Memphis, TN, 2011.

2185
Kings Grant Foundation ✧
c/o Courtney Desisto
P.O. Box 897
Tampa, FL 33601-0897

Established in 2001 in RI.
Donors: Dennis Hardiman; Lisa Hardiman; Advanced Financial Services, Inc.; Embrace Home Loans Inc.
Foundation type: Independent foundation.
Financial data (yr. ended 06/30/13): Assets, $5,521,698 (M); gifts received, $2,300,000; expenditures, $2,079,153; qualifying distributions, $2,023,147; giving activities include $2,023,147 for 16 grants (high: $500,000; low: $5,000).
Fields of interest: Higher education; Christian agencies & churches.
Limitations: Applications not accepted. Giving primarily in the U.S., with emphasis on AZ, FL, RI, and TX. No grants to individuals.
Application information: Contributes only to pre-selected organizations.
Trustees: Courtney Desisto; Lisa Hardiman.
EIN: 050520607

2186
The Thomas M. & Irene B. Kirbo Charitable Foundation ✧
2720 Park St., Ste. 211
Jacksonville, FL 32205 (904) 384-0440
Contact: R. Murray Jenks, Pres.

Established in 1980 in FL.
Donor: City of Bainbridge.
Foundation type: Independent foundation.
Financial data (yr. ended 12/31/13): Assets, $42,086,905 (M); expenditures, $2,035,753; qualifying distributions, $1,827,044; giving activities include $1,752,000 for 125 grants (high: $150,000; low: $2,000).
Fields of interest: Literature; Arts; Education, special; Education; Health care; Health organizations, association; Youth development, centers/clubs; Human services; United Ways and Federated Giving Programs; Science; Christian agencies & churches; Religion.
Limitations: Applications accepted. Giving primarily in Jacksonville, FL. No grants to individuals.
Application information: Application form required.
Initial approach: Completed application form
Deadline(s): None
Officers: Bruce W. Kirbo, Chair.; R. Murray Jenks, Pres.
Trustees: Charles H. Kirbo, Jr.; Martha J. Sawyer.
EIN: 596197946
Selected grants: The following grants are a representative sample of this grantmaker's funding activity:
$20,000 to Arc Jacksonville, Jacksonville, FL, 2011. For general contribution.
$6,000 to Jacksonville Zoological Society, Jacksonville, FL, 2011.

2187
The Kislak Family Fund, Inc. ✧
7900 Miami Lakes Dr. W.
Miami Lakes, FL 33016-5897
Contact: Stephanie Chace
FAX: (305) 821-1267; E-mail: schace@kislak.com

Established in 1992 in FL.
Donors: Jay I. Kislak; J.I. Kislak, Inc.
Foundation type: Independent foundation.
Financial data (yr. ended 12/31/12): Assets, $20,236,741 (M); gifts received, $1,612,639; expenditures, $894,992; qualifying distributions, $825,018; giving activities include $805,297 for 65 grants (high: $100,000; low: $25).
Purpose and activities: Giving primarily for human services, animal welfare, and to Jewish agencies.
Fields of interest: Museums; Museums (art); Museums (marine/maritime); Museums (specialized); Higher education; Animal welfare; United Ways and Federated Giving Programs; Jewish agencies & synagogues.
Limitations: Applications not accepted. Giving primarily in FL. No grants to individuals.
Application information: Contributes only to pre-selected organizations.
Officers and Directors:* Jay I. Kislak,* Pres.; Jean Kislak,* Secy.; Thomas Bartelmo, Treas.; Philip Thomas Kislak; Paula Mangravite.
EIN: 650350930

2188
Klorfine Foundation ✧
2700 N. Ocean Dr., Apt. 2103A
Riviera Beach, FL 33404
Main URL: http://www.klorfinefoundation.org/

Established in 1993 in PA.
Donors: Leonard Klorfine; Norma E. Klorfine.
Foundation type: Independent foundation.
Financial data (yr. ended 11/30/13): Assets, $23,044,254 (M); expenditures, $1,410,255; qualifying distributions, $1,363,006; giving activities include $1,345,125 for 36 grants (high: $509,000; low: $5).
Purpose and activities: Giving for the arts, medicine, fire prevention, political research, and the environment.
Fields of interest: Arts; Environment; Health care, formal/general education; Disasters, fire prevention/control; Recreation, camps.
Type of support: General/operating support; Continuing support; Annual campaigns; Capital campaigns; Building/renovation; Endowments; Emergency funds.
Limitations: Applications not accepted. Giving primarily in Philadelphia, PA and Seattle, WA. No grants to individuals.
Application information: Unsolicited requests for funds not accepted.
Trustees: Leonard Klorfine; Norma E. Klorfine.
EIN: 227743385
Selected grants: The following grants are a representative sample of this grantmaker's funding activity:
$252,750 to Museum of Glass, Tacoma, WA, 2011.
$251,200 to Bellevue Arts Museum, Bellevue, WA, 2011.
$59,870 to Philadelphia Museum of Art, Philadelphia, PA, 2011.
$25,000 to Seattle Art Museum, Seattle, WA, 2011.
$18,000 to Forest Ethics, San Francisco, CA, 2011.
$11,000 to Climate Solutions, Seattle, WA, 2011.

$11,000 to Forterra, Seattle, WA, 2011.
$10,000 to Artist Trust, Seattle, WA, 2011.
$10,000 to Bark, Portland, OR, 2011.
$10,000 to Duwamish River Cleanup Coalition-Technical Advisory Group, Seattle, WA, 2011.

2189
The Samuel Aba and Sisel Klurman Foundation, Inc. ✧
(formerly The Klurman Foundation, Inc.)
4000 Hollywood Blvd., Ste. 530N
Hollywood, FL 33021-6744

Established in 1984 in FL.
Donors: Samuel A. Klurman†; Sisel Klurman; Matan Ben-Aviv; Ganot Corp.; The Debbie Klurman 1994 Trust.
Foundation type: Independent foundation.
Financial data (yr. ended 12/31/13): Assets, $11,978,944 (M); gifts received, $133,600; expenditures, $748,610; qualifying distributions, $680,897; giving activities include $679,952 for 57 grants (high: $283,333; low: $1).
Fields of interest: Education; Health organizations, association; Human services; Jewish federated giving programs; Jewish agencies & synagogues.
International interests: Israel.
Type of support: General/operating support.
Limitations: Applications not accepted. Giving primarily in FL and NY. No grants to individuals.
Application information: Contributes only to pre-selected organizations.
Officers and Directors:* Zipora Ben-Aviv,* Pres.; Matan Ben-Aviv,* V.P.; Harvey L. Lichtman, Secy.-Treas.
EIN: 592532272

2190
KMD Foundation ✧
2424 N. Federal Hwy., No. 454
Boca Raton, FL 33431-7746

Established in 1981 in MI.
Donors: Irving A. Smokler; Toba Smokler Trust; Carol S. Smokler.
Foundation type: Independent foundation.
Financial data (yr. ended 12/31/13): Assets, $2,468,948 (M); gifts received, $1,103,839; expenditures, $700,428; qualifying distributions, $635,001; giving activities include $634,501 for 27 grants (high: $100,000; low: $120).
Purpose and activities: Giving primarily to Jewish agencies, temples, schools, and federated giving programs.
Fields of interest: Education; Hospitals (general); Human services; Jewish federated giving programs; Jewish agencies & synagogues.
Limitations: Applications not accepted. Giving primarily in FL, MI, and NY; some funding also in MA. No grants to individuals; no loans or program-related investments.
Application information: Contributes only to pre-selected organizations.
Trustees: Carol S. Smokler; Irving A. Smokler.
EIN: 382378958

2191
John S. and James L. Knight Foundation ✧
(formerly Knight Foundation)
200 S. Biscayne Blvd., Ste. 3300
Miami, FL 33131-2349 (305) 908-2600
Contact: Grant Admin.
FAX: (305) 908-2698;
E-mail: web@knightfoundation.org; Additional tel. for publication requests: (305) 908-2630; Main URL: http://www.knightfoundation.org
Community foundations guide for developing a Giving Day: http://www.givingdayplaybook.org/
Facebook: http://www.facebook.com/knightfdn
Grant Assessments: http://knightfoundation.org/publications/browse/?q=%22%22&page=1&selected_facets=pubtype_exact:%22Grant%20Assessments%22
KnightBlog: http://www.knightblog.org/
Pinterest: http://pinterest.com/knightfnd/pins/
RSS Feed: http://www.knightfoundation.org/rss/
Twitter: http://www.twitter.com/knightfdn
Vimeo: http://www.vimeo.com/knightfdn/videos

Incorporated in 1950 in OH.
Donors: John S. Knight†; James L. Knight†; and their families.
Foundation type: Independent foundation.
Financial data (yr. ended 12/31/13): Assets, $2,395,608,862 (M); expenditures, $135,987,628; qualifying distributions, $120,694,865; giving activities include $107,825,135 for grants, $10,928,230 for foundation-administered programs and $1,941,500 for loans/program-related investments.
Purpose and activities: The foundation advances journalism in the digital age and invests in the vitality of communities where the Knight brothers owned newspapers. The foundation focuses on projects that promote informed, engaged communities and that lead to transformational change. The foundation promotes these goals through its journalism, communities and national programs.
Fields of interest: Media, print publishing; Media, journalism; Arts; Education; Children, services; Family services; Civil rights, race/intergroup relations; Community development, neighborhood development; Economic development; Public affairs, citizen participation; African Americans/Blacks.
Type of support: General/operating support; Management development/capacity building; Capital campaigns; Building/renovation; Endowments; Emergency funds; Program development; Seed money; Curriculum development; Fellowships; Technical assistance; Program evaluation; Program-related investments/loans; Employee matching gifts; Matching/challenge support; Mission-related investments/loans.
Limitations: Applications accepted. Giving limited to projects serving the 26 communities where the Knight brothers published newspapers for communities and local grants: Long Beach and San Jose, CA, Boulder, CO, Bradenton, Miami, Palm Beach County, and Tallahassee, FL, Columbus, Macon, and Milledgeville, GA, Fort Wayne and Gary, IN, Wichita, KS, Lexington, KY, Detroit, MI, Duluth and St. Paul, MN, Biloxi, MS, Charlotte, NC, Grand Forks, ND, Akron, OH, Philadelphia and State College, PA, Columbia and Myrtle Beach, SC, and Aberdeen, SD; international for Journalism. No support for organizations whose mission is to prevent, eradicate and/or alleviate the effects of a specific disease; hospitals, unless for community-wide capital campaigns; activities to propagate a religious faith or restricted to one religion or denomination; political candidates; international programs, except U.S.-based organizations supporting free press around the world; charities operated by service clubs; or activities that are the responsibility of government (the foundation will in selective cases, join with units of government in supporting special projects). No grants to individuals, or for fundraising events; second requests for previously funded capital campaigns; operating deficits; general operating support; films, videos, or television programs; honoraria for distinguished guests-except in initiatives of the foundation in all three cases; group travel; memorials; medical research; or conferences.
Publications: Newsletter.
Application information: Please do not submit a proposal until you have been invited to do so by the Grants Admin. or a Prog. Off. Journalism and media grantees are required to disclose the identities of major donors and amounts contributed. The requirement applies to gifts of at least $5,000. Application form required.
Initial approach: Online inquiry
Copies of proposal: 1
Deadline(s): None, except for special initiatives (approximately 6-month grant cycle)
Board meeting date(s): Mar., June, Sept., and Dec.
Final notification: Full proposal: 1 month
Officers and Trustees:* John Palfrey,* Chair.; Alberto Ibarguen,* C.E.O. and Pres.; Carol Coletta, V.P., Community and National Initiatives; Terese Coudreaut Curiel, V.P., HR and Admin.; Juan J. Martinez, V.P., C.F.O. and Treas.; Dennis Scholl, V.P., Arts and Prog. Dir., Miami; Jorge Martinez, V.P., Inf. Systems; Jennifer Preston, V.P., Journalism; Andrew Sherry, V.P., Comm.; Elena Stetsenko, Cont.; Christopher M. Austen; Stephanie Bell-Rose; Francisco L. Borges; William Considine; James N. Crutchfield; Chris Hughes; Joi Ito; Susan D. Kronick; Anna Spangler Nelson; Beverly Knight Olson; Ray Rodriguez; E. Roe Stamps IV; Paul Steiger.
Number of staff: 61 full-time professional; 1 part-time professional.
EIN: 650464177
Selected grants: The following grants are a representative sample of this grantmaker's funding activity:
$6,000,000 to University Park Alliance, Akron, OH, 2012. For core engagement and partnership work and to launch efforts to provide sustainable long-term income.
$5,020,000 to Code for America Labs, San Francisco, CA, 2012. To focus on rewiring govemrnent to engage with citizens using innovative technology solutions.
$5,000,000 to Miami Foundation, Miami, FL, 2012. To create Knight Miami Ballet Fund to expand repertoire and commission new works under new artistic director.
$5,000,000 to Miami Foundation, Miami, FL, 2012. To create Knight Ideas Fund innovative program at Wolfsonian focused on increasing digital and physical access to collection including creation of Ideas event.
$3,150,000 to International Center for Journalists, Washington, DC, 2012. To launch new Knight International Journalism Fellows.
$3,120,000 to New York University, New York, NY, 2012. To develop multi-school, multi-disciplinary network of students, faculty and professionals

working to design and implement ways of using technology for citizen engagement.
$3,000,000 to Connect to Compete, Washington, DC, 2012. For Connect2Compete national public-private coalition to make internet services, equipment and training affordable for low-income families, with focus on Knight communities.
$2,888,000 to Foundation for the Carolinas, Charlotte, NC, 2012. To provide laptops to K-5 students.
$2,261,000 to Mercer University, Macon, GA, 2012. To continue work of College Hill Alliance and establish Innovation Corridor to attract and retain entrepreneurial businesses.
$2,250,000 to Community Foundation for Southeast Michigan, Detroit, MI, 2012. To create Knight Foundation Digital Innovation Fund to support Detroit Symphony Orchestra's expanded capacity for digital experimentation.
$2,250,000 to Community Foundation for Southeast Michigan, Detroit, MI, 2012. To create Knight Detroit Museum Fund to support increased community engagement using new models at Detroit Institute of Arts.
$2,250,000 to University of Michigan, Ann Arbor, MI, 2012. For artistic instruction by professional artists from key organizations such as Sphinx, Mosaic Theater, Michigan Opera and Detroit School of Arts.
$2,000,000 to Miami Foundation, Miami, FL, 2012. To create Knight Miami Classical Music donor-advised fund to support expansion of Cleveland Orchestra presence in Miami.
$2,000,000 to Pro Publica, New York, NY, 2012. For rapid response news applications team and associated training programs.

2192
Koch Foundation, Inc. ✧
4421 N.W. 39th Ave., Bldg. 1, Ste. 1
Gainesville, FL 32606-7211 (352) 373-7491
Contact: Carolyn A. Young, Exec. Dir.
E-mail: staff@thekochfoundation.org; Main URL: http://www.thekochfoundation.org

Incorporated in 1979 in FL.
Donors: Carl E. Koch‡; Paula Koch‡.
Foundation type: Independent foundation.
Financial data (yr. ended 03/13/14): Assets, $118,729,669 (M); expenditures, $7,887,324; qualifying distributions, $7,498,808; giving activities include $6,965,112 for 526 grants (high: $1,000,000; low: $1,500).
Purpose and activities: Grants only for Roman Catholic organizations that propagate the faith. Grants are made for direct evangelization programs, preparation of evangelists, Roman Catholic schools in resource-poor areas, and where the schools are the principal means of evangelization, and a Roman Catholic presence in the media.
Fields of interest: Catholic agencies & churches.
Type of support: Conferences/seminars; Curriculum development; Equipment; General/operating support; Matching/challenge support; Program development; Publication.
Limitations: Applications accepted. Giving on a national and international basis. No support for political funding, motor vehicles, or for medicine or pharmaceutical purposes. No grants to individuals, or for endowment funds, deficit financing, operating expenses, seed money, capital campaigns, or for scholarships or fellowships; no loans.
Publications: Application guidelines; Annual report.
Application information: All applicants outside the U.S. must list a diocese or religious congregation in the U.S. to act as Fiscal Agent through which funds may be distributed. The fiscal agent must be an organization listed in the Official Catholic Directory (OCD). The foundation currently has a moratorium on funds for international construction. Application form required.
Initial approach: Letter of request for an application that briefly describes the project; submit between Jan. 1 and May 1. All requests must be made in English. Fax, telephone, or e-mail requests will not be accepted
Copies of proposal: 1
Deadline(s): 90 days after receipt of application
Board meeting date(s): Feb.
Final notification: 1 month after Feb. board meeting
Officers and Directors:* William A. Bomberger,* Pres.; Inge L. Vraney,* V.P.; Rachel A. Bomberger,* Secy.; Dorothy C. Bomberger, Treas.; Carolyn A. Young, Exec. Dir.; Carolyn L. Bomberger; Matthew A. Bomberger; Michelle H. Bomberger; Charlotte L. Spacinsky; Jeffrey Vraney; Lawrence E. Vraney, Jr.; Lori A. Vraney; Maura J. Vraney.
Number of staff: 2 full-time professional; 3 full-time support.
EIN: 591885997
Selected grants: The following grants are a representative sample of this grantmaker's funding activity:
$30,000 to Lamp Ministries, Bronx, NY, 2013. For evangelization outreach program to the homeless.
$25,000 to Dismas Ministry, Milwaukee, WI, 2013. For prison outreach program.
$25,000 to Our Lady of Victory Church Maria Lanakila Parish, Lahaina, HI, 2013. For the purchase of kitchen equipment for a school.
$25,000 to Poor Clare Sisters of Omaha, Omaha, NE, 2013. For the purchase of kitchen equipment for a new monastery.
$25,000 to Saint Joseph School, Wakefield, MA, 2013. For the renovation and expansion of a Catholic school.
$20,000 to Catholic Archdiocese of Trichur, India, 2013. For daily living expenses and education for seminarians.
$20,000 to Cistercian Monastery of Our Lady of Phuoc Hat, Ba Ria, Vietnam, 2013. For daily living expenses, education and formation for women religious.
$20,000 to Sacred Heart Major Seminary, Detroit, MI, 2013. For daily living expenses and education of seminarians.
$15,000 to Apostolic Vicariate of Benghazi, Benghazi, Libya, 2013. For the living expenses and pastoral efforts of men and women religious and laity in Libya.
$15,000 to Congregation of Holy Cross, North Easton, MA, 2013. For the formation of seminarians in Peru.

2193
The Korf Family Foundation, Inc. ✧
200 S. Biscayne Blvd., Ste. 5500
Miami, FL 33131-2333

Established in 2006 in FL.
Donor: Mordechai Korf.
Foundation type: Independent foundation.
Financial data (yr. ended 11/30/13): Assets, $204,959 (M); gifts received, $2,368,000; expenditures, $2,354,718; qualifying distributions, $2,351,155; giving activities include $2,351,155 for 25 grants (high: $1,208,265; low: $350).
Purpose and activities: Giving primarily to Jewish agencies, temples, and schools.
Fields of interest: Education; Jewish federated giving programs; Jewish agencies & synagogues.
Limitations: Applications not accepted. Giving primarily in FL and NY.
Application information: Contributes only to pre-selected organizations.
Officers: Mordechai Y. Korf, C.E.O. and Pres.; Nechama A. Korf, V.P.
EIN: 203942766

2194
The KPS Charitable Foundation ✧
202 Gomez Rd.
Hobe Sound, FL 33455-2513

Established in 2000 in NJ.
Donors: Frank Bongrazio; Krishna P. Singh; Martha J. Singh; S. Amy Singh; Harbor Associates.
Foundation type: Independent foundation.
Financial data (yr. ended 09/30/13): Assets, $4,443,208 (M); expenditures, $8,159,384; qualifying distributions, $8,105,500; giving activities include $8,105,500 for 4 grants (high: $8,000,000; low: $500).
Purpose and activities: Giving primarily to a university's center for nanotechnology.
Fields of interest: Higher education; Human services.
Type of support: General/operating support.
Limitations: Applications not accepted. Giving primarily in Philadelphia, PA; some giving in IL. No grants to individuals.
Application information: Contributes only to pre-selected organizations.
Officers: Krishna P. Singh, Pres.; Martha J. Singh, Secy.; Frank Bongrazio, Treas.
EIN: 522211755

2195
C. L. C. Kramer Foundation, Inc. ✧
3840 Prairie Dunes Dr.
Sarasota, FL 34238-2816
E-mail: rzabelle@verizon.net; Tel./fax: (941) 924-2533; Main URL: http://www.clckramerfoundation.org

Established in 1966.
Donor: Catherine Kramer‡.
Foundation type: Independent foundation.
Financial data (yr. ended 09/30/13): Assets, $7,579,245 (M); expenditures, $607,040; qualifying distributions, $486,790; giving activities include $451,000 for 31 grants (high: $60,000; low: $500).
Purpose and activities: Giving primarily for hospitals, as well as to an organization for people who are blind; funding also for the performing arts and Jewish organizations.
Fields of interest: Performing arts; Hospitals (general); Medical research, institute; Human services; Jewish federated giving programs.
Type of support: General/operating support; Continuing support.
Limitations: Applications not accepted. Giving primarily in New York, NY. No grants to individuals.
Publications: IRS Form 990 or 990-PF printed copy available upon request.

Application information: Contributes only to pre-selected organizations.
Officers: Robert Zabelle, Pres.; Lawrence Rothenberg, Secy.; Erica Harold, Treas.
EIN: 136226513
Selected grants: The following grants are a representative sample of this grantmaker's funding activity:
$60,000 to Lighthouse International, New York, NY, 2011. For general support.
$25,000 to Mount Sinai Medical Center, New York, NY, 2011. For general support.
$25,000 to Saint Francis Hospital, Roslyn, NY, 2011. For general support.
$20,000 to Sarasota Ballet of Florida, Sarasota, FL, 2011. For general support.
$15,000 to Alvin Ailey Dance Foundation, New York, NY, 2011. For general support.
$15,000 to Chamber Music Society of Lincoln Center, New York, NY, 2011. For general support.
$10,000 to Philharmonic-Symphony Society of New York, New York, NY, 2011. For general support.
$5,000 to Columbia University, New York, NY, 2011. For general support.
$5,000 to Roundabout Theater Company, New York, NY, 2011. For general support.
$2,500 to Prime Time House, Torrington, CT, 2011. For general support.

2196
Krouse Family Foundation, Inc. ✧
c/o Sun Capital Partners, Inc.
5200 Town Center Cir., Ste. 650
Boca Raton, FL 33486-1045
Contact: Donna Wohlfarth

Donors: Rodger Krouse; Hillary Krouse.
Foundation type: Independent foundation.
Financial data (yr. ended 09/30/13): Assets, $8,562,954 (M); gifts received, $10,000,000; expenditures, $2,345,762; qualifying distributions, $2,323,888; giving activities include $2,322,333 for 10 grants (high: $1,100,000; low: $1,000).
Fields of interest: Education; Human services; Foundations (private grantmaking).
Limitations: Applications not accepted. Giving primarily in Boca Raton, FL; some funding also in New York, NY, and Philadelphia, PA.
Application information: Contributes only to pre-selected organizations.
Officers and Directors:* Rodger R. Krouse,* Pres.; Hillary Krouse,* Secy.; Marc J. Leder,* Treas.
EIN: 261514117
Selected grants: The following grants are a representative sample of this grantmaker's funding activity:
$200,000 to University of Pennsylvania, Philadelphia, PA, 2011.

2197
The Laber Foundation, Inc. ✧
1521 Alton Rd., No. 133
Miami Beach, FL 33131

Established in 2006 in DE.
Donor: Uri Laber.
Foundation type: Independent foundation.
Financial data (yr. ended 11/30/13): Assets, $18,454 (M); gifts received, $750,000; expenditures, $740,247; qualifying distributions, $738,200; giving activities include $738,200 for 20 grants (high: $160,000; low: $1,600).
Fields of interest: Education; Jewish federated giving programs; Jewish agencies & synagogues.
Limitations: Applications not accepted. Giving primarily in NJ and NY.
Application information: Contributes only to pre-selected organizations.
Officers: Uri Laber, Pres. and C.E.O.; Mordechai Y. Korf, V.P.; Bassie Laber, Secy.
EIN: 203925774

2198
Constance C. and Linwood A. Lacy, Jr. Foundation ✧
c/o Bank of America, N.A.
P.O. Box 40200, FL9-100-10-19
Jacksonville, FL 32203-0200
Application address: c/o Sarah D. Kay, Bank of America, 1111 E. Main St., 12th Fl., Richmond, VA 23219, tel.: (804) 887-8773

Established in 1998 in VA.
Donors: Linwood A. Lacy, Jr.; Constance C. Lacy; The Linwood A. Lacy Charitable Lead Annuity Trust.
Foundation type: Independent foundation.
Financial data (yr. ended 12/31/13): Assets, $4,070,467 (M); expenditures, $535,281; qualifying distributions, $512,388; giving activities include $498,500 for 35 grants (high: $100,000; low: $3,000).
Fields of interest: Arts; Higher education; Housing/shelter, development; Boys & girls clubs; Human services; Salvation Army; Children/youth, services; Christian agencies & churches.
Limitations: Applications accepted. Giving primarily in Richmond and Charlottesville, VA.
Application information: Application form required.
Initial approach: Letter
Deadline(s): None
Officers: Linwood A. Lacy, Jr., Pres.; Constance C. Lacy, Secy.
Directors: Adam M. Lacy; Christopher L. Lacy.
EIN: 541919627
Selected grants: The following grants are a representative sample of this grantmaker's funding activity:
$20,000 to FeedMore, Richmond, VA, 2012. For Food Bank/Meals on Wheels.

2199
Patricia A. & William E. LaMothe Foundation ✧
6169 Victory Dr.
Ave Maria, FL 34142 (239) 472-2067
Contact: Patricia A. LaMothe, Pres. and Tr.

Established in 1986 in MI.
Donors: Patricia A. LaMothe; William E. LaMothe; Sydney McManus.
Foundation type: Independent foundation.
Financial data (yr. ended 12/31/13): Assets, $6,962,827 (M); gifts received, $1,211,300; expenditures, $548,252; qualifying distributions, $535,874; giving activities include $532,491 for 89 grants (high: $25,000; low: $100).
Purpose and activities: Giving primarily for higher education, Roman Catholic organizations, and conservation.
Fields of interest: Education; Environment, natural resources; Health organizations, association; Human services; Catholic agencies & churches.
Limitations: Applications accepted. Giving primarily in Battle Creek and Kalamazoo, MI.
Application information:
Initial approach: Letter
Deadline(s): None
Officers and Trustees:* Patricia A. LaMothe,* Pres.; Alexis LaMothe,* V.P.; Sydney McManus,* Secy.; William E. LaMothe,* Treas.
EIN: 386517929
Selected grants: The following grants are a representative sample of this grantmaker's funding activity:
$1,000 to Boy Scouts of America, SW Michigan Council, Kalamazoo, MI, 2012. For general programs.

2200
The Lampert Foundation ✧
(formerly The Edward and Kinga Lampert Foundation)
1170 Kane Concourse
Bay Harbor, FL 33154

Established in CT.
Donor: Edward Lampert.
Foundation type: Independent foundation.
Financial data (yr. ended 12/31/13): Assets, $44,525,784 (M); expenditures, $1,163,900; qualifying distributions, $1,161,850; giving activities include $1,155,800 for grants (high: $534,800; low: $1,000).
Fields of interest: Cancer; Heart & circulatory diseases; Breast cancer research; Human services.
Limitations: Applications not accepted. Giving primarily in Greenwich, CT; some funding also in Minneapolis, MN, and Toronto, Ontario, Canada.
Application information: Unsolicited requests for funds not accepted.
Trustees: Edward S. Lampert; Kinga Keh Lampert.
EIN: 205436006

2201
George H. Langenfelder Charitable Trust ✧
c/o Bank of America, N.A.
P.O. Box 40200, FL9-100-10-19
Jacksonville, FL 32203-0200

Established in 2005 in MD.
Donor: G.H. Langenfelder Marital Trust.
Foundation type: Independent foundation.
Financial data (yr. ended 06/30/13): Assets, $13,051,226 (M); expenditures, $701,320; qualifying distributions, $572,076; giving activities include $572,076 for grants.
Fields of interest: Health care; Health organizations; Human services.
Limitations: Applications not accepted. Giving primarily in MD. No grants to individuals.
Application information: Contributes only to pre-selected organizations.
Trustees: Barbara Ann Spicer; Bank of America, N.A.
EIN: 546548865
Selected grants: The following grants are a representative sample of this grantmaker's funding activity:
$64,049 to Joseph Richey House, Baltimore, MD, 2011. For general funds.

$64,049 to United Way of Central Maryland, Baltimore, MD, 2011. For general funds.

2202
Frances Langford Foundation ✧
P.O. Box 96
Jensen Beach, FL 34958-0096 (918) 744-5222
Contact: Evans Crary, Jr., Tr.; John B. Turner, Tr.

Established in 1989 in FL.
Donor: Frances Langford Stuart.
Foundation type: Independent foundation.
Financial data (yr. ended 12/31/13): Assets, $15,821,223 (M); expenditures, $2,751,564; qualifying distributions, $2,307,450; giving activities include $2,307,450 for 44 grants (high: $525,000; low: $1,000).
Fields of interest: Museums (marine/maritime); Historic preservation/historical societies; Higher education; Hospitals (specialty); Human services; American Red Cross; Children/youth, services; Christian agencies & churches.
Limitations: Applications accepted. Giving primarily in Stuart, FL. No grants to individuals.
Application information: Application form not required.
Initial approach: Letter
Copies of proposal: 1
Deadline(s): None
Trustees: Evans Crary, Jr.; John B. Turner.
EIN: 656041900
Selected grants: The following grants are a representative sample of this grantmaker's funding activity:
$245,500 to Capernaum Ministries, Indian Lake Estates, FL, 2011.
$100,000 to Boys and Girls Club of Martin County, Hobe Sound, FL, 2011.

2203
Larson Foundation ✧ ☆
4931 Bonita Bay Blvd., Ste. 1802
Bonita Springs, FL 34134-1705

Established in 1988 in MN.
Donors: Kenneth R. Larson; Slumberland, Inc.
Foundation type: Independent foundation.
Financial data (yr. ended 12/31/13): Assets, $1,908,683 (M); gifts received, $1,489,862; expenditures, $688,025; qualifying distributions, $688,025; giving activities include $688,000 for 35 grants (high: $150,000; low: $1,000).
Purpose and activities: Emphasis on Christian education and agencies.
Fields of interest: Christian agencies & churches.
Type of support: General/operating support; Fellowships.
Limitations: Applications not accepted. Giving on a national basis.
Application information: Unsolicited requests for funds not accepted.
Officers: Kenneth R. Larson, Pres. and Secy.; Barbara J. Larson, V.P.
Number of staff: None.
EIN: 411605601
Selected grants: The following grants are a representative sample of this grantmaker's funding activity:
$50,000 to Minnehaha Academy, Minneapolis, MN, 2011. For general support.
$25,000 to Rockpoint Church, Lake Elmo, MN, 2011. For general support.
$5,000 to Hope for the City, Saint Louis Park, MN, 2011. For general support.

2204
Lattner Family Foundation, Inc. ✧
777 E. Atlantic Ave., Ste. 317
Delray Beach, FL 33483-5352 (561) 278-3781
Contact: Patty Gerhart, Fund Mgr.
E-mail: lattner@bellsouth.net; Main URL: http://www.lattnerfoundation.org

Established in 2006 in FL with assets from the Forrest C. Lattner Foundation.
Foundation type: Independent foundation.
Financial data (yr. ended 12/31/12): Assets, $78,032,683 (M); expenditures, $4,850,441; qualifying distributions, $4,205,500; giving activities include $4,205,500 for grants.
Purpose and activities: Giving primarily in the areas of education, environment, health and social services, arts and humanities, and religion, including Christian organizations that provide health and social services. Special emphasis on the following geographical areas related to where the trustees live: Palm Beach County, Florida, Kansas, Rhode Island, Texas, and Georgia.
Fields of interest: Humanities; Arts; Education; Environment; Health care; Community/economic development; Christian agencies & churches; Religion.
Type of support: General/operating support.
Limitations: Applications accepted. Giving primarily in Palm Beach County, FL, GA, KS, RI, and TX.
Publications: Application guidelines.
Application information: The foundation is not accepting any unsolicited grants from organizations unless they have received a grant in the past. See foundation web site for specific application guidelines which must be followed. The foundation does not accept grant requests via e-mail, fax or phone. Please mail in all grant requests for review. Upon receipt, each request will be reviewed on a preliminary basis. Application form not required.
Initial approach: Letter
Copies of proposal: 1
Deadline(s): Mar. 1 and Sept. 1
Board meeting date(s): Late spring and fall
Final notification: Notification letters are sent out approximately twelve weeks after board meetings
Officer and Trustees:* Martha L. Walker,* Chair.; Janet Barnes; Forrest C. Brown, M.D.; Andrew L. Harris; Richard M. Harris; Thomas Shoof; Susan B. Funke Walker.
EIN: 203100839

2205
Forrest C. & Frances H. Lattner Foundation ✧
198 N.E. 6th Ave.
Delray Beach, FL 33483-5423 (561) 266-9494
Contact: Susan L. Lloyd, Chair.
E-mail: fcfhlattner@bellsouth.net

Established in 2006 in FL with assets from the Forrest C. Lattner Foundation.
Foundation type: Independent foundation.
Financial data (yr. ended 12/31/12): Assets, $77,179,579 (M); expenditures, $4,817,067; qualifying distributions, $4,131,208; giving activities include $3,952,902 for 101 grants (high: $250,000; low: $2,000).
Purpose and activities: Giving primarily in the areas of education, environment, and health and social services.
Fields of interest: Arts; Education; Environment; Health care; Human services; Community/economic development.
Type of support: General/operating support.
Limitations: Giving primarily in CA, FL, GA, PA, RI, and VT.
Application information: Contributes mostly to pre-selected organizations.
Officer: Susan L. Lloyd, Chair.
Trustees: David W. Hollenbeck; Douglas Hollenbeck; Drew Hollenbeck.
EIN: 203106502

2206
Lavin Family Foundation ✧
(formerly Leonard H. Lavin Foundation)
5001 S.W. 27th Ave.
Ocala, FL 34474-0109 (708) 450-3434
Contact: Leonard H. Lavin, Pres.

Established around 1964.
Donor: Leonard H. Lavin.
Foundation type: Independent foundation.
Financial data (yr. ended 12/31/13): Assets, $69,949,595 (M); expenditures, $4,539,564; qualifying distributions, $4,140,500; giving activities include $4,140,500 for 64 grants (high: $1,000,000; low: $500).
Purpose and activities: Giving primarily for higher and other education, and for human services.
Fields of interest: Higher education; Education; Medical research, institute; Human services.
Limitations: Applications accepted. Giving primarily in Chicago, IL. No grants to individuals.
Application information: Application form not required.
Initial approach: Letter
Deadline(s): None
Officers: Leonard H. Lavin, Pres.; Carol L. Bernick, V.P.
EIN: 366106074
Selected grants: The following grants are a representative sample of this grantmaker's funding activity:
$400,000 to Art Institute of Chicago, Chicago, IL, 2011.
$25,000 to Art Institute of Chicago, Chicago, IL, 2011.
$10,000 to Chicago Symphony Orchestra, Chicago, IL, 2011.
$7,500 to Junior Achievement of Chicago, Chicago, IL, 2011.
$7,500 to Posse Foundation, New York, NY, 2011.
$5,000 to Boys and Girls Clubs of Chicago, Chicago, IL, 2011.
$5,000 to Chamber of Commerce Foundation, Chicagoland, Chicago, IL, 2011.
$1,000 to Food for the Poor, Coconut Creek, FL, 2011.

2207
The Bennett and Geraldine LeBow Foundation Inc. ✧
c/o CBIZ MHM LLC
1200 Brickell Ave., Ste. 700
Miami, FL 33131-3256
Application address: c/o Stephanie Don, 667 Madison Ave., 14th Fl., New York, NY 10065, tel.: (212) 319-4400

Established in 1997 in FL.
Foundation type: Independent foundation.
Financial data (yr. ended 12/31/13): Assets, $488,666 (M); expenditures, $703,024; qualifying distributions, $677,596; giving activities include $675,000 for 6 grants (high: $500,000; low: $5,000).
Fields of interest: Education; Community/economic development; Religion.
Limitations: Applications accepted. Giving primarily in Washington, DC, FL, NY and PA.
Application information: Application form required.
Initial approach: Letter
Deadline(s): None
Officers: Bennett S. LeBow, Pres.; Karen Eisenbud, Secy.
Director: Stephanie Don.
EIN: 650755022

2208
Leclerc Charity Fund ✧
P.O. Box 110205
Naples, FL 34108-0104

Established in 1968 in MA.
Donors: Raymond Leclerc; Ray Plastic, Inc.
Foundation type: Independent foundation.
Financial data (yr. ended 12/31/13): Assets, $11,405,714 (M); expenditures, $686,366; qualifying distributions, $553,056; giving activities include $553,056 for 58 grants (high: $50,000; low: $456).
Purpose and activities: Giving primarily for human services, and for Roman Catholic agencies and schools.
Fields of interest: Education; Health organizations, association; Human services; Catholic agencies & churches.
Type of support: General/operating support.
Limitations: Applications not accepted. No grants to individuals.
Application information: Contributes only to pre-selected organizations.
Officer: Raymond Leclerc, Mgr.
Trustees: Diana Moore; Francis S. Wyman.
EIN: 046183548
Selected grants: The following grants are a representative sample of this grantmaker's funding activity:
$10,000 to Samaritans Purse, Boone, NC, 2011.
$10,000 to Smile Train, New York, NY, 2011.
$10,000 to Special Olympics, Washington, DC, 2011.

2209
Marc J. Leder Foundation, Inc. ✧
c/o Sun Capital Partners, Inc., Attn.: Donna Wohlfarth
5200 Town Center Cir., Ste. 650
Boca Raton, FL 33486-1045

Established in FL.
Donors: Marc Leder; Leder Family Foundation, Inc.
Foundation type: Independent foundation.
Financial data (yr. ended 09/30/13): Assets, $4,892,600 (M); gifts received, $4,948,634; expenditures, $1,342,465; qualifying distributions, $1,312,648; giving activities include $1,311,100 for 5 grants (high: $1,100,000; low: $100).
Fields of interest: Higher education; Education; Foundations (private grantmaking).
Limitations: Applications not accepted. Giving in the U.S., with emphasis on FL. No grants to individuals.
Application information: Unsolicited requests for funds not accepted.
Officers and Directors:* Marc J. Leder,* Pres.; Kevin J. Calhoun,* Secy.; Rodger R. Krouse,* Treas.
EIN: 271815293

2210
Lennar Foundation ✧
700 N.W. 107th Ave., Ste. 400
Miami, FL 33172-3139 (305) 229-6400
Contact: Marshall Ames, Pres. and Dir.
E-mail: marshall.ames@lennar.com; Main URL: http://www.lennar.com/

Established in 1989 in FL.
Donor: Lennar Corp.
Foundation type: Company-sponsored foundation.
Financial data (yr. ended 11/30/13): Assets, $47,790,381 (M); expenditures, $3,116,327; qualifying distributions, $1,893,007; giving activities include $1,482,244 for 38 grants (high: $455,000; low: $1,325).
Purpose and activities: The foundation supports organizations involved with education, water resources, cancer, multiple sclerosis, disaster relief, and human services. Special emphasis is directed toward programs designed to assist people who are less fortunate.
Fields of interest: Middle schools/education; Higher education; Education, services; Education; Environment, water resources; Health care, patient services; Health care; Cancer; Multiple sclerosis; Disasters, preparedness/services; Children/youth, services; Children, foster care; Homeless, human services; Human services; United Ways and Federated Giving Programs; Economically disadvantaged.
Type of support: General/operating support; Seed money.
Limitations: Applications accepted. Giving primarily in CA, Miami, FL, Las Vegas, NV, SC, and TX. No grants to individuals.
Application information: Application form required.
Initial approach: Letter
Deadline(s): None
Officers and Directors:* Marshall Ames,* Pres.; Samantha Fels,* Secy.; Jim Carr; Ezra Katz; Waynewright Malcolm; Stuart A. Miller; Allan J. Pekor; Shelley Rubin.
EIN: 650171539

2211
Levitetz Family Foundation, Inc ✧ ☆
5300 Broken Sound Blvd. N.W., Ste. 110
Boca Raton, FL 33487-3519 (800) 323-6838
Contact: Alan Rutner, V.P.

Donors: Jeffery A. Levitetz; Barry M. Smith Trust.
Foundation type: Independent foundation.
Financial data (yr. ended 06/30/13): Assets, $6,426,714 (M); gifts received, $1,010,000; expenditures, $477,550; qualifying distributions, $446,617; giving activities include $442,650 for 29 grants (high: $50,000; low: $1,000).
Fields of interest: Arts; Education; Recreation; Science.
Type of support: General/operating support.
Limitations: Applications accepted. Giving primarily in AL, CO and FL.
Application information: Application form required.
Initial approach: Letter
Deadline(s): None
Officers and Directors:* Jeffery A. Levitetz,* Pres.; Alan Rutner,* V.P., Secy.-Treas.; David Groomes,* V.P.; Tyler Levitetz; Zachary Levitetz.
EIN: 273533930

2212
Frank J. Lewis Foundation, Inc. ✧
P.O. Box 9726
Riviera Beach, FL 33419-9726

Established in 1996 in FL.
Donor: Philip D. Lewis.
Foundation type: Independent foundation.
Financial data (yr. ended 12/31/12): Assets, $7,484,128 (M); gifts received, $872,343; expenditures, $687,851; qualifying distributions, $538,218; giving activities include $530,300 for 39 grants (high: $35,000; low: $1,300).
Purpose and activities: Giving primarily for education, human services, and Roman Catholic churches and agencies.
Fields of interest: Higher education; Education; Health organizations, association; Human services; Catholic agencies & churches.
Type of support: General/operating support.
Limitations: Giving primarily in FL, IL, and IN; some funding also in NY.
Trustees: Megan Lewis Daly; Diana Lewis; Edward D. Lewis; M. Patricia Lewis; Philip D. Lewis; Timothy P. Lewis.
EIN: 650652107

2213
Libra Foundation, Inc. ✧
96 N.E. 4th Ave.
Delray Beach, FL 33483-4597

Established in 1994 in FL.
Donors: Jane E. Werly†; Charles M. Werly†.
Foundation type: Independent foundation.
Financial data (yr. ended 12/31/13): Assets, $43,608,999 (M); expenditures, $2,332,225; qualifying distributions, $2,026,596; giving activities include $1,953,000 for 40 grants (high: $100,000; low: $3,000).
Purpose and activities: Giving primarily for human services.
Fields of interest: Education; Human services; Children, services; Family services.
Limitations: Applications not accepted. Giving primarily in FL and MA. No grants to individuals.
Application information: Contributes only to pre-selected organizations.
Directors: Horace S. Nichols; Thomas A. Smith; J. Jeffrey Thistle.
EIN: 650469849

2214
The Lichtenberger Foundation ✧
508 N.W. Winters Creek Rd.
Palm City, FL 34990-8096

Established in 1997 in CT.
Donors: H. William Lichtenberger; Patricia A. Lichtenberger; HWL Incestements, LLC; H. William Lichtenberger Four Year Charitable Lead Annuity Trust; H. William Lichtenberger Eight Year Charitable Lead Annuity Trust; H. William Lichtenberger Twelve Year Charitable Lead Annuity Trust.
Foundation type: Independent foundation.
Financial data (yr. ended 12/31/13): Assets, $5,598,455 (M); gifts received, $1,106,778; expenditures, $668,518; qualifying distributions, $602,585; giving activities include $602,585 for 58 grants (high: $70,000; low: $100).
Fields of interest: Higher education; Cancer; Alzheimer's disease; Health organizations; Boy scouts; American Red Cross; Salvation Army; United Ways and Federated Giving Programs.
Type of support: General/operating support.
Limitations: Applications not accepted. Giving primarily in CT and FL. No grants to individuals.
Application information: Contributes only to pre-selected organizations.
Trustees: Lisa Krass; Erich T. Lichtenberger; H. William Lichtenberger; Patricia A. Lichtenberger.
EIN: 061483820
Selected grants: The following grants are a representative sample of this grantmaker's funding activity:
$25,000 to Homes for Our Troops, Taunton, MA, 2012. For Housing for Military Personnel.
$15,000 to UNICEF, New York, NY, 2012. To assist Needy Children.
$10,000 to Walsingham Academy, Williamsburg, VA, 2012. For general educational purposes.
$5,000 to Child Development Resources, Norge, VA, 2012. To provide Services to Children.
$4,000 to Sigma Nu Educational Foundation, Lexington, VA, 2012. To provide scholarships.
$4,000 to Wounded Warrior Project, Jacksonville, FL, 2012. To assist Wounded Military Personnel.
$1,000 to Library Foundation of Martin County, Stuart, FL, 2012. To promote literacy.
$600 to Feed the Children, Oklahoma City, OK, 2012. To provide Food for Hungry Children.
$456 to Compassion International, Colorado Springs, CO, 2012. For general charitable purposes.

2215
Lois Pope Life Foundation Inc. ✧
6274 Linton Blvd., Ste. 103
Delray Beach, FL 33484-6508 (561) 865-0955
FAX: (561) 865-0938; E-mail: life@life-edu.org; Main URL: http://www.life-edu.org/

Established in FL.
Donor: The Lois Pope Life Foundation.
Foundation type: Independent foundation.
Financial data (yr. ended 12/31/12): Assets, $4,032,904 (M); expenditures, $993,611; qualifying distributions, $945,821; giving activities include $650,250 for 19 grants (high: $250,000; low: $500).
Purpose and activities: Giving primarily for animal welfare, medical research, education, summer camp programs, humanitarian relief, and the performing arts.
Fields of interest: Performing arts; Education; Animals/wildlife; Medical research, institute; Recreation, camps; Human services; Military/veterans' organizations.
Type of support: Scholarships—to individuals.
Limitations: Applications not accepted. Giving primarily in FL.
Publications: Newsletter.
Application information: Unsolicited requests for funds not accepted.
Officers: Lois B. Pope, Chair.; Paul D. Pope, Pres.; Robert C. Miller, Secy.; Elsa Johnson, Treas.
EIN: 273158367
Selected grants: The following grants are a representative sample of this grantmaker's funding activity:
$500 to Busch Wildlife Sanctuary, Jupiter, FL, 2012. For wildlife welfare.

2216
The Liman Foundation, Inc. ✧ ☆
c/o Rampell & Rampell, P.A.
223 Sunset Ave., Ste. 200
Palm Beach, FL 33480-3855
Application address: c/o Anne Hennessy, US Trust, Bank of America Private Wealth Mgmt., 114 W. 47th St., New York, NY 10036

Established in 2000 in NY, as a result of a transfer of assets from the Joe and Emily Lowe Foundation.
Foundation type: Independent foundation.
Financial data (yr. ended 12/31/13): Assets, $6,530,469 (M); expenditures, $638,267; qualifying distributions, $542,667; giving activities include $538,600 for 67 grants (high: $50,000; low: $1,000).
Purpose and activities: Giving primarily for the arts, education, legal services, medical research, the environment and Jewish philanthropy.
Fields of interest: Arts; Education; Legal services; Jewish agencies & synagogues.
Limitations: Applications accepted. Giving primarily in the New York, NY metropolitan area. No grants to individuals.
Application information: Application form required.
Initial approach: Letter of request
Deadline(s): None
Officers: Ellen Liman, Pres. and Treas.; Douglas Liman, V.P.; Emily Liman, V.P.; Lewis Liman, Secy.
EIN: 134062758
Selected grants: The following grants are a representative sample of this grantmaker's funding activity:
$100,000 to Columbia University, New York, NY, 2011.
$20,000 to Jewish Museum, New York, NY, 2011.
$15,000 to Park Avenue Synagogue, New York, NY, 2011.
$10,000 to Legal Aid Society, New York, NY, 2011.
$9,000 to Spelman College, Atlanta, GA, 2011.
$5,000 to Museum of Arts and Design, New York, NY, 2011.
$5,000 to New York Botanical Garden, Bronx, NY, 2011.
$5,000 to Publicolor, New York, NY, 2011.
$2,000 to Educational Alliance, New York, NY, 2011.
$1,000 to Marthas Vineyard Hebrew Center, Vineyard Haven, MA, 2011.

2217
Lindemann Charitable Foundation II ✧
505 S. Flagler Dr., No. 900
West Miami Beach, FL 33401-5923

Established in FL.
Donor: George L. Lindemann.
Foundation type: Independent foundation.
Financial data (yr. ended 06/30/13): Assets, $21,355,089 (M); gifts received, $1,313,964; expenditures, $1,577,025; qualifying distributions, $1,570,500; giving activities include $1,570,500 for 19 grants (high: $1,000,000; low: $500).
Fields of interest: Performing arts; Performing arts, opera; Arts; Education; Human services; United Ways and Federated Giving Programs; Jewish federated giving programs.
Limitations: Applications not accepted. Giving primarily in FL and NY.
Application information: Contributes only to pre-selected organizations.
Officers: George L. Lidemann, Pres.; Frayda B. Lindemann, V.P.; Sloan N. Lindemann, Secy.; George L. Lindemann, Jr., Treas.
EIN: 582119083
Selected grants: The following grants are a representative sample of this grantmaker's funding activity:
$957,319 to Metropolitan Opera, New York, NY, 2011.
$400,000 to Brown University, Providence, RI, 2011.
$80,203 to United Way of Miami-Dade, Miami, FL, 2011.
$32,000 to Ballet Theater Foundation, New York, NY, 2011.
$25,000 to Gotham Chamber Opera, New York, NY, 2011.
$25,000 to Mount Vernon Ladies Association, Mount Vernon, VA, 2011.
$25,000 to United Way of Palm Beach County, Boynton Beach, FL, 2011.
$10,000 to Opera America, New York, NY, 2011.
$5,815 to Martina Arroyo Foundation, New York, NY, 2011.
$5,000 to Cushman School, Miami, FL, 2011.

2218
Litowitz Foundation Inc. ✧
11401 Bird Rd., Ste. 370
Miami, FL 33165-3340

Established in1997 in FL.
Donor: Robert Litowitz.
Foundation type: Independent foundation.
Financial data (yr. ended 12/31/13): Assets, $18,397,701 (M); expenditures, $753,124; qualifying distributions, $706,069; giving activities include $698,065 for 37 grants (high: $253,360; low: $7).
Purpose and activities: Giving primarily for public radio, animal and environmental protection, higher education, health and medical services, and for Jewish religious institutes.
Fields of interest: Media, radio; Higher education; Environment; Animal welfare; Health care; Jewish agencies & synagogues.
Limitations: Applications not accepted. Giving on a national basis; with emphasis on FL. No grants to individuals.
Application information: Unsolicited requests for funds not accepted.
Board meeting date(s): Quarterly

Officers: Robert Litowitz, Pres. and Treas.; Donna Litowitz, V.P. and Secy.; Budd Litowitz, V.P.
Directors: Arthur Litowitz; Susan Litowitz.
Number of staff: None.
EIN: 650763609

2219
London Foundation Inc. ✧ ☆
c/o Howard M. Amdur C.P.A., P.A.
4780 S.W. 64th Ave., Ste. 104
Davie, FL 33314-4400

Established in 1997 in FL.
Foundation type: Independent foundation.
Financial data (yr. ended 12/31/13): Assets, $706,548 (M); expenditures, $637,554; qualifying distributions, $628,362; giving activities include $628,362 for 3 grants (high: $577,362; low: $1,000).
Fields of interest: Foundations (private grantmaking).
Limitations: Applications not accepted. Giving in the U.S., with emphasis on CA.
Application information: Unsolicited requests for funds not accepted.
Directors: Meredith Borden; David London; Valerie London; Stuart L. Morris; Elizabeth L. Rogers.
EIN: 650358176

2220
The Alan S. Lorberbaum Family Foundation ✧
c/o M. Shue, Bessemer Trust
801 Brickell Ave.
Miami, FL 33131-2951
Application address: c/o Suzanne L. Helen, Tr., 9605 E. Poundstone Pl., Englewood, CO 80111, tel.: (561) 362-7024

Established in 1998 in FL.
Donor: Alan S. Lorberbaum.
Foundation type: Independent foundation.
Financial data (yr. ended 12/31/13): Assets, $22,372,162 (M); expenditures, $561,489; qualifying distributions, $558,439; giving activities include $557,639 for 6 grants (high: $552,639; low: $1,000).
Purpose and activities: Giving primarily to a gift fund.
Fields of interest: Education; Foundations (private grantmaking).
Limitations: Applications accepted. Giving primarily in NJ.
Application information: Application form required.
Initial approach: Written summary (not more than 2 pages)
Deadline(s): None
Trustees: Suzanne L. Helen; Jeffrey Lorberbaum; Mark Lorberbaum.
EIN: 586368036
Selected grants: The following grants are a representative sample of this grantmaker's funding activity:
$1,000 to Bright School, Chattanooga, TN, 2011. For operating fund.
$1,000 to Chattanooga Symphony and Opera, Chattanooga, TN, 2011. For operating fund.
$1,000 to Creative Discovery Museum, Chattanooga, TN, 2011. For operating fund.
$1,000 to Hunter Museum of Art, Chattanooga, TN, 2011. For operating fund.

2221
E. M. Lynn Foundation ✧
1905 N.W. Corporate Blvd.
Boca Raton, FL 33431-7303 (561) 994-1900

Established in 1977.
Donors: E.M. Lynn‡; Mrs. E.M. Lynn; The Christopher E. and Krista Mary DaSilva Charitable Lead Annuity Trust.
Foundation type: Independent foundation.
Financial data (yr. ended 10/31/13): Assets, $180,478,553 (M); expenditures, $9,300,494; qualifying distributions, $8,289,250; giving activities include $8,289,250 for 72 grants (high: $5,700,000; low: $25).
Purpose and activities: Giving primarily for education and health care, particularly to a hospital.
Fields of interest: Higher education; Hospitals (general); Health care; Medical research, institute; Spine disorders research; Human services.
Type of support: General/operating support.
Limitations: Applications not accepted. Giving primarily in FL. No grants to individuals.
Application information: Contributes only to pre-selected organizations.
Trustee: Christine E. Lynn.
EIN: 591788859
Selected grants: The following grants are a representative sample of this grantmaker's funding activity:
$5,700,000 to Buoniconti Fund to Cure Paralysis, Miami, FL, 2013. For research on spinal cord injury.
$500,000 to Lynn University, Boca Raton, FL, 2013. For International Business Center.
$500,000 to Stetson University, DeLand, FL, 2013. For Student Center.
$250,000 to Florida Atlantic University Foundation, Boca Raton, FL, 2013. For Faculty Retention Fund.
$150,000 to South Florida Bone Marrow/Stem Cell Transplant Institute, Boynton Beach, FL, 2013. For stem cell cancer research.
$100,000 to Florida Atlantic University Foundation, Boca Raton, FL, 2013. For general support.
$100,000 to Florida Atlantic University Foundation, Boca Raton, FL, 2013. For Schmidt College of Medicine.
$100,000 to Florida Atlantic University Foundation, College of Medicine, Boca Raton, FL, 2013.
$80,000 to Buoniconti Fund to Cure Paralysis, Miami, FL, 2013. For programs to support people with spinal cord injuries.
$50,000 to American College International Foundation, Claymont, DE, 2013. For general support.

2222
Daniel M. Lyons & Bente S. Lyons Foundation ✧
13685 Rivoli Dr.
Palm Beach Gardens, FL 33410-1239 (561) 627-1573
Contact: Bente S. Lyons, Tr.

Established in 1984 in FL.
Donors: Bente S. Lyons; Daniel M. Lyons‡.
Foundation type: Independent foundation.
Financial data (yr. ended 12/31/13): Assets, $3,216,474 (M); gifts received, $336; expenditures, $932,761; qualifying distributions, $826,164; giving activities include $784,600 for 5 grants (high: $335,000; low: $5,000).
Fields of interest: Jewish federated giving programs; Jewish agencies & synagogues.
Limitations: Applications accepted. Giving primarily in FL and NY. No grants to individuals.
Application information:
Initial approach: Letter
Deadline(s): Aug. 1
Board meeting date(s): As needed
Trustee: Bente S. Lyons.
EIN: 592315047
Selected grants: The following grants are a representative sample of this grantmaker's funding activity:
$100,000 to Jewish Federation of Palm Beach County, West Palm Beach, FL, 2010. For general charitable purpose.
$25,000 to World Union for Progressive Judaism, Jerusalem, Israel, 2011. For general charitable purposes.
$24,000 to Brooklyn College Foundation, Brooklyn, NY, 2010. For general charitable purpose.

2223
Dr. John T. Macdonald Foundation, Inc. ✧
1550 Madruga Ave., Ste. 215
Coral Gables, FL 33146-3017 (305) 667-6017
FAX: (305) 667-9135;
E-mail: info@jtmacdonaldfdn.org; Contact for application procedures: Kim Greene, Exec. Dir., e-mail: kgreene@tjmacdonaldfdn.org; Main URL: http://www.jtmacdonaldfdn.org
Facebook: https://www.facebook.com/DrJohnTMacDonaldFoundation
Twitter: http://www.twitter.com/drjtmacdonaldfn

Established in 1992 in FL; converted from sale of Doctors' Hospital to HEALTHSOUTH Rehabilitation Corporation; became a private foundation in 1992.
Donor: Adele H. Goddard Trust.
Foundation type: Independent foundation.
Financial data (yr. ended 12/31/13): Assets, $26,702,217 (M); gifts received, $40,103; expenditures, $3,117,026; qualifying distributions, $2,948,845; giving activities include $2,678,900 for 41 grants (high: $1,500,000; low: $1,000).
Purpose and activities: To provide funding for programs and projects designed to improve, preserve or restore the health and health care of the people in Miami-Dade County, FL.
Fields of interest: Medical school/education; Health care; Mental health/crisis services; Human services.
Type of support: General/operating support; Continuing support; Equipment; Program development; Seed money; Scholarship funds; Technical assistance; Program evaluation.
Limitations: Applications accepted. Giving limited to Miami-Dade County, FL. No support for projects that promote religious faith, political candidates or campaigns, national projects which would result in funding leaving Miami-Dade County, for-profit organizations, or other grantmaking foundations. No grants to individuals directly, or for fundraising campaigns.
Publications: Application guidelines; Annual report; Grants list.
Application information: Application form and deadlines are available on foundation web site. Application form required.
Initial approach: Letters of inquiry submitted online, through foundation web site. Selected applicants are then invited to fill out application
Copies of proposal: 1
Deadline(s): Feb. 1 to Apr. 15

Board meeting date(s): Quarterly
Final notification: June
Officers and Directors:* Steven S. Pabalan, M.D.*, Chair.; Thomas M. Mark, M.D.*, Vice-Chair.; Karl Smiley,* Secy.; Kim Greene, Exec. Dir.; Robert G. Breier; Aldo C. Busot, M.D.; Gary W. Dix; Charles A. Dunn, M.D.; R. Rodney Howell, M.D.; George D. Mekras, M.D.; John C. Nordt III, M.D.; R. Latanae Parker, Jr., M.D.; Dean H. Roller, M.D.; Stuart H. Savedoff, D.D.S.; Dazelle D. Simpson, M.D.; Margaret C. Starner; David A. Wolfberg.
Number of staff: 1 full-time professional; 1 part-time professional.
EIN: 590818918
Selected grants: The following grants are a representative sample of this grantmaker's funding activity:
$75,000 to Lotus House Womens Shelter, Miami, FL, 2011. For counselor and resource coordinators at Lotus House.
$75,000 to Open Door Health Center, Homestead, FL, 2011. For operating support.
$55,000 to Nova Southeastern University, College of Dental Medicine, Davie, FL, 2011. For preventive oral health services in North Miami Beach elementary schools.
$50,000 to Camillus Health Concern, Miami, FL, 2011. For full-time Benefits Employment Specialist to coordinate local SSI/SSDI Outreach, Access and Recovery (SOAR) initiative.
$50,000 to Florida International University, Herber Wertheim College of Medicine, Miami, FL, 2011. For scholarships for medical students.
$50,000 to Miami Lighthouse for the Blind and Visually Impaired, Miami, FL, 2011. For Heiken Children's Vision Program in schools of DJTMF School Health Initiative.
$50,000 to Theodore R. Gibson Memorial Fund, Miami, FL, 2011. For Maximizing Health Status for at Risk Minority Seniors A Matter of Life and Death program.
$35,650 to Florida International University, College of Nursing and Health Sciences, Miami, FL, 2011. For scholarships for students enrolled in Nursing and Health Sciences Program.
$35,000 to Hearing Research Institute, South Miami, FL, 2011. To purchase hearing testing equipment and hearing aids for needy children and adults.
$30,000 to Coral Gables Womans Club May Van Sickle Childrens Dental Clinic, Coral Gables, FL, 2011. For operation of dental clinic to provide services to indigent children in Miami-Dade County.

2224
Gloria C. Mackenzie Foundation, Inc. ✧ ☆
4483 Glen Kernan Pkwy. E.
Jacksonville, FL 32224-5629 (904) 281-0080
Application address: c/o Hammock & Assocs., PLLC, 4237 Salisbury Rd., Bldg, 1, No. 100, Jacksonville, FL 32216, tel.: (904) 281-0080

Established in FL.
Donor: Gloria Mackenzie.
Foundation type: Independent foundation.
Financial data (yr. ended 12/31/13): Assets, $18,990,632 (M); expenditures, $1,032,119; qualifying distributions, $1,000,000; giving activities include $1,000,000 for 1 grant.
Fields of interest: Community/economic development.
Limitations: Applications accepted. Giving primarily in East Millinocket, ME.
Application information: Application form required.
Initial approach: Letter
Deadline(s): None
Directors: Gloria C. Mackenzie; Melinda A. Mackenzie; Jaimie A. Weinberg.
EIN: 463375435

2225
Chesley G. Magruder Foundation ✧
c/o SunTrust Bank
200 S. Orange Ave., SOAB 10
Orlando, FL 32801

Established in 1979 in FL.
Donor: Chesley G. Magruder Trust.
Foundation type: Independent foundation.
Financial data (yr. ended 06/30/13): Assets, $16,624,596 (M); expenditures, $823,146; qualifying distributions, $742,350; giving activities include $742,350 for grants.
Purpose and activities: Giving primarily for education and human services, and to Christian agencies and churches.
Fields of interest: Arts; Higher education; Education; Housing/shelter, development; Human services; Residential/custodial care; Christian agencies & churches.
Type of support: Scholarship funds; In-kind gifts; General/operating support; Endowments; Continuing support; Building/renovation.
Limitations: Applications accepted. Giving limited to central FL, including Orange and Seminole counties. No grants to individuals.
Application information: Application form required.
Initial approach: Completed Application Form
Copies of proposal: 6
Deadline(s): None
Board meeting date(s): Mar., June, Oct., and Dec.
Trustees: SunTrust Bank; Robert N. Blackford, Esq.; G.Brock Magruder, Sr., M.D.
Officers: Scott Greenwood, M.D., Pres.; Allen K. Holcomb, M.D., V.P.; Leon H. Handley, Esq., Secy.-Treas.
EIN: 591920736
Selected grants: The following grants are a representative sample of this grantmaker's funding activity:
$10,000 to Childrens Home Society of Florida, Winter Park, FL, 2010. For general charitable purpose.
$10,000 to Childrens Home Society of Florida, Winter Park, FL, 2011. For general charitable purpose.
$10,000 to Gathering USA, Orlando, FL, 2010. For general charitable purpose.
$10,000 to Gathering USA, Orlando, FL, 2011. For general charitable purpose.
$7,500 to A Gift for Teaching, Orlando, FL, 2010. For general charitable purpose.
$7,500 to A Gift for Teaching, Orlando, FL, 2011. For general charitable purpose.
$6,960 to Canine Companions for Independence, Santa Rosa, CA, 2010. For general charitable purpose.
$6,000 to Retired and Senior Volunteer Program, Washington, DC, 2010. For general charitable purpose.
$5,000 to Best Buddies International, Miami, FL, 2010. For general charitable purpose.
$5,000 to Canine Companions for Independence, Santa Rosa, CA, 2011. For general charitable purpose.
$5,000 to United Negro College Fund, Fairfax, VA, 2010. For general charitable purpose.

2226
The Harry T. Mangurian, Jr. Foundation, Inc. ✧
(formerly The Mangurian Foundation, Inc.)
3696 N. Federal Hwy., Ste. 300
Fort Lauderdale, FL 33308-6263 (954) 491-1722

Established in 1999 in NY.
Donor: Harry T. Mangurian, Jr.‡.
Foundation type: Independent foundation.
Financial data (yr. ended 12/31/13): Assets, $149,584,594 (M); expenditures, $8,125,061; qualifying distributions, $6,668,780; giving activities include $6,078,495 for 71 grants (high: $1,650,000; low: $250).
Fields of interest: Higher education; Hospitals (general); Health care; Children/youth, services; Human services.
Limitations: Applications not accepted. Giving primarily in FL and NY; some funding also in MA. No grants to individuals.
Application information: Contributes only to pre-selected organizations.
Officers and Directors:* Stephen G. Mehallis,* Chair. and Pres.; Beth P. Piana, V.P., Finance and Secy.-Treas.; Gordon W. Latz,* V.P., Grants; Nora Gillary.
EIN: 161578255
Selected grants: The following grants are a representative sample of this grantmaker's funding activity:
$1,650,000 to Ohio State University Foundation, Columbus, OH, 2012. For research for Medical School and construction and scholarships for Business School.
$1,050,090 to Holy Cross Hospital, Fort Lauderdale, FL, 2012. For program support.
$602,000 to Leukemia & Lymphoma Society, Southern Florida Chapter, Hollywood, FL, 2012. For research.
$525,000 to Syracuse University, Syracuse, NY, 2012. For Performing Arts College and Athletics Program.
$346,500 to American Red Cross, Plantation, FL, 2012. For drowning prevention initiative that provides swimming lessons to at-risk children in Broward County.
$250,000 to Mayo Clinic Jacksonville, Jacksonville, FL, 2012. For program support.
$250,000 to University of Texas M.D. Anderson Cancer Center, Houston, TX, 2012. To ensure highest quality research for the treatment and care of childhood leukemia.
$134,448 to American Heart Association, Marietta, GA, 2012. For CPR Anytime training to Broward County public school children.
$100,000 to Cleveland Clinic Florida Weston, Weston, FL, 2012. To create Neurology Research Fellowship Program to study Alzheimer's disease, dementias and cognitive disorders.
$50,000 to Lewy Body Dementia Association, Lilburn, GA, 2012. For program support.

2227
Thomas H. Maren Foundation ✧
c/o Emily Maren
621 S.W. 26th Pl.
Gainesville, FL 32601-9014 (352) 373-5305
Contact: Emily Maren, Tr.

Established in 1999 in FL.
Donor: Maren Royalty Trust.
Foundation type: Independent foundation.
Financial data (yr. ended 12/31/12): Assets, $223,730 (M); gifts received, $914,288; expenditures, $838,911; qualifying distributions, $838,761; giving activities include $838,761 for grants.
Purpose and activities: Giving primarily for education, particularly a biological laboratory research fellowship program for high school and undergraduate college students, health care, including hospices, and a cancer-specific exercise program for cancer patients and survivors, and human services; funding also for Roman Catholic and Protestant organizations and ministries.
Fields of interest: Arts; Education, public education; Elementary/secondary education; Higher education; Education; Environment; Physical therapy; End of life care; Health care; Human services; Children/youth, services; Community/economic development; Biology/life sciences; Protestant agencies & churches; Catholic agencies & churches.
Limitations: Applications accepted. Giving primarily in AZ, FL, and ME; some funding nationally, with emphasis on RI. No grants to individuals.
Application information: Application form not required.
Initial approach: Proposal
Deadline(s): None
Trustees: Susan Fellner; Leon Goldstein; David K. Maren; Emily Maren; James Maren; Peter Maren; Erik Swenson.
EIN: 133855243

2228
Martin Family Foundation, Inc. ✧ ☆
801 S. Delaware Ave.
Tampa, FL 33606-2914 (813) 478-7453
Contact: Allan S. Martin, Treas.; Marie Martin, Pres.

Established in 2007 in FL.
Donors: Allan S. Martin; Marie B. Martin.
Foundation type: Independent foundation.
Financial data (yr. ended 12/31/13): Assets, $4,126,633 (M); gifts received, $3,025,061; expenditures, $1,345,279; qualifying distributions, $1,341,434; giving activities include $1,340,173 for 21 grants (high: $152,000; low: $5,000).
Fields of interest: Education; Catholic agencies & churches.
Limitations: Applications accepted. Giving primarily in Tampa, FL.
Application information: Application form required.
Initial approach: Letter
Deadline(s): None
Officers: Marie B. Martin, Pres.; Allan S. Martin, Treas.
Directors: David Boudreaux; Martin A. Benjamin.
EIN: 261416403

2229
The Martin Foundation, Inc. ✧
5051 Castello Sq., Ste. 204
Naples, FL 34103-8985
Contact: Geraldine F. Martin, Pres.

Incorporated in 1953 in IN.
Donors: Ross Martin†; Esther Martin†; Lee Martin; Geraldine F. Martin.
Foundation type: Independent foundation.
Financial data (yr. ended 06/30/13): Assets, $32,190,526 (M); expenditures, $1,769,699; qualifying distributions, $1,553,000; giving activities include $1,553,000 for 57 grants (high: $150,000; low: $1,500).
Fields of interest: Media/communications; Museums; Arts; Education, early childhood education; Higher education; Adult/continuing education; Libraries/library science; Education, reading; Education; Environment, natural resources; Environment; Animal welfare; Animals/wildlife, preservation/protection; Health care, clinics/centers; Reproductive health, family planning; Medical care, rehabilitation; Mental health/crisis services; Housing/shelter, development; Boys & girls clubs; Human services; Youth, services; Family services; Women, centers/services; Minorities/immigrants, centers/services; Community/economic development; United Ways and Federated Giving Programs; Population studies; Public affairs.
Limitations: Applications accepted. Giving primarily in FL; some funding also in NY. No support for religious or political organizations. No grants to individuals.
Publications: Annual report (including application guidelines).
Application information: Application form not required.
Initial approach: Letter requesting guidelines
Copies of proposal: 1
Deadline(s): None
Board meeting date(s): As required
Final notification: 4 to 8 weeks
Officers: Geraldine F. Martin, Pres.; Casper Martin, Secy.-Treas.
Directors: Jennifer L. Martin; Elizabeth Martin.
EIN: 351070929
Selected grants: The following grants are a representative sample of this grantmaker's funding activity:
$30,000 to Earthjustice, San Francisco, CA, 2011. For operations.
$30,000 to Indiana University, Bloomington, IN, 2011. For operations.
$25,000 to Environmental Defense Fund, New York, NY, 2011. For operations.
$25,000 to World Wildlife Fund, Washington, DC, 2011. For operations.
$7,500 to American Bird Conservancy, The Plains, VA, 2011. For operations.
$2,880 to American Diabetes Association, Alexandria, VA, 2011. For operations.

2230
Edwin and Jeanette May Foundation ✧ ☆
(formerly The Edwin J. May Foundation)
4731 Bonita Bay, Blvd., PH 302 N.
Bonita Springs, FL 28262
Application address: c/o Brian S. May, 615 Abbey St., Birmingham, MI 48009, tel.: (248) 723-9033

Established in 1994 in FL.
Donors: Daniel May; Dianne L. May; Daniel May Charitable Lead Unitrust; Jeanette May Charitable Lead Unitrust.
Foundation type: Independent foundation.
Financial data (yr. ended 12/31/13): Assets, $2,812,971 (M); gifts received, $893,375; expenditures, $2,182,901; qualifying distributions, $2,165,000; giving activities include $2,165,000 for 3 grants (high: $2,065,000; low: $50,000).
Fields of interest: Elementary/secondary education; Higher education, college; American Red Cross; International relief.
International interests: Haiti.
Type of support: General/operating support.
Limitations: Applications accepted. Giving primarily in DC, FL, and NC. No grants to individuals.
Application information: Application form not required.
Initial approach: Proposal
Deadline(s): None
Trustees: Brian S. May; Daniel May; Dianne L. May.
EIN: 650501566
Selected grants: The following grants are a representative sample of this grantmaker's funding activity:
$450,000 to Lees-McRae College, Banner Elk, NC, 2011. For general support.
$50,000 to Seacrest Country Day School, Naples, FL, 2011.

2231
James and Tara McCahill Family Foundation, Inc. ✧
c/o Ed Falzarano
6131 Louise Cove Dr.
Windermere, FL 34786-8939

Established in FL.
Donors: James McCahill; Tara McCahill.
Foundation type: Independent foundation.
Financial data (yr. ended 12/31/13): Assets, $438,857 (M); gifts received, $700,000; expenditures, $686,147; qualifying distributions, $684,050; giving activities include $684,050 for 38 grants (high: $280,000; low: $100).
Fields of interest: Hospitals (general); Health organizations; Housing/shelter; Human services.
Limitations: Applications not accepted. Giving in the U.S., with some emphasis on FL, NJ, and NY.
Application information: Unsolicited requests for funds not accepted.
Officers: James J. McCahill, Pres.; Tara F. McCahill, V.P.; Elizabeth McCahill, Secy.-Treas.
EIN: 800312628

2232
Joy McCann Foundation, Inc. ✧
(formerly Culverhouse Family Foundation, Inc.)
1700 S. MacDill Ave., Ste. 360
Tampa, FL 33629-5244 (813) 805-2775
Contact: Lynn Collingsworth
FAX: (813) 805-6603;
E-mail: info@mccannfoundation.org; Main URL: http://www.mccannfoundation.org

Established in 1996 in FL.
Foundation type: Independent foundation.
Financial data (yr. ended 12/31/13): Assets, $14,277,547 (M); expenditures, $1,247,647; qualifying distributions, $961,669; giving activities

include $812,514 for 47 grants (high: $54,832; low: $500).
Purpose and activities: Giving primarily for: 1) efforts to build a more vibrant Tampa Bay Area, Florida, community, 2) excellence in medical, nursing and science education, research and patient care, 3) educational programs that nurture individual achievement, and 4) the role of the visual and performing arts in enhancing community life.
Fields of interest: Arts; Higher education; Medical research, institute; Boys & girls clubs; Youth development; Human services; YM/YWCAs & YM/YWHAs.
Limitations: Applications accepted. Giving primarily in FL. No support for start-up organizations. No grants to individuals, or for scholarships, or capital campaigns.
Publications: IRS Form 990 or 990-PF printed copy available upon request.
Application information: Application form required.
Initial approach: Letter
Deadline(s): Feb. 1 and Aug. 1
Officers and Directors:* Christopher Chapman,* Co-Chair.; Joy McCann Culverhouse,* Co-Chair.; Scott D. Lynch.
EIN: 593166283

2233
R. Cathleen Cox McFarlane Charitable Foundation, Inc. ✧
622 N. Flagler Dr., Ste. 201
West Palm Beach, FL 33401-4011

Established in 1999 in FL.
Donor: R. Cathleen Cox McFarlane.
Foundation type: Independent foundation.
Financial data (yr. ended 04/30/13): Assets, $23,723,547 (M); gifts received, $855,793; expenditures, $1,038,709; qualifying distributions, $609,848; giving activities include $609,848 for grants.
Purpose and activities: Giving primarily for Roman Catholic agencies and churches as well as other religious organizations.
Fields of interest: Arts; Animal welfare; Health care; Health organizations; Human services; Children, services; Catholic agencies & churches; Religion.
Limitations: Applications not accepted. Giving primarily in FL. No grants to individuals.
Application information: Contributes only to pre-selected organizations.
Officers and Directors:* Walter M. Ross,* Pres.; Christy L. Peterson,* Secy.; Denis P. Coleman,* Treas.; Bridget Cathleen Healey; Jeff Smith.
EIN: 650856300
Selected grants: The following grants are a representative sample of this grantmaker's funding activity:
$1,000 to Food for the Poor, Coconut Creek, FL, 2011.

2234
McKeen Fund ✧
c/o Bessemer Trust Co. of FL
222 Royal Palm Way
Palm Beach, FL 33480-4303 (561) 655-4030
Contact: James J. Daly, Tr.

Established in 1993 in FL.
Foundation type: Independent foundation.
Financial data (yr. ended 12/31/13): Assets, $12,834,307 (M); expenditures, $934,442; qualifying distributions, $829,727; giving activities include $643,900 for 63 grants (high: $100,000; low: $400).
Purpose and activities: Giving primarily to hospitals, universities, social welfare organizations, and cultural institutions; of particular interest is providing for the maintenance and care of the aged and infirm, retarded and mentally disabled, and for the education of persons studying for the priesthood.
Fields of interest: Higher education; Hospitals (general); American Red Cross; Catholic agencies & churches.
Limitations: Applications accepted. Giving primarily in FL and NY. No grants to individuals.
Application information: Application form required.
Initial approach: Completed application form
Copies of proposal: 2
Deadline(s): Within 45 days
Trustees: Beth A. Daly; James J. Daly.
EIN: 137002920
Selected grants: The following grants are a representative sample of this grantmaker's funding activity:
$5,000 to Nature Conservancy, Arlington, VA, 2011.
$2,000 to National Coalition Building Institute, Washington, DC, 2011.
$1,000 to Achilles International, New York, NY, 2011.

2235
The Evelyn F. McKnight Brain Research Foundation ✧
(also known as The McKnight Brain Research Foundation)
(formerly McKnight Brain Research Foundation)
c/o The SunTrust Bank
P.O. Box 620005
Orlando, FL 32862-0005 (407) 237-4485
Contact: Melanie Cianciotto, 1st V.P.
Main URL: http://www.tmbrf.org

Established in 1998 in FL.
Donor: Evelyn Franks McKnight†.
Foundation type: Independent foundation.
Financial data (yr. ended 06/30/13): Assets, $44,288,551 (M); expenditures, $2,713,854; qualifying distributions, $2,434,496; giving activities include $2,087,173 for 3 grants (high: $1,000,000; low: $87,173).
Purpose and activities: The purpose of the foundation is to promote research and investigation of the brain in the fundamental mechanisms that underlie the neurobiology of memory with clinical relevance to the problems of age related memory loss. The foundation strives to: 1) Lead in generating interest and support of scientific research in the understanding and alleviation of age-related memory loss and inspire commitment and shared vision in the understanding and alleviation of age-related memory loss; 2) Partner with research scientists, institutions, and organizations to promote research to understand and alleviate age-related memory loss; 3) Promote collaboration and communication among research scientists, institutions, and organizations engaged in research in age-related memory loss, and nurture scientists dedicated to the exploration and innovative research in the understanding and alleviation of age-related memory loss; and 4) Recognize and Reward achievement in discoveries leading to the understanding and alleviation of age-related memory loss.
Fields of interest: Brain research; Medical research; Aging.
Type of support: Research.
Limitations: Giving on a national basis. No grants for bricks and mortar operating costs, or for equipment (including computers), maintenance or indirect overhead costs, endowments, conferences, administrative expenses, travel or honoria for distinguished guests.
Application information: The foundation will consider only those research proposals which will meet the purpose of the foundation. Application form not required.
Initial approach: See foundation web site
Copies of proposal: 6
Deadline(s): None
Officer and Trustees:* Melanie Cianciotto,* 1st V.P.; John Clarkson, M.D.; Dr. J. Lee Dockery; Michael L. Dockery, M.D.; Dr. Nina Ellenbogen Raim; Dr. Gene Ryerson; SunTrust Bank.
EIN: 656301255

2236
McMurtry Family Foundation of 2003 ✧
(formerly McMurtry Family Foundation)
101 W. Venice Ave.
Venice, FL 34285-1902

Established in 2003 in FL.
Donors: Ann McMurtry; Burton McMurtry; Ann Kathryn McMurtry Charitable Lead Trust of 2003; Octave West LLC.
Foundation type: Independent foundation.
Financial data (yr. ended 12/31/13): Assets, $17,505,665 (M); gifts received, $2,385,602; expenditures, $1,054,623; qualifying distributions, $991,625; giving activities include $990,500 for 29 grants (high: $110,000; low: $1,500).
Fields of interest: Higher education; Education; Human services.
Type of support: General/operating support.
Limitations: Applications not accepted. Giving primarily in CA. No grants to individuals.
Application information: Contributes only to pre-selected organizations.
Trustees: Jill Choate; Robert Goldman; Michael Hartley; Jill A. Lervold; Ann K. McMurtry; Burton J. McMurtry; Cathryn McMurtry; John McMurtry; Michael Tillman.
EIN: 510478343
Selected grants: The following grants are a representative sample of this grantmaker's funding activity:
$10,000 to WildAid, San Francisco, CA, 2012. To further and promote animal welfare.
$5,000 to Reading Partners, Oakland, CA, 2012. To further and promote educational purposes.
$2,000 to Council on Foreign Relations, New York, NY, 2012. To further and promote charitable efforts.

2237
The Melville Foundation ✧
11556 Turtle Beach Rd.
North Palm Beach, FL 33408-3345

Established in 1986 in CT.
Donors: Harry Burn III; Jean Burn.
Foundation type: Independent foundation.

Financial data (yr. ended 12/31/13): Assets, $25,275,566 (M); gifts received, $5,523,630; expenditures, $525,180; qualifying distributions, $525,180; giving activities include $504,750 for 32 grants (high: $210,000; low: $750).
Fields of interest: Higher education; Education; Health organizations; Human services.
Limitations: Applications not accepted. Giving primarily in CT and VA. No grants to individuals.
Application information: Contributes only to pre-selected organizations.
Trustees: Harry Burn III; Jean Burn.
EIN: 222777140

2238
Miami Foundation, The ✧
(formerly Dade Community Foundation)
200 South Biscayne Blvd., Ste. 505
Miami, FL 33131-5330 (305) 371-2711
Contact: Pamelo Olmo, V.P., Finance and C.F.O.; For grants: Charisse L. Grant, Sr. V.P., Progs.; For communications: Matthew Beatty, Comms. Off.; For development: Julie Bindeutel, Devel. Off.
FAX: (305) 371-5342;
E-mail: info@miamifoundation.org; Additional e-mail: cgrant@miamifoundation.org; Main URL: http://www.miamifoundation.org
E-Newsletter: http://visitor.r20.constantcontact.com/d.jsp?llr=jvilmidab&p=oi&m=1103014240937
LinkedIn: http://www.linkedin.com/companies/dade-community-foundation
For Miami Fellows: Tamaya Garcia (305) 357-2094

Established in 1967 in Miami, FL.
Foundation type: Community foundation.
Financial data (yr. ended 12/31/13): Assets, $204,796,955 (M); gifts received, $35,029,818; expenditures, $26,146,994; giving activities include $22,289,643 for grants.
Purpose and activities: The foundation seeks to encourage philanthropy and charitable giving by developing a permanent endowment to meet current and future emerging charitable needs. Grants are made in broad program areas including education, health, human services, arts and culture, the environment, and community and economic development. In addition, field of interest and special funding initiatives have enabled significant grantmaking addressing the issues of abused and neglected children, immigrants and refugees, AIDS, homelessness, social justice, African-American affairs, care of animals, and heart disease.
Fields of interest: Arts, multipurpose centers/programs; Visual arts; Arts; Education; Environment; Animal welfare; Health care; Health organizations, association; Heart & circulatory diseases; AIDS; Alzheimer's disease; Crime/violence prevention, child abuse; Housing/shelter; Disasters, 9/11/01; Youth development; Children/youth, services; Homeless, human services; Human services; Civil/human rights, minorities; Civil/human rights, LGBTQ; Civil/human rights; Community development, neighborhood development; Economic development; Community/economic development; Aging; African Americans/Blacks; AIDS, people with; Crime/abuse victims; Immigrants/refugees; Economically disadvantaged; Homeless; LGBTQ.
Type of support: General/operating support; Management development/capacity building; Building/renovation; Equipment; Land acquisition; Endowments; Emergency funds; Program development; Publication; Seed money; Scholarship funds; Research; Technical assistance; Consulting services; Program evaluation; Program-related investments/loans; Scholarships—to individuals; Matching/challenge support.
Limitations: Applications accepted. Giving limited to Miami-Dade County, FL. No grants to individuals (except through scholarship funds), or for memberships, fundraising, memorials, deficit financing, or conferences.
Publications: Application guidelines; Annual report; Newsletter; Occasional report.
Application information: Visit foundation web site for application Cover form, Budget form, and guidelines. E-mailed or faxed proposals are not accepted. New applicants are encouraged to contact the Program Department staff prior to submitting an application. The foundation conducts a free information workshop about the Community Grants Program; call foundation to register. Application form required.
Initial approach: Mail application Cover form, Budget form, and proposal
Copies of proposal: 2
Deadline(s): Oct. 1 through Nov. 15 for community grants; varies for others
Board meeting date(s): Feb., May, Sept., and Nov.
Final notification: Feb. for community grants; 8 to 12 weeks for others
Officers and Governors:* Michael A. Marquez,* Chair.; Alex Fraser,* Vice-Chair.; Javier Alberto Soto, C.E.O. and Pres.; Charisse L. Grant, Sr. V.P., Progs.; Pamela Olmo, V.P., Finance and C.F.O.; Juan Martinez,* Treas. and Secy.; Christopher Williams, Cont.; Maria C. Alonso; Mitchell Bierman; Pablo Cejas; Barron Channer; Manuel Diaz; Joseph A. Fernandez; John Fumagalli; Richard Giusto; Marlon A. Hill; Melissa Krinzman; Ana Lopez-Blazquez; Dr. Michael N. Rosenberg; Rafael Saldana; David Samson; Penny S. Shaffer; Allison P. Shipley; Bruce Turkel; Raul G. Valdes-Fauli.
Number of staff: 17 full-time professional.
EIN: 650350357
Selected grants: The following grants are a representative sample of this grantmaker's funding activity:
$500,000 to University of Pennsylvania, Center for High Impact Philanthropy, Philadelphia, PA, 2012. For general support.
$300,000 to Jackson Memorial Foundation, Miami, FL, 2012. For general support.
$152,549 to Foundation for End-of-Life Care, Hollywood, FL, 2012. For scholarship.
$125,998 to University of Miami, Coral Gables, FL, 2012. For general support.
$15,000 to Planned Parenthood of South Florida and the Treasure Coast, West Palm Beach, FL, 2012. To implement the Teen Outreach Program (TOP), evidence-based approach that has great efficacy in increasing academic success, preventing teen pregnancy, and reducing other negative behaviors, TOP to be implemented for 200 youth ages 12-17 in Miami-Dade County with interactive sessions, community service activities, and parental engagement.
$12,500 to Jewish Community Services of South Florida, North Miami, FL, 2012. For general support.
$9,628 to Womens Fund of Miami-Dade County, Coral Gables, FL, 2012. For partnership with The Children's Trust for A Future. Not a Past (AFNAP), a campaign to increase general public awareness about girls under the age of 18 being sold for sex in the community to launch Phase II of the public awareness campaign by expanding the distribution of language appropriate materials on how to identify warning signs for trafficked girls and actions citizens can take to engage law enforcement if trafficking of a minor is suspected.
$6,250 to Miami Gay and Lesbian Film Festival, Miami Beach, FL, 2012. For general support.
$5,000 to Florida International University Foundation, Miami, FL, 2012. For general support.

2239
The J. S. & S. Michaan Foundation ✧
150 Bradley Pl., Ste. 106
Palm Beach, FL 33480-3804

Established in 1995 in FL.
Donors: Joseph Michaan; Suzanne Michaan.
Foundation type: Operating foundation.
Financial data (yr. ended 06/30/13): Assets, $5,163,657 (M); expenditures, $1,908,609; qualifying distributions, $1,846,647; giving activities include $1,842,725 for 63 grants (high: $311,000; low: $25).
Purpose and activities: Giving primarily to Jewish organizations.
Fields of interest: Human services; Jewish federated giving programs; Jewish agencies & synagogues.
Limitations: Applications not accepted. Giving primarily in FL and NY. No grants to individuals.
Application information: Contributes only to pre-selected organizations.
Trustees: Allen Michaan; Suzanne Michaan.
EIN: 650635890
Selected grants: The following grants are a representative sample of this grantmaker's funding activity:
$100,000 to Hospice Foundation of Palm Beach County, Palm Beach, FL, 2011. For general support.
$100,000 to Jewish Federation of Palm Beach County, West Palm Beach, FL, 2011. For general support.

2240
Mill Park Foundation, Inc. ✧
(formerly P & M Charities, Inc.)
9045 Strada Stell Ct., Ste. 500
Naples, FL 34109-4344

Established in 2002 in FL.
Donors: Isabel Collier†; Miles C. Collier; Isabel Collier Read Trust; Read 2009 Qtip Trust.
Foundation type: Independent foundation.
Financial data (yr. ended 12/31/12): Assets, $89,004,341 (M); gifts received, $22,549,612; expenditures, $15,322,639; qualifying distributions, $14,713,834; giving activities include $14,711,500 for 24 grants (high: $12,000,000; low: $250).
Fields of interest: Higher education; Health care; Human services.
Type of support: General/operating support.
Limitations: Applications not accepted. Giving primarily in FL, MT, NY, and VT. No grants to individuals.
Application information: Contributes only to pre-selected organizations.
Officers and Directors:* Miles C. Collier,* C.E.O.; Parker J. Collier,* Pres.; William E. Thomas,* Exec. V.P.; Michael B. Lenzner, V.P.; Sandra D. Walker, Secy.-Treas.
EIN: 010644503

Selected grants: The following grants are a representative sample of this grantmaker's funding activity:
$2,000,000 to Eckerd College, Saint Petersburg, FL, 2011. For general support.
$250,000 to Icahn School of Medicine at Mount Sinai, New York, NY, 2011. For general support.
$133,000 to Florida Agriculture Center and Horse Park Authority, Ocala, FL, 2011. For general support.
$100,000 to Trinity-by-the-Cove Episcopal Church, Naples, FL, 2011. For general support.
$75,000 to Immokalee Foundation, Naples, FL, 2011. For general support.
$50,000 to Hospital for Special Surgery, New York, NY, 2011. For general support.
$50,000 to University of Florida, Gainesville, FL, 2011. For general support.

2241
Miller Foundation, Inc. ✧
(formerly Miller Family Foundation, Inc.)
700 N.W. 107th Ave., 4th Fl.
Miami, FL 33172-3161

Established in 1984 in FL.
Donors: Leonard Miller; Susan Miller; Miller Charitable Fund LLLP.
Foundation type: Independent foundation.
Financial data (yr. ended 11/30/13): Assets, $11,147,452 (M); expenditures, $6,493,082; qualifying distributions, $6,475,868; giving activities include $6,470,307 for 37 grants (high: $3,333,551; low: $5,000).
Purpose and activities: Giving primarily for higher education as well as to Jewish organizations; some giving also for the arts including a performing arts center, and health and social services.
Fields of interest: Museums (art); Performing arts, orchestras; Education; Human services; Children/youth, services; United Ways and Federated Giving Programs; Jewish federated giving programs; Jewish agencies & synagogues.
Limitations: Applications not accepted. Giving primarily in FL, with emphasis on Miami and Miami Beach; some giving also in Cleveland, OH. No grants to individuals.
Application information: Contributes only to pre-selected organizations.
Officers: Susan Miller, Pres.; Brian Bilzin, V.P.
Directors: Jeffrey Miller; Stuart Miller; Leslie Saiontz.
EIN: 592474323

2242
The John A. Moran Charitable Trust ✧ ☆
125 Worth Ave., Ste. 202
Palm Beach, FL 33480-4466 (561) 659-0075
Contact: John A. Moran, Tr.

Established in 1988 in FL.
Donor: John A. Moran.
Foundation type: Independent foundation.
Financial data (yr. ended 12/31/13): Assets, $23,217,801 (M); expenditures, $4,111,082; qualifying distributions, $4,019,236; giving activities include $4,019,236 for 19 grants (high: $1,505,000; low: $1,000).
Fields of interest: Museums (art); Hospitals (general); Prostate cancer; Human services.
Limitations: Giving primarily in CA, FL, and NY. No grants to individuals.
Application information: Application form not required.
Initial approach: Letter
Deadline(s): None
Trustees: Kellie Dawn Hudson; Carole O. Moran; John A. Moran; Elizabeth Moran; Marisa Moran Sullivan.
EIN: 650066880

2243
The Jim Moran Foundation, Inc. ✧
100 Jim Moran Blvd.
Deerfield Beach, FL 33442-1702 (954) 429-2122
FAX: (954) 429-2699;
E-mail: information@jimmoranfoundation.org; Main URL: http://www.jimmoranfoundation.org/
Grants List: http://www.jimmoranfoundation.org/Grants2014.aspx
Multimedia: http://www.jimmoranfoundation.org/Videos.aspx

Established in 2000 in FL.
Donors: James M. Moran‡; Janice M. Moran; JM Family Enterprises, Inc.; Jim Moran & Associates, Inc.; Automotive Management Services, Inc.; AutoNation.
Foundation type: Company-sponsored foundation.
Financial data (yr. ended 12/31/13): Assets, $119,468,200 (M); gifts received, $14,261,131; expenditures, $9,994,645; qualifying distributions, $9,570,378; giving activities include $9,570,378 for 119 grants (high: $550,000; low: $4,500).
Purpose and activities: The foundation supports programs designed improve quality of life for youth and families in Florida through initiatives and opportunities that meet ever-changing needs of the community. Special emphasis is directed towards education programs designed to provide academic enrichment and opportunities for quality learning; elder care programs designed to improve quality of life for at-risk seniors; family strengthening programs designed to provide safety and stability to children and families, including food security; and youth transitional living programs designed to help at-risk youth and young adults achieve self-sufficiency.
Fields of interest: Secondary school/education; Higher education; Education, reading; Education; Food services; Big Brothers/Big Sisters; Salvation Army; Children/youth, services; Family services; Aging, centers/services; Human services; Community/economic development; Youth; Aging; Economically disadvantaged.
Type of support: General/operating support; Continuing support; Equipment; Program development; Scholarship funds.
Limitations: Applications accepted. Giving primarily in FL, with emphasis on Broward, Palm Beach, and Duval counties. No grants to individuals, or for administrative or overhead costs, capital campaigns, capacity building, healthcare or medical research, or event sponsorships.
Publications: Application guidelines; Grants list; Newsletter.
Application information: A full application may be requested at a later date. No consecutive year funding, except for multi-year grants. Application form required.
Initial approach: Complete online letter of inquiry form
Deadline(s): None
Final notification: 90 days
Officers and Directors:* Janice M. Moran,* Chair. and Pres.; Larry D. McGinnes,* V.P.; Melanie A. Burgess,* Secy. and Exec. Dir.; Thomas K. Blanton,* Treas.; George Gadson; Irvin A, Kiffin; Lucia C. Lopez; Dom Pino; Melvin T. Stith.
EIN: 651058044
Selected grants: The following grants are a representative sample of this grantmaker's funding activity:
$425,000 to Florida State University Foundation, College of Business, Tallahassee, FL, 2011. To provide expanded outreach of Jim Moran Institute for Global Entrepreneurship into South Florida through Entrepreneurial University Program..
$340,000 to Childrens Services Council of Broward County, Lauderhill, FL, 2011. For collaborative funding to support a holistic system of care in Broward County for at-risk young adults transitioning into independent living from foster care.
$338,768 to Family Central, North Lauderdale, FL, 2011. For Community for Quality Early Learning and Literacy (C-QuELL) Project, which holistically supports children's early learning by engaging the family, child care centers, elementary schools and communities in Broward County..
$225,000 to United Way of Broward County, Fort Lauderdale, FL, 2011. For Project Lifeline, hunger relief initiative which provides for purchase and distribution of nutritious groceries to food pantries throughout Broward County.
$219,960 to Boys and Girls Clubs of Broward County, Fort Lauderdale, FL, 2011. To provides transportation directly from schools to Boys and Girls Clubs throughout Broward County for a safe place to learn with healthy snacks and a nutritious dinner.
$154,616 to Housing Opportunities, Mortgage Assistance, and Effective Neighborhood Solutions, Fort Lauderdale, FL, 2011. For Transition to Independent Living (TIL) Youth Apartment Rental Program, which provides safe housing and compassionate support for former foster-care or kin-care youth transitioning into adulthood in Broward County.
$116,015 to I. M. Sulzbacher Center for the Homeless, Jacksonville, FL, 2011. For Emergency Shelter Services for Homeless Families, program to provide transitional housing, case management and life skills training to equip families for self-sufficiency.
$75,000 to SOS Childrens Village of Florida, Coconut Creek, FL, 2011. For After-Care Program, which provides teens in foster care and transitioning young adults with the tools necessary to improve their life skills, academic outcomes and career development with support and coaching from an after-care coordinator.
$50,000 to Network for Teaching Entrepreneurship, Miami, FL, 2011. For Building the Entrepreneurial Community Program, which provides entrepreneurial training to students at Stranahan and Hallandale high schools in Broward County.
$50,000 to PACE Center for Girls of Palm Beach County, West Palm Beach, FL, 2011. For SPIRITED GIRLS! program which provides young women with academics and essential life skills for more successful futures.

2244
The Morby Family Charitable Foundation, Inc. ✧ ☆
18 S. Island Dr.
Key Largo, FL 33037-3606

Established in 1986 in MA.
Donors: Jacqueline C. Morby; Jeffrey Morby.
Foundation type: Independent foundation.
Financial data (yr. ended 11/30/13): Assets, $22,953,334 (M); gifts received, $1,007,095; expenditures, $1,153,238; qualifying distributions, $1,096,026; giving activities include $1,088,776 for grants.
Fields of interest: Museums (specialized); Performing arts, theater; Arts; Higher education; Education; Animals/wildlife; Hospitals (general); Alzheimer's disease research; United Ways and Federated Giving Programs.
Limitations: Applications not accepted. No grants to individuals.
Application information: Unsolicited requests for funds not accepted.
Officers and Directors:* Jacqueline C. Morby,* Pres.; Jeffrey L. Morby,* Treas.
EIN: 042943793

2245
John M. & Susan Morrison Family Foundation ✧

(formerly Morrison Family Foundation)
3093 Fort Charles Dr.
Naples, FL 34102-7920

Established in 1997 in FL.
Donors: John M. Morrison; Susan M. Morrison; Fosta-Tek Optics; Central Financial Svcs., Inc.
Foundation type: Independent foundation.
Financial data (yr. ended 06/30/14): Assets, $562,119 (M); gifts received, $400,081; expenditures, $507,309; qualifying distributions, $505,535; giving activities include $505,535 for 15 grants (high: $199,991; low: $500).
Fields of interest: Higher education; Education; Health care; Catholic agencies & churches.
Limitations: Applications not accepted. Giving primarily in Minneapolis-St. Paul, MN and Naples, FL. No grants to individuals.
Application information: Unsolicited requests for funds not accepted.
Officer: Janice Graser, V.P.
Trustees: Jeanne M. Cook; Julie Morrison; John M. Morrison; John M. Morrison, Jr.; Mary S. Morrison; Susan M. Morrison.
EIN: 656254131
Selected grants: The following grants are a representative sample of this grantmaker's funding activity:
$3,750 to Conservancy of Southwest Florida, Naples, FL, 2013. For fund raising event.
$2,000 to Abbott Northwestern Hospital Foundation, Minneapolis, MN, 2013. For Medicine Ball.
$1,000 to Catholic Community Foundation, Saint Paul, MN, 2013. For Community Priorities Fund No. 25100A.
$1,000 to Malta Human Services Foundation, New York, NY, 2013. For fund for grants.

2246
Frank and Carol Morsani Foundation, Inc. ✧

16007 N. Florida Ave.
Lutz, FL 33549-6128

Established in FL.
Donors: Frank L. Morsani; Carol D. Morsani.
Foundation type: Independent foundation.
Financial data (yr. ended 08/31/13): Assets, $6,465,288 (M); gifts received, $5,000; expenditures, $971,216; qualifying distributions, $850,000; giving activities include $850,000 for 4 grants (high: $500,000; low: $50,000).
Purpose and activities: Giving primarily for higher education.
Fields of interest: Higher education.
Limitations: Applications not accepted. Giving primarily in FL. No grants to individuals.
Application information: Contributes only to pre-selected organizations.
Directors: Alan Higbee; Carol D. Morsani; Frank L. Morsani.
EIN: 593543872

2247
Cherna Moskowitz Foundation ✧

1250 E. Hallandale Beach Blvd., Ste. 1000
Hallandale Beach, FL 33009-4647 (305) 531-4559
Contact: Cherna Moskowitz, Pres. and Secy.-Treas.

Established in 2008 in DE.
Donor: Cherna Moskowitz.
Foundation type: Independent foundation.
Financial data (yr. ended 12/31/13): Assets, $35,837,531 (M); gifts received, $5,341,000; expenditures, $5,197,384; qualifying distributions, $5,154,130; giving activities include $5,154,130 for 63 grants (high: $1,495,000; low: $100).
Fields of interest: Education; Health care; Food banks; Athletics/sports, academies; Jewish agencies & synagogues.
Limitations: Applications accepted. Giving primarily in CA, FL, NJ and NY.
Application information:
Initial approach: Letter or telephone
Officer: Cherna Moskowitz, Pres. and Secy.-Treas.
EIN: 262547583
Selected grants: The following grants are a representative sample of this grantmaker's funding activity:
$1,676,000 to Central Fund of Israel, New York, NY, 2010.
$1,185,000 to Central Fund of Israel, New York, NY, 2011.
$1,000,000 to American Friends of the College of Judea and Samaria, Encinitas, CA, 2011.
$1,000,000 to Bar-Ilan University in Israel, New York, NY, 2011.
$1,000,000 to Friends of Ir David, Brooklyn, NY, 2010. For education.
$1,000,000 to Friends of Ir David, Brooklyn, NY, 2011.
$900,000 to National Council of Young Israel, Brooklyn, NY, 2010. For educational programs.
$500,000 to Nefesh B'Nefesh - Jewish Souls United, Paramus, NJ, 2011.
$400,000 to Nefesh B'Nefesh - Jewish Souls United, Paramus, NJ, 2010.
$350,000 to American Friends of Ateret Cohanim - Jerusalem Reclamation Project, New York, NY, 2010. For higher education.
$210,000 to One Israel Fund, Hewlett, NY, 2010. For the welfare and safety of people in Judea and Samaria.
$200,000 to International Israel Allies Caucus Foundation, Washington, DC, 2010. To promote Judeo-Christian values.
$160,000 to One Israel Fund, Hewlett, NY, 2011.
$150,000 to Second Thought, Jerusalem, Israel, 2010.
$150,000 to Western Wall Heritage Foundation, New York, NY, 2011.
$100,000 to American Friends of Bnei Akiva Yeshivas in Israel, New York, NY, 2010. To collect and distribute funds to educational institutions.
$100,000 to American Friends of Mercaz Harav Kook, Brooklyn, NY, 2011.
$100,000 to Ohr Somayach International, Brooklyn, NY, 2010.
$50,000 to Friends of Yeshivat Nir Kiryat Arba, New York, NY, 2011.
$50,000 to Israel Independence Fund, New York, NY, 2011.

2248
The Stephen and Sandra Muss Foundation, Inc. ✧

(formerly The Stephen Muss Foundation, Inc.)
9100 S. Dadeland Blvd., Ste. 1500
Miami, FL 33156-7816 (305) 531-4848
Contact: Stephen Muss, Pres.

Established in DE.
Donor: Stephen Muss.
Foundation type: Independent foundation.
Financial data (yr. ended 10/31/12): Assets, $14,522,596 (M); expenditures, $1,177,357; qualifying distributions, $1,128,800; giving activities include $1,128,800 for 18 grants (high: $390,000; low: $1,000).
Purpose and activities: Giving primarily to Jewish agencies, temples, schools, and federated giving programs.
Fields of interest: Performing arts, orchestras; Education; Health organizations; Jewish federated giving programs; Jewish agencies & synagogues.
Limitations: Giving primarily in FL. No grants to individuals.
Application information:
Initial approach: Letter
Deadline(s): None
Officers: Stephen Muss, Pres.; Sandra Muss, V.P. and Secy.; Brian Bilzin, Treas.
EIN: 237424763

2249
Nanci's Animal Rights Foundation, Inc. ✧

2831 N. Ocean Blvd., Ste. 1101N
Fort Lauderdale, FL 33308-7581 (954) 474-7600

Established in 2004.
Donor: Nanci Alexander.
Foundation type: Independent foundation.
Financial data (yr. ended 06/30/13): Assets, $31,927,396 (M); expenditures, $3,103,113; qualifying distributions, $3,100,000; giving activities include $3,100,000 for 3 grants (high: $1,500,000; low: $100,000).
Purpose and activities: Giving primarily for animal rights.
Fields of interest: Animals/wildlife, equal rights; Animal welfare.
Limitations: Applications not accepted. Giving primarily in Washington, DC and VA. No grants to individuals.
Application information: Contributes only to pre-selected organizations.

Officer: Nanci Alexander, Pres.
EIN: 651174489
Selected grants: The following grants are a representative sample of this grantmaker's funding activity:
$2,500,000 to PCRM Foundation, Washington, DC, 2012. For general support.
$2,500,000 to People for the Ethical Treatment of Animals, Norfolk, VA, 2012. For general support.
$1,500,000 to PCRM Foundation, Washington, DC, 2013. For general support.
$1,500,000 to People for the Ethical Treatment of Animals, Norfolk, VA, 2013. For general support.
$100,000 to Performing Animal Welfare Society, Galt, CA, 2013. For general support.
$1,000 to New York Coalition for Healthy School Lunches, Mamaroneck, NY, 2012. For general support.

2250
The William & Anita Newman Foundation ✧

1400 S. Ocean Blvd., Ste. 1606
Boca Raton, FL 33432-8527

Established in 1985 in NY.
Donors: William Newman; Anita Newman; Debra Bernstein.
Foundation type: Independent foundation.
Financial data (yr. ended 09/30/13): Assets, $12,248,084 (M); gifts received, $150,000; expenditures, $677,727; qualifying distributions, $645,078; giving activities include $645,078 for 4 + grants (high: $251,260).
Purpose and activities: Giving primarily for Jewish organizations.
Fields of interest: Education; Human services; Jewish federated giving programs; Jewish agencies & synagogues.
Type of support: General/operating support.
Limitations: Applications not accepted. Giving in Boca Raton, FL. No grants to individuals.
Application information: Unsolicited requests for funds not accepted.
Officers: William Newman, Pres.; Melvin David Newman, V.P.; Debra Bernstein, Secy.
EIN: 133352983

2251
NextEra Energy Foundation, Inc. ✧

(formerly FPL Group Foundation, Inc.)
700 Universe Blvd.
Juno Beach, FL 33408-2683

Established in 1987 in FL.
Donor: Florida Power & Light Co.
Foundation type: Company-sponsored foundation.
Financial data (yr. ended 12/31/13): Assets, $10,206,828 (M); gifts received, $6,073,261; expenditures, $1,545,338; qualifying distributions, $1,541,190; giving activities include $1,492,890 for 258 grants (high: $100,000; low: $50).
Purpose and activities: The foundation supports organizations involved with arts and culture, education, the environment, health, animals and wildlife, affordable housing, human services, neighborhood development, economic development, government administration, and economically disadvantaged people.
Fields of interest: Arts; Higher education; Education; Environment, energy; Environmental education; Environment; Animal welfare; Animals/wildlife; Health care; Housing/shelter; Salvation Army; Aging, centers/services; Homeless, human services; Human services; Community development, neighborhood development; Economic development; United Ways and Federated Giving Programs; Government/public administration; Economically disadvantaged.
Type of support: Employee volunteer services; Capital campaigns; Endowments; Curriculum development; Employee matching gifts.
Limitations: Applications accepted. Giving primarily in areas of company operations, with emphasis on the east coast of FL and the west coast from Bradenton to Naples. No support for religious organizations, political or lobbying groups, United Way-affiliated agencies, or discriminatory organizations. No grants to individuals, or for school events, travel, or conferences, or endowments.
Publications: Application guidelines.
Application information: Application form required.
Initial approach: Completed application form
Copies of proposal: 1
Deadline(s): None
Final notification: 4 to 6 weeks
Officers and Directors:* James L. Robo,* Chair.; Eric E. Silagy,* Pres. and Treas.; Deborah H. Caplan, V.P.; Paul I. Cutler, V.P.; John W. Ketchum,* V.P.; W. Scott Seeley, Secy.; Charles E. Sieving.
Number of staff: 2 part-time support.
EIN: 650031452

2252
The Nommontu Foundation, Inc. ✧ ☆

(formerly Marisa Muller Charitable Foundation, Inc.)
c/o Fiduciary Trust
200 S. Biscayne, Ste. 3050
Miami, FL 33131-5337

Donor: Joyce Ann Mueller‡.
Foundation type: Independent foundation.
Financial data (yr. ended 12/31/13): Assets, $7,066,645 (M); expenditures, $602,958; qualifying distributions, $492,152; giving activities include $470,417 for 5 grants (high: $250,417; low: $50,000).
Fields of interest: AIDS; United Ways and Federated Giving Programs.
Limitations: Applications not accepted. Giving primarily in NY.
Application information: Unsolicited requests for funds not accepted.
Directors: Hans Muller; Joyce Muller; Marisa Muller.
EIN: 311787455
Selected grants: The following grants are a representative sample of this grantmaker's funding activity:
$200,000 to Acumen Fund, New York, NY, 2011. For program support.
$19,200 to Institute for Philanthropy US, New York, NY, 2011. For program support.

2253
Ocean Reef Community Foundation, Inc. ✧

(formerly Ocean Reef Foundation, Inc.)
200 Anchor Dr., Ste. B
Key Largo, FL 33037-5202 (305) 367-4707
Contact: Yurianna Mikolay, Exec. Dir.
FAX: (305) 367-6327;
E-mail: foundation@oceanreef.com; Additional e-mail: ymikolay@oceanreef.com; Main URL: http://www.orfound.org

Established in 1994 in FL.
Foundation type: Community foundation.
Financial data (yr. ended 10/31/13): Assets, $27,497,599 (M); gifts received, $5,954,343; expenditures, $5,403,322; giving activities include $4,719,324 for 54+ grants (high: $959,925).
Purpose and activities: The Ocean Reef Community Foundation is an independent, charitable, and not-for-profit organization. It was established to enhance responsible and effective philanthropy throughout the community.
Fields of interest: Historic preservation/historical societies; Arts; Education; Environment; Hospitals (general); Health care; Human services; Community/economic development; Aging.
Limitations: Applications accepted. Giving primarily in Ocean Reef, FL. No support for religious activities or programs that serve predominantly one denomination. No grants to individuals, or for general operating expenses, or endowment or memorial funds.
Publications: Application guidelines; Newsletter.
Application information: Visit foundation web site for application form and guidelines. If an organization would like to determine if its project is eligible prior to submitting a complete application, it may submit an optional pre-application form for review; see web site for electronic submission form. Application form required.
Initial approach: Mail or e-mail application form and attachments
Deadline(s): Dec.
Final notification: By Apr. 30
Officers and Directors:* William Nutt,* Chair.; Steven A. Markel,* Pres.; Tom N. Davidson,* V.P.; Yurianna Mikolay,* Secy.; Larry Brady,* Treas.; Alan J. Goldstein,* Chair.-Emeritus; Paul Astbury; Marlene Boll; Michael Berman; James F. Dicke II; Richard T. Farmer; Edmund A. Hajim; Nancy Harrington; Kenneth Karl; Nicola Lanni; Cynthia Lee; Donald McClure; David Ritz; Robert Schmetterer; Janie Sims; Nelson Sims; Adelaide Skoglund; Jill Sullivan; Gayle Tallardy; Donald Waite; Stevie Wishnak; Carla Wood.
EIN: 650509255

2254
Esther B. O'Keeffe Charitable Foundation ✧ ☆

P.O. Box 5357
Deerfield Beach, FL 33442

Established in 1990 in FL.
Donor: Esther B. O'Keeffe.
Foundation type: Independent foundation.
Financial data (yr. ended 12/31/13): Assets, $40,880,622 (M); expenditures, $2,494,832; qualifying distributions, $1,920,080; giving activities include $1,920,000 for 12 grants (high: $350,000; low: $20,000).
Fields of interest: Biomedicine research.
Limitations: Applications not accepted. Giving primarily in FL.
Application information: Contributes only to pre-selected organizations.
Trustees: Brian O'Keeffe; Clare O'Keeffe.
EIN: 650244287

2255
The Paiko Foundation ✧ ☆
2070 Gordon Dr.
Naples, FL 34102-7560

Established in FL.
Donor: Ray D. Berry.
Foundation type: Independent foundation.
Financial data (yr. ended 12/31/12): Assets, $41,630,716 (M); gifts received, $17,000,000; expenditures, $1,596,823; qualifying distributions, $1,000,000; giving activities include $1,000,000 for 1 grant.
Purpose and activities: Giving primarily to a foundation for the purpose of cancer research.
Fields of interest: Cancer research.
Limitations: Applications not accepted. Giving primarily in Palo Alto, CA.
Application information: Unsolicited requests for funds not accepted.
Trustee: Ray D. Berry.
EIN: 306282543

2256
Paul Palank Memorial Foundation, Inc. ✧
70 Bay Colony Ln.
Fort Lauderdale, FL 33308-2004
E-mail: palankfoundation@bellsouth.net; Main URL: http://www.palankfoundation.org

Established in 2000 in FL.
Donor: Angelica Palank.
Foundation type: Independent foundation.
Financial data (yr. ended 10/31/13): Assets, $13,018,114 (M); gifts received, $1,360; expenditures, $659,028; qualifying distributions, $600,050; giving activities include $595,708 for 18 grants (high: $115,000; low: $5,000).
Purpose and activities: The foundation will strive to facilitate creative, effective programming that addresses the immediate needs of children in crisis while seeking long term solutions to the abuse, neglect, and abandonment problems facing the children of our economy.
Fields of interest: Human services; Children/youth, services.
Limitations: Applications accepted. Giving primarily in Dade and Broward counties, FL.
Publications: Application guidelines.
Application information: Application form required.
Initial approach: Use pre-application form on foundation web site
Deadline(s): See foundation web site for deadlines
Directors: Angelica Palank-Sharlet; Anne Richards Rothe; Lisa Collins Stamp.
EIN: 651050806
Selected grants: The following grants are a representative sample of this grantmaker's funding activity:
$147,800 to Kristi House, Miami, FL, 2011. For general support.
$80,000 to Helping Abused, Neglected, Disadvantaged Youth, Fort Lauderdale, FL, 2011. For general support.
$50,000 to Childrens Harbor, Pembroke Pines, FL, 2011. For general support.
$20,100 to Foster Care Review, Miami, FL, 2011. For general support.
$15,000 to Neat Stuff, Miami, FL, 2011. For general support.

2257
Pamphalon Foundation, Inc. ✧
P.O. Box 357237
Gainesville, FL 32635

Established in 2003 in FL.
Foundation type: Independent foundation.
Financial data (yr. ended 12/31/13): Assets, $3,710,922 (M); expenditures, $506,629; qualifying distributions, $500,315; giving activities include $500,035 for 57 grants (high: $55,000; low: $400).
Purpose and activities: Giving primarily to Christian organizations and churches, and also for education, and social services.
Fields of interest: Education; Housing/shelter, development; Human services; Christian agencies & churches; Protestant agencies & churches.
Limitations: Applications not accepted. Giving primarily in FL.
Application information: Unsolicited requests for funds not accepted.
Officers: Rolf E. Hummel, Pres.; Daniel Maico, V.P.; Waltrude E. Hummel, Secy.
EIN: 141876459
Selected grants: The following grants are a representative sample of this grantmaker's funding activity:
$58,000 to Gainesville Community Ministry, Gainesville, FL, 2012. For Emergency food, clothing, assistance 501(c), FIN 59-172-4202.
$10,000 to Alachua Conservation Trust, Gainesville, FL, 2012. For organization for land conservation tax exempt under 501(c)(3).
$10,000 to Arbor House, Gainesville, FL, 2012. For Home for homeless single mothers + children.
$10,000 to Child Advocacy Center, Gainesville, FL, 2012. For Combination of agencies to assist children in need, 501(c)(3), 31-170 5396.
$8,000 to Chimp Haven, Keithville, LA, 2012. For Organization. to save and house former medical research chimps 501(a), 501(c)(3), EIN No. 74-2766663.
$6,000 to Amnesty International USA, New York, NY, 2012. For International Human Rights Organization.
$4,000 to Grier School, Tyrone, PA, 2012. For Middle school and High school, geared toward arts, Tax exempt No. 75-08659-2.
$570 to Concordia Language Villages, Moorhead, MN, 2012. For Part of Concordia College, Connected to Lutheran Church of America.
$100 to UNICEF, New York, NY, 2012. For International Help Organization.

2258
Paul S. Pariser Foundation, Inc. ✧
155 Flanders, Apt. D
Delray Beach, FL 32812 (406) 388-7715
Contact: Paul S. Pariser, Dir.

Established in 2006 in MT.
Donor: Paul S. Pariser.
Foundation type: Independent foundation.
Financial data (yr. ended 12/31/12): Assets, $104,987 (M); gifts received, $113,434; expenditures, $922,719; qualifying distributions, $830,532; giving activities include $90,008 for 83 grants (high: $22,369; low: $18).
Fields of interest: Hospitals (general); Cancer research; Human services; Jewish agencies & synagogues.
International interests: Israel.
Limitations: Applications accepted. Giving primarily in NY; some giving also in MD and Israel. No grants to individuals.
Application information: Application form not required.
Initial approach: Proposal
Deadline(s): None
Directors: Alan D. Pariser; Benjamin S. Pariser; Paul S. Pariser; Eli Schlossberg; Robert M. Schwartz.
EIN: 562066991
Selected grants: The following grants are a representative sample of this grantmaker's funding activity:
$1,080 to Aleh Negev Foundation, New York, NY, 2012. For the Care of Severely Disabled Jewish Children.
$828 to Bascom Palmer Eye Institute, Miami, FL, 2012. To Help Needy People with Eye Problems.
$756 to One Israel Fund, Hewlett, NY, 2012. For Welfare and Safety of Citizens in Judea and Samraia.
$549 to Chabad of South Beach, Miami Beach, FL, 2012. To help the needy.
$378 to Muscular Dystrophy Association, Boynton Beach, FL, 2012. For serves muscular dystrophy.
$270 to Ohr Somayach International, Brooklyn, NY, 2012. For helps the needy.
$216 to Chabad Lubavitch of Utah, Salt Lake City, UT, 2012. For Religious Institution Serves the Needy.
$180 to Southern Poverty Law Center, Montgomery, AL, 2012. For serves fighting religious crimes.
$162 to Yellowstone Public Radio, Billings, MT, 2012. For Helps Public Radio.

2259
Drs. Kiran & Pallavi Patel Family Foundation, Inc. ✧
5600 Mariner St., Ste. 227
Tampa, FL 33609-3471
Contact: Kiran C. Patel M.D., Secy.-Treas.

Established in 2006 in FL.
Donors: Kiran C. Patel, M.D.; Pallavi C. Patel, M.D.; Ace Endowment Fund; Bay Area Primary Care; The Aids Institute, Inc.; Glance HR LLC.
Foundation type: Independent foundation.
Financial data (yr. ended 06/30/13): Assets, $7,058,381 (M); gifts received, $1,369,610; expenditures, $1,478,454; qualifying distributions, $1,424,430; giving activities include $1,386,894 for 15 grants (high: $1,000,000; low: $1,008).
Fields of interest: Performing arts centers; Education; Health care; Human services; International development; International relief; International human rights.
International interests: India.
Type of support: General/operating support; Program development; Scholarships—to individuals.
Limitations: Applications accepted. Giving primarily in FL; some funding also in India.
Application information:
Initial approach: Proposal
Deadline(s): None
Officers: Pallavi C. Patel, M.D., Pres.; Shilen Patel, V.P.; Kiran C. Patel, M.D., Secy.-Treas.
Trustees: Sonali Judd; Sheetal Patel.
EIN: 203916634
Selected grants: The following grants are a representative sample of this grantmaker's funding activity:
$2,500 to Childrens Home, Tampa, FL, 2011.

2260
The Patterson Foundation ✧
2 N. Tamiami Trail, Ste. 206
Sarasota, FL 34236-5574 (941) 952-1413
Contact: Carol Lipp
FAX: (941) 952-1435;
E-mail: clipp@thepattersonfoundation.org; Main URL: http://www.thepattersonfoundation.org
Blog: http://www.thepattersonfoundation.org/blog/
Facebook: http://www.facebook.com/pages/The-Patterson-Foundation/233909564806
Google Plus: https://plus.google.com/u/0/+ThepattersonfoundationOrg/posts
Twitter: http://twitter.com/ThePattersonFdn
YouTube: http://www.youtube.com/user/ThePattersonFdn

Established in 1997 in FL.
Donors: Dorothy Clarke Patterson†; James J. Patterson†; Dorothy C. Patterson Trust.
Foundation type: Independent foundation.
Financial data (yr. ended 06/30/13): Assets, $222,423,695 (M); expenditures, $12,557,541; qualifying distributions, $10,498,134; giving activities include $4,961,681 for 23 grants (high: $1,500,000; low: $1,250).
Purpose and activities: The foundation believes that through communications, technology, and financial innovations, improvements may be achieved that transcend any single issue, entity, or geographic area. The foundation provides resources to facilitate, expedite, and share methods, techniques, and tools, joining with others in creating New Realities. Current initiatives focus on aging, diabetes, arthritis, and educational opportunities in the community.
Fields of interest: Higher education; Arthritis; Diabetes; Human services; Aging, centers/services; Aging.
Limitations: Applications not accepted. Giving primarily FL, with emphasis on Sarasota. No grants to individuals.
Application information: Contributes only to pre-selected organizations.
Officer: Debra M. Jacobs, C.E.O. and Pres.
Designation Committee: John T. Berteau, Chair.; Charles D. Bailey, Jr.; Ric Gregoria.
Trustee: Northern Trust Bank.
EIN: 656230256
Selected grants: The following grants are a representative sample of this grantmaker's funding activity:
$2,500,000 to Community Foundation of Sarasota County, Sarasota, FL, 2011. For Donor Advised Fund.
$1,014,437 to University of South Florida Foundation, Tampa, FL, 2011. For Diabetes Initiative.
$530,000 to Community Foundation of Sarasota County, Sarasota, FL, 2011. For Season of Sharing.
$400,000 to Arthritis Foundation, Florida Chapter, Bradenton, FL, 2011. For Jingle Bell Run Walk Matching Funds.
$390,500 to Sarasota Memorial Healthcare Foundation, Sarasota, FL, 2011. For Health Safety Net.
$334,000 to Community Foundation of Sarasota County, Sarasota, FL, 2011. For Match Day 2012.
$250,000 to Arthritis Foundation, Florida Chapter, Bradenton, FL, 2011. For JBRW Matching Gift.
$250,000 to Community Foundation of Northeast Alabama, Anniston, AL, 2011. For challenge grant.
$210,000 to Community Foundation of Sarasota County, Sarasota, FL, 2011. For Pay It Forward.
$100,000 to Community Foundation of Sarasota County, Sarasota, FL, 2011. For one-time grant to support emerging opportunities.

2261
The Patterson Foundation ✧ ☆
11410 Dickey Ln.
P.O. Box 790
Captiva, FL 33924-0790

Established in 2007 in MO.
Donor: Neal Patterson.
Foundation type: Independent foundation.
Financial data (yr. ended 12/31/13): Assets, $7,961,348 (M); gifts received, $408,031; expenditures, $429,842; qualifying distributions, $424,200; giving activities include $424,200 for 7 grants (high: $200,000; low: $2,000).
Fields of interest: Higher education; Human services.
Limitations: Applications not accepted. Giving primarily in KS and MO. No grants to individuals.
Application information: Contributes only to pre-selected organizations.
Trustees: Jeanne Patterson; Neal Patterson.
EIN: 207550081

2262
Albert F. Patton Trust ✧
c/o Bank of America, N.A.
P.O. Box 40200, FL9-100-10-19
Jacksonville, FL 32203-0200

Foundation type: Independent foundation.
Financial data (yr. ended 12/31/13): Assets, $11,293,906 (M); expenditures, $699,189; qualifying distributions, $596,283; giving activities include $549,017 for 5 grants (high: $199,642; low: $49,911).
Purpose and activities: Giving primarily to Presbyterian organizations, including churches, seminaries, and a home for senior citizens.
Fields of interest: Higher education; Theological school/education; Residential/custodial care, senior continuing care; Protestant agencies & churches.
Limitations: Applications not accepted. Giving primarily in VA.
Application information: Contributes only to pre-selected organizations.
Trustee: Bank of America, N.A.
EIN: 546033518
Selected grants: The following grants are a representative sample of this grantmaker's funding activity:
$182,789 to Hampden-Sydney College, Hampden Sydney, VA, 2010. For general funding.
$149,732 to Sunnyside Presbyterian Home, Harrisonburg, VA, 2011. For general funding.
$91,394 to Union Presbyterian Seminary, Richmond, VA, 2010.
$45,697 to Union Presbyterian Seminary, Richmond, VA, 2010. For general funding.

2263
Peacock Foundation, Inc. ✧
100 S.E. 2nd St., Ste. 2370
Miami, FL 33131-2127 (305) 373-1386
Contact: Joelle Allen, Exec. Dir.
Main URL: http://www.peacockfoundationinc.org

Incorporated in 1947 in FL.
Donor: Henry B. Peacock, Jr.†.
Foundation type: Independent foundation.
Financial data (yr. ended 11/30/13): Assets, $47,520,701 (M); expenditures, $2,587,456; qualifying distributions, $2,131,964; giving activities include $1,804,380 for 52 grants (high: $100,000; low: $2,500).
Purpose and activities: The foundation's priorities include: supporting educational programs in the arts and the environment, as well as special education for disabled persons; contributing to medical research, healthcare organizations, and hospitals; and making grants to human services providers that promote youth development, assist abused or neglected children, women, and the elderly, and seek to reduce abuse, prevent homelessness, and end hunger.
Fields of interest: Arts education; Education; Environmental education; Hospitals (general); Mental health/crisis services; Health organizations, association; Medical research, institute; Human services; Youth, services.
Type of support: General/operating support; Continuing support; Program development; Research; Matching/challenge support.
Limitations: Giving primarily in the southeast FL communities located in Broward, Miami-Dade, and Monroe counties. No support for political lobbying or religious organizations unless project benefits entire community. No grants to individuals or for construction campaigns, deficit financing or debt reduction, conferences, or fundraising/special/athletic events.
Application information:
Initial approach: Letter of inquiry
Board meeting date(s): Quarterly
Officers and Directors:* Robin Reiter-Faragalli,* Pres.; Jan Griffin,* V.P.; Charles P. Sacher, Secy.-Treas.; Joelle Allen, Exec. Dir.
Number of staff: 3 full-time professional.
EIN: 590999759
Selected grants: The following grants are a representative sample of this grantmaker's funding activity:
$50,000 to Guardianship Program of Dade County, Miami, FL, 2013. For Young Adult Case Management.
$50,000 to Miami Art Museum of Dade County, Miami, FL, 2013. For education and outreach Program.
$50,000 to Network for Teaching Entrepreneurship, Miami, FL, 2013. For Transform and Expand Entrepreneurship.
$40,000 to YMCA of Greater Miami, Miami, FL, 2013. For Active Older Adult Program.
$25,000 to Miami City Ballet, Miami Beach, FL, 2013. For Complimentary Ticket Program and Ballet for Young People.
$20,000 to New World Symphony, Miami Beach, FL, 2013. For Kids in the Concert Hall.
$4,000 to Florida Philanthropic Network, Tampa, FL, 2013. For 2013 support contributions.

2264
The Dr. M. Lee Pearce Foundation, Inc. ✧
5601 N. Dixie Hwy., Ste. 411
Fort Lauderdale, FL 33334-4147

Established in 1984 in DE and FL.
Donor: M. Lee Pearce, M.D.
Foundation type: Independent foundation.
Financial data (yr. ended 12/31/12): Assets, $11,869,685 (M); gifts received, $537,918; expenditures, $1,269,368; qualifying distributions, $958,658; giving activities include $954,818 for 56 grants (high: $450,250; low: $1,000).
Purpose and activities: Giving primarily for the arts, education, health and human services.
Fields of interest: Performing arts; Arts; Higher education; Education; Hospitals (general); Medical research, institute; Human services.
Limitations: Applications not accepted. Giving in the U.S., with some emphasis on Washington, DC, FL and NY. No grants to individuals.
Application information: Contributes only to pre-selected organizations.
Officers and Directors:* M. Lee Pearce, M.D.*, Chair. and C.E.O.; Charles Douglas, Vice-Chair. and Pres.; Robert Potts,* Sr. V.P.; Scott Kent,* V.P.; Tim Lincoln, Secy.; Jose Valle,* Treas.; Robert L. Achor; Jeffrey Bivins; Dale Rusted.
EIN: 592424272

2265
The Pechter Family Foundation ✧
8230 210 St. S.
Boca Raton, FL 33433-1600 (561) 982-7770
Contact: Jack H. Pechter, Dir.

Established in 2005 in FL.
Donors: Jack H. Pechter; Lisa Pechter; Marilyn A. Pechter; Marty Pechter; Shelley Pechter Himmerich; Melissa Pechter; Pechter Family Foundation; Carlton Investments, LP; Danielle Pechter, LP; JSP Investments, LP; Zach Pechter, LP; The Melissa Pechter Irrev. Trust; Coley Pechter, LP.
Foundation type: Independent foundation.
Financial data (yr. ended 12/31/13): Assets, $15,078,634 (M); expenditures, $1,378,394; qualifying distributions, $688,021; giving activities include $599,977 for 43 grants (high: $110,000; low: $25).
Purpose and activities: Giving primarily for Jewish agencies and temples, as well as for education, health organizations and hospitals, and children, youth, and social services.
Fields of interest: Education; Hospitals (general); Health organizations, association; Human services; Children/youth, services; Jewish agencies & synagogues.
Limitations: Applications accepted. Giving primarily in FL and MD.
Application information: Application form not required.
Initial approach: Proposal
Deadline(s): None
Officers: Shelly Pechter Himmelrich, Pres.; Jeffrey S. Pechter, V.P.; Martin H. Pechter, V.P.; Renee McGovern, Secy.-Treas.
Directors: Darrell Friedman; R. Brady Osborne, Jr.; Jack H. Pechter; Marilyn A. Pechter; Mitchell D. Schepps.
EIN: 050618996
Selected grants: The following grants are a representative sample of this grantmaker's funding activity:
$110,010 to Boca Raton Regional Hospital, Boca Raton, FL, 2011.
$15,000 to University of Miami, Miami, FL, 2011.
$10,000 to Bnos Yisroel of Baltimore, Baltimore, MD, 2011.
$10,000 to SOS Childrens Village of Florida, Coconut Creek, FL, 2011.
$5,000 to Hebrew Immigrant Aid Society, New York, NY, 2011.
$5,000 to Shoresh, Baltimore, MD, 2011.
$2,500 to Jemicy School, Owings Mills, MD, 2011.
$2,500 to Ner Israel Rabbinical College, Baltimore, MD, 2011.
$1,000 to Keene State College, Keene, NH, 2011.
$1,000 to Lynn University, Boca Raton, FL, 2011.

2266
Claudia and Steven Perles Family Foundation ✧ ☆
5700 Collins Ave., Ste. PH-A
Miami Beach, FL 33140 (305) 864-8465
Contact: Claudia Kendrew Perles, Pres.

Established in DC.
Donors: Claudia Perles; Steven Perles.
Foundation type: Independent foundation.
Financial data (yr. ended 12/31/13): Assets, $5,012,594 (M); expenditures, $851,632; qualifying distributions, $677,366; giving activities include $677,366 for 25 grants (high: $218,466; low: $500).
Fields of interest: Arts; Education; Health organizations.
Limitations: Applications accepted. Giving primarily in NY; funding also in MA.
Application information: Application form not required.
Initial approach: Proposal
Deadline(s): None
Officer: Claudia Kendrew Perles, Pres.
Directors: Steven Perles; William D. Simon.
EIN: 311810212
Selected grants: The following grants are a representative sample of this grantmaker's funding activity:
$150,000 to Multiple Sclerosis Society, National, New York, NY, 2011.
$65,000 to Multiple Sclerosis Society, National, Waltham, MA, 2010.
$35,000 to United States Holocaust Memorial Museum, Washington, DC, 2010.
$32,000 to Miami City Ballet, Miami Beach, FL, 2011.
$25,000 to College of William and Mary, Williamsburg, VA, 2010.
$10,000 to Alzheimers Association, Chicago, IL, 2010.
$10,000 to Days End Farm Horse Rescue, Lisbon, MD, 2010.
$10,000 to Institute for the Study of War, Washington, DC, 2010.
$5,000 to Boston Symphony Orchestra, Boston, MA, 2011.
$5,000 to Shakespeare and Company, Lenox, MA, 2011.
$5,000 to Shakespeare and Company, Lenox, MA, 2010.
$5,000 to University of Miami, Coral Gables, FL, 2010.
$3,500 to W L R N, Friends of, Miami, FL, 2011.
$2,500 to Amigos de las Americas, Houston, TX, 2010.
$2,000 to Craft Emergency Relief Fund, Montpelier, VT, 2011.
$1,000 to Humane Society of Greater Miami, North Miami Beach, FL, 2010.

2267
The Patricia Price Peterson Foundation ✧
c/o AUREOS
P.O. Box 25331
Miami, FL 33102-5331
Contact: Erik Peterson, Pres.
E-mail: pppfoundation@gmail.com

Established about 1964.
Donor: Rudolph A. Peterson†.
Foundation type: Independent foundation.
Financial data (yr. ended 12/31/13): Assets, $11,026,617 (M); expenditures, $726,758; qualifying distributions, $717,518; giving activities include $717,518 for 17 grants (high: $235,000; low: $10,000).
Purpose and activities: The purpose of the foundation is to support the implementation of initiatives to solve social challenges faced by disadvantaged communities. The foundation believes that by enhancing educational opportunities and promoting a positive development of youth, it can foster long lasting impact that can boost social development. It pursues this mission by awarding grants and supporting projects and organizations that share this vision and work in the areas of education and youth development. It is particularly interested in working closely with communities in the Central American region, and in particular, Panama.
Fields of interest: Teacher school/education; Education; Environment, natural resources; Agriculture; Physically disabled.
International interests: Central America.
Type of support: General/operating support; Management development/capacity building; Equipment; Land acquisition; Emergency funds; Program development; Professorships; Seed money; Scholarship funds.
Limitations: Giving limited to Central America and Panama.
Application information: Application form not required.
Initial approach: E-mail
Copies of proposal: 1
Deadline(s): None
Board meeting date(s): Mid-year
Officers: Stephen W. Bennett, Pres. and Secy.; Erik Peterson, Treas.
Directors: Merrill K. Bennett; R. Price Peterson; Dr. Peter Sterling.
EIN: 946109098

2268
Petway Family Foundation Inc. ✧ ☆
(formerly The Universal Foundation, Inc.)
8230 Nations Way
Jacksonville, FL 32256-0830

Established in FL.
Donors: Thomas F. Petway III; Zurich Insurance Sevices Inc.
Foundation type: Independent foundation.
Financial data (yr. ended 06/30/13): Assets, $82,964 (M); gifts received, $400,000; expenditures, $457,312; qualifying distributions,

$456,000; giving activities include $456,000 for grants.
Fields of interest: Higher education; Human services; Residential/custodial care, hospices.
Limitations: Applications not accepted. Giving primarily in Jacksonville, FL. No grants to individuals.
Application information: Contributes only to pre-selected organizations.
Officers: Thomas F. Petway III, Chair. and Treas.; Elizabeth P. Petway, Vice-Chair.; Brette E. Petway, Pres.; Thomas F. Petway IV, Secy.
EIN: 592735054
Selected grants: The following grants are a representative sample of this grantmaker's funding activity:
$75,000 to Shining Mountain Waldorf School, Boulder, CO, 2011. For general contribution.
$33,333 to Western State College Foundation, Gunnison, CO, 2011. For general contribution.
$7,500 to Museum of Contemporary Art Jacksonville, Jacksonville, FL, 2011. For general contribution.
$5,000 to Humane Society, Jacksonville, Jacksonville, FL, 2011. For general contribution.
$5,000 to Mission House, Jacksonville Beach, FL, 2011. For general contribution.
$5,000 to Teach for America, New York, NY, 2011. For general contribution.

2269
Pinellas County Community Foundation ✧

5200 East Bay Dr., Ste. 202
Clearwater, FL 33764 (727) 531-0058
Contact: Julie Scales, Exec. Dir.
FAX: (727) 531-0053; E-mail: info@pinellasccf.org;
Main URL: http://www.pinellasccf.org
Blog: http://pinellasccf.wordpress.com/
Facebook: https://www.facebook.com/pinellasccf?skip_nax_wizard=true

Established in 1969 in FL by trust agreement.
Foundation type: Community foundation.
Financial data (yr. ended 12/31/13): Assets, $85,607,432 (M); gifts received, $544,516; expenditures, $2,730,528; giving activities include $1,993,271 for grants.
Purpose and activities: The purpose of the foundation is to receive donations from people and organizations interested in helping their community and to oversee the investment of those funds by monitoring the work of the trustees and then to distribute the income to sound charitable organizations that meet community needs. Primary areas of interest include family services, the disadvantaged, low income, handicapped, and other social services.
Fields of interest: Arts; Education; Environment; Animal welfare; Health care; Substance abuse, services; Mental health/crisis services; Crime/violence prevention, abuse prevention; Housing/shelter; Children/youth, services; Family services; Aging, centers/services; Developmentally disabled, centers & services; Women, centers/services; Human services; Religion; Children/youth; Adults; Aging; Disabilities, people with; Blind/visually impaired; Deaf/hearing impaired; Mentally disabled; Economically disadvantaged; Homeless.
Type of support: General/operating support; Continuing support; Building/renovation; Equipment; Scholarship funds; Scholarships—to individuals.
Limitations: Applications accepted. Giving limited to Pinellas County, FL area. No grants for endowment funds, or for research, fellowships, or matching gifts; no loans.
Publications: Application guidelines; Annual report (including application guidelines); Informational brochure; Newsletter; Occasional report.
Application information: Only agencies receiving Operating Grants from the foundation are eligible to apply for Competitive Grants; visit foundation web site for application information. Application form required.
Initial approach: Telephone
Copies of proposal: 1
Deadline(s): Oct. 1 for Operating Grants; June 15 and Oct. 1 for Competitive Grants
Board meeting date(s): Feb., Sept., and Dec.
Final notification: 2 months
Officers and Governors:* Sallie Parks,* Chair.; Byron Smith,* Vice-Chair.; Julie Scales, Exec. Dir.; Louis N. Adcock, Jr.; Sandra F. Diamond; Maria N. Edmonds; Robert Entel, M.D.; Joseph W. Fleece III; Peggy O'Shea; Judith Powers; Virginia Rowell; David Sietsma; Irene Sullivan; Sarah Williams, Esq.
Trustee Banks: Bank of America, N.A.; Fifth Third Bank; Merrill Lynch Trust Co.; Northern Trust Bank of Florida, N.A.; Raymond James Trust Co.; Regions Morgan Keegan Trust; Sabal Co.; SunTrust Bank; Synovus Trust Co.; Wachovia Bank, N.A.
Number of staff: 1 full-time professional; 1 part-time support.
EIN: 237113194

2270
Plangere Foundation, Inc. ✧

S. Quail Ridge
3829 Partridge Pl.
Boynton Beach, FL 33436-5413

Established in 1997 in FL.
Donors: Jules L. Plangere, Jr.; Alfred Colantoni; The Plangere KCA Charitable Trust; The Plangere KRDJ Charitable Trust.
Foundation type: Independent foundation.
Financial data (yr. ended 04/30/13): Assets, $7,383,391 (M); gifts received, $628,460; expenditures, $1,638,768; qualifying distributions, $1,609,415; giving activities include $1,565,500 for 24 grants (high: $1,025,000; low: $1,000).
Fields of interest: Higher education; Human services; Community/economic development.
Limitations: Applications not accepted. Giving primarily in NJ. No grants to individuals.
Application information: Contributes only to pre-selected organizations.
Officers and Directors:* Jules Plangere, Jr.,* Chair.; E. Donald Lass, Secy.; Jules L. Plangere III, Treas.; Wendy Bickart; Alfred Colantoni; John C. Conover III.
EIN: 650747053
Selected grants: The following grants are a representative sample of this grantmaker's funding activity:
$1,000,000 to Monmouth University, West Long Branch, NJ, 2012.
$5,000 to Memorial Sloan-Kettering Cancer Center, New York, NY, 2012.
$4,000 to Achievement Centers for Children and Families, Delray Beach, FL, 2011.
$3,000 to CRC Recovery Foundation, Delray Beach, FL, 2012.

2271
Anila Sarswati and Parmanand Vijay Poonai Charitable Foundation, Inc. ✧ ☆

2723 Eagle Cliff Dr.
Kissimme, FL 34746-3182

Established in 2001 in FL.
Donors: Anila Poonai; Parmanand V. Poonai.
Foundation type: Independent foundation.
Financial data (yr. ended 12/31/13): Assets, $0 (M); gifts received, $704,219; expenditures, $793,712; qualifying distributions, $793,712; giving activities include $793,251 for 1 grant.
Fields of interest: Religion.
Limitations: Applications not accepted. No grants to individuals.
Application information: Unsolicited requests for funds not accepted.
Officers: Parmanand V. Poonai, Pres.-Secy.
Director: Jaswa Rajen; Hemraj Shivdarsan; Premnath Poonai.
EIN: 311792596

2272
The Lois Pope Life Foundation

1720 S. Ocean Blvd.
Manalapan, FL 33462-6222 (561) 582-8083
FAX: (561) 582-8086; E-mail: life@life-edu.org; Main URL: http://www.life-edu.org

Established in 1996 in FL.
Donors: Lois B. Pope; The Cessna Aircraft Co.
Foundation type: Independent foundation.
Financial data (yr. ended 12/31/11): Assets, $0 (M); expenditures, $545,058; qualifying distributions, $510,735; giving activities include $439,015 for 18 grants (high: $175,000; low: $365).
Purpose and activities: Giving primarily for education, health associations, social services, and to disabled veterans' organizations.
Fields of interest: Education; Animal welfare; Health organizations, association; Human services; Children/youth, services; Military/veterans' organizations.
Limitations: Applications not accepted. Giving primarily in FL; funding also in CA and NY.
Publications: Newsletter.
Application information: Unsolicited requests for funds not accepted.
Trustees: Elsa G. Johnson; Lois B. Pope; Michele Ritter.
EIN: 137086087

2273
The Preik Family Foundation, Inc. ✧

7 Sound Point Ct.
Fernandina Beach, FL 32034-6443

Established in 2007 in FL.
Donors: Reinhold Preik; Jennifer Preik.
Foundation type: Independent foundation.
Financial data (yr. ended 12/31/13): Assets, $8,470,355 (M); gifts received, $600; expenditures, $576,277; qualifying distributions, $525,150; giving activities include $525,150 for 10 grants (high: $325,950; low: $5,000).
Fields of interest: Health organizations; Human services; Religion.
Limitations: Applications not accepted. Giving primarily in FL, GA and TX. No grants to individuals.

Application information: Unsolicited requests for funds not accepted.
Officers and Trustees:* Reinhold Preik,* Pres.; Jennifer Preik,* V.P.; Diana Huynen, Secy.-Treas.; Erin Lee; Austin Preik; Curtis Preik.
EIN: 261590815

2274
The Prentice Family Foundation ✧
1805 Osceola St.
Jacksonville, FL 32204-4607

Established in 2007 in IL.
Donors: Bryant Prentice III; Marc C. Hutchinson.
Foundation type: Independent foundation.
Financial data (yr. ended 12/31/13): Assets, $15,467,206 (M); gifts received, $509,259; expenditures, $847,148; qualifying distributions, $739,068; giving activities include $664,752 for 2 grants (high: $443,188; low: $221,564).
Fields of interest: Higher education; Scholarships/financial aid.
Limitations: Applications not accepted. Giving primarily in Buffalo, NY.
Application information: Unsolicited requests for funds not accepted.
Officers: Bryant H. Prentice III, Pres.; Joan P. Prentice, V.P.; Colette P. Pike, Secy.; Marc C. Hutchinson, Treas.; Gail Johnstone, Exec. Dir.
Director: Robert Zak.
EIN: 202557712

2275
Publix Super Markets Charities ✧
(formerly George W. Jenkins Foundation, Inc.)
3300 Publix Corporate Pkwy.
Lakeland, FL 33811-3311 (863) 686-8754
Contact: Kelly Williams-Puccio, Exec. Dir.
Application address: P.O. Box 407, Lakeland, FL 33802-0407

Incorporated in 1967 in FL.
Donor: George W. Jenkins‡.
Foundation type: Independent foundation.
Financial data (yr. ended 12/31/13): Assets, $728,769,589 (M); gifts received, $50; expenditures, $36,885,401; qualifying distributions, $34,601,341; giving activities include $34,562,391 for 3,110 grants (high: $2,200,000; low: $100).
Purpose and activities: Giving primarily for education, children and youth, and the United Way and its agencies.
Fields of interest: Education; Children/youth, services; Children, services; Youth, services; United Ways and Federated Giving Programs.
Type of support: General/operating support; Capital campaigns; Building/renovation; Equipment; Program development; Employee matching gifts.
Limitations: Applications accepted. Giving primarily in AL, FL, GA, SC, and TN. No grants to individuals.
Application information:
Initial approach: Letter of request
Copies of proposal: 1
Deadline(s): None
Board meeting date(s): Monthly
Final notification: 6 to 8 weeks
Officers and Directors:* Carol Barnett,* Chair. and C.E.O.; Hoyt Barnett,* V.P.; John Attaway, Secy.; Tina Johnson, Treas.; Kelly Williams-Puccio,* Exec. Dir.; Barbara Hart; Sharon Miller.
Number of staff: 3 full-time professional.
EIN: 596194119
Selected grants: The following grants are a representative sample of this grantmaker's funding activity:
$2,100,000 to United Way of Metropolitan Atlanta, Atlanta, GA, 2012.
$1,600,000 to United Way of Central Florida, Highland City, FL, 2012.
$400,000 to Florida Southern College, Lakeland, FL, 2012.
$210,000 to University of South Florida Foundation, Tampa, FL, 2012.
$100,500 to United Way of Citrus County, Crystal River, FL, 2012.
$100,000 to Youth and Family Alternatives, New Port Richey, FL, 2012.
$50,000 to Junior Achievement of South Florida, Coconut Creek, FL, 2012.
$15,000 to Girls Inc. of Pinellas, Pinellas Park, FL, 2012.
$12,500 to YMCA, Sarasota Family, Sarasota, FL, 2012.
$10,000 to Academy Prep Center of Saint Petersburg, Saint Petersburg, FL, 2012.

2276
Quantum Foundation ✧
2701 N. Australian Ave., Ste. 200
West Palm Beach, FL 33407-4526 (561) 832-7497
Contact: Eric Kelly, Pres.
FAX: (561) 832-5794;
E-mail: tmay@quantumfnd.org; Main URL: http://www.quantumfnd.org
Facebook: http://www.facebook.com/pages/West-Palm-Beach-FL/Quantum-Foundation/131113414501
Foundation News Feed: http://www.quantumfnd.org/index.cfm?fuseaction=news.main&rss=true&x=9836582
Grants Database: http://www.cybergrants.com/cybergrants/plsql/quantum.grant_search.search_page
LinkedIn: http://www.linkedin.com/groups?home=&gid=2342204&trk=anet_ug_hm
Twitter: http://twitter.com/quantumfnd

Established in 1995 in FL; converted from sale of John F. Kennedy Hospital to Columbia/HCA.
Foundation type: Independent foundation.
Financial data (yr. ended 12/31/12): Assets, $139,453,453 (M); expenditures, $8,569,297; qualifying distributions, $7,446,051; giving activities include $6,268,578 for 197 grants (high: $650,000; low: $400).
Purpose and activities: The foundation works in Palm Beach County to increase health care access, improve science and health education, and enhance the health care workforce.
Fields of interest: Education; Health care; Community/economic development; Children; Adults; Economically disadvantaged.
Type of support: General/operating support; Management development/capacity building; Capital campaigns; Building/renovation; Equipment; Emergency funds; Program development; Seed money; Technical assistance; Consulting services; Program evaluation; Employee matching gifts; Matching/challenge support.
Limitations: Applications accepted. Giving limited to Palm Beach County, FL. No support for religious organizations for religious purposes, health research, or for political organizations or causes. No grants to individuals, or individual requests for scholarships, or for endowments, operating deficits or retirement of debt.
Publications: Application guidelines; Annual report; Grants list; Newsletter; Occasional report.
Application information: Letters of Inquiry are received and reviewed on an on-going basis. If your LOI is approved to move forward in the review process, you will be invited to submit a full proposal. If you are invited to submit a full proposal, you will be directed to the foundation's online proposal form. All areas to address in your full proposal will be clearly identified. The foundation invites submission of full proposals at least three times per year. Full proposals must be submitted online and must be received by close of business on the full proposal due date. Application form required.
Initial approach: Submit a letter of inquiry online at foundation's web site
Deadline(s): See foundation web site for current full proposal due dates
Board meeting date(s): Year-round
Final notification: 3-4 weeks
Officers and Trustees:* William A. Meyer,* Chair.; Denis P. Coleman, Jr.,* Vice-Chair.; Eric M. Kelly, Pres.; Joe Paskoski, C.F.O.; Jeannette M. Corbett; Kerry A. Diaz; Michael J. Dixon; James P. Kintz; Anthony J. McNicholas III; Stephen C. Moore; Donna A. Mulholland; Gerald J. O'Connor; Richard Sussman; Ethel Isaacs Williams.
Number of staff: 6 full-time professional; 2 full-time support.
EIN: 590812783
Selected grants: The following grants are a representative sample of this grantmaker's funding activity:
$1,000,000 to University of Florida Foundation, Gainesville, FL, 2012. For Palm Beach School District STEM Initiative, payable over 3.25 years.
$900,000 to South Florida Science Museum, West Palm Beach, FL, 2012. For The Breakthrough Project, payable over 3.50 years.
$625,000 to Genesis Community Health, Boynton Beach, FL, 2012. For core operating support.
$500,000 to Caridad Center, Boynton Beach, FL, 2013. For upgrade and expansion project.
$500,000 to Florida Atlantic University Foundation, Boca Raton, FL, 2013. For research and service partnership at Community Health Center, which provides culturally sensitive health care to underserved people in the area, payable over 2.00 years.
$379,293 to Mental Health Association of Palm Beach County, West Palm Beach, FL, 2013. For Be Merge for Infants and Children (BMIC). Be Merge is a training initiative for mental health professionals to help them identify and respond to potential and current mental health issues that exist within infants, children and adolescents, payable over 2.00 years.
$315,000 to Center for Child Counseling, West Palm Beach, FL, 2013. To train professionals in early childhood mental heath intervention, payable over 2.00 years.
$300,000 to True Fast Outreach Ministries, West Palm Beach, FL, 2012. For Health Care Navigator Program and other health and wellness basic needs programs, payable over 2.00 years.
$240,000 to South Florida Science Museum, West Palm Beach, FL, 2012. For Science on a Sphere, payable over 3.00 years.

$185,658 to Vita Nova, West Palm Beach, FL, 2012. For Youth Advocacy Center, payable over 3.00 years.
$175,000 to Palm Beach Atlantic University, West Palm Beach, FL, 2012. For Center for Integrative Science Learning, payable over 2.75 years.
$171,839 to University of Miami, Miller School of Medicine, Miami, FL, 2013. To train Palm Beach County medical residents and practicing physicians in laparoscopic surgery.
$135,000 to Trust for Public Land, Southeast Florida Office, South Miami, FL, 2013. To develop Fitness Zones in Palm Beach County, payable over 2.00 years.
$100,000 to Florida Atlantic University Foundation, Boca Raton, FL, 2012. For Healthcare Careers Outreach Program.
$100,000 to Girl Scouts of the U.S.A., Oakland Park, FL, 2012. For Engaging Girls in STEM, payable over 2.00 years.
$100,000 to Palm Beach County Food Bank, Lantana, FL, 2013. For Nutrition XPress food delivery program, payable over 2.00 years.
$100,000 to Parent-Child Center, Riviera Beach, FL, 2013. For Coordinated Trauma Care Program, payable over 2.00 years.
$25,000 to First Baptist Church of Lantana, Lantana, FL, 2013. For outreach to provide food and clothing to needy.
$25,000 to Light House Cafe Ministries of the Glades, Pahokee, FL, 2012. For Feeding the Hungry.
$25,000 to Renewed Deliverance Christian Ministry, Lake Park, FL, 2013. For Feeding the Flock Community Food Pantry.

2277
The Querrey Simpson Charitable Foundation ✧
700 Kings Town Dr.
Naples, FL 34102-7831
Contact: Kimberly Querry, Tr.

Established in 2007 in IL.
Donors: Louis A. Simpson; Kimberly Querrey.
Foundation type: Independent foundation.
Financial data (yr. ended 12/31/12): Assets, $1,860,814 (M); gifts received, $4,968,430; expenditures, $7,190,081; qualifying distributions, $7,136,102; giving activities include $7,136,102 for 23 grants (high: $6,000,000; low: $2,000).
Fields of interest: Museums; Education.
Limitations: Giving primarily in Chicago, IL; some giving also in CA and NY.
Application information: Application form not required.
Initial approach: Letter
Deadline(s): None
Trustee: Kimberly Querrey.
EIN: 261346418

2278
Philip E. and Carole R. Ratcliffe Foundation, Inc. ✧ ☆
64 Isla Bahia Dr.
Fort Lauderdale, FL 33316 (954) 327-0324
Contact: Carole R. Ratcliffe, Pres. and Secy.

Established in 2003.
Donors: Philip E. Ratcliffe; Carole R. Ratcliffe.
Foundation type: Independent foundation.
Financial data (yr. ended 12/31/13): Assets, $32,994,711 (M); gifts received, $38,650; expenditures, $1,601,795; qualifying distributions, $1,435,000; giving activities include $1,435,000 for 8 grants (high: $600,000; low: $10,000).
Fields of interest: Higher education, college; Health care; Human services.
Limitations: Applications accepted. Giving primarily in FL and MD.
Application information: Application form required.
Initial approach: Letter
Deadline(s): None
Officers: Carole R. Ratcliffe, Pres. and Secy.; James D. Wright, V.P. and Treas.
EIN: 820568453
Selected grants: The following grants are a representative sample of this grantmaker's funding activity:
$150,000 to Anne Arundel Community College, Arnold, MD, 2011.
$10,000 to Baldwin-Wallace College, Berea, OH, 2011.

2279
The Rawlings Foundation, Inc. ✧
2554 Players Ct.
Wellington, FL 33414-6286

Established in 2001 in FL.
Donors: George R. Rawlings; James L. Saylor II; George Halstead; John Rawlings; Lionel Martin; The Rawlings Co., LLC; Rawlings and Assocs., PLLC; Baptist Bible College West.
Foundation type: Operating foundation.
Financial data (yr. ended 12/31/12): Assets, $58,417,915 (M); gifts received, $13,277,313; expenditures, $12,073,267; qualifying distributions, $13,669,520; giving activities include $1,722,918 for 33 grants (high: $540,000; low: $299), $9,772,963 for foundation-administered programs and $1,802,734 for loans/program-related investments.
Fields of interest: Higher education; Education; Human services; Christian agencies & churches.
Type of support: General/operating support; Program-related investments/loans.
Limitations: Applications not accepted. Giving primarily in KY, MO, TN, TX, and VA.
Application information: Unsolicited requests for funds not accepted.
Officers and Directors:* George R. Rawlings,* Pres.; Beverly S. Rawlings,* V.P. and Secy.; Herbert M. Rawlings,* Treas.
EIN: 651051638

2280
The Rayni Foundation, Inc. ✧
c/o Raul F. Rodriguez
300 S.W. 124 Ave.
Miami, FL 33184-1418

Established in 2000 in FL.
Donor: Raul F. Rodriguez.
Foundation type: Operating foundation.
Financial data (yr. ended 12/31/12): Assets, $8,337,240 (M); expenditures, $1,048,423; qualifying distributions, $1,017,225; giving activities include $799,914 for 38 grants (high: $312,900; low: $330), and $14,050 for 3 grants to individuals (high: $7,000; low: $3,000).
Fields of interest: Higher education; Scholarships/financial aid.
Limitations: Applications not accepted. Giving primarily in Miami, FL.
Application information: Unsolicited requests for funds not accepted.
Directors: Nidia Maldonado Rodriguez; Raul Francisco Rodriguez.
EIN: 650838191

2281
The Rayonier Foundation ✧
(formerly The ITT Rayonier Foundation)
1301 Riverplace Blvd., Ste. 2300
Jacksonville, FL 32207-9062 (904) 357-9100
Contact: Charles H. Hood, Pres.

Incorporated in 1952 in NY.
Donors: ITT Rayonier Inc.; Rayonier Inc.
Foundation type: Company-sponsored foundation.
Financial data (yr. ended 12/31/13): Assets, $6,015,905 (M); gifts received, $100,000; expenditures, $750,924; qualifying distributions, $725,070; giving activities include $725,070 for 38 grants (high: $3,000; low: $1,250).
Purpose and activities: The foundation supports organizations involved with arts and culture, education, the environment, health, human services, community economic development, civic affairs, and science and awards college scholarships to individuals.
Fields of interest: Museums; Performing arts; Arts; Elementary/secondary education; Higher education; Engineering school/education; Education, reading; Education; Environment, natural resources; Environment, forests; Environmental education; Environment; Hospitals (general); Health care; American Red Cross; Children/youth, services; Human services; Community/economic development; United Ways and Federated Giving Programs; Chemistry; Engineering/technology; Science; Public affairs.
Type of support: General/operating support; Continuing support; Annual campaigns; Capital campaigns; Equipment; Program development; Conferences/seminars; Scholarship funds; Employee-related scholarships; Scholarships—to individuals; Matching/challenge support.
Limitations: Applications accepted. Giving primarily in areas of company operations in Nassau County, FL, Wayne County, GA, and the Olympic Peninsula, WA, area. No support for religious organizations, advocacy organizations, fraternal or political organizations, or discriminatory organizations. No grants for chairs or professorships, courtesy or goodwill advertising for festival participation, tickets, telethons, raffles, auction, or memberships.
Publications: Application guidelines.
Application information: Grants range from $250 to $2,500. Application form required.
Initial approach: Completed application form
Copies of proposal: 1
Deadline(s): Oct. 31 for northwest recipients; Dec. 13 for southeast recipients
Board meeting date(s): Feb.
Final notification: May. 1
Officers and Directors:* Paul G. Boynton,* Chair.; Charles H. Hood,* Pres.; W. Edwin Frazier III,* Secy.; Macdonald Auguste, Co-Treas.; Hans E. Vanden Noort, Cont. and Co-Treas.; Jack Kriesel; Charles Margiotta; Helen Rowan; Lynn N. Wilson.
EIN: 136064462

Selected grants: The following grants are a representative sample of this grantmaker's funding activity:
$101,182 to United Way of Northeast Florida, Jacksonville, FL, 2011.
$83,471 to United Way, South Georgia, Waycross, GA, 2011.
$4,000 to Altamaha Technical College, Jesup, GA, 2011.
$2,500 to Georgia Southern University, Statesboro, GA, 2011.
$2,500 to University of Georgia, Athens, GA, 2011.
$2,500 to Valdosta State University, Valdosta, GA, 2011.
$2,500 to Western Washington University, Bellingham, WA, 2011.
$2,000 to Stetson University, DeLand, FL, 2011.
$1,300 to United Way of Clallam County, Port Angeles, WA, 2011.
$1,000 to Community Foundation, Jacksonville, FL, 2011.

2282
Carmen Rebozo Foundation, Inc. ✧
6274 S.W. 35th St.
Miami, FL 33155-4934
Contact: Olga Guilarte, V.P.

Established in 1985 in FL.
Donors: Charles G. Rebozo†; Mary Bouterse†.
Foundation type: Independent foundation.
Financial data (yr. ended 06/30/13): Assets, $18,314,578 (M); expenditures, $967,527; qualifying distributions, $867,125; giving activities include $867,125 for grants.
Purpose and activities: Giving primarily for a boys and girls club, as well as for education and children, youth and social services.
Fields of interest: Education; Boys & girls clubs; Human services; Children/youth, services.
Limitations: Applications not accepted. Giving primarily in FL.
Application information: Contributes only to pre-selected organizations.
Officers: Charles F. Rebozo, Pres.; James Bernhardt, V.P.; E. Andres Guilarte, V.P.; Olga Guilarte, V.P.; Teresa Rebozo Hood, V.P.; Michael Rebozo, V.P.; Thomas Rebozo, Jr., V.P.; William Rebozo, Jr., V.P.
EIN: 592667397

2283
Regal Foundation Inc. ✧ ☆
2300 Jetport Dr.
Orlando, FL 32809-7800

Established in 1984 in FL.
Donors: Regal Marine; Gene Kandel; Paul Kuck Trust; Youth With A Mission; Timothy Kuck; Regal Marine Industries, Inc.
Foundation type: Independent foundation.
Financial data (yr. ended 07/31/13): Assets, $13,496,737 (M); gifts received, $616,706; expenditures, $660,341; qualifying distributions, $629,939; giving activities include $607,880 for 22 grants (high: $450,000; low: $250), and $15,703 for foundation-administered programs.
Purpose and activities: Giving primarily for Christian organizations, and organizations that assist needy poor people.
Fields of interest: Human services; Community/economic development; Christian agencies & churches.
Limitations: Applications not accepted. Giving primarily in FL, GA and TX. No grants to individuals.
Application information: Unsolicited requests for funds not accepted.
Officers: Duane Kuck, Pres.; Tim Kuck, V.P. and Secy.; Pam Biddle, Treas.
EIN: 581662076
Selected grants: The following grants are a representative sample of this grantmaker's funding activity:
$34,260 to One Mission Society, Greenwood, IN, 2011.
$25,000 to Marriage and Family Foundation, Norcross, GA, 2011.
$12,000 to Frontline Outreach, Orlando, FL, 2011.
$10,000 to Prison Fellowship Ministries, Lansdowne, VA, 2010.
$5,200 to Campus Crusade for Christ International, Orlando, FL, 2011.
$5,000 to Care Net, Lansdowne, VA, 2011.
$5,000 to Champions for Life, Dallas, TX, 2011.
$5,000 to Florida Family Council, Tampa, FL, 2011.
$3,000 to Fellowship of Christian Athletes, Winter Park, FL, 2011.
$1,000 to Choose Life, Ocala, FL, 2011.
$1,000 to Liberty Counsel, Orlando, FL, 2011.

2284
The Revs Institute for Automotive Research, Inc. ✧
2500 S. Horseshoe Dr.
Naples, FL 34104-6119 (239) 643-5783
FAX: (239) 643-7167;
E-mail: info@revsinstitute.org; Main URL: http://www.revsinstitute.org/

Established in FL.
Donors: Miles C. Collier; Martin D. Gruss; Mill Park Foundation, Inc.
Foundation type: Operating foundation.
Financial data (yr. ended 12/31/12): Assets, $716,530 (M); gifts received, $2,968,374; expenditures, $2,430,037; qualifying distributions, $2,838,197; giving activities include $2,000,000 for 1 grant, and $838,197 for 2 foundation-administered programs.
Purpose and activities: Giving primarily to Leland Stanford Junior University for the Revs program.
Fields of interest: Education.
Limitations: Applications not accepted. Giving primarily in Stanford, CA.
Application information: Unsolicited requests for funds not accepted.
Officers: Miles C. Collier, Chair. and Pres.; William E. Thomas, Exec. V.P.; L. Scott George, V.P.; Sandra D. Walker, Secy.; Michael B. Lenzner, Treas.
EIN: 263056526

2285
Marshall and Vera Lea Rinker Foundation, Inc. ✧
380 Columbia Dr., Ste. 110
West Palm Beach, FL 33409-1977

Reincorporated in 1998 in FL.
Foundation type: Independent foundation.
Financial data (yr. ended 12/31/13): Assets, $31,581,922 (M); expenditures, $1,620,621; qualifying distributions, $1,351,052; giving activities include $1,231,981 for 7 grants (high: $53,181; low: $10,000).
Fields of interest: Higher education; Human services.
Type of support: Capital campaigns; Building/renovation; Land acquisition.
Limitations: Applications not accepted. Giving primarily in FL, with emphasis on south and central FL. No grants to individuals.
Application information: Contributes only to pre-selected organizations.
Officers and Directors:* John J. Rinker,* Pres.; Sheila A. Rinker,* V.P.; Michael J. Stevens,* Secy.-Treas.; R. Hagan Kohler; R. Michael Strickland.
EIN: 311610196
Selected grants: The following grants are a representative sample of this grantmaker's funding activity:
$925,000 to Palm Beach Atlantic University, West Palm Beach, FL, 2012. For athletic complex capital campaign.
$258,391 to Palm Beach Atlantic University, West Palm Beach, FL, 2012. For athletic complex endowment fund.
$10,000 to Rollins College, Winter Park, FL, 2012. For Tennis Scholarship Endowment Fund.
$10,000 to Rollins College, Winter Park, FL, 2012. For Marshall and Vera Lea Rinker Admissions Building Endowment.

2286
Marshall E. Rinker, Sr. Foundation, Inc. ✧
310 Okeechobee Blvd., No. 100
West Palm Beach, FL 33401-6419
Contact: Fdn. Admin.

Established in 1998 in FL.
Donor: M.E. Rinker, Sr.
Foundation type: Independent foundation.
Financial data (yr. ended 12/31/13): Assets, $30,633,127 (M); expenditures, $1,591,264; qualifying distributions, $1,400,251; giving activities include $1,286,560 for 30 grants (high: $250,000; low: $400).
Purpose and activities: Giving primarily for higher education.
Fields of interest: Higher education; Education; Health care; Community/economic development; Religion.
Type of support: Capital campaigns; Endowments.
Limitations: Applications not accepted. Giving primarily in FL. No grants to individuals.
Application information: Unsolicited requests for funds not accepted.
Board meeting date(s): Quarterly
Officers and Directors:* David B. Rinker,* Pres.; Leighan R. Rinker,* 1st V.P.; Paul C. Bremer,* Secy.-Treas.; Marshall M. Criser; Richard A. Krause; Christopher R. Rinker; David S. Rinker.
EIN: 650871532

2287
River Branch Foundation ✧
177 4th Ave. N., 2nd Fl.
Jacksonville, FL 32250-7016 (904) 396-5831
E-mail: JLeroux@RiverBranchFoundation.org; Main URL: http://riverbranchfoundation.org/

Trust established in 1963 in NJ.

Donors: J. Seward Johnson 1951 and 1961 Charitable Trusts; The Atlantic Foundation; Jennifer Johnson Duke.
Foundation type: Independent foundation.
Financial data (yr. ended 12/31/12): Assets, $17,813,732 (M); gifts received, $8,105; expenditures, $1,270,573; qualifying distributions, $1,135,848; giving activities include $1,135,848 for grants.
Purpose and activities: Giving primarily for human services, children's services, education, the arts and the environment.
Fields of interest: Higher education; Environment; Children/youth, services.
Limitations: Applications accepted. Giving primarily in the Jacksonville, FL, area. No grants to individuals.
Publications: Application guidelines.
Application information: Application form not required.
Initial approach: Letter
Copies of proposal: 1
Deadline(s): None
Director: Jennifer Johnson Duke.
Trustees: Jason Gregg; Simon Gregg; Judith Leroux.
EIN: 226054887

2288
Riverside Hospital Foundation Inc. ✧
(formerly Riverside Foundation, Inc.)
9090 Barrister Ct.
Jacksonville, FL 32257-5068 (904) 982-3676
Contact: Helen Werking, Exec. Dir.
Main URL: http://riversidehospitalfdn.org/

Established in 1992 in FL.
Foundation type: Independent foundation.
Financial data (yr. ended 12/31/13): Assets, $12,860,015 (M); expenditures, $634,390; qualifying distributions, $540,893; giving activities include $540,893 for 1 grant.
Purpose and activities: Giving primarily to healthcare organizations.
Fields of interest: Health care; Health organizations, association; Foundations (community).
Limitations: Applications accepted. Giving limited to the five-county area of northeast FL. No grants to individuals.
Application information: Application form required.
Initial approach: Contact foundation for application form
Deadline(s): None
Board meeting date(s): Quarterly
Officers: W. Randall Mann, Pres.; William J. Knauer, V.P.; Katy Towers, Treas.; Helen Werking, Exec. Dir.
Directors: James H. Abernathy; Catherine Bauman; Robert Colyer; Mark Constantine; Lorraine H. Dajani; Clint Dawkins; Robert S. Franco; H. Thomas Platt; Gresham Stoneburner; Alonzo Walton; David Williams.
EIN: 593057267

2289
RJKB Family Charitable Foundation, Inc.
4000 Ponce De Leon Blvd.
Coral Gables, FL 33146 (305) 443-3354
Contact: E. Richard Yulman, Dir.
Application address: 555 Leucadendra Dr., Coral Gables, FL 33516, tel.: (305) 443-3354

Established in 2006 in FL.
Donors: Janet K. Yulman; E. Richard Yulman; Beth Karmin Kaplan.
Foundation type: Independent foundation.
Financial data (yr. ended 12/31/12): Assets, $16,818,899 (M); gifts received, $1,000,000; expenditures, $1,083,708; qualifying distributions, $916,000; giving activities include $916,000 for 11 grants (high: $547,000; low: $500).
Fields of interest: Jewish federated giving programs; Jewish agencies & synagogues.
Limitations: Applications accepted. Giving primarily in Miami, FL.
Application information: Application form required.
Initial approach: Contact foundation
Deadline(s): None
Directors: Kate J. Williamson; E. Richard Yulman.
EIN: 205161254

2290
J. David and Kathleen A. Roberts Family Foundation, Inc ✧ ☆
6744 Pelican Bay Blvd.
Naples, FL 34108-8211

Established in 2001 in OH.
Donors: J. David Roberts; Kathleen A. Roberts.
Foundation type: Independent foundation.
Financial data (yr. ended 12/31/13): Assets, $0 (M); expenditures, $1,047,682; qualifying distributions, $1,041,749; giving activities include $1,041,749 for 9 grants (high: $990,749; low: $1,500).
Fields of interest: Education; Human services; Philanthropy/voluntarism.
Limitations: Applications not accepted. No grants to individuals.
Application information: Unsolicited requests for funds not accepted.
Officers and Directors:* J. David Roberts,* Pres. and Treas.; Kathleen A. Roberts,* V.P. and Secy.; Adam J. Roberts; Jill D. Roberts; Megan E. Roberts; Scott D. Roberts.
EIN: 311808573
Selected grants: The following grants are a representative sample of this grantmaker's funding activity:
$5,000 to Smile Train, New York, NY, 2011.

2291
C. J. Robinson Trust ✧
P.O. Box 1908
Orlando, FL 32802-1908

Supporting organization of Church Schools in the Diocese of Virginia, the Diocese of Virginia Episcopal Church Trustees Fund, George Mason University Foundation, and the Protestant Episcopal Theological Seminary.
Foundation type: Independent foundation.
Financial data (yr. ended 12/31/13): Assets, $18,554,857 (M); expenditures, $1,015,814; qualifying distributions, $911,812; giving activities include $828,672 for 4 grants (high: $414,336; low: $103,584).
Fields of interest: Higher education; Protestant agencies & churches.
Limitations: Applications not accepted. Giving limited to VA. No grants to individuals.
Application information: Contributes only to pre-selected organizations.
Trustee: SunTrust Banks, Inc.
EIN: 546209842
Selected grants: The following grants are a representative sample of this grantmaker's funding activity:
$99,177 to Protestant Episcopal Theological Seminary in Virginia, Alexandria, VA, 2011. For general charitable purpose.

2292
Rooms to Go Children's Fund ✧
11540 Hwy. 92 E.
Seffner, FL 33584-7346 (813) 623-5400
Contact: Lewis Stein, V.P.

Established in 1998 in FL.
Donors: Jeffrey Seaman; Julie Seaman; Rooms To Go, Inc.; roomstogo.com.
Foundation type: Independent foundation.
Financial data (yr. ended 12/31/12): Assets, $1,027,361 (M); gifts received, $1,000,000; expenditures, $522,908; qualifying distributions, $500,689; giving activities include $500,689 for grants.
Purpose and activities: Giving primarily for health organizations, and children, youth and social services.
Fields of interest: Hospitals (general); Health organizations, association; Cancer research; Human services; Children/youth, services.
Type of support: General/operating support.
Limitations: Applications accepted. Giving in the U.S., with emphasis on FL.
Application information: Application form not required.
Initial approach: Proposal
Deadline(s): None
Officers and Directors:* Jeffrey Seaman,* Pres.; Lewis Stein,* V.P.; J. Michael Kettle,* Secy.-Treas.
EIN: 650878894

2293
Root Family Foundation ✧ ☆
275 Clyde Morris Blvd.
Ormond Beach, FL 32174-5977

Established in 1997 in FL.
Donor: Susan Root Feibleman.
Foundation type: Independent foundation.
Financial data (yr. ended 12/31/13): Assets, $1,727,534 (M); gifts received, $1,187,110; expenditures, $572,432; qualifying distributions, $564,698; giving activities include $561,691 for 11 grants (high: $527,191; low: $500).
Fields of interest: Museums (art); Arts; Human services.
Type of support: General/operating support.
Limitations: Applications not accepted. Giving primarily in FL. No grants to individuals.
Application information: Unsolicited requests for funds not accepted.
Trustee: William J. Voges.
EIN: 593485274

2294
The Harris Rosen Foundation, Inc. ✧
9840 International Dr.
Orlando, FL 32819-8293

Established in 1987 in FL.

Donors: Harris Rosen; Daytona International Speedway; Florida Hospital Medical Center; Southern Area of The Links, Inc.; Wayne M. Densch Charitable Trust; National Council of Negro Women; The Procter & Gamble Co.; The Links, Inc.; Rosen Hotels & Resorts, Inc.; Busch Entertainment Corp.; Diocese of Orlando; Southern Wine & Spirits of Florida, Inc.; Coca Cocal Bottling.
Foundation type: Independent foundation.
Financial data (yr. ended 12/31/13): Assets, $14,266,302 (M); gifts received, $153,176; expenditures, $1,288,485; qualifying distributions, $1,288,485; giving activities include $1,284,109 for 68 grants (high: $500,000; low: $100).
Fields of interest: Higher education; Education; Jewish federated giving programs.
Type of support: Scholarship funds.
Limitations: Applications not accepted. Giving primarily in FL.
Application information: Contributes only to pre-selected organizations.
Officers and Directors:* Harris Rosen,* Pres.; Frank Santos,* Secy.-Treas.; S. Ashley Bacot.
EIN: 592890420
Selected grants: The following grants are a representative sample of this grantmaker's funding activity:
$1,000 to Orange County Sheriffs Office, Orlando, FL, 2012. For Sheriff Community Safety Expo.
$250 to Headstrong Foundation, Holmes, PA, 2012. For cancer research fund.

2295
The Stanley and Susan Rosenblatt Family Foundation ✧

c/o Susan Rosenblatt, Esq.
201 S. Biscayne Blvd., Rm. 1318
Miami, FL 33131-4333

Established in 2001 in FL.
Donors: Stanley M. Rosenblatt; Susan Rosenblatt.
Foundation type: Operating foundation.
Financial data (yr. ended 12/31/13): Assets, $721,898 (M); gifts received, $150,360; expenditures, $471,520; qualifying distributions, $448,849; giving activities include $448,849 for 96 grants (high: $36,000; low: $36).
Fields of interest: Elementary/secondary education; Higher education; Education; Medical research, institute; Human services; Children/youth, services; Developmentally disabled, centers & services; Jewish federated giving programs; Jewish agencies & synagogues; Economically disadvantaged.
Limitations: Applications not accepted. Giving primarily in FL and New York, NY. No grants to individuals.
Application information: Contributes only to pre-selected organizations.
Officers and Trustees: Stanley M. Rosenblatt,* Pres.; Susan Rosenblatt,* Secy.
EIN: 656355846

2296
The Roskamp Foundation Irrevocable Trust ✧

1226 N. Tamiami Trail. Ste. 302
Sarasota, FL 34236-2461

Established in 1996 in AZ and FL.
Donors: Robert G. Roskamp; David Hagelstein; Daniel Flores; Rebecca John Flores; Dr. Gary Kompothecras; Diane Sampson Roskamp; Music Festival for Mental Health; Vanguard Charitable Endowment Program; Roskamp Charities, Inc.; SCW Communities, LLC; Kompo Family Company, LLC; International Mental Health Research Organization; Star Scientific.
Foundation type: Independent foundation.
Financial data (yr. ended 12/31/12): Assets, $21,796,729 (M); gifts received, $462,500; expenditures, $2,253,075; qualifying distributions, $1,718,729; giving activities include $1,718,729 for grants.
Fields of interest: Education; Mental health/crisis services.
Type of support: General/operating support.
Limitations: Applications not accepted. Giving primarily in FL. No grants to individuals.
Application information: unsolicited requests for funds not accepted.
Officer: Robert G. Roskamp, Pres.
Trustee: Diane Sampson Roskamp.
Director: Mike Mullan.
EIN: 656206042

2297
Rothberg Family Charitable Foundation for Children's Diseases ✧ ☆

7551 Isla Verde Way
Delray Beach, FL 33446-4346
Contact: M. Rothberg

Established in CT.
Donors: Jonathan M. Rothberg; Henry M. Rothberg; Lilliam R. Rothberg.
Foundation type: Independent foundation.
Financial data (yr. ended 12/31/13): Assets, $27,052,194 (M); expenditures, $1,077,346; qualifying distributions, $1,074,700; giving activities include $1,070,000 for 6 grants (high: $400,000; low: $50,000).
Purpose and activities: Giving primarily for the support of research relating to, and the development of medications for the treatment and cure of Tuberous Sclerosis Complex (TSC).
Fields of interest: Education; Health organizations; Medical research.
Type of support: Research.
Limitations: Applications not accepted. Giving primarily in CT, MD and PA. No grants to individuals.
Application information: Unsolicited requests for funds not accepted.
Trustees: Jonathan M. Rothberg; Michael J. Rothberg.
EIN: 061519674
Selected grants: The following grants are a representative sample of this grantmaker's funding activity:
$200,000 to Carnegie Mellon University, Pittsburgh, PA, 2013. To further TSC research.
$200,000 to Tuberous Sclerosis Alliance, Silver Spring, MD, 2013. To further TSC research.
$150,000 to Yale University, New Haven, CT, 2013. To further TSC research.
$70,000 to University of Pennsylvania, Philadelphia, PA, 2013. To further TSC research.
$50,000 to LAM Foundation, Cincinnati, OH, 2013. For LAM Research.

2298
Rothman Foundation Inc. ✧

201 N. Franklin St., Ste. 2800
Tampa, FL 33602

Established in 2006 in FL; a successor to The Rothman Foundation.
Donors: The Rothman Foundation; Robert Rothman.
Foundation type: Independent foundation.
Financial data (yr. ended 12/31/12): Assets, $2,087,643 (M); gifts received, $2,071,349; expenditures, $982,365; qualifying distributions, $975,000; giving activities include $975,000 for 5 grants (high: $500,000; low: $50,000).
Purpose and activities: Giving primarily for higher education.
Fields of interest: Museums (art); Museums (history); Higher education; Cancer.
Limitations: Applications not accepted. Giving primarily in Tampa, FL. No grants to individuals.
Application information: Unsolicited requests fopr funds not accepted.
Trustees: Margaret Rothman; Robert Rothman.
EIN: 161779570

2299
J. M. Rubin Foundation, Inc. ✧

505 S. Flagler Dr., Ste. 1320
West Palm Beach, FL 33401-5951 (561) 833-3309
FAX: (561) 833-3647; E-mail: info@jmrf.org; Main URL: http://www.jmrf.org

Established in 1973 in FL.
Donor: Jacob M. Rubin†.
Foundation type: Independent foundation.
Financial data (yr. ended 11/30/13): Assets, $55,034,521 (M); expenditures, $3,071,752; qualifying distributions, $2,363,493; giving activities include $860,500 for 49 grants (high: $200,000; low: $500), and $1,107,025 for grants to individuals.
Purpose and activities: Giving primarily for scholarships to residents of Palm Beach County, FL, to use at any recognized educational institution.
Fields of interest: Higher education; Human services.
Type of support: Scholarship funds.
Limitations: Giving primarily in Palm Beach, FL; scholarships limited to U.S. citizens who are residents of Palm Beach County, FL.
Publications: Application guidelines.
Application information: Scholarships are paid directly to the educational institution. Application form required.
Initial approach: Complete online application
Deadline(s): Mar. 1 for scholarships; June 1 for on-line renewal applications
Final notification: May
Officers and Trustees:* Robert T. Owens,* Chair.; Mary S. Harper,* C.E.O. and Pres.; Kimberly L. Harris, V.P. and Treas.; Edward R. Griffin,* Secy.
EIN: 591958240
Selected grants: The following grants are a representative sample of this grantmaker's funding activity:
$200,000 to Palm Beach Atlantic University, West Palm Beach, FL, 2011.
$25,000 to Adopt-A-Family of the Palm Beaches, Lake Worth, FL, 2011.

2300
Walter and Lucille Rubin Foundation Inc. ✧
2101 N.W. Corporate Blvd., Ste. 317
Boca Raton, FL 33431-7319

Established in 2007 in FL.
Donors: Roberta Rubin Trust; Richard Rubin Trust; Ronald Rubin Trust; Randi Rubin Trust; Rubin Trust UAD; GI Research Institute; John Hopkins Medicine; BRRH Foundation; American Tinnitus Association; Mayo Clinic; Larger than Life USA; UM Dept. of Neurology Epilepsy Research; Jarc Endowment fund; Smithsonian; Epilepsy Foundation.
Foundation type: Independent foundation.
Financial data (yr. ended 12/31/13): Assets, $14,075,424 (M); expenditures, $1,007,860; qualifying distributions, $699,150; giving activities include $699,150 for 34 grants (high: $250,000; low: $500).
Fields of interest: Arts; Health organizations; Human services; Jewish federated giving programs.
Limitations: Applications not accepted.
Application information: Unsolicited requests for funds not accepted.
Directors: Lucille Rubin; Walter Rubin.
EIN: 260369836
Selected grants: The following grants are a representative sample of this grantmaker's funding activity:
$175,000 to Mayo Clinic, Rochester, MN, 2011.
$100,000 to Brain and Behavior Research Foundation, New York, NY, 2011.
$1,000 to Alzheimers Association, Atlanta, GA, 2011.

2301
Robert Russell Memorial Foundation ✧
c/o Norman H. Lipoff, Esq.
1221 Brickell Ave., 17th Fl.
Miami, FL 33131-2804 (305) 579-0503
Contact: Norman H. Lipoff, Chair.
FAX: (305) 961-5503; E-mail: Lipoffn@Gtlaw.com

Established in 1984 in FL.
Donor: Robert Russell†.
Foundation type: Independent foundation.
Financial data (yr. ended 08/31/13): Assets, $15,647,581 (M); expenditures, $1,141,767; qualifying distributions, $968,470; giving activities include $808,000 for 77 grants (high: $250,000; low: $1,000).
Purpose and activities: Support primarily for Jewish and Israeli programs and agencies, including education, social or research programs, capital projects, religious tolerance, Middle East studies, Jewish leadership development, and interfaith activity.
Fields of interest: Jewish federated giving programs.
International interests: Israel.
Type of support: General/operating support; Continuing support; Annual campaigns; Capital campaigns; Building/renovation; Program development; Fellowships; Scholarship funds; Matching/challenge support.
Limitations: Applications accepted. Giving primarily in the Miami-Dade County, FL, area; limited giving also in Israel. No grants to individuals.
Publications: Application guidelines.
Application information: Application form required.
Initial approach: Letter
Copies of proposal: 5
Deadline(s): Mar. 31
Board meeting date(s): May
Final notification: Following board meeting
Officer and Trustees:* Norman H. Lipoff,* Chair.; Joel Goldman; Bill Lehman; Jacob Solomon; Harry Weitzer; Northern Trust Bank, N.A.
EIN: 592486579
Selected grants: The following grants are a representative sample of this grantmaker's funding activity:
$250,000 to Jewish Federation, Greater Miami, Miami, FL, 2011.
$36,000 to Jewish Federation, Greater Miami, Miami, FL, 2011.
$35,000 to Alexander Muss Institute for Israel Education, Rockville Centre, NY, 2011. For general support.
$20,000 to Camp Ramah Darom, Atlanta, GA, 2011.
$20,000 to Hillel: The Foundation for Jewish Campus Life, Gainesville, FL, 2011. For general support.
$15,000 to Friends of Yemin Orde, Bethesda, MD, 2011. For general support.
$10,000 to Jewish Telegraphic Agency, New York, NY, 2011. For general support.
$6,000 to Pardes Institute of Jewish Studies North America, New York, NY, 2011.
$5,000 to New Israel Fund, Washington, DC, 2011.
$5,000 to Schechter Institutes, Philadelphia, PA, 2011.

2302
The Ryder System Charitable Foundation, Inc. ✧
11690 N.W. 105th St.
Miami, FL 33178-1103 (305) 500-3031
E-mail: foundation@ryder.com; Main URL: http://www.ryder.com/aboutus_cinfo_arc.shtml

Established in 1984 in FL.
Donor: Ryder System, Inc.
Foundation type: Company-sponsored foundation.
Financial data (yr. ended 12/31/13): Assets, $224,851 (M); gifts received, $1,163,411; expenditures, $1,089,141; qualifying distributions, $1,089,141; giving activities include $1,089,141 for 91 grants (high: $137,500; low: $50).
Purpose and activities: The foundation supports organizations involved with arts and culture, education, health, disaster relief, human services, community development, and civic affairs.
Fields of interest: Performing arts; Arts; Higher education; Education; Hospitals (general); Health care; Disasters, preparedness/services; Boy scouts; American Red Cross; Salvation Army; Human services; Community/economic development; United Ways and Federated Giving Programs; Public affairs.
Type of support: General/operating support; Annual campaigns; Capital campaigns; Building/renovation; Scholarship funds; Employee volunteer services; Sponsorships; Employee matching gifts; Employee-related scholarships; Grants to individuals; In-kind gifts.
Limitations: Applications accepted. Giving primarily in areas of company operations in Los Angeles, CA, southern FL, Atlanta, GA, St. Louis, MO, Cincinnati, OH, and Dallas, TX.
Publications: Application guidelines; Corporate giving report.
Application information: Application form required.
Initial approach: Proposal
Copies of proposal: 1
Deadline(s): None
Board meeting date(s): Annually and as needed
Final notification: Within 60 days
Officers and Directoes: Gregory T. Swienton,* Chair., Pres., and C.E.O.; David B. Bruce, C.A.O. and Exec. Dir.; Robert D. Fatovic,* V.P. and Corp. Secy.; W. Daniel Susik, V.P. and Treas.; Art A. Garcia,* V.P.; Gregory F. Greene,* V.P.
Number of staff: 1 full-time professional; 1 full-time support.
EIN: 592462315
Selected grants: The following grants are a representative sample of this grantmaker's funding activity:
$5,000 to University of Virginia, Darden School, Charlottesville, VA, 2012.

2303
Sack Family Foundation Irrevocable Trust ✧
415 L'Ambiance Dr., Apt. PH-D
Longboat Key, FL 34228-3916

Established in 1996 in FL.
Donor: Burton M. Sack.
Foundation type: Independent foundation.
Financial data (yr. ended 12/31/13): Assets, $5,656,196 (M); expenditures, $544,141; qualifying distributions, $455,600; giving activities include $455,600 for 52 grants (high: $400,000; low: $50).
Purpose and activities: Giving primarily for higher education and medical-related purposes.
Fields of interest: Performing arts; Higher education; Education, services; Health care; Human services; Children/youth, services; Military/veterans' organizations.
Type of support: Annual campaigns; Capital campaigns; Building/renovation.
Limitations: Applications not accepted. Giving in the U.S., with emphasis on FL, MA, and NY. No grants to individuals.
Application information: Contributes only to pre-selected organizations.
Board meeting date(s): Varies
Trustee: Burton M. Sack.
EIN: 656217967
Selected grants: The following grants are a representative sample of this grantmaker's funding activity:
$100,100 to Gulf Coast Community Foundation, Gulfport, MS, 2011.

2304
The Sage & Dice Foundation ✧
c/o William C. Stone
425 Gulf Shore Blvd. N.
Naples, FL 34102-5548

Established in 2005 in CT.
Donor: William C. Stone.
Foundation type: Independent foundation.
Financial data (yr. ended 12/31/12): Assets, $1,563,921 (M); expenditures, $1,253,398; qualifying distributions, $1,251,242; giving activities include $1,250,523 for 8 grants (high: $1,000,000; low: $300).
Fields of interest: Education; United Ways and Federated Giving Programs.
Type of support: General/operating support.

Limitations: Applications not accepted. Giving primarily in CT and IN. No grants to individuals.
Application information: Contributes only to pre-selected organizations.
Trustees: Mary R. Stone; William C. Stone.
EIN: 206771152
Selected grants: The following grants are a representative sample of this grantmaker's funding activity:
$1,000,000 to Archdiocese of Hartford, Hartford, CT, 2012. For Inner City Parochial Schools.
$139,223 to Celebrate Windsor, Windsor, CT, 2012. For general support.

2305
Lawrence A. Sanders Foundation, Inc. ✧
c/o Brede
1900 Corporate Blvd. N.W., Ste. 201E
Boca Raton, FL 33431

Established in 1991 in FL.
Donors: Lawrence Sanders Enterprises; Lawrence A. Sanders Rev. Trust; Lawrence A. Sanders Trust.
Foundation type: Independent foundation.
Financial data (yr. ended 12/31/13): Assets, $20,570,740 (M); expenditures, $1,126,378; qualifying distributions, $1,039,823; giving activities include $990,538 for 67 grants (high: $52,500; low: $100).
Purpose and activities: Giving primarily for organizations involved with education and human services, some funding for the arts.
Fields of interest: Arts; Education; Human services; YM/YWCAs & YM/YWHAs; Foundations (community); United Ways and Federated Giving Programs; Catholic agencies & churches.
Limitations: Applications not accepted. Giving primarily in FL. No grants to individuals.
Application information: Unsolicited requests for funds not accepted.
Directors: J. Daniel Brede, Esq.; Helen Brede; Timothy Devlin.
EIN: 650270066
Selected grants: The following grants are a representative sample of this grantmaker's funding activity:
$25,000 to Kiwanis Club of West Palm Beach Foundation, West Palm Beach, FL, 2012. For Contribution Designated to Scholarship Fund.
$5,000 to United Way of Palm Beach County, Boynton Beach, FL, 2012. For contribution to General Fund to Support Charitable Mission.

2306
Harvey and Phyllis Sandler Foundation, Inc. ✧
2080 N.W. Boca Raton Blvd., Ste. 6
Boca Raton, FL 33431-7445

Established in 1993 in FL.
Donor: Harvey Sandler.
Foundation type: Independent foundation.
Financial data (yr. ended 12/31/13): Assets, $9,003,340 (M); gifts received, $167,524; expenditures, $901,840; qualifying distributions, $481,315; giving activities include $481,315 for 60 grants (high: $180,350; low: $20).
Fields of interest: Education; Hospitals (general); Medical research, institute; Human services; Jewish federated giving programs.
Limitations: Applications not accepted. Giving primarily in FL and New York, NY. No grants to individuals.
Application information: Contributes only to pre-selected organizations.
Officers and Directors:* Harvey Sandler,* Pres.; Phyllis Sandler,* Secy.
EIN: 650452582
Selected grants: The following grants are a representative sample of this grantmaker's funding activity:
$1,531,910 to Boca Raton Regional Hospital, Boca Raton, FL, 2010.
$1,516,020 to Boca Raton Regional Hospital, Boca Raton, FL, 2011.
$500,815 to Jewish Federation of South Palm Beach County, Boca Raton, FL, 2011.
$10,000 to Janet Burros Memorial Foundation, New York, NY, 2011.
$10,000 to Jewish Community Center in Manhattan, New York, NY, 2010.

2307
Sansing Foundation, Inc. ✧
6200 Pensacola Blvd.
Pensacola, FL 32505-2214

Established in 1995 in FL.
Donors: Robert C. Sansing; Peggy L. Sansing.
Foundation type: Independent foundation.
Financial data (yr. ended 12/31/13): Assets, $488,710 (M); gifts received, $1,000,000; expenditures, $1,011,480; qualifying distributions, $1,008,293; giving activities include $1,008,293 for 70 grants (high: $250,000; low: $100).
Purpose and activities: Giving primarily for education, health organizations, children, youth, and social services, Christian organizations, and to Baptist organizations and churches.
Fields of interest: Education; Health organizations, association; Human services; Children/youth, services; Christian agencies & churches; Protestant agencies & churches.
Limitations: Applications not accepted. Giving in the U.S., with emphasis on AL and FL. No grants to individuals.
Application information: Unsolicited requests for funds not accepted.
Officers and Trustees:* Robert C. Sansing,* Pres.; Peggy L. Sansing,* V.P.; Thomas M. Bizzell.
EIN: 593284550
Selected grants: The following grants are a representative sample of this grantmaker's funding activity:
$5,500 to Smile Train, Washington, DC, 2011. For general fund.

2308
The Saunders Foundation ✧
P.O. Box 10477
Tampa, FL 33679-0477 (813) 229-0804
Contact: Kathleen J. Belmonte, Tr.

Established in 1970 in FL.
Donors: William N. Saunders†; Ruby Lee Saunders†.
Foundation type: Independent foundation.
Financial data (yr. ended 12/31/13): Assets, $15,383,347 (M); expenditures, $847,458; qualifying distributions, $739,730; giving activities include $672,500 for 31 grants (high: $150,000; low: $2,000).
Purpose and activities: Giving primarily for the performing arts and museums; funding also for higher education, and health organizations.
Fields of interest: Museums (history); Museums (science/technology); Performing arts centers; Performing arts, theater; Arts; Higher education; Health organizations, association; Human services.
Type of support: Building/renovation; Program development; Scholarship funds; Matching/challenge support.
Limitations: Applications accepted. Giving primarily in the Tampa Bay, FL area. No support for organizations that promote sports or athletic competition. No grants to individuals, or for fellowships, travel projects, or operating funds.
Publications: Application guidelines.
Application information: Application form required.
Initial approach: Contact foundation for application form
Copies of proposal: 2
Deadline(s): None
Board meeting date(s): 1st Wed. of each month
Trustees: Kathleen J. Belmonte; Fred Dobbins; George B. Howell III; Solon F. O'Neal, Jr.
EIN: 596152326
Selected grants: The following grants are a representative sample of this grantmaker's funding activity:
$150,000 to University of Tampa, Tampa, FL, 2012. For grant award for nursing skills laboratory pursuant to board of trustees' approval 1/4/12.
$25,000 to Boy Scouts of America, Gulf Ridge Council, Tampa, FL, 2012. For Matching Funds grant award for scoutreach Program pursuant to board of trustees' approval 4/6/12.
$25,000 to Lowry Park Zoological Society of Tampa, Tampa, FL, 2012. For grant award for upgrades and renovation to manatee and aquatic center and David A. Straz Jr. Manatee hospital, pursuant to board of trustees' approval 10/12/12.
$25,000 to Metropolitan Ministries, Tampa, FL, 2012. For grant award for phase 1 of Miracle Place pursuant to board of trustees' approval 8/1/12.
$25,000 to Metropolitan Ministries, Tampa, FL, 2012. For Balance of grant award for phase 1 of Miracle Place pursuant to board of trustees' approval 8/1/12.
$12,500 to Champions for Children, Tampa, FL, 2012. For grant award for Kids on the Block Program pursuant to board of trustees' approval 6/6/12.
$10,000 to OASIS Network of New Tampa, Tampa, FL, 2012. For grant award for purchase of socks and underwear for 1,000 needy students in Hillsborough County pursuant to board of trustees' approval 2/1/12.
$3,000 to Metropolitan Ministries, Tampa, FL, 2012. For grant award for children's holiday needs pursuant to board of trustees' approval 12/5/12.
$2,500 to Tampa Bay History Center, Tampa, FL, 2012. For Sustaining Founder Membership pursuant to board of trustees' approval 12/5/12.

2309
Scaife Family Foundation ✧
777 S. Flagler Dr.
West Tower, Ste. 903
West Palm Beach, FL 33401-6161 (561) 659-1188
Contact: David A. Zywiec, Pres.
Main URL: http://www.scaifefamily.org

Established in 1983 in PA.
Donor: Sarah Mellon Scaife†.
Foundation type: Independent foundation.
Financial data (yr. ended 12/31/12): Assets, $79,224,592 (M); expenditures, $3,755,158; qualifying distributions, $3,298,236; giving activities include $2,751,500 for 75 grants (high: $250,000; low: $1,500).
Purpose and activities: Grants to support and develop programs that strengthen families, address issues surrounding the health and welfare of women and children, promote animal welfare, and that demonstrate the beneficial interaction between humans and animals; Support also for conservation, and early intervention and prevention efforts in the area of drug and alcohol addiction.
Fields of interest: Animal welfare; Health care; Substance abuse, prevention.
Type of support: General/operating support; Program development.
Limitations: Applications accepted. Giving primarily in FL, NY and PA. No grants to individuals. Generally, no grants for event sponsorships, endowments, capital campaigns, renovations or government agencies; no loans.
Publications: Annual report; Grants list; IRS Form 990 or 990-PF printed copy available upon request.
Application information: Application form not required.
Initial approach: Letter
Copies of proposal: 1
Deadline(s): Grant applications are normally considered quarterly; no set deadline
Board meeting date(s): Quarterly
Final notification: Following board meetings
Officers and Trustees:* Jennie K. Scaife,* Chair.; David A. Zywiec, Pres. and Secy.-Treas.; Beth H. Genter,* V.P.; Mary T. Walton,* V.P.
Number of staff: 1 full-time professional; 1 full-time support.
EIN: 251427015

2310
The John F. Scarpa Foundation ✧
1676 S. Ocean Blvd.
Palm Beach, FL 33480-4040

Established in 1997 in FL.
Donor: John F. Scarpa.
Foundation type: Independent foundation.
Financial data (yr. ended 12/31/12): Assets, $4,545,208 (M); gifts received, $400,387; expenditures, $889,688; qualifying distributions, $863,355; giving activities include $863,355 for grants.
Purpose and activities: Giving primarily for education, health organizations, and social services.
Fields of interest: Law school/education; Education; Health care; Health organizations, association; Human services; Foundations (private grantmaking).
Limitations: Applications not accepted. Giving primarily in FL, NJ and PA.
Application information: Contributes only to pre-selected organizations.
Officers and Directors:* John F. Scarpa,* Pres.; Michael P. Haney, Secy.; Michael B. Azeez,* Treas.
EIN: 232939489

2311
Rowland & Sylvia Schaefer Family Foundation, Inc. ✧
555 S. Federal Hwy., Ste. 340
Boca Raton, FL 33432-5542 (561) 620-3233
Contact: Rowland Schaefer

Established in 1996 in FL.
Donor: Rowland Schaefer.
Foundation type: Independent foundation.
Financial data (yr. ended 08/31/13): Assets, $13,341,624 (M); expenditures, $934,715; qualifying distributions, $818,530; giving activities include $818,530 for grants.
Fields of interest: Health organizations, association; Medical research, institute; Human services; Jewish federated giving programs; Jewish agencies & synagogues.
Limitations: Applications accepted. Giving primarily in Miami, FL, and New York, NY.
Application information: Application form not required.
Initial approach: Proposal
Deadline(s): None
Directors: Eileen Bonnie Schaefer; Marla Schaefer Weishoff.
EIN: 650757807
Selected grants: The following grants are a representative sample of this grantmaker's funding activity:
$160,000 to Simon Wiesenthal Center, Los Angeles, CA, 2011.
$10,000 to Planned Parenthood Federation of America, New York, NY, 2011.

2312
The Schemel Family Foundation, Inc. ✧
823 Lands End Rd.
Lantana, FL 33462 (561) 496-4440
Contact: Robert G. Schemel, Dir.

Established in 2007 in FL.
Donors: Richard G. Schemel; Robert G. Schemel.
Foundation type: Independent foundation.
Financial data (yr. ended 12/31/13): Assets, $58,572 (M); gifts received, $500,000; expenditures, $465,670; qualifying distributions, $465,000; giving activities include $465,000 for 6 grants (high: $200,000; low: $5,000).
Purpose and activities: Giving primarily for education, particularly to a Roman Catholic high school, as well as for youth and social services.
Fields of interest: Secondary school/education; Education; Human services; Youth, services.
Limitations: Giving primarily in IL; funding also in FL.
Application information: Application form not required.
Initial approach: Letter
Deadline(s): None
Directors: Elizabeth A. Schemel; Gregory S. Schemel; Robert G. Schemel; Robert G. Schemel II.
EIN: 208007821
Selected grants: The following grants are a representative sample of this grantmaker's funding activity:
$200,000 to Leo High School, Chicago, IL, 2011.
$100,000 to Leo High School, Chicago, IL, 2011.
$10,000 to Florida Atlantic University Foundation, Boca Raton, FL, 2011.
$5,000 to Boys and Girls Clubs of Manatee County, Bradenton, FL, 2011.
$5,000 to HOPE Family Services, Bradenton, FL, 2011.
$5,000 to Southeastern Guide Dogs, Palmetto, FL, 2011.

2313
The Schoenbaum Family Foundation, Inc. ✧
P.O. Box 1908
Orlando, FL 32802-1908

Established in 1988 in FL.
Donor: Alex Schoenbaum†.
Foundation type: Independent foundation.
Financial data (yr. ended 12/31/13): Assets, $15,384,683 (M); expenditures, $910,076; qualifying distributions, $816,167; giving activities include $792,047 for 31 grants (high: $105,000; low: $1,000).
Purpose and activities: Grants for health, education and welfare.
Fields of interest: Human services; Jewish federated giving programs.
Type of support: Program development; Scholarship funds.
Limitations: Applications not accepted. Giving on a national basis, with emphasis on FL and WV.
Application information: Contributes only to pre-selected organizations.
Board meeting date(s): Varies
Officers: Betty Jane Schoenbaum, Pres.; Joann Schoenbaum Miller, V.P.; Emily Schoenbaum, V.P.; Raymond D. Schoenbaum, Secy.; Jeffry F. Schoenbaum, Treas.
Number of staff: 1 part-time support.
EIN: 650043921

2314
The Seaman Family Foundation, Inc. ✧
11540 Highway 92 E.
Seffner, FL 33584-7346 (813) 623-5400
Contact: Lewis Stein, Treas.

Established in 1999 in FL.
Donor: Jeffrey Seaman.
Foundation type: Independent foundation.
Financial data (yr. ended 12/31/12): Assets, $4,013,560 (M); gifts received, $4,000,000; expenditures, $3,076,965; qualifying distributions, $3,071,400; giving activities include $3,071,400 for grants.
Fields of interest: Higher education, university; Hospitals (general); Health organizations; Jewish federated giving programs; Jewish agencies & synagogues.
Limitations: Giving primarily in GA and PA.
Application information:
Initial approach: Letter
Officers and Directors:* Jeffrey Seaman,* Pres.; Julie Seaman,* Secy.; Lewis Stein,* Treas.
EIN: 593631102

2315
SeaWorld & Busch Gardens Conservation Fund ✧
9205 SouthPark Center Loop, Ste. 400
Orlando, FL 32819-8651
Contact: Brad F. Andrews, Pres. and Exec. Dir.
E-mail: mail@swbgfund.org; Application address for Environmental Excellence Awards: c/o SeaWorld

Orlando Education Dept., 7007 SeaWorld Dr., Orlando, FL 32821, tel.: (877) 792-4332 or (407) 363-2389, e-mail: buschgardenseducation@gmail.com; Main URL: http://www.swbg-conservationfund.org/
E-Newsletter: http://cs.silverpop.com/abec/preferences/index.sp?pid=WOD
Facebook: http://www.facebook.com/SeaWorldBuschGardensFund
Grants Database: http://www.swbg-conservationfund.org/SuccessStoriesArticle.aspx?search=1
Twitter: http://twitter.com/JulieScardina

Established in 2003 in DE and MO.
Donors: SeaWorld Parks and Entertainment; Busch Entertainment Corp.
Foundation type: Company-sponsored foundation.
Financial data (yr. ended 12/31/13): Assets, $412,993 (M); gifts received, $1,099,117; expenditures, $1,284,972; qualifying distributions, $1,258,600; giving activities include $1,258,600 for 85 grants (high: $75,000; low: $2,000).
Purpose and activities: The foundation supports programs designed to promote species research; habitat protection; animal rescue and rehabilitation; and conservation education.
Fields of interest: Elementary/secondary education; Environment, water resources; Environmental education; Environment; Animals/wildlife, research; Animals/wildlife, public education; Animal welfare; Animals/wildlife, preservation/protection; Animals/wildlife, fisheries; Animals/wildlife, sanctuaries; Animals/wildlife.
Type of support: General/operating support; Continuing support; Program development; Research; Grants to individuals.
Limitations: Applications accepted. Giving on a national and international basis in areas of company operations. No grants to individuals (except for Environmental Excellence Awards); generally, no grants for capital campaigns, building, or construction that would outlive the project supported by the Fund or ex-situ captive breeding efforts.
Publications: Application guidelines; Annual report; Financial statement; Newsletter.
Application information: Grants range from $5,000 to $25,000. A site visit may be requested. Color photographs, brochures, videos, CD's, Websites, news articles, posters, t-shirts, and buttons are encouraged for the Environmental Excellence Awards. Application form required.
Initial approach: Complete online application; mail a 300-word letter and a 5 minute video on a CD or flash drive to application address for Environmental Excellence Awards for schools; post and email a video nomination on YouTube for Environmental Excellence Awards for individuals
Deadline(s): Sept. to Dec. 1; Mar. 2 for Environmental Excellence Awards for schools; Mar. 5 for Environmental Excellence Awards for individuals
Board meeting date(s): Once a year in Spring
Final notification: Apr. and May
Officers and Directors: Brad F. Andrews,* Pres. and Exec. Dir.; Howard Demsky, Secy.; Marc G. Swanson, Treas.; James D. Atchison; Virginia M. Busch; Jim Dean; David Grabe; Jack Hanna; Julie Scardina; Hugh Share; Judy St. Leger; Shiela Voss; Glenn Young.
EIN: 113692807

2316
William G. Selby and Marie Selby Foundation ✧

1800 2nd St., Ste. 954
Sarasota, FL 34236-5930 (941) 957-0442
Contact: Evan Jones, Grants Mgr.
FAX: (941) 957-3135; E-mail: ejones@selbyfdn.org; Main URL: http://www.selbyfdn.org/

Trust established in 1955 in FL.
Donors: William G. Selby†; Marie Selby†.
Foundation type: Independent foundation.
Financial data (yr. ended 05/31/13): Assets, $69,415,321 (M); expenditures, $3,593,894; qualifying distributions, $3,222,201; giving activities include $2,002,187 for grants, and $811,820 for grants to individuals.
Purpose and activities: The foundation seeks to make capital grants that will improve the quality of life in Sarasota County, FL, and its bordering counties. Scholarships are also given to students who can demonstrate financial need, who maintain a 3.0 (unweighted) GPA, who are residents of Sarasota, Manatee, Charlotte or DeSoto counties in FL, and who are pursuing a bachelors degree from a four-year college or university. Scholarships will be awarded up to $7,000 per year.
Fields of interest: Visual arts; Performing arts; Historic preservation/historical societies; Arts; Child development, education; Elementary school/education; Secondary school/education; Higher education; Education; Housing/shelter, development; Recreation, parks/playgrounds; Human services; Youth, services; Child development, services; Aging, centers/services; Community/economic development; Physical/earth sciences; Aging.
Type of support: Capital campaigns; Building/renovation; Equipment; Land acquisition; Scholarships—to individuals.
Limitations: Applications accepted. Giving limited to Charlotte, DeSoto, Manatee, and Sarasota counties, FL. No support for private K-12 schools, public schools, childcare facilities, or churches and their individual ministries. No grants to individuals (except through Selby Scholars Program), or for debt reduction, annual campaigns, deficit financing, operating budgets, endowment funds, surveys, program advertising, research, seminars, workshops, travel, fundraising, or conferences; no loans.
Publications: Application guidelines; Grants list; Informational brochure (including application guidelines).
Application information: Application must be submitted using the foundation's guidelines and online system. No applications for amounts under $10,000. Application guidelines and form for Selby Scholars available on foundation web site. Application form required.
Initial approach: Letter
Copies of proposal: 1
Deadline(s): Feb. 1 and Aug. 1 for grants; Apr. 1 for scholarships
Board meeting date(s): Apr. and Nov.
Final notification: May 15 and Dec. 15
Officer: Sarah Pappas, Pres.
Trustee: Wells Fargo, N.A.
Number of staff: 1 full-time professional; 2 full-time support.
EIN: 596121242

2317
Selevan Family Foundation, Inc. ✧

4030 Phillips Hwy.
Jacksonville, FL 32207-6835 (904) 733-9311
Contact: Russell Selevan, V.P. and Secy.

Established in 1986 in FL.
Donors: Russell Selevan; Jack Selevan; Gardens of Mount Carmel; General Trading USA, Inc.
Foundation type: Independent foundation.
Financial data (yr. ended 12/31/13): Assets, $643,070 (M); gifts received, $260,000; expenditures, $516,310; qualifying distributions, $516,310; giving activities include $516,310 for 16 grants (high: $145,000; low: $250).
Purpose and activities: Giving primarily for Jewish organizations.
Fields of interest: Human services; United Ways and Federated Giving Programs; Jewish federated giving programs; Jewish agencies & synagogues.
Limitations: Applications accepted. Giving primarily in Jacksonville, FL. No grants to individuals.
Application information: Application form required.
Initial approach: Proposal
Deadline(s): None
Officers: Jack Selevan, Pres. and Treas.; Russell Selevan, V.P. and Secy.
Trustees: Andrew Selevan; Marc Selevan.
EIN: 592742007
Selected grants: The following grants are a representative sample of this grantmaker's funding activity:
$110,000 to River Garden Foundation, Jacksonville, FL, 2011.
$100,000 to Jacksonville Jewish Center, Jacksonville, FL, 2011.
$75,000 to Jewish National Fund, Clearwater, FL, 2011.
$27,604 to Jewish Community Alliance, Jacksonville, FL, 2011.
$13,000 to Jewish Family and Community Services, Jacksonville, FL, 2011.
$12,500 to Jewish Federations of North America, New York, NY, 2011.
$10,000 to American Cancer Society, Jacksonville, FL, 2011.
$5,000 to OneJax, Jacksonville, FL, 2011.
$2,325 to American Friends of Carmel School, New York, NY, 2011.

2318
The Bruce & Cynthia Sherman Charitable Foundation, Inc. ✧

5150 Tamiami Trail N., Ste. 505
Naples, FL 34103-2822

Established in 2005 in FL.
Donors: Bruce S. Sherman; Cynthia L. Sherman.
Foundation type: Independent foundation.
Financial data (yr. ended 12/31/13): Assets, $17,201,858 (M); expenditures, $709,055; qualifying distributions, $471,100; giving activities include $471,100 for 19 grants (high: $210,000; low: $100).
Fields of interest: Arts; Higher education, university; Botanical gardens; Medical research, institute; Human services.
Limitations: Applications not accepted. Giving primarily in Naples, FL, and New York, NY. No grants to individuals.
Application information: Contributes only to pre-selected organizations.

Officers: Bruce S. Sherman, Pres.; Cynthia L. Sherman, Treas.
EIN: 050629744
Selected grants: The following grants are a representative sample of this grantmaker's funding activity:
$125,000 to New York University, New York, NY, 2011.
$20,000 to Naples, City of, Naples, FL, 2011.
$15,000 to Naples Botanical Garden, Naples, FL, 2011.
$14,250 to Foundation for AIDS Research, New York, NY, 2011.
$10,000 to Lung Cancer Research Foundation, New York, NY, 2011.
$10,000 to Mountain Mission School, Grundy, VA, 2011.

2319
Sherman Family Foundation ✧
(formerly The Betsy R. and George M. Sherman Private Foundation)
7292 Fisher Island Dr.
Miami Beach, FL 33109-0764

Established in 1994 in MD.
Donor: George M. Sherman.
Foundation type: Independent foundation.
Financial data (yr. ended 12/31/12): Assets, $28,884,885 (M); gifts received, $5,477,340; expenditures, $2,301,664; qualifying distributions, $2,287,937; giving activities include $2,287,937 for grants.
Fields of interest: Arts; Education; Health organizations, association; Human services; Foundations (private grantmaking); United Ways and Federated Giving Programs.
Type of support: General/operating support.
Limitations: Applications not accepted. Giving primarily in Miami, FL, and Baltimore, MD. No grants to individuals.
Application information: Contributes only to pre-selected organizations.
Trustee: George M. Sherman.
EIN: 526723302

2320
SHIFT ✧
(formerly Aaron & Martha Schecter Private Foundation)
3900 Hollywood Blvd., Apt. PH-N
Hollywood, FL 33021-1244

Established in 1981 in FL.
Donors: Aaron Schecter; Martha Schecter†; Laurie Schecter; Julie Schecter.
Foundation type: Independent foundation.
Financial data (yr. ended 09/30/13): Assets, $13,976,365 (M); expenditures, $2,012,013; qualifying distributions, $1,826,000; giving activities include $1,826,000 for 10 grants (high: $1,000,000; low: $5,000).
Purpose and activities: Giving primarily for international affairs, public policy groups promoting peace and social responsibility, and civil rights organizations.
Fields of interest: Arts; Scholarships/financial aid; International peace/security; International affairs; Civil/human rights; Philanthropy/voluntarism; Public policy, research.
Limitations: Applications not accepted. Giving in the U.S., with emphasis on CA and NY. No grants to individuals.
Application information: Contributes only to pre-selected organizations.
Trustees: Carol Goloff; Julie Schecter; Laurie Schecter.
EIN: 592185762
Selected grants: The following grants are a representative sample of this grantmaker's funding activity:
$665,000 to Tides Center, San Francisco, CA, 2013. For unrestricted donation.

2321
Leon J. Simkins Charitable Foundation ✧
c/o Berkowitz Pollack Brant
200 S. Biscayne Blvd., 6th Fl.
Miami, FL 33131-2310

Established in 1986 in FL.
Donor: Leon J. Simkins.
Foundation type: Independent foundation.
Financial data (yr. ended 08/31/13): Assets, $12,670,617 (M); expenditures, $608,051; qualifying distributions, $545,900; giving activities include $545,900 for 19 grants (high: $256,150; low: $500).
Fields of interest: Health care; Health organizations; Diabetes research; Foundations (community).
Limitations: Applications not accepted. Giving primarily in Aspen, CO; funding also in FL. No grants to individuals.
Application information: Contributes only to pre-selected organizations.
Trustees: Michelle Simkins Rubell; Albert Simkins; David Simkins; Leon J. Simkins; Michael Simkins; Ronald Simkins.
EIN: 592757208

2322
The Sidney, Milton and Leoma Simon Foundation-Florida ✧
101 Plaza Real S., Ste. 930
Boca Raton, FL 33432-4852 (561) 368-8666
Contact: Joseph Warner, Tr.

Established in FL.
Donor: Sidney, Milton & Leoma Simon Foundation.
Foundation type: Independent foundation.
Financial data (yr. ended 05/31/13): Assets, $16,481,188 (M); expenditures, $1,046,719; qualifying distributions, $846,820; giving activities include $644,000 for 67 grants (high: $15,000; low: $3,000).
Purpose and activities: Giving primarily for the arts, health, human services, and Jewish organizations.
Fields of interest: Performing arts; Arts; Health organizations, association; Human services; Jewish agencies & synagogues.
Application information: Application form required.
Initial approach: Letter on organization letterhead
Deadline(s): None
Trustees: Burt Bergenfield; Joseph Warner; Meryll Warner.
EIN: 656282105
Selected grants: The following grants are a representative sample of this grantmaker's funding activity:
$3,000 to Alliance for Eating Disorders Awareness, West Palm Beach, FL, 2011.

2323
The Raj & Neera Singh Charitable Foundation, Inc. ✧
23 Indian Creek Island Rd.
Indian Creek Village, FL 33154-2901

Established in 2006 in FL.
Donors: Rajendra Singh; Neera Singh; RF Investors, LLC.
Foundation type: Independent foundation.
Financial data (yr. ended 12/31/13): Assets, $18,201 (M); gifts received, $2,597,514; expenditures, $2,606,563; qualifying distributions, $2,603,442; giving activities include $2,603,442 for 2 grants (high: $2,004,798; low: $598,644).
Fields of interest: Higher education; Education.
Limitations: Applications not accepted. Giving primarily in CA and PA. No grants to individuals.
Application information: Contributes only to pre-selected organizations.
Officers: Rajendra Singh, Pres.; Serge Martin, V.P.; Neera Singh, Secy.; Margaret Keast, Treas.
Directors: Hersh Singh; Samir Singh.
EIN: 205198104

2324
The Gertrude E. Skelly Charitable Foundation ✧
4600 N. Ocean Blvd., Ste. 206
Boynton Beach, FL 33435-7365 (561) 276-1008
Contact: Erik Edward Joh, Tr.
E-mail: skelly@erikjoh.com

Established in 1991 in FL.
Donor: Gertrude E. Skelly†.
Foundation type: Independent foundation.
Financial data (yr. ended 12/31/12): Assets, $15,124,697 (M); expenditures, $1,052,705; qualifying distributions, $906,372; giving activities include $765,000 for 47 grants (high: $30,000; low: $5,000).
Purpose and activities: The foundation's primary mission is to provide educational opportunities, mainly at colleges and universities, and needed medical care for those who are unable to afford them. All grants must affect multiple individuals and meet some educational, medical or emergency need.
Fields of interest: Scholarships/financial aid; Education; Hospitals (general).
Type of support: Emergency funds; Fellowships; Internship funds; Scholarship funds; Research; Matching/challenge support.
Limitations: Applications accepted. Giving on a national basis. No support for political or advocacy groups, or for organizations similar to the United Way which called funds for distribution to other charities. No grants to individuals.
Publications: Application guidelines.
Application information: Application form not required.
Initial approach: Contact foundation for complete guidelines
Copies of proposal: 7
Deadline(s): June 30
Board meeting date(s): Oct.
Trustees: Erik Edward Joh; SunTrust Bank.

Number of staff: 1 full-time professional; 1 part-time support.
EIN: 656085406
Selected grants: The following grants are a representative sample of this grantmaker's funding activity:
$30,000 to American Academy of Nursing, Washington, DC, 2012. For annual nursing meeting and conference.
$30,000 to Smithsonian Institution, Washington, DC, 2012. For How Things Fly Web Site.
$20,000 to Briarwood-Brookwood, Brookshire, TX, 2012. For medical program.
$20,000 to Duke University, Durham, NC, 2012. For Dean's Emergency Fund.
$15,000 to Meharry Medical College, Nashville, TN, 2012. For Medical and Dental Scholarships.
$15,000 to North Dallas Shared Ministries, Dallas, TX, 2012. For prescription medications and lab.
$15,000 to West Palm Beach Library Foundation, West Palm Beach, FL, 2012. For ABE/GED Classes.
$10,000 to Caridad Center, Boynton Beach, FL, 2012. For Chronic Disease Pet Program.
$10,000 to Ursuline College, Pepper Pike, OH, 2012. For emergency grants.

2325
Sontag Foundation, Inc. ✧
c/o Frederick Sontag
816 A1A North, Ste. 201
Ponte Vedra Beach, FL 32082-8213
E-mail: kverble@sontagfoundation.com; Main URL: http://www.sontagfoundation.com
E-Newsletter: http://www.sontagfoundation.com/display.aspx?page=newsletter

Established in 2000 in FL.
Donor: Frederick B. Sontag.
Foundation type: Independent foundation.
Financial data (yr. ended 12/31/12): Assets, $53,483,785 (M); expenditures, $3,569,986; qualifying distributions, $3,236,660; giving activities include $2,910,812 for 41 grants (high: $784,286; low: $250).
Purpose and activities: Giving primarily for brain cancer and brain tumor research, rheumatoid arthritis research, and grants to programs that help individuals in northeast FL to become more self-sufficient.
Fields of interest: Brain research; Arthritis research; Human services.
Type of support: General/operating support.
Limitations: Applications not accepted. Giving primarily in northeast FL, with emphasis on Baker, Clay, Duval, Flagler, Nassau, Putnam, and St. John's counties. No grants to individuals or for building funds, capital campaigns, sponsorship of fundraising events, long range program support.
Application information: See foundation web site for the application guidelines and procedures which must be followed.
Officers and Directors:* Frederick B. Sontag,* Pres.; Frederick T. Sontag,* V.P.; Daniel M. Ryan,* Secy.-Treas.; Kay W. Verble, Exec. Dir.; Jeffrey Hudgins; Bradley D. Mottier; Susan T. Sontag; John D. Strom.
EIN: 593634325

2326
The Richard W. Sorenson Family Foundation, Inc. ✧
2727 Aqua Vista Blvd.
Fort Lauderdale, FL 33301-1552

Established in 1984 in CT; reincorporated in 1990 in FL.
Donors: Carlingswitch, Inc.; Carling Technologies, Inc.
Foundation type: Independent foundation.
Financial data (yr. ended 12/31/13): Assets, $2,950,173 (M); gifts received, $475,000; expenditures, $459,245; qualifying distributions, $456,000; giving activities include $456,000 for 4 grants (high: $300,000; low: $1,000).
Fields of interest: Higher education; Education; Hospitals (general).
Limitations: Applications accepted. Giving primarily in CT and MA. No grants to individuals.
Application information: Application form required.
Initial approach: Request application form
Deadline(s): July 1
Directors: Barbara Forasiere; Edward D. Rosenthal; Richard W. Sorenson.
EIN: 222547323

2327
The Southwest Florida Community Foundation, Inc. ✧
8771 College Pkwy., Bldg. 2, Ste. 201
Fort Myers, FL 33919 (239) 274-5900
FAX: (239) 274-5930;
E-mail: info@floridacommunity.com; Sanibel office: 455 Periwinkle Way, Sanibel, FL 33957; Main URL: http://www.floridacommunity.com
Facebook: https://www.facebook.com/SWFLCF
Twitter: https://twitter.com/SWFLCFnd

Incorporated in 1976 in FL.
Donors: Dorothy M. Beall†; Beryl Berry†; Marguerite Covington†; Herbert E. Hussey†; Isabel Kirkpatrick†; Leonard Santini†; Earl Riggs†; Mrs. Earl Riggs†; Daniel J. Berktold; Jane H. Berktold; Betty Houkom; Lillia Hodges; Richard T. Thompson.
Foundation type: Community foundation.
Financial data (yr. ended 06/30/13): Assets, $69,750,445 (M); gifts received, $4,545,963; expenditures, $5,582,325; giving activities include $3,841,584 for 140+ grants (high: $1,015,226), and $263,950 for 68 grants to individuals.
Purpose and activities: The goals of the foundation are: 1) to significantly strengthen the ability of existing institutions to reach a broader segment of the community; 2) to provide innovative responses to community needs which do not unnecessarily duplicate other efforts; and 3) to create a sense of community through neighborhood involvement and outreach. Emphasis also on organizational capacity-building for area nonprofit organizations.
Fields of interest: Historic preservation/historical societies; Arts; Higher education; Education; Environment; Animal welfare; Health care; Mental health/crisis services; Safety/disasters; Children/youth, services; Human services; Community/economic development; Infants/toddlers; Children/youth; Children; Youth; Young adults; Disabilities, people with; Physically disabled; Blind/visually impaired; Deaf/hearing impaired; Mentally disabled; Minorities; Substance abusers; AIDS, people with; Single parents; Crime/abuse victims; Immigrants/refugees; Economically disadvantaged; Homeless.
Type of support: Technical assistance; Management development/capacity building; Capital campaigns; Building/renovation; Equipment; Endowments; Emergency funds; Program development; Scholarship funds; Consulting services; Scholarships—to individuals; Matching/challenge support.
Limitations: Applications accepted. Giving limited to Charlotte, Collier, Glades, Hendry and Lee counties, FL. No support for fraternal organizations, societies, or orders, or religious organizations for sectarian purposes (except where designated by a fund donor). No grants to individuals (except for scholarships), or for operating budgets, research, annual funds, debt retirement, feasibility studies, sports team travel, class trips, or fundraising events; no loans.
Publications: Application guidelines; Annual report (including application guidelines); Financial statement; Grants list; Informational brochure; Newsletter; Occasional report; Program policy statement; Program policy statement (including application guidelines); Quarterly report.
Application information: Visit foundation website for the online application portal and application guidelines. Application form required.
Initial approach: Complete online application
Deadline(s): Varies
Board meeting date(s): Quarterly
Final notification: Several days after board meetings
Officers and Trustees:* Joe Mazurkiewicz, Jr., Ph. D*, Chair.; Guy E. Whitesman,* Vice-Chair.; Sarah Owen,* C.E.O. and Pres.; Gay Thompson,* Secy.-Treas.; Deborah M. Braendle; Carolyn E. Conant; Patricia K. Dobbins; Dawn-Marie Driscoll; Kevin L. Erwin; Craig Folk; John Gamba; Charles Green; Archie B. Hayward, Jr.; Christopher Hill, CFA; Larry A. Hobbs, M.D.; Hugh Kinsey; Li-Su Huang Javedan; Howard Leland; Alan Mandel; Sarah Owen; Darren Robertshaw; Sandy Robinson; Robbie B. Roepstorff; Karson Turner; Myra Hale Walters; A. Scott White; Steven R. Whitley.
Number of staff: 6 full-time professional; 3 full-time support; 1 part-time support.
EIN: 596580974
Selected grants: The following grants are a representative sample of this grantmaker's funding activity:
$140,297 to Captiva Chapel By the Sea, Captiva, FL, 2012. For program/operating support.
$80,549 to Habitat for Humanity of Lee and Hendry Counties, North Fort Myers, FL, 2012. For program/operating support.
$75,513 to Charitable Foundation of the Islands, Sanibel, FL, 2012. For program support.
$72,100 to Lee Memorial Health System Foundation, Fort Myers, FL, 2012. For program/operating support.
$66,230 to Foundation for Lee County Public Schools, Fort Myers, FL, 2012. For scholarship programs.
$51,000 to Childrens Advocacy Center of Southwest Florida, Fort Myers, FL, 2012. For operating support.
$31,915 to Boy Scouts of America, Southwest Florida Council, Fort Myers, FL, 2012. For program/operating support.
$30,187 to Southwest Florida Symphony Orchestra and Chorus Association, Fort Myers, FL, 2012. For program/operating support.
$18,000 to Peace By Piece Learning Center, Fort Myers, FL, 2012. For renovation.

$15,000 to HOPE Clubhouse of Southwest Florida, Fort Myers, FL, 2012. For program/operating support.

2328
Roy M. Speer Foundation ✧
2535 Success Dr.
Odessa, FL 33556-3401
Contact: Lynnda L. Speer, Tr.

Established in 1986 in FL.
Donors: Richard W. Baker; Roy M. Speer†.
Foundation type: Independent foundation.
Financial data (yr. ended 06/30/13): Assets, $32,414,151 (M); gifts received, $20,089,627; expenditures, $1,089,385; qualifying distributions, $1,001,383; giving activities include $669,500 for 15 grants (high: $297,000; low: $2,500).
Fields of interest: Medical school/education; Hospitals (general); Hospitals (specialty); Heart & circulatory diseases; Health organizations; Religious federated giving programs; Protestant agencies & churches.
Limitations: Applications accepted. Giving primarily in FL. No grants to individuals.
Application information: Application form not required.
Initial approach: Letter
Deadline(s): None
Trustees: Lynnda L. Speer; Richard M. Speer.
EIN: 592785945
Selected grants: The following grants are a representative sample of this grantmaker's funding activity:
$30,000 to Boys and Girls Clubs of the Suncoast, Largo, FL, 2011.

2329
Mary M. and Sash A. Spencer Foundation Inc. ✧ ☆
c/o Nostro Jones PA
1441 Brickell Ave., No. 1230
Miami, FL 33131

Established in FL.
Donor: Mary M. Spencer.
Foundation type: Independent foundation.
Financial data (yr. ended 12/31/13): Assets, $4,794,342 (M); expenditures, $2,571,579; qualifying distributions, $2,551,685; giving activities include $2,500,000 for 2 grants (high: $1,500,000; low: $1,000,000).
Fields of interest: Eye research.
Limitations: Applications not accepted. Giving primarily in Miami, FL.
Application information: Unsolicited requests for funds not accepted.
Officers: Mary M. Spencer, Pres.; James W. Donaghy, V.P.; Louis Nostro, Secy.; Maureen McLaughlin, Treas.
EIN: 263034777

2330
The Spurlino Foundation ✧
7214 N. Mobley Rd.
Odessa, FL 33556-2303 (813) 926-9311
Contact: Cyrus Spurlino, Tr.

Established in 1986 in FL.
Donor: Cyrus W. Spurlino.
Foundation type: Independent foundation.
Financial data (yr. ended 12/31/13): Assets, $53,824,369 (M); gifts received, $9,761,719; expenditures, $2,771,820; qualifying distributions, $2,605,055; giving activities include $2,603,000 for 58 grants (high: $500,000; low: $1,000).
Purpose and activities: Giving for children's services, higher education, and federated giving programs.
Fields of interest: Higher education, university; Libraries/library science; Animals/wildlife, preservation/protection; Health organizations, association; YM/YWCAs & YM/YWHAs; Children/youth, services; United Ways and Federated Giving Programs.
Limitations: Applications accepted. Giving primarily in Tampa, FL. No grants to individuals.
Application information: Application form not required.
Initial approach: Proposal
Deadline(s): None
Officer and Trustee:* Cyrus W. Spurlino,* Fdn. Mgr.
EIN: 596875441
Selected grants: The following grants are a representative sample of this grantmaker's funding activity:
$400,000 to Florida Aquarium, Tampa, FL, 2011.
$200,000 to United Way Suncoast, Tampa, FL, 2011. For general operating support.
$45,000 to Canine Companions for Independence, Orlando, FL, 2010. For general operating support.
$40,000 to Nature Conservancy, Arlington, VA, 2011.
$40,000 to Oxfam America, Boston, MA, 2011.
$40,000 to Room to Read, San Francisco, CA, 2011. For general operating support.
$40,000 to Water for People, Denver, CO, 2011. For general operating support.
$30,000 to Childhood League Center, Columbus, OH, 2011. For general operating support.
$30,000 to FINCA International, Washington, DC, 2011. For general operating support.
$25,000 to Doctors Without Borders USA, New York, NY, 2010. For general operating support.
$25,000 to International Fund for Animal Welfare, Yarmouth Port, MA, 2011. For general operating support.
$25,000 to United Way of Southern Nevada, Las Vegas, NV, 2011. For general operating support.
$20,000 to Abe Brown Ministries, Tampa, FL, 2010. For general operating support.
$20,000 to Boys and Girls Clubs of Tampa Bay, Tampa, FL, 2010. For general operating support.
$15,000 to Childrens Cancer Center, Tampa, FL, 2010.

2331
The St. Joe Community Foundation Inc. ✧ ☆
(formerly Northwest Florida Improvement Foundation, Inc.)
133 S. Watersound Pkwy.
Watersound, FL 32413-7280
Main URL: http://www.stjcf.com
Grants List: http://www.stjcf.com/Grants.html

Established in 1999 in FL.
Foundation type: Company-sponsored foundation.
Financial data (yr. ended 12/31/13): Assets, $2,246,387 (M); expenditures, $931,516; qualifying distributions, $892,266; giving activities include $892,266 for 41 grants (high: $30,000; low: $2,000).
Purpose and activities: The foundation seeks to enrich the quality of life of the people who live, work, and play in northwest Florida.
Fields of interest: Arts; Education; Health care.
Type of support: Management development/capacity building; Capital campaigns; Building/renovation; Equipment; Endowments; Program development; Professorships; Publication; Seed money; Curriculum development; Fellowships; Scholarship funds; Research.
Limitations: Applications not accepted. Giving limited to Bay, Calhoun, Franklin, Gadsden, Gulf, Jefferson, Leon, Liberty, Wakulla, and Walton counties, FL. No support for sectarian or religious activities. No grants to individuals, or for fundraising events, health initiatives other than regional healthcare delivery, or individual sports teams.
Application information: Unsolicited requests for funds not accepted.
Board meeting date(s): Quarterly
Board Members: Ken Borick; Park Brady; Jorge Gonzalez; Janet Greeno.
Number of staff: 1 full-time professional.
EIN: 593576402

2332
St. Petersburg Times Fund, Inc. ✧
(formerly St. Petersburg Times Scholarship Fund)
P.O. Box 1121
St. Petersburg, FL 33731-1121
Contact: Nancy Waclawek, Tr.
FAX: (727) 892-2257;
E-mail: waclawek@tampabay.com; Application address: Times Fund Inc., 490 1st Ave. S., St. Petersburg, FL 33701-4204; Main URL: http://www.tampabay.com/company/times-fund/

Incorporated in 1953 in DC.
Donors: Henrietta M. Poynter†; Nelson Poynter†; Congressional Quarterly; Times Publishing Co.; Godbold Foundation.
Foundation type: Independent foundation.
Financial data (yr. ended 12/31/12): Assets, $11,576,695 (M); gifts received, $62,739; expenditures, $695,494; qualifying distributions, $674,338; giving activities include $360,271 for 50 + grants (high: $48,500), and $156,800 for grants to individuals.
Purpose and activities: The fund provides grants to non-profit organizations in these general categories: education, arts/culture, social services and journalism. The focus is primarily on helping to improve the quality of life in West Central Florida, specifically the counties of Pinellas, Hillsborough, Pasco, Hernando, and Citrus.
Fields of interest: Media/communications; Media, print publishing; Arts; Education; Human services; Minorities.
Type of support: Capital campaigns; Fellowships; Scholarship funds; Employee matching gifts; Scholarships—to individuals; Matching/challenge support.
Limitations: Applications accepted. Giving limited to west central FL: Pinellas, Hillsborough, Pasco, and Hernando, and Citrus counties. No support for religious or political organizations, or for fraternal groups, athletic teams, bands, school newspapers or yearbooks, veterans organizations, or volunteer firefighter groups. No grants for annual fund drives, golf tournaments or raffles; no loans.
Publications: Application guidelines; Financial statement; Grants list.

Application information: Grant applicants may submit only 1 request per calendar year (Jan. 1 to Dec. 31). Application information available on foundation web site. Application form required.
Initial approach: Concept letter (no more than 2 pages) or see foundation web site
Copies of proposal: 1
Deadline(s): See foundation web site for current deadline dates
Board meeting date(s): Apr. and Nov.
Final notification: Within 30 days
Officers and Trustees:* Paul Tash,* Pres.; Andrew P. Corty,* Secy.; Jana Jones,* Treas.; Neil Brown; Stephen Buckley; Sebastian Dortch; Jennifer Orsi; Nancy Waclawek.
Number of staff: 1 full-time professional; 1 full-time support.
EIN: 596142547

2333
Festus and Helen Stacy Foundation, Inc. ✧
5200 N. Federal Hwy.
P.M.B. 1065
Fort Lauderdale, FL 33308-3848 (954) 776-3386
Contact: Sharon Bizzell, Grants Mgr.
FAX: (954) 776-6469; E-mail: grants@fsfnd.org; Sharon Bizzell e-mail: sbizzell@fsfnd.org; Main URL: http://www.fsfnd.org

Established in 1980 in FL.
Donors: Festus Stacy†; Helen Stacy Charitable Trust.
Foundation type: Independent foundation.
Financial data (yr. ended 10/31/13): Assets, $49,257,844 (M); gifts received, $436,907; expenditures, $3,167,982; qualifying distributions, $2,289,812; giving activities include $1,577,927 for 35 grants (high: $621,663; low: $250), and $47,872 for foundation-administered programs.
Purpose and activities: Support of charitable works that are consistent with making a genuine Christian impact benefiting mankind.
Fields of interest: Human services; Children/youth, services; International development; Foundations (community); Christian agencies & churches.
International interests: Africa; Asia; Europe.
Type of support: Seed money; In-kind gifts; Matching/challenge support.
Limitations: Giving primarily in Broward County, FL; some giving on a national and international basis. No support for No support to secular organizations or for for-profit organizations, national organizations that do not cover the U.S., or do not have a national focus, as well as to churches other than those that the trustees are personally involved with, or those who are proposing unified multi-church outreaches, or seminaries. No grants to individuals, or for endowments, scholarship funds, long term Christian education, disaster or emergency funds, general operating budgets and/or capital expenditures to churches, expensive low-impact investments, or denominational concerns.
Publications: Application guidelines.
Application information: Having a prior connection at the foundation will help in the application process. Application guidelines and form available on foundation web site. Application form required.
Initial approach: Telephone or e-mail requesting application form or download form from web site
Copies of proposal: 3
Deadline(s): None
Board meeting date(s): Feb. and June
Final notification: 60 days
Officers and Directors:* Douglas A. Stepelton,* Pres.; Brett S. Stepelton,* V.P.; Sean D. Stepelton,* V.P.; Virlee Stacy Stepelton,* Secy.-Treas.
EIN: 311706311
Selected grants: The following grants are a representative sample of this grantmaker's funding activity:
$333,333 to Operation Mobilization USA, Tyrone, GA, 2011.
$147,000 to Christian Community Foundation of South Florida, Fort Lauderdale, FL, 2011.
$39,500 to Haggai Institute for Advanced Leadership Training, Norcross, GA, 2011.

2334
Festus & Helen Stacy Foundation II ✧
701 E. Commercial Blvd., Ste. 300
Fort Lauderdale, FL 33334-3392

Established in 2006 in FL.
Foundation type: Independent foundation.
Financial data (yr. ended 10/31/13): Assets, $11,829,010 (M); expenditures, $599,556; qualifying distributions, $466,277; giving activities include $454,617 for 2 grants (high: $451,667; low: $2,950).
Fields of interest: Youth development; Christian agencies & churches; Religion.
Limitations: Applications not accepted. Giving primarily in FL; some funding also in PA. No grants to individuals.
Application information: Unsolicited requests for funds not accepted.
Officers and Trustees:* Douglas A. Stepelton,* Pres.; Brett S. Stepelton,* Secy.; Sean D. Stepelton; Virlee S. Stepelton.
EIN: 206712263
Selected grants: The following grants are a representative sample of this grantmaker's funding activity:
$62,000 to Sheridan House, Davie, FL, 2011.
$41,000 to Mission India, Grand Rapids, MI, 2011.
$36,000 to Onehope, Inc., Pompano Beach, FL, 2011.
$35,560 to Kanakuk Ministries, Branson, MO, 2011.
$25,000 to Banner Communications, Gainesville, FL, 2011.
$1,500 to Holy Cross Hospital, Fort Lauderdale, FL, 2011.

2335
The Star Family Foundation ✧
(formerly Stanley A. Star Foundation)
400 5th Ave. S., Ste. 201
Naples, FL 34102-7713 (239) 435-9008
Contact: Stanley A. Star, Tr.

Established in 1996 in FL.
Donors: Stanley A. Star; CliffStar Corp.; Elizabeth Star.
Foundation type: Independent foundation.
Financial data (yr. ended 12/31/13): Assets, $1,820 (M); gifts received, $1,040,000; expenditures, $1,040,000; qualifying distributions, $1,040,000; giving activities include $1,040,000 for 2 grants (high: $1,000,000; low: $40,000).
Purpose and activities: Giving primarily to a law school; some funding also for education and to a cancer center.
Fields of interest: Law school/education; Education; Cancer.
Type of support: General/operating support; Scholarship funds.
Limitations: Applications accepted. Giving primarily in NC.
Application information: Application form not required.
Initial approach: Proposal
Deadline(s): None
Trustees: Elizabeth A. Star; Richard Star; Stanley A. Star; Elizabeth Star Winer.
EIN: 650712086
Selected grants: The following grants are a representative sample of this grantmaker's funding activity:
$715,000 to Duke University, School of Law, Durham, NC, 2012. For educational.
$20,000 to Iron Dukes, Durham, NC, 2012. For Duke University Athletics.

2336
Bill and Linda Stavropoulos Family Foundation ✧
8665 Bay Colony Dr., Unit 803
Naples, FL 34108-6769

Established in 2006 in FL.
Donors: S. William Stavropoulos; I. Linda Stavropoulos; Garden City Charitable Trust.
Foundation type: Independent foundation.
Financial data (yr. ended 12/31/13): Assets, $6,598,772 (M); gifts received, $2,609,225; expenditures, $627,819; qualifying distributions, $619,150; giving activities include $619,150 for 33 grants (high: $400,000; low: $200).
Fields of interest: Higher education; Health care; Human services; Foundations (private grantmaking).
Limitations: Applications not accepted. Giving in the U.S., with emphasis on FL and MI; funding also in Notre Dame, IN. No grants to individuals.
Application information: Contributes only to pre-selected organizations.
Officers: I. Linda Stavropoulos, Pres.; Angela Laurite, Secy.; S. William Stavropoulos, Treas.
EIN: 450547094

2337
David A. Stein Foundation Inc. ✧ ☆
(formerly Stein Family Foundation)
220 Ponte Vedra Park Dr., Ste. 160
Ponte Vedra Beach, FL 32082-6616 (904) 543-7073
Contact: David A. Stein, Chair.

Established in 1949 in FL.
Donors: David A. Stein; Martin Stein†; King Provision Corp.; Southern Industrial Corp.; Linda Stein.
Foundation type: Independent foundation.
Financial data (yr. ended 12/31/13): Assets, $8,016,472 (M); gifts received, $1,000,022; expenditures, $1,743,092; qualifying distributions, $1,339,352; giving activities include $1,332,408 for 59 grants (high: $223,000; low: $40).
Fields of interest: Museums; Performing arts; Arts; Elementary/secondary education; Zoos/zoological societies; Hospitals (general); Cancer; Heart &

circulatory diseases; Youth development; Human services; Aging, centers/services; Community development, neighborhood development; Foundations (community); United Ways and Federated Giving Programs; Jewish federated giving programs; Jewish agencies & synagogues.
Limitations: Applications accepted. Giving primarily in Jacksonville, FL. No grants to individuals.
Application information: Application form required.
Initial approach: Letter
Copies of proposal: 1
Deadline(s): None
Officers: David A. Stein, Chair.; Tracey Stein, Treas.
Trustees: Allison S. Robbins; Linda B. Stein.
EIN: 596152351

2338
Jay and Deanie Stein Foundation Trust ✧
(formerly Jay Stein Foundation Trust)
1200 Riverplace Blvd., 10th Fl.
Jacksonville, FL 32207-9046

Established in FL.
Donor: Jay Stein.
Foundation type: Independent foundation.
Financial data (yr. ended 06/30/13): Assets, $22,978,357 (M); expenditures, $1,346,735; qualifying distributions, $1,321,125; giving activities include $1,292,556 for 37 grants (high: $444,000; low: $400).
Purpose and activities: Giving primarily for the arts, education, Jewish organizations, and medical research.
Fields of interest: Arts; Higher education; Education; Medical research, institute; Human services; Jewish federated giving programs; Jewish agencies & synagogues.
Limitations: Applications not accepted. Giving primarily in FL and NY. No grants to individuals.
Application information: Contributes only to pre-selected organizations.
Trustee: Jay Stein.
EIN: 311585141
Selected grants: The following grants are a representative sample of this grantmaker's funding activity:
$20,000 to Metropolitan Museum of Art, New York, NY, 2013. To support arts.
$5,000 to KIPP Foundation, San Francisco, CA, 2013. For Students in Underserved Communities with a College-Preparatory Education.
$4,000 to City Rescue Mission, Jacksonville, FL, 2013. For Serving the Needs of the Homeless and Needy in the Jacksonville Area.
$500 to Jacksonville University, Jacksonville, FL, 2013.

2339
Steve and Bonnie Stern Foundation, Inc. ✧
(formerly Gustav and Irene Stern Foundation, Inc.)
184 Bradley Pl.
Palm Beach, FL 33480-3705

Established in 1980.
Donors: Roy Stern; Steven Stern.
Foundation type: Independent foundation.
Financial data (yr. ended 03/31/13): Assets, $7,486,792 (M); expenditures, $647,908; qualifying distributions, $647,908.
Purpose and activities: Giving primarily to Jewish agencies and temples, and for education and the arts.
Fields of interest: Performing arts; Performing arts, opera; Higher education; Education; Human services; Jewish federated giving programs; Jewish agencies & synagogues.
Limitations: Applications not accepted. Giving primarily in New York, NY. No grants to individuals.
Application information: Unsolicited requests for funds not accepted.
Officer and Director:* Steven E. Stern,* Pres. and Secy.-Treas.
EIN: 136121155

2340
The Stiles-Nicholson Foundation ✧
4600 Military Trail, Ste. 222
Jupiter, FL 33458-4813

Established in 1992 in FL.
Donor: David J.S. Nicholson.
Foundation type: Independent foundation.
Financial data (yr. ended 12/31/13): Assets, $17,488,528 (M); expenditures, $543,388; qualifying distributions, $473,995; giving activities include $473,995 for grants.
Purpose and activities: Giving for economic literacy, with special focus on educational programs related to teaching free enterprise and the capitalist system.
Fields of interest: Education; Youth, services; Economics.
Limitations: Applications not accepted. Giving primarily in Washington, DC, and FL. No grants to individuals.
Application information: Contributes only to pre-selected organizations.
Trustees: Leeanne S. Labanz; C. Lynn Nicholson; David J.S. Nicholson.
EIN: 656103072

2341
David A. Straz, Jr. Foundation ✧
4401 W. Kennedy Blvd., Ste 150
Tampa, FL 33609-2000 (813) 639-0155
Contact: David A. Straz, Jr., Tr.

Established in 1983 in WI.
Donors: David A. Straz, Jr.; David A. Straz, Sr.†.
Foundation type: Independent foundation.
Financial data (yr. ended 12/31/13): Assets, $54,249,135 (M); gifts received, $2,000; expenditures, $2,045,223; qualifying distributions, $1,578,997; giving activities include $1,377,620 for 32 grants (high: $620,250; low: $50).
Fields of interest: Performing arts centers; Performing arts, opera; Arts; Higher education; Education; Hospitals (general); Human services.
Type of support: Annual campaigns; Capital campaigns; Building/renovation.
Limitations: Applications accepted. Giving primarily in Tampa, FL; some funding also in New York, NY, and WI.
Application information:
Initial approach: Proposal
Deadline(s): None
Trustee: David A. Straz, Jr.
Number of staff: 1 full-time professional.
EIN: 391776211
Selected grants: The following grants are a representative sample of this grantmaker's funding activity:
$1,191,500 to David A. Straz, Jr. Center for the Performing Arts, Tampa, FL, 2011. For annual support.
$135,000 to Lowry Park Zoological Society of Tampa, Tampa, FL, 2011. For annual support.

2342
Roberta Leventhal Sudakoff Foundation, Inc. ✧
1800 2nd St., Ste. 954
Sarasota, FL 34236-5930
Contact: Lori A. Andrew, Trust Off.
Main URL: http://www.selbyfdn.org/roberta-leventhal-sudakoff-foundation.aspx

Established in 1997 in FL.
Donor: Roberta L. Sudakoff†.
Foundation type: Independent foundation.
Financial data (yr. ended 12/31/13): Assets, $19,529,687 (M); expenditures, $1,165,940; qualifying distributions, $1,165,940; giving activities include $932,596 for 21 grants (high: $185,000; low: $5,000).
Purpose and activities: Giving primarily for programs and capital projects in: the arts, community, education for children and youth, the environment, human services for families and seniors, and science. Scholarships also for local students with limited financial means so that they may pursue a higher education with the goal of not only achieving a meaningful career, but also helping their community.
Fields of interest: Performing arts, theater; Higher education; YM/YWCAs & YM/YWHAs; Community/economic development.
Type of support: Scholarships—to individuals.
Limitations: Applications accepted. Giving limited to Charlotte, DeSoto, Manatee and Sarasota counties in FL. No grants to individuals (except for scholarships), endowments, debt reduction, operating support, conferences, seminars, annual campaigns, and research.
Publications: Application guidelines.
Application information: Application form required.
Initial approach: Use online grant application process on foundation web site
Deadline(s): By 5:00pm on Feb.1 or Aug. 1 (for grants); Apr. 1 (for scholarships)
Officers: Gary A. Bucholtz, Pres. and Treas.; Larry Hietbrink, V.P.; William T. Harrison, Jr., Secy.
EIN: 311483381

2343
Sullivan Family Fund ✧ ☆
c/o Joseph D. Sullivan
11290 Old Harbour Rd.
North Palm Beach, FL 33408-3420

Established in 1986 in OH.
Donors: Pine Fund Corp.; Joseph D. Sullivan.
Foundation type: Independent foundation.
Financial data (yr. ended 12/31/12): Assets, $2,175,648 (M); gifts received, $3,195,316; expenditures, $1,111,789; qualifying distributions, $1,108,637; giving activities include $1,108,637 for 54 grants (high: $800,000; low: $15).
Fields of interest: Arts; Health care; Human services; Foundations (private grantmaking).

Type of support: General/operating support.
Limitations: Applications not accepted. Giving primarily in OH, with emphasis on Cleveland. No grants to individuals.
Application information: Unsolicited requests for funds not accepted.
Trustees: Joseph D. Sullivan; Joseph D. Sullivan, Jr.; Sandra H. Sullivan.
EIN: 341537311

2344
Sun Capital Partners Foundation, Inc. ✧
c/o Donna Wohlfarth
5200 Town Center Cir., Ste. 650
Boca Raton, FL 33486-1015

Established in 2008 in FL.
Donors: Leder Family Foundation, Inc.; Krouse Family Foundation, Inc.; Marc J. Leder Foundation, Inc.
Foundation type: Independent foundation.
Financial data (yr. ended 09/30/13): Assets, $969,259 (M); gifts received, $2,200,000; expenditures, $1,346,307; qualifying distributions, $1,346,307; giving activities include $1,339,548 for 133 grants (high: $125,000; low: $100).
Fields of interest: Education; Health organizations; Human services; Jewish federated giving programs.
Limitations: Applications not accepted. Giving in the U.S., with emphasis on CA, FL, and NY.
Application information: Unsolicited requests for funds not accepted.
Officers and Directors:* Marc J. Leder,* Pres.; Rodger R. Krouse,* Secy.; Kevin J. Calhoun,* Treas.
EIN: 261513089
Selected grants: The following grants are a representative sample of this grantmaker's funding activity:
$100,000 to Operation Homefront, San Antonio, TX, 2011.
$30,000 to University of Arizona, Tucson, AZ, 2011.
$29,800 to Rush Philanthropic Arts Foundation, New York, NY, 2011.
$21,500 to UJA-Federation of New York, New York, NY, 2011.
$13,250 to American Jewish Committee, New York, NY, 2011.
$10,800 to Boca Raton Rotary Fund, Boca Raton, FL, 2011. For scholarship fund.
$10,000 to National Hemophilia Foundation, Glenside, PA, 2011.
$10,000 to Siena Francis House, Omaha, NE, 2011.
$10,000 to World Vision, Federal Way, WA, 2011.
$9,250 to Boca Raton Regional Hospital Foundation, Boca Raton, FL, 2011.

2345
SunTrust Bank Charitable Trust ✧ ☆
(formerly Crestar Bank Charitable Trust)
P.O. Box 1908
Orlando, FL 32802-1908
Contact: Cheryl Hechler
Application address: 919 E. Main St., Richmond, VA 23219

Established in 1964 in VA.
Donor: Crestar Bank.
Foundation type: Company-sponsored foundation.
Financial data (yr. ended 12/31/13): Assets, $12,518,569 (M); expenditures, $1,726,048; qualifying distributions, $1,561,733; giving activities include $1,528,958 for 1 grant.
Purpose and activities: The trust supports corporate foundations and organizations involved with historic preservation and community economic development.
Fields of interest: Historic preservation/historical societies; Community/economic development; Foundations (corporate).
Type of support: General/operating support; Continuing support.
Limitations: Applications accepted. Giving primarily in VA. No support for government-supported organizations or political, religious, or national health organizations. No grants to individuals, or for scholarships or fellowships; no loans.
Publications: Application guidelines.
Application information: Application form required.
Initial approach: Letter
Copies of proposal: 1
Deadline(s): Oct.
Board meeting date(s): Semiannually, and as required
Trustee: SunTrust Bank.
Number of staff: 3
EIN: 546054608
Selected grants: The following grants are a representative sample of this grantmaker's funding activity:
$25,000 to Florida Community Loan Fund, Orlando, FL, 2011. For general charitable purpose.

2346
The Jake and Jeanne Sweeney Foundation ✧ ☆
4331 Bayshore Blvd., N.E.
St. Petersburg, FL 33703-5527

Established in OH.
Donor: C. Jeanne Sweeney.
Foundation type: Independent foundation.
Financial data (yr. ended 12/31/13): Assets, $636,542 (M); expenditures, $574,342; qualifying distributions, $572,500; giving activities include $572,500 for 3 grants (high: $560,000; low: $2,500).
Fields of interest: Crime/law enforcement; Youth development.
Limitations: Applications not accepted. Giving primarily in Cincinnati, OH and Tampa, FL.
Application information: Unsolicited requests for funds not accepted.
Officers and Trustees:* Mary S. Sweeney, Pres. and Secy.; Deborah Cassinelli,* V.P.; Susan S. Kreuzmann,* V.P.; Elizabeth S. Loper,* V.P.; Gregory Sweeney,* V.P.; Pamela S. Schneider,* V.P.
EIN: 311601553

2347
SWS Charitable Foundation, Inc. ✧
1600 N.W. 163rd St.
Miami, FL 33169-5641
Contact: Robert M. Hersh

Established in 2000 in FL.
Donor: Southern Wine & Spirits of America, Inc.
Foundation type: Company-sponsored foundation.
Financial data (yr. ended 12/31/12): Assets, $462,333 (M); gifts received, $3,462,108; expenditures, $3,547,272; qualifying distributions, $3,546,094; giving activities include $3,546,094 for grants.
Purpose and activities: The foundation supports organizations involved with arts and culture, education, health, medical research, and human services.
Fields of interest: Arts; Education; Health care; Medical research; Human services.
Type of support: Annual campaigns; Emergency funds; Employee matching gifts; General/operating support; Matching/challenge support; Sponsorships.
Limitations: Applications not accepted. Giving primarily in KY, NV, NY, PA, SC, and WA, with emphasis on FL. No grants to individuals (except for employee-related disaster relief grants).
Application information: Contributes only to pre-selected organizations.
Officers: Harvey R. Chaplin, Chair.; Wayne E. Chaplin, Pres.; Steven R. Becker, Exec. V.P. and Treas.; Melvin A. Dick, Sr. V.P.; Lee Hager, Secy.
Director: Paul B. Chaplin.
Number of staff: None.
EIN: 651054944
Selected grants: The following grants are a representative sample of this grantmaker's funding activity:
$250,000 to American Red Cross, Int'L Fund/Haiti, 2010.
$125,000 to Jewish Federation, Greater Miami, Miami, FL, 2010.
$100,000 to Blessings in a Backpack, Louisville, KY, 2012.
$100,000 to Chopin Foundation of the United States, Miami, FL, 2010.
$75,000 to University of Louisville, Louisville, KY, 2010.
$68,500 to D-FY-IT, Miami, FL, 2010.
$68,000 to Nonprofit Enterprise and Self-Sustainability Team, San Francisco, CA, 2010.
$50,450 to American Cancer Society, Atlanta, GA, 2012.
$50,000 to Food Bank for New York City, New York, NY, 2012.
$40,000 to Child Help, Maui, HI, 2012.
$40,000 to Epicurean Charitable Foundation, Las Vegas, NV, 2010.
$35,000 to American Cancer Society, Atlanta, GA, 2010.
$34,500 to Boys Town of Italy, New York, NY, 2012.
$31,300 to Kids in Distress, Fort Lauderdale, FL, 2012.
$25,000 to Nevada Cancer Institute, Las Vegas, NV, 2010.
$25,000 to Smile Train, New York, NY, 2010.
$20,000 to Injured Police Officers Fund, Las Vegas, NV, 2012.
$17,500 to American Heart Association, Dallas, TX, 2012.
$15,000 to Florida International University, Miami, FL, 2012.
$10,000 to Make-A-Wish Foundation of Metro New York, Lake Success, NY, 2012.

2348
Harcourt M. and Virginia W. Sylvester Foundation, Inc. ✧
c/o Wells Fargo Bank, N.A.
255 S. Country Rd.
Palm Beach, FL 33480-4255 (561) 820-1012
Contact: Jayne Malfitano, Pres. and Secy.

Established in 1980 in FL.

Donors: Harcourt M. Sylvester‡; Virginia W. Sylvester‡.
Foundation type: Independent foundation.
Financial data (yr. ended 07/31/13): Assets, $33,559,090 (M); expenditures, $2,184,654; qualifying distributions, $1,904,400; giving activities include $1,904,400 for 23 grants (high: $1,276,900; low: $1,000).
Fields of interest: Education; Human services; United Ways and Federated Giving Programs; Infants/toddlers; Children/youth; AIDS, people with; Economically disadvantaged.
Type of support: Matching/challenge support; Research; Equipment; Capital campaigns; Building/renovation; Endowments.
Limitations: Applications not accepted. Giving primarily in FL. No grants to individuals.
Application information: Unsolicited requests for funds not accepted.
Officers and Directors:* Jayne Malfitano,* Pres. and Secy.; Laura Cameron,* V.P.; Harcourt M. Sylvester II,* Pres. Emeritus.
EIN: 592018824
Selected grants: The following grants are a representative sample of this grantmaker's funding activity:
$250,000 to University of Miami, Coral Gables, FL, 2011.
$125,000 to Deerfield Academy, Deerfield, MA, 2011.
$125,000 to Proctor Academy, Andover, NH, 2011.
$25,000 to Childrens Place at Home Safe, Lake Worth, FL, 2011.
$10,000 to Boca Raton Regional Hospital, Boca Raton, FL, 2011.
$10,000 to Food for the Poor, Coconut Creek, FL, 2011.
$10,000 to Lords Place, West Palm Beach, FL, 2011.
$5,000 to Little Smiles, West Palm Beach, FL, 2011.
$4,500 to Junior League of Boca Raton, Boca Raton, FL, 2011.
$1,000 to Caridad Center, Boynton Beach, FL, 2011.

2349
The Taft Foundation ✧
1322 S.E. 17th St.
Fort Lauderdale, FL 33316-1708

Established in 2004 in DE and FL.
Donor: Don Taft.
Foundation type: Independent foundation.
Financial data (yr. ended 12/31/12): Assets, $134,671,070 (M); gifts received, $107,000,000; expenditures, $8,164,487; qualifying distributions, $7,804,495; giving activities include $7,781,000 for 17 grants (high: $7,000,000; low: $1,000).
Fields of interest: Historic preservation/historical societies; Arts; Higher education; Education; Human services; Jewish agencies & synagogues.
Limitations: Applications not accepted. Giving primarily in FL.
Application information: Contributes only to pre-selected organizations.
Officers and Directors:* Howard Rothman,* Pres.; Britt-Louise Gilder,* V.P.
EIN: 201232852

2350
The Taishoff Family Foundation, Inc. ✧
5025 Castello Dr., Ste. 203
Naples, FL 34103-8900 (239) 261-2660

Donors: LBT Trust 1; LBT Trust 2.
Foundation type: Independent foundation.
Financial data (yr. ended 12/31/12): Assets, $32,028,528 (M); gifts received, $1,178,378; expenditures, $2,053,317; qualifying distributions, $1,678,045; giving activities include $1,488,285 for 49 grants (high: $250,000; low: $55).
Fields of interest: Higher education; Education; Hospitals (general); Health organizations, association; Christian agencies & churches; Jewish agencies & synagogues.
Limitations: Giving primarily in DC, FL, MD, NY, and VA.
Application information:
Initial approach: Letter
Officers: Robert P. Taishoff, Pres.; Laurie B. Taishoff, V.P.; Martha Taishoff, V.P.; Joel Miller, Secy.
EIN: 263582609

2351
Tangelo Park Pilot Program Inc. ✧
9840 International Dr.
Orlando, FL 32819-8111
Main URL: http://www.tangeloparkprogram.com/

Established in 2004 in FL.
Donors: Harris Rosen; Joaquin Bacardi; Sonia Bacardi; The Harris Rosen Foundation Inc.; Rosen Family Charitable Trust; Helmsbriscoe; Bacardi; Florida Hospital Medical Center; Wade's World Foundation Inc.; Fraternal Order of Angeles Charity Foundation.
Foundation type: Independent foundation.
Financial data (yr. ended 12/31/13): Assets, $53,281 (M); gifts received, $502,500; expenditures, $509,344; qualifying distributions, $509,344; giving activities include $165,033 for 11 grants (high: $55,193; low: $225), and $333,960 for 9 grants to individuals (high: $37,440; low: $34,920).
Purpose and activities: Giving to programs that improve the quality of life for students of Tangelo Park Elementary School, in Florida.
Fields of interest: Elementary/secondary education.
Type of support: General/operating support.
Limitations: Applications not accepted.
Application information: Unsolicited requests for funds not accepted.
Officers: Diondra Woodard, Chair.; Juanita Reed, Secy.; Harris Rosen, Treas.
Directors: Jeri Adkinson; Robert Allen.
EIN: 593224659

2352
Amy E. Tarrant Foundation Inc. ✧
12750 W. Hwy. 40
Ocala, FL 34481-1237 (603) 471-9909
Contact: Ronald L. Roberts
Application address: 360 Rt. 201, Ste. 3A, Bedford, NH 03110, tel.: (603) 471-9909

Established in 2000 in VT.
Donor: Amy E. Tarrant.
Foundation type: Independent foundation.
Financial data (yr. ended 12/31/12): Assets, $12,771,497 (M); expenditures, $985,795; qualifying distributions, $818,500; giving activities include $818,500 for 46 grants (high: $50,000; low: $1,000).
Purpose and activities: Giving primarily to educational organizations and to organizations which provide care and assistance to the needy, the indigent, and to those who cannot help themselves.
Fields of interest: Arts; Education; Housing/shelter, development; Human services; Children/youth, services; Family services; Aging, centers/services.
Limitations: Applications accepted. Giving primarily in Chittenden County, VT.
Application information: Application form not required.
Initial approach: Letter
Deadline(s): None
Directors: Amy E. Tarrant; Brian Tarrant; Jeremiah Tarrant; Richard E. Tarrant, Jr.
EIN: 020514457

2353
Jerry Taylor & Nancy Bryant Foundation ✧
1 Las Olas Cir., No. 1003
Fort Lauderdale, FL 33316-1635

Established in 1999 in FL.
Donors: Galen D. Taylor Charitable Lead Trust; Gerald Taylor; Nancy Bryant.
Foundation type: Independent foundation.
Financial data (yr. ended 12/31/13): Assets, $11,697,326 (M); gifts received, $199,497; expenditures, $598,685; qualifying distributions, $518,806; giving activities include $496,529 for 29 grants (high: $67,000; low: $500).
Purpose and activities: Giving primarily for human services.
Fields of interest: Higher education; Human services; Children/youth, services; Foundations (community).
Type of support: General/operating support; Emergency funds; Program development.
Limitations: Applications not accepted. No grants to individuals.
Application information: Contributes only to pre-selected organizations.
Board meeting date(s): Nov.
Trustees: Nancy Bryant; Diem Chau Taylor; Galen D. Taylor; Gerald Taylor.
EIN: 522134053

2354
Jack Taylor Family Foundation, Inc. ✧
P.O. Box 402309
Miami Beach, FL 33140

Established in 1968.
Donors: Taylor Development Corp.; Jack Taylor; Mitchell Taylor; and other members of the Taylor family.
Foundation type: Independent foundation.
Financial data (yr. ended 12/31/13): Assets, $8,244,596 (M); expenditures, $459,410; qualifying distributions, $426,296; giving activities include $426,296 for 10 grants (high: $201,000; low: $500).
Purpose and activities: Giving primarily for health organizations, as well as for the arts, education, and human services.

Fields of interest: Arts; Higher education; Health organizations; Medical research, institute; Human services; American Red Cross; Foundations (private grantmaking).
Limitations: Applications not accepted. No grants to individuals.
Application information: Unsolicited requests for funds not accepted.
Officers and Directors:* Elizabeth Taylor,* Pres.; Mitchell Taylor,* V.P. and Secy.-Treas.; Seth D. Rosen, M.D.
EIN: 596205187

2355
Max B. Tharpe Charitable Foundation, Inc. ✧
2081 N.E. 56 St., Ste. 205
Fort Lauderdale, FL 33308-2533

Donor: Max B. Tharpe Irrevocable Trust.
Foundation type: Independent foundation.
Financial data (yr. ended 12/31/12): Assets, $1,984,117 (M); gifts received, $30,000; expenditures, $784,336; qualifying distributions, $420,140; giving activities include $420,140 for 5 grants (high: $300,000; low: $3,500).
Fields of interest: Protestant agencies & churches.
Limitations: Applications not accepted.
Application information: Unsolicited requests for funds not accepted.
Officer: Barbara Morin, Pres.
EIN: 261569652

2356
Samuel E. & Mary W. Thatcher Foundation, Inc. ✧
9130 S. Dadeland Blvd., Ste. 1901
Miami, FL 33156

Established in 1982 in FL.
Donors: John W. Thatcher; Mary W. Thatcher‡; Mary Thatcher Irrevocable Trust.
Foundation type: Independent foundation.
Financial data (yr. ended 12/31/13): Assets, $16,954,376 (M); gifts received, $188,730; expenditures, $2,245,779; qualifying distributions, $2,040,013; giving activities include $2,040,013 for 59 grants (high: $264,000; low: $1,000).
Purpose and activities: Support primarily for religious ministries, particularly for youth; giving also for higher education.
Fields of interest: Higher education; Education; Youth, services; Christian agencies & churches.
Limitations: Applications not accepted. Giving primarily in FL. No grants to individuals.
Application information: Contributes only to pre-selected organizations.
Directors: Jacqueline L. Eads; William R. Jordan III; David M. Richardson; Paul M. Stokes.
EIN: 592230243

2357
William and Helen Thomas Charitable Trust ✧
c/o U.S. Trust, Bank of America, N.A.
900 S.E. Federal Hwy., 2nd Fl., M/C: FL5-359-02-6
Stuart, FL 34994-3733 (772) 403-1623
Contact: Bonney A. Johnson, Sr. V.P., U.S. Trust
FAX: (772) 403-1617;
E-mail: bonney.johnson@ustrust.com; Main URL: http://fdnweb.org/thomas

Established in 1990 in FL.
Donors: William A. Thomas‡; Helen S. Thomas; Emily Thomas‡.
Foundation type: Independent foundation.
Financial data (yr. ended 12/31/13): Assets, $23,201,745 (M); expenditures, $1,666,497; qualifying distributions, $1,433,107; giving activities include $1,327,000 for 54 grants (high: $100,000; low: $5,000).
Purpose and activities: Giving primarily for: 1) Educational opportunities for deserving and needy students; 2) Preservation and protection of the natural environment; 3) Medical research and care for the treatment, prevention and cure of arthritis, blindness and diabetes; 4) Assistance for the poor, especially those of Appalachia and those of American Indian ancestry; and 5) Assistance and care for orphaned children who are unlikely to be adopted because of age, handicap, or for other reasons.
Fields of interest: Education; Environment; Health organizations, association; Human services; Children/youth, services; Disabilities, people with; Blind/visually impaired; Native Americans/American Indians.
Type of support: General/operating support; Continuing support; Annual campaigns; Capital campaigns; Building/renovation; Equipment; Endowments; Program development; Curriculum development; Scholarship funds; Matching/challenge support.
Limitations: Applications accepted. Giving primarily in FL and Appalachia. No grants to individuals.
Application information: Applicants are encouraged to submit applications in advance of the deadline. Application form required.
Initial approach: Use online application on foundation web site
Deadline(s): Sept. 15
Board meeting date(s): Nov.
Final notification: Within 3 months
Trustees: Dennis Blanz; James H. Elam; James Keffler; Marilyn Moore; U.S. Trust Co., N.A.
Number of staff: 1
EIN: 366917007
Selected grants: The following grants are a representative sample of this grantmaker's funding activity:
$125,000 to Hospice of Martin and Saint Lucie, Stuart, FL, 2012. For third installment of four year capital commitment totalling $500,000 for the counseling center.
$100,000 to Indian River State College Foundation, Fort Pierce, FL, 2012. For STEM Center.
$60,000 to Safespace, Stuart, FL, 2012. For general operations of the organization.
$50,000 to Indian River State College Foundation, Fort Pierce, FL, 2012. For William and Helen Thomas Nursing Scholarship Fund.
$50,000 to LifeBuilders of the Treasure Coast, Fort Pierce, FL, 2012. For general operations of the organization.
$50,000 to Miami Lighthouse for the Blind and Visually Impaired, Miami, FL, 2012. For Braille Literacy and Technology program.
$50,000 to Palm Beach Atlantic University, West Palm Beach, FL, 2012. For School of Nursing Scholarships.
$25,000 to Exchange Club Center for the Prevention of Child Abuse of Fort Pierce, Fort Pierce, FL, 2012. For Safe Families program.
$25,000 to Martin Memorial Foundation, Stuart, FL, 2012. For The William and Helen Thomas Charitable Trust Nursing Education Fund.
$20,000 to Place of Hope, Palm Beach Gardens, FL, 2012. For general operations of the organization.

2358
The Thompson Family Charitable Foundation Inc. ✧
P.O. Box 1370
Loxahatchee, FL 33470-1370
Application address: c/o Shannon Thompson, P.O. Box 679, Camilla, GA 31730, tel.: (229) 336-1761

Established in 2007 in FL.
Donor: Joe Kay Thompson.
Foundation type: Independent foundation.
Financial data (yr. ended 12/31/13): Assets, $160,800 (M); gifts received, $508,860; expenditures, $508,385; qualifying distributions, $508,385; giving activities include $507,500 for 16 grants (high: $100,000; low: $1,000).
Fields of interest: Religion.
Limitations: Applications accepted. Giving primarily in FL, IL and NC.
Application information: Application form required.
Initial approach: Letter
Deadline(s): None
Directors: Michael W. Shiver; Aaron Thompson; Joe E. Thompson, Jr.; Kara Thompson; Kay H. Thompson; Shannon Thompson.
EIN: 260849782
Selected grants: The following grants are a representative sample of this grantmaker's funding activity:
$100,000 to Billy Graham Evangelistic Association, Charlotte, NC, 2012. For Spread the Gospel of Jesus Christ.
$100,000 to Focus on the Family, Colorado Springs, CO, 2012. To promote Biblical Truths Worldwide.
$20,000 to Bible Study Fellowship, San Antonio, TX, 2012. For International Bible Study.
$12,000 to American Missionary Fellowship, Villanova, PA, 2012. For Stateside Missions.
$5,000 to In Touch Ministries, Atlanta, GA, 2012. For Worldwide Spread of Jesus Christ.
$5,000 to Mastermedia International, Redlands, CA, 2012. For Christian Media Leaders.

2359
Thompson-Hartford Foundation, Inc. ✧ ☆
P.O. Box 1288
Tampa, FL 33601-1288

Established in 2006 in FL.
Donors: Harold Hartford; Nylah J. Thompson; Eleanor S. Thompson Charitable Lead Annuity Trust I; James R. Thompson Charitable Lead Annuity Trust I.
Foundation type: Independent foundation.
Financial data (yr. ended 12/31/13): Assets, $7,589,761 (M); expenditures, $504,032; qualifying distributions, $455,000; giving activities include $455,000 for 10 grants (high: $100,000; low: $5,000).
Fields of interest: Higher education, university.
Limitations: Applications not accepted. Giving primarily in FL.

Application information: Unsolicited requests for funds not accepted.
Officers: Nylah J. Thompson, Pres. and Secy.; Harold L. Hartford, V.P. and Treas.
Director: Lisa M. Nicholas.
EIN: 204662640
Selected grants: The following grants are a representative sample of this grantmaker's funding activity:
$285,000 to Seminole Boosters, Tallahassee, FL, 2011.
$100,000 to Mercy Ministries of America, Nashville, TN, 2011.

2360
The Thornburgh Family Foundation ✧
14 Golfview Rd.
Palm Beach, FL 33480

Established in 2005 in NY.
Donor: Richard E. Thornburgh.
Foundation type: Independent foundation.
Financial data (yr. ended 12/31/12): Assets, $6,643,451 (M); gifts received, $1,505,282; expenditures, $1,919,295; qualifying distributions, $1,902,130; giving activities include $1,902,000 for 9 grants (high: $1,275,000; low: $5,000).
Fields of interest: Education; Environment; Human services; Christian agencies & churches.
Limitations: Applications not accepted. Giving primarily in CT and NY. No grants to individuals.
Application information: Contributes only to pre-selected organizations.
Trustees: Cornelia P. Thornburgh; Richard E. Thornburgh.
EIN: 203950886

2361
Louise B. Blackman Tollefson Family Foundation ✧ ☆
400 Royal Palm Way, Ste. 304
Palm Beach, FL 33480-4117

Established in 2001 in FL.
Donors: Bennett H. Tollefson; Louise B. Tollefson; The Jean Keller & Robert Carros Foundation.
Foundation type: Independent foundation.
Financial data (yr. ended 12/31/12): Assets, $11,186,759 (M); gifts received, $725,420; expenditures, $644,157; qualifying distributions, $450,000; giving activities include $450,000 for grants.
Fields of interest: Health organizations; Medical research; Human services.
Limitations: Applications not accepted. Giving primarily in CT, FL, and NY. No grants to individuals.
Application information: Contributes only to pre-selected organizations.
Trustee: Robert G. Simses.
EIN: 066503680

2362
Tsunami Foundation ✧
c/o Anson M. Beard, Jr.
421 Peruvian Ave.
Palm Beach, FL 33480-4518

Established in 1993 in CT.
Donor: Anson McCook Beard, Jr.
Foundation type: Independent foundation.
Financial data (yr. ended 12/31/13): Assets, $30,195,600 (M); gifts received, $2,250,000; expenditures, $1,342,700; qualifying distributions, $1,129,025; giving activities include $1,110,000 for 25 grants (high: $90,000; low: $5,000).
Purpose and activities: Giving primarily for education, conservation, health, and human services.
Fields of interest: Arts; Education; Environment, natural resources; Health care; Human services.
Limitations: Applications not accepted. Giving primarily in NY and PA. No grants to individuals.
Application information: Contributes only to pre-selected organizations.
Trustees: Anson H. Beard; Anson McCook Beard, Jr.; Debra Beard; James M. Beard; Veronica M. Beard; Veronica S. Beard.
EIN: 137019761

2363
Tupperware Brands Foundation ✧
(formerly Tupperware Children's Foundation)
14901 S. Orange Blossom Trail
Orlando, FL 32837-6600

Established in 2003 in FL.
Donors: Tupperware U.S., Inc.; Tupperware Brands Corp.
Foundation type: Company-sponsored foundation.
Financial data (yr. ended 12/31/13): Assets, $30,521 (M); gifts received, $318,868; expenditures, $425,535; qualifying distributions, $425,535; giving activities include $418,358 for 17 grants (high: $250,000; low: $25,000), and $7,050 for 5 grants to individuals (high: $500; low: $250).
Purpose and activities: The foundation supports programs designed to educate and empower women and girls.
Fields of interest: Boys & girls clubs; Youth development, business; Women; Girls.
Type of support: General/operating support; Capital campaigns.
Limitations: Applications not accepted. Giving primarily in Lakeland and Orlando, FL. No grants to individuals.
Application information: Contributes only to pre-selected organizations.
Officers and Directors:* Lillian D. Garcia,* Pres.; Josef Hajek, Secy.; Michael Poteshman,* Treas.; Yolanda Londono, Exec. Dir.; Thomas M. Roehlk*.
Trustee: Tupperware Brands Corp.
EIN: 550824285

2364
Two Eagles Foundation Inc. ✧
307 Santander Ct.
Punta Gorda, FL 33950-8043

Established in 2004 in FL.
Donors: David C. Orlowski; Delta Christine Orlowski.
Foundation type: Independent foundation.
Financial data (yr. ended 12/31/13): Assets, $34,275,552 (M); gifts received, $86,496; expenditures, $2,457,452; qualifying distributions, $2,306,204; giving activities include $2,300,000 for 69 grants (high: $50,000; low: $7,500).
Purpose and activities: Giving primarily to Roman Catholic schools.
Fields of interest: Education.
Limitations: Applications not accepted. Giving primarily in FL, IL, MI, TN and WI. No grants to individuals.
Application information: Contributes only to pre-selected organizations.
Officers and Directors:* David C. Orlowski,* Pres.; Delta Christine Orlowski,* Secy.-Treas.; Michael Navarro; Doris A. Orlowski; Michael W. Orlowski.
EIN: 830399899

2365
The TWS Foundation ✧
c/o Thomas W. Smith
2200 Butts Rd., No. 320
Boca Raton, FL 33431-7453 (561) 314-0800
Contact: Thomas W. Smith, Tr.

Established in 1984 in NY.
Donor: Thomas W. Smith.
Foundation type: Independent foundation.
Financial data (yr. ended 12/31/12): Assets, $6,845,959 (M); gifts received, $6,327,750; expenditures, $5,884,565; qualifying distributions, $5,826,514; giving activities include $5,619,287 for grants.
Fields of interest: Arts; Education; Health care; Health organizations, association; Human services; Community/economic development; Public policy, research.
Type of support: General/operating support; Scholarship funds.
Limitations: Giving primarily in CT, ID, NY, RI, and VA. No grants to individuals.
Application information:
Initial approach: Letter
Deadline(s): None
Trustee: Thomas W. Smith.
EIN: 133258067

2366
Albert L. Ueltschi Foundation ✧
481 Indian Harbor Rd.
Vero Beach, FL 32963-3512
Albert Lee Ueltschi's Giving Pledge Profile: http://glasspockets.org/philanthropy-in-focus/eye-on-the-giving-pledge/profiles/ueltschi

Established in 2003 in FL as a successor to the original Albert L. Ueltschi Foundation (Irvine, CA).
Donors: Albert L. Ueltschi†; James T. Ueltschi.
Foundation type: Independent foundation.
Financial data (yr. ended 12/31/13): Assets, $198,067,161 (M); gifts received, $187,470,678; expenditures, $7,003,006; qualifying distributions, $7,002,975; giving activities include $7,000,000 for 2 grants (high: $5,000,000; low: $2,000,000).
Fields of interest: Eye diseases.
Limitations: Applications not accepted. Giving primarily in Boston, MA. No grants to individuals.
Application information: Contributes only to pre-selected organizations.
Trustee: James T. Ueltschi.
EIN: 550838858

2367
Thomas J. and Sandra L. Usher Charitable Foundation ✧
26124 Fawnwood Ct.
Bonita Springs, FL 34134-8690

Established in 1999 in PA.
Donors: Thomas J. Usher; Sandra L. Usher.
Foundation type: Independent foundation.
Financial data (yr. ended 12/31/13): Assets, $16,184,182 (M); expenditures, $1,232,821; qualifying distributions, $1,046,382; giving activities include $1,046,382 for 139 grants (high: $250,000; low: $100).
Fields of interest: Education; Offenders/ex-offenders, services; Youth development; Human services; Family services; Christian agencies & churches.
Limitations: Applications not accepted. Giving primarily in PA; some funding nationally. No grants to individuals.
Application information: Contributes only to pre-selected organizations.
Trustees: Sandra L. Usher; Thomas J. Usher.
EIN: 256681379

2368
Van Vleet Foundation ✧
P.O. Box 1908
Orlando, FL 32802-1908

Established in 1962 in TN.
Donor: Harriet Smith Van Vleet‡.
Foundation type: Independent foundation.
Financial data (yr. ended 12/31/13): Assets, $10,705,821 (M); expenditures, $551,864; qualifying distributions, $517,882; giving activities include $487,180 for 4 grants (high: $283,665; low: $13,875).
Purpose and activities: Grants to local area universities, as well as to a children's hospital.
Fields of interest: Higher education; Hospitals (specialty).
Type of support: Equipment; Endowments; Fellowships; Scholarship funds.
Limitations: Applications not accepted. Giving limited to Memphis, TN. No grants to individuals.
Application information: Contributes only to pre-selected organizations.
Advisors: B. Snowden Boyle, Jr.; William L. Richmond.
Trustee: SunTrust Banks, Inc.
EIN: 626034067
Selected grants: The following grants are a representative sample of this grantmaker's funding activity:
$256,638 to University of Tennessee Medical Group, Memphis, TN, 2010. For general charitable purposes.
$124,190 to University of Memphis, Memphis, TN, 2011. For general charitable purpose.
$80,539 to Saint Jude Childrens Research Hospital, Memphis, TN, 2010. For general charitable purposes.
$13,485 to Rhodes College, Memphis, TN, 2011. For general charitable purposes.

2369
Van Voorhis Family Foundation ✧ ☆
13 Maria Pl.
Ponte Vedra Beach, FL 32082-2314

Established in 2000 in OH.
Donor: Samuel D. Van Voorhis.
Foundation type: Independent foundation.
Financial data (yr. ended 12/31/13): Assets, $773,202 (M); expenditures, $732,050; qualifying distributions, $723,080; giving activities include $723,080 for 23 grants (high: $110,000; low: $1,000).
Purpose and activities: Giving to Worthington, Ohio, Christian schools.
Fields of interest: Education.
Type of support: Scholarship funds.
Limitations: Applications not accepted. Giving in the U.S., with some emphasis on GA. No grants to individuals.
Application information: Unsolicited requests for funds not accepted.
Directors: Tom Anglea; Steven McCollum; John A. Van Voorhis; Julie A. Van Voorhis; Samuel D. Van Voorhis.
EIN: 311743340

2370
Vanneck-Bailey Foundation ✧ ☆
c/o William P. Vanneck
217 West Indies Dr.
Palm Beach, FL 33480-3408

Established in 1971 in NY through the consolidation of The Vanneck Foundation, incorporated in 1949 in NY, and The Frank and Marie Bailey Foundation.
Donors: John Vanneck‡; Barbara Bailey Vanneck.
Foundation type: Independent foundation.
Financial data (yr. ended 12/31/13): Assets, $7,157,944 (M); expenditures, $457,994; qualifying distributions, $449,604; giving activities include $422,000 for 12 grants (high: $50,000; low: $10,000).
Fields of interest: Elementary/secondary education; Higher education; Environment, natural resources; Botanical gardens; Hospitals (general); Health care; Cancer; Medical research; Children/youth, services; Community/economic development; Protestant agencies & churches.
Limitations: Applications not accepted. Giving primarily in the greater metropolitan New York, NY, area and CT; giving also in CA, FL, IL, MA, TX, and VT. No grants to individuals.
Application information: Contributes only to pre-selected organizations.
Officers: Barbara V. May, Pres.; William P. Vanneck, V.P.; Domenick A. Salsa, Secy.-Treas.
EIN: 237165285
Selected grants: The following grants are a representative sample of this grantmaker's funding activity:
$30,000 to Brooklyn Botanic Garden, Brooklyn, NY, 2011. For general unrestricted use.
$25,000 to New York-Presbyterian Hospital, New York, NY, 2011. For general unrestricted use.
$15,000 to Columbia University, College of Physicians and Surgeons, New York, NY, 2011. For general unrestricted use.
$15,000 to Memorial Sloan-Kettering Cancer Center, New York, NY, 2011. For general unrestricted use.
$15,000 to Rockefeller University, New York, NY, 2011. For general unrestricted use.
$15,000 to Ronald McDonald House Charities, Oak Brook, IL, 2011. For general unrestricted use.
$10,000 to Kids in Crisis, Cos Cob, CT, 2011. For general unrestricted use.
$7,500 to Freedom Institute, New York, NY, 2011. For general unrestricted use.
$7,500 to Hole in the Wall Gang Fund, New Haven, CT, 2011. For general unrestricted use.
$1,500 to University of Vermont, Burlington, VT, 2011. For general unrestricted use.

2371
The Joan & John Vatterott Family Foundation ✧
1144 Gulf Shores Blvd.
Naples, FL 34102-7051

Established in 2006 in FL.
Foundation type: Independent foundation.
Financial data (yr. ended 12/31/12): Assets, $2,934,184 (M); expenditures, $651,877; qualifying distributions, $448,698; giving activities include $448,698 for grants.
Fields of interest: Elementary/secondary education; Education; Human services; Foundations (private grantmaking).
Limitations: Applications not accepted. Giving primarily in St. Louis, MO; some funding also in CA. No grants to individuals.
Application information: Unsolicited requests for funds not accepted.
Trustees: Kathleen Vatterott Crider; Maria Vatterott Fitzgerald; Genevieve Vatterott Haas; Joan M. Vatterott; John C. Vatterott; John C. Vatterott, Jr.; Patrick Vatterott; Timothy Vatterott.
EIN: 204789447

2372
Vinik Family Foundation ✧
914 S. Golf View St.
Tampa, FL 33629-5222 (813) 251-1302
Contact: Jeffrey N. Vinik, Tr.

Established in 1998 in MA.
Donor: Jeffrey N. Vinik.
Foundation type: Independent foundation.
Financial data (yr. ended 12/31/12): Assets, $212,357,560 (M); expenditures, $10,787,645; qualifying distributions, $10,783,232; giving activities include $9,594,854 for 51 grants (high: $3,050,000; low: $100).
Fields of interest: Museums; Education; Human services.
Limitations: Applications not accepted. Giving primarily in MA. No grants to individuals.
Application information: Contributes only to pre-selected organizations.
Trustees: Jeffrey N. Vinik; Mary Penny Vinik.
EIN: 911917506
Selected grants: The following grants are a representative sample of this grantmaker's funding activity:
$3,050,000 to Meadowbrook School, Weston, MA, 2012. For general support.
$1,615,000 to Duke University, Durham, NC, 2012. For general support.
$1,250,000 to Presbyterian Conference Association, Holmes, NY, 2012. For general support.
$850,000 to Brigham and Women's Hospital, Boston, MA, 2012. For general support.
$500,000 to Tampa Bay Host Committee, Tampa, FL, 2012. For general support.
$300,000 to Combined Jewish Philanthropies of Greater Boston, Boston, MA, 2012. For general support.
$230,000 to Worcester Academy, Worcester, MA, 2012. For general support.
$110,000 to Newton-Wellesley Hospital, Newton, MA, 2012. For general support.
$100,000 to Red Sox Foundation, Boston, MA, 2012. For general support.
$30,000 to Riverdale Country School, Bronx, NY, 2012. For general support.

2373
Vollmer Foundation, Inc. ✧
c/o Claudia Sanchez Prodek, Inc.
10900 N.W. 21st St., Unit 190
Miami, FL 33172-2024

Incorporated in 1965 in NY.
Donor: Alberto F. Vollmer†.
Foundation type: Independent foundation.
Financial data (yr. ended 12/31/13): Assets, $424,861,511 (M); expenditures, $3,308,816; qualifying distributions, $3,148,687; giving activities include $3,105,412 for 58 grants.
Purpose and activities: Giving primarily for health, higher and other education, and social services in Venezuela.
Fields of interest: Higher education; Education; Health care; Youth development; Children/youth, services; Community/economic development; Science, research.
International interests: Venezuela.
Type of support: General/operating support; Continuing support; Research.
Limitations: Applications not accepted. Giving primarily in Venezuela. No grants to individuals, or for building funds or matching gifts; no loans.
Application information: Contributes only to pre-selected organizations. Unsolicited requests for funds not considered.
Board meeting date(s): As required
Officers and Directors:* Gustavo J. Vollmer,* Pres.; Ana Luisa Estrada Wallis,* V.P. and Treas.; Carolina Vollmer-Eseverri, Secy.; Gustavo A. Vollmer.
Number of staff: 1 full-time professional; 1 part-time professional.
EIN: 132620718

2374
Don & Zelma Waggoner Foundation ✧
1252 Gordon River Trail N.
Naples, FL 34105-2773

Established in 1994 in FL.
Donors: Don Waggoner; Zelma Waggoner.
Foundation type: Independent foundation.
Financial data (yr. ended 12/31/13): Assets, $5,030,043 (M); gifts received, $1,500,000; expenditures, $794,028; qualifying distributions, $759,411; giving activities include $759,411 for 23 grants (high: $400,000; low: $100).
Purpose and activities: Giving primarily for education, human services, and to Christian agencies and churches.
Fields of interest: Arts; Higher education; Housing/shelter, development; Human services; Children/youth, services; Christian agencies & churches.
Limitations: Applications not accepted. Giving primarily in FL and SC. No grants to individuals.
Application information: Contributes only to pre-selected organizations.
Trustees: Don Waggoner; Zelma Waggoner.
EIN: 656141632
Selected grants: The following grants are a representative sample of this grantmaker's funding activity:
$100,178 to Habitat for Humanity of Collier County, Naples, FL, 2011.
$20,000 to South Carolina District Church of the Nazarene, West Columbia, SC, 2011.
$19,000 to Metropolitan Arts Council, Greenville, SC, 2011.
$5,000 to Trevecca Nazarene University, Nashville, TN, 2011.
$2,000 to Limestone College, Gaffney, SC, 2011.
$2,000 to Sistercare, Columbia, SC, 2011.
$1,000 to Epilepsy Foundation, Landover, MD, 2011.
$1,000 to Glenforest School, West Columbia, SC, 2011.
$1,000 to Make-A-Wish Foundation of South Carolina, Greenville, SC, 2011.
$1,000 to Marine Toys for Tots Foundation, Triangle, VA, 2011.

2375
The Walter Foundation ✧
(formerly Jim Walter Corporation Foundation)
13623 N. Florida Ave.
Tampa, FL 33613-3216 (813) 961-0530
Contact: Steven L. Myers, Tr.

Established in 1966 in FL.
Donor: Walter Industries, Inc.
Foundation type: Company-sponsored foundation.
Financial data (yr. ended 08/31/14): Assets, $17,489,334 (M); expenditures, $1,079,189; qualifying distributions, $877,400; giving activities include $877,400 for 59 grants (high: $75,000; low: $2,500).
Purpose and activities: The foundation supports hospitals and organizations involved with orchestras, historical activities, secondary and higher education, mental health and crisis services, hunger, human services, and Christianity.
Fields of interest: Performing arts, orchestras; Historical activities; Secondary school/education; Higher education; Hospitals (general); Mental health/crisis services; Food distribution, meals on wheels; Boys & girls clubs; Salvation Army; Children, services; Residential/custodial care; Developmentally disabled, centers & services; Human services; Christian agencies & churches.
Type of support: General/operating support.
Limitations: Applications accepted. Giving primarily in FL. No grants to individuals.
Application information: Application form not required.
Initial approach: Proposal
Deadline(s): None
Trustees: W.K. Baker; S.L. Myers; A.J. Walter; R.A. Walter.
EIN: 596205802
Selected grants: The following grants are a representative sample of this grantmaker's funding activity:
$100,000 to University of Tampa, Tampa, FL, 2010.
$100,000 to University of Tampa, Tampa, FL, 2011.
$75,000 to Florida Orchestra, Saint Petersburg, FL, 2011.
$50,000 to Idlewild Baptist Church, Lutz, FL, 2010.
$37,000 to Idlewild Baptist Church, Lutz, FL, 2011.
$30,000 to Tampa General Hospital Foundation, Tampa, FL, 2011.
$25,000 to American Red Cross, Tampa, FL, 2010.
$25,000 to Florida Orchestra, Saint Petersburg, FL, 2010.
$25,000 to Tampa Bay History Center, Tampa, FL, 2011.
$25,000 to Tampa Bay History Center, Tampa, FL, 2010.
$25,000 to Tampa General Hospital Foundation, Tampa, FL, 2010.
$15,000 to University of South Florida Foundation, Tampa, FL, 2010.
$15,000 to University of South Florida Foundation, Tampa, FL, 2011.
$10,000 to HARC, Tampa, FL, 2010.
$10,000 to HARC, Tampa, FL, 2011.
$10,000 to Metropolitan Ministries, Tampa, FL, 2011.
$10,000 to Tampa General Hospital Foundation, Tampa, FL, 2010.
$10,000 to Tampa Lighthouse for the Blind, Tampa, FL, 2010.
$10,000 to Tampa Lighthouse for the Blind, Tampa, FL, 2011.
$10,000 to Vanderbilt University, Nashville, TN, 2011.

2376
Edna Wardlaw Charitable Trust ✧
P.O. Box 1908
Orlando, FL 32802-1908
Application address: c/o SunTrust Bank, P.O. Box 4655, Atlanta, GA 30302

Established in 1992 in GA.
Donor: Edna Wardlaw.
Foundation type: Independent foundation.
Financial data (yr. ended 12/31/13): Assets, $17,459,039 (M); expenditures, $1,015,245; qualifying distributions, $954,212; giving activities include $929,000 for 81 grants (high: $42,500; low: $1,000).
Fields of interest: Education; Environment, natural resources; Reproductive health, family planning; Children/youth, services; Family services; Homeless, human services; International affairs, goodwill promotion; International peace/security; International human rights.
Limitations: Applications accepted. Giving on a national basis.
Application information:
Initial approach: Letter
Copies of proposal: 1
Deadline(s): None
Trustee: SunTrust Banks, Inc.
EIN: 586278167
Selected grants: The following grants are a representative sample of this grantmaker's funding activity:
$10,000 to Adaptive Design Association, New York, NY, 2011. For general charitable purpose.
$5,000 to A. J. Muste Memorial Institute, New York, NY, 2011. For general charitable purpose.
$3,500 to San Francisco Conservation Corps, San Francisco, CA, 2011. For general charitable purpose.

2377
The Gertrude and William C. Wardlaw Fund ✧
P.O. Box 1908
Orlando, FL 32802-1908
Contact: Gertrude Wardlaw

Established in 1936 in GA; incorporated in 1951.
Donors: Gertrude Wardlaw; William C. Wardlaw, Jr.†.
Foundation type: Independent foundation.
Financial data (yr. ended 12/31/13): Assets, $19,921,855 (M); expenditures, $720,497; qualifying distributions, $640,580; giving activities include $603,504 for 60 grants (high: $50,004; low: $1,000).
Purpose and activities: Giving primarily to educational, health-related, and arts-related public charities.

Fields of interest: Arts; Education; Health care; Homeless.
Type of support: General/operating support.
Limitations: Applications accepted. Giving primarily in Atlanta, GA. No grants to individuals.
Application information: Application form required.
Initial approach: Letter
Copies of proposal: 1
Deadline(s): None
Board meeting date(s): Mar.
Officer and Trustees:* Chris Beyers,* Secy.; Charlotte C. Hoffman; William C. Wardlaw III; SunTrust Bank.
EIN: 586026065

2378
The Ware Foundation ✧
5825 Sunset Dr., Ste. 306
South Miami, FL 33143-5222
E-mail: info@warefoundation.org; Application address: 6609 S.W. 65th St., Miami, FL 33143, tel.: (305) 662-5002; Main URL: http://www.warefoundation.org

Trust established in 1950 in PA.
Donor: John H. Ware, Jr.‡.
Foundation type: Independent foundation.
Financial data (yr. ended 12/31/12): Assets, $19,432,030 (M); expenditures, $1,062,615; qualifying distributions, $841,923; giving activities include $678,508 for 31 grants (high: $75,000; low: $1,000).
Purpose and activities: The foundation's mission is to promote social responsibility by providing grants that improve the quality of people's lives, particularly the lives of children.
Fields of interest: Higher education; Education; Environment, water resources; Environment; Medical research; Crime/violence prevention, child abuse; Human services.
Limitations: Giving primarily in CO and FL. No support for private foundations. No grants to individuals.
Publications: Application guidelines.
Application information: When forwarding an application or correspondence electronically please put a copy in the mail. Telephone inquiries are not accepted. Application form not required.
Initial approach: Letter or proposal, no more than 2 pages
Final notification: Positive responses only; up to 6 months from receipt of letter
Officer: Mark Edwards, Secy.-Treas.
Trustees: Elizabeth Eason; John Edwards; James Odom; Morgan Ware-Soumah.
EIN: 237286585
Selected grants: The following grants are a representative sample of this grantmaker's funding activity:
$75,000 to Florida International University, Miami, FL, 2012. For Eg Ware Foundation - Neuro Engineering Professorship.
$50,000 to Phoenix Multisport, Boulder, CO, 2012. For operation cost of staff, equipment and Programs.
$33,250 to Florida International University, Miami, FL, 2012. For Award- Underage Drinking C- Birg.
$25,000 to Kristi House, Miami, FL, 2012. To support Victims of Sex Trafficking.
$15,000 to Atlanta International School, Atlanta, GA, 2012. For financial aid assistance.
$10,000 to Atlanta International School, Atlanta, GA, 2012. For Technology Programs, Assist in Purchasing 10 Laptops for Financial Aid Students.
$2,245 to Kristi House, Miami, FL, 2012. To assist in Project Gold -Drop in Center/Shelter.

2379
E. G. Watkins Family Foundation ✧
c/o Goodrich, LLC
525 Okeechobee Blvd., Ste. 1000
West Palm Beach, FL 33401-6357

Established in 1998 in MA.
Donors: Edward G. Watkins; C Black Hills Trust; K Black Hills Trust.
Foundation type: Independent foundation.
Financial data (yr. ended 12/31/12): Assets, $876,005 (M); gifts received, $3,700,000; expenditures, $3,746,723; qualifying distributions, $3,744,500; giving activities include $3,744,500 for grants.
Purpose and activities: Giving primarily to hospitals and education.
Fields of interest: Historic preservation/historical societies; Education; Hospitals (general).
Limitations: Applications not accepted. Giving primarily in MA. No grants to individuals.
Application information: Contributes only to pre-selected organizations.
Trustees: Stanley L. Clark; Douglas Dubiel; Joseph Marzilli; Edward G. Watkins; Jennifer Wynne.
EIN: 311612983

2380
The William R. Watts Foundation, Inc. ✧
(formerly The Watts Foundation, Inc.)
P.O. Box 39238
Fort Lauderdale, FL 33339-9238
Contact: Wilson B. Greaton, Jr., Pres.

Established in 1992 in FL.
Donor: William R. Watts, Sr.‡.
Foundation type: Independent foundation.
Financial data (yr. ended 10/31/13): Assets, $22,509,400 (M); expenditures, $1,299,433; qualifying distributions, $1,187,229; giving activities include $1,100,000 for 36 grants (high: $110,000; low: $5,000).
Purpose and activities: The foundation supports charities in Broward County and Miami-Dade counties, FL.
Fields of interest: Higher education, university; Boys & girls clubs; Salvation Army; United Ways and Federated Giving Programs; Children; Blind/visually impaired; Economically disadvantaged.
Type of support: General/operating support; Continuing support; Annual campaigns; Capital campaigns; Building/renovation; Endowments; Debt reduction; Scholarship funds.
Limitations: Applications accepted. Giving limited to Miami-Dade and Broward counties, FL. No grants to individuals, or for memberships, fundraising events or memorials.
Publications: Application guidelines; Financial statement.
Application information: Bound or faxed proposals are not accepted. Application form not required.
Initial approach: Cover letter on organization's letterhead, plus a narrative consisting of no more than 3 typewritten pages
Copies of proposal: 1
Deadline(s): Aug. 1
Board meeting date(s): Sept.
Final notification: Oct. 31
Officers and Directors:* Wilson B. Greaton, Jr.,* Pres.; Elizabeth G. Stephany,* V.P. and Secy.-Treas.; Richard G. Coker, Jr.; Paul E. Daly; Mary E. Donworth; Nancy Jones; Alan Loehr; William J. Rotella.
Number of staff: None.
EIN: 591971220

2381
Barton and Shirley Weisman Foundation, Inc. ✧
17603 Lake Estates Dr.
Boca Raton, FL 33496-1425

Established in 2004 in FL.
Donors: Barton Weisman; Shirley Weisman.
Foundation type: Independent foundation.
Financial data (yr. ended 12/31/13): Assets, $7,809,045 (M); gifts received, $313,980; expenditures, $597,820; qualifying distributions, $584,140; giving activities include $584,140 for 21 grants (high: $253,000; low: $500).
Fields of interest: Human services; Jewish agencies & synagogues.
Limitations: Applications not accepted. Giving primarily in FL. No grants to individuals.
Application information: Contributes only to pre-selected organizations.
Directors: Marcia Langley; Andrew Weisman; Barton Weisman; Shirley Weisman.
EIN: 202825536

2382
The John F. Welch, Jr. Foundation ✧
11935 Lost Tree Way
North Palm Beach, FL 33408

Established in 1986 in CT.
Donors: John F. Welch, Jr.; Executive Focus International; General Electric, Inc.
Foundation type: Independent foundation.
Financial data (yr. ended 12/31/13): Assets, $10,018,851 (M); expenditures, $1,446,925; qualifying distributions, $1,432,125; giving activities include $1,432,125 for 62 grants (high: $500,000; low: $500).
Purpose and activities: Giving primarily for human services, higher education, and hospitals.
Fields of interest: Higher education; Hospitals (general); Health organizations; Human services; Children/youth, services; Catholic agencies & churches.
Limitations: Applications not accepted. Giving primarily in CT, MA and NY. No grants to individuals.
Application information: Contributes only to pre-selected organizations.
Trustee: John F. Welch, Jr.
EIN: 222801492
Selected grants: The following grants are a representative sample of this grantmaker's funding activity:
$500,000 to Sacred Heart University, Fairfield, CT, 2011. For general operating support.
$50,000 to Boys and Girls Club of Greater Salem, Salem, MA, 2011. For general operating support.
$50,000 to First Presbyterian Church, North Palm Beach, FL, 2011. For general operating support.

$50,000 to Pomfret School, Pomfret, CT, 2011. For general operating support.
$40,000 to Belmont Hill School, Belmont, MA, 2011. For general operating support.
$25,000 to Sankaty Head Foundation, Siasconset, MA, 2011.
$20,000 to Gateway High School, San Francisco, CA, 2011. For general operating support.
$10,000 to Graham-Windham, New York, NY, 2011. For general operating support.
$10,000 to Sconset Trust, Siasconset, MA, 2011.
$9,200 to Nantucket Golf Club Foundation, Siasconset, MA, 2011. For general operating support.

2383
Lillian S. Wells Foundation, Inc. ✧
600 Sagamore Rd.
Fort Lauderdale, FL 33301-2215
Contact: Patricia F. Mulvaney, Exec. Dir.
E-mail: patricia.mulvaney@thewellsfamily.net

Established around 1976 in FL.
Donors: Barbara S. Wells; Preston A. Wells, Jr.‡.
Foundation type: Independent foundation.
Financial data (yr. ended 12/31/12): Assets, $42,507,627 (M); expenditures, $2,763,894; qualifying distributions, $2,451,316; giving activities include $2,451,316 for 9 grants (high: $1,000,000; low: $25,000).
Purpose and activities: Giving primarily for medical research, with emphasis on brain cancer research, women's health, substance abuse, and at-risk youth. Additional funding for education and the arts.
Fields of interest: Arts, cultural/ethnic awareness; Humanities; Arts; Higher education; Education; Hospitals (general); Health organizations; Medical research, institute; Youth development, services; Children/youth, services; Philanthropy/voluntarism, research; Children/youth; Mentally disabled; Women; Young adults, male.
Type of support: General/operating support; Continuing support; Management development/capacity building; Capital campaigns; Building/renovation; Equipment; Endowments; Program development; Conferences/seminars; Professorships; Scholarship funds; Research; Matching/challenge support.
Limitations: Applications not accepted. Giving primarily in Fort Lauderdale, FL and Chicago, IL.
Application information: Contributes only to pre-selected organizations.
Board meeting date(s): Quarterly, in Jan., Apr., July, and Oct.
Officers and Directors:* Barbara S. Wells,* Pres.; Ellen McPherson,* Treas.; Walter W. Bell; James Ulmer.
Number of staff: 1 full-time professional.
EIN: 237433827

2384
The Welsh Family Foundation, Inc. ✧
c/o Patrick Welsh
7 Sea Ct.
Vero Beach, FL 32963-3466

Established in 1994 in NJ.
Donors: Patrick J. Welsh; Carol A. Welsh.
Foundation type: Independent foundation.
Financial data (yr. ended 12/31/13): Assets, $7,733,244 (M); gifts received, $1,530,853; expenditures, $1,012,247; qualifying distributions, $978,000; giving activities include $978,000 for 40 grants (high: $500,000; low: $1,000).
Purpose and activities: Giving primarily for hospitals and children services, including children's health care.
Fields of interest: Hospitals (general); Health care; Human services; Children/youth, services; Foundations (private grantmaking).
Limitations: Giving primarily in NJ. No grants to individuals.
Application information:
Initial approach: Letter requesting application format
Deadline(s): None
Trustees: Carol A. Welsh; Eric A. Welsh; Patrick J. Welsh.
EIN: 223331136
Selected grants: The following grants are a representative sample of this grantmaker's funding activity:
$5,000 to American Heart Association, Dallas, TX, 2011.
$2,000 to World Wildlife Fund, Washington, DC, 2011.
$1,000 to Nature Conservancy, Arlington, VA, 2011.
$1,000 to Trout Unlimited, Arlington, VA, 2011.
$1,000 to United States Olympic Committee, Colorado Springs, CO, 2011.

2385
Whitehall Foundation, Inc. ✧
P.O. Box 3423
Palm Beach, FL 33480-1623 (561) 655-4474
Contact: George M. Moffett II, Pres.; Catherine M. Thomas, Asst. Treas.
FAX: (561) 655-1296; E-mail: email@whitehall.org; Express mail address: 125 Worth Ave., Ste. 220, Palm Beach, FL 33480; Main URL: http://www.whitehall.org
Grants List: http://www.whitehall.org/recipients/

Incorporated in 1937 in NJ.
Donor: George M. Moffett‡.
Foundation type: Independent foundation.
Financial data (yr. ended 09/30/13): Assets, $110,067,523 (M); expenditures, $5,562,385; qualifying distributions, $5,246,636; giving activities include $4,959,158 for 125 grants (high: $300,000; low: $5,000).
Purpose and activities: Support for scholarly research in the life sciences, with emphasis on behavioral neuroscience and invertebrate neurophysiology; innovative and imaginative projects preferred. Research grants are paid to sponsoring institutions, rather than directly to individuals.
Fields of interest: Biology/life sciences.
Type of support: Equipment; Program development; Research.
Limitations: Applications accepted. Giving limited to the U.S. No support for investigators who already have, or expect to receive, substantial support from other quarters. No grants for salary support for principal investigator, travel to conferences or for consultation, secretarial or office expenses, construction projects or laboratory renovations, or tuition or fellowships.
Publications: Application guidelines; Grants list.
Application information: See foundation web site for specific application guidelines. Though the foundation encourages use of electronic mail, the letter of intent must be submitted in hard copy, via U.S. mail, on institutional letterhead. Foundation telephone available 9:00am-12:00pm, weekdays.
Initial approach: 2-page letter of intent
Deadline(s): Letter of intent: Jan. 15, Apr. 15, and Oct. 1; Application: Feb. 15, June 1, and Sept. 1
Board meeting date(s): 3 grant review sessions per year
Final notification: May 15, Aug. 15, and Dec. 1
Officers and Trustees:* George M. Moffett II,* Pres. and Treas.; J. Wright Rumbough, Jr.,* V.P.; Peter Gibbons Neff,* Assoc. V.P.; Catherine M. Thomas, Corp. Secy.; Kenneth S. Beall, Jr.; E. Anthony Newton.
Number of staff: 1 full-time professional; 1 part-time professional.
EIN: 135637595

2386
Wildflower Foundation ✧ ☆
P.O. Box 10370
Naples, FL 34101-0370

Established in 1983 in OH.
Donor: Hanna O. Rice‡.
Foundation type: Independent foundation.
Financial data (yr. ended 06/30/13): Assets, $6,584,195 (M); expenditures, $485,543; qualifying distributions, $458,377; giving activities include $455,000 for 1 grant.
Fields of interest: Human services.
Type of support: General/operating support.
Limitations: Applications not accepted. Giving primarily in Akron and Canton, OH. No grants to individuals.
Application information: Contributes only to pre-selected organizations.
Trustee: Robert R. Rice.
EIN: 341436725

2387
The Wildflower Foundation, Inc. ✧
1441 Brickell Ave., Ste. 1230
Miami, FL 33131-4328

Donor: Christine Stiefel.
Foundation type: Independent foundation.
Financial data (yr. ended 12/31/13): Assets, $44,046,245 (M); expenditures, $2,350,148; qualifying distributions, $2,241,390; giving activities include $2,221,100 for 29 grants (high: $260,000; low: $1,100).
Fields of interest: Arts; Education; Environment; Human services.
Limitations: Applications not accepted. Giving primarily in CA, DC, FL, IL, MA, NJ, NY, and VA.
Application information: Contributes only to pre-selected organizations.
Officers and Directors:* Christine E. Stiefel,* Pres. and Treas.; Barbara A. Stiefel,* V.P.; Louis Nostro,* Secy.
EIN: 270406313

2388
Edna Sproull Williams Foundation ✧
c/o James Burke
2046 Eventide Rd.
Switzerland, FL 32259

Established in 1976.

Donor: Edna Sproull Williams†.
Foundation type: Independent foundation.
Financial data (yr. ended 12/31/13): Assets, $17,355,669 (M); expenditures, $986,987; qualifying distributions, $794,990; giving activities include $714,500 for 61 grants (high: $40,000; low: $2,500).
Purpose and activities: Giving primarily to Christian causes.
Fields of interest: Arts; Higher education; Theological school/education; Hospitals (general); Health organizations, association; Youth development, centers/clubs; Youth, services; Christian agencies & churches.
Limitations: Applications not accepted. Giving primarily in FL, with emphasis on Jacksonville. No grants to individuals.
Application information: Contributes only to pre-selected organizations.
Trustees: Susan W. Brodeur; James W. Burke; Edward McCarthy, Jr.; David F. Williams; Patrick M. Williams.
EIN: 510198606

2389
Windsor Foundation Trust ✧
(formerly Quincy Cole Trust)
P.O. Box 40200, FL9-100-10-19
Jacksonville, FL 32203-0200 (804) 788-2673
Contact: Sarah Kay
Application address: 1111 E. Main St., VA-300-12-92, Richmond, VA 23219

Established in 1969 in VA.
Donor: Quincy Cole†.
Foundation type: Independent foundation.
Financial data (yr. ended 06/30/13): Assets, $11,723,927 (M); expenditures, $699,853; qualifying distributions, $570,000; giving activities include $570,000 for grants.
Fields of interest: Performing arts; Performing arts, orchestras; Arts; Education.
Limitations: Applications accepted. Giving limited to the metropolitan Richmond, VA, area.
Application information: Application form required.
Initial approach: Letter
Deadline(s): Apr. 1 and Oct. 1
Board meeting date(s): May and Nov.
Trustee: Bank of America, N.A.
EIN: 546086247
Selected grants: The following grants are a representative sample of this grantmaker's funding activity:
$100,000 to Maymont Foundation, Richmond, VA, 2013. For Improvements to Children's Farm.
$40,000 to Faison School for Autism, Richmond, VA, 2013. To support construction.
$40,000 to Virginia Historical Society, Richmond, VA, 2013. For Murals Restoration and Conservation.
$35,000 to Historic Polegreen Church Foundation, Mechanicsville, VA, 2013. For facility lighting project.
$25,000 to Fan Free Clinic, Richmond, VA, 2013. To support Health Outcomes Program.
$25,000 to Full Circle Grief Center, Richmond, VA, 2013. For Hands Healing Program.
$10,000 to Art 180, Richmond, VA, 2013. To support Youth Curators Program.

2390
Winter Park Health Foundation ✧
(formerly Winter Park Memorial Hospital Association, Inc.)
220 Edinburgh Dr.
Winter Park, FL 32792-4160 (407) 644-2300
FAX: (407) 644-0174; Main URL: http://www.wphf.org
E-Newsletter: http://feedburner.google.com/fb/a/mailverify?uri=WinterParkHealthFoundation
Facebook: https://www.facebook.com/WinterParkHealthFoundation
Flickr: https://www.flickr.com/photos/109856427@N08/
LinkedIn: http://www.linkedin.com/company/winter-park-health-foundation?trk=tyah&trkInfo=tas%3Awinter+park+health+foundation%2Cidx%3A1-1-1
Pinterest: http://www.pinterest.com/WPHealthFdn/
Twitter: https://twitter.com/WPHealthFdn
Vimeo: http://vimeo.com/user4160462/videos
YouTube: http://www.youtube.com/user/WPHealthFdn

Established in 1951 as Winter Park Memorial Hospital Association; name changed in 1994.
Donors: Lola E. Nowers Fund; Carl J. Brunoehler Scholarship Fund.
Foundation type: Independent foundation.
Financial data (yr. ended 12/31/13): Assets, $126,025,965 (M); gifts received, $139,970; expenditures, $6,551,413; qualifying distributions, $5,321,137; giving activities include $2,915,658 for 186 grants (high: $553,092; low: $200), and $1,115,419 for foundation-administered programs.
Purpose and activities: Giving primarily for children and youth, community health, and older adults.
Fields of interest: Education; Health care; Human services; Children/youth; Youth; Adults; Aging.
Type of support: Management development/capacity building; Emergency funds; Program development; Conferences/seminars; Scholarship funds; Research; Consulting services; Program evaluation; Matching/challenge support.
Limitations: Applications not accepted. Giving primarily in the greater Winter Park, FL, area. No support for political purposes, lobbying, electioneering, or for-profit organizations. No grants to individuals.
Publications: Grants list; Informational brochure; Newsletter; Occasional report.
Application information: Unsolicited applications not accepted.
Board meeting date(s): Quarterly
Officers and Trustees:* George H. Herbst,* Chair.; Toni Jennings, Vice-Chair., Children and Youth; Eddie Needham, M.D., FAAFP, Vice-Chair., Community Health; Joyce Swain,* Vice-Chair., Older Adults; Patricia Maddox,* C.E.O. and Pres.; Harold W. Barley,* Secy.; Marisa Carnevale-Henderson,* Treas.; Ron Lambert, C.F.O.; Rita Bornstein, Ph.D.; Debbie Chang; Matthew M. Davies; W. Marvin Hardy IV, M.D.; Christine Jablonski, M.D.; Christopher Jacobs; Barbara Jenkins, Ed.D.; Jean D. Leuner; Joseph D. Portoghese, M.D.; David Stanley; J. Kurt Wood.
Number of staff: 6 full-time professional; 1 part-time professional; 3 full-time support.
EIN: 590669460

2391
The Betty K. Wolfe Foundation ✧ ☆
24600 S. Tamiami Trail 212
PMB 122
Bonita Springs, FL 34134-7022 (239) 961-1515
Contact: Jon Hileman, Tr.

Established in 1992 in TX.
Donors: Betty K. Wolfe; Betty K. Wolfe Administrative Trust.
Foundation type: Operating foundation.
Financial data (yr. ended 12/31/13): Assets, $0 (M); gifts received, $1,049,200; expenditures, $909,237; qualifying distributions, $900,000; giving activities include $900,000 for 9 grants (high: $500,000; low: $50,000).
Purpose and activities: Giving for public affairs and policy institutes.
Fields of interest: Arts; Human services; Civil/human rights.
Type of support: General/operating support; Grants to individuals.
Limitations: Applications accepted. Giving primarily in VA, and Washington, DC.
Application information: Application form required.
Initial approach: Letter
Deadline(s): None
Trustees: Jon Hileman; Philis Hileman.
EIN: 756423068

2392
Mitchell Wolfson, Sr. Foundation ✧
c/o Akerman Senterfitt
1 S.E. 3rd Ave., 28th Fl.
Miami, FL 33131-1714 (305) 373-0123

Established in 1984 in FL; supporting organization of Association of Small Foundations, Best Buddies, Boy Scouts of America, Channel 2, Congregation B'nai Zion, Crime Watch of America, Dade Community Foundation, Daily Bread Food Bank, Diabetes Research Institute University, Florida Lions Eyebank, Florida House, Greater Miami Jewish Federation, Health Foundation of South Florida, Hillel at Syracuse University, International Council of the Museum of Art, Miami Dade Community College, Miami Jewish Home and Hospital for the Aged, Mt. Sinai Hospital of Greater Miami, University of Miami School of Medicine, Wolfsonian - FIU Foundation, Princeton University, and YMCA.
Foundation type: Independent foundation.
Financial data (yr. ended 02/28/13): Assets, $221,720,193 (M); expenditures, $13,314,531; qualifying distributions, $9,209,460; giving activities include $8,881,289 for 37 grants (high: $7,177,919; low: $500).
Fields of interest: Arts; Higher education, college (community/junior); Higher education, college; Hospitals (general).
Type of support: Scholarship funds.
Limitations: Applications not accepted. Giving primarily in FL and NY. No grants to individuals.
Application information: Contributes only to pre-selected organizations.
Trustees: Arthur Hertz; Sylvan Myers; Joseph T. Natoli; Jeri Louise Waxenberg Wolfson; Louis Wolfson III; Mitchell Wolfson, Jr.
EIN: 592390240
Selected grants: The following grants are a representative sample of this grantmaker's funding activity:

$7,177,919 to Miami Dade College, Miami, FL, 2013. For general support.
$890,893 to University of Miami, School of Medicine, Miami, FL, 2013. To fund medical education in south Florida.
$441,450 to Miami Jewish Health Systems, Miami, FL, 2013. For general support.
$88,289 to Mount Sinai Medical Center, Miami Beach, FL, 2013. For general support.
$10,000 to Advertising Federation of Greater Miami Scholarship Foundation, Miami, FL, 2013. For general support.
$10,000 to Bascom Palmer Eye Institute, Miami, FL, 2013. For operating support.

2393
Wollowick Family Foundation ✧ ☆

(formerly Rubin and Gladys Wollowick Foundation, Inc.)
c/o Golomb, Schwartz & Cove, P.A.
2000 N.W. 150th Ave., Ste. 2106
Pembroke Pines, FL 33028-2870 (954) 889-0075

Established in 1984 in FL.
Donor: Gladys Wollowick‡.
Foundation type: Independent foundation.
Financial data (yr. ended 01/31/13): Assets, $4,104,242 (M); expenditures, $676,452; qualifying distributions, $601,193; giving activities include $589,550 for 96 grants (high: $150,000; low: $800).
Purpose and activities: Giving primarily for education, hospitals and health organizations, social services, and Jewish organizations.
Fields of interest: Higher education; Hospitals (general); Health organizations, association; Medical research, institute; Human services; American Red Cross; Jewish federated giving programs; Jewish agencies & synagogues.
International interests: Israel.
Type of support: General/operating support; Annual campaigns; Equipment; Emergency funds; Research; Matching/challenge support.
Limitations: Applications accepted. Giving primarily in Boca Raton and Miami, FL. No grants to individuals.
Application information: Application form not required.
Initial approach: Letter
Deadline(s): Sept. 30
Board meeting date(s): Varies
Directors: Megan Lowe; Richard Lowe; Sandra Lois Lowe; Jason Stein; Rhoda Stein; Ronnit Stein; Dr. Robert Tesher; Janet Amy Wollowick.
Trustee: BNY Mellon, N.A.
EIN: 592469452
Selected grants: The following grants are a representative sample of this grantmaker's funding activity:
$17,500 to Mount Sinai Medical Center, 2010.
$15,000 to Mount Sinai Medical Center, 2010.
$10,500 to Appalshop, Whitesburg, KY, 2010.
$10,000 to Jewish Federation of Broward County, Fort Lauderdale, FL, 2010.
$5,000 to University of Miami, Coral Gables, FL, 2011.
$5,000 to University of Miami, Coral Gables, FL, 2011.
$5,000 to Yeshiva University, New York, NY, 2011.
$1,000 to University of Miami, Coral Gables, FL, 2011.

2394
Working Partners Foundation ✧

400 Royal Palm Way, Ste. 304C
Palm Beach, FL 33480-4117
E-mail: info@wpfint.org; Main URL: http://www.wpfint.org

Established in 2005 in CO.
Donor: The New Millennium Trust.
Foundation type: Independent foundation.
Financial data (yr. ended 12/31/12): Assets, $340,233 (M); gifts received, $134,560; expenditures, $1,454,029; qualifying distributions, $1,357,657; giving activities include $1,246,750 for 2 grants (high: $1,218,250; low: $28,500).
Purpose and activities: The goal of the foundation is to improve basic health and living conditions for people in need through health care, micro-economic financing, sanitation and water, education, food, prevention and a magnitude of other community development assistance programs around the globe.
Fields of interest: International agricultural development; International economic development; International relief.
International interests: Africa; Global Programs.
Limitations: Applications not accepted. Giving primarily to U.S-based organizations with international focus.
Application information: Contributes only to pre-selected organizations.
Director: Robert G. Simses.
EIN: 201783302

2395
Worrell Foundation, Inc. ✧ ☆

(formerly The Dharma Foundation III, Inc.)
14 S. Swinton Ave.
Delray Beach, FL 33444-3654

Established in 1990 in DE and FL.
Donors: Thomas E. Worrell, Jr.; Odette A. Worrell; The Shaffer Worrell Charitable Lead Trust; First Union National Bank; Dharma Holdings, Ltd.
Foundation type: Independent foundation.
Financial data (yr. ended 11/30/13): Assets, $765,334 (M); expenditures, $1,011,607; qualifying distributions, $1,000,000; giving activities include $1,000,000 for 1 grant.
Fields of interest: Environment, water resources; Human services; Foundations (community).
Limitations: Applications not accepted. Giving primarily in CA and Charlottesville, VA; funding also in Ghana. No grants to individuals.
Application information: Contributes only to pre-selected organizations.
Officers and Director:* Thomas E. Worrell, Jr.,* Chair.; Kimberly A. Goodyear, Pres.
EIN: 650239353

2396
Jerome A. Yavitz Charitable Foundation, Inc. ✧

777 Arthur Godfrey Rd., Ste. 320
Miami Beach, FL 33140-3447 (305) 532-3200
Contact: Stephen Cypen, Pres.

Established in 2002 in FL.
Donor: Jerome A. Yavitz‡.
Foundation type: Independent foundation.
Financial data (yr. ended 05/31/13): Assets, $18,581,007 (M); expenditures, $1,127,851; qualifying distributions, $860,798; giving activities include $730,289 for grants.
Purpose and activities: Giving primarily for Jewish organizations, higher education, and human services.
Fields of interest: Arts; Higher education; Health organizations; Human services; Foundations (private grantmaking); Jewish agencies & synagogues.
Limitations: Applications accepted. Giving primarily in FL, with emphasis on Miami and Miami Beach. No grants to individuals.
Application information: Application form not required.
Initial approach: Proposal
Deadline(s): None
Officer: Stephen H. Cypen, Pres.
EIN: 030473333
Selected grants: The following grants are a representative sample of this grantmaker's funding activity:
$58,001 to University of Miami, Coral Gables, FL, 2011.
$10,000 to Chai Lifeline, New York, NY, 2011.
$5,000 to Alzheimers Association, Chicago, IL, 2011.
$1,000 to Nature Conservancy, Arlington, VA, 2011.

2397
James P. and Margaret L. Zehnder Foundation, Inc. ✧ ☆

28709 Tanner Dr.
Wesley Chapel, FL 33543-5406

Established in FL.
Donors: James P. Zehnder; Margaret L. Zehnder; Trinity Logistics Corp.
Foundation type: Independent foundation.
Financial data (yr. ended 12/31/12): Assets, $103,604 (M); gifts received, $451,958; expenditures, $474,239; qualifying distributions, $452,043; giving activities include $452,043 for grants.
Fields of interest: Libraries (special); Housing/shelter; Human services; Military/veterans' organizations; Christian agencies & churches.
Limitations: Applications not accepted. No grants to individuals.
Application information: Contributes only to pre-selected organizations.
Officers and Directors:* James P. Zehnder,* Pres.; Daniel J. Zehnder,* V.P.; Barbara J. Zehnder,* Secy.; Margaret L. Zehnder,* Treas.; Mary J. Cajthaml.
EIN: 562334965

GEORGIA

2398
Addison Hines Charitable Trust ✧
c/o Liszewski
P.O. Box 4608
Canton, GA 30114-0019

Established in 2005 in FL.
Donors: Addison Hines Trust; Addison Hines Declaration of Trust.
Foundation type: Independent foundation.
Financial data (yr. ended 12/31/13): Assets, $22,794,789 (M); expenditures, $1,512,774; qualifying distributions, $1,244,750; giving activities include $1,212,500 for 19 grants (high: $175,000; low: $25,000).
Fields of interest: Higher education; Hospitals (specialty); Medical research, institute; Human services.
Limitations: Applications not accepted. Giving primarily in FL.
Application information: Contributes only to pre-selected organizations.
Trustees: James H. Murray, Jr.; Robert J. Liszewski.
EIN: 201679943
Selected grants: The following grants are a representative sample of this grantmaker's funding activity:
$175,000 to Elwyn, Elwyn, PA, 2012. For Space Conversion to Outpatient Health Center.
$100,000 to American Red Cross, West Palm Beach, FL, 2012. To support Emergency Services Fund to Aid Local Disaster Relief.
$52,500 to American Heart Association, West Palm Beach, FL, 2012. For funding of Aha Heroes Summer Camp.
$50,000 to Norton Museum of Art, West Palm Beach, FL, 2012. To support Educational Programming for 2012-2013 Season.
$25,000 to Masonic Medical Research Laboratory, Utica, NY, 2012. To support of Cardiac Research.

2399
The Aflac Foundation, Inc. ✧
1932 Wynnton Rd.
Columbus, GA 31999-0001
Contact: Francine Medley, Admin.
FAX: (706) 320-2288;
E-mail: corporatephilanthropy@aflac.com; Main URL: http://www.aflac.com/us/en/aboutaflac/communityinvolvement.aspx

Established in 1999 in GA.
Donor: American Family Life Assurance Co. of Columbus.
Foundation type: Company-sponsored foundation.
Financial data (yr. ended 12/31/13): Assets, $2,356,381 (M); gifts received, $5,258,435; expenditures, $5,994,772; qualifying distributions, $5,994,435; giving activities include $5,994,435 for 82 grants (high: $2,000,000; low: $1,000).
Purpose and activities: The foundation supports programs designed to promote health; education; youth; and the arts.
Fields of interest: Museums; Arts; Higher education; Libraries (public); Education; Environment; Health care, clinics/centers; Health care; Cancer; Cancer research; Children/youth, services; Human services; Community/economic development; United Ways and Federated Giving Programs; Minorities.
Type of support: General/operating support; Annual campaigns; Capital campaigns; Endowments; Program development; Fellowships; Scholarship funds; Research; Cause-related marketing; Employee volunteer services.
Limitations: Applications accepted. Giving primarily in areas of company operations in NE, NY, and SC with emphasis on the greater Atlanta, GA, area. No support for religious or political organizations or private secondary schools. No grants to individuals.
Publications: Application guidelines.
Application information: Support is limited to 1 contribution per organization during any given year. Application form not required.
Initial approach: Download application form and mail to foundation
Copies of proposal: 1
Deadline(s): None
Board meeting date(s): Bi-monthly
Officers: Kathleen V. Amos, Pres.; Audrey Tilman, V.P.; Alfred O. Blackmar, Secy.; Teresa White, Treas.
EIN: 582509396
Selected grants: The following grants are a representative sample of this grantmaker's funding activity:
$2,000,000 to Childrens Healthcare of Atlanta, Aflac Cancer and Blood Disorders Center, Atlanta, GA, 2013.
$375,000 to United Way, 2013.
$375,000 to United Way, 2013.
$359,000 to Community Foundation of the Chattahoochee Valley, Columbus, GA, 2013.
$265,000 to American Association for Cancer Research, Philadelphia, PA, 2013.
$250,000 to Cora Reid Greene Home for Children, Phenix City, AL, 2013.
$125,000 to Columbus State University, Columbus, GA, 2013.
$25,000 to Columbus State University, Columbus, GA, 2013.
$20,000 to National Childrens Cancer Society, Saint Louis, MO, 2013.
$10,000 to Methodist Home of the South Georgia Conference, Macon, GA, 2013.

2400
AGL Resources Private Foundation, Inc. ✧
P.O. Box 4569, M.C. 1080
Atlanta, GA 30302-4569 (404) 584-3791
Contact: Melanie Platt, Pres.
For organizations in the Nicor Gas service territory contact: amartinez@aglresources.com; Main URL: http://www.aglresources.com/community/guidelines.aspx

Established in 1998 in GA.
Donors: Georgia Gas Co.; AGL Foundation; AGL Resources Inc.
Foundation type: Company-sponsored foundation.
Financial data (yr. ended 12/31/12): Assets, $1,802,897 (M); expenditures, $3,528,249; qualifying distributions, $3,519,154; giving activities include $3,507,559 for 298 grants (high: $500,000; low: $100).
Purpose and activities: The foundation supports organizations involved with arts and culture, K-12 and higher education, literacy, the environment, economic development, business, science, mathematics, leadership development, senior citizens, minorities, women, and economically disadvantaged people.
Fields of interest: Arts; Secondary school/education; Higher education; Education, reading; Environment, air pollution; Environment, natural resources; Environment, energy; Environment, beautification programs; Economic development; Business/industry; United Ways and Federated Giving Programs; Science, formal/general education; Mathematics; Leadership development; Aging; Minorities; Women; Economically disadvantaged.
Type of support: Annual campaigns; Capital campaigns; Building/renovation; Endowments; Emergency funds; Program development; Seed money; Scholarship funds; Sponsorships.
Limitations: Applications accepted. Giving primarily in areas of company operations in FL, GA, IL, MD, NJ, TN, TX, and VA. No support for religious organizations or private K-12 schools. No grants to individuals.
Publications: Application guidelines; Program policy statement.
Application information: Visit website for application addresses. Application form required.
Initial approach: Download application form and mail application form and proposal to application address
Deadline(s): Education, Environmental Stewardship, and Organizational and Supplier Diversity applications are reviewed in Quarter 1; Community Enrichment Quarter 2; and Energy Assistance in Quarter 3
Board meeting date(s): Quarterly
Officers and Trustees: Melanie M. Platt, Pres.; Beth Reese, V.P.; Myra Bierria, Secy.; Bryan E. Seas, Treas.; Bryan Baston; SunTrust Bank.
EIN: 582399946
Selected grants: The following grants are a representative sample of this grantmaker's funding activity:
$400,000 to United Way of Metropolitan Atlanta, Atlanta, GA, 2010.
$100,000 to Grady Memorial Hospital Corporation, Atlanta, GA, 2010.
$75,000 to BeltLine Partnership, Atlanta, GA, 2010. For program support.
$37,500 to Habitat for Humanity in Atlanta, Atlanta, GA, 2010.
$30,000 to Chamber of Commerce Foundation of Georgia, Atlanta, GA, 2010.
$30,000 to Salvation Army, 2010.
$25,000 to Sustainable Atlanta, Atlanta, GA, 2010.
$25,000 to University of Houston-University Park, C.T. Bauer College of Business, Houston, TX, 2010.
$20,000 to Houston Livestock Show and Rodeo, Houston, TX, 2010.
$15,000 to Hispanic Scholarship Fund, Gardena, CA, 2011. For general charitable purposes.
$15,000 to Special Olympics Virginia, Richmond, VA, 2011. For general charitable purposes.
$13,500 to Girl Scouts of the U.S.A., 2010.
$10,000 to American Association of Blacks in Energy, Washington, DC, 2011. For general charitable purposes.
$7,500 to Nature Conservancy, Arlington, VA, 2011. For general charitable purposes.
$5,000 to Chesapeake Bay Foundation, Annapolis, MD, 2011. For general charitable purposes.
$5,000 to Empty Stocking Fund, Atlanta, GA, 2011. For general charitable purposes.
$5,000 to Susan G. Komen for the Cure, Dallas, TX, 2011. For general charitable purposes.

$5,000 to Teach for America, New York, NY, 2011. For general charitable purposes.
$5,000 to United Negro College Fund, Fairfax, VA, 2011. For general charitable purposes.
$4,000 to Junior Achievement of Georgia, Atlanta, GA, 2011. For general charitable purposes.

2401
Daniel P. Amos Family Foundation
(formerly Daniel P. and Shannon L. Amos Foundation, Inc.)
c/o Selection Comm.
P.O. Box 5346
Columbus, GA 31906-0346
E-mail: CCBradshaw@AmosFamilyFoundation.org; Main URL: http://amosfamilyfoundation.org/danielhome.html

Established in 1992 in GA.
Donors: Daniel P. Amos; Paul Amos Trust; Jean Amos Trust; Paul S. and Jean R. Amos Trust.
Foundation type: Independent foundation.
Financial data (yr. ended 12/31/12): Assets, $140,670,140 (M); gifts received, $7,147,917; expenditures, $8,105,347; qualifying distributions, $6,772,000; giving activities include $6,772,000 for 58 grants (high: $1,500,000; low: $500).
Purpose and activities: Giving primarily to Christian organizations whose goals, activities, and operating principles are consistent with the foundation's Statement of Faith.
Fields of interest: Higher education; Human services; Christian agencies & churches; Protestant agencies & churches.
Type of support: Building/renovation.
Limitations: Applications accepted. Giving primarily in Columbus, GA. No grants to individuals.
Application information: Application forms available on foundation web site. Application form required.
Initial approach: Complete appropriate application form
Officer and Trustee:* Daniel P. Amos, Pres.
EIN: 582005391

2402
The Paul and Courtney Amos Foundation, Inc. ✧
P.O. Box 5120
Columbus, GA 31906-0120

Established in 2002 in GA.
Donors: Paul S. Amos II; Courtney Amos.
Foundation type: Independent foundation.
Financial data (yr. ended 12/31/12): Assets, $5,386,188 (M); expenditures, $666,828; qualifying distributions, $633,010; giving activities include $633,010 for 25 grants (high: $275,000; low: $100).
Fields of interest: Elementary/secondary education; Cancer; Protestant agencies & churches.
Type of support: Capital campaigns; General/operating support.
Limitations: Applications not accepted. Giving primarily in Columbus, GA. No grants to individuals.
Application information: Contributes only to pre-selected organizations.
Officers: Paul S. Amos II, Pres.; Courtney G. Amos, V.P.
EIN: 721555644

2403
The Peyton Anderson Foundation, Inc. ✧
577 Mulberry St., Ste. 830
Macon, GA 31201-8223 (478) 743-5359
Contact: Karen J. Lambert, Pres.
FAX: (478) 742-5201; E-mail: grants@pafdn.org; Main URL: http://www.peytonanderson.org/
Peyton Anderson Scholarship tel. (Scholarship Mgr.): (478) 314-0948, e-mail: scholarships@pafdn.org

Incorporated in 1988 in GA; funded in 1989.
Donor: Peyton Tooke Anderson, Jr.†.
Foundation type: Independent foundation.
Financial data (yr. ended 12/31/13): Assets, $98,315,107 (M); gifts received, $23,000; expenditures, $5,506,593; qualifying distributions, $4,694,936; giving activities include $3,493,739 for 46 grants (high: $568,650; low: $250), and $277,750 for grants to individuals.
Purpose and activities: Giving primarily for community development and human services; funding also for the arts. Scholarships have also been established to help fund the college education of highly promising high school students in Bibb County, GA, who have been residents for the past 2 years and who are graduating high school seniors with a 2.0 GPA, who are graduating from a Bibb County public high school or private high school accredited by the Southern Association of Colleges and Schools (SACS), and demonstrate academic promise, strong character, community involvement, and financial need. All scholarship recipients must register as full-time students in an undergraduate degree program at one of the following Georgia schools: Central Georgia Technical College, Fort Valley State University, Georgia College and State University, Georgia Institute of Technology, Georgia Southern University, Georgia State University, Kennesaw State University, Macon State College, Mercer University, Middle Georgia Technical College, University of Georgia, or Wesleyan College. Scholarships are paid directly to the school and not the individual.
Fields of interest: Performing arts, theater; Arts; Higher education; Scholarships/financial aid; Education; Human services; Children/youth, services; Community/economic development.
Type of support: Program development; Seed money; Matching/challenge support.
Limitations: Applications accepted. Giving limited to Bibb County and Macon, GA. No support for private foundations, private schools, sports related events, or churches. No grants to individuals directly, or for endowments, festivals, trips or special events.
Publications: Application guidelines; Grants list; Informational brochure (including application guidelines).
Application information: Specific application guidelines and form available on foundation web site. Information and application guidelines and form for Peyton Anderson Scholars maybe be found on http://www.peytonandersonscholars.org. Application forms may also be obtained at high school guidance counselor's office. Peyton Anderson Scholarship may be combined with the HOPE scholarship and other financial aid awards. Application form required.
Initial approach: Use online application form, or letter or telephone requesting guidelines and form
Deadline(s): Apr. 1 and Aug. 1 for grants; see foundation web site for current scholarship deadline
Board meeting date(s): 2 times per year
Final notification: Grants awarded twice a year
Officers and Trustees:* Ed S. Sell III,* Chair.; Tom Johnson,* V.P.; Karen J. Lambert, Pres.; R. Kirby Godsey, Secy.; R. Reid Hanson,* Treas.; John D. Comer,* Chair. Emeritus.
Number of staff: 1 full-time professional; 2 full-time support.
EIN: 581803562

2404
Ray C. Anderson Foundation, Inc. ✧
P.O. Box 723656
Atlanta, GA 31139-0656
Main URL: http://www.raycandersonfoundation.org/

Established in 1991 in GA.
Donor: Ray C. Anderson†.
Foundation type: Independent foundation.
Financial data (yr. ended 12/31/13): Assets, $40,937,387 (M); gifts received, $3,200; expenditures, $1,699,667; qualifying distributions, $1,219,338; giving activities include $964,302 for 46 grants (high: $310,000; low: $300).
Purpose and activities: Giving primarily for environmental education.
Fields of interest: Higher education; Education; Environment, natural resources; United Ways and Federated Giving Programs.
Limitations: Applications not accepted. No grants to individuals.
Application information: Unsolicited requests for funds not accepted.
Officers: Harriet A. Langford, Pres.; Maryanne A. Lanier, V.P. and Secy.; Patricia A. Anderson, Treas.
EIN: 581867303
Selected grants: The following grants are a representative sample of this grantmaker's funding activity:
$50,000 to David Suzuki Foundation, Vancouver, Canada, 2011.
$20,000 to Worldwatch Institute, Washington, DC, 2011.
$10,000 to Captain Planet Foundation, Atlanta, GA, 2011.
$8,500 to LaGrange Academy, LaGrange, GA, 2011.
$6,000 to Smile Train, New York, NY, 2011.
$5,000 to American Horse Trials Foundation, Centreville, MD, 2011.
$5,000 to Atlanta Community Food Bank, Atlanta, GA, 2011.
$5,000 to National Wildlife Federation, Reston, VA, 2011.
$5,000 to Womens Network for a Sustainable Future, New York, NY, 2011.
$2,500 to Biomimicry Institute, Missoula, MT, 2011.

2405
The Argo Family Fund ✧
c/o Robert Arogeti
5 Concourse Pkwy., Ste. 1000
Atlanta, GA 30328-6132

Established in 1993 in GA.
Donors: James Arogeti; Jeanette Arogeti; Jane A. Durham; Barbara Arogeti; Joel Arogeti; Robert J. Arogeti; Beth Arogeti; Argo Associates, LLP.
Foundation type: Independent foundation.

Financial data (yr. ended 12/31/13): Assets, $10,605,209 (M); gifts received, $50; expenditures, $586,032; qualifying distributions, $487,750; giving activities include $487,750 for 20 grants (high: $307,250; low: $1,000).
Purpose and activities: Giving for Jewish federated giving programs and health care organizations.
Fields of interest: Education; Health care; Jewish federated giving programs; Jewish agencies & synagogues.
Limitations: Applications not accepted. Giving primarily in Atlanta, GA. No grants to individuals.
Application information: Unsolicited requests for funds not accepted.
Trustees: Joel Arogeti; Robert Arogeti.
EIN: 582069120

2406
Atlanta Foundation ✧
c/o Wachovia Bank, N.A.
100 Terminus Building, Ste. 400
3280 Peachtree Rd., N.W., Ste. 400, MC GA8023
Atlanta, GA 30305-2422 (888) 234-1999
E-mail: grantadministration@wellsfargo.com; Main URL: https://www.wellsfargo.com/privatefoundationgrants/atlanta

Established in 1921 in GA by bank resolution and declaration of trust.
Foundation type: Independent foundation.
Financial data (yr. ended 12/31/13): Assets, $19,202,440 (M); expenditures, $1,165,985; qualifying distributions, $995,842; giving activities include $941,558 for 107 grants (high: $35,000; low: $1,000).
Purpose and activities: The foundation provides assistance to charitable and educational institutions to promote education and improve local living conditions. Primary areas of interest include education, cultural programs, housing, and other general charitable activities in Fulton and DeKalb counties, Georgia.
Fields of interest: Arts; Adult education—literacy, basic skills & GED; Education, reading; Education; Hospitals (general); Health care; Housing/shelter, development; Recreation; Human services; Youth, services; Community/economic development; United Ways and Federated Giving Programs.
Type of support: General/operating support; Capital campaigns; Building/renovation; Equipment; Program development.
Limitations: Applications accepted. Giving limited to Fulton and DeKalb counties, GA. No grants to individuals, or for scholarships or fellowships; no loans.
Publications: Application guidelines; Grants list.
Application information: Guidelines available on foundation web site. Application form required.
Initial approach: Use online application via foundation web site
Copies of proposal: 1
Deadline(s): Mar. 1 or Sept. 1
Board meeting date(s): Apr. and Oct.
Final notification: Sept. 1
Committee Members: Elaine B. Alexander; Linda Selig; Ty Smith; Dom H. Wyant.
Trustee: Wells Fargo Bank, N.A.
EIN: 586026879
Selected grants: The following grants are a representative sample of this grantmaker's funding activity:
$20,000 to Piedmont Park Conservancy, Atlanta, GA, 2012. For Piedmont Park Expansion Area Operating Expenses (26 acres).
$18,000 to Boy Scouts of America, Atlanta Area Council, Atlanta, GA, 2012. For Scouting character education Program.
$15,000 to Atlanta Volunteer Lawyers Foundation, Atlanta, GA, 2012. For Domestic Violence Project-Safe Families Office.
$15,000 to Jewish Federation of Greater Atlanta, Atlanta, GA, 2012. For Health and Wellness Programs for the Georgia NORC Initiative.
$12,500 to YWCA of Greater Atlanta, Atlanta, GA, 2012. For Women in Transition.
$10,000 to Create Your Dreams, Atlanta, GA, 2012. For CYD Core Programs.
$10,000 to East Lake Foundation, Atlanta, GA, 2012. For CREW (Creating responsible, Educated, Working) Teens.
$10,000 to Project GRAD Atlanta, Atlanta, GA, 2012. For Graduation Really Achieves Dreams: Operating Support for Project GRAD Atlanta.
$8,000 to Camp Twin Lakes, Atlanta, GA, 2012. For Camper Scholarship Program.
$7,500 to Refugee Family Services, Stone Mountain, GA, 2012. For Refugee Youth After School Program.

2407
The Chantal and Tommy Bagwell Family Foundation Inc. ✧
4705 Leland Dr.
Cumming, GA 30041-3991

Established in 1996 in GA.
Donors: Thomas N. Bagwell; Solon Investments, LP; American Proteins.
Foundation type: Independent foundation.
Financial data (yr. ended 12/31/13): Assets, $35,368,281 (M); gifts received, $2,935; expenditures, $1,441,233; qualifying distributions, $1,291,500; giving activities include $1,291,500 for 14 grants (high: $1,000,000; low: $2,500).
Fields of interest: Education; Christian agencies & churches.
Type of support: Building/renovation.
Limitations: Applications not accepted. Giving primarily in GA. No grants to individuals.
Application information: Contributes only to pre-selected organizations.
Officers: Thomas N. Bagwell, Pres. and C.E.O.; Chantal Bagwell, C.F.O. and Treas.
EIN: 582176142

2408
The Beard-Payne Family Foundation ✧ ☆
3288 Northside Dr. N.W.
Atlanta, GA 30305-1900

Established in 2007 in GA.
Donor: William P. Payne.
Foundation type: Independent foundation.
Financial data (yr. ended 12/31/13): Assets, $152,754 (M); expenditures, $497,960; qualifying distributions, $492,410; giving activities include $492,410 for 42 grants (high: $250,000; low: $25).
Fields of interest: Higher education; Human services; Community/economic development; Protestant agencies & churches.
Limitations: Applications not accepted. Giving primarily in GA.
Application information: Unsolicited requests for funds not accepted.
Officers: Martha B. Payne, Pres.; William P. Payne, Secy.
EIN: 261441249

2409
Beech Foundation, Inc. ✧
2461 O'Neal Rd.
Conyers, GA 30094-6027
E-mail: jeff@thebeechfoundation.org; Tel./fax: (678) 413-2136; additional e-mail: greta@thebeechfoundation.org; Main URL: http://www.thebeechfoundation.org

Established 2002 in GA.
Donors: Greta Beech; Jeff Beech; Alton Housworth.
Foundation type: Operating foundation.
Financial data (yr. ended 12/31/12): Assets, $0 (M); gifts received, $1,372,518; expenditures, $1,276,993; qualifying distributions, $1,248,523; giving activities include $387,052 for grants, and $861,471 for grants to individuals.
Purpose and activities: The foundation provides management and economic assistance to new and established organizations that deliver: 1) development, medical, and spiritual assistance to the disadvantaged areas of the world, 2) family and child assistance with an emphasis on those with special needs or who are medically fragile, and 3) programs to develop service and stewardship capabilities in young people. The foundation also provides scholarship opportunities for those committed to nonprofit career callings.
Fields of interest: Human services; Children/youth, services; Economically disadvantaged.
Type of support: General/operating support; Scholarships—to individuals.
Limitations: Applications not accepted. Giving primarily in GA.
Application information: Unsolicited requests for funds not accepted.
Officers and Directors:* Jeff Beech,* Pres.; Greta Beech,* Secy.; Allen A. Beech, Jr.; Randy Beech; Saxon Dasher; Kevin Kraus; Neil Young.
EIN: 611405192

2410
S.E. Belcher, Jr. Private Foundation No. 2 ✧
c/o Synovus Trust
P.O. Box 23024
Columbus, GA 31902-3024
Application address: c/o Robert Ingram, Jr., 2200 Jack Warner Pkwy., Ste. 300, Tuscaloosa, AL 35406; tel.: (205)345-8440

Donor: S.E. Belcher, Jr.†.
Foundation type: Independent foundation.
Financial data (yr. ended 12/31/13): Assets, $28,080,731 (M); expenditures, $3,567,531; qualifying distributions, $3,161,500; giving activities include $3,161,500 for 11 grants (high: $1,019,000; low: $17,500).
Fields of interest: Education; Human services; Christian agencies & churches.
Limitations: Applications accepted. Giving primarily in AL; funding also in AR and CO.
Application information: Application form not required.

Initial approach: Proposal
Deadline(s): None
Governors: Ashley Belcher Ferry; Sam P. Faucett; Robert L. Ingram, Jr.
Trustee: Synovus Trust Co. N.A.
EIN: 631259859

2411
Beloco Foundation, Inc. ✧
P.O. Box 140
Columbus, GA 31902-0140 (706) 571-6040
Contact: Lovick P. Corn, Pres.
Application address: P.O. Box 23024, Columbus, GA 31902-3024, tel.: (706) 571-6040

Established in 1967 in GA.
Donors: Lovick P. Corn; Elizabeth T. Corn.
Foundation type: Independent foundation.
Financial data (yr. ended 06/30/13): Assets, $14,408,673 (M); gifts received, $149,226; expenditures, $912,075; qualifying distributions, $622,338; giving activities include $622,338 for grants.
Purpose and activities: Giving primarily for education, health, and human services.
Fields of interest: Higher education; Education; Health care; Human services; Children/youth, services; Foundations (private grantmaking).
Type of support: General/operating support; Continuing support; Capital campaigns.
Limitations: Applications accepted. Giving primarily in GA; some funding nationally. No grants to individuals.
Application information: Application form required.
Initial approach: Letter
Deadline(s): None
Officers: Lovick P. Corn, Pres.; Elizabeth T. Corn, V.P.; Elizabeth C. Ogie, V.P.; Polly C. Miller, Secy.; Katherine C. Foster, Treas.; Phyllis Wagner, Admin.
Trustees: Abby C. Irby; Gilbert B. Miller; Susan C. Wainwright.
EIN: 586065378
Selected grants: The following grants are a representative sample of this grantmaker's funding activity:
$100,000 to Wesleyan College, Macon, GA, 2013. For general use of donee.

2412
The Sara Blakely Foundation Inc. ✧ ☆
c/o Kim Jones
3344 Peachtree Rd.
Atlanta, GA 30326

Donors: Sara Blakely; Spanx, Inc.; Neiman Marcus Group.
Foundation type: Independent foundation.
Financial data (yr. ended 12/31/13): Assets, $23,342,184 (M); gifts received, $4,005,500; expenditures, $782,958; qualifying distributions, $613,520; giving activities include $613,520 for 30 grants (high: $100,000; low: $1,000).
Fields of interest: Arts; Education; Human services.
Limitations: Applications not accepted.
Application information: Unsolicited requests for funds not accepted.
Officers and Directors:* Sara Blakely,* Pres.; John Blakely,* V.P.; Laurie Ann Goldman,* Secy.
EIN: 205088833

2413
The Arthur M. Blank Family Foundation ✧
3223 Howell Mill Rd. N.W.
Atlanta, GA 30327-4105 (404) 367-2100
Contact: Penelope "Penny" McPhee, Pres.
FAX: (404) 367-2059; Main URL: http://www.blankfoundation.org
Annual reports: http://www.blankfoundation.org/annual-reports
Arthur Blank's Giving Pledge Profile: http://glasspockets.org/philanthropy-in-focus/eye-on-the-giving-pledge/profiles/blank
Facebook: http://www.facebook.com/ArthurBlankFamilyFoundation
Grants List: http://www.blankfoundation.org/2011-grants
RSS Feed: http://blankfoundation.org/feed.xml
Twitter: http://twitter.com/blankfoundation
YouTube: http://www.youtube.com/user/BlankFoundation

Established in 1995 in GA.
Donor: Arthur M. Blank.
Foundation type: Independent foundation.
Financial data (yr. ended 12/31/12): Assets, $39,718,177 (M); gifts received, $4,762,418; expenditures, $5,766,036; qualifying distributions, $5,873,997; giving activities include $4,761,024 for 221 grants (high: $275,000; low: $25), and $201,814 for 4 foundation-administered programs.
Purpose and activities: The mission going forward is to promote positive change in people's lives and to build and enhance the communities in which they live. The foundation has an especially strong interest in supporting innovative endeavors leading to better circumstances for low-income youth and their families. The foundation seeks to learn from their investments, share what they have learned, and inspire others in the public and private sectors to make similar commitments. The foundation has established two primary initiatives: 1) Fostering Opportunity - to support efforts that help create access to opportunity and improve life chances for low-income young people and their families; and 2) Enhancing Quality of Life - to preserve green space and parks, and sustain a vibrant arts community.
Fields of interest: Performing arts, theater; Education; Environment; Youth development, services.
Type of support: Research; Employee matching gifts.
Limitations: Applications not accepted. Giving primarily in Maricopa County, AZ, Atlanta, GA, and Beaufort County, SC. No support for government agencies, municipalities, parochial or private schools, houses of worship, or therapeutic programs. No grants to individuals, or for events.
Publications: Annual report.
Application information: Within the scope of its strategic plan, the Blank Family Foundation will identify and invite potential partners to apply for grants around its specific initiatives. The foundation will seek partners from all sectors - public, private and nonprofit. The foundation will no longer accept unsolicited grant requests.
Board meeting date(s): Aug. and Dec.
Officers and Trustees:* Arthur M. Blank,* Chair.; Penelope "Penny" McPhee,* Pres.; John Bare, V.P.; Frank Fernandez, V.P., Community Development; Dena Kimball; Kenny Blank; Michael Blank; Nancy Blank; Josh Kimball; Danielle Thomsen.
Number of staff: 8 full-time professional; 1 part-time professional; 3 full-time support.
EIN: 586292769
Selected grants: The following grants are a representative sample of this grantmaker's funding activity:
$275,000 to Outward Bound, Garrison, NY, 2012. For Operating Support.
$250,000 to Pace Academy, Atlanta, GA, 2012. For Capital Support.
$200,000 to First Tee, Saint Augustine, FL, 2012. To provide direct services.
$200,000 to Grady Memorial Hospital Corporation, Atlanta, GA, 2012. To provide direct services.
$200,000 to National Center for Civil and Human Rights, Atlanta, GA, 2012. For capital support.
$131,000 to Boys and Girls Clubs of Hall County, Gainesville, GA, 2012. To provide direct services.
$75,000 to Jewish Community Foundation of Greater Phoenix, Scottsdale, AZ, 2012. To provide direct services.
$60,000 to City of Refuge, Atlanta, GA, 2012. For Capital Support and Direct Services.
$25,000 to Outward Bound California, San Francisco, CA, 2012. For Operating Support.
$10,000 to Pace Academy, Atlanta, GA, 2012. For Operating Support.

2414
Bradley-Turner Foundation, Inc. ✧
P.O. Box 140
Columbus, GA 31902-0140 (706) 571-6040
Contact: Phyllis Wagner, Exec. Secy.

Incorporated in 1943 in GA as W.C. and Sarah H. Bradley Foundation; in 1982 absorbed the D.A. and Elizabeth Turner Foundation, Inc., also of GA.
Donors: W.C. Bradley†; D.A. Turner†; Elizabeth B. Turner†; Elizabeth T. Corn; Sarah T. Butler Charity Lead Annuity Trust.
Foundation type: Independent foundation.
Financial data (yr. ended 12/31/13): Assets, $138,914,362 (M); gifts received, $2,740,206; expenditures, $5,842,640; qualifying distributions, $5,416,209; giving activities include $5,416,209 for 105 grants (high: $315,923; low: $1,000).
Purpose and activities: Giving primarily for higher education, religious associations, community funds, and youth and social service agencies; support also for cultural and health-related programs.
Fields of interest: Arts; Higher education; Education; Health care; Health organizations, association; Human services; Youth, services; Religion.
Type of support: General/operating support.
Limitations: Applications accepted. Giving primarily in GA, with emphasis on Columbus. No grants to individuals.
Application information: Application form not required.
Initial approach: Letter
Copies of proposal: 2
Deadline(s): None
Board meeting date(s): Quarterly
Final notification: None
Officers and Trustees:* Steve Butler,* Interim Chair.; William B. Turner, Treas.; Chris Ball; Betty Corn; Katie Krieg; Gilbert Miller; Marie Moshell; Elizabeth Ogie; Wilds Ogie; Betsy Ramsay; Lane Riley; John Turner; Sue Marie Turner; Susan Wainwright; Sarah West; Worth Williams; Katherine C. Wilson.
EIN: 586032142
Selected grants: The following grants are a representative sample of this grantmaker's funding activity:

$317,356 to Community Foundation of the Chattahoochee Valley, Columbus, GA, 2012. For grant in form of stock for general and operating.
$251,891 to Brookstone School, Columbus, GA, 2012. For grant in form of stock for general and operating.
$225,000 to Teen Challenge International, Columbus, GA, 2012. For general and operating.
$200,000 to Saint Francis Hospital, Columbus, GA, 2012. For general and operating.
$139,675 to United Way of the Chattahoochee Valley Foundation, Columbus, GA, 2012. For grant in form of stock for general and operating.
$134,280 to UPtown Columbus, Columbus, GA, 2012. For grant in form of stock for general and operating.
$109,486 to Pastoral Institute, Columbus, GA, 2012. For general and operating.
$50,380 to MidTown, Inc., Columbus, GA, 2012. For grant in form of stock for general and operating.
$25,382 to Mercymed of Columbus, Columbus, GA, 2012. For grant in form of stock for general and operating.
$16,369 to Marist School, Atlanta, GA, 2012. For grant in form of stock for general and operating.

2415
The Benjamin F. Brady Charitable Foundation ✧

P.O. Box 1200
Cumming, GA 30028-1200

Established in GA.
Donor: Benjamin F. Brady†.
Foundation type: Independent foundation.
Financial data (yr. ended 12/31/13): Assets, $12,355,920 (M); expenditures, $686,409; qualifying distributions, $616,100; giving activities include $568,100 for 26 grants (high: $130,000; low: $500).
Fields of interest: Education; Environment, natural resources; Human services; YM/YWCAs & YM/YWHAs.
Limitations: Applications not accepted. Giving primarily in GA. No grants to individuals.
Application information: Contributes only to pre-selected organizations.
Trustees: Phillip Bettis; Eric S. Chofnas; James J. Myers; Ronald H. Pilcher.
EIN: 582413726
Selected grants: The following grants are a representative sample of this grantmaker's funding activity:
$50,000 to Special Operations Warrior Foundation, Tampa, FL, 2012. To Fund Special Operations Women's Fund.
$10,000 to Salvation Army, Atlanta, GA, 2012. To Fund Angel Tree Christmas.

2416
Frances Hollis Brain Foundation, Inc. ✧

1219 Clifton Rd.
Atlanta, GA 30307-1231 (404) 371-9389
Contact: Diane Bryant, Secy.
FAX: (404) 377-1754;
E-mail: diane@fhbfoundation.org; Maine inquiries: c/o John Watson, 32 Orchard St., Portland, ME 04102, tel.: (207) 774-3968; e-mail: john@fhbfoundation.org; Main URL: http://www.fhbfoundation.org

Established in 1992 in KY.
Donors: David L. Brain; Frances H. Brain.
Foundation type: Independent foundation.
Financial data (yr. ended 08/31/13): Assets, $9,629,830 (M); expenditures, $657,486; qualifying distributions, $596,970; giving activities include $500,348 for 59 grants (high: $125,000; low: $2,500).
Purpose and activities: Giving primarily for education, human services, the increase of access to health care, and for the promotion of self-sufficiency and the availability to provide for self, family, and the community. The foundation places priority on organizations and projects that: 1) support the underserved, the disadvantaged, or those who do not have the resources to provide opportunities for themselves, and 2) demonstrate a broad base of community support.
Fields of interest: Education; Health care; Human services.
Type of support: General/operating support; Continuing support; Capital campaigns; Emergency funds; Matching/challenge support.
Limitations: Giving primarily in GA, KY, and ME. No grants to individuals, or for conferences, annual fund appeals, seminars, tickets to charitable events or dinners, or to sponsor special events, productions or performances.
Publications: Application guidelines; Grants list; Program policy statement; Program policy statement (including application guidelines).
Application information: Full proposals are by invitation only, upon review of initial letter of inquiry. Maine Philanthropy Center Common Grant Application Form accepted. Complete application information available on foundation web site. Application form not required.
Initial approach: Letter of inquiry to Diane Bryant if located in GA or KY, and John Watson if located in ME, or telephone or e-mail
Copies of proposal: 1
Deadline(s): May 1 and Oct. 1
Board meeting date(s): Aug. and Nov.
Final notification: Aug. 31 and Dec. 31
Officers and Directors:* Nancy R. Brain,* Pres. and Treas.; Diane Bryant,* Secy. and Co-Exec. Dir.; John C. Watson, Co-Exec. Dir.; David L. Brain; Kathryn H. Bryant; Michael D. Bryant; Jessica R.R. Hauser; Christopher J. Watson.
Number of staff: 2 part-time professional.
EIN: 611227049
Selected grants: The following grants are a representative sample of this grantmaker's funding activity:
$10,000 to Four Directions Development Corporation, Orono, ME, 2010.
$10,000 to Sisters of Charity Health System, Lewiston, ME, 2011.
$10,000 to Wesley Community Centers, Atlanta, GA, 2011.
$8,000 to 24 7 Gateway LLC, Atlanta, GA, 2011.
$8,000 to Mid-Maine Homeless Shelter, Waterville, ME, 2011. For capital campaign.
$7,500 to Coastal Enterprises, Wiscasset, ME, 2011.
$7,500 to Trinity United Methodist Church, Atlanta, GA, 2010.
$5,000 to Literacy Action, Atlanta, GA, 2011.
$5,000 to Living Room, Atlanta, GA, 2011.
$5,000 to Opportunity Alliance, Portland, ME, 2011.
$5,000 to Senior Connections, Chamblee, GA, 2011.
$5,000 to Southern Maine Agency on Aging, Scarborough, ME, 2010.
$5,000 to Visiting Nurse Health System, Atlanta, GA, 2011.

2417
Walter and Frances Bunzl Foundation ✧

780 Johnson Ferry Rd., Ste. 325
Atlanta, GA 30342-1434

Established in 1981 GA.
Donors: Walter Y. Bunzl†; Frances B. Bunzl.
Foundation type: Independent foundation.
Financial data (yr. ended 11/30/13): Assets, $835,583 (M); expenditures, $762,609; qualifying distributions, $752,975; giving activities include $750,000 for 4 grants (high: $500,000; low: $50,000).
Fields of interest: Museums (art); Education; Jewish agencies & synagogues.
Type of support: General/operating support.
Limitations: Applications not accepted. Giving primarily in Atlanta, GA. No grants to individuals.
Application information: Unsolicited requests for funds not accepted.
Officers: Frances B. Bunzl, Pres. and C.E.O.; Bennett L. Kight, V.P. and C.O.O.; William C. Lankford, Jr., V.P., C.F.O., and Secy.
EIN: 581458440
Selected grants: The following grants are a representative sample of this grantmaker's funding activity:
$150,000 to High Museum of Art, Atlanta, GA, 2011. For Annual Fund.
$50,000 to High Museum of Art, Atlanta, GA, 2011.
$25,000 to High Museum of Art, Atlanta, GA, 2011.
$10,000 to Atlanta Symphony Orchestra, Atlanta, GA, 2011. For Annual Fund.

2418
Fuller E. Callaway Foundation ✧

209 Broome St.
P.O. Box 790
LaGrange, GA 30241-0014 (706) 884-7348
Contact: H. Speer Burdette III, Genl. Mgr.
FAX: (706) 884-0201; Main URL: http://www.callawayfoundation.org/fecf_entry.php
Application address for George E. Sims Nursing Scholarship: c/o Gaylene Deason, West Georgia Health, 1514 Vernon Rd., LaGrange, GA 30240-4131, tel.: (706) 845-3722, e-mail: deasong@wghealth.org

Incorporated in 1917 in GA.
Donors: Fuller E. Callaway, Sr.†; Callaway Foundation, Inc.; Members of the Callaway family.
Foundation type: Independent foundation.
Financial data (yr. ended 12/31/13): Assets, $55,149,275 (M); gifts received, $3,323; expenditures, $3,211,536; qualifying distributions, $2,473,661; giving activities include $861,835 for 7 grants (high: $750,000; low: $250), and $304,920 for grants to individuals.
Purpose and activities: Giving primarily for religious, charitable, and educational organizations; scholarships for worthy students; modest gifts toward operating expenses of community welfare agencies, including youth programs, and health organizations.
Fields of interest: Education; Hospitals (general); Health care; Health organizations, association; Human services; Youth, services.

Type of support: Capital campaigns; Building/renovation; Equipment; Scholarships—to individuals; Matching/challenge support.
Limitations: Applications accepted. Giving primarily in the city of LaGrange and Troup County, GA. No grants for endowment funds; no loans.
Publications: Informational brochure.
Application information: Application form required only for scholarship program. Applicants for scholarship awards must have been residents of Troup County, Georgia, for at least two years. See foundation web site for complete application guidelines.
Copies of proposal: 1
Deadline(s): End of the month preceding board meeting for grants; Feb. 15 for college scholarships; May 15 for graduate school scholarships
Board meeting date(s): Jan., Apr., July, and Oct.
Final notification: 60 to 90 days
Officers: H. Speer Burdette III, Pres. and Genl. Mgr.; D. Ray McKenzie, Jr., V.P.; Esther S. Rainey, Secy.-Treas.
Trustees: Jane Alice Craig; Ellen H. Harris; Charles D. Hudson, Jr.; Ida H. Russell.
EIN: 580566148
Selected grants: The following grants are a representative sample of this grantmaker's funding activity:
$153,961 to Hatton Lovejoy Graduate Studies Fund, LaGrange, GA, 2012. For Graduate Studies Scholarships to Individual Students.

2419
Callaway Foundation, Inc. ✧
209 Broome St.
P.O. Box 790
LaGrange, GA 30241-0014 (706) 884-7348
Contact: H. Speer Burdette, III, Pres.
FAX: (706) 884-0201; E-mail: (for H. Speer Burdette, III) hsburdette@callaway-foundation.org; Main URL: http://www.callawayfoundation.org

Incorporated in 1943 in GA.
Donors: Textile Benefit Assn.; Callaway Mills; Callaway Institute, Inc.
Foundation type: Independent foundation.
Financial data (yr. ended 09/30/13): Assets, $208,270,211 (M); expenditures, $10,317,756; qualifying distributions, $8,756,420; giving activities include $8,200,444 for 47 grants (high: $5,000,000; low: $1,000).
Purpose and activities: Giving for elementary, higher, and secondary education, including libraries and buildings, and equipment; health and hospitals; community funds; care for the aged; community development; historic preservation; and church support.
Fields of interest: Historic preservation/historical societies; Elementary school/education; Secondary school/education; Higher education; Libraries/library science; Education; Hospitals (general); Health care; Health organizations, association; Aging, centers/services; Community/economic development; Christian agencies & churches; General charitable giving; Aging.
Type of support: Program-related investments/loans; General/operating support; Continuing support; Annual campaigns; Capital campaigns; Building/renovation; Equipment; Land acquisition; In-kind gifts; Matching/challenge support.
Limitations: Applications accepted. Giving primarily in GA, with emphasis on the City of LaGrange and Troup County. No grants to individuals, or for endowment funds, deficit financing, scholarships, or fellowships; no loans (except for program-related investments).
Publications: Annual report (including application guidelines).
Application information: Requests from churches outside Troop County, GA, are not considered. Application form not required.
Initial approach: Letter
Copies of proposal: 1
Deadline(s): End of month preceding board meetings
Board meeting date(s): Jan., Apr., July, and Oct.
Final notification: 2 months
Officers: H. Speer Burdette III, Pres. and Genl. Mgr.; D. Ray McKenzie, Jr., V.P.; Esther S. Rainey, Secy.-Treas.
Trustees: Jane Alice Hudson Craig; Ellen Hudson Harris; Charles D. Hudson, Jr.; Ida Hudson Russell.
EIN: 580566147
Selected grants: The following grants are a representative sample of this grantmaker's funding activity:
$5,000,000 to West Georgia Health Foundation, LaGrange, GA, 2013. To develop Community Cancer Center.
$4,391,258 to LaGrange College, LaGrange, GA, 2012. To purchase land and to make improvements to housing for students.
$500,000 to University of Georgia Foundation, Athens, GA, 2013. For renovation of Carnegie Library.
$430,000 to Boy Scouts of America, Chattahoochee Council, Columbus, GA, 2013. To develop waterfront and aquatics program.
$400,000 to Georgia Tech Athletic Association, Atlanta, GA, 2012. For construction of McCamish Pavilion.
$273,088 to LaGrange College, LaGrange, GA, 2012. For renovations to Lamar Dodd Art Center.
$270,500 to LaGrange Art Museum, LaGrange, GA, 2013. For capital improvements in the Center for Creative Learning.
$205,387 to Explorations in Antiquity Center, LaGrange, GA, 2012. For construction of theater and Biblical artifact gallery.
$167,194 to Lafayette Society for Performing Arts, LaGrange, GA, 2013. For operating support.
$150,064 to Community Action for Improvement, LaGrange, GA, 2012. To build parking lot for Head Start Center.
$150,000 to New Horizon Community Theater, West Point, GA, 2013. For renovations.
$115,000 to LaGrange Art Museum, LaGrange, GA, 2012. For operating support.
$110,245 to Lafayette Society for Performing Arts, LaGrange, GA, 2012. For operating support.
$109,920 to LaGrange Art Museum, LaGrange, GA, 2013. For operating support.
$105,875 to West Georgia Technical College Foundation, LaGrange, GA, 2012. For renovations to Callaway Conference Center.
$105,000 to LaGrange Symphony Orchestra, LaGrange, GA, 2013. For operating support.
$100,000 to Point University, West Point, GA, 2013. For capital improvements to Fine Arts Center.
$82,222 to LaGrange Symphony Orchestra, LaGrange, GA, 2012. For operating support.
$62,000 to Troup County Historical Society, LaGrange, GA, 2012. For operating support.
$62,000 to Troup County Historical Society, LaGrange, GA, 2013. For operating support.

2420
J. Bulow Campbell Foundation
3050 Peachtree Rd., N.W., Ste. 270
Atlanta, GA 30305-2212 (404) 658-9066
Contact: Betsy Hamilton Verner, Assoc. Dir.
FAX: (404) 659-4802; Main URL: http://www.jbcf.org

Trust established in 1940 in GA.
Donors: J. Bulow Campbell†; Virginia Campbell Courts†.
Foundation type: Independent foundation.
Financial data (yr. ended 12/31/13): Assets, $553,795,187 (M); expenditures, $36,902,243; qualifying distributions, $26,506,863; giving activities include $25,306,787 for 41 grants (high: $5,000,000; low: $50,000).
Purpose and activities: Broad purposes include, but are not limited to, privately-supported education, human welfare, youth development, the arts, Christian church-related agencies and agencies of the Presbyterian Church (not congregations) operating within the foundation's giving area. Concern for improving quality of spiritual and intellectual life, preferably projects of permanent nature or for capital funds. Gives anonymously and requests no publicity.
Fields of interest: Arts; Secondary school/education; Higher education; Education; Youth development; Human services; Children/youth, services; Family services; Christian agencies & churches; Protestant agencies & churches.
Type of support: Capital campaigns; Building/renovation; Land acquisition; Endowments; Matching/challenge support.
Limitations: Applications accepted. Giving primarily in GA; very limited giving in AL, FL, NC, SC, and TN. No support for local church congregations. No grants to individuals, or for current scholarships, fellowships, operating budgets, or recurring items; no loans.
Publications: Application guidelines; Informational brochure (including application guidelines).
Application information: Submit 1-page proposal, 1 copy of tax information. Application form not required.
Initial approach: Letter of inquiry or telephone
Copies of proposal: 1
Deadline(s): 1st of Jan., Apr., July, and Oct.
Board meeting date(s): Jan., Apr., July, and Oct.
Final notification: Within 1 week of board meetings
Officers and Trustees:* Bickerton W. Cardwell, Jr., Chair.; Richard C. Parker, Vice-Chair.; John W. Stephenson, Exec. Dir.; David B. Allman; Malon W. Courts; George H. Lane III; James B. Patton; William C. Warren IV, M.D.; S. Zachary Young.
Number of staff: 2 full-time professional; 3 full-time support.
EIN: 580566149
Selected grants: The following grants are a representative sample of this grantmaker's funding activity:
$5,000,000 to Grady Memorial Hospital Corporation, Grady Health System, Atlanta, GA, 2011. To establish a new cardiac center.
$2,000,000 to Kings Ridge Christian School, Alpharetta, GA, 2011. Toward construction of a new upper school building.
$1,000,000 to Atlanta Botanical Garden, Atlanta, GA, 2011. Toward Phase II of the New Seasons campaign.

$1,000,000 to Big Brothers Big Sisters of Metro Atlanta, Atlanta, GA, 2011. Toward purchase and renovation of new headquarters.
$1,000,000 to National Infantry Foundation, Columbus, GA, 2011. Toward campaign toward new campus.
$600,000 to Goodwill Industries of Middle Georgia, Macon, GA, 2011. Toward construction of Helms Career Institute in Augusta.
$600,000 to Springer Opera House Arts Association, Columbus, GA, 2011. Toward capital campaign.
$500,000 to First Presbyterian Day School, Macon, GA, 2011. Toward a $3.2 million capital campaign.
$400,000 to Jacobs Ladder Neurodevelopmental Learning Center, Roswell, GA, 2011. Toward campaign to purchase current facility.
$175,000 to Paul Anderson Youth Home, Vidalia, GA, 2011. Toward cottage renovations and campus redesign.

2421
Camp-Younts Foundation ✧
c/o SunTrust Bank
P.O. Box 4655, MC 221
Atlanta, GA 30302-4655
Contact: Emily Butler, Grants Mgr., SunTrust Banks
E-mail: fdnsvsc.ga@suntrust.com; Main URL: http://fdnweb.org/campyounts

Established in 1955 in GA.
Donors: Charles Younts†; Willie Camp Younts†.
Foundation type: Independent foundation.
Financial data (yr. ended 12/31/13): Assets, $45,655,856 (M); expenditures, $2,130,893; qualifying distributions, $2,029,000; giving activities include $1,947,399 for grants.
Purpose and activities: Giving primarily for education, with emphasis on higher and secondary educational institutions (including colleges and universities), and social services; support also for youth, Protestant giving, and health associations and hospitals with focus on helping poor and needy people.
Fields of interest: Arts, alliance/advocacy; Secondary school/education; Higher education; Education; Hospitals (general); Health organizations, association; Human services; Youth, services; Protestant agencies & churches; Children/youth; Children; Young adults.
Type of support: Management development/capacity building; General/operating support; Emergency funds; Capital campaigns; Annual campaigns.
Limitations: Applications accepted. Giving primarily in GA (only for operating and program grants) and VA. No grants to individuals.
Application information: In Georgia, only operating and non-capital grants will be considered. Application form not required.
Initial approach: Use application form on foundation web site; organizations outside of Metro Atlanta that wish to be considered should submit requests via U.S. mail to Franklin, VA, address
Copies of proposal: 1
Deadline(s): Aug. 31
Board meeting date(s): Dec.
Final notification: 3 months
Trustees: Harold S. Atkinson; John M. Camp, Jr.; John R. Marks; Gilford Walker; SunTrust Bank.
EIN: 586026001

Selected grants: The following grants are a representative sample of this grantmaker's funding activity:
$10,000 to Back on My Feet, Philadelphia, PA, 2011. For Atlanta Chapter Launch.
$10,000 to George West Mental Health Foundation, Atlanta, GA, 2011. For financial aid program.
$10,000 to Robert W. Woodruff Arts Center, Atlanta, GA, 2011. For annual corporate campaign.
$10,000 to Wesleyan School, Norcross, GA, 2011. For scholarship and financial aid endowment.
$10,000 to Year Up Atlanta, Atlanta, GA, 2011. For operating support.
$10,000 to YWCA of Greater Atlanta, Atlanta, GA, 2011. For Women In Transition, Cascade House.
$7,500 to Breakthrough Atlanta, Atlanta, GA, 2011. For scholarships.
$5,000 to Atlanta Opera, Atlanta, GA, 2011. For educational program for children and youth in metro Atlanta.
$5,000 to Our House, Decatur, GA, 2011. For general support for award-winning programs for homeless children and families.
$5,000 to Posse Foundation, Atlanta, GA, 2011. For general operating support.

2422
The Thalia N. and Chris M. Carlos Foundation, Inc. ✧ ☆
1 National Dr. S.W.
Atlanta, GA 30336-1631

Established in GA.
Foundation type: Independent foundation.
Financial data (yr. ended 12/31/13): Assets, $240,534 (M); gifts received, $1,035,810; expenditures, $834,000; qualifying distributions, $834,000; giving activities include $834,000 for 7 grants (high: $287,000; low: $5,000).
Fields of interest: Museums (specialized); Arts; Higher education, university; Education; Zoos/zoological societies; Religion.
Limitations: Applications not accepted. Giving primarily in GA.
Application information: Unsolicited requests for funds not accepted.
Officers: Chris M. Carlos, Pres. and Treas.; John L. Taylor, Jr., V.P. and Secy.
EIN: 454196053

2423
The Cawood Foundation, Inc. ✧
c/o TWA
103 Clover Green
Peachtree City, GA 30269-1672

Established in 1977 in GA.
Donors: Frank Cawood; Gayle Cawood.
Foundation type: Independent foundation.
Financial data (yr. ended 12/31/13): Assets, $93,801,758 (M); expenditures, $4,681,557; qualifying distributions, $4,310,850; giving activities include $4,310,850 for 22 grants (high: $1,500,000; low: $3,000).
Purpose and activities: Giving for education and Christian organizations.
Limitations: Applications not accepted.
Application information: Unsolicited requests for funds not accepted.
Officers: Frank Cawood, Pres.; Gayle Cawood, Secy.
Directors: Tim Anders; Benjamin Cawood; Joseph Cawood; Mimi Cawood; Mark Cruver; Natalie Cruver.
EIN: 581295620

2424
The Challenge Foundation ✧
c/o Habif, Arogeti & Wynne, LLP
5 Concourse Pkwy., Ste. 1000
Atlanta, GA 30328-5350
Contact: William J. Steinbrook, Jr., Exec. Dir.
E-mail: information@challengefoundation.org; Main URL: http://www.challengefoundation.org

Established in 1989 in GA.
Donor: John D. Bryan.
Foundation type: Independent foundation.
Financial data (yr. ended 12/31/12): Assets, $47,756,890 (M); gifts received, $7,540,874; expenditures, $5,007,218; qualifying distributions, $1,761,320; giving activities include $1,761,320 for 29 grants (high: $50,000; low: $5,765).
Purpose and activities: The foundation's mission is to support model educational initiatives that make it possible for every American child to attain a high school education that produces literate, factually aware, and thinking graduates second to none in the world. To do this the foundation provides start-up grants and support for charter schools.
Fields of interest: Education, association; Elementary/secondary education; Education, early childhood education; Elementary school/education; Secondary school/education; Education.
Type of support: Equipment; Program development; Conferences/seminars; Seed money; Curriculum development; Scholarship funds; Technical assistance; Consulting services; Program evaluation; Matching/challenge support.
Limitations: Applications not accepted. Giving on a national basis. No grants to individuals, or for general operating funds, fundraising, debt reduction, endowments, construction, land purchases or renovations.
Application information: Unsolicited requests for funds not accepted. Grant proposals are received only at the foundation's request.
Board meeting date(s): Apr. and Nov.
Officer: William J. Steinbrook, Jr., Exec. Dir.
Trustees: John D. Bryan; Martha Bryan.
Number of staff: 3 full-time professional; 1 part-time professional.
EIN: 581817816
Selected grants: The following grants are a representative sample of this grantmaker's funding activity:
$100,000 to Barry Goldwater Institute for Public Policy Research, Phoenix, AZ, 2012. For Two-part grant: (1) $50,000 to support the Goldwater Institute's Center for Constitutional Litigation in protecting individual liberty and constraints on government power in the Arizona Constitution, and (2) $50,000 to support the Goldwater Program to adv..
$50,000 to Arizona Charter Schools Association, Phoenix, AZ, 2012. For professional development services for Arizona charter school educators. The services will focus on three Program areas: (1) Free Professional Development for ACSA Member Charter Schools, (2) Customized intensive Professional Development for Sch.
$50,000 to Cato Institute, Washington, DC, 2012. For General operating support for Cato's mission to promote Libertarian principles of limited government, free markets, and individual liberty.

$50,000 to Foundation for Excellence in Education, Tallahassee, FL, 2012. For the National Summit on Education Reform Initiatives. The two-day conference will focus on improving education policy around the nation, state-by-state, by providing strategic support to Governors, state education chiefs, lawmakers and policymaking.
$40,000 to Parents for Educational Freedom in North Carolina, Raleigh, NC, 2012. For Ongoing support to help Parents for Educational Freedom in NC promote a comprehensive parental school choice policy that will allow all children in North Carolina to access greater school choice. The grant will help educate and engage parents, business.
$25,000 to Institute for Justice, Arlington, VA, 2012. For ongoing support for the Institute for Justice's legal cause to vindicate the constitutionality of school choice.
$25,000 to Irvington Community School, Indianapolis, IN, 2012. For a full-time Special Education classroom teacher for students that were recently transferred to Irvington Community School as the result of the December 16, 2011 closing of the Stonegate Early College High School.
$8,255 to Thomas A. Edison High School, Portland, OR, 2012. For 45 Apple iPods and related equipment for Edison High School's audio library to enhance reading skills of students with learning disabilities.
$5,765 to Jesuit High School, Portland, OR, 2012. For student financial aid in response to annual appeal at the 2012 Financial Aid Luncheon.

2425
Anne Cox Chambers Foundation, Inc. ✧
(formerly Anncox Foundation, Inc.)
P.O. Box 105720
Atlanta, GA 30348-5720

Incorporated in 1960 in GA.
Donor: Anne Cox Chambers.
Foundation type: Independent foundation.
Financial data (yr. ended 12/31/13): Assets, $55,778,107 (M); gifts received, $4,399; expenditures, $3,041,439; qualifying distributions, $2,826,440; giving activities include $2,826,440 for 127 grants (high: $333,000; low: $12).
Purpose and activities: Giving primarily for museums and education, animal welfare, health, and human services.
Fields of interest: Museums; Education; Environment, natural resources; Animal welfare; Animals/wildlife, preservation/protection; Health organizations, association; Human services.
Limitations: Applications not accepted. Giving primarily in GA, and the greater metropolitan New York, NY, area. No grants to individuals.
Application information: Contributes only to pre-selected organizations.
Officers and Trustees:* Anne Cox Chambers, Chair. and Pres.; James Cox Chambers,* V.P.; Alexander C. Taylor,* V.P.; Nancy K. Rigby, Secy.-Treas.
EIN: 586033966

2426
CLC Foundation Inc. ✧
450 E. Paces Ferry Rd.
Atlanta, GA 30305-3301
Contact: David Jones, Dir.
Application address: 412 King Rd., N.W., Atlanta, GA 30342

Established in 1983 in GA.
Donors: C.L. Chandler, Jr.†; C.L. Chandler, Jr. Charitable Remainder Trust; Bailey Johnson Heights Inc.
Foundation type: Independent foundation.
Financial data (yr. ended 12/31/13): Assets, $10,377,279 (M); expenditures, $606,960; qualifying distributions, $523,000; giving activities include $523,000 for 63 grants (high: $252,000; low: $500).
Purpose and activities: Giving primarily for education and Protestant organizations.
Fields of interest: Higher education; Education; Boy scouts; United Ways and Federated Giving Programs; Protestant agencies & churches.
Type of support: General/operating support; Scholarship funds.
Limitations: Applications accepted. Giving primarily in GA.
Application information: Application form required.
Initial approach: Letter
Deadline(s): None
Directors: Mark Chandler; Walker Chandler; Carol Dew; David Jones; Tommy Jones; Neal Quirk.
EIN: 581457649
Selected grants: The following grants are a representative sample of this grantmaker's funding activity:
$155,000 to Georgia State University, Atlanta, GA, 2010.
$4,000 to Alexs Lemonade Stand Foundation, Wynnewood, PA, 2010. For general operating funds.
$2,000 to Agnes Scott College, Decatur, GA, 2010.
$2,000 to Helen Keller International, New York, NY, 2011. For general operating funds.

2427
Ty Cobb Educational Fund ✧
P.O. Box 937
Sharpsburg, GA 30277-0937
Contact: Cathy Scott, Schol. Coord.
E-mail: tycobb@mindspring.com; Main URL: http://www.tycobbfoundation.com

Trust established in 1953 in GA.
Donor: Tyrus R. Cobb†.
Foundation type: Independent foundation.
Financial data (yr. ended 12/31/13): Assets, $14,323,458 (M); expenditures, $686,855; qualifying distributions, $624,349; giving activities include $520,000 for grants to individuals.
Purpose and activities: The foundation was established by the late Tyrus R. Cobb for the purpose of assisting capable and deserving residents of GA (who have resided in GA for at least 2 years prior to attending college, or have graduated from high school in GA), who need financial assistance in completing their college education. Foundation scholarships are granted to qualified students who have completed at least 30 semester hours or 45 quarter hours, with a 3.0 GPA or better, for the purpose of attending an accredited college or university full time. Professional students pursuing their dentistry or MD degrees, who are residents of GA, and have demonstrated financial need are eligible to apply.
Fields of interest: Higher education; Medical school/education; Dental care.
Type of support: Scholarships—to individuals.
Limitations: Giving limited to GA residents. No grants for building or endowment funds, operating budgets, special projects, or matching gifts; no loans.
Publications: Application guidelines; Informational brochure.
Application information: Application must include a letter of recommendation from student's academic dean or advisor and transcripts of all college studies; transcripts must be received by June 15th. Application form maybe downloaded from a PDF file on the foundation web site. Funds are paid directly to the applicant's institution. Application form required.
Initial approach: Letter or e-mail for guidelines between Mar. 15 and June 10 (postmark date), or see foundation web site
Copies of proposal: 1
Deadline(s): June 15
Board meeting date(s): Jan. and July
Final notification: Within 5 business days
Officers and Scholarship Board:* Francis J. Tedesco, M.D.,* Chair.; Cathy Cox; Sherm Day; Dr. Harry S. Downs; Bill Gerspacher; Dr. Valerie Hepburn; Hank Huckaby.
Trustee: SunTrust Bank.
Number of staff: 1 part-time support.
EIN: 586026003
Selected grants: The following grants are a representative sample of this grantmaker's funding activity:
$3,000 to Johns Hopkins University, School of Medicine, Baltimore, MD, 2012. For scholarships.

2428
The Coca-Cola Foundation, Inc. ✧
1 Coca-Cola Plaza, N.W.
Atlanta, GA 30313-2420 (404) 676-2568
Contact: Helen Smith Price, Exec. Dir.
FAX: (404) 676-8804;
E-mail: cocacolacommunityrequest@coca-cola.com; Additional tel.: (404) 676-3525; Main URL: http://www.thecoca-colacompany.com/citizenship/foundation_coke.html
Grants List: http://assets.coca-colacompany.com/c0/91/5c8a678246dd96470f4e306938ed/2011_grants_contributions_paid.pdf

Incorporated in 1984 in GA.
Donor: The Coca-Cola Co.
Foundation type: Company-sponsored foundation.
Financial data (yr. ended 12/31/12): Assets, $191,508,505 (M); expenditures, $70,331,780; qualifying distributions, $69,658,157; giving activities include $64,103,179 for 3,644 grants (high: $5,250,000; low: $10,000), and $5,554,978 for employee matching gifts.
Purpose and activities: The foundation supports programs designed to promote water stewardship; healthy and active lifestyles; community recycling, and education.
Fields of interest: Higher education; Scholarships/financial aid; Education, services; Education, drop-out prevention; Education; Environment, water pollution; Environment, recycling; Environment, water resources; Hospitals (general); Public health, obesity; Public health, physical fitness; Public health, clean water supply; Public health, sanitation; AIDS; Nutrition; Disasters, preparedness/services; Big Brothers/Big Sisters; Girl scouts; Youth development; Economic development; Community/economic development; Women.
International interests: Africa; Europe; Latin America.
Type of support: General/operating support; Continuing support; Emergency funds; Program

development; Fellowships; Scholarship funds; Sponsorships; Employee matching gifts.
Limitations: Applications accepted. Giving on a national and international basis in areas of company operations, with emphasis on CA, Washington, DC, Atlanta, GA, New York, NY, TX, VA, Africa, Australia, Chile, China, Colombia, Europe, Italy, Japan, Latin America, Philippines, and Russia. No support for discriminatory organizations, political, legislative, or lobbying organizations, fraternal organizations, athletic teams, or U.S. based local schools, including charter schools, pre-schools, elementary schools, middle schools, or high schools. No grants to individuals (except for the Coca-Cola First Generation Scholarship), or for movie, film, or television documentaries, website development, concerts or other entertainment events, beauty contests, fashion shows, or hair shows, local sports, travel or organized field trips, family reunions, marketing sponsorships, cause marketing, or advertising projects, land, building, or equipment, or construction or renovation projects.
Publications: Application guidelines; Grants list; Program policy statement.
Application information: Faxed or e-mailed applications are not accepted. Application form required.
Initial approach: Complete online application form; contact participating universities for Coca-Cola First Generation Scholarship
Copies of proposal: 1
Deadline(s): None
Board meeting date(s): Quarterly
Final notification: 60 days
Officers and Directors:* Lisa M. Borders, Chair.; Alexander B. Cummings, Secy.; Gary P. Fayard,* Treas.; Lawton Hawkins, Genl. Legal Counsel; William Hawkins,* Genl. Tax Counsel; Helen Smith Price,* Exec. Dir.; Ahmet C. Bozer; Beatriz Perez; Sonya Soutus; Dominique Reiniche; Clyde C. Tuggle.
Number of staff: 6 full-time professional; 5 full-time support.
EIN: 581574705
Selected grants: The following grants are a representative sample of this grantmaker's funding activity:
$7,000,000 to Global Environment and Technology Foundation, Arlington, VA, 2013. For Replenish Africa Initiative (RAIN). Supports a five-year, $30 million project to provide access to water and sanitation to two million people on the African continent. Grant made through Coca-Cola Africa Foundation.
$2,000,000 to United Nations Development Programme, New York, NY, 2013. For Every Drop Matters: Community-Based Water Management Programs. Supports water access and education programs in Armenia, Azerbaijani, Bangladesh, Belarus, Bulgaria, Georgia, Iraq, Jordan, Kazakhstan, Lebanon, Nepal, Pakistan, Palestinian Territories, Romania, Russian Federation, Sri Lanka, Turkey, Ukraine and Uzbekistan.
$1,450,000 to Institute Doe Seu Lixo, Rio de Janeiro, Brazil, 2013. For Recycling Cooperative Management Capability Program. Supports a program to reduce solid waste through recycling and provides economic opportunities for communities in Brazil. Grant made through Instituto Coca-Cola Brasil.
$1,340,000 to Keep America Beautiful, Stamford, CT, 2013. For Transforming Chicago Recycling With Curbside Recycling Carts. Support to expand awareness and activation of curbside recycling services to more than 25,000 homes in Chicago, Illinois.
$528,000 to City University London, Friends of, Cass Business School, Wilmington, DE, 2013. For Coca Cola Scholars At Cass Business School. Provides scholarships to eight undergraduate students attending the Cass Business School who have met academic requirements and need financial assistance.
$500,000 to Charities Aid Foundation-Russia, Moscow, Russia, 2013. For Street Workout Russia - Be Active. Funding for 13 Street Workout sports facilities in six cities throughout Russia.
$125,000 to University of Illinois at Urbana-Champaign, Urbana, IL, 2013. For Coca-Cola First Generation Scholarship Program. Provides $24,000 scholarships ($6,000 each year for four years) to 20 students who are the first in their families to attend college.
$120,000 to John Tung Foundation, Taipei, Taiwan, 2013. For 2013 Rope Skipping For Healthy Lifestyles. Supports for rope skipping classes and competitions to promote active healthy lifestyles to 24,000 students in 12 schools throughout Taipei, Taiwan.
$100,000 to ALE Coalition, Astana, Kazakhstan, 2013. For Green Technology Training For Rural Citizens. Supports rural economic development efforts utilizing green technologies in Akmolinskaya and Almatinskaya, Kazakhstan.
$100,000 to Junior Achievement Ecuador, Quito, Ecuador, 2013. For Apuntate A Jugar Plus (Sign Up To Play Plus). Funding for physical education equipment kits for 9,200 students, ages 6 to 12, at 25 public schools in Quito, Ecuador.

2429
Susanne Marcus Collins Foundation, Inc. ✧

1266 W. Paces Ferry Rd., Ste. 615
Atlanta, GA 30327-2306

Established in 1998 in GA.
Foundation type: Independent foundation.
Financial data (yr. ended 12/31/13): Assets, $7,299,402 (M); expenditures, $1,945,716; qualifying distributions, $1,909,614; giving activities include $1,637,000 for 6 grants (high: $1,000,000; low: $7,000).
Fields of interest: Arts; Health care; Human services.
Limitations: Applications not accepted. Giving primarily in Boston, MA. No grants to individuals.
Application information: Contributes only to pre-selected organizations.
Officer: Susanne Collins, Chair. and Exec. Dir.
Directors: Martina G. Barnes; Martin Collins; Rachel Collins; Jo Pitkin; Grant Smith.
EIN: 582396540

2430
Colonial Foundation, Inc. ✧

P.O. Box 576
Savannah, GA 31402-0576 (912) 236-1331
Contact: Frances A. Brown, V.P. and Treas.
Application address: 1010 N. Lathrop Ave., Savannah, GA 31415

Established in 1986 in GA.
Donor: Colonial Oil Industries, Inc.
Foundation type: Company-sponsored foundation.
Financial data (yr. ended 12/31/13): Assets, $7,806,987 (M); gifts received, $150,000; expenditures, $1,041,494; qualifying distributions, $999,371; giving activities include $999,371 for 82 grants (high: $200,000; low: $100).
Purpose and activities: The foundation supports organizations involved with arts and culture, education, health, cancer, hunger, human services, and business promotion.
Fields of interest: Museums; Historic preservation/historical societies; Arts; Elementary/secondary education; Higher education; Engineering school/education; Education; Health care; Cancer; Food services; Youth development, business; YM/YWCAs & YM/YWHAs; Human services; Community development, business promotion; United Ways and Federated Giving Programs.
Type of support: General/operating support; Annual campaigns; Scholarship funds; Sponsorships; Employee matching gifts.
Limitations: Applications accepted. Giving primarily in Savannah, GA. No grants to individuals.
Application information: Application form required.
Initial approach: Letter
Deadline(s): None
Officers: Robert H. Demere, Jr., Pres. and Secy.; Frances A. Brown, V.P. and Treas.; William A. Baker, Jr., V.P.
EIN: 581693323
Selected grants: The following grants are a representative sample of this grantmaker's funding activity:
$200,000 to Telfair Museum of Art, Savannah, GA, 2011.
$101,500 to United Way, Greater Twin Cities, Minneapolis, MN, 2011.
$100,000 to Coastal Heritage Society, Savannah, GA, 2011.
$100,000 to Saint Andrews School, Barrington, RI, 2011.
$100,000 to Saint Josephs Candler Health System, Savannah, GA, 2011.
$100,000 to Savannah Country Day School, Savannah, GA, 2011.
$3,000 to Abilities Unlimited, Westerville, OH, 2011.

2431
Communities of Coastal Georgia Foundation, Inc.

1626 Frederica Rd., Ste. 201
Saint Simons Island, GA 31522 (912) 268-4442
Contact: Valerie A. Hepburn, Pres. and C.E.O.; For grant inquiries: Ellen E. Post, Grants and Opers. Mgr.
FAX: (912) 268-2316;
E-mail: vhepburn@coastalgeorgiafoundation.org; Grant inquiry tel.: (912) 268-2561, and e-mail: epost@coastalgeorgiafoundation.org; Main URL: http://www.coastalgeorgiafoundation.org
Facebook: https://www.facebook.com/pages/Communities-of-Coastal-Georgia-Foundation-Inc/503084426417621

Established in 2005 in GA.
Foundation type: Community foundation.
Financial data (yr. ended 12/31/13): Assets, $12,711,007 (M); gifts received, $3,169,060; expenditures, $787,592; giving activities include $490,404 for 23+ grants (high: $50,000).
Purpose and activities: The mission of the foundation is to improve the quality of life in Coastal Georgia by promoting and increasing responsible,

effective philanthropy now and for future generations.
Fields of interest: Arts; Education, early childhood education; Education; Environment; Animals/wildlife; Health care; Youth development; Human services; Community development, neighborhood development; Community/economic development.
Type of support: Management development/capacity building; Equipment; Program development; Conferences/seminars; Curriculum development; Technical assistance; Consulting services; Program evaluation.
Limitations: Applications accepted. Giving limited to Glynn, McIntosh, and Camden counties, GA. No support for medical or academic research, religious purposes, or international NGOs. No grants to individuals, or for annual fundraising campaigns, debt or deficit reduction, capital building campaigns, general operating support, endowments, grants for re-granting or retroactive funding.
Publications: Application guidelines; Annual report; Financial statement; Grants list; Informational brochure; Newsletter.
Application information: Visit foundation web site for application deadlines and guidelines. Full proposals accepted through invitation only, following letter of intent. Application form required.
Initial approach: Letter of intent
Copies of proposal: 1
Deadline(s): Feb. 13
Board meeting date(s): First Wed. of June
Final notification: Approx. 4 weeks for RFP invitation; Early June for grant determination
Officers and Directors:* Rees Sumerford,* Chair.; Arthur M. Lucas,* Vice-Chair. and Secy.; Jeff Barker,* Treas.; Frank DeLoach, Jr., Dir. Emeritus; Jack Dinos, Dir. Emeritus; Bill Jones III, Dir. Emeritus; Claude Booker, At-Large; Jeanne Manning, At-Large; Bonney Stamper Shuman, At-Large; Edward Andrews, Jr.; Ellen Fleming; S. Michael Hardy; Jack C. Kilgore; Diane Laws; Michael Maloy; William Bernard McCloud; Diana M. Murphy; S. Lloyd Newberry, Jr., Ph.D.; Mary T. Root; Alfred Sams III; Janet A. Shirley; Bill Stembler.
Number of staff: 2 full-time professional.
EIN: 202454729
Selected grants: The following grants are a representative sample of this grantmaker's funding activity:
$5,000 to Camden Community Crisis Center, Saint Marys, GA, 2011. For computer equipment and network training.
$5,000 to Southeast Youth Development Academies, Brunswick, GA, 2011. For equipment for Beyond the Horizon program.
$5,000 to YMCA of Coastal Georgia, Savannah, GA, 2011. To implement Health Management Lab for Activate America program.
$4,700 to McIntosh County Sustainable Environmental and Economic Development, Darien, GA, 2011. For extension of Project YELL youth education program and addition of college fairs.
$4,400 to Communities in Schools of Glynn County, Brunswick, GA, 2011. For professional development of Executive Director and new staff.
$4,000 to Americas Second Harvest of Coastal Georgia, Savannah, GA, 2011. For website construction update and social networking development.
$4,000 to McIntosh County Family Connection, Darien, GA, 2011. For technology and equipment upgrades.
$3,000 to Bryan-Lang Foundation, Woodbine, GA, 2011. For strategic plan and board development.
$3,000 to Grace House of Brunswick, Brunswick, GA, 2011. For computer equipment.
$3,000 to Safe Harbor Childrens Shelter, Brunswick, GA, 2011. For equipment and technology upgrades for new outreach program.
$2,500 to CASA Glynn, Brunswick, GA, 2011. For training for Executive Director and staff.
$2,400 to Mcintosh Art Association, GA, 2011. For educational outreach program.
$2,000 to Ferst Foundation for Childhood Literacy, Madison, GA, 2011. For cost of books to be mailed into homes of registered children to encourage early literacy.
$2,000 to Southern Technological Advocacy Resources Foundation, Brunswick, GA, 2011. For computer equipment.

2432
The Community Foundation for Greater Atlanta ✧

(formerly Metropolitan Atlanta Community Foundation, Inc.)
50 Hurt Plz., Ste. 449
Atlanta, GA 30303-2915 (404) 688-5525
Contact: Alicia Philipp, Pres.
FAX: (404) 688-3060;
E-mail: info@cfgreateratlanta.org; Main URL: http://www.cfgreateratlanta.org
E-Newsletter: http://www.cfgreateratlanta.org/Sign-Up-Now.aspx
Facebook: http://www.facebook.com/cfgreateratlanta
Flickr: http://www.flickr.com/photos/cfgreateratlanta
LinkedIn: http://www.linkedin.com/companies/the-community-foundation-for-greater-atlanta
YouTube: http://www.youtube.com/user/cfgreateratlanta
Scholarship information e-mail: scholarships@cfgreateratlanta.org

Incorporated in 1977 as successor to Metropolitan Foundation of Atlanta established in 1951 in GA by bank resolution and declaration of trust.
Foundation type: Community foundation.
Financial data (yr. ended 12/31/13): Assets, $929,200,310 (M); gifts received, $198,279,399; expenditures, $147,974,002; giving activities include $124,456,642 for grants.
Purpose and activities: The foundation strengthens the region by providing quality services to donors and innovative leadership on community issues.
Fields of interest: Arts education; Arts; Education; Environment, natural resources; Health care; AIDS; Housing/shelter, development; Housing/shelter; Youth development; Youth, services; Family services; Family services, parent education; Women, centers/services; Homeless, human services; Human services; Community development, neighborhood development; Community/economic development; General charitable giving; Children/youth; Women; AIDS, people with; Homeless.
Type of support: General/operating support; Management development/capacity building; Advocacy; Program development; Scholarship funds; Technical assistance; Consulting services; Program-related investments/loans; Scholarships—to individuals; Mission-related investments/loans.
Limitations: Applications accepted. Giving limited to the 23-county metropolitan area of Atlanta, GA. No support for religious education or services (except through donor-advised funds), or operating expenses for private and publicly funded schools (K-12) and institutions of higher learning. No grants to individuals (except for scholarships), or for endowment funds, fundraising and marketing events, or capital campaign contributions.
Publications: Application guidelines; Annual report; Grants list; Informational brochure; Newsletter; Occasional report; Program policy statement.
Application information: Visit foundation web site for application guidelines per grant type and orientation schedule. The foundation reviews all Letters of Intent for the Common Good Funds and invites approximately 30 organizations to submit final applications. Application form required.
Initial approach: Submit Letter of Intent
Copies of proposal: 1
Deadline(s): Apr. 16 for Common Good Funds Letters of Intent; June 16 for Common Good Fund final applications (invitation only); varies for others
Board meeting date(s): Feb., Apr., May and Oct.
Final notification: Late Oct. for Common Good Funds grants; varies for others
Officers and Directors:* Suzanne E. Boas,* Chair.; Alicia Philipp, Pres.; Lesley Grady, Sr. V.P., Community Partnerships; Christie Brown, V.P., Finance and Opers.; Kristin Dunstan, V.P., Mktg. and Comms.; Rob Smulian, V.P., Philanthropic Svcs.; Antoinette Maddox, Cont.; Benjamin T. White, Legal Counsel; Kenneth Bernhardt; Becky Blalock; Kenneth Britt; Robert L. Brown; Ann W. Cramer; Edward Croft; Brian Friedman; Carol Hatfield; Dr. Sivan Hines; Lynn Huntley; Tad Hutcheson; Donata Russell Major; Michael A. Nadal; Roger Chip Patterson, Jr.; Katy Patillo; Jagdish Sheth, Ph.D.; Hon. Ronit Walker.
Number of staff: 27 full-time professional; 1 part-time professional; 4 full-time support; 2 part-time support.
EIN: 581344646
Selected grants: The following grants are a representative sample of this grantmaker's funding activity:
$8,301,285 to Grady Memorial Hospital Corporation, Atlanta, GA, 2011.
$4,400,000 to Young Harris College, Young Harris, GA, 2012.
$3,000,000 to Ida Cason Callaway Foundation, Pine Mountain, GA, 2012.
$2,000,000 to Childrens Healthcare of Atlanta Foundation, Atlanta, GA, 2012.
$1,350,000 to Rollins Child Development Center, Atlanta, GA, 2011.
$1,237,775 to PATH Foundation, Atlanta, GA, 2011.
$1,000,000 to Peachtree Road United Methodist Church, Atlanta, GA, 2012.
$800,000 to Marcus Institute for Development and Learning, Atlanta, GA, 2012.
$500,000 to BeltLine Partnership, Atlanta, GA, 2012.
$500,000 to General Conference of Seventh-Day Adventists, Silver Spring, MD, 2011.
$500,000 to Paul and Debbie Chelko Foundation, Atlanta, GA, 2011.
$200,000 to CORE, Decatur, GA, 2011.
$50,000 to StoryCorps, Brooklyn, NY, 2011. For in memory of Phillip Rush and for Story Booth Atlanta.
$50,000 to StoryCorps, Brooklyn, NY, 2011. For in memory of Phillip Rush and Story Booth Atlanta.
$6,250 to Smile Train, New York, NY, 2011. For general support.

$5,000 to Atlanta Botanical Garden, Atlanta, GA, 2012.
$4,940 to Good Shepherd Clinic, Morrow, GA, 2012.
$4,000 to American Farm School, New York, NY, 2012.
$3,600 to Hebrew Benevolent Congregation of Atlanta, Atlanta, GA, 2012.
$3,500 to Darlington School, Rome, GA, 2011.
$3,400 to Church at Northside, Armuchee, GA, 2011.
$3,000 to Smile Train, New York, NY, 2011. For general support.
$2,500 to Visiting Nurse Health System, Atlanta, GA, 2011.
$2,500 to Youth Villages, Memphis, TN, 2011.

2433
Community Foundation for Northeast Georgia ✧

6500 Sugarloaf Pkwy., Ste. 220
Duluth, GA 30097 (770) 813-3380
Contact: Margaret Bugbee, Dir., Finance
FAX: (770) 813-3375; E-mail: info@cfneg.org; Main URL: http://www.cfneg.org
Facebook: https://www.facebook.com/pages/Community-Foundation-for-Northeast-Georgia/190357550996590
Twitter: https://twitter.com/CFNEG

Incorporated in 1985 in GA.
Foundation type: Community foundation.
Financial data (yr. ended 12/31/12): Assets, $26,680,210 (M); gifts received, $3,409,949; expenditures, $4,218,983; giving activities include $3,701,318 for 51+ grants.
Purpose and activities: The foundation seeks to: 1) provide a cost-effective bridge for all donors to our community's changing needs; 2) serve as a leader, catalyst, and resource for philanthropy; 3) produce an expanding pool of permanent endowment funds for now and all time; 4) Improve the quality of life with grants and technical assistance to local charities; and 5) partner with and be an advocate for the endowment of local charities.
Fields of interest: Performing arts; Arts; Education; Health care; Human services; Community/economic development; Children/youth; Youth; Aging.
Type of support: Capital campaigns; Building/renovation; Equipment; Emergency funds; Program development; Seed money.
Limitations: Applications accepted. Giving limited to organizations or services directly benefiting citizens of northeast GA. No support for religious purposes, or commonly accepted community services. No grants for individuals, or for endowment support, debt reduction, fundraising or annual campaigns, membership contributions, research, travel, or ongoing operating support.
Publications: Annual report (including application guidelines); Grants list; Newsletter.
Application information: Visit foundation web site for application cover sheet and guidelines. Faxed applications are not accepted. Application form required.
Initial approach: Submit grant proposal cover sheet and attachments
Copies of proposal: 15
Deadline(s): Mar. 1
Board meeting date(s): 5 times annually
Final notification: June
Officers and Directors:* Robert D. Fowler,* Chair.; William R. Short,* Pres.; Greg Shumate,* V.P.; Richard B. Chandler, Jr.,* Secy.; William E. McLendon,* Treas.; Judy Waters, Exec. Dir.; Tom Abernathy; Ethel D. Anderson; Julie Keeton Arnold; Doug Bridges; Stephen K. Hill; Barbara Howard; Dan Kaufman; James Pack; Scott Phelan; Maxie Price, Jr.; Karen Fine Saltiel; Ruth Strickland; Sandra Strickland; Perry Tindol; T. Michael Tennant; Kathryn Willis; A. Ray Weeks, Jr.
Number of staff: 2 full-time professional; 2 part-time support.
EIN: 581557995

2434
Community Foundation for the Central Savannah River Area ✧

(formerly CSRA Community Foundation, Inc.)
1450 Greene St., Ste. 228
Augusta, GA 30901-5234 (706) 724-1314
Contact: R. Lee Smith, Jr., C.E.O.
FAX: (706) 724-1315; E-mail: info@cfcsra.org; Mailing address: P.O. Box 31358, Augusta, GA 30903; Main URL: http://www.cfcsra.org

Established in 1995 in GA.
Donors: Norman Shapiro; Mrs. Norman Shapiro.
Foundation type: Community foundation.
Financial data (yr. ended 12/31/13): Assets, $64,058,339 (M); gifts received, $8,161,073; expenditures, $10,530,488; giving activities include $9,871,823 for grants.
Purpose and activities: The mission of the foundation is to encourage and promote philanthropy through education, responsible management of charitable contributions and the distribution of these funds, and to provide the structure for this to be accomplished by individuals, companies and organizations.
Fields of interest: Arts; Higher education; Education; Environment; Health care; Children, services; Youth, services; Family services; Human services; Community development, neighborhood development; Economic development; Community/economic development; Government/public administration; Religion.
Type of support: Annual campaigns; Capital campaigns; Seed money; Scholarship funds; Matching/challenge support.
Limitations: Applications accepted. Giving limited to the greater Augusta, GA, area, including Burke, Columbia, McDuffie, and Richmond counties, GA, and Aiken and Edgefield counties, SC. No support for fraternal organizations or professional associations. No grants to individuals, or for building campaigns, deficit financing, debt reduction, endowments, fundraisers, surveys, travel, or for film and video production.
Publications: Application guidelines; Grants list; Informational brochure; Newsletter; Occasional report (including application guidelines).
Application information: Visit foundation web site for application form and instructions. Applications submitted by fax are not accepted or considered. The foundation holds a free grantmaker session/seminar for organizations that wish to apply for funding; reservations are limited, please call or e-mail foundation. Application form required.
Initial approach: Submit application form and attachments
Copies of proposal: 8
Deadline(s): Aug. 29
Board meeting date(s): Quarterly
Final notification: Dec.
Officers and Directors:* James M. Hull,* Chair.; R. Lee Smith, Jr.,* C.E.O. and Pres.; C.P. Boardman III,* V.P., Investment Comm.; Abram Serotta,* V.P., Grants Comm.; Braye C. Boardman,* Secy.-Treas.; D. Douglas Barnard, Jr.,* Honorary Dir.; Charles H. Bellmann, Honorary Dir.; William S. Morris III,* Honorary Dir.; James J. Bernstein; Shell Knox Berry; Thomas M. Blanchard, Jr.; C.G. "Pete" Caye, Jr.; Zack O. Daffin; Lafeye Hargrove, Ph.D.; Duncan N. Johnson, Jr.; Brian J. Marks; Mason H. McKnight III; E.G. Meybohm; Russell V. Mobley; Susan G. Nicholson; H.M. Osteen, Jr.; N. Turner Simkins; Barry L. Storey; James B. Trotter; William H. Tucker; Kenneth L. Usry.
Number of staff: 2 full-time professional; 1 full-time support.
EIN: 582184345

2435
Community Foundation of Central Georgia, Inc. ✧

277 Martin Luther King, Jr. Blvd., Ste. 303
Macon, GA 31201-3489 (478) 750-9338
FAX: (478) 738-9214; E-mail: info@cfcga.org; Additional tel.: (866) 750-9338; Grant inquiry e-mail: grants@cfcga.org; Main URL: http://www.cfcga.org
Blog: http://www.cfcga.org/Page.aspx?pid=333
Facebook: http://www.facebook.com/CFCGA
Instagram: http://instagram.com/cfcentralga
Twitter: http://twitter.com/CFCGA
YouTube: http://www.youtube.com/user/CFCGa

Established in 1993 in GA.
Foundation type: Community foundation.
Financial data (yr. ended 06/30/13): Assets, $69,296,540 (M); gifts received, $6,014,739; expenditures, $5,574,154; giving activities include $4,141,746 for 107 grants (high: $107,298; low: $42), and $198,767 for 88 grants to individuals.
Purpose and activities: The foundation seeks to enhance the quality of life for the people of Central Georgia. To accomplish its mission, the foundation has five primary goals: 1) to be a catalyst for the establishment of endowments to benefit the community now and for all time; 2) to provide leadership and resources in identifying and meeting local needs; 3) to serve donors' varied interests and needs; 4) to promote local philanthropy; and 5) to serve as stewards of funds.
Fields of interest: Historic preservation/historical societies; Arts; Education; Environment; Animal welfare; Health care; Human services; Economic development; Community/economic development; Disabilities, people with; Economically disadvantaged.
Type of support: General/operating support; Management development/capacity building; Capital campaigns; Building/renovation; Equipment; Program development; Scholarship funds; Matching/challenge support.
Limitations: Applications accepted. Giving limited to central GA. No support for sectarian religious purposes.
Publications: Annual report; Financial statement.
Application information: Visit foundation web site for guidelines and online application form. Hardcopy, faxed, e-mailed, and/or incomplete applications will not be considered. Application form required.
Initial approach: Submit online application form and required attachments

Deadline(s): June 30 and Dec. 31 for Community Grants; varies for others
Final notification: Sept. and Mar.
Officers and Directors:* G. Boone Smith III,* Chair.; Kathryn H. Dennis, Pres.; Jacqueline G. Scott,* Secy.; Ronnie Rollins,* Treas.; Julie G. Baldwin; Beverly Blake; Charlotte Bogle; Malcom S. Burgess, Jr.; Mark Byrd; Dave Carty; Donald J. Cornett; Tiena Fletcher; Robert F. Hatcher, Jr.; Terry A. Henderson; Camille Hope; John D. Houser; Ruth A. Knox; Eleanor Lane; Jeff Manley; James A. Manley III; W. John O'Shaughnessey; Terry Parker; Billy Pitts; Albert P. Reichert; Chris R. Sheridan, Jr.; F. Tredway Shurling; Scott W. Spivey; Neal Talton.
Number of staff: 5 full-time professional; 1 part-time support.
EIN: 582053465

2436
Community Foundation of Northwest Georgia, Inc. ✧

714 S. Thorton Ave., Ste. 5
P.O. Box 942
Dalton, GA 30722-0942 (706) 275-9117
Contact: David Aft, Pres.
FAX: (706) 275-9118;
E-mail: thefoundation@communityfoundationnwga.org; Additional e-mail: david.aft@communityfoundationwga.org; Main URL: http://www.communityfoundationnwga.org
Facebook: https://www.facebook.com/CommunityFoundationNWGA

Established in 1998 in GA.
Foundation type: Community foundation.
Financial data (yr. ended 12/31/13): Assets, $32,301,848 (M); gifts received, $9,575,638; expenditures, $3,890,257; giving activities include $3,138,656 for 234+ grants (high: $282,507; low: $76).
Purpose and activities: The foundation seeks to enhance the quality of life in the northwest GA region for both present and future generations by: 1) promoting philanthropy; 2) building and maintaining permanent endowment funds to be used for the broad charitable needs of the region; 3) serving as a leader in identifying and prioritizing needs in the community; 4) serving as a catalyst in developing effective responses to community issues; 5) encouraging collaboration between organizations and agencies to shape solutions; and 6) serving as a steward of the funds in the endowment.
Fields of interest: Historic preservation/historical societies; Arts; Education; Environment; Animal welfare; Health care; Youth development; Children/youth, services; Human services; Community/economic development; Religion.
Type of support: Program development; Seed money; Matching/challenge support.
Limitations: Applications accepted. Giving limited to Bartow, Catoosa, Chattooga, Dade, Fannin, Floyd, Gilmer, Gordon, Murray, Pickens, Walker, and Whitfield, GA.
Publications: Application guidelines; Annual report; Informational brochure.
Application information: Visit foundation web site for online application and guidelines. Application form required.
Initial approach: Submit online application or call foundation
Deadline(s): Mar. 31 and Oct. 1
Board meeting date(s): Jan., Mar., May, July, Sept., and Nov.
Final notification: 30 to 60 days
Officers and Directors:* Harris R. Thompson,* Chair.; David Aft, Pres.; Vance D. Bell; Jim Bethel; Linda Blackman; Ed Brush; George Crowley; Bill Davies; Bryan McAllister.
Number of staff: 1 full-time professional; 1 full-time support; 1 part-time support.
EIN: 582360356

2437
Community Foundation of South Georgia, Inc. ✧

(formerly Community Foundation of Southwest Georgia, Inc.)
135 N. Broad St., Ste. 202
Thomasville, GA 31792-8103 (229) 228-5088
Contact: David M. Carlton, Pres.; Randae Davis, Dir., Donor Svcs.
FAX: (229) 228-0848; E-mail: cfsga@rose.net; Additional tel.: (888) 544-2317; Main URL: http://www.cfsga.net/

Established in 1995 in GA.
Foundation type: Community foundation.
Financial data (yr. ended 12/31/12): Assets, $55,007,443 (M); gifts received, $5,464,223; expenditures, $5,751,630; giving activities include $4,662,150 for grants, and $118,493 for 121 grants to individuals.
Purpose and activities: The foundation seeks to: 1) be a catalyst for the establishment of charitable funds which benefit the community for generations to come; 2) serve the varied interests and needs of donors; 3) promote local philanthropy; 4) serve as a steward of funds; and 5) provide leadership and resources in identifying and meeting local needs.
Fields of interest: Arts; Education; Health care; Human services.
Type of support: Scholarships—to individuals.
Limitations: Applications not accepted. Giving primarily in southwest GA.
Publications: Annual report; Grants list; Informational brochure.
Application information: Unsolicited requests for funds are currently not accepted.
Board meeting date(s): Mar., June, Sept., and Dec.
Officers and Trustees:* Alston Watt,* Chair.; Vann K. Parrott,* Vice-Chair.; David Carlton,* Pres.; George Lilly II,* Secy.; W. Ralph Rodgers, Jr.,* Treas.; Lisa Hitt, Cont.; Jimmy Allen; Bill Burke; John M. Carlton, Jr.; David Cone; Russ Henry; Ann Hopkins; James M. Jeter; Bruce W. Kirbo, Jr.; John McTier; John Prince III; E.J. Vann IV; Randy Wages; Jo Stott Wingate.
Number of staff: 3 full-time professional; 1 part-time professional.
EIN: 582210876

2438
Community Foundation of the Chattahoochee Valley ✧

1340 13th St.
Columbus, GA 31901-2345 (706) 320-0027
Contact: Betsy W. Covington, C.E.O.
FAX: (706) 320-9331; E-mail: info@cfcv.com; Additional e-mail: bcovington@cfcv.com; Main URL: http://www.cfcv.com
Facebook: http://www.facebook.com/pages/The-Community-Foundation-of-the-Chattahoochee-Valley/204884916208685

Established in 1998 in GA.
Foundation type: Community foundation.
Financial data (yr. ended 09/30/13): Assets, $99,720,097 (M); gifts received, $9,827,506; expenditures, $10,747,835; giving activities include $9,971,023 for 296+ grants (high: $1,680,968).
Purpose and activities: The foundation is a nonprofit charitable organization dedicated to strengthening the Chattahoochee Valley's diverse community for both present and future generations. It promotes philanthropy, builds and maintains a permanent collection of endowment funds, and serves as a trustworthy partner and leader in shaping effective responses to community needs and opportunities.
Fields of interest: Arts; Education; Environment, natural resources; Youth development; Children/youth, services; Human services; Community/economic development.
Type of support: Program evaluation.
Limitations: Applications not accepted. Giving limited to the Chattahoochee Valley Region in west central GA and east central AL.
Application information: The foundation is not currently accepting grant applications.
Officers and Trustees:* Gwendolyn H. Ruff,* Chair.; Kenneth M. Henson, Jr.,* Vice-Chair. and Chair., Funds Devel.; Betsy W. Covington,* C.E.O. and Pres.; Marquette M. McKnight,* Secy.; D. Raines Jordan,* Treas.; Lawrence R. "Larry" Heisler, Cont.; Anthony D. Link,* Chair., Investments; Lane M. Riley, Chair., Distributions; Amos "Ted" Beason; Dr. Frank D. Brown; Cecil M. Cheves; Dr. James C. Elder, Jr.; Frank S. Etheridge III; Kerry W. Hand; Joey M. Loudermilk; Rodney K. Mahone; LaRae Dixon Moore; Melanie V. Slaton; Murray L. Solomon; Mathews D. Swift; Tyler A. Townsend; Billy G. Turner.
Number of staff: 2 full-time professional; 1 part-time professional; 1 full-time support.
EIN: 582381589
Selected grants: The following grants are a representative sample of this grantmaker's funding activity:
$800,000 to Columbus Museum, Columbus, GA, 2012. For Ele Acquisition.
$130,847 to Community Foundation, Jacksonville, FL, 2012. For Ball Family Fund.
$100,000 to Pastoral Institute, Columbus, GA, 2012. For capital campaign.
$69,876 to Muscogee County School District, Columbus, GA, 2012. For Programming Coordinator and support staff.
$52,847 to Muscogee County School District, Columbus, GA, 2012. For Children's Services.
$10,000 to United Way of the Chattahoochee Valley, Columbus, GA, 2012. For general support.
$3,000 to Believers Church, Douglasville, GA, 2012. For $2,000 for Believers Church and $1,000 for Meet the Believers.
$2,500 to University of Georgia Foundation, Athens, GA, 2012. For Georgia Museum of Art.
$1,500 to Valley Rescue Mission, Columbus, GA, 2012. For general support.
$1,000 to Columbus Museum, Columbus, GA, 2012.

2439
Community Foundation of West Georgia ✧
807 South Park St.
Carrollton, GA 30117 (770) 832-1462
Contact: Kim B. Jones, Pres.
E-mail: info@cfwg.net; Additional E-mail: kim@cfwg.net; Main URL: http://www.cfwg.net
Facebook: http://www.facebook.com/pages/Community-Foundation-of-West-Georgia/102933456439561
Twitter: https://twitter.com/CFWGA
YouTube: http://www.youtube.com/cfwga

Established in 2003 in GA.
Foundation type: Community foundation.
Financial data (yr. ended 12/31/13): Assets, $39,456,898 (M); gifts received, $6,288,954; expenditures, $6,845,642; giving activities include $6,599,996 for 74+ grants (high: $1,738,820).
Purpose and activities: The foundation seeks to enhance the quality of life for the people of the West Georgia area.
Fields of interest: Arts; Education; Environment; Health care; Residential/custodial care, hospices; Human services; Economic development; Community/economic development.
Limitations: Applications accepted. Giving primarily in Carroll, Haralson, and Heard counties, GA. No support for religious organizations (unless there are no religious requirements), for-profit organizations, or charities operated by service clubs or organizations that in turn make grants to others. No grants to individuals, or for annual fundraising campaigns, fundraising events, operating deficits, endowments, or memorials.
Publications: Application guidelines; Annual report; Financial statement; Grants list; Informational brochure; Newsletter.
Application information: Visit foundation web site for application form and guidelines. Late, e-mailed, or faxed applications will not be accepted. Application form required.
Initial approach: Submit application form and attachments online
Deadline(s): Aug. 1 for Community Impact Grants
Board meeting date(s): Bi-monthly
Final notification: 60 days
Officers and Directors:* Gelon Wasdin,* Chair.; Bill Stone,* Vice-Chair.; Kim B. Jones,* Pres.; Fred O'Neal,* Secy.-Treas.; Kirby Butler; Steve Davis; Laurie Fleck; Andrew Lovvorn; Ann Newman; Will Parrish; Jackie Pate; L. Richard Plunkett; Denney Rogers; Deidre Rouse; Zachary Steed; Amy Velasquez.
Number of staff: 1 full-time professional; 1 full-time support.
EIN: 030472714

2440
The Correll Family Foundation, Inc. ✧
191 Peachtree St., Ste. 4050
Atlanta, GA 30303-1786 (404) 478-6779

Established in 2006 in GA.
Donors: Alston D. Correll; Ada L. Correll.
Foundation type: Independent foundation.
Financial data (yr. ended 06/30/14): Assets, $41,146,453 (M); gifts received, $3,027,817; expenditures, $6,697,121; qualifying distributions, $6,366,834; giving activities include $6,366,834 for 20 grants (high: $3,833,334; low: $1,000).
Purpose and activities: Giving primarily for higher education, and children, youth and social services.
Fields of interest: Higher education; Environment, natural resources; Health care; Boys & girls clubs; Human services; Children/youth, services; United Ways and Federated Giving Programs.
Limitations: Applications not accepted. Giving primarily in Atlanta, GA; some funding also in ME. No grants to individuals.
Application information: Contributes only to pre-selected organizations.
Officers and Directors:* Ada F. Correll,* Secy.; Alston D. Correll,* Treas.; Alston D. Correll III; Elizabeth Richards.
EIN: 134311179
Selected grants: The following grants are a representative sample of this grantmaker's funding activity:
$500,000 to Emory University, Atlanta, GA, 2011.
$500,000 to Georgia Aquarium, Atlanta, GA, 2011.
$400,000 to University of Maine, Orono, ME, 2011. For scholarships.
$15,000 to Atlanta Education Fund, Atlanta, GA, 2011. For general fund.
$5,000 to Our House, Decatur, GA, 2011. For general fund.
$1,250 to Atlanta History Center, Atlanta, GA, 2011. For general fund.

2441
Courts Foundation, Inc. ✧
3050 Peachtree Rd., N.W., Ste. 270
Atlanta, GA 30305-2212 (404) 658-9066
Contact: John W. Stephenson, Exec. Dir.

Incorporated in 1950 in GA.
Donors: Richard W. Courts†; Virginia Campbell Courts†; Malon C. Courts†; Richard W. Courts II; Atlantic Realty Co.
Foundation type: Independent foundation.
Financial data (yr. ended 12/31/13): Assets, $73,998,915 (M); expenditures, $4,774,908; qualifying distributions, $4,790,488; giving activities include $4,720,500 for 19 grants (high: $1,750,000; low: $25,000).
Purpose and activities: Support primarily for education, religion, health care, human services, and arts and culture.
Fields of interest: Arts; Higher education; Education; Health care; Children/youth, services; Christian agencies & churches.
Type of support: Capital campaigns; Building/renovation; Land acquisition; Endowments.
Limitations: Applications accepted. Giving primarily in Atlanta, GA, with a secondary emphasis on Georgia-based organizations. No grants to individuals.
Publications: Informational brochure (including application guidelines).
Application information: Application form not required.
Initial approach: Letter
Copies of proposal: 1
Deadline(s): Mar. 1, June 1, Sept. 1, Dec. 1
Board meeting date(s): Mar., June, Sept., and Dec.
Final notification: 1 month
Officers and Trustees:* Richard W. Courts II,* Pres.; John B. Ellis,* V.P.; Malon W. Courts,* Secy. and Treas.; John W. Stephenson, Exec. Dir.; Clay L. Courts; Richard W. Courts IV; T. Bradbury Courts; William A. Parker, Jr.
Number of staff: 2 part-time professional; 3 part-time support.
EIN: 586036859
Selected grants: The following grants are a representative sample of this grantmaker's funding activity:
$4,135,000 to Community Foundation for Greater Atlanta, Atlanta, GA, 2012. For Donor-Advised Fund.
$200,000 to KIPP Metro Atlanta Collaborative, Atlanta, GA, 2012.
$150,000 to Pace Academy, Atlanta, GA, 2012.
$100,000 to Kings Ridge Christian School, Alpharetta, GA, 2012.
$100,000 to Woodward Academy, College Park, GA, 2012.
$50,000 to Teach for America, Atlanta, GA, 2012. For general operating support.
$25,000 to United Way of Metropolitan Atlanta, Atlanta, GA, 2012. For general operating support.
$25,000 to University of Georgia Foundation, Athens, GA, 2012.
$6,000 to Southeastern Council of Foundations, Atlanta, GA, 2012.

2442
The Cousins Foundation, Inc. ✧
3445 Peachtree Rd., Ste. 175
Atlanta, GA 30326-1234

Incorporated in 1963 in GA.
Donors: Thomas G. Cousins; Ann D. Cousins; Cousins Charitable Lead Annuity Trust; Thomas G. Cousins Life Insurance Trust.
Foundation type: Independent foundation.
Financial data (yr. ended 12/31/12): Assets, $39,792,895 (M); gifts received, $489,146; expenditures, $2,573,321; qualifying distributions, $2,139,385; giving activities include $2,134,669 for 35 grants (high: $1,000,000; low: $500).
Purpose and activities: The foundation supports organizations that strengthen the spiritual, mental and moral fiber of a community. There is a special focus on children, and an emphasis on programs that seek to break the cycle of poverty.
Fields of interest: Arts; Higher education; Education; Health organizations, association; Human services; Children/youth, services; Community/economic development; Christian agencies & churches.
Type of support: General/operating support; Annual campaigns; Capital campaigns; Building/renovation; Endowments; Program development; Program evaluation.
Limitations: Applications not accepted. Giving primarily in the South, with emphasis on GA, particularly Atlanta. No grants to individuals; or for scholarships.
Application information: Unsolicited requests for funds not accepted.
Officers and Trustees:* Lillian C. Giornelli,* Pres.; William C. Wren,* V.P.; Amy Clarke, Secy.-Treas.; Ann D. Cousins; Grady Cousins.
EIN: 586043765

2443
Cousins Properties Foundation, Inc. ✧ ☆
c/o Cousins Properties Inc.
191 Peachtree St., Ste. 500
Atlanta, GA 30303-1757 (404) 407-1000
Contact: Pamela F. Roper

Established in 2005 in GA.
Donor: Cousins Real Estate Corp.
Foundation type: Company-sponsored foundation.

Financial data (yr. ended 12/31/13): Assets, $4,695,309 (L); expenditures, $508,489; qualifying distributions, $451,083; giving activities include $451,083 for 24 grants (high: $200,000; low: $250).
Purpose and activities: The foundation supports community foundations and organizations involved with arts and culture, education, health, cancer, and community economic development.
Fields of interest: Education; Human services; Community/economic development.
Type of support: General/operating support; Program development.
Limitations: Applications accepted. Giving primarily in the Atlanta, GA, area; giving also in other parts of southeast and southwest. No grants to individuals.
Application information: Application form not required.
Initial approach: Proposal
Deadline(s): None
Officers and Directors:* Larry L. Gellerstedt III,* Pres. and C.E.O; Gregg Adzema,* Exec. V.P. and C.F.O.
EIN: 203982777

2444
The Covenant Foundation, Inc. ✧
(formerly The Davis Foundation)
1 National Dr.
Atlanta, GA 30336-1631

Established in 1960.
Donors: Alfred M. Davis; Jay M. Davis; Ann Davis; ADP Rental Co.; Raleigh Linen Svc., Inc.; Servitex, Inc.; Truck Rental Co.; National Distributing Co., Inc.; and subsidiaries.
Foundation type: Independent foundation.
Financial data (yr. ended 07/31/13): Assets, $9,376,131 (M); gifts received, $499,982; expenditures, $1,282,969; qualifying distributions, $1,261,545; giving activities include $1,261,515 for 114 grants (high: $150,000; low: $36).
Purpose and activities: Grants primarily for Jewish welfare funds and temple support; funding also for cultural programs.
Fields of interest: Arts; Education; Health care; Human services; United Ways and Federated Giving Programs; Jewish federated giving programs; Jewish agencies & synagogues.
Limitations: Applications not accepted. Giving primarily in Atlanta, GA.
Application information: Contributes only to pre-selected organizations.
Officers: Jay M. Davis, Pres.; Ann Davis, V.P.
EIN: 586035088

2445
The James M. Cox Foundation of Georgia, Inc. ✧
6205 Peachtree Dunwoody Rd.
Atlanta, GA 30328 (678) 645-0929
Contact: Nancy K. Rigby, Treas.
FAX: (678) 645-1708;
E-mail: coxfoundation@coxinc.om; Main URL: http://coxenterprises.com/corporate-responsibility/giving/foundations.aspx

Incorporated in 1957 in GA.
Donor: Cox Enterprises, Inc.
Foundation type: Company-sponsored foundation.
Financial data (yr. ended 12/31/12): Assets, $260,080,087 (M); gifts received, $70,000,000; expenditures, $8,176,849; qualifying distributions, $6,450,432; giving activities include $6,411,998 for grants.
Purpose and activities: The James M. Cox Foundation provides funding for capital campaigns and special projects in communities where Cox Enterprises Inc. does business. The Foundation concentrates its community support in several priority areas: Conservation and Environment; Early Childhood Education; Empowering Families and Individuals for Success; and Health.
Fields of interest: Education, early childhood education; Environment, natural resources; Environment, beautification programs; Public health, physical fitness; Health care; Medical research; Recreation, parks/playgrounds; Human services.
Type of support: Capital campaigns; Program development.
Limitations: Applications accepted. Giving primarily in areas of company operations, with emphasis on Atlanta, GA. No support for religious, political, or discriminatory organizations. No grants to individuals, or for general operating purposes, seed money, endowment funds, events, or sponsorships.
Publications: Application guidelines.
Application information: If located outside metropolitan Atlanta, a letter of support from general manager (or equivalent) at local Cox business is required. Application form required.
Initial approach: Complete online eligibility quiz and application
Copies of proposal: 1
Deadline(s): Mar. 1, July 1, and Nov. 1
Board meeting date(s): Apr., Aug., and Dec.
Final notification: May 15, Sept. 15, and Dec. 31
Officers and Trustees:* Anne Cox Chambers,* Chair.; James C. Kennedy,* Pres.; James C. Kennedy, Jr.,* V.P.; Alexander C. Taylor,* V.P.; Shauna Sullivan Muhl, Secy.; Nancy K. Rigby, Treas.
EIN: 586032469

2446
Jim Cox, Jr. Foundation ✧
3414 Peachtree Rd., Ste. 722
Atlanta, GA 30326-1166
Contact: Larry B. Hooks, Tr.

Established in 1995 in GA.
Foundation type: Independent foundation.
Financial data (yr. ended 12/31/13): Assets, $20,711,264 (M); expenditures, $1,049,416; qualifying distributions, $882,294; giving activities include $811,550 for 10 grants (high: $300,000; low: $10,000).
Fields of interest: Museums; Performing arts, orchestras; Arts; Higher education; Education.
Type of support: Program development; General/operating support; Curriculum development; Continuing support; Capital campaigns; Building/renovation; Annual campaigns.
Limitations: Applications not accepted. Giving primarily in metropolitan Atlanta, GA. No grants for endowments.
Application information: Unsolicited requests for funds not accepted.
Board meeting date(s): Annually, generally in May or June
Trustee: Larry B. Hooks.
Number of staff: 1 part-time professional.
EIN: 586285853

Selected grants: The following grants are a representative sample of this grantmaker's funding activity:
$261,000 to Emory University, School of Medicine, Atlanta, GA, 2012. For Fund Holland Chair of Neurology.
$100,000 to Emory University, School of Medicine, Atlanta, GA, 2012. For neurological research.
$22,661 to Rhode Island Hospital, Providence, RI, 2012. To fund observerships.

2447
Creel-Harison Foundation Inc. ✧
(formerly The Creel Foundation, Inc.)
P.O. Box 15967
Augusta, GA 30919
Contact: Robbie T. White, Dir.

Established in 2003 in GA.
Donor: The Creel Foundation.
Foundation type: Independent foundation.
Financial data (yr. ended 12/31/13): Assets, $18,596,306 (M); expenditures, $1,016,378; qualifying distributions, $841,516; giving activities include $734,950 for 50 grants (high: $75,000; low: $465).
Fields of interest: Arts; Education; Human services; Salvation Army.
Limitations: Applications accepted. Giving primarily in Augusta, GA; some giving also in Pueblo, CO.
Application information: Application form required.
Initial approach: Contact foundation for application form
Deadline(s): Oct. 1
Director: Robbie T. White.
Trustees: W.A. Copenhaver; Julie M. Harison; Phil S. Harison, Jr.; Eleanor H. Taylor.
EIN: 223875267

2448
Cecil B. Day Foundation, Inc. ✧
4725 Peachtree Corners Cir., Ste. 300
Norcross, GA 30092-2574 (770) 446-1500
Contact: Edward L. White, Jr., Pres.

Incorporated in 1968 in GA.
Donors: Cecil B. Day‡; Deen Day Sanders.
Foundation type: Independent foundation.
Financial data (yr. ended 12/31/13): Assets, $16,089,693 (M); expenditures, $2,396,078; qualifying distributions, $2,107,749; giving activities include $1,877,039 for grants.
Purpose and activities: Grants to Christian churches, especially Baptist churches, for evangelism, missions, and discipleships, and for Pastor's Leadership Training.
Fields of interest: Christian agencies & churches; Protestant agencies & churches.
Type of support: General/operating support; Continuing support; Capital campaigns; Building/renovation; Equipment; Emergency funds; Seed money; Matching/challenge support.
Limitations: Applications accepted. Giving primarily in the New England states; special consideration for GA, primarily in the metropolitan Atlanta area. No grants to individuals, or for deficit financing, endowment funds, scholarships, or fellowships.
Publications: Informational brochure.
Application information: Initial meeting is required for preliminary assessment. If requirements meet

foundation guidelines, online application will be granted by invitation only.
Initial approach: Letter requesting program brochure
Copies of proposal: 1
Deadline(s): None
Board meeting date(s): Annually
Officers and Trustees:* Deen Day Sanders,* Vice-Chair.; Edward L. White, Jr.,* Pres.; R.D. Spear,* V.P.; Joann F. Dollar, Secy.; Charles A. Sanders,* Treas.; C. Burke Day; C. Parke Day; C. Peyton Day; Clinton M. Day; Kathie Day.
EIN: 581030351
Selected grants: The following grants are a representative sample of this grantmaker's funding activity:
$40,000 to National Day of Prayer Task Force, Colorado Springs, CO, 2012. For evangelism, ministry.

2449
R. Howard Dobbs, Jr. Foundation, Inc.
(formerly Helen and Howard Dobbs Foundation, Inc.)
133 Peachtree St. N.E., Ste. 4950
Atlanta, GA 30303-1861 (404) 574-2970
FAX: (404) 574-2971; E-mail: dgray@rhdobbs.net; Main URL: http://www.dobbsfoundation.org

Established in 1959.
Donor: R. Howard Dobbs, Jr.‡.
Foundation type: Independent foundation.
Financial data (yr. ended 12/31/12): Assets, $66,076,520 (M); expenditures, $2,726,435; qualifying distributions, $2,419,558; giving activities include $1,871,285 for 51 grants (high: $250,000; low: $100).
Purpose and activities: The mission of the foundation is to improve the quality of life for individuals, families and communities by supporting educational opportunities, improving access to health services, promoting environmental stewardship, and enriching the arts. The foundation is committed to honoring the life and impact of R. Howard Dobbs, Jr. through its grant-making activities. In the field of education, the foundation seeks to improve teacher quality and classroom outcomes by investing in the development of new and veteran educators with an emphasis on innovative teaching practices and the delivery of a 21st century education. The foundation will place priority on projects with potential for scaling and replication. In its environmental giving, the foundation focuses on land conservation and watershed protection with particular interest in the coastal Georgia and longleaf pine ecosystems. Health priorities include age related macular degeneration (ARMD) research, access to basic health services including low vision services. The foundation does not support medical research outside of ARMD. Arts funding is limited to mid-size organizations with an operating budget less than $2,000,000. Maximum award amount is $40,000. The foundation will support requests for discrete capital purchases that improve content delivery or increase organizational capacity; or requests that support cultural opportunities for school groups.
Fields of interest: Arts; Education; Environment; Health care.
Limitations: Giving primarily in the metropolitan Atlanta, GA area. Consideration will also be given to proposals that serve other parts of the state of GA as well as states in which the Life Insurance Company of Georgia operated. Giving outside of GA is by invitation only and must be strongly aligned with stated interests. No support for churches or religious organizations. No grants or loans to individuals, or for endowments, special events, performances, dinners, booster clubs, or for reduction of debts/deficits.
Publications: Application guidelines; Grants list.
Application information: Unsolicited full proposals will not be reviewed. See foundation web site for application guidelines and application form. Although the foundation prefers the use of its application form, it is not required. However when not using the foundation's form, please ensure all questions on the form are addressed in your proposal. Application form not required.
Initial approach: Letter of inquiry
Copies of proposal: 1
Deadline(s): Dec. 1, Mar. 1, June 1 and Sept. 1
Board meeting date(s): Jan., Apr., July, and Oct.
Final notification: The board will vote on the grant generally two months after the receipt of an invited proposal and following a site visit.
Officers and Trustees:* E. Cody Laird, Jr.,* Chair.; David Weitnauer, Pres.; Nancy L. Crosswell,* Secy.; C. Mark Crosswell,* Treas.; William Clarkson IV; Ciannat M. Howett; Nancy Clair Laird McInaney; Dorothy L. Williams; Laird M. Williams.
Number of staff: 2 full-time professional.
EIN: 586033186
Selected grants: The following grants are a representative sample of this grantmaker's funding activity:
$200,000 to PATH Foundation, Atlanta, GA, 2012. For Capital Campaign, payable over 3.00 years.
$150,000 to Atlanta Botanical Garden, Atlanta, GA, 2013. For Smithgall Woodland Garden. Grant supports a $21 million campaign to construct infrastructure and native woodland gardens on a 185 acre parcel of donated land in Hall County.
$125,000 to Southern Environmental Law Center, Atlanta, GA, 2013. For Coastal Initiative. Grant supports its continued efforts to protect the coast of Georgia against ill-conceived development and violations of existing laws and regulations.
$100,000 to A. G. Rhodes Home, Atlanta, GA, 2013. For Nurses Stations. For the renovation of four nurses' stations in effort to de-institutionalize the facility's environment to make it more competitive in the nursing home market.
$100,000 to Bartow Health Access, Cartersville, GA, 2013. For Electronic Medical Record system. For the purchase and implementation of electronic medical record system.
$100,000 to Junior Achievement Worldwide, Junior Achievement of Georgia, Colorado Springs, CO, 2013. For JA Biztown/JA Finance Park. Grant supports a $5.2 million capital campaign to create Atlanta simulation center for its financial literacy curriculum.
$100,000 to Teach for America, Atlanta, GA, 2013. For Operating Support. Teach for America requests support for its general operations, payable over 2.00 years.
$75,000 to Georgia River Network, Athens, GA, 2013. For Operating Support. Grant supports general operations of the Georgia River Network as it strives to strengthen the state's local watershed advocacy efforts, payable over 3.00 years.
$75,000 to KIPP Metro Atlanta Collaborative, Atlanta, GA, 2013. For Teacher Fellows Program. Grant supports the KIPP Metro Atlanta Collaborative's Teacher Fellows Program which provides practical training and mentorship for people entering the teaching profession with a commitment to teaching in high-poverty urban schools.
$55,000 to Our House, Decatur, GA, 2013. For Activity Vehicle. Grant supports the purchase of a new vehicle used to transport children for educational field trips.
$50,000 to Good Samaritan Health Center of Cobb, Austell, GA, 2013. For Property Acquisition. Good Samaritan Health Center of Cobb requests support to purchase a parcel of land adjacent to its current location in order to expand the Center's facilities.

2450
The Frances and Beverly DuBose Foundation, Inc. ✧
4200 Northside Pkwy. N.W., Bldg. 14, Ste. 100
Atlanta, GA 30327-3081

Established in 1990 in GA.
Donors: Frances W. DuBose; DuBose Family Charitable Annuity Trust.
Foundation type: Independent foundation.
Financial data (yr. ended 06/30/13): Assets, $14,348,858 (M); expenditures, $814,685; qualifying distributions, $677,833; giving activities include $677,833 for grants.
Purpose and activities: Giving primarily for the arts, particularly historical preservation and historical societies; some funding for higher education.
Fields of interest: Historic preservation/historical societies; Arts; Higher education; Education.
Type of support: Annual campaigns; Capital campaigns; Building/renovation; Land acquisition; Endowments; Conferences/seminars; Seed money; Internship funds; Research.
Limitations: Applications not accepted. Giving primarily in GA, with emphasis on Atlanta and Savannah; some funding nationally. No grants to individuals.
Publications: Annual report.
Application information: Contributes only to pre-selected organizations.
Officers and Trustees:* Frances W. DuBose,* Chair.; Dean DuBose Smith,* Secy.; Mr. Beverly M. DuBose III,* Treas.; Eileen Erickson DuBose; Elizabeth Egleston DuBose; Thomas Edward Lewis; H. Bronson Smith.
EIN: 581901090
Selected grants: The following grants are a representative sample of this grantmaker's funding activity:
$25,000 to Georgia Trust for Historic Preservation, Atlanta, GA, 2013. For Preservation of Rhodes Hall Renovation of Hay House.
$25,000 to Ossabaw Island Foundation, Savannah, GA, 2013. For Wet Biology Lab.
$25,000 to Southern Center for International Studies, Atlanta, GA, 2013. For funding for Cataloging of Archives.
$25,000 to Southern Environmental Law Center, Charlottesville, VA, 2013. For Legal Environmental Issues.
$25,000 to Telfair Museum of Art, Savannah, GA, 2013. To design Phase for Reinterpretation of the Owens Thomas House.
$10,000 to Atlanta History Center, Atlanta, GA, 2013. For operating cost.
$10,000 to Civil War Preservation Trust, Washington, DC, 2013. For Preservation of Fleetwood Hill Site.
$5,000 to Mercer University, Macon, GA, 2013. For Scholarships for Medical Students.

2451
Robert and Polly Dunn Foundation, Inc. ✧
3248 Paces Ferry Cir.
Smyrna, GA 30080-0194 (770) 444-0071
Contact: Karen Wilbanks, Exec. Dir.
E-mail: kwilbanks@lawnet.org

Established in 1986 in GA.
Foundation type: Independent foundation.
Financial data (yr. ended 12/31/13): Assets, $12,494,197 (M); expenditures, $765,162; qualifying distributions, $572,967; giving activities include $572,967 for 52 grants (high: $50,000; low: $250).
Fields of interest: Education; Health care; Human services; Children/youth, services.
Type of support: General/operating support; Scholarship funds.
Limitations: Applications accepted. Giving limited to the southeast, with emphasis on the metropolitan Atlanta, GA, area. No support for private schools. No grants to individuals, or for endowment funds, capital campaigns, buildings, or day care; no loans or program-related investments.
Publications: Application guidelines.
Application information: Application form required.
Initial approach: Letter
Copies of proposal: 1
Deadline(s): None
Officer: Karen C. Wilbanks,* Exec. Dir.
Trustees: Richard B Freeman; Preston Hayes; Andrew Perry.
Number of staff: 1 part-time professional.
EIN: 581671255

2452
The Jim Ellis Foundation Inc. ✧
5901 Peachtree Industrial Blvd.
Atlanta, GA 30341-1630

Established in 1999 in GA.
Donors: James W. Ellis, Jr.; Jim Ellis.
Foundation type: Independent foundation.
Financial data (yr. ended 06/30/13): Assets, $7,073,068 (M); gifts received, $600,000; expenditures, $711,435; qualifying distributions, $710,050; giving activities include $710,050 for grants.
Fields of interest: Hospitals (general); Human services; Christian agencies & churches.
Limitations: Applications not accepted. Giving primarily in GA. No grants to individuals.
Application information: Contributes only to pre-selected organizations.
Officers and Trustees:* James W. Ellis, Jr.,* Pres.; Billie S. Ellis,* Secy.; James E. Ellis,* Treas.; Karen E. Black; Kristi E. Cohron.
EIN: 582500810
Selected grants: The following grants are a representative sample of this grantmaker's funding activity:
$305,000 to Gwinnett Hospital System Foundation, Lawrenceville, GA, 2011. For general support.
$5,000 to Campus Crusade for Christ International, Orlando, FL, 2011. For general support.

2453
The Florence C. and Harry L. English Memorial Fund ✧
c/o SunTrust Bank
P.O. Box 4418, MC041
Atlanta, GA 30302-4655 (404) 588-8250
Contact: Kirby A. Thompson, Secy.
FAX: (404) 724-3082; Main URL: http://www.suntrust.com/microsites/foundation/application_info.htm

Established in 1964 in GA.
Donor: Florence Cruft English†.
Foundation type: Independent foundation.
Financial data (yr. ended 12/31/13): Assets, $16,411,910 (M); expenditures, $512,188; qualifying distributions, $464,318; giving activities include $431,000 for 13 grants (high: $90,000; low: $6,000).
Purpose and activities: Grants only for education, health, general welfare, and culture, with emphasis on assisting the aged and chronically ill, the blind, and those persons generally designated as being underprivileged.
Fields of interest: Arts; Higher education; Education; Community/economic development.
Type of support: Building/renovation; Capital campaigns; Equipment; Land acquisition.
Limitations: Applications accepted. Giving limited to the metropolitan Atlanta, GA, area. No support for veterans' organizations or organizations which have not been operating without a deficit for at least a year. No grants to individuals, or for general operating support, maintenance, or for debt service; no loans.
Application information: Application form required.
Initial approach: On-line application
Copies of proposal: 1
Deadline(s): Mar. 31, Aug. 31, and Nov. 30
Board meeting date(s): Jan., May and Oct.
Trustee: SunTrust Bank, Inc.
Number of staff: 1 full-time professional.
EIN: 586045781
Selected grants: The following grants are a representative sample of this grantmaker's funding activity:
$200,000 to Zoo Atlanta, Atlanta, GA, 2012. For general support.
$60,000 to BeltLine Partnership, Atlanta, GA, 2010. For general charitable purpose.
$50,000 to Georgia State University, Atlanta, GA, 2010. For general charitable purpose.
$40,000 to Henry W. Grady Health System Foundation, Atlanta, GA, 2010. For general charitable purpose.
$37,500 to YMCA of Metropolitan Atlanta, Atlanta, GA, 2010. For general charitable purpose.
$25,000 to Boy Scouts of America, Atlanta Area Council, Atlanta, GA, 2010. For general charitable purpose.
$25,000 to Camp Twin Lakes, Atlanta, GA, 2010. For general charitable purpose.
$20,000 to Atlanta Lyric Theater, Atlanta, GA, 2010. For general charitable purpose.
$20,000 to Atlanta Neighborhood Development Partnership, Development Partnership Inc, Atlanta, GA, 2010. For general charitable purpose.
$20,000 to Kennesaw State University, Kennesaw, GA, 2010. For general charitable purpose.
$15,000 to Atlanta International School, Atlanta, GA, 2012. For general support.
$10,000 to Arthritis Foundation, Georgia Chapter, Atlanta, GA, 2010. For general charitable purpose.

2454
The Entelechy Foundation ✧ ☆
P.O. Box 57343
Atlanta, GA 30343-1343

Donor: John C. Portman, Jr.
Foundation type: Independent foundation.
Financial data (yr. ended 12/31/13): Assets, $166 (M); gifts received, $3,500,000; expenditures, $3,500,819; qualifying distributions, $3,500,819; giving activities include $3,500,000 for 2 grants (high: $2,500,000; low: $1,000,000).
Fields of interest: Higher education.
Limitations: Applications not accepted. Giving primarily in GA and MA.
Application information: Unsolicited requests for funds not accepted.
Directors: Alvis E. Campbell; Bruce MacEwen; John C. Portman, Jr.
EIN: 461115236

2455
Equifax Foundation ✧
1550 Peachtree St. N.W.
Atlanta, GA 30309-2468
Contact: Robert W. Kamerschen, Sr. V.P.; Ann Chakales

Trust established in 1978 in GA.
Donors: Retail Credit Co.; Equifax Inc.
Foundation type: Company-sponsored foundation.
Financial data (yr. ended 12/31/13): Assets, $8,143,702 (M); gifts received, $1,350,000; expenditures, $1,817,866; qualifying distributions, $1,817,742; giving activities include $1,817,742 for 1,006 grants (high: $75,000).
Purpose and activities: The foundation supports organizations involved with arts and culture, education, economics, civic affairs, and youth. Special emphasis is directed toward programs that serve the needy, and K-12 education for underserved youth.
Fields of interest: Arts; Education; Human services; Economics; Children/youth; Youth; Economically disadvantaged.
Type of support: General/operating support; Management development/capacity building; Capital campaigns; Building/renovation; Land acquisition; Scholarship funds; Technical assistance; Employee matching gifts; Matching/challenge support.
Limitations: Applications accepted. Giving primarily in Atlanta, GA; limited giving in cities with field offices. No support for religious, political, fraternal, or social organizations. No grants to individuals, or for debt reduction, fellowships, publications, or travel.
Publications: Corporate report.
Application information: Application form not required.
Initial approach: Proposal; letter of inquiry
Copies of proposal: 1
Deadline(s): Rolling
Board meeting date(s): Quarterly
Final notification: 60 days
Officer and Trustees:* Robert W. Kamerschen,* Secy.; J. Dann Adams; Lee Adrean; Kent Mast; Coretha Rushing; Richard F. Smith.
Number of staff: 1 part-time professional; 1 part-time support.
EIN: 581296807

Selected grants: The following grants are a representative sample of this grantmaker's funding activity:
$227,024 to United Way of Metropolitan Atlanta, Atlanta, GA, 2011.
$37,500 to Habitat for Humanity in Atlanta, Atlanta, GA, 2011.
$25,000 to KIPP Metro Atlanta Collaborative, Atlanta, GA, 2011.
$25,000 to Teach for America, Atlanta, GA, 2011.
$15,000 to Atlanta Community Food Bank, Atlanta, GA, 2011.
$15,000 to Breakthrough Atlanta, Atlanta, GA, 2011.
$2,000 to Families First, Atlanta, GA, 2011.
$1,000 to Georgia Center for Nonprofits, Atlanta, GA, 2011.
$1,000 to Georgia Consortium for Personal Financial Literacy, Atlanta, GA, 2011.

2456
The EZ Agape Foundation
12850 Highway 9, Ste. 600, PMB 328
Alpharetta, GA 30004-4248 (404) 633-9360
Contact: Nancy Walker, Fdn. Mgr.
E-mail: grantrequest@ezagapefoundation.org

Established in 1994 in GA.
Donors: Mary Louise Brown Jwell; Nancy Louise Brown Markham; Elizabeth Irene Brown Dixon.
Foundation type: Independent foundation.
Financial data (yr. ended 12/31/12): Assets, $8,813,504 (M); expenditures, $892,490; qualifying distributions, $776,702; giving activities include $776,702 for 76 grants (high: $25,000; low: $1,500).
Purpose and activities: Giving primarily for those who are poor, disabled and needy; funding also for smaller charities, and helping handicapped children and adults.
Fields of interest: Housing/shelter, development; Human services; Children, services; Children; Women; Homeless.
Type of support: General/operating support; Building/renovation; Program development; Scholarship funds.
Limitations: Applications accepted. Giving primarily in Atlanta, GA. No grants to individuals.
Application information: Application form not required.
Initial approach: E-mail
Copies of proposal: 1
Deadline(s): None
Board meeting date(s): Generally in the 1st quarter, summer, and fall; however no set schedule.
Officer: Nancy Walker, Mgr.
Trustees: Elizabeth Irene Brown Dixon; Nancy Louise Brown Markham.
EIN: 586289241

2457
Betty and Davis Fitzgerald Foundation, Inc. ✧
P.O. Box 11749
Atlanta, GA 30355-1749
Contact: Jackie Stradley, Exec. Dir.
E-mail: jackiestradley@bettyanddavisfitzgerald.org; Application e-mail: Cathy Hall, Grantmaking Assoc., cathyhall@bettyanddavisfitzgerald.org; Main URL: http://bettyanddavisfitzgerald.org

Established in GA.
Donors: Betty Fitzgerald†; Davis Fitzgerald†.
Foundation type: Independent foundation.
Financial data (yr. ended 12/31/12): Assets, $24,533,412 (M); expenditures, $1,512,495; qualifying distributions, $1,086,858; giving activities include $893,200 for 30 grants (high: $250,000; low: $200), and $36,524 for 31 employee matching gifts.
Purpose and activities: Giving to organizations dedicated to making a difference in the lives of others, primarily through the education and health care of the disadvantaged residents of Metro Atlanta and Georgia.
Fields of interest: Education; Health care; Economically disadvantaged.
Limitations: Applications accepted. Giving primarily in GA, with emphasis on Atlanta. No support for churches or religious organizations, or for booster clubs or lobbying. No grants to individuals or for dinners, research, conferences and seminars, sponsoring productions or to retire debt.
Publications: Application guidelines.
Application information: If the foundation determines that further consideration is to be given to the proposed project, additional information will be requested. Application form not required.
Initial approach: 1-page letter or e-mail
Copies of proposal: 1
Deadline(s): Feb. 15, May 15, Aug. 15 and Nov. 15
Officer: Jackie Stradley, Exec. Dir.
Number of staff: 1 full-time professional.
EIN: 581669823

2458
Porter Fleming Foundation ✧
c/o Suntrust Company Bank
P.O. Box 4418
Atlanta, GA 30302
Application address: c/o Suntrust Bank of Augusta, P.O. Box 927, Augusta, GA 30903, tel.: (706) 821-3093

Established in GA.
Foundation type: Independent foundation.
Financial data (yr. ended 12/31/13): Assets, $11,073,376 (M); expenditures, $533,000; qualifying distributions, $520,759; giving activities include $519,509 for 9 grants (high: $350,000; low: $78).
Fields of interest: Museums (history); Arts; Elementary/secondary education; Human services.
Limitations: Applications accepted. Giving primarily in Augusta, GA. No grants to individuals.
Application information: Application form not required.
Initial approach: Proposal
Deadline(s): None
Trustee: SunTrust Bank.
EIN: 586042191

2459
William Howard Flowers, Jr. Foundation, Inc. ✧
P.O. Box 6100
Thomasville, GA 31758-6100

Established in 1991 in GA.
Donors: William H. Flowers, Jr.†; Maury Flowers Shields; McFadden Trust; Parker Trust; Maury Tice Flowers Trust.
Foundation type: Independent foundation.
Financial data (yr. ended 12/31/12): Assets, $74,908,885 (M); gifts received, $388,866; expenditures, $3,694,031; qualifying distributions, $3,450,501; giving activities include $3,450,501 for grants.
Fields of interest: Arts; Education; Health care; Legal services; Human services; YM/YWCAs & YM/YWHAs; Children/youth, services; Christian agencies & churches.
Type of support: General/operating support.
Limitations: Applications not accepted. Giving primarily in FL and GA. No grants to individuals.
Application information: Contributes only to pre-selected organizations.
Board meeting date(s): Twice yearly
Officers: Daphne F. Wood, Pres.; Taliaferro F. Crozer, V.P.; Kaye Reynolds, Secy.; Maury Flowers Shields, Treas.
Number of staff: 1 full-time professional; 1 part-time professional.
EIN: 581399036

2460
Mildred Miller Fort Foundation, Inc. ✧
P.O. Box 2665
Columbus, GA 31902-2665 (706) 341-6662
Contact: Alan F. Rothschild, Jr., Pres. and Tr.
FAX: (706) 320-3828;
E-mail: fortfoundation@bellsouth.net

Established in 1992 in GA.
Donors: Mildred Miller Fort†; Mildred Fort Irrevocable Trust No. 1.
Foundation type: Independent foundation.
Financial data (yr. ended 12/31/13): Assets, $47,080,520 (M); expenditures, $3,670,175; qualifying distributions, $3,623,453; giving activities include $3,500,000 for 20 grants (high: $1,000,000; low: $10,000).
Purpose and activities: Giving primarily for education and health care, including a hospital; funding also for environmental protection and beautification, and relief of the underserved.
Fields of interest: Arts; Education; Environment; Hospitals (general); Health care.
Limitations: Applications not accepted. Giving primarily in Columbus, GA.
Application information: Unsolicited requests for funds not accepted.
Officers and Trustees:* Alan F. Rothschild, Jr.,* Pres.; J. Kyle Spencer,* V.P.; Sally B. Hatcher,* Secy.; William C. Woolfolk III,* Treas.; Warner Neal.
Number of staff: 1 part-time professional.
EIN: 581991612

2461
Foundation for a Better World, Inc. ✧ ☆
1282 Timberland Dr.
Marietta, GA 30067-5123

Donor: Thomas Claugus.
Foundation type: Independent foundation.
Financial data (yr. ended 12/31/13): Assets, $415,576 (M); gifts received, $1,000,000; expenditures, $584,464; qualifying distributions, $583,964; giving activities include $498,265 for 16 grants (high: $120,000; low: $2,000).

Fields of interest: Education; Health care; Community/economic development.
Limitations: Applications not accepted. Giving primarily in MA, OH and Washington, DC.
Application information: Unsolicited requests for funds not accepted.
Officers and Directors:* Beatriz Illescas,* Pres.; Thomas Claugus,* V.P.; Melissa Claugus,* Secy.; Thomas Claugus II,* Treas.
EIN: 462385457

2462
John and Mary Franklin Foundation, Inc. ✧

P.O. Box 725429
Atlanta, GA 31139-2429 (770) 842-8000
Contact: Marilu H. McCarty, Exec. Secy.
E-mail: FranklinFoundation@bellsouth.net

Incorporated in 1955 in GA.
Donors: John Franklin†; Mary O. Franklin†.
Foundation type: Independent foundation.
Financial data (yr. ended 12/31/13): Assets, $35,465,103 (M); expenditures, $2,021,606; qualifying distributions, $1,816,866; giving activities include $1,743,730 for 291 grants (high: $60,000; low: $130).
Purpose and activities: Giving primarily for education, scientific research, health, youth services, and the arts.
Fields of interest: Historical activities; Arts; Higher education; Education; Health care; Health organizations, association; Boys clubs; Boys & girls clubs; Children/youth, services; United Ways and Federated Giving Programs; Science, research; Infants/toddlers; Children/youth; Children; Youth; Young adults; Disabilities, people with; Physically disabled; Blind/visually impaired; Deaf/hearing impaired; Mentally disabled; Minorities; Hispanics/Latinos; Immigrants/refugees; Economically disadvantaged; Homeless.
Type of support: General/operating support; Continuing support; Annual campaigns; Capital campaigns; Building/renovation; Scholarship funds; Research.
Limitations: Applications accepted. Giving primarily in GA, with emphasis on the metropolitan Atlanta area. No support for religious organizations, political organizations or private schools (except under specific conditions). No grants to individuals.
Application information: Application form not required.
Initial approach: Varies
Copies of proposal: 1
Deadline(s): Dec. 31
Board meeting date(s): Apr. and Dec., and as needed
Final notification: Mar. of the following year
Officer and Trustees:* Marilu H. McCarty,* Exec. Secy.; John B. Carter, Jr.; John B. Ellis; Marion B. Glover; Elizabeth Jones; Frank M. Malone, Jr.; Jerry W. Nix; E. Kendrick Smith.
Number of staff: 1 part-time professional; 1 part-time support.
EIN: 586036131
Selected grants: The following grants are a representative sample of this grantmaker's funding activity:
$60,000 to Georgia Institute of Technology, Atlanta, GA, 2012. For John McCarty Chair for Electrical Engineering.
$50,000 to Georgia State University Foundation, Atlanta, GA, 2012. For Parker Pefit Science Building.
$50,000 to University of Georgia Foundation, Athens, GA, 2012. For Coverdell Center Neuroimaging.
$25,000 to Brenau University, Gainesville, GA, 2012. For general support.
$25,000 to George West Mental Health Foundation, Skyland Trail, Atlanta, GA, 2012. For general support.
$15,000 to Robert W. Woodruff Arts Center, Atlanta, GA, 2012. For general support.
$5,000 to Fernbank Museum of Natural History, Atlanta, GA, 2012. For general support.

2463
The Fraser-Parker Foundation ✧

3050 Peachtree Rd. N.W., Ste. 270
Atlanta, GA 30305-2212
Contact: John Stephenson

Established in 1987 in GA.
Donors: William A. Parker, Jr.; Nancy F. Parker†; AGT Lewis H. Beck Educational Foundation.
Foundation type: Independent foundation.
Financial data (yr. ended 12/31/13): Assets, $23,928,457 (M); gifts received, $5,099,156; expenditures, $1,087,391; qualifying distributions, $973,646; giving activities include $884,500 for 47 grants (high: $100,000; low: $2,500).
Purpose and activities: Support primarily for organizations that are traditionally supported by the family, including the arts and education.
Fields of interest: Museums; Secondary school/education; Education; Medical research, institute; Youth, services; Religion.
Type of support: General/operating support; Continuing support; Capital campaigns.
Limitations: Applications accepted. Giving primarily in the metropolitan Atlanta, GA, area. No grants to individuals, or for emergency funds, deficit financing, or deficit operating budgets; no loans.
Publications: Informational brochure (including application guidelines).
Application information: Application form not required.
Initial approach: Proposal
Deadline(s): None
Directors: Richard W. Courts II; T. Brad Courts; Katharine G. Farnham; Isobel P. Mills; Richard Carlyle Parker; William A. Parker, Jr.; William A. Parker III.
Trustee: SunTrust Bank.
Number of staff: 2 part-time professional; 2 part-time support.
EIN: 586212344

2464
J. B. Fuqua Foundation, Inc. ✧

3350 Riverwood Pkwy., Ste. 700
Atlanta, GA 30339-3351
Contact: J. Rex Fuqua, Pres.

Incorporated in 1970 in GA.
Donors: J.B. Fuqua†; J.B. Fuqua Family Charitable Lead Unitrust.
Foundation type: Independent foundation.
Financial data (yr. ended 12/31/13): Assets, $52,347,729 (M); gifts received, $20,690,954; expenditures, $3,323,016; qualifying distributions, $2,503,163; giving activities include $2,378,850 for 42 grants (high: $333,334; low: $1,750).
Fields of interest: Education; Health care; Human services.
Limitations: Applications not accepted. Giving primarily in GA and Durham, NC. No support for partisan political programs. No grants to individuals.
Application information: Contributes only to pre-selected organizations.
Officers and Directors:* J. Rex Fuqua,* Pres.; Dorothy C. Fuqua,* V.P.; B. Clayton Rolader,* V.P.; James A. Stanley, Secy.; James M. Stevens, Jr., Treas.; Anne Sterchi, Exec. Dir.; Duvall S. Fuqua.
Number of staff: 1 full-time professional; 1 part-time support.
EIN: 237122039

2465
Richard and Barbara Gaby Foundation ✧

c/o Bridges and Dunn-Rankin, LLP
400 Galleria Pkwy., No. 1050
Atlanta, GA 30339-5980

Established in 2005 in GA.
Donors: Richard Gaby; Barbara Van Andel Gaby; Jay and Betty Van Andel Foundation; Jay Van Andel Irrevocable Trust; Gaby Investments, L.P.
Foundation type: Independent foundation.
Financial data (yr. ended 12/31/12): Assets, $85,018,307 (M); expenditures, $9,482,879; qualifying distributions, $6,759,309; giving activities include $6,759,309 for 81 grants (high: $1,000,000; low: $17).
Purpose and activities: Giving primarily to Christian organizations and churches.
Fields of interest: Human services; Christian agencies & churches.
Limitations: Applications not accepted. Giving primarily in Atlanta, GA; some funding also in Washington, DC.
Application information: Contributes only to pre-selected organizations.
Trustees: Richard Gaby; Barbara Van Andel-Gaby.
EIN: 202110682

2466
Courtney Knight Gaines Foundation ✧

15 Lake St., Ste. 210
Savannah, GA 31411

Established in 1998 in GA.
Donor: Courtney Knight Gaines.
Foundation type: Independent foundation.
Financial data (yr. ended 12/31/12): Assets, $9,030,501 (M); expenditures, $533,049; qualifying distributions, $453,666; giving activities include $453,666 for 42 grants (high: $33,333; low: $1,500).
Purpose and activities: Giving primarily for education, the environment, health organizations and children and social services.
Fields of interest: Higher education, university; Education; Environment, natural resources; Health organizations, association; Human services; American Red Cross; Children/youth, services; Residential/custodial care, hospices.
Limitations: Applications not accepted. Giving primarily in GA. No grants to individuals.
Application information: Contributes only to pre-selected organizations.
Officers: Ezekiel B. Gaines III, Pres.; Christopher E. Klein, Secy.

Trustees: Courtney Gaines Fetz; William B. Gaines; Grace Gaines Gattis; James Thomas Gattis.
EIN: 582398209
Selected grants: The following grants are a representative sample of this grantmaker's funding activity:
$69,500 to Hospice of Savannah, Savannah, GA, 2010. For general charitable purposes.
$26,000 to Wesley Monumental United Methodist Church, Savannah, GA, 2010. For general charitable purposes.
$25,000 to Lake Junaluska Assembly, Lake Junaluska, NC, 2010. For general charitable purposes.
$25,000 to Pine Woods Retreat, Savannah, GA, 2010. For general charitable purposes.
$20,000 to Ossabaw Island Foundation, Savannah, GA, 2010. For general charitable purposes.
$15,000 to Americas Second Harvest, Topeka, KS, 2010. For general charitable purposes.
$15,000 to Leukemia & Lymphoma Society, 2010. For general charitable purposes.
$15,000 to Leukemia & Lymphoma Society, White Plains, NY, 2011. For general charitable purposes.
$15,000 to Savannah Music Festival, Savannah, GA, 2010. For general charitable purposes.
$10,000 to Savannah Country Day School, Savannah, GA, 2010. For general charitable purposes.
$2,500 to Muscular Dystrophy Association, Tucson, AZ, 2011. For general charitable purposes.

2467
The Roderick S., Flossie R., & Helen M. Galloway Foundation ✧

7000 Peachtree Dunwoody Rd., Bldg. 1
Atlanta, GA 30328-1655

Established in 1994 in GA.
Donor: Roderick S. Galloway.
Foundation type: Independent foundation.
Financial data (yr. ended 07/31/13): Assets, $10,806,605 (M); expenditures, $799,101; qualifying distributions, $521,000; giving activities include $521,000 for 54 grants (high: $250,000; low: $1,000).
Fields of interest: Higher education; Health care; Human services.
Limitations: Applications not accepted. Giving primarily in Atlanta, GA; some giving also in Ames, IA, and NY. No grants to individuals.
Application information: Contributes only to pre-selected organizations.
Trustees: Richard M. Ambery; James H. Mobley, Jr.; Mark G. Weinstein.
EIN: 582140070
Selected grants: The following grants are a representative sample of this grantmaker's funding activity:
$250,000 to Iowa State University Foundation, Ames, IA, 2011.
$35,000 to Shepherd Center, Atlanta, GA, 2011.
$30,000 to Childrens Healthcare of Atlanta, Atlanta, GA, 2011.
$30,000 to Leukemia & Lymphoma Society, Atlanta, GA, 2011.
$20,000 to Duke University, Durham, NC, 2011.
$15,000 to CURE Childhood Cancer, Atlanta, GA, 2011.
$10,000 to Dream House for Medically Fragile Children, Snellville, GA, 2011.
$10,000 to Foster Care Support Foundation, Roswell, GA, 2011.
$10,000 to Jenkins Clinic, Atlanta, GA, 2011.
$10,000 to Visiting Nurse Health System, Atlanta, GA, 2011.

2468
Georgia Power Foundation, Inc.

241 Ralph McGill Blvd., N.E., Bin 10131
Atlanta, GA 30308-3374 (404) 506-6784
Contact: Susan M. Carter, Secy. and Exec. Dir.
FAX: (404) 506-1485;
E-mail: gpfoundation@southernco.com; Main URL: http://www.georgiapower.com/in-your-community/charitable-giving/overview-and-focus.cshtml

Established in 1986 in GA.
Donors: Georgia Power Co.; Savannah Electric Foundation, Inc.
Foundation type: Company-sponsored foundation.
Financial data (yr. ended 12/31/12): Assets, $128,972,580 (M); gifts received, $10,000,000; expenditures, $8,621,772; qualifying distributions, $8,016,375; giving activities include $8,016,375 for 547 grants (high: $1,330,000; low: $250).
Purpose and activities: The foundation supports organizations involved with arts and culture, education, the environment, cancer, diversity, and workforce planning.
Fields of interest: Arts; Higher education; Education; Environment, air pollution; Environment, water pollution; Environment, natural resources; Environment; Health care; Cancer; Salvation Army; Human services; Community development, neighborhood development.
Type of support: General/operating support; Continuing support; Annual campaigns; Capital campaigns; Equipment; Emergency funds; Program development; Conferences/seminars; Scholarship funds; Sponsorships; Employee matching gifts.
Limitations: Applications accepted. Giving primarily in GA. No support for private foundations, political or religious organizations, private elementary or secondary schools, or non-public charities. No grants to individuals, or for political campaigns or causes.
Publications: Application guidelines; Informational brochure (including application guidelines).
Application information: Support is limited to 1 contribution per organization during any given year. Multi-year funding is not automatic. Video submissions are not encouraged. Application form not required.
Initial approach: Complete online application form or mail proposal to foundation
Copies of proposal: 1
Deadline(s): Feb. 15, May 15, Aug. 15, and Nov. 15 for requests over $25,000
Board meeting date(s): Mar., June, Sept., and Dec.
Final notification: 1 month following board meetings for requests over $25,000
Officers and Directors:* Michael K. Anderson,* Pres. and C.E.O.; Susan M. Carter, Secy. and Exec. Dir.; Roger S. Steffens, Treas.; W. Ron Hinson, C.F.O.; W. Craig Barrs; Brad J. Gates; Valerie D. Searcy; Anthony L. Wilson.
EIN: 581709417
Selected grants: The following grants are a representative sample of this grantmaker's funding activity:
$1,330,000 to United Way of Metropolitan Atlanta, Atlanta, GA, 2010. For annual campaign.
$750,000 to Grady Memorial Hospital Corporation, Grady Health System, Atlanta, GA, 2010. For Greater Grady Campaign.
$750,000 to Grady Memorial Hospital Corporation, Grady Health System, Atlanta, GA, 2011. For future payment - final payment of 2 year pledge - $325M Greater Grady Campaign.
$450,000 to Robert W. Woodruff Arts Center, Atlanta, GA, 2010. For annual campaign and corporate challenge.
$250,000 to National Center for Civil and Human Rights, Atlanta, GA, 2010. For future payment - final of two year pledge for design and construction campaign.
$222,223 to Zoo Atlanta, Atlanta, GA, 2011. For capital campaign for Zoo renovations and expansion of the Amphibian and Reptile Complex and the Animal Health Complex.
$130,000 to University of Georgia Foundation, Athens, GA, 2011. For Georgia Power Developing Scholar Program ($80K) and support for relocation of Public Health to Health Sciences Campus ($50K).
$125,000 to Arch Foundation for the University of Georgia, Athens, GA, 2010. For UGA needs based undergraduate scholarship program and Terry College of Business programs.
$125,000 to Community Foundation for Greater Atlanta, Atlanta, GA, 2010. For City of Atlanta Financial Panels Review Fund.
$105,000 to United Way of the Coastal Empire, Savannah, GA, 2010. For annual campaign.
$100,000 to Communities in Schools of Georgia, Atlanta, GA, 2010. To support local affiliates, Performance Learning Centers, and graduation coaches.
$100,000 to Georgia Partnership for Excellence in Education, Atlanta, GA, 2010. For operating expenses.
$100,000 to United Negro College Fund, Atlanta, GA, 2010. For corporate campaign.
$80,000 to Nature Conservancy, Atlanta, GA, 2011. To support conservation work in Georgia.

2469
Georgia-Pacific Foundation, Inc. ✧

133 Peachtree St. N.E., 39th FL
Atlanta, GA 30303-1808 (404) 652-4000
Contact: Curley M. Dossman, Jr., Pres.
FAX: (404) 749-2754;
E-mail: GPFoundation@gapac.com; Additional contact: Charmaine Ward, Dir., Community Affairs, tel.: (404) 652-5302; e-mail for Bucket Brigade: gpbucketbrigade@gapac.com; Main URL: http://www.gp.com/gpfoundation/index.html

Incorporated in 1958 in OR.
Donor: Georgia-Pacific Corp.
Foundation type: Company-sponsored foundation.
Financial data (yr. ended 12/31/12): Assets, $249,025 (M); gifts received, $3,303,617; expenditures, $4,161,881; qualifying distributions, $4,161,881; giving activities include $4,134,739 for 405 grants (high: $398,145; low: $100).
Purpose and activities: The foundation supports programs designed to promote education; environment; community enrichment; and entrepreneurship.
Fields of interest: Arts; Elementary/secondary education; Higher education; Education, reading; Education; Environment, air pollution; Environment, recycling; Environment, natural resources; Environment, land resources; Environmental education; Environment; Employment, training;

Employment; Housing/shelter, development; Housing/shelter; Disasters, preparedness/services; Disasters, fire prevention/control; Safety/disasters; Youth development, business; Youth development; Family services, domestic violence; Social entrepreneurship; Community development, small businesses; Community/economic development; United Ways and Federated Giving Programs; Youth; Minorities; Women.
Type of support: General/operating support; Continuing support; Management development/capacity building; Annual campaigns; Capital campaigns; Building/renovation; Equipment; Program development; Conferences/seminars; Scholarship funds; Employee volunteer services; Sponsorships; Employee-related scholarships; In-kind gifts.
Limitations: Applications accepted. Giving limited to areas of company operations in AL, AR, AZ, CA, Washington, DC, DE, FL, GA, IA, IL, IN, KS, KY, LA, MA, MI, MN, MO, MS, NH, NJ, NM, NV, NY, NC, OH, OK, OR, PA, SC, TN, VA, WA, WI, WV, WY, and Africa, Asia, Europe, and South America. No support for discriminatory organizations, political candidates, churches or religious denominations, religious or theological schools, social, labor, veterans', alumni, or fraternal organizations not of direct benefit to the entire community, athletic associations, national organizations with local chapters already receiving support, medical or nursing schools, or pass-through organizations. No grants to individuals (except for employee-related scholarships), or for emergency needs for general operating support, political causes, legislative lobbying, or advocacy efforts, goodwill advertising, sporting events, general operating support for United Way member agencies, tickets or tables for testimonials or similar benefit events, named academic chairs, social sciences or health science programs, fundraising events, or trips or tours.
Publications: Application guidelines; Program policy statement.
Application information: Extraneous proposal materials are not encouraged. Photos, videos, CD's, and DVD's are not encouraged. Firefighting units must process applications through their local GP facility contact. Application form not required.
Initial approach: Complete online eligibility quiz and mail application or proposal to foundation; download application form for Bucket Brigade
Copies of proposal: 1
Deadline(s): Between Jan. 1 and Oct. 31; Apr. 1 to July 11 for Bucket Brigade
Board meeting date(s): As required
Final notification: Within 60 days; Sept. for Bucket Brigade
Officers and Directors:* Curley M. Dossman, Jr.,* Pres.; Gerald Shirk, V.P. and Treas.; Mark Berry,* Secy.; Philip Ellender; Shiela Weidman.
Number of staff: 5 full-time professional; 1 full-time support.
EIN: 936023726

2470
Jack and Anne Glenn Charitable Foundation ✧
c/o SunTrust Bank
P.O. Box 4655, MC221
Atlanta, GA 30302-4655 (404) 813-2021
Contact: Emily Butler, Grants Mgr., SunTrust Bank
E-mail: fdnsvcs.ga@suntrust.com; Main URL: http://fdnweb.org/glenn

Established in 2004 in FL.
Donors: Anne Glenn; Jack Glenn; John Fitten Glen†.
Foundation type: Independent foundation.
Financial data (yr. ended 12/31/13): Assets, $12,006,191 (M); expenditures, $533,938; qualifying distributions, $498,822; giving activities include $478,665 for 20 grants (high: $130,000; low: $4,000).
Fields of interest: Elementary/secondary education; Environment; Health care; Human services; Community/economic development.
Type of support: Scholarship funds; Endowments; Program development.
Limitations: Applications accepted. Giving primarily in Atlanta, GA. No grants to individuals.
Application information:
Initial approach: Proposal
Copies of proposal: 1
Deadline(s): Feb. 15 and July 15
Board meeting date(s): Spring and Fall
Directors: Alston Glenn; Jack Glenn; Lewis Glenn; Robert Glenn.
Trustee: SunTrust Bank.
EIN: 200545315
Selected grants: The following grants are a representative sample of this grantmaker's funding activity:
$50,000 to Darlington School, Rome, GA, 2011. For Glenn Teaching and Learning Center and Ron Clark Academy Student Scholarship.
$50,000 to Emory University, Eye Center, Atlanta, GA, 2011. For pediatric ophthalmology section - treatment of children in need of cornea transplants.
$50,000 to Emory University, School of Medicine, Atlanta, GA, 2011. For research efforts in the Department of Neurosurgery.
$50,000 to Lovett School, Atlanta, GA, 2011. For Jack and Anne Glenn Character Education Speakers Fund.
$25,000 to George West Mental Health Foundation, Skyland Trail, Atlanta, GA, 2011. For Financial Aid Program.
$25,000 to Piedmont Hospital, Atlanta, GA, 2011.
$15,000 to Acworth Parks and Recreation Department, Acworth, GA, 2011. For Expanding Horizons Program.
$10,000 to Atlanta Youth Academies Foundation, Atlanta, GA, 2011. To enhance existing endowment, which will provide income that will significantly contribute to the schools sustainability.
$10,000 to Forward Arts Foundation, Atlanta, GA, 2011. For Fashion Show.
$9,000 to Center for the Visually Impaired, Atlanta, GA, 2011. For CVI Contact Center and Customer Service Training Program.

2471
The Wilbur and Hilda Glenn Family Foundation
(formerly Bluegrass Foundation)
42 Lenox Pointe
Atlanta, GA 30324-3170 (678) 608-4983
Contact: Suzanna Stribling, Exec. Dir.
FAX: (404) 214-9758; Main URL: http://www.glennfamilyfdn.org

Established in 1996 in GA.
Donors: Thomas K. Glenn II; Wilbur Glenn Irrevocable Trust.
Foundation type: Independent foundation.
Financial data (yr. ended 12/31/13): Assets, $142,808,459 (M); expenditures, $8,120,335; qualifying distributions, $7,320,014; giving activities include $7,015,500 for 34 grants (high: $2,500,000; low: $5,000).
Purpose and activities: To enhance the quality of human life by making grants that reflect the keen interests and passions of the foundation's trustees and which are structured to achieve significant impact.
Fields of interest: Education; Health care; Human services.
Limitations: Applications not accepted. Giving primarily in Atlanta, GA. No grants to individuals.
Application information: Unsolicited requests for funds not accepted.
Board meeting date(s): Mar.
Officers and Trustees:* Thomas K. Glenn II,* Chair.; Louise R. Glenn,* Vice-Chair.; Louisa Glenn D'Antignac,* Secy.; Rand Glenn Hagen,* Treas.; Suzanna Stribling, Exec. Dir.
Number of staff: 1 full-time professional.
EIN: 586328896

2472
The Evelyn and Frank Gordy Foundation ✧
3330 Cumberland Blvd., Ste. T-40
Atlanta, GA 30339-5985
Contact: Steven H. Simms, Tr.
E-mail: stevesimms@thevarsity.com

Established in 1997 in GA.
Donor: Evelyn Gordy Rankin†.
Foundation type: Independent foundation.
Financial data (yr. ended 04/30/13): Assets, $10,535,092 (M); gifts received, $13,144; expenditures, $647,617; qualifying distributions, $420,000; giving activities include $420,000 for grants.
Fields of interest: Higher education; Education; Health care; Human services; Children/youth, services; Christian agencies & churches.
Limitations: Applications accepted. Giving primarily in the Atlanta and Marietta, GA, area. No grants to individuals.
Application information: Application form required.
Initial approach: Letter
Deadline(s): None
Board meeting date(s): Apr. 25
Trustees: Caroline Muir Browne; Douglas Gordon Muir III; Nancy Gordy Simms; Steven H. Simms.
Number of staff: 1 full-time professional; 1 part-time professional.
EIN: 586343707
Selected grants: The following grants are a representative sample of this grantmaker's funding activity:
$141,000 to Feed My Lambs, Marietta, GA, 2011.
$50,000 to Childrens Healthcare of Atlanta Foundation, Atlanta, GA, 2011.
$50,000 to Reinhardt University, Waleska, GA, 2011.
$30,000 to Good Samaritan Health Center, Atlanta, GA, 2011.
$20,000 to Atlanta Union Mission, Atlanta, GA, 2011.
$10,000 to Foster Care Support Foundation, Roswell, GA, 2011.
$10,000 to Foundation of Wesley Woods, Atlanta, GA, 2011.
$5,000 to Center for the Visually Impaired, Atlanta, GA, 2011.
$5,000 to Eagle Ranch, Flowery Branch, GA, 2011.

2473
Griffith Family Charitable Foundation, Inc. ✧
6304 Peake Rd.
Macon, GA 31210-3960

Established in 1993 in GA.
Donor: Benjamin W. Griffith III.
Foundation type: Independent foundation.
Financial data (yr. ended 12/31/13): Assets, $3,821,440 (M); expenditures, $826,127; qualifying distributions, $823,692; giving activities include $823,692 for 34 grants (high: $500,000; low: $250).
Purpose and activities: Giving primarily for higher education; some giving for children and social services, and Baptist organizations.
Fields of interest: Higher education; Human services; Children, services; Protestant agencies & churches.
Limitations: Applications not accepted. Giving primarily in Macon, GA. No grants to individuals.
Application information: Contributes only to pre-selected organizations.
Officers: Benjamin W. Griffith III, Pres. and Treas.; Teresa M. Griffith, Secy.
EIN: 582075742
Selected grants: The following grants are a representative sample of this grantmaker's funding activity:
$250,000 to Mercer University, Macon, GA, 2012. For Mercer University Press and General Fund.
$16,027 to Macon Arts Alliance, Macon, GA, 2012. For Summer Arts Program.

2474
Grizzard Family Foundation Inc. ✧
4500 Hugh Howell Rd., Apt. 620E
Tucker, GA 30084-4110

Established in 2000 in GA.
Donor: Claude H. Grizzard, Sr.
Foundation type: Independent foundation.
Financial data (yr. ended 07/31/13): Assets, $17,490,844 (M); gifts received, $4,772,732; expenditures, $426,492; qualifying distributions, $419,906; giving activities include $419,906 for grants.
Fields of interest: Elementary school/education; Health care; Boys & girls clubs; Human services; Protestant agencies & churches.
Limitations: Applications not accepted. No grants to individuals.
Application information: Contributes only to pre-selected organizations.
Trustees: Claude H. Grizzard, Sr.; Elizabeth H. Grizzard.
EIN: 311732808
Selected grants: The following grants are a representative sample of this grantmaker's funding activity:
$64,000 to Young Life, Atlanta, GA, 2011. For general support.
$50,000 to Boy Scouts of America, Atlanta, GA, 2011. For general support.
$30,000 to Action Ministries, Atlanta, GA, 2011. For general support.
$20,000 to Denver Dumb Friends League, Denver, CO, 2011. For general support.
$20,000 to Kiwanis Foundation of Atlanta, Atlanta, GA, 2011. For general support.
$20,000 to Mission of Hope, Bolivia, Charlottesville, VA, 2011. For general support.
$15,000 to Habitat for Humanity in Atlanta, Atlanta, GA, 2011. For general support.
$15,000 to Lovett School, Atlanta, GA, 2011. For general support.
$15,000 to Peachtree Road United Methodist Church, Atlanta, GA, 2011. For general support.
$5,000 to Rescue Missions Ministries, Durham, NC, 2011. For general support.

2475
Guanacaste Ventures U.S., Inc. ✧
P.O. Box 1047
Decatur, GA 30031-1047

Established in 2005 in GA.
Donors: H.G. Pattillo; John J. McMahon, Jr.
Foundation type: Independent foundation.
Financial data (yr. ended 12/31/13): Assets, $606,432 (M); gifts received, $3,100; expenditures, $657,329; qualifying distributions, $657,000; giving activities include $657,000 for 3 grants (high: $560,000; low: $42,000).
Fields of interest: Higher education; United Ways and Federated Giving Programs.
Limitations: Applications not accepted. Giving primarily in GA; funding also in Santa Cruz, Costa Rica.
Application information: Contributes only to pre-selected organizations.
Officers and Trustees:* H.G. Pattillo,* Pres.; Bree Patillo, V.P.; Carolyn Wagnon, Secy.-Treas.; Jack Guynn.
EIN: 203885468

2476
The Hanley Family Foundation, Inc. ✧
485 Winfield Glen Ct.
Atlanta, GA 30342-1437
Contact: Michael J. Hanley, Pres.
E-mail: info@hanleyfamilyfoundation.org; Main URL: http://www.hanleyfamilyfoundation.org

Established in 1986 in FL.
Donors: John W. Hanley, Sr.; John W. Hanley, Jr.; Michael J. Hanley, Sr.; Susan Hanley Myers; Mary Reel Hanley.
Foundation type: Independent foundation.
Financial data (yr. ended 05/31/13): Assets, $14,760,581 (M); expenditures, $873,247; qualifying distributions, $778,648; giving activities include $675,000 for 3 grants (high: $635,000; low: $10,000).
Purpose and activities: Giving limited strictly to non-profit organizations whose primary mission is the treatment of alcoholism or chemical dependency.
Fields of interest: Substance abuse, treatment; Alcoholism; Substance abusers.
Type of support: Capital campaigns; Building/renovation; Program development; Seed money; Matching/challenge support.
Limitations: Giving on a national basis.
Publications: Financial statement; Multi-year report (including application guidelines).
Application information: The foundation is not currently accepting applications.
Board meeting date(s): As required
Officers and Directors:* John W. Hanley, Jr.,* Chair.; Michael J. Hanley,* Pres. and Treas.; Linda H. Hanley, Secy.; Jack Hanley; John W. Hanley, Sr.; Kristen Hanley; Mary Jane Hanley; Michael J. Hanley, Jr.; Mimi Hanley; Sondra Hanley; Susan H. Myers; Stephen Roegiers; Amy H. Rothermel; Andrew Rothermel; George Stickney; Lara J. Stickney; Douglas Tieman.
Number of staff: 1 full-time professional.
EIN: 592745187

2477
John H. and Wilhelmina D. Harland Charitable Foundation, Inc. ✧
2 Piedmont Ctr., Ste. 710
Atlanta, GA 30305-1567 (404) 264-9912
Contact: Jane G. Hardesty, Exec. Dir.
Main URL: http://harlandfoundation.org

Incorporated in 1972 in GA.
Donors: John H. Harland†; Miriam H. Conant†; John A. Conant†.
Foundation type: Independent foundation.
Financial data (yr. ended 12/31/13): Assets, $29,434,403 (M); expenditures, $1,523,233; qualifying distributions, $1,213,751; giving activities include $920,100 for 46 grants (high: $100,000; low: $10,000).
Purpose and activities: Support for youth services, arts and culture, and community services. The focus is local rather than regional or national, and priority is given to institutions in metropolitan Atlanta, Georgia.
Fields of interest: Arts; Education, early childhood education; Adult education—literacy, basic skills & GED; Children/youth, services; Child development, services; Children/youth; Disabilities, people with.
Type of support: General/operating support; Capital campaigns; Building/renovation; Equipment; Program development; Matching/challenge support.
Limitations: Applications accepted. Giving limited to GA, with emphasis on DeKalb and Fulton counties in metropolitan Atlanta. No support for private, primary, or secondary schools, except for those serving the handicapped. No grants to individuals, or for annual campaigns or special events; no loans.
Publications: Annual report (including application guidelines).
Application information: 21-month waiting period for new grant proposals from previously considered applicants. Application form required.
Initial approach: Telephone call preferred
Copies of proposal: 1
Deadline(s): Mar. 15 and Oct. 1
Board meeting date(s): June 1 and Dec. 1
Final notification: 3 to 4 weeks after board meeting
Officers: Margaret C. Reiser, Pres.; Winifred S. Davis, V.P. and Treas.; Robert E. Reiser, Jr., Secy.; Jane G. Hardesty, Exec. Dir.
Trustees: Kathleen B. Patillo; Joseph E. Patrick, Jr.; Sam Pettway.
Number of staff: 1 full-time professional; 1 full-time support; 2 part-time support.
EIN: 237225012

2478
William M. Harris Family Foundation ✧
(formerly Foundation for Advancement of Chiropractic Education, Inc.)
600 Houze Way, Ste. D-9
Roswell, GA 30076-1434 (770) 641-1927
Contact: Jane Goodwin, Secy.-Treas.
E-mail: eaglesfounda@mindspring.com

Established in 1986 in GA.
Donor: Dr. William T. Harris‡.
Foundation type: Independent foundation.
Financial data (yr. ended 12/31/13): Assets, $8,095,754 (M); expenditures, $786,651; qualifying distributions, $734,372; giving activities include $708,344 for 16 grants (high: $356,244; low: $100).
Purpose and activities: The organization promotes chiropractic education and research through grants to various chiropractic colleges and educational organizations.
Fields of interest: Medical school/education; Chiropractic; Medical research, institute.
Type of support: Research.
Limitations: Applications accepted. Giving primarily in IL. No grants to individuals.
Application information: Application form not required.
Initial approach: Proposal
Deadline(s): None
Officers: Vincent Erario, Vice-Chair.; Deane Mink, Pres.; Jane Goodwin, Secy.-Treas.
Board Members: Jerry Hardee; James McDonald; Tom Morgan; Edwin Staub.
EIN: 581422604

2479
Clarence E. Harris Foundation, Inc. ✧
6 Concourse Pkwy., Ste. 600
Atlanta, GA 30328-5351

Established in 1985 in GA.
Foundation type: Independent foundation.
Financial data (yr. ended 12/31/12): Assets, $13,577,688 (M); expenditures, $742,721; qualifying distributions, $567,000; giving activities include $567,000 for grants.
Fields of interest: Hospitals (general); Human services; Children/youth, services.
Type of support: General/operating support; Continuing support; Endowments; Program development; Matching/challenge support.
Limitations: Applications not accepted. Giving limited to Calhoun, GA, and Chattanooga, TN. No grants to individuals.
Application information: Unsolicited requests for funds not accepted.
Officers: Bobbye F. Harris,* Pres.; George W. Hillegass, V.P.; Joel B. Piassick,* V.P.
Directors: Carolyn Rice; G. McKittrick Simmons, Jr.
EIN: 581674685

2480
Dr. J. Harold Harrison Foundation, Inc. ✧
P.O. Box 129
Bartow, GA 30413-2201

Established in GA.
Donor: J. Harold Harrison.
Foundation type: Independent foundation.
Financial data (yr. ended 12/31/12): Assets, $22,578,969 (M); expenditures, $1,445,473; qualifying distributions, $1,337,350; giving activities include $1,337,350 for 9 grants (high: $1,000,000; low: $2,000).
Fields of interest: Higher education; Medical school/education.
Limitations: Applications not accepted. Giving limited to GA. No grants to individuals.
Application information: Contributes only to pre-selected organizations.
Officers: Sue W. Harrison, Chair. and Treas.; Robert G. Woodward, Vice-Chair.; James B. Osborne, Sr., Secy.
EIN: 586076185

2481
The Luther & Susie Harrison Foundation, Inc. ✧
3414 Peachtree Rd. N.E., Ste. 722
Atlanta, GA 30326-1166 (404) 842-1870
Contact: Larry B. Hooks, Mgr.

Established in 1994 in GA.
Donor: Robert Harold Harrison‡.
Foundation type: Independent foundation.
Financial data (yr. ended 12/31/13): Assets, $82,733,184 (M); expenditures, $3,612,038; qualifying distributions, $3,034,604; giving activities include $2,928,435 for 57 grants (high: $500,000; low: $725).
Purpose and activities: Giving to enhance lives through education, faith, and health, primarily in north Georgia.
Fields of interest: Education; Health care; Mental health/crisis services; Health organizations, association; Medical research, institute; Protestant agencies & churches.
Type of support: Annual campaigns; Building/renovation; Capital campaigns; Curriculum development; Equipment; Professorships; Program development; Scholarship funds.
Limitations: Applications accepted. Giving limited to within a 60-mile radius of Bethlehem, GA. No support for political organizations or cultural programs.
Publications: Application guidelines.
Application information: No more than 1 grant request per grantee per year. Application form required.
Initial approach: Narrative letter, telephone for application
Copies of proposal: 6
Deadline(s): Feb. 15 and Aug. 15
Board meeting date(s): Apr. and Oct.
Final notification: Following board meetings
Officer: Larry B. Hooks, Mgr.
Directors: J. Curtis Pruett; Virginia S. Pruett; Bobbie Ann Reynolds; Rev. Jay Tenney; Anne Marie Tison; Kelley H. Tison.
Number of staff: 1 part-time professional.
EIN: 582169694
Selected grants: The following grants are a representative sample of this grantmaker's funding activity:
$575,000 to Emmanuel Episcopal Church, Athens, GA, 2011.
$250,000 to Atlanta Union Mission, Atlanta, GA, 2011.
$45,000 to Make-A-Wish Foundation of Georgia and Alabama, Atlanta, GA, 2011.

2482
Healthcare Georgia Foundation, Inc.
191 Peachtree St. N.E., Ste. 2650
Atlanta, GA 30303-1769 (404) 653-0990
Contact: Javier Sanchez, Grants Mgr.
FAX: (404) 577-8386;
E-mail: info@healthcaregeorgia.org; Main URL: http://www.healthcaregeorgia.org/
E-Newsletter: http://www.healthcaregeorgia.org/publications-and-research/issues-category.cfm/type/Catalyst#signup
Facebook: https://www.facebook.com/HealthcareGeorgiaFoundation
Grant Applicants Survey: http://www.healthcaregeorgia.org/grantmaking/grant-applicants-survey.cfm
Grants Database: http://www.healthcaregeorgia.org/grantees/grants-search.cfm
Podcasts: http://www.healthcaregeorgia.org/news-and-information/news-details.cfm/news_id/D2CDF3B7-3048-7C59-19EA37D285C896B0
Twitter: https://twitter.com/HealthcareGA

Established in 1999 in GA; converted from the merger of Blue Cross Blue Shield of Georgia with Wellpoint Health Networks.
Donor: Blue Cross and Blue Shield of Georgia, Inc.
Foundation type: Independent foundation.
Financial data (yr. ended 12/31/13): Assets, $119,125,630 (M); expenditures, $7,502,625; qualifying distributions, $5,936,410; giving activities include $4,318,696 for 100 grants (high: $215,000; low: $2,000), and $153,761 for foundation-administered programs.
Purpose and activities: The foundation's mission is to advance the health of all Georgians and to expand access to affordable, quality health care for underserved individuals and communities. Specific goals include protecting and promoting the health of individuals, families and communities; improving the availability, quality, appropriateness and financing of health care services; and integrating and coordinating efforts to improve health and health care services. The foundation has also established the following grantmaking priorities: 1) addressing health disparities; 2) strengthening nonprofit health organizations; and 3) expanding access to primary health care.
Fields of interest: Public health; Health care.
Type of support: Publication; General/operating support; Income development; Management development/capacity building; Program development; Conferences/seminars; Research; Technical assistance; Program evaluation.
Limitations: Applications accepted. Giving limited to GA. No support for sectarian programs (benefiting only one religious organization). No grants to individuals (except for award program), or for capital campaigns, or major equipment.
Publications: Application guidelines; Annual report; Grants list; Informational brochure (including application guidelines); Occasional report; Program policy statement.
Application information: The foundation is currently reviewing its Grantmaking Priorities and Guidelines. Please visit its web site for more information. The foundation engages in both proactive (solicited) and responsive (unsolicited) grantmaking. Proactive grantmaking will be carried out through an RFP process that addresses specific areas within the foundation's funding priorities. Responsive grantmaking will allow the foundation to support unsolicited proposals that fit its mission and fall within its funding priorities. See foundation web site for full application requirements and guidelines. Application form required.
Initial approach: Potential applicants should view pre-application webinar on foundation web

site. All applications should be submitted online via web site
Copies of proposal: 2
Deadline(s): See foundation web site for current deadline
Board meeting date(s): Quarterly
Final notification: Within 3 months for letters of inquiry; within 8 to 9 months for proposals; declinations are announced quarterly
Officers and Directors:* Diane Zabak Weems, M.D.*, Chair.; Francis Tedesco, M.D.*, Vice-Chair.; Gary D. Nelson, Ph.D., Pres.; Lynn Thogerson,* Secy.; Teri Hartman,* Treas.; Michael J. Sweeney III, C.F.O.; Cheryl Christian; Floyd M. Dukes; Gene Godfrey; Anne Griffith Hennessy; Scott Kroell; Pierluigi Mancini, Ph.D.; Steven P. Merz; Robert Nesbit, M.D.; Charles T. Stafford, M.D.
Number of staff: 8 full-time professional; 1 full-time support.
EIN: 582418091
Selected grants: The following grants are a representative sample of this grantmaker's funding activity:
$500,000 to Emory University, Atlanta, GA, 2012. To implement school-based health center demonstration project in three elementary schools in Georgia, payable over 1.50 years.
$130,000 to TechBridge, Atlanta, GA, 2012. For technology implementation, network management, network maintenance, program support and training efforts for use of HealthTecDL for Healthcare Georgia Foundation's Distance Learning program.
$60,000 to Georgia Southern University Research and Service Foundation, Statesboro, GA, 2012. For work of Jiann-Ping Hsu College of Public Health to complete cross-site and site-specific evaluation of Georgia Childhood Asthma Management Program and to publish and disseminate evaluation results.
$48,000 to Georgia Coalition Against Domestic Violence, Decatur, GA, 2012. To provide training to the Public Health District health care providers and domestic violence shelters in Southwest Georgia, payable over 1.50 years.
$48,000 to Northwest Georgia Healthcare Partnership, Dalton, GA, 2012. To implement a Community Health Worker-Promotoras de Salud Program in Whitfield and Murray counties, payable over 1.50 years.
$48,000 to Positive Impact, Atlanta, GA, 2012. To expand HIV counseling, testing and linkage services to high risk men.
$48,000 to Saint Josephs Mercy Care Services, Atlanta, GA, 2012. To implement health promotion program designed to facilitate early detection and treatment of diabetes at Atlanta clinic.

2483
The Helton Foundation ✧
c/o W. Frank Drewry
3945 Holcomb Bridge Rd., Ste. 200
Norcross, GA 30092
Application assress: c/o The Helton Foundation, 8720 E. 127th Ct., Brighton, CO 80206

Established in 2005 in CO.
Donors: Todd L. Helton; Christy B. Helton; Encana Cares USA Foundation.
Foundation type: Independent foundation.
Financial data (yr. ended 12/31/13): Assets, $13,392,923 (M); gifts received, $12,300; expenditures, $603,308; qualifying distributions, $535,094; giving activities include $535,094 for 1 grant.
Fields of interest: Christian agencies & churches.
Limitations: Applications accepted. Giving primarily in CA and CO.
Application information: Application form required.
Initial approach: Letter
Deadline(s): None
Officers: Todd L. Helton, Pres.; Rodney Helton, V.P.; Christy B. Helton, Secy.
Directors: Robert R. Davies; Mike Moye.
EIN: 203694022

2484
Douglas J. Hertz Family Foundation ✧
5500 United Dr. S.E.
Smyrna, GA 30082

Established in GA.
Donors: Hertz Family Foundation Inc.; United Distributors Inc.; Douglas J. Hetz; Jennings Hertz‡.
Foundation type: Independent foundation.
Financial data (yr. ended 12/31/12): Assets, $6,980,065 (M); gifts received, $8,406; expenditures, $1,183,302; qualifying distributions, $1,135,816; giving activities include $1,133,566 for 52 grants (high: $800,000; low: $250).
Purpose and activities: Giving primarily for higher education.
Fields of interest: Higher education; Foundations (private grantmaking).
Limitations: Applications not accepted. Giving primarily in Atlanta, GA, and New Orleans, LA.
Application information: Unsolicited requests for funds not accepted.
Officers: Douglas Hertz, Pres.; Lila Hertz, V.P.; Amy H. Agami, Secy.; Michael Hertz, Treas.
EIN: 262792485

2485
The Holder Construction Foundation ✧
3333 Riverwood Pkwy., Ste. 400
Atlanta, GA 30339-3304 (770) 988-3280
Contact: J.C. Pendrey, Jr., Tr.

Donor: Holder Construction Co.
Foundation type: Company-sponsored foundation.
Financial data (yr. ended 12/31/13): Assets, $5,551,288 (M); gifts received, $1,510,000; expenditures, $903,229; qualifying distributions, $900,729; giving activities include $900,729 for 64 grants (high: $230,000; low: $500).
Purpose and activities: The foundation supports zoos and organizations involved with arts and culture, education, health, human services, and business.
Fields of interest: Museums (art); Performing arts, ballet; Arts; Elementary/secondary education; Higher education; Education; Zoos/zoological societies; Health care; Children/youth, services; Human services; Business/industry; United Ways and Federated Giving Programs.
Type of support: General/operating support.
Limitations: Applications accepted. Giving in the greater metropolitan Atlanta, GA, area.
Application information: Application form required.
Initial approach: Letter or telephone
Deadline(s): None
Trustee: J.C. Pendrey, Jr.
EIN: 586412965

2486
The Scott Hudgens Family Foundation, Inc. ✧
3425 Duluth Park Ln., Ste. A
Duluth, GA 30096-3259
Main URL: http://www.hudgensfoundation.org/

Established in 2001 in GA.
Donor: D. Scott Hudgens, Jr.‡.
Foundation type: Independent foundation.
Financial data (yr. ended 12/31/13): Assets, $82,542,714 (M); expenditures, $5,719,002; qualifying distributions, $5,047,600; giving activities include $5,020,000 for 82 grants (high: $865,050; low: $5,000).
Purpose and activities: The foundation funds public charities with missions related to: 1) Improving the lives of individuals who through physical, mental or socio-economic disadvantages are unable to help themselves, including a) services for the developmentally handicapped; b) services for homeless individuals and families; c) services for veterans; d) hospice care and services for the elderly; and e) alcoholism and substance abuse; 2) Promoting self-sufficiency through educational programs and projects, including technical training programs; and 3) Community development projects impacting education, health care and the arts. Whenever practical, the foundation will consider capital campaign contributions in order to enhance the long-term impact of grant making.
Fields of interest: Arts; Education; Health care; Substance abuse, services; Human services; Family services; Residential/custodial care, hospices; Aging, centers/services; Homeless, human services; Military/veterans; Economically disadvantaged.
Limitations: Applications accepted. Giving primarily in GA. No grants to individuals.
Application information: Application form required.
Initial approach: Use online qualification process on foundation web site
Officers and Directors:* Dallas S. Hudgens III,* Chair.; William A. Brogdon, Exec. Dir.; Richard Mayberry.
EIN: 582513020

2487
The Imlay Foundation, Inc. ✧
945 E. Paces Ferry Rd., Ste. 2450
Atlanta, GA 30326-1125 (404) 239-1777
Contact: Mary Ellen Imlay, V.P. and Exec. Dir.
FAX: (404) 239-1779; Main URL: http://theimlayfoundation.org
Grants List: http://theimlayfoundation.org/pdf/imlay-recipients.pdf

Established in 1989 in GA.
Donor: John P. Imlay, Jr.
Foundation type: Independent foundation.
Financial data (yr. ended 12/31/12): Assets, $21,523,481 (M); expenditures, $1,642,844; qualifying distributions, $1,497,268; giving activities include $1,490,812 for 91 grants (high: $100,000; low: $5,000).
Purpose and activities: Giving primarily for health care, and children, youth and social services.
Fields of interest: Botanical gardens; Hospitals (general); Health care; Human services; Children/youth, services; Foundations (community).
Type of support: General/operating support; Annual campaigns; Capital campaigns; Building/

renovation; Program development; Curriculum development; Scholarship funds; Research.
Limitations: Giving primarily in Atlanta, GA and Hilton Head, SC; some funding also in Scotland. No grants to individuals.
Application information: Applications may be hand delivered or mailed. The foundation does not accept e-mailed applications because of the required attachments. Application form not required.
Initial approach: Letter of intent
Deadline(s): Feb. 1, June 1, and Oct. 1
Board meeting date(s): Apr., Sept., and Dec.
Officers: John P. Imlay, Jr., Chair.; Mary Ellen Imlay, Pres.; I. Sigmund Mosley, Jr., V.P. and Secy.
Directors: John Dayton; Wimberly Charlotte Dayton; William Evans; Donald Hardie; Cindy Imlay; John P. "Scott" Imlay III; Cori Zubay.
Number of staff: 1 part-time professional; 1 part-time support.
EIN: 581868936

2488
Indiana Charitable Trust ✧ ☆
14072 Scenic Hwy.
Lookout Mountain, GA 30750-4101

Established in IN.
Donor: Richard J. Schilling.
Foundation type: Independent foundation.
Financial data (yr. ended 12/31/13): Assets, $3,908,209 (M); expenditures, $1,781,306; qualifying distributions, $1,770,770; giving activities include $1,770,770 for 22 grants (high: $1,043,000; low: $100).
Fields of interest: Human services; Protestant agencies & churches.
Limitations: Applications not accepted.
Application information: Unsolicited requests for funds not accepted.
Trustees: Richard J. Schilling; James A. Cheney.
EIN: 457024527

2489
The Invisible Hand Foundation, Inc. ✧ ☆
737 Kennesaw Due West Rd.
Kennesaw, GA 30152-4068
Main URL: http://theinvisiblehand.org/

Established in 2006 in GA.
Donors: Robert E. Matthews; Matthew D. Burton; Christopher Braaksma; Narwhal Capital Management.
Foundation type: Independent foundation.
Financial data (yr. ended 12/31/13): Assets, $425,845 (M); gifts received, $100,000; expenditures, $579,895; qualifying distributions, $576,784; giving activities include $575,600 for 5 grants (high: $475,600; low: $10,000).
Fields of interest: Education; Human services.
Limitations: Applications not accepted. No grants to individuals.
Application information: Unsolicited requests for funds not accepted.
Directors: Matthew D. Burton; David Hall.
EIN: 205791133
Selected grants: The following grants are a representative sample of this grantmaker's funding activity:
$1,726 to Reach for Excellence, Atlanta, GA, 2012. For grant Purposes Are Religious.

2490
Horace B. Jackson Test Charitable Trust ✧
P.O. Box 1127
Bainbridge, GA 39818-1127

Donor: Horace B. Jackson.
Foundation type: Independent foundation.
Financial data (yr. ended 12/31/13): Assets, $7,893,015 (M); gifts received, $34,850; expenditures, $2,890,777; qualifying distributions, $2,877,606; giving activities include $2,877,606 for 19 grants (high: $577,876; low: $2,215).
Fields of interest: Human services; Christian agencies & churches; Protestant agencies & churches.
Limitations: Applications not accepted. Giving primarily in AL, GA, MN, and TX.
Application information: Unsolicited requests for funds not accepted.
Trustees: Glaphrey Jackson; Edward T. Mitchell; Richard Y. Youmans.
EIN: 276807572

2491
Charles H. Jones Family Foundation, Inc. ✧
P.O. Box 7345
Macon, GA 31209-7345 (478) 471-2520
Contact: Dwight C. Jones, Dir.

Established in 1985 in GA.
Donors: Charles H. Jones†; Dwight C. Jones; Ocmulgee Fields, Inc.; Landmark Developers of Macon.
Foundation type: Independent foundation.
Financial data (yr. ended 05/31/13): Assets, $12,572,935 (M); gifts received, $5,600; expenditures, $762,933; qualifying distributions, $582,753; giving activities include $582,753 for grants.
Fields of interest: Elementary/secondary education; Higher education; Alzheimer's disease; Human services.
Limitations: Applications accepted. Giving primarily in Macon, GA. No grants to individuals.
Application information: Application form required.
Initial approach: Letter
Deadline(s): None
Directors:* Lindsey Crosby; Charles J. Jones; Dwight C. Jones; Ves Jones; John Kitchens.
EIN: 581678452
Selected grants: The following grants are a representative sample of this grantmaker's funding activity:
$110,000 to Campus Crusade for Christ, Athens, GA, 2011. For general support of programs.

2492
The Jordan Foundation Inc. ✧
6001 River Rd., Ste. 100
Columbus, GA 31904-2949 (706) 322-5105
Contact: Viki B. Gilmore, Secy.-Treas.

Donors: Helen S. Jordan†; Randolph Swift Jordan Charitable Lead Annuity Trust; Helen S. Jordan Charitable Lead Annuity Trust.
Foundation type: Independent foundation.
Financial data (yr. ended 12/31/13): Assets, $4,589,322 (M); gifts received, $2,663,877; expenditures, $985,926; qualifying distributions, $973,121; giving activities include $973,121 for 43 grants (high: $378,000; low: $100).
Fields of interest: Arts; Elementary/secondary education; Higher education; Animal welfare; YM/YWCAs & YM/YWHAs; Developmentally disabled, centers & services; Protestant agencies & churches.
Type of support: Capital campaigns; General/operating support.
Limitations: Applications accepted. Giving primarily in Columbus, GA.
Application information: Application form required.
Initial approach: Letter
Deadline(s): None
Officers: Helen S. Olnick, Pres.; Katherine J. Waddell, V.P.; Viki B. Gilmore, Secy.-Treas.
Trustees: Gardiner W. Garrard; Lenora Garrard; Wright Waddell.
EIN: 586039423

2493
David & Jennifer Kahn Family Foundation, Inc. ✧
(formerly The David B. Kahn Foundation, Inc.)
3755 Atlanta Industrial Pkwy.
Atlanta, GA 30331-1027

Established in 1999 in GA.
Donor: David B. Kahn.
Foundation type: Independent foundation.
Financial data (yr. ended 12/31/13): Assets, $21,208,389 (M); gifts received, $3,500; expenditures, $519,882; qualifying distributions, $428,150; giving activities include $428,150 for 31 grants (high: $325,000; low: $50).
Fields of interest: Arts; Education; Health care; Human services; Children/youth, services.
Limitations: Applications not accepted. Giving primarily in Atlanta, GA. No grants to individuals.
Application information: Contributes only to pre-selected organizations.
Officers: David B. Kahn, Chair.; Jennifer M. Kahn, Vice-Chair.
EIN: 582472876

2494
Abraham J. & Phyllis Katz Foundation ✧
c/o Alexander S. Katz
1579F Monroe Dr., Ste. 933
Atlanta, GA 30324-5016
Contact: Peter A. Katz, Tr.
E-mail: contact@katzfoundation.org; Main URL: http://katzfoundation.org/
Grants List: http://katzfoundation.org/recent_grants.html

Established in 1994 in NY.
Donors: Abraham J. Katz†; Phyllis Katz†; Peter A. Katz; Kason Industries, Inc.; World Trade Ventures, Ltd.
Foundation type: Operating foundation.
Financial data (yr. ended 12/31/12): Assets, $67,944,440 (M); gifts received, $28,863; expenditures, $3,799,545; qualifying distributions, $3,696,674; giving activities include $3,376,647 for 33 grants.
Purpose and activities: Giving to support young musicians both in performance and composition, and for scientific and medical research. Medical research projects must be related to the use of cord blood to promote wellness, prevent disease or save lives. Of particular interest to the foundation are

programs that benefit low-income and under-resourced populations.
Fields of interest: Performing arts, music; Higher education; Medical school/education; Hospitals (general).
Limitations: Applications accepted. Giving primarily in NY and OH. The Small Grants Program is limited to organizations located in the City of Atlanta, GA and the counties of Coweta, DeKalb, Fayette, and Fulton, GA. No grants to individuals or government agencies; no funding for events.
Application information: To be considered, organizations must have at least one paid staff member. Complete application guidelines available on foundation web site. Application form required.
Initial approach: For medical research requests: 1-page Letter of Intent outlining proposed research
Deadline(s): Varies; application deadlines available on foundation web site
Board meeting date(s): Jan. and Apr.
Trustees: Ellen B. Doft; Alexander S. Katz; David Katz; Esther Katz.
Number of staff: 1 part-time professional.
EIN: 116442077

2495
J. C. Kennedy Foundation, Inc. ✧
(formerly JCK Foundation, Inc.)
P.O. Box 105720
Atlanta, GA 30348

Established in 2003 in GA.
Donor: James C. Kennedy.
Foundation type: Independent foundation.
Financial data (yr. ended 12/31/13): Assets, $23,289,228 (M); expenditures, $902,079; qualifying distributions, $624,044; giving activities include $624,044 for 46 grants (high: $75,000; low: $200).
Purpose and activities: Giving primarily for athletics, including a tennis center; support also for health organization, education, and the environment.
Fields of interest: Education; Environment; Health care; Athletics/sports, racquet sports; Human services.
Limitations: Applications not accepted. Giving primarily in GA. No grants to individuals.
Application information: Contributes only to pre-selected organizations.
Officers and Directors:* James C. Kennedy,* Pres.; Barbara K. Harty,* V.P.; James C. Kennedy, Jr.,* Secy.-Treas.; Macon Cherp; Clay K. Kennedy.
EIN: 200424251
Selected grants: The following grants are a representative sample of this grantmaker's funding activity:
$5,000 to Montana Wilderness Association, Helena, MT, 2011.
$2,500 to Special Olympics Georgia, Atlanta, GA, 2011.
$1,000 to American Rivers, Washington, DC, 2011.
$1,000 to American Rivers, Washington, DC, 2011.
$1,000 to National Parks Conservation Association, Washington, DC, 2011.

2496
Donald and Marilyn Keough Foundation ✧
(formerly Donald R. Keough Foundation)
c/o Michael Keough
200 Galleria Pkwy., Ste. 970
Atlanta, GA 30339-5945
E-mail: dmkfdn@aol.com

Established in 1986 in GA.
Donor: Donald R. Keough.
Foundation type: Independent foundation.
Financial data (yr. ended 12/31/13): Assets, $11,283,718 (M); expenditures, $499,164; qualifying distributions, $493,725; giving activities include $493,000 for 71 grants (high: $37,500; low: $1,000).
Purpose and activities: Support primarily for higher education.
Fields of interest: Performing arts, opera; Higher education; Girl scouts; Catholic agencies & churches.
Type of support: General/operating support; Continuing support; Scholarship funds.
Limitations: Applications not accepted. Giving on a national basis. No grants to individuals.
Application information: Contributes only to pre-selected organizations.
Officers and Trustees:* Donald R. Keough,* Chair.; Marilyn M. Keough,* Pres.
EIN: 581709967
Selected grants: The following grants are a representative sample of this grantmaker's funding activity:
$6,000 to Creighton University, Nursing School, Omaha, NE, 2012. For general.

2497
The Klaus Family Foundation ✧
1330 Monte Carlo Dr.
Atlanta, GA 30327-3803

Established in 2006 in GA.
Donor: Christopher W. Klaus.
Foundation type: Independent foundation.
Financial data (yr. ended 09/30/13): Assets, $13,484,454 (M); expenditures, $680,498; qualifying distributions, $639,776; giving activities include $639,776 for 5 grants (high: $558,276; low: $500).
Fields of interest: Arts; Education; United Ways and Federated Giving Programs.
Limitations: Applications not accepted. Giving primarily in Atlanta, GA, and Albany, NY. No grants to individuals.
Application information: Contributes only to pre-selected organizations.
Trustee: Christopher Klaus.
EIN: 205529710
Selected grants: The following grants are a representative sample of this grantmaker's funding activity:
$25,000 to Atlanta Speech School, Atlanta, GA, 2011.
$25,000 to Sophia Academy, Atlanta, GA, 2011.
$2,500 to Atlanta International School, Atlanta, GA, 2011.

2498
The Knox Foundation ✧
3133 Washington Rd. N.W.
Thomson, GA 30824-5451 (706) 595-1907
Contact: Boone A. Knox, Tr.

Established in 1981 in GA.
Donors: Boone A. Knox†; Julia P.R. Knox; The George Ann Knox Charitable Lead Annuity Trust; The Pat Knox Charitable Lead Annuity Trust; Knox, Ltd.; Folkstone Ltd.; The Pat Knox Charitable Lead Annuity Trust.
Foundation type: Independent foundation.
Financial data (yr. ended 12/31/12): Assets, $64,880,599 (M); gifts received, $337,292; expenditures, $3,436,654; qualifying distributions, $2,891,130; giving activities include $2,719,387 for 121 grants (high: $360,000; low: $600).
Fields of interest: Arts; Higher education; Human services.
Type of support: General/operating support; Continuing support; Annual campaigns; Capital campaigns; Building/renovation; Endowments; Program development; Matching/challenge support.
Limitations: Applications accepted. Giving generally primarily in Augusta and Thomson, GA. No grants to individuals.
Application information: Application form not required.
Initial approach: Letter
Copies of proposal: 2
Deadline(s): None
Board meeting date(s): Apr. and Oct.
Final notification: Feb. 15 and Aug. 15
Director: Jefferson B.A. Knox.
EIN: 586163728

2499
The Sartain Lanier Family Foundation, Inc. ✧
950 Joseph E. Lowery Blvd. N.W.
25 Puritan Mill
Atlanta, GA 30318-5279 (404) 564-1259
Contact: Mark B. Riley, Dir.; Patricia E. Lummus, Assoc. Dir.
FAX: (404) 564-1251;
E-mail: plummus@lanierfamilyfoundation.org; Main URL: http://www.lanierfamilyfoundation.org

Established in 1963 in GA.
Donor: Sartain Lanier†.
Foundation type: Independent foundation.
Financial data (yr. ended 12/31/13): Assets, $112,145,346 (M); expenditures, $5,483,231; qualifying distributions, $4,444,855; giving activities include $4,318,034 for 98 grants (high: $1,022,769; low: $1,000).
Purpose and activities: The foundation will focus the majority of new grantmaking on education, which has traditionally been primary to the foundation's mission. Specifically the foundation will focus on educational organizations which have broad, systemic impact with the aim of enhancing available options for K-12 education in the metro Atlanta area. The foundation will not be establishing new relationships with private schools at this time, but may continue to make grants to private schools which have received grants from the foundation in the past. In the areas of health and human services, arts, environment and community development, special consideration will continue to be given to institutions that were supported by Mr. Lanier during

his lifetime and that his family has supported since his death.
Fields of interest: Arts; Elementary/secondary education; Education; Environment; Human services; Community/economic development.
Type of support: General/operating support; Capital campaigns; Building/renovation; Endowments; Program development; Program-related investments/loans.
Limitations: Giving primarily in New grants will be limited to organizations in the metro Atlanta, GA area. There will be a few grants each year to organizations outside Atlanta, but those will be based on commitments to organizations with which the foundation has had a lengthy history. No support for churches or religious organizations (for projects that primarily benefit their own members), or for partisan political purposes. No grants to individuals, or for tickets to charitable events or dinners, or to sponsor special events or fundraisers.
Publications: Application guidelines.
Application information: Applications are by invitation only. See foundation web site for further information. Application form not required.
Initial approach: E-mail or telephone
Copies of proposal: 1
Deadline(s): No deadlines, but those invited to submit are encouraged to apply by Apr. 1 for the May meeting and Oct. 1 for the Nov. meeting
Board meeting date(s): May and Dec.
Final notification: Within 1 week of Board of Trustees meeting in May and Nov.
Officers and Trustees:* J. Hicks Lanier,* Chair.; Cecil D. Conlee,* Vice-Chair.; Julie W. Lanier Balloun; Liza Lanier Jancik; Stephen S. Lanier; V. Whitson Lanier, Jr.; Claudia M. Livingston; E. Jenner Wood III.
Director: Mark B. Riley.
Number of staff: 2 part-time professional; 1 part-time support.
EIN: 586045056
Selected grants: The following grants are a representative sample of this grantmaker's funding activity:
$1,228,603 to Vanderbilt University, Nashville, TN, 2012.
$500,000 to University of Alabama, School of Medicine, Department of Neurology, Birmingham, AL, 2012. For parkinson's disease research.
$250,000 to Emory University, Atlanta, GA, 2012. For Vance Lanier Chair of Neurology.
$175,000 to United Way of Metropolitan Atlanta, Atlanta, GA, 2012.
$85,000 to Robert W. Woodruff Arts Center, Atlanta, GA, 2012.
$75,000 to KIPP Metro Atlanta Collaborative, Atlanta, GA, 2012.
$75,000 to Teach for America, Atlanta, GA, 2012.
$70,000 to Atlanta Speech School, Atlanta, GA, 2012.

2500
Wade L. Layton Charitable Trust ✧
1808 Walthour Rd.
Savannah, GA 31410

Established in 2007 in GA.
Donors: Wade Layton Trust; Elizabeth Layton†.
Foundation type: Independent foundation.
Financial data (yr. ended 12/31/12): Assets, $11,810,847 (M); expenditures, $629,859; qualifying distributions, $529,882; giving activities include $480,000 for 6 grants (high: $150,000; low: $10,000).
Purpose and activities: Giving primarily to Baptist churches and schools.
Fields of interest: Elementary/secondary education; Protestant agencies & churches.
Limitations: Applications not accepted. Giving in Savannah, GA.
Application information: Contributes only to pre-selected organizations.
Trustees: Francis A. Brown; Bennie Faulk.
EIN: 208572571

2501
Murray Lender Family Foundation Inc. ✧ ☆
c/o Pathstone Family Office
P.O. Box 52047
Atlanta, GA 30355-0047

Established in 1994.
Donor: Murray Lender.
Foundation type: Independent foundation.
Financial data (yr. ended 12/31/12): Assets, $175 (M); gifts received, $533; expenditures, $482,917; qualifying distributions, $481,600; giving activities include $481,600 for grants.
Purpose and activities: Giving primarily for Jewish federated giving programs and organizations, higher education, hospitals, health associations, and human services.
Fields of interest: Arts; Education; Community/economic development.
Limitations: Applications not accepted. Giving primarily in CT.
Application information: Unsolicited requests for funds not accepted.
Officers: Marvin Lender, Chair. and Pres.; Haris Lender, Secy.
Trustees: Carl M. Lender; Jay G. Lender.
EIN: 061403607

2502
Dorothy V. & Logan Lewis Foundation, Inc. ✧
c/o Edward J. Harrell
240 3rd St.
Macon, GA 31201-3310
E-mail: ejharrell@martinsnow.com

Established in 1979.
Donor: Dorothy V. Lewis†.
Foundation type: Independent foundation.
Financial data (yr. ended 12/31/13): Assets, $64,337,080 (M); expenditures, $3,872,946; qualifying distributions, $3,274,401; giving activities include $3,260,901 for 19 grants (high: $1,304,351; low: $5,000).
Purpose and activities: Giving primarily for the promotion of academic excellence in Catholic education.
Fields of interest: Elementary/secondary education; Catholic agencies & churches; African Americans/Blacks; Women; Adults, women; Men; Adults, men.
Type of support: Scholarships—to individuals; Scholarship funds; Endowments; Conferences/seminars.
Limitations: Applications accepted. Giving limited to middle GA, with emphasis on Macon. No support for private foundations.
Publications: Annual report; Financial statement; Grants list; Multi-year report; Program policy statement; Quarterly report.
Application information: No more than 3 supplemental pages may be attached to proposal. Application form required.
Initial approach: Proposal
Copies of proposal: 7
Deadline(s): Apr. 1 and Nov. 15
Board meeting date(s): Apr. and Dec.
Officers and Directors:* David G. Jeffords III,* Pres.; Edward J. Harrell,* Exec. V.P. and C.F.O.; Fr. John Cuddy; John T. McGoldrick, Jr.; Chris R. Sheridan.
EIN: 581365128
Selected grants: The following grants are a representative sample of this grantmaker's funding activity:
$146,000 to Community Foundation of Central Georgia, Macon, GA, 2011.
$100,000 to Georgia Trust for Historic Preservation, Atlanta, GA, 2011.

2503
J. C. Lewis Foundation, Inc. ✧
P.O. Box 13666
Savannah, GA 31416-0666
Application address: c/o Charles E. Izlar, P.O. Box 60759, Savannah, GA 31420, tel.: (912) 925-0234

Established in 1951 in GA.
Donors: John C. Lewis, Jr.†; Sara McAdoo Coy; Lewis Broadcasting Corp.; J.C. Lewis Motor Co.
Foundation type: Independent foundation.
Financial data (yr. ended 12/31/13): Assets, $17,661,378 (M); expenditures, $825,482; qualifying distributions, $787,806; giving activities include $770,950 for 111 grants (high: $200,000; low: $500).
Purpose and activities: Giving primarily to evangelical Christian agencies and churches; some giving for health and human services.
Fields of interest: Health organizations, association; Human services; Residential/custodial care, hospices; United Ways and Federated Giving Programs; Christian agencies & churches; Protestant agencies & churches; Jewish agencies & synagogues; General charitable giving.
Limitations: Applications accepted. Giving primarily in Savannah, GA.
Application information: Application form required.
Initial approach: Letter
Deadline(s): None
Officers: J.C. Lewis, Jr., Chair. and Pres.; J.C. Lewis III, V.P. and Secy.; Charles E. Izlar, V.P. and Treas.; D. Scott Lewis, V.P.; J. Christian Lewis, V.P.; Nancy V. Lewis, V.P.; S. Wistar Lewis, V.P.; Walter N. Lewis, V.P.
EIN: 586043785
Selected grants: The following grants are a representative sample of this grantmaker's funding activity:
$1,000 to YMCA of Coastal Georgia, Savannah, GA, 2012. For Financial Support of Charitable Organization.

2504
The LittleJohn Family Foundation ✧
18 W. Harris St.
Savannah, GA 31401

Donor: Angus C. LittleJohn, Jr.
Foundation type: Independent foundation.
Financial data (yr. ended 12/31/13): Assets, $3,564,692 (M); gifts received, $1,251,500; expenditures, $969,316; qualifying distributions, $948,000; giving activities include $948,000 for 10 grants (high: $550,000; low: $2,500).
Purpose and activities: Giving primarily for education.
Fields of interest: Elementary/secondary education; Higher education.
Limitations: Applications not accepted. Giving primarily in CT and TN. No grants to individuals.
Application information: Contributes only to pre-selected organizations.
Officer: Angus C. LittleJohn, Pres.
EIN: 133948281

2505
Lockwood Partners Foundation, Inc. ✧
(formerly Amos-Cheves Foundation, Inc.)
6867 Mountainbrook Dr., Ste. 107
Columbus, GA 31904-3379

Established in 2002 in GA.
Donors: Olivia D. Amos; Bettye A. Cheves; Cecil M. Cheves; Elizabeth Cheves Meeks; Olivia D. Amos Charitable Lead Trust.
Foundation type: Independent foundation.
Financial data (yr. ended 12/31/13): Assets, $21,994,958 (M); gifts received, $580,280; expenditures, $1,759,768; qualifying distributions, $1,757,509; giving activities include $1,713,832 for 79 grants (high: $750,000; low: $100), and $37,400 for 27 grants to individuals (high: $4,380; low: $500).
Purpose and activities: Giving primarily for Christian-based education, youth programs, and human services.
Fields of interest: Higher education; Youth development; Human services; YM/YWCAs & YM/YWHAs; Children/youth, services; International relief; Christian agencies & churches; Economically disadvantaged.
Type of support: Building/renovation; Equipment; Program development; Scholarship funds; Grants to individuals; Scholarships—to individuals.
Limitations: Applications not accepted. Giving primarily in GA; some giving also in AL, SC, and TN.
Application information: Unsolicited requests for funds not accepted.
Officers: Cecil M. Cheves, Chair.; Bettye A. Cheves, Pres. and Secy.-Treas.
Board Members: Olivia C. Blanchard; William R. Blanchard; Elizabeth C. Meeks; Ryan L. Meeks; Avery C. Wolff; Luther H. Wolff III.
EIN: 582634947

2506
Charles Loridans Foundation, Inc. ✧ ☆
c/o Margaret W. Scott, Alston & Bird
1 Atlantic Ctr., 1201 W. Peachtree St., Ste. 4200
Atlanta, GA 30309-3424

Incorporated in 1952 in GA.
Donors: Charles Loridans†; A.T. Arnold.
Foundation type: Independent foundation.
Financial data (yr. ended 12/31/13): Assets, $9,157,050 (M); expenditures, $526,394; qualifying distributions, $466,459; giving activities include $451,848 for 26 grants (high: $100,000; low: $2,500).
Purpose and activities: Support for local educational institutions lacking access to general sources of support. The foundation also funds small to medium-size arts and cultural institutions in the metropolitan Atlanta, GA, area.
Fields of interest: Arts; Education; Human services.
Type of support: Building/renovation; Equipment; Land acquisition; Endowments; Emergency funds; Professorships; Seed money; Scholarship funds; Matching/challenge support.
Limitations: Applications not accepted. Giving primarily in GA, with strong emphasis on the metropolitan Atlanta area. No grants for operating budgets, continuing support, annual campaigns, deficit financing, research, publications, or conferences; no loans.
Application information: Unsolicited requests for funds not accepted.
Board meeting date(s): June and Dec.
Officers: Robert G. Edge, Esq., Chair.; Margaret W. Scott, Secy.-Treas.
Trustees: B. Harvey Hill, Jr.; Ben F. Johnson III; Della A. Wells; Benjamin T. White; R. Mark Williamson.
EIN: 580871627

2507
The Loudermilk Family Christian Foundation Inc. ✧
1186 Mayo Rd.
Ellerslie, GA 31807-5442 (706) 582-2346
Contact: Joey M. Loudermilk, Pres. and Treas.

Established in 1999 in GA.
Donor: Joey M. Loudermilk.
Foundation type: Independent foundation.
Financial data (yr. ended 12/31/13): Assets, $7,094,038 (M); gifts received, $435,751; expenditures, $775,935; qualifying distributions, $775,093; giving activities include $774,250 for 24 grants (high: $700,000; low: $100).
Fields of interest: Education; Human services; Children/youth, services; Christian agencies & churches; Protestant agencies & churches.
Limitations: Applications accepted. Giving primarily in GA. No grants to individuals.
Application information: Application form not required.
Initial approach: Proposal
Deadline(s): None
Officers: Joey M. Loudermilk, Pres. and Treas.; Ramona L. Loudermilk, V.P. and Secy.
Trustees: J. Matthew Loudermilk; Jenny M. Loudermilk; Justin M. Loudermilk.
EIN: 582510681

2508
Gay and Erskine Love Foundation, Inc. ✧
2800 Overlook Pkwy., NE
Atlanta, GA 30339-6240 (404) 691-5830
Contact: Gay M. Love, Chair.
E-mail: Foundation@Printpack.com; Application address: P.O. Box 723608, Atlanta, GA 31139; Main URL: http://www.printpack.com/Who-We-Are/Community/The-Gay-and-Erskine-Love-Foundation.aspx

Established in 1976 in GA.
Donors: Printpack Inc.; Love Family Charitable Lead Trust.
Foundation type: Company-sponsored foundation.
Financial data (yr. ended 12/31/12): Assets, $4,850,572 (M); gifts received, $862,819; expenditures, $3,881,049; qualifying distributions, $3,944,687; giving activities include $3,844,687 for 77 grants (high: $1,210,400; low: $250).
Purpose and activities: The foundation supports organizations involved with arts and culture, health, heart disease, youth development, human services, community development, civic affairs, and religion. Special emphasis is directed toward education.
Fields of interest: Performing arts; Arts; Elementary/secondary education; Higher education; Theological school/education; Education; Health care; Heart & circulatory diseases; Boy scouts; Youth development; Children, services; Human services; Community development, service clubs; Community/economic development; United Ways and Federated Giving Programs; Public affairs; Christian agencies & churches; Religion.
Type of support: General/operating support; Program development; Scholarship funds.
Limitations: Applications accepted. Giving primarily in areas of company operations, with emphasis on Atlanta, GA. No grants to individuals.
Publications: Application guidelines.
Application information: Application form not required.
Initial approach: Mail or e-mail proposal to foundation
Deadline(s): None
Board meeting date(s): Quarterly
Officers: Gay M. Love, Chair.; Dennis M. Love, Pres.; Dellmer B. Seitter III, Secy.
EIN: 510198585
Selected grants: The following grants are a representative sample of this grantmaker's funding activity:
$265,000 to American Heart Association, Dallas, TX, 2011.
$1,000 to Cystic Fibrosis Foundation, Bethesda, MD, 2011.

2509
The Thomas H. and Jarman F. Lowder Foundation ✧
c/o Pathstone Family Office
P.O. Box 52047
Atlanta, GA 30355-0047

Established in 1995 in AL.
Donors: Thomas H. Lowder; Jarman F. Lowder; Catherine Lowder†; Charlotte Lowder.
Foundation type: Independent foundation.
Financial data (yr. ended 12/31/13): Assets, $22,811,411 (M); expenditures, $1,574,279; qualifying distributions, $1,287,971; giving activities include $1,287,971 for 11 grants (high: $500,000; low: $4,000).
Purpose and activities: Giving primarily for education, health organizations, social services, federated giving programs, and Roman Catholic organizations and churches.
Fields of interest: Education; Health organizations; Human services; United Ways and Federated Giving Programs; Catholic agencies & churches.
Limitations: Applications not accepted. Giving primarily in Birmingham, AL. No grants to individuals.
Application information: Contributes only to pre-selected organizations.

Officers: Thomas H. Lowder, Pres. and Treas.; Susan C. Carrington, V.P. and Secy.; Heather Anne Lowder, V.P.; James K. Lowder, V.P.
EIN: 631139498
Selected grants: The following grants are a representative sample of this grantmaker's funding activity:
$10,000 to John Carroll Catholic High School, Birmingham, AL, 2012. For Forevermore Campaign.
$2,500 to Appalachia Service Project, Johnson City, TN, 2012. To fund general program expenditures.
$100 to Auburn University Foundation, Auburn, AL, 2012. For School of Nursing Jarman Lowder Endowed Scholarship Award.

2510
Ma-Ran Foundation ✧
(formerly The Peggy and Randall Rollins Foundation)
c/o RFA Mgmt. Co., LLC
1908 Cliff Valley Way
Atlanta, GA 30329-2472

Established in 1991 in GA.
Donor: R. Randall Rollins.
Foundation type: Independent foundation.
Financial data (yr. ended 12/31/12): Assets, $74,703,924 (M); gifts received, $7,029,544; expenditures, $3,141,618; qualifying distributions, $3,019,999; giving activities include $3,019,999 for 15 grants (high: $1,885,023; low: $5,000).
Fields of interest: Education; Health organizations, association; Human services; Foundations (community); Protestant agencies & churches.
Limitations: Applications not accepted. Giving primarily in DE and Atlanta, GA. No grants to individuals.
Application information: Contributes only to pre-selected organizations.
Trustees: Gary W. Rollins; Margaret H. Rollins; R. Randall Rollins.
EIN: 586263945

2511
The Marcus Foundation, Inc. ✧
1266 W. Paces Ferry Rd., No. 615
Atlanta, GA 30327-2306
Contact: Jay Kaiman, Exec. Dir.
Bernie and Billi Marcus's Giving Pledge Profile: http://glasspockets.org/philanthropy-in-focus/eye-on-the-giving-pledge/profiles/marcus
GiveSmart: http://www.givesmart.org/Stories/Donors/Bernie-Marcus

Established in 1989 in GA.
Donor: Bernard Marcus.
Foundation type: Independent foundation.
Financial data (yr. ended 12/31/12): Assets, $105,307,446 (M); gifts received, $98,418; expenditures, $46,246,211; qualifying distributions, $45,441,488; giving activities include $40,881,572 for 200 grants (high: $4,910,105; low: $500).
Purpose and activities: Support primarily for human services, mental health, Jewish federated giving programs, education, and public affairs.
Fields of interest: Education; Health care; Mental health, treatment; Jewish agencies & synagogues.
Type of support: Program-related investments/loans.
Limitations: Applications not accepted. Giving primarily in Atlanta, GA. No grants to individuals.
Application information: Contributes only to pre-selected organizations.
Officers and Directors:* Bernard Marcus,* Chair.; Michael Leven,* Vice-Chair.; Frederick Slagle, Secy.-Treas.; Douglas D. Napoli, C.F.O.; Jay Kaiman, Exec. Dir.; Lisa Brill; Dennis Cooper; James Grien; Doug Hertz; Jeffrey Koplan; Ken Langone; Frederick R. Marcus; Michael Morris; Larry Smith.
Number of staff: 15 full-time professional.
EIN: 581815651
Selected grants: The following grants are a representative sample of this grantmaker's funding activity:
$2,000,000 to Foundation for the Defense of Democracies, Washington, DC, 2012. For consolidated grant.
$1,760,000 to University of Pennsylvania, Philadelphia, PA, 2012. For The Penn Ovarian Cancer Research Immunotherapy Program-Personalized Immunotherapy for Ovarian Cancer.
$1,128,750 to Mitral Foundation, New York, NY, 2012. For Mitral Education Center Program Costs.
$719,139 to City of Hope, Duarte, CA, 2012. For Central Memory T Cell Adoptive Therapy for CD19 Lymphomas and Leukemias.
$641,000 to Institute for Humane Studies, Arlington, VA, 2012. For Liberty Expansion in Academia Project (aka LEAP).
$100,000 to Cleveland Clinic Florida Weston, Weston, FL, 2012. For Department of Colorectal Surgery Research and Education Fund.
$100,000 to Foundation for the Defense of Democracies, Washington, DC, 2012. For Human Rights Project.
$30,000 to Yeshiva High School, Atlanta, GA, 2012. For Tuition Scholarships.

2512
MARTA Charity Club ✧
2424 Piedmont Rd. N.E.
Atlanta, GA 30324-3311

Established in GA.
Foundation type: Independent foundation.
Financial data (yr. ended 12/31/13): Assets, $333,940 (M); gifts received, $642,844; expenditures, $683,721; qualifying distributions, $586,980; giving activities include $586,980 for grants.
Fields of interest: United Ways and Federated Giving Programs.
Limitations: Applications not accepted. Giving primarily in the greater metropolitan Atlanta, GA, area. No grants to individuals.
Application information: Unsolicited requests for funds not accepted.
Officers: Warren McMichael, C.E.O.; Phyllis Spencer, C.F.O. and Treas.; Tia DeLoach, Secy.
EIN: 581576346

2513
The Carlos and Marguerite Mason Fund ✧
c/o Wells Fargo Bank, N.A.
3280 Peachtree Rd. N.E., MAC G0141-041
Atlanta, GA 30305-2430
Contact: Joyce Yamaato, V.P. and Sr. Trust and Fiduciary Specialist in Philanthropic Svcs.; Lydia Whitman
Main URL: https://www.wellsfargo.com/privatefoundationgrants/mason

Established in 1991 in GA.
Donor: Marguerite F. Mason‡.
Foundation type: Independent foundation.
Financial data (yr. ended 12/31/12): Assets, $92,551,805 (M); expenditures, $4,885,894; qualifying distributions, $4,257,830; giving activities include $4,056,963 for 8 grants (high: $2,068,000; low: $25,000).
Purpose and activities: Support only for Georgia organizations involved with organ transplantation and related research.
Fields of interest: Health care, organ/tissue banks; Organ research.
Type of support: Equipment; Program development; Professorships; Research.
Limitations: Applications accepted. Giving limited to GA. No support for indirect or overhead expenses for projects at colleges, universities, governmental units, or other established organizations. No grants to individuals, or for general goodwill advertising, or grants that would replace existing sources of funding.
Publications: Application guidelines.
Application information: Application form not required.
Initial approach: Proposal
Copies of proposal: 3
Deadline(s): June 1
Board meeting date(s): Sept.
Final notification: Sept. 30
Officer and Advisory Committee:* George W.P. Atkins,* Chair.; Carol Hoffman; John Libby; Alice Sheets; Joyce Yamaato.
Trustee: Wells Fargo Bank, N.A.
EIN: 581996431

2514
Masters Tournament Foundation Inc. ✧
P.O. Box 2444
Augusta, GA 30903-2444

Established in GA.
Donors: William Patrick Battle; Edward D. Herlihy; James H. Armstrong, Jr.; Robert L. Johnston; James E. Rohr; Fred S. Ridley; Timothy P. Neher; Stanley F. Druckenmiller; W.B. Harrison, Jr.; Anne S. Harrison; Jefferson Knox; Charles Knox; Lee J. Styslinger III; Kelly Styslinger; Charles William Griffin; Lynn E. Griffin; George Davis; Kelly Davis; Dr. W. Howard Hudson; Mrs. Howard Hudson; Clayton P. Boardman III; M. James Gorrie; Claude B. Nielsen; Charles G. Caye, Jr.; Michael D. Thompson; David M. Ratcliffe; James Dixon Robinson III; James D. Robinson IV; Katie Jacobs Robinson; Samuel J. Palmisano; Gaier N. Palmisano; Thomas R. Wall IV; Thomas M. Blanchard, Jr.; Lynda P. Blanchard; Herbert Allen; J. Haley Roberts, Jr.; Paul M. Hazen; Cassandra Hazen; Robert Chapman; Nick Evans; Grey B. Murray; Barry L. Storey; Craig L. Heatley; Tom Nelson; Thomas M. Ryan; James E. Reinhart; Ronald Cross; Dessey L. Kuhlke; Beard Payne Family Foundation; The Aileen K. and Brian L. Roberts Foundation; John W. Harris Family Foundation; Cypress Foundation, Inc.; David and Wendy Novak Foundation; The Davis Family Foundation, Inc.; Leslie C. Quick, Jr. and Regina A. Quick Charitable Trust Foundation; Augusta National Inc.; Morris Communications Company, LLC; Bradford M. Freeman Foundation; Chattooga Partners Fund; Roberts Foundation; Bell Family Foundation; Jim &

Karen Hull Fund; William D. McKnight Stock Fund; J. Smith Lanier & Co., Inc.; Toby S. Wilt Family Foundation; The Tripp and Blair Rackley Family Foundation; Thomas J. and Sandra L. Usher Charitable Foundation; The Charles and Ann Johnson Foundation.
Foundation type: Independent foundation.
Financial data (yr. ended 12/31/12): Assets, $8,014,288 (M); gifts received, $4,268,557; expenditures, $1,785,470; qualifying distributions, $1,718,000; giving activities include $1,718,000 for grants.
Fields of interest: Athletics/sports, golf.
Limitations: Applications not accepted. Giving primarily in FL and GA.
Application information: Contributes only to pre-selected organizations.
Officers: William Porter Payne, Chair.; Hugh L. McColl, Jr., C.E.O. and Pres.; Robert L. Johnston, Secy.-Treas.
Directors: James H. Armstrong, Jr.; Joe T. Ford; Craig Heatley; Edward D. Herlihy; Claude B. Nielsen; Fred S. Ridley; Brian L. Roberts.
EIN: 274452110

2515
James T. Jr. & Carolyn T. McAfee Foundation ✧
6501 Peake Rd., Bldg. 800
Macon, GA 31210-8050

Established in 1988 in GA.
Donors: James T. McAfee, Jr.; Raymond C. Townsend; Carolyn T. McAfee.
Foundation type: Independent foundation.
Financial data (yr. ended 12/31/13): Assets, $8,837,123 (M); gifts received, $572,000; expenditures, $979,167; qualifying distributions, $925,026; giving activities include $885,000 for 3 grants (high: $500,000; low: $25,000).
Fields of interest: Higher education; Christian agencies & churches.
Limitations: Applications not accepted. Giving primarily in GA. No grants to individuals.
Application information: Contributes only to pre-selected organizations.
Trustee: Carolyn T. McAfee.
Advisory Committee: James T. McAfee III.
EIN: 586219512
Selected grants: The following grants are a representative sample of this grantmaker's funding activity:
$500,000 to Mercer University, Macon, GA, 2012. For School of Music.
$360,000 to Celebrating Grace, Macon, GA, 2012. For exempt function.

2516
McKenna Long & Aldridge Foundation, Inc. ✧
303 Peachtree St., Ste. 5300
Atlanta, GA 30308-3265

Established in 2006 in GA.
Donors: McKenna, Long and Aldridge, LLP; Howard Dean.
Foundation type: Independent foundation.
Financial data (yr. ended 12/31/13): Assets, $4,522 (M); gifts received, $572,476; expenditures, $707,764; qualifying distributions, $688,622; giving activities include $688,622 for 106 grants (high: $94,000; low: $90).
Fields of interest: Health organizations; Legal services; Human services.
Limitations: Applications not accepted. Giving primarily in Washington, DC, and Atlanta, GA; some funding also in CA.
Application information: Unsolicited requests for funds not accepted.
Officers: Clay C. Long, Chair.; Jeffrey K. Haidet, C.E.O.; Megan McCamey, Secy.; Roger Rushing, Treas.
Board Members: John C. Callan, Jr.; Christopher F. Graham; Maryscott Greenwood; Christian D. Humphreys; Joann G. Jones; Kurt L. Kicklighter; Mark J. Meagher; Susan A. Mitchell.
EIN: 208042671
Selected grants: The following grants are a representative sample of this grantmaker's funding activity:
$10,000 to Make-A-Wish Foundation of San Diego, San Diego, CA, 2012. For general purpose of the charity.
$500 to Georgia Justice Project, Atlanta, GA, 2012. For general purposes of the charity.

2517
Mohawk Carpet Foundation, Inc. ✧
1975 W. Oak Cir.
Marietta, GA 30062 (706) 278-8000
Contact: Robert Webb, C.E.O.
Main URL: http://mohawkind.com/pdf/MohawkCarpetFoundationTools.pdf

Established in 1991 in GA.
Donor: Mohawk Industries, Inc.
Foundation type: Company-sponsored foundation.
Financial data (yr. ended 12/31/13): Assets, $313,286 (M); gifts received, $900,000; expenditures, $1,054,259; qualifying distributions, $1,049,790; giving activities include $1,049,790 for 103 grants (high: $130,000; low: $250).
Purpose and activities: The foundation improves the quality of life for Mohawk employees and their families through partnerships with nonprofit service providers.
Fields of interest: Arts; Higher education; Health care; Youth development; Community/economic development.
Type of support: General/operating support; Annual campaigns; Building/renovation; Emergency funds; Employee matching gifts; Matching/challenge support.
Limitations: Applications accepted. Giving primarily in AL, GA, NC, SC, and VA in communities where the company operates manufacturing facilities. No support for houses of worship, individual schools or political organizations. No grants, loans, or scholarships to individuals, or for professorships, fellowships, internship funds, or land acquisition.
Application information: Application form required.
Initial approach: Letter
Copies of proposal: 1
Deadline(s): None
Officers: Robert Webb, C.E.O.; Frank Boykin, C.F.O.; Barbara Goetz, Secy.
EIN: 581902607
Selected grants: The following grants are a representative sample of this grantmaker's funding activity:
$25,000 to Creative Arts Guild, Dalton, GA, 2012. For cultural arts.
$25,000 to Family Support Council, Dalton, GA, 2012. For family advocacy.
$3,000 to Caregivers of Rockingham County, Reidsville, NC, 2012. For Services for older adults and persons with disabilities.
$2,500 to Rockbridge Area Hospice, Lexington, VA, 2012. For hospice.
$2,000 to Boy Scouts of America, Southern District Stonewall Jackson Area, Waynesboro, VA, 2012. For youth development.
$1,500 to Boy Scouts of America, Cape Fear Council, Wilmington, NC, 2012. For youth development.
$1,000 to Boy Scouts of America, East Carolina Council, Kinston, NC, 2012. For youth development.
$250 to Emory University, Goizueta Business School, Atlanta, GA, 2012. For educational.

2518
Kenneth H. Montgomery Foundation, Inc. ✧
2340 Perimeter Park Dr., No. 100
Atlanta, GA 30341-1318

Established in 1990 in GA.
Foundation type: Independent foundation.
Financial data (yr. ended 10/31/13): Assets, $11,352,482 (M); expenditures, $833,325; qualifying distributions, $445,960; giving activities include $445,960 for 45 grants (high: $36,700; low: $750).
Fields of interest: Secondary school/education; Higher education; Protestant agencies & churches.
Limitations: Applications not accepted. Giving in the U.S., with some emphasis on AL, GA, MA, MO, NE, OH, OK, and TX. No grants to individuals.
Application information: Contributes only to pre-selected organizations.
Officers: L.J. Montgomery, C.E.O.; L.J. Montgomery III, Pres.; Mary Montgomery, Treas.
Directors: Beverly Edmundson Bennett; Elizabeth Montgomery Scheine.
EIN: 581928906
Selected grants: The following grants are a representative sample of this grantmaker's funding activity:
$31,500 to Georgia Tech Foundation, Atlanta, GA, 2011.
$20,000 to Literacy Volunteers of Troup County, LaGrange, GA, 2011.
$20,000 to Montgomery Catholic High School, Montgomery, AL, 2011.
$17,500 to Handley High School, Roanoke, AL, 2011.
$6,000 to University of Georgia, Athens, GA, 2011.
$6,000 to University of Mississippi, University, MS, 2011.
$5,000 to Circle for Children, Atlanta, GA, 2011.
$5,000 to Doniphan High School, Doniphan, MO, 2011.
$5,000 to United Methodist Childrens Home, Decatur, GA, 2011.
$5,000 to Woodward Academy, College Park, GA, 2011.

2519
The Sara Giles Moore Foundation ✧
1355 Peachtree St., Ste. 1560
Atlanta, GA 30309-3275 (404) 249-2800
Contact: Lisa B. Williams, Exec. Dir.

E-mail: lwilliams@thesaragilesmoorefoundation.org; Main URL: http://www.thesaragilesmoorefoundation.org
Grants List: http://thesaragilesmoorefoundation.org/recent-grants/

Established in 1997 in GA.
Donor: Sara Giles Moore†.
Foundation type: Independent foundation.
Financial data (yr. ended 12/31/13): Assets, $39,557,792 (M); expenditures, $2,158,790; qualifying distributions, $1,717,006; giving activities include $1,559,500 for 59 grants (high: $150,000; low: $2,000).
Purpose and activities: Giving to art and cultural institutes.
Fields of interest: Visual arts; Museums; Education, early childhood education.
Type of support: General/operating support; Management development/capacity building; Annual campaigns; Capital campaigns; Building/renovation; Emergency funds; Scholarship funds; Matching/challenge support.
Limitations: Applications accepted. Giving primarily in Atlanta, GA.
Application information: Application form required.
Initial approach: E-mail
Copies of proposal: 1
Board meeting date(s): Oct. and May
Final notification: 3 to 6 months
Officers and Trustees:* Sara A. Hehir,* Chair.; Elizabeth Pritchard, Secy.; Frank Butterfield,* Treas.; Lisa B. Williams, Exec. Dir.; Frank McGaughey; Kathleen Riley.
Number of staff: 1 part-time professional.
EIN: 586343477

2520
James Starr Moore Memorial Foundation ✧
3290 Northside Pkwy., Ste. 390
Atlanta, GA 30327-2273

Incorporated in 1953 in GA.
Donors: Sara Giles Moore†; Starr Moore.
Foundation type: Independent foundation.
Financial data (yr. ended 12/31/13): Assets, $14,585,024 (M); expenditures, $717,156; qualifying distributions, $630,739; giving activities include $608,000 for 56 grants (high: $80,300; low: $1,000).
Fields of interest: Arts; Education; Reproductive health, family planning; Health care; Human services.
Type of support: General/operating support; Annual campaigns; Capital campaigns; Building/renovation; Endowments; Scholarship funds; Matching/challenge support.
Limitations: Applications not accepted. Giving primarily in Atlanta, GA. No grants to individuals.
Application information: Unsolicited requests for funds not accepted.
Officers and Trustees:* Starr Moore,* Chair.; Barbara M. Stewart,* Secy.; Rick Flinn.
EIN: 586033190

2521
Morgens West Foundation ✧
3562 Knollwood Dr.
Atlanta, GA 30305-1022

Established around 1968 in GA.
Donor: Morgens West Charitable Lead Annuity Trust.
Foundation type: Independent foundation.
Financial data (yr. ended 12/31/13): Assets, $15,978,419 (M); gifts received, $350,360; expenditures, $999,392; qualifying distributions, $741,128; giving activities include $706,109 for 56 grants (high: $129,500; low: $500).
Fields of interest: Museums; Arts; Higher education; Education; Environment, natural resources; Environment, land resources; Human services; United Ways and Federated Giving Programs; Protestant agencies & churches.
Limitations: Applications not accepted. Giving primarily in Atlanta, GA. No grants to individuals.
Application information: Contributes only to pre-selected organizations.
Directors: E.H. Morgens; James H. Morgens; S.F. Morgens.
EIN: 316090957

2522
Katherine John Murphy Foundation ✧
c/o SunTrust Bank
P.O. Box 4655, MC GA-ATL-0221
Atlanta, GA 30302-4655
Contact: Emily Butler, Grants Mgr., SunTrust Bank
E-mail: info@murphyfoundation.org; E-mail for questions regarding grantmaking: fdnsvcs.ga@suntrust.com; Main URL: http://www.murphyfoundation.org/

Trust established in 1954 in GA.
Donor: Katherine Murphy Riley†.
Foundation type: Independent foundation.
Financial data (yr. ended 12/31/13): Assets, $17,023,482 (M); expenditures, $948,545; qualifying distributions, $848,923; giving activities include $820,000 for 32 grants (high: $170,000; low: $5,000).
Fields of interest: Arts; Higher education; Environment; Health care; Children/youth, services.
International interests: Latin America.
Limitations: Applications not accepted. Giving primarily in Atlanta, GA. No grants to individuals, or for research, or matching gifts; no loans.
Application information: The foundation has suspended grantmaking for the foreseeable future. Please check foundation web site for updates.
Board meeting date(s): Annually, and as necessary
Officer and Trustees:* Martin Gatins,* Chair.; Dameron Black III; Phillip Gatins.
Number of staff: None.
EIN: 586026045

2523
Stuart & Eulene Murray Foundation ✧
c/o Joel Reed
2800 Century Pkwy., Ste. 900
Atlanta, GA 30345-3140

Established in 1991 in GA.
Donor: Eulene H. Murray†.
Foundation type: Independent foundation.
Financial data (yr. ended 06/30/13): Assets, $47,331,568 (M); expenditures, $2,651,489; qualifying distributions, $2,212,963; giving activities include $2,210,834 for 12 grants (high: $1,000,000; low: $2,000).
Fields of interest: Arts; Education; Human services.
Limitations: Applications not accepted. Giving primarily in GA, with some emphasis on Atlanta. No grants to individuals.
Application information: Contributes only to pre-selected organizations.
Trustees: Joe McDonald, Jr.; Joel Reed; Marilyn Rowland.
EIN: 581936483
Selected grants: The following grants are a representative sample of this grantmaker's funding activity:
$1,000,000 to Murray Arts Center Foundation, Kennesaw, GA, 2011. For building fund.
$510,000 to Buckhead Christian Ministry, Atlanta, GA, 2012.
$250,000 to Frederica Academy, Saint Simons Island, GA, 2012.
$160,000 to Good Samaritan Health Center, Atlanta, GA, 2012.
$50,000 to Reinhardt University, Waleska, GA, 2012.
$10,000 to Lovett School, Atlanta, GA, 2012.

2524
NCR Foundation ✧
3095 Satellite Blvd. Bldg. 800, 3rd Fl.
Duluth, GA 30096-5814
Contact: Yvonne Whitaker

Incorporated in 1953 in OH.
Donor: NCR Corp.
Foundation type: Company-sponsored foundation.
Financial data (yr. ended 12/31/13): Assets, $15,875,842 (M); gifts received, $3,000,000; expenditures, $875,262; qualifying distributions, $724,884; giving activities include $724,884 for 17 grants (high: $200,000; low: $3,300).
Purpose and activities: The foundation supports organizations involved with arts and culture, education, health, human services, and civic affairs.
Fields of interest: Arts; Housing/shelter; Human services.
Limitations: Applications accepted. Giving primarily in areas of company operations, with emphasis on Dayton, OH. No support for religious or political organizations. No grants to individuals, or loans, or for athletic programs.
Application information: Application form required.
Initial approach: Letter
Copies of proposal: 1
Deadline(s): None
Board meeting date(s): July and Dec.
Officer: Bo Sawyer, Treas.
Trustees: Peter Dorsman; Elise Kirban; Andrea Ledford; Bob Fishman.
Number of staff: 1 part-time professional; 1 part-time support.
EIN: 316030860

2525
North Georgia Community Foundation ✧
615F Oak St., Ste. 1300
Gainesville, GA 30501-8562 (770) 535-7880
FAX: (770) 503-0439; E-mail: info@ngcf.org; Additional tel.: (866) 535-7880; Grant application e-mail: grants@ngcf.org; Main URL: http://www.ngcf.org
Facebook: http://www.facebook.com/pages/Gainesville-GA/North-Georgia-Community-Foundation/128405248648

Established in 1985 in GA.
Foundation type: Community foundation.
Financial data (yr. ended 12/31/13): Assets, $48,250,366 (M); gifts received, $5,158,386; expenditures, $6,088,476; giving activities include $5,005,198 for 130+ grants (high: $616,000), and $164,250 for 128 grants to individuals.
Purpose and activities: The foundation supports nonprofit organizations and donors by building, distributing and preserving philanthropic assets to enhance the spirit of community and the quality of life of the region.
Fields of interest: Arts; Education; Environment; Health care; Human services; Economic development; Community/economic development; Philanthropy/voluntarism; Religion.
Type of support: General/operating support; Management development/capacity building; Equipment; Program development; Seed money; Technical assistance; Program evaluation; Matching/challenge support.
Limitations: Applications accepted. Giving limited to the 15-county area of northeast GA for discretionary funding. No grants to individuals (except for scholarships), or for annual fund campaigns.
Publications: Application guidelines; Annual report; Financial statement; Informational brochure; Occasional report.
Application information: Visit foundation Web site for RFP announcements and application guidelines. Application form not required.
Initial approach: Submit application letter (not to exceed two type-written pages)
Copies of proposal: 1
Deadline(s): June 16 for Community Impact grants
Board meeting date(s): 2nd Wed. monthly
Final notification: Late July for Community Impact grants
Trustees: James McCoy,* Chair.
Trustees: Strother Randolph,* Vice-Chair.; James E. Mathis, Jr.,* C.E.O.
Trustees: Julie Ferguson,* Secy.; Henry Ridgon,* Treas.; Loveanne Addison; Richard M. Asbill; Jeff Ash; Kathleen Carter; Jim Coyle; Tim Darrah; Rob Fowler; Chip Frierson; Haines Hill; Ronnie Hopkins; Rusty Hopkins; Mary Helen McGruder; Cara Mitchell; Virgilio Perez Pascoe; Lona Pope; Helen Ray; Lydia Starke; Kevin Tallant; Daren Wayne.
Number of staff: 4 full-time professional.
EIN: 581610318

2526
The Pechter Foundation ✧
1266 Bellaire Ln.
Atlanta, GA 30319-3391

Established in 1993 in NJ and DE.
Donor: Richard S. Pechter.
Foundation type: Independent foundation.
Financial data (yr. ended 12/31/13): Assets, $1,970,033 (M); expenditures, $442,209; qualifying distributions, $434,375; giving activities include $434,375 for 40 grants (high: $194,500; low: $100).
Fields of interest: Arts; Higher education; Education; Health organizations, association; Human services.
Limitations: Applications not accepted. Giving primarily in NJ and NY. No grants to individuals.
Application information: Contributes only to pre-selected organizations.
Officer: Richard S. Pechter, Pres. and Secy.-Treas.
EIN: 133711334

2527
Patricia G. Pelling Foundation Inc. ✧ ☆
2137 McKinley Rd. N.W.
Atlanta, GA 30318-1707

Established in GA.
Donor: Patricia G. Pelling.
Foundation type: Independent foundation.
Financial data (yr. ended 12/31/12): Assets, $3,802,713 (M); gifts received, $1,450; expenditures, $543,462; qualifying distributions, $500,000; giving activities include $500,000 for 1 grant.
Fields of interest: Human services; Children.
Limitations: Applications not accepted. Giving primarily in Baltimore, MD. No grants to individuals.
Application information: Unsolicited requests for funds not accepted.
Officers: Patricia G. Pelling, Pres.; Thomas Pelling, Treas.
Trustee: Katherine Pelling.
EIN: 273800561
Selected grants: The following grants are a representative sample of this grantmaker's funding activity:
$500,000 to Catholic Relief Services, Baltimore, MD, 2012. For Children Behind Project in Kenya.

2528
Pickett & Hatcher Educational Fund, Inc. ✧
6001 River Rd., Ste. 408
Columbus, GA 31904-4558 (800) 864-8308, ext. 100
FAX: (706) 324-6788; E-mail: info@phef.org; Mailing address: P.O. Box 8169, Columbus, GA 31908-8169; tel.: (706) 327-6586; e-mail for Scholarships: info@phef.org; Main URL: http://www.phef.org
Facebook: https://www.facebook.com/phefinc

Incorporated in 1938 in GA.
Donor: Claud A. Hatcher‡.
Foundation type: Independent foundation.
Financial data (yr. ended 09/30/13): Assets, $47,057,882 (M); gifts received, $1,000; expenditures, $4,087,428; qualifying distributions, $3,929,669; giving activities include $3,376,752 for 520 loans to individuals.
Purpose and activities: The fund makes student loans to U.S. citizens who are full-time students (12 hours per term), who are enrolled in classroom instructional credit hours on the campus of a 4-year college or university in the U.S., who are enrolled in a bachelor's degree program with a broad liberal education component, who possess a good credit history (or have no credit), and who have a GPA no less than 2.0 on a 4.0 scale (per term and overall). Entering freshmen must have a minimum composite ACT score of 20 or combined verbal/critical reading and math score of 950 on the SAT. Loans are available to medical health care students studying nursing, physical therapy, etc.
Fields of interest: Economically disadvantaged.
Type of support: Student loans—to individuals.
Limitations: Applications accepted. Giving limited to the U.S. No support for students planning to enter career fields of medicine, law, or the ministry. No grants for any purpose other than educational loans.
Publications: Application guidelines; Informational brochure (including application guidelines).
Application information: Loans cannot be made if applicant will be enrolled in a vocational or technical school/college, a 2-year college, at a branch campus, or an online-program. See foundation web site for current application guidelines, procedures and deadlines. Application form required.
Initial approach: Use online application on foundation web site
Copies of proposal: 1
Deadline(s): Varies based on availability of funds
Board meeting date(s): Feb., May, Aug. and Nov.
Final notification: Usually 1-2 weeks
Officers and Directors:* William B. Hardegree, Jr.,* Chair.; Kenneth R. Owens, Pres.; Margaret G. Zollo,* Secy.; Frank D. Brown, Ph.D.; Frank S. Etheridge III; Donna S. Hand; Anne H. Matthews; Jerry M. Smith.
Number of staff: 1 full-time professional; 3 full-time support; 2 part-time support.
EIN: 580566216

2529
William I. H. and Lula E. Pitts Foundation ✧
c/o SunTrust Bank, Atlanta
P.O. Box 4655, MC 221
Atlanta, GA 30302-4655 (404) 813-2021
Contact: Emily Butler, Grants Mgr., SunTrust Bank
E-mail: fdnsvcs.ga@suntrust.com; Additional tel.: (404) 588-7347; Main URL: http://www.pittsfoundation.org

Trust established in 1941 in GA.
Donors: William I.H. Pitts‡; Margaret A. Pitts.
Foundation type: Independent foundation.
Financial data (yr. ended 12/31/13): Assets, $86,411,305 (M); expenditures, $3,940,639; qualifying distributions, $3,685,697; giving activities include $3,570,872 for 13 grants (high: $1,042,936; low: $5,000).
Purpose and activities: Giving exclusively to organizations affiliated with the United Methodist Church; specific areas of interest include education, children's homes, charitable hospitals, and care of the elderly.
Fields of interest: Higher education; Human services; Residential/custodial care; Aging, centers/services; Protestant agencies & churches; Children; Aging.
Type of support: General/operating support; Continuing support; Building/renovation; Equipment; Conferences/seminars; Professorships; Scholarship funds.
Limitations: Applications accepted. Giving limited to GA. No grants to individuals, or for endowment funds, research, scholarships, fellowships, or matching gifts; no loans.
Publications: Application guidelines.
Application information: Application form required.
Initial approach: Use online grant application form on foundation web site
Copies of proposal: 1
Deadline(s): Mar. 1
Board meeting date(s): Apr.
Officers and Directors:* Bishop L. Bevel Jones III,* Chair.; Allen Mast, Secy.; Columbus Gilmore; Dan McAlexander; Philip Millians; Ralph R. Morrison; Elizabeth C. Ogie; David Seyle; E. Jenner Wood III.
Trustee: SunTrust Bank.
EIN: 586026047

Selected grants: The following grants are a representative sample of this grantmaker's funding activity:
$1,042,936 to Andrew College, Cuthbert, GA, 2012. For William I. H. and Lula E. Pitts Foundation Grant.
$1,042,936 to LaGrange College, LaGrange, GA, 2012. For Margaret Adger Pitts Scholarship Fund.
$250,000 to Wesleyan College, Macon, GA, 2012. For the construction of Pierce Chapel, a new 300-seat facility on the Wesleyan College Campus.
$200,000 to Epworth By The Sea, Saint Simons Island, GA, 2012. To assist in funding programming needs and property improvements as well as help to complete the debt of Epworth's Booth Gate property purchase.
$150,000 to Wesleyan College, Macon, GA, 2012. For Margaret A. Pitts Endowed Scholarship for Methodist Students.
$125,000 to Magnolia Manor, Americus, GA, 2012. For Installation of Smart Chart Documentation.
$125,000 to Reinhardt University, Waleska, GA, 2012. To support its unrestricted annual scholarship fund to support the financial needs of qualifying students.
$99,000 to Methodist Home of the South Georgia Conference, Macon, GA, 2012. For We Are Seeking Support for Project Hope (Healthy Opportunities for People Everyday). Funding Will Support the Overall Operations for Our Various Programs and Services.
$75,000 to Young Harris College, Young Harris, GA, 2012. For Margaret A. Pitts Expendable Scholarships.
$15,000 to Vashti Center for Children and Families, Thomasville, GA, 2012. For Vashti Will Not Turn a Child Away If Treatment Services Are Essential. We Seek Help in Recouping Over $2000 Per Month of Indigent Care.

2530
The Pittulloch Foundation, Inc. ✧
5830 E. Ponce de Leon Ave.
Stone Mountain, GA 30083-1504

Established in 1985 in GA.
Donors: Stone Mountain Industrial Park, Inc.; Pattillo Split Interest Trust; Rockdale Industries, Inc.; Genuine Parts Co.; Peter Winters.
Foundation type: Independent foundation.
Financial data (yr. ended 12/31/13): Assets, $37,154,647 (M); gifts received, $576,000; expenditures, $1,653,660; qualifying distributions, $1,580,502; giving activities include $1,572,500 for 30 grants (high: $500,000; low: $500).
Purpose and activities: Support primarily for mental health services for children and for education.
Fields of interest: Education, early childhood education; Higher education; Education, reading; Mental health, treatment; Human services; Leadership development; Children/youth.
Limitations: Applications not accepted. Giving primarily in GA. No grants to individuals.
Application information: Contributes only to pre-selected organizations.
Officers and Directors:* Lynn L. Pattillo-Cohen, Chair.; Michael G. Kerman, Secy.; Robert C. Goddard; Anita Kern.
EIN: 581651352

2531
Parker Poe Charitable Trust ✧ ☆
P.O. Box 1116
Thomasville, GA 31799-1116

Established in 1991 in GA.
Donor: Parker Poe†.
Foundation type: Independent foundation.
Financial data (yr. ended 03/31/13): Assets, $9,610,498 (M); expenditures, $715,317; qualifying distributions, $540,064; giving activities include $537,904 for 24 grants (high: $125,000; low: $1,500).
Purpose and activities: Giving primarily for the arts, education, health, and social services.
Fields of interest: Arts; Education; Human services.
Limitations: Applications not accepted. Giving primarily in GA; funding also in FL and ME. No grants to individuals.
Application information: Contributes only to pre-selected organizations.
Trustees: M.H. Allen; Nancy Stahl.
EIN: 596968647
Selected grants: The following grants are a representative sample of this grantmaker's funding activity:
$119,000 to Thomasville Cultural Center, Thomasville, GA, 2011.
$100,000 to Thomas University, Thomasville, GA, 2011.
$62,500 to Tall Timbers Research, Tallahassee, FL, 2011.
$25,000 to Bowdoin College, Brunswick, ME, 2011.
$16,667 to Maine Coast Heritage Trust, Topsham, ME, 2011. For general support.
$10,000 to Abraham Baldwin Agricultural College, Tifton, GA, 2011.
$1,500 to Thomasville Antiques Show Foundation, Thomasville, GA, 2011. For general support.
$1,500 to Thomasville Landmarks, Thomasville, GA, 2011. For general support.

2532
John S. and Katherine R. Poindexter Charitable Foundation ✧
c/o Richard R. Lazard
19 Cove Dr.
Savannah, GA 31419-9579

Established in 2007 in GA.
Donor: Katherine Poindexter†.
Foundation type: Independent foundation.
Financial data (yr. ended 12/31/13): Assets, $7,655,456 (M); expenditures, $3,144,427; qualifying distributions, $3,138,340; giving activities include $3,134,000 for 7 grants (high: $1,042,000; low: $8,400).
Fields of interest: Higher education, college; American Red Cross; Salvation Army; Christian agencies & churches.
Limitations: Applications not accepted. Giving primarily in GA, NC and TN.
Application information: Contributes only to pre-selected organizations.
Trustees: Richard R. Lazard; John S. Poindexter III.
EIN: 311608481

2533
James Hyde Porter Testamentary Trust ✧
P.O. Box 4248
Macon, GA 31208-4248
Application address: c/o SunTrust Bank, Middle Georgia, 606 Cherry St., Macon, GA 31201, tel.: (478) 755-5133

Established in 1949 in GA.
Donor: James Hyde Porter†.
Foundation type: Independent foundation.
Financial data (yr. ended 12/31/13): Assets, $10,716,451 (M); expenditures, $612,276; qualifying distributions, $580,233; giving activities include $580,233 for 36 grants (high: $151,800; low: $500).
Purpose and activities: Giving primarily for the arts, education, youth, social services and civic affairs.
Fields of interest: Arts; Higher education; Education; Youth development; Human services; Community/economic development.
Type of support: Building/renovation; Seed money; Matching/challenge support.
Limitations: Applications accepted. Giving strictly limited to Bibb County, GA. No grants to individuals, or for endowment funds, research programs, scholarships, or fellowships; no loans.
Publications: Application guidelines.
Application information: Application form not required.
Initial approach: Completed application form
Deadline(s): Apr. 20
Board meeting date(s): June
Officers: Keith Ellis, Mgr.; Doug Gilbreath, Mgr.; Samual Hart, Sr., Mgr.; Ronnie Johnston, Mgr.; Fleetwood Maddox, Mgr.; Sandy Matson, Mgr.; Kathy Morgan, Mgr.; Dr. Henry Patton, Mgr.; Elizabeth J. Pope, Mgr.; Starr Purdue, Mgr.; Mayor Robert Reichert, Mgr.
Trustee: SunTrust Bank Middle GA, N.A.
EIN: 586034882
Selected grants: The following grants are a representative sample of this grantmaker's funding activity:
$76,800 to Wesleyan College, Macon, GA, 2011. For operation grant.
$40,000 to NewTown Macon, Macon, GA, 2011. For operation grant.
$35,000 to Mercer University, Macon, GA, 2011. For operation grant.
$30,000 to Museum of Arts and Sciences, Macon, GA, 2011. For operation grant.
$25,000 to Macon Volunteer Clinic, Macon, GA, 2011. For operation grant.
$15,000 to Girl Scouts of the U.S.A., Lizella, GA, 2011. For operation grant.
$15,000 to Macon Symphony Orchestra, Macon, GA, 2011. For operation grant.
$15,000 to Rebuilding Macon, Macon, GA, 2011. For operation grant.
$7,500 to Alzheimers Association, Macon, GA, 2011. For operation grant.
$5,912 to Macon Rescue Mission, Macon, GA, 2011. For operation grant.

2534
The Primerica Foundation Inc. ✧
3120 Breckinridge Blvd.
Duluth, GA 30099
E-mail: PRIFoundation@primerica.com; Main URL: http://www.primerica.com/public/foundation/index.html
Grants List: http://www.primerica.com/public/foundation/primerica-foundation-grant-awards.html

Established in GA.
Donor: Primerica Inc.
Foundation type: Company-sponsored foundation.
Financial data (yr. ended 12/31/13): Assets, $709,418 (M); gifts received, $1,025,000; expenditures, $1,019,970; qualifying distributions, $1,017,379; giving activities include $995,000 for 36 grants (high: $100,000; low: $10,000).
Purpose and activities: The foundation supports programs designed to promote self-sufficiency for low- to moderate-income families and individuals.
Fields of interest: Secondary school/education; Education, drop-out prevention; Education; Health care; Employment; Housing/shelter, expense aid; Housing/shelter; Children/youth, services; Family services; Human services, financial counseling; Human services; Economically disadvantaged; Homeless.
Type of support: General/operating support; Management development/capacity building; Program development.
Limitations: Applications not accepted. Giving primarily in GA. No support for religious, political, veteran or fraternal organizations. No grants to individuals, or for advertising, special events, dinners, telethons, benefits, memorials, pass-through funding, or general fundraising activities.
Publications: Grants list.
Application information: The foundation practices an invitation only process of giving.
Officers: Karen Fine Saltiel, Chair. and Pres.; Anne Soutter, Vice-Chair. and V.P.; Margaret Halbert, Secy.; William J. Nemetz, Treas.
EIN: 274689647

2535
Realan Foundation, Inc. ✧
3350 Riverwood Pkwy., Ste. 700
Atlanta, GA 30339-3467

Established in 1985 in GA.
Donors: J. Rex Fuqua; JRF Charitable Lead Unitrust; JRF Charitable Lead Unitrust 99.
Foundation type: Independent foundation.
Financial data (yr. ended 12/31/13): Assets, $13,195,855 (M); gifts received, $266,764; expenditures, $978,073; qualifying distributions, $719,498; giving activities include $688,334 for 57 grants (high: $50,000; low: $1,500).
Purpose and activities: Giving primarily for education, children and youth, and human services.
Fields of interest: Education; Human services; Children/youth, services.
Limitations: Applications not accepted. Giving primarily in Middletown, DE and Atlanta, GA. No grants to individuals.
Application information: Unsolicited requests for funds not accepted.
Officers and Directors:* J. Rex Fuqua,* Pres.; Duvall S. Fuqua,* V.P.; B. Clayton Rolader,* V.P.; James A. Stanley, Secy.; James M. Stevens, Jr., Treas.; Anne Sterchi, Exec. Dir.
EIN: 581648407

2536
The Mabel Dorn Reeder Foundation ✧
P.O. Box 468404
Atlanta, GA 31146-8404 (404) 885-3344

Established in 2007 in GA.
Donor: Mable Dorn Reeder†.
Foundation type: Independent foundation.
Financial data (yr. ended 12/31/13): Assets, $1,481,960 (M); expenditures, $624,767; qualifying distributions, $613,000; giving activities include $613,000 for 11 grants (high: $250,000; low: $3,000).
Fields of interest: Performing arts, orchestras; Arts; Higher education; Medical school/education; Botanical gardens; Zoos/zoological societies; Health care; Christian agencies & churches.
Limitations: Applications accepted. Giving primarily in GA and MO.
Application information: Application form not required.
Initial approach: Letter
Deadline(s): None
Trustees: Brian H. Frank; Mabel L. Purkerson, M.D.
EIN: 586470265
Selected grants: The following grants are a representative sample of this grantmaker's funding activity:
$500,000 to Atlanta Symphony Orchestra, Atlanta, GA, 2012. For general operating support.
$500,000 to Opera Theater of Saint Louis, Saint Louis, MO, 2012. For general operating support.
$500,000 to Zoo Atlanta, Atlanta, GA, 2012. For general operating support.
$400,000 to Missouri History Museum, Saint Louis, MO, 2012. For general operating support.
$250,000 to Animal Protective Association of Missouri, Brentwood, MO, 2012. For general operating support.
$250,000 to Radio Arts Foundation, Saint Louis, Saint Louis, MO, 2012. For general operating support.
$200,000 to Atlanta Botanical Garden, Atlanta, GA, 2012. For general operating support.
$100,000 to Washington University, School of Medicine, Saint Louis, MO, 2012. For general operating support.
$50,000 to Atlanta History Center, Atlanta, GA, 2012. For general operating support.
$50,000 to Marist School, Atlanta, GA, 2012. For general operating support.

2537
The Rich Foundation, Inc. ✧
11 Piedmont Ctr., Ste. 204
3495 Piedmont Rd. N.E.
Atlanta, GA 30305-1738 (404) 312-2619
Contact: Thomas J. Asher, Pres.
E-mail: tasher@richfoundationatlanta.org; Main URL: http://www.richfoundationatlanta.org

Incorporated in 1943 in GA.
Donor: Rich's, Inc.
Foundation type: Independent foundation.
Financial data (yr. ended 01/31/13): Assets, $46,126,709 (M); expenditures, $2,528,778; qualifying distributions, $2,000,411; giving activities include $1,942,301 for 76 grants (high: $150,000; low: $1).
Purpose and activities: Giving to benefit non-profit organizations in the field of arts, civic, education, health, environment and social welfare in the metropolitan Atlanta, Georgia area.
Fields of interest: Performing arts, theater; Arts; Higher education; Environment; Hospitals (general); Health care; Health organizations, association; Medical research; Human services; Children/youth, services; Residential/custodial care, hospices; Homeless, human services; Children/youth; Youth; Aging; Disabilities, people with; Physically disabled; Blind/visually impaired; AIDS, people with; Economically disadvantaged; Homeless.
Type of support: General/operating support; Annual campaigns; Capital campaigns; Building/renovation; Equipment; Endowments; Research; Technical assistance.
Limitations: Applications accepted. Giving limited to the metropolitan Atlanta, GA area. No support for religious, political or fraternal organizations. No grants to individuals, or for matching gifts, conferences and seminars, legislative or lobbying efforts, fundraising luncheons or dinners, sporting events, and accumulated debt; no loans.
Publications: Application guidelines.
Application information: Only 1 request for funding may be submitted in a 12-month period. Only 1 copy of IRS determination letter and audited financial statement is needed. Correspondence by USPS, FedEx or UPS not accepted. See foundation web site for specific application guidelines. Application form required.
Initial approach: 1-page letter of request
Copies of proposal: 5
Deadline(s): Dec. 15, Mar. 15, June 15, and Sept. 15
Board meeting date(s): Feb., May, Aug., and Nov.
Final notification: 2 weeks after quarterly meeting
Officers and Trustees:* Thomas J. Asher,* Pres.; David S. Baker, V.P. and Secy.; Juliet Asher Golden, M.D.; Anthony Montag.
EIN: 586038037
Selected grants: The following grants are a representative sample of this grantmaker's funding activity:
$150,000 to Robert W. Woodruff Arts Center, Atlanta, GA, 2011.
$125,000 to Emory University, Atlanta, GA, 2011.
$100,000 to Central Atlanta Progress, Atlanta, GA, 2011.
$25,000 to All About Developmental Disabilities, Decatur, GA, 2011.
$25,000 to Alliance Theater Company, Atlanta, GA, 2011.
$5,000 to Adaptive Learning Center for Infants and Children, Marietta, GA, 2011.

2538
Richards Family Foundation ✧ ☆
1030 Stevens Creek Rd.
Augusta, GA 30907-3204

Established in 1997 in GA.
Donor: John W. Richards, Jr.
Foundation type: Independent foundation.
Financial data (yr. ended 12/31/13): Assets, $10,535,932 (M); expenditures, $613,409; qualifying distributions, $590,812; giving activities include $585,515 for 21 grants (high: $267,000; low: $100).

Fields of interest: Health organizations; Civil liberties, freedom of religion; Christian agencies & churches.
Limitations: Applications not accepted. Giving primarily in GA and SC. No grants to individuals.
Application information: Contributes only to pre-selected organizations.
Officers: John W. Richards, Jr., Pres.; Nancy Richards, V.P.
Board Member: John W. Richards III.
EIN: 582238827

2539
The Richards Foundation, Inc. ✧ ☆
(also known as Judy Windom)
(formerly Roy Richards, Jr. Foundation for Charitable Giving)
P.O. Box 800
Carrollton, GA 30112-0015 (770) 832-4097
Contact: Roy Richards, Dir.
FAX: (770) 832-5265;
E-mail: Judy_Windom@southwire.com

Established in 1990 in GA.
Donor: Roy Richards, Jr.
Foundation type: Independent foundation.
Financial data (yr. ended 12/31/12): Assets, $7,263,365 (M); gifts received, $1,997,420; expenditures, $1,183,424; qualifying distributions, $1,180,562; giving activities include $1,143,000 for 12 grants (high: $500,000; low: $1,000).
Fields of interest: Education; Environment, natural resources; Environment, land resources; Foundations (community).
Limitations: Applications accepted. Giving primarily in Charleston, SC; funding also in Carroll County, GA, and surrounding counties.
Application information:
Initial approach: Letter
Copies of proposal: 1
Deadline(s): Ongoing
Director: Roy Richards.
EIN: 581933598

2540
The Rockdale Foundation Inc. ✧
(formerly Rockdale Fund for Social Investment, Inc.)
916 Joseph E. Lowery Blvd. N.W., Ste. 4
Atlanta, GA 30318-5280

Established in GA.
Donor: Kathleen M. Barksdale.
Foundation type: Independent foundation.
Financial data (yr. ended 12/31/13): Assets, $5,551,866 (M); expenditures, $660,498; qualifying distributions, $521,263; giving activities include $439,865 for 44 grants (high: $89,590; low: $100).
Fields of interest: Education; Human services; Children, services; International migration/refugee issues; Foundations (community); Economically disadvantaged.
Limitations: Applications not accepted. Giving primarily in Atlanta, GA. No grants to individuals.
Application information: Contributes only to pre-selected organizations.
Officers: Kathleen M. Barksdale, Pres.; Winsome Hawkins, Secy.; Jody Stephenson, C.F.O.
Board Members: Joanna Adams; Beverly Hall.
EIN: 582668065

Selected grants: The following grants are a representative sample of this grantmaker's funding activity:
$105,875 to UNICEF, Atlanta, GA, 2012. To advocate for Children's Rights.
$50,000 to International Rescue Committee, New York, NY, 2012. For opportunities for refugees.
$50,000 to Teach for America, Atlanta, GA, 2012. To eliminate Educational Inequity.
$2,750 to University of Colorado Foundation, Boulder, CO, 2012. For Institute of Higher Education.
$2,500 to Marion Medical Mission, Marion, IL, 2012. For Mission Work in Africa.
$500 to Columbia Theological Seminary, Decatur, GA, 2012. To support Theological Education.
$500 to Paideia School, Atlanta, GA, 2012. For Diversified Education Institution.
$500 to University of Georgia Foundation, Athens, GA, 2012. For Institute of Higher Education.

2541
The Rod and Leslie Aycox Foundation, Inc. ✧
3440 Preston Ridge Rd., Ste. 500
Alpharetta, GA 30005-3823

Established in GA.
Donors: Leslie Aycox; Roderick Aycox.
Foundation type: Independent foundation.
Financial data (yr. ended 12/31/11): Assets, $2,930,445 (M); gifts received, $572,000; expenditures, $855,359; qualifying distributions, $850,363; giving activities include $837,200 for 51 grants (high: $200,000; low: $450), and $13,163 for foundation-administered programs.
Fields of interest: Education; Health care; Protestant agencies & churches.
Limitations: Applications not accepted. Giving in the U.S., with some emphasis on GA, NY, and TX.
Application information: Unsolicited requests for funds not accepted.
Directors: Leslie Aycox; Roderick Aycox; Sarah Johnson.
EIN: 263920026

2542
The Gary W. Rollins Foundation ✧
(formerly The Gary W. and Ruth M. Rollins Foundation)
c/o RFA Mgmt. Co.
1908 Cliff Valley Way
Atlanta, GA 30329-2479

Established in 1991 in GA.
Donor: Gary W. Rollins.
Foundation type: Independent foundation.
Financial data (yr. ended 12/31/13): Assets, $85,334,560 (M); gifts received, $6,960,885; expenditures, $2,361,698; qualifying distributions, $2,264,000; giving activities include $2,264,000 for 25 grants (high: $2,000,000; low: $1,000).
Fields of interest: Museums; Higher education; Education; Community/economic development; Protestant agencies & churches.
Type of support: Annual campaigns.
Limitations: Applications not accepted. Giving primarily in Atlanta, GA. No grants to individuals.
Application information: Contributes only to pre-selected organizations.
Trustees: Amy Rollins Kreisler; Gary W. Rollins; Pamela R. Rollins; R. Randall Rollins; Ruth M. Rollins.
EIN: 586263946
Selected grants: The following grants are a representative sample of this grantmaker's funding activity:
$200,000 to High Museum of Art, Atlanta, GA, 2012. For MOMA Series.
$5,000 to Pace Academy, Atlanta, GA, 2012. For ATM High Campaign.
$2,000 to High Museum of Art, Atlanta, GA, 2012. For Margaret and Terry Stent Lecture Series Endowment.

2543
O. Wayne Rollins Foundation ✧
c/o RFA Mgmt. Co., Inc.
1908 Cliff Valley Way
Atlanta, GA 30329-2479 (404) 888-2472
Contact: Amy Rollins Kreisler, Exec. Dir.; Aliya Carnes, Admin.
FAX: (404) 486-4658; E-mail: akreisler@rfallc.com; Tel. for Aliya Carnes: (404) 486-4658, e-mail: acarnes@rfallc.com

Established in 1967 in GA.
Donors: O. Wayne Rollins†; Grace C. Rollins†.
Foundation type: Independent foundation.
Financial data (yr. ended 12/31/13): Assets, $530,007,004 (M); expenditures, $24,952,360; qualifying distributions, $20,893,596; giving activities include $20,792,811 for 50 grants (high: $6,000,000; low: $500).
Purpose and activities: The mission of the foundation is to improve the physical, mental, and spiritual well being of people, predominantly in the state of Georgia.
Fields of interest: Arts; Elementary school/education; Higher education; Education; Speech/hearing centers; Public health; Health care; Learning disorders; Medical research, institute; Children/youth, services; Community/economic development; Foundations (community); Protestant agencies & churches.
Type of support: Building/renovation; Scholarship funds.
Limitations: Applications not accepted. Giving primarily in GA. No grants to individuals.
Application information: Contributes only to pre-selected organizations.
Board meeting date(s): Jan., Apr., Jul. and Oct.
Officer: Amy Rollins Kreisler, Exec. Dir.
Trustees: Gary W. Rollins; Pam Rollins; R. Randall Rollins; Henry Tippie.
EIN: 586066677
Selected grants: The following grants are a representative sample of this grantmaker's funding activity:
$6,000,000 to Emory University, Rollins School of Public Health, Atlanta, GA, 2012. For Rollins School of Public Health Expansion.
$5,000,000 to Peachtree Road United Methodist Church, Atlanta, GA, 2012. For Building Fund.
$3,000,000 to Emory University, Chandler School of Theology, Atlanta, GA, 2012. For Chandler School of Theology Building Phase I.
$2,195,000 to Horatio Alger Association of Distinguished Americans, Alexandria, VA, 2012. For capital campaign.
$2,000,000 to PATH Foundation, Atlanta, GA, 2012. For park and trail improvement.

$2,000,000 to Young Harris College, Young Harris, GA, 2012. For Campus Computer Center.
$500,000 to Lovett School, Atlanta, GA, 2012. For education.
$500,000 to Westminster Schools, Atlanta, GA, 2012. For Teaching for Tomorrow capital campaign.
$225,000 to Emory University, Atlanta, GA, 2012. For leadership in Rollins School of Public Health.

2544
Rosenberg Family Foundation Inc. ✧
1 National Dr.
Atlanta, GA 30336-1631

Established in 1995 in GA.
Donors: H. Jerome Rosenberg III; Dulcy D. Rosenberg; H. Alan Rosenberg; Michele Rosenberg; Karen Rosenberg; Kenneth Rosenberg; Karen R. Percy; National Distributing Co., Inc.
Foundation type: Independent foundation.
Financial data (yr. ended 12/31/13): Assets, $4,085,618 (M); gifts received, $1,300,000; expenditures, $589,678; qualifying distributions, $574,083; giving activities include $574,083 for 32 grants (high: $179,000; low: $100).
Purpose and activities: Giving primarily for Jewish federated giving programs, organizations, and temples; funding also for education, health associations, and human services.
Fields of interest: Education; Health organizations, association; Human services; Jewish federated giving programs; Jewish agencies & synagogues.
Limitations: Applications not accepted. Giving primarily in Atlanta, GA.
Application information: Contributes only to pre-selected organizations.
Trustees: Dulcy D. Rosenberg; H. Jerome Rosenberg III.
EIN: 582166389

2545
Murray & Sydell Rosenberg Foundation, Inc. ✧
(formerly Murray M. Rosenberg Foundation)
3330 Cumberland Blvd., Ste. 900
Atlanta, GA 30339-5998

Established in 1991 in GA.
Donor: Greystone Funding Corp.
Foundation type: Company-sponsored foundation.
Financial data (yr. ended 06/30/13): Assets, $39,860 (M); gifts received, $4,308,010; expenditures, $4,218,900; qualifying distributions, $4,215,084; giving activities include $4,215,084 for 65 grants (high: $429,632; low: $500).
Purpose and activities: The foundation supports programs designed to help impoverished Jewish families.
Fields of interest: Education; Jewish agencies & synagogues; Economically disadvantaged.
International interests: Israel.
Type of support: General/operating support; Grants to individuals.
Limitations: Applications not accepted. Giving primarily in NJ and NY, and in Israel.
Application information: Contributes only to pre-selected organizations and individuals.
Directors: Lisa Lifshitz; Cheryl Rosenberg; Stephen Rosenberg.
Number of staff: 3 full-time professional.
EIN: 581947342

2546
The Sapelo Foundation, Inc. ✧
(formerly Sapelo Island Research Foundation, Inc.)
4503 New Jesup Hwy.
Brunswick, GA 31520-1798 (912) 265-0520
Contact: Phyllis Bowen, Exec. Dir.
FAX: (912) 265-1888;
E-mail: sapelofoundation@mindspring.com; Main URL: http://www.sapelofoundation.org
Grants List: http://sapelofoundation.org/resources

Incorporated in 1949 in GA.
Donor: Richard J. Reynolds, Jr.†.
Foundation type: Independent foundation.
Financial data (yr. ended 06/30/13): Assets, $34,567,452 (M); expenditures, $1,937,743; qualifying distributions, $1,533,340; giving activities include $891,045 for 61 grants (high: $80,000; low: $344), and $119,750 for grants to individuals.
Purpose and activities: The foundation promotes progressive social change affecting, in particular, vulnerable populations, rural communities and the natural environment. Scholarships also to financially needy residents of McIntosh County, GA, who are graduates of McIntosh County Academy, and who have a 2.0 GPA or better, for attendance at accredited colleges, universities, or technical colleges.
Fields of interest: Higher education; Environment, public policy; Environment, air pollution; Environment, toxics; Environment, water resources; Environment, forests; Animals/wildlife, preservation/protection; Crime/violence prevention, youth; Legal services, public interest law; Civil liberties, due process; Civil/human rights.
Type of support: General/operating support; Continuing support; Annual campaigns; Program development; Matching/challenge support.
Limitations: Applications accepted. Giving limited to rural and statewide GA (with the exception of the Metro Atlanta area). No support for projects focusing on and/or implemented in the Metro Atlanta, GA, area, or for indirect or overhead expenses for projects at colleges, universities, public schools or governmental units. No grants or scholarships to individuals directly, or for capital, emergency, or endowment funds, deficit financing, or publications; no loans.
Publications: Application guidelines; Annual report; Financial statement; Grants list.
Application information: The foundation will not fund 100 percent of any organization or project. Applicants may include only 1-3 pages of news articles, letters of support, or other information. Such information must be formatted on an easy-to-copy 8.5" x 11" page. Attachments in color must be mailed to the Sapelo Foundation (15 copies). See foundation web site for complete and specific application guidelines and procedures, as incomplete proposals are not accepted. Application form required.
Initial approach: For grants use online application system on foundation web site; For scholarships use application form on foundation web site and send via U.S. mail
Deadline(s): Sept 1. for grants and Mar. 1 for both grants and scholarships
Board meeting date(s): May and Nov.
Final notification: Within two weeks following board meeting
Officers and Trustees:* Irene Reynolds Schier,* Pres.; Nicole Bagley,* V.P.; Hon. Nan Grogan Orrock,* Secy.; Bettieanne Hart,* Treas.; Phyllis Bowen, Exec. Dir.; William K. Broker; Henry H. Carey; Philip N. Carey; Jerry Gonzalez; Katharine R. Grant; Michael Grant; Midge Sweet.
Number of staff: 2 full-time professional.
EIN: 580827472

2547
Helen and Harry Saul Foundation, Inc. ✧ ☆
2100 Fiber Park Dr.
Dalton, GA 30720-3739

Established in 1993 in GA.
Donor: Harry I. Saul†.
Foundation type: Independent foundation.
Financial data (yr. ended 12/31/12): Assets, $3,373,668 (M); expenditures, $438,688; qualifying distributions, $436,440; giving activities include $436,440 for grants.
Fields of interest: Arts; Elementary/secondary education; Higher education; Education; United Ways and Federated Giving Programs; Jewish federated giving programs; Jewish agencies & synagogues.
Type of support: General/operating support.
Limitations: Applications not accepted. Giving primarily in GA and TN. No grants to individuals.
Application information: Contributes only to pre-selected organizations.
Trustees: Julian D. Saul; Linda S. Schejola.
EIN: 582063931

2548
The Savannah Community Foundation ✧
(formerly The Savannah Foundation)
7393 Hodgson Memorial Dr., Ste. 204
Savannah, GA 31406-1507 (912) 921-7700
Contact: K. Russell Simpson, Pres.
E-mail: russ@savfoundation.org; Additional e-mails: russ@savfoundation.org and grants@savfoundation.org; Main URL: http://www.savfoundation.org

Established in 1953 in GA; re-incorporated as a community foundation in 1986.
Foundation type: Community foundation.
Financial data (yr. ended 06/30/13): Assets, $19,056,716 (M); gifts received, $3,702,102; expenditures, $3,227,861; giving activities include $2,910,973 for 55+ grants (high: $1,021,600).
Purpose and activities: The foundation supports organizations involved with arts, education, health, human services, and religion.
Fields of interest: Arts; Education; Health care; Health organizations, association; Medical research, institute; Human services; Religion.
Type of support: Scholarships—to individuals; Endowments; Equipment; Emergency funds; Conferences/seminars; Scholarship funds; In-kind gifts.
Limitations: Applications accepted. Giving limited primarily to southeastern GA, but Donor-Advised Funds may support any qualified U.S. charity. No grants to individuals (except for scholarships).
Publications: Application guidelines; Financial statement; Grants list; Informational brochure (including application guidelines).
Application information: Visit foundation web site for application information. Application form required.
Initial approach: E-mail
Deadline(s): None

Board meeting date(s): Feb., May, Aug., and Nov.
Final notification: Varies
Officers and Directors:* Michael Traynor,* Chair.; K. Russell Simpson,* Pres.; John C. Helmken II,* V.P.; Stephen W. Schwarz,* Secy.; Christopher Cay,* Treas.; Michael F. Kemp,* Asst. Treas.; Jennifer Abshire; Dale C. Critz, Jr.; Linda J. Evans; Justin A. Godchaux; James R. Hungerpiller; Russell C. Jacobs III; Michael F. Kemp; Al Kennickell, Jr.; Stephen S. Leonard; Frank S. Macgill; Melanie L. Marks; Michael Traynor.
Number of staff: 1 part-time professional; 1 part-time support.
EIN: 586033468

2549
The Selig Foundation Inc. ✧
1100 Spring St. N.W., Ste. 550
Atlanta, GA 30309-2857 (404) 876-5511
Contact: S. Stephen Selig III, Pres.

Established in 1968.
Donors: Cathy Selig; S. Stephen Selig III; Selig Enterprises Inc.
Foundation type: Independent foundation.
Financial data (yr. ended 12/31/13): Assets, $74,243 (M); gifts received, $730,000; expenditures, $704,925; qualifying distributions, $703,710; giving activities include $703,710 for 61 grants (high: $444,250; low: $25).
Purpose and activities: Giving primarily for Jewish organizations and federated giving programs; funding also for the arts, education and health associations.
Fields of interest: Museums (art); Arts; Higher education; Education; Health organizations, association; Jewish federated giving programs; Jewish agencies & synagogues.
Limitations: Applications accepted. Giving primarily in Atlanta, GA. No grants to individuals.
Application information: Application form required.
Initial approach: Letter
Deadline(s): None
Officers: S. Stephen Selig III, Pres.; Cathy Selig, Treas.
EIN: 586074209

2550
Servant's Heart Foundation, Inc. ✧
(formerly For HIS Adopted Children, Inc.)
3414 Peachtree Rd. N.E., Ste. 1144
Atlanta, GA 30326-1153

Established in 1995 in GA.
Donors: Paul A. Neff; Verne Murray; Kathy Neff; Saffell Family Trust.
Foundation type: Independent foundation.
Financial data (yr. ended 12/31/11): Assets, $8,739,297 (M); gifts received, $15,000; expenditures, $850,895; qualifying distributions, $744,102; giving activities include $629,949 for 26 grants (high: $344,302; low: $75).
Purpose and activities: Giving primarily to Christian churches and ministries.
Fields of interest: Higher education; Education; Human services; Christian agencies & churches.
Limitations: Applications not accepted. Giving primarily in CA; some funding also in GA. No grants to individuals.
Application information: Contributes only to pre-selected organizations.
Officers: Becky Bean, Secy.; Richard Haugen, Treas.
Directors: Kathy A. Neff; Paul A. Neff.
EIN: 582218044

2551
Lewis Hall and Mildred Sasser Singletary Foundation Inc. ✧
126 N. Broad St.
P.O. Box 1095
Thomasville, GA 31799-1095 (229) 226-1011
Contact: Lewis Hall Singletary II, Secy.; Mildred Sasser

Established in 1990.
Donor: Lewis Hall Singletary†.
Foundation type: Independent foundation.
Financial data (yr. ended 12/31/13): Assets, $27,198,327 (M); expenditures, $1,654,519; qualifying distributions, $1,494,345; giving activities include $1,450,000 for 40 grants (high: $123,800; low: $1,500).
Purpose and activities: Giving primarily for kids at risk mainly in the Southeast and primarily in southwest GA.
Fields of interest: Libraries (public); Libraries (special); Environmental education; YM/YWCAs & YM/YWHAs; Children, adoption.
Type of support: Capital campaigns; Seed money; Matching/challenge support.
Limitations: Applications accepted. Giving primarily in the southeastern U.S., with emphasis on Thomas County, GA. No grants to individuals.
Application information: Application form required.
Initial approach: Proposal
Copies of proposal: 1
Deadline(s): Aug. 31
Officers: J. Philip Leabo, Jr., Pres.; Michael Hamil, V.P.; Lewis Hall Singletary II, Secy.; Richard L. Singletary, Jr., Treas.
Directors: Greg Hamil; Jeanne S. Hamil; J. Philip Leabo; Karen S. Leabo; Lisa Leabo; Julia Singletary; Karen L. Singletary; Rebecca Singletary; Richard L. Singletary; Timothy Singletary.
Number of staff: 1 part-time professional.
EIN: 581906094

2552
Snell Family Foundation, Inc. ✧
1785 Oak Rd.
Snellville, GA 30078-2233

Established in GA.
Donor: E.R. Snell Contractor, Inc.
Foundation type: Independent foundation.
Financial data (yr. ended 12/31/13): Assets, $4,318,171 (M); expenditures, $684,816; qualifying distributions, $678,906; giving activities include $677,500 for 71 grants (high: $100,000; low: $350).
Fields of interest: Education; Human services; Religion.
Limitations: Applications not accepted.
Application information: Unsolicited requests for funds not accepted.
Officers: Robin J. Snell, Pres.; David E. Snell, V.P.; Fred B. Snell, Jr., Secy.; Brian T. Snell, Treas.
EIN: 263894877

2553
The Kerri and Jeffrey Snow Family Private Foundation, Inc. ✧ ☆
1118 Houston Mill Rd.
Atlanta, GA 30329-3830

Established in GA.
Donors: Sylvia Snow; Jeffrey Snow; Kerri Snow.
Foundation type: Independent foundation.
Financial data (yr. ended 12/31/13): Assets, $2,534,309 (M); gifts received, $799; expenditures, $1,099,432; qualifying distributions, $1,096,276; giving activities include $1,096,276 for 21 grants (high: $1,000,000; low: $180).
Fields of interest: Education; Health care; Food banks; Jewish agencies & synagogues; Religion.
Limitations: Applications not accepted. Giving primarily in Atlanta, GA. No grants to individuals.
Application information: Unsolicited requests for funds not accepted.
Officers: Jeffrey Snow, Pres.; Adam B. Snow, V.P.; Kerri K. Snow, V.P.
Directors: David Price; Eileen Price; Denise Snow.
EIN: 582365263
Selected grants: The following grants are a representative sample of this grantmaker's funding activity:
$17,500 to Greenfield Hebrew Academy, Atlanta, GA, 2011.
$10,000 to Scheie Eye Institute, Philadelphia, PA, 2011.
$10,000 to Torah Day School of Atlanta, Atlanta, GA, 2011.
$7,500 to Batya-Friends of United Hatzalah, New York, NY, 2011.
$7,500 to Vi and Milton Weinstein Hospice, Atlanta, GA, 2011.
$4,000 to Young Israel of Toco Hills, Atlanta, GA, 2011.
$2,500 to Atlanta Community Food Bank, Atlanta, GA, 2011.

2554
Southern Company Charitable Foundation, Inc.
241 Ralph McGill Blvd., N.E., BIN 10131
Atlanta, GA 30308-3374 (404) 506-6784
Contact: Susan M. Carter, Secy.
FAX: (404) 506-1485; Main URL: http://www.southerncompany.com/corporate-responsibility/social-responsibility/communityInvolvement.aspx

Established in 1999 in GA.
Donor: The Southern Co.
Foundation type: Company-sponsored foundation.
Financial data (yr. ended 12/31/13): Assets, $51,933,635 (M); expenditures, $1,572,818; qualifying distributions, $1,301,591; giving activities include $1,301,111 for 17 grants (high: $260,000; low: $5,000).
Purpose and activities: The foundation supports organizations involved with education, the environment, and disaster relief.
Fields of interest: Education; Environment; Disasters, preparedness/services.
Type of support: Annual campaigns; Capital campaigns; Continuing support; Emergency funds; General/operating support; Grants to individuals; Program development.
Limitations: Applications accepted. Giving primarily in AL, FL, GA, and MS. No support for religious

organizations or private or secondary schools or non-public foundations. No grants to individuals (except for employee-related emergency assistance grants).
Application information: Multi-year funding is not automatic. Application form not required.
Initial approach: Proposal
Copies of proposal: 1
Deadline(s): None
Board meeting date(s): May
Final notification: 1 month
Officers and Directors:* Michael K. Anderson,* Pres.; Susan M. Carter, Secy.; Roger S. Steffens, Treas.; Arthur P. Beattie; Mark S. Lantrip; Christopher C. Womack.
EIN: 582514027

2555
The Spring Foundation, Inc. ✧
3060 Peachtree Rd., N.W., Ste. 1415
Atlanta, GA 30305-2485

Donors: Michael Masters; Suzanne Masters.
Foundation type: Independent foundation.
Financial data (yr. ended 12/31/13): Assets, $63,513,760 (M); gifts received, $9,000,000; expenditures, $4,524,026; qualifying distributions, $4,451,093; giving activities include $4,450,000 for 5 grants (high: $3,000,000; low: $100,000).
Fields of interest: Higher education; Community/economic development; Christian agencies & churches.
Limitations: Applications not accepted. Giving primarily in DC, GA, and TN.
Application information: Unsolicited requests for funds not accepted.
Officers: Suzanne Masters, Pres.; Michael Masters, Treas.
EIN: 271498037

2556
The Synovus Foundation ✧
(formerly CB&T Charitable Trust)
P.O. Box 23024
Columbus, GA 31902-3024

Established in 1969.
Donors: Columbus Bank & Trust Co.; Synovus Financial Corp.; Total System Services, Inc.
Foundation type: Company-sponsored foundation.
Financial data (yr. ended 12/31/13): Assets, $380,658 (M); expenditures, $462,875; qualifying distributions, $459,933; giving activities include $459,933 for 33 grants (high: $100,000; low: $600).
Purpose and activities: The foundation supports museums and organizations involved with education, health, human services, and community economic development.
Fields of interest: Arts; Education; Human services.
Type of support: General/operating support; Annual campaigns; Capital campaigns; Building/renovation.
Limitations: Applications not accepted. Giving primarily in the Columbus, GA area. No support for religious organizations. No grants to individuals.
Application information: Unsolicited requests for funds not accepted.
Board meeting date(s): Monthly
Officers and Directors:* Rebecca W. Rumer,* Chair.; William R. Blanchard,* Secy.; Teresa T. Abell, Treas.; R. Dallas Copeland; George G. Flowers; Audrey Hollingsworth.
Number of staff: 7
EIN: 237024198

2557
The Thoresen Foundation ✧
2725 Woodridge Chase
Canton, GA 30114-6861
Contact: Michael W. Thoresen, Tr.

Established in 1952 in IL.
Donors: William E. Thoresen†; Catherine E. Thoresen†.
Foundation type: Independent foundation.
Financial data (yr. ended 12/31/13): Assets, $41,200,011 (M); expenditures, $2,556,076; qualifying distributions, $2,242,773; giving activities include $2,116,000 for 59 grants (high: $200,000; low: $5,000).
Purpose and activities: Giving primarily for higher education, the environment and wildlife conservation, and to health associations.
Fields of interest: Performing arts, theater; Higher education; Education; Environment; Animals/wildlife, preservation/protection; Health organizations, association; Cancer research; Children; Aging; Young adults; Disabilities, people with; Physically disabled; Blind/visually impaired; Deaf/hearing impaired; Women; Military/veterans; Terminal illness, people with; Homeless.
Type of support: Capital campaigns; Building/renovation; Equipment; Land acquisition; Program development; Scholarship funds; Research; Technical assistance; Matching/challenge support.
Limitations: Applications not accepted. Giving on a national basis. No support for political organizations. No grants or scholarships to individuals.
Application information: Contributes only to pre-selected organizations. Unsolicited requests for funds not accepted. Applications are considered only after an invitation from the foundation.
Board meeting date(s): As required
Officers and Trustees:* Michael W. Thoresen,* C.E.O.; Paul V. O'Connell,* C.F.O.
EIN: 366102493

2558
Thunder Bay Foundation, Inc. ✧
171 17th St., Ste. 900
Atlanta, GA 30363-1072

Established in 2007 in GA.
Donors: Peter Kight; Teresa Kight; Thunder Bay Charities Foundation.
Foundation type: Independent foundation.
Financial data (yr. ended 12/31/13): Assets, $21,456,413 (M); expenditures, $906,960; qualifying distributions, $835,500; giving activities include $835,500 for 3 grants (high: $810,000; low: $500).
Fields of interest: Elementary/secondary education; Health care; Boys & girls clubs.
Limitations: Applications not accepted. Giving primarily in CA and GA.
Application information: Unsolicited requests for funds not accepted.
Officers and Director:* Teresa J. Kight,* Pres.; Peter J. Kight, Secy.-Treas.
EIN: 261172656
Selected grants: The following grants are a representative sample of this grantmaker's funding activity:
$501,250 to Healthcare Foundation Northern Sonoma County, Healdsburg, CA, 2011. For general support.
$50,000 to Trout Unlimited, Arlington, VA, 2011. For general support.
$5,500 to Boys and Girls Clubs of Metro Atlanta, Atlanta, GA, 2011. For general support.

2559
Tillotson-Menlo Charitable Foundation ✧
c/o Jeffrey Richardson
P.O. Box 389
Menlo, GA 30731-0389

Established in 2005 in GA.
Donor: Neil Tillotson Trust.
Foundation type: Independent foundation.
Financial data (yr. ended 12/31/13): Assets, $9,718,177 (M); expenditures, $499,595; qualifying distributions, $456,338; giving activities include $456,338 for 51 grants (high: $28,800; low: $500).
Fields of interest: Historic preservation/historical societies; Arts; Education; Recreation, parks/playgrounds; Children/youth, services; Community/economic development, government agencies; Community/economic development.
Type of support: Building/renovation; Equipment.
Limitations: Applications not accepted. Giving primarily in GA. No grants to individuals.
Application information: Contributes only to pre-selected organizations.
Officers: Theresa Canada, Pres.; Arch Farrar, Secy.; Jeffrey Richardson, Treas.
Directors: Bill Alico; Paula Buice; Robert McWhorter; Janet Munchak; Jon Payne; Eddie Robertson.
EIN: 203918578
Selected grants: The following grants are a representative sample of this grantmaker's funding activity:
$5,000 to Gaylesville High School, Gaylesville, AL, 2012. For Gaylesville Enterprise Newspaper.
$5,000 to Mercy Senior Care, Rome, GA, 2012. For Grands Who Care.

2560
Trailsend Foundation ✧
(formerly James M. Cox, Jr. Foundation, Inc.)
c/o Cox Enterprises, Inc.
6205 Peachtree Dunwoody Rd., N.E.
Atlanta, GA 30328-4524
Contact: Nancy K. Rigby, Treas.

Established in 1969 in OH.
Donors: James M. Cox, Jr.†; Cox Enterprises, Inc.
Foundation type: Independent foundation.
Financial data (yr. ended 12/31/12): Assets, $102,228,740 (M); gifts received, $8,187,768; expenditures, $2,767,342; qualifying distributions, $2,262,500; giving activities include $2,262,500 for 35 grants (high: $1,000,000; low: $2,500).
Purpose and activities: Giving primarily for conservation, environment and education.
Fields of interest: Higher education; Education; Environment, natural resources; Environment, beautification programs.
Type of support: Capital campaigns; Building/renovation; Program development.

Limitations: Applications not accepted.
Application information: Unsolicited requests for funds not accepted.
Officers and Trustees:* James C. Kennedy,* Chair.; Blair Parry-Okeden,* Pres.; Jimmy W. Hayes,* V.P.; Shauna Sullivan Muhl, Secy.; Nancy K. Rigby, Treas.
EIN: 237256190

2561
The Tull Charitable Foundation ✧
191 Peachtree St. N.E., Ste. 3950
Atlanta, GA 30303-1740 (404) 659-7079
Contact: Barbara Cleveland, Secy.-Treas and Exec. Dir.
E-mail: bobbi@tullfoundation.org; Main URL: http://www.tullfoundation.org

Trust established in 1952 in GA as The J.M. Tull Foundation; reorganized under current name in 1984 with the Tull Charitable Foundation.
Donors: J.M. Tull‡; J.M. Tull Metal and Supply Co., Inc.
Foundation type: Independent foundation.
Financial data (yr. ended 12/31/13): Assets, $84,576,473 (M); expenditures, $4,624,660; qualifying distributions, $3,634,248; giving activities include $2,870,500 for 60 grants (high: $250,000; low: $1,000), and $268,370 for 145 employee matching gifts.
Purpose and activities: Giving to assist Georgia nonprofit organizations with one-time capital costs associated with the implementation of strategic growth initiatives.
Fields of interest: Museums; Performing arts; Arts; Secondary school/education; Higher education; Education; Environment; Health care; Housing/shelter, development; Youth development; Human services; Children/youth, services; Residential/custodial care; Homeless, human services; Children/youth; Youth; Economically disadvantaged; Homeless.
Type of support: Capital campaigns; Building/renovation.
Limitations: Applications accepted. Giving limited to organizations based in and serving GA. No support for government agencies, churches, projects of religious organizations that primarily benefit their own adherents, PTAs or Booster Clubs. No grants to individuals or for conferences or seminars; scientific research, purchase of tickets to benefit events; sponsorship of performances; program or project support; operating support; to retire accumulated debt; or for scholarships (except for scholarship endowments); no loans.
Publications: Informational brochure (including application guidelines).
Application information: The foundation does not accept grant proposals via e-mail. Application form not required.
Initial approach: Letter of intent
Copies of proposal: 1
Deadline(s): None for letters of intent; see foundation web site for current proposal deadlines
Board meeting date(s): Jan., Apr., July, and Oct.
Final notification: 1 week after board meeting, in writing
Officers and Trustees:* Larry L. Prince,* Chair.; Warren Y. Jobe,* Vice-Chair.; Barbara Cleveland, Secy.-Treas. and Exec. Dir.; Clair (Yum) Arnold; Sylvia Dick; Lillian C. Giornelli; Jack Guynn; B. Harvey Hill, Jr.
Agent: SunTrust Bank.
Number of staff: 1 full-time professional; 1 full-time support.
EIN: 581687028
Selected grants: The following grants are a representative sample of this grantmaker's funding activity:
$500,000 to Agnes Scott College, Decatur, GA, 2012. For renovation of Campbell Hall, payable over 3.00 years.
$400,000 to Oglethorpe University, Atlanta, GA, 2012. For construction of new Student Center.
$250,000 to Atlanta History Center, Atlanta, GA, 2012. For facility and exhibition renovations and endowment, The Campaign for The Atlanta History Center, payable over 2.00 years.
$250,000 to East Lake Foundation, Atlanta, GA, 2013. For capital campaign for Drew Charter School.
$150,000 to Habitat for Humanity in Atlanta, Atlanta, GA, 2013. To purchase and renovate property for administrative offices.
$150,000 to University of Georgia Foundation, Athens, GA, 2013. For renovations to Carnegie Library.
$150,000 to YMCA of Metropolitan Atlanta, Atlanta, GA, 2013. For Outdoor Vision Capital Campaign for camp improvements and expansion.
$125,000 to Center for Puppetry Arts, Atlanta, GA, 2012. For facility expansion and renovation.
$125,000 to Marcus Institute for Development and Learning, Marcus Autism Center, Atlanta, GA, 2012. For technology upgrade.
$125,000 to Wellspring Living, Tyrone, GA, 2013. For White Umbrella Capital Campaign for purchase and renovation of new facility for girls and upgrades to women's facility.
$100,000 to Atlanta Botanical Garden, Atlanta, GA, 2012. For Smithgall Woodland Garden Master Plan for Gainesville.
$100,000 to Covenant House Georgia, Atlanta, GA, 2013. For building acquisition, renovation and repair.
$100,000 to PATH Foundation, Atlanta, GA, 2012. For Make the Connection capital campaign.
$100,000 to Woodward Academy, College Park, GA, 2012. For construction of humanities building for Upper School (final phase of Campaign Woodward).
$100,000 to Young Harris College, Young Harris, GA, 2012. For construction of Rollins Center.
$75,000 to Junior Achievement of Georgia, Atlanta, GA, 2013. For creation of JA BizTown and JA Finance Park site for financial and economic education programs.
$75,000 to Marist School, Atlanta, GA, 2013. For capital campaign, The Way, The Hope, The Promise which will be used for construction of new academic building.
$50,000 to Chastain Park Conservancy, Atlanta, GA, 2013. To develop natural play area for children.
$1,500 to Midtown Assistance Center, Atlanta, GA, 2013. For end of year contribution.
$1,000 to Jewish Family and Career Services, Atlanta, GA, 2012. For end of year contribution, for Ben Massell Dental Clinic.

2562
The Turner Family Foundation Inc. ✧
384 Westview Dr.
Athens, GA 30606-4636

Established in 1995 in GA.
Donor: Hoyt J. Turner.
Foundation type: Independent foundation.
Financial data (yr. ended 12/31/12): Assets, $14,432,219 (M); gifts received, $208,661; expenditures, $754,511; qualifying distributions, $681,100; giving activities include $681,100 for grants.
Fields of interest: Performing arts, orchestras; Higher education, university; Education; Animal welfare; Medical research, institute; Crime/violence prevention, child abuse; Boys & girls clubs; Boy scouts; Girl scouts; Salvation Army; YM/YWCAs & YM/YWHAs; United Ways and Federated Giving Programs; Religion, association.
Limitations: Applications not accepted. Giving primarily in GA, with some giving in PA. No grants to individuals.
Application information: Contributes only to pre-selected organizations.
Officers: James C. Turner, Pres.; Barbara A. Turner, V.P.; Elbert N. Whitmire III, Secy.; James A. Hickey, Treas.
Trustee: Paul Bowles III.
EIN: 582145915

2563
Turner Foundation, Inc. ✧
c/o Raymond Goodreau
133 Luckie St. N.W., 2nd Fl.
Atlanta, GA 30303-2038
Contact: Michael Finley, Pres.
FAX: (404) 681-0172; Main URL: http://www.turnerfoundation.org
GiveSmart: http://www.givesmart.org/Stories/Donors/Ted-Turner
Ted Turner's Giving Pledge Profile: http://glasspockets.org/philanthropy-in-focus/eye-on-the-giving-pledge/profiles/turner

Established in 1990 in GA.
Donor: R.E. "Ted" Turner III.
Foundation type: Independent foundation.
Financial data (yr. ended 12/31/13): Assets, $12,200,379 (M); gifts received, $12,382,151; expenditures, $12,512,031; qualifying distributions, $12,423,876; giving activities include $10,352,874 for 358 grants (high: $509,249; low: $250).
Purpose and activities: The foundation is committed to preventing damage to the natural systems - water, air, and land - on which all life depends.
Fields of interest: Environment, natural resources; Environment, water resources; Environment, energy; Animals/wildlife, preservation/protection; Animals/wildlife; Population studies; Children/youth; Children; Youth; Young adults; Hispanics/Latinos; Women; Girls; Young adults, female; Young adults, male.
Type of support: General/operating support; Continuing support; Program development; Research; Technical assistance; Matching/challenge support.
Limitations: Applications not accepted. Giving primarily on a regional and national basis; priority consideration to programs in FL, GA, MT, NM, and SC. No grants to individuals, or for buildings, land acquisition, endowments, start-up funds, films, books, magazines, and other specific media projects.
Application information: The foundation has implemented an invitation-only grantmaking process. Letters of inquiry and unsolicited proposals are not accepted.
Board meeting date(s): April, Aug., and Dec.

Officers and Trustees:* R.E. "Ted" Turner III,* Chair.; Michael Finley,* Pres. and Treas.; J. Rutherford Seydel II, Secy.; Jennie Turner Garlington; Laura Lee Turner Seydel; Beau Turner; Rhett Lee Turner; Teddy Turner.
Number of staff: 7 full-time professional.
EIN: 581924590
Selected grants: The following grants are a representative sample of this grantmaker's funding activity:
$509,250 to Turner Endangered Species Fund, Bozeman, MT, 2012.
$300,000 to League of Conservation Voters Education Fund, Washington, DC, 2012.
$265,000 to Upper Chattahoochee Riverkeeper Fund, Atlanta, GA, 2012.
$250,000 to Better World Fund, Washington, DC, 2012.

2564
Turner Global Foundation ✧
133 Luckie St.
Atlanta, GA 30303-2038
Ted Turner's Giving Pledge Profile: http://glasspockets.org/philanthropy-in-focus/eye-on-the-giving-pledge/profiles/turner

Established in 2004 in FL.
Donor: R.E. "Ted" Turner III.
Foundation type: Independent foundation.
Financial data (yr. ended 12/31/13): Assets, $31,801,437 (M); expenditures, $50,030,150; qualifying distributions, $50,000,000; giving activities include $50,000,000 for 1 grant.
Purpose and activities: Support for United Nations Foundation and Better World Fund, Inc.
Fields of interest: Human services.
Limitations: Applications not accepted. Giving limited to Washington, DC. No grants to individuals.
Application information: Contributes only to pre-selected organizations.
Trustee: R.E. "Ted" Turner III.
EIN: 900230253
Selected grants: The following grants are a representative sample of this grantmaker's funding activity:
$43,000,000 to United Nations Foundation, Washington, DC, 2011. For general support.
$7,000,000 to Better World Fund, Washington, DC, 2011. For general support.

2565
U.S. Poultry & Egg/Harold E. Ford Foundation, Inc. ✧
(formerly Southeastern Poultry & Egg/Harold E. Ford Foundation)
1530 Cooledge Rd.
Tucker, GA 30084-7303 (770) 493-9401
Contact: Donald Dalton, Pres.
FAX: (770) 493-9257;
E-mail: bjenkins@poultryegg.org; Main URL: http://www.poultryfoundation.org/

Established in 1994 in GA.
Donors: U.S. Poultry & Egg Association Inc.; CTB, Inc.; Southern Poultry Science Society; Monty Henderson; US Paultry.
Foundation type: Company-sponsored foundation.
Financial data (yr. ended 09/30/13): Assets, $7,231,525 (M); gifts received, $2,178,103; expenditures, $916,362; qualifying distributions, $571,259; giving activities include $571,259 for 31 grants (high: $101,196; low: $1,000).
Purpose and activities: The foundation supports programs and research designed to promote the poultry and egg industry.
Fields of interest: Education; Recreation; Human services.
Type of support: General/operating support; Program development; Research.
Limitations: Applications accepted. Giving primarily in AL, AR, CA, GA, MS, and TX. No grants to individuals.
Publications: Application guidelines.
Application information: Application form required.
Initial approach: Letter
Deadline(s): None
Officer: John Starkey, Pres.
Directors: James Denton; Elton Maddox; Sherman Miller; Mark Waller.
EIN: 582098298
Selected grants: The following grants are a representative sample of this grantmaker's funding activity:
$134,188 to Auburn University, Auburn, AL, 2011.
$132,941 to North Carolina State University, Raleigh, NC, 2011.
$53,432 to Ohio State University, Columbus, OH, 2011.
$29,499 to Texas A & M University, College Station, TX, 2011.
$19,043 to University of Arkansas, Fayetteville, AR, 2011.
$16,334 to University of Georgia, Athens, GA, 2011.
$15,295 to Texas A & M University, College Station, TX, 2011.
$7,000 to Jones County Junior College, Ellisville, MS, 2011.
$6,500 to Modesto Junior College, Modesto, CA, 2011.
$5,422 to Louisiana State University and A & M College, Baton Rouge, LA, 2011.

2566
The UPS Foundation ✧
55 Glenlake Pkwy., N.E.
Atlanta, GA 30328-3474 (404) 828-6374
FAX: (404) 828-7435; Main URL: http://community.ups.com/UPS+Foundation

Incorporated in 1951 in DE.
Donor: United Parcel Service of America, Inc.
Foundation type: Company-sponsored foundation.
Financial data (yr. ended 12/31/13): Assets, $1,058,798 (M); gifts received, $42,895,860; expenditures, $45,327,025; qualifying distributions, $42,910,467; giving activities include $42,895,860 for 1,713 grants (high: $7,840,542; low: $100).
Purpose and activities: The foundation supports programs designed to promote diversity; volunteerism; community safety; and the environment.
Fields of interest: Higher education; Education, reading; Education; Environment, climate change/global warming; Environment, natural resources; Environment, energy; Environment, forests; Environmental education; Environment; Food services; Disasters, preparedness/services; Safety, automotive safety; Safety/disasters; Boys & girls clubs; Youth development, adult & child programs; Girl scouts; American Red Cross; Salvation Army; Children/youth, services; Human services, financial counseling; Human services; International relief; Civil/human rights, equal rights; Civil/human rights; Social entrepreneurship; Microfinance/microlending; Nonprofit management; Community/economic development; Voluntarism promotion; United Ways and Federated Giving Programs; Leadership development; Minorities; Women; Economically disadvantaged.
International interests: Brazil; Canada; China; Mexico; South Africa.
Type of support: Continuing support; Management development/capacity building; Endowments; Program development; Publication; Scholarship funds; Research; Technical assistance; Employee volunteer services; Employee matching gifts; Employee-related scholarships; In-kind gifts.
Limitations: Applications not accepted. Giving on a national basis and in Brazil, Canada, China, England, Mexico, the Philippines, and South Africa; giving also to statewide, regional, national, and international organizations. No support for religious organizations not of direct benefit to the entire community. No grants to individuals (except for employee-related scholarships); generally, no grants for capital campaigns, endowments, or general operating support.
Publications: Annual report; Informational brochure.
Application information: Unsolicited requests for funds not accepted.
Board meeting date(s): Oct. and Nov.
Officers and Trustees:* John McDevitt,* Chair.; Eduardo Martinez,* Pres.; Frank Romeo, V.P.; David P. Abney,* Secy.; Kurt P. Kuehn,* Treas.; Daniel J. Brutto; Alan Gershenhorn; Teri Plummer McClure.
Number of staff: 7 full-time professional; 4 full-time support.
EIN: 136099176
Selected grants: The following grants are a representative sample of this grantmaker's funding activity:
$7,179,208 to United Way Worldwide, Alexandria, VA, 2012.
$1,618,175 to National Merit Scholarship Corporation, Evanston, IL, 2012.
$875,000 to Urban League, National, New York, NY, 2012.
$820,000 to Boys and Girls Clubs of America, Atlanta, GA, 2012.
$650,000 to Nature Conservancy, Arlington, VA, 2012.
$650,000 to United States Fund for UNICEF, New York, NY, 2012. Toward support in 2012 for UNICEF's Emergency Fund ($100,000), Supply Chain Stock Replenishment Enhancement Program and transportation study ($450,000), and toward Dan Brutto's board requirement ($100,000).
$15,000 to Foundation Center, New York, NY, 2012.
$10,000 to Saint Charles Community College, Cottleville, MO, 2012.
$5,000 to YWCA of Greater Miami and Dade County, Miami, FL, 2012.

2567
Stanley D. and Kay B. Walker Foundation ✧
27 City Sq., Ste. 5
P.O. Box 781
Hoschton, GA 30548-2062

Established in 1999 in GA.
Donors: Stanley D. Walker, Jr.; Kay B. Walker.
Foundation type: Independent foundation.

Financial data (yr. ended 12/31/13): Assets, $542,363 (M); expenditures, $457,114; qualifying distributions, $447,998; giving activities include $444,250 for 11 grants (high: $100,000; low: $12,000).
Fields of interest: Christian agencies & churches.
Limitations: Applications not accepted. Giving primarily in FL, GA, and TX. No grants to individuals.
Application information: Contributes only to pre-selected organizations.
Officers: Stanley D. Walker, Jr., Chair.; Kay B. Walker, Vice-Chair.
Trustees: Victor Logan; Ronald D. Morris, Jr.; S. Benton Walker III.
EIN: 582491026

2568
Watkins Christian Foundation, Inc. ✧
1958 Monroe Dr. N.E.
Atlanta, GA 30324-4844

Established in 1983 in GA.
Donors: Bill Watkins†; Watkins Associated Industries, Inc.; Midway Kids Village LLC.
Foundation type: Independent foundation.
Financial data (yr. ended 12/31/13): Assets, $56,395,028 (M); expenditures, $2,805,602; qualifying distributions, $2,510,719; giving activities include $2,510,689 for 46 grants (high: $525,000; low: $5,000).
Purpose and activities: Grants for evangelism, churches, ministries, and a variety of religious organizations, including those providing support for human welfare and feeding the hungry.
Fields of interest: Food services; Human services; Religious federated giving programs; Christian agencies & churches.
Limitations: Applications not accepted. Giving primarily in FL and GA. No grants to individuals.
Application information: Contributes only to pre-selected organizations.
Officers and Trustees:* George C. Watkins,* Chair.; Michael L. Watkins,* Pres.; W. Neal Freeman,* V.P.; Eric S. Wahlen, Secy.-Treas.; John C. Watkins; Kimberly Watkins.
EIN: 581494832

2569
Watson-Brown Foundation, Inc. ✧
310 Tom Watson Way
Thomson, GA 30824-0037 (706) 595-8886
Contact: Tad Brown, Pres.
FAX: (706) 595-3948;
E-mail: tbrown@watson-brown.org; Main URL: http://www.watson-brown.org/
Facebook: http://www.facebook.com/pages/Watson-Brown-Foundation/277102390498?ref=ts
Scholarship contact: Sarah Katherine Drury, Dir., Scholarships & Alumni Rels., tel.: (706) 872-6972, e-mail: skdrury@watson-brown.org

Established in 1970 in GA.
Donor: Walter J. Brown†.
Foundation type: Independent foundation.
Financial data (yr. ended 12/31/12): Assets, $108,975,271 (M); gifts received, $1,692; expenditures, $4,835,605; qualifying distributions, $6,044,739; giving activities include $2,490,198 for 173 grants (high: $252,000; low: $825), and $3,375,351 for foundation-administered programs.
Purpose and activities: The foundation focuses its giving within the Southeast by funding nonprofit organizations and institutions that advance education. Most grants to colleges and universities are to fund programs in the areas of history, literature, law, agricultural education, and historic preservation. The foundation also provides college scholarships of $3,000 and $5,000 for students from communities in and near the Savannah River valley.
Fields of interest: History/archaeology; Literature; Historic preservation/historical societies; Higher education; Law school/education; Agriculture.
Type of support: General/operating support; Capital campaigns; Building/renovation; Program development; Conferences/seminars; Publication; Fellowships; Scholarship funds; Research; Scholarships—to individuals; Matching/challenge support.
Limitations: Applications accepted. Giving limited to the Southeast, primarily in GA and SC. No support for religious programs. No grants for debt reduction, advertising or marketing efforts, or for social events such as sports tournaments or galas.
Publications: Application guidelines; Newsletter.
Application information: Scholarship awards paid directly to the individual recipient's educational institution. See foundation web site for full scholarship application guidelines. The foundation's grant program is currently suspended. Refer to foundation web site for updates. Application form required.
Initial approach: Letter
Copies of proposal: 7
Deadline(s): Feb. 15 for scholarships
Board meeting date(s): Quarterly
Final notification: Within 1 month of Board's 3rd quarter meeting
Officers and Trustees:* Tad Brown,* Pres.; R. Byron Attridge; Wyche Fowler, Jr.; Joab Lesesne; John Woodham.
Number of staff: 4 full-time professional; 9 full-time support; 1 part-time support.
EIN: 237097393

2570
The Joseph and Felicia Weber Family Foundation, Inc. ✧
7000 Peachtree Dunwoody Rd., Bldg. 1
Atlanta, GA 30328-1660

Established in 2003 in GA.
Donor: Joseph F. Weber.
Foundation type: Independent foundation.
Financial data (yr. ended 06/30/13): Assets, $8,755,433 (M); expenditures, $744,524; qualifying distributions, $689,360; giving activities include $688,500 for 27 grants (high: $150,000; low: $1,000).
Fields of interest: Education; Human services; Jewish federated giving programs; Jewish agencies & synagogues.
Limitations: Applications not accepted. Giving primarily in Atlanta, GA. No grants to individuals.
Application information: Contributes only to pre-selected organizations.
Officer and Trustee:* Joseph F. Weber,* Chair.
EIN: 200510704

2571
Joseph B. Whitehead Foundation ✧ ☆
191 Peachtree St., N.E., Ste. 3540
Atlanta, GA 30303-1799 (404) 522-6755
Contact: P. Russell Hardin, Pres.
FAX: (404) 522-7026; E-mail: fdns@woodruff.org; Main URL: http://www.jbwhitehead.org
Grants List: http://jbwhitehead.org/grants-program/previous-grants/

Established in 1937 in GA.
Donor: Joseph B. Whitehead, Jr.†.
Foundation type: Independent foundation.
Financial data (yr. ended 12/31/13): Assets, $1,432,190,285 (M); expenditures, $37,627,104; qualifying distributions, $36,606,202; giving activities include $36,345,000 for 36 grants (high: $21,330,000; low: $50,000).
Purpose and activities: The foundation focuses on the following program areas: human services (particularly for children and youth), elementary and secondary education, health care and education, economic development and civic affairs, and literacy and vocational training; preference is given to one-time capital projects of established private charitable organizations.
Fields of interest: Elementary/secondary education; Child development, education; Education; Environment; Health care; Health organizations, association; Children/youth, services; Child development, services; Aging, centers/services; Economic development; Government/public administration; Aging.
Type of support: Capital campaigns; Building/renovation; Equipment; Land acquisition; Program development; Seed money.
Limitations: Applications accepted. Giving limited to the metropolitan Atlanta, GA area. No grants to individuals, or for endowment funds, research, scholarships, fellowships, or matching gifts; generally, no support for operating expenses; no loans.
Publications: Application guidelines; Grants list; Informational brochure (including application guidelines).
Application information: The foundation generally grants only to existing partners; contact foundation before submitting letters of intent to determine eligibility. Application form not required.
Initial approach: Letter
Copies of proposal: 1
Deadline(s): Feb. 1 and Sept. 1
Board meeting date(s): Apr. and Nov.
Final notification: Within 30 days of trustee meeting
Officers and Trustees:* James B. Williams,* Chair.; James M. Sibley,* Vice-Chair.; P. Russell Hardin,* Pres.; Erik Johnson, Secy.-Treas.; Marti Morton, Cont.; Charles H. McTier.
EIN: 586001954
Selected grants: The following grants are a representative sample of this grantmaker's funding activity:
$13,000,000 to Childrens Healthcare of Atlanta, Atlanta, GA, 2011. For construction of a pediatric research building and support of the Marcus Autism Center's efforts to establish a comprehensive autism center.
$5,000,000 to United Way of Metropolitan Atlanta, Atlanta, GA, 2011. For continued support of Smart Start Georgia.
$3,000,000 to United Way of Metropolitan Atlanta, Atlanta, GA, 2011. For priority projects of the Regional Commission on Homelessness.

$1,450,000 to Georgia Partnership for Excellence in Education, Atlanta, GA, 2011. For continued support of core programs, program support for the Georgia Leadership Institute for School Improvements and support for a plan to grow the Teach for America corps in Atlanta.
$1,200,000 to Communities in Schools of Georgia, Atlanta, GA, 2011. To support of core programs and planning costs associated with expansion of the PLC model.
$1,000,000 to United Way of Metropolitan Atlanta, Atlanta, GA, 2011. For continued support for high quality early childhood education through SmartStart Georgia.
$800,000 to Center for the Visually Impaired, Atlanta, GA, 2011. For establishment of telephone call center to employ CVI clients and create a revenue stream.
$750,000 to Visiting Nurse Health System, Atlanta, GA, 2011. For ten-month pilot of home healthcare program to reduce re-hospitalization of older patients on Medicare and second year of home healthcare partnership with Grady Health System.
$425,000 to Good Samaritan Health Center, Atlanta, GA, 2011. For capital needs, including conversion to electronic medical records system and construction of a teaching kitchen.
$410,000 to Families First, Atlanta, GA, 2011. For implementation of a Placement to Permanency Program model.

2572
Williams Family Foundation of Georgia, Inc. ✧

P.O. Box 1577
Thomasville, GA 31799-1577 (229) 228-1828

Established in 1980 in GA.
Donors: Diane W. Parker; Marguerite N. Williams†; Thomas L. Williams III; Bennie G. Williams†.
Foundation type: Independent foundation.
Financial data (yr. ended 11/30/13): Assets, $62,852,225 (M); expenditures, $3,198,043; qualifying distributions, $2,903,379; giving activities include $2,692,000 for 80 grants (high: $250,000; low: $500).
Purpose and activities: Giving primarily for education and historic preservation.
Fields of interest: Visual arts; Museums; Performing arts; Historic preservation/historical societies; Arts; Secondary school/education; Higher education; Libraries/library science; Education; Environment, natural resources; Environment; Animals/wildlife, preservation/protection; Family services; Community/economic development; Government/public administration; Children/youth; Economically disadvantaged.
Type of support: General/operating support; Building/renovation; Program development; Matching/challenge support.
Limitations: Applications accepted. Giving primarily in GA, with emphasis on Thomasville and Thomas County. No grants to individuals.
Publications: Application guidelines; Corporate giving report; Informational brochure (including application guidelines).
Application information: New contributions limited due to numerous commitments. Application form required.
Initial approach: Letter
Copies of proposal: 1
Deadline(s): Feb. 1 and Sept. 1
Board meeting date(s): May and Nov.
Final notification: June 10 and Nov. 10
Officers and Directors:* Mrs. Alston Parker Watt, Pres. and Exec. Dir.; Diane W. Parker,* Secy.; Stephen T. Parker,* V.P.; Bernard Lanigan, Jr.,* Treas.; Joseph E. Beverly; Frederick E. Cooper; Lawrence A. Harmon; Thomas W. Parker; Thomas H. Vann, Jr.; Ashlyn W. Williams; Joseph Neel Williams; Thomas Lyle Williams IV.
Number of staff: 1 part-time professional; 1 part-time support.
EIN: 581414850

2573
Jesse Parker Williams Foundation, Inc.

3050 Peachtree Rd. N.W., Ste. 260
Atlanta, GA 30305-2212 (404) 658-1112
Contact: Mary H. Judson
FAX: (404) 842-1311;
E-mail: mary.judson@jpwf.org; Main URL: http://www.jpwf.org

Established in 1992.
Foundation type: Independent foundation.
Financial data (yr. ended 12/31/13): Assets, $32,880,852 (M); expenditures, $1,894,133; qualifying distributions, $1,894,133; giving activities include $1,689,962 for 22 grants (high: $250,000; low: $1,500; average: $50,000–$100,000).
Purpose and activities: The mission of the Jesse Parker Williams Foundation is to support highly effective organizations that emphasize preventative, comprehensive health opportunities and enhance access to health services for women and children. It focuses especially on those serving populations with limited financial means and predominately in the five-county metropolitan Atlanta, Georgia, area (Fulton, DeKalb, Cobb, Gwinnett and Clayton.).
Fields of interest: Dental care; Health care; Mental health/crisis services; Children; Women.
Limitations: Applications accepted. Giving limited to the metropolitan Atlanta, GA, area (Fulton, DeKalb, Cobb, Gwinnett and Clayton counties.). No support for sectarian religious activities or lobbying activities. No grants to individuals, or for clinical research or trials; treatment or research related to specific diseases, endowment funds or capital campaigns, event sponsorships or camps.
Application information: Direct contact with the trustees is strongly discouraged, but the trustees do encourage potential applicants to communication with foundation staff prior to submission of any proposal. Application form not required.
Initial approach: Letter of inquiry
Copies of proposal: 1
Deadline(s): Jan. 15 and July 15
Board meeting date(s): Feb., May, Aug. and Dec.
Final notification: Letters of inquiry will be reviewed at the Feb. and Aug. meetings of the Board of Trustees and response will take place shortly thereafter.
Officers: Larry L. Gellerstedt III, Chair.; Lucy C. Vance, Vice-Chair.; Mary Humann Judson, Secy. and Exec. Dir.
Trustees: Eleanor H. Ridley; Richard A. Schneider; E. Jenner Wood III.
EIN: 580601653
Selected grants: The following grants are a representative sample of this grantmaker's funding activity:
$250,000 to Childrens Healthcare of Atlanta Foundation, Atlanta, GA, 2012. For Primary Care Clinic at Children's Healthcare at Hughes Spalding.
$150,000 to Jewish Family and Career Services, Atlanta, GA, 2012. For operating support for Ben Massell Dental Clinic.
$100,000 to Families First, Atlanta, GA, 2012. For mental health services for low-income families.
$100,000 to Good Samaritan Health Center, Atlanta, GA, 2012. For medical and mental health care of women and children.
$100,000 to Good Samaritan Health Center of Cobb, Austell, GA, 2012. For Chronic Disease Program.
$100,000 to Planned Parenthood Southeast, Atlanta, GA, 2012. For Affordable Reproductive Healthcare Project.
$100,000 to Presbyterian Village, Atlanta, GA, 2012. For long-term quality care initiatives.
$100,000 to Visiting Nurse Health System, Atlanta, GA, 2012. For Physician House Call program.
$96,290 to Emory Healthcare, Fuqua Center for Late-Life Depression, Atlanta, GA, 2012. For Geriatric Psychiatry Services in Low Income Housing.
$95,416 to Community Advanced Practice Nurses, Atlanta, GA, 2012. For primary care and mental health services for homeless women and children.
$80,000 to A. G. Rhodes Home, Atlanta, GA, 2012. For of the services provided to female patients under the 1971 Operating Agreement.
$80,000 to Foundation of Wesley Woods, Atlanta, GA, 2012. For the services provided to female residents under the 1970 Operating Agreement.
$67,879 to Center for the Visually Impaired, Atlanta, GA, 2012. For integrated low vision services and community-based vision rehabilitation services for women with severe vision loss.
$50,000 to Project Healthy Grandparents, Atlanta, GA, 2012. For Project Healthy Grandparents.

2574
James M. Williams, Jr. Family Foundation, Inc. ✧

2442 Francis Rd., Ste. 160
Alpharetta, GA 30004

Established in 1996 in GA.
Donor: James M. Williams, Jr.
Foundation type: Operating foundation.
Financial data (yr. ended 12/31/13): Assets, $11,453,423 (M); expenditures, $748,284; qualifying distributions, $599,100; giving activities include $599,100 for 22 grants (high: $320,000; low: $250).
Purpose and activities: Giving primarily to Baptist churches.
Fields of interest: Youth development; Human services; Protestant agencies & churches.
Limitations: Applications not accepted. Giving primarily in GA. No grants to individuals.
Application information: Contributes only to pre-selected organizations.
Officers: James M. Williams, Jr., Pres.; Barbara Williams Bowling, Secy.-Treas.
Directors: Dondi Anne Bosson; Candace Cheri O'Neal; Linda Sue Williams.
EIN: 582275806

2575
A. L. Williams, Jr. Family Foundation Inc. ✧
3473 Satellite Blvd., Ste. 211
Duluth, GA 30096-8691 (770) 813-0090
Contact: Frank M. Sato

Incorporated 1985 in GA.
Donors: Arthur L. Williams, Jr.; Angela H. Williams; Boe Adams.
Foundation type: Independent foundation.
Financial data (yr. ended 12/31/12): Assets, $63,470,798 (M); expenditures, $1,792,619; qualifying distributions, $1,349,895; giving activities include $1,210,000 for 33 grants (high: $210,000; low: $3,000).
Purpose and activities: Giving primarily for Protestant ministries and organizations, as well as for education, social services, and to a hospital foundation.
Fields of interest: Higher education; Education; Hospitals (general); Human services; Christian agencies & churches; Protestant agencies & churches.
Limitations: Giving primarily in FL and GA.
Application information: Application form required.
Initial approach: Letter
Deadline(s): None
Officers and Trustees:* Angela H. Williams,* Pres. and Treas.; James E. Kelly,* Exec. V.P.; April Williams Demoss,* V.P.; Arthur R. Williams III,* V.P.; Gloice Y. Crim, Secy.; Elizabeth W. Carter; Georgia A. Demoss; Alex L. Williams; Andrew L. Williams; Arthur R. Williams IV.
EIN: 581650389

2576
The Frances Wood Wilson Foundation, Inc. ✧
4500 Hugh Howell Rd., Ste. 370
Tucker, GA 30084-4729 (770) 270-9083
Contact: Donna Moseley, Secy.-Treas.
FAX: (770) 270-9829; E-mail: fwwf@bellsouth.net; Mailing address: P.O. Box 349, Tucker GA 30085

Incorporated in 1954 in GA.
Donors: Fred B. Wilson†; Mrs. Frances W. Wilson†; St. Louis-San Francisco Railroad.
Foundation type: Independent foundation.
Financial data (yr. ended 05/31/14): Assets, $41,823,209 (M); expenditures, $2,029,263; qualifying distributions, $1,845,790; giving activities include $1,594,000 for 144 grants (high: $62,000; low: $1,000).
Purpose and activities: Grants largely for child welfare, religious, civic, health, and higher educational organizations; support also for college scholarship funds.
Fields of interest: Higher education; Health care; Health organizations, association; Children/youth, services; Religion.
Type of support: General/operating support; Continuing support; Annual campaigns; Capital campaigns; Building/renovation; Equipment; Land acquisition; Scholarship funds.
Limitations: Applications accepted. Giving limited to GA, except for programs carried on by Chestnut Hill Benevolent Assn. in Boston, MA. No grants to individuals, directly or for endowment funds; no loans.
Publications: Application guidelines.
Application information: Application form not required.
Initial approach: Proposal
Copies of proposal: 1
Deadline(s): Mar. 1 and Sept. 1
Board meeting date(s): Apr. and Oct.
Officers and Trustees:* J.B. Edmunds, Jr.,* Chair.; B.A. Bird,* Pres.; Donna Moseley,* Secy.-Treas.; W.T. Wingfield,* Chair., Exec. Committee; D.G. Loggins; Lawton Stephens.
Number of staff: 1 part-time support.
EIN: 586035441
Selected grants: The following grants are a representative sample of this grantmaker's funding activity:
$25,000 to Young Life, Colorado Springs, CO, 2011.
$16,500 to Emory University, Atlanta, GA, 2011.
$12,000 to Mercer University, Macon, GA, 2011.
$5,000 to American Cancer Society, Atlanta, GA, 2011.
$5,000 to Arthritis Foundation, Atlanta, GA, 2011.
$5,000 to National Kidney Foundation, New York, NY, 2011.
$2,000 to Learning Ally, Princeton, NJ, 2011.

2577
WinShape Foundation, Inc. ✧
(formerly WinShape Centre, Inc.)
5200 Buffington Rd.
Atlanta, GA 30349-2998
FAX: (706) 238-7742;
E-mail: rskelton@winshape.org; Additional address: P.O. Box 490009, Mt. Berry, GA 30149-0009, tel.: (877) 977-3873, e-mail: info@winshape.org; Main URL: http://www.winshape.org
Scholarship application address: c/o Berry College, P.O. Box 490159, Mt. Berry, GA 30149-0009, tel.: (706) 236-2215,
e-mail: admissions@berry.edu,
collegeprogram@winshape.org

Established as a company-sponsored operating foundation in 1984 in GA.
Donors: Chick-fil-A, Inc.; S. Truett Cathy; CFA Properties, Inc.
Foundation type: Operating foundation.
Financial data (yr. ended 12/31/12): Assets, $71,523,969 (M); gifts received, $20,973,966; expenditures, $26,372,699; qualifying distributions, $17,165,351; giving activities include $569,547 for 2 grants (high: $507,547; low: $62,000), and $20,519,733 for 4 foundation-administered programs.
Purpose and activities: The foundation supports programs involved with education, children and youth, families, marriage enrichment, and religion; also awards college scholarships to undergraduate students attending Berry College.
Fields of interest: Child development, education; Secondary school/education; Education; Youth development; Children/youth, services; Child development, services; Family services; Christian agencies & churches; Religion; Children/youth; Children.
Type of support: Continuing support; Scholarships—to individuals.
Limitations: Applications accepted. Giving primarily in GA.
Publications: Application guidelines; Informational brochure (including application guidelines).
Application information: Unsolicited requests accepted only for scholarship program. An interview may be required for scholarships. Scholarship applicants must apply to the WinShape College Program and to Berry College. Application form required.
Initial approach: Complete online application form or contact foundation for application form for scholarships
Deadline(s): Feb. 1 for scholarships
Board meeting date(s): Varies
Final notification: Apr. 15 for scholarships
Officers and Directors: S. Truett Cathy, Pres.; Donald M. Cathy, V.P.; John W. White, III, V.P.; James B. McCabe, Secy.-Treas.; Robert M. Skelton, Exec. Dir.; Brett Whorton.
Number of staff: 62 full-time professional.
EIN: 581595471

2578
J. W. & Ethel I. Woodruff Foundation, Inc. ✧
c/o J. Barnett Woodruff
P.O. Box 750
Columbus, GA 31902-0750

Established in 1960 in GA.
Donors: Ethel I. Woodruff; James W. Woodruff; J. Barnett Woodruff; members of the Woodruff family.
Foundation type: Independent foundation.
Financial data (yr. ended 07/31/13): Assets, $31,660,411 (M); expenditures, $1,538,535; qualifying distributions, $1,434,006; giving activities include $1,430,000 for 58 grants (high: $350,000; low: $2,000).
Fields of interest: Performing arts, opera; Arts; Higher education; Education; Health care; Health organizations, association; Boys & girls clubs; Human services; Children/youth, services.
Limitations: Applications not accepted. Giving primarily in GA, with emphasis on Columbus. No grants to individuals; no loans.
Application information: Contributes only to pre-selected organizations.
Officers and Directors:* Katherine F. Woodruff,* Chair. and C.E.O.; Christopher S. Woodruff, Secy.-Treas.; Timothy L. Decamp; Stephen E. Draper; Dina Woodruff; James W. Woodruff III.
EIN: 586049589
Selected grants: The following grants are a representative sample of this grantmaker's funding activity:
$105,000 to Springer Opera House Arts Association, Columbus, GA, 2011.

2579
Robert W. Woodruff Foundation, Inc. ✧
(formerly Trebor Foundation, Inc.)
191 Peachtree N.W., Ste. 3540
Atlanta, GA 30303-1799 (404) 522-6755
Contact: P. Russell Hardin, Pres.
FAX: (404) 522-7026; E-mail: fdns@woodruff.org; Main URL: http://woodruff.org/
Grants List: http://woodruff.org/grants-program/previous-grants/

Incorporated in 1937 in DE.
Donors: Robert W. Woodruff†; The Acmaro Securities Corp.; and others.
Foundation type: Independent foundation.
Financial data (yr. ended 12/31/13): Assets, $3,119,096,039 (M); expenditures, $158,366,166; qualifying distributions,

$156,739,995; giving activities include $155,816,887 for 46 grants (high: $79,999,887; low: $25,000).

Purpose and activities: To enhance the quality of life for citizens in Georgia by investing in the health, education, economic opportunity and the vitality of the community.

Fields of interest: Arts; Elementary/secondary education; Higher education; Education; Environment, natural resources; Environment; Health care; Human services; Children/youth, services; Aging, centers/services; Economic development; Public affairs; Aging.

Type of support: General/operating support; Management development/capacity building; Capital campaigns; Building/renovation; Equipment; Land acquisition; Program development.

Limitations: Applications accepted. Giving limited to GA, with emphasis on the metropolitan Atlanta area. No support for church denominational programs, or human services outside Atlanta, GA. No grants to individuals, or for annual campaigns, endowments, conferences, festivals or performances, films and documentaries, or seed money; no loans.

Publications: Application guidelines; Grants list; IRS Form 990 or 990-PF printed copy available upon request; Program policy statement; Program policy statement (including application guidelines).

Application information: The foundation shares offices and administrative staff with the Joseph B. Whitehead Foundation, Lettie Pate Whitehead Foundation, Inc., Lettie Pate Evans Foundation, Inc., Ichauway, Inc., and the Robert W. Woodruff Health Sciences Center Fund, Inc. Grant inquiries or proposals submitted to the Robert W. Woodruff Foundation, Inc. may also be considered by one or more of the foundations sharing this common administrative arrangement. It is not necessary to communicate separately with more than one of these foundations in seeking information or requesting grant support. Application form not required.

Initial approach: Letter
Copies of proposal: 1
Deadline(s): Feb. 1 and Sept. 1
Board meeting date(s): Apr. and Nov.
Final notification: Within 30 days of trustee meeting

Officers and Trustees:* James B. Williams,* Chair.; James M. Sibley,* Vice-Chair.; P. Russell Hardin, Pres.; Erik S. Johnson, Secy. and General Counsel; J. Lee Tribble, Treas.; Wilton D. Looney; Charles H. McTier; E. Jenner Wood III.

EIN: 581695425

Selected grants: The following grants are a representative sample of this grantmaker's funding activity:

$79,999,887 to Emory University, Atlanta, GA, 2013. To redevelop outpatient facilities of the Woodruff Health Sciences Center. Grant redirected for construction of a 210-bed hospital tower across Clifton Road.

$50,000,011 to Emory University, Atlanta, GA, 2012. For endowment to grow and enhance the Woodruff Scholars Program in Emory College.

$25,000,000 to Emory University, Atlanta, GA, 2013. To endow new scholarship programs.

$7,500,000 to Robert W. Woodruff Arts Center, Atlanta, GA, 2012. For capital needs support.

$6,000,000 to East Lake Foundation, Atlanta, GA, 2012. For construction of combined middle/high school building for Drew Charter School.

$5,000,000 to Georgia State University, College of Law, Atlanta, GA, 2013. For creation of new facility at John Wesley Dobbs and Park Place. Grant is contingent on state funding and receipt of final construction contract.

$5,000,000 to Ichauway, Newton, GA, 2012. For capital and operating support.

$5,000,000 to Saint Simons Land Trust, Saint Simons Island, GA, 2012. For acquisition of Cannon's Point, a 617-acre tract on Saint Simons Island. Grant will be paid when all funds necessary to retire the debt have been committed.

$2,500,000 to Atlanta Botanical Garden, Atlanta, GA, 2013. To implement Master Plan for Smithgall Woodland Garden in Gainesville. Grant is contingent on raising additional grant funds by June 30, 2013.

$2,242,500 to Ichauway, Newton, GA, 2012. For capital and operating support.

$1,500,000 to BeltLine Partnership, Atlanta, GA, 2012. To construct extension of Eastside Trail and Gateway Entrance to Historic Fourth Ward Park.

$1,500,000 to BeltLine Partnership, Atlanta, GA, 2013. To construct extension of Eastside Trail and Gateway Entrance to Historic Fourth Ward Park.

$1,250,000 to Shepherd Center, Atlanta, GA, 2013. For operating support for work to establish Shepherd Transition Services Program to improve discharge care and support.

$1,000,000 to CDC Foundation, Atlanta, GA, 2013. For operating support for Phase II of initiative to articulate the role and value of the Centers for Disease Control (CDC) to private sector leadership.

$1,000,000 to Ichauway, Newton, GA, 2013. For capital and operating support.

$1,000,000 to Interdenominational Theological Center, Atlanta, GA, 2013. For capital improvements and deferred maintenance.

$750,000 to Georgia Military College, Milledgeville, GA, 2013. For construction of Health and Wellness Center.

$750,000 to Project GRAD Atlanta, Atlanta, GA, 2012. For scholarships and college counseling services for Atlanta high school students. $250,000 for operating support and community study; $500,000 for last-dollar scholarships.

2580
David, Helen, and Marian Woodward Fund ✧

(also known as Marian W. Ottley Trust-Atlanta)
c/o Wells Fargo Bank, N.A.
3280 Peachtree Rd., N.E., Ste. 400, MAC G0141-041
Atlanta, GA 30305-2422 (888) 234-1999
Contact: Joyce Yamaato
FAX: (877) 746-5889;
E-mail: grantadministration@wellsfargo.com; Main URL: https://www.wellsfargo.com/privatefoundationgrants/woodward

Established in 1975 in GA.

Donor: Marian W. Ottley‡.

Foundation type: Independent foundation.

Financial data (yr. ended 05/31/13): Assets, $48,680,409 (M); expenditures, $2,501,914; qualifying distributions, $2,164,739; giving activities include $2,080,500 for 46 grants (high: $150,000; low: $7,500).

Fields of interest: Arts; Education; Health organizations; Human services.

Type of support: Capital campaigns; Building/renovation; Equipment.

Limitations: Giving primarily in the metropolitan Atlanta, GA, area. No grants to individuals, or for scholarships or student loans.

Publications: Application guidelines.

Application information: Application form required.

Initial approach: Use online application form on foundation web site
Deadline(s): Apr. 1 and Sept. 1
Board meeting date(s): May and Nov.

Officers and Distribution Committee:* Benjamin T. White,* Chair.; Crawford F. Barnett, Jr., M.D.; Mike Donnelly; Florida Huff; Horace Sibley.

Trustee: Wells Fargo Bank, N.A.

Number of staff: 1 full-time professional; 1 full-time support.

EIN: 586222004

Selected grants: The following grants are a representative sample of this grantmaker's funding activity:

$200,000 to United Way of Metropolitan Atlanta, Atlanta, GA, 2011.

$150,000 to Grady Memorial Hospital Corporation, Atlanta, GA, 2011.

$120,000 to Robert W. Woodruff Arts Center, Atlanta, GA, 2011.

$25,000 to Big Brothers Big Sisters of Metro Atlanta, Atlanta, GA, 2011.

2581
The Vasser Woolley Foundation, Inc. ✧

c/o David C. Lawrence, Jr.
1 Atlantic Ctr.
1201 W. Peachtree St., Ste. 4200
Atlanta, GA 30309-3424
Contact: Margaret Scott, Secy.-Treas.
E-mail: margaret.scott@alston.com

Incorporated in 1961 in GA.

Donor: Vasser Woolley‡.

Foundation type: Independent foundation.

Financial data (yr. ended 12/31/13): Assets, $12,580,754 (M); expenditures, $677,548; qualifying distributions, $529,973; giving activities include $498,333 for 14 grants (high: $100,000; low: $15,000).

Purpose and activities: Support for charitable organizations in the metropolitan Atlanta, GA area, with focus on those serving the general welfare, education, arts and youth development.

Fields of interest: Performing arts; Arts; Elementary/secondary education; Higher education; Recreation, parks/playgrounds; Youth; Homeless.

Type of support: Annual campaigns; Capital campaigns; Building/renovation; Equipment; Land acquisition; Emergency funds; Professorships; Seed money; Scholarship funds; Matching/challenge support.

Limitations: Applications not accepted. Giving primarily in the metropolitan Atlanta, GA, area. No grants to individuals, or for operating budgets, continuing support, annual campaigns, deficit financing, special projects, research, publications, or conferences; no loans.

Application information: Contributes only to pre-selected organizations.

Board meeting date(s): May and Nov.

Officers and Trustees:* L. Neil Williams, Jr.,* Chair.; David C. Lawrence, Jr., Secy.-Treas.; Susan Seydel Cofer; M. Hill Jeffries, Jr.; Michael T. Petrik; J. Rutherford Seydel II.

EIN: 586034197

2582
Jane H. & William D. Young Foundation ✧
1271 Tacoma Dr.
Atlanta, GA 30318-4145

Established in 1992 in GA.
Donors: Jane H. Young; William D. Young, Sr.
Foundation type: Independent foundation.
Financial data (yr. ended 06/30/13): Assets, $9,449,395 (M); gifts received, $3,094,188; expenditures, $468,730; qualifying distributions, $466,500; giving activities include $466,500 for grants.
Fields of interest: Museums; Arts; Education; Youth development, services; Human services; Protestant agencies & churches.
Limitations: Applications not accepted. Giving primarily in AR, AZ and GA. No grants to individuals.
Application information: Contributes only to pre-selected organizations.
Trustees: Jane H. Young; William D. Young.
EIN: 582021302
Selected grants: The following grants are a representative sample of this grantmaker's funding activity:
$200,000 to Peachtree Presbyterian Church, Atlanta, GA, 2011.
$100,000 to Translational Genomics Research Institute, Phoenix, AZ, 2011.
$1,500 to Translational Genomics Research Institute, Phoenix, AZ, 2011.

2583
Zaban Foundation, Inc. ✧ ☆
3475 Lenox Rd. N.E., Ste. 950
Atlanta, GA 30326-3220

Established in 1960 in GA.
Donors: Erwin Zaban; Zaban Investments, L.P.
Foundation type: Independent foundation.
Financial data (yr. ended 06/30/13): Assets, $9,596,401 (M); expenditures, $501,566; qualifying distributions, $451,367; giving activities include $447,550 for 39 grants (high: $135,000; low: $1,000).
Purpose and activities: Giving primarily to Jewish agencies and temples; funding also for human services and education.
Fields of interest: Education; Human services; United Ways and Federated Giving Programs; Jewish federated giving programs; Jewish agencies & synagogues.
Limitations: Applications not accepted. Giving primarily in Atlanta, GA. No grants to individuals.
Application information: Contributes only to pre-selected organizations.
Officers: Judy Zaban, Chair. and Treas.; Stephen M. Berman, Secy.
Directors: Carol Z. Cooper; Laura Z. Dinerman; Sara Z. Franco.
EIN: 586034590
Selected grants: The following grants are a representative sample of this grantmaker's funding activity:
$5,000 to Project Interchange, Washington, DC, 2011.
$5,000 to Teach for America, New York, NY, 2011.
$3,000 to American Jewish Committee, New York, NY, 2011.

2584
Zeist Foundation, Inc. ✧
3715 Northside Pkwy. N.W., Ste. 3-195
Atlanta, GA 30327-2812 (404) 949-3176
FAX: (404) 949-3161; E-mail: info@zfo.net; Main URL: http://www.zeistfoundation.org/

Established in 1989 in GA.
Donors: George W. Brumley, Jr.†; Jean S. Brumley†; Elizabeth Stanback†.
Foundation type: Independent foundation.
Financial data (yr. ended 12/31/12): Assets, $230,773,616 (M); expenditures, $12,559,950; qualifying distributions, $10,864,244; giving activities include $9,256,927 for 67 grants, and $192,639 for 1 foundation-administered program.
Fields of interest: Arts; Education; Health organizations, association; Human services; Foundations (community).
Type of support: General/operating support; Annual campaigns; Capital campaigns; Building/renovation; Land acquisition; Debt reduction; Conferences/seminars; Curriculum development; Internship funds; Research; Technical assistance; Consulting services; Program evaluation; Matching/challenge support.
Limitations: Applications not accepted. Giving limited to the metropolitan Atlanta, GA, area. No grants to individuals.
Publications: Informational brochure.
Application information: Contributes only to pre-selected organizations.
Board meeting date(s): Quarterly
Officers and Directors:* Nancy J. Brumley-Robitaille,* Pres.; R. Brad Foster,* V.P.; Marie B. Foster, Secy.-Treas.; Kappy Kellett deButts, Exec. Dir.
Number of staff: 1 full-time professional; 1 full-time support.
EIN: 581890927
Selected grants: The following grants are a representative sample of this grantmaker's funding activity:
$3,042,000 to Community Foundation for Greater Atlanta, Atlanta, GA, 2012.
$1,025,000 to Childrens Healthcare of Atlanta Foundation, Atlanta, GA, 2012.
$500,000 to Atlanta Speech School, Atlanta, GA, 2012.
$380,000 to Fernbank Museum of Natural History, Atlanta, GA, 2012.
$330,000 to KIPP Metro Atlanta Collaborative, Atlanta, GA, 2012.
$225,000 to Families First, Atlanta, GA, 2012.
$100,000 to DonorsChoose.org, New York, NY, 2012.
$50,000 to Center for Puppetry Arts, Atlanta, GA, 2012.
$50,000 to Refugee Family Services, Stone Mountain, GA, 2012.
$50,000 to United Way of Metropolitan Atlanta, Atlanta, GA, 2012.

HAWAII

2585
The Lanie Albrecht Foundation ✧
(formerly The Lanie Foundation)
P.O. Box 5046
Kaneohe, HI 96744-9046

Established in 2001 in NV.
Donor: Ralph W. Albrecht, Sr.
Foundation type: Independent foundation.
Financial data (yr. ended 12/31/13): Assets, $1,401,367 (M); gifts received, $891,000; expenditures, $897,601; qualifying distributions, $825,100; giving activities include $825,100 for 20 grants (high: $280,000; low: $1,000).
Purpose and activities: Giving primarily for human services.
Fields of interest: Human services.
Limitations: Applications not accepted. Giving primarily in Sacramento, CA and in HI; some giving in Brazil. No grants to individuals.
Application information: Contributes only to pre-selected organizations.
Officer and Directors: Sharon Wong, Chair.; Dana Christy; Michael Gibson.
EIN: 880431967

2586
Atherton Family Foundation ✧
c/o Hawaii Community Foundation
827 Fort Street Mall
Honolulu, HI 96813-4317 (808) 537-6333
Contact: Amy Luersen, Dir., Philanthropic Svcs., HCF
FAX: (808) 521-6286;
E-mail: foundations@hcf-hawaii.org; Toll free tel.: (888) 731-3863 (Hawaii and neighbor islands only); Contact if applicant is not able to submit proposal online: Pam Funai, tel.: (808) 566-5537, e-mail: pfunai@hcf-hawaii.org; Main URL: http://www.athertonfamilyfoundation.org

Incorporated in 1975 in HI as successor to Juliette M. Atherton Trust established in 1915; F. C. Atherton Trust merged into the foundation in 1976.
Donors: Juliette M. Atherton†; Frank C. Atherton†.
Foundation type: Independent foundation.
Financial data (yr. ended 12/31/13): Assets, $99,658,833 (M); expenditures, $5,391,502; qualifying distributions, $4,666,178; giving activities include $4,258,359 for 218 grants (high: $200,000; low: $500), and $131,790 for 33 grants to individuals (high: $8,000; low: $510).
Purpose and activities: The foundation is concerned with education, human services, culture and the arts, health, religion, and the environment. Focus also on programs that benefit the people of Hawaii. Scholarships for the postgraduate education of Protestant ministers, Protestant ministers' children for undergraduate study, and for graduate theological education at a Protestant seminary. Foundation staff and grants administration is provided by the Hawaii Community Foundation.
Fields of interest: Humanities; Arts; Theological school/education; Education; Environment; Health care; Health organizations, association; Youth development; Human services; Community/economic development; Protestant agencies & churches.
Type of support: Management development/capacity building; Annual campaigns; Capital campaigns; Building/renovation; Equipment; Program development; Seed money; Curriculum development; Research; Technical assistance; Program evaluation; Scholarships—to individuals; Matching/challenge support.
Limitations: Applications accepted. Giving limited to HI; student aid for HI residents only. Generally, no support for private foundations, or for lobbying, individual Department of Education schools, or for organizations engaged in fundraising for the purpose of distributing grants to recipients of their own choosing, or to the University of Hawai`i other than an annual grant to the University of Hawai`i Foundation. No grants to individuals (except for scholarships), generally no giving for endowment funds, or for annual operating support or funds for re-granting; no conferences, festivals or one-time events; no loans.
Publications: Annual report; Financial statement; Grants list.
Application information: Application form required for scholarships and automation grants. See foundation web site for application details. If an organization applies through a fiscal sponsor, the fiscal sponsor must agree that the purpose of the grant is charitable, to monitor the grant project, control the expenditure of grant funds, and ensure compliance with the terms and conditions of the grant. Application form required.
Initial approach: Applicant must first establish an online account with the Hawaii Community Foundation in order to access the online application at: https://nexus.hawaiicommunityfoundation.org/SSLPage.aspx?pid=330
Copies of proposal: 1
Deadline(s): Jan. 2, Apr. 1, July 1, and Oct. 1
Board meeting date(s): Mar., June, Sept., and Dec.
Final notification: 2 to 3 months
Officers and Directors:* Judith M. Dawson,* Pres.; Joan H. Rohlfing,* V.P. and Secy.; Frank C. Atherton,* V.P. and Treas.; Patricia R. Giles,* V.P.; Robin S. Midkiff,* V.P.; Paul F. Morgan,* V.P.
Agent: Bank of Hawaii.
EIN: 510175971

2587
Priscilla and Michael Baldwin Foundation ✧
1003 Bishop St., Ste. 1200
Honolulu, HI 96813-6436

Established in 2006 in CO.
Donors: Michael C. Baldwin; Priscilla V. Baldwin.
Foundation type: Independent foundation.
Financial data (yr. ended 12/31/12): Assets, $49,062 (M); gifts received, $970,496; expenditures, $922,755; qualifying distributions, $921,445; giving activities include $901,833 for 22 grants (high: $134,360; low: $2,500).
Fields of interest: Museums.
Limitations: Applications not accepted. Giving primarily in Tucson, AZ. No grants to individuals.
Application information: Contributes only to pre-selected organizations.
Officers: Priscilla V. Baldwin, Pres.; Michael C. Baldwin, Secy.-Treas.
Directors: Gary Brothers; Robert Edison; Wendy Moore; Theodore Rachlin.
EIN: 205265903
Selected grants: The following grants are a representative sample of this grantmaker's funding activity:
$10,619 to Arizona-Sonora Desert Museum, Tucson, AZ, 2012. For Baldwin Education Building.
$5,000 to Arizona-Sonora Desert Museum, Tucson, AZ, 2012. For ASDM VC Painting Jaguarundi by Carel p. Brest Van Kempen.
$3,000 to Arizona-Sonora Desert Museum, Tucson, AZ, 2012. For ASDM VC Painting Fresh Water Musselsby Scott Fraser Inc.
$2,500 to Arizona-Sonora Desert Museum, Tucson, AZ, 2012. For ASDM VC Painting Tel Hicks Mexican by Eco Wear and Publishing.

2588
Bank of Hawaii Foundation ✧
(formerly Bancorp Hawaii Charitable Foundation)
Foundation Admin. No. 758
P.O. Box 3170
Honolulu, HI 96802-3170 (808) 538-4944
Contact: Elaine Moniz, Trust Specialist
FAX: (808) 538-4006; E-mail: emoniz@boh.com; Additional contacts: Flora Williams, Asst. V.P., tel.: (808) 694-4393, e-mail: flora.williams@boh.com; Paula Boyce, Grants Admin., tel.: (808) 538-4945, e-mail: pboyce@boh.com; Main URL: https://www.boh.com/customer-service/689.asp

Established in 1981 in HI.
Donors: Bank of Hawaii; Allan R. Landon.
Foundation type: Company-sponsored foundation.
Financial data (yr. ended 12/31/13): Assets, $11,712,661 (M); gifts received, $712,627; expenditures, $1,682,029; qualifying distributions, $1,662,374; giving activities include $1,554,649 for 106 grants (high: $79,483; low: $120).
Purpose and activities: The foundation supports organizations involved with arts and culture, education, health, hunger, housing, human services, and community development. Special emphasis is directed toward programs designed serve children and youth, indigenous peoples, and economically disadvantaged people; and strengthen low- to moderate-income communities.
Fields of interest: Arts education; Arts; Higher education; Education; Health care; Food services; Housing/shelter; Salvation Army; Human services, financial counseling; Human services; Economic development; Community/economic development; Children/youth; Indigenous peoples; Economically disadvantaged.
Type of support: General/operating support; Continuing support; Annual campaigns; Capital campaigns; Building/renovation; Equipment; Endowments; Emergency funds; Program development; Scholarship funds; Technical assistance; Matching/challenge support.
Limitations: Applications accepted. Giving primarily in areas of company operations in American Samoa, Guam, HI, and Saipan. No support for pass-through organizations. No grants to individuals, or for deficit budgets, general fundraising campaigns, religious purposes, or trips or tours.
Publications: Application guidelines; Informational brochure.
Application information: Grants range from $1,000 to $25,000. Letters of inquiry are strongly encouraged for unsolicited ideas or projects. Executive summaries should be no longer than 1 page and include a summary of the proposal and a brief overview of the organization. A full formal proposal may be requested at a later date. Support

is limited to 1 contribution per organization during any given year. Application form required.

Initial approach: Download letter of inquiry cover sheet and mail cover sheet and executive summary to foundation

Copies of proposal: 1

Deadline(s): Postmarked by Jan. 15 or July 15

Board meeting date(s): Biannually

Final notification: 60 days

Officers and Directors:* Donna A. Tanoue,* Pres.; Stafford J. Kiguchi, V.P.; Peter S. Ho,* V.P.; Cynthia G. Wyrick, Secy.; Kent Lucien,* Treas.; S. Haunani Apoliona; Mary G.F. Bitterman; Mark A. Burak; Michael J. Chun, Ph.D.; Clinton R. Churchill; David A. Heenan; Robert A. Huret; Alton T. Kuioka; Martin A. Stein; Donald M. Takaki; Barbara J. Tanabe; Robert W. Wo, Jr.

Trustee: Bank of Hawaii.

EIN: 990210467

2589
Paul & Irene Buehner - Joan B. Merrill Family Foundation ✧ ☆

(formerly Paul & Irene Buehner Foundation)
50 Pu'U Anoano St., No. 11201
Lahaina, HI 96761-1954 (808) 667-6608
Contact: Joan B. Merrill, Dir.

Established in 2007 in UT.

Foundation type: Independent foundation.

Financial data (yr. ended 05/31/13): Assets, $595,876 (M); expenditures, $2,258,456; qualifying distributions, $2,239,212; giving activities include $2,239,212 for 13 grants (high: $585,056; low: $1,000).

Fields of interest: Cancer; Family services; United Ways and Federated Giving Programs.

Limitations: Applications accepted. Giving primarily in CA, ID and UT. No grants to individuals.

Application information: Application form not required.

Initial approach: Letter

Deadline(s): None

Directors: Joan B. Merrill; Mark B. Merrill; Scott B. Merrill.

EIN: 260272154

Selected grants: The following grants are a representative sample of this grantmaker's funding activity:

$40,000 to California Family Foundation, Palo Alto, CA, 2012.

$15,000 to Brigham Young University-Hawaii, Laie, HI, 2012.

$5,000 to Giving Circle, Saratoga Springs, NY, 2012.

2590
The Julia Burke Foundation ✧

73-1397 Hamiha St.
Kailua Kona, HI 96740-9213 (808) 960-1705
Contact: Joy Johnson, Exec. Dir.
FAX: (866) 437-8579;
E-mail: Projects@JuliaBurkeFoundation.com; E-mail address for Joy Johnson, Exec. Dir.: Joy_Johnson@burkefoundation.org; Main URL: http://www.juliaburkefoundation.com/

Established in 1998 in CA.

Donors: Gerald P. Burke; Marilyn Burke; Janice Hamill; Stephen Hamill.

Foundation type: Independent foundation.

Financial data (yr. ended 11/30/13): Assets, $7,019,168 (M); gifts received, $604,632; expenditures, $861,229; qualifying distributions, $858,577; giving activities include $610,807 for 16 grants (high: $200,000; low: $2,000).

Fields of interest: Medical school/education; Scholarships/financial aid; Education; Family services, parent education; International peace/security; International affairs.

Limitations: Applications accepted. Giving worldwide, with an emphasis on CA. No grants to individuals.

Publications: Newsletter.

Application information: See foundation web site for specific policies and guidelines. Application form required.

Initial approach: E-mail

Deadline(s): None

Officers: Marilyn C. Burke, Pres. and Secy.; Gerald P. Burke, V.P. and Treas.; Joy Johnson, Exec. Dir.

Members: Donald M. Burke; Robert M. Burke; Michelle Campion; Timothy J. Campion; Jonathan E. Cowperthwait; Robbie Murphy; Eric S. Zampol.

Number of staff: 1 full-time professional.

EIN: 943314266

Selected grants: The following grants are a representative sample of this grantmaker's funding activity:

$56,000 to Woodward Academy, College Park, GA, 2013. For The Building of Three Classrooms, Five Faculty Houses and Two Permanent Dormitories on Behalf of the Terranova School in Mazabuka, Zambia.

$44,429 to University of San Francisco, San Francisco, CA, 2013. For School Expenses for Scholarship Recipient.

$35,000 to Mindful Schools, Oakland, CA, 2013. For Supporting Graduates with Materials and Resources.

2591
The Cades Foundation ✧

c/o E.Gunner Schull
1000 Bishop St., Ste. 1500
Honolulu, HI 96813-4210 (808) 521-9200
Contact: E. Gunner Schull Esq., V.P., Secy. and Dir.

Established in 1982 in HI.

Donors: Milton Cades†; J. Russell Cades†; Charlotte M. Cades†.

Foundation type: Independent foundation.

Financial data (yr. ended 12/31/13): Assets, $12,220,189 (M); expenditures, $602,533; qualifying distributions, $531,634; giving activities include $490,250 for 51 grants (high: $50,000; low: $500).

Purpose and activities: Giving primarily to educational and cultural institutions.

Fields of interest: Museums; Performing arts; Arts; Higher education; Education; Human services; Children/youth, services.

Limitations: Applications accepted. Giving primarily in Honolulu, HI.

Application information: Application form not required.

Initial approach: Proposal

Deadline(s): None

Officers and Directors:* James S. Campbell,* Pres.; E. Gunner Schull,* V.P. and Secy.; Larry Takumi,* V.P. and Treas.; Rhonda Griswold,* V.P.; Ian McLean Cooke.

EIN: 990285922

2592
James & Abigail Campbell Family Foundation ✧

(formerly James & Abigail Campbell Foundation)
1001 Kamokila Blvd., Ste. 200
Kapolei, HI 96707-2030 (808) 674-3167
Contact: D. Keola Lloyd, Grants Mgr.
FAX: (808) 674-3349;
E-mail: keolal@jamescampbell.com; Main URL: http://www.campbellfamilyfoundation.org

Established in 1980 in HI.

Donor: Members of the Campbell family.

Foundation type: Independent foundation.

Financial data (yr. ended 12/31/12): Assets, $20,183,041 (M); gifts received, $676,432; expenditures, $1,186,519; qualifying distributions, $912,009; giving activities include $772,426 for 27 grants (high: $150,000; low: $5,000).

Purpose and activities: Giving primarily for: 1) programs that address the challenges of young people; 2) public schools, early childhood education and environmental stewardship; and 3) programs that promote values and the health and welfare of Hawaiians.

Fields of interest: Education; Human services; Children/youth, services.

Type of support: Continuing support; Building/renovation; Equipment; Program development; Seed money; Curriculum development; Scholarship funds.

Limitations: Applications accepted. Giving limited to HI, with emphasis on West Oahu: Ewa/Ewa Beach, Kapolei, Makakilo and the Wai'anae Coast. No support for sectarian or religious programs. No grants to individuals, or for endowments, or highly technical research projects; no loans.

Publications: Annual report; Grants list.

Application information: The foundation considers 1 request per organization per calendar year. Application guidelines available on foundation web site. Application form not required.

Initial approach: Proposal (2-3 pages)

Copies of proposal: 1

Deadline(s): Feb. 1 and Aug. 1

Board meeting date(s): Last working day of Apr. and Oct.

Final notification: 2 weeks after board meeting

Officers and Directors:* Wendy B. Crabb,* Pres.; Alice K. Shingle,* V.P.; Alice F. Guild,* Secy.; Jonathan E. Staub,* Treas.; Richard J. Dahl; Kapi 'Olani K. Marignoli; Dorna M. Robinson; Juliette K. Sheehan; Cynthia K. Sorenson.

Number of staff: 2 part-time professional; 1 part-time support.

EIN: 990203078

Selected grants: The following grants are a representative sample of this grantmaker's funding activity:

$150,000 to Island Pacific Academy, Kapolei, HI, 2012. For grant for gymnasium.

$30,000 to University of Hawaii, Honolulu, HI, 2012. For annual request school.

$28,000 to Kapolei High School, Kapolei, HI, 2012. For Engineering and Robotics Program.

$25,000 to Hawaii Community Foundation, Honolulu, HI, 2012. For Dalai Lama Visit.

$20,000 to Family Programs Hawaii, Honolulu, HI, 2012. For Ho ' Omalu O Na Kamali ' I Program.

2593
Harold K. L. Castle Foundation ✧
1197 Auloa Rd.
Kailua, HI 96734-4658 (808) 263-7073
Contact: Ann Matsukado, Cont.
FAX: (808) 261-6918;
E-mail: jguerrero@castlefoundation.org; E-mail for Ann Matsukado:
amatsukado@castlefoundation.org; Main URL: http://www.castlefoundation.org
Facebook: http://www.facebook.com/pages/Kailua-HI/Harold-KL-Castle-Foundation/56297956988?ref=ts
Twitter: http://twitter.com/HaroldKLCastle
YouTube: https://www.youtube.com/user/hklcastle

Incorporated in 1962 in HI.
Donors: Harold K.L. Castle†; Mrs. Harold K.L. Castle†.
Foundation type: Independent foundation.
Financial data (yr. ended 12/31/12): Assets, $165,470,137 (M); expenditures, $11,980,744; qualifying distributions, $8,032,561; giving activities include $5,948,273 for 105 grants (high: $750,000; low: $190).
Purpose and activities: As the largest private foundation in the state of Hawaii, the foundation grants approximately $7,000,000 per year to organizations that serve Hawaii. The foundation is currently focusing on three strategic program areas: 1) Public Education Redesign and Enhancement; 2) Near-Shore Marine Resource Conservation; and 3) Windward Oahu.
Fields of interest: Education, management/technical assistance; Education, public policy; Education, reform; Education, public education; Elementary school/education; Elementary/secondary school reform; Education; Environment, public policy; Environment, water resources; Environment; Youth development; Community/economic development.
Type of support: Management development/capacity building; Program development; Seed money; Technical assistance; Program evaluation.
Limitations: Applications accepted. Giving limited to HI with priority given to Windward Oahu. No grants to individuals, or for ongoing operating expenses, endowments, annual fund drives, vehicles, or sponsorships or special events.
Application information: Within one month of receipt of inquiry, the foundation will contact applicant either to invite a full proposal or to inform applicant that the foundation will be unable to consider the request due to a mismatch with current foundation priorities. If applicant does not receive notification within a month after submitting online application, please contact Elizabeth Murph, Grants Mgr., at tel.: (808) 263-7073 or e-mail: bmurph@castlefoundation.org. Additionally, all prospective applicants must submit information explaining the extent to which the proposed project will help the foundation achieve its strategic goals. Application form required.
Initial approach: Submit online inquiry on foundation's web site
Copies of proposal: 1
Deadline(s): None
Board meeting date(s): Bimonthly
Final notification: Within 1 month of scheduled meeting
Officers and Directors:* H. Mitchell D'Olier,* Chair.; Terrence R. George, C.E.O. and Pres.; Carlton K.C. Au, C.F.O., V.P., and Treas.; Ann Matsukado, Cont.; Dr. Claire L. Asam; Dr. Kittredge A. Baldwin; Corbett A.K. Kalama; James C. McIntosh; Eric K. Yeaman.
Number of staff: 2 full-time professional; 2 part-time professional; 2 full-time support.
EIN: 996005445
Selected grants: The following grants are a representative sample of this grantmaker's funding activity:
$750,000 to Le Jardin Academy, Kailua, HI, 2012. For matching grant for phase 2 of capital campaign.
$500,000 to Nature Conservancy of Hawaii, Honolulu, HI, 2012. For invasive algae removal and reintroduction of native sea urchins to restore reefs of Kaneohe Bay.
$400,000 to Nature Conservancy of Hawaii, Honolulu, HI, 2012. To protect and restore Hawaii's Marine Resources.
$333,252 to University of Hawaii Foundation, Honolulu, HI, 2012. For Hawaii P-20 Partnerships for Education to use data, policy research and communications to increase college enrollment.
$300,000 to New Teacher Center, Santa Cruz, CA, 2012. For Hawaii New Teacher Induction Network.
$250,000 to Bishop Museum, Honolulu, HI, 2012. For challenge grant for educational exhibits in new Pacific Hall.
$250,000 to Castle Medical Center, Kailua, HI, 2012. For capital renovation and renewal to strengthen hospital's ability to provide high-quality health services to Windward Oahu residents.
$200,000 to University of Hawaii Foundation, Honolulu, HI, 2012. For challenge grant for UH Maui College Hawaiian Music Institute.
$50,000 to Hawaiian Educational Council, Honolulu, HI, 2012. To establish Malama Honua Learning Center Charter School and Education Leadership Institute.
$30,000 to Malama Maunalua, Honolulu, HI, 2012. To build community-based plan for marine resources in Maunalua Bay.

2594
Samuel N. and Mary Castle Foundation ✧
Pacific Guardian Ctr., Makai Twr.
733 Bishop St., Ste. 1275
Honolulu, HI 96813-4019 (808) 522-1101
Contact: Alfred L. Castle, Exec. Dir.
FAX: (802) 522-1103;
E-mail: snandmarycastle@hawaii.rr.com; Main URL: http://foundationcenter.org/grantmaker/castle/

Founded as S.N. Castle Memorial Trust in 1894; incorporated as a foundation in 1925 in HI.
Donors: Mary Castle†; Samuel N. Castle†.
Foundation type: Independent foundation.
Financial data (yr. ended 12/31/13): Assets, $47,043,222 (M); expenditures, $2,251,179; qualifying distributions, $1,983,762; giving activities include $1,715,500 for 69 grants (high: $175,000; low: $2,000).
Purpose and activities: The foundation is committed to providing resources to improve the life of Hawaii's children and families by improving the quality and quantity of early education, K-12, independent schools, and arts and cultural institutions. Preference is given to pre-schools, K-12 independent schools and other organizations which improve the lives of low income children and families.
Fields of interest: Historical activities; Arts; Education, early childhood education; Elementary school/education; Teacher school/education; Child development, services; Children/youth; Children; Economically disadvantaged.
Type of support: Capital campaigns; Building/renovation; Equipment; Program development; Seed money; Curriculum development; Scholarship funds; Technical assistance; Program evaluation; Matching/challenge support.
Limitations: Applications accepted. Giving generally limited to HI. Generally, no support for publicly funded organizations, public and government funded charter schools, or for lobbying organizations. No grants to individuals, or for continuing support; generally, no support for general operating budgets, endowment funds, more than 30 percent of total project cost, projects in which parents and community have not been properly involved in planning and funding, annual campaigns, scholarships, or research; no loans.
Publications: Application guidelines; Annual report; Annual report (including application guidelines); Financial statement; Grants list; Occasional report; Program policy statement.
Application information: Major capital requests of $25,000 or more considered at Dec. meeting only, with preferences given to organizations with which trustees are involved or that trustees have invited to apply. Application form not required.
Initial approach: Contact Exec. Dir. by mail, e-mail, telephone or in-person visit prior to submitting a proposal
Copies of proposal: 2
Deadline(s): Feb. 1, June 1, and Oct. 1
Board meeting date(s): Apr., Aug., and Dec.
Final notification: 2 months
Officers and Trustees:* Dr. Robert G. Peters,* Pres.; Kitt Baldwin,* V.P.; James C. McIntosh,* V.P.; Cynthia Quisenberry,* Secy.; Alfred L. Castle,* Treas. and Exec. Dir.
Number of staff: 1 full-time professional; 1 part-time support.
EIN: 996003321
Selected grants: The following grants are a representative sample of this grantmaker's funding activity:
$35,000 to University of Hawaii Foundation, Honolulu, HI, 2012. For Pre-K-3 Data Entry and Assessment.
$15,000 to Kokua Kalihi Valley Comprehensive Family Services, Honolulu, HI, 2012. For Early Childhood Program and Expansion to Linapuni K-l School.
$1,446 to Maui Economic Opportunity, Wailuku, HI, 2012. For emergency pre-school staff (raining.

2595
Central Pacific Bank Foundation ✧ ☆
c/o Scott Hino
220 S. King St.
Honolulu, HI 96813-4526 (808) 544-3673
Main URL: https://www.centralpacificbank.com/About-CPB/Works-For-You/In-Our-Community.aspx

Established in 2007 in HI.
Donors: John Dean; Central Pacific Bank.
Foundation type: Company-sponsored foundation.
Financial data (yr. ended 12/31/12): Assets, $9,113,651 (M); gifts received, $3,579,664; expenditures, $530,640; qualifying distributions, $434,417; giving activities include $434,417 for grants.
Purpose and activities: The foundation supports programs designed to promote education and community development.

Fields of interest: Education; Housing/shelter, home owners; American Red Cross; Youth, services; Community/economic development.
Type of support: General/operating support; Program development.
Limitations: Giving primarily in areas of company operations Honolulu, HI. No support for political action committees or candidates, fraternal or alumni organizations, private non-operating foundations, athletic teams, social groups, or discriminatory organizations. No grants to individuals or for sponsorships.
Application information:
Initial approach: Contact foundation for updated application guidelines
Officers: Denis K. Isono, Chair. and Pres.; Glenn Ching, V.P. and Secy.; Reid A. Gushiken, V.P. and Treas.; Wayne H. Kirihara, V.P.; Catherine Ngo, V.P.; Donna Takeda, V.P.
EIN: 392068708

2596
The Clarence T. C. Ching Foundation ✧
1001 Bishop St., Ste. 770
Honolulu, HI 96813-3406 (808) 521-0344
Contact: R. Stevens Gilley, Pres.
E-mail: admin@chingfoundation.org; Main URL: http://www.clarencetcchingfoundation.org/

Established in 1967.
Donors: Loyalty Development Co., Ltd.; Kukui Gardens Corporation.
Foundation type: Company-sponsored foundation.
Financial data (yr. ended 12/31/12): Assets, $107,426,446 (M); expenditures, $6,366,632; qualifying distributions, $5,592,989; giving activities include $5,079,285 for 11 grants (high: $1,000,000; low: $15,000).
Purpose and activities: The foundation supports organizations involved with arts and culture, education, health care, and science. Special emphasis is directed toward programs designed to serve the needy, sick, or aged.
Fields of interest: Performing arts, music; Literature; Arts; Higher education; Education; Hospitals (general); Health care; YM/YWCAs & YM/YWHAs; Science; Economically disadvantaged.
Type of support: General/operating support; Capital campaigns; Building/renovation; Program development; Scholarship funds; Research; Matching/challenge support.
Limitations: Applications accepted. Giving primarily in Honolulu, HI. No support for political organizations or candidates. No grants to individuals, or for government services, publications, films, or videos, commercial or business development, conferences or seminars, benefit events, annual campaigns, or endowments.
Publications: Application guidelines.
Application information: Faxed and e-mailed submissions are not accepted. Letters of inquiry should be two to three pages. Organizations receiving support are asked to submit an interim report and a final report.
Initial approach: Letter of inquiry
Deadline(s): Jan. 31 and July 31
Board meeting date(s): Mar. and Sept.
Officers and Trustees:* John K. Tsui,* Chair.; Raymond J. Tam, Vice-Chair. and Secy.; R. Stevens Gilley, Pres.; Peter P.J. Ng,* Treas.; Catherine H.Q. Ching; Kenneth T. Okamoto.
EIN: 996014634

Selected grants: The following grants are a representative sample of this grantmaker's funding activity:
$1,000,000 to Saint Louis School, Honolulu, HI, 2012. For program support.
$714,285 to Chaminade University of Honolulu, Honolulu, HI, 2012. For capital improvements.
$600,000 to Maryknoll Schools, Honolulu, HI, 2012. For capital improvements.
$500,000 to Catholic Charities Hawaii, Honolulu, HI, 2012. For capital improvements.
$500,000 to Punahou School, Honolulu, HI, 2012. For program support.
$500,000 to Saint Francis School, Honolulu, HI, 2012. For capital improvements.
$400,000 to Palolo Chinese Home, Honolulu, HI, 2012. For capital improvements.
$300,000 to Saint John the Baptist Catholic School, Honolulu, HI, 2012. For capital improvements.
$300,000 to Salvation Army of Hawaiian Islands, Hawaiian and Pacific Islands Divison, Honolulu, HI, 2012. For capital improvement.
$250,000 to Hanahauoli School, Honolulu, HI, 2012. For program support.

2597
Cooke Foundation, Ltd. ✧
827 Fort St. Mall
Honolulu, HI 96813-4317 (808) 566-5524
Contact: Amy Luersen
FAX: (808) 521-6286;
E-mail: foundations@hcf-hawaii.org; Contact if applicant cannot submit proposal online: Terry Savage, tel.: (808) 566-5508, e-mail: tsavage@hcf-hawaii.org; toll-free tel. from neighboring islands: (888) 731-3863, ext. 508; Main URL: http://www.cookefdn.org

Trust established in 1920 in HI; incorporated in 1971.
Donor: Anna C. Cooke†.
Foundation type: Independent foundation.
Financial data (yr. ended 06/30/13): Assets, $22,040,871 (M); expenditures, $1,415,237; qualifying distributions, $1,228,727; giving activities include $1,070,885 for 65 grants (high: $100,000; low: $4,000).
Purpose and activities: Giving to assure the continuance of, and also to expand and extend all worthy endeavors for the betterment and welfare of the people of Hawaii.
Fields of interest: Humanities; Education; Environment; Health care; Health organizations, association; Human services.
Type of support: Management development/capacity building; Capital campaigns; Building/renovation; Equipment; Program development; Seed money; Technical assistance; Consulting services; Program evaluation; Matching/challenge support.
Limitations: Applications accepted. Giving limited to HI and to organizations serving the people of HI. No support for religious organizations, unless the forebears were involved with them, or to supporting organizations classified under section 509(a)(3). No grants to individuals, or for scholarships, fellowships, general operations, or endowment funds; no loans.
Publications: Application guidelines; Annual report (including application guidelines); Financial statement; Grants list.
Application information: Applicants must first establish an online account with the Hawaii Community Foundation to access the online application. If the applicant is requesting an account for the first time, it may take two to three days to receive the account information. It is recommended to request an account early enough in order to allow adequate time to complete the application by the submission deadline. Applicants must be in existence for 5 years and be in stable financial condition. Applications from a unit of the University of Hawai'i must be submitted through the University of Hawai'i Foundation. Requests for more than $20,000 must be sponsored by a trustee. Requests for more than $5,000 should demonstrate that the Cooke Foundation portion of the budget does not exceed 30 percent of the total project budget. Application form required.
Initial approach: Use online application process on foundation web site
Copies of proposal: 1
Deadline(s): See foundation web site for current deadlines
Board meeting date(s): May and Nov.
Final notification: Early June for Mar. submissions, and early Dec. for Sept. submissions
Officers and Trustees:* Dale S. Bachman,* Pres.; Caroline Bond Davis,* V.P. and Secy.; Charles C. Spalding, Jr.,* V.P. and Treas.; Catherine Cooke,* V.P.; Lissa Dunford,* V.P.; Lynne Johnson,* V.P.
EIN: 237120804

2598
First Hawaiian Bank Foundation ✧
(formerly First Hawaiian Foundation)
999 Bishop St.
Honolulu, HI 96813-4423 (808) 525-7777
Contact: Sharon Shiroma Brown, Pres.
FAX: (808) 525-8708;
E-mail: FHBFoundation@fhb.com; Main URL: http://www.fhb.com/about-corp-giving.htm

Established in 1975 in HI.
Donors: First Hawaiian Bank; BancWest Corp.
Foundation type: Company-sponsored foundation.
Financial data (yr. ended 12/31/13): Assets, $12,708,089 (M); gifts received, $2,004; expenditures, $1,494,531; qualifying distributions, $1,482,614; giving activities include $1,482,614 for 66 grants (high: $200,000; low: $1,000).
Purpose and activities: The foundation supports programs designed to meet community needs; improve access to health care; provide educational opportunities; serve youth and children; and enrich life through culture and the arts.
Fields of interest: Arts; Elementary/secondary education; Education; Hospitals (general); Health care; Children/youth, services; Residential/custodial care, hospices; Human services; Community/economic development; Foundations (community); United Ways and Federated Giving Programs; Religion.
Type of support: Management development/capacity building; Continuing support; Annual campaigns; Capital campaigns; Building/renovation; Equipment; Endowments; Program development; Employee volunteer services; Sponsorships.
Limitations: Applications accepted. Giving primarily in areas of company operations in Honolulu, HI. No grants for ongoing general operating support, endowments, sponsorships, conferences, or special events.
Publications: Application guidelines.
Application information: Application form required.

Initial approach: Complete online application
Deadline(s): E-mail foundation for deadline dates
Board meeting date(s): Quarterly

Officers and Directors:* Robert S. Harrison,* Chair.; Sharon Shiroma Brown,* Pres.; Gary L. Caulfield,* V.P.; William E. Atwater III,* Secy.; Albert M. Yamada,* Treas.; Alan H. Arisumi; Winston K.H. Chow; Brandt G. Farias; Robert T. Fujioka; Anthony R. Guerrero, Jr.; Donald G. Horner; Corbett A.K. Kalama; Iris Y. Matsumoto; Kristi L. Maynard; Robin S. Midkiff; James W. Mills; Melvin W.Y. Mow; Raymond S. Ono; Curt T. Otaguro; Lily K. Yao.
EIN: 237437822

Selected grants: The following grants are a representative sample of this grantmaker's funding activity:
$50,000 to Hospice of Hilo, Hilo, HI, 2012. To support construction of Medicare-certified hospice in-patient facility.
$20,000 to Hanalani Schools, Mililani, HI, 2012. To support $2 5 million capital campaign to add classrooms and make upgrades.

2599
Frost Family Foundation ✧ ☆
c/o Horizon Financial
353 Hanamau St., Ste. 21
Kahului, HI 96732-2474 (808) 524-8099
Contact: Karin A. Frost, Tr.

Donor: Karin A. Frost.
Foundation type: Independent foundation.
Financial data (yr. ended 08/31/13): Assets, $10,234,391 (M); expenditures, $585,730; qualifying distributions, $545,039; giving activities include $524,000 for 8 grants (high: $252,000; low: $15,000).
Fields of interest: Foundations (community).
Limitations: Applications accepted. Giving primarily in HI.
Application information: Application form required.
Initial approach: Proposal
Deadline(s): None
Trustee: Karin A. Frost.
EIN: 273374284

2600
Victoria S. & Bradley L. Geist Foundation ✧
c/o Hawaii Community Foundation
827 Fort Street Mall
Honolulu, HI 96813-4317 (808) 537-6333
Contact: Amy Luersen, Dir. of Philanthropic Svcs., Hawaii Community Foundation
E-mail: foundations@hcf-hawaii.org; Main URL: http://www.hawaiicommunityfoundation.org

Established in 1975 in HI.
Donor: Bradley L. Geist Trust.
Foundation type: Independent foundation.
Financial data (yr. ended 12/31/13): Assets, $41,922,951 (M); expenditures, $2,446,381; qualifying distributions, $2,235,981; giving activities include $1,799,087 for 30 grants (high: $300,000; low: $5,824), and $175,875 for 76 grants to individuals (high: $5,000; low: $500).
Purpose and activities: The foundation has particular interest in programs involving the recruitment, initial and follow-up training, or retention of foster parents, sibling connectivity projects and supporting transitioning foster youth. The foundation also provides grants for medical research, and to support researchers to investigate key health issues within the context of both national research trends, and the reality of conducting studies in today's high-cost environment.
Fields of interest: Higher education; Education; Human services; Children/youth, services.
Type of support: Program development; Seed money; Research; Consulting services; Program evaluation; Scholarships—to individuals.
Limitations: Applications accepted. Giving limited to HI residents and organizations. No grants for capital projects, endowment funds, or for on-going or general operating costs.
Publications: Application guidelines.
Application information: Application form required.
Initial approach: Use online application process on foundation web site
Copies of proposal: 1
Deadline(s): See foundation web site for current deadlines
Board meeting date(s): Mar., July, and Nov. for Transitioning Foster Youth and Foster Parent funds; and May and Nov. for Medical Research
Trustees: Charman J. Akina; Gary S. Morimoto; Bank of Hawaii.
EIN: 990163400

2601
The Hau'oli Mau Loa Foundation ✧
701 Bishop St.
Honolulu, HI 96813-4814 (808) 545-4212
Contact: General inquiries:: Anela Shimizu, Opers. Mgr.
FAX: (808) 440-0061;
E-mail: info@hauolimauloa.org; Main URL: http://www.hauolimauloa.org

Established in 1990 in NY.
Donors: Helga Glaesel-Hollenback†; Edwin Hollenback†; Edwin Hollenback 1998 Trust; Helga Glaesel-Hollenback 1990 Trust.
Foundation type: Independent foundation.
Financial data (yr. ended 12/31/12): Assets, $138,402,848 (M); expenditures, $8,096,046; qualifying distributions, $6,594,177; giving activities include $5,091,223 for 33 grants (high: $445,182; low: $25,000).
Purpose and activities: Giving primarily to help the less fortunate, especially children, and to enhance stewardship, preservation, and protection of the environment.
Fields of interest: Environment; Children/youth, services; International relief.
Type of support: General/operating support.
Limitations: Applications not accepted. Giving primarily in HI. No grants to individuals.
Publications: Informational brochure; Occasional report; Program policy statement.
Application information: Contributes only to pre-selected organizations.
Officers and Directors:* Hans Bertram-Nothnagel,* Pres.; Wayne M. Pitluck,* V.P.; Janis A. Reischmann, Exec. Dir.
Number of staff: 4 full-time professional; 1 full-time support.
EIN: 133588071

2602
Hawaii Community Foundation ✧
(formerly The Hawaiian Foundation)
827 Fort St. Mall
Honolulu, HI 96813 (808) 537-6333
Contact: Kelvin H. Taketa, C.E.O.
FAX: (808) 521-6286; E-mail: info@hcf-hawaii.org; Additional tel.: (888) 731-3863; Main URL: http://www.hawaiicommunityfoundation.org
Facebook: http://www.facebook.com/pages/Hawaii-Community-Foundation/31768973510
Flickr: http://www.flickr.com/photos/hcfhawaii
GiveSmart: http://www.givesmart.org/Stories/Donors/Kelvin-Taketa
LinkedIn: http://www.linkedin.com/in/hcfhawaii
Twitter: http://twitter.com/hcfhawaii
YouTube: http://www.youtube.com/hcfhawaii
Scholarship inquiry e-mail: scholarships@hcf-hawaii.org

Established in 1916 in HI by trust resolution; incorporated in 1987; reorganized in 1988.
Foundation type: Community foundation.
Financial data (yr. ended 12/31/12): Assets, $426,636,217 (M); gifts received, $23,901,041; expenditures, $37,161,178; giving activities include $25,843,999 for 462+ grants (high: $1,477,422), and $1,517,980 for 1,431 grants to individuals.
Purpose and activities: The foundation helps people make a difference by inspiring the spirit of giving and by investing in people and solutions to benefit every island community.
Fields of interest: Historic preservation/historical societies; Arts; Adult/continuing education; Education, reading; Education; Environment, natural resources; Environmental education; Environment; Health care; Mental health, treatment; Medical research, institute; Residential/custodial care; Aging, centers/services; Human services; Nonprofit management; Community/economic development; Leadership development; Aging; Economically disadvantaged.
Type of support: Travel awards; Management development/capacity building; Program development; Scholarship funds; Research; Technical assistance; Consulting services; Scholarships—to individuals.
Limitations: Applications accepted. Giving limited to HI. No grants to individuals (except for scholarships), or for annual campaigns, emergency support, endowments, major capital projects, ongoing operating support, tuition aid programs, or deficit financing; no loans.
Publications: Application guidelines; Annual report; Financial statement; Informational brochure; Newsletter; Program policy statement.
Application information: Application procedures vary with the foundation's different grantmaking programs. Visit foundation web site for application instructions, application forms, and specific deadlines. Application form required.
Initial approach: Contact foundation
Copies of proposal: 1
Deadline(s): Varies
Board meeting date(s): Varies
Final notification: Within 3 months of proposal deadline
Officers and Board Members:* Paul Kosasa,* Chair.; Deborah Berger,* Vice-Chair.; Kelvin H. Taketa, C.E.O. and Pres.; Wally Chin, V.P. and C.F.O.; Tom Kelly, V.P., Knowledge, Evaluation and Learning; Joseph Martyak, V.P., Comms.; Tammi Chun, V.P., Progs.; Curtis Saiki, V.P., Philanthropy

and Genl. Counsel; Myles Shibata, V.P., Mktg. Initiatives; Chris van Bergeijk, V.P. and C.O.O.; Gary Caulfield,* Secy.; Cathy Luke,* Treas.; Robert R. Bean; Mary G.F. Bitterman; Michael Broderick; Kimberly W. Dey; Elizabeth Rice Grossman; Richard W. Gushman II; Robert S. Harrison; Dorothy "Honey Bun" Haynes; Peter Ho; Tyrie Lee Jenkins; Micah A. Kane; Katherine G. Richardson; Jennifer Goto Sabas; Barry K. Taniguchi; James Wei; Eric K. Yeaman.
Number of staff: 39 full-time professional; 3 part-time professional; 12 full-time support; 1 part-time support.
EIN: 990261283
Selected grants: The following grants are a representative sample of this grantmaker's funding activity:
$2,260,797 to Research Corporation of the University of Hawaii, Honolulu, HI, 2012. For Office of Information Management and Technology to research and develop effective plans for statewide information technology activities.
$1,000,000 to Punahou School, Honolulu, HI, 2012. For six year $6M matching grant; up to $1m per year for no more than 6 years/$6m to support the construction of the K-1 neighborhood.
$907,272 to Hawaii Leadership Forum, Honolulu, HI, 2012. For operating support for Omidyar Fellows Program of the Hawaii Leadership Forum.
$388,000 to Kapiolani Health Foundation, Honolulu, HI, 2012. For LEED building renovations for the NICU/PICU.
$200,000 to Collaborative Leaders Network, Honolulu, HI, 2012. For efforts to develop effective statewide plans for early childhood development in Hawaii.
$200,000 to Kanu Hawaii, Honolulu, HI, 2012. For general support funding.
$118,804 to Honolulu Theater for Youth, Honolulu, HI, 2012. For Artists in the Schools.
$113,023 to Childrens Research Triangle, Chicago, IL, 2012. For Improving Birth Outcomes: Prevention and Early Intervention for Alcohol/Drug Use in Pregnancy.
$7,000 to Salvation Army of Hawaiian Islands, Honolulu, HI, 2012. For unrestricted support.
$6,500 to Kalani High School, Honolulu, HI, 2012. For Kipuka Kalani'iki Sustainability Program.

2603
Hawaiian Electric Industries Charitable Foundation ✧

(also known as H.E.I. Charitable Foundation)
P.O. Box 730
Honolulu, HI 96808-0730 (808) 543-7960
Contact: Denise Tanaka
FAX: (808) 203-1390; E-mail: heicf@hei.com; Main URL: http://www.hei.com/phoenix.zhtml?c=101675&p=charitable-foundation

Established in 1984 in HI.
Donor: Hawaiian Electric Industries, Inc.
Foundation type: Company-sponsored foundation.
Financial data (yr. ended 12/31/12): Assets, $2,573,271 (M); expenditures, $1,579,993; qualifying distributions, $1,575,958; giving activities include $1,539,164 for 68 grants (high: $440,000; low: $1,000), and $36,794 for employee matching gifts.
Purpose and activities: The foundation supports programs designed to promote educational excellence, economic growth, and environmental sustainability.
Fields of interest: Education; Environment; Family services; Community/economic development.
Type of support: Employee volunteer services; General/operating support; Continuing support; Capital campaigns; Program development; Employee matching gifts.
Limitations: Applications accepted. Giving limited to HI. No support for political, religious, veterans', fraternal, or labor organizations. No grants to individuals or for advertising, dinners, or tournaments.
Publications: Application guidelines; Annual report.
Application information: Support is limited to 1 contribution per organization during any given year. Organizations receiving support are asked to submit a final report. Application form required.
Initial approach: Download application form and mail proposal and application form to foundation
Copies of proposal: 1
Deadline(s): Jan. 1, Apr. 1, July 1, and Oct. 1
Board meeting date(s): Quarterly
Officers and Directors:* Alan Oshima,* Chair.; Constance H. Lau,* Pres.; James A. Ajello, V.P., Finance and Treas.; Chester A. Richardson,* Secy.; Richard M. Rosenblum; Richard F. Wacker; Jeffrey N. Watanabe.
Number of staff: 1 full-time professional; 1 full-time support.
EIN: 990230697

2604
HMSA Foundation ✧

(also known as Hawaii Medical Service Association Foundation)
P.O. Box 860
Honolulu, HI 96808-0860 (808) 948-5585
Contact: Mark L. Forman, Exec. Admin.
FAX: (808) 948-6860;
E-mail: mark_forman@hmsa.com; Main URL: http://www.hmsafoundation.org

Established in 1997 in HI.
Donors: Pacific Century Trust; American Healthways; Hawaii Community Services Council; Hawaii Institute for Integrative Healthcare Research; University of California, San Francisco; Health Plan Hawaii Foundation; The Robert Wood Johnson Foundation; The Queen's Medical Centers; Hale Makua; Hawaii State Center for Nursing.
Foundation type: Independent foundation.
Financial data (yr. ended 12/31/12): Assets, $24,715,718 (M); gifts received, $25; expenditures, $1,749,063; qualifying distributions, $1,335,209; giving activities include $1,335,209 for 40 grants (high: $150,000; low: $2,000).
Purpose and activities: The purpose of the foundation is to provide access to cost-effective healthcare services; health promotion, education, and research; and the promotion of social welfare.
Fields of interest: Higher education; Hospitals (general); Medical care, outpatient care; Health care; Health organizations, association; Medical research, institute; Human services; Children, services; Community/economic development.
Type of support: General/operating support; Scholarship funds.
Limitations: Applications accepted. Giving primarily in Honolulu, HI. No grants to individuals; or for scholarship funds, lobbying, voter registration, capital projects, endowments, development campaigns or multi-year commitments.
Publications: Application guidelines; Annual report; Grants list.
Application information: Application information and cover sheet available on foundation web site.
Initial approach: Letter or telephone at least 2 weeks before application due date
Copies of proposal: 1
Deadline(s): Jan. 1 for Mar. review, Apr. 1 for June review, July 1 for Sept. review, and Oct. 1 for Dec. review
Officers and Directors:* Robert P. Hiam,* Chair.; Michael A. Gold,* Pres.; Tim Johns, V.P.; Elisa Yadao, Secy.; Steve Van Ribbink, Treas.; Elena Cabatu; Robin Campaniano; Andrew I.T. Chang; Michael J. Chun, Ph.D.; Terry George; Marvin B. Hall; Gary Kajiwara; Maile Kanemaru.
EIN: 990250429
Selected grants: The following grants are a representative sample of this grantmaker's funding activity:
$150,000 to Aloha Medical Mission, Honolulu, HI, 2012. To enable Aloha Medical Mission to continue and hygiene essentials care to the underserved people of Hawaii.
$130,000 to Hawaii Health Systems Foundation, Honolulu, HI, 2012. To provide statewide palliative and hospice care training at state hospitals.
$120,000 to University of Hawaii Foundation, Honolulu, HI, 2012. For Hawaii Initiative for Childhood Obesity Research and Education and Hawaii 5210 Initiative Let's Go! project to create environments that support healthy eating and active living for children and families.
$100,000 to Rehabilitation Hospital of the Pacific Foundation, Honolulu, HI, 2012. To renovate existing wing to be the new suite of exam rooms for physiatrists.
$100,000 to Special Olympics Hawaii, Honolulu, HI, 2012. For Creation of a multi-purpose sports, education, fitness and wellness facility in Kapolei with emphasis on providing accessible facilities to persons with intellectual disabilities to showcase their abilities.
$100,000 to University of Hawaii Foundation, Honolulu, HI, 2012. To improve oral health for native Hawaiian prenatal mothers and children Develop and implement culturally appropriate project to target native Hawaiians to provide hands on oral health educational sessions and screenings for 3rd and 7th grade students and pr.
$60,000 to Hospice of Hilo, Hilo, HI, 2012. For Palliative Care Center in-patient hospice facility that will serve the entire island of Hawaii.
$50,000 to Planned Parenthood of Hawaii, Honolulu, HI, 2012. To expand health care services to the island of Kauai by offering free or low-cost family and hygiene essentials teens and low-income individuals.
$50,000 to YMCA of Honolulu, Honolulu, HI, 2012. For N E W Kids Addressing Hawaii's Childhood Obesity Crisis a Program to work with severely obese children that will result in a decrease in medical complications for the highest risk population.
$25,000 to Child and Family Service, Ewa Beach, HI, 2012. To create adaption of the Trauma Informed Care curriculum by integrating native Hawaiian practices in and hygiene essentials impact among native Hawaiian clients.

2605
Teresa F. Hughes Trust ✧ ☆
c/o Bank of Hawaii, No. 758
P.O. Box 3170
Honolulu, HI 96802-3170
Contact: Paula Boyce, Asst. V.P., Bank of Hawaii
E-mail for Paula Boyce: paula.boyce@boh.com; Main URL: http://www.boh.com/philanthropy

Established in 1991 in HI.
Donor: Teresa F. Hughes†.
Foundation type: Independent foundation.
Financial data (yr. ended 03/31/14): Assets, $8,372,179 (M); expenditures, $646,470; qualifying distributions, $581,380; giving activities include $510,000 for 19 grants (high: $50,000; low: $10,000).
Purpose and activities: Grants restricted to support programs and projects that serve adults at least 70 years of age who are physically or mentally ill, and children under 18 years of age who have been abused, neglected or abandoned or reside in a household where abuse has occurred. Also provides block grants to community-based service organizations, which in turn distribute funds in the form of financial assistance to eligible adults and children who are residents of Hawaii only.
Fields of interest: Human services; Children/youth, services; Family services; Aging, centers/services; Aging; Economically disadvantaged.
Type of support: Emergency funds; Program development.
Limitations: Applications accepted. Giving limited to HI.
Publications: Application guidelines.
Application information: Signed cover sheet must accompany proposal. Application form required.
Initial approach: Proposal for grants (not to exceed 3 pages)
Copies of proposal: 3
Deadline(s): Apr. 30 for persons in need and Sept. 1 for program support
Final notification: Ninety days after deadline
Trustees: Suzanne Smith Churchill; Bank of Hawaii.
EIN: 990042494
Selected grants: The following grants are a representative sample of this grantmaker's funding activity:
$50,000 to Family Programs Hawaii, Honolulu, HI, 2013. For PIN for Children (Enhancements).
$20,000 to Molokai General Hospital, Kaunakakai, HI, 2013. For PIN for Adults and Children.
$10,000 to Rehabilitation Hospital of the Pacific Foundation, Honolulu, HI, 2013. For PIN for Adults.

2606
Island Insurance Foundation ✧
1022 Bethel St.
Honolulu, HI 96813-4302
Contact: Franklin M. Tokioka, Chair.

Established in 2002 in HI; classified as a company-sponsored operating foundation in 2003.
Donors: Island Insurance Co., Ltd.; Tradewind Capital Group Inc.
Foundation type: Operating foundation.
Financial data (yr. ended 12/31/13): Assets, $12,685,198 (M); gifts received, $976,000; expenditures, $640,122; qualifying distributions, $640,122; giving activities include $579,370 for 100 grants (high: $58,630; low: $25).
Purpose and activities: The foundation supports organizations involved with arts and culture, K-12 and higher education, health, children and youth, family services, community development, and other areas.
Fields of interest: Arts; Education; Health care.
Type of support: Continuing support; Capital campaigns; Program development; Employee matching gifts; Matching/challenge support.
Limitations: Applications accepted. Giving primarily in HI.
Application information: Application form required.
Initial approach: Letter
Deadline(s): None
Officers and Directors:* Franklin M. Tokioka,* Chair.; Tyler M. Tokioka,* Pres. and Secy.; Colbert M. Matsumoto,* V.P.; Nolan N. Kawano, Treas.; John F. Schapperle; Lionel Y. Tokioka.
EIN: 710894475

2607
The Kosasa Foundation ✧
766 Pohukaina St.
Honolulu, HI 96813-5307 (808) 591-2550
Contact: Paul J. Kosasa, Pres.

Established in 1994 in HI.
Donors: Gloria J. Gainsley; Stephen E. Gainsley; Lisa C. Kosasa; Minnie Kosasa; Sidney S. Kosasa; Paul J. Kosasa; Susan M. Kosasa; Thomas S. Kosasa; Wilfred Nishi; Atlanta/Sosnoff Capital Corp.; Central Pacific Bank; Island Insurance Foundation.
Foundation type: Independent foundation.
Financial data (yr. ended 07/31/13): Assets, $15,495,157 (M); gifts received, $2,000; expenditures, $806,926; qualifying distributions, $725,500; giving activities include $725,500 for grants.
Purpose and activities: Giving primarily for the arts, education, and children, youth, and social services.
Fields of interest: Arts; Education; Health care; Human services; Children/youth, services.
Limitations: Giving primarily in Honolulu, HI.
Application information: Application form not required.
Initial approach: Letter
Deadline(s): None
Officers and Directors:* Paul J. Kosasa,* Pres. and Treas.; Minnie Kosasa,* V.P.; Gloria Gainsley,* V.P.; Susan M. Kosasa,* Secy.; Sidney S. Kosasa, Chair. Emeritus; Thomas S. Kosasa.
EIN: 990313279
Selected grants: The following grants are a representative sample of this grantmaker's funding activity:
$60,000 to Punahou School, Honolulu, HI, 2013. For K-1 Renovation Fund.
$50,000 to Central Union Church, Honolulu, HI, 2013. For Preschool and Rebuilding of Admin Building and Classrooms.
$50,000 to Damien Memorial School, Honolulu, HI, 2013. For E Ho ' Opa ' a Capital Campaign.
$50,000 to Japanese Cultural Center of Hawaii, Honolulu, HI, 2013. For Okage Sama De - a Living Legacy Campaign.
$25,000 to Bishop Museum, Honolulu, HI, 2013. For Pacific Hall Restoration Project.
$25,000 to Castle Medical Center, Kailua, HI, 2013. For Comprehensive Renovation and Revitalization Project.
$25,000 to Rehabilitation Hospital of the Pacific Foundation, Honolulu, HI, 2013. To support Rehab Programs.
$25,000 to Sacred Hearts Academy, Honolulu, HI, 2013. To support the Clarence T.C. Ching Student Center.
$15,000 to Visitor Aloha Society of Hawaii, Honolulu, HI, 2013. For Staffing Expansion Program.
$10,000 to Palama Settlement, Honolulu, HI, 2013. To support Blackfield and Friends Education Scholarship Program.

2608
The Kutler Family Foundation ✧
68-1022 Honokaope St.
Kamuela, HI 96743-8600

Established in 1997 in CA.
Donor: Jon B. Kutler.
Foundation type: Independent foundation.
Financial data (yr. ended 12/31/13): Assets, $168,104 (M); gifts received, $523,379; expenditures, $543,020; qualifying distributions, $542,325; giving activities include $542,325 for 14 grants (high: $500,400; low: $225).
Fields of interest: Education.
Limitations: Applications not accepted. Giving primarily in CA. No grants to individuals.
Application information: Unsolicited requests for funds not accepted.
Officers: Jon B. Kutler, Pres.; Sara L. Kutler, C.F.O.
EIN: 954661920

2609
Robert F. Lange Foundation ✧
P.O. Box 3170, Dept. 715
Honolulu, HI 96802-3170

Established in 1972 in HI.
Donors: Anna Lange†; Nora E. Lange†.
Foundation type: Independent foundation.
Financial data (yr. ended 12/31/13): Assets, $9,393,492 (M); expenditures, $578,685; qualifying distributions, $474,804; giving activities include $450,000 for 2 grants (high: $225,000; low: $225,000).
Purpose and activities: Giving primarily for Asian art and services for children.
Fields of interest: Arts, cultural/ethnic awareness; Museums; Children/youth, services; Family services.
Type of support: Program development.
Limitations: Applications not accepted. Giving limited to Honolulu, HI. No grants to individuals.
Application information: Contributes only to pre-selected organizations.
Board meeting date(s): Mar.
Officers and Directors:* John Lockwood,* Pres.; David Franklin,* V.P.; Patti Lyons,* V.P.; Ruedi F. Thoeni,* V.P.; Mary F. Williamson,* V.P.; Marilynn Matsumoto,* Secy.-Treas.
EIN: 237241511
Selected grants: The following grants are a representative sample of this grantmaker's funding activity:
$215,000 to Child and Family Service, Ewa Beach, HI, 2011.
$215,000 to Honolulu Academy of Arts, Honolulu, HI, 2011.

2610
The Learning Coalition ✧ ☆
900 Fort St., No. 1800
Honolulu, HI 96813-3779

Donors: Deborah K. Berger; William H. Reeves.
Foundation type: Independent foundation.
Financial data (yr. ended 12/31/12): Assets, $241,809 (M); gifts received, $925,714; expenditures, $895,878; qualifying distributions, $457,254; giving activities include $457,254 for grants.
Fields of interest: Education; Human services; Foundations (community); Public affairs.
Limitations: Applications not accepted. Giving primarily in HI.
Application information: Unsolicited requests for funds not accepted.
Officers and Directors:* Deborah K. Berger,* Pres. and Secy.; William H. Reeves,* V.P. and Treas.; Matt Lorin, V.P.; Lori L. Nelson.
EIN: 800253359

2611
LGA Family Foundation ✧
(formerly Leburta Atherton Foundation)
c/o Bank of Hawaii
P.O. Box 3170, Dept. 715
Honolulu, HI 96802-3170

Established in 1997 in HI.
Donor: Leburta G. Atherton 2003 Charitable Lead Trust.
Foundation type: Independent foundation.
Financial data (yr. ended 12/31/13): Assets, $16,848,172 (M); expenditures, $689,421; qualifying distributions, $677,523; giving activities include $667,500 for 22 grants (high: $100,000; low: $1,000).
Fields of interest: Education; Health care; Cancer research; Human services.
Limitations: Applications not accepted. Giving primarily in Long Beach, CA, and HI.
Application information: Unsolicited requests for funds not accepted.
Officers and Directors:* Leburta G. Atherton,* Pres.; Marjory A. Newell,* V.P.; Frank C. Atherton II,* Secy.; Balbi A. Brooks,* Treas.
EIN: 943260209
Selected grants: The following grants are a representative sample of this grantmaker's funding activity:
$100,000 to American Cancer Society, Honolulu, HI, 2011.
$100,000 to Central Union Church, Honolulu, HI, 2011.
$30,000 to Cystic Fibrosis Foundation, Bethesda, MD, 2011.
$25,000 to American Red Cross, Hawaii Chapter, Honolulu, HI, 2011.
$25,000 to Children's Defense Fund, Washington, DC, 2011.
$25,000 to Parker School, Kamuela, HI, 2011.
$20,000 to Food Allergy Research and Education, McLean, VA, 2011.
$10,000 to Child Guidance Center, Santa Ana, CA, 2011.
$2,000 to Colorado School of Mines Foundation, Golden, CO, 2011.

2612
McInerny Foundation ✧
c/o Bank of Hawaii, Fdn. Admin.
P.O. Box 3170
Honolulu, HI 96802-3170
Contact: Paula Boyce, Asst. V.P.
FAX: (808) 694-4006;
E-mail: paula.boyce@boh.com; Additional contact: Elaine Moniz, Trust Specialist, tel.: (808) 694-4944, fax: (808) 694-4006, e-mail: elaine.moniz@boh.com; Toll-free tel. from neighbor islands: 1 (800) 272-7262; Main URL: https://www.boh.com/apps/foundations/FoundationDetails.aspx?foundation=7&show=0

Trust established in 1937 in HI.
Donors: William H. McInerny†; James D. McInerny†; Ella McInerny†.
Foundation type: Independent foundation.
Financial data (yr. ended 09/30/13): Assets, $73,107,190 (M); gifts received, $1,143,624; expenditures, $4,891,022; qualifying distributions, $3,760,554; giving activities include $3,551,955 for 92 grants (high: $256,000; low: $5,000).
Purpose and activities: Giving primarily for arts and culture, community, education, the environment, health, and human services.
Fields of interest: Arts; Education; Environment; Health care; Health organizations, association; AIDS; Human services; Youth, services.
Type of support: General/operating support; Continuing support; Capital campaigns; Building/renovation; Equipment; Program development; Seed money; Scholarship funds; Matching/challenge support.
Limitations: Applications accepted. Giving limited to HI. No support for religious institutions. No grants to individuals, or for endowment funds, deficit financing, the purchase of real estate, or research; no loans.
Publications: Application guidelines; Grants list; Occasional report (including application guidelines).
Application information: Application guidelines with specific instructions and cover sheet available on foundation web site. Application form required.
Initial approach: Proposal (3 pages maximum) with cover sheet
Copies of proposal: 7
Deadline(s): None
Board meeting date(s): Distribution Committee generally meets monthly
Final notification: 3-4 months
Officers and Distribution Committee:* Peter Ho,* Chair.; Thurston Twigg-Smith, Vice-Chair.; Paula Boyce, Grants Admin. Off.; Mrs. Gerry Ching.
Trustee: Bank of Hawaii.
EIN: 996002356

2613
The Larry & Celia Moh Foundation ✧
(also known as A North Carolina Exempt Organization)
(formerly The Celia Moh Foundation)
702 S. Beretania St.
Honolulu, HI 96813-2599

Established in 2002 in NC.
Donors: Sorgente No. 3 Trust; Sorgente Investments LLC.
Foundation type: Independent foundation.
Financial data (yr. ended 12/31/13): Assets, $30,622,940 (M); expenditures, $2,160,036; qualifying distributions, $2,034,251; giving activities include $2,034,251 for 11 grants (high: $1,250,000; low: $15,000).
Purpose and activities: Scholarship funds for students in fields related to furniture provided through the qualified institutions.
Fields of interest: Higher education; Scholarships/financial aid.
Type of support: Scholarship funds.
Limitations: Applications accepted. Giving primarily in CA, MI, and NC.
Application information: Application form required.
Initial approach: Request application form
Deadline(s): None
Officers: Peggy Moh, Pres.; Celia Moh, V.P.; Michael Moh, V.P.
Directors: Alexander Thompson; Robert W. Wo, Jr.
EIN: 680492736
Selected grants: The following grants are a representative sample of this grantmaker's funding activity:
$50,000 to Institute for Families, Los Angeles, CA, 2012. For children with illnesses.

2614
The Schuler Family Foundation ✧
(formerly The James and Patricia Schuler Foundation)
c/o First Hawaiian Bank
828 Fort St., Ste. 310
Honolulu, HI 96813-4321

Established in 1995 in HI.
Donors: James K. Schuler; Patricia T. Schuler.
Foundation type: Independent foundation.
Financial data (yr. ended 12/31/12): Assets, $20,435,471 (M); expenditures, $1,075,226; qualifying distributions, $992,375; giving activities include $992,375 for 92 grants (high: $100,000; low: $2,500).
Fields of interest: Education; Animal welfare; Cancer; Human services; Children/youth, services.
Type of support: General/operating support; Research.
Limitations: Applications not accepted. Giving primarily in Honolulu, HI and WA.
Application information: Contributes only to pre-selected organizations.
Officers: James K. Schuler, Pres.; Pamela S. Jones, V.P.
Directors: Christopher T. Schuler; Mark J. Schuler; Jeffery S. Whiteman.
EIN: 990316347

2615
The Shaw "U.S." Foundation ✧
c/o Kobayashi, Kanetoku, Doi, Lum & Yasuda, CPAs, LLC
745 Fort St., Ste. 2100
Honolulu, HI 96813-3820

Established in 1995 in DE and HI.
Donors: Sir Run Run Shaw; Kapiolani Properties Corp.; Mandarin Theaters Corp.
Foundation type: Independent foundation.
Financial data (yr. ended 12/31/13): Assets, $48,186,595 (M); gifts received, $3,841,106; expenditures, $9,376,510; qualifying distributions, $9,357,847; giving activities include $9,352,986 for 6 grants (high: $7,741,436; low: $322,310).
Purpose and activities: Giving primarily for higher education in China and Hong Kong.

Fields of interest: Higher education; Engineering school/education.
Limitations: Applications not accepted. Giving primarily in Hong Kong and China. No grants to individuals.
Application information: Contributes only to pre-selected organizations.
Officers: Roger Epstein, Secy.; Jerry Rajakulendran, Treas.
Directors: Venus Choy; Mona Fong; Kit Yee Jenny Li; Choy Meage.
EIN: 990291105
Selected grants: The following grants are a representative sample of this grantmaker's funding activity:
$322,310 to Chizhou University, Chizhou, China, 2012. For operating support.
$322,310 to Jilin University of Finance and Economics, Jilin, China, 2012. For operating support.
$322,310 to Taiyuan Institute of Technology, Taiyuan City, China, 2012. For operating support.
$322,310 to Tongren University, Tongren, China, 2012. For operating support.
$322,310 to Xian University of Technology, Xian, China, 2012. For operating support.

2616
The Patrick N. C. Shin Foundation ✧ ☆
3170 Noela St.
Honolulu, HI 96815-4515

Established in 2005 in HI.
Donors: Patrick N.C. Shin; NAN, Inc.; Nan C. Shin.
Foundation type: Independent foundation.
Financial data (yr. ended 12/31/13): Assets, $1,982,263 (M); expenditures, $1,355,903; qualifying distributions, $1,348,079; giving activities include $1,348,079 for 11 grants (high: $1,000,000; low: $1,080).
Fields of interest: Higher education, university; Education; Health care; Human services.
Limitations: Applications not accepted. Giving primarily in HI and OH. No grants to individuals.
Application information: Contributes only to pre-selected organizations.
Officers and Directors:* Nan C. Shin,* Pres. and Treas.; Siriporn Newsham,* V.P. and Secy.; Jinny Miranda.
EIN: 203306898

2617
The Strong Foundation ✧
c/o Bank of Hawaii
P.O. Box 3170
Honolulu, HI 96802-3170
Contact: Carol Tom, Secy.
E-mail: carol.tom@boh.com; Tel. for neighbor islands: (800) 272-7262; Main URL: https://www.boh.com/apps/foundations/FoundationDetails.aspx?foundation=12&show=1
Grants List: https://www.boh.com/files/foundations/Strong_GrantList.pdf

Established in 1995 in HI.
Foundation type: Independent foundation.
Financial data (yr. ended 08/31/13): Assets, $27,761,136 (M); expenditures, $1,669,119; qualifying distributions, $1,468,427; giving activities include $1,455,400 for 22 grants (high: $100,000; low: $10,000).
Fields of interest: Arts; Education; Human services; Community/economic development.
Limitations: Giving limited to HI. No grants to individuals.
Publications: Application guidelines.
Application information: Each submission must indicate the name of the foundation trustee who has agreed to serve as the applicant's sponsor. Sponsorship generally includes trustee involvement with the charity or the program. See foundation web site for guidelines.
Copies of proposal: 9
Deadline(s): Mar. 1
Officers and Trustees:* Anne Strong Carter,* Pres.; Samuel A. Cooke,* V.P.; Charles M. Holland,* V.P.; Carol L. Tom, Secy.; Paul L. Wysard,* Treas.; Edward Baldwin; Peter S. Ho; Henry F. Rice; William G. Philpotts.
EIN: 990090807
Selected grants: The following grants are a representative sample of this grantmaker's funding activity:
$100,000 to Haleakala Waldorf School, Kula, HI, 2013. For Renovation and furnishing of Matsumoto Cottage for high school.
$100,000 to Hui Noeau Visual Arts Center, Makawao, HI, 2013. To protect the Past, Enrich the Future preservation and restoration project.
$75,000 to Variety School of Hawaii, Honolulu, HI, 2013. For Renovation of structures and landscaping for new high school Program.
$50,000 to Bishop Museum, Honolulu, HI, 2013. For Restoration of Pacific Hall.
$50,000 to Easter Seals Hawaii, Honolulu, HI, 2013. For Renovation of Maui Campus for Disability Services.
$50,000 to Hawaii Alliance of Nonprofit Organizations, Honolulu, HI, 2013. To build capacity to deliver on HANO's mission and sustainability.
$50,000 to Historic Hawaii Foundation, Honolulu, HI, 2013. For Programs and service lines of the Preservation Resource Center.
$50,000 to Pacific Aviation Museum Pearl Harbor, Honolulu, HI, 2013. For Restoration of Aerological tower portion of historic Ford Island Control Tower complex.
$50,000 to Palolo Chinese Home, Honolulu, HI, 2013. For Capital improvements for campus redevelopment project.
$50,000 to Waipa Foundation, Hanalei, HI, 2013. For Construct the Waipa Kitchen, Poi Mill and Hale Imu.

2618
Maurice and JoAnna Sullivan Family Foundation ✧
737 Bishop St., Ste. 2990
Honolulu, HI 96813

Established in 2003 in HI.
Donor: Joanna Sullivan.
Foundation type: Independent foundation.
Financial data (yr. ended 12/31/13): Assets, $8,847,736 (M); expenditures, $1,132,700; qualifying distributions, $1,098,200; giving activities include $1,098,200 for 6 grants (high: $1,000,000; low: $10,000).
Fields of interest: Arts; Elementary/secondary education; Higher education, university.
Type of support: General/operating support.
Limitations: Applications not accepted. Giving primarily in Honolulu, HI. No grants to individuals.
Application information: Contributes only to pre-selected organizations.
Trustees: Elliot Loden; Joanna Sullivan.
EIN: 481259090
Selected grants: The following grants are a representative sample of this grantmaker's funding activity:
$700,000 to Chaminade University of Honolulu, Honolulu, HI, 2011.
$40,000 to Hawaii Rotary Youth Foundation, Honolulu, HI, 2011. For scholarship endowment.
$10,000 to Iolani School, Honolulu, HI, 2011. For scholarship endowment.

2619
Thomas J. Vincent Foundation, Inc. ✧
44-447 Kaneohe Bay Dr.
Kaneohe, HI 96744-2611

Established in HI.
Donors: Thomas J. Vincent; Thomas J. Vincent Foundation.
Foundation type: Independent foundation.
Financial data (yr. ended 12/31/13): Assets, $20,948,373 (M); gifts received, $293,602; expenditures, $1,045,421; qualifying distributions, $1,035,060; giving activities include $1,035,060 for 12 grants (high: $670,000; low: $160).
Fields of interest: Higher education; Education; Engineering/technology; Christian agencies & churches.
Limitations: Applications not accepted. Giving primarily in CO, HI, IL, and MA. No grants to individuals.
Application information: Contributes only to pre-selected organizations.
Officers and Directors:* Thomas J. Vincent, Pres.; Manoucher Elison,* V.P.; Judith Chester-Tomiyasu, Secy.; Peter A. Roney; Ronald L. Shaw.
EIN: 912140465

2620
J. Watumull Fund ✧
(formerly J. Watumull Estate, Inc.)
P.O. Box 3708
Honolulu, HI 96811
Contact: Galub Watumull, Pres. and Dir.
Application address: Watumull Bldg., 307 Lewers St., 6th Fl., Honolulu, HI 96815

Established in 1980 in HI.
Donors: Jhamandos Watumull‡; Watumull Bros., Ltd.
Foundation type: Independent foundation.
Financial data (yr. ended 12/31/12): Assets, $11,632,454 (M); gifts received, $100,000; expenditures, $604,043; qualifying distributions, $530,613; giving activities include $515,450 for 240 grants (high: $50,000; low: $450).
Purpose and activities: Giving primarily for the arts, education, health, and human services.
Fields of interest: Arts; Higher education; Health care; Human services; Family services.
International interests: India.
Type of support: General/operating support; Capital campaigns; Building/renovation; Endowments; Program development; Fellowships; Scholarship funds; Scholarships—to individuals.
Limitations: Applications accepted. Giving primarily in HI, and nationally to organizations interested in

India, as well as some funding also in Mumbai, India.
Application information: Application form required.
Initial approach: Proposal
Copies of proposal: 1
Deadline(s): None
Board meeting date(s): Apr., June, and Nov.
Officers and Directors:* Gulab Watumull,* Pres.; Jaidev Watumull,* V.P.; Jyoti Watumull,* Secy.; Vikram Watumull,* Treas.
EIN: 510205431

2621
George N. Wilcox Trust ✧
c/o Bank of Hawaii, Fdn. Admin.
P.O. Box 3170, Dept. 715
Honolulu, HI 96802-3170
Contact: Paula Boyce, Asst. V.P.
FAX: (808) 694-4006;
E-mail: paula.boyce@boh.com; Additional contact: Elaine Moniz, Trust Specialist, e-mail: elaine.moniz@boh.com; Main URL: http://www.boh.com/philanthropy

Trust established in 1916 in HI.
Donor: George N. Wilcox†.
Foundation type: Independent foundation.
Financial data (yr. ended 12/31/13): Assets, $21,588,588 (M); expenditures, $1,303,908; qualifying distributions, $1,279,737; giving activities include $1,207,625 for 92 grants (high: $50,000; low: $1,600).
Purpose and activities: Primary areas of interest include social services, child welfare, family services, education, and health. Support also for literacy programs, the elderly, arts and culture, hospices, AIDS services and education, community funds, delinquency and crime prevention, and Protestant church support. No multi-year pledges.
Fields of interest: Arts; Adult education—literacy, basic skills & GED; Education, reading; Education; Health care; Health organizations, association; AIDS; Crime/violence prevention, youth; Crime/law enforcement; Human services; Children/youth, services; Family services; Residential/custodial care, hospices; Aging, centers/services; Protestant agencies & churches; Religion.
Type of support: General/operating support; Building/renovation; Equipment; Program development; Seed money; Scholarship funds; Matching/challenge support.
Limitations: Applications accepted. Giving limited to HI, with emphasis on the Island of Kauai. No support for government agencies or organizations substantially supported by government funds. No grants to individuals, or for endowment funds, reserve funds, research, or deficit financing; no direct student aid or scholarships; no loans.
Publications: Occasional report.
Application information: Schools' scholarship requests considered at Mar. meeting (Feb. 15 deadline for submission); the trust accepts unsolicited applications from Hawaii only. Application form required.
Initial approach: Letter (no more than 3 pages)
Copies of proposal: 4
Deadline(s): Jan 1, Apr. 1, July 1, and Oct. 1
Board meeting date(s): Mar., June, Sept., and Dec.
Final notification: 3 months
Committee on Beneficiaries: Katherine Anderson, Chair.; Gale Fisher Carswell; Aletha Kaohi.
Trustee: Bank of Hawaii.
EIN: 996002445
Selected grants: The following grants are a representative sample of this grantmaker's funding activity:
$45,000 to Boys and Girls Club of Hawaii, Honolulu, HI, 2012. For Award for Katicu Island - General.
$30,000 to Waikiki Health Center, Honolulu, HI, 2012. For Primary Care Service Expansion to Uninsured/Underinsured Patients in 2012.
$25,000 to Nature Conservancy of Hawaii, Honolulu, HI, 2012. For Protecting Kauai's Native Forests.
$17,000 to Church of the Pacific, UCC, Princeville, HI, 2012. For Food Pantry Program in 2013.
$16,200 to Academy of the Pacific, Honolulu, HI, 2012. For Campus Improvements - Asplialt Paying and Signage.
$15,000 to Arc of Hilo, Hilo, HI, 2012. For Purchase Equipment for Expansion of Commercial Laundry Services.
$15,000 to Hana Arts, Hana, HI, 2012. For Creaine today School Program for SY August 2012 May 2013.
$15,000 to Junior Achievement of Hawaii, Honolulu, HI, 2012. For General Operating - FYI 6/30/2013.
$12,000 to YWCA of Kauai, Lihue, HI, 2012. For Food Pantry for Family Violence Shelter - FYE 6/30/2013.
$10,000 to Kauai Historical Society, Lihue, HI, 2012. For Preserving Kekalia Sugar Plumation Collection.

2622
Harry Chow & Nee-Chang Chock Wong Foundation ✧
1164 Bishop St., Ste. 530
Honolulu, HI 96813-2815

Established about 1970 in HI.
Donors: Harry C. Wong†; Nee-Chang Chock Wong†.
Foundation type: Independent foundation.
Financial data (yr. ended 12/31/13): Assets, $11,985,122 (M); expenditures, $675,778; qualifying distributions, $532,520; giving activities include $458,120 for 66 grants (high: $250,000; low: $60).
Fields of interest: Higher education; Education; Human services; Christian agencies & churches.
Type of support: General/operating support; Continuing support; Curriculum development; Scholarship funds.
Limitations: Applications not accepted. Giving limited to HI. No grants to individuals.
Application information: Contributes only to pre-selected organizations.
Officers and Directors:* Robert H.Y. Leong,* Pres. and Secy.-Treas.; Maxine W. Leong,* V.P.; Toni L. Parastie,* V.P.
EIN: 996012585

2623
The Zierk Family Foundation ✧ ☆
c/o Kukio
72-3207 Manini' Owali Dr.
Kailua-Kona, HI 96740

Established in HI.
Donor: David K. Zierk.
Foundation type: Independent foundation.
Financial data (yr. ended 12/31/13): Assets, $10,305,396 (M); gifts received, $8,500,000; expenditures, $429,244; qualifying distributions, $424,200; giving activities include $424,200 for 14 grants (high: $250,000; low: $1,000).
Fields of interest: Health care; Human services; Community/economic development.
Limitations: Applications not accepted. Giving primarily in CA; funding also in HI.
Application information: Unsolicited requests for funds not accepted.
Officers: David K. Zierk, Pres. and Treas.; Davn M. Zierk, V.P. and Secy.
EIN: 462243181

2624
Hans and Clara Davis Zimmerman Foundation ✧
c/o Bank of Hawaii
P.O. Box 3170, Dept. 715
Honolulu, HI 96802-3170
Scholarship contact: Hawai'i Community Foundation, tel.: (808) 566-5570, toll-free tel. from neighbor islands: (888) 731-3863,
e-mail: scholarships@hcf-hawaii.org

Established in 1963 in HI.
Donors: Hans Zimmerman†; Clara Zimmerman†.
Foundation type: Independent foundation.
Financial data (yr. ended 12/31/13): Assets, $14,647,175 (M); expenditures, $808,401; qualifying distributions, $667,400; giving activities include $573,970 for 246 grants to individuals (high: $6,300; low: $825).
Purpose and activities: Giving scholarships to assist Hawaiian residents who wish to pursue an education in a health-related field (not including sports medicine, psychology [unless clinical], and social work). Applicants must be a college junior, senior or graduate student, have a minimum GPA of 3.0, be enrolled full-time, demonstrate financial need, and attend an accredited 2- or 4-year college or university in the U.S. Scholarships also for Hawaiian residents who have a major in Education with an emphasis on classroom teaching. Applicants in this area should have a minimum GPA of 2.8, and preference is given to those who have 2 or more years of classroom teaching experience and are returning to school. Applicants must also provide information about their teaching philosophy and how that philosophy is being applied in the classroom today. Applicants must be full-time students, demonstrate financial need, and attend an accredited 2- or 4-year college or university as either an undergraduate or graduate student. The foundation allows the Hawai'i Community Foundation's scholarship program to administer its scholarship funds.
Fields of interest: Higher education; Scholarships/financial aid.
Type of support: Scholarships—to individuals.
Limitations: Giving limited to residents of HI.
Application information: Application form required.
Initial approach: Use application process on the Hawai'i Community Foundation web site: http://www.hawaiicommunityfoundation.org/scholarships
Board meeting date(s): May
Trustee: Bank of Hawaii.
EIN: 996006669

IDAHO

2625
Adiuvo, Inc. ✧
P.O. Box 730
Fruitland, ID 83619

Foundation type: Independent foundation.
Financial data (yr. ended 12/31/12): Assets, $8,736,049 (M); expenditures, $747,394; qualifying distributions, $600,000; giving activities include $600,000 for grants.
Fields of interest: Higher education.
Limitations: Applications not accepted. Giving primarily in ID, KY, and UT.
Application information: Unsolicited requests for funds not accepted.
Officers: Lewis L. Hall, Pres.; Carrol Lee Lawhorn, Exec. Dir.
Board Member: John L. Magdiel.
EIN: 820342341

2626
J. A. & Kathryn Albertson Foundation, Inc. ✧
501 Baybrook Ct.
P.O. Box 70002
Boise, ID 83707-0102 (208) 424-2600
Contact: Jamie MacMillian, Exec. Dir.
Main URL: http://www.jkaf.org
Go On Idaho Initiative Facebook: http://www.facebook.com/GoOnIdaho?sk=wall
Go On Idaho Initiative Twitter: http://twitter.com/go_on_idaho
Go On Idaho Initiative YouTube: http://www.youtube.com/user/IdahoGoOn

Established in 1966 in ID.
Donors: J.A. Albertson‡; Kathryn Albertson‡.
Foundation type: Independent foundation.
Financial data (yr. ended 12/31/12): Assets, $650,068,822 (M); gifts received, $53,874,675; expenditures, $34,875,619; qualifying distributions, $29,881,276; giving activities include $28,862,561 for 90 grants (high: $11,173,178; low: $1,000).
Purpose and activities: The vision and mission of the foundation is to discover, develop and expand environments of limitless learning for all Idahoans.
Fields of interest: Elementary/secondary education; Education, early childhood education; Higher education, college (community/junior).
Type of support: Program development; Conferences/seminars; Curriculum development.
Limitations: Applications not accepted. Giving primarily in ID. No grants to individuals.
Publications: Annual report; Informational brochure; Newsletter.
Application information: Unsolicited requests for funds not accepted. All giving done through RFPs or invitations to apply. Check web site for current initiatives and programs.
Board meeting date(s): Quarterly
Officers and Directors:* Joseph B. Scott,* Chair.; Brady Panatopoulos,* C.E.O.; Jamie MacMillian,* Pres.; Brian Naeve,* V.P. and Secy.-Treas.; Rex Butler, Cont.; Roger Quarles, Exec. Dir.; Gary Michael; Toby Prehn; Brian Scott; J.L. Scott.
Number of staff: 6 full-time professional; 1 part-time support.
EIN: 826012000
Selected grants: The following grants are a representative sample of this grantmaker's funding activity:
$11,173,718 to Idaho State Department of Education, Boise, ID, 2012. For general operating support.
$2,344,248 to Boise State University, Boise, ID, 2012. For General Operating Support.
$2,300,000 to Northwest Nazarene University, Nampa, ID, 2012. For General Operating Support.
$2,000,000 to Idaho Education Network, Boise, ID, 2012. For General Operating Support.
$1,820,229 to College of Western Idaho, Nampa, ID, 2012. For General Operating Support.
$450,000 to Idaho Youth ChalleNGe Academy, Pierce, ID, 2012. For General Operating Support.
$400,000 to Idaho State Department of Education, Boise, ID, 2012. For General Operating Support.
$326,000 to Colorado Succeeds, Denver, CO, 2012. For General Operating Support.
$260,000 to American Heritage Charter School, Idaho Falls, ID, 2012. For General Operating Support.
$40,000 to Fairmont Junior High School, Boise, ID, 2012. For General Operating Support.

2627
Blue Cross of Idaho Foundation for Health, Inc. ✧ ☆
3000 E. Pine Ave.
Meridian, ID 83642-5995 (208) 387-6817
E-mail: info@bcidahofoundation.org; Additional address: P.O. Box 8419, Boise, ID 83707, tel.: (866) 482-2252, e-mail: grants@bcidahofoundation.org; Main URL: http://www.bcidahofoundation.org/
Facebook: http://www.facebook.com/BlueCrossOfIdahoFoundation

Established in 2001 in ID.
Donors: Blue Cross of Idaho Health Service, Inc.; American Legacy Foundation.
Foundation type: Company-sponsored foundation.
Financial data (yr. ended 12/31/13): Assets, $20,927,151 (M); gifts received, $61,568; expenditures, $1,054,220; qualifying distributions, $1,046,533; giving activities include $495,073 for 21+ grants (high: $100,000).
Purpose and activities: The foundation supports programs and organizations that work to improve the health and wellness of all Idahoans.
Fields of interest: Nursing school/education; Education; Hospitals (general); Public health; Public health, obesity; Public health, physical fitness; Health care; Mental health, smoking; Health organizations; Food services; Nutrition; Children, day care; Children; Economically disadvantaged.
Type of support: Continuing support; Annual campaigns; Program development; Curriculum development; Research; Sponsorships; Program evaluation; Donated equipment; Matching/challenge support.
Limitations: Applications accepted. Giving limited to ID. No grants to individuals.
Publications: Application guidelines.
Application information: Funding amounts are typically $10,000 and under. Proposals should be no longer than 2 pages.
Initial approach: E-mail proposal to foundation
Deadline(s): Feb. 7 and Aug. 8
Final notification: 60 days
Officers and Directors: Zelda Geyer-Sylvia, Chair. and Pres.; Dave Jeppesen, Vice-Chair.; David Slonaker, Treas.; Scott Whipple, Genl. Counsel; Gary Dyer; Tim Olson.
Number of staff: 1 full-time professional.
EIN: 260024334

2628
John H. & Orah I. Brandt Foundation ✧
203 11th Ave. S.
Nampa, ID 83651-3920 (208) 466-7821
Contact: Donald K. Brandt, Tr.

Established in 1990 in ID.
Donor: John H. Brandt.
Foundation type: Independent foundation.
Financial data (yr. ended 12/31/13): Assets, $15,325,885 (M); expenditures, $991,704; qualifying distributions, $544,000; giving activities include $544,000 for 17 grants (high: $65,000; low: $5,000).
Fields of interest: Higher education, college; Higher education, university; Theological school/education; Salvation Army; Christian agencies & churches.
Limitations: Applications accepted. Giving primarily in Nampa, ID.
Application information: Application form not required.
Initial approach: Proposal
Deadline(s): None
Trustees: Donald K. Brandt; Lawrence V. Gray; Jerry Hess; J.R. Schiller; Dan Symms.
EIN: 943124992

2629
Greg Carr Foundation, Inc. ✧
c/o Ryan Kirkham
313 N. Water St.
Idaho Falls, ID 83402-3716 (208) 529-4785
Contact: Gregory C. Carr, Pres.

Established in 2009 in DE and MA.
Donors: Gregory C. Carr; E.O. Wilson Biodiversity Foundation; The Community Foundation; Betty Carr.
Foundation type: Independent foundation.
Financial data (yr. ended 12/31/13): Assets, $36,677,071 (M); gifts received, $4,923,201; expenditures, $6,224,717; qualifying distributions, $7,143,365; giving activities include $4,239,728 for 19 grants (high: $3,277,918; low: $200).
Fields of interest: Arts; Education; Environment, natural resources.
Limitations: Applications accepted. Giving primarily in Washington DC and Cambridge, MA; some giving in ID.
Application information: Application form required.
Initial approach: Contact foundation for application form
Deadline(s): None
Officers and Director:* Gregory C. Carr,* Pres.; Ryan P. Kirkham, Secy.-Treas.
EIN: 270564755

2630
Laura Moore Cunningham Foundation, Inc. ✧
P.O. Box 1157
Boise, ID 83701-1157
Contact: Harry Bettis, Pres.
E-mail: lmcf_idaho@msn.com; Main URL: http://www.lauramoorecunningham.org

Incorporated in 1964 in ID.
Donors: Harry Bettis; Laura Moore Cunningham‡; Doreen Moore‡; Anna Parsons‡.
Foundation type: Independent foundation.
Financial data (yr. ended 08/31/13): Assets, $103,685,169 (M); gifts received, $110,000; expenditures, $4,188,646; qualifying distributions, $4,113,828; giving activities include $4,102,985 for 63 grants (high: $500,004; low: $1,000).
Purpose and activities: Emphasis on higher and other education, particularly for scholarship funds; support also for hospitals, child welfare, and educational programs.
Fields of interest: Arts; Higher education; Health care; Human services; Children/youth, services; Children/youth; Economically disadvantaged.
Type of support: General/operating support; Building/renovation; Equipment; Endowments; Program development; Seed money; Scholarship funds.
Limitations: Applications accepted. Giving limited to ID. No grants to individuals.
Publications: Informational brochure (including application guidelines).
Application information: The foundation only accepts unsolicited grant applications from tax-exempt organizations within the State of ID. Unsolicited applications from outside ID, from individuals, or from organizations not providing proof of current tax exempt status will not be reviewed or acknowledged. Application form required.
Initial approach: Request application via e-mail
Copies of proposal: 2
Deadline(s): May 15
Board meeting date(s): Summer
Final notification: By Aug. 31
Officers: Harry L. Bettis, Pres. and Treas.; Janelle A. Wise, V.P.; Laura MacGregor Bettis, Secy.
Number of staff: None.
EIN: 826008294

2631
Gorongosa Restoration Project, Inc. ✧ ☆
(formerly Gregory C. Carr Foundation)
313 N. Water Ave.
Idaho Falls, ID 83402-3716
E-mail: MLgray@prodigy.net

Established in 1999 in MA.
Donors: Gregory C. Carr; Jan Sousa; Academy for Education Development; United States Agency for International Development; IPAD; Fundacao Ciocle AE Tecnologia; Graig Carr Foundation; USAID.
Foundation type: Independent foundation.
Financial data (yr. ended 12/31/12): Assets, $428,857 (M); gifts received, $2,956,613; expenditures, $8,704,910; qualifying distributions, $8,704,570; giving activities include $8,144,947 for 1 grant.
Purpose and activities: Giving primarily to further public education in the area of human rights, African development, and health care in rural areas.
Fields of interest: Environment.
Limitations: Applications not accepted. Giving primarily in Mozambique.
Application information: Contributes only to pre-selected organizations.
Officers: Gregory C. Carr, Pres.; Jessica Greenston, Secy.; James Glasgow, Treas.
Board of Directors: Terezinha Da Silva; Jennifer Garvey; Mateous Mutenba; Bob Poole; Rob Pringle.
EIN: 043452643

2632
Idaho Community Foundation ✧
210 W. State St.
Boise, ID 83702-6052 (208) 342-3535
Contact: Holly Motes, Cont.
FAX: (208) 342-3577; E-mail: info@idcomfdn.org; Additional tel.: (800) 657-5357; Additional E-mail: hmotes@idcomfdn.org; Grant inquiry E-mail: grants@idcomfdn.org; Main URL: http://www.idcomfdn.org
Facebook: http://www.facebook.com/pages/Idaho-Community-Foundation/261769331685?ref=ts
Twitter: http://twitter.com/idahocf
YouTube: http://www.youtube.com/user/IDCommFoundation

Incorporated in 1988 in ID.
Foundation type: Community foundation.
Financial data (yr. ended 12/31/13): Assets, $115,383,200 (M); gifts received, $6,202,046; expenditures, $5,805,639; giving activities include $4,655,732 for grants.
Purpose and activities: The mission of the foundation is to enrich the quality of life throughout ID.
Fields of interest: Humanities; Arts; Libraries/library science; Education; Environment; Animals/wildlife; Health care; Recreation; Human services, emergency aid; Human services; Community development, neighborhood development.
Type of support: General/operating support; Continuing support; Management development/capacity building; Building/renovation; Equipment; Emergency funds; Program development; Seed money; Curriculum development; Scholarship funds; Matching/challenge support.
Limitations: Applications accepted. Giving primarily in ID. No support for religious purposes, or organizations typically funded by the government, or national organizations, unless monies expended are for sole benefit of ID citizens. No grants to individuals (except for scholarships), or for debt reduction, fundraising projects, travel, conferences or seminars, or endowments.
Publications: Application guidelines; Annual report; Financial statement; Grants list; Informational brochure (including application guidelines); Newsletter; Program policy statement.
Application information: Visit foundation web site for application and guidelines. Application form required.
Initial approach: Complete online grant application
Copies of proposal: 1
Deadline(s): Jan. 15 for northern region, Apr. 1 for eastern region, and July 1 for southwestern region
Board meeting date(s): Feb., May, Aug., and Nov.
Final notification: May for northern region; Aug. for eastern region; Nov. for southwestern region
Officers and Directors:* Mike McBride,* Chair.; Bill Berg,* Vice-Chair.; Bob Hoover,* C.E.O. and Pres.; Sue Thilo,* Secy.; Greg Braun,* Treas.; Holly Motes, Cont.; Bill Allen; Candice Allphin; Steve Carr; Trent Clark; Gerard Connelly; Frances Ellsworth; Jean Elsaesser; Shannon E.H. Erstad; Mary Lynn Hartwell; C. K. Haun; C. Timothy Hopkins; Tom Killingsworth; Dan Klocko; Joe Marshall; Mike McBride; Mark Nye; Debra Riedel; Brenda Sanford; Denise Smith; Tricia Swartling; Alan Van Orden; Marc Wallace; Linda Watkins; Ray Wolfe; Robert J. Yuditsky.
Number of staff: 5 full-time professional; 2 part-time professional; 2 full-time support; 1 part-time support.
EIN: 820425063
Selected grants: The following grants are a representative sample of this grantmaker's funding activity:
$125,000 to College of Western Idaho Foundation, Nampa, ID, 2013.
$69,752 to Panhandle Alliance for Education, Sandpoint, ID, 2013.
$64,732 to YMCA, Treasure Valley Family, Boise, ID, 2013.
$63,000 to Boise Philharmonic Association, Boise, ID, 2013.
$48,161 to HDR Engineering, Omaha, NE, 2013.
$37,256 to Saint Lukes Health Foundation, Boise, ID, 2013.
$2,800 to Sun Valley Performing Arts Center, Ketchum, ID, 2013.
$2,340 to Kids Alive International, Valparaiso, IN, 2013.
$2,000 to Syringa General Hospital, Grangeville, ID, 2013.
$2,000 to University of Idaho Foundation, Moscow, ID, 2013.

2633
Jeker Family Trust ✧
199 N. Capitol Blvd., Ste. 502
Boise, ID 83701-5964

Established in 2006 in ID.
Foundation type: Independent foundation.
Financial data (yr. ended 12/31/12): Assets, $15,210,314 (M); expenditures, $1,057,266; qualifying distributions, $794,037; giving activities include $574,805 for 56 grants (high: $85,463; low: $500).
Purpose and activities: Giving primarily for scholarships and higher education, as well as for health, and children, youth and social services.
Fields of interest: Higher education; Health organizations, association; Human services; Children/youth, services.
Type of support: Scholarships—to individuals.
Limitations: Applications not accepted. Giving primarily to residents of ID, with emphasis on Boise, Eagle and Moscow.
Application information: Unsolicited requests for funds not accepted.
Directors: Diane M. Bagley; Catherine Parkinson; Charles Winder.
Trustees: E. Don Copple; Terry Copple.
EIN: 204120889

2634
The Julius C. Jeker Foundation, Inc. ✧
199 N. Capitol Blvd., Ste. 502
Boise, ID 83702-5963

Established in 2005 in ID.
Donor: Julius C. Jeker.
Foundation type: Independent foundation.
Financial data (yr. ended 12/31/13): Assets, $19,297,892 (M); expenditures, $1,215,786; qualifying distributions, $873,843; giving activities include $629,761 for 30 grants (high: $70,000; low: $5,000).
Fields of interest: Food banks; Human services; YM/YWCAs & YM/YWHAs; Homeless.
Type of support: General/operating support; Continuing support; Program development; Consulting services; Matching/challenge support.
Limitations: Applications not accepted. Giving limited to southwestern ID.
Application information: Unsolicited requests for funds not accepted.
Officers: E. Don Copple, Pres.; Jon Miller, V.P.; Terry C. Copple, Secy.; John C. Travis, Treas.
Number of staff: 1 full-time professional.
EIN: 203902260

2635
The Julius M. Kleiner Memorial Park Trust ✧ ☆

217 W. Georgia Ave. , Ste. 100
Nampa, ID 83686-6812

Established in 2008 in ID.
Donor: Eugene M. Kleiner.
Foundation type: Operating foundation.
Financial data (yr. ended 03/31/13): Assets, $463,306 (M); expenditures, $8,565,592; qualifying distributions, $9,185,340; giving activities include $8,495,126 for 1 grant.
Fields of interest: Human services.
Limitations: Applications not accepted.
Application information: Contributes only to pre-selected organizations.
Trustees: Elden Gray; Michael E. Huter; Eugene M. Kleiner; Michael Kleiner.
EIN: 260366794

2636
The Lightfoot Foundation ✧

(also known as The E.L. & B.G. Lightfoot Foundation)
c/o U.S. Bank, N.A.
P.O. Box 7928
Boise, ID 83707-1928 (208) 383-7215
FAX: (208) 383-7171;
E-mail: info@lightfootfoundation.com; Main URL: http://www.lightfootfoundation.com
Scholarship contact: Mary Frazer, tel.: (208) 383-7215, e-mail: mary.frazer@usbank.com

Established in 1992 in ID.
Donors: Elma Lightfoot Newgen‡; The Elma L. Newgen Family Trust.
Foundation type: Independent foundation.
Financial data (yr. ended 02/28/13): Assets, $32,417,993 (M); gifts received, $9; expenditures, $1,711,329; qualifying distributions, $1,405,385; giving activities include $1,232,170 for 60 grants (high: $281,313; low: $1,500), and $91,300 for 73 grants to individuals (high: $2,000; low: $250).
Purpose and activities: The foundation assists students in the Treasure Valley region of Idaho and Oregon who wish to further their education, organizations engaged in the protection and preservation of our environment, and homeless shelters and family housing organizations that help those in need. Scholarships are available to students who reside in any of the 58 towns and cities in the Treasure Valley area for at least 1-year, who have a 2.5 cumulative GPA, and whose household gross income does not exceed over $90,000 per year.
Fields of interest: Education; Environment, natural resources; Housing/shelter; Human services.
Type of support: Grants to individuals.
Limitations: Applications accepted. Giving limited to southern ID and eastern OR.
Application information: Scholarship forms and guidelines available on foundation web site. The foundation no longer accepts paper applications. Application form required.
Initial approach: Refer to procedures indicated on foundation web site
Deadline(s): Dec. 1 for Environment and Housing; Apr. 15 for scholarships
Charitable Committee: Maureen L. Howe; Sydney L. Mitchell; Albert W. Wilson III.
Trustee: U.S. Bank, N.A.
EIN: 820454166

2637
Micron Technology Foundation, Inc. ✧

8000 S. Federal Way, MS 1-407
P.O. Box 6
Boise, ID 83707-0006
Contact: Kami Faylor, Community Rels. Mgr.
E-mail: mtf@micron.com; E-mail for Micron's K-12 Programs: k-12programs@micron.com; Main URL: http://www.micron.com/foundation
Micron Students site: http://students.micron.com/
The Micron Bulletin: http://bulletin.micron.com/
Twitter: http://twitter.com/Micron_Giving

Established in 1999 in ID.
Donors: Micron Technology, Inc.; Micron Semiconductor Products, Inc.; Blue Cross of Idaho Health Service, Inc.
Foundation type: Company-sponsored foundation.
Financial data (yr. ended 12/31/12): Assets, $86,805,324 (M); expenditures, $5,756,844; qualifying distributions, $5,192,051; giving activities include $4,340,124 for 328 grants (high: $1,500,000; low: $25).
Purpose and activities: The foundation supports organizations involved with K-12 and higher education. Special emphasis is directed toward programs designed to promote education in the areas of engineering, science, chemistry, mathematics, and computer science.
Fields of interest: Education, research; Elementary/secondary education; Secondary school/education; Higher education; Teacher school/education; Engineering school/education; Education; Science, formal/general education; Chemistry; Mathematics; Engineering/technology; Computer science.
International interests: Italy; Singapore.
Type of support: Continuing support; Program development; Professorships; Curriculum development; Fellowships; Scholarship funds; Research; Employee volunteer services; Sponsorships; Employee matching gifts; Scholarships—to individuals.
Limitations: Applications accepted. Giving limited to areas of company operations in Boise, ID, Manassas, VA, Avezzano, Italy, and Singapore. No support for religious, fraternal, veterans', or political organizations, discriminatory organizations, pass-through organizations, or private foundations. No grants to individuals (except for scholarships), or for general operating support, luncheons, dinners, auctions, or events, travel or related expenses, courtesy advertisements, endowments, annual campaigns, or lobbying activities.
Publications: Application guidelines.
Application information: University participation in the University Partnerships program is by invitation only. Applications for Chip Camp require a teacher recommendation. Application form required.
Initial approach: Download application form and mail proposal and application form to foundation for Community and K-12 Grants; visit website for Chip Camp
Deadline(s): None for Community and K-12 Grants; Apr. 15 for Chip Camp
Final notification: Monthly
Officers and Directors:* Mark D. Duncan,* Chair.; Kipp A. Bedard,* Pres.; Roderick W. Lewis,* Secy.; Tom L. Laws, Treas.; Dee K. Mooney, Exec. Dir.; Jay L. Hawkins.
Number of staff: 8 full-time professional; 2 part-time professional.
EIN: 820516178
Selected grants: The following grants are a representative sample of this grantmaker's funding activity:
$1,500,000 to College of Western Idaho Foundation, Nampa, ID, 2012.
$422,170 to University of Idaho Foundation, Moscow, ID, 2012.
$170,500 to Iowa State University, Ames, IA, 2012.
$150,600 to Boise State University, Boise, ID, 2012.
$112,500 to George Mason University, Fairfax, VA, 2012.
$111,121 to Nanyang Technological University, Singapore, 2012.
$106,525 to Northwest Nazarene University, Nampa, ID, 2012.
$100,000 to University of Bristol, Bristol, England, 2012.
$61,500 to Prince William County Public Schools Education Foundation, Manassas, VA, 2012.
$26,070 to Universita degli Studi di Catania, Department of Electrical Engineering, Electronics, and Informatics, Catania, Italy, 2012.

2638
Morrison Center Endowment Foundation, Inc. ✧ ☆

827 Park Blvd., Ste. 200
Boise, ID 83706-7782 (208) 345-5225
Contact: Justin Wilkerson, Co-Pres.

Foundation type: Independent foundation.
Financial data (yr. ended 12/31/13): Assets, $15,261,945 (M); gifts received, $1,600; expenditures, $948,470; qualifying distributions, $912,539; giving activities include $900,110 for 9 grants (high: $601,600; low: $4,100).
Fields of interest: Arts; Education.
Limitations: Applications accepted. Giving primarily in Boise, ID.
Application information: Application form required.
Initial approach: Letter
Deadline(s): None
Officers: Velma V. Morrison, Chair.; Mary B. Smith, Co-Pres.; Justin Wilkerson, Co-Pres.
Directors: Michelle M. Bauer; Scott M. Hayes; Eugene D. Heil; David S. Taylor; Bonnie Wilkerson.
EIN: 820381185

2639
The John F. Nagel Foundation ✧
435 E. Shore Dr., Ste. 130
Eagle, ID 83616-5754
Contact: Curt Goldgrabe, Secy.
E-mail: curt@nagelfoundation.com; Main URL: http://www.nagelfoundation.com

Established in 1989 in ID.
Donors: Mildred E. Nagel†; Annie Nagel Matthews†; Nagel Beverage Co., Inc.
Foundation type: Independent foundation.
Financial data (yr. ended 12/31/13): Assets, $24,279,959 (M); expenditures, $1,783,592; qualifying distributions, $1,314,452; giving activities include $1,099,199 for 33 grants (high: $150,000; low: $2,500).
Purpose and activities: The mission of the foundation is to fund organizations in southwest Idaho whose purpose is to help those who would otherwise be unable to help themselves. The selection of grant recipients is based primarily on need.
Fields of interest: Education; Health care; Human services; Children/youth, services; Family services.
Type of support: Equipment; Program development; Scholarship funds.
Limitations: Applications accepted. Giving in southwestern ID, with emphasis on the Boise area.
Publications: Annual report.
Application information: Application guidelines available on web site. Application form required.
Initial approach: Using the online application form on foundation web site is the preferred method
Copies of proposal: 1
Deadline(s): Annually, on Oct. 31
Board meeting date(s): Annually, in Nov.
Final notification: Nov. 30
Officers and Directors:* Vance Miller,* Pres.; Curt Goldgrabe,* Secy.; William E. Morris,* Treas.; Ryan Fornstrom.
Number of staff: 1 full-time professional.
EIN: 820431505
Selected grants: The following grants are a representative sample of this grantmaker's funding activity:
$150,000 to Boise Rescue Mission, Boise, ID, 2013.
$100,500 to Boise Rescue Mission, Boise, ID, 2013.
$100,000 to Boise State University, Boise, ID, 2013.
$100,000 to Northwest Nazarene University, Nampa, ID, 2013.
$60,000 to Big Brothers Big Sisters of Southwest Idaho, Boise, ID, 2013.
$52,500 to Society of Saint Vincent de Paul, Meridian, ID, 2013.
$50,000 to Camp Rainbow Gold, Boise, ID, 2013.
$41,500 to Boys and Girls Clubs of Ada County, Garden City, ID, 2013.
$40,000 to Culinary Skills Training Center, Life's Kitchen, Boise, ID, 2013.
$37,500 to Boys and Girls Club of Nampa, Nampa, ID, 2013.

2640
The Rebholtz Family Foundation Inc. ✧
1555 Shoreline Dr., 3rd Fl.
Boise, ID 83702-9106

Established in 1996 in ID.
Donors: Dorothy Rebholtz; Agri Beef Co.
Foundation type: Independent foundation.
Financial data (yr. ended 09/30/13): Assets, $1,660,708 (M); expenditures, $706,500; qualifying distributions, $680,000; giving activities include $680,000 for 4 grants (high: $250,000; low: $30,000).
Fields of interest: Human services; Foundations (private grantmaking).
Type of support: General/operating support; Grants to individuals.
Limitations: Applications not accepted. Giving primarily in ID and MN.
Application information: Unsolicited requests for funds not accepted.
Officers: Dorothy Rebholtz, Pres.; Teresa A. Cleary, Secy.; Thomas M. Rebholtz, Treas.
EIN: 820496018

2641
The Arthur B. Schultz Foundation ✧
P.O. Box 5339
Ketchum, ID 83340-5339 (307) 714-5665
Contact: Erik B. Schultz, Chair.; Rachael K. Richards, Exec. Dir.
E-mail: info@absfoundation.org; E-mail for Erik B. Schultz: ebs@absfoundation.org.; Main URL: http://www.absfoundation.org
Facebook: http://www.facebook.com/pages/The-Arthur-B-Schultz-Foundation/103668762718
Grants List: http://www.absfoundation.org/index.php?id=3

Established in 1985 in CA.
Donor: Arthur B. Schultz.
Foundation type: Independent foundation.
Financial data (yr. ended 12/31/13): Assets, $5,677,962 (M); gifts received, $216,665; expenditures, $642,865; qualifying distributions, $604,547; giving activities include $438,348 for 26 grants (high: $250,000; low: $1,000), and $27,044 for 2 loans/program-related investments.
Purpose and activities: Advancing opportunities for women, entrepreneurs, and people with disabilities.
Fields of interest: Elementary/secondary education; Higher education; Physical therapy; Economic development; Young adults; Disabilities, people with; Physically disabled; Women; Girls; Economically disadvantaged.
International interests: Cambodia; Central America; East Jerusalem; Israel; Kenya; Rwanda; Tanzania; Vietnam; West Bank/Gaza (Palestinian Territories).
Type of support: General/operating support; Continuing support; Income development; Management development/capacity building; Equipment; Program development; Seed money; Scholarship funds; Program-related investments/loans; Matching/challenge support.
Limitations: Applications accepted. Giving primarily in the developing world. No support for strictly religious organizations. No grants to individuals.
Publications: Application guidelines; Financial statement; Grants list; Program policy statement; Program policy statement (including application guidelines).
Application information: Electronic submission only. Application guidelines are available on foundation web site; unsolicited letter of inquiry are accepted but unsolicited proposals are not accepted. Other publications available online include grant guidelines, program descriptions and selected grant descriptions. The foundation requires letters of inquiry received by e-mail, with attachments in MS Office (Word, Excel, etc.), and/or Adobe PDF format. Eligible organizations will be invited to submit a full proposal.
Initial approach: See foundation web site for letter of inquiry guidelines. Letter of inquiry required; electronic submissions only.
Copies of proposal: 1
Deadline(s): Varies
Board meeting date(s): Annually, typically in the spring or early summer
Final notification: For letters of inquiry, no response if guidelines are not met.
Officers and Director:* Erik B. Schultz, Chair.; Rachael K. Richards, Exec. Dir.
Number of staff: 1 full-time professional; 1 part-time professional.
EIN: 953980014
Selected grants: The following grants are a representative sample of this grantmaker's funding activity:
$250,000 to Rogue Initiative for a Vital Economy, Ashland, OR, 2013. For Pay-it-Forward loan to small business entrepreneurs.
$16,000 to Northern Kenya Fund, Kenya, 2013. For North Horr All Girls High School and University Level Scholarships in Nairobi.
$15,000 to A Leg to Stand On, New York, NY, 2013. For mobility aids and rehabilitation for children in Cambodia.
$15,000 to Akili Dada, Nairobi, Kenya, 2013.
$15,000 to Prosthetics Outreach Foundation, Seattle, WA, 2012. For Vietnam Clubfoot Program.
$13,000 to Akilah Institute for Women, Kigali, Rwanda, 2012. For entrepreneur students.
$8,000 to Creativity for Peace, Santa Fe, NM, 2013. For scholarships.
$7,500 to Kenya Paraplegic Organization, Kenya, 2012. For Wheelchair Project.

2642
Seagraves Foundation, Inc. ✧
P.O. Box 1292
Twin Falls, ID 83303-1292
Application Address: c/o Penelope Parker, 320 Main Ave., Twin Falls, ID 83301, tel.: (208) 735-8812

Established in 2000 in ID.
Donor: Janice K. Seagraves Charitable Lead Trust.
Foundation type: Independent foundation.
Financial data (yr. ended 12/31/13): Assets, $19,936,233 (M); gifts received, $942,375; expenditures, $991,110; qualifying distributions, $878,844; giving activities include $722,204 for 62 grants (high: $99,000; low: $500).
Purpose and activities: Giving primarily for organizations that benefit terminally ill children, impoverished children, humane treatment of animals, Christian purposes, and post-secondary academic education.
Fields of interest: Historical activities; Secondary school/education; Higher education; Animal welfare; Disasters, fire prevention/control; Recreation, parks/playgrounds; Human services; Children, services; Christian agencies & churches.
Limitations: Applications accepted. Giving primarily in Hailey and Twin Falls, ID.
Application information: Application form required.
Initial approach: Letter
Deadline(s): None
Directors: Larry D. Braga; Barry Crow; Cindy Crow; Emerald Crow; Penny Parker; Jack G. Seagraves; Judy Seagraves.
EIN: 820511735

Selected grants: The following grants are a representative sample of this grantmaker's funding activity:
$2,000 to Yellowstone Park Foundation, Bozeman, MT, 2012. To preserve nature.

2643
J. R. Simplot Company Foundation, Inc. ✧
P.O. Box 27
Boise, ID 83707-0027

Established in 2000 in ID.
Donor: J.R. Simplot Co.
Foundation type: Company-sponsored foundation.
Financial data (yr. ended 03/31/13): Assets, $28,100,614 (M); expenditures, $1,878,494; qualifying distributions, $1,663,932; giving activities include $1,646,376 for 60+ grants (high: $529,103).
Purpose and activities: The foundation supports organizations involved with arts and culture, secondary and higher education, health, agriculture and food, human services, and community development.
Fields of interest: Health care; Human services; Religion.
Limitations: Applications not accepted. Giving primarily in Boise, ID. No grants to individuals.
Application information: Contributes only to pre-selected organizations.
Officers and Directors:* Gay C. Simplot,* Pres.; John Edward Simplot,* V.P.; Terry T. Uhling, Secy.; Annette Elg, Treas.; Debbie S. McDonald; Scott R. Simplot.
EIN: 820522113

2644
Smeed Memorial Foundation ✧ ☆
1201 S. Kimball Ave.
Caldwell, ID 83605-4626
E-mail: rcoffman@cableone.net; Application address: c/o Smeed Memorial Foundation, 3509 Malibu Pl., Caldwell, ID 83605 tel.: (208) 455-9040

Donor: Ralph E. Smeed†.
Foundation type: Independent foundation.
Financial data (yr. ended 12/31/13): Assets, $4,988,074 (M); gifts received, $2,901,695; expenditures, $498,591; qualifying distributions, $435,500; giving activities include $435,500 for 8 grants (high: $250,000; low: $5,000).
Fields of interest: Education; Human services.
Type of support: General/operating support.
Limitations: Applications accepted. Giving primarily in ID and TX.
Application information: Application form required.
Initial approach: Completed Application form
Deadline(s): None
Officers: Rick Coffman, Pres.; Dan Symms, V.P.; Elizabeth Allan-Hodge, Secy.; Dick Anderson, Treas.
Directors: Maurice Clements; Chris Derry; Stan Hawkins; Phil Hurley; Laird Maxwell; Monte Munn; Theron Nelson; Steve Symms.
EIN: 453753483
Selected grants: The following grants are a representative sample of this grantmaker's funding activity:
$130,000 to Idaho Freedom Foundation, Boise, ID, 2012. To Help Underwrite Speaker for Fund Raising and General Operating Expenses.
$5,000 to National Humanities Institute, Bowie, MD, 2012. For Maintain Current Programs, Including Publishing Constitutional History Curriculum and Website.

2645
Harold E. & Phyllis S. Thomas Foundation ✧
12549 W. Bowmont Ct.
Boise, ID 83713-0023
Contact: Judy Rasmussen, Dir.

Established in 1995 in ID.
Donors: Harold Thomas; Phyllis Thomas; Patrick W. Feenstra.
Foundation type: Independent foundation.
Financial data (yr. ended 12/31/13): Assets, $0 (M); gifts received, $1,391,097; expenditures, $512,203; qualifying distributions, $440,823; giving activities include $440,823 for 28+ grants (high: $50,000).
Purpose and activities: Grants are awarded for Christian evangelical work with particular consideration for missions and organizations engaged in missionary teachings and work. Some giving also for other religious philanthropic organizations.
Fields of interest: Christian agencies & churches.
Limitations: Applications not accepted. Giving in the U.S., with emphasis on ID and WA.
Application information: Contributes only to pre-selected organizations. Unsolicited requests for funds not accepted.
Director: Judy Rasmussen.
Trustees: Don Anderson; Dave Hills; James Mitchell; Robert Renfro; Harold E. Thomas; Rick Thomas.
EIN: 820477243
Selected grants: The following grants are a representative sample of this grantmaker's funding activity:
$15,000 to Expansion International, Meridian, ID, 2012. To fund religious activity.
$15,000 to Idaho Mountain Ministries, Boise, ID, 2012. To fund religious activities.

2646
The Robert I. Wishnick Foundation ✧
(doing business as The William Wishnick Foundation)
(formerly The Witco Foundation)
P.O. Box 447
Ponderay, ID 83852

Incorporated in 1951 in IL.
Donor: William Wishnick.
Foundation type: Independent foundation.
Financial data (yr. ended 12/31/13): Assets, $7,960,551 (M); expenditures, $480,656; qualifying distributions, $444,372; giving activities include $433,400 for 66 grants (high: $67,500; low: $150).
Fields of interest: Arts; Animal welfare; Human services; Jewish federated giving programs; Jewish agencies & synagogues.
Type of support: General/operating support; Annual campaigns; Capital campaigns; Endowments; Research.
Limitations: Applications not accepted. Giving primarily in UT. No grants to individuals.
Application information: Contributes only to pre-selected organizations.
Board meeting date(s): 4 to 5 times a year
Officers: Lisa Wishnick, Pres. and Treas.; Ami Jo Gibson, Secy.
Directors: Kendall Wishnick Adams; Gina Grossman; Howard Schur.
EIN: 136068668
Selected grants: The following grants are a representative sample of this grantmaker's funding activity:
$10,000 to Washington State University, Pullman, WA, 2011.
$8,500 to American Friends of the Hebrew University, New York, NY, 2011.
$3,000 to New York City Ballet, New York, NY, 2011.

ILLINOIS

2647
2010 McKaco Charitable Foundation Trust ✧ ☆
10 S. Dearborn St., IL1-0117
Chicago, IL 60603-2300

Established in DE.
Donors: Mickaco 2003 CRT; Mac Dunwoody.
Foundation type: Independent foundation.
Financial data (yr. ended 12/31/13): Assets, $16,098 (M); expenditures, $578,395; qualifying distributions, $570,895; giving activities include $567,800 for 24 grants (high: $255,000; low: $100).
Fields of interest: Education; Human services; Foundations (private grantmaking).
Limitations: Applications not accepted. Giving primarily in CA, MA, and TX. No grants to individuals.
Application information: Unsolicited requests for funds not accepted.
Trustees: Cindri Carrick; JPMorgan Chase Bank, N.A.
EIN: 386938924

2648
The Clara Abbott Foundation ✧
1175 Tri-State Pkwy., Ste. 200
Gurnee, IL 60031-9141 (800) 972-3859
Contact: Christy Wistar, V.P. and Exec. Dir.
FAX: (847) 938-6511;
E-mail: claraabbottfoundation@abbott.com;
Additional tel.: (847) 937-1090; Main URL: http://clara.abbott.com

Established in 1940 in IL.
Donors: Clara Abbott†; Louis B. Kyle; Joseph Miller, Jr.; Mrs. Joseph Miller, Jr.; Marie Wilkinson; Jack Moss Trust for Euluos Moss; Rieker Charitable Remainder Trust; Charles S. Brown; Mrs. Charles S. Brown; Marcia Thomas; John C. Kane; Bernard Semler; Gary P. Coughlan; W. Thomas Brady; Lucilee Heine.
Foundation type: Independent foundation.
Financial data (yr. ended 12/31/13): Assets, $251,190,467 (M); expenditures, $7,002,507; qualifying distributions, $6,476,048; giving activities include $3,352,267 for grants to individuals.
Purpose and activities: The mission of the foundation is to efficiently and responsibly provide needed assistance to Abbott families worldwide. Grants, loans, financial education and counseling services are made to Abbott Laboratories employees and retirees for financial aid due to financial hardships. Educational grants are made only to dependents of Abbott Laboratories employees (of at least one year) and retirees based on a financial need criteria.
Fields of interest: Education; Human services; Aging; Economically disadvantaged.
Type of support: Continuing support; Emergency funds; Consulting services; Program-related investments/loans; Employee-related scholarships; Grants to individuals; Scholarships—to individuals.
Limitations: Applications accepted. Giving primarily to Abbott Laboratories employees (of at least one year) and retirees worldwide.
Publications: Annual report (including application guidelines); Financial statement; Informational brochure.
Application information: Application and guidelines available on foundation's web site. Application form required.
Deadline(s): Varies
Board meeting date(s): Apr. and Oct.
Final notification: 5 business days of receiving application.
Officers and Directors:* Stephen R. Fussell,* Pres.; Christy Wistar, V.P. and Exec. Dir.; Sheri Keith, Treas.; Hubert Allen; Charles M. Brock; Jaime Contreras; Charles D. Foltz; Robert Funck; Lawrence Kraus; Greg Linder; Mary Moreland; Corlis Murray; William H. Preece; Robert E. Tweed; Grice E. Williams; Valentine Yien; Brian Yoor.
Number of staff: 25 full-time professional; 4 part-time professional; 12 full-time support; 1 part-time support.
EIN: 366069632

2649
Abbott Fund ✧
(formerly Abbott Laboratories Fund)
100 Abbott Park Rd., D379/AP6D
Abbott Park, IL 60064-3500 (847) 937-7075
Main URL: http://www.abbottfund.org

Incorporated in 1951 in IL.
Donor: Abbott Laboratories.
Foundation type: Company-sponsored foundation.
Financial data (yr. ended 12/31/13): Assets, $195,272,643 (M); gifts received, $40,110,931; expenditures, $23,036,393; qualifying distributions, $22,952,171; giving activities include $11,064,922 for 71 grants (high: $1,800,005; low: $1,000), and $3,766,687 for employee matching gifts.
Purpose and activities: The fund supports organizations involved with arts and culture, education, water conservation, health, HIV/AIDS, diabetes, tropical diseases, hunger, nutrition, disaster relief, human services, community development, science, children, minorities, women, and economically disadvantaged people. Special emphasis is directed toward programs designed to promote science and medical innovation; expand access to healthcare; and strengthen communities around the globe.
Fields of interest: Museums; Museums (science/technology); Arts; Elementary/secondary education; Higher education; Libraries (public); Education; Environment, water resources; Medical care, community health systems; Hospitals (general); Health care, clinics/centers; Health care, infants; Health care, rural areas; Reproductive health, OBGYN/Birthing centers; Public health, physical fitness; Health care; AIDS; Diabetes; Tropical diseases; Food services; Food banks; Nutrition; Disasters, preparedness/services; American Red Cross; Family services; Homeless, human services; Human services; Community/economic development; United Ways and Federated Giving Programs; Mathematics; Engineering/technology; Science; Children; Minorities; Women; Economically disadvantaged.
Type of support: General/operating support; Continuing support; Management development/capacity building; Building/renovation; Program development; Conferences/seminars; Faculty/staff development; Curriculum development; Scholarship funds; Research; Sponsorships; Employee matching gifts.
Limitations: Applications not accepted. Giving on a national and international basis in areas of company operations, with emphasis on AR, CA, CT, Washington, DC, IL, IN, MA, NH, NY, OH, OR, PR, TX, VA, Afghanistan, Africa, Brazil, Haiti, India, Kenya, and Tanzania; giving also to national and international organizations. No support for social organizations, political parties or candidates, sectarian religious organizations, or trade or business associations. No grants to individuals, or for scholarships, advertising journals or booklets, capital campaigns, congresses, symposiums, or meetings, medical research that supports Abbott products, political activities, fundraising events, ticket purchases, sporting events, travel, trips, tours, or cultural exchange programs; no employee volunteer services.
Application information: The foundation is currently not accepting unsolicited applications. Visit website to view future opportunities for funding.
Officers and Directors:* Paul K. Magill,* Pres.; Katherine Pickus, V.P.; John Berry, Secy.; Stephen R. Fussel; Joellen Medley; Miles D. White.
Number of staff: 1 full-time professional; 1 part-time professional; 1 full-time support; 1 part-time support.
EIN: 366069793
Selected grants: The following grants are a representative sample of this grantmaker's funding activity:
$1,800,005 to Rockefeller Philanthropy Advisors, Philanthropic Collaborative, New York, NY, 2013. For Cardiovascular Fellowship Program.
$1,000,000 to Northwestern University, Evanston, IL, 2013. For Abbott Pavilion.
$932,509 to Boston University, Boston, MA, 2013. For The Abbott Fund Institute of Nutrition Science: Advancing Clinical Nutrition in Vietnam.
$750,000 to John G. Shedd Aquarium Society, Chicago, IL, 2013. For Making Waves: The Campaign for Shedd Aquarium.
$500,000 to United States Department of State, Washington, DC, 2013. For Health and Education for Women and Girls in Burma.
$400,000 to Ann and Robert H. Lurie Children's Hospital of Chicago, Chicago, IL, 2013. For Heroes for Life: Campaign for Ann and Robert H. Lurie Children's Hospital of Chicago.
$400,000 to Direct Relief International, Santa Barbara, CA, 2013. For Funding for Afghan Institute of Learning, Diabetes Care and Nutrition Programs.
$200,000 to AmeriCares, Stamford, CT, 2013. To support of the Vietnam Pediatric Nutrition Project.
$100,000 to Direct Relief International, Santa Barbara, CA, 2013. For Typhoon Haiyan Response.
$95,000 to Faraja Trust Fund, Morogoro, Tanzania, 2013. For Integrated Care, Coping, Legal and Human Rights in Morogoro, Tanzania.

2650
The Abbvie Patient Assistance Foundation ✧
(formerly The Abbott Patient Assistance Foundation)
200 Abbott Park Rd., D-031C AP31-3NW
Abbott Park, IL 60064-6214 (800) 222-6885
Main URL: http://www.abbviepaf.org/

Established in 2007 in IL.
Donor: Abbott Laboratories.
Foundation type: Operating foundation.

Financial data (yr. ended 12/31/13): Assets, $53,271,158 (M); gifts received, $810,053,325; expenditures, $787,981,527; qualifying distributions, $787,981,527; giving activities include $783,366,952 for grants to individuals.
Purpose and activities: The foundation provides Abbott medications, medical nutritionals, and diabetes care products to economically disadvantaged individuals living below the federal poverty line and to individuals lacking prescription drug coverage.
Fields of interest: Health care; Diabetes; Economically disadvantaged.
Type of support: Grants to individuals; Donated products.
Limitations: Applications accepted. Giving on a national basis, with emphasis on CA, IL, KY, and NJ.
Publications: Application guidelines.
Application information: Visit website for application addresses. Application form required.
Initial approach: Download application form and mail to application address or contact foundation for application form
Deadline(s): None
Officers and Directors: John Pilotte, Pres.; Thad Smith, V.P.; Kathleen Scheidt, Secy.; Denis Tian, Treas.; Kevin Buckbee; Kevin Dolan; Daryl Dorcy; Russell Garich; Kelly Ingold; Dale Johnson; Angela Sekston.
EIN: 261215559

2651
Abt Family Charitable Foundation ✧ ☆
1200 Milwaukee Ave.
Glenview, IL 60025-2416
Contact: Robert J. Abt, Tr.

Established in 1987 in IL.
Donor: ABT Electronics, Inc.
Foundation type: Company-sponsored foundation.
Financial data (yr. ended 12/31/12): Assets, $4,177,195 (M); gifts received, $7,000,000; expenditures, $2,931,642; qualifying distributions, $2,927,200; giving activities include $2,927,200 for grants.
Purpose and activities: The foundation supports organizations involved with cancer, medical research, karate, human services, and Judaism.
Fields of interest: Cancer; Diabetes research; Medical research; Athletics/sports, amateur leagues; Developmentally disabled, centers & services; Human services; Jewish federated giving programs; Jewish agencies & synagogues.
Type of support: General/operating support; Scholarship funds.
Application information: Application form not required.
Initial approach: Letter
Deadline(s): None
Trustees: Michael Abt; Richard L. Abt; Robert J. Abt; William P. Abt.
EIN: 363583929

2652
G.A. Ackermann Memorial Fund ✧ ☆
c/o US Trust, Bank of America, N.A.
231 S. LaSalle St., IL1-231-13-32
Chicago, IL 60604-1426 (312) 828-4154
Contact: George Thorn, Market Dir.
E-mail: ilgrantmaking@ustrust.com; Main URL: https://www.bankofamerica.com/philanthropic/grantmaking.go

Established in 1937.
Foundation type: Independent foundation.
Financial data (yr. ended 12/31/13): Assets, $25,182,997 (M); expenditures, $922,758; qualifying distributions, $801,635; giving activities include $700,000 for 7 grants (high: $175,000; low: $30,000).
Purpose and activities: Giving to Catholic and Protestant church-affiliated organizations.
Fields of interest: Secondary school/education; Theological school/education; Human services; Salvation Army; Catholic federated giving programs; Protestant federated giving programs; Catholic agencies & churches.
Limitations: Giving limited to organizations that are geographically located within the city limits of New York City, NY or Chicago, IL.
Application information: Application form not required.
Initial approach: Online
Deadline(s): Jan. 15 and June 1
Trustee: Bank of America, N.A.
EIN: 366039158
Selected grants: The following grants are a representative sample of this grantmaker's funding activity:
$100,000 to Advocate Charitable Foundation, Downers Grove, IL, 2011. For Advocate Trinity Hospital Community Health Program - Partnering with Faith Communities.
$100,000 to Episcopal Charities and Community Services of the Diocese of Chicago, Chicago, IL, 2011. For general operating support.
$100,000 to Holy Family Ministries, Chicago, IL, 2011. For Holy Family School, opens the door to education for low-income families.
$100,000 to Lutheran Social Services of Illinois, Des Plaines, IL, 2011. For Steps to Life.
$100,000 to Misericordia Heart of Mercy Center, Chicago, IL, 2011. For general operations.
$100,000 to Presence Home Care Services, Des Plaines, IL, 2011. For general operating support.
$100,000 to Saint Bernard Hospital and Health Care Center, Chicago, IL, 2011. For St. Bernard Hospital Dental Center.
$100,000 to Saint Vincent de Paul Center, Chicago, IL, 2011. For general operations.
$100,000 to Swedish Covenant Hospital, Chicago, IL, 2011. For Chronic Disease Care Transitions Program Expansion.
$50,000 to Catholic Charities of the Archdiocese of Chicago, Chicago, IL, 2011. For general operations.

2653
The Adjuvant Foundation ✧
(formerly Irving Harris Foundation B)
191 N. Wacker Dr., Ste. 1500
Chicago, IL 60606-1899

Established in 1993 in IL.
Donors: Virginia H. Polsky; Irving B. Harris‡; Richard M. Polsky Trust; Jack Polsky Investment Trust; Richard Polsky.
Foundation type: Independent foundation.
Financial data (yr. ended 12/31/13): Assets, $22,137,964 (M); expenditures, $1,203,525; qualifying distributions, $712,088; giving activities include $695,408 for 18 grants (high: $350,000; low: $408).
Purpose and activities: Giving primarily for hospitals, and youth enrichment programs.
Fields of interest: Education; Hospitals (general); Youth development.
Type of support: General/operating support; Program-related investments/loans.
Limitations: Applications not accepted. Giving primarily in Boston, MA, New York, NY, and Providence, RI. No grants to individuals.
Application information: Contributes only to pre-selected organizations.
Officers and Directors:* Virginia H. Polsky,* Pres. and Secy.; Charles Polsky,* V.P.; George Polsky,* V.P.; Jack Polsky,* V.P.; James Polsky,* V.P.; Jean Polsky,* V.P.; Richard Polsky,* V.P.; Beth Stephens, Treas.
EIN: 363866528

2654
J.R. Albert Charitable Foundation ✧
55 S. Main St., Ste. 307
Naperville, IL 60540-5372 (630) 335-7098
Contact: Patricia Belle Robb, C.E.O. and Pres.
E-mail: staff@jralbertfoundation.org; Main URL: http://www.jralbertfoundation.org/
Grants List: http://www.jralbertfoundation.org/recent.htm

Foundation type: Independent foundation.
Financial data (yr. ended 12/31/13): Assets, $36,689,703 (M); expenditures, $2,134,817; qualifying distributions, $1,943,484; giving activities include $1,670,475 for 90 grants (high: $100,000; low: $1,000).
Purpose and activities: Giving primarily to: 1) increase access to healthy foods by developing local food delivery systems, increasing distribution of fresh foods, and work in sustainable agriculture, urban farms, and community gardens; 2) provide food to those who are in need, by supporting large regional food banks; and 3) provide nutrition and wellness education and opportunities, particularly in economically disadvantaged populations.
Fields of interest: Arts; Education; Health care.
Limitations: Giving primarily in IL, KS, MI, MO, and WI. No support for programs outside of the foundation's geographic area, or for those with political affiliations or for religious organizations' operating expenses. Generally, no grants for conferences, seminars, forums, summits, or think-tanks; no support for museum or art exhibits or for private school tuition.
Application information: As of June 2013, the Board is not accepting unsolicited applications, but has decided to focus on multi-year commitments to several of the foundation's existing grantees. See foundation web site for updates and application guidelines.
Officers and Directors:* B. Joanne Sante,* Chair.; Trish Robb, C.E.O. and Pres.; Carol Deese; Harry Robb; Patty Robb; Sandy Robb; Sue Robb; Mike Sante.
EIN: 260147405
Selected grants: The following grants are a representative sample of this grantmaker's funding activity:
$100,000 to Public Health Solutions, New York, NY, 2012. For School Food Focus Umrll.
$62,100 to University of Missouri, Columbia, MO, 2012. For Early Sprouts.
$53,000 to University of Missouri, Columbia, MO, 2012. For Effect of Fructose Consumption on Cardiovascular Health in Adolescents.

$50,000 to Growing Home, Chicago, IL, 2012. For Urban Ag and Econ Development. in Englewood.
$50,000 to Healthy Schools Campaign, Chicago, IL, 2012. For Go for the Gold.
$40,000 to Youth Farm and Market Project, Minneapolis, MN, 2012. For Youth Led Food Movement.
$25,000 to Eastern Illinois Foodbank, Urbana, IL, 2012. For Cold Storage Expansion.
$25,000 to Faith in Place, Chicago, IL, 2012. For Building Community Through Gardens.
$20,000 to Philabundance, Philadelphia, PA, 2012. For Delaware Valley Hunger Relief.
$5,000 to University of Missouri, Columbia, MO, 2012. For Mizzou South Farm.

2655
Fred & Jean Allegretti Foundation, Inc.

830 W. Rte. 22, Ste. 119
Lake Zurich, IL 60047-2389 (224) 655-6405
Contact: Carol Allegretti, Pres.; Lynn Larson, Fdn. Admin.
FAX: (224) 677-4992;
E-mail: fjallegrettifoundation@gmail.com; Toll-free tel.: (866) 819-3301; Main URL: http://allegrettifoundation.org

Established in 1997 in IL.
Donors: Jean Allegretti†; Carol Allegretti; Joseph Zielinski†.
Foundation type: Operating foundation.
Financial data (yr. ended 10/31/13): Assets, $22,033,385 (M); gifts received, $2,831,771; expenditures, $926,264; qualifying distributions, $735,500; giving activities include $735,500 for 81 grants (high: $30,000; low: $500).
Purpose and activities: The foundation provides financial support to various domestic charitable organizations that work to improve the lives, minds, health and well being of children, adults, the elderly, animals, those who are physically challenged, and veterans. It is our goal to provide a quality of life and dignity through humanitarian support, medical treatment, housing, education, and the arts.
Fields of interest: Arts; Education; Animals/wildlife, preservation/protection; Health care; Housing/shelter; Human services; Children/youth, services; Residential/custodial care; Military/veterans' organizations; Aging; Military/veterans; Economically disadvantaged.
Type of support: Program development; Advocacy.
Limitations: Applications accepted. Giving primarily in CO, FL, and IL; some funding nationally. No grants to individuals, or for endowments or international grants.
Application information: Online application process accessed from foundation web site. Application guidelines available on foundation web site.
Initial approach: Letter of Inquiry—through online application system on foundation web site
Deadline(s): For new organizations: May 31 for Letter of Inquiry, July 31 for application. For renewal applications: June 30
Board meeting date(s): Aug.
Final notification: Varies
Officers: Carol Allegretti, Pres.; Thomas Bucaro, Secy.; James Allegretti, Treas.
Directors: Karen Allegretti; Kim Allegretti.
EIN: 364110761
Selected grants: The following grants are a representative sample of this grantmaker's funding activity:
$15,000 to Northern Illinois Food Bank, Geneva, IL, 2013.
$10,000 to Alzheimers Association, Florida Gulf Coast Chapter, Clearwater, FL, 2013.
$10,000 to Bravehearts Therapeutic Riding and Educational Center, Harvard, IL, 2013.
$10,000 to Community Cooperative Ministries, Fort Myers, FL, 2013.
$10,000 to Florida Repertory Company, Fort Myers, FL, 2013.
$10,000 to Habitat for Humanity of Lee and Hendry Counties, North Fort Myers, FL, 2013.
$10,000 to Housing Opportunities and Maintenance for the Elderly, Chicago, IL, 2013.
$10,000 to La Rabida Children's Hospital, Chicago, IL, 2013.
$10,000 to Misericordia Home, Chicago, IL, 2013.
$10,000 to Womens Bean Project, Denver, CO, 2013.
$5,000 to Code 3 Associates, Erie, CO, 2013.
$5,000 to Hope House of Colorado, Arvada, CO, 2013.
$5,000 to Nurture, Sun Valley, ID, 2013.
$5,000 to Pioneer Center for Human Services, McHenry, IL, 2013.
$5,000 to Storycatchers Theatre, Chicago, IL, 2013.

2656
Allen Foundation ✧

c/o JPMorgan Chase Bank, N.A.
10 S. Dearborn St., No. 21
Chicago, IL 60603-2300

Established in 1991 in WI.
Donors: Marion M. Allen; Harris G. Allen Trust.
Foundation type: Independent foundation.
Financial data (yr. ended 07/31/13): Assets, $17,721,785 (M); expenditures, $996,721; qualifying distributions, $843,409; giving activities include $843,409 for grants.
Fields of interest: Education; Health organizations; Human services; Aging, centers/services.
Type of support: Program development.
Limitations: Applications not accepted. Giving primarily in WI. No grants to individuals.
Application information: Contributes only to pre-selected organizations.
Officer and Governors:* David Casarotto, Chair.; Hugh H. Bell; Allan Brinkerhoff; Fr. James McEnery; Morgan R. Redwine, Jr.
Trustee: JPMorgan Chase Bank, N.A.
EIN: 391708035
Selected grants: The following grants are a representative sample of this grantmaker's funding activity:
$578,604 to National Philanthropic Trust, Jenkintown, PA, 2011. For program support.

2657
The Allstate Foundation ✧

2775 Sanders Rd., Ste. F4
Northbrook, IL 60062-6127 (847) 402-7849
Contact: Patricia Lara Garza, Dir., Strategic Philanthropy
FAX: (847) 402-7568; E-mail: Grants@Allstate.com; Additional e-mails: Jan Epstein - jepstein@allstate.com; Sue Duchak - sue.duchak@allstate.com; Jennifer McGrath - jennifermcgrath@allstate.com; Chindaly Griffith - chindaly.griffith@allstate.com; e-mail for High School Award: KeeptheDrive@allstate.com; Main URL: http://www.allstatefoundation.org/
Act Out Loud on Facebook: http://www.facebook.com/pages/Act-Out-Loud/184625609915
Click To Empower - Home: http://www.clicktoempower.org/
Click to Empower Domestic Violence Survivors on Facebook: http://www.facebook.com/purplepurse?fref=ts
Click to Empower Domestic Violence Survivors on Twitter: http://twitter.com/ClickToEmpower
Keep the Drive on Youtube: http://www.youtube.com/watch?v=3NB5Pt7IuPA
Purple Purse: http://www.facebook.com/purplepurse
YouTube: http://www.youtube.com/allstatenews
E-mail for High School Award: KeeptheDrive@allstate.com

Incorporated in 1952 in IL.
Donors: The Allstate Corp.; Allstate Insurance Co.; Allstate New Jersey Insurance Co.
Foundation type: Company-sponsored foundation.
Financial data (yr. ended 12/31/12): Assets, $65,952,209 (M); gifts received, $36,275,138; expenditures, $19,764,214; qualifying distributions, $19,764,214; giving activities include $17,065,547 for 3,165 grants (high: $825,515; low: $25), $203,580 for employee matching gifts, and $17,065,547 for 6 foundation-administered programs.
Purpose and activities: The foundation supports programs designed to address teen safe driving and domestic violence. Additionally, the Foundation also supports programs designed to promote safe and vital communities; economic empowerment; and tolerance, inclusion, and diversity.
Fields of interest: Crime/violence prevention, youth; Employment, services; Employment, training; Employment; Disasters, preparedness/services; Safety, automotive safety; Safety/disasters; Youth, services; Family services, domestic violence; Human services, financial counseling; Civil/human rights, equal rights; Civil rights, race/intergroup relations; Community development, neighborhood development; Economic development; Children/youth; Disabilities, people with; Minorities; Asians/Pacific Islanders; African Americans/Blacks; Hispanics/Latinos; Native Americans/American Indians; Economically disadvantaged; LGBTQ; Gay men; Bisexual.
Type of support: Pro bono services - technology infrastructure; Pro bono services - strategic management; Pro bono services - marketing/branding; Pro bono services - legal; Pro bono services - interactive/website technology; Pro bono services - human resources; Pro bono services - financial management; Pro bono services - communications/public relations; Pro bono services; Technical assistance; Research; Loaned talent; Emergency funds; Cause-related marketing; Conferences/seminars; Curriculum development; Employee matching gifts; Employee volunteer services; Film/video/radio; General/operating support; Grants to individuals; Management development/capacity building; Program development.
Limitations: Giving in on a national basis in areas of company operations, in AK, AL, AR, AZ, CA, CO, CT, DC, DE, FL, GA, HI, IA, ID, IL, IN, KS, KY, LA, MA, MD, ME, MI, MN, MO, MS, MT, NC, ND, NE, NH, NJ, NM, NV, NY, OH, OK, OR, PA, RI, SC, TN, TX, UT, VA, VT, WA, WI, WV, and WY; giving also to regional and

national organizations. No support for religious organizations not of direct benefit to the entire community. Also, ONLY 501(c)3 tax status organizations are eligible. No grants to individuals (except for Keep the Drive High School Journalism Awards), or for fundraising events or sponsorships, equipment not part of a community outreach program, athletic events, memorials, travel, or audio, film, or video production.
Publications: Application guidelines; Program policy statement.
Application information: Application form required.
Initial approach: Complete online eligibility quiz and application; For Teen Safe Driving programs complete online application for Keep the Drive High School Journalism Awards and Act Out Loud
Deadline(s): Varies for Teen Safe Driving, Domestic Violence, Safe and Vital Communities, Economic Empowerment, and Tolerance, Inclusion, and Diversity; None; Oct. 1 to Mar. 1 for Keep the Drive High School Journalism Awards; Oct. 14 to Jan. 31 for Act Out Loud registration
Board meeting date(s): Aug. and Nov.
Final notification: Varies
Officers and Trustees:* Thomas J. Wilson,* Chair. and Pres.; Joan H. Walker, Exec. V.P. and Secy.; Judith P. Greffin,* Exec. V.P. and C.I.O; Susie Lees, Exec. Dir. and Genl. Counsel; Mario Rizzo, Sr. V.P. and Treas.; D. Scott Harper, Sr. V.P.; Don Civgin; Michele C. Mayes; Mathew E. Winter.
EIN: 366116535
Selected grants: The following grants are a representative sample of this grantmaker's funding activity:
$825,515 to National Safety Council, Itasca, IL, 2012. For Drive it Home Multi-City Launch.
$500,000 to United Way of Metropolitan Chicago, Chicago, IL, 2012. For Promoting Financial Stability for Domestic Violence Survivors.
$425,000 to Facing History and Ourselves National Foundation, Brookline, MA, 2012. For Community Conversations.
$400,000 to Junior Achievement, National, Colorado Springs, CO, 2012. For Title Sponsorship Renewal JA Economics for Success, $ave USA and Teens and Personal Finance Survey, and technology/operating support.
$400,000 to National Network to End Domestic Violence, Washington, DC, 2012. For NNEDV/TAF Economic Empowerment Project.
$35,000 to White Plains Library Foundation, White Plains, NY, 2012. For Allstate Readiness Series.
$1,000 to Boys and Girls Club of the Columbia Basin, Moses Lake, WA, 2012. For Agency Owner Volunteerism.
$1,000 to Boys and Girls Clubs of the Tennessee Valley, Knoxville, TN, 2012. For Agency Owner Volunteerism.
$1,000 to Community School of the Arts, Marion, IN, 2012. For Agency Owner Volunteerism.
$1,000 to Mississippi Childrens Museum, Jackson, MS, 2012. For Agency Owner Volunteerism.
$1,000 to Shelter for Abused Women of Collier County, Naples, FL, 2012. For Agency Owner Volunteerism.
$1,000 to YMCA, Shenango Valley, Hermitage, PA, 2012. For Agency Owner Volunteerism.

2658
Alphawood Foundation ✧
(formerly WPWR-TV Channel 50 Foundation)
P.O. Box 146340
Chicago, IL 60614-8544 (773) 477-8984
Contact: Agnes Meneses, Prog. Off. and Grants Mgr.
FAX: (773) 477-9019;
E-mail: info@alphawoodfoundation.org; Main URL: http://www.alphawoodfoundation.org/

Established in 1991 in IL.
Donors: Fred Eychaner; Newsweb Corp.
Foundation type: Independent foundation.
Financial data (yr. ended 02/28/13): Assets, $169,408,379 (M); gifts received, $6,883,616; expenditures, $12,356,541; qualifying distributions, $11,788,820; giving activities include $11,349,545 for 208 grants (high: $1,000,000; low: $5,000).
Purpose and activities: The foundation provides general operating support to nonprofit organizations whose primary mission involves the arts, arts education for children, institutional advocacy for social change, domestic violence intervention/prevention, and architecture and historical preservation. Arts education funding is specifically for children only.
Fields of interest: Arts education; Visual arts; Performing arts, dance; Performing arts, theater; Performing arts, music; Performing arts (multimedia); Literature; Historic preservation/historical societies; Arts; Family services, domestic violence.
Type of support: General/operating support.
Limitations: Giving primarily in the metropolitan Chicago, IL, area and northwestern IN. No support for religious or fraternal purposes, political campaigns or for public schools. No grants to individuals, or for scholarships, underwriting or tables for events, capital campaigns, or special projects.
Publications: Program policy statement (including application guidelines).
Application information: New proposals from organizations not currently being funded are by invitation only. Prospective new applications for funding must demonstrate a very strong match between their work and the foundation's priorities and guidelines; in order to be invited to apply contact foundation for more information.
Board meeting date(s): Varies
Officers and Directors:* Fred Eychaner,* Pres. and Treas.; Don Hilliker,* Secy.; Barbara Richardson; Tom Yoder.
Number of staff: 2 full-time professional.
EIN: 363805338
Selected grants: The following grants are a representative sample of this grantmaker's funding activity:
$1,000,000 to Four Freedoms Park Conservancy, Franklin D. Roosevelt Four Freedoms Park, New York, NY, 2013. For Four Freedoms Park.
$533,250 to University of Chicago, Chicago, IL, 2013. For Wuhan University Medical Education Reform (WUMER) Project in Wuhan, China. WUMER Project is a university-wide initiative that provides technical assistance to Wuhan University for comprehensive reform of their medical education curriculum and methodology, with a special emphasis on infectious diseases and public health.
$360,295 to University of Central Florida Research Foundation, Department of Anthropology, Winter Springs, FL, 2013. For Caracol Archeological Project in Belize.
$217,675 to Pennsylvania State University, Department of Entomology, University Park, PA, 2013. For research on Asian Longhorn Beetles (ALB) and how they affect trees and forests.
$150,000 to Center on Halsted, Chicago, IL, 2013. For general operations.
$89,525 to Kennesaw State University, Kennesaw, GA, 2013. For Pacbitun Regional Archaeological Project (PRAP) in Belize.
$50,000 to Abraham Lincoln Presidential Library Foundation, Springfield, IL, 2013. For general operations - 2nd payment of 3 year pledge.
$40,000 to Save the Dunes Conservation Fund, Michigan City, IN, 2013. For general operations.
$25,000 to Access Living of Metropolitan Chicago, Chicago, IL, 2013. For general operating support for advocacy activities.
$25,000 to Lira Ensemble, Chicago, IL, 2013. For general operations.

2659
Alsdorf Foundation ✧
209 E. Lake Shore Dr., Ste. 15W
Chicago, IL 60611-1307

Incorporated in 1944 in IL.
Donor: James W. Alsdorf†.
Foundation type: Independent foundation.
Financial data (yr. ended 12/31/13): Assets, $6,076,725 (M); expenditures, $729,863; qualifying distributions, $534,791; giving activities include $534,227 for 41 grants (high: $503,072; low: $15).
Purpose and activities: Giving primarily for the arts, particularly art museums, and for education.
Fields of interest: Arts; Education.
Type of support: Annual campaigns; Capital campaigns; Endowments.
Limitations: Applications not accepted. Giving primarily in Chicago, IL. No grants to individuals, or for scholarships, fellowships, or prizes; no loans.
Application information: Contributes only to pre-selected organizations.
Board meeting date(s): Dec. and as required
Officers: Marilynn B. Alsdorf, Pres. and Secy.; Robert N. Grant, V.P. and Secy.; Jeffrey A. Alsdorf, V.P.
Directors: Bridgette Alsdorf; Julius Lewis.
Number of staff: 1 full-time professional; 1 full-time support.
EIN: 366065388
Selected grants: The following grants are a representative sample of this grantmaker's funding activity:
$1,000 to Rush University Medical Center, Chicago, IL, 2012. For Healthcare.

2660
Amicus Foundation ✧
c/o Pete Ericson
98 E. Chicago Ave., Ste. 201
Westmont, IL 60559-1559

Established in 1985 in IL.
Donors: Joan C. Erickson; Peter E. Erickson; Hubbard H. Erickson, Jr.; Peggy Bigelow; Peter H. Erickson; Michael G. Beemer; John Erickson.
Foundation type: Independent foundation.
Financial data (yr. ended 12/31/13): Assets, $20,214,875 (M); expenditures, $1,030,106; qualifying distributions, $901,740; giving activities

include $900,736 for 2 grants (high: $900,000; low: $736).
Fields of interest: Human services; Philanthropy/ voluntarism.
Limitations: Applications not accepted. Giving primarily in OH, some giving in IL. No grants to individuals.
Application information: Contributes only to pre-selected organizations.
Officers and Directors:* Hubbard H. Erickson,* Pres.; Karen E. Cronin, V.P.; Joanne E. Smith, V.P.; Zachary Erickson,* Secy.; Peter H. Erickson,* Treas.; John H. Erickson; Joan C. Erickson.
EIN: 363378462

2661
Andrew Family Foundation ✧
14628 John Humphrey Dr.
Orland Park, IL 60462-2642

Established in 1993 in IL.
Donors: Edward J. Andrew; Edward J. Andrew, Jr.; Laurel J. Andrew; Edith G. Andrew; Richard G. Andrew; William V. Andrew; Kathryn A. Willett; Whitecap Investments G.P.
Foundation type: Independent foundation.
Financial data (yr. ended 10/31/13): Assets, $16,044,346 (M); expenditures, $636,940; qualifying distributions, $589,646; giving activities include $514,066 for 116 grants (high: $100,000; low: $200).
Fields of interest: Elementary/secondary education; Higher education; Education; Human services; Children/youth, services.
Type of support: General/operating support; Annual campaigns; Capital campaigns; Building/ renovation; Scholarship funds.
Limitations: Applications not accepted. Giving in the U.S., with emphasis on IL. No support for religious programs.
Application information: Unsolicited requests for funds not accepted.
Board meeting date(s): Quarterly
Officers and Directors:* Edward J. Andrew, Jr.,* Pres.; Richard G. Andrew,* V.P.; Kathryn A. Willett,* Secy.; Laurel J. Andrew,* Treas.; Edith G. Andrew; Edward J. Andrew; William V. Andrew.
EIN: 363926511
Selected grants: The following grants are a representative sample of this grantmaker's funding activity:
$150,000 to Reading in Motion, Chicago, IL, 2011.
$100,000 to Reading in Motion, Chicago, IL, 2011.
$45,000 to Meadows School, Las Vegas, NV, 2011.
$42,500 to Lutheran General Health System, Park Ridge, IL, 2010.
$20,000 to Benet Academy, Lisle, IL, 2011.
$20,000 to Lied Discovery Childrens Museum, Las Vegas, NV, 2011.
$15,000 to Valley Youth Theater, Phoenix, AZ, 2011.
$6,000 to Great Arizona Puppet Theater, Phoenix, AZ, 2011.
$6,000 to Southwest Chicago Christian School Association, Palos Heights, IL, 2010.
$4,833 to Northwestern University, Evanston, IL, 2011.
$2,625 to Great Arizona Puppet Theater, Phoenix, AZ, 2011.
$2,500 to Neighborhood Health Clinic, Naples, FL, 2010.
$2,300 to Great Arizona Puppet Theater, Phoenix, AZ, 2011.

2662
Aileen S. Andrew Foundation ✧
10701 Winterset Dr.
Orland Park, IL 60467-1106 (708) 349-4445
Contact: Robert E. Hord, Jr., Pres.
Facebook: http://www.facebook.com/pages/ Aileen-S-Andrew-Foundation/160805170607286

Incorporated in 1946 in IL.
Donors: Edward J. Andrew; Richard G. Andrew; Juanita A. Hord; Andrew Corp.
Foundation type: Independent foundation.
Financial data (yr. ended 11/30/13): Assets, $55,493,667 (M); expenditures, $2,948,951; qualifying distributions, $2,356,010; giving activities include $2,006,245 for 362 grants (high: $100,000; low: $50), and $46,650 for 7 grants to individuals (high: $10,184; low: $2,902).
Purpose and activities: Giving for higher education, including scholarships for children of Andrew Corp. employees and graduates of a local high school; support also for health organizations and hospitals, youth and social services, and Christian and Protestant churches.
Fields of interest: Higher education; Education; Hospitals (general); Health organizations, association; Cancer; Human services; Children/ youth, services; Christian agencies & churches; Protestant agencies & churches.
Type of support: General/operating support; Employee-related scholarships.
Limitations: Giving primarily in Orland Park, IL. No support for taxable corporations, political organizations or private foundations. No grants to individuals (except scholarships); no loans.
Application information: Application forms are available for scholarship program.
Initial approach: Letter of intent
Deadline(s): None for grants; generally at the beginning of Apr. for scholarships, but refer to application form for exact deadline date
Board meeting date(s): Several times per year
Final notification: May 1 for scholarships
Officers and Directors:* Robert E. Hord, Jr.,* Pres.; Joyce Smith, V.P.; Aileen H. Daly,* Secy.; Richard L. Dybala, Treas.; Laurel J. Andrew; Richard G. Andrew; Juanita A. Hord.
EIN: 366049910

2663
Paul M. Angell Family Foundation ✧
4140 W. Fullerton Ave.
Chicago, IL 60639-2106 (773) 628-6980
Contact: Kim Van Horn, Chief Admin. Off.
E-mail: kim@pmangellfamfound.org; Main URL: http://pmangellfamfound.org
Grants List: http://pmangellfamfound.org/ Fall_2013_Grants.html

Donor: Charles T. Angell.
Foundation type: Independent foundation.
Financial data (yr. ended 12/31/13): Assets, $418,155 (M); gifts received, $2,596,149; expenditures, $2,515,532; qualifying distributions, $2,498,884; giving activities include $2,411,500 for 103 grants (high: $150,000; low: $5,000).
Purpose and activities: Giving primarily for: 1) Conservation, particularly the protection of the world's oceans and species. The foundation is interested in site-specific projects designed to improve the health of ocean habitats and to enhance their ability to withstand the challenges of climate change. The foundation also supports efforts to fund species protection, particularly regarding the seas' apex predators. Eligible projects include research, conservation and/or restoration. Grants for other types of water-related conservation efforts may be considered on a limited basis; 2) Performing Arts, primarily classical music and theater; and 3) Social Causes, particularly to support efforts that address the root causes of poverty and inequality, particularly in urban areas. Priority will be given to programs that emphasize evidence-based early intervention and prevention approaches. The foundation seeks to support efforts designed to help alter the life trajectories of socioeconomically disadvantaged individuals and families. Specific areas of interest include early childhood education, teenage pregnancy prevention, school completion for at-risk youth, workforce preparedness, and African-American male achievement. Although not limited exclusively to Chicago, grant making in Social Causes will focus on the Chicago area.
Fields of interest: Museums (natural history); Arts; Environment; Youth development; Community/ economic development.
Limitations: Applications accepted. Giving primarily in CA, Washington, DC and IL. No support for religious institutions. No grants for debt reeducation, fundraising events, or endowments.
Application information: Applications are by invitation only, upon review of Letter of Inquiry. Application form required.
Initial approach: Create an account on the foundation's web site, then use the online Letter of Inquiry process
Deadline(s): See foundation web site for current deadlines
Officers: Charles T. Angell, Pres.; James S . Angell, Secy.; Michael T. Angell, Treas.
EIN: 274818015

2664
Lester and Edward Anixter Family Foundation ✧
(formerly L. & R. Anixter Foundation)
1300 N. State Pkwy., Unit 803
Chicago, IL 60610-8657

Established in 1985 in IL.
Donor: Lester J. Anixter Trust.
Foundation type: Independent foundation.
Financial data (yr. ended 12/31/13): Assets, $18,629,408 (M); expenditures, $1,064,149; qualifying distributions, $929,612; giving activities include $851,666 for 45 grants (high: $175,000; low: $500).
Fields of interest: Museums; Arts; Higher education; Education; Human services; Children/ youth, services; Jewish federated giving programs; Science, research; Jewish agencies & synagogues.
Limitations: Applications not accepted. Giving primarily in Chicago, IL and New York, NY. No grants to individuals.
Application information: Unsolicited requests for funds not accepted.
Officers: Steven Anixter, Pres.; Jo Ann Anixter Silva, V.P.; Jack Ehrlich, Secy.-Treas.
EIN: 363458779

2665
Ansari Family Foundation, Inc. ✧ ☆
802 Normandy Ln.
Glenview, IL 60025
Application address: Mohsin Ansari, 1530 Central Pkwy., Glenview, IL 60025, tel.: (414) 350-7739

Established in 2001 in WI.
Donors: Mohsin Ansari; Faizah Syed.
Foundation type: Independent foundation.
Financial data (yr. ended 12/31/13): Assets, $426,391 (M); expenditures, $1,188,154; qualifying distributions, $1,187,454; giving activities include $1,187,454 for 18 grants (high: $750,000; low: $650).
Fields of interest: Education; Islam.
Limitations: Applications accepted. Giving primarily in IL and VA.
Application information: Application form not required.
Initial approach: Proposal
Deadline(s): None
Officers: Mohsin Ansari, Pres.; Faizah Syed, V.P.
Director: Husam Ansari.
EIN: 800015664

2666
Anschel Eilian Family Charitable Foundation ✧ ☆
c/o C. Eilian
3470 N. Lake Shore Dr., Ste. 27
Chicago, IL 60657-2892

Established in 2002 in IL.
Donors: Trude Anschel; Jonathan Eilian.
Foundation type: Independent foundation.
Financial data (yr. ended 12/31/13): Assets, $1,288,046 (M); expenditures, $439,539; qualifying distributions, $436,812; giving activities include $436,812 for 40 grants (high: $102,000; low: $100).
Fields of interest: Human services; Jewish federated giving programs; Jewish agencies & synagogues.
Limitations: Applications not accepted. Giving primarily in IL and NY. No grants to individuals.
Application information: Contributes only to pre-selected organizations.
Officers: Charlene Eilian, Pres. and Treas; Daniel Anschel, Secy.
EIN: 320002986
Selected grants: The following grants are a representative sample of this grantmaker's funding activity:
$25,000 to New Yorkers for Children, New York, NY, 2012. To provide funds for underprivileged children.
$10,000 to Georgetown University, Washington, DC, 2012. For funds for school.
$1,100 to Shalva, Chicago, IL, 2012. To provide funds for abused women.
$1,000 to Creighton University, Omaha, NE, 2012. To provide funds for school.
$600 to Chicago Symphony Orchestra, Chicago, IL, 2012. For the Support of the Chicago Symphony Orchestra.
$500 to Memorial Sloan-Kettering Cancer Center, New York, NY, 2012. For funds for cancer research.
$300 to ARS Viva Symphony Orchestra, Libertyville, IL, 2012. For Funds for the Orchestra.
$250 to University of Chicago, Chicago, IL, 2012. For Funds for the School.
$200 to Maot Chitim of Greater Chicago, Lincolnwood, IL, 2012. For Funds to Provide Food for the Poor.

2667
Aon Foundation ✧
(formerly Combined International Foundation)
200 East Randolph
Chicago, IL 60601-6419 (312) 381-3555
Contact: Carolyn Barry Frost, Pres. and Treas.
FAX: (312) 381-6166;
E-mail: aon_foundation@aon.com; Main URL: http://www.aon.com/about-aon/global-citizenship/giving.jsp

Established in 1984 in IL.
Donor: Aon Corp.
Foundation type: Company-sponsored foundation.
Financial data (yr. ended 12/31/12): Assets, $50,035 (M); gifts received, $10,024,731; expenditures, $9,431,769; qualifying distributions, $9,431,769; giving activities include $9,431,769 for 3,082 grants (high: $500,000; low: $25).
Purpose and activities: The Aon Foundation is the principal vehicle for Aon's philanthropic programs in the U.S. and focuses on empowering people and working with communities at risk. Aon invests in educational programs that make a marked difference in the academic achievement of young people, as well as in organizations that help develop the future workforce.
Fields of interest: Arts; Education; Environment; Disasters, preparedness/services; Youth development; American Red Cross; Human services; Community/economic development; Youth; Disabilities, people with; Minorities; Economically disadvantaged.
Type of support: General/operating support; Program development; Employee volunteer services; Employee matching gifts.
Limitations: Applications not accepted. Giving on a national basis in areas of company operations, with emphasis on Chicago, IL. No support for fraternal, labor, political, religious, or discriminatory organizations. No grants to individuals.
Publications: Corporate giving report.
Application information: Contributes only to pre-selected organizations. The foundation utilizes an invitation only process for giving.
Board meeting date(s): 3 times per year
Officers and Directors: Carolyn Barry Frost, Pres. and Treas.; Ram Padmanabhan, Secy.; Gregory J. Besio; Gregory C. Case; Christa Davies.
Number of staff: 4
EIN: 363337340
Selected grants: The following grants are a representative sample of this grantmaker's funding activity:
$333,334 to Virginia Mason Health System, Seattle, WA, 2012.
$296,000 to United Way of Metropolitan Chicago, Chicago, IL, 2012.
$250,000 to Facing History and Ourselves National Foundation, Chicago, IL, 2012.
$200,000 to China Literacy Foundation, Hong Kong, China, 2012.
$100,000 to Covenant House New Jersey, Newark, NJ, 2012.
$75,000 to American Diabetes Association, Chicago, IL, 2012.
$10,000 to Suzuki-Orff School for Young Musicians, Chicago, IL, 2012.
$3,500 to Allies Friends Foundation, Newtown, PA, 2012. For providing comforting stuffed animals to emergency medical assistance teams throughout the united states to children in medical emergencies.
$3,000 to Baptist Health System Foundation, Jacksonville, FL, 2012. To conduct education, to be advocates for issues related to the aged and to promote public health issues for persons of all ages.
$2,000 to University of Wisconsin-Stout Foundation, Menomonie, WI, 2012. To solicit ensure and manage contributions from the private sector (primarily individuals corporations, and philanthropic foundations) for the benefit of the university, institution of higher education.

2668
The Appleby Foundation ✧
c/o Northern Trust
P.O. Box 803878
Chicago, IL 60682
Application address: The Appleby Foundation, c/o The Northern Trust Co., P.O. Box 4097, Sarasota, FL 34230, tel.: (941) 329-2628

Established in 1958 in DC.
Donor: Scott B. Appleby†.
Foundation type: Independent foundation.
Financial data (yr. ended 12/31/13): Assets, $12,058,533 (M); expenditures, $677,488; qualifying distributions, $539,833; giving activities include $513,250 for 26 grants (high: $120,000; low: $1,000).
Purpose and activities: Giving primarily for higher education, as well as for arts and cultural programs, environmental conservation and protection, medical research, including a foundation for research in aging, and for youth and social services.
Fields of interest: Performing arts; Arts; Higher education; Education; Environment; Animals/wildlife, preservation/protection; Reproductive health, family planning; Health organizations, association; Multiple sclerosis; Medical research; Human services; Children/youth, services; Residential/custodial care, hospices.
Type of support: General/operating support; Scholarship funds.
Limitations: Applications accepted. Giving primarily in FL, GA, NY, and WY.
Application information:
Initial approach: Letter
Deadline(s): None
Trustees: Benjamin M. Colby; F. Jordan Colby; Sarah Rob Colby Pierce; The Northern Trust Co.
Number of staff: 1 part-time support.
EIN: 526026971

2669
Edith Marie Appleton Foundation ✧
1028 Seneca Rd.
Wilmette, IL 60091-1255

Established in 1999 in IL.
Donor: Edith Marie Appleton†.
Foundation type: Independent foundation.
Financial data (yr. ended 12/31/13): Assets, $7,387,219 (M); expenditures, $812,377; qualifying distributions, $710,000; giving activities include $710,000 for 20 grants (high: $255,000; low: $5,000).

Purpose and activities: Giving primarily for the performing arts in the Chicago, Illinois, area.
Fields of interest: Museums (art); Performing arts, theater; Arts; Human services; Women.
Limitations: Applications not accepted. Giving primarily in Chicago, IL. No grants to individuals.
Application information: Contributes only to pre-selected organizations.
Board meeting date(s): Annually
Officers and Directors:* Albert I. Goodman,* Pres. and Treas.; Cathy Smerch,* V.P.; Jane Hannon,* Secy.; Robert Dunagan; Maria Goodman.
EIN: 364329167

2670
ArcelorMittal USA Foundation, Inc. ✧
(formerly Mittal Steel USA Foundation, Inc.)
c/o Paul Liebenson
1 S. Dearborn St., 19th Fl.
Chicago, IL 60603-2307
Contact: William C. Steers, Pres.

Established in 2000 in IN.
Donors: Mittal Steel USA Inc.; ArcelorMittal USA, Inc.
Foundation type: Company-sponsored foundation.
Financial data (yr. ended 12/31/13): Assets, $16,869 (M); gifts received, $852,034; expenditures, $1,177,565; qualifying distributions, $1,177,550; giving activities include $1,177,550 for 13 grants (high: $500,000; low: $1,500).
Purpose and activities: The foundation supports organizations involved with education, animal welfare, disaster relief, and to the United Way.
Fields of interest: Education; Animal welfare; Disasters, preparedness/services; United Ways and Federated Giving Programs.
Type of support: Scholarship funds; General/operating support; Program development.
Limitations: Applications accepted. Giving in the U.S., with emphasis on IN and MN.
Application information: Application form required.
Initial approach: Proposal
Deadline(s): None
Officers: William C. Steers, Pres.; Paul Liebenson, Secy.; Martha Gonzalez, Treas.
Directors: Josephine Heil; Gary Lefko; Heather Loebner; Cordell Petz.
EIN: 352121803
Selected grants: The following grants are a representative sample of this grantmaker's funding activity:
$700,000 to National Fish and Wildlife Foundation, Bloomington, MN, 2011.
$300,000 to United Way, Lake Area, Griffith, IN, 2011.
$195,000 to United Way of Greater Cleveland, Cleveland, OH, 2011.
$175,000 to United Way of Porter County, Valparaiso, IN, 2011.
$165,635 to Legacy Foundation, Merrillville, IN, 2011.
$75,776 to United Way of Chester County, West Chester, PA, 2011.
$30,000 to United Way of Metropolitan Chicago, Chicago, IL, 2011.
$23,000 to United Way of the Capital Region, Enola, PA, 2011.
$20,000 to United Way of Weirton, Weirton, WV, 2011.
$15,000 to United Way of Greater Philadelphia and Southern New Jersey, Philadelphia, PA, 2011.

2671
Jacqueline G. Archer Charitable Trust ✧
10 S. Dearborn IL1-0117
Chicago, IL 60603

Established in 2002 in CO.
Foundation type: Independent foundation.
Financial data (yr. ended 12/31/13): Assets, $14,340,493 (M); expenditures, $729,691; qualifying distributions, $631,102; giving activities include $603,000 for 26 grants (high: $120,000; low: $6,000).
Fields of interest: Education; Human services; Children/youth, services; Aging, centers/services; Christian agencies & churches.
Limitations: Applications not accepted. Giving in the U.S., with emphasis on CO, particularly Colorado Springs. No grants to individuals.
Application information: Contributes only to pre-selected organizations.
Trustee: JPMorgan Chase Bank, N.A.
EIN: 686218949

2672
ARIA Foundation, Inc. ✧
c/o TG Tax & Accounting Svcs., LLC
1710 Waters Edge Dr.
Minooka, IL 60447-8201

Established in 1991 in VT.
Donors: Adam Albright; Rachel Albright.
Foundation type: Independent foundation.
Financial data (yr. ended 10/31/13): Assets, $36,281,366 (M); expenditures, $1,668,117; qualifying distributions, $1,442,641; giving activities include $1,433,205 for 49 grants (high: $252,060; low: $800).
Purpose and activities: Giving primarily for the protection and preservation of our natural resources and the global environment.
Fields of interest: Education; Environment, natural resources; Environment; Children/youth, services; Family services; Women; LGBTQ.
Limitations: Applications not accepted. Giving in the U.S., with emphasis on New York, NY. No grants to individuals.
Application information: Contributes only to pre-selected organizations.
Officers: Adam Albright, Pres.; Rachel Albright, V.P.; Ruth S. Flynn, Secy.; Elliott M. Friedman, Treas.
Director: Mika Albright.
EIN: 133603275

2673
The Arthur Foundation ✧
(formerly MacNeal Health Foundation)
19 Riverside Rd., Ste. 6
Riverside, IL 60546-2606
Main URL: http://www.arthurfdn.org/

Established in 2000 in IL; converted from MacNeal Memorial Hospital; changed its name to The Arthur Foundation in 2006.
Foundation type: Independent foundation.
Financial data (yr. ended 12/31/12): Assets, $104,003,022 (M); expenditures, $8,622,839; qualifying distributions, $7,764,772; giving activities include $7,266,170 for 16 grants (high: $2,000,000; low: $10,000).
Purpose and activities: The foundation aims to improve the health of the community by supporting accessible, affordable and appropriate health services to vulnerable populations. The foundation recognizes that actual health care or health related service is only one of the factors determining the health status of individuals and families of these same communities. The health of the people is also determined by the educational status of its people, especially its youth. Therefore, the foundation will also consider grant requests that foster and improve education and educational opportunities for the citizens of the area it seeks to serve.
Fields of interest: Medical school/education; Nursing school/education; Education, ESL programs; Education; Health care; Children/youth; Children; Adults; Young adults; Disabilities, people with; Physically disabled; Blind/visually impaired; Deaf/hearing impaired; Mentally disabled; Hispanics/Latinos; Immigrants/refugees; Economically disadvantaged.
Type of support: General/operating support; Continuing support; Income development; Management development/capacity building; Building/renovation; Equipment; Endowments; Program development; Professorships; Curriculum development; Fellowships; Internship funds; Scholarship funds; Research; Program evaluation; Matching/challenge support.
Limitations: Applications not accepted. Giving primarily in Berwyn and Cicero, IL for education grants. Health care grants for western Cook County, IL. No support for organizations without charitable status, political parties or candidates, sponsorship of service clubs, sport teams, fraternal organizations, advocacy or lobby groups, or for foreign organizations. No grants to individuals, or for operating budgets for pre-existing programs, organization overhead expenses not directly applicable to a grant project, salaries for participants with faculty appointments at institutions of higher learning, programs normally funded by governmental agencies, fundraising events (including advertising, tickets, raffles and dinners), debt reduction, stand-alone research, individual scholarship support, conferences/seminars, books/periodicals, memberships, travel expenses not connected to a funded program, any attempt to influence legislation, sectarian religious activities, foreign expenditures, telephone solicitations; no loans.
Publications: Financial statement.
Application information: Unsolicited requests for funds not accepted.
Board meeting date(s): Semi-annually
Officers and Board Members:* Luke McGuiness,* Chair.; William J. Hank,* Vice-Chair. and V.P.; Michael P. Kenahan,* Pres.; Jeffrey P. Huml, M.D., Secy.; Raymond Nootens, M.D., Treas.; Rolf Gunnar, M.D.; Allen B. Hank; Roxanne Martino; Carmen Velasquez.
Number of staff: 2 full-time professional.
EIN: 364324067
Selected grants: The following grants are a representative sample of this grantmaker's funding activity:
$2,000,000 to University of Notre Dame, Mendoza College of Business, Notre Dame, IN, 2012. To endow fellowships for Masters of Business Administration (MBA) students.
$1,250,000 to University of Notre Dame, Mendoza College of Business, Notre Dame, IN, 2012. For Masters of Business Administration (MBA) in Executive Education.
$750,000 to University of Notre Dame, Institute for Latino Studies, Notre Dame, IN, 2012. For

assessment for Berwyn/Cicero, IL and leadership identification, capacity building and education advice.
$738,400 to Loyola University of Chicago, Chicago, IL, 2012. For enhancements for nursing faculty and building.
$500,000 to Loyola University Health System, Maywood, IL, 2012. To construct Nursing School.
$500,000 to University of Notre Dame, Mendoza College of Business, Notre Dame, IN, 2012. For fellowships for Masters of Nonprofit Administration (MNA) students.
$480,000 to Loyola University of Chicago, College of Education, Chicago, IL, 2012. For LUChoice program and Center for Catholic School Effectiveness.
$250,000 to Northeastern Illinois University, Chicago Teachers' Center/Center for College Access and Success, Chicago, IL, 2012. To implement Initiative for Education Excellence in Berwyn and Cicero, IL.
$250,000 to University of Notre Dame, Mendoza College of Business, Notre Dame, IN, 2012. To endow Chair in Nonprofit Administration.
$30,000 to Seguin Services, Cicero, IL, 2012. For Entrepreneur Education programs for developmentally disabled.

2674
Mary Frost Ashley Charitable Trust ✧
c/o Tax Div.
111 W. Monroe St., Ste. 10C
Chicago, IL 60603-4026

Established in 2007 in IL.
Donor: Mary Frost Ashley Trust.
Foundation type: Independent foundation.
Financial data (yr. ended 06/30/13): Assets, $10,992,190 (M); expenditures, $682,592; qualifying distributions, $558,504; giving activities include $558,504 for grants.
Fields of interest: Education; Human services; Residential/custodial care, hospices.
Limitations: Applications not accepted. No grants to individuals.
Application information: Contributes only to pre-selected organizations.
Trustees: Patricia F. Callahan; Floyd D. Perkins; James Seymour; BMO Harris Bank, N.A.
EIN: 261417061
Selected grants: The following grants are a representative sample of this grantmaker's funding activity:
$160,000 to Kenosha Unified School District No. 1, Kenosha, WI, 2011.
$50,000 to Hospice Alliance, Pleasant Prairie, WI, 2011.
$50,000 to University of Wisconsin-Parkside, Kenosha, WI, 2011.
$35,000 to ELCA Urban Outreach Center, Kenosha, WI, 2011.
$30,000 to Armitage Academy, Kenosha, WI, 2011.
$25,000 to YMCA, Kenosha, Kenosha, WI, 2011.
$20,000 to Kenosha Achievement Center, Kenosha, WI, 2011.
$12,500 to Boys and Girls Club of Kenosha, Kenosha, WI, 2011.
$12,500 to Women and Childrens Horizons, Kenosha, WI, 2011.
$6,000 to Kenosha Public Museum, Kenosha, WI, 2011.

2675
Astellas USA Foundation ✧
(formerly Yamanouchi USA Foundation)
1 Astellas Way
Northbrook, IL 60062-6111 (224) 205-8979
Main URL: http://www.astellasusafoundation.org

Established in 1993 in DC.
Donor: Fujisawa USA Charitable Trust Fund.
Foundation type: Independent foundation.
Financial data (yr. ended 12/31/13): Assets, $28,142,282 (M); expenditures, $1,973,805; qualifying distributions, $1,957,872; giving activities include $1,947,000 for 37 grants (high: $400,000; low: $5,000).
Purpose and activities: Giving primarily for global initiatives to improve the quality of life and medical care for patients; basic scientific research in areas of future therapeutic interest to Astellas; and to civic and community organizations located in areas where Astellas, Inc. has offices that focus on local needs.
Fields of interest: Education; Botanical gardens; Health organizations, association; Medical research, institute; Human services.
Limitations: Giving in the U.S., with emphasis on IL; funding also in Canada. The foundation will give strong preference to programs that are located in an area where Astellas has employees and/or facilities. No support for continuing medical education grants, educational activities for healthcare professionals or patients that relate to an Astellas Therapeutic area of interest, professional medical associations or societies, academic medical centers, or political or religious organizations. No grants to individuals, or for medical fellowships or residencies, endowments, lobbying, applied research in any area, or general operating expenses.
Application information:
Initial approach: Register on foundation web site to submit an online application
Deadline(s): 90 days in advance of the need for funds
Final notification: 90 days (minimum)
Officers: Collette Taylor, Pres.; Robin Andrews, Secy.; Steve Knowles, Treas.
Directors: Yasuo Ishii; Sef Kurstjens; Yoshirou Miyokawa; Masafumi Nogimori; Steven Ryder; Masao Yoshida.
EIN: 521820099
Selected grants: The following grants are a representative sample of this grantmaker's funding activity:
$100,000 to Biotechnology Institute, Arlington, VA, 2011.
$35,000 to National Association of Japan-America Societies, Washington, DC, 2011.

2676
Robert and Martha and John Atherton Foundation ✧
(formerly Robert & Martha Atherton Foundation)
2100 S. Wolf Rd.
Des Plaines, IL 60018-1932

Established in 1989 in IL.
Donors: Martha A. Atherton; John C. Atherton; Robert C. Atherton.
Foundation type: Independent foundation.
Financial data (yr. ended 12/31/13): Assets, $1,696,068 (M); gifts received, $354,144; expenditures, $1,016,334; qualifying distributions, $985,665; giving activities include $985,665 for 16 grants (high: $200,000; low: $1,000).
Fields of interest: Higher education; Education; Health care; Cystic fibrosis; Cancer; Human services; Foundations (private grantmaking); United Ways and Federated Giving Programs; Christian agencies & churches.
Type of support: General/operating support; Scholarship funds.
Limitations: Applications not accepted. Giving primarily in IL. No grants to individuals.
Application information: Contributes only to pre-selected organizations.
Trustees: Linda Anderson; John C. Atherton; Martha A. Atherton; John C. Boecher; Marshall G. Lobin.
EIN: 363679194
Selected grants: The following grants are a representative sample of this grantmaker's funding activity:
$10,000 to Emanuel Medical Center Foundation, Portland, OR, 2011. For general support.
$8,150 to Portland Rescue Mission, Portland, OR, 2011. For general support.
$5,000 to Opportunity International, Oak Brook, IL, 2011. For general support.

2677
The Sidley Austin Foundation ✧
c/o Timothy F. Bergen
1 S. Dearborn St., Ste. 2300
Chicago, IL 60603-2302

Established in 2005 in IL.
Donors: Sidley Austin; Sidley Austin, LLP.
Foundation type: Company-sponsored foundation.
Financial data (yr. ended 12/31/12): Assets, $12,808,940 (M); gifts received, $6,200,000; expenditures, $3,231,496; qualifying distributions, $3,231,496; giving activities include $3,231,126 for 431 grants (high: $208,200; low: $100).
Purpose and activities: Giving primarily for higher education, particularly law schools, as well as for the arts, and youth and social services.
Fields of interest: Arts; Higher education; Law school/education; Environment; Legal services; Human services; Children/youth, services; Economic development; United Ways and Federated Giving Programs; Jewish federated giving programs.
Limitations: Applications not accepted. Giving primarily in IL, MA, and NY. No grants to individuals.
Application information: Contributes only to pre-selected organizations.
Officers and Directors:* Charles H. Douglas,* Pres.; Timothy F. Bergen,* Secy.; Christian Cooley,* Treas.; Joseph W. Armbrust, Jr.; Theodore N. Miller.
EIN: 203980527

2678
Bacca Foundation ✧ ☆
c/o J.P. Morgan Trust Co. of DE
10 S. Dearborn St., IL1-0111
Chicago, IL 60603-2024

Established in DE.
Donors: The Gibson Trust; Brett M. Berry; Winston B. Berry.
Foundation type: Independent foundation.
Financial data (yr. ended 12/31/13): Assets, $22,972,930 (M); gifts received, $3,000,000; expenditures, $4,171,158; qualifying distributions,

$4,108,972; giving activities include $4,047,333 for 5 grants (high: $1,700,000; low: $14,000).
Fields of interest: Arts; Higher education; Hospitals (general); Cancer research; Christian agencies & churches.
Limitations: Applications not accepted. Giving primarily in CA, CO, and MA.
Application information: Unsolicited requests for funds not accepted.
Trustees: Brett M. Berry; Winston B. Berry.
EIN: 386981808
Selected grants: The following grants are a representative sample of this grantmaker's funding activity:
$1,000,000 to Massachusetts General Hospital, Boston, MA, 2012. For Maternal, Newborn and Child Health Initiative.
$250,000 to ETown, Boulder, CO, 2012. To Educate, Entertain and Inspire a Diverse Audience Through Music.
$10,000 to University of Colorado Foundation, Boulder, CO, 2012. For the University of Colorado.
$10,000 to University of Pennsylvania, Philadelphia, PA, 2012. For the University of Pennsylvania.

2679
G. Carl Ball Family Foundation ✧
c/o N. Kaskovich
622 Town Rd.
West Chicago, IL 60185-2614

Established in 2003 in IL.
Donors: G. Carl Ball‡; Ball Investments LP.
Foundation type: Independent foundation.
Financial data (yr. ended 12/31/13): Assets, $49,845,855 (M); expenditures, $3,193,401; qualifying distributions, $3,081,775; giving activities include $3,078,750 for 11 grants (high: $2,800,000; low: $500).
Fields of interest: Education; Human services.
Limitations: Applications not accepted. Giving primarily in Mayer, AZ, and IL.
Application information: Contributes only to pre-selected organizations.
Officers and Directors:* Anna C. Ball,* Pres. and Secy.; Susannah P. Ball,* V.P. and Treas.; Jane Mann.
EIN: 830366015
Selected grants: The following grants are a representative sample of this grantmaker's funding activity:
$250,000 to YMCA, Ryall, Glen Ellyn, IL, 2011. To support operations.

2680
A.N. and Pearl G. Barnett Family Foundation ✧
20 N. Wacker Dr., Ste. 1416
Chicago, IL 60606-2906

Established in 1989 in IL.
Donors: Marjorie C. Barnett; Marjorie C. Barnett Trust No. 1.
Foundation type: Independent foundation.
Financial data (yr. ended 12/31/13): Assets, $1,689,061 (M); expenditures, $744,398; qualifying distributions, $718,996; giving activities include $710,811 for 15 grants (high: $150,615; low: $500).
Fields of interest: Performing arts, music; YM/YWCAs & YM/YWHAs; Jewish agencies & synagogues.
Limitations: Applications not accepted. Giving primarily in Chicago, IL and New York, NY. No grants to individuals.
Application information: Unsolicited requests for funds not accepted.
Officers: Milton G. Lefton, Pres.; Jane Nicholl Sahlins, V.P.; Christine K. Buck, Secy.
EIN: 363663240

2681
Gertrude A. Barnett Foundation ✧
P.O. Box 803878
Chicago, IL 60680-3878

Established in 1997 in FL.
Foundation type: Independent foundation.
Financial data (yr. ended 12/31/13): Assets, $11,259,563 (M); expenditures, $606,941; qualifying distributions, $520,644; giving activities include $510,852 for 10 grants (high: $91,064; low: $45,532).
Purpose and activities: Giving primarily for higher education, human services, United Methodist churches, and children and youth services, including a children's hospital.
Fields of interest: Higher education; Hospitals (specialty); Human services; Children/youth, services; Protestant agencies & churches.
Limitations: Applications not accepted. Giving primarily in FL. No grants to individuals.
Application information: Contributes only to pre-selected organizations.
Trustee: The Northern Trust Co.
EIN: 656245681
Selected grants: The following grants are a representative sample of this grantmaker's funding activity:
$79,454 to University of Miami, Coral Gables, FL, 2011. For general support.
$49,727 to Florida United Methodist Childrens Home, Children's Home, Deltona, FL, 2010. For general support.
$49,727 to Florida United Methodist Childrens Home, Deltona, FL, 2011. For general support.
$39,727 to Florence Fuller Child Development Center, Children's Dev Center, Boca Raton, FL, 2010. For general support.
$39,727 to Florida Sheriffs Youth Ranches, Live Oak, FL, 2011. For general support.
$39,727 to Illinois Masonic Home, Sullivan, IL, 2010. For general support.
$39,727 to Miami Childrens Hospital, Miami, FL, 2011. For general support.
$39,727 to Saint Labre Indian Catholic School, Ashland, MT, 2010. For general support.
$39,727 to Salvation Army of Naples, Naples, FL, 2010. For general support.

2682
Barney Family Foundation ✧
(formerly Chester Foundation)
c/o Kristen Barney Adams
130 S. Canal St., Ste. 9T
Chicago, IL 60606-3919 (312) 632-0000
Contact: Kristen Barney Adams, Tr.
FAX: (312) 632-1000; Main URL: http://barneyfamilyfoundation.org/

Established in 1998; supporting organization of Opportunity International, the Focus Fund, the Heritage Foundation, CATO Institute, Shriners Hospital for Crippled Children, the American Institute for Cancer Research, Catholic Bishop of Chicago, Hillsdale College, DePauw University, Chicago Community Trust, Children's Scholarship Fund, and Alzheimer's Disease International.
Foundation type: Independent foundation.
Financial data (yr. ended 12/31/12): Assets, $36,043,186 (M); expenditures, $1,667,061; qualifying distributions, $1,365,186; giving activities include $1,319,500 for 32 grants (high: $400,000; low: $10,000).
Fields of interest: Elementary/secondary education; Higher education; Medical research, institute; Foundations (private grantmaking); Foundations (public).
Limitations: Applications accepted. Giving in the U.S., with some emphasis on Chicago, IL. No grants to individuals; or for governmental organizations.
Publications: Application guidelines.
Application information:
Initial approach: Contact the foundation for formal application form
Trustees: Kristen Barney Adams; Lynne C. Barney; Stephen M. Barney, Sr.; Stephen M. Barney, Jr.
EIN: 367195126

2683
Julie and Roger Baskes Charitable Trust ✧
(formerly Bernard and Rochelle Zell Charitable Trust)
980 N. Michigan Ave., Ste. 1380
Chicago, IL 60611-4501

Established in 1986 in IL.
Donor: Rochelle Zell‡.
Foundation type: Independent foundation.
Financial data (yr. ended 04/30/13): Assets, $5,451,982 (M); expenditures, $736,762; qualifying distributions, $736,762; giving activities include $672,561 for 46 grants (high: $219,137; low: $100).
Fields of interest: Performing arts; Performing arts, opera; Arts; Higher education; Libraries/library science; Education; Human services; Jewish federated giving programs; Jewish agencies & synagogues.
Limitations: Applications not accepted. Giving primarily in Chicago, IL; funding also in New York, NY. No grants to individuals.
Application information: Contributes only to pre-selected organizations.
Trustees: Julie Z. Baskes; Roger S. Baskes.
EIN: 363440025
Selected grants: The following grants are a representative sample of this grantmaker's funding activity:
$400,470 to Newberry Library, Chicago, IL, 2011.
$110,000 to Chicago Opera Theater, Chicago, IL, 2011.
$33,200 to Chicago Symphony Orchestra, Chicago, IL, 2011.
$17,000 to Goodman Theater, Chicago, IL, 2011.
$14,090 to Santa Fe Opera, Santa Fe, NM, 2011.
$6,815 to Lyric Opera of Chicago, Chicago, IL, 2011.
$5,000 to Music and Dance Theater Chicago, Chicago, IL, 2011.
$2,500 to Folger Shakespeare Library, Washington, DC, 2011.
$2,109 to Library of Congress, Washington, DC, 2011.

$1,250 to Chicago Public Library Foundation, Chicago, IL, 2011.

2684
Baskes Family Foundation ✧
980 N. Michigan Ave., No. 1380
Chicago, IL 60611-4528

Established in 2004 in IL.
Foundation type: Independent foundation.
Financial data (yr. ended 07/31/13): Assets, $6,569,874 (M); expenditures, $2,464,958; qualifying distributions, $2,436,196; giving activities include $2,376,080 for 59 grants (high: $1,580,000; low: $90).
Fields of interest: Performing arts, opera; Arts; Higher education; Libraries/library science; Libraries (special); Education; Human services; Children/youth, services; Jewish federated giving programs; Jewish agencies & synagogues.
Limitations: Applications not accepted. Giving primarily in Chicago, IL, and New York, NY.
Application information: Contributes only to pre-selected organizations.
Officers and Directors:* Julie Z. Baskes,* Pres.; Daniel L. Baskes,* V.P.; Jeremy A. Baskes,* V.P.; Laura Baskes Litwin,* V.P.; Roger S. Baskes,* Secy.-Treas.
EIN: 300257951
Selected grants: The following grants are a representative sample of this grantmaker's funding activity:
$1,000 to Harvard University, Law School, Cambridge, MA, 2013. For Unrestricted Cash Donation to 501 C 3 Organizations.
$140 to Museum of Modern Art, New York, NY, 2013. For Unrestricted Cash Donation to 501 C 3 Organizations.

2685
Samuel J. Baskin Charitable Trust ✧
2 N. Lasalle St., Ste. 2300
Chicago, IL 60602-3975 (312) 726-0083
Contact: Sheldon Baskin, Mgr.

Established in 1963 in IL.
Donors: Samuel J. Baskin†; Hadassah Baskin; Baskin Family Charitable Lead Trust.
Foundation type: Operating foundation.
Financial data (yr. ended 08/31/13): Assets, $618,252 (M); gifts received, $766,283; expenditures, $861,289; qualifying distributions, $859,502; giving activities include $859,502 for 127 grants (high: $50,000; low: $20).
Fields of interest: Education; Human services; Foundations (private operating); Jewish federated giving programs.
Type of support: General/operating support.
Limitations: Applications accepted. Giving primarily in CO, IL, NY and Washington, DC.
Application information: Application form not required.
Initial approach: Proposal
Deadline(s): None
Officer: Sheldon L. Baskin, Mgr.
EIN: 366118260
Selected grants: The following grants are a representative sample of this grantmaker's funding activity:
$50,000 to Stop Cancer, Los Angeles, CA, 2013. For The Alli Fund.
$25,000 to Partners in Health, Boston, MA, 2013. For Project Mireblais Hospital-Haiti (one charge= $50K).
$25,000 to Partners in Health, Boston, MA, 2013. For Project Butaro Hospital-Rwanda (one charge= $50K).
$25,000 to RefugeeOne, Chicago, IL, 2013. For Creating opportunity for refugees.
$20,000 to Solid Ground, Seattle, WA, 2013. For Building community to end poverty.
$10,000 to Merit School of Music, Chicago, IL, 2013. For Highest quality music education.
$10,000 to Sargent Shriver National Center on Poverty Law, Chicago, IL, 2013. For social justice.
$5,000 to Partners in Health, Boston, MA, 2013. For Providing a preferential option for the poor in health care.
$1,000 to Community Renewal Society, Chicago, IL, 2013. For Improving school system.
$1,000 to Maysles Institute, New York, NY, 2013. For DeFriest Project.

2686
The Bill Bass Foundation ✧
c/o Louis A. Rascia, Griffith & Jacobson, LLC
55 W. Monroe St., Ste. 3550
Chicago, IL 60603-5000

Established in 2005 in IL.
Donor: William Bass Trust.
Foundation type: Independent foundation.
Financial data (yr. ended 12/31/13): Assets, $16,519,944 (M); expenditures, $854,135; qualifying distributions, $684,281; giving activities include $596,000 for 53 grants (high: $100,000; low: $1,000).
Fields of interest: Higher education, university; Health organizations; Jewish federated giving programs.
Limitations: Applications not accepted. Giving primarily in IL. No grants to individuals.
Application information: Contributes only to pre-selected organizations.
Trustees: Melinda Jacobson; Marc Schwartz.
EIN: 616314816

2687
M. R. Bauer Foundation ✧
300 S. Wacker Dr., No. 500
Chicago, IL 60606-6680 (312) 924-4241
Contact: Kent Lawrence, Pres. and Exec. Dir.
FAX: (312) 372-2389; E-mail: klawrence@lksu.com

Established in 1995 in IL.
Donors: Modestus R. Bauer†; Evalyn M. Bauer†.
Foundation type: Independent foundation.
Financial data (yr. ended 12/31/13): Assets, $16,555,245 (M); expenditures, $890,790; qualifying distributions, $955,264; giving activities include $680,200 for 48 grants (high: $192,000; low: $300), and $150,000 for 1 loan/ program-related investment.
Fields of interest: Reproductive health, family planning; Medical research; Courts/judicial administration.
Type of support: Land acquisition; General/ operating support; Continuing support; Endowments; Conferences/seminars; Research; Program evaluation.
Limitations: Applications not accepted. Giving primarily in IL. No grants to individuals.
Application information: Unsolicited requests for funds not accepted.
Board meeting date(s): Quarterly
Officers and Directors:* Kent Lawrence,* Pres. and Exec. Dir.; Roy Svenson,* V.P.; Kathleen A. Lawrence,* Secy.-Treas.; Mitchell B. Goldberg; Steve Meeks.
Number of staff: None.
EIN: 363980782
Selected grants: The following grants are a representative sample of this grantmaker's funding activity:
$300,000 to Center for Conflict Resolution, Chicago, IL, 2012.
$80,000 to Planned Parenthood of Illinois, Chicago, IL, 2012.
$40,000 to Brandeis University, Waltham, MA, 2012.
$22,600 to National Council of Jewish Women, Los Angeles, CA, 2012.
$20,000 to Natural Land Institute, Rockford, IL, 2012.

2688
Modestus Bauer Foundation ✧
c/o Robert J. Lawrence
300 S. Wacker Dr., Ste. 500
Chicago, IL 60606-6758

Established in 2001 in IL.
Foundation type: Independent foundation.
Financial data (yr. ended 12/31/13): Assets, $16,928,729 (M); expenditures, $947,552; qualifying distributions, $875,988; giving activities include $839,600 for 125 grants (high: $75,000; low: $100).
Fields of interest: Education; Health care; Religion.
Limitations: Applications not accepted. Giving primarily in Chicago, IL. No grants to individuals.
Application information: Contributes only to pre-selected organizations.
Officers and Directors:* Robert J. Lawrence,* Pres.; Lawrence A. Reich,* V.P.; David Reich,* Secy.; Linda N. Lawrence.
EIN: 364473662

2689
The Alvin H. Baum Family Fund ✧
c/o Joel M. Friedman
500 W. Madison St.
Chicago, IL 60661
Main URL: http://www.alvinbaumfamilyfund.org/

Trust established in 1945; incorporated in 1952 in IL.
Donors: Alvin H. Baum†; and members of the Baum family.
Foundation type: Independent foundation.
Financial data (yr. ended 12/31/13): Assets, $54,047,750 (M); expenditures, $2,843,190; qualifying distributions, $2,405,667; giving activities include $2,049,238 for 124 grants (high: $333,333; low: $100).
Purpose and activities: Giving primarily for children and youth services; some giving also to religious and medical organizations.
Fields of interest: Higher education; Hospitals (general); Health organizations, association; AIDS; Human services; Youth, services; Residential/ custodial care; Christian agencies & churches; Jewish agencies & synagogues.

Limitations: Applications not accepted. Giving primarily in Chicago, IL. No grants to individuals.
Application information: Unsolicited requests for funds not accepted.
Board meeting date(s): Annually
Officers and Directors:* Joel M. Friedman,* Pres.; Ross Friedman,* V.P.; Iris Friedman,* Secy.; Kevin Friedman.
EIN: 366063093

2690
The Baxter International Foundation ✧
(formerly The Baxter Allegiance Foundation)
1 Baxter Pkwy.
Deerfield, IL 60015-4633 (847) 948-4605
Contact: Donna Namath, Secy. and Exec. Dir.
FAX: (847) 948-4559; E-mail: fdninfo@baxter.com; Additional tel.: (847) 948-2000; Main URL: http://www.baxter.com/about_baxter/sustainability/international_foundation/index.html
Foundation Grants Video: http://video.baxter.com/wmv/foundation_pd/grant_video.wmv
Prize Programs Video: http://video.baxter.com/wmv/foundation_pd/prize_video.wmv
Recent Grants: http://www.baxter.com/about_baxter/sustainability/international_foundation/recent_foundation_grants.html

Established in 1982 in IL.
Donors: Baxter International Inc.; American Hospital Supply Corp.; Allegiance Corp.
Foundation type: Company-sponsored foundation.
Financial data (yr. ended 12/31/12): Assets, $65,029,300 (M); gifts received, $30,000,000; expenditures, $3,228,624; qualifying distributions, $3,053,481; giving activities include $2,246,437 for 112 grants (high: $210,000; low: $200), and $625,378 for employee matching gifts.
Purpose and activities: The foundation supports programs designed to improve access, quality, and cost-effectiveness of direct healthcare. Special emphasis is directed toward programs designed to expand access to direct healthcare services to disadvantaged or underserved populations in communities where a significant number of Baxter employees live and work.
Fields of interest: Dental care; Health care, insurance; Health care, cost containment; Health care; Substance abuse, services; Mental health/crisis services; Crime/violence prevention, domestic violence; Crime/violence prevention, child abuse; Crime/violence prevention, sexual abuse; Aging; Disabilities, people with; Military/veterans; Economically disadvantaged.
Type of support: Continuing support; Program development; Employee volunteer services; Employee matching gifts; Employee-related scholarships.
Limitations: Applications accepted. Giving on a national and international basis in areas of company operations, including CA, Cook, Lake, and McHenry County, IL, IN, China, Ireland, and Mexico. No support for disease or condition-specific organizations, hospitals, lobbying or political organizations, or organizations with a limited constituency, such as fraternal, veterans', or religious organizations. No grant to individuals (except for employee-related scholarships) or for capital or endowment campaigns, non-healthcare activities at educational institutions, general operating support or maintenance of effort, magazines, professional journals, documentaries, film, video, radio, or website productions, medical missions, advertising, tickets to dinners, benefits, social or fund-raising events, sponsorships or promotional materials, or research.
Publications: Application guidelines; Grants list; IRS Form 990 or 990-PF printed copy available upon request.
Application information: Multi-year funding is not automatic. The majority of grants are awarded based on recommendations from Baxter facilities' staff and employees. Organizations receiving support are asked to provide an interim report and a final report. Application form not required.
Initial approach: Complete online application
Copies of proposal: 1
Deadline(s): Feb. Jan 1 to Feb. 11; May 1 to June 11; Sept. 1 to Oct. 11
Board meeting date(s): Three times a year
Final notification: Following board meetings
Officers and Directors: Robert J. Hombach, Pres.; Donna Namath, Secy. and Exec. Dir.; Charles W. Thurman, Treas.; Katherine Azuara; Alice J. Campbell; Robert M. Davis; Douglas Hunt; Shaun Newlon; Peter Nicklin.
Number of staff: 1 full-time professional; 1 full-time support.
EIN: 363159396

2691
Paul Bechtner Foundation ✧
c/o Paul Weaver
660 Pine St.
Winnetka, IL 60093

Established around 1994.
Donors: Everett P. Weaver; Everett Weaver Living Trust; Marjorie Weaver; Martha Weaver; Helen Kinniard; Annemarie Weaver; Paul Weaver; Robert Weaver; William Weaver.
Foundation type: Independent foundation.
Financial data (yr. ended 12/31/13): Assets, $17,713,867 (M); gifts received, $826,519; expenditures, $825,516; qualifying distributions, $756,750; giving activities include $756,750 for 70 grants (high: $70,000; low: $500).
Fields of interest: Arts; Higher education; Human services.
Limitations: Applications not accepted. Giving primarily in IL. No grants to individuals.
Application information: Contributes only to pre-selected organizations.
Officer and Directors:* Paul Weaver,* Pres. and Treas.; Helen W. Kinnaird; Annamarie F. Weaver; Martha J. Weaver; Robert P. Weaver; William T. Weaver.
EIN: 363973429

2692
Francis Beidler Foundation ✧
53 W. Jackson Blvd., Ste. 530
Chicago, IL 60604-3422 (312) 922-3792
Contact: Francis Beidler III, Tr.

Established in 1999 in IL.
Foundation type: Independent foundation.
Financial data (yr. ended 12/31/13): Assets, $16,192,035 (M); expenditures, $887,731; qualifying distributions, $756,769; giving activities include $736,730 for 139 grants (high: $46,500; low: $500).
Purpose and activities: Giving primarily for human services.
Fields of interest: Museums (children's); Higher education; Education; Health organizations; Human services; YM/YWCAs & YM/YWHAs; Children/youth, services; Children, services; United Ways and Federated Giving Programs; Public affairs.
Limitations: Applications accepted. Giving primarily in Chicago, IL. No grants to individuals.
Application information: Application form required.
Initial approach: Letter
Deadline(s): None
Trustees: Francis Beidler III; Thomas B. Dorris; Elizabeth Tisdahl.
EIN: 364260449

2693
Bellebyron Foundation ✧
c/o Briar Hall LLC
200 W. Madison St., Ste. 3400
Chicago, IL 60606-3600

Established in 1983 in IL.
Donor: Harold Byron Smith, Jr.
Foundation type: Independent foundation.
Financial data (yr. ended 12/31/13): Assets, $944,126 (M); expenditures, $900,094; qualifying distributions, $897,789; giving activities include $897,264 for 2 grants (high: $645,771; low: $251,493).
Fields of interest: Historic preservation/historical societies; Botanical gardens; Aquariums; Hospitals (general).
Limitations: Applications not accepted. Giving primarily in CA and FL. No grants to Individuals.
Application information: Contributes only to pre-selected organizations.
Officers and Directors:* Stephen B. Smith,* Pres.; David B. Smith,* Secy.; Christopher B. Smith.
EIN: 366058056
Selected grants: The following grants are a representative sample of this grantmaker's funding activity:
$200,008 to Rush University Medical Center, Chicago, IL, 2011. For general purpose.

2694
The Berner Charitable and Scholarship Foundation ✧
P.O. Box 06560
Chicago, IL 60606-6560 (312) 782-5885
Contact: Ruben R. Vernof, Tr.

Established in 1994 in IL.
Foundation type: Independent foundation.
Financial data (yr. ended 12/31/13): Assets, $8,877,543 (M); expenditures, $992,235; qualifying distributions, $842,647; giving activities include $331,938 for 32 grants (high: $161,413; low: $1,000), and $510,709 for 63 grants to individuals (high: $20,000; low: $992).
Purpose and activities: Giving primarily for education and health associations. Scholarship awards to residents of the U.S. who are attending, or who are planning to attend, any U.S. college or university. Selection shall be based on scholastic achievements, or the potential to make scholastic achievements, financial need, and demonstrated quality of leadership. Applicants who are seeking a scholarship for undergraduate degree must have graduated from high school with a "C" average or

better. Applicants who are seeking a scholarship for a graduate degree, must have graduated from college with a "C" average or better. Applicants must enroll as full-time students and carry a full-time course load.
Fields of interest: Education; Health care; Human services.
Type of support: General/operating support; Scholarships—to individuals.
Limitations: Applications accepted. Giving primarily in Chicago, IL and GA; support also in AL.
Application information: Application form required.
Initial approach: Letter
Deadline(s): None
Trustees: Linda Neylon; Ruben R. Vernof.
EIN: 363923844
Selected grants: The following grants are a representative sample of this grantmaker's funding activity:
$15,000 to American Cancer Society, Chicago, IL, 2012. For Cancer Research, Prevention and Education.
$15,000 to American Heart Association, Chicago, IL, 2012. For Research of Heart Disease and Its Prevention.
$5,000 to Organ Transplant Support, Naperville, IL, 2012. To Provide Support, Counseling, Education and Informational Programs and Materials on Transplantation For.
$2,000 to Epilepsy Foundation, Landover, MD, 2012. For awareness, education and research for epilepsy.

2695
The Howard B. Bernick Foundation ✧
c/o Bernick Holdings, Inc.
401 N. Michigan Ave., Ste. 1818
Chicago, IL 60611-4225 (312) 464-1188
Contact: Howard B. Bernick, Tr.

Donor: Howard B. Bernick.
Foundation type: Independent foundation.
Financial data (yr. ended 12/31/13): Assets, $2,914,179 (M); gifts received, $413,775; expenditures, $839,672; qualifying distributions, $825,486; giving activities include $823,661 for 45 grants (high: $150,000; low: $1,000).
Fields of interest: Health organizations, association; Diabetes research; Jewish federated giving programs; Jewish agencies & synagogues.
Limitations: Giving primarily in Chicago, IL. No support for non-501(c)(3) organizations.
Application information:
Initial approach: Letter
Deadline(s): None
Distribution Committee: Craig Bernick; Elizabeth Bernick; Howard B. Bernick; Peter Bernick.
EIN: 208042481

2696
Alfred Bersted Foundation ✧
c/o US Trust
231 S. LaSalle St., IL1-231-13-32
Chicago, IL 60697-0001 (312) 828-4154
Contact: Debra Grand, Sr. V.P.
E-mail to discuss application process or for questions: ilgrantmaking@ustrust.com (the name of the foundation must be indicated in subject line); Main URL: http://www.bankofamerica.com/grantmaking

Established in 1972 in IL.
Donor: Alfred Bersted†.
Foundation type: Independent foundation.
Financial data (yr. ended 12/31/13): Assets, $21,945,266 (M); expenditures, $1,110,226; qualifying distributions, $967,258; giving activities include $822,200 for 59 grants (high: $25,000; low: $5,000).
Purpose and activities: The foundation was established in 1972 to support and promote quality educational, human services, and health care programming for underserved populations. It specifically serves the people of DeKalb, DuPage, Kane, and McHenry counties in Illinois.
Fields of interest: Health organizations; Human services; Children/youth, services.
Type of support: General/operating support; Continuing support; Building/renovation; Technical assistance.
Limitations: Applications accepted. Giving limited to DeKalb, DuPage, Kane, and McHenry counties, in IL. No support for religious houses of worship, degree-conferring institutions of higher learning or for organizations that are testing for public safety. No grants to individuals; or for endowment funds exclusively, deficit financing or political campaigns.
Application information: Application form and guidelines available online. Application form required.
Initial approach: Online application
Deadline(s): Apr. 15 and Sept. 15
Final notification: June 30 (for the Apr. deadline), and Dec. 15 (for the Sept. deadline)
Trustee: Bank of America, N.A.
EIN: 366493609
Selected grants: The following grants are a representative sample of this grantmaker's funding activity:
$35,000 to Edward Hospital, Naperville, IL, 2011. For renovation and expansion of Neonatal and Pediatric Department with naming of a Special Procedure Room.
$30,000 to Catholic Charities of DuPage County, Lombard, IL, 2011. For Homeless Prevention Program.
$25,000 to Boys and Girls Clubs of Elgin, Elgin, IL, 2011. For general operating support.
$25,000 to Hope Haven of DeKalb County, DeKalb, IL, 2011. For capital campaign.
$25,000 to Northern Illinois Food Bank, Geneva, IL, 2011. For general operating support.
$25,000 to One Hope United, Chicago, IL, 2011. For Aurora Early Learning Center.
$20,000 to Central DuPage Hospital Association, Winfield, IL, 2011. For Home Care Physicians.
$20,000 to Community Crisis Center, Elgin, IL, 2011. For Bi-lingual Case Manager position.
$15,000 to Ben Gordon Center, DeKalb, IL, 2011. For reconfiguration of office and counseling space.
$10,000 to Regional Access and Mobilization Project, Rockford, IL, 2011. For Youth Advocacy and Education Program and to develop a Teens in Transition Program.

2697
Best Portion Foundation ✧
c/o William Thomas
111 S. Wacker Dr.
Chicago, IL 60606-4302

Established in 2007 in IL.
Donors: Timothy Schwertfeger; Gail Waller.
Foundation type: Independent foundation.
Financial data (yr. ended 12/31/12): Assets, $17,758,449 (M); gifts received, $7,500; expenditures, $1,939,800; qualifying distributions, $1,799,625; giving activities include $1,791,875 for 13 grants (high: $665,875; low: $1,000).
Purpose and activities: Giving primarily for education.
Fields of interest: Arts; Education.
Limitations: Applications not accepted. Giving primarily in IL, with emphasis on Chicago. No grants to individuals.
Application information: Contributes only to pre-selected organizations.
Officers: M. Gail Waller, Pres.; Timothy Schwertfeger, V.P. and Secy.-Treas.
Director: Andrew Schwertfeger.
EIN: 260894840
Selected grants: The following grants are a representative sample of this grantmaker's funding activity:
$10,000 to School Year Abroad, North Andover, MA, 2012. For All Contributions Made For Unrestricted Use.

2698
The Bielfeldt Foundation ✧
(formerly The Gary K. and Carlotta J. Bielfeldt Foundation)
4700 N. Prospect Rd., No. A3
Peoria Heights, IL 61616-6469 (309) 685-6050
Contact: Carlotta J. Bielfeldt, Exec. Dir.

Established in 1985 in IL.
Donor: Gary K. Bielfeldt.
Foundation type: Independent foundation.
Financial data (yr. ended 12/31/13): Assets, $15,663,477 (M); expenditures, $1,425,598; qualifying distributions, $1,228,815; giving activities include $1,090,552 for 5 grants (high: $663,052; low: $2,500).
Fields of interest: Zoos/zoological societies; United Ways and Federated Giving Programs.
Limitations: Applications accepted. Giving primarily in Peoria, IL. No grants to individuals.
Application information: Application form required.
Initial approach: Request application form
Deadline(s): None
Board meeting date(s): End of Mar., June, Oct., and Dec.
Officers: Douglas G. Stewart, Pres.; Jane B. Converse, V.P.; Gary Anna, Secy.-Treas.; Carlotta Biefeldt, Exec. Dir.
Director: William R. Barrick.
Number of staff: 1
EIN: 371188243

2699
William Blair & Company Foundation ✧
222 W. Adams St., 28th Fl.
Chicago, IL 60606-5307
Contact: E. David Coolidge III, V.P.

Established in 1980 in IL.
Donor: William Blair & Co., L.L.C.
Foundation type: Company-sponsored foundation.
Financial data (yr. ended 12/31/13): Assets, $9,290,286 (M); gifts received, $1,576,575; expenditures, $849,567; qualifying distributions, $834,480; giving activities include $834,480 for 191 grants (high: $75,000; low: $75).

Purpose and activities: The foundation supports organizations involved with arts and culture, higher education, health, cancer, human services, civic affairs, Christianity, and Judaism.
Fields of interest: Arts; Higher education; Hospitals (general); Health care; Cancer; Cancer research; Children/youth, services; Human services; Government/public administration; Public affairs; Catholic agencies & churches; Jewish agencies & synagogues.
Type of support: Annual campaigns; Building/renovation; Capital campaigns; Continuing support; Endowments; Fellowships; General/operating support; Internship funds; Scholarship funds.
Limitations: Applications accepted. Giving primarily in the metropolitan Chicago, IL, area. No grants to individuals.
Application information: Application form not required.
Initial approach: Proposal
Copies of proposal: 1
Deadline(s): None
Officers: Edgar D. Jannotta, Pres.; E. David Coolidge III, V.P.; Michelle S. Seitz, V.P.; Thomas W. Pace, Secy.; John R. Ettelson, Treas.
EIN: 363092291
Selected grants: The following grants are a representative sample of this grantmaker's funding activity:
$75,000 to Greater Chicago Food Depository, Chicago, IL, 2011. For general purposes.
$15,000 to Chicago Council on Global Affairs, Chicago, IL, 2011. For general purposes.
$15,000 to Chicago Summer Business Institute, Chicago, IL, 2011. For general purposes.
$15,000 to Chicago Symphony Orchestra, Chicago, IL, 2011. For general purposes.
$10,000 to American Jewish Committee, New York, NY, 2011. For general purposes.
$10,000 to Chicago Public Library Foundation, Chicago, IL, 2011. For general purposes.
$7,000 to Cystic Fibrosis Foundation, Bethesda, MD, 2011. For general purposes.
$5,000 to Catholic Charities of the Archdiocese of Chicago, Chicago, IL, 2011. For general purposes.
$5,000 to Infant Welfare Society of Chicago, Chicago, IL, 2011. For general purposes.
$2,500 to Chicago Community Trust, Chicago, IL, 2011. For general purposes.

2700
Blair Foundation ✧
c/o The Northern Trust Co.
P.O. Box 803878
Chicago, IL 60680-3878

Established in FL.
Donors: Dorothy Blair†; Dorothy Blair Trust.
Foundation type: Independent foundation.
Financial data (yr. ended 12/31/12): Assets, $87,096,273 (M); gifts received, $1,231,459; expenditures, $4,976,785; qualifying distributions, $4,709,605; giving activities include $4,510,000 for 26 grants (high: $450,000; low: $10,000).
Purpose and activities: Giving primarily for higher education, conservation, animals and wildlife, as well as for health, human services, and children and family services, as well as to reproductive choice causes.
Fields of interest: Museums; Education; Environment, natural resources; Animals/wildlife; Reproductive health, family planning; Health care; Human services; Children/youth, services; Family services; Community/economic development.
Limitations: Applications not accepted. Giving primarily in FL, with emphasis on Naples; some giving also in Washington, DC, and NC. No grants to individuals.
Application information: Contributes only to pre-selected organizations.
Trustees: James Laurion; Richard Rieman; The Northern Trust Co.
EIN: 656072965

2701
George and June Block Family Foundation ✧
7310 W. Wilson Ave.
Harwood Heights, IL 60706-4708

Established in 1999 in IL.
Donors: George P. Block; June E. Block; George P. Block Charitable Lead Annuity Trust; Carstens, Inc.
Foundation type: Independent foundation.
Financial data (yr. ended 12/31/13): Assets, $15,631,101 (M); gifts received, $1,000,000; expenditures, $841,265; qualifying distributions, $734,000; giving activities include $734,000 for 54 grants (high: $100,000; low: $500).
Purpose and activities: Giving primarily for education, medical research, particularly pancreatic cancer research, and human services.
Fields of interest: Education; Health organizations; Medical research, institute; Cancer research; Human services; Youth, services; Christian agencies & churches.
Limitations: Applications not accepted. Giving primarily in Chicago, IL; some funding nationally, particularly in CA. No grants to individuals.
Application information: Contributes only to pre-selected organizations.
Officers: Barbara Block Vanderkloot, Pres.; George P. Block, Jr., V.P.; Mathew Vanderkloot, Treas.
EIN: 364294119

2702
The Blowitz-Ridgeway Foundation
1701 E. Woodfield Rd., Ste. 201
Schaumburg, IL 60173-5127 (847) 330-1020
Contact: Serena L. Moy, Admin.; Laura Romero, Prog. Assoc.
FAX: (847) 330-1028;
E-mail: laura@blowitzridgeway.org; Main URL: http://www.blowitzridgeway.org/

Status changed from public charity to private foundation in 1984; converted from Ridgeway Hospital.
Foundation type: Independent foundation.
Financial data (yr. ended 09/30/13): Assets, $23,437,664 (M); expenditures, $1,706,033; qualifying distributions, $1,582,591; giving activities include $1,137,679 for 56 grants (high: $50,000; low: $2,000), and $100,000 for 1 loan/program-related investment.
Purpose and activities: Giving through program, general operating capital, and research grants primarily in the areas of health, mental and physical disability, and social services, with emphasis on children and youth.
Fields of interest: Health care; Mental health/crisis services; Medical research, institute; Human services; Children/youth, services; Children/youth; Youth; Adults; Aging; Young adults; Disabilities, people with; Physically disabled; Mentally disabled; Women; Adults, women; Young adults, female; Adults, men; Young adults, male; Terminal illness, people with; Economically disadvantaged.
Type of support: General/operating support; Continuing support; Capital campaigns; Program development; Research; Program-related investments/loans.
Limitations: Applications accepted. Giving generally limited to IL, except for medical research grants. No support for government agencies, religious purposes, or organizations that subsist mainly on third-party funding. No grants to individuals, or for production or writing of audio-visual materials.
Publications: Annual report; Annual report (including application guidelines); Grants list; Informational brochure (including application guidelines).
Application information: See foundation web site for application guidelines and forms. Return applicants are required to submit their final report for the previous grant, before the new grant request can be reviewed. In addition, the foundation is requiring all grant applicants to include, with their grant application, a copy of the Schedule A form from the IRS form 990. Application form required.
Initial approach: Letter or telephone requesting guidelines
Copies of proposal: 5
Deadline(s): Ongoing
Board meeting date(s): Monthly
Final notification: 3-6 months
Officers and Trustees:* Daniel L. Kline,* Pres.; Pierre R. LeBreton, Ph.D., V.P.; Sandra Swantek, M.D.*, Secy.; Thomas P. FitzGibbon, Jr.,* Treas.; Rev. Barbara Bolsen; Anthony M. Dean; Marvin J. Pitluk, Ph.D.; Marva E. Williams, Ph.D.
Number of staff: 1 full-time professional; 1 full-time support.
EIN: 362488355

2703
Blue Foundation ✧
5 S. Wabash Ave., Ste. 2110
Chicago, IL 60603-3041
Application address: c/o Clare Munana, 150 N. Michigan Ave., Ste. 2800, Chicago, IL 60601, tel.: (312) 624-7685

Donors: Clare M. Munana; Niamogue Foundation.
Foundation type: Independent foundation.
Financial data (yr. ended 12/31/13): Assets, $3,950,178 (M); gifts received, $303,020; expenditures, $626,809; qualifying distributions, $597,197; giving activities include $590,872 for 93 grants (high: $60,000; low: $40).
Fields of interest: Arts; Higher education; Medical research, institute.
Limitations: Applications accepted. Giving primarily in IL and NY.
Application information: Application form required.
Initial approach: Proposal
Deadline(s): None
Officer and Directors:* Clare Munana,* Pres.; Charles McCartney; Madeleine McCartney; Ric Estrada.
EIN: 261919507

2704
The Bluhm Family Charitable Foundation ✧
900 N. Michigan Ave., Ste. 1600
Chicago, IL 60611-6543

Established in 2007 in IL.
Donors: Neil G. Bluhm; Andrew G. Bluhm; Leslie N. Bluhm; Meredith A. Bluhm-Wolf; Lamb Company, LLC; Lamb Partners.
Foundation type: Independent foundation.
Financial data (yr. ended 12/31/13): Assets, $17,346,033 (M); gifts received, $6,861,550; expenditures, $7,133,003; qualifying distributions, $7,099,030; giving activities include $7,099,015 for 41 grants (high: $2,100,000; low: $1,500).
Purpose and activities: Giving primarily for museums, education, social services, and children and youth services, including a children's hospital.
Fields of interest: Museums (art); Education; Hospitals (specialty); Health organizations, association; Human services; Children/youth, services; Jewish agencies & synagogues.
Limitations: Applications not accepted. Giving primarily in Chicago, IL. No grants to individuals.
Application information: Contributes only to pre-selected organizations.
Trustees: Andrew G. Bluhm; Leslie N. Bluhm; Neil G. Bluhm; Meredith A. Bluhm-Wolf.
EIN: 261572776
Selected grants: The following grants are a representative sample of this grantmaker's funding activity:
$1,033,750 to Art Institute of Chicago, Chicago, IL, 2011.
$300,000 to Northwestern University, Evanston, IL, 2011.
$250,000 to Ann and Robert H. Lurie Children's Hospital of Chicago, Chicago, IL, 2011.
$200,000 to Chicago Cares, Chicago, IL, 2011.
$52,500 to Museum of Contemporary Art, Chicago, IL, 2011.
$25,000 to Rush NeuroBehavioral Center, Skokie, IL, 2011.
$24,000 to United States Holocaust Memorial Museum, Washington, DC, 2011.
$20,000 to Merit School of Music, Chicago, IL, 2011.
$10,000 to Santa Monica Museum of Art, Santa Monica, CA, 2011.
$10,000 to Teach for America, Chicago, IL, 2011.

2705
The Nathan and Emily S. Blum Fund ✧
c/o BMO Harris Bank N.A.
111 W. Monroe St., Tax Div. 10C
Chicago, IL 60603-4096 (312) 461-5154

Established in 1980.
Donor: Nathan Blum†.
Foundation type: Independent foundation.
Financial data (yr. ended 12/31/13): Assets, $12,007,702 (M); expenditures, $641,905; qualifying distributions, $560,015; giving activities include $560,000 for 6 grants (high: $168,000; low: $6,975).
Fields of interest: Law school/education; Health care, single organization support; Human services; Family services; United Ways and Federated Giving Programs; Jewish federated giving programs.
Limitations: Applications accepted. Giving primarily in Chicago, IL. No grants to individuals.
Application information: Application form required.
Initial approach: Proposal
Deadline(s): None
Trustee: BMO Harris Bank, N.A.
EIN: 366706638
Selected grants: The following grants are a representative sample of this grantmaker's funding activity:
$159,000 to Jewish Federation of Metropolitan Chicago, Chicago, IL, 2011.
$159,000 to Michael Reese Health Trust, Chicago, IL, 2011.
$79,500 to Metropolitan Family Services, Chicago, IL, 2011.
$79,500 to United Way of Metropolitan Chicago, Chicago, IL, 2011.
$6,600 to Reading is FUNdamental in Chicago, River Grove, IL, 2011.

2706
Blum-Kovler Foundation ✧
875 N. Michigan Ave., Ste. 3400
Chicago, IL 60611-1958 (312) 664-5050

Incorporated in 1953 in IL.
Donors: Harry Blum†; Everett Kovler.
Foundation type: Independent foundation.
Financial data (yr. ended 12/31/12): Assets, $93,603,281 (M); expenditures, $5,687,244; qualifying distributions, $5,065,606; giving activities include $4,700,050 for 236 grants (high: $829,596; low: $100).
Purpose and activities: Giving primarily for social services, Jewish welfare funds, higher education, health services and medical research, and cultural programs; support also for youth and child welfare agencies and public interest and civic affairs groups.
Fields of interest: Arts; Higher education; Education; Health organizations; Medical research, institute; Human services; Children/youth, services; Jewish federated giving programs; Jewish agencies & synagogues.
Type of support: General/operating support.
Limitations: Applications accepted. Giving primarily in the Chicago, IL, area, as well as Washington, DC.
Application information: Application form not required.
Initial approach: Written proposal (1-2 pages)
Copies of proposal: 1
Deadline(s): Mid-Nov.
Board meeting date(s): As required
Final notification: Varies
Officers and Directors:* Peter Kovler,* Chair.; H. Jonathan Kovler,* Pres. and Treas.; Hymen Bregar,* Secy.; Brian T. Burke, Cont.
Number of staff: 4 full-time professional; 1 part-time professional; 3 part-time support.
EIN: 362476143

2707
The Bobolink Foundation ✧
(formerly Henry M. & Wendy J. Paulson, Jr. Foundation)
c/o Robbins and Assocs. LLC
333 W. Wacker Dr., Ste. 830
Chicago, IL 60606-1225

Established in 1985 in IL.
Donors: Henry M. Paulson, Jr.; Goldman Sachs & Co.
Foundation type: Independent foundation.
Financial data (yr. ended 03/31/13): Assets, $76,534,456 (M); expenditures, $19,327,856; qualifying distributions, $19,039,146; giving activities include $18,869,486 for 49 grants (high: $12,641,986; low: $5,000).
Purpose and activities: Support primarily for environmental conservation and wildlife preservation.
Fields of interest: Environment, natural resources; Animals/wildlife, preservation/protection; Animals/wildlife, bird preserves.
Limitations: Applications not accepted. Giving primarily in New York, NY, Washington, DC, Chicago, IL, Arlington, VA, and Boston, MA. No grants to individuals; no loans.
Application information: Contributes only to pre-selected organizations.
Trustees: Amanda Clark Paulson; Henry M. Paulson, Jr.; Henry Merritt Paulson III; Wendy J. Paulson.
EIN: 942988627

2708
The Boler Family Foundation ✧
(formerly The Boler Company Foundation)
500 Park Blvd., Ste. 1010
Itasca, IL 60143-1285

Established in 1987 in IL.
Donors: The Boler Co., Inc.; John M. Boler; James W. Boler; Matthew J. Boler; Michael J. Boler; Judith B. McCormack; Jill B. McCormack.
Foundation type: Company-sponsored foundation.
Financial data (yr. ended 12/31/13): Assets, $35,874,836 (M); gifts received, $4,500,000; expenditures, $1,237,986; qualifying distributions, $1,137,905; giving activities include $1,135,000 for 8 grants (high: $600,000; low: $10,000).
Purpose and activities: The foundation supports organizations involved with education, health, autism, and children with special needs.
Fields of interest: Higher education; Education; Health care, clinics/centers; Health care; Human services.
Type of support: General/operating support; Program development.
Limitations: Applications not accepted. Giving limited to IL. No grants to individuals.
Application information: Contributes only to pre-selected organizations.
Trustees: John M. Boler; Jill B. McCormack; Judith B. McCormack.
EIN: 366854134
Selected grants: The following grants are a representative sample of this grantmaker's funding activity:
$350,000 to World Gospel Mission, Marion, IN, 2011. For general fund.
$267,000 to American Red Cross, Chicago, IL, 2011. For general fund.
$182,653 to Rush University Medical Center, Chicago, IL, 2011. For general fund.
$150,000 to Heights Foundation, Fort Myers, FL, 2011. For general fund.
$150,000 to Saint Vincent Charity Medical Center Foundation, Cleveland, OH, 2011. For general fund.
$50,000 to Yampa Valley Autism Program, Steamboat Springs, CO, 2011. For general fund.

2709
Bond Family Foundation ✧
233 E. Prairie Ave.
Wheaton, IL 60187-3529

Established in 2006 in IL.
Donors: Harold B. Bond; Kimberly A. Bond.
Foundation type: Independent foundation.
Financial data (yr. ended 12/31/13): Assets, $8,363,532 (M); gifts received, $1,100,000; expenditures, $746,235; qualifying distributions, $715,000; giving activities include $715,000 for 6 grants (high: $360,000; low: $10,000).
Purpose and activities: Giving primarily for Christian education.
Fields of interest: Secondary school/education.
Limitations: Applications not accepted. Giving primarily in IL and MO. No grants to individuals.
Application information: Contributes only to pre-selected organizations.
Officers and Directors:* Harold B. Bond,* Pres.; Kimberly A. Bond,* V.P. and Secy.; William Bond,* Treas.
EIN: 208100744

2710
The Bondi Foundation ✧
10 S. Dearborn St., IL1-0117
Chicago, IL 60603-2300
Application address: c/o JP Morgan Chase Bank, N.A., 270 Park Ave., 18th Fl., New York, NY 10017-2014

Established in 1998 in DE.
Donors: Geoffrey C. Bible; Sara Bible.
Foundation type: Independent foundation.
Financial data (yr. ended 12/31/13): Assets, $16,851,296 (M); expenditures, $480,366; qualifying distributions, $433,113; giving activities include $431,248 for 10 grants (high: $160,000; low: $10,000).
Purpose and activities: Giving primarily for health care and medical research; funding also for human services.
Fields of interest: Health care; Human services.
Limitations: Applications accepted. Giving primarily in AZ, CT and NY.
Application information: Application form required.
Initial approach: Letter
Deadline(s): None
Officers: Thomas Bible, Pres.; Sara Bible, V.P.; Geoffrey Bible, Secy.
EIN: 134015931
Selected grants: The following grants are a representative sample of this grantmaker's funding activity:
$250,000 to Save the Children Federation, Fairfield, CT, 2011.
$115,000 to Haitian Health Foundation, Norwich, CT, 2011.
$25,000 to HealthCare Chaplaincy, New York, NY, 2011.

2711
Martin and Mary L. Boyer Foundation ✧
709 Carlyle Ct.
Northbrook, IL 60062-2262

Established in 2007 in IL.
Donors: Martin Boyer†; Boyer Marital Trust; Boyer Residence Trust.
Foundation type: Independent foundation.
Financial data (yr. ended 12/31/12): Assets, $11,751,566 (M); gifts received, $1,549,231; expenditures, $529,186; qualifying distributions, $477,000; giving activities include $477,000 for 37 grants (high: $50,000; low: $5,000).
Fields of interest: Media, television; Education; Cancer research; Human services; Residential/custodial care, senior continuing care; Christian agencies & churches; Jewish agencies & synagogues; Children.
Limitations: Applications not accepted. Giving primarily in IL and TN. No grants to individuals.
Application information: Contributes only to pre-selected organizations.
Officers and Directors:* Alan I. Boyer,* Pres.; Louis S. Harrison,* Secy.; Craig Boyer,* Treas.
EIN: 260587477
Selected grants: The following grants are a representative sample of this grantmaker's funding activity:
$50,000 to Chicago Center for Jewish Genetic Disorders, Chicago, IL, 2011.
$50,000 to North Shore Senior Center, Northfield, IL, 2011.
$25,000 to Birthright Israel Foundation, New York, NY, 2011.
$15,000 to Jewish United Fund of Metropolitan Chicago, Chicago, IL, 2011.
$5,000 to Africare, Washington, DC, 2011.
$5,000 to Childrens Organ Transplant Association, Bloomington, IN, 2011.
$5,000 to City of Hope, Chicago, IL, 2011.
$5,000 to Scholarship America, Minneapolis, MN, 2011.
$5,000 to United Cerebral Palsy Association of Greater Chicago, Chicago, IL, 2011.
$2,000 to Ark, The, Chicago, IL, 2011.

2712
Helen V. Brach Foundation ✧
104 S. Michigan Ave., Ste. 1310
Chicago, IL 60603-6114 (312) 372-4417
Contact: John P. Hagnell, Assoc. Dir.

Established in 1974 in IL.
Donor: Helen Brach†.
Foundation type: Independent foundation.
Financial data (yr. ended 03/31/14): Assets, $122,603,508 (M); expenditures, $7,454,801; qualifying distributions, $6,826,566; giving activities include $5,448,900 for 408 grants (high: $75,000; low: $500), and $637,550 for 153 employee matching gifts.
Purpose and activities: The foundation's charter provides that it should operate for the following purposes: charitable, educational, literary, prevention of cruelty to animals, prevention of cruelty to children, promotion of music, arts and theater, religious and scientific.
Fields of interest: Arts; Secondary school/education; Higher education; Education; Environment; Animal welfare; Housing/shelter; Youth development, services; Human services; Children/youth, services; Homeless, human services; Disabilities, people with; Economically disadvantaged.
Type of support: General/operating support; Annual campaigns; Building/renovation; Equipment; Program development; Conferences/seminars; Publication; Scholarship funds.
Limitations: Applications accepted. Giving primarily in the Chicago, IL, metropolitan area. No grants outside continental U.S. No support for political organizations. No grants to individuals, or to organizations with less than one year of budget history.
Publications: Application guidelines; Biennial report (including application guidelines).
Application information: No grants under $5,000. Prior year's minimum expenses must have been $50,000. Application form required.
Initial approach: Letter. Faxed applications or inquiries not accepted
Copies of proposal: 6
Deadline(s): Dec. 31 (earlier preferred)
Board meeting date(s): Quarterly; grants considered at Mar. meeting
Final notification: Mar. and Apr.
Officers and Directors:* Raymond F. Simon,* Chair.; R. Matthew Simon,* Pres.; Richard Curry; James J. O'Connor; John J. Sheridan; Charles A. Vorhees.
Number of staff: 3 full-time professional.
EIN: 237376427

2713
Robert N. Brewer Family Foundation ✧
115 W. Jefferson St., Ste. 200
Bloomington, IL 61702-3217
Application address: 2 North Park Ave., Herrin, IL 62948

Established in 1997 in IL.
Donors: Robert N. Brewer†; Robert D. Brewer†.
Foundation type: Independent foundation.
Financial data (yr. ended 12/31/13): Assets, $18,809,864 (M); gifts received, $342,484; expenditures, $1,399,552; qualifying distributions, $1,159,522; giving activities include $400,200 for 2 grants (high: $400,000; low: $200), and $688,500 for 159 grants to individuals (high: $6,375; low: $2,125).
Purpose and activities: Giving primarily for scholarships for post-secondary education to graduates of Harrin and Marion High Schools in Illinois, who have achieved a cumulative G.P.A. of C or better; funding also for lung disease research.
Fields of interest: Education; Lung research.
Type of support: Scholarships—to individuals.
Limitations: Applications accepted. Giving primarily in IL, with emphasis on Herrin and Marion.
Application information: Application form required.
Initial approach: Proposal
Deadline(s): None
Directors: David L. Gename; Marie A. Delaney; Christopher B. Osman.
EIN: 364129119
Selected grants: The following grants are a representative sample of this grantmaker's funding activity:
$400,000 to Mayo Foundation, Rochester, MN, 2011.

2714
Bright Future International NFP Inc. ✧ ☆
1 Overlook Point, Ste. 110
Lincolnshire, IL 60069-4303 (847) 821-6068
Contact: Anthony Melikhov
FAX: (224) 676-1531; E-mail: grants@usabfi.org; Main URL: http://www.brightfutureinternational.org/
Facebook: https://www.facebook.com/BrightFutureInternational

Flickr: https://www.flickr.com/photos/79979434@N04/sets/
Twitter: https://twitter.com/brightfutureint
YouTube: http://www.youtube.com/user/BrightFutureInt

Donor: Anthony S. Melikhov.
Foundation type: Independent foundation.
Financial data (yr. ended 03/31/13): Assets, $4,057,571 (M); gifts received, $6,775,242; expenditures, $3,134,490; qualifying distributions, $3,140,256; giving activities include $1,678,649 for 13 grants (high: $559,640; low: $614).
Purpose and activities: Giving primarily to help underprivileged children around the world achieve a better future. The foundation funds arts and educational enrichment programs through partnerships with local and international organizations.
Fields of interest: Arts; Children/youth, services.
Limitations: Giving on a national basis, and in Chelyabinsk, Russia. No support for political or religious groups, or for projects and/or programs that are strictly revenue based.
Application information: The foundation is currently not accepting new applications. See foundation web site for updates in this area, as well as for full application guidelines.
Officers and Directors:* Anthony Melikhov,* Pres.; Karen Lodygowski,* Secy.; Maya Gumirov; Dr. Andrew Ivanchenko; David Loewenguth.
EIN: 800621924

2715
The Brinson Foundation
737 N. Michigan Ave., Ste. 1850
Chicago, IL 60611-6707 (312) 799-4500
FAX: (312) 799-4310;
E-mail: mail@brinsonfoundation.org; Main URL: http://www.brinsonfoundation.org

Established in 2000 in IL. Grantmaking operations commenced in the spring of 2001.
Foundation type: Independent foundation.
Financial data (yr. ended 12/31/13): Assets, $102,811,041 (M); expenditures, $4,683,176; qualifying distributions, $4,683,176; giving activities include $3,878,500 for 138 grants (high: $100,000; low: $200).
Purpose and activities: Grantmaking priorities are: 1) Education, which falls into seven focus areas: Financial Literacy; Health Care Career Development; High School and College Access; Liberty, Citizenship and Free Enterprise; Literacy; Science, Technology, Engineering and Math (STEM); and Student Health; and 2) Scientific research, including astrophysics, cosmology, evolutionary development biology, and geophysics, as well as specific areas of medical research selected from time to time by the Board of Directors.
Fields of interest: Education; Medical research; Physical/earth sciences.
Type of support: General/operating support; Continuing support; Management development/capacity building; Program development; Fellowships; Scholarship funds; Research; Technical assistance.
Limitations: Giving on a national basis for medical and scientific research. Education grants are generally made to organizations that serve individuals and communities in the greater Chicago, IL area. No support for promotion of religion or religious content, voter registration, political or lobbying activity, or for programs limited to members of a specific race, gender, religion or ethnic group. No grants for capital improvements, endowments, or fundraising events.
Publications: Application guidelines; Annual report; Grants list.
Application information: Unsolicited grant applications are not accepted. Full applications accepted by invitation only, upon review of Grantseeker Information Form. The foundation does not accept grantseeker inquiries in medical research. Information regarding the submission of Grantseeker Information Forms and the application process is provided on the foundation's web site. Application form required.
Initial approach: Use Grantseeker Information Form on foundation web site
Copies of proposal: 1
Board meeting date(s): May and Oct.
Officers and Directors:* Gary P. Brinson,* Chair.; James D. Parsons, Pres.; Tally S. Melone,* Secy.; Suzann A. Brinson; Monique B. Demery; Thomas R. Demery; Andrew H. Melone.
Number of staff: 4 full-time professional.
EIN: 680656415

2716
T. Kimball Brooker Foundation ✧ ☆
21 S. Clark St., Ste. 3990
Chicago, IL 60603-2008

Incorporated in 1986 in IL.
Donors: T. Kimball Brooker; Barbara Oil Co.
Foundation type: Independent foundation.
Financial data (yr. ended 10/31/13): Assets, $2,473,994 (M); gifts received, $1,490,704; expenditures, $494,759; qualifying distributions, $487,485; giving activities include $487,485 for 11 grants (high: $195,500; low: $25).
Purpose and activities: Giving primarily for private and university libraries.
Fields of interest: Museums; Arts; Higher education, university; Libraries (school); Libraries (academic/research).
Limitations: Applications not accepted. Giving primarily in Chicago, IL, and New York, NY. No grants to individuals.
Application information: Contributes only to pre-selected organizations.
Officers: T. Kimball Brooker, Pres. and Treas.
EIN: 363481541
Selected grants: The following grants are a representative sample of this grantmaker's funding activity:
$55,000 to Newberry Library, Chicago, IL, 2011.
$52,000 to Pierpont Morgan Library, New York, NY, 2011.
$50,000 to Field Museum of Natural History, Chicago, IL, 2011.
$2,000 to University of Chicago, Chicago, IL, 2011.
$1,010 to Grolier Club of the City of New York, New York, NY, 2011.

2717
The Bruning Foundation ✧
c/o Larry J. Brooks
787 Berkshire Ln.
Des Plaines, IL 60016-7545

Established in 1960.
Donors: Herbert F. Bruning; Paul J. Bruning.
Foundation type: Independent foundation.
Financial data (yr. ended 12/31/13): Assets, $19,402,873 (M); expenditures, $1,001,003; qualifying distributions, $820,400; giving activities include $820,400 for 72 grants (high: $75,000; low: $1,000).
Purpose and activities: Giving primarily for education and human services.
Fields of interest: Education; Environment; Health care.
Type of support: General/operating support.
Limitations: Applications not accepted. Giving primarily in IL. No grants to individuals.
Application information: Contributes only to pre-selected organizations.
Officers and Directors:* Charles Bruning III,* Pres.; Kathleen Bruning, Secy.; Edwin C. Bruning,* Treas.; Larry J. Brooks, Mgr.; Tracy Bruning; Kim Donahue; Jeanne Joseph; Christopher Silge; Susan Wulff.
EIN: 366068626
Selected grants: The following grants are a representative sample of this grantmaker's funding activity:
$1,000 to Allendale Shelter Club, Lake Forest, IL, 2011.

2718
Fred J. Brunner Foundation ✧
9300 King Ave.
Franklin Park, IL 60131-2114 (847) 678-3232
Contact: Pamela Brunner Schwegal, V.P.

Incorporated in 1955 in IL.
Donor: Fred J. Brunner†.
Foundation type: Independent foundation.
Financial data (yr. ended 12/31/13): Assets, $40,397,365 (M); expenditures, $2,223,489; qualifying distributions, $2,027,056; giving activities include $1,757,226 for 110 grants (high: $185,000; low: $1,226).
Purpose and activities: Giving primarily for education and health.
Fields of interest: Education; Health care; Health organizations, association; Human services; Children/youth, services; Catholic agencies & churches.
Type of support: General/operating support; Continuing support; Annual campaigns; Building/renovation; Equipment; Seed money; Research; Matching/challenge support.
Limitations: Giving primarily in IL. No grants to individuals, or for endowment funds, scholarships, fellowships, or matching gifts; no loans.
Application information: Application form not required.
Initial approach: Proposal or letter
Copies of proposal: 1
Deadline(s): Aug. 1
Officers and Directors:* Fred M. Brunner,* Pres.; Pamela Schwegel,* V.P.; Robert B. Wolf, Secy.-Treas.; Michele Cronin.
Number of staff: 1 part-time professional.
EIN: 366066471
Selected grants: The following grants are a representative sample of this grantmaker's funding activity:
$10,000 to Elim Christian Services, Palos Heights, IL, 2012. For religious organizations.
$5,000 to Wonder Works, Oak Park, IL, 2012. For educational organizations.

2719
William & Catherine Bryce Memorial Fund ✧
10 S. Dearborn St., IL1-0117
Chicago, IL 60603-2300

Established in 1944 in TX.
Foundation type: Independent foundation.
Financial data (yr. ended 09/30/13): Assets, $19,422,631 (M); expenditures, $1,000,629; qualifying distributions, $869,141; giving activities include $834,700 for 13 grants (high: $250,000; low: $10,000).
Purpose and activities: Giving primarily for education, health organizations, children and social services, and to a Baptist theological seminary.
Fields of interest: Higher education; Theological school/education; Education; Health organizations; Human services.
Limitations: Applications accepted. Giving limited to TX, with emphasis on the Fort Worth area. No grants to individuals.
Application information: Application form required.
Initial approach: Proposal
Copies of proposal: 1
Deadline(s): Sept.
Board meeting date(s): Nov.
Trustee: JPMorgan Chase Bank, N.A.
EIN: 756013845
Selected grants: The following grants are a representative sample of this grantmaker's funding activity:
$75,000 to Brite Divinity School, Fort Worth, TX, 2011. For program support.
$70,000 to Arts Council of Fort Worth and Tarrant County, Fort Worth, TX, 2011. For program support.
$30,000 to Cassata High School, Fort Worth, TX, 2011. For program support.
$30,000 to Catholic Charities Diocese of Fort Worth, Fort Worth, TX, 2011. For program support.
$30,000 to Saint Andrews Episcopal Church, Fort Worth, TX, 2011. For program support.
$20,000 to Mothers Milk Bank of North Texas, Fort Worth, TX, 2011. For program support.
$15,000 to Austin College, Sherman, TX, 2011. For program support.
$10,000 to AIDS Outreach Center, Fort Worth, TX, 2011. For program support.
$10,000 to Happy Hill Farm Childrens Home and Academy, Granbury, TX, 2011.
$10,000 to Ladder Alliance, Fort Worth, TX, 2011. For program support.

2720
The Buchanan Family Foundation ✧
222 E. Wisconsin Ave.
Lake Forest, IL 60045-1701

Established in 1967 in IL.
Donors: D.W. Buchanan, Sr.†; D.W. Buchanan, Jr.
Foundation type: Independent foundation.
Financial data (yr. ended 12/31/13): Assets, $50,086,082 (M); expenditures, $2,544,845; qualifying distributions, $2,402,111; giving activities include $2,235,000 for 102 grants (high: $85,000; low: $2,500).
Purpose and activities: Giving primarily for cultural programs, hospitals and health associations, education, social services, community funds, and environmental associations.
Fields of interest: Museums; Performing arts; Arts; Elementary/secondary education; Higher education; Environment; Hospitals (general); Human services; United Ways and Federated Giving Programs.
Limitations: Applications not accepted. Giving primarily in IL, with emphasis on Chicago and Lake Forest. No grants to individuals.
Application information: Contributes only to pre-selected organizations.
Board meeting date(s): Fall
Officers: Kenneth H. Buchanan, Pres.; G.M. Walsh, V.P. and Secy.; Huntington Eldridge, Jr., Treas.
Directors: John A. Andersen; Margaux Buchanan; Hunt Eldridge III; Charles F. Kane, Jr.
EIN: 366160998
Selected grants: The following grants are a representative sample of this grantmaker's funding activity:
$250,000 to Lake Forest College, Lake Forest, IL, 2011.

2721
The Henry and Gilda Buchbinder Family Foundation ✧ ☆
875 N. Michigan Ave., 31st Fl.
Chicago, IL 60611-7500

Established in 2003 in IL.
Donors: Henry Buchbinder; Gilda Buchbinder.
Foundation type: Independent foundation.
Financial data (yr. ended 12/31/13): Assets, $3,838,511 (M); gifts received, $675,760; expenditures, $570,068; qualifying distributions, $568,600; giving activities include $568,600 for 24 grants (high: $290,000; low: $500).
Fields of interest: Museums (art); Performing arts; Performing arts, opera; Historic preservation/historical societies; Arts; Secondary school/education; Medical research, association; Genetic diseases and disorders research.
Limitations: Applications not accepted. Giving primarily in IL and MD. No grants to individuals.
Application information: Contributes only to pre-selected organizations.
Officers and Directors:* Gilda Buchbinder,* Pres.; Henry Buchbinder,* V.P.; Bradley Buchbinder; Leslie Buchbinder.
EIN: 364452084

2722
Buckeye Foundation ✧
c/o F & H Assoc., LLP
1313 W. 175th St.
P.O. Box 1055
Homewood, IL 60430-4606

Established in 1994 in IL.
Donors: Marilyn M. Patrick; Thomas H. Patrick; City Spire Mgmt. Holidings, Inc.
Foundation type: Independent foundation.
Financial data (yr. ended 12/31/12): Assets, $34,130,662 (M); expenditures, $1,582,035; qualifying distributions, $1,128,877; giving activities include $1,125,112 for 26 grants (high: $429,224; low: $250).
Purpose and activities: Giving primarily for education, hospitals, particularly children's hospitals, and human services.
Fields of interest: Higher education; Education; Hospitals (general); Hospitals (specialty); Human services; Children/youth, services.
Limitations: Applications not accepted. Giving primarily in IL and NY; giving also in OH. No grants to individuals.
Application information: Contributes only to pre-selected organizations.
Officers: Thomas H. Patrick, Pres.; Marilyn M. Patrick, Secy.; Mary Karen Patrick-Philip, Treas.
EIN: 363999865

2723
John & Jacolyn Bucksbaum Family Foundation ✧
c/o MB Investments, LLC
180 N. Wacker Dr., Ste. 001
Chicago, IL 60606-1511

Established in 2007 in IL.
Donors: John Bucksbaum; Jacolyn Bucksbaum; The Matthew and Carolyn Bucksbaum Family Foundation.
Foundation type: Independent foundation.
Financial data (yr. ended 12/31/13): Assets, $7,303,479 (M); gifts received, $1,706,273; expenditures, $2,243,073; qualifying distributions, $2,212,815; giving activities include $2,171,267 for 17 grants (high: $1,015,000; low: $25,000).
Fields of interest: Education; Human services; Jewish agencies & synagogues.
Limitations: Applications not accepted. Giving primarily in IL.
Application information: Contributes only to pre-selected organizations.
Officers and Directors:* John Bucksbaum,* Pres.; Jacolyn Bucksbaum,* V.P.; E. Michael Greaves,* Secy.; Richard B. Dennert, Treas.
EIN: 260450497
Selected grants: The following grants are a representative sample of this grantmaker's funding activity:
$50,000 to USA Cycling Development Foundation, Colorado Springs, CO, 2012. For All Contributions Made for the Intent Established By the Various Charities.

2724
Matthew and Carolyn Bucksbaum Family Foundation ✧
(formerly Matthew Bucksbaum Family Foundation)
c/o MB Investments, LLC
180 N. Wacker Dr., Ste. 001
Chicago, IL 60606-1648

Established in 1994 in IA.
Donors: Matthew Bucksbaum; Carolyn Bucksbaum; John Bucksbaum; Ann B. Friedman; Orly D. Friedman; Thomas L. Friedman; Jacolyn Bucksbaum; Ann B. and Thomas L. Friedman Family Foundation; General Trust Co.
Foundation type: Independent foundation.
Financial data (yr. ended 12/31/13): Assets, $44,687,669 (M); expenditures, $8,849,842; qualifying distributions, $7,263,595; giving activities include $7,263,595 for 4+ grants (high: $6,150,000).
Fields of interest: Museums (art); Arts; Higher education; Human services.
Limitations: Applications not accepted. Giving primarily in Chicago, IL; some funding also in Aspen, CO. No grants to individuals.
Application information: Contributes only to pre-selected organizations.

Officers and Directors:* John Bucksbaum,* Pres.; Carolyn Bucksbaum,* V.P.; E. Michael Greaves, Secy.; Rick B. Dennert, Treas.; Ann B. Friedman; Thomas L. Friedman.
EIN: 421425846

2725
Leo R. Buder Foundation Trust ✧
231 S. LaSalle St., IL1-231-10-05
Chicago, IL 60697

Donors: Leo R. Buder Special Trust No. 1; Leo R. Buder Special Trust No. 2; Leo R. Buder Special Trust No. 3.
Foundation type: Independent foundation.
Financial data (yr. ended 09/30/13): Assets, $18,433,795 (M); gifts received, $52,653; expenditures, $765,882; qualifying distributions, $731,791; giving activities include $714,720 for grants.
Fields of interest: Health organizations, association; Youth development, scouting agencies (general); Human services; Salvation Army; Children/youth, services; United Ways and Federated Giving Programs.
Limitations: Applications not accepted. Giving primarily in St. Louis, MO.
Application information: Contributes only to pre-selected organizations.
Trustees: Cheryl Mills; Bank of America, N.A.
EIN: 436023142
Selected grants: The following grants are a representative sample of this grantmaker's funding activity:
$17,167 to Evangelical Childrens Home, Saint Louis, MO, 2011.
$17,167 to Missouri Botanical Garden, Saint Louis, MO, 2011.
$17,167 to Shriners Hospitals for Children, Tampa, FL, 2011.
$17,167 to United Way of Greater Saint Louis, Saint Louis, MO, 2011.
$8,584 to American Diabetes Association, Alexandria, VA, 2011.
$8,584 to American Lung Association of Eastern Missouri, Saint Louis, MO, 2011.
$8,584 to Boys and Girls Town of Missouri, Saint Louis, MO, 2011.
$8,584 to Central Institute for the Deaf, Saint Louis, MO, 2011.
$8,584 to Humane Society of Missouri, Saint Louis, MO, 2011.
$8,584 to Saint Louis Society for Children and Adults with Physical Disabilities, Saint Louis, MO, 2011.

2726
Howard G. Buffett Foundation ✧
145 N. Merchant St.
Decatur, IL 62523-1442 (217) 423-9286
Main URL: http://www.thehowardgbuffettfoundation.org/
Multimedia: http://www.thehowardgbuffettfoundation.org/media/

Established in 1999 in IL and NE.
Donors: Warren E. Buffett; Susan T. Buffett‡.
Foundation type: Independent foundation.
Financial data (yr. ended 12/31/13): Assets, $275,916,946 (M); gifts received, $140,551,996; expenditures, $113,651,674; qualifying distributions, $122,236,393; giving activities include $103,284,879 for 147 grants (high: $21,167,401; low: $275), and $7,024,655 for 3 foundation-administered programs.
Purpose and activities: The foundation's mission is to improve the standard of living and quality of life for the world's most impoverished and marginalized populations. It works to achieve its mission by focusing its funding in three core areas: 1) food security; 2) water security; and 3) conflict resolution, management and post-conflict development.
Fields of interest: Education; Environment; Public health, clean water supply; Agriculture; Agriculture, farmlands; Human services; International conflict resolution.
Limitations: Applications not accepted. Giving primarily in GA, IL and MD, and in England and Italy. No grants to individuals.
Application information: Contributes only to pre-selected organizations.
Officers and Directors:* Howard G. Buffett,* Chair. and C.E.O.; Ann M. Kelly, Pres.; Trisha A. Cook, V.P., Opers. and Treas.; Devon G. Buffett,* Exec. V.P. and Secy.; Howard W. Buffett, Exec. Dir.; Nicolette DeBruyn; Erin M. Morgan; Michael D. Walter; Chelsea M. Zillmer.
EIN: 470824756
Selected grants: The following grants are a representative sample of this grantmaker's funding activity:
$3,637,320 to Virunga Fund, Brooklyn, NY, 2012. For Ranger Capacity Building.
$2,861,409 to Feeding America, Chicago, IL, 2012. For Hunger Study.
$2,834,923 to World Food Programme, Rome, Italy, 2012. For Purchase for Progress - Cent America.
$1,954,111 to Catholic Relief Services, Baltimore, MD, 2012. For Global Water Initiative - Central America.
$1,690,000 to Catholic Relief Services, Baltimore, MD, 2012. For Kivu Specialty Coffee - Kahawa Bora.
$1,556,542 to Partners for Seed In Africa Fund, Nairobi, Kenya, 2012. For Seed System to Improve Food Security - Sudan.
$500,000 to New Venture Fund, Washington, DC, 2012. For Bridgeway Special Project Fund - Central African Republic and South Sudan.
$302,600 to Virunga Fund, Brooklyn, NY, 2012. For Operational Support.
$128,308 to Virunga Fund, Brooklyn, NY, 2012. For Peacebuilding Thorugh Public Works.
$92,328 to Pennsylvania State University, State College, PA, 2012. For Agricultural Research.

2727
Rebecca Susan Buffett Foundation ✧
c/o L. Bettanin
548 Hyacinth Pl.
Highland Park, IL 60035-1262

Established in 1998 in IL.
Donor: Pamela Buffett.
Foundation type: Independent foundation.
Financial data (yr. ended 12/31/12): Assets, $14,052,213 (M); gifts received, $10,306,472; expenditures, $3,469,306; qualifying distributions, $3,431,954; giving activities include $3,431,954 for 40 grants (high: $1,095,362; low: $300).
Purpose and activities: Giving primarily for education, health, and human services.
Fields of interest: Higher education; Hospitals (general); Mental health/crisis services, single organization support; Human services; Civil liberties, reproductive rights; Girls.
Limitations: Applications not accepted. Giving primarily in CA, IL, NE, and NY. No grants to individuals.
Application information: Unsolicited requests for funds not accepted.
Officers and Directors:* Pamela Buffett,* Pres. and Treas.; Allen Greenberg,* Secy.; Sarah Buffett.
EIN: 364201771

2728
Bunning Family Foundation ✧
(also known as The Sunshine Charitable Foundation)
225 E. Deerpath Rd., Ste. 210
Lake Forest, IL 60045-5302

Established in 2005 in IL.
Donor: David G. Bunning.
Foundation type: Independent foundation.
Financial data (yr. ended 06/30/13): Assets, $53,930,830 (M); expenditures, $4,057,630; qualifying distributions, $7,524,105; giving activities include $3,870,058 for 45 grants (high: $1,611,558; low: $1,000).
Purpose and activities: Giving primarily for education and food allergy research.
Fields of interest: Elementary/secondary education; Higher education; Health care, fund raising/fund distribution; Hospitals (specialty); Allergies; Food services.
Limitations: Applications not accepted. Giving primarily in IL and New York, NY. No grants to individuals.
Application information: Contributes only to pre-selected organizations.
Officers and Directors:* David G. Bunning,* Pres.; Denise A. Bunning,* V.P.; Michael Hughes,* Secy.; David Popovich,* Treas.
EIN: 201919538

2729
Butler Family Foundation ✧
1550 Northwest Hwy., Ste. 108-D
Park Ridge, IL 60068-1482 (847) 299-2244
Contact: Rhett W. Butler, Tr.

Established in 1953 in IL.
Donor: Gladys A. Butler Charitable Lead Trust.
Foundation type: Independent foundation.
Financial data (yr. ended 12/31/13): Assets, $17,559,296 (M); gifts received, $292,917; expenditures, $700,247; qualifying distributions, $594,562; giving activities include $577,300 for 102 grants (high: $50,000; low: $500).
Purpose and activities: Giving primarily for education and health and human services.
Fields of interest: Arts; Theological school/education; Education; Environment; Medical research, institute; Human services; Protestant agencies & churches; Children/youth; Children; Aging; Disabilities, people with; Physically disabled; Blind/visually impaired; Deaf/hearing impaired; Mentally disabled; African Americans/Blacks; Crime/abuse victims; Terminal illness, people with; Economically disadvantaged.
Type of support: General/operating support; Continuing support; Annual campaigns; Capital campaigns; Building/renovation; Endowments; Program development; Fellowships; Internship

funds; Scholarship funds; Research; Program-related investments/loans; Matching/challenge support.
Limitations: Applications accepted. Giving primarily in Chicago, IL; some giving also in AZ and NY. No grants to individuals.
Publications: Application guidelines.
Application information: Application form not required.
Initial approach: Letter
Deadline(s): None
Board meeting date(s): 3 times per year
Trustees: Lynne G. Butler Adams; Rhett W. Butler.
Number of staff: 1 part-time professional; 1 part-time support.
EIN: 366101775
Selected grants: The following grants are a representative sample of this grantmaker's funding activity:
$2,000 to West Valley Child Crisis Center, Glendale, AZ, 2012. For All the above contributions were made for the general charitable, religious, educational or scientific purpose of each donee organization.

2730
C.W.B. Foundation ✧ ☆
1252 Bell Valley Rd., Ste. 300
Rockford, IL 61108-4439

Established in 1986 in IL.
Donor: Cedric W. Blazer†.
Foundation type: Independent foundation.
Financial data (yr. ended 12/31/13): Assets, $19,812,121 (M); gifts received, $2,720,515; expenditures, $932,171; qualifying distributions, $841,095; giving activities include $797,600 for 26 grants (high: $500,000; low: $500).
Fields of interest: Arts; Education; Hospitals (general); Human services; Independent living, disability.
Limitations: Applications not accepted. Giving primarily in Rockford, IL. No grants to individuals.
Application information: Contributes only to pre-selected organizations.
Directors: Mark Blazer; James W. Keeling; Jay Maddox; Patrick Shaw; Jim Vitale; Bob Yocum.
EIN: 363480054

2731
The John P. Calamos, Sr. Foundation ✧
c/o Calamos Family Office
2020 Calamos Ct.
Naperville, IL 60563-2793

Established in 2004 in IL.
Donors: John P. Calamos, Sr.; John P. Calamos, Jr.
Foundation type: Independent foundation.
Financial data (yr. ended 12/31/13): Assets, $11,555,986 (M); expenditures, $1,116,809; qualifying distributions, $1,105,013; giving activities include $1,105,013 for 2 grants (high: $1,005,013; low: $100,000).
Fields of interest: Higher education.
Type of support: General/operating support; Scholarship funds.
Limitations: Applications not accepted. Giving primarily in IL. No grants to individuals.
Application information: Contributes only to pre-selected organizations.
Trustee: John P. Calamos, Sr.
EIN: 201383344

2732
Apollos Camp and Bennet Humiston Trust ✧
223 N. Mill St.
P.O. Box 837
Pontiac, IL 61764-1906 (815) 842-1400
Contact: Louis Lyons, Tr.

Established in 1925 in IL.
Foundation type: Independent foundation.
Financial data (yr. ended 04/30/13): Assets, $10,662,539 (M); expenditures, $587,178; qualifying distributions, $450,284; giving activities include $450,284 for grants.
Purpose and activities: Giving primarily for children, youth, social services, community development, and for the benefit of the residents of Pontiac, Illinois.
Fields of interest: Education; Environment, natural resources; Health care; Boys & girls clubs; Human services; Children/youth, services; Community/economic development.
Type of support: General/operating support; Building/renovation; Equipment.
Limitations: Applications accepted. Giving limited to Pontiac, IL.
Application information: Application form required.
Initial approach: Letter
Deadline(s): None
Trustees: Patrick Crowley; Mark Eppel; Sara Gschwendtner; David R. Harding; Louis Lyons.
EIN: 370701044
Selected grants: The following grants are a representative sample of this grantmaker's funding activity:
$34,369 to Boys and Girls Club of Livingston County, Pontiac, IL, 2011.

2733
The Canning Foundation ✧
1650 W. Dublin Ct.
Inverness, IL 60067-4726

Established in 1993 in IL.
Donors: John A. Canning, Jr.; Rita Canning.
Foundation type: Independent foundation.
Financial data (yr. ended 11/30/13): Assets, $4,680,374 (M); gifts received, $3,159,372; expenditures, $2,137,835; qualifying distributions, $2,118,051; giving activities include $2,115,389 for 84 grants (high: $198,787; low: $341).
Purpose and activities: Giving primarily for the arts and education, including Roman Catholic education; funding also for human services.
Fields of interest: Museums; Arts; Secondary school/education; Higher education; Education; Health organizations, association; Human services; Foundations (private grantmaking).
Limitations: Applications not accepted. Giving primarily in IL. No grants to individuals.
Application information: Contributes only to pre-selected organizations.
Officers and Directors:* John A. Canning, Jr.,* Pres. and Treas.; Rita J. Canning,* V.P. and Secy.; Sharon J. Kulak; Elizabeth Canning Lupo; John F. Podjasek III.
EIN: 363913323
Selected grants: The following grants are a representative sample of this grantmaker's funding activity:
$347,582 to Hales Franciscan High School, Chicago, IL, 2011.
$237,866 to Field Museum of Natural History, Chicago, IL, 2011.
$194,171 to Museum of Science and Industry, Chicago, IL, 2011.
$186,984 to Northwest Community Healthcare Foundation, Arlington Heights, IL, 2011.

2734
Gerald & Janet Carrus Foundation ✧
c/o Bank of America, N.A.
231 S. LaSalle St.
Chicago, IL 60697-0001 (312) 828-6763
Contact: George Thorn

Established in 1997 in NH.
Donors: Janet Carrus; Gerald Carrus†.
Foundation type: Independent foundation.
Financial data (yr. ended 12/31/13): Assets, $12,373,438 (M); gifts received, $22; expenditures, $1,669,376; qualifying distributions, $1,616,438; giving activities include $1,470,322 for 9 grants (high: $1,000,000; low: $1,336).
Fields of interest: Arts; Health organizations; Human services; Native Americans/American Indians.
Limitations: Applications accepted. Giving primarily in NY. No grants to individuals.
Application information: Application form not required.
Initial approach: Proposal
Deadline(s): None
Officers and Directors:* Janet Carrus,* Pres.; Irving Sitnick,* V.P. and Secy.; Cathey Romano, Exec. Dir.; Robin Miller; Michelle Peperone; Renee Peperone.
EIN: 133929249
Selected grants: The following grants are a representative sample of this grantmaker's funding activity:
$80,000 to Shinnecock Indian Nation, Southampton, NY, 2012. For Life Skills Enhancement Project.
$20,000 to WonderWork, New York, NY, 2012. For Founding Donors Match Program.

2735
Carylon Foundation ✧
2500 W. Arthington St.
Chicago, IL 60612-4108
Contact: Marcie Hemmelstein, Dir.
Main URL: http://www.carylon corp.com/

Established in 1956 in IL.
Donors: Julius Hemmelstein; Ace Pipe Cleaning, Inc.; Bionomic Services Inc.; Beary Properties Inc.; Mobile Dredging & Pumping Co.; National Industrial Maintenance Services; National Plant Services, Inc.; National Water Main Cleaning Co.; Robinson Pipe Cleaning Co.; Metropolitan Environmental Services; Specialized Maintenance Services; National Power Rodding; Video Pipe Services; Odesco Industrial Services; Deep South Industrial Services; Deep South Solutions, Inc; National Industrial Maintenance - MI; Video Industrial Services; Sewer System Evaluations Inc.
Foundation type: Independent foundation.
Financial data (yr. ended 06/30/13): Assets, $22,884,832 (M); gifts received, $1,051,100; expenditures, $1,146,903; qualifying distributions, $1,045,590; giving activities include $1,045,590 for 3 grants (high: $747,550; low: $49,740).

Purpose and activities: The foundation supports Jewish agencies and temples and organizations involved with arts and culture, education, health, and human services.
Fields of interest: Hospitals (general); Human services; Jewish federated giving programs; Jewish agencies & synagogues.
Limitations: Applications accepted. Giving on a national basis. No grants to individuals.
Application information: Application form required.
Initial approach: Letter
Deadline(s): None
Directors: Julius Hemmelstein; Marcie Hemmelstein.
EIN: 366033583
Selected grants: The following grants are a representative sample of this grantmaker's funding activity:
$100,000 to Israel Center for Excellence Through Education, Chicago, IL, 2011.

2736
Paul & Pearl Caslow Foundation ✧
950 Milwaukee Ave., Ste. 327
Glenview, IL 60025

Donor: Pearl Caslow Irrevocable Trust.
Foundation type: Independent foundation.
Financial data (yr. ended 12/31/13): Assets, $3,080,121 (M); expenditures, $1,390,455; qualifying distributions, $1,187,911; giving activities include $1,162,550 for 247 grants (high: $155,500; low: $200).
Fields of interest: Human services; Jewish agencies & synagogues.
Limitations: Applications not accepted. No grants to individuals.
Application information: Contributes only to pre-selected organizations.
Officers: Betty Breslaw, Pres.; Esther Mann, V.P.; David Mann, Secy.
EIN: 366065830
Selected grants: The following grants are a representative sample of this grantmaker's funding activity:
$10,000 to Aleph Institute, Surfside, FL, 2011.
$10,000 to Jewish United Fund of Metropolitan Chicago, Chicago, IL, 2011.
$5,000 to Aleph Institute, Surfside, FL, 2011.
$1,000 to Aleph Institute, Surfside, FL, 2011.
$1,000 to Jewish National Fund, Rockville Centre, NY, 2011.
$1,000 to Jewish United Fund of Metropolitan Chicago, Chicago, IL, 2011.

2737
Catch the Dream Foundation ✧
P.O. Box 803878
Chicago, IL 60680

Donor: David R. Whitwam.
Foundation type: Independent foundation.
Financial data (yr. ended 12/31/13): Assets, $1,348,645 (M); expenditures, $463,916; qualifying distributions, $457,500; giving activities include $457,500 for 5 grants (high: $400,000; low: $10,000).
Fields of interest: Community/economic development.
Limitations: Applications not accepted. Giving primarily in MI.
Application information: Unsolicited requests for funds not accepted.
Officers: David R. Whitwam, Pres.; Barbara L. Whitwam, Secy.; Mark D. Whitwam, Treas.
EIN: 460848195

2738
Caterpillar Foundation ✧
100 N.E. Adams St.
Peoria, IL 61629-4295 (309) 675-4464
Contact: Jennifer Zammuto, V.P.
Main URL: http://www.cat.com/foundation

Established in 1952 in IL.
Donor: Caterpillar Inc.
Foundation type: Company-sponsored foundation.
Financial data (yr. ended 12/31/13): Assets, $42,018,553 (M); gifts received, $58,276,000; expenditures, $57,564,907; qualifying distributions, $57,564,907; giving activities include $55,998,836 for 1,151 grants (high: $6,225,421; low: $50).
Purpose and activities: The foundation supports programs designed to promote education, the environment, and emergency relief. Special emphasis is directed toward programs designed to spiral poverty into a path to prosperity through women and girls.
Fields of interest: Arts; Education, early childhood education; Higher education; Education; Environment, natural resources; Environment, water resources; Environment, land resources; Environment, forests; Environment; Hospitals (general); Health care; Breast cancer; Employment, services; Food services; Nutrition; Housing/shelter; Disasters, preparedness/services; Youth development, business; American Red Cross; Human services; Community/economic development; United Ways and Federated Giving Programs; Mathematics; Engineering/technology; Science; Public policy, research; Leadership development; Women; Girls; Economically disadvantaged.
Type of support: General/operating support; Annual campaigns; Capital campaigns; Building/renovation; Equipment; Program development; Curriculum development; Scholarship funds; Employee volunteer services; Sponsorships; Employee matching gifts; Matching/challenge support.
Limitations: Applications not accepted. Giving primarily in areas of company operations in North Little Rock, AR, Tucson, AZ, San Diego, CA, Griffin, LaGrange, and Spalding, GA, Aurora, Decatur, Joliet, and Pontiac, IL, Franklin and Lafayette, IN, Wamego, KS, Danville, KY, Minneapolis, MN, Boonville and West Plains, MO, Boonville, Corinth, and Prentiss, MS, Cary, Clayton, Morgantown, Sanford, and Winston-Salem, NC, Fargo, ND, Sumter, SC, Victoria, TX, and Milwaukee, WI, with emphasis on Peoria, IL. No support for fraternal organizations or exclusive membership societies, hospitals, political action committees or candidates, private foundations, religious organizations not of direct benefit to the entire community, or discriminatory organizations. No grants to individuals, or for graduate student scholarships or fellowships, capital campaigns, building construction, debt reduction, development or production of books, videos, films, or television programs, research papers or articles in professional journals, endowments, general operating or agency programs funded by the United Way, political causes, research, sponsorships, tickets, or advertising for fund-raising, or travel; no product or service donations; no loans.
Application information: The foundation currently practices an invitation only process for giving.
Officers and Directors:* Michelle Sullivan, Pres.; Jennifer L. Zammuto, Exec. V.P. and Mgr.; M. H. Collier, V.P.; P. G. Holcombe, Secy,; Robin D. Beran, Treas.; James B. Buda; Kathryn D. Karol.
EIN: 376022314
Selected grants: The following grants are a representative sample of this grantmaker's funding activity:
$6,291,050 to United Way, Heart of Illinois, Peoria, IL, 2012.
$3,801,634 to International Youth Foundation, Baltimore, MD, 2012.
$3,000,000 to World Resources Institute, Washington, DC, 2012.
$2,021,846 to Akshaya Patra Foundation, Bangalore, India, 2012.
$1,379,332 to Bradley University, Peoria, IL, 2012.
$100,000 to Give2Asia, San Francisco, CA, 2012.
$25,000 to United Way Worldwide, Alexandria, VA, 2012.
$5,000 to Vermont Technical College, Randolph Center, VT, 2012.

2739
Cedar Hill Foundation ✧
10 S. Dearborn, IL1-0117
Chicago, IL 60603

Established in 1997 in DE and NY.
Foundation type: Independent foundation.
Financial data (yr. ended 12/31/13): Assets, $14,941,748 (M); expenditures, $709,772; qualifying distributions, $681,789; giving activities include $676,000 for 15 grants (high: $125,000; low: $12,000).
Purpose and activities: Giving for education and human services.
Fields of interest: Arts; Elementary/secondary education; Education; Environment, natural resources; Animals/wildlife; Substance abuse, services; Human services; Children/youth, services.
Limitations: Applications not accepted. Giving primarily in NY; some giving also in Washington DC.
Application information: Unsolicited requests for funds not accepted.
Officers: Clare P. Potter, Pres.; William Parsons, Jr., Esq., V.P. and Treas.
Director: Julia Thieriot.
EIN: 133948444

2740
Harry F. and Elaine Chaddick Foundation, Inc. ✧
2623 N. Lakewood Ave., Ste. 515
Chicago, IL 60614-5373

Established in 1986 in IL.
Donors: Harry F. Chaddick†; Elaine M. Chaddick†.
Foundation type: Independent foundation.
Financial data (yr. ended 06/30/13): Assets, $10,157,685 (M); expenditures, $1,216,911; qualifying distributions, $937,358; giving activities include $670,675 for 67 grants (high: $128,250; low: $100).
Purpose and activities: Giving primarily for higher education, health associations, particularly for

cancer, children, youth, and social services, and to Catholic organizations and churches.
Fields of interest: Media, radio; Higher education; Education; Zoos/zoological societies; Health care; Health organizations, association; Cancer research; Human services; Children/youth, services; Christian agencies & churches.
Type of support: Continuing support; Building/renovation; Equipment; Program development; Conferences/seminars; Curriculum development; Scholarship funds; Research.
Limitations: Applications not accepted. Giving primarily in the metropolitan Chicago, IL, area and Asheville, NC. No grants to individuals.
Application information: Unsolicited requests for funds not accepted.
Board meeting date(s): June and as necessary
Officers and Directors:* Mari Hatzenbuehler Craven,* Pres.; Suzanne Sikes,* V.P.; Wayne Moretti,* Treas.
Number of staff: 1 part-time professional; 1 full-time support.
EIN: 363320988
Selected grants: The following grants are a representative sample of this grantmaker's funding activity:
$120,000 to DePaul University, Chicago, IL, 2011.
$55,000 to Diana Wortham Theater, Asheville, NC, 2011.
$20,000 to Pisgah Legal Services, Asheville, NC, 2011.
$18,500 to Sacred Heart Schools, Chicago, IL, 2011.
$10,250 to MemoryCare, Inc., Asheville, NC, 2011.
$10,000 to Bears Care, Lake Forest, IL, 2011.
$10,000 to Park Ridge Hospital, Hendersonville, NC, 2011.
$10,000 to Riverlink, Asheville, NC, 2011.
$5,000 to Buncombe County Council on Aging, Asheville, NC, 2011.
$5,000 to Special Olympics of North Carolina, Morrisville, NC, 2011.

2741
Ting Tsung and Wei Fong Chao Foundation ✧
10 S. Dearborn St., IL1-0111
Chicago, IL 60603-2300

Foundation type: Independent foundation.
Financial data (yr. ended 12/31/12): Assets, $8,491,549 (M); gifts received, $1,672,000; expenditures, $8,561,505; qualifying distributions, $8,495,588; giving activities include $8,473,667 for 75 grants (high: $3,090,000; low: $2,500).
Fields of interest: Arts; Higher education; Animal welfare; Hospitals (general); Buddhism.
Limitations: Applications not accepted. Giving primarily in Houston, TX; some giving nationally.
Application information: Contributes only to pre-selected organizations.
Officers: Albert Chao, Pres.; Dorothy Jenkins, Secy.
Directors: Wei-Fong Chu Chao; James Chao.
Trustee: JPMorgan.
EIN: 300005201

2742
Charleston Area Charitable Foundation ✧
6029 Park Dr.
P.O. Box 677
Charleston, IL 61920-9400 (217) 345-2128

Established in 1985 in IL.
Donors: Blanche Linder Trust; Mary Linder Trust; Lewis Linder Trust; Dorothy M. Woodyard Trust; Virginia L. Moore; Dolly McFarland.
Foundation type: Independent foundation.
Financial data (yr. ended 06/30/13): Assets, $10,738,376 (M); gifts received, $300; expenditures, $502,114; qualifying distributions, $471,131; giving activities include $471,131 for grants.
Purpose and activities: Giving primarily for community development, education, the arts, and children and youth services.
Fields of interest: Performing arts, orchestras; Arts; Elementary/secondary education; Higher education; Education; Recreation, community; Children/youth, services; Community/economic development; United Ways and Federated Giving Programs; Government/public administration.
Type of support: General/operating support; Annual campaigns; Building/renovation; Scholarship funds; Exchange programs.
Limitations: Giving limited to Charleston and the Coles County, IL, area. No grants to individuals.
Publications: Application guidelines.
Application information: Application form required.
Initial approach: Letter
Copies of proposal: 1
Deadline(s): Jan. 15, Apr. 15, July 15, and Oct. 15
Board meeting date(s): 1st Mon. in Feb., May, Aug., and Nov.
Officers: Michael J. Metzger, Pres.; Henry E. Kramer, V.P.; Mark Bluhm, Secy.; Richard J. Williams, Treas.
Directors: Carol Adams; Jan Grewell; Jeff Horn; Dolly McFarland; Chris Thomason.
Number of staff: None.
EIN: 371172293
Selected grants: The following grants are a representative sample of this grantmaker's funding activity:
$40,000 to Sarah Bush Lincoln Health Foundation, Mattoon, IL, 2013. For Funding the Future Campaign.
$25,000 to United Way of Coles County, Mattoon, IL, 2013. For annual funding.
$15,000 to Eastern Illinois University Foundation, Charleston, IL, 2013. For Business Solutions Center.

2743
The Charlevoix Foundation ✧
P.O. Box 178
Hinsdale, IL 60522-0178 (630) 320-5955
Contact: Andre Radandt, Pres. and Treas.
Application address: 118 E. 3rd St. Hinsdale, IL 60521; tel: (630) 320-5955

Donor: Andre M. Radandt.
Foundation type: Independent foundation.
Financial data (yr. ended 12/31/12): Assets, $4,060,921 (M); gifts received, $4,000,000; expenditures, $3,495,033; qualifying distributions, $3,444,804; giving activities include $3,439,536 for 15 grants (high: $900,000; low: $45,000).
Fields of interest: Education; Health care; Youth development.
Limitations: Applications accepted. Giving primarily in Chicago, IL; some giving also in Phoenix, AZ and Colorado Springs, CO.
Application information: Application form required.
Initial approach: Letter
Deadline(s): None
Officers: Andre Radandt, Pres. and Treas.; Lisa Radandt, V.P. and Secy.
Trustee: Brett Verkaik.
EIN: 412264569
Selected grants: The following grants are a representative sample of this grantmaker's funding activity:
$300,000 to Northwestern College, Orange City, IA, 2012. For contribution to Be Used for Charitable Purposes.

2744
The Chartered Foundation ✧ ☆
5430 W. Roosevelt Rd., Ste. 232
Chicago, IL 60644-1493

Established in 1998 in IL.
Donor: James R. Swanson.
Foundation type: Independent foundation.
Financial data (yr. ended 06/30/13): Assets, $2,829,108 (M); expenditures, $1,319,498; qualifying distributions, $1,116,855; giving activities include $1,095,922 for 3 grants (high: $960,922; low: $10,000).
Purpose and activities: Giving to provide students, children, and adults with opportunities and incentives to improve their competitive positions in society; to provide food, clothing, housing, transportation, health care, nutrition, child care, job placement, and counseling for students and their families; and to provide scholarships to certain students who might benefit from them.
Fields of interest: Health care; Boys & girls clubs; Youth development, services; Human services; Family services; Community/economic development.
Limitations: Applications not accepted. Giving primarily in FL and IL. No grants to individuals.
Application information: Contributes only to pre-selected organizations.
Officer: James R. Swanson, Pres.
Director: Mark T. Swanson.
EIN: 364239391
Selected grants: The following grants are a representative sample of this grantmaker's funding activity:
$25,000 to HighSight, Chicago, IL, 2011.

2745
Elizabeth F. Cheney Foundation ✧
120 S. LaSalle St., Ste. 1740
Chicago, IL 60603-3568 (312) 782-1234
Contact: Elisabeth Geraghty, Exec. Dir.
FAX: (312) 782-1242;
E-mail: egeraghty@cheneyfoundation.org; Main URL: http://www.cheneyfoundation.org
Grants List: http://www.cheneyfoundation.org/grants2012-2013.pdf

Established in 1985 in IL.
Donor: Elizabeth F. Cheney Trust.
Foundation type: Independent foundation.
Financial data (yr. ended 05/31/13): Assets, $10,814,662 (M); expenditures, $1,180,832; qualifying distributions, $1,002,706; giving activities include $1,002,706 for grants.
Purpose and activities: The Elizabeth F. Cheney Foundation is a private independent foundation. Its principal focus is to support the arts and cultural organizations. Organizations supported include, but are not limited to, musical performance

organizations, theater and dance companies, historical societies and museums. The overall grant making focus of the foundation is on artistic achievement in presentation or performance rather than education enrichment or outreach.
Fields of interest: Visual arts; Museums; Performing arts, dance; Performing arts, theater; Performing arts, music; Literature.
Type of support: Program development.
Limitations: Applications accepted. Giving primarily in the metropolitan Chicago, IL, area. No grants to individuals.
Publications: Application guidelines; Annual report; Grants list.
Application information: See foundation web site for complete application guidelines. Application form required.
Initial approach: See website for application form
Copies of proposal: 1
Deadline(s): 30 days prior to meeting based on programmatic schedule
Board meeting date(s): Mar., May, July, Sept., and Nov.
Officers: Lawrence L. Belles, Pres.; Howard M. McCue III, Secy.; Allan R. Drebin, Treas.; Elisabeth Geraghty, Exec. Dir.
Number of staff: 1 part-time professional.
EIN: 363375377
Selected grants: The following grants are a representative sample of this grantmaker's funding activity:
$100,000 to Art Institute of Chicago, Chicago, IL, 2013. For Impressionism and Fashion Catalogue.
$46,700 to Chicago Symphony Orchestra, Chicago, IL, 2013. For Civic broadcast, Muti open rehearsal.
$35,000 to Lyric Opera of Chicago, Chicago, IL, 2013. For Singer sponsorship.
$25,000 to Newberry Library, Chicago, IL, 2013. For Realizing the Newberry Exhibit.
$20,000 to Chicago Chamber Musicians, Chicago, IL, 2013. For Britten Centennial Festival.
$20,000 to Joffrey Ballet, Chicago, IL, 2013. For Mavericks of Dance.
$10,000 to Roosevelt University, Chicago, IL, 2013. For Live broadcast on WFMT.
$6,500 to Chicago Symphony Orchestra, Chicago, IL, 2013. For civic scholarship.
$1,000 to Cornell University, Ithaca, NY, 2013. For Goldman Family Scholarship Fund.
$1,000 to University of Michigan, Ann Arbor, MI, 2013. For Directors discretionary of matching grant.

2746
The Chicago Community Trust ✧

225 N. Michigan Ave.
Chicago, IL 60601 (312) 616-8000
Contact: For grants: Ms. Sandy Phelps, Dir., Grants Mgmt.
FAX: (312) 616-7955; E-mail: info@cct.org; TDD: (312) 856-1703; Grant inquiries e-mail: grants@cct.org; Main URL: http://www.cct.org
Facebook: http://www.facebook.com/thechicagocommunitytrust
Grants Database: http://www.cct.org/grants/grant-list
RSS Feed: http://www.cct.org/news/updates
Twitter: http://twitter.com/ChiTrust

Established in 1915 in IL by bank resolution and declaration of trust.
Donors: Albert W. Harris; and members of the Harris family.
Foundation type: Community foundation.
Financial data (yr. ended 09/30/13): Assets, $2,087,011,848 (M); gifts received, $138,759,785; expenditures, $176,675,532; giving activities include $150,313,429 for grants.
Purpose and activities: The trust's mission is to lead and inspire philanthropic efforts that measurably improve the quality of life and the prosperity of the region. With new strategic focus, the trust seeks to advance four overarching goals in the community: 1) advancing opportunities for human and economic development; 2) securing conditions for healthy, safe, just and caring communities; 3) promoting civic and cultural vitality; and 4) transforming the region through sustainable development.
Fields of interest: Visual arts; Performing arts; Humanities; Arts; Child development, education; Elementary school/education; Secondary school/education; Education; Environment; Health care; Employment, training; Agriculture/food; Housing/shelter, development; Youth development, services; Children/youth, services; Child development, services; Aging, centers/services; Women, centers/services; Minorities/immigrants, centers/services; Homeless, human services; Human services; Economic development; Nonprofit management; Community/economic development; Public policy, research; Government/public administration; Leadership development; Children/youth; Children; Adults; Aging; Young adults; Disabilities, people with; Blind/visually impaired; Minorities; Asians/Pacific Islanders; African Americans/Blacks; Hispanics/Latinos; Native Americans/American Indians; Indigenous peoples; Women; Girls; Adults, women; Young adults, female; Men; Boys; Adults, men; Young adults, male; Offenders/ex-offenders; Immigrants/refugees; Economically disadvantaged; Homeless; Migrant workers; LGBTQ.
Type of support: General/operating support; Continuing support; Income development; Management development/capacity building; Capital campaigns; Building/renovation; Equipment; Land acquisition; Program development; Curriculum development; Research; Technical assistance; Consulting services; Program evaluation; Employee matching gifts; Matching/challenge support.
Limitations: Applications accepted. Giving primarily in Cook County and the adjacent 5 counties of northeastern, IL. No support for sectarian purposes or support of single-disease oriented research, treatment or care. No grants to individuals (except for limited fellowship programs), or for reducing operating deficits or liquidating existing debt, or for the sole purpose of writing, publishing, producing or distributing audio, visual or printing material, or for conducting conferences, festivals, exhibitions or meetings.
Publications: Application guidelines; Annual report; Financial statement; Grants list.
Application information: Visit foundation web site for strategic grant opportunities, guidelines, RFPs and to access online application system. Application form required.
Initial approach: Create online account to submit application
Copies of proposal: 1
Deadline(s): Varies
Board meeting date(s): Jan., May, and Sept.
Officers and Executive Committee:* Frank M. Clark,* Chair.; Terry Mazany, C.E.O. and Pres.; Carol Y. Crenshaw, V.P., Finance; Jamie Phillippe, V.P., Devel. and Donor Svcs.; Frank Soo Hoo, Cont.; Tom Irvine, C.I.O.; Leslie Bluhm; Carol L. Brown; Martin R. Castro; John "Jack" Catlin; William M. Daley; Shawn M. Donnelley; Michael W. Ferro, Jr.; Denise Gardner; King W. Harris; Christopher G. Kennedy; Audrey R. Peeples; Mary B. Richardson-Lowry; John W. Rowe; Jesse H. Ruiz; Michael Tang; Linda S. Wolf.
Trustees: Bank of America, N.A.; BMO Harris Bank, N.A.; JPMorgan Chase Bank, N.A.; The Northern Trust Company; U.S. Bank, N.A.
Number of staff: 32 full-time professional; 11 full-time support.
EIN: 362167000
Selected grants: The following grants are a representative sample of this grantmaker's funding activity:
$817,500 to University of Illinois at Chicago, Learning Sciences Research Institute, Chicago, IL, 2012. For strengthening of mathematics instruction in 32 south and west suburban Cook County districts.
$600,000 to Scholarship America, Saint Peter, MN, 2012. For distribution of the William J. Cook Scholarship Fund.
$400,000 to Metropolis Strategies, Chicago, IL, 2012. For core priorities of regional economic development, environmental sustainability, and justice system reform and to support the economic growth strategy for Cook County.
$226,000 to Big Shoulders Fund, Chicago, IL, 2012. For the partnership with the University of Chicago Center for Elementary Math and Science Education to strengthen math instruction in seven schools.
$220,000 to Safer Foundation, Chicago, IL, 2012. To train and place re-entering ex-offenders in metal working occupations.
$150,000 to Health and Disability Advocates, Chicago, IL, 2012. For Starting Strong in Illinois.
$150,000 to Health and Medicine Policy Research Group, Chicago, IL, 2012. For Strengthening Health Systems and Healthcare Access.
$150,000 to Woodstock Institute, Chicago, IL, 2012. To convene and coordinate the lead partners of the Regional Homeownership Preservation Initiative.
$90,000 to Arts Alliance Illinois, Chicago, IL, 2012. For its leadership in promoting analysis, awareness and use of the Cultural Vitality Indicators.
$40,000 to Chicago Dancing Company, Lombard, IL, 2012. For participation in the SMART Growth Program.

2747
The Children's Care Foundation ✧

333 N. Michigan Ave., Ste. 2131
Chicago, IL 60601-4110 (312) 201-0540
Contact: Robert L. Campbell, Exec. Dir.
Main URL: http://www.childrenscarefoundation.org

Established in 1990 in IL.
Donors: Mary L. Medlock Trust; William J. Watson Trust; C. Lydia Frederick Trust; Hobart W. Williams Trust; Ava W. Farwell Trust; Robert & Janet McMurdy Fund; George J. Williams Charitable Trust; The Chicago Community Trust; Caroline Williams Charitable Trust.
Foundation type: Independent foundation.
Financial data (yr. ended 06/30/13): Assets, $48,356,310 (M); gifts received, $363,427; expenditures, $2,543,910; qualifying distributions, $2,308,459; giving activities include $1,977,000 for 24 grants (high: $530,000; low: $5,000).

Purpose and activities: Support limited to organizations that benefit children in the state of Illinois. Funding interests include programmatic services that give accountable results addressing such issues as: access to primary pediatric and related child health care, child abuse, educational and youth development, social services and delinquency prevention. Priority is given to community-based health care and health services for medically underserved poor children living in metropolitan Chicago, Illinois.
Fields of interest: Hospitals (general); Human services; Children/youth, services.
Type of support: Program-related investments/loans; Matching/challenge support.
Limitations: Applications accepted. Giving limited to metropolitan Chicago, IL. No support for political organizations or governmental entities. No grants to individuals, or for endowments, capital campaigns, general operating support, advocacy, start-up projects, research, lobbying groups, fundraising benefits, or courtesy advertisements.
Publications: Application guidelines; Informational brochure (including application guidelines).
Application information: Full proposals are by invitation only, upon review of letter of inquiry. Electronic submissions, including faxes and e-mails, are not accepted. Organizations that expend more than fifteen percent of their annual revenue for administration, overhead and fundraising will usually not be considered for funding. Application guidelines available on foundation web site. Application form not required.
Initial approach: Letter of inquiry
Copies of proposal: 1
Deadline(s): None
Board meeting date(s): Twice a year
Final notification: 30 days
Officers and Directors:* Anthony Pertile,* Chair.; Joseph S. Johnson,* Pres.; Edward X. Clinton, V.P.; Bruce E. Huey,* V.P.; George S. Trees, Jr.,* V.P.; Roxanne M. Warble,* V.P.; Justin A. Stanley, Jr., Secy.-Treas.; Robert L. Campbell,* Exec. Dir.; Marvin Kamensky; Michael E. Reed; Samuel H. Young.
Number of staff: 1 full-time professional.
EIN: 366088708
Selected grants: The following grants are a representative sample of this grantmaker's funding activity:
$511,818 to Saint Bernard Hospital and Health Care Center, Chicago, IL, 2011. For general support.
$300,000 to Loyola University Medical Center, Children's Hospital, Maywood, IL, 2011. For general support.
$82,000 to Chicago Youth Programs, Chicago, IL, 2011. For general support.
$40,000 to Mount Sinai Medical Center, New York, NY, 2011. For general support.
$30,000 to BBF Family Services, Chicago, IL, 2011. For general support.
$30,000 to Young Mens Educational Network, Chicago, IL, 2011. For general support.
$25,000 to Illinois College of Optometry, Chicago, IL, 2011. For general support.
$25,000 to Jesse White Tumbling Team, Chicago, IL, 2011. For general support.
$25,000 to Lyric Opera of Chicago, Chicago, IL, 2011. For general support.
$24,000 to Chicago Jesuit Academy, Chicago, IL, 2011. For general support.

2748
The Christopher Family Foundation ✧
(formerly Jay and Doris Christopher Foundation)
P.O. Box 133
Western Springs, IL 60558-0133

Established around 1995 in IL.
Donors: Jay Christopher; Julie Christopher; Kelley Christopher Schueler.
Foundation type: Independent foundation.
Financial data (yr. ended 12/31/13): Assets, $23,209,740 (M); expenditures, $2,655,408; qualifying distributions, $2,487,659; giving activities include $2,346,449 for 80 grants (high: $500,000; low: $400).
Purpose and activities: The foundation supports initiatives that strengthen Christian faith, that educate, that encourage health and family well being, and that inspire creativity.
Fields of interest: Museums (children's); Higher education; Education; Human services; Children/youth, services; Family services; Protestant agencies & churches.
Limitations: Applications not accepted. Giving primarily in IL. No grants to individuals.
Application information: Contributes only to pre-selected organizations.
Officer and Trustees:* Kelley Christopher Schueler,* Exec. Dir.; Jay W. Christopher.
EIN: 367092282
Selected grants: The following grants are a representative sample of this grantmaker's funding activity:
$220,000 to Lutheran Social Services of Illinois, Des Plaines, IL, 2012. For Transforming Foster Care Children's Lives with Lifebooks-Research, Marketing, Broader Implementation.
$50,000 to Wheat Ridge Ministries, Itasca, IL, 2012. For Strategic Future Summit.
$35,000 to CARA Program, Chicago, IL, 2012. For The Cara Programs Traditional Job Training, Placement and Retention Program.
$30,000 to Lutheran Music Program, Minneapolis, MN, 2012. For 30 Years - 3 Good Reasons - A 3-Year Commitment Project.
$30,000 to Robert Crown Center for Health Education, Hinsdale, IL, 2012. For FIT An Obesity Prevention Program.
$25,000 to Augustana College, Rock Island, IL, 2012. For Service Learning at Home Abroad.
$25,000 to Timothy Christian Schools, Elmhurst, IL, 2012. For His Faithfulness Continues Campaign.
$20,000 to Inspiration Corporation, Chicago, IL, 2012. For Inspiration Cafe.
$15,000 to Concordia Place, Chicago, IL, 2012. For Preschool Arts Connect Math and Science.
$5,000 to Auburn University Foundation, Auburn, AL, 2012. For Chicago Auburn Club-Scholarship Program.

2749
Circle of Service Foundation ✧
P.O. Box 8529
Northfield, IL 60093-8529 (847) 716-2111
Contact: Adam Levine, Pres.
FAX: (847) 716-2177;
E-mail: info@cosfoundation.org; Main URL: http://www.cosfoundation.org

Established in 1997 in IL.
Donor: Michael P. Krasny.
Foundation type: Independent foundation.
Financial data (yr. ended 12/31/13): Assets, $518,796,996 (M); gifts received, $2,479,995; expenditures, $28,676,920; qualifying distributions, $26,618,857; giving activities include $25,225,731 for 558 grants (high: $2,075,000; low: $150), $2,170 for 7 in-kind gifts, and $82,434 for foundation-administered programs.
Purpose and activities: Giving primarily for human services, education, medical research and Jewish concerns.
Fields of interest: Education; Health organizations, association; Medical research; Human services; Children/youth, services.
Type of support: Management development/capacity building; General/operating support; Continuing support; Annual campaigns; Capital campaigns; Building/renovation; Equipment; Program-related investments/loans; Matching/challenge support.
Limitations: Applications accepted. Giving primarily in Cook and Lake counties, IL, with funding also in Chicago. No support for political organizations or lobbying. No grants to individuals, or for travel or international purposes, or for the funding of policy research.
Publications: Application guidelines; Program policy statement.
Application information: If your pre-application is accepted, you will be sent a link to a full application. Unsolicited pre-applications are accepted for: Community Services and Jewish Community in Cook County and/or Lake County. Pre-applications are not accepted for Medical Research. Application form required.
Initial approach: Online pre-application
Copies of proposal: 1
Deadline(s): None
Board meeting date(s): 4 times a year
Final notification: Pre-application: within 45 days. Application: within 90-120 days
Officer and Directors:* Michael P. Krasny,* Chair.; Adam Levine,* Pres. and Secy.-Treas.; Michael S. Tepper,* V.P.; Michelle Collins; Gary Kash; Janet Krasny; Steven S. Lowenstein; Amy B. Stein.
Number of staff: 6 full-time professional; 1 part-time professional.
EIN: 364185939
Selected grants: The following grants are a representative sample of this grantmaker's funding activity:
$1,000,000 to Center for Enriched Living, Riverwoods, IL, 2012. For Opening the Doors at The Center for Enriched Living - Challenge Grant, payable over 3.25 years.
$750,000 to Bnai Brith Youth Organization, Washington, DC, 2012. For 2013-2015 Support for BBYO Midwest Region, Panim Institute, and BBYO Summer Experiences- Challenge Grant, payable over 3.00 years.
$600,000 to Academy for Urban School Leadership, Chicago, IL, 2012. For General Operating Support and Transitions and Tracking Initiative - Challenge Grant, payable over 2.00 years.
$600,000 to American Israel Education Foundation, Washington, DC, 2012. For AIPAC Synagogue Initiative - Challenge Grant, payable over 2.00 years.
$90,000 to Chicago Arts Partnerships in Education, Chicago, IL, 2012. For Arts Education Design Seminar Program - Challenge Grant, payable over 2.00 years.
$35,000 to Jewish Outreach Institute, New York, NY, 2012. For Public Space Judaism Program Coordinator Chicago - Challenge Grant.

$18,000 to Ida Crown Jewish Academy, Chicago, IL, 2012. For Ira Korman Special Needs Fund.
$17,500 to Resonate, Chicago, IL, 2012. For Spark Chicago Youth Apprenticeship Program - Challenge Grant.
$15,000 to Franciscan Outreach Association, Chicago, IL, 2012. For Streets to Home Initiative - Challenge Grant.
$10,000 to Special Olympics Illinois, Chicago, IL, 2012. For in honor of Windy City Circus.

2750
Mary D. Clapham Charitable Trust ✧
10 S. Dearborn St., IL1-0117
Chicago, IL 60603-2300

Established in 2006 in DE.
Donors: Mary Clapham 1997 Rev. Trust; Mary D. Clapham Trust No. 1.
Foundation type: Independent foundation.
Financial data (yr. ended 11/30/13): Assets, $49,517,254 (M); expenditures, $2,502,598; qualifying distributions, $2,280,773; giving activities include $2,199,996 for 18 grants (high: $574,000; low: $57,444).
Fields of interest: Health care; Health organizations, association; Cancer; Human services; Catholic agencies & churches.
Limitations: Applications not accepted. Giving primarily in MA, NJ, and NY.
Application information: Contributes only to pre-selected organizations.
Trustee: JPMorgan Chase Bank, N.A.
EIN: 516570085

2751
The Clark Family Foundation ✧
2333 Waukegan Rd., Ste. 160
Bannockburn, IL 60015-1541

Established in 1986 in IL.
Donors: Donald C. Clark, Sr.; Jean W. Clark.
Foundation type: Independent foundation.
Financial data (yr. ended 12/31/13): Assets, $5,807,853 (M); expenditures, $811,815; qualifying distributions, $800,825; giving activities include $742,300 for 26 grants (high: $325,000; low: $1,000).
Purpose and activities: Giving primarily for higher education, human services, health organizations, and to Presbyterian churches.
Fields of interest: Planetarium; Higher education; Theological school/education; Health organizations; Human services; Children/youth, services; Protestant agencies & churches.
Limitations: Applications not accepted. Giving primarily in IL, NJ and NY. No grants to individuals.
Application information: Unsolicited requests for funds not accepted.
Officers: Donald C. Clark, Sr., Pres.; Jean W. Clark, V.P.; Thomas R. Clark, Secy.; Barbara Clark Lopresti, Treas.
EIN: 363487579
Selected grants: The following grants are a representative sample of this grantmaker's funding activity:
$18,000 to West Virginia University, School of Dentistry Development, Morgantown, WV, 2012. For unrestricted.

2752
Clearing Corporation Charitable Foundation ✧
227 W. Monroe St., Ste. 1500
Chicago, IL 60606-5053

Established in 2007 in IL.
Donor: Clearing Corporation Trust Fund.
Foundation type: Independent foundation.
Financial data (yr. ended 12/31/11): Assets, $13,625,760 (M); expenditures, $541,093; qualifying distributions, $488,875; giving activities include $488,860 for 18 grants (high: $75,000; low: $5,000).
Fields of interest: Higher education; Human services; Public affairs, ethics.
Limitations: Applications not accepted. Giving primarily in IL and Washington, D.C.
Application information: Contributes only to pre-selected organizations.
Officer and Directors:* Kevin R. McClear,* Admin.; Gerald F. Corcoran; Michael C. Dawley; Ronald Filler; David Johnson; Wendall A. Kapustiak; James G. McCormick; Ira Polk; Peter Reitz.
EIN: 205258907

2753
Cless Family Foundation ✧
(formerly Karl Cless Foundation)
2100 Mallard Dr.
Northbrook, IL 60062-6643

Established in 1991 in IL.
Donor: Gerhard Cless.
Foundation type: Independent foundation.
Financial data (yr. ended 12/31/13): Assets, $19,761,062 (M); gifts received, $1,813,225; expenditures, $428,405; qualifying distributions, $426,528; giving activities include $426,500 for 9 grants (high: $220,000; low: $3,000).
Purpose and activities: Giving primarily for education and medical research.
Fields of interest: Higher education; Education; Medical research.
Limitations: Applications not accepted. Giving primarily in IL; some funding in FL and NC. No grants to individuals.
Application information: Contributes only to pre-selected organizations.
Officers and Directors:* Gerhard Cless,* Pres. and Treas.; Ruth I. Cless,* V.P. and Secy.; Bryan C. Cless; Martin Cless; Stephen G. Cless; Jennifer U. Zehr.
EIN: 363796675
Selected grants: The following grants are a representative sample of this grantmaker's funding activity:
$250,000 to Duke University, Durham, NC, 2011.
$170,000 to University of Illinois at Urbana-Champaign, Urbana, IL, 2011.
$100,000 to University of Illinois at Urbana-Champaign, Urbana, IL, 2010.
$55,000 to Chicago Lighthouse for People Who Are Blind or Visually Impaired, Chicago, IL, 2011.
$10,000 to Boys and Girls Club of Collier County, Naples, FL, 2011.
$10,000 to Lambs Foundation, Libertyville, IL, 2011.
$8,000 to Tutoring Chicago, Chicago, IL, 2011.
$5,000 to Childrens Hospital Los Angeles, Los Angeles, CA, 2011.
$3,000 to Chicago Youth Centers, Chicago, IL, 2011.
$2,500 to Childcare Network of Evanston, Evanston, IL, 2011.
$2,500 to YMCA, McGaw, Evanston, IL, 2011.

2754
The Clinton Family Fund ✧
5824 S. Nashville Ave.
Chicago, IL 60638-3323

Established in 1996 in IL.
Donors: Bruce E. Clinton; Regents Park Trust.
Foundation type: Independent foundation.
Financial data (yr. ended 12/31/13): Assets, $21,980,633 (M); expenditures, $1,085,736; qualifying distributions, $975,919; giving activities include $971,580 for 114 grants (high: $100,000; low: $100).
Purpose and activities: Giving for the arts and education, and to Protestant churches.
Fields of interest: Media, television; Media, radio; Performing arts, dance; Performing arts, music; Performing arts, orchestras; Arts; Higher education; Education; Protestant agencies & churches.
Type of support: General/operating support; Annual campaigns; Matching/challenge support.
Limitations: Applications not accepted. Giving primarily in CO, FL, IL, and NY. No grants to individuals.
Application information: Contributes only to pre-selected organizations.
Officers and Directors:* Bruce E. Clinton,* Pres. and C.E.O.; Mark Honings, V.P., Finance; L. Andrew Martin,* V.P.; Martha O. Clinton,* Secy.
EIN: 363994361
Selected grants: The following grants are a representative sample of this grantmaker's funding activity:
$145,000 to New World Symphony, Miami Beach, FL, 2012. For Annual Fund/Wallcasts/Gala.
$50,000 to Plymouth Congregational Church, Coconut Grove, FL, 2012. For Pastor's Discretionary Fund/General Operations.
$15,000 to Seraphic Fire, Miami, FL, 2012. For Portable Baroque.
$10,000 to Hyde Park Art Center, Chicago, IL, 2012. For Working Capital Reserve/Guest Housing.
$10,000 to Poudre Wilderness Volunteers, Fort Collins, CO, 2012. For Firefighter Support.
$5,000 to Fairchild Tropical Botanic Garden, Coral Gables, FL, 2012. For President's Discretionary Fund.
$5,000 to Plymouth Congregational Church, Coconut Grove, FL, 2012. For United Negro College Fund Campaign.
$5,000 to Rochester Art Center, Rochester, MN, 2012. For Boys and Girls Club/President's Discretionary Fund.
$3,000 to Fairchild Tropical Botanic Garden, Coral Gables, FL, 2012. To underwrite Table for Splendor in the Garden.
$2,000 to Seraphic Fire, Miami, FL, 2012. For Gospel Brunch.

2755
CME Group Community Foundation ✧
(formerly New York Mercantile Exchange Charitable Foundation)
20 S. Wacker Dr.
Chicago, IL 60606-7499 (312) 559-4966
Contact: Nancy Choi

E-mail: Nancy.Choi@cmegroup.com; Main URL: http://www.cmegroup.com/company/corporate-citizenship/cme-foundation.html

Established in 1989 in NY.
Donors: New York Mercantile Exchange, Inc.; Steven Berkson; Chicago Mercantile Exchange, Inc.; Madison Tyler LLC; MF Global.
Foundation type: Company-sponsored foundation.
Financial data (yr. ended 12/31/13): Assets, $711,894 (M); gifts received, $885,128; expenditures, $739,861; qualifying distributions, $727,046; giving activities include $727,046 for grants.
Purpose and activities: The foundation supports organizations involved with children in need, education, and health and human services.
Fields of interest: Education; Health care; Disasters, preparedness/services; Children/youth, services; Human services.
Type of support: General/operating support; Annual campaigns; Building/renovation; Equipment; Emergency funds; Program development; Seed money; Scholarship funds; Research; Sponsorships; Employee matching gifts.
Limitations: Applications not accepted. Giving primarily in areas of company operations, with emphasis on Chicago, IL and New York, NY. No support for exclusionary organizations, private foundations, political candidates or lobbying organizations, religious, fraternal, social, or other membership organizations providing services to their own constituencies, or athletic teams. No grants to individuals, or for general operating costs, capital expenses, memorials, endowments, multi-year pledges, fundraising, special events including conferences, symposia, or sports tournaments, or video/film production.
Application information: Unsolicited applications are not accepted.
Officers: Terrance A. Duffy, Pres.; Meg Wright, Secy.; Jill A. Harley,* Treas.
Directors: Neil Citrone; Bryan T. Durkin; Phupinder S. Gill; Hilda Harris Piell; Kristin K. Wood; Meg Wright.
EIN: 133586378

2756
CME Group Foundation ✧
20 S. Wacker Dr.
Chicago, IL 60606-7431 (312) 930-3292
Contact: Kassie Davis, Exec. Dir.
E-mail: kassie.davis@cmegroupfoundation.org; Main URL: http://www.cmegroupfoundation.org

Established in 2008 in IL.
Donor: Chicago Mercantile Exchange Trust.
Foundation type: Company-sponsored foundation.
Financial data (yr. ended 12/31/12): Assets, $17,238,849 (M); gifts received, $3,897,660; expenditures, $3,285,475; qualifying distributions, $3,099,716; giving activities include $3,099,716 for grants.
Purpose and activities: Giving primarily in the Chicago, Illinois region to promote research, teaching and learning specific to financial markets; to promote the education of children and youth; and to promote the health and education of young children.
Fields of interest: Elementary/secondary education; Higher education; Education; Youth development; Human services.
Limitations: Applications not accepted. Giving primarily in the Chicago, IL region. No support for political campaigns or for organizations not in compliance with all applicable anti-terrorist financing and asset control laws. No grants to individuals, or for deficit reduction, debt, benefit events or advertising.
Application information: Contributes only to pre-selected organizations.
Officers and Directors:* Howard J. Siegel,* Chair.; Charles P. Carey,* Vice-Chair.; Terrance A. Duffy,* Vice-Chair.; Phupinder Gill,* Vice-Chair.; Leo Melamed,* Vice-Chair.; John F. Sandner,* Vice-Chair.; James E. Oliff,* Secy.-Treas.; Kassie Davis,* Exec. Dir.
EIN: 450575574

2757
The Code Family Foundation ✧
c/o Promus Capital
30 S. Wacker Dr., Ste. 1600
Chicago, IL 60606-7407 (312) 876-3945
Contact: Andrew W. Code, Pres.

Established in 1997 in IL.
Donors: Adam Code; Andrew W. Code; David Code; Susan K. Code.
Foundation type: Independent foundation.
Financial data (yr. ended 12/31/13): Assets, $23,606,262 (M); gifts received, $4,993,667; expenditures, $3,434,810; qualifying distributions, $4,241,608; giving activities include $3,125,290 for 60 grants (high: $575,000; low: $250).
Fields of interest: Education; Health organizations, association; Children/youth, services; Christian agencies & churches.
Limitations: Applications accepted. Giving primarily in IL. No support for organizations that the foundation is not involved with or connected to in some way.
Application information: Application form required.
Initial approach: Proposal
Deadline(s): None
Officers: Andrew W. Code, Pres.; Paige P. Walsh, V.P.; Susan K. Code, Secy.; Blake Thoele, Treas.
Director: Kevin Code.
Number of staff: None.
EIN: 364159492

2758
Cole-Crone Family Foundation, Inc. ✧
68 Buckingham Ct.
Deerfield, IL 60015-4872
Contact: Marvin Crone, Pres.
E-mail: marvin526@aol.com

Established in 1995 in IL.
Donors: Jerome J. Cole; Ilene S. Cole.
Foundation type: Independent foundation.
Financial data (yr. ended 12/31/13): Assets, $19,584,151 (M); gifts received, $250,024; expenditures, $1,028,004; qualifying distributions, $902,145; giving activities include $892,000 for 27 grants (high: $100,000; low: $1,000).
Purpose and activities: Giving primarily to hospitals and health associations.
Fields of interest: Hospitals (general); Health organizations, association; Medical research, association; Human services; Jewish federated giving programs.
Limitations: Applications accepted. Giving primarily in Chicago, IL; some funding also in FL and NY. No grants to individuals.
Application information: Application form not required.
Initial approach: E-mail or letter
Copies of proposal: 1
Deadline(s): None
Final notification: 30 days
Officers and Directors:* Marvin R. Crone,* Pres. and Treas.; Ilene S. Cole,* V.P.; Julie Cole Crone,* Secy.; Brian Genrich, Mgr.
EIN: 364039363
Selected grants: The following grants are a representative sample of this grantmaker's funding activity:
$100,000 to Rush Hospice Partners, Hillside, IL, 2011.

2759
The Coleman Foundation, Inc.
651 W. Washington Blvd., Ste. 306
Chicago, IL 60661-2134 (312) 902-7120
Contact: Michael W. Hennessy, C.E.O. and Pres.
FAX: (313) 902-7124;
E-mail: info@colemanfoundation.org; Main URL: http://www.colemanfoundation.org
Blog: http://colemanfoundation.typepad.com/cfi_blog/

Trust established in 1951 in IL.
Donors: J.D. Stetson Coleman†; Dorothy W. Coleman†.
Foundation type: Independent foundation.
Financial data (yr. ended 12/31/13): Assets, $165,992,413 (M); expenditures, $7,561,088; qualifying distributions, $6,658,720; giving activities include $5,482,084 for 111 grants (high: $780,500; low: $1,000).
Purpose and activities: Giving for postsecondary, community, secondary and elementary education programs which focus on developing awareness of self-employment, and other selected postsecondary, secondary, and elementary education projects. Support also for cancer care and research well as for programs to aid the developmentally disabled in the metropolitan Chicago area.
Fields of interest: Elementary school/education; Secondary school/education; Higher education; Business school/education; Adult/continuing education; Education; Medical care, rehabilitation; Cancer; Cancer research; Human services; Community development, small businesses; Community/economic development; Disabilities, people with; Economically disadvantaged.
Type of support: General/operating support; Income development; Capital campaigns; Building/renovation; Equipment; Program development; Conferences/seminars; Professorships; Curriculum development; Scholarship funds; Research; Program-related investments/loans; Matching/challenge support.
Limitations: Applications accepted. Giving primarily in the Midwest, with emphasis on the metropolitan Chicago, IL, area; support outside the Midwest is only for selected programs. No support for religious or political organizations. No grants to individuals, or for deficit financing, ticket purchases, or student loans to individuals.
Publications: Application guidelines; Financial statement; Grants list; Occasional report.

Application information: Brochures, videotapes, CDs and other attachments should not be sent with the letter of inquiry. Full grant proposals should only be submitted upon invitation by the foundation. Refer to website for application requirements. Application form available on website. Application form required.

Initial approach: Concise letter of inquiry. The foundation may then contact the applicant for a full application
Copies of proposal: 1
Deadline(s): Rolling deadline schedule with quarterly consideration
Board meeting date(s): Usually in Feb., May, Aug., and Nov.
Final notification: 3 months

Officers and Directors:* Michael W. Hennessy,* C.E.O. and Pres.; James H. Jones,* Secy.; Trevor C. Davies,* C.F.O. and Treas.; John E. Hughes,* Chair. Emeritus; R. Michael Furlong; Daniel Wanzenberg.
Number of staff: 4 full-time professional; 1 full-time support.
EIN: 363025967
Selected grants: The following grants are a representative sample of this grantmaker's funding activity:
$250,000 to National Association for Community College Entrepreneurship, Springfield, MA, 2012. For General Operating Support.
$220,000 to Almost Home Kids, Naperville, IL, 2012. For Capital Support.
$200,000 to American Cancer Society, Chicago, IL, 2012. For Program Support.
$200,000 to Seguin Services, Cicero, IL, 2012. For Program Support.
$108,300 to Almost Home Kids, Naperville, IL, 2012. For Capital Support.
$100,000 to Gildas Club Chicago, Chicago, IL, 2012. For General Operating Support.
$100,000 to University of Illinois at Chicago, Department of Disability and Human Development (MC 726), College of Applied Health Sciences, Chicago, IL, 2012. For Program Support.
$79,500 to Cancer Center for Healthy Living, Peoria, IL, 2012. For Program Support.
$47,100 to Ray Graham Association for People with Disabilities, Downers Grove, IL, 2012. For Program Support.
$18,000 to Quincy University, Quincy, IL, 2012. For Program Support.

2760
The Comer Foundation ✧
c/o Neal Gerber & Eisenberg
2 N. LaSalle St.
Chicago, IL 60602-3702

Established in 1986 in IL.
Donors: Gary C. Comer‡; Frances Comer.
Foundation type: Independent foundation.
Financial data (yr. ended 12/31/13): Assets, $7,073,842 (M); expenditures, $899,662; qualifying distributions, $858,636; giving activities include $800,100 for 46 grants (high: $137,500; low: $300).
Purpose and activities: Giving primarily for environmental protection, medicine, arts and cultural organizations, human services, and education.
Fields of interest: Museums; Arts; Libraries/library science; Education; Environment, natural resources; Zoos/zoological societies; Hospitals (general); Public health; AIDS; Human services; Children/youth, services.
Type of support: General/operating support; Continuing support; Program development; Internship funds.
Limitations: Applications not accepted. Giving primarily in Chicago, IL. No grants to individuals.
Application information: Contributes only to pre-selected organizations.
Officers: Stephanie Comer, Pres.; Frances Comer, V.P.; Vicki Kalnins, Secy.; William T. Schleicher, Treas.
Director: Guy Comer.
Number of staff: 1 full-time professional.
EIN: 363522486

2761
Comer Science & Education Foundation ✧
c/o Lawrence Richman
2 N. LaSalle St.
Chicago, IL 60602-3963

Established in 1998 in IL.
Donors: The Comer Foundation; Gary C. Comer‡; The Chicago Community Trust; UBS AG; After School Matters; United States Department of Education; State of Illinois Dept. of Human Services; State Farm Mutual Auto Insurance Co.; Access Community Health Network; Illinois State Board of Education; Department of Family Support Services; McDougal Family Foundation; Noble Network of Charter Schools; U.S. Department of Agriculture; Greater Auburn Gresham Development; Bel Brands USA Inc.; Walton Family Foundation; Uhlich Children's Advantage Network.
Foundation type: Independent foundation.
Financial data (yr. ended 12/31/13): Assets, $123,478,257 (M); gifts received, $1,351,787; expenditures, $8,200,443; qualifying distributions, $6,362,428; giving activities include $456,301 for 17 grants (high: $157,096; low: $1,000).
Purpose and activities: Giving primarily for climate change and the redevelopment of a Chicago neighborhood.
Fields of interest: Museums (natural history); Higher education; Education; Hospitals (general); Urban/community development.
Type of support: General/operating support; Program development.
Limitations: Applications not accepted. Giving primarily in Chicago, IL. No grants to individuals.
Application information: Contributes only to pre-selected organizations.
Officers: Guy Comer, Pres.; Stephanie Comer, V.P.; William T. Schleicher, Jr., Secy.; Vicki Kalnins, Treas.; Karen Powell, Cont.; Gregory Mooney, Exec. Dir.
Number of staff: 20
EIN: 364244783

2762
Community Foundation for the Land of Lincoln ✧
(formerly Sangamon County Foundation)
205 S. 5th St., Ste. 930
Springfield, IL 62701 (217) 789-4431
Contact: John Stremsterfer, C.E.O. and Pres.; Stacy Reed, V.P., Progs.
FAX: (217) 789-4635; E-mail: info@cfll.org; Main URL: http://www.cfll.org
Facebook: http://www.facebook.com/CFLL1

Established in 1924 in IL.
Foundation type: Community foundation.
Financial data (yr. ended 12/31/13): Assets, $18,587,261 (M); gifts received, $1,743,139; expenditures, $1,584,327; giving activities include $883,726 for 41+ grants (high: $110,550), and $69,420 for 23 grants to individuals.
Purpose and activities: The foundation's primary function is providing a service to other charities and philanthropists in the local community.
Fields of interest: Recreation; General charitable giving; Aging; Disabilities, people with; Women; Girls.
Limitations: Applications accepted. Giving primarily in Sangamon County, IL. Also serving needs in surrounding counties of Cass, Christian, Logan, Menard, Montgomery, and Morgan in IL.
Application information: Visit foundation web site for online application and guidelines. Application form required.

Initial approach: Complete online application
Deadline(s): Sept. 1 for Community Grant Program; varies for others
Final notification: Nov. 1

Officers and Directors:* Katherine S. Germeraad,* Chair.; John Stremsterfer,* C.E.O. and Pres.; Stacy Reed,* V.P., Progs.; Harry J. Berman; Carolyn A. Blackwell; Arthur H. Bunn; G. Virginia Conlee; Janet S. Costello; Kevin W. Crumly; Saul J. Morse; Bruce A. Sommer; Roe Stone; Martha S. Sumner; Bruce E. Thompson.
EIN: 204191391

2763
Community Foundation of Central Illinois ✧
(formerly Peoria Area Community Foundation)
331 Fulton St., Ste. 310
Peoria, IL 61602-1449 (309) 674-8730
Contact: Mark Roberts, C.E.O.
FAX: (309) 674-8754;
E-mail: mark@communityfoundationci.org; Main URL: http://www.communityfoundationci.org
Facebook: http://www.facebook.com/pages/Community-Foundation-of-Central-Illinois/322998507749395
Twitter: https://twitter.com/CFCIllinois

Incorporated in 1987 in IL.
Foundation type: Community foundation.
Financial data (yr. ended 06/30/13): Assets, $22,776,804 (M); gifts received, $567,607; expenditures, $1,233,327; giving activities include $802,973 for 81+ grants (high: $38,500).
Purpose and activities: The foundation seeks to serve the Central Illinois area by providing an intelligent bridge between needs and resources through a growing endowment, entrepreneurial grantmaking service to the nonprofit sector, and promotion of philanthropy. Primary areas of interest include community development, the arts and humanities, education, health, and human services.
Fields of interest: Arts education; Visual arts; Museums; Performing arts; Performing arts, dance; Performing arts, music; Humanities; Historic preservation/historical societies; Arts; Education, early childhood education; Child development, education; Elementary school/education; Secondary school/education; Higher education; Adult/continuing education; Adult education—literacy, basic skills & GED; Education, reading; Education; Environment, natural resources;

Environment; Animal welfare; Animals/wildlife, preservation/protection; Reproductive health, family planning; Medical care, rehabilitation; Health care; Substance abuse, services; Mental health/crisis services; Health organizations, association; Cancer; Heart & circulatory diseases; AIDS; Alcoholism; Cancer research; Heart & circulatory research; AIDS research; Crime/violence prevention, youth; Food services; Nutrition; Recreation; Youth development, services; Children/youth, services; Child development, services; Family services; Aging, centers/services; Homeless, human services; Human services; Civil/human rights; Urban/community development; Community/economic development; Voluntarism promotion; United Ways and Federated Giving Programs; Social sciences; Government/public administration; Leadership development; Aging; Disabilities, people with; Minorities; Women; Economically disadvantaged; Homeless.
Type of support: General/operating support; Capital campaigns; Equipment; Program development; Conferences/seminars; Seed money; Scholarship funds; Employee matching gifts; In-kind gifts; Matching/challenge support.
Limitations: Applications accepted. Giving limited to the central IL area. No support for sectarian religious purposes. No grants to individuals (except for scholarships), or for annual campaigns or endowments; no loans.
Publications: Application guidelines; Annual report (including application guidelines); Financial statement; Informational brochure; Newsletter.
Application information: Visit foundation web site for application form and application guidelines. Application form required.
Initial approach: Submit application and attachments
Copies of proposal: 17
Deadline(s): Mar. 1 for Community Arts Grants and Jean M. Ligon Animal Welfare Grant; Sept. 1 for Community Needs Grants
Board meeting date(s): Monthly
Final notification: Within 1 month
Officers and Directors:* Bashir Ali,* Chair.; Cathy Butler,* Vice-Chair. and Treas.; Mark Roberts,* C.E.O.; Donna Marcacci,* Secy.; Nathan Bach; Alma Brown; Ray Busam; Christopher Glynn; Dawn Harris Jeffries; Ron Miller; Debbie Ritschel; Sarah Stabler-Cordis; Karen Stumpe; Dr. Maxine Wortham; David Wynn.
Number of staff: 2 full-time professional; 1 part-time professional.
EIN: 371185713

2764
The Community Foundation of Decatur/Macon County ✧

125 N. Water St., Ste. 200
Decatur, IL 62523-1309 (217) 429-3000
Contact: Missy Batman, V.P., Opers. and Finance
FAX: (217) 429-3001;
E-mail: wegi@endowdecatur.org; Additional e-mail: mbatman@endowdecatur.org; Main URL: http://www.endowdecatur.org

Established in 1998 in IL.
Foundation type: Community foundation.
Financial data (yr. ended 12/31/13): Assets, $27,525,860 (M); gifts received, $2,588,502; expenditures, $3,304,957; giving activities include $2,657,490 for 650+ grants (high: $754,625), and $600 for grants to individuals.
Purpose and activities: The foundation seeks to increase the permanent charitable capital available in Decatur and Macon County, IL.
Fields of interest: Arts; Education; Environment; Health care; Community/economic development; Youth.
Limitations: Applications accepted. Giving primarily in Decatur and Macon County, IL.
Publications: Application guidelines; Annual report; Financial statement; Grants list; Informational brochure; Newsletter; Occasional report; Program policy statement.
Application information: Visit foundation web site for application guidelines. Application form not required.
Initial approach: Telephone or e-mail
Board meeting date(s): Quarterly
Officers and Directors:* Kevin Breheny,* Chair.; Bruce Nims,* Vice-Chair.; Louise Ferry Stewart,* Pres.; Missy Batman,* V.P., Opers. and Finance; Kathleen Locke,* Secy.; Larry Altenbaumer,* Treas.; Dave Brandon; Walt Hupe; Mark E. Jackson; Cathy Mansur; James R. Neff; James L. Wade, M.D.; Melissa Watson; Hon. Lisa Holder White.
Number of staff: 1 full-time professional; 1 part-time professional.
EIN: 371372729

2765
Community Foundation of East Central Illinois ✧

(formerly Community Foundation of Champaign County)
307 W. University Ave.
Champaign, IL 61820 (217) 359-0125
Contact: Joan M. Dixon, C.E.O.
E-mail: info@cfeci.org; Main URL: http://www.cfeci.org
Facebook: https://www.facebook.com/CFECI
Twitter: https://twitter.com/CFECI

Incorporated in 1972 in IL.
Foundation type: Community foundation.
Financial data (yr. ended 12/31/13): Assets, $14,732,982 (M); gifts received, $1,002,697; expenditures, $1,194,830; giving activities include $777,298 for 30+ grants (high: $143,651).
Purpose and activities: The foundation seeks to raise the quality of life throughout east central Illinois.
Fields of interest: Humanities; Arts; Education; Environment; Health care; Health organizations, association; Crime/violence prevention, abuse prevention; Youth, services; Human services; Urban/community development; Aging; Disabilities, people with; African Americans/Blacks; Economically disadvantaged; Homeless; LGBTQ.
Type of support: Building/renovation; Equipment; Scholarship funds.
Limitations: Applications accepted. Giving limited to programs that benefit east central IL. No support for sectarian purposes unless program or project is open to the entire community regardless of religious belief. No grants to individuals, or for annual budgets, endowments, scholarships, for-profit entities, start-up costs for new agencies, staffing costs, operations, non-capital items, or travel expenses.
Publications: Application guidelines; Annual report; Grants list; Informational brochure; Newsletter.
Application information: Visit foundation web site for application information. Application form required.
Initial approach: Telephone
Copies of proposal: 11
Deadline(s): Last Friday of Aug.
Board meeting date(s): Monthly
Final notification: Nov.
Officers and Trustees:* Jeff Davis,* Chair.; Brooke Didier Starks,* Vice-Chair.; Joan M. Dixon, C.E.O. and Pres.; Menah Pratt-Clarke,* Secy.; Tom Costello,* Treas.; Katie Bermingham; Tom Brown; Wade Hampton; Charles Hundley; Bonnie Kemper; Jeff Livesay; Brenda Timmons; Rebecca McBride; Alan Nudo; Bradley Uken; Steve Whitsitt; Rick Winkel.
Number of staff: 1 full-time professional; 1 part-time professional.
EIN: 237176723

2766
Community Foundation of Northern Illinois ✧

(formerly Rockford Community Foundation)
946 N. 2nd St.
Rockford, IL 61107-3005 (815) 962-2110
FAX: (815) 962-2116; E-mail: info@cfnil.org; Grant application tel.: (815) 962-2110, ext. 15 and e-mail: bnelson@cfnil.org; Main URL: http://www.cfnil.org
Facebook: http://www.facebook.com/cfnil
Twitter: http://twitter.com/resources4ever

Established in 1953 in IL.
Foundation type: Community foundation.
Financial data (yr. ended 06/30/13): Assets, $79,088,107 (M); gifts received, $27,485,890; expenditures, $2,832,587; giving activities include $1,712,291 for 81+ grants (high: $225,061), and $153,038 for 91 grants to individuals.
Purpose and activities: The foundation seeks to serve the four-county area through philanthropy, to provide leadership in meeting charitable needs, and to be a responsible steward to donors of the endowment. Giving primarily for social services; support also for arts and culture, education, health services, and housing, neighborhoods, economic and community development, youth, children, and families. The "In Youth We Trust" group of the foundation supports programs initiated by and operated for people under 21.
Fields of interest: Humanities; Historic preservation/historical societies; Arts; Education; Health care; Housing/shelter; Youth, services; Child development, services; Family services; Human services; Economic development; Community/economic development; Children; Youth; Disabilities, people with; Economically disadvantaged.
Type of support: Management development/capacity building; Equipment; Emergency funds; Program development; Seed money; Scholarship funds; Research; Technical assistance; Program evaluation; Program-related investments/loans; Scholarships—to individuals; Matching/challenge support.
Limitations: Applications accepted. Giving primarily in the metropolitan Rockford, IL, area, including Boone, Ogle, Stephenson, and Winnebago counties. No grants to individuals (except for scholarships), or for ongoing project support or operating support, annual or capital campaigns, budget deficit, endowments, or regranting of funds.

Publications: Application guidelines; Annual report; Grants list; Informational brochure (including application guidelines); Newsletter; Program policy statement.
Application information: Visit foundation web site for online application and additional guidelines per grant type. Applicant may attend a Grant Seekers meeting held on the 1st Tues. of every May and Nov.; call for reservations. Application form required.
Initial approach: Complete Grant Application Pre-Approval Form
Copies of proposal: 1
Deadline(s): Sept. 1 and May 1
Board meeting date(s): Feb., Apr., May, Aug., Sept., Oct., and Nov.
Final notification: 2 1/2 months
Officers and Trustees:* Nancy Hyzer,* Chair.,; Larry Bridgeland,* Vice-Chair.; Gloria Lundin,* Pres. and Secy.; Jon Bates,* Exec. V.P.; Roger Reithmeier,* Treas.; Jonathan Whitlock,* Asst. Secy.; Richard Leighton, Tr. Emeritus; Thomas S. Johnson, Legal Counsel; Cheryl Balsam; Judith A. Barnard; Williard C. Brenner; Edward Clift; Russ Dennis; James Hansberry; Chris Janke; Kathy Kwiat-Hess; Jeffrey Layng; Erin Maggio-Calkins; Fayrene Muhammad; William Reilly II; Thomas R. Walsh; Janice Westlund; Michael White, Jr.; Brenten Witherby.
Trustee Bank: JPMorgan Chase Bank, N.A.
Number of staff: 8 full-time professional.
EIN: 364402089
Selected grants: The following grants are a representative sample of this grantmaker's funding activity:
$20,000 to Girl Scouts of the U.S.A., Rock River Valley Council, Rockford, IL, 2011. For aMAZE Violence Prevention Program.
$20,000 to Northern Illinois Food Bank, Geneva, IL, 2011. For Senior Food Box Program.
$17,420 to Boys and Girls Club of Rockford, Rockford, IL, 2011. For Operation Respect Rockford.
$15,000 to Regional Access and Mobilization Project, Rockford, IL, 2011. For Teens in Transition Program.
$10,000 to Arc of Winnebago, Boone and Ogle Counties, Rockford, IL, 2011. For heating system.
$10,000 to Rockford MELD, Rockford, IL, 2011. For education for self sufficiency for youth mothers.
$7,430 to Childrens Safe Harbor, Rockford, IL, 2011. For Neutral Exchange Program.
$6,750 to Rockford Police Department, Rockford, IL, 2011. For Police Youth Academy.
$5,000 to Discovery Center Museum of Rockford, Rockford, IL, 2011. For outreach.
$5,000 to Senior Resource Center in Freeport, Freeport, IL, 2011. For senior transportation program.

2767
Community Foundation of the Fox River Valley ✧
(formerly The Aurora Foundation)
111 W. Downer Pl., Ste. 312
Aurora, IL 60506-5136 (630) 896-7800
Contact: Sharon Stredde, C.E.O.
FAX: (630) 896-7811;
E-mail: info@CommunityFoundationFRV.org;
Additional e-mails:
sstredde@communityfoundationfrv.org and grant@communityfoundationfrv.org; Main URL: http://www.communityfoundationfrv.org
Facebook: https://www.facebook.com/cffrv
Twitter: https://twitter.com/CFFRVfoundation
E-mail for scholarship:
Sch@CommunityFoundationFRV.org

Incorporated in 1948 in IL.
Foundation type: Community foundation.
Financial data (yr. ended 12/31/13): Assets, $7,995,415 (M); gifts received, $4,929,045; expenditures, $6,121,215; giving activities include $4,334,816 for 80+ grants (high: $797,675), and $872,600 for 455 grants to individuals.
Purpose and activities: The foundation is a non-profit philanthropic organization that administers individual charitable funds from which grants and scholarships are distributed to benefit the citizens of the Greater Aurora Area, the TriCities and Kendall County, Illinois.
Fields of interest: Humanities; Arts; Higher education; Education; Hospitals (general); Health care; Health organizations, association; Children/youth, services; Human services.
Type of support: Capital campaigns; Building/renovation; Equipment; Seed money; Scholarship funds; Scholarships—to individuals; Matching/challenge support.
Limitations: Applications accepted. Giving limited to City of Aurora, Southern Kane County, and Kendall County, IL. No support for private foundations, sectarian or religious purposes, or for organizations operated primarily for the benefit of their own membership. No grants to individuals (except for scholarships), or for operating budgets, research, annual campaigns, continuing support, endowments, contingency funds, reserves, deficits, benefit tickets, or national fundraising efforts.
Publications: Application guidelines; Annual report; Newsletter.
Application information: Visit foundation web site for application guidelines.
Initial approach: Telephone or e-mail
Copies of proposal: 8
Deadline(s): May 1 and Nov. 3
Board meeting date(s): Mar. and Sept.; Exec. Comm. meets as required
Officers and Directors:* Mark E. Truemper,* Chair.; Hedy K. Lindgren,* Vice-Chair.; Sharon Stredde,* Pres. and C.E.O.; William B. Skoglund,* Treas.; Duncan Alexander; Christina S.T. Anderson; Austin M. Dempsey; John Diederich; Patricia Fabian; Rick Guzman; Jane W. Harris; Frank R. Miller; Katherine Navota; Robert J. O'Connor; Timothy J. Reuland; Edward H. Schmitt, Jr.; Scott Voris; Donna J. Williams; Kyle D. Witt.
Number of staff: 1 full-time professional; 1 full-time support.
EIN: 366086742

2768
Community Health Foundation of Warren ✧
717 N. 11th St.
Monmouth, IL 61462
Application address: c/o Greg McClintock, 707 N. 11th St., Monmouth, IL 61462, tel.: (309) 734-5214

Established in 2007 in IL.
Foundation type: Independent foundation.
Financial data (yr. ended 12/31/13): Assets, $15,759,515 (M); expenditures, $964,769; qualifying distributions, $900,000; giving activities include $900,000 for 3 grants (high: $650,000; low: $100,000).
Fields of interest: Health care.
Limitations: Applications accepted. Giving primarily in IL.
Application information: Application form not required.
Initial approach: Proposal
Deadline(s): None
Officers: Greg McClintock, Chair.; Gary Heaton, Vice-Chair.; Dorothy Ricketts, Secy.
Directors: James Battenburg; Mike Connell; Jon Ferguson; Don Gladfelter; Mary Reed; Spud Riley; Carol Shaw.
EIN: 208070870
Selected grants: The following grants are a representative sample of this grantmaker's funding activity:
$13,875 to Warren Achievement Center, Monmouth, IL, 2011.

2769
Community Memorial Foundation ✧
15 Spinning Wheel Rd., Ste. 326
Hinsdale, IL 60521-2986 (630) 654-4729
Contact: Deb Kustra, Grants Mgr.
FAX: (630) 654-3402; E-mail: info@cmfdn.org; Main URL: http://cmfdn.org/
Facebook: https://www.facebook.com/CommunityMemorialFoundation

Established in 1995 in IL; converted from sale of La Grange Memorial Hospital to Columbia/HCA.
Donors: Helen Prempas Trust; LaGrange Memorial Health System; Marion O. Crion Trust; Harris Associates.
Foundation type: Independent foundation.
Financial data (yr. ended 12/31/13): Assets, $93,924,311 (M); gifts received, $817,250; expenditures, $4,900,842; qualifying distributions, $4,256,317; giving activities include $3,277,117 for 89 grants (high: $1,000,000; low: $175), and $548,097 for 2 foundation-administered programs.
Purpose and activities: The foundation is dedicated to measurably improving the health of people who live and work in the western suburbs of Chicago, Illinois.
Fields of interest: Health care, clinics/centers; Dental care; Health care; Substance abuse, services; Mental health, clinics; Mental health, counseling/support groups; Housing/shelter, temporary shelter; Housing/shelter, homeless; Housing/shelter, services.
Type of support: Management development/capacity building; General/operating support; Continuing support; Program development; Technical assistance; Consulting services; Program evaluation; Matching/challenge support.
Limitations: Applications accepted. Giving limited to the 27 communities of Bridgeview, Broadview, Brookfield, Burr Ridge, Clarendon Hills, Countryside, Darien, Downers Grove, Hickory Hills, Hinsdale, Hodgkins, Indian Head Park, Justice, La Grange, LaGrange Park, Lyons, McCook, North Riverside, Oak Brook, Riverside, Stickney, Summit, Westchester, Western Springs, Westmont, Willow Springs and Willowbrook in the western suburbs of Chicago, IL. No support for organizations which limit services to any one religious group or members of a specific sectarian perspective. No grants to individuals, or for endowments, in-patient care, capital projects, sponsoring dinners, or advertising space.

Publications: Application guidelines; Financial statement; Grants list; Informational brochure; Newsletter; Program policy statement.
Application information: See foundation web site for downloadable General Grant Application Packet. Application form required.
Copies of proposal: 1
Deadline(s): See foundation web site for current deadlines
Board meeting date(s): Varies
Final notification: June and Dec.
Officers and Directors:* Jeffrey Simmons,* Chair.; Beth Prohaska,* Vice-Chair. and Treas.; Gregory DiDomenico,* C.E.O and Pres.; Neil James,* Secy.; Michael Bruni; Deborah Daro, Ph.D.; Gustavo Espinosa; Grace B. Hou; Anthony Perry, M.D.; Hon. Patrick Rogers; Ruby Roy, M.D.; Richard Shanley.
Number of staff: 5 full-time professional.
EIN: 364012380

2770
The Conduit Foundation ✧
c/o Strategic Philanthropy
1700 W. Irving Park Rd., No. 203
Chicago, IL 60613-2599 (773) 360-5998
Main URL: http://www.theconduitfoundation.org

Established in 2002.
Donor: Oak Tree Trust.
Foundation type: Independent foundation.
Financial data (yr. ended 12/31/12): Assets, $21,003,442 (M); expenditures, $1,617,796; qualifying distributions, $2,561,374; giving activities include $1,548,000 for 3 grants.
Purpose and activities: Giving primarily for Jewish education.
Fields of interest: Elementary/secondary education.
Limitations: Applications not accepted. Giving primarily in CT, MA and NY. No grants to individuals.
Application information: Contributes only to pre-selected organizations.
Officers: William M. Doyle, Jr., Pres. and Secy.; Dennis J. Kelly, Treas.; Betsy Brill, Exec. Dir.
EIN: 043684566
Selected grants: The following grants are a representative sample of this grantmaker's funding activity:
$992,000 to Fidelity Investments Charitable Gift Fund Foundation, Boston, MA, 2012. For general support.
$520,000 to Carmel Academy, Greenwich, CT, 2012. For general support.
$36,000 to Chabad Lubavitch of Greenwich, Greenwich, CT, 2012. For general support.

2771
Robert J. & Loretta W. Cooney Family Foundation ✧
c/o Robert J. Cooney, Jr.
120 N. LaSalle St., 30th Fl.
Chicago, IL 60602-2492

Established in 2000 in IL.
Donors: Loretta W. Cooney; Robert J. Cooney; Robert J. Cooney, Jr.
Foundation type: Independent foundation.
Financial data (yr. ended 12/31/13): Assets, $8,234,304 (M); expenditures, $838,339; qualifying distributions, $797,783; giving activities include $797,783 for 33 grants (high: $360,000; low: $500).
Fields of interest: Arts; Education; Human services; Foundations (private grantmaking).
Limitations: Applications not accepted. Giving primarily in IL. No grants to individuals.
Application information: Contributes only to pre-selected organizations.
Directors: Loretta W. Cooney; Robert J. Cooney, Jr.
EIN: 364408645
Selected grants: The following grants are a representative sample of this grantmaker's funding activity:
$328,500 to Boston College, Chestnut Hill, MA, 2011.
$142,857 to Fenwick High School, Oak Park, IL, 2010.
$12,000 to Chicago Jesuit Academy, Chicago, IL, 2011.
$2,500 to 100 Club, Houston, TX, 2010.

2772
Abe and Ida Cooper Foundation ✧ ☆
P.O. Box 48
Glencoe, IL 60022-0048

Established in 1982.
Donors: Fred Cooper; Abe Cooper Trust; Ida Cooper Trust.
Foundation type: Independent foundation.
Financial data (yr. ended 12/31/13): Assets, $25,168,934 (M); expenditures, $1,438,764; qualifying distributions, $1,169,200; giving activities include $1,169,200 for 16 grants (high: $1,000,000; low: $1,000).
Fields of interest: Arts; Higher education; Education; Jewish agencies & synagogues; Religion.
Type of support: General/operating support.
Limitations: Applications not accepted. Giving primarily in Chicago, IL. No grants to individuals.
Application information: Unsolicited requests for funds not accepted.
Officer: Arthur Callistein, Pres.
Directors: Fern Callistein; Bartholomew O' Toole.
EIN: 363219529

2773
Philip H. Corboy Foundation ✧
33 N. Dearborn St., Ste. 2100
Chicago, IL 60611
Main URL: http://www.corboyfoundation.org/

Established in 1983 in IL.
Donors: Philip H. Corboy; James Epstein Investment Trust.
Foundation type: Independent foundation.
Financial data (yr. ended 12/31/13): Assets, $6,956,991 (M); expenditures, $1,421,374; qualifying distributions, $1,343,742; giving activities include $1,343,742 for 46 grants (high: $466,667; low: $100).
Purpose and activities: Support primarily for education, health associations, and children, youth, and social services; funding also for Roman Catholic agencies and churches.
Fields of interest: Elementary/secondary education; Higher education; Health organizations, association; Human services; Children/youth, services; Foundations (private grantmaking); Catholic agencies & churches.
Limitations: Applications not accepted. Giving primarily in Chicago, IL. No grants to individuals.
Application information: Contributes only to pre-selected organizations.
Officers and Directors:* Mary A. Dempsey,* Pres.; Marcy A. Twardak,* Secy.; Daniel M. Kotin.
EIN: 363211607

2774
Alverin M. Cornell Foundation ✧
495 Central Ave., Ste. 101
Northfield, IL 60093-3044

Established in 2001 in IL.
Donor: Alverin Cornell Marital Trust.
Foundation type: Independent foundation.
Financial data (yr. ended 12/31/13): Assets, $10,678,039 (M); expenditures, $804,785; qualifying distributions, $706,832; giving activities include $675,941 for 33 grants (high: $130,000; low: $1,000).
Fields of interest: Education; Health organizations, association; Christian agencies & churches; Protestant agencies & churches.
Limitations: Applications not accepted. Giving primarily in IL. No grants to individuals.
Application information: Contributes only to pre-selected organizations.
Officers: William H. Brewer, Pres.; Wendy Brewer, Secy.; Gregory Ciokajlo, Treas.
EIN: 367371436

2775
Dominique Cornwell and Peter Mann Foundation ✧ ☆
10 S. Dearborn St., IL1-0117
Chicago, IL 60603-2300

Donors: Victoria Mann; Dominique Cornwell.
Foundation type: Independent foundation.
Financial data (yr. ended 09/30/13): Assets, $785,993 (M); expenditures, $546,000; qualifying distributions, $543,000; giving activities include $500,000 for 9 grants (high: $100,000; low: $25,000).
Fields of interest: Cancer research; Parasitic diseases research; Human services.
Limitations: Applications not accepted. Giving primarily in the U.S., support also in London, England.
Application information: Unsolicited requests for funds not accepted.
Trustees: Dominique Cornwell; Helen Lovely Francis; Peter Mann.
EIN: 266848909

2776
A. G. Cox Charity Trust ✧
10 S. Dearborn St., 8th Fl., IL1-0117
Chicago, IL 60603-2300 (312) 732-3568
Contact: Timothy Fitzgibbon

Established in 1924 in IL.
Foundation type: Independent foundation.
Financial data (yr. ended 12/31/13): Assets, $24,322,865 (M); expenditures, $1,062,005; qualifying distributions, $1,031,048; giving activities include $1,026,125 for 54 grants (high: $150,000; low: $2,000).

Purpose and activities: Giving primarily for education and human services.
Fields of interest: Higher education; Hospitals (general); Health care; Health organizations, association; Cancer; Human services; American Red Cross; Children/youth, services.
Limitations: Applications accepted. Giving in the U.S., with emphasis on IL, particularly Chicago. No grants to individuals.
Application information:
Initial approach: Letter
Deadline(s): None
Trustee: JPMorgan Chase Bank, N.A.
EIN: 366011498
Selected grants: The following grants are a representative sample of this grantmaker's funding activity:
$50,000 to Northwestern University, Evanston, IL, 2012. For grant: Kellogg Grad School.
$50,000 to Rush University Medical Center, Chicago, IL, 2012. For grant: Nursing Training.
$50,000 to Santa Catalina Island Conservancy, Avalon, CA, 2012. For grant: Eagles Nest Lodge Restoration.
$10,000 to Heartland Alliance for Human Needs and Human Rights, Chicago, IL, 2012. For grant: Travelers Aid.

2777
Coypu Foundation ✧ ☆
10 S. Dearborn St., IL1-0117
Chicago, IL 60603-2300
E-mail: ElizabethMAry@jpmorgan.com

Established in 1988 in LA.
Donor: John S. McIlhenny.
Foundation type: Independent foundation.
Financial data (yr. ended 12/31/13): Assets, $19,382,558 (M); expenditures, $1,112,364; qualifying distributions, $908,826; giving activities include $882,111 for 20 grants (high: $100,000; low: $10,000).
Fields of interest: Education; Environment; Animals/wildlife; Medical research.
Type of support: Program development; Conferences/seminars; Professorships; Research.
Limitations: Giving primarily in LA. No grants to individuals.
Application information: See http://www.jpmorgan.com/onlinegrants for guidelines.
Trustees: William Callihan; Chris Hale; Eugenie Schwartz; JPMorgan Chase Bank, N.A.; Whitney National Bank.
EIN: 581795856
Selected grants: The following grants are a representative sample of this grantmaker's funding activity:
$125,000 to NOCCA Institute, New Orleans, LA, 2011. For operating funds.
$100,000 to Tulane University, New Orleans, LA, 2010.
$97,000 to Trust for Public Land, New Orleans, LA, 2011.
$96,500 to Southeastern Louisiana University, Hammond, LA, 2011.
$85,000 to LSU Foundation, Baton Rouge, LA, 2011.
$75,000 to Pennington Biomedical Research Center, Baton Rouge, LA, 2011.
$50,000 to International Crane Foundation, Baraboo, WI, 2010. For operating funds.
$35,000 to Defenders of Wildlife, Washington, DC, 2011.
$28,800 to Chimp Haven, Keithville, LA, 2011. For operating funds.
$20,000 to Nicholls State University, Thibodaux, LA, 2011.
$18,540 to Bayou Land Resource Conservation and Development Council, Metairie, LA, 2011. For operating funds.
$15,000 to Historic New Orleans Collection, New Orleans, LA, 2010.
$14,150 to Peregrine Fund, Boise, ID, 2011. For operating funds.

2778
Crain-Maling Foundation ✧
c/o Beatrice G. Crain
505 N. Lake Shore Dr., Ste. 1105
Chicago, IL 60611-6405

Established in 2007 from the division of the Joseph and Bessie Feinberg Foundation.
Donor: Reuben Feinberg†.
Foundation type: Independent foundation.
Financial data (yr. ended 10/31/13): Assets, $41,153,045 (M); expenditures, $1,563,276; qualifying distributions, $1,181,829; giving activities include $811,100 for 10 grants (high: $701,275; low: $1,000).
Fields of interest: Higher education; Jewish federated giving programs; Jewish agencies & synagogues.
Limitations: Applications not accepted. Giving primarily in IL and NY; some funding also in AR. No grants for individuals.
Application information: Unsolicited requests for funds not accepted.
Officers and Directors:* Beatrice G. Crain,* Chair. and C.E.O.; Michael S. Maling,* Pres.; Elise A. Maling,* Secy.; Manssa Iancu,* Treas.
EIN: 204310219
Selected grants: The following grants are a representative sample of this grantmaker's funding activity:
$239,000 to Friends of Refugees of Eastern Europe, Brooklyn, NY, 2011.
$100,000 to Hendrix College, Conway, AR, 2011.
$50,000 to Associated Talmud Torahs, Chicago, IL, 2011.
$50,000 to Hebrew Theological College, Skokie, IL, 2011.
$15,220 to American Jewish Committee, Chicago, IL, 2011.
$10,000 to Lyric Opera of Chicago, Chicago, IL, 2011.
$9,000 to Chicago Loop Synagogue, Chicago, IL, 2011.
$7,500 to American Friends of Yad Eliezer, Brooklyn, NY, 2011.
$5,000 to Jewish National Fund, Rockville Centre, NY, 2011.

2779
The Bryan C. & Christina I. Cressey Foundation ✧ ☆
c/o Rosen & Cohen
5 Revere Dr., Ste. 350
Northbrook, IL 60062-1566
Contact: Bryan C. Cressey, Pres. and Treas.

Established in 1986 in IL.
Donors: Bryan C. Cressey; Christina I. Cressey.
Foundation type: Independent foundation.
Financial data (yr. ended 12/31/13): Assets, $2,284,733 (M); expenditures, $948,019; qualifying distributions, $937,438; giving activities include $937,438 for 66 grants (high: $250,000; low: $25).
Fields of interest: Planetarium; Higher education; Business school/education; Law school/education; Education; Human services; Protestant agencies & churches.
Type of support: General/operating support.
Limitations: Applications accepted. Giving primarily in the Chicago, IL, area. No grants to individuals.
Application information: Application form not required.
Initial approach: Proposal
Deadline(s): None
Officers: Bryan C. Cressey, Pres. and Treas.; Christina I. Cressey, V.P. and Secy.
EIN: 363486617
Selected grants: The following grants are a representative sample of this grantmaker's funding activity:
$25,000 to Cathedral Shelter of Chicago, Chicago, IL, 2011.
$1,000 to American Liver Foundation, New York, NY, 2010.

2780
Susan Crown Exchange Inc. ✧
(also known as SCE)
4 E. Ohio St., No. 30
Chicago, IL 60611-2783
E-mail: info@scefdn.org; Main URL: http://www.scefdn.org
Twitter: http://www.twitter.com/#!/scefdn

Donor: Susan Crown.
Foundation type: Independent foundation.
Financial data (yr. ended 12/31/12): Assets, $2,509,986 (M); gifts received, $2,459,328; expenditures, $3,039,448; qualifying distributions, $3,029,197; giving activities include $2,688,000 for 34 grants (high: $1,862,000; low: $1,000).
Purpose and activities: The foundation aspires to become a hub for ideas, people, services, and innovation in the service of public good. Areas of interest include, but are not limited to, women and girls, social entrepreneurship, change agents, and health care.
Fields of interest: Health care; Social entrepreneurship; Women; Girls.
Limitations: Applications not accepted.
Application information: Contributes only to pre-selected organizations.
Officers: Susan Crown, Chair.; William C. Kunkler III, Secy.-Treas.
Trustees: Eli Evans; Jennifer Jacoby Hurd; Paul Jansen; Martha Minow.
EIN: 262991942

2781
Arie and Ida Crown Memorial ✧
(doing business as Crown Family Philanthropies)
222 N. LaSalle St., Ste. 1000
Chicago, IL 60601-1109 (312) 750-6671
Contact: Caren Yanis, Exec. Dir.
FAX: (312) 984-1499;
E-mail: aicm@crown-chicago.com; Main URL: http://www.crownmemorial.org/

Incorporated in 1947 in IL.

Donor: members of the Crown family.
Foundation type: Independent foundation.
Financial data (yr. ended 12/31/12): Assets, $670,711,031 (M); gifts received, $15,979,096; expenditures, $28,155,593; qualifying distributions, $23,627,848; giving activities include $22,915,737 for 444 grants (high: $1,125,000; low: $15).
Purpose and activities: Giving primarily for arts and culture, civic affairs, education, the environment, health, human services, and Jewish causes.
Fields of interest: Arts; Education; Environment; Health care; Human services; Public affairs; Jewish agencies & synagogues.
International interests: Israel.
Type of support: General/operating support; Continuing support; Annual campaigns; Capital campaigns; Building/renovation; Equipment; Endowments; Program development; Professorships; Fellowships; Scholarship funds; Employee matching gifts; Matching/challenge support.
Limitations: Applications accepted. Giving primarily in metropolitan Chicago, IL, with some giving in NY. No support for government-sponsored programs, or to organizations with budgets under $200,000. No grants to individuals, or for film, video, exhibitions, conference, associations or coalitions.
Publications: Application guidelines.
Application information: Application guidelines available on foundation web site. Application form not required.
Initial approach: E-mail letter of intent (2 pages maximum)
Copies of proposal: 1
Deadline(s): See web site deadlines for specific program areas
Board meeting date(s): Spring and fall
Officers and Directors:* Susan Crown, Pres.; A. Steven Crown,* V.P.; James S. Crown,* V.P.; Rebecca Crown,* V.P.; William Crown,* V.P.; Charles Goodman, V.P.; Barbara Goodman Manilow,* V.P.; Sara Crown Star,* V.P.; Arnold Weber,* V.P.; Lester Crown, Treas.; Caren Yanis, Exec. Dir.
Number of staff: 6 full-time professional.
EIN: 366076088
Selected grants: The following grants are a representative sample of this grantmaker's funding activity:
$1,125,000 to Covenant Foundation, New York, NY, 2012.
$514,200 to Nature Conservancy, Arlington, VA, 2012.
$220,000 to Jerusalem Foundation, New York, NY, 2012.
$200,000 to Heartland Alliance for Human Needs and Human Rights, Chicago, IL, 2012.
$200,000 to Rush University Medical Center, Chicago, IL, 2012.
$115,000 to American Friends of the Israel Museum, New York, NY, 2012.
$100,000 to Center for Neighborhood Technology, Chicago, IL, 2012.
$35,000 to Chicago Coalition for the Homeless, Chicago, IL, 2012.
$30,000 to Yale University, New Haven, CT, 2012.
$25,000 to Lyric Opera of Chicago, Chicago, IL, 2012.

2782
Joe and Jessie Crump Fund ✧
c/o JPMorgan Chase Bank, N.A.
10 S. Dearborn St.
Chicago, IL 60603-2300

Trust established in 1965 in TX.
Foundation type: Independent foundation.
Financial data (yr. ended 09/30/13): Assets, $40,579,350 (M); expenditures, $2,191,609; qualifying distributions, $1,996,578; giving activities include $1,389,671 for 8 grants (high: $888,900; low: $10,000), and $500,000 for loans/program-related investments.
Purpose and activities: Giving primarily for health organizations and foundations, including children's health organizations; support also for an Episcopal theological seminary.
Fields of interest: Theological school/education; Health organizations, association; Health organizations, fund raising/fund distribution; Medical research, institute; Children, services; Foundations (private grantmaking).
Type of support: Curriculum development; Scholarship funds; Research; Program-related investments/loans.
Limitations: Applications not accepted. Giving primarily in TX. No grants to individuals, or for building or endowment funds, matching gifts, or general purposes.
Application information: Contributes only to pre-selected organizations.
Board meeting date(s): As required
Trustee: JPMorgan Chase Bank, N.A.
EIN: 756045044

2783
The Cuneo Foundation ✧
111 Person St., Ste. 1500
Chicago, IL 60611-2077 (312) 915-6400

Incorporated in 1945 in IL.
Donors: John F. Cuneo; Milwaukee Golf Development Corp.
Foundation type: Independent foundation.
Financial data (yr. ended 12/31/13): Assets, $11,852,844 (M); expenditures, $635,560; qualifying distributions, $547,526; giving activities include $491,000 for 18 grants (high: $56,000; low: $7,000).
Purpose and activities: Giving primarily for Roman Catholic church support and church-related organizations; funding also for health care, education, and children, youth and social services.
Fields of interest: Elementary/secondary education; Higher education; Health care; Health organizations, association; Human services; Children/youth, services; Catholic agencies & churches; Blind/visually impaired.
Type of support: General/operating support; Continuing support; Building/renovation; Equipment; Scholarship funds; Matching/challenge support.
Limitations: Applications accepted. Giving primarily in the metropolitan Chicago, IL, area. No grants to individuals, or for fellowships, or research projects; no loans.
Publications: Annual report.
Application information: Application form required.
Initial approach: Letter
Deadline(s): None
Final notification: 2 months
Officers and Directors:* Michael J. Garanzini,* Co-Chair.; Andrea Hasten,* Co-Chair.; Katherine White, Secy.; Joan E. Steel,* Treas.; Kenneth J. Velo.
EIN: 362261606

2784
D and R Fund ✧
c/o James J. Glasser
500 W. Monroe St., Ste. 2660
Chicago, IL 60661-3769

Incorporated in 1951 in IL.
Donors: Samuel R. Rosenthal†; Marie-Louise Rosenthal; Carolyn S. Dreyfus†; Alice L. Dreyfus†; Samuel Rosenthal Trust A.
Foundation type: Independent foundation.
Financial data (yr. ended 12/31/12): Assets, $27,481,157 (M); expenditures, $1,792,538; qualifying distributions, $1,129,000; giving activities include $1,129,000 for 33 grants (high: $125,000; low: $6,000).
Purpose and activities: Giving primarily for the arts, education, community development, and Jewish organizations.
Fields of interest: Museums; Arts; Education; Human services; Community/economic development; Jewish federated giving programs; Jewish agencies & synagogues.
Limitations: Applications not accepted. Giving primarily in the Chicago, IL, metropolitan area. No grants to individuals, or for building or endowment funds or operating budgets.
Application information: Contributes only to pre-selected organizations.
Board meeting date(s): As necessary
Officer and Directors:* James J. Glasser,* Treas.; Emily Glasser; Louise R. Glasser; Babette H. Rosenthal; Samuel L. Rosenthal.
EIN: 366057159

2785
Davee Foundation ✧
c/o Charles A. Stern - Wildman, Harrold, Allen
225 W. Wacker Dr., 30th Fl.
Chicago, IL 60606-1229 (312) 268-4156

Established in 1964 in IL.
Donor: Ken M. Davee.
Foundation type: Independent foundation.
Financial data (yr. ended 12/31/13): Assets, $124,211,103 (M); expenditures, $6,819,215; qualifying distributions, $6,419,920; giving activities include $6,331,000 for 88 grants (high: $1,325,000; low: $1,000).
Purpose and activities: Giving primarily for higher education, health care and the arts.
Fields of interest: Arts; Higher education; Hospitals (general); Health organizations, association; Medical research, institute; Human services.
Type of support: General/operating support; Professorships; Research.
Limitations: Applications not accepted. Giving primarily in IL, with emphasis on Chicago. No grants to individuals.
Application information: Contributes only to pre-selected organizations.
Officer: J.W. Dugdale, Jr., Pres.
Directors: Sharon Kushiner; Charles A. Stern.
EIN: 366124598

Selected grants: The following grants are a representative sample of this grantmaker's funding activity:
$1,205,000 to Northwestern University, School of Music, Evanston, IL, 2012. For general support.
$500,000 to Northwestern University, Evanston, IL, 2012. For general support.
$430,000 to Chicago Shakespeare Theater, Chicago, IL, 2012. For general support.
$350,000 to United States Fund for UNICEF, Chicago, IL, 2012. For general support.
$320,000 to Rehabilitation Institute of Chicago, Chicago, IL, 2012. For general support.
$300,000 to Lincoln Park Zoo, Chicago, IL, 2012. For research.
$100,000 to International House of Blues Foundation in Chicago, Chicago, IL, 2012. For general support.
$25,000 to CARE USA, Atlanta, GA, 2012. For general support.
$15,000 to Planned Parenthood of Illinois, Chicago, IL, 2012. For general support.
$15,000 to Shimer College, Chicago, IL, 2012. For general support.

2786
Davis Foundation ✧
10 S. Dearborn St., IL1-0117
Chicago, IL 60603-2300
Application address: c/o JPMorgan Chase Bank, Attn.: NCAA, 2200 Ross Ave., Dallas, TX 75201, tel.: (866) 300-6222

Established in OH.
Donors: David Davis†; Velma Davis†; Velma Davis Irrevocable Trust.
Foundation type: Independent foundation.
Financial data (yr. ended 12/31/13): Assets, $44,370,301 (M); expenditures, $2,699,655; qualifying distributions, $2,155,998; giving activities include $2,039,010 for 44 grants (high: $500,000; low: $5,000).
Purpose and activities: Giving primarily to Evangelical Christian agencies and churches; funding also for Christian higher education.
Fields of interest: Higher education; Theological school/education; Human services; YM/YWCAs & YM/YWHAs; Christian agencies & churches.
Limitations: Applications accepted. Giving primarily in GA and OH.
Application information:
Initial approach: Letter
Deadline(s): None
Trustee: JPMorgan Chase Bank, N.A.
EIN: 346566892

2787
Doris & Victor Day Foundation, Inc. ✧
1800 3rd Ave., Ste. 302
Rock Island, IL 61201-9019 (309) 788-2300
Contact: Dave Geenen, Exec. Dir.
FAX: (309) 788-3298;
E-mail: day.rauch@sbcglobal.net; E-mail for Dave Geenen: dave@dayfoundation.org; Main URL: http://www.dayfoundation.org
Facebook: https://www.facebook.com/Day/Foundation

Established in 1965 in IL.
Donors: Doris D. Day†; Victor B. Day†.
Foundation type: Independent foundation.
Financial data (yr. ended 06/30/14): Assets, $15,710,800 (M); expenditures, $922,730; qualifying distributions, $841,200; giving activities include $705,016 for grants.
Purpose and activities: Giving primarily for social services, including child welfare and the homeless.
Fields of interest: Education; Health organizations, association; Employment, services; Employment, training; Housing/shelter, development; Youth development, adult & child programs; Human services; Children/youth, services; Homeless, human services; Children/youth; Adults; Minorities; Homeless; LGBTQ.
Type of support: Capital campaigns; General/operating support; Building/renovation; Equipment; Emergency funds; Seed money; Scholarship funds.
Limitations: Applications accepted. Giving limited to Scott County, IA, and Rock Island County, IL. No support for religious purposes (except for non-sectarian, community serving programs of religious organizations). No grants to individuals, or for endowment funds.
Publications: Application guidelines; Annual report (including application guidelines); Grants list; IRS Form 990 or 990-PF printed copy available upon request.
Application information: Application form required.
Initial approach: See foundation web site or telephone
Copies of proposal: 1
Deadline(s): May 1
Final notification: Sept. 1
Officers and Directors:* William R. Stengel, Jr.,* Pres.; Stacie Fidlar, V.P.; Kai Swanson, Secy.; Daniel Fetes, Treas.; Dave Geenen, Exec. Dir.; Samuel M. Gilman, Dir. Emeritus; Charles Wilson, Dir. Emeritus; Walter Braud.
Number of staff: 1 full-time professional; 1 part-time professional.
EIN: 366131596
Selected grants: The following grants are a representative sample of this grantmaker's funding activity:
$79,747 to Rock Island/Milan School District No. 41, Rock Island, IL, 2011. For truancy and community coordinator staffing.
$75,000 to Supplemental Emergency Assistance Program, Bettendorf, IA, 2011. For emergency assistance.
$35,000 to Iowa Abortion Action Fund, Cedar Rapids, IA, 2011. For medical assistance for women of Scott County, IA and Rock Island County, IL.
$30,000 to Child Abuse Council, Rock Island, IL, 2011. For educational enrichment of free day camp for children.
$27,500 to Western Illinois University, Quad Cities, Moline, IL, 2011. For scholarships.
$25,000 to Child Abuse Council, Rock Island, IL, 2011. For seed funding for QC Alliance for Immigrants and Refugees.
$25,000 to YouthBuild, Rock Island, IL, 2011. For building trades and educational programs.
$20,000 to Churches United of the Quad City Area, Bettendorf, IA, 2011. For food pantry and women's shelter operations.
$20,000 to Rock Island Parks and Recreation Department, Rock Island, IL, 2011. For staffing for free day camps.
$15,000 to Project Now, Rock Island, IL, 2011. For customer assistance.
$12,000 to Bethany for Children and Families, Moline, IL, 2011. For Ways to Work auto loan program.

2788
The de Kay Foundation ✧
10 S. Dearborn St., IL1-0117
Chicago, IL 60603
Contact: Yvette Boisnier MSW, Prog. Dir.
Application address: c/o JPMorgan Chase Bank, N.A., Attn.: Daniel Ordan, V.P., 270 Park Ave., New York, NY 10017; tel.: (212) 648-1489

Established in 1967 in CT.
Donor: Helen M. de Kay†.
Foundation type: Independent foundation.
Financial data (yr. ended 02/28/13): Assets, $32,797,098 (M); expenditures, $1,307,556; qualifying distributions, $1,107,961; giving activities include $700,000 for 3 grants (high: $350,000; low: $175,000), and $351,794 for grants to individuals.
Purpose and activities: The foundation traditionally awards monthly stipends directly to elderly individuals and couples to help them remain in their home in safety and comfort, to protect their dignity and individuality, and to encourage them to continue contributing to their community. Stipendiary program applicants must be 65 years of age or older and must be referred by social service agencies and have an assigned social worker. Applicants must demonstrate a history of self-sufficiency and minimal dependence on private charitable or government assistance. Individuals should also demonstrate a history of volunteering or engaging in civic or cultural activities. Applicants may have assets up to $25,000, excluding their primary residence.
Fields of interest: Hospitals (specialty); Aging.
Type of support: Grants to individuals.
Limitations: Applications accepted. Giving limited to the New York, NY metropolitan area, including the five boroughs of New York City, Westchester, Rockland, and Nassau counties, NY, Fairfield County, CT, and Essex, Bergen, Hudson, and Passaic counties, NJ. No grants for building or endowment funds, scholarships, fellowships, or matching gifts; no loans.
Publications: Application guidelines.
Application information: Monthly stipends range from $150-$1,000. Application form required.
Initial approach: Application form
Copies of proposal: 1
Deadline(s): None
Board meeting date(s): Quarterly
Final notification: 3 months
Trustee: JPMorgan Chase Bank, N.A.
EIN: 136203234

2789
The Dean Foundation, Inc. ✧ ☆
P.O. Box 803878
Chicago, IL 60680-3878

Established in 1995 in TX.
Donors: Jimmy Dean; Donna Dean; Jimmy Dean Revocable Trust.
Foundation type: Independent foundation.
Financial data (yr. ended 07/31/13): Assets, $1,500,943 (M); gifts received, $5,081,190; expenditures, $4,160,694; qualifying distributions, $4,158,750; giving activities include $4,150,000 for 3 grants (high: $4,000,000; low: $50,000).
Fields of interest: Higher education; Human services.

Limitations: Applications not accepted. Giving primarily in Plainview, TX, and Richmond, VA. No grants to individuals.
Application information: Unsolicited requests for funds not accepted.
Officer and Directors:* Donna Dean,* Pres.; T. Craig Harmon,* Secy.; Jack A. Bartlett,* Treas.
EIN: 752637602

2790
John Deere Foundation ✧
1 John Deere Pl.
Moline, IL 61265-8010
FAX: (309) 748-7953; Main URL: http://www.deere.com/en_US/globalcitizenship/socialinvestment/index.html

Incorporated in 1948 in IL.
Donor: Deere & Co.
Foundation type: Company-sponsored foundation.
Financial data (yr. ended 10/31/13): Assets, $176,086,308 (M); gifts received, $20,000,000; expenditures, $12,794,828; qualifying distributions, $12,296,901; giving activities include $12,083,063 for grants, and $303,559 for 1 foundation-administered program.
Purpose and activities: The foundation supports programs designed to promote education; community development; and solutions for world hunger.
Fields of interest: Arts; Higher education; Adult/continuing education; Education; Agriculture, sustainable programs; Food services; Food banks; Agriculture/food; Disasters, preparedness/services; Youth development, business; American Red Cross; Human services; Community development, business promotion; Community development, small businesses; Community/economic development; Mathematics; Engineering/technology; Science; Minorities; Economically disadvantaged.
International interests: Africa; Global Programs.
Type of support: General/operating support; Continuing support; Annual campaigns; Building/renovation; Emergency funds; Program development; Scholarship funds; Research; Employee volunteer services; Employee matching gifts.
Limitations: Applications accepted. Giving primarily in areas of company operations in Augusta, GA, Des Moines, Dubuque, Iowa Quad cities, Ottumwa, and Waterloo, IA, Quad City Region, IL, Coffeyville and Greater Kansas City, KS, Thibodaux, LA, Cary and Fuquay-Varina, NC, Fargo and Valley City, ND, Greeneville, TN, and Horicon and Madison, WI; giving also to Africa and global programs. No support for religious organizations, athletic organizations, political organizations, foundations, tax-supported organizations, or fraternal organizations or sororities. No grants to individuals, or for sports programs, political campaigns, advertising, or marketing; no loans; no in-kind equipment donations.
Publications: Application guidelines; Corporate report.
Application information: Application form required.
Initial approach: Complete online eligibility quiz and application
Deadline(s): None
Board meeting date(s): Quarterly
Final notification: 30 days following board meetings
Officers and Directors:* Samuel R. Allen,* Chair.; Mara L. Sovey,* Pres.; C. Nathan Clark, V.P.; Gregory R. Noe, Secy.; Thomas Spitzfaden, Treas.; Frances B. Emerson; James M. Field; Max Guinn; Mary K. W. Jones; Rajesh Kalathur.
Number of staff: 2.5 full-time professional.
EIN: 366051024
Selected grants: The following grants are a representative sample of this grantmaker's funding activity:
$1,250,000 to Opportunity International, Oak Brook, IL, 2012. For Solutions for World Hunger.
$1,100,000 to PYXERA Global, Washington, DC, 2012. For Community Betterment.
$1,000,000 to Waterloo Development Corporation, Waterloo, IA, 2012. For Community Betterment.
$850,000 to United Way of the Quad Cities Area, Davenport, IA, 2012. For Community Betterment.
$500,000 to World Food Program USA, Washington, DC, 2012. For Solutions for World Hunger.
$243,980 to Rock Island-Milan Education Foundation, Rock Island, IL, 2012.
$175,000 to Feeding America, Chicago, IL, 2012. For Solutions for World Hunger.
$90,000 to Foods Resource Bank, Western Springs, IL, 2012. For Solutions for World Hunger.
$27,000 to United Fund of Coffeyville, Coffeyville, KS, 2012. For Community Betterment.
$3,000 to Western Michigan University Foundation, Kalamazoo, MI, 2012.

2791
Deering Foundation ✧
410 N. Michigan Ave., Rm. 590
Chicago, IL 60611-4220

Incorporated in 1956 in IL.
Donors: Barbara D. Danielson; Richard E. Danielson, Jr.; Marion D. Campbell; Miami Corp.
Foundation type: Independent foundation.
Financial data (yr. ended 11/30/13): Assets, $15,968,233 (M); expenditures, $953,958; qualifying distributions, $701,598.
Fields of interest: Arts; Higher education; Education; Human services; Foundations (private grantmaking).
Type of support: General/operating support.
Limitations: Applications not accepted. Giving primarily in Chicago, IL; some giving also in Miami, FL. No grants to individuals, or for scholarships or fellowships; no loans.
Application information: Contributes only to pre-selected organizations.
Officers and Directors:* John Rau,* Pres.; Barbara S. Danielson,* V.P.; Candida D. Burnap,* V.P.; Susan D. Pattock, Secy.-Treas.; Charles E. Seitz; Stephen M. Strachan; Jocelyn D. Tennille.
EIN: 366051876

2792
DeKalb County Community Foundation (IL) ✧
475 DeKalb Ave.
Sycamore, IL 60178 (815) 748-5383
Contact: Daniel P. Templin, Executive Director; Anita Zurbrugg, Prog. Dir.
FAX: (815) 748-5873; E-mail: dan@dekalbccf.org; Main URL: http://www.dekalbccf.org
E-Newsletter: http://visitor.constantcontact.com/manage/optin/ea?v=001VUyJZcZ—frU09m5m_4P1g==
Facebook: http://www.facebook.com/pages/DeKalb-County-Community-Foundation/IL/92913581842

Established in 1991 in IL; re-incorporated in 1993 under current name.
Foundation type: Community foundation.
Financial data (yr. ended 12/31/13): Assets, $44,112,367 (M); gifts received, $1,144,258; expenditures, $1,844,710; giving activities include $1,332,910 for 45+ grants (high: $151,398; low: $625).
Purpose and activities: The foundation seeks to enhance the quality of life for the citizens of DeKalb County, IL, by: 1) serving donors in achieving their philanthropic objectives; 2) creating and building a lasting source of revenue to benefit the residents of the local community; and 3) providing leadership and resources in addressing community needs.
Fields of interest: Arts; Education; Environment; Health care; Human services; Community/economic development.
Type of support: Building/renovation; Equipment; Seed money; Matching/challenge support.
Limitations: Applications accepted. Giving primarily in DeKalb County, IL. No support for religious purposes, political campaigns, or direct support to individuals. Generally no grants for operational phases of established programs, debt reduction, or advertising.
Publications: Application guidelines; Annual report; Financial statement; Grants list; Informational brochure; Newsletter; Occasional report.
Application information: Visit foundation Web site for application forms and guidelines. Application form required.
Initial approach: Contact foundation
Copies of proposal: 7
Deadline(s): Mar. 1 and Sept. 1 for Community Needs Grant
Board meeting date(s): Jan., Apr., July, and Oct.
Final notification: Approx. 60 days for Community Needs Grant
Officers and Directors:* Tim Suter,* Pres.; Donna Larson,* V.P.; Daniel P. Templin,* Secy. and Exec. Dir.; Frank Roberts,* Treas.; Marcy Billington; Larry D. Bolles; Kevin Buick; Amie Carey; Tim Dunlop; Patricia A. Foster; Kevin Fuss; Kristina Garcia; Marcia Goodrich; Lana Haines; Alethia Hummel; Dean Lundeen; Kevin McArtor; Charles McCormick; Penny Rosenow; Donna Turner; Beth White.
Number of staff: 2 full-time professional; 2 part-time professional.
EIN: 363788167

2793
Beatrice P. Delany Charitable Trust ✧
c/o JPMorgan Chase Bank, N.A.
10 S. Dearborn St., ILI-0117
Chicago, IL 60603-2300
Application address: John J. Powers, c/o JPMorgan Chase Bank, N.A., 270 Park Ave., 16th Fl., New York, NY 10017-2014

Trust established about 1977 in NY.
Donor: Beatrice P. Delany‡.
Foundation type: Independent foundation.
Financial data (yr. ended 10/31/13): Assets, $57,052,143 (M); expenditures, $8,298,043; qualifying distributions, $7,972,612; giving activities include $7,900,000 for 117 grants (high: $1,000,000; low: $2,500).

Purpose and activities: Giving primarily for education, especially higher education, and to Roman Catholic schools. Giving also to hospitals, health organizations, Roman Catholic and Episcopal churches, and cultural programs.
Fields of interest: Arts; Higher education; Education; Hospitals (general); Health care; Health organizations, association; Protestant agencies & churches; Catholic agencies & churches.
Type of support: General/operating support.
Limitations: Applications accepted. Giving primarily in the metropolitan Chicago, IL, area. No grants to individuals.
Application information: Application form not required.
Initial approach: Proposal
Deadline(s): None
Trustee: JPMorgan Chase Bank, N.A.
EIN: 136748171

2794
Dew Foundation ✧ ☆
2702 Southlawn Dr.
Bloomington, IL 61705-4154

Donors: DEW Building; DEW Texas Building; Dale Walsh; Ednamae Walsh.
Foundation type: Independent foundation.
Financial data (yr. ended 12/31/13): Assets, $28,747,484 (M); gifts received, $183,857; expenditures, $1,423,909; qualifying distributions, $1,175,375; giving activities include $1,108,464 for grants.
Fields of interest: Arts; Education; Human services.
Limitations: Applications not accepted.
Application information: Unsolicited requests for funds not accepted.
Officers: Dale Walsh, Pres.; Ednamae Walsh, Secy.; Sharron Edberg, Co-Treas.; Joyce Hagberg, Co-Treas.
EIN: 262169255
Selected grants: The following grants are a representative sample of this grantmaker's funding activity:
$30,000 to National Parkinson Foundation, Miami, FL, 2011.
$20,000 to Los Angeles Parks Foundation, Los Angeles, CA, 2011.
$10,000 to Alliance for School Choice, Washington, DC, 2010.
$10,000 to Food Bank of Northern Nevada, McCarran, NV, 2010.
$10,000 to Mayo Clinic, Rochester, MN, 2011.
$10,000 to Nevada Discovery Museum, Reno, NV, 2010.
$5,000 to Focus on the Family, Colorado Springs, CO, 2011.

2795
The Harriet F. Dickenson Foundation ✧
(formerly The Harriet Ford Dickenson Foundation)
10 S. Dearborn St., IL1-0117
Chicago, IL 60603-2300
Application address: c/o James Largey, V.P., JPMorgan Philanthropic Svcs., 270 Park Ave., 16th Fl., New York, NY 10017-2014, tel: (212) 464-1937.

Established about 1958 in NY.
Donor: Harriet Ford Dickenson†.
Foundation type: Independent foundation.
Financial data (yr. ended 12/31/12): Assets, $6,759,744 (M); expenditures, $8,505,909; qualifying distributions, $8,476,966; giving activities include $8,470,000 for 46 grants (high: $4,100,000; low: $1,000).
Purpose and activities: Giving primarily for the arts, botanical gardens, hospitals, a community foundation, and human services.
Fields of interest: Museums; Performing arts; Arts; Botanical gardens; Hospitals (general); Human services.
Limitations: Applications accepted. Giving primarily in New York, NY, area. No grants to individuals.
Application information: Application form not required.
Initial approach: Letter
Copies of proposal: 1
Deadline(s): None
Board meeting date(s): Late spring and late fall
Advisory Committee: Gillian Attfield; Anne A. Hubbard; David J. Hubbard; Thomas J. Hubbard.
Trustee: JPMorgan Chase Bank, N.A.
EIN: 136047225
Selected grants: The following grants are a representative sample of this grantmaker's funding activity:
$4,100,000 to New York City Ballet, New York, NY, 2012.
$2,501,000 to Smith College, Northampton, MA, 2012. For landscape design.
$1,000,000 to United Church of Christ, Cornwall, CT, 2012. For endowment.
$200,000 to New York Botanical Garden, Bronx, NY, 2012.
$150,000 to Metropolitan Opera, New York, NY, 2012.
$75,000 to Preservation League of New York State, Albany, NY, 2012.
$10,000 to Cornwall Historical Society, Cornwall, CT, 2012.

2796
Dillon Foundation ✧
P.O. Box 537
Sterling, IL 61081-0537 (815) 626-9000
Contact: Peter W. Dillon, Pres.

Incorporated in 1953 in IL.
Donor: members of the Dillon family.
Foundation type: Independent foundation.
Financial data (yr. ended 10/31/13): Assets, $63,649,799 (M); expenditures, $4,252,963; qualifying distributions, $3,178,959; giving activities include $3,082,039 for 150 grants (high: $511,485; low: $250).
Purpose and activities: Support for local community economic development and civic and urban affairs; technology and other education; social services and youth; historic preservation and museums; recreation; and libraries in and around Sterling, IL.
Fields of interest: Museums; Historic preservation/historical societies; Vocational education, post-secondary; Libraries/library science; Education; Recreation; Human services; Children/youth, services; Community/economic development; Government/public administration.
Type of support: General/operating support; Continuing support; Annual campaigns; Capital campaigns; Building/renovation; Equipment; Land acquisition; Endowments; Emergency funds; Program development; Seed money; Scholarship funds; In-kind gifts; Matching/challenge support.
Limitations: Applications accepted. Giving primarily in the Sterling, IL, area. No grants to individuals; no loans.
Application information: Application form not required.
Initial approach: Letter
Copies of proposal: 1
Deadline(s): None
Board meeting date(s): Feb. and Aug.
Final notification: As soon as possible
Officers and Directors:* Peter W. Dillon,* Pres.; Patrick Dillon,* V.P.; James M. Boesen,* Secy.; John Van Osdol, Treas.; Margo Dillon; Deborah D. Haglund; Gale D. Inglee; Mark Inglee; Thomas Lexvold.
Number of staff: 1 part-time support.
EIN: 366059349

2797
The James and Judith K. Dimon Foundation ✧
10 S. Dearborn, IIL1-0117
Chicago, IL 60603

Established in 1996 in NY.
Donors: James Dimon; Judith K. Dimon; JD 2006 Charitable Lead Trust.
Foundation type: Independent foundation.
Financial data (yr. ended 11/30/13): Assets, $26,334,007 (M); gifts received, $1,837,718; expenditures, $1,744,806; qualifying distributions, $1,423,750; giving activities include $1,423,000 for grants.
Purpose and activities: Giving primarily for education, health, and children, youth, and social services.
Fields of interest: Arts; Higher education; Hospitals (general); Health organizations; Human services; Children/youth, services.
Limitations: Applications not accepted. Giving primarily in New York, NY. No grants to individuals.
Application information: Contributes only to pre-selected organizations.
Officers: James Dimon, Pres.; Theodore Dimon, Secy.; Judith K. Dimon, Treas.
EIN: 133922199
Selected grants: The following grants are a representative sample of this grantmaker's funding activity:
$100,000 to New York University Langone Medical Center, New York, NY, 2011. For general support.
$100,000 to Prep for Prep, New York, NY, 2011. For general support.
$50,000 to Child Mind Institute, New York, NY, 2011. For general support.
$40,000 to SEED Foundation, Washington, DC, 2011. For general support.
$25,000 to Lincoln Center for the Performing Arts, New York, NY, 2011. For general support.
$25,000 to New York Psychoanalytic Society and Institute, New York, NY, 2011. For general support.
$25,000 to New York University Langone Medical Center, New York, NY, 2011. For general support.
$10,000 to Light of the World Charities, Palm City, FL, 2011. For general support.
$10,000 to Women for Women International, Washington, DC, 2011. For general support.
$5,000 to YM-YWHA, 92nd Street, New York, NY, 2011. For general support.

2798
DiSomma Family Foundation ✧
600 W. Chicago Ave., Ste. 825
Chicago, IL 60654-2528

Donors: William DiSomma; Mary DiSomma.
Foundation type: Independent foundation.
Financial data (yr. ended 12/31/13): Assets, $28,616,762 (M); expenditures, $5,078,643; qualifying distributions, $5,011,000; giving activities include $5,011,000 for 2 grants (high: $5,000,000; low: $11,000).
Purpose and activities: Giving primarily for advancement in medicine.
Fields of interest: Health care, formal/general education; Hospitals (specialty).
Limitations: Applications not accepted. Giving primarily in IL.
Application information: Contributes only to pre-selected organizations.
EIN: 263859966
Selected grants: The following grants are a representative sample of this grantmaker's funding activity:
$5,000,000 to OSF Healthcare Foundation, Peoria, IL, 2012.

2799
Domanada Foundation ✧
209 E. Liberty Dr., 2nd Fl.
Wheaton, IL 60187-5413 (630) 221-9130
FAX: (630) 221-9223; E-mail: info@domanada.com; Main URL: http://www.domanada.com

Established in 1989 in IL.
Donors: Donald E. Sveen; Marjorie L. Sveen.
Foundation type: Independent foundation.
Financial data (yr. ended 12/31/12): Assets, $28,207,454 (M); expenditures, $1,463,983; qualifying distributions, $1,250,244; giving activities include $822,467 for 51 grants (high: $87,000; low: $1,000).
Purpose and activities: Giving to Christian ministries and organizations.
Fields of interest: Higher education; Theological school/education; Hospitals (general); Human services; Religious federated giving programs; Christian agencies & churches.
Limitations: Applications accepted. Giving on a national and international basis, primarily in Chicago, IL, and Central and Eastern Europe. No support for larger non-profit organizations and ministries, organizations the foundation cannot visit on a regular basis, or organizations whose funding exceeds 5% of their annual budget. No grants to individuals, or for scholarships, building projects, endowments, salaries, multi-year proposals, or to address financial problems within an organization.
Publications: Application guidelines.
Application information: Application form not required.
Initial approach: Telephone call
Trustees: Nancy L. Jackson; David E. Sveen; Donald E. Sveen; Marjorie L. Sveen.
Number of staff: None.
EIN: 366916790

2800
Gaylord and Dorothy Donnelley Foundation ✧
35 E. Wacker Dr., Ste. 2600
Chicago, IL 60601-2102 (312) 977-2700
Contact: Susan Clark, Grants Mgr.
FAX: (312) 977-1686; E-mail: info@gddf.org; Address for Lowcountry Charleston office: 4 N. Atlantic Wharf, Charleston, SC 29401, tel. and fax: (843) 651-3793; mailing address: 5465 Huntington Marsh Rd., Murrells Inlet, SC 29576; Main URL: http://www.gddf.org
Blog: http://gddf.org/blog
E-Newsletter: http://gddf.org/signup/

Incorporated in 1952 in IL.
Donors: Gaylord Donnelley‡; Dorothy Ranney Donnelley‡.
Foundation type: Independent foundation.
Financial data (yr. ended 12/31/12): Assets, $167,911,567 (M); expenditures, $8,665,514; qualifying distributions, $8,126,341; giving activities include $6,061,021 for 363 grants (high: $250,000; low: $2,500), and $61,736 for 49 employee matching gifts.
Purpose and activities: Primary areas of interest include conservation and environment, and arts and culture.
Fields of interest: Arts; Environment, natural resources; Environment.
Type of support: General/operating support; Program development; Program-related investments/loans; Employee matching gifts; Mission-related investments/loans.
Limitations: Applications accepted. Giving primarily in the Chicago, IL, area and in the Lowcountry area of SC. No support for religious purposes. No grants to individuals, or for pledges, endowments, capital campaigns, benefits, conferences, meetings, eradication of deficits, research, or studies, publications, films, videos or fundraising events; no loans (except for program-related investments).
Publications: Application guidelines; Grants list; Occasional report; Occasional report (including application guidelines).
Application information: Complete guidelines for each program are available on the foundation web site. Application form required.
Initial approach: Telephone or e-mail prior to applying online
Copies of proposal: 1
Deadline(s): Generally, Apr., July and Dec. See web site for exact dates
Board meeting date(s): Mar., July, and Nov.
Final notification: 1 month
Officers and Directors:* Laura Donnelley,* Chair.; Shawn M. Donnelley,* Secy.-Treas.; J. David Farren, Exec. Dir.; Julia Antonatos; Timothy H. Brown; Peter R. Crane; Ceara Donnelley; Vivian Donnelley; Charles Lane; Cheryl Mayberry McKissack; Dr. John Rashford; Alex Shuford; Max E. Wheeler; Mimi Wheeler.
Number of staff: 4 full-time professional; 3 full-time support.
EIN: 366108460
Selected grants: The following grants are a representative sample of this grantmaker's funding activity:
$360,000 to Chicago Community Trust, Chicago, IL, 2013. For Arts Work Fund, payable over 2.00 years.
$200,000 to Terrafirma, Burlington, VT, 2012. To complete the required capitalization of Terrafirma.
$190,000 to Ducks Unlimited, Charleston, SC, 2013. For Low Country Land Conservation Partnership, payable over 2.00 years.
$190,000 to Lowcountry Open Land Trust, Charleston, SC, 2013. For Low Country Land Conservation Partnership, payable over 2.00 years.
$190,000 to Nature Conservancy, Columbia, SC, 2013. For Low Country Land Conservation Partnership, payable over 2.00 years.
$190,000 to South Carolina Coastal Conservation League, Charleston, SC, 2013. For Low Country Land Conservation Partnership, payable over 2.00 years.
$180,000 to Chicago Community Trust, Chicago, IL, 2012. For Arts Work Fund.
$180,000 to Chicago Community Trust, Chicago, IL, 2012. For Arts Work Fund for Organizational Development.
$167,500 to University of South Carolina Educational Foundation, Columbia, SC, 2013. For Historical Aerial Photographs of the Low Country, payable over 3.00 years.
$150,000 to New Venture Fund, Washington, DC, 2012. For Fresh Taste in Chicago, payable over 3.00 years.
$130,000 to Land Trust Alliance, Washington, DC, 2012. For facilitation of the Chicago Region Land Trust Coalition, payable over 2.00 years.
$100,000 to Conservation Foundation, Naperville, IL, 2012. For a major donor development plan, payable over 1.50 years.
$90,000 to DuSable Museum of African American History, Chicago, IL, 2013. For two assistants' salaries and appropriate storage materials to inventory, catalog, and rehouse the Museum's collection.
$75,000 to Save the Dunes Conservation Fund, Michigan City, IN, 2013. For Calumet Land Conservation Partnership, payable over 3.00 years.
$75,000 to South Carolina Historical Society, Charleston, SC, 2013. For relocation of the Society's collection to the College of Charleston.
$70,000 to South Carolina Coastal Conservation League, Charleston, SC, 2012. For GrowFood Carolina, payable over 2.00 years.
$55,000 to Wetlands Initiative, Chicago, IL, 2012. For Phase II of the Lobelia Meadows restoration project.
$50,000 to Family Farmed Organization, Oak Park, IL, 2012. For the Green Chicago Restaurant Coalition Local Food project.
$16,000 to Charleston Regional Alliance for the Arts, Charleston, SC, 2013. For general operations.
$15,000 to Music and Dance Theater Chicago, Chicago, IL, 2012. For Learning Lab.

2801
R. R. Donnelley Foundation ✧
111 S. Wacker Dr., 38th Fl
Chicago, IL 60601-4301 (312) 322-6946
Contact: Kamala L. Martinez, Mgr., Community Rels.
E-mail: communityrelations@rrd.com; Application address: 3075 Highland Pkwy., Downers Grove, IL 60515; Main URL: http://www.rrdonnelley.com/about/external-affairs/community-relations.aspx

Established in 2000 in IL.
Donor: R.R. Donnelley & Sons Co.
Foundation type: Company-sponsored foundation.
Financial data (yr. ended 12/31/13): Assets, $6,158 (M); gifts received, $628,000; expenditures, $636,712; qualifying distributions,

$636,712; giving activities include $630,697 for 39 grants (high: $192,021; low: $850).
Purpose and activities: The foundation supports programs designed to promote youth, education, inclusion, and diversity.
Fields of interest: Museums; Secondary school/education; Higher education; Libraries (public); Education, reading; Education; Boys & girls clubs; YM/YWCAs & YM/YWHAs; Children/youth, services; Human services; Civil/human rights, equal rights; United Ways and Federated Giving Programs; Youth.
Type of support: General/operating support; Employee volunteer services; Sponsorships; Employee-related scholarships.
Limitations: Applications accepted. Giving in areas of company operations, with emphasis on Bolingbrook and Chicago, IL, Reno, NV, and New York, NY; giving also to national organizations. No support for religious or political organizations or hospitals. No grants to individuals (except for employee-related scholarships), or for printing, television, radio, film, video, clinical care, medical research, or equipment.
Publications: Application guidelines.
Application information: Application form not required.
Initial approach: Download application form and e-mail to foundation
Copies of proposal: 1
Deadline(s): None
Board meeting date(s): Quarterly
Officers and Directors:* Damayanti P. Vasudevan,* Pres.; Suzanne S. Bettman,* Secy.; Daniel N. Leib, Treas.; Thomas J. Quinlan.
EIN: 364398696

2802
The Donnelley Foundation ✧
c/o Thomas E. Donnelley, II
333 N. Michigan Ave., Ste. 2200
Chicago, IL 60601-4048
FAX: (312) 827-1234; E-mail: donnelleyt@aol.com

Incorporated in 1954 in IL.
Donors: Elliott Donnelley†; Ann S. Donnelley Hardy†; Thomas E. Donnelley II; James R. Donnelley; Barbara C. Donnelley; Nina H. Donnelley; Robert G. Donnelley; Miranda S. Donnelley; David E. Donnelley.
Foundation type: Independent foundation.
Financial data (yr. ended 12/31/13): Assets, $15,621,087 (M); gifts received, $8,500; expenditures, $890,167; qualifying distributions, $774,595; giving activities include $748,800 for 70 grants (high: $64,250; low: $250).
Purpose and activities: Giving primarily to wildlife conservation, youth welfare, libraries, historic preservation, and educational and medical institutions with which the foundation directors have long-term relationships and/or serve on the boards.
Fields of interest: Museums; Historic preservation/historical societies; Libraries/library science; Education; Animals/wildlife, preservation/protection; Hospitals (general); Children/youth, services.
Type of support: General/operating support; Continuing support; Annual campaigns; Capital campaigns; Building/renovation; Endowments; Seed money; Matching/challenge support.
Limitations: Applications not accepted. Giving primarily in CA, CT, IL, MA, MT, OR and VT. No support for political organizations. No grants to individuals, or for pledges or multi-year grants.
Application information: Contributes only to pre-selected organizations.
Board meeting date(s): As required
Officers and Directors:* Thomas E. Donnelley II,* Pres.; James R. Donnelley,* 1st V.P.; David E. Donnelley,* V.P. and Secy.; Robert G. Donnelley,* V.P. and Treas.
EIN: 366066894
Selected grants: The following grants are a representative sample of this grantmaker's funding activity:
$5,000 to University of Chicago, Laboratory School, Chicago, IL, 2012. For unrestricted.

2803
The Dover Foundation ✧ ☆
3005 Highland Pkwy., Ste. 200
Downers Grove, IL 60515
E-mail: info@doverfoundation.org; Main URL: http://www.doverfoundation.org
Scholarship address: The Dover Sons and Daughters Scholarship Program, P.O. Box 648, Naperville, IL 60566, tel.: (630) 428-2412

Foundation type: Independent foundation.
Financial data (yr. ended 12/31/13): Assets, $8,333 (L); expenditures, $1,045,374; qualifying distributions, $1,045,824; giving activities include $680,765 for 64 grants (high: $525,000; low: $100), and $247,500 for grants to individuals.
Purpose and activities: Giving to assist Dover companies and their employees in their efforts to become active members in communities in which the organization operates. The foundation also assists Dover employees by providing educational scholarship opportunities for their children. Extra consideration is given to applicants interested in pursuing studies that focus on technical or vocational programs in the areas of science and engineering.
Fields of interest: Museums (science/technology); Higher education; Education; Human services.
Type of support: Scholarships—to individuals.
Limitations: Giving in areas where Dover Corporation does business. No support for religious organizations for religious purposes, political organizations, non-qualified military veteran organizations, fraternal orders or labor groups. No grants for trips, tours, dinners, tickets or advertising, or equipment or products.
Publications: Application guidelines; IRS Form 990 or 990-PF printed copy available upon request.
Application information: See foundation web site for application process for scholarships. Application form required.
Deadline(s): See foundation web site for current scholarship deadline
Officers: Adrian Sakowicz, Pres.; Raymond Cabrera, V.P.; Scott Greenhouse, V.P.; Sarah Chomiak, Secy.; Kevin Buchanan, Treas.
Directors: John Hartner; Jay Kloosterboer; Joseph Schmidt; William Spurgeon.
EIN: 453137541

2804
William and Kathy Doyle Foundation ✧
150 Thorn Tree Ln.
Winnetka, IL 60093-3732

Established in 2005 in IL.
Donor: William J. Doyle.
Foundation type: Independent foundation.
Financial data (yr. ended 12/31/13): Assets, $5,132,302 (M); gifts received, $3,500,000; expenditures, $3,202,602; qualifying distributions, $3,166,415; giving activities include $3,161,900 for 12 grants (high: $3,000,000; low: $100).
Fields of interest: Higher education; Education; Health organizations; Human services.
Limitations: Applications not accepted. Giving primarily in Washington, DC. No grants to individuals.
Application information: Contributes only to pre-selected organizations.
Officers and Directors:* William J. Doyle,* Pres. and Treas.; Kathy A. Doyle,* Secy.; Erin Doyle.
EIN: 352260044
Selected grants: The following grants are a representative sample of this grantmaker's funding activity:
$1,400,000 to Georgetown University, Washington, DC, 2011. For general support.
$480,000 to Georgetown University, Washington, DC, 2011. For general support.
$100,000 to Big Shoulders Fund, Chicago, IL, 2011. For general support.

2805
The Richard H. Driehaus Foundation ✧
737 N. Michigan Ave., Ste. 2000
Chicago, IL 60611-6745 (312) 641-5772
FAX: (312) 641-5736; Contact for arts and culture groups with budgets under $500,000: Richard Cahan, Prog. Off., e-mail: RichardCahan@aol.com, tel.: (847) 722-9244; Contact for small theater and dance companies with budgets under $150,000, Peter Handler, Prog. Dir., e-mail: peterhandler@driehausfoundation.org; E-mail for general inquiries, Kim Romero, Admin.: kimromero@driehausfoundation.org; Main URL: http://www.driehausfoundation.org
Grants Database: http://www.driehausfoundation.org/grants/?ya=1989&yb=2014&r=5&aa=0&ab=100000
RSS Feed: http://www.driehausfoundation.org/rss.xml
YouTube: http://www.youtube.com/user/DriehausFoundation

Established in 1983 in IL.
Donors: Richard H. Driehaus; John D. and Catherine T. MacArthur Foundation; Reva and David Logan Foundation; Leveraging Investment in Creativity.
Foundation type: Independent foundation.
Financial data (yr. ended 12/31/13): Assets, $78,833,375 (M); gifts received, $126,117; expenditures, $6,541,227; qualifying distributions, $5,504,723; giving activities include $4,484,782 for grants.
Purpose and activities: The foundation benefits individuals and communities primarily by supporting the preservation and enhancement of the built and natural environments through historic preservation, encouragement of quality architectural and landscape design, and conserving open space. The foundation also supports the performing and visual arts, investigative reporting and government accountability, and makes grants to organizations that provide opportunities for working families who remain poor.
Fields of interest: Visual arts, design; Historic preservation/historical societies; Arts; Housing/

shelter, development; Human services; Economic development.
International interests: Scotland.
Type of support: General/operating support; Capital campaigns; Emergency funds; Program development; Publication; Seed money; Grants to individuals; Matching/challenge support.
Limitations: Giving primarily in the metropolitan Chicago, IL, area which includes Cook, DuPage, Lake, McHenry, Kane and Will counties. Generally, no support for arts education or arts outreach, community theater or community dance, public, private or parochial education, or health care.
Publications: Application guidelines; Biennial report; Multi-year report.
Application information: Applications accepted only for MacArthur grants. Application guidelines and form are available on foundation web site. Faxed proposals are not accepted. Application form required.
Initial approach: Letter of inquiry or telephone for Built Environment, Economic Opportunity for the Working Poor, Government Accountability/Investigative Reporting, Small Museums and Cultural Centers funding areas; Arts and culture groups with budgets under $500,000, and small theater and dance companies with budgets under $150,000 may apply online through foundation web site
Copies of proposal: 2
Deadline(s): See foundation web site for current deadlines in each funding area
Final notification: 4 - 5 months
Officers and Directors:* Richard H. Driehaus,* Pres.; Elizabeth Driehaus,* Secy.; Dorothy Mellin,* Treas.; Kim Coventry, Exec. Dir.
Number of staff: 2 full-time professional; 1 full-time support.
EIN: 363261347

2806
Walter S. and Lucienne Driskill Charitable Foundation ✧
430 W. Erie, Ste. 512
Chicago, IL 60654-2619 (312) 266-2484
Contact: June D. Barnard, Exec. Dir.
FAX: (312) 266-1797;
E-mail: kmm@driskillfoundation.com; Main URL: http://www.driskillfoundation.com

Established in 1986 in FL.
Donors: Walter S. Driskill†; Lucienne Driskill†.
Foundation type: Independent foundation.
Financial data (yr. ended 12/31/12): Assets, $29,886,799 (M); expenditures, $9,291,927; qualifying distributions, $8,673,810; giving activities include $8,598,946 for 13 grants (high: $3,412,500; low: $15,000).
Purpose and activities: The objectives of the foundation are to benefit research, development and use of medical treatments and medicines used in such treatments. Also, the foundation will seek to provide assistance to relieve and eliminate child abuse and provide assistance to infants and children who are without proper homes.
Fields of interest: Health care; Medical research; Crime/violence prevention, child abuse; Children/youth, services.
Limitations: Applications accepted. Giving on a national basis. No support for religious institutions, or for sports organizations, political organizations or performing arts organizations. No grants to individuals, or for endowments, or capital improvements.
Publications: Application guidelines.
Application information: Summary proposal form available on foundation web site. Formal proposals accepted by invitation only. Application form required.
Deadline(s): Nov. 1 for summary proposals. Feb. 1 for formal application
Final notification: Foundation will request formal applications by Jan. 1
Officer and Directors:* June D. Barnard,* Exec. Dir.; Laura F. Gutierrez; Katie McGovern; James Sutherland; Katie Trowbridge.
EIN: 061190296
Selected grants: The following grants are a representative sample of this grantmaker's funding activity:
$3,412,500 to Northwestern University, Evanston, IL, 2012. For medical research.
$2,050,000 to Oregon Health and Science University, Portland, OR, 2012. For medical research.
$1,300,990 to Alzheimers Association National Headquarters, Chicago, IL, 2012. For medical research.
$733,419 to Mayo Clinic, Rochester, MN, 2012. For medical research.
$417,676 to University of Colorado, Boulder, CO, 2012. For medical research.
$324,076 to National Headache Foundation, Chicago, IL, 2012. For medical research.
$101,436 to Fox Chase Cancer Center, Philadelphia, PA, 2012. For medical research.
$50,000 to Memorial Sloan-Kettering Cancer Center, New York, NY, 2012. For medical research.
$25,000 to Miracle Flights for Kids, Henderson, NV, 2012. For medical research.
$25,000 to National Jewish Health, Denver, CO, 2012. For medical research.

2807
DRW Trading Group Foundation ✧
c/o Jim Lange
540 W. Madison St., Ste. 2500
Chicago, IL 60661-2555

Established in 2004 in IL.
Donor: DRW Holdings LLC.
Foundation type: Company-sponsored foundation.
Financial data (yr. ended 12/31/12): Assets, $2,826,040 (M); gifts received, $2,232,010; expenditures, $594,996; qualifying distributions, $594,996; giving activities include $594,582 for 23 grants (high: $404,000; low: $100).
Purpose and activities: The foundation supports food banks and organizations involved with education, health, spine disorders, medical research, recreation, and human services.
Fields of interest: Education; Health care; Medical research.
Type of support: General/operating support; Program development.
Limitations: Applications not accepted.
Application information: Contributes only to pre-selected organizations.
Officers: Jeffery Levoff, Pres.; Donald R. Wilson, Jr., V.P. and Secy.; Kevin Kroger, Treas.
EIN: 201734765
Selected grants: The following grants are a representative sample of this grantmaker's funding activity:
$52,188 to Greater Chicago Food Depository, Chicago, IL, 2011.
$30,000 to Cabrini Connections, Chicago, IL, 2011.
$25,000 to ECON Illinois, DeKalb, IL, 2011.
$25,000 to Invest for Kids, Chicago, IL, 2011.
$25,000 to Noble Network of Charter Schools, Chicago, IL, 2011.
$21,600 to Urban Initiatives, Chicago, IL, 2011.
$17,200 to American Refugee Committee, Minneapolis, MN, 2011.
$17,200 to Reading in Motion, Chicago, IL, 2011.
$13,500 to West Town Bikes, Chicago, IL, 2011.
$10,000 to Achilles International, New York, NY, 2011.

2808
Edward T. & Ellen K. Dryer Charitable Foundation ✧ ☆
P.O. Box 803878
Chicago, IL 60680-3878

Donor: Ellen Dryer†.
Foundation type: Independent foundation.
Financial data (yr. ended 11/30/13): Assets, $2,621,770 (M); expenditures, $1,180,076; qualifying distributions, $1,155,000; giving activities include $1,140,000 for 6 grants (high: $1,000,000; low: $15,000).
Fields of interest: Education, public education; Education; Health care; Human services; Blind/visually impaired.
Type of support: General/operating support.
Limitations: Applications not accepted. Giving primarily in MI. No grants to individuals.
Application information: Contributes only to pre-selected organizations.
Trustees: Joseph Drobot; Judy Drobot; Elizabeth Mower Gandelot; Jon B. Gandelot.
EIN: 371451429

2809
The Duchossois Family Foundation ✧
(formerly The Duchossois Foundation)
1515 W. 22nd St., Ste. 650
Oak Brook, IL 60523

Established in 1984 in IL.
Donors: Duchossois Industries, Inc.; Thrall Car Manufacturing Co.; Duchossois Technology Partners, LLC; The Chamberlain Group, Inc.; The Duchossois Group, Inc.
Foundation type: Company-sponsored foundation.
Financial data (yr. ended 12/31/13): Assets, $1,384,863 (M); gifts received, $2,000,000; expenditures, $804,940; qualifying distributions, $803,939; giving activities include $779,449 for 63 grants (high: $100,000; low: $1,000).
Purpose and activities: The foundation supports organizations involved with mental health, cancer, and human services.
Fields of interest: Education; Health organizations; Human services.
Type of support: General/operating support; Annual campaigns; Capital campaigns; Research; Employee matching gifts.
Limitations: Applications not accepted. Giving primarily in the metropolitan Chicago, IL, area.
Application information: Contributes only to pre-selected organizations.
Board meeting date(s): 4 times per year

Officers and Directors:* Kimberly T. Duchossois,* Pres.; Craig J. Duchossois,* V.P. and Treas.; Richard L. Duchossois,* Secy.
Number of staff: 1 part-time professional; 1 part-time support.
EIN: 363327987
Selected grants: The following grants are a representative sample of this grantmaker's funding activity:
$1,000,000 to American Cancer Society, Chicago, IL, 2011.
$50,000 to American Cancer Society, Chicago, IL, 2011.
$50,000 to American Cancer Society, Chicago, IL, 2011.
$25,000 to American Cancer Society, Chicago, IL, 2011.
$25,000 to Metropolitan Family Services, Chicago, IL, 2011.
$12,000 to Center for Independent Futures, Evanston, IL, 2011.
$10,000 to Metropolitan Family Services, Chicago, IL, 2011.
$10,000 to Naples Children and Education Foundation, Naples, FL, 2011.
$5,000 to American Cancer Society, Chicago, IL, 2011.
$5,000 to Operation Homefront, San Antonio, TX, 2011.

2810
Dunard Fund USA, Ltd. ✧

555 Skokie Blvd., Ste. 555
Northbrook, IL 60062-2845

Established around 1993 in IL.
Donors: Consolidated Electrical Distributors, Inc.; LCR-M Corp.; Carol C. Hogel.
Foundation type: Company-sponsored foundation.
Financial data (yr. ended 12/31/12): Assets, $34,331,373 (M); gifts received, $15,005,000; expenditures, $3,464,471; qualifying distributions, $3,186,803; giving activities include $3,171,445 for 23 grants (high: $1,332,950; low: $8,930).
Purpose and activities: The foundation supports organizations involved with arts and culture and education.
Fields of interest: Museums; Performing arts, music; Performing arts, orchestras; Performing arts, opera; Performing arts, education; Arts; Higher education.
Type of support: Matching/challenge support; General/operating support; Continuing support; Annual campaigns; Endowments; Program development; Scholarship funds.
Limitations: Applications not accepted. Giving primarily in CA, New York, NY, and Philadelphia, PA. No grants to individuals.
Application information: Contributes only to organizations referred by known and highly respected figures.
Board meeting date(s): Weekly
Officers and Directors:* Carol C. Hogel,* Pres. and Treas.; David T. Bradford, Secy.; Catherine C. Hogel; Elisabeth Hogel.
EIN: 980087034

2811
The Dunham Fund ✧

8 E. Galena Blvd., Ste. 202
Aurora, IL 60506-4161 (630) 844-2774
FAX: (630) 844-4405;
E-mail: info@dunhamfund.org; Main URL: http://www.dunhamfund.org
Facebook: https://www.facebook.com/DunhamFund
Twitter: https://twitter.com/DunhamFund
Wordpress: http://dunhamfund.wordpress.com/
YouTube: https://www.youtube.com/user/DunhamFund?feature=mhee

Established in 2007 in IL.
Donor: John C. Dunham Trust.
Foundation type: Independent foundation.
Financial data (yr. ended 12/31/12): Assets, $76,764,979 (M); expenditures, $3,282,530; qualifying distributions, $2,858,603; giving activities include $2,358,603 for 30 grants (high: $535,000; low: $2,250).
Purpose and activities: The mission of the fund is to honor the legacy of John C. Dunham. In that spirit, the fund supports organizations that work to make the world a safer and more comfortable place for mankind to live and prosper, giving special consideration to Aurora, Illinois-area organizations engaged in providing education and to organizations engaged in assisting individuals to attain heights they may not have attained without the benefit of such assistance. Areas of interest include: education within formal academic settings such as licensed early childhood education, K-12, college, and graduate school, including STEM (Science, Technology, Mathematics and Science) education, workforce development, and other accredited professional certifications; and community development, which the fund describes as the expansion of infrastructure, capital, resources, human capital or aggregate capability available to the community on a long term basis that provides support for stronger social or economic interaction and performance.
Fields of interest: Vocational education; Education; Housing/shelter.
Type of support: Scholarship funds; Program-related investments/loans.
Limitations: Giving primarily in the Aurora, IL area; the fund gives preference to applicants located within Kane, DuPage and Kendall Counties, more specifically, the geography bounded on the north by Illinois State Route 38 and on the south by U.S. Route 34; on the east by Illinois State Route 59 and on the west by Illinois State Route 47.
Publications: Application guidelines.
Application information: Full grant applications by invitation only, upon review of letter of inquiry. The fund prefers to provide one-time, startup funding for new or uniquely enhanced educational or community development programs and capital projects. See foundation web site for detailed application information.
Initial approach: Use online grant application on foundation web site
Deadline(s): Feb. 1 and June 1
Officers and Directors:* Mark Treumper, Chair.; Robert W. Vaughn, Exec. Dir.; Stewart Beach; Wendy Hirsch; Ryan Maley; Michael J. Morcos; Christine Tunney.
EIN: 376416138
Selected grants: The following grants are a representative sample of this grantmaker's funding activity:
$510,000 to Community Foundation of the Fox River Valley, Aurora, IL, 2011.
$456,900 to Community Foundation of the Fox River Valley, Aurora, IL, 2011.
$350,000 to Paramount Arts Center, Aurora, IL, 2011.
$205,000 to Provena Mercy Medical Center, Aurora, IL, 2011.
$100,000 to North Central College, Naperville, IL, 2011.
$50,000 to Urban League, Quad County, Aurora, IL, 2011.
$45,500 to Mutual Ground, Aurora, IL, 2011.
$35,000 to United Way, Fox Valley, Aurora, IL, 2011.
$17,100 to Rosary High School, Aurora, IL, 2011.

2812
The DuPage Community Foundation ✧

104 E. Roosevelt Rd., Ste. 204
Wheaton, IL 60187-5200 (630) 665-5556
Contact: David M. McGowan, Pres.; For grants: Barb Szczepaniak, Dir., Progs.
FAX: (630) 665-9571; E-mail: dmm@dcfdn.org; Grant application e-mail: barbs@dcfdn.org; Main URL: http://www.dcfdn.org
Facebook: http://www.facebook.com/pages/The-DuPage-Community-Foundation/101853007709
LinkedIn: http://www.linkedin.com/company/the-dupage-community-foundation
Twitter: https://twitter.com/DCFDN

Established in 1986 in IL as fund of Chicago Community Trust; became a separate entity in 1994.
Foundation type: Community foundation.
Financial data (yr. ended 06/30/13): Assets, $47,016,028 (M); gifts received, $4,412,199; expenditures, $3,351,925; giving activities include $2,360,061 for 97+ grants (high: $250,000).
Purpose and activities: The foundation was created to benefit the residents of DuPage County, IL. It receives contributions and bequests into a permanent endowment that continues to grow and help meet the needs of its community. Priorities in grantmaking are arts and culture, environment, education, health, and human services.
Fields of interest: Arts; Education; Environment, pollution control; Environmental education; Environment; Animals/wildlife, preservation/protection; Health care; Mental health/crisis services; Children/youth, services; Human services.
Type of support: General/operating support; Building/renovation; Equipment; Program development; Seed money; Scholarship funds; Matching/challenge support.
Limitations: Applications accepted. Giving primarily in DuPage County, IL. No support for religious purposes, disease-specific organizations, historic societies and foundations, food pantries for the purchase of food, hospitals, private foundations or private operating foundations. No grants to individuals, or for endowments.
Publications: Application guidelines; Annual report; Grants list; Informational brochure; Newsletter; Occasional report.
Application information: Visit foundation web site for application form and guidelines. The foundation accepts requests for up to $2,500 for Community Needs mini-grants, and $20,000 for Community Needs general grants. Application form required.
Initial approach: Telephone

Copies of proposal: 2
Deadline(s): 1st Fri. in Mar. for Health and Human Services and 1st Fri. in Sept. for Arts and Culture, Education, and Environment
Board meeting date(s): Bimonthly
Final notification: 10 weeks

Officers and Trustees:* Stephen M. Burt,* Chair.; Joan S. Morrissey,* Vice-Chair.; David M. McGowan,* Pres.; Denice A. Gierach,* Secy.; Ernest J. Mrozek,* Treas.; Betsy K. Brosnan; Phillip R. Cabrera; Brett M. Dale; Marilyn K. Gaston; Janet A. Hodge; Frank C. Hudetz; Christopher M. Janc; William J. Kennedy; Mary Kay Kluge; Richard W. Kuhn; Bruce K. Lee; Daniel Maguire; Charles B. McKenna; Charles G. Mueller; Nathaniel P. Wasson; Joyce A. Webb; Joseph L. Weidenbach.
Number of staff: 5 full-time professional; 1 part-time support.
EIN: 363978733
Selected grants: The following grants are a representative sample of this grantmaker's funding activity:
$15,000 to Community House, Hinsdale, IL, 2012. To subsidize fees for Willowbrook Corner After School and Summer Camp programs which serve at-risk youth.
$15,000 to Northern Illinois Food Bank, Geneva, IL, 2012. To purchase 25,000 lbs. of food for distribution to DuPage partner food pantries.
$12,500 to Green Earth Institute, Naperville, IL, 2012. To complete well and cistern reservoir to support vegetable farm to serve as educational venue.
$10,000 to Bridge Communities, Glen Ellyn, IL, 2012. For Transitional Housing Program.
$10,000 to Family Shelter Service, Wheaton, IL, 2012. For Residential Program to provide emergency shelter and intermediated housing, counseling and case management for victims of domestic violence and their children.
$10,000 to Teen Parent Connection, Glen Ellyn, IL, 2012. For Adolescent Family Strengthening Program (Doula Services, Childbirth Education Classes, Healthy Families Program and Group Services).
$7,805 to DuPage Childrens Museum, Naperville, IL, 2012. For When Learning Comes into Play collaborative project with DuPage Head Start programs designed to nurture children's creativity and problemsolving through integrated hands-on experiences.
$7,500 to Addison Community Switchboard, Addison, IL, 2012. To expand short-term emergency assistance program.
$7,500 to Naperville Community Outreach Youth and Family Services, Naperville, IL, 2012. For therapist salaries in Counseling Program for low-income children, families and adults.
$7,250 to College of DuPage Foundation, Glen Ellyn, IL, 2012. For contract expenses of featured performers in SchoolStage Series, collection of curriculum-based performances targeted to students pre-kindergarten through eighth grade.

2813
David F. Dury Foundation ✧
339 Sheridan Rd.
Winnetka, IL 60093-4227

Established in 1995 in IL.
Donors: David F. Dury; Option Opportunites.
Foundation type: Independent foundation.
Financial data (yr. ended 12/31/12): Assets, $5,254 (M); gifts received, $675,000; expenditures, $720,111; qualifying distributions, $720,111; giving activities include $720,100 for 14 grants (high: $654,000; low: $300).
Purpose and activities: Giving for education and health services.
Fields of interest: Education; Human services; Christian agencies & churches.
Limitations: Applications not accepted. Giving limited to IL. No grants to individuals.
Application information: Contributes only to pre-selected organizations.
Director: David F. Dury.
EIN: 367088062
Selected grants: The following grants are a representative sample of this grantmaker's funding activity:
$2,500 to Bernard P. Floriani Foundation, Bernie's Book Bank, Lake Forest, IL, 2011.
$1,000 to Holy Trinity High School, Chicago, IL, 2011.

2814
Eddema Foundation ✧
700 N. Linden Ave.
Oak Park, IL 60302-1560

Established in 1991 in IL.
Donor: Edward Petrick.
Foundation type: Independent foundation.
Financial data (yr. ended 12/31/13): Assets, $26,475,438 (M); gifts received, $2,779,000; expenditures, $950,604; qualifying distributions, $647,230; giving activities include $647,230 for 3 grants (high: $620,000; low: $7,230).
Fields of interest: Arts education; Environment, land resources; Foundations (community).
Limitations: Applications not accepted. Giving primarily in IL and MI. No grants to individuals.
Application information: Contributes only to pre-selected organizations.
Officer: Edward Petrick, Mgr.
EIN: 363781866
Selected grants: The following grants are a representative sample of this grantmaker's funding activity:
$14,630 to Interlochen Center for the Arts, Interlochen, MI, 2011.
$10,000 to Grand Traverse Regional Land Conservancy, Traverse City, MI, 2011.

2815
Edlis-Neeson Foundation ✧
175 E. Delaware Pl., No. 5116
Chicago, IL 60611-1756

Established in 2007 in IL.
Donor: Stefan Edlis.
Foundation type: Independent foundation.
Financial data (yr. ended 12/31/13): Assets, $19,062,247 (M); expenditures, $2,316,547; qualifying distributions, $2,237,038; giving activities include $2,227,150 for 46 grants (high: $446,000; low: $1,000).
Fields of interest: Arts education; Museums (art); Human services; Social sciences.
Limitations: Applications not accepted. Giving primarily in CO, Washington, DC, IL, and NY.
Application information: Contributes only to pre-selected organizations.
Directors: Stefan Edlis; Jack Guthman; Heather Gael Neeson.
EIN: 208986573
Selected grants: The following grants are a representative sample of this grantmaker's funding activity:
$2,400,000 to Museum of Contemporary Art, Chicago, IL, 2011.
$466,000 to Art Institute of Chicago, Chicago, IL, 2011.
$428,000 to Aspen Institute, Washington, DC, 2011.
$406,000 to Solomon R. Guggenheim Museum, New York, NY, 2011.
$100,000 to American Civil Liberties Union Foundation, New York, NY, 2011.
$100,000 to Chicago Public Media, Chicago, IL, 2011.
$55,000 to Aspen Art Museum, Aspen, CO, 2011.
$55,000 to People for the American Way, Washington, DC, 2011.
$50,500 to Chicago Opera Theater, Chicago, IL, 2011.
$20,000 to Theater Aspen, Aspen, CO, 2011.

2816
Edwardson Family Foundation ✧
(formerly 747 Foundation)
301 Sheridan Rd.
Winnetka, IL 60093-4227

Established in 1990 in IL.
Donors: John A. Edwardson; Catharine O. Edwardson.
Foundation type: Independent foundation.
Financial data (yr. ended 12/31/13): Assets, $13,013,883 (M); gifts received, $545,850; expenditures, $1,196,138; qualifying distributions, $1,176,000; giving activities include $1,176,000 for 32 grants (high: $635,000; low: $250).
Purpose and activities: Giving primarily for human services, higher education, and for health organizations.
Fields of interest: Museums (art); Arts; Higher education; Human services.
Limitations: Applications not accepted. Giving primarily in IL, with emphasis on Chicago. No grants to individuals.
Application information: Contributes only to pre-selected organizations.
Trustee: John A. Edwardson.
EIN: 363757845
Selected grants: The following grants are a representative sample of this grantmaker's funding activity:
$400,000 to University of Chicago, Chicago, IL, 2011. For general operations.
$200,000 to Art Institute of Chicago, Chicago, IL, 2011. For general operations.
$30,000 to American Red Cross, Chicago, IL, 2011. For general operations.
$25,000 to Greater Chicago Food Depository, Chicago, IL, 2011. For general operations.
$25,000 to United Synagogue of Chicago, Chicago, IL, 2011. For general operations.
$16,667 to Chicago Symphony Orchestra, Chicago, IL, 2011. For general operations.
$10,000 to Erikson Institute, Chicago, IL, 2011. For general operations.
$5,000 to Ann and Robert H. Lurie Children's Hospital of Chicago Foundation, Chicago, IL, 2011. For general operations.

$5,000 to New Schools for Chicago, Chicago, IL, 2011. For general operations.
$2,500 to Children's Home and Aid Society of Illinois, Chicago, IL, 2011. For general operations.

2817
Greater Edwardsville Area Community Foundation ✧
(also known as Your Community Foundation)
P.O. Box 102
Edwardsville, IL 62025-1911 (855) 464-3223
Contact: Mary Westerhold, Chair.
E-mail: contact@edwardsvillefoundation.org; Main URL: http://www.geacf.org/
Blog: http://www.geacf.org/category/news/
E-Newsletter: http://edwardsvillefoundation.us2.list-manage.com/subscribe?u=9401e8e863419e971bb8aad42&id=356341c88c
Facebook: http://www.facebook.com/edwardsvillecommunityfoundation
Twitter: http://twitter.com/TheGEACF

Established in 1997 in IL.
Foundation type: Community foundation.
Financial data (yr. ended 12/31/12): Assets, $1,697,395 (M); gifts received, $463,984; expenditures, $547,196; giving activities include $445,315 for 14+ grants (high: $170,000), and $68,950 for 58 grants to individuals.
Purpose and activities: The foundation's mission is to enhance the quality of life in the Greater Edwardsville area by: 1) leading the development of collaboration and understanding among all members of the community; 2) ascertaining community needs and opportunities; 3) providing a flexible permanent vehicle for donors with diverse interests; 4) protecting the community's endowment through prudent investment and effective stewardship; 5) expanding the community's endowment through appropriate solicitations; and 6) acting as an informed grant maker.
Fields of interest: Arts; Education; Environment; Health care; Human services; Community/economic development.
Type of support: Building/renovation; Equipment; Land acquisition; Emergency funds; Program development; Conferences/seminars; Curriculum development; Consulting services; Scholarships—to individuals.
Limitations: Applications accepted. Giving primarily in Edwardsville, Glen Carbon, Hamel, Worden, Dorsey, and Moro, IL. No support for sectarian religious programs. No grants for operating budgets, basic municipal services, basic educational functions, or endowment campaigns.
Publications: Informational brochure; Newsletter.
Application information: Visit foundation web site for application form and guidelines. Application form required.
Initial approach: Submit application form and attachments
Copies of proposal: 1
Deadline(s): Oct. 1
Board meeting date(s): Jan., Mar., May, July, Sept., and Nov.
Final notification: Nov.
Officers and Directors:* Mary Westerhold,* Chair.; Patty Thiede,* Vice-Chair., Chair, Gifts and Funds Comm., and Treas.; Chad Abernathy,* Chair., Community Awareness Comm.; Suzanne Weiss,* Chair., Education Comm.; Scott Weber,* Chair., Grants Review Comm.; Steve Mudge,* Secy.; Calvin Brown; Greg Coffey; Faye Coffman; Jill Dorsey; Pete Fornof; David Gerber; Phil Lading; Linda Lynch; Joseph Malench; Carol Mestemacher; John Motley; Will Shashack.
EIN: 367146151

2818
EFS Foundation ✧
(formerly Elgin Financial Foundation)
1695 Larkin Ave.
Elgin, IL 60123-5944 (847) 289-0513
Contact: Ursula Wilson, Exec. Dir.
E-mail: efsfoundation@efsfoundation.org; Main URL: http://www.efsfoundation.org/

Established in 1998 in DE and IL as the Elgin Financial Foundation; current name adopted in 2004.
Donors: Elgin Financial Savings Bank; EFC Bancorp, Inc.
Foundation type: Company-sponsored foundation.
Financial data (yr. ended 12/31/13): Assets, $11,453,100 (M); expenditures, $676,514; qualifying distributions, $556,215; giving activities include $540,945 for 76 grants (high: $15,000; low: $250).
Purpose and activities: The foundation supports programs designed to promote community development; and support community organizations that contribute to the quality of life in Elgin and surrounding communities. Special emphasis is directed toward programs designed to promote housing for low or moderate-income individuals; benefit local performing art groups; promote educational initiatives that enhance and expand youth development; and provide scholarship funds to local, deserving students.
Fields of interest: Performing arts; Higher education; Education; Health care; Housing/shelter, home owners; Housing/shelter; Boys & girls clubs; Youth development; Human services; Community/economic development; Economically disadvantaged.
Type of support: Continuing support; Program development; Scholarship funds.
Limitations: Applications accepted. Giving limited to Carpentersville, East Dundee, Elgin, Hampshire, Huntley, South Elgin, and West Dundee, IL. No support for discriminatory organizations or religious organizations not of direct benefit to the entire community. No grants for budget deficits, operating expenses for established programs, fundraising events by an organization for the benefit of another organization.
Publications: Application guidelines.
Application information: Letters of inquiry should be no longer than 2 pages. A full proposal may be requested at a later date. If submitting proposals via mail, six individual packets must be submitted. Multi-year funding is not automatic. Support is limited to 1 contribution per organization during any given year. Application form required.
Initial approach: E-mail or mail letter of inquiry; full proposal if invited
Deadline(s): Feb. 15. May 15, and Aug. 15 for letters of inquiry; Mar. 31, June 30, and Sept. 30 for proposals
Board meeting date(s): May, Aug., and Nov.
Final notification: Mid-May, Mid-Aug., and Mid-Nov. for proposals
Officers: Leo M. Flanagan, Jr., Vice-Chair.; Eric J. Fernandez, Pres.; James J. Kovac, Treas.; Ursula Wilson, Exec. Dir.
Directors: James A. Alpeter; Thomas I. Anderson; Randy W. Brittain; Ralph W. Helm; Larry M. Narum; Barrett J. O'Connor; Thomas S. Rakow; Jack Shales; Peter A. Traeger.
Number of staff: 1 part-time professional.
EIN: 364219647

2819
George M. Eisenberg Foundation for Charities ✧
(formerly Eisenberg Foundation for Charities)
2340 S. Arlington Heights Rd., Ste. 615
Arlington Heights, IL 60005-4512 (847) 981-0545

Established in 1989 in IL.
Donor: George M. Eisenberg†.
Foundation type: Independent foundation.
Financial data (yr. ended 12/31/13): Assets, $58,127,475 (M); expenditures, $3,926,056; qualifying distributions, $3,562,095; giving activities include $3,308,400 for 177 grants (high: $1,000,000; low: $1,000).
Purpose and activities: Giving primarily for medicine, health, education, and physical, emotional, and social assistance for the benefit of underprivileged youth and the elderly.
Fields of interest: Elementary/secondary education; Higher education; Hospitals (general); Hospitals (specialty); Medical care, rehabilitation; Public health; Medical research, institute; Youth development, services; Human services; Children/youth, services; Residential/custodial care; Aging, centers/services; Religion.
Type of support: General/operating support; Capital campaigns.
Limitations: Applications accepted. Giving limited to IL and MN, with emphasis on metropolitan Chicago and DuPage County, IL, and Rochester, MN. No support for political organizations, elementary or secondary schools, public colleges or universities (unless related to medical care), churches, or religious education. No grants to individuals, or for endowment funds, advertising, or purchasing of tickets for fundraising.
Application information: Application form not required.
Initial approach: 1- to 2-page letter
Deadline(s): May 15
Board meeting date(s): Eight or more times per year
Final notification: Nov. or Dec.
Officers and Directors:* Dean J. Marousis, Pres.; Erin K. O' Brien-Cahill, V.P.; Thomas C. Spelsberg, Jr., Secy.; James K. Marousis,* Treas.; Thomas E. O'Brien; Katie Owens; Nancy T. Spelsberg; Thomas C. Spelsberg.
EIN: 363689650

2820
Gail G. Ellis Foundation, Inc. ✧
c/o David Friedlander, FGMK
2801 Lakeside Dr., 3rd Fl.
Bannockburn, IL 60015-1275

Established in 1995 in IL.
Donor: Gail G. Ellis.
Foundation type: Independent foundation.

Financial data (yr. ended 12/31/12): Assets, $10,454,677 (M); expenditures, $628,058; qualifying distributions, $489,550; giving activities include $489,550 for 112 grants (high: $50,000; low: $100).
Fields of interest: Arts; Higher education; Education; Health care; Health organizations, association; Human services.
Limitations: Applications not accepted. No grants to individuals.
Application information: Unsolicited requests for funds not accepted.
Directors: Gail G. Ellis; Brian C. Sullivan; Carrie E. Sullivan.
EIN: 364076867

2821
The Ellis Foundation Inc. ✧
c/o The Northern Trust Co.
P.O. Box 803878
Chicago, IL 60680-3878

Established in 1997 in GA.
Donors: W.D. Ellis, Jr.; Chatham Investment Partners, LLC; Florida S. Ellis; Laura Maddox†; John Oglesby.
Foundation type: Independent foundation.
Financial data (yr. ended 12/31/13): Assets, $4,202,988 (M); gifts received, $948,294; expenditures, $958,291; qualifying distributions, $944,266; giving activities include $928,266 for 51 grants (high: $325,000; low: $116).
Fields of interest: Higher education; Higher education, university; Education; Religion, association.
Limitations: Applications not accepted. Giving primarily in the metropolitan Atlanta, GA, area.
Application information: Unsolicited requests for funds not accepted.
Officers: Florida Smith Ellis, Pres.; W.D. Ellis, Jr., Secy.; Florida Ellis Huff, Treas.
EIN: 586362281

2822
Emerson Directors & Officers Charitable Trust ✧
c/o The Northern Trust Co.
P.O. Box 803878
Chicago, IL 60680-3878

Established in 1986 in MO.
Donors: Cynthia Heath; Frank Dellaquila; Patrick Sly; David Farr; Walter Galvin; Paul McNight; Craig Ashmore; Matt Levatich; Emerson Electric Co.; Edgar Purvis, Jr.; Frank Steves; Richard Schlueter.
Foundation type: Independent foundation.
Financial data (yr. ended 12/31/13): Assets, $5,611,879 (M); gifts received, $2,338,874; expenditures, $1,316,313; qualifying distributions, $1,316,313; giving activities include $1,316,313 for 179 grants (high: $500,000; low: $50).
Fields of interest: Arts; Higher education; United Ways and Federated Giving Programs; Christian agencies & churches; Protestant agencies & churches.
Type of support: Continuing support; Annual campaigns; Endowments.
Limitations: Applications not accepted. Giving primarily in St. Louis, MO.
Application information: Contributes only to pre-selected organizations.
Trustee: The Northern Trust Co.
EIN: 436316003

2823
Ende Menzer Walsh & Quinn Retirees' Widows' & Children's Assistance Fund ✧
20 S. Clark St., Rm. 1400
Chicago, IL 60603-1802
Main URL: http://www.widowsandchildren.org/
Facebook: https://www.facebook.com/emwqfund?ref=tn_tnmn
LinkedIn: http://www.linkedin.com/company/2632435
RSS Feed: http://www.widowsandchildren.org/1/feed
Twitter: https://twitter.com/emwqfund

Established in 2007 in IL.
Donors: Fireman's Annuity and Benefit Fund of Chicago; City of Chicago Charitable Giving Program; BMO Harris Bank, N.A.; Ignite the Spirit; Firemens Association of Chicago; Chicago Blackhawks Alumni Association; Fraternal Order of Police; Calumet City Firefighters Association; Chicago Board of Trade Foundation.
Foundation type: Operating foundation.
Financial data (yr. ended 12/31/13): Assets, $223,142 (M); gifts received, $729,172; expenditures, $743,101; qualifying distributions, $682,756; giving activities include $40,000 for 6 grants (high: $15,000; low: $2,000), and $642,756 for grants to individuals.
Purpose and activities: The sole purpose of the foundation is to provide financial assistance annually to the neediest widows and orphans of members of the Chicago Fire Department from the resources accumulated by the organization.
Fields of interest: Children; Women; Economically disadvantaged.
Type of support: Grants to individuals.
Limitations: Applications not accepted. Giving in the U.S., with emphasis on IL.
Publications: Financial statement; IRS Form 990 or 990-PF printed copy available upon request.
Application information: Unsolicited requests for funds not accepted.
Officers and Directors:* Anthony R. Martin,* Pres.; Michael Shanahan,* Secy.; Kenneth Kaczmarz,* Treas.; Susana Mendoza; Jose Santiago.
EIN: 205045585

2824
Energizer Charitable Trust ✧
c/o The Northern Trust Co.
P.O. Box 803878
Chicago, IL 60680-3878

Established in 2000 in MO.
Donors: Ralston Purina Trust Fund; Energizer Holdings, Inc.
Foundation type: Company-sponsored foundation.
Financial data (yr. ended 09/30/13): Assets, $6,744,253 (M); expenditures, $3,023,115; qualifying distributions, $3,016,615; giving activities include $3,015,615 for 409 grants (high: $1,500,000; low: $25).
Purpose and activities: The trust supports museums and organizations involved with education, animal welfare, diabetes, housing development, youth development, human services, and economically disadvantaged people.
Fields of interest: Museums; Museums (art); Elementary/secondary education; Education, special; Higher education; Libraries (public); Scholarships/financial aid; Education, services; Education; Animal welfare; Diabetes; Housing/shelter, development; Boys & girls clubs; Youth development, business; Youth development; Children/youth, services; Human services; United Ways and Federated Giving Programs; Economically disadvantaged.
Type of support: General/operating support; Continuing support; Program development; Scholarship funds; Employee matching gifts.
Limitations: Applications not accepted. Giving primarily in St. Louis, MO and other areas of company operations in CT, IL, KY, NC, NY, and OH. No support for veterans' or fraternal organizations not of direct benefit to the entire community. No grants to individuals, or for religious or politically partisan purposes, investment funds, tickets for dinners, benefits, exhibits, conferences, sports events, or other short term activities, advertisements, or debt reduction or post-event needs; no loans.
Application information: Unsolicited requests for funds not accepted.
Trustees: Buron Buffkin; Jacqueline E. Burwitz; Dan Carpenter; William C. Fox; Mark A. Schafale; Joseph J. Tisone; Jeff Ziminski.
EIN: 367324191

2825
Dan J. Epstein Family Foundation ✧
3270 N. Lake Shore Dr., Ste. 12B
Chicago, IL 60657-3917

Established in IL.
Donors: Dan J. Epstein; Epstein Charitable Remainder Trust; Epstein Residuary Trust.
Foundation type: Independent foundation.
Financial data (yr. ended 12/31/13): Assets, $8,813,515 (M); expenditures, $588,703; qualifying distributions, $465,405; giving activities include $465,405 for 20 grants (high: $250,000; low: $300).
Fields of interest: Arts; Education; Civil/human rights.
Limitations: Applications not accepted. Giving primarily in IL.
Application information: Unsolicited requests for funds not accepted.
Officers and Director:* Dan J. Epstein,* Pres. and Treas.; William Pinsof, V.P.; Michael Friedberg, Secy.
EIN: 263807997
Selected grants: The following grants are a representative sample of this grantmaker's funding activity:
$5,200 to Princeton University, Princeton, NJ, 2012. To further the educational works of the organization.
$2,500 to City of Hope, Chicago, IL, 2012. For the Charitable Works of the Organization.
$1,000 to Fordham University, School of Law, New York, NY, 2012. To further the educational works of the organization.
$1,000 to Rush University Medical Center, Chicago, IL, 2012. To further the educational works of the organization.
$150 to Jump Rhythm Jazz Project, Chicago, IL, 2012. To further the artistic works of the organization.

2826
Evanston Community Foundation ✧
1560 Sherman Ave., Ste. 535
Evanston, IL 60201 (847) 492-0990
Contact: Sara L. Schastok Ph.D., C.E.O.; For grants: Marybeth Schroeder, V.P., Progs.
FAX: (847) 492-0904;
E-mail: info@evanstonforever.org; Additional e-mail: schastok@evanstonforever.org; Grant inquiry e-mail: schroeder@evanstonforever.org; Grant inquiry tel.: (847) 492-0990; Main URL: http://www.evanstonforever.org
Facebook: https://www.facebook.com/evanstonforever
Twitter: http://www.twitter.com/evanstonforever

Established in 1986 in IL.
Foundation type: Community foundation.
Financial data (yr. ended 12/31/12): Assets, $17,138,221 (M); gifts received, $2,050,801; expenditures, $2,333,103; giving activities include $1,404,948 for 45+ grants (high: $108,250).
Purpose and activities: The foundation was established as a publicly supported philanthropic organization. Helping Evanston thrive now and forever as a vibrant, inclusive, and just community, the Evanston Community Foundation builds, connects, and distributes resources and knowledge through local organizations for the common good.
Fields of interest: Arts; Education, early childhood education; Education; Environment; Health care; Health organizations, association; AIDS; Employment, services; Housing/shelter, development; Youth development, services; Children/youth, services; Family services; Aging, centers/services; Minorities/immigrants, centers/services; Homeless, human services; Human services; Community development, neighborhood development; Community/economic development; Public affairs, citizen participation; Leadership development; Infants/toddlers; Children/youth; Youth; Aging; Disabilities, people with; Minorities; Women; Girls; Boys; Economically disadvantaged; Homeless.
Type of support: Income development; Management development/capacity building; Program development; Seed money; Curriculum development; Program evaluation.
Limitations: Applications accepted. Giving limited to organizations serving the Evanston, IL community. No grants to individuals.
Publications: Annual report; Grants list; Informational brochure; Newsletter; Occasional report.
Application information: Visit foundation web site for applications and guidelines per grant type. Application form required.
Initial approach: Create an online eGrant account
Copies of proposal: 15
Deadline(s): Jan. 28 for Responsive Grants program; varies for others
Board meeting date(s): Jan., Mar., May, June, Sept., Nov., and Dec.
Final notification: Varies
Officers and Directors:* Joan Gunzberg,* Chair.; Mike Brody,* 1st Vice-Chair.; Judith Aiello-Fantus,* 2nd Vice-Chair.; Sara L. Schastok, Ph.D.*, Pres. and C.E.O.; Gwen Jessen,* V.P., Philanthropy; Marybeth Schroeder,* V.P., Progs.; Anne Murdoch,* Secy.; Bill Blanchard,* Treas.; Jan Fischer,* C.F.O.; Lisa Altenbernd; Lun Ye Crim Barefield; Julie Chernoff; Diana Cohen; Pete Henderson; Burgie Howard; Bill Logan; John McCarthy; Kevin Mott; Richard Peach; Patty Reece; Eric Robison; Penelope Sachs; Keith Sarpolis, M.D.; Gene Servillo; Sandra Waller Shelton, C.P.A.; Larry Singer; Keith Terry; Judy Witt.
Number of staff: 4 full-time professional; 3 part-time professional.
EIN: 363466802

2827
Exelon Foundation ✧
P.O. Box 5408
Chicago, IL 60680-5408 (312) 394-2200
E-mail: exelonfoundation@exeloncorp.com; Main URL: http://www.exelonfoundation.org

Established in 2007 in IL.
Donor: Exelon Corporation.
Foundation type: Company-sponsored foundation.
Financial data (yr. ended 12/31/12): Assets, $69,144,969 (M); gifts received, $18,000; expenditures, $3,818,396; qualifying distributions, $3,285,371; giving activities include $3,252,500 for 29 grants (high: $250,000; low: $37,500).
Purpose and activities: The foundation supports programs designed to promote the environment and conservation; innovative math and science education; and diversity and tolerance.
Fields of interest: Education; Environment, natural resources; Environment, land resources; Environment, energy; Environment; Recreation, parks/playgrounds; Civil/human rights, equal rights; Mathematics; Science; Public affairs.
Type of support: Program development.
Limitations: Giving primarily in areas of company operations in IL, MA, MD, PA, and TX. No grants to individuals.
Publications: Application guidelines.
Application information: Letters of inquiry should be brief. Generally, the foundation does not accept unsolicited proposals. Full proposals are accepted by invitation only.
Initial approach: E-mail letter of inquiry
Deadline(s): None
Board meeting date(s): Quarterly
Officers and Directors:* John W. Rowe,* Chair.; Steven J. Solomon, Pres.; Joseph Dominquez, V.P.; James Firth,* V.P.; Michelle McConnell, Secy.; Matthew F. Hilzinger,* Treas.; Douglass J. Brown; Frank Clark; Katherine Combs; Christopher M. Crane; Ruth Ann M. Gillis; Denis O'Brien; John M. Palms, Ph.D.; Williamson C. Richardson, Ph.D.; William A. Van Hoene, Jr.; Andrea Zopp.
EIN: 830499473

2828
Farnham Foundation ✧
c/o Joel Ashmus
315 Quail Ridge Dr.
Westmont, IL 60559-6144

Established in 1989 in IL.
Donor: Viola D. Hank‡.
Foundation type: Independent foundation.
Financial data (yr. ended 12/31/13): Assets, $4,580,937 (M); expenditures, $446,440; qualifying distributions, $439,000; giving activities include $439,000 for 4 grants (high: $200,000; low: $3,000).
Fields of interest: Arts; Education; Religion.
Type of support: General/operating support.
Limitations: Applications not accepted. Giving primarily in Chicago, IL and IN. No grants to individuals.
Application information: Unsolicited requests for funds not accepted.
Officer: Celeste Hank Wright, Chair.
Trustees: Allen B. Hank; John C. Hank; J. Luke McGuinness; Cynthia H. Stark.
EIN: 363684134
Selected grants: The following grants are a representative sample of this grantmaker's funding activity:
$25,000 to University of Notre Dame, Notre Dame, IN, 2011. For operating expenses.
$20,000 to Benet Academy, Lisle, IL, 2011. For operating expenses.
$20,000 to Fenwick High School, Oak Park, IL, 2011. For operating expenses.
$1,500 to Sovereign Military Order of Malta, Washington, DC, 2011. For operating expenses.
$1,000 to Arizona State University, Tempe, AZ, 2011. For operating expenses.

2829
FDC Foundation ✧
1415 W. 55th St., Ste. 202
Countryside, IL 60525-6543 (847) 235-2170
Contact: John C. Doyle, Pres.
E-mail: fcluck@fdcfoundation.org; Additional e-mail: jdoyle@fdcfoundation.org; Main URL: http://www.fdcfoundation.org/

Foundation type: Independent foundation.
Financial data (yr. ended 12/31/13): Assets, $10,101,019 (M); expenditures, $717,183; qualifying distributions, $576,600; giving activities include $576,600 for 28 grants (high: $100,000; low: $2,600).
Purpose and activities: Giving primarily for: 1) Health, particularly to organizations that support a) improved nutrition for Americans, including organizations supplying food and food supplements to people in need as well as those providing education regarding proper nutrition; b) the treatment of persons with diabetes, including education, nutrition, medication and supplies for persons who either now have or who are at high risk of developing diabetes; and c) the expanded use of alternative medicines, including all forms of non-traditional therapies and medications that offer promise of improving the lives of people, whether healthy or ill; 2) Education, particularly to organizations that support a) early childhood development programs, including but not limited to educational institutions currently doing outstanding work in the field; b) programs for returning scholars, supporting organizations that provide financial support (such as reimbursement of tuition, fees, cost of books and additional living expenses) incurred by persons who return to school to continue their education later in life; and c) literary achievement, specifically organizations (such as colleges and universities) offering financial support or programs to gifted individuals pursuing the creation of meritorious literary works (poetry, fiction, drama, non-fiction prose, or translation) over a specific time period (such as one year); and 3) Housing, particularly to organizations that provide opportunities to those who have difficulty finding housing or achieving home ownership. The organizations may support construction of new housing, rehabilitation of existing housing, or financing of housing for people having unusual needs or facing extraordinary challenges. The foundation may also offer grants to organizations supporting education for careers within the real

estate industry, such as the endowment of a chair with the business department of a university.
Fields of interest: Education, early childhood education; Education; Health care; Diabetes; Nutrition; Housing/shelter; Human services.
Limitations: Applications accepted. Giving primarily in IL. No support for international organizations, or for-profit businesses.
Application information: Application form required.
Initial approach: Letter
Deadline(s): See foundation web site for current deadlines
Final notification: Within 3 months
Officers: Frank D. Cluck, Jr., Chair. and Treas.; John C. Doyle, Pres.; Bruce W. Cluck, V.P.; Cynthia Heynen, V.P.; Susan Patke, V.P.; Maria Begona Pulido, Secy.
EIN: 263349582
Selected grants: The following grants are a representative sample of this grantmaker's funding activity:
$30,000 to American Diabetes Association, Chicago, IL, 2012. For Aid/Education Childhood Diabetics Camp.
$30,000 to Together We Cope, Tinley Park, IL, 2012. For emergency food/housing assistance.
$20,000 to Old Irving Park Community Clinic, Chicago, IL, 2012. For General operations of a Free Health Clinic.
$15,000 to Irving Park Community Food Pantry, Chicago, IL, 2012. For food distribution/nutrition training.

2830
Joseph and Bessie Feinberg Foundation ✧
415 E. North Water St., Ste. 2301
Chicago, IL 60611-5834

Established in 1969 in IL.
Donor: Reuben Feinberg‡.
Foundation type: Independent foundation.
Financial data (yr. ended 12/31/13): Assets, $36,254,751 (M); expenditures, $1,396,694; qualifying distributions, $1,264,237; giving activities include $1,237,150 for 118 grants (high: $50,000; low: $50), and $132 for 1 in-kind gift.
Purpose and activities: Giving primarily for education, health and Jewish welfare.
Fields of interest: Education; Public health, obesity; Health organizations; Human services; Jewish federated giving programs.
Limitations: Applications not accepted. Giving primarily in IL, with emphasis in Chicago. No grants to individuals.
Application information: Contributes only to pre-selected organizations.
Officers: Janice Feinberg, Pres. and Treas.; Joseph Feinberg, V.P. and Secy.
Directors: Paul Goldberg; Rhonda Feinberg.
EIN: 237028857

2831
The Field Foundation of Illinois, Inc. ✧
200 S. Wacker Dr., Ste. 3860
Chicago, IL 60606-5848 (312) 831-0910
Contact: Aurie A. Pennick, Exec. Dir.; Beatrice Young, Opers./Grants Mgr.
FAX: (312) 831-0961;
E-mail: byoung@fieldfoundation.org; Main URL: http://www.fieldfoundation.org

Incorporated in 1960 in IL.
Donor: Marshall Field IV‡.
Foundation type: Independent foundation.
Financial data (yr. ended 04/30/13): Assets, $60,814,807 (M); expenditures, $2,087,156; qualifying distributions, $3,361,186; giving activities include $2,462,250 for 143 grants (high: $25,000), and $106,875 for 87 employee matching gifts.
Purpose and activities: The foundation seeks to provide support for community, civic, and cultural organizations in the Chicago, Illinois area, enabling both new and established programs to test innovations, to expand proven strengths or to address specific, time-limited operational needs. The foundation supports giving in the fields of health, community welfare, primary and secondary education, cultural activities, conservation, and urban and community affairs.
Fields of interest: Museums; Arts; Education, early childhood education; Elementary school/education; Secondary school/education; Adult education—literacy, basic skills & GED; Education; Environment; Health care; Substance abuse, services; Mental health/crisis services; AIDS; Employment; Food services; Human services; Children/youth, services; Aging, centers/services; Homeless, human services; Civil rights, race/intergroup relations; Community/economic development; Public policy, research; Public affairs; Children/youth; Youth; Aging; Disabilities, people with; Minorities; Women; Girls; Offenders/ex-offenders; AIDS, people with; Crime/abuse victims; Immigrants/refugees; Economically disadvantaged; Homeless; LGBTQ.
Type of support: General/operating support; Capital campaigns; Building/renovation; Equipment; Land acquisition; Emergency funds; Program development; Seed money; Curriculum development; Technical assistance; Employee matching gifts; Matching/challenge support.
Limitations: Applications accepted. Giving primarily in the Chicago, IL, metropolitan area. No support for member agencies of community funds, medical research, national health agencies, neighborhood health clinics, small cultural groups, or religious purposes. No grants to individuals, or for endowment funds, continuing operating support, conferences, operating support of day care centers, fundraising events, advertising, scholarships, printed materials or video equipment, or fellowships; no loans.
Publications: Biennial report; Informational brochure (including application guidelines); Occasional report.
Application information: Application guidelines available on foundation web site. Application form not required.
Initial approach: Proposal, including Self-Certification Checklist
Copies of proposal: 1
Deadline(s): Jan. 15, May 15, and Sept. 15 (if these dates fall on a weekend, the deadline is the following Monday)
Board meeting date(s): 3 times per year
Final notification: Within 4 months
Officers and Directors:* Lyle Logan, Chair.; Sarah Linsley,* Secy.; Aurie A. Pennick, Treas. and Exec. Dir.; Judith S. Block; Gloria Castillo; Marshall Field V; Rita A. Fry; Philip Wayne Hummer; F. Oliver Nicklin; George A. Ranney, Jr.
Number of staff: 4 full-time professional; 1 full-time support; 1 part-time support.
EIN: 366059408

2832
Finnegan Family Foundation ✧
(formerly Finnegan Foundation)
c/o Albert W. McCally, III
500 Davis St., Ste. 508
Evanston, IL 60201
Main URL: http://www.finneganfamilyfdn.org/

Established in 1998 in IL.
Donors: Paul J. Finnegan; Mary M. Finnegan.
Foundation type: Independent foundation.
Financial data (yr. ended 12/31/13): Assets, $39,426,744 (M); gifts received, $1,791,594; expenditures, $1,681,002; qualifying distributions, $1,412,837; giving activities include $1,330,137 for 66 grants (high: $241,000; low: $1,000).
Purpose and activities: Giving primarily for education, health and human services.
Fields of interest: Higher education; Education; Health organizations; Human services.
Limitations: Applications not accepted. Giving in the U.S., with emphasis on CA, IL, and NY. No grants to individuals.
Application information: Contributes only to pre-selected organizations.
Officers and Directors:* Paul J. Finnegan,* Chair. and Treas.; Albert Ward McCally III,* Pres.; Mary M. Finnegan,* V.P. and Secy.
EIN: 364221334
Selected grants: The following grants are a representative sample of this grantmaker's funding activity:
$282,000 to Teach for All, New York, NY, 2012. For Regional Hub in Africa.
$125,000 to Ounce of Prevention Fund, Chicago, IL, 2012. For $25,000 to support Early Learning Executive Council, $100,000 Unrestricted.
$100,000 to Erie Family Health Center, Chicago, IL, 2012. For Launch of Evanston/Skokie federally-qualified health center.
$35,000 to Metropolitan Family Services, Chicago, IL, 2012. For Evanston/Skokie Valley Family Support and Prevention Program, Evanston/Skokie Community Center, North Children's Center.
$30,000 to Teach for America, New York, NY, 2012. For Good to Great Research Project on Teacher Effectiveness.
$29,000 to Peer Health Exchange, Chicago, IL, 2012. For Chicago Program.
$25,000 to Citizen Schools, Boston, MA, 2012. For Launch of Chicago Program.
$25,000 to University of Minnesota, Minneapolis, MN, 2012. For Midwest Expansion of the Child-Parent Center Education Program, i3 matching funds.
$10,000 to Youth Technology Corps, Chicago, IL, 2012. For Evanston, Illinois Operation.
$5,000 to Noble Network of Charter Schools, Chicago, IL, 2012. For Right Angle Program.

2833
First Bank of Highland Park Foundation ✧
(formerly Lionel Takiff and Rosella Takiff Charities, Ltd.)
1835 First St.
Highland Park, IL 60035-3101
Contact: Jill Takiff Hirsh, Dir.

Established in IL.
Donors: Rosella Takiff; Lionel Takiff; Bank of Highland Park Financial Corp.; First Bank of Highland Park.
Foundation type: Independent foundation.

Financial data (yr. ended 12/31/13): Assets, $1,297,755 (M); gifts received, $73,000; expenditures, $454,084; qualifying distributions, $454,004; giving activities include $452,389 for 153 grants (high: $50,000; low: $50).
Fields of interest: Education; Medical research, institute; Recreation; Human services; Jewish federated giving programs.
Limitations: Applications accepted. Giving primarily in Chicago, IL.
Application information: Application form not required.
Initial approach: Proposal
Deadline(s): None
Director: Jill Takiff Hirsh.
Trustee: Randy Green.
EIN: 363310459
Selected grants: The following grants are a representative sample of this grantmaker's funding activity:
$7,500 to Multiple Sclerosis Society, National, New York, NY, 2011. For research.
$5,000 to ACCION Chicago, Chicago, IL, 2011.
$2,800 to Greater Chicago Food Depository, Chicago, IL, 2011.
$2,500 to Boys and Girls Clubs of Chicago, Chicago, IL, 2011.
$2,500 to Rebuilding Together, Washington, DC, 2011.
$1,100 to Cystic Fibrosis Foundation, Bethesda, MD, 2011. For research.
$1,000 to DePaul University, Chicago, IL, 2011.

2834
Andrew and Alice Fischer Charitable Trust ✧
c/o First American Bank
218 W. Main St.
Dundee, IL 60118-2093
Contact: Kathryn Hector, Trust Off., First American Bank

Established in IL.
Donor: Joanne Meyers Charitable Trust.
Foundation type: Operating foundation.
Financial data (yr. ended 12/31/13): Assets, $11,466,083 (M); expenditures, $492,152; qualifying distributions, $461,389; giving activities include $429,200 for 33 grants (high: $25,000; low: $4,700).
Purpose and activities: Giving primarily for educational funding for challenged individuals, programs benefiting U.S. veterans, and programs benefitting children and senior citizens.
Fields of interest: Higher education.
Limitations: Applications accepted. Giving primarily in the greater Chicagoland area, IL.
Application information: Application form not required.
Initial approach: Proposal
Deadline(s): Apr. 1 and Oct. 1
Trustee: First American Bank.
EIN: 206792124
Selected grants: The following grants are a representative sample of this grantmaker's funding activity:
$25,000 to One Hope United, Lake Villa, IL, 2012. For 2nd payment of 3 year grant.
$20,000 to Esperanza Community Services, Chicago, IL, 2012. For Coleridge adult day Program.
$10,000 to College Bound Opportunities, Riverwoods, IL, 2012. For 3rd payment of 4 year grant.
$10,000 to LYDIA Home Association, Chicago, IL, 2012. For Urban Academy.
$5,000 to TriCity Family Services, Geneva, IL, 2012. For children and adolescents.

2835
J. & V. Flynn Foundation ✧
c/o William R. Pillman
1921 W. Altorfer Dr.
Peoria, IL 61615-1801 (309) 713-2812
Contact: William R. Pillman, Pres.

Established in 1999 in IL.
Donor: Virginia Flynn‡.
Foundation type: Independent foundation.
Financial data (yr. ended 05/31/13): Assets, $11,198,387 (M); expenditures, $563,793; qualifying distributions, $481,000; giving activities include $481,000 for grants.
Fields of interest: Higher education; Protestant agencies & churches.
Limitations: Applications accepted. Giving primarily in IL.
Application information: Application form not required.
Initial approach: Proposal
Deadline(s): None
Officer: William R. Pillman, Pres.
Trustees: William Campbell; Sally A. Pillman.
EIN: 371387143
Selected grants: The following grants are a representative sample of this grantmaker's funding activity:
$75,000 to Eureka College, Eureka, IL, 2012.
$18,000 to Lakeview Museum of Arts and Sciences, Peoria, IL, 2012.
$15,000 to Bradley University, Peoria, IL, 2012.
$10,000 to Red Cloud Indian School, Pine Ridge, SD, 2012.
$9,000 to Illinois Wesleyan University, Bloomington, IL, 2012.
$2,000 to Childrens Hospital of Illinois, Peoria, IL, 2012.
$1,000 to University of the Cumberlands, Williamsburg, KY, 2012.

2836
The Fogelson Foundation ✧
1455 S. Michigan Ave., Ste. 100
Chicago, IL 60605-2815

Established in 2005 in IL.
Donors: Gerald W. Fogelson; Georgia B. Fogelson.
Foundation type: Independent foundation.
Financial data (yr. ended 12/31/13): Assets, $3,765,402 (M); expenditures, $597,574; qualifying distributions, $550,533; giving activities include $508,904 for 43 grants (high: $75,000; low: $100).
Fields of interest: Museums (art); Education; Cancer; Medical research; Religion.
Limitations: Applications not accepted. Giving primarily in CA and IL. No grants to individuals.
Application information: Unsolicited requests for funds not accepted.
Officers: Gerald W. Fogelson, Pres.; Tamara L. Trock, V.P. and Secy.-Treas.
Director: Georgia B. Fogelson.
EIN: 202902485
Selected grants: The following grants are a representative sample of this grantmaker's funding activity:
$75,000 to Eisenhower Medical Center, Rancho Mirage, CA, 2012. For EMC Expansion Campaign.

2837
Foglia Family Foundation ✧
190 S. LaSalle St., Ste. 1700
Chicago, IL 60603-3411

Established in 1993 in IL.
Donor: Vincent W. Foglia.
Foundation type: Independent foundation.
Financial data (yr. ended 09/30/13): Assets, $73,911,868 (M); gifts received, $75,020,000; expenditures, $7,226,910; qualifying distributions, $7,017,080; giving activities include $7,017,080 for 94 grants (high: $750,000; low: $300).
Fields of interest: Higher education; Education; Hospitals (general); Health care; Human services; YM/YWCAs & YM/YWHAs; Children/youth, services; Residential/custodial care, hospices.
Limitations: Applications not accepted. Giving primarily in Chicago, IL. No grants to individuals.
Application information: Contributes only to pre-selected organizations.
Officers and Directors:* Patricia A. Foglia,* Pres.; Vincent W. Foglia,* Secy.-Treas.; Kymberly A. Foglia; Vincent J. Foglia.
EIN: 363925857
Selected grants: The following grants are a representative sample of this grantmaker's funding activity:
$800,000 to JourneyCare, Barrington, IL, 2012.
$525,000 to Family Health Partnership Clinic, Woodstock, IL, 2012.
$250,000 to University of Chicago, Chicago, IL, 2012.
$226,400 to By the Hand Club for Kids, Chicago, IL, 2012.
$175,000 to Wellness Place, Palatine, IL, 2012.
$100,000 to Samaritan Institute, Winnetka, IL, 2012.
$64,000 to Neighborhood Health Clinic, Naples, FL, 2012.
$50,000 to Boys Hope Girls Hope of Illinois, Wilmette, IL, 2012.
$50,000 to Christ the King Jesuit College Preparatory School, Chicago, IL, 2012.
$25,000 to Boy Scouts of America, Barrington Hills, IL, 2012.

2838
Peggy and Steve Fossett Foundation ✧
(formerly Challenger Oceanographic Foundation)
401 S. LaSalle St., Ste. 200
Chicago, IL 60605-2999 (312) 786-5054
Contact: David Maier, Secy.-Treas.

Established in 2006 in IL.
Donor: J. Stephen Fossett‡.
Foundation type: Operating foundation.
Financial data (yr. ended 12/31/13): Assets, $23,485,918 (M); gifts received, $90; expenditures, $1,345,706; qualifying distributions, $1,129,072; giving activities include $988,000 for 45 grants (high: $110,000; low: $1,000).

Fields of interest: Museums; Arts; Education; Aquariums; Human services.
Limitations: Applications accepted. Giving primarily in CO and MO.
Application information:
Initial approach: Letter
Deadline(s): None
Officers: Peggy V. Fossett, Pres.; David Maier, Secy.-Treas.
Directors: Abraham J. Stern; Thomas Viehland.
EIN: 204521801
Selected grants: The following grants are a representative sample of this grantmaker's funding activity:
$100,000 to Museum of Flight, Seattle, WA, 2011. For general support.
$50,000 to Steadman Philippon Research Institute, Vail, CO, 2011. For general support.
$25,000 to Field Museum of Natural History, Chicago, IL, 2011. For general support.
$25,000 to Vail Valley Medical Center Foundation, Vail, CO, 2011. For general support.
$25,000 to Washington University, Saint Louis, MO, 2011. For general support.
$20,000 to Himalayan Cataract Project, Waterbury, VT, 2011. For general support.
$10,000 to Donald Danforth Plant Science Center, Saint Louis, MO, 2011. For general support.
$5,000 to Big Sur Land Trust, Monterey, CA, 2011. For general support.
$5,000 to Community Human Services, Monterey, CA, 2011. For general support.
$5,000 to Food Bank for Monterey County, Salinas, CA, 2011. For general support.

2839
Foundation for Retinal Research ✧
666 Dundee Rd., Ste. 1104
Northbrook, IL 60062-2735 (224) 927-5063
Contact: David Brint, Pres.
FAX: (847) 562-9401; E-mail: info@tfrr.org; Main URL: http://www.tfrr.org/
Facebook: http://www.facebook.com/pages/Foundation-for-Retinal-Research/132181800132766

Established in 1998 in IL.
Donors: Claire Cortessi; Richard Cortessi; William Dutton; Brinshore Development, LLC; Alan Schwartz; Jimmy Brendle; Heather Brendle.
Foundation type: Independent foundation.
Financial data (yr. ended 12/31/12): Assets, $769,816 (M); gifts received, $708,736; expenditures, $703,158; qualifying distributions, $434,871; giving activities include $434,871 for 6 grants (high: $150,000; low: $14,315).
Purpose and activities: Giving primarily for research to find treatments and cures for retinal degenerative diseases and for the support of affected families.
Fields of interest: Eye diseases; Medical research, institute; Eye research.
Limitations: Applications accepted. Giving primarily in CA, MA, MD, ME and Netherlands. No grants to individuals.
Application information: Requests should be in standard format for medical research; written or electronic formats are acceptable.
Deadline(s): None
Officers: David Brint, Pres.; Elizabeth Brint, V.P.; Michael Cornell, V.P.; Alan G. Schwartz, Secy.-Treas.
EIN: 364232603

2840
J. S. Frank Foundation ✧
666 Garland Pl.
Des Plaines, IL 60016-4725

Established in IL.
Donors: James S. Frank; Frank Consolidated Enterprises.
Foundation type: Independent foundation.
Financial data (yr. ended 12/31/13): Assets, $1,128,490 (M); gifts received, $1,550,000; expenditures, $1,012,386; qualifying distributions, $1,012,365; giving activities include $1,012,350 for 59 grants (high: $115,000; low: $250).
Purpose and activities: Giving primarily for higher education and the arts, as well as to a medical center.
Fields of interest: Arts; Higher education; Hospitals (general); Human services; Children/youth, services; United Ways and Federated Giving Programs.
Limitations: Applications accepted. Giving primarily in IL. No grants to individuals.
Application information: Application form required.
Initial approach: Letter
Deadline(s): None
Officers: James S. Frank, Pres.; Karen Frank, Secy.
EIN: 237376410
Selected grants: The following grants are a representative sample of this grantmaker's funding activity:
$500,000 to University of Chicago, Chicago, IL, 2011.
$200,000 to University of Chicago, Chicago, IL, 2011.
$140,000 to University of Chicago, Chicago, IL, 2011.
$75,000 to Teach for America, New York, NY, 2011.
$5,000 to Chicago Theological Seminary, Chicago, IL, 2011.
$2,500 to University of Chicago, Chicago, IL, 2011.
$2,500 to University of Chicago, Chicago, IL, 2011.

2841
Franke Family Charitable Foundation ✧
676 N. Michigan Ave., Ste. 2920
Chicago, IL 60611-2861 (312) 573-2743
Contact: Richard J. Franke, Tr.

Established in 1989 in IL.
Donors: Richard J. Franke; Barbara E. Franke.
Foundation type: Independent foundation.
Financial data (yr. ended 06/30/13): Assets, $48,389,705 (M); expenditures, $772,849; qualifying distributions, $668,160; giving activities include $604,275 for 43 grants (high: $50,000; low: $75).
Purpose and activities: Giving primarily for higher education and the arts.
Fields of interest: Arts education; Museums (art); Performing arts; Humanities; Arts; Higher education; Education.
Type of support: Annual campaigns; Capital campaigns.
Limitations: Applications accepted. Giving primarily in IL, with emphasis on Chicago; some giving also in New Haven, CT and New York, NY. No grants to individuals.
Application information: Application form required.
Initial approach: Letter
Deadline(s): None
Trustees: Barbara E. Franke; Katherine Franke; Jane Franke-Molner; Richard J. Franke.
EIN: 363662848
Selected grants: The following grants are a representative sample of this grantmaker's funding activity:
$75,000 to New York Community Trust, New York, NY, 2011.
$25,000 to Chicago Humanities Festival, Chicago, IL, 2011.
$25,000 to Chicago Shakespeare Theater, Chicago, IL, 2011.
$25,000 to Court Theater, Chicago, IL, 2011.
$14,000 to Court Theater, Chicago, IL, 2011.
$10,000 to American Cancer Society, New York, NY, 2011.
$10,000 to Greater Chicago Food Depository, Chicago, IL, 2011.
$10,000 to Salvation Army, Chicago, IL, 2011.
$10,000 to University of Chicago, Chicago, IL, 2011.
$9,500 to Golden Apple Foundation, Chicago, IL, 2011.

2842
Frankel Family Foundation ✧
c/o Peter Frankel
1700 W. Irving Park Rd., Ste. 203
Chicago, IL 60613-2599 (773) 360-5412
FAX: (773) 224-5187;
E-mail: info@frankelfamilyfoundation.org; Main URL: http://www.frankelfamilyfoundation.org/index.aspx
Grants Database: http://www.frankelfamilyfoundation.org/grantlist.aspx

Established in 2000 in IL.
Donors: Bernard Frankel; Peter Frankel; Miriam Frankel; Frankel Family LP; Matthew Frankel Living Trust.
Foundation type: Independent foundation.
Financial data (yr. ended 10/31/13): Assets, $10,294,467 (M); expenditures, $701,746; qualifying distributions, $606,519; giving activities include $530,000 for 40 grants (high: $100,000; low: $1,000).
Purpose and activities: Giving primarily for the environment, a democratic and peaceful Israel as a homeland for Jews, fighting anti-Semitism wherever it exists, and for providing education for refugees and displaced persons.
Fields of interest: Arts; Education; Environment; Human services; Children/youth, services; Jewish federated giving programs.
Type of support: General/operating support; Continuing support; Annual campaigns; Capital campaigns; Building/renovation; Equipment; Land acquisition; Endowments; Debt reduction; Emergency funds; Program development; Conferences/seminars; Professorships; Publication; Seed money; Curriculum development; Fellowships; Internship funds; Scholarship funds; Research; Technical assistance; Consulting services; Matching/challenge support.
Limitations: Giving primarily in Chicago and Evanston, IL; some funding nationally, particularly in NY. No grants to individuals.
Publications: Application guidelines.
Application information: Full proposals by invitation only; if invited to submit a full proposal, the submission deadline will be specified in the

invitation letter. Application guidelines available on foundation web site.
Initial approach: Letter of inquiry via foundation web site
Officers and Directors:* Peter Frankel,* Pres.; Miriam Frankel,* V.P.; Bernard Frankel,* Treas.; Marya Frankel; Matthew Frankel.
EIN: 367337220

2843
Julius N. Frankel Foundation ✧
(formerly Frankel Foundation)
111 W. Monroe St., Tax Div. 10C
Chicago, IL 60603-4096 (312) 461-5154

Established in 1959 in IL.
Donors: Gerald Frankel†; Gustav Frankel†; Julius N. Frankel†.
Foundation type: Independent foundation.
Financial data (yr. ended 10/31/13): Assets, $60,646,783 (M); expenditures, $3,488,011; qualifying distributions, $2,494,099; giving activities include $2,232,064 for 39 grants (high: $200,000; low: $15,000).
Purpose and activities: Giving primarily for the arts, education, and human services.
Fields of interest: Performing arts; Arts; Higher education; Education; Human services; Children/youth, services.
Limitations: Applications accepted. Giving primarily in Chicago, IL. No grants to individuals.
Application information: Application form required.
Initial approach: Letter
Deadline(s): None
Board meeting date(s): At least 5 times annually
Final notification: Immediately following meetings
Trustees: John L. Georgas; BMO Harris Bank, N.A.
EIN: 366765844
Selected grants: The following grants are a representative sample of this grantmaker's funding activity:
$200,000 to Northwestern Memorial Foundation, Chicago, IL, 2011.
$170,000 to Night Ministry, Chicago, IL, 2011.
$155,000 to Lyric Opera of Chicago, Chicago, IL, 2011.
$150,000 to Chicago Symphony Orchestra, Chicago, IL, 2011.
$125,000 to Jacksonville Symphony Orchestra, Jacksonville, FL, 2011.
$101,376 to Rehabilitation Institute of Chicago, Chicago, IL, 2011.
$50,000 to Thresholds, Chicago, IL, 2011.
$45,000 to Music of the Baroque, Chicago, IL, 2011.
$40,000 to Lawrence Hall Youth Services, Chicago, IL, 2011.
$30,000 to Little Sisters of the Poor, Chicago, IL, 2011.

2844
Frechette Family Foundation ✧
c/o The Northern Trust Co.
P.O. Box 803878
Chicago, IL 60680-3878

Established in 1997 in IL.
Donor: Peter L. Frechette.
Foundation type: Independent foundation.
Financial data (yr. ended 12/31/13): Assets, $11,835,405 (M); expenditures, $587,467; qualifying distributions, $517,025; giving activities include $516,000 for 19 grants (high: $152,000; low: $2,000).
Fields of interest: Higher education; Education; AIDS; Diabetes; Neuroscience; Health organizations; Recreation, camps; Boy scouts; Human services; Children/youth, services.
Type of support: General/operating support.
Limitations: Applications not accepted. Giving primarily in Avon, CO and Chicago, IL, and Williamsburg, VA. No grants to individuals.
Application information: Contributes only to pre-selected organizations.
Directors: Patricia Frechette; Kathy Tenula*; Peter Tenula*; Bill Woolfolk*; Kristy Woolfolk.
Officer: Peter L. Frechette, Pres.
EIN: 311530248
Selected grants: The following grants are a representative sample of this grantmaker's funding activity:
$10,000 to Field School, Washington, DC, 2011. For general support.
$10,000 to University of Wisconsin Foundation, Madison, WI, 2011. For general support.

2845
Abel and Judy Friedman Charitable Foundation ✧
4231 W. Grove St.
Skokie, IL 60076-1843

Donors: Abel Friedman; Judy Friedman.
Foundation type: Independent foundation.
Financial data (yr. ended 12/31/13): Assets, $430,024 (M); gifts received, $250,000; expenditures, $528,225; qualifying distributions, $523,400; giving activities include $523,400 for 35 + grants (high: $150,000).
Fields of interest: Education; Health care; Health organizations, association; Jewish federated giving programs; Jewish agencies & synagogues.
Limitations: Applications not accepted. Giving primarily in DC and IL.
Application information: Contributes only to pre-selected organizations.
Officers: Abel Friedman, Pres.; Judy Friedman, Secy.
EIN: 262647690
Selected grants: The following grants are a representative sample of this grantmaker's funding activity:
$500 to American Heart Association, Chicago, IL, 2012. For Health and Human $ Services.

2846
Ann B. and Thomas L. Friedman Family Foundation ✧
c/o MB Investments, LLC
180 N. Wacker Dr., Ste. 001
Chicago, IL 60606-1648

Established in 2004 in IL.
Donors: Thomas L. Friedman; Mary B. Friedman; Ann B. Friedman; Matthew & Carolyn Bucksbaum Family Foundation; Ann Bucksbaum; Tom Bucksbaum.
Foundation type: Independent foundation.
Financial data (yr. ended 12/31/13): Assets, $18,961,784 (M); gifts received, $2,250,000; expenditures, $1,605,736; qualifying distributions, $1,541,504; giving activities include $1,541,504 for 11 grants (high: $700,000; low: $20,000).
Fields of interest: Higher education; Education; Human services; Foundations (private grantmaking); Jewish agencies & synagogues.
Limitations: Applications not accepted. Giving in the U.S., with emphasis on Washington, DC and VA. No grants to individuals.
Application information: Contributes only to pre-selected organizations.
Officers and Directors:* Ann B. Friedman,* Pres.; Thomas L. Friedman,* V.P.; E. Michael Greaves, Secy.; Richard B. Dennert, Treas.
EIN: 432057377

2847
Philip M. Friedmann Family Charitable Trust ✧
2430 N. Lakeview Ave.
Chicago, IL 60614-2877

Established in 1998 in IL.
Donors: Philip M. Friedmann; Recycled Paper Greetings, Inc.
Foundation type: Independent foundation.
Financial data (yr. ended 12/31/13): Assets, $25,599,452 (M); expenditures, $1,414,586; qualifying distributions, $1,117,910; giving activities include $1,117,910 for 180 grants (high: $150,000; low: $50).
Purpose and activities: Giving primarily for education, medical research, youth and social services, and Jewish organizations.
Fields of interest: Education; Health organizations; Medical research, institute; Youth development, services; Human services; Public affairs; Jewish agencies & synagogues.
Limitations: Applications not accepted. Giving primarily in Chicago, IL area, and the greater metropolitan Washington, DC, area.
Application information: Contributes only to pre-selected organizations.
Trustee: Philip M. Friedmann.
EIN: 367252117

2848
Helen V. Froehlich Foundation ✧
c/o The Northern Trust Co.
P.O. Box 803878
Chicago, IL 60680-3878

Established in 1993 in IL.
Foundation type: Independent foundation.
Financial data (yr. ended 05/31/13): Assets, $25,547,754 (M); expenditures, $2,059,943; qualifying distributions, $1,964,859; giving activities include $1,883,500 for 6 grants (high: $420,000; low: $209,500).
Purpose and activities: Giving primarily to botanical gardens, and for natural resource conservation.
Fields of interest: Environment, natural resources; Environment, water resources; Environment, land resources; Botanical gardens.
Limitations: Applications not accepted. Giving primarily in IL, and NY, with emphasis on Brooklyn and Lake George. No grants to individuals.
Application information: Contributes only to pre-selected organizations.
Trustee: The Northern Trust Co.
EIN: 367033137
Selected grants: The following grants are a representative sample of this grantmaker's funding activity:

$450,000 to Brooklyn Botanic Garden, Brooklyn, NY, 2011. For general support.
$410,000 to Chicago Horticultural Society, Glencoe, IL, 2011. For general support.
$220,000 to Rensselaer Polytechnic Institute, Troy, NY, 2011. For general support.
$200,000 to Lake George Land Conservancy, Bolton Landing, NY, 2011. For general support.

2849
Lloyd A. Fry Foundation
120 S. LaSalle St., Ste. 1950
Chicago, IL 60603-3419 (312) 580-0310
Contact: Unmi Song, Pres. and Secy.
FAX: (312) 580-0980;
E-mail: usong@fryfoundation.org; Main URL: http://www.fryfoundation.org

Established in 1959 in IL.
Donor: Lloyd A. Fry†.
Foundation type: Independent foundation.
Financial data (yr. ended 06/30/13): Assets, $164,492,986 (M); expenditures, $10,109,550; qualifying distributions, $9,181,748; giving activities include $7,389,379 for 276 grants (high: $150,000; low: $200).
Purpose and activities: The foundation supports organizations with the strength and commitment to address persistent problems of urban Chicago resulting from poverty, violence, ignorance and despair. The foundation seeks to build the capacity of individuals and the systems that serve them. The vision is of a Chicago that offers education, prosperity and hope for all.
Fields of interest: Arts; Elementary school/education; Secondary school/education; Education; Health care; AIDS; Employment; Minorities/immigrants, centers/services; Children/youth; Children; Adults; Young adults; Minorities; Asians/Pacific Islanders; African Americans/Blacks; Hispanics/Latinos; Women; Girls; Adults, women; Young adults, female; Men; Boys; Adults, men; Young adults, male; AIDS, people with; Immigrants/refugees; Economically disadvantaged.
Type of support: General/operating support; Continuing support; Program development; Curriculum development; Technical assistance; Program evaluation.
Limitations: Applications accepted. Giving generally limited to Chicago, IL. No support for medical research, religious purposes, governmental bodies, or tax-supported educational institutions for services that fall within their responsibilities. No grants to individuals, or for general operating support for new grantees, annual campaigns, emergency funds, deficit financing, building funds, fundraising benefits, land acquisition, renovation projects, or endowment funds; no loans.
Publications: Application guidelines; Annual report (including application guidelines); Financial statement; Grants list.
Application information: Organizations outside of Chicago, IL are rarely funded. The foundation now requires demographic information from applicant organizations. Chicago Area Grant Application Form accepted. Application form not required.
Initial approach: Letter of inquiry
Copies of proposal: 1
Deadline(s): Mar. 1, June 1, Sept. 1, and Dec. 1
Board meeting date(s): Feb., May, Aug., and Nov.
Final notification: 3 months
Officers and Directors:* Howard M. McCue III,* Chair.; Lloyd A. Fry III,* Vice-Chair.; Unmi Song, Pres. and Secy.; Stephanie Pace Marshall,* V.P.; Graham C. Grady, Treas.; Diane Sotiros, Cont.; Amina J. Dickerson; David A. Donovan.
Number of staff: 5 full-time professional; 2 full-time support; 1 part-time support.
EIN: 366108775
Selected grants: The following grants are a representative sample of this grantmaker's funding activity:
$250,000 to Big Shoulders Fund, Chicago, IL, 2012. For the Extended Day Program, payable over 2.00 years.
$250,000 to Ingenuity Chicago, Chicago, IL, 2012. For Ingenuity Incorporated to implement strategies to expand arts learning in Chicago, payable over 2.00 years.
$160,000 to Community Renewal Society, Chicago, IL, 2012. For Catalyst Chicago and the Chicago Reporter, payable over 2.00 years.
$120,000 to Women Employed Institute, Chicago, IL, 2012. For Career Pathways and Student Support initiatives, payable over 2.00 years.
$80,000 to Lawndale Christian Health Center, Chicago, IL, 2012. For the Medical Home Advancement Project, payable over 2.00 years.
$70,000 to Posse Foundation, Chicago, IL, 2012. For the Pre-Collegiate Training Program, payable over 2.00 years.
$60,000 to Latino Union of Chicago, Chicago, IL, 2012. For the Day Laborer Program at the Albany Park Workers Center, payable over 2.00 years.
$40,000 to Northeastern Illinois University, Chicago, IL, 2012. For the Studio Thinking and American Art project.

2850
Fulk Family Foundation, Inc. ✧
10 S. Wacker Dr., Ste. 2675
Chicago, IL 60606-7475 (312) 236-2233

Established in 1989 in NE.
Donors: Wilma B. Fulk†; Robert W. Fulk; Fulk Farms, Inc.
Foundation type: Independent foundation.
Financial data (yr. ended 07/31/13): Assets, $26,636,952 (M); gifts received, $1,538,774; expenditures, $1,080,843; qualifying distributions, $913,185; giving activities include $910,000 for 32 grants (high: $100,000; low: $1,000).
Fields of interest: Arts; Education; Health care; Medical research; Human services.
Limitations: Giving in the U.S., with emphasis on IL.
Application information:
Initial approach: Letter to the Board
Deadline(s): Dec. 1
Final notification: Dec. 31
Officer and Directors:* Robert W. Fulk,* Pres. and Treas.; Alice Brunner; Marcia Coffman; N. Jane Morrison.
EIN: 470732237
Selected grants: The following grants are a representative sample of this grantmaker's funding activity:
$500,000 to Mayo Clinic Jacksonville, Jacksonville, FL, 2011.
$10,000 to Tabitha, Lincoln, NE, 2011.

2851
Full Circle Foundation ✧
P.O. Box 387
Richmond, IL 60071-0387
Contact: Russell Foszcz, V.P.
E-mail: grants@fullcircleinc.org; Main URL: http://fullcircleinc.org/

Established in 1998 in IL.
Donors: Russell Foszcz; Sara Foszcz.
Foundation type: Independent foundation.
Financial data (yr. ended 12/31/13): Assets, $1,290,775 (M); gifts received, $500,000; expenditures, $464,033; qualifying distributions, $456,262; giving activities include $449,125 for 33 grants (high: $100,000; low: $1,000).
Purpose and activities: The foundation focuses its grants on educational opportunities, environmental and natural resource issues, health organizations, housing and shelter, and basic human services.
Fields of interest: Education; Environment, natural resources; Health organizations; Housing/shelter, development; Human services.
Type of support: General/operating support.
Limitations: Applications accepted. Giving emphasis is strongly on local organizations in McHenry County, IL, but some grants are awarded to national organizations. No support for religious organizations. No grants to individuals.
Application information: Grant applicants must submit a grant request form obtained from the foundation. Do not share grant request forms as they are dated and coded. Forms (and proposals) submitted without code will be automatically rejected. Application form required.
Initial approach: Letter or e-mail
Copies of proposal: 1
Deadline(s): Nov. 30
Board meeting date(s): Dec. 15
Final notification: 60 days
Officers: Sara Foszcz, Pres.; Russell Foszcz, V.P.
Directors: Cooper Foszcz; Joshua Foszcz.
Number of staff: None.
EIN: 364265265
Selected grants: The following grants are a representative sample of this grantmaker's funding activity:
$45,000 to Southern Poverty Law Center, Montgomery, AL, 2012. For Aid to prevent racial discrimination.
$25,000 to Family Health Partnership Clinic, Woodstock, IL, 2012. To Provide insurance to uninsured.
$12,500 to Wetlands Initiative, Chicago, IL, 2012. To restore wetlands resources.
$10,000 to Algebra Project, Cambridge, MA, 2012. For Training opportunities to improve the delivery of math.
$10,000 to Chicago Lights, Chicago, IL, 2012. For opportunity for the poverty.
$10,000 to Emergency Fund, Chicago, IL, 2012. To Provide small loans with little bureaucracy to those in need quickly.
$10,000 to Seven Generations Ahead, Oak Park, IL, 2012. For Promotes ecologically sustainable and healthy communities.
$5,000 to Sarah's Circle, Chicago, IL, 2012. For serves homeless or at risk women.
$5,000 to Uhlich Children's Advantage Network, Chicago, IL, 2012. For assistance with troubled children.
$1,000 to Chicago Coalition for the Homeless, Chicago, IL, 2012. For Homeless shelter support.

2852
Galashiels Fund, Ltd. ✧
555 Skokie Blvd., Ste. 555
Northbrook, IL 60062-2845

Established in 1988 in IL.
Donors: Consolidated Electrical Distributors, Inc.; RCK Properties; Rolled Alloys, Inc.; Elizabeth W. Colburn Trust.
Foundation type: Independent foundation.
Financial data (yr. ended 12/31/13): Assets, $112,210,618 (M); expenditures, $7,070,693; qualifying distributions, $6,101,904; giving activities include $6,070,625 for 33 grants (high: $1,025,000; low: $15,000).
Purpose and activities: Giving primarily for education, and public policy research; funding also for the arts, with emphasis on theater, and to a charitable gift fund.
Fields of interest: Arts; Secondary school/ education; Education; Foundations (public); Social sciences, public policy.
Type of support: General/operating support; Continuing support.
Limitations: Applications not accepted. Giving primarily in Boston, MA, IL, and Exeter, NH; funding also in CA and IN.
Application information: Contributes only to pre-selected organizations.
Officers and Directors:* Keith W. Colburn,* Pres. and Treas.; Betsy P. Colburn,* V.P.; David T. Bradford,* Secy.
EIN: 943059858
Selected grants: The following grants are a representative sample of this grantmaker's funding activity:
$2,275,000 to Fidelity Charitable Gift Fund, Boston, MA, 2011. For general support.
$500,000 to Phillips Exeter Academy, Exeter, NH, 2011. For scholarship fund.
$300,000 to Greater Educational Opportunities Foundation, Indianapolis, IN, 2011. For annual support.
$200,000 to Holy Family Ministries, Chicago, IL, 2011. For debt redemption.
$200,000 to Wellesley College, Wellesley, MA, 2011. For endowment.
$100,000 to Holy Family Ministries, Chicago, IL, 2011. For annual support.
$100,000 to Writers Theater, Glencoe, IL, 2011. For annual support.
$98,000 to Cristo Rey Jesuit High School, Chicago, IL, 2011. For O'Halleran Scholarship.
$50,000 to Chicago Shakespeare Theater, Chicago, IL, 2011. For annual support.
$32,000 to Steppenwolf Theater Company, Chicago, IL, 2011. For annual support.

2853
Galesburg Community Foundation ✧ ☆
(formerly Cottage Health Care Foundation)
246 E. Main St., Ste. 101
Galesburg, IL 61401 (309) 344-8898
Contact: Joshua D. Gibb, Exec. Dir.
FAX: (309) 344-8890;
E-mail: info@ahealthycommunity.org; Main URL: https://www.ahealthycommunity.org

Established in 1984 in IL.
Foundation type: Community foundation.
Financial data (yr. ended 12/31/13): Assets, $23,863,317 (M); gifts received, $1,884,863; expenditures, $1,468,327; giving activities include $636,101 for 25+ grants (high: $93,000), and $13,750 for 12 grants to individuals.
Purpose and activities: The foundation develops resources to equip and empower residents and nonprofit organizations to create a healthy community by building endowed and non-endowed funds, granting to nonprofit organizations, promoting collaboration, and addressing community priorities through the investment of resources.
Fields of interest: Arts; Education; Public health, physical fitness; Health care.
Limitations: Applications accepted. Giving primarily in the greater Knox County area, IL.
Application information: Competitive Grants are available once annually. Discretionary Small grants (not to exceed $500) are available. Visit foundation website for more information. Application form required.
Initial approach: Submit application
Deadline(s): Apr. 1 for Helen H. Wetherbee Nursing Scholarship. Mar. 15 for John E. Bohan Excellence in Athletics Scholarship.
Officers and Directors:* Carl Nixon,* Chair.; Joel Estes,* Vice-Chair.; Mark Kleine,* Secy.; David Pearson, Treas.; Joshua D. Gibb,* Exec. Dir.; Harry Bulkeley; Joyce Coffman; Nancy Erickson; Lance Humphreys; Thomas Maloney; Carol Simpson; Carol St. Amant.
EIN: 371159944

2854
The Robert E. Gallagher Charitable Trust ✧
c/o Arthur J. Gallagher & Co.
2 Pierce Pl.
Itasca, IL 60143-3141

Established in 1997 in IL.
Donors: Robert E. Gallagher†; Robert E. Gallagher Marital Trust.
Foundation type: Operating foundation.
Financial data (yr. ended 12/31/11): Assets, $36,802,553 (M); gifts received, $3,333,530; expenditures, $1,485,921; qualifying distributions, $1,350,893; giving activities include $1,272,500 for 35 grants (high: $831,000; low: $500).
Purpose and activities: Giving primarily to Roman Catholic education, organizations, and churches.
Fields of interest: Elementary/secondary education; Higher education, university; Catholic agencies & churches.
Limitations: Applications not accepted. Giving primarily in Chicago, IL. No grants to individuals.
Application information: Contributes only to pre-selected organizations.
Trustee: Robert E. Gallagher, Jr.
EIN: 367180671

2855
Arthur J. Gallagher Foundation ✧
2 Pierce Pl.
Itasca, IL 60143-3141

Donor: Arthur J. Gallagher & Co.
Foundation type: Independent foundation.
Financial data (yr. ended 12/31/13): Assets, $9,820,509 (M); gifts received, $1,016,989; expenditures, $2,761,200; qualifying distributions, $1,016,246; giving activities include $1,012,779 for 1,255 grants (high: $100,000; low: $50).
Purpose and activities: The foundation disburses employee-matching gifts only.
Fields of interest: Arts; Education; Environment; Human services; Christian agencies & churches; Disabilities, people with.
Type of support: Employee matching gifts.
Limitations: Applications not accepted. Giving on a national basis. No support for domestic animal shelters. No grants to individuals.
Publications: Informational brochure.
Application information: Contributes only to pre-selected organizations.
Board meeting date(s): Quarterly
Trustees: J. Patrick Gallagher, Jr.; Robert E. Gallagher, Jr.; Douglas K. Howell.
Number of staff: 1 part-time support.
EIN: 366082304
Selected grants: The following grants are a representative sample of this grantmaker's funding activity:
$1,000 to University of Chicago, Divinity School, Chicago, IL, 2012. For general exempt purpose.

2856
Christopher B. Galvin Family Foundation ✧
33 Indian Hill Rd.
Winnetka, IL 60093-3940

Established in 2004 in IL.
Donor: Christopher B. Galvin.
Foundation type: Independent foundation.
Financial data (yr. ended 12/31/12): Assets, $5,104,051 (M); gifts received, $500,000; expenditures, $571,906; qualifying distributions, $496,500; giving activities include $496,500 for grants.
Fields of interest: Arts; Higher education; Public affairs.
Limitations: Applications not accepted. Giving primarily in Washington, DC, IL and VA. No grants to individuals.
Application information: Contributes only to pre-selected organizations.
Trustees: Christopher B. Galvin; Cynthia Galvin.
EIN: 550887504

2857
Robert W. Galvin Foundation ✧
71 S. Wacker Dr., Ste. 3575
Chicago, IL 60606-4610 (312) 376-0100
Contact: Christopher B. Galvin, Pres.

Incorporated in 1953 in IL.
Donor: Robert W. Galvin†.
Foundation type: Independent foundation.
Financial data (yr. ended 12/31/12): Assets, $43,516,537 (M); expenditures, $1,312,564; qualifying distributions, $615,000; giving activities include $615,000 for grants.
Purpose and activities: Giving primarily for higher and other education as well as for the arts, and children, youth, and social services.
Fields of interest: Museums (history); Arts; Higher education; Education; Human services; Children/ youth, services; United Ways and Federated Giving Programs.
Limitations: Applications accepted. Giving in the U.S., with emphasis on IL, particularly Chicago. No grants to individuals.
Application information: Application form not required.

Initial approach: Proposal
Deadline(s): None
Board meeting date(s): Annually
Officers: Christopher B. Galvin, Pres.; Michael P. Galvin, V.P.; Mary G. Galvin, Secy.-Treas.
EIN: 366065560

2858
Paul Galvin Memorial Foundation Trust ✧
(formerly Helen M. Galvin Charitable Trust)
71 S. Wacker Dr., Ste. 3575
Chicago, IL 60606-4637

Established in 1989 in AZ.
Donor: Helen M. Galvin‡.
Foundation type: Independent foundation.
Financial data (yr. ended 12/31/12): Assets, $64,484,997 (M); expenditures, $4,655,148; qualifying distributions, $3,750,025; giving activities include $3,748,150 for 105 grants (high: $1,100,000; low: $150).
Purpose and activities: Giving primarily for health associations, and human services.
Fields of interest: Museums (children's); Arts; Higher education; Hospitals (general); Health organizations, association; Medical research, institute; Children/youth, services.
Limitations: Applications not accepted. Giving primarily IL; some funding also in Pasadena, CA, and Washington, DC. No grants to individuals.
Application information: Contributes only to pre-selected organizations.
Trustees: Christopher Galvin; Michael Galvin.
EIN: 866182808

2859
Gates Charitable Trust ✧
c/o John S. Gates, Jr.
410 N. Michigan Ave., Ste. 333
Chicago, IL 60611-4213

Established in 1997 in IL.
Donor: John S. Gates, Jr.
Foundation type: Independent foundation.
Financial data (yr. ended 12/31/13): Assets, $6,744,752 (M); expenditures, $785,154; qualifying distributions, $735,366; giving activities include $701,732 for 34 grants (high: $388,750; low: $200).
Purpose and activities: Giving primarily for education, human services, and for children services, including a children's hospital.
Fields of interest: Higher education; Education; Hospitals (specialty); Human services; Children/youth, services.
Limitations: Applications not accepted. Giving primarily in Chicago, IL; some funding also in Hartford, CT. No grants to individuals.
Application information: Contributes only to pre-selected organizations.
Trustee: John S. Gates, Jr.
EIN: 367193328

2860
James & Zita Gavin Foundation ✧
701 Park Dr.
Kenilworth, IL 60043-1008

Established in 1983 in IL.
Donors: James J. Gavin, Jr.; Zita C. Gavin; Mission Society of Mandeville; William Gavin; Zita C. Gavin Irrevocable Trust.
Foundation type: Independent foundation.
Financial data (yr. ended 12/31/13): Assets, $14,800,993 (M); gifts received, $100,000; expenditures, $688,069; qualifying distributions, $679,718; giving activities include $679,250 for 21 grants (high: $135,000; low: $4,000).
Purpose and activities: Support primarily for Roman Catholic organizations and ministries.
Fields of interest: Education; Human services; Catholic agencies & churches.
Limitations: Applications not accepted. Giving primarily in IL and OH. No grants to individuals.
Application information: Contributes only to pre-selected organizations.
Officers: Zita C. Gavin, Pres.; William Gavin, V.P.; Steven J. Gavin, Secy.; James L. Gavin, Treas.
EIN: 363256613
Selected grants: The following grants are a representative sample of this grantmaker's funding activity:
$265,000 to Lumen Christi Institute, Chicago, IL, 2012. For grant expense.

2861
Elizabeth Morse Genius Charitable Trust ✧
c/o US Trust, Philanthropic Solutions
231 S. LaSalle St., IL 1-231-13-32
Chicago, IL 60697-0001 (312) 828-1029
Contact: Kristin Carlson Vogen, Sr. V.P.
E-mail: ilgrantmaking@ustrust.com; Main URL: http://www.emgeniustrust.org

Established in 1992 in IL.
Foundation type: Independent foundation.
Financial data (yr. ended 11/30/13): Assets, $62,177,443 (M); expenditures, $3,304,755; qualifying distributions, $2,736,722; giving activities include $2,261,094 for 29 grants (high: $500,000; low: $5,000).
Purpose and activities: Giving primarily for individual self-reliance, the relief of human suffering, and the fostering of individual self-worth, with an emphasis on the classical fine arts, the development of physical health and spiritual well-being, and the promotion of world peace through the improvement of travel.
Fields of interest: Education; Health organizations; Human services; Children/youth, services.
Limitations: Applications accepted. Giving limited to Chicago, IL, metropolitan area. No grants to individuals, or for capital campaigns or endowments.
Publications: Application guidelines.
Application information: Letter of Inquiry must be written in font size no smaller than Times New Roman 12-point, with standard, 1-inch margins and double spaced. Letters exceeding 3 pages will not be considered. Full proposals are by invitation only, upon review of Letter of Inquiry. Applicants who have previously received a grant from the trust must, prior to submitting a Letter of Inquiry, timely submit a report on the prior grant in accordance with its grant letter. Application form required.
Initial approach: Letter of Inquiry (no more than 3 pages)
Copies of proposal: 2
Deadline(s): None
Board meeting date(s): Ongoing
Final notification: 1-4 months (for Letter of Inquiry)
Trustees: James L. Alexander; Bank of America, N.A.
EIN: 367010559
Selected grants: The following grants are a representative sample of this grantmaker's funding activity:
$262,500 to Reading in Motion, Chicago, IL, 2012. For Area One Expansion Project and Benchmarks Program.
$250,000 to Lyric Opera of Chicago, Chicago, IL, 2012. For production of Show Boat and Elektra for following year.
$250,000 to Metropolis Strategies, Chicago, IL, 2012. For general operating support.
$200,000 to Lutheran Social Services of Illinois, Des Plaines, IL, 2012. For Steps to Life, Connections, and Project IMPACT programs.
$150,000 to Chicago Historical Society, Chicago History Museum, Chicago, IL, 2012. For challenge grant to support the exhibition LGBT Chicago.
$100,000 to Ann and Robert H. Lurie Children's Hospital of Chicago Foundation, Chicago, IL, 2012. For Bridges Palliative Care program and Heroes for Life: Campaign for Ann and Robert H. Lurie Children's Hospital of Chicago.
$50,000 to Chicago Historical Society, Chicago History Museum, Chicago, IL, 2012. For challenge grant to support the exhibition LGBT Chicago.
$50,000 to Juvenile Protective Association, Chicago, IL, 2012. For Building Bridges to North Lawndale (BBNL) pilot project.
$25,000 to Chicago Public Library Foundation, Chicago, IL, 2012. For Honorary Grant.
$25,000 to Sarah's Circle, Chicago, IL, 2012. For general operating support.

2862
Joseph L. & Emily K. Gidwitz Memorial Foundation ✧
(formerly Division Fund)
200 S. Wacker Dr., Ste. 4000
Chicago, IL 60606-1274
Contact: Kevin O'Keefe

Established in 1983 as the Division Foundation.
Donor: Joseph L. Gidwitz.
Foundation type: Independent foundation.
Financial data (yr. ended 12/31/13): Assets, $21,198,138 (M); expenditures, $793,843; qualifying distributions, $525,010; giving activities include $525,010 for 11 grants (high: $150,000; low: $5).
Purpose and activities: Giving primarily to Jewish federated giving programs.
Fields of interest: Museums; Human services; Jewish federated giving programs.
Limitations: Applications accepted. Giving primarily in Chicago, IL.
Application information: Application form required.
Initial approach: Letter
Deadline(s): None
Officers: Betsy R. Gidwitz, Pres.; Ronald J. Gidwitz, Secy.
Director: Richard M. Horwood.
EIN: 363209007

2863
The Gies Foundation ✧
500 W. Madison St., Ste. 3890
Chicago, IL 60661-4593

Established in 2004 in IL.
Donors: Beth G. Gies; Larry W. Gies, Jr.; Madison GMT, LLC; Larry W. Gies.
Foundation type: Independent foundation.
Financial data (yr. ended 12/31/13): Assets, $7,416,406 (M); expenditures, $737,337; qualifying distributions, $724,726; giving activities include $721,570 for 8 grants (high: $525,000; low: $1,000).
Fields of interest: Education; Medical research; Children/youth, services.
Limitations: Applications not accepted. Giving primarily in IL. No grants to individuals.
Application information: Contributes only to pre-selected organizations.
Officers and Directors:* Larry W. Gies,* Pres.; Beth G. Gies,* Secy.; Brian F. Richards.
EIN: 201685394
Selected grants: The following grants are a representative sample of this grantmaker's funding activity:
$374,000 to Chicago Jesuit Academy, Chicago, IL, 2011.
$36,585 to Holy Trinity High School, Chicago, IL, 2011.
$25,000 to Teach for America, New York, NY, 2011.
$15,000 to Glenwood School, Glenwood, IL, 2011.
$7,500 to Royal Family Kids Camp, Santa Ana, CA, 2011.

2864
Gilmore Foundation ✧ ☆
416 Main St., Ste. 1125
Peoria, IL 61602-1154 (309) 671-9600

Donors: Jean Gilmore; Robert E. Gilmore.
Foundation type: Independent foundation.
Financial data (yr. ended 12/31/13): Assets, $1,112,282 (M); gifts received, $400,000; expenditures, $526,630; qualifying distributions, $520,109; giving activities include $518,750 for 27 grants (high: $260,000; low: $250).
Fields of interest: Arts; Higher education; Human services; Christian agencies & churches.
Application information: Application form not required.
Initial approach: Proposal
Deadline(s): None
Officers and Directors :* Robert E. Gilmore, Pres.; Douglas Oberhelman,* V.P.; Nathan R. Miller,* Secy.; Lawrence Williams IV,* Treas.; Dan Daly.
EIN: 271400179
Selected grants: The following grants are a representative sample of this grantmaker's funding activity:
$250,000 to Peoria Riverfront Museum, Peoria, IL, 2011.

2865
GKN Foundation ✧
(formerly Interlake Foundation)
550 davey Rd., Ste. 300
Woodridge, IL 60517-5064 (630) 737-1456
Contact: Hugo Perez, Treas. and Dir.

Incorporated in 1951 in IL.
Donor: The Interlake Corp.
Foundation type: Company-sponsored foundation.
Financial data (yr. ended 12/31/13): Assets, $2,827,840 (M); expenditures, $704,214; qualifying distributions, $689,810; giving activities include $668,500 for 281 grants (high: $30,000; low: $250), and $21,310 for 33 employee matching gifts.
Purpose and activities: The foundation supports community foundations and organizations involved with arts and culture, education, health, cancer, diabetes, human services, and community economic development.
Fields of interest: Animals/wildlife; Community/economic development; Religion.
Limitations: Applications accepted. Giving primarily in areas of company operations, with emphasis on IL. No support for political, religious, or athletics organizations.
Application information: Application form required.
Initial approach: Letter
Deadline(s): Jan. 1 for Scholarships
Officers and Directors:* Paul J. Westman,* Pres.; John M. O'Donnell,* V.P. and Genl. Counsel; Barbara A. Gustafson, Secy.; Hugo Perez,* Treas.
EIN: 362590617
Selected grants: The following grants are a representative sample of this grantmaker's funding activity:
$10,000 to Salesmanship Club of Dallas, Dallas, TX, 2011.
$5,000 to American Cancer Society, Atlanta, GA, 2011.
$5,000 to Childrens Hospital Medical Center, Cincinnati, OH, 2011.
$5,000 to College of DuPage Foundation, Glen Ellyn, IL, 2011.
$5,000 to Orangewood Childrens Foundation, Santa Ana, CA, 2011.
$5,000 to United Way of Long Island, Deer Park, NY, 2011.
$2,500 to Hospice of Cincinnati, Cincinnati, OH, 2011.
$2,500 to Safe Kids Worldwide, Washington, DC, 2011.
$2,000 to Hunger Task Force, Milwaukee, WI, 2011.
$1,000 to Art Institute of Chicago, Chicago, IL, 2011.

2866
Sidney and Lisa Glenner Foundation ✧
5454 W. Fargo Ave.
Skokie, IL 60077-3210 (847) 674-5454
Contact: Sidney Glenner, Pres.

Established in 1986 in IL.
Donors: Sidney Glenner; Wi-Fi Wheeling and Dealing, LLC.
Foundation type: Independent foundation.
Financial data (yr. ended 11/30/13): Assets, $3,609,227 (M); gifts received, $2,166,319; expenditures, $1,955,736; qualifying distributions, $1,950,641; giving activities include $1,931,506 for 589 grants (high: $250,000; low: $10).
Purpose and activities: Giving primarily to Jewish temples, organizations, and schools.
Fields of interest: Education; Jewish federated giving programs; Jewish agencies & synagogues.
Type of support: General/operating support.
Limitations: Applications accepted. Giving primarily in IL, NJ, NY, and Israel.
Application information: Application form required.
Initial approach: Letter
Deadline(s): None
Officers and Directors:* Sidney Glenner,* Pres.; Lisa Glenner,* Secy.
EIN: 363557155
Selected grants: The following grants are a representative sample of this grantmaker's funding activity:
$65,000 to Central Fund of Israel, New York, NY, 2011. For unrestricted purposes.
$50,000 to Central Fund of Israel, New York, NY, 2011. For unrestricted purposes.
$10,400 to Arie Crown Hebrew Day School, Skokie, IL, 2011. For unrestricted purposes.
$10,000 to KESHET, Northbrook, IL, 2011. For unrestricted purposes.
$10,000 to KESHET, Northbrook, IL, 2011. For unrestricted purposes.
$10,000 to KESHET, Northbrook, IL, 2011. For unrestricted purposes.
$10,000 to KESHET, Northbrook, IL, 2011. For unrestricted purposes.
$10,000 to KESHET, Northbrook, IL, 2011. For unrestricted purposes.
$5,000 to Hebrew Theological College, Skokie, IL, 2011. For unrestricted purposes.
$1,800 to Hebron Fund, Brooklyn, NY, 2011. For unrestricted purposes.

2867
Walter & Karla Goldschmidt Foundation ✧
465 Lakeside Terr.
Glencoe, IL 60022-1760 (847) 835-4655

Established in 1974 in IL.
Donors: Walter Goldschmidt; Karla Goldschmidt; WMG, Inc. Pension Plan; Goldschmidt IRA at Morgan Stanley; Goldschmidt IRA at Baird; The Karla Goldschmidt Trust; W.M.G., Inc.; Walter Goldschmidt Trust.
Foundation type: Independent foundation.
Financial data (yr. ended 11/30/13): Assets, $25,031,080 (M); expenditures, $1,302,830; qualifying distributions, $1,009,384; giving activities include $1,001,030 for 103 grants (high: $188,750; low: $125).
Fields of interest: Arts; Education; Health organizations, association; Boys & girls clubs; Human services.
Limitations: Applications accepted. Giving primarily in the Chicago, IL, area.
Application information: Application form not required.
Initial approach: Letter
Deadline(s): None
Officers and Directors:* Susan Goldschmidt,* Pres. and Secy.; Miles Taub,* V.P. and Treas.; Jane Deal; James Goldschmidt.
EIN: 237410867
Selected grants: The following grants are a representative sample of this grantmaker's funding activity:
$25,000 to Boys and Girls Clubs of America, Atlanta, GA, 2011.
$1,000 to Boys and Girls Clubs of Kern County, Bakersfield, CA, 2011.

2868
Goodman Family Foundation ✧
4711 W. Golf Rd., Ste. 1000
Skokie, IL 60076-1235 (847) 674-1400
FAX: (847) 674-8157;
E-mail: sbaum@llgoogmanfdn.org; Main URL: http://www.llgoodmanfdn.org/

Established in 1994 in IL.
Donors: Lawrence Goodman; Cebrin Goodman†; Goodman Real Estate Partnership; Lawrence Goodman Revocable Trust; Alliance Bernstein, L.P.; Sharyn Johnson; Ilyse Lopatin.
Foundation type: Independent foundation.
Financial data (yr. ended 12/31/13): Assets, $20,216,290 (M); gifts received, $2,819,720; expenditures, $1,400,988; qualifying distributions, $1,220,024; giving activities include $1,002,251 for 31+ grants (high: $760,000).
Purpose and activities: Giving primarily for Jewish causes and to secular organizations which address hunger issues and promote the prevention of drug abuse.
Fields of interest: Substance abuse, prevention; Food banks; Jewish federated giving programs; Jewish agencies & synagogues.
International interests: Israel.
Limitations: Giving primarily in Chicago, IL; some funding also in West Palm Beach, FL. Funding also in the area of Be'er Sheva, Israel and the surrounding Negev. No support for political campaigns, or to organizations that aspire to build or renovate places of business, or purchase or refurbish capital as needed. No grants to individuals, or for conferences, festivals, exhibitions, or debt reduction.
Application information: Unsolicited proposals are not accepted. Letters of inquiry and full proposals are by invitation only, upon review of grant inquiry form.
Initial approach: Use grant inquiry form on foundation web site
Final notification: For grant inquiry form submissions: within 60 days
Officers: Lawrence Goodman, Pres.; Lawrence Etchell, Secy.-Treas.; Susan Rifkin, Mgr.
Director: Sharyn Johnson.
EIN: 363956748

2869
The Ellis Goodman Family Foundation ✧
(formerly Gillian and Ellis Goodman Foundation)
69 Park Ave.
Glencoe, IL 60022-1333

Established in 1987 in IL.
Donors: Gillian Goodman; Ellis M. Goodman; Paul Goodman; Cathy Green.
Foundation type: Independent foundation.
Financial data (yr. ended 12/31/13): Assets, $9,672,599 (M); gifts received, $500,000; expenditures, $1,021,456; qualifying distributions, $957,273; giving activities include $957,273 for 60 grants (high: $260,200; low: $50).
Fields of interest: Arts; Education; Botanical gardens; Health organizations, association; Human services; Jewish federated giving programs.
Limitations: Applications not accepted. Giving primarily in IL and NY; funding also in London, England. No grants to individuals.
Application information: Contributes only to pre-selected organizations.
Officers: Ellis M. Goodman, Pres. and Treas.; Gillian Goodman, V.P. and Secy.
EIN: 363566590
Selected grants: The following grants are a representative sample of this grantmaker's funding activity:
$89,750 to Writers Theater, Glencoe, IL, 2011.
$25,000 to Portland Trust, London, England, 2011.
$15,000 to Environmental Law and Policy Center of the Midwest, Chicago, IL, 2011.
$15,000 to Family Farmed Organization, Oak Park, IL, 2011.
$10,000 to Christopher House, Chicago, IL, 2011.
$2,500 to Lake Forest College, Lake Forest, IL, 2011.
$1,000 to Eisenhower Medical Center, Rancho Mirage, CA, 2011.
$1,000 to Rehabilitation Institute of Chicago, Chicago, IL, 2011.
$1,000 to Salvation Army, Chicago, IL, 2011.

2870
William and Karen Goodyear Foundation ✧
c/o Bank of America, N.A.
231 S. LaSalle St.
Chicago, IL 60697-0001
Application address: 30 S. Wacker Dr., Ste. 3550, Chicago, IL 60606

Established in 1997.
Donors: Karen E. Goodyear; William M. Goodyear.
Foundation type: Independent foundation.
Financial data (yr. ended 04/30/13): Assets, $289,082 (M); gifts received, $400,000; expenditures, $868,090; qualifying distributions, $867,950; giving activities include $867,950 for grants.
Fields of interest: Museums; Higher education; Hospitals (general); Human services; Catholic agencies & churches.
Limitations: Applications accepted. Giving primarily in Chicago, IL.
Application information: Application form not required.
Initial approach: Letter
Deadline(s): None
Trustees: Karen E. Goodyear; William M. Goodyear.
EIN: 364157874
Selected grants: The following grants are a representative sample of this grantmaker's funding activity:
$260,000 to University of Notre Dame, Notre Dame, IN, 2013. For MBA Fellowship.
$225,000 to Museum of Science and Industry, Chicago, IL, 2013. For Science Rediscovered.
$200,000 to Rush University Medical Center, Chicago, IL, 2013. For Rush University Medical Center.
$20,000 to University of Notre Dame, Notre Dame, IN, 2013. For Malpass Scholars Program.
$1,200 to Chicago Symphony Orchestra, Chicago, IL, 2013. For Women's Board.

2871
Gore Family Memorial Foundation ✧
P.O. Box 803878
Chicago, IL 60680-3878

Trust established in 1973 in FL.
Donor: R.H. Gore Trust.
Foundation type: Independent foundation.
Financial data (yr. ended 01/31/14): Assets, $22,114,411 (M); expenditures, $914,406; qualifying distributions, $809,918; giving activities include $553,199 for 23 grants (high: $50,000; low: $1,650).
Purpose and activities: Aid to the needy and handicapped; aid to the needy restricted to Broward County, FL; scholarships restricted to Broward County residents, except for severely handicapped applicants.
Fields of interest: Higher education; Disabilities, people with; Economically disadvantaged.
Type of support: General/operating support; Grants to individuals; Scholarships—to individuals.
Limitations: Applications not accepted. Giving primarily in Fort Lauderdale, FL.
Application information: Unsolicited requests for funds not accepted.
Trustees: Lorena Gore Dunlap; Charles H. Gore; David S. Gore; Paul A. Gore; Theodore Thomas Gore, Jr.; Steve Knapp; Nancy G. Saravia; Patricia Palmer Schiff; Kathleen P. Whitney.
Number of staff: 2 full-time support.
EIN: 596497544
Selected grants: The following grants are a representative sample of this grantmaker's funding activity:
$12,806 to University of Miami, Miller School of Science Department of Otolaryngology, Miami, FL, 2013. For U.M. Ear Institute Medical Aid to the Handicapped - Honor G.H. Gore.
$7,500 to University of South Dakota, Sanford School of Medicine, Vermillion, SD, 2013. For Scholarship Funds for Disabled Student.
$5,000 to Salvation Army of Broward County, Fort Lauderdale, FL, 2013. For Emergency Food Replenishment for Pantry - Assistance to aged/needy.
$4,433 to University of Central Florida, Orlando, FL, 2013. For Scholarship Funds for Disabled Student.

2872
Grace Foundation ✧
407 S. 3rd St., No. 230
Geneva, IL 60134-2741

Established in 1985 in IL.
Donors: Robert Van Kampen†; Sola Scriptura.
Foundation type: Independent foundation.
Financial data (yr. ended 12/31/12): Assets, $21,983,509 (M); gifts received, $551,080; expenditures, $4,669,695; qualifying distributions, $4,611,300; giving activities include $4,611,300 for grants.
Fields of interest: Foundations (private grantmaking); Christian agencies & churches.
Limitations: Applications not accepted. Giving in the U.S., with emphasis on FL, IL, MI, and NC. No grants to individuals.
Application information: Contributes only to pre-selected organizations.
Officers: Dean H. Tisch, V.P.; Jerald A. Trannel, Treas.; Scott Pierre, Exec. Dir.
Directors: Judith Van Kampen; Karla Van Kampen-Pierre; Kristen Wisen.
EIN: 363374325

2873
Graham Foundation for Advanced Studies in the Fine Arts ✧
4 W. Burton Pl.
Chicago, IL 60610-1416
Contact: Sarah C. Herda, Exec. Dir.
E-mail: info@grahamfoundation.org; Main URL: http://www.grahamfoundation.org
Facebook: http://www.facebook.com/pages/Graham-Foundation-for-Advanced-Studies-in-the-Fine-Arts/72868252843
Grants Database: http://www.grahamfoundation.org/grantees
Twitter: http://www.twitter.com/grahamfound/

Incorporated in 1956 in IL.
Donor: Ernest R. Graham†.
Foundation type: Independent foundation.
Financial data (yr. ended 12/31/13): Assets, $46,298,849 (M); expenditures, $2,529,249; qualifying distributions, $2,112,149; giving activities include $448,417 for 46 grants (high: $20,000; low: $1,417), and $484,467 for 79 grants to individuals (high: $20,000; low: $100).
Purpose and activities: Founded in 1956, the Graham Foundation for Advanced Studies in the Fine Arts makes project-based grants to individuals and organizations and produces public programs to foster the development and exchange of diverse and challenging ideas about architecture and its role in the arts, culture, and society.
Fields of interest: Visual arts; Visual arts, architecture.
Type of support: Grants to individuals; Program development; Publication; Research.
Limitations: Applications accepted. Giving primarily in the U.S. and internationally. No grants for endowments, general operating expenses, capital projects, scholarship aid or for work in pursuit of an academic degree (except for the Carter Manny Award), debt or expenses incurred prior to the date of grant request.
Publications: Application guidelines; Annual report (including application guidelines); Grants list.
Application information: Full proposals by invitation only. Application guidelines available on foundation web site. After Inquiry Forms are reviewed, applicants whose projects best match the foundation's priorities and interests are invited to submit a Proposal Form and supplementary materials. Applicants who are not invited to submit a Proposal Form are sent a decline letter at this stage. Decisions are based on: Priority of the proposed project as related to our mission and interests; Potential impact of the project; Availability of Graham Foundation funds. Grant Decision: Funding recommendations are presented to the Board of Trustees for consideration. If a grant is awarded to an applicant, he or she will be asked to sign a Grant Agreement that outlines the conditions of the award, such as annual reporting. Application form not required.
Initial approach: Inquiry form (submitted electronically)
Copies of proposal: 1
Deadline(s): Individuals must apply at the fall deadline and organizations must apply at the spring deadline. For Individuals: Inquiry Form deadline: Sept. 15. For organizations, inquiry form deadline: Feb. 25th. Deadline for the Carter Manny Award: March 15th
Board meeting date(s): Spring and Summer
Final notification: 4 months for Carter Manny Award; 5 months for other grants
Officers and Trustees:* Hamza Walker,* Pres.; Ross Wimer,* V.P.; Chandra Goldsmith Gray,* Secy.; Rena Conti,* Treas.; Theaster Gates; Sean Keller; Randall Kroszner; Eric T. McKissack; John Ronan; Bruce Sagan; John Syvertsen.
Director: Sarah Herda.
Number of staff: 5 full-time professional.
EIN: 362356089
Selected grants: The following grants are a representative sample of this grantmaker's funding activity:
$25,000 to Institute for Urban Design, New York, NY, 2012. For Spontaneous Interventions Design Actions for the Common Good.
$20,000 to Art Institute of Chicago, Chicago, IL, 2012. For Building Inside Studio Gang Architects.
$15,000 to Artists Space, New York, NY, 2012. For Bernadette Corporation 2000 Wasted Years.
$15,000 to Harvard University, Department of Visual and Environmental Studies, Cambridge, MA, 2012. For Brute.
$15,000 to Storefront for Art and Architecture, New York, NY, 2012. For Critical History Project.
$15,000 to Yale University, Yale School of Architecture, New Haven, CT, 2012. For Palladio Virtuel Inventing the Palladian Project.
$10,000 to Architectural League of New York, New York, NY, 2012. For Form, Idea, Resonance Thirty Years of Architectural League Emerging Voices.
$10,000 to MAK Center for Art and Architecture, West Hollywood, CA, 2012. For Schindler Lab.
$10,000 to Southern California Institute of Architecture, Los Angeles, CA, 2012. For A Confederacy of Heretics The Architecture Gallery, Venice, 1979.
$5,000 to Archeworks, Chicago, IL, 2012. For Archeworks New Practice Program.

2874
The Grainger Foundation Inc. ✧
100 Grainger Pkwy.
Lake Forest, IL 60045-5201 (847) 535-1000
Contact: Gloria J. Sinclair, V.P. and Secy.

Incorporated in 1967 in IL as successor to the Grainger Charitable Trust established in 1949.
Donors: William W. Grainger†; Hally W. Grainger†; David W. Grainger.
Foundation type: Independent foundation.
Financial data (yr. ended 12/31/13): Assets, $445,096,516 (M); gifts received, $230,860,000; expenditures, $58,019,938; qualifying distributions, $54,710,239; giving activities include $54,710,239 for 809 grants (high: $24,938,241; low: $1,000).
Purpose and activities: Emphasis on capital funds, and special program funds for education, cultural institutions (museums, the arts, and symphony orchestras), hospitals, and human service organizations.
Fields of interest: Museums; Arts; Education; Health care; Medical research; Human services; Engineering; Science.
Type of support: General/operating support; Continuing support; Capital campaigns; Building/renovation; Equipment; Endowments; Program development; Professorships; Fellowships; Scholarship funds; Research.
Limitations: Applications not accepted. Giving on a national basis. No grants to individuals, or for seed money, emergency funds, deficit financing, publications, conferences, or matching gifts; no loans.
Application information: The foundation contributes only to pre-selected charitable organizations as determined by its directors and officers. For this reason, and due to staffing constraints, grant requests received from organizations other than those first contacted by The Grainger Foundation cannot be acknowledged.
Board meeting date(s): Periodically
Officers and Directors:* David W. Grainger,* Pres.; Gloria J. Sinclair, V.P. and Secy.; William B. Hayden, V.P.; Chris J. Bellmore, Treas.; John S. Chapman; John L. Howard; David L. Kendall.
Number of staff: 4 part-time professional; 1 part-time support.
EIN: 366192971
Selected grants: The following grants are a representative sample of this grantmaker's funding activity:
$3,514,108 to Field Museum of Natural History, Chicago, IL, 2012. For Grainger Digital Initiative and Fund for Science. Grant made in form of stock.
$3,011,390 to Rush University Medical Center, Chicago, IL, 2012. For Dual Control da Vinci si Surgical System. Grant made in form of stock.
$2,520,450 to Museum of Science and Industry, Chicago, IL, 2012. For Amazing Fractals Mirror Maze. Grant made in form of stock.
$2,508,216 to Rehabilitation Institute of Chicago, Chicago, IL, 2012. For Grainger Pediatric Ability Lab. Grant made in form of stock.
$2,496,481 to Yale University, New Haven, CT, 2012. For Engineering, Land Conservation, Art Conservation, Asian Studies. Grant made in form of stock.
$2,022,312 to Window to the World Communications, Chicago, IL, 2012. For Capital Campaign, Media Center. Grant made in form of stock.
$75,000 to North Chicago Community Partners, Lake Bluff, IL, 2012. For Unrestricted -Community School Program.
$10,000 to Florida State College Foundation, Jacksonville, FL, 2012. For Logistics and Supply Chain Management Program.
$10,000 to Irving Healthcare Foundation, Irving, TX, 2012. For Program Support.
$10,000 to YMCA of Central Ohio, Columbus, OH, 2012. For YMCA Performing Arts Summer Camp.

2875
Grand Victoria Foundation ✧
230 W. Monroe St., Ste. 2530
Chicago, IL 60606-5048 (312) 609-0200
Contact: Nancy Fishman, Exec. Dir.; Mary Kay Francel, Dir., Opers.
FAX: (312) 658-0738;
E-mail: nancyf@grandvictoriafdn.org; Application address for Elgin Grantworks: 50 S. Grove Ave. Ste. A, Elgin, IL 60120, tel.: (847) 289-8575, fax: (847) 289-8576; Additional e-mail: info@grandvictoriafdn.org; E-mail for Vital Lands Illinois: vitallandsillinois@grandvictoriafdn.org; Main URL: http://www.grandvictoriafdn.org
Grants List: http://www.grandvictoriafdn.org/grants-list

Established in 1996 in IL.
Donors: Grand Victoria Casino; Elgin Riverboat Resort.
Foundation type: Company-sponsored foundation.
Financial data (yr. ended 12/31/12): Assets, $100,440,477 (M); gifts received, $7,365,721; expenditures, $9,520,891; qualifying distributions,

$9,374,356; giving activities include $7,551,131 for 129 grants (high: $578,000; low: $275), and $7,160 for 10 employee matching gifts.
Purpose and activities: The foundation supports programs designed to strengthen educational opportunities for children and adults; foster economic vitality of neighborhoods, cities, and regions; and restore and preserve natural resources.
Fields of interest: Education, early childhood education; Elementary/secondary school reform; Environment, air pollution; Environment, natural resources; Environment, water resources; Environment, land resources; Environment, plant conservation; Community/economic development, public policy; Public affairs, reform; Transportation.
Type of support: General/operating support; Continuing support; Management development/ capacity building; Land acquisition; Program development; Technical assistance; Employee matching gifts.
Limitations: Applications accepted. Giving limited to the Chicago metropolitan region, Elgin, and statewide efforts. No support for religious or political purposes; or to support programs that are beyond the scope of the Foundation's mission and strategies. No grants to individuals, or for endowments, capital campaigns, fundraising events, debt reduction, research, or planning projects.
Publications: Application guidelines; Financial statement; Grants list; Informational brochure; Occasional report; Program policy statement.
Application information: Application form required.
Initial approach: Letter of inquiry; Core Grant Program: Download guidelines, follow instructions, prepare and send letter of inquiry; Elgin Grantworks: download guidelines/ application form and send proposal with application to 50A S. Grove, Elgin, IL 60120; Vital Land Illinois: Download guidelines, prepare application and email to vitallandsillinois@grandvictoriafdn.org
Deadline(s): 1st Fri. in May and Oct. for Education, Economic Development, and Environment; 1st Fri. in Feb., Jun., and Oct. for Elgin Grantworks; None for Vital Lands Illinois
Board meeting date(s): Quarterly
Final notification: 20 working days for letter of inquiry; Elgin Grantworks: 8-10 weeks for grant decision; Vital Lands Illinois: 5-10 weeks from receipt of full proposal
Officers and Directors:* Nicholas J. Pritzker, Pres.; Richard L. Schulze, Exec. V.P.; Daniel Azark,* V.P.; Phyllis James, Secy.; Corey Sanders,* Treas.; Nancy Fishman, Exec. Dir.; Taffy Hoffer; Will Martin; Eric T. McKissack.
Number of staff: 7 full-time professional; 2 full-time support.
EIN: 364107162
Selected grants: The following grants are a representative sample of this grantmaker's funding activity:
$335,000 to Openlands, Chicago, IL, 2012. For challenge grant.
$268,830 to Openlands, Chicago, IL, 2012. For program support.
$268,000 to Chicago Jobs Council, Chicago, IL, 2012. For general operating support.
$200,000 to Ounce of Prevention Fund, Chicago, IL, 2012. For general operating support.
$115,000 to Metropolitan Planning Council, Chicago, IL, 2012. For general operating support.
$85,000 to Advance Illinois, Chicago, IL, 2012. For general operating support.
$85,000 to Woodstock Institute, Chicago, IL, 2012. For general operating support.
$75,000 to Liberty Prairie Conservancy, Grayslake, IL, 2012. For program support.
$27,000 to Elgin Academy, Elgin, IL, 2012. For scholarships.
$25,000 to One Hope United, Lake Villa, IL, 2012. For general operating support.

2876
Grant Healthcare Foundation ✧
500 N. Western Ave., Ste. 204
Lake Forest, IL 60045-1955 (847) 735-1590
Contact: Joan Eldridge Ridell, Exec. Dir.
FAX: (847) 735-8770;
E-mail: koconnor@granthealthcare.org; Main URL: http://www.granthealthcare.org
Grants List: http://www.granthealthcare.org/awards.html

Established in 1996 in IL.
Foundation type: Independent foundation.
Financial data (yr. ended 12/31/13): Assets, $17,974,122 (M); gifts received, $392,882; expenditures, $1,494,306; qualifying distributions, $1,175,000; giving activities include $1,175,000 for 41 grants (high: $100,000; low: $7,000).
Purpose and activities: Giving primarily for healthcare organizations in the greater Chicago, IL, area.
Fields of interest: Reproductive health; Health care; Substance abuse, services; Economically disadvantaged.
Type of support: Matching/challenge support; General/operating support; Seed money.
Limitations: Applications accepted. Giving only in Chicago, IL, and the surrounding metropolitan area. No support for religious and political organizations. No grants to individuals.
Publications: Application guidelines; Grants list.
Application information: Grant applications are not to be submitted without prior approval of preliminary grant inquiry. Application form required.
Initial approach: Preliminary grant inquiry—must be submitted electronically
Copies of proposal: 1
Deadline(s): See foundation web site for current deadlines
Board meeting date(s): May, June, Aug., Oct., Nov. and Dec.
Final notification: Dec. 15
Officers and Directors:* Robert Friedlander,* Chair.; Richard M. Norton,* Secy.-Treas.; Kate Grubbs O'Connor, Exec. Dir.; Joseph S. Carr; George M. Covington; Richard Ross, Jr.
Number of staff: 1 full-time professional.
EIN: 362167090
Selected grants: The following grants are a representative sample of this grantmaker's funding activity:
$100,000 to Planned Parenthood of Illinois, Chicago, IL, 2012. For general operating support.
$100,000 to University of Chicago, Chicago, IL, 2012. For Project ECHO to improve access to specialty care in Chicago south side primary care clinics.
$53,063 to Ann and Robert H. Lurie Children's Hospital of Chicago, Chicago, IL, 2012. For Fellowship in Palliative Medicine.
$35,000 to Childrens Research Triangle, Chicago, IL, 2012. To assess and treat children impacted by fetal alcohol syndrome.
$30,000 to Chicago Family Health Center, Chicago, IL, 2012. For operating support of primary care clinic on Chicago's south side.
$30,000 to Saint Joseph Hospital, Chicago, IL, 2012. For uninsured patients at Laboure' Clinic.
$25,000 to American Indian Health Service of Chicago, Chicago, IL, 2012. For primary care clinic for Native Americans.
$25,000 to Hospice Foundation of Northeastern Illinois, Barrington, IL, 2012. For pediatric palliative care.
$25,000 to Juvenile Protective Association, Chicago, IL, 2012. For Building Bridges to North Lawndale project provide mental health sevices in primary schools.
$20,000 to Lawndale Christian Health Center, Chicago, IL, 2012. For prenatal program.

2877
Grant Thornton Foundation ✧
c/o Allison Moran
175 W. Jackson Blvd.
Chicago, IL 60604

Established in 2007 in IL.
Donor: Grant Thornton LLP.
Foundation type: Company-sponsored foundation.
Financial data (yr. ended 07/31/13): Assets, $1,000 (M); gifts received, $824,245; expenditures, $824,245; qualifying distributions, $824,245; giving activities include $812,266 for 101 grants (high: $50,000; low: $200).
Fields of interest: Higher education.
Type of support: General/operating support.
Limitations: Applications not accepted. Giving primarily in areas of company operations in AK, AL, AR, AZ, CA, CO, CT, DC, FL, GA, HI, IL, KS, KY, MA, MD, ME, MI, MN, MO, MS, NC, ND, NH, NJ, NM, NY, OH, OK, OR, PA, RI, SC, TN, UT, VA, WA, WI, and WV.
Application information: Contributes only to pre-selected organizations.
Officers and Directors:* Michael McGuire,* Pres.; Maureen Aidsani,* Secy.; Russell G. Wieman,* Treas.; Dorsey Baskin; Janet Malzone.
EIN: 300438415
Selected grants: The following grants are a representative sample of this grantmaker's funding activity:
$5,600 to Pace University, New York, NY, 2011.

2878
Richard and Mary Gray Foundation ✧
875 N. Michigan Ave., Ste. 2503
Chicago, IL 60611-3103
Contact: Richard Gray, Pres.
FAX: (312) 642-8488;
E-mail: rgray@richardgraygallery.com

Established in 1987 in IL.
Donors: Richard Gray; Graycor, Inc.
Foundation type: Independent foundation.
Financial data (yr. ended 12/31/12): Assets, $13,920,792 (M); expenditures, $938,904; qualifying distributions, $802,324; giving activities include $802,310 for 144 grants (high: $150,000; low: $25).
Purpose and activities: Giving for arts and culture and human services.

Fields of interest: Visual arts, architecture; Museums; Performing arts; Performing arts, music; Historic preservation/historical societies; Arts; Higher education.
Type of support: General/operating support; Annual campaigns; Capital campaigns; Endowments.
Limitations: Applications not accepted. Giving primarily in Chicago, IL. No grants to individuals.
Application information: Unsolicited requests for funds not accepted.
Officers: Richard Gray, Pres.; Mary L. Gray, V.P.
EIN: 363485580

2879
Florence C. Gregory Charitable Trust ✧
111 W. Monroe St., Tax Div. 10C
Chicago, IL 60603-4026

Established in IL; supporting organization of Clay County Hospital, Saint Anthony Hospital, Swedish American Hospital, Rockford Memorial Hospital, EAA Aviation Foundation Endowment, Salvation Army, and YMCA.
Foundation type: Independent foundation.
Financial data (yr. ended 09/30/13): Assets, $18,834,742 (M); expenditures, $999,690; qualifying distributions, $902,941; giving activities include $827,894 for 7 grants (high: $124,184; low: $82,790).
Fields of interest: Hospitals (general); Salvation Army; YM/YWCAs & YM/YWHAs.
Limitations: Applications not accepted. Giving primarily in IL.
Application information: Unsolicited requests for funds not accepted.
Trustee: BMO Harris Bank, N.A.
EIN: 367338985
Selected grants: The following grants are a representative sample of this grantmaker's funding activity:
$43,210 to EAA Aviation Foundation, Oshkosh, WI, 2011. For program support.

2880
David F. and Margaret T. Grohne Family Foundation ✧
4908 Lawn Ave.
Western Springs, IL 60558-1731
Contact: David Grohne, Pres.

Established in 1995 in IL.
Donors: David Grohne; Margaret Grohne.
Foundation type: Independent foundation.
Financial data (yr. ended 12/31/12): Assets, $60,838,629 (M); gifts received, $10,000,000; expenditures, $4,132,469; qualifying distributions, $3,822,500; giving activities include $3,822,500 for 30 grants (high: $2,000,000; low: $500).
Fields of interest: Animals/wildlife, preservation/protection; Health organizations; Human services.
Limitations: Giving primarily in Chicago, IL, MN, and TN. No grants to individuals.
Application information: Application form not required.
Deadline(s): None
Officers: David Grohne, Pres.; Margaret Grohne, V.P.
Directors: Jeffrey Grohne; Jennifer Huber; Patricia Tassone.
EIN: 364061509

2881
The Growmark Foundation ✧
1701 Towanda Ave.
P.O. Box 2500
Bloomington, IL 61702-2500

Established in IL.
Donor: Growmark, Inc.
Foundation type: Company-sponsored foundation.
Financial data (yr. ended 12/31/13): Assets, $7,050,129 (M); gifts received, $1,432,413; expenditures, $750,015; qualifying distributions, $738,950; giving activities include $738,950 for 89 grants (high: $75,000; low: $100).
Purpose and activities: The foundation supports food banks and organizations involved with higher education, plant conservation, health, and agriculture.
Fields of interest: Education; Agriculture/food; Community/economic development.
Type of support: General/operating support; Scholarship funds.
Limitations: Applications not accepted. Giving primarily in IL. No grants to individuals.
Application information: Contributes only to pre-selected organizations.
Directors: Marshall P. Bohbrink; Brent D. Bostrom; Steve Buckalew; Kevin Carroll; Brent Ericson; Shelly Kruse; Jeffrey M. Solberg; James Spradlin.
EIN: 371401632
Selected grants: The following grants are a representative sample of this grantmaker's funding activity:
$75,000 to Midwest Food Bank, Bloomington, IL, 2012. To support of Food Donations.
$60,000 to United Way of McLean County, Bloomington, IL, 2012. To support of Charitable Organizations.
$10,000 to Trees Forever, Marion, IA, 2012. To support of Tree Planting Activities.
$5,000 to Farm Safety 4 Just Kids, Urbandale, IA, 2012. To support of Child Farm Safety Programs.
$1,000 to Beyond the Books Educational Foundation, Bloomington, IL, 2012. To support of Education.
$1,000 to Ecology Action Center, Normal, IL, 2012. To support of Ecology Preservation Activities.
$1,000 to Illinois Agricultural Leadership Foundation, Macomb, IL, 2012. To support of Agricultural Leadership Activities.
$1,000 to Living History Farms Foundation, Urbandale, IA, 2012. To support of Agricultural Museums.
$500 to Personal Assistance Telephone Help, Bloomington, IL, 2012. To support of Community Charitable Activities.
$50 to Habitat for Humanity of McLean County, Bloomington, IL, 2012. For charitable organization.

2882
The Leo S. Guthman Fund ✧
c/o Iris Krieg Assocs.
333 N. Michigan Ave., No. 510
Chicago, IL 60601-3901 (312) 641-6330
FAX: (312) 641-5736; E-mail: iriskrieg1@aol.com; Additional e-mail: Lauren Krieg, Prog. Off., EQUIP Dir.: lauren@ikriegassoc.com; Main URL: http://www.lsgfchicago.org
Grants List: http://www.lsgfchicago.org/our_grantees0.aspx

Established in 2004 in IL.
Foundation type: Independent foundation.
Financial data (yr. ended 12/31/13): Assets, $2,620,343 (M); expenditures, $2,295,435; qualifying distributions, $2,286,681; giving activities include $2,210,921 for grants.
Purpose and activities: Giving primarily for the arts, education, children, youth and social services, women's organizations, and Jewish organizations.
Fields of interest: Arts education; Museums; Performing arts, theater; Arts; Zoos/zoological societies; Human services; Children/youth, services; Jewish agencies & synagogues; Children/youth; Youth; Economically disadvantaged.
Type of support: General/operating support; Continuing support; Management development/capacity building; Program development; Seed money; Technical assistance; Matching/challenge support.
Limitations: Applications accepted. Giving primarily in Making general grants in Chicago, IL, and elsewhere by trustee discretion. No support for political organizations. No grants to individuals; no scholarships.
Application information: Full proposals are by invitation only. Application form not required.
Initial approach: Brief letter or telephone call
Copies of proposal: 1
Deadline(s): Jan. 15 and Aug. 31
Board meeting date(s): Mar. and Oct.
Final notification: 3 months
Trustees: Lynne Rosenthal; Patti Silver.
EIN: 611459002

2883
The H.B.B. Foundation ✧
75 Executive Dr., Ste. 459
Aurora, IL 60654

Established in 1964 in IL.
Donor: Elizabeth Babson Tieken Charitable Lead Trust.
Foundation type: Independent foundation.
Financial data (yr. ended 12/31/13): Assets, $16,643,395 (M); gifts received, $909,966; expenditures, $788,991; qualifying distributions, $662,176; giving activities include $629,400 for 37 grants (high: $200,000; low: $400).
Purpose and activities: Giving primarily for health services, the arts, and children and youth services.
Fields of interest: Museums; Arts; Education; Environment; Health organizations, association; Human services; Children/youth, services.
Limitations: Applications not accepted. Giving primarily in CO, IL, MA, and VA. No grants to individuals.
Application information: Contributes only to pre-selected organizations.
Officers: Taylor Kirkpatrick, Co-Pres.; Theodore D. Tieken, Jr., Co-Pres.; Elizabeth Kirkpatrick, V.P.; Mark Stephenitch, Secy.- Treas.
Director: Nancy B. Tieken.
EIN: 366104969
Selected grants: The following grants are a representative sample of this grantmaker's funding activity:
$100,000 to Harvard College Association for U.S.-China Relations, Cambridge, MA, 2011.
$40,000 to Habitat for Humanity of Metro Denver, Denver, CO, 2011.
$10,000 to Montpelier Foundation, Montpelier Station, VA, 2011.

2884
Daniel P. Haerther Charitable Trust ✧
c/o Burke, Warren, Mackay & Serritell
330 N. Wabash Ave., 22nd Fl.
Chicago, IL 60611-3607

Established in 2007 in IL.
Donor: Haerther Living Trust.
Foundation type: Independent foundation.
Financial data (yr. ended 12/31/12): Assets, $40,140,232 (M); expenditures, $2,136,472; qualifying distributions, $1,774,816; giving activities include $1,774,816 for grants.
Fields of interest: Higher education, university; Aquariums.
Limitations: Applications not accepted. Giving primarily in IL.
Application information: Unsolicited requests for funds not accepted.
Trustees: Mary L. Burke; Richard W. Burke, Jr.; Richard W. Burke, Sr.; Jerome R. Prassas.
EIN: 261225450

2885
Patricia S. and William J. Hagenah Foundation ✧
c/o William J. Hagenah
1 Northfield Plz., Ste. 300
Northfield, IL 60093-1214

Established in 2003 in IL.
Donor: William J. Hagenah.
Foundation type: Independent foundation.
Financial data (yr. ended 12/31/13): Assets, $4,352,371 (M); expenditures, $531,024; qualifying distributions, $522,415; giving activities include $520,000 for 4 grants (high: $200,000; low: $20,000).
Fields of interest: Higher education; Horticulture/garden clubs; Hospitals (general).
Type of support: General/operating support.
Limitations: Applications not accepted. Giving primarily in IL. No grants to individuals.
Application information: Unsolicited requests for funds not accepted.
Trustee: William J. Hagenah.
EIN: 320087646

2886
John R. Halligan Charitable Fund ✧
c/o Neal, Gerber & Eisenberg, LLP
2 N. LaSalle St., Ste. 1700
Chicago, IL 60602-4000
Contact: Norman J. Gantz, Pres.
E-mail: ngantz@ngelaw.com

Established in 1963 in IL.
Donor: John R. Halligan†.
Foundation type: Independent foundation.
Financial data (yr. ended 12/31/12): Assets, $22,579,064 (M); expenditures, $1,745,416; qualifying distributions, $1,503,754; giving activities include $1,393,305 for 75 grants (high: $183,505; low: $3,000).
Purpose and activities: Giving for the arts, civic and cultural institutes.
Fields of interest: Museums; Historic preservation/historical societies; Arts; Animals/wildlife.
Type of support: General/operating support; Continuing support; Annual campaigns.
Limitations: Applications not accepted. Giving primarily in Honolulu, HI, and Chicago, IL. No grants to individuals.
Application information: Contributes only to pre-selected organizations.
Officers and Directors:* Norman J. Gantz,* Pres.; Lawrence Richman,* V.P.; Norman Kellerman,* Treas.
EIN: 366078591

2887
D.A. Hamel Family Charitable Trust ✧
10 S. Dearborn St., 21st Fl.
Chicago, IL 60603-2003

Established in 1986 in NY.
Donor: Dana A. Hamel.
Foundation type: Independent foundation.
Financial data (yr. ended 11/30/13): Assets, $18,090,321 (M); expenditures, $924,801; qualifying distributions, $834,517; giving activities include $810,800 for 49 grants (high: $400,000; low: $500).
Purpose and activities: Giving primarily for the arts, health organizations and human services.
Fields of interest: Historic preservation/historical societies; Arts; Libraries (public); Education; Health organizations; Recreation, centers; Human services; Children, services.
Type of support: General/operating support; Building/renovation.
Limitations: Applications not accepted. Giving primarily in NH. No grants to individuals.
Application information: Unsolicited requests for funds not accepted.
Trustees: Dana A. Hamel; JPMorgan Chase Bank, N.A.
EIN: 136873334

2888
Hamill Family Foundation ✧
(formerly Happy Hollow Fund)
c/o Briar Hall LLC
200 W. Madison St., Ste. 3400
Chicago, IL 60606-3600

Established in 1963.
Donors: Corwith Hamill; Joan B. Hamill†; Jonathan C. Hamill; Nancy H.C. Winter; Elizabeth C. Bramsen.
Foundation type: Independent foundation.
Financial data (yr. ended 12/31/12): Assets, $11,127,869 (M); gifts received, $197,328; expenditures, $2,046,339; qualifying distributions, $1,959,167; giving activities include $1,956,600 for 250 grants (high: $500,000; low: $200).
Purpose and activities: Giving primarily for the environment and animal welfare; giving also for education, the arts, and health and human services.
Fields of interest: Arts; Higher education; Environment; Zoos/zoological societies; Animals/wildlife; Athletics/sports, equestrianism; Human services; Christian agencies & churches.
Type of support: General/operating support; Continuing support; Capital campaigns; Endowments; Debt reduction; Matching/challenge support.
Limitations: Applications not accepted. Giving primarily in IL. No grants to individuals.
Application information: Contributes only to pre-selected organizations.
Officers and Directors:* Corwith Hamill,* Chair.; Jonathan C. Hamill,* Pres. and Treas.; Elizabeth C. Bramsen,* V.P. and Secy.; Nancy C.H. Winter,* V.P.
EIN: 366096808
Selected grants: The following grants are a representative sample of this grantmaker's funding activity:
$1,500,000 to Jo Daviess Conservation Foundation, Elizabeth, IL, 2011. For unrestricted support.
$1,000,000 to Chicago Zoological Society, Brookfield, IL, 2011. For unrestricted support.
$1,000,000 to Nature Conservancy, Arlington, VA, 2011. For unrestricted support.
$500,000 to Masters School, Dobbs Ferry, NY, 2011. For unrestricted support.
$437,000 to Openlands, Chicago, IL, 2011. For unrestricted support.
$68,640 to Northwestern University, Evanston, IL, 2011. For unrestricted support.
$50,000 to John G. Shedd Aquarium, Chicago, IL, 2011. For unrestricted support.
$20,250 to Northwestern University, Evanston, IL, 2011. For unrestricted support.
$20,000 to Center for Whole Communities, Fayston, VT, 2011. For unrestricted support.
$12,500 to Chicago Zoological Society, Brookfield, IL, 2011. For unrestricted support.

2889
Hansen-Furnas Foundation, Inc. ✧
(formerly Furnas Foundation, Inc.)
28 S. Water St., Ste. 310
Batavia, IL 60510-3103 (630) 761-1390

Incorporated in 1960 in IL.
Donors: W.C. Furnas†; Leto M. Furnas†; Leto M. Furnas Trust.
Foundation type: Independent foundation.
Financial data (yr. ended 12/31/12): Assets, $848,063 (M); gifts received, $485,000; expenditures, $489,605; qualifying distributions, $489,053; giving activities include $432,789 for 95 grants (high: $30,138; low: $100).
Purpose and activities: Emphasis on higher education, including a scholarship program for undergraduate study; support also for health and family agencies, hospices, and community funds.
Fields of interest: Higher education; Health care; Family services; Residential/custodial care, hospices.
Type of support: Annual campaigns; Capital campaigns; Building/renovation; Equipment; Scholarships—to individuals; Matching/challenge support.
Limitations: Applications accepted. Giving primarily in IA and IL; giving limited to Clarke County, IA, and within 12 miles of Batavia, IL, for scholarships. No grants to individuals (except for scholarships); no loans.
Publications: Application guidelines; Informational brochure; Program policy statement.
Application information: Application form required.
Initial approach: Request application form
Copies of proposal: 1
Deadline(s): Mar. 15
Board meeting date(s): Jan., Apr., July, and Oct.
Officers: Joanne B. Hansen, Pres.; Thomas F. Caughlin, V.P.; Robert F. Peterson, Secy.-Treas.
Directors: Kirsten Hansen Barkley; James Hansen; Lisa Hansen; Richard W. Hansen; Scott Hansen.
EIN: 366049894

2890
Alice G. Hanson Family Foundation ✧ ☆
P.O. Box 803878
Chicago, IL 60680-3878

Established in FL and IL.
Foundation type: Independent foundation.
Financial data (yr. ended 12/31/13): Assets, $9,152,974 (M); expenditures, $657,785; qualifying distributions, $573,250; giving activities include $440,000 for 3 grants (high: $300,000; low: $40,000).
Purpose and activities: Giving primarily for Jewish organizations as well as to a charitable gift fund; funding also for a children's hospital.
Fields of interest: Hospitals (specialty); Human services; Children/youth, services; Foundations (public); Jewish agencies & synagogues.
Limitations: Applications not accepted. Giving primarily in MA and NY, with some giving in IL and NM. No grants to individuals.
Application information: Contributes only to pre-selected organizations.
Officers and Directors:* Burton Rottman,* Pres.; Howard Rottman,* Secy.; Michael Rottman,* Treas.
EIN: 363215192

2891
Kenneth L. Harder Declaration of Trust ✧ ☆
1515 N. Astor St., Ste. 5C
Chicago, IL 60610-5792

Established in IL.
Foundation type: Independent foundation.
Financial data (yr. ended 12/31/13): Assets, $110,466 (M); expenditures, $1,734,578; qualifying distributions, $1,550,000; giving activities include $1,550,000 for 5 grants (high: $500,000; low: $150,000).
Purpose and activities: Giving primarily to an opera company, and for the environment, particularly to a university lab for the study and research of birds.
Fields of interest: Performing arts, opera; Environment; Animals/wildlife, research.
Limitations: Applications not accepted. Giving primarily in Denver, CO, Chicago, IL, and New York, NY; funding also in Zurich, Switzerland.
Application information: Unsolicited requests for funds not accepted.
Trustee: Scott E. Harder.
EIN: 276840273

2892
Harris Family Foundation ✧
150 S. Wacker Dr., Ste. 3275
Chicago, IL 60606-4217 (312) 831-4130

Incorporated in 1957 in IL.
Donors: Scott C. Friend; William J. Friend; Bette D. Harris†; King W. Harris; Katherine P. Harris; Neison Harris†; Toni H. Paul; Pam F. Szokol; KPH Trust; KWWH Trust; THP Trust.
Foundation type: Independent foundation.
Financial data (yr. ended 02/28/13): Assets, $155,278,850 (M); gifts received, $1,134,520; expenditures, $11,267,923; qualifying distributions, $10,508,384; giving activities include $10,283,615 for 230 grants (high: $2,280,000; low: $22).
Purpose and activities: Giving primarily for Jewish charities, early childhood education, education, cultural institutions and museums, social services, hospitals/medical centers, housing and economic development in Chicago, IL and Washington DC.
Fields of interest: Arts; Higher education; Education; Botanical gardens; Zoos/zoological societies; Hospitals (general); Medical care, rehabilitation; Health organizations, association; Medical research, institute; Human services; Children/youth, services; Family services; Jewish federated giving programs; Jewish agencies & synagogues.
Type of support: General/operating support; Continuing support; Annual campaigns; Capital campaigns; Building/renovation; Conferences/seminars; Professorships; Internship funds; Scholarship funds.
Limitations: Applications accepted. Giving primarily in the Chicago, IL, and Washington DC areas. No grants to individuals.
Application information: Application form not required.
Initial approach: Letter
Copies of proposal: 1
Deadline(s): None
Board meeting date(s): May and Nov.
Final notification: 30 days
Officers and Directors:* King W. Harris,* Pres.; Katherine P. Harris,* V.P.; Toni H. Paul,* V.P.; Pam F. Szokol,* V.P.; Edward Schwartz,* Secy.-Treas.
EIN: 366054378
Selected grants: The following grants are a representative sample of this grantmaker's funding activity:
$2,280,000 to Museum of Contemporary Art, Chicago, IL, 2013. For general operating support.
$1,000,000 to Chicago Community Trust, Chicago, IL, 2013. For general operating support.
$1,000,000 to Rehabilitation Institute of Chicago, Chicago, IL, 2013. For general operating support.
$990,000 to Jewish United Fund of Metropolitan Chicago, Chicago, IL, 2013. For general operating support.
$250,000 to Phillips Academy, Andover, MA, 2013. For general operating support.
$205,000 to Field Museum of Natural History, Chicago, IL, 2013. For general operating support.
$75,000 to Chicago Community Trust, Chicago, IL, 2013. For general operating support.
$12,000 to Rehabilitation Institute of Chicago, Women's Board, Chicago, IL, 2013. For general operating support.
$10,000 to Maria High School, Chicago, IL, 2013. For general operating support.
$10,000 to Music Institute of Chicago, Wilmette, IL, 2013. For general operating support.

2893
Irving Harris Foundation
(formerly The Harris Foundation)
191 N. Wacker Dr., Ste. 1500
Chicago, IL 60606-1899 (312) 621-0566
Contact: For all other proposals: June Matayoshi, Grants Mgr.
FAX: (312) 621-9179; For J. Matayoshi, e-mail: jmatayoshi@irvingharrisfdn.org

Incorporated in 1945 in MN.
Donor: Members of the Harris family.
Foundation type: Independent foundation.
Financial data (yr. ended 12/31/12): Assets, $248,192,006 (M); expenditures, $19,988,038; qualifying distributions, $14,535,603; giving activities include $13,263,835 for 308 grants (high: $659,000; low: $50).
Purpose and activities: The mission of the foundation is to enhance quality of life through the creation and development of innovative programs, preventive practices, and public policies that promote social justice, address inequity and create opportunities for creative expression. The foundation does this by making targeted investments toward the healthy development of very young children and their families, and communities where the foundation is located and where it sees need. The foundation takes a strategic proactive approach to funding in the areas of early childhood development/child and family policy; the arts, humanities and culture; community-based giving; and Jewish philanthropy in the U.S. and in Israel.
Fields of interest: Arts; Education, early childhood education; Child development, education; Human services; Child development, services; Community/economic development; Jewish federated giving programs; Infants/toddlers; Children/youth; Minorities; Women; Girls; Single parents.
Type of support: General/operating support; Program development; Employee matching gifts; Matching/challenge support.
Limitations: Applications not accepted. Giving on a national basis, with an emphasis on Chicago and some specific grant giving in Israel. No grants to individuals, or for emergency or endowment funds, deficit financing, land acquisition, renovations, scholarships, or fellowships; no loans.
Application information: Contributes only to pre-selected organizations.
Board meeting date(s): May/June and Sept./Oct.
Officers and Trustees:* Nancy Meyer, Chair.; Joan W. Harris, Pres.; Alicia Lieberman; Daniel Meyer; Harriet Meyer; George Polsky; Jack Polsky; Jean Polsky.
Number of staff: 3 full-time professional; 3 full-time support.
EIN: 366055115
Selected grants: The following grants are a representative sample of this grantmaker's funding activity:
$659,000 to Music and Dance Theater Chicago, Chicago, IL, 2012.
$500,000 to Ounce of Prevention Fund, Chicago, IL, 2012.
$500,000 to University of Chicago, Chicago, IL, 2012.
$250,000 to Erikson Institute, Chicago, IL, 2012.
$230,000 to Zero to Three: National Center for Infants, Toddlers and Families, Washington, DC, 2012.
$100,000 to Center for Reproductive Rights, New York, NY, 2012.
$45,000 to University of Illinois Foundation, Urbana, IL, 2012.
$40,000 to National Latina Institute for Reproductive Health, New York, NY, 2012.
$25,000 to Emergency Fund, Chicago, IL, 2012.
$5,000 to Chicago Historical Society, Chicago, IL, 2012.

2894
Fred G. Harrison Foundation ✧ ☆
101 S. Park Ave.
Herrin, IL 62948-3609 (618) 942-6666

Established in 1969 in IL.
Donors: Julia Harrison Bruce†; Fred G. Harrison†.

Foundation type: Independent foundation.
Financial data (yr. ended 12/31/13): Assets, $16,154,373 (M); expenditures, $1,389,326; qualifying distributions, $808,890; giving activities include $575,998 for 8 grants (high: $283,000; low: $1,000), and $4,000 for 4 grants to individuals (high: $1,000; low: $1,000).
Fields of interest: Education; Community/economic development.
Type of support: General/operating support; Scholarships—to individuals.
Limitations: Applications accepted. Giving primarily in Herrin, IL.
Application information: Application form required.
Initial approach: Letter
Deadline(s): None
Advisors: Carl Goodwin; Clay Goodwin; Ed Goodwin; Barbara Jacobs.
Trustee: The Bank of Herrin, N.A.
EIN: 376085205

2895
The Mary A. Harrison Foundation ✧
10 S. Dearborn St., IL1-0117
Chicago, IL 60603

Established in VA.
Foundation type: Independent foundation.
Financial data (yr. ended 09/30/13): Assets, $13,124,417 (M); expenditures, $608,314; qualifying distributions, $600,150; giving activities include $533,930 for 7 grants (high: $200,000; low: $430).
Purpose and activities: Giving primarily for education; some funding also for health organizations, particularly a cancer center, and to a children's museum.
Fields of interest: Museums (children's); Historic preservation/historical societies; Higher education; Education; Cancer; Health organizations.
Limitations: Applications not accepted. Giving primarily in Richmond, VA; some funding also in Chapel Hill, NC.
Application information: Unsolicited requests for funds not accepted.
Officers: George A. Harrison, Pres.; Cindy Harrison, V.P.
EIN: 260433030

2896
Helen M. Harrison Foundation Inc. ✧
c/o T. Carroll
333 W. Wacker Dr., Ste. 1700
Chicago, IL 60606-1247

Incorporated in 2005 in IL as successor to Helen M. Harrison Foundation established in 1986 in IL.
Donor: Helen M. Harrison Foundation.
Foundation type: Independent foundation.
Financial data (yr. ended 12/31/13): Assets, $14,257,061 (M); expenditures, $702,229; qualifying distributions, $562,365; giving activities include $487,500 for 1+ grant.
Fields of interest: Arts; Secondary school/education; Higher education; Libraries/library science; Hospitals (general); Health organizations; Diabetes; Children/youth, services; Community/economic development; Foundations (community); Christian agencies & churches.
Limitations: Applications not accepted. Giving primarily in the Chicago, IL, area. No grants to individuals.
Application information: Contributes only to pre-selected organizations.
Directors: Katherine Burno; Philip M. Burno; Timothy G. Carroll; Raymond Kratzer.
EIN: 421668546

2897
The Selma J. Hartke Community Foundation ✧
c/o U.S. Bank, N.A.
P.O. Box 19264
Springfield, IL 62794-9264

Established in 2001 in IL.
Donor: Selma Hartke†.
Foundation type: Independent foundation.
Financial data (yr. ended 03/31/13): Assets, $9,035,718 (M); expenditures, $737,914; qualifying distributions, $573,299; giving activities include $573,299 for grants.
Purpose and activities: Giving primarily for social services including food services for the homeless and needy, and heating services for low-income families. Also giving scholarships for higher education.
Fields of interest: Education; Food banks; Human services; Developmentally disabled, centers & services; Christian agencies & churches.
Type of support: Scholarships—to individuals.
Limitations: Applications not accepted. Giving limited to the greater Litchfield, IL, area.
Application information: Unsolicited requests for funds not accepted.
Board of Directors: Dorothy A. Ernst; Paul Ernst; Carrie Hardt; Edwin E. Hardt; Joshua Hardt; Karl W. Hardt.
EIN: 371406237

2898
The Robert & Debra F. Hartman Family Foundation ✧
(formerly Hartman Family Foundation)
6633 N. Lincoln Ave.
Lincolnwood, IL 60712-3625

Established in 1991 in IL.
Donors: Robert Hartman; Hartman Family Trust.
Foundation type: Independent foundation.
Financial data (yr. ended 12/31/12): Assets, $372,845 (M); gifts received, $770,000; expenditures, $1,041,319; qualifying distributions, $702,477; giving activities include $702,477 for grants.
Purpose and activities: Giving primarily to Jewish agencies, temples, and schools.
Fields of interest: Elementary/secondary education; Theological school/education; Jewish agencies & synagogues.
Limitations: Applications not accepted. No grants to individuals.
Application information: Contributes only to pre-selected organizations.
Officers: Robert Hartman, Pres.; Debra F. Hartman, Secy.
EIN: 364120697

2899
The Morris A. Hazan Family Foundation ✧
P.O. Box 803878
Chicago, IL 60680-3878

Established in 1967 in CA.
Donors: Morris A. Hazan†; Morris A. Hazan Trust.
Foundation type: Independent foundation.
Financial data (yr. ended 12/31/13): Assets, $22,056,004 (M); expenditures, $1,496,369; qualifying distributions, $1,396,188; giving activities include $1,394,250 for grants.
Purpose and activities: Giving primarily for the arts, education, and to Jewish agencies and temples.
Fields of interest: Arts; Higher education; Health organizations, association; Human services; Foundations (private grantmaking); Jewish federated giving programs; Jewish agencies & synagogues.
Limitations: Applications not accepted. Giving primarily in CA, with emphasis on Los Angeles. No grants to individuals.
Application information: Contributes only to pre-selected organizations.
Officers: Morris A. Hazan, Jr., Pres.; Judy Carmel, Secy.; Lovee Arum, C.F.O.
EIN: 956220356

2900
Healthcare Foundation of Northern Lake County ✧
114 S. Genesee St., Ste. 505
Waukegan, IL 60085-5607 (847) 377-0525, ext. 25
Contact: Ernest Vasseur, Exec. Dir.
FAX: (847) 782-8351; E-mail: evasseur@hfnlc.org; Angela Baran, M.S., Prog. Off. e-mail: angela.baran@hfnlc.org; Main URL: http://www.hfnlc.org
Facebook: https://www.facebook.com/HFNLC

Established in 2006 in IL.
Donors: Lake County; Victory Wind-Down Company.
Foundation type: Independent foundation.
Financial data (yr. ended 05/31/13): Assets, $54,400,973 (M); gifts received, $1,748,842; expenditures, $2,231,098; qualifying distributions, $2,060,179; giving activities include $1,673,990 for 39 grants (high: $160,250; low: $6,750).
Purpose and activities: The foundation provides financial support for primary care services (including direct medical, dental, vision, and mental health care), medical supplies, pharmaceuticals, and health care equipment; community health education; and postsecondary education scholarship programs that prepare Lake County, Illinois residents to pursue health-related careers and to work in underserved Lake County communities.
Fields of interest: Medicine/medical care, public education; Health care, formal/general education; Medical care, community health systems; Dental care; Optometry/vision screening; Health care; Mental health, treatment; Mental health, counseling/support groups; Economically disadvantaged.
Limitations: Applications accepted. Giving primarily in northern Lake County, IL, with emphasis on Antioch, Fox Lake, Grayslake-Third Lake, Great Lakes, Gurnee, Lake Villa-Lindenhurst, North Chicago, Round Lake, Wadsworth, Waukegan and Zion. No support for biomedical research, patient

financial aid, and services provided by unqualified persons.
Publications: Application guidelines; Biennial report; Financial statement; Grants list.
Application information: Application guidelines available on foundation web site. Application form required.
Initial approach: Letter of inquiry (not exceeding 2 pages)
Copies of proposal: 1
Deadline(s): Feb. 1 (for May meeting) and Aug. 1 (for Nov. meeting)
Board meeting date(s): Feb., May, Sept., and Nov.
Officers and Directors:* William Ensing, Esq.*, Chair.; Jorge Ortiz, Vice-Chair.; Diane Klotnia, Esq.*, Secy.; Nadine Johnson,* Treas.; Ernest Vasseur, Exec. Dir.; Rev. Reginald Blount, Ph.D.; Mary Dominiak; Gerard Goshgarian, M.D.; Tim Harrington; John Joanem, Esq.; Jacquelyn Kendall; Rodrigo Manjarres, LCPC; Gust Petropoulos; Wendy Rheault, Ph.D.; Maria C. Schwartz, Ph.D., PT.
EIN: 205253008
Selected grants: The following grants are a representative sample of this grantmaker's funding activity:
$121,900 to Rosalind Franklin University of Medicine and Science, North Chicago, IL, 2011.
$100,000 to Lake County Community Foundation, Waukegan, IL, 2011.

2901
Bernard Heerey Family Foundation ✧
c/o Nathaniel I. Grey
1 N. LaSalle St., Ste. 1100
Chicago, IL 60602-3904

Established in 2006 in IL.
Donor: Bernard A. Heerey†.
Foundation type: Independent foundation.
Financial data (yr. ended 12/31/13): Assets, $69,929,852 (M); expenditures, $4,728,619; qualifying distributions, $3,116,564; giving activities include $2,972,111 for 16 grants (high: $516,840; low: $25,750).
Fields of interest: Education; Human services; Catholic agencies & churches; Jewish agencies & synagogues.
Limitations: Applications not accepted. Giving primarily in Chicago, IL.
Application information: Contributes only to pre-selected organizations.
Directors: Charles E. Dobrusin; Martin D. Kerpel.
EIN: 141840613

2902
Heisley Family Foundation ✧
70 W. Madison St., Ste. 5600
Chicago, IL 60602-4211 (312) 580-7844
Contact: Judith F. Heisley Bishop, Pres.

Established in 1997 in IL.
Donors: Michael E. Heisley, Jr.; Michael E. Heisley, Sr.; Emily Heisley Stoeckel.
Foundation type: Independent foundation.
Financial data (yr. ended 12/31/13): Assets, $188,925 (M); gifts received, $575,000; expenditures, $780,200; qualifying distributions, $780,015; giving activities include $780,000 for 10 grants (high: $275,000; low: $10,000).
Fields of interest: Education; Catholic agencies & churches.
Limitations: Applications accepted. Giving primarily in Washington, DC, IL, and TN; some giving also in India. No grants to individuals.
Application information: Application form required.
Initial approach: Telephone or U.S. mail
Deadline(s): None
Officers: Judith F. Heisley Bishop, Pres.; Agnes M. Heisley, V.P.; Barbara Rogers, Secy.; Emily Heisley Stoeckel, Treas.
Directors: Michael E. Heisley, Sr.; Michael E. Heisley, Jr.; Theresa Nesbitt.
EIN: 364120052
Selected grants: The following grants are a representative sample of this grantmaker's funding activity:
$10,000 to Duke University, Fuqua School of Business, Durham, NC, 2012. For unrestricted.

2903
Diane and David B. Heller Charitable Foundation ✧
c/o Diane Heller
414 W. Grant Pl.
Chicago, IL 60614-3807

Established in 2005 in IL.
Donors: David B. Heller; Diane B. Heller.
Foundation type: Independent foundation.
Financial data (yr. ended 12/31/13): Assets, $1,879,167 (M); expenditures, $1,214,986; qualifying distributions, $1,203,609; giving activities include $1,196,000 for 23 grants (high: $300,000; low: $100).
Fields of interest: Museums (art); Elementary/secondary education; Higher education; Health organizations.
Limitations: Applications not accepted. Giving primarily in Chicago and Evanston, IL, and Charlottesville, VA. No grants to individuals.
Application information: Contributes only to pre-selected organizations.
Officers and Directors:* Diane B. Heller,* Pres.; Matthew W. Dougherty,* Secy.-Treas.; Lee E. Heller.
EIN: 202387089

2904
Walter E. Heller Foundation ✧ ☆
c/o Bank of America, N.A.
231 S. LaSalle St.
Chicago, IL 60697-0001 (312) 828-6763
Contact: George Thorn

Incorporated in 1955 in IL.
Donors: Walter E. Heller†; Whico, Inc.; Heller Residuary Trust for Alyce.
Foundation type: Independent foundation.
Financial data (yr. ended 12/31/13): Assets, $13,879,981 (M); expenditures, $591,021; qualifying distributions, $487,850; giving activities include $442,000 for 41 grants (high: $94,000; low: $500).
Purpose and activities: Support for cultural programs, primarily for an opera and symphony orchestra.
Fields of interest: Media, television; Performing arts; Performing arts, orchestras; Performing arts, opera; Arts; Jewish federated giving programs.
Type of support: General/operating support.
Limitations: Giving primarily in the Chicago, IL, area. No grants to individuals.
Application information: Application form not required.
Initial approach: Letter
Deadline(s): None
Officers and Director:* M. Catherine Ryan, V.P. and Treas.; Mary J. Tremondt, Secy.; Allan C. Ryan IV; Carol Sonnschein Sadow.
EIN: 366058986
Selected grants: The following grants are a representative sample of this grantmaker's funding activity:
$125,000 to Art Institute of Chicago, Chicago, IL, 2011.
$50,000 to Lyric Opera of Chicago, Chicago, IL, 2011.
$25,000 to Chicago High School for the Arts, Chicago, IL, 2011.
$25,000 to Chicago Public Library Foundation, Chicago, IL, 2011.
$25,000 to Dominican University, River Forest, IL, 2011.
$10,000 to Field Museum of Natural History, Chicago, IL, 2011.
$5,000 to Dominican University, River Forest, IL, 2011.
$1,000 to Dominican University, River Forest, IL, 2011.
$1,000 to Storycatchers Theatre, Chicago, IL, 2011. For general support.
$1,000 to University of Chicago, Chicago, IL, 2011. For general support.

2905
Carl R. Hendrickson Family Foundation ✧ ☆
c/o US Trust
231 S. LaSalle St., IL1-231-13-32
Chicago, IL 60697-0001 1-(312) 828-2055
Contact: Debra Grand, Sr. V.P.
E-mail: ilgrantmaking@ustrust.com; Main
URL: http://www.bankofamerica.com/grantmaking

Established in 1991 in IL.
Donor: Virginia Hendrickson†.
Foundation type: Independent foundation.
Financial data (yr. ended 12/31/13): Assets, $11,550,148 (M); expenditures, $610,598; qualifying distributions, $522,985; giving activities include $421,575 for 38 grants (high: $25,000; low: $5,000).
Purpose and activities: To support and promote quality educational, human services, and health care programming for underserved populations. Special consideration is given to charitable organizations that help individuals meet their basic needs while also addressing their spiritual needs. Preference is given to organizations or programs that approach their mission from an entrepreneurial perspective.
Fields of interest: Higher education; Health organizations, association; Human services; Christian agencies & churches.
Limitations: Applications accepted. Giving primarily in IL. No grants for capital projects or endowments.
Application information: The foundation has an online application process. See foundation web site for complete application guidelines. Application form required.
Copies of proposal: 2
Deadline(s): July 31
Final notification: Dec.
Officers: Charles Slamar, Jr., Pres.; David J. Zeller, Secy.; Kristin Carlson Vogen, Treas.

Trustee: Bank of America, N.A.
EIN: 366736213
Selected grants: The following grants are a representative sample of this grantmaker's funding activity:
$20,000 to Jobs for Youth/Chicago, Chicago, IL, 2011. For JFY Occupational Training Program.
$20,000 to Wheaton College, Wheaton, IL, 2011. For Human Need and Global Resources Program Scholarship.
$18,855 to Philosophia International, Boise, ID, 2011.
$17,500 to Child Evangelism Fellowship, Warrenton, MO, 2011. For Hendrickson Missionary.
$15,000 to Easter Seals Metropolitan Chicago, Chicago, IL, 2011. For Vocational Training and Support through HarrysButtons.com Microenterprise at Easter Seals.
$15,000 to Interfaith House, Chicago, IL, 2011. For general operating support.
$15,000 to Little City Foundation, Palatine, IL, 2011. For Center for Health and Wellness.
$15,000 to LYDIA Home Association, Chicago, IL, 2011. For Lydia Urban Academy, which serves up to 40 students annually that are at risk due to poverty, homelessness, truancy or criminal history, pregnant, or psychiatric history.
$10,000 to Saint Vincent de Paul Center, Chicago, IL, 2011. For Child Development Program.
$10,000 to WorldVenture, Littleton, CO, 2011.

2906
The Henry Foundation Inc. ✧
102 N. Westgate Ave.
Jacksonville, IL 62650

Established in 1986 in FL.
Foundation type: Independent foundation.
Financial data (yr. ended 12/31/13): Assets, $13,707,212 (M); expenditures, $745,314; qualifying distributions, $673,590; giving activities include $547,292 for 99 grants (high: $173,500; low: $250).
Purpose and activities: Giving primarily for education, coral reef conservation and for animal welfare.
Fields of interest: Secondary school/education; Higher education; Environment, water resources; Animals/wildlife, preservation/protection; Mental health/crisis services.
International interests: Caribbean.
Type of support: Program development; Conferences/seminars; Publication; Seed money; Matching/challenge support.
Limitations: Applications not accepted. Giving primarily in FL and Washington, DC. No grants to individuals, or for capital campaigns or endowments.
Application information: Unsolicited requests for funds not accepted.
Officer: C. Wolcott Henry III, Pres.
Directors: Nancy H. McKelvy; H. Alexander Henry.
Number of staff: 1 part-time professional.
EIN: 592827461

2907
The Heritage Foundation of First Security Federal Savings Bank, Inc. ✧ ☆
2329 W. Chicago Ave.
Chicago, IL 60622-4723 (773) 486-6645
Contact: Julian E. Kulas, Pres.

Established in 1997 in IL.
Donors: First Security Federal Savings Bank; Maria Olijnyk.
Foundation type: Company-sponsored foundation.
Financial data (yr. ended 12/31/13): Assets, $13,349,921 (M); expenditures, $558,002; qualifying distributions, $452,760; giving activities include $452,760 for 51 grants (high: $55,000; low: $250).
Purpose and activities: The foundation supports programs designed to preserve Ukrainian culture and heritage; and promote democracy and a free market economy.
Fields of interest: Arts; Education; Human services.
International interests: Ukraine.
Type of support: General/operating support; Program development; Conferences/seminars; Publication.
Limitations: Applications accepted. Giving primarily in IL. No grants to individuals.
Application information: Application form not required.
Initial approach: Proposal
Deadline(s): None
Officers: Julian E. Kulas,* Pres.; Paul Nadzikewycz, V.P.; Terry Gawryk, Secy.
Trustees: Taras Drozd; Dmytro Shtohryn; Chrysta Wereszczak.
Number of staff: 1 part-time support.
EIN: 364135415
Selected grants: The following grants are a representative sample of this grantmaker's funding activity:
$60,000 to American Ukrainian Youth Association, Chicago, IL, 2011.
$25,000 to Ukrainian Institute of Modern Art, Chicago, IL, 2011.
$25,000 to Ukrainian National Museum, Chicago, IL, 2011.
$10,000 to American Foreign Policy Council, Washington, DC, 2011.
$5,000 to Ukrainian Catholic Archdiocese of Philadelphia, Philadelphia, PA, 2011.
$5,000 to Ukrainian Museum-Archives, Cleveland, OH, 2011.
$3,550 to Ukrainian National Womens League of America, New York, NY, 2011.
$2,500 to Columbia University, New York, NY, 2011.

2908
The Grover Hermann Foundation ✧
908 Kenmare Dr.
Burr Ridge, IL 60527-7091 (630) 908-7800
Contact: Paul K. Rhoads, Pres.

Incorporated in 1955 in IL.
Donor: Grover M. Hermann.
Foundation type: Independent foundation.
Financial data (yr. ended 12/31/13): Assets, $15,902,019 (M); expenditures, $1,742,548; qualifying distributions, $1,636,656; giving activities include $1,486,000 for 74 grants (high: $255,000; low: $2,500).
Purpose and activities: Giving primarily for higher education, social services, community development, health, public policy organizations, and religious organizations, solely for assistance in furthering well-defined secular causes.
Fields of interest: Arts; Higher education; Health care; Health organizations, association; Human services; Community/economic development; Public policy, research; Religion.
Type of support: General/operating support; Annual campaigns; Building/renovation; Equipment; Endowments; Program development; Seed money; Scholarship funds.
Limitations: Applications accepted. Giving limited to the Chicago, IL, metropolitan area. No support for fraternal, athletic, or foreign organizations or private foundations. No grants to individuals; generally no support for operating budgets, except for national health organizations.
Publications: Application guidelines.
Application information: Application form required.
Initial approach: Letter
Copies of proposal: 3
Deadline(s): None
Board meeting date(s): Quarterly; Mar., June, Sept. and Dec.
Officers and Directors:* Paul K. Rhoads,* Pres.; Katheryn V. Rhoads,* Exec. Dir.; Marianne K. Calhoun.
EIN: 366064489
Selected grants: The following grants are a representative sample of this grantmaker's funding activity:
$255,000 to Heritage Foundation, Huntsville, AL, 2011.
$250,000 to Community Foundation for Monterey County, Monterey, CA, 2011.
$30,000 to Alice Lloyd College, Pippa Passes, KY, 2011.
$5,000 to Alexian Brothers Bonaventure House, Chicago, IL, 2011.

2909
The Herr Foundation ✧ ☆
1130 Lake Shore Dr., Ste. 6E
Chicago, IL 60611-1048

Established in 1986 in IL.
Donor: Jeffrey M. Herr.
Foundation type: Independent foundation.
Financial data (yr. ended 11/30/13): Assets, $2,616,062 (M); gifts received, $2,086,158; expenditures, $1,535,969; qualifying distributions, $1,530,400; giving activities include $1,530,400 for 7 grants (high: $1,500,000; low: $300).
Fields of interest: Museums (ethnic/folk arts); Education; Human services.
Type of support: General/operating support; Emergency funds.
Limitations: Applications not accepted. Giving primarily in the Chicago, IL, area; some funding also in Washington, DC. No grants to individuals.
Application information: Unsolicited requests for funds not accepted.
Officers: Jeffrey M. Herr, Pres.; Toby Herr, Treas.
Director: Julie Herr.
EIN: 363482112
Selected grants: The following grants are a representative sample of this grantmaker's funding activity:
$55,000 to Erikson Institute, Chicago, IL, 2011. For general contribution.
$2,100 to Project Match - Families in Transition, Chicago, IL, 2011. For general contribution.
$2,000 to Business and Professional People for the Public Interest, Chicago, IL, 2011. For general contribution.
$1,500 to Chicago Public Media, Chicago, IL, 2011. For general contribution.
$1,500 to Special Childrens Charities, Chicago, IL, 2011. For general contribution.

$1,000 to United Way of Elgin, South Elgin, IL, 2011. For general contribution.

2910
The David Herro Charitable Foundation ✧
65 E. Goethe St., Ste. 3W
Chicago, IL 60610-7259

Established in IL.
Donors: David Herro; John Raitt; Mary Raitt.
Foundation type: Independent foundation.
Financial data (yr. ended 12/31/13): Assets, $8,092,418 (M); gifts received, $3,000,000; expenditures, $4,720,476; qualifying distributions, $4,682,680; giving activities include $4,682,680 for 17 grants (high: $2,000,000; low: $7,150).
Fields of interest: Arts; Education.
Limitations: Applications not accepted. Giving primarily in IL and WI.
Application information: Contributes only to pre-selected organizations.
Trustee: David Herro.
EIN: 364121681
Selected grants: The following grants are a representative sample of this grantmaker's funding activity:
$10,000 to Hubbard Street Dance Chicago, Chicago, IL, 2012. For new carpeting and decorating.

2911
Hintz Family Fund, Inc. ✧ ☆
10 S. Dearborn St., IL1-0117
Chicago, IL 60603-2300

Established in DE.
Donors: JPMorgan Services, Inc.; Hintz 2008-2017 Non-Grantor Trust; Hintz 2008-2020 Non-Grantor Trust.
Foundation type: Independent foundation.
Financial data (yr. ended 12/31/13): Assets, $23,138,919 (M); gifts received, $2,081,698; expenditures, $955,924; qualifying distributions, $826,318; giving activities include $826,096 for 31 grants (high: $251,000; low: $250).
Fields of interest: Museums; Arts; Education; Health organizations; Human services.
Limitations: Applications accepted. Giving primarily in the U.S., with some emphasis on MA and NY.
Application information: Application form not required.
Initial approach: Proposal
Deadline(s): None
Officers: Edward R. Hintz, Pres.; Helen S. Hintz, V.P. and Treas.; Virginia Hintz Remmey, Secy.
Members: Elizabeth Hintz; Kathryn S. Hintz.
EIN: 263843309

2912
Irma T. Hirschl Trust ✧
c/o JPMorgan Chase Bank, N.A.
10 S. Dearborn St., IL1-0117
Chicago, IL 60603-2300

Trust established in 1973 in NY.
Donor: Irma T. Hirschl†.
Foundation type: Independent foundation.
Financial data (yr. ended 10/31/13): Assets, $45,618,202 (M); expenditures, $2,374,223; qualifying distributions, $2,261,265; giving activities include $2,157,000 for grants.
Purpose and activities: Giving primarily for higher education, particularly medical school education, as well as for other health organizations, including a children's hospital; funding also for Jewish organizations.
Fields of interest: Higher education; Medical school/education; Hospitals (specialty); Health care; Medical research, institute; Human services; United Ways and Federated Giving Programs; Jewish federated giving programs.
Type of support: Scholarship funds; Research.
Limitations: Applications not accepted. Giving primarily in New York, NY. No support for private foundations. No grants to individuals (except for Medical Scholar Program).
Application information: Unsolicited requests for funds not accepted.
Trustees: Leo L. Schmolka, Esq.; JPMorgan Chase Bank, N.A.; Weil, Gottshalk & Manges.
EIN: 136356381

2913
His First Foundation ✧
P.O. Box 50
Mossville, IL 61552-0050 (309) 686-4048
Contact: John S. Wieland, Dir.

Established in 2001.
Donors: MH Logistics; MH Equipment Co.
Foundation type: Company-sponsored foundation.
Financial data (yr. ended 12/31/13): Assets, $2,545,456 (M); gifts received, $1,005,100; expenditures, $463,063; qualifying distributions, $459,000; giving activities include $459,000 for 23 grants (high: $255,000; low: $1,000).
Purpose and activities: The foundation supports programs designed to promote areas of faith, secular good works, and acts of kindness.
Fields of interest: Education; Health care; Children/youth, services; Homeless, human services; Human services; Christian agencies & churches.
Type of support: General/operating support.
Limitations: Applications accepted. Giving primarily in Peoria, IL. No grants to individuals.
Application information: Application form required.
Initial approach: Letter
Deadline(s): None
Directors: Clyde Wieland; John S. Wieland; Julie Wieland.
EIN: 371414330

2914
The Hobbs Foundation ✧
102 N. Westgate Ave., Ste. A
Jacksonville, IL 62650-1718

Established in 1986 in AL.
Donor: Ioka Fund.
Foundation type: Independent foundation.
Financial data (yr. ended 12/31/13): Assets, $14,116,346 (M); expenditures, $622,401; qualifying distributions, $606,247; giving activities include $603,150 for 148 grants (high: $43,000; low: $100).
Purpose and activities: Giving primarily for the arts, education, health association, children, youth and social services, and to Christian and Protestant churches.
Fields of interest: Arts; Higher education; Education; Health organizations, association; Boys & girls clubs; Human services; Children/youth, services; Christian agencies & churches; Protestant agencies & churches.
Type of support: Capital campaigns; Building/renovation.
Limitations: Applications not accepted. Giving primarily in Montgomery, AL. No grants to individuals.
Application information: Contributes only to pre-selected organizations.
Officer: Truman M. Hobbs, Jr., Pres.
Directors: Joyce C. Hobbs; Truman M. Hobbs.
EIN: 630952482

2915
Hochberg Family Foundation ✧
400 Skokie Blvd., Ste. 800
Northbrook, IL 60062-7908

Established in 1981 in IL.
Donors: Larry J. Hochberg; Joseph Hochberg; Sanford Cantor; Andrew S. Hochberg; John Lowenstein.
Foundation type: Independent foundation.
Financial data (yr. ended 11/30/13): Assets, $6,434,483 (M); gifts received, $1,218,000; expenditures, $752,664; qualifying distributions, $712,766; giving activities include $712,766 for 49 grants (high: $106,286; low: $500).
Purpose and activities: Giving primarily for education, community services, and Jewish institutions.
Fields of interest: Education; Human services; Jewish federated giving programs; Jewish agencies & synagogues.
Limitations: Applications not accepted. Giving primarily in Chicago, IL and in WI.
Application information: Unsolicited requests for funds not accepted.
Directors: Andrew S. Hochberg; Larry J. Hochberg.
EIN: 363152002
Selected grants: The following grants are a representative sample of this grantmaker's funding activity:
$175,700 to Israel Emergency Alliance, Los Angeles, CA, 2011.
$95,000 to Friends of the Israel Defense Forces, New York, NY, 2011.
$75,000 to Foundation for the Defense of Democracies, Washington, DC, 2011.
$50,000 to Hebrew Union College-Jewish Institute of Religion, New York, NY, 2011.
$15,500 to Jewish Funders Network, New York, NY, 2011.
$12,500 to Hillel: The Foundation for Jewish Campus Life, Washington, DC, 2011.
$7,500 to Illinois Holocaust Museum and Education Center, Skokie, IL, 2011.
$2,500 to Madison Project, Santa Monica, CA, 2011.
$2,500 to Middle East Forum, Philadelphia, PA, 2011.
$1,500 to American Society for Technion-Israel Institute of Technology, New York, NY, 2011.

2916
The Hoehn Family Charitable Trust ✧
c/o Catheryn E. Hoehn, Thomas James, NT
50 S. LaSalle St., Ste B-3
Chicago, IL 60603-1008

Established in 1998 in IL.
Donors: Dorothy Hoehn; Catheryn Emily Hoehn; Dorothy S. Hoehn Trust.
Foundation type: Independent foundation.
Financial data (yr. ended 12/31/13): Assets, $45,928,381 (M); gifts received, $5,990; expenditures, $2,257,268; qualifying distributions, $2,102,987; giving activities include $2,100,000 for 68 grants (high: $300,000; low: $10,000).
Purpose and activities: Giving primarily for education, health organizations, and human services.
Fields of interest: Higher education, university; Zoos/zoological societies; Health organizations, association; Human services.
Limitations: Applications not accepted. Giving primarily in CA and WI. No grants to individuals.
Application information: Contributes only to pre-selected organizations.
Trustee: Catheryn Emily Hoehn.
EIN: 364235135
Selected grants: The following grants are a representative sample of this grantmaker's funding activity:
$25,000 to Disabled American Veterans, Cold Spring, KY, 2011.

2917
Helen Hoffritz Charitable Trust ✧
c/o JPMorgan Chase Bank, N.A.
10 S. Dearborn St., IL1-0117
Chicago, IL 60603-2317

Established in 1994 in NY.
Donor: Helen Hoffritz†.
Foundation type: Independent foundation.
Financial data (yr. ended 12/31/13): Assets, $16,603,455 (M); expenditures, $837,401; qualifying distributions, $715,558; giving activities include $676,000 for 12 grants (high: $95,000; low: $30,000).
Purpose and activities: Financial assistance for individuals in need of medical equipment. Priority is given to hospital-based programs that target patients preparing for discharge or those in rehabilitation centers; and community-based programs that help people with disabilities or degenerative illnesses. The trust also provides annual grants to four organizations named by the donor.
Fields of interest: Hospitals (general); Health care; Medical research.
Limitations: Applications not accepted. Giving primarily in New York City and Long Island, NY. No grants to individuals; no loans or matching gifts.
Publications: Grants list.
Application information: Contributes only to pre-selected organizations.
Trustee: JPMorgan Chase Bank, N.A.
EIN: 136655406

2918
Renate, Hans & Maria Hofmann Trust ✧
(formerly Hofmann Article 5 Charitable Trust)
10 S. Dearborn St., IL1-0117
Chicago, IL 60603-6089

Established in 1996 in NY.
Donor: Renate Hofmann†.
Foundation type: Independent foundation.
Financial data (yr. ended 06/30/13): Assets, $45,091,141 (M); expenditures, $2,561,677; qualifying distributions, $2,398,221; giving activities include $1,123,722 for 12 grants (high: $550,000; low: $6,000).
Purpose and activities: Giving primarily to a Roman Catholic diocese in Germany; funding also for the arts.
Fields of interest: Arts; Catholic agencies & churches.
International interests: Germany.
Limitations: Applications not accepted. Giving primarily in Germany; some giving also in New York, NY. No grants to individuals.
Application information: Contributes only to pre-selected organizations.
Trustees: Patricia A. Gallagher, Esq.; Robert S. Warshaw, Esq.; JPMorgan Chase Bank, N.A.
EIN: 137102172
Selected grants: The following grants are a representative sample of this grantmaker's funding activity:
$30,000 to Art Education for the Blind, New York, NY, 2011. For general support.
$25,000 to Fountain House, New York, NY, 2011. For general support.
$25,000 to Henry Street Settlement, New York, NY, 2011. For general support.
$15,000 to Graham-Windham, New York, NY, 2011. For general support.
$12,500 to Baruch College Fund, New York, NY, 2011. For general support.
$10,000 to United States Fund for UNICEF, New York, NY, 2011. For general support.
$2,000 to Painting Center, New York, NY, 2011. For general support.

2919
B. H. Homan, Jr. Trust ✧ ☆
c/o JPMorgan Chase Bank, N.A.
10 S. Dearborn St., 21st Fl.
Chicago, IL 60603-2300
Contact: Erin K. Hogan
FAX: (212) 464-2305;
E-mail: Erin.k.hogan@jpmorgan.com

Trust established in 1978 in NY.
Donor: Benjamin Homan, Jr.†.
Foundation type: Independent foundation.
Financial data (yr. ended 05/31/13): Assets, $22,212,041 (M); expenditures, $1,144,011; qualifying distributions, $1,032,488; giving activities include $1,000,002 for 6 grants (high: $166,667; low: $166,667).
Fields of interest: Higher education; Medical school/education.
Type of support: General/operating support.
Limitations: Applications not accepted. Giving primarily in New York, NY. No grants to individuals or for matching gifts.
Application information: Contributes only to pre-selected organizations.
Trustee: JPMorgan Chase Bank, N.A.
EIN: 136741112
Selected grants: The following grants are a representative sample of this grantmaker's funding activity:
$190,000 to Icahn School of Medicine at Mount Sinai, New York, NY, 2011. For program support.
$190,000 to New York Medical College, Valhalla, NY, 2011. For program support.
$190,000 to Weill Medical College of Cornell University, New York, NY, 2011. For program support.

2920
Hoogland Family Foundation ✧
1022 E. Adams St.
Springfield, IL 62703-1028

Established in 2000 in IL.
Donors: Charles R. Hoogland; Kathleen Hoogland; Family Video Inc.
Foundation type: Independent foundation.
Financial data (yr. ended 12/31/12): Assets, $14,537,644 (M); gifts received, $382,692; expenditures, $1,092,992; qualifying distributions, $723,752; giving activities include $723,752 for grants.
Purpose and activities: Giving primarily for higher education and to an arts center.
Fields of interest: Arts, multipurpose centers/programs; Higher education; YM/YWCAs & YM/YWHAs.
Limitations: Applications not accepted. Giving primarily in Springfield, IL, Hillsdale, MI, and Nashville, TN. No grants to individuals.
Application information: Contributes only to pre-selected organizations.
Directors: Charles E. Hoogland; Charles R. Hoogland; Kathleen Hoogland; Keith A. Hoogland.
EIN: 364427146

2921
Hospira Foundation ✧
275 N. Field Dr., Dept. 051N, Bldg. H-1
Lake Forest, IL 60045-2579 (866) 806-8996
E-mail: HospiraFoundation@easygive.com; Main URL: http://www.hospira.com/InTheCommunity/default.aspx

Established in 2004 in IL.
Donor: Hospira, Inc.
Foundation type: Company-sponsored foundation.
Financial data (yr. ended 11/30/13): Assets, $18,120,619 (M); expenditures, $955,264; qualifying distributions, $859,547; giving activities include $742,970 for grants.
Purpose and activities: The foundation supports organizations involved with health and other areas. Special emphasis is directed toward programs designed to advance wellness.
Fields of interest: Health care, clinics/centers; Public health; Health care; Cancer; Nutrition; General charitable giving; Economically disadvantaged.
Type of support: Program development; Scholarship funds.
Limitations: Applications accepted. Giving primarily in San Jose CA, Boulder, CO, Lake Forest, IL, McPherson, KS, Clayton and Rocky Mount, NC, Austin, TX, and Pleasant Prairie, WI; giving also to national organizations. No support for veterans', labor, or political organizations, fraternal, athletic, or social organizations, or organizations posing a

conflict of interest with Hospira's code of business conduct or corporate policies. No grants to individuals, or for capital campaigns, endowments, general operating support, equipment, charity event attendance, debt reduction, political campaigns, or religious or sectarian causes; no loans.
Publications: Application guidelines; Corporate report; Corporate giving report.
Application information: Proposals should be no longer than 2 pages and the minimum dollar request for all proposal is $5,000. E-mailed proposals and telephone solicitations will not be accepted or reviewed. Multi-year funding is not automatic. Application form not required.
Initial approach: Complete online application
Copies of proposal: 1
Deadline(s): None
Board meeting date(s): Quarterly
Final notification: 6 weeks for national organizations and organizations located in Lake County, IL, and Kenosha County, WI
Officers and Directors:* Stacey Eisen,* Pres.; Royce Bedward, V.P. & Secy.; Ken Meyers,* V.P.; Mike Chialdikas, Treas.; Rohit Vishnoi.
EIN: 202039190

2922
The John R. Houlsby Foundation ✧
212 Bridle Path Cir.
Oak Brook, IL 60523-2615 (630) 986-5645
Contact: Judith Louthan

Established in 1996 in IL.
Donor: John R. Houlsby†.
Foundation type: Independent foundation.
Financial data (yr. ended 12/31/13): Assets, $5,458,641 (M); expenditures, $904,020; qualifying distributions, $828,786; giving activities include $722,400 for 48 grants (high: $50,000; low: $2,500).
Purpose and activities: Giving primarily for community welfare, including the arts and youth services.
Fields of interest: Arts; Mental health, treatment; Health organizations, association; Children, services; Community/economic development.
Type of support: Continuing support; Emergency funds; Program development; Scholarship funds.
Limitations: Applications accepted. Giving limited to Cook and Lake counties, IL. No grants to individuals.
Application information: Application form required.
Initial approach: Letter of inquiry
Deadline(s): None
Board meeting date(s): 6 times a year
Officers and Directors:* David E. Mason,* Pres.; Katherine L. Fox, Secy.; Maree G. Bullock, Treas.; Stanley Ferguson; Mary L. Fox.
Number of staff: 1 full-time professional.
EIN: 363915186
Selected grants: The following grants are a representative sample of this grantmaker's funding activity:
$35,000 to Boys and Girls Clubs of Chicago, Chicago, IL, 2011.
$30,000 to Sarah's Circle, Chicago, IL, 2011.
$25,000 to Horizon Hospice and Palliative Care, Chicago, IL, 2011.
$25,000 to Lawyers' Committee for Better Housing, Chicago, IL, 2011.
$20,000 to CommunityHealth, Chicago, IL, 2011.
$20,000 to Housing Opportunities and Maintenance for the Elderly, Chicago, IL, 2011.
$17,500 to Chicago Jesuit Academy, Chicago, IL, 2011.
$15,000 to Children's Home and Aid Society of Illinois, Chicago, IL, 2011.
$12,000 to Infant Welfare Society of Chicago, Chicago, IL, 2011.
$10,000 to North Park University, Chicago, IL, 2011.

2923
Hargrove Hudson Charitable Trust ✧
c/o JPMorgan Chase Bank, N.A.
10 S. Dearborn St., 21st Fl.
Chicago, IL 60603-2317

Established in 1981 in WI; supporting organization of The Sisters of Charity of the Incarnate Word, The Sisters of the Sorrowful Mother, and The Sisters of the Good Shepard with affiliated order of the Sisters of the Cross.
Foundation type: Independent foundation.
Financial data (yr. ended 07/31/13): Assets, $61,902,302 (M); expenditures, $4,271,935; qualifying distributions, $2,530,343; giving activities include $2,461,603 for 5 grants (high: $965,285; low: $142,599).
Purpose and activities: Giving primarily to Roman Catholic communities of women religious.
Fields of interest: Catholic agencies & churches.
Limitations: Applications not accepted. Giving primarily in MO, NY, TX and WI.
Application information: Unsolicited requests for funds not considered or acknowledged.
Trustee: JPMorgan Chase Bank, N.A.
EIN: 731128665

2924
Huizenga Foundation ✧
2215 York Rd., Ste. 500
Oak Brook, IL 60523-4014

Established in 1988 in IL.
Donors: Peter H. Huizenga; HCM Energy Holdings, LLC.
Foundation type: Independent foundation.
Financial data (yr. ended 12/31/12): Assets, $1,248,938 (M); gifts received, $25,000; expenditures, $1,082,331; qualifying distributions, $1,042,788; giving activities include $1,042,788 for 146 grants (high: $202,175; low: $50).
Purpose and activities: Giving primarily to Christian organizations and churches, as well as for higher education, and children, youth, and social services.
Fields of interest: Arts; Elementary/secondary education; Higher education; Theological school/education; Human services; Family services; Christian agencies & churches.
Limitations: Applications not accepted. Giving primarily in IL and MI. No grants to individuals.
Application information: Contributes only to pre-selected organizations. Unsolicited requests for funds not accepted.
Officers and Directors:* Peter H. Huizenga,* Pres.; David A. Bradley, Secy.; Heidi A. Huizenga,* Treas.; Betsy Bradley; Greta Giesen; P.J. Huizenga; Tim Huizenga.
EIN: 363582536

2925
Hull Family Foundation ✧
141 W. Jackson Blvd., Ste. 340
Chicago, IL 60604
E-mail: info@hullfamilyfoundation.org; Main URL: http://www.hullfamilyfoundation.org/

Donor: M. Blair Hull, Jr.
Foundation type: Independent foundation.
Financial data (yr. ended 12/31/12): Assets, $20,880,092 (M); expenditures, $1,298,534; qualifying distributions, $1,146,314; giving activities include $1,011,744 for 145 grants (high: $50,000; low: $50).
Fields of interest: Education; Environment; Human services.
Limitations: Applications not accepted. Giving in the U.S., with emphasis on CA.
Application information: Unsolicited requests for funds not accepted.
Officersnd Directors:* Kristin Hull,* Pres.; Blair Hull; Courtney Hull; Jeffrey Hull; Megan Hull.
EIN: 260170419
Selected grants: The following grants are a representative sample of this grantmaker's funding activity:
$50,000 to Tides Foundation, San Francisco, CA, 2012. For youth engagement fund.
$50,000 to United Republic Education Fund, Florence, MA, 2012. For Purpose Action Factory Project.
$20,000 to New Organizing Institute Education Fund, Washington, DC, 2012. For Sum Of Us Program.
$18,000 to New Organizing Institute Education Fund, Washington, DC, 2012. For Citizen Engagement Lab Program.
$18,000 to New Organizing Institute Education Fund, Washington, DC, 2012. For Citizen Engagement Lab.
$15,000 to Tides Foundation, San Francisco, CA, 2012. For Latino Engagement Fund.
$10,000 to Movement Strategy Center, Oakland, CA, 2012. For Rebuild the Dream Innovation Fund.
$10,000 to New Organizing Institute Education Fund, Washington, DC, 2012. For Color of Change Program.
$5,000 to Solidago Foundation, Northampton, MA, 2012. For Criminal Justice Initiative (CJI) Division.
$5,000 to Tides Foundation, San Francisco, CA, 2012. For New Media Ventures Division.

2926
Hunter Family Foundation ✧
c/o Financial Investments Corp.
50 E. Washington St., No. 400
Chicago, IL 60602-2100

Established in 1995 in IL.
Donors: Thomas B. Hunter III; Maxine M. Hunter Charitable Lead Annuity Trust.
Foundation type: Independent foundation.
Financial data (yr. ended 12/31/12): Assets, $24,738,740 (M); gifts received, $1,521,229; expenditures, $1,248,442; qualifying distributions, $966,925; giving activities include $966,925 for grants.
Purpose and activities: Giving primarily for the arts, education, the environment, and social services.
Fields of interest: Performing arts; Arts; Elementary/secondary education; Higher education; Education; Environment; Hospitals (general); Human services; Protestant agencies & churches.

Limitations: Applications not accepted. Giving primarily in IL, with emphasis on Chicago and Lake Forest, and New York, NY. No grants to individuals.
Application information: Contributes only to pre-selected organizations.
Trustees: Maxine Hunter; Thomas B. Hunter III; Thomas B. Hunter IV; Willard M. Hunter.
EIN: 363959347

2927
Perkins Malo Hunter Foundation ✧
311 S. Wacker Dr., Ste. 6000
Chicago, IL 60606-6696

Established in 1996 in IL.
Donors: Robert H. Perkins; Nancy A. Perkins; Kenneth V. Perkins; Patrick Perkins; Greg Wolf; Todd Perkins; Gregory Grosh; Curtis L. Stine; Jill Perkins; Laurie Perkins; Robert Morgridge; N. Theodore Hans; Nancy Perkins Trust; Robert H. Perkins Trust; Phillip Perkins Trust; Todd Perkins Trust.
Foundation type: Independent foundation.
Financial data (yr. ended 12/31/13): Assets, $53,227,818 (M); gifts received, $3,712,000; expenditures, $2,558,133; qualifying distributions, $2,395,338; giving activities include $2,395,338 for 40 grants (high: $350,546; low: $500).
Purpose and activities: Giving primarily for education and human services.
Fields of interest: Elementary/secondary education; Education; Human services; Children/youth, services; Christian agencies & churches.
Limitations: Applications not accepted. Giving primarily in IL. No grants to individuals.
Application information: Contributes only to pre-selected organizations.
Directors: Jill Perkins; Laurie Perkins; Phillip M. Perkins; Robert H. Perkins; Todd Perkins; Curtis L. Stine.
EIN: 364098513
Selected grants: The following grants are a representative sample of this grantmaker's funding activity:
$312,085 to Marcy-Newberry Association, Chicago, IL, 2011. For general use.
$215,000 to New Schools for Chicago, Chicago, IL, 2011.
$120,000 to Cambridge School of Chicago, Chicago, IL, 2011. For tuition assistance.
$100,000 to Erie Elementary Charter School, Chicago, IL, 2011.
$90,000 to Entrepreneurship Preparatory School, Cleveland, OH, 2011.
$75,000 to Back of the Yards Neighborhood Council, Chicago, IL, 2011. For general use.
$75,000 to Citizens Academy, Cleveland, OH, 2011.
$55,000 to Boys and Girls Club of Greater Holland, Holland, MI, 2011. For general use.
$25,000 to Boys and Girls Clubs of Grand Rapids Youth Commonwealth, Grand Rapids, MI, 2011. For general use.
$1,200 to Henry Booth House, Chicago, IL, 2011. For general use.

2928
The James Huntington Foundation ✧
c/o Samuel H. Ellis
10 S. Wacker Dr., Ste. 2675
Chicago, IL 60606-7475

Established in 1987 in IL.
Donor: Samuel H. Ellis.
Foundation type: Independent foundation.
Financial data (yr. ended 12/31/13): Assets, $19,007,313 (M); expenditures, $1,508,952; qualifying distributions, $913,500; giving activities include $913,500 for 82 grants (high: $200,000; low: $500).
Purpose and activities: Giving primarily for the arts and human services.
Fields of interest: Arts; Elementary/secondary education; Higher education; Environment, natural resources; Animals/wildlife, preservation/protection; Hospitals (general); Health organizations, association; Human services; Salvation Army.
Limitations: Applications not accepted. Giving primarily in IL. No grants to individuals.
Application information: Contributes only to pre-selected organizations.
Trustee: Samuel H. Ellis.
EIN: 363553345

2929
Gladys & Ed E. Hurley Endowment Foundation ✧
10 S. Dearborn St., IL1-0117
Chicago, IL 60603-2300

Supporting organization of Centenary College of Louisiana, Centenary College - Hurley Center, Centenary College - Great Teachers, First United Methodist Church, Union College, Methodist Children's Home, Shreveport Symphony Society, American Bible Society, and Shreveport Rescue Mission.
Foundation type: Independent foundation.
Financial data (yr. ended 12/31/13): Assets, $22,381,502 (M); expenditures, $1,405,309; qualifying distributions, $1,287,554; giving activities include $1,256,837 for 7 grants (high: $1,237,337; low: $500).
Fields of interest: Higher education, college.
Limitations: Applications not accepted. Giving primarily in Shreveport, LA.
Application information: Contributes only to pre-selected organizations.
Trustee: JPMorgan Chase Bank, N.A.
EIN: 766017128
Selected grants: The following grants are a representative sample of this grantmaker's funding activity:
$1,201,339 to Centenary College of Louisiana, Shreveport, LA, 2012. For grant: Teaching Chairs.

2930
Hurvis Charitable Foundation, Inc. ✧
4065 Commercial Dr.
Northbrook, IL 60062-1828

Established in 2003 in IL.
Donor: J. Thomas Hurvis.
Foundation type: Independent foundation.
Financial data (yr. ended 12/31/12): Assets, $129,021,640 (L); gifts received, $124,291,607; expenditures, $4,311,304; qualifying distributions, $4,310,454; giving activities include $4,012,800 for 42 grants (high: $750,000; low: $10,000).
Fields of interest: Higher education; Education; Human services.
Type of support: General/operating support.
Limitations: Applications not accepted. Giving primarily in IL. No grants to individuals.
Application information: Contributes only to pre-selected organizations.
Officers and Directors:* J. Thomas Hurvis,* Pres.; Julie A. Hurvis,* V.P. and Secy.; Christina Hurvis; Sara Hurvis-Younkin.
EIN: 710935903
Selected grants: The following grants are a representative sample of this grantmaker's funding activity:
$3,000,000 to Lawrence University, Appleton, WI, 2011. For enhancements to film studies program.
$2,000,000 to Lawrence University, Appleton, WI, 2011. For enhancements to film studies program.
$500,000 to World Wildlife Fund, Washington, DC, 2011. For Tiger Network Initiative.
$415,000 to New Schools for Chicago, Chicago, IL, 2011. For challenge grant for marketing, communications and community organizing activities.
$335,000 to New Schools for Chicago, Chicago, IL, 2011. For challenge grant for marketing, communications and community organizing activities.
$100,000 to Chicago High School for the Arts, Chicago, IL, 2011. For startup support.
$50,000 to Lawrence University, Appleton, WI, 2011. For Lawrence Fellow in Spanish.
$50,000 to Merit School of Music, Chicago, IL, 2011. For Solo Voice program.
$50,000 to Muttville, San Francisco, CA, 2011. For capital support for new headquarters.
$50,000 to New Schools for Chicago, Chicago, IL, 2011. For matching grant for community organizing activities.

2931
I and G Charitable Foundation ✧
c/o Gary Holzman
225 W. Washington St., Ste. 1650
Chicago, IL 60606-3486

Incorporated in 1945 in IL.
Donors: Roger O. Brown; Barbara Brown; GB 30 Year Charitable Trust; Roger O. Brown Charitable Trust.
Foundation type: Independent foundation.
Financial data (yr. ended 12/31/12): Assets, $7,338,241 (M); expenditures, $655,175; qualifying distributions, $549,000; giving activities include $549,000 for grants.
Purpose and activities: Giving primarily for human services.
Fields of interest: Education; Human services; Children/youth, services; Jewish federated giving programs.
Limitations: Applications not accepted. No grants to individuals.
Application information: Contributes only to pre-selected organizations.
Officers: Owen Brown, Pres. and Treas.; Gail Feiger Brown, V.P. and Secy.; Joan Jensen, V.P.
Directors: Andrew Brown; Henry Brown; Jeffrey R. Brown; Vanessa J.B. McGuire.
EIN: 366069174

2932
IDP Foundation, Inc. ✧
321 N. Clark St., Ste. 2350
Chicago, IL 60654-4784 (312) 321-4000
Contact: Alison Ehlke, Admin. and Grants Mgr.; Anne Schumacher, Prog. Mgr., IDP Rising Schools Prog.
FAX: (312) 755-0386;
E-mail: info@idpfoundation.org; Additional address: 51 Madison Ave., Ste. 2100, New York, NY 10010;
Main URL: http://www.idpfoundation.org
E-Newsletter: http://idpfoundation.us1.list-manage.com/subscribe?u=b4f2abb075ed4830f7d64a21a&id=874bee3ac5
Facebook: http://www.facebook.com/IDPFoundation
LinkedIn: http://www.linkedin.com/in/idpfoundation
Twitter: http://twitter.com/IDPFoundation

Established in 2008 in DE, but registered to do business in IL.
Foundation type: Independent foundation.
Financial data (yr. ended 12/31/13): Assets, $50,884,731 (M); gifts received, $4,991,939; expenditures, $1,804,771; qualifying distributions, $1,540,447; giving activities include $572,563 for 13 grants (high: $150,000; low: $1,000), $1,247,166 for 1 foundation-administered program and $125,000 for 1 loan/program-related investment.
Purpose and activities: The foundation's mission is to mobilize resources and strategic support to increase educational opportunities, striving to support and create successful educational advancement at all levels, from pre-school to post-doctoral scientific and medical research.
Fields of interest: Elementary/secondary education; Higher education; Graduate/professional education; Education; International development; Children/youth; Children; Youth; Economically disadvantaged.
International interests: Africa; Ghana; Global Programs.
Limitations: Applications not accepted. Giving primarily in Chicago, IL and in Ghana. No support for lobbying, or for religious missionary or indoctrination activities. No grants to individuals, or for endowments, capital construction, or deficit financing.
Application information: The foundation is currently not accepting unsolicited letters of inquiry.
Officers: Irene Pritzker, Pres.; Liesel Pritzker Simmons, V.P. and Dir. Prog. Development.
EIN: 262753703

2933
Illinois Children's Healthcare Foundation ✧
1200 Jorie Blvd., Ste. 301
Oak Brook, IL 60523-2269 (630) 571-2555
FAX: (630) 571-2566; E-mail for Tammy Lemke: tammylemke@ilchf.org; Main URL: http://www.ilchf.org

Established in 2002 in IL.
Donors: Health Care Services Corp.; Peter E. Doris, M.D.; C. William Pollard.
Foundation type: Independent foundation.
Financial data (yr. ended 12/31/13): Assets, $136,293,450 (M); expenditures, $6,013,467; qualifying distributions, $5,643,447; giving activities include $4,669,253 for 26 grants (high: $557,500; low: $7,000).
Purpose and activities: The foundation (ILCHF) has a single mission: to ensure that every child in Illinois has the opportunity to grow up healthy. As such, its grant making is designed to close the gap between children who have access to care and those who are underserved. At the current time, ILCHF focuses its giving in two focus areas: 1) improving the oral health of children; and 2) addressing the mental health needs of children, specifically through system of care modeling. In addition, the foundation monitors emerging and other compelling health issues that the board of directors may select as focus areas in the future.
Fields of interest: Dental care; Health care; Mental health/crisis services; Children.
Type of support: Building/renovation; Equipment; Emergency funds; Program development; Research; Program evaluation.
Limitations: Applications accepted. Giving limited to IL. No support for partisan, lobbying, political or denominational organizations, or for organizations not determined to be public charities. No grants to individuals, or for endowments or, general medical research.
Publications: Annual report; Financial statement; Grants list; IRS Form 990 or 990-PF printed copy available upon request; Program policy statement.
Application information: Funding is through either an open RFP (see foundation web site for RFP information) or via invitation. Funding requests by invitation are initiated by a phone call to ILCHF. Application form required.
Initial approach: Telephone call or letter of inquire in response to a specific RFP
Copies of proposal: 1
Board meeting date(s): Generally six times per year
Officers and Directors:* Kathleen L. Halloran,* Chair.; J. Kevin Dorsey, M.D., Ph.D.*, Vice-Chair.; Heather Higgins Alderman, Pres.; Terry F. Hatch, M.D.*, Secy.; Floyd D. Perkins,* Treas.; C. William Pollard, Dir. Emeritus; Jim Ryan, Dir. Emeritus; Billie Wright Adams, M.D.; Hon. Charles E. Box; Philip S. Cali; Louise Coleman, Ed.D.; Peter E. Doris, M.D.; Peter Flynn, Ph.D.; John Jasinski; Michael Parker; Ruth B. Rosenthal, M.D.; Christine Hehmeyer Rosso; Kay L. Saving, M.D.; James L. Schroeder, M.D.
Number of staff: 4 full-time professional.
EIN: 030503425

2934
Illinois Tool Works Foundation ✧
3600 W. Lake Ave.
Glenview, IL 60025-5811 (847) 724-7500
Contact: Rosemary Matzl, Secy. and Dir. of Community Rels.
FAX: (847) 657-4505; Main URL: http://www.itw.com/social-responsibility/community-relations/itw-foundation/

Incorporated in 1954 in IL.
Donor: Illinois Tool Works Inc.
Foundation type: Company-sponsored foundation.
Financial data (yr. ended 12/31/13): Assets, $8,918,313 (M); expenditures, $21,048,727; qualifying distributions, $20,939,634; giving activities include $12,790,676 for 647 grants (high: $5,780,951; low: $10), and $8,124,548 for 7,255 employee matching gifts.
Purpose and activities: The foundation supports organizations involved with arts and culture, education, the environment, health, human services, and youth. Special emphasis is directed towards science, technology, engineering, and mathematics.
Fields of interest: Museums (history); Museums (science/technology); Performing arts; Performing arts, theater; Performing arts, orchestras; Arts; Elementary/secondary education; Higher education; Business school/education; Education; Botanical gardens; Horticulture/garden clubs; Environment, beautification programs; Environment; Hospitals (general); Health care, clinics/centers; Health care; Food services; Food banks; Youth development, centers/clubs; Boys & girls clubs; Youth development, business; American Red Cross; YM/YWCAs & YM/YWHAs; Residential/custodial care, hospices; Human services; United Ways and Federated Giving Programs; Science; Youth.
Type of support: General/operating support; Continuing support; Annual campaigns; Capital campaigns; Building/renovation; Program development; Scholarship funds; Employee volunteer services; Employee matching gifts; Employee-related scholarships.
Limitations: Applications accepted. Giving primarily in areas of company operations, with emphasis on Chicago, IL; giving also to national organizations. No support for political organizations or candidates or religious organizations. No grants to individuals (except for employee-related scholarships), or for endowments or research; no loans.
Publications: Application guidelines; Corporate giving report.
Application information: Preference is given to organizations with an established relationship with an ITW employee or business unit. Application form required.
Initial approach: Complete online application
Deadline(s): None
Board meeting date(s): May and Dec.
Officers and Directors: Sharon M. Brady, Pres.; Rosemary Matzl, Secy. and Dir. of Community Rels.; Maria C. Green; Michael M. Larsen; David C. Parry; Ernest Scott Santi.
Number of staff: 1 full-time support.
EIN: 366087160
Selected grants: The following grants are a representative sample of this grantmaker's funding activity:
$605,225 to Scholarship America, Saint Peter, MN, 2012. For general support.
$200,000 to Ann and Robert H. Lurie Children's Hospital of Chicago Foundation, Chicago, IL, 2012. For general support.
$200,000 to Field Museum of Natural History, Chicago, IL, 2012. For general support.
$200,000 to United Way of Metropolitan Chicago, Chicago, IL, 2012. For general support.
$100,000 to Chicago Horticultural Society, Chicago Botanic Garden, Glencoe, IL, 2012. For general support.
$100,000 to La Rabida Childrens Hospital, Chicago, IL, 2012. For general support.
$50,000 to Ralph Wilson Youth Clubs, Temple, TX, 2012. For general support.
$25,000 to Teach for America, Chicago, IL, 2012. For general support.
$10,000 to Ravinia Festival Association, Highland Park, IL, 2012. For general support.
$5,000 to United Way of Eastern La Salle County, Ottawa, IL, 2012. For general support.

2935
William P. Ingersoll Trust ✧
10 S. Dearborn St., ILI1-0117
Chicago, IL 60603-2300

Foundation type: Independent foundation.
Financial data (yr. ended 09/30/13): Assets, $38,691,285 (M); expenditures, $2,112,794; qualifying distributions, $1,903,550; giving activities include $1,851,941 for 17 grants (high: $370,388; low: $23,149).
Fields of interest: Recreation, parks/playgrounds; Human services; American Red Cross; Salvation Army; YM/YWCAs & YM/YWHAs; Children/youth, services; Protestant agencies & churches.
Limitations: Applications not accepted. Giving primarily in Canton, IL.
Application information: Contributes only to pre-selected organizations.
Trustee: JPMorgan Chase Bank, N.A.
EIN: 366584340
Selected grants: The following grants are a representative sample of this grantmaker's funding activity:
$376,111 to Canton Park District, Canton, IL, 2011. For program support.
$94,028 to Graham Hospital Association, Canton, IL, 2011. For program support.

2936
Irwin Family Foundation ✧
2825 Denton Ct.
Westchester, IL 60154-5637 (708) 751-5597
Contact: Robert W. Lynch, Tr.

Established in 1977.
Donors: Richard D. Irwin Trust No. 1; Richard D. Irwin Charitable Remainder Annuity Trust.
Foundation type: Independent foundation.
Financial data (yr. ended 12/31/13): Assets, $11,608,495 (M); expenditures, $1,196,010; qualifying distributions, $1,165,800; giving activities include $1,140,000 for 6 grants (high: $500,000; low: $25,000).
Purpose and activities: Giving primarily for higher education.
Fields of interest: Higher education; Hospitals (general); Cancer research; Human services.
Type of support: Capital campaigns; Program development; Fellowships; Scholarship funds.
Limitations: Giving primarily in IL. No grants to individuals.
Application information: Application form not required.
Initial approach: Proposal
Deadline(s): None
Board meeting date(s): As required
Trustees: Robert E. Hamilton; Robert W. Lynch; Jacques Murphy; Jacqueline Pipher.
EIN: 362913193
Selected grants: The following grants are a representative sample of this grantmaker's funding activity:
$500,000 to University of Illinois at Urbana-Champaign, Urbana, IL, 2011.
$250,000 to Ingalls Memorial Hospital, Harvey, IL, 2011.
$240,000 to University of Illinois at Urbana-Champaign, Urbana, IL, 2011. For scholarships.
$200,000 to Literacy Council of Bonita Springs, Bonita Springs, FL, 2011. For program funding.
$60,000 to Cornerstone Academy, Chicago, IL, 2011. For program funding.
$25,000 to Glenwood School, Glenwood, IL, 2011. For program funding.
$2,000 to Respond Now, Chicago Heights, IL, 2011. For program funding.

2937
Marion Gardner Jackson Charitable Trust ✧
c/o U.S. Trust, Philanthropic Solutions
231 S. LaSalle St., IL4-135-14-19
Chicago, IL 60604-1426 (312) 828-4154
Contact: Debra Grand, Sr. V.P.
E-mail: ilgrantmaking@ustrust.com (indicate the foundation name in subject line); Main URL: http://www.bankofamerica.com/grantmaking

Foundation type: Independent foundation.
Financial data (yr. ended 12/31/13): Assets, $11,423,983 (M); expenditures, $624,358; qualifying distributions, $556,359; giving activities include $492,101 for 19 grants (high: $85,950; low: $5,000).
Purpose and activities: Giving primarily to aid religious, charitable, scientific, literary, and educational organizations in the Quincy, Illinois area and surrounding communities in Adams County, Illinois. Additionally, applicants may apply for 1- to 5-year grants to support capital projects. The project must support the mission of the organization and/or the stated outcome of a program or project. Applicants with organizational budgets of $1 million or less may apply for grants of up to $25,000 per year, for up to 3 years, for program or general operating support. For program support grants, the yearly request may not be more than 50 percent of the program's budget.
Fields of interest: Higher education; Education; Big Brothers/Big Sisters; Youth development; Human services; Community/economic development.
Type of support: Building/renovation.
Limitations: Giving primarily in Quincy, IL, and surrounding communities in Adams County. No grants to individuals.
Application information: Application guidelines available on Trust web site.
Initial approach: Online through Trust web site
Deadline(s): July 31
Final notification: Jan. 15
Trustee: Bank of America, N.A.
EIN: 046010559
Selected grants: The following grants are a representative sample of this grantmaker's funding activity:
$37,500 to John Wood Community College Foundation, Quincy, IL, 2011. For student activity center.
$25,000 to Good Samaritan Home, Quincy, IL, 2011. For Code Alert Wireless System.
$25,000 to Quincy Art Center, Quincy, IL, 2011. For Art Mentor Program.
$25,000 to Quincy Society of Fine Arts, Quincy, IL, 2011. To increase access to the arts and foster artistic excellence.
$21,380 to YMCA of Quincy, Quincy, IL, 2011. For Baseball Field Relocation Project.
$21,185 to Cornerstone Foundations for Families, Quincy, IL, 2011. For roof and gutter repair.
$20,000 to Community Foundation of the Quincy Area, Quincy, IL, 2011. For staff salaries primarily for Program Coordinator and support staff positions and partial funding for the purchase and implementation of online grant management software.
$18,200 to Great River Recovery Resources, Quincy, IL, 2011. For two furnaces and condensers.
$16,700 to Quincy Museum, Quincy, IL, 2011. For Exterior Restoration Project.
$11,980 to Cheerful Home, Quincy, IL, 2011. For replacement windows and ADA approved doors.

2938
Reinhardt H. & Shirley R. Jahn Foundation Trust ✧
2737 Eastwood Ave.
Evanston, IL 60201-1544

Established in 2003 in IL.
Foundation type: Independent foundation.
Financial data (yr. ended 12/31/13): Assets, $11,860,280 (M); expenditures, $841,448; qualifying distributions, $785,000; giving activities include $785,000 for 7 grants (high: $300,000; low: $10,000).
Fields of interest: Arts education; Medical school/education; Boys & girls clubs; Youth development.
Type of support: General/operating support; Land acquisition.
Limitations: Applications not accepted. Giving primarily in Chicago, IL, MI, and WI. No grants to individuals.
Application information: Contributes only to pre-selected organizations.
Trustees: Carolyn L. Jahn; Charles L. Jahn; Reinhardt E. Jahn.
EIN: 426643394
Selected grants: The following grants are a representative sample of this grantmaker's funding activity:
$30,000 to Art Resources in Teaching, Chicago, IL, 2012. For programs and operations.

2939
Jephson Educational Trust No. 2 ✧
c/o JPMorgan Srvs., Inc.
P.O. Box 6089
Chicago, IL 60603
Contact: Casey E. Burgess, Prog. off., JPMorgan Chase Bank, N.A.
E-mail: casey.e.burgess@jpmchase.com

Trust established in 1979 in NY.
Donor: Lucretia Davis Jephson†.
Foundation type: Independent foundation.
Financial data (yr. ended 09/30/13): Assets, $11,178,664 (M); expenditures, $590,344; qualifying distributions, $535,797; giving activities include $446,500 for 38 grants (high: $70,000; low: $2,500).
Purpose and activities: Giving primarily for the arts and education.
Fields of interest: Performing arts; Arts; Secondary school/education; Higher education.
Type of support: Scholarship funds.
Limitations: Applications not accepted. Giving in the U.S., with emphasis on NY. No grants to individuals, or for matching gifts; no loans.
Publications: Grants list; Informational brochure.
Application information: Contributes only to pre-selected organizations.
Trustees: John F. Parkin; Robert D. Taisey, Esq.; JPMorgan Chase Bank, N.A.

Number of staff: 1
EIN: 136777236
Selected grants: The following grants are a representative sample of this grantmaker's funding activity:
$15,000 to Learning Ally, Princeton, NJ, 2011. For general support.
$10,000 to Clarke School for the Deaf, Northampton, MA, 2011. For general support.

2940
JNT Foundation ✧
10 S. Dearborn St., IL1-0117
Chicago, IL 60603-2300

Established in 1999 in IA.
Foundation type: Independent foundation.
Financial data (yr. ended 08/31/13): Assets, $15,853,190 (M); gifts received, $130,000; expenditures, $1,701,486; qualifying distributions, $1,612,077; giving activities include $1,581,000 for 18 grants (high: $300,000; low: $25,000).
Fields of interest: Higher education; Health care; Agriculture; Human services; American Red Cross; Salvation Army; Children, services; Family services, domestic violence.
Limitations: Applications not accepted. Giving primarily in IA. No grants to individuals.
Application information: Contributes only to pre-selected organizations.
EIN: 421493980

2941
Lowell N. Johnson Charitable Foundation ✧ ☆
1610 5th Ave.
Moline, IL 61265-7909 (309) 762-3643
Contact: Daniel Churchill, Pres.

Established in 2002 in IL.
Donors: Lowell N. Johnson; Lowell N. Johnson Trust.
Foundation type: Independent foundation.
Financial data (yr. ended 12/31/13): Assets, $11,095,734 (M); expenditures, $602,271; qualifying distributions, $528,710; giving activities include $455,550 for 32 grants (high: $100,000; low: $500).
Fields of interest: Higher education; Education; Christian agencies & churches.
Limitations: Applications accepted. Giving primarily in IL. No grants to individuals, political, labor or fraternal organizations.
Application information: Application form required.
Initial approach: Letter
Deadline(s): None
Officer: Daniel Churchill, Pres.
EIN: 460484573
Selected grants: The following grants are a representative sample of this grantmaker's funding activity:
$75,000 to University of Illinois Foundation, College of Business, Champaign, IL, 2011.
$55,000 to Augustana College Foundation, Rock Island, IL, 2011.
$50,000 to Saint Ambrose University, Davenport, IA, 2011.
$20,000 to Christian Friendliness Association, Moline, IL, 2011.
$10,000 to Quad-City Music Guild, Moline, IL, 2011.
$2,500 to Child Abuse Council, Rock Island, IL, 2011.
$2,500 to Childrens Therapy Center of the Quad Cities, Moline, IL, 2011.
$2,500 to Niabi Zoological Society, Coal Valley, IL, 2011.
$2,000 to Moline Foundation, Moline, IL, 2011.
$1,000 to Arrowhead Ranch, Coal Valley, IL, 2011.

2942
Violet M. Johnson Family Foundation ✧
P.O. Box 803878
Chicago, IL 60680-3878

Foundation type: Independent foundation.
Financial data (yr. ended 07/31/13): Assets, $15,557,610 (M); expenditures, $637,247; qualifying distributions, $508,000; giving activities include $508,000 for grants.
Fields of interest: Medical research, institute; Human services; Children/youth, services.
Limitations: Applications not accepted. Giving primarily in AZ and CO.
Application information: Contributes only to pre-selected organizations.
Officers: Loren Thomas Halverstadt, Jr., Pres. and Treas.; Karen Halverstadt Miller, V.P.
Director: Douglas Halverstadt.
EIN: 200128534
Selected grants: The following grants are a representative sample of this grantmaker's funding activity:
$20,000 to DonorsChoose.org, New York, NY, 2011. For general support.
$10,000 to Boys and Girls Clubs of Greater Scottsdale, Scottsdale, AZ, 2011. For general support.

2943
Julie Ann Johnson Foundation ✧ ☆
1511 Lexington
Arlington Heights, IL 60004-2811

Foundation type: Independent foundation.
Financial data (yr. ended 12/31/13): Assets, $134,899 (M); expenditures, $836,098; qualifying distributions, $815,270; giving activities include $815,270 for 5 grants (high: $500,000; low: $40,270).
Purpose and activities: Giving primarily for a railway museum, a Christian church, and a center for transgender equality; funding also for health organizations.
Fields of interest: Museums (specialized); Health organizations; Human services; Christian agencies & churches.
Limitations: Applications not accepted. Giving primarily in IL; some funding also in Washington, DC. No grants to individuals.
Application information: Unsolicited Requests for funds not accepted.
Officers: Deanna Reed, Pres.; Laura DeVries, Secy.-Treas.
EIN: 452956492

2944
Mead Johnson Nutrition Foundation ✧
2701 Patriot Blvd.
Glenview, IL 60026 (847) 832-2420
Main URL: http://www.meadjohnson.com/corporate-citizenship/nurturing-communities

Donor: Mead Johnson Nutrition Company.
Foundation type: Company-sponsored foundation.
Financial data (yr. ended 12/31/13): Assets, $2,645,960 (M); expenditures, $426,030; qualifying distributions, $426,030; giving activities include $425,900 for 4 grants (high: $125,000; low: $100,000).
Purpose and activities: Giving primarily to support infants and children in fragile circumstances.
Fields of interest: Children, services; Human services; Infants/toddlers.
Application information: Application form not required.
Initial approach: Proposal
Deadline(s): None
Officers and Directors:* Stanley Burhans, V.P.; Michael Cascella, V.P.; Tom de Weerdt, V.P.; Peter Leemputte, V.P.; Eryk Spytek, V.P.; Kasper Jakobsen,* Chair.; Charles M. Urbain, Vice-Chair.; William C. P'Pool,* V.P. and Secy.; Kevin Wilson,* V.P. and Treas.; Christopher Perille, Exec. Dir.
EIN: 274243966

2945
The Jordan Family Sports Foundation ✧
875 N. Michigan Ave., Ste. 4020
Chicago, IL 60611

Established in IL.
Donors: John W. Jordan II Revocable Trust; The Jordan Companies; Jordan Industries, Inc.; John W. Jordan II.
Foundation type: Independent foundation.
Financial data (yr. ended 12/31/13): Assets, $2,376 (M); gifts received, $663,000; expenditures, $693,399; qualifying distributions, $619,800; giving activities include $619,800 for 36 grants (high: $360,559; low: $67).
Fields of interest: Athletics/sports, football.
Type of support: Equipment.
Limitations: Applications not accepted. Giving primarily in IL and NY.
Application information: Unsolicited requests for funds not accepted.
Directors: Jennifer L. Jordan; John W. Jordan II; John W. Jordan III.
EIN: 262516641
Selected grants: The following grants are a representative sample of this grantmaker's funding activity:
$25,000 to Josephinum Academy, Chicago, IL, 2012. For Salary of Physical Education Teacher.
$7,352 to Leo High School, Chicago, IL, 2012. For Sports Equipment Contributed to School.
$1,888 to Maria High School, Chicago, IL, 2012. For Sports Equipment Contributed to the School.
$1,395 to Maria High School, Chicago, IL, 2012. For contribution to Fund Gymnasium Floor Renovation.

2946
The Joyce Foundation ✧
c/o Dir. Communication
321 North Clark Street, Ste. 1500
Chicago, IL 60654-4714 (312) 782-2464
Contact: Dir. Comms.
FAX: (312) 595-1350; E-mail: info@joycefdn.org;
Main URL: http://www.joycefdn.org
LinkedIn: http://www.linkedin.com/company/122729
Twitter: https://twitter.com/joyceawards

Incorporated in 1948 in IL.
Donor: Beatrice Joyce Kean‡.
Foundation type: Independent foundation.
Financial data (yr. ended 12/31/13): Assets, $936,451,953 (M); expenditures, $46,720,403; qualifying distributions, $42,383,163; giving activities include $35,040,827 for 315 grants (high: $550,000; low: $1,000), and $40,910 for employee matching gifts.
Purpose and activities: The foundation supports the development of policies that both improve the quality of life for people in the Great Lakes region and serve as models for the rest of the country. The foundation focuses on today's most pressing problems while also informing the public policy decisions critical to creating opportunity and achieving long-term solutions. The work is based on sound research and is focused on where the foundation can add the most value. The foundation encourages innovative and collaborative approaches with a regional focus and the potential for a national reach.
Fields of interest: Arts; Education; Environment; Crime/violence prevention; Crime/violence prevention, gun control; Employment; Public affairs, finance; Public affairs, political organizations.
Type of support: General/operating support; Continuing support; Program development; Conferences/seminars; Research; Program evaluation; Employee matching gifts.
Limitations: Applications accepted. Giving primarily in the Great Lakes region, specifically the states of Illinois, Indiana, Michigan, Minnesota, Ohio, and Wisconsin. A limited number of environment grants are made to organizations in Canada. Education grant making in K-12 focuses on Chicago, Indianapolis, and Minneapolis. The Employment Program primarily focuses on federal and state policy grants, but will make some grants to support targeted metro-level progress in Chicago, Indianapolis, and Minneapolis/St. Paul. Culture grants are primarily focused on the Chicago metropolitan area, except for the Joyce Awards, which extend to other Midwest cities. No support for religious activities, or for political organizations. No grants to individuals or for endowment campaigns, scholarships, direct service programs, commercial ventures, or capital proposals.
Publications: Annual report (including application guidelines); Financial statement; Newsletter; Occasional report.
Application information: Program policy and grant proposal guidelines reviewed annually in Dec. Proposals in all program areas will be considered at each board meeting. Applicants are encouraged to submit their proposals for the Apr. or July meeting, since most grant funds will be distributed at those times. Proposal cover sheet available on foundation web site. Online proposals will not be considered. Application form required.

Initial approach: Contact foundation for application guidelines prior to submitting 2- to 3-page letter of inquiry
Copies of proposal: 1
Deadline(s): Letter of inquiry required at least 6 to 8 weeks before proposal deadlines. For formal proposals: Apr. 8 (for July meeting); Aug. 13 (for Dec. meeting). For Joyce Awards: Apr. 4 for letter of inquiry and June 16 for proposal (if requested by foundation)
Board meeting date(s): Apr., July, and Dec.
Final notification: 2 weeks after meeting

Officers and Directors:* Roger R. Fross,* Chair.; Charles U. Daly, Vice-Chair.; Ellen S. Alberding,* Pres.; Deborah Gillespie, V.P., Finance and Admin. and Treas.; Beth Swanson, V.P., Prog(s). and Strategy; Gil M. Sarmiento, Cont.; Jane R. Paterson, C.I.O.; Jose B. Alvarez; John T. Anderson; Roger G. Bottoms; Michael F. Brewer; Anthony S. Earl; Carlton L. Guthrie; Daniel P. Kearney; Tracey L. Meares; Margot M. Rogers; Paula Wolff.
Number of staff: 17 full-time professional; 2 part-time professional; 8 full-time support.
EIN: 366079185
Selected grants: The following grants are a representative sample of this grantmaker's funding activity:
$1,500,000 to Southeastern Wisconsin Watersheds Trust, Milwaukee, WI, 2012. For its project to achieve clean water in the Greater Milwaukee watersheds, payable over 3.00 years.
$1,208,142 to WestEd, San Francisco, CA, 2013. To support training of regional Certified Coach Trainers as part of scaling implementation of Kindergarten Individual Development Survey (KIDS) in Illinois to support early literacy instruction, payable over 2.00 years.
$1,000,000 to Aspen Institute, Washington, DC, 2012. For continued support for the Aspen Prize for Community College Excellence, payable over 2.00 years.
$850,000 to National Skills Coalition, Washington, DC, 2012. For federal policy efforts, technical assistance to Midwest state advocates, strategic communications, and a national Workforce Data Quality Campaign, payable over 2.00 years.
$700,000 to EmployIndy, Indianapolis, IN, 2013. To launch Hire Up Indy, payable over 2.00 years.
$650,000 to Harvard University, Cambridge, MA, 2012. To conduct firearms research, disseminate findings, and conduct the Means Matter campaign.
$500,000 to Environmental Defense Fund, New York, NY, 2013. For work to improve water quality in the Western Lake Erie basin, payable over 2.00 years.
$500,000 to Harvard University, Cambridge, MA, 2013. For grant to School of Public Health in Boston for work to support Preventing Firearm Violence project, payable over 1.50 years.
$455,000 to Brennan Center for Justice, New York, NY, 2012. For its Midwest policy and legal work in the areas of redistricting, campaign finance, fair courts, and voting rights, payable over 2.00 years.
$300,000 to Chicago Theater Group, Chicago, IL, 2012. For artistic development and diversity initiatives, payable over 2.00 years.
$300,000 to Civic Consulting Alliance, Chicago, IL, 2013. To provide strategic consulting to the City of Chicago and the State of Illinois in the areas of education and workforce development, payable over 2.00 years.
$272,500 to Bellwether Education Partners, Wellesley, MA, 2013. To support expansion of work on teacher pension reform issues through key policy reports and engagement of teachers and other education reform stakeholders.
$150,000 to Global Philanthropy Partnership, Chicago, IL, 2013. To scale up energy efficiency retrofits in the health care and higher education sectors in Chicago.
$150,000 to Manufacturing Renaissance, Chicago, IL, 2012. To advocate for expanded and improved advanced manufacturing workforce development in the Chicago area, and to support expansion of such work beyond the Chicago area, payable over 2.00 years.
$150,000 to Nature Conservancy, Arlington, VA, 2012. For Western Lake Erie Basin project.
$150,000 to Policy Innovators in Education Network, Minneapolis, MN, 2012. For state-level policy changes needed to improve teacher quality, close achievement gaps, and ensure that all student graduates are world ready.
$125,000 to Educational Fund to Stop Gun Violence, Washington, DC, 2012. For building national gun violence prevention coalitions, to implement recommendations from the communications framing process, and to build expertise on the intersection of gun violence and mental health issues.
$100,000 to Aspen Institute, Washington, DC, 2013. To support Skills for Americas Future, employer-led policy initiative of the Economic Opportunities Program at the Aspen Institute. SAF identifies solutions in which education and training providers work together with employers to prepare individuals with the skills that will allow American businesses to be more productive, innovative and competitive.
$100,000 to Northwestern University, Evanston, IL, 2013. To support evaluation of reform initiatives of the Chicago Police Department.
$100,000 to Proteus Fund, Amherst, MA, 2013. To increase communications capacity of fair courts and money in politics reform organizations in the Great Lakes region, payable over 2.00 years.

2947
Mayer and Morris Kaplan Family Foundation ✧

1780 Green Bay Rd., Ste. 205
Highland Park, IL 60035-3276 (847) 926-8350
Contact: Dinaz Mansuri, Exec. Dir.
FAX: (847) 681-1363;
E-mail: dmansuri@kapfam.com; Main URL: http://www.kapfam.com/

Incorporated in 1957 in IL.
Donors: Burton B. Kaplan‡; Morris Kaplan‡.
Foundation type: Independent foundation.
Financial data (yr. ended 12/31/13): Assets, $38,591,785 (M); gifts received, $517,001; expenditures, $3,744,551; qualifying distributions, $3,301,097; giving activities include $2,990,132 for 154 grants (high: $500,000; low: $500).
Purpose and activities: Giving primarily for education and the environment.
Fields of interest: Education; Environment.
Type of support: General/operating support; Management development/capacity building; Program development.
Limitations: Giving in Los Angeles, CA, and Chicago, IL, for Education Grants; and CO and WY for Environment Grants. No support for religious organizations, organizations that accept abstinence-only educational funding; employment, housing and emergency services organizations, national organizations, health care institutions, or medical, scientific, or academic research. No grants to individuals, or for capital campaigns, building funds, equipment or materials, research, publications, meetings, ticket purchases, films or recordings.
Publications: Application guidelines; Annual report; Financial statement; Grants list.
Application information:

Initial approach: Refer to foundation web site for specific guidelines
Deadline(s): See foundation web site for current deadlines
Board meeting date(s): 2 times per year

Officers and Directors:* Curt Kaplan,* Chair.; Beth Kaplan Karmin,* Pres.; Anne Kaplan,* V.P.; Jessica Kaplan Lundevall,* Secy.; Michael Kaplan,* Treas.; Dinaz Mansuri, Exec. Dir.; Aura de la Fuente; Charles Kaplan; David Kaplan; Jean Kaplan; Robert Kaplan; Hilary Kaplan Loretta; Kaja Lundevall; Tellef Lundevall; Sarah Kaplan Moore.
Number of staff: 3 full-time professional.
EIN: 366099675

2948
Elaine & William Kaplan Family Private Foundation ✧
10 S. Dearborn IL1-0117
Chicago, IL 60603

Established in 1990 in NY.
Foundation type: Independent foundation.
Financial data (yr. ended 12/31/12): Assets, $7,476,710 (M); expenditures, $772,672; qualifying distributions, $770,486; giving activities include $724,455 for 26 grants (high: $400,000; low: $750).
Purpose and activities: Giving primarily for health organizations and human services.
Fields of interest: Education; Employment; Human services.
Type of support: General/operating support.
Limitations: Applications not accepted. Giving primarily in Newburgh, NY. No grants to individuals.
Application information: Contributes only to pre-selected organizations.
Officers: Joan P. Kaplan, Pres.; Amy Kaplan, V.P.; Sheila Kaplan, V.P.; Deborah K. Sergi, V.P.; Richard J. Drake, Secy.; David Marks, Treas.
Directors: Richard J. Bauer; Harold Kaplan; A. Vincent Mazzie.
EIN: 141736469

2949
Kaplan Foundation ✧
25 Lakewood Pl.
Highland Park, IL 60035-5007
Mailing address: c/o Chicago Community Trust, 111 E. Wacker Dr., Ste. 1400, Chicago, IL 60601; tel.: (312) 616-8000, fax: (312) 616-7955, e-mail: info@cct.org

Established in 1991 in IL.
Donor: Edward Kaplan.
Foundation type: Independent foundation.
Financial data (yr. ended 12/31/12): Assets, $20,249,242 (M); expenditures, $1,545,344; qualifying distributions, $1,428,435; giving activities include $1,426,604 for 15 grants (high: $1,400,000; low: $500).
Fields of interest: Human services; Foundations (community); Jewish agencies & synagogues.
Limitations: Applications not accepted. Giving primarily in Chicago, IL. No grants to individuals.
Application information: Contributes only to pre-selected organizations. Unsolicited requests for funds not accepted.
Officers: Carol K. Kaplan, Pres.; Edward Kaplan, Secy.-Treas.
Directors: Alan Kaplan; Martin Kaplan.
EIN: 363796516

2950
John and Editha Kapoor Charitable Foundation ✧
(formerly Kapoor Charitable Foundation)
100 North Field Dr., Ste. 150
Lake Forest, IL 60045-2597
Contact: Mary Gauwitz, Exec. Dir.
FAX: (847) 295-8680;
E-mail: mgauwitz@ejfinancial.com

Established in 1990 in IL.
Donors: Editha Sue Kapoor‡; John N. Kapoor.
Foundation type: Independent foundation.
Financial data (yr. ended 12/31/13): Assets, $9,688,824 (M); gifts received, $456,873; expenditures, $2,141,882; qualifying distributions, $2,070,270; giving activities include $1,201,791 for 26 grants (high: $367,439; low: $1,000).
Purpose and activities: Giving primarily for education and human services.
Fields of interest: Education; Cancer; AIDS; Cancer research; AIDS research; Food banks; Nutrition; Human services; Youth, pregnancy prevention; Homeless.
Limitations: Applications accepted. Giving primarily in AZ, IL and NY, as well as India. No grants to individuals.
Application information: CAGA Chicago Area Grant Application Form accepted. Application form required.
Initial approach: Letter
Copies of proposal: 1
Deadline(s): None
Officer: Mary Gauwitz, Exec. Dir.
Trustee: John N. Kapoor.
Number of staff: 1 full-time professional.
EIN: 366923817
Selected grants: The following grants are a representative sample of this grantmaker's funding activity:
$163,270 to IMD Guest House Foundation, Chicago, IL, 2012. For Four Rooms for Patient Rehab in Addition to 2 Parking Units and Recliners Window Coverings for the 4 Rooms and Counter Tops of 2 Rooms.
$5,000 to Midtown Educational Foundation, Chicago, IL, 2012. For Inner City Youth.
$2,000 to SeaShare, Bainbridge Island, WA, 2012. For High Protein in Seafood Products for Americans.

2951
Katten Muchin Rosenman Foundation, Inc. ✧
(formerly Katten Muchin Zavis Rosenman Foundation, Inc.)
525 W. Monroe St., Ste. 1900
Chicago, IL 60661-3693 (312) 902-5200
FAX: (312) 902-1061; Main URL: http://www.kattenlaw.com/katten-cares

Established in 1982 in IL.
Donors: Katten Muchin Zavis; Katten Muchin Zavis Rosenman; Katten Muchin Rosenman LLP; Wander Revocable Trust.
Foundation type: Company-sponsored foundation.
Financial data (yr. ended 12/31/13): Assets, $233,930 (M); gifts received, $1,974,220; expenditures, $2,052,681; qualifying distributions, $2,052,681; giving activities include $2,052,681 for 337 grants (high: $100,000; low: $25).
Purpose and activities: The foundation supports organizations involved with arts and culture, education, health, cancer, heart disease, legal aid, human services, international relief, civil rights, Judaism, and women.
Fields of interest: Museums; Performing arts; Performing arts, theater; Arts; Higher education; Law school/education; Education; Health care, volunteer services; Hospitals (general); Health care; Cancer; Cancer, leukemia; Heart & circulatory diseases; Legal services; Boys & girls clubs; Children/youth, services; Human services; International relief; Civil/human rights; United Ways and Federated Giving Programs; Jewish agencies & synagogues; Women.
Type of support: General/operating support.
Limitations: Applications not accepted. Giving primarily in the Chicago, IL, area. No grants to individuals.
Application information: Contributes only to pre-selected organizations.
Officers: Vincent A.F. Sergi, Pres.; Herbert S. Wander, Secy.; Howard S. Lanznar, Treas.
Directors: David J. Bryant; Henry Bregstein; Roger P. Furey; Daniel S. Huffenus; David H. Kistenbroker; Laura Keidan Martin; Kenneth E. Noble; Joshua S. Rubenstein; Stuart P. Shulruff; Ross O. Silverman; Steven P. Solow; Joshua D. Wayser.
EIN: 363165216
Selected grants: The following grants are a representative sample of this grantmaker's funding activity:
$62,733 to Jewish United Fund of Metropolitan Chicago, Chicago, IL, 2011.
$52,000 to Action Against Hunger USA, New York, NY, 2010.
$45,920 to American Heart Association, Dallas, TX, 2011.
$45,900 to Chicago Bar Foundation, Chicago, IL, 2011.
$26,950 to American Ireland Fund, Boston, MA, 2011.
$25,000 to Art Institute of Chicago, Chicago, IL, 2011.
$23,250 to Youth, I.N.C., Washington, DC, 2011.
$16,667 to Lyric Opera of Chicago, Chicago, IL, 2011.
$13,600 to City of Hope, Duarte, CA, 2011.
$10,000 to Pro Bono Partnership, White Plains, NY, 2011.
$9,000 to Alliance for Childrens Rights, Los Angeles, CA, 2010.
$2,135 to American Cancer Society, Atlanta, GA, 2011.

2952
Ben E. Keith Foundation Trust ✧
10 S. Dearborn St., 21st Fl., IL1-0117
Chicago, IL 60603-2300

Established in 1951 in TX.
Foundation type: Independent foundation.
Financial data (yr. ended 06/30/13): Assets, $16,222,665 (M); expenditures, $969,116; qualifying distributions, $880,220; giving activities include $855,295 for 79 grants (high: $100,000; low: $500).
Fields of interest: Museums (art); Performing arts; Performing arts centers; Performing arts, orchestras; Arts; Elementary/secondary education; Higher education; Education; Health care; Human services; Children/youth, services; Aging, centers/services; Community/economic development.
Type of support: General/operating support; Continuing support; Annual campaigns; Capital campaigns; Building/renovation; Equipment; Land

acquisition; Endowments; Debt reduction; Emergency funds; Seed money; Matching/challenge support.
Limitations: Applications not accepted. Giving limited to TX, with emphasis on the Dallas-Fort Worth metropolitan area. No grants to individuals, or for scholarships or fellowships; no loans.
Application information: Unsolicited requests for funds not accepted.
Board meeting date(s): Jan., Mar., June, and Oct.
Trustee: JPMorgan Chase Bank, N.A.
EIN: 756013955
Selected grants: The following grants are a representative sample of this grantmaker's funding activity:
$3,000 to Shakespeare Festival of Dallas, Dallas, TX, 2013. For contribution.
$2,000 to Dallas Wind Symphony, Dallas, TX, 2013. For contribution.
$1,000 to University of Texas System, Austin, TX, 2013. For grant- UT Austin.

2953
The Joseph Kellman Family Foundation ✧
(formerly The Kellman Foundation)
1512 S. Pulaski Rd.
Chicago, IL 60623-1952
E-mail: kellman14@aol.com

Established in 1999 in IL.
Donors: Joseph Kellman‡; LouAnne Kellman.
Foundation type: Independent foundation.
Financial data (yr. ended 12/31/12): Assets, $20,445,388 (M); expenditures, $2,152,721; qualifying distributions, $1,693,856; giving activities include $1,471,465 for 9 grants (high: $1,240,000; low: $1,500).
Purpose and activities: Giving primarily for education and youth services.
Fields of interest: Elementary/secondary education; Youth, services.
Type of support: General/operating support.
Limitations: Applications not accepted. Giving primarily in IL. No support for religious, political or healthcare organizations. No grants to individuals.
Application information: Contributes only to pre-selected organizations.
Officers: Jack Kellman, Pres.; Troy Ratliff, V.P. and Secy.; Lorrie Jones, Treas.
Board Members: Sherry Johns; Collette Kellman; Allan Munchin.
Number of staff: 1 full-time professional.
EIN: 367336206

2954
Kemper Educational and Charitable Fund ✧
1001 Green Bay Rd.
PMB Box 186
Winnetka, IL 60093-1721

Incorporated in 1961 in IL.
Donor: James Scott Kemper‡.
Foundation type: Independent foundation.
Financial data (yr. ended 12/31/12): Assets, $10,374,062 (M); expenditures, $686,083; qualifying distributions, $481,322; giving activities include $481,322 for grants.
Purpose and activities: Giving primarily for education and children, youth and social services; some funding for health associations and the arts.
Fields of interest: Arts; Education; Botanical gardens; Health organizations, association; Human services; Children/youth, services; Family services; Christian agencies & churches.
Type of support: General/operating support; Continuing support; Building/renovation; Equipment; Program development; Curriculum development; Scholarship funds; Research.
Limitations: Applications not accepted. No grants to individuals; no loans.
Application information: Unsolicited requests for funds not accepted.
Board meeting date(s): Annually and as required
Officers: John Van Cleave, Chair.; Dale Park, Jr., Secy.
Trustees: Brian Van Cleave; Lynn Van Cleave; Patricia Van Cleave.
Number of staff: 1 part-time professional; 1 part-time support.
EIN: 366054499

2955
James S. Kemper Foundation ✧
20 N. Wacker Dr., Ste. 1823
Chicago, IL 60606-2905 (312) 332-3114
Contact: Ryan LaHurd, Pres. and Exec. Dir.
E-mail: dmattison@jskemper.org; Main URL: http://www.jskemper.org

Incorporated in 1942 in IL.
Donors: James Scott Kemper‡; Lumbermens Mutual Casualty Co.; American Motorists Insurance Co.; American Manufacturers Mutual Insurance Co.
Foundation type: Independent foundation.
Financial data (yr. ended 07/31/13): Assets, $37,277,368 (M); expenditures, $1,936,154; qualifying distributions, $1,720,965; giving activities include $1,017,474 for 66 grants (high: $100,000; low: $250).
Purpose and activities: The mission of the James S. Kemper Foundation is to promote liberal arts education as an ideal preparation for life and work, especially in administration and business. The foundation focuses primarily on small, private liberal arts colleges, though it maintains a secondary commitment to undergraduate opportunities at Chicago's cultural organizations. The foundation partners with sixteen private colleges in a special scholarship/internship program, the Kemper Scholars Program, and it also makes project grants to small private colleges and some of Chicago's cultural organizations.
Fields of interest: Arts; Higher education, college.
Type of support: Program development; Conferences/seminars; Seed money; Curriculum development; Internship funds.
Limitations: Giving on a national basis to colleges and universities. Giving for arts limited to Chicago, IL. No support for public institutions, large universities, cultural organizations outside of Chicago, or international organizations. No grants to individuals or for capital purposes.
Publications: Application guidelines; Annual report; Grants list; Program policy statement.
Application information: Currently, because of the severe limitation of funds, the foundation has discontinued accepting uninvited proposals or letters of interest. Only invited proposals will be accepted. The foundation unfortunately cannot respond to uninvited letters of inquiry or proposals. The Kemper Scholars Grant program is administered by selection committees at participating colleges and universities. The committee on each campus publicizes the program to enrolled freshman students who are oriented toward a career in business, accepts applications, and screens the applicants. Liberal Arts colleges are given preference. Application information also available on foundation web site. Full proposals will be accepted by invitation only. Publications are only available via web site. Application form not required.
Copies of proposal: 1
Deadline(s): Dec. 1 for invited proposals
Board meeting date(s): Feb., May, and Nov.
Final notification: Early Mar.
Officers and Trustees:* David B. Mathis,* Chair.; Ryan LaHurd, Pres. and Exec. Dir.; John K. Conway,* Secy.; E.B. Smith, Jr., Treas.; Genl. John T. Chain, Jr.; J. Reed Coleman; Peter B. Hamilton; George R. Lewis; John E. Porter.
Number of staff: 2 full-time professional; 1 part-time professional.
EIN: 366007812

2956
George R. Kendall Foundation ✧
10 S. Dearborn IL1-0117
Chicago, IL 60603
Application address: c/o Susan Berkun, JPMorgan Chase Bank, N.A., 1101 Skokie Blvd., Ste. 260, Northbrook, IL 60062, tel.: (847) 239-8309

Trust established in 1969 in IL.
Donor: George R. Kendall, Sr.‡.
Foundation type: Independent foundation.
Financial data (yr. ended 11/30/13): Assets, $14,742,113 (M); expenditures, $825,839; qualifying distributions, $642,336; giving activities include $588,060 for 9 grants (high: $148,060; low: $15,000).
Purpose and activities: Giving primarily for higher education and human services.
Fields of interest: Higher education; Human services; Salvation Army.
Type of support: General/operating support; Program development; Curriculum development.
Limitations: Applications accepted. Giving primarily in the North Shore suburbs, north of Chicago, IL. No grants to individuals, or for endowment funds, scholarships, fellowships, or matching gifts; no loans.
Application information: Application form required.
Initial approach: Letter
Copies of proposal: 1
Deadline(s): Mar. 1
Board meeting date(s): Oct.
Trustees: George P. Kendall, Jr.; Helen R. Kendall; Thomas C. Kendall; JPMorgan Chase Bank, N.A.
EIN: 366403376
Selected grants: The following grants are a representative sample of this grantmaker's funding activity:
$137,600 to Saint Marys University of Minnesota, Winona, MN, 2011.
$117,000 to Harding University, Searcy, AR, 2011. For program support.
$81,000 to United Negro College Fund, Fairfax, VA, 2011. For program support.
$70,000 to Berea College, Berea, KY, 2011.
$59,800 to Christ the King Jesuit College Preparatory School, Chicago, IL, 2011.
$54,000 to Salvation Army, Chicago, IL, 2011.
$39,000 to YMCA of Snohomish County, Everett, WA, 2011.
$35,000 to Family Matters, Chicago, IL, 2011.

$25,500 to Saint Martin de Porres High School, Waukegan, IL, 2011.
$15,000 to Winona Volunteer Services, Winona, MN, 2011. For program support.

2957
The Kensington Square Foundation ✧
1418 N. Lake Shore Dr., No. 9
Chicago, IL 60610-1642

Established in 1999 in IL.
Donors: Richard C. Carr; Ann K. Carr.
Foundation type: Independent foundation.
Financial data (yr. ended 12/31/13): Assets, $10,516,303 (M); gifts received, $15; expenditures, $1,110,311; qualifying distributions, $1,100,900; giving activities include $1,100,900 for 68 grants (high: $600,000; low: $1,000).
Purpose and activities: Giving primarily for Roman Catholic education; support also for a Roman Catholic home for developmentally disabled children and adults.
Fields of interest: Arts; Higher education; Education; Human services; Catholic federated giving programs; Catholic agencies & churches.
Limitations: Applications not accepted. Giving primarily in IL. No grants to individuals.
Application information: Contributes only to pre-selected organizations.
Officers and Directors:* Richard C. Carr,* Pres.; Ann K. Carr,* Secy.
EIN: 367291505
Selected grants: The following grants are a representative sample of this grantmaker's funding activity:
$100,000 to Misericordia Home, Chicago, IL, 2011. For general support.
$30,000 to Old Saint Patricks Church, Chicago, IL, 2011. For general support.
$25,000 to GoodCity, Chicago, IL, 2011. For general support.
$21,000 to Near North Montessori School, Chicago, IL, 2011. For general support.
$20,000 to CARA Program, Chicago, IL, 2011. For general support.
$18,000 to Phoenix Symphony Association, Phoenix, AZ, 2011. For general support.
$10,000 to Dominican Sisters of Springfield, Springfield, IL, 2011. For general support.
$5,000 to American Indian College Fund, Denver, CO, 2011. For general support.
$2,500 to Art Institute of Chicago, Chicago, IL, 2011. For general support.
$1,000 to Valley of the Sun Hospice Association, Phoenix, AZ, 2011. For general support.

2958
Kern Foundation Trust ✧
c/o The Northern Trust Co.
P.O. Box 803878
Chicago, IL 60680-3878

Established in 1959 in IL.
Donors: Herbert A. Kern†; John C. Kern; Theosophical Society in America; Krotona Institute of Theosophy; Happy Valley School; The Theosophical Book Gift Institute; Theosophical Order of Service.
Foundation type: Independent foundation.
Financial data (yr. ended 12/31/13): Assets, $22,230,358 (M); expenditures, $1,630,091; qualifying distributions, $1,506,444; giving activities include $1,381,246 for 5 grants (high: $1,228,500; low: $5,000).
Purpose and activities: Giving to aid the spiritual enlightenment of as many people as practical by exposing them to the theosophical philosophy, particularly through support of the Theosophical Society in America and the Krotona Institute of Theosophy.
Fields of interest: Religion.
Limitations: Applications not accepted. Giving primarily in CA and IL. No grants to individuals, or for building funds.
Publications: Program policy statement.
Application information: Contributes only to pre-selected organizations.
Trustees: John C. Kern; The Northern Trust Co.
EIN: 366107250

2959
Khesed Foundation ✧
c/o The Northern Trust Co.
P.O. Box 803878
Chicago, IL 60680-3878

Established in 2001 in IL.
Donors: Janet Willis; Scott Willis.
Foundation type: Independent foundation.
Financial data (yr. ended 01/31/12): Assets, $3,603,690 (M); expenditures, $1,152,977; qualifying distributions, $1,148,400; giving activities include $1,129,400 for 34 grants (high: $501,000; low: $400).
Purpose and activities: Giving primarily to Christian ministries.
Fields of interest: Christian agencies & churches.
Type of support: General/operating support; Program-related investments/loans.
Limitations: Applications not accepted. Giving in the U.S., with emphasis on IL. No grants to individuals.
Application information: Contributes only to pre-selected organizations.
Officers: Duane Scott Willis, Pres.; Janet Willis, Secy.-Treas.
Directors: Amy Moody; Daniel Willis; Toby Willis.
EIN: 260036863

2960
The King Family Foundation ✧
(formerly Flagg Creek Foundation)
c/o Salt Creek Ventures, LLC
1415 W. 22nd St., Ste. 400
Oak Brook, IL 60523-2023

Established in 1995 in IL.
Donors: Robert E. King; Emily King.
Foundation type: Independent foundation.
Financial data (yr. ended 09/30/13): Assets, $10,882,480 (M); gifts received, $9,000,000; expenditures, $686,777; qualifying distributions, $659,192; giving activities include $653,921 for 38 grants (high: $137,500; low: $400).
Purpose and activities: Giving primarily for the arts, education, and health. The grantmaker also gives toward African Wildlife Foundation scholarships.
Fields of interest: Performing arts; Arts; Education; Health care; Human services; Children; Youth; Physically disabled; African Americans/Blacks; Hispanics/Latinos; Native Americans/American Indians; Indigenous peoples; Military/veterans; Terminal illness, people with; Economically disadvantaged.
International interests: Africa.
Type of support: General/operating support; Continuing support; Management development/capacity building; Annual campaigns; Capital campaigns; Building/renovation; Endowments; Emergency funds; Program development; Curriculum development; Internship funds; Scholarship funds; Technical assistance; Program evaluation; Matching/challenge support.
Limitations: Applications not accepted. Giving primarily in IL. No grants to individuals.
Application information: Contributes only to pre-selected organizations.
Officers: Emily H. King, Pres.; Robert E. King, Jr., V.P.
Directors: Lizzie King Alden; Robert E. King; Heather K. Pines.
Number of staff: None.
EIN: 363991717

2961
Klaff Family Foundation ✧
180 N. Michigan Ave., Ste. 300
Chicago, IL 60601

Established in 2004 in IL.
Donor: Hersch M. Klaff.
Foundation type: Independent foundation.
Financial data (yr. ended 12/31/13): Assets, $6,193,589 (M); expenditures, $664,496; qualifying distributions, $573,582; giving activities include $573,582 for 49 grants (high: $100,000; low: $100).
Fields of interest: Arts; Education; Human services; Children/youth, services; Jewish agencies & synagogues.
Limitations: Applications not accepted. Giving primarily in IL and NY; some funding also in Johannesburg, South Africa. No grants to individuals.
Application information: Contributes only to pre-selected organizations.
Directors: Avril R. Klaff; Hersch M. Klaff; Allan J. Reich.
EIN: 611480716

2962
Gerald A. & Karen A. Kolschowsky Foundation, Inc. ✧
5235 Walnut Ave., Ste. 1
Downers Grove, IL 60515-4064

Incorporated in 1986 in IL.
Donors: Gerald A. Kolschowsky; Karen A. Kolschowsky.
Foundation type: Independent foundation.
Financial data (yr. ended 12/31/13): Assets, $8,400,356 (M); gifts received, $3,985,518; expenditures, $1,670,937; qualifying distributions, $1,662,665; giving activities include $1,595,722 for 172 grants (high: $260,000; low: $100).
Purpose and activities: Giving primarily for Lutheran churches; support also for health associations and hospitals, and social services, including child welfare.
Fields of interest: Higher education; Hospitals (general); Health organizations, association; Human services; Children/youth, services; Protestant agencies & churches.

Type of support: General/operating support.
Limitations: Applications not accepted. Giving primarily in IL. No grants to individuals.
Application information: Contributes only to pre-selected organizations.
Officers: Timothy J. Kolschowsky, Pres.; Michael J. Kolschowsky, V.P. and Secy.-Treas.
Directors: Gerald A. Kolschowsky; Karen A. Kolschowsky.
EIN: 363505302
Selected grants: The following grants are a representative sample of this grantmaker's funding activity:
$1,000 to African Wildlife Foundation, Washington, DC, 2011.

2963
Russell & Josephine Kott Memorial Charitable Trust ✧
231 S. LaSalle St., IL1-231-13-32
Chicago, IL 60697-0001

Established in 2002 in IL.
Donors: Kott Grandchildren Charitable Trust; Josephine Kott Trust; Russell Kott Trust.
Foundation type: Independent foundation.
Financial data (yr. ended 11/30/13): Assets, $31,825,671 (M); expenditures, $1,706,661; qualifying distributions, $1,570,953; giving activities include $1,431,743 for 33 grants (high: $250,000; low: $5,000).
Purpose and activities: Giving for organizations that improve the livelihood of individuals, especially through education or medical services, with an emphasis on such services for the elderly.
Fields of interest: Human services.
Limitations: Giving primarily in IL. No grants to individuals.
Trustees: Michael Steven Kott; Craig Lusthoff; Bank of America, N.A.
Number of staff: None.
EIN: 597229565

2964
Kovler Family Foundation ✧
(formerly Harry and Maribel G. Blum Foundation)
875 N. Michigan Ave., Ste. 3400
Chicago, IL 60611-1958 (312) 664-5050

Established in 1967 in IL.
Donors: Harry Blum†; Everett Kovler.
Foundation type: Independent foundation.
Financial data (yr. ended 12/31/13): Assets, $51,420,615 (M); expenditures, $2,396,568; qualifying distributions, $2,143,225; giving activities include $2,082,676 for 52 grants (high: $725,300; low: $200).
Purpose and activities: Giving primarily for the arts, education, medical research, particularly for diabetes research, as well as for children and youth services.
Fields of interest: Arts; Higher education; Education; Diabetes; Medical research, institute; Human services; Children/youth, services; Jewish federated giving programs.
Type of support: General/operating support; Research.
Limitations: Applications accepted. Giving primarily in Chicago, IL. No grants to individuals.
Application information:
Initial approach: Letter or proposal (1-2 pages)
Copies of proposal: 1
Deadline(s): Mid-Nov.
Officers and Directors:* Peter Kovler,* Chair.; Jonathan Kovler,* Pres. and Treas.; Benjamin Kovler,* Secy.; Judy L. Lansing.
Number of staff: 2 full-time professional; 2 part-time professional.
EIN: 366152744
Selected grants: The following grants are a representative sample of this grantmaker's funding activity:
$99,014 to Francis W. Parker School, Chicago, IL, 2012. For Education-To aid in achieving the exempt purpose of the various donee organizations. Donated 1,800shs of stock DHR @ average price of $54.73 per share on 12/14/12 Cash amount $500.
$5,000 to Publicolor, New York, NY, 2012. For Children's Welfare-To aid in achieving the exempt purpose of the various donee organizations.
$2,500 to University of Pennsylvania, Philadelphia, PA, 2012. For Medical-To aid in achieving the exempt purpose of the various donee organizations.
$1,000 to Desert Community Foundation, Palm Desert, CA, 2012. For General Welfare-To aid in achieving the exempt purpose of the various donee organizations.
$1,000 to Joffrey Ballet, Chicago, IL, 2012. For Cultural and Civic-To aid in achieving the exempt purpose of the various donee organizations.
$1,000 to University of Chicago, Laboratory School, Chicago, IL, 2012. For Education-To aid in achieving the exempt purpose of the various donee organizations.

2965
Marcia Turner Kreyling Charitable Foundation ✧ ☆
c/o The Northern Trust Company
P.O. Box 803878
Chicago, IL 60680-3878

Donor: Marcia Kreyling 2001 Trust.
Foundation type: Independent foundation.
Financial data (yr. ended 01/31/14): Assets, $11,430,891 (M); gifts received, $535,418; expenditures, $689,209; qualifying distributions, $608,089; giving activities include $596,834 for 7 grants (high: $197,080; low: $2,986).
Fields of interest: Arts; Health care; Human services.
Limitations: Applications not accepted. Giving primarily in IN.
Application information: Unsolicited requests for funds not accepted.
Trustee: The Northern Trust Company.
EIN: 276584006
Selected grants: The following grants are a representative sample of this grantmaker's funding activity:
$124,628 to Mayo Clinic, Rochester, MN, 2012. For general support.
$3,777 to Willard Library Foundation, Evansville, IN, 2012.
$3,777 to Youth Resources of Southwestern Indiana, Evansville, IN, 2012.
$1,888 to Evansville Philharmonic Orchestra, Evansville, IN, 2012.

2966
Landau Family Foundation ✧ ☆
P.O. Box 577880
Chicago, IL 60657-7880

Established in 1955 in IL.
Donor: Howard M. Landau†.
Foundation type: Independent foundation.
Financial data (yr. ended 11/30/13): Assets, $8,640,894 (M); expenditures, $518,731; qualifying distributions, $430,000; giving activities include $430,000 for 26 grants (high: $50,000; low: $3,000).
Purpose and activities: Support primarily for social and economic justice.
Fields of interest: Legal services, public interest law; Human services; Civil/human rights; Jewish federated giving programs; Public affairs; Jewish agencies & synagogues; Immigrants/refugees; Economically disadvantaged.
International interests: Israel; Middle East.
Type of support: General/operating support; Continuing support; Emergency funds; Program development; Seed money; Program-related investments/loans.
Limitations: Applications accepted. Giving primarily in Chicago, IL. No grants to individuals.
Application information: Application form not required.
Initial approach: Proposal
Deadline(s): None
Officers and Directors:* Kay Berkson,* Pres.; Kenneth J. Landau,* Secy.; Sidney Hollander,* Treas.; Daniel Berkson.
EIN: 366089098

2967
Orville H. and Shirley I. Larson Charitable Trust ✧ ☆
21 E. Main St.
Galesburg, IL 61401-4525

Donor: Orville H. Larson†.
Foundation type: Independent foundation.
Financial data (yr. ended 12/31/13): Assets, $8,179,212 (M); expenditures, $501,345; qualifying distributions, $426,000; giving activities include $426,000 for 4 grants (high: $142,003; low: $70,997).
Fields of interest: Health organizations; Religion.
Limitations: Applications not accepted. Giving primarily in IL.
Application information: Unsolicited requests for funds not accepted.
Trustees: Lynn Bowman; Farmers & Mechanics Bank.
EIN: 367517145
Selected grants: The following grants are a representative sample of this grantmaker's funding activity:
$132,389 to Evangelical Lutheran Church in America, Chicago, IL, 2012. For Further Donee's Charitable Purpose.

2968
Harry and Sadie Lasky Foundation ✧
c/o Chuhak & Tecson
30 S. Wacker Dr., Ste. 2600
Chicago, IL 60606-7512 (312) 855-4356
Contact: Mitchell Feinberg, Secy. and Dir.

Incorporated in 1958 in IL.
Donor: Sadie E. Lasky.
Foundation type: Independent foundation.
Financial data (yr. ended 12/31/13): Assets, $13,185,820 (M); expenditures, $693,239; qualifying distributions, $558,330; giving activities include $510,000 for 24 grants (high: $120,000; low: $2,500).
Purpose and activities: Giving primarily for Jewish organizations.
Fields of interest: Higher education; Education; Jewish federated giving programs; Jewish agencies & synagogues.
Limitations: Applications accepted. Giving primarily in Chicago, IL. No grants to individuals.
Application information: Application form not required.
Initial approach: Proposal
Deadline(s): None
Officers and Directors:* Phyllis Handelsman,* Pres.; Mitchell Feinberg,* Secy.; Bobbe Hirsh,* Treas.
EIN: 366105123

2969
John J. Lawless Testamentary Trust B ✧
c/o Edgar County Bank and Trust Co.
P.O. Box 400
Paris, IL 61944-0400

Foundation type: Independent foundation.
Financial data (yr. ended 09/30/13): Assets, $14,917,285 (M); expenditures, $773,371; qualifying distributions, $487,945; giving activities include $477,860 for grants.
Fields of interest: Higher education.
Limitations: Applications not accepted. Giving primarily in St. Louis, MO.
Application information: Contributes only to pre-selected organizations.
Trustee: Edgar County Bank & Trust Co.
EIN: 376308433
Selected grants: The following grants are a representative sample of this grantmaker's funding activity:
$200,265 to Saint Louis University, Saint Louis, MO, 2011.

2970
Lea Charitable Trust ✧
1500 Primrose Ln.
Glenview, IL 60026-7772

Established in 1986 in IL.
Donors: L. Bates Lea; Marcia W. Lea.
Foundation type: Independent foundation.
Financial data (yr. ended 12/31/13): Assets, $15,749,934 (M); gifts received, $5,225,935; expenditures, $561,392; qualifying distributions, $504,879; giving activities include $501,500 for 22 grants (high: $130,000; low: $1,000).
Fields of interest: Arts education; Visual arts; Performing arts, orchestras; Arts; Education; Cancer; Human services; Foundations (community); United Ways and Federated Giving Programs.
Type of support: General/operating support.
Limitations: Applications not accepted. Giving primarily in IL and FL. No grants to individuals.
Application information: Contributes only to pre-selected organizations.
Trustees: Christopher G. Lea; Jennifer Ann Lea; L. Bates Lea; Marcia W. Lea; Victoria Lea.
EIN: 363486285
Selected grants: The following grants are a representative sample of this grantmaker's funding activity:
$40,000 to Chicago House and Social Service Agency, Chicago, IL, 2011. For general support.
$35,000 to Southern Methodist University, Dallas, TX, 2011. For general support.
$25,000 to Strings Music Festival, Steamboat Springs, CO, 2011. For general support.
$25,000 to Yampa Valley Community Foundation, Steamboat Springs, CO, 2011. For general support.
$20,000 to University of Michigan, Ann Arbor, MI, 2011. For general support.
$16,000 to Glenview Community Church, Glenview, IL, 2011. For general support.
$10,000 to A Call to College, Newark, OH, 2011. For general support.
$10,000 to Massachusetts Institute of Technology, Cambridge, MA, 2011. For general support.
$10,000 to Vanderbilt University, Nashville, TN, 2011. For general support.
$6,000 to Ravinia Festival Association, Highland Park, IL, 2011. For general support.

2971
The Lefkofsky Family Foundation ✧
600 W. Chicago Ave., Ste. 775
Chicago, IL 60654-2526
E-mail: info@lffoundation.com; Main URL: http://www.lefkofskyfoundation.com
Liz and Eric Lefkofsky's Giving Pledge Profile: http://glasspockets.org/philanthropy-in-focus/eye-on-the-giving-pledge/profiles#l

Established in 2006 in IL.
Donors: Elizabeth Lefkofsky; Eric Lefkofsky.
Foundation type: Independent foundation.
Financial data (yr. ended 12/31/13): Assets, $13,693,134 (M); expenditures, $4,344,956; qualifying distributions, $4,156,380; giving activities include $4,026,612 for 101 grants (high: $781,337; low: $50).
Fields of interest: Arts; Education; Medical research; Civil/human rights.
Limitations: Applications not accepted. Giving primarily in IL.
Application information: Unsolicited requests for funds not accepted.
Trustees: Dawn Denberg; Bradley Keywell; Kim Keywell; Manuel Kramer; Susan Kramer; Elizabeth K. Lefkofsky; Eric P. Lefkofsky; Sandra Lefkofsky; Steven Lefkofsky; William Lefkofsky; Jodi Neff.
EIN: 207066362

2972
John S. Lehmann Charitable Trust ✧
c/o Bank of America, N.A.
231 S. LaSalle St., IL1-231-10-05
Chicago, IL 60697-0001

Established in 2005 in MO.
Donor: J.S. Lehmann Trust.
Foundation type: Independent foundation.
Financial data (yr. ended 08/31/13): Assets, $15,913,644 (M); expenditures, $1,436,223; qualifying distributions, $1,338,549; giving activities include $1,286,830 for 2 grants (high: $643,415; low: $643,415).
Fields of interest: Higher education, university; Botanical gardens.
Limitations: Applications not accepted. Giving primarily in St. Louis, MO. No grants to individuals.
Application information: Contributes only to pre-selected organizations.
Trustee: Bank of America, N.A.
EIN: 597268792
Selected grants: The following grants are a representative sample of this grantmaker's funding activity:
$351,923 to Missouri Botanical Garden, Saint Louis, MO, 2011. For general support.
$351,923 to Washington University, Saint Louis, MO, 2011. For general support.

2973
Sheldon L. and Pearl R. Leibowitz Foundation ✧
2800 Lakeside Dr.
Bannockburn, IL 60015-1246

Established in 1986 in IL.
Donors: Sheldon L. Leibowitz; Pearl R. Leibowitz.
Foundation type: Independent foundation.
Financial data (yr. ended 09/30/13): Assets, $495,545 (M); gifts received, $500,000; expenditures, $692,949; qualifying distributions, $692,949; giving activities include $692,927 for 140 grants (high: $100,000; low: $200).
Purpose and activities: Giving for human services, Jewish federated programs, and health associations.
Fields of interest: Arts; Theological school/education; Education; Health organizations, association; Human services; Children/youth, services; Jewish federated giving programs; Jewish agencies & synagogues.
Limitations: Applications not accepted. Giving primarily in Chicago, IL. No grants to individuals.
Application information: Contributes only to pre-selected organizations.
Directors: Dale Leibowitz; Lew Leibowitz; Todd Leibowitz.
EIN: 363480213
Selected grants: The following grants are a representative sample of this grantmaker's funding activity:
$5,000 to Chicago Child Care Society, Chicago, IL, 2011.
$5,000 to Missionaries of Charity, Bronx, NY, 2011.
$5,000 to Northwestern University, Evanston, IL, 2011.
$3,986 to Rehabilitation Institute of Chicago, Chicago, IL, 2011.
$3,000 to Chicago Child Care Society, Chicago, IL, 2011.
$3,000 to Lyric Opera of Chicago, Chicago, IL, 2011.
$3,000 to United Negro College Fund, Fairfax, VA, 2011.
$2,000 to Cystic Fibrosis Foundation, Bethesda, MD, 2011.
$1,000 to Chicago Heart Association, Chicago, IL, 2011.
$1,000 to Joffrey Ballet, Chicago, IL, 2011.

2974
Phillip and Edith Leonian Foundation ✧
(formerly Paul & Gabriella Rosenbaum Foundation)
1723 S. Michigan Ave.
Chicago, IL 60616-1211 (312) 987-9500
Contact: Phillip Leonian, Treas.

Established in 1983 in IL.
Donors: Gabriella Rosenbaum; Gabriella Rosenbaum Trust; Edith Leonian; Phillip Leonian.
Foundation type: Independent foundation.
Financial data (yr. ended 09/30/13): Assets, $9,013,423 (M); gifts received, $1,198,603; expenditures, $607,496; qualifying distributions, $559,635; giving activities include $425,159 for 7 grants (high: $125,000; low: $10,000).
Fields of interest: Museums (art); Museums (specialized); Recreation, parks/playgrounds.
Limitations: Applications accepted. Giving primarily in Chicago, IL.
Application information: Application form required.
Initial approach: Proposal
Deadline(s): None
Officers: Edith Leonian, Pres.; Phillip Leonian, Treas.
Director: Allan J. Riech.
EIN: 363204862
Selected grants: The following grants are a representative sample of this grantmaker's funding activity:
$200,000 to Museum of Fine Arts, Houston, Houston, TX, 2011.
$166,000 to Jewish Museum, New York, NY, 2011.
$65,000 to International Center of Photography, New York, NY, 2011.
$60,000 to Art Institute of Chicago, Chicago, IL, 2011.
$41,178 to Chicago Park District, Chicago, IL, 2011.
$10,000 to Childrens Place Association, Chicago, IL, 2011.

2975
Eugene & Janet Lerner Family Foundation Inc. ✧
1831 Mission Hills Rd., Ste. 510
Northbrook, IL 60062-5746

Established in 1990 in IL.
Donors: Eugene Lerner; Janet Lerner.
Foundation type: Independent foundation.
Financial data (yr. ended 12/31/13): Assets, $13,208,230 (M); gifts received, $5,018,330; expenditures, $642,293; qualifying distributions, $564,319; giving activities include $564,319 for 57 grants (high: $120,000; low: $20).
Purpose and activities: Giving primarily to Jewish agencies.
Fields of interest: Arts; Higher education; Education; Human services; Jewish federated giving programs; Jewish agencies & synagogues.
Limitations: Applications not accepted. Giving primarily in IL. No grants to individuals.
Application information: Contributes only to pre-selected organizations.
Officers: Eugene Lerner, Pres.; Susan L. Cohn, Secy.; Janet Lerner, Treas.
EIN: 363674212

2976
Levi, Ray & Shoup Foundation ✧ ☆
2401 W. Monroe St.
Springfield, IL 62704-1439

Established in 2001 in IL.
Donor: Levi, Ray & Shoup, Inc.
Foundation type: Company-sponsored foundation.
Financial data (yr. ended 07/31/13): Assets, $12,761,043 (M); gifts received, $1,000,000; expenditures, $517,663; qualifying distributions, $494,650; giving activities include $494,650 for 37 grants (high: $100,000; low: $250).
Purpose and activities: The foundation supports health centers and organizations involved with education, human services, and homelessness.
Fields of interest: Secondary school/education; Higher education; Education, reading; Education; Health care, clinics/centers; Health care; Children/youth, services; Homeless, human services; Human services; Homeless.
Type of support: Building/renovation; Program development; General/operating support.
Limitations: Applications not accepted. Giving primarily in Springfield, IL. No grants to individuals.
Application information: Contributes only to pre-selected organizations.
Trustees: Agnes E. Levi; Richard H. Levi; Ryan M. Levi; Lindsay M. Matthews.
EIN: 326007063
Selected grants: The following grants are a representative sample of this grantmaker's funding activity:
$51,500 to Eastern Illinois University Foundation, Charleston, IL, 2011.
$25,000 to SPARC, Springfield, IL, 2011.
$11,000 to Memorial Medical Center Foundation, Springfield, IL, 2011.
$11,000 to Springfield College in Illinois, Springfield, IL, 2011.
$10,000 to Lincoln Land Community College Foundation, Springfield, IL, 2011.
$1,000 to Central Illinois Foodbank, Springfield, IL, 2011.
$1,000 to Childrens Miracle Network, Springfield, IL, 2011.
$1,000 to Leukemia & Lymphoma Society, White Plains, NY, 2011.
$1,000 to Ricky King Foundation, Naples, FL, 2011.
$1,000 to Saint Johns Hospital, Springfield, IL, 2011.

2977
Daniel Levin Charitable Fund ✧
650 Warrenville Rd., Ste. 500
Lisle, IL 60532-4318

Established in 1998 in IL.
Donor: Daniel E. Levin.
Foundation type: Operating foundation.
Financial data (yr. ended 12/31/13): Assets, $1,006,825 (M); gifts received, $1,300,000; expenditures, $845,015; qualifying distributions, $844,390; giving activities include $842,500 for 5 grants (high: $250,000; low: $50,000).
Purpose and activities: Giving primarily for education, including a rabbinical college, as well as to other Jewish organizations.
Fields of interest: Theological school/education; Education; Environment, public policy; Jewish federated giving programs; Social sciences, public policy; Jewish agencies & synagogues.
Limitations: Applications not accepted. Giving primarily in Chicago, IL, and PA. No grants to individuals.
Application information: Contributes only to pre-selected organizations.
Directors: Mark D. Anderson; Daniel E. Levin; Fay Hartog Levin.
EIN: 364265104
Selected grants: The following grants are a representative sample of this grantmaker's funding activity:
$250,000 to Reconstructionist Rabbinical College, Wyncote, PA, 2011.
$50,000 to Environmental Law and Policy Center of the Midwest, Chicago, IL, 2011.
$10,000 to Illinois Holocaust Museum and Education Center, Skokie, IL, 2011.

2978
Donald Levin Family Foundation ✧ ☆
c/o Donald Levin
2301 Ravine Way
Glenview, IL 60025-7627

Established in 1984 in IL.
Donors: Donald R. Levin; DRL Enterprises.
Foundation type: Independent foundation.
Financial data (yr. ended 09/30/13): Assets, $23,697,238 (M); gifts received, $20,000,000; expenditures, $1,305,245; qualifying distributions, $1,251,500; giving activities include $1,251,500 for 5 grants (high: $1,000,000; low: $500).
Purpose and activities: Giving to animal welfare agencies, health related issues, youth services, and Jewish agencies.
Fields of interest: Education; Animal welfare; Animals/wildlife; Youth development; Children/youth, services; Human services; Jewish agencies & synagogues.
Limitations: Applications not accepted. Giving primarily in IL. No grants to individuals.
Application information: Contributes only to pre-selected organizations.
Officers and Directors:* Donald R. Levin,* Pres.; Allan Kandelman,* Secy.; Alan M. Berry,* Treas.
EIN: 363329401

2979
J. Edward Lewis Scholarship Trust ✧ ☆
10 S. Dearborn IL1-0117
Chicago, IL 60603-2024

Foundation type: Independent foundation.
Financial data (yr. ended 12/31/13): Assets, $15,327,814 (M); expenditures, $576,766; qualifying distributions, $502,271; giving activities include $479,270 for 1 grant.
Fields of interest: Higher education.
Limitations: Applications not accepted. Giving primarily in Lexington, VA.
Application information: Unsolicited requests for funds not accepted.
Trustee: JPMorgan Chase Bank, N.A.
EIN: 556138391

2980
Lewis-Sebring Family Foundation ✧
2735 Sheridan Rd.
Evanston, IL 60201-1727

Established in 1996 in IL.
Donors: Charles A. Lewis; Penny Bender Sebring.
Foundation type: Independent foundation.
Financial data (yr. ended 12/31/13): Assets, $10,102,428 (M); gifts received, $250,000; expenditures, $1,336,143; qualifying distributions, $1,310,338; giving activities include $1,309,323 for 64 grants (high: $405,000; low: $100).
Purpose and activities: Giving primarily for education and children and social services.
Fields of interest: Higher education; Education; Human services; Children/youth, services.
Limitations: Applications not accepted. Giving primarily in Evanston and Chicago, IL. No grants to individuals.
Application information: Contributes only to pre-selected organizations.
Officers and Directors:* Charles A. Lewis,* Chair.; Penny Bender Sebring,* Pres.; Lisa S. Carreras,* V.P.; Kathryn Lewis Varela,* Secy.; Peter C. Lewis,* Treas.
EIN: 364120411
Selected grants: The following grants are a representative sample of this grantmaker's funding activity:
$842,500 to University of Chicago, Chicago, IL, 2012. For Bowman Society of University of Chicago Pritzker School of Medicine Capital Campaign UEI Pledge - 12/09-12/13.
$137,500 to Amherst College, Amherst, MA, 2012. For Lewis-Sebring Careers in Education Professions Fund.
$62,000 to University of Chicago, Chicago, IL, 2012. For CCEPP Pledge.
$60,000 to University of Chicago, Chicago, IL, 2012. For Capital Campaign JDRE Biological Science Div. pledge.
$22,900 to University of Chicago, Chicago, IL, 2012. For COE/Hong.
$10,000 to Amherst College, Amherst, MA, 2012. For Annual Fund (from PCL).
$10,000 to Amherst College, Amherst, MA, 2012. For Annual Fund (from CAL).
$5,000 to Teach for America, Chicago, IL, 2012. For Chicago Benefit Dinner (deductible amount) Annual Fund.
$1,850 to Kingswood-Oxford School, West Hartford, CT, 2012. For T-Shirts.
$1,500 to Kingswood-Oxford School, West Hartford, CT, 2012. For Composer Colloquy Series.

2981
The Libra Foundation

1700 W. Irving Park Rd., Ste. 203
Chicago, IL 60613-2599 (773) 325-1235
Contact: Hilda Vega, Sr. Prog. Off.; Betsy Brill, Exec. Dir.; Leah Zamora, Grant Admin.
E-mail: info@thelibrafoundation.org; Main URL: http://www.thelibrafoundation.org
The Libra Foundation's Philanthropy Promise: http://www.ncrp.org/philanthropys-promise/who

Established in 2002 in IL.
Donors: Rhoda Pritzker†; Nicholas J. Pritzker; Pritzker Foundation.
Foundation type: Independent foundation.
Financial data (yr. ended 12/31/13): Assets, $174,815,450 (M); gifts received, $15,138,888; expenditures, $4,189,215; qualifying distributions, $3,479,604; giving activities include $3,239,397 for 72 grants (high: $200,000; low: $500).
Purpose and activities: The foundation funds organizations that integrate human rights into their work in and across the following priority areas: women's rights, with an emphasis on reproductive rights and the elevation of women's rights as human rights; environmental sustainability, with an emphasis on promoting social justice within climate change mitigation and adaptation strategies; social justice, with an emphasis on fair application of the law, government accountability and human rights field-building; and drug policy reform, focusing on protecting rights and advancing reforms that lessen the social and economic impacts of the "war on drugs".
Fields of interest: International human rights; Civil/human rights, alliance/advocacy; Civil/human rights, public policy; Civil/human rights, reform; Civil/human rights, advocacy; Civil liberties, advocacy; Civil liberties, reproductive rights; Civil liberties, due process; Environmental and resource rights; Civil/human rights; Economically disadvantaged.
International interests: Africa; Asia; Europe; Latin America.
Type of support: General/operating support; Management development/capacity building; Emergency funds; Seed money; Program evaluation; Matching/challenge support.
Limitations: Giving is limited to state-specific work in CA and IL, for projects with national level impact and for work covering multiple regions outside of the U.S. (but funded through a U.S. home office). The foundation does not fund international work directly, nor does it fund international work focused on a single country. No support for international organizations not registered in the U.S., or for organizations that are heavily supported by the government (except for specific advocacy or public policy projects of interest). No grants to individuals, or for fundraising events, capital fund drives or campaigns, debt reduction, international work that focuses on a single country or on a small set of countries, or for religious activities.
Publications: Application guidelines; Grants list.
Application information: The foundation does not accept unsolicited proposals. Brief letters of inquiry are accepted however, on a rolling basis. Letters must be submitted via our website. Paper inquiries will not be accepted. Refer to foundation web site for complete application information and guidelines. Application form required.
Initial approach: Letter of Inquiry, with a preference for brief phone discussion first to determine alignment.
Deadline(s): None
Board meeting date(s): June and Dec.
Final notification: Letters of inquiry are reviewed on a monthly basis.
Officers and Directors:* Nicholas J. Pritzker,* C.E.O.; Susan S. Pritzker,* Pres. and Treas.; Regan Pritzker,* V.P. and Secy.; Thomas Dykstra, V.P.; Betsy Brill, Exec. Dir.; Isaac Pritzker; Jacob Pritzker; Joseph Pritzker.
Number of staff: 1 full-time professional; 1 part-time professional; 1 part-time support.
EIN: 300031117
Selected grants: The following grants are a representative sample of this grantmaker's funding activity:
$400,000 to Shared Interest, New York, NY, 2012. For Campaign for the Next Generation.
$120,000 to Fund for Global Human Rights, Washington, DC, 2013. For Strengthening Frontline Human Rights Activism Worldwide.
$100,000 to Global Greengrants Fund, Boulder, CO, 2013. For Environment and Human Rights Grassroots Support.
$100,000 to Opportunity Agenda, New York, NY, 2013. For Communications Tools, Training, and Support to Enhance the Impact of U.S. Human Rights Advocates.
$100,000 to Planned Parenthood Federation, International, New York, NY, 2012. For Building the Movement: Public Policy/Youth Mobilization.
$100,000 to Shared Interest, New York, NY, 2013. For Capacity Building for Economic Empowerment.
$83,333 to Planned Parenthood of Illinois, Chicago, IL, 2012. For Conversion to Electronic Records.
$75,000 to Children and Family Justice Center, Chicago, IL, 2012. For Illinois Coalition for the Fair Sentencing of Children.
$75,000 to Environmental Law and Policy Center of the Midwest, Chicago, IL, 2012. For ELPC's Global Warming Solutions Project.
$75,000 to Opportunity Agenda, New York, NY, 2012. For Human Rights in the Public Dialogue: Research and Support to Enhance Field Communications Capacity.
$60,000 to Environmental Law and Policy Center of the Midwest, Chicago, IL, 2013. For Midwest Climate Change Solutions.
$50,000 to Global Fund for Women, San Francisco, CA, 2013. For Advancing Women's Rights Worldwide.
$50,000 to Law Enforcement Against Prohibition Educational Fund, Medford, MA, 2013.
$50,000 to Planned Parenthood Federation, International, New York, NY, 2012. For Expanding Advocacy Initiatives to Advance Sexual and Reproductive Health and Rights in the Caribbean.
$45,000 to Human Rights First, New York, NY, 2013. For Promoting National Security Policies that Comport with U.S. Values and Human Rights Laws.
$40,000 to Law Enforcement Against Prohibition Educational Fund, Medford, MA, 2012. For General Support.
$40,000 to United States International Council on Disabilities, Washington, DC, 2012.
$35,000 to International Development Exchange, San Francisco, CA, 2012. For The IDEX Way: Authentic and Transformational International Human Rights Partnerships.
$30,000 to Pacific Forest Trust, San Francisco, CA, 2013. For Leveraging Forest Conservation to Combat Climate Change.
$25,000 to Urban Justice Center, New York, NY, 2013.

2982
Dolores Zohrab Liebmann Fund ✧

10 S. Dearborn St., ILI-0117
Chicago, IL 60603-2300
Application address: Dan Ordan, 270 Park Ave., New York, NY 10017, tel.: (212) 648-1489

Established in NY.
Foundation type: Independent foundation.
Financial data (yr. ended 12/31/13): Assets, $23,467,353 (M); expenditures, $1,501,334; qualifying distributions, $1,306,091; giving activities include $1,247,120 for 83 grants to individuals (high: $35,716; low: $1,250).
Purpose and activities: Giving to support educational development.
Fields of interest: Higher education.
Type of support: Scholarships—to individuals.

Limitations: Applications accepted. Giving in the U.S., with emphasis on CA.
Committee Members: Carol Aslanian; Kevork Bardakjian; Missak Heigentz; Nina Garsoian; Dr. Kevork Maksoudian.
Trustee: JPMorgan Chase Bank, N.A.
EIN: 133682433

2983
Reva and David Logan Foundation ✧
c/o Jonathan Logan
980 N. Michigan Ave., Ste. 1122
Chicago, IL 60611-4522 (312) 664-3350
Contact: Peter Handler, Exec. Dir.
FAX: (312) 664-9103; E-mail: jon@loganfdn.org; Peter Handler, Exec. Dir., contact for Letters of Inquiry, tel.: (312) 664-3350, e-mail: peter@loganfdn.org; Main URL: http://www.loganfdn.org
Grants List: http://www.loganfdn.org/grants.html

Established in 1965 in IL.
Donors: David Logan; Daniel Logan; Richard Logan; Jonathan Logan.
Foundation type: Independent foundation.
Financial data (yr. ended 12/31/12): Assets, $2,614,017 (M); gifts received, $2,042,000; expenditures, $590,334; qualifying distributions, $548,538; giving activities include $418,499 for 19 grants (high: $125,000; low: $2,000), and $100,018 for 1 employee matching gift.
Purpose and activities: Giving primarily for education, community and social welfare, Jewish life and concerns, public service and civil society, the upkeep and support of a library of modern illustrated and photographic books, and investigative reporting.
Fields of interest: Media/communications; Literature; Arts; Journalism school/education; Education; Aging, centers/services; Philanthropy/voluntarism; Leadership development; Jewish agencies & synagogues; Children; Aging; LGBTQ.
Type of support: General/operating support; Annual campaigns; Building/renovation; Endowments; Publication; Curriculum development; Research; Matching/challenge support.
Limitations: Giving primarily in the metropolitan areas of San Francisco, CA, and Chicago, IL. No grants to individuals.
Application information: Unsolicited proposals are not accepted.
Initial approach: Letter of Inquiry or telephone call
Officers and Directors:* Jonathan Logan,* Pres.; Richard Logan,* Secy.; Cecelia Simmons,* Treas.; Peter Handler, Exec. Dir.; Daniel Logan; Ben Rothblatt.
Number of staff: None.
EIN: 366139439
Selected grants: The following grants are a representative sample of this grantmaker's funding activity:
$100,018 to University of California, Berkeley, CA, 2012. For Investigative Reporting (matching gift).
$50,000 to University of California, Berkeley, CA, 2012. For Logan Symposium.
$25,000 to Burgundy Farm Country Day School, Alexandria, VA, 2012. For campus renewal initiative.
$5,000 to American Red Cross, Chicago, IL, 2012. For Disaster Relief Fund.

2984
Michael W. Louis Charitable Trust ✧
135 S. LaSalle St., Ste. 2350
Chicago, IL 60603

Established in 1998 in IL.
Donors: Michael W. Louis†; Henrietta J. Louis Charitable Trust.
Foundation type: Independent foundation.
Financial data (yr. ended 12/31/13): Assets, $20,165,743 (M); expenditures, $1,840,148; qualifying distributions, $1,489,625; giving activities include $1,489,625 for 14 grants (high: $250,000; low: $40,000).
Purpose and activities: Giving primarily for higher education, social services, and children and youth services, including aid to a children's hospital.
Fields of interest: Higher education; Hospitals (specialty); Human services; Children/youth, services; Foundations (private independent).
Limitations: Applications not accepted. Giving primarily in AZ and IL. No grants to individuals.
Application information: Contributes only to pre-selected organizations.
Trustee: Herbert J. Louis.
EIN: 367216588
Selected grants: The following grants are a representative sample of this grantmaker's funding activity:
$500,000 to National-Louis University, Chicago, IL, 2011. For general support.
$100,000 to First Tee of Phoenix, Phoenix, AZ, 2011. For general support.
$75,000 to Translational Genomics Research Institute Foundation, Phoenix, AZ, 2011. For general support.
$65,000 to AmeriCares, Stamford, CT, 2011. For general support.
$60,000 to Center for Life Specific Design, Park City, UT, 2011. For general support.
$50,000 to Arizona Womens Board, Paradise Valley, AZ, 2011. For general support.
$50,000 to Foundation Fighting Blindness, Denver, CO, 2011. For general support.
$50,000 to Lycee Francais de Chicago, Chicago, IL, 2011. For general support.
$45,000 to Colorado College, Colorado Springs, CO, 2011. For general support.

2985
Josephine P. & John J. Louis Foundation ✧
(formerly John J. Louis, Jr. Foundation)
1 S. Wacker Dr., Ste. 800
Chicago, IL 60606-4900 (312) 634-3400
Contact: Josephine P. Louis, V.P. and Dir.; Edward Fellin McGladrey

Established in 1992 in IL as partial successor to John J. Louis Foundation.
Donors: John J. Louis, Jr.†; Josephine P. Louis; John J. Louis Foundation; Henrietta J Louis Trust; John J. Louis, Jr. Trust; John J. Louis, Jr. Charitable Annuity Trust; Michael W. Louis Trust; Henrietta J. Louis Charitable Trust; Henrietta J. Lewis Charitable Annuity Trust; Michael W. Louis Charitable Trust.
Foundation type: Independent foundation.
Financial data (yr. ended 12/31/13): Assets, $9,839,912 (M); gifts received, $577,264; expenditures, $1,082,456; qualifying distributions, $997,593; giving activities include $995,100 for 52 grants (high: $250,000; low: $100).
Purpose and activities: Giving primarily for the arts, education, the environment, health, and human services.
Fields of interest: Arts; Higher education; Education; Botanical gardens; Environment; Health care; Medical research, institute; Human services; Foundations (private grantmaking).
Type of support: General/operating support; Continuing support; Annual campaigns; Capital campaigns; Building/renovation; Endowments.
Limitations: Applications accepted. Giving primarily in the Chicago, IL, area, including Evanston. No grants, fellowships or scholarships to individuals.
Application information: Application form not required.
Initial approach: Letter
Deadline(s): None
Board meeting date(s): Mid to late Oct.
Officers and Directors:* Josephine P. Louis,* V.P.; Walter W. Bell, Secy.; Tracy Louis Merrill; Kimberly Louis Stewart.
EIN: 363837993

2986
The Lumpkin Family Foundation ✧
121 S. 17th St.
Mattoon, IL 61938-3915 (217) 235-3361
Contact: Bruce Karmazin, Exec. Dir.
FAX: (217) 258-8444;
E-mail: info@lumpkinfoundation.org; Main URL: http://www.lumpkinfoundation.org/
Grant Locations: http://www.lumpkinfoundation.org/WHEREwegive/GrantLocations/tabid/62/cid/2/cat/Outside%20East%20Central%20Illinois/Default.aspx

Incorporated in 1953 in IL.
Donors: Besse Adamson Lumpkin†; Mary G. Lumpkin†; Richard Adamson Lumpkin†; Illinois Consolidated Telephone Co.; Richard Anthony Lumpkin; Mary Lee Sparks; Margaret L. Keon; Elizabeth Lumpkin Celio; Benjamin I. Lumpkin.
Foundation type: Independent foundation.
Financial data (yr. ended 12/31/13): Assets, $48,752,384 (M); gifts received, $218,978; expenditures, $2,622,219; qualifying distributions, $2,326,738; giving activities include $1,872,718 for 191 grants (high: $345,000; low: $25), and $92,918 for foundation-administered programs.
Purpose and activities: The foundation supports people pursuing innovation and long-lasting improvements in the environment, health, education, and community access to the arts.
Fields of interest: Arts; Libraries (public); Education; Environment, natural resources; Health care; Human services; Children, services.
Type of support: General/operating support; Management development/capacity building; Annual campaigns; Program development; Seed money; Internship funds; Technical assistance; Program evaluation; Employee matching gifts; Matching/challenge support.
Limitations: Applications accepted. Giving primarily in East Central IL; some funding nationally, see foundation web site for locations outside of IL. No support for religious organizations, political causes, or organizations who influence legislation. No grants to individuals.
Publications: Application guidelines; Annual report; Grants list.
Application information: Online application process. See complete application guidelines on foundation web site. Application form required.

Initial approach: Online letter of inquiry
Deadline(s): For Regional Grants Program, Apr. 4 for Letter of Inquiry and May 30 for invited applications; for Lumpkin Family Foundation, see calendar on foundation web site for deadlines
Board meeting date(s): Feb., Apr., June, Sept. and Nov.
Final notification: May, July and Nov.
Officers and Directors:* Christina Duncan,* Pres.; Richard DeWyngaert,* V.P.; Barbara Federico,* V.P.; Steve L. Grissom,* Secy.; Richard Anthony Lumpkin,* Treas.; Bruce Karmazin, Exec. Dir.; Lisa Barr; Elizabeth Celio; Susan DeWyngaert; Joseph Dively.
Number of staff: 2 full-time professional; 1 full-time support.
EIN: 237423640

2987
Ann and Robert H. Lurie Foundation ✧
(formerly Ann and Robert H. Lurie Family Foundation)
2 N. Riverside Plz., Ste. 1240
Chicago, IL 60606-2657

Established in 1986 in IL.
Donors: Ann Lurie; Robert Lurie†; Robert H. & Ann Lurie Trust.
Foundation type: Independent foundation.
Financial data (yr. ended 12/31/13): Assets, $4,471,010 (M); gifts received, $10,006,775; expenditures, $14,934,169; qualifying distributions, $14,858,015; giving activities include $14,858,000 for 5 grants (high: $13,000,000; low: $25,000).
Purpose and activities: Giving primarily to a children's hospital, as well as for higher education.
Fields of interest: Higher education; Hospitals (specialty); Children.
Type of support: Endowments.
Limitations: Applications not accepted. Giving primarily in Chicago, IL. No grants to individuals.
Application information: Contributes only to pre-selected organizations.
Officers and Directors:* Ann Lurie,* Pres. and Treas.; Sheli Z. Rosenberg,* V.P. and Secy.; Andrew Lurie,* V.P.; Benjamin Lurie,* V.P.; Elizabeth Lurie, V.P.
EIN: 363486274

2988
Charles J. Lynn Trust ✧
10 S. Dearborn IL1-0117
Chicago, IL 60603

Established in IN.
Foundation type: Independent foundation.
Financial data (yr. ended 12/31/13): Assets, $52,318,147 (M); expenditures, $2,667,235; qualifying distributions, $2,346,463; giving activities include $2,262,538 for 7 grants (high: $678,791; low: $226,254).
Fields of interest: Higher education; Health care; YM/YWCAs & YM/YWHAs; Residential/custodial care, senior continuing care.
Limitations: Applications not accepted. Giving primarily in IN, with some emphasis on Indianapolis.
Application information: Contributes only to pre-selected organizations.
Trustee: JPMorgan Chase Bank, N.A.
EIN: 356009281

2989
The John D. and Catherine T. MacArthur Foundation
140 S. Dearborn St., Ste. 1200
Chicago, IL 60603-5285 (312) 726-8000
Contact: Richard J. Kaplan, Assoc. V.P., Institutional Research and Grants Mgmt.
FAX: (312) 920-6258;
E-mail: 4answers@macfound.org; TDD: (312) 920-6285; Main URL: http://www.macfound.org
E-Newsletter: http://www.macfound.org/site/c.lkLXJ8MQKrH/b.4357343/k.7FF4/Subscribe_to_eNews__Custom/apps/ka/ct/contactcustom.asp
Grants Database: http://www.macfound.org/site/c.lkLXJ8MQKrH/b.4979973/k.8E29/Recent_Grants.htm
Knowledge Center: http://www.macfound.org/site/c.lkLXJ8MQKrH/b.2722017/k.62D0/What_We_Have_Learned.htm
RSS Feed: http://feeds.feedburner.com/macfound
Spotlight on Digital Media and Learning: http://spotlight.macfound.org/blog
Twitter: http://www.twitter.com/macfound
YouTube: http://www.youtube.com/macfound

Incorporated in 1970 in IL.
Donors: John D. MacArthur†; Catherine T. MacArthur†.
Foundation type: Independent foundation.
Financial data (yr. ended 12/31/13): Assets, $6,323,307,217 (M); expenditures, $285,953,112; qualifying distributions, $267,823,606; giving activities include $206,842,721 for 1,578 grants (high: $2,500,000; low: $143), and $11,700,000 for 117 grants to individuals (high: $100,000; low: $100,000).
Purpose and activities: The John D. and Catherine T. MacArthur Foundation supports creative people and effective institutions committed to building a more just, verdant, and peaceful world. In addition to selecting the MacArthur Fellows, the foundation works to defend human rights, advance global conservation and security, make cities better places, and understand how technology is affecting children and society.
Fields of interest: Media/communications; Media, film/video; Education, public education; Higher education; Environment, natural resources; Reproductive health; Mental health/crisis services, public policy; Crime/violence prevention, youth; International peace/security; International human rights; Community development, neighborhood development; Public policy, research.
International interests: India; Mexico; Nigeria; Russia.
Type of support: General/operating support; Program development; Fellowships; Research; Program-related investments/loans; Employee matching gifts; Matching/challenge support.
Limitations: Applications accepted. Giving on a national and international basis. No support for religious programs, political activities or campaigns. No grants for fundraising appeals, institutional benefits, honorary functions or similar projects, tuition expenses, scholarships, or fellowships (other than those sponsored by the foundation).
Publications: Annual report; Newsletter.
Application information: Please do not send the letter of inquiry by fax. Send it by mail to the office of Grants Management or by e-mail. Direct applications for MacArthur Fellows programs not accepted. Grants increasingly initiated by the board. Application form not required.
Initial approach: Letter of inquiry (2 to 3 pages) and one-page summary
Copies of proposal: 1
Deadline(s): None
Board meeting date(s): Mar., June, Sept., and Dec.
Final notification: 8 to 10 weeks
Officers and Directors:* Marjorie M. Scardino,* Chair.; Julia Stasch, Pres.; Marc P. Yanchura, V.P., and C.F.O.; Susan E. Manske, V.P. and C.I.O.; Joshua J. Mintz, V.P. and Genl. Counsel; Cecilia Conrad, V.P., MacArthur Fellows Prog.; Elspeth A. Revere, V.P., Media, Culture and Special Initiatives; Andrew Solomon, V.P., Public Affairs; Elizabeth Kane, Secy.; Kevin Doherty, Cont.; John Seely Brown; Jack Fuller; Jamie S. Gorelick; Mary Graham; Donald R. Hopkins, M.D.; Daniel Huttenlocher; Joi Ito; Julie T. Katzman; Paul Klingenstein; Martha Minow; Mario J. Molina; Sendhil Mullainathan; Claude M. Steele.
Number of staff: 92 full-time professional; 85 full-time support.
EIN: 237093598
Selected grants: The following grants are a representative sample of this grantmaker's funding activity:
$9,672,000 to Richard H. Driehaus Foundation, Chicago, IL, 2012. For the MacArthur Fund for Arts and Culture and the Small Theater and Dance Group Program, payable over 5.00 years.
$8,000,000 to Local Initiatives Support Corporation, Chicago, IL, 2012. For the New Communities Program, payable over 3.00 years.
$6,000,000 to Pew Charitable Trusts, Philadelphia, PA, 2012. To deepen the work of the Results First Initiative, helping states use cost-benefit analysis for setting policy directions and budget priorities, payable over 3.00 years.
$5,000,000 to New York University, New York, NY, 2013. For MacArthur Research Network on Opening Governance, payable over 3.00 years.
$4,900,000 to University of California, Irvine, CA, 2013. For Research Network on Connected Learning, payable over 4.00 years.
$3,550,000 to Public Interest Projects, New York, NY, 2012. For a multi-state campaign to promote juvenile justice systems reform nationally.
$3,500,000 to Public Interest Projects, New York, NY, 2013. For a multi-state campaign to promote juvenile justice systems reform nationally.
$3,300,000 to Institute of Play, New York, NY, 2012. For new games, assessment, and innovation learning center (over three years), payable over 3.00 years.
$3,060,000 to University of California, Irvine, CA, 2013. For the Digital Media and Learning Competition (over two years), payable over 2.00 years.
$2,500,000 to Bipartisan Policy Center, Washington, DC, 2012. To finalize and promote the Housing Commission's recommendations for housing finance and policy reform.
$1,500,000 to National Security Archive Fund, Washington, DC, 2013. For the work in international human rights and on nuclear security (over three years), payable over 3.00 years.
$1,000,000 to Family Care International, New York, NY, 2012. For institutional support.
$1,000,000 to International Institute for Population Sciences, Mumbai, India, 2013. For the fourth round of the national demographic survey in India called the National Health and Family Welfare Survey, payable over 1.50 years.

$1,000,000 to NatureServe, Arlington, VA, 2013. For innovation seed fund and enhanced communications capacity.
$750,000 to Womens Rights Advancement and Protection Alternative, Abuja, Nigeria, 2013. To complete the construction of a Resource Centre and equip and furnish it.
$480,000 to Center for Change and Community Development, Abuja, Nigeria, 2013. To produce a film and community advocacy campaign to increase demand for girls' secondary education in northern Nigeria (over two years), payable over 2.00 years.
$300,000 to Coalition for Juvenile Justice, Washington, DC, 2013. To sustain and spread Models for Change juvenile justice system reforms through its networks of state-based juvenile justice advisory and advocacy groups, payable over 2.00 years.
$300,000 to EastWest Institute, New York, NY, 2012. For the Sanya Initiative, a track 2 U.S.-China dialogue, payable over 2.00 years.

2990
Roderick MacArthur Foundation ✧
9333 N. Milwaukee Ave.
Niles, IL 60714-1303 (847) 966-0143

Established in 1976 in IL.
Donors: J. Roderick MacArthur‡; Solange D. MacArthur; Bradford Exchange, Ltd.
Foundation type: Independent foundation.
Financial data (yr. ended 12/31/12): Assets, $12,752,062 (M); gifts received, $3,585,000; expenditures, $5,933,861; qualifying distributions, $5,838,376; giving activities include $5,697,400 for 3 grants (high: $4,500,000; low: $215,400).
Purpose and activities: The primary aims of the foundation in fulfilling its charitable, scientific, literary and educational purposes are to protect and encourage freedom of expression, human rights, civil liberties and social justice.
Fields of interest: Civil/human rights.
Type of support: General/operating support; Program development; Publication; Seed money.
Limitations: Applications not accepted. Giving on a national basis.
Publications: Grants list.
Application information: Unsolicited requests for funds not considered or acknowledged. A major commitment has been made to 3 specific projects.
Board meeting date(s): Approximately every 2 months
Officers and Directors:* John R. MacArthur,* Chair. and Secy.; Solange D. MacArthur,* Chair.; Robert Cordova,* Vice-Chair.; James D. Liggett,* Pres.; Marylou Bane, Treas. and Admin.
Number of staff: 1 full-time professional.
EIN: 510214450
Selected grants: The following grants are a representative sample of this grantmaker's funding activity:
$4,500,000 to Harpers Magazine Foundation, New York, NY, 2012. For operating support.
$982,000 to American Dance Institute, Rockville, MD, 2012. For program support.
$215,400 to Death Penalty Information Center, Washington, DC, 2012. For general support.

2991
Flora Ethel Maddux Trust 819 ✧ ☆
c/o First National Bank
891 Fairfax St.
Carlyle, IL 62231-1809

Established in IL.
Foundation type: Independent foundation.
Financial data (yr. ended 12/31/13): Assets, $1,559,792 (M); expenditures, $1,093,759; qualifying distributions, $1,084,813; giving activities include $1,072,062 for 1 grant.
Fields of interest: Libraries (public); Education.
Limitations: Applications not accepted. Giving limited to Carlyle, IL.
Application information: Unsolicited requests for funds not accepted.
Trustee: First National Bank.
EIN: 376189508

2992
Madigan Family Foundation ✧
c/o Madden, Jiganti, Moore & Sinars
190 S. LaSalle St., Ste. 1700
Chicago, IL 60603-3496

Established in 1997 in IL.
Donor: John W. Madigan.
Foundation type: Independent foundation.
Financial data (yr. ended 03/31/13): Assets, $1,901,044 (M); gifts received, $500,923; expenditures, $844,098; qualifying distributions, $838,418; giving activities include $838,418 for grants.
Purpose and activities: Giving primarily for the arts, education, health organizations, and social services.
Fields of interest: Arts; Education; Hospitals (general); Health organizations, association; Human services; Children/youth, services; International affairs, foreign policy; Christian agencies & churches; Catholic agencies & churches.
Limitations: Applications not accepted. Giving primarily in IL. No grants to individuals.
Application information: Contributes only to pre-selected organizations.
Officers and Directors:* Holly W. Madigan,* Pres.; John W. Madigan,* Secy.-Treas.; John J. Jiganti.
EIN: 364155300
Selected grants: The following grants are a representative sample of this grantmaker's funding activity:
$25,000 to Chicago Council on Global Affairs, Chicago, IL, 2011.
$25,000 to Chicago Foundation for Education, Chicago, IL, 2011.
$25,000 to Civic Committee of the Commercial Club of Chicago, Chicago, IL, 2011.
$25,000 to Paley Center for Media, New York, NY, 2011.
$25,000 to United Way of Metropolitan Chicago, Chicago, IL, 2011.
$20,000 to Chicago Council on Global Affairs, Chicago, IL, 2011.
$10,000 to Aspen Institute, Washington, DC, 2011.
$10,000 to Chicago Council on Global Affairs, Chicago, IL, 2011.
$10,000 to Paley Center for Media, New York, NY, 2011.
$10,000 to University of Michigan, Ann Arbor, MI, 2011.

2993
Magnus Charitable Trust ✧
600 W. Rand Rd., Ste. A-104
Arlington Heights, IL 60004-2355 (847) 255-1100
Contact: Delores Dorethy
FAX: (847) 632-0616;
E-mail: info@magnuscharitable.org; Toll free tel.: (888) 259-5044; Main URL: http://www.magnuscharitable.org

Established in 1995 in IL.
Donors: Alexander B. Magnus, Jr.‡; The Magnus Asset Management Trust.
Foundation type: Independent foundation.
Financial data (yr. ended 12/31/12): Assets, $9,865,836 (M); expenditures, $1,444,082; qualifying distributions, $498,266; giving activities include $479,388 for 10 grants (high: $180,000; low: $1,997).
Purpose and activities: The mission of the Trust is to make a positive impact on the world by helping to educate those that are greatly in need. Since its inception, the trust has partnered with many organizations to help eliminate hunger and obstacles to obtaining education. Giving primarily for education scholarships to needy individuals; some funding for higher education, health and human services.
Fields of interest: Higher education; Education; Health organizations, association; Human services; International human rights.
Limitations: Applications accepted. Giving in the U.S., with emphasis on IL.
Application information: Application form required.
Deadline(s): Apr. 18
Director: Victoria Magnus.
EIN: 364049284

2994
Makray Family Foundation ✧
c/o Harrison & Held, LLP
333 W. Wacker Dr., Ste. 1700
Chicago, IL 60606-1247

Established in IL.
Donors: Paul Makray, Sr.‡; Elise Makray‡.
Foundation type: Independent foundation.
Financial data (yr. ended 01/31/14): Assets, $16,653,476 (M); expenditures, $7,831,646; qualifying distributions, $7,692,612; giving activities include $7,692,612 for 13 grants (high: $7,352,112; low: $2,000).
Purpose and activities: Giving primarily to a philanthropy fund, as well as for natural resource conservation, and animal welfare.
Fields of interest: Education; Animals/wildlife; Health care; Foundations (public).
Limitations: Applications not accepted. Giving primarily in FL, IL, and NJ. No grants to individuals.
Application information: Contributes only to pre-selected organizations.
Officers and Directors:* Paul Makray, Jr.,* Pres. and Treas.; Carol Donohoe,* V.P. and Secy.
EIN: 364298517
Selected grants: The following grants are a representative sample of this grantmaker's funding activity:
$60,000 to Ravenswood Community Daycare, Chicago, IL, 2011.
$55,635 to University of California, Berkeley, CA, 2011.
$30,000 to Lincoln Park Zoo, Chicago, IL, 2011.

$25,000 to Alzheimers Association, Northern California and Northern Nevada, Mountain View, CA, 2011.
$25,000 to International Crane Foundation, Baraboo, WI, 2011.
$20,000 to Geneva Lake Conservancy, Fontana, WI, 2011.
$10,000 to Beloit College, Beloit, WI, 2011.
$6,000 to Adopt-A-Family of the Palm Beaches, Lake Worth, FL, 2011.
$5,000 to From the Top, Boston, MA, 2011.

2995
Edward Mallinckrodt, Jr. Foundation ✧

114 Forest Grove Dr.
Glen Carbon, IL 62034-1361 (618) 520-2977
Contact: Becki Blankenship
E-mail: emjf.org@gmail.com; Main URL: http://www.emallinckrodtfoundation.org/

Incorporated in 1953 in MO.
Donor: Edward Mallinckrodt, Jr.‡.
Foundation type: Independent foundation.
Financial data (yr. ended 09/30/13): Assets, $46,556,112 (M); gifts received, $10,000,000; expenditures, $2,820,683; qualifying distributions, $2,712,930; giving activities include $2,656,316 for 43 grants to individuals.
Purpose and activities: Grants largely for domestic biomedical education and research. The foundation's mission is to support early stage investigators engaged in biomedical research that has the potential to significantly advance the understanding, diagnosis, or treatment of disease.
Fields of interest: Medical research, institute; Biomedicine research.
Type of support: Annual campaigns; Capital campaigns; Conferences/seminars; Scholarship funds; Research.
Limitations: Giving in the U.S., with some emphasis on MO and PA. No grants for overhead.
Publications: Application guidelines; Annual report.
Application information: See foundation web site for specific application instructions which must be followed including page limitations and font size. Application form required.
Initial approach: Proposal via e-mail in one .pdf file to Becki Blankenship
Copies of proposal: 7
Deadline(s): None
Board meeting date(s): Feb. or Mar., June, and Sept.
Final notification: 3 to 6 weeks following board meeting
Officers and Directors:* Spencer Burke, Pres.; Bill Polk, V.P.; Marian Mehan, Secy.; Dr. Thomas Cori; Stuart A. Kornfeld, M.D.; Lila Solnica-Krezel; Alan Schwartz.
EIN: 436030295
Selected grants: The following grants are a representative sample of this grantmaker's funding activity:
$200,000 to University of Pennsylvania, Philadelphia, PA, 2013. For scholar program.
$120,000 to Columbia University Medical Center, New York, NY, 2013. To study of How Notch Regulates Hepatic Glucose and Lipid Metabolism.
$120,000 to Stanford University, Stanford, CA, 2013. For Coronary Artery Smooth Muscle Cells.
$120,000 to University of Utah, Salt Lake City, UT, 2013. To study of a Molecular Code Governing Neural Circuit Assembly.
$120,000 to University of Utah, School of Medicine, Salt Lake City, UT, 2013. To study of the Discovery of Novel Bacteria Molecules to Treat Autoimmune Disease.
$75,000 to California Institute of Technology, Pasadena, CA, 2013. For scholar program.
$75,000 to University of Pittsburgh, Pittsburgh, PA, 2013. For scholar program.
$60,000 to Baylor College of Medicine, Houston, TX, 2013. For Role of Sirtuins in Aging and Disease.
$60,000 to Duke University, Durham, NC, 2013. For Novel Mechanism of Protein Acetylation.
$60,000 to Duke University, School of Medicine, Durham, NC, 2013. For Cellular Substrate of Odor Perception.

2996
Malott Family Foundation ✧

(formerly Camalott Charitable Foundation)
200 E. Randolph Dr.
Chicago, IL 60601-6436

Established in 1989 in IL.
Donor: Robert H. Malott.
Foundation type: Independent foundation.
Financial data (yr. ended 12/31/12): Assets, $45,332,063 (M); gifts received, $3,942,144; expenditures, $1,216,496; qualifying distributions, $1,004,137; giving activities include $916,217 for 89 grants (high: $170,000; low: $150).
Purpose and activities: Giving primarily for the arts, particularly museums, education, and human services.
Fields of interest: Museums; Performing arts; Arts; Higher education; Education; Environment, association; Environment; Hospitals (general); Human services; Children/youth, services; United Ways and Federated Giving Programs; Public policy, research.
Limitations: Applications not accepted. Giving primarily in IL. No support for religious organizations. No grants to individuals.
Application information: Unsolicited requests for funds not considered.
Officers: Robert H. Malott, Pres.; Barbara H. Malott Kizziah, Secy.
Directors: Robert Deane Malott; Elizabeth Malott Pohle.
Number of staff: 1 full-time professional; 1 part-time professional.
EIN: 363680666

2997
The Manaaki Foundation ✧

c/o Pascale Kichler, William A. Gee IV
10 S. Dearborn, IL1-0117
Chicago, IL 60603
Application address: JPMorgan Chase Bank, N.A., 2200 Ross Ave., 5th Fl., Dallas, TX 75201-2787, tel.: (214) 965-2910

Established in 2010.
Donor: William A. Gee IV.
Foundation type: Independent foundation.
Financial data (yr. ended 07/31/13): Assets, $11,058,660 (M); expenditures, $568,444; qualifying distributions, $500,255; giving activities include $500,230 for grants.
Fields of interest: Media/communications; Education.
Limitations: Applications accepted. Giving primarily in CT, FL, and IL.
Application information: Application form required.
Initial approach: Telephone Call
Deadline(s): None
Officers and Directors:* William A. Gee IV,* Pres.; Susan Crothers Gee,* Secy.; Pascale Kichler.
EIN: 271371242
Selected grants: The following grants are a representative sample of this grantmaker's funding activity:
$50,000 to Chicago Public Media, Chicago, IL, 2011. For program support.
$50,000 to Foundation for National Progress, San Francisco, CA, 2011. For program support.
$30,000 to Education and Hope, Norwalk, CT, 2011. For program support.
$5,000 to Carter Center, Atlanta, GA, 2011. For program support.
$5,000 to Chicago Academy of Sciences, Chicago, IL, 2011.
$5,000 to Doctors Without Borders USA, New York, NY, 2011. For program support.
$5,000 to Growing Power, Milwaukee, WI, 2011. For program support.
$5,000 to Heshima Kenya, Chicago, IL, 2011.
$5,000 to Planned Parenthood Federation of America, New York, NY, 2011.
$5,000 to Seven Generations Ahead, Oak Park, IL, 2011. For program support.

2998
Walter S. Mander Foundation

c/o Charles Wolf/Vedder, Price, PC
222 N. LaSalle St.
Chicago, IL 60601-1003
Contact: General Inquiries: Theresa G. Lipo, Fdn. Consultant
E-mail: tglipo@sbcglobal.net; Main URL: http://waltermanderfoundation.org/

Established in 1994 in IL.
Donor: Walter S. Mander‡.
Foundation type: Independent foundation.
Financial data (yr. ended 03/31/14): Assets, $10,315,231 (M); expenditures, $794,171; qualifying distributions, $632,460; giving activities include $632,460 for 34 grants (high: $225,000; low: $300).
Purpose and activities: The foundation has four major areas of focus: 1) Chicago community development; 2) issues associated with food and agriculture; 3) cancer research (by invitation only); and 4) Jewish organizations and causes.
Fields of interest: Agriculture/food, alliance/advocacy; Agriculture/food, public policy; Agriculture/food, public education; Youth development, agriculture; Human services; Community development, neighborhood development; Community development, citizen coalitions; Community development, public/private ventures; Jewish federated giving programs; Jewish agencies & synagogues; Children/youth; Adults; Minorities; Economically disadvantaged.
Type of support: General/operating support; Management development/capacity building; Program development; Consulting services; Program evaluation.
Limitations: Applications not accepted. Giving primarily limited to the city of Chicago, IL and surrounding area with the exception of some discretionary funding and Jewish causes. No grants to individuals.

Application information: Contributes only to pre-selected organizations. Organizations matching the foundation's areas of interest may submit 1-2 page program descriptions. The foundation will respond if interested in receiving additional information.
Officers and Directors:* Charles B. Wolf,* Pres.; James J. Stevens,* V.P.; Peter E. Goschi,* Secy.; Peter Wolf.
EIN: 363961599
Selected grants: The following grants are a representative sample of this grantmaker's funding activity:
$20,000 to Association House of Chicago, Chicago, IL, 2013. For Center for Working Families.
$10,000 to Bethel New Life, Chicago, IL, 2013. For Community and Economic Development programming.

2999
The Manitoba Foundation ✧
10 S. Dearborn St., Fl. 21
Chicago, IL 60603

Established in 1996 in DE and NY.
Foundation type: Independent foundation.
Financial data (yr. ended 12/31/12): Assets, $12,275,622 (M); expenditures, $638,710; qualifying distributions, $597,874; giving activities include $595,000 for 5 grants (high: $400,000; low: $25,000).
Fields of interest: Human services; Jewish federated giving programs; Jewish agencies & synagogues.
Limitations: Applications not accepted. Giving primarily in NY; funding also in London, England. No grants to individuals.
Application information: Unsolicited requests for funds not accepted.
Directors: Jean De Gunzburg; Terry De Gunzburg; Alan Halperin; Samuel Minzberg.
EIN: 133775261

3000
Mansueto Foundation ✧ ☆
c/o Bank of America, N.A.
231 S. LaSalle St., Ste. 1332
Chicago, IL 60604-1435
Joe and Rika Mansueto's Giving Pledge Profile: http://glasspockets.org/philanthropy-in-focus/eye-on-the-giving-pledge/profiles/mansueto

Established in IL.
Donor: Joseph D. Mansueto.
Foundation type: Independent foundation.
Financial data (yr. ended 12/31/13): Assets, $5,304,278 (M); gifts received, $4,975,419; expenditures, $1,002,262; qualifying distributions, $987,531; giving activities include $987,531 for 1 grant.
Fields of interest: Philanthropy/voluntarism.
Limitations: Applications not accepted. Giving primarily in Chicago, IL.
Application information: Contributes only to pre-selected organizations.
Officers: Joseph D. Mansueto, Pres.; Rika Yoshida, V.P.
EIN: 271895175

3001
Charles E. Marks, Jr. Charitable Trust ✧
c/o Stanley R. Weinberg
203 N. LaSalle St., Ste. 1620
Chicago, IL 60601-1225

Established in 2006 in IL.
Donors: Charles E. Marks, Sr. Trust; Charles E. Marks, Jr. Trust.
Foundation type: Independent foundation.
Financial data (yr. ended 12/31/12): Assets, $26,248,907 (M); expenditures, $3,954,596; qualifying distributions, $3,776,500; giving activities include $3,579,556 for 20 grants (high: $741,645; low: $25,000).
Fields of interest: Education; Children/youth, services.
Limitations: Applications not accepted. Giving primarily in Chicago, IL. No grants to individuals.
Application information: Unsolicited requests for funds not accepted.
Trustees: Jonathan Levine; Stanley R. Weinberger.
EIN: 207240974
Selected grants: The following grants are a representative sample of this grantmaker's funding activity:
$25,000 to Voices for Illinois Children, Chicago, IL, 2012. To provide Health, Welfare, and Educational Services to Children.

3002
Bert W. Martin Foundation ✧
c/o The Northern Trust Co.
P.O. Box 803878
Chicago, IL 60680-3878
Application address: 940 S. Orange Ave., Ste. 101, Orlando, FL 32806-1242

Incorporated in 1946 in IL.
Donors: Bert W. Martin; Ada La May Martin; Bert Martin Charitable Fund; Ada Martin Trust.
Foundation type: Independent foundation.
Financial data (yr. ended 12/31/13): Assets, $47,768,072 (M); gifts received, $268,576; expenditures, $1,931,867; qualifying distributions, $1,838,547; giving activities include $1,810,000 for 18 grants (high: $300,000; low: $5,000).
Purpose and activities: Giving primarily for higher education, health care, and human services.
Fields of interest: Museums; Higher education; Hospitals (general); Health care; Human services.
Limitations: Applications accepted. Giving primarily in AZ and FL. No grants to individuals.
Application information: Application form not required.
Initial approach: Letter
Deadline(s): Jan. 31
Officers: Winifred M. Warden, Pres.; Chandler D. Warden, V.P.; Thomas M. James, Secy.; F. Andrew Warden, Treas.
EIN: 366060591

3003
Charlotte Y. Martin Foundation Trust ✧
c/o BMO Harris Bank, N.A.
111 W. Monroe St., Ste. 10C
Chicago, IL 60603-4026
E-mail: info@charlottemartin.org; Main URL: http://www.charlottemartin.org

Established in 1988 in WA.
Donor: Charlotte Y. Martin†.
Foundation type: Independent foundation.
Financial data (yr. ended 03/31/13): Assets, $23,041,833 (M); expenditures, $969,138; qualifying distributions, $863,804; giving activities include $625,107 for 90 grants (high: $208,157; low: $1,000).
Purpose and activities: Giving primarily for youth-focused athletics, culture, education, and wildlife and habitat preservation.
Fields of interest: Visual arts; Performing arts; Elementary/secondary education; Higher education; Environment, natural resources; Animals/wildlife, fisheries; Animals/wildlife, sanctuaries; Athletics/sports, school programs; Children/youth.
Type of support: General/operating support; Continuing support; Building/renovation; Equipment; Land acquisition; Program development; Seed money; Curriculum development; Matching/challenge support.
Limitations: Applications accepted. Giving limited to the Pacific Northwest. No support for private foundations, or for social services, pre-kindergarten programs, programs for college students, programs whose goals are primarily social services, artists in residence programs, international exchange programs, or for organizations whose mission statement does not include wildlife and habitat preservation. No grants to individuals, or for multi-year grants, films, videos, books, travel costs and lodging for conference or event attendance, fitness, wellness, nutrition, or health, the rental or purchase of buses, capital projects, hardware, technology, the purchase of computers or textbooks, the rental of facilities, marketing, pass though funding, students or paid internships, curriculum development, children's testing or test preparation, passive participation by youth, preservation of small isolated parcels of land or of land solely valued for recreational purposes, wildlife rehabilitation, captive breeding, city parks, or for zoos or aquariums.
Publications: Application guidelines; Annual report; Grants list; IRS Form 990 or 990-PF printed copy available upon request; Program policy statement.
Application information: Application form and information available on web site. Application form required.
Initial approach: All applications accepted through web site only. No applications or letter of intent accepted by mail
Deadline(s): See foundation web site for current deadlines
Board meeting date(s): Quarterly
Final notification: 1-6 months
Officers and Committee Members:* Tom Campbell,* Chair.; Sheila Kelly,* Secy.; Peter Galloway,* Treas.; Joan Gagliardi; C'Ardiss Gardner Gleser; Bonnie Sachatello-Sawyer.
Trustee: BMO Harris Bank, N.A.
Number of staff: 1 part-time professional.
EIN: 916294504
Selected grants: The following grants are a representative sample of this grantmaker's funding activity:
$10,000 to Inland Northwest Land Trust, Spokane, WA, 2013. For Wild Lifelines.
$6,000 to Bark, Portland, OR, 2013. For Monitoring Program for Mt Hood National Forest Project.
$5,000 to Arts Central, Bend, OR, 2013. For Tri-County Youth Arts Education Program.
$5,000 to Associated Recreation Council, Seattle, WA, 2013. For All Girl Everything Ultimate Program.

$5,000 to Film Action Oregon, Portland, OR, 2013. For Project Youth Doc.
$5,000 to First Place, Seattle, WA, 2013. For First Place Education Program.
$5,000 to Longview Stageworks, Longview, WA, 2013. For The C A S T Project.
$5,000 to MAC Foundation, Madras, OR, 2013. For BuffEnuff FC Project.
$5,000 to Salem Schools Foundation, Salem, OR, 2013. For Roots of Hip Hop Dance and Culture Education.
$5,000 to Salish Sea Expeditions, Bainbridge Island, WA, 2013. For Salish Sea Expeditions' Sound and Source Science and Environmental Education Program.

3004
Master Educational Assistance Foundation ✧

747 S. Euclid Ave.
Oak Park, IL 60304-1243 (847) 431-5590
Contact: James F. Zangrilli, Exec. Dir.

Established in 1987 in IL.
Donor: Valerian Schultz.
Foundation type: Independent foundation.
Financial data (yr. ended 12/31/13): Assets, $7,797,326 (M); expenditures, $911,588; qualifying distributions, $890,566; giving activities include $644,704 for 21+ grants (high: $102,950; low: $2,873), and $166,900 for grants to individuals.
Purpose and activities: Giving primarily for education and for scholarship awards and other educational assistance to financially disadvantaged and/or physically or mentally disabled inner-city residents; support also for health care.
Fields of interest: Education; Human services; Foundations (private operating); Physically disabled; Mentally disabled; Economically disadvantaged.
Type of support: General/operating support; Scholarships—to individuals.
Limitations: Applications accepted. Giving primarily to residents of IL.
Application information: Application form required.
Initial approach: Letter
Deadline(s): None
Officer: James F. Zangrilli, Exec. Dir.
EIN: 363542174
Selected grants: The following grants are a representative sample of this grantmaker's funding activity:
$99,111 to Chicago Police Memorial Foundation, Chicago, IL, 2011.

3005
Oscar G. and Elsa S. Mayer Family Foundation ✧

c/o Barbara J. Pope, P.C.
190 S. LaSalle St., Ste. 610
Chicago, IL 60603-3557

Established in 1996 in IL.
Foundation type: Independent foundation.
Financial data (yr. ended 12/31/12): Assets, $15,708,529 (M); expenditures, $1,022,342; qualifying distributions, $764,334; giving activities include $687,977 for 63 grants (high: $94,300; low: $200).
Fields of interest: Education; Children/youth, services.
Type of support: Program development.
Limitations: Applications not accepted. Giving in the U.S., with emphasis on IL, OR and WI. No grants to individuals.
Application information: Applications only accepted from organizations a foundation director is involved with. Unsolicited requests for funds not accepted.
Board meeting date(s): Feb.
Officers and Directors:* Harold F. Mayer,* Pres.; William E. Mayer,* V.P.; Allison M. Shetter,* Secy.-Treas.; Allan C. Mayer, Jr.; Oscar H. Mayer; Richard A. Mayer; Scott T. Mayer.
Number of staff: 1 part-time support.
EIN: 364035204

3006
Robert & Beatrice C. Mayer Foundation ✧

160 E. Pearson St., No. 3103
Chicago, IL 60611-2308

Established in 1952.
Donors: Robert B. Mayer‡; Beatrice C. Mayer.
Foundation type: Independent foundation.
Financial data (yr. ended 12/31/12): Assets, $0 (M); gifts received, $730,787; expenditures, $585,471; qualifying distributions, $585,471; giving activities include $575,155 for grants.
Fields of interest: Museums; Arts; Higher education.
Limitations: Applications not accepted. Giving primarily in Chicago, IL. No grants to individuals.
Application information: Contributes only to pre-selected organizations.
Officers: Beatrice C. Mayer, Pres. and Co-Secy.; Robert N. Mayer, V.P.; Ruth Mayer Durchslag, Co-Secy.
EIN: 366051068

3007
Mazza Foundation ✧

30 S. Wacker Dr., Ste. 2600
Chicago, IL 60606-7512 (312) 855-4055
Contact: Mary Jane Rubinelli, Pres.

Incorporated in 1957 in IL.
Donors: Leonard M. Lavezzorio‡; Louise T. Mazza Trust; Tina Lavezzorio‡; Walter D. Lavezzorio Residuary Trust.
Foundation type: Independent foundation.
Financial data (yr. ended 11/30/13): Assets, $38,252,286 (M); gifts received, $4,766,490; expenditures, $1,680,298; qualifying distributions, $1,449,530; giving activities include $1,420,000 for 39 grants (high: $250,000; low: $5,000).
Purpose and activities: Giving primarily for education, health associations, children and youth services, including a children's hospital, as well as for social services, and Roman Catholic organizations.
Fields of interest: Historic preservation/historical societies; Arts; Elementary/secondary education; Higher education; Education; Hospitals (general); Hospitals (specialty); Health care; Health organizations, association; Human services; Children/youth, services; Catholic agencies & churches.
Limitations: Applications accepted. Giving primarily in Chicago, IL.
Application information: Application form not required.
Initial approach: Proposal
Deadline(s): None
Officers and Directors:* Mary Jane Rubinelli,* Pres.; Joan Lavezzorio Schniedwind,* V.P.; Joseph O. Rubinelli, Jr.,* Secy.; Nicholas J. Lavezzorio,* Treas.
EIN: 366054751

3008
MB Financial Charitable Foundation ✧

6111 N. River Rd., Ste. 1100
Rosemont, IL 60018
Contact: Sue Lepore, Pres.
Main URL: http://www.mbfinancial.com/AboutMBFinancialBank/MBinYourCommunity/MBFinancialCharitableFoundation/tabid/171/Default.aspx

Established in 2006 in IL.
Donor: MB Financial Bank, N.A.
Foundation type: Company-sponsored foundation.
Financial data (yr. ended 12/31/12): Assets, $1,793,348 (M); expenditures, $644,359; qualifying distributions, $627,314; giving activities include $619,814 for 169 grants (high: $50,500; low: $150).
Purpose and activities: The foundation supports organizations involved with preservation, health, mental health, housing, human services, community economic development, and civic affairs. Special emphasis is directed toward programs designed to serve low- and moderate-income communities and households.
Fields of interest: Historic preservation/historical societies; Health care; Mental health/crisis services; Housing/shelter, development; Housing/shelter, rehabilitation; Housing/shelter; Family services; Human services, financial counseling; Human services; Community development, neighborhood development; Community development, business promotion; Community development, small businesses; Community/economic development; Public affairs; Economically disadvantaged.
Type of support: General/operating support; Program development.
Limitations: Applications accepted. Giving primarily in the areas of company operations, with emphasis on the greater Chicagoland area, IL. No support for religious or fraternal organizations (unless for a secular project of benefit to the entire community). No grants to individuals, or for dinner or galas tickets, golf fees, membership dues, publicity or advertising.
Application information: Application form not required.
Initial approach: Proposal
Deadline(s): None
Officers: Sue Lepore, Pres.; Vicky Arroyo, V.P.; Lesly Flores, Secy.; Patricia Basan, Treas.
EIN: 203216854

3009
Raymond F. and Judith K. McCaskey 2003 Charitable Trust ✧ ☆

2450 N. Lakeview, Ste. 6
Chicago, IL 60614

Donor: Raymond F. McCaskey.
Foundation type: Independent foundation.

Financial data (yr. ended 12/31/13): Assets, $7,100,241 (M); gifts received, $803,400; expenditures, $1,035,772; qualifying distributions, $1,001,715; giving activities include $1,000,000 for 1 grant.
Fields of interest: Arts; Human services.
Limitations: Applications not accepted.
Application information: Unsolicited requests for funds not accepted.
Trustee: Raymond F. McCaskey.
EIN: 276362159

3010
Chauncey and Marion Deering McCormick Foundation ✧
410 N. Michigan Ave., Ste. 590
Chicago, IL 60611-4220

Incorporated in 1957 in IL.
Donors: Brooks McCormick‡; Brooks McCormick Trust; Charles Deering McCormick Trust; Roger McCormick Trust; Lisa Collins Meaney; Conor McCormick O'Neil.
Foundation type: Independent foundation.
Financial data (yr. ended 07/31/13): Assets, $69,613,162 (M); gifts received, $415,777; expenditures, $3,261,962; qualifying distributions, $3,140,688; giving activities include $3,121,741 for 94 grants (high: $650,000; low: $1,500).
Purpose and activities: Giving primarily for higher education, hospitals, and art museums; support also for child welfare.
Fields of interest: Museums (art); Arts; Higher education; Education; Hospitals (general); Human services; YM/YWCAs & YM/YWHAs; Children/youth, services.
Type of support: General/operating support.
Limitations: Applications accepted. Giving primarily in Chicago, IL. No grants to individuals.
Application information: Application form not required.
Initial approach: Proposal
Deadline(s): None
Officers and Trustees:* Christopher Hunt,* Chair.; Abby McCormick O'Neil,* Vice-Chair.; John Rau,* Pres.; Blair Collins Maus,* V.P.; Hilary H. McCutcheon,* V.P.; Lisa Collins Meaney,* V.P.; Susan D. Pattock,* Secy.-Treas.; Ian C. Hunt; Fiona McMillan; Conor O'Neil; Nancy M. Vella.
EIN: 366054815

3011
Ronald L. McDaniel Foundation ✧
c/o Ronald L. McDaniel
8005 Woodside Ln.
Burr Ridge, IL 60527-8052

Established in 1995 in IL.
Donor: Ronald L. McDaniel.
Foundation type: Independent foundation.
Financial data (yr. ended 12/31/13): Assets, $16,192,084 (M); gifts received, $1,575,000; expenditures, $739,245; qualifying distributions, $662,947; giving activities include $662,947 for 12 grants (high: $400,000; low: $1,000).
Purpose and activities: Giving primarily for social services, as well as for higher education, children and youth services, and to a YMCA.
Fields of interest: Higher education; Human services; YM/YWCAs & YM/YWHAs; Children/youth, services.
Limitations: Applications not accepted. Giving primarily in IL and IN. No grants to individuals.
Application information: Unsolicited requests for funds not accepted.
Officers: Ronald McDaniel, Pres.; Barbara Gulick, V.P.; Julia Vincer, Secy.; Brenda Jacobs, Treas.
EIN: 364012153

3012
McDonald's Foundation ✧ ☆
1 Kroc Dr.
Oak Brook, IL 60523-2275

Established in IL.
Donor: McDonald's Corporation.
Foundation type: Independent foundation.
Financial data (yr. ended 12/31/13): Assets, $180 (M); gifts received, $97,656; expenditures, $1,097,656; qualifying distributions, $1,075,000; giving activities include $1,075,000 for 1 grant.
Fields of interest: Recreation, parks/playgrounds; Children/youth, services.
Limitations: Applications not accepted. Giving primarily in Washington, DC; funding also in Chicago, IL.
Application information: Unsolicited requests for funds not accepted.
Officers and Directors:* Gloria Santona,* Pres.; Karen A. Matusinec,* V.P. and Secy.; Robert L. Switzer,* V.P.
EIN: 460706440

3013
McDougal Family Foundation ✧
737 N. Michigan Ave., Ste. 1040
Chicago, IL 60611-7014 (312) 255-0916
Contact: Peter Mich
FAX: (312) 255-0936;
E-mail: pmich@mcdougalfamilyfoundation.org

Established in 1994.
Donors: Alfred L. McDougal; The Chicago Community Trust.
Foundation type: Independent foundation.
Financial data (yr. ended 12/31/11): Assets, $15,022,681 (M); expenditures, $821,655; qualifying distributions, $715,621; giving activities include $489,262 for grants.
Purpose and activities: The foundation seeks to foster the efforts of a small number of Chicago, Illinois organizations in their efforts to assist students in grades 6 through 12 achieve school success. The goal is to increase the number of students graduating from Chicago Public Schools.
Fields of interest: Elementary/secondary education; Teacher school/education.
Type of support: Continuing support; Program development; Conferences/seminars; Curriculum development.
Limitations: Applications not accepted. Giving primarily in Chicago, IL. No support for individual schools. No grants for scholarships for individuals, special events, or capital campaigns.
Publications: Grants list.
Application information: Unsolicited requests for funds not accepted.
Board meeting date(s): Varies
Officers: Alfred L. McDougal, Pres. and Treas.; Nancy A. Lauter, V.P.; Thomas McDougal, Secy.
Directors: Sarah Duncan; Jan McDougal; Stephen McDougal.
Number of staff: 1 part-time support.
EIN: 363943431

3014
William G. McGowan Charitable Fund, Inc. ✧
212 N. Sangamon St., Ste. 1D
Chicago, IL 60607-1722 (312) 243-3198
Contact: Diana Spencer, Exec. Dir.
FAX: (312) 243-3199;
E-mail: info@mcgowanfund.rg; E-mail (for Diana Spencer): diana.spencer@mcgowanfund.org; Main URL: http://www.mcgowanfund.org
LinkedIn: William G. McGowan Scholars Alumni: http://www.linkedin.com/groupInvitation?gid=154411

Established in 1992 in DC.
Donor: William G. McGowan‡.
Foundation type: Independent foundation.
Financial data (yr. ended 06/30/13): Assets, $167,843,396 (M); gifts received, $10,108; expenditures, $9,089,973; qualifying distributions, $8,128,715; giving activities include $7,363,203 for grants, and $186,646 for employee matching gifts.
Purpose and activities: Giving in the areas of education to improve high school graduation rates, healthcare in the area of childhood obesity/cardiac health prevention; human services for vulnerable populations. Giving is limited to specific geographic regions.
Fields of interest: Elementary/secondary education; Education, early childhood education; Education; Heart & circulatory research; Medical research; Human services; Economically disadvantaged.
Type of support: General/operating support; Continuing support; Equipment; Program development; Scholarship funds; Research; Technical assistance; Matching/challenge support.
Limitations: Applications accepted. Giving limited to the Washington, DC, area, Chicago, IL, KS, western and upstate NY, northeastern PA, and northern VA, Denver and Eagle counties, CO and Reno, NV (but does not apply to colleges and universities seeking McGowan Scholar grants). No support for political causes, events, campaigns, or for organizations supporting the arts. No grants to individuals or for sponsorships.
Publications: Application guidelines; Biennial report; Occasional report.
Application information: Full proposals will be accepted by invitation only. The foundation has closed the McGowan Scholars Program. Unsolicited proposals from MD and VA (including Washington DC) are no longer accepted. Application form required.
Initial approach: Only online applications are accept. Application acceptance varies by geographic region. See web site
Deadline(s): Letter of inquiry deadlines: Nov. 15, Mar. 15 and July 15. Application deadlines: Jan. 2, May 1 and Sept. 1
Board meeting date(s): Mar., July, and Nov.
Final notification: Following board meeting
Officers and Trustees:* Sue Gin McGowan,* Pres.; A. Joseph Rosica,* Secy.; Diana K. Spencer, Exec. Dir.; V. Orville Wright, Emeritus; Michael N. Cachine, Sr.; Mary Alice Gin; Sherilyn Kingsbury; Gertrude McGowan; Leo McGowan; Tim McGowan; William P. McGowan; MaryPat McGowan-Swartz; Daniel

Rosica; Kathryn Rosica; Mark Rosica; John Worthington.
Number of staff: 1 full-time professional; 1 part-time support.
EIN: 521829785
Selected grants: The following grants are a representative sample of this grantmaker's funding activity:
$1,279,410 to American Heart Association, National Office, Dallas, TX, 2013. For Healthy Way to Grow child care technical assistance program.
$750,000 to University of Pittsburgh, McGowan Institute for Regenerative Medicine, Pittsburgh, PA, 2013. For medical research grants.
$441,536 to University of Pittsburgh, McGowan Institute for Regenerative Medicine, Pittsburgh, PA, 2013. For medical research grants.
$297,488 to Marywood University, Scranton, PA, 2013. For Student Academic Success and Inspiring Excellence (SASIE) Program.
$250,000 to National Technical Institute for the Deaf at Rochester Institute of Technology, Rochester, NY, 2013. For Sebastian and Lenore Rosica Hall.
$150,000 to Center for Inspired Teaching, Washington, DC, 2013. For education grants.
$150,000 to Foundation for the National Archives, Washington, DC, 2013. For William G McGowan Theater Program and Audience Development.
$125,000 to Gerard Place Housing Development Fund Company, Buffalo, NY, 2013. For Community Center general operating support.
$40,000 to Catholic Education Foundation of Northeast Kansas, Kansas City, KS, 2013. For Scholarships for Wyandotte County under-resourced youth.
$20,000 to Uplift Organization, Kansas City, MO, 2013.

3015
McGraw Foundation ✧

653 Landwehr Rd.
Northbrook, IL 60062-2309 (847) 291-9810
Contact: Gordon LaBounty, V.P.
FAX: (847) 291-9811;
E-mail: info@maxmcgrawfoundation.org; Main URL: http://www.maxmcgrawfoundation.org

Incorporated in 1948 in IL.
Donors: Alfred Bersted†; Carol Jean Root†; Maxine Elrod†; Donald S. Elrod†; Max McGraw†; Richard F. McGraw†; McGraw-Edison Co.; and others.
Foundation type: Independent foundation.
Financial data (yr. ended 12/31/13): Assets, $9,268,502 (M); expenditures, $944,968; qualifying distributions, $830,921; giving activities include $671,215 for 109 grants (high: $200,000; low: $50).
Purpose and activities: The primary focus of the foundation is on education at all levels, with an emphasis on higher education in the fields of science and environment. In addition, grants are made to social service agencies, emphasizing those dealing with children. The foundation also occasionally makes grants in the areas of health, medical research and the arts.
Fields of interest: Humanities; Arts; Education, special; Higher education; Education; Environment; Animals/wildlife; Medical research; Human services; Science.
Type of support: General/operating support; Continuing support; Annual campaigns; Professorships; Seed money; Scholarship funds; Research; Employee matching gifts; Matching/challenge support.
Limitations: Applications accepted. Giving primarily in the Chicago, IL, area and in the Midwest. No support for religious purposes, theater groups or public or private high schools. No grants to individuals, seminars or conferences.
Publications: Application guidelines; Program policy statement.
Application information: Application form required.
Initial approach: Proposal
Copies of proposal: 1
Deadline(s): Feb. 1
Board meeting date(s): June; grant committee meets annually in Mar.
Officers and Directors:* Jerry D. Jones,* Pres.; Gordon LaBounty,* V.P., Secy.-Treas. and Exec. Dir.; James F. Quilter; J. Bradley Davis; Scott M. Elrod; Dennis W. Fitzgerald; Terence Graunke; William W. Mauritz; Daphne Monroy; Carol E. Moorman; Catherine Nelson; James F. Quilter; Bernard B. Rinella.
Number of staff: 2 full-time professional; 1 full-time support.
EIN: 362490000
Selected grants: The following grants are a representative sample of this grantmaker's funding activity:
$250,000 to University of Michigan, Ann Arbor, MI, 2011.
$200,000 to Max McGraw Wildlife Foundation, Dundee, IL, 2011.
$60,000 to Associated Colleges of Illinois, Chicago, IL, 2011.
$25,000 to Allendale Association, Lake Villa, IL, 2011.
$25,000 to Max McGraw Wildlife Foundation, Dundee, IL, 2011.
$20,000 to Associated Colleges of Illinois, Chicago, IL, 2011.
$15,000 to Max McGraw Wildlife Foundation, Dundee, IL, 2011.
$5,000 to Experimental Station, Chicago, IL, 2011.
$5,000 to New Leaders for New Schools, Chicago, IL, 2011.
$5,000 to PADS to Hope, Palatine, IL, 2011.

3016
McIntosh Foundation, Inc. ✧

525 Sheridan Rd.
Kenilworth, IL 60043-1222

Established in 1985 in IL.
Donor: William A. McIntosh.
Foundation type: Independent foundation.
Financial data (yr. ended 04/30/13): Assets, $15,479,891 (M); expenditures, $749,634; qualifying distributions, $733,000; giving activities include $733,000 for grants.
Purpose and activities: Giving primarily for Roman Catholic churches, schools, and charities; funding also for other education and social services.
Fields of interest: Performing arts, ballet; Higher education; Education; Human services; Catholic agencies & churches.
Limitations: Applications not accepted. Giving in the U.S., with strong emphasis on IL, particularly Chicago; some emphasis also in CT and New York, NY. No grants to individuals.
Application information: Contributes only to pre-selected organizations.
Officers: William A. McIntosh, Pres. and Treas.; Kathleen M. Clarke, V.P. and Secy.
Directors: Anne Atzeff; David McIntosh; Michael McIntosh; Julia A. Smith.
EIN: 363358483
Selected grants: The following grants are a representative sample of this grantmaker's funding activity:
$100,000 to Fairfield University, Fairfield, CT, 2012.
$85,000 to American Ballet Theater, New York, NY, 2012.
$75,000 to Missionaries of Charity, Bronx, NY, 2012.
$50,000 to Big Shoulders Fund, Chicago, IL, 2012.
$40,000 to Saint Benedict the African Parish, Chicago, IL, 2012.
$25,000 to John Marshall Law School, Chicago, IL, 2012.
$20,000 to Chicago Jesuit Academy, Chicago, IL, 2012.
$20,000 to Tulane University, New Orleans, LA, 2012.
$7,500 to Saint Marys Mission School, Redlake, MN, 2012.

3017
The McNamara Purcell Foundation ✧

(formerly The Anne McNamara Purcell Foundation)
27 W. 332 Churchill Rd.
Winfield, IL 60190

Established in 1999 in IL.
Donors: Philip J. Purcell; Anne McNamara Purcell.
Foundation type: Independent foundation.
Financial data (yr. ended 12/31/13): Assets, $14,708,406 (M); expenditures, $674,326; qualifying distributions, $657,665; giving activities include $654,250 for 49 grants (high: $60,000; low: $1,000).
Purpose and activities: Giving primarily for education and health.
Fields of interest: Higher education, university; Education; Hospitals (general); Medical research, institute.
Limitations: Applications not accepted. Giving primarily in Chicago, IL; some funding nationally. No grants to individuals.
Application information: Contributes only to pre-selected organizations.
Officer: Philip J. Purcell, Mgr.
Trustees: David P. Purcell; Michael J. Purcell; Paul M. Purcell.
EIN: 367293187
Selected grants: The following grants are a representative sample of this grantmaker's funding activity:
$202,500 to Multiple Sclerosis Society, National, New York, NY, 2010.
$90,000 to J. E. Cosgriff Memorial Catholic School, Salt Lake City, UT, 2011.
$50,000 to Myelin Repair Foundation, Saratoga, CA, 2011.
$50,000 to University of Notre Dame, Notre Dame, IN, 2011.
$25,000 to Boys Club of New York, New York, NY, 2011.
$18,000 to Peggy Notebaert Nature Museum, Chicago, IL, 2011.
$10,000 to Food Allergy Research and Education, New York, NY, 2011.
$10,000 to Hospital for Special Surgery, New York, NY, 2011.
$10,000 to Multiple Sclerosis Society, National, Greater Illinois Chapter, Chicago, IL, 2011.

$10,000 to Susan G. Komen for the Cure, Dallas, TX, 2011.
$10,000 to University of San Diego, San Diego, CA, 2011.
$5,000 to Pathways Awareness Foundation, Chicago, IL, 2010.

3018
Adeline & George McQueen Foundation ✧ ☆
10 S. Dearborn St., IL1-0117
Chicago, IL 60603-2024
Application address: c/o JPMorgan Chase Bank, N.A., P.O. Box 2050, Fort Worth, TX 76113, tel.: (817) 884-4772

Established in 1960 in TX.
Foundation type: Independent foundation.
Financial data (yr. ended 06/30/13): Assets, $21,352,441 (M); expenditures, $728,848; qualifying distributions, $478,814; giving activities include $431,000 for 21 grants (high: $125,000; low: $1,000).
Fields of interest: Alzheimer's disease; Human services; Children/youth, services.
Limitations: Applications accepted. Giving primarily in Dallas and Fort Worth, TX. No grants to individuals.
Application information: Application form required.
Initial approach: Letter
Copies of proposal: 1
Deadline(s): None
Board meeting date(s): Nov.
Trustee: JPMorgan Chase Bank, N.A.
EIN: 756014459
Selected grants: The following grants are a representative sample of this grantmaker's funding activity:
$250,000 to James L. West Presbyterian Special Care Center, Fort Worth, TX, 2011.
$40,000 to SafeHaven of Tarrant County, Hurst, TX, 2011. For program support.
$13,000 to Camp Fire USA, Fort Worth, TX, 2011. For program support.

3019
The Medline Foundation ✧
1 Medline Pl.
Mundelein, IL 60060-4486 (847) 643-4343

Established in 2002 in IL.
Donors: Medline Industries, Inc.; James Abrams; Wendy Abrams.
Foundation type: Company-sponsored foundation.
Financial data (yr. ended 12/31/12): Assets, $3,416,018 (M); gifts received, $519,750; expenditures, $714,773; qualifying distributions, $710,752; giving activities include $624,577 for 2 + grants (high: $612,077), and $82,900 for 1 grant to an individual.
Purpose and activities: The foundation supports general charitable giving and awards disaster relief grants, welfare grants, and scholarships to employees and children of employees of Medline.
Limitations: Applications accepted. Giving primarily in areas of company operations.
Application information: Application form required.
Initial approach: Letter
Copies of proposal: 1
Deadline(s): None
Officers: Andrew J. Mills, Pres.; Ann Ford, V.P.; Alex Liberman, V.P.; Laura Knudson, Secy.-Treas.
Director: James D. Abrams.
EIN: 421563666

3020
Mary L. Medlock Trust ✧ ☆
10 S. Dearborn, IL1-0117
Chicago, IL 60603

Established in IL.
Foundation type: Independent foundation.
Financial data (yr. ended 12/31/13): Assets, $10,307,713 (M); expenditures, $633,787; qualifying distributions, $570,566; giving activities include $550,987 for 8 grants (high: $82,648; low: $27,549).
Fields of interest: Arts; Education; Cancer; Health organizations; Blind/visually impaired; Boys.
Limitations: Applications not accepted. Giving primarily in IL, FL and OK.
Application information: Unsolicited requests for funds not accepted.
Trustee: JPMorgan Chase Bank, N.A.
EIN: 366034925

3021
Edward Arthur Mellinger Educational Foundation, Inc. ✧
1025 E. Broadway
Monmouth, IL 61462-1983 (309) 734-2419
FAX: (309) 734-4435; E-mail: info@mellinger.org; Main URL: http://www.mellinger.org/

Incorporated in 1959 in DE.
Donor: Inez M. Hensleigh†.
Foundation type: Independent foundation.
Financial data (yr. ended 12/31/12): Assets, $19,973,976 (M); gifts received, $1,130; expenditures, $1,602,457; qualifying distributions, $1,414,211; giving activities include $406,160 for 5 grants (high: $400,000; low: $160), $895,660 for 730 grants to individuals, and $7,500 for loans to individuals.
Purpose and activities: The Mellinger foundation is committed to the support of education. Accordingly, the foundation devotes a major portion of its resources to providing scholarship and loan assistance to young men and women from western Illinois who attend colleges and universities throughout the nation. In addition, the foundation offers support to a variety of educational organizations and programs in its local area.
Fields of interest: Higher education; Education; Young adults.
Type of support: Seed money; Scholarships—to individuals; Student loans—to individuals.
Limitations: Applications accepted. Giving limited to students residing in any of the 6 western IL counties of Fulton, Henderson, Knox, McDonough, Mercer and Warren.
Publications: Application guidelines; Program policy statement.
Application information: Application information available on foundation web site. Application form required.
Initial approach: Request application form
Copies of proposal: 1
Deadline(s): Applications are accepted from Feb. 1 to May 1 only
Board meeting date(s): Scholarship committee meets in June
Final notification: Early July
Officers and Trustees:* Tom Johnson,* Pres.; Gary D. Willhardt, Ph.D.*, V.P.; Daniel G. Kistler,* Secy.; Debra L. Grand; Gary Martin.
Number of staff: 1 part-time professional; 4 part-time support.
EIN: 362428421

3022
Richard & Martha Melman Foundation ✧
c/o Lettuce Entertain You Entertainment
5419 N. Sheridan Rd.
Chicago, IL 60640-1964

Established in 1996 in IL.
Donor: Richard Melman.
Foundation type: Independent foundation.
Financial data (yr. ended 12/31/13): Assets, $60,339 (M); gifts received, $875,436; expenditures, $847,248; qualifying distributions, $844,653; giving activities include $844,653 for 13 grants (high: $650,000; low: $500).
Purpose and activities: Giving primarily for hospitals, youth services, and Jewish organizations.
Fields of interest: Hospitals (general); Human services; Children/youth, services; Jewish agencies & synagogues.
Limitations: Applications not accepted. Giving primarily in Chicago, IL. No grants to individuals.
Application information: Unsolicited requests for funds not accepted.
Directors: Martha Melman; Richard Melman; R.J. Melman.
EIN: 364140849

3023
The Meyer Charitable Foundation ✧
100 W. University Ave., Ste. 401
Champaign, IL 61820-8800

Established in 1996 in IL.
Donor: A.C. Meyer, Jr.
Foundation type: Independent foundation.
Financial data (yr. ended 05/31/13): Assets, $24,587,850 (M); gifts received, $1,241,111; expenditures, $1,048,932; qualifying distributions, $967,650; giving activities include $967,650 for grants.
Fields of interest: Higher education; Education; Health organizations; Human services; Children/youth, services; United Ways and Federated Giving Programs.
Limitations: Applications not accepted. Giving primarily in CA, and Champaign, IL. No grants to individuals.
Application information: Contributes only to pre-selected organizations.
Officers: Karen H. Meyer, Pres.; Gregory A. Kimmel, V.P.; A.C. Meyer, Jr., Secy.-Treas.
EIN: 364152268
Selected grants: The following grants are a representative sample of this grantmaker's funding activity:
$142,000 to Atlas Economic Research Foundation, Washington, DC, 2011.
$101,000 to Carle Foundation Hospital, Urbana, IL, 2011.

3024
Glen and Wendy Miller Family Foundation ✧ ☆
2500 Telegraph Rd.
Bannockburn, IL 60015

Established in 2007 in IL.
Donor: Glen Miller.
Foundation type: Independent foundation.
Financial data (yr. ended 12/31/13): Assets, $6,463,712 (M); gifts received, $211,500; expenditures, $494,237; qualifying distributions, $468,825; giving activities include $468,800 for 10 grants (high: $260,000; low: $1,000).
Fields of interest: Medical school/education; Alzheimer's disease; Alzheimer's disease research; Jewish agencies & synagogues.
Limitations: Applications not accepted. Giving primarily in IL. No grants to individuals.
Application information: Contributes only to pre-selected organizations.
Directors: Lauren Izaks; Glen Miller; Wendy Miller.
EIN: 208365083
Selected grants: The following grants are a representative sample of this grantmaker's funding activity:
$2,500 to Clearbrook, Arlington Heights, IL, 2012. For human services.
$1,000 to KESHET, Northbrook, IL, 2012. For Services for Disabled Children.

3025
The Harvey L. Miller Family Foundation ✧
485 E. Half Day Rd., Ste. 350
Buffalo Grove, IL 60089-8806 (847) 883-8414
Contact: Elizabeth Versten, Exec. Dir.

Established in 1991.
Donor: Harvey L. Miller.
Foundation type: Independent foundation.
Financial data (yr. ended 12/31/13): Assets, $61,521 (M); gifts received, $2,100,000; expenditures, $2,586,840; qualifying distributions, $2,584,675; giving activities include $2,331,495 for 59 grants (high: $794,128; low: $2,000).
Purpose and activities: Giving primarily to Jewish organizations providing social services and addressing issues of higher education, anti-Semitism, and Conservative Judaism. The foundation is also interested in children's services, health research, and a local aquarium.
Fields of interest: Education; Health care; Human services; Jewish agencies & synagogues; Children.
Type of support: General/operating support; Capital campaigns; Endowments; Program development; Curriculum development; Scholarship funds.
Limitations: Applications not accepted. Giving primarily in the Chicago, IL, area. No support for local organizations outside of Chicago (unless national in scope).
Publications: Grants list.
Application information: Contributes only to pre-selected organizations.
Board meeting date(s): As necessary
Officers and Directors:* H. L. Miller,* Pres.; R. Miller,* V.P.; E. Versten,* Exec. Dir.; E. Achepohl,* Treas.; L. Khanuk; J. Miller; S. Miller.
Number of staff: None.
EIN: 363771211

3026
Jack Miller Family Foundation ✧
(formerly Jack and Goldie Wolfe Miller Foundation)
485 Half Day Rd., Ste. 200
Buffalo Grove, IL 60089-8806 (847) 883-9700
Contact: Alicia Oberman, Dir.
FAX: (847) 883-9960;
E-mail: jmffinfo@tbgfoundations.org; Main URL: http://www.gojmff.org/

Established in 2004 in IL.
Donors: Audrey and Jack Miller Family Charitable Foundation; Jack Miller Charitable Trust; Jack Miller.
Foundation type: Independent foundation.
Financial data (yr. ended 12/31/13): Assets, $1,332,133 (M); gifts received, $4,531,531; expenditures, $4,030,185; qualifying distributions, $4,029,486; giving activities include $3,572,960 for 122 grants (high: $400,000; low: $250).
Purpose and activities: The foundation generally supports organizations whose missions fall within the following areas: Jewish Community, Health, Education, Arts and Culture, and Community Development.
Fields of interest: Arts; Education; Health care; Community/economic development; Jewish agencies & synagogues.
Limitations: Applications not accepted. Giving primarily in IL, with emphasis on Chicago. No grants to individuals.
Application information: Unsolicited requests for funds not accepted.
Board meeting date(s): Quarterly
Officers and Directors:* Jack Miller,* Chair. and Pres.; Goldie Wolfe Miller,* V.P. and Secy.; Eric F. Achepohl, Treas.; Judith N. Joy; Alicia Schuyler Oberman; Bethany Shiner.
EIN: 201930514

3027
James Millikin Trust A ✧
P.O. Box 77
Decatur, IL 62525-0077
Application address: c/o James Uhl, 295 N. Franklin St., Decatur, IL 62523, tel.: (217) 429-2391

Established in 1910 in IL.
Donor: James Millikin†.
Foundation type: Independent foundation.
Financial data (yr. ended 12/31/13): Assets, $18,018,157 (M); expenditures, $943,024; qualifying distributions, $813,964; giving activities include $760,000 for 14 grants (high: $300,000; low: $1,000).
Purpose and activities: Giving primarily for higher education.
Fields of interest: Higher education; Human services.
Type of support: General/operating support.
Limitations: Giving primarily in Decatur, IL.
Application information: Application information available in trust's brochure. Application form required.
Initial approach: Proposal
Deadline(s): None
Board meeting date(s): 3rd Wed. of each month
Trustees: David Butts; Edward Elliott; James E. Masey; Lucy Murphy; Troy Swinford; David G. Weber.
EIN: 370661226

3028
Mills Charitable Foundation ✧
(formerly James Mills Charitable Foundation)
500 N. Green Bay Rd.
Lake Forest, IL 60045-2146

Established in 2005 in IL.
Donors: James Mills; Charles Mills.
Foundation type: Independent foundation.
Financial data (yr. ended 12/31/13): Assets, $5,969,491 (M); gifts received, $2,898,683; expenditures, $1,755,246; qualifying distributions, $1,754,710; giving activities include $1,754,695 for 59 grants (high: $305,000; low: $500).
Purpose and activities: Giving primarily for education, health organizations, particularly a children's hospital, human services, Jewish organizations, and to an opera company.
Fields of interest: Performing arts, opera; Higher education; Education; Hospitals (specialty); Health organizations; Human services; Children/youth, services; United Ways and Federated Giving Programs; Jewish federated giving programs.
Limitations: Applications not accepted. Giving primarily in IL. No grants to individuals.
Application information: Contributes only to pre-selected organizations.
Trustees: Charles Mills; James Mills.
EIN: 203972275
Selected grants: The following grants are a representative sample of this grantmaker's funding activity:
$120,000 to United Way of Lake County, Gurnee, IL, 2011.
$113,300 to Ann and Robert H. Lurie Children's Hospital of Chicago, Chicago, IL, 2011.
$78,000 to Lake Forest Academy, Lake Forest, IL, 2011.
$55,000 to Glenkirk Foundation, Northbrook, IL, 2011.
$50,000 to Northwestern Lake Forest Hospital, Lake Forest, IL, 2011.
$45,000 to Boys and Girls Clubs of Chicago, Chicago, IL, 2011.
$28,625 to Lake Forest Country Day School, Lake Forest, IL, 2011.
$11,000 to Rush University, Chicago, IL, 2011.
$10,000 to University of Illinois Foundation, Urbana, IL, 2011.
$5,000 to Allendale Association, Lake Villa, IL, 2011.

3029
Mills Family Charitable Foundation ✧
1600 Eastwood Ave.
Highland Park, IL 60035-2110

Established in 2001 in IL.
Donors: James D. Abrams; Andrew J. Mills; Jonathan M. Mills; Lois Mills.
Foundation type: Independent foundation.
Financial data (yr. ended 12/31/13): Assets, $1,659,983 (M); gifts received, $1,008,695; expenditures, $1,797,955; qualifying distributions, $1,785,778; giving activities include $1,785,778 for 79 grants (high: $1,000,000; low: $20).
Fields of interest: Arts; Education; Health care; Human services; Jewish agencies & synagogues.
Limitations: Applications not accepted. Giving primarily in IL. No grants to individuals.
Application information: Contributes only to pre-selected organizations.

Trustee: Jonathan M. Mills.
EIN: 306000363
Selected grants: The following grants are a representative sample of this grantmaker's funding activity:
$5,000 to University of Pennsylvania, School of Medicine, Philadelphia, PA, 2012. For general funding.

3030
Miner Charitable Foundation, Inc. ✧ ☆
1455 N. 1750 E. Rd.
Watseka, IL 60970-6606 (815) 474-4404
Contact: Michael Miner, Pres.

Established in 2003 in IL.
Foundation type: Independent foundation.
Financial data (yr. ended 12/31/13): Assets, $7,437,763 (M); expenditures, $869,807; qualifying distributions, $710,047; giving activities include $633,336 for 62 grants (high: $307,308; low: $2), and $31,750 for 59 grants to individuals (high: $1,000; low: $500).
Fields of interest: Education; Health care; Christian agencies & churches.
Limitations: Applications accepted. Giving primarily in IL.
Application information: Application form required.
Initial approach: Proposal
Deadline(s): None
Officers and Directors:* Michael Miner, Pres.; Charles Hopkins, Secy.; Michael J. Miner,* Treas.; Darrin Fischer.
EIN: 510476676

3031
The Stuart Frankel and Rita Mirman Family Foundation Trust ✧ ☆
3433 N. Seeley Ave.
Chicago, IL 60618-6113

Established in IL.
Donors: Stuart Frankel; Rita Mirman.
Foundation type: Independent foundation.
Financial data (yr. ended 12/31/13): Assets, $257 (M); expenditures, $935,633; qualifying distributions, $935,390; giving activities include $935,390 for 6 grants (high: $923,800; low: $500).
Fields of interest: Health care; Health organizations; Human services.
Limitations: Applications not accepted. Giving primarily in IL.
Application information: Unsolicited requests for funds not accepted.
Trustees: Stuart Frankel; Rita Mirman.
EIN: 266671557

3032
The Jerome Mirza Foundation ✧
(formerly The Mirza Foundation for Advocacy and Justice)
202 N. Center St., Ste. 1A
Bloomington, IL 61701-4105

Established in 1999 in IL.
Donor: Jerome Mirza†.
Foundation type: Independent foundation.
Financial data (yr. ended 12/31/13): Assets, $18,422,893 (M); gifts received, $400,000; expenditures, $1,038,288; qualifying distributions, $888,518; giving activities include $782,781 for 13 grants (high: $200,000; low: $5,000).
Fields of interest: Family services; Foundations (community); Law/international law.
Limitations: Applications not accepted. Giving primarily in IL. No grants to individuals.
Application information: Unsolicited requests for funds not accepted.
Officers and Directors:* Deborah D. Peters,* Pres.; Thomas M. Harris, Jr.,* Secy.; Candace R. Mirza.
EIN: 371392755

3033
The Moline Foundation ✧
817 11th Ave.
Moline, IL 61265-1222 (309) 736-3800
Contact: Joy Boruff, Exec. Dir.
FAX: (309) 736-3721;
E-mail: molinefoundation@qconline.com; Main URL: http://www.molinefoundation.org
Facebook: https://www.facebook.com/pages/Moline-Foundation/104847132915358
Scholarship e-mail: ldaily@qconline.com

Established in 1953 in IL.
Foundation type: Community foundation.
Financial data (yr. ended 09/30/13): Assets, $17,230,778 (M); gifts received, $866,262; expenditures, $1,143,814; giving activities include $777,378 for 18+ grants (high: $325,428), and $35,750 for 20 grants to individuals.
Purpose and activities: The foundation is a community-based, nonprofit organization which provides grants to health, human services, education, community development, the arts, and other charitable organizations which benefit the citizens of Moline and the Quad Cities, IL, region.
Fields of interest: Arts; Education; Health care; Employment; Human services; Community development, neighborhood development; Economic development.
Type of support: Scholarship funds.
Limitations: Applications accepted. Giving limited to the Quad Cities area of eastern IA and western IL.
Publications: Annual report; Grants list; Newsletter.
Application information: Visit foundation web site for grant application guidelines. Application form not required.
Initial approach: Letter
Copies of proposal: 11
Deadline(s): Apr. 15, and Sept. 30
Board meeting date(s): Scheduled as needed
Final notification: Within 2 weeks of interview
Officers and Trustees:* Sandra Kramer,* Chair.; Darcy Callas,* Vice-Chair.; Ann Millman,* Secy.; Stephen Krause,* Treas.; Joy Boruff, Exec. Dir.; Gene Blanc; Dennis Fox; Dr. Kerry Humes; Mary Lagerblade; Dr. David Markward; Larry Meeske.
EIN: 800664860

3034
The Mondelez International Foundation ✧
(formerly The Kraft Foods Foundation)
3 Pkwy. North Blvd.
Deerfield, IL 60015-2504
Main URL: http://www.mondelezinternational.com/well-being/community-partnerships

Established in 2005 in IL.
Donor: Kraft Foods Global, Inc.
Foundation type: Company-sponsored foundation.
Financial data (yr. ended 12/31/12): Assets, $35,740,779 (M); gifts received, $12,000,219; expenditures, $3,309,359; qualifying distributions, $3,309,071; giving activities include $1,552,689 for grants, and $1,756,382 for employee matching gifts.
Purpose and activities: The foundation supports programs designed to empower families and communities to lead healthier lives; offer nutrition education; promote active play; and provide access to fresh foods.
Fields of interest: Public health, obesity; Public health, physical fitness; Health care; Agriculture; Food services; Food banks; Nutrition; Disasters, preparedness/services; American Red Cross; Salvation Army; YM/YWCAs & YM/YWHAs; Human services; Community/economic development; Children; African Americans/Blacks; Hispanics/Latinos.
Type of support: General/operating support; Continuing support; Program development; Employee volunteer services; Sponsorships; Employee matching gifts; Donated products; In-kind gifts.
Limitations: Applications not accepted. Giving on a national and international basis in areas of company operations, with emphasis on CA, CO, Washington, DC, FL, GA, IA, IL, MN, MO, NJ, NY, PA, TX, VA, WI, Argentina, Australia, Brazil, Canada, China, France, Germany, India, Indonesia, Italy, Mexico, Philippines, Spain, Russia, and the United Kingdom.
Application information: Contributes only to pre-selected organizations.
Officers and Directors:* Nicole R. Robinson,* Pres.; Carol J. Ward, V.P. and Secy.; Kim Harris Jones, V.P., Treas., and Cont.; Ernest L. Duplessis, V.P.; Marc S. Firestone,* V.P.; Julia Gin, V.P.; Joseph Klauke, Counsel; James Portnoy, Counsel.
EIN: 203881590
Selected grants: The following grants are a representative sample of this grantmaker's funding activity:
$2,092,617 to Save the Children Federation, Fairfield, CT, 2011.
$1,000,000 to KaBOOM, Washington, DC, 2010.
$1,000,000 to Project Concern International, San Diego, CA, 2011.
$800,000 to Food Trust, Philadelphia, PA, 2010.
$800,000 to YMCA of the U.S.A., Chicago, IL, 2010.
$736,565 to Alicia Foundation, Barcelona, Spain, 2011.
$715,398 to Helen Keller International, New York, NY, 2011.
$568,000 to Parkways Foundation, Chicago, IL, 2011.
$524,891 to Red Cross of France, Paris, France, 2011.
$400,000 to Kids Against Hunger, New Hope, MN, 2010.
$360,000 to Chicago Public Library Foundation, Chicago, IL, 2010.
$275,000 to KaBOOM, Washington, DC, 2010.
$166,046 to Klasse2000, Nuremberg, Germany, 2011.
$105,000 to International Federation of Red Cross and Red Crescent Societies at the United Nations, New York, NY, 2011.
$100,000 to International Federation of Red Cross and Red Crescent Societies at the United Nations, New York, NY, 2010.
$100,000 to Save the Children Mexico, Mexico City, Mexico, 2011.

$25,000 to International Federation of Red Cross and Red Crescent Societies, Geneva, Switzerland, 2010.
$5,000 to Atlanta Community Food Bank, Atlanta, GA, 2011.
$5,000 to Catholic Charities of the Diocese of Saint Cloud, Saint Cloud, MN, 2010.
$5,000 to Mid-Ohio Foodbank, Grove City, OH, 2010.

3035
Kenneth & Harle Montgomery Foundation ✧
c/o Bell & Anderson
135 S. LaSalle St., Ste. 2350
Chicago, IL 60603-4153

Established in 1993 in IL.
Donors: Harle G. Montgomery; Harle G. Montgomery Post Mortem Trust.
Foundation type: Independent foundation.
Financial data (yr. ended 12/31/13): Assets, $9,323,692 (M); gifts received, $4,500; expenditures, $1,062,501; qualifying distributions, $916,000; giving activities include $916,000 for 42 grants (high: $125,000; low: $1,500).
Purpose and activities: Giving primarily for the arts, education, and public policy research and initiatives.
Fields of interest: Museums; Performing arts, theater; Historic preservation/historical societies; Arts; Elementary school/education; Higher education; Law school/education; Education; Children/youth, services; Public policy, research.
Limitations: Applications not accepted. Giving primarily in Chicago, IL and CA. No grants to individuals.
Application information: Contributes only to pre-selected organizations.
Officers and Directors:* Bryant G. Garth,* Pres.; Walter W. Bell,* V.P. and Secy.; Cynthia Kobel,* V.P.; Linda Landreth, Treas.
EIN: 363871012
Selected grants: The following grants are a representative sample of this grantmaker's funding activity:
$100,000 to La Jolla Historical Society, La Jolla, CA, 2011.
$50,000 to San Diego Public Library, San Diego, CA, 2011.
$50,000 to Western Golf Association, Golf, IL, 2011.
$40,000 to Southern California Public Radio, Pasadena, CA, 2011.
$30,000 to Southwestern University School of Law, Los Angeles, CA, 2011.
$25,000 to American Civil Liberties Union Foundation of San Diego and Imperial Counties, San Diego, CA, 2010. For general support.
$25,000 to John Howard Association, Chicago, IL, 2011.
$20,000 to John Howard Association, Chicago, IL, 2011.
$10,000 to Facets Multimedia, Chicago, IL, 2011.
$10,000 to Northeastern Illinois University, Chicago, IL, 2011.
$10,000 to Southwestern University School of Law, Los Angeles, CA, 2011.
$3,000 to John Howard Association, Chicago, IL, 2010. For general support.

3036
The Monticello College Foundation ✧
c/o The Evergreens
5800 Godfrey Rd.
Godfrey, IL 62035-2426 (618) 468-2370
Contact: Linda K. Nevlin, Exec. Dir.
E-mail: lnevlin@lc.edu; Main URL: http://monticellofound.org/
Grants List: http://monticellofound.org/awards.cfm

Incorporated in 1843 in IL as Monticello College; reorganized as a foundation in 1971.
Donors: Lucile Porter Charitable Trust; Patricia Adams Elliott Trust.
Foundation type: Independent foundation.
Financial data (yr. ended 06/30/13): Assets, $14,088,729 (M); gifts received, $12,388; expenditures, $717,122; qualifying distributions, $647,810; giving activities include $647,810 for grants.
Purpose and activities: Support for programs that assist in advancing education for women.
Fields of interest: Higher education; Education; Women; Young adults, female.
Type of support: Endowments; Fellowships; Internship funds; Scholarship funds.
Limitations: Applications accepted. No support for foreign schools or foreign-based American schools, or for social service agencies. No grants to individuals, or for capital, bricks and mortar, operating expenses, or for endowed chairs and exchange students.
Publications: Application guidelines; Annual report (including application guidelines); Financial statement; Grants list.
Application information: Proposals may be stapled. Please do not place proposals in folders or other binders. Application form required.
Initial approach: Letter (2-pages maximum)
Copies of proposal: 18
Deadline(s): Feb. 28 (for spring meeting), and Aug. 31 (for fall meeting)
Board meeting date(s): Oct. and Apr.
Officers and Board Members: Janet Biermann,* Chair.; Alice Norton,* Vice-Chair.; Dianne P. Saul,* Secy.; Karl K. Hoagland, Jr.,* Treas.; Linda K. Nevlin, Exec. Dir.; Mary Dell Pritzlaff, Tr. Emeritus; Sara Anschuetz; Sarah Hoagland; Christopher Kreid; Cathy Maude; Barbara P. Pierce; Enola Proctor; Jenny Levis Sadow; Janet A. Schweppe; Mary Anschuetz Vogt; Julie Jones Williams.
Number of staff: 1 part-time professional.
EIN: 370681538
Selected grants: The following grants are a representative sample of this grantmaker's funding activity:
$25,200 to Newberry Library, Chicago, IL, 2013. For research fellowship.
$20,000 to MacMurray College, Jacksonville, IL, 2013. For scholarships for women.
$18,000 to Illinois State Museum Society, Springfield, IL, 2013. For museum internship.
$13,000 to Alice Lloyd College, Pippa Passes, KY, 2013. For Workshops for Women.
$12,500 to Regional Dance America, Reston, VA, 2013. For choreography scholarships.
$12,000 to Beloit College, Beloit, WI, 2013. For science scholarships.
$12,000 to California Institute of Technology, Pasadena, CA, 2013. For summer internships.
$7,000 to Lawrence University, Appleton, WI, 2013. For Summer Science Research.
$6,900 to Luther College, Decorah, IA, 2013. For Student Summer Research.
$6,700 to Central College, Pella, IA, 2013. For science research project.

3037
Morrison Family Foundation ✧
1125 E. 48th St.
Chicago, IL 60615-1903

Established in 1997.
Donors: William L. Morrison; Kate B. Morrison; Ann Morrison; Ellen Morrison; Sarah Morrison; William B. Morrison.
Foundation type: Independent foundation.
Financial data (yr. ended 12/31/13): Assets, $10,716,363 (M); expenditures, $510,031; qualifying distributions, $482,370; giving activities include $482,370 for 93 grants (high: $31,700; low: $500).
Fields of interest: Performing arts, music; Arts, services; Higher education; Libraries/library science; Medical care, in-patient care; Health organizations, association; Human services; Children/youth, services; Community/economic development.
Limitations: Applications not accepted. No grants to individuals.
Application information: Contributes only to pre-selected organizations.
Officer and Directors:* Kate Morrison,* Secy.-Treas.; Ann Morrison; Ellen Morrison; Sarah Morrison; William B. Morrison.
EIN: 364151134
Selected grants: The following grants are a representative sample of this grantmaker's funding activity:
$10,000 to University of Chicago, Laboratory School, Chicago, IL, 2012. For In each case the donee was a publicly expanded organization exempt funders 501(c)(3) and in each case to purpose use to contribute to the general financial support by the public to the donee.
$5,000 to Reading Partners, Oakland, CA, 2012. For In each case the donee was a publicly expanded organization exempt funders 501(c)(3) and in each case to purpose use to contribute to the general financial support by the public to the donee.
$5,000 to University of Chicago, Laboratory School, Chicago, IL, 2012. For In each case the donee was a publicly expanded organization exempt funders 501(c)(3) and in each case to purpose use to contribute to the general financial support by the public to the donee.
$2,000 to University of Chicago, Laboratory School, Chicago, IL, 2012. For In each case the donee was a publicly panded organization exempt funders 501 (c)(3) and in each case to purpose use to contribute to the general financial support by the public to the donee.
$1,000 to University of Chicago, Laboratory School, Chicago, IL, 2012. For In each case the donee was a publicly expanded organization exempt funders 501(c)(3) and in each case to purpose use to contribute to the general financial support by the public to the donee.

3038
Harold M. and Adeline S. Morrison Family Foundation ✧
50 E. Washington St., Ste. 430
Chicago, IL 60602-2152

Established in 1994 in IL.
Donors: Adeline S. Morrison; Harold M. Morrison; Margot Brinley; Amy Heinrich; Helen Morrison; Lois L. Morrison.
Foundation type: Independent foundation.
Financial data (yr. ended 12/31/13): Assets, $11,190,367 (M); gifts received, $11,582; expenditures, $674,236; qualifying distributions, $591,546; giving activities include $498,111 for 65 grants (high: $116,000; low: $500).
Purpose and activities: Giving primarily for education, inner-city development, music, and medical research.
Fields of interest: Media, radio; Performing arts, music; Historic preservation/historical societies; Higher education, university; Education; Environment, forests; Environment; Hospitals (general); Medical research, institute; Urban/community development; Community/economic development; Foundations (private grantmaking); Foundations (community).
Limitations: Applications not accepted. Giving primarily in IL and VA.
Application information: Contributes only to pre-selected organizations.
Officer: Lois Morrison, Exec. Dir.
Directors: Bruce Boyd; Charles Brinley; Margot Brinley; Justin Daab; Amy Heinrich; Rob Heinrich; Helen Morrison.
Trustees: Adeline S. Morrison; Harold M. Morrison.
EIN: 367090069
Selected grants: The following grants are a representative sample of this grantmaker's funding activity:
$1,000 to Yellowstone Park Foundation, Bozeman, MT, 2012. For All Contributions Were to Further the Donee's Exempt Purpose.

3039
The Elizabeth Morse Charitable Trust ✧

208 S. LaSalle St., Ste. 1660
Chicago, IL 60604-1226 (312) 739-0326
Contact: Melissa Workman, Prog. Asst.
E-mail: OfficeAdm@Morsetrust.org; Main URL: http://www.morsetrust.org

Established in 1992 in IL.
Donor: Richard M. Genius, Jr.
Foundation type: Independent foundation.
Financial data (yr. ended 12/31/13): Assets, $52,393,833 (M); expenditures, $2,530,269; qualifying distributions, $2,197,516; giving activities include $1,818,625 for 59 grants (high: $350,000; low: $3,500).
Purpose and activities: Giving primarily to encourage the principles of individual self-reliance, self sacrifice, thrift, industry, and humility; relieve human suffering: through scientific research and education regarding disease; assisting youth with troubled childhoods and emotional disorders; addressing the concerns of the elderly; and helping humankind during time of natural and human-made disasters; foster individual self-worth and dignity, with a broad emphasis on the classical fine arts; develop physical health and spiritual well-being through vigorous athletic activity; and promote world peace and understanding through the improvement of national and international means of travel by air, rail, and sea.
Fields of interest: Museums; Arts; Education; Health care; Housing/shelter; Human services; Children/youth, services.
Type of support: Management development/capacity building; General/operating support; Continuing support; Program development; Seed money; Technical assistance; Program evaluation; Matching/challenge support.
Limitations: Giving primarily in the Chicago/Cook County, IL. No support for religious or political organizations. No grants to individuals, or for scholarships, capital campaigns, endowments, or for benefits; no loans.
Publications: Application guidelines.
Application information: See the trust's web site for application guidelines and procedures. Letter of Inquiry must be mailed or hand delivered; no faxed or e-mailed Letters of Inquiry are accepted. Full proposals are by invitation only. Application form not required.
Initial approach: Letter of inquiry (no more than 3 pages; double-spaced, and written in Times New Roman 12 point font with standard, one-inch margins)
Copies of proposal: 1
Deadline(s): None
Trustees: James L. Alexander; JPMorgan Chase Bank, N.A.
Number of staff: 1 full-time professional; 1 part-time support.
EIN: 366999365
Selected grants: The following grants are a representative sample of this grantmaker's funding activity:
$220,000 to Fourth Presbyterian Church, Chicago, IL, 2012. For Project Second Century.
$200,000 to Chicago Historical Society, Chicago, IL, 2012. For the OUT in Chicago exhibition.
$50,000 to Lawrence Hall Youth Services, Chicago, IL, 2012. For the Wellness Center of the Residential Treatment Center.
$50,000 to Museum of Contemporary Art, Chicago, IL, 2012. For the Teen Creative Agency.
$25,000 to Grant Park Orchestral Association, Chicago, IL, 2012. For the 50th anniversary of the Grant Park Chorus.

3040
Mark Morton Memorial Fund ✧

c/o Schiff Hardin LLP
233 S. Wacker Dr., Ste. 6600
Chicago, IL 60606-6360 (312) 258-5588

Established in 1951 in IL.
Foundation type: Independent foundation.
Financial data (yr. ended 12/31/12): Assets, $17,075,845 (M); expenditures, $1,339,248; qualifying distributions, $1,214,738; giving activities include $759,000 for 16 grants (high: $175,000; low: $2,000), and $244,488 for 72 grants to individuals (high: $10,656; low: $140).
Purpose and activities: Grants to individuals are limited to those who have been verifiable employees of the Morton Salt Co. before June 30, 1971, to assist with hospital, medical, and surgical expenses, as well as assistance to the aged, blind, or disabled. Organizational support focuses on the environment and human services, with emphasis on women and domestic violence.
Fields of interest: Crime/violence prevention, domestic violence; Human services; Catholic federated giving programs; Catholic agencies & churches; Women.
Type of support: Grants to individuals.
Limitations: Giving primarily in IL, with emphasis on Chicago.
Application information: Grant requests from people who are not employees of Morton Salt Company will not be accepted or acknowledged.
Officers and Directors:* Sarah K. Severson,* Pres.; Molly Gallo,* V.P.; Arthur J. McGivern,* V.P.; Davis H. Roenisch,* V.P.; John Venhuizen,* V.P.; Leonard E. Zak,* V.P.
Number of staff: 2
EIN: 237181380

3041
George & Julie Mosher Family Foundation ✧

P.O. Box 803878
Chicago, IL 60680-3878

Established in 1995 in WI.
Donors: George Mosher; Julie Mosher; George A. Mosher Charitable Lead Annuity Trust; Mosher Charitable Trust; The Northern Trust Co.; Julie A. Mosher Charitable Lead Annuity Trust.
Foundation type: Independent foundation.
Financial data (yr. ended 12/31/13): Assets, $823,373 (M); gifts received, $500,000; expenditures, $551,754; qualifying distributions, $546,000; giving activities include $545,000 for grants.
Fields of interest: Arts; Higher education; Education; Environment; Health organizations, association; Human services; Children/youth, services.
Type of support: General/operating support.
Limitations: Applications not accepted. Giving primarily in Milwaukee, WI. No grants to individuals.
Application information: Contributes only to pre-selected organizations.
Trustees: George Mosher; Julie Mosher.
EIN: 396620969
Selected grants: The following grants are a representative sample of this grantmaker's funding activity:
$5,000 to Milwaukee Public Schools, Milwaukee, WI, 2011. For general support.

3042
Motorola Mobility Foundation ✧

(formerly Motorola Foundation)
600 N. U.S. Hwy. 45
Libertyville, IL 60048-1286
Contact: Eileen Sweeney, V.P.
E-mail: giving@motorola.com; Main URL: http://responsibility.motorola.com/
Empowerment Grants Recipients: http://responsibility.motorola.com/index.php/community/empowermentgrants/egrecipients2012/
YouTube: http://www.youtube.com/MotorolaMobilityFdn

Donor: Motorola Solutions Foundation.
Foundation type: Company-sponsored foundation.
Financial data (yr. ended 12/31/12): Assets, $7,836,627 (M); expenditures, $3,467,410; qualifying distributions, $3,462,310; giving activities include $3,275,086 for 1,230 grants (high: $250,000; low: $50).
Purpose and activities: The foundation supports programs designed to promote education, community, health and wellness, and disaster response.

Fields of interest: Arts; Elementary/secondary education; Higher education; Education; Environmental education; Environment; Health care; Disasters, preparedness/services; Human services; United Ways and Federated Giving Programs; Science, formal/general education; Engineering/technology; Science; Youth.
Type of support: General/operating support; Equipment; Program development; Curriculum development; Employee volunteer services; Employee matching gifts.
Limitations: Applications accepted. Giving primarily on a national and international basis in areas of company operations, with emphasis on CA, Washington, DC, FL, GA, IL, MA, MD, NJ, NY, OR, PA, TX, Afghanistan, Argentina, Brazil, China, England, and Mexico. No support for political or lobbying organizations, political candidates, trade schools, or private foundations. No grants to individuals or for political campaigns, endowments, sports sponsorships, fundraising events, conferences, benefits, sponsorships, dinners, tickets, courtesy advertising, capital campaigns, or media projects; no product or equipment donations (except for disaster relief situations).
Publications: Application guidelines; Grants list.
Application information: Application form required.
Initial approach: Complete online application for Empowerment Grants
Deadline(s): Mar. 23 for Empowerment Grants
Board meeting date(s): Monthly and as required
Final notification: May for Empowerment Grants
Officers: Sanjay Jha, Pres.; Carol Forsyte, V.P. and Secy.; Marc Rothman, V.P. and Treas.; Marshall Brown, V.P.; Jennifer Weyrauch Erickson, V.P.; Daniel M. Moloney, V.P.; Eileen Sweeney, V.P.
EIN: 272451177

3043
Motorola Solutions Foundation ✧
(formerly Motorola Foundation)
1303 East Algonquin Rd.
Schaumburg, IL 60196-4041 (847) 538-7639
Contact: Matt Blakely, Dir.
FAX: (847) 538-1456;
E-mail: foundation@motorolasolutions.com; Main URL: http://responsibility.motorolasolutions.com/index.php/solutions-for-community/com02-foundation/
Facebook: http://www.facebook.com/MSIFoundation
Innovation Generation Grant Recipients: http://responsibility.motorolasolutions.com/images/downloads_page/2013_Innovation_Generation_Grant_Descriptions.pdf
International Grant Recipients: http://responsibility.motorolasolutions.com/images/downloads_page/2013_Motorola_Solutions_Foundation_International_Grants.pdf
Motorola Responsibility Blog: http://communities.motorolasolutions.com/blogs/corporate_responsibility/
Public Safey Grant Recipients: http://responsibility.motorolasolutions.com/images/downloads_page/2013_Motorola_Solutions_Foundation_Public_Safety_Grants.pdf
Twitter: http://twitter.com/msifoundation

Established in 1953 in IL.
Donors: Motorola, Inc.; Motorola Solutions, Inc.
Foundation type: Company-sponsored foundation.
Financial data (yr. ended 12/31/12): Assets, $61,362,029 (M); gifts received, $61,362,029; expenditures, $17,037,678; qualifying distributions, $16,904,625; giving activities include $16,672,432 for 353 grants (high: $2,000,000; low: $143).
Purpose and activities: The Motorola Solutions Foundation focuses its funding on education, especially science, technology, engineering, and math programming; public safety; disaster relief and preparedness; and employee involvement.
Fields of interest: Museums (science/technology); Education, formal/general education; Elementary/secondary education; Education; Disasters, preparedness/services; Disasters, fire prevention/control; Safety/disasters; American Red Cross; Human services; Mathematics; Engineering/technology; Science; Youth; Minorities; Girls.
Type of support: General/operating support; Equipment; Program development; Curriculum development; Employee volunteer services.
Limitations: Applications accepted. Giving primarily on a national and international basis in areas of company operations, with emphasis on CA, Washington, DC, FL, GA, IL, MA, MD, NJ, NY, Argentina, Belgium, Brazil, Canada, China, England, France, Mexico, Poland, and Singapore. No support for political or lobbying organizations, political candidates, religious organizations, or private foundations described under the U.S. IRS Code Section 509(a). No grants to individuals, or for endowments, sports sponsorships, or capital campaigns; no Motorola Solutions product or equipment donations.
Publications: Application guidelines; Grants list; Program policy statement.
Application information: Support is limited to 1 contribution per organization during any given year. Organizations receiving support are asked to submit a program evaluation. Application form required.
Initial approach: Complete online eligibility quiz and application
Deadline(s): None for general grants; Jan. to Apr. 11 for Innovation Generation Grants; Mar. to June for International Grants for International Countries; May to July for Public Safety Grans
Board meeting date(s): Monthly and as required
Final notification: June for Innovation Generation Grants
Director: Matt Blakely, Dir.
Number of staff: 1 full-time professional; 3 part-time professional; 1 full-time support.
EIN: 366109323

3044
MRB Foundation ✧
c/o Walter W. Bell
135 S. Lasalle St. Ste. 2350
Chicago, IL 60603

Established in 1993 in IL.
Donor: John P. Bent Charitable Annuity Trust.
Foundation type: Independent foundation.
Financial data (yr. ended 12/31/13): Assets, $16,316,821 (M); gifts received, $900,668; expenditures, $813,796; qualifying distributions, $616,000; giving activities include $616,000 for 37 grants (high: $151,000; low: $1,000).
Fields of interest: Education; Environment; Health care; Human services.
Limitations: Applications not accepted. Giving primarily in CA, IL, NY, and VA. No grants to individuals.
Application information: Contributes only to pre-selected organizations.
Officers and Directors:* John P. Bent, Jr.,* Pres.; Stephen P. Bent,* V.P.; Walter W. Bell, Secy.-Treas.
EIN: 363920061

3045
W. B. Munson Foundation ✧ ☆
c/o JPMorgan Chase Bank, N.A.
10 S. Dearborn St.
Chicago, IL 60603-2300
Application address: c/o JPMorgan Chase Bank, N.A., 2200 Ross Ave., 7th Fl., Dallas, TX 75201

Trust established in 1943 in TX.
Foundation type: Independent foundation.
Financial data (yr. ended 12/31/13): Assets, $8,361,882 (M); expenditures, $556,530; qualifying distributions, $488,915; giving activities include $454,260 for 11 grants (high: $212,000; low: $2,500), and $16,000 for 15 grants to individuals (high: $2,000; low: $1,000).
Purpose and activities: Giving primarily for health care, the arts and education, including scholarship awards to high school graduates from Denison, Texas.
Fields of interest: Performing arts; Arts; Higher education; Libraries (public); Education; Hospitals (general); Reproductive health, family planning; Recreation, camps; Athletics/sports, school programs; Human services; American Red Cross; Salvation Army; Children/youth, services; Community/economic development.
Type of support: General/operating support; Building/renovation; Equipment; Endowments; Employee matching gifts; Scholarships—to individuals.
Limitations: Giving primarily in Grayson County, TX.
Application information: Application form required.
Initial approach: Letter
Copies of proposal: 7
Deadline(s): None
Board meeting date(s): Quarterly
Trustee: JPMorgan Chase Bank, N.A.
EIN: 756015068
Selected grants: The following grants are a representative sample of this grantmaker's funding activity:
$200,000 to Denison Independent School District, Denison, TX, 2012. For Renovation and rebuilding of the West/Home Grandstands of Munson Stadium, owned, operated and maintained by Denison ISD.
$45,500 to Denison Public Library Endowment Fund, Denison, TX, 2012. For Read to Win.
$20,000 to Greater Texoma Health Clinic, Denison, TX, 2012. For GTHC Electronic Health Records System Upgrade Note Org budget is without in-kind.
$12,000 to Denison Independent School District, Denison, TX, 2012. For AP Incentives Program.
$2,000 to Abilene Christian University, Abilene, TX, 2012. For Paid Abilene Christian University Jessica Eller Spring and Fall 2012.
$2,000 to University of Texas at Dallas, Richardson, TX, 2012. For Paid University of Texas at Dallas Nadia Dunkerton Spring 2012 and Spring 2013 (Student Hadn't Requested Funds from Prior Spring).
$1,000 to Columbia University, New York, NY, 2012. For Paid Columbia University Jaycee Parker Fall 2012.

$1,000 to Texas Christian University, Fort Worth, TX, 2012. For Paid Texas Christian University Brandon Parker Wood Spring 2013.
$1,000 to Texas Christian University, Fort Worth, TX, 2012. For Paid Texas Christian University Deanna Catherine Word Spring 2013.
$1,000 to Texas State University, San Marcos, TX, 2012. For Paid Texas State University April S Braxton Spring 2012.

3046
Natural Health Research Foundation ✧
3200 W. Higgins Rd.
Hoffman Estates, IL 60169-2064

Donors: Mercola Foundation; Mercola.com Natural Health Resource.
Foundation type: Independent foundation.
Financial data (yr. ended 06/30/13): Assets, $474,864 (M); gifts received, $1,225,000; expenditures, $1,267,801; qualifying distributions, $1,266,263; giving activities include $1,266,263 for grants.
Fields of interest: Animal welfare; Health care, information services; Public health, environmental health; Health organizations, association.
Limitations: Applications not accepted. Giving primarily in VA.
Application information: Unsolicited requests for funds not accepted.
Officers: Steven Rye, C.E.O.; Joseph M. Mercola, Pres.; James Larsen, V.P.; Janet Selvig, Secy.; Amalia Legaspi, Treas.
EIN: 223936343
Selected grants: The following grants are a representative sample of this grantmaker's funding activity:
$160,000 to National Vaccine Information Center, Vienna, VA, 2011.
$10,000 to Consumers for Dental Choice, Washington, DC, 2011.

3047
The Negaunee Foundation ✧
555 Skokie Blvd., Ste. 555
Northbrook, IL 60062-2854
Contact: Richard W. Colburn, Pres.

Established in 1987 in IL.
Foundation type: Independent foundation.
Financial data (yr. ended 12/31/11): Assets, $80,374,981 (M); gifts received, $6,280,000; expenditures, $6,066,811; qualifying distributions, $4,484,341; giving activities include $4,464,586 for grants.
Purpose and activities: Giving primarily for museums and the performing arts.
Fields of interest: Performing arts, music; Arts; Higher education; Human services.
Type of support: General/operating support; Continuing support; Endowments.
Limitations: Applications not accepted. Giving primarily in Chicago, IL and vicinity. No support for racist appeals. No grants to individuals; no loans.
Application information: Contributes only to pre-selected organizations. Unsolicited requests for funds not considered.
Board meeting date(s): Dec.
Officers and Directors:* Richard W. Colburn,* Pres.; Robin Tennant Colburn,* V.P. and Treas.; Ewa Jones, Secy.; Elizabeth Corey.
Number of staff: 1 part-time professional.
EIN: 363555046

3048
The Neisser Family Foundation ✧
20 S. Clark St., Ste. 1650
Chicago, IL 60603-1845

Established in 1964 in IL.
Donors: Edward Neisser; Judith E. Neisser.
Foundation type: Independent foundation.
Financial data (yr. ended 12/31/13): Assets, $332,694 (M); gifts received, $384,116; expenditures, $687,485; qualifying distributions, $652,650; giving activities include $652,650 for grants.
Purpose and activities: Giving primarily for the arts and education.
Fields of interest: Museums; Performing arts; Performing arts, music; Arts; Higher education; Health organizations, association.
Limitations: Applications not accepted. Giving primarily in Chicago, IL. No grants to individuals.
Application information: Contributes only to pre-selected organizations.
Officers and Directors:* Judith E. Neisser,* Pres. and Treas.; Katherine M. Neisser,* V.P.; Sherwin A. Zuckerman,* Secy.; Nathan M. Grossman.
EIN: 366054300
Selected grants: The following grants are a representative sample of this grantmaker's funding activity:
$2,500 to Yale University, New Haven, CT, 2012. For Public Charity Support.

3049
James & Aune Nelson Foundation ✧
P.O. Box 5146
Godfrey, IL 62035-5146

Established in IL.
Donor: Aune Nelson‡.
Foundation type: Independent foundation.
Financial data (yr. ended 12/31/13): Assets, $20,826,211 (M); expenditures, $888,107; qualifying distributions, $694,500; giving activities include $680,820 for 14 grants (high: $294,500; low: $2,000).
Purpose and activities: Giving primarily for conservation and the environment.
Fields of interest: Environment, natural resources; Environment, land resources.
Type of support: General/operating support; Land acquisition; Program development.
Limitations: Applications not accepted. Giving primarily in IL and CA. No grants to individuals.
Application information: Contributes only to pre-selected organizations.
Officers: Judy Hoffman, Pres.; Richard Keating, V.P.; Robert McClellan, Treas.
Directors: Laura Asher; Anita Cooper; Karen Eckert; Mark Maggos; Jeff Weber; John Williams.
EIN: 371371840

3050
Jerome Nerenberg 2000 Charitable Trust ✧
c/o The Northern Trust Co.
P.O. Box 803878
Chicago, IL 60680-3878

Foundation type: Independent foundation.
Financial data (yr. ended 12/31/13): Assets, $17,234,377 (M); expenditures, $1,777,671; qualifying distributions, $1,662,347; giving activities include $1,651,744 for 13 grants (high: $255,424; low: $51,084).
Fields of interest: Performing arts, opera; Higher education; Theological school/education; Arthritis; Cancer research; Medical research; Salvation Army; Human services.
Limitations: Applications not accepted. Giving primarily in Chicago, IL and New York, NY; some giving also in Stamford, CT, Newton, MA, Cincinnati, OH, and Austin, TX.
Application information: Contributes only to pre-selected organizations.
Trustee: Northern Trust.
EIN: 266307600
Selected grants: The following grants are a representative sample of this grantmaker's funding activity:
$117,422 to Arthritis Foundation, Newton, MA, 2012. For General - Applies to All.

3051
Nesbitt Foundation ✧
P.O. Box 803878
Chicago, IL 60680-3878

Established in CA.
Donor: Patricia Nesbitt Knight‡.
Foundation type: Independent foundation.
Financial data (yr. ended 12/31/13): Assets, $6,815,725 (M); expenditures, $846,387; qualifying distributions, $786,925; giving activities include $780,000 for 13 grants (high: $175,000; low: $20,000).
Fields of interest: Arts; Food banks; Youth development, services; Human services; Children/youth, services.
Limitations: Applications not accepted. Giving primarily in Los Angeles, CA. No grants to individuals.
Application information: Contributes only to pre-selected organizations.
Trustee: Northern Trust, N.A.
EIN: 956092682

3052
New Prospect Foundation ✧
c/o KKP Group LLC
1603 Orrington Ave., Ste. 1275
Evanston, IL 60201-5026 (847) 328-2288
Contact: Frances Lehman, Pres.

Established in 1969 in IL.
Donors: Elliot Lehman; Frances Lehman; Fel-Pro Inc.; Fel Pro Mecklenburger Foundation.
Foundation type: Independent foundation.
Financial data (yr. ended 12/31/12): Assets, $673,008 (M); expenditures, $1,319,699; qualifying distributions, $1,295,991; giving activities include $1,295,991 for 165 grants (high: $100,000; low: $50).
Purpose and activities: Support for advocacy directed toward the improvement of housing, employment, welfare, and the economic viability of urban and inner-city neighborhoods. Funding priority given to organizations with modest budgets that may not qualify for traditional sources of financial assistance; also supports efforts undertaken in the

public interest through legal services. Additional areas of interest include human and civil rights, and Chicago, IL, public school reform.
Fields of interest: Arts; Health care; Legal services; Employment, single organization support; Human services; Civil liberties, reproductive rights; United Ways and Federated Giving Programs; Women.
Type of support: General/operating support; Continuing support; Program development; Seed money.
Limitations: Giving primarily in the metropolitan Chicago, IL, area. Generally no funding for the arts, higher education, health care, or human services. No grants to individuals, or for capital or endowment funds, basic research, scholarships, or fellowships; no loans.
Publications: Informational brochure.
Application information: Chicago Area Grant Application Form accepted. Application form not required.
Initial approach: Letter
Deadline(s): None
Officers: Frances Lehman, Pres.; Elliot Lehman, V.P.; Philip Fontana, Secy-Treas.
Number of staff: 1 part-time professional.
EIN: 237032384

3053
NIB Foundation ✧
1140 W. Erie St.
Chicago, IL 60622-5848

Established in 2001 in IL.
Donors: Sonia Florian; William C. Florian.
Foundation type: Independent foundation.
Financial data (yr. ended 08/31/13): Assets, $8,049,248 (M); expenditures, $1,068,338; qualifying distributions, $1,039,501; giving activities include $863,500 for 25 grants (high: $250,000; low: $2,000).
Purpose and activities: Giving primarily for the performing arts.
Fields of interest: Performing arts, ballet; Performing arts, opera; Arts; Environment; Human services.
Limitations: Applications not accepted. Giving primarily in Chicago, IL. No grants to individuals.
Application information: Contributes only to pre-selected organizations.
Officers and Directors:* William C. Florian,* Pres.; Sonia Florian,* Secy.
EIN: 364464875

3054
John D. & Alexandria C. Nichols Family Foundation ✧
900 Mt. Pleasant Rd.
Winnetka, IL 60093-3613

Established in 1992 in IL.
Donors: John D. Nichols; Alexandra Trust; Nichols Family Investment, LP; Nichols Family Ltd. Partnership.
Foundation type: Independent foundation.
Financial data (yr. ended 12/31/12): Assets, $52,671,405 (M); gifts received, $19,900; expenditures, $3,661,220; qualifying distributions, $3,339,131; giving activities include $3,289,153 for 111 grants (high: $2,500,000; low: $65).
Purpose and activities: Giving primarily for the arts and for education.
Fields of interest: Arts education; Arts; Human services.
Limitations: Applications not accepted. Giving primarily in Chicago, IL. No grants to individuals.
Application information: Contributes only to pre-selected organizations.
Trustees: Alexandra C. Nichols; John D. Nichols.
EIN: 363858388

3055
Don Nierling Memorial Foundation ✧
c/o Peter Smith, JPMorgan Chase Bank
10 S. Dearborn St., 21st Fl., IL1-0117
Chicago, IL 60603

Established in AZ.
Foundation type: Independent foundation.
Financial data (yr. ended 04/30/13): Assets, $12,143,399 (M); expenditures, $661,910; qualifying distributions, $548,818; giving activities include $512,684 for 18 grants (high: $87,635; low: $8,500).
Fields of interest: Education; Health organizations; Human services; Children/youth, services.
Limitations: Applications not accepted.
Application information: Unsolicited requests for funds not accepted.
Trustees: Peter Smith; A.L. Wartner; JPMorgan Chase Bank, N.A.
EIN: 866083347

3056
John J. Nierling, Jr. Charitable Trust ✧
10 S. Dearborn, IL1-0117
Chicago, IL 60603-2300

Established in 2008 in AZ.
Foundation type: Independent foundation.
Financial data (yr. ended 08/31/13): Assets, $11,603,407 (M); expenditures, $624,982; qualifying distributions, $547,498; giving activities include $522,692 for 11 grants (high: $130,673; low: $26,134).
Fields of interest: Hospitals (general); Human services; Protestant agencies & churches; Children.
Limitations: Applications not accepted. Giving primarily in AZ, MN and ND.
Application information: Contributes only to pre-selected organizations.
Trustee: JPMorgan Chase Bank, N.A.
EIN: 866034609
Selected grants: The following grants are a representative sample of this grantmaker's funding activity:
$125,469 to Shriners Hospitals for Children, Minneapolis, MN, 2011. For program support.

3057
Night Owl Foundation ✧ ☆
485 Half Day Rd., Ste. 350
Buffalo Grove, IL 60089-8806
Contact: Elizabeth Versten, Exec. Dir.

Established in 2006 in IL.
Donors: L. Khanuk; HLM and JM 2006 Charitable Lead Trust.
Foundation type: Independent foundation.
Financial data (yr. ended 12/31/13): Assets, $7,697,118 (M); gifts received, $1,316,326; expenditures, $489,967; qualifying distributions, $482,032; giving activities include $428,000 for 15 grants (high: $75,000; low: $5,000).
Purpose and activities: The foundation aims to support effective organizations that foster innovative research and development in medicine, with an emphasis on pediatrics and cancer, and organizations that provide assistance to Jewish refugees and immigrants from the former Soviet Union to the Chicago, Illinois area and Israel.
Fields of interest: Health care; Human services.
Limitations: Applications not accepted. No grants to individuals.
Application information: Contributes only to pre-selected organizations.
Officers and Directors:* L. Khanuk,* Pres.; T. Khanuk,* V.P. and Secy.; E. Achepohl,* Treas.
EIN: 205905161
Selected grants: The following grants are a representative sample of this grantmaker's funding activity:
$30,000 to Israel Cancer Research Fund, New York, NY, 2012. To support Organization's Program.
$5,000 to Jewish United Fund of Metropolitan Chicago, Chicago, IL, 2012. To support Organization's Program.

3058
Dellora A. & Lester J. Norris Foundation ✧
303 E. Main St.
P.O. Box 4325
St. Charles, IL 60174-2057 (630) 584-2500
Contact: Thomas Wright, Co-Treas.

Established in 1979 in IL.
Donors: Dellora A. Norris†; Lester J. Norris†.
Foundation type: Independent foundation.
Financial data (yr. ended 12/31/13): Assets, $37,608,850 (M); expenditures, $2,144,012; qualifying distributions, $1,762,600; giving activities include $1,762,600 for 77 grants (high: $170,000; low: $1,000).
Purpose and activities: Giving primarily for the arts, education, health organizations, YMCAs, and Protestant agencies and churches.
Fields of interest: Arts; Elementary/secondary education; Higher education; Health care; Health organizations; Autism; YM/YWCAs & YM/YWHAs; Protestant agencies & churches.
Limitations: Giving primarily in AZ, CO, FL, IL, and TX. No grants to individuals.
Application information: Application form not required.
Initial approach: Letter
Deadline(s): None
Board meeting date(s): Quarterly
Officers and Directors:* George N. Gaynor,* Chair.; Pamela Norris,* Pres.; Phillip N. Collins,* V.P.; Edward F. Rodenbach, Secy.; Eugene W. Butler, Co-Treas.; Thomas Wright, Co-Treas.; Robert A. Norris.
EIN: 363054939
Selected grants: The following grants are a representative sample of this grantmaker's funding activity:
$3,000 to Valley Presbyterian Church, Paradise Valley, AZ, 2012. For Grants to the Dellora A. Norris Cultural Arts Center - a controlled supporting organization; expenditure responsibility is being exercised and grant was not treated as a qualifying distribution pursuant to IRC sections 4945(d)(4)(A)(ii) and (B) and 4942(g.

3059
The Northern Trust Company Charitable Trust ✧
50 S. LaSalle St., L7
Chicago, IL 60675-0001 (312) 630-1762
Contact: Chasity Davis, Community Affairs
E-mail: northern_trust_charitable_trust@ntrs.com; Additional address: P.O. Box 803878, Chicago, IL 60680; Main URL: http://www.northerntrust.com/about-us/corporate-social-responsibility/community-affairs/charitable-trust

Trust established in 1966 in IL.
Donor: The Northern Trust Co.
Foundation type: Company-sponsored foundation.
Financial data (yr. ended 12/31/12): Assets, $3,645,981 (M); gifts received, $4,651,913; expenditures, $4,308,574; qualifying distributions, $4,308,414; giving activities include $4,308,399 for 192 grants.
Purpose and activities: The trust supports organizations involved with arts and culture, education, and social welfare. Special emphasis is directed toward programs designed to advance the well being of disadvantaged women and children and people with disabilities.
Fields of interest: Arts education; Arts; Teacher school/education; Education; Environment; Health care; Employment, training; Food services; Housing/shelter; Family services; Human services; Community/economic development; Children; Disabilities, people with; Women; Economically disadvantaged.
Type of support: General/operating support; Continuing support; Annual campaigns; Capital campaigns; Building/renovation; Endowments; Program development; Employee volunteer services; Employee matching gifts.
Limitations: Applications accepted. Giving limited to Cook County, IL, primarily in the Chicago neighborhoods of Chatham, Englewood, Humboldt Park, Logan Square, Loop, Washington Park, and West Town. No support for United Way-supported organizations (over 5 percent of budget), national health organizations or the local affiliates of national health organizations or research or disease advocacy organizations, political, labor, or fraternal organizations or civic clubs, religious organizations not of direct benefit to the entire community, individual pre-K-12 schools, or organizations established less than 2 years ago. No grants to individuals, or for scholarships or fellowships, fundraising events, advertising or marketing, sports, athletic events, or athletic programs, travel-related events, book, film, video, or television development or production, memorial campaigns, or multi-year general operating support.
Publications: Application guidelines; Annual report (including application guidelines); Corporate giving report (including application guidelines).
Application information: A full application may be requested at a later date. Support is limited to 3 consecutive years, with 1 year off before an organization is eligible to apply again. Multi-year funding is not automatic. A site visit may be requested. Application form required.
Initial approach: Complete online questionnaire and letter of inquiry form for new applicants; complete online application form for previous grantees
Deadline(s): Nov. 14 and June 19 for Social Welfare; Mar. 6 for Arts and Culture and Education for new applicants; Jan. 2 and Aug. 7 for Social Welfare for previous grantees; May 7 for Arts and Culture and Education for previous grantees
Board meeting date(s): Late Mar., July, and Oct.
Final notification: Following review
Officers and Directors:* Timothy P. Moen,* Chair.; Deborah Liverett, Secy.; Gregg D. Behrens; William A. Osborn; Alison Winter.
Trustee: The Northern Trust Co.
Number of staff: 2 full-time professional; 1 part-time professional; 1 full-time support; 1 part-time support.
EIN: 366147253

3060
Bill Nygren Foundation ✧ ☆
(formerly William & Sara Nygren Charitable Foundation)
2 N. LaSalle St., Ste. 500
Chicago, IL 60602-3703

Established in 1994 in IL.
Donors: William C. Nygren; Sara Nygren.
Foundation type: Independent foundation.
Financial data (yr. ended 12/31/13): Assets, $11,482,188 (M); expenditures, $631,712; qualifying distributions, $599,680; giving activities include $599,680 for 26 grants (high: $243,000; low: $500).
Purpose and activities: Giving primarily for education, children, youth and social services, and federated giving programs.
Fields of interest: Higher education; Education; Human services; Children/youth, services; United Ways and Federated Giving Programs.
Limitations: Applications not accepted. Giving primarily in Chicago, IL; some funding also in WI. No grants to individuals.
Application information: Unsolicited requests for funds not accepted.
Officer and Directors:* William C. Nygren,* Pres. and Treas.; Henry Berghoef; Robert Levy.
EIN: 363987600

3061
Oak Park/River Forest Community Foundation ✧
1049 Lake St., No. 204
Oak Park, IL 60301-6708 (708) 848-1560
Contact: Kristin C. Vogen, Pres.
FAX: (708) 848-1531; E-mail: kcvogen@oprfcf.org; Main URL: http://www.oprfcf.org
Facebook: https://www.facebook.com/OPRFCF

Established in 1958 in IL.
Foundation type: Community foundation.
Financial data (yr. ended 12/31/13): Assets, $27,176,331 (M); gifts received, $2,976,407; expenditures, $2,454,206; giving activities include $939,029 for 30+ grants (high: $87,707), and $781,802 for 336 grants to individuals.
Purpose and activities: The foundation serves the community by: 1) stimulating and facilitating individual philanthropy; 2) being accountable and prudent managers of donor funds; 3) making responsive and informed grants; and 4) convening resources to address community priorities and interests.
Fields of interest: Arts; Education; Environment; Health care; Crime/violence prevention; Housing/shelter; Recreation; Family services; Human services; Community development, neighborhood development; Community/economic development; Children/youth; Aging; Disabilities, people with; Minorities.
Type of support: Advocacy; General/operating support; Income development; Management development/capacity building; Program development; Seed money; Consulting services; Scholarships—to individuals; Matching/challenge support.
Limitations: Applications accepted. Giving limited to Oak Park and River Forest, IL, for discretionary grantmaking. No grants to individuals (except for specific funds designated for scholarships), or for endowments, capital campaigns or for debt retirement.
Publications: Application guidelines; Annual report (including application guidelines); Grants list; Informational brochure; Newsletter; Occasional report.
Application information: Visit foundation web site for application form and guidelines. Applications are sent to an extensive mailing list of Oak Park and River Forest organizations; to be placed on the list, organizations can call the foundation or e-mail staff. E-mailed or faxed applications are not accepted. Application form required.
Initial approach: Telephone or e-mail
Copies of proposal: 3
Deadline(s): July 18 for Community grants; Varies for others
Board meeting date(s): 2nd Tues. in Jan., Mar., May, Sept., and Nov.
Officers and Directors:* Sheila Price,* Pres.; Clare Golla,* V.P.; Donna Myers,* Secy.; Matthew Grote,* Treas.; Sophia Lloyd, Exec. Dir.; Case Hoogendoorn, Counsel; Cuyler Brown; Susan Conti; Michele Donley; Sonny Ginsberg; Janet Hanley; John Hedges; John Houseal; Phillip Jimenez; Annese Piazza; Brian Plain; Pravin Rao; Mary Jo Schuler; Michelle Vanderlaan; Barbara Watkins; Eric Weinheimer; Stacey Williams.
Number of staff: 3 full-time professional; 1 part-time professional; 1 full-time support.
EIN: 364150724

3062
The Offield Family Foundation ✧
400 N. Michigan Ave., Rm. 407
Chicago, IL 60611-4159 (312) 444-3854

Incorporated in 1940 in IL.
Donors: Dorothy Wrigley Offield; Offield Charitable Lead Unitrust; James Offield Charitable Lead Unitrust; Paxon Offield Charitable Lead Unitrust.
Foundation type: Independent foundation.
Financial data (yr. ended 06/30/12): Assets, $82,199,450 (M); gifts received, $1,547,808; expenditures, $6,384,785; qualifying distributions, $5,950,046; giving activities include $5,727,500 for 72 grants (high: $1,350,000; low: $2,500).
Purpose and activities: Emphasis on hospitals, education, and cultural programs.
Fields of interest: Arts; Education; Hospitals (general).
Limitations: Applications not accepted. Giving primarily in CA and MI. No grants to individuals.
Application information: Contributes only to pre-selected organizations.
Officers and Directors:* Paxson H. Offield,* Pres.; James S. Offield,* V.P. and Treas.; Gail Hodge,* Secy.; Chase Offield; Meighan Offield.
EIN: 366066240

Selected grants: The following grants are a representative sample of this grantmaker's funding activity:
$1,350,000 to Northern Michigan Hospital Foundation, Petoskey, MI, 2012. For general support.
$500,000 to Planned Parenthood of West and Northern Michigan, Grand Rapids, MI, 2012. For general support.
$450,000 to International Game Fish Association, Dania, FL, 2012. For general support.
$300,000 to Peregrine Fund, Boise, ID, 2012. For general support.
$250,000 to Oregon Health and Science University, Portland, OR, 2012. For general support.
$250,000 to Santa Catalina Island Conservancy, Avalon, CA, 2012. For general support.
$100,000 to Little Traverse Conservancy, Harbor Springs, MI, 2012. For general support.
$85,000 to Billfish Foundation, Fort Lauderdale, FL, 2012. For general support.
$50,000 to J. F. Shea Therapeutic Riding Center, San Juan Capistrano, CA, 2012. For general support.
$30,000 to Instituto Health Sciences Career Academy, Chicago, IL, 2012. For general support.

3063
Omron Foundation, Inc. ✧

c/o Omron Managment Center of America
55 Commerce Dr.
Schaumburg, IL 60173-5302 (224) 520-7650
Contact: James P. Eberhart, Treas.
FAX: (224) 520-7680; E-mail: OFI@omron.com; Main URL: http://www.omronfoundation.omron.com/

Established in 1989 in IL.
Donors: Omron Electronics Inc.; Omron Electronics LLC; Omron Healthcare, Inc.; Omron Electronics Components, LLC; Omron Automotive Electronics, Inc.
Foundation type: Company-sponsored foundation.
Financial data (yr. ended 03/31/14): Assets, $644,899 (M); gifts received, $232,878; expenditures, $633,353; qualifying distributions, $633,353; giving activities include $633,338 for 212 grants (high: $75,000; low: $12).
Purpose and activities: The foundation supports food banks and organizations involved with arts and culture, education, health, breast cancer, heart disease, housing development, disaster relief, human services, the disabled, and the elderly.
Fields of interest: Arts, cultural/ethnic awareness; Arts; Secondary school/education; Higher education; Engineering school/education; Education; Health care; Breast cancer; Heart & circulatory diseases; Food banks; Housing/shelter, development; Disasters, preparedness/services; American Red Cross; Aging, centers/services; Developmentally disabled, centers & services; Human services; United Ways and Federated Giving Programs; Disabilities, people with.
Type of support: General/operating support; Continuing support; Building/renovation; Endowments; Program development; Scholarship funds; Employee matching gifts; Employee-related scholarships.
Limitations: Applications accepted. Giving primarily in CA, IL, NY, and TX. No support for political, fraternal, veterans', athletic, or lobbying organizations, or religious organizations not of direct benefit to the entire community. No grants to individuals (except for employee-related scholarships), or for travel funds, tours, expeditions, or trips by individuals or groups, dues or gifts to national or local alumni groups, clubs or fraternities, institutional memberships, subscription fees for publications, donations for benefit events, or raffle tickets or fundraising efforts that involve value returned to the donor.
Publications: Application guidelines.
Application information: Applicants must be invited by the Foundation Board to send a full proposal. Preference will be given to applicants that adhere to the BBB Wise Give Alliance's "Standards for Charity Accountability". Funding approved for one year only. Submission should include a cover letter of no more than one page in length and a narrative no more than three pages. Application form required.
Initial approach: E-Mail applications and full proposals
Deadline(s): None
Board meeting date(s): Quarterly
Officers and Directors: Nigel Blakeway,* Pres. and V.P.; K. Blake Thatcher,* Secy.; James P. Eberhart, Treas.; Yutaka Miyanaga.
EIN: 363644055
Selected grants: The following grants are a representative sample of this grantmaker's funding activity:
$75,700 to Little City Foundation, Palatine, IL, 2011.
$57,000 to Illinois State University, Normal, IL, 2011.
$50,000 to Northern Illinois University, DeKalb, IL, 2011.
$41,980 to American Red Cross, Des Moines, IA, 2011.
$36,899 to Northern Illinois Food Bank, Geneva, IL, 2011.
$16,000 to North Central College, Naperville, IL, 2011.
$15,000 to Safe Alternatives to Violent Environments, Fremont, CA, 2011.
$12,400 to Narconon International, Los Angeles, CA, 2011.
$10,810 to Houston Food Bank, Houston, TX, 2011.
$10,000 to Gleaners Community Food Bank, Detroit, MI, 2011.

3064
Edmond and Alice Opler Foundation ✧

(formerly Edmond Opler Foundation)
P.O. Box 547
Oak Lawn, IL 60454-0547

Established in 1981in IL.
Donor: Edmond Opler.
Foundation type: Independent foundation.
Financial data (yr. ended 12/31/13): Assets, $19,952,472 (M); expenditures, $1,175,555; qualifying distributions, $1,007,351; giving activities include $842,000 for 66 grants (high: $50,000; low: $2,500).
Purpose and activities: Giving primarily for health organizations, hospitals, and children and social services.
Fields of interest: Hospitals (general); Hospitals (specialty); Health organizations, association; Human services; Children/youth, services; Blind/visually impaired.
Limitations: Applications not accepted. Giving primarily in Chicago, IL.
Application information: Contributes only to pre-selected organizations.
Officers: Rita Egan, Pres.; Rosemary Morris, Secy.; Lyle Olson, Treas.
Director: Barbara Kupferberg.
EIN: 363137745

3065
Leo Oppenheimer and Flora Oppenheimer Haas Trust ✧

10 S. Dearborn, IL1-0117
Chicago, IL 60603

Trust established in 1950 in NY.
Donor: Flora Oppenheimer Haas†.
Foundation type: Independent foundation.
Financial data (yr. ended 12/31/13): Assets, $18,843,588 (M); expenditures, $960,789; qualifying distributions, $807,459; giving activities include $763,200 for 16 grants (high: $110,000; low: $1,200).
Purpose and activities: Giving to programs and agencies that provide care, aid and comfort to needy Jewish children; particular interest in helping Jewish children recovering from illness; funding also for other Jewish organizations.
Fields of interest: Health organizations, association; Cancer; Children/youth, services; Jewish federated giving programs; Jewish agencies & synagogues.
Type of support: General/operating support.
Limitations: Applications not accepted. Giving primarily in the New York, NY, metropolitan area. No support for hospitals. No grants to individuals, or for matching gifts; no loans.
Publications: Grants list.
Application information: Unsolicited requests for funds not accepted.
Board meeting date(s): June and Dec.
Trustee: JPMorgan Chase Bank, N.A.
EIN: 136013101

3066
The Oppenheimer Family Foundation ✧

c/o E.H. Oppenheimer
1501 N. State Pkwy., Ste. 11B
Chicago, IL 60610-5737
Application address: c/o E.H. Oppenheimer, P.O. Box 14771, Chicago, IL 60614; fax: (312) 943-9472

Incorporated in 1953 in IL.
Donors: Seymour Oppenheimer†; Edward H. Oppenheimer; James K. Oppenheimer; Harry D. Oppenheimer.
Foundation type: Independent foundation.
Financial data (yr. ended 12/31/13): Assets, $4,590,326 (M); gifts received, $200; expenditures, $500,936; qualifying distributions, $437,625; giving activities include $437,625 for 202 grants (high: $26,000; low: $300).
Purpose and activities: Giving primarily for the arts, education, the environment, and social services.
Fields of interest: Arts education; Media/communications; Arts; Education; Environment; Human services; Jewish federated giving programs.
Limitations: Applications accepted. Giving primarily in Chicago, IL.
Application information: Guidelines for the Teacher Incentive Grant may be found at: http://www.offtig.org/contactus.php. Application form required.
Initial approach: Letter

Copies of proposal: 1
Deadline(s): None
Officers: Edward H. Oppenheimer, Pres.; Harry J. Oppenheimer, V.P.; James Oppenheimer, V.P.; William J. Garmisa, Secy.
EIN: 366054015
Selected grants: The following grants are a representative sample of this grantmaker's funding activity:
$100,000 to Lake Forest College, Lake Forest, IL, 2011.

3067
Oprah Winfrey Charitable Foundation ✧
110 N. Carpenter St.
Chicago, IL 60607-2104

Established in 2010 in IL.
Donor: Oprah Winfrey.
Foundation type: Independent foundation.
Financial data (yr. ended 12/31/12): Assets, $239,950,811 (M); gifts received, $18,000,000; expenditures, $20,332,744; qualifying distributions, $19,054,139; giving activities include $18,778,000 for 5 grants (high: $17,717,307; low: $64,304).
Fields of interest: Education; Youth development.
Limitations: Applications not accepted. Giving primarily in IL.
Application information: Unsolicited request for funds not accepted.
Trustees: Robert Greene; Gayle King; Oprah G. Winfrey.
EIN: 266908382

3068
The Owens Foundation ✧
(formerly Thomas M. & Mary M. Owens Foundation)
7804 College Dr., Ste. 3SW
Palos Heights, IL 60463-1473 (708) 361-8845
Contact: Mary M. Owens, Pres.

Established in 1985 in IL.
Donor: Thomas M. Owens.
Foundation type: Independent foundation.
Financial data (yr. ended 12/31/12): Assets, $20,754,396 (M); expenditures, $1,601,777; qualifying distributions, $1,176,233; giving activities include $1,069,775 for 2+ grants.
Purpose and activities: Giving primarily in three areas: 1) programs that work with the homeless, the poor, and other disadvantaged populations, particularly those programs that deal with self-sufficiency through self-help, and programs that provide basic support, food, shelter and clothing, along with job training and employment, are given high priority; 2) homeless prevention - emergency funds administered independently by each agency for rents, mortgage payments, utilities, and food, etc.; 3) private education, primarily secondary education for use for scholarships for poor and deserving students.
Fields of interest: Secondary school/education; Housing/shelter, development; Human services; Economically disadvantaged; Homeless.
Type of support: General/operating support; Emergency funds; Scholarship funds.
Limitations: Giving primarily in Chicago, IL. No grants to individuals directly, or for capital campaigns, building funds, or raffles.
Publications: Application guidelines; Program policy statement.
Application information: Application form required.
Initial approach: Letter or telephone requesting application guidelines
Copies of proposal: 1
Deadline(s): None
Board meeting date(s): Quarterly
Officers and Directors:* Mary M. Owens,* Pres. and Secy.; Thomas M. Owens,* V.P. and Treas.; Julie Owens Mineman; Katie M. Mulcahy; Michael Owens; Thomas M. Owens, Jr.; Sharon Owens.
Number of staff: 1 part-time professional; 1 part-time support.
EIN: 363429160

3069
The John C. & Carolyn Noonan Parmer Private Foundation ✧
9 Woodley Rd.
Winnetka, IL 60093-3735

Established in 1997 in IL.
Donor: Carolyn N. Parmer.
Foundation type: Independent foundation.
Financial data (yr. ended 12/31/13): Assets, $29,411,029 (M); expenditures, $1,386,943; qualifying distributions, $1,259,495; giving activities include $1,247,500 for 44 grants (high: $50,000; low: $500).
Purpose and activities: Giving primarily for education, health and social services, and to Roman Catholic agencies and churches.
Fields of interest: Higher education; Education; Health care; Human services; Catholic agencies & churches.
Limitations: Applications not accepted. Giving primarily in IL. No grants to individuals.
Application information: Contributes only to pre-selected organizations.
Trustees: Carolyn L. Parmer LaRochelle; Carolyn Noonan Parmer; James W. Parmer; John F. Parmer; Raymond C. Parmer; Phyllis M. Parmer Plummer.
EIN: 364153563

3070
Martha Sue Parr Trust ✧
c/o JPMorgan Chase Bank, N.A.
10 S. Dearborn St., IL1-0117
Chicago, IL 60603-2300
Application address: c/o JPMorgan Chase Bank, N.A.; Attn.: Larry Bothe, 420 Throckmorton St., Fort Worth, TX 76102-3700, tel.: (817) 884-4022

Established in TX.
Donor: Martha Sue Parr†.
Foundation type: Independent foundation.
Financial data (yr. ended 03/31/13): Assets, $26,713,084 (M); expenditures, $1,298,224; qualifying distributions, $1,134,238; giving activities include $1,085,000 for 9 grants (high: $200,000; low: $5,000).
Purpose and activities: Giving primarily for children and youth services.
Fields of interest: Health care, association; Hospitals (general); Hospitals (specialty); Children, services; Residential/custodial care.
Limitations: Applications accepted. Giving primarily in Fort Worth, TX.
Application information:
Initial approach: Letter
Deadline(s): None
Trustee: JPMorgan Chase Bank, N.A.
EIN: 416519559
Selected grants: The following grants are a representative sample of this grantmaker's funding activity:
$250,000 to Cook Childrens Medical Center, Fort Worth, TX, 2011. For program support.
$200,000 to All Saints Health Foundation, Fort Worth, TX, 2011. For program support.
$200,000 to Cumberland Presbyterian Childrens Home, Denton, TX, 2011. For program support.
$100,000 to Ronald McDonald House of Fort Worth, Fort Worth, TX, 2011. For program support.
$75,000 to Fort Worth Junior Golf Foundation, Fort Worth, TX, 2011. For program support.
$50,000 to Tarrant County Academy of Medicine, Fort Worth, TX, 2011. For program support.
$35,000 to Cornerstone Assistance Network, Fort Worth, TX, 2011. For program support.
$25,000 to United Way of Tarrant County, Fort Worth, TX, 2011. For program support.
$20,000 to Fortress Youth Development Center, Fort Worth, TX, 2011. For program support.
$12,500 to Texas Girls Choir, Fort Worth, TX, 2011. For program support.

3071
Pasquinelli Family Foundation ✧
535 Plainfield Rd., Ste. B.
Willowbrook, IL 60527-7608 (630) 455-5400
Contact: Bruno A. Pasquinelli, Dir.

Established in 1997 in IL.
Donors: Anthony R. Pasquinelli; Bruno A. Pasquinelli; Portrait Homes-North Carolina, LLC; Pasquinelli Homebuilding, LP.
Foundation type: Independent foundation.
Financial data (yr. ended 12/31/11): Assets, $3,912,564 (M); expenditures, $525,256; qualifying distributions, $494,095; giving activities include $476,205 for grants.
Purpose and activities: Giving for the arts, education, health organizations, and human services.
Fields of interest: Arts; Higher education; Education; Health organizations, association; Human services; Community/economic development.
Type of support: Employee matching gifts.
Limitations: Applications accepted. Giving primarily in IL.
Application information: Application form not required.
Initial approach: Letter
Deadline(s): May 1 and Nov. 1
Directors: Anthony R. Pasquinelli; Bruno A. Pasquinelli.
EIN: 364157643

3072
The Pattee Foundation ✧
51 Public Sq.
P.O. Box 647
Monmouth, IL 61462-1755 (309) 734-5105
Contact: Marcum A. Spears, V.P.

Established in IL.
Foundation type: Independent foundation.

Financial data (yr. ended 12/31/13): Assets, $32,400,035 (M); expenditures, $2,176,532; qualifying distributions, $1,536,305; giving activities include $1,450,000 for 8 grants (high: $450,000; low: $15,000).
Purpose and activities: Support primarily for education and the YMCA.
Fields of interest: Higher education; Recreation; YM/YWCAs & YM/YWHAs.
Type of support: General/operating support.
Limitations: Applications accepted. Giving primarily in Monmouth, IL. No grants to individuals.
Application information: Application form required.
Initial approach: Proposal
Deadline(s): None
Officers: Raymond E. Defenbaugh, Pres.; Marcum A. Spears, V.P.; Larry Lee Spears, Secy.-Treas.
EIN: 371138998
Selected grants: The following grants are a representative sample of this grantmaker's funding activity:
$125,000 to YMCA of Warren County, Monmouth, IL, 2011.

3073
Frank E. Payne and Seba B. Payne Foundation ✧
c/o Bank of America, N.A.
135 S. LaSalle St., IL4-135-14-19
Chicago, IL 60603-4177 (312) 828-1785
Contact: M. Catherine Ryan, Sr. V.P., Bank of America, N.A.

Trust established in 1962 in IL.
Donor: Seba B. Payne†.
Foundation type: Independent foundation.
Financial data (yr. ended 06/30/14): Assets, $144,658,893 (M); expenditures, $7,332,177; qualifying distributions, $6,859,828; giving activities include $6,543,816 for 54 grants (high: $3,000,000; low: $5,000).
Purpose and activities: Support for education, hospitals, and cultural and religious programs; support also for the prevention of cruelty to children or animals.
Fields of interest: Arts; Education; Animal welfare; Hospitals (general); AIDS; AIDS research; Housing/shelter, development; Children/youth, services.
Type of support: General/operating support; Building/renovation; Equipment.
Limitations: Applications accepted. Giving primarily in Bethlehem, PA. No grants to individuals, or for fellowships; generally no support for endowments; no loans.
Publications: Application guidelines.
Application information: Application form required.
Initial approach: Proposal
Copies of proposal: 1
Deadline(s): Mar. 15 and Oct. 15
Board meeting date(s): May and Nov., and as required
Final notification: 4 months
Trustees: Susan Hurd Cummings; Priscilla Payne Hurd; Bank of America, N.A.
EIN: 237435471
Selected grants: The following grants are a representative sample of this grantmaker's funding activity:
$1,775,000 to Moravian Village of Bethlehem, Bethlehem, PA, 2012. For memory support and assisted living center.
$1,000,000 to DeSales University, Center Valley, PA, 2013. For Gambet Center for Business and Healthcare Education.
$1,000,000 to National Disaster Search Dog Foundation, Ojai, CA, 2012. For National Training Center.
$1,000,000 to Visiting Nurse Association of Eastern Pennsylvania - Home, Health and Hospice, Bethlehem, PA, 2013. For in-patient hospice care and patient rooms at Black River Road.
$604,000 to Project Hospitality, Staten Island, NY, 2013. For Hurricane Sandy relief efforts.
$500,000 to National Museum of Industrial History, Bethlehem, PA, 2012. For capital campaign.
$400,000 to Nature Conservancy, Arlington, VA, 2013. For matching grant for Urban Conservation Work Challenge Fund.
$250,000 to Visiting Nurse Association of Eastern Pennsylvania - Home, Health and Hospice, Bethlehem, PA, 2013. For A Legacy of Caring Hospice Endowment Fund.
$200,000 to Upper Bucks Regional Emergency Medical Services, Revere, PA, 2013. For general operating support.
$150,000 to Bethlehem Area Public Library, Bethlehem, PA, 2012. For renovations to South Side Branch.
$120,000 to Associated Colleges of Illinois, Chicago, IL, 2012. For general operating support.
$120,000 to Associated Colleges of Illinois, Chicago, IL, 2013. For general operating support.
$100,000 to American Red Cross of the Greater Lehigh Valley, Bethlehem, PA, 2012. For general support.
$100,000 to Lehigh Valley PBS, Bethlehem, PA, 2012. For broadcast of childrens programs.
$75,000 to Turning Point of the Lehigh Valley, Allentown, PA, 2013. For general operating support.
$50,000 to United Negro College Fund, Chicago, IL, 2012. For annual campaign.
$50,000 to United Negro College Fund, Chicago, IL, 2013. For Annual Campaign.
$30,000 to Civic Theater of Allentown, Allentown, PA, 2012. For Digital Cinema Campaign.
$29,800 to Community Health and Education Outreach, Collingdale, PA, 2013. For Hope Program.
$25,000 to Episcopal Ministries of the Diocese of Bethlehem, Bethlehem, PA, 2012. For general operating support.

3074
Pepper Family Foundation ✧
c/o Richard S. Pepper
643 N. Orleans St.
Chicago, IL 60654-3608

Established in 1987 in IL.
Donors: Richard S. Pepper; Roxelyn M. Pepper; The Pepper Cos., Inc.; Richard S. Pepper Trust.
Foundation type: Independent foundation.
Financial data (yr. ended 12/31/13): Assets, $6,452,769 (M); gifts received, $2,279,842; expenditures, $5,824,758; qualifying distributions, $5,779,506; giving activities include $5,779,506 for grants.
Fields of interest: Arts; Elementary/secondary education; Higher education; Hospitals (general); Foundations (public); Christian agencies & churches.
Type of support: General/operating support; Scholarship funds.
Limitations: Applications not accepted. Giving primarily in IL, with emphasis on Chicago and Barrington. No grants to individuals.
Application information: Contributes only to pre-selected organizations.
Officers and Directors:* Richard S. Pepper,* Pres. and Treas.; Roxelyn M. Pepper,* V.P.; Thomas M. O'Leary, Exec. V.P. and Secy.; J. David Pepper; Lisa Pepper.
EIN: 363540747
Selected grants: The following grants are a representative sample of this grantmaker's funding activity:
$35,000 to Northwestern University, Athletic Department, Evanston, IL, 2012. For operating funds.

3075
Nancy Allison Perkins Foundation ✧
1424 Dartmouth Ave.
Flossmoor, IL 60422-1915

Established in IL.
Donors: Brett Allison; Candi Allison; Jody Allison; Jerry Berard; Suzanne Allison; Joan Berard; Robert Chisser; Leigh Lehmann; Bob Morgridge; Rhonda Morgridge; Lindsay Vail; Wade Allison; Sandee Johnson; Jean Chisser; Scott Kazmierczak; Dean Palmateer; Lindsay Vail; Joan Jerry Berard; Robert Jean Chisser; Brett Candi Allison; Jody Allison; Suzanne Allison; Sandee Johnson; Wade Allison Trust; Leigh Lehmann; Leigh Allison; Jerome Berard; Burt Engelberg.
Foundation type: Independent foundation.
Financial data (yr. ended 12/31/13): Assets, $9,485,458 (M); gifts received, $212,500; expenditures, $824,687; qualifying distributions, $821,842; giving activities include $821,842 for 22 grants (high: $500,000; low: $150).
Purpose and activities: Giving primarily for education, animal welfare, and human services, particularly to an organization for underserved blind people.
Fields of interest: Education; Animal welfare; Eye diseases; Health organizations; Human services; Blind/visually impaired.
Limitations: Applications not accepted. Giving primarily in IL, KS, VT, and WI.
Application information: Unsolicited requests for funds not accepted.
Officers and Directors:* Nancy Allison Perkins,* Pres.; Brett Allison,* Secy.; Lindsay Vail,* Treas.; Jody Allison; Suzanne Allison-Vail; Leigh Lehmann.
EIN: 710947614
Selected grants: The following grants are a representative sample of this grantmaker's funding activity:
$20,000 to Doctors Without Borders USA, New York, NY, 2011. For general use.

3076
The Perlman Family Foundation ✧
(formerly Louis & Anita Perlman Family Foundation)
c/o Havi Group, LP
3500 Lacey Rd., Ste. 600
Downers Grove, IL 60515

Established in 1969 in IL.
Donors: David Schulman; Carol Schulman; Ruth Harter; Marilyn Perlman; Harriette Perlman.
Foundation type: Independent foundation.

Financial data (yr. ended 12/31/13): Assets, $2,419,219 (M); gifts received, $835,080; expenditures, $840,384; qualifying distributions, $808,670; giving activities include $808,670 for 35 grants (high: $110,000; low: $200).
Purpose and activities: Giving primarily for Jewish welfare funds and higher education.
Fields of interest: Arts; Higher education; Human services; Jewish federated giving programs.
Limitations: Applications not accepted. Giving primarily in IL and NY. No grants to individuals.
Application information: Contributes only to pre-selected organizations.
Officers: Theodore F. Perlman, Pres.; Harriette L. Perlman, V.P. and Secy.; Dorene Dunkleman, Treas.
EIN: 362670190
Selected grants: The following grants are a representative sample of this grantmaker's funding activity:
$5,750 to Wellness House, Hinsdale, IL, 2012. For civic and social.

3077
Richard A. Perritt Charitable Foundation ✧
P.O. Box 433
Barrington, IL 60011-0433

Established in 1993 in IL.
Donor: Richard A. Perritt Char. Trust.
Foundation type: Independent foundation.
Financial data (yr. ended 12/31/13): Assets, $4,538,801 (M); gifts received, $1,150,735; expenditures, $1,460,949; qualifying distributions, $1,366,291; giving activities include $1,366,291 for 24 grants (high: $297,130; low: $1,000).
Purpose and activities: Giving primarily for health associations, with an emphasis on cancer research, and services for people who are visually impaired; funding also for children, youth and social services.
Fields of interest: Higher education; Medical school/education; Hospitals (general); Hospitals (specialty); Health care; Cancer research; Human services; Children/youth, services.
Limitations: Applications not accepted. Giving primarily in IL. No grants to individuals.
Application information: Contributes only to pre-selected organizations.
Officers and Directors:* Ronald A. Tyrpin,* Pres.; Diane A. Tyrpin,* V.P. and Secy.-Treas.; John C. Tyrpin,* V.P.; Mark A. Tyrpin,* V.P.
EIN: 363896125
Selected grants: The following grants are a representative sample of this grantmaker's funding activity:
$30,000 to Little Sisters of the Poor, Chicago, IL, 2012. For assistance for needy aged residents.
$25,000 to Barrington Area Council on Aging, Barrington, IL, 2012. For needy elderly individuals.
$6,000 to Countryside Association for People with Disabilities, Palatine, IL, 2012. For Vocational assistance for disabled.
$5,000 to Saint Columbanus Church, Chicago, IL, 2012. For Feeding hungry disadvantaged persons.

3078
Esper A. Petersen Foundation ✧ ☆
1 E. Belvidere Rd.
Grayslake, IL 60030-3328 (847) 336-0900
Contact: Esper A. Petersen, Pres.

Incorporated in 1944 in IL.
Donor: Esper A. Petersen†.
Foundation type: Independent foundation.
Financial data (yr. ended 12/31/13): Assets, $8,169,897 (M); expenditures, $1,362,805; qualifying distributions, $1,032,371; giving activities include $1,032,371 for 34 grants (high: $500,000; low: $500).
Fields of interest: Museums; Performing arts, opera; Arts; Education; Health care; Food services; Recreation, parks/playgrounds; Human services; Community/economic development.
Type of support: General/operating support; Building/renovation; Research.
Limitations: Applications accepted. Giving primarily in CA and IL. No grants to individuals.
Publications: Application guidelines.
Application information: Application form not required.
Initial approach: Letter
Deadline(s): None
Board meeting date(s): July and Dec.
Final notification: Dec. 31
Officers and Directors:* Esper A. Petersen,* Pres. and Treas.; Ann Petersen,* V.P.; Daniel Winkowski, Secy.; Leslie Pam.
EIN: 366125570
Selected grants: The following grants are a representative sample of this grantmaker's funding activity:
$18,600 to Friends of Robinson Gardens, Beverly Hills, CA, 2012. To preserve and restore the Virginia Robinson gardens and estate.
$7,500 to American Cancer Society, Lincolnshire, IL, 2012. To raise awareness about cancer-related issues while helping fight the disease through research, education, advocacy and services.
$5,000 to Los Angeles Regional Food Bank, Los Angeles, CA, 2012. For charitable distribution of food.
$1,600 to Ganna Walska Lotusland, Santa Barbara, CA, 2012. To help provide the gardens and home of Lotusland as a place for the public to enjoy as a botanical destination and a learning experience.

3079
Albert Pick, Jr. Fund ✧
333 N. Michigan Ave., Ste. 510
Chicago, IL 60601-3749 (312) 236-1192
E-mail: iris@albertpickjrfund.org; Main URL: http://www.albertpickjrfund.org

Incorporated in 1947 in IL.
Donor: Albert Pick, Jr.†.
Foundation type: Independent foundation.
Financial data (yr. ended 12/31/13): Assets, $22,462,757 (M); expenditures, $1,118,186; qualifying distributions, $877,650; giving activities include $857,775 for 53 grants (high: $30,000; low: $7,500).
Purpose and activities: Support within four major program categories: 1) Civic and community, including programs which enhance the environment, address the needs of minorities and the physically disabled, and/or promote good government and human relations; 2) Cultural organizations, especially projects which seek to expand audience access or educate new audiences through outreach activities; 3) Educational improvement and reform at the precollegiate level, especially early childhood education, tutoring, at-risk intervention, and in-job training and re-training; and 4) Health and human services, including wellness programs, community-based health care delivery, youth, family planning, or geriatric services, mental health, physical rehabilitation and shelter care services.
Fields of interest: Arts; Education; Health care; Human services; Community/economic development.
Type of support: General/operating support; Continuing support; Program development; Technical assistance.
Limitations: Applications accepted. Giving limited to IL. No support for political or religious purposes, hospitals or local chapters of single-disease agencies, umbrella organizations, fraternal, veterans', labor, or athletic organizations, or local chapters of state, regional, or national organizations, professional groups with volunteer service programs, or for individual elementary or secondary schools. No grants to individuals, or for scholarships, building or endowment funds, capital campaigns, deficit financing, long-term projects, travel, sponsorship, advertising, scholarships, or fundraising.
Publications: Application guidelines; Grants list.
Application information: The fund will not review incomplete or late applications. Application guidelines and form available on fund's web site. Application form required.
Initial approach: Letter
Copies of proposal: 1
Deadline(s): Jan. 21, Apr. 1, July 1, and Oct. 1
Board meeting date(s): Mar., June, Sept., and Dec. Cultural proposals considered only at Sept. meeting; other categories considered at all meetings
Final notification: Within 3 weeks of board meetings
Officers and Directors:* Robert B. Lifton,* Pres.; Gwendolyn M. Rice,* Secy.; Howard A. Sulkin,* Treas.; Iris J. Krieg, Exec. Dir.; Shelley A. Davis; James W. Mabie.
Number of staff: 3 part-time support.
EIN: 366071402
Selected grants: The following grants are a representative sample of this grantmaker's funding activity:
$20,000 to Robert Crown Center for Health Education, Hinsdale, IL, 2011.
$12,000 to Jewish Federation of Metropolitan Chicago, Chicago, IL, 2011.
$10,000 to Art Institute of Chicago, Chicago, IL, 2011.
$10,000 to Chicago Historical Society, Chicago History Museum, Chicago, IL, 2011.
$10,000 to Chicago Opera Theater, Chicago, IL, 2011.
$10,000 to Literacy Works, Chicago, IL, 2011.
$10,000 to North Lawndale College Preparatory Charter High School, Chicago, IL, 2011.
$10,000 to Rape Victim Advocates, Chicago, IL, 2011.
$10,000 to Working in the Schools, Chicago, IL, 2011.

3080
The Pierce Family Charitable Foundation
(doing business as Pierce Family Foundation)
c/o Pierce and Assocs.
1 N. Dearborn St., Ste. 1300
Chicago, IL 60602-4321
Contact: Heather D. Parish, Prog. Dir.; Marianne Philbin, Exec. Dir.
Main URL: http://www.piercefamilyfoundation.org
Facebook: https://www.facebook.com/thepiercefamilyfoundation

Established in 2007 in DE and IL.
Donors: Denis Pierce; Martha V. Pierce.
Foundation type: Independent foundation.
Financial data (yr. ended 12/31/12): Assets, $10,607,961 (M); gifts received, $2,249,780; expenditures, $1,893,321; qualifying distributions, $1,779,943; giving activities include $1,095,171 for 149 grants (high: $55,741; low: $200), and $564,564 for foundation-administered programs.
Purpose and activities: The foundation supports nonprofit organizations providing essential social services in the areas of housing and opportunities for homeless people.
Fields of interest: Environment, natural resources; Housing/shelter; Human services; Family services; Homeless, human services; Protestant agencies & churches; Homeless.
Type of support: Management development/capacity building; General/operating support.
Limitations: Applications not accepted. Giving primarily in Chicago, IL, as well as to select programs in MI. No grants to individuals.
Application information: Contributes only to pre-selected organizations.
Officers and Director:* Denis Pierce,* Pres.; Martha V. Pierce, Secy.; Marianne Philbin, Exec. Dir.
EIN: 261459612
Selected grants: The following grants are a representative sample of this grantmaker's funding activity:
$50,000 to Connections for the Homeless, Evanston, IL, 2011.
$25,000 to Deborahs Place, Chicago, IL, 2011.
$25,000 to Resurrection Lutheran Church, Franklin Park, IL, 2011.
$20,000 to Chicago Foundation for Women, Chicago, IL, 2011.
$15,000 to SEEDS, Traverse City, MI, 2011.
$10,000 to Michigan Land Use Institute, Traverse City, MI, 2011.
$6,170 to Interfaith House, Chicago, IL, 2011.
$5,000 to JJs List, Wilmette, IL, 2011.
$2,500 to Crossroads Fund, Chicago, IL, 2011.
$2,000 to Resurrection Lutheran Church, Franklin Park, IL, 2011.

3081
A. Franklin Pilchard Foundation ✧
P.O. Box 2690
Palatine, IL 60078-2690 (847) 963-6762
Contact: Robert C. Pacilio, Treas.

Established in 1990 in IL.
Donor: A. Franklin Pilchard.
Foundation type: Independent foundation.
Financial data (yr. ended 06/30/13): Assets, $18,265,194 (M); expenditures, $752,588; qualifying distributions, $1,400,300; giving activities include $559,403 for grants to individuals.
Purpose and activities: Scholarships awarded only to students who attend participating educational institutions in Illinois.
Fields of interest: Education.
Type of support: Scholarship funds.
Limitations: Applications accepted. Giving limited to residents of IL.
Application information: Application form required.
Initial approach: Request application form
Deadline(s): Oct. 31
Officers and Directors:* Kevin J. Ryan,* Pres.; Donald R. Pawelski,* Secy.; Robert C. Pacilio,* Treas.
EIN: 363723290

3082
Ploughshares Foundation ✧
108 W. Grand Ave.
Chicago, IL 60654-5206
Contact: Donald M. Ephraim, Pres.

Established in 1990 in IL.
Foundation type: Independent foundation.
Financial data (yr. ended 12/31/13): Assets, $53,897,915 (M); expenditures, $2,741,495; qualifying distributions, $2,433,500; giving activities include $2,433,500 for 288 grants (high: $88,000; low: $1,000).
Fields of interest: Environment; AIDS; Human services; Civil rights, race/intergroup relations; Homeless.
Type of support: General/operating support.
Limitations: Applications accepted. Giving on a national basis. No grants to individuals.
Application information: Application form not required.
Initial approach: Letter
Deadline(s): None
Officer and Directors:* Donald M. Ephraim,* Pres.; Eliot S. Ephraim; David M. Ephraim.
EIN: 363739577

3083
The Poetry Foundation ✧
(formerly The Modern Poetry Association)
61 W. Superior St.
Chicago, IL 60654-5457 (312) 787-7070
Contact: Stephen Young, Prog. Dir.
FAX: (312) 787-6650;
E-mail: mail@poetryfoundation.org; Main URL: http://www.poetryfoundation.org
Blog: http://www.poetryfoundation.org/harriet/
E-Newsletter: http://www.poetryfoundation.org/archive/signup.html
Facebook: http://www.facebook.com/poetryfoundation
Knowledge Center: http://www.poetryfoundation.org/learning/index.html
Twitter: http://twitter.com/poetryfound

Founded in 1941.
Donors: Eleanor Wood Prince Remainder Trust; Art Institute of Chicago; Mid Atlantic Arts Foundation.
Foundation type: Operating foundation.
Financial data (yr. ended 12/31/13): Assets, $238,760,639 (M); gifts received, $1,275,208; expenditures, $9,017,516; qualifying distributions, $6,988,052; giving activities include $717,000 for 130 grants (high: $200,000; low: $50), $242,200 for grants to individuals, and $4,235,242 for foundation-administered programs.
Purpose and activities: The foundation awards fellowships and prizes to students of creative writing or English who are enrolled in a university or college. The foundation is dedicated to promoting the understanding and appreciation of poetry worldwide.
Fields of interest: Literature.
Type of support: Grants to individuals; Fellowships.
Limitations: Applications accepted. Giving on a national basis.
Publications: Financial statement.
Application information:
Initial approach: Letter
Deadline(s): None
Officers and Trustees:* John Kenney,* Chair.; Charlie Pierce,* Vice-Chair.; Robert Wedgeworth,* Vice-Chair.; Robert Polito,* Pres.; Benna Wilde,* Secy.; Caren F. Skoulas, C.F.O.; Thomas C. Cronin; and 8 additional trustees.
EIN: 362490808
Selected grants: The following grants are a representative sample of this grantmaker's funding activity:
$10,000 to Academy of American Poets, New York, NY, 2012. For National Poetry Month.
$10,000 to Brooklyn Arts Council, Brooklyn, NY, 2012. For Alzheimer's Poetry Project.
$10,000 to National Poetry Series, Princeton, NJ, 2012. For publication support.
$5,000 to Snow City Arts Foundation, Chicago, IL, 2012. For poetry programs.
$1,250 to American Poetry Review, Philadelphia, PA, 2012. For Stephen Berg Project.
$1,000 to Small Press Distribution, Berkeley, CA, 2012. For Sponsorship for The Bee-In.

3084
Polk Bros. Foundation, Inc. ✧
20 W. Kinzie St., Ste. 1110
Chicago, IL 60654-5815 (312) 527-4684
Contact: Sheila A. Robinson, Grant Admin.
FAX: (312) 527-4681; E-mail: info@polkbrosfdn.org; E-mail for Sheila A. Robinson:srobinson@polkbrosFdn.org; Main URL: http://www.polkbrosfdn.org/
Grants Database: http://www.polkbrosfdn.org/grants.asp

Incorporated in 1957 in IL.
Donors: David D. Polk†; Harry Polk†; Morris G. Polk†; Samuel H. Polk†; Sol Polk†; Rand Realty and Development Co.; Polk Bros., Inc.; and members of the Polk family.
Foundation type: Independent foundation.
Financial data (yr. ended 08/31/13): Assets, $434,206,007 (M); expenditures, $23,353,181; qualifying distributions, $22,998,209; giving activities include $19,464,480 for 455 grants (high: $350,000; low: $100), and $1,357,985 for 453 employee matching gifts.
Purpose and activities: The mission is to improve the quality of life for the people of Chicago. The foundation partners with local nonprofit organizations that work to reduce the impact of poverty and provide area residents with better access to quality education, preventive health care and basic human services. Through its grantmaking, the foundation strives to make Chicago a place where all people have the opportunity to reach their full potential.
Fields of interest: Museums; Performing arts; Performing arts, theater; Arts; Education, early childhood education; Child development, education; Vocational education; Higher education; Adult/continuing education; Adult education—literacy, basic skills & GED; Education, reading; Education; Health care; Mental health/crisis services; Health organizations, association; AIDS; Crime/violence prevention, domestic violence; Legal services; Employment; Youth development, services; Human services; Children/youth, services; Child development, services; Family services; Women, centers/services; Minorities/immigrants, centers/services; Homeless, human services; Civil rights, race/intergroup relations; Urban/community development; Community/economic development; Jewish federated giving programs; Leadership development; Jewish agencies & synagogues; Disabilities, people with; Minorities; Women; Economically disadvantaged; Homeless.

Type of support: Pro bono services - legal; Management development/capacity building; General/operating support; Continuing support; Equipment; Program development; Curriculum development; Scholarship funds; Technical assistance; Program evaluation; Employee matching gifts.
Limitations: Applications accepted. Giving primarily in Chicago, IL. No support for political organizations or religious institutions seeking support for programs whose participants are restricted by religious affiliation, or for tax-generating entities (municipalities and school districts) for services within their normal responsibilities. No grants to individuals, or for medical, scientific or academic research, or purchase of dinner or raffle tickets.
Publications: Annual report (including application guidelines).
Application information: An organization that is new to the foundation or has not received a grant from the foundation in the last five years should review the foundation's program area guide before submitting a pre-application form. Current grantees or those that have received a grant from the foundation within the last five years may call or e-mail the foundation for an application packet. Proposals for health-related services are not reviewed at the Feb., May and Nov. board meeting. Application form required.
Initial approach: Letter of inquiry and online pre-application request
Copies of proposal: 1
Deadline(s): None
Board meeting date(s): Feb., May, Aug., and Nov.
Final notification: 3 - 4 weeks
Officers and Directors:* Sandra P. Guthman,* Chair.; Gillian Darlow, C.E.O.; Evette M. Cardona, V.P., Progs.; Raymond F. Simon,* V.P.; Gordon S. Prussian,* Secy.; Theodore S. Weymouth, C.F.O.; Sidney Epstein,* Treas.; Bruce R. Bachmann; Howard J. Polk; Cherryl T. Thomas.
Number of staff: 9 full-time professional; 2 part-time professional; 2 full-time support.
EIN: 366108293
Selected grants: The following grants are a representative sample of this grantmaker's funding activity:
$300,000 to Black Ensemble Theater Corporation, Chicago, IL, 2011.
$250,000 to Big Shoulders Fund, Chicago, IL, 2011.
$250,000 to Chicago High School for the Arts, Chicago, IL, 2011. For general support.
$250,000 to Chicago Project for Violence Prevention, Chicago, IL, 2011. For general support.
$220,000 to Heartland International Health Center, Chicago, IL, 2011.
$200,000 to Old Town School of Folk Music, Chicago, IL, 2011. For general support.
$175,000 to Chicago Community Loan Fund, Chicago, IL, 2011.
$150,000 to Christopher House, Chicago, IL, 2011.
$125,000 to Metropolitan Tenants Organization, Chicago Housing Initiative, Chicago, IL, 2011. For general support.
$100,000 to Jewish Council for Youth Services, Chicago, IL, 2011. For general support.
$75,000 to Ingenuity Chicago, Chicago, IL, 2011. For general support.
$40,000 to Chicago Scholars Foundation, Chicago, IL, 2011.
$40,000 to Ladder Up, Chicago, IL, 2011.
$40,000 to Poder Learning Center, Chicago, IL, 2011. For general support.
$35,000 to Howard Area Community Center, Chicago, IL, 2011. For general support.
$30,000 to Chicago Childrens Museum, Chicago, IL, 2011.
$30,000 to ETA Creative Arts Foundation, Chicago, IL, 2011. For general support.

3085
Popular Community Bank Foundation ✧ ☆
(formerly Banco Popular Foundation, Inc.)
9600 W. Bryn Mawr Ave.
Rosemont, IL 60018-5209 (787) 725-8861
Contact: Beatriz Polhamus, Exec. Dir.

Established in 2005 in IL.
Donors: Banco Popular North America; Richard C. Peterson; Michelle Imbasciani; Cesar Medina; Chris A. McFadden; Banco Popular Foundation, Inc.; Popular Community Foundation, Inc.; Carlos Vazouez; Brian Doran; Popular Community Bank.
Foundation type: Company-sponsored foundation.
Financial data (yr. ended 12/31/13): Assets, $2,036,764 (M); gifts received, $713,794; expenditures, $711,211; qualifying distributions, $683,699; giving activities include $683,699 for 45 grants (high: $265,000; low: $3,000).
Purpose and activities: The foundation supports programs designed to strengthen the social and economic well-being of communities.
Fields of interest: Education; Housing/shelter, development; Housing/shelter; Youth development, business; Family services; Developmentally disabled, centers & services; Minorities/immigrants, centers/services; Human services; Business/industry; Community/economic development.
Type of support: General/operating support; Continuing support; Program development; Scholarship funds.
Limitations: Applications accepted. Giving primarily in CA, FL, IL, and NY. No support for religious or political organizations. No grants to individuals, or for fundraising events, table purchases, event sponsorships, or capital campaigns.
Publications: Application guidelines.
Application information: Application form required.
Initial approach: Proposal
Deadline(s): None
Officers and Directors:* Richard L. Carrion,* Chair.; Carlos J. Vasquez,* Vice-Chair.; Brian F. Doran, Secy.; Eduardo J. Negron,* Treas.; Beatriz Polhamus, Exec. Dir.; Manuel Chinea; Pamela Kulnis.
EIN: 753175825

3086
Leo Potishman Foundation ✧
10 S. Dearborn St., IL1-0117
Chicago, IL 60603-2300
Application address: c/o JPMorgan Chase Bank, N.A., Attn. Eric Hy, 420 Throckmorton St., Fort Worth, TX 76102-3700, tel.: (817) 884-4165

Established in 1983 in TX.
Foundation type: Independent foundation.
Financial data (yr. ended 06/30/13): Assets, $9,195,651 (M); expenditures, $1,034,884; qualifying distributions, $936,837; giving activities include $916,000 for 13 grants (high: $300,000; low: $5,000).
Purpose and activities: Giving primarily for education, health, and human services.
Fields of interest: Museums; Higher education; Education; Health organizations, association; Human services; YM/YWCAs & YM/YWHAs; Children/youth, services.
Type of support: Continuing support; Annual campaigns; Capital campaigns; Equipment.
Limitations: Applications accepted. Giving primarily in TX, with emphasis on Fort Worth. No grants to individuals.
Application information: Application form required.
Initial approach: Proposal
Copies of proposal: 1
Deadline(s): None
Board meeting date(s): As needed
Trustee: JPMorgan Chase Bank, N.A.
EIN: 756314202
Selected grants: The following grants are a representative sample of this grantmaker's funding activity:
$236,000 to Texas Christian University, Fort Worth, TX, 2011. For program support.
$196,000 to Texas Christian University, Fort Worth, TX, 2010. For program support.
$125,000 to Carter BloodCare, Bedford, TX, 2010. For program support.
$125,000 to Carter BloodCare, Bedford, TX, 2011. For program support.
$100,000 to Fort Worth Opera Association, Fort Worth, TX, 2011. For program support.
$55,000 to Fort Worth Opera Association, Fort Worth, TX, 2010. For program support.
$50,000 to Casa Manana, Fort Worth, TX, 2011. For program support.
$50,000 to Southwestern University, Georgetown, TX, 2010. For program support.
$50,000 to Southwestern University, Georgetown, TX, 2011. For program support.
$50,000 to Texas Ballet Theater, Fort Worth, TX, 2010. For program support.
$40,000 to Fort Worth Airpower Foundation, Fort Worth, TX, 2010. For program support.
$35,000 to Score a Goal in the Classroom, Fort Worth, TX, 2011. For program support.
$30,000 to Lena Pope Home, Fort Worth, TX, 2011. For program support.
$30,000 to SafeHaven of Tarrant County, Hurst, TX, 2010. For program support.
$25,000 to Fort Worth Art Association, Modern Art Museum of Fort Worth, Fort Worth, TX, 2010. For program support.
$25,000 to Jarvis Christian College, Hawkins, TX, 2010. For program support.
$25,000 to Lena Pope Home, Fort Worth, TX, 2010. For program support.
$25,000 to Partners Together for Health, Fort Worth, TX, 2011. For program support.
$25,000 to Tarrant County College Foundation, Fort Worth, TX, 2011. For program support.
$10,000 to Love Never Fails International, Fort Worth, TX, 2011. For program support.

3087
Justin & Valere Potter Foundation ✧
c/o Bank of America, N.A.
231 S. LaSalle St., IL1-231-10-05
Chicago, IL 60697
Application address: c/o Portia Wells, V.P., U.S. Trust/Bank of America, 414 Union St., 3rd Fl., Nashville, TN 37219; tel.: (615) 749-3176

Established in 1953.

Foundation type: Independent foundation.
Financial data (yr. ended 12/31/13): Assets, $18,613,126 (M); expenditures, $960,467; qualifying distributions, $907,328; giving activities include $884,240 for 17 grants (high: $250,000; low: $5,000).
Fields of interest: Health organizations, association; Cancer; Human services.
Limitations: Applications accepted. Giving primarily in Nashville, TN.
Application information: Application form required.
Initial approach: Letter
Deadline(s): None
Trustee: Bank of America, N.A.
Committee Members: Marianne Byrd; Albert L. Menefee III; Valere Menefee.
EIN: 626306577
Selected grants: The following grants are a representative sample of this grantmaker's funding activity:
$250,000 to Vanderbilt-Ingram Cancer Center, Nashville, TN, 2011. For general support.
$125,000 to Catholic Charities of Tennessee, Nashville, TN, 2011. For general support.
$50,000 to Boy Scouts of America, Middle Tennessee Council, Nashville, TN, 2011. For general support.
$50,000 to Nashville Rescue Mission, Nashville, TN, 2011. For general support.
$20,000 to Downtown Ministry Center, Nashville, TN, 2011. For general support.
$15,000 to Rochelle Center, Nashville, TN, 2011. For general support.
$10,000 to Tennessee Wildlife Federation, Nashville, TN, 2011. For general support.
$10,000 to United States Sportsmens Alliance Foundation, Columbus, OH, 2011. For general support.
$5,000 to PENCIL Foundation, Nashville, TN, 2011. For general support.

3088
Abra Prentice Foundation, Inc. ✧
980 N. Michgan Ave., Ste. 1360
Chicago, IL 60611-4591

Established in 1980 in IL.
Donors: Abra Prentice Wilkin; Abra Prentice Revocable Trust.
Foundation type: Independent foundation.
Financial data (yr. ended 12/31/13): Assets, $37,779,159 (M); gifts received, $2,003,041; expenditures, $1,828,856; qualifying distributions, $1,527,636; giving activities include $1,500,000 for 27 grants (high: $300,000; low: $5,000).
Purpose and activities: Giving primarily to: 1) maintain and improve the quality and availability of health care; 2) increase and promote knowledge through educational, scientific or literary endeavors in secondary, college, professional schools, etc.; 3) provide for the special needs of children, the elderly, the disabled, and the impoverished; 4) improve social conditions and cultural development in the U.S. and elsewhere; and 5) promote international peace and understanding and achieve other charitable purposes which the foundation recognizes as especially worthy of its support.
Fields of interest: Higher education; Medical school/education; Education; Human services.
Type of support: General/operating support; Building/renovation.
Limitations: Applications not accepted. Giving primarily in Watertown, CT and Chicago, IL. No grants to individuals.
Application information: Unsolicited requests for funds not accepted.
Officers and Directors:* Abra Prentice Wilkin,* Pres.; Louis S. Harrison, Secy.; James Wilken,* Treas.
EIN: 363092281

3089
Prince Charitable Trusts ✧
140 S. Dearborn St., Ste. 1410
Chicago, IL 60603-5208 (312) 419-8700
Contact: Benna Wilde, Prog. Dir.; For Chicago and RI Proposals: Sharon Robison, Grants Mgr.
FAX: (312) 419-8558;
E-mail: tfron@prince-trusts.org; Additional address: 816 Connecticut Ave. N.W., Washington, DC 2006, tel.: (202) 728-0646, fax: (202) 466-4726. Proposals should be addressed to: Charles C. Twichell, Mgr. Dir. (Chicago office); Main URL: http://princetrusts.org

Frederick Henry Prince Trust dated July 9, 1947 established in 1947 in IL. Frederick Henry Prince Testamentary Trust established in 1947 in RI. Abbie Norman Prince Trust established in 1949 in IL.
Donor: Frederick Henry Prince†.
Foundation type: Independent foundation.
Financial data (yr. ended 12/31/13): Assets, $152,240,728 (M); expenditures, $6,871,132; qualifying distributions, $6,573,113; giving activities include $5,232,640 for 342 grants (high: $165,000; low: $200).
Purpose and activities: Support for cultural programs, youth organizations, social services, hospitals, hospital morale, rehabilitation, and environment.
Fields of interest: Arts; Education, early childhood education; Environment, natural resources; Environment; Hospitals (general); Reproductive health, family planning; Medical care, rehabilitation; Health care; Human services; Children/youth, services; Children/youth; Children; Minorities; Economically disadvantaged; Homeless.
Type of support: General/operating support; Continuing support; Capital campaigns; Program development; Seed money; Technical assistance; Program-related investments/loans; Employee matching gifts.
Limitations: Applications accepted. Giving limited to local groups in Washington, DC, Chicago, IL, and RI, with emphasis on Aquidneck Island. No support for national organizations, or for religious or political organizations. No grants to individuals.
Publications: Application guidelines.
Application information: The DC office will not be accepting unsolicited proposals - applications by invitation only. Some funding areas for the Chicago office are via invitation only- applicants should check web site prior to applying. Application form not required.
Initial approach: On-line proposal (4 to 6 pages for proposal) to be submitted via http://www.egrant.net. Check foundation web site for application guidelines
Copies of proposal: 1
Deadline(s): Chicago: Jan. 13 for Social Svcs., May 1 for Health, June 2 for Arts/Culture, Environment and Capital; Rhode Island: May 1
Board meeting date(s): Chicago: spring and fall; Rhode Island: fall; Washington, DC: late spring and late fall
Final notification: Within 5 months of proposal deadline
Trustees: Frederick Henry Prince IV; Patrick B. Wood-Prince.
Number of staff: 4 full-time professional; 1 part-time professional; 2 full-time support.
Selected grants: The following grants are a representative sample of this grantmaker's funding activity:
$250,000 to Latin School of Chicago, Chicago, IL, 2012. For endowment.
$200,000 to Aquidneck Island Land Trust, Middletown, RI, 2012. For challenge grant to support lots 3 and 8 on St Mary's campus, Portsmouth, RI.
$75,000 to Hubbard Street Dance Chicago, Chicago, IL, 2012. For Prince Prize for commissioning of original work.
$40,000 to Child and Family Services of Newport County, Middletown, RI, 2012. To complete installation of Essential EHR and IT program and match $150,000 Fidelity Foundation Challenge Grant.
$40,000 to Josie King Foundation, Baltimore, MD, 2012. For Resiliency in Stressful Events (RISE) Program.
$25,000 to Alliance for the Great Lakes, Chicago, IL, 2012. For Chicago Coastal Open Space Program.
$25,000 to Erie Family Health Center, Chicago, IL, 2012. For staff morale improvement project.
$20,000 to Martin Luther King Community Center, Newport, RI, 2012. For general operating support.
$20,000 to Music and Dance Theater Chicago, Chicago, IL, 2012. For general operating support.
$15,000 to Sacred Heart Schools, Chicago, IL, 2012. For general operating support for Children of the Heart.

3090
Prince Foundation ✧
140 S. Dearborn St., Ste. 1410
Chicago, IL 60603 (312) 419-8700
Main URL: http://www.princetrusts.org/chicago.html

Incorporated in 1955 in IL.
Donors: F.H. Prince & Co., Inc.; John D. MacArthur Foundation; Catherine T. MacArthur Foundation.
Foundation type: Company-sponsored foundation.
Financial data (yr. ended 12/31/13): Assets, $2,537,476 (M); gifts received, $1,635,000; expenditures, $1,611,830; qualifying distributions, $1,609,180; giving activities include $1,363,000 for 46 grants (high: $40,000; low: $20,000).
Purpose and activities: The foundation supports organizations involved with arts and culture and children and youth.
Fields of interest: Museums; Performing arts, dance; Performing arts, theater; Performing arts, orchestras; Performing arts, opera; Performing arts, music (choral); Arts; Elementary/secondary education; Children/youth, services.
Type of support: General/operating support; Employee matching gifts.
Limitations: Applications accepted. Giving primarily in IL. No grants to individuals.
Application information: Application form required.
Initial approach: Letter
Deadline(s): None

Officers and Trustees:* Patrick Wood-Prince,* Pres.; Randall M. Highley, V.P.; Frederick Henry Prince,* V.P.
EIN: 366116507
Selected grants: The following grants are a representative sample of this grantmaker's funding activity:
$25,000 to Chicago Human Rhythm Project, Chicago, IL, 2012. For one-time grant for consulting assistance with executive search and capital fund development.
$20,000 to International Latino Cultural Center of Chicago, Chicago, IL, 2012. For one-time grant to hire associate director of development and marketing.
$20,000 to Maywood Fine Arts Association, Maywood, IL, 2012. For one-time grant for architectural assessment and master building plan.
$20,000 to Swedish American Museum Association of Chicago, Chicago, IL, 2012. For one-time grant for a comprehensive marketing plan.
$5,000 to Hyde Park Art Center, Chicago, IL, 2012. For one-time grant to support Kate Lorenz' attendance at the Harvard Business School Strategic Perspectives in Nonprofit Management course.

3091
Colonel (IL) James N. Pritzker Charitable Distribution Fund ✧
(doing business as The Tawani Foundation)
104 S. Michigan Ave., Ste. 525
Chicago, IL 60603-5950 (312) 374-9390
E-mail: www.info@tawanifoundation.net; Main URL: http://www.tawanifoundation.org/

Established in 2002 in IL.
Donors: James Pritzker; Pritzker Foundation; Pritzker Cousins Foundation.
Foundation type: Independent foundation.
Financial data (yr. ended 12/31/13): Assets, $52,977,195 (M); gifts received, $10,598,411; expenditures, $12,959,329; qualifying distributions, $12,566,838; giving activities include $12,178,719 for 289+ grants (high: $3,500,000).
Purpose and activities: Giving primarily for historical preservation of military heritage, projects that provide access to public spaces and services that enhance and improve quality of life, conservation and preservation of historic sites, as well as the foundation provides cadet awards for JROTC and ROTC units, and supports programs that reward, study and document the promotion of the citizen soldier ideal and military service.
Fields of interest: Museums; Historical activities; Education.
Type of support: Capital campaigns; Building/renovation; Program development; Publication; Research; Matching/challenge support.
Limitations: Applications not accepted. Giving primarily in Chicago, IL. No support for political campaigns. No grants to individuals, or for building endowments or scholarships.
Application information: Letters of inquiry and applications are by invitation only.
Board meeting date(s): Fall and spring
Directors: Lew Collens; Charles E. Dobrusin; Mary Parthe; Col. David Pelizzon; Tal Hava Pritzker.
Number of staff: 5 full-time professional.
EIN: 300040386
Selected grants: The following grants are a representative sample of this grantmaker's funding activity:
$250,000 to Field Museum of Natural History, Chicago, IL, 2012. For Polar Exhibition Fund.
$183,250 to College Options Foundation, Lees Summit, MO, 2012.
$100,000 to Ride 2 Recovery, Calabasas, CA, 2012.
$50,000 to United States Naval Institute, Annapolis, MD, 2012.
$40,000 to Salvation Army, Metropolitan Division Headquarters, Chicago, IL, 2012.
$15,000 to Ann and Robert H. Lurie Children's Hospital of Chicago, Chicago, IL, 2012.
$10,000 to American Red Cross National Headquarters, Washington, DC, 2012.
$10,000 to Honor Flight Chicago, Chicago, IL, 2012.
$5,000 to George C. Marshall Research Foundation, Lexington, VA, 2012.
$5,000 to Tulane University, AROTC, New Orleans, LA, 2012.

3092
The Anthony Pritzker Family Foundation ✧
111 S. Wacker Dr., Ste. 4000
Chicago, IL 60606-4309

Established in 2002 in CA and IL.
Donors: Pritzker Foundation; Pritzker Cousins Foundation; Colson Trust.
Foundation type: Independent foundation.
Financial data (yr. ended 12/31/12): Assets, $45,893,622 (M); gifts received, $14,455,571; expenditures, $6,119,669; qualifying distributions, $5,619,546; giving activities include $5,494,000 for 76 grants (high: $1,127,600; low: $500).
Purpose and activities: Giving primarily for education, health organizations, social services, Jewish organizations, and to an art museum.
Fields of interest: Museums (art); Elementary/secondary education; Higher education; Hospitals (general); Health organizations, association; Human services; Jewish federated giving programs; Jewish agencies & synagogues.
Limitations: Applications not accepted. Giving primarily in CA. No grants to individuals.
Application information: Contributes only to pre-selected organizations.
Officers and Directors:* Anthony N. Pritzker,* Pres.; Judy Schroffel, Secy.-Treas.; Jay Robert Pritzker; Jeanne Pritzker.
EIN: 300039840

3093
Margot & Thomas Pritzker Family Foundation ✧
71 S. Wacker Dr., Ste. 4700
Chicago, IL 60606-4716

Established in IL.
Donor: Colson Trust.
Foundation type: Independent foundation.
Financial data (yr. ended 10/31/13): Assets, $66,685,028 (M); expenditures, $2,205,946; qualifying distributions, $1,629,537.
Fields of interest: Museums (art); Arts; Higher education, university; International affairs; Philanthropy/voluntarism.
Type of support: General/operating support.
Limitations: Applications not accepted. Giving in the U.S., with emphasis on CA, Chicago, IL, and New York, NY. No grants to individuals.
Application information: Contributes only to pre-selected organizations.
Board meeting date(s): Nov., and as necessary
Officers and Directors:* Thomas J. Pritzker,* Pres.; Charles J. Barron, V.P. and Secy.; Scott Stevens, V.P. and Treas.; Glen Miller,* V.P.; Margot Pritzker,* V.P.
EIN: 363852559

3094
Robert and Mayari Pritzker Family Foundation ✧
1 N. Franklin St., Ste. 2420
Chicago, IL 60606-3435

Established in 2006 in IL.
Donors: James N. Pritzker; Karen Pritzker; Michael Vlock; Jay Pritzker Foundation; CIBC Trust Co., Ltd.
Foundation type: Independent foundation.
Financial data (yr. ended 12/31/12): Assets, $3,359,370 (M); gifts received, $653,176; expenditures, $727,279; qualifying distributions, $694,950; giving activities include $694,950 for 23 grants (high: $245,000; low: $500).
Fields of interest: Engineering school/education; Human services; Social sciences, research.
Limitations: Applications not accepted. No grants to individuals.
Application information: Unsolicited requests for funds not accepted.
Directors: Michael A. Lovallo; Mayari S. Pritzker; Rebecca L. Spooner.
EIN: 203829597

3095
The Pritzker Family Foundation ✧
(also known as J.B. and M.K. Pritzker Family Foundation)
111 S. Wacker Dr., Ste. 4000
Chicago, IL 60606-4309

Established in 2002 in CA and IL.
Donors: Pritzker Foundation; Pritzker Cousins Foundation; CIBC Trust Co. (Bahamas) Ltd.
Foundation type: Independent foundation.
Financial data (yr. ended 12/31/12): Assets, $18,605,846 (M); gifts received, $14,455,571; expenditures, $13,549,078; qualifying distributions, $12,944,829; giving activities include $12,497,800 for 162 grants (high: $1,000,000; low: $250).
Fields of interest: Higher education; Education; Health organizations, association; Human services; Children/youth, services; Jewish federated giving programs; Jewish agencies & synagogues.
Limitations: Applications not accepted. Giving primarily in IL. No grants to individuals.
Application information: Contributes only to pre-selected organizations.
Officers and Directors:* Jay Robert Pritzker,* Pres.; Jen Levine, Secy.-Treas.; Anthony N. Pritzker; Mary Kathryn Pritzker.
EIN: 300039820
Selected grants: The following grants are a representative sample of this grantmaker's funding activity:
$1,000,000 to Bill, Hillary and Chelsea Clinton Foundation, Little Rock, AR, 2012. For general support.
$700,000 to University of South Dakota, Vermillion, SD, 2012. For general support.

$503,000 to Chicago Community Trust, Chicago, IL, 2012. For general support.
$500,000 to Ounce of Prevention Fund, Chicago, IL, 2012. For general support.
$375,000 to Jewish United Fund of Metropolitan Chicago, Chicago, IL, 2012. For general support.
$360,800 to United States Holocaust Memorial Museum, Washington, DC, 2012. For general support.
$250,000 to Virgin Unite USA, New York, NY, 2012. For general support.
$200,000 to American Israel Education Foundation, Washington, DC, 2012. For general support.
$25,000 to Center for Enriched Living, Riverwoods, IL, 2012. For general support.
$25,000 to University of Vermont, College of medicine, Burlington, VT, 2012. For general support.

3096
Pritzker Foundation ✧
300 N. LaSalle St., Ste. 1500
Chicago, IL 60654-3413 (312) 873-4884

Incorporated in 1944 in IL.
Donors: Members of the Pritzker family; H. Group Holding, Inc. and Subsidiaries; Marmon Holdings, Inc. and Subsidiaries.
Foundation type: Independent foundation.
Financial data (yr. ended 12/31/12): Assets, $384,212,520 (M); expenditures, $14,243,023; qualifying distributions, $8,876,744; giving activities include $8,848,000 for 41 grants (high: $2,500,000; low: $500).
Purpose and activities: Grants largely for higher education, including medical education, and religious welfare funds; giving also for hospitals, temple support, and cultural programs.
Fields of interest: Arts; Higher education; Higher education, university; Medical school/education; Hospitals (general); Human services; Foundations (private grantmaking); Philanthropy/voluntarism; Religious federated giving programs; Jewish agencies & synagogues.
Limitations: Applications not accepted. Giving primarily in Chicago, IL. No grants to individuals.
Application information: Contributes only to pre-selected organizations.
Board meeting date(s): Dec. and as required
Officers and Directors:* Gigi Pritzker Pucker,* Pres.; Ronald D. Wray, V.P. and Secy.; Nicholas J. Pritzker,* V.P.; Thomas J. Pritzker,* V.P.; Brian S. Traubert,* V.P.
EIN: 366058062
Selected grants: The following grants are a representative sample of this grantmaker's funding activity:
$2,500,000 to University of Chicago, Chicago, IL, 2012. For general operating support.
$1,010,000 to Millennium Park, Chicago, IL, 2012. For general operating support.
$1,000,000 to Conservation International, Arlington, VA, 2012. For general operating support.
$1,000,000 to Stanford University, Stanford, CA, 2012. For general operating support.
$614,000 to Chicago Public Education Fund, Chicago, IL, 2012. For general operating support.
$300,000 to Columbia College, Chicago, IL, 2012. For general operating support.
$250,000 to Academy for Urban School Leadership, Chicago, IL, 2012. For general operating support.
$250,000 to Old Town School of Folk Music, Chicago, IL, 2012. For general operating support.
$250,000 to Urban Gateways: Center for Arts Education, Chicago, IL, 2012. For general operating support.
$100,000 to New-York Historical Society, New York, NY, 2012. For general operating support.

3097
The Pritzker Pucker Family Foundation ✧
(formerly The Vince Club Family Foundation)
71 S. Wacker Dr., Ste. 4700
Chicago, IL 60606-4716

Established in 2002 in IL.
Foundation type: Independent foundation.
Financial data (yr. ended 12/31/13): Assets, $71,931,873 (M); expenditures, $3,392,572; qualifying distributions, $2,478,802; giving activities include $2,438,895 for 83 grants (high: $673,333; low: $200).
Fields of interest: Arts; Higher education; Education; Health organizations; Jewish agencies & synagogues.
Limitations: Applications not accepted. Giving primarily in IL; with emphasis on Chicago. No grants to individuals.
Application information: Contributes only to pre-selected organizations.
Officers and Directors:* GiGi Pritzker Pucker,* Pres.; Charles Barron, V.P. and Secy.; Michael Pucker, V.P. and Treas.; Glen Miller, V.P.; Scott Stevens, V.P.; Julie Wilen, V.P.
EIN: 300036022

3098
The Pritzker Traubert Family Foundation
(formerly The Bryan Traubert and Penny Pritzker Charitable Foundation)
300 N. La Salle St., Ste. 1500
Chicago, IL 60654-3413
Contact: Jody Boutell, Grants Mgr.
E-mail: jboutell@ptffoundation.org; Main URL: http://www.ptffoundation.org/

Established in 2000 in IL.
Donors: Bryan Traubert; Penny Pritzker.
Foundation type: Independent foundation.
Financial data (yr. ended 12/31/13): Assets, $203,997,870 (M); gifts received, $2,659,260; expenditures, $12,072,334; qualifying distributions, $10,062,259; giving activities include $9,881,490 for 119 grants (high: $5,800,000; low: $250).
Purpose and activities: Giving primarily for education, health and fitness, and art and culture programs.
Fields of interest: Arts; Education; Public health.
Limitations: Applications not accepted. Giving primarily in Chicago, IL. No grants to individuals.
Application information: Contributes only to pre-selected organizations.
Board meeting date(s): Annually
Officers and Directors:* Bryan S. Traubert, M.D.*, Pres.; Ronald D. Wray, V.P. and Secy.; Penny Pritzker,* V.P.; Kevin Poorman,* Treas.
EIN: 364347781
Selected grants: The following grants are a representative sample of this grantmaker's funding activity:
$383,520 to Noble Network of Charter Schools, Chicago, IL, 2011. For general operating support.
$300,000 to Stanford University, Stanford, CA, 2011. For general operating support.
$217,500 to University of Chicago, Chicago, IL, 2011. For general operating support.
$150,000 to Aspen Institute, Washington, DC, 2011. For general operating support.
$140,000 to Brookings Institution, Washington, DC, 2011. For general operating support.
$105,000 to Chicago Youth Running Initiative, Chicago, IL, 2011. For general operating support.
$100,000 to Renaissance Society at the University of Chicago, Chicago, IL, 2011. For general operating support.
$75,000 to Yale University, New Haven, CT, 2011. For general operating support.
$61,000 to John F. Kennedy Center for the Performing Arts, Washington, DC, 2011. For general operating support.
$30,000 to City Year, Boston, MA, 2011. For general operating support.

3099
The Lawrence Pucci Wedgwood Society of Chicago ✧
P.O. Box 8177
Chicago, IL 60680-8177

Donors: A. Robert Abboud; Dawn Davis; J.R. Davis; J.R. Davis III; Richard Davis; Lester McKeever, Jr.; Caryl Pucci Rettaliata; Wacker Michigan Corporation; Wacker Springfield Corporation; Lawrence M. Pucci Revocable Trust.
Foundation type: Independent foundation.
Financial data (yr. ended 12/31/13): Assets, $79,875,651 (M); gifts received, $4,155; expenditures, $15,759,945; qualifying distributions, $15,555,284; giving activities include $12,845,000 for 45 grants (high: $10,000,000; low: $100).
Fields of interest: Arts; Education; Health care; Health organizations, association.
Limitations: Applications not accepted. Giving primarily in Chicago, IL.
Application information: Contributes only to pre-selected organizations.
Officers: J.R. Davis, Co-Chair. and Secy.-Treas.; Caryl Pucci Rettaliata, Co-Chair.; Dawn Davis, Vice-Chair. and Pres.
Directors: A. Robert Abboud; J.R. Davis III; Richard Davis; Lester McKeever, Jr.
EIN: 363092220

3100
George M. Pullman Educational Foundation ✧
55 W. Monroe St., Ste. 3460
Chicago, IL 60603-5086 (312) 422-0444
Contact: Robin Redman, Exec. Dir.
FAX: (312) 422-0448;
E-mail: info@pullmanfoundation.org; Main URL: http://www.pullmanfoundation.org
Facebook: https://www.facebook.com/pages/George-M-Pullman-Educational-Foundation/141896812511358
LinkedIn: http://www.linkedin.com/groups?gid=4239215&trk=hb_side_g
Twitter: https://twitter.com/pullmanfdn

Incorporated in 1949 in IL.
Donors: George Mortimer Pullman†; Harriet Sanger Pullman†.

Foundation type: Independent foundation.
Financial data (yr. ended 07/31/13): Assets, $27,740,913 (M); gifts received, $76,590; expenditures, $1,539,850; qualifying distributions, $1,201,842; giving activities include $559,683 for 161 grants to individuals (high: $6,000; low: $300).
Purpose and activities: The foundation was established in 1949 to support qualified individuals primarily for post-secondary education. Graduating high school seniors who are residents of Cook County, IL are eligible for consideration for scholarships for college.
Fields of interest: Education.
Type of support: Program development; Scholarship funds.
Limitations: Giving primarily to residents of Cook County, IL. No grants to individuals directly.
Publications: Informational brochure.
Application information: Scholarship applicants must be residents of Cook County, IL. Awards are paid directly to the scholar's chosen college or university. Application information available on the foundation's website. Application form required.
Initial approach: Online application available at foundation's website
Deadline(s): Mar. 31
Board meeting date(s): Quarterly
Officers and Directors:* Barbara H. Miller,* Pres.; John P. Hergert, V.P.; Rev. Sam A. Portaro, Jr.,* Secy.; Marc Christman,* Treas.; Robin Redmond, Exec. Dir.; Robert W. Bennett; Edward McCormick Blair, Jr.; Peter Braxton; Robert W. Fioretti; Kimberley Freedman; Alejandra Garza; Richard J. Hoskins; Warren Pullman Miller; Harry M. Oliver, Jr.
Number of staff: 4 full-time professional; 2 full-time support.
EIN: 362216171

3101
Purcell Charitable Foundation ✧ ☆
825 S. Washington St.
Hinsdale, IL 60521-4530 (630) 655-9901
Contact: Paul E. Purcell, Pres.

Established in 1998 in IL.
Donor: Paul E. Purcell.
Foundation type: Independent foundation.
Financial data (yr. ended 12/31/13): Assets, $3,531,764 (M); gifts received, $4,919; expenditures, $489,292; qualifying distributions, $424,173; giving activities include $421,598 for 40 grants (high: $100,000; low: $450).
Fields of interest: Higher education; Education; United Ways and Federated Giving Programs.
Type of support: General/operating support.
Limitations: Applications accepted. Giving primarily in IL and WI. No grants to individuals.
Application information: Application form not required.
Initial approach: Proposal
Deadline(s): None
Officers: Paul E. Purcell, Pres.; Carolann P. Purcell, V.P.; Paul E. Purcell, Jr., V.P.; Patricia W. Purcell, Secy.
EIN: 364221916
Selected grants: The following grants are a representative sample of this grantmaker's funding activity:
$12,000 to Hazelden Foundation, Center City, MN, 2012. For rehab.

3102
R H Taylor for Princeton University ✧
10 S. Dearborn St., IL1-0117
Chicago, IL 60603-2300

Foundation type: Independent foundation.
Financial data (yr. ended 12/31/13): Assets, $46,169,848 (M); expenditures, $2,232,986; qualifying distributions, $1,971,093; giving activities include $1,900,593 for 1 grant.
Fields of interest: Higher education.
Limitations: Applications not accepted. Giving primarily in Princeton, NJ.
Application information: Contributes only to pre-selected organizations.
Trustee: JPMorgan Chase Bank, N.A.
EIN: 136745231
Selected grants: The following grants are a representative sample of this grantmaker's funding activity:
$1,958,156 to Princeton University, Princeton, NJ, 2012. For grant: Firestone Library, English Department, General.

3103
Rajchenbach Family Foundation ✧
6633 N. Lincoln Ave.
Lincolnwood, IL 60712-3625

Established in 1995 in IL.
Donors: Jack Rajchenbach; Judith Rajchenbach; JLR Management Corp.; J & J Partnership.
Foundation type: Independent foundation.
Financial data (yr. ended 12/31/12): Assets, $50,000 (M); gifts received, $1,052,802; expenditures, $1,052,931; qualifying distributions, $1,047,487; giving activities include $1,047,487 for 836+ grants (high: $50,000).
Purpose and activities: Giving primarily to Jewish organizations, temples, and schools.
Fields of interest: Elementary/secondary education; Theological school/education; Human services; Jewish agencies & synagogues.
Limitations: Applications not accepted. No grants to individuals.
Application information: Contributes only to pre-selected organizations.
Officers: Jack Rajchenbach, Pres.; Judith Rajchenbach, V.P.
EIN: 363990464

3104
Ranch Spur Charitable Trust ✧
P.O. Box 503
Wayne, IL 60184-0503
Contact: Frank Bauer, Tr.

Established in 2007 in IL.
Donor: Frank Bauer.
Foundation type: Independent foundation.
Financial data (yr. ended 12/31/13): Assets, $8,747,707 (M); gifts received, $122,875; expenditures, $628,626; qualifying distributions, $602,270; giving activities include $580,300 for 42 grants (high: $75,000; low: $1,000).
Fields of interest: Higher education, university; International affairs.
Type of support: Scholarships—to individuals.
Limitations: Applications accepted. Giving primarily in Washington, DC, IL and NY.
Application information: Application form required.
Initial approach: Letter
Deadline(s): None
Trustees: Frank Bauer; Joyce Bauer.
EIN: 266121636

3105
Rauner Family Foundation ✧
720 Rosewood Ave.
Winnetka, IL 60093-2031

Established in IL.
Donors: Bruce V. Rauner; Diana M. Rauner.
Foundation type: Independent foundation.
Financial data (yr. ended 12/31/12): Assets, $46,921,705 (M); expenditures, $6,372,468; qualifying distributions, $6,292,000; giving activities include $6,292,000 for 53 grants (high: $800,000; low: $2,000).
Fields of interest: Higher education; Education; Environment, natural resources; Human services; Children/youth, services; Community/economic development.
Limitations: Applications not accepted. Giving primarily in Chicago, IL; some funding also in Hanover, NH. No grants to individuals.
Application information: Contributes only to pre-selected organizations.
Officers: Bruce V. Rauner, Pres.; Diana M. Rauner, V.P. and Secy.-Treas.
Director: David R. Casper.
EIN: 363993405

3106
The Rawley Foundation ✧
c/o JPMorgan Chase Bank, N.A.
10 S. Dearborn St., M/S IL1-0111
Chicago, IL 60603-2300
Application address: c/o Stanley T. Rawley, 5400 Mesa Dr., Houston, TX 77028; tel.: (713) 635-4200

Established in 1997 in TX.
Donors: Stanley T. Rawley; Pipe Distributors, Inc.
Foundation type: Independent foundation.
Financial data (yr. ended 12/31/13): Assets, $8,609,755 (M); gifts received, $680,000; expenditures, $618,605; qualifying distributions, $586,312; giving activities include $565,000 for 21 grants (high: $70,000; low: $30,000).
Fields of interest: Higher education; Hospitals (general); Health organizations, association; Children/youth, services; Insurance, providers; Deaf/hearing impaired.
Type of support: General/operating support.
Limitations: Applications accepted. Giving primarily in TX, with emphasis on Houston.
Application information: Application form not required.
Initial approach: Proposal
Deadline(s): None
Trustees: Stanley T. Rawley; JPMorgan Chase Bank, N.A.
EIN: 766124547
Selected grants: The following grants are a representative sample of this grantmaker's funding activity:
$180,870 to Gateway Community Church, Houston, TX, 2011.
$50,000 to Texas Childrens Hospital, Houston, TX, 2011.
$45,000 to Houston Baptist University, Houston, TX, 2011.

$40,000 to Alzheimers Association, Houston, TX, 2011.
$30,000 to Center for Hearing and Speech, Houston, TX, 2011.
$25,000 to Boy Scouts of America, Houston, TX, 2011.
$25,000 to Bridge Over Troubled Waters, Pasadena, TX, 2011.
$25,000 to Salvation Army of Houston, Houston, TX, 2011.
$25,000 to Star of Hope Mission, Houston, TX, 2011.

3107
REAM Foundation ✧
485 Half Day Rd., Ste. 350
Buffalo Grove, IL 60089-8806
Contact: Elizabeth Versten, Exec. Dir.
Main URL: http://reamfoundation.org/

Established in 2006 in IL.
Donors: S. Miller; HLM & JM Charitable Lead Trust.
Foundation type: Independent foundation.
Financial data (yr. ended 12/31/13): Assets, $4,223,478 (M); gifts received, $716,326; expenditures, $540,511; qualifying distributions, $534,703; giving activities include $480,000 for 38 grants (high: $50,000; low: $5,000).
Purpose and activities: The foundation is committed to a world where children are cherished and nurtured to reach their full potential, and where health, education, and the arts are enriched for everyone. Giving is to those organizations that are doing the most effective work in: helping children reach their full potential, with an emphasis on preventing abuse; improving access to and quality of education; supporting advances in medicine and improving health; and nurturing the arts and cultural endeavors.
Fields of interest: Arts education; Performing arts; Arts; Education; Health care; Human services; Children.
Limitations: Giving primarily in IL.
Application information: Unsolicited applications not accepted. Submit Letter of Inquiry first.
Initial approach: Letter of Inquiry may be submitted through foundation web site
Officers and Directors:* D. Miller,* Pres.; S. Miller,* V.P. and Secy.; E. Achepohl,* Treas.
EIN: 205905128

3108
Redhill Foundation - Sam and Jean Rothberg Family Charitable Trust ✧
(also known as Redhill Foundation - Rothberg Family Charitable Trust)
c/o Kavanagh, Scully, Sudow, White & Frederick, P.C.
301 S.W. Adams St., Ste. 700
Peoria, IL 61602-1570 (309) 676-1381
Contact: Karen M. Stumpe Esq.

Established in 1987 in IL.
Donors: Samuel Rothberg; Lee Patrick Rothberg; Kathleen M. Barnett; Heidi B. Munday; Jean Rothberg; Samuel Rothberg Trust.
Foundation type: Independent foundation.
Financial data (yr. ended 12/31/13): Assets, $148,882,102 (M); expenditures, $8,991,121; qualifying distributions, $6,152,311; giving activities include $6,152,296 for 5 grants (high: $6,100,000; low: $40).
Purpose and activities: Giving primarily for Jewish organizations and for human services.
Fields of interest: Human services; United Ways and Federated Giving Programs; Jewish federated giving programs; Jewish agencies & synagogues.
Type of support: General/operating support; Scholarship funds; Research.
Limitations: Giving primarily in Peoria, IL and New York, NY. No grants to individuals.
Application information:
Initial approach: Letter
Deadline(s): None
Trustees: Kathleen M. Barnett; Heidi B. Rothberg; Jean C. Rothberg; Lee Patrick Rothberg; Michael Rothberg.
EIN: 371217165

3109
John & Cynthia Reed Foundation ✧
c/o The Northern Trust Co.
P.O. Box 803878
Chicago, IL 60680-3878

Established in 2000 in NY.
Donors: John S. Reed; Cynthia Reed.
Foundation type: Independent foundation.
Financial data (yr. ended 12/31/13): Assets, $1,176,355 (M); expenditures, $1,884,745; qualifying distributions, $1,856,585; giving activities include $1,855,000 for 30 grants (high: $590,000; low: $5,000).
Purpose and activities: Giving primarily for education and arts and culture.
Fields of interest: Museums (art); Performing arts, theater; Higher education; Higher education, university; Animals/wildlife, preservation/protection; Recreation, parks/playgrounds; Big Brothers/Big Sisters.
Type of support: General/operating support; Continuing support; Annual campaigns; Capital campaigns; Building/renovation; Land acquisition; Program development.
Limitations: Applications not accepted. Giving primarily in the greater metropolitan New York, NY, area, NJ and MA.
Application information: Unsolicited requests for funds not accepted.
Trustees: Cynthia Reed; John S. Reed.
Number of staff: 1 part-time professional; 1 part-time support.
EIN: 137219392
Selected grants: The following grants are a representative sample of this grantmaker's funding activity:
$500,000 to Massachusetts Institute of Technology, Cambridge, MA, 2012. For CMS, Hyper Studio and Shakespeare Initiatives.
$200,000 to Washington and Jefferson College, Washington, PA, 2012. For general support.
$180,000 to Concord Academy, Concord, MA, 2012.
$120,000 to Bard College, Annandale on Hudson, NY, 2012. For programs for at-risk students.
$100,000 to American Philosophical Society, Philadelphia, PA, 2012. For research.
$100,000 to MDRC, New York, NY, 2012. For general support.
$100,000 to RAND Corporation, Santa Monica, CA, 2012. For James Q. Wilson Tribute Fund.
$70,000 to Boston Symphony Orchestra, Boston, MA, 2012. For general support.
$50,000 to Bay Farm Montessori Academy, Duxbury, MA, 2012. For general support.
$50,000 to Celebrity Series of Boston, Boston, MA, 2012. For general support.

3110
Michael Reese Health Trust ✧
(formerly Michael Reese Hospital Foundation)
150 N. Wacker Dr., Ste. 2320
Chicago, IL 60606-1608 (312) 726-1008
Contact: Gregory S. Gross Ed.D., Pres.; Jennifer M. Rosenkranz, Sr. Prog. Off., Responsive Grants
FAX: (312) 726-2797;
E-mail: wpalmer@healthtrust.net; E-mail for Responsive Grant Program: jrosenkranz@healthtrust.net (Jennifer Rosenkranz); Main URL: http://www.healthtrust.net
Knowledge Center: http://www.healthtrust.net/index.php?option=com_content&task=view&id=14&Itemid=43

Established in 1995 in IL; converted from sale of Michael Reese Hospital to Humana (now Columbia/HCA).
Donors: Foreman Trust; Lazarus Charitable Fund; Kirchheimer Trust; Blum Trust; Alice Schimberg.
Foundation type: Independent foundation.
Financial data (yr. ended 06/30/13): Assets, $135,030,710 (M); gifts received, $443,143; expenditures, $7,844,624; qualifying distributions, $6,804,140; giving activities include $5,927,374 for 150 grants (high: $417,000; low: $700), and $199,260 for foundation-administered programs.
Purpose and activities: The trust is committed to improving the health of the Chicago area's most vulnerable residents: the poor, children and youth, people with disabilities, the elderly, immigrants and refugees, and the uninsured. Its grants and initiatives support the work of organizations serving these populations, as well as efforts to achieve lasting change in the region's healthcare delivery system.
Fields of interest: Education, public education; Public health; Health care; Medical research, institute; Children/youth, services; Civil/human rights, disabled; Jewish agencies & synagogues; Aging; Disabilities, people with; Military/veterans; Immigrants/refugees.
Type of support: General/operating support; Program development; Research; Technical assistance; Program evaluation.
Limitations: Applications accepted. Giving limited to the metropolitan Chicago, IL, area with emphasis on the city of Chicago. No support for private foundations, secular purposes or for durable medical equipment. No grants to individuals, or for capital campaigns, endowment funds, fundraising events, debt reduction, or scholarships.
Publications: Financial statement; Grants list; Multi-year report.
Application information: If an organization's letter of inquiry is accepted, a full proposal will be invited. Online application process. Application form not required.
Initial approach: Use online Letter of Inquiry found on foundation web site
Deadline(s): Dec. 15 and June 15 for receipt of letter of inquiry
Board meeting date(s): Twice per year
Final notification: Approx. 5-6 weeks after deadlines for letters of inquiry; approx. 3 months for proposals

Officers and Trustees:* Herbert S. Wander,* Chair.; Hon. Howard W. Carroll,* Vice-Chair.; Gregory S. Gross, Ed.D.*, Pres.; Walter R. Nathan,* Secy.; Ellard Pfaelzer, Jr.,* Treas.; Harvey J. Barnett; John F. Benjamin; Andrew K. Block; Bechara Choucair, M.D.; Nancy Glick; Ann-Louise Kleper; Gregory C. Mayer; Mally Z. Rutkoff; Michelle R. B. Saddler; Max R. Schrayer II; Michael B. Tarnoff; Joseph F. West, ScD; Andrea Rozran Yablon.
Number of staff: 4 full-time professional.
EIN: 362170910

3111
The Regenstein Foundation ✧

225 W. Wacker Dr., Ste. 1500
Chicago, IL 60606-1235 (312) 917-1833
Contact: Susan L. Regenstein, Chair. and Pres.

Incorporated in 1950 in IL as the Joseph & Helen Regenstein Foundation; in 1981 merged into Regenstein Foundation which was incorporated in DE.
Donors: Joseph Regenstein†; Helen Regenstein†; Velsicol Corporation; Arvey Corporation.
Foundation type: Independent foundation.
Financial data (yr. ended 12/31/13): Assets, $77,282,920 (M); expenditures, $4,533,788; qualifying distributions, $3,329,727; giving activities include $3,227,500 for 40 grants (high: $1,000,000; low: $2,500).
Fields of interest: Arts; Botanical gardens; Zoos/zoological societies; Hospitals (specialty); Human services; Children/youth, services.
Type of support: Capital campaigns; Building/renovation; Equipment; Program development; Research.
Limitations: Applications accepted. Giving primarily in the metropolitan Chicago, IL, area. No grants to individuals, or for scholarships, fellowships, annual campaigns, seed money, emergency funds, deficit financing, publications, conferences, or matching gifts; no loans.
Publications: Application guidelines; Program policy statement.
Application information: Most grants made on the initiative of the directors. Historically, the foundation has concentrated the majority of its grants toward one-time capital projects. Grants for continuing annual operations are limited and selective in scope. Application form required.
Initial approach: Proposal with foundation Grant Questionnaire
Copies of proposal: 1
Deadline(s): Mar. 31 and Sept. 30
Board meeting date(s): May and as required
Final notification: 30 days
Officers: Susan L. Regenstein, Chair. and Pres.; Joseph Regenstein III, Secy.-Treas.
Directors: Marshall Field V; Robert N. LaTour; F. Oliver Nicklin, Jr.
Number of staff: 3 full-time professional; 1 part-time support.
EIN: 363152531

3112
Robert and Jean Reid Family Foundation ✧ ☆

111 W. Monroe St., Tax Div. 10C
Chicago, IL 60603-4096

Established in WA.
Donor: Jean Reid Survivors Trust.
Foundation type: Independent foundation.
Financial data (yr. ended 12/31/13): Assets, $8,755,806 (M); gifts received, $10,000,000; expenditures, $1,502,411; qualifying distributions, $1,500,000; giving activities include $1,500,000 for 10 grants (high: $580,000; low: $10,000).
Fields of interest: Higher education; Hospitals (specialty); Health organizations; Human services.
Limitations: Applications not accepted. Giving primarily in Bellevue and Seattle, WA.
Application information: Unsolicited requests for funds not accepted.
Trustee: BMO Harris Bank, N.A.
EIN: 467048885

3113
The Retirement Research Foundation ✧

8765 W. Higgins Rd., Ste. 430
Chicago, IL 60631-4170 (773) 714-8080
Contact: Irene Frye, Exec. Dir.
FAX: (773) 714-8089; E-mail: info@rrf.org; Main URL: http://www.rrf.org
Grants List: http://www.rrf.org/about-rrf/grant-awards
The Retirement Research Foundation's Philanthropy Promise: http://www.ncrp.org/philanthropys-promise/who

Incorporated in 1950 in MI.
Donor: John D. MacArthur†.
Foundation type: Independent foundation.
Financial data (yr. ended 12/31/13): Assets, $134,295,217 (M); expenditures, $9,994,823; qualifying distributions, $6,757,283; giving activities include $5,104,975 for 121 grants (high: $451,319; low: $1,000), and $161,010 for 99 employee matching gifts.
Purpose and activities: The foundation is dedicated to improving quality of life for our nation's older population. It awards grants each year in support of programs, research, advocacy, and training to improve the quality of life for older Americans.
Fields of interest: Health care, home services; Mental health, addictions; Mental health/crisis services; Geriatrics; Geriatrics research; Employment, retraining; Housing/shelter, aging; Human services, public policy; Residential/custodial care, senior continuing care; Aging, centers/services; Civil/human rights, public policy; Nonprofit management; Gerontology.
Type of support: Research; Technical assistance; Program evaluation.
Limitations: Applications accepted. Giving limited to FL, IL, IN, IA, KY, MO and WI for direct service requests. Giving on a national basis for research, advocacy, education, and training. No support for governmental agencies except for area agencies on aging, state universities and the Veterans Administration. Generally, no grants to individuals, construction, general operating expenses of established organizations, endowment or developmental campaigns, deficit financing, land acquisition, scholarships, media productions, conferences, dissertation research, annual campaigns or biomedical research.
Publications: Application guidelines; Grants list; Informational brochure; Occasional report.
Application information: All proposals must relate to aged population. The foundation accepts the Chicago Area Grant Application Form. Application information and form available on foundation web site. Application form required.
Initial approach: E-mail, letter or telephone
Copies of proposal: 2
Deadline(s): Submit proposal preferably in Jan., Apr., or July; deadlines Feb. 1, May 1, and Aug. 1
Board meeting date(s): Feb., May, Aug., and Nov.
Final notification: Up to 6 months
Officers and Trustees:* Nathaniel P. McParland, M.D.*, Chair.; Ruth Ann Watkins,* Secy.; Downey R. Varey,* Treas.; Irene Frye, Exec. Dir.; Marvin Meyerson, Tr. Emeritus; John F. Santos, Ph.D., Tr. Emeritus; Sr. Stella Louise Slomka, C.S.F.N., Tr. Emeritus; Marilyn Hennessey; Kathleen Kolodgy; Thomas Prohaska, Ph.D.; Michael J. Starshak; Cheryl Woodson, M.D.
Number of staff: 4 full-time professional; 1 part-time professional; 3 full-time support; 1 part-time support.
EIN: 362429540
Selected grants: The following grants are a representative sample of this grantmaker's funding activity:
$139,812 to Nova Southeastern University, Davie, FL, 2012. For research on non-pharmacologic intervention, managed by family caregivers, to improve sleep in persons with dementia.
$124,828 to Council on Aging of Martin County, Stuart, FL, 2012. For geriatric health clinic co-located within senior center.
$99,546 to American Geriatrics Society, New York, NY, 2012. To disseminate up-to-date information about medications that are dangerous for older adults.
$77,484 to Council on Social Work Education, Alexandria, VA, 2012. To assess and prepare Aging Network workforce in areas of cultural competence, person-centered care and participant direction.
$75,000 to Pension Rights Center, Washington, DC, 2012. To provide training and technical assistance to regional Pension Counseling and Information across the country.
$50,000 to Pillars, La Grange Park, IL, 2012. For PEARLS, treatment program to reduce depression in older adults.
$45,000 to National People's Action, Chicago, IL, 2012. For advocacy campaign to end predatory payday lending practices targeting seniors.
$40,075 to Catholic Charities of the Archdiocese of Chicago, Chicago, IL, 2012. To train home care aides and seniors they serve about proper nutrition and healthy meal preparation.
$33,000 to Korean American Community Services, Chicago, IL, 2012. For program that trains recently retired Korean-Americans to assist low-income Korean seniors with applications for public benefits.
$30,000 to Asian Health Coalition of Illinois, Chicago, IL, 2012. For program to reduce disparities in colorectal cancer among older Asian Americans.

3114
J. Christopher and Anne N. Reyes Foundation ✧

6250 N. River Rd., Ste. 9000
Rosemont, IL 60018-4241

Established in 2007 in IL.
Donors: J. Christopher Reyes; Anne N. Reyes.
Foundation type: Independent foundation.
Financial data (yr. ended 12/31/13): Assets, $333,771 (M); gifts received, $3,505,250; expenditures, $4,337,555; qualifying distributions, $4,309,400; giving activities include $4,306,760 for 73 grants (high: $3,100,000; low: $500).

Fields of interest: Arts; Higher education; Education; Health organizations; Children/youth, services.
Limitations: Applications not accepted. Giving primarily in IL.
Application information: Contributes only to pre-selected organizations.
Trustees: Anne N. Reyes; J. Christopher Reyes.
EIN: 207532299

3115
The Rhoades Foundation ✧
(formerly Otto L. and Hazel T. Rhoades Fund)
233 S. Wacker Dr., Ste. 8000
Chicago, IL 60606-6448

Established in 1978 in IL.
Donors: Otto L. Rhoades†; Hazel T. Rhoades†.
Foundation type: Independent foundation.
Financial data (yr. ended 12/31/13): Assets, $14,125,748 (M); expenditures, $1,377,672; qualifying distributions, $1,172,520; giving activities include $1,172,520 for 140 grants (high: $200,000; low: $100).
Fields of interest: Museums (art); Performing arts; Performing arts, theater; Performing arts, opera; Arts; Higher education; Education; Hospitals (general); Health care; Food banks; Human services; Children/youth, services; Christian agencies & churches; Disabilities, people with.
Limitations: Applications not accepted. Giving primarily in IL. No grants to individuals.
Application information: Contributes only to pre-selected organizations.
Board meeting date(s): 1st week of Mar. and Dec.
Officers and Directors:* Julius Lewis,* Pres.; H. Allan Stark,* V.P. and Secy.; James F. Oates,* Treas.
EIN: 362994856

3116
Daniel F. and Ada L. Rice Foundation ✧
(also known as Rice Foundation)
8600 Gross Point Rd.
Skokie, IL 60077-2151 (847) 581-9999
Contact: Peter Nolan, Pres.

Incorporated in 1947 in IL.
Donors: Daniel F. Rice†; Ada Rice†.
Foundation type: Independent foundation.
Financial data (yr. ended 12/31/13): Assets, $76,240,798 (M); expenditures, $5,473,789; qualifying distributions, $4,666,965; giving activities include $3,990,232 for 101 grants (high: $1,000,000; low: $200).
Fields of interest: Higher education; Botanical gardens; Environment; Animal welfare; Hospitals (general); Health care; Human services; Children/youth, services.
Type of support: General/operating support.
Limitations: Applications accepted. Giving primarily in IL. No grants to individuals.
Application information:
Initial approach: Proposal
Deadline(s): Sept. 1
Officers and Directors:* Peter G. Nolan,* Pres.; Robin G. Nolan, V.P.; Celia A. Persson,* Secy.
EIN: 366043160

3117
Murray and Harriet Richards Private Foundation ✧ ☆
c/o The Northern Trust Company
P.O. Box 803878
Chicago, IL 60680-3878

Foundation type: Independent foundation.
Financial data (yr. ended 12/31/13): Assets, $5,056,550 (M); expenditures, $526,931; qualifying distributions, $471,209; giving activities include $464,400 for 1 grant.
Fields of interest: Human services.
Limitations: Applications not accepted. Giving primarily in CA.
Application information: Unsolicited requests for funds not accepted.
Trustee: Northern Trust Company.
EIN: 901027106

3118
Elyse Meredith Roberts and Raymond John Roberts Charitable Foundation ✧
88 Brinker Rd.
Barrington, IL 60010-5135

Established in 2001 in IL.
Donors: Elyse Meredith Roberts; Raymond J. Roberts; Allison Roberts Greene.
Foundation type: Independent foundation.
Financial data (yr. ended 07/31/13): Assets, $8,926,201 (M); gifts received, $69,443; expenditures, $464,058; qualifying distributions, $449,000; giving activities include $449,000 for 39 grants (high: $76,000; low: $500).
Purpose and activities: Giving primarily for the arts, education, and human services.
Fields of interest: Arts; Education; Health care; Athletics/sports, equestrianism; Human services; Children/youth, services.
Limitations: Applications not accepted. Giving primarily in IL, with some emphasis on Chicago. No grants to individuals.
Application information: Contributes only to pre-selected organizations.
Directors: Allison Roberts Greene; Elyse Meredith Roberts.
EIN: 522333799

3119
Margaret A. Roberts Charitable Foundation ✧
c/o Janice Rodgers
300 N. Lasalle St., Ste. 4000
Chicago, IL 60654-3422

Established in 1998 in IL.
Donor: Margaret A. Roberts.
Foundation type: Independent foundation.
Financial data (yr. ended 12/31/13): Assets, $14,020,324 (M); expenditures, $697,411; qualifying distributions, $628,251; giving activities include $598,000 for 41 grants (high: $100,000; low: $1,000).
Fields of interest: Higher education; Health organizations, association; Human services; Christian agencies & churches.
Type of support: General/operating support.
Limitations: Applications not accepted. Giving primarily in IL and KS. No grants to individuals.
Application information: Contributes only to pre-selected organizations.
Trustees: Thomas G. Hesse; Michael J. Roberts; Susan Shawn Roberts; Thomas H. Roberts III; Catherine Roberts-Suskin.
EIN: 367238483
Selected grants: The following grants are a representative sample of this grantmaker's funding activity:
$15,000 to Wichita State University Foundation, Wichita, KS, 2011.
$5,000 to Call to Action, Chicago, IL, 2011. For general operating support.
$1,500 to A Better Choice, Wichita, KS, 2011. For general operating support.
$1,000 to Wichita Childrens Home, Wichita, KS, 2011. For general operating support.

3120
Roy H. and Natalie C. Roberts Family Foundation ✧
P.O. Box 803878
Chicago, IL 60680-3878

Established in 2005 in FL.
Donor: Roy Roberts Trust.
Foundation type: Independent foundation.
Financial data (yr. ended 03/31/14): Assets, $38,738,144 (M); expenditures, $2,043,446; qualifying distributions, $1,936,317; giving activities include $1,730,500 for 51 grants (high: $300,000; low: $1,000).
Purpose and activities: Giving primarily for higher education, particularly for a medical school, as well as for the arts, health, and human services.
Fields of interest: Arts; Higher education; Dental school/education; Medical school/education; Health organizations; Human services.
Limitations: Applications not accepted. Giving primarily in MI and WA. No grants to individuals.
Application information: Contributes only to pre-selected organizations.
Officers: John H. Roberts, Pres.; Anne W. Roberts, V.P.; Rebecca Roberts, Secy.; David Roberts, Treas.
EIN: 656269008
Selected grants: The following grants are a representative sample of this grantmaker's funding activity:
$300,000 to University of Michigan, School of Medicine, Ann Arbor, MI, 2013. For general.
$300,000 to University of Michigan, School of Dentistry, Ann Arbor, MI, 2013. For general.

3121
Dora Roberts Foundation ✧
10 S. Dearborn St., IL1-0117
Chicago, IL 60603-2300 (817) 884-5155

Established in 1948 in TX.
Donors: Dora Roberts†; Eloise Canter Taylor.
Foundation type: Independent foundation.
Financial data (yr. ended 06/30/13): Assets, $69,088,284 (M); expenditures, $3,629,657; qualifying distributions, $2,806,859; giving activities include $2,686,680 for 31 grants (high: $350,000; low: $5,000).
Fields of interest: Arts; Education; Health care; Human services; Salvation Army.
Type of support: General/operating support.
Limitations: Applications accepted. Giving limited to TX, with emphasis on Big Spring.

Application information: Application form not required.
Initial approach: Proposal
Copies of proposal: 1
Deadline(s): Sept. 30
Board meeting date(s): Annually in Oct. or Nov.
Officers: Jimmy Tayler, Pres.; Sue Garrett Partee, Secy.-Treas.
Trustee: JPMorgan Chase Bank, N.A.
Board Members: Lisa Canter; Bob Moore; Stan Partee; Eloise Waters; R.H. Weaver.
EIN: 756013899
Selected grants: The following grants are a representative sample of this grantmaker's funding activity:
$241,400 to Dora Roberts Rehabilitation Center, Big Spring, TX, 2011. For program support.
$187,500 to Heritage Museum of Big Spring, Big Spring, TX, 2011. For program support.
$156,000 to First United Methodist Church, Big Spring, TX, 2011. For program support.
$100,000 to Humane Society of Big Spring, Big Spring, TX, 2011. For program support.
$80,000 to Howard County Council on Aging, Big Spring, TX, 2011. For program support.
$70,000 to Sibley Environmental Learning Center Foundation, Midland, TX, 2011. For program support.
$60,000 to Rape Crisis Services of Big Spring, Big Spring, TX, 2011. For program support.
$50,000 to Northside Community Action League, Big Spring, TX, 2011. For program support.
$50,000 to YMCA of Big Spring, Big Spring, TX, 2011. For program support.
$35,000 to University of Texas of the Permian Basin, Odessa, TX, 2011. For program support.

3122
Maurice R. Robinson Fund ✧ ☆
10 S. Dearborn St., IL1-0117
Chicago, IL 60603-2300
Application address: c/o Marian Steffens, Secy., Scholastic Inc., 557 Broadway, New York, NY 10012

Established in 1960 in NY.
Donors: Maurice R. Robinson‡; Florence L. Robinson‡; Robinson Family; Scholastic Inc.
Foundation type: Independent foundation.
Financial data (yr. ended 06/30/13): Assets, $7,286,039 (M); gifts received, $194,309; expenditures, $792,158; qualifying distributions, $789,104; giving activities include $780,000 for 3 grants (high: $750,000; low: $10,000).
Purpose and activities: Giving primarily for the arts and education.
Fields of interest: Arts, alliance/advocacy; Arts; Higher education.
Type of support: Program development; Seed money; Curriculum development; Internship funds; Scholarship funds; Program-related investments/loans.
Limitations: Applications accepted. Giving primarily on the East Coast, with emphasis on the metropolitan New York, NY, area. No grants to individuals.
Application information: Application form required.
Initial approach: Letter
Deadline(s): None
Board meeting date(s): Varies
Officers: Ernie Fleishman, Pres.; Rebecca Bondor, V.P.; Claudia Cohl, V.P.; Karen Proctor, V.P.; Marian Steffens, Secy.; John Quinn, Treas.
Number of staff: 3 part-time professional.
EIN: 136161094
Selected grants: The following grants are a representative sample of this grantmaker's funding activity:
$10,000 to Trinity College, Hartford, CT, 2011. For general support.

3123
Renee and Edward Ross Foundation ✧
c/o Edward Ross
35 E. Wacker Dr., Ste. 3300
Chicago, IL 60601-2306

Established in 1989 in IL.
Donors: Edward Ross; Renee Ross.
Foundation type: Independent foundation.
Financial data (yr. ended 12/31/13): Assets, $9,959,305 (M); expenditures, $525,648; qualifying distributions, $474,435; giving activities include $469,420 for 47 grants (high: $125,000; low: $100).
Fields of interest: Higher education; Health organizations, association; Diabetes research; Children, services; Jewish federated giving programs; Jewish agencies & synagogues.
Limitations: Applications not accepted. Giving primarily in Chicago, IL. No grants to individuals.
Application information: Unsolicited requests for funds not accepted.
Trustees: Edward Ross; Renee Ross.
Directors: Nanci Agostini; Patrice Alpert; Ilene Ross; William Ross.
EIN: 366914759
Selected grants: The following grants are a representative sample of this grantmaker's funding activity:
$5,000 to Rush University Medical Center, Chicago, IL, 2012. For As Needed.

3124
Hulda B. & Maurice L. Rothschild Foundation
c/o The Northern Trust Co., Attn.: Carol Grant, St. V.P.
50 S. LaSalle St., B-2
Chicago, IL 60603-1008 (312) 642-7060
Contact: Robert N. Mayer Ph.D., Pres.
E-mail: robtmayer@gmail.com; Main URL: http://www.therothschildfoundation.us/

Established in 1981 in IL.
Donor: Hulda B. Rothschild‡.
Foundation type: Independent foundation.
Financial data (yr. ended 12/31/13): Assets, $15,502,495 (M); expenditures, $711,700; qualifying distributions, $639,826; giving activities include $459,583 for 16 grants (high: $151,945; low: $1,400).
Purpose and activities: The foundation is a private national philanthropy with primary interest in improving the quality of life for elders in long term care communities, as well as a commitment to person-centered care in the United States. The foundation has created a number of regulatory task forces which are in the process of crafting new and/or revised national codes and standards which will help improve the quality of life for residents of long term care communities.
Fields of interest: Arts; Health care, patient services; Health care; Health organizations, administration/regulation; Residential/custodial care, senior continuing care; Aging.
Type of support: Program development; Publication; Seed money; Research; Matching/challenge support.
Limitations: Applications accepted. Giving primarily for programs with a national impact. No support for projects outside the U.S. No grants to individuals, or for general purposes, operating budgets, endowment or development campaigns, or scholarships; no loans.
Publications: Application guidelines; Program policy statement.
Application information: Application guidelines available on foundation web site.
Initial approach: The foundation prefers to receive a letter of inquiry or an e-mail prior to a formal grant application.
Copies of proposal: 1
Deadline(s): None
Final notification: Usually within 30 days
Officer: Robert N. Mayer, Pres.
Trustees: Beatrice C. Mayer; Debra Weese-Mayer.
EIN: 366752787

3125
Rotonda Foundation ✧
(formerly Irving Harris Foundation A)
191 N. Wacker Dr., Ste. 1500
Chicago, IL 60606-1899

Established in 1993 in IL.
Donors: Roxanne H. Frank; Irving B. Harris; Mako Foundation; Nancy Meyer; Marc Weiss.
Foundation type: Independent foundation.
Financial data (yr. ended 12/31/13): Assets, $10,734,412 (M); expenditures, $2,031,786; qualifying distributions, $1,654,415; giving activities include $1,645,500 for 55 grants (high: $1,000,000; low: $1,000).
Fields of interest: Museums (art); Arts; Higher education; Health organizations, association; Human services; Jewish federated giving programs; Jewish agencies & synagogues.
Limitations: Applications not accepted. Giving primarily in St. Louis, MO, and New York, NY. No grants to individuals.
Publications: Annual report.
Application information: Contributes only to pre-selected organizations.
Officers and Directors:* Roxanne H. Frank,* Pres. and Secy.; Daniel Meyer,* V.P.; Nancy Meyer,* V.P.; Thomas Meyer,* V.P.; Jack Polsky, V.P.; Beth Stephens, Treas.
EIN: 363866527

3126
Paul A. and Joan S. Rubschlager Foundation ✧
800 N. Michigan Ave., Unit 5902
Chicago, IL 60611-2153

Established in 1986 in IL.
Donors: Paul A. Rubschlager; Joan S. Rubschlager.
Foundation type: Independent foundation.
Financial data (yr. ended 10/31/13): Assets, $21,201,641 (M); gifts received, $1,666,390; expenditures, $767,250; qualifying distributions, $757,700; giving activities include $757,700 for 34 grants (high: $323,200; low: $1,600).

Fields of interest: Health care; Health organizations, association; Human services.
Limitations: Applications not accepted. Giving primarily in Chicago, IL. No grants to individuals.
Application information: Contributes only to pre-selected organizations.
Trustees: Joan S. Rubschlager; Paul A. Rubschlager.
EIN: 363487448
Selected grants: The following grants are a representative sample of this grantmaker's funding activity:
$255,000 to Museum of Broadcast Communications, Chicago, IL, 2011.
$38,200 to Les Turner Amyotrophic Lateral Sclerosis Foundation, Skokie, IL, 2011.
$30,000 to Alzheimers Association, Chicago, IL, 2011.
$13,100 to United States Fund for UNICEF, Chicago, IL, 2011.
$10,000 to American Red Cross, Chicago, IL, 2011.
$10,000 to Goodwill Industries of Chicago, Chicago, IL, 2011.
$8,625 to University of Chicago, Chicago, IL, 2011.
$5,500 to Multiple Sclerosis Society, National, Chicago, IL, 2011.
$5,000 to Rush University Medical Center, Chicago, IL, 2011.
$3,800 to Field Museum of Natural History, Chicago, IL, 2011.

3127
Ruggles Family Foudation ✧ ☆
c/o Northern Trust, N.A.
P.O. Box 803878
Chicago, IL 60680-3878

Donor: Ruth C. Ruggles Charitable Lead Annuity Trust A.
Foundation type: Independent foundation.
Financial data (yr. ended 04/30/13): Assets, $887,029 (M); gifts received, $821,391; expenditures, $656,075; qualifying distributions, $653,658; giving activities include $652,500 for 36 grants (high: $100,000; low: $2,500).
Fields of interest: Higher education; Education; Health care; Youth development.
Limitations: Applications not accepted. Giving primarily in IL, MA and NC.
Application information: Unsolicited requests for funds not accepted.
Trustees: Rudy Ruggles, Jr.; Leslie Rylee; Whitney Savignano; Northern Trust, N.A.
EIN: 266381931
Selected grants: The following grants are a representative sample of this grantmaker's funding activity:
$75,000 to NorthShore University HealthSystem Foundation, Evanston, IL, 2012.
$50,000 to Organization for Tropical Studies, Durham, NC, 2012.
$25,000 to Childrens Hospital Trust, Boston, MA, 2012.
$25,000 to Vincent Club, Boston, MA, 2012.
$20,000 to Founders Hall Foundation, Ridgefield, CT, 2012.
$10,000 to Childrens Hospital Trust, Boston, MA, 2012.
$10,000 to GO Project, New York, NY, 2012.
$10,000 to Harlem Childrens Zone, New York, NY, 2012.
$5,000 to Beverly Bootstraps Community Services, Beverly, MA, 2012.
$5,000 to New York Times Neediest Cases Fund, New York, NY, 2012.

3128
Joyce and Donald Rumsfeld Foundation ✧
(formerly D.H.R. Foundation)
c/o RALLC Tax Dept.
P.O. Box 3016
Chicago, IL 60654-0016

Established in IL.
Donors: Donald H. Rumsfeld; Joyce P. Rumsfeld.
Foundation type: Independent foundation.
Financial data (yr. ended 12/31/12): Assets, $4,396,446 (M); expenditures, $676,629; qualifying distributions, $625,300; giving activities include $625,300 for 115 grants (high: $107,500; low: $300).
Purpose and activities: Giving primarily for education and human services.
Fields of interest: Higher education; Education; Human services.
Limitations: Applications not accepted. Giving primarily in CA, Washington, DC, IL, with emphasis on Chicago, Taos, NM, and New York, NY. No grants to individuals.
Application information: Contributes only to pre-selected organizations.
Officers and Directors:* Donald H. Rumsfeld,* Pres.; Joyce P. Rumsfeld,* V.P.; James M. Denny,* Secy.-Treas.
EIN: 364283822

3129
S. Orville Ryan Family Foundation ✧
135 Thornbrook Rd.
DeKalb, IL 60115-2314

Established in 1997 in IL.
Donor: Richard O. Ryan.
Foundation type: Independent foundation.
Financial data (yr. ended 12/31/13): Assets, $1,027,830 (M); expenditures, $654,235; qualifying distributions, $652,125; giving activities include $650,000 for 2 grants (high: $450,000; low: $200,000).
Fields of interest: Performing arts, music; Arts; Higher education; Human services; Children/youth, services; Christian agencies & churches.
Limitations: Applications not accepted. Giving primarily in Chicago and DeKalb, IL. No grants to individuals.
Application information: Contributes only to pre-selected organizations.
Officers and Directors:* Richard O. Ryan,* Pres.; William M. Elsbury,* Secy.; Susan M. Dye; Kiera R. Kelly.
EIN: 364157632

3130
Patrick G. & Shirley W. Ryan Foundation ✧
150 N. Michigan Ave., Ste. 2100
Chicago, IL 60601-7559

Established in 1984 in IL.
Donors: Patrick G. Ryan; Shirley W. Ryan; Ryan Holding Corp. of Illinois; Ryan Enterprises Corp. of Illinois.
Foundation type: Independent foundation.
Financial data (yr. ended 11/30/13): Assets, $31,239,805 (M); gifts received, $9,808,507; expenditures, $6,428,833; qualifying distributions, $6,385,549; giving activities include $6,361,962 for 110 grants (high: $1,500,000; low: $100).
Purpose and activities: Giving primarily for education, the arts, Roman Catholic churches and schools, and children and youth services.
Fields of interest: Performing arts; Arts; Elementary/secondary education; Higher education; Education; Youth development, services; Human services; Children/youth, services; Residential/custodial care, hospices; United Ways and Federated Giving Programs; Catholic agencies & churches.
Limitations: Applications not accepted. Giving primarily in IL, with emphasis on Chicago. No grants to individuals.
Application information: Contributes only to pre-selected organizations.
Officers and Directors:* Patrick G. Ryan,* Chair. and V.P.; Shirley W. Ryan, Pres. and Treas.; Dawn Moore, Secy.; Corbett M.W. Ryan; Patrick G. Ryan, Jr.; Robert J.W. Ryan.
EIN: 363305162
Selected grants: The following grants are a representative sample of this grantmaker's funding activity:
$2,780,000 to Alain Locke Initiative, Chicago, IL, 2012. For general operating support.
$1,500,000 to Alain Locke Initiative, Chicago, IL, 2013. For general operating support.
$1,000,000 to Big Shoulders Fund, Chicago, IL, 2013. For general operating support.
$943,000 to Art Institute of Chicago, Chicago, IL, 2012. For general operating support.
$900,000 to Art Institute of Chicago, Chicago, IL, 2013. For general operating support.
$650,000 to Pathways Foundation, Glenview, IL, 2013. For general operating support.
$560,500 to Lyric Opera of Chicago, Chicago, IL, 2013.
$550,000 to Lyric Opera of Chicago, Chicago, IL, 2012. For Magnificent Art Form Continuation.
$525,000 to Big Shoulders Fund, Chicago, IL, 2012. For general operating support.
$175,000 to Chicago Council on Global Affairs, Chicago, IL, 2013. For strategic plan.
$50,000 to American Ireland Fund, Boston, MA, 2013. For general operating support.
$50,000 to Chicago Foundation for Education, Chicago, IL, 2012. For general operating support.
$50,000 to University of Notre Dame, Notre Dame, IN, 2012. For general operating support.
$50,000 to W T T W Channel 11, Chicago, IL, 2012. For To Celebrate American Song.
$25,230 to Donors Forum of Chicago, Chicago, IL, 2012. For educational support.
$25,000 to Aurora University, Aurora, IL, 2012. For Music by the Lake.
$25,000 to Music and Dance Theater Chicago, Chicago, IL, 2012. For general operating support.
$25,000 to Music Institute of Chicago, Wilmette, IL, 2013. For general operating support.
$25,000 to University of Notre Dame, Notre Dame, IN, 2013. For general operating support.
$10,000 to Mayo Clinic, Rochester, MN, 2013.

3131
Sacks Family Foundation ✧
1850 2nd St., Ste. 201
Highland Park, IL 60035-3176 (312) 506-6501
Contact: Michael Sacks

Established in 2001 in IL.
Donors: Michael Sacks; Judd Malkin; Stephen S. Malkin; Cari A. Sacks; Barry Malkin; Jodi Malkin; Karen Malkin.
Foundation type: Independent foundation.
Financial data (yr. ended 12/31/13): Assets, $2,142,050 (M); gifts received, $6,650,010; expenditures, $5,491,801; qualifying distributions, $5,489,513; giving activities include $5,489,513 for 99 grants (high: $720,000; low: $500).
Purpose and activities: Giving primarily for the arts, education, children and social services, health, and Jewish organizations and temples.
Fields of interest: Museums (art); Arts; Education; Health care; Human services; Children/youth, services; Jewish federated giving programs; Jewish agencies & synagogues.
Limitations: Giving primarily in Chicago, IL.
Application information:
Initial approach: Letter
Deadline(s): None
Officers: Michael Sacks, Pres. and Treas.; Kenneth Sacks, Secy.
Director: A. Lee Sacks.
EIN: 364053778

3132
Sall Family Foundation, Inc. ✧
10 S. Dearborn IL1-0117
Chicago, IL 60603-2300 (866) 888-5157
Contact: John Phillip Sall, Chair.
John and Ginger Sall's Giving Pledge Profile: http://glasspockets.org/philanthropy-in-focus/eye-on-the-giving-pledge/profiles/sall

Established in 1993 in NC.
Donors: John Phillip Sall; Virginia B. Sall.
Foundation type: Independent foundation.
Financial data (yr. ended 12/31/13): Assets, $13,017,302 (M); gifts received, $7,000,000; expenditures, $8,466,726; qualifying distributions, $8,435,750; giving activities include $8,435,000 for 9 grants (high: $4,750,000; low: $10,000).
Purpose and activities: Giving primarily for health, education, environmental protection, and community development.
Fields of interest: Education; Environment, natural resources; Health care; Community/economic development.
Limitations: Applications accepted. Giving primarily in Washington DC, CA, and VA. No grants to individuals.
Application information:
Initial approach: Letter
Deadline(s): Sept. 30
Officers: John Phillip Sall, Pres.; Virginia B. Sall, Secy.-Treas.
Board Members: Ben Abram; Jason Haggins; Sophie Harthorn; John McMillan; William B. Messer; Elizabeth A. Sall; English Sall; Leslie C. Sall; William Sall; Mary Tschirhart.
Agent: JPMorgan Chase Bank, N.A.
EIN: 582016050
Selected grants: The following grants are a representative sample of this grantmaker's funding activity:
$4,550,000 to CARE USA, Atlanta, GA, 2012. For general support.
$1,500,000 to Nature Conservancy, Arlington, VA, 2012. For general support.
$1,475,000 to World Wildlife Fund, Washington, DC, 2012. For general support.

3133
Gene A. Salmon Charitable Trust ✧
c/o Busey Trust Co.
P.O. Box 260
Champaign, IL 61824-0260

Established in IL.
Donor: Gene A. Salmon‡.
Foundation type: Independent foundation.
Financial data (yr. ended 12/31/13): Assets, $9,810,457 (M); expenditures, $529,111; qualifying distributions, $443,513; giving activities include $443,513 for 1 grant.
Fields of interest: Theological school/education; Christian agencies & churches.
Limitations: Applications not accepted. Giving primarily in Champaign, IL. No grants for individuals.
Application information: Contributes only to pre-selected organizations.
Trustee: Busey Trust Co.
EIN: 207135495

3134
Sangre De Christo Charitable Trust ✧
(formerly Bernard J. and Joyce M. Hank, Jr. Charitable Trust)
3630 71st St. Ct.
Moline, IL 61265-8011

Established in 1993 in IL.
Donors: Bernard J. Hank, Jr.; Joyce M. Hank; Viola Hank‡.
Foundation type: Independent foundation.
Financial data (yr. ended 12/31/13): Assets, $3,218,236 (M); expenditures, $508,289; qualifying distributions, $490,515; giving activities include $490,500 for 11 grants (high: $300,000; low: $2,500).
Fields of interest: Higher education; Education; Catholic agencies & churches.
Limitations: Applications not accepted. Giving primarily in Moline, IL and South Bend, IN. No grants to individuals.
Application information: Contributes only to pre-selected organizations.
Trustees: Bernard J. Hank, Jr.; Joyce M. Hank.
EIN: 367042588
Selected grants: The following grants are a representative sample of this grantmaker's funding activity:
$500,000 to University of Notre Dame, Notre Dame, IN, 2011. For unrestricted grant.
$25,000 to YMCA, Two Rivers, Moline, IL, 2011. For unrestricted grant.
$10,000 to Junior Achievement of the Heartland, Moline, IL, 2011. For unrestricted grant.
$10,000 to Saint Ambrose University, Davenport, IA, 2011. For unrestricted grant.
$10,000 to Saint Marys College, Notre Dame, IN, 2011. For unrestricted grant.
$5,000 to University of Notre Dame, Notre Dame, IN, 2011. For unrestricted grant.

3135
The Santreece Foundation ✧
100 E. Huron St., Ste. 4503
Chicago, IL 60611

Established in 2001 in DE.
Donors: Sandra M. Reece; Thomas L. Reece; Heather K. Reece.
Foundation type: Independent foundation.
Financial data (yr. ended 11/30/13): Assets, $8,294,775 (M); expenditures, $480,528; qualifying distributions, $480,528; giving activities include $441,500 for 26 grants (high: $75,000; low: $5,000).
Fields of interest: Arts; Education; Crime/violence prevention, abuse prevention; Human services; YM/YWCAs & YM/YWHAs.
Type of support: General/operating support; Program development.
Limitations: Applications not accepted. Giving on a national basis. No grants to individuals.
Application information: Contributes only to pre-selected organizations.
Officers and Directors:* Thomas L. Reece,* Pres.; Sandra Reece,* V.P.; Heather K. Reece, Secy. and Admin.; Leslie A. Littlejohn,* Treas.; Paul D. Littlejohn.
Number of staff: None.
EIN: 311809798
Selected grants: The following grants are a representative sample of this grantmaker's funding activity:
$30,000 to Family and Childrens Services, Kalamazoo, MI, 2011.
$15,000 to Farmers Alley Theater, Kalamazoo, MI, 2011. For general operating support.
$15,000 to Unitarian Universalist Service Committee, Cambridge, MA, 2011.
$10,000 to Catholic Family Services, Kalamazoo, MI, 2011. For general operating support.
$10,000 to Colorado Bright Beginnings, Denver, CO, 2011. For general operating support.
$10,000 to Greenhope Services for Women, New York, NY, 2011. For general operating support.
$10,000 to Kalamazoo Institute of Arts, Kalamazoo, MI, 2011.
$5,000 to Advocates for Victims of Assault, Frisco, CO, 2011.
$2,500 to Walden Family Services, San Diego, CA, 2011. For general operating support.

3136
The Satter Foundation ✧
500 N. Michigan Ave., Ste. 1700
Chicago, IL 60611-3751

Established in 1997 in NY.
Donors: Kristen Hertel; Muneer A. Satter.
Foundation type: Independent foundation.
Financial data (yr. ended 12/31/13): Assets, $70,423,924 (M); expenditures, $8,163,536; qualifying distributions, $6,251,449; giving activities include $5,709,583 for 87 grants (high: $515,000; low: $250).
Fields of interest: Higher education; Environment, natural resources; Hospitals (general); Health organizations, association; Human services; Civil/human rights; Foundations (private grantmaking).
Limitations: Applications not accepted. Giving in the U.S., with emphasis on IL, MA, and NY. No grants to individuals.
Application information: Contributes only to pre-selected organizations.
Trustees: Kristen Hertel; Muneer A. Satter.
EIN: 133936468

3137
Mary Bucksbaum Scanlan Family Foundation ✧
c/o MB Investments LLC
180 N. Wacker Dr., No. 001
Chicago, IL 60601-1648

Established in 2002 in IL.
Donor: Mary Bucksbaum Scanlan.
Foundation type: Independent foundation.
Financial data (yr. ended 12/31/12): Assets, $13,725,304 (M); expenditures, $6,563,846; qualifying distributions, $6,456,330; giving activities include $6,456,300 for 13+ grants (high: $4,000,000; low: $25,000).
Fields of interest: Museums (art); Arts; Education; Human services.
Limitations: Applications not accepted. Giving in the U.S., with emphasis on CO and NY. No grants to individuals.
Application information: Contributes only to pre-selected organizations.
Officers and Directors:* Mary Bucksbaum Scanlan,* Pres.; Michael Greaves, V.P.; Patrick Scanlan,* Secy.; Melva Bucksbaum,* Treas.
EIN: 527240192

3138
The Clarence W. and Marilyn G. Schawk Family Foundation ✧
c/o Clarence W. Schawk
1695 River Rd.
Des Plaines, IL 60018-2205

Established in 1995 in IL.
Donors: Clarence W. Schawk; Marilyn G. Schawk.
Foundation type: Independent foundation.
Financial data (yr. ended 12/31/13): Assets, $4,378,218 (M); gifts received, $400,000; expenditures, $1,213,627; qualifying distributions, $1,210,859; giving activities include $1,208,548 for 49 grants (high: $803,818; low: $100).
Purpose and activities: Giving primarily to Christian and Protestant agencies, as well as for education and human services.
Fields of interest: Higher education; Education; Hospitals (general); Human services; United Ways and Federated Giving Programs; Christian agencies & churches; Protestant agencies & churches.
Limitations: Applications not accepted. Giving primarily in Minneapolis, MN and IL. No grants to individuals.
Application information: Contributes only to pre-selected organizations.
Trustees: Clarence W. Schawk; Marilyn G. Schawk.
EIN: 363996543

3139
Schmidt Family Foundation ✧
c/o JPMorgan Chase Bank
10 S. Dearborn St., IL1-0117
Chicago, IL 60603-2317
Application address: c/o Maria Levix, 399 N.W. Boca Raton Blvd., Boca Raton, FL 33432

Established in 1982 in FL.
Donors: Charles E. Schmidt†; Charles E. Smith 1994 Revocable Trust.
Foundation type: Independent foundation.
Financial data (yr. ended 12/31/12): Assets, $46,542,559 (M); expenditures, $8,139,332; qualifying distributions, $7,891,699; giving activities include $7,661,821 for 57 grants (high: $5,402,170; low: $1,192).
Purpose and activities: Giving primarily for the arts, education, health, and children, youth, and social services.
Fields of interest: Arts; Higher education; Education; Hospitals (general); Health organizations, association; Human services; Children/youth, services.
Type of support: General/operating support; Scholarship funds; Matching/challenge support.
Limitations: Giving primarily in southern FL. No grants to individuals.
Application information: Application form not required.
Initial approach: Letter
Copies of proposal: 1
Deadline(s): None
Board meeting date(s): Apr., Sept., and Jan.
Trustees: Barbara M. Schmidt; Catherine B. Schmidt; Richard L. Schmidt; Raymond Webb; JPMorgan Chase Bank, N.A.
Number of staff: 1 part-time professional.
EIN: 136808881

3140
Arthur J. Schmitt Foundation ✧
P.O. Box 340
LaGrange, IL 60525-0340 (708) 522-9361
Contact: Patricia A. Shevlin, Exec. Dir.
E-mail: schmittfoundation@gmail.com; Main URL: http://www.schmittfoundation.org

Incorporated in 1941 in IL.
Donor: Arthur J. Schmitt†.
Foundation type: Independent foundation.
Financial data (yr. ended 06/30/13): Assets, $15,965,294 (M); expenditures, $1,115,375; qualifying distributions, $980,616; giving activities include $891,000 for 14 grants (high: $100,000; low: $15,000).
Purpose and activities: Giving for institutional scholarship support to universities for undergraduate and graduate studies, and to organizations that sponsor and mentor under-privileged students attending Catholic high schools. Funding also for organizations that develop and support learning and leadership in students of various learning levels.
Fields of interest: Education; Human services.
Type of support: General/operating support; Continuing support; Fellowships; Scholarship funds.
Limitations: Giving primarily in the metropolitan Chicago, IL, area. No grants to individuals, or for capital or building funds, research, or matching gifts; no loans.
Publications: Informational brochure.
Application information: The foundation does not encourage new grant applications at this time.
Board meeting date(s): Sept., Dec., Mar., and June
Officers and Directors:* John J. Gearen,* Pres.; Mary M. Dwyer,* Treas.; Daniel E. Mayworm,* V.P.; Peter J. Wrenn,* V.P.; Patricia A. Shevlin, Exec. Dir.; Richard C. Becker, Pres. and Board Member Emeritus; Patrick C. Eilers; Carol H. Sullivan.
Number of staff: 1 part-time professional.
EIN: 362217999

3141
Dr. Scholl Foundation ✧
1033 Skokie Blvd., Ste. 230
Northbrook, IL 60062-4109 (847) 559-7430
Contact: Pamela Scholl, Chair. and Pres.
Main URL: http://www.drschollfoundation.com

Incorporated in 1947 in IL.
Donor: William M. Scholl, M.D.†.
Foundation type: Independent foundation.
Financial data (yr. ended 12/31/12): Assets, $154,250,553 (M); expenditures, $9,864,858; qualifying distributions, $8,426,050; giving activities include $6,964,464 for 334 grants (high: $1,000,000; low: $1,000).
Purpose and activities: Support for private education at all levels, including elementary, secondary, and postsecondary schools, colleges and universities, and medical and nursing institutions; general charitable programs, including grants to hospitals, and programs for children, the developmentally disabled, and senior citizens; and civic, cultural, social welfare, economic, and religious activities.
Fields of interest: General charitable giving.
Type of support: Continuing support; Equipment; Program development; Fellowships; Internship funds; Scholarship funds; Research.
Limitations: Applications accepted. Giving primarily in the U.S., with some emphasis on the Chicago, IL area. No support for public education, political organizations, or political action committees. No grants to individuals, or for deficit financing, or unrestricted purposes, or to endowments, or capital campaigns, event sponsorship, liquidation of debt; no loans.
Publications: Application guidelines; Informational brochure.
Application information: Applications sent by fax or e-mail not accepted; only one request per organization, per year is permitted. Application form required.
Initial approach: Letter on organization letterhead
Copies of proposal: 1
Deadline(s): Mar. 1
Board meeting date(s): Feb., May, Aug., and Nov.
Final notification: Nov.
Officers and Directors:* Pamela Scholl,* Chair. and Pres.; Anne Moseley, V.P.; Jeanne M. Scholl,* Secy.; John A. Nitschke, Treas.; Mary Ann Hynes; Stephen Meer; Richard B. Patterson; Daniel Scholl; Susan Scholl.
Number of staff: 3 full-time professional; 3 full-time support.
EIN: 366068724
Selected grants: The following grants are a representative sample of this grantmaker's funding activity:
$1,000,000 to Rosalind Franklin University of Medicine and Science, College of Podiatric Medicine, North Chicago, IL, 2012. For $500,000 for scholarships for Dr. William M Scholl College of Podiatric Medicine and the remainder to be used for scholarships for other health profession colleges.
$420,000 to American Committee for the Weizmann Institute of Science, Chicago, IL, 2012. For water and climate research.
$100,000 to Christie Charity, Manchester, England, 2012. For positions of Physiotherapist and Occupational Therapist.
$100,000 to Mount Vernon Ladies Association, Mount Vernon, VA, 2012. To restore Large Dining Room.

$70,000 to Broader Urban Involvement and Leadership Development, Chicago, IL, 2012. To support use of Cluster Model programs.
$15,000 to Nature Conservancy, Chicago, IL, 2012. For river science project.
$10,000 to CommunityHealth, Chicago, IL, 2012. For free clinic visits for medical and dental patients.
$10,000 to Teach for America, Chicago, IL, 2012. For early childhood education initiative.
$7,000 to International Hearing Dog, Henderson, CO, 2012. For training and placement of hearing dog.
$5,000 to Musical Offering, Evanston, IL, 2012. For scholarship program.

3142
John and Kathleen Schreiber Foundation ✧

682 Bank Ln., Ste. 200
Lake Forest, IL 60045-1885

Established in 2005 in IL.
Donors: John G. Schreiber; SB Westridge, Inc.
Foundation type: Independent foundation.
Financial data (yr. ended 12/31/13): Assets, $34,541,777 (M); gifts received, $3,912,792; expenditures, $1,887,242; qualifying distributions, $1,817,022; giving activities include $1,751,383 for grants.
Fields of interest: Higher education; Education; Health organizations; Human services; Children/youth, services; Catholic agencies & churches.
Limitations: Applications not accepted. Giving primarily in IL.
Application information: Contributes only to pre-selected organizations.
Officers: John G. Schreiber, Pres.; Kathleen A. Schreiber, Treas.
Director: Heather E. Sannes.
EIN: 421684377
Selected grants: The following grants are a representative sample of this grantmaker's funding activity:
$180,000 to Big Shoulders Fund, Chicago, IL, 2011.
$60,670 to Church of Saint Mary, Lake Forest, IL, 2011.
$50,100 to Catholic Charities of Lake County, Waukegan, IL, 2011.
$50,000 to Ann and Robert H. Lurie Children's Hospital of Chicago Foundation, Chicago, IL, 2011.
$50,000 to Loyola Academy, Wilmette, IL, 2011.
$25,000 to Academy for Urban School Leadership, Chicago, IL, 2011.
$25,000 to Mercy Housing Lakefront, Chicago, IL, 2011.
$18,000 to Deborahs Place, Chicago, IL, 2011.
$16,667 to Cornell University, Ithaca, NY, 2011.
$5,000 to Alexian Brothers Bonaventure House, Chicago, IL, 2011.

3143
Schuler Family Foundation ✧

28161 N. Keith Dr.
Lake Forest, IL 60045-4528
E-mail: info@schulerprogram.org; Main URL: http://www.schulerfoundation.org/
Blog: http://www.schulerscholar.blogspot.com
Facebook: https://www.facebook.com/schulerprogram
Google Plus: https://plus.google.com/107506573411218462200/posts
LinkedIn: http://www.linkedin.com/company/schuler-scholar-program
Twitter: https://www.twitter.com/SchulerScholar
YouTube: http://www.youtube.com/channel/UCVxXfByTFbtCjW5JqCuNc5A

Established in 1997 in IL.
Donors: Jack W. Schuler; AmeriCorps.
Foundation type: Independent foundation.
Financial data (yr. ended 12/31/13): Assets, $150,154,388 (M); gifts received, $10,443,419; expenditures, $5,442,969; qualifying distributions, $4,906,253; giving activities include $2,050 for 4 grants (high: $1,000; low: $50), $846,810 for grants to individuals, and $846,960 for foundation-administered programs.
Purpose and activities: The foundation sponsors a scholarship program to motivate and change behavior of high potential students to strive towards a goal of graduating from college, recognizing that even high potential students are vulnerable to outside influences during high school and college years. Schuler Scholars are Illinois students selected at the end of the freshman year in high school. They are offered a 4 year college scholarship provided they maintain the requirements of the Scholar program for their remaining 3 years of high school and 4 years of college. Each student will have a team of advisors, including her/his parents to help him or her navigate through high school and college. At Highland Park and Maine East high schools, applications will be accepted from 8th grade students only; at Waukegan High School, applications will be accepted from Freshman only; at Round Lake and Warren Township high schools, applications will be accepted from both 8th grade and Freshman students.
Fields of interest: Arts; Higher education; Health care; Human services; Children/youth, services; Women, centers/services.
Type of support: Scholarships—to individuals.
Limitations: Giving primarily in IL.
Application information: Contributes only to pre-selected organizations for general grants. See foundation web site for Schuler Scholar guidelines and application. Application form required.
Deadline(s): Varies
Officers: Jack W. Schuler, Pres. and Secy.; Therese H. Hoffman, V.P.; Tino H. Schuler, V.P.; Tanya E. Sharman, V.P.; Renate R. Schuler, Treas.; Candace A. Browdy, Exec. Dir.
EIN: 364154510
Selected grants: The following grants are a representative sample of this grantmaker's funding activity:
$1,000 to Annie Wright School, Tacoma, WA, 2011. For general support.
$1,000 to Bravewell Collaborative, Minneapolis, MN, 2011. For general support.
$1,000 to Heritage Foundation, Washington, DC, 2011. For general support.
$1,000 to Wallin Education Partners, Minneapolis, MN, 2011. For general support.

3144
The Eleanor Schwartz Charitable Foundation ✧

c/o Rodolphe Hamel, Stephen B. Boies, Joan Lavella
10 S. Dearborn St., IL1-0117
Chicago, IL 60603-2300

Established in 2008 in DE.
Donor: Eleanor Schwartz‡.
Foundation type: Independent foundation.
Financial data (yr. ended 07/31/13): Assets, $34,184,662 (M); expenditures, $1,829,038; qualifying distributions, $1,638,838; giving activities include $1,515,000 for 13 grants (high: $300,000; low: $50,000).
Fields of interest: Higher education; Ear, nose & throat research; Human services; Biology/life sciences.
Limitations: Applications not accepted. Giving primarily in New York, NY; funding also in MA.
Application information: Contributes only to pre-selected organizations.
Trustees: Stephen Boies; Rodolphe Hamel; Joan Lavella; JPMorgan Chase Bank, N.A.
EIN: 516593287
Selected grants: The following grants are a representative sample of this grantmaker's funding activity:
$200,000 to Cold Spring Harbor Laboratory, Cold Spring Harbor, NY, 2011. For general purpose fund.
$100,000 to Trudeau Institute, Saranac Lake, NY, 2011. For general purpose fund.

3145
Theodore G. Schwartz Family Foundation ✧

(formerly Theodore G. and M. Christine Schwartz Family Foundation)
c/o TCS Group, LLC
1 N. Wacker Dr., Ste. 3605
Chicago, IL 60606-2834

Established in 1996 in IL.
Donors: Theodore G. Schwartz; M. Christine Schwartz.
Foundation type: Independent foundation.
Financial data (yr. ended 12/31/13): Assets, $186,839 (M); gifts received, $350,000; expenditures, $595,030; qualifying distributions, $595,000; giving activities include $595,000 for 8 grants (high: $350,000; low: $4,000).
Purpose and activities: Giving to 1) promote self-esteem, self-confidence and a sense of pride in Jewish youth, emphasizing Jewish identity and historical accomplishments, and to promote causes to benefit the State of Israel; 2) to encourage measures for raising standards of research and prevention or suppression of mental illness and related disorders, including establishing or maintaining transitional living resources for afflicted individuals, to assist them in building confidence and the necessary tools for successful re-entry into the mainstream; 3) to promote resources to enable and empower deserving youth in broken homes and dysfunctional environments to develop self-esteem and self-confidence while assisting them to become productive adults; 4) to promote alternative transitional resources to enable and empower people in abusive relationships to develop self-esteem, and to allow them to productively improve their lives and eliminate abuse; 5) to promote conservation of natural resources, and the advancement of farming, by providing education to deserving students and funding research to benefit responsible farmers; 6) to encourage measures for preservation and conservation of wildlife, including the enhancement of animal life and promotion of animal welfare; 7) to match resources with the homeless whose private resources are inadequate, including financial assistance for the erection and

operation of housing, and the opportunity for a better future; 8) to promote education by providing resources and financial assistance to enable motivated responsible individuals to secure an education; 9) to promote scientific and medical research for the alleviation of human suffering, including promoting a better quality of life and sense of dignity when encountering adversity; 10) to encourage measures for raising standards of medical care, research and prevention or suppression of disease; and 11) to promote public appreciation of literature, music, painting, dance and other fine arts.
Fields of interest: Higher education; Health organizations; Human services; Community/economic development; Jewish agencies & synagogues.
Limitations: Applications not accepted. Giving primarily in IL, with emphasis on Chicago. No grants to individuals; or for political campaigns.
Application information: Contributes only to pre-selected organizations.
Officers and Directors:* M. Christine Schwartz,* Pres.; Tracy Ward,* Secy.; Theodore G. Schwartz,* Treas.; Todd Schwartz.
EIN: 311490195
Selected grants: The following grants are a representative sample of this grantmaker's funding activity:
$1,930,419 to United Jewish Communities of MetroWest, Whippany, NJ, 2011.

3146
The Seabury Foundation ✧
1111 N. Wells St., Ste. 503
Chicago, IL 60610-7633 (312) 587-7146
Contact: Boyd McDowell III
FAX: (312) 587-7332;
E-mail: bmcdowell@seaburyfoundation.org; Main URL: http://www.seaburyfoundation.org

Trust established in 1947 in IL.
Donors: Charles Ward Seabury†; Louise Lovett Seabury†.
Foundation type: Independent foundation.
Financial data (yr. ended 12/31/13): Assets, $24,899,012 (M); expenditures, $1,290,964; qualifying distributions, $969,349; giving activities include $775,160 for 89 grants (high: $32,000; low: $904).
Purpose and activities: Giving primarily for community and social services.
Fields of interest: Arts education; Arts; Elementary/secondary education; Education, early childhood education; Child development, education; Middle schools/education; Secondary school/education; Vocational education; Vocational education, post-secondary; Higher education; Higher education, college (community/junior); Adult education—literacy, basic skills & GED; Education, ESL programs; Education, drop-out prevention; Education, computer literacy/technology training; Education; Environment, formal/general education; Environment; Employment, services; Employment, job counseling; Employment, training; Employment, retraining; Infants/toddlers; Children/youth; Adults; Young adults; Economically disadvantaged.
Type of support: Curriculum development; Continuing support; Program development; Scholarship funds; Matching/challenge support.
Limitations: Applications accepted. Giving primarily in Chicago, IL; giving also in various states where family member sponsors organization and proposal. No support for religious organizations. No grants to individuals, or for annual campaigns, private research or benefit events.
Publications: Application guidelines; Grants list; Program policy statement; Program policy statement (including application guidelines).
Application information: All submissions must be made to The Seabury Foundation office by e-mail and one mailed hard copy of the LOI or proposal, and both must be received by the close of business (4:30 p.m., Central Time) on the due dates. The hard copy should be addressed to the Foundation Director, with the e-mail copy being sent to lstigsen@seaburyfoundation.org. Full proposals accepted by invitation only following letter of inquiry. The foundation makes no multi-year grants, although organizations may apply up to three years in a row. It mostly funds program support, as opposed to general operating expenses. See foundation web site for details. Application form not required.
Initial approach: 1-2-page letter of inquiry at least 45 days in advance of deadlines
Copies of proposal: 1
Deadline(s): For Letters of Inquiry: Sept. 15, Jan. 15 and June 15; for Proposals: Nov. 1, Mar. 1, and Aug. 1
Board meeting date(s): Feb., May, and Oct.
Final notification: Feb. 28, May 31, and Oct. 31
Officers and Trustees:* Robert S. Boone,* Chair. and Exec. Dir.; Fanny Boone Zeddies,* Exec. Secy.; Sarah Boone; William C. Fisk; Seabury J. Hibben; Louise Fisk Morris; David G. Seabury.
Director: Boyd McDowell III.
Number of staff: 2 full-time professional.
EIN: 366027398
Selected grants: The following grants are a representative sample of this grantmaker's funding activity:
$25,000 to Indianapolis Zoological Society, Indianapolis, IN, 2012.
$19,718 to Julian Center, Indianapolis, IN, 2012.
$18,000 to Providence Cristo Rey High School, Indianapolis, IN, 2012.
$16,000 to University of Arizona, Tucson, AZ, 2012.
$12,000 to East Village Youth Program, Chicago, IL, 2012.
$10,000 to 826CHI, Chicago, IL, 2012.
$10,000 to Chicago Coalition for the Homeless, Chicago, IL, 2012.
$10,000 to Lakeside Shakespeare Theater, Frankfort, MI, 2012.
$7,500 to Chicago Coalition for the Homeless, Chicago, IL, 2012.
$4,000 to Berea College, Berea, KY, 2012.

3147
Segal Family Foundation ✧
(formerly Segal Family Foundation II)
1474 Techny Rd.
Northbrook, IL 60062-5447

Established in 2000 in IL.
Donors: Carole B. Segal; Christopher S. Segal; Robert Segal; Katherine E.S. Frekko; Gordon I. Segal Income Trust; Segal Family Trust; Gordon Segal.
Foundation type: Independent foundation.
Financial data (yr. ended 12/31/13): Assets, $30,306,010 (M); gifts received, $1,483,745; expenditures, $2,608,593; qualifying distributions, $2,530,947; giving activities include $2,530,947 for 77 grants (high: $1,000,000; low: $1,000).
Fields of interest: Arts; Higher education; Theological school/education; Education; Hospitals (general); Health organizations, association; Human services; Foundations (private grantmaking); Jewish agencies & synagogues.
Limitations: Applications not accepted. Giving primarily in Chicago, IL. No grants to individuals.
Application information: Contributes only to pre-selected organizations.
Officers: Carole B. Segal, Pres. and Treas.; Harvey J. Silverstone, Secy.
Directors: Katherine Frekko; Robert Segal.
EIN: 364330990

3148
Barbara and Barre Seid Foundation ✧
(formerly Barre Seid Foundation)
1111 W. 35th St., 12th Fl.
Chicago, IL 60609-1404

Established in 1985 in IL.
Donor: Barre Seid.
Foundation type: Independent foundation.
Financial data (yr. ended 12/31/13): Assets, $1,730,370 (M); gifts received, $1,550,000; expenditures, $2,151,932; qualifying distributions, $2,149,254; giving activities include $2,147,120 for 40 grants (high: $966,000; low: $100).
Purpose and activities: Support primarily for education, cultural organizations and the arts, and philanthropic associations.
Fields of interest: Performing arts, music; Performing arts, opera; Arts; Higher education; Education; Human services; Jewish federated giving programs; Jewish agencies & synagogues.
Limitations: Applications not accepted. Giving primarily in Chicago, IL. No grants to individuals.
Application information: Contributes only to pre-selected organizations.
Officers: Barre Seid, Pres. and Treas.; Barbara Landis-Seid, Secy.
Director: Joan Frontczak.
EIN: 363342443

3149
SF Foundation ✧
(formerly Simon Family Foundation)
27 N. Wacker Dr., Ste. 458
Chicago, IL 60606-2800

Established in 1997 in IL.
Donors: Daniel L. Simon; S. Simon.
Foundation type: Independent foundation.
Financial data (yr. ended 12/31/13): Assets, $29,797,796 (M); gifts received, $2,522,609; expenditures, $1,789,277; qualifying distributions, $1,553,500; giving activities include $1,553,500 for 10 grants (high: $1,000,000; low: $1,000).
Purpose and activities: Giving primarily for higher education; funding also for human services.
Fields of interest: Secondary school/education; Higher education; Human services; Family services; Economically disadvantaged.
Limitations: Applications not accepted. Giving primarily in IL and MN; some funding in New York, NY. No grants to individuals.
Application information: Contributes only to pre-selected organizations.
Directors: K. Hondru; Joseph Simon; Paul G. Simon; Sandra Simon.
EIN: 364146804

3150
Lester & Edna Shapiro Family Foundation ✧
799 Central Ave., Ste. 350
Highland Park, IL 60035-5640

Established in 1968.
Donors: Lester Shapiro†; Nathan Shapiro; Norton Shapiro; Robert Shapiro; Daniel Shapiro; Sherwin Begoun; Steven Shapiro; NS Associates, Inc.; New Horizon Enterprises, Inc.
Foundation type: Independent foundation.
Financial data (yr. ended 09/30/13): Assets, $454,474 (M); gifts received, $287,390; expenditures, $660,732; qualifying distributions, $648,041; giving activities include $648,041 for 1 + grant.
Fields of interest: Elementary/secondary education; Jewish agencies & synagogues.
Limitations: Applications not accepted. No grants to individuals.
Application information: Contributes only to pre-selected organizations.
Officers: Nathan Shapiro, Pres.; Daniel Shapiro, Secy.-Treas.
Trustees: Norton Shapiro; Robert Shapiro.
EIN: 363985971

3151
Charles and M. R. Shapiro Foundation, Inc. ✧
(formerly Fern G. Shapiro, Morris R. Shapiro, and Charles Shapiro Foundation, Inc.)
191 N. Wacker Dr., Ste. 1800
Chicago, IL 60606-1615

Incorporated in 1958 in IL.
Donors: Charles Shapiro†; Mary Shapiro†; Molly Shapiro†; Morris R. Shapiro†.
Foundation type: Independent foundation.
Financial data (yr. ended 07/31/13): Assets, $39,141,096 (M); expenditures, $2,045,767; qualifying distributions, $1,911,351; giving activities include $1,722,020 for 84 grants (high: $154,520; low: $5,000).
Purpose and activities: Giving primarily to Jewish organizations and for human services; funding also for higher education.
Fields of interest: Arts; Higher education; Health organizations, association; Medical research, institute; Human services; Youth, services; Jewish federated giving programs; Jewish agencies & synagogues.
Limitations: Applications not accepted. Giving primarily in Chicago, IL; funding also in New York, NY. No grants to individuals.
Application information: Contributes only to pre-selected organizations.
Officers and Directors:* Norman A. Shubert,* Pres.; Joan Pines,* V.P. and Secy.; Robert Kaufman; Judy Rosen.
EIN: 366109757
Selected grants: The following grants are a representative sample of this grantmaker's funding activity:
$135,000 to Board of Jewish Education of Chicago, Chicago, IL, 2011. For general support.

3152
Earl & Brenda Shapiro Foundation ✧
111 E. Wacker Dr., Ste. 2607
Chicago, IL 60601-4211 (312) 552-7660
Contact: Benjamin Shapiro, V.P. and Treas.

Established in 2003 in IL.
Donors: Earl W. Shapiro; Soretta Shapiro; Soretta and Henry Shapiro Family Foundation; Brenda M. Shapiro; Matthew I. Shapiro; Benjamin M. Shapiro; Alexandra E. F. Shapiro.
Foundation type: Independent foundation.
Financial data (yr. ended 12/31/12): Assets, $27,926,003 (M); gifts received, $2,000,000; expenditures, $3,240,885; qualifying distributions, $3,127,068; giving activities include $3,107,000 for 45 grants (high: $500,000; low: $2,500).
Fields of interest: Arts; Higher education; Environment, natural resources; Jewish federated giving programs.
Type of support: General/operating support.
Limitations: Applications accepted. Giving primarily in Chicago, IL and New York, NY. No grants to individuals.
Application information: Application form not required.
Initial approach: Letter
Deadline(s): None
Officers and Directors:* Brenda M. Shapiro,* Pres.; Matthew I. Shapiro,* V.P. and Secy.; Alexandra E. F. Shapiro, V.P. and Co-Treas.; Benjamin M. Shapiro,* V.P. and Co-Treas.
EIN: 450524597

3153
The Howard and Jackie Shapiro Foundation ✧
(formerly Howard Shapiro Foundation)
26 N. Halsted St.
Chicago, IL 60661-2107

Established in 2006 in IL.
Donors: Howard Shapiro†; Weigel Broadcasting Co.
Foundation type: Independent foundation.
Financial data (yr. ended 12/31/13): Assets, $10,767,205 (M); expenditures, $640,964; qualifying distributions, $633,790; giving activities include $633,790 for 14 grants (high: $105,000; low: $790).
Fields of interest: Jewish federated giving programs; Jewish agencies & synagogues.
Limitations: Applications not accepted. Giving primarily in IL. No grants to individuals.
Application information: Unsolicited requests for funds not accepted.
Directors: Fred Bishop; Norman Shapiro.
EIN: 134331684
Selected grants: The following grants are a representative sample of this grantmaker's funding activity:
$185,000 to Jewish Federation of Metropolitan Chicago, Chicago, IL, 2011.
$40,000 to Doctors Without Borders USA, New York, NY, 2011.
$10,000 to Northwestern University, Evanston, IL, 2011.
$10,000 to Wayland Academy, Beaver Dam, WI, 2011.

3154
The Walden W. & Jean Young Shaw Foundation ✧
131 S. Deerborn St., Ste. 2400
Chicago, IL 60603-5577

Established in 1967 in IL.
Donors: Walden W. Shaw; Jean Young Shaw.
Foundation type: Independent foundation.
Financial data (yr. ended 06/30/13): Assets, $8,212,445 (M); expenditures, $632,711; qualifying distributions, $558,578; giving activities include $496,450 for 11 grants (high: $115,000; low: $5,000).
Purpose and activities: Giving primarily for hospitals and other medical facilities, including medical facilities for children, as well as for other children's services.
Fields of interest: Hospitals (general); Hospitals (specialty); Mental health, treatment; Cancer; Medical research, institute; Cancer research; Children/youth, services.
Limitations: Applications not accepted. Giving primarily in Chicago, IL, CA, and OR. No grants to individuals.
Application information: Contributes only to pre-selected organizations.
Officers: Donald Carey Iler, Pres. and Exec. Dir.; Robert Gordon Iler, Jr., V.P.; Walter Roth, Secy.-Treas.
Directors: N. Carey Iler, Jr.; Robert Gordon Iler, Jr.; Cheryl Kennedy; Sharon Jean Kirby.
EIN: 366162196
Selected grants: The following grants are a representative sample of this grantmaker's funding activity:
$38,000 to Burn Institute, San Diego, CA, 2013. For general funds.

3155
The Sheba Foundation ✧
1225 Corporate Blvd.
Aurora, IL 60505

Established in 1994 in IL.
Donors: Sheldon Lavin; Sylvia Lavin.
Foundation type: Independent foundation.
Financial data (yr. ended 12/31/13): Assets, $22,739,419 (M); gifts received, $5,050,000; expenditures, $2,637,166; qualifying distributions, $2,563,088; giving activities include $2,561,900 for 14 grants (high: $1,020,000; low: $100).
Purpose and activities: Giving primarily for health, particularly children's health, as well as for Jewish federated giving programs.
Fields of interest: Performing arts, theater; Hospitals (specialty); Health organizations, association; Medical research, institute; Children/youth, services; Jewish federated giving programs.
Limitations: Applications not accepted. Giving primarily in IL. No grants to individuals.
Application information: Contributes only to pre-selected organizations.
Officers and Directors:* Sheldon Lavin,* Pres.; Steven Lavin,* Secy.-Treas.; Deborah Rosenberg.
EIN: 363976909
Selected grants: The following grants are a representative sample of this grantmaker's funding activity:
$2,500,000 to Rush University Medical Center, Chicago, IL, 2012. For cancer center at new medical facility.

3156
Peggy and Bill Shiffick Charitable Foundation ✧
P.O. Box 803878
Chicago, IL 60680-1285

Established in 1996 in TX.
Donors: Margaret Shiffick; William Shiffick†.
Foundation type: Independent foundation.
Financial data (yr. ended 12/31/13): Assets, $12,648,786 (M); expenditures, $733,652; qualifying distributions, $592,753; giving activities include $580,346 for 3 grants (high: $232,138; low: $174,104).
Fields of interest: Higher education.
Limitations: Applications not accepted. Giving limited to TX. No grants to individuals.
Application information: Unsolicited requests for funds not accepted.
Trustees: Christine Herrforth Groccia; Northern Trust Bank, N.A.
EIN: 766112561
Selected grants: The following grants are a representative sample of this grantmaker's funding activity:
$237,107 to University of Saint Thomas, Houston, TX, 2011.
$177,830 to Rice University, Houston, TX, 2011.
$177,830 to University of Houston System, Houston, TX, 2011.

3157
Daniel & Louise M. Shipman Charity ✧
231 S. LaSalle St., IL1-231-10-05
Chicago, IL 60604-1426

Established in IL.
Foundation type: Independent foundation.
Financial data (yr. ended 04/30/13): Assets, $12,800,987 (M); expenditures, $857,455; qualifying distributions, $740,975; giving activities include $740,975 for grants.
Purpose and activities: Giving primarily to a school for boys, as well as for hospitals, and to a retirement community.
Fields of interest: Education; Hospitals (general); Health care; Aging.
Limitations: Applications not accepted. Giving primarily in the Chicago, IL, area. No grants to individuals.
Application information: Unsolicited requests for funds not accepted.
Trustee: Bank of America, N.A.
EIN: 366038534
Selected grants: The following grants are a representative sample of this grantmaker's funding activity:
$125,991 to Admiral at the Lake, Chicago, IL, 2012.
$125,991 to Glenwood School, Glenwood, IL, 2012.
$125,991 to Northwestern Memorial Foundation, Chicago, IL, 2012.
$118,408 to Rush University Medical Center, Chicago, IL, 2012.

3158
Russell and Betty Shirk Foundation ✧
P.O. Box 1549
Bloomington, IL 61702-1549
Application address: c/o James A. Shirk, 103 N. Robinson St., Bloomington, IL 61701-5424, tel.: (309) 827-8580

Established in 1968.
Donors: Russell O. Shirk; James A. Shirk; Betty J. Shirk; Linda S. Shirk.
Foundation type: Independent foundation.
Financial data (yr. ended 12/31/13): Assets, $10,952,160 (M); gifts received, $234,000; expenditures, $600,067; qualifying distributions, $527,452; giving activities include $491,750 for 15 grants (high: $250,000; low: $250).
Purpose and activities: Giving primarily for higher education, as well as to a YMCA; funding also for social services.
Fields of interest: Higher education; Education; Health organizations, association; Human services; YM/YWCAs & YM/YWHAs.
Type of support: General/operating support; Scholarship funds.
Limitations: Applications accepted. Giving primarily in McLean County, IL. No grants to individuals.
Application information: Application form required.
Initial approach: Contact foundation for application form
Deadline(s): May 1 and Oct. 1
Officers and Directors:* James A. Shirk,* Pres.; Linda S. Shirk,* Treas.; Betty J. Shirk; Cynthia L. Shirk; Lia Valerio Shirk.
EIN: 237022709
Selected grants: The following grants are a representative sample of this grantmaker's funding activity:
$280,000 to Illinois Wesleyan University, Bloomington, IL, 2012. For athletic complex.
$5,000 to United Way of McLean County, Bloomington, IL, 2012. To support of Local Charities.

3159
Simmons Mesothelioma Foundation ✧
1 Court St.
Alton, IL 62002-6267 (877) 309-6376
E-mail: info@simmonsmesotheliomafoundation.org; Main URL: http://www.simmonsmesotheliomafoundation.org

Donor: Simmons Browder Gianaris Angelides.
Foundation type: Independent foundation.
Financial data (yr. ended 12/31/12): Assets, $2,474 (M); gifts received, $796,325; expenditures, $697,321; qualifying distributions, $697,321; giving activities include $680,195 for 9 grants (high: $229,920; low: $5,000).
Purpose and activities: The foundation will provide much-needed financial, organizational, volunteer, and other resources, to support the national efforts of medical experts and researchers, hospitals, universities, patient caregivers, advocates, and philanthropic organizations in the pursuit of improved quality of life for patients and, ultimately, finding of a cure for mesothelioma.
Fields of interest: Cancer research; Lung research.
Limitations: Applications not accepted. Giving primarily in Chicago, IL, New York, NY, and PA.
Application information: Contributes only to pre-selected organizations.
Officers and Directors:* John Simmons,* Pres.; Michael Angelides,* V.P.; Gregg Kirkland,* Secy.; Mark Motley.
EIN: 271278566

3160
The Simon Family Foundation ✧
843 Bluff St.
Glencoe, IL 60022-1572 (847) 835-9195
Contact: Albert Simon III, Pres.

Established in 2000 in IL.
Donors: Albert Simon, Jr.†; Albert Simon III.
Foundation type: Independent foundation.
Financial data (yr. ended 12/31/13): Assets, $65,996,489 (M); gifts received, $2,940,370; expenditures, $2,746,263; qualifying distributions, $2,641,260; giving activities include $2,545,986 for 55 grants (high: $178,745; low: $5,000).
Fields of interest: Arts; Agriculture/food; Human services.
Limitations: Applications accepted. Giving primarily in IL. No grants to individuals.
Application information: Application form required.
Initial approach: Letter
Deadline(s): None
Officers: Albert Simon III, Pres.; Judith Simon, V.P.
EIN: 364325958

3161
The Alexandrine and Alexander L. Sinsheimer Fund ✧
10 S. Dearborn St., IL1-0117
Chicago, IL 60603-2300
Application address: c/o Wing Wilson, V.P., 270 Park Ave., 16th Fl., New York, NY 10017-2014; tel.: (212) 464-1497

Established in 1959 in NY.
Donors: Alexander L. Sinsheimer†; Alexandrine Sinsheimer†.
Foundation type: Independent foundation.
Financial data (yr. ended 04/30/13): Assets, $10,222,378 (M); expenditures, $534,287; qualifying distributions, $453,890; giving activities include $430,000 for 7 grants (high: $100,000; low: $50,000).
Purpose and activities: Grants to medical schools to support scientific research relating to the prevention and cure of human diseases.
Fields of interest: Medical school/education; Medical research, institute.
Type of support: Research.
Limitations: Giving primarily in the metropolitan New York, NY, area; some funding also in Rochester, and Syracuse, NY.
Application information: Application form required.
Deadline(s): Feb. 15
Final notification: Apr. 30
Trustee: JPMorgan Chase Bank, N.A.
EIN: 136047421
Selected grants: The following grants are a representative sample of this grantmaker's funding activity:
$547,000 to Yeshiva University, New York, NY, 2011.

3162
The Siragusa Foundation ✧
1 E. Wacker Dr., Ste 2910
Chicago, IL 60601-1474 (312) 755-0064
Contact: Irene S. Phelps, Pres.
FAX: (312) 755-0069; E-mail: info@siragusa.org;
Main URL: http://www.siragusa.org
Grants List: http://www.siragusa.org/pages/recent_grants_2013/176.php

Trust established in 1950 in IL; incorporated in 1980.
Donor: Ross D. Siragusa†.
Foundation type: Independent foundation.
Financial data (yr. ended 12/31/13): Assets, $26,141,212 (M); gifts received, $1,000; expenditures, $1,916,359; qualifying distributions, $1,535,472; giving activities include $1,100,216 for 137 grants (high: $32,000; low: $500), and $20,458 for employee matching gifts.
Purpose and activities: The foundation strives to improve the quality of life for people living in the metropolitan Chicago, IL, area, by funding projects and programs that help care for those in need, as well as nurture the environments in which they live, work and play. Building on the foundation's founder Ross D. Siragusa's compassion and generosity, the foundation believes in working with organizations, communities and other philanthropic entities to connect people with people, engage people in issues and bridge people to services, all with the purpose of fulfilling their basic needs, enhancing their lives, and fostering a sense of community. The foundation supports charitable organizations that reflect the founder's special interests in arts and culture, education, the environment, health services and medical research, and human services.
Fields of interest: Humanities; Arts; Higher education; Education; Environment; Hospitals (general); Health care; Medical specialties; Youth, services; Child development, services; Aging, centers/services; Homeless, human services; Human services; Infants/toddlers; Children/youth; Children; Youth; Adults; Aging; Young adults; Disabilities, people with; Physically disabled; Blind/visually impaired; Mentally disabled; Minorities; African Americans/Blacks; Hispanics/Latinos; Native Americans/American Indians; Women; Girls; Military/veterans; Offenders/ex-offenders; AIDS, people with; Immigrants/refugees; Economically disadvantaged; Homeless.
Type of support: General/operating support; Continuing support; Emergency funds; Program development; Fellowships; Scholarship funds; Technical assistance; Employee matching gifts.
Limitations: Applications not accepted. Giving primarily in the metropolitan Chicago, IL, area. No support for political advocacy programs. No grants to individuals, or for endowment funds or medical research; no loans.
Publications: Annual report; Financial statement; Grants list; IRS Form 990 or 990-PF printed copy available upon request.
Application information: Unsolicited requests for funds not accepted. Refer to foundation web site for further information.
Board meeting date(s): Apr. and Nov.
Officers and Directors:* John E. Hicks, Jr., Chair.; Ross D. Siragusa III,* Vice-Chair.; Irene S. Phelps, C.E.O. and Pres.; Sinclair C. Siragusa,* Secy.; John R. Siragusa III,* Treas.; James Durkan; Caitlyn Hicks; Alisa Perrotte; Andrew Perrotte; Melvyn H. Schneider; Alexander C. Siragusa; Isabel Siragusa.
Number of staff: 2 full-time professional; 1 full-time support.
EIN: 363100492

3163
Sirius Fund ✧
(formerly Peter and Virginia Foreman Family Foundation)
225 W. Washington St., Ste. 1650
Chicago, IL 60606-3486 (312) 443-5240
Contact: Peter B. Foreman, Pres.

Established in 1990 in IL.
Donors: Christopher Foreman; Peter B. Foreman.
Foundation type: Independent foundation.
Financial data (yr. ended 06/30/13): Assets, $15,982,919 (M); gifts received, $6,000; expenditures, $874,335; qualifying distributions, $869,859; giving activities include $825,236 for 94 grants (high: $205,200; low: $25).
Purpose and activities: Giving primarily for the arts, education, health, and human services; also support for Jewish organizations and the environment.
Fields of interest: Museums; Performing arts, theater; Arts; Higher education; Education; Environment, natural resources; Botanical gardens; Hospitals (general); Health care; Health organizations, association; Recreation, parks/playgrounds; Human services; Children/youth, services; Women, centers/services; Community development, neighborhood development; Jewish federated giving programs.
Limitations: Applications accepted. Giving primarily in ID and IL. No grants to individuals.
Application information: Application form not required.
Initial approach: Letter of inquiry
Deadline(s): None
Officers: Peter B. Foreman, Co-Pres.; Virginia Foreman, Co-Pres.; Rhonda Keysor, V.P.
Directors: Chris Foreman; Jeff Foreman.
EIN: 363712587
Selected grants: The following grants are a representative sample of this grantmaker's funding activity:
$55,200 to Art Institute of Chicago, Chicago, IL, 2011.
$45,000 to National Forest Foundation, Missoula, MT, 2011.
$37,500 to PADS Lake County, Waukegan, IL, 2011.
$31,150 to Chicago Horticultural Society, Glencoe, IL, 2011.
$12,215 to Ravinia Festival Association, Highland Park, IL, 2011.
$11,000 to Sun Valley Summer Symphony, Ketchum, ID, 2011.
$10,000 to Chicago Symphony Orchestra, Chicago, IL, 2011.
$10,000 to Field Museum of Natural History, Chicago, IL, 2011.
$10,000 to Merit School of Music, Chicago, IL, 2011.
$5,000 to 500 Clown, Chicago, IL, 2011.

3164
H. D. Smith Foundation ✧
3063 Fiat Ave.
Springfield, IL 62703-5930

Established in IL.
Donors: Joseph Conda; Henry Dale Smith, Jr.; James Christopher Smith; Rogers Smith; Andrew Smith; Emmanuel Watson; Robert Mcnew; George Grimes; Christian Herrington; Walnut Foundation; H.D. Smith Wholesale Drug Corp.
Foundation type: Independent foundation.
Financial data (yr. ended 12/31/13): Assets, $15,742,404 (M); gifts received, $1,025,058; expenditures, $1,076,482; qualifying distributions, $1,042,320; giving activities include $1,042,320 for 90 grants (high: $105,000; low: $1,000).
Fields of interest: Education; Human services; Protestant agencies & churches; Catholic agencies & churches.
Limitations: Applications not accepted. Giving primarily in IL, PA, and VT.
Application information: Contributes only to pre-selected organizations.
Officers: Henry Dale Smith, Jr., Pres.; James Christopher Smith, V.P. and Secy.-Treas.; D. Andrew Smith, 2nd V.P.
EIN: 452487072
Selected grants: The following grants are a representative sample of this grantmaker's funding activity:
$16,400 to Amigos en Cristo, Bonita Springs, FL, 2012. For charitable and religious.

3165
Harry L. & John L. Smysor Memorial Fund ✧
c/o First Mid-Illinois Bank & Trust
P.O. Box 529
Mattoon, IL 61938-0529
Contact: Laura Walk
Application address: c/o First Mid-Illinois Bank & Trust, 1515 Charleston Ave., Mattoon, IL 61938-3932, tel.: (217) 258-0633

Established in 1982 in IL.
Donors: Catherine H. Smysor†; John L. Smysor†.
Foundation type: Independent foundation.
Financial data (yr. ended 05/31/13): Assets, $13,754,204 (M); expenditures, $891,945; qualifying distributions, $569,526; giving activities include $552,484 for 160 grants to individuals (high: $6,364; low: $1,591).
Purpose and activities: Awards scholarships to high school students for higher education.
Fields of interest: Higher education.
Type of support: Scholarships—to individuals.
Limitations: Applications accepted. Giving primarily to residents of IL.
Application information: Application form required.
Initial approach: Proposal
Deadline(s): Apr. 15
Trustees: Gary Boske; Orris Seng; First Mid-Illinois Bank & Trust.
EIN: 371160678

3166
Fred B. Snite Foundation ✧
550 W. Frontage Rd., Ste. 3745
Northfield, IL 60093-1289 (847) 446-7705
Contact: Margaret Sackley, Pres.

Incorporated in 1945 in IL.
Donors: Fred B. Snite†; Local Loan Co.
Foundation type: Independent foundation.

Financial data (yr. ended 06/30/13): Assets, $17,996,581 (M); expenditures, $904,905; qualifying distributions, $734,000; giving activities include $734,000 for grants.
Purpose and activities: Giving primarily for Roman Catholic church support and church-related educational institutions; funding also for social services.
Fields of interest: Higher education; Education; Human services; Catholic agencies & churches.
Limitations: Applications accepted. Giving in the U.S., with emphasis on IL. No grants to individuals.
Application information: Application form required.
Initial approach: Letter
Deadline(s): None
Officers: Margaret Sackley, Pres.; Teresa Bratton, V.P.; Katherine B. Miszklevitz, V.P.; Theresa Rassas, V.P.; Patrick Sackley, V.P.; Joanne Ward, V.P.; Lance Williams, V.P.; Patricia Nahigian, Secy.; Robert Wott, Treas.
EIN: 366084839
Selected grants: The following grants are a representative sample of this grantmaker's funding activity:
$100,000 to Big Shoulders Fund, Chicago, IL, 2011.
$15,000 to Lambs Farm, Libertyville, IL, 2011.

3167
Soderstrom Family Charitable Trust ✧
4909 N. Glen Park Pl.
Peoria, IL 61614-4689 (309) 674-7546
Contact: Carl W. Soderstrom, Jr. M.D., Tr.

Established in 1997 in IL.
Donors: Carl W. Soderstrom; Carl D. Soderstrom.
Foundation type: Independent foundation.
Financial data (yr. ended 12/31/13): Assets, $2,205,688 (M); expenditures, $625,053; qualifying distributions, $612,650; giving activities include $610,000 for 10 grants (high: $510,000; low: $500).
Fields of interest: Health organizations.
Limitations: Applications accepted. Giving primarily in IL; some giving in TX and MN. No grants to individuals.
Application information: Application form not required.
Initial approach: Proposal
Deadline(s): None
Trustees: Carl D. Soderstrom; Carl W. Soderstrom, Jr., M.D.; Robert W. Soderstrom.
EIN: 367187407

3168
Souder Family Foundation ✧
P.O. Box 803878
Chicago, IL 60680

Established in 1986 in FL.
Donors: Susanna J. Souder; William F. Souder, Jr. Charitable Lead Trust; Susanna Souder Charitable Lead Trust.
Foundation type: Independent foundation.
Financial data (yr. ended 12/31/13): Assets, $22,192,146 (M); gifts received, $743,666; expenditures, $1,081,969; qualifying distributions, $912,050; giving activities include $910,550 for 58 grants (high: $100,000; low: $500).
Fields of interest: Museums (children's); Historic preservation/historical societies; Education; Aquariums; Hospitals (general); Human services; Protestant agencies & churches.
Type of support: General/operating support; Annual campaigns; Building/renovation.
Limitations: Applications not accepted. Giving primarily in FL, IL, MI, and WI. No grants to individuals.
Application information: Unsolicited requests for funds not accepted.
Directors: Susanna J. Souder; William F. Souder, Jr.; Eric J. Vainder.
EIN: 391560019

3169
Southeastern Illinois Community Foundation ✧ ☆
300 E. Washington Ave.
P.O. Box 1211
Effingham, IL 62401 (217) 342-4988
Contact: For grants: Joedy Hightower, Pres. and C.E.O.
FAX: (217) 342-4995;
E-mail: info@enrichingourcommunity.org; Additional e-mail: jhightower@enrichingourcommunity.org; Main URL: http://www.enrichingourcommunity.org/
YouTube: https://www.youtube.com/user/southeasternilcf?feature=watch

Established in 1999 in IL.
Foundation type: Community foundation.
Financial data (yr. ended 12/31/13): Assets, $16,381,479 (M); gifts received, $2,036,290; expenditures, $1,199,933; giving activities include $522,045 for 13+ grants (high: $68,544), and $82,496 for 61 grants to individuals.
Purpose and activities: The foundation provides services to donors interested in providing charitable funding, providing financial support for qualified nonprofit organizations and other charitable purpose in the regional area.
Fields of interest: Arts; Education; Health care; Human services.
Type of support: Capital campaigns; Equipment; Program development.
Limitations: Applications accepted. Giving primarily in Effingham County, IL.
Publications: Annual report; Informational brochure (including application guidelines).
Application information: Visit foundation web site for application information. Application form required.
Initial approach: Submit application
Deadline(s): May for Effing County, June 27 for Colcs County
Board meeting date(s): Jan., Mar., May, July, Sept. and Nov.
Final notification: Sept. 1
Officers and Directors:* Scott Lensink,* Chair.; Brian Titus,* Vice-Chair.; Joedy Hightower,* Pres. and C.E.O.; James Schultz,* Secy.; Richard Siemer,* Treas.; Mark Bolander; Bill Elliott; Brett Kingery.
Number of staff: 1 part-time professional.
EIN: 371390271

3170
Albert J. & Claire R. Speh Foundation ✧
10700 W. Higgins Rd., Ste. 250
Rosemont, IL 60018-3711 (847) 299-7011
Contact: Kevin Malinger, Exec. Dir.
FAX: (847) 299-7044; E-mail: info@speh.org; Main URL: http://www.speh.org
Grants List: http://www.speh.org/grantees.php

Established in 1996 in IL.
Donors: Albert J. Speh, Jr.†; Claire R. Speh.
Foundation type: Independent foundation.
Financial data (yr. ended 12/31/13): Assets, $9,993,033 (M); expenditures, $902,750; qualifying distributions, $740,889; giving activities include $537,982 for 34 grants (high: $120,000; low: $2,500).
Purpose and activities: Giving for programs that directly impact youth between the ages of 13 and 19.
Fields of interest: Education; Youth development; Children/youth, services; Family services.
Type of support: General/operating support; Continuing support; Management development/capacity building; Annual campaigns; Capital campaigns; Building/renovation; Equipment; Emergency funds; Program development; Seed money; Curriculum development; Internship funds; Scholarship funds; Technical assistance; Consulting services; Employee-related scholarships; Matching/challenge support.
Limitations: Applications accepted. Giving primarily in the metropolitan Chicago, IL, area. Generally, no grants to individuals, government agencies, medical/healthcare agencies and programs, or for research or political activity.
Publications: Grants list; Informational brochure (including application guidelines).
Application information: Letter of intent must be submitted 60 days prior to grant application deadline. Full proposals are by invitation only, upon review of letter of interest. Chicago Area Grant Application Form accepted, and can be downloaded from foundation web site (if full proposal is requested). Organizations that are not approved for grants are welcome to submit a new letter of interest the subsequent year. Application form required.
Initial approach: Letter of interest (no longer than 2 typewritten pages, via e-mail. Attachments, brochures, reports, articles, etc., will not be accepted)
Copies of proposal: 1
Deadline(s): Mar. 15 and July 15 for applications
Board meeting date(s): Feb., June, and Oct.
Final notification: June 30 and Oct. 30
Officers and Members:* Kevin Malinger,* Exec. Dir.; Alanna Golden,* Prog. Off.; Justin Bennett; Lorene Caravello; Erik Jorgenson; Megan Jorgenson; Lynette Malinger; Shannon Neal; Matthew Sharko; Michelle Sharko; Albert J. Speh IV; Michael Speh.
Executive Committee: Jonathan Speh; Kathleen M. Malinger.
Number of staff: 2 full-time professional; 1 part-time support.
EIN: 364118596
Selected grants: The following grants are a representative sample of this grantmaker's funding activity:
$15,000 to Target Hope, Matteson, IL, 2012. For Brue9380 - 04/29/13 02 24PM Worksheet Private Foundation.
$10,000 to By the Hand Club for Kids, Chicago, IL, 2012. For College Readiness Initiative.
$10,000 to Family Matters, Chicago, IL, 2012. For Postsecondary Readiness Initiative.
$5,000 to Literature for All of Us, Evanston, IL, 2012. For Simpson Academy of Young Women.

3171
The Spencer Foundation ✧
625 N. Michigan Ave., Ste. 1600
Chicago, IL 60611-3109 (312) 337-7000
Contact: Michael S. McPherson, Pres.
FAX: (312) 337-0282; E-mail: pres@spencer.org;
Main URL: http://www.spencer.org
Grants List: http://www.spencer.org/content.cfm/foundation-reports

Incorporated in 1962 in IL.
Donor: Lyle M. Spencer†.
Foundation type: Independent foundation.
Financial data (yr. ended 03/31/14): Assets, $530,519,280 (M); expenditures, $21,559,614; qualifying distributions, $19,708,631; giving activities include $13,953,673 for 194 grants (high: $1,591,687; low: $1,500), $240,863 for employee matching gifts, and $475,315 for foundation-administered programs.
Purpose and activities: The foundation is committed to supporting high-quality investigation of education through its research programs and to strengthening and renewing the educational research community through its fellowship and by strengthening the connections among education research, policy and practice through its communication and networking.
Fields of interest: Education, research.
Type of support: Fellowships; Research; Employee matching gifts.
Limitations: Applications accepted. Giving on a national and international basis. No grants to individuals, or for capital funds, general purposes, operating or continuing support, sabbatical supplements, work in instructional or curriculum development, any kind of training or service program, scholarships, travel fellowships, endowment funds, or pre-doctoral research; no loans.
Publications: Annual report; Financial statement; Grants list; Informational brochure; Newsletter.
Application information: Application information for specific foundation programs available on foundation website. Submit full proposal only upon request. Information on program and application forms required for NAEd/Spencer Postdoctoral Fellowships or NAEd/Spencer Dissertation Fellowships should be requested from the National Academy of Education, 500 5th St. N.W., Washington, DC 20001. Application form not required.
Initial approach: See foundation web site for program-specific guidelines
Deadline(s): See program-specific deadlines on foundation website
Board meeting date(s): Jan., June, and Oct.
Final notification: Program-specific dates available on foundation website
Officers and Directors:* Deborah Lowenberg Ball,* Chair.; Pamela Grossman,* Vice-Chair.; Michael S. McPherson,* Pres.; Diana Hess, Sr. V.P.; Elizabeth Carrick, V.P., Admin. and Chief of Staff; Julie Hubbard, C.F.O.; Mary J. Cahillane, C.I.O.; Carol R. Johnson; Richard Murnane; Stephen Raudenbush; C. Cybele Raver; Mario Small; T. Dennis Sullivan; Mark Vander Ploeg.
Number of staff: 11 full-time professional; 10 full-time support; 2 part-time support.
EIN: 366078558
Selected grants: The following grants are a representative sample of this grantmaker's funding activity:
$1,577,217 to National Academy of Education, Washington, DC, 2013. For NAEd/Spencer Postdoctoral Fellowship Program (Cohorts 12-13, 13-14, 14-15).
$1,054,264 to National Academy of Education, Washington, DC, 2013. For NAEd/Spencer Dissertation Fellowship Program.
$340,550 to Harvard University, Cambridge, MA, 2013. For Do Individual Differences in Executive Function Predict the Young Child's Ability to Learn Biology?.
$277,550 to University of California, Santa Cruz, CA, 2013. For Ethical Issues in Equity-Oriented Collaborative Community-Based Research.
$267,450 to Graduate Center, City University of New York, New York, NY, 2013. For Mainstreaming Mathematics Remedial Students A Random Assignment Experiment.
$247,400 to University of Sydney, Sydney, Australia, 2013. For The Civic Network: A Comparative Study of the Use of Social Media for Enhancing Young People's Political Engagement.
$40,000 to New York University, New York, NY, 2013. For The Extreme Goes Mainstream? School Bans and New Right-Wing Extremist Forms in Germany.
$40,000 to RAND Corporation, Santa Monica, CA, 2013. For An Audit Study of the Labor Market's Perception of For-Profit College Graduates.
$39,950 to University of Minnesota, Minneapolis, MN, 2013. For The Sociocultural Construction of Out-of-School Suspensions: The Experiences of African American Children, their Parents and Educators.
$39,880 to Biological Sciences Curriculum Study, Colorado Springs, CO, 2013. For PCK (Pedagogical Content Knowledge) Summit.

3172
The Otho S. A. Sprague Memorial Institute ✧
P.O. Box 806214
Chicago, IL 60680-4123 (847) 475-0034
Contact: James N. Alexander, Exec. Dir.
Main URL: http://www.spragueinstitute.org

Incorporated in 1910 in IL.
Donor: Members of the Sprague family.
Foundation type: Independent foundation.
Financial data (yr. ended 12/31/13): Assets, $36,926,689 (M); expenditures, $1,742,319; qualifying distributions, $1,508,207; giving activities include $1,239,975 for 12 grants (high: $205,000; low: $2,525).
Purpose and activities: Giving for the investigation of the causes of disease and the prevention and relief of human suffering. In accordance with the wishes of the founder, support is restricted to nonprofits and programs within Chicago, IL.
Fields of interest: Health care, reform; Public health; Health care; Pediatrics research; American Red Cross.
Type of support: General/operating support; Program development; Publication; Seed money; Curriculum development; Research; Technical assistance.
Limitations: Applications not accepted. Giving limited to Chicago, IL. No grants to individuals, or for building or endowment funds, general purposes, scholarships, fellowships, or matching gifts; no loans.
Publications: Annual report.
Application information: Unsolicited requests for funds not accepted. Application by invitation only.
Board meeting date(s): May and Dec.
Officers and Directors:* William E. Bennett,* Pres.; Edward K. Chandler,* V.P.; Rebecca M. Wurtz, M.D., MPH*, Secy.; John A. Svoboda,* Treas.; James N. Alexander, Exec. Dir.; Whitney Wood Addington, M.D.*, Life Dir.; Vernon Armour, Life Dir.; Charles F. Clarke, Jr., Life Dir.; Stewart S. Dixon, Life Dir.; Ada Mary Gugenheim, Life Dir.; Thomas J. Behrens; Tariq H. Butt, M.D.; Michelle L. Collins; Caswell A. Evans, D.D.S.; Lee Francis, M.D., MPH; Julian G. Posada; T. Sands Thompson; Bryan S. Traubert, M.D.; Kevin B. Weiss.
Number of staff: 1 part-time professional.
EIN: 366068723
Selected grants: The following grants are a representative sample of this grantmaker's funding activity:
$220,000 to Smart Chicago Collaborative, Chicago, IL, 2011. For Smart Health Chicago providing technology to underserved patients in clinical waiting rooms, community centers and Chicago Public Library branches enabling them to access their electronic medical records and search the web for linguistically and culturally competent health and wellness information.
$176,858 to Heartland Health Outreach, Chicago, IL, 2011. For general operating support for Chicago Community Oral Health Forum.
$125,000 to CommunityHealth, Chicago, IL, 2011. For MedAccess Chicago, pharmaceutical distribution program.
$80,000 to University of Chicago, Chicago, IL, 2011. For C3, initiative linking and networking Chicago's translational research centers.
$54,100 to Medical Home Network, Chicago, IL, 2012. For pilot testing telemedical links to hypertensive patients enrolled in this network.
$50,000 to Ann and Robert H. Lurie Children's Hospital of Chicago, Chicago, IL, 2011. For 10th Anniversary Projects for CLOCC, The Consortium to Lower Obesity in Chicago Children.
$2,254 to Donors Forum of Chicago, Chicago, IL, 2011. For general operating support.

3173
Square One Foundation ✧
(formerly Kersten Family Foundation)
701 W. Erie St.
Chicago, IL 60610-3973

Established in 1959 in IL.
Donors: Samuel Kersten, Jr.†; Steven Kersten; Priscilla Kersten.
Foundation type: Independent foundation.
Financial data (yr. ended 12/31/12): Assets, $38,222,262 (M); gifts received, $5,000,000; expenditures, $1,432,958; qualifying distributions, $818,542; giving activities include $818,542 for 38 grants (high: $250,000; low: $300).
Purpose and activities: Giving primarily for Jewish federated giving programs, Jewish agencies, higher education and human services.
Fields of interest: Arts; Higher education; Education; Health organizations, association; Human services; Jewish federated giving programs; Jewish agencies & synagogues.
Limitations: Applications not accepted. Giving primarily in Chicago, IL. No grants to individuals.
Application information: Contributes only to pre-selected organizations.

Officers and Directors:* Priscilla Kersten,* Pres.; Steven A. Kersten,* Secy.-Treas.; Walter Roth.
EIN: 366068835

3174
State Farm Companies Foundation ✧
1 State Farm Plz.
Bloomington, IL 61710-0001 (309) 994-0280
Contact: Ed Woods, Asst. Secy.
FAX: (309) 766-2314; Main URL: http://www.statefarm.com/aboutus/community/grants/foundation/foundation.asp

Incorporated in 1963 in IL.
Donor: State Farm Mutual Automobile Insurance Co.
Foundation type: Company-sponsored foundation.
Financial data (yr. ended 12/31/13): Assets, $4,790,799 (M); gifts received, $17,010,089; expenditures, $17,362,818; qualifying distributions, $17,189,637; giving activities include $14,209,305 for 496+ grants (high: $4,106,358), and $2,980,332 for employee matching gifts.
Purpose and activities: The foundation supports key initiatives and scholarships, as well as associate-directed programs, including grants supporting volunteerism and matching gifts to two- and four-year colleges and universities.
Fields of interest: Higher education; Education, drop-out prevention; Education; Voluntarism promotion.
International interests: Canada.
Type of support: General/operating support; Scholarship funds; Employee volunteer services; Employee matching gifts; Employee-related scholarships.
Limitations: Applications not accepted. Giving on a national basis and in Canada. No support for Houses of Worship or organizations established for religious, political, or special interest purposes, veterans', fraternal, or social organizations under Section 501(c)(4), professional organizations under Section 501(c)(6), discriminatory organizations, or nonprofit, tax-exempt organizations under Section 501(c)(3) of the U.S. Internal Revenue Code that are not private foundations because they are described in Code Section 509(a)(3) or 509(a)(4). No grants to individuals.
Application information: Contributes only through employee matching gifts, scholarships, and volunteerism.
Officers and Directors:* Edward B. Rust, Jr.,* Chair. and Pres.; Mary Crego, V.P. and Secy.; Kellie Clapper, V.P., Progs.; Joseph P. Young, V.P., Fixed Income; David Beigie, V.P.; Duane Farrington, V.P.; Mary Schmidt, V.P.; Michael L. Tipsord, V.P.; Paul J. Smith, Treas.; W.H. Knight, Jr.; Susan M. Phillips.
EIN: 366110423
Selected grants: The following grants are a representative sample of this grantmaker's funding activity:
$3,105,358 to Illinois Wesleyan University, Bloomington, IL, 2012.
$1,796,034 to National Merit Scholarship Corporation, Evanston, IL, 2012.
$905,730 to Illinois State University Foundation, Normal, IL, 2012.
$545,000 to University of Illinois at Urbana-Champaign, Urbana, IL, 2012.
$500,000 to Community Cancer Center Foundation, Normal, IL, 2012.
$334,484 to United Way of McLean County, Bloomington, IL, 2012.
$240,703 to United Way of McLean County, Bloomington, IL, 2012.
$65,000 to Scholarship America, Saint Peter, MN, 2012.
$63,734 to United Way of Metropolitan Dallas, Dallas, TX, 2012.
$24,046 to United Way of Weld County, Greeley, CO, 2012.

3175
Steans Family Foundation ✧
50 E. Washington St., Ste. 410
Chicago, IL 60602-2152 (312) 467-5900
Contact: Wendy Vendel, Grants Mgr./Prog. Assoc.
FAX: (312) 467-1229; E-mail: wvendel@fic-sff.com; Main URL: http://www.steansfamilyfoundation.org

Established in 1986 in IL.
Donors: Harrison Steans; Lois Steans; Heather Steans; Jennifer W. Steans; Robin Steans.
Foundation type: Independent foundation.
Financial data (yr. ended 12/31/12): Assets, $17,663,821 (M); gifts received, $1,214,214; expenditures, $4,130,532; qualifying distributions, $3,847,430; giving activities include $2,448,485 for 137 grants (high: $136,903; low: $110), and $367,333 for foundation-administered programs.
Purpose and activities: The foundation's mission is to focus its grantmaking and programs in North Lawndale, IL, a revitalizing neighborhood on Chicago, IL's, west side, and working in partnership with local residents and institutions to build and enhance the North Lawndale community. Giving primarily for education, birth-college access, including early childhood and school-based funding.
Fields of interest: Education; Infants/toddlers; Children/youth; Children; Youth; Young adults; Minorities; African Americans/Blacks; Infants/toddlers, female; Girls; Young adults, female; Infants/toddlers, male; Boys; Young adults, male.
Type of support: Program evaluation; General/operating support; Continuing support; Management development/capacity building; Program development; Seed money; Curriculum development; Technical assistance; Program-related investments/loans; Matching/challenge support.
Limitations: Applications not accepted. Giving primarily in the North Lawdale neighborhood of Chicago, IL. No support for political or religious organizations. No grants to individuals.
Publications: Annual report.
Application information: Unsolicited requests for funds not accepted.
Board meeting date(s): Quarterly and as needed
Officers and Trustees:* Harrison I. Steans,* C.E.O.; Pat Ford, Exec. Dir.; Leonard A. Gail; Reginald Jones; James P. Kastenholz; Leo A. Smith; Heather Steans; Jennifer Steans; Lois M. Steans; Robin M. Steans.
Number of staff: 1 full-time professional; 1 part-time professional; 1 full-time support.
EIN: 363486843
Selected grants: The following grants are a representative sample of this grantmaker's funding activity:
$63,750 to Carole Robertson Center for Learning, Chicago, IL, 2012. For Birth Through Five Program.
$50,000 to Juvenile Protective Association, Chicago, IL, 2012. For Building Bridges to North Lawndale Demonstration Project.
$50,000 to Resonate, Chicago, IL, 2012. For Spark Chicago North Lawndale Youth Apprenticeship Program.
$35,000 to Children First Fund: The Chicago Public Schools Foundation, Chicago, IL, 2012. For area and traditional neighborhood schools.
$30,000 to Community Services West, Chicago, IL, 2012. For CSW Career Academy's Culinary Arts Program.
$25,000 to Free Spirit Media, Chicago, IL, 2012. For digital media across North Lawndale.
$20,000 to Frazier Preparatory Academy, IL, 2012. For after school academic program.
$20,000 to Old Town School of Folk Music, Chicago, IL, 2012. For Wiggleworms in Residence Program.
$20,000 to Teach for America, Chicago, IL, 2012. To increase Teach for Americ's impace in North Lawndale.
$15,000 to Catalyst Charter School-Howland, Chicago, IL, 2012. For general operating support.
$10,000 to Academy for Urban School Leadership, Chicago, IL, 2012. For emergency scholarship fund.

3176
Gerald D. & Helen M. Stephens Foundation ✧ ☆
493 E. High Point Dr.
Peoria, IL 61614-2243

Established in 1987 in IL.
Donor: Gerald D. Stephens.
Foundation type: Independent foundation.
Financial data (yr. ended 12/31/13): Assets, $761,259 (M); gifts received, $1,377; expenditures, $1,598,346; qualifying distributions, $1,598,346; giving activities include $1,596,969 for 1 grant.
Fields of interest: Education.
Limitations: Applications not accepted. Giving limited to Peoria, IL. No grants to individuals.
Application information: Unsolicited requests for funds not accepted.
Officers and Directors:* Gerald D. Stephens,* Pres.; Helen M. Stephens,* Secy.; Janet Stephens; Jeffrey Stephens; Edward F. Sutkowski.
EIN: 371224611
Selected grants: The following grants are a representative sample of this grantmaker's funding activity:
$50,000 to Mayo Clinic, Rochester, MN, 2011.
$35,000 to University of Wisconsin, Stevens Point, WI, 2011.
$5,000 to Center for Prevention of Abuse, Peoria, IL, 2011.

3177
Irvin Stern Foundation
4 E. Ohio St., Studio 22
Chicago, IL 60611-2783
Contact: Christine Flood, Grants Admin.
E-mail: christine@irvinstern.org; Main URL: http://www.irvinstern.org

Established in 1957 in IL.
Donor: Irvin Stern†.
Foundation type: Independent foundation.
Financial data (yr. ended 09/30/13): Assets, $13,476,782 (M); expenditures, $1,008,111; qualifying distributions, $880,962; giving activities include $798,000 for 56 grants (high: $120,000; low: $1,000).
Purpose and activities: Grants for human services, particularly aid to the underserved, the poor and disadvantaged, via innovative social service

programs, physical and mental health outreach, literacy and vocational training; civic affairs aimed at improving the quality of life in urban communities through grass roots and neighborhood organizations; and for the enhancement of the Jewish community through education and spirituality.
Fields of interest: Education; Mental health/crisis services; Health organizations; Food services; Human services; Homeless, human services; Jewish federated giving programs; Public affairs; Jewish agencies & synagogues.
International interests: Israel.
Type of support: General/operating support; Continuing support; Equipment; Program development; Seed money.
Limitations: Applications accepted. Giving primarily in Chicago, IL. Some giving in New York by invitation only. No support for organizations outside of Chicago, IL without an invitation from the foundation. No grants to individuals, or for endowment funds, deficit financing, building funds, capital campaigns, construction projects, medical research, or advertising or program books.
Publications: Application guidelines.
Application information: Letter of inquiry form and application guidelines available on foundation web site. All requests for funding from outside the City of Chicago are by invitation only. Unsolicited requests for funds accepted only from applicants in Chicago. Application form required.
Initial approach: Brief letter of inquiry form available on foundation web site
Copies of proposal: 1
Deadline(s): Submit proposal preferably by Mar. 1 or Sept. 1
Board meeting date(s): Apr./May and Oct./Nov.
Final notification: Up to 90 days
Trustees: Heidi Boncher; Kristen Boncher; Ian Epstein; Jeffrey R. Epstein; Nicholas Epstein; Samantha Epstein; Stuart A. Epstein; Arthur Winter; Dorothy Winter; Emma Winter.
Number of staff: 1 part-time professional.
EIN: 366047947

3178
Stewart Foundation ✧ ☆
c/o The Northern Trust Co.
P.O. Box 803878
Chicago, IL 60680-3878

Established in 1984 in IL.
Donors: John Alexander; Thomas S. Alexander; Alexander S. Rudolph; Geoffrey E. Rudolph; Emily H. Alexander; Martha J. Alexander; Brett W. Barnes; Kenneth W. Barnes; Eliza A. Cummings; Walter Alexander; Chris Barnes; Barbara A. Harty; American Livestock Insurance Co.; Alexander-Stewart Lumber Co.; Alexander Building Co.
Foundation type: Independent foundation.
Financial data (yr. ended 08/31/13): Assets, $965,838 (M); expenditures, $1,584,842; qualifying distributions, $1,566,015; giving activities include $1,565,000 for 5 grants (high: $1,275,000; low: $20,000).
Fields of interest: Arts education; Higher education, college; Higher education, university; Environment; Zoos/zoological societies; Aquariums; Animals/wildlife; Catholic agencies & churches.
Limitations: Applications not accepted. Giving primarily in CT, FL, IL, MA, MN, and NY. No grants to individuals.
Application information: Contributes only to pre-selected organizations.
Officers and Directors:* John Alexander,* Pres.; Duncan M. Alexander,* V.P.; Emily H. Alexander,* Secy.-Treas.; Eliza A. Cummings; Margaret A. Pemberton; Martha A. Porter; Emily A. Strong.
EIN: 363339135
Selected grants: The following grants are a representative sample of this grantmaker's funding activity:
$200,000 to Lemur Conservation Foundation, Myakka City, FL, 2011. For general support.
$100,000 to Mayo Clinic, Rochester, MN, 2011. For general support.
$60,000 to Lincoln Park Zoo, Chicago, IL, 2011. For general support.
$50,000 to Project Native, Housatonic, MA, 2011. For general support.
$50,000 to Sharon Audubon Center, Sharon, CT, 2011. For general support.
$25,000 to American Prairie Foundation, Bozeman, MT, 2011. For general support.
$25,000 to Nature Conservancy, Boston, MA, 2011. For general support.
$10,000 to Wetlands Initiative, Chicago, IL, 2011. For general support.
$5,000 to Chicago Zoological Society, Brookfield, IL, 2011. For general support.
$5,000 to Ducks Unlimited, Memphis, TN, 2011. For general support.

3179
Roger and Susan Stone Family Foundation ✧
c/o Roger Stone
1101 Skokie Blvd., Ste. 300
Northbrook, IL 60062-4124

Established in 1969 in IL.
Donor: Roger Stone.
Foundation type: Independent foundation.
Financial data (yr. ended 12/31/13): Assets, $88,387,211 (M); expenditures, $5,062,282; qualifying distributions, $4,983,248; giving activities include $4,977,983 for 129 grants (high: $2,000,000; low: $100).
Purpose and activities: Giving for primarily for health and education; funding also for children and social services.
Fields of interest: Arts; Education; Health care; Health organizations; Human services; Children/youth, services; Jewish federated giving programs.
Limitations: Applications not accepted. Giving primarily in Chicago, IL; some funding also in Washington DC. No grants to individuals.
Application information: Contributes only to pre-selected organizations.
Officers and Directors:* Roger Stone,* Pres. and Treas.; Susan Stone,* Secy.; Karen Stone Kaplan; Jennifer Lynn Stone; Lauren Gail Stone.
EIN: 237026711
Selected grants: The following grants are a representative sample of this grantmaker's funding activity:
$5,000 to Northwestern University, Kellogg School, Evanston, IL, 2012.

3180
W. Clement & Jessie V. Stone Foundation ✧
1100 Lake St., Ste. 202
Oak Park, IL 60301-1015 (800) 288-4859
FAX: (415) 561-0927;
E-mail: Brian@wcstonefnd.org; Main URL: http://www.wcstonefnd.org
Grants List: http://www.wcstonefnd.org/grantees/index.html
Knowledge Center: http://www.wcstonefnd.org/reports.html

Incorporated in 1958 in IL.
Donors: W. Clement Stone†; Jessie V. Stone†.
Foundation type: Independent foundation.
Financial data (yr. ended 12/31/13): Assets, $120,561,100 (M); expenditures, $5,870,028; qualifying distributions, $5,288,282; giving activities include $4,415,584 for 101 grants (high: $150,000; low: $500).
Purpose and activities: The foundation is committed to providing the educational and developmental opportunities to disadvantaged children and young people that enable them to fulfill their potential. Its grantmaking programs in education, youth development and early childhood development are designed to tackle the problems children and youth face in obtaining an excellent education, accessing the skills that will serve them as they transition into adulthood, and experiencing quality developmental experiences in their earliest years. It seeks to work with great leaders doing promising work that has the potential for advancing the knowledge and practice in its grantmaking fields.
Fields of interest: Education; Youth development.
Type of support: General/operating support; Management development/capacity building; Program development; Curriculum development; Scholarship funds; Program evaluation.
Limitations: Applications not accepted. Giving limited to Chicago, IL, the San Francisco Bay Area, CA, New York, NY, and Boston, MA. No grants to individuals.
Publications: Annual report; Grants list.
Application information: Contributes only to pre-selected organizations. See foundation web site for further information.
Board meeting date(s): May and Oct.
Officers and Directors:* Norman C. Stone, Ph.D.*, Pres.; Steven Stone, J.D.*, 1st V.P. and Treas.; Michael A. Stone,* V.P. and Secy.; Barbara Samuels, V.P.; Tony Smith, Exec. Dir.; Jeff Donoghue, C.O.O.; Alexander Knecht; Amy M. Stone; Barbara West Stone; David Stone; Deborah Stone; Jennifer Stone; Norah Sharpe Stone, J.D.; Sandra Stone; Sara Stone; Chad Tingley.
Number of staff: 3 full-time professional.
EIN: 362498125

3181
STS Foundation ✧
c/o The Northern Trust Co.
P.O. Box 803878
Chicago, IL 60680-3878

Established in 2007 in WY.
Foundation type: Independent foundation.
Financial data (yr. ended 12/31/13): Assets, $9,798,834 (M); expenditures, $500,050; qualifying distributions, $442,148; giving activities include $436,000 for 145 grants (high: $25,000; low: $1,000).

Fields of interest: Museums; Higher education; Education.
Limitations: Applications not accepted. No grants to individuals.
Application information: Contributes only to pre-selected organizations.
Officers: Jennifer H. Wilson, Pres.; Virginia Bartholomay, V.P.; Phelps H. Swift, Secy.
EIN: 202045581

3182
Stuart Family Foundation ✧
(formerly The Barbara and Robert Stuart Foundation)
150 Field Dr., Ste. 100
Lake Forest, IL 60045-2597

Established in 1985 in IL.
Donor: Robert D. Stuart, Jr.
Foundation type: Independent foundation.
Financial data (yr. ended 12/31/13): Assets, $11,089,861 (M); gifts received, $5,001,772; expenditures, $2,941,947; qualifying distributions, $2,840,341; giving activities include $2,515,550 for 108 grants (high: $200,000; low: $500).
Fields of interest: Media/communications; Arts; Education; International affairs, goodwill promotion; Civil rights, race/intergroup relations.
Type of support: General/operating support; Continuing support; Annual campaigns; Capital campaigns.
Limitations: Applications not accepted. Giving primarily in Chicago, IL. No grants to individuals.
Application information: Contributes only to pre-selected organizations.
Officers and Directors:* Robert D. Stuart, Jr.,* Pres.; Marian S. Pillsbury,* V.P.; Alexander D. Stuart,* V.P.; Teresa Acuna,* Treas.; Catherine A. Bertini; Blair Pillsbury Enders; Trevor Potter; James M. Stuart; Maren M. Stuart.
Number of staff: 1 full-time professional; 3 part-time professional.
EIN: 363422731

3183
Supera Family Foundation ✧
2001 N. Halsted St., 3rd Fl.
Chicago, IL 60614-4365

Established in 1986 in IL.
Donors: Michael Supera; Michael Supera Charitable Lead Trust 1; Michael Supera Charitable Lead Trust 2; Executive Planning, Inc.; Michael Supera Trust Dated 11/1/2008; Michael Supera Trust Dated 3/31/2005; Michael Supera Trust Dated 3/31/20008; Michael Supera Trust Dated 9/1/2006.
Foundation type: Independent foundation.
Financial data (yr. ended 11/30/13): Assets, $2,469,336 (M); gifts received, $680,694; expenditures, $717,155; qualifying distributions, $713,690; giving activities include $713,690 for 32 grants (high: $305,000; low: $500).
Purpose and activities: Giving primarily for Jewish federated giving programs and temples; funding also for health organizations, education and human services.
Fields of interest: Education; Health organizations, association; Human services; Jewish federated giving programs; Jewish agencies & synagogues.
Limitations: Applications not accepted. Giving primarily in Chicago, IL. No grants to individuals.
Application information: Contributes only to pre-selected organizations.
Officers: Michael Supera, Pres.; Roslynne Supera, Secy.-Treas.
Director: John Supera.
EIN: 363013584
Selected grants: The following grants are a representative sample of this grantmaker's funding activity:
$50,000 to Latin School of Chicago, Chicago, IL, 2011.
$5,000 to Working in the Schools, Chicago, IL, 2011.
$4,000 to Friends of the Israel Defense Forces, Chicago, IL, 2011.
$1,200 to Council for Jewish Elderly, Chicago, IL, 2011.
$1,000 to Alzheimers Association, Chicago, IL, 2011.
$1,000 to Menomonee Club for Boys and Girls, Chicago, IL, 2011.
$1,000 to Posse Foundation, Chicago, IL, 2011.

3184
Robert and Jamie Taylor Foundation ✧
312 Woodley Rd.
Winnetka, IL 60093-3741

Established in 2005 in IL.
Donors: Robert A. Taylor; Jamie T. Taylor.
Foundation type: Independent foundation.
Financial data (yr. ended 12/31/13): Assets, $1,715,972 (M); gifts received, $641,747; expenditures, $578,133; qualifying distributions, $576,969; giving activities include $574,650 for 30 grants (high: $100,000; low: $1,000).
Fields of interest: Performing arts, dance; Education; Health care; Lupus research; Children/youth, services.
Limitations: Applications not accepted. Giving primarily in Washington, DC, and IL. No grants to individuals.
Application information: Contributes only to pre-selected organizations.
Directors: Jamie T. Taylor; Robert A. Taylor.
EIN: 203971327
Selected grants: The following grants are a representative sample of this grantmaker's funding activity:
$100,000 to AmeriCares, Stamford, CT, 2011.
$50,000 to Special Olympics, Washington, DC, 2011.
$30,000 to LEARN Charter School, Chicago, IL, 2011.
$25,000 to Holy Trinity High School, Chicago, IL, 2011.
$25,000 to Teach for America, Chicago, IL, 2011.
$10,000 to AIDS Cycle, Chicago, IL, 2011.
$10,000 to Big Shoulders Fund, Chicago, IL, 2011.
$10,000 to Japan Society, New York, NY, 2011.
$10,000 to Multiple Sclerosis Society, National, Washington, DC, 2011.
$1,000 to American Cancer Society, Chicago, IL, 2011.

3185
Tellabs Foundation ✧
1415 W. Diehl Rd.
Naperville, IL 60563-2349
Contact: Meredith Hilt, Exec. Dir.
FAX: (630) 798-4778;
E-mail: meredith.hilt@tellabs.com

Established in 1997 in IL.
Donor: Tellabs, Inc.
Foundation type: Company-sponsored foundation.
Financial data (yr. ended 12/31/12): Assets, $25,193,354 (M); expenditures, $1,551,578; qualifying distributions, $1,301,665; giving activities include $1,301,665 for 35 grants (high: $200,000; low: $1).
Purpose and activities: The foundation supports organizations involved with education, the environment, and health.
Fields of interest: Engineering school/education; Education; Environment, waste management; Environment, natural resources; Environment, water resources; Environment, land resources; Environmental education; Environment; Hospitals (general); Health care, clinics/centers; Public health; Health care; Mathematics; Science.
International interests: China; Finland.
Type of support: Management development/ capacity building; Building/renovation; Program development; Conferences/seminars; Seed money; Curriculum development; Research.
Limitations: Applications accepted. Giving primarily in areas of company operations, with emphasis on Santa Clara, CA, Chicago, and Naperville, IL, and Dallas, TX, and in China and Finland. No support for political or lobbying organizations, labor unions or organizations, service organizations raising money for community purposes, local or national alumni groups, clubs or fraternities, individual churches or synagogues or other religious organizations, or organizations not of direct benefit to the entire community, or discriminatory organizations. No grants to individuals, or for local athletic or sports programs, travel, tours, expeditions, or trips, institutional memberships or subscription fees for publications, or benefit events, raffle tickets, or fundraising efforts returning value to the donor; no product or equipment donations.
Publications: Application guidelines; IRS Form 990 or 990-PF printed copy available upon request.
Application information: Letters of inquiry should be no longer than 1 to 2 pages. Letters of inquiry are not accepted by fax or e-mail. A full proposal may be requested at a later date. Application form not required.
Initial approach: Letter of inquiry
Deadline(s): Jan. 1, Apr. 1., July 1, and Oct. 1
Board meeting date(s): Jan., Apr., July, and Oct.
Officers: Michael J. Birck, Pres. and Treas.; Denise Callarman, V.P.; Carol Gavin, V.P.; Stephanie Pace Marshall, V.P.; Meredith Hilt,* Secy. and Exec. Dir.
Number of staff: 1 part-time support.
EIN: 364037547

3186
Terra Foundation for American Art ✧
120 E. Erie St., Chicago
Chicago, IL 60611-3154 (312) 664-3939
Contact: Amy Zinck, V.P.
FAX: (312) 664-2052;
E-mail: grants@terraamericanart.org; Additional e-mail: contact@terraamericanart.org and tsr@terraamericanart.org; Main URL: http://www.terraamericanart.org
E-Newsletter: http://www.terraamericanart.org/about/e-newsletter-sign-up-form-archive/
Grants List: http://www.terraamericanart.org/grants/grants-awarded/

Classified as a private operating foundation in 1981 in IL.
Donors: Daniel J. Terra†; Lawter Intl.; James D. Terra.
Foundation type: Operating foundation.
Financial data (yr. ended 06/30/13): Assets, $331,633,281 (M); expenditures, $16,978,564; qualifying distributions, $15,663,104; giving activities include $7,190,605 for 76 grants (high: $435,546; low: $5,000), and $66,300 for 9 grants to individuals (high: $15,000; low: $5,000).
Purpose and activities: The foundation is dedicated to fostering exploration, understanding, and enjoyment of the visual arts of the United States for national and international audiences. Recognizing the importance of experiencing original works of art, the foundation provides opportunities for interaction and study, beginning with the presentation and growth of its own art collection in Chicago. To further cross-cultural dialogue on American art, the foundation supports and collaborates on innovative exhibitions, research, and educational programs. The foundation's grant areas are Exhibition, Academic and Public Programs, Chicago K-12 Education, and Publication. Publication grants will provide support for publication projects on historical American art (circa 1500 to 1980) that make a significant contribution to scholarship and have an international dimension.
Fields of interest: Arts, multipurpose centers/programs; Arts education; Visual arts; Museums (art).
International interests: Asia; Europe; South America.
Type of support: Program development; Fellowships.
Limitations: Applications accepted. Giving in the U.S., with emphasis on Chicago, IL, and internationally. No support for artwork conservation.
Publications: Application guidelines; Annual report; Grants list.
Application information: Application guidelines available on foundation web site. Formal proposals accepted by invitation only, after review of letter of inquiry. Application form not required.
Initial approach: Letter of inquiry (1 copy only, 3 pages maximum, written in English and e-mailed to Grants Mgr.)
Copies of proposal: 5
Deadline(s): See foundation web site for current deadlines
Board meeting date(s): 3 times annually
Final notification: Within 3 weeks
Officers and Trustees:* Gerhard Casper, Chair.; Elizabeth Glassman, C.E.O. and Pres.; Donald Ratner, Exec. V.P. and C.F.O.; Amy Zinck, V.P.; Max N. Berry; Ruth Fine; Mimi Gardner Gates; Chet Gougis; Peter Krikovich; Michael Leja; Henri Loyrette; Peter Lunder; Clare Munana; Larry Richman; Gloria Scoby; Michael Shapiro; Marilynn Thoma; Greg Williamson.
Number of staff: 20 full-time professional.
EIN: 362999442
Selected grants: The following grants are a representative sample of this grantmaker's funding activity:
$25,000 to High Museum of Art, Atlanta, GA, 2013. For art education.

3187
Edward N. & Della L. Thome Memorial Foundation ✧

c/o US Trust, Philanthropic Solutions
231 S. LaSalle St., IL1-231-13-32
Chicago, IL 60604-1426
Contact: George Thorn, V.P.
E-mail: ilgrantmaking@ustrust.com; Main URL: http://www.bankofamerica.com/grantmaking

Established in 2003 in MD.
Donor: Robert P. Thome.
Foundation type: Independent foundation.
Financial data (yr. ended 12/31/13): Assets, $104,480,102 (M); expenditures, $7,529,144; qualifying distributions, $6,930,520; giving activities include $6,365,000 for 20 grants (high: $2,000,000; low: $7,500).
Purpose and activities: The foundation supports dignified treatment of older adults as well as medical research on diseases affecting older adults.
Fields of interest: Nursing care; Geriatrics; Human services; Aging.
Type of support: General/operating support.
Limitations: Applications accepted. Giving on a national basis, with emphasis on MD and MI. No grants to individuals.
Application information: See foundation web site for complete application guidelines.
Deadline(s): June 15, rolling (check website for more details)
Trustee: Bank of America, N.A.
EIN: 597241019
Selected grants: The following grants are a representative sample of this grantmaker's funding activity:
$2,000,000 to Easter Seals Greater Washington-Baltimore Region, Silver Spring, MD, 2013. For the Edward N. and Della L. Thome Campus for the Well-Being and Care of Individuals Living with Alzheimer's Disease and Other Age-Related Disorders and Their Caregivers.
$500,000 to Presbyterian Villages of Michigan Foundation, Southfield, MI, 2013. For Implementation of Community Connections of Michigan (CCM) Known As 'senior Village Alliance' in Original Proposal.
$250,000 to Boston University, Boston, MA, 2013. For Genetic Mechanisms shared by Eye and Brain Diseases as Novel Therapeutic Targets for Age-Related Macular Degeneration.
$250,000 to Brigham and Women's Hospital, Boston, MA, 2013. For Indigneous Microglia and Recruited Monocytes in Amd: Role in Pathogenesis and Immunotherapy By Specific Immune Targeting.
$250,000 to Duke University, Durham, NC, 2013. For contribution of Complement Dysregulation to Amd Pathogenesis.
$250,000 to Stanford University, Stanford, CA, 2013. For Modulating Metabolism in Mice to Understand and Treat Amd.
$250,000 to University of Rochester, Rochester, NY, 2013. For Adaptive Optics Imaging of Geographic Atrophy Progression in Macular Degeneration.
$250,000 to Washington University, Saint Louis, MO, 2013. For a Novel Mouse Model of Dry Type Age-Related Macular Degeneration.
$250,000 to Yale University, New Haven, CT, 2013. For Inducing Vessel Quiescence in Age-Related Macular Degeneration.
$150,000 to Jewish Family Services of Washtenaw County, Ann Arbor, MI, 2013. For Older Adult Services.

3188
The Timken Company Charitable Trust ✧

c/o JPMorgan Chase
10 S. Dearborn St., Ste. IL1-0111
Chicago, IL 60603-2300
E-mail: timken.trust@timken.com; Main URL: http://www.timken.com/en-us/about/citizenship/CharitableTrust/Pages/default.aspx

Trust established in 1947 in OH.
Donor: The Timken Co.
Foundation type: Company-sponsored foundation.
Financial data (yr. ended 12/31/13): Assets, $6,223 (M); expenditures, $582,067; qualifying distributions, $574,692; giving activities include $563,517 for 47 grants (high: $150,000; low: $500).
Purpose and activities: The foundation supports organizations involved with arts and culture, education, and community and economic development and programs designed to improve quality of life in communities where Timken associates live and work.
Fields of interest: Arts; Human services; Community/economic development.
Type of support: General/operating support; Income development; Building/renovation.
Limitations: Applications accepted. Giving primarily in areas of company operations, with some emphasis on GA, IL, NC, NH, OH, SC, and VA. No grants to individuals, or for health-related research, capital projects, or national programs.
Publications: Application guidelines; Corporate report.
Application information: Application form not required.
Initial approach: Proposal
Deadline(s): None
Trustee: JPMorgan Chase Bank, N.A.
Number of staff: 3 full-time professional; 3 full-time support.
EIN: 346534265

3189
Tracy Family Foundation ✧

P.O. Box 25, Highway 99 South
Mount Sterling, IL 62353-0025
Contact: Kim Bielik, Grants Mgr.
E-mail: kbielik@tracyfoundation.org; Additional contact: Jean Buckley, Pres., e-mail: jbuckley@tracyfoundation.org; Main URL: http://www.tracyfoundation.org

Established in 1997 in IL.
Donor: Dot Foods, Inc.
Foundation type: Company-sponsored foundation.
Financial data (yr. ended 12/31/13): Assets, $10,613,334 (M); gifts received, $3,467,130; expenditures, $2,657,214; qualifying distributions, $2,646,267; giving activities include $2,336,737 for 239 grants (high: $260,719; low: $1).
Purpose and activities: The foundation supports programs designed to promote education; youth and families; leadership; and economic development. Additional support is given to address pre-k to grade 12 academics; youth development; and the unmet needs of at-risk families.
Fields of interest: Elementary/secondary education; Education, early childhood education; Education, services; Education; Youth development; YM/YWCAs & YM/YWHAs; Children/youth, services; Family services; Human services;

Community/economic development; Leadership development; Catholic agencies & churches.
Type of support: General/operating support; Management development/capacity building; Annual campaigns; Capital campaigns; Program development; Curriculum development; Scholarship funds; Employee matching gifts.
Limitations: Applications accepted. Giving primarily in Adams, Brown, Cass, Greene, Hancock, McDonough, Morgan, Pike, Schuyler, and Scott County, IL. No grants to individuals.
Publications: Application guidelines; IRS Form 990 or 990-PF printed copy available upon request; Program policy statement.
Application information: Organizations receiving Formal Funding, Capacity Building, Brown County T.E.A.C.H.E.R. Fund, or Catholic School grants are asked to submit a final report. Final Reports are due within 1 year of receipt of the grant. Application form required.
Initial approach: Complete online pre-application for Formal Funding Grant Program, Brown County T.E.A.C.H.E.R. Fund, and Catholic School Grants; complete online application for Capacity Building Grant
Deadline(s): Jan 1, May 1, and Sept. 1 for Formal Funding Grant Program and Brown County T.E.A.C.H.E.R. Fund; Sept. 1 for Catholic Schools Grants; None for Capacity Building Grant
Board meeting date(s): Feb., June, and Oct.
Final notification: Apr., Aug., and Dec. for Formal Funding Grant Program and Brown County T.E.A.C.H.E.R. Fund; Dec. for Catholic School Grants
Officers: Jean C. Buckley, Pres. and C.E.O.; Pat Smith, V.P.; John Oliver, Secy.; Rob Tracy, Treas.
Directors: Mary Sullivan; Alex Tracy; Don Tracy; Jane Tracy; Linda Tracy; Liz Tracy.
EIN: 364163760
Selected grants: The following grants are a representative sample of this grantmaker's funding activity:
$7,500 to Fordham University, Law School, New York, NY, 2012. For capital campaign.
$1,500 to Quincy Notre Dame High School, Quincy, IL, 2012. For Underwriting of a Fundraiser.

3190
Tricord Foundation ✧
225 W. Washington, 28th Fl.
Chicago, IL 60606

Established in 1997 in IL.
Foundation type: Independent foundation.
Financial data (yr. ended 12/31/13): Assets, $4,709,115 (M); expenditures, $481,916; qualifying distributions, $453,027; giving activities include $453,002 for 6 grants (high: $151,000; low: $2).
Fields of interest: Education; Environment, natural resources; Environment, land resources; Animals/wildlife, preservation/protection; Hospitals (general); Christian agencies & churches.
Limitations: Applications not accepted. Giving primarily in CO, IL, MI, and VA. No grants to individuals.
Application information: Contributes only to pre-selected organizations.
Officers: Marion S. Searle, Pres.; Louise S. Klarr, V.P.; Elizabeth B. Searle, V.P.; Ron Bailitz, Secy.-Treas.
Directors: Michael W. Branham; S. Gunnar Klarr.
Number of staff: 2 full-time professional; 1 full-time support.
EIN: 364198123

3191
Trio Foundation ✧ ☆
45 Indian Hill Rd.
Winnetka, IL 60093-3939

Established in 2007 in IL.
Donors: John P. Amboian, Jr.; Ann L. Amboian.
Foundation type: Independent foundation.
Financial data (yr. ended 12/31/13): Assets, $4,800,485 (M); expenditures, $480,590; qualifying distributions, $435,500; giving activities include $435,500 for 7 grants (high: $200,000; low: $500).
Fields of interest: Higher education, university; Hospitals (specialty); Pediatrics; Boys & girls clubs.
Limitations: Applications not accepted. Giving primarily in IL. No grants to individuals.
Application information: Contributes only to pre-selected organizations.
Officers and Directors:* Ann L. Amboian,* Pres.; John P. Amboian, Jr., V.P. and Treas.; Michael S. Lee,* Secy.; Andrew L. Amboian.
EIN: 261115900
Selected grants: The following grants are a representative sample of this grantmaker's funding activity:
$1,500 to Academy for Urban School Leadership, Chicago, IL, 2012. For general - unrestricted.

3192
The Trott Family Foundation ✧
P.O. Box 3016, RALLC Tax Dept.
Chicago, IL 60654-0016

Established in 1996 in IL.
Donor: Byron D. Trott.
Foundation type: Independent foundation.
Financial data (yr. ended 08/31/13): Assets, $13,776,317 (M); gifts received, $392,181; expenditures, $3,142,743; qualifying distributions, $3,069,275; giving activities include $3,054,100 for 44 grants (high: $500,000; low: $500).
Purpose and activities: Giving primarily for the arts, as well as for education, health organizations and social services.
Fields of interest: Museums (art); Arts; Education, association; Elementary/secondary education; Education; Health organizations, association; Human services.
Limitations: Applications not accepted. Giving primarily in IL, with emphasis on Chicago; some funding also in OH, Nashville, TN and VA. No grants or scholarships to individuals; no loans.
Application information: Contributes only to pre-selected organizations.
Trustees: Byron D. Trott; Tina L. Trott.
EIN: 133919816

3193
Trustmark Foundation ✧
(formerly BTL Foundation)
400 Field Dr.
Lake Forest, IL 60045-4809
Contact for Impact Educator Grant Program: Cindy Gallaher, tel.: (847) 283-4065,
E-mail: cindy.gallaher@trustmarkins.com; Main URL: http://www.trustmarkins.com/internet/corporate/aboutus_205.html

Established in 1985.
Donor: Trustmark Insurance Co.
Foundation type: Company-sponsored foundation.
Financial data (yr. ended 12/31/13): Assets, $762,539 (M); gifts received, $1,244,977; expenditures, $1,075,779; qualifying distributions, $1,075,779; giving activities include $1,075,614 for 191 grants (high: $118,750; low: $45).
Purpose and activities: The foundation supports organizations involved with arts and culture, education, health, safety, and human services.
Fields of interest: Arts; Education; Health care, clinics/centers; Health care; Pediatrics; Nutrition; Safety/disasters; Children/youth, services; Residential/custodial care, hospices; Human services; United Ways and Federated Giving Programs.
Type of support: General/operating support; Program development; Employee volunteer services; Employee-related scholarships; In-kind gifts.
Limitations: Applications accepted. Giving primarily in IL. No grants to individuals (except for employee-related scholarships).
Publications: Application guidelines.
Application information: Application form not required.
Initial approach: Complete online application for Impact Educator Grant Program
Deadline(s): Oct. 17 for Impact Educator Grant Program
Final notification: Dec. for Impact Educator Grant Program
Officer and Trustees:* Karin Lowry, Chair.; Kim Croisant; Kendra Fuson; Kelly Marsh; Elizabeth O'Brien; Lloyd Sarrel; J. Grover Thomas, Jr.
EIN: 363330631
Selected grants: The following grants are a representative sample of this grantmaker's funding activity:
$125,000 to United Way of Lake County, Mentor, OH, 2010.
$30,000 to Interfaith House, Chicago, IL, 2011.
$15,000 to Kennedy Krieger Foundation, Baltimore, MD, 2011.
$15,000 to Recreation Unlimited Foundation, Ashley, OH, 2011.
$10,000 to Actuarial Foundation, Schaumburg, IL, 2011.
$10,000 to Forgotten Harvest, Oak Park, MI, 2011.
$10,000 to Midwest Palliative and Hospice CareCenter, Glenview, IL, 2011.
$7,500 to Be The Match Foundation, Minneapolis, MN, 2011.
$7,500 to Tongue River Childs Place, Ranchester, WY, 2010.
$5,000 to American Cancer Society, Atlanta, GA, 2011.
$5,000 to Lambs Farm, Libertyville, IL, 2011.
$5,000 to Together We Cope, Tinley Park, IL, 2011.

3194
The Tulsa Foundation ✧
c/o JPMorgan Chase Bank, N.A.
10 S. Dearborn St., 21st Fl.
Chicago, IL 60603-2300

Established in 1919 in OK.
Foundation type: Independent foundation.

Financial data (yr. ended 12/31/13): Assets, $21,144,974 (M); expenditures, $1,116,415; qualifying distributions, $971,199; giving activities include $900,663 for 19 grants (high: $188,075; low: $2,000).
Purpose and activities: Support to organizations that provide services that enhance the quality of life for the citizens of Tulsa, OK.
Fields of interest: Goodwill Industries; Salvation Army; YM/YWCAs & YM/YWHAs; Human services; Community/economic development; Boys.
Limitations: Applications not accepted. Giving limited to Tulsa, OK, area. No grants to individuals.
Application information: Contributes only to pre-selected organizations.
Trustee: JPMorgan Chase Bank, N.A.
EIN: 736090617

3195
Tyndale House Foundation ✧
351 Executive Dr.
Carol Stream, IL 60188-2420 (630) 790-9532
Contact: Mary Kleine Yehling, Exec. Dir.
FAX: (630) 790-2446;
E-mail: foundation@tyndalehousefdn.org; Main URL: http://www.TyndaleHouseFdn.org

Established in 1964 in IL.
Donors: Howard A. Elkind‡; Kenneth N. Taylor‡; ENB Charitable Trust; Elizabeth Taylor Char. Trust.
Foundation type: Independent foundation.
Financial data (yr. ended 12/31/13): Assets, $67,395,634 (M); expenditures, $4,766,941; qualifying distributions, $4,450,504; giving activities include $4,151,350 for 276 grants (high: $200,000; low: $1,000).
Purpose and activities: Giving to promote the Gospel through Christian literature projects, Bible translations, and Christian services and activities in the U.S. and abroad. The main area of interest is Christian literature and media.
Fields of interest: Language/linguistics; Literature; Human services; Religious federated giving programs; Christian agencies & churches; Protestant agencies & churches.
Type of support: General/operating support; Program development; Conferences/seminars; Publication; Matching/challenge support.
Limitations: Applications accepted. Giving in the U.S.; international projects are funded through U.S.-based organizations. No grants to individuals, or for building or endowment funds, scholarships, fellowships, or personnel support.
Publications: Application guidelines; Financial statement; Informational brochure (including application guidelines).
Application information: The foundation only accepts online applications. Organizations that apply need to have a faith-based component. See foundation web site for instructions. Application form required.
Initial approach: Online eligibility quiz and application on foundation web site
Deadline(s): Dec. 1
Board meeting date(s): Apr. for grantmaking; as required for administrative business
Final notification: May of the subsequent year
Officers and Directors:* C. Douglas McConnell,* Chair.; Edward A. Elliott,* Vice-Chair.; Mark D. Taylor,* C.E.O. and Pres.; Mary Kleine Yehling, V.P. and Exec. Dir.; David M. Howard; Ted Noble; Jeremy P. Taylor; Peter W. Taylor; Rebecca Wilson.
Number of staff: 1 full-time professional; 1 full-time support; 5 part-time support.
EIN: 362555516
Selected grants: The following grants are a representative sample of this grantmaker's funding activity:
$200,000 to Wycliffe Seed Company, Arlington, TX, 2012. To build capacity for national-led accelerated bible translation.
$75,000 to Oasis International, Wheaton, IL, 2012. To create first Protestant Bible with help and applications written by Africans for the African context.
$50,000 to Biblica, Colorado Springs, CO, 2012. For China Scripture Outreach.
$50,000 to Langham Partnership, Milpitas, CA, 2012. To equip Evangelical Leaders for Church in Francophone Africa.
$50,000 to Pioneers, Inc., Orlando, FL, 2012. To empower national believers in developing South to excel in their roles as church planters and leaders of global church.
$40,000 to CLC Ministries International, PA, 2012. For Rejuvenation Christian Bookstore and expansion of distribution in Kyrgyzstan, printing in Myamar, distribution in Mindanao, Philippines, Ciraq Bookstore in Azerbaijan, bookstore in Minsk, Belarus and printing in Russian Bibles.
$40,000 to World Relief, DuPage Office, Wheaton, IL, 2012. For DuPage Early Childhood ESL at College Church.
$40,000 to WorldVenture, Littleton, CO, 2012. To develop Doctoral Program and Women's School and furnishings for new Education Center.
$35,000 to Gospel Light Publications, Ventura, CA, 2012. To legally produce first children's Bible storybooks in mainland China: God's Story for Me and help children in China enter and grow in personal relationship with Jesus Christ through culturally relevant children's Bible study and curriculum.

3196
Ubben Foundation ✧
9 Briar Ln.
Glencoe, IL 60022-1801

Established in 1987 in IL.
Donors: Timothy H. Ubben; Jeffrey W. Ubben.
Foundation type: Independent foundation.
Financial data (yr. ended 01/31/13): Assets, $20,610,945 (M); gifts received, $1,500,000; expenditures, $1,486,572; qualifying distributions, $1,308,700; giving activities include $1,308,700 for grants.
Purpose and activities: Giving primarily for higher education and youth services; some funding also for the arts.
Fields of interest: Performing arts, theater; Elementary/secondary education; Higher education; Boys & girls clubs.
Type of support: General/operating support.
Limitations: Applications not accepted. Giving primarily in San Francisco, CA, Chicago and Evanston, IL, and New York, NY. No grants to individuals.
Application information: Contributes only to pre-selected organizations.
Officers: Timothy H. Ubben, Pres.; Sharon W. Ubben, V.P.; Pamela Wisinski, Secy.; Jeffrey W. Ubben, Treas.
EIN: 363496530
Selected grants: The following grants are a representative sample of this grantmaker's funding activity:
$100,000 to American Conservatory Theater, San Francisco, CA, 2012. For general support.
$100,000 to University of Wisconsin, Madison, WI, 2012. For general support.
$77,500 to Pepperdine University, Malibu, CA, 2012. For general support.
$75,000 to Edgewood Center for Children and Families, San Francisco, CA, 2012. For general support.
$50,000 to Posse Foundation, Chicago, IL, 2012. For general support.
$30,000 to Philharmonic Center for the Arts, Naples, FL, 2012. For general support.
$25,000 to Bay Citizen, San Francisco, CA, 2012. For general support.
$10,000 to Northwestern University, Evanston, IL, 2012. For general support.
$10,000 to Tourette Syndrome Association, Bayside, NY, 2012. For general support.
$7,500 to Summer Search Foundation, San Francisco, CA, 2012. For general support.

3197
Ed Uihlein Family Foundation ✧
(formerly Little Owl Foundation)
736 N. Western Ave., Ste. 339
Lake Forest, IL 60045-1820

Established in 2006 in IL.
Donor: Richard Uihlein.
Foundation type: Independent foundation.
Financial data (yr. ended 12/31/13): Assets, $11,313,453 (M); gifts received, $9,736,503; expenditures, $8,443,386; qualifying distributions, $8,414,068; giving activities include $8,412,630 for 122 grants (high: $800,000; low: $100).
Fields of interest: Theological school/education; Education; Animals/wildlife; Public policy, research.
Limitations: Applications not accepted. Giving primarily in IL and VA. No grants to individuals.
Application information: Contributes only to pre-selected organizations.
Officers and Directors:* Richard E. Uihlein,* Pres.; Lucia Uihlein Higgins,* Secy.; Fredericka Anne Goldenberg,* Treas.
EIN: 205723621
Selected grants: The following grants are a representative sample of this grantmaker's funding activity:
$250,000 to Media Research Center, Reston, VA, 2011. For general support.
$150,000 to Leadership Institute, Arlington, VA, 2011. For general support.
$68,000 to Clare Boothe Luce Policy Institute, Herndon, VA, 2011. For general support.
$40,000 to Institute for Humane Studies, Arlington, VA, 2011. For general support.
$20,000 to Daniel Murphy Scholarship Fund, Chicago, IL, 2011. For general support.
$17,000 to Kenosha Public Museum, Kenosha, WI, 2011. For general support.
$13,000 to Accuracy in Media, Washington, DC, 2011. For general support.
$10,000 to Lake Forest College, Lake Forest, IL, 2011. For general support.
$10,000 to Northwestern Lake Forest Hospital, Lake Forest, IL, 2011. For general support.
$10,000 to Washington Legal Foundation, Washington, DC, 2011. For general support.

3198
John Ullrich Foundation Trust ✧
c/o Busey Trust Co.
130 N. Water St.
Decatur, IL 62523-1310

Foundation type: Independent foundation.
Financial data (yr. ended 12/31/13): Assets, $30,192,152 (M); expenditures, $1,645,463; qualifying distributions, $1,205,000; giving activities include $1,205,000 for 23 grants (high: $250,000; low: $1,000).
Purpose and activities: Giving primarily for higher education, and federated giving programs.
Fields of interest: Higher education; Youth development; Human services; United Ways and Federated Giving Programs.
Type of support: General/operating support.
Limitations: Applications not accepted. Giving primarily in IL. No grants to individuals.
Application information: Contributes only to pre-selected organizations.
Trustee: Busey Trust Co.
EIN: 376279232

3199
United Airlines Foundation ✧
(formerly UAL Foundation)
P.O. Box 66100
Chicago, IL 60666-0100
FAX: (847) 700-7345; Main URL: http://www.united.com/web/en-US/content/company/globalcitizenship/community.aspx

Incorporated in 1951 in IL.
Donor: United Air Lines, Inc.
Foundation type: Company-sponsored foundation.
Financial data (yr. ended 12/31/12): Assets, $3,431,228 (M); gifts received, $1,704,914; expenditures, $1,786,051; qualifying distributions, $1,566,543; giving activities include $1,566,543 for 117 grants (high: $144,611; low: $1,000).
Purpose and activities: The foundation supports organizations involved with disaster relief and humanitarian aid. Special emphasis is directed toward programs designed to address youth potential, arts and culture, and health initiatives.
Fields of interest: Museums; Performing arts, ballet; Performing arts, theater; Performing arts, music; Arts; Education; Health care; Food services; Disasters, preparedness/services; Youth development, business; Youth development; Human services; Youth.
Type of support: General/operating support; Annual campaigns; Program development; Scholarship funds; Research; Employee volunteer services.
Limitations: Applications not accepted. Giving primarily in areas of company operations in Los Angeles and San Francisco, CA, Denver, CO, Chicago, IL, Newark, NJ, New York, NY, Cleveland, OH, and Houston, TX. No support for political or fraternal organizations, United Way-supported organizations, religious organizations, or individual public or private schools. No grants to individuals, or for capital campaigns or development campaigns; no air transportation for fundraising events.
Publications: Corporate giving report.
Application information: The foundation is not accepting grant proposals at this time.
Board meeting date(s): Mar., June, Sept., and Dec.
Officers and Directors:* Mark Anderson,* Chair.; Sonya Y. Jackson, Pres.; Jeffrey T. Foland, V.P.; Peter D. McDonald, V.P.; Thomas J. Sabatino, Jr., Secy.; John R. Gebo, Treas.; John H. Walker.
Number of staff: 2
EIN: 366109873

3200
United States Gypsum Foundation, Inc. ✧
(formerly USG Foundation, Inc.)
550 W. Adams St.
Chicago, IL 60661-3676 (312) 436-4000
Contact: Jeffrey P. Rodewald, Pres. and Dir.

Incorporated in 1978 in IL.
Donors: USG Corp.; Chicago Tourism Fund.
Foundation type: Company-sponsored foundation.
Financial data (yr. ended 12/31/13): Assets, $2,545,647 (M); gifts received, $2,000,000; expenditures, $561,718; qualifying distributions, $561,718; giving activities include $528,786 for 64 grants (high: $77,500; low: $100), and $32,932 for 3 employee matching gifts.
Purpose and activities: The foundation supports organizations involved with arts and culture, higher education, health, human services, community development, and civic affairs.
Fields of interest: Performing arts; Arts; Higher education; Hospitals (general); Health care; Heart & circulatory diseases; American Red Cross; Children/youth, services; Human services; Community/economic development; United Ways and Federated Giving Programs; Public affairs.
Type of support: General/operating support; Continuing support; Annual campaigns; Capital campaigns; Building/renovation; Equipment; Program development; Scholarship funds; Research; Technical assistance; Employee matching gifts.
Limitations: Applications accepted. Giving primarily in areas of company operations. No support for sectarian organizations not of direct benefit to the entire community, political organizations, fraternal or veterans' organizations, or primary or secondary schools; generally, no support for united fund-supported organizations. No grants to individuals, or for courtesy advertising; no loans.
Publications: Application guidelines.
Application information: Application form required.
Initial approach: Letter
Copies of proposal: 1
Deadline(s): None
Board meeting date(s): Quarterly
Officers and Directors:* Jeffrey P. Rodewall,* Pres.; Stanley L. Ferguson,* V.P. and Secy.; Brian J. Cook,* V.P. and Treas.; Brendan J. Deely,* V.P.; James S. Metcalf,* V.P.; Jennifer F. Scanlon,* V.P.
Number of staff: 1 full-time professional.
EIN: 362984045
Selected grants: The following grants are a representative sample of this grantmaker's funding activity:
$30 to Brown University, Providence, RI, 2012. To help fund college costs.

3201
United Stationers Charitable Trust ✧
1 Pkwy. North Blvd., Ste. 100
Deerfield, IL 60015-2559 (847) 627-7000
Contact: Tracey Horwich, Exec. Dir.

Established in 2005 in IL.
Donors: Richard Gochnauer; Daniel Good; Frederick Hegi, Jr.; Jeff Scheck; Todd Shelton; Stephen Schultz; John Zillmer; Brooklace, Inc.; Fresh Products, Inc.; Henson Sales Group; Lagasse, Inc.; Procter & Gamble; Reckitt Benckiser PLC; Rubbermaid Commercial Products; Unger Industrial, LLC; Waterbury Companies, Inc.; Robert Kelderhouse; Golden State Foods; Newwell Rubbermaid; ACCO; Fellowes; Dematic; Reign Print Soutions; Robert J. Kelderhouse; 3M Center Building; International Paper; ACCO Brands Corporation; NewellRubbermaid.
Foundation type: Independent foundation.
Financial data (yr. ended 12/31/13): Assets, $1,430,494 (M); gifts received, $1,760,215; expenditures, $1,802,820; qualifying distributions, $1,613,332; giving activities include $937,975 for 458 grants (high: $137,702; low: $50).
Purpose and activities: Giving primarily for education, social services and medical research.
Fields of interest: Higher education; Education; Medical research, institute; Human services; Foundations (private grantmaking).
Limitations: Applications accepted. Giving primarily in CA and IL.
Application information: Application form not required.
Initial approach: Proposal
Deadline(s): None
Officers: Timothy Connolly, Pres.; Marsha Rubin, Secy.; Jing Xing, Treas.; Tracey Horwich, Exec. Dir.
Trustees: Jason Barr; Paul Barrett; Helen Brewer; Meg Dolan; Shelly Flanagan; Robert Kelderhouse; George Killian, Jr.; David Leinart; Lawrence Miller; Stephen Morgan; Elliott Motta; Megan Ogden; Maren Okrzynski; Tom Patterson; Mickey Wayne Scott, Jr.
EIN: 066547406
Selected grants: The following grants are a representative sample of this grantmaker's funding activity:
$1,120 to American Heart Association, Syracuse, NY, 2012. For Medical - Heart Disease.
$1,000 to Black Ensemble Theater Corporation, Chicago, IL, 2012. For Social Services - Education.
$1,000 to Blue Star Mothers of America, Tulsa, OK, 2012. For military.
$1,000 to Emergency Infant Services, Tulsa, OK, 2012. For Social Services - Children.
$750 to Greater Salem Caregivers, Salem, NH, 2012. For Social Services - Other.
$500 to Cystic Fibrosis Foundation, Indianapolis, IN, 2012. For medical - other.
$500 to Free Wheelchair Mission, Irvine, CA, 2012. For Social Services - Basic Needs.
$500 to March of Dimes Foundation, White Plains, NY, 2012. For Medical - Childhood Disease.
$500 to NuPath, Woburn, MA, 2012. For Social Services - Medical.
$500 to Woburn Council of Social Concern, Woburn, MA, 2012. For needs.

3202
Donna Van Eekeren Foundation ✧
P.O. Box 589
Lansing, IL 60438-0589

Established in IL.
Donor: Donna Van Eekeren.
Foundation type: Independent foundation.
Financial data (yr. ended 12/31/13): Assets, $370,795 (M); gifts received, $503,615; expenditures, $807,812; qualifying distributions,

$801,815; giving activities include $800,000 for 2 grants (high: $450,000; low: $350,000).
Fields of interest: Performing arts, theater; Performing arts, opera; Arts; Down syndrome.
Limitations: Applications not accepted. Giving primarily in Chicago, IL.
Application information: Contributes only to pre-selected organizations.
Officers: Donna Van Eekeren, Pres.; David Van Eekeren, V.P.
Directors: Daniel Sharpe; Bridget Van Eekeren; Kevin Van Eekeren; Kathryn Van Eekeren-Sharpe.
EIN: 260493191
Selected grants: The following grants are a representative sample of this grantmaker's funding activity:
$422,000 to Lyric Opera of Chicago, Chicago, IL, 2011.
$350,000 to Chicago Shakespeare Theater, Chicago, IL, 2011.
$40,000 to Lyric Opera of Chicago, Chicago, IL, 2010.
$25,000 to Chicago Shakespeare Theater, Chicago, IL, 2010.
$10,000 to Art Institute of Chicago, Chicago, IL, 2010.

3203
The Vaughn Foundation ✧
(formerly Jim M. Vaughn Foundation)
10 S. Dearborn IL1-0117
Chicago, IL 60603-6089
Application address: c/o Marc Irvin, 712 Main St., 11th Fl., Houston, TX 77002-3201, tel.: (713) 216-4515

Established in 1952 in TX.
Donors: Edgar H. Vaughn†; Lillie Mae Vaughn†; John Willie Bell Trust; Sarah Mosely Motes Curt.
Foundation type: Independent foundation.
Financial data (yr. ended 12/31/13): Assets, $8,154,895 (M); expenditures, $502,089; qualifying distributions, $461,700; giving activities include $449,500 for 47 grants (high: $25,000; low: $1,000).
Fields of interest: Performing arts, ballet; Performing arts, theater; Performing arts, orchestras; Arts; Elementary school/education; Higher education; Hospitals (general); Health organizations, association; Human services; Children/youth, services; United Ways and Federated Giving Programs; Christian agencies & churches; Protestant agencies & churches.
Type of support: General/operating support.
Limitations: Applications accepted. Giving primarily in Houston and Tyler, TX. No grants to individuals.
Application information: Application form not required.
Initial approach: Proposal
Deadline(s): None
Trustee: JPMorgan Chase Bank, N.A.
Number of staff: 1 part-time support.
EIN: 756008953
Selected grants: The following grants are a representative sample of this grantmaker's funding activity:
$50,000 to University of Texas, Tyler, TX, 2010.
$40,000 to University of Texas Medical Branch, Galveston, TX, 2011. For general support.
$25,000 to University of Texas M.D. Anderson Cancer Center, Anderson Cancer Center, Houston, TX, 2010.
$20,000 to Texas Childrens Hospital, Houston, TX, 2011. For general support.
$15,000 to Alley Theater, Houston, TX, 2011. For general support.
$15,000 to Duchesne Academy of the Sacred Heart, Houston, TX, 2011. For general support.
$15,000 to Houston Ballet Foundation, Houston, TX, 2011. For general support.
$15,000 to Houston Friends of Chamber Music, Houston, TX, 2011. For general support.
$15,000 to Houston Grand Opera, Houston, TX, 2011. For general support.
$15,000 to Houston International Dance Coalition, Houston, TX, 2011. For general support.
$15,000 to Ronald McDonald House of Houston, Houston, TX, 2011. For general support.
$15,000 to W. Oscar Neuhaus Memorial Foundation, Bellaire, TX, 2011. For general support.
$10,000 to First Presbyterian Church of Houston, Houston, TX, 2010.
$10,000 to Meals on Wheels, Bay Area, Houston, TX, 2010.
$5,000 to American Cancer Society, Houston, TX, 2010.
$5,000 to Houston Parks Board, Houston, TX, 2010.

3204
Ventana Charitable Foundation ✧
77 E. Walton St., Ste. 28C
Chicago, IL 60611-2299

Established in IL.
Foundation type: Independent foundation.
Financial data (yr. ended 12/31/13): Assets, $13,182,871 (M); gifts received, $2,009; expenditures, $801,629; qualifying distributions, $779,351; giving activities include $777,342 for 23 grants (high: $150,000; low: $250).
Fields of interest: Arts; Education; Human services.
Limitations: Applications not accepted. Giving primarily in the Chicago, IL, area, as well as in San Miguel de Allende, Mexico. No grants to individuals.
Application information: Unsolicited requests for funds not accepted.
Officers: John Patience, Pres. and Treas.; Diane Patience, V.P. and Secy.
EIN: 261224721

3205
Vermilion Healthcare Foundation ✧
P.O. Box 1853
Danville, IL 61834-1853 (217) 431-7021
Contact: Valeria Saikley

Established in 1994 in IL.
Foundation type: Independent foundation.
Financial data (yr. ended 09/30/13): Assets, $10,810,971 (M); expenditures, $695,462; qualifying distributions, $625,114; giving activities include $615,800 for 4 grants (high: $238,600; low: $50,000).
Fields of interest: Education; Hospitals (general).
Limitations: Applications accepted. Giving limited to Danville, IL. No grants to individuals.
Publications: Application guidelines; Program policy statement.
Application information: Grant guidelines are available from foundation upon request. Application form required.
Initial approach: Request application form
Copies of proposal: 8
Deadline(s): Mar. 15, June 15, Sept. 15, and Dec. 15
Board meeting date(s): Last Wed. in Jan., Apr., July, and Oct.
Officers: Neal M. Ehrlich, Chair.; Curtis D. Towne, Vice-Chair.; Michael Kiddoo, Secy.-Treas.
Directors: Michael L. Brown; Kathy Houpt; Michael Hulvey; Donald A. McLaughlin; Michael J. O'Brien; Maruti Seth; W. John Shane; Lesley Shore; Tom Wodetzki.
EIN: 371225688
Selected grants: The following grants are a representative sample of this grantmaker's funding activity:
$50,000 to Danville Area Community College, Danville, IL, 2011.
$50,000 to Danville Area Community College, Danville, IL, 2011.

3206
VNA Foundation ✧
(doing business as Visiting Nurse Association of Chicago)
20 N. Wacker Dr., Ste. 3118
Chicago, IL 60606-3101 (312) 214-1521
Contact: Robert N. DiLeonardi, Exec. Dir.; Claudia Baier, Sr. Prog. Off.; Ann C. Schaefer, Prog. Assoc.
FAX: (312) 214-1529;
E-mail: info@vnafoundation.net; Main URL: http://www.vnafoundation.net
LinkedIn: http://www.linkedin.com/company/vna-foundation
Twitter: https://twitter.com/vnafoundation
YouTube: http://www.youtube.com/user/VNAFoundation

Established in 1995 in IL; converted from the transfer of VNA-C operations to CareMed Chicago; status changed to a private foundation in July 1998.
Foundation type: Independent foundation.
Financial data (yr. ended 06/30/13): Assets, $48,808,866 (M); gifts received, $32,816; expenditures, $3,174,890; qualifying distributions, $2,800,722; giving activities include $2,361,172 for 67 grants (high: $150,000; low: $305).
Purpose and activities: The grantmaking goal of the foundation is to support home- and community-based health care and health services for the medically underserved in Cook and the collar counties, IL, with a focus on Chicago. Capital, program and general operating grants to support home, health, community and school-based services, prevention and health promotion, and early intervention are available to nonprofits. Priority is given to programs in which care is provided by nurses. The population targeted by the program must be medically underserved.
Fields of interest: Dental care; Health care, support services; Nursing care; Health care, home services; Health care; Economically disadvantaged; Homeless.
Type of support: General/operating support; Capital campaigns; Equipment; Program development; Seed money; Program evaluation; Matching/challenge support.
Limitations: Applications accepted. Giving primarily in Cook, DuPage, Kane, Lake, Will, and McHenry counties, IL. No support for profit organizations. No grants for research or inpatient services.
Publications: Application guidelines; Financial statement; Grants list.

Application information: Both unsolicited and solicited applicants are invited to submit grant ideas via a Letter of Intent. Full proposals must be invited, with invitations offered following foundation's review of letter of inquiry. The foundation uses an online grants management system that can be accessed through its website. Letters of Intent and proposals submitted to the foundation through means other than the online grants management system will not be considered. Application form required.

Initial approach: Telephone calls, (encouraged) and letter of intent submitted through the foundation's online system.

Copies of proposal: 1

Deadline(s): Call for deadlines or see foundation web site.

Board meeting date(s): Quarterly

Final notification: 7 weeks

Officers and Directors:* M. Catherine Ryan, Chair.; Sandra Wilks, MS, RN, Vice-Chair.; Brigid E. Kenney,* Secy.; Dian Langenhorst, Treas.; Robert N. DiLeonardi, Exec. Dir.; Marie W. Harris; Arlene Michaels Miller, Ph.D., RN, FAAN; Katherine H. Miller; Denise Palmer; David R. Rutter; Nancy Scinto.

Number of staff: 2 full-time professional; 1 part-time professional.

EIN: 362167943

Selected grants: The following grants are a representative sample of this grantmaker's funding activity:

$75,000 to AIDS Foundation of Chicago, Chicago, IL, 2013. Toward salary and benefits of Chief Clinical Officer who works to improve the local HIV care system.

$60,000 to Beloved Community Family Wellness Center, Chicago, IL, 2013. Toward salary of Chronic Care Nurse at this expanding FQHC in Englewood.

$50,000 to DuPage Health Coalition, Access DuPage, Carol Stream, IL, 2013. To secure pro-bono specialty care consultation and treatment for low-income, uninsured DuPage county residents.

$50,000 to Goldies Place, Chicago, IL, 2013. Toward it's dental care program that serves homeless adults, with services provided free of charge by volunteer dentists and students at the UIC College of Dentistry.

$50,000 to Inner-City Muslim Action Network, Chicago, IL, 2013. For expansion of IMAN's Free Health Clinic, to support a part-time family nurse practitioner to provide free patient care, health education, and initiative pediatric services.

$40,000 to Communities in Schools of Chicago, Chicago, IL, 2013. To assist CISC with connecting Chicago Public School students to a range of essential healthcare services and strengthening the role of nurses in its school network.

$40,000 to Instituto Health Sciences Career Academy, Chicago, IL, 2013. For full time school nurse.

$35,000 to American Cancer Society, Illinois Division, Chicago, IL, 2013. For Patient Navigation Services for cancer patients at John A. Stroger Hospital of Cook County.

$25,000 to Teen Parent Connection, Glen Ellyn, IL, 2013.

$10,000 to Chicago Jesuit Academy, Chicago, IL, 2013. For School Nurse Services for Students on Chicago's Westside, funding will assist the Academy in providing medically underserved students and their families.

3207
Voice of Peace Foundation, Inc. ✧ ☆

(formerly Voice of Peace, Inc.)
630 Lively Blvd.
Elk Grove Village, IL 60007-2016

Donors: Martin M. Selak; MS Management Company LLC.

Foundation type: Independent foundation.

Financial data (yr. ended 12/31/13): Assets, $221,038 (M); gifts received, $929,681; expenditures, $1,035,855; qualifying distributions, $1,035,855; giving activities include $926,276 for 3 grants (high: $770,000; low: $30,000), and $98,926 for 5 grants to individuals (high: $50,000; low: $2,000).

Fields of interest: Education; Human services.

Type of support: Scholarships—to individuals.

Limitations: Applications not accepted.

Application information: Unsolicited requests for funds not accepted.

Officers: Martin M. Selak, Pres. and Treas.; Nancy Dedic, Secy.

Board Member: George Selak.

EIN: 364129474

3208
Leona Stanford Vollintine Charitable Trust ✧

2218 Augusta Dr.
Springfield, IL 62704-3105
Contact: Richard Lansden

Established in 1999 in CO.

Donors: Leona S. Vollintine; Reward Oil.

Foundation type: Independent foundation.

Financial data (yr. ended 12/31/13): Assets, $11,545,431 (M); expenditures, $623,161; qualifying distributions, $499,000; giving activities include $499,000 for 24 grants (high: $35,000; low: $10,000).

Fields of interest: Higher education; Blind/visually impaired.

Type of support: Scholarship funds.

Limitations: Applications not accepted. Giving primarily in CO and IL. No grants to individuals.

Application information: Contributes only to pre-selected organizations.

Officers and Trustees: Roger Hickman,* Treas.; Richard U. Lansden,* Exec. Dir.

EIN: 841524918

Selected grants: The following grants are a representative sample of this grantmaker's funding activity:

$23,000 to University of Illinois, Springfield, IL, 2011.

3209
Walgreen Benefit Fund ✧

102 Wilmot Rd., Ste. 1242
Deerfield, IL 60015-5121 (847) 315-4662
Contact: John Gremer, V.P. and Dir.
FAX: (847) 368-6647; Application address: 104 Wilmot Rd., Ste. 1457, Deerfield, IL 60015, tel.: (847) 315-4662; Main URL: http://www.walgreens.com/topic/sr/sr_walgreens_benefit.jsp

Incorporated in 1939 in IL.

Donors: Touro University; Walgreen Co.; C.R. Walgreen, Jr.; L. Daniel Jorndt; Ohio Northwestern University; Texas Tech University.

Foundation type: Company-sponsored foundation.

Financial data (yr. ended 04/30/14): Assets, $25,449,712 (M); gifts received, $238,855; expenditures, $2,264,527; qualifying distributions, $2,239,351; giving activities include $2,235,873 for 1,199 grants to individuals (high: $8,000; low: $12).

Purpose and activities: The fund awards grants to employees and former employees and the family members of employees and former employees of Walgreen who have experienced hardship cause by long illnesses, accidents, natural disasters, and other situations.

Fields of interest: Economically disadvantaged.

Type of support: Grants to individuals.

Limitations: Applications accepted. Giving primarily in areas of company operations in Deerfield, IL.

Publications: Application guidelines; Annual report.

Application information: Application form required.

Initial approach: Contact foundation for application form

Copies of proposal: 1

Deadline(s): None

Board meeting date(s): Monthly

Officers and Directors:* K.E. Dimitriou,* Pres.; Timothy Engstrom,* V.P.; John Gremer,* V.P.; C.O. Knupp,* Secy.-Treas.; R.J. Hans; M.D. Oettinger; Wayne Orvis; M.A. Wattley.

Number of staff: 1 part-time professional; 1 part-time support.

EIN: 366051130

3210
Walgreens Assistance, Inc. ✧

300 Wilmot Rd., M.S. 3301
Deerfield, IL 60015
Main URL: http://www.walgreens.com/topic/sr/sr_giving_back_flu_shot.jsp

Donor: Walgreen Co. and Subsidiaries.

Foundation type: Operating foundation.

Financial data (yr. ended 08/31/13): Assets, $0; gifts received, $7,587,000; expenditures, $7,587,000; qualifying distributions, $7,587,000; giving activities include $7,587,000 for grants to individuals.

Purpose and activities: The foundation provides flu shot vouchers to the uninsured or underinsured ill, needy, and infants to prevent influenza and improve health.

Fields of interest: Health care; Infants/toddlers; Economically disadvantaged.

Type of support: Grants to individuals; Donated products; In-kind gifts.

Limitations: Applications not accepted. Giving on a national basis and in Laos.

Application information: The foundation partners with the U.S. Department of Health and Human Services to distribute flu vaccine vouchers to local health agencies and community partners.

Officers and Directors:* John Gremer,* Pres.; John Mann,* V.P.; Robert Silverman,* Secy.; Rick Hans,* Treas.

EIN: 274521750

3211
Jay P. Walker Charitable Trust ✧
10 S. Dearborn, IL1-0117
Chicago, IL 60603-3038

Established in 1970; supporting organization of Berkeley Hall School, Holland Hall, the University of Tulsa, and the Principia Corporation.
Foundation type: Independent foundation.
Financial data (yr. ended 09/30/13): Assets, $10,610,149 (M); expenditures, $642,386; qualifying distributions, $516,889; giving activities include $490,288 for 9 grants (high: $201,581; low: $19,198).
Fields of interest: Education; Salvation Army; YM/YWCAs & YM/YWHAs.
Limitations: Applications not accepted. Giving limited to Los Angeles, CA, Tulsa, OK, and St. Louis, MO.
Application information: Contributes only to pre-selected organizations; unsolicited requests for funds not considered or acknowledged.
Trustee: JPMorgan Chase Bank, N.A.
EIN: 736110880
Selected grants: The following grants are a representative sample of this grantmaker's funding activity:
$201,581 to Principia Corporation, Saint Louis, MO, 2013. For Contribution: Operations History Teaching.
$134,387 to University of Tulsa, Tulsa, OK, 2013. For Contribution Operating Not Capital.
$28,797 to Berkeley Hall School Foundation, Los Angeles, CA, 2013. For Contribution: Operating Not Capital.
$19,198 to YMCA of Greater Tulsa, Tulsa, OK, 2013. For Contribution Operating But Not Capital.

3212
The Walsh Foundation ✧
c/o Madden, Jiganti, Moore & Sinars
190 S. LaSalle St., Ste. 1700
Chicago, IL 60603-3496

Established around 1995 in IL.
Donors: The Walsh Construction Co. of Illinois; A-W Contractors; Archer Western Contractors.
Foundation type: Independent foundation.
Financial data (yr. ended 12/31/12): Assets, $190,412,539 (M); expenditures, $8,332,293; qualifying distributions, $7,281,250; giving activities include $7,281,250 for 82 grants (high: $2,000,000; low: $1,000).
Purpose and activities: Giving primarily for the arts, education, Roman Catholic churches and schools, social services, and children services, including a children's hospital.
Fields of interest: Arts; Secondary school/education; Higher education; Education; Hospitals (specialty); Human services; Children, services; Catholic agencies & churches.
Limitations: Applications not accepted. Giving primarily in IL, with emphasis on Chicago; some funding also in Notre Dame, IN. No grants to individuals.
Application information: Contributes only to pre-selected organizations.
Officers and Directors:* Matthew M. Walsh,* C.E.O.; Daniel J. Walsh, Pres.; Patricia R. Walsh,* Secy.; Joyce S. Walsh,* Treas.; E. Bryan Dunigan.
EIN: 363994447
Selected grants: The following grants are a representative sample of this grantmaker's funding activity:
$2,000,000 to University of Notre Dame, School of Architecture, Notre Dame, IN, 2012.
$500,000 to Mission of Our Lady of Mercy, Mercy Home for Boys and Girls, Chicago, IL, 2012.
$500,000 to Mother McAuley Liberal Arts High School, Chicago, IL, 2012.
$400,000 to Chicago Jesuit Academy, Chicago, IL, 2012.
$100,000 to Catholic Church Extension Society of the U.S.A., Chicago, IL, 2012.
$100,000 to Saint Vincent de Paul Center, Chicago, IL, 2012.
$100,000 to University of Notre Dame, School of Architecture, Dean's Fund, Notre Dame, IN, 2012.
$75,000 to Children at the Crossroads Foundation, Chicago, IL, 2012.
$50,000 to Old Saint Patricks Church, Chicago, IL, 2012.
$12,500 to Peggy Notebaert Nature Museum, Chicago, IL, 2012.

3213
Byron L. Walter Family Trust ✧ ☆
c/o JPMorgan Chase Bank, N.A.
10 S. Dearborn St., IL1-0117
Chicago, IL 60603-2300 (312) 732-7553
Contact: Mackenzie Currans, Trust Off., JPMorgan Chase Bank, N.A.

Established in 1981 in WI.
Donor: Arlene B. Walter‡.
Foundation type: Independent foundation.
Financial data (yr. ended 04/30/13): Assets, $13,241,388 (M); expenditures, $702,300; qualifying distributions, $595,165; giving activities include $562,552 for 14 grants (high: $77,552; low: $5,000).
Fields of interest: Arts; Higher education; Nursing school/education; Education; Health care; Human services; YM/YWCAs & YM/YWHAs; Children/youth, services; Foundations (private grantmaking).
Type of support: Capital campaigns; Building/renovation; Equipment; Program development.
Limitations: Applications accepted. Giving limited to Brown County, WI. No grants to individuals, or for matching gifts; no loans.
Publications: Application guidelines.
Application information: Application form not required.
Initial approach: Letter
Copies of proposal: 2
Deadline(s): None
Board meeting date(s): Jan., Apr., June, Sept., and Dec.
Final notification: 6 months
Trustees: Richard J. Blahnik; JPMorgan Chase Bank, N.A.
EIN: 396346563
Selected grants: The following grants are a representative sample of this grantmaker's funding activity:
$50,000 to Saint Norbert College, De Pere, WI, 2011.
$40,000 to NEW Curative Rehabilitation, Green Bay, WI, 2011.
$25,000 to Bellin College of Nursing, Green Bay, WI, 2011.
$10,000 to Bellin Foundation, Green Bay, WI, 2011.
$1,000 to Greater Green Bay Community Foundation, Green Bay, WI, 2011.

3214
Riaz H. Waraich Charitable Foundation ✧
4065 Commercial Ave.
Northbrook, IL 60062-1851

Established in 1990 in IL.
Donors: Riaz H. Waraich; Qaiser F. Waraich.
Foundation type: Independent foundation.
Financial data (yr. ended 12/31/13): Assets, $120,790 (M); gifts received, $2,247,000; expenditures, $2,748,030; qualifying distributions, $2,748,030; giving activities include $2,748,030 for 38 grants (high: $1,000,000; low: $50).
Fields of interest: Higher education, university; Education; Cancer; Islam.
Limitations: Applications not accepted. Giving primarily in IL. No grants to individuals.
Application information: Contributes only to pre-selected organizations.
Officer: Tommy Pappas, Mgr.
Trustees: J. Thomas Hurvis; Riaz H. Waraich.
EIN: 363766283

3215
Eugenie Phyllis Ward Charity Trust ✧
c/o The Northern Trust Co.
P.O. Box 803878
Chicago, IL 60680-3878

Established in 1977.
Foundation type: Independent foundation.
Financial data (yr. ended 08/31/13): Assets, $18,651,959 (M); expenditures, $1,372,637; qualifying distributions, $1,229,439; giving activities include $1,215,326 for 3 grants (high: $616,442; low: $299,442).
Fields of interest: Residential/custodial care, group home.
Limitations: Applications not accepted. Giving primarily in NE and in Paris, France.
Application information: Contributes only to pre-selected organizations; unsolicited requests for funds not considered or acknowledged.
Trustee: The Northern Trust Co.
EIN: 366027626
Selected grants: The following grants are a representative sample of this grantmaker's funding activity:
$291,257 to Boys Town, Boys Town, NE, 2011. For general support.

3216
A. Montgomery Ward Foundation ✧
c/o Bank of America, N.A.
231 S. LaSalle St. IL1-231-13-32
Chicago, IL 60604-1206
E-mail: ilgrantmaking@ustrust.com; Main URL: https://www.bankofamerica.com/philanthropic/grantmaking.go

Trust established in 1959 in IL.
Donor: Marjorie Montgomery Ward Baker‡.
Foundation type: Independent foundation.
Financial data (yr. ended 06/30/13): Assets, $15,155,469 (M); expenditures, $853,693; qualifying distributions, $693,461; giving activities include $562,627 for 40 grants (high: $66,000; low: $1,848).
Purpose and activities: The foundation's grantmaking emphasizes those institutions in the Chicago, IL, area which provide its many citizens

with high-quality, well established educational and cultural activities, with emphasis on museums; funding also for children, youth, families, women, and social services including recordings for the blind and dyslexic, and treatment for families where child abuse and neglect have occurred, focusing on children from birth to 5 years.
Fields of interest: Museums; Museums (natural history); Planetarium; Arts; Education; Hospitals (general); Health care; Human services; Children/youth, services; Community/economic development.
Type of support: General/operating support; Capital campaigns; Scholarship funds.
Limitations: Giving primarily in Chicago, IL, and surrounding metropolitan areas. No grants to individuals.
Publications: Application guidelines.
Application information: Application guidelines and form available on foundation web site. Application form required.
Initial approach: Proposal
Copies of proposal: 2
Deadline(s): Apr. 15, and Oct. 15
Board meeting date(s): May and Nov.
Final notification: June 30 and Dec. 31
Trustees: Jack Hutchings; Richard Oloffson; Bank of America, N.A.
EIN: 362417437
Selected grants: The following grants are a representative sample of this grantmaker's funding activity:
$100,000 to Museum of Science and Industry, Chicago, IL, 2011. For new Body Human programs and exhibits.
$65,000 to Associated Colleges of Illinois, Chicago, IL, 2011. For A. Montgomery Ward Foundation Scholarship.
$55,868 to Josephinum Academy, Chicago, IL, 2011. For Gymnasium Renovation Project.
$27,980 to Avenues to Independence, Park Ridge, IL, 2011. For Fire Sprinkler Systems.
$25,000 to Little City Foundation, Palatine, IL, 2011. For Children's Village Initiative.
$25,000 to WINGS Program, Schaumburg, IL, 2011. For WINGS Van Purchase.
$20,000 to Chicago Childrens Museum, Chicago, IL, 2011. For Access Initiatives to eliminate barriers to visiting the museum and engaging in array of educational programs offered on site. Includes free admission opportunities, discounted membership and admission programs.
$15,000 to Catholic Charities of the Archdiocese of Chicago, Chicago, IL, 2011. For St. Francis DePaula Interim Family Shelter Renovation. The Shelter provides interim housing and intensive case management services to homeless families with children.
$10,000 to Chicago Family Health Center, Chicago, IL, 2011. For Back to School Health Fairs. Host fairs at clinics in southeast Chicago with the goal to provide school physicals and dental screenings to school-aged children. They provide lunch for the whole family, entertainment and backpacks.
$10,000 to Harbour, The, Park Ridge, IL, 2011. For Safe Harbour Emergency Shelter.

3217
Washington Square Health Foundation, Inc. ✧

875 N. Michigan Ave., Ste. 3516
Chicago, IL 60611-1957 (312) 664-6488
Contact: Howard Nochumson, Exec. Dir.; Catherine Baginski, Prog. Dir.
FAX: (312) 664-7787; E-mail: washington@wshf.org; Main URL: http://www.wshf.org
Facebook: https://www.facebook.com/WashingtonSquareHealthFoundation

Established in 1985 in IL; converted from Henrotin Hospital.
Donors: Henrotin Hospital; George Zendt Charitable Trust.
Foundation type: Independent foundation.
Financial data (yr. ended 09/30/13): Assets, $20,702,949 (M); gifts received, $11,353; expenditures, $1,200,472; qualifying distributions, $1,448,977; giving activities include $426,344 for 72 grants (high: $30,000; low: $200), and $350,000 for 1 loan/program-related investment.
Purpose and activities: Giving to promote and maintain access to adequate primary health care, through grants for medical and nursing education scholarships, medical research, and direct healthcare services.
Fields of interest: Medical school/education; Nursing school/education; Nursing care; Nursing home/convalescent facility; Health care; AIDS; Medical research, institute; AIDS research; Crime/violence prevention, domestic violence; Aging; Disabilities, people with; Minorities; Women; AIDS, people with; Immigrants/refugees; Homeless; LGBTQ.
Type of support: Equipment; Program development; Seed money; Fellowships; Scholarship funds; Research; Program-related investments/loans; Matching/challenge support.
Limitations: Applications accepted. Giving primarily in the Chicago, IL, area for direct healthcare services; giving nationally for medical research and education grants. No grants to individuals, or for general operating or administrative expenses, land acquisition, or construction.
Publications: Application guidelines; Annual report; Grants list.
Application information: Application form required.
Initial approach: Use online grant form on foundation web site
Board meeting date(s): Feb., May, and July
Officers and Directors:* William N. Werner, M.D., Pres.; Richard B. Patterson, DPM, MSPH*, V.P.; William B. Friedeman,* Secy.; James M. Snyder,* Treas.; Howard Nochumson,* Exec. Dir.; Barbara Berendt; Catherine M. Creticos Poulos, M.D.
Number of staff: 2 full-time professional; 1 part-time support.
EIN: 361210140

3218
Arthur K. Watson Charitable Trust ✧

c/o JPMorgan Chase Bank, N.A.
10 S. Dearborn St., 21st Fl.
Chicago, IL 60603-2300
Application address: c/o James Largey, JP Morgan Chase Bank, N.A., 270 Park Ave., 18th Fl., New York, NY 10017; tel.: (212) 464-1937

Donor: Thomas J. Watson Foundation.
Foundation type: Independent foundation.
Financial data (yr. ended 05/31/12): Assets, $14,682,278 (M); expenditures, $707,300; qualifying distributions, $628,277; giving activities include $620,000 for 19 grants (high: $100,000; low: $7,500).
Purpose and activities: Giving primarily for medical research and for the provision of non-governmental education programs.
Fields of interest: Education; Health care; Medical research, institute.
Limitations: Giving primarily in AZ, ME and MA. No grants to individuals.
Application information: Application form not required.
Initial approach: Letter
Deadline(s): None
Advisory Committee: Ann W. Bresnahan; Caroline W. Morong; Jane W. Stetson; Arthur K. Watson, Jr.; David J. Watson; Stuart H. Watson.
Trustees: Ann H. Symington; JPMorgan Chase Bank, N.A.
EIN: 132989468
Selected grants: The following grants are a representative sample of this grantmaker's funding activity:
$40,000 to Northeastern University, Boston, MA, 2013. For grant; Ne Students for Giving.

3219
The Thomas J. & Olive C. Watson Foundation ✧

c/o JPMorgan Chase Bank, N.A.
10 S. Dearborn St., IL1-0117
Chicago, IL 60603-2317
Application address: c/o Sarah Rubin, 270 Park Ave., 16th Fl., New York, NY 10017-2014; tel.: (212) 464-2599

Established in 2002 in NY.
Donors: Thomas J. Watson, Jr.; Olive C. Watson Marital Trust.
Foundation type: Independent foundation.
Financial data (yr. ended 07/31/13): Assets, $30,260,374 (M); expenditures, $1,472,819; qualifying distributions, $1,256,885; giving activities include $1,226,081 for 2 grants (high: $1,183,558; low: $42,523).
Fields of interest: Higher education.
Limitations: Giving in RI.
Application information:
Initial approach: Letter
Deadline(s): None
Advisory Committee: David E. McKinney; Daniel L. Mosley; Thomas J. Watson III.
Trustee: JPMorgan Chase Bank, N.A.
EIN: 137371044
Selected grants: The following grants are a representative sample of this grantmaker's funding activity:
$1,029,263 to Brown University, Providence, RI, 2011. For general support.

3220
Wavering Family Charitable Foundation ✧

P.O. Box 803878
Chicago, IL 60680-3878

Established in 1990 in IL.
Donor: Emer H. Wavering.
Foundation type: Independent foundation.

Financial data (yr. ended 12/31/13): Assets, $13,929,025 (M); expenditures, $644,118; qualifying distributions, $585,179; giving activities include $582,120 for 7 grants (high: $300,000; low: $3,500).
Fields of interest: Historic preservation/historical societies; Education; Environment, natural resources.
Limitations: Applications accepted. Giving primarily in FL and IL.
Application information: Application form not required.
Initial approach: Proposal
Deadline(s): None
Trustee: The Northern Trust Co.
EIN: 366940417
Selected grants: The following grants are a representative sample of this grantmaker's funding activity:
$25,000 to Naples Botanical Garden, Naples, FL, 2012. For Sustaining Leadership Council.

3221
The Weberg Trust ✧
(formerly Weberg Foundation)
P.O. Box 803878
Chicago, IL 60680-8378
E-mail: jwebarg@netcom.com

Established in 1999 in CO; reorganized in 2004. The entity was originally known as Weberg Foundation.
Donors: John P. Weberg; Jacqueline Weberg.
Foundation type: Independent foundation.
Financial data (yr. ended 12/31/13): Assets, $13,554,391 (M); expenditures, $4,982,943; qualifying distributions, $4,834,607; giving activities include $4,777,000 for 5 grants (high: $1,200,000; low: $555,996).
Purpose and activities: Support for microenterprise development worldwide.
Fields of interest: International economic development.
Limitations: Applications not accepted. Giving in the U.S., with some emphasis on CA and IL. No grants to individuals.
Application information: Contributes only to pre-selected organizations.
Grant Committee: Karen Sue Allen; Linda Lair; Russ Lair; Claudia Weberg; Gary Weberg; Jacqueline Weberg; John P. Weberg.
Trustee: The Northern Trust Co.
EIN: 206382151
Selected grants: The following grants are a representative sample of this grantmaker's funding activity:
$1,300,000 to Freedom from Hunger, Davis, CA, 2012. For general support.
$1,200,000 to Pro Mujer, New York, NY, 2012. For general support.
$900,000 to Opportunity International, Oak Brook, IL, 2012. For general support.
$600,000 to MicroPlanet Technologies, Washington, DC, 2012. For general support.

3222
The Weezie Foundation ✧
10 S. Dearborn St., IL1-0117
Chicago, IL 60603-2300
Application address: c/o James Vinograd, 270 Park Ave. 28th Fl. New York, NY 10017

Trust established in 1961 in NY.
Donor: Adelaide T. Corbett†.
Foundation type: Independent foundation.
Financial data (yr. ended 12/31/13): Assets, $25,932,892 (M); expenditures, $1,252,182; qualifying distributions, $1,109,739; giving activities include $1,063,170 for 16 grants (high: $100,000; low: $6,670).
Purpose and activities: Giving primarily for education and human services.
Fields of interest: Arts; Education; Human services; Youth, services.
Limitations: Applications accepted. Giving primarily in MA and New York, NY.
Application information: Application form required.
Initial approach: Letter
Deadline(s): None
Advisory Committee: Elizabeth Carroll; Abigail Fiske; Elaine Fiske; Kirke T. Hall; Lucille Hays; Tyler P. Hoffman; Katherine McBride; William Parsons, Jr., Esq.
Trustee: JPMorgan Chase Bank, N.A.
EIN: 136090903

3223
Judd A. and Marjorie G. Weinberg Family Foundation ✧
401 N. Michigan Ave., Ste. 3050
Chicago, IL 60611-5515

Established in 1977.
Donors: Marjorie G. Weinberg; Judd A. Weinberg; and other members of the Weinberg family.
Foundation type: Independent foundation.
Financial data (yr. ended 12/31/12): Assets, $6,478,370 (M); expenditures, $654,548; qualifying distributions, $651,602; giving activities include $611,058 for 65 grants (high: $200,100; low: $50).
Purpose and activities: Giving primarily for higher education; funding also for medical research, the arts and Jewish welfare.
Fields of interest: Arts; Higher education; Medical research, institute; Cancer research; Human services; Jewish federated giving programs; Jewish agencies & synagogues.
Limitations: Applications not accepted. Giving primarily in IL, with emphasis on Chicago. No grants to individuals.
Application information: Contributes only to pre-selected organizations.
Officers: Judd A. Weinberg, Chair.; Richard G. Weinberg, Pres.; David B. Weinberg,* V.P. and Secy.-Treas.; Jack A. Weinberg,* V.P.
EIN: 362934515

3224
William L. and Josephine B. Weiss Family Foundation ✧
c/o SBC
225 W. Randolph St., Ste. 27A
Chicago, IL 60606-7406

Established in 1986 in IL.
Donors: William L. Weiss; Josephine B. Weiss.
Foundation type: Independent foundation.
Financial data (yr. ended 12/31/12): Assets, $8,035,594 (M); expenditures, $523,908; qualifying distributions, $461,000; giving activities include $461,000 for grants.
Fields of interest: Higher education; Human services; Children/youth, services.
Limitations: Applications not accepted. Giving primarily in FL and PA. No grants to individuals.
Application information: Contributes only to pre-selected organizations.
Officers: David W. Weiss,* Pres.; William L. Weiss,* V.P. and Secy.-Treas.; Steven P. Weiss,* V.P.; Susan L. Miller; Josephine B. Weiss.
EIN: 363478679

3225
Herbert C. Wenske Foundation ✧
c/o Howard Stone
1 S. Wacker Dr., Ste. 800
Chicago, IL 60606-4650

Established in 1957 in IL.
Donors: Florence Wenske; Herbert C. Wenske†; Wenske Enterprises, Inc.
Foundation type: Independent foundation.
Financial data (yr. ended 12/31/13): Assets, $5,658,327 (M); expenditures, $734,199; qualifying distributions, $661,526; giving activities include $568,000 for 41 grants (high: $165,000; low: $1,000).
Purpose and activities: Giving primarily for Jewish religious and educational purposes; support also for hospitals and health care.
Fields of interest: Education; Hospitals (general); Health organizations, association; Children/youth, services; Jewish federated giving programs; Protestant agencies & churches; Jewish agencies & synagogues.
Limitations: Applications accepted. Giving primarily in Chicago, IL. No grants to individuals.
Application information: Application form not required.
Initial approach: Proposal
Deadline(s): None
Officers: Howard L. Stone, Pres.; Loren R. Stone, Secy.; Harvey Gaffen, Treas.
EIN: 366055643

3226
Ernest Wentcher Educational Fund ✧ ☆
P. O. Box 11079
Chicago, IL 60611-0079 (312) 321-5100

Established in 1997 in IL.
Donor: Ernest C. Wentcher†.
Foundation type: Independent foundation.
Financial data (yr. ended 06/30/13): Assets, $11,975,666 (M); gifts received, $476,797; expenditures, $631,406; qualifying distributions, $534,566; giving activities include $534,566 for 34 grants (high: $112,500; low: $7,500).
Purpose and activities: Giving for education of Chicago public school seniors, and Oakton Community College students.
Fields of interest: Education.
Type of support: General/operating support.
Limitations: Applications accepted. Giving primarily in IL, with emphasis on Chicago. No grants to individuals directly.
Application information: Application form required.
Deadline(s): End of Feb. (for Chicago Public Schools Dept. of College Preparation); spring (for Oakton Community College Student Aid Dept.)

Officers: Brian Fitzpatrick, Pres.; Norma Berfield, Secy.-Treas.
Directors: A. Vincent Agnew; Marilyn Appelson; Richard Helmholz; Lucy Tuck.
EIN: 364170236
Selected grants: The following grants are a representative sample of this grantmaker's funding activity:
$52,500 to University of Illinois at Urbana-Champaign, Urbana, IL, 2011.
$48,023 to Oakton Community College, Des Plaines, IL, 2011.
$45,000 to DePaul University, Chicago, IL, 2011.
$30,000 to Northeastern Illinois University, Chicago, IL, 2011.
$30,000 to University of Illinois at Chicago, Chicago, IL, 2011.
$18,750 to Howard University, Washington, DC, 2011.
$15,000 to Loyola University of Chicago, Chicago, IL, 2011.
$15,000 to University of Illinois at Urbana-Champaign, Urbana, IL, 2011.
$15,000 to University of Wisconsin, Madison, WI, 2011.
$7,500 to Fisk University, Nashville, TN, 2011.

3227
Wessner Foundation ✧
c/o Harrizon & Held, LLP
333 W. Wacker Dr., Ste. 1700
Chicago, IL 60606-1220

Established in 1994 in MN.
Donor: Norma C. Wessner.
Foundation type: Independent foundation.
Financial data (yr. ended 12/31/13): Assets, $8,853,697 (M); gifts received, $297,950; expenditures, $710,629; qualifying distributions, $634,535; giving activities include $634,500 for 9 grants (high: $209,500; low: $5,000).
Fields of interest: Higher education; Christian agencies & churches.
Limitations: Applications not accepted. Giving primarily in IL. No grants to individuals.
Application information: Contributes only to pre-selected organizations.
Officers and Directors:* David K. Wessner,* Pres.; Barbara W. Anderson,* V.P. and Secy.; Ross E. Anderson,* Treas.; Patricia A. Wessner.
EIN: 363480120
Selected grants: The following grants are a representative sample of this grantmaker's funding activity:
$200,000 to Wheaton College, Wheaton, IL, 2011. For general support.
$65,000 to Development Associates International, Colorado Springs, CO, 2011. For general support.
$15,000 to Mustard Seed Ministries, Springfield, IL, 2011. For general support.

3228
Westlake Health Foundation ✧
1 Lincoln Ctr.
18 W. 140 Butterfield Rd., Ste. 1660
Oakbrook Terrace, IL 60181-4257 (630) 495-3800
Contact: Leonard J. Muller, Chair.
E-mail: info@westlakehf.com; Additional e-mail: rosewesolek@aol.com; Main URL: http://www.westlakehf.com

Established in 1998 in IL; converted from Westlake Hospital.
Donor: Westlake Hospital.
Foundation type: Independent foundation.
Financial data (yr. ended 12/31/13): Assets, $115,313,240 (M); expenditures, $5,842,126; qualifying distributions, $5,042,817; giving activities include $4,387,623 for 55 grants (high: $500,000; low: $100).
Purpose and activities: The foundation supports and encourages the development of healthcare services by making grants to nonprofit community organizations.
Fields of interest: Health care.
Limitations: Applications accepted. Giving primarily in west suburban Cook County, IL. No support for political organizations, direct religious activities or for fraternal societies. No grants to individuals; or for endowment campaigns, campaigns or lobbying activities, fundraising or for telephone solicitations.
Publications: Application guidelines.
Application information: See web site for application guidelines.
Deadline(s): May 1 and Nov. 1
Board meeting date(s): June and Dec.
Officers and Trustees:* Leonard J. Muller,* Chair. and C.E.O.; David R. Hey,* Pres. and C.O.O.; J. Melvin Smith, M.D.*, Secy.; Richard M. Montalbano, Sr.; Saundra L. Spiloto; Fred M. Tomera, M.D.; Raul Villasuso, M.D.
EIN: 363104071

3229
W. P. and H. B. White Foundation ✧
540 Frontage Rd., Ste. 3240
Northfield, IL 60093-1232 (847) 446-1441
Contact: Steven R. White, Pres. and Exec. Dir.

Incorporated in 1953 in IL.
Donors: William P. White†; Hazel B. White†.
Foundation type: Independent foundation.
Financial data (yr. ended 12/31/13): Assets, $27,799,305 (M); expenditures, $1,092,557; qualifying distributions, $981,972; giving activities include $696,505 for 64 grants (high: $22,000; low: $5).
Purpose and activities: Funding to organizations in the metropolitan Chicago, IL area that contribute to the future good of society, primarily in the areas of education, health, and human services, with an emphasis on helping those most in need. Since there are limits to the number of proposals that the foundation can fund, selection in no way reflects on the merits of those not given support.
Fields of interest: Secondary school/education; Adult/continuing education; Education; Health care; Housing/shelter, development; Human services; Children/youth, services; Minorities; Economically disadvantaged.
Type of support: General/operating support; Continuing support; Annual campaigns; Program development; Scholarship funds.
Limitations: Applications accepted. Giving primarily in the metropolitan Chicago, IL, area. No grants to individuals, or for land acquisition, endowments, fundraising events, publications, conferences, deficit financing, or visual or performing arts; no loans.
Publications: Application guidelines.
Application information: Application form not required.
Initial approach: Proposal
Copies of proposal: 1
Deadline(s): Feb. 1, May 1, Aug. 1, Nov. 1
Board meeting date(s): Mar., June, Sept., and Dec.
Final notification: Several weeks
Officers and Directors:* Steven R. White,* Pres. and Exec. Dir.; Philip O. White,* V.P. and Treas.; John J. McCortney,* Secy.; Roger B. White; William P. White III.
Number of staff: 1 full-time professional; 1 full-time support.
EIN: 362601558
Selected grants: The following grants are a representative sample of this grantmaker's funding activity:
$20,000 to Our Lady of Tepeyac High School, Chicago, IL, 2012. For needs based financial aid.
$15,000 to De La Salle Institute, Chicago, IL, 2012. For Student Financial Assistance Program.
$15,000 to Target Hope, Matteson, IL, 2012. For STEM Initiative.
$14,000 to LYDIA Home Association, Chicago, IL, 2012. For Safe Families Program.
$14,000 to Saint Patrick High School, Chicago, IL, 2012. For financial assistance program.
$12,000 to Casa Central, Chicago, IL, 2012. For La Posada.
$12,000 to Mother McAuley Liberal Arts High School, Chicago, IL, 2012. For tuition assistance for 8 minority students.
$12,000 to Mount Carmel High School, Chicago, IL, 2012. For McDermott-Doyle Program.
$10,000 to Lambs Farm, Libertyville, IL, 2012. For Comprehensive Vocational Services.
$10,000 to Logan Square Neighborhood Association, Chicago, IL, 2012. For school programs.

3230
G. R. White Trust ✧
10 S. Dearborn St., IL1-0117
Chicago, IL 60603
Application address: c/o JPMorgan Chase Bank, N.A., 420 Throckmorton St., Forth Worth, TX 76102, tel.: (817) 884-4022

Established in 1965 in TX.
Donor: G.R. White†.
Foundation type: Independent foundation.
Financial data (yr. ended 09/30/13): Assets, $22,052,157 (M); expenditures, $1,543,584; qualifying distributions, $1,068,330; giving activities include $1,052,325 for 43 grants (high: $182,453; low: $2,000).
Purpose and activities: Giving primarily for higher and other education.
Fields of interest: Museums (history); Higher education; Libraries/library science; Education; Environment; Agriculture/food, formal/general education; Disasters, fire prevention/control; Youth development, agriculture; Human services; Community/economic development; Protestant agencies & churches.
Type of support: General/operating support; Building/renovation; Equipment; Professorships; Scholarship funds.
Limitations: Applications accepted. Giving limited to TX. No grants to individuals.
Application information: Application form required.
Initial approach: Proposal
Copies of proposal: 1
Deadline(s): Sept.
Board meeting date(s): Fall

Trustee: JPMorgan Chase Bank, N.A.
EIN: 756094930
Selected grants: The following grants are a representative sample of this grantmaker's funding activity:
$155,000 to Texas Tech Foundation, Lubbock, TX, 2011.
$70,000 to Baylor Health Care System, Dallas, TX, 2011. For program support.
$50,000 to Texas and Southwestern Cattle Raisers Foundation, Fort Worth, TX, 2011.
$40,000 to Saint Stephens Episcopal School, Austin, TX, 2011.
$28,000 to Saint Stephens Episcopal School, Austin, TX, 2011. For program support.
$12,500 to Parkland Foundation, Dallas, TX, 2011. For program support.
$5,000 to Southwestern Baptist Theological Seminary, Fort Worth, TX, 2011. For scholarship program.

3231
Wieboldt Foundation
53 W. Jackson Blvd., Ste. 1252
Chicago, IL 60604-3611 (312) 786-9377
Contact: Carmen Prieto
E-mail for letter of inquiry: awards@wieboldt.org.; Main URL: http://www.wieboldt.org
Wieboldt Foundation's Philanthropy Promise: http://www.ncrp.org/philanthropys-promise/who

Incorporated in 1921 in IL.
Donors: William A. Wieboldt†; Anna Krueger Wieboldt†.
Foundation type: Independent foundation.
Financial data (yr. ended 12/31/13): Assets, $19,302,752 (M); expenditures, $1,019,806; qualifying distributions, $930,790; giving activities include $629,530 for grants, and $25,000 for 1 loan/program-related investment.
Purpose and activities: The foundation's highest priority is the support of multi-issue community organizations that work in low-income neighborhoods, that are accountable to neighborhood residents, and through which people are empowered to have a major voice in shaping decisions that affect their lives. A second priority is given to organizations that support community organizations through training, technical assistance, legal strategies, coalition building, advocacy, and policy development. The foundation's recognition of community organizing or community action as its prime concern is promoted by its conviction that a sense of powerlessness and the apathy and alienation bred of this sense are at the root of many of the ills of our time. It believes that funding those efforts that give people hope that they can exercise a degree of control over their lives and that involve them working together toward jointly defined ends is an important contribution to the resolution of social ills.
Fields of interest: Urban/community development.
Type of support: General/operating support; Continuing support; Program-related investments/loans.
Limitations: Applications accepted. Giving limited to the metropolitan Chicago, IL, area. No grants to individuals, or for endowment funds, studies and research, capital campaigns, scholarships, fellowships, conferences, direct service projects, or economic development.
Publications: Application guidelines; Annual report (including application guidelines); Grants list.
Application information: Complete application guidelines available on foundation web site. Application form required.
Initial approach: Letter of inquiry via e-mail for general grant requests; telephone regarding Program Related Investments
Copies of proposal: 1
Deadline(s): See foundation web site for current deadlines
Board meeting date(s): Monthly, except Apr., Aug., and Dec.
Officers and Directors:* Jennifer Corrigan,* Pres.; Ben Darrow,* V.P.; John S. Darrow,* Treas.; Regina McGraw, Exec. Dir.; Jessica Darrow; Bill Davis; T. Lawrence Doyle; Carol Larson; Maureen Loughnane; Janet Smith; Nancy Wieboldt.
Number of staff: 2 full-time professional.
EIN: 362167955
Selected grants: The following grants are a representative sample of this grantmaker's funding activity:
$15,000 to United African Organization, Chicago, IL, 2012. For All Grants Are for General Operations.

3232
Wilemal Fund ✧
c/o Briar Hall, LLC
200 W. Madison St., Ste. 3400
Chicago, IL 60603-3600

Established in 1964.
Donors: Elizabeth Byron Brown; Malcolm M. Brown; William G. Brown; Dr. John Reppas; Dr. Solange Brown.
Foundation type: Independent foundation.
Financial data (yr. ended 12/31/13): Assets, $28,596,254 (M); gifts received, $1,267,911; expenditures, $1,753,107; qualifying distributions, $1,715,003; giving activities include $1,704,978 for 28 grants (high: $775,000; low: $1,000).
Purpose and activities: Giving primarily for the arts, education, and social services.
Fields of interest: Arts education; Arts; Higher education; Education; Environment, natural resources; Hospitals (general); Human services.
Limitations: Applications not accepted. Giving primarily in IL, with emphasis on Chicago, and Winston-Salem, NC. No grants to individuals.
Application information: Contributes only to pre-selected organizations. Unsolicited requests for funds not accepted.
Officers and Directors:* William Gardner Brown,* Pres. and Secy.; Solange Stephanie Pezon Brown,* V.P. and Treas.; Georges Pezon Brown.
EIN: 366098849
Selected grants: The following grants are a representative sample of this grantmaker's funding activity:
$10,000 to Tulane University, New Orleans, LA, 2012. For the General Scientific Or Education Purpose.
$6,500 to American Symphony Orchestra League, New York, NY, 2012. For the General, Scientific Or Education Purpose.

3233
Hobart W. Williams ✧
231 S. LaSalle St., IL1-231-10-05
Chicago, IL 60697-0001

Foundation type: Independent foundation.
Financial data (yr. ended 09/30/13): Assets, $22,912,118 (M); expenditures, $1,495,397; qualifying distributions, $1,336,714; giving activities include $1,291,460 for 10 grants (high: $129,146; low: $129,146).
Fields of interest: Higher education; Children, services; Residential/custodial care, senior continuing care.
Limitations: Applications not accepted. Giving primarily in IL.
Application information: Contributes only to pre-selected organizations.
Trustee: Bank of America, N.A.
EIN: 366039360
Selected grants: The following grants are a representative sample of this grantmaker's funding activity:
$72,780 to Chicago Child Care Society, Chicago, IL, 2011.
$72,780 to Illinois College, Jacksonville, IL, 2011.
$72,780 to Illinois Wesleyan University, Bloomington, IL, 2011.
$72,780 to Millikin University, Decatur, IL, 2011.
$72,780 to Monmouth College, Monmouth, IL, 2011.
$72,780 to Rockford College, Rockford, IL, 2011.

3234
Nell Williams Family Foundation ✧
444 N. Michigan Ave., Ste. 3530
Chicago, IL 60611-3902

Established in 2006 in IL.
Donors: Elrick Williams; Paula Williams Madison; CME Group Inc.
Foundation type: Independent foundation.
Financial data (yr. ended 12/31/12): Assets, $9,650,036 (M); gifts received, $270,000; expenditures, $671,102; qualifying distributions, $659,503; giving activities include $659,503 for grants.
Fields of interest: Secondary school/education; Higher education; Civil/human rights; Public affairs.
Limitations: Applications not accepted. Giving primarily in NY. No grants to individuals.
Application information: Contributes only to pre-selected organizations.
Trustees: Paula Williams Madison; Elrick Williams.
EIN: 207182883

3235
Willow Springs Charitable Trust ✧
c/o Jenny B. Stoddard, Tr.
10897 S. Rte. 78
Mount Carroll, IL 61053-9522

Established in 2006 in IL.
Foundation type: Independent foundation.
Financial data (yr. ended 12/31/13): Assets, $56,703,730 (M); expenditures, $4,091,638; qualifying distributions, $2,425,518; giving activities include $2,425,518 for 58 grants (high: $400,000; low: $5,000).
Fields of interest: Arts; Higher education; Education; Health organizations; Human services; Children/youth, services; Residential/custodial care, hospices.
Limitations: Applications not accepted. Giving primarily in IL.

Application information: Contributes only to pre-selected organizations.
Trustees: Kent Brodie; Sara Smock Foszcz; Jenny B. Stoddard; Suzy Brodie Vogler.
EIN: 204383299

3236
Jasper L. & Jack Denton Wilson Charitable Foundation ✧
10 S. Dearborn IL1-0117
Chicago, IL 60603

Established in 1989 in TX.
Donors: Mrs. Jack D. Wilson; Jasper L. Wilson.
Foundation type: Independent foundation.
Financial data (yr. ended 12/31/13): Assets, $15,713,183 (M); expenditures, $796,702; qualifying distributions, $680,250; giving activities include $628,486 for 3 grants (high: $350,000; low: $78,486).
Fields of interest: Cancer research.
Limitations: Applications not accepted. Giving primarily in TX. No grants to individuals.
Application information: Contributes only to pre-selected organizations.
Trustees: J. Denton DeWitt; Dinah Gaspard; James L. Gaspard; Timothy R. Vaughan; JPMorgan Chase Bank, N.A.
EIN: 760285403

3237
Anne Potter Wilson Foundation ✧
c/o Bank of America, N.A.
231 S. LaSalle St., IL1-231-10-05
Chicago, IL 60697-1411
Application address: c/o Portia Wells, Bank of America, N.A., 414 Union St., Nashville, TN 37219-1697, tel.: (615) 749-4344

Established in 1996 in TN.
Foundation type: Independent foundation.
Financial data (yr. ended 12/31/13): Assets, $26,048,191 (M); expenditures, $1,119,403; qualifying distributions, $1,073,067; giving activities include $1,048,492 for 24 grants (high: $125,000; low: $5,000).
Purpose and activities: Giving primarily for education, including a music school, and human services.
Fields of interest: Arts education; Performing arts, music; Higher education; Education; Human services.
Limitations: Applications accepted. Giving primarily in Nashville, TN. No grants to individuals.
Application information: Application form required.
Initial approach: Letter
Deadline(s): None
Trustee: Bank of America, N.A.
Committee Members: Blair J. Wilson; Justin P. Wilson; William M. Wilson.
EIN: 626306576
Selected grants: The following grants are a representative sample of this grantmaker's funding activity:
$125,000 to Ensworth School, Nashville, TN, 2011.
$40,000 to Vanderbilt University, Nashville, TN, 2011.
$29,000 to Boy Scouts of America, Nashville, TN, 2011.
$25,000 to Fund for American Studies, Washington, DC, 2011.
$25,000 to University School of Nashville, Nashville, TN, 2011.
$15,000 to Tennessee State Collaborative on Reforming Education, Nashville, TN, 2011.
$12,000 to Montgomery Bell Academy, Nashville, TN, 2011.
$10,784 to Teach for America, New York, NY, 2011.
$10,000 to Cumberland Trail Conference, Crossville, TN, 2011.
$10,000 to Helping Hands Clinic, Morristown, TN, 2011.

3238
Wohlers Family Foundation ✧
c/o The Northern Trust Co.
P.O. Box 803878
Chicago, IL 60680-3878
Application address: c/o Natalie Malik, 21 E. Huron, Ste. 2202, Chicago, IL 60611, tel.: (312) 643-2213

Donors: Albert H. Wohlers; Janet L. Wohlers.
Foundation type: Independent foundation.
Financial data (yr. ended 12/31/13): Assets, $32,020,084 (M); gifts received, $2,000,000; expenditures, $1,169,371; qualifying distributions, $1,041,734; giving activities include $925,268 for 19 grants (high: $200,000; low: $2,500).
Fields of interest: Education; Health organizations; Human services.
Limitations: Applications accepted. Giving primarily in IL.
Application information: Application form required.
Initial approach: Contact foundation
Officers: Albert H. Wohlers, Chair.; Nancy W. Malik, Pres.; Natalie Jane Malik, Secy. and Exec. Dir.; Andrew James Malik, Treas.
Board Members: Daniel James Malik; Molly Jane Pearson.
Advisor: Philip Boersma.
EIN: 260530001

3239
Wonderful Life Foundation ✧
(formerly M. Jude & Lori W. Reyes Foundation)
6250 N. River Rd., Ste. 9000
Rosemont, IL 60018-4241

Established in 2000 in VA.
Donors: M. Jude Reyes; Lori W. Reyes.
Foundation type: Independent foundation.
Financial data (yr. ended 12/31/13): Assets, $1,049,554 (M); gifts received, $4,605,250; expenditures, $4,771,304; qualifying distributions, $4,764,140; giving activities include $4,761,500 for 50 grants (high: $2,500,000; low: $1,000).
Purpose and activities: Giving primarily for education, health organizations, and social services.
Fields of interest: Higher education; Education; Hospitals (specialty); Medical care, rehabilitation; Health organizations, association; Human services; Protestant agencies & churches.
Limitations: Applications not accepted. Giving primarily in IL. No grants to individuals.
Application information: Contributes only to pre-selected organizations.
Directors: Lori W. Reyes; M. Jude Reyes.
EIN: 541995591
Selected grants: The following grants are a representative sample of this grantmaker's funding activity:
$202,500 to Grace Presbyterian Church, Fort Mill, SC, 2011. For general support.
$150,000 to Ann and Robert H. Lurie Children's Hospital of Chicago Foundation, Chicago, IL, 2011.
$125,000 to Field Museum of Natural History, Chicago, IL, 2011. For general support.

3240
Woodbury Foundation ✧
c/o Christine M. Rhode
222 N. LaSalle St., 24th Fl.
Chicago, IL 60601-1003
Application address: c/o Dean of Admissions, Warren Wilson College, Swannanoa, NC 28778, tel.: (704) 298-3325

Established in 1990 in IL.
Donors: Christiana L. Ransom†; Christiana Ransom Irrevocable Trust.
Foundation type: Independent foundation.
Financial data (yr. ended 05/31/13): Assets, $19,852,676 (M); expenditures, $1,005,443; qualifying distributions, $905,238; giving activities include $905,238 for grants.
Purpose and activities: Scholarships for study at Warren Wilson College, preference given to students from Charlevoix, Emmet, Cheboygan and Antrim counties, MI. Giving also for churches and drug rehabilitation centers.
Fields of interest: Historic preservation/historical societies; Higher education; Substance abuse, services; Substance abuse, treatment; Human services; Children, services.
Type of support: General/operating support; Building/renovation; Endowments; Scholarships—to individuals.
Limitations: Applications not accepted. Giving on a national basis.
Application information: Scholarship application available only from Warren Wilson College. Unsolicited requests for funds are not accepted.
Board meeting date(s): April
Officers and Directors:* Myron P. Boon,* Pres.; F. Conrad Fischer,* V.P.; Sophia Iannaccone, Secy.; Christina Lopez,* Treas.; Priscilla M. Anderson; Jennifer Melton; Earl Ransom.
Number of staff: None.
EIN: 363715828
Selected grants: The following grants are a representative sample of this grantmaker's funding activity:
$180,628 to Warren Wilson College, Asheville, NC, 2013. For Woodbury Scholarship Fund.
$60,000 to University of Chicago, Laboratory School, Chicago, IL, 2013. For Peer Aggression Program.
$25,000 to Stanford University, Stanford, CA, 2013. For Triple Negative Research Program.
$10,000 to Westtown School, West Chester, PA, 2013. For operations; capital improvements.

3241
The Woods Foundation ✧
306 Clinton St.
Lincoln, IL 62656-2702 (217) 735-1234

Established in 1998 in IL.
Donors: Joan Jarrett Woods; Robert J. Woods.
Foundation type: Independent foundation.
Financial data (yr. ended 12/31/13): Assets, $17,382,778 (M); expenditures, $1,019,725;

qualifying distributions, $944,327; giving activities include $886,173 for 59 grants (high: $120,000; low: $30).
Fields of interest: Higher education; Education; Health care; Human services.
Type of support: Matching/challenge support.
Limitations: Applications accepted. Giving limited to Logan County, IL, and surrounding counties in central IL. No support for political or fraternal organizations. No grants to individuals.
Application information: Application form required.
Initial approach: Proposal
Deadline(s): None
Officers: William B. Bates, Pres.; David L. Golwitzer, Secy.-Treas.
Directors: William B. Bates, Jr.; Christopher L. Golwitzer.
EIN: 364196899

3242
Woods Fund of Chicago
35 E. Wacker Dr., Ste. 1760
Chicago, IL 60601-2271 (312) 782-2698
Contact: Deborah D. Clark, Grants and Opers. Mgr.
FAX: (312) 782-4155;
E-mail: application@woodsfund.org; Main URL: http://www.woodsfund.org
Facebook: https://www.facebook.com/pages/Woods-Fund-Chicago/426945720738370
Twitter: https://twitter.com/WoodsFundChi
Woods Fund of Chicago's Philanthropy Promise: http://www.ncrp.org/philanthropys-promise/who

Established in 1994 in IL.
Donors: Woods Charitable Fund, Inc.; The Ford Foundation; East Chicago Development Foundation, Inc.; Twin City Education Foundation, Inc.
Foundation type: Independent foundation.
Financial data (yr. ended 12/31/12): Assets, $59,510,240 (M); expenditures, $3,469,913; qualifying distributions, $3,126,073; giving activities include $2,337,545 for 104 grants (high: $65,000; low: $245).
Purpose and activities: Woods Fund Chicago is a grantmaking foundation committed to the promotion of social, economic, and racial justice through the support of community organizing and public policy advocacy that engages people that are most impacted. Working primarily as a funding partner with nonprofit organizations, the fund values community organizing and public policy advocacy efforts that lead to comprehensive, authentic, relevant, and sustainable solutions. The fund believes systemic change is the only way to eradicate poverty and structural racism. People most affected by economic and racial inequity should be the leaders and participants in the process of addressing issues that impact them. The fund asserts communities have greater strength, authority, and power through collaborative practice and collective voice. The fund commits to be an active partner and catalyst with organizations that share our mission and values.
Fields of interest: Community/economic development, public policy; Community development, citizen coalitions; Community development, neighborhood associations; Public policy, research; Welfare policy/reform; Public affairs.
Type of support: General/operating support; Continuing support; Program development; Research.
Limitations: Applications accepted. Giving limited to the metropolitan Chicago, IL, area. No support for social services, residential care, counseling programs, clinics, recreation programs, housing construction or rehabilitation, religious programs, business or economic development practitioners, healthcare institutions, or programs in or for individual schools. No grants to individuals, or for capital campaigns and projects, fundraising benefits, program advertising, endowments, scholarships, fellowships, or medical and scientific research.
Publications: Application guidelines; Annual report; Biennial report; Grants list.
Application information: See foundation web site for application information updates. Application guidelines and inquiry form are available on the foundation's web site. All forms must be submitted in electronic format to application@woodsfund.org. Application form required.
Initial approach: Prospective applicants should first submit an inquiry form. Current grantees submit an intent to apply form. Full applications accepted by invitation only
Deadline(s): 1st Fri. in Dec. and the last business day in May
Board meeting date(s): June and Dec.
Final notification: 3rd Fri. in Dec. and 2nd Fri. in June; Mar. and Sept. for final grant decisions
Officers and Directors:* Patrick M. Sheahan, Ph.D.*, Chair.; Beth E. Richie,* Vice-Chair.; Grace B. Hou, Pres.; Deborah D. Clark, Corp. Secy.; Suzanne R. Boyle, Treas.; Lee Bey; Amina J. Dickerson; Ricardo (Ric) Estrada; Josina Morita.
Number of staff: 2 full-time professional; 2 part-time professional; 1 full-time support.
EIN: 363917968
Selected grants: The following grants are a representative sample of this grantmaker's funding activity:
$80,000 to Albany Park Neighborhood Council, Chicago, IL, 2011. For general operating support, payable over 2.00 years.
$40,000 to Alianza Leadership Institute, Chicago, IL, 2011. For general operating support.
$40,000 to Illinois Asset Building Group, Chicago, IL, 2011. For general operating support.
$40,000 to Target Area Development Corporation, Chicago, IL, 2011. For general operating support.
$35,000 to United African Organization, Chicago, IL, 2011. For general operating support.
$30,000 to Housing Action Illinois, Chicago, IL, 2011. For general operating support.
$30,000 to Juvenile Justice Initiative, Evanston, IL, 2011. For general operating support.
$30,000 to Supportive Housing Providers Association, Springfield, IL, 2011. For general operating support.
$20,000 to A Just Harvest/Northside P.O.W.E.R., Chicago, IL, 2011. For Northside P.O.W.E.R..
$20,000 to Albany Park Theater Project, Chicago, IL, 2011. For general operating support.
$20,000 to Gilloury Institute, Silk Road Theater Project, Chicago, IL, 2011. For Silk Road Rising's Mosque Alert Project.
$20,000 to Illinois Action for Children, Chicago, IL, 2011. For Child Care Provider Leadership/Public Policy program on the south side of Chicago.
$20,000 to Storycatchers Theatre, Chicago, IL, 2011. For art and advocacy work with incarcerated youth.

3243
Woodward Charitable Trust ✧
5001 N. 2nd St.
Rockford, IL 61125-7001
Contact: Pam Cappitelli; Jennifer Ray; Jackie Kleino; Demie Garcia; David Berkley; Romy Kuklin; Rick Holm
Application address: 1000 E. Drake Rd., Fort Collins, Co 80525; 700 N. Centennial St., Zeeland, MI 49464; 201 Forrester Dr., Ste. 1A, Greenville, SC 29607; 7320 N. Linder Ave., Skokie, IL 60077; 25200 W. Rye Canyon Rd., Santa Clarita, CA 91355

Established in 1947 in IL.
Donors: Woodward, Inc.; Woodward Governor Co.
Foundation type: Company-sponsored foundation.
Financial data (yr. ended 12/31/13): Assets, $23,332,371 (M); gifts received, $200,000; expenditures, $850,650; qualifying distributions, $762,545; giving activities include $759,000 for 59 grants (high: $250,000; low: $1,000).
Purpose and activities: The trust supports organizations involved with arts and culture, education, health, mental health, hunger, housing, human services, community development, disabled people, homeless people, and economically disadvantaged people.
Fields of interest: Museums; Arts; Higher education; Education; Health care, clinics/centers; Health care; Substance abuse, services; Mental health/crisis services; Food services; Food banks; Housing/shelter; YM/YWCAs & YM/YWHAs; Children/youth, services; Family services, domestic violence; Homeless, human services; Human services; Community/economic development; United Ways and Federated Giving Programs; Disabilities, people with; Economically disadvantaged; Homeless.
Type of support: General/operating support; Continuing support; Annual campaigns; Capital campaigns; Equipment; Emergency funds; Seed money.
Limitations: Giving primarily in areas of company operations, with emphasis on Fort Collins, CO, Rockford, IL, and Stevens Point, WI. No grants to individuals, or for endowments, research, scholarships, fellowships, special projects, publications, or conferences; no loans; no matching gifts.
Application information: Application form not required.
Initial approach: Letter
Copies of proposal: 1
Deadline(s): None
Board meeting date(s): As required
Final notification: 8 weeks
Officers and Trustees:* Marty Glass,* Pres.; Lori Swan, Secy.; Karen Pinch, Treas.; Julia Buchanan; Jay Evans; A. Christopher Fawzy; Dan Loescher; Phil Turner.
EIN: 846025403
Selected grants: The following grants are a representative sample of this grantmaker's funding activity:
$4,000 to Muscular Dystrophy Association, Tucson, AZ, 2011.
$3,612 to United Way of Northwest Illinois, Freeport, IL, 2011.
$2,500 to Habitat for Humanity, Fort Collins, Fort Collins, CO, 2011.

3244
Wm. Wrigley Jr. Company Foundation ✧
410 N. Michigan Ave.
Chicago, IL 60611-4213
Contact: Maureen Jones, Exec. Dir. and Mgr.
FAX: (312) 644-0015; Main URL: http://www.wrigley.com/global/principles-in-action/foundation.aspx

Established in 1986 in IL.
Donor: Wm. Wrigley Jr. Co.
Foundation type: Company-sponsored foundation.
Financial data (yr. ended 12/31/12): Assets, $65,801,405 (M); expenditures, $4,806,511; qualifying distributions, $4,735,070; giving activities include $4,443,470 for 33 grants (high: $1,118,250; low: $600), and $291,600 for employee matching gifts.
Purpose and activities: The foundation supports programs designed to improve the health of people and the planet through sustainable initiatives focused on oral health, environmental stewardship, and healthy communities.
Fields of interest: Elementary/secondary education; Higher education; Education; Environment, waste management; Environment, natural resources; Environment, land resources; Environmental education; Environment; Dental care; Public health, physical fitness; Health care; Nutrition; Disasters, preparedness/services; Youth development; American Red Cross; Children/youth, services; United Ways and Federated Giving Programs.
Type of support: General/operating support; Continuing support; Building/renovation; Program development; Scholarship funds; Employee volunteer services; Employee matching gifts.
Limitations: Applications not accepted. Giving on a national basis in areas of company operations with emphasis on IL, MD, and VA; giving also internationally in Australia, China, India, and Ireland. No support for athletic teams or hospitals. No grants to individuals, or for artistic or cultural activities (unless related to educational programming), sports, or research or support services related to specific medical conditions or diseases.
Application information: Unsolicited applications are currently not accepted.
Officers and Directors:* Martin Radvan,* Pres.; Andrew Pharaoh,* V.P.; Ritu Vig, Secy.; Anthony Gedeller, Treas.; Maureen Jones, Exec. Dir. and Mgr.; Ian Burton; Casey Keller; Martin Schlatter; Tomek Suchecki; Melissa Weber; Michael Yeung.
EIN: 363486958
Selected grants: The following grants are a representative sample of this grantmaker's funding activity:
$750,000 to Save the Children Federation, Fairfield, CT, 2011.
$750,000 to Save the Children Federation, Fairfield, CT, 2011.
$220,000 to United Way of Metropolitan Chicago, Chicago, IL, 2011.
$208,750 to Keep America Beautiful, Stamford, CT, 2011.
$160,112 to International Youth Foundation, Baltimore, MD, 2011.
$10,000 to Keep Chicago Beautiful, Chicago, IL, 2011.
$7,500 to Friends of the Chicago River, Chicago, IL, 2011.

3245
Youth Improved, Inc ✧
10255 W. Higgins Rd., Ste. 900
Rosemont, IL 60018-5638 (847) 627-3251
Contact: Christopher Moore

Donors: Kraft Foods, Inc.; Lala Gilsa Products and Services; Leprino Foods; General Mills; New England Dairy and Food Council; National Dairy Council; Children's Hunger Alliance; Dean's Foods; Domino's Pizza; Quaker Oats; Stoneyfield Farm, Inc; American Dairy Association Mideast; American Dairy Assoc & Dairy Council; Dairy Council of Arizona; Indiana Diary and Nutrition Council; Dairy Farmers of Florida; Dairy Max; ID Diary Council United Dairymen of ID; Maine Dairy Promotion Board; Mid-Atlantic Dairy Association; Midwest Dairy Council; Oregon Dairy Products Commission; SUDIA; United Diary Industry of Michigan; Washington State Diary Council; Western Dairy Association; Dairy Management, Inc; Utah Dairy Commission; Agri-Mark Cabot; Atlanta Fixture & Sales Co., Inc; Borden Dairy Co.; Borton and Sons, Inc; Chelan Fresh Marketing; CHOBANI; Dole Food Company; First Fruits; Food Marketing Institute Foundation; Garelick Farms; Hewlett Packard; HP Hood, LLC; Iowa Farm Bureau Federation; J.S.B. Foundation; Land O'Lakes, Inc; Leprino; McDonald's Twin Cities Co-Op; Monsanto; Nike, Inc; Prairie Pizza; Rainer Fruit; Xbox.
Foundation type: Independent foundation.
Financial data (yr. ended 12/31/12): Assets, $3,374,555 (M); gifts received, $7,421,525; expenditures, $6,001,624; qualifying distributions, $5,970,307; giving activities include $4,232,902 for 769 grants (high: $121,871; low: $200).
Fields of interest: Public health; Agriculture/food, formal/general education; Nutrition; Children/youth, services.
Limitations: Applications accepted. Giving primarily in IL.
Application information:
Deadline(s): Varies
Officer: Thomas Gallagher, Chair.
Directors: Pete Abitante; Patrick Doyle; Richard Edelman; Roger Goodell; Carla Hall; Les Hardesty; Larry Jensen; Rhonda Jordan; Howie Long; Steve McCormick; and 9 additional trustees.
EIN: 270988546

3246
Morton & Helen Yulman Charitable Trust ✧
(formerly Yulman Foundation)
c/o The Northern Trust Co.
P.O. Box 803878
Chicago, IL 60680-3878

Established in 1955.
Donors: Morton Yulman; Helen Yulman.
Foundation type: Independent foundation.
Financial data (yr. ended 12/31/12): Assets, $13,467,149 (M); expenditures, $841,355; qualifying distributions, $570,111; giving activities include $525,121 for 30 grants (high: $100,000; low: $500).
Purpose and activities: Giving primarily to Jewish organizations.
Fields of interest: Museums (art); Human services; United Ways and Federated Giving Programs; Jewish federated giving programs; Jewish agencies & synagogues.
Limitations: Applications not accepted. Giving primarily in FL and NY. No grants to individuals.
Application information: Contributes only to pre-selected organizations.
Trustees: Nedra Y. Oren; E. Richard Yulman; Helen B. Yulman.
EIN: 146015572

3247
Zell Family Foundation ✧
(formerly Samuel Zell Family)
2 N. Riverside Plz., Ste. 600
Chicago, IL 60606-2639 (312) 466-3852

Established in 1986 in IL.
Donor: Samuel Zell.
Foundation type: Independent foundation.
Financial data (yr. ended 12/31/13): Assets, $58,225,154 (M); gifts received, $33,427,508; expenditures, $14,801,072; qualifying distributions, $14,744,201; giving activities include $14,739,900 for 88 grants (high: $2,000,000; low: $1,000).
Purpose and activities: Giving primarily for the arts, education, medicine, cancer research, recreation, youth development, and human service organizations.
Fields of interest: Museums (art); Arts; Education; Health care; Cancer research; Recreation; Youth development; Human services.
Limitations: Applications not accepted. Giving primarily in Chicago, IL, with some giving in MI. No grants to individuals.
Application information: Contributes only to pre-selected organizations.
Officers and Directors:* Samuel Zell,* Pres.; Philip Tinkler, V.P.; Helen H. Zell,* V.P.; Joann L. Zell,* V.P.; Kellie Zell,* V.P.; Matthew M. Zell,* V.P.; Carleen Schreder, Secy.; James Bunegar, Treas.
EIN: 363487811
Selected grants: The following grants are a representative sample of this grantmaker's funding activity:
$2,000,000 to Museum of Contemporary Art, Chicago, IL, 2013.
$1,000,000 to Chicago Symphony Orchestra, Chicago, IL, 2013.
$1,000,000 to Northwestern University, Evanston, IL, 2013. For Lurie Cancer Center in Chicago.
$1,000,000 to Teach for America, New York, NY, 2013.
$1,000,000 to University of Michigan, Ann Arbor, MI, 2013. For ZEAL Program.
$200,000 to PKD Foundation, Kansas City, MO, 2013.
$200,000 to Planned Parenthood of Illinois, Chicago, IL, 2013.
$100,000 to University of Michigan, Ann Arbor, MI, 2013. For Entrepreneurial Studies at Ross.
$50,000 to Imagination Productions, Jerusalem U, New York, NY, 2013.
$50,000 to University of California San Francisco Foundation, San Francisco, CA, 2013.

3248
Zerrusen Family Foundation ✧
902 W. Main St.
Teutopolis, IL 62467-1329

Established in 2003 in IL.
Donor: Three Z Printing Co.

Foundation type: Company-sponsored foundation.
Financial data (yr. ended 12/31/13): Assets, $8,777,757 (M); expenditures, $671,715; qualifying distributions, $670,600; giving activities include $670,600 for 18 grants (high: $250,000; low: $100).
Purpose and activities: The foundation supports organizations involved with human services and Christianity.
Fields of interest: Human services; Christian agencies & churches.
Type of support: General/operating support.
Limitations: Applications not accepted. Giving primarily in IL. No grants to individuals.
Application information: Contributes only to pre-selected organizations.
Trustee: Lorraine E. Zerrusen.
EIN: 200484359

3249
Zita Charitable Trust ✧ ☆
10 S. Dearborn, 21st Fl.
Chicago, IL 60603-2300

Donors: Rand H. Falbaum; Bobby J. Hollingsworth; Virginia Murphy; Lee Ann Hollingsworth; David H. Hoover; Gary Loftin; Marianne Loftin; James C. Reeves; Byron E. Johnson; Cynthia J. Rehig; The Alta Franks Foundation; The John Franks Foundation; Don Walker; Sadie Walker; Elaine T. Potter-Talbert; June E. Goldston Family Trust; Sam Pack; Carol Pack; Anita D. Sonfield; Don D. Martinson; Margaret A. Martinson; Dwight L. Pugh; Donna W. Crawford; Hiram W. Watson‡; Robert E. Carignan; Catherine L. Carrignan; Juliana C. Morelli; Dan Scurlock; Nancy Scurlock; Gary Loftin; Marianne Loftin; Arkansas Baptist Foundation; John W. Dean; Lori Dean; George Lukacs; James Crysdale; Lakshmi Kovvali; Venkata R. Kovvali; Karol Willy Raines; Karol Kreymerofkreymer Investments; Terry Rich; Linda Rich; John Hall; Marjorie-Padula Hall; Tea Ranch (June Goldston Family Trust); Joan Lukaacs; Richard A. Owen.
Foundation type: Independent foundation.
Financial data (yr. ended 12/31/13): Assets, $18,913,858 (M); gifts received, $825,117; expenditures, $892,701; qualifying distributions, $602,960; giving activities include $511,829 for 1 grant.
Fields of interest: Education.
Limitations: Applications not accepted. Giving primarily in Shreveport, LA.
Application information: Unsolicited requests for funds not accepted.
Trustee: JPMorgan Chase Bank.
EIN: 205177582

3250
Roberta L. Zuhlke Trust ✧
10 S. Dearborn St., IL1-0117
Chicago, IL 60603-2300

Established in 1972; supporting organization of the American Red Cross, National Association of Mental Health, New York Presbyterian Hospital, Lincoln Center, The Salvation Army, International Center for the Disabled, The Humane Society of the USA, and Planned Parenthood.
Foundation type: Independent foundation.
Financial data (yr. ended 11/30/13): Assets, $35,796,049 (M); expenditures, $1,784,209; qualifying distributions, $1,609,567; giving activities include $1,566,554 for 10 grants (high: $313,311; low: $93,993).
Fields of interest: Arts, single organization support; Animal welfare; Hospitals (general); Reproductive health, family planning; Mental health/crisis services, single organization support; American Red Cross; Salvation Army; Developmentally disabled, centers & services.
Limitations: Applications not accepted. Giving on a national basis. No grants to individuals.
Application information: Contributes only to pre-selected organizations; unsolicited requests for funds not considered or acknowledged.
Trustee: JPMorgan Chase Bank, N.A.
EIN: 136374227
Selected grants: The following grants are a representative sample of this grantmaker's funding activity:
$244,635 to American Society for the Prevention of Cruelty to Animals, New York, NY, 2011. For program support.
$122,318 to New York-Presbyterian Hospital, New York, NY, 2011. For program support.
$73,390 to Lincoln Center for the Performing Arts, New York, NY, 2011. For program support.

INDIANA

3251
1st Source Foundation ✧
P.O. Box 1602
South Bend, IN 46634-1602

Established in 1952 in IN.
Donors: 1st Source Corp.; 1st Source Bank Charitable Trust; 1st Source Capital.
Foundation type: Company-sponsored foundation.
Financial data (yr. ended 12/31/13): Assets, $25,957,257 (M); gifts received, $195,676; expenditures, $1,199,337; qualifying distributions, $1,072,128; giving activities include $1,072,128 for 238 grants (high: $100,000; low: $183).
Purpose and activities: The foundation supports organizations involved with arts and culture, education, social welfare and human services, community development, and civic affairs.
Fields of interest: Media, television; Museums (history); Arts; Elementary school/education; Higher education; Education; Hospitals (general); Crime/violence prevention; YM/YWCAs & YM/YWHAs; Human services; Community development, neighborhood development; Community/economic development; Foundations (community); United Ways and Federated Giving Programs; Public affairs.
Type of support: General/operating support.
Limitations: Applications accepted. Giving primarily in area of company operations in IN, with emphasis on South Bend.
Publications: Application guidelines; Corporate report.
Application information: Application form required.
Initial approach: Request application form
Deadline(s): None
Directors: Terry Gerber; Wellington D. Jones III; Rex Martin; Christopher J. Murphy III.
Trustee: 1st Source Bank.
EIN: 356034211
Selected grants: The following grants are a representative sample of this grantmaker's funding activity:
$49,479 to United Way of Saint Joseph County, South Bend, IN, 2011.
$17,000 to Community Action of Northeast Indiana, Fort Wayne, IN, 2011.
$15,000 to Boys and Girls Club of Benton Harbor, Benton Harbor, MI, 2011.
$12,000 to Habitat for Humanity, Saint Joseph County, South Bend, IN, 2011.
$11,000 to Bethel College, Mishawaka, IN, 2011.
$10,000 to South Bend Symphony Orchestra, South Bend, IN, 2011.
$10,000 to Urban League of Fort Wayne, Fort Wayne, IN, 2011.
$5,029 to United Way of Porter County, Valparaiso, IN, 2011.
$3,000 to South Bend Heritage Foundation, South Bend, IN, 2011.
$1,000 to Indiana University, South Bend, IN, 2011.

3252
The Ackerman Foundation ✧
280 E. 96th St., Ste. 350
Indianapolis, IN 46240-3858 (317) 663-0205
Contact: John F. Ackerman, Tr.
FAX: (317) 663-0215;
E-mail: jdisbro@cardinalep.com; Main URL: http://ackermanfoundation.com/

Established in 1992 in IN.
Donor: James F. Ackerman.
Foundation type: Independent foundation.
Financial data (yr. ended 12/31/12): Assets, $8,192,086 (M); expenditures, $618,008; qualifying distributions, $439,900; giving activities include $439,900 for 49 grants (high: $50,000; low: $1,000).
Purpose and activities: Giving primarily to central Indiana organizations as well as a few national medical research institutions. Specifically, the foundation focuses on Indiana cultural institutions and organizations benefiting health and human services, community development, and education.
Fields of interest: Arts; Higher education; Health care; Health organizations, association; Medical research; Human services; United Ways and Federated Giving Programs; Jewish federated giving programs; Jewish agencies & synagogues; Aging.
Type of support: General/operating support; Continuing support; Annual campaigns; Capital campaigns; Building/renovation; Equipment; Endowments.
Limitations: Giving primarily in IN, with some giving on a national basis. No grants to individuals.
Publications: Application guidelines; Financial statement; Grants list.
Application information: Application form not required.
Initial approach: Brief one or two page letter describing proposal
Copies of proposal: 1
Deadline(s): Thirty days prior to the meeting date
Board meeting date(s): The business day that falls on or closest to June 15 and Dec. 15
Trustee: John F. Ackerman.
Number of staff: 2 full-time professional.
EIN: 356567579

3253
Adams County Community Foundation ✧ ☆
102 N. 2nd St.
Decatur, IN 46733-1660 (260) 724-3939
Contact: Coni Mayer, Exec. Dir.
FAX: (260) 724-2299;
E-mail: accfoundation@earthlink.net; Main URL: http://www.adamscountyfoundation.org

Established in 1991 in Indiana.
Foundation type: Community foundation.
Financial data (yr. ended 12/31/13): Assets, $15,724,421 (M); gifts received, $1,536,339; expenditures, $845,174; giving activities include $313,094 for 8+ grants (high: $33,246), and $238,687 for 348 grants to individuals.
Purpose and activities: The foundation seeks to build partnerships between donors and community organizations to enrich and enhance the quality of life in Adams County, IN.
Fields of interest: Arts; Elementary/secondary education; Education, early childhood education; Secondary school/education; Education, special; Higher education; Scholarships/financial aid; Hospitals (general); Health care; Employment; Children/youth, services; Aging, centers/services; Human services; Community/economic development.
Type of support: Equipment; Seed money; Scholarship funds; Scholarships—to individuals.
Limitations: Applications accepted. Giving limited to Adams County, IN. No support for sectarian religious purposes. No grants for endowments, or trips that do not benefit the community.
Publications: Annual report.
Application information: Visit foundation web site for grant information and application form. Application form required.
Initial approach: Submit application form
Copies of proposal: 10
Deadline(s): 2nd Thurs. in Jan., Apr., July, and Oct.; 1st Thurs. in Feb. for scholarships
Board meeting date(s): 4th Wed. of each month
Officers and Directors:* Greg Fleming,* Pres.; Dr. Michael Johnson,* V.P.; Cathy Stucky,* Secy.; Louise Ray,* Asst. Secy.; Matthew Subler,* Treas.; Coni Mayer, Exec. Dir.; Chris Biggs-Pierce; Andrew Briggs; Becky Cochran; Rebecca Durbin; Fred Macke; Adam Miller; Wayne Porter; Alice Rhoades.
Number of staff: 1 full-time professional; 1 part-time support.
EIN: 351834664

3254
ADL Charitable Trust ✧
9400 Hunt Club Rd.
Zionsville, IN 46077-8451
Contact: Alexander C. Lange, Tr.

Established in 1997 in IN.
Donor: Alexander C. Lange.
Foundation type: Independent foundation.
Financial data (yr. ended 12/31/12): Assets, $4,521,961 (M); gifts received, $242,348; expenditures, $479,038; qualifying distributions, $465,906; giving activities include $454,374 for 29 grants (high: $201,500; low: $50).
Fields of interest: Elementary/secondary education; Education; Human services; Christian agencies & churches.
Limitations: Applications accepted. Giving primarily in IN, with emphasis on Carmel and Indianapolis. No grants to individuals.
Application information: Application form not required.
Initial approach: Proposal
Deadline(s): None
Trustees: Alexander C. Lange; Cynthia M. Lange; Dorothea L. Morton.
EIN: 352033079

3255
John W. Anderson Foundation ✧
402 Wall St., Ste. 12
Valparaiso, IN 46383-2562 (219) 462-4611
Contact: William N. Vinovich, Vice-Chair.
E-mail: info@andersonfnd.com

Trust established in 1967 in IN.
Donor: John W. Anderson†.
Foundation type: Independent foundation.
Financial data (yr. ended 12/31/13): Assets, $258,456,169 (M); expenditures, $10,530,272; qualifying distributions, $9,433,569; giving activities include $8,635,020 for 243 grants (high: $2,400,000; low: $320).
Purpose and activities: Giving primarily to organizations serving youth; higher educational institutions; community funds; scientific or medical

research for the purpose of alleviating suffering; care of needy, crippled or orphaned children; care of needy persons who are sick, aged or helpless; improving the health, and quality of life of all persons; human services; and the arts and humanities.
Fields of interest: Arts; Higher education; Health care; Medical research, institute; Medical research; Human services; Children/youth, services; Developmentally disabled, centers & services; Community development, neighborhood development; United Ways and Federated Giving Programs.
Type of support: Equipment; Scholarship funds; Research; Program development; General/operating support; Continuing support; Annual campaigns.
Limitations: Applications accepted. Giving primarily in Lake and Porter counties in northwest IN. No support for elementary, secondary and charter schools, or for business or any for-profit organization, or for supporting organizations classified as 509(a)3. No grants to individuals, or for endowment funds, multi-year grants, fundraising events, advertising, seed money, deficit financing; no loans.
Publications: Application guidelines; Informational brochure (including application guidelines).
Application information: Applications sent by fax not considered. Application form not required.
Initial approach: Letter
Copies of proposal: 6
Deadline(s): Jan. 20, Mar. 20, May 20, July 20, Sept. 20, and Nov. 20
Board meeting date(s): Feb., Apr., June, Aug., Oct., and Dec.
Final notification: In writing, 10-15 days after board meeting
Officers and Trustees:* Bruce W. Wargo,* Chair.; William N. Vinovich,* Vice-Chair.; Clyde D. Compton,* Secy.; Charles W. Conover; John J. Diederich.
Number of staff: 2 full-time professional; 3 part-time professional; 1 part-time support.
EIN: 356070695
Selected grants: The following grants are a representative sample of this grantmaker's funding activity:
$2,900,000 to Boys and Girls Clubs of Northwest Indiana, Gary, IN, 2012. For capital support.
$100,000 to Crisis Center, Gary, IN, 2012. For operating support and capital support.
$100,000 to Northwest Indiana Public Broadcasting, Merrillville, IN, 2012. For operating support.
$75,000 to Brothers Keeper, Gary, IN, 2012. For operating support and capital support.
$45,000 to Meals on Wheels of Northwest Indiana, Merrillville, IN, 2012.
$35,000 to Food Bank of Northwest Indiana, Gary, IN, 2012.
$35,000 to Indiana University-Purdue University Indianapolis, School of Medicine, Indianapolis, IN, 2012. For research.
$15,000 to Harold Hal Kelley Respite Foundation, Valparaiso, IN, 2012. For operating support.
$15,000 to Mental Health America of Lake County, Crown Point, IN, 2012. For operating support.
$15,000 to South Shore Arts, Munster, IN, 2012.
$5,000 to Gary Literacy Coalition, Gary, IN, 2012.

3256
The R. B. Annis Educational Foundation ✧
11999 Lakeside Dr.
Fishers, IN 46038-1316

Established in 1996 in IN.
Donors: Robert B. Annis†; Ralph Stahl.
Foundation type: Independent foundation.
Financial data (yr. ended 12/31/13): Assets, $13,763,608 (M); expenditures, $698,992; qualifying distributions, $644,800; giving activities include $585,000 for 34 grants (high: $172,500; low: $500).
Purpose and activities: Giving primarily for education and human services.
Fields of interest: Museums; Arts; Higher education; Zoos/zoological societies; Human services.
Limitations: Applications not accepted. Giving primarily in IN, with emphasis on Indianapolis. No grants to individuals.
Application information: Unsolicited requests for funds not accepted.
Trustees: Charles D. Angus; Elmira F. Annis; Wayne E. Weber; C. Daniel Yates.
EIN: 356627460
Selected grants: The following grants are a representative sample of this grantmaker's funding activity:
$172,500 to Indianapolis Zoological Society, Indianapolis, IN, 2011.
$100,000 to Interlochen Center for the Arts, Interlochen, MI, 2011.
$87,500 to Grand Valley State University, Grand Rapids, MI, 2011.
$12,000 to Cathedral Trustees, Indianapolis, IN, 2011.
$4,000 to University of the Cumberlands, Williamsburg, KY, 2011.
$1,400 to Saint Marys Child Center, Indianapolis, IN, 2011.
$1,000 to Brown County Art Gallery Foundation, Nashville, IN, 2011.

3257
Anthem Foundation
(formerly WellPoint Foundation, Inc.)
120 Monument Cir.
Indianapolis, IN 46204-4906
Contact: Lance Chrisman, Exec. Dir.
E-mail: wellpoint.foundation@wellpoint.com; Additional e-mail: communityrelations@wellpoint.com; Main URL: http://www.anthemcorporateresponsibility.com/cr/foundation/
Tumblr: http://wellpointfoundation.tumblr.com/
Twitter: https://twitter.com/@wellpointfdn_Pr

Established in 2000 in IN.
Donors: Anthem Insurance Cos., Inc.; Anthem Health Plans of New Hampshire, Inc.; Anthem, Inc.; WellPoint, Inc.; Howard Cashion Living Trust.
Foundation type: Company-sponsored foundation.
Financial data (yr. ended 12/31/12): Assets, $123,585,891 (M); expenditures, $11,590,892; qualifying distributions, $10,983,238; giving activities include $7,699,508 for 45 grants (high: $1,643,481; low: $3,000), and $1,939,562 for employee matching gifts.
Purpose and activities: The foundation supports programs designed to enhance the health and well-being of individuals and families. Special emphasis is directed toward programs designed to promote healthy generations.
Fields of interest: Hospitals (general); Health care, infants; Reproductive health, prenatal care; Public health; Public health, communicable diseases; Public health, obesity; Public health, physical fitness; Health care, insurance; Health care; Mental health, smoking; Cancer; Heart & circulatory diseases; Diabetes; Disasters, preparedness/services; Boys & girls clubs; American Red Cross; YM/YWCAs & YM/YWHAs; Public policy, research.
Type of support: General/operating support; Continuing support; Emergency funds; Program development; Scholarship funds; Research; Employee volunteer services; Sponsorships; Employee matching gifts.
Limitations: Applications accepted. Giving primarily in areas of company operations in AZ, CA, CO, CT, FL, GA, IN, KS, KY, LA, MD, ME, MO, NV, NH, NJ, NM, NY, OH, TN, TX, UT, VA, WA, and WI. No support for private charities or foundations, religious organizations not of direct benefit to the entire community, political candidates or organizations, discriminatory organizations, or association memberships. No grants to individuals, or for political causes or campaigns, lobbying activities, endowments, film, music, TV, video, or media production projects or broadcast program underwriting, fundraising events, sports sponsorships, performing arts tours, or requests that provide benefit to WellPoint, Inc. or WellPoint employees.
Publications: Application guidelines.
Application information: Organizations receiving support are asked to submit an interim and a final report. Unsolicited applications for capital projects, initiatives, or campaigns are not accepted. Research and policy grants are by invitation only and must align with the Healthy Generations signature initiative. Organizations with research or policy projects should e-mail the foundation with a brief summary. Application form required.
Initial approach: Complete online eligibility quiz and application
Deadline(s): May 9 and Sept. 12
Board meeting date(s): Quarterly
Final notification: 4 to 6 months
Officers and Directors:* Kathleen S. Kiefer, Secy.; Wayne S. DeVeydt,* C.F.O.; R. David Kretschmer, Treas.; Lance Chrisman, Exec. Dir.; Angela F. Braly; Randal L. Brown; Lisa Moriyama; Samuel R. Nussbaum, M.D.
EIN: 352122763
Selected grants: The following grants are a representative sample of this grantmaker's funding activity:
$1,643,481 to Boys and Girls Clubs of America, National Headquarters, Atlanta, GA, 2012. For youth health promotion as part of Healthy Generations Campaign.
$1,481,850 to OASIS Institute, Saint Louis, MO, 2012. To promote adult activity as part of Healthy Generations Campaign.
$500,000 to American Cancer Society, Atlanta, GA, 2012. For Patient Navigator.
$485,600 to American Heart Association, Dallas, TX, 2012. For Hands-Only Cardiopulmonary Resuscitation (CPR) White Suit promotional and fundraising campaign.
$334,000 to March of Dimes Foundation, White Plains, NY, 2012. For prenatal care as part of Healthy Generations Campaign.

$300,000 to American Enterprise Institute for Public Policy Research, Washington, DC, 2012. For health policy research.
$245,050 to Cancer Care, New York, NY, 2012. To provide Web-enabled support for cancer caregivers.
$95,000 to Saint Francis Medical Center of Lynwood Foundation, Lynwood, CA, 2012. For Health Options for Patient Empowerment (HOPE) Program.
$75,000 to Susan G. Komen for the Cure, Los Angeles County Affiliate, Los Angeles, CA, 2012. For African-American breast health initiative.
$10,000 to Childrens Healthcare of Atlanta, AFLAC Cancer Center, Atlanta, GA, 2012. For Director's Fund grant for operating support.

3258
Apgar Foundation Inc. ✧
c/o Dares LLC
8520 Allison Pointe Blvd., Ste. 220
Indianapolis, IN 46250-5700

Established in 2001 in NJ.
Donor: Martha B. Apgar.
Foundation type: Independent foundation.
Financial data (yr. ended 12/31/13): Assets, $325,747 (M); gifts received, $400,000; expenditures, $660,305; qualifying distributions, $646,759; giving activities include $528,033 for 28 grants (high: $25,000; low: $5,000).
Fields of interest: Higher education; Human services.
Type of support: General/operating support.
Limitations: Applications not accepted. Giving in the U.S., with emphasis on VA. No grants to individuals.
Application information: Unsolicited requests for funds not accepted.
Officers and Trustees:* Martha B. Apgar,* Pres.; Karl W. Apgar,* V.P.; Marian H. McGrath,* Secy.; John N. Apgar IV,* Treas.; Edward A. Capano; John J. Miller; Jay S. Nordlinger.
EIN: 223772118
Selected grants: The following grants are a representative sample of this grantmaker's funding activity:
$25,000 to Florida State University, Tallahassee, FL, 2012. For Stavros Center Program Support.
$25,000 to Furman University, Greenville, SC, 2012. For Tocqueville Program.
$25,000 to Linfield College, McMinnville, OR, 2012. For Frederick Douglas Forum for Law, Right and Justice.
$25,000 to Monterey Peninsula College Foundation, Monterey, CA, 2012. For Great Books Program.
$25,000 to Rockford College, Rockford, IL, 2012. For Center for Ethics and Entrepreneurship.
$25,000 to Troy University, Troy, AL, 2012. For Manuel H Johnson Center for Political Economy/ Beaulier.
$25,000 to University of Arizona Foundation, Tucson, AZ, 2012. For Center for the Study of American Ideals and Culture.
$22,950 to Emory University, Atlanta, GA, 2012. For Epex 0000017564 - Program in Democracy and Citizenship.
$22,500 to Florida State University, Tallahassee, FL, 2012. For Stavros Center-Multimedia Course Econ for Non-Economics Majors.
$22,000 to Ohio University Foundation, Athens, OH, 2012. For George Washington Forum.

3259
Asante Foundation, Inc. ✧
211 W. Washington St., Ste. 2400
South Bend, IN 46601-1708

Established in 2005 in IN.
Donors: Michael Joines; Connie V. Joines; Matthew E. Edmonds; Sharon Edmonds; Thomas F. Veldman; Anita Veldman; Kranenburg, LLC.
Foundation type: Independent foundation.
Financial data (yr. ended 12/31/13): Assets, $60,015,097 (M); expenditures, $2,533,254; qualifying distributions, $2,053,235; giving activities include $1,808,790 for 26 grants (high: $250,000; low: $10,000).
Fields of interest: Higher education; Health organizations, association; Human services; Women, centers/services.
Limitations: Applications not accepted. Giving primarily in IN. No grants to individuals.
Application information: Contributes only to pre-selected organizations.
Officers and Directors:* Thomas F. Veldman,* Pres.; Wilma Veldman,* V.P. and Secy.; Sharon Edmonds,* V.P. and Treas.; Matthew E. Edmonds,* V.P.; Connie V. Joines,* V.P.; Michael A. Joines,* V.P.; Anita J. Veldman,* V.P.; Peter Veldman,* V.P.; Nancy Ickler, Exec. Dir.
EIN: 203554641

3260
Edward D. & Ione Auer Foundation ✧
c/o Monarch Capital, Attn.: David Meyer
127 W. Berry St., Ste. 402
Fort Wayne, IN 46802-2310 (260) 415-5743
E-mail: AuerFoundation@MonarchCapitalMgmt.com;
Main URL: http://www.auerfoundation.org/

Established in IN.
Donor: Ione Breeden Auer Irrevocable Trust.
Foundation type: Independent foundation.
Financial data (yr. ended 12/31/12): Assets, $33,200,571 (M); expenditures, $5,102,305; qualifying distributions, $4,873,758; giving activities include $4,779,000 for 59 grants (high: $1,000,000; low: $4,000).
Purpose and activities: Some emphasis in the foundation's giving includes literature, music, art, education, and parks.
Fields of interest: Performing arts; Performing arts, orchestras; Arts; Higher education; Libraries (public); Zoos/zoological societies; Human services; Children/youth, services.
Type of support: Equipment; Land acquisition.
Limitations: Giving limited to Fort Wayne, IN. No support for individual public schools or school districts. No grants to individuals, or for scholarships (unless through an endowment), travel, conferences, deficits, sponsorships, special events, advertising, or annual appeals.
Publications: Application guidelines.
Application information: Full proposals are by invitation only, upon review of initial concept letter. Refer to foundation web site for Application Packet.
Initial approach: 1-page concept letter (with print no smaller than an 11 point font)
Deadline(s): Jan. 15, Apr. 15, July 15, and Oct. 15 for concept letters
Board meeting date(s): Feb. 1, May 1, Aug. 1, and Nov. 1
Trustees: David Meyer; Lake City Bank.
EIN: 311097946
Selected grants: The following grants are a representative sample of this grantmaker's funding activity:
$1,120,964 to Fort Wayne Philharmonic Orchestra, Fort Wayne, IN, 2011. For endowment.
$1,000,000 to Allen County Public Library Foundation, Fort Wayne, IN, 2011. For endowment.
$1,000,000 to Arts United of Greater Fort Wayne, Fort Wayne, IN, 2010. To purchase building.
$1,000,000 to Fort Wayne Zoological Society, Fort Wayne, IN, 2011. For endowment.
$1,000,000 to Indiana University-Purdue University Fort Wayne, Fort Wayne, IN, 2011. For endowment.
$750,000 to Allen County Public Library Foundation, Fort Wayne, IN, 2010. For endowment.
$750,000 to Fort Wayne Philharmonic Orchestra, Fort Wayne, IN, 2010. For endowment.
$750,000 to Fort Wayne Zoological Society, Fort Wayne, IN, 2010. For endowment.
$750,000 to Indiana University-Purdue University Fort Wayne, Fort Wayne, IN, 2010. For endowment.
$50,000 to Questa Foundation for Education, Fort Wayne, IN, 2011. For education programs.
$25,000 to Embassy Theater Foundation, Fort Wayne, IN, 2011. For building project.
$25,000 to Fort Wayne Civic Theater, Fort Wayne, IN, 2011. For Growth Initiative Campaign.
$25,000 to Lincoln Endowment, Fort Wayne, IN, 2010. For endowment.
$25,000 to Science Central, Fort Wayne, IN, 2010. For program support.
$25,000 to Science Central, Fort Wayne, IN, 2011. For program support.
$20,000 to Embassy Theater Foundation, Fort Wayne, IN, 2010. For building project.
$20,000 to Fort Wayne Museum of Art, Fort Wayne, IN, 2010. For American Art Initiative.
$20,000 to W F W A-TV 39, Fort Wayne, IN, 2010. For production of local programs.
$15,000 to Lifeline Youth and Family Services, Fort Wayne, IN, 2011. For alternative education program expansion.
$10,000 to C2G Music Hall Corporation, Fort Wayne, IN, 2011. For music program.

3261
Hazel & Walter T. Bales Foundation ✧ ☆
630 Broadway
Jeffersonville, IN 47130-8203
Application address: c/o Lori Lewis, 1507 Fox Run Tr., Jeffersonville, IN 47130, tel.: (812) 282-2586

Established in 1989 in IN.
Donors: Walter T. Bales; Hazel Bales†.
Foundation type: Independent foundation.
Financial data (yr. ended 12/31/13): Assets, $13,544,456 (M); expenditures, $575,584; qualifying distributions, $512,584; giving activities include $510,000 for 53 grants (high: $97,000; low: $500).
Fields of interest: Hospitals (general); Human services; American Red Cross; Salvation Army; YM/YWCAs & YM/YWHAs; Children/youth, services; Protestant agencies & churches.
Type of support: Continuing support; Building/renovation; Curriculum development; Matching/challenge support.
Limitations: Applications accepted. Giving limited to Clark and Floyd counties, IN, and Jefferson County, KY. No grants to individuals.
Publications: Financial statement.
Application information: Application form not required.

Initial approach: Proposal
Deadline(s): None
Officers: Lori Lewis, Pres.; Les Albro, V.P.; Judy Adamson, Secy.
Number of staff: 1 part-time support.
EIN: 351783030

3262
Ball Brothers Foundation ✧
P.O. Box 1408
Muncie, IN 47308-1408 (765) 741-5500
Contact: Jud Fisher, C.O.O. and Pres.
FAX: (765) 741-5518; E-mail: info@ballfdn.org; Additional address: 222 S. Mulberry St., Muncie, IN 47305. Additional e-mail: donna.munchel@ballfdn.org; Main URL: http://www.ballfdn.org
Ball Brothers News: http://www.ballfdn.org/news/
E-Newsletter: http://www.ballfdn.org/publications/e-newsletter/
Grants List: http://www.ballfdn.org/grant-info/grant-award-announcements/

Incorporated in 1926 in IN.
Donors: Edmund B. Ball†; Edmund F. Ball†; Frank C. Ball†; George A. Ball†; Lucius L. Ball, M.D.†; Janice B. Fisher†; John W. Fisher†; Virginia B. Ball†; William A. Ball†.
Foundation type: Independent foundation.
Financial data (yr. ended 12/31/12): Assets, $145,711,100 (M); expenditures, $7,681,594; qualifying distributions, $6,812,155; giving activities include $6,252,541 for 120 grants (high: $2,599,500; low: $1,000; average: $1,000–$250,000).
Purpose and activities: Support for the environment, humanities and cultural programs, higher and other education, health and medical education, youth, and family and social services.
Fields of interest: Museums; Humanities; Arts; Elementary school/education; Secondary school/education; Higher education; Medical school/education; Adult education—literacy, basic skills & GED; Education, reading; Education; Environment; Hospitals (general); Health care; Health organizations, association; Human services; Children/youth, services; Family services; Community/economic development; Public affairs.
Type of support: Program evaluation; Annual campaigns; Building/renovation; Capital campaigns; Conferences/seminars; Consulting services; Curriculum development; Endowments; Equipment; General/operating support; In-kind gifts; Management development/capacity building; Matching/challenge support; Professorships; Program development; Publication; Research; Technical assistance.
Limitations: Applications accepted. Giving limited to IN. No support for non-secular religious programs or booster organizations. No grants to individuals.
Publications: Application guidelines; Annual report; Grants list.
Application information: Applications now accepted via foundation web site. Application form required.
Initial approach: Submit letter of inquiry via web site
Copies of proposal: 1
Deadline(s): Letters of inquiry: Feb. 15 and July 15
Board meeting date(s): Quarterly and as necessary
Final notification: Varies
Officers and Directors:* James A. Fisher,* Chair.; Frank E. Petty,* Vice-Chair.; Jud Fisher,* C.O.O. and Pres.; Terry L. Walker,* Secy.; Tammy Phillips, Treas.; William M. Bracken; Stephanie Duckmann; Douglas J. Foy; Nancy B. Keilty; Terri E. Matchett; Judith F. Oetinger; Scott Shockley.
Number of staff: 2 full-time professional; 1 part-time professional; 1 full-time support.
EIN: 350882856
Selected grants: The following grants are a representative sample of this grantmaker's funding activity:
$2,749,500 to Minnetrista Cultural Foundation, Muncie, IN, 2012.
$250,000 to Ivy Tech Foundation, Muncie, IN, 2012.
$125,000 to Energize-ECI, Muncie, IN, 2012.
$125,000 to Project Leadership, Marion, IN, 2012.
$115,000 to Habitat for Humanity, Greater Muncie, Muncie, IN, 2012.
$105,000 to Cardinal Greenway, Muncie, IN, 2012.
$100,000 to Riley Childrens Foundation, Indianapolis, IN, 2012.
$80,000 to Ross Community Center, Muncie, IN, 2012.
$60,000 to Soil and Water Conservation District, Delaware County, Muncie, IN, 2012.
$50,000 to Second Harvest Food Bank of East Central Indiana, Muncie, IN, 2012.

3263
Edmund F. and Virginia B. Ball Foundation, Inc. ✧
P.O. Box 1408
Muncie, IN 47308-1408 (765) 741-5500
Contact: Kris Gross

Established in 1994 in IN.
Donors: Edmund F. Ball†; Virginia B. Ball†.
Foundation type: Independent foundation.
Financial data (yr. ended 09/30/13): Assets, $26,661,180 (M); expenditures, $1,473,597; qualifying distributions, $1,319,454; giving activities include $1,297,000 for 20 grants (high: $232,000; low: $5,000).
Fields of interest: Arts; Higher education; Education; Health organizations; Children/youth, services.
Limitations: Applications accepted. Giving primarily in MI and IN. No grants to individuals.
Application information: Application form required.
Initial approach: Proposal
Deadline(s): June 30
Officers and Directors:* Frank E. Ball,* Chair. and Pres.; Robert B. Ball,* V.P.; Douglas J. Foy,* Secy.-Treas.; Michael J. Fisher, Jr., Exec. Dir.; Charles F. Ball; Lauren E. Conner; Nancy B. Keilty; Stacy McHenry.
EIN: 351911169
Selected grants: The following grants are a representative sample of this grantmaker's funding activity:
$100,000 to Interlochen Center for the Arts, Interlochen, MI, 2013. For Creative Writing Contest.
$75,000 to Munson Healthcare Regional Foundation, Traverse City, MI, 2013. For Restoration Kids Creek.
$50,000 to Community Enhancement Projects, Muncie, IN, 2013. For White River Dam Renovation.
$50,000 to Leelanau Conservancy, Leland, MI, 2013. For Farmland Preservation Projects.
$25,000 to Yale University, New Haven, CT, 2013. For Global Inst Sustaining Forestry.
$20,000 to Indiana Youth Institute, Indianapolis, IN, 2013. For Virginia B Ball Library.
$5,000 to Traverse Symphony Orchestra, Traverse City, MI, 2013. For family concerts.

3264
George and Frances Ball Foundation ✧
P.O. Box 1408
Muncie, IN 47308-1408 (765) 741-5500
Contact: Kris Gross, Exec. Asst.
FAX: (765) 741-5518; E-mail: tcbracken@att.net; Additional address: 222 S. Mulberry St., Muncie, IN 47305

Incorporated in 1937 in IN.
Donor: George A. Ball†.
Foundation type: Independent foundation.
Financial data (yr. ended 12/31/13): Assets, $102,568,075 (M); expenditures, $4,821,229; qualifying distributions, $4,349,045; giving activities include $4,136,000 for 32 grants (high: $1,671,040; low: $2,500).
Purpose and activities: Emphasis on higher education and community programs.
Fields of interest: Arts; Education; Environment, natural resources; Environment; Health care; Human services; Community development, neighborhood development.
Type of support: Scholarship funds; Capital campaigns; Building/renovation; Equipment; Program development; Professorships; Matching/challenge support.
Limitations: Applications accepted. Giving primarily in Muncie and Delaware County, IN. No support for religious or political organizations. No grants to individuals.
Publications: Application guidelines.
Application information: Application form not required.
Initial approach: Letter and proposal
Copies of proposal: 1
Deadline(s): None
Board meeting date(s): Varies (4 times per year)
Final notification: Following board review
Officers and Directors:* Frank A. Bracken,* Pres.; Stefan S. Anderson,* V.P.; Joan H. McKee,* Secy.; Tamara S. Phillips, CPA, Treas.; Thomas C. Bracken, Exec. Dir.; Norman E. Beck; Ronald K. Fauquher; Douglas J. Foy; Jon H. Moll; Robert M. Smitson; Joseph F. "Ted" Wiese.
Number of staff: 1 full-time professional.
EIN: 356033917
Selected grants: The following grants are a representative sample of this grantmaker's funding activity:
$1,580,000 to Ball State University Foundation, Muncie, IN, 2012. For Immersive Learning/Honors College.
$1,110,500 to Minnetrista Cultural Foundation, Muncie, IN, 2012. For operating support.
$200,000 to Ivy Tech Foundation, Indianapolis, IN, 2012. For Associate Faculty Development Institute.
$200,000 to United Way of Delaware County, Muncie, IN, 2012. For annual campaign.
$75,000 to Community Foundation of Muncie and Delaware County, Muncie, IN, 2012. For B5 Early Childhood Initiative.
$75,000 to Energize-ECI, Muncie, IN, 2012. For operating support.
$60,000 to Community Arts and Building Foundation, Cornerstone Center for the Arts, Muncie, IN, 2012. For operating support.

$60,000 to Delaware Advancement Corporation, Muncie, IN, 2012. For economic development.
$50,000 to Keuka College, Keuka Park, NY, 2012. For George Harvey Ball Scholarship.
$50,000 to Riley Childrens Foundation, Indianapolis, IN, 2012. For juvenile diabetes.

3265
The Blue River Community Foundation, Inc. ✧
(formerly The Blue River Foundation, Inc.)
54 W. Bdwy. St., Ste. 1
P.O. Box 808
Shelbyville, IN 46176-1267 (317) 392-7955
Contact: For grant applications: Lynne Ensminger, Prog. Admin.
FAX: (317) 392-4545;
E-mail: brf@blueriverfoundation.com; Grant application E-mail: lensminger@blueriverfoundation.com; Main URL: http://www.blueriverfoundation.com
Facebook: http://www.facebook.com/pages/Blue-River-Community-Foundation/217727811593029
Flickr: http://www.flickr.com/photos/blue_river_cf/

LinkedIn: http://www.linkedin.com/company/blue-river-community-foundation
Twitter: http://twitter.com/bluerivercf
YouTube: http://www.youtube.com/user/BlueRiverCF?feature=mhee

Established in 1988 in IN.
Foundation type: Community foundation.
Financial data (yr. ended 12/31/13): Assets, $30,582,257 (M); gifts received, $1,752,687; expenditures, $1,848,478; giving activities include $878,245 for 29+ grants (high: $100,000), and $195,613 for 100 grants to individuals.
Purpose and activities: The foundation seeks to serve and assist charitable endeavors in Shelby County, IN, and to promote leadership to address community issues.
Fields of interest: Arts; Education; Environment, beautification programs; Health care; Recreation; Children/youth, services; Aging, centers/services; Human services; Community/economic development; Children/youth; Aging; Disabilities, people with.
Type of support: Capital campaigns; Building/renovation; Equipment; Endowments; Program development; Seed money; Curriculum development; Scholarship funds; Technical assistance; Consulting services; Grants to individuals; Scholarships—to individuals; In-kind gifts; Matching/challenge support.
Limitations: Applications accepted. Giving limited to Shelby County, IN. No support for religious organizations for religious purposes, or for projects which are considered part of a regular school curriculum. No grants to individuals (except for scholarships), or for annual campaign drives, travel or endowments (generally).
Publications: Application guidelines; Annual report; Financial statement; Informational brochure.
Application information: Visit foundation web site for application form and guidelines. If grant request meets the foundation's funding guidelines, the organization will be invited to submit a formal "Grant Application Form". Please do not submit an application with out first discussing it with the foundation's Program Admin. Application form required.
Initial approach: Submit Grant Interest form
Copies of proposal: 1
Deadline(s): May. 1 and Sept. 1
Board meeting date(s): 4th Wed. of each month
Final notification: One month after deadline
Officers and Directors:* Greg Gerline,* Pres.; Tom Rosenfeld,* V.P.; Judy Montgomery,* Secy.; Rod Meyerholtz,* Treas.; Amy Haacker, Exec. Dir.; Jeff Beaty; John DePrez, Jr.; Brent Sandman; Nancy Smith; Terry Smith; Brent Thoman; Judy Yeager.
Number of staff: 2 full-time professional; 1 part-time professional; 1 part-time support.
EIN: 351756331

3266
Blue Sky Foundation, Inc. ✧
P.O. Box 1407
New Albany, IN 47151-1407 (812) 944-6733
Main URL: http://www.blueskynetwork.org/

Established in 2001 in IN.
Donor: John B. Shine.
Foundation type: Independent foundation.
Financial data (yr. ended 12/31/13): Assets, $2,866,575 (M); expenditures, $1,465,178; qualifying distributions, $1,256,825; giving activities include $1,256,825 for 25+ grants (high: $300,000).
Purpose and activities: The foundation encourages individuals and communities to imagine and work toward a world with a higher quality of life, education and economic and technological development.
Fields of interest: Education; Environment, water resources; Animal welfare; Youth, services; Community/economic development; Engineering/technology; Christian agencies & churches.
Type of support: General/operating support.
Limitations: Applications not accepted. Giving primarily in IN. No grants to individuals.
Application information: Contributes only to pre-selected organizations.
Officers and Directors:* John B. Shine,* Pres.; Bryce Butler, Exec. Dir.; Jane Shine.
EIN: 352153383

3267
The Boren Foundation, Inc. ✧
P.O. Box 218
Upland, IN 46989-0218
Application address: c/o Sally Brodkorb, P.O. Box 548, Upland, IN 46989; tel.: (765) 998-8100

Established in 1982 in IN.
Donors: Leland E. Boren; LaRita R. Boren†.
Foundation type: Independent foundation.
Financial data (yr. ended 09/30/13): Assets, $13,059,844 (M); expenditures, $584,846; qualifying distributions, $517,219; giving activities include $458,500 for 28 grants (high: $100,000; low: $1,000).
Fields of interest: Elementary school/education; Education; Children/youth, services.
Type of support: General/operating support; Capital campaigns; Matching/challenge support.
Limitations: Applications accepted. Giving primarily in IN. No grants to individuals.
Publications: Financial statement; Program policy statement (including application guidelines).
Application information: Telephone calls are not accepted. Application form not required.
Initial approach: Typewritten letter
Copies of proposal: 1
Deadline(s): None
Board meeting date(s): Apr. and Sept.
Final notification: 60-90 days
Officers: Marty Songer, Pres.; Lael Boren, V.P.; Angela Darlington, Secy.; Pat Smith, Treas.; Lori L. Meyers, Exec. Dir.
Directors: Leland E. Boran; Tom Logan; Jay Ross.
Number of staff: None.
EIN: 351557058
Selected grants: The following grants are a representative sample of this grantmaker's funding activity:
$25,000 to Heartland Truly Moving Pictures, Indianapolis, IN, 2011.
$5,000 to Indiana State Museum, Indianapolis, IN, 2011.
$4,000 to Gilead Ministries, Jonesboro, IN, 2011.
$1,000 to Indiana Historical Society, Indianapolis, IN, 2011.

3268
Brotherhood Mutual Foundation Inc. ✧ ☆
6400 Brotherhood Way
Fort Wayne, IN 46825-4235

Established in 2005 in IN.
Donor: Brotherhood Mutual Insurance Co.
Foundation type: Company-sponsored foundation.
Financial data (yr. ended 12/31/13): Assets, $418,858 (M); gifts received, $735,528; expenditures, $523,684; qualifying distributions, $523,401; giving activities include $523,401 for 75 grants (high: $60,500; low: $125).
Purpose and activities: The foundation supports organizations involved with higher education, housing development, human services, international relief, and Christianity.
Fields of interest: Higher education; Housing/shelter, development; Human services; International relief; United Ways and Federated Giving Programs; Christian agencies & churches; Religion.
Type of support: General/operating support; Annual campaigns; Capital campaigns; Building/renovation; Program development; Sponsorships.
Limitations: Applications not accepted. Giving primarily in IN. No grants to individuals.
Application information: Contributes only to pre-selected organizations.
Officers: James A. Blum, Chair.; Mark A. Robison, Pres.; Hugh W. White, V.P.; Matthew G. Hirschy, Treas.
EIN: 203618117
Selected grants: The following grants are a representative sample of this grantmaker's funding activity:
$35,000 to Youth for Christ, Fort Wayne, IN, 2011.
$30,000 to Taylor University, Upland, IN, 2011.
$3,500 to University of Saint Francis, Fort Wayne, IN, 2011.

3269
Brown County Community Foundation, Inc. ✧
91 W. Mound St. Unit 4
P.O. Box 191
Nashville, IN 47448 (812) 988-4882
Contact: Judy Bowling, Office and Financial Mgr.

FAX: (812) 988-0299; E-mail: jenise@bccfin.org;
Main URL: http://www.bccfin.org/
Facebook: https://www.facebook.com/bccfin
Twitter: https://twitter.com/BCCFIN

Established in 1993 in IN.
Foundation type: Community foundation.
Financial data (yr. ended 12/31/13): Assets, $9,345,547 (M); gifts received, $572,566; expenditures, $863,889; giving activities include $596,260 for 20+ grants (high: $124,382), and $27,105 for 20 grants to individuals.
Purpose and activities: The foundation seeks to receive, hold, and distribute funds for charity. Primary areas of focus include arts and humanities, education, the environment, health care, human services, and community development.
Fields of interest: Humanities; Arts; Higher education; Education; Environment; Health care; Human services; Community/economic development; Children/youth; Youth; Adults; Disabilities, people with; Physically disabled; Women; Adults, women; Substance abusers.
Type of support: Continuing support; Capital campaigns; Building/renovation; Equipment; Land acquisition; Emergency funds; Program development; Conferences/seminars; Film/video/radio; Publication; Seed money; Scholarship funds; Technical assistance; Scholarships—to individuals; Matching/challenge support.
Limitations: Applications accepted. Giving primarily in Brown County, IN. No support for religious organizations. No grants for operating expenses (generally).
Publications: Application guidelines; Annual report; Financial statement; Informational brochure (including application guidelines); Newsletter.
Application information: Visit foundation web site for application information. Application form required.
Initial approach: Attend a mandatory grants workshop meeting
Copies of proposal: 1
Deadline(s): Late May for grants; Jan. for scholarships
Board meeting date(s): 4th Monday of every month
Final notification: Late June or July.
Officers and Trustees:* Michael Laros,* Chair.; Robert Andrew,* Vice-Chair.; Larry Pejeau,* C.E.O.; Shirley Boardman,* Secy.; Bill Lloyd, Legal Counsel; Karen Avery; Timothy Burke; Mark LindenLaub; Jack Winn.
Number of staff: 2 full-time professional; 1 part-time professional.
EIN: 351960379
Selected grants: The following grants are a representative sample of this grantmaker's funding activity:
$6,500 to Brown County Historical Society, Nashville, IN, 2011. For roof repairs.
$6,250 to South Central Community Action Program (SCCAP), Nashville, IN, 2011. For A Hand Up (heating asst).
$5,000 to Dance Kaleidoscope, Indianapolis, IN, 2011. For Opera performed in Brown County Schools.
$3,569 to Jackson Township Fire Department Station 5, Nashville, IN, 2011. For tank and pump.
$3,078 to Brown County Art Guild, Nashville, IN, 2011. For Marie Goth Painting Preservation.
$2,050 to Brown County Literacy Coalition, Nashville, IN, 2011. For client education.
$2,000 to Dolly Parton Imagination Library, Nineveh, IN, 2011. For book funding.
$1,656 to Career Resource Center of Brown County, Nashville, IN, 2011. For classroom enclosure.
$1,000 to Return to the Wild, Nashville, IN, 2011. For security monitoring system.
$500 to Early Music in Motion, Bloomington, IN, 2011. For traditional music performed in Nashville, IN.

3270
Carmichael Foundation, Inc. ✧
P.O. Box 1602
South Bend, IN 46601-1630
Application address: c/o Lee Morton, 1st Source Bank, 100 N. Michigan St., South Bend, IN 46601-1600

Incorporated in 1967 in IN.
Donors: Christopher J. Murphy III; Carmen C. Murphy.
Foundation type: Independent foundation.
Financial data (yr. ended 12/31/12): Assets, $4,165,759 (M); expenditures, $3,418,718; qualifying distributions, $3,409,399; giving activities include $3,409,399 for 4 grants (high: $1,961,830; low: $13,000).
Purpose and activities: Giving primarily for higher education.
Fields of interest: Higher education; Education; Human services.
Limitations: Applications accepted. Giving primarily in South Bend, IN. No grants to individuals.
Application information: Application form not required.
Initial approach: Proposal
Deadline(s): None
Trustee: 1st Source Bank.
EIN: 356069904
Selected grants: The following grants are a representative sample of this grantmaker's funding activity:
$5,000 to Medical Education Foundation, South Bend, IN, 2011.

3271
Cass County Community Foundation, Inc. ✧
417 N. St., Ste. 102
P.O. Box 441
Logansport, IN 46947-3172 (574) 722-2200
Contact: Deanna Crispen, Pres.
FAX: (574) 753-7501;
E-mail: cccf@casscountycf.org; Main URL: http://www.casscountycf.org

Established in 1993 in IN.
Foundation type: Community foundation.
Financial data (yr. ended 12/31/13): Assets, $16,690,901 (M); gifts received, $1,195,603; expenditures, $792,164; giving activities include $354,451 for 16+ grants (high: $30,226), and $137,124 for 90 grants to individuals.
Purpose and activities: The foundation honors the spirit of giving and assists donors in building enduring sources of charitable assets to promote education, enhance humanity and advance community development throughout Cass County, IN.
Fields of interest: Education; Human services; Community/economic development.
Type of support: Seed money; Matching/challenge support; Equipment; Program development; Scholarships—to individuals.
Limitations: Applications accepted. Giving primarily in Cass County, IN. No support for public schools. No grants to individuals (except for scholarships), travel expenses, ongoing operating expenses, advocacy, or endowments; no loans.
Publications: Application guidelines; Annual report; Informational brochure; Newsletter.
Application information: Visit foundation web site for application form and information. Scholarship Orientation Session mandatory for scholarships. Application form required.
Initial approach: Contact foundation
Copies of proposal: 7
Deadline(s): Feb. 27 for Scholarship
Board meeting date(s): Monthly
Officers and Board Members:* Thillia Reynolds,* Chair.; Paul Kroeger,* Vice-Chair.; Deanna Crispen,* Pres.; Deb Shanks,* Secy.; Keith Cole,* Treas.; Lucy Burns; Randy Head; Tom Heckard; Dan Layman; Susan Platt; Dr. Herb Price; Burton Reed; Dr. Sue Ridlen; Jesse Robinson.
Number of staff: 1 full-time professional; 1 part-time professional; 1 full-time support.
EIN: 352125727

3272
Central Indiana Community Foundation, Inc. ✧
615 N. Alabama St., Ste. 119
Indianapolis, IN 46204-1498 (317) 634-2423
Contact: Brian Payne, C.E.O.
FAX: (317) 684-0943; E-mail: info@cicf.org;
Additional tel.: (317) 634-7497; Grant application e-mail: applications@cicf.org; Main URL: http://www.cicf.org
E-Newsletter: http://www.cicf.org/page26606.cfm
LinkedIn: http://www.linkedin.com/companies/central-indiana-community-foundation
Twitter: https://twitter.com/cicfoundation

Established in 1997 in IN through a partnership between the Indianapolis Foundation and the Legacy Fund of Hamilton County.
Foundation type: Community foundation.
Financial data (yr. ended 12/31/13): Assets, $705,654,058 (M); gifts received, $125,883,451; expenditures, $44,189,151; giving activities include $35,371,279 for grants.
Purpose and activities: The foundation is committed to improving and strengthening the metropolitan region community, with grantmaking focused on helping where the needs are greatest and the benefits to the region are most extensive.
Fields of interest: Arts, cultural/ethnic awareness; Arts; Education; Health care; Mental health/crisis services; Health organizations, association; Housing/shelter; Children/youth, services; Family services; Human services, emergency aid; Aging, centers/services; Human services; Community development, neighborhood development; Economic development; Economic development, visitors/convention bureau/tourism promotion; Community development, business promotion; Community/economic development; Philanthropy/voluntarism; Government/public administration; Disabilities, people with.
Type of support: Mission-related investments/loans; General/operating support; Annual campaigns; Capital campaigns; Building/

renovation; Equipment; Land acquisition; Emergency funds; Program development; Conferences/seminars; Publication; Seed money; Curriculum development; Scholarship funds; Technical assistance; Consulting services; Program evaluation; Scholarships—to individuals; Matching/challenge support.
Limitations: Applications accepted. Giving limited to the central IN region. No support for religious or sectarian purposes, or for post-event or after-the-fact situations. No grants to individuals (except for scholarships), or for long-term operating support, endowment funds, medical, scientific or academic research, publications, travel, fundraising events, annual appeals, or membership contributions.
Publications: Application guidelines; Annual report; Financial statement; Grants list; Informational brochure; Newsletter.
Application information: Visit foundation web site for online grants management system and application guidelines. Application form required.
Initial approach: Complete online application
Copies of proposal: 1
Deadline(s): Feb. 28 and July 31
Board meeting date(s): Feb., May., Sept., and Nov.
Final notification: By year-end for both cycles
Officers and Directors:* Charles P. Sutphin,* Chair.; Cynthia Simon Skjodt,* Vice-Chair.; Brian Payne,* C.E.O. and Pres.; Rob MacPherson, V.P., Devel.; Liz Tate, V.P., Community Investment; Gregory F. Hahn,* Secy.; Jennifer K. Bartenbach, C.F.O.; Brenda Delaney, Cont.; Elaine Bedel; Michael Daugherty; Kathy Davis; Traci M. Dolan; Henry L. Fernandez; Marianne Glick; Mark E. Hill; Alan A. Levin; Myrta Pulliam; Marisol Sanchez; Jerry D. Semler; Michael Simmons; Joseph L. Smith, Jr.; Corby D. Thompson; Milton O. Thompson; Lee White.
EIN: 351793680
Selected grants: The following grants are a representative sample of this grantmaker's funding activity:
$12,160,203 to Community Foundation of Greater Fort Wayne, Fort Wayne, IN, 2012.
$1,570,565 to Boys and Girls Clubs of Indianapolis, Indianapolis, IN, 2012.
$1,250,000 to TradeWinds Rehabilitation Center, Gary, IN, 2012. For Building purchase.
$392,000 to United Way of Central Indiana, Indianapolis, IN, 2012. For Focus School Strategy at IPS No. 51.
$314,109 to Indiana Repertory Theater, Indianapolis, IN, 2012. For distribution.
$23,253 to National Philanthropic Trust, Jenkintown, PA, 2012. For Transfer for Funds.
$20,000 to Milligan College, Milligan College, TN, 2012. For Forward Ever campaign.
$20,000 to Pacers Foundation, Indianapolis, IN, 2012. For Ticket Donation.
$15,000 to Kalapriya Foundation Center for Indian Performing Art, Chicago, IL, 2012. For general operating support.
$15,000 to Perry Senior Citizens Services, Indianapolis, IN, 2012. For services to the homebound seniors.

3273
Champagne Family Charitable Trust ✧
c/o LM Henderson and Co.
450 E. 96th St., Ste. 200
Indianapolis, IN 46240-3797

Established in 2005 in IN.
Donor: ITT Educational Services Inc.
Foundation type: Independent foundation.
Financial data (yr. ended 06/30/13): Assets, $2,953,101 (M); gifts received, $8,700,000; expenditures, $9,640,570; qualifying distributions, $9,640,195; giving activities include $9,640,195 for grants.
Fields of interest: Education; United Ways and Federated Giving Programs.
Limitations: Giving primarily in CT, FL, and MD. No grants to individuals.
Application information: Unsolicited requests for funds not accepted.
Trustees: Rene R. Champagne; Teresa I. Champagne.
EIN: 206262204
Selected grants: The following grants are a representative sample of this grantmaker's funding activity:
$10,000 to Marco Island Discovery Center, Marco Island, FL, 2012. For public charter high school.
$2,200 to American Cancer Society, Atlanta, GA, 2012. For dedicated to eliminating cancer.

3274
Allen Whitehill Clowes Charitable Foundation, Inc. ✧
320 N. Meridian St., Ste. 811
Indianapolis, IN 46204-1731 (317) 955-0138
Contact: William H. Marshall, Pres.

Established in 1990 in IN.
Donor: Allen W. Clowes†.
Foundation type: Independent foundation.
Financial data (yr. ended 12/31/13): Assets, $103,499,442 (M); expenditures, $4,535,337; qualifying distributions, $4,372,499; giving activities include $4,042,312 for 67 grants (high: $1,800,000; low: $4,000).
Purpose and activities: The foundation supports charitable organizations that promote or preserve the arts and humanities. Priority will be given, primarily, to those located in central Indiana.
Fields of interest: Humanities; Arts.
Type of support: General/operating support; Building/renovation; Equipment; Program development; Publication; Research; Program evaluation; Matching/challenge support.
Limitations: Applications accepted. Giving primarily in central IN. No grants for endowments.
Publications: Application guidelines.
Application information: Application form required.
Initial approach: Letter
Copies of proposal: 2
Deadline(s): Jan. 31
Officer: William H. Marshall, Pres.
Directors: Ben W. Blanton; Danny R. Dean; James B. Lemler; Thomas M. Lofton; Betty Roberts; Beth Slaninka; Anna Seim White.
Number of staff: 1 part-time professional; 1 part-time support.
EIN: 351812631

3275
The Clowes Fund, Inc. ✧
320 N. Meridian St., Ste. 316
Indianapolis, IN 46204-1722 (317) 833-0144
Contact: Elizabeth A. Casselman, Exec. Dir.
FAX: (317) 833-0145; E-mail: staff@clowesfund.org; Additional tel.: (800) 943-7209; additional fax: (800) 943-7286; Main URL: http://www.clowesfund.org

Incorporated in 1952 in Indianapolis, IN.
Donors: Edith W. Clowes†; George H.A. Clowes†; Allen W. Clowes†; George H.A. Clowes, Jr.†.
Foundation type: Independent foundation.
Financial data (yr. ended 12/31/12): Assets, $64,447,387 (M); expenditures, $3,472,680; qualifying distributions, $3,058,153; giving activities include $2,607,150 for 180 grants (high: $120,000; low: $50).
Purpose and activities: The Clowes Fund, a family foundation, seeks to enhance the common good by encouraging organizations and projects that help to build a just and equitable society, create opportunities for initiative, foster creativity and the growth of knowledge, and promote appreciation of the natural environment.
Fields of interest: Performing arts; Performing arts, music; Arts; Elementary/secondary education; Employment; Human services.
Limitations: Giving in the greater Indianapolis, IN, area, defined as Marion County and the seven contiguous counties (for social services and education); Seattle, WA (for the arts and art education); and in the greater Boston, MA, area and parts of northern New England (for social services, education and art education). No support for foreign organizations, colleges or universities, programs promoting specific religious doctrine, or for organizations classified as Type III Supporting Organizations. No grants to individuals, or for fundraising events or operating support; no loans.
Publications: Application guidelines; Grants list; Program policy statement; Program policy statement (including application guidelines).
Application information: See foundation web site for current application information.
Officers and Directors:* Dr. Alexander W. Clowes,* Pres.; Jonathan J. Clowes,* V.P.; Margaret C. Bowles,* Secy.; William H. Marshall,* Treas.; Elizabeth A. Casselman, Exec. Dir.; Margaret Clowes, Dir. Emeritus; Ben W. Blanton; Douglas S. Clowes; Carolyn Osteen; Dr. Donna L. Wiley.
Number of staff: 2 full-time professional; 1 full-time support; 1 part-time support.
EIN: 351079679

3276
Olive B. Cole Foundation, Inc. ✧
6207 Constitution Dr.
Fort Wayne, IN 46804-1517
Contact: Maclyn T. Parker, Pres.
E-mail: gwentip@ligtel.com

Incorporated in 1954 in IN.
Donors: Richard R. Cole†; Olive B. Cole†.
Foundation type: Independent foundation.
Financial data (yr. ended 03/31/13): Assets, $30,527,314 (M); expenditures, $1,535,774; qualifying distributions, $1,378,634; giving activities include $977,393 for grants, and $229,706 for 194 grants to individuals (high: $1,200; low: $500).
Purpose and activities: Grants largely for education, including student aid for graduates of Noble County, IN, high schools, hospitals, civic affairs, youth agencies, and cultural programs.
Fields of interest: Arts; Higher education; Hospitals (general); Youth, services; Government/public administration.

Type of support: General/operating support; Continuing support; Building/renovation; Equipment; Land acquisition; Seed money; Scholarships—to individuals; Matching/challenge support.
Limitations: Giving limited to Noble County, IN, and immediate adjacent areas in northern IN. No grants for endowment funds or research.
Publications: Application guidelines; Program policy statement.
Application information: Scholarship applications available through foundation and at all Noble and LaGrange County, IN, secondary schools. Application form required.
Initial approach: Letter
Copies of proposal: 7
Deadline(s): None
Board meeting date(s): Feb., May, Aug., and Nov.
Final notification: 4 months
Officers and Directors:* John N. Pichon, Jr.,* Chair.; Maclyn T. Parker,* Pres.; Emily E. Pichon, Secy.; Michael Barranda; Kristi P. Celico; Jack Hunter; John Riemke; Tracy Tipton.
Scholarship Administrator: Gwen I. Tipton.
Number of staff: 1 full-time professional; 1 full-time support.
EIN: 356040491
Selected grants: The following grants are a representative sample of this grantmaker's funding activity:
$100,000 to Fort Wayne Childrens Zoo, Fort Wayne, IN, 2011.
$100,000 to Northeast Indiana Innovation Center, Fort Wayne, IN, 2011.
$100,000 to YMCA, Cole Center Family, Kendallville, IN, 2011.
$31,000 to Junior Achievement of Northern Indiana, Fort Wayne, IN, 2011. For program support.
$20,000 to Ligonier Parks and Recreation Department, Ligonier, IN, 2011.
$15,000 to DeKalb County Fair Association, Auburn, IN, 2011.
$11,250 to American Red Cross of Northeast Indiana, Fort Wayne, IN, 2011.
$5,000 to Early Childhood Alliance, Fort Wayne, IN, 2011.
$5,000 to Kendallville Park and Recreation Department, Kendallville, IN, 2011.
$5,000 to Kendallville Park and Recreation Department, Kendallville, IN, 2011.

3277
Community Foundation Alliance, Inc. ✧

5000 E. Virginia St., Ste. 4
Evansville, IN 47715 (812) 429-1191
Contact: Jill Tullar, Exec. Dir.
FAX: (812) 429-0840; E-mail: info@alliance9.org; Toll free tel.: (877) 429-1191; Main URL: http://www.alliance9.org

Established in 1991 in IN.
Foundation type: Community foundation.
Financial data (yr. ended 06/30/13): Assets, $69,896,856 (M); gifts received, $2,024,033; expenditures, $3,269,135; giving activities include $1,505,876 for 55+ grants (high: $66,500), and $205,755 for 182 grants to individuals.
Purpose and activities: The alliance seeks to provide leadership and support for member community foundations as they promote philanthropy and build endowments to serve their communities.
Fields of interest: Humanities; Arts; Education; Environment, beautification programs; Environment; Health care; Recreation; Youth development; Human services; Community/economic development.
Type of support: Management development/capacity building; Program development; Program evaluation; Scholarships—to individuals.
Limitations: Applications accepted. Giving limited to Daviess, Gibson, Knox, Perry, Pike, Posey, Spencer, Vanderburgh, and Warrick counties, IN. No support for religious organizations for religious purposes. No grants for endowment creation or debt reduction, operating costs, capital campaigns, annual appeals or membership contributions, or travel requests for groups or individuals such as bands, sports teams, or classes.
Publications: Application guidelines; Annual report; Financial statement; Grants list; Informational brochure; Newsletter.
Application information: Visit foundation web site or contact foundation for application forms, deadlines, and guidelines. Application form required.
Initial approach: Telephone
Deadline(s): Varies according to county
Board meeting date(s): 2nd Tues. of each month, except for July and Dec.
Officers and Directors:* Chris Harmon,* Chair.; Jody Giles,* Vice-Chair.; Jill Tullar,* Secy. and Exec. Dir.; Dave Osmon,* Treas.; Jean Blanton; Shane Bonaparte; John Dudenhoeffer; Bill Gillenwater; Jim Gislason; Bill Goedde; Randall Haaff; Tim Hayden; Kim Keene; Carla Kidwell; Pam Lock; Jim Pearson; Mason Seay; Paul Singleton; Grant Taylor; Wil Teague; Carolyn Veale; Tom Virgin.
Number of staff: 2 full-time professional; 13 full-time support; 4 part-time support.
EIN: 351830262

3278
Community Foundation of Bloomington and Monroe County, Inc. ✧

(formerly Bloomington Community Foundation, Inc.)
101 W. Kirkwood Ave., Ste. 321
Bloomington, IN 47404-6129 (812) 333-9016
Contact: Tina Peterson, Pres. and CEO; For grants: Renee Chambers, Prog. Dir.
FAX: (812) 333-1153; E-mail: info@cfbmc.org; Grant inquiry e-mail: renee@cfbmnc.org; Main URL: http://www.cfbmc.org
Facebook: https://www.facebook.com/CommunityFoundationBloomingtonMonroeCounty
LinkedIn: http://www.linkedin.com/pub/community-foundation-of-bloomington-and-monroe-county/17/454/47a
RSS Feed: http://www.cfbmc.org/feed/
Twitter: https://twitter.com/CoFoundationBMC

Established in 1990 in IN.
Foundation type: Community foundation.
Financial data (yr. ended 06/30/13): Assets, $22,062,280 (M); gifts received, $979,852; expenditures, $1,188,927; giving activities include $691,638 for 31+ grants (high: $100,000), and $14,208 for 13 grants to individuals.
Purpose and activities: The foundation seeks to champion enduring and effective philanthropy that enhances the local quality of life. The foundation accomplishes this through: 1) partnering with donors to build and steward permanent endowments; 2) addressing community needs through grants; and 3) providing inclusive community leadership on issues of local importance.
Fields of interest: Arts councils; Historic preservation/historical societies; Arts; Higher education; Hospitals (general); Health care; Children/youth, services; Family services; Human services; Community/economic development; Christian agencies & churches; Protestant agencies & churches.
Type of support: Emergency funds; Scholarships—to individuals; Building/renovation; Equipment; Program development; Seed money; Scholarship funds; Program-related investments/loans.
Limitations: Applications accepted. Giving limited to Bloomington and Monroe County, IN. No support for sectarian religious organizations. No grants to individuals (except for scholarships), or for general operating support, endowment campaigns, or for previously incurred debts.
Publications: Application guidelines; Annual report; Informational brochure; Newsletter.
Application information: Visit foundation web site for application form and guidelines. Application form required.
Initial approach: Letter
Copies of proposal: 12
Deadline(s): Varies
Board meeting date(s): Monthly
Final notification: End of month following deadline
Officer and Directors:* Edward Najam, Jr.,* Chair.; Kevin Theile,* Vice-Chair.; Margaret Frisbie,* Secy.; Dr. Thomas A. Morrison,* Treas.; Tina Peterson,* C.E.O. and Pres.; Mark Bradford; Chris Cockerham; Tim DeBruicker; Jean Emery; Dottie Frapwell; Denise Howard; Randy Lloyd; E. Mayer Maloney; W. David Martin; MaryFrances McCourt; Laurie Burns McRobbie; Vi Simpson; Lon Stevens; Jimmy Stewart; Jennie Vaughan; Brian D. Yeley.
Number of staff: 1 full-time professional; 1 part-time support.
EIN: 351811149

3279
Community Foundation of Boone County, Inc. ✧

102 N. Lebanon St., Ste. 200
Lebanon, IN 46052 (317) 873-0210
Contact: For grants: Barbara J. Schroeder, Prog. Dir.; Jen Pendleton, Pres. and C.E.O.
FAX: (317) 873-0219;
E-mail: info@communityfoundationbc.org; Additional tel.: (765)-482-0024; Main URL: http://www.communityfoundationbc.org
Facebook: http://www.facebook.com/CFBooneCo
RSS Feed: http://www.communityfoundationbc.org/feed/
Twitter: http://twitter.com/cfbooneco

Established in 1991 in IN.
Foundation type: Community foundation.
Financial data (yr. ended 12/31/13): Assets, $20,674,876 (M); gifts received, $985,003; expenditures, $1,645,282; giving activities include $738,666 for 24+ grants (high: $97,149), and $167,087 for 52 grants to individuals.
Purpose and activities: The foundation was established in order to serve as the central philanthropic vehicle to address the needs of the Boone County, Indiana community.
Fields of interest: Arts; Education; Environment; Health care; Recreation; Youth development; Children/youth, services; Human services;

Community/economic development; Youth; Adults; Aging; Disabilities, people with; Economically disadvantaged.
Type of support: General/operating support; Management development/capacity building; Endowments; Program development; Seed money; Scholarship funds; Technical assistance; Matching/challenge support.
Limitations: Applications accepted. Giving limited to the residents of Boone County, IN, area. No support for religious organizations which address specific needs directly related to the promotion or teaching of doctrine. No grants for international travel, first-class air fare; luxury accommodations; and hospitality for purposes other than those directly related to meeting program objectives as defined in the proposal. The foundation will consider granting for operating expenses only in special circumstances.
Publications: Application guidelines; Annual report; Informational brochure; Newsletter.
Application information: Visit foundation web site for application format and guidelines. Applications for grants of $10,000 or less should be submitted on the "Short Form Application". Application form required.

Initial approach: Submit application
Copies of proposal: 1
Deadline(s): Apr. 15 and Oct. 14
Board meeting date(s): 10 times annually
Final notification: Within 6 weeks

Officers and Directors:* Steve David,* Pres.; Marc Applegate,* V.P.; Jen Pendleton,* C.E.O. and Pres.; Mark Ransom,* Secy.; Jack Jones,* Scholarship Committee Co-Chair.; Wayne Adams; Beth Casselman; Mike Harlos; Gary Heck; Ray Ingham; Karen Milam; Laura Miller; Suzy Rich; Beth Sease.
Number of staff: 1 full-time professional; 3 part-time professional.
EIN: 351829585

3280
Community Foundation of Grant County ✧

505 W. 3rd St.
Marion, IN 46952-3748 (765) 662-0065
Contact: Dawn Brown, Exec. Dir.; For grants and scholarships: Ashley McKnight, Prog. Mgr.
FAX: (765) 662-1438;
E-mail: QuickQuestion@GiveToGrant.org; Main URL: http://www.comfdn.org
Blog: http://givetogrant.org/read-all-about-us/blogs/
Facebook: http://www.facebook.com/comfdn
Twitter: http://twitter.com/comfdn

Incorporated in 1984 in IN.
Foundation type: Community foundation.
Financial data (yr. ended 03/31/13): Assets, $19,465,148 (M); gifts received, $970,260; expenditures, $2,105,587; giving activities include $562,155 for 150 grants (high: $110,792; low: $100), and $350,412 for 266 grants to individuals (high: $29,941; low: $500).
Purpose and activities: The foundation offers creative and imaginative grantmaking, coupled with strict volunteer review that assures responsible funding.
Fields of interest: Arts; Education; Environment, beautification programs; Health care; Mental health/crisis services; Recreation, parks/playgrounds; Youth development, services; Youth development; Children/youth, services; Family services; Family services, domestic violence; Aging, centers/services; Human services; Community development, neighborhood associations; Economic development; Community/economic development; Philanthropy/voluntarism.
Type of support: Building/renovation; Equipment; Emergency funds; Program development; Conferences/seminars; Seed money; Technical assistance; Matching/challenge support.
Limitations: Applications accepted. Giving limited to Grant County, IN. No support for sectarian or religious purposes. No grants for endowments or salaries.
Publications: Application guidelines; Annual report; Financial statement; Newsletter.
Application information: Visit foundation web site for proposal summary form and guidelines. Application form required.

Initial approach: Letter of intent
Copies of proposal: 12
Deadline(s): Prior to noon on the last Friday in Jan, Apr, July, and Oct.
Board meeting date(s): Feb., May, Aug., and Nov.
Final notification: Feb., May, Aug., and Nov. - approximately one month after deadline date

Officers and Directors:* Martin Harker,* Pres.; Chad Leighty,* V.P.; Mary Eckerle,* Secy.; Karen Behnke,* Treas.; Dawn Brown, Exec. Dir.; Sherri Rush,* C.F.O.; Dennis Banks; Janet Barnett; Jackie Certain; Mike Cline; Trent Dailey; Mike Falder; Judy Fitzgerald; John Jones; Dru McCoy; Jane Merchant; Georgette Miller; Reggie Nevels; Chris Oliver; Kyle Persinger; Dave Raabe; Nedra Sutter; Steven A. Wampner.
Number of staff: 7 full-time professional; 3 full-time support; 2 part-time support.
EIN: 311117791

3281
Community Foundation of Greater Fort Wayne, Inc. ✧

(formerly Fort Wayne Community Foundation)
555 E. Wayne St.
Fort Wayne, IN 46802-2013 (260) 426-4083
Contact: David J. Bennett, Exec. Dir.; For grant application: Christine Meek, Dir., Progs.
FAX: (260) 424-0114; E-mail: info@cfgfw.org; Additional e-mail: dbennett@cfgfw.org; Grant application tel.: (260) 426-4083, ext. 318, e-mail: cmeek@cfgfw.org; Main URL: http://www.cfgfw.org
Facebook: https://www.facebook.com/CFGFW

Incorporated in 1956 in IN.
Foundation type: Community foundation.
Financial data (yr. ended 12/31/13): Assets, $139,551,027 (M); gifts received, $3,903,504; expenditures, $5,181,180; giving activities include $4,529,481 for grants.
Purpose and activities: The foundation encourages requests that are developed in consultation with other agencies and planning groups, increase coordination and cooperation among agencies, and reduce unnecessary duplication of services. Preference is given to funding requests that: address priority community concerns; encourage more effective use of community resources; test or demonstrate new approaches and techniques in the solution of community problems; are intended to strengthen the management capabilities of agencies; and promote volunteer participation and citizen involvement in community affairs.
Fields of interest: Arts; Education, early childhood education; Business school/education; Adult education—literacy, basic skills & GED; Education; Health care; Substance abuse, services; Health organizations, association; Food services; Youth development, services; Youth, services; Family services; Homeless, human services; Human services; Community/economic development; Voluntarism promotion; Science; Leadership development; Infants/toddlers; Children/youth; Adults; Aging; Young adults; Disabilities, people with; Physically disabled; Blind/visually impaired; Deaf/hearing impaired; Mentally disabled; Minorities; African Americans/Blacks; Hispanics/Latinos; Offenders/ex-offenders; Substance abusers; AIDS, people with; Single parents; Crime/abuse victims; Terminal illness, people with; Immigrants/refugees; Economically disadvantaged; Homeless; LGBTQ.
Type of support: General/operating support; Continuing support; Management development/capacity building; Building/renovation; Equipment; Land acquisition; Emergency funds; Program development; Seed money; Scholarship funds; Technical assistance; Consulting services; Program evaluation; Scholarships—to individuals; Matching/challenge support.
Limitations: Applications accepted. Giving primarily in the Fort Wayne and Allen County, IN, areas. No support for religious purposes, hospitals, or private, public, or parochial schools. No grants to individuals (except for scholarships), or for operating budgets, continuing support, annual campaigns, deficit financing, endowment funds (except for Endowment-Building matching grants for funds), fellowships, medical or academic research, sponsorships, special events, advertising, films or videos, television programs, conferences, or group uniforms or group trips; no loans.
Publications: Application guidelines; Annual report; Financial statement; Grants list; Informational brochure; Informational brochure (including application guidelines); Newsletter; Occasional report; Occasional report (including application guidelines).
Application information: Visit foundation web site for concept letter fact sheet, guidelines, and specific deadlines; application by invitation only after consideration of concept letter. Faxed or e-mailed concept letters are not accepted. Application form required.

Initial approach: Mail concept letter
Copies of proposal: 5
Deadline(s): Varies
Board meeting date(s): Feb., April, May, Aug., Oct. and Nov.
Final notification: 3 months for grant determination

Officers and Board Members:* Jane Gerardot,* Pres.; Chris Rupp,* V.P.; Thomas Trent,* Secy.; Shannon Hardiek,* Treas.; David J. Bennett, Exec. Dir.; Michael Barranda; Ian Boyce; Bob Francis; Jonathan Hancock; Trois Hart; Greg Johnson; Kathy Kolb; Carol Lindquist; Deb McMahon; Bruce Menshy; Don Steininger; Rise Taylor.
Number of staff: 4 full-time professional; 3 full-time support; 3 part-time support.
EIN: 351119450
Selected grants: The following grants are a representative sample of this grantmaker's funding activity:
$788,060 to Partners for Workforce Solutions, Fort Wayne, IN, 2012. For allocation for incumbent worker training.
$447,390 to Purdue University, West Lafayette, IN, 2012. For IPFW Systems Engineering Labs.

$50,000 to Lutheran Social Services of Indiana, Fort Wayne, IN, 2012. For general operating support.
$50,000 to Turnstone Center for Disabled Children and Adults, Fort Wayne, IN, 2012. For general operating support.
$50,000 to YMCA of Greater Fort Wayne, Metropolitan, Fort Wayne, IN, 2012. For Renaissance Pointe YMCA and Youth Service Bureau programs.
$5,000 to Urban League of Fort Wayne, Fort Wayne, IN, 2012. For playground equipment and installation for the Thurgood Marshall Leadership Academy.
$3,800 to University of Saint Francis, Fort Wayne, IN, 2012. For performance rights and production material for The Will Rogers Follies.

3282
The Community Foundation of Greater Lafayette ✧

1114 E. State St.
Lafayette, IN 47905-1219 (765) 742-9078
Contact: Marianne Rose, C.E.O.
FAX: (765) 742-2428; E-mail: info@cfglaf.org; Main URL: http://www.cfglaf.org
Facebook: http://www.facebook.com/pages/Lafayette-IN/The-Community-Foundation-of-Greater-Lafayette/109336922422126

Established in 1970 in IN.
Foundation type: Community foundation.
Financial data (yr. ended 12/31/13): Assets, $43,253,424 (M); gifts received, $1,802,450; expenditures, $1,802,590; giving activities include $1,000,012 for 45+ grants (high: $120,775), and $116,000 for 72 grants to individuals.
Purpose and activities: The mission of the foundation is to inspire, nurture, and practice philanthropy, stewardship, and leadership in local community.
Fields of interest: Performing arts, music; Performing arts, education; Humanities; Arts; Higher education; Education; Environment, beautification programs; Environment; Health care; Substance abuse, services; Mental health/crisis services; Food services; Housing/shelter, homeless; Housing/shelter; Children, day care; Human services; Community development, neighborhood development; Youth.
Type of support: Capital campaigns; Equipment; Emergency funds; Seed money; Scholarship funds; Program-related investments/loans; Scholarships—to individuals.
Limitations: Applications accepted. Giving primarily in Tippecanoe County and the greater Lafayette, IN, area, including the surrounding counties. No support for government agencies or public institutions, or sectarian or religious purposes. No grants to individuals (except for scholarships), or for ongoing expenses, endowments, special events, multi-year grants, debt or deficit reduction, or operating support.
Publications: Application guidelines; Annual report; Grants list; Informational brochure; Newsletter.
Application information: Visit foundation web site for application form and guidelines. Application form required.
Initial approach: Mail grant proposal form and attachments
Deadline(s): Discretionary Grants: Apr. 1 for grants over $15,000; Sept. 2 for grants over $7,500; none for grants under $7,500
Board meeting date(s): Last Thurs. of each month except June and Dec.
Final notification: Discretionary Grants: May 31 for grants over $15,000; Oct. 31 for grants over $7,500; within 4 weeks for grants under $7,500
Officers and Directors:* Dave Luhman,* Chair.; Jim Bodenmiller,* Vice-Chair.; Marianne Curtis Rose,* C.E.O. and Pres.; George Ramsey,* Secy.; Charlie Shook,* Treas.; Maryann Santos de Barona; Carolyn Gery; Scott Hanback; Sue Holder-Price; Steve Horne; Jeff Love; John Martin; Sonya Margerum; Amy Moulton; Rick Olson.
Number of staff: 3 full-time professional; 1 full-time support.
EIN: 237147996

3283
The Community Foundation of Howard County, Inc. ✧

215 W. Sycamore
Kokomo, IN 46901 (765) 454-7298
Contact: For grants: Kim Abney, V.P., Progs.
FAX: (765) 868-4123; E-mail: info@cfhoward.org; Additional tel.: (800) 964-0508; Grant application e-mail: kim@cfhoward.org; Main URL: http://www.cfhoward.org
E-Newsletter: http://www.cfhoward.org/enews_signup.html
Facebook: https://www.facebook.com/pages/Community-Foundation-Serving-Howard-Clinton-Carroll-Counties/112393758833133

Established in 1991 in IN.
Foundation type: Community foundation.
Financial data (yr. ended 12/31/12): Assets, $44,632,435 (M); gifts received, $601,103; expenditures, $2,016,035; giving activities include $1,064,773 for 47+ grants (high: $146,935), and $398,524 for 168 grants to individuals.
Purpose and activities: The foundation seeks to improve the quality of life in the community through the accumulation and stewardship of enduring the charitable gifts. Primary areas of interest include health and medical, social services, education, cultural affairs, civic affairs and community beautification.
Fields of interest: Historic preservation/historical societies; Arts; Elementary/secondary education; Education, early childhood education; Education, special; Higher education; Education; Environment, beautification programs; Hospitals (general); Health care; Employment; Youth, services; Human services; Community/economic development; Leadership development.
Type of support: Capital campaigns; Building/renovation; Equipment; Program development; Seed money; Scholarship funds; Scholarships—to individuals; Matching/challenge support.
Limitations: Applications accepted. Giving limited to Carroll, Clinton, and Howard counties, IN. No support for sectarian religious purposes. No grants to individuals (except for scholarships), or for seminars, equipment, normal operating expenses or salaries, or endowments.
Publications: Application guidelines; Annual report (including application guidelines); Informational brochure; Newsletter.
Application information: Visit foundation web site for application form and guidelines. First-time applicants must contact the foundation to discuss grant proposals prior to submission. Application form required.
Initial approach: Mail, e-mail, or fax letter of Inquiry
Copies of proposal: 21
Deadline(s): Jan. 24, May 9, Aug. 1 and Oct. 3 for letter of inquiry; Feb. 21, May 30, Sept. 5 and Oct. 31 for full application
Board meeting date(s): Monthly
Final notification: Letters of inquiry will receive a prompt response. Grant determination within 1 month of full application deadline
Officers and Directors:* Scott McClelland,* Chair.; Rick Smith,* Vice-Chair.; Hilda Burns,* Pres.; Kim Abney,* V.P., Progs.; Bob Hingst,* Secy.-Treas.; Nanette Bowling; Joe Dunbar; Melissa Ellis; Brian Hayes; Betsy Hoshaw; Brad Howell; Beth MacDonald; Paul Manning; James B. McIntyre; Dr. Greg Norman; Stan Rebber; Steve Rothenberger; Laura Sheets; John Shoup; Mike Ullery; Doug Vaughn; J.D. Young; and 6 additional directors.
Number of staff: 1 full-time professional.
EIN: 351844891

3284
The Community Foundation of Jackson County, Inc. ✧ ☆

107 Community Dr.
P.O. Box 1231
Seymour, IN 47274 (812) 523-4483
Contact: Dan Davis, Pres. and C.E.O.
FAX: (812) 523-1433;
E-mail: info@cfjacksoncounty.org; Additional e-mails: president@cfjacksoncounty.org, vicepresident@cfjacksoncounty.org, accounting@cfjacksoncounty.org and development@cfjacksoncounty.org; Main URL: http://www.cfjacksoncounty.org
Facebook: https://www.facebook.com/CFJacksonCounty

Established in 1992 in IN.
Foundation type: Community foundation.
Financial data (yr. ended 12/31/13): Assets, $10,106,924 (M); gifts received, $1,425,121; expenditures, $1,520,023; giving activities include $638,903 for 9+ grants (high: $44,543), and $69,297 for 68 grants to individuals.
Purpose and activities: The foundation seeks to promote philanthropy in Jackson County. It is a community-focused organization dedicated to: 1) building visionary partnerships with donors and local service organizations; 2) trustworthy stewardship of gifts; 3) providing funds to enhance the quality of life across Jackson County; 4) and being a catalyst for change in the community.
Fields of interest: Arts; Education; Environment; Youth development; Human services; Community/economic development; Children/youth; Adults; Deaf/hearing impaired; Homeless.
Type of support: Income development; Management development/capacity building; Building/renovation; Emergency funds; Seed money; Curriculum development; Scholarship funds; Technical assistance; Consulting services; Program evaluation; Employee-related scholarships; Scholarships—to individuals; Matching/challenge support.
Limitations: Applications accepted. Giving limited to Jackson County, IN. No support for sectarian programs. No grants for seminars, trips, endowments, or state or national fundraising efforts.

Publications: Application guidelines; Annual report; Financial statement; Informational brochure (including application guidelines); Newsletter.
Application information: Visit foundation web site application form and guidelines. Application form required.
Initial approach: Submit application form
Copies of proposal: 1
Deadline(s): July 31
Board meeting date(s): 3rd Wed. of Jan., Apr., July and Oct.
Final notification: 30 days
Officers and Directors:* Denise Connell,* Chair.; Gary Meyer,* Vice-Chair.; Dan Davis,* C.E.O. and Pres.; Sue Smith,* V.P., Prog. and Admin.; Priscilla Wischmeier,* Secy.; Ray Eakins,* Treas.; John Beatty; Susan Bevers; Patricia Butt; Kevin Gabbard; Ron Harrison; Jim Johnson; Tom Lantz; Sue Nehrt; Darrell Persinger; Jim Plump; Andy Royalty; Ron Sibert.
Number of staff: 2 full-time professional; 1 full-time support; 1 part-time support.
EIN: 311119856

3285
Community Foundation of Madison and Jefferson County, Inc. ✧

416 W. St., Ste. B
P.O. Box 306
Madison, IN 47250-0306 (812) 265-3327
Contact: Bill Barnes, Pres. and C.E.O.
FAX: (812) 273-0181; E-mail: info@cfmjc.org; Main URL: http://www.cfmjc.org
Facebook: http://www.facebook.com/cfmjc
Scholarship e-mail: kelly@cfmjc.org

Established in 1992 in IN.
Foundation type: Community foundation.
Financial data (yr. ended 12/31/12): Assets, $18,126,846 (M); gifts received, $273,207; expenditures, $731,134; giving activities include $369,584 for 19+ grants (high: $42,615), and $71,845 for 51 grants to individuals.
Purpose and activities: The mission of the foundation is to build a strong, vibrant community by helping donors provide perpetual funding for the people, projects and passions of Jefferson County, IN.
Fields of interest: Arts; Education; Environment; Animal welfare; Health organizations, association; Human services; Community/economic development; Youth; Aging.
Type of support: Management development/capacity building; Capital campaigns; Building/renovation; Equipment; Endowments; Emergency funds; Program development; Conferences/seminars; Seed money; Scholarship funds; Technical assistance; Consulting services; Scholarships—to individuals; Matching/challenge support.
Limitations: Applications accepted. Giving limited to Jefferson County, IN. No support for religious purposes or programs requiring religious participation, public or private educational institutions, or government agencies. No grants to individuals (except for scholarships), or for debt reduction, annual appeals or membership contribution, ongoing operating expenses or regular programming of well-established agencies, or travel expenses.
Publications: Application guidelines; Annual report; Financial statement; Grants list; Informational brochure; Newsletter; Program policy statement.
Application information: Visit foundation web site for the Initial Proposal form and application information. Application form required.
Initial approach: Contact foundation
Deadline(s): Aug. 1 for Initial Proposal, Sept. 5 for full application
Board meeting date(s): 1st Wed. of each month
Final notification: Mar. 19
Officers and Directors:* Bonnie Hare,* Chair.; Carri Dirksen,* Vice-Chair.; Bill Barnes,* C.E.O. and Pres.; Donn Vecchie-Campbell,* Secy.; Charles McKay,* Treas.; Mark Wynn, Counsel; Anthony D. Brandon; Dr. Ben Canida; Clifford Carnes; Darleen Connolly; Al Huntington; Eric Phagan; Michael Robinson; Margaret Seifert-Russell; Steve Telfer.
Number of staff: 2 full-time professional; 1 full-time support; 1 part-time support.
EIN: 351847297

3286
The Community Foundation of Muncie and Delaware County, Inc. ✧

201 E. Jackson St.
Muncie, IN 47305 (765) 747-7181
FAX: (765) 289-7770; E-mail: info@cfmdin.org; Mailing address: PO Box 807, Muncie, IN 47308-0807; Main URL: http://www.cfmdin.org
Facebook: http://www.facebook.com/pages/The-Community-Foundation-of-Muncie-and-Delaware-County-Inc/98358219043
Twitter: http://twitter.com/CFofMuncieDelCo

Incorporated in 1985 in IN.
Foundation type: Community foundation.
Financial data (yr. ended 12/31/13): Assets, $52,239,700 (M); gifts received, $1,135,022; expenditures, $2,525,747; giving activities include $1,753,348 for 56+ grants (high: $108,000), and $101,352 for grants to individuals.
Purpose and activities: The foundation seeks to encourage philanthropy, assist donors in building and enduring source of charitable assets, and exercise leadership in directing resources to enhance the quality of life of the residents of Muncie and Delaware County, Indiana.
Fields of interest: Arts; Education; Human services; Community development, neighborhood development; Economic development; Children/youth; Children; Adults; Aging; Young adults; Disabilities, people with; Women; Men; Economically disadvantaged; Homeless.
Type of support: General/operating support; Capital campaigns; Building/renovation; Equipment; Emergency funds; Program development; Conferences/seminars; Seed money; Curriculum development; Scholarship funds; Technical assistance; Consulting services; Scholarships—to individuals; In-kind gifts; Matching/challenge support.
Limitations: Applications accepted. Giving limited to Muncie and Delaware County, IN. No support for religious purposes or public agency projects. No grants to individuals (except for scholarships), or for endowment support, travel, fundraising events, or budget deficits.
Publications: Application guidelines; Annual report; Financial statement; Grants list; Informational brochure; Newsletter; Occasional report.
Application information: Visit foundation web site for application form and specific guidelines per grant type. Application form required.
Initial approach: Telephone
Copies of proposal: 2
Deadline(s): Jan. 8, Apr. 10, July 10, and Oct. 9 for the quarterly competitive grants; varies for others
Board meeting date(s): 3rd Mon. of each month
Final notification: 3rd Mon. of Feb., May, Aug., and Nov. for the quarterly competitive grants; varies for others
Officers and Board Members:* Mark A. Ervin,* Chair.; Marianne Vorhees,* Vice-Chair.; Kelly Shrock,* Pres.; Suzanne Kadinger,* V.P.; Catharine P. Stewart,* Treas.; Mary L. Dollison; Jud Fisher; Michael B. Galliher; Mark K. Hardwick; Jeffrey R. Lang; Michael O. Lunsford.
Number of staff: 3 full-time professional; 1 part-time professional; 2 full-time support.
EIN: 351640051
Selected grants: The following grants are a representative sample of this grantmaker's funding activity:
$32,000 to Huffer Memorial Childrens Center, Muncie, IN, 2011.
$27,770 to Red-Tail Conservancy, Muncie, IN, 2011.
$25,046 to Gateway Health Clinic, Muncie, IN, 2011.
$20,000 to Community Arts and Building Foundation, Muncie, IN, 2011.
$20,000 to Motivate Our Minds, Muncie, IN, 2011.
$20,000 to Muncie Civic Theater, Muncie, IN, 2011.
$17,500 to Animal Rescue Fund, Muncie, IN, 2011.
$15,000 to Second Harvest Food Bank of East Central Indiana, Muncie, IN, 2011.
$12,375 to Back to School Teachers Store, Muncie, IN, 2011.
$10,000 to First Choice for Women, Muncie, IN, 2011.

3287
Community Foundation of Randolph County, Inc. ✧ ☆

213 S. Main St.
Winchester, IN 47394-1824 (765) 584-9077
Contact: Ruth B. Mills, Exec. Dir.
FAX: (765) 584-7710;
E-mail: info@cfrandolphcounty.org; Additional e-mail: rmills@cfrandolphcounty.org; Main URL: http://www.randolphcountyfoundation.org/
Facebook: https://www.facebook.com/#!/pages/Community-Foundation-of-Randolph-County/205746446129959
Twitter: http://www.twitter.com/CFofRC

Established in 1992 in IN.
Foundation type: Community foundation.
Financial data (yr. ended 12/31/13): Assets, $8,262,514 (M); gifts received, $725,251; expenditures, $628,515; giving activities include $314,860 for 23+ grants (high: $57,888), and $126,169 for 68 grants to individuals.
Purpose and activities: The Community Foundation of Randolph County, Inc. seeks to bring people and resources together to enrich the lives of Randolph County residents.
Fields of interest: Historic preservation/historical societies; Arts; Higher education; Scholarships/financial aid; Education; Environment; Health care;

Human services; Economic development; Community/economic development; Youth; Aging.
Type of support: Program development; Curriculum development; Scholarship funds.
Limitations: Applications accepted. Giving limited to Randolph County, IN. No support for religious or sectarian purposes. No grants to individuals (except for scholarships), or for make-up of operating deficits, post-event or after-the-fact situations, or endowments campaigns.
Publications: Application guidelines; Annual report; Newsletter; Occasional report (including application guidelines).
Application information: Visit foundation web site for application cover sheet and guidelines. Completed typewritten application forms should be sent or delivered to the foundation's office. Applications cannot be submitted online. Application form required.
Initial approach: Submit application
Copies of proposal: 11
Deadline(s): Mar. 31 and Sept. 30
Board meeting date(s): 3rd Thursday of each month
Final notification: 4 to 6 weeks
Officers and Directors:* Chip Loney,* Pres.; Cheryl Jones,* V.P.; Sheryl Thurston,* Secy.; Lisa Jennings,* Treas.; Ruth B. Mills, Exec. Dir.; Christen Commers; Dick Gause; Richard Gough; Jane Grove; Joyce Husmann; James Meinerding; Janice Powers; Ronn Shumaker; Cathy Stephen; Kent Thornburg; Linda Wilcox.
Number of staff: 2 full-time professional.
EIN: 351903148

3288
Community Foundation of Southern Indiana ✧

4104 Charlestown Rd.
New Albany, IN 47150-9538 (812) 948-4662
Contact: For grants: Crystal Gunther, Grants and Prog. Off.
FAX: (812) 948-4678;
E-mail: lspeed@cfsouthernindiana.com; Grant inquiry e-mail: cgunther@cfsouthernindiana.com; Main URL: http://www.cfsouthernindiana.com
Facebook: https://www.facebook.com/cfsouthernindiana
Twitter: https://twitter.com/CFofSI
YouTube: http://www.youtube.com/user/cfsouthernindiana

Established in 1991 in IN.
Foundation type: Community foundation.
Financial data (yr. ended 06/30/13): Assets, $29,476,399 (M); gifts received, $452,214; expenditures, $3,942,768; giving activities include $2,562,778 for grants.
Purpose and activities: The foundation builds enduring charitable resources used to positively impact the community by: 1) serving as a partner and resource for donors, their advisors, and area nonprofits; 2) making it simple for donors to fulfill their individual goals in giving back; 3) providing stewardship of donor gifts and charitable intent for generations to come; and 4) fulfilling a leadership role on important community issues.
Fields of interest: Arts; Education; Environment; Health care; Recreation; Youth development; Human services; Community/economic development.
Type of support: Management development/capacity building; Capital campaigns; Building/renovation; Emergency funds; Program development; Conferences/seminars; Seed money; Scholarship funds; Scholarships—to individuals; Matching/challenge support.
Limitations: Applications accepted. Giving limited to Clark and Floyd counties, IN. No support for medical, scientific or academic research, or for religious or sectarian purposes. No grants to individuals (except for designated scholarship funds), or for annual appeals, endowment funds, membership contributions, fundraising events, existing obligations, travel expenses, long-term operating support, or multi-year grants or repeat funding; no loans.
Publications: Annual report (including application guidelines); Financial statement; Informational brochure; Newsletter.
Application information: Visit foundation web site for application forms and guidelines. Application form required.
Initial approach: Submit online application and attachments
Copies of proposal: 2
Deadline(s): Sept. 1 for competitive grant cycle
Board meeting date(s): Bimonthly
Final notification: Late Oct.
Officers and Directors:* Julie Larner,* Chair.; Susie Stewart,* Vice-Chair.; Linda S. Speed,* C.E.O. and Pres.; Gary Banet,* Secy.; Phillip Beaman,* Treas.; Jessica Bergman; Helen Bryant; Bill Hanson; Tom Hardy; Jorge Lanz; Leslie Lewis-Sheets; Pat More; Greg Neely; Kyle Ridout; Sue Sanders; Andrew Takami; Bill White.
Number of staff: 4 full-time professional; 2 part-time professional; 1 full-time support; 1 part-time support.
EIN: 351827813

3289
Community Foundation of St. Joseph County

205 W. Jefferson Blvd., Ste. 610
P.O. Box 837
South Bend, IN 46624-0837 (574) 232-0041
Contact: Angela Butiste, Prog. Dir.
FAX: (574) 233-1906; E-mail: info@cfsjc.org; Additional e-mail: angela@cfsjc.org; Grant application e-mail: grants@cfsjc.org; Main URL: http://www.cfsjc.org
Knowledge Center: http://cfsjc.org/publications/
YouTube: http://www.youtube.com/user/cfsjc

Established in 1991 in IN.
Foundation type: Community foundation.
Financial data (yr. ended 06/30/14): Assets, $146,885,950 (M); gifts received, $3,021,444; expenditures, $6,691,430; giving activities include $5,124,112 for grants, $269,367 for grants to individuals, and $5,835,672 for foundation-administered programs.
Purpose and activities: The foundation seeks to improve the quality of life for the citizens of St. Joseph County and their succeeding generations.
Fields of interest: Arts; Higher education; Education; Health care; Recreation, parks/playgrounds; Recreation; Human services; Community development, neighborhood development; Youth.
Type of support: Management development/capacity building; Capital campaigns; Building/renovation; Equipment; Scholarships—to individuals; Matching/challenge support.
Limitations: Applications accepted. Giving limited to St. Joseph County, IN. No support for religious organizations for religious purposes, or development or public relations activities. No grants to individuals (except for scholarships), or for endowment campaigns, retirement of debts, camperships, annual appeals or membership contributions, travel, post-event or after the fact situations, or computers (unless presented as a necessary component of larger program or objective).
Publications: Application guidelines; Financial statement; Grants list; Newsletter.
Application information: Visit foundation web site for application Cover Sheet and guidelines. Application form required.
Initial approach: E-mail Grant Cover Sheet and attachments
Copies of proposal: 1
Deadline(s): Varies
Board meeting date(s): Mar., June, Sept., and Dec.
Final notification: Varies
Officers and Directors:* Timothy Sexton,* Chair.; Jeffrey Costello,* Vice-Chair.; Rose Meissner,* C.E.O. and Pres.; Anita Echevarria, V.P., Admin.; Brad Beutter,* Secy.; Patricia Hackett,* Treas.; John S. Abernethy; Jose Alvarez; Carl Bossung; Pamela Burish; Dr. Virginia Calvin; Roland Chamblee, Jr.; Richard Currey; Mary Jan Hedman; Vincent Henderson; Nancy Ickler; Marcia Jones; Christopher Karam; James Keenan; Nancy King; Greta Roemer Lewis; Tina Patton; Richard Pfeil; Jeffrey Rea; Greta Roemer Lewis; Jo Ann Wittenbach.
Number of staff: 8 full-time professional.
EIN: 237365930
Selected grants: The following grants are a representative sample of this grantmaker's funding activity:
$359,383 to South Bend Symphony Orchestra, South Bend, IN, 2011. For unrestricted support, ArtsEverywhere Series, MLK Day Celebration.
$250,000 to Family Connection of Saint Joseph County, South Bend, IN, 2011. For early childhood initiative.
$112,125 to Foundation of Saint Joseph Regional Medical Center, South Bend, IN, 2011. For unrestricted support, scholarship.
$98,969 to Center for the Homeless, South Bend, IN, 2011. For unrestricted support.
$74,225 to University of Notre Dame, Notre Dame, IN, 2011. For charitable initiatives.
$60,000 to University of Notre Dame, Major Venture Grant to Robinson Community Learning Center, Notre Dame, IN, 2012. To expand outreach of Robinson Shakespeare Company to schools within South Bend Community School Corporation, include afterschool program in class collaborative teaching and professional development for teachers.
$57,500 to Real Services of Saint Joseph County, South Bend, IN, 2012. To continue to build Care Transition model in collaboration with Saint Joseph Regional Medical Center.
$45,000 to Housing Authority of the City of South Bend, South Bend, IN, 2011. For Lead Abatement Program.
$27,170 to Michiana Public Broadcasting Corporation, South Bend, IN, 2011. For unrestricted support, Center for Public Media Wall of Helping Hands, Leighton Award Special Recognition.

$25,000 to La Casa de Amistad, South Bend, IN, 2011. For program support.
$20,000 to CASIE Center, South Bend, IN, 2011. For Establishment of Child-Friendly Medical Clinic.
$20,000 to South Bend Civic Theater, South Bend, IN, 2012. For season support.
$18,480 to Saint Marys College, Notre Dame, IN, 2011. For unrestricted support, scholarships.
$13,434 to Logan Community Resources, South Bend, IN, 2012. To purchase new furniture for Logan's group living homes.
$10,000 to Fischoff National Chamber Music Association, Notre Dame, IN, 2012. For free community outreach programs for children and youth presented by Fischoff Competition alumni and local professional musicians.
$5,000 to Michiana Public Broadcasting Corporation, WNIT Public Television, South Bend, IN, 2012. To experience Michiana new daily show, airing at 6:30 pm on WNIT and 8:00 pm on InFocus Monday through Friday.
$5,000 to Musical Arts Indiana, IN, 2012. For three concerts of the Vesper Chorale during 20th Anniversary season.
$4,000 to Mainstage Theater Company, Eugene, OR, 2012. For production of Broadway musical Legally Blonde.
$2,500 to South Bend Jazz Festival, IN, 2012. For free public stage part of European-style jazz festival to be held in conjunction with Art Beat.
$1,500 to Good Shepherd Montessori School, South Bend, IN, 2012. For outdoor sculpture project for students grades 1-8 bird sculpture will be constructed step-by-step by students with assistance of local artists who act as artist-in-residence.

3290
Community Foundation of Wabash County ✧

(formerly North Manchester Community Foundation)
218 E. Main St.
P.O. Box 7
North Manchester, IN 46962 (260) 982-4824
Contact: Patty Grant, Exec. Dir.; For grants: Julie Garber, Prog. Dir.
FAX: (260) 982-8644; E-mail: info@cfwabash.org; Grant inquiry e-mail: julie@cfwabash.org; Main URL: http://www.cfwabash.org
Facebook: https://www.facebook.com/pages/Community-Foundation-of-Wabash-County/82489716455

Established in 1954 in IN as North Manchester Community Foundation; current name adopted in 1992.
Foundation type: Community foundation.
Financial data (yr. ended 12/31/13): Assets, $33,642,815 (M); gifts received, $814,011; expenditures, $1,600,349; giving activities include $833,963 for 17+ grants (high: $242,350), and $87,114 for 113 grants to individuals.
Purpose and activities: The foundation serves the citizens of Wabash County by implementing their charitable aspirations, making grants, investing and safeguarding charitable assets, providing information regarding charitable endeavors, and convening citizens and linking resources to address issues confronting residents' shared lives.
Fields of interest: Arts; Higher education; Education; Environment; Health care; Recreation; Human services; Economic development; Community/economic development; Social sciences.
Type of support: General/operating support; Continuing support; Building/renovation; Equipment; Endowments; Program development; Seed money; Curriculum development; Scholarship funds; Technical assistance; Program evaluation; Scholarships—to individuals; Matching/challenge support.
Limitations: Applications accepted. Giving limited to Wabash County, IN. No support for religious activities, or for national organizations (except for local chapters serving Wabash County). No grants to individuals (except for scholarships), or for start-ups.
Publications: Application guidelines; Annual report (including application guidelines); Grants list; Informational brochure; Newsletter; IRS Form 990 or 990-PF printed copy available upon request.
Application information: Visit foundation web site for application form and additional guidelines per grant type. Application form required.
Initial approach: Mail application form and attachments
Copies of proposal: 9
Deadline(s): Mar. 15 and July 15 for Good Deeds Grants; Jan. for strategic initiatives
Board meeting date(s): Quarterly
Final notification: One month after deadline
Officers and Directors:* Steve Hentgen,* Pres.; Chris Garber,* V.P.; Dave Mann,* Secy.; Cindy Seitz,* Treas.; Patty Grant, Exec. Dir.; Mark Coppler; Dick Dubois; Cathy Gatchel; Brian Howenstine; Stan Leland; Joe Messer; Josh Petruniw; Lola Smith; Amy Sullivan.
Number of staff: 3 full-time professional.
EIN: 356019016

3291
Crown Point Community Foundation ✧

115 S. Court St.
Crown Point, IN 46307 (219) 662-7252
Contact: Patricia Huber, Pres.
FAX: (219) 662-9493; E-mail: info@thepcf.org; Mailing address: P.O. Box 522, Crown Point, IN 46308-0522; Main URL: http://www.crownpointcommunityfoundation.org
Facebook: http://www.facebook.com/CrownPointCommunityFoundation
YouTube: http://www.youtube.com/TheCPCFoundation

Established in 1990 in IN.
Foundation type: Community foundation.
Financial data (yr. ended 12/31/13): Assets, $21,548,175 (M); gifts received, $2,059,484; expenditures, $985,735; giving activities include $369,932 for 20+ grants (high: $52,667), and $259,136 for 115 grants to individuals.
Purpose and activities: The foundation's mission is to enrich the quality of life in Crown Point and Northwest Indiana, serving as a well-managed agent for giving and receiving to the local community.
Fields of interest: Historic preservation/historical societies; Arts; Higher education; Education; Environment; Health care; Crime/violence prevention; Housing/shelter; Recreation; Youth development; Human services; Community/economic development; Philanthropy/voluntarism; Public affairs; Religion.
Type of support: General/operating support; Continuing support; Annual campaigns; Capital campaigns; Equipment; Emergency funds; Scholarship funds; Scholarships—to individuals.
Limitations: Applications accepted. Giving limited to northwestern IN, including the Crown Point area. No support for religious organizations for religious purposes. No grants for endowments.
Publications: Application guidelines; Annual report; Informational brochure; Newsletter.
Application information: Visit foundation web site for application form and guidelines. Application form required.
Initial approach: Submit application
Copies of proposal: 8
Deadline(s): Feb. 1, June 1, and Sept. 1
Board meeting date(s): 3 times per-year, plus annual dinner meeting
Final notification: 1 month
Officers and Directors:* Dave Batusic,* Chair.; Greg Forsythe,* 1st Vice-Chair.; Patricia Huber,* Pres.; Darryl Miller,* Treas.; Linda Armstrong; Ben Ballou; Mark Bates; John Barney; Jeff Bryner; Nancy Cowan-Eksten; Mike Dexter; Larry Geisen; Jon Harts; Marilyn Kaper; Jim Larsen; Tom Liss; Karen Raab; Daniel R. Root; Dick Sauerman; Stephanie Schrage.
Number of staff: 1 full-time professional; 3 part-time support.
EIN: 310247014

3292
The Cummins Foundation ✧

(formerly Cummins Engine Foundation)
500 Jackson St.
M.C. 60113
Columbus, IN 47201 (812) 377-3114
FAX: (812) 377-7897;
E-mail: Cummins.Foundation@cummins.com; Additional tel.: (812) 377-3746; Main URL: http://www.cummins.com/cmi/navigationAction.do?nodeId=1003&siteId=1&nodeName=Corporate+Responsibility&menuId=1003
Grants List: http://cmipef.cummins.com/CMIPEFMIG/CumminsNA/SiteContent/en/BinaryAsset/Attachments/Sustainability/Cummins_Contributions_2012_2013.pdf

Incorporated in 1954 in IN.
Donors: Cummins Engine Co., Inc.; Fleetguard, Inc.; Cummins Inc.
Foundation type: Company-sponsored foundation.
Financial data (yr. ended 12/31/13): Assets, $36,506,530 (M); gifts received, $5,100; expenditures, $8,345,021; qualifying distributions, $7,190,373; giving activities include $7,190,373 for 171 grants (high: $1,260,363; low: $48).
Purpose and activities: The foundation supports programs designed to promote education, the environment, and social justice; and programs designed to improve communities in which Cummins does business.
Fields of interest: Visual arts, architecture; Elementary/secondary education; Higher education; Engineering school/education; Education, services; Education; Environment, climate change/global warming; Environment, natural resources; Environment, water resources; Environment, energy; Environment; Employment, services; Disasters, preparedness/services; Youth, services; Human services; Civil/human rights; Business/industry; Community/economic development; United Ways and Federated Giving Programs; Mathematics; Engineering/technology; Science; Economically disadvantaged.

International interests: Brazil; China; India; Mexico; South Africa.
Type of support: General/operating support; Continuing support; Annual campaigns; Building/renovation; Equipment; Endowments; Emergency funds; Program development; Publication; Curriculum development; Scholarship funds; Technical assistance; Sponsorships; Employee matching gifts; Matching/challenge support.
Limitations: Applications accepted. Giving primarily in areas of company operations, with emphasis on Lake Mills, IA, the Columbus and Seymour, IN, areas, Fridley, MN, Jamestown, NY, Rocky Mount, NC, Findlay, OH, Charleston, SC, Cookeville, Memphis, and Nashville, TN, El Paso, TX, Stoughton, WI and in Brazil, China, India, Mexico, and South Africa; giving also to national organizations. No support for sectarian religious organizations, political candidates, or medical or disease-related organizations. No grants to individuals, or for capital campaigns, business start-up needs or political causes; no loans or product donations.
Publications: Application guidelines; Corporate giving report; Grants list; IRS Form 990 or 990-PF printed copy available upon request.
Application information: Additional information may be requested at a later date. Organizations receiving support are asked to submit a final report.
Initial approach: Proposal
Copies of proposal: 1
Deadline(s): None
Board meeting date(s): Quarterly
Final notification: Varies by board meeting cycle
Officers and Directors:* Theodore M. Solso,* Chair.; Mark Levett, C.E.O.; Mary Chandler, Secy.; Marsha Allamanno, Treas.; Thomas Linebarger; William I. Miller; Marya M. Rose; Patrick J. Ward.
Number of staff: 2 full-time professional; 1 full-time support.
EIN: 356042373
Selected grants: The following grants are a representative sample of this grantmaker's funding activity:
$1,190,624 to United Way of Bartholomew County, Columbus, IN, 2012. For employee matching grants.
$250,000 to Save the Children Federation, Fairfield, CT, 2012. For Children in Emergencies Fund to support Education in Emergencies.
$222,270 to Courage Center, Minneapolis, MN, 2012. To elevate the Courage Center AT program to a national level of prominence.
$175,000 to Ivy Tech Community College Columbus, Columbus, IN, 2012. For Graduation Coaches Program.
$88,000 to GlobalGiving Foundation, Washington, DC, 2012. For Patronato Pro Regeneracion del Parque Juan H Sanchez to improve water quality of Parque Morales Boating Lake in downtown San Luis Potosi.
$36,100 to Bartholomew Consolidated School Corporation, Columbus, IN, 2012. For Project Manager for Bartholomew Consolidated Schools.
$25,661 to United Way of Putnam County, Cookeville, TN, 2012. For employee matching grants.
$25,000 to Family Nurturing Center, Asheville, NC, 2012. For matching grant.
$17,000 to Food Bank of Eastern New Mexico, Clovis, NM, 2012. To reduce electrical utilization/reduce carbon foot print.
$5,000 to GlobalGiving Foundation, Hocsung Orphanage, Washington, DC, 2012. For General Support for the Orphange.

3293
Dearborn Community Foundation ✧
(formerly Dearborn County Community Foundation)
322 Walnut St.
Lawrenceburg, IN 47025 (812) 539-4115
Contact: Fred McCarter, Exec. Dir.; For grants: Denise Sedler, Dir., Progs.
FAX: (812) 539-4119;
E-mail: fmccarter@dearborncf.org; Grant information e-mail: dsedler@comcast.net; Main URL: http://www.dearborncf.org
Facebook: http://www.facebook.com/DearbornCommunityFoundation

Established in 1997 in IN.
Donors: The Greater Cincinnati Foundation; Lilly Endowment; Rising Sun Regional Foundation.
Foundation type: Community foundation.
Financial data (yr. ended 12/31/13): Assets, $16,628,760 (M); gifts received, $4,168,548; expenditures, $3,892,513; giving activities include $3,154,806 for 12+ grants (high: $370,909), and $325,000 for 209 grants to individuals.
Purpose and activities: The foundation is a catalyst to connect people who care with causes that improve the quality of life in the community by advancing cultural, educational and social opportunities, while preserving its heritage and helping donors to create a permanent legacy in Dearborn County.
Fields of interest: Arts; Elementary/secondary education; Education; Environment, natural resources; Environment; Hospitals (general); Health care; Crime/law enforcement, government agencies; Human services; Community/economic development; Children/youth.
Type of support: Building/renovation; Equipment; Program development; Seed money; Scholarships—to individuals; Matching/challenge support.
Limitations: Applications accepted. Giving limited to Dearborn County, IN. No support for sectarian or religious purposes. No grants to individuals (except for scholarships), or exclusively for endowment creation or debt reduction, or for travel expenses or after-the-fact funding.
Publications: Application guidelines; Annual report; Newsletter.
Application information: Visit foundation web site for application cover form, guidelines, and specific deadline per grant type. Application form required.
Initial approach: Submit grant application cover form and attachments
Copies of proposal: 8
Deadline(s): Varies
Board meeting date(s): Last Thurs. of every month except Apr., July, and Dec.
Final notification: Varies
Officers and Directors:* Jim Stock,* Chair.; Perry Taylor,* Pres.; David Wismann,* V.P.; Mary Ewbank,* Secy.; John Rumsey,* Treas.; Fred McCarter, Exec. Dir.; Lisa DeHart Lehner, Counsel; Tami Bovard; Paula Bruner; Dave Deddens; Mark Graver; Deanna Hacker; Mike Hornbach; Becky Lyons; Barry Nanz; Jon Strautman; Judy Ullrich.
Number of staff: 4 full-time professional; 1 full-time support.
EIN: 352036110

3294
Christel DeHaan Family Foundation ✧
(formerly RCI Foundation)
c/o Joe Schneider
10 W. Market St., Ste. 1990
Indianapolis, IN 46204-2973 (317) 464-2038
Contact: Melynne Klaus, Exec. Dir.
E-mail: mklaus@cde-ltd.com; Main URL: http://www.christeldehaanfamilyfoundation.org/

Established in 1992 in IN.
Donor: Christel DeHaan.
Foundation type: Independent foundation.
Financial data (yr. ended 12/31/12): Assets, $43,358,672 (M); expenditures, $1,160,899; qualifying distributions, $776,694; giving activities include $662,650 for 64 grants (high: $80,000; low: $100).
Purpose and activities: Giving to meaningfully preserve and enhance for future generations the rich artistic and cultural fabric of the Indianapolis, Indiana community.
Fields of interest: Arts.
Type of support: General/operating support; Continuing support; Annual campaigns; Program development; Matching/challenge support.
Limitations: Giving primarily in central IN. No support for religious organizations, political candidates, parties or lobbyists, federal/state/local governmental bodies, or for other private foundations. No grants for individual artistic endeavors, media advertising, or public awareness campaigns.
Publications: IRS Form 990 or 990-PF printed copy available upon request.
Application information: Full applications are accepted by invitation only, upon consideration of initial tel., e-mail or letter. See foundation web site for additional information. Application form required.
Initial approach: Tel., e-mail or letter to request additional information and funding guidelines
Copies of proposal: 1
Board meeting date(s): June and Dec.
Officers and Directors:* Christel DeHaan,* Pres.; Cheryl J. Wendling,* Sr. V.P. and Secy.; Keith A. DeHaan,* V.P.; Kirsten A. DeHaan,* V.P.; Timothy E. DeHaan,* V.P.; Joe Schneider, Treas.; Melynne Klaus, Exec. Dir.; Mark Willis, C.I.O.; Nelson Hitchcock; Jim Reed.
Number of staff: 1 part-time professional.
EIN: 351939960
Selected grants: The following grants are a representative sample of this grantmaker's funding activity:
$50,000 to Indiana University Foundation, Bloomington, IN, 2012. To support opera Akhnaten at Clowes Hall.
$50,000 to Indianapolis Symphony Orchestra, Indianapolis, IN, 2012. For Christmas Concert.
$25,000 to Central Indiana Community Foundation, Indianapolis, IN, 2012. To support 2012 Spotlight Event.
$16,700 to Indianapolis Chamber Orchestra, Indianapolis, IN, 2012. To support ICO string instructor at schools.
$15,000 to Big Car Media, Indianapolis, IN, 2012. To support Big Car event and winning presenter.
$10,000 to Culver Educational Foundation, Culver, IN, 2012. For General Operating and Scholarship Support.
$10,000 to Indianapolis Museum of Art, Indianapolis, IN, 2012. For general operating support.

$5,000 to Arts Council of Indianapolis, Indianapolis, IN, 2012. For Start With Art luncheon.
$5,000 to Encore Vocal Arts, Indianapolis, IN, 2012. For The Myth, The Hero, and The Legend concert.
$2,500 to Indiana University Foundation, Bloomington, IN, 2012. To support 2012 Spirit and Place Festival.

3295
DeKalb County Community Foundation, Inc. ✧ ☆
700 S. Main St.
P.O. Box 111
Auburn, IN 46706-0111 (260) 925-0311
Contact: Wendy Oberlin, Exec. Dir.; For grants: Diane Wilson, Grant and Scholarship Mgr.
FAX: (260) 925-0383;
E-mail: woberlin@dekalbfoundation.org; Additional tel.: (888) 727-3834; Grant application e-mail: dwilson@dekalbfoundation.org; Main URL: http://www.dekalbfoundation.org
Scholarship application e-mail: scholarships@dekalbfoundation.org

Established in 1996 in IN.
Foundation type: Community foundation.
Financial data (yr. ended 12/31/13): Assets, $14,041,958 (M); gifts received, $794,433; expenditures, $1,112,341; giving activities include $486,546 for grants.
Purpose and activities: The foundation promotes community philanthropy by offering local citizens the opportunity to leave a charitable legacy that will sustain and improve life in DeKalb County.
Fields of interest: Arts; Education; Environment; Health care; Youth development; Human services; Community/economic development.
Type of support: General/operating support; Capital campaigns; Building/renovation; Equipment; Program development; Technical assistance; Scholarships—to individuals; Matching/challenge support.
Limitations: Applications accepted. Giving limited to projects/programs that benefit residents of DeKalb County, IN.
Publications: Application guidelines; Annual report; Financial statement; Grants list; Newsletter.
Application information: Visit foundation web site for application form and guidelines. Handwritten proposals are not accepted. The foundation offers free 60-minute workshops to help grantseekers understand the application process and how to submit a request; contact Prog. Mgr. to register. Application form required.
Initial approach: Contact foundation to schedule meeting
Copies of proposal: 1
Deadline(s): July 1
Board meeting date(s): Varies
Officers and Directors:* W. Erik Weber,* Pres.; Holly Albright,* V.P.; Wendy Oberlin, Exec. Dir.; Matthew A. Bechdol; Wayne E. Funk; Michael W. Hasselman; Don B. Hollman; Ken McCrory; Ian Mercer; Michael C. Payne; Dennis D. Post; Terry Rayle; Vanessa Sterling; Trenton Stuckey; Kathie O. Swaim; Marcia K. Weller.
Number of staff: 2 full-time professional; 4 part-time support.
EIN: 351992897

3296
Dekko Foundation, Inc. ✧
P.O. Box 548
Kendallville, IN 46755-0548 (260) 347-1278
Contact: Thomas Leedy, Pres.
FAX: (260) 347-7103;
E-mail: dekko@dekkofoundation.org; Main URL: http://www.dekkofoundation.org

Established in 1981 in IN.
Donor: Chester E. Dekko‡.
Foundation type: Independent foundation.
Financial data (yr. ended 08/31/13): Assets, $227,541,363 (M); gifts received, $1,396,730; expenditures, $12,286,527; qualifying distributions, $11,063,533; giving activities include $9,737,926 for 118 grants (high: $2,000,000; low: $100), and $325,971 for 3 foundation-administered programs.
Purpose and activities: The foundation believes that positive child development experiences are the basis for building independent, economically free citizens. Every grant the foundation makes is designed to give young people the developmental experiences that they need to thrive. Foundation grantmaking is concentrated in the following areas: Early childhood development (birth through age five); Middle childhood development (ages six through twelve); Adolescent development (ages thirteen through eighteen); and Community development (related to the advancement of children and young people).
Fields of interest: Education, early childhood education; Elementary school/education; Secondary school/education; Education; Youth development.
Type of support: General/operating support; Continuing support; Management development/capacity building; Capital campaigns; Building/renovation; Equipment; Land acquisition; Endowments; Program development; Conferences/seminars; Seed money; Curriculum development; Technical assistance; Consulting services; Matching/challenge support.
Limitations: Applications accepted. Giving primarily in Limestone County, AL, Collier County, FL, DeKalb, LaGrange, Kosciusko, Noble, Steuben and Whitley counties, IN, Clarke, Decatur, Lucas, Ringgold and Union counties, IA and the Ada community, MN. No grants to individuals.
Publications: Application guidelines; Annual report.
Application information: Application form available online, but not required. Application form not required.
Initial approach: Check eligibility on foundation web site
Copies of proposal: 1
Deadline(s): None
Board meeting date(s): Feb., Apr., Jun., Aug., Oct. and Dec.
Final notification: 3-4 months
Officers and Directors: Thomas Leedy, Pres.; Robin McCormick, Cont.; Erica D. Dekko; Tad Dekko; Phil Salsbery.
Number of staff: 8 full-time professional; 1 part-time professional; 3 part-time support.
EIN: 351528135
Selected grants: The following grants are a representative sample of this grantmaker's funding activity:
$2,000,000 to Oak Farm School, Avilla, IN, 2013. For operating support.
$1,778,850 to Oak Farm School, Avilla, IN, 2013. For capital support.
$1,050,000 to YMCA of Dekalb County, Auburn, IN, 2013. For capital support and operating support.
$750,000 to Athens-Limestone Public Library, Athens, AL, 2013. For capital support.
$353,750 to Oak Farm School, Avilla, IN, 2013. For program support.
$200,000 to Waterloo Grant Township Public Library, Waterloo, IN, 2013. For capital support.
$173,500 to Indiana Youth Institute, Indianapolis, IN, 2013. For operating support.
$101,500 to Life and Family Services, Kendallville, IN, 2013. For endowment and capacity building.
$97,100 to Early Childhood Alliance, Fort Wayne, IN, 2013. For program support.
$60,000 to Mayflower Heritage Christian School, Creston, IA, 2013. For program support and capacity building.

3297
Duneland Health Council, Inc. ✧ ☆
P.O. Box 9327
Michigan City, IN 46361-9327 (219) 874-4193

Established in 1997 in IN.
Donor: Alverno Health Care Corp.
Foundation type: Independent foundation.
Financial data (yr. ended 12/31/13): Assets, $7,554,523 (M); expenditures, $581,872; qualifying distributions, $428,073; giving activities include $428,073 for 23 grants (high: $57,000; low: $500).
Purpose and activities: To improve the health and general welfare of the greater Michigan City, IN, community.
Fields of interest: Nursing school/education; Education; Health care, clinics/centers; Health care; Human services; Salvation Army; Family services; Children's rights; Community/economic development.
Type of support: Advocacy.
Limitations: Applications accepted. Giving primarily in the metropolitan Michigan City, IN, area. No support for religious organizations. No grants to individuals, or for fund-raising, endowments, or advertising.
Application information: Duneland Health Council Grant Application Form required. Application form required.
Initial approach: Proposal
Deadline(s): None
Officers: Gil Pontius, Chair.; George R. Averitt, Vice-Chair.; Tom Cipares, Secy.; H. Fred Miller, Treas.; Norman D. Steider, Exec. Dir.
Directors: Linda Anast-May; Linda Bechinski; Barbara Eason-Watkins; Judy Jacobi; Allan Whitlow.
EIN: 352021548

3298
Elkhart County Community Foundation, Inc. ✧
101 S. Main St., 1st Fl.
P.O. Box 2932
Elkhart, IN 46515 (574) 295-8761
Contact: For grants: Shannon Oakes, Dir., Grants Admin.
FAX: (574) 389-7497; E-mail: info@elkhartccf.org; Main URL: http://www.elkhartccf.org
Facebook: http://www.facebook.com/pages/Elkhart-County-Community-Foundation/202040020314
Twitter: http://twitter.com/eccf1989

Established in 1987 in IN; incorporated in 1989.
Foundation type: Community foundation.
Financial data (yr. ended 06/30/13): Assets, $197,402,382 (M); gifts received, $143,539,993; expenditures, $5,900,036; giving activities include $3,638,701 for grants.
Purpose and activities: The foundation seeks to maintain funding in the areas of arts and culture, community development, education, health, and human services.
Fields of interest: Historic preservation/historical societies; Arts; Education; Environment; Animals/wildlife; Dental care; Health care; Youth development; Aging, centers/services; Human services; Community/economic development; Aging.
Type of support: Grants to individuals; Emergency funds; Building/renovation; General/operating support; Continuing support; Management development/capacity building; Equipment; Program development; Seed money; Scholarship funds; Technical assistance; Scholarships—to individuals; In-kind gifts; Matching/challenge support.
Limitations: Applications accepted. Giving limited to organizations that serve Elkhart County, IN. No support for religious or sectarian purposes. No grants to individuals (except for scholarships), or for operating budgets or budget deficits, annual funds, conferences, scholarly research, endowments, personal travel, fundraising campaigns, underwriting special events, or films.
Publications: Application guidelines; Annual report (including application guidelines); Grants list; Informational brochure; Newsletter; Occasional report.
Application information: Before applicant submits first request for funding, contact Dir., Grants Administration to set up a meeting to discuss organization. Visit foundation web site for additional information. Application form required.
Initial approach: Register at the foundation's online Charitable Catalog
Copies of proposal: 1
Deadline(s): May 1 and Nov. 1 for online Letters of Interest; Jan. 1 and July 1 for application form
Board meeting date(s): Quarterly
Final notification: 1 month for Letter of Interest; Apr. and Oct. for grant determination
Officers and Directors:* Rick Jenkins,* Chair.; Dzung Nguyen,* Vice-Chair.; Dr. Pete McCown, McCown*, Pres.; Megan Baughman,* Secy.; Cole Patuzzi,* C.F.O. and Cont.; Jodi Spataro, C.A.O.; Mike Schoeffler,* Treas.; Brian Smith, Chair.-Emeritus; Rebecca Ball-Miller; Randy Christophel; Rob Cripe; Steve Fidler; David Findlay; Levon Johnson; Del King; Levi King; Sharon Liegl; Sue Miller; Gordon Moore; Jill Richardson; Jill Sigsbee; Bob Schrock; David Weed; Jeff Wells.
Number of staff: 4 full-time professional; 2 full-time support.
EIN: 311255886
Selected grants: The following grants are a representative sample of this grantmaker's funding activity:
$200,000 to Horizon Educational Alliance, Elkhart, IN, 2012.
$150,000 to Goshen, City of, Goshen, IN, 2012. For Fidler's Pond.
$134,000 to Elkhart Community Schools, Elkhart, IN, 2012.
$115,000 to Premier Arts, Elkhart, IN, 2012.
$70,000 to Crossing National, Elkhart, IN, 2012.
$30,000 to Habitat for Humanity of Elkhart County, Goshen, IN, 2012.
$23,674 to Elkhart County Sheriffs Department, Elkhart, IN, 2012.
$20,000 to Elkhart County Council on Aging, Elkhart, IN, 2012.
$20,000 to Ethos, Elkhart, IN, 2012.
$15,000 to Elkhart County Womens Shelter, Elkhart, IN, 2012.

3299
English-Bonter-Mitchell Foundation ✧
c/o PNC Bank, N.A.
110 W. Berry St., Ste. 900
Fort Wayne, IN 46802-2316 (260) 461-6218
Contact: Margaret A. Sturm
FAX: (260) 461-6198;
E-mail: margaret.sturm@pnc.com; Main URL: http://www.englishbontermitchell.org

Established in 1972 in IN.
Donors: Mary Tower English; Louise Bonter; and others.
Foundation type: Independent foundation.
Financial data (yr. ended 12/31/13): Assets, $130,840,288 (M); expenditures, $6,236,768; qualifying distributions, $5,895,148; giving activities include $5,211,500 for 119 grants (high: $300,000; low: $2,500).
Purpose and activities: Giving primarily for cultural programs and programs for youth; support also for higher education, hospitals, churches and religious organizations, social services, health, and community development.
Fields of interest: Arts; Higher education; Hospitals (general); Health care; Health organizations, association; Human services; Children/youth, services; Community/economic development; Christian agencies & churches.
Limitations: Applications accepted. Giving primarily in Fort Wayne, IN. No grants to individuals.
Publications: Annual report; Grants list.
Application information: See foundation web site for additional application information. Application form required.
Initial approach: Online application
Copies of proposal: 1
Deadline(s): Apr. 15 and Sept. 15
Board meeting date(s): May and Dec.
Trustee: PNC Bank, N.A.
EIN: 356247168
Selected grants: The following grants are a representative sample of this grantmaker's funding activity:
$300,000 to Arts United of Greater Fort Wayne, Fort Wayne, IN, 2012. For general support.
$170,000 to Indiana University-Purdue University at Fort Wayne Foundation, Fort Wayne, IN, 2012. For student services program and Library Complex.
$160,000 to Junior Achievement of Northern Indiana, Fort Wayne, IN, 2012. For general support.
$150,000 to Turnstone Center for Disabled Children and Adults, Fort Wayne, IN, 2012. For general support.
$132,000 to Mad Anthonys Childrens Foundation, Fort Wayne, IN, 2012. For expansion of Children's Hope.
$60,000 to Allen County Education Partnership, Fort Wayne, IN, 2012. For Project Reads Program.
$42,000 to Big Brothers Big Sisters of Northeast Indiana, Fort Wayne, IN, 2012. For general support.
$30,000 to Fort Wayne Ballet, Fort Wayne, IN, 2012. For general support.
$25,000 to Early Childhood Alliance, Fort Wayne, IN, 2012. For program for low-income children.
$15,000 to Community Action of Northeast Indiana, Fort Wayne, IN, 2012. For program, Covering Kids and Families of Northeast Indiana.

3300
Eskenazi Family Foundation, Inc. ✧
10689 N. Pennsylvania St.
Indianapolis, IN 46208-5728

Established in IN.
Donor: Sidney Lois Eskenazi.
Foundation type: Independent foundation.
Financial data (yr. ended 09/30/12): Assets, $3,076,095 (M); gifts received, $910,000; expenditures, $924,105; qualifying distributions, $889,754; giving activities include $889,754 for grants.
Fields of interest: Health organizations, association; Human services; Foundations (private grantmaking); Jewish agencies & synagogues.
Limitations: Applications not accepted. Giving primarily in Indianapolis, IN.
Application information: Unsolicited requests for funds not accepted.
Officers: Sidney Eskenazi, Pres.; Lois Eskenazi, Secy.; Sandra Eskenazi, Mgr.; Dori Meyers, Mgr.
EIN: 371500990

3301
Richard M. Fairbanks Foundation, Inc. ✧
(formerly Fairbanks Foundation, Inc.)
9292 N. Meridian St., Ste. 304
Indianapolis, IN 46260-1828 (317) 846-7111
Contact: Betsy Bikoff, V.P. and Chief Grantmaking Off.
FAX: (317) 844-0167; E-mail (for Betsy Bikoff): bikoff@rmff.org; Main URL: http://www.rmff.org
CEP Study: http://www.rmff.org/page.aspx?PageID=f82d510d-d596-41e7-8848-704060f2d6dd&ParentPageID=814be4f6-2d1d-46f5-acef-8235b323be12

Established in 1986 in IN.
Donor: Richard M. Fairbanks†.
Foundation type: Independent foundation.
Financial data (yr. ended 12/31/13): Assets, $304,516,332 (M); gifts received, $455,761; expenditures, $19,469,168; qualifying distributions, $15,609,207; giving activities include $14,812,039 for 89 grants (high: $2,700,000; low: $980), and $87,350 for 58 employee matching gifts.
Purpose and activities: Support primarily for health care, the vitality of Indianapolis, sustainable employment as well as organizations historically supported by the foundation.
Fields of interest: Health care; Employment, services; Human services; Community/economic development.
Type of support: General/operating support; Continuing support; Management development/capacity building; Annual campaigns; Capital campaigns; Building/renovation; Equipment; Endowments; Program development; Seed money; Fellowships; Research; Technical assistance; Program evaluation; Matching/challenge support.
Limitations: Applications accepted. Giving primarily in greater Indianapolis, IN, with an emphasis on Marion County. No support for political

organizations. No grants to individuals, or for conference, seminars, media events, or workshops unless they are an integral part of a broader program, and no grants to for-profit organizations.
Publications: Application guidelines; Financial statement; Grants list.
Application information: Proposals should be submitted to the foundation only upon request. Unsolicited full proposals will not be accepted. Application form not required.
Initial approach: Telephone or letter of inquiry (2-3 pages)
Copies of proposal: 1
Deadline(s): No
Board meeting date(s): Spring, summer, and fall
Final notification: Day after board meetings
Officers and Directors:* Leonard J. Betley,* Chair., C.E.O. and Pres.; Mary E. "Betsy" Bikoff, V.P. and Chief Grantmaking Off.; Ellen White Quigley, Secy. and Grants Off.; Roger S. Snowdon,* Treas.; Steffanie Rhinesmith, C.I.O.; Daniel C. Appel; Christopher M. Callahan, M.D.; Jonathan B. Fairbanks; Elizabeth N. Mann; Bryan A. Mills; Thomas H. Ristine.
Number of staff: 4 full-time professional; 1 part-time professional; 2 part-time support.
EIN: 311189885
Selected grants: The following grants are a representative sample of this grantmaker's funding activity:
$10,000,000 to Butler University, Department of Science, Indianapolis, IN, 2013. For program support, payable over 5.00 years.
$5,000,000 to Marian University, College of Osteopathic Medicine, Indianapolis, IN, 2012. For operating gap funding, payable over 2.00 years.
$2,400,000 to Mind Trust, Indianapolis, IN, 2012. For general operating support, payable over 3.00 years.
$2,209,145 to Central Indiana Corporate Partnership Foundation, Indianapolis, IN, 2012. For general operating support for BioCrossroads, economic development initiative in the life sciences field, payable over 3.00 years.
$1,590,000 to Teach for America, Indianapolis, Indianapolis, IN, 2012. For Principal Fellowship and Corps and Alumni growth, payable over 3.00 years.
$1,091,460 to Learning Well, Indianapolis, IN, 2013. To provide health services in Charter Schools.
$1,087,371 to Learning Well, Indianapolis, IN, 2012. For school year support.
$1,000,000 to Fairbanks Hospital, Indianapolis, IN, 2012. For Phase I of long-term facility project, payable over 2.00 years.
$250,000 to Planned Parenthood of Indiana and Kentucky, Indianapolis, IN, 2013. To implement Electronic Health Records (EHR) Project.
$180,000 to Indiana University-Purdue University Indianapolis, School of Medicine, Indianapolis, IN, 2013. To reorganize Fairbanks Institute for Healthy Communities.
$150,000 to Jane Pauley Community Health Center, Indianapolis, IN, 2013. For general operating support, payable over 3.00 years.
$150,000 to Mind Trust, Indianapolis, IN, 2013. For Community Engagement Plan.
$140,000 to Community Health Network Foundation, Indianapolis, IN, 2013. For pilot school-based health services in Charter School.
$125,000 to Mary Rigg Neighborhood Center, Indianapolis, IN, 2012. For computer training and career skills programs.
$100,000 to DonorsChoose Indiana, Indianapolis, IN, 2013. For Double Your Impact Challenge Grant, payable over 2.00 years.
$75,000 to Eskenazi Health Foundation, Indianapolis, IN, 2012. For World Burn Congress hosted by Eskenazi Hospital in Indianapolis.
$25,000 to Reach Out and Read, Boston, MA, 2013. For general operating support for Reach Out and Read programs in Marion County.
$20,000 to Fairbanks Hospital, Indianapolis, IN, 2012. For general operating support.
$15,000 to Central Indiana Corporate Partnership Foundation, Indianapolis, IN, 2012. For annual dues for BioCrossroads, economic development initiative in the life sciences field.

3302
The J.E. Fehsenfeld Family Foundation Inc. ✧
5400 W. 86th St.
Indianapolis, IN 46268-1502
Contact: Debra Ann Baker, Secy.

Established in 1999 in IN.
Donors: Mac Fehsenfeld; Fred Fehsenfeld; Frank Fehsenfeld; The Heritage Group.
Foundation type: Independent foundation.
Financial data (yr. ended 12/31/13): Assets, $1,165,461 (M); gifts received, $711,958; expenditures, $630,820; qualifying distributions, $630,452; giving activities include $590,000 for 68 grants (high: $32,000; low: $333).
Fields of interest: Arts; Education; Animal welfare; Health care; Human services.
Application information: Application form not required.
Initial approach: Proposal
Deadline(s): None
Officers: Shannon Burns, Pres.; Judee Fehsenfeld, V.P.; Debra Ann Baker, Secy.
Directors: Ashlee Fehsenfeld; Robin Fehsenfeld; Jason Immekus; Sarah Immekus; Nancy Smith; Steve Stuk.
EIN: 352091086
Selected grants: The following grants are a representative sample of this grantmaker's funding activity:
$17,000 to Riley Childrens Foundation, Indianapolis, IN, 2011.
$15,000 to Charles A. Tindley Accelerated School, Indianapolis, IN, 2011.
$15,000 to Leukemia & Lymphoma Society, Indianapolis, IN, 2011.
$15,000 to Neighborhood House, Portland, OR, 2011.
$15,000 to Opera Grand Rapids, Grand Rapids, MI, 2011.
$11,000 to Traditional Chinese Medicine World Foundation, New York, NY, 2011.
$10,000 to Ducks Unlimited, Ridgeland, MS, 2011.
$10,000 to Villages of Indiana, Indianapolis, IN, 2011.
$5,000 to Family Focus, Chicago, IL, 2011.
$5,000 to Reading and Beyond, Fresno, CA, 2011.

3303
Finish Line Youth Foundation, Inc. ✧
3308 N. Mitthoeffer Rd.
Indianapolis, IN 46235-2332 (317) 899-1022
Contact: Marty Posch, Exec. Dir.
Main URL: http://www.finishline.com/

Established in 1998 in IN.
Donors: The Finish Line, Inc.; The Sablosky Family Foundation, Inc.; Reebok International Ltd.; The Cohen Family Foundation, Inc.; Adidas; Nike, Inc.; PUMA; GE; Sam and Janet Sato.
Foundation type: Company-sponsored foundation.
Financial data (yr. ended 12/31/13): Assets, $8,274,847 (M); gifts received, $2,620,840; expenditures, $2,784,024; qualifying distributions, $2,685,762; giving activities include $2,242,830 for 93 grants (high: $1,500,000; low: $1,000).
Purpose and activities: The foundation supports organizations involved with athletics and youth development. Special emphasis is directed toward programs designed to promote active lifestyles and team building skills; and camps designed to promote sports and active lifestyles, and serve disadvantaged and special needs kids.
Fields of interest: Arts; Education; Health care; Recreation, camps; Athletics/sports, amateur leagues; Youth development; Human services; Youth; Disabilities, people with; Economically disadvantaged.
Type of support: Capital campaigns; Building/renovation; Equipment; Emergency funds; Program development; Scholarship funds.
Limitations: Applications accepted. Giving on a national basis in areas of company operations. No support for discriminatory organizations, religious organizations not of direct benefit to the entire community, fraternal, veterans', or labor organizations, or foundations affiliated with a for-profit entity. No grants to individuals, or for political campaigns, endowments, general operating support, start-up needs, debt reduction, beauty or talent contests, team sponsorships, special events, or fundraising activities, medical, scientific, or academic research, or travel.
Publications: Application guidelines.
Application information: Application form required.
Initial approach: See website for application form
Deadline(s): Quarterly basis
Board meeting date(s): Jan., Apr., July, and Oct.,
Officers: Chad Edmundson, Pres.; Ed Wilhelm, V.P.; Mark Clark, Secy.; Linda Disher, Treas.; Marty Posch, Exec. Dir.
Directors: Greg Beidler; Greg Davis; Danny Dean; Melissa Greenwell; Mike Grimes; Jason Kish; Terry Ledbetter; Cindie Norris; Mike Northrop; Danielle Quatrochi; Curt Simic.
EIN: 352059749

3304
Foellinger Foundation, Inc. ✧
520 E. Berry St.
Fort Wayne, IN 46802-2002 (260) 422-2900
Contact: Cheryl K. Taylor, C.E.O. and Pres.; Terry Stevens, Exec. and Prog. Specialist
FAX: (260) 422-9436; E-mail: info@foellinger.org; E-mail for Cheryl K. Taylor: cheryl@foellinger.org. E-mail for Terry Stevens: terry@foellinger.org; Main URL: http://www.foellinger.org

Incorporated in 1958 in IN.
Donors: Esther A. Foellinger†; Helene R. Foellinger†.
Foundation type: Independent foundation.
Financial data (yr. ended 08/31/13): Assets, $172,748,697 (M); expenditures, $9,294,455; qualifying distributions, $7,920,656; giving activities include $6,939,909 for 126 grants (high: $893,000; low: $3,000), and $139,846 for 4 foundation-administered programs.

Purpose and activities: Giving in Allen County, IN, for early childhood development, youth development and family development, especially the most in need with the least opportunity, and organizational effectiveness.
Fields of interest: Children/youth, services; Family services; Children/youth; Youth; Economically disadvantaged.
Type of support: General/operating support; Continuing support; Management development/ capacity building; Program development; Research; Technical assistance; Consulting services; Program evaluation.
Limitations: Applications accepted. Giving in Allen County, IN, area. Generally, no grants for religious groups for religious purposes, elementary or secondary schools independent of their school systems, or purposes taxpayers are expected to support. No grants to individuals, or for endowments, deficit financing, sponsorships, camperships, special events, conferences, commercial advertising, capital projects, annual campaigns or appeals, or for capital projects.
Publications: Application guidelines; Annual report; Grants list; Occasional report.
Application information: See foundation's web site for downloadable grant guideline packet. Not currently accepting applications for capital support. Only 1 application for operation or program support per organization per year. Application form required.
Initial approach: Grant application
Copies of proposal: 1
Deadline(s): No deadline for grants for Inspire, Renew or Transform grant applications. First Mon. in Feb. for Community Interests; First Mon. in Aug. for Early Childhood Development and Family Development; First Mon. in Nov. for Youth Development; and as invited for all other foundation-invited initiatives
Board meeting date(s): Quarterly in Feb., May, Aug., and Nov.
Final notification: One week after board meeting
Officers and Directors:* David A. Bobilya,* Chair.; Robert N. Taylor,* Vice-Chair. and Secy.; Cheryl K. Taylor,* C.E.O. and Pres.; Helen J. Murray, Treas.; Darryl R. Olson, C.F.O.; Hon. Thomas J. Felts; Carolyn R. Hughes; Richard B. Pierce; Todd C. Rumsey, M.D.; Sarah Strimmenos, CPA.
Number of staff: 3 full-time professional; 3 full-time support.
EIN: 356027059
Selected grants: The following grants are a representative sample of this grantmaker's funding activity:
$893,000 to Taylor University, Upland, IN, 2013. For program support.
$290,000 to Allen County Public Library Foundation, Fort Wayne, IN, 2013. For program support.
$190,000 to Catholic Charities Fort Wayne-South Bend Diocese, Fort Wayne, IN, 2013. For operating support.
$185,000 to Big Brothers Big Sisters of Northeast Indiana, Fort Wayne, IN, 2013. For operating support.
$100,000 to Allen County Public Library Foundation, Fort Wayne, IN, 2013. For program support.
$66,500 to Fort Wayne Museum of Art, Fort Wayne, IN, 2013. For operating support.
$45,000 to Community Transportation Network, Fort Wayne, IN, 2013. For operating support.
$32,500 to Power House Youth Center, New Haven, IN, 2013. For operating support.
$15,000 to Public Broadcasting of Northeast Indiana, Fort Wayne, IN, 2013. For operating support.

3305
Ford Meter Box Foundation, Inc. ✧ ☆
775 Manchester Ave.
P.O. Box 443
Wabash, IN 46992-0443 (260) 563-3171
Contact: Marta D. Gidley, Secy.

Established in 1988 in IN.
Donor: The Ford Meter Box Co., Inc.
Foundation type: Company-sponsored foundation.
Financial data (yr. ended 12/31/13): Assets, $864,790 (M); expenditures, $737,490; qualifying distributions, $737,430; giving activities include $737,430 for 37 grants (high: $500,000; low: $150).
Purpose and activities: The foundation supports organizations involved with arts and culture, education, health, youth development, children and youth, family services, residential care, and community development.
Fields of interest: Education; Health care; Human services.
Type of support: General/operating support; Annual campaigns; Capital campaigns; Building/ renovation; Endowments.
Limitations: Applications accepted. Giving primarily in Wabash County, IN.
Publications: Application guidelines.
Application information: Application form required.
Initial approach: Letter
Copies of proposal: 1
Deadline(s): None
Officers: Daniel H. Ford, Chair.; Thomas G. Vanosdol, Vice-Chair.; Marta D. Gidley, Secy.; Mark S. Ford, Treas.
EIN: 351253080
Selected grants: The following grants are a representative sample of this grantmaker's funding activity:
$10,000 to Living Well In Wabash County CoA, Wabash, IN, 2012. For and 2013 Annual Fund.
$10,000 to Water for People, Denver, CO, 2012. For new office headquarters.
$2,000 to North Manchester Historical Society, North Manchester, IN, 2012. For facility upgrades.
$2,000 to Wabash Friends Church, Wabash, IN, 2012. For Day of Healing Conference.
$1,100 to Wabash Valley Music Association, Wabash, IN, 2012. For program ad.
$1,000 to Wabash Area Community Theater, Wabash, IN, 2012. For Annie.
$1,000 to Wabash Valley Dance Theater, Wabash, IN, 2012. For Annual Ballet Christmas Festival.
$500 to Indianapolis Symphony Orchestra, Indianapolis, IN, 2012. For Young People's Discovery Concerts.
$250 to Family Service Society, Marion, IN, 2012. For Wabash County Hands of Hope.
$150 to Wabash County Hospital Foundation, Wabash, IN, 2012. For Golf Scramble.

3306
The Foundations of East Chicago, Inc. ✧
100 West Chicago Ave.
East Chicago, IN 46312-3260 (219) 392-4225
Contact: Russel G. Taylor, Exec. Dir.
FAX: (219) 392-4245; Contact for RFPs: Rosie Pena, rpena@foundationsec.org; Main URL: http://www.foundationsec.org
Collaboration Grants Recipients: http://foundationsofeastchicago.net/strategic-plan-at-work/spring-2013-collaborations-grants-awarded
E-Newsletter: http://foundationsofeastchicago.net/subpage.php?subpid=27
Facebook: https://www.facebook.com/foundationsec
Foundations of East Chicago Blog: http://foundationsofeastchicago.net/blog/
Grants List: http://foundationsofeastchicago.org/track-record/2012-programs-funded
Scholarship Recipients: http://foundationsofeastchicago.org/education/meet-current-scholars
Twitter: https://twitter.com/foundationsec
YouTube: https://www.youtube.com/channel/UCWhpTO8i2He4P87f_LPcvwg

Donor: Ameristar East Chicago.
Foundation type: Company-sponsored foundation.
Financial data (yr. ended 12/31/12): Assets, $28,251,619 (M); gifts received, $3,832,474; expenditures, $7,338,295; qualifying distributions, $6,162,068; giving activities include $5,490,441 for 195 grants (high: $2,000,000; low: $360).
Purpose and activities: The foundation supports programs designed to promote education; public safety; youth development; family support; health; financial independence and community economic development; and awards college scholarships.
Fields of interest: Arts; Elementary/secondary education; Vocational education; Education, drop-out prevention; Education, reading; Education; Public health; Health care; Crime/violence prevention; Employment, services; Employment, training; Food services; Food banks; Safety/disasters; Youth development; Children/youth, services; Family services; Human services, financial counseling; Human services; Community development, neighborhood development; Community/economic development.
Type of support: General/operating support; Management development/capacity building; Capital campaigns; Building/renovation; Scholarship funds; Scholarships—to individuals.
Limitations: Applications accepted. Giving limited to East Chicago, IN.
Publications: Application guidelines; Financial statement; Grants list; Newsletter (including application guidelines); Program policy statement.
Application information: Additional information may be requested at a later date. An interview may be requested for scholarships. Organizations receiving support are asked to submit an interim report and a final report.
Initial approach: Complete online application form; visit website for scholarship information; e-mail proposals for RFPs
Copies of proposal: 1
Deadline(s): Oct. for General Support Grants; Sept. for Collaboration Grants; Varies for scholarships and RFPs
Final notification: Mid-Nov. for General Support and Collaboration Grants
Officers and Directors:* Nadyne Kokot,* Pres.; Peter Smith, Secy.; Mario Palacios, Treas.; Russel G. Taylor, Exec. Dir.; Cedric Gamble; Sylvia Morrisroe; Joseph Verduzco.
EIN: 208445003

Selected grants: The following grants are a representative sample of this grantmaker's funding activity:
$150,000 to Saint Josephs Carmelite Home, East Chicago, IN, 2011.
$13,500 to International Community Alliance, East Chicago, IN, 2011.
$10,000 to East Chicago Education Foundation, East Chicago, IN, 2011.

3307
The Froderman Foundation, Inc. ✧
4325 U.S. Highway 41
P.O. Box 10039
Terre Haute, IN 47802-4406
Contact: Mark Fuson, Pres.
FAX: (812) 232-8414;
E-mail: markfuson@drivefuson.com; Main URL: http://www.frodermanfoundation.com

Established in 1962 in IN.
Donors: Harvey Froderman†; Mrs. Harvey Froderman.
Foundation type: Independent foundation.
Financial data (yr. ended 06/30/13): Assets, $10,989,878 (M); expenditures, $561,847; qualifying distributions, $463,373; giving activities include $463,373 for 20 grants (high: $90,000; low: $925).
Purpose and activities: The foundation's mission is to provide funds to qualified applicants whose emphasis is to promote religious, educational, medical, and/or charitable causes.
Fields of interest: Higher education; Health organizations, association; Human services; Christian agencies & churches.
Type of support: Building/renovation; Equipment; Publication; Scholarship funds.
Limitations: Applications accepted. Giving primarily in Indianapolis and Terre Haute, IN. No grants to individuals, or for operating budgets.
Application information: Application form required.
Initial approach: Request application
Copies of proposal: 1
Deadline(s): None
Board meeting date(s): Apr., June, Sept., and Dec.
Officers: Mark Fuson, Pres.; Carl Froderman, V.P.; Chris Froderman, Secy.; Brad Fuson, Treas.
EIN: 356025283
Selected grants: The following grants are a representative sample of this grantmaker's funding activity:
$200,000 to Union Hospital Foundation, Terre Haute, IN, 2011.
$75,000 to Saint Vincent Hospital Foundation, Indianapolis, IN, 2011.
$50,500 to Crossroads Rehabilitation Center, Indianapolis, IN, 2011.
$50,000 to Bosma Industries for the Blind, Indianapolis, IN, 2011.
$21,000 to Rehabilitation Hospital of Indiana, Indianapolis, IN, 2011.
$20,000 to Oaks Academy, Indianapolis, IN, 2011.
$15,000 to Vigo County School Corporation, Terre Haute, IN, 2011.
$14,600 to Dayspring Center, Indianapolis, IN, 2011.
$8,000 to Indiana State University Foundation, Terre Haute, IN, 2011.

3308
Gagan Family Foundation, Inc. ✧
(formerly Friendship Foundation, Inc.)
P.O. Box 14189
Merrillville, IN 46411-4189
Contact: Sarah P. Cavan, Exec. V.P.

Established in 1985 in IN.
Donors: James L. Gagan; United Consumers Club, Inc.
Foundation type: Independent foundation.
Financial data (yr. ended 07/31/13): Assets, $4,553,662 (M); expenditures, $887,359; qualifying distributions, $869,725; giving activities include $869,725 for grants.
Purpose and activities: Giving primarily for education, health, and human services.
Fields of interest: Higher education; Health care; Health organizations, association; Human services; Salvation Army.
Limitations: Applications accepted. Giving primarily in CA and IN. No support for pass-through agencies. No grants to individuals.
Application information:
Initial approach: Letter
Deadline(s): None
Officers: James L. Gagan, Chair.; Claire Gagan, Pres.; Sarah P. Cavan, Exec. V.P.; Pamela M. Gagan, Secy.; Eugene H. Deutsch, Treas.
EIN: 311150302
Selected grants: The following grants are a representative sample of this grantmaker's funding activity:
$100,000 to Scripps Health Foundation, San Diego, CA, 2011.
$50,000 to Bighorn Behind A Miracle, Palm Desert, CA, 2011.
$50,000 to Friends of the Cultural Center, Palm Desert, CA, 2011.
$50,000 to Opportunity Enterprises, Valparaiso, IN, 2011.
$25,000 to Eisenhower Medical Center, Rancho Mirage, CA, 2011.
$25,000 to Link Unlimited, Chicago, IL, 2011.
$10,000 to Food for the Poor, Coconut Creek, FL, 2011.
$10,000 to Smile Train, New York, NY, 2011.
$10,000 to University of San Diego, San Diego, CA, 2011.
$6,000 to Catholic Charities of the Archdiocese of Chicago, Chicago, IL, 2011.

3309
The Garatoni Family Foundation ✧
4100 Edison Lakes Pkwy., Ste. 260
Mishawaka, IN 46545-3470

Foundation type: Independent foundation.
Financial data (yr. ended 12/31/12): Assets, $23,141,243 (M); expenditures, $997,158; qualifying distributions, $614,767; giving activities include $614,767 for 33 grants (high: $295,000; low: $25).
Fields of interest: Education; Human services; Catholic agencies & churches.
Limitations: Applications not accepted. Giving primarily in IN.
Application information: Contributes only to pre-selected organizations.
Trustees: Judith A. Garatoni; Lawrence A. Garatoni.
EIN: 262866592

3310
Eugene and Marilyn Glick Foundation Corporation ✧
P.O. Box 40177
Indianapolis, IN 46240-0177 (317) 469-5877
Contact: David O. Barrett, C.E.O. and Pres.

Established in 1982 in IN.
Donors: Eugene B. Glick†; Marilyn K. Glick†.
Foundation type: Independent foundation.
Financial data (yr. ended 11/30/13): Assets, $167,733,905 (M); gifts received, $2,543,167; expenditures, $2,994,089; qualifying distributions, $1,571,407; giving activities include $1,518,661 for 134 grants (high: $347,000; low: $750).
Fields of interest: Arts; Higher education; Education; Eye research; Human services; Children/youth, services; Foundations (community).
Type of support: General/operating support; Capital campaigns; Program development; Matching/challenge support.
Limitations: Applications accepted. Giving primarily in Indianapolis, IN. No grants to individuals.
Application information:
Initial approach: Letter
Deadline(s): None
Officers and Directors:* David O. Barrett,* Vice-Chair., C.E.O. and Pres.; Marianne Glick,* Vice-Chair.; James T. Bisesi,* Secy.; Anita S. Smith,* C.F.O. and Treas.; Sharon Kibbe, Exec. Dir.; Thomas J. Grande,* C.I.O.; Jacqueline Barrett; Arlene Grande; Alice Meshbane; Lynda Schwartz.
Number of staff: 1 full-time professional.
EIN: 351549707
Selected grants: The following grants are a representative sample of this grantmaker's funding activity:
$347,000 to Childrens Bureau of Indianapolis, Indianapolis, IN, 2013.
$148,461 to Indianapolis Art Center, Indianapolis, IN, 2013. For outreach programs.
$115,000 to Childrens Bureau of Indianapolis, PRO-100, Indianapolis, IN, 2013. For program support.
$100,000 to Marian University, Indianapolis, IN, 2013. For ECO Lab.
$100,000 to United Way of Central Indiana, Indianapolis, IN, 2013. For program support.
$89,710 to Central Indiana Community Foundation, Indianapolis, IN, 2013. For Indianapolis Cultural Trail.
$50,000 to Indiana University Foundation, Bloomington, IN, 2013. For Varsity Club.
$30,000 to Butler University, Indianapolis, IN, 2013. For fundraiser.
$25,000 to Providence Cristo Rey High School, Indianapolis, IN, 2013.
$10,000 to Lords Place, West Palm Beach, FL, 2013.

3311
Pierre F. and Enid Goodrich Foundation ✧
(formerly Thirty Five Twenty, Inc.)
8335 Allison Pointe Trail, Ste. 300
Indianapolis, IN 46250-1687 (317) 842-0880
Contact: Emilio J. Pacheco, Pres.

Incorporated in 1965 in IN.
Donors: Enid Goodrich†; Pierre F. Goodrich†.
Foundation type: Independent foundation.
Financial data (yr. ended 04/30/13): Assets, $20,788,374 (M); expenditures, $1,056,894;

qualifying distributions, $805,000; giving activities include $805,000 for grants.
Purpose and activities: The foundation makes grants for general support and special projects that support further educational activities that are concerned with human liberty and individual freedom within a free society.
Fields of interest: Humanities; Education; Economics; Political science.
Type of support: General/operating support; Program development; Conferences/seminars; Research.
Limitations: Applications accepted. Giving on a national basis. No support for government agencies, or schools and universities, hospitals or medical research facilities. No grants to individuals, or for annual campaigns, emergency funds, deficit financing, capital or endowment funds, scholarships, fellowships, matching gifts, or demonstration projects; no loans.
Application information: Application form required.
Initial approach: Letter
Copies of proposal: 1
Deadline(s): None
Board meeting date(s): Apr. and Oct.
Final notification: Within 1 month, if denied
Officers and Directors:* T. Alan Russell,* Chair.; Emilio J. Pacheco,* Pres.; Sandra J. Schaller, Secy. and Cont.; Chris L. Talley,* Treas.; Ruth E. Connolly; Richard W. Duesenberg; Helen W. Garlotte.
Number of staff: 5 part-time professional; 2 part-time support.
EIN: 356056960
Selected grants: The following grants are a representative sample of this grantmaker's funding activity:
$10,000 to Brown University, Providence, RI, 2013. For Political Theory Project.

3312
Cecil A. and Mabel Lene Hamman Foundation, Inc. ✧
2709 Washington Ave., Ste. 18
Evansville, IN 47714-2450

Established in IN.
Donor: Mabel Lene Hamman.
Foundation type: Independent foundation.
Financial data (yr. ended 12/31/13): Assets, $17,801,225 (M); gifts received, $1,500; expenditures, $834,999; qualifying distributions, $834,999; giving activities include $706,100 for 54 grants (high: $55,000; low: $1,000).
Fields of interest: Human services.
Type of support: General/operating support; Capital campaigns.
Limitations: Applications not accepted. Giving primarily in IN.
Application information: Unsolicited requests for funds not accepted.
Officers: Wilfred C. Bussing III, Pres.; Steven G. Kuester, V.P.; Mary Ann Wise, Secy.-Treas.
EIN: 262724931

3313
Hancock County Community Foundation, Inc. ✧ ☆
312 E. Main St.
Greenfield, IN 46140-2348 (317) 462-8870
Contact: Mary Gibble, Pres.; For grants: Kara Harrison, Community Investment and Grants Off.
FAX: (317) 467-3330;
E-mail: info@givehcgrowhc.org; Grant inquiry e-mail: kharrison@giveHCgrowHC.org; Main URL: http://givehcgrowhc.org/
Facebook: https://www.facebook.com/HancockCountyCommunityFoundation
RSS Feed: http://www.givehcgrowhc.org/feed
Twitter: https://twitter.com/HancockCountyCF
YouTube: http://www.youtube.com/user/HCCFGreenfield

Established in 1992 in IN.
Foundation type: Community foundation.
Financial data (yr. ended 12/31/13): Assets, $25,204,807 (M); gifts received, $1,041,392; expenditures, $1,322,267; giving activities include $364,126 for 21+ grants (high: $19,949), and $166,119 for 134 grants to individuals.
Purpose and activities: The foundation provides philanthropic leadership to effectively manage and direct the resources of community donors in ways which enrich and enhance the quality of life in Hancock County, IN.
Fields of interest: Arts; Education; Health care; Human services; Community/economic development; Youth.
Type of support: Program development; Equipment; Conferences/seminars; Seed money; Curriculum development; Scholarship funds; Technical assistance; Consulting services; Matching/challenge support.
Limitations: Applications accepted. Giving limited to Hancock County, IN. No support for sectarian religious purposes. No grants to individuals (except for scholarships), or for endowments, deficit financing, or fundraising.
Publications: Application guidelines; Annual report; Informational brochure; Newsletter.
Application information: Visit foundation web site for application guidelines per grant type. Application form required.
Initial approach: Attend Grant Workshop
Deadline(s): Sept. 11 for Fall Grants; Feb. 28 for Scholarships
Board meeting date(s): 3rd Thurs. of each month
Officers and Directors:* Tom Seng,* Chair.; Teri Dunlavy,* Vice-Chair.; Mary Gibble,* Pres.; Fred Powers,* Secy.; P. Jon Miller,* Treas.; Wayne Beck; Bob Bogigian; Barbara Campbell; Tim Clark; Josh Daugherty; David Dellacca; Lorraine Ewing; Jim Greig; Debi Hill; Leah Janes; Chris McQueeney; Florence May; Sandy Miller; Linda Muegge; Susan Nichter; Adam Schultz; Bill Weldon; Stephenie White-Longworth.
Number of staff: 4 full-time professional.
EIN: 351837729

3314
Harrison County Community Foundation, Inc. ✧
1523 Foundation Way
Corydon, IN 47112-2272 (812) 738-6668
Contact: Steven A. Gilliland, C.E.O.; For grants: Anna Curts, Grants Mgr.
FAX: (812) 738-6864;
E-mail: steveg@hccfindiana.org; Additional e-mail: staff@hccfindiana.org; Grant inquiry e-mail: annac@hccfindiana.org; Mailing address: P. O. Box 279 Corydon, IN 47112-0279; Main URL: http://www.hccfindiana.org
E-Newsletter: http://www.hccfindiana.org/category/httpwww-icontact-archive-comcmi0k5-gqgmskpcbq5hwlgjr-dvfqxmj03i6m_6sjlywrk8bp-d0ojwww3/
Facebook: http://www.facebook.com/pages/Harrison-County-Community-Foundation/155052747849474
RSS Feed: http://www.hccfindiana.org/feed/
Scholarship inquiry e-mail: heathers@hccfindiana.org

Established in 1996 in IN.
Foundation type: Community foundation.
Financial data (yr. ended 12/31/13): Assets, $146,536,171 (M); gifts received, $11,189,787; expenditures, $5,298,850; giving activities include $4,660,063 for grants.
Purpose and activities: The foundation was established for the receipt of donations and distribution of income from permanent endowments for the philanthropic purposes of Harrison County, IN. Giving primarily for arts and culture, human services, recreation, government, health and safety, historical preservation, community projects, education and environment.
Fields of interest: Historic preservation/historical societies; Arts; Secondary school/education; Higher education; Adult education—literacy, basic skills & GED; Scholarships/financial aid; Education; Environment; Health care; Recreation; Youth development; Human services; Community/economic development; Government/public administration; Aging.
Type of support: General/operating support; Continuing support; Management development/capacity building; Capital campaigns; Building/renovation; Equipment; Land acquisition; Emergency funds; Program development; Conferences/seminars; Publication; Seed money; Curriculum development; Research; Consulting services; Program evaluation; Employee-related scholarships; Scholarships—to individuals; Matching/challenge support.
Limitations: Applications accepted. Giving limited to Harrison County, IN. No support for religious organizations for the purpose of furthering their religion. No grants to individuals (except for scholarships), or for reimbursement for previously purchased items or previously incurred expenses, or to purchase souvenirs or other personal items or real estate that has not been identified and appraised.
Publications: Application guidelines; Annual report; Financial statement; Grants list; Informational brochure; Multi-year report; Newsletter; Program policy statement (including application guidelines).
Application information: Visit foundation web site for application forms and guidelines. All applicants are strongly encouraged to attend formal training sessions as announced, typically in May and Nov. Application form required.
Initial approach: Submit online application
Deadline(s): Jan. 15 and July 15
Board meeting date(s): Monthly, first Mon.
Final notification: Mar. 15 and Sept. 15
Officers and Directors:* Heather Clunie,* Chair.; Chad Coffman,* Vice-Chair.; Steve A. Gilliland, C.E.O. and Pres.; Cheryl Fisher,* Secy.-Treas.; Paul Beckort; Kevin Burch; Steven Day; Scott Estes; Cheryl Fisher; Jim Isbell; Phyllis J. Krush; Barbara Middleton; Shirley Raymond; joe Shireman; Brett Stilwell; Sharon Uhl; Glenn Walker.
Number of staff: 5 full-time professional; 1 full-time support.
EIN: 351986569

Selected grants: The following grants are a representative sample of this grantmaker's funding activity:
$252,101 to Lanesville Youth Baseball and Softball League, Lanesville, IN, 2011. For construction of two new diamonds and one Pee Wee field.
$73,457 to Harrison County Parks and Recreation, Corydon, IN, 2011. To build a log cabin at the Battle of Corydon Park.
$32,306 to Blue River Services, Corydon, IN, 2011. To construct a basketball court at the Wyandotte House Youth shelter, and matching funds.
$20,523 to Morgan Elementary School, Palmyra, IN, 2011. To purchase Leveled Readers books and quizzes.
$5,000 to Indiana University Southeast, New Albany, IN, 2011. For family and children's programming at the IUS Ogle Center.

3315
Hart N. and Simona Hasten Family Foundation, Inc. ✧

3901 W. 86th St., Ste. 470
Indianapolis, IN 46268-3700 (317) 872-9901
Contact: Hart N. Hasten, Dir.

Established in 1996 in IN.
Donors: Hart N. Hasten; Anna Ruth Hasten; Simona Hasten.
Foundation type: Independent foundation.
Financial data (yr. ended 12/31/12): Assets, $13,663,295 (M); expenditures, $905,327; qualifying distributions, $674,639; giving activities include $674,639 for grants.
Purpose and activities: Giving primarily to Jewish agencies.
Fields of interest: Higher education; Education; Jewish agencies & synagogues.
Limitations: Giving primarily in IN, NY and Israel.
Application information: Application form not required.
Initial approach: Letter
Deadline(s): None
Officers and Directors:* Renee Hasten Halevy,* Pres.; Joshua Hasten,* V.P.; Bernard Hasten,* Secy.-Treas.; Hart N. Hasten; Simona Hasten.
EIN: 351998919

3316
Mark and Anna Ruth Hasten Family Foundation, Inc. ✧

3901 W. 86th St., Ste. 470
Indianapolis, IN 46268-3700 (317) 872-9901
Contact: Mark Hasten, Dir.

Established in 1996 in IN.
Donors: Mark Hasten; Anna Ruth Hasten; Edward Hasten; Michael Hasten.
Foundation type: Independent foundation.
Financial data (yr. ended 12/31/12): Assets, $5,885,450 (M); gifts received, $110,000; expenditures, $907,389; qualifying distributions, $801,358; giving activities include $801,358 for 175 grants (high: $75,000; low: $25).
Fields of interest: Education; Jewish federated giving programs; Jewish agencies & synagogues.
International interests: Israel.
Limitations: Applications accepted. Giving primarily in Indianapolis, IN, New York, NY, and Israel.
Application information: Application form not required.
Initial approach: Proposal
Deadline(s): None
Officers and Directors:* Edward Hasten,* Pres.; Judith Hasten,* V.P.; Michael Hasten,* V.P.; Monica Hasten Rosenfeld,* Secy.; Anna Ruth Hasten; Mark Hasten.
EIN: 351998923

3317
The Health Foundation of Greater Indianapolis, Inc. ✧

429 E. Vermont St., Ste. 400
Indianapolis, IN 46202-3732 (317) 630-1805
Contact: Betty H. Wilson, C.E.O. and Pres.
FAX: (317) 630-1806; E-mail: betty@thfgi.org; Additional e-mail: info@thfgi.org; Main URL: http://www.thfgi.org

Established as a private foundation in 1985 in IN; converted from an HMO, Metro Health.
Donors: Deborah Simon; James Spain; Wm. Kingston; David Suess; Betty H. Wilson; Mary D. Richardson; Steven Reeves; AIDSERVE Indiana; Anthem, Inc.; Broadway Cares; Cooke Investment Group; Community Hospitals of Indiana; Indiana Thrift for AIDS; Endagered Species Chocolate; The National Bank of Indianapolis; National City Bank; Efromyson Fund; Central Indiana Community Foundation; Christel DeHaan Family Foundation; Joseph F. Miller Foundation; Indiana State Dept. of Health; Marion County Health Department; Indy Pride; St. Francis Hospital; The Indianapolis Foundation; Wishard Hospital; Health and Hospital Corp.; Samerian Foundation; Baker and Daniels, LLP; Bose McKinney, Attorneys; Bingham McHale, LLP; Back Home Again Foundation; Financial Partners.
Foundation type: Independent foundation.
Financial data (yr. ended 12/31/13): Assets, $21,718,157 (M); gifts received, $608,886; expenditures, $3,052,373; qualifying distributions, $2,625,331; giving activities include $1,893,935 for 43 grants (high: $365,000; low: $500).
Purpose and activities: Primary areas of focus are adolescent health, including childhood obesity and school-based health clinics, and HIV/AIDS education and services. Grants will be made to neighborhood-based service centers such as neighborhood health centers, multi-service centers, churches, and other nonprofit agencies and organizations.
Fields of interest: Health care; AIDS; Nutrition; Human services; Children/youth, services; Minorities; African Americans/Blacks; Hispanics/Latinos; Women; AIDS, people with; Economically disadvantaged.
Type of support: Program evaluation; Management development/capacity building; Consulting services; General/operating support; Continuing support; Equipment; Program development; Conferences/seminars; Seed money; Technical assistance.
Limitations: Applications not accepted. Giving limited to Marion County, IN and the seven contiguous counties. No support for sectarian or religious purposes. No grants to individuals, or for advertising, event tickets, research, payment of financial deficit, production and design of educational materials that are currently available for purchase, endowments, or short- or long- term loans.
Publications: Grants list; Informational brochure; Occasional report.
Application information: Unsolicited requests for funds not accepted.
Board meeting date(s): 2nd Wed. of Jan., Mar., May, July, Sept. and Nov.
Officers and Directors:* David Suess,* Chair.; Anne Belcher,* Vice-Chair.; Betty H. Wilson, C.E.O. and Pres.; Teresa Craig, C.P.A.*, Secy.; David Kelleher,* Treas.; Michael Carter; John Hall; Kenneth Hull; Monica Medina; Robert D. Robinson, M.D.; James Trulock.
Number of staff: 3 full-time professional; 2 full-time support.
EIN: 356203550
Selected grants: The following grants are a representative sample of this grantmaker's funding activity:
$5,000 to Washington Township Schools Foundation, Indianapolis, IN, 2012. To promote wellness.

3318
Helping Fund ✧

P.O. Box 334
Zionsville, IN 46077-0334 (317) 873-2311
Contact: Rollin M. Dick, Tr.

Established in 1992 in IN.
Donors: Rollin M. Dick; Helen E. Dick‡; Cheryl J. Dick.
Foundation type: Independent foundation.
Financial data (yr. ended 12/31/13): Assets, $3,912,973 (M); expenditures, $494,497; qualifying distributions, $450,829; giving activities include $450,829 for 29 grants (high: $101,000; low: $351).
Purpose and activities: Giving only to public charities, educational institutions or governmental agencies.
Fields of interest: Arts; Higher education; Health organizations; Human services.
Limitations: Applications accepted. Giving primarily in Indianapolis, IN. No grants to individuals or private foundations.
Application information: Application form required.
Initial approach: Letter
Deadline(s): None
Trustees: Cheryl J. Dick; Rollin M. Dick.
EIN: 351872573
Selected grants: The following grants are a representative sample of this grantmaker's funding activity:
$213,370 to Center for the Performing Arts, Carmel, IN, 2012. For contribution to arts, civic or cultural organizations for the purpose of furthering their arts and cultural missions.
$5,000 to American Institute of Business, Des Moines, IA, 2012. For Contributions to educational institutions for the purpose of furthering their educational and building Programs.

3319
Hendricks County Community Foundation ✧

(formerly The White Lick Heritage Community Foundation, Inc.)
6319 E. U.S. Hwy. 36, Ste. 211
Avon, IN 46123 (317) 268-6240
Contact: William A. Rhodehamel, Exec. Dir.
FAX: (317) 268-6164;
E-mail: info@hendrickscountycf.org; Additional

e-mail: william@hendrickscountycf.org; Main URL: http://www.hendrickscountycf.org/
Alternate URL: http://www.HCGives.orgs
E-Newsletter: http://www.hendrickscountycf.org/signup/
Facebook: http://facebook.com/pages/Hendricks-County-Community-Foundation/103732686862
Scholarship inquiry e-mail: eric@hendrickscountycf.org

Established in 1996 in IN.
Foundation type: Community foundation.
Financial data (yr. ended 12/31/13): Assets, $9,708,075 (M); gifts received, $1,406,449; expenditures, $1,428,857; giving activities include $758,402 for 13+ grants (high: $49,686), and $181,257 for 305 grants to individuals.
Purpose and activities: The foundation is a vehicle for people of all means to make a difference in the Hendricks County, IN, community. The foundation seeks to: 1) professionally manage and distribute revenues from charitable contributions and bequests in a manner consistent with the donor's specific or general interests; 2) maintain and enhance the educational, social, cultural, health and civic resources of the community through support of appropriate community organizations; and 3) provide philanthropic leadership and promote efforts to improve the quality of life in the community.
Fields of interest: Arts; Education; Environment; Health care; Youth development; Human services; Community/economic development.
Type of support: Continuing support; Building/renovation; Equipment; Land acquisition; Emergency funds; Program development; Seed money; Curriculum development; Research; Grants to individuals; Scholarships—to individuals; Matching/challenge support.
Limitations: Applications accepted. Giving limited to Hendricks County, IN. No support for projects aimed at promoting a particular religion or construction projects for religious institutions. No grants to individuals (except for scholarships), bands, sports teams or other groups without a philanthropic project, annual appeals, galas, or membership contributions, fundraising events, post-event, after-the-fact situations or debt retirement, or medical, scientific or academic research.
Publications: Annual report; Financial statement; Informational brochure; Newsletter.
Application information: Visit foundation web site for application guidelines. Application form not required.
Initial approach: E-mail grant application
Copies of proposal: 1
Deadline(s): Mar. 4 for Opportunity Fund grants
Board meeting date(s): Monthly
Officers and Board Members:* Judy Wyeth,* Pres.; Rhonda Wiles,* V.P.; Jim Hall,* Secy.; Carrie Hanni,* Treas.; William A. Rhodehamel, Exec. Dir.; David Durell; Steve Eichenberger; Janie Hardin; Matt Howrey; Terri McCoy; Alice McColgin; Larry Paynter; Teresa Ray; Melaney Sargent; Marland Villanueva; Dan Whipple; Dan Young.
Number of staff: 1 part-time professional; 2 part-time support.
EIN: 351878973

3320
Henry County Community Foundation, Inc. ✧
700 S. Memorial Dr.
P.O. Box 6006
New Castle, IN 47362-6006 (765) 529-2235
Contact: Beverly Matthews, Pres.
FAX: (765) 529-2284;
E-mail: info@henrycountycf.org; Additional e-mail: beverly@henrycountycf.org; Main URL: http://www.henrycountycf.org
E-Newsletter: http://www.henrycountycf.org/index.php?src=forms&ref=enews
Facebook: http://www.facebook.com/pages/Henry-Community-Foundation/32495688002

Established in 1985 in IN.
Foundation type: Community foundation.
Financial data (yr. ended 12/31/13): Assets, $33,863,393 (M); gifts received, $746,945; expenditures, $1,733,597; giving activities include $555,608 for 20+ grants (high: $27,118), and $277,999 for 225 grants to individuals.
Purpose and activities: The mission of the foundation is to help where the needs are greatest, and the benefits to the community and its citizens are most substantial. The foundation seeks to provide public-spirited donors a vehicle for using their gifts in the best possible way now and in the future, and to provide stewardship for those gifts.
Fields of interest: Arts; Education; Health care; Mental health/crisis services; Recreation; Children/youth, services; Developmentally disabled, centers & services; Human services; Community/economic development; Government/public administration; Infants/toddlers; Children/youth; Disabilities, people with; Physically disabled; Women; Men; Economically disadvantaged; Homeless.
Type of support: Technical assistance; Continuing support; Capital campaigns; Building/renovation; Equipment; Endowments; Emergency funds; Program development; Conferences/seminars; Publication; Seed money; Scholarship funds; Research; Consulting services; Exchange programs; Matching/challenge support.
Limitations: Applications accepted. Giving limited to Henry County, IN. No support for sectarian religious purposes. No grants to individuals (except for scholarships), or for endowments or operating costs including salaries.
Publications: Application guidelines; Annual report; Financial statement; Grants list; Informational brochure (including application guidelines); Newsletter.
Application information: Visit foundation web site for grant application workshop dates, application forms and additional guidelines. Application form not required.
Initial approach: Attend Spring or Fall Grant Workshop
Copies of proposal: 15
Deadline(s): Feb. 28 and Aug. 29
Board meeting date(s): Monthly
Final notification: Within 30 days
Officers and Directors:* Susan Falck Neal,* Chair.; Dick Armstrong,* 1st Vice-Chair.; Duke Hamm,* 2nd Vice-Chair.; Beverly Matthews, Pres. and Exec. Dir.; Debi Ware,* Treas.; Herb Bunch, Dir., Emeritus; Danny Danielson, Dir., Emeritus; Patty Danielson, Dir., Emeritus; Morris Edwards, Dir., Emeritus; Judy Melton, Dir., Emeritus; Dick Myers, Dir., Emeritus; Rex Slick, Dir., Emeritus; Mike Broyles; Jeff Galyen; Soni Jones; Steve Pfenninger; Jim Ray; Steve Weidert; and 5 additional Directors.
Number of staff: 3 full-time professional; 1 full-time support; 1 part-time support.
EIN: 311170412

3321
Heritage Fund - The Community Foundation of Bartholomew County ✧
(formerly Heritage Fund of Bartholomew County, Inc.)
538 Franklin St.
P.O. Box 1547
Columbus, IN 47202-1547 (812) 376-7772
Contact: For grants: Kristin Munn, Community Grants and Outreach Mgr.
FAX: (812) 376-0051;
E-mail: info@heritagefundbc.org; Grant application e-mail: kmunn@heritagefundbc.org; Main URL: http://www.heritagefundbc.com
Facebook: http://www.facebook.com/pages/Heritage-Fund-The-Community-Foundation-of-Bartholomew-County/112620139694
Twitter: http://twitter.com/heritagefundbc
YouTube: http://www.youtube.com/heritagefundbc

Incorporated in 1976 in IN.
Foundation type: Community foundation.
Financial data (yr. ended 12/31/13): Assets, $61,653,828 (M); gifts received, $2,759,770; expenditures, $3,928,419; giving activities include $2,147,477 for 41+ grants (high: $386,775), and $268,470 for 116 grants to individuals.
Purpose and activities: The foundation primarily: 1) provides responsible stewardship of gifts donated for broad charitable purposes; 2) develops leadership to address community issues; 3) serves as a catalyst for positive change in partnership with others; and 4) promotes philanthropy broadly within the community.
Fields of interest: Arts; Education, early childhood education; Education; Health care; Health organizations, association; Employment; Children/youth, services; Aging, centers/services; Human services; Civil rights, race/intergroup relations; Economic development; Community/economic development; Public affairs; Youth; Aging.
Type of support: Management development/capacity building; Capital campaigns; Building/renovation; Equipment; Land acquisition; Emergency funds; Program development; Conferences/seminars; Publication; Seed money; Scholarship funds; Research; Technical assistance; Consulting services; Matching/challenge support.
Limitations: Applications accepted. Giving limited to Bartholomew County, IN. No support for sectarian religious purposes. No grants to individuals (except for scholarships and special educational programs), or for annual campaigns, endowment funds, seminars or trips (unless there are special circumstances which will benefit the community), or operating support (generally); no loans.
Publications: Application guidelines; Annual report; Grants list; Informational brochure; Newsletter; Program policy statement.
Application information: Visit foundation web site for application form and guidelines. An organization will be invited to submit a formal request based on initial contact with the foundation. Grant application form, logic chart, annual/project budgets, and board list should be e-mailed to Prog. Off.; additional material may be mailed or hand delivered. Application form required.
Initial approach: Contact foundation
Copies of proposal: 1

Deadline(s): Quarterly: Mar. 1, June 1, Sept. 1, and Dec. 1
Board meeting date(s): Quarterly
Final notification: 60 - 90 days

Officers and Directors:* Mickey Kim, Chair.; Kevina A. Schumaker,* Vice-Chair.; Tracy Hamilton Souza,* C.E.O. and Pres.; Amber Fischvogt, V.P., Devel.; Jesse Brand,* Secy.; John M. Burnett,* Treas.; David S. Barker; Jeffrey N. Brown; Mayor Kristen Brown; Diane Doup; Mark S. Elwood; Rich Freeland; Tony Gambaiani; Brian Hannasch; Tom Harmon; Ryan C. Hou; Laura Hurt; Carl Lienhoop; Lynne M. Maguire; Joseph Mathew; Angie May; Nobu Nakajima; John B. Quick; Brian P. Russell; Lorraine Smith; Mark Stewart; Tom Vujovich; Pat Ward; Ro Whittington.
Number of staff: 4 full-time professional; 3 part-time professional.
EIN: 351343903

3322
Holiday Management Foundation, Inc. ✧

(formerly Holiday Home Foundation of Evansville, Inc.)
1202 W. Buena Vista Rd., No. 200
Evansville, IN 47710-5191

Established in 1974 in IN.
Donors: Sharon Dunigan; Larry Dunigan; Holiday Home Health Care Corp. of Evansville; Holiday Retirement Village; NSPB Corp.; 3-D Corp.; NFrame, Inc.; Mitchell Dunigan Trust.
Foundation type: Independent foundation.
Financial data (yr. ended 09/30/13): Assets, $14,137,118 (M); gifts received, $240,748; expenditures, $849,062; qualifying distributions, $818,136; giving activities include $815,393 for 29 grants (high: $221,500; low: $250).
Purpose and activities: Giving primarily for education, youth organizations, and human services.
Fields of interest: Elementary/secondary education; Higher education; Youth development; Human services; YM/YWCAs & YM/YWHAs; Christian agencies & churches.
Limitations: Applications not accepted. Giving primarily in Evansville, IN. Generally no grants to individuals.
Application information: Contributes only to pre-selected organizations. Unsolicited requests for funds not considered.
Officers: Larry Dunigan, Pres.; Derek Dunigan, V.P.; Sharon Dunigan, Secy.-Treas.
EIN: 237414999
Selected grants: The following grants are a representative sample of this grantmaker's funding activity:
$100,833 to Evansville Day School, Evansville, IN, 2011.
$71,429 to University of Evansville, Evansville, IN, 2011.
$46,904 to Tri-State Food Bank, Evansville, IN, 2011.
$20,000 to Lampion Center, Evansville, IN, 2011.
$18,000 to Albion Fellows Bacon Center, Evansville, IN, 2011.
$10,000 to Evansville Christian Life Center, Evansville, IN, 2011.
$6,100 to Evansville Rescue Mission, Evansville, IN, 2011.
$5,000 to Patchwork Central, Evansville, IN, 2011.

3323
Hoover Family Foundation ✧

860 E. 86th St., Ste. 5
Indianapolis, IN 46240-6860 (317) 815-9553
Contact: David C. Hoover, Pres., Indianapolis, IN; Glen H. Friedman, Exec. Dir, Portland, OR
FAX: (317) 815-9663; OR address: P.O. Box 551, West Linn, OR 97068, Attn: Glen Friedman, Exec. Dir., Oregon, tel.: (503) 699-1363; Main URL: http://www.gosw.org/hff/

Established in 1992 in IN.
Donors: James E. Hoover; Katherine C. Hoover†; Mildred M. Hoover†.
Foundation type: Independent foundation.
Financial data (yr. ended 06/30/13): Assets, $13,714,303 (M); expenditures, $1,214,943; qualifying distributions, $1,163,829; giving activities include $895,172 for 84 grants (high: $350,000; low: $2,000).
Purpose and activities: Giving primarily for human services and promoting self-sufficiency.
Fields of interest: Education; Human services; Economically disadvantaged.
Limitations: Applications accepted. Giving primarily in Indianapolis, IN, and Portland, OR. No support for religious or sectarian organizations. No grants to individuals, or for operating budgets, continuous support, capital campaigns, event (or post event) funding, multi-year funding, college scholarships, medical research, private foundations or endowment funds, or for long term funding.
Publications: Application guidelines.
Application information: Only grantseekers in IN should contact the foundation's IN office, and grantseekers in the metropolitan Portland, OR, area should contact the OR office. Applications for the Indianapolis, North Webster and Syracuse, IN, area are accepted by invitation only. Unsolicited applications from these areas will not be considered. See foundation web site for specific guidelines which must be followed. Application form required.
Initial approach: Use format and cover sheet which is available on foundation web site
Copies of proposal: 3
Board meeting date(s): Jan., May, and Sept.
Final notification: 3-4 months

Officers and Directors:* David C. Hoover,* Pres.; Cynthia K. Hoover,* V.P.; Glen H. Friedman, Exec. Dir., Oregon; Anne Hoover.
Number of staff: 2 full-time professional; 1 part-time professional.
EIN: 351873953
Selected grants: The following grants are a representative sample of this grantmaker's funding activity:
$15,000 to Indianapolis Parks Foundation, Indianapolis, IN, 2011.
$10,000 to Center for Leadership Development, Indianapolis, IN, 2011.
$10,000 to Dayspring Center, Indianapolis, IN, 2011.
$10,000 to Kids Voice of Indiana, Indianapolis, IN, 2011.
$10,000 to Net Literacy, Carmel, IN, 2011.
$10,000 to United Way of Central Indiana, Indianapolis, IN, 2011.
$8,000 to Albertina Kerr Centers, Portland, OR, 2011.
$8,000 to Innovative Housing, Portland, OR, 2011.
$7,500 to Childrens Cancer Association, Portland, OR, 2011.
$7,500 to Young Audiences of Indiana, Indianapolis, IN, 2011.

3324
Huntington County Community Foundation, Inc. ✧ ☆

(formerly Heritage Fund of Huntington County, Inc.)
356 W. Park Dr.
P.O. Box 5037
Huntington, IN 46750-2636 (260) 356-8878
Contact: Michael Howell, Exec. Dir.
FAX: (260) 356-0921;
E-mail: info@huntingtonccf.org; Main URL: http://huntingtonccf.org
Facebook: http://www.facebook.com/pages/Huntington-County-Community-Foundation/241568909220594
Scholarship e-mail: scholarship@huntingtonccf.org

Established in 1991 in IN.
Foundation type: Community foundation.
Financial data (yr. ended 12/31/13): Assets, $13,786,715 (M); gifts received, $315,416; expenditures, $663,525; giving activities include $338,538 for 4+ grants (high: $100,000), and $83,438 for 108 grants to individuals.
Purpose and activities: The foundation funds charitable projects that will make a positive impact on Huntington County, IN, and its people, and is particularly interested in ideas that shed new light on local needs and provide innovative, long term solutions. Grantmaking areas of interest include arts and culture, community development, education, environment, health, human services, and youth development.
Fields of interest: Arts; Elementary/secondary education; Higher education; Education; Environment; Health care; Recreation; Youth development; Human services; Community/economic development.
Type of support: Management development/capacity building; Annual campaigns; Building/renovation; Equipment; Land acquisition; Endowments; Program development; Conferences/seminars; Professorships; Publication; Seed money; Curriculum development; Scholarship funds; Technical assistance; Consulting services; Program evaluation; Program-related investments/loans; Scholarships—to individuals; Matching/challenge support.
Limitations: Applications accepted. Giving primarily in Huntington County, IN. No grants for operating funds.
Publications: Application guidelines; Annual report; Annual report (including application guidelines); Financial statement; Grants list; Informational brochure; Informational brochure (including application guidelines); Newsletter; Newsletter (including application guidelines); Program policy statement; Program policy statement (including application guidelines).
Application information: Visit foundation web site for application form and guidelines. Application form required.
Initial approach: Submit application
Copies of proposal: 8
Deadline(s): Apr. 15 and Oct. 15
Board meeting date(s): Bimonthly
Final notification: 2 weeks

Officers and Directors:* Jim Scheiber,* Pres.; Rick Delaney,* 1st V.P.; Steve Eisenhut, 2nd V.P.; John Mignone,* Secy.-Treas.; Michael Howell, Exec. Dir.; Scott Berry; Gina Canady; David Daugherty; Midge

Decker; Roger Dyson; Bill Hancher; Steve Kimmel; John Niederman; Fred Scheiber.
Number of staff: 1 full-time professional; 1 part-time professional; 1 part-time support.
EIN: 351838709

3325
The Hux Family Charitable Trust ✧
P.O. Box 1027
Riley, IN 47871-1027
Application address: c/o Cynthia S. Martin, P.O. Box 129, Riley, IN 47871-0129, tel.: (812) 894-2096

Established in 1992 in IN.
Donor: Vernon E. Hux†.
Foundation type: Independent foundation.
Financial data (yr. ended 09/30/13): Assets, $5,954,012 (M); expenditures, $626,506; qualifying distributions, $597,172; giving activities include $597,172 for 59 grants (high: $88,251; low: $50).
Purpose and activities: Giving primarily for education, hospitals, human services, and Protestant and Roman Catholic organizations and churches.
Fields of interest: Elementary/secondary education; Higher education; Education; Hospitals (general); Health organizations, association; Human services; Children/youth, services; Protestant agencies & churches; Catholic agencies & churches.
Type of support: General/operating support; Scholarship funds.
Limitations: Applications accepted. Giving primarily in FL and IN. No grants to individuals.
Application information: Application form required.
Initial approach: Letter
Deadline(s): None
Trustees: Cynthia S. Martin; Kathy A. Perry.
EIN: 356562911
Selected grants: The following grants are a representative sample of this grantmaker's funding activity:
$88,200 to Union Hospital, Terre Haute, IN, 2011. For general use.
$60,000 to Saint Mary of the Woods, Saint Mary of the Woods, IN, 2011.
$55,000 to Saint Patrick Church, Terre Haute, IN, 2011. For general use.
$38,456 to Saint Mary of the Woods, Saint Mary of the Woods, IN, 2011. For scholarship.
$16,000 to Vigo County School Corporation, Terre Haute, IN, 2011. For general use.
$10,000 to Ivy Tech Foundation, Terre Haute, IN, 2011.
$7,500 to Ivy Tech Foundation, Terre Haute, IN, 2011. For scholarships.
$5,000 to Lords Place, West Palm Beach, FL, 2011.
$2,000 to Nicklaus Childrens Health Care Foundation, North Palm Beach, FL, 2011. For general use.
$2,000 to Quantum House, West Palm Beach, FL, 2011. For general use.

3326
Imburgia Foundation Inc. ✧ ☆
c/o Anthony Imburgia
13821 N. Layton Mills Ct.
Camby, IN 46113-8774 (317) 281-1494
Contact: Anthony Imburgia, Pres.
E-mail: info@imburgiafoundation.org; Main URL: http://imburgiafoundation.org/

Established in IN.
Donors: Anthony Jessica Imburgia; XFMRS Inc.
Foundation type: Independent foundation.
Financial data (yr. ended 12/31/12): Assets, $156,184 (M); gifts received, $371,388; expenditures, $929,987; qualifying distributions, $929,524; giving activities include $918,399 for 2 grants (high: $859,493; low: $58,906).
Fields of interest: Religion.
Application information: Application form required.
Initial approach: Use online application form on foundation web site
Deadline(s): None
Officers:* Anthony Imburgia, Pres.; Jessica Imburgia, V.P. and Secy.
EIN: 211280734

3327
Indiana Chemical Trust ✧
P.O. Box 207
Evansville, IN 47702 (812) 462-7459
Contact: Julie Schlosser
Application address: c/o Old National Trust, P.O. Box 1447, Terre Haute, IN 47808 Tel.: (812) 462-7459

Established in 1953 in IN.
Donors: Terre Haute Gas Corp.; Indiana Gas and Chemical Corp.; Tribune-Star Publishing Co.
Foundation type: Company-sponsored foundation.
Financial data (yr. ended 12/31/13): Assets, $10,177,834 (M); expenditures, $494,437; qualifying distributions, $444,143; giving activities include $442,000 for 44 grants (high: $125,000; low: $2,000).
Purpose and activities: The foundation supports museums and hospitals and organizations involved with historic preservation, education, animal welfare, patient services, housing development, and human services.
Fields of interest: Education; Human services; Religion.
Type of support: General/operating support.
Limitations: Applications accepted. Giving primarily in areas of company operations in Terre Haute, IN. No grants to individuals.
Application information: Application form not required.
Initial approach: Proposal
Deadline(s): None
Board meeting date(s): Dec.
Committee Members: W. Curtis Brighton; Anton Hulman George; Mari Hulman George.
Trustee: Old National Trust Co.
EIN: 356024816
Selected grants: The following grants are a representative sample of this grantmaker's funding activity:
$5,000 to Best Buddies International, Miami, FL, 2011.

3328
Indiana Pathology Endowment, Inc. ✧
(formerly University Clinical Pathology Associates, Inc.)
5610 Crawfordsville Rd., Ste. 2002
Indianapolis, IN 46224-3714

Established in 1975; supporting organization of the Indiana University School of Medicine.
Foundation type: Operating foundation.
Financial data (yr. ended 12/31/13): Assets, $11,312,085 (M); expenditures, $717,255; qualifying distributions, $659,170; giving activities include $585,000 for 2 grants (high: $575,000; low: $10,000).
Fields of interest: Higher education, university.
Limitations: Applications not accepted. Giving limited to Indianapolis, IN. No grants to individuals.
Application information: Contributes only to pre-selected organizations; unsolicited requests for funds not considered or acknowledged.
Officers: John N. Eble, M.D., Pres. and Treas.; David Grignon, M.D., V.P.; Thomas M. Ulbright, M.D., Secy.
EIN: 351331530

3329
The Ethan and Joyce Jackson Family Charitable Foundation Inc. ✧
6900 S. Gray Rd.
Indianapolis, IN 46237-3209

Established in IN.
Donor: Ethan I. Jackson.
Foundation type: Independent foundation.
Financial data (yr. ended 12/31/13): Assets, $121,462 (M); gifts received, $496,365; expenditures, $573,493; qualifying distributions, $573,302; giving activities include $573,302 for 56 grants (high: $130,760; low: $200).
Fields of interest: Human services; Christian agencies & churches.
Limitations: Applications not accepted. Giving in the U.S., with emphasis on FL and IN. No grants to individuals.
Application information: Contributes only to pre-selected organizations.
Officer: Mary Beth Jackson, Pres.
Directors: Blake A. Jackson; Ethan I. Jackson; Joyce A. Jackson; Kyle E. Jackson; Wessley E. Jackson.
EIN: 351899729

3330
Johnson County Community Foundation, Inc. ✧
(formerly Greater Johnson County Community Foundation)
398 S. Main St.
P.O. Box 217
Franklin, IN 46131 (317) 738-2213
Contact: Gail Richards, C.E.O.; For grants and scholarships: Stephanie Walls, Prog. Assoc., Grants and Scholarships
FAX: (317) 738-9113; E-mail: frontdesk@jccf.org; Grant and scholarship inquiries e-mail: stephaniew@jccf.org; Main URL: http://www.jccf.org
Facebook: http://www.facebook.com/jccfindiana
Twitter: https://twitter.com/JCCFIndiana
YouTube: http://www.youtube.com/jccfindiana

Established in 1991 in IN.
Foundation type: Community foundation.
Financial data (yr. ended 12/31/13): Assets, $20,713,844 (M); gifts received, $1,969,504; expenditures, $1,438,673; giving activities include $652,649 for 36+ grants (high: $132,464), and $209,627 for 101 grants to individuals.
Purpose and activities: The foundation exists to encourage local philanthropy and to improve the quality of life in the Johnson County community through leadership and grant support to local

nonprofit organizations. Scholarships are awarded to high school seniors from specific high schools primarily in Johnson County, IN, and/or students enrolled at specific IN colleges or universities.
Fields of interest: Arts; Higher education; Education; Environment; Health care; Agriculture; Disasters, preparedness/services; Human services; Community/economic development.
Type of support: General/operating support; Management development/capacity building; Building/renovation; Equipment; Emergency funds; Program development; Seed money; Scholarship funds; Technical assistance; Consulting services; Program evaluation; Scholarships—to individuals; Matching/challenge support.
Limitations: Applications accepted. Giving limited to Johnson County, IN, and vicinity. No support for sectarian or religious programs, or for medical research. No grants to individuals (except for scholarships), or for endowments, conferences, travel, publications or media projects, annual campaigns, capital campaigns, ongoing operating budgets, fundraising events, deficit funding, equipment, construction and renovation, land acquisition, public school services required by state law, repeat funding supported through prior grants, or athletic leagues or teams.
Publications: Application guidelines; Annual report (including application guidelines); Grants list; Informational brochure (including application guidelines); Newsletter.
Application information: Visit foundation web site for application guidelines. If the grant request meets funding guidelines, the foundation will invite the organization to submit a full application. Application form required.
Initial approach: E-mail letter of inquiry
Copies of proposal: 1
Deadline(s): Apr. 4 and Aug. 1 for letter of inquiry; Apr. 26 and Aug. 30 for full grant application
Board meeting date(s): 6 times per year
Final notification: Within 30-60 days
Officers and Directors:* Andy Walker,* Chair.; Gail Richards, C.E.O. and Pres.; Kim Minton, V.P., Devel.; Erin Smith,* Secy.; Steve Sonntag,* Treas.; John Shell,* Chair.-Elect; Dean Abplanalp; Brian V. Biehn; Susie Bixler; Chris Cosner; Don Cummings; Virginia Davis; Ed Deiwert; Bill Kiesel; Amy Kelsay; Courtney Krudy; Seth Perigo; Bob Romack; Loren Snyder; Joe Waltermann; Richard Wertz; Brooke Worland.
Number of staff: 3 full-time professional.
EIN: 351797437

3331
Arthur Jordan Foundation ✧ ☆
1230 N. Delaware St.
Indianapolis, IN 46202-2531 (317) 631-1888
Contact: Margaret Sallee
FAX: (317) 632-5488;
E-mail: msallee@arthurjordanfoundation.org; Main URL: http://www.arthurjordanfoundation.org/

Trust established in 1928 in IN.
Donor: Arthur Jordan‡.
Foundation type: Independent foundation.
Financial data (yr. ended 12/31/13): Assets, $17,250,017 (M); expenditures, $778,065; qualifying distributions, $630,473; giving activities include $482,219 for 36 grants (high: $210,500; low: $1,300).
Purpose and activities: Giving primarily for the arts and education, as well as historic landmarks.
Fields of interest: Arts; Higher education.
Type of support: General/operating support; Annual campaigns; Capital campaigns; Building/renovation; Matching/challenge support.
Limitations: Applications accepted. Giving limited to Marion County, IN. No support for medical research, or primary or secondary educational institutions. No grants to individuals, or for endowment funds, multi-year grants, seed money, research, scholarships, or fellowships; no loans.
Publications: Application guidelines; Grants list.
Application information: Application guidelines and cover sheet available on foundation web site. Application form required.
Initial approach: Letter (2-3 pages)
Copies of proposal: 1
Deadline(s): Mar. 1
Board meeting date(s): May
Officers: Sara B. Cobb, Chair.; Thomas A. King, Vice-Chair.; Samuel L. Odle, Secy.; Joseph D. Barnette, Jr., Treas.
Trustees: Dan R. DeMars; Thomas P. Ewbank.
Number of staff: 1 full-time professional.
EIN: 350428850

3332
Journal-Gazette Foundation, Inc. ✧
701 S. Clinton St., Ste. 104
Fort Wayne, IN 46802-1883
Contact: Jerry D. Fox, Secy.-Treas.

Established in 1985 in IN.
Donors: Journal-Gazette Co.; Richard G. Inskeep; Harriett J. Inskeep; Julie Inskeep.
Foundation type: Company-sponsored foundation.
Financial data (yr. ended 12/31/13): Assets, $12,276,707 (M); gifts received, $12,000; expenditures, $547,870; qualifying distributions, $547,870; giving activities include $478,836 for 82 grants (high: $109,675; low: $50).
Purpose and activities: The foundation supports zoological societies, parks and playgrounds, and food banks and organizations involved with arts and culture, education, health, cancer, child welfare, and human services.
Fields of interest: Arts; Education; Human services.
Type of support: General/operating support; Capital campaigns; Scholarship funds.
Limitations: Applications accepted. Giving limited to northeastern IN and northeastern OH. No grants to individuals.
Application information: Application form required.
Initial approach: Letter
Deadline(s): None
Board meeting date(s): Quarterly
Officers and Directors:* Harriett J. Inskeep,* Pres.; Jerry D. Fox, Secy.-Treas.; Gilmore S. Haynie, Jr.; Thomas R. Inskeep; Julie Inskeep Simpson.
EIN: 311134237

3333
Kendrick Foundation, Inc. ✧
(formerly Kendrick Memorial Hospital, Inc.)
c/o The Academy Bldg.
250 N. Monroe St.
Mooresville, IN 46158-1551 (317) 831-1232
FAX: (317) 831-2854;
E-mail: info@kendrickfoundation.org; Toll free tel.: (855) 280-3095 (tel. is in c/o the Community Foundation of Morgan County, Inc.); Main URL: http://www.kendrickfoundation.org

Established in 2001 in IN from proceeds of the sale of Kendrick Memorial Hospital.
Foundation type: Independent foundation.
Financial data (yr. ended 06/30/13): Assets, $29,315,922 (M); expenditures, $1,852,868; qualifying distributions, $1,708,119; giving activities include $1,212,270 for 36 grants (high: $200,000; low: $1,500), and $378,113 for 43 grants to individuals (high: $15,000; low: $1,144).
Purpose and activities: The foundation supports healthcare programs in Morgan County, IN.
Fields of interest: Medical school/education; Health care.
Type of support: Land acquisition; Equipment; Scholarships—to individuals.
Limitations: Applications accepted. Giving limited to Morgan County, IN.
Publications: Application guidelines; Annual report; Financial statement.
Application information: Full proposals for grants will not be accepted. Only those who have their Letters of Intent approved may submit a full proposal. Scholarship application form available on foundation web site. Letters of Intent are accessible on foundation web site for a limited amount of time during the opening of the grant cycle. Paper applications are not accepted. Application form required.
Initial approach: Letter of intent for grants via foundation web site; fill out application form for scholarships
Copies of proposal: 6
Deadline(s): See foundation web site for current deadlines
Board meeting date(s): Quarterly
Final notification: 60 days
Officer: Shelley D. Voelz, Chair. and Pres.; Mae Cooper, Secy.-Treas.
Directors: Alicia Boyd; Lynn Gordon; Greg McKelfresh; R. Barry Melbert, M.D.
EIN: 351124905
Selected grants: The following grants are a representative sample of this grantmaker's funding activity:
$60,000 to First Presbyterian Church, Martinsville, IN, 2011.
$35,000 to Jackson Center for Conductive Education, Mooresville, IN, 2011.
$5,000 to Hemophilia of Indiana, Indianapolis, IN, 2011.

3334
Koch Foundation, Inc. ✧
(formerly George Koch Sons Foundation, Inc.)
10 S. 11th Ave.
Evansville, IN 47744-0001
Contact: Jennifer K. Slade, Secy.
Main URL: http://www.kochenterprises.com/foundation

Incorporated in 1945 in IN.
Donors: George Koch Sons, Inc.; George Koch Sons, LLC; Gibbs Die Casting Corp.; Koch Enterprises, Inc.
Foundation type: Company-sponsored foundation.
Financial data (yr. ended 12/31/13): Assets, $29,722,060 (M); gifts received, $902,000; expenditures, $1,085,457; qualifying distributions, $1,000,699; giving activities include $1,000,546 for 112 grants (high: $202,500; low: $50).
Purpose and activities: The foundation supports organizations involved with arts and culture, education, health, human services, civic affairs, and religion. Special emphasis is directed toward

organizations with which employees of Koch Enterprises are involved.
Fields of interest: Arts; Education; Health care; Human services; Public affairs; Religion.
Type of support: Annual campaigns; Capital campaigns; Building/renovation; Program development; Research; Employee volunteer services; Sponsorships; Employee matching gifts; Employee-related scholarships; Matching/challenge support.
Limitations: Applications accepted. Giving limited to IN, KY, MO, Elko, NV, Schertz, TX, Beckley, WV, and Casper, WY, with emphasis on the Evansville and the Vanderburgh County, IN, area. No grants to individuals (except for employee-related scholarships).
Publications: Application guidelines.
Application information: Application form not required.
Initial approach: Proposal
Copies of proposal: 1
Deadline(s): None
Final notification: 3 months
Officers and Directors:* Robert L. Koch II,* Pres.; Kevin R. Koch, V.P.; James H. Muehlbauer,* V.P.; Jennifer K. Slade, Secy.; Susan E. Parsons, Treas.; Steve A. Church; Josh Gilberg; David M. Koch; Glen J. Muehlbauer; Brad J. Muehlbauer; Christopher L. Slade.
Number of staff: 2 part-time support.
EIN: 356023372
Selected grants: The following grants are a representative sample of this grantmaker's funding activity:
$206,000 to University of Evansville, Evansville, IN, 2012. For Capital Campaign and Scholarships.
$33,000 to YMCA of Southwestern Indiana, Evansville, IN, 2012. For Capital Campaign and Charitable Operations.
$2,300 to University of Southern Indiana, Evansville, IN, 2012. For Charitable Operations and Scholars.
$1,600 to Boy Scouts of America, Buffalo Trace Council, Evansville, IN, 2012. For charitable operations.

3335
Kosciusko 21st Century Foundation, Inc. ✧

(also known as K21 Health Foundation)
2170 N. Pointe Dr.
Warsaw, IN 46581-1810 (574) 269-5188
FAX: (574) 269-5193;
E-mail: rhaddad@k21foundation.org; Mailing address: c/o Richard Haddad, C.E.O. and Pres., P.O. Box 1810, Warsaw, IN 46581-1810; Main URL: http://www.k21foundation.org
Facebook: http://www.facebook.com/pages/K21-Health-Foundation/107302855974304
Grants List: http://www.k21foundation.org/what-weve-done/index.cfm

Established in 1999 in IN from the proceeds of the sale of Kosciusko Community Hospital to Quorum Health Group, Inc.
Foundation type: Independent foundation.
Financial data (yr. ended 12/31/13): Assets, $71,915,313 (M); gifts received, $273,851; expenditures, $3,675,944; qualifying distributions, $3,395,201; giving activities include $2,558,038 for 75 grants (high: $806,156; low: $335).
Purpose and activities: The foundation exists for the benefit of Kosciusko County, Indiana citizens to ensure healthcare services are provided, and to advance prevention and healthy lifestyles. This will be accomplished by identifying health needs in our community and maintaining an endowment so funding is available, through investments and grants, for those needs.
Fields of interest: Medical care, community health systems; Medical care, rehabilitation; Physical therapy; Health care, EMS; Pharmacy/prescriptions; Health care; Mental health/crisis services; Cancer; Crime/violence prevention, domestic violence; Disasters, preparedness/services; Residential/custodial care, hospices.
Type of support: Capital campaigns; Building/renovation; Equipment; Program development; Scholarship funds; Matching/challenge support.
Limitations: Applications accepted. Giving primarily in Kosciusko County, IN.
Publications: Application guidelines; Annual report; Grants list; Newsletter.
Application information: Application form required.
Initial approach: Use online application form and/or online program to see if the applicant qualifies. See foundation web site for details
Copies of proposal: 1
Deadline(s): Feb. 1, May 1, Aug. 1, and Nov. 1 for grants
Board meeting date(s): Quarterly
Final notification: 2 months
Officers and Directors:* Dr. Jennifer Lucht, Chair.; Jim Tinkey, Vice-Chair.; Richard A. Haddad,* C.E.O. and Pres.; Shari Boyle, Secy.; Mr. Dana L. Krull,* Treas.; Karen Boling; David C. Cates; Dr. David Dick; Becky Doll; Steve Grill; Dr. David Haines; Officer Joe Hawn; Rosy Jansma; Max Mock; Jon Sroufe; Scott Tucker; Valerie Warner.
Number of staff: 2 full-time professional; 1 full-time support; 1 part-time support.
EIN: 351187105
Selected grants: The following grants are a representative sample of this grantmaker's funding activity:
$2,000,000 to YMCA, Kosciusko Community, Warsaw, IN, 2012. For new facility construction.
$717,749 to Kosciusko Health Services Pavilion, Warsaw, IN, 2012.
$350,000 to Kosciusko Home Care and Hospice, Warsaw, IN, 2012.
$200,000 to Kosciusko County Community Foundation, Warsaw, IN, 2012.
$200,000 to Kosciusko Home Care and Hospice, Warsaw, IN, 2012.
$50,000 to Heartline Pregnancy Center, Warsaw, IN, 2012.
$15,000 to Childrens Hope, Mad Anthonys Childrens Hope House, Fort Wayne, IN, 2012.

3336
Kosciusko County Community Foundation, Inc. ✧

102 E. Market St.
Warsaw, IN 46580-2806 (574) 267-1901
Contact: Suzanne M. Light, Exec. Dir.
FAX: (574) 268-9780; E-mail: kcf@kcfoundation.org; Main URL: http://www.kcfoundation.org
Facebook: https://www.facebook.com/gotoKCCF
RSS Feed: http://kcfoundation.org/feed/
Twitter: https://twitter.com/koscocommfdtn

Established in 1968 by the Warsaw Chamber of Commerce as the Greater Warsaw Foundation. In 1972, after reorganization to include the entire county, the name was changed. In 2002, the current name was adopted.
Foundation type: Community foundation.
Financial data (yr. ended 06/30/13): Assets, $44,536,243 (M); gifts received, $2,193,144; expenditures, $3,213,789; giving activities include $1,096,466 for 533 grants, and $638,137 for 2,075 grants to individuals.
Purpose and activities: By bringing caring people and charitable endeavors together, the foundation makes donors dreams shine for the good of the community by serving as the vehicle for donors' charitable dreams, awarding grants to charitable projects and organizations, and addressing community needs as a catalyst and convener.
Fields of interest: Arts; Education; Environment; Health care; Recreation; Human services; Public affairs.
Type of support: Management development/capacity building; Capital campaigns; Building/renovation; Equipment; Program development; Seed money; Scholarships—to individuals; Matching/challenge support.
Limitations: Applications accepted. Giving limited to Kosciusko County, IN. No support for sectarian or religious groups, or national organizations (unless the monies are to be used solely to benefit citizens of Kosciusko County). No grants to individuals (except for scholarships), or for endowment funds, fundraising projects, or long-term funding.
Publications: Application guidelines; Annual report; Newsletter.
Application information: Visit foundation web site for application form and guidelines. Application form required.
Initial approach: Telephone
Copies of proposal: 7
Deadline(s): Jan. 15, May 15, and Sept. 15 for Community Fund Grants
Board meeting date(s): Every 2 months
Final notification: 9 weeks after deadline
Officers and Directors:* Jerry Yeager,* Pres.; Jim McFadden,* V.P.; Rob Parker,* Secy.; Stephen Snyder,* Treas.; Suzanne M. Light,* Exec. Dir.; Ceaneh Alexis; Ron Baumgartner; Robert Bishop; Jerry Clevenger; Kevin Deardorff; Jennifer Hollar; Zoe Howard; Mike Kinsey; Dana Krull; Vern Landis; Sally Mahnken; Ron Manahan; Allison McSherry; Marlene Mulero-Betances; John Roberts; Christine Sands; Sharon Sommers; Kip Tom; John Warren.
Number of staff: 5 full-time professional; 2 full-time support.
EIN: 356086777
Selected grants: The following grants are a representative sample of this grantmaker's funding activity:
$5,351,403 to Orthopedics Capital Foundation, Warsaw, IN, 2011. For general support of supporting organization initiatives.
$7,430 to American Cancer Society, Northwest Indiana Office, Mishawaka, IN, 2011. For general support.

3337
Legacy Foundation, Inc. ✧
1000 E. 80th Pl.
Merrillville, IN 46410 (219) 736-1880
FAX: (219) 736-1940; E-mail: legacy@legacyfdn.org; Main URL: http://www.legacyfdn.org
E-Newsletter: http://www.legacyfoundationlakeco.org/emailsignup.html
Facebook: http://www.facebook.com/pages/Merrillville-IN/Legacy-Foundation/314525729630
Flickr: http://www.flickr.com/photos/legacyfdn/sets/
Twitter: http://twitter.com/legacyfdn

Established in 1992 in IN.
Foundation type: Community foundation.
Financial data (yr. ended 06/30/13): Assets, $46,819,671 (M); gifts received, $2,116,606; expenditures, $2,791,918; giving activities include $1,796,037 for 87+ grants (high: $40,000), and $157,023 for 152 grants to individuals.
Purpose and activities: The mission of the foundation is to enhance the quality of life for all citizens of Lake County, IN, now and for generations to come. The mission is achieved by building a community endowment, addressing needs through grantmaking, and by providing leadership on key community issues.
Fields of interest: Arts; Education; Environment; Public health; Health care; Youth, services; Human services; Community development, neighborhood development; Community/economic development; Philanthropy/voluntarism; Public affairs.
Type of support: Building/renovation; Equipment; Program development; Seed money; Scholarship funds; Technical assistance; Scholarships—to individuals; Matching/challenge support.
Limitations: Applications accepted. Giving primarily in Lake County, IN. No support for sectarian religious programs or basic municipal or educational functions and services. No grants to individuals (except through designated scholarship funds), or for operating budgets, endowment funds, debt reduction, continuing support, general operating expenses (except for start up), annual campaigns, fundraising events, or travel; no multi-year grants or scholarly research grants.
Publications: Application guidelines; Annual report; Grants list; Informational brochure; Newsletter.
Application information: Visit foundation Web site for application forms and guidelines. If application deadline falls on a non-business day, proposals must be received on the last business day prior to the deadline. Application form required.
Initial approach: Contact foundation
Copies of proposal: 1
Deadline(s): Mar. 1, May 1, Sept. 1, and Nov. 1
Board meeting date(s): 1st Tues. of Feb., Apr., June, Aug., Oct., and Dec.
Final notification: Approx. 6 weeks
Officers and Directors:* Nancy L. Clifford,* Chair.; Robert Johnson,* Vice-Chair.; Carolyn Saxton,* Pres.; Sandra Snearly-Vosberg,* Treas.; Dave Austgen; Benjamin Bochnowski; Margot Clark; Danette Garza; Matthew Glaros; Gregory Gordon; Amy Han, Ph.D.; J. Brian Hittinger; Debara Howe; Jill Jones; Tom Keilman; Shar Miller; Janet Moran; Dana Rifai; Marti Rivas-Ramos; Dave Ryan; Michael Suggs; Alexis Vazquez-Dedelow; Chris White.
Number of staff: 4 full-time professional; 1 part-time professional; 1 full-time support.
EIN: 351872803

3338
Judd Leighton Foundation, Inc. ✧
211 W. Washington Ave., Ste. 2400
South Bend, IN 46601-1708 (574) 232-5970
Contact: Charles F. Nelson, Exec. Dir.
E-mail: CNelson@juddleightonfoundation.org; Main URL: http://www.juddleightonfoundation.org/

Established in 2000 in IN.
Donor: Judd Leighton.
Foundation type: Independent foundation.
Financial data (yr. ended 12/31/12): Assets, $97,051,165 (M); gifts received, $1,525,500; expenditures, $5,802,021; qualifying distributions, $4,767,533; giving activities include $4,501,209 for 34 grants (high: $1,671,109; low: $350).
Purpose and activities: Giving primarily to enhance the quality of life in St. Joseph County, IN, by providing funds for health, education, and economic development.
Fields of interest: Higher education; Medical research, institute; Heart & circulatory research; Human services.
Limitations: Giving primarily in St. Joseph County, IN. No support for programs that are sectarian or religious in nature, political organizations or candidates or organizations without 501 (c) (3) designation. No grants to individuals.
Publications: Application guidelines.
Application information: Application guidelines available on foundation web site. Application form required.
Initial approach: Use online application on foundation web site
Deadline(s): By the end of the month preceding a Board Meeting month
Board meeting date(s): Mar., June, Sept., and Dec.
Officers: James F. Keenan, Pres. and Treas.; John M. Pycik, V.P. and Secy.; Charles F. Nelson, Exec. Dir.
Directors: Mary Stanfield; Donald F. Walter.
EIN: 352120550

3339
The Len-Ari Foundation, Inc. ✧
5642 Coventry Ln.
Fort Wayne, IN 46804-7140

Established in 2004 in IN.
Donors: Omnisource Corporation; Leonard Rifkin.
Foundation type: Independent foundation.
Financial data (yr. ended 12/31/13): Assets, $16,537,571 (M); expenditures, $800,460; qualifying distributions, $649,457; giving activities include $649,457 for 33 grants (high: $110,000; low: $1,000).
Fields of interest: Arts; Eye diseases; United Ways and Federated Giving Programs; Jewish agencies & synagogues.
Limitations: Applications not accepted. Giving primarily in FL, IN and WY. No grants to individuals.
Application information: Unsolicited requests for funds not accepted.
Officers: Richard Rifkin, Pres.; Ariela Rifkin, Secy.; Jennifer L. Wilson, Treas.
EIN: 201317221

3340
Eli Lilly and Company Foundation ✧
(also known as Lilly Foundation)
Lilly Corporate Ctr., D.C. 1627
Indianapolis, IN 46285-0001 (317) 276-2000
Contact: Robert Lee Smith, Pres.
FAX: (371) 277-6719; Main URL: http://www.lillyfoundation.org

Incorporated in 1968 in IN.
Donors: Eli Lilly and Co.; Edmund A Cyrol Trust.
Foundation type: Company-sponsored foundation.
Financial data (yr. ended 12/31/13): Assets, $105,476,499 (M); gifts received, $40,000,000; expenditures, $26,648,855; qualifying distributions, $26,245,760; giving activities include $14,315,163 for 217 grants (high: $2,428,986; low: $50), and $11,883,972 for 1,576 employee matching gifts.
Purpose and activities: The foundation supports programs designed to improve the lives of people who lack the resources to obtain quality healthcare, with a focus on low and middle-income countries; and strengthen public education, with an emphasis on science and math education.
Fields of interest: Arts; Elementary/secondary education; Higher education; Public health; Public health, communicable diseases; Health care; Mental health, depression; Mental health, schizophrenia; Mental health/crisis services; Cancer; Nerve, muscle & bone diseases; Diabetes; Disasters, preparedness/services; Youth development; American Red Cross; Community/economic development; United Ways and Federated Giving Programs; Mathematics; Engineering/technology; Science; Public policy, research; Economically disadvantaged.
Type of support: General/operating support; Continuing support; Annual campaigns; Capital campaigns; Equipment; Curriculum development; Scholarship funds; Employee volunteer services; Employee matching gifts; Donated products; Matching/challenge support.
Limitations: Applications not accepted. Giving on a national and international basis, with emphasis on areas of company operations, including Indianapolis, IN. No support for religious or sectarian organizations not of direct benefit to the entire community, fraternal, labor, athletic, or veterans' organizations, political organizations or candidates, legislative organizations, or discriminatory organizations. No grants to individuals, or for scholarships or travel, endowments or capital campaigns (exceptions made by invitation only), debt reduction, medical missions, beauty or talent contests, fundraising activities related to individual sponsorship, conferences or media production, or memorials; no loans.
Publications: Corporate giving report.
Application information: Unsolicited requests are currently not accepted. The foundation develops and initiates partnerships in specific areas of interest.
Board meeting date(s): 1st quarter and 3rd quarter
Officer and Directors:* Robert Lee Smith,* Pres.; Robert A. Armitage; Enrique A. Contero; Maria Crowe; Stephen F. Frye; John C. Lechleiter, Ph.D.; Jan Lundberg; Susan Mahony; Anne Nobles; Bart Peterson; Derica W. Rice; David A. Ricks; Jeffrey N. Simmons; Jacques Tapiero; Fionnuala Walsh.
Number of staff: 1 full-time professional; 3 full-time support.
EIN: 356202479

Selected grants: The following grants are a representative sample of this grantmaker's funding activity:
$2,454,831 to United Way International, Alexandria, VA, 2012. For Lilly MDR-TB Partnership Grant Payments and Fees.
$1,000,000 to YMCA of Greater Indianapolis, Indianapolis, IN, 2012. For North of South YMCA.
$750,000 to Mind Trust, Indianapolis, IN, 2012. For Grow What Works Campaign.
$500,000 to Riley Childrens Foundation, Indianapolis, IN, 2012. For Riley Children's Hospital.
$250,000 to Childrens Museum of Indianapolis, Indianapolis, IN, 2012. For Terra Cotta Warriors: The Emperor's Painted Army.
$250,000 to Eskenazi Health Foundation, Indianapolis, IN, 2012. For The New Wishard Hospital.
$250,000 to Heifer Project International, Little Rock, AR, 2012. For Elanco/Heifer International Hunger Relief Projects.
$58,662 to CARE USA, Atlanta, GA, 2012. For Treatment Adherence and Follow up of MDR-TB Patients.
$50,000 to Christel House Academy, Indianapolis, IN, 2012. For Christel House Academy Watanabe High School.
$17,500 to La Plaza, Indianapolis, IN, 2012. For Night of the Americas and Fiesta Indianapolis.

3341
Lilly Cares Foundation, Inc. ✧
c/o Eli Lilly and Co.
Lilly Corp. Ctr.
Indianapolis, IN 46285-0001 (800) 545-6962
Application address: P.O. Box 230999, Centerville, VA 20120, fax: (703) 310-2534; Main URL: http://www.lilly.com/Responsibility/patients/Pages/PatientAssistance.aspx

Established as a company-sponsored operating foundation in 1996 in IN.
Donor: Eli Lilly and Co.
Foundation type: Operating foundation.
Financial data (yr. ended 12/31/13): Assets, $0; gifts received, $697,004,928; expenditures, $697,004,928; qualifying distributions, $697,004,928; giving activities include $697,004,928 for grants to individuals.
Purpose and activities: The foundation distributes pharmaceuticals to ill and economically disadvantaged people - including infants - who are below the federal poverty level and who are not eligible for any third-party medication payment assistance.
Fields of interest: Economically disadvantaged.
Type of support: Grants to individuals; Donated products.
Limitations: Applications accepted. Giving on a national basis.
Publications: Application guidelines; Informational brochure.
Application information: Application form required.
Initial approach: Telephone foundation for application form or download application form and fax or mail to application address
Deadline(s): None
Final notification: 4 weeks
Officers and Directors:* Steven Stapleton,* Chair. and Pres.; Tamara Cooper, V.P.; Jamie Haney, Secy.; Thomas W. Grein, Treas.; Terrence M. Lyons; Alonzo Weems; Brad Woodward.
EIN: 352027985

3342
Lilly Endowment Inc.
2801 N. Meridian St.
P.O. Box 88068
Indianapolis, IN 46208-0068 (317) 924-5471
Contact: Ronni Kloth, Comm. Dir.
FAX: (317) 926-4431; Main URL: http://www.lillyendowment.org

Incorporated in June 1937 in IN.
Donors: J.K. Lilly, Sr.†; Eli Lilly†; J.K. Lilly, Jr.†; Ruth Lilly†.
Foundation type: Independent foundation.
Financial data (yr. ended 12/31/13): Assets, $7,699,211,116 (M); expenditures, $294,868,788; qualifying distributions, $270,300,000; giving activities include $270,300,000 for grants.
Purpose and activities: The endowment supports religion, education, and community development, with special emphasis on initiatives that benefit youth, that foster philanthropic leadership among nonprofit institutions, and that promote the causes of philanthropy and volunteerism.
Fields of interest: Museums; Historic preservation/historical societies; Arts; Education, research; Elementary/secondary education; Higher education; Theological school/education; Education; Housing/shelter; Safety/disasters; Recreation; Youth development, services; Human services; Community/economic development; Philanthropy/voluntarism, research; Voluntarism promotion; Philanthropy/voluntarism; Public policy, research; Religion, research; Religion; Infants/toddlers; Children/youth; Children; Youth; Adults; Aging; Young adults; Disabilities, people with; Physically disabled; Mentally disabled; Minorities; African Americans/Blacks; Hispanics/Latinos; Native Americans/American Indians; Women; Infants/toddlers, female; Girls; Adults, women; Young adults, female; Men; Infants/toddlers, male; Boys; Adults, men; Young adults, male; Military/veterans; Economically disadvantaged; Homeless.
Type of support: General/operating support; Continuing support; Management development/capacity building; Annual campaigns; Capital campaigns; Building/renovation; Equipment; Land acquisition; Endowments; Emergency funds; Program development; Conferences/seminars; Professorships; Publication; Seed money; Curriculum development; Fellowships; Internship funds; Scholarship funds; Research; Technical assistance; Consulting services; Program evaluation; Employee matching gifts; Matching/challenge support.
Limitations: Applications accepted. Giving limited to IN, with emphasis on Indianapolis, for community development projects (including the arts, preservation, capital building funds, operating funds, and social services). Education funding focused principally on Indiana under invitational grant programs. National giving in religion, philanthropic studies, leadership education, and selected higher education initiatives, principally to increase educational opportunities for minorities. Generally, no support for healthcare programs, mass media projects, libraries, individual elementary/secondary schools, or for individual churches (except as part of invitational grant programs). No grants to individuals (except for fellowships awarded under special programs) or for endowments (except in the context of special initiatives).
Publications: Application guidelines; Annual report (including application guidelines); Occasional report.
Application information: Proposals submitted via fax or e-mail will not be considered. Application form not required.
Initial approach: Letter (no more than 2 pages)
Copies of proposal: 1
Deadline(s): None
Board meeting date(s): Mar., June, Sept., Nov., and Dec.
Final notification: Generally 3 to 6 months after formal proposal is submitted
Officers and Directors:* Thomas M. Lofton,* Chair.; N. Clay Robbins,* C.E.O. and Pres.; Sara B. Cobb, V.P., Education; Christopher L. Coble, V.P., Religion; Diane M. Stenson, V.P. and Treas.; E.G. White, V.P., Finance; Ace Yakey, V.P., Community Devel.; David D. Biber, Secy.; Daniel P. Carmichael; Craig R. Dykstra; William G. Enright, Ph.D.; Charles E. Golden; Eli Lilly II; Mary K. Lisher; David N. Shane.
Number of staff: 18 full-time professional; 17 full-time support.
EIN: 350868122
Selected grants: The following grants are a representative sample of this grantmaker's funding activity:
$11,500,000 to Independent Colleges of Indiana, Indianapolis, IN, 2012. For Lilly Endowment Community Scholarship Program.
$10,000,000 to Indiana Department of Natural Resources, Indianapolis, IN, 2012. For Indiana Bicentennial Nature Trust.
$8,100,000 to Christian Theological Seminary, Indianapolis, IN, 2012. To establish Center for Pastoral Excellence.
$6,300,000 to Indianapolis Neighborhood Housing Partnership, Indianapolis, IN, 2012. For general support.
$5,000,000 to Calvin College, Grand Rapids, MI, 2012. For continuing support for Calvin Institute of Christian Worship programs.
$5,000,000 to Protestant Episcopal Cathedral Foundation of the District of Columbia, Washington, DC, 2012. To repair and restore Washington National Cathedral.
$5,000,000 to United Way Worldwide, Alexandria, VA, 2012. For Hurricane Sandy Recovery Fund.
$4,200,000 to THIRTEEN, New York, NY, 2012. For 16th season of Religion and Ethics Newsweekly.
$3,800,000 to United Way of Central Indiana, Indianapolis, IN, 2012. For campaign.
$2,400,000 to Indiana Youth Institute, Indianapolis, IN, 2012. For general operating support.

3343
Ruth Lilly Philanthropic Foundation ✧
c/o PNC Bank, N.A.
101 W. Washington St., No. 600E
Indianapolis, IN 46255-5000 (317) 267-3731
Contact: Regina Smith
FAX: (317) 267-3959; E-mail for Regina Smith: regina.smith@pnc.com

Established in 2006 in OH.
Donor: Ruth Lilly†.
Foundation type: Independent foundation.

Financial data (yr. ended 12/31/12): Assets, $154,094,161 (M); gifts received, $54,878,842; expenditures, $17,114,238; qualifying distributions, $16,611,836; giving activities include $16,311,285 for 130 grants (high: $2,876,876; low: $1,000).
Purpose and activities: Giving primarily for the arts, higher education and youth development.
Fields of interest: Arts; Higher education; Boys & girls clubs; Youth development.
Limitations: Applications not accepted. Giving fifty percent to IN charities, and fifty percent is unrestricted.
Application information: Unsolicited requests for funds not accepted.
Trustee: PNC Bank, N.A.
EIN: 347206415
Selected grants: The following grants are a representative sample of this grantmaker's funding activity:
$2,876,876 to Indiana University Foundation, Center of Philanthropy, Indianapolis, IN, 2012. For General Support.
$1,550,000 to United Way of Central Indiana, Indianapolis, IN, 2012. For General Support.
$958,959 to American Red Cross, Indianapolis, IN, 2012. For General Support.
$958,959 to Indiana University Foundation, Herron School of Art, Indianapolis, IN, 2012. For General Support.
$958,959 to Ruth Lilly Health Education Center, Indianapolis, IN, 2012. For Life Leadership.
$875,000 to Duke University, Durham, NC, 2012. For General Support.
$250,000 to United Way of Central Indiana, Indianapolis, IN, 2012. For General Support.
$40,000 to Mind Trust, Indianapolis, IN, 2012. For General Support.
$30,000 to Cape Cod Center For Women, North Falmouth, MA, 2012. For Funding for the Child Advocacy Specialist with the Balance for General Repair and Maintenance.
$25,000 to Woodstock Historical Foundation, Indianapolis, IN, 2012. For General Support.

3344
Lincoln Financial Foundation ✧

(formerly Lincoln Financial Group Foundation)
1300 S. Clinton St.
P.O. Box 7863
Fort Wayne, IN 46801-7863
FAX: (260) 455-4004; Application contact: Deb Washler, Prog. Off., tel.: (260) 455-3868, e-mail: Deb.Washler@LFG.com; Main URL: http://www.lincolnfinancial.com/LincolnPageServer?LFGPage=/lfg/lfgclient/abt/fingrp/index.html
Grants List: http://www.lfg.com/LincolnPageServer?LFGPage=/lfg/lfgclient/abt/fingrp/rec/index.html

Established in 1962 in IN as a company-sponsored operating foundation.
Donors: Lincoln National Corp.; The Lincoln National Life Insurance Co.
Foundation type: Company-sponsored foundation.
Financial data (yr. ended 12/31/13): Assets, $5,862,499 (M); gifts received, $8,305,100; expenditures, $9,324,166; qualifying distributions, $9,312,492; giving activities include $9,312,492 for 1,307 grants (high: $270,000; low: $50).
Purpose and activities: The foundation supports programs designed to promote the arts; youth education; human services; and workforce and economic development.
Fields of interest: Arts, cultural/ethnic awareness; Arts education; Performing arts, music; Arts; Elementary/secondary education; Education, early childhood education; Adult/continuing education; Adult education—literacy, basic skills & GED; Education, ESL programs; Education, services; Education, drop-out prevention; Education, reading; Education; Employment, training; Employment; Food services; Food banks; Housing/shelter, temporary shelter; Housing/shelter; Family services, domestic violence; Human services, financial counseling; Homeless, human services; Independent living, disability; Human services; Economic development; Business/industry; United Ways and Federated Giving Programs; Leadership development; Children; Aging; Economically disadvantaged.
Type of support: Building/renovation; Equipment; Program development; Scholarship funds; Employee volunteer services; Sponsorships; Employee matching gifts; Matching/challenge support.
Limitations: Applications accepted. Giving limited to areas of company operations, with emphasis on Hartford, CT, Fort Wayne, IN, Greensboro, NC, Omaha, NE, Concord, NH, and Philadelphia, PA. No support for religious organizations, public or private elementary or secondary schools or school foundations, hospitals, hospital foundations, fraternal, political, veterans', or sports organizations. No grants to individuals, or for endowments, continuing support, general operating support, capital campaigns, debt reduction, marketing programs, sporting events or tournaments, fundraising for national organizations, or national walks; generally, no grants for tickets, corporate tables, or testimonial events.
Publications: Application guidelines; Grants list.
Application information: Applications are reviewed by local Charitable Contribution Committees. Visit website for nearest application address. Support is limited to 1 contribution per organization during any given year. Application form required.
Initial approach: Complete online application form for specified cities
Copies of proposal: 1
Deadline(s): Mar. 11 for Education; June 17 for Human Services; Sept. 16 for Workforce and Economic Development; and Dec. 3 for Arts
Board meeting date(s): Quarterly
Final notification: 3 to 4 months
Officers and Directors:* Lisa M. Buckingham,* Chair.; Anne T. Rogers,* Pres.; Sharon M. Jeffers, Secy.; Jeffrey D. Coutts, Treas.; Adam G. Ciongoli; Charles C. Cornelio; Mark E. Konen.
Number of staff: 1 full-time professional; 5 part-time professional; 1 full-time support.
EIN: 356042099
Selected grants: The following grants are a representative sample of this grantmaker's funding activity:
$490,000 to Teach for America, New York, NY, 2012. For National STEM, payable over 2.00 years.
$270,000 to United Way of Allen County, Fort Wayne, IN, 2012. For Community Campaign, Learn United, Case Coordination System.
$150,000 to United Way of Greater Philadelphia and Southern New Jersey, Philadelphia, PA, 2012. For Success By 6.
$140,000 to Arts United of Greater Fort Wayne, Fort Wayne, IN, 2012. For Annual Fund Drive and Nonprofit Arts Internship Initiative.
$100,000 to Eagles Charitable Foundation, Philadelphia, PA, 2012. For Eagles Eye Mobile and Eagles Book Mobile.
$18,000 to Junior Achievement of Central North Carolina, Greensboro, NC, 2012. For K-12 Full STEM Ahead: Skills for a Global Economy.
$1,500 to Dallas Symphony Association, Dallas, TX, 2012.
$1,300 to Jewish Federation of Greater Atlanta, Atlanta, GA, 2012.
$625 to East Wayne Street Center, Fort Wayne, IN, 2012.
$500 to University of Rochester, Rochester, NY, 2012.

3345
Lumina Foundation ✧

P.O. Box 1806
Indianapolis, IN 46206-1806 (317) 951-5300
Contact: Juan Suarez, Sr. V.P., External Affairs; Lucia Anderson, Comms. Dir.
FAX: (317) 951-5063;
E-mail: jsuarez@luminafoundation.org; E-mail for Lucia Anderson: landerson@luminafoundation.org. Toll free: (800) 834-5756; Main URL: http://www.luminafoundation.org
E-Newsletter: http://www.luminafoundation.org/subscribe
Grants Database: http://www.luminafoundation.org/grants/database/
iTunes: http://itunes.apple.com/podcast/lumina-foundation-for-education/id311515249
Jamie Merisotis on Twitter: http://twitter.com/jamieindy/
Knowledge Center: http://www.luminafoundation.org/publications.html
Multimedia: http://www.luminafoundation.org/newsroom/multimedia.html
Twitter: http://twitter.com/LuminaFound

Established in 2000.
Donors: USA Group, Inc.; SLM Holding Corp.
Foundation type: Independent foundation.
Financial data (yr. ended 12/31/13): Assets, $1,258,939,683 (M); expenditures, $83,118,897; qualifying distributions, $75,274,689; giving activities include $49,852,400 for 150 grants (high: $2,000,000; low: $20,000), $1,995,039 for 606 employee matching gifts, and $13,750,934 for 4 foundation-administered programs.
Purpose and activities: The foundation's primary goal is to raise the proportion of the U.S. adult population who earn college degrees to 60 percent by 2025. The foundation is dedicated to expanding access and success in education beyond high school.
Fields of interest: Higher education; Youth; Adults; Young adults; Minorities; Asians/Pacific Islanders; African Americans/Blacks; Hispanics/Latinos; Native Americans/American Indians; Immigrants/refugees.
Type of support: General/operating support; Continuing support; Management development/capacity building; Program development; Conferences/seminars; Film/video/radio; Publication; Seed money; Research; Technical assistance; Consulting services; Program evaluation; Employee matching gifts; Matching/challenge support.
Limitations: Applications accepted. Giving on a national basis. No support for P-12 education reform, discipline-specific schools of study and training or religious activities (except for activities

that promote educational access and success and that serve diverse recipients without regard to their religious background); no grants that support single institutions; and no support for electioneering or lobbying activities. No grants to individuals (except for employee matching gifts), or for scholarships, fundraisers, corporate sponsorships, meetings and conferences (except for those related to a strategic initiative of the foundation), capital campaigns, or endowment funds.
Publications: Application guidelines; Financial statement; Grants list; Informational brochure (including application guidelines); Newsletter; Occasional report.
Application information: See foundation web site for LOI instructions. Only selected LOIs will receive a response. Application form required.
Initial approach: Online letter of inquiry
Copies of proposal: 1
Deadline(s): None
Board meeting date(s): Mar., Jun., Sept., and Nov.
Final notification: 3 to 6 months
Officers and Directors:* James C. Lintzenich,* Chair.; Jamie P. Merisotis, C.E.O. and Pres.; J. David Maas, V.P., Finance and Investments and C.F.O.; Danette Howard, V.P., Policy and Mobilization; Dewayne Matthews, V.P., Policy and Strategy; Samuel D. Cargile, V.P., Sr. Advisor to C.E.O.; Kiko Suarez, V.P., Comm. and Innovation; David A. Brown, Cont.; Holiday Hart McKiernan, Chief of Staff and Genl. Counsel; Frank D. Alvarez; Kathy Davis; Allan Hubbard; F. Joseph Loughrey; Marie V. McDemmond; J. Bonnie Newman; Laura Palmer Noone; Michael L. Smith; Belle S. Wheelan; Mark G. Yudof.
Number of staff: 27 full-time professional; 9 full-time support.
EIN: 351813228
Selected grants: The following grants are a representative sample of this grantmaker's funding activity:
$1,700,000 to SPEC Associates, Detroit, MI, 2012. To gain a deep understanding of the effectiveness of the Strategy Labs Network approach that Lumina has settled on with grantee partners for effecting policy- and systems-level change around a defined agenda of policy and practice, the Four Steps to Finishing First.
$1,600,000 to Georgetown University, Washington, DC, 2012. For the Georgetown University Center on Education and the Workforce's mission to strengthen the alignment of postsecondary education and workforce via research and technical assistance.
$1,596,900 to Tides Center, San Francisco, CA, 2012. For supporting Lumina Foundation's multi-state, multi-year Productivity Grant initiative by managing contracts with states focused on incentivizing college completion to encourage graduation of many more Americans with high-quality degrees and credentials.
$1,200,000 to Achieving the Dream, Silver Spring, MD, 2012. For attainment of degrees and credentials by community college students nationally through Achieving the Dream, Inc.
$1,140,000 to Excelencia in Education, Washington, DC, 2012. To strengthen the knowledge sharing, cultural competency, place-based collaboration, technical assistance, and communications strategies among thirteen communities striving to increase Latino student success.
$1,108,000 to Tides Center, San Francisco, CA, 2012. For supporting Lumina Foundation's multi-state, multi-year Productivity Grant initiative by managing contracts with states focused on restructuring costs of administrative and academic services to expand capacity to educate college students.
$70,000 to CEOs for Cities, Chicago, IL, 2012. To expand the reach, elevate the message and support urban leaders to move from insight to action on the Talent Dividend.

3346
Madison County Community Foundation ✧
33 W. 10th St., Ste. 600
P.O. Box 1056
Anderson, IN 46015-1056 (765) 644-0002
Contact: Sally A. DeVoe, Exec. Dir.
FAX: (765) 644-3392; E-mail: info@madisonccf.org; Additional e-mail: sdevoe@madisonccf.org; Main URL: http://www.madisonccf.org
Facebook: https://www.facebook.com/madisonccf

Established in 1992 in IN.
Foundation type: Community foundation.
Financial data (yr. ended 12/31/12): Assets, $15,132,719 (M); gifts received, $692,216; expenditures, $1,177,407; giving activities include $657,631 for grants.
Purpose and activities: The foundation seeks to enhance the quality of life of the citizens of Madison County, IN, by attracting charitable gifts, making philanthropic grants, providing responsible financial stewardship and community leadership.
Fields of interest: Arts; Education; Health care; Human services; Economic development; Public affairs.
Type of support: General/operating support; Capital campaigns; Building/renovation; Equipment; Emergency funds; Program development; Curriculum development; Scholarship funds; Scholarships—to individuals; Matching/challenge support.
Limitations: Applications accepted. Giving limited to Madison County, IN. No support for religious or sectarian activities. No grants to individuals (except for scholarships), for budget deficits, annual fund campaigns, capital debt reduction, endowments, medical, scientific, or health research, or travel; no student loans.
Publications: Annual report (including application guidelines); Informational brochure; Newsletter.
Application information: Visit foundation web site for application form and guidelines. Application form required.
Initial approach: Submit application
Copies of proposal: 8
Deadline(s): May 9 and Nov. 5 for General Grants; varies for others
Board meeting date(s): 6 times a year
Final notification: Within 6 weeks
Officers and Directors:* Tom Cassidy,* Pres.; Craig Dunkin,* V.P.; Lynn Rowley,* Secy.; Tom Beeman,* Treas.; Sally A. DeVoe,* Exec. Dir.; James F. Ault; Sherri Contos; Gary Erskine; Gloria Gaither; Joe Kilmer; Rob Loose; Bob Pensec; Marcia Simmermon; Chuck Staley.
Number of staff: 1 full-time professional; 1 part-time professional; 1 full-time support.
EIN: 351859959

3347
Marian Wayside Shrine Foundation Inc. ✧ ☆
10630 Wicker Ave.
St. John, IN 46373-8809

Established in IN.
Donors: Frank Schilling; Shirley Schilling; Jerry Corcoran; Gail Corcoran; Francine Demma; Crown Point Community Foundation; James J. Depaoli; Schilling Brothers Lumber.
Foundation type: Operating foundation.
Financial data (yr. ended 12/31/13): Assets, $8,992,774 (M); gifts received, $387,786; expenditures, $2,263,545; qualifying distributions, $1,434,980; giving activities include $1,000,000 for 1 grant, and $1,389,159 for 1 foundation-administered program.
Fields of interest: Religion.
Limitations: Applications not accepted. Giving primarily in Green Bay, WI.
Application information: Unsolicited requests for funds not accepted.
Officers: Frank E. Schilling, Pres.; Sammie L. Maletta, V.P.; Shirley Schilling, Secy.
Directors: Frank Keilman; Tom Kirsch; Dean Schilling; Gregory Schilling; Jeffrey Schilling; Todd Schilling; Steve Teibel.
EIN: 300111349

3348
Marshall County Community Foundation, Inc. ✧
2701 N. Michigan St.
P.O. Box 716
Plymouth, IN 46563 (574) 935-5159
FAX: (574) 936-8040;
E-mail: info@marshallcountycf.org; Main URL: http://www.marshallcountycf.org
Facebook: https://www.facebook.com/pages/Marshall-County-Community-Foundation/218830374800800
RSS Feed: http://marshallcountycf.org/feed/

Established in 1991 in IN.
Foundation type: Community foundation.
Financial data (yr. ended 06/30/13): Assets, $28,632,675 (M); gifts received, $725,507; expenditures, $1,106,755; giving activities include $649,183 for 26 grants (high: $63,109).
Purpose and activities: The foundation seeks to enhance the quality of life in Marshall County by providing funds through a grant making process for humanitarian, cultural, educational, recreational and environmental activities. The general policy of the foundation is to make grants for innovative and creative projects serving Marshall County, and to programs which are responsive to changing community needs.
Fields of interest: Arts; Secondary school/education; Higher education; Libraries (public); Scholarships/financial aid; Education; Environment; Animals/wildlife, preservation/protection; Hospitals (general); Health care; Recreation, parks/playgrounds; Recreation; Family services; Human services; Community/economic development; Government/public administration; Children/youth.
Type of support: Building/renovation; Equipment; Emergency funds; Program development; Publication; Seed money; Research; Technical assistance; Consulting services; Scholarships—to individuals; Matching/challenge support.

Limitations: Applications accepted. Giving limited to Marshall County, IN. No support for sectarian or religious purposes. No grants to individuals (except for scholarships), or for operating expenses, long-term funding or for endowments.
Publications: Application guidelines; Annual report (including application guidelines); Financial statement; Grants list; Informational brochure (including application guidelines); Newsletter; Program policy statement.
Application information: Visit foundation web site for application form and guidelines. Application form required.
Initial approach: Submit application form and attachments
Copies of proposal: 3
Deadline(s): Feb. 1 and Aug. 1
Board meeting date(s): Jan., Mar., May, July, Sept., and Nov.
Final notification: Within 90 days
Officers and Directors:* Jerry Gates,* Chair.; Patti Kitch,* Vice-Chair.; Jayne Gibson,* V.P., Opers.; Carolyn Kline,* Secy.; Jared Weidner,* Treas.; Richard Parker,* Co-Treas.; Linda K. Yoder, Exec. Dir.; Derek Jones, Legal Counsel; Brian Baker; Don Balka; Kevin Boyer; Tim Harman; Joan Hunt; Connie Lemler; Louise Mason; Amy Middaugh; Ginny Munroe; Don Newton; Paul Nye; Michael Overmyer; John Small, Jr.; Beth Styers; Don Thompson; Barbara Winters; John Zeglis; Ron Zeltwanger; and 4 additional Directors.
Number of staff: 2 part-time professional; 1 full-time support; 2 part-time support.
EIN: 351826870

3349
Marten Charitable Trust ✧ ☆
210 W. 77th St.
Indianapolis, IN 46260-3608

Donor: Virginia A. Marten.
Foundation type: Independent foundation.
Financial data (yr. ended 12/31/13): Assets, $983,499 (M); gifts received, $119,794; expenditures, $476,646; qualifying distributions, $466,322; giving activities include $466,322 for 1 grant.
Fields of interest: Human services; Foundations (private grantmaking); Catholic agencies & churches.
Limitations: Applications not accepted. Giving primarily in IN. No grants to individuals.
Application information: Contributes only to pre-selected organizations.
Trustees: Virginia M. Hupfer; David K. Marten; James W. Marten; Virginia A. Marten; Alicia M. O'Connor.
EIN: 356596974

3350
Rex and Alice A. Martin Foundation ✧
1516 Middlebury St.
Elkhart, IN 46516-4740

Established in 2000 in IN.
Donors: Rex Martin; Alice A. Martin; NIBCO, Inc.; Alexis Martin; Ashley Martin.
Foundation type: Operating foundation.
Financial data (yr. ended 06/30/13): Assets, $11,958,931 (M); expenditures, $829,573; qualifying distributions, $734,155; giving activities include $543,000 for 11 grants (high: $200,000; low: $5,000).
Fields of interest: Higher education; Human services; Community/economic development; Foundations (community).
Limitations: Applications not accepted. Giving primarily in Chicago, IL, and IN, with emphasis on Elkhart. No grants to individuals.
Application information: Contributes only to pre-selected organizations.
Officer and Directors:* Alice A. Martin,* Pres.; Alexis Martin; Ashley Martin; Rex Martin.
EIN: 352117025
Selected grants: The following grants are a representative sample of this grantmaker's funding activity:
$150,000 to Elkhart, City of, Elkhart, IN, 2011.
$83,000 to Elkhart County Community Foundation, Elkhart, IN, 2011.

3351
Alfred J. McAllister and Dorothy N. McAllister Foundation ✧
2310 N. 725 E.
Lafayette, IN 47905-9693

Established in 2000 in IN.
Donor: Dorothy N. McAllister.
Foundation type: Independent foundation.
Financial data (yr. ended 12/31/13): Assets, $11,747,727 (M); expenditures, $625,299; qualifying distributions, $512,062; giving activities include $422,000 for 16 grants (high: $72,500; low: $2,000).
Fields of interest: Education; Animals/wildlife; Human services.
Limitations: Applications not accepted. Giving primarily in Lafayette, IN. No grants to individuals.
Application information: Contributes only to pre-selected organizations.
Trustees: Charles Max Layden; William J. McCaw; J. David Webb; Wayne E. Weber.
EIN: 352050825
Selected grants: The following grants are a representative sample of this grantmaker's funding activity:
$50,000 to Ivy Tech Foundation, Lafayette, IN, 2011.
$25,000 to Wabash Center, Lafayette, IN, 2011.
$20,000 to Tippecanoe Arts Federation, Lafayette, IN, 2011.
$15,000 to Natalie's Second Chance Dog Shelter, Lafayette, IN, 2011.
$12,500 to Art Museum of Greater Lafayette, Lafayette, IN, 2011.

3352
McMillen Foundation, Inc. ✧
6610 Mutual Dr.
Fort Wayne, IN 46825-4236
Contact: Dorothy J. Robinson, Secy.-Treas.
Application contact: John F. McMillen, Pres.

Incorporated in 1947 in IN.
Donors: Dale W. McMillen‡; and members of the McMillen family.
Foundation type: Independent foundation.
Financial data (yr. ended 12/31/12): Assets, $30,855,372 (M); expenditures, $1,735,515; qualifying distributions, $1,579,896; giving activities include $1,550,842 for 24 grants (high: $425,000; low: $1,102).
Purpose and activities: Emphasis on recreation associations and youth agencies; some support also for education, and health associations.
Fields of interest: Education; Health care; Health organizations, association; Recreation; Children/youth, services; Community/economic development; Children/youth.
Type of support: Capital campaigns; Building/renovation; Endowments; Program development; Matching/challenge support.
Limitations: Applications accepted. Giving limited to Fort Wayne and Allen County, IN. No support for churches or religious groups. No grants to individuals.
Publications: Application guidelines.
Application information: Application form not required.
Initial approach: Letter
Copies of proposal: 1
Deadline(s): None
Board meeting date(s): Annual meeting in midsummer; and executive committee meets near year end
Final notification: 6 months
Officers and Directors:* John F. McMillen,* Pres.; Thomas M. Shoaff,* V.P.; Dorothy J. Robinson, Secy.-Treas.; Thomas A. Irmscher; Dale W. McMillen III; N. Reed Silliman.
Number of staff: 1 part-time support.
EIN: 356021003
Selected grants: The following grants are a representative sample of this grantmaker's funding activity:
$200,000 to Indiana Institute of Technology, Fort Wayne, IN, 2012. For Capital Campaign - McMillen Library Component.
$200,000 to University of Saint Francis, Fort Wayne, IN, 2012. For Cap Building Campaign.
$50,000 to Junior Achievement of Northern Indiana, Fort Wayne, IN, 2012. For economics program.
$50,000 to Science Central, Fort Wayne, IN, 2012. For Science on a Sphere Exhibit.
$13,225 to East Wayne Street Center, Fort Wayne, IN, 2012. For New Carpet and Flooring.

3353
Met Foundation, Inc. ✧
7406 N. Washington Blvd.
Indianapolis, IN 46240-3090

Established in 1997 in IN.
Donors: Sue Anne McVie; Susan M. Tolbert.
Foundation type: Independent foundation.
Financial data (yr. ended 12/31/13): Assets, $12,761,122 (M); expenditures, $587,678; qualifying distributions, $540,374; giving activities include $525,035 for 66 grants (high: $53,500; low: $100).
Purpose and activities: Giving for the arts, youth services, and animal welfare.
Fields of interest: Museums; Higher education; Environment, natural resources; Environment, land resources; Animals/wildlife, preservation/protection; Alzheimer's disease; Boy scouts; Youth, services; Protestant agencies & churches.
Limitations: Applications not accepted. Giving primarily in Indianapolis, IN.
Application information: Contributes only to pre-selected organizations.

Officers and Directors:* Susan M. Tolbert,* Pres. and Treas.; Douglas S. McVie,* V.P.; Alexander S. McVie,* Secy.
EIN: 351995120
Selected grants: The following grants are a representative sample of this grantmaker's funding activity:
$53,593 to Sky Island Alliance, Tucson, AZ, 2011. For operating support.
$30,000 to Methodist Health Foundation, Indianapolis, IN, 2011. For operating support.
$25,000 to Second Presbyterian Church, Indianapolis, IN, 2011. For operating support.
$25,000 to United Way of Central Indiana, Indianapolis, IN, 2011. For operating support.
$25,000 to Wabash College, Crawfordsville, IN, 2011. For operating support.
$20,000 to National Sports Center for the Disabled, Denver, CO, 2011. For operating support.
$12,000 to Boy Scouts of America, Denver, CO, 2011. For operating support.
$11,243 to Habitat for Humanity of Greater Indianapolis, Indianapolis, IN, 2011. For operating support.
$5,000 to Defenders of Wildlife, Washington, DC, 2011. For operating support.
$5,000 to Indianapolis Museum of Art, Indianapolis, IN, 2011. For operating support.

3354
Michigan City Community Enrichment Corporation ✧

100 E. Michigan Blvd.
Michigan City, IN 46360-3265 (219) 873-1400 x382
E-mail: mccomenrich@yahoo.com; Application address: P.O. Box 526, Michigan City, IN 46361; Main URL: http://www.emichigancity.com/cityhall/boards/mccec/index.htm

Established in 1998 in IN.
Donor: Blue Chip Casino, Inc.
Foundation type: Company-sponsored foundation.
Financial data (yr. ended 12/31/13): Assets, $517,224 (M); gifts received, $705,673; expenditures, $649,994; qualifying distributions, $649,994.
Purpose and activities: The foundation supports zoos and organizations involved with education, health, hunger, and human services. Special emphasis is directed toward programs designed to benefit children.
Fields of interest: Elementary school/education; Education; Zoos/zoological societies; Health care; Food distribution, meals on wheels; Boys & girls clubs; Youth development, business; American Red Cross; YM/YWCAs & YM/YWHAs; Children/youth, services; Family services; Homeless, human services; Human services; Children.
Type of support: Capital campaigns; Building/renovation; Equipment; Program development.
Limitations: Applications accepted. Giving primarily in Michigan City, IN. No support for churches or sectarian religious organizations. No grants to individuals, or for endowments, debt reduction, general operating support, or basic municipal or educational functions or services.
Application information: Organizations receiving support are asked to submit quarterly grant reports. Support is limited to 1 contribution per organization during any given year. Additional information may be requested at a later date. Application form required.
Initial approach: Download application form and mail to foundation or contact foundation for an application form
Copies of proposal: 9
Deadline(s): Varies
Officers and Directors: Andy Swan, Pres.; Charles Sheerin, V.P.; Brenda Tillman, Treas.; Chris Carter; George Kazmierczak; Michael McKervey; Shirley St. Arnaud; Susan Webster; Joan Wiseman; Jack VanEtten.
EIN: 352036426
Selected grants: The following grants are a representative sample of this grantmaker's funding activity:
$35,000 to Stepping Stone Shelter for Women, Michigan City, IN, 2011.
$25,000 to Reins of Life, South Bend, IN, 2011.
$15,000 to Jack and Shirley Lubeznik Center for the Arts, Michigan City, IN, 2011.
$15,000 to Open Door Health Center, Michigan City, IN, 2011.
$15,000 to Social and Learning Institute for the Disadvantaged, Michigan City, IN, 2011.
$10,000 to Samaritan Counseling Centers, Michigan City, IN, 2011.
$10,000 to Shirley Heinze Land Trust, Michigan City, IN, 2011.
$3,000 to Festival Players Guild, Michigan City, IN, 2011.

3355
Dr. Dane & Mary Louise Miller Foundation, Inc. ✧

(formerly The Biomet Foundation, Inc.)
700 Park Ave., Ste. G
Winona Lake, IN 46590-1066
Contact: Cindy Helper, Secy. and Dir.

Established in 1990 in IN.
Donors: Biomet, Inc.; Dane A. Miller; Mrs. Dane A. Miller; Jerry L. Ferguson; Mrs. Jerry L. Ferguson.
Foundation type: Company-sponsored foundation.
Financial data (yr. ended 12/31/13): Assets, $18,183,961 (M); expenditures, $992,782; qualifying distributions, $992,782; giving activities include $729,090 for 58 grants (high: $250,000; low: $100), and $219,000 for 73 grants to individuals (high: $3,000; low: $3,000).
Purpose and activities: The foundation supports organizations involved with arts and culture, education, breast cancer research, recreation, human services, and Christianity.
Fields of interest: Media, television; Arts; Secondary school/education; Higher education; Education; Breast cancer research; Recreation, fairs/festivals; Recreation; Children/youth, services; Family services, adolescent parents; Pregnancy centers; Developmentally disabled, centers & services; Human services; United Ways and Federated Giving Programs.
Type of support: Matching/challenge support; General/operating support; Annual campaigns; Program development; Scholarship funds; Sponsorships; Employee-related scholarships.
Limitations: Applications accepted. Giving primarily in Kosciusko County, IN. No support for political or religious organizations.
Publications: Informational brochure.
Application information: Application form required.
Initial approach: Completed application form
Copies of proposal: 1
Deadline(s): Mar. 15
Officers and Directors:* Dane A. Miller,* Pres.; Mary Louise Miller,* V.P.; Cindy Hepler,* Secy.; Daniel P. Hann; Kimberly Vansessen; Darlene K. Whaley.
EIN: 351806314

3356
Montgomery County Community Foundation ✧

119 E. Main St.
P.O. Box 334
Crawfordsville, IN 47933-1709 (765) 362-1267
Contact: Kelly Taylor, Exec. Dir.
FAX: (765) 361-0562; E-mail: ann@mccf-in.org; Main URL: http://www.mccf-in.org
Facebook: http://www.facebook.com/pages/Montgomery-County-Community-Foundation/174910159217873
Scholarship inquiry e-mail: marty@mccf-in.org

Established in 1991 in IN.
Foundation type: Community foundation.
Financial data (yr. ended 12/31/13): Assets, $38,194,030 (M); gifts received, $920,961; expenditures, $1,877,792; giving activities include $1,207,350 for 23+ grants (high: $734,827), and $242,650 for 206 grants to individuals.
Purpose and activities: The foundation provides grants and scholarships to the Montgomery County community.
Fields of interest: Historic preservation/historical societies; Arts; Higher education; Education; Environment, recycling; Environment, energy; Environment; Health care; Human services; Community/economic development; Children/youth; Disabilities, people with.
Type of support: Annual campaigns; Capital campaigns; Building/renovation; Equipment; Program development; Conferences/seminars; Seed money; Scholarship funds; Scholarships—to individuals; Matching/challenge support.
Limitations: Applications accepted. Giving limited to Montgomery County, IN. No support for religious organizations. No grants to individuals (except for scholarships), or for endowments, operating budgets, special events, existing obligations, parades, festivals, or sporting events.
Publications: Application guidelines; Annual report; Grants list; Informational brochure (including application guidelines); Newsletter.
Application information: Visit foundation web site for application forms and guidelines. Application form required.
Initial approach: Submit online application
Copies of proposal: 10
Deadline(s): Apr. 15
Board meeting date(s): June and Nov.
Final notification: Aug.
Officers and Directors:* Steve McLaughlin,* Pres.; Tom Mellish,* V.P.; Heather Dennison,* Secy.; Dale Petrie,* Treas.; Kelly Taylor, Exec. Dir.; Amy Cooper; Tony Cosenza; Larry Griffith; Sheridan Hadley; Mike Mitchell; Sharon O'Dell-Keedy; Janet Rucker; Anita Rupar; Nancy Sennett; John Tidd; Tom Utley.
Number of staff: 3 full-time professional; 1 part-time professional; 1 part-time support.
EIN: 351836315

3357
MTI Foundation, Inc. ✧
1401 S. Grandstaff Dr.
Auburn, IN 46706-2664

Established in 2004 in IN.
Donor: Metal Technologies, Inc.
Foundation type: Independent foundation.
Financial data (yr. ended 12/31/13): Assets, $789,941 (M); gifts received, $1,170,000; expenditures, $898,638; qualifying distributions, $896,610; giving activities include $896,610 for 24 grants (high: $400,000; low: $50).
Fields of interest: Arts; Higher education; Libraries (public); Education; Human services; YM/YWCAs & YM/YWHAs; Foundations (community).
Limitations: Applications not accepted. Giving primarily in IL and IN. No grants to individuals.
Application information: Contributes only to pre-selected organizations.
Officers: Rick L. James, Pres.; Jeffrey L. Turner, Secy.-Treas.
EIN: 352114344

3358
National Recreation Foundation, Inc. ✧
P.O. Box 8007
Bloomington, IN 47407-8007 (812) 855-1342
FAX: (812) 855-0061; E-mail: mobley@indiana.edu; Main URL: http://nationalrecreationfoundation.org

Supporting organization of Abraham Lincoln Council, American Trauma Society, Appalachian Sustainable, Asphalt Gree, Big Picture Alliance, Boys and Girls Clubs, Boys and Girls Clubs of Peninsula, Chicago Youth Centers, City Wild, Community Prepartory School, Conservancy of SW FL, Durango Nature Studies, Focus: Hope, Good Sports Inc., Greater Newark Conservatory, Gulf of Marine Institute, Illinois State Museum Society, International City/ County Management, Irvine Nature Center, James Beckworth Mtn., KERA, Kidpower, Kids at Hope, King Street Youth Center, Lefroy Springs & Co., Lyman Allen Art Center, Mann Center for the Performing Arts, Miller Middle School, Museum of African Art, National Recreation & Park Association, Nature Discovery Museum, Norris Square Neighborhood, Parkland Foundation, Pogasa Springs Park, Portland Museum of Art, Proyecto Pastoral at Delores, Tanglewood 4-H Camp, The Family Center, The PA Horticultural, The Village Foundation, Trust for Public Land, Ujoma Student Development.
Foundation type: Independent foundation.
Financial data (yr. ended 12/31/12): Assets, $38,543,505 (M); expenditures, $2,260,453; qualifying distributions, $2,076,835; giving activities include $1,851,115 for 31 grants (high: $200,000; low: $5,000).
Fields of interest: Environment; Boys & girls clubs; Human services; Children/youth, services.
Limitations: Applications not accepted.
Publications: Financial statement.
Application information: Unsolicited requests for funds not considered or acknowledged.
Officers and Trustees:* Kathryn A. Porter,* Pres.; Francis P. Pandolfi, V.P.; Robert A. Stuart, Jr.,* 2nd V.P.; Jonathan D. Scott,* Treas.; Tony A. Mobley, Exec. Dir.; Joseph B. Anderson, Jr.; Lynne M. O. Brickner; David H. Carleton; Robert W. Crawford, Jr.; John L. Crompton, Ph.D.; Endicott P. Davidson, Jr.; James R. Donnelley; Robert Jaunich II; Elsie Crum McCabe-Thompson; John W. McCarter, Jr.; J. James Pearce, Jr.; Nicholas G. Penniman IV; Edith R. Perez; Timothy L. Richardson; Robert D. Rogers; Jon J. Seal; John M. Templeton, Jr., M.D.; R. Thayer Tutt, Jr.; Alfred A. Valenzuela.
EIN: 136172514
Selected grants: The following grants are a representative sample of this grantmaker's funding activity:
$200,000 to Cristo Rey Network, Chicago, IL, 2012. To help pilot the Healthy Lifestyles Program.
$150,000 to Stonington Community Center, Stonington, CT, 2012. To support of their scholarship Program.
$50,000 to National Guard Youth Foundation, Alexandria, VA, 2012. For the National Guard Youth Challenge Program (Crawford Award).
$45,000 to Byerschool Foundation, Philadelphia, PA, 2012. To help pilot the Ours for Life Program.
$30,000 to Boothbay Region Land Trust, Boothbay Harbor, ME, 2012. For the development and implementation of the Osprey Program.
$30,000 to Friends of City Park, New Orleans, LA, 2012. To assist in expanding outreach of LOOP Program.
$30,000 to METROsquash, Chicago, IL, 2012. To enable growth in Program enrollment and support more athletic instruction and fitness Programming.
$30,000 to Neighborhood Youth Association, Venice, CA, 2012. For the NYA Personal Best Program which assists the prevention of anti-social behavior and encourages proactive lifestyles and healthy values for at-risk youth.
$25,000 to Urban Youth Ministries, Denver, CO, 2012. For Programs seeking to fill the gap in parenting resources that exist in single parent households of at-risk youth in the Denver area.
$15,000 to Catamount Institute, Colorado Springs, CO, 2012. To maintain and expand its award winning Youth Environmental Stewards (YES) Program.

3359
Noble County Community Foundation ✧
1599 Lincolnway S.
Ligonier, IN 46767-9731 (260) 894-3335
Contact: Linda Speakman-Yerick, Exec. Dir.; For grants: Margarita White, Prog. Off.
FAX: (260) 894-9020;
E-mail: info@noblecountycf.org; Grant inquiry e-mail: margarita@noblecountycf.org; Grant inquiry tel.: (260) 894-3335; Main URL: http://www.noblecountycf.org/
Facebook: https://www.facebook.com/pages/Noble-County-Community-Foundation/486692855042
RSS Feed: http://noblecountycf.org/feed/

Established in 1991 in IN.
Foundation type: Community foundation.
Financial data (yr. ended 12/31/13): Assets, $24,843,990 (M); gifts received, $1,727,777; expenditures, $1,407,896; giving activities include $644,597 for grants.
Purpose and activities: The foundation seeks to improve the quality of life in Noble County by serving as a catalyst for positive change, enabling donors to carry out charitable intent, and making grants. Primary areas of interest include health, human services, education, arts and culture, and civic affairs.
Fields of interest: Arts, cultural/ethnic awareness; Arts; Education; Health care; Safety/disasters; Youth development, services; Family services, parent education; Human services; Community/ economic development; Public affairs; Girls.
Type of support: Management development/ capacity building; In-kind gifts; Building/renovation; Capital campaigns; Conferences/seminars; Consulting services; Emergency funds; Equipment; General/operating support; Land acquisition; Matching/challenge support; Program development; Scholarship funds; Scholarships—to individuals; Seed money; Technical assistance.
Limitations: Applications accepted. Giving primarily limited to Noble County, IN. No support for sectarian religious purposes, or for conduit organizations. No grants for annual fund campaigns, routine operating support for ongoing programs, multi-year funding, travel, augmenting endowments, deficit spending, underwriting for fundraising events, or research; no loans.
Publications: Application guidelines; Annual report; Grants list; Informational brochure (including application guidelines); Newsletter.
Application information: Visit foundation Web site for application guidelines. Faxed proposals are not accepted. The foundation offers a free grant writing workshop from time to time; e-mail or call Prog. Off. to register. Application form not required.
Initial approach: Telephone or letter of intent
Copies of proposal: 1
Deadline(s): Mar. 2, May 2, July 2, and Nov. 2
Board meeting date(s): 4th Wed. in Feb., Apr., June, Aug., Oct., and 3rd Wed. in Dec.
Final notification: 60 days after deadline
Officers and Directors:* Valerie Hague,* Pres.; Dr. Doug Jansen,* V.P.; Jolene Durham,* Secy.; Monte Egolf,* Treas.; Linda Speakman-Yerick, Exec. Dir.; Jim Abbs; Arthur Grawcock; Gary Leatherman; Jonthan Leman; Craig Lichlyter; Josh Munson; Leigh Pranger; Jarrod Ramer; Rodney Schoon; Janet Sweeney.
Number of staff: 3 full-time professional; 1 full-time support; 1 part-time support.
EIN: 351827247

3360
Northern Indiana Community Foundation, Inc. ✧
715 Main St.
P.O. Box 807
Rochester, IN 46975-1543 (574) 223-2227
Contact: Jay Albright, Exec. Dir.
FAX: (574) 224-3709; E-mail: jay@nicf.org; Additional tel.: (877) 432-6423; additional e-mail: jay@nicf.org; Main URL: http://www.nicf.org
Facebook: http://www.facebook.com/pages/Northern-Indiana-Community-Foundation/207271679290731

Established in 1993 in IN.
Foundation type: Community foundation.
Financial data (yr. ended 12/31/12): Assets, $23,704,972 (M); gifts received, $1,664,358; expenditures, $2,608,434; giving activities include $1,163,556 for 28+ grants (high: $150,000), and $230,563 for 293 grants to individuals.
Purpose and activities: The foundation seeks to improve the quality of life in the community by assisting donors in fulfilling their charitable wishes.
Fields of interest: Arts; Education; Environment; Health organizations, association; Recreation; Youth development; Human services; Community/ economic development; Youth.

Type of support: General/operating support; Building/renovation; Equipment; Endowments; Emergency funds; Program development; Seed money; Scholarship funds; Consulting services; Matching/challenge support.
Limitations: Applications accepted. Giving limited to Fulton, Miami, and Starke counties, IN. No support for sectarian or religious organizations operated primarily for the benefit of their own members. No grants to individuals (except for scholarships), or for annual fundraisers or campaigns, ongoing operating expenses, deficits, direct or grass-roots lobbying, sponsorships, special events, commercial advertising, films or videos, television, conferences, or group uniforms or trips.
Publications: Application guidelines; Annual report; Informational brochure; Newsletter.
Application information: Visit foundation web site for specific county application forms, guidelines, and deadlines. Application form required.
Initial approach: Telephone or fax
Copies of proposal: 1
Deadline(s): Varies
Board meeting date(s): 3rd Wed. of each month
Final notification: Approx. 6 weeks
Officers and Directors:* Ron Douglas,* Pres.; Jennifer Gappa,* V.P.; Judy Climie,* Secy.; Gene Miles,* Treas.; Jay Albright, Exec. Dir.; Suzy Bishop; Larry Cunningham; Jeff Finke; Evan Gottschalk; Jerry Gurrado; Max Hattery; Leon Huskey; Gene Ladd; Tom McKaig; Marcia Minard; Pat Mitchell; Susie Perkins; Kirk Robinson; Marilyn Wickert; Jim Yates.
Number of staff: 1 full-time professional; 4 full-time support.
EIN: 351912317

3361
Nicholas H. Noyes, Jr. Memorial Foundation, Inc. ✧
1950 E. Greyhound Pass, No. 18-356
Carmel, IN 46033-7730 (317) 844-8009
Contact: Kelly Mills, Exec. Admin.
FAX: (317) 844-8099;
E-mail: admin@noyesfoundation.org; Letter of inquiry contact: Sue Richardson, Prog. Off., e-mail: SLSR28@yahoo.com; Main URL: http://www.noyesfoundation.org

Incorporated in 1951 in IN.
Donors: Nicholas H. Noyes†; Marguerite Lilly Noyes†.
Foundation type: Independent foundation.
Financial data (yr. ended 12/31/13): Assets, $42,594,924 (M); expenditures, $1,711,194; qualifying distributions, $1,609,415; giving activities include $1,467,500 for 140 grants (high: $60,000; low: $1,000).
Purpose and activities: Giving primarily for the arts, civic and community development, k-12 and higher education, environmental preservation and improvement, health and human services, and religious initiatives.
Fields of interest: Museums; Performing arts; Arts; Education, early childhood education; Elementary school/education; Secondary school/education; Higher education; Education; Hospitals (general); Health care; Health organizations, association; Human services; Children/youth, services; Family services; Community/economic development; Disabilities, people with; Minorities; Economically disadvantaged.
Type of support: General/operating support; Continuing support; Annual campaigns; Capital campaigns; Program development; Scholarship funds.
Limitations: Applications accepted. Giving primarily in the greater Indianapolis, IN, area with emphasis on Marion County. No support for political organizations or lobbying organizations. No grants to individuals, or for endowments, matching grants, or multi-year grants; no loans.
Publications: Application guidelines.
Application information: Specific application policies and form available on foundation web site. Application form required.
Initial approach: Letter of Inquiry via e-mail to Sue Richardson, Prog. Off.
Deadline(s): See foundation web site for current deadlines
Board meeting date(s): Semiannually
Officers and Directors:* Nicholas S. Noyes,* Pres.; Avery Augustine,* V.P. and Secy.; L. Gene Tanner,* Treas.; Nancy Ayres; Clay Carrington; David Harris; Dan Noyes; Elizabeth H. Noyes; Henry S. Noyes; Zeb Portanova; Robert H. Reynolds.
Number of staff: 1 full-time professional; 1 part-time professional.
EIN: 351003699
Selected grants: The following grants are a representative sample of this grantmaker's funding activity:
$100,000 to Eskenazi Health Foundation, Indianapolis, IN, 2011.
$50,000 to Independent Colleges of Indiana, Indianapolis, IN, 2011.
$50,000 to United Way of Central Indiana, Indianapolis, IN, 2011. For annual support.
$42,500 to Indiana Symphony Society, Indianapolis, IN, 2011. For annual support.
$30,000 to Nature Conservancy, Indianapolis, IN, 2011. For annual support.
$20,000 to Boy Scouts of America, Crossroads of America Council, Indianapolis, IN, 2011. For annual support.
$20,000 to Goodwill Industries of Central Indiana, Indianapolis, IN, 2011. For annual support.
$20,000 to Noble, Inc., Indianapolis, IN, 2011. For annual support.
$16,000 to Special Olympics Indiana, Indianapolis, IN, 2011. For annual support.
$6,500 to Diabetes Youth Foundation of Indiana, Indianapolis, IN, 2011.

3362
Paul Ogle Foundation, Inc. ✧
321 E. Court Ave.
Jeffersonville, IN 47130-3411
Contact: Kent W. Lanum, Exec. Dir.
Mailing address: P.O. Box 845, Jeffersonville, IN 47131-0845; contact for K. Lanum, tel.: (812) 280-8372, ext. 2; e-mail: klanum@ogle-fdn.org; Main URL: http://www.ogle-fdn.org

Established in 1980 in IN.
Donor: Paul W. Ogle†.
Foundation type: Independent foundation.
Financial data (yr. ended 12/31/12): Assets, $63,977,396 (M); expenditures, $3,274,258; qualifying distributions, $3,044,255; giving activities include $2,653,281 for 33 grants (high: $300,000; low: $2,500).
Purpose and activities: The primary categories of funding by the foundation are education (primarily higher education), civic, economic development, humanities and health and general welfare. Historically, the foundation has supported projects with an emphasis on bricks and mortar, equipment purchases, and pre-selected scholarship funds.
Fields of interest: Arts; Higher education; Education; Human services; Community/economic development.
Type of support: Building/renovation; Equipment; Land acquisition; Endowments; Program development; Scholarship funds; Matching/challenge support.
Limitations: Applications accepted. Giving primarily in southern IN (Clark, Floyd, Harrison, Scott, Switzerland and Washington counties), as well as Jefferson County, KY. Only nonprofits in these areas may apply. No support for research programs, churches and related activities, private foundations, or public or private elementary or secondary school programs. No grants to individuals, or for ongoing, general operating expenses or existing deficits; no loans.
Publications: Application guidelines.
Application information: Application guidelines available on foundation web site. Based on review of the letter of inquiry, the foundation may request a full proposal. Applicants may apply for grant funds only once in 36 months. Application form required.
Initial approach: Letter of inquiry on organization letterhead, not exceeding 5-6 pages.
Copies of proposal: 1
Deadline(s): None
Board meeting date(s): Bimonthly
Final notification: 6 months
Officers and Directors:* Robert W. Lanum,* Chair.; Kent W. Lanum,* C.E.O. and Pres.; Willis Charles,* V.P.; Roy W. Nett,* Secy.-Treas.; Cecile A. Blau; Norman Pfau; John Ragland.
Number of staff: 1 full-time professional; 1 part-time professional; 1 part-time support.
EIN: 310988988

3363
Old National Bank Foundation, Inc.
c/o Janet H. Baas, Fdn. Pres.
1 Main St.
Evansville, IN 47708 (812) 464-1515
Contact: Janet Heldt Baas, Pres.; Linda Ford, Fdn. Prog. Admin.
E-mail: grants&sponsorships@oldnational.com; Additional tel.: (812) 468-1991; Main URL: http://www.oldnational.com/giving

Established in 2006.
Donors: Old National Bank; Old National Bancorp.
Foundation type: Company-sponsored foundation.
Financial data (yr. ended 12/31/13): Assets, $1,163,858 (M); gifts received, $1,200,000; expenditures, $1,226,737; qualifying distributions, $1,221,292; giving activities include $1,154,167 for grants.
Purpose and activities: The foundation supports organizations involved with arts and culture, health, and human services. Special emphasis is directed toward programs designed to promote community and economic development and education.
Fields of interest: Arts, cultural/ethnic awareness; Elementary/secondary education; Education, early childhood education; Higher education; Adult/continuing education; Adult education—literacy, basic skills & GED; Education, ESL programs; Education, continuing education; Education, reading; Education; Housing/shelter, rehabilitation; Housing/shelter, home owners; Youth

development; Human services, financial counseling; Community development, neighborhood development; Economic development; Urban/ community development; Rural development; Community development, small businesses; Microfinance/microlending; Community/economic development; Leadership development; Children/ youth; Disabilities, people with; Economically disadvantaged.

Type of support: Employee matching gifts; Capital campaigns; Continuing support; Curriculum development; In-kind gifts; Program development.

Limitations: Applications accepted. Giving limited to areas of company operations in IL, IN, KY, and MI. No support for school clubs/organizations, including, but not limited to bands, athletic or academic teams, booster clubs, or PTO/PTA, summer camps, political, labor, military, veterans', international, or fraternal organizations, discriminatory organizations, or programs administered by religious organizations for religious purposes. No grants to individuals, or for scholarships, endowments, salaries or general operating support, meals, tickets, dues, memberships, fees, travel, tuition, subscriptions, or other tangible benefits, childcare fees/subsidies or K-12 tuition, meetings, conferences, or workshops, debt retirement, contests, competitions, athletic events, beauty pageants, or talent contests, operating costs or capital campaigns for faith-based organizations, sponsorships, fundraisers, races, telethons, marathons, benefits, banquets, galas, golf tournaments, festivals or other events, or scholarly or medical research, feasibility studies, project research or development phases, including the cost of hiring consultants or planners.

Publications: Application guidelines; Corporate giving report; Grants list.

Application information: A full proposal may be required at a later date. Support is limited to 1 contribution per organization during any given year. Application form required.

Initial approach: Complete online application or letter of intent
Copies of proposal: 1
Deadline(s): For Developing Partnerships (previous grantees) — Jan. 30, Apr. 30, and July 31; for Community Investments (new applicants) — Aug. 31.
Board meeting date(s): Spring and Fall
Final notification: 8-9 weeks from submission to final decision for Developing Partnerships; 2-4 weeks after "letter of intent" submission for Community Investments to determine if a full application is needed.

Officers: Janet Heldt Baas, Pres.; Doug Gregurich, V.P.; Linda Ford, Secy.; Jackie Russell, Treas.

EIN: 260130059

Selected grants: The following grants are a representative sample of this grantmaker's funding activity:

$15,000 to Junior Achievement of Southwest Indiana, Evansville, IN, 2013.
$10,000 to Girls Inc. of Greater Indianapolis, Indianapolis, IN, 2012. For Smart College and Career Planning.
$7,500 to Boys and Girls Clubs of Fort Wayne, Fort Wayne, IN, 2012. For Project Lean Program.
$5,000 to Keep Indianapolis Beautiful, Indianapolis, IN, 2013. To implement Youth Tree Team program.

3364
The OneAmerica Foundation, Inc. ✧

(formerly AUL Foundation, Inc.)
1 American Sq.
P.O. Box 368
Indianapolis, IN 46206-0368 (317) 285-1877
Contact: Jim Freeman, V.P.

Established in 1985 in IN.

Donor: American United Life Insurance Co.

Foundation type: Company-sponsored foundation.

Financial data (yr. ended 12/31/12): Assets, $9,268,106 (M); expenditures, $630,272; qualifying distributions, $622,141; giving activities include $622,141 for 49 grants (high: $321,366; low: $100).

Purpose and activities: The foundation supports museums and zoological societies and organizations involved with orchestras, education, human services, and leadership development.

Fields of interest: Museums; Performing arts, orchestras; Higher education; Education; Zoos/ zoological societies; American Red Cross; Children, services; Human services; Leadership development.

Type of support: General/operating support.

Limitations: Applications accepted. Giving limited to the Indianapolis, IN, area. No grants to individuals.

Application information: Application form required.

Initial approach: Letter
Deadline(s): Sept. 30

Officers and Directors:* Dayton H. Molendorp,* Chair. and Pres.; James W. Freeman, V.P.; Thomas M. Zurek,* Secy.; Douglas W. Collins, Treas.; J. Scott Davison; Jeffrey D. Holley; John C. Mason; Mark C. Roller.

EIN: 311146437

3365
Orange County Community Foundation, Inc. ✧

112 W. Water St.
Paoli, IN 47454-1347 (812) 723-4150
Contact: Imojean Dedrick, Exec. Dir.
FAX: (812) 723-7304;
E-mail: contact@orangecountycommunityfoundation.org; Main URL: http://occf-in.org/
Facebook: https://www.facebook.com/orangecountycf
Twitter: http://twitter.com/OrangeCountyCF

The foundation was incorporated in 2000 in IN.

Foundation type: Community foundation.

Financial data (yr. ended 09/30/13): Assets, $9,313,706 (M); gifts received, $1,486,933; expenditures, $1,538,663; giving activities include $863,874 for grants.

Purpose and activities: The goal of the foundation is to provide a pool of funds to help meet the needs of Orange County, IN, citizens and, in so doing, to help donors carry out their philanthropic purposes as effectively as possible.

Fields of interest: Humanities; Historical activities; Arts; Education; Environment; Animals/wildlife; Health care; Recreation; Human services; Children/ youth; Terminal illness, people with.

Type of support: Building/renovation; Equipment; Program development; Conferences/seminars; Film/video/radio; Publication; Curriculum development; Research; Technical assistance; Consulting services; Program evaluation; Scholarships—to individuals.

Limitations: Applications accepted. Giving limited to Orange County, IN. No support for religious purposes. No grants to individuals (except for scholarships), or for operating revenue, endowment creation, debt reduction, or travel expenses; no loans.

Publications: Application guidelines; Annual report; Financial statement; Grants list; Informational brochure; Newsletter.

Application information: Visit foundation web site for application form and additional information. Application form required.

Initial approach: Contact foundation
Copies of proposal: 7
Deadline(s): Varies
Board meeting date(s): 4th Thurs. of every month
Final notification: Varies

Officers and Directors:* Carolyn Clements,* Pres.; Peter Grigsby,* V.P.; Larry Hollan,* Secy.; Mary Jane Harrison,* Treas.; Imojean Dedrick, Exec. Dir.; Hon. Larry Blanton; Brett Busick; Pete Conrad; Donnie Crockett; Linda Gerkin; Barbara Gilliatt; Todd Hitchcock; Kay Lynn Kaiser; Glenda Lamb; Louanne Lashbrook; Timothy Leehe.

Number of staff: 3 full-time professional; 1 part-time support.

EIN: 352117084

Selected grants: The following grants are a representative sample of this grantmaker's funding activity:

$70,452 to Orange County Emergency Management Agency (OCEMA), 2011. Toward digital banding radio upgrades.
$35,000 to Habitat for Humanity of Orange County, Paoli, IN, 2011. For building materials for Paoli High School building trades classes for construction project for Habitat homes.
$25,000 to Pivotal People of Southern Indiana, IN, 2011. For restoration of former Central Baptist Church building for use as public venue.
$15,000 to Hoosier Uplands Economic Development Corporation, Mitchell, IN, 2011. For furnishings for College Hill public auditorium.
$12,229 to Orange County Historical Society, Orange, VA, 2011. For museum expenses and upkeep.
$11,284 to Paoli, Town of, Paoli, IN, 2011. To furnish playground equipment for renovation of JayCee Park.
$9,829 to Orange County Sheriffs Department, Santa Ana, CA, 2011. For Drunk, Drugged and Distracted Driving and bullying programs in county schools.

3366
Parke County Community Foundation, Inc. ✧

115 N. Market St.
P.O. Box 276
Rockville, IN 47872-1719 (765) 569-7223
Contact: Brad C. Bumgardner, Exec. Dir.
FAX: (765) 569-5383; E-mail: parkeccf@yahoo.com;
Main URL: http://www.parkeccf.org
Facebook: https://www.facebook.com/pages/Parke-County-Community-Foundation/188650397850473
RSS Feed: http://www.parkeccf.org/newsreleases.html?rss

Established in 1993 in IN.

Foundation type: Community foundation.

Financial data (yr. ended 12/31/13): Assets, $12,945,888 (M); gifts received, $831,399;

expenditures, $864,280; giving activities include $344,085 for 11+ grants (high: $35,268), and $208,593 for 166 grants to individuals.
Purpose and activities: The foundation's mission is to assist donors in meeting charitable need in Parke County and to build community capacity, thereby, enhancing the quality of life in Parke County.
Fields of interest: Performing arts, theater; Historic preservation/historical societies; Elementary/secondary education; Higher education; Education; Animal welfare; Health organizations, association; Disasters, fire prevention/control; Human services; Community/economic development; Protestant agencies & churches; Cemeteries/burial services.
Type of support: General/operating support; Program development; Scholarship funds; Scholarships—to individuals.
Limitations: Applications accepted. Giving primarily in Parke County, IN.
Publications: Financial statement; Newsletter.
Application information: Visit foundation web site for application form and guidelines. For requests $1,000 or undera one-page letter or email will suffice. Application form required.
Initial approach: Submit application
Deadline(s): None
Final notification: Within 90 days
Officers and Directors:* Nathan Adams,* Chair.; Wilma Wooten,* Vice-Chair.; Donna McVay,* Secy.; Tom Rohr,* Treas.; Brad C. Bumgardner, Exec. Dir.; Andrew Allen; Jana Crites; Mark Davis; Renee Hartman; Jenn Kersey; Cliff Kunze; Barbara Livezey; Nellie Myers; Gary Staadt.
EIN: 351881810

3367
Robert J. Harriet A. and David T. Parrish Foundation ✧ ☆

c/o Tower Trust Company
P.O. Box 11080
Fort Wayne, IN 46855-1080

Donor: Robert J. Parrish.
Foundation type: Independent foundation.
Financial data (yr. ended 12/31/13): Assets, $4,113,911 (M); expenditures, $845,673; qualifying distributions, $823,782; giving activities include $809,100 for 14 grants (high: $153,000; low: $7,500).
Fields of interest: Environment; Food services; Human services; Disabilities, people with.
Limitations: Applications not accepted. Giving primarily in Fort Wayne, IN.
Application information: Unsolicited requests for funds not accepted.
Trustee: Sharon Peters.
EIN: 277078826

3368
Mary K. Peabody Foundation ✧

c/o Tower Trust Co.
P.O. Box 11080
Fort Wayne, IN 46855-1080

Established in 1991 in IN.
Foundation type: Independent foundation.
Financial data (yr. ended 07/31/11): Assets, $982,651 (M); expenditures, $2,013,774; qualifying distributions, $1,999,618; giving activities include $1,957,710 for 1 grant.
Fields of interest: Foundations (community).
Type of support: Building/renovation; Equipment.
Limitations: Applications not accepted. Giving primarily in Manchester, IN. No grants to individuals.
Application information: Contributes only to pre-selected organizations.
Distribution Committee: Frances H. Fisher; Robert Wagner.
Trustee: Tower Bank.
EIN: 356546371
Selected grants: The following grants are a representative sample of this grantmaker's funding activity:
$1,957,710 to Community Foundation of Wabash County, North Manchester, IN, 2011. For operating support.

3369
Porter County Community Foundation, Inc. ✧

57 S. Franklin St., Ste. 207
P.O. Box 302
Valparaiso, IN 46384 (219) 465-0294
Contact: For grants: Brenda Sheetz, V.P., Opers.
FAX: (219) 464-2733;
E-mail: info@portercountyfoundation.org; Grant inquiry e-mail: bsheetz@portercountyfoundation.org;
Main URL: http://www.portercountyfoundation.org
Facebook: http://www.facebook.com/pages/Porter-County-Community-Foundation/133136959185
LinkedIn: http://www.linkedin.com/company/porter-county-community-foundation
Twitter: https://twitter.com/pccfoundation

Established in 1996 in IN.
Foundation type: Community foundation.
Financial data (yr. ended 12/31/13): Assets, $39,699,668 (M); gifts received, $5,537,049; expenditures, $2,746,496; giving activities include $1,829,499 for 80+ grants (high: $110,627), and $13,000 for 13 grants to individuals.
Purpose and activities: The foundation provides resources and ideas by which donors can make lasting contributions to humanitarian, cultural, educational, recreational and environmental causes in Porter County, IN, and provides asset management which maximizes the effectiveness of these gifts.
Fields of interest: Arts; Education; Environment; Human services.
Type of support: Capital campaigns; Emergency funds; Management development/capacity building; Program development; Equipment.
Limitations: Applications accepted. Giving primarily in Porter County, IN. No support for programs that are sectarian or religious in nature. No grants to individuals (except scholarships from scholarship funds), operational funding, annual appeals or membership contributions, event sponsorship, endowment campaigns (except for endowment building grants), debt reduction, camp scholarships or fees related to camp programs, or travel for bands, sports teams, or similar groups.
Publications: Application guidelines; Annual report; Grants list; Newsletter.
Application information: Visit foundation web site for application cover sheet and specific guidelines. Application form required.
Initial approach: Proposal
Copies of proposal: 1
Deadline(s): Feb. 16 and Aug. 17
Final notification: 60 days after deadline
Officers and Directors:* Barbara A. Young,* Pres.; William A. Higbie, V.P., Devel.; Brenda A. Sheetz,* V.P., Opers.; Kim Abbett; Andrew Arnold; Jan Barsophy; Rick Calinski; Laura Campbell; Laura Elliott; Dr. John Felton; Stephanie Gerdes; Minaski Ghuman; Carol Hall; John Hannon; Heather Harrigan-Hitz; Joe Jaskowiak; Stephanie Jones; Susan Kelly-Johnson; Geoff Laciak; Judy Leetz; William P. Maar; Kent Mishler; Ralph Neff; Douglas Olson; Desila Rosetti; Gregory Sobkowski; Jacki Stutzman; Spero Valavanis; John Walsh; Katharine Wehling.
EIN: 352000788

3370
The Portland Foundation ✧

112 E. Main St.
Portland, IN 47371-2105 (260) 726-4260
Contact: Douglas L. Inman, Exec. Dir.; For grant applications: Jessica L. Cook, Prog. Off.
FAX: (260) 726-4273;
E-mail: tpf@portlandfoundation.org; Main URL: http://www.portlandfoundation.org
Facebook: https://www.facebook.com/pages/The-Portland-Foundation/138673816247793

Established in 1951 in IN.
Foundation type: Community foundation.
Financial data (yr. ended 12/31/13): Assets, $28,720,250 (M); gifts received, $2,131,715; expenditures, $994,196; giving activities include $442,316 for grants, and $191,487 for grants to individuals.
Purpose and activities: The foundation provides support for all aspects of the quality of life in the Jay County, IN, community.
Fields of interest: Arts; Child development, education; Higher education; Libraries/library science; Education; Animal welfare; Health care; Children/youth, services; Family services; Human services, emergency aid; Aging, centers/services; Human services; Community/economic development; Youth; Disabilities, people with.
Type of support: Capital campaigns; Building/renovation; Equipment; Program development; Seed money; Scholarship funds; Scholarships—to individuals; Matching/challenge support.
Limitations: Applications accepted. Giving limited to Jay County, IN. No support for religious or sectarian purposes. No grants to individuals (except through designated scholarship funds); generally no grants for regular operating budgets, operating costs, operating deficits, after-the-fact funds, endowments, or long-term funding; no loans.
Publications: Application guidelines; Annual report; Newsletter; IRS Form 990 or 990-PF printed copy available upon request.
Application information: Visit foundation web site for application form and guidelines. Applications must be typed; handwritten copies will not be accepted. Application form required.
Initial approach: Submit application form and attachments
Copies of proposal: 1
Deadline(s): Jan. and July
Board meeting date(s): Bimonthly
Final notification: Feb. and Aug.
Officers and Trustees:* Mary Davis,* Pres.; Dean Jetter,* V.P.; Emily Goodrich Roberts,* Secy.-Treas.; Douglas L. Inman, Exec. Dir.; Pat Bennett; David Fullenkamp; Rex Journay; Ronald Laux; John Moore; Stephanie Robinson.

Number of staff: 1 full-time professional; 1 part-time support.
EIN: 356028362

3371
Myrta J. Pulliam Charitable Trust ✧ ☆
c/o Holly Pantzer, BKD LLP
201 N. Illinois St., Ste. 700
Indianapolis, IN 46204-4224

Established in 2001 in IN.
Donors: Myrta J. Pulliam; Jane B. Pulliam†.
Foundation type: Independent foundation.
Financial data (yr. ended 12/31/13): Assets, $11,389,074 (M); expenditures, $633,099; qualifying distributions, $588,012; giving activities include $583,012 for 28 grants (high: $500,000; low: $72).
Fields of interest: Arts; Education; Animals/wildlife.
Type of support: Program development; Scholarship funds.
Limitations: Applications not accepted. Giving primarily in IN. No grants to individuals.
Application information: Contributes only to pre-selected organizations.
Trustee: Myrta J. Pulliam.
EIN: 356712560

3372
Nina Mason Pulliam Charitable Trust ✧
135 N. Pennsylvania St., Ste. 1200
Indianapolis, IN 46204-2484 (317) 231-6075
Contact: Mary K. Price, Dir., Grants Admin.
FAX: (317) 231-9208; E-mail: mprice@nmpct.org; Application address for Arizona organizations: 2201 E. Camelback Rd., Ste. 600B, Phoenix, AZ 85016, tel.: (602) 955-3000, fax: (602) 955-8029; Main URL: http://www.ninapulliamtrust.org
E-Newsletter: http://www.ninapulliamtrust.org/index.php/news/connections-newsletter/
Grants List: http://www.ninapulliamtrust.org/index.php/grantees/

Established in 1997.
Foundation type: Independent foundation.
Financial data (yr. ended 12/31/12): Assets, $352,882,000 (M); expenditures, $19,711,255; qualifying distributions, $17,186,507; giving activities include $13,870,000 for 179 grants (high: $2,000,000; low: $500; average: $10,000–$100,000).
Purpose and activities: The trust seeks to help people in need, especially women, children and families; to protect animals and nature; and to enrich community life in the metropolitan areas of Indianapolis, IN, and Phoenix, AZ.
Fields of interest: Arts, cultural/ethnic awareness; Education; Environment, recycling; Environmental education; Animal welfare; Animal population control; Health care, clinics/centers; Health care; Eye diseases; Employment, training; Food banks; Housing/shelter; Human services; Children/youth, services; Children, foster care; Family services; Community development, neighborhood development; Children/youth; Adults; Disabilities, people with; Blind/visually impaired; Hispanics/Latinos; Immigrants/refugees; Economically disadvantaged; Homeless.
Type of support: General/operating support; Management development/capacity building; Equipment; Program development; Curriculum development; Scholarship funds.
Limitations: Applications accepted. Giving primarily in Phoenix, AZ, and Indianapolis, IN. No grants to individuals, or for academic research, capital campaigns (building or endowments) non-operating private foundations, or international activities.
Publications: Application guidelines; Annual report (including application guidelines); Financial statement; Grants list; Newsletter.
Application information: The trust will not accept unsolicited proposals for capital campaigns, either for building or endowment purposes. See the foundation's web site for application process. Requests for funding are limited to one request per organization per year. Proposals must be submitted online via the foundation's web site. Application form required.
Initial approach: Before submitting a proposal, consult with a program officer one month prior to proposal deadline
Deadline(s): Proposal: Feb. 4 and Aug. 1.
Board meeting date(s): Mar., May, July, Sept., Nov. and Dec.
Final notification: Mar. 31 and Nov. 29
Officers: Gene D'Adamo, C.E.O. and Pres.; Robert L. Lowry, Exec. V.P. and C.F.O.; Ryan C. Hammons, Cont.
Trustees: Kent E. Agness; Carol P. Schilling; Lisa Shover Kackley.
Number of staff: 9 full-time professional; 8 full-time support.
EIN: 356644088
Selected grants: The following grants are a representative sample of this grantmaker's funding activity:
$2,000,000 to Petsmart Charities, Phoenix, AZ, 2012. For the collaborative initiative of the Alliance for Companion Animals of Maricopa County to conduct a three-year campaign to significantly reduce the intake and euthanasia of dogs and cats by increasing spay/neuter procedures and adoptions through community awareness and coordinated activities.
$742,264 to Arizona State University Foundation for a New American University, Tempe, AZ, 2012. For Nina Mason Pulliam Legacy Scholars program.
$490,282 to Goodwill Industries of Central Arizona, Phoenix, AZ, 2012. For the Goodwill Training and Employment Network, a partnership with Maricopa Community Colleges to provide occupational skills training, services and job matching opportunities to 300 individuals with barriers to employment.
$300,000 to Desert Botanical Garden, Phoenix, AZ, 2012. For the Conservation Alliance, a collaboration of stakeholders committed to studying, restoring and promoting the mountain park preserves of the Phoenix area, a system encompassing over 186,000 acres of open space.
$250,000 to Eiteljorg Museum of American Indians and Western Art, Indianapolis, IN, 2012. To restore the Southwest Summer Showers sculpture, install a plumbing system to have water flowing over the sculpture, renovate and upgrade the sculpture niche, and to create a permanent restoration fund in honor of Frank and Nancy Russell.
$75,000 to Indiana Recycling Coalition, Indianapolis, IN, 2012. To increase recycling efforts in at least 100 central Indiana schools and develop a marketing campaign targeting 100 businesses to begin recycling.
$55,000 to Stepping Stone Foundation, Phoenix, AZ, 2012. For preschool classrooms for approximately 35 children, ages 3 and 4, from low-income families at Westwood Elementary School in the Alhambra School District.
$50,000 to Mount Carmel Community Life Center, Indianapolis, IN, 2012. For over 1,000 youth with a variety of recreational and social development programs at the community center located on the far eastside of Indianapolis.
$50,000 to Southwest Wildlife Rehabilitation and Educational Foundation, Scottsdale, AZ, 2012. To construct three habitat enclosures for new arrivals to the Mexican Gray Wolf Recovery Program to assist the national captive breeding program for this highly endangered subspecies.

3373
The Putnam County Community Foundation ✧
2 S. Jackson St.
P.O. Box 514
Greencastle, IN 46135-0514 (765) 653-4978
Contact: M. Elaine Peck, Exec. Dir.
FAX: (765) 653-6385;
E-mail: info@pcfoundation.org; Additional e-mail: epeck@pcfoundation.org; Main URL: http://www.pcfoundation.org
E-Newsletter: http://www.pcfoundation.org/about_newsletter.html
Facebook: https://www.facebook.com/pages/Putnam-County-Community-Foundation/128261640565285?ref=ts
Scholarship e-mail: dgambill@pcfoundation.org

Established in 1985 in IN.
Foundation type: Community foundation.
Financial data (yr. ended 12/31/13): Assets, $24,798,640 (M); gifts received, $707,202; expenditures, $1,248,793; giving activities include $644,162 for 18+ grants (high: $100,000), and $185,206 for 150 grants to individuals.
Purpose and activities: The foundation partners with those who give to enrich life and strengthen community for current and future generations.
Fields of interest: Arts; Education; Environment; Animals/wildlife; Public health, obesity; Health care; Recreation; Children/youth, services; Human services; Economic development; Community/economic development; Public affairs, citizen participation; Transportation; Youth; Aging.
Type of support: Income development; Building/renovation; Program development; Seed money; Scholarship funds; Technical assistance; Consulting services; Program-related investments/loans; Matching/challenge support.
Limitations: Applications accepted. Giving limited to Putnam County, IN. No support for sectarian religious purposes, or national or state-wide fundraising projects. No grants to individuals (except for scholarships), or for salaries, utilities or rent, projects normally fully funded by units of government, endowment funds, fundraising projects, or retroactive funding.
Publications: Application guidelines; Annual report; Financial statement; Grants list; Informational brochure; Newsletter.
Application information: Visit foundation web site for application forms and guidelines. To be considered for funding, organizations must first submit a Preliminary Grant Application form; eligible organizations will then be mailed application materials and an invitation in writing to submit a full application. Application form required.
Initial approach: Submit 1-page Preliminary Grant Application form

Copies of proposal: 1
Deadline(s): Feb. 2 and Aug. 1 for preliminary application; Mar. 1 and Sept. 1 for full application
Board meeting date(s): Monthly
Final notification: Feb. 15 and Aug. 15 for full application invitation; 3 months for funding decisions

Officer and Directors:* Ellie Ypma,* Pres.; M. Todd Lewis,* V.P.; Nancy Wells,* Secy.; David Archer,* Treas.; M. Elaine Peck, Exec. Dir.; Keith Archer; Keith Brackney; Debbi Christy; Ellen Dittmer; Ken Eitel; Brad Hayes; Karen Nelson Heavin; Scott Herrick; Susan Lemon; Carolyn Mann; Susan Price; Vivian Whitaker; Rodger Winger.
Number of staff: 4 full-time professional.
EIN: 311159916

3374
Carl Marshall Reeves and Mildred Almen Reeves Foundation, Inc. ✧
c/o Larry Nunn
3435 Duffer Dr.
Columbus, IN 47203-2714 (812) 343-1787
Contact: Mary Ann Nunn, Secy.-Treas.
E-mail: manunn@carlandmildredreevesfoundation.org; Main URL: http://www.carlandmildredreevesfoundation.org/

Established in 1997 in IN.
Foundation type: Independent foundation.
Financial data (yr. ended 12/31/13): Assets, $14,638,555 (M); expenditures, $693,842; qualifying distributions, $645,012; giving activities include $638,109 for 22 grants (high: $128,983; low: $400).
Purpose and activities: Giving primarily for research in macular degeneration of the eyes, as well as for education, and children, youth and social services.
Fields of interest: Secondary school/education; Medical school/education; Education; Health care; Eye diseases; Human services; Children/youth, services.
Limitations: Applications accepted. Giving primarily in the Columbus, IN, area.
Application information: Application form required.
Initial approach: Completed application form
Copies of proposal: 6
Deadline(s): Prior to semi-annual meeting
Board meeting date(s): Semi-annually
Officers: Larry E. Nunn, Pres.; Mary Ann Nunn, Secy.-Treas.
Directors: Tom Bigley; W. George Brueggemann; Emily A. Mabe; Mary Lu Orr.
EIN: 352026200
Selected grants: The following grants are a representative sample of this grantmaker's funding activity:
$109,721 to Vanderbilt University, Nashville, TN, 2012. For Macular Degeneration of the Eye Research Study.
$50,000 to University of Wisconsin, Department of Othalmology and Visual Sciences, Madison, WI, 2012. For Macular Degeneration of the Eye Research Study.
$30,000 to Foundation for Youth, Columbus, IN, 2012. For Real Estate Acquisition Costs.
$7,927 to Volunteers in Medicine, Columbus, IN, 2012. For Diabetes Testing - Medical Supplies and Equipment.
$6,000 to Columbus Indiana Architectural Archives, Columbus, IN, 2012. For Production of Documentaries.
$5,154 to Columbus East High School, Columbus, IN, 2012. For High School Band Musical Equipment.
$5,000 to Bartholomew Consolidated School Corporation, Columbus, IN, 2012. For Equipment for Early Learning Center.
$100 to Hospice of South Central Indiana, Columbus, IN, 2012. For hospice care.

3375
Regenstrief Foundation, Inc. ✧
9292 N. Meridian, Ste. 202
Indianapolis, IN 46260-1828
Contact: Susan Luse, Secy.

Established in IN in 1969.
Foundation type: Independent foundation.
Financial data (yr. ended 06/30/13): Assets, $165,175,602 (M); expenditures, $10,666,192; qualifying distributions, $8,951,025; giving activities include $8,735,573 for 2 grants (high: $5,780,361; low: $2,955,212).
Purpose and activities: Giving for innovative research directed toward improving the efficiency, quality, and accessibility of health care.
Fields of interest: Higher education; Medical research, institute; Medical research, information services; Medical research, formal/general education.
Type of support: Research.
Limitations: Applications not accepted. Giving primarily in Indianapolis, IN.
Application information: Unsolicited requests for funds not considered.
Board meeting date(s): Jan. and June
Officers and Directors:* Jack Snyder,* Chair.; Jack R. Shaw, C.E.O., Pres., and Treas.; Susan M. Luse, Secy.; Daniel Appel; Leonard J. Betley; D. Craig Brater; Richard Buckius; Allan L. Cohn; Ronald W. Dollens; Harvey Feigenbaum, M.D.; Stephen L. Ferguson; David W. Knall; Sally F. Mason, Ph.D.; Lesley B. Olswang, Ph.D.; Bart Peterson.
Number of staff: 4 part-time professional; 2 part-time support.
EIN: 356066023
Selected grants: The following grants are a representative sample of this grantmaker's funding activity:
$5,780,361 to Regenstrief Institute, Indianapolis, IN, 2013. For medical research.
$2,955,212 to Purdue University, West Lafayette, IN, 2013. For medical research.

3376
Gilmore & Golda Reynolds Foundation ✧ ☆
c/o Steve Gloyd
136 S. Buckeye St.
Osgood, IN 47037-1302

Established in 1990 in IN.
Donor: Golda Reynolds.
Foundation type: Independent foundation.
Financial data (yr. ended 12/31/13): Assets, $24,268,481 (M); expenditures, $919,730; qualifying distributions, $911,530; giving activities include $721,026 for 10 grants (high: $480,362; low: $1,000).
Purpose and activities: Giving for community volunteer services.
Fields of interest: Secondary school/education; Safety/disasters, volunteer services; Disasters, fire prevention/control; Human services; Community/economic development.
Type of support: Program-related investments/loans; General/operating support.
Limitations: Applications not accepted. Giving primarily in Osgood, IN. No grants to individuals.
Application information: Contributes only to pre-selected organizations.
Officers: Stephen Michael Black, Pres.; Dwight Hooton, V.P.; Neil Comer, Secy.; Douglas Thayer, Treas.; Steve Gloyd, Exec. Dir.
EIN: 356525698
Selected grants: The following grants are a representative sample of this grantmaker's funding activity:
$584,690 to Osgood, Town of, Osgood, IN, 2011.
$125,000 to Osgood, Town of, Osgood, IN, 2011. For general fund.
$4,400 to Chamber of Commerce, Ripley County, Versailles, IN, 2011.

3377
Rick L. and Vicki L .James Foundation Inc. ✧ ☆
1401 S. Grandstaff Dr.
Auburn, IN 46706-2664

Donors: Rick James; Vicki james.
Foundation type: Independent foundation.
Financial data (yr. ended 12/31/13): Assets, $1,199,469 (M); gifts received, $3,000,000; expenditures, $3,336,940; qualifying distributions, $3,325,586; giving activities include $3,324,586 for 16 grants (high: $2,200,000; low: $15,000).
Fields of interest: Higher education; Education; Christian agencies & churches.
Limitations: Applications not accepted. Giving primarily in FL and IN.
Application information: Unsolicited request for funds not accepted.
Directors: Rick James; Vicki James.
EIN: 452195649
Selected grants: The following grants are a representative sample of this grantmaker's funding activity:
$1,500,000 to Trine University, Angola, IN, 2012. For Furth Center Pledge.

3378
Rifkin Family Foundation ✧ ☆
5642 Coventry Ln.
Fort Wayne, IN 46804-7140

Established in 1986 in IN.
Donors: Daniel M. Rifkin; Richard S. Rifkin; Martin S. Rifkin; OmniSource Corp.; Gopher Smelting & Refining Corp.; Associated Media Group LLC; Mezuman Associates LLC.
Foundation type: Independent foundation.
Financial data (yr. ended 12/31/13): Assets, $8,234,478 (M); expenditures, $474,130; qualifying distributions, $420,172; giving activities include $420,172 for 52 grants (high: $107,900; low: $100).
Purpose and activities: Giving primarily for education, children and social services, and Jewish organizations.
Fields of interest: Education; Health organizations; Human services; Children/youth, services; Jewish

federated giving programs; Jewish agencies & synagogues.
Limitations: Applications not accepted. Giving primarily in Fort Wayne, IN. No grants to individuals.
Application information: Contributes only to pre-selected organizations.
Trustee: Daniel M. Rifkin.
EIN: 311192429
Selected grants: The following grants are a representative sample of this grantmaker's funding activity:
$10,000 to Boston University, School of Management, Boston, MA, 2012. For education.
$5,000 to Erins House for Grieving Children, Fort Wayne, IN, 2012. For bereavement support services.
$5,000 to Fort Wayne Sports Foundation, Fort Wayne, IN, 2012. To Provide Sports Activities for Youth.
$5,000 to Teach Our Children Fund, Fort Wayne, IN, 2012. For education learning disadvantaged children.
$5,000 to Trine University, Angola, IN, 2012. For Student Scholarship Fund.
$3,000 to Historic Fort Wayne, Fort Wayne, IN, 2012. For Installation of Audio System at Old Fort.
$3,000 to Junior Achievement of Northern Indiana, Fort Wayne, IN, 2012. For education scholarship fund.
$1,000 to Helping Hands Ministries, Tallulah Falls, GA, 2012. For medical projects.
$1,000 to Project Linus, Fort Wayne, IN, 2012. To Provide Blankets for Children in Community.
$500 to Zeta Beta Tau Foundation, Indianapolis, IN, 2012. For Education-Scholarships and Leadership Programs.

3379
Ripley County Community Foundation, Inc. ✧☆
4 S. Park, Ste. 210
Batesville, IN 47006 (812) 933-1098
Contact: Sally Morris, Exec. Dir.
FAX: (812) 933-0096; E-mail: office@rccfonline.org; Additional tel.: (887) 234-5220; Additional e-mail: smorris@rccfonline.org and office@rccfonline.org; Main URL: http://rccfonline.org/
Facebook: https://www.facebook.com/RipleyCountyCommunityFoundation?fref=ts

Established in 1997 in IN.
Foundation type: Community foundation.
Financial data (yr. ended 12/31/13): Assets, $9,883,875 (M); gifts received, $846,046; expenditures, $1,036,378; giving activities include $486,263 for 8+ grants (high: $17,418), and $174,382 for grants to individuals.
Purpose and activities: The foundation seeks to: 1) assist donors to build an enduring source of charitable assets to benefit Ripley County; 2) provide responsible stewardship of the gifts donated; 3) promote leadership in addressing Ripley County's issues; and 4) to make grants in the fields of community service, social service, education, health, environment, and the arts.
Fields of interest: Arts; Education; Environment; Health care; Human services; Community/economic development.
Type of support: General/operating support; Seed money; Matching/challenge support.
Limitations: Applications accepted. Giving limited to Ripley County, IN. No support for sectarian religious purposes. No grants to individuals (except for scholarships), or for seminars, trips, or endowments.
Publications: Application guidelines; Annual report.
Application information: Visit foundation web site for application form and guidelines. Application form required.
Initial approach: Submit application
Deadline(s): First Friday of Apr., June, Sept. and Nov. for small projects grants for amounts up to $500; Aug. 2 for larger projects grants for amounts of $500 to $5,000.
Officers and Board Members:* Amy Kellerman Streator,* Pres.; Mark Collier,* V.P.; Linda Chandler,* Secy.; Eric Benz,* Treas.; Marie Dausch; Tim Dietz; John Kellerman II; Jenny Miles; Chris Nichols; Alesha Neal; Herman Struewing.
EIN: 352048001

3380
Roehm Charitable Trust ✧☆
127 W. Berry St.
Fort Wayne, IN 46802

Donor: Roehm Charitable Remainder Unitrust.
Foundation type: Independent foundation.
Financial data (yr. ended 12/31/12): Assets, $0 (M); expenditures, $528,212; qualifying distributions, $521,678; giving activities include $521,678 for 4 grants (high: $447,797; low: $10,000).
Fields of interest: Education; Health care; Religion.
Limitations: Applications not accepted. Giving primarily in IN.
Application information: Unsolicited requests for funds not accepted.
Trustee: Star Financial Bank.
EIN: 456829239

3381
Ian & Mimi Rolland Foundation ✧
110 W. Berry St., Ste. 2400
Fort Wayne, IN 46802 (260) 461-6285
Contact: Ian Rolland, Pres.

Established in 1995 in IN.
Donors: Ian Rolland; Miriam Rolland.
Foundation type: Independent foundation.
Financial data (yr. ended 06/30/13): Assets, $6,201,051 (M); expenditures, $505,216; qualifying distributions, $450,388; giving activities include $450,388 for grants.
Purpose and activities: Giving for the arts, education, social services and the environment.
Fields of interest: Arts; Education; Human services; Children/youth; Children; Youth; Disabilities, people with; Physically disabled; Minorities; African Americans/Blacks; Economically disadvantaged; Homeless.
Type of support: General/operating support; Annual campaigns; Capital campaigns; Building/renovation; Endowments; Emergency funds; Program development; Scholarship funds; Research; Matching/challenge support.
Limitations: Applications accepted. Giving primarily in IN, with emphasis on Fort Wayne. No support for religious or political organizations. No grants to individuals.
Application information: Application form not required.
Initial approach: Proposal
Copies of proposal: 1
Deadline(s): None
Board meeting date(s): Quarterly
Officers: Ian Rolland, Pres.; Miriam Rolland, V.P.; Thomas D. Wright, Secy.-Treas.
Number of staff: None.
EIN: 351944302

3382
The Madge Rothschild Foundation ✧
c/o Tower Trust Company
P.O. Box 11080
Fort Wayne, IN 46855-1080

Established in 1999 in IN.
Foundation type: Independent foundation.
Financial data (yr. ended 12/31/13): Assets, $3,241,473 (M); expenditures, $1,658,326; qualifying distributions, $1,618,269; giving activities include $1,582,500 for 13 grants (high: $275,000; low: $2,500).
Fields of interest: Arts; Education; Health organizations; Human services; Youth, services.
Type of support: General/operating support.
Limitations: Applications not accepted. Giving primarily in Fort Wayne, IN. No grants to individuals.
Application information: Contributes only to pre-selected organizations.
Trustee: Tower Trust Company.
EIN: 356685311
Selected grants: The following grants are a representative sample of this grantmaker's funding activity:
$150,000 to Fort Wayne Museum of Art, Fort Wayne, IN, 2012. For American Art Initiative.
$125,000 to Arts United of Greater Fort Wayne, Fort Wayne, IN, 2012. For a Home for the Arts Capital Campaign.
$125,000 to SCAN, Fort Wayne, IN, 2012. For Second Installment for Healthy Families Program.
$100,000 to Northeast Indiana Public Radio, Fort Wayne, IN, 2012. For operating support campaign.
$10,000 to Headwaters Park Alliance, Fort Wayne, IN, 2012. For Gift for Landscape Project.

3383
Saltsburg Fund Charitable Trust ✧
P.O. Box 836
Carmel, IN 46082-0836 (317) 846-9290
Contact: Donald W. Buttrey, Tr.
Application address: P.O. Box 40669, Indianapolis, IN 46240-0669

Established in 2000 in IN.
Donors: Donald W. Buttrey; Karen Lake Buttrey.
Foundation type: Independent foundation.
Financial data (yr. ended 12/31/12): Assets, $3,564,301 (M); expenditures, $656,351; qualifying distributions, $640,734; giving activities include $636,014 for 78 grants (high: $236,914; low: $100).
Fields of interest: Arts; Higher education; Human services; Christian agencies & churches.
Limitations: Applications accepted. Giving primarily in Indianapolis, IN and PA. No grants to individuals.
Application information: Application form required.
Initial approach: Letter
Deadline(s): None
Trustee: Donald W. Buttrey.
EIN: 912044415

3384
Samerian Foundation, Inc. ✧ ☆
9650 Commerce Dr., Ste. 532
Carmel, IN 46032-8512 (317) 802-9220
Contact: Fonda Crandall, Secy.-Treas.

Established in 2002 in IN.
Donors: Cynthia Simon Skjodt; Simon 5 Year Charitable Lead Annuity Trust; Simon 10 Year Charitable Lead Annuity Trust; Simon 12 Year Charitable Lead Annuity Trust; Simon 15 Year Charitable Lead Annuity Trust.
Foundation type: Independent foundation.
Financial data (yr. ended 12/31/13): Assets, $5,986,433 (M); gifts received, $6,350,000; expenditures, $930,552; qualifying distributions, $892,583; giving activities include $892,583 for 87 grants (high: $100,000; low: $100).
Fields of interest: Elementary school/education; Higher education; Scholarships/financial aid; Environment; Health organizations, association; Children, services; Jewish agencies & synagogues.
Type of support: General/operating support; Continuing support; Annual campaigns; Capital campaigns; Grants to individuals; Scholarships—to individuals.
Limitations: Applications accepted. Giving primarily in IN. No support for political organizations.
Application information: Application form required.
Initial approach: Letter
Deadline(s): None
Officers: Paul Skjodt, Chair.; Cynthia Simon Skjodt, Pres.; Fonda Crandall, Secy.-Treas.
Directors: Erik Skjodt; Ian Skjodt; Samantha Skjodt.
Number of staff: None.
EIN: 371439047
Selected grants: The following grants are a representative sample of this grantmaker's funding activity:
$25,000 to American Heart Association, Indianapolis, IN, 2011. For contribution to general fund.
$10,000 to Jewish Federation of Greater Indianapolis, Indianapolis, IN, 2011. For contribution to general fund.
$3,000 to Damien Center, Indianapolis, IN, 2011. For contribution to general fund.
$2,500 to Saint Joseph Institute for the Deaf, Indianapolis, IN, 2011. For contribution to general fund.

3385
David E. Simon & Jacqueline S. Simon Charitable Foundation ✧
10555 Hussey Ln.
Carmel, IN 46032-7921

Established in 2003 in IN.
Donors: David E. Simon; Jacqueline S. Simon; 5-Year Charitable Trust; 10-Year Charitable Trust; 12-Year Charitable Trust; 15-Year Charitable Trust.
Foundation type: Independent foundation.
Financial data (yr. ended 12/31/13): Assets, $3,955,848 (M); gifts received, $4,100,000; expenditures, $1,145,851; qualifying distributions, $1,129,732; giving activities include $1,123,408 for 38 grants (high: $300,000; low: $25).
Purpose and activities: Giving primarily for education, human services, and Jewish organizations.
Fields of interest: Higher education; Education; Health organizations; Human services; Children/youth, services; Jewish federated giving programs; Jewish agencies & synagogues.
Limitations: Applications not accepted. Giving primarily in Indianapolis, IN. No grants to individuals.
Application information: Unsolicited requests for funds not accepted.
Trustees: David E. Simon; Jacqueline S. Simon.
EIN: 141859319

3386
The Joshua Max Simon Charitable Foundation ✧
(formerly The Max Simon Charitable Foundation)
10110 Ditch Road
Carmel, IN 46032-9613

Established in 1999 in IN.
Donors: Deborah Simon; Melvin Simon†; Cynthia Simon Skjodt; Sam W. Klein Charitable Foundation.
Foundation type: Independent foundation.
Financial data (yr. ended 12/31/12): Assets, $4,811,672 (M); gifts received, $26,259; expenditures, $527,297; qualifying distributions, $505,000; giving activities include $505,000 for grants.
Purpose and activities: Giving primarily for a health care center, as well as to a film festival.
Fields of interest: Media, film/video; Health care; Human services; Foundations (private grantmaking).
Type of support: General/operating support; Annual campaigns; Scholarship funds.
Limitations: Applications not accepted. Giving primarily in Indianapolis, IN.
Application information: Unsolicited requests for funds not accepted.
Trustees: Tamme Simon McCauley; Bren Simon.
EIN: 356692310

3387
The Melvin and Bren Simon Charitable Foundation Number One ✧
10110 Ditch Rd.
Carmel, IN 46032-9613 (317) 844-9467

Established in 1998 in IN.
Donors: Melvin Simon†; Melvin Simon and Associates, Inc.
Foundation type: Independent foundation.
Financial data (yr. ended 12/31/12): Assets, $23,850,329 (M); gifts received, $1,000,000; expenditures, $2,596,243; qualifying distributions, $2,485,833; giving activities include $2,485,833 for grants.
Purpose and activities: Giving primarily for the arts, higher education, health, human services, and Jewish organizations.
Fields of interest: Museums (art); Arts; Higher education; Health organizations; Foundations (private grantmaking); Jewish federated giving programs; Jewish agencies & synagogues; Children.
Limitations: Applications not accepted. Giving primarily in Indianapolis, IN; some funding also in Los Angeles, CA. No grants to individuals.
Application information: Contributes only to pre-selected organizations.
Trustee: Bren Simon.
EIN: 352049367

3388
Smithville Charitable Foundation ✧ ☆
P.O. Box 68
Ellettsville, IN 47429
Application Address: c/o Darby A. McCarthy, 808 W. Temperance, Ellettsville, IN 47429, tel.: (336) 747-8190

Established in IN.
Foundation type: Independent foundation.
Financial data (yr. ended 10/31/13): Assets, $23,244,540 (M); gifts received, $33,033; expenditures, $1,052,643; qualifying distributions, $1,014,107; giving activities include $975,451 for 29 grants (high: $200,000; low: $1,300).
Fields of interest: Education; Foundations (community).
Limitations: Applications accepted. Giving primarily in IN.
Application information: Application form required.
Initial approach: Letter
Deadline(s): None
Board Members: Richard O. Kissel II; Cullen H. McCarthy; Darby A. McCarthy.
Trustee: Wolfrum Capital Management Group.
EIN: 462100122

3389
The Steel Dynamics Foundation, Inc. ✧
7575 W. Jefferson Blvd.
Fort Wayne, IN 46804-4131
Contact: Beth Burke
Main URL: http://www.steeldynamicsfoundation.org/

Donor: Steel Dynamics, Inc.
Foundation type: Company-sponsored foundation.
Financial data (yr. ended 12/31/13): Assets, $2,929,218 (M); gifts received, $650,000; expenditures, $1,286,292; qualifying distributions, $1,272,749; giving activities include $1,272,749 for 30 grants (high: $30,000; low: $10,000).
Purpose and activities: The foundation supports organizations involved with children and family services. Special emphasis is directed toward programs designed to promote economic development, including education in business and technology fields.
Fields of interest: Business school/education; Children/youth, services; Family services; Economic development.
Type of support: Equipment; Building/renovation; Capital campaigns; Sponsorships; General/operating support.
Limitations: Applications accepted. Giving primarily in areas of company operations in Wayne, IN.
Publications: Application guidelines.
Application information: General grant requests should be submitted to the division general manager who will determine if the request is suited for the foundation.
Initial approach: Contact local general management for general grants; complete online eligibility form for major impact grants
Deadline(s): None
Officers and Directors: Theresa E. Wagler, Pres. and Secy.; Richard A. Poinsatte, Treas.; Keith E. Busse; Mark Millet.
Number of staff: None.
EIN: 263012038

3390
Steuben County Community Foundation ✧
1701 N. Wayne St.
Angola, IN 46703-2356 (260) 665-6656
Contact: Jennifer Danic, Pres. and C.E.O.; For grants: Bill Stockberger, Prog. Off.
FAX: (260) 665-8420;
E-mail: sccf@steubenfoundation.org; Grant application e-mail: bstockberger@steubenfoundation.org; Main URL: http://www.steubenfoundation.org

Established in 1992 in IN.
Foundation type: Community foundation.
Financial data (yr. ended 06/30/13): Assets, $19,411,692 (M); gifts received, $3,570,112; expenditures, $1,453,977; giving activities include $1,029,867 for 30+ grants (high: $514,475).
Purpose and activities: The foundation works to preserve and enhance the lifestyle and assets of Steuben County, IN, for all current and future generations by providing ongoing assessment and financial support of identified needs through philanthropic giving and endowment building.
Fields of interest: Arts; Higher education; Education; Environment; Health care; Recreation; Human services; Community/economic development; Children/youth; Children; Adults; Aging; Disabilities, people with; Women; Girls; Adults, women; Men; Adults, men; Homeless.
Type of support: General/operating support; Management development/capacity building; Building/renovation; Equipment; Land acquisition; Endowments; Emergency funds; Program development; Conferences/seminars; Seed money; Curriculum development; Scholarship funds; Technical assistance; Program evaluation; Scholarships—to individuals; In-kind gifts; Matching/challenge support.
Limitations: Applications accepted. Giving limited to Steuben County, IN. No support for private schools, or religious or sectarian causes. No grants to individuals (except for scholarships), or for fundraising activities, second- or multi-year funding, budget deficits, travel, advertising, debt reduction, or annual campaigns; no loans.
Publications: Application guidelines; Annual report; Financial statement; Informational brochure (including application guidelines); Newsletter; Occasional report.
Application information: Visit foundation web site for Grant Application Cover Sheet and application guidelines. Application form required.
Initial approach: Telephone
Copies of proposal: 1
Deadline(s): Last day of July, Oct., Jan., and Apr.
Board meeting date(s): 3rd Thurs. of each month
Final notification: Generally 3 weeks
Officers and Directors:* Hope Korte,* Chair.; Kevin Stoy,* Vice-Chair.; Jennifer Danic,* Pres. and C.E.O.; Marla Toigo,* Secy.; James Burns,* Treas.; Greg Burns; Marylyn Ernsberger; Dave Goodwin; Sherry Holiday; Jim Ingledue; Phil Meyer; Julie Troyer; Randy White; Jan Williams.
Number of staff: 3 full-time professional; 1 part-time professional.
EIN: 351857065

3391
Tipton County Foundation, Inc. ✧
1020 W. Jefferson St.
P.O. Box 412
Tipton, IN 46072-0412 (765) 675-8480
Contact: Frank M. Giammarino, Pres. and C.E.O.
FAX: (765) 675-8488; E-mail: tcf@tiptoncf.org; Grant e-mail: grants@tiptoncf.org; Main URL: http://www.tiptoncf.org
Blog: http://tiptoncountyfoundation.blogspot.in/
Facebook: https://www.facebook.com/tiptoncountyfoundation
YouTube: http://www.youtube.com/intiptoncounty
Scholarship e-mail: scholars@tiptoncf.org

Established in 1986 in IN.
Foundation type: Community foundation.
Financial data (yr. ended 12/31/13): Assets, $33,093,612 (M); gifts received, $3,895,275; expenditures, $1,211,817; giving activities include $656,278 for 18+ grants (high: $229,323), and $150,377 for 109 grants to individuals.
Purpose and activities: The foundation is a nonprofit public charity established to serve donors, award grants, and provide leadership to improve the quality of life in Tipton County.
Fields of interest: Arts; Education; Recreation; Youth development; Human services; Community/economic development; Public affairs.
Type of support: Income development; Management development/capacity building; Annual campaigns; Capital campaigns; Building/renovation; Equipment; Emergency funds; Program development; Conferences/seminars; Seed money; Curriculum development; Scholarship funds; Consulting services; Scholarships—to individuals; Matching/challenge support.
Limitations: Applications accepted. Giving limited to Tipton County, IN. No support for religious purposes. No grants for individuals (except for scholarships), or for ongoing operating expenses, debt reduction, annual appeals or membership contributions, travel, or endowment building.
Publications: Application guidelines; Annual report; Financial statement; Grants list; Informational brochure; Newsletter; Occasional report; IRS Form 990 or 990-PF printed copy available upon request.
Application information: Visit foundation web site for application form and guidelines. Application form required.
Initial approach: Mail or e-mail letter of intent
Copies of proposal: 1
Deadline(s): Apr. 1, Aug. 1 and Sept. 15 for full proposals, letters of intent should be submitted a few weeks beforehand
Board meeting date(s): Feb., May, Sept., and Dec.
Officers and Directors:* Mark Raver,* Chair.; Jan Henderson,* Vice-Chair.; Frank M. Giammarino,* C.E.O. and Pres.; Nancy A. Nicholson,* Secy.; Mark Baird,* Treas.; Dr. Kevin Condict; Lary Graves; Ben B. Hobbs; Tom McKinney; JoAnn McQuinn; Anabeth Rayl; Dr. Mike Smith; Sharon Smith.
Number of staff: 1 full-time professional; 1 part-time support.
EIN: 311175045

3392
Transformation Trust, Inc. ✧
P. O. Box 80007
Indianapolis, IN 46280-0007 (317) 580-2002

Established in 1997 in IN.
Donors: Edwin H. Klink; Sheila K. Klink; Edwin Howard Klink†.
Foundation type: Independent foundation.
Financial data (yr. ended 12/31/12): Assets, $32,618,328 (M); expenditures, $1,801,335; qualifying distributions, $1,616,446; giving activities include $1,505,600 for 40 grants (high: $200,000; low: $1,600).
Fields of interest: Arts; Education; Health care, public policy; Employment, research; Human services; International affairs; United Ways and Federated Giving Programs; Spirituality.
Limitations: Applications accepted. Giving primarily in CA, IL, IN, VA, and WA.
Application information: Contributes only to pre-selected organizations.
Board Members: Elizabeth Hamilton; Patsy Heard; Sheila K. Klink.
EIN: 352024586

3393
Unity Foundation of La Porte County, Inc. ✧
115 E. 4th St.
Michigan City, IN 46360 (219) 879-0327
Contact: Margaret A. Spartz, Pres.
FAX: (219) 210-3881; E-mail: info@uflc.net; Mailing address: P.O. Box 527 Michigan City, IN 46361; Additional tel.: (888) 89-UNITY; Main URL: http://www.uflc.net
Facebook: https://www.facebook.com/pages/The-Unity-Foundation/241204849231027
LinkedIn: http://www.linkedin.com/company/unity-foundation-of-la-porte-county
Twitter: http://twitter.com/unityfndtn
YouTube: http://www.youtube.com/user/UnityFound

Established in 1992 in IN.
Foundation type: Community foundation.
Financial data (yr. ended 12/31/12): Assets, $23,797,446 (M); gifts received, $3,143,116; expenditures, $1,741,174; giving activities include $744,995 for 369+ grants, and $142,629 for grants to individuals.
Purpose and activities: The foundation seeks to accept and pool charitable contributions from a variety of resources, and use the proceeds to support other charitable activities and organizations to benefit the residents of La Porte County, IN. The foundation makes discretionary and field of interest grants to charitable organizations in the area of the arts, education, health and human services, the environment, and the community.
Fields of interest: Historic preservation/historical societies; Arts; Libraries/library science; Education, reading; Education; Environment; Animals/wildlife; Health care; Mental health/crisis services; Housing/shelter, homeless; Housing/shelter; Recreation; Youth development; Children/youth, services; Human services; Community/economic development.
Type of support: Building/renovation; Equipment; Land acquisition; Endowments; Program development; Conferences/seminars; Seed money; Scholarship funds; Technical assistance; Employee matching gifts.
Limitations: Applications accepted. Giving limited to residents of La Porte County, IN. No support for sectarian religious programs. No grants to individuals (except for scholarship funds), or for operating budgets, basic municipal or educational

functions and services, debt reduction, long-term funding, or after-the-fact funding.
Publications: Application guidelines; Annual report; Annual report (including application guidelines); Financial statement; Grants list; Newsletter.
Application information: Community fund grant requests should be no more than $3000. Visit foundation web site for application forms and guidelines. Application form required.
Initial approach: Submit letter and attachments
Copies of proposal: 1
Deadline(s): July 20
Board meeting date(s): 1st Mon. of month
Final notification: Mid-Sept.
Officers and Directors:* Michael Brennan,* Co-Chair.; Edward Volk,* Co-Chair.; Margaret A. Spartz,* Pres.; Sandy Gleim,* V.P.; Elizabeth Bernel; Daryl Crockett; Jon Gilmore; Jim Jessup; Jack L. Jones; Jerry Kabelin; Vidya Kora, M.D.; Daniel E. Lewis; Mary Lou Linnen; Ronald J. Ragains; Burton B. Ruby; Kim Sauers; Marti Swanson; Michele Thompson.
Number of staff: 2 full-time professional; 1 part-time professional; 3 part-time support.
EIN: 351658674

3394
Vectren Foundation, Inc. ✧
(formerly Indiana Energy Foundation, Inc.)
1 Vectren Sq.
Evansville, IN 47708-1251 (812) 491-4176
Contact: Mark Miller, Mgr., Community Affairs
E-mail: mmiller@vectren.com; Additional application address and contact: Lynda Hoffman, Community Affairs, Mgr., Vectren Corp., 120 W. 2nd St., Ste. 1212, Dayton, OH 45402-1685, tel.: (937) 222-2936, e-mail:lkhoffman@vectren.com; Main URL: http://www.vectrenfoundation.org/

Established in 2000 in IN.
Donors: Indiana Energy, Inc.; Vectren Corp.
Foundation type: Company-sponsored foundation.
Financial data (yr. ended 12/31/13): Assets, $2,514,523 (M); gifts received, $1,100; expenditures, $2,176,687; qualifying distributions, $2,176,687; giving activities include $2,158,415 for 451 grants (high: $100,000).
Purpose and activities: The foundation supports programs designed to promote community development; energy conservation and environmental stewardship; and education. Special emphasis is directed toward programs designed to contribute to sustainable future.
Fields of interest: Elementary/secondary education; Higher education; Education, services; Education, reading; Education; Environment, natural resources; Environment, energy; Environmental education; Environment; Health care, clinics/centers; Health care; Employment, training; Employment; Housing/shelter, development; Housing/shelter; Youth development, adult & child programs; American Red Cross; YM/YWCAs & YM/YWHAs; Children/youth, services; Economic development; Community/economic development; Foundations (community); United Ways and Federated Giving Programs; Leadership development; Public affairs.
Type of support: General/operating support; Capital campaigns; Equipment; Program development; Employee volunteer services; Sponsorships; Employee matching gifts.
Limitations: Applications accepted. Giving limited to areas of company operations in IN and west central OH. No support for political, religious, fraternal, labor, or veterans' organizations or issue-oriented organizations. No grants to individuals or for scholarships.
Publications: Application guidelines; Annual report.
Application information: Application form required.
Initial approach: Complete online application
Deadline(s): None
Final notification: 90 days
Officers and Directors:* Jeffrey W. Whiteside,* Pres.; Ronald E. Christian,* V.P.; Joshua Claybourn, Secy.; Jerome A. Benkert, Jr.; Carl L. Chapman; J. Bradley Ellsworth; Colleen Ryan.
EIN: 351950691
Selected grants: The following grants are a representative sample of this grantmaker's funding activity:
$100,000 to University of Evansville, Evansville, IN, 2011.
$50,690 to United Way of Southwestern Indiana, Evansville, IN, 2011.
$50,000 to Japan-America Society of Indiana, Indianapolis, IN, 2011.
$35,000 to Nature Conservancy, Arlington, VA, 2011.
$25,000 to Habitat of Evansville, Evansville, IN, 2011.
$25,000 to Hollys House, Evansville, IN, 2011.
$19,600 to Dayton Art Institute, Dayton, OH, 2011.
$15,000 to Boys and Girls Club of Evansville, Evansville, IN, 2011.
$15,000 to Evansville Christian Life Center, Evansville, IN, 2011.
$10,000 to American Gas Foundation, Washington, DC, 2011.

3395
Volo Non Valeo Foundation Inc. ✧ ☆
7274 Hunt Club Ln.
Zionsville, IN 46077

Established in 1999 in IN.
Donors: Robert N. Postlethwait; Kathleen D. Postlethwait.
Foundation type: Independent foundation.
Financial data (yr. ended 06/30/13): Assets, $0 (M); expenditures, $590,363; qualifying distributions, $587,153; giving activities include $587,153 for 5 grants (high: $460,236; low: $2,500).
Fields of interest: Education; Health organizations; Human services.
Type of support: General/operating support.
Limitations: Applications accepted. Giving primarily in IN and OH. No grants to individuals.
Application information: Application form not required.
Initial approach: Letter
Deadline(s): None
Officers: Kathleen D. Postlethwait, Pres.; Robert N. Postlethwait, V.P.
Directors: Caitlin L. Postlethwait; Megan L. Postlethwait.
EIN: 352089820

3396
Wabash Valley Community Foundation, Inc. ✧
2901 Ohio Blvd., Ste. 153
Terre Haute, IN 47803-2239 (812) 232-2234
Contact: Beth A.A. Tevlin, Exec. Dir.; Kate Kollinger, Financial Mgr.
FAX: (812) 234-4853; E-mail: info@wvcf.com; Additional tel.: (877) 232-2230; Additional e-mails: beth@wvcf.com, kate@wvcf.com; Main URL: http://www.wvcf.com
Facebook: http://www.facebook.com/pages/Wabash-Valley-Community-Foundation/134088539978330
RSS Feed: http://161.58.109.117/wvcf-news/rss.php?category=1,8&number=10
Twitter: https://twitter.com/WVCFoundation
YouTube: http://www.youtube.com/user/WVCFoundation

Established in 1991 in IN.
Foundation type: Community foundation.
Financial data (yr. ended 09/30/13): Assets, $41,510,929 (M); gifts received, $1,378,742; expenditures, $2,139,708; giving activities include $859,467 for 165+ grants (high: $23,553; low: $30), and $526,767 for grants to individuals.
Purpose and activities: The foundation's mission is to promote community investment for a better tomorrow. Giving primarily for arts and culture, education, human services, community development, and religion in west central IN, specifically in Clay, Sullivan and Vigo counties.
Fields of interest: Arts; Education; Health care; Youth, services; Human services; Community/economic development; Religion.
Type of support: General/operating support; Capital campaigns; Building/renovation; Equipment; Endowments; Emergency funds; Seed money; Scholarship funds; Scholarships—to individuals; Matching/challenge support.
Limitations: Applications accepted. Giving primarily in Clay, Sullivan, and Vigo counties, IN; requests from other counties occasionally considered. No support for religious purposes. No grants for endowments, deficit funding, annual appeals and membership contributions, travel for groups such as bands, sports teams and classes, conferences, publications, films, television, or radio programs (unless integral to the project for which the grant is sought).
Publications: Application guidelines; Annual report; Financial statement; Grants list; Informational brochure; Newsletter.
Application information: Visit foundation web site for application guidelines, varying per grant type. 17 to 22 copies depending on grant cycle. Application form required.
Initial approach: Letter of Intent (1 page)
Copies of proposal: 1
Deadline(s): June 1 for Clay, Sullivan, and Vigo counties' letters of intent, Nov. 1 for Vigo County letter of intent; Feb. 1 for Vigo County full proposal, Aug. 1 for Clay, Sullivan, and Vigo counties' full proposals
Board meeting date(s): Jan., Mar., May, July, Sept., and Nov.
Final notification: Approx. 1 month for letter of intent determination; Approx. 4 months for full grant proposals
Officers and Directors:* Fred Nation,* Pres.; Michael Lawson,* V.P.; Jeff Perry,* Secy.; David Doti,* Treas.; Beth A.A. Tevlin, Exec. Dir.; Daryl Andrews; Cynthia Cox; Lant Davis; Jo Einstandig; Jon

Ford; Judy Harris; Jackie Lower; Malinda Medsker; Dave Piker; Lakshmi Reddy; Nancy Rogers; Dr. Randall Stevens; Renee Stewart; Dick Vining.
Number of staff: 2 full-time professional; 1 part-time professional; 1 part-time support.
EIN: 351848649

3397
Walther Cancer Foundation, Inc. ✧
(formerly Walther Cancer Institute Foundation, Inc.)
9292 N. Meridian St., Ste. 300
Indianapolis, IN 46260-1828 (317) 708-6101
Contact: James E. Ruckle Ph.D., C.E.O. and Pres.
FAX: (317) 708-6102; E-mail: info@walther.org; Main URL: http://www.walther.org
Grants List: http://www.walther.org/grants-and-programs/active-grant-list.aspx

Established in 1985 in IN; The grantmaker changed its status from Public Charity to Private Foundation in 2007.
Foundation type: Independent foundation.
Financial data (yr. ended 06/30/13): Assets, $146,183,284 (M); gifts received, $10,407; expenditures, $5,979,879; qualifying distributions, $5,185,036; giving activities include $4,755,643 for 147 grants (high: $333,334; low: $32).
Purpose and activities: The mission of the foundation is to eliminate cancer as a cause of suffering and death through interdisciplinary and inter-institutional basic laboratory, clinical, and behavioral cancer research initiatives.
Fields of interest: Cancer research.
Type of support: Research.
Limitations: Applications not accepted. Giving limited to the U.S., with emphasis on IN. No grants for building/renovation, debt reduction, emergency funds, land acquisition, equipment, or technical assistance; no loans.
Publications: Grants list; IRS Form 990 or 990-PF printed copy available upon request.
Application information: Unsolicited requests for funds not accepted.
Board meeting date(s): Second Tues. of each month
Officers and Directors:* Leonard J. Betley,* Chair.; Gregory L. Pemberton,* Vice-Chair.; James E. Ruckle, Ph.D., C.E.O. and Pres.; D. Craig Brater, M.D., V.P., Progs.; Donald C. Danielson,* Secy.; Sue Peebles, C.F.O.; Stephen C. Gaerte,* Treas.; Steffanie Rhinesmith, C.I.O.; Daniel Appel; Mary Beth Gadus; Richard Gaynor, M.D.; Thomas W. Grein; Bryan A. Mills; Sharon Pierce; Nancy Yaw.
Number of staff: 2 full-time professional; 2 part-time professional; 1 full-time support.
EIN: 351650570
Selected grants: The following grants are a representative sample of this grantmaker's funding activity:
$1,200,000 to Indiana University, Bloomington, IN, 2012. For organization and operation of Indiana University Simon Cancer Center (IUSCC) AMPATH-Oncology Institute (AOI) in Eldoret, Kenya, payable over 3.00 years.
$900,000 to Indiana University, School of Public Health, Bloomington, IN, 2012. For infrastructure development to expand cancer prevention and survivorship through community engagement, payable over 3.00 years.
$706,454 to Indiana University, Bloomington, IN, 2012. For Behavioral Cooperative Oncology Group (BCOG) Center for Symptom Management, which was formed to foster cooperation among Midwest regional academic/medical center researchers and community practitioners. In addition to researchers and practitioners, members include project personnel and students from many fields, ranging from nursing to music therapy. Center will develop cost-effective interventions that can be used to alleviate or prevent symptom burden associated with a cancer diagnosis and its treatment. Pre and post-doctoral fellows as well as junior faculty will be trained to develop and sustain a program of symptom science research that can be translated into practice for the benefit of cancer patients and their families, payable over 3.00 years.
$414,099 to Indiana University, Bloomington, IN, 2012. To recruit Director of Pediatric Neuro-Oncology at Riley Hospital for Children in Indianapolis, payable over 5.00 years.
$400,780 to University of Notre Dame, Notre Dame, IN, 2012. For program support for Harper Cancer Research Institute.
$400,000 to University of Notre Dame, Notre Dame, IN, 2012. For Harper Cancer Research Institute Advancing Basic Cancer (ABC) Research, initiative to stimulate novel multi-disciplinary integrative cancer research, seed collaborative interactions between at least 2 scientific fields, provide a cross-disciplinary training environment for a post-doctoral fellow and to generate high quality preliminary data for an extramural funding application., payable over 2.00 years.
$337,556 to Michigan State University, East Lansing, MI, 2012. For Behavioral Cooperative Oncology Group (BCOG) Center for Symptom Management, which was formed to foster cooperation among Midwest regional academic/medical center researchers and community practitioners. In addition to researchers and practitioners, members include project personnel and students from many fields, ranging from nursing to music therapy. Center will develop cost-effective interventions that can be used to alleviate or prevent symptom burden associated with a cancer diagnosis and its treatment. Pre and post-doctoral fellows as well as junior faculty will be trained to develop and sustain a program of symptom science research that can be translated into practice for the benefit of cancer patients and their families, payable over 3.00 years.
$333,333 to Indiana University, Bloomington, IN, 2012. For Invest in Success Campaign to establish Basic Science Cancer Center at IU-Bloomington, payable over 5.50 years.
$203,684 to University of Michigan, Ann Arbor, MI, 2012. For Behavioral Cooperative Oncology Group (BCOG) Center for Symptom Management, which was formed to foster cooperation among Midwest regional academic/medical center researchers and community practitioners. In addition to researchers and practitioners, members include project personnel and students from many fields, ranging from nursing to music therapy. Center will develop cost-effective interventions that can be used to alleviate or prevent symptom burden associated with a cancer diagnosis and its treatment. Pre and post-doctoral fellows as well as junior faculty will be trained to develop and sustain a program of symptom science research that can be translated into practice for the benefit of cancer patients and their families, payable over 3.00 years.
$30,000 to Indiana University, Bloomington, IN, 2012. To create a web intervention which will increase colorectal and breast cancer screening in women.

3398
Washington County Community Foundation, Inc. ✧
1707 N. Shelby St., Ste. 100
P.O. Box 50
Salem, IN 47167-0050 (812) 883-7334
Contact: Judy Johnson, Exec. Dir.
FAX: (812) 883-9464; E-mail: info@wccf.biz; Additional e-mail: director@wccf.biz; Main URL: http://www.wccf.biz/
Facebook: https://www.facebook.com/pages/Washington-County-Community-Foundation/125868960809517?v=wall
RSS Feed: http://www.wccf.biz/News/rss_display.html

Established in 1993 in IN.
Foundation type: Community foundation.
Financial data (yr. ended 12/31/12): Assets, $17,775,448 (M); gifts received, $681,995; expenditures, $817,523; giving activities include $504,140 for 8+ grants (high: $22,951).
Purpose and activities: The goal of the foundation is to improve the quality of life in Washington County, IN. Giving for education, health, arts and cultural projects, community development and other civic efforts.
Fields of interest: Historical activities; Arts; Education; Health care; Recreation; Community/economic development.
Type of support: Scholarship funds; Conferences/seminars; Capital campaigns; Management development/capacity building; Building/renovation; Equipment; Program development; Seed money; Curriculum development; Consulting services; Scholarships—to individuals.
Limitations: Applications accepted. Giving limited to Washington County, IN. No support for sectarian religious purposes. No grants for debt reduction, exchange programs, fellowships, operating expenses, endowments, internships, or professorships; no loans.
Publications: Application guidelines; Annual report; Grants list; Informational brochure; Newsletter.
Application information: Visit foundation web site for application information. Each grant cycle begins with a public meeting; application forms, guidelines, and deadlines may be obtained at this meeting; dates are announced in the local papers and on the local radio station. Application form required.
Initial approach: Letter or telephone
Copies of proposal: 9
Deadline(s): Mar. and Sept.
Board meeting date(s): Monthly
Final notification: Within 1 month
Officers and Directors:* John Roberts,* Pres.; Jeff Souder,* V.P.; Adrian Brown,* Secy.; Kim Scifres,* Treas.; Judy Johnson, Exec. Dir.; Shirley Batt; Amy Birkla; Janet Bowling; Linda Chastain; Marvin Clark; Karen Davis; Rita Elliott; Rita Haub; Sue Hawkins; Judy Hedrick; Steve Miller; David Morris; Jeanette Nolan; Andrew Wright.
Number of staff: 1 full-time professional; 1 full-time support; 1 part-time support.
EIN: 351883377

3399
Waterfield Foundation, Inc. ✧
7221 Engle Rd., Ste. 250
Fort Wayne, IN 46804-2237 (260) 434-8512
Contact: Howard L. Chapman, Pres.; Becky Teagarden, Exec. Dir.

FAX: (260) 434-8332;
E-mail: beckyt@waterfieldcapital.com; Main URL: http://waterfieldcapital.com/foundation.html

Established in 1992 in IN.
Donors: Anne K. Waterfield‡; Elizabeth W. Chapman; Frances L. Swanson; Richard D. Waterfield; Stephen Chapman; Richard R. Waterfield; J. Randall Waterfield; Jill L. Waterfield.
Foundation type: Independent foundation.
Financial data (yr. ended 12/31/13): Assets, $4,987,565 (M); gifts received, $226,414; expenditures, $3,457,797; qualifying distributions, $3,368,165; giving activities include $3,362,318 for 74 grants (high: $2,000,000; low: $50).
Purpose and activities: Giving primarily for housing, recreation, youth development, the environment, and services for people who are handicapped.
Fields of interest: Arts, cultural/ethnic awareness; Performing arts; Education; Environment; Housing/shelter, development; Housing/shelter; Recreation, parks/playgrounds; Athletics/sports, training; Youth development, centers/clubs; Disabilities, people with; Physically disabled; Offenders/ex-offenders.
Type of support: General/operating support; Continuing support; Annual campaigns; Capital campaigns; Building/renovation; Equipment; Land acquisition; Endowments; Emergency funds; Program development; Seed money; Scholarship funds; Exchange programs.
Limitations: Applications accepted. Giving primarily in northeastern IN. No support for non-501(c)(3) organizations.
Publications: Application guidelines.
Application information: Application form required.
Initial approach: Written requests only (via foundation web site)
Copies of proposal: 1
Deadline(s): Based upon when the next meeting is held
Board meeting date(s): Quarterly
Final notification: After quarterly board meeting, only to approved grant applicants
Officers and Directors:* Richard D. Waterfield,* Chair. and Treas.; Howard L. Chapman, Pres.; Frances L. Swanson,* V.P.; Elizabeth W. Chapman,* Secy.; Becky Teagarden, Exec. Dir.
Number of staff: 1 part-time professional.
EIN: 351872984

3400
Wayne County, Indiana Foundation, Inc. ✧
(also known as Wayne County Foundation)
33 S. 7th St., Ste. 1
Richmond, IN 47374-5423 (765) 962-1638
Contact: Steven C. Borchers, Exec. Dir.
E-mail: steve@waynecountyfoundation.org; Main URL: http://www.waynecountyfoundation.org
E-Newsletter: https://wayne.giftlegacy.com/?DID=3353&pageID=36
Facebook: https://www.facebook.com/WayneCountyFoundation
LinkedIn: https://www.linkedin.com/company/wayne-county-foundation?trk=fc_badge
Twitter: http://twitter.com/waynecountyfdtn

Established in 1979 in IN.
Foundation type: Community foundation.
Financial data (yr. ended 12/31/13): Assets, $37,212,046 (M); gifts received, $3,369,154; expenditures, $2,425,952; giving activities include $1,371,106 for grants.
Purpose and activities: The foundation exists to foster and encourage private philanthropic giving, to enhance the spirit of community, and to improve the quality of life in the Wayne County, IN, area now and for future generations. Scholarships through restricted funds are awarded to deserving graduates of Wayne County, IN, high schools.
Fields of interest: Media, television; Visual arts; Museums; Performing arts; Humanities; Historic preservation/historical societies; Arts; Vocational education; Higher education; Adult/continuing education; Adult education—literacy, basic skills & GED; Libraries/library science; Student services/organizations; Scholarships/financial aid; Education, services; Education, reading; Education; Environment; Animal welfare; Health care; Mental health/crisis services; Health organizations, association; Cancer research; Crime/violence prevention, youth; Crime/violence prevention, child abuse; Youth development, centers/clubs; Youth development; Children/youth, services; Human services; Community/economic development; Leadership development; Children; Youth; Aging; Disabilities, people with.
Type of support: Equipment; Program development; Conferences/seminars; Publication; Seed money; Scholarship funds; Scholarships—to individuals; Matching/challenge support.
Limitations: Applications accepted. Giving limited to Wayne County, IN. No support for religious organizations for sectarian purposes, organizations normally funded by the government, or for operating costs of non-public schools. No grants to individuals (except through restricted funds and scholarships), or for annual campaigns or operating funds, endowment funds, travel, or operating deficits or capital debt reduction.
Publications: Application guidelines; Annual report; Financial statement; Grants list; Newsletter; Program policy statement (including application guidelines).
Application information: Visit foundation web site for grant application Cover Sheet and guidelines. Application form required.
Initial approach: Submit application Cover Sheet and proposal
Copies of proposal: 6
Deadline(s): Apr. 1 for Improving Quality of Life, July 31 for Enhancing the Spirit of Community and Aug. 28 Challenge Match Program
Board meeting date(s): 3rd Thurs. of each month
Final notification: May 15 for Improving Quality of Life, Sept. 18 for Enhancing the Spirit of Community and Oct. 16 Challenge Match Program
Officers and Directors:* Chris Hardie,* Chair.; Darla Lane,* Vice-Chair.; Jill King,* Secy.; John Zetzl,* Treas.; Stephen C. Borchers, Exec. Dir.; Len Clark; J. Roger Green; Steve Higinbotham; Greg Janzow; David Jetmore, M.D.; John McBride; Amy Noe; Sabrina Pennington; Jim Tanner; Bonita Washington-Lacey.
Number of staff: 5 full-time professional.
EIN: 351406033

3401
Weaver Popcorn Foundation, Inc. ✧
14470 Bergen Blvd., Ste. 100
Noblesville, IN 46060-3377 (317) 292-4763
Contact: Brian Hamilton

Established in 1997 in IN.
Donor: Weaver Popcorn Co., Inc.
Foundation type: Company-sponsored foundation.
Financial data (yr. ended 12/31/13): Assets, $3,285,656 (M); gifts received, $464,935; expenditures, $550,322; qualifying distributions, $533,600; giving activities include $533,600 for 43 grants (high: $100,000; low: $400).
Purpose and activities: The foundation supports organizations involved with education, health, youth development, and human services, and awards educational scholarships to residents of Huntington, IN.
Fields of interest: Secondary school/education; Higher education; Education; Health care; Boy scouts; YM/YWCAs & YM/YWHAs; Children/youth, services; Family services, domestic violence; Human services.
Type of support: General/operating support; Scholarships—to individuals.
Limitations: Applications accepted. Giving primarily in IN.
Application information: Application form not required.
Initial approach: Proposal
Deadline(s): None
Officers and Directors:* Michael E. Weaver,* Chair.; William M. Weaver,* V.P.; Rebecca J. Weaver,* Secy.; Thomas M. Shoaff.
EIN: 352026043
Selected grants: The following grants are a representative sample of this grantmaker's funding activity:
$3,000 to Benton Community Foundation, Fowler, IN, 2012. For donations health and safety.
$3,000 to Indiana School for the Blind, Indianapolis, IN, 2012. For donations youth and education.
$2,000 to Taylor University, Upland, IN, 2012. For Donations Scholarship Bob Staight Scholarship.
$1,250 to Ball State University, Muncie, IN, 2012. For Donations Scholarship Weaver Scholarship.

3402
Welborn Baptist Foundation, Inc. ✧
(formerly Welborn Foundation, Inc.)
21 S.E. 3rd St., Ste. 610
Evansville, IN 47708-1418
Contact: Gary W. Bauer, C.F.O.
FAX: (812) 437-8269; E-mail: info@welbornfdn.org; Main URL: http://www.welbornfdn.org
Grants List: http://www.welbornfdn.org/news/funded-projects
Knowledge Center: http://www.welbornfdn.org/community-resources/publications

Established in 1999 in IN; converted from Welborn Hospital.
Donor: WBH Evansville, Inc.
Foundation type: Independent foundation.
Financial data (yr. ended 12/31/12): Assets, $110,263,986 (M); gifts received, $1,156,100; expenditures, $6,885,324; qualifying distributions, $6,570,847; giving activities include $3,657,791 for 117 grants (high: $425,000; low: $24).
Purpose and activities: Giving primarily in support of improved community health, well being and quality of life for all members of the Tri-State Community, particularly in the areas of 1) Promotion of Early Childhood Education, 2) Faith Based Initiatives, 3) Promotion of Healthy Adolescent Development, 4) Improvements in Community Health Status, and 5) School Based Health Programs. The foundation will apply Christian principles when evaluating and selecting applications for granting.

Fields of interest: Health care; Substance abuse, services; Crime/violence prevention; Nutrition; Youth development; Community/economic development; Religion.
Type of support: Building/renovation; Capital campaigns; Conferences/seminars; Curriculum development; Equipment; Matching/challenge support; Program development.
Limitations: Giving limited to Gallatin, Saline, Wabash, Wayne and White counties, IL; Dubois, Gibson, Perry, Pike, Posey, Spencer, Vanderburgh, and Warrick counties, IN; and Henderson County, KY. No support for basic scientific research. No grants to individuals, or for endowments, annual fund drives, debt service, deficit spending, scholarships, fellowships, general operating costs, venture capital or fund-raising; no loans.
Publications: Application guidelines; Annual report; Financial statement; Multi-year report; Program policy statement.
Application information: Applications are not accepted via U.S. Mail, e-mail or any other method apart from the foundation's online process.
Initial approach: Use application process on foundation web site
Deadline(s): See foundation web site for current deadline
Board meeting date(s): Varies
Officers: Daniel Schenk, Ph.D., Chair.; Ellis S. Redd, 1st Vice-Chair.; John C. Schroeder, 2nd Vice-Chair.; Kevin Bain, C.E.O. and Exec. Dir.; Connie K. Nass, Secy.; Lisa N. Collins, Treas.; Gary W. Bauer, C.F.O.
Directors: Norm Bafunno; Linda Bennett, Ph.D.; W. Harold Calloway; Don Chaudoin; John M. Dunn; Carrie Ellspermann; C. Mark Hubbard; E. Lynn Johnson; Thomas A. Kazee, Ph.D; Marilyn Klenck; David L. Knapp; James Muehlbauer; John Pulcini, M.D.; Ronald Romain; Jaleigh J. White.
Number of staff: 8 full-time professional; 3 part-time professional; 1 full-time support.
EIN: 352056722

3403
The Wells County Foundation, Inc. ✧

360 N. Main St., Ste. C
Bluffton, IN 46714 (260) 824-8620
Contact: Tammy Slater, C.E.O.
FAX: (260) 824-3981;
E-mail: wellscountyfound@wellscountyfound.org; Additional e-mail: tslater@wellscountyfound.org; Additional E-mail: light@wellscountyfound.org; Main URL: http://www.wellscountyfound.org

Established in 1957 in IN.
Foundation type: Community foundation.
Financial data (yr. ended 12/31/13): Assets, $19,768,368 (M); gifts received, $1,638,377; expenditures, $713,324; giving activities include $256,370 for 14+ grants (high: $44,254), and $195,304 for 78 grants to individuals.
Purpose and activities: The foundation seeks to enhance the quality of life of the Wells County, IN, community through the generation and prudent administration of entrusted donor funds to meet present and future changing community needs. Grantmaking fields of interest include arts and culture, education, economic and community development, health and human services, and other charitable purposes.
Fields of interest: Arts; Scholarships/financial aid; Education; Environment; Animals/wildlife; Health care; Recreation; Children/youth, services; Human services; Economic development; Community/economic development; Public affairs.
Type of support: Building/renovation; Equipment; Emergency funds; Program development; Seed money; Technical assistance; Scholarships—to individuals; Matching/challenge support.
Limitations: Applications accepted. Giving primarily in Wells County, IN. No support for religious organizations for religious purposes, or private or parochial schools. No grants to individuals (except for scholarships), or for operating support, financial deficits, or travel; no multi-year funding.
Publications: Application guidelines; Annual report; Informational brochure; IRS Form 990 or 990-PF printed copy available upon request.
Application information: Visit foundation web site for grant application format and guidelines. Scholarships only to residents of Wells County, IN; application guidelines available upon request. Application form not required.
Initial approach: Telephone
Copies of proposal: 1
Deadline(s): Feb. 14, June 16, and Oct. 15
Officers and Directors:* Laura Gentis,* Pres.; Tammy Slater,* C.E.O.; Alan Gunkel,* V.P. and Chair., Finance Comm.; Chuck King,* Secy.; Trent Bucher,* Treas.; Amy Greiner,* Chair., Mktg. Comm.; Jeremy Todd,* Chair., Grants Comm.; Tim Babcock; Barbara Barbieri; Ginny Fenstermaker; Adam Harder; Mitch Harnish; Mike Kracium; Olivia Reeves; Greg Roembke; Tammy Schaffer; Pat Trant.
Number of staff: 1 full-time professional.
EIN: 356042815

3404
West Foundation, Inc. ✧ ☆

c/o JPMorgan Chase Bank, N.A.
111 Monument Cir., Ste. 220
Indianapolis, IN 46204-5168
Application address: c/o Emily West, 4120 N. Illinois St., Indianapolis, IN 46208, tel.: (317) 283-5525

Established in 1954.
Donors: Stephen R. West; Phyllis M. West.
Foundation type: Independent foundation.
Financial data (yr. ended 12/31/13): Assets, $6,273,664 (M); expenditures, $579,126; qualifying distributions, $536,221; giving activities include $480,000 for 29 grants (high: $30,000; low: $5,000).
Purpose and activities: Giving primarily for international community development and human service agencies.
Fields of interest: Health care; Human services; International economic development.
International interests: Africa; Europe; South America.
Type of support: General/operating support; Annual campaigns; Capital campaigns; Matching/challenge support.
Limitations: Applications accepted. Giving primarily in the U.S. with some emphasis on CA and NY. No grants to individuals.
Publications: Application guidelines.
Application information: Application form not required.
Copies of proposal: 1
Deadline(s): None
Board meeting date(s): Feb., May, Aug., and Nov.
Officers: Phyllis M. West, V.P.; Emily A. West, Exec. Dir.
EIN: 237416727
Selected grants: The following grants are a representative sample of this grantmaker's funding activity:
$20,000 to African Wildlife Foundation, Washington, DC, 2012. For Easements for Education Program.
$20,000 to Shared Interest, New York, NY, 2012. To work in South Africa.
$20,000 to Village Enterprise Fund, San Carlos, CA, 2012. For Business In A Box Program.
$16,000 to Project MedSend, Stratford, CT, 2012. For Part/time Development Staff Member in CA.
$15,000 to Boys Hope Girls Hope, Bridgeton, MO, 2012. For Guatemalan and Brazilian Home Programs.
$15,000 to Children International, Kansas City, MO, 2012. For Training Program Quito, Ecuador.
$14,400 to BlueEnergy, San Francisco, CA, 2012. For Latrine Feasibility Study.
$12,000 to Blue Planet Network, Redwood City, CA, 2012. For Cambodia with East Meets West.
$12,000 to Prosthetics Outreach Foundation, Seattle, WA, 2012. To work in Sierra Leone.
$10,000 to CURE International, Lemoyne, PA, 2012. For Hydrocephalus Program In Mozambique.

3405
The Bruce and Beth White Family Foundation ✧

701 E. 83rd Ave.
Merrillville, IN 46410-9202

Established in 2006 in IN.
Donors: Bruce W. White; Elizabeth E. White.
Foundation type: Independent foundation.
Financial data (yr. ended 12/31/13): Assets, $8,877,174 (M); gifts received, $1,000; expenditures, $590,555; qualifying distributions, $573,477; giving activities include $490,225 for 9 grants (high: $250,000; low: $2,725).
Fields of interest: Higher education; Higher education, university; Health care, clinics/centers; Medical research; Foundations (community); United Ways and Federated Giving Programs.
Type of support: General/operating support.
Limitations: Applications not accepted. Giving primarily in IL, IN, MI, MN, PA and WY. No grants to individuals.
Application information: Contributes only to pre-selected organizations.
Officers: Bruce W. White, Pres.; Elizabeth E. White, V.P.; Carol Ann Bowman, Secy.-Treas.
EIN: 208107053
Selected grants: The following grants are a representative sample of this grantmaker's funding activity:
$50,000 to Mayo Clinic, Rochester, MN, 2012. For J Willard Marriott Jr Fund in Cardiovascular Diseases Research.

3406
Dean & Barbara White Family Foundation, Inc. ✧

1000 E. 80th Pl., Ste. 700N
Merrillville, IN 46410-5676

Established in 1997.
Donors: Dean V. White; Barbara E. White; Craig White; Cynthia Biestek; Christopher White.
Foundation type: Independent foundation.

Financial data (yr. ended 12/31/13): Assets, $29,174,598 (M); gifts received, $2,000,000; expenditures, $8,746,978; qualifying distributions, $8,391,064; giving activities include $8,371,642 for 24 grants (high: $2,000,000; low: $1,000).
Purpose and activities: Giving primarily for community and social services.
Fields of interest: Arts; Higher education; Zoos/zoological societies; Health organizations, association; Human services; Children/youth, services; Community/economic development.
Limitations: Applications not accepted. Giving primarily in IN. No grants to individuals.
Application information: Contributes only to pre-selected organizations.
Board meeting date(s): Dec.
Officers: Dean V. White, Pres.; Craig White, V.P. and Secy.; Barbara E. White, V.P. and Treas.
EIN: 352015808
Selected grants: The following grants are a representative sample of this grantmaker's funding activity:
$2,000,000 to Crown Point Youth Sports Commission, Crown Point, IN, 2013. For operating support.
$2,000,000 to Indianapolis Zoological Society, Indianapolis Zoo, Indianapolis, IN, 2013. For operating support.
$1,500,000 to National Ability Center, Park City, UT, 2013. For operating support.
$1,000,000 to Indiana State Museum Foundation, Indianapolis, IN, 2013. For matching grant for Lincoln Financial Foundation Collection.
$500,000 to Bosma Visionary Opportunities Foundation, Indianapolis, IN, 2013. For operating support.
$500,000 to Crown Point Community Foundation, Crown Point, IN, 2013. For operating support.
$250,000 to Crown Point Youth Sports Commission, Crown Point, IN, 2013. For operating support.
$50,000 to Bosma Visionary Opportunities Foundation, Indianapolis, IN, 2013. For matching grant.
$50,000 to Bosma Visionary Opportunities Foundation, Indianapolis, IN, 2013. For matching grant.
$15,000 to South Shore Arts, Munster, IN, 2013. For operating support.

3407
Whitley County Community Foundation ✧

400 N. Whitley St.
P.O. Box 527
Columbia City, IN 46725 (260) 244-5224
Contact: September McConnell, Exec. Dir.; For grant applications: John Slavich, Prog. Off.
FAX: (260) 244-5724; E-mail: sepwccf@gmail.com; Main URL: http://whitleycountycommunityfoundation.org
Facebook: https://www.facebook.com/WhitleyCountyCommunityFoundation
Twitter: https://twitter.com/#!/WhitleyCountyCF

Established in 1992 in IN.
Foundation type: Community foundation.
Financial data (yr. ended 12/31/13): Assets, $20,181,240 (M); gifts received, $1,367,710; expenditures, $1,681,700; giving activities include $1,002,140 for 27+ grants (high: $55,969), and $85,715 for 132 grants to individuals.
Purpose and activities: The mission of the foundation is to champion the spirit of philanthropy and grow permanent endowments. Utilizing collaborative leadership, it will assess and address local needs and direct funding to best meet community aspirations. Funding categories include: arts and culture, health, civic affairs, recreation, community development, welfare, and education.
Fields of interest: Arts; Education; Health care; Recreation; Human services; Community development, neighborhood development; Community/economic development; Voluntarism promotion; Public affairs; Youth; Women.
Type of support: Capital campaigns; Endowments; Emergency funds; Seed money; Scholarships—to individuals; Matching/challenge support; Student loans—to individuals.
Limitations: Applications accepted. Giving limited to Whitley County, IN. No support for private schools, or religious or sectarian causes. No grants for operating budgets, budget deficits, annual campaigns, advertising, or debt retirement.
Publications: Application guidelines; Biennial report; Grants list; Informational brochure (including application guidelines); Newsletter.
Application information: Visit foundation web site for application form and guidelines. Application form required.
Initial approach: Submit application form and attachments
Copies of proposal: 1
Deadline(s): May 1 and Dec. 1
Board meeting date(s): 2nd Thurs. of each month
Officers and Directors:* Laurie Steill,* Pres.; Sharlene Berkshire,* Secy.; September McConnell, Exec. Dir.; Dale Duncan; Greg Fahl; Rhonda Jones; John Lefever; Rob Marr; Aileen Meier; Harold Norman; Bill Overdeer; David Smith; John Whiteleather.
Number of staff: 2 full-time professional; 1 part-time professional; 1 full-time support.
EIN: 351860518

3408
Word & Deed Foundation of IMMI, Inc. ✧

(formerly IMMI Word & Deed Foundation, Inc.)
c/o Anthony M. Schelonka
1919 E. 191st St.
Westfield, IN 46074-9245
Contact: Suzanne Wilhelm, Dir.

Established in 1991 in IN.
Donors: Indiana Mills & Manufacturing, Inc.; Beverly S. Anthony; James R. Anthony; James T. Anthony; Mary Elizabeth Gordon; Suzanne A. Wilhelm; Shellie Anthony; Providential, LLC; Anthony Charitable Lead Annuity Trust; Uniform Hood Lace; Valley Christian.
Foundation type: Independent foundation.
Financial data (yr. ended 11/30/13): Assets, $6,741,399 (M); gifts received, $704,861; expenditures, $1,288,616; qualifying distributions, $1,266,532; giving activities include $1,261,455 for 93 grants (high: $573,950; low: $100), and $2,087 for foundation-administered programs.
Purpose and activities: The foundation supports organizations involved with Christianity.
Fields of interest: Christian agencies & churches.
Limitations: Applications not accepted. Giving in the U.S., with some emphasis on FL and IN. No grants to individuals.
Application information: Applications are by invitation only.
Officers: James R. Anthony, Pres.; Beverly S. Anthony, Secy.
Directors: James T. Anthony; Mary Elizabeth Gordon; Suzanne A. Wilhelm.
EIN: 351859427
Selected grants: The following grants are a representative sample of this grantmaker's funding activity:
$19,200 to Mission to Ukraine, Carmel, IN, 2011.
$16,500 to Fellowship of Christian Athletes, Indianapolis, IN, 2011.
$14,500 to Samaritans Purse, Boone, NC, 2011.
$6,000 to Care Center, Indianapolis, IN, 2011.
$5,000 to Indiana Wesleyan University, Marion, IN, 2011.
$5,000 to Moms in Touch International, Poway, CA, 2011.

IOWA

3409
AEGON Transamerica Foundation ✧
(formerly AEGON USA Charitable Foundation, Inc.)
c/o Tax Dept.
4333 Edgewood Rd., N.E.
Cedar Rapids, IA 52499-3210
E-mail: shaegontransfound@aegonusa.com; Application contact for organizations in Baltimore, MD: Transamerica Foundation Baltimore, 100 Light St., Fl. B1, Baltimore, MD 21202-2559, Attn: Veronica Mouring, #3237, e-mail: TransamericaFoundationBaltimore@Transamerica.com; Main URL: http://www.transamerica.com/about_us/aegon_transamerica_foundation.asp

Established around 1994.
Donors: AEGON USA, Inc.; Life Investors Insurance Co. of America; Transmerica Financial Life Insurance Co.
Foundation type: Company-sponsored foundation.
Financial data (yr. ended 12/31/12): Assets, $122,717,445 (M); gifts received, $602,215; expenditures, $5,164,627; qualifying distributions, $4,594,667; giving activities include $4,339,031 for 256 grants (high: $226,282; low: $250), and $255,636 for 503 employee matching gifts.
Purpose and activities: The foundation supports programs designed to promote arts and culture; civic and community; education and literacy; and health and welfare.
Fields of interest: Museums; Performing arts; Performing arts, music; Arts; Secondary school/education; Higher education; Education, reading; Education; Health care; Employment; Nutrition; Housing/shelter, homeless; Housing/shelter; Disasters, preparedness/services; Athletics/sports, golf; American Red Cross; Children/youth, services; Family services; Human services, financial counseling; Human services; Business/industry; Community/economic development; United Ways and Federated Giving Programs; Leadership development; Public affairs.
Type of support: General/operating support; Capital campaigns; Building/renovation; Equipment; Program development; Employee volunteer services; Employee matching gifts.
Limitations: Applications accepted. Giving primarily in areas of company operations, with emphasis on Little Rock, AR, Los Angeles, CA, St. Petersburg, FL, Atlanta, GA, Cedar Rapids, IA, Louisville, KY, Baltimore, MD, Harrison, NY, Exton, PA, and Bedford and Plano, TX. No support for athletes or athletic organizations, fraternal organizations, political parties or candidates, religious organizations not of direct benefit to the entire community, or social organizations. No grants to individuals, or for conferences, seminars, or trips, courtesy or goodwill advertising, fellowships, K-12 school fundraisers or events, or political campaigns.
Publications: Application guidelines; Annual report.
Application information: Organizations receiving support are asked to submit a semi-annual report and a final report. Visit website for company facility addresses.
Initial approach: Download application form and mail to nearest company facility; download application form and e-mail to application address for organizations located in Baltimore, MD
Deadline(s): Varies per location
Final notification: Varies per location
Officers and Directors:* Mark William Mullen,* Chair.; David Blankenship, Pres.; Cynthia Nodorft, V.P.; Lonny Olejniczak, V.P.; David Schulz, V.P.; Greg Tucker, V.P.; Craig D. Vermie, Secy.; Diane Meiners, Treas.
EIN: 421415998

3410
The Claude W. & Dolly Ahrens Foundation ✧
1510 Penrose St.
P.O. Box 284
Grinnell, IA 50112-1203
FAX: (641) 236-5590;
E-mail: info@ahrensfamilyfoundation.org; Main URL: http://www.ahrensfamilyfoundation.org/
Facebook: http://www.facebook.com/pages/Claude-W-Dolly-Ahrens-Foundation-Ahrens-Park-Foundation/122607224452384
Twitter: https://twitter.com/CDAFoundation

Established in 1993 in IA.
Donor: Claude W. Ahrens†.
Foundation type: Independent foundation.
Financial data (yr. ended 10/31/13): Assets, $13,403,210 (M); gifts received, $425; expenditures, $1,262,675; qualifying distributions, $1,131,983; giving activities include $507,756 for 13 grants (high: $425,111; low: $1,433).
Purpose and activities: Giving primarily for education, health, and parks and recreation.
Fields of interest: Arts; Education; Health care; Recreation, parks/playgrounds; Human services; Youth, services.
Type of support: Capital campaigns; Building/renovation; Equipment; Program development; Conferences/seminars; Seed money; Technical assistance; Matching/challenge support.
Limitations: Applications not accepted. Giving limited to central IA. No support for religious and political organizations. No grants to individuals, or for scholarships, general operating support, or international.
Publications: Annual report; Grants list; Informational brochure.
Application information: Unsolicited requests for funds not accepted.
Board meeting date(s): Jan., Mar., May, July, Sept., and Nov.
Officers and Trustees:* Julie Gosselink,* C.E.O. and Pres.; Susan E. Ahrens Witt,* V.P.; Shannon Fitzgerald-Schultz, Secy.-Treas.; Chad W. Ahrens; David Clay.
Number of staff: 3 full-time professional.
EIN: 391906775

3411
Aviva Charitable Foundation ✧
(formerly AmerUs Group Charitable Foundation)
7700 Mills Civic Pkwy.
West Des Moines, IA 50266-3862 (515) 342-3910
Contact: Karen Lynn, V.P.
E-mail: AvivaFoundation@avivausa.com; E-mail for Karen Lynn: karen.lynn@avivausa.com

Established in 1994 in IA.
Donors: American Mutual Life Insurance Co.; AmerUs Group Co.; Aviva Life and Annuity Co.
Foundation type: Company-sponsored foundation.
Financial data (yr. ended 12/31/13): Assets, $3,261,150 (M); gifts received, $1,000,000; expenditures, $2,038,618; qualifying distributions, $2,038,618; giving activities include $2,038,618 for 162 grants (high: $1,504,382; low: $25).
Purpose and activities: The foundation supports organizations involved with arts and culture, education, community development, and civic affairs.
Fields of interest: Media, television; Visual arts; Museums; Performing arts; Arts; Higher education; Education; Health care, association; Health care; Human services; Community/economic development; United Ways and Federated Giving Programs; Economics; Public affairs.
Type of support: General/operating support; Continuing support; Scholarship funds; Employee volunteer services; Employee matching gifts.
Limitations: Applications accepted. Giving primarily in areas of company operations in Des Moines, IA, Indianapolis, IN, Topeka, KS, Quincy, MA, and Woodbury, NY. No support for athletes or athletic organizations, fraternal organizations, hospitals or health care facilities, K-8 schools, military or veterans' groups, pass-through organizations, political parties, candidates, or organizations, private foundations, sectarian, religious or denominational organizations, social organizations, trade, industry, or professional associations, or United Way organizations seeking funds for operating expenses of United Way-funded programs. No grants to individuals, or for conference or seminar attendance, courtesy or goodwill advertising, endowments, fellowships, festival participation, or political campaigns.
Publications: Application guidelines.
Application information: Support is limited to 1 contribution per organization during any given year. Multi-year funding is not automatic. Organizations receiving support are asked to provide a final report. Application form required.
Initial approach: Contact foundation for application form
Copies of proposal: 1
Deadline(s): None
Board meeting date(s): Three times per year
Final notification: 8 weeks
Officers and Director:* Christopher J. Littlefield, Pres.; Karen Lynn, V.P.; Michael H. Miller, Secy.; Brenda J. Cushing, Treas.
Number of staff: 2 part-time professional.
EIN: 421431745
Selected grants: The following grants are a representative sample of this grantmaker's funding activity:
$10,000 to Youth Homes of Mid-America, Johnston, IA, 2012. For civic and community.

3412
Harold R. Bechtel Charitable Trust ✧
201 W. 2nd St., Ste. 1000
Davenport, IA 52801-1817 (563) 328-3353
Contact: R. Richard Bittner, Tr.

Foundation type: Independent foundation.
Financial data (yr. ended 04/30/13): Assets, $38,057,443 (M); expenditures, $1,768,157; qualifying distributions, $1,603,658; giving activities include $1,535,558 for 29 grants (high: $366,000; low: $2,000).

Fields of interest: Museums; Arts; Education; YM/YWCAs & YM/YWHAs; United Ways and Federated Giving Programs.
Limitations: Applications accepted. Giving primarily in Scott County, IA.
Application information: Application form required.
Initial approach: Letter or telephone requesting application form
Deadline(s): None
Officers and Trustee:* R. Richard Bittner,* Pres.; Lucille Oseland, Secy.
EIN: 261284636
Selected grants: The following grants are a representative sample of this grantmaker's funding activity:
$125,000 to Putnam Museum of History and Natural Science, Davenport, IA, 2013. For funding for improvements for the Science, Technology, Engineering and Mathematics Learning Center.
$87,500 to United Way of the Quad Cities Area, Davenport, IA, 2013. For New pre-school facility at Scott County Family Y.
$40,000 to Iowa Public Television, Johnston, IA, 2013. For funding for the Quad City Ballet televised production of The Nutcracker Ballet at the Adler Theatre in Davenport, Iowa.
$35,000 to Big Brothers Big Sisters of the Mississippi Valley, Davenport, IA, 2013. For Challenge grant funding to transition away from dependence on federal and state funding.
$30,000 to Augustana College, Rock Island, IL, 2013. For Scholarship Program for Scott County, Iowa residents.
$30,000 to Bastyr University, Kenmore, WA, 2013. For Scholarship Program for the benefit of students of naturopathic medicine from the Midwest region of the United States.
$30,000 to Quad City Arts, Rock Island, IL, 2013. For funding for 2012 Festival of Trees which raises charitable funds contributing to arts and culture with emphasis on youth.
$30,000 to Quad City Arts, Rock Island, IL, 2013. For funding for the 2013 Youth Metro Arts Summer Youth Employment Program.
$18,500 to Christian Friendliness Association, Moline, IL, 2013. For Funding to build a new water system building at Camp Summit in order to meet state code.
$10,000 to Bettendorf Public Library Foundation, Bettendorf, IA, 2013. For Funding to renovate and update facilities to increase functional areas within the library.

3413
Marie H. Bechtel Charitable Trust ✧
201 W. 2nd St., Ste. 1000
Davenport, IA 52801 (563) 328-2222
Contact: R. Richard Bittner, Pres. and Tr.

Established in IA.
Foundation type: Independent foundation.
Financial data (yr. ended 12/31/13): Assets, $42,084,597 (M); expenditures, $2,072,490; qualifying distributions, $1,847,824; giving activities include $1,750,948 for 31 grants (high: $300,000; low: $3,000).
Fields of interest: Arts; Education; Human services.
Limitations: Applications accepted. Giving primarily in Scott County, IA.
Application information: Application form required.
Initial approach: Request application form
Deadline(s): None
Officers and Trustee:* R. Richard Bittner,* Pres.; Jeffrey S. Bittner, Exec. V.P.; Lucille Oseland, Secy.
EIN: 260745711

3414
Brownell Family Foundation ✧
c/o Frank R. Brownell III
200 S. Front St.
Montezuma, IA 50171-1000

Established in 1986.
Donors: Frank R. Brownell III; Brownells, Inc.
Foundation type: Independent foundation.
Financial data (yr. ended 12/31/12): Assets, $90,750 (M); gifts received, $425,000; expenditures, $479,014; qualifying distributions, $477,740; giving activities include $477,740 for grants.
Purpose and activities: Giving to Christian agencies, higher education, the arts, and medical centers.
Fields of interest: Arts; Higher education; Hospitals (general); Christian agencies & churches.
Limitations: Applications not accepted. No grants to individuals.
Application information: Contributes only to pre-selected organizations.
Trustee: Frank R. Brownell III.
EIN: 421276134

3415
The Butler Family Foundation ✧
P.O. Box 28
Dubuque, IA 52004-0028

Established in 1994 in IA.
Donors: John E. Butler; Alice L. Butler; Andrew J. Butler; Debra Butler; Cottingham & Butler Insurance.
Foundation type: Independent foundation.
Financial data (yr. ended 12/31/13): Assets, $19,083,301 (M); gifts received, $520,430; expenditures, $1,520,950; qualifying distributions, $1,441,561; giving activities include $1,441,561 for 56 grants (high: $1,000,000; low: $100).
Purpose and activities: Giving primarily for education and youth services.
Fields of interest: Arts; Elementary/secondary education; Higher education; Health organizations; Youth development; Human services.
Limitations: Applications not accepted. Giving primarily in Dubuque, IA. No grants to individuals.
Application information: Contributes only to pre-selected organizations.
Officers: John E. Butler, Chair.; Alice L. Butler, Vice-Chair.; Timothy L. Berns, Secy.-Treas.
EIN: 421429940

3416
Roy J. Carver Charitable Trust ✧
202 Iowa Ave.
Muscatine, IA 52761-3733 (563) 263-4010
Contact: Troy K. Ross Ph.D., Exec. Admin.
FAX: (563) 263-1547; E-mail: info@carvertrust.org;
Main URL: http://www.carvertrust.org
Grants List: http://www.carvertrust.org/index.php?page=recent20082009

Established in 1982 in IA.
Donor: Roy J. Carver, Sr.†.
Foundation type: Independent foundation.
Financial data (yr. ended 04/30/13): Assets, $286,567,469 (M); expenditures, $15,293,819; qualifying distributions, $14,238,789; giving activities include $13,200,122 for 88 grants (high: $3,200,000; low: $3,054).
Purpose and activities: Support primarily for biomedical and scientific research and programs addressing the educational needs of youth.
Fields of interest: Elementary/secondary education; Higher education; Libraries/library science; Biomedicine; Medical research, institute; Youth development; Science, research.
Type of support: Capital campaigns; Building/renovation; Equipment; Program development; Conferences/seminars; Professorships; Seed money; Curriculum development; Scholarship funds; Research.
Limitations: Applications accepted. Giving primarily in IA, with some funding in IL. No support for religious activities or political organizations. No grants to individuals, or for endowments, fundraising benefits, program advertising, annual operating support.
Publications: Application guidelines; Grants list; Informational brochure (including application guidelines).
Application information: Proposals must be accompanied by a standardized cover sheet available on trust web site. Application form not required.
Initial approach: Letter (no more than 2 pages)
Copies of proposal: 1
Deadline(s): Feb. 15, May 15, Aug. 15, and Nov. 15
Board meeting date(s): 3rd Fri. of Jan., Apr., July, and Oct.
Officers and Trustees:* Roy J. Carver, Jr.,* Chair.; J. Larry Griffith,* Vice-Chair.; Willard L. Boyd; John A. Carver; Martin G. Carver; D. Scott Ingstad; David M. Utley.
Number of staff: 3 full-time professional; 1 full-time support; 1 part-time support.
EIN: 421186589
Selected grants: The following grants are a representative sample of this grantmaker's funding activity:
$7,500,000 to Iowa State University, Ames, IA, 2012. For a major initiative in the field of biomolecular structure.
$3,000,000 to University of Iowa, Iowa City, IA, 2012. For Naming Gift Payout.
$750,000 to University of Iowa, Iowa City, IA, 2012. For research and outreach program to address health issues among Muscatine middle school students.
$427,386 to University of Illinois at Urbana-Champaign, Urbana, IL, 2012. For factors in tissue regeneration using fruit fly as a laboratory model.
$376,882 to Iowa State University, Ames, IA, 2012. For research study on human disease-related biochemical signaling pathway using marine worm laboratory model.
$358,502 to University of Northern Iowa, Cedar Falls, IA, 2012. To update departmental microscopy resources.
$218,233 to University of Northern Iowa, Cedar Falls, IA, 2012. To update instructional laboratories in pre-health disciplines.
$200,000 to Drake University, Des Moines, IA, 2012. For technology learning center for science education.

$150,000 to Quad City Helicopter Emergency Medical Service, Bettendorf, IA, 2012. To purchase mobile training unit.
$60,000 to Griswold Public Library, Griswold, IA, 2012. To construct library extension.

3417
The Greater Cedar Rapids Community Foundation ✧

(formerly The Greater Cedar Rapids Foundation)
324 3rd St. SE
Cedar Rapids, IA 52401-1841 (319) 366-2862
Contact: For grants: Karla Twedt-Ball, V.P., Progs.
FAX: (319) 366-2912; E-mail: info@gcrcf.org; Additional e-mail: karla.twedt-ball@gcrcf.org; Main URL: http://www.gcrcf.org
Facebook: https://www.facebook.com/GCRCF
Flickr: http://www.flickr.com/photos/gcrcf
LinkedIn: http://www.linkedin.com/company/the-greater-cedar-rapids-community-foundation
Vimeo: http://vimeo.com/26034494
YouTube: http://www.youtube.com/TheGCRCF
Scholarship inquiry e-mail: scholarships@gcrcf.org

Established in 1949 in IA.
Foundation type: Community foundation.
Financial data (yr. ended 12/31/12): Assets, $123,375,167 (M); gifts received, $6,980,461; expenditures, $7,555,404; giving activities include $5,582,377 for 78 grants (high: $256,910).
Purpose and activities: The foundation seeks to connect donors to the priorities they care about and to the needs of the community, to increase charitable giving, and to provide leadership on important community issues. The foundation serves as one of the most important resources in Linn County, funding activities in four essential program areas: Arts and Culture, Community Development and the Environment, Education, and Health and Human Services.
Fields of interest: Historic preservation/historical societies; Arts; Education; Environment; Health care; AIDS; Human services; Community development, neighborhood development; Community/economic development.
Type of support: Capital campaigns; Building/renovation; Equipment; Emergency funds; Program development; Conferences/seminars; Publication; Seed money; Curriculum development; Scholarship funds; Technical assistance; Consulting services; Matching/challenge support.
Limitations: Applications accepted. Giving limited to the greater Cedar Rapids and surrounding Linn County, IA, area. No support for religious activities of religious organizations (including parochial schools), or for crisis intervention. No grants to individuals (except for scholarships), or for annual operating budgets or travel; generally no grants for capital campaigns, endowment campaigns, one-time events, fundraising, equipment, scientific research, debt retirement, or deficit financing.
Publications: Application guidelines; Annual report; Informational brochure; Newsletter.
Application information: The foundation asks one person act as the grant administrator for an organization, who will have access to submit online applications, check the status of application, review grant histories and submit final reports. Visit foundation web site for instructions on how to become a grant administrator and for additional guidelines per grant type. Application form required.
Initial approach: Email foundation
Copies of proposal: 12
Deadline(s): Feb. 14, July 16, and Oct. 15 for Program grants and Organizational Development Capacity grants; varies for others
Board meeting date(s): Bimonthly
Final notification: Approx. 8 weeks
Officers and Directors:* Chris Skogman,* Chair.; Kevin Welu,* Vice-Chair. and Chair.-Elect; Dr. Leslie H. Garner, Jr., C.E.O. and Pres.; Karla Twedt-Ball, Sr. V.P.; Michelle Beisker, V.P., Devel.; Jean Brenneman, C.F.O.; Katie Oberbroeckling,* Treas.; Emmylou Ball, Cont.; Karl Casell; John Chaimov; Terri Chrisoffersen; Brent Cobb; Patrick DePalma; Greg Dunn; Tiffany Earl; Sara B. Fisette; Peggy Herdesty; Maureen Kenney; Amy Lynch; Thomas Moore; Julie Nosek; John Osako; Oather Taylor.
Number of staff: 7 full-time professional; 1 part-time professional; 1 full-time support.
EIN: 426053860

3418
The Clarinda Foundation ✧

114 E. Washington St.
P.O. Box 273
Clarinda, IA 51632 (712) 542-4412
Contact: Pam Herzberg, Exec. Dir.
FAX: (712) 542-4412;
E-mail: clarindafound@iowatelecom.net; Main URL: http://www.clarindafoundation.com

Established in 1986 in IA.
Foundation type: Community foundation.
Financial data (yr. ended 12/31/13): Assets, $4,420,085 (M); gifts received, $1,404,313; expenditures, $1,162,599; giving activities include $1,034,038 for 23+ grants (high: $207,322), and $41,503 for 32 grants to individuals.
Purpose and activities: The foundation seeks to provide prospective donors an effective way to invest in the future of Clarinda, IA, and to maximize tax savings to the donors and their estates.
Fields of interest: Education; Health care; Human services; Community/economic development; Public affairs.
Type of support: Building/renovation; Equipment; Program development; Scholarship funds; Scholarships—to individuals; Exchange programs.
Limitations: Applications accepted. Giving limited to within 15 miles of Clarinda, IA.
Publications: Application guidelines; Annual report; Newsletter.
Application information: Visit foundation web site for grant application form. Application form required.
Initial approach: Mail application form
Copies of proposal: 1
Deadline(s): Apr. 1
Board meeting date(s): 3rd Thursday of every month
Final notification: Within 90 days
Officers and Directors:* Jennifer McCall,* Pres.; Martin Mattes,* 1st V.P.; Sandy Geer,* 2nd V.P.; Scott Sump,* 3rd V.P.; Belinda Lane,* Co-Secy.; Connie Richardson,* Co-Secy.; Jon Baier,* Treas.; Pam Herzberg,* Exec. Dir.; Ed Brown; Scott Brown; Lisa Hull; Dale McAllister; Tom McAndrews; Teresa Nook; Carl Sonksen; Laura Swanson; Lynn Whitmore.
Number of staff: 1 part-time professional; 1 part-time support.
EIN: 421285187

3419
Community Foundation of Fort Dodge and United Way ✧

24 N 9th St., Ste. B
Fort Dodge, IA 50501 (515) 573-3179
Contact: For grants: Randy Kuhlman, C.E.O.
FAX: (515) 955-5421;
E-mail: mail.fdfoundation@frontier.com; Main URL: http://www.fd-foundation.org/
Facebook: http://www.facebook.com/pages/Fort-Dodge-Community-Foundation-and-United-Way/163888696985010

Established in IA in 1995.
Foundation type: Community foundation.
Financial data (yr. ended 12/31/12): Assets, $2,507,113 (M); gifts received, $1,209,561; expenditures, $935,238; giving activities include $696,162 for 18+ grants (high: $70,000).
Purpose and activities: The foundation's mission is to serve as a catalyst for charitable giving - developing charitable resources to support important community programs, services and projects that will benefit the public good and improve the quality of life of all citizens, families and youth in Fort Dodge, Webster County and North Central Iowa.
Fields of interest: Arts; Education, reading; Education; Environment, beautification programs; Environment; Health care; Crime/violence prevention; Recreation, parks/playgrounds; Recreation; Youth development; Human services, emergency aid; Human services; Community/economic development.
Limitations: Applications accepted. Giving primarily in Fort Dodge, Webster County, and North Central Iowa.
Publications: Annual report.
Application information: All applications are to submitted in hard-copy form and electronically. Visit foundation web site for application form and additional information. Application form required.
Initial approach: Submit application
Deadline(s): Oct. 31 for Community Development Funds
Officers and Board Members:* Randy Kuhlman,* C.E.O.; Timothy J. Carmody,* Pres.; John Bruner,* V.P.; Deb Johnson,* Secy.; Scott Johnson,* Treas.; Tim Burns; Nick Cochrane; Jim Humes; Susan Ahlers Leman; Troy Martens; Scott McQueen; Don Schnurr; Troy K. Shaner; Lin Simpson; Bill Thatcher; Lisa Wilson; Karen Wood.
EIN: 421439853

3420
Community Foundation of Greater Des Moines ✧

(formerly Des Moines Community Foundation)
1915 Grand Ave.
Des Moines, IA 50309-3311 (515) 883-2626
Contact: For grants: Angela Dethlefs-Trettin, V.P., Community Investment and Initiatives
FAX: (515) 883-2630;
E-mail: info@desmoinesfoundation.org; Grant inquiry e-mail: trettin@demoinesfoundation.org; Grant request tel.: (515) 244-0340; Main URL: http://www.desmoinesfoundation.org
Facebook: http://www.facebook.com/communityfoundationdesmoines
Google Plus: https://plus.google.com/109270311669777363643/

RSS Feed: http://www.desmoinesfoundation.org/rss/rssFeed.aspx?group=News
Twitter: https://twitter.com/cfdesmoines

Incorporated in 1969 in IA.
Foundation type: Community foundation.
Financial data (yr. ended 12/31/12): Assets, $225,538,295 (M); gifts received, $37,707,482; expenditures, $32,309,822; giving activities include $25,228,667 for grants.
Purpose and activities: The Community Foundation of Greater Des Moines is a donor-driven public foundation whose purpose is to improve the quality of life in Greater Des Moines through philanthropy.
Fields of interest: Arts; Education; Health care; Employment; Children/youth, services; Human services; Community/economic development.
Type of support: Management development/capacity building; Building/renovation; Program development; Seed money; Scholarship funds; Research; Technical assistance; Scholarships—to individuals; Matching/challenge support.
Limitations: Applications accepted. Giving primarily in the greater Des Moines, Iowa area and through Iowa. No support for sectarian religious purposes through the foundation's discretionary grantmaking. No grants to individuals (except for scholarships), or for annual operating expenses.
Publications: Application guidelines; Annual report; Financial statement.
Application information: Select projects will be invited to submit a full grant application based on Letter of Intent. The Community Foundation will continue to advance its Leadership Agenda through Leadership Grants, Capacity Building Grants and nonprofit training opportunities; visit foundation web site for application guidelines per grant type. Application form required.
Initial approach: Letter of Intent
Deadline(s): Semi-annually
Board meeting date(s): Five times annually
Final notification: Varies
Officers and Directors:* Cara Heiden,* Chair.; Richard Deming, M.D.*, Vice-Chair.; Kristi Knous, Pres.; Angela Dethlefs-Trettin, V.P., Community Investment and Initiatives; Gordon R. Fischer, V.P., Gift Planning Strategies; Karla Jones-Weber, V.P., Finance and Admin. and C.F.O.; Sheila Kinman, V.P., Advancement; Fred W. Weitz,* Secy.-Treas.; Kris Pete-Swanson, Cont.; Peg Armstrong-Gustafson; Margo Blumenthal; Roger K. Brooks; Frederick V. Buie; Suzie Glazer Burt; Teree Caldwell-Johnson; Sandy Hatfield Clubb; Jim Cownie; Johnny Danos; Nora Evertt; Peggy Fisher; Allison Fleming; N. Brian Gentry; J. Barry Griswell; H. Lynn Horak; Fred S. Hubbell; Kyle Krause; Stephen M. Lacy; Loree Miles; Christopher E. Nelson, Ph.D.; Mary O'Keefe; Mark Oman; Alfredo Parrish; Alejandro H. Piedras; Suku Radia; Doug Reichardt; Robert G. "Bob" Riley, Jr.; Janis Ruan; Mark Rupprecht; Thomas Urban.
Number of staff: 13 full-time professional; 3 full-time support.
EIN: 426139033

3421
Community Foundation of Greater Dubuque ✧

700 Locust St., Ste. 195
Dubuque, IA 52001-6824 (563) 588-2700
Contact: Nancy Van Milligen, C.E.O.; For grants: Katie Foust, Grant Mgmt. Asst.; For grants: Kari McCann, Dir., Philanthropic and Nonprofit Partnerships
FAX: (563) 583-6619;
E-mail: office@dbqfoundation.org; Grant inquiry and information e-mails: katie@dbqfoundation.org and kari@dbqfoundation.org; Main URL: http://www.dbqfoundation.org
Facebook: http://www.facebook.com/pages/Community-Foundation-of-Greater-Dubuque/119274054070?ref=mf
Google Plus: https://plus.google.com/111491904102395018243
LinkedIn: http://www.linkedin.com/companies/community-foundation-of-greater-dubuque
RSS Feed: http://www.dbqfoundation.org/news-events/news/feed
Twitter: https://twitter.com/dbqfoundation
YouTube: http://www.youtube.com/user/yapperscfgd

Established in 2001 in IA.
Foundation type: Community foundation.
Financial data (yr. ended 06/30/13): Assets, $44,671,360 (M); gifts received, $10,732,491; expenditures, $4,338,633; giving activities include $2,890,592 for 68+ grants (high: $352,328), and $5,537 for 35 grants to individuals.
Purpose and activities: The foundation works to improve the quality of life in the Dubuque region by: serving donors, making grants and providing community leadership through convening and collaboration.
Fields of interest: Community/economic development; Children/youth; Youth; Aging; Physically disabled; Economically disadvantaged.
Type of support: General/operating support; Management development/capacity building; Seed money; Scholarship funds; Technical assistance; Consulting services.
Limitations: Applications accepted. Giving limited to northeast IA. No support for religious purposes. No grants for operating support, annual and capital campaigns, budget deficit, endowments, or equipment (unless it is essential for the program).
Publications: Application guidelines; Annual report; Grants list; Informational brochure; Newsletter.
Application information: Visit foundation web site for applications and guidelines per grant type. Application form required.
Initial approach: Complete online application for Community Impact Grants
Deadline(s): Dec. 31 for Community Impact Grants; varies for others
Board meeting date(s): 4 times a year
Final notification: Early Oct. for Community Impact Grants; varies for others
Officers and Directors:* Tim Conlon,* Chair.; John O'Connor,* Vice-Chair.; Nancy Van Milligen,* C.E.O. and Pres.; Eric Dregne,* V.P., Strategic Initiatives; Amy Manternach,* V.P., Philanthropic Srvs.; Ken Furst,* Secy.; Rebecca Kruse, Cont.; Brian Kane,* Treas.; Dr. Ed Alt; Jesus Aviles; Chad Chandlee; Charlie Glab; Sarah Harris; Jane Hasek; Bob Hoefer; William R. Klauer, Jr.; Keith Kramer; Jeanne Lauritsen; Phillip Ruppel; Jim Theisen; Teri Zuccaro.
Number of staff: 5 full-time professional; 8 part-time professional; 1 full-time support; 1 part-time support.
EIN: 421526614

3422
Community Foundation of Johnson County ✧

325 E. Washington St.
Iowa City, IA 52240-3968 (319) 337-0483
Contact: Michael L. Stoffregen, Exec. Dir.
FAX: (319) 338-9958;
E-mail: info@communityfoundationofjohnsoncounty.com; Main URL: http://www.communityfoundationofjohnsoncounty.org/

Established in 2000 in IA.
Foundation type: Community foundation.
Financial data (yr. ended 06/30/13): Assets, $14,006,210 (M); gifts received, $4,973,336; expenditures, $1,129,028; giving activities include $803,526 for 33+ grants (high: $132,500).
Purpose and activities: The organization provides a means for citizens to make gifts to specific organizations, general areas of concern or the common good, to pool and manage endowment funds for local nonprofit organizations, and to distribute funds to benefit the community.
Fields of interest: Arts; Education; Environment; Animals/wildlife; Health care; Youth development; Human services.
Limitations: Applications accepted. Giving limited to the Johnson County, IA, area.
Publications: Annual report; Grants list; Newsletter.
Application information: Visit web site for application form and guidelines. Application form required.
Initial approach: Create online profile
Deadline(s): July 15
Officers and Directors:* Tim Krumm,* Pres.; John Schneider,* V.P.; Steve Atkins,* Secy.; Dean Price,* Treas.; Michael L. Stoffregen, Exec. Dir.; Betsy Boyd; Chuck Coulter; Maggie Elliott; Bart Floyd; Pat Harney; Michael Heinrich; Sarah Maiers; Sharon Oglesby; Nancy Richardson; Chuck Skaugstad, Jr.; Greg Turner; Anne Vandenberg; Steve Weeber; Joe Wegman; Mary Westbrook; Nancy Williams.
EIN: 421508117

3423
Community Foundation of Northeast Iowa ✧

(formerly Community Foundation of Waterloo/Cedar Falls and Northeast Iowa)
425 Cedar St., Ste. 310
Waterloo, IA 50701-1351 (319) 287-9106
Contact: Kaye Englin, C.E.O. and Pres.
FAX: (319) 287-5015; E-mail: kenglin@cfneia.org; Main URL: http://www.cfneia.org
Facebook: https://www.facebook.com/CFNEIA?ref=ts&fref=ts

Incorporated in 1956 in IA.
Foundation type: Community foundation.
Financial data (yr. ended 12/31/13): Assets, $76,786,500 (M); gifts received, $8,790,203; expenditures, $6,265,444; giving activities include $5,081,247 for 703+ grants (high: $277,995; low: $18).
Purpose and activities: The foundation's mission is to: 1) respond to the current and future charitable needs of Northeast Iowa; 2) secure and serve as the custodian of endowment funds contributed by many donors; 3) create other mechanisms, which will channel charitable money, goods and services to meet community need; and 4) serve as a convener

to examine and determine community needs and facilitate a solution.
Fields of interest: Historic preservation/historical societies; Arts; Child development, education; Libraries/library science; Education; Environment, natural resources; Environment; Health care; Disasters, Hurricane Katrina; Recreation; Children/youth, services; Child development, services; Family services; Minorities/immigrants, centers/services; Human services; Community/economic development.
Type of support: General/operating support; Continuing support; Management development/capacity building; Capital campaigns; Building/renovation; Equipment; Endowments; Emergency funds; Program development; Conferences/seminars; Publication; Seed money; Scholarship funds; Research; Program evaluation; Exchange programs; Matching/challenge support.
Limitations: Applications accepted. Giving primarily in northeastern IA. No support for religious organizations. No grants to individuals (except for scholarships), or for annual campaigns.
Publications: Application guidelines; Annual report; Financial statement; Grants list; Informational brochure (including application guidelines); Newsletter.
Application information: Visit foundation web site for Grant Request form and application guidelines per grant type. Application form required.
Initial approach: Telephone
Deadline(s): Varies
Board meeting date(s): 1st Wed. in June and Dec.
Final notification: June and Dec.
Officers and Trustees:* Marlene Behn,* Chair.; Jay Bullerman,* Vice-Chair.; Kaye Englin, C.E.O. and Pres.; Stacy Robinson, V.P., Finance and Opers.; Aaron Sannes, Chair., Investment; Deb Giarusso,* Secy.; Charley Perry, Treas.; Robert Bradford; Stacie Brass; Camille Hogan; Jeff Hassman; Lori Johnson; Rudy Jones; Darcy Knights; Becky Mudd; Mark Rolinger; Ellen Young.
Number of staff: 8 full-time professional; 2 full-time support.
EIN: 426060414

3424
Community Foundation of the Great River Bend ✧
(formerly Davenport Area Foundation)
852 Middle Rd., Ste. 100
Bettendorf, IA 52722-4100 (563) 326-2840
Contact: Susan S. Skora, C.E.O.
FAX: (563) 326-2870; E-mail: info@cfgrb.org; Additional e-mail: susanskora@cfgrb.org; Main URL: http://www.cfgrb.org
Facebook: https://www.facebook.com/cfgrb?ref=ts&fref=ts
Twitter: http://twitter.com/CFGRB
Scholarship inquiry e-mail: scholarships@cfgrb.org

Established in 1964 in IA.
Foundation type: Community foundation.
Financial data (yr. ended 12/31/13): Assets, $105,244,950 (M); gifts received, $9,064,815; expenditures, $6,371,537; giving activities include $5,052,650 for grants.
Purpose and activities: The foundation seeks to enhance the quality of life in the communities served by encouraging permanent charitable giving to meet the needs of present and future generations. Giving primarily for cultural activities, educational programs, health and human services, and economic development.
Fields of interest: Arts; Scholarships/financial aid; Education; Environment; Health care; Youth development, services; Human services; Economic development; Community/economic development; Philanthropy/voluntarism; Youth.
Type of support: Continuing support; Management development/capacity building; Capital campaigns; Building/renovation; Equipment; Emergency funds; Conferences/seminars; Publication; Seed money; Technical assistance; Consulting services; Matching/challenge support.
Limitations: Applications accepted. Giving limited to eastern IA and western IL. No support for sectarian purposes. No grants to individuals (except for scholarships), or for annual fundraising, endowment funds, or deficit financing; generally no multi-year grants.
Publications: Application guidelines; Annual report; Grants list; Informational brochure; Newsletter.
Application information: Visit foundation web site for online application forms and additional guidelines per grant type. Application form required.
Initial approach: Create account on the foundation's web site
Deadline(s): Varies
Board meeting date(s): 1st Tues. of each month
Final notification: Varies
Officers and Trustees:* Deann R. Thoms,* Chair.; Pete Wessels,* 1st Vice-Chair.; Luann Rickert,* 2nd Vice-Chair.; Sherry Ristau, C.E.O. and Pres.; Kathy Graves, V.P., Finance and Admin.; Barbara J. Melbourne, V.P., Devel.; Matt Mendenhall, V.P., Progs.; Jill McLaughlin,* Secy.; Ray Allen,* Treas.; Dan Ellard; Michael K. Drymiller; Paul Koch; Randy Moore; Jean Moran; Linda Neuman; David Nuernberger; William Storm; Terry Wilson.
Number of staff: 4 full-time professional; 2 part-time professional; 1 full-time support; 3 part-time support.
EIN: 426122716

3425
W. T. and Edna M. Dahl Trust ✧
699 Walnut St., Ste. 1600
Des Moines, IA 50309-3944 (515) 246-4513
Contact: Paul R. Tyler, Tr.

Established in 2007 in IA.
Donor: W.T. Dahl†.
Foundation type: Independent foundation.
Financial data (yr. ended 12/31/13): Assets, $9,632,413 (M); expenditures, $887,715; qualifying distributions, $780,875; giving activities include $743,000 for 20 grants (high: $100,000; low: $3,000).
Fields of interest: Arts; Human services; Residential/custodial care, senior continuing care; Foundations (private grantmaking).
Limitations: Applications accepted. Giving primarily in IA. No grants to individuals.
Application information: Application form required.
Initial approach: Completed application form
Deadline(s): None
Trustees: Jerry G. Jones; Paul R. Tyler.
EIN: 206983203
Selected grants: The following grants are a representative sample of this grantmaker's funding activity:
$100,000 to ChildServe Foundation, Johnston, IA, 2011.

3426
Greater Delaware County Community Foundation ✧ ☆
200 E. Main St.
Manchester, IA 52057 (563) 927-4141
E-mail: macc@manchesteriowa.org; Main URL: http://www.manchesteriowa.org/GDCCF/index.html

Established in 1976 in IA.
Foundation type: Community foundation.
Financial data (yr. ended 10/31/13): Assets, $2,903,457 (M); gifts received, $1,017,930; expenditures, $556,780; giving activities include $435,168 for 8+ grants (high: $123,485), and $65,278 for 352 grants to individuals.
Purpose and activities: Giving for scholarships and community development.
Fields of interest: Higher education; Education; Community/economic development.
Type of support: Scholarships—to individuals.
Limitations: Giving primarily in IA.
Officers and Trustees:* John E. Tyrrell,* Chair.; Cheryl Stufflebeaum,* Vice-Chair.; Jack Klaus,* Secy.; Tom Allyn; Kay Harris; Fred Phelps; Ed Poynor; Doug Tuetken.
EIN: 421045184

3427
James K. and Pauline C. Durgin Foundation ✧
1301 19th Ave., NW
Clinton, IA 52732-2752 (563) 243-4204
Application address: c/o James K. Durgin, 814 13th Ave. N., Clinton, IA 52732l tel: (563) 243-4204

Established in 1993.
Donor: James K. Durgin.
Foundation type: Independent foundation.
Financial data (yr. ended 12/31/11): Assets, $62,578 (M); expenditures, $2,141,137; qualifying distributions, $2,123,800; giving activities include $2,123,800 for 26 grants (high: $400,000; low: $500).
Fields of interest: Higher education, college.
Limitations: Applications accepted. Giving primarily in Clinton, IA.
Application information: Application form required.
Initial approach: Letter or telephone
Deadline(s): None
Trustees: James K. Durgin; Pauline C. Durgin.
EIN: 421394666
Selected grants: The following grants are a representative sample of this grantmaker's funding activity:
$10,000 to Alzheimers Foundation of America, New York, NY, 2011.
$5,000 to Midwest Lumber Museum, Clinton, IA, 2011.

3428
EMC Insurance Foundation ✧
(formerly Employers Mutual Charitable Foundation)
P.O. Box 712
Des Moines, IA 50303-0712 (515) 345-7390
Contact: Sean Pelletier, Exec. Dir.
Main URL: http://www.emcins.com/AboutEMC/Community_Involvement.aspx

Established in 1989 in IA.
Donor: Employers Mutual Casualty Co.

Foundation type: Company-sponsored foundation.
Financial data (yr. ended 12/31/13): Assets, $8,868,640 (M); gifts received, $2,338,126; expenditures, $1,215,809; qualifying distributions, $1,180,607; giving activities include $1,180,607 for 91 grants (high: $249,640; low: $2).
Purpose and activities: The foundation supports organizations involved with arts and culture, education, health, human services, and insurance education.
Fields of interest: Performing arts, orchestras; Arts; Elementary/secondary education; Higher education; Education; Health care; American Red Cross; Children/youth, services; Human services; Community development, civic centers; Business/industry; United Ways and Federated Giving Programs.
Type of support: General/operating support.
Limitations: Applications accepted. Giving primarily in areas of company operations in IA. No grants to individuals.
Application information: Application form required.
Initial approach: Proposal
Deadline(s): None
Officers: Bruce G. Kelley,* C.E.O. and Pres.; Richard Hoffmann, Secy.; Ronald D. Herman, Treas.; Sean Pelletier,* Exec. Dir.
Directors: John C. Burgeson; David J. Fisher; Frederick Schiek; Philip T. Van Ekeren.
EIN: 421343474
Selected grants: The following grants are a representative sample of this grantmaker's funding activity:
$1,500 to YMCA of Greater Des Moines, Des Moines, IA, 2012. For All contributions are made either for the general support or for a capital fund drive of the respective organization.

3429
Gabus Family Foundation ✧ ☆
c/o Iowa State Bank/Steve Hoeksema
2301 128th St.
Urbandale, IA 50323-1818

Established in 1995 in IA.
Donors: Charles Gabus; Gene Gabus.
Foundation type: Independent foundation.
Financial data (yr. ended 12/31/13): Assets, $1,838,151 (M); gifts received, $171,577; expenditures, $2,779,393; qualifying distributions, $2,745,900; giving activities include $2,745,900 for 11 grants (high: $1,000,000; low: $2,400).
Fields of interest: Performing arts, orchestras; Higher education; Protestant federated giving programs; Science; Protestant agencies & churches.
Limitations: Applications not accepted. Giving primarily in Urbandale, IA, and Peru, NE. No grants to individuals.
Application information: Unsolicited requests for funds not accepted.
Officers: Patricia Peterson, Pres.; Jan Gabus, V.P.; Gene Gabus, Treas.
EIN: 421448004

3430
The Gerdin Charitable Foundation ✧
901 N. Kansas Ave.
North Liberty, IA 52317-4725

Established in 1996 in IA.
Donors: Russell A. Gerdin; Ann S. Gerdin.
Foundation type: Independent foundation.
Financial data (yr. ended 12/31/13): Assets, $89,390,351 (M); gifts received, $2,400,000; expenditures, $4,030,426; qualifying distributions, $3,851,750; giving activities include $3,851,750 for 3 grants (high: $3,200,000; low: $151,750).
Purpose and activities: Giving primarily for educational foundations, as well as for other charitable purposes, including a cancer organization.
Fields of interest: Higher education; Cancer research; Foundations (public).
Limitations: Applications not accepted. Giving primarily in IA and MN, with emphasis on Cedar Rapids. No grants to individuals.
Application information: Contributes only to pre-selected organizations.
Officers: Ann S. Gerdin, Pres. and Secy.-Treas.; Michael J. Gerdin, V.P.; Julie J. Durr, V.P.; Angela K. Janssen, V.P.
EIN: 421462088

3431
John P. and Lawrence J. Giacoletto Foundation ✧ ☆
1175 8th Ave.
Marion, IA 52302-3503 (319) 363-1910
FAX: (319) 377-9406; E-mail: info@giacoletto.org; Main URL: http://www.giacoletto.org

Donor: Giacoletto Living Trust.
Foundation type: Operating foundation.
Financial data (yr. ended 12/31/13): Assets, $8,165,745 (M); expenditures, $492,836; qualifying distributions, $492,836; giving activities include $422,500 for 30 grants (high: $100,000; low: $1,000).
Fields of interest: Libraries/library science; Libraries (public); Education; United Ways and Federated Giving Programs.
Limitations: Applications accepted. Giving primarily in IA and IN.
Application information: See foundation web site for complete application guidelines. Application form required.
Deadline(s): Quarterly
Trustees: Barbara Robison; E. Wayne Scott; Alex Taylor.
EIN: 201777917

3432
Gilchrist Foundation ✧
P.O. Box 147
Sioux City, IA 51102-0147

Established in 1998 in IA.
Donor: Jocelyn Gilchrist‡.
Foundation type: Independent foundation.
Financial data (yr. ended 12/31/13): Assets, $37,513,540 (M); expenditures, $1,944,223; qualifying distributions, $1,670,912; giving activities include $1,670,912 for 30 grants (high: $125,000; low: $5,890).
Purpose and activities: Giving primarily for the arts, education, the environment, health, animal welfare, and children, youth and social services.
Fields of interest: Arts; Higher education; Environment, natural resources; Animal welfare; Health care; Human services; American Red Cross; Children/youth, services.
Type of support: General/operating support.
Limitations: Applications not accepted. Giving primarily in Sioux City, IA and IL. No grants to individuals.
Application information: Contributes only to pre-selected organizations.
Trustee: Security National Bank.
EIN: 426578668

3433
The Jeffrey W. Glazer Foundation ✧ ☆
3737 River Oaks Dr.
Des Moines, IA 50312-4614

Established in 1985 in IA.
Donors: Jeffrey W. Glazer; Madelyn Levitt; Lisa Braun-Glazer.
Foundation type: Independent foundation.
Financial data (yr. ended 12/31/13): Assets, $8,861,062 (M); gifts received, $15,000; expenditures, $481,780; qualifying distributions, $480,180; giving activities include $480,180 for 19 + grants (high: $125,100).
Fields of interest: Education; Jewish federated giving programs; Jewish agencies & synagogues.
Type of support: General/operating support.
Limitations: Applications not accepted. Giving primarily in CA and VA. No grants to individuals.
Application information: Contributes only to pre-selected organizations.
Officers: Jeffrey W. Glazer, Pres.; Lisa Braun-Glazer, Secy.
Directors: Julia Braun-Glazer; Anna Glazer.
EIN: 421258464
Selected grants: The following grants are a representative sample of this grantmaker's funding activity:
$50,000 to Institute for Shipboard Education, Charlottesville, VA, 2011. For general fund.
$12,400 to Institute for Jewish Spirituality, New York, NY, 2011. For general fund.

3434
Susan J. Glazer Foundation ✧
3737 River Oaks Dr.
Des Moines, IA 50312-4614

Established in 1985 in IA.
Donors: Susan J. Burt; Madelyn L. Glazer.
Foundation type: Independent foundation.
Financial data (yr. ended 12/31/13): Assets, $6,966,312 (M); expenditures, $546,367; qualifying distributions, $543,280; giving activities include $543,280 for 23 grants (high: $400,000; low: $100).
Fields of interest: Health care; Boys & girls clubs; Human services; Residential/custodial care, hospices.
Type of support: General/operating support; Scholarship funds.
Limitations: Applications not accepted. Giving primarily in Des Moines, IA. No grants to individuals.
Application information: Unsolicited Requests for funds not accepted.
Officers: Susan Glazer Burt, Pres.; Gregory Burt, Treas.
EIN: 421258466
Selected grants: The following grants are a representative sample of this grantmaker's funding activity:

$200,000 to Drake University, Des Moines, IA, 2011.
$53,800 to Boys and Girls Club of Central Iowa, West Des Moines, IA, 2011.
$9,100 to University of Iowa, Iowa City, IA, 2011.
$3,000 to Des Moines Public Schools, Des Moines, IA, 2011.
$2,719 to Tifereth Israel Synagogue, Des Moines, IA, 2011.

3435
Global Invincibility Foundation ✧

c/o Swartz Co.
200 W. Washington Ave.
Fairfield, IA 52556-3318
Contact: Rafael David, Pres.

Donor: Rafael David.
Foundation type: Independent foundation.
Financial data (yr. ended 12/31/11): Assets, $3,869,989 (M); expenditures, $563,761; qualifying distributions, $559,500; giving activities include $559,500 for 4 grants (high: $275,000; low: $32,000).
Fields of interest: Higher education; International peace/security.
Limitations: Applications accepted. Giving primarily in IA.
Application information: Application form required.
Initial approach: Proposal
Deadline(s): None
Officers: Rafael David, Pres.; Nancy Diamond, Secy.-Treas.
Director: Steve Brittingham.
EIN: 263418616

3436
Leonard A. Good Trust ✧

713 W. Cherry
Ogden, IA 50212 (515) 275-2427
Contact: Doug Nebbe, Tr.

Established in 1990 in IA.
Foundation type: Independent foundation.
Financial data (yr. ended 12/31/13): Assets, $10,767,044 (M); expenditures, $598,400; qualifying distributions, $577,374; giving activities include $572,761 for 29 grants (high: $165,000; low: $2,000).
Purpose and activities: Giving primarily for public affairs and human services.
Fields of interest: Elementary/secondary education; Human services; Public affairs, government agencies.
Limitations: Applications accepted. Giving primarily in Boone County, IA. No support for political organizations. No grants to individuals.
Application information: Application form required.
Initial approach: Telephone
Copies of proposal: 4
Deadline(s): None
Board meeting date(s): Varies
Trustees: J. Dale Burman; Helen Miller; Douglas E. Nebbe; Randall C. Reutter.
EIN: 426453227
Selected grants: The following grants are a representative sample of this grantmaker's funding activity:
$5,000 to United Way of Boone County, Boone, IA, 2011.
$2,600 to Camp Hertko Hollow, Des Moines, IA, 2011.
$1,000 to Four-H Foundation, Iowa, Ames, IA, 2011.

3437
Max and Helen Guernsey Charitable Foundation ✧

P.O. Box 1172
Waterloo, IA 50704-1172 (319) 226-3434
Contact: Soo Greiman, Exec. Dir.
E-mail: GuernseyFoundatn@aol.com; Physical address to apply in person for a grant: Regions Bank Building, 100 E. Park Ave., Ste. 230, Waterloo, IA; Main URL: http://www.guernseyfoundation.com

Established in 1996 in IA.
Donors: Helen Guernsey; Max E. Guernsey†; Waverly Plastics, Inc.
Foundation type: Independent foundation.
Financial data (yr. ended 06/30/13): Assets, $18,825,315 (M); gifts received, $5,000; expenditures, $1,322,757; qualifying distributions, $1,098,794; giving activities include $1,098,794 for 92 grants (high: $50,000; low: $500).
Purpose and activities: The foundation's mission is to work in partnership with others to improve the vitality of the community, addressing issues important now and in the future. The foundation focuses its support on a broad spectrum of needs including education that builds character, programs that enhance family life, key social issues, science, programs that aim for community betterment, health and life skills, sports, fitness, and activities that recognize the value of people.
Fields of interest: Museums; Education; Botanical gardens; Crime/law enforcement, police agencies; YM/YWCAs & YM/YWHAs; Children/youth, services; Children, services; Family services.
Type of support: General/operating support; Continuing support; Annual campaigns; Capital campaigns; Building/renovation; Endowments; Emergency funds; Conferences/seminars.
Limitations: Applications accepted. Giving primarily in the Cedar Valley, IA, area. No support for national health organizations and their local affiliates, veteran, labor and political organizations or campaigns, or fraternal, athletic, and social clubs; no operating expenses of organizations supported by United Way. No grants to individuals, or for business ventures, endowments, advertising, loans or debt retirements, conferences, seminars, trips or similar events; no grants for religious purposes or to sectarian programs for religious purposes.
Publications: Application guidelines; Informational brochure.
Application information: Brochures and application forms are available at the foundation office. Application form required.
Initial approach: Telephone Exec. Dir. to determine appropriateness of request
Copies of proposal: 1
Deadline(s): Mar. 15 and Aug. 15
Board meeting date(s): Spring and Fall
Final notification: June 1 and Nov. 1
Officers and Directors:* Thomas R. Paulsen,* Pres.; Helen Guernsey,* V.P.; Shirley Kreger,* Secy.; Gary Nelson,* Treas.; Soo Greiman, Exec. Dir.; Harold B. Strever, Jr.
EIN: 421460664
Selected grants: The following grants are a representative sample of this grantmaker's funding activity:
$20,000 to Afro-American Community Broadcasting, Waterloo, IA, 2011.
$20,000 to Big Brothers Big Sisters, Waterloo, IA, 2011.
$20,000 to Boy Scouts of America, Waterloo, IA, 2011.
$20,000 to Cedar Valley Hospice, Waterloo, IA, 2011.
$20,000 to Grout Museum, Waterloo, IA, 2011.
$15,000 to Northeast Iowa Food Bank, Waterloo, IA, 2011.
$11,000 to Friends of Hartman Reserve, Cedar Falls, IA, 2011.
$10,000 to Hawkeye Community College, Waterloo, IA, 2011.
$5,500 to Waterloo Police Department, Waterloo, IA, 2011.
$2,500 to United Way, Cedar Valley, Waterloo, IA, 2011.

3438
The GuideOne Insurance Foundation, Inc. ✧

1111 Ashworth Rd., M.S. A27
West Des Moines, IA 50265-3544
Contact: Sarah Buckley, V.P., Corp. Comms. and Mktg.
Main URL: http://www.guideone.com/AboutUs/foundation.htm

Established in 2000 in IA as a company-sponsored operating foundation.
Donor: GuideOne Life Insurance Co.
Foundation type: Operating foundation.
Financial data (yr. ended 12/31/12): Assets, $2,151,567 (M); gifts received, $72,517; expenditures, $425,577; qualifying distributions, $425,577; giving activities include $425,577 for 35 grants (high: $161,898; low: $1,000).
Purpose and activities: The foundation supports food banks and organizations involved with housing development, human services, community development, and Christianity. Special emphasis is directed toward programs designed to promote mission and community development; provide assistance for immediate needs; and promote prevention of drinking and driving and underage drinking.
Fields of interest: Crime/law enforcement, DWI; Food banks; Housing/shelter, development; Disasters, preparedness/services; Safety, automotive safety; American Red Cross; Children/youth, services; Human services; Community/economic development; United Ways and Federated Giving Programs; Christian agencies & churches.
Type of support: General/operating support; Emergency funds; Program development; Sponsorships.
Limitations: Giving primarily in IA; giving also to national organizations. No grants to individuals.
Officers and Directors:* James D. Wallace,* Chair. and Pres.; Brian Hughes, Treas.; Tom Fischer.
EIN: 391910630

3439
The Hall-Perrine Foundation ✧

(formerly The Hall Foundation, Inc.)
115 3rd St., S.E., Ste. 803
Cedar Rapids, IA 52401-1222 (319) 362-9079
Contact: Kristin Novak, Prog. Off.; Jack Evans, Pres.

FAX: (319) 362-7220;
E-mail: kristin@Hallperrine.org; Main URL: http://www.hallperrine.org/

Incorporated in 1953 in IA.
Donor: Members of the Hall family.
Foundation type: Independent foundation.
Financial data (yr. ended 12/31/12): Assets, $109,995,615 (M); expenditures, $6,194,121; qualifying distributions, $5,595,424; giving activities include $5,422,878 for 17+ grants (high: $1,000,000), and $100,000 for 1 loan/program-related investment.
Purpose and activities: The foundation is dedicated to improving the quality of life for people in Linn County, IA by responding to changing social, economic, and cultural needs. Primary areas of interest include the arts, higher education, social services, community funds, and health care. Support also for cultural programs, including fine and performing art groups, youth agencies, and health services.
Fields of interest: Arts; Higher education; Health care; Youth, services; Human services.
Type of support: Capital campaigns; Building/renovation; Matching/challenge support.
Limitations: Applications accepted. Giving limited to Linn County, IA. No support for churches or their programs, or elementary or secondary schools. No grants to individuals, or for deficit financing, endowment funds, continuing operating support, benefits, special events, conferences, or fellowships; no loans.
Publications: Application guidelines; Informational brochure.
Application information: Application form required.
Initial approach: Letter or in-person conversation
Copies of proposal: 1
Deadline(s): Varies according to meeting dates
Board meeting date(s): Quarterly
Final notification: After board meetings
Officers and Directors:* Jack B. Evans,* Pres.; Darrel A. Morf,* V.P.; Iris E. Muchmore,* Secy.; Charles M. Peters,* Treas.; Dee Baird; Todd M. Bergen; Dennis L. Boatman, M.D.; Ernie Buresh; Kathy E. Eno; Carleen Grandon; Alex A. Meyer.
Number of staff: 2 full-time professional.
EIN: 426057097
Selected grants: The following grants are a representative sample of this grantmaker's funding activity:
$1,000,000 to Coe College, Cedar Rapids, IA, 2012. For renovations to Science Building.
$1,000,000 to National Czech and Slovak Museum and Library, Cedar Rapids, IA, 2012. For renovations.
$800,000 to Cedar Rapids City Market, Cedar Rapids, IA, 2012. For construction.
$600,000 to Cedar Rapids Public Library Foundation, Cedar Rapids, IA, 2012. For new library.
$550,000 to United Way of East Central Iowa, Cedar Rapids, IA, 2012. For Annual Campaign.
$504,800 to Cedar Rapids, City of, Cedar Rapids, IA, 2012. For Amphitheater.
$250,000 to Cedar Rapids, City of, Cedar Rapids, IA, 2012. For Convention Center.
$250,000 to Saint Lukes Health Care Foundation, Cedar Rapids, IA, 2012. For Hospice Unit.
$250,000 to Waypoint Services for Women, Children, and Families, Cedar Rapids, IA, 2012. For renovations.
$60,000 to Cedar Rapids Symphony Orchestra Association, Orchestra Iowa, Cedar Rapids, IA, 2012. For operating support.

3440
William M. and Patricia A. Hansen Charitable Foundation ✧ ☆

2050 Woodland Dr.
New Hampton, IA 50659-9225

Established in IA.
Donors: Willis M. Hansen; Patricia A. Hansen.
Foundation type: Independent foundation.
Financial data (yr. ended 12/31/13): Assets, $1,534,570 (M); gifts received, $35,845; expenditures, $535,217; qualifying distributions, $524,585; giving activities include $523,000 for 9 grants (high: $500,000; low: $1,000).
Fields of interest: Education; Health care; Religion.
Limitations: Applications not accepted. Giving primarily in IA.
Application information: Unsolicited requests for funds not accepted.
Officers: Willis M. Hansen, Pres. and Treas.; Patricia A. Hansen, V.P. and Secy.
Directors: Robert H. Hansen; Roger M. Hansen; Thomas L. Hansen; Carmen R. Stenhaug.
EIN: 262252106

3441
The John K. & Luise V. Hanson Foundation ✧

(formerly The Hanson Foundation)
c/o Linda Kay
P.O. Box 450
Forest City, IA 50436-0450 (641) 582-2825
Contact: Linda Kay, Secy.-Treas.

Established in 1971 in IA.
Foundation type: Independent foundation.
Financial data (yr. ended 06/30/13): Assets, $56,226,133 (M); expenditures, $2,041,250; qualifying distributions, $1,644,250; giving activities include $1,644,250 for 150 grants (high: $314,000; low: $500).
Purpose and activities: Giving primarily to provide the means of enhancing the quality of life in the north central Iowa, area, through activities involving youth, parks, recreation, and governmental agencies.
Fields of interest: Historical activities; Arts; Higher education; Education; Health care; Recreation; Human services; Children/youth, services; Community/economic development; Public affairs, government agencies.
Type of support: Matching/challenge support.
Limitations: Applications not accepted. Giving primarily in north central IA. No support for religious organizations, or political organizations. No grants to individuals.
Application information: Contributes only to pre-selected organizations.
Board meeting date(s): Mar., June, Sept., Dec.
Officers and Directors:* John V. Hanson,* Pres.; Linda Kay, Secy.-Treas.; Mary Jo Boman; Paul D. Hanson.
Number of staff: 1 part-time support.
EIN: 421343843

3442
The Amy Helpenstell Foundation Inc. ✧

852 Middle Rd., Ste. 100
Bettendorf, IA 52722-4100 (563) 326-2840
Main URL: http://www.amyhelpenstell.org

Established in 2005 in IL.
Donor: Amy Helpenstell‡.
Foundation type: Independent foundation.
Financial data (yr. ended 12/31/12): Assets, $7,051,239 (M); expenditures, $723,171; qualifying distributions, $684,921; giving activities include $634,500 for 49 grants (high: $50,000; low: $2,000).
Purpose and activities: The mission of the foundation is to improve the quality of life in the Quad Cities area by funding educational programs and by funding grants for health, community development, youth development, and cultural activities.
Fields of interest: Performing arts; Arts; Higher education; Health care; Youth development; Human services; Children/youth, services; Community/economic development; Protestant agencies & churches.
Limitations: Applications not accepted. Giving limited to Davenport and Bettendorf, IA, and Moline and Rock Island, IL. No grants to individuals, endowment funds.
Publications: Annual report.
Application information: Unsolicited requests for funds not accepted. Applicants must be invited to apply. See foundation web site for further information.
Board meeting date(s): Oct., Jan., Apr. and July
Officers: Franz Helpenstell, Pres.; Esta R. Helpenstell, V.P. and Secy.-Treas.
Directors: Mark Evers; Bonnie Helpenstell; Eric Helpenstell; Heidi Huiskamp; Denise Ormsby; Bruce Strunk; Janet Helpenstell Strunk.
EIN: 200563962

3443
HNI Charitable Foundation ✧

(formerly HON INDUSTRIES Charitable Foundation)
P.O. Box 1109
Muscatine, IA 52761-0071 (563) 252-7503
Contact: Dianna Stelzner, Secy.-Treas.
FAX: (563) 264-7217; Application address: 408 W. Second St., Muscatine, IA 52761 tel.: (563) 252-7503

Established in 1985 in IA.
Donors: HON Industries Inc.; HNI Corp.
Foundation type: Company-sponsored foundation.
Financial data (yr. ended 12/31/13): Assets, $2,710,190 (M); gifts received, $460,625; expenditures, $725,893; qualifying distributions, $695,513; giving activities include $695,513 for 82 grants (high: $200,000; low: $50).
Purpose and activities: The foundation supports organizations involved with arts and culture, education, health, disaster preparedness, and human services.
Fields of interest: Historic preservation/historical societies; Arts; Higher education; Libraries (public); Education, services; Education; Hospitals (general); Health care, clinics/centers; Health care; Disasters, preparedness/services; Disasters, fire prevention/control; Boy scouts; YM/YWCAs & YM/YWHAs; Human services; United Ways and Federated Giving Programs.
Type of support: General/operating support; Capital campaigns; Building/renovation.
Limitations: Applications accepted. Giving limited to areas of company operations, with emphasis on IA, IL, KY, MN, NC and WA. No support for national, statewide, or religious organizations. No grants to individuals.

Application information: Application form not required.
Initial approach: Proposal
Copies of proposal: 1
Deadline(s): None
Officers: Stan A. Askren,* Pres.; Gary L. Carlson,* V.P.; Dianna Stelzner, Secy.-Treas.; Tim Heth; Jack Michaels; Karen Olderog.
Number of staff: 1 full-time professional.
EIN: 421246787

3444
Holthues Trust ✧
209 Iowa Ave.
Muscatine, IA 52761-3730

Established in 1997 in IA.
Donor: The Stanley Foundation.
Foundation type: Independent foundation.
Financial data (yr. ended 12/31/13): Assets, $28,974,145 (M); expenditures, $1,146,255; qualifying distributions, $993,967; giving activities include $987,000 for 35 grants (high: $120,000; low: $5,000).
Purpose and activities: Giving primarily for projects that will advance the goals of peace, security, freedom and justice globally, as well as community services locally in Iowa.
Fields of interest: Education; Human services; International peace/security; International human rights; International affairs; Civil/human rights; Community/economic development.
Limitations: Applications not accepted. Giving in the U.S., with emphasis on Washington, DC, IA, MA, MN, and NY. No support for private foundations. No grants to individuals.
Application information: Contributes only to pre-selected organizations.
Officers and Directors:* Richard H. Stanley, Pres.; Joseph H. Stanley,* V.P.; Betty Anders, Secy.; Dana W. Pittman, Treas.; Brian Hanson; Elizabeth Shriver; Lincoln Stanley; Lynne E. Stanley; Sarah Stanley.
EIN: 421466786

3445
Fred and Charlotte Hubbell Foundation ✧
453 7th St.
Des Moines, IA 50309-4110 (515) 245-2965
Contact: Mindy Nussbaum-Bell

Established in 1997 in IA.
Donors: Charlotte Hubbell; Frederick S. Hubbell.
Foundation type: Independent foundation.
Financial data (yr. ended 12/31/13): Assets, $2,800,911 (M); expenditures, $684,960; qualifying distributions, $672,262; giving activities include $662,001 for 101 grants (high: $102,600; low: $100).
Purpose and activities: Giving primarily for education, the environment and the arts; support also for a federated giving program.
Fields of interest: Arts; Higher education; Environment, association; Human services; International affairs; Foundations (community); United Ways and Federated Giving Programs.
Limitations: Applications accepted. Giving primarily in IA, with emphasis on Des Moines.
Application information: Application form required.
Initial approach: Letter
Deadline(s): None
Trustee: Bankers Trust Co.
EIN: 391878112

3446
Hubbell-Waterman Foundation ✧
c/o Lane & Waterman LLP
220 N. Main St., Ste. 600
Davenport, IA 52801-1987 (563) 333-6608
Contact: C.D. Waterman III
FAX: (563) 324-1616;
E-mail: dwaterman@l-wlaw.com; Main URL: http://www.hubbellwaterman.org

Established in 1967 in IA.
Donors: Mary H. Waterman; Mary H. Waterman Trust; Mary H. Waterman Charitable Lead Unitrust.
Foundation type: Independent foundation.
Financial data (yr. ended 12/31/13): Assets, $33,907,231 (M); gifts received, $663,709; expenditures, $1,618,482; qualifying distributions, $1,493,994; giving activities include $1,432,500 for 17 grants (high: $500,000; low: $5,000).
Purpose and activities: Giving primary for the citizens of the Quad Cities by financially supporting areas of need in culture and the arts, early childhood education and social welfare.
Fields of interest: Arts; Education; Human services; Foundations (private grantmaking).
Type of support: Building/renovation; Capital campaigns.
Limitations: Applications accepted. Giving primarily in the Quad Cities geographic area of Scott County, IA and Rock Island County, IL. No grants to individuals; or for debt retirement, membership campaigns, conferences, medical, scientific, or academic research, or for political and religious doctrine.
Publications: Application guidelines.
Application information: Scanned documents accompanying the proposal must be in .tif, .jpg, .bmp, or .pdf formats. Please do not use folders, notebooks or binders, or include videotapes or additional materials that are not specifically requested. If mailing proposal, submit all materials printed single sided on 8 1/2 x 11 paper. Faxed proposals are not accepted. Application form required.
Initial approach: Use form on foundation web site
Copies of proposal: 1
Deadline(s): Sept. 1
Board meeting date(s): October
Trustees: Leslie Waterman Banks; Lynn Waterman Blum; Peter L. L. Lundy; Larned A. Waterman, Jr.; Ann E. Waterman; C. Dana Waterman III; Robert V.P. Waterman, Jr.; Wells Fargo Bank Nebraska, N.A.
EIN: 426126467
Selected grants: The following grants are a representative sample of this grantmaker's funding activity:
$50,000 to Boy Scouts of America, Illowa Council, Davenport, IA, 2012. For general support grant.

3447
Iowa West Foundation
25 Main Pl., Ste. 550
Council Bluffs, IA 51503-0700 (712) 309-3000
Contact: Deb Debbaut, Grants. Mgr.
E-mail: grantinfo@iowawest.com; Main URL: http://www.iowawestfoundation.org
Facebook: https://www.facebook.com/IowaWestFoundation
Grants List: http://www.iowawestfoundation.org/grantmaking/grant-archive/
Twitter: https://twitter.com/IowaWestFdn

Established in 1992 in IA, began grant operations in 1994.
Donor: Iowa West Racing Assn.
Foundation type: Independent foundation.
Financial data (yr. ended 12/31/13): Assets, $375,014,583 (M); gifts received, $7,993,209; expenditures, $20,057,279; qualifying distributions, $16,583,705; giving activities include $14,184,381 for 203 grants (high: $990,441; low: $2,000), and $1,042,629 for 2 foundation-administered programs.
Purpose and activities: The mission of the foundation is to improve lives and strengthen communities for present and future generations. The foundation strives to provide leadership, create partnerships, leverage resources and serve as a catalyst in identifying and supporting community needs. The foundation has a special interest in the areas of community development and beautification, economic development, education, and human and social needs. Current focus includes assisting local schools to reduce the dropout rate, and to improve neighborhoods in Pottawattamie County, IA.
Fields of interest: Education; Human services; Community/economic development.
Type of support: General/operating support; Management development/capacity building; Capital campaigns; Building/renovation; Equipment; Program development; Seed money; Curriculum development; Consulting services; Scholarships—to individuals; Matching/challenge support.
Limitations: Applications accepted. Giving primarily in southwest IA and eastern NE. No support for medical research or church-affiliated organizations for religious purposes. No grants for fundraising, benefit, and social events, capital requests (for improvements to school property or for hospitals, medical facilities, assisted living projects, nursing homes, independent care, and extended care facilities), operating deficits or long-term operating support, publications, films, books, seminars, symposia or for conferences.
Publications: Application guidelines; Annual report; Quarterly report.
Application information: After foundation staff review letter of inquiry, they notify each prospective applicant usually within one business day and only by foundation invitation are applicants requested to complete an on-line proposal. Application form required.
Initial approach: Complete on-line eligibility quiz and, if eligible, submit an on-line letter of inquiry via foundation's web site
Copies of proposal: 1
Deadline(s): For letter of inquiry: Feb. 15, June 15 and Oct. 15. For application: Mar. 15, July 15 and Nov. 15
Final notification: 3 months from application deadline
Officers and Directors:* Sue M. Miller,* Chair.; Rick Crowl, Vice-Chair.; Peter Tulipana, C.E.O. and Pres.; Jerry Mathiasen, Sr. V.P; Tim Miller, V.P., Finance; Kathleen Rapp, V.P., Grants and Initiatives; Rick Killion, Secy.-Treas.; Amy Crawford; Mark Genereux; John P. Nelson; Suellen Overton; Robert Schlott; Warren Weber.
Number of staff: 9 full-time professional.
EIN: 421391990

Selected grants: The following grants are a representative sample of this grantmaker's funding activity:
$3,406,685 to Council Bluffs, City of, Parks, Recreation and Public Property Department, Council Bluffs, IA, 2012. For River's Edge Park.
$2,066,058 to Pottawattamie County Community Foundation, Council Bluffs, IA, 2012. For Pottawattamie County Community Endowment.
$2,000,000 to Council Bluffs, City of, Council Bluffs, IA, 2012. For Bunge Facilities Acquisition and Demolition.
$1,120,357 to Pottawattamie County Development Corporation, Council Bluffs, IA, 2012. For Downtown Revitalization/Redevelopment.
$1,019,400 to Council Bluffs Community School District, Council Bluffs, IA, 2012. For Education Phase I Initiative.
$326,250 to FAMILY, Council Bluffs, IA, 2012. For Pottawattamie County Young Families Support Initiative.
$288,000 to Habitat for Humanity of Council Bluffs, Council Bluffs, IA, 2012. For projects.
$26,250 to Glenwood Public Library, Glenwood, IA, 2012. For Living Literacy Lab.
$24,750 to Minden, City of, Minden, IA, 2012. For City of Minden Park Revitalization.

3448
Richard O. Jacobson Foundation, Inc. ✧
4201 Westown Pkwy., Ste. 124
West Des Moines, IA 50266-6720

Established in 1976.
Donor: Richard O. Jacobson.
Foundation type: Independent foundation.
Financial data (yr. ended 10/31/13): Assets, $1,311,003 (M); expenditures, $4,069,074; qualifying distributions, $4,063,770; giving activities include $4,063,770 for 9 grants (high: $2,000,000; low: $1,750).
Purpose and activities: Giving primarily for health care and medical research.
Fields of interest: Education; Health care; Medical research, institute; Youth development; Human services; Foundations (private grantmaking).
Limitations: Applications not accepted. Giving primarily in Rochester, MN. No grants to individuals.
Application information: Contributes only to pre-selected organizations.
Officer: Richard O. Jacobson, Pres.
EIN: 510192624
Selected grants: The following grants are a representative sample of this grantmaker's funding activity:
$1,025,000 to Iowa State University Foundation, Ames, IA, 2012. For general support.
$1,000,000 to Iowa State Fair Blue Ribbon Foundation, Des Moines, IA, 2012. For general support.
$200,000 to Science Center of Iowa, Des Moines, IA, 2012. For general support.
$50,000 to Junior Achievement, 2012. For general support.
$25,000 to Pinellas County Education Foundation, Largo, FL, 2012. For general support.
$15,000 to Des Moines Area Youth Track Club and Youth Development, Des Moines, IA, 2012. For general support.
$12,000 to Harbor of Hope Mission, Des Moines, IA, 2012. For general support.

3449
Zach Johnson Foundation ✧ ☆
P.O. Box 2336
Cedar Rapids, IA 52406-2336 (319) 730-3734
Contact: Tracey Myers, Admin.
E-mail: tmyers@zachjohnsongolf.com; Main URL: http://www.zachjohnsongolf.com/foundation.page
Facebook: https://www.facebook.com/pages/Zach-Johnson-Foundation/122406031136754
Twitter: https://twitter.com/ZJFClassic

Donors: Gary Rozek; David Ekland; William Mowery; Patrick Cobb; SFX Escrow - Blood PSA; TrueNorth Companies; DSD Realty, Inc.; Cedar Rapids Bank & Trust; Infinity Contact; AEGON Transamerica Foundation; PGA of America; Zach Johnson; Kimala Johnson; Pat Baird.
Foundation type: Independent foundation.
Financial data (yr. ended 12/31/13): Assets, $1,739,988 (M); gifts received, $759,940; expenditures, $803,187; qualifying distributions, $524,845; giving activities include $524,845 for 4 grants (high: $437,477; low: $2,500).
Purpose and activities: Giving primarily to help Cedar Rapids, Iowa children and their families lead happy, healthy lives.
Fields of interest: Children/youth, services; Family services; Human services; United Ways and Federated Giving Programs; Children.
Limitations: Giving primarily in IA.
Publications: Annual report; IRS Form 990 or 990-PF printed copy available upon request.
Officers and Directors:* Patrick Cobb,* Chair.; Zach Johnson,* Pres.; Kimala Johnson,* V.P.; Craig Vermie, Secy.; Patrick Baird,* Treas.; Brad Buffoni; Larry Gladson; Craig Hotchkiss; Beth Malicki; Lon Olejniczak.
EIN: 272683100
Selected grants: The following grants are a representative sample of this grantmaker's funding activity:
$19,100 to Community Health Free Clinic, Cedar Rapids, IA, 2012. To support children and families in need of health care.
$2,500 to Discovery Land Company Foundation, Beverly Hills, CA, 2012. To Support youth mentoring Programs.

3450
Kent Corporation Charitable Foundation ✧
(formerly Kent-Stein Foundation)
c/o Grain Processing Corp.
1600 Oregon St.
Muscatine, IA 52761-1404 (563) 264-4227

Established in 1945 in IA.
Donors: Grain Processing Corp.; Kent Nutrition Group, Inc.; Kent Precision Foods Group.
Foundation type: Independent foundation.
Financial data (yr. ended 12/31/13): Assets, $444,814 (M); gifts received, $720,000; expenditures, $492,516; qualifying distributions, $491,383; giving activities include $491,383 for 19 grants (high: $200,000; low: $1,000).
Fields of interest: Elementary/secondary education; Higher education; Education; Human services; Community/economic development; United Ways and Federated Giving Programs.
Limitations: Applications accepted. Giving primarily in IA, with some emphasis on Muscatine. No grants to individuals.
Application information: Application form not required.
Initial approach: Letter
Deadline(s): 3 months prior to date funds are needed
Trustees: Jeffrey W. Bohling; Gage A. Kent.
EIN: 426058939
Selected grants: The following grants are a representative sample of this grantmaker's funding activity:
$235,000 to Simpson College, Indianola, IA, 2011. For general operations.
$125,000 to Iowa College Foundation, Des Moines, IA, 2011. For general operations.
$50,000 to United Way of Muscatine, Muscatine, IA, 2011. For general operations.
$15,000 to Iowa Wesleyan College, Mount Pleasant, IA, 2011. For general operations.
$10,000 to Pearl City Outreach, Muscatine, IA, 2011. For general operations.
$4,350 to Historic Muscatine, Muscatine, IA, 2011. For general operations.

3451
Kinney-Lindstrom Foundation Inc. ✧
P.O. Box 520
Mason City, IA 50401-0520 (641) 269-5703

Incorporated in 1957 in IA.
Foundation type: Independent foundation.
Financial data (yr. ended 12/31/13): Assets, $8,047,915 (M); expenditures, $1,056,619; qualifying distributions, $734,886; giving activities include $728,935 for 49 grants (high: $200,000; low: $500).
Purpose and activities: Giving primarily for education, health, and children, youth and social services.
Fields of interest: Higher education; Education; Hospitals (general); Human services; Children/youth, services.
Type of support: Building/renovation; Equipment.
Limitations: Applications accepted. Giving primarily within a 25-mile radius of Mason City, IA. No grants to individuals, or for endowment funds, operating budgets, or research; no loans.
Application information: Application form required.
Initial approach: Letter
Deadline(s): None
Board meeting date(s): Four meetings annually
Officers: John H. Greve, Secy.-Treas.; Kent A Hall, Fdn. Mgr.
Trustee: Pat Hall.
Number of staff: 1 full-time professional.
EIN: 426037351

3452
William C. Knapp Charitable Foundation ✧
(formerly Iowa Realty Charitable Foundation)
5000 Westown Pkwy., Ste. 400
West Des Moines, IA 50266-6704

Established in 1987 in IA.
Donors: Roger Brooks; Dennis Elwell; William C. Knapp; Allied Development; Knapp Realty Co.; Civic Parkway Assocs.; Denny Elwell Companies; Cownie Charitable Trust; WCKLC-2, L.C.
Foundation type: Independent foundation.
Financial data (yr. ended 12/31/13): Assets, $568,059 (M); gifts received, $640,759; expenditures, $867,807; qualifying distributions,

$847,535; giving activities include $844,795 for 78 grants (high: $200,000; low: $100).
Purpose and activities: Giving primarily for education, health organizations, and youth and social services.
Fields of interest: Elementary/secondary education; Education; Health organizations, association; Human services; Children/youth, services; Community/economic development; Foundations (community); Christian agencies & churches.
Limitations: Applications not accepted. Giving primarily in Des Moines, IA. No grants to individuals.
Application information: Contributes only to pre-selected organizations.
Officers and Directors:* William C. Knapp,* Pres.; William C. Knapp II,* V.P.; Gerard D. Neugent,* Secy.-Treas.
EIN: 421234012
Selected grants: The following grants are a representative sample of this grantmaker's funding activity:
$37,500 to Community Foundation of Greater Des Moines, Des Moines, IA, 2011. For program support.

3453
Thomas and Linda Koehn Foundation ✧
412 S. 26th St.
West Des Moines, IA 50265-5514

Established in 1987 in IA.
Donors: Thomas Koehn; Linda Koehn.
Foundation type: Independent foundation.
Financial data (yr. ended 11/30/13): Assets, $13,287,980 (M); gifts received, $2,468,511; expenditures, $503,027; qualifying distributions, $498,550; giving activities include $497,750 for 17 grants (high: $131,000; low: $250).
Fields of interest: Performing arts, orchestras; Performing arts, opera; Arts; Foundations (community); United Ways and Federated Giving Programs; Science.
Limitations: Applications not accepted. Giving primarily in Des Moines, IA. No grants to individuals.
Application information: Contributes only to pre-selected organizations.
Officers: Thomas Koehn, Pres.; Linda Koehn, Secy.
EIN: 421293625
Selected grants: The following grants are a representative sample of this grantmaker's funding activity:
$150,000 to Naples Children and Education Foundation, Naples, FL, 2011. For general operating fund.
$121,500 to Science Center of Iowa, Des Moines, IA, 2011. For general operating fund.
$30,000 to Cornell College, Mount Vernon, IA, 2011.
$30,000 to Des Moines Pastoral Counseling Center, West Des Moines, IA, 2011. For general operating fund.
$10,000 to Des Moines Art Center, Des Moines, IA, 2011. For general operating fund.
$5,000 to Civic Center of Greater Des Moines, Des Moines, IA, 2011. For general operating fund.

3454
Krause Gentle Foundation ✧
6400 Westown Pkwy.
West Des Moines, IA 50266-7709

Established in 1994 in IA.
Donors: William A. Krause; KG Investments; Krause Gentle Corporation; Kum & Go LC; Cheiftain.
Foundation type: Independent foundation.
Financial data (yr. ended 12/31/12): Assets, $3,940,125 (M); expenditures, $452,769; qualifying distributions, $452,010; giving activities include $437,225 for 108 grants (high: $152,500; low: $40).
Purpose and activities: Giving primarily for Catholic schools, churches and organizations; giving also for youth services and programs and for education.
Fields of interest: Arts; Elementary/secondary education; Higher education; Multiple sclerosis; YM/YWCAs & YM/YWHAs; Youth, services; Community/economic development; United Ways and Federated Giving Programs; Protestant agencies & churches; Catholic agencies & churches.
Limitations: Applications not accepted. Giving primarily in IA. No grants to individuals.
Application information: Contributes only to pre-selected organizations.
Directors: Dennis Folden; William A. Krause.
EIN: 421414004
Selected grants: The following grants are a representative sample of this grantmaker's funding activity:
$250 to Wounded Warrior Project, Topeka, KS, 2012. For civic purpose.

3455
Kruidenier Charitable Foundation ✧
1501 42nd St.
West Des Moines, IA 50266

Established in 1984 in IA.
Donors: Elizabeth Kruidenier; Lisa Kruidenier.
Foundation type: Independent foundation.
Financial data (yr. ended 12/31/13): Assets, $3,369,797 (M); expenditures, $813,473; qualifying distributions, $775,000; giving activities include $775,000 for 8 grants (high: $200,000; low: $25,000).
Purpose and activities: Giving primarily for community foundations, and arts and culture; funding also for human services, and religion.
Fields of interest: Arts; Higher education; Human services; Foundations (community); Religion.
Type of support: General/operating support.
Limitations: Applications not accepted. Giving primarily in Des Moines, IA. No support for religious or political organizations. No grants to individuals.
Application information: Contributes only to pre-selected organizations.
Officers: Lisa Kruidenier, Pres.; Thomas Macklin, Treas.
Number of staff: 1 full-time professional.
EIN: 421255071

3456
Peter H. and E. Lucille Gaass Kuyper Foundation ✧
617 Franklin Pl., Ste. 200
Pella, IA 50219-2147 (641) 621-3834
Contact: Stan Van Wyk
Main URL: http://www.kuyperfoundation.org

Established in 1970 in IA.
Donors: Peter H. Kuyper†; E. Lucille Gaass Kuyper†; Joan Kuyper Farver.
Foundation type: Independent foundation.
Financial data (yr. ended 12/31/13): Assets, $12,621,425 (M); expenditures, $505,023; qualifying distributions, $475,921; giving activities include $475,921 for 64 grants (high: $55,000; low: $250).
Purpose and activities: Primarily general charitable giving, including the arts, education, Christian agencies, and health.
Fields of interest: Arts; Higher education; Hospitals (general).
Type of support: Annual campaigns; Building/renovation; Capital campaigns; Endowments; Equipment; Scholarship funds.
Limitations: Applications accepted. Giving limited to organizations that exist in communities where substantial numbers of Pella team members reside, primarily in: Macomb, IL, Carroll, Pella, Shenandoah, Sioux Center, IA, Murray, KY, Fairfield, OH, Portland, OR, Gettysburg, PA, and Columbia, SC. No grants to individuals.
Publications: Application guidelines.
Application information: Application form required.
Initial approach: See website
Copies of proposal: 1
Deadline(s): None
Officers and Directors:* Joan Kuyper Farver,* Chair. and Pres.; Charles Farver, V.P.; Mary Griffith,* V.P.; Peter C. Kuyper, V.P.; Kathy Schipper,* Secy.-Treas.; Amy G. Charters; Adam Farver; Benjamin Farver; Charles Jacob Farver; Melissa Farver; James W. Griffith, Jr.; Jacqueline Kuyper; Jill Kuyper; Aaron Ralston; Mary E. Ralston.
EIN: 237068402

3457
Lee Foundation ✧
201 N. Harrison St., Ste. 600
Davenport, IA 52801-1918

Incorporated in 1962 in IA.
Donor: Lee Enterprises, Inc.
Foundation type: Company-sponsored foundation.
Financial data (yr. ended 09/30/12): Assets, $4,705,308 (M); expenditures, $589,054; qualifying distributions, $575,723; giving activities include $571,703 for 116 grants (high: $100,000; low: $300).
Purpose and activities: The foundation supports organizations involved with arts and culture, education, and business and industry.
Fields of interest: Arts; Education; Human services.
Type of support: Capital campaigns; Building/renovation; Endowments.
Limitations: Applications not accepted. Giving primarily in areas of company operations in CA, ID, IA, IL, IN, KY, MN, MT, ND, NE, NV, NY, OR, PA, SC, SD, WA, WI, and WY. No grants to individuals.
Application information: Unsolicited requests for funds not accepted.
Officers and Directors:* Mary E. Junck,* Pres.; Carl G. Schmidt,* Secy.; Daniel K. Hayes; Gregory P. Schermer; Greg Veon.
Number of staff: 1 part-time support.
EIN: 426057173
Selected grants: The following grants are a representative sample of this grantmaker's funding activity:
$35,426 to Quad Cities Golf Classic Charitable Foundation, East Moline, IL, 2011. For general support.
$20,000 to Boys and Girls Clubs of the Mississippi Valley, Moline, IL, 2011. For general support.

$20,000 to Madison Community Foundation, Madison, WI, 2011. For general support.
$12,500 to Yellowstone Art Museum, Billings, MT, 2011. For general support.
$10,000 to Montana Meth Project, Missoula, MT, 2011. For general support.
$10,000 to Montana State University, Billings, MT, 2011. For general support.
$10,000 to University of Kentucky, Lexington, KY, 2011. For general support.
$5,000 to Billings Clinic Foundation, Billings, MT, 2011. For general support.
$5,000 to Georgetown University, Washington, DC, 2011. For general support.
$2,500 to Hill School, Pottstown, PA, 2011. For general support.

3458
Madelyn M. Levitt Foundation ✧
(formerly Madelyn L. Glazer Foundation)
3737 River Oaks Dr.
Des Moines, IA 50312-4614

Established in 1957 in IA.
Donor: Madelyn M. Levitt†.
Foundation type: Independent foundation.
Financial data (yr. ended 12/31/13): Assets, $15,340,151 (M); expenditures, $514,347; qualifying distributions, $475,618; giving activities include $474,000 for 2 grants (high: $280,000; low: $194,000).
Purpose and activities: Giving primarily for the arts, education, and to a community foundation.
Fields of interest: Arts; Higher education; Boys & girls clubs; Children/youth, services; Foundations (community).
Limitations: Applications not accepted. Giving primarily in Des Moines, IA. No grants to individuals.
Application information: Contributes only to pre-selected organizations.
Officers: Susan G. Burt, Pres.; Jeffrey W. Glazer, V.P.; Ellen G. Ziegler, Secy.; Linda G. Toohey, Treas.
EIN: 426052426
Selected grants: The following grants are a representative sample of this grantmaker's funding activity:
$200,000 to Community Foundation of Greater Des Moines, Des Moines, IA, 2011.
$100,000 to Jewish Community Foundation, San Diego, CA, 2011.
$16,666 to Iowa State Fair Blue Ribbon Foundation, Des Moines, IA, 2011.
$10,000 to Civic Center of Greater Des Moines, Des Moines, IA, 2011.

3459
Mansfield Charitable Foundation ✧
(formerly Wesley & Irene Mansfield Charitable Foundation)
1211 Brendell Hill Dr. N.W.
Cedar Rapids, IA 52405-1565 (319) 444-3285
Contact: Larry Schlue, Tr.
Application address: P.O. Box 283, Belle Plaine, IA 52208, tel.: (319) 444-3285

Established in 1984 in IA.
Foundation type: Independent foundation.
Financial data (yr. ended 07/31/13): Assets, $13,224,244 (M); expenditures, $759,713; qualifying distributions, $550,000; giving activities include $550,000 for grants.
Purpose and activities: Giving primarily for education and human services.
Fields of interest: Higher education; Education; Human services; Community/economic development.
Type of support: General/operating support; Building/renovation; Scholarship funds.
Limitations: Applications accepted. Giving primarily in IA; some funding also in NE. No grants to individuals.
Application information: Application form required.
Initial approach: Proposal
Copies of proposal: 1
Deadline(s): June 1
Trustees: M.D. Dreilbelbis; Larry Schlue; Eugene Severson.
EIN: 421226535
Selected grants: The following grants are a representative sample of this grantmaker's funding activity:
$10,000 to Boone County Fitness Center, Albion, NE, 2011. For general purposes.

3460
The F. Maytag Family Foundation ✧
(formerly The F. Maytag Family Foundation)
P.O. Box 366
Newton, IA 50208
Contact: Edna Parrish, Secy.

Trust established in 1945 in IA.
Donors: Fred Maytag II†; and members of the Maytag family.
Foundation type: Independent foundation.
Financial data (yr. ended 12/31/12): Assets, $56,066,191 (M); expenditures, $6,302,524; qualifying distributions, $6,044,084; giving activities include $6,028,696 for 81 grants (high: $1,100,000; low: $500).
Purpose and activities: Giving primarily for higher and other education, arts and culture, public affairs, social services, health, and aid for the handicapped.
Fields of interest: Arts; Higher education; Education; Environment, natural resources; Health care; Health organizations, association; Human services; Community/economic development; Public affairs; Disabilities, people with.
Type of support: General/operating support; Continuing support; Annual campaigns; Capital campaigns; Building/renovation; Equipment; Land acquisition; Endowments; Emergency funds; Program development; Conferences/seminars; Professorships; Publication; Seed money; Curriculum development; Fellowships; Internship funds; Scholarship funds; Research; Technical assistance; Matching/challenge support.
Limitations: Applications accepted. Giving primarily in Des Moines and Newton, IA. No grants to individuals, or for emergency funds, deficit financing, scholarships, fellowships, demonstration projects, or conferences; no loans.
Publications: Application guidelines.
Application information: Application form not required.
Initial approach: Telephone or write for guidelines
Copies of proposal: 3
Deadline(s): None
Officer and Directors:* Kenneth P. Maytag,* Pres.; Frederick L. Maytag III,* Vice-Pres.; Edna Parrish, Secy.; William C. Weinsheimer.
Number of staff: 1 full-time support.
EIN: 421444870

3461
R. J. McElroy Trust ✧
425 Cedar St., Ste. 312
Waterloo, IA 50701-1351 (319) 287-9102
Contact: Stacy Van Gorp, Exec. Dir.
FAX: (319) 287-9105;
E-mail: vangorp@mcelroytrust.org; Additional e-mail: office@mcelroytrust.org; Main URL: http://www.mcelroytrust.org
Blog: http://mcelroytrust.org/news/
Grants List: http://mcelroytrust.org/grants/previous-grants/

Established in 1965 in IA; private foundation status attained in 1984.
Donor: R.J. McElroy†.
Foundation type: Independent foundation.
Financial data (yr. ended 12/31/13): Assets, $45,017,751 (M); expenditures, $2,691,296; qualifying distributions, $2,051,201; giving activities include $1,794,173 for grants.
Purpose and activities: Primary emphasis on education, especially scholarship and loan programs; public secondary education, particularly for the disadvantaged; early childhood and elementary education and programs for minorities; and youth, including internships. The trust awards scholarships to 1-3 high school seniors in each of the school districts in the trust's 19-county area. Scholarship selection is made locally, not by the trust. Giving also for the arts, recreation, and the environment; some support through matching funds and fellowships for graduate study.
Fields of interest: Visual arts; Performing arts; Arts; Education, early childhood education; Child development, education; Elementary school/education; Secondary school/education; Higher education; Education; Environment; Recreation; Youth development, services; Human services; Children/youth, services; Child development, services; Leadership development; Infants/toddlers; Children/youth; Children; Youth; Young adults.
Type of support: General/operating support; Capital campaigns; Building/renovation; Equipment; Emergency funds; Program development; Professorships; Seed money; Fellowships; Internship funds; Scholarship funds; Research; Matching/challenge support.
Limitations: Applications accepted. Giving primarily in 15 counties in northeast IA, (Allamakee, Black Hawk, Bremer, Buchanan, Butler, Chickasaw, Clayton, Delaware, Dubuque, Fayette, Floyd, Grundy, Howard, Tama, and Winneshiek). No support for religious organizations for religious education. No grants to individuals (except for fellowship and scholarship programs that are already established).
Publications: Application guidelines; Grants list; Informational brochure; Informational brochure (including application guidelines); Program policy statement; Program policy statement (including application guidelines).
Application information: Application guidelines and form available on foundation web site. Application form required.
Initial approach: E-mail or telephone to Exec. Dir.
Copies of proposal: 1
Deadline(s): None
Board meeting date(s): Monthly
Officers and Trustees:* James B. Waterbury,* Chair.; Stacy Van Gorp, Exec. Dir.; Raleigh D. Buckmaster; Rick Young.

Number of staff: 1 full-time professional; 1 full-time support.
EIN: 426173496
Selected grants: The following grants are a representative sample of this grantmaker's funding activity:
$500,000 to Waterloo Development Corporation, Waterloo, IA, 2012. For Cedar Valley SportsPlex (Payment 2 of 8).
$95,000 to University of Northern Iowa Foundation, Cedar Falls, IA, 2012. For GBPAC Improvements (Payment 3 of 3).
$60,000 to University of Northern Iowa Foundation, Cedar Falls, IA, 2012. For Naming of the Student Business Incubator (Payment 1 o.
$30,000 to University of Northern Iowa Foundation, Cedar Falls, IA, 2012. For Reading Recovery Teacher Training (Payment 3 of 5).
$30,000 to Waterloo Development Corporation, Waterloo, IA, 2012. For Cedar Valley SportsPlex (Additional Year End Payment.
$20,000 to Iowa College Foundation, Des Moines, IA, 2012. For Student/Faculty Research Program.
$15,000 to Robey Memorial Library, Waukon, IA, 2012. For library expansion.
$10,000 to University of Northern Iowa Foundation, Cedar Falls, IA, 2012. For JPEC Student Fellowships/Unique Support.
$3,000 to Volunteer Center of Cedar Valley, Waterloo, IA, 2012. For Service Learning and After School Youth Volunteer Program.
$500 to Volunteer Center of Cedar Valley, Waterloo, IA, 2012. For Mayor's Top Teen Awards.

3462
The McIntyre Foundation ✧
210 Candlestick Dr. N.E.
P.O. Box 232
Mount Vernon, IA 52314-1577

Established in 1996 in IA.
Donors: J. Scott McIntyre, Jr.; Mildred McIntyre; United Fire & Casualty Co.
Foundation type: Independent foundation.
Financial data (yr. ended 06/30/13): Assets, $13,746,892 (M); expenditures, $691,934; qualifying distributions, $632,700; giving activities include $632,700 for grants.
Fields of interest: Arts; Higher education; Human services; YM/YWCAs & YM/YWHAs; United Ways and Federated Giving Programs.
Limitations: Applications not accepted. Giving primarily in Cedar Rapids, IA. No grants to individuals.
Application information: Contributes only to pre-selected organizations.
Officers: John A. Rife, Pres.; Dee Ann McIntyre, V.P.; Kaye M. Drahzal, Secy.
EIN: 391876841
Selected grants: The following grants are a representative sample of this grantmaker's funding activity:
$105,250 to United Way of East Central Iowa, Cedar Rapids, IA, 2011. For general purposes.
$40,000 to Cedar Rapids Public Library Foundation, Cedar Rapids, IA, 2011. For general purposes.
$36,250 to Four Oaks, Cedar Rapids, IA, 2011. For general purposes.
$17,000 to Cedar Rapids Museum of Art, Cedar Rapids, IA, 2011. For general purposes.
$15,000 to Community Health Free Clinic, Cedar Rapids, IA, 2011. For general purposes.
$10,000 to Coe College, Cedar Rapids, IA, 2011. For general purposes.
$7,500 to Indian Creek Nature Center, Cedar Rapids, IA, 2011. For general purposes.
$5,000 to Cedar Rapids, City of, Cedar Rapids, IA, 2011. For general purposes.
$5,000 to Goodwill Industries of the Heartland, Cedar Rapids, IA, 2011. For general purposes.
$5,000 to Junior Achievement of Eastern Iowa, Cedar Rapids, IA, 2011. For general purposes.

3463
Meredith Corporation Foundation ✧
1716 Locust St.
Des Moines, IA 50309-3023
Contact: Cheri Cipperley, Fdn. Mgr.

Established around 1994 in IA.
Donor: Meredith Corp.
Foundation type: Company-sponsored foundation.
Financial data (yr. ended 06/30/14): Assets, $21,575,234 (L); gifts received, $1,500,000; expenditures, $1,751,254; qualifying distributions, $1,725,232; giving activities include $1,725,232 for 846 grants (high: $152,100; low: $25).
Purpose and activities: The foundation supports organizations involved with arts and culture, education, and human services.
Fields of interest: Media, print publishing; Media, journalism; Visual arts; Performing arts; Arts; Higher education; Journalism school/education; Education; Children/youth, services; Family services; Human services; United Ways and Federated Giving Programs; Children; Aging; Disabilities, people with; Economically disadvantaged.
Type of support: General/operating support; Annual campaigns; Capital campaigns; Program development; Employee volunteer services; Employee matching gifts.
Limitations: Applications accepted. Giving primarily in the metropolitan Des Moines, IA, area. No support for religious or political organizations. No grants to individuals, or for fundraising events or sports or health-related programs.
Publications: Application guidelines.
Application information: Telephone requests are not accepted. Application form not required.
Initial approach: Proposal
Deadline(s): Quarterly during fiscal year
Board meeting date(s): Apr. and Oct.
Officers and Directors:* Mell Meredith Frazier,* Chair.; Stephen M. Lacy,* Pres.; John S. Zieser,* Secy.; Kevin Wagner, Treas.; Joseph H. Ceryanec.
EIN: 421426258

3464
Edwin T. Meredith Foundation ✧ ☆
1716 Locust St.
Des Moines, IA 50309-3023

Incorporated in 1946 in IA.
Donors: Meredith Publishing Co.; Katherine Meredith.
Foundation type: Independent foundation.
Financial data (yr. ended 12/31/13): Assets, $17,173,920 (M); expenditures, $867,826; qualifying distributions, $806,365; giving activities include $804,400 for 24 grants (high: $200,000; low: $100).
Purpose and activities: Grants largely for youth agencies, higher education, cultural programs, and a historic preservation area; some support for hospitals and health agencies, as well as for conservation.
Fields of interest: Arts; Higher education; Environment, natural resources; Health care; Children/youth, services; Science.
Type of support: Annual campaigns; Capital campaigns; Building/renovation; Endowments.
Limitations: Applications not accepted. Giving primarily in IA. No grants to individuals.
Application information: Unsolicited requests for funds not accepted.
Board meeting date(s): June
Officers: Katherine C. Meredith, Pres.; D. Mell Frazier, V.P.; E.T. Meredith IV, V.P.; John S. Zieser, Secy.; Cheri A. Cipperley, Treas.
EIN: 426059818

3465
MidAmerican Energy Foundation ✧
(formerly Midwest Foundation)
P.O. Box 657 (DMR8)
Des Moines, IA 50306-0657
E-mail: kmkunert@midamerican.com

Established as a company-sponsored foundation in 1990 in IA; status changed to public charity; status changed to company-sponsored foundation in 2004.
Donors: Midamerican Energy Holdings Co. LTTP; MHC Investment Co.
Foundation type: Company-sponsored foundation.
Financial data (yr. ended 12/31/13): Assets, $23,993,547 (M); gifts received, $5,000,349; expenditures, $807,568; qualifying distributions, $737,568; giving activities include $737,380 for 306 grants (high: $125,000; low: $25).
Purpose and activities: The foundation supports fairs and civic centers and organizations involved with arts and culture, higher education, cancer, baseball, and human services.
Fields of interest: Education; Housing/shelter; Human services.
Type of support: Annual campaigns; Capital campaigns; Building/renovation; Scholarship funds; Sponsorships; Employee matching gifts.
Limitations: Applications accepted. Giving primarily in IA.
Application information: Application form required.
Initial approach: Letter
Copies of proposal: 1
Deadline(s): None
Board meeting date(s): Quarterly
Officers and Director:* Gregory E. Abel,* Pres.; Tim Grabinski, Secy.; Calvin D. Haack, Treas.
EIN: 421338550
Selected grants: The following grants are a representative sample of this grantmaker's funding activity:
$5,000 to Greater Cedar Rapids Community Foundation, Cedar Rapids, IA, 2011.
$5,000 to Greater Cedar Rapids Community Foundation, Cedar Rapids, IA, 2011.
$3,100 to Cystic Fibrosis Foundation, Bethesda, MD, 2011.
$1,740 to American Cancer Society, Atlanta, GA, 2011.
$1,280 to University of Nebraska Foundation, Lincoln, NE, 2011.

3466
Mid-Iowa Health Foundation ✧
3900 Ingersoll Ave., Ste. 104
Des Moines, IA 50312-3535 (515) 277-6411
Contact: Suzanne Mineck, Pres.
E-mail: info@midiowahealth.org; Main URL: http://www.midiowahealth.org
Twitter: https://twitter.com/midiahealthfdn

Established in 1983 in IA; converted from Northwest Community Hospital.
Foundation type: Independent foundation.
Financial data (yr. ended 12/31/13): Assets, $15,849,796 (M); expenditures, $897,139; qualifying distributions, $739,076; giving activities include $464,842 for 26 grants (high: $40,000; low: $500).
Purpose and activities: The foundation will be a catalyst for and sustainer of preventive health services for vulnerable populations in Des Moines, IA, and the surrounding communities.
Fields of interest: Medical care, community health systems; Health care, clinics/centers; Health care.
Type of support: General/operating support; Program development; Technical assistance.
Limitations: Applications accepted. Giving limited to Polk, Warren, and Dallas counties, IA. No support for scientific or medical research, health camps, or religious organizations. No grants to individuals, or for research, fundraisers, conferences, endowments, debt reduction, capital campaigns, film, or for computer equipment.
Publications: Application guidelines; Annual report; Grants list; Informational brochure (including application guidelines).
Application information: Applications only accepted for Community Response Program. Application guidelines and form available on foundation web site. Application form required.
Initial approach: See website for application form
Deadline(s): Oct. 1
Board meeting date(s): Mar., June, Sept., and Dec.
Officers: Becky Miles-Polka, Chair.; Rob Hayes, Vice-Chair.; Suzanne Mineck, Pres.; Cheryl Harding, Secy.-Treas.
Directors: Terry Caldwell-Johnson; Nolden Gentry; Libby Jacobs; Thomas Jeschke; Matthew McGarvey; Judith Vogel, C.F.A.; Scott L. Wilson.
Number of staff: 2 full-time professional.
EIN: 421235348

3467
The Nelson Foundation ✧ ☆
4105 Timberwood Dr.
West Des Moines, IA 50265-5366 (515) 266-2111
Contact: Mary Nelson, V.P.

Established in 1983 in IA.
Donors: R.W. Nelson; Mary Nelson.
Foundation type: Independent foundation.
Financial data (yr. ended 12/31/13): Assets, $1,970,209 (M); expenditures, $1,876,422; qualifying distributions, $1,866,844; giving activities include $1,845,169 for 13 grants (high: $400,000; low: $5,000), and $20,000 for 4 grants to individuals (high: $5,000; low: $5,000).
Fields of interest: Higher education; United Ways and Federated Giving Programs; Christian agencies & churches.
Type of support: Continuing support; Employee-related scholarships.
Limitations: Applications accepted. Giving primarily in IA.
Publications: Annual report.
Application information: Application form required.
Initial approach: Request application form
Deadline(s): None
Board meeting date(s): Jan.
Officers: R.W. Nelson, Pres. and Treas.; Mary A. Nelson, V.P. and Secy.
EIN: 421207818

3468
New Hope Foundation ✧
2610 Park Ave.
Muscatine, IA 52761-5639

Established in 1992 in IA.
Donors: David M. Stanley; Jean Leu Stanley; E & M Charities; Pearl Management Company; Tax Education Support Organization.
Foundation type: Independent foundation.
Financial data (yr. ended 12/31/12): Assets, $15,235,615 (M); gifts received, $107,769; expenditures, $1,208,784; qualifying distributions, $1,169,615; giving activities include $730,600 for 110 grants (high: $179,000; low: $100), and $326,149 for foundation-administered programs.
Purpose and activities: Giving primarily for education, social services, and Christian and United Methodist churches and organizations.
Fields of interest: Education; Health organizations, association; Human services; Children/youth, services; Family services; United Ways and Federated Giving Programs; Christian agencies & churches; Protestant agencies & churches.
Limitations: Applications not accepted. Giving primarily in IA. No grants to individuals.
Application information: Unsolicited requests for funds not accepted.
Officers and Directors: David Stanley,* Chair.; Robert H. Solt,* Vice-Chair. and Secy.-Treas.; Andrea S. Failor,* Pres.; Daniel G. Steele,* V.P.; Charlene Knutsen; Harry L. Knusten; C. Diane Norton; Thomas K. Norton; Dana D. Solt; Jean Leu Stanley; Linda A. Steele.
EIN: 421395902
Selected grants: The following grants are a representative sample of this grantmaker's funding activity:
$179,000 to Institute on Religion and Democracy, Washington, DC, 2012. For Religious, Educational, Human Rights.
$50,000 to Good News, Wilmore, KY, 2012. For Religious, Educational, Church Renewal.
$12,000 to Face to Face International, Scottsdale, AZ, 2012. For religious, missions.
$10,000 to American Family Association, Tupelo, MS, 2012. For Educational, Charitable, Religious, Pro-marriage, Pro-family.
$10,000 to Asbury Theological Seminary, Wilmore, KY, 2012. For Educational, Religious, Christian Seminary.
$10,000 to Family Research Council, Holland, MI, 2012. For educational, religious, pro-family.
$2,000 to Marriage Savers, Potomac, MD, 2012. For charitable, educational, pro-marriage.
$1,000 to Northwestern College, Orange City, IA, 2012. For Educational, Religious, Christian College.
$1,000 to Tax Education Support Organization, Muscatine, IA, 2012. For Educational, Human Rights, Taxpayer Protection, Limited Government.
$1,000 to Wycliffe Bible Translators, Orlando, FL, 2012. For Religious, Educational, Bible Translation.

3469
Northeast Iowa Charitable Foundation ✧
P.O. Box 203
Oelwein, IA 50662-0203 (319) 283-1056

Established in 1989 in IA.
Donor: Churchill Williams.
Foundation type: Independent foundation.
Financial data (yr. ended 12/31/12): Assets, $8,984,415 (M); expenditures, $521,216; qualifying distributions, $508,964; giving activities include $469,736 for 27 grants (high: $113,000; low: $1,000).
Fields of interest: Libraries (public); Education; Human services.
Type of support: Equipment; Scholarship funds; Scholarships—to individuals.
Limitations: Applications accepted. Giving limited to northeast IA.
Application information: Application form required.
Initial approach: Letter
Deadline(s): None
Officers: Maureen Nolan, Pres.; Char DeHaven, Secy.; James R. Ridihalgh, Treas.
Directors: Todd Bradley; Andrew Cubit; Marilyn Dahl; Alan Jamison; Carol Tousley; Marvall Williams.
EIN: 421341188

3470
Ochylski Family Foundation ✧
300 Walnut St., Ste. 295A
Des Moines, IA 50309-2212 (515) 244-6040

Established in 1996 in IL.
Donors: Edward Ochylski; Mrs. Edward Ochylski.
Foundation type: Independent foundation.
Financial data (yr. ended 12/31/13): Assets, $4,116,602 (M); gifts received, $2,104,864; expenditures, $1,383,413; qualifying distributions, $1,360,000; giving activities include $1,360,000 for 11 grants (high: $600,000; low: $25,000).
Purpose and activities: Giving primarily for Roman Catholic organizations.
Fields of interest: Education; Human services; Children/youth, services; Catholic agencies & churches.
International interests: Holy See.
Limitations: Applications accepted. Giving primarily in FL, IL, and Warsaw, Poland.
Application information: Application form not required.
Initial approach: Letter
Deadline(s): Oct. 1
Officers: Jessica Stark, Pres.; Daniel Ochylski, V.P.; Juliana Summers, V.P.; Gabrielle Klein, Secy.; Kathy Hovey, Treas.
EIN: 364110483

3471
On His Path ✧
604 N. Parkway St.
Wayland, IA 52654-7638 (319) 256-5656
E-mail: info@onhispath.com; Main URL: http://www.onhispath.com/
Blog: http://blog.onhispath.com/
Facebook: https://www.facebook.com/pages/On-His-Path/203691329662316

Established in IA.
Donor: M.D. Orthopaedics Inc.
Foundation type: Independent foundation.

Financial data (yr. ended 12/31/12): Assets, $48,409 (M); gifts received, $840,121; expenditures, $817,527; qualifying distributions, $766,604; giving activities include $638,228 for 36 grants (high: $157,581; low: $70), $23,535 for 8 grants to individuals (high: $13,308; low: $227), and $92,651 for 4 foundation-administered programs.
Purpose and activities: Giving primarily for children and social services, particularly for the manufacturing and distribution of a superior low-cost clubfoot brace to developing countries. Support also for research on devices and techniques to more effectively treat and care for a variety of pediatric and adult conditions and deformities. The foundation is also focused on bringing potable water and adequate nutrition to the developing world.
Fields of interest: Health care; Human services; Children/youth, services; International relief.
Limitations: Applications accepted. Giving in the U.S., with some emphasis on IA.
Application information: Application form available on foundation web site. Application form required.
Officers: John Mitchell, Pres.; Jean Mitchell, V.P.; Emily Ferguson, Secy.-Treas.
EIN: 271354039
Selected grants: The following grants are a representative sample of this grantmaker's funding activity:
$34,400 to Compassion International, Colorado Springs, CO, 2012. For Unsponsored Children Fund, LDP Support of 4 Students for 1 Year.
$31,749 to Wycliffe Bible Translators, Orlando, FL, 2012. For Columbia Sign Language Match.
$10,000 to Mercy Ships, Lindale, TX, 2012. For Clubfoot Program in Sierra Leone.
$5,000 to English Language Institute in China, Fort Collins, CO, 2012. For China Missionary Support.
$5,000 to Prosthetics Outreach Foundation, Seattle, WA, 2012. For Vietnam Ponseti Clubfoot Program.
$1,680 to LifeBridge Health, Baltimore, MD, 2012. For Limb Deformity Event.

3472
John & Mary Pappajohn Scholarship Foundation ✧ ☆
666 Walnut St.
2116 Financial Center
Des Moines, IA 50309-3907

Established in 1996 in IA.
Foundation type: Independent foundation.
Financial data (yr. ended 09/30/13): Assets, $929,216 (M); expenditures, $470,467; qualifying distributions, $469,343; giving activities include $468,350 for 35 grants (high: $142,500; low: $100).
Fields of interest: Higher education; Scholarships/financial aid; Religion.
Limitations: Applications not accepted. Giving primarily in Des Moines, IA. No grants to individuals.
Application information: Contributes only to pre-selected organizations.
Directors: John Pappajohn; Mary Pappajohn; Ann Vassiliou.
EIN: 421645551

3473
Pella Rolscreen Foundation ✧
102 Main St.
Pella, IA 50219-2147
Contact: Mary A. Van Zante, Secy. and Exec. Dir.
FAX: (641) 621-6950; E-mail: mavzante@pella.com; Main URL: http://www.pellarolscreen.com/

Trust established in 1952 in IA.
Donor: Pella Corp.
Foundation type: Company-sponsored foundation.
Financial data (yr. ended 12/31/13): Assets, $10,984,069 (M); gifts received, $507,062; expenditures, $1,293,735; qualifying distributions, $1,191,806; giving activities include $1,191,806 for 600 grants (high: $375,050; low: $25).
Purpose and activities: The foundation supports organizations involved with arts and culture, education, the environment, human services, and civic affairs.
Fields of interest: Arts; Higher education; Education; Environment; Human services; Public affairs.
Type of support: Building/renovation; Capital campaigns; Employee matching gifts; Employee volunteer services; Employee-related scholarships; Program development; Scholarship funds.
Limitations: Applications accepted. Giving primarily in areas of company manufacturing operations in Carroll, Pella, Shenandoah, and Sioux Center, IA, Macomb, IL, Murray, KY, Portland, OR, Gettysburg, PA, and Wylie, TX. No support for religious or political organizations or organizations with a narrow scope. No grants to individuals (except for employee-related scholarships); no loans.
Publications: Application guidelines; Annual report; Program policy statement.
Application information: Application form required.
Initial approach: Download application form and mail to foundation
Copies of proposal: 1
Deadline(s): None
Board meeting date(s): Quarterly
Final notification: 1 to 4 months
Officers and Directors:* Pat Meyer,* Chair. and Pres.; Mary A. Van Zante, Secy. and Exec. Dir.; Charles Farver,* Treas.; Joan Farver.
Number of staff: 2 part-time support.
EIN: 237043881

3474
Pioneer Hi-Bred International, Inc. Foundation ✧ ☆
P.O. Box 1000
Johnston, IA 50131-1000 (515) 535-6677
Contact: Michelle Gowdy, Pres.
Main URL: http://www.pioneer.com/home/site/about/business/pioneer-giving/

Established in 1992.
Donor: Pioneer Hi-Bred International, Inc.
Foundation type: Company-sponsored foundation.
Financial data (yr. ended 12/31/12): Assets, $671,895 (M); gifts received, $3,163,250; expenditures, $2,538,877; qualifying distributions, $2,538,877; giving activities include $2,538,877 for 149 grants (high: $469,912; low: $25).
Purpose and activities: The foundation supports programs designed to promote science education; food security; and community betterment.
Fields of interest: Elementary/secondary education; Education; Health care; Agriculture; Agriculture, sustainable programs; Agriculture, farmlands; Food services; Nutrition; Community/economic development; Science, formal/general education; Science.
Type of support: Equipment; Program development; Conferences/seminars; Scholarship funds; Research; Employee matching gifts; Scholarships—to individuals; Matching/challenge support.
Limitations: Applications accepted. Giving primarily in areas of company operations in the U.S and in Argentina, Brazil, Canada, Chile, China, India, Indonesia, Mexico, Philippines, and Turkey. No support for religious or political organizations, discriminatory organizations, or athletic teams. No grants to individuals (except for scholarships), or for marketing or advertising, or athletic events.
Publications: Application guidelines.
Application information: Application form required.
Initial approach: Complete online eligibility quiz and application
Deadline(s): None
Board meeting date(s): Quarterly
Officers: Michelle Gowdy, Pres.; Jeffrey A. Austin, V.P.; Nita Seelinger, Secy.; David Martin, Treas.
Directors: Paul E. Schickler; Laurie Conslato.
EIN: 421388269
Selected grants: The following grants are a representative sample of this grantmaker's funding activity:
$10,000 to Bioversity International, Rome, Italy, 2011.

3475
Greater Poweshiek Community Foundation ✧
1510 Penrose St.
P.O. Box 344
Grinnell, IA 50112-1203 (641) 236-5518
FAX: (641) 236-5590; E-mail: gpcf@greaterpcf.org; Main URL: http://www.greaterpcf.org
Facebook: http://www.facebook.com/pages/Greater-Poweshiek-Community-Foundation/119322154783442

Established in 1989 in IA.
Foundation type: Community foundation.
Financial data (yr. ended 12/31/11): Assets, $4,789,200 (M); gifts received, $1,368,895; expenditures, $1,174,916; giving activities include $805,338 for 5+ grants (high: $395,258), and $37,865 for grants to individuals.
Purpose and activities: The foundation seeks to strengthen the community by building charitable endowments, assisting donors, making effective grants and providing for county needs. The foundation's directors look for projects that: 1) increase citizens' commitment to meet community needs; 2) eliminate duplication of services and encourage cooperations; 3) develop self-reliance or eliminate dependency; 4) address new and emerging needs or incorporate new approaches to meeting recognized needs; 5) address themselves to prevention as well as to treatment; 6) are models that have a strong possibility for replication, or have demonstrated significant success elsewhere; 7) increase the managerial and financial capabilities of non-profit organizations and public agencies; and 8) develop, disseminate, or follow up on seed research concerning the region and its people.
Fields of interest: Arts; Libraries (public); Education; Environment; Health care; Agriculture/food; Human services; Community/economic development; Public affairs.

Type of support: Endowments; Program development; Seed money; Scholarship funds; Scholarships—to individuals.
Limitations: Applications accepted. Giving primarily in Poweshiek County, IA. No grants for debt reduction, conferences, or annual meetings; no loans.
Application information: Application form required.
Initial approach: Contact foundation
Board meeting date(s): Quarterly
Officers and Directors:* Nancy Maly,* Pres.; Catherine Wilson,* V.P.; Marilyn Kennett,* Secy.; Chris Hansen,* Treas.; David Arendt; Julie Augustine; Rachel Bly; Matt Buckingham; Jessica Dillon; Tim Douglas; Al Henderson; Mike Mahaffey; Laura Manatt; Bob Mann; Tom Marshall; Martha Pinder; Jodie Ryan; Jo Wells.
EIN: 421298055

3476
Principal Financial Group Foundation, Inc. ✧

711 High St.
Des Moines, IA 50392-0150 (515) 247-7227
Contact: Andrew Allen, Community Rels.
FAX: (515) 246-5475;
E-mail: allen.andrew@principal.com; Main URL: http://www.principal.com/corporate-social-responsibility/giving/

Established in 1987 in IA.
Donor: Principal Life Insurance Co.
Foundation type: Company-sponsored foundation.
Financial data (yr. ended 12/31/12): Assets, $127,821,844 (M); gifts received, $61,155,974; expenditures, $8,276,718; qualifying distributions, $8,103,138; giving activities include $8,103,138 for 142 grants (high: $1,500,000; low: $500).
Purpose and activities: The foundation supports organizations involved with arts and culture, education, the environment, health, substance abuse, diseases, employment training, nutrition, housing, recreation and tourism, youth development, human services, community development, civic affairs, babies, and senior citizens.
Fields of interest: Arts, equal rights; Arts, cultural/ethnic awareness; Arts; Education, equal rights; Child development, education; Higher education; Business school/education; Education; Environment; Health care, equal rights; Public health; Health care; Substance abuse, services; Health organizations, public education; Geriatrics; Employment, training; Nutrition; Housing/shelter; Disasters, preparedness/services; Recreation; Youth development, adult & child programs; Youth development; Family services; Human services, financial counseling; Human services; Economic development, visitors/convention bureau/tourism promotion; Community/economic development; Computer science; Public affairs; Infants/toddlers; Aging.
Type of support: General/operating support; Continuing support; Annual campaigns; Capital campaigns; Building/renovation; Program development; Professorships; Seed money; Curriculum development; Scholarship funds; Program evaluation; Employee matching gifts.
Limitations: Applications accepted. Giving limited to Des Moines, IA, and areas of company operations in Wilmington, DE, Cedar Falls, Mason City, and Ottumwa, IA, Grand Island, NE, Spokane, WA, and Appleton, WI. No support for athletes or athletic organizations, fraternal organizations, individual K-12 schools, libraries, pass-through organizations, partisan political organizations, private foundations, retirement communities or nursing homes, sectarian, religious, or denominational organizations, social organizations, tax-supported city, county, or state organizations, trade, industry, or professional associations, or veterans' organizations. No grants to individuals, or for conference or seminar attendance, courtesy or goodwill advertising in benefit publications, endowments or memorials, fellowships, festival participation, hospital or healthcare facility capital campaigns, or United Way-funded programs.
Publications: Application guidelines; Corporate giving report; Grants list; Program policy statement.
Application information: Visit website for application mailing addresses. Support is limited to 1 contribution per organization during any given year. Multi-year funding is not automatic. Organizations receiving support are asked to submit a grant evaluation form. Capital requests require a separate application and are considered mainly in Des Moines, IA and on a limited case-by-case basis. Video, CD, or DVD submissions are not accepted. Application form required.
Initial approach: Download application form and mail proposal and application form to nearest company facility; download application form and mail proposal and application form to foundation for organizations located in Des Moines, IA
Copies of proposal: 11
Deadline(s): June 1 for organizations located outside of Des Moines, IA; Mar. 1 for Health and Human Services, June 1 for Education, Sept. 1 for Arts and Culture, and Dec. 1 for Civic, Community, and Environment for organizations located in Des Moines, IA
Board meeting date(s): Quarterly
Final notification: 10 weeks
Officers and Directors:* Mary O'Keefe,* Chair. and Pres.; Andrew Allen, Secy.; Jed A. Fisk,* Treas.; Pat Barry; Nora Everett; Joyce Hoffman; Terrance J. Lillis; Renee Schaaf; Larry Zimpleman.
EIN: 421312301
Selected grants: The following grants are a representative sample of this grantmaker's funding activity:
$1,500,000 to Community Foundation of Greater Des Moines, Des Moines, IA, 2012. For RiverWalk.
$1,100,000 to Community Foundation of Greater Des Moines, Des Moines, IA, 2012. For RiverWalk.
$1,000,000 to Community Foundation of Greater Des Moines, Des Moines, IA, 2012. For Principal Charity Classic.
$1,000,000 to Community Foundation of Greater Des Moines, Des Moines, IA, 2012. For RiverWalk.
$1,000,000 to Community Foundation of Greater Des Moines, Des Moines, IA, 2012.
$590,306 to Truist, Washington, DC, 2012.
$375,000 to Truist, Washington, DC, 2012.
$200,000 to Truist, Washington, DC, 2012.
$20,000 to Community Foundation of Greater Des Moines, Des Moines, IA, 2012. For general support.
$15,000 to Bidwell Riverside Center, Des Moines, IA, 2012.

3477
Rockwell Collins Charitable Corporation ✧

400 Collins Rd., N.E., M.S. 124-302
Cedar Rapids, IA 52498-0001 (319) 295-8122
Contact: Jennifer Becker, Exec. Dir.
FAX: (319) 295-9374;
E-mail: jlbecker@rockwellcollins.com; Additional e-mail: communityrelations@rockwellcollins.com; Contact for Green Communities Prog.: Joan Schaffer, Community Rels., tel.: (319) 295-5131, e-mail: jmschaff@rockwellcollins.com; Main URL: http://www.rockwellcollins.com/Our_Company/Corporate_Responsibility/Community_Overview/Charitable_Giving.aspx

Established in 2001 in IA.
Donor: Rockwell Collins, Inc.
Foundation type: Company-sponsored foundation.
Financial data (yr. ended 09/30/13): Assets, $385,095 (M); gifts received, $4,450,000; expenditures, $4,596,751; qualifying distributions, $4,531,828; giving activities include $4,107,750 for 151 grants, and $424,078 for employee matching gifts.
Purpose and activities: The foundation supports organizations involved with the environment, health, human services, and civic affairs. Special emphasis is directed toward programs designed to promote math, science, engineering, and technology education; and arts and culture with a focus on youth educational initiatives.
Fields of interest: Arts education; Arts; Engineering school/education; Education; Environment, natural resources; Environment, water resources; Environment, land resources; Environment; Youth development; Science, formal/general education; Mathematics; Engineering/technology; Science; Youth.
Type of support: Capital campaigns; Continuing support; Employee matching gifts; General/operating support; Program development; Scholarship funds.
Limitations: Applications accepted. Giving in the U.S. in areas of company operations, with emphasis on Tustin, CA, Melbourne, FL, IA, Portland, OR, and Richardson, TX; giving also to international organizations in Australia, Canada, France, and the United Kingdom for the Green Communities Program. No support for private foundations, political candidates or organizations, religious organizations not of direct benefit to the entire community, fraternal or social organizations, or discriminatory organizations. No grants to individuals, or for memorials, endowments, annual campaigns, debt reduction, federated campaigns, political campaigns, sports events or scholarships for designated athletes, gifts, door prizes, or raffles, equipment or playground funding, classroom donations, or school fundraisers.
Publications: Application guidelines.
Application information: All grant applications should be preceded by an e-mail or telephone inquiry. Applicants for Green Communities Program must be teamed with a Rockwell Collins employee or retiree. Organizations receiving Green Communities grants may be asked to provide interim reports and a final report. Application form required.
Initial approach: Telephone or e-mail foundation; download application form and mail to foundation for organizations located in IA or mail to nearest company facility for organizations located outside IA; download application form and e-mail form to contact for Green Communities Program
Copies of proposal: 1
Deadline(s): Apr. 1 to Apr. 30 and Aug. 1 to Aug. 30; Feb. 14 for Green Communities Program

Board meeting date(s): Oct. and July
Final notification: 3 months; Apr. for Green Communities Program
Officers and Directors:* Martha May,* Pres.; Gary R. Chadick,* V.P. and Secy.; Patrick E. Allen, V.P. and Treas.; Jennifer Becker, Exec. Dir.; Robert K. Ortberg.
Number of staff: None.
EIN: 421526774

3478
John Ruan Foundation Trust ✧
666 Grand Ave., 1700 Ruan Ctr.
Des Moines, IA 50309-2520 (515) 245-2555
Contact: John Ruan III, Tr.

Established in 1955 in IA.
Donors: Ruan Transport Corp.; Elizabeth Ruan Trust; John Ruan III.
Foundation type: Company-sponsored foundation.
Financial data (yr. ended 06/30/14): Assets, $16,999,169 (M); gifts received, $300,000; expenditures, $656,299; qualifying distributions, $638,211; giving activities include $637,883 for 85 grants (high: $190,000; low: $250).
Purpose and activities: The foundation supports community foundations and organizations involved with arts and culture, education, health, mental health, employment, and human services.
Fields of interest: Performing arts; Performing arts, theater; Performing arts, orchestras; Arts; Elementary/secondary education; Higher education; Higher education, college (community/junior); Education; Health care; Mental health/crisis services; Employment, services; Big Brothers/Big Sisters; Children/youth, services; Family services; Residential/custodial care; Developmentally disabled, centers & services; Human services; Foundations (community).
Type of support: General/operating support; Building/renovation.
Limitations: Applications accepted. Giving primarily in Des Moines, IA. No grants to individuals.
Application information: Application form not required.
Initial approach: Proposal
Deadline(s): None
Trustee: John Ruan III.
EIN: 426059463
Selected grants: The following grants are a representative sample of this grantmaker's funding activity:
$40,000 to Youth Homes of Mid-America, Johnston, IA, 2011.
$12,500 to Culver Educational Foundation, Culver, IN, 2011.
$12,500 to Des Moines Playhouse, Des Moines, IA, 2011.
$12,500 to Employee and Family Resources, Des Moines, IA, 2011.
$12,500 to Orchard Place, Des Moines, IA, 2011.
$10,000 to Des Moines Symphony, Des Moines, IA, 2011.
$10,000 to Drake University, Des Moines, IA, 2011.
$10,000 to Link Associates, Des Moines, IA, 2011.
$10,000 to University of Iowa Foundation, Iowa City, IA, 2011.
$2,500 to Science Center of Iowa, Des Moines, IA, 2011.

3479
The Seidler Foundation ✧
c/o Harvey Kadlec
P.O. Box 1297
Des Moines, IA 50305-1297
Contact: Stanley B. Seidler, Pres.

Established in 1982 in IA.
Donors: Iowa Periodicals, Inc.; Stanley B. Seidler; Excell Mktg., LLC; Evelyn G. Seidler.
Foundation type: Company-sponsored foundation.
Financial data (yr. ended 12/31/13): Assets, $10,587,464 (M); gifts received, $450,000; expenditures, $515,602; qualifying distributions, $499,858; giving activities include $496,435 for 96 grants (high: $143,000; low: $175).
Purpose and activities: The foundation supports organizations involved with arts and culture, higher education, education services, children, and Judaism.
Fields of interest: Education; Human services; Religion.
Type of support: General/operating support; Scholarship funds; Scholarships—to individuals.
Limitations: Applications accepted. Giving primarily in IA and WY.
Application information: Application form required.
Initial approach: Letter
Deadline(s): None
Officer: Stanley B. Seidler, Pres.
Directors: Carol Seidler Mavrakis; Susan Seidler Nerman.
EIN: 421209825
Selected grants: The following grants are a representative sample of this grantmaker's funding activity:
$5,000 to Cornell College, Mount Vernon, IA, 2012. For Gamer Renovation.
$1,000 to University of Iowa, Iowa City, IA, 2012. For scholarship.

3480
Siouxland Community Foundation ✧
(formerly Siouxland Foundation)
505 5th St., Ste. 412
Sioux City, IA 51101-1507
FAX: (712) 293-3303;
E-mail: office@siouxlandcommunityfoundation.org;
Main URL: http://www.siouxlandcommunityfoundation.org
Facebook: https://www.facebook.com/pages/Siouxland-Community-Foundation/163191497219881
LinkedIn: https://www.linkedin.com/company/siouxland-community-foundation?trk=biz-companies-cym
Twitter: https://twitter.com/SiouxlandCF

Established in 1988 in IA.
Foundation type: Community foundation.
Financial data (yr. ended 12/31/12): Assets, $15,937,837 (M); gifts received, $1,819,406; expenditures, $2,195,307; giving activities include $1,791,197 for 60 grants (high: $602,422), and $217,275 for 72 grants to individuals.
Purpose and activities: The foundation awards grants to social service agencies that offer assistance with addiction, domestic violence and other issues. Giving also for arts and culture, education, civic affairs, and health.
Fields of interest: Arts education; Museums; Performing arts, dance; Performing arts, theater; Performing arts, music; Arts; Education, early childhood education; Child development, education; Medical school/education; Adult education—literacy, basic skills & GED; Education, reading; Education; Nursing care; Health care; Substance abuse, services; Mental health/crisis services; Health organizations, association; Alcoholism; Crime/violence prevention, domestic violence; Safety/disasters; Recreation, parks/playgrounds; Recreation; Children/youth, services; Child development, services; Family services; Aging, centers/services; Minorities/immigrants, centers/services; Human services; Community/economic development; Government/public administration; Youth; Aging; Disabilities, people with; Minorities; Asians/Pacific Islanders; African Americans/Blacks; Hispanics/Latinos; Native Americans/American Indians; Economically disadvantaged; Homeless.
Type of support: Building/renovation; Equipment; Program development; Conferences/seminars; Seed money; Scholarship funds; Research; Employee-related scholarships; Scholarships—to individuals.
Limitations: Applications accepted. Giving limited to the greater Sioux City, IA, tri-state area (within a 50-mile radius of Sioux City, including NE and SD). No support for religious purposes. No grants to individuals (except for scholarships), or for endowment funds, deficit financing, fundraising campaigns, capital campaigns, general operating support, or school playground equipment or uniforms.
Publications: Application guidelines; Annual report; Annual report (including application guidelines); Grants list; Informational brochure; Newsletter.
Application information: Visit foundation web site for application cover sheet and guidelines. Foundation grants do not generally exceed $5,000. Application form required.
Initial approach: Letter or telephone
Copies of proposal: 2
Deadline(s): Jan. 16 and May 15
Board meeting date(s): Mar., June, Sept., and Dec.
Final notification: Late Mar. and late June
Officers and Directors:* Matthew J. Basye,* Chair., Grant Review Committee and V.P.; Richard J. Dehner,* Chair., Investment/Finance Comm.; Laura A. Schiltz,* Chair., Mktg. and Devel. Comm.; Lesley M. Bartholomew,* Pres.; Barbara F. Orzechowski,* Secy.; Paul A. Bergmann,* Treas.; Rebecca Krohn, Exec. Dir.; Marie L. Buckley; Todd DeMoss; Lance D. Ehmcke; Marilyn J. Hagberg; Robert W. Houlihan; Charles A. Knoepfler; Matthew J. Lawler; Robert F. Meis; Pam Miller; Michael H. Prosser; Leon D. Rozeboom; Garrett K. Smith; Richard G. Wagner; Charese E. Yanney.
Number of staff: 1 full-time professional; 1 part-time professional; 1 part-time support.
EIN: 421323904

3481
South Central Iowa Community Foundation ✧
108 North Grand
Chariton, IA 50049 (641) 217-9105
Contact: Diane Bear, C.E.O.
E-mail: scicf.diane@mediacombb.net; Main URL: http://www.scicf.org
Facebook: https://www.facebook.com/pages/South-Central-Iowa-Community-Foundation/167804839939700

Twitter: https://twitter.com/SCICF1

Established in 1993 in IA.
Foundation type: Community foundation.
Financial data (yr. ended 06/30/13): Assets, $11,225,942 (M); gifts received, $2,027,184; expenditures, $1,314,555; giving activities include $1,128,543 for 41+ grants (high: $50,000).
Purpose and activities: The foundation's mission is to contribute to a better life for people of South Central Iowa by helping donors to carry out their charitable intent and by providing responsible stewardship of gifts for community purposes.
Fields of interest: Arts; Education; Human services; Community/economic development.
Limitations: Applications accepted. Giving primarily in Clarke, Decatur, Lucas, Ringgold, and Union counties, IA. No grants for existing debts, operating expenses or salaries, or consumable items.
Application information: Visit foundation web site for application form and guidelines. Application form required.
Initial approach: Submit application form and attachments
Copies of proposal: 6
Deadline(s): Varies
Officers and Directors:* Betty Hansen,* Chair.; Lori Borcherding,* Vice-Chair.; Diane Bear,* Pres. and C.E.O.; Michell Ricker,* Secy.; Kay Herring,* Treas.; Peg Anderson; Adam Bahr; Sue Beck; Pennie Gonseth Cheers; Kevin Creveling; Mike Frost; Jason Gibbs; Dennis Jeter; Mellony Klemesrud; Jan Knock; Gloria Salsman; Mary Seales; Don Sheridan; Melissa Snell; Clinton Spurrier; Barb Stephens; Mary Stierwalt; Ray Thurlby; Jim Wright; and 2 additional directors.
Number of staff: 1 full-time professional; 1 full-time support.
EIN: 421411234

3482
Stine Family Foundation ✧
22555 Laredo Trail
Adel, IA 50003-4570

Established in 1999 in IA.
Donors: Harry H. Stine; Midwest Oilseeds Inc.
Foundation type: Independent foundation.
Financial data (yr. ended 06/30/13): Assets, $14,835,017 (M); expenditures, $689,711; qualifying distributions, $658,000; giving activities include $658,000 for grants.
Fields of interest: Higher education; Education; Human services.
Type of support: General/operating support.
Limitations: Applications not accepted. Giving primarily in IA. No grants to individuals.
Application information: Contributes only to pre-selected organizations.
Officers and Directors:* Molly S. Stine,* Pres.; Jerald L. Reichling, C.F.O.; Harry H. Stine,* V.P. and Treas.; Michael L. Peterson.
EIN: 421497513
Selected grants: The following grants are a representative sample of this grantmaker's funding activity:
$334,500 to Buena Vista University, Storm Lake, IA, 2013. For funds for student research in a university setting.
$310,000 to Character Counts in Iowa, Des Moines, IA, 2013. For The Institute's mission is to recognize, enhance and sustain the positive qualities of Iowans in order to provide civility through character development.

3483
The Sukup Family Foundation ✧
1379 Beeds Lake Dr.
Hampton, IA 50441-7437

Established in 1999 in IA.
Donors: Eugene Sukup; Mary Sukup; Charles Sukup; Sukup Mfg. Co.; Eugene Sukup Trust; Mary E. Sukup Trust.
Foundation type: Independent foundation.
Financial data (yr. ended 12/31/12): Assets, $1,322,418 (M); gifts received, $1,560,000; expenditures, $2,581,269; qualifying distributions, $2,579,587; giving activities include $2,579,587 for 47 grants (high: $900,000; low: $2,000).
Purpose and activities: Giving primarily for Christian, Lutheran, and United Methodist churches and organizations.
Fields of interest: Human services; Salvation Army; Children, day care; Christian agencies & churches; Protestant agencies & churches.
Limitations: Applications not accepted. Giving primarily in IA. No grants to individuals.
Application information: Contributes only to pre-selected organizations.
Officers: Eugene Sukup, Pres.; Charles Sukup, V.P.; Mary Sukup, Secy.; Steven Sukup, Treas.
EIN: 421488675

3484
Martha-Ellen Tye Foundation ✧
16 E. Main St., Ste. 260
Marshalltown, IA 50158-4936 (641) 752-8340
FAX: (641) 752-8341;
E-mail: info@marthaellentyefoundation.org; Main URL: http://www.marthaellentyefoundation.org
Grants List: http://www.marthaellentyefoundation.org/2009_Grants_List.pdf

Established in 1976 in IA.
Donor: Martha-Ellen Tye†.
Foundation type: Independent foundation.
Financial data (yr. ended 12/31/13): Assets, $29,259,451 (M); gifts received, $3,826; expenditures, $1,650,889; qualifying distributions, $1,519,010; giving activities include $1,298,108 for 63 grants (high: $200,000; low: $252).
Purpose and activities: Giving primarily for arts and culture, and education; funding also human service needs, and community betterment.
Fields of interest: Humanities; Arts; Education; Human services; Public affairs; Hispanics/Latinos.
Type of support: General/operating support; Capital campaigns; Building/renovation; Equipment; Program development; Curriculum development; Scholarship funds; Matching/challenge support.
Limitations: Applications accepted. Giving primarily in Marshalltown, IA, and the surrounding county. No support for religious organizations. No grants to individuals, or for annual campaigns, sponsorships, advertising, or film or video production.
Publications: Application guidelines; Grants list; Program policy statement.
Application information: Application information available on foundation web site; accepting applications only from Marshalltown, Iowa and surrounding Marshall County. Application form not required.
Initial approach: Letter, telephone or e-mail
Copies of proposal: 1
Deadline(s): Mar. 1, June 1, Sept.1, and Dec. 1
Board meeting date(s): Mid May and late Oct.
Final notification: Within 1 month of application deadline
Officers and Directors:* Dennis A. O'Toole,* Pres.; Joel Greer,* Secy.-Treas.; Karn Gregoire, Exec. Dir.; Matt Fisher; John Hermanson; Jim Lowrance; Thomas O'Toole; David Tank; Steven Tye; Deb Vogeler.
Number of staff: 2 full-time professional.
EIN: 421055988
Selected grants: The following grants are a representative sample of this grantmaker's funding activity:
$135,250 to Iowa Valley Community College District, Marshalltown, IA, 2012. For Educational Partnership, 2012 Performance Series and Challenge Grant.
$85,000 to Quakerdale-Whites Iowa Institute, New Providence, IA, 2012. For General Operating Fund, Scholarships, Promise Academy.
$66,712 to Community Foundation of Northeast Iowa, Waterloo, IA, 2012. For Commitment to Development Program, Advised Fund.
$56,000 to Church of the Resurrection, San Antonio, TX, 2012. For General Operating Fund, Children's Center and Community Hall.
$49,000 to Marshalltown Community Schools, Marshalltown, IA, 2012. For General Operating Fund, Technology Upgrade, Swim Timing System.
$37,000 to San Antonio Symphony, San Antonio, TX, 2012. For General Operating Fund and Concerts.
$22,500 to Marshalltown Community College Foundation, Marshalltown, IA, 2012. For scholarships, general operating fund.
$15,000 to Marshalltown Community College, Marshalltown, IA, 2012. For General Operating Fund, Library, Tye Teaching Excellence.
$5,175 to Iowa River Hospice, Marshalltown, IA, 2012. For IRH Equipment/Supplies.
$5,000 to American Red Cross in Greater New York, New York, NY, 2012. For Super Storm Sandy Relief Fund.

3485
United Fire Group Foundation ✧
118 2nd Ave. S.E.
Cedar Rapids, IA 52401-1212

Established in 2001 in IA.
Donors: United Fire & Casualty Co.; United Life Insurance Co.
Foundation type: Company-sponsored foundation.
Financial data (yr. ended 12/31/13): Assets, $16,947 (M); gifts received, $42,359; expenditures, $722,510; qualifying distributions, $704,172; giving activities include $599,335 for 53 grants (high: $175,000; low: $25), and $98,000 for 25 grants to individuals (high: $4,000; low: $2,000).
Purpose and activities: The foundation supports museums and organizations involved with theater, education, employment, and human services and awards grants to individuals for higher education and disaster relief.
Fields of interest: Museums; Performing arts, theater; Higher education; Business school/education; Libraries (public); Education; Goodwill Industries; YM/YWCAs & YM/YWHAs; Children,

services; Residential/custodial care; Residential/custodial care, hospices; Developmentally disabled, centers & services; Human services; United Ways and Federated Giving Programs.
Type of support: Emergency funds; General/operating support; Program development; Grants to individuals.
Limitations: Applications not accepted. Giving primarily in IA.
Application information: Contributes only to pre-selected organizations and individuals.
Officers: Randy A. Ramlo, Pres.; Michael T. Wilkens, Secy.; Dianne M. Lyons, Treas.
Director: Jack Evans.
EIN: 421492320

3486
Vermeer Charitable Foundation ✧
1210 Vermeer Rd. E.
Pella, IA 50219-7660 (641) 628-3141
Contact: Lois J. Vermeer, Secy. and Dir.

Established in 1977 in IA.
Donors: Vermeer Manufacturing Co.; Vermeer Farms, Inc.
Foundation type: Company-sponsored foundation.
Financial data (yr. ended 12/31/13): Assets, $8,513,843 (M); gifts received, $5,140,000; expenditures, $1,990,058; qualifying distributions, $1,946,159; giving activities include $1,946,159 for 129 grants (high: $500,000; low: $100).
Purpose and activities: The foundation supports projects designed to bring honor and praise to God. Special emphasis is directed toward projects designed to promote the quality of life for Vermeer employees and communities; inspire Vermeer employees to use their skills and resources; and utilize Vermeer products and expertise.
Fields of interest: Elementary/secondary education; Higher education; Education; Recreation; Human services; Christian agencies & churches.
Type of support: Building/renovation; Seed money; Scholarship funds; Sponsorships; Employee-related scholarships.
Limitations: Applications accepted. Giving primarily in the Pella, IA, area. No grants to individuals (except for employee-related scholarships), or for endowments; no loans.
Publications: Application guidelines.
Application information: Application form required.
Initial approach: Letter
Copies of proposal: 2
Deadline(s): None
Board meeting date(s): Apr., Oct., and as required
Officers and Directors:* Robert Vermeer,* Pres.; Lois J. Vermeer,* Secy.; Mindi Vanden Bosch,* Treas.; Dale J. Andringa; Mary Vermeer Andringa; Derek Dehaan; Allison van Wyngarden; David Vermeer; Matilda Vermeer; Tricia Vermeer.
Number of staff: 1 part-time professional; 2 part-time support.
EIN: 421087640

3487
Vogel Charities Inc. ✧
P.O. Box 440
Orange City, IA 51041-0440

Established in 1973 in IA.
Donors: Vogel Paint & Wax; Marwin Paints; Frank Vogel; Iowa State Bank.
Foundation type: Independent foundation.
Financial data (yr. ended 12/31/12): Assets, $6,727,533 (M); gifts received, $147,500; expenditures, $685,995; qualifying distributions, $655,000; giving activities include $655,000 for 5 grants (high: $250,000; low: $5,000).
Purpose and activities: Giving primarily for Christian organizations and for education.
Fields of interest: Arts; Secondary school/education; Higher education; Health care; Health organizations, association; Human services; Community development, neighborhood development; United Ways and Federated Giving Programs; Christian agencies & churches.
Type of support: Building/renovation; Scholarship funds.
Limitations: Applications not accepted. Giving primarily in IA, NE and SD. No grants to individuals.
Application information: Contributes only to pre-selected organizations.
Officer: Frank Vogel, Pres.
EIN: 237169167

3488
Wallace Research Foundation ✧
c/o RSM McGladrey, Inc., Attn.: Kay Hegarty
221 3rd Ave. S.E., Ste. 300
Cedar Rapids, IA 52401-1525

Established in 1996 in IA.
Donors: H.B. Wallace‡; Jocelyn M. Wallace; Henry D. Wallace; Linda Wallace-Gray; H.A. Wallace‡; Eric Gilchrist Charitable Trust.
Foundation type: Independent foundation.
Financial data (yr. ended 12/31/13): Assets, $81,399,500 (M); gifts received, $5,521; expenditures, $3,410,105; qualifying distributions, $2,922,773; giving activities include $2,894,773 for 42 grants (high: $250,000; low: $16,397).
Purpose and activities: Giving primarily for education, the environment, and medical research.
Fields of interest: Higher education; Environment, natural resources; Animal welfare; Medical research, institute.
Type of support: General/operating support; Endowments; Research.
Limitations: Applications not accepted. Giving primarily in the U.S., with some emphasis on AZ. No support for religious or political purposes. No grants to individuals.
Publications: Annual report.
Application information: Contributes only to pre-selected organizations.
Officers: Henry D. Wallace, Pres.; Linda Wallace-Gray, V.P. and Secy.-Treas.
Directors: Alex Gilchrist; Angus Gilchrist.
EIN: 426540579

3489
Weathertop Foundation ✧
(formerly Thomas Nelson Urban, Jr. and Mary Bright Urban Foundation)
5320 Grand Ave.
Des Moines, IA 50312-2124

Established in 1994 in IA.
Donors: Thomas Nelson Urban; Mary Bright Urban.
Foundation type: Independent foundation.
Financial data (yr. ended 07/31/13): Assets, $11,272,721 (M); gifts received, $2,550; expenditures, $477,825; qualifying distributions, $442,675; giving activities include $436,880 for 66 grants (high: $120,000; low: $250).
Fields of interest: Performing arts, orchestras; Arts; Higher education; Education; Botanical gardens; Health organizations; Human services; Foundations (community); United Ways and Federated Giving Programs; Christian agencies & churches.
Type of support: General/operating support.
Limitations: Applications not accepted. Giving primarily in FL, IA, OH, and MA.
Application information: Unsolicited requests for funds not accepted.
Board meeting date(s): Aug.
Officers: Thomas Nelson Urban, Jr., Chair. and Pres.; Mary Bright Urban, V.P.; Victoria Urban Broer, Secy.; William G. Urban, Treas.
Directors: Cornelia Urban Sawczuk; Thomas N. Urban III.
EIN: 421431036
Selected grants: The following grants are a representative sample of this grantmaker's funding activity:
$20,000 to Concord Academy, Concord, MA, 2011. For general operations.
$16,000 to Cleveland Botanical Garden, Cleveland, OH, 2011. For general operations.
$15,000 to Georgia Research Alliance, Atlanta, GA, 2011. For general operations.
$11,000 to Georgia Biomedical Partnership, Atlanta, GA, 2011. For general operations.
$10,000 to United Way of Central Iowa, Des Moines, IA, 2011. For general operations.
$7,500 to Childrens Miracle Network, Salt Lake City, UT, 2011.
$5,000 to Des Moines Pastoral Counseling Center, West Des Moines, IA, 2011. For general operations.
$5,000 to Multiple Sclerosis Society, National, New York, NY, 2011. For general operations.
$5,000 to Society of the Four Arts, Palm Beach, FL, 2011.
$5,000 to Stanford University, Stanford, CA, 2011.

3490
The Wellmark Foundation ✧
(formerly The IASD Health Care Foundation)
1331 Grand Ave., Station 3W739
Des Moines, IA 50309-2551 (515) 376-4819
Contact: Stephanie Perry, Interim Dir.
FAX: (515) 376-9082;
E-mail: wmfoundation@wellmark.com; Contact for Stephanie Perry: (605) 373-7429, e-mail: perryss@wellmark.commcgarveym@wellmark.com; Additional contact: Mike Gerrish, Corporate & Mktg. Comms, (515) 376-4611, e-mail gerrishm@wellmark.com; Main URL: http://www.wellmark.com/foundation/index.asp
Grants List: http://www.wellmark.com/foundation/grants/grant_awards.htm

Established in 1991 in IA.
Donors: Blue Cross and Blue Shield of Iowa; Blue Cross and Blue Shield of South Dakota; Wellmark, Inc.
Foundation type: Company-sponsored foundation.
Financial data (yr. ended 12/31/13): Assets, $67,548,986 (M); gifts received, $13,297,686; expenditures, $3,044,960; qualifying distributions, $2,423,328; giving activities include $2,423,328 for 11+ grants (high: $79,679).
Purpose and activities: The foundation supports programs designed to improve the health of Iowans, South Dakotans, and their communities. Special emphasis is directed toward childhood obesity

prevention; and community-based wellness and prevention.
Fields of interest: Elementary/secondary education; Dental care; Reproductive health; Reproductive health, prenatal care; Public health; Public health, obesity; Public health, physical fitness; Health care; Food services; Nutrition; Family services, parent education; United Ways and Federated Giving Programs; Children.
Type of support: Employee volunteer services; Continuing support; Management development/ capacity building; Program development; Publication; Seed money; Curriculum development.
Limitations: Applications accepted. Giving limited to IA and SD. No support for for-profit organizations. No grants to individuals, or for biomedical research not of direct benefit to local residents, uncompensated care for direct clinical services, or services that are billable for third-party reimbursement, capital campaigns, equipment, organizations indirect/ overhear costs, debt reduction, annual campaigns, fundraising events, or endowments.
Publications: Application guidelines; Annual report; Grants list; Newsletter.
Application information: Proposals for Healthy Communities Small Grants should be no longer than 4 pages. A full proposal may be requested at a later date for MATCH grants. Application form required.
Initial approach: Proposal for Healthy Communities Small Grants; letter of interest for MATCH grants
Copies of proposal: 4
Deadline(s): Mar. 3 for Healthy Communities Small Grants; May 6 for MATCH grants
Board meeting date(s): Mar. 30, May 24, Aug. 11, and Nov. 1
Final notification: Late Apr. for Healthy Communities Small Grants; early Aug. for MATCH grants
Officers and Directors: John D. Forsyth, Chair.; Janet Griffin, Secy.; Christa Kuennen, Treas.; Theodore J. Boesen, Jr.; Ruth Litchfield; Edward R. Lynn; Robert E. O'Connell; Robert J. Richard; Sheila Riggs; Roberta Wattlesworth.
Number of staff: 2 full-time professional; 1 part-time professional.
EIN: 421368650

3491
The William J. Zimmerman Foundation ✧
1603 Pleasant Plain Rd.
Fairfield, IA 52556

Established in 1983 in IL.
Donor: Zimmerman Family Trust, No. 1.
Foundation type: Independent foundation.
Financial data (yr. ended 12/31/13): Assets, $14,411,311 (M); expenditures, $867,362; qualifying distributions, $659,763; giving activities include $596,000 for 16 grants (high: $160,000; low: $1,000).
Fields of interest: Education; Human services.
Limitations: Applications not accepted. Giving primarily in CA. No grants to individuals.
Application information: Contributes only to pre-selected organizations.
Officers and Directors:* David J. Johnson, Pres.; John E. Mallard, V.P.; William M. Doyle, Jr.,* Secy.; Susan E. Chroman; Christopher J. Podoll.
EIN: 421223262

KANSAS

3492
Ash Grove Charitable Foundation ✧
P.O. Box 25900
Overland Park, KS 66225-5900 (913) 451-8900

Established in 1997 in KS.
Donor: Ash Grove Cement Co.
Foundation type: Company-sponsored foundation.
Financial data (yr. ended 12/31/13): Assets, $14,496,199 (M); gifts received, $3,546,213; expenditures, $577,807; qualifying distributions, $448,506; giving activities include $448,356 for 100 grants (high: $33,821; low: $350).
Purpose and activities: The foundation supports community foundations and organizations involved with education, conservation, cancer, crime and violence prevention, human services, and community development.
Fields of interest: Education; Human services; Community/economic development.
Limitations: Applications accepted. Giving primarily in areas of company operations in AR, ID, KS, MO, MT, NE, OR, and WA. No support for secondary schools.
Publications: Grants list.
Application information: Application form not required.
Initial approach: Proposal
Copies of proposal: 1
Deadline(s): None
Board meeting date(s): As needed
Officers: Kenton W. Sunderland, Pres. and Treas.; Charles T. Sunderland, V.P.; M. Meads, Secy.
Number of staff: 1 part-time professional.
EIN: 431765963
Selected grants: The following grants are a representative sample of this grantmaker's funding activity:
$600 to Foundation for Public Affairs, Washington, DC, 2012. For donation.

3493
Baughman Foundation ✧
P.O. Box 1356
Liberal, KS 67905-1356 (620) 624-1371
Contact: Carol Feather-Francis, Pres.

Incorporated in 1958 in KS.
Donors: Robert W. Baughman†; The John W. Baughman Farms Co.
Foundation type: Independent foundation.
Financial data (yr. ended 12/31/13): Assets, $30,607,938 (M); expenditures, $1,763,350; qualifying distributions, $1,422,695; giving activities include $1,370,706 for 40 grants (high: $322,000; low: $1,125).
Fields of interest: Arts; Higher education; Human services; Community/economic development; Foundations (private grantmaking); United Ways and Federated Giving Programs.
Type of support: General/operating support; Building/renovation; Endowments; Program development; Scholarship funds.
Limitations: Applications accepted. Giving primarily in southwest KS; some funding also in the OK Panhandle area. No support for private foundations. No grants to individuals.
Application information: Application form required.
Initial approach: Proposal
Copies of proposal: 3
Deadline(s): Monthly Board Meeting
Board meeting date(s): Monthly
Officers: Carol Feather-Francis, Pres.; Richard R. Yoxall, V.P.; James R. Yoxall, Secy.-Treas.
Number of staff: 1 part-time support.
EIN: 486108797

3494
The Ross and Marianna Beach Foundation, Inc. ✧
P.O. Box 1752
Lawrence, KS 66044-8752
Contact: Carrie Edwards
E-mail: beachfoundation@gmail.com

Established in 2001 in KS.
Donors: Marianna Beach; Ross Beach.
Foundation type: Independent foundation.
Financial data (yr. ended 09/30/13): Assets, $12,037,359 (M); expenditures, $604,619; qualifying distributions, $558,643; giving activities include $527,853 for 25 grants (high: $100,000; low: $500).
Purpose and activities: The foundation is dedicated to the enrichment of Kansans, specifically through the support of education, the arts, and the environment, and to the enhancement of the lives of children and adults with special needs.
Fields of interest: Arts; Education, early childhood education; Child development, education; Education, special; Human services; Civil/human rights, disabled; Disabilities, people with; Mentally disabled.
Type of support: General/operating support; Building/renovation; Endowments.
Limitations: Applications accepted. Giving limited to KS. No grants to individuals.
Publications: Annual report.
Application information: The foundation prefers email contact.
Officers and Directors:* Marianna Beach,* Pres.; Terry Edwards,* Secy.-Treas.; Elizabeth Jane Hipp.
Number of staff: 1 part-time support.
EIN: 431947099
Selected grants: The following grants are a representative sample of this grantmaker's funding activity:
$100,000 to Lawrence Public Library Foundation, Lawrence, KS, 2013. For Establishment of Author Series.
$15,000 to Heartland Community Foundation, Hays, KS, 2013. To establish First Call for Help Fund.
$10,000 to Elizabeth Ballard Community Center, Lawrence, KS, 2013. For Tuition Reduction for Programs.
$1,500 to Hutchinson Community Foundation, Hutchinson, KS, 2013. For Fund for Hutchinson.

3495
Israel Henry Beren Charitable Trust ✧
c/o Robert M. Beren
2020 N. Bramblewood St.
Wichita, KS 67206-1094

Established in 1995 in OH.
Donor: Israel Henry Beren†.
Foundation type: Independent foundation.
Financial data (yr. ended 12/31/13): Assets, $51,988,091 (M); expenditures, $2,919,337; qualifying distributions, $2,520,220; giving activities include $2,519,000 for 7 grants (high: $2,100,000; low: $1,000).
Fields of interest: Education; Human services; Jewish agencies & synagogues.
Limitations: Applications not accepted. Giving primarily in NY; some funding also in FL and TX. No grants to individuals.
Application information: Contributes only to pre-selected organizations.
Trustee: Robert M. Beren.
EIN: 486337836
Selected grants: The following grants are a representative sample of this grantmaker's funding activity:
$500,000 to Ner Israel Rabbinical College, Baltimore, MD, 2012. For Food Service Building Project.
$40,000 to Yeshiva University, New York, NY, 2012. For Stern Campus, Beren Campus Flags and Banners.

3496
Robert M. Beren Foundation, Inc. ✧
2020 N. Bramblewood St.
Wichita, KS 67206-1094

Established in 1984 in KS.
Donors: Adolph Beren†; Robert M. Beren.
Foundation type: Independent foundation.
Financial data (yr. ended 10/31/13): Assets, $67,535,586 (M); expenditures, $3,212,611; qualifying distributions, $2,725,780; giving activities include $2,693,455 for 58 grants (high: $620,000; low: $50).
Purpose and activities: Giving primarily for higher education, human services, and Jewish agencies and temples.
Fields of interest: Higher education; Education; Human services; Jewish federated giving programs; Jewish agencies & synagogues.
Type of support: General/operating support; Annual campaigns; Building/renovation; Emergency funds; Fellowships.
Limitations: Applications not accepted. Giving primarily in FL and NY; some giving also in MA. No grants to individuals.
Application information: Contributes only to pre-selected organizations.
Officers: Robert M. Beren, Pres. and Treas.; Charles B. Spradlin, Jr., Secy.
EIN: 480990309

3497
Blue Cross and Blue Shield of Kansas Foundation, Inc. ✧
1133 S.W. Topeka Blvd.
Topeka, KS 66629-0001 (785) 291-7246
Contact: Marlou Wegener, C.O.O.
FAX: (785) 291-8997;
E-mail: marlou.wegener@bcbsks.com; Toll Free: (800) 432-0216 ext. 7246; Main URL: http://www.bcbsks.com/AboutUs/Foundation/index.htm
Grants List: http://www.bcbsks.com/AboutUs/Foundation/pdf/2013_HHFL_Recipients.pdf

Established in 2005 in KS.
Donor: Blue Cross and Blue Shield of Kansas, Inc.
Foundation type: Company-sponsored foundation.

Financial data (yr. ended 12/31/13): Assets, $14,239,770 (M); expenditures, $812,614; qualifying distributions, $645,901; giving activities include $641,636 for 259 grants (high: $50,000; low: $82).
Purpose and activities: The foundation supports programs designed to promote health improvement, health access, health education, healthy behaviors, and prevention initiatives.
Fields of interest: Health care, clinics/centers; Public health; Public health, obesity; Public health, physical fitness; Health care, insurance; Health care, patient services; Health care.
Type of support: General/operating support; Program development; Curriculum development.
Limitations: Applications accepted. Giving in areas of company operations in KS. No support for religious organizations or parent-teacher organizations. No grants to individuals, or for sponsorships of sports or athletic teams, capital or renovation campaigns, or political campaigns, events, or activities.
Publications: Application guidelines.
Application information: Grant applications are limited to the application form and a maximum of four additional pages for the written proposal. Application form required.
Initial approach: Completed application form
Deadline(s): Oct. 10 for Healthy Habits for Life
Officers and Directors:* Andrew C. Corbin,* Pres.; Marlou Wegener,* C.O.O.; Scott H. Raymond, Secy.; Ronald D. Simmons,* Treas.; Robin R. LacKamp; Beryl Lowery-Born; Louis E. Mosiman.
EIN: 203085640
Selected grants: The following grants are a representative sample of this grantmaker's funding activity:
$30,000 to Kansas Learning Center for Health, Halstead, KS, 2012. For On the Road to Better Health.
$5,000 to Oral Health Kansas, Topeka, KS, 2012. For Oral health education Programs in KS.
$3,000 to Salina Family Healthcare Center, Salina, KS, 2012. For clinic grants.
$2,500 to American Red Cross, Topeka, KS, 2012. For Harveyville tornado relief fund.
$2,500 to YMCA of Topeka, Topeka, KS, 2012. For Strong Kids Program support.
$1,739 to Kansas Learning Center for Health, Halstead, KS, 2012. For Fueling My Body Program Frisbees for Wichita public schools fourth grade students.
$1,500 to YWCA of Topeka, Topeka, KS, 2012. For Girls on the Run Program.
$1,000 to Northeast Kansas Area Agency on Aging, Hiawatha, KS, 2012. For Northeast Kansas Area Agency on Aging 2012 Expo.

3498
Capitol Federal Foundation ✧
700 S. Kansas Ave., Ste. 517
Topeka, KS 66603-3809 (785) 270-6041
Contact: Tammy Dishman, Pres. and Exec. Dir.
Additional tel.: (785) 270-6040; Main URL: http://www.capfed.com/site/en/home/community.html

Established in 1999 in KS.
Donor: Capitol Federal Financial.
Foundation type: Company-sponsored foundation.
Financial data (yr. ended 12/31/12): Assets, $94,589,305 (M); expenditures, $3,689,163; qualifying distributions, $3,277,708; giving activities include $3,162,245 for 394 grants (high: $300,000; low: $37).
Purpose and activities: The foundation supports performing art centers and organizations involved with education, health, affordable housing, human services, and community development.
Fields of interest: Performing arts centers; Higher education; Education; Health care; Housing/shelter; Boys & girls clubs; Big Brothers/Big Sisters; Youth, services; Human services; Community/economic development; Foundations (community); United Ways and Federated Giving Programs.
Type of support: General/operating support; Continuing support; Income development; Management development/capacity building; Annual campaigns; Capital campaigns; Building/renovation; Equipment; Emergency funds; Program development; Conferences/seminars; Professorships; Seed money; Fellowships; Internship funds; Scholarship funds; Technical assistance; Employee volunteer services; Employee matching gifts; Matching/challenge support.
Limitations: Applications accepted. Giving limited to areas of company operations in central and northeastern KS. No support for religious or political organizations.
Application information: Application form not required.
Initial approach: Letter or telephone
Copies of proposal: 1
Deadline(s): None
Board meeting date(s): Quarterly
Final notification: 90 to 120 days
Officers: John C. Dicus, Chair.; Tammy Dishman, Pres. and Exec. Dir.; John B. Dicus, Secy.-Treas.
Number of staff: 1 full-time professional.
EIN: 481214952
Selected grants: The following grants are a representative sample of this grantmaker's funding activity:
$100,000 to Kansas University Endowment Association, Lawrence, KS, 2012.
$77,480 to Kansas University Endowment Association, Lawrence, KS, 2012.
$77,480 to Kansas University Endowment Association, Lawrence, KS, 2012.
$45,000 to Wichita State University Foundation, Wichita, KS, 2012.
$39,500 to Emporia State University Foundation, Emporia, KS, 2012.
$25,000 to Flint Hills Technical College Foundation, Emporia, KS, 2012.
$25,000 to Kansas University Endowment Association, Lawrence, KS, 2012.
$20,000 to Washburn University Foundation, Topeka, KS, 2012.
$10,000 to Shawnee Mission Education Foundation, Shawnee Mission, KS, 2012.

3499
Barton P. & Mary Davidson Cohen Charitable Fund Part II ✧
5901 College Blvd., Ste. 100
Overland Park, KS 66211-1834 (913) 319-0391
Contact: Mary Davidson Cohen, Tr.
Main URL: http://cohentrust.org/

Established in KS.
Foundation type: Independent foundation.
Financial data (yr. ended 12/31/12): Assets, $10,681,151 (M); expenditures, $729,830; qualifying distributions, $598,433; giving activities include $533,773 for 25 grants (high: $200,000; low: $3,000).
Purpose and activities: Giving primarily for charitable projects in Wyandotte and/or Johnson County, Kansas, and related to Jewish, American, regional, and/or local history.
Fields of interest: Historical activities; Arts; Libraries/library science; Education; Youth development; Jewish agencies & synagogues.
Limitations: Applications accepted. Giving primarily in Wyandotte and Johnson Counties, KS.
Application information: Application guidelines and form available on foundation web site. Application form required.
Initial approach: Telephone call to determine whether program fits foundation guidelines
Deadline(s): None
Trustees: Mary Cohen; Midwest Trust Co.
EIN: 266205956
Selected grants: The following grants are a representative sample of this grantmaker's funding activity:
$10,000 to Jewish Family Services, Overland Park, KS, 2012. To support and Strengthen the Jewish Communities By Providing Quality Programs and Services.
$5,000 to American Jewish Archives, Cincinnati, OH, 2012. For Preserving American Jewish History.
$5,000 to Kauffman Center for the Performing Arts, Kansas City, MO, 2012. For Educate, Nurture, and Inspire the Community Through the Performance of Art.

3500
Barton P. and Mary Davidson Cohen Charitable Fund Part One ✧
5901 College Blvd., Ste. 100
Overland Park, KS 66211-1834 (913) 319-0391
Contact: Mary Davidson Cohen
E-mail: MCohen@midwesttrust.com; Main URL: http://cohentrust.org/

Established in KS.
Donor: Barton P. Cohen†.
Foundation type: Independent foundation.
Financial data (yr. ended 12/31/12): Assets, $10,452,397 (M); gifts received, $215; expenditures, $680,574; qualifying distributions, $575,413; giving activities include $510,514 for 16 grants (high: $204,350; low: $1,000).
Fields of interest: Arts; Education; Jewish agencies & synagogues.
Limitations: Applications accepted. Giving primarily in Kansas City, Overland Park, and Johnson and Wyandotte counties, KS.
Publications: Grants list.
Application information: Applicants are encouraged to contact the foundation prior to submitting an application to determine if their program fits the foundation's guidelines. Application form required.
Initial approach: Use application form on foundation web site
Deadline(s): None
Trustees: Mary Cohen; Midwest Trust Co.
EIN: 266205947
Selected grants: The following grants are a representative sample of this grantmaker's funding activity:
$30,000 to Kansas City Symphony, Kansas City, MO, 2012. For Community Outreach Through Music.

$25,000 to Nelson-Atkins Museum of Art, Kansas City, MO, 2012. For Dedicated to the Enjoyment of the Visual Arts and Cultural Education.
$20,000 to Barton County Community College, Great Bend, KS, 2012. To Provide Higher Education.

3501
Coleman Family Foundation, Inc. ✧
610 E. Jefferson
Pittsburg, KS 66762-5913 (620) 231-8050
Contact: H. Richard Coleman, Pres. and Treas.

Established in 2002 in KS and MO.
Donors: Faith P. Coleman; H. Richard Coleman.
Foundation type: Independent foundation.
Financial data (yr. ended 12/31/13): Assets, $5,888,400 (M); gifts received, $1,930,000; expenditures, $1,614,206; qualifying distributions, $1,572,895; giving activities include $1,567,350 for 47 grants (high: $500,000; low: $200).
Fields of interest: Higher education; Education; Human services; Children/youth, services; Foundations (community).
Limitations: Applications accepted. Giving primarily in Pittsburg, KS.
Application information: Application form required.
Initial approach: Letter
Deadline(s): None
Officers and Directors:* H. Richard Coleman,* Pres. and Treas.; Faith P. Coleman,* V.P.; Marcia A. Sorrick, Secy.
EIN: 431947299
Selected grants: The following grants are a representative sample of this grantmaker's funding activity:
$500,000 to Pittsburg State University Foundation, Pittsburg, KS, 2012. For Fine Arts Center Fund.
$150,000 to University of Minnesota Foundation, Minneapolis, MN, 2012. For athletic scholarships.
$100,000 to Community Foundation of Southeast Kansas, Pittsburg, KS, 2012. For Stilwell Heritage and Educational Endowment.
$100,000 to Pittsburg State University Foundation, Pittsburg, KS, 2012. For Brian Hutchins Endowed Scholarship.
$30,000 to University of Minnesota Foundation, Minneapolis, MN, 2012. For program sponsor.
$10,000 to Center for Learning Tree Institute, Girard, KS, 2012. For Abernathy Science Education Center.
$5,000 to Community Foundation of Southeast Kansas, Pittsburg, KS, 2012. For Pittsburg Public Library Foundation.
$2,500 to Pittsburg State University Foundation, Pittsburg, KS, 2012. For KRPS Public Radio.
$500 to Big Brothers Big Sisters of Crawford County, Pittsburg, KS, 2012. For event sponsor.
$200 to Boy Scouts of America, Ozark Trails Council, Springfield, MO, 2012. For general fund.

3502
Community Foundation of Southwest Kansas ✧
(formerly Dodge City Area Foundation)
208 W.Wyatt Earp Blvd, Ste 200
P.O. Box 1313
Dodge City, KS 67801-1313 (620) 225-0959
Contact: Pat Hamit, Exec. Dir.
FAX: (620) 225-4946; E-mail: cfsk@sbcglobal.net;
Main URL: http://www.communityfoundationswks.com

Established in 1992 in KS.
Foundation type: Community foundation.
Financial data (yr. ended 12/31/13): Assets, $23,487,752 (M); gifts received, $897,562; expenditures, $812,948; giving activities include $385,245 for 15+ grants (high: $42,521), and $189,000 for 167 grants to individuals.
Purpose and activities: The foundation gives citizens of the area the opportunity to make a lasting gift to a community which has been good to them. It pools the assets and represents the ideas and interests of people who want to increase the impact of their philanthropy.
Fields of interest: Community development, neighborhood development; Economic development; Children/youth; Youth; Aging; Physically disabled; Women.
Type of support: Endowments; Matching/challenge support; Scholarships—to individuals.
Limitations: Applications accepted. Giving primarily in southwestern KS.
Publications: Application guidelines; Annual report; Grants list; Informational brochure; Newsletter; Occasional report.
Application information: Visit foundation web site for application form and guidelines. Application form required.
Initial approach: Mail application and attachments
Copies of proposal: 1
Deadline(s): Oct. 1
Board meeting date(s): 3rd Wed. of each month
Final notification: 30 to 45 days
Officers and Directors:* Jeff Thorpe,* Chair.; Darrin Golliher,* Vice-Chair.; Rolland Werner,* Treas.; Pat Hamit, Exec. Dir.; Martha Barnhardt; Larry Burk; Mindy Burkhart; Floris Jean Hampton; Craig Mock; David Snapp; Dana Waters; Lu Ann Wetmore.
Number of staff: 1 full-time professional; 2 part-time professional.
EIN: 481117413

3503
The Cooper-Clark Foundation ✧
P.O. Box 2707
Liberal, KS 67905-2707 (620) 624-7699
Contact: Kimberly Hay

Established in 1983.
Donors: James Clark†; Lucille Clark†.
Foundation type: Independent foundation.
Financial data (yr. ended 12/31/13): Assets, $13,400,385 (M); expenditures, $641,373; qualifying distributions, $521,725; giving activities include $482,353 for 108 grants (high: $65,000; low: $100).
Purpose and activities: Giving primarily for social services.
Fields of interest: Arts; Elementary/secondary education; Human services; Aging, centers/services; Community/economic development; Aging.
Type of support: General/operating support; Continuing support; Building/renovation; Equipment; Land acquisition; Emergency funds; Conferences/seminars; Seed money; Research; Technical assistance.
Limitations: Applications accepted. Giving limited to Baca, Cheyenne, Kiowa, Kit Carson, and Lincoln counties, CO, and Grant, Haskell, Morton, Seward, and Stanton counties, KS. No grants to individuals.
Application information: Application form required.
Deadline(s): None
Board meeting date(s): Quarterly
Officers: Lee Anderson, Pres.; Bob Todd, V.P.; Jay Hay, Secy.-Treas.
Directors: Kay Hay; Sharon Todd.
Number of staff: 1 part-time professional.
EIN: 742252034
Selected grants: The following grants are a representative sample of this grantmaker's funding activity:
$20,000 to Seward County Council on Aging, Liberal, KS, 2012. For new roof.
$10,000 to Walsh Healthcare Center, Walsh, CO, 2012. For operation expenses.
$5,189 to Prairie Family Center, Burlington, CO, 2012. For expenses.
$5,000 to Southwest Medical Center, Liberal, KS, 2012. For Community health fair.
$4,881 to Baker Arts Center, Liberal, KS, 2012. For Windows.
$2,250 to Baker Arts Center, Liberal, KS, 2012. For security system.
$1,500 to Stepping Stone Shelter, Liberal, KS, 2012. For food.

3504
Damon Family Foundation ✧ ☆
5601 S.W. Barrington Ct. S.
Topeka, KS 66614-2560 (785) 273-7722
Contact: Karen L. Damon, Pres.
Main URL: http://www.damonfamilyfoundation.org/
Facebook: https://www.facebook.com/damonfamilyfoundation

Established in KS.
Donors: Donald H. Damon; Kathleen J. Damon.
Foundation type: Independent foundation.
Financial data (yr. ended 12/31/13): Assets, $2,087,037 (M); expenditures, $2,412,877; qualifying distributions, $2,334,565; giving activities include $2,238,000 for 8 grants (high: $500,000; low: $3,000), and $96,565 for grants to individuals.
Fields of interest: Safety/disasters; Human services; Economically disadvantaged.
Type of support: Grants to individuals; General/operating support.
Limitations: Applications accepted. Giving primarily in KA.
Application information: See foundation website for complete application guidelines. Application form required.
Officers and Directors:* Karen L. Damon,* Pres.; Alan E. Streit,* V.P.; Kelly Strayer, Secy.; Donald H. Damon, Treas.; Carla Damm; Brenden A. Damon; Kathleen J. Damon.
EIN: 271568326

3505
DeBoer Family Foundation ✧
8621 E. 21st St. N., Ste. 250
Wichita, KS 67206-2965

Established in 1984 in KS.
Donors: Jack P. DeBoer; Penny K. DeBoer; Colony Club Apartments LLc.
Foundation type: Independent foundation.
Financial data (yr. ended 12/31/12): Assets, $146,357 (M); gifts received, $747,636; expenditures, $793,588; qualifying distributions,

$525,613; giving activities include $525,613 for 50 grants (high: $189,186; low: $500).
Fields of interest: Human services; Community/economic development; Christian agencies & churches.
Type of support: General/operating support.
Limitations: Applications not accepted. Giving primarily in Wichita, KS. No grants to individuals.
Application information: Contributes only to pre-selected organizations.
Trustees: Annie Baalman-DeBoer; Alexander DeBoer; Christopher DeBoer; Jack P. DeBoer; Marilyn S. DeBoer; Penny K. DeBoer; Skyler S. DeBoer; Cary Paine; Mary Rogers; Robert Seiple.
Officer and Director:* Paul Fritz Kling,* Pres.
EIN: 480988194

3506
Ronald D. Deffenbaugh Foundation ✧
c/o Charles E. Wetzler
4501 W. 135th St.
Leawood, KS 66224

Donors: Ronald Deffenbaugh, Sr. Mgmt. Trust; Ronald Deffenbaugh, Sr. Irrevocable Trust.
Foundation type: Independent foundation.
Financial data (yr. ended 12/31/13): Assets, $17,239,195 (M); gifts received, $3,297,068; expenditures, $2,397,398; qualifying distributions, $2,325,321; giving activities include $2,320,000 for 4 grants (high: $2,260,000; low: $5,000).
Fields of interest: Higher education; Community/economic development; Christian agencies & churches.
Limitations: Applications not accepted. Giving primarily in KS; some giving also in MO.
Application information: Contributes only to pre-selected organizations.
Trustees: George McGrew; Mark O. Rosenau; Charles E. Wetzler.
EIN: 266095573

3507
Delta Dental of Kansas Foundation, Inc. ✧
(formerly Delta Dental Plan of Kansas Foundation)
1619 N. Waterfront Pkwy.
Wichita, KS 67278 (316) 264-1099 ext. 114
Contact: Nancy Wiebe, Exec. Dir.
FAX: (316) 462-3393;
E-mail: nwiebe@deltadentalks.com; Additional contact: Tammy Penrow, Fdn. Asst., tel.: (913) 327-3728, e-mail: tpenrow@deltadentalks.com; Main URL: http://www.deltadentalksfoundation.org
Facebook: http://www.facebook.com/DeltaDentalKSFoundation

Established in 2004 in KS.
Donor: Delta Dental Plan of Kansas, Inc.
Foundation type: Company-sponsored foundation.
Financial data (yr. ended 12/31/12): Assets, $2,680,515 (M); gifts received, $1,244,692; expenditures, $754,845; qualifying distributions, $743,868; giving activities include $618,288 for 98 grants (high: $83,004; low: $21).
Purpose and activities: The foundation supports programs designed to increase access to dental care by underserved populations; build the capacity to provide dental care; increase public awareness of oral health; and promote the prevention of oral disease. Special emphasis is directed toward programs that emphasize prevention; have significant and/or large impact; and are sustainable solutions.
Fields of interest: Dental school/education; Health care, clinics/centers; Dental care; Employment, training; Children; Aging; Economically disadvantaged.
Type of support: Building/renovation; Equipment; Program development; Seed money; Scholarship funds; Program evaluation; Employee matching gifts; Donated products.
Limitations: Applications accepted. Giving limited to areas of company operations in KS. No support for political, lobbying, or religious organizations. No grants or dental treatment funds for individuals, or for administrative costs, salaries, fundraising events, ongoing programs, general operating expenses, or existing deficits.
Publications: Application guidelines; Annual report; Annual report (including application guidelines); Grants list.
Application information: Faxed or e-mailed applications are not accepted. Additional information may be requested at a later date. Organizations receiving support are asked to provide periodic reports. Application form required.
Initial approach: Download application form and mail proposal and application form to foundation for Community Dental Health Grants and Toothbrush Kit Program
Copies of proposal: 10
Deadline(s): May 1 for Community Dental Health Grants; Aug. 27 for Toothbrush Kit Program
Board meeting date(s): Apr. to Dec.
Final notification: June for Community Dental Health Grants
Officers and Directors:* Lucynda Raben, Chair.; Jill Quigley, Vice-Chair.; Greg Peppes, Secy.; Nancy Wiebe, Exec. Dir.; Barbara Bollier; Michael Herbert; Brick Scheer; R. Wayne Thompson; Bruce Witt.
Number of staff: 1 full-time professional; 1 part-time professional.
EIN: 680554527

3508
The Deramus Foundation Inc. ✧
(formerly Southern Foundation, Inc.)
9401 Indian Creek Pkwy., Ste. 700
Overland Park, KS 66210-2005 (816) 292-8152
Contact: David N. Zimmerman

Established in 1966 in MO.
Foundation type: Independent foundation.
Financial data (yr. ended 12/31/13): Assets, $17,037,298 (M); expenditures, $1,075,830; qualifying distributions, $1,065,259; giving activities include $1,058,300 for 42 grants (high: $125,000; low: $1,000).
Fields of interest: Higher education; Education; Health organizations, association; Human services.
Limitations: Applications accepted. Giving primarily in MO, with emphasis on Kansas City. No grants to individuals.
Application information: Application form required.
Initial approach: Letter
Deadline(s): None
Officers and Directors:* William N. Deramus IV,* Pres. and Secy.; Patricia D. Bunch,* V.P. and Treas.; Jill D. Dean,* V.P.; Jean D. Wagner,* V.P.
EIN: 436066776

3509
Douglas County Community Foundation ✧
900 Massachusetts St., Ste. 406
Lawrence, KS 66044-2868 (785) 843-8727
Contact: Chip Blaser, Exec. Dir.; For grants: Marilyn Hull, Prog. Off.
FAX: (785) 843-8735;
E-mail: dccfoundation@sbcglobal.net; Additional tel.: (785) 843-8735; Grant proposal e-mail: marilynhull@dccfoundation.org; Main URL: http://www.dccfoundation.org
Facebook: https://www.facebook.com/pages/Douglas-County-Community-Foundation/236784366389403
Twitter: http://twitter.com/DCCFoundation

Established in 2000 in KS.
Foundation type: Community foundation.
Financial data (yr. ended 12/31/13): Assets, $33,001,758 (M); gifts received, $10,245,923; expenditures, $2,167,769; giving activities include $1,826,536 for 57+ grants (high: $1,283,981), and $8,000 for 8 grants to individuals.
Purpose and activities: The foundation connects the diverse citizens and communities of Douglas County, KS through charitable action. Their mission is to enrich the quality of life by: 1) building philanthropic resources and relationships; 2) providing attractive options for donors to make philanthropist contributions; and 3) being a catalyst for the betterment of the lives of the citizens of Douglas County.
Fields of interest: Arts; Education; Environment; Health care; Housing/shelter; Children/youth, services; Youth, services; Human services; Community/economic development; United Ways and Federated Giving Programs; Children/youth.
Type of support: Management development/capacity building; Building/renovation; Equipment; Emergency funds; Program development; Publication; Curriculum development; Program evaluation; Scholarships—to individuals; Matching/challenge support.
Limitations: Applications accepted. Giving primarily in Douglas County, KS. No support for religious purposes. No grants to individuals (except for scholarships), or for administrative or general operating expenses, tickets, marketing plans or projects, annual campaigns, endowment funds, or debt retirement.
Publications: Application guidelines; Annual report; Annual report (including application guidelines); Grants list.
Application information: Visit foundation web site for application form and guidelines. Faxed applications are not considered. Application form required.
Initial approach: Submit application form and attachments
Copies of proposal: 12
Deadline(s): Jan. 29
Board meeting date(s): 9 to 12 times per year
Final notification: Early Apr.
Officers and Directors:* Web Golden,* Chair.; John Elmore,* Vice-Chair.; Chip Blaser, Exec. Dir.; Harry Gibson; Pat Long; Mike McGrew; Vickie Randel; Reggie Robinson; Dan Sabatini; Dolph Simons, Jr.; Evan Williams.
Number of staff: 2 part-time professional.
EIN: 481209687

3510
Barry L. & Paula M. Downing Foundation ✧
1625 N. Waterfront Pkwy., Ste. 100
Wichita, KS 67206-6622 (316) 260-3353
FAX: (316) 260-3356; Main URL: http://www.downingfoundation.org

Established in 1993 in KS.
Donors: Barry L. Downing; Elizabeth Koch; Bill Hanna; Janice Hanna; Dan Carney; Gayla Carney; Paul Jackson; Lisa Jackson; Cargill Meat Solutions Corp.; INTRUST Bank, N.A.; AT&T; Koch Industries.
Foundation type: Independent foundation.
Financial data (yr. ended 12/31/13): Assets, $5,738,064 (M); gifts received, $1,500,000; expenditures, $1,735,837; qualifying distributions, $1,380,753; giving activities include $1,380,753 for 30 grants (high: $500,000; low: $300).
Purpose and activities: The foundation supports initiatives that impact the quality of life for a community or for a significant number of members of a community on a lasting basis, focusing specifically on projects that lead to self-sufficiency and future success. The foundation favors projects involving the arts, children's causes, community development and enrichment, early education, and service to the underprivileged.
Fields of interest: Arts, multipurpose centers/programs; Museums (art); Higher education; Education; Animal welfare; Zoos/zoological societies; Human services; Children/youth, services.
Limitations: Giving primarily in Wichita, KS. No support for government, political, legislative, or lobbying entities, specific physical, medical or psychological conditions, social or fraternal organizations, or for-profit organizations. No grants to individuals, or for medical research.
Publications: Application guidelines.
Application information: Application guidelines and forms available on foundation web site. Application form required.
Initial approach: Submit Letter of Inquiry through foundation web site
Deadline(s): Mar. 31, June 30, Sept. 30, and Dec. 31
Trustees: Barry L. Downing; Paula M. Downing; Lisa Jackson.
EIN: 481134459
Selected grants: The following grants are a representative sample of this grantmaker's funding activity:
$1,000 to Loma Linda University Medical Center, Loma Linda, CA, 2012. For contribution to operations/research.
$1,000 to Special Olympics Kansas, Wichita, KS, 2012. For contribution to operations.

3511
Leo J. & Albina Dreiling Charitable Trust ✧ ☆
1008 Cody Ave.
P.O. Box 550
Hays, KS 67601-2431 (785) 625-8327
Contact: Joseph A. Hess, Tr.

Established in 1980 in KS.
Donors: Leo J. Dreiling‡; Anita Feltes.
Foundation type: Independent foundation.
Financial data (yr. ended 09/30/13): Assets, $8,978,710 (M); expenditures, $513,040; qualifying distributions, $455,000; giving activities include $455,000 for 9 grants (high: $200,000; low: $5,000).
Fields of interest: Secondary school/education; Education; Cancer.
Type of support: General/operating support; Building/renovation; Scholarship funds.
Limitations: Applications accepted. Giving primarily in Ellis County, KS, area. No grants to individuals.
Application information: Application form required.
Initial approach: Letter
Deadline(s): None
Trustees: Dennis L. Bieker; Joseph A. Hess.
EIN: 480916752
Selected grants: The following grants are a representative sample of this grantmaker's funding activity:
$50,000 to Hays Medical Center Foundation, Hays, KS, 2011.
$10,000 to Hays Arts Council, Hays, KS, 2011.

3512
The Dreiseszun Family Foundation ✧
c/o Debbie Pate
P.O. Box 12545
Overland Park, KS 66282-2545

Established in 1985 in MO.
Donors: Richard Dreiseszun; Sherman Dreiseszun; Irene Dreiseszun; Richard J. Dreiseszun Grantor Trust.
Foundation type: Independent foundation.
Financial data (yr. ended 11/30/13): Assets, $52,826,107 (M); gifts received, $92,163; expenditures, $2,789,211; qualifying distributions, $2,575,655; giving activities include $2,575,655 for 60 grants (high: $375,000; low: $250).
Fields of interest: Arts; Education; Hospitals (general); Hospitals (specialty); Health organizations, association; Medical research, association; Human services; Children/youth, services; Jewish federated giving programs; Jewish agencies & synagogues.
Limitations: Giving primarily in KS and MO. No grants to individuals.
Application information: Application form not required.
Initial approach: Letter
Deadline(s): None
Trustees: Helene Abrahams; Irene Dreiseszun; Erica Fisher; Brooke Levy.
EIN: 481021776
Selected grants: The following grants are a representative sample of this grantmaker's funding activity:
$353,010 to National Philanthropic Trust, Jenkintown, PA, 2011.
$350,000 to Village Shalom, Overland Park, KS, 2011.
$268,509 to Kehilath Israel Synagogue, Overland Park, KS, 2011.
$105,000 to Jewish Federation of Greater Kansas City, Overland Park, KS, 2011.
$100,000 to Torah Learning Center, Overland Park, KS, 2011.
$16,000 to Jewish Family Services, Overland Park, KS, 2011.
$15,000 to Caring for Kids, Clayton, MO, 2011.
$5,000 to Make-A-Wish Foundation, Washington, DC, 2011.
$2,500 to Temple Sinai, Denver, CO, 2011.

3513
John & Ruth Elliott Foundation, Inc. ✧
5400 W. 100 St.
Overland Park, KS 66207

Established in KS.
Donor: John A. Elliott.
Foundation type: Independent foundation.
Financial data (yr. ended 12/31/12): Assets, $0 (M); gifts received, $200,000; expenditures, $429,536; qualifying distributions, $428,610; giving activities include $428,610 for 35 grants (high: $135,250; low: $50).
Fields of interest: Youth development; Human services; Philanthropy/voluntarism.
Limitations: Applications accepted. Giving primarily in KS. No grants to individuals.
Application information: Unsolicited requests for funds not accepted. Application form not required.
Officers: Karen E. Tierney, Pres.; Roger D. Elliott, Secy.; J. Nelson Elliott, Treas.
EIN: 486143360
Selected grants: The following grants are a representative sample of this grantmaker's funding activity:
$500 to Andover Advantage Foundation, Andover, KS, 2012. To improve public education.
$250 to Trash Mountain Project, Topeka, KS, 2012. To assist youth and families.
$200 to American Red Cross, Wichita, KS, 2012. For charitable efforts.
$100 to Union Rescue Mission, Wichita, KS, 2012. To assist homeless and poor.
$50 to Youth Horizons, Wichita, KS, 2012. For serving at risk youth.

3514
Emporia Community Foundation ✧
527 Commercial St., Ste. 501
Emporia, KS 66801 (620) 342-9304
E-mail: emporiacf@emporiacf.org; Main URL: http://emporiacf.org/
Facebook: https://www.facebook.com/emporiacommunityfoundation?fref=ts

Established in 1996 in KS.
Foundation type: Community foundation.
Financial data (yr. ended 12/31/12): Assets, $11,981,273 (M); gifts received, $1,879,459; expenditures, $2,642,851; giving activities include $2,328,825 for grants to individuals.
Purpose and activities: The mission of the foundation is to improve the quality of life in the Emporia area, consisting of Lyon County and those six counties that are contiguous to Lyon County: Chase, Morris, Coffey, Greenwood, Osage and Wabaunsee counties.
Fields of interest: Arts; Education; Health care; Recreation; Human services; Children/youth; Blind/visually impaired; Deaf/hearing impaired.
Limitations: Applications accepted. Giving primarily in Chase, Morris, Coffey, Greenwood, Lyon, Osage and Wabaunsee counties. No grants for operational expenses.
Publications: Application guidelines; Annual report.
Application information: Application form required.
Copies of proposal: 9
Deadline(s): Feb. 15
Final notification: Approx. 45 days
Officers and Trustees:* Mark Schreiber,* Chair.; Cynthia Kraft,* Vice-Chair.; Shirley M. Antes,* Exec. Dir. and C.O.O.; Bill Barnes; Tom Bell; Ken Buchele; Jeff DeBauge; Skip Evans; Eddie Gilpin; D.J. Glaser;

Jim Kessler; Mary Kretsinger; Dr. Thomas Kriss; Kay Lauer; Janis Meyer; Larry Putnam; Sally Sanchez; Bob Symmonds; Jennell Tebbetts; Nancy Thomas; Bobby Thompson.
Officers and Directors:* Ken Buchele, Pres.; Mark Schreiber,* V.P.; Jeff DeBauge,* Treas.; Ken Calhoun, Emeritus; Elvin Perkins, Emeritus; Cynthia Kraft; Kay Lauer; Bob Symmonds.
EIN: 481169158

3515
R. E. French Family Educational Foundation ✧

P.O. Box 203
Gridley, KS 66852-0203

Established in KS.
Donor: Members of the R.E. French family.
Foundation type: Independent foundation.
Financial data (yr. ended 06/30/13): Assets, $11,437,233 (M); gifts received, $500; expenditures, $619,424; qualifying distributions, $430,591; giving activities include $430,591 for grants.
Purpose and activities: The foundation provides scholarships to graduates of Kansas high schools, who have demonstrated the desire to attend a college or university, or who seek vocational training in an accredited vocational training institution. The foundation also awards grants to Kansas schools, libraries, and other educational institutions to provide or improve facilities, equipment, or books.
Fields of interest: Education.
Type of support: Equipment; Scholarships—to individuals.
Limitations: Applications accepted. Giving limited to KS.
Application information: Completion of application form required for scholarships. Application form required.
Initial approach: E-mail
Deadline(s): None
Trustees: Gregory L. Arnold; Sarah K. Grimm; Joann Osborn; Max V. Snodgrass.
EIN: 480926521

3516
Jean and Willard Garvey Fund ✧

c/o Heritage Group LC
7309 E. 21st St. N., Ste. 120
Wichita, KS 67206-1178

Established in 1989 in KS.
Donors: Jean K. Garvey; Willard W. Garvey; Willard W. Garvey Charitable Trust No. 1; Willard W. Garvey Charitable Trust No. 2; Garvey, Inc.; Jean K. Garvey Revocable Trust; Willard W. Garvey Revocable Trust.
Foundation type: Independent foundation.
Financial data (yr. ended 12/31/13): Assets, $429,384 (M); gifts received, $900,000; expenditures, $871,405; qualifying distributions, $868,979; giving activities include $862,843 for 7 grants (high: $250,000; low: $52,779).
Fields of interest: Performing arts; Arts; Higher education; Education; Human services; Salvation Army; Community development, neighborhood development.
Type of support: General/operating support; Building/renovation; Endowments; Scholarship funds.
Limitations: Applications not accepted. Giving in the U.S., with emphasis on Wichita, KS, as well as CA and MA. No grants to individuals.
Application information: Contributes only to pre-selected organizations.
Trustees: James W. Garvey; Julie R.G. Sheppard.
EIN: 481068307
Selected grants: The following grants are a representative sample of this grantmaker's funding activity:
$1,600 to Cedars Camps, Manchester, MO, 2012. For operating fund for religious organization.
$1,000 to Wichita Art Museum, Wichita, KS, 2012. For operating fund for community funds.
$100 to United States Olympic Committee, Colorado Springs, CO, 2012. For operating fund for other public charity.

3517
HANDinHAND Christian Adoption, Inc. ✧ ☆

18318 Mimosa Ct.
Gardner, KS 66030-8802 (913) 248-5015
E-mail: handinhandadopt@gmail.com; Main URL: http://www.handinhandadopt.org/

Established in 2007 in KS.
Donors: Doug Evans; Bruce Pearson; Charles Way; Daniel Gunn; DKS Foundation; Evangelical Free Church of Mankato; Giving Hope Worldwide Foundation; Jeremy Zebroski; Kirsten Carter; Lifesong for Orphan; Mark Dunn; Praise Assembly; The Bench Online, LLC.
Foundation type: Operating foundation.
Financial data (yr. ended 12/31/13): Assets, $279,338 (M); gifts received, $869,354; expenditures, $857,334; qualifying distributions, $820,470; giving activities include $820,470 for 203 grants (high: $11,975; low: $9).
Purpose and activities: The organization's mission is to help children become part of "forever" families by using God-given resources to financially help those who have been called to adopt.
Fields of interest: Children/youth, services; Children, adoption.
Type of support: Grants to individuals; Matching/challenge support.
Application information: Application form and guidelines available on foundation web site. Application form required.
Initial approach: Letter or telephone
Deadline(s): None
Officers and Directors:* Trudy George,* Pres.; Doug Evans,* V.P.
EIN: 260851443
Selected grants: The following grants are a representative sample of this grantmaker's funding activity:
$4,660 to Christian Services of Oklahoma, Edmond, OK, 2012. For adoption expense.
$1,150 to Lutheran Social Service of the South, Austin, TX, 2012. For adoption expense.

3518
Dane G. Hansen Foundation ✧

P.O. Box 187
Logan, KS 67646-0187 (785) 689-4832
Contact: Don Stahr, Tr.
FAX: (785) 689-4833; Main URL: http://www.danehansenfoundation.org

Incorporated in 1965 in KS.
Donors: Dane G. Hansen†; Dane G. Hansen Trust.
Foundation type: Independent foundation.
Financial data (yr. ended 09/30/13): Assets, $161,755,823 (M); gifts received, $380,857; expenditures, $7,067,413; qualifying distributions, $6,211,097; giving activities include $5,527,436 for 132 grants (high: $500,398; low: $333).
Purpose and activities: Grants largely for higher education, including undergraduate, graduate, theological, and vocational scholarships to individuals, civic affairs and public interest groups, youth agencies, services for the handicapped, and hospitals.
Fields of interest: Vocational education; Higher education; Hospitals (general); Youth, services; Public policy, research; Government/public administration; Disabilities, people with.
Type of support: General/operating support; Continuing support; Building/renovation; Equipment; Publication; Scholarship funds; Scholarships—to individuals.
Limitations: Giving primarily in Logan, Phillips County, and northwestern KS; scholarships limited to residents of 26 northwestern KS counties, which include: Cheyenne, Cloud, Decatur, Ellis, Ellsworth, Gove, Graham, Jewell, Lincoln, Logan, Mitchell, Norton, Osborne, Ottawa, Phillips, Rawlins, Republic, Rooks, Russell, Saline, Sheridan, Sherman, Smith, Thomas, Trego and Wallace.
Application information: Scholarship application information and form available on foundation web site. Application form required.
Deadline(s): See web site for latest deadlines
Board meeting date(s): Monthly
Final notification: Within 2 weeks for grants to organizations; 30 days after graduation for scholarships
Officers and Trustees:* Doyle D. Rahjes,* Pres.; F. Doyle Fair,* V.P.; Robert Hartman,* Secy.-Treas.; Douglas M. Albin; Carol Bales; Charles I. Moyer; Gary Poore; Don Stahr.
Number of staff: 7 full-time support.
EIN: 486121156

3519
Hartley Family Foundation ✧

2112 Tomahawak Rd.
Mission Hills, KS 66208-1949 (913) 236-8473
Contact: Laura H. Lintecum, Pres.

Established in 1997 in KS.
Donor: W.C. Hartley.
Foundation type: Independent foundation.
Financial data (yr. ended 12/31/13): Assets, $6,658,766 (M); expenditures, $652,654; qualifying distributions, $471,807; giving activities include $456,080 for 68 grants (high: $75,000; low: $50).
Fields of interest: Arts; Higher education; Human services; Protestant agencies & churches.
Limitations: Giving primarily in KS. No grants to individuals.
Application information: Application form not required.
Initial approach: Proposal
Deadline(s): None
Officers: Patricia Hartley, Chair.; Laura H. Lintecum, Pres.; Elizabeth H. Winetroub, V.P.
Board Member: Ann H. Bush.
EIN: 742822359

Selected grants: The following grants are a representative sample of this grantmaker's funding activity:
$115,000 to Kansas University Endowment Association, Lawrence, KS, 2011.
$25,000 to Kauffman Center for the Performing Arts, Kansas City, MO, 2011.
$25,000 to Saint Lukes Hospital Foundation, Kansas City, MO, 2011.
$20,000 to Saint Andrews Episcopal Church, Kansas City, MO, 2011.
$10,000 to Family Conservancy, Kansas City, KS, 2011.
$10,000 to Village Presbyterian Church, Prairie Village, KS, 2011.
$5,000 to Angel Flight Central, Kansas City, MO, 2011.
$5,000 to Lakemary Center, Paola, KS, 2011.
$5,000 to Liberty Memorial Association, Kansas City, MO, 2011.
$5,000 to Operation Breakthrough, Kansas City, MO, 2011.

3520
Horejsi Charitable Foundation, Inc. ✧
2121 E. Crawford Pl.
Salina, KS 67401-3719

Established in 1998 in KS.
Donors: Stewart Horejsi; Horejsi, Inc.
Foundation type: Independent foundation.
Financial data (yr. ended 12/31/13): Assets, $23,614,651 (M); expenditures, $1,015,286; qualifying distributions, $922,032; giving activities include $921,231 for 49 grants (high: $475,000; low: $500).
Fields of interest: Higher education; Education; Health care.
Limitations: Applications not accepted. Giving primarily in AZ and KS. No grants to individuals.
Application information: Unsolicited requests for funds not accepted.
Officers and Directors:* Stewart Horejsi,* Pres.; Laura Rhodenbaugh, V.P. and Secy.-Treas.; Stephen Miller, V.P.; Susan Ciciora; John Horejsi.
EIN: 460447536
Selected grants: The following grants are a representative sample of this grantmaker's funding activity:
$100,000 to Grand Canyon Association, Grand Canyon, AZ, 2012. For Trail Project.
$100,000 to Scottsdale Healthcare Foundation, Scottsdale, AZ, 2012. For grant for Heart and Vascular Program.
$10,000 to University of Colorado Foundation, Boulder, CO, 2012. For music department.
$5,000 to Emory University, Atlanta, GA, 2012. For Brooker Fund for Eye Education.
$5,000 to Missoula Art Museum, Missoula, MT, 2012. For Gift - General Fund.
$2,500 to Big Brothers Big Sisters of Metropolitan Chicago, Chicago, IL, 2012. For child development programs.
$2,400 to Aurora University, Aurora, IL, 2012. For music education.

3521
Hutchinson Community Foundation ✧
1 N. Main St., Ste. 501
P.O. Box 298
Hutchinson, KS 67504-0298 (620) 663-5293
Contact: Aubrey Abbott Patterson, Pres.; For grants: Eileen Yamauchi, Donor Svcs. Assoc.
FAX: (620) 663-9277; E-mail: info@hutchcf.org; Grant inquiry e-mail: eileen@hutchcf.org; Main URL: http://www.hutchcf.org
Facebook: https://www.facebook.com/Hutchcf
Twitter: http://twitter.com/hutchcf

Established in 1989 in KS.
Foundation type: Community foundation.
Financial data (yr. ended 12/31/13): Assets, $47,630,280 (M); gifts received, $9,553,493; expenditures, $3,859,376; giving activities include $2,590,562 for 58+ grants (high: $134,200).
Purpose and activities: The foundation connects donors to community needs and opportunities, increases philanthropy and provides community leadership. Giving primarily for arts, education, health care, mental health/crisis services, health associations, housing/shelter development, human services, children and youth services, hospices, aging centers and services, civil rights, community development, voluntarism promotion, federated giving programs, disabled, aging, economically disadvantaged, and general charitable giving.
Fields of interest: Visual arts; Performing arts; Performing arts, theater; Arts; Education, early childhood education; Higher education; Education; Health care; Substance abuse, services; Mental health/crisis services; Health organizations, association; Housing/shelter, development; Youth development; Children/youth, services; Child development, services; Residential/custodial care, hospices; Aging, centers/services; Human services; Civil/human rights; Economic development; Community/economic development; Voluntarism promotion; United Ways and Federated Giving Programs; Aging; Disabilities, people with; Men; Economically disadvantaged.
Type of support: Scholarships—to individuals; General/operating support; Continuing support; Annual campaigns; Capital campaigns; Equipment; Endowments; Debt reduction; Program development; Conferences/seminars; Seed money; Curriculum development; Scholarship funds; Technical assistance; Matching/challenge support.
Limitations: Applications accepted. Giving primarily in Reno County, KS. No grants to individuals (except for scholarships).
Publications: Application guidelines; Annual report; Financial statement; Grants list; Informational brochure; Newsletter; Occasional report; Program policy statement.
Application information: Visit foundation web site for application form and guidelines. Application form required.
Initial approach: Submit application
Copies of proposal: 13
Deadline(s): Aug. 1
Board meeting date(s): Quarterly
Final notification: Nov. 14
Officers and Directors:* Marilyn Bolton,* Chair.; Aubrey Abbott Patterson,* Pres. and Exec. Dir.; Terri L. Eisiminger,* V.P., Admin. and Secy.; Paul W. Dillon,* Co-Treas.; Kenneth E. Vogel,* Co-Treas.; Chelsea Barker; Susan Buttram; Ryan Diehl; David Dick; Dan Garber; Wendy C. Hobart; Kory Jackson; John D. Montgomery; Richard Russell; Bill Southern; Dell Marie Shanahan Swearer; Mark Trotman.
Number of staff: 4 full-time professional; 1 part-time support.
EIN: 481076910

3522
INTRUST Bank Charitable Trust ✧ ☆
(formerly First National Bank in Wichita Charitable Trust)
c/o INTRUST Bank, N.A.
P.O. Box 1
105 North Main
Wichita, KS 67201-5001 (316) 383-1489
Contact: Diane Iseman, V.P., Corp. Comms.
FAX: (316) 383-5801;
E-mail: Diane.Iseman@intrustbank.com; Main URL: https://www.intrustbank.com/about/community-commitment.aspx

Established in 1952 in KS.
Donor: INTRUST Bank, N.A.
Foundation type: Company-sponsored foundation.
Financial data (yr. ended 12/31/13): Assets, $835,294 (M); gifts received, $420,000; expenditures, $483,623; qualifying distributions, $483,286; giving activities include $482,948 for 28 grants (high: $230,184; low: $360).
Purpose and activities: The foundation supports organizations involved with arts and culture, higher education, and human services.
Fields of interest: Arts; Higher education; Children/youth, services; Human services; United Ways and Federated Giving Programs.
Type of support: Continuing support; Capital campaigns; General/operating support; Building/renovation.
Limitations: Applications accepted. Giving limited to KS, with emphasis on Wichita.
Publications: Application guidelines.
Application information: Application form not required.
Initial approach: Proposal
Copies of proposal: 1
Deadline(s): None
Final notification: 6 weeks
Trustees: Jill Beckman; Charles Q. Chandler IV; J.V. Lentell; Rodney D. Pitts; Susan Sullivan; Lyndon Wells.
EIN: 486102412

3523
Walter S. and Evan C. Jones Foundation ✧
(also known as Jones Foundation, Inc.)
2501 W. 18th Ave., Ste. D
Emporia, KS 66801-6195 (620) 342-1714
Contact: Sharon L. Tidwell, Exec. Dir.
FAX: (620) 342-4701; E-mail: dir@jonesfdn.org; Main URL: http://www.jonesfdn.org

Established in 1974 in KS.
Donor: Walter S. and Evan C. Jones Trust.
Foundation type: Independent foundation.
Financial data (yr. ended 06/30/13): Assets, $30,191 (M); gifts received, $2,282,500; expenditures, $2,253,951; qualifying distributions, $2,089,761; giving activities include $2,076,361 for grants.
Purpose and activities: Grants awarded are limited to educational and medical expenses of children of 3 specified counties who have resided there continuously for a minimum of 1 year.

Fields of interest: Education; Health care; Children/youth, services; Economically disadvantaged.
Type of support: Grants to individuals; Scholarships—to individuals.
Limitations: Applications accepted. Giving limited to children who have resided continuously for a minimum of one year in Osage, Coffey, or Lyon counties, KS. No support for non U.S. citizens.
Publications: Informational brochure; Program policy statement.
Application information: Applicants must contact office prior to submitting an application. Must be under 21 for medical grants. Medical services must be pre-approved generally, except in emergency cases. Individuals who move to Coffey, Lyon or Osage County and attend a post-secondary institution prior to fulfilling the residency requirement are not eligible for medical or educational assistance. Copy of current federal income tax return (both personal and business, if applicable), a minimum of 1 month's pay stubs, proof of all other income, and a copy of insurance card (if applicable) are required with application. Application form required.
Initial approach: Telephone
Deadline(s): None
Board meeting date(s): Monthly
Final notification: 1-2 months
Officers: Tom Thomas, Pres.; Jeff Larson, V.P.; Max Stewart, Jr., Secy.; Megan A. Evans, Treas.; Sharon L. Tidwell, Exec. Dir.
Trustees: Greg Bachman; Jeff Longbine; Cheryl Mussato.
Number of staff: 1 full-time professional; 1 full-time support; 1 part-time support.
EIN: 237384087

3524
Kansas Health Foundation ✧
(formerly Kansas Health Foundation/Kansas Health Trust)
309 E. Douglas
Wichita, KS 67202-3405
Contact: Valerie Black, Information Technoloy Specialist; Chris Power, V.P., Comms.
FAX: (316) 262-2044; E-mail: info@khf.org; Additional tel.: (800) 373-7681; E-mail for Valerie Black: vblack@khf.org; Main URL: http://www.kansashealth.org
Blog: http://www.kansashealth.org/blog
E-Newsletter: http://www.kansashealth.org/publications/happenings
Facebook: http://www.facebook.com/pages/Kansas-Health-Foundation/131838311319
Grants Database: http://www.kansashealth.org/grantmaking/grants
Twitter: https://twitter.com/kansashealthorg

Established in 1978 in KS as the Wesley Medical Endowment Foundation; converted from funds resulting from the sale of Wesley Medical Center to HCA in 1985; current name adopted in 1991.
Foundation type: Independent foundation.
Financial data (yr. ended 12/31/13): Assets, $526,124,315 (M); expenditures, $19,614,737; qualifying distributions, $24,589,164; giving activities include $12,058,318 for 212 grants (high: $547,932; low: $1,272), and $934,770 for 4 foundation-administered programs.
Purpose and activities: The foundation is driven by a mission to improve the health of all Kansans. The foundation joins with the World Health Organization in defining health, believing that health is a state of complete physical, mental and social well-being and not merely the absence of disease or infirmity.
Fields of interest: Public health; Children/youth, services; Leadership development; Children/youth; Adults.
Type of support: General/operating support; Continuing support; Management development/capacity building; Program development; Technical assistance; Program evaluation; Matching/challenge support.
Limitations: Applications accepted. Giving limited to KS. No support for political campaigns or political advocacy. No grants to individuals, or for medical research, deficit or debt retirement, endowments not initiated by the foundation, vehicles, construction projects, mental health or for direct medical services.
Publications: Application guidelines; Annual report (including application guidelines); Grants list; Informational brochure; Newsletter; Occasional report.
Application information: Application forms required for Recognition Grants. Forms are available on foundation web site. Application form required.
Initial approach: Application through Recognition Grant program form on web site
Deadline(s): Mar. 15 and Sept. 15 for Recognition Grants
Board meeting date(s): Quarterly
Final notification: 60 days for Recognition Grants
Officers and Directors:* Shelly Buhler,* Chair.; Steve Coen,* C.E.O. and Pres.; Evan Meyers, V.P. and C.F.O.; Christopher Power, V.P., Admin.; Blythe Thomas, V.P., Comms.; Jeffrey Willett, V.P., Progs.; Matt Allen; Claudia Bakely; Mollie H. Carter; Junetta Everett; Jeffrey L. Jack; Michael Lennen; Donna Shank; Andy Tompkins.
Number of staff: 12 full-time professional; 8 full-time support; 2 part-time support.
EIN: 480873431
Selected grants: The following grants are a representative sample of this grantmaker's funding activity:
$1,500,000 to Kansas University Endowment Association, Lawrence, KS, 2012. To contribute funds toward endowment for the development of the School of Public Health, payable over 3.00 years.
$718,000 to Kansas Association of the Medically Underserved, Topeka, KS, 2012. For funding opportunities for all safety net clinics to build capacity at the administrative level, and to provide technical assistance to clinics in addressing the three clinical preventive measures in which Kansas clinics were ranked very low, and to assist FQHC's in the implementation of new Health and Human Services Uniform Data System (UDS) performance measures, payable over 3.00 years.
$472,084 to Hutchinson Community Foundation, Hutchinson, KS, 2012. To fund the Kansas Association of Community Foundations to provide training to the Kansas community foundation field that will help support the goals and objectives of GROW II and provide technical assistance to the foundations participating in the GROW II endowment building program to ensure their success, payable over 5.00 years.
$400,000 to National Recreation and Park Association, Ashburn, VA, 2012. To provide grants to five Kansas communities to implement the NRPA's Serving Kansas Communities Initiative which includes the following components: Provides financial resources to park and recreation agencies that allow them to serve more children healthy meals by funding summer food service program staff, community outreach, transportation for kids, refrigerators and heating units and other basic needs for their summer feeding program. Offer children through these park and recreation agencies nutritional education with behavior change outcomes to create lifelong healthy habits. Provides funding to expand or create community gardens at these sites as a means of connecting children to nature, gardening, fresh food, and nutritional education through community-based edible garden programs.
$308,000 to Kansas Department of Health and Environment, Topeka, KS, 2012. For funding to the KDHE Bureau of Health Promotion to conduct the Kansas Adult Tobacco Survey.
$40,000 to Council on Foundations, Arlington, VA, 2012. For annual membership.
$25,000 to Dental Lifeline Network, Denver, CO, 2012. To link eligible applicants-generally elderly and disabled individuals who can't afford dental treatment-with volunteer dental professionals who provide the patients with needed dental services.
$25,000 to Menorah Legacy Foundation, Kansas City, MO, 2012. To help reduce the risk of chronic disease and increase access to healthy foods for residents of Wyandotte and Johnson Counties through the Kansas City Beans and Greens Program.
$25,000 to Pittsburg State University, Pittsburg, KS, 2012. For the formation of a campus wide task force for the purpose of moving the campus to a tobacco-free environment, payable over 1.75 years.

3525
Kao Family Foundation ✧
1200 E. 151st St.
Olathe, KS 66062-3426

Established in 2004 in KS.
Donor: Min-Hwan Kao.
Foundation type: Independent foundation.
Financial data (yr. ended 12/31/13): Assets, $16,980,309 (M); expenditures, $911,510; qualifying distributions, $870,000; giving activities include $870,000 for 18 grants (high: $148,600; low: $200).
Fields of interest: Performing arts, orchestras; Higher education, university; United Ways and Federated Giving Programs.
Limitations: Applications not accepted. Giving primarily in KS and MO. No grants to individuals.
Application information: Contributes only to pre-selected organizations.
Officers and Directors:* Min-Hwan Kao,* Pres.; Kenneth Kao,* V.P. and Secy.; Yu-Fan C. Kao,* Treas.; Jennifer Kao.
EIN: 202014620

3526
Kelly Family Foundation ✧
10393 S. Highland Cir.
Olathe, KS 66061-8441 (913) 764-6495
Contact: Bonnie Kelly, Tr.

Donors: Bonnie Kelly; Gerald Kelly; Gerald A. Kelly, Jr.
Foundation type: Independent foundation.
Financial data (yr. ended 12/31/13): Assets, $31,979,884 (M); expenditures, $1,796,247; qualifying distributions, $1,653,510; giving activities include $1,653,510 for 45 grants (high: $375,000; low: $200).

Fields of interest: Education; Health care; Cancer; Human services.
Limitations: Applications accepted. Giving primarily in DC, KS, and MO.
Application information: Application form not required.
Initial approach: Proposal
Deadline(s): None
Trustees: Ryane Delka; Bonnie Kelly; Gerald A. Kelly, Jr.
EIN: 276825262

3527
Kirk Foundation ✧
(formerly Kirk Family Charitable Trust)
6125 Reinhardt Dr.
Fairway, KS 66205-3336 (816) 292-8136
Contact: Michael C. Kirk, Tr.

Established in 1986 in KS.
Donors: Andrew M. Kirk; David Kirk; Frank Kirk; James C. Kirk; James Philip Kirk, Sr.; Kristin Kirk; Natalie Kirk; Melinda Sanders; Michael Kirk.
Foundation type: Independent foundation.
Financial data (yr. ended 12/31/13): Assets, $16,199,218 (M); expenditures, $588,670; qualifying distributions, $515,677; giving activities include $511,500 for 40 grants (high: $134,000; low: $1,000).
Purpose and activities: Giving primarily for the arts, education, health care and research, and a variety of human service organizations.
Fields of interest: Arts; Libraries (public); Education; Health care; Human services; YM/YWCAs & YM/YWHAs.
Limitations: Applications accepted. Giving primarily in the bi-state Kansas City area. No grants to individuals.
Application information: Application form required.
Initial approach: Proposal
Deadline(s): None
Trustees: David Kirk; Frank H. Kirk; Michael C. Kirk.
EIN: 481030766

3528
David H. Koch Charitable Foundation ✧
c/o Kara Washington
4111 E. 37th St., N.
Wichita, KS 67220-3203
Contact: Vonda Holliman, Treas.
E-mail: inquiries@kochfamilyfoundations.org; Additional address: P.O. Box 2256, Wichita, KS 67201-2256; Main URL: http://www.kochfamilyfoundations.org/FoundationsDHK.asp

Established in 1982 in KS.
Donors: David H. Koch; Fred C. Koch Trusts for Charity.
Foundation type: Independent foundation.
Financial data (yr. ended 12/31/12): Assets, $60,567,797 (M); expenditures, $10,504,239; qualifying distributions, $10,502,790; giving activities include $10,500,000 for 2 grants (high: $10,000,000; low: $500,000).
Fields of interest: Arts; Higher education; Hospitals (specialty); Prostate cancer research; Science, formal/general education; Science; Public affairs.
Type of support: Research.
Limitations: Applications not accepted. Giving primarily in Washington, DC and New York, NY. No grants to individuals, for deficit financing, exchange programs, land acquisition, seed money or professorships; no loans.
Application information: Contributes only to pre-selected organizations.
Officers and Director:* David H. Koch,* Pres.; Ruth E. Williams, Secy.; Vonda Holliman, Treas.
EIN: 480926946
Selected grants: The following grants are a representative sample of this grantmaker's funding activity:
$10,000,000 to City Center of Music and Drama, New York, NY, 2012. For renovations to New York State Theatre Building also called the David H. Koch Theater.
$500,000 to New York City Opera, New York, NY, 2012. For general operating support.

3529
The Fred C. and Mary R. Koch Foundation, Inc. ✧
(formerly The Fred C. Koch Foundation)
4111 E. 37th St. N.
Wichita, KS 67220-3203
Contact: Grant Admin.
E-mail: email@fmkfoundation.org; Main URL: http://www.fmkfoundation.org/
Scholarship e-mail: scholarships@fmkfoundation.org

Incorporated in 1953 in KS.
Donors: Fred C. Koch†; Mary R. Koch†; Koch Industries, Inc.
Foundation type: Independent foundation.
Financial data (yr. ended 12/31/12): Assets, $31,775,151 (M); gifts received, $408,000; expenditures, $2,127,153; qualifying distributions, $2,043,000; giving activities include $1,638,000 for 22 grants (high: $626,000; low: $2,500), and $405,000 for 204 grants to individuals (high: $2,000; low: $2,000).
Purpose and activities: Grants for the arts and art education, environmental stewardship, human services, the enablement of at-risk youth, and education in KS. Scholarships are limited to dependents of full-time employees of Koch Industries, Inc. and its subsidiaries.
Fields of interest: Arts; Higher education; Environment; Children/youth, services.
Type of support: General/operating support; Continuing support; Program development; Scholarship funds; Research; Employee-related scholarships.
Limitations: Giving primarily in KS. No support for athletic associations or sports teams, or for political or fraternal organizations. No grants to individuals (except for dependents of Koch Industries employees); or for venture capital grants, fundraising events, trips, tours, endowment funds, or for capital campaigns (unless the organization has received previous grants from the foundation).
Publications: Application guidelines.
Application information: Application required for scholarships. Application form not required.
Initial approach: Letter for grants (3 pages maximum); scholarship applicants should send for guidelines or refer to foundation web site
Copies of proposal: 1
Deadline(s): Submit proposal preferably Oct. 1; Mar. 1 deadline for scholarship
Board meeting date(s): Mar.
Officers and Directors:* Elizabeth B. Koch,* Pres.; Susan Addington, Secy.; Heather Love, Treas.; Richard Fink; Charles G. Koch; David H. Koch.
EIN: 486113560

3530
Harry J. Lloyd Charitable Trust ✧
(formerly Share Foundation)
7200 W. 132nd St., Ste. 190
Overland Park, KS 66213-1136 (913) 851-2174
FAX: (913) 851-4892; E-mail: ltrust@ltrust.org; Main URL: http://www.hjltrust.org/

Established in 1965 in MO.
Donors: House of Lloyd, Inc.; Harry J. Lloyd†.
Foundation type: Independent foundation.
Financial data (yr. ended 12/31/12): Assets, $92,101,581 (M); expenditures, $10,924,121; qualifying distributions, $10,545,415; giving activities include $9,486,685 for 158 grants (high: $200,000; low: $500).
Purpose and activities: The foundation concentrates its support on projects that have a spiritual dimension, with special attention given to evangelical work, especially in the foreign mission field. Interest also in human services and educational organizations that are Christian-based.
Fields of interest: Education; Health care; Cancer; Cancer research; Food services; Christian agencies & churches.
International interests: Africa; China; India; Middle East.
Type of support: Capital campaigns; Equipment; Program development; Seed money; Scholarship funds.
Limitations: Applications accepted. Giving worldwide. No support for the arts, organizations that support or prohibit abortion or abortion rights, or for political organizations.
Publications: Application guidelines.
Application information: The foundation's web site is restricted to information on and applications for melanoma research related grants. Not more than one application per institution in each of the three melanoma grant type categories will be funded. See foundation's web site for complete melanoma research grant application policies, guidelines and forms. Application form required.
Initial approach: Online for melanoma grants. Proposal for Evangelism/General Christian Purposes
Deadline(s): Feb. 1 for melanoma research grants
Board meeting date(s): Quarterly
Final notification: May for melanoma research grants
Officer: Russell Brown, Pres.
Trustees: Don Carson; Dan Doty; G. Richard Hastings; Jami Kay; Demi Lloyd; Jeanette Lloyd; Jane Overstreet.
Number of staff: 6 full-time support.
EIN: 436689416
Selected grants: The following grants are a representative sample of this grantmaker's funding activity:
$385,778 to City Union Mission, Kansas City, MO, 2012. For general support.
$200,000 to Strategic Global Assistance, Elkhart, IN, 2012. For evangelism.
$183,500 to Alpha USA, Bannockburn, IL, 2012. For evangelism.
$180,000 to Redeemer City to City, Medina, WA, 2012. For evangelism.

$150,000 to Care for Children, Evanston, IL, 2012. For general support.
$125,000 to University of Maryland-Baltimore, Baltimore, MD, 2012. For medical research.
$125,000 to University of Southern California, Los Angeles, CA, 2012. For medical research.
$100,000 to Wistar Institute of Anatomy and Biology, Philadelphia, PA, 2012. For medical research.
$50,000 to Disciple Nations Alliance, Phoenix, AZ, 2012. For evangelism.
$28,000 to Viva Network North America, Seattle, WA, 2012. For general support.

3531
Edward G. & Kathryn E. Mader Foundation B ✧

c/o Midwest Trust Co.
5901 College Blvd., Ste. 100
Overland Park, KS 66211-1834
E-mail: Application@MaderFoundation.org; Application address: c/o Midwest Philanthropic & Institutional Services, Overland Park, KS 66211, Attn: Mark J. Drake, V.P., tel.: (913) 319-0317; Main URL: http://www.maderfoundation.org

Established in 2006 in MO.
Donor: Kathryn E. Mader†.
Foundation type: Independent foundation.
Financial data (yr. ended 12/31/12): Assets, $15,085,336 (M); expenditures, $984,476; qualifying distributions, $824,721; giving activities include $812,400 for 28 grants (high: $250,000; low: $5,000).
Purpose and activities: Giving to benefit children in the Greater Kansas City, Missouri, area in the arts, education, as well as for their medical care and welfare.
Fields of interest: Arts; Education; Hospitals (specialty); Health care; Children.
Limitations: Applications accepted. Giving primarily in the greater Kansas City, MO, area.
Publications: Application guidelines.
Application information:
Initial approach: Refer to instructions on foundation web site
Deadline(s): May 1
Committe Members: Melissa D. Mader-Schaefer; David A. Schaefer; Katheryn D. Schaefer.
Trustee: Midwest Trust Co.
EIN: 206728720
Selected grants: The following grants are a representative sample of this grantmaker's funding activity:
$25,000 to Cystic Fibrosis Foundation, Mission, KS, 2012. For Kc Great Strides Walk to Raise Funds to Develop Cf Drugs and Therapy.
$5,400 to Kansas City Symphony, Kansas City, MO, 2012. For youth education and outreach Programs for children to provide access to the arts.
$5,000 to Metropolitan Lutheran Ministry, Kansas City, MO, 2012. To support of Art for Good Program for art day camps for disadvantaged children and youth.
$5,000 to Powell Gardens, Kingsville, MO, 2012. To support of youth education Programs in the Heartland Harvest Garden.

3532
Greater Manhattan Community Foundation ✧

555 Poyntz Avenue, Ste. 269
P.O. Box 1127
Manhattan, KS 66505-1127
E-mail: foundation@mcfks.org; Main URL: http://www.mcfks.org/
Facebook: https://www.facebook.com/GreaterManhattanCommunityFoundation?ref=ts&fref=ts

Established in 1999 in KS.
Foundation type: Community foundation.
Financial data (yr. ended 12/31/13): Assets, $45,504,090 (M); gifts received, $1,463,781; expenditures, $1,470,929; giving activities include $1,108,804 for 29+ grants (high: $97,250).
Purpose and activities: The mission of the foundation is to enhance quality of life in the Greater Manhattan area, both today and in the future, by: 1) enabling donors to fulfill their charitable desires; 2) building a permanent endowment; 3) facilitating prudent management and care of funds; and 4) meeting needs through grants, awards, and scholarships.
Fields of interest: Humanities; Arts; Education; Environment; Health care; Mental health/crisis services; Safety/disasters; Human services; Community/economic development; Youth; Aging.
Type of support: Capital campaigns; Equipment; Program development.
Limitations: Applications accepted. Giving primarily in greater Manhattan, KS. No support for religious organizations for religious purposes. No grants for annual appeals in membership drives.
Publications: Annual report; Informational brochure.
Application information: Visit foundation web site for application guidelines. Application form required.
Initial approach: Contact foundation
Copies of proposal: 3
Deadline(s): Varies
Officers and Trustees:* James Gordon,* Pres.; Neil Horton,* V.P.; Jodi Kaus,* Secy.; Tom Fryer,* Treas.; Jerry Banaka; Matt Crocker; Cheryl Grice; Neal Helmick; Vern Henricks; Jo Lyle; Dennis Mullin; Bill Richter; Karen Roberts; Jim Armendariz; Bahr Bahr.
EIN: 481215574

3533
Don C. and Florence M. McCune Foundation ✧

P.O. Box 198
Salina, KS 67402-0198 (785) 827-7251
Contact: Sidney A. Reitz, Pres.
Application address: 119 W. Iron Ave., United Bldg., 10th Fl., Salina, KS 67401-2600, tel.: (785) 827-7251

Established in 1995 in KS.
Donor: Florence M. McCune.
Foundation type: Independent foundation.
Financial data (yr. ended 06/30/13): Assets, $11,826,854 (M); expenditures, $600,473; qualifying distributions, $507,360; giving activities include $507,360 for grants.
Purpose and activities: Giving primarily for higher education, as well as to an education foundation; funding also for a community foundation and Presbyterian churches.
Fields of interest: Arts; Higher education; Education; Human services; Foundations (community); Protestant agencies & churches.
Limitations: Giving primarily in Salina, KS. No grants to individuals.
Application information:
Initial approach: Letter
Deadline(s): None
Board meeting date(s): Varies
Officers: Sidney A. Reitz, Pres.; Susan N. Reitz, Secy.
EIN: 481164218
Selected grants: The following grants are a representative sample of this grantmaker's funding activity:
$157,300 to Greater Salina Community Foundation, Salina, KS, 2013. For Community Recreation Center Fund.
$6,500 to Rolling Hills Wildlife Adventure, Salina, KS, 2013. For Dream Night for Special Needs Children.
$5,000 to Kansas State University Foundation, Manhattan, KS, 2013. For Hrimd Culinary Education Workshop.
$5,000 to Rolling Hills Wildlife Adventure, Salina, KS, 2013. For Penguin Landing Exhibit.
$3,000 to Salina Animal Shelter, Salina, KS, 2013. For operating budget assistance.

3534
McPherson County Community Foundation ✧

206 S. Main
P.O. Box 616
McPherson, KS 67460 (620) 245-9070
Contact: Becky Goss, C.E.O.
FAX: (620) 245-0238;
E-mail: info@mcphersonfoundation.org; Toll Free Tel.: (866) 245-9070; Grant deadlines and information e-mail: sharon@mcphersonfoundation.org; Main URL: http://www.mcphersonfoundation.org/
Facebook: https://www.facebook.com/mcphersoncountycommunityfoundation
RSS Feed: http://www.mcphersonfoundation.org/feed/
Twitter: https://twitter.com/McPFoundation

Established in 2001 in KS.
Foundation type: Community foundation.
Financial data (yr. ended 08/31/13): Assets, $11,371,038 (M); gifts received, $1,267,646; expenditures, $2,338,293; giving activities include $1,587,106 for 30+ grants (high: $1,012,859), and $253,052 for 339 grants to individuals.
Purpose and activities: The foundation seeks to leave a legacy through the endowment for the future of McPherson County, KS, residents.
Fields of interest: Arts; Education; Environment; Animals/wildlife; Health care; Mental health/crisis services; Human services; Philanthropy/voluntarism; Religion.
Type of support: General/operating support; Continuing support; Income development; Management development/capacity building; Annual campaigns; Capital campaigns; Building/renovation; Equipment; Land acquisition; Emergency funds; Program development; Conferences/seminars; Professorships; Publication; Seed money; Curriculum development; Fellowships; Internship funds; Scholarship funds; Research; Technical assistance; Consulting

services; Program evaluation; Program-related investments/loans; Employee matching gifts; Grants to individuals; Scholarships—to individuals; Exchange programs; Matching/challenge support.
Limitations: Applications accepted. Giving primarily in McPherson County, KS. No grants to individuals (except for scholarships), or for operating deficits or retirement of debt, or annual appeals in membership drives.
Publications: Application guidelines; Annual report; Financial statement; Grants list; Informational brochure; Newsletter.
Application information: Visit foundation web site for guidelines. Application form not required.
Initial approach: Submit one page narrative
Copies of proposal: 1
Deadline(s): Ongoing unless a specific project is announced
Board meeting date(s): 2nd Wed. of Jan., Mar., May, Aug., Sept., and Nov.
Final notification: Within 30 days
Officers and Directors:* Becky Goss,* Pres. and C.E.O.; Terri Bornholdt; Jerry Fithian; Bill Gately; Zac Hoppes; Bob Kohrs, Jr.; Julie Milleson; Cyndi Ratzlaff; Fred Schrag; Glen Snell; Megan Spencer; Kathy Steiner; Rick Tuxhorn.
Number of staff: 1 full-time professional; 1 part-time professional; 1 part-time support.
EIN: 481238797

3535
Miller Family Foundation, Inc. ✧
610 E. Jefferson St.
Pittsburg, KS 66762-5913

Established in 2001 in KS.
Donor: Richard G. Miller.
Foundation type: Independent foundation.
Financial data (yr. ended 12/31/13): Assets, $30,678,591 (M); gifts received, $4,000,000; expenditures, $1,354,107; qualifying distributions, $1,057,455; giving activities include $1,050,300 for 42 grants (high: $300,000; low: $500).
Fields of interest: Elementary/secondary education; Higher education; Human services; Foundations (private grantmaking); Catholic agencies & churches.
Limitations: Applications not accepted. Giving primarily in Pittsburg, KS, and Columbia, MO. No grants to individuals.
Application information: Contributes only to pre-selected organizations.
Officers: Richard G. Miller, Pres.; H. Richard Coleman, V.P.; Marcia Sorrick, Secy.-Treas.
EIN: 431943960
Selected grants: The following grants are a representative sample of this grantmaker's funding activity:
$105,000 to Mount Carmel Foundation, Pittsburg, KS, 2012. For Via Christi Women's Center.
$20,000 to University of Missouri, Columbia, MO, 2012. For Show-Me State Games.
$19,000 to Pittsburg State University, Pittsburg, KS, 2012. For Football Letterman Scholarship Fund.
$2,000 to Habitat for Humanity of Crawford County, Pittsburg, KS, 2012. For Cornerstone Builders Program.
$1,700 to Boy Scouts of America, Great Rivers Council, Columbia, MO, 2012. For general fund.
$500 to Boy Scouts of America, Ozark Trails Council, Springfield, MO, 2012. For general fund.

3536
The Morgan Family Foundation ✧
P.O. Box 129
Shawnee Mission, KS 66201-0129 (913) 831-2996
Contact: Amanda K. Morgan, Co-Secy.; Erika R. Velasquez, Co-Secy.

Incorporated in 1985 in MO.
Donors: Frank Morgan; Frank Morgan Trust; Frank Morgan Charitable Lead Annuity Trust; Frank Morgan Charitable Lead Unitrust.
Foundation type: Independent foundation.
Financial data (yr. ended 11/30/13): Assets, $35,482,699 (M); expenditures, $1,897,656; qualifying distributions, $1,610,500; giving activities include $1,610,500 for 125 grants (high: $211,000; low: $650).
Purpose and activities: Giving primarily for Jewish organizations, health organizations, and social services.
Fields of interest: Hospitals (general); Health organizations, association; Human services; Jewish federated giving programs; Jewish agencies & synagogues.
Limitations: Applications accepted. Giving primarily in Overland Park, KS and Kansas City, MO. No grants to individuals.
Application information: Application form required.
Initial approach: Letter
Deadline(s): Nov. 30 for next fiscal year
Officers and Directors:* Thomas S. Morgan,* Co-Pres.; Todd D. Morgan,* Co-Pres.; Michael B. Morgan,* V.P.; Amanda K. Morgan,* Co-Secy.; Erika R. Velasquez,* Co-Secy.; Mark A. Morgan,* Treas.; Chad Feingold; Brian J. Morgan; Marilyn J. Morgan.
EIN: 481024615

3537
Mark and Bette Morris Family Foundation ✧
5500 S.W. 7th St.
Topeka, KS 66606-2531
Contact: Bette M. Morris, Pres.
Additional address: 5500 S.W. 7th St., Topeka, KS 66606

Established in 1989 in KS.
Donors: Mark L. Morris, Jr.†; Bette M. Morris; Mark L. Morris, Jr. Trust.
Foundation type: Independent foundation.
Financial data (yr. ended 12/31/12): Assets, $55,540,769 (M); expenditures, $3,732,591; qualifying distributions, $3,009,300; giving activities include $3,009,300 for 26 grants (high: $2,089,000; low: $2,900).
Purpose and activities: Support only to pre-selected organizations that encourage the healthy development and well-being of persons and animals, and that are personally known by the donors.
Fields of interest: Performing arts, theater; Performing arts, music; Higher education; Theological school/education; Animal welfare; Children/youth, services; United Ways and Federated Giving Programs; Protestant agencies & churches; Children/youth.
Limitations: Applications not accepted. Giving primarily in CO, KS and MO. No grants to individuals.
Application information: Contributes only to pre-selected organizations that are personally known by the donors. Unsolicited requests for funds not considered.
Officer: Bette M. Morris, Pres.
EIN: 481077121

3538
Ethel and Raymond F. Rice Foundation ✧
1617 St. Andrews Dr., No. 200A
Lawrence, KS 66047-1701
Contact: Robert C. Johnson, Pres.
FAX: (785) 841-9964;
E-mail: ricefdn@sunflower.com

Established in 1972.
Foundation type: Independent foundation.
Financial data (yr. ended 12/31/13): Assets, $16,715,924 (M); expenditures, $843,971; qualifying distributions, $809,255; giving activities include $696,500 for 23 grants (high: $210,000; low: $1,000).
Purpose and activities: Giving primarily for education and human services.
Fields of interest: Arts; Higher education; Human services; Children/youth, services; Children/youth.
Type of support: General/operating support; Capital campaigns; Building/renovation; Equipment; Scholarship funds; Research.
Limitations: Applications accepted. Giving primarily in the Douglas County, KS, area. No support for political organizations. No grants to individuals or for pledges for future support.
Publications: Annual report; Informational brochure (including application guidelines).
Application information: Applicants will be notified of the receipt of their application. Grants are made in Dec. Application form required.
Initial approach: Letter
Copies of proposal: 1
Deadline(s): Sept. 1
Board meeting date(s): Quarterly
Officers and Trustees:* Robert C. Johnson,* Pres.; Peter Curran,* V.P. and Treas.; James W. Paddock, Secy.
Number of staff: 1 part-time professional; 1 part-time support.
EIN: 237156608
Selected grants: The following grants are a representative sample of this grantmaker's funding activity:
$220,000 to University of Kansas, Lawrence, KS, 2012. For scholarships.
$75,000 to Salvation Army of Lawrence, Lawrence, KS, 2012. For food assistance.
$40,000 to Lawrence Schools Foundation, Lawrence, KS, 2012. For early childhood education.
$27,000 to Humane Society, Lawrence, Lawrence, KS, 2012. For building repairs and remodeling.
$15,000 to Meals on Wheels, Lawrence, Lawrence, KS, 2012. For general support.
$10,000 to Nature Conservancy of Kansas, Kansas Chapter, Topeka, KS, 2012. For general support.

3539
Riverside Health Foundation ✧
P.O. Box 9527
Wichita, KS 67277-0527

Established in 2006 in KS.
Donor: Riverside Health System, Inc.
Foundation type: Independent foundation.
Financial data (yr. ended 09/30/13): Assets, $17,573,341 (M); expenditures, $1,004,603; qualifying distributions, $853,237; giving activities

include $850,000 for 10 grants (high: $500,000; low: $2,000).
Fields of interest: Hospitals (general); Health organizations, association.
Limitations: Applications not accepted. Giving primarily in Wichita, KS.
Application information: Unsolicited requests for funds not accepted.
Officers and Directors:* Randy Coonrod,* Chair.; Jerry Gaston,* Vice-Chair.; Ron Stephen,* Secy.-Treas.; Les Donovan; Terry Fry; Jon Kirkpatrick; Dan McCarty; Carolina Soria; Ronnie Troy.
EIN: 481142989
Selected grants: The following grants are a representative sample of this grantmaker's funding activity:
$165,000 to Guadalupe Clinic, Wichita, KS, 2011.
$71,000 to Mental Health Association of South Central Kansas, Wichita, KS, 2011.
$20,000 to United Methodist Open Door, Wichita, KS, 2011.

3540
Greater Salina Community Foundation ✧
119 W. Iron, 8th Floor
P.O. Box 2876
Salina, KS 67402-2876 (785) 823-1800
Contact: Betsy Wearing, Pres.
FAX: (785) 823-9370;
E-mail: betsywearing@gscf.org; Main URL: http://www.gscf.org

Established in 1999 in KS.
Foundation type: Community foundation.
Financial data (yr. ended 06/30/13): Assets, $120,836,202 (M); gifts received, $37,366,772; expenditures, $5,442,256; giving activities include $4,784,518 for 79+ grants (high: $1,913,173), and $129,987 for 248 grants to individuals.
Purpose and activities: The foundation seeks to enhance quality of life, both today and in the future, by enabling donors to fulfill their charitable desires, building a permanent endowment, facilitating prudent management and care of funds, and meeting needs through grants, awards, and scholarships.
Fields of interest: Visual arts; Performing arts; Arts; Scholarships/financial aid; Education; Environment; Health care; Employment, training; Human services; Spirituality.
Type of support: General/operating support; Management development/capacity building; Capital campaigns; Equipment; Endowments; Emergency funds; Program development; Conferences/seminars; Publication; Seed money; Scholarship funds; Grants to individuals; Scholarships—to individuals.
Limitations: Applications accepted. Giving primarily in Saline County, KS, and the surrounding area. No grants for operating deficits or retirement of debt.
Publications: Annual report; Financial statement; Newsletter.
Application information: Visit foundation web site for application forms and additional guidelines per grant type. Contact the foundation for specific deadlines for the Fund for Greater Salina grants. Application form required.
Initial approach: Submit application form
Copies of proposal: 15
Deadline(s): Dec./Jan. and July/Aug. for the Fund for Greater Salina grants; none for others
Board meeting date(s): Bi-monthly
Final notification: Spring and fall for Fund for Greater Salina grants
Officers and Directors:* Dan Mendicina,* Chair.; Betsy Wearing,* Pres. and Exec. Dir.; Ray Perez,* Secy.-Treas.; Mark Berkley; Stephanie Klingzell Carlin; Ruth Cathcart-Rake; Olaf Frandsen; Frieda Mai-Weis; Rex Matlack; Dusty Moshier; Peter L. Peterson; Susy Reitz; Martha Rhea; Mark Speer; Glenn Stroer; Galen Swenson; Paula Tomlins; Susan Young.
Number of staff: 1 full-time professional; 4 part-time professional; 1 part-time support.
EIN: 481215503

3541
Sarli Family Foundation ✧
8101 Mission Rd., Apt. 214
Prairie Village, KS 66205-5246

Established in 2002 in KS.
Donors: Ralph Sarli; Mary Helen Sarli; Ralph S. Sarli Crat.
Foundation type: Independent foundation.
Financial data (yr. ended 12/31/13): Assets, $29,203,693 (M); gifts received, $8,949,985; expenditures, $918,279; qualifying distributions, $850,334; giving activities include $800,000 for 16 grants (high: $50,000; low: $50,000).
Fields of interest: Education; Hospitals (specialty); Health organizations; Human services; Children/youth, services; Children.
Limitations: Applications not accepted. Giving primarily in Kansas City, MO. No grants to individuals.
Application information: Contributes only to pre-selected organizations.
Directors: Lisa Wehrle; Mary Helen Sarli; Melinda Wehrle; W. Rodger Marsh, Jr.
EIN: 331020940
Selected grants: The following grants are a representative sample of this grantmaker's funding activity:
$50,000 to Camps for Kids, Kansas City, MO, 2011.
$50,000 to Childrens Center for the Visually Impaired, Kansas City, MO, 2011.
$50,000 to Childrens Mercy Hospital, Kansas City, MO, 2011.
$50,000 to Childrens TLC-Easter Seals, Kansas City, MO, 2011.
$50,000 to Crittenton Childrens Center, Kansas City, MO, 2011.
$50,000 to Kansas City Autism Training Center, Prairie Village, KS, 2011.
$50,000 to Saint Lukes Hospital Foundation, Kansas City, MO, 2011.
$50,000 to TLC for Children and Families, Olathe, KS, 2011.

3542
Schowalter Foundation, Inc. ✧
900 N. Poplar St., Ste. 200
Newton, KS 67114-1969 (316) 283-3720

Incorporated in 1953 in KS.
Donor: J.A. Schowalter‡.
Foundation type: Independent foundation.
Financial data (yr. ended 12/31/13): Assets, $24,776,219 (M); expenditures, $1,299,887; qualifying distributions, $978,946; giving activities include $930,001 for 73 grants (high: $40,000; low: $250).
Purpose and activities: Giving to assist retired ministers and missionaries, and theological seminaries and church-related schools (including scholarships); grants also for peace and international cooperation, and for technical assistance abroad, and other activities of the 2 Mennonite denominations related to the foundation (the Mennonite Church USA, and the Church of God in Christ, Mennonite).
Fields of interest: Education; Protestant agencies & churches.
Limitations: Applications accepted. Giving primarily in OH, IN and KS. No support for private or elementary schools, or for retirement centers. No grants to individuals (except for scholarships), or for endowment funds, fellowships, operating budgets, travel, or matching gifts; no loans.
Application information: Applicants not using the foundation's format will be asked to resubmit their application, or may not be considered. Application form required.
Initial approach: Letter requesting application form
Copies of proposal: 2
Deadline(s): Mar. 1 and Sept. 1
Officers: Mitchell Kingsley, Chair.; William Koehn, Vice-Chair.; Jerre Bontrager, Pres.; Heber Ramer, Secy.; Sue Ann Jantz, Treas.
Directors: Ron Goertzen; John Mark Koehn.
EIN: 480623544
Selected grants: The following grants are a representative sample of this grantmaker's funding activity:
$1,000 to American Bible Society, New York, NY, 2012. For Harvey County Homeless Shelter.

3543
Scott Community Foundation ✧
303 Court St., 3rd Fl.
Scott City, KS 67871 (620) 872-3790
Contact: For grants: Ryan Roberts, Exec. Dir.
E-mail: ryan@scottcf.org; Additional e-mail: jennifer@scottcf.org; Main URL: http://www.scottcf.org/
Facebook: https://www.facebook.com/scottcommunityfoundation

Established in 1987 in KS.
Foundation type: Community foundation.
Financial data (yr. ended 12/31/13): Assets, $6,415,046 (M); gifts received, $880,512; expenditures, $709,928; giving activities include $364,861 for 10+ grants (high: $138,371), and $55,000 for 3 grants to individuals.
Purpose and activities: The foundation is dedicated to preserving local wealth so the communities in and around Scott County will forever remain attractive places to live, work, and raise a family.
Fields of interest: Education; Health care; Recreation; Community/economic development.
Limitations: Applications accepted. Giving primarily in Scott County, KS and the surrounding area. No grants to individuals (except for scholarships), or for debt reduction, capital campaigns, or endowment programs.
Application information: Applications for grants from the General Fund and non-restricted component funds are available in the Fall of each year; visit foundation web site for updates. Application form required.

Board of Trustees:* Lori Krause,* Chair.; Karma Huck,* Vice-Chair.; James Rodenbeek,* Secy.; Dorothy Hutchins, Treas.; Ryan Roberts, Exec. Dir.; Natalie Armantrout; Josh Bailey; Nancy Hess; Kelly Hoeme; Cody Palen; Clint Pearson; Myles Vulgamore.
EIN: 480995697

3544
Security Benefit Life Insurance Company Charitable Trust ✧
1 Security Benefit Pl.
Topeka, KS 66636-1000 (785) 438-3000
Contact: Michael Kiley, Tr.; Michel Cole, Corp. Comms.

Established in 1976 in KS.
Donor: Security Benefit Life Insurance Co.
Foundation type: Company-sponsored foundation.
Financial data (yr. ended 12/31/13): Assets, $176,249 (M); gifts received, $728,400; expenditures, $608,258; qualifying distributions, $608,258; giving activities include $608,258 for 236 grants (high: $185,293; low: $25).
Purpose and activities: The foundation supports organizations involved with arts and culture, higher education, cancer, HIV/AIDS research, hunger, human services, women, economically disadvantaged people, and homeless people.
Fields of interest: Performing arts; Arts; Higher education; Cancer; AIDS research; Food services; Children/youth, services; Human services; Voluntarism promotion; Youth; Young adults; Physically disabled; Women; Economically disadvantaged; Homeless.
Type of support: Annual campaigns; Capital campaigns; Continuing support; Employee matching gifts; Equipment; Program-related investments/loans.
Limitations: Applications accepted. Giving limited to the Topeka, KS, area.
Application information: Application form not required.
Initial approach: Proposal
Copies of proposal: 1
Deadline(s): None
Trustee: Michael Kiley.
Number of staff: None.
EIN: 486211612
Selected grants: The following grants are a representative sample of this grantmaker's funding activity:
$170,082 to United Way of Greater Topeka, Topeka, KS, 2012.
$50,000 to NEA Foundation for the Improvement of Education, Washington, DC, 2012. For Kansas State Department of Education for improving teaching and learning in public schools, colleges and universities nationwide.
$35,000 to Friends of the Topeka Zoo, Topeka, KS, 2012.
$23,420 to Topeka Performing Arts Center, Topeka, KS, 2012.
$7,820 to Washburn University, Topeka, KS, 2012.

3545
The Ken and Jan Shannon Family Foundation ✧ ☆
P.O. Box 3903
Wichita, KS 67201-3903

Established in KS.
Donor: Kenneth F. Shannon.
Foundation type: Independent foundation.
Financial data (yr. ended 06/30/13): Assets, $80,984 (M); gifts received, $550,000; expenditures, $545,071; qualifying distributions, $545,000; giving activities include $545,000 for 12 grants (high: $263,000; low: $2,000).
Fields of interest: Human services; YM/YWCAs & YM/YWHAs; Children, services; Pregnancy centers; International affairs; United Ways and Federated Giving Programs; Christian agencies & churches.
Limitations: Applications not accepted. Giving primarily in Colorado Springs, CO and Wichita, KS. No grants to individuals.
Application information: Unsolicited requests for funds not accepted.
Officers and Directors:* Janet A. Shannon,* Pres.; Ken Shannon,* Secy.-Treas.; John Melhorn; Julie E. Melhorn; David J. Shannon; Kirsten Shannon.
EIN: 200438918

3546
The Shumaker Family Foundation ✧
1948 E. Santa Fe St., Ste. G
Olathe, KS 66062-1894
Contact: Judy Wright, Exec. Dir.
E-mail: request@shumakerfamilyfoundation.net; Tel./fax: (913) 764-1772; Main URL: http://www.shumakerfamilyfoundation.org

Established in 2005 in KS.
Donors: Paul K. Shumaker‡; Dianne C. Shumaker.
Foundation type: Independent foundation.
Financial data (yr. ended 12/31/13): Assets, $19,030,203 (M); expenditures, $955,502; qualifying distributions, $811,475; giving activities include $710,500 for 72 grants (high: $55,000; low: $100).
Purpose and activities: The foundation exists to promote social justice, environmental justice, and education. Within social justice, the foundation emphasizes domestic violence prevention and the development of leadership among inner-city youth. Within environmental justice, the foundation supports projects that promote animal rights, animal welfare, and that address global warming. Within education, the foundation favors projects that show the fascination and potentiality of math, physical science, engineering, and the arts to children who otherwise might not receive such exposure. The foundation also funds projects that address the education of children 0-3 years of age. The foundation prefers innovative projects led by people and organizations with a history of successful innovation; projects that connect 2 or more of foundation funding areas; and projects that can demonstrate significant outcomes within 3 years.
Fields of interest: Arts, public education; Education, early childhood education; Engineering school/education; Education; Environment; Animal welfare; Animals/wildlife, preservation/protection; Crime/violence prevention, domestic violence; International peace/security; Civil/human rights; Science; Religion, interfaith issues.
Type of support: Management development/capacity building; Capital campaigns; Curriculum development; Program evaluation.
Limitations: Applications accepted. Giving primarily in the greater bi-state Kansas City area; national and international giving for environmental and animal rights. No support for non 501(c)3 organizations, or for churches, or organizations that discriminate or promote violence (including to the environment). In general, no support for schools, except for select organizations. No grants to individuals, or for bricks and mortar, annual campaigns, capital campaigns or for special events.
Publications: Application guidelines; Grants list.
Application information: Application form available on foundation web site. Requests for $10,000 or less need only a letter description plus the required documentation. Application form required.
Initial approach: Letter, telephone or e-mail inquiry to ensure applicant's request fits the foundation's criteria
Copies of proposal: 1
Deadline(s): Mar. 15 for Spirituality and Environmental Justice; July 15 for Social Justice and Education
Board meeting date(s): Feb., Apr., July and Nov.
Final notification: Within 6 weeks of decision
Trustees: Dianne C. Shumaker; Eric A. Shumaker; Megan I. Shumaker.
Number of staff: 1 full-time professional.
EIN: 656406193

3547
Kenneth L. & Eva S. Smith Foundation ✧
c/o Thomas K. Jones
11000 King St., Ste. 200, Bldg. C
Overland Park, KS 66210-1233

Established in 1968 in KS.
Donors: Kenneth L. Smith‡; Eva S. Smith‡.
Foundation type: Independent foundation.
Financial data (yr. ended 12/31/13): Assets, $7,480,561 (M); expenditures, $669,963; qualifying distributions, $555,117; giving activities include $530,000 for 13 grants (high: $160,000; low: $5,000).
Fields of interest: Education; Hospitals (general); Residential/custodial care.
Type of support: Continuing support.
Limitations: Applications not accepted. Giving primarily in KS, and the greater Kansas City, MO, area. No grants to individuals.
Application information: Contributes only to pre-selected organizations.
Trustee: Thomas K. Jones.
EIN: 486142517

3548
Smoot Charitable Foundation ✧
P.O. Box 678
Salina, KS 67402-0678
Contact: Robert W. Weber M.D., Pres.

Established in 1976.
Foundation type: Independent foundation.
Financial data (yr. ended 06/30/13): Assets, $10,324,491 (M); expenditures, $763,549; qualifying distributions, $591,500; giving activities include $591,500 for grants.
Fields of interest: Arts; Higher education; Human services; YM/YWCAs & YM/YWHAs; Children/youth, services; United Ways and Federated Giving Programs.
Limitations: Applications accepted. Giving limited to Saline County, KS. No grants to individuals.
Application information: Application form required.
Initial approach: Letter
Deadline(s): None

Officers: Robert W. Weber, M.D., Pres.; George W. Yarnevich, V.P.; Janice L. Doherty, Secy.; Tom A. Williamson, Treas.
EIN: 480851141
Selected grants: The following grants are a representative sample of this grantmaker's funding activity:
$50,000 to Kansas Wesleyan University, Salina, KS, 2013. For Student Activities Center.
$5,000 to Salina Education Foundation, Salina, KS, 2013. For Grow Your Teacher/Lift Program.

3549
Sprint Foundation ✧
(formerly United Telecommunications Foundation)
6220 Sprint Pkwy.
Overland Park, KS 66251-6118
FAX: (913) 624-3490;
E-mail: communityrequests@sprint.com; E-mail for Sprint Local Grant Program:
Local_giving_program@sprint.com; Main
URL: http://www.sprint.com/responsibility/sprint_foundation/index.html

Established in 1989 in KS.
Donors: Sprint Corp.; Sprint Nextel Corp.; The United Telephone Co. of Pennsylvania; Sprint Communications Co., LP.
Foundation type: Company-sponsored foundation.
Financial data (yr. ended 12/31/12): Assets, $1,596,881 (M); gifts received, $1,860,000; expenditures, $4,180,361; qualifying distributions, $4,131,334; giving activities include $4,131,334 for 790 grants (high: $612,673; low: $25).
Purpose and activities: The foundation supports organizations involved with arts and culture, K-12 and business education, environmental stewardship, youth development, community development, and civic affairs.
Fields of interest: Visual arts; Museums; Performing arts; Performing arts, theater; Performing arts, orchestras; Arts; Elementary/secondary education; Business school/education; Environment; Boys & girls clubs; Youth development, adult & child programs; Big Brothers/Big Sisters; Boy scouts; Girl scouts; Camp Fire; Youth development, services; Youth development; American Red Cross; Community/economic development; Leadership development; Public affairs; Youth.
Type of support: General/operating support; Continuing support; Annual campaigns; Program development; Scholarship funds; Employee volunteer services; Employee matching gifts; Donated equipment; In-kind gifts.
Limitations: Applications accepted. Giving primarily in areas of company operations in Overland Park, KS and Kansas City, MO; giving also in Denver, CO, Atlanta, GA, NJ, and New York, NY, and Dallas and Fort Worth, TX for the Sprint Local Grant Program. No support for discriminatory organizations, political organizations, religious organizations, private charities or foundations, international organizations, or school-affiliated teams, bands, or choirs. No grants to individuals, or for endowments, capital campaigns, memorials, construction, or renovation projects, travel, film, music, television, video, or media production projects, school-affiliated events, marketing, sports, or event sponsorships; no donations of Sprint products or services.
Publications: Application guidelines; Program policy statement.
Application information: Finalists for the Sprint Local Grant Program must submit a three-minute video showcasing the program that will receive funding. Application form required.
Initial approach: Complete online application form
Deadline(s): Jan. 3 to Nov. 18; May 1 to June 15 for Sprint Local Grant Program
Board meeting date(s): Quarterly
Final notification: 90 days; Sept. 28 for Sprint Local Grant Program
Officers and Directors:* Ralph Reid, Pres. and Exec. Dir.; Tim O'Grady, Secy.; Greg Block,* Treas.; Steve Gaffney; Bill White.
EIN: 481062018
Selected grants: The following grants are a representative sample of this grantmaker's funding activity:
$612,673 to United Way of Greater Kansas City, Kansas City, MO, 2012.
$328,019 to American Red Cross National Headquarters, Washington, DC, 2012.
$208,175 to Kansas University Endowment Association, Lawrence, KS, 2012.
$125,000 to Boys and Girls Clubs of Greater Kansas City, Kansas City, MO, 2012.
$103,737 to K C P T-Kansas City Public Television Channel 19, Kansas City, MO, 2012.
$15,000 to Denver Kids, Denver, CO, 2012.
$5,702 to United Way of Central Carolinas, Charlotte, NC, 2012.
$5,000 to Coterie Theater, Kansas City, MO, 2012.
$2,500 to Messmer Catholic Schools, Milwaukee, WI, 2012.

3550
The Stowers Foundation ✧
6731 W. 121 St., Ste. 206
Leawood, KS 66209-2003

Donors: James E. Stowers; Ryan Contillo; Lauren Contillo; Alex Johnson; Layne Stowers; James Stowers IV.
Foundation type: Independent foundation.
Financial data (yr. ended 05/31/13): Assets, $77,100,825 (M); gifts received, $11,309,176; expenditures, $1,410,273; qualifying distributions, $1,167,153; giving activities include $1,150,000 for 2 grants (high: $850,000; low: $300,000).
Fields of interest: Medical research; Community/economic development.
Limitations: Applications not accepted. Giving primarily in Kansas City, MO.
Application information: Contributes only to pre-selected organizations.
Trustees: Wendy B. Marvin; Kathleen Stowers Potter; James E. Stowers III; Linda Stowers; Virginia G. Stowers.
EIN: 326176805

3551
Sunderland Foundation ✧
(formerly Lester T. Sunderland Foundation)
P.O. Box 25900
Overland Park, KS 66225-5900 (913) 451-8900
Contact: Kent Sunderland, Pres.
E-mail: sunderlandfoundation@ashgrove.com; Main
URL: http://www.sunderlandfoundation.org
Grants List: http://www.sunderlandfoundation.org/2009Contributions.asp

Incorporated in 1945 in MO.
Donors: Lester T. Sunderland‡; Paul Sunderland‡.
Foundation type: Independent foundation.
Financial data (yr. ended 12/31/13): Assets, $103,522,183 (M); expenditures, $5,903,299; qualifying distributions, $5,469,140; giving activities include $5,434,000 for 98 grants (high: $250,000; low: $5,000).
Purpose and activities: Areas of interest include higher education, youth serving agencies, health facilities, community buildings, museums, civic projects, and low maintenance, energy efficient housing projects sponsored by qualified tax-exempt organizations.
Fields of interest: Arts; Higher education; Hospitals (general); Health care; Children/youth, services.
Type of support: General/operating support; Continuing support; Annual campaigns; Capital campaigns; Building/renovation; Equipment; Land acquisition; Endowments; Emergency funds.
Limitations: Applications accepted. Giving primarily in geographic areas that have connections to the Ash Grove Cement Co., particularly AR, Western IA, KS, Western MO and NE, and, to a lesser extent, ID, MT, OR, UT, and WA. No grants to individuals, or for programs, endowments, special events, scholarships or operating expenses; no loans.
Publications: Application guidelines; Financial statement; Grants list; Program policy statement.
Application information: Application guidelines available on foundation web site. Application form not required.
Initial approach: Proposal via U.S. mail or e-mail as a PDF file
Copies of proposal: 1
Deadline(s): None
Board meeting date(s): As required
Officers and Trustees:* Kent Sunderland,* Pres.; James P. Sunderland,* Secy.; Charles Sunderland,* Treas.; William Sunderland, Ph.D.
Number of staff: 1 part-time support.
EIN: 446011082

3552
Topeka Community Foundation ✧
5431 S.W. 29th St., Ste. 300
Topeka, KS 66614-4483 (785) 272-4804
Contact: Roger K. Viola, Pres.; For grants: Marsha Pope, V.P.
FAX: (785) 273-4644;
E-mail: info@topekacommunityfoundation.org; Grant inquiry e-mail:
pope@topekacommunityfoundation.org; Main
URL: http://www.topekacommunityfoundation.org
Facebook: https://www.facebook.com/pages/Topeka-Community-Foundation/124452534291100

Incorporated in 1983 in KS.
Foundation type: Community foundation.
Financial data (yr. ended 12/31/12): Assets, $43,295,040 (M); gifts received, $3,571,443; expenditures, $3,622,108; giving activities include $2,484,310 for 46 grants (high: $250,000), and $147,052 for 150 grants to individuals.
Purpose and activities: The foundation seeks to connect donors with their interests and community needs, increasing charitable giving in our community, providing leadership on key community issues and ensuring stewardship and accountability for effective community investment of donor dollars.
Fields of interest: Performing arts; Arts; Education, early childhood education; Education; Environment, natural resources; Environment; Public health; Substance abuse, services; Children/youth, services; Family services; Homeless, human

services; Human services; Community/economic development; Government/public administration; Children/youth; Youth; Adults; Disabilities, people with; Mentally disabled; Women; Adults, women; Homeless.
Type of support: General/operating support; Continuing support; Annual campaigns; Capital campaigns; Building/renovation; Emergency funds; Program development; Seed money; Scholarship funds; Employee matching gifts; Employee-related scholarships; Scholarships—to individuals; In-kind gifts; Matching/challenge support.
Limitations: Applications accepted. Giving limited to Topeka and Shawnee County, KS. No support for religious organizations for religious purposes. No grants to individuals (directly), or for ongoing general operating expenses or existing deficits, endowments, or fundraising events.
Publications: Application guidelines; Annual report; Financial statement; Informational brochure; Informational brochure (including application guidelines); Newsletter; Quarterly report.
Application information: Visit foundation web site for application forms and attachments. Faxed or e-mailed applications are not accepted. Application form required.
Initial approach: Submit application and attachments
Copies of proposal: 17
Deadline(s): Varies
Board meeting date(s): Quarterly, 3rd Thurs. of Feb., May, Aug. and Nov.
Final notification: Varies
Officers and Directors:* Grace A. Morrison, M.D.*, Chair.; Nancy Lewis,* Vice-Chair.; Roger K. Viola,* Pres.; Marsha Pope,* V.P.; James Schmank,* Secy.; Brad Owen,* Treas.; Steve Briman; Mary Brownback; Shelly Buhler; Dan Crow; John B. Dicus; Tim Etzel; Cathy McCoy; Chris McGee; Maynard Oliverius; Larry Robbins; Ford Ross; Stephen Tempero, M.D.; Susan Krenbiel William; C. Patrick Woods; Lambert Wu.
Number of staff: 2 full-time professional; 2 full-time support.
EIN: 480972106

3553
Westar Energy Foundation ✧
(formerly Western Resources Foundation, Inc.)
818 S. Kansas Ave.
Topeka, KS 66612-1203 (785) 575-1544
Contact: Cynthia McCarvel, Pres.

Established in 1991 in KS.
Donors: Western Resources, Inc.; Westar Energy, Inc.
Foundation type: Company-sponsored foundation.
Financial data (yr. ended 12/31/13): Assets, $2,936,518 (M); gifts received, $200,000; expenditures, $927,546; qualifying distributions, $911,823; giving activities include $851,174 for 221 grants (high: $133,333; low: $100), and $60,649 for 36 employee matching gifts.
Purpose and activities: The foundation supports programs designed to improve academic performance of youth; and prepare youth for the world of work and community leadership.
Fields of interest: Education; Human services; Religion.
Limitations: Applications accepted. Giving primarily in areas of company operations in KS. No support for organizations supported by the United Way, tax-supported institutions, fraternal, ethnic, church, or social organizations, local youth or athletic groups including scout troops, 4-H clubs, or athletic teams, or political organizations. No grants to individuals, or for building fund drives, capital campaigns, primary or secondary school-related functions, medical research, disease campaigns, fundraising walks, or conferences, conventions, or meeting sponsorships.
Publications: Application guidelines; Informational brochure.
Application information: Application form required.
Initial approach: Letter
Copies of proposal: 1
Deadline(s): None
Officers: Cynthia McCarvel, Pres.; Pamela J. Ketter, Secy.; John M. Grace, Treas.
Directors: John T. Bridson; Kelly B. Harrison; James J. Ludwig; Anthony D. Somma.
Number of staff: 2 full-time professional; 1 full-time support.
EIN: 481099341
Selected grants: The following grants are a representative sample of this grantmaker's funding activity:
$13,553 to United Way of Johnson County, Lenexa, KS, 2012. For corporate donation.
$6,000 to Topeka Youth Project, Topeka, KS, 2012. For JYA.
$5,000 to Exploration Place, Wichita, KS, 2012. For Star Wars Exhibit.
$5,000 to Sunflower Music Festival, Topeka, KS, 2012. For festival sponsorship.
$5,000 to Topeka Association for Retarded Citizens, Topeka, KS, 2012. For Winter Wonderland.
$5,000 to YWCA of Topeka, Topeka, KS, 2012. For Girls on the Run.
$2,500 to Lawrence Arts Center, Lawrence, KS, 2012. For Elk Co Art Classes.
$2,500 to Van Go Mobile Arts, Lawrence, KS, 2012. For Jams.
$2,500 to Wichita Symphony Society, Wichita, KS, 2012. For Young People's concert.
$1,500 to Salina Rescue Mission, Salina, KS, 2012. For upgrades.

3554
Western Kansas Community Foundation ✧
402 N. Main
Garden City, KS 67846
Contact: For grants: Melissa Gallegos, Opers. Mgr.
E-mail: wkcf@wkcf.org; Grant inquiry e-mail: melissa@wkcf.org; Main URL: http://www.wkcf.org/
E-Newsletter: http://wkcf.org/news/newsletters
Facebook: https://www.facebook.com/pages/Western-Kansas-Community-Foundation/115598408500639

Established in 1996 in KS.
Foundation type: Community foundation.
Financial data (yr. ended 12/31/13): Assets, $25,517,574 (M); gifts received, $2,152,009; expenditures, $1,539,044; giving activities include $886,012 for 40+ grants (high: $90,030), and $99,200 for 48 grants to individuals.
Purpose and activities: The foundation enriches western Kansas life through philanthropy, collaboration and leadership.
Fields of interest: General charitable giving.
Type of support: Program development.
Limitations: Applications accepted. Giving primarily in the 15-county service area of Western Kansas: Greeley, Wichita, Scott, Lane, Hamilton, Kearny, Finney, Stanton, Grant, Haskell, Gray, Morton, Stevens, Seward, and Meade counties, KS. No support for religious organizations for religious purposes. No grants to individuals (except for scholarship funds), or operating or maintenance expenses, medical or scholarly research, membership fees, banquet or luncheon expenses, ticket sales or fundraising efforts, travel expenses, capital debt reduction, endowments, or marketing tools.
Publications: Application guidelines; Newsletter.
Application information: Visit foundation web site for additional information. Application form required.
Initial approach: Submit application
Copies of proposal: 1
Deadline(s): Feb. 1, May 1, Aug. 1, Nov. 1
Officer and Directors:* Shea Sinclair, Exec. Dir.; Michael Cearley; Troy Dirks; Neil Hawley; Sharla Krenzel; Bob Kreutzer; Pat LeClerc; Marlene Lee; Don Linville; Emily Miller; Martin Nusser; Brenda Reeve; Liz Sosa; Bill Stewart.
EIN: 481184667

3555
Wichita Community Foundation ✧
(formerly Greater Wichita Community Foundation)
301 N. Main, Ste. 100
Wichita, KS 67202 (316) 264-4880
Contact: Sherry Prichard, C.E.O.
FAX: (316) 264-7592; E-mail: wcf@wichitacf.org; Additional e-mail: sprichard@wichitacf.org; Main URL: http://www.wichitacf.org
Facebook: https://www.facebook.com/wichitacf
Twitter: https://twitter.com/WichitaCF

Incorporated in 1986 in KS.
Foundation type: Community foundation.
Financial data (yr. ended 06/30/13): Assets, $57,430,588 (M); gifts received, $7,063,887; expenditures, $6,516,405; giving activities include $5,500,751 for 85+ grants (high: $778,000), and $242,069 for 748 grants to individuals.
Purpose and activities: The foundation was established to build charitable endowments and help donors create funds that reflect their charitable goals. It consists of numerous permanent funds in its endowment built by many thoughtful individuals, families, and companies who care about the Wichita region. Grants are made from endowment earnings to a wide variety of nonprofit organizations to enhance life in the community.
Fields of interest: Humanities; Arts; Education; Environment, natural resources; Environment; Health care; Human services.
Type of support: Scholarships—to individuals; Matching/challenge support.
Limitations: Applications accepted. Giving limited to the greater Wichita, KS, area. No support for religious organizations for religious purposes. No grants to individuals (except for scholarships), or for building projects, endowments, fellowships, debt reduction, administrative overhead, or fundraising campaigns.
Publications: Application guidelines; Annual report; Financial statement; Informational brochure; Newsletter.
Application information: Visit foundation web site for guidelines. Application form not required.
Initial approach: Letter (no longer than 2 pages)
Deadline(s): None
Board meeting date(s): Apr. and Oct.
Final notification: Within 90 days
Officers and Directors:* Sheryl L. Wohlford,* Chair.; Barry Schwan,* Vice-Chair.; Shelly Chenowith

Prichard,* C.E.O. and Pres.; Ed Healy,* Secy.; Justin Healy, C.F.O.; Steve Houlik,* Treas.; Jerry Aaron; Pamela Ammar; Clark Bastian; Brian A. Black; Noreen Carrocci; Cokie Diggs; Jeff Fluhr; Gary Gamm; William "Skip" Hidlay; Thomas Martin; Mary Lynn Oliver; Ron Paulseen; Charles Stark; Lynn Stephan; Lyndon Wells.
Number of staff: 1 full-time professional; 1 part-time professional; 1 full-time support.
EIN: 481022361
Selected grants: The following grants are a representative sample of this grantmaker's funding activity:
$314,900 to United Way of the Plains, Wichita, KS, 2012. For general purposes, Tornado Fund Grants.
$275,000 to Doc's Friends, Wichita, KS, 2012. For general purposes.
$235,548 to Wichita Business Coalition on Health Care, Wichita, KS, 2012. For Worksite Wellness Grant.
$187,788 to Wichita State University Foundation, Wichita, KS, 2012. For general purposes, band instrument and restoration, to establish a track and field scholarship, for physics lectures, National Advisory Council, Shirley Beggs Ballroom Renovation, and Walter A. Verwiebe Scholarship/Fellowship.
$135,000 to Wichita Downtown Development Corporation, Wichita, KS, 2012. For Project Downtown.
$69,259 to Salvation Army of Wichita, Wichita, KS, 2012. For general purposes, Share the Season, yearly distribution, disaster assistance.
$26,750 to E.C. Tyree Health and Dental Clinic, Wichita, KS, 2012. For general purposes, underwrite clinic's planned expansion.
$18,150 to Wichita Childrens Home, Wichita, KS, 2012. For general purposes, challenge grant for shuttle van.
$12,000 to Orpheum Performing Arts Center, Wichita, KS, 2012. For general purposes, 90th Anniversary Concert.
$10,000 to Christ the Savior Academy, Wichita, KS, 2012. For general purposes.

3556
Wyandotte Health Foundation ✧

c/o George Howell
755 Minnesota Ave.
Kansas City, KS 66117-2703
Application address: c/o Greater Kansas City Community Foundation, 1055 Broadway, Ste. 130, Kansas City, MO 64105; tel.: (816) 627-3403

Established in 1997; converted from the assets of Bethany Medical Center.
Donors: Kathryn A. Powers‡; Eleanor Redbeck Trust; Elmer Williams Trust.
Foundation type: Independent foundation.
Financial data (yr. ended 09/30/13): Assets, $41,735,198 (M); expenditures, $2,961,616; qualifying distributions, $2,442,858; giving activities include $2,040,151 for 29 grants (high: $380,000; low: $5,000).
Purpose and activities: The foundation's mission is to promote and improve the health of Wyandotte County citizens, particularly the indigent, through grants and collaborative efforts. Therefore, the foundation seeks to achieve this mission by focusing its grant making into two major categories: Primary Health Care; Prevention, Intervention and Education.
Fields of interest: Health care; Human services.
Type of support: General/operating support; Continuing support; Building/renovation; Equipment; Emergency funds; Program development; Publication; Technical assistance; Matching/challenge support.
Limitations: Applications accepted. Giving limited to Wyandotte and Johnson counties, KS, and Jackson County, MO. No support for sectarian or religious organizations. No grants or scholarships to individuals, directly or for budget deficits or debt reduction, to directly influence legislation or support candidates for office, annual fund drives or events, building or capital campaigns or for medical research.
Publications: Application guidelines; Grants list; Informational brochure.
Application information: Application form required.
Initial approach: E-mail
Deadline(s): June 30
Board meeting date(s): 4th Thur. of each month
Final notification: Oct.
Officers: Raymond L. Daniels, Ph.D., Chair.; William C. Tempel, 1st Vice-Chair.; Trudie Hall, 2nd Vice-Chair.; William Eppenheimer, Pres.; George S. Howell,* V.P.; James White, Secy.; Leon C. Logan, Treas.
Directors: Patricia Gaunce; John J. Jurcyk, Jr.; W. Jackson Letts; Ramon Murguia; Clarence Small; Charles W. Thurston, Jr.
Number of staff: 2 full-time professional; 1 full-time support.
EIN: 480547722
Selected grants: The following grants are a representative sample of this grantmaker's funding activity:
$127,500 to Kansas University Endowment Association, Lawrence, KS, 2011.
$110,000 to Childrens Mercy Hospital Foundation, Kansas City, MO, 2011.
$100,000 to University of Kansas Medical Center Research Institute, Kansas City, KS, 2011.

KENTUCKY

3557
The Augusta Brown Holland Philanthropic Foundation, Inc. ✧ ☆
c/o Atlas Brown
333 E. Main St., Ste. 400
Louisville, KY 40202-1259

Established in KY.
Donor: Sara S. Brown.
Foundation type: Independent foundation.
Financial data (yr. ended 11/30/13): Assets, $11,546,314 (M); expenditures, $763,128; qualifying distributions, $662,258; giving activities include $651,112 for 56 grants (high: $102,158; low: $1,000).
Fields of interest: Arts; Education; Human services; Community/economic development.
Limitations: Applications not accepted.
Application information: Unsolicited requests for funds not accepted.
Directors: Brooke Brown Barzun; Christina Lee Brown; Owsley Brown III; Augusta Brown Holland.
EIN: 274432220

3558
J. Rogers Badgett, Sr. Foundation Inc. ✧
1822 N. Main St., Bldg. A
Madisonville, KY 42431-9401

Established in 2001 in KY.
Donor: J. Rodgers Badgett, Sr.‡.
Foundation type: Independent foundation.
Financial data (yr. ended 10/31/12): Assets, $19,772,975 (M); gifts received, $400,000; expenditures, $2,789,852; qualifying distributions, $1,466,503; giving activities include $1,415,796 for 11 grants (high: $525,000; low: $1,500).
Fields of interest: Higher education.
Limitations: Applications not accepted. Giving primarily in KY; funding also in CO. No grants to individuals.
Application information: Contributes only to pre-selected organizations.
Officers and Directors:* Bentley F. Badgett II,* Pres.; Thomas J. Edwards,* V.P.; Claude R. Badgett,* Secy.-Treas.; Mary Rheaetta Ashby.
EIN: 311755149
Selected grants: The following grants are a representative sample of this grantmaker's funding activity:
$126,922 to Murray State University Foundation, Murray, KY, 2011.
$86,000 to Madisonville Community College, Madisonville, KY, 2011.
$20,000 to American Red Cross, Madisonville, KY, 2011.

3559
The Brooke Brown Barzun Philanthropic Foundation, Inc. ✧ ☆
c/o Atlas Brown
333 E. Main St., Ste. 400
Louisville, KY 40202-1259

Donor: Sara S. Brown.
Foundation type: Independent foundation.
Financial data (yr. ended 11/30/13): Assets, $11,724,251 (M); expenditures, $578,420; qualifying distributions, $477,684; giving activities include $466,417 for 16 grants (high: $223,444; low: $1,000).
Fields of interest: Museums (art); Performing arts, orchestras; Arts; Education; Community/economic development.
Type of support: General/operating support.
Limitations: Applications not accepted.
Application information: Unsolicited requests for funds not accepted.
Directors: Brooke Brown Barzun; Christina Lee Brown; Owsley Brown III; Augusta Brown Holland.
EIN: 274432411

3560
Blue Grass Community Foundation, Inc. ✧
(formerly Blue Grass Foundation, Inc.)
499 E. High St., Ste. 112
Lexington, KY 40507 (859) 225-3343
Contact: For grants: Kassie L. Branham, Dir., Grants and Scholarships
FAX: (859) 243-0770; E-mail: info@bgcf.org; Grant inquiry e-mail: kbranham@bgcf.org; Main URL: http://www.bgcf.org
Blog: http://bgcf.org/engage/news-events/
Facebook: http://www.facebook.com/bgcf.org
Flickr: http://www.flickr.com/photos/bgcf/
LinkedIn: http://www.linkedin.com/companies/blue-grass-community-foundation
RSS Feed: http://bgcf.org/feed/
Twitter: http://twitter.com/BGCF
YouTube: http://www.youtube.com/bluegrasscf

Incorporated in 1967 in KY.
Foundation type: Community foundation.
Financial data (yr. ended 06/30/13): Assets, $65,790,534 (M); gifts received, $13,605,326; expenditures, $9,936,019; giving activities include $7,799,413 for 147 grants (high: $2,500,000), and $113,686 for 56 grants to individuals.
Purpose and activities: The foundation receives gifts and gives grants to people and causes in central and eastern Kentucky.
Fields of interest: Arts; Education, early childhood education; Education, reading; Education; Environment; Animal welfare; Health care; Health organizations, association; Housing/shelter, homeless; Housing/shelter; Disasters, Hurricane Katrina; Children/youth, services; Human services; Economic development; Community/economic development; Public affairs; Religion; Infants/toddlers.
Type of support: General/operating support; Management development/capacity building; Building/renovation; Equipment; Endowments; Program development; Seed money; Scholarship funds; Technical assistance; Consulting services; Employee-related scholarships; Scholarships—to individuals; Matching/challenge support.
Limitations: Applications accepted. Giving limited to central and eastern KY.
Publications: Application guidelines; Annual report; Financial statement; Grants list; Quarterly report.
Application information: The foundation's grant committee will review all letters of inquiry and decide which agencies will be asked to complete a full application for Community Grants. Visit foundation web site for application forms and guidelines per grant type. Application form required.
Initial approach: E-mail Letter of inquiry (1 to 2 pages) for Community Grants
Copies of proposal: 1
Deadline(s): Aug. 15 for Community Grants; varies for others
Board meeting date(s): Quarterly
Final notification: Varies
Officers and Directors:* Buckner Woodford IV,* Chair.; Arthur R. Salomon,* Vice-Chair.; Lisa Adkins,* Pres. and C.E.O.; Madonna Turner,* Secy.; James Rouse,* Treas.; Jonathan Barker; Eunice Beatty; Garland H. Barr III; Bruce Florence; Rufus Friday; Phil Holoubek; Logan Marskbury; John Milward; Travis Musgrave; P.G. Peeples, Sr.; Ashley Robbins; Joe Rosenberg; Dr. Ronald Saykaly; Brandi Skirvin; Fran Taylor; Nancy Allen Turner; Griffin VanMeter; Bud Watson; Tracee Whitley.
Number of staff: 4 full-time professional.
EIN: 616053466

3561
Ina B. Bond Ashbourne Charitable Fund Inc. ✧
4969 US Hwy. 42, Ste. 2000
Louisville, KY 40222-6391

Established in 2011 in KY.
Donors: The Cockayne Fund, Inc.; The Ina Brown Bond Charitable Lead Annuity Trust.
Foundation type: Independent foundation.
Financial data (yr. ended 12/31/13): Assets, $33,356,828 (M); gifts received, $1,253,304; expenditures, $1,703,769; qualifying distributions, $1,659,973; giving activities include $1,658,846 for grants.
Fields of interest: Museums (specialized); Civil rights, race/intergroup relations.
Limitations: Applications not accepted. Giving primarily in Louisville, KY.
Application information: Unsolicited requests for funds not accepted.
Officers: Ina Brown Bond, Chair. and Pres.; W. Austin Musselman, Jr., Secy.-Treas.
Director: Elaine G. Musselman.
EIN: 452809797

3562
Owsley Brown Charitable Foundation ✧
c/o Zelkova Strategic Partners, LLC
333 E. Main St., Ste. 401
Louisville, KY 40202-1297

Established in 1990 in KY.
Donors: Owsley Brown II‡; Mrs. W.L. Lyons Brown; Sara S. Brown; Augusta Brown Holland; Brooke Brown Barzun; Christina Lee Brown 2012 Charitable Lead Annuity Trust.
Foundation type: Independent foundation.
Financial data (yr. ended 12/31/13): Assets, $29,072,297 (M); gifts received, $8,156,710; expenditures, $2,803,732; qualifying distributions, $2,700,805; giving activities include $2,688,554 for 76 grants (high: $540,000; low: $100).
Purpose and activities: Giving primarily for the arts and education.
Fields of interest: Arts; Education; Religion.
Type of support: Annual campaigns; Capital campaigns.
Limitations: Applications not accepted. Giving primarily in KY. No grants to individuals.
Application information: Contributes only to pre-selected organizations.

Officers and Directors:* Christina Lee Brown,* Pres. and Secy.; Brooke Brown Barzun,* Treas.; Owsley Brown III; Augusta Brown Holland.
EIN: 611189915

3563
James Graham Brown Foundation, Inc. ✧
4350 Brownsboro Rd., Ste. 200
Louisville, KY 40207-1681 (502) 896-2440
Contact: Mason B. Rummel, Pres. and Treas.
FAX: (502) 896-1774; E-mail: grants@jgbf.org; Additional tel.: (866) 896-5423. E-mail for Mason B. Rummel : mason@jgbf.org; Main URL: http://www.jgbf.org
Grants List: http://www.jgbf.org/grants-paid/

Trust established in 1943 in KY; incorporated in 1954.
Donors: J. Graham Brown‡; Agnes B. Duggan‡.
Foundation type: Independent foundation.
Financial data (yr. ended 12/31/12): Assets, $336,587,494 (M); expenditures, $23,146,729; qualifying distributions, $19,492,826; giving activities include $18,725,108 for 35 grants (high: $2,666,666; low: $500).
Purpose and activities: Giving for higher education, civic organizations, community and economic development, human service organizations, culture and humanities, and health.
Fields of interest: Museums; Historic preservation/historical societies; Higher education; Education; Health care; Human services; Youth, services; Urban/community development.
Type of support: Building/renovation; Capital campaigns; Equipment; Land acquisition; Matching/challenge support; Research.
Limitations: Applications accepted. Giving limited to KY, with emphasis on the Jefferson County and Louisville metropolitan areas. No support for private foundations or the performing arts, primary or secondary schooling, religious institutions for religious purposes, including theological seminaries, or political or national organizations. No grants to individuals.
Publications: Application guidelines; Grants list; Informational brochure (including application guidelines).
Application information: Application form required if board approves request for permission to apply. Application form required.
Initial approach: Online Pre-Grant Request
Copies of proposal: 1
Deadline(s): Social Services: July 7; Culture and Civic: May 5; Education: Mar. 3
Board meeting date(s): Six annually
Final notification: Grants paid Dec. 31
Officers and Trustees:* R. Alex Rankin,* Chair. and C.E.O.; Mason B. Rummel, Pres.; W. Barrett Nichols,* V.P.; Kathy Kotcamp, Treas.; Alice Houston; Fr. Ron Knott; J.A. Paradis, III; Robert W. Rounsavall III; R. Ted Steinbock, M.D.
Number of staff: 4 full-time professional; 1 part-time professional.
EIN: 610724060
Selected grants: The following grants are a representative sample of this grantmaker's funding activity:
$4,000,000 to University of Louisville, Louisville, KY, 2011. For a strategic partnership withthe J. Graham Brown Cancer Center.
$2,666,666 to 21st Century Parks, Louisville, KY, 2011. Toward support of the Floyds Fork Greenway Project development and land acquisition.
$1,000,000 to Bellarmine University, Louisville, KY, 2011. Toward Grad Rate 2020, a multi-faceted student retention and faculty development initiative.
$1,000,000 to United Way, Metro, Louisville, KY, 2011. Toward annual campaign.
$532,418 to University of Kentucky, Lexington, KY, 2011. Toward the Next Generation Leadership Academy.
$500,000 to Kentucky Christian University, Grayson, KY, 2011. Toward the development of a biology/pre-professional degree program.
$500,000 to Western Kentucky University, Bowling Green, KY, 2011. Toward support of i4 Initiative to promote a culture of innovation through a series of outreach and programming opportunities that instills a sense of importance of STEM education.
$250,000 to Young Adult Development in Action, YouthBuild Louisville, Louisville, KY, 2011. Toward a capital campaign to centralize YouthBuild program components on one campus in the Smoketown neighborhood.
$13,000 to Southeastern Council of Foundations, Atlanta, GA, 2011. Toward membership and support of the 2011 Conference.

3564
W. L. Lyons Brown Foundation ✧
Waterfront Plz., Ste. 1110
325 W. Main St.
Louisville, KY 40202-4254
Contact: Susan V. Nicholson, Admin.
E-mail: wllb@cflouisville.org

Established in 1962 in KY.
Donors: W.L. Lyons Brown‡; Sara S. Brown‡.
Foundation type: Independent foundation.
Financial data (yr. ended 12/31/13): Assets, $73,577,842 (M); expenditures, $2,946,601; qualifying distributions, $2,801,741; giving activities include $2,779,551 for 54 grants (high: $450,694; low: $250).
Purpose and activities: Giving primarily to organizations seeking to improve quality of life, including museums, parks, educational institutions, and organizations supporting the arts.
Fields of interest: Museums; Arts; Higher education; Environment, natural resources.
Type of support: General/operating support; Annual campaigns; Capital campaigns; Building/renovation; Land acquisition.
Limitations: Applications not accepted. No support for sectarian projects. No grants to individuals, or for scholarships or annual appeals; no loans.
Application information: Unsolicited requests for funds not accepted.
Board meeting date(s): Oct.
Officers and Trustees:* Ina B. Bond,* Pres.; Cary Brown,* V.P.; Owsley Brown III,* V.P.; Martin S. Brown,* Treas.
EIN: 610598511

3565
W. L. Lyons Brown, Jr. Charitable Foundation ✧
c/o Wyatt ET AL, T. Berry
500 W. Jefferson St., Ste. 2800
Louisville, KY 40202-2813

Established in 1993 in KY.
Donors: Mrs. W.L. Lyons Brown; Sara Shallenberger Brown.
Foundation type: Independent foundation.
Financial data (yr. ended 12/31/13): Assets, $25,311,950 (M); expenditures, $1,307,011; qualifying distributions, $1,174,960; giving activities include $1,167,926 for 51 grants (high: $207,500; low: $100).
Fields of interest: Historic preservation/historical societies; Arts; Higher education; Libraries (public); Education; Botanical gardens.
Limitations: Applications not accepted. Giving primarily in NY; some funding also in VA. No grants to individuals.
Application information: Contributes only to pre-selected organizations.
Officers and Directors:* Alice Cary Brown,* Pres.; Stuart R. Brown, Secy.-Treas.; W.L. Lyons Brown III; W.L. Lyon Brown, Jr.; A. Cary Brown Epstein.
EIN: 611233038

3566
The C.E. & S. Foundation, Inc. ✧
101 S. 5th St., Ste. 1650
Louisville, KY 40202-3122 (502) 583-0546
Contact: Bruce A. Maza, Exec. Dir.
FAX: (502) 583-7648;
E-mail: Bruce@cesfoundation.com; Main URL: http://www.cesfoundation.com

Established in 1984 in FL.
Donors: David A. Jones; and family.
Foundation type: Independent foundation.
Financial data (yr. ended 12/31/13): Assets, $71,993,766 (M); expenditures, $3,788,069; qualifying distributions, $3,502,411; giving activities include $3,060,831 for 103 grants (high: $500,000; low: $500).
Purpose and activities: Giving primarily for higher education, (with a focus on undergraduate liberal arts programs in Louisville, KY), as well as for colleges and universities, and for disaster relief and prevention, international cooperation, Louisville's urban environment, and special projects initiated by the grants committee. The foundation will give priority to organizations and programs that: 1) have demonstrated effectiveness, proven management, clear plans and a high level of competence; 2) are committed to measuring outcomes and examining the lasting impact of their efforts; 3) have strong levels of funding from other donors; and 4) offer unique, highly innovative solutions to recognized social problems.
Fields of interest: Education; Safety/disasters; International affairs, goodwill promotion; Urban/community development.
Type of support: General/operating support; Income development; Management development/capacity building; Capital campaigns; Land acquisition; Endowments; Emergency funds; Program development; Seed money; Internship funds; Scholarship funds; Research; Technical assistance; Consulting services; Program-related investments/loans.
Limitations: Applications accepted. Giving primarily in Louisville, KY. No support for medical research organizations, or for political organizations. No grants to individuals, or for scholarships.
Publications: Application guidelines; Annual report; Grants list; Program policy statement.
Application information: Letters sent to the foundation that propose projects outside of the guidelines are immediately declined. Application form not required.

Initial approach: Letter, telephone, or web site for guidelines
Copies of proposal: 1
Deadline(s): None
Board meeting date(s): Jan., May, Sept. and Nov.
Final notification: Up to two months
Officers and Trustee:* David A. Jones,* Pres.; Bruce A. Maza, Exec. Dir.
Number of staff: 3 full-time professional.
EIN: 592466943

3567
Carson-Myre Charitable Foundation ✧
2616 Broadway
P.O. Box 194
Paducah, KY 42002-0194

Established in 2006 in KY.
Donor: Jane Carson Myre†.
Foundation type: Independent foundation.
Financial data (yr. ended 12/31/13): Assets, $78,599,970 (M); expenditures, $4,645,176; qualifying distributions, $4,079,780; giving activities include $4,079,780 for 72 grants (high: $515,000; low: $3,477).
Purpose and activities: Giving primarily for social services, and for Christian organizations and churches.
Fields of interest: Hospitals (general); Human services; Christian agencies & churches.
Limitations: Applications not accepted. Giving primarily in KY, with emphasis on Paducah. No grants to individuals.
Application information: Contributes only to pre-selected organizations.
Trustees: J. William Howerton; W. Clay Howerton; J. Robert Milford; Mary Allison Ogden; J. Lane Peck; Paducah Bank and Trust Co.
EIN: 364597768

3568
Larry R. Coffey Charitable Trust ✧ ☆
504 Bedfordshire Rd.
Louisville, KY 40222-5509 (502) 426-2751
Contact: Joan B. Coffey

Established in 1989 in KY.
Donor: Larry R. Coffey.
Foundation type: Independent foundation.
Financial data (yr. ended 12/31/13): Assets, $8,952,086 (M); gifts received, $250,000; expenditures, $549,840; qualifying distributions, $540,026; giving activities include $511,975 for 31 grants (high: $250,000; low: $500).
Fields of interest: Higher education; Libraries (special); Protestant agencies & churches.
Type of support: Capital campaigns.
Limitations: Applications accepted. Giving primarily in FL and Louisville, KY and VA. No grants to individuals.
Application information: Application form required.
Initial approach: Proposal
Deadline(s): None
Trustee: Larry R. Coffey.
EIN: 616168546
Selected grants: The following grants are a representative sample of this grantmaker's funding activity:
$10,000 to YMCA of Greater Louisville, Louisville, KY, 2011.
$5,000 to American Red Cross, Louisville, KY, 2011. For general fund.
$2,000 to Kentucky Historical Society, Frankfort, KY, 2011.
$1,000 to Neighborhood House, Louisville, KY, 2011. For general fund.

3569
The Community Foundation of Louisville, Inc. ✧
(formerly Louisville Community Foundation, Inc.)
Waterfront Plz. Bldg.
325 W. Main St., Ste. 1110
Louisville, KY 40202-4251 (502) 585-4649
Contact: For scholarships: Meredith Zahirovic, Community Leadership Assoc.
FAX: (502) 587-7484;
E-mail: giving@cflouisville.org; Main URL: http://www.cflouisville.org
Facebook: http://www.facebook.com/cflouisville
Flickr: http://www.flickr.com/photos/cflouisville/
LinkedIn: http://www.linkedin.com/company/community-foundation-of-louisville
Twitter: http://twitter.com/cflouisville
YouTube: http://www.youtube.com/user/cflouisville
Scholarship URL: http://scholarship.cflouisville.org; Scholarship inquiry
e-mail: meredithz@cflouisville.org

Established in 1916 in KY; reorganized in 1984.
Foundation type: Community foundation.
Financial data (yr. ended 06/30/13): Assets, $378,320,066 (M); gifts received, $26,506,832; expenditures, $33,882,389; giving activities include $28,285,522 for grants.
Purpose and activities: To strengthen the region through inspired philanthropy and outstanding stewardship by: 1) partnering with donors and others to ensure last impact; 2) leveraging knowledge of communities; and 3) offering constituents an unmatched level of personal engagement.
Fields of interest: Humanities; Historic preservation/historical societies; Arts; Education; Environment; Public health; Health care; Family services; Human services; Community/economic development.
Type of support: General/operating support; Continuing support; Annual campaigns; Building/renovation; Equipment; Emergency funds; Program development; Publication; Seed money; Scholarship funds; Research; Technical assistance; Employee matching gifts; Scholarships—to individuals; Matching/challenge support; Mission-related investments/loans.
Limitations: Applications accepted. Giving primarily in Louisville and Jefferson County, KY. No grants to individuals (except for scholarships), or operations.
Publications: Annual report; Informational brochure; Newsletter; Program policy statement.
Application information: The foundation does not accept unsolicited grant proposals or requests. The foundation seeks out partnerships and charitable investments that align with their strategic plan, rather than requesting projects or programs from local nonprofit organizations. So, there is not an application or proposal process for nonprofit organizations looking for financial support from the Community Foundation. Application form required.
Deadline(s): Aug. 21
Board meeting date(s): Mar., June, Sept., and Dec.
Officers and Directors:* Marshall Bradley, Jr.,* Chair.; Eric W. Taylor,* Vice-Chair.; Susan A. Barry, C.E.O. and Pres.; Matthew L. Bacon, V.P. and C.F.O.; Angie M. Evans, V.P., Community Leadership; Cara Baribeau, V.P., Mktg. and Comms.; Mike Schultz, V.P., Devel. and Stewardship; Maria G. Hampton,* Secy.; Julie LaValle "Valle" Jones,* Treas.; James Hill, Cont.; Claire Alagia; Henry "Sonny" M. Altman, Jr.; Stephanie Bateman; Suzanne Bergmeister; Robert P. Bordogna; Pedro A. Bryant; Mark A. Campisano; Toni Clem; Jacqueline C. Gibbs; Charles J. Kane, Jr.; Audrey D. Kline, Ph.D.; Nirupama "Nima" Kulkarni; Harriet Lair; William R. Mapother; Michael Masick; Deborah Moessner; William O. Price; Dorothy S. "Dot" Ridings; Robert "Bob" Smedley; Stephanie H. Smith; Bill Strench; Patricia G. Swope; David Tachau; James H. Taylor; Gary Ulmer; Mimi Zinniel.
Number of staff: 10 full-time professional; 5 full-time support.
EIN: 310997017
Selected grants: The following grants are a representative sample of this grantmaker's funding activity:
$17,385,500 to 21st Century Parks, Louisville, KY, 2012.
$2,998,329 to San Francisco Foundation, San Francisco, CA, 2012.
$993,000 to Muhammad Ali Museum and Education Center, Louisville, KY, 2012.
$893,367 to Louisville Free Public Library Foundation, Louisville, KY, 2012.
$736,250 to Yale University, New Haven, CT, 2012.
$118,090 to Community Foundation of Louisville Corporate Depository, Louisville, KY, 2012.
$66,700 to Louisville Olmsted Parks Conservancy, Louisville, KY, 2012.
$25,000 to Louisville Metropolitan Parks Foundation, Louisville, KY, 2012.
$25,000 to National Museum of Patriotism, Atlanta, GA, 2012.
$18,500 to Brescia University, Owensboro, KY, 2012.

3570
Community Foundation of West Kentucky ✧
(formerly Paducah Area Community Foundation)
333 Broadway, Ste. 615
P.O. Box 7
Paducah, KY 42002-0007 (270) 442-8622
Contact: Tony Watkins, C.E.O.
FAX: (270) 442-8623; E-mail: info@cfwestky.org; Main URL: http://www.cfwestky.org

Established in 1995 in KY.
Foundation type: Community foundation.
Financial data (yr. ended 12/31/12): Assets, $16,972,502 (M); gifts received, $1,639,229; expenditures, $1,249,485; giving activities include $670,350 for 30+ grants (high: $25,000), and $42,000 for 35 grants to individuals (high: $2,000; low: $500).
Purpose and activities: The foundation supports areas of art and culture, community development, education, environment, health and social needs.
Fields of interest: Arts, cultural/ethnic awareness; Arts; Education; Environment; Public health; Health care; Human services; Community/economic development.
Type of support: Equipment; General/operating support; Annual campaigns; Capital campaigns;

Endowments; Debt reduction; Emergency funds; Program development; Scholarship funds.
Limitations: Applications not accepted. Giving primarily in western KY and Massac County, IL.
Publications: Annual report; Informational brochure; Newsletter.
Application information:
Board meeting date(s): Quarterly in Feb., May, Aug., and Nov.
Officers and Directors:* Tony Watkins,* C.E.O.; Scott Powell,* Pres.; Vicki Brantley,* Secy.-Treas.; Carney Allen; Chris Black; Terry Bunnell; Eugenia Drossos; Joseph H. Framptom; B.A. Hamilton; Mark Hequembourg; Chris Hutson; Ronald Jackson; Eugene Katterjohn, Jr.; Robin Kelly; C. Thomas Miller; Gerry Montgomery; Bonnie Schrock; Jerr Severns; George Shaw; Chris Smith; Tim Thomas; Ken Wheeler.
Number of staff: 1 full-time professional; 1 full-time support; 1 part-time support.
EIN: 611304905

3571
The Cralle Foundation, Inc. ✧
614 W. Main St., Ste. 2500
Louisville, KY 40202-4252
Contact: James T. Crain, Jr., Exec. Dir.
FAX: (502) 581-1937;
E-mail: jcrain37@bellsouth.net

Incorporated in 1990 in KY as successor foundation to the Cralle Foundation.
Foundation type: Independent foundation.
Financial data (yr. ended 12/31/13): Assets, $10,108,216 (M); expenditures, $873,779; qualifying distributions, $789,007; giving activities include $651,203 for 85 grants (high: $25,000; low: $1,000).
Purpose and activities: Giving primarily for education and human services.
Fields of interest: Museums; Higher education; Education; Human services; Children/youth, services; Community/economic development; Children/youth; Aging; Disabilities, people with; Physically disabled; Blind/visually impaired; Deaf/hearing impaired; Mentally disabled; Minorities; Women; Girls; Men; Boys; Substance abusers; Single parents; Crime/abuse victims; Terminal illness, people with; Immigrants/refugees; Economically disadvantaged; Homeless.
Type of support: General/operating support; Continuing support; Capital campaigns; Building/renovation; Equipment; Endowments; Program development; Seed money; Scholarship funds; Matching/challenge support.
Limitations: Applications accepted. Giving primarily in KY, with emphasis on Louisville. No grants to individuals.
Application information: Application form required.
Initial approach: Letter requesting application form
Copies of proposal: 4
Deadline(s): Mar. 1 and Sept. 1
Board meeting date(s): Apr. and Oct.
Officer and Trustees:* James T. Crain, Jr.,* Exec. Dir.; Carolyn Day; Joan Cralle Day; Susan Day.
Number of staff: 1 full-time professional; 1 part-time support.
EIN: 611179672
Selected grants: The following grants are a representative sample of this grantmaker's funding activity:
$25,000 to Shively Area Ministries, Louisville, KY, 2012. For Vision25.
$15,000 to USA Cares, Radcliff, KY, 2012. For Warrior Treatment Today Program.
$10,000 to Cabbage Patch Settlement House, Louisville, KY, 2012. For Bridge the Gap' Program.
$10,000 to Georgetown College, Georgetown, KY, 2012. For Renovation of Hall of Fame Room in Lee E Cralle Student Building.
$10,000 to Kentucky Historical Society, Frankfort, KY, 2012. For internship program.
$10,000 to Lighthouse Promise, Louisville, KY, 2012. Toward Construction of New Building.
$10,000 to Meredith-Dunn School, Louisville, KY, 2012. For Financial Assistance for Needy Families.
$10,000 to Project One, Louisville, KY, 2012. For Talented and Gifted Scholars' Program.
$7,250 to New Opportunity School for Women, Berea, KY, 2012. For Career/Education Counselor.
$3,000 to Blue Apple Players, Louisville, KY, 2012. For bullying program.

3572
R. C. Durr Foundation, Inc. ✧
541 Buttermilk Pike, Ste. 544
P.O. Box 175710
Covington, KY 41017-5710
Contact: Jean H. Mize
E-mail: JMize@DurrFoundation.com; E-mail for Jean Mize, Asst. to the Pres.: JMize@DurrFoundation.com; Main URL: http://www.durrfoundation.com

Established in 1994 in KY.
Donor: R.C. Durr‡.
Foundation type: Independent foundation.
Financial data (yr. ended 12/31/13): Assets, $67,189,264 (M); gifts received, $4,066,101; expenditures, $3,055,220; qualifying distributions, $2,741,177; giving activities include $2,634,842 for 165 grants (high: $322,350; low: $25).
Purpose and activities: The foundation is dedicated to celebrating the life and legacy of its benefactor by providing philanthropic support to improve the quality of life of the larger Northern Kentucky region and its people, with a particular emphasis on education, social services and community development. Secondary consideration is also given to health care, particularly to public health care, in the same geographic area. Priority is given to new or innovative projects and programs that make the larger Northern Kentucky community a better place to live, learn and work; that are measurable with stated goals and objectives; that demonstrate effectiveness and innovation, or great potential for such; that are models for others; that demonstrate collaboration; and that can eventually be self-supporting or show evidence of long-term viability and impact.
Fields of interest: Arts; Education; Medical research; Recreation; Human services; Aging, centers/services; Community/economic development.
Limitations: Applications accepted. Giving primarily in the larger Northern Kentucky area, including: Boone, Bracken, Campbell, Carroll, Gallatin, Grant, Harrison, Kenton, Mason, Owen, Pendleton, and Robertson counties. No support for religious organizations (unless they are engaged in programs benefiting the entire community), organizations that discriminate, private foundations or endowments, walks, runs, golf outings, or neighborhood- or school-specific events. No grants to individuals, or for fundraising or donor cultivation events, sponsorships, raffle tickets or tables for fund raising events, or for courtesy advertising.
Publications: Application guidelines.
Application information: Prospective applicants are advised to familiarize themselves with foundation guidelines prior to applying, and can send queries via a 1-page pre-application summary proposal. Telephone calls not accepted. Application form not required.
Initial approach: Grant request via letter or e-mail
Deadline(s): None
Final notification: Within 90 days
Officers: Wilbert L. Ziegler, C.E.O. and Pres.; Robert W. Zapp, V.P.; Robert C. Ziegler, Secy.
EIN: 611249998
Selected grants: The following grants are a representative sample of this grantmaker's funding activity:
$20,000 to Housing Opportunities of Northern Kentucky, Covington, KY, 2011. For general support.

3573
Ray and Kay Eckstein Charitable Trust ✧
4965 Village Square Dr., Ste. A
Paducah, KY 42001-6722
Application address: c/o Heather J. Baer, P.O. Box 7606, Paducah, KY 42002-7606, tel.: (270) 534-8930; Main URL: http://ecksteincharity.org/

Established in 2005 in WI.
Donors: Ray A. Eckstein; Kathryn A. Eckstein.
Foundation type: Independent foundation.
Financial data (yr. ended 12/31/13): Assets, $72,573,270 (M); gifts received, $2,944,093; expenditures, $3,416,003; qualifying distributions, $2,897,975; giving activities include $2,748,500 for 18 grants (high: $2,000,000; low: $2,000).
Purpose and activities: Giving primarily to Roman Catholic Church-affiliated organizations, and educational, missionary and ministry programs (Catholic and non-Catholic).
Fields of interest: Higher education; Catholic agencies & churches.
Limitations: Applications accepted. Giving primarily in WI. No grants to individuals.
Application information: Application form required.
Initial approach: Letter
Deadline(s): Oct.
Trustees: Kathryn A. Eckstein; Ray A. Eckstein; Teresa R. Eckstein; Cynthia L. Erickson; Susan F. Homra.
EIN: 396786592

3574
The Fischer Family Foundation 2008 ✧
P.O. Box 17160
Fort Mitchell, KY 41017-0160

Established in KY.
Foundation type: Independent foundation.
Financial data (yr. ended 11/30/13): Assets, $46,423,985 (M); expenditures, $1,645,521; qualifying distributions, $1,400,000; giving activities include $1,400,000 for 54 grants (high: $300,000; low: $50).
Purpose and activities: Giving primarily for education, children, youth and social services, Roman Catholic organizations, and to a children's hospital.

Fields of interest: Education; Hospitals (specialty); Human services; Children/youth, services; Catholic agencies & churches.
Limitations: Applications not accepted. Giving primarily in KY and OH. No grants to individuals.
Application information: Contributes only to pre-selected organizations.
Trustees: Elaine M. Fischer; Henry K. Fischer.
EIN: 386863779

3575
Foundation for the Tri-State Community, Inc. ✧
(formerly Greater Ashland Area Cultural and Economic Development Foundation, Inc.)
855 Central Ave., Ste. 300
P.O. Box 2096
Ashland, KY 41105-2096 (606) 324-3888
Contact: Mary Witten Wiseman, Pres.
FAX: (606) 324-5961;
E-mail: info@tristatefoundation.org; Huntington office: 916 Fifth Ave., Suite 403, P.O. Box 7932, Huntington, WV 25701; Main URL: http://www.tristatefoundation.org
Facebook: https://www.facebook.com/pages/Foundation-for-the-Tri-State-Community/223290124515555
Twitter: https://twitter.com/FoundationTSC

Incorporated in 1972 in KY.
Foundation type: Community foundation.
Financial data (yr. ended 12/31/13): Assets, $20,825,308 (M); gifts received, $686,007; expenditures, $1,349,270; giving activities include $674,018 for 4+ grants (high: $26,141), and $56 for grants to individuals.
Purpose and activities: The foundation makes grants for charitable, cultural, educational, and scientific purposes and seeks to respond to a wide variety of needs in the community.
Fields of interest: Arts; Education; Science.
Type of support: Building/renovation; Equipment; Emergency funds; Program development; Seed money; Scholarship funds; Technical assistance; Consulting services; Matching/challenge support.
Limitations: Applications accepted. Giving limited to Boyd and Greenup counties, KY; Lawrence County, OH; and Cabell and Wayne counties, WV. No support for sectarian activities of religious organizations. No grants to individuals, or for deficit financing, operating support, or endowment funds.
Publications: Application guidelines; Annual report; Grants list; Informational brochure.
Application information: Applications reviewed quarterly. Visit foundation web site for application information. Application form required.
Initial approach: Letter, telephone, or proposal
Copies of proposal: 1
Deadline(s): Jan. 15, Apr. 15, July 15, and Oct. 15
Board meeting date(s): Quarterly
Officers and Trustees:* J. Patrick Jones,* Chair.; Cassie Landers,* Vice-Chair.; Jodi Rowe-Collins,* Vice-Chair.; April Russell Perry,* Vice-Chair.; Mary Whitten Wiseman,* Pres.; Geoffery S. Sheils,* Secy.-Treas.; Curtis B. Anderson; Donald R. Capper; Nick Carter; Rebecca M. Craig; Evan H. Jenkins; Kimberly S. McCann; H. Edward Neely; James W. St. Clair; Laurel Sewell Timberlake.
Number of staff: 3 full-time professional; 1 full-time support.
EIN: 610729266

3576
Annie Gardner Foundation ✧
620 S. 6th St.
Mayfield, KY 42066-2316
Contact: Nancy H. Sparks, Dir.

Established in 1941 in KY.
Donor: Ed Gardner Trust.
Foundation type: Operating foundation.
Financial data (yr. ended 05/31/13): Assets, $10,202,510 (M); gifts received, $690,786; expenditures, $1,129,699; qualifying distributions, $1,365,762; giving activities include $784,253 for grants to individuals.
Purpose and activities: Support primarily for the disadvantaged, including grants for rent, medical care, clothing, and other necessities; also awards educational loans, maximum of $3,000 and $4,000 per-year for undergraduate and graduate students of Graves County High School or Mayfield High School in Kentucky. Students attending summer school may receive an additional $500.
Fields of interest: Education; Human services; Economically disadvantaged.
Type of support: Grants to individuals; Student loans—to individuals.
Limitations: Applications accepted. Giving limited to residents of Graves County, KY.
Application information: Student loan application available from foundation. Application form required.
Deadline(s): July 1
Officer: Edward Elder, Exec. Dir.
Director: Nancy Sparks.
Trustees: Jim Heath; Barry McDonald; Don Sparks; Kelly Weber.
EIN: 610564889

3577
The Gheens Foundation, Inc. ✧
401 W. Main St., Ste. 705
Louisville, KY 40202-2937 (502) 584-4650
Contact: Carl M. Thomas, Pres.
FAX: (502) 584-4652;
E-mail: carl@gheensfoundation.org; Main URL: http://www.gheensfoundation.org

Incorporated in 1957 in KY.
Donors: C. Edwin Gheens†; Mary Jo Gheens Hill†.
Foundation type: Independent foundation.
Financial data (yr. ended 10/31/13): Assets, $123,333,385 (M); expenditures, $6,800,277; qualifying distributions, $5,886,160; giving activities include $5,607,021 for 138 grants (high: $250,000; low: $2,500).
Purpose and activities: Emphasis on higher and secondary education, ongoing teacher education, social service agencies, health associations, programs for the physically and mentally handicapped, and cultural programs.
Fields of interest: Arts; Secondary school/education; Higher education; Education; Mental health/crisis services; Health organizations, association; Human services; Children/youth; Disabilities, people with; Economically disadvantaged.
Type of support: General/operating support; Capital campaigns; Building/renovation; Equipment; Program development; Scholarship funds; Research.
Limitations: Applications accepted. Giving primarily in Louisville, KY, and LaFourche and Terrebone parishes, LA. No support for private high schools. No grants to individuals.
Publications: Application guidelines; Grants list.
Application information: Application form, guidelines and information is available on foundation web site. Application form required.
Initial approach: Ask for application by letter, phone, fax, or e-mail
Copies of proposal: 7
Deadline(s): One week before the last business day of the month prior to board meeting
Board meeting date(s): Quarterly
Final notification: Within 30 days after board meeting
Officers and Trustees:* Michael B. Mountjoy,* Chair. and C.E.O.; Carl M. Thomas, Pres. and Treas.; William G. Duncan, Jr., Secy.; Morton Boyd; John R. Crockett III; Dr. Laman A. Gray, Jr.; Phoebe A. Wood.
Number of staff: 2 full-time professional; 2 full-time support.
EIN: 616031406

3578
Good Samaritan Foundation, Inc. ✧
c/o Grant Review Comm.
7400 Floydsburg Rd.
Crestwood, KY 40014-8202 (800) 530-7236
E-mail: gsf@kyumc.org; Main URL: http://kyumc.org/gsf
Facebook: https://www.facebook.com/KentuckyAnnualConference

Established in 1888 in KY, Incorporated as Good Samaritan Hospital of KY in 1929; Good Samaritan Foundation is a hospital conversion foundation.
Donors: Thomas Clark†; F.W. Rickard†; Elisabeth Spanton†.
Foundation type: Independent foundation.
Financial data (yr. ended 06/30/13): Assets, $19,076,591 (M); gifts received, $31,437; expenditures, $1,175,170; qualifying distributions, $860,000; giving activities include $860,000 for 28 grants (high: $180,456; low: $2,500).
Purpose and activities: The foundation initiates, participates in, and supports activities which focus on improving the health status of Kentuckians. Primary/preventive health care proposals serving low income and uninsured individuals in underserved areas of KY are a priority for funding.
Fields of interest: Health care.
Type of support: General/operating support; Equipment; Seed money; Curriculum development; Fellowships; Scholarship funds; Research.
Limitations: Applications accepted. Giving limited to KY. No support for indirect costs, or for fraternal or veterans' organizations. No grants to individuals, or capital improvements, endowment funds. charitable tournaments, meal functions, team sponsorships, ticket purchases, or athletic activities.
Publications: Application guidelines; Informational brochure (including application guidelines); Newsletter; Occasional report.
Application information: In addition to the online applications, applicants must mail both a paper copy of all attachments and a CD containing a pdf file which contains all attachments. All attachments should be placed in one pdf file and not in multiple files. See foundation web site for complete application requirements. Application form required.
Initial approach: Use online application on foundation web site
Copies of proposal: 2

Deadline(s): See web site for current deadline
Final notification: May 31
Officers: Jackson Brewer, Chair.; William Martin Moore, Vice-Chair.; Marian Bensema, Secy.; Joni B. Way, Treas.
Directors: Carlyle Ackley; Randy Capps; Leanne Diakov; Frank Fitzpatrick; Paul Fryman; Terry L. Reffett; Marian R. Smith; Tukea Talbert.
Number of staff: 1 full-time support.
EIN: 311087598

3579
The Virginia Clark Hagan Charitable Foundation Inc. ✧
250 W. Main St., Ste. 1600
Lexington, KY 40507-1726

Established in 2002 in KY.
Donors: Virginia Clark Hagan†; Hagan Unitrust.
Foundation type: Independent foundation.
Financial data (yr. ended 12/31/13): Assets, $16,490,845 (M); expenditures, $791,977; qualifying distributions, $689,957; giving activities include $663,000 for 10 grants (high: $150,000; low: $15,000).
Purpose and activities: Giving primarily for education and human services.
Fields of interest: Higher education; Adult education—literacy, basic skills & GED; Human services; Salvation Army.
Limitations: Applications not accepted. Giving primarily in Lexington, KY.
Application information: Unsolicited requests for funds not accepted.
Officers and Directors:* Herbert D. Sledd,* Pres.; Sarah Clark,* V.P.; Charles L. Shearer,* Secy.; Elizabeth Blackford.
EIN: 611184780
Selected grants: The following grants are a representative sample of this grantmaker's funding activity:
$90,260 to International Book Project, Lexington, KY, 2012. For Literacy Initiative.
$80,000 to Central Music Academy, Lexington, KY, 2012. For youth music education.
$21,748 to Shriners Hospitals for Children, Lexington, KY, 2012. For children health education.
$20,000 to American Red Cross, Lexington, KY, 2012. For Disaster Education Program.
$10,000 to National Christian Foundation, Alpharetta, GA, 2012. For education and literacy.

3580
The Claude and Betty Harris Foundation, Inc. ✧
295 N. Hubbards Ln., Ste. 203
Louisville, KY 40207-8230

Established in 2002 in KY.
Donors: Claude Harris; Harris Charitable Lead Trust; Harris Family Charitable Lead Trust No. 2.
Foundation type: Independent foundation.
Financial data (yr. ended 12/31/13): Assets, $47,638,014 (M); gifts received, $1,260,000; expenditures, $2,728,949; qualifying distributions, $2,408,244; giving activities include $2,357,600 for 74 grants (high: $88,000; low: $1,000).
Fields of interest: Health care, clinics/centers; Food banks; Housing/shelter, development; Human services; Children/youth, services; Women, centers/services; Christian agencies & churches.
Limitations: Applications not accepted. Giving in the U.S., with some emphasis on AR. No grants to individuals.
Application information: Contributes only to pre-selected organizations.
Officers: Theresa Jean Harris Moore, Chair.; David Harris, Vice-Chair. and Treas.; Paula Harris Stansell, Secy.
Directors: Don Harris; Gary Harris; Gayla Harris; Timothy Harris.
EIN: 611400416

3581
Mildred V. Horn Foundation ✧
South Highway 53, Ste. 3
PMB 2028
La Grange, KY 40031-9119
Contact: H. Scott Davis, Jr., Tr.

Established in 1988 in KY.
Donor: Mildred V. Horn†.
Foundation type: Independent foundation.
Financial data (yr. ended 12/31/13): Assets, $35,917,602 (M); expenditures, $1,778,072; qualifying distributions, $1,715,770; giving activities include $1,461,289 for 145 grants (high: $168,550; low: $500).
Purpose and activities: Giving primarily for the preservation of historic homes (1760-1860) which are open to the public and located in Kentucky or its contiguous states; giving also for homeless shelters and schools in Kentucky.
Fields of interest: Museums; Historic preservation/historical societies; Elementary/secondary education; Higher education; Human services; Family services; Homeless.
Type of support: General/operating support; Building/renovation.
Limitations: Applications accepted. Giving primarily in KY (for homeless shelters and education) and historic homes (built between 1760-1860) open to the public in KY, IL, IN, MO, OH, TN, VA, and WV. No grants to individuals or for endowments or multi-year grants.
Publications: Application guidelines.
Application information: Application form not required.
Initial approach: 1-to 2-page letter for requests under $5,000; 4-page form may be required for grants over $5,000
Copies of proposal: 1
Deadline(s): Dec. 31
Board meeting date(s): Varies
Final notification: Usually 14 days
Trustees: Walter T. Crutcher; H. Scott Davis, Jr.; Louisa M. Gaines.
Number of staff: 1 full-time professional; 2 part-time professional.
EIN: 616166544
Selected grants: The following grants are a representative sample of this grantmaker's funding activity:
$48,000 to University of Pikeville, Pikeville, KY, 2012. For Feasibility Study of Dental School.
$33,000 to Center for Nonprofit Excellence, Louisville, KY, 2012. For general support/server/succession plan.
$15,000 to National Society Sons of the American Revolution, Louisville, KY, 2012. For Expansion Main St Property.
$7,500 to Jefferson County Historical Society, Madison, IN, 2012. For photo copier.
$5,500 to Neighborhood House, Louisville, KY, 2012. For after-school/preschool/sr. adults.
$5,000 to American Red Cross, Louisville, KY, 2012. For Storm Sandy Disaster.
$5,000 to Coalition for the Homeless, Louisville, KY, 2012. For education initiative.
$3,190 to Cedar Ridge Camp, Louisville, KY, 2012. For Balance on Van/Autumn Under Cedar.
$1,000 to Belmont Mansion Association, Nashville, TN, 2012. To restore Master Bedroom.

3582
The Humana Foundation, Inc. ✧
500 W. Main St., Ste. 208
Louisville, KY 40202-2946 (502) 580-4140
Contact: Barbara Wright; Virginia K. Judd, Exec. Dir.
FAX: (502) 580-1256;
E-mail: bwright@humana.com; Additional e-mail: HumanaFoundation@humana.com; Main URL: http://www.humanafoundation.org
Grants List: http://www.humanafoundation.org/philanthropy/examples.asp

Incorporated in 1981 in KY.
Donor: Humana Inc.
Foundation type: Company-sponsored foundation.
Financial data (yr. ended 12/31/12): Assets, $140,674,968 (M); expenditures, $6,658,014; qualifying distributions, $6,658,014; giving activities include $6,658,014 for 137 grants (high: $774,635; low: $500).
Purpose and activities: The foundation supports programs designed to promote healthy lives and healthy communities, with a focus on the needs of children, families, and seniors. Special emphasis is directed toward programs designed to promote childhood health and education; health literacy; and active lifestyles and wellness.
Fields of interest: Arts; Elementary school/education; Education; Public health, obesity; Public health, physical fitness; Health care; Nutrition; Disasters, preparedness/services; Children, services; Family services; Human services; Public affairs; Aging; Economically disadvantaged.
Type of support: General/operating support; Continuing support; Annual campaigns; Capital campaigns; Building/renovation; Program development; Professorships; Curriculum development; Scholarship funds; Employee volunteer services; Employee matching gifts; Employee-related scholarships; Matching/challenge support.
Limitations: Applications accepted. Giving primarily in areas of company operations in Phoenix, AZ, San Diego and San Francisco, CA, Denver, CO, CT, FL, GA, Bloomington, Chicago, Peoria, and Rockford, IL, Indianapolis, IN, Louisville, KY, New Orleans, LA, Boston, MA, Baltimore, MD, Detroit, MI, Kansas City and St. Louis, MO, Charlotte, NC, NJ, Las Vegas, NV, NY, Cincinnati, OH, Philadelphia and Pittsburgh, PA, Columbia, SC, Nashville, TN, Austin, Dallas, and Houston, TX, Salt Lake City, UT, VA, and Green Bay and Milwaukee, WI. No support for social, labor, political, veterans', or fraternal organizations, lobbying efforts, or mission-focused activities. No grants for start-up needs or seed money, salary expenses or other administrative costs, general operating support for religious organizations, or for construction or renovation of sanctuaries.
Publications: Application guidelines; Grants list; Informational brochure; Newsletter.

Application information: Support is limited to 1 contribution per organization during any given year. Application form required.

Initial approach: Complete online application form
Copies of proposal: 1
Deadline(s): Nov. 1 through Jan. 15
Board meeting date(s): March
Final notification: April through May

Officers and Directors:* Michael B. McCallister,* Chair., C.E.O., and Pres.; James H. Bloem, Sr. V.P., C.F.O., and Treas.; George G. Bauernfeind, V.P.; Joan O. Lenahan, Secy.; Virginia K. Judd, Exec. Dir.; David A. Jones; David A. Jones, Jr.
EIN: 611004763

3583
Independence Foundation, Inc. ✧
2425 Frederica St.
P.O. Box 988
Owensboro, KY 42302 (270) 686-1776

Donors: Independence Bank; Ernie Davis.
Foundation type: Company-sponsored foundation.
Financial data (yr. ended 12/31/13): Assets, $183,953 (M); gifts received, $493,247; expenditures, $424,474; qualifying distributions, $424,474; giving activities include $413,750 for 365 grants (high: $25,000; low: $40), and $10,724 for 6 grants to individuals (high: $3,900; low: $293).
Purpose and activities: The foundation supports service clubs and organizations involved with education, cancer, housing development, recreation, youth, and community development; provides relief grants to employees of Independence Bank; and awards college scholarships to high school seniors from a seven county area.
Fields of interest: Education; Recreation; Community/economic development.
Type of support: General/operating support; Equipment; Emergency funds; Program development; Scholarship funds; Sponsorships; Grants to individuals; Scholarships—to individuals.
Limitations: Applications accepted. Giving primarily in areas of company operations in KY, with emphasis on Daviess, Hancock, Henderson, McLean, McCracken, Warren, and Webster counties.
Application information: Application form required.

Initial approach: Letter
Deadline(s): 20th of each month for general funding

Officer: Cathy R. Switzer, Admin.
Directors: Christopher Reid; Marjorie A. Reid.
EIN: 261568393
Selected grants: The following grants are a representative sample of this grantmaker's funding activity:
$10,175 to Diocese of Owensboro, Owensboro, KY, 2012. To assist with directory of services provided throughout Diocese assist with funding of 75th Anniversary showcasing history and services provided.
$10,000 to International Bluegrass Music Museum, Owensboro, KY, 2012. To support local music bluegrass festival.
$5,000 to Riverpark Center, Owensboro, KY, 2012. For international Mystery Writers Festival.
$4,750 to Owensboro Symphony Orchestra, Owensboro, KY, 2012. For funding to bring music awareness to general public and schools Assist with operating costs.
$2,500 to Paducah Symphony Orchestra, Paducah, KY, 2012. To sponsor events for community with musical diversity assist with expense for Youth Orchestra.
$1,600 to Western Kentucky Botanical Garden, Owensboro, KY, 2012. For membership contributing to operating costs Dazzling Daylilly Festival providing educational opportunities for schools and adults.
$144 to National Child Safety Council, Jackson, MI, 2012. For safety and drug awareness education.

3584
The J & L Foundation ✧
(formerly The Joan and Lee Thomas Foundation, Inc.)
2602 Grassland Dr.
Louisville, KY 40299-2524 (502) 495-1958
Contact: Lee B. Thomas, Dir.

Established in 1989 in KY.
Donors: Lee B. Thomas; Joan Thomas.
Foundation type: Independent foundation.
Financial data (yr. ended 06/30/13): Assets, $20,492,143 (M); expenditures, $1,270,539; qualifying distributions, $1,230,167; giving activities include $1,208,000 for 28 grants (high: $125,000; low: $5,000).
Purpose and activities: Giving primarily for human services and education.
Fields of interest: Higher education; Education; Human services; Children/youth, services; Family services; Religion, interfaith issues.
Limitations: Applications accepted. Giving primarily in Louisville, KY; some funding also in Washington, DC. No grants to individuals.
Application information: Application form not required.

Deadline(s): None

Officers and Directors:* Lee B. Thomas,* Chair. and Treas.; Glenn E. Thomas, Pres. and Secy.
EIN: 611166955
Selected grants: The following grants are a representative sample of this grantmaker's funding activity:
$5,000 to Westtown School, West Chester, PA, 2013. To Be Used Within Exempt Function.

3585
Dr. Kirti Jain Family Foundation, Inc. ✧
243 Bellefonte Cir.
Ashland, KY 41101-2195
Contact: Kirti Jain

Established in 2004.
Donors: Kirti Jain; Asha Jain.
Foundation type: Independent foundation.
Financial data (yr. ended 12/31/12): Assets, $10,960,603 (M); expenditures, $505,147; qualifying distributions, $501,351; giving activities include $501,351 for 8 grants (high: $450,000; low: $21).
Fields of interest: Education; Human services; International relief.
Application information: Application form not required.

Initial approach: Letter

Officers: Kirti Jain, Pres.; Asha Jain, Secy.
Director: Anshu Jain.
EIN: 201729881

3586
LG&E and KU Foundation Inc. ✧
(formerly E.ON U.S. Foundation Inc.)
220 W. Main St.
Louisville, KY 40202-1395 (502) 627-3337
FAX: (502) 627-3629; Application address: P.O. Box 32030, Louisville, KY 40232; Main URL: http://www.lge-ku.com/foundation/default.asp

Established in 1994 in KY.
Donors: LG&E Energy Corp.; LG&E Energy LLC; E.ON U.S. LLC.
Foundation type: Company-sponsored foundation.
Financial data (yr. ended 12/31/13): Assets, $12,533,481 (M); expenditures, $875,165; qualifying distributions, $839,948; giving activities include $839,948 for 43 grants (high: $296,545; low: $41).
Purpose and activities: The foundation supports programs designed to promote education, the environment, health, human services, and diversity.
Fields of interest: Arts; Education; Human services.
Type of support: General/operating support; Annual campaigns; Building/renovation; Program development; Scholarship funds; Employee matching gifts; Employee-related scholarships; Matching/challenge support.
Limitations: Applications accepted. Giving primarily in areas of company operations in KY. No support for political, fraternal, labor, or religious organizations or United Way or Fund for the Arts agencies. No grants to individuals, or for pageants or travel expenses, capital campaigns, medical research or disease campaigns/walks, or athletic sponsorships; no support of raffles or prizes.
Publications: Application guidelines; Program policy statement.
Application information: Support is limited to 1 contribution per organization during any given year. Application form required.

Initial approach: Download application and mail to foundation
Copies of proposal: 1
Deadline(s): Nov. 15
Board meeting date(s): Annually

Officers and Directors:* Victor A. Staffieri,* Pres.; Gerald A. Reynolds,* V.P. and Secy.; Laura M. Douglas, V.P.; S. Bradford Rives,* V.P.; Daniel K. Arbough, Treas.; Kent W. Blake; Mary C. Whelan.
Number of staff: 1 full-time professional.
EIN: 611257368

3587
Lift A Life Foundation, Inc. ✧
(formerly The David C. and Wendy L. Novak Foundation, Inc.)
4350 Brownsboro Rd., Ste. 110
Louisville, KY 40207-1681 (502) 893-4540
E-mail: info@listalifefoundation.org; Main URL: http://www.liftalifefoundation.org
Facebook: https://www.facebook.com/LiftALifeFoundation
LinkedIn: http://www.linkedin.com/company/lift-a-life-foundation?trk=top_nav_home
Twitter: https://twitter.com/LiftALifeFdtn

Established in 1999 in KY.
Donors: David C. Novak; Wendy L. Novak.
Foundation type: Independent foundation.
Financial data (yr. ended 12/31/12): Assets, $34,938,198 (M); gifts received, $9,535,542; expenditures, $4,511,363; qualifying distributions,

$4,239,950; giving activities include $4,239,950 for 27 grants (high: $500,000; low: $5,000).
Purpose and activities: Giving primarily to organizations that impact individuals and families in need in the areas of hunger, education, leadership, juvenile diabetes research and family support programs, and youth and family issues.
Fields of interest: Diabetes research; Food services; Human services; Family services; Christian agencies & churches; Youth.
Limitations: Giving primarily in KY; some funding also in Washington, DC. No support for political activities. No grants to individuals, or for travel, surveys or fundraising activities (unless exception is made by the foundation's Board of Directors).
Application information: Full proposals are by invitation only, upon review of Partnership Interest Form. Proposals submitted without a request from the foundation will not be considered.
Initial approach: Submit Partnership Interest Form through foundation web site
Deadline(s): See foundation web site for current deadlines
Officers and Directors:* David C. Novak,* Pres.; Wendy L. Novak,* V.P. and Secy.-Treas.; Ashley Novak Butler; Susan B. Novak.
EIN: 611359337

3588
The Marshall Charitable Foundation Inc. ✧
P.O. Box 7066
Louisville, KY 40257-0066

Established in 1998 in KY.
Donors: Homestead Co.; Louisville Timber Co.; Maggie T. Marshall.
Foundation type: Independent foundation.
Financial data (yr. ended 12/31/13): Assets, $23,273,379 (M); expenditures, $1,099,719; qualifying distributions, $1,065,114; giving activities include $1,048,200 for 49 grants (high: $105,000; low: $1,000).
Purpose and activities: Giving primarily for education, health organizations, and children, youth and social services.
Fields of interest: Education; Health care; Human services; Children/youth, services.
Limitations: Applications not accepted. Giving primarily in Louisville, KY. No grants to individuals.
Application information: Contributes only to pre-selected organizations.
Officers and Directors: Phillip H. Marshall, Sr.,* Pres.; Frank H. Thiemann III,* V.P.; Sue Ellen Marshall,* Secy.; Robert Wood Marshall, Jr.,* Treas.; Andrew M. Davidson; Bruce K. Dudley; Lydia M. Hess; April W. Marshall; Phillip H. Marshall, Jr.
EIN: 611308522

3589
Mercy Foundation, Inc. ✧ ☆
8820 Bankers St.
Florence, KY 41042-4212

Established in 2002.
Donors: Kheder Kutmah; Mohamed Zineddin; Rula Abdulrazzak; Fatema Zuhayll.
Foundation type: Independent foundation.
Financial data (yr. ended 12/31/12): Assets, $798,192 (M); gifts received, $315,664; expenditures, $1,558,340; qualifying distributions, $1,527,646; giving activities include $1,527,646 for 2+ grants (high: $1,355,000).
Fields of interest: Health care; Islam.
Type of support: General/operating support.
Limitations: Applications not accepted. Giving primarily in KY. No grants to individuals.
Application information: Unsolicited requests for funds not accepted.
Directors: Rula Abdulrazzak; Kheder Kutmah; Mohamed Zineddin.
EIN: 320013422

3590
The Mt. Brilliant Foundation ✧
(formerly HGG Family Foundation)
3314 Huffman Mill Pike
Lexington, KY 40511-9557

Established in 2007 in TX.
Donors: Harold G. Goodman; Bo Goodman; Hannah Goodman; Hutton Goodman; Mary Jane Goodman.
Foundation type: Independent foundation.
Financial data (yr. ended 12/31/13): Assets, $3,313,063 (M); gifts received, $800,000; expenditures, $869,819; qualifying distributions, $849,002; giving activities include $842,913 for 24 grants (high: $300,000; low: $160).
Fields of interest: Elementary/secondary education; Higher education; Cancer research.
Limitations: Applications not accepted. Giving primarily in KY; funding also in TX.
Application information: Unsolicited requests for funds not accepted.
Officers and Directors:* Hutton Gregory Goodman,* Chair.; Gay Bredin, Secy.; Rebecca Goodman,* Treas.; H. Viterbo Goodman; Hannah Jane Goodman; Harold G. Goodman; Mary Jane Goodman.
EIN: 261093418
Selected grants: The following grants are a representative sample of this grantmaker's funding activity:
$216,564 to Sayre School, Lexington, KY, 2012. For general support/debt reduction.
$53,600 to Kentucky Horse Park Foundation, Lexington, KY, 2012. For General Support/Barn Complex/Literacy Program.

3591
W.O. and Lois Newell Charitable Trust ✧
c/o Cumberland Security Bank
107 S. Main St.
Somerset, KY 42501-2005

Foundation type: Independent foundation.
Financial data (yr. ended 12/31/13): Assets, $16,266,469 (M); expenditures, $796,519; qualifying distributions, $713,380; giving activities include $713,380 for 13 grants (high: $178,345; low: $14,268).
Fields of interest: Education; Human services; Protestant agencies & churches.
Limitations: Applications not accepted. Giving primarily in KY.
Application information: Unsolicited requests for funds not accepted.
Trustee: Cumberland Security Bank.
EIN: 263939254

3592
The Norton Foundation Inc. ✧
(formerly The George W. Norton Foundation, Inc.)
4350 Brownsboro Rd., Ste. 133
Louisville, KY 40207-1679 (502) 893-9549
Contact: Lucy Crawford, Exec. Dir.
FAX: (502) 896-9378;
E-mail: lcrawford@nortonfoundation.com

Incorporated in 1958 in KY.
Donor: Mrs. George W. Norton†.
Foundation type: Independent foundation.
Financial data (yr. ended 12/31/12): Assets, $11,828,825 (M); expenditures, $901,773; qualifying distributions, $602,100; giving activities include $602,100 for grants.
Purpose and activities: The foundation's mission is to contribute to the improvement of the quality of life, and foster a favorable business climate in the company's communities in North America, consistent with and supportive of business objectives.
Fields of interest: Arts education; Education, early childhood education; Elementary school/education; Secondary school/education; Education, reading; Education; Human services; Children/youth, services; Family services; Minorities/immigrants, centers/services; Economically disadvantaged.
Type of support: General/operating support; Continuing support; Program development; Seed money; Scholarship funds.
Limitations: Applications accepted. Giving limited to the Louisville, KY, area. No grants to individuals.
Publications: Application guidelines; Financial statement; Grants list.
Application information: Application form required.
Initial approach: Proposal
Copies of proposal: 5
Deadline(s): Quarterly
Board meeting date(s): Quarterly
Officers: Jane Norton Newton, Pres.; Robert W. Dulaney, V.P.; Lucy Crawford,* Exec. Dir.
Director: Richard H.C. Clay.
Number of staff: 1 full-time professional.
EIN: 616024040

3593
Opera House Fund, Inc. ✧
c/o Doug Dean
106 W. Vine St., Ste. 600
Lexington, KY 40507-1679

Established in 1983 in KY.
Donor: William T. Young, Jr.
Foundation type: Independent foundation.
Financial data (yr. ended 06/30/13): Assets, $7,027,558 (M); gifts received, $17,500; expenditures, $638,782; qualifying distributions, $592,281; giving activities include $586,385 for 15 grants (high: $103,955; low: $1,957).
Purpose and activities: The fund supports performing arts groups that use the Lexington Opera House.
Fields of interest: Arts education; Performing arts; Performing arts, dance; Performing arts, ballet; Performing arts, theater; Performing arts, music; Recreation, parks/playgrounds.
Limitations: Applications not accepted. Giving limited to Lexington, KY. No grants to individuals.
Application information: Contributes only to pre-selected organizations.
Officers and Directors:* William T. Young, Jr.,* Pres.; Linda Carey,* V.P.; Doug Dean,*

Secy.-Treas.; W. James Host; Bob Warren; Christopher Young.
EIN: 510180177

3594
The Orleton Trust Fund ✧
303 Eden Ave., Unit 4A
Bellevue, KY 41073-1170

Trust established in 1944 in OH.
Donor: Mary E. Johnston†.
Foundation type: Independent foundation.
Financial data (yr. ended 12/31/13): Assets, $7,282,089 (M); expenditures, $708,807; qualifying distributions, $608,124; giving activities include $597,225 for 12 grants (high: $119,451; low: $23,890).
Fields of interest: Foundations (private grantmaking); Foundations (community).
Type of support: General/operating support; Building/renovation; Scholarship funds.
Limitations: Applications not accepted. Giving in the U.S., with emphasis on CA and OH. No grants to individuals.
Application information: Contributes only to pre-selected organizations.
Board meeting date(s): As required
Trustee: John Sawyer.
EIN: 316024543

3595
Owsley Brown Ii Cockayne Fund, Inc. ✧ ☆
c/o Zelkova Strategic Partners, LLC
333 E. Main St., Ste. 401
Louisville, KY 40202-1297

Established in KY.
Donor: Martin Shallenberger†.
Foundation type: Independent foundation.
Financial data (yr. ended 12/31/13): Assets, $35,407,973 (M); expenditures, $1,340,009; qualifying distributions, $1,302,102; giving activities include $1,278,321 for 37 grants (high: $330,000; low: $200).
Fields of interest: Arts; Education; Human services.
Limitations: Applications not accepted. Giving in the U.S., with some emphasis on Louisville, KY.
Application information: Unsolicited request for funds not accepted.
Officers and Directors:* Christina Lee Brown,* Pres.; Owsley Brown III,* V.P.; Augusta Brown Holland,* Secy.; Brooke Brown Barzun,* Treas.
EIN: 452961442

3596
Raymond B. Preston Family Foundation ✧
P.O. Box 5
Henderson, KY 42419-0005

Established in 1989 in MD.
Donors: Hattie L. Preston; Raymond B. Preston; Ohio Valley Bancorp.
Foundation type: Independent foundation.
Financial data (yr. ended 12/31/13): Assets, $11,492,132 (M); expenditures, $649,759; qualifying distributions, $588,714; giving activities include $559,557 for 41 grants (high: $59,000; low: $100).
Purpose and activities: Giving primarily for education and social services.
Fields of interest: Performing arts, music; Arts; Elementary/secondary education; Higher education; Hospitals (general); Human services; Residential/custodial care, hospices; Christian agencies & churches.
Type of support: General/operating support; Building/renovation.
Limitations: Applications not accepted. Giving primarily in KY, with emphasis on Henderson and Bowling Green. No grants to individuals.
Application information: Contributes only to pre-selected organizations.
Officers and Directors:* Charlotte Critser,* Pres.; Connie Walaskay,* V.P. and Secy.; Kay Smith, Recording Secy.; Chris Melton, Treas.; Gary Critser; Kent Preston; Phillip Brigham; and 3 additional directors.
EIN: 521676236
Selected grants: The following grants are a representative sample of this grantmaker's funding activity:
$50,000 to Western Kentucky University, Bowling Green, KY, 2011.
$25,000 to Saint Anthonys Hospice of Henderson County, Henderson, KY, 2010.
$22,000 to Saint Pauls Episcopal Church, Henderson, KY, 2011.
$15,000 to Henderson Area Arts Alliance, Henderson, KY, 2011.
$10,000 to Bainbridge Schools Foundation, Bainbridge Island, WA, 2011.
$10,000 to Chemical Educational Foundation, Arlington, VA, 2011.
$10,000 to Interfaith Homeless Network, Chattanooga, TN, 2010.
$8,000 to Community Foundation of Louisville, Louisville, KY, 2011.
$5,000 to Chemical Educational Foundation, Arlington, VA, 2011.
$4,000 to University of Southern Indiana, Evansville, IN, 2011. For scholarship.
$2,000 to University of Southern Indiana, Evansville, IN, 2011.
$1,500 to Henderson Community College, Henderson, KY, 2011. For scholarship.

3597
Public Life Foundation of Owensboro ✧ ☆
(formerly The Community Life Foundation of Owensboro, KY)
401 Frederica St., Bldg. B, Ste. 203
Owensboro, KY 42301 (270) 685-2652
FAX: (270) 685-6074; Main URL: http://www.plfo.org/

Established in 1995 in KY.
Donors: Frankie Hager; John S. Hager; Larry Hager Jr.; Marjorie Hager.
Foundation type: Operating foundation.
Financial data (yr. ended 12/31/13): Assets, $8,262,804 (M); gifts received, $91,102; expenditures, $822,623; qualifying distributions, $742,908; giving activities include $440,000 for 12 grants (high: $255,000; low: $25).
Purpose and activities: The foundation will support two broad categories of projects: (a) the exploration of the relationship of values and public life in the Owensboro, Kentucky area, and (b) education, especially for at-risk children and their parents. Proposals may be either research-oriented, with preference in the research area given to projects with the potential for improving the quality of public life in the Owensboro, Kentucky area.
Fields of interest: Education; Human services; Community/economic development.
Type of support: Endowments; Program development; Research; Technical assistance.
Limitations: Applications not accepted. Giving primarily in KY.
Publications: Annual report.
Application information: Unsolicited requests for funds not accepted.
Officers and Directors:* Sarah Hager Wood,* Chair.; Bruce William Hager,* Vice-Chair.; Rodney Berry, Pres.; Kathy Strobel, Secy.; Susan Hager Alford,* Treas.; John Stewart Hager, Jr.; William G. Speciale.
Number of staff: 1 full-time professional; 1 full-time support.
EIN: 616232654

3598
E. O. Robinson Mountain Fund ✧
P.O. Box 54930
Lexington, KY 40555-4930 (859) 269-2624
Contact: Juanita Stollings, Secy.-Treas.

Incorporated in 1922 in KY.
Donors: Edward O. Robinson†; University of Kentucky.
Foundation type: Independent foundation.
Financial data (yr. ended 06/30/13): Assets, $15,974,540 (M); expenditures, $777,875; qualifying distributions, $637,814; giving activities include $422,717 for grants.
Purpose and activities: Giving to promote the general welfare of the people of eastern KY in the areas of education, health care, and community programs.
Fields of interest: Humanities; Arts; Higher education; Scholarships/financial aid; Education; Health care; Human services; Economic development.
Type of support: General/operating support; Continuing support; Building/renovation; Equipment; Scholarship funds; Technical assistance; Matching/challenge support.
Limitations: Applications accepted. Giving limited to 30 counties in eastern KY. No support for political or religious organizations, substance abuse programs, or national organizations, even if for local projects. No grants to individuals, or for salaries, or endowments.
Publications: Application guidelines; Informational brochure.
Application information: Application form required.
Initial approach: Letter
Copies of proposal: 1
Deadline(s): Mar. 1 and Sept. 1
Board meeting date(s): Apr. and Oct.
Officers: William Engle III, Chair.; J. Hagan Codell, Vice-Chair.; Juanita Stollings, Secy.-Treas.
Directors: Sara Walter Combs; Susan Duff; Ronald M. Johnson; James L. Hurley; Harold H. Mullis.
Number of staff: 1 full-time professional; 3 full-time support.
EIN: 610449642
Selected grants: The following grants are a representative sample of this grantmaker's funding activity:
$25,000 to Alice Lloyd College, Pippa Passes, KY, 2011.
$14,000 to Alice Lloyd College, Pippa Passes, KY, 2011. For scholarships.

3599
Ephraim Roseman Foundation, Inc. ✧ ☆
2025 Fred Fackler Rd.
Brandenburg, KY 40108-9425

Established in 1961 in KY.
Donor: Wilma S. Roseman.
Foundation type: Independent foundation.
Financial data (yr. ended 12/31/13): Assets, $12,361,886 (M); gifts received, $10,673; expenditures, $810,234; qualifying distributions, $621,000; giving activities include $621,000 for 16 grants (high: $100,000; low: $1,000).
Purpose and activities: Support for ovarian cancer and a children's hospital.
Fields of interest: Health care; ALS research; Alzheimer's disease research; Medical research; Human services.
Limitations: Applications not accepted. No grants to individuals.
Application information: Unsolicited requests for funds not accepted.
Officer: Linda K. Shelman, Pres.
Directors: Dana S. Flaherty; Leslie K. Ory; Alicia J. Shelman.
EIN: 616027248

3600
The Charles E. and Mary Elizabeth Scripps Foundation, Inc. ✧
250 Grandview Ave., Ste. 400
Fort Mitchell, KY 41017-5634

Established in 2007 in KY.
Donors: Charles E. Scripps‡; Mary Elizabeth Scripps Byrne.
Foundation type: Independent foundation.
Financial data (yr. ended 12/31/13): Assets, $10,992,116 (M); expenditures, $552,683; qualifying distributions, $482,847; giving activities include $482,500 for 24 grants (high: $65,000; low: $5,000).
Fields of interest: Arts; Higher education; Education; Human services.
Limitations: Applications not accepted. Giving in the U.S., with emphasis on FL. No grants to individuals.
Application information: Contributes only to pre-selected organizations.
Officers and Directors:* Mary Elizabeth Scripps Byrne,* Pres.; Bruce W. Sanford,* Secy.; Ben Breslin,* Treas.; Andrew Breslin.
EIN: 261541507
Selected grants: The following grants are a representative sample of this grantmaker's funding activity:
$20,000 to Ave Maria University, Ave Maria, FL, 2012. For Financial Aid for Students.
$20,000 to Maysville Players, Maysville, KY, 2012. To support and Expansion of Youth Summer Theater Experience.
$10,000 to Holy Name Cathedral, Chicago, IL, 2012. For general purposes.
$10,000 to Kentucky Gateway Museum Center, Maysville, KY, 2012. For Read on Program.

3601
Smith Foundation ✧
(formerly Edward P. and Mary Klein Smith Charitable Trust)
111 Lookout Farm Dr.
Crestview Hills, KY 41017

Foundation type: Independent foundation.
Financial data (yr. ended 12/31/13): Assets, $15,499,206 (M); expenditures, $747,320; qualifying distributions, $653,231; giving activities include $653,231 for 33 grants (high: $65,323; low: $13,065).
Fields of interest: Education; Health care; Human services.
Limitations: Applications not accepted. Giving primarily in KY.
Application information: Unsolicited requests for funds not accepted.
Trustee: The Bank of Kentucky, Inc.
EIN: 900587749

3602
The Spray Foundation, Inc. ✧
(formerly ACK Foundation, Inc.)
P.O. Box 22828
Lexington, KY 40522-2828

Established in 1995 in GA.
Donors: James G. Kenan; Anne R. Kenan; Brutus C. Kenan.
Foundation type: Independent foundation.
Financial data (yr. ended 12/31/12): Assets, $61,382,017 (M); gifts received, $931,616; expenditures, $3,153,557; qualifying distributions, $3,000,000; giving activities include $3,000,000 for grants.
Purpose and activities: Giving primarily for education, the environment, health care, and children, youth and social services.
Fields of interest: Higher education; Education; Environment, natural resources; Health care; Human services; Children/youth, services.
Type of support: General/operating support; Annual campaigns; Capital campaigns; Endowments; Program development; Matching/challenge support.
Limitations: Applications not accepted. Giving primarily in Atlanta, GA, Harrodsburg and Lexington, KY, and PA. No grants to individuals.
Application information: Contributes only to pre-selected organizations.
Officers and Directors:* James G. Kenan III, Chair., Pres. and Treas.; Angela Thomas,* Secy.; George Branch; Sarah K. Kennedy; Clay Kenan Kirk; Hazel Nystrom.
EIN: 582219018

3603
Sam Swope Family Foundation, Inc. ✧
10 Swope Auto Ctr.
Louisville, KY 40299-1862

Established in 2002 in KY.
Donor: Samuel G. Swope.
Foundation type: Independent foundation.
Financial data (yr. ended 12/31/12): Assets, $14,606,325 (M); gifts received, $3,350,000; expenditures, $602,656; qualifying distributions, $579,087; giving activities include $554,962 for 23 grants (high: $155,612; low: $1,000).
Fields of interest: Higher education, university; Animal welfare; Hospitals (general); Boy scouts; Human services; Christian agencies & churches.
Type of support: General/operating support.
Limitations: Applications not accepted. Giving primarily in FL and KY. No grants to individuals.
Application information: Contributes only to pre-selected organizations.
Directors: Patricia G. Swope; Samuel G. Swope; Susan Swope.
EIN: 920186097

3604
Vanhoose Stewart Foundation, Inc. ✧ ☆
P.O. Box 2439
Ashland, KY 41105-2439

Established in 2002 in KY.
Donors: John C. Stewart, Jr.; Robert W. Vanhoose.
Foundation type: Independent foundation.
Financial data (yr. ended 06/30/13): Assets, $910,744 (M); expenditures, $969,063; qualifying distributions, $947,966; giving activities include $947,966 for 22 grants (high: $900,000; low: $100).
Fields of interest: Education; Agriculture/food; Human services.
Limitations: Applications not accepted. No grants to individuals.
Application information: Unsolicited requests for funds not accepted.
Officers: Robert W. Vanhoose, Pres.; J. Michael Delaney, Treas.
EIN: 383655991
Selected grants: The following grants are a representative sample of this grantmaker's funding activity:
$8,000 to University of Kentucky, Lexington, KY, 2012.
$2,000 to Ohio State University, Columbus, OH, 2012.

3605
Ventas Charitable Foundation, Inc. ✧ ☆
10350 Ormsby Park Pl., Ste. 300
Louisville, KY 40223-6177
Main URL: http://www.ventasreit.com/corporate-responsibility/charitable-giving

Established in 2005 in KY.
Foundation type: Company-sponsored foundation.
Financial data (yr. ended 12/31/13): Assets, $12,742,361 (M); expenditures, $524,581; qualifying distributions, $435,801; giving activities include $435,801 for 54 grants (high: $47,600; low: $250).
Purpose and activities: The foundation supports organizations involved with arts and culture, education, and human services.
Fields of interest: Visual arts, art conservation; Museums; Arts; Education; Recreation, parks/playgrounds; Recreation; American Red Cross; Family services; Human services.
Type of support: General/operating support; Program development.
Limitations: Applications not accepted. No grants to individuals.
Application information: Contributes only to pre-selected organizations.
Officers and Directors:* Richard A. Schweinhart, Pres.; Kristen M. Benson, Secy.; Brian K. Wood, Treas.
EIN: 203959500
Selected grants: The following grants are a representative sample of this grantmaker's funding activity:
$50,000 to Cystic Fibrosis Foundation, Bethesda, MD, 2011.

$10,000 to 21st Century Parks, Louisville, KY, 2011.
$10,000 to DePaul University, Chicago, IL, 2011.
$9,250 to High Jump, Chicago, IL, 2011.
$8,000 to Daniel Murphy Scholarship Fund, Chicago, IL, 2011.
$5,000 to Center for Women and Families, Louisville, KY, 2011.
$5,000 to Envision Unlimited, Chicago, IL, 2011.
$2,550 to YMCA of Metropolitan Chicago, Chicago, IL, 2011.

3606
WCA Charitable Foundation ✧ ☆

2100 Gardiner Ln., Ste. 207
Louisville, KY 40205-2948
Contact: Stephen J. Evans

Established in 1998 in KY.
Donor: Wayne T. Smith.
Foundation type: Independent foundation.
Financial data (yr. ended 12/31/13): Assets, $1,946,906 (M); gifts received, $1,003,617; expenditures, $1,273,794; qualifying distributions, $1,270,111; giving activities include $1,270,111 for 2 grants (high: $1,000,000; low: $270,111).
Fields of interest: Nursing home/convalescent facility; Health care; Religion.
Limitations: Applications not accepted. Giving primarily in AL. No grants to individuals.
Application information: Unsolicited request for funds not accepted.
Trustee: Stephen J. Evans.
EIN: 611328465
Selected grants: The following grants are a representative sample of this grantmaker's funding activity:
$5,000 to Gildas Club Louisville, Louisville, KY, 2011.

3607
Marilyn & William Young Charitable Foundation, Inc. ✧

(formerly Marilyn & William Young Foundation)
P.O. Box 825
Owensboro, KY 42302-0549 (270) 926-1860
Contact: Sara Hemingway

Established in 1993 in KY.
Donor: Marilyn F. Young‡.
Foundation type: Independent foundation.
Financial data (yr. ended 12/31/13): Assets, $12,534,516 (M); expenditures, $663,637; qualifying distributions, $586,396; giving activities include $535,037 for 42 grants (high: $100,000; low: $500).
Purpose and activities: Giving primarily for the arts, particularly to museums; funding also for health and social services.
Fields of interest: Museums; Museums (art); Museums (specialized); Performing arts centers; Performing arts, orchestras; Arts; Education; Boys & girls clubs; Human services; Developmentally disabled, centers & services; Community/economic development.
Type of support: General/operating support; Capital campaigns; Building/renovation; Equipment; Program development; Scholarship funds; Consulting services; Matching/challenge support.
Limitations: Applications accepted. Giving primarily in Owensboro, KY. No support for political organizations.
Application information: Application form not required.
Initial approach: Proposal
Deadline(s): None
Directors: Gayle S. Dorsey; E. Phillips Malone; Joe Overby; William R. Young III.
Number of staff: 1 part-time professional.
EIN: 616175836

3608
Yum! Brands Foundation, Inc. ✧

(formerly Tricon Foundation, Inc.)
P.O. Box 35910
Louisville, KY 40232-5910 (502) 874-2203
Contact: Angela Osting, Mgr.
Additional address: 1441 Gardiner Lane, Louisville, KY 40213; Main URL: http://www.yum.com/responsibility/foundation.asp

Established in 1998 in KY and TX.
Donors: Tricon Global Restaurants, Inc.; Yum! Brands, Inc.
Foundation type: Company-sponsored foundation.
Financial data (yr. ended 12/31/13): Assets, $10,158,048 (M); gifts received, $9,293,643; expenditures, $7,686,460; qualifying distributions, $7,623,691; giving activities include $7,444,001 for 478 grants (high: $3,428,250; low: $25), and $20,500 for 8 grants to individuals (high: $5,000; low: $500).
Purpose and activities: The foundation supports programs designed to promote hunger relief, youth development, and the arts.
Fields of interest: Performing arts, theater; Arts; Higher education; Education; Diabetes; Food services; Food banks; Disasters, preparedness/services; Youth, services; Human services; United Ways and Federated Giving Programs.
Type of support: Grants to individuals; General/operating support; Continuing support; Annual campaigns; Program development; Employee volunteer services; Employee matching gifts.
Limitations: Applications not accepted. Giving primarily in areas of company operations, with some emphasis on Louisville, KY; giving also to national organizations.
Application information: Unsolicited applications are currently not accepted.
Officers and Directors:* David C. Novak,* Chair. and C.E.O.; Jonathan Blum, Pres.; Christian L. Campbell,* V.P. and Secy.; Pat Grismer,* V.P. and Treas.; Donald Phillips, V.P.; W. Lawrence Gathof, C.F.O.; Laura Melilo Barnum, Exec. Dir. and Admin.; Roger Eaton; Anne Byerlein.
EIN: 611327140
Selected grants: The following grants are a representative sample of this grantmaker's funding activity:
$3,069,852 to World Food Program USA, Washington, DC, 2012. For unrestricted support.
$1,054,688 to Juvenile Diabetes Research Foundation International, Louisville, KY, 2012. For unrestricted support.
$955,682 to United Way, Metro, Louisville, KY, 2012. For unrestricted support.
$609,487 to Fund for the Arts, Louisville, KY, 2012. For unrestricted support.
$400,000 to World Food Program USA, Washington, DC, 2012. For unrestricted support.
$52,600 to Muhammad Ali Museum and Education Center, Louisville, KY, 2012. For unrestricted support.
$51,000 to Juvenile Diabetes Research Foundation International, Louisville, KY, 2012. For unrestricted support.
$15,600 to Kentucky Center for African American Heritage, Louisville, KY, 2012. For unrestricted support.
$13,491 to World Food Program USA, Washington, DC, 2012. For unrestricted support.
$11,600 to Louisville Science Center, Louisville, KY, 2012. For unrestricted support.

LOUISIANA

3609
Albemarle Foundation ✧
451 Florida St.
Baton Rouge, LA 70801-1700 (225) 388-7552
Contact: Sandra M. Holub, Mgr.
E-mail: AlbemarleFoundation@albemarle.com;
E-mail for Sandra Holub:
sandra_holub@albemarle.com; Main URL: http://www.albemarle.com/Sustainability/Albemarle-Foundation-42.html
Grants List: http://www.albemarle.com/Sustainability/2013-Giving-by-Agency-838C42.html
YouTube: https://www.youtube.com/watch?feature=player_embedded&v=BJnANeuLUD8

Established in 2006 in VA.
Donors: M. Rohr; J. Steitz; L. Kissam; Albemarle Corp.
Foundation type: Company-sponsored foundation.
Financial data (yr. ended 12/31/12): Assets, $10,121,573 (M); gifts received, $11,070,282; expenditures, $3,883,642; qualifying distributions, $3,591,091; giving activities include $3,591,091 for 675 grants (high: $281,487; low: $50).
Purpose and activities: The foundation supports programs designed to promote future workforce and education; social and health services; and cultural resources and advocacy.
Fields of interest: Arts education; Arts; Charter schools; Adult/continuing education; Education; Hospitals (general); Health care; Employment, services; Food banks; Housing/shelter, development; Disasters, preparedness/services; Children/youth, services; Family services; Human services; Community/economic development; Engineering/technology.
Type of support: General/operating support; Annual campaigns; Building/renovation; Program development; Curriculum development; Employee volunteer services; Employee matching gifts; Employee-related scholarships.
Limitations: Applications accepted. Giving limited to communities in which Albemarle Corporation operates in Magnolia, AR, Baton Rouge, LA, South Haven, MI, Twinsburg, OH, Tyrone, PA, Orangeburg, SC, and Bayport, Clearlake, and Pasadena, TX. No support for discriminatory organizations or legislative organizations. No grants for telephone solicitations.
Publications: Application guidelines; Grants list; Informational brochure.
Application information: Grant requests of $5,000 and less are forwarded to site councils for review. Grant requests of $5,001 must be approved by the Board of Directors at the January meeting. Organizations receiving support are asked to submit a final report. Application form required.
Initial approach: Complete online application
Deadline(s): Feb. to Nov.
Board meeting date(s): First week of May and Nov.
Final notification: 4 to 12 weeks
Officers and Directors:* Luke Kissam,* Pres.; Nicole C. Daniel, Secy.; Richard G. Fishman, Treas.; Mark C. Rohr, Pres.; John M. Steitz; Ron Zumstein.
EIN: 204798471

3610
The Almar Foundation ✧
601 Poydras St., Ste. 1726
New Orleans, LA 70130-6039
Contact: Susan Couvillon, Mgr.
FAX: (504) 524-8519;
E-mail: almar_foundation@yahoo.com

Established in 1997 in LA.
Foundation type: Independent foundation.
Financial data (yr. ended 12/31/13): Assets, $20,619,765 (M); expenditures, $788,246; qualifying distributions, $724,538; giving activities include $688,550 for 70 grants (high: $100,000; low: $250).
Purpose and activities: Giving primarily for education and services to the economically disadvantaged in New Orleans, LA, as well as for the re-building of New Orleans, post Hurricane Katrina.
Fields of interest: Education; Disasters, Hurricane Katrina; Religion.
Type of support: General/operating support; Endowments; Seed money; Scholarship funds.
Limitations: Giving primarily in New Orleans, LA. No support for political organizations. No grants to individuals.
Application information: Generally does not accept unsolicited request for funds.
Initial approach: Letter
Copies of proposal: 1
Deadline(s): None
Board meeting date(s): May, Nov. and Feb.
Manager: Susan Couvillon.
Trustees: Alden Laborde; James Laborde; John Laborde; Stephanie Laborde; Jane Roussel.
Number of staff: 1 part-time professional.
EIN: 721371702
Selected grants: The following grants are a representative sample of this grantmaker's funding activity:
$80,000 to Loyola University, New Orleans, LA, 2012. For English Department and Education.
$3,368 to Jesuit High School, New Orleans, LA, 2012. For Capital Campaign and Annual Giving.
$1,250 to Baton Rouge Area Foundation, Baton Rouge, LA, 2012. For Animal TransportJazz Coalition.

3611
The Azby Fund ✧
650 Poydras St., Ste. 2521
New Orleans, LA 70130-6191

Established in 1969 in LA.
Donors: Marion W. Harvey†; Herbert J. Harvey, Jr.†; Erminia Wadsworth†.
Foundation type: Independent foundation.
Financial data (yr. ended 12/31/13): Assets, $24,817,593 (M); expenditures, $1,737,114; qualifying distributions, $1,253,272; giving activities include $1,181,897 for 60 grants (high: $406,184; low: $1,000).
Purpose and activities: Giving primarily for education, community development, botanical gardens, youth services, and Roman Catholic churches and organizations; funding also for the arts, and historic preservation.
Fields of interest: Arts; Education; Human services.
Limitations: Applications not accepted. Giving primarily in New Orleans, LA. No grants to individuals.
Application information: Contributes only to pre-selected organizations.
Officers: Ann Fitzmorris, Pres.; Stewart Farnet, V.P.; Thomas B. Lemann, Secy.-Treas.; Michael S. Liebaert, Exec. Dir.
Director: Samuel S. Farnet, Jr.
EIN: 726049781
Selected grants: The following grants are a representative sample of this grantmaker's funding activity:
$264,353 to River Road Historical Society, Destrehan, LA, 2012. For historical.
$55,000 to Tulane University, School of Architecture, New Orleans, LA, 2012. For education.

3612
Baptist Community Ministries
(formerly Christian Health Ministries)
400 Poydras St., Ste. 2950
New Orleans, LA 70130-3245 (504) 593-2323
Contact: Charles Beasley, Interim C.E.O. and Pres.
FAX: (504) 593-2301; E-mail: info@bcm.org; Main URL: http://www.bcm.org

Established in 1996 in LA; converted from the sale of the assets of Mercy + Baptist Medical Center. In 2009, the organization changed their name following a merger with the original Baptist Community Ministries.
Donors: C.E. McFarland Trust; D.A. McFarland Trust; Baptist Community Ministries; Christian Health Ministries Foundation.
Foundation type: Independent foundation.
Financial data (yr. ended 09/30/13): Assets, $263,002,185 (M); gifts received, $1,096,641; expenditures, $14,705,458; qualifying distributions, $13,577,081; giving activities include $8,385,686 for 120 grants (high: $332,500; low: $280), and $1,719,693 for foundation-administered programs.
Purpose and activities: Baptist Community Ministries is committed to the development of a healthy community offering a wholesome quality of life to its residents and to improving the physical, mental, and spiritual health of the individuals it serves.
Fields of interest: Education; Health care; Crime/violence prevention; Public affairs, citizen participation.
Type of support: General/operating support; Continuing support; Program development; Seed money; Curriculum development; Research; Technical assistance; Program evaluation; Matching/challenge support.
Limitations: Applications accepted. Giving primarily in Jefferson, Orleans, Plaquemines, St. Bernard and St. Tammany parishes, LA. No support for operating budgets of individual churches. No grants to individuals, or for capital grants.
Publications: Application guidelines; Annual report (including application guidelines); Informational brochure.
Application information: Provide material on standard 8-1/2 by 11 inch paper with 2 filing holes punched at top and secured with binder clips. Do not use staples, binders or folders. Application form required.
Initial approach: Check foundation web site for updated application information before applying. Application form available on foundation web site
Copies of proposal: 3
Deadline(s): Spring: Feb. 15 - Feb. 28. Fall: Aug. 15 - Aug. 31

Board meeting date(s): May and Nov.
Final notification: May and Nov.

Officers and Trustees:* H. Merritt Lane III,* Chair.; David Guidry,* Vice-Chair.; Charles E. Beasley, C.E.O. and Pres.; Laurie G. DeCuir, Sr. V.P. and C.F.O.; Frances L. Hawkins, R.N., V.P., Congregational Wellness; James E. Hightower, Jr., Ed. D., V.P., Chaplaincy; Luceia LeDoux, V.P., Public Safety and Gov. Oversight; Jennifer P. Roberts, V.P., Education; Elizabeth L. Scheer, V.P., Health; Patricia M. Prechter, Ed.D., M.S.N*, Secy.-Treas.; Herschel L. Abbott, Jr.; Dianne C. Boazman; Tina S. Clark; Richard Estrada; John J. Graham; Robert A. "Drew" Jardine, Jr.; Hans B. Jonassen; Frank Kelly; Kenneth E. Pickering; Jerry St. Pierre, M.D.; Rep. James Tucker.
Number of staff: 11 full-time professional; 3 full-time support; 1 part-time support.
EIN: 720423887
Selected grants: The following grants are a representative sample of this grantmaker's funding activity:
$638,850 to School Leadership Center of Greater New Orleans, New Orleans, LA, 2012. For School Leadership Building Program.
$570,000 to Healthy Lifestyle Choices, New Orleans, LA, 2012. For Children's Health Education Program.
$149,250 to Youth Empowerment Project, New Orleans, LA, 2012. For Disconnected Youth Mentoring and Support Services Program.
$145,926 to New Orleans Police and Justice Foundation, New Orleans, LA, 2012. For Fully-Integrated Justice Information System/ MOTION.
$100,250 to Libertys Kitchen, New Orleans, LA, 2012. For Youth Development Program.
$85,000 to Reconcile New Orleans, New Orleans, LA, 2012. For program to improve and expand job readiness.
$75,079 to Junior Achievement of Greater New Orleans, New Orleans, LA, 2012. For Capstone Challenge Campaign.
$65,000 to New Orleans Bayou Steppers Social Aid and Pleasure Club, Silence is Violence, New Orleans, LA, 2012. For Victim Allies Project.
$36,240 to Tulane University, New Orleans, LA, 2012. For Faces and Voices of Community Moms, initiative to encourage breastfeeding.
$21,038 to Jefferson Chamber Foundation, Metairie, LA, 2012. For Jefferson Chamber Foundation Academy.

3613
Baton Rouge Area Foundation

402 N. 4th St.
Baton Rouge, LA 70802-5506 (225) 387-6126
Contact: John G. Davies, C.E.O.
FAX: (225) 387-6153; E-mail: mverma@braf.org; Additional tel.: (877) 387-6126; Grant information e-mail: lsmyth@braf.org; Main URL: http://www.braf.org
Facebook: https://www.facebook.com/BRAreaFoundation
Twitter: https://twitter.com/BRFdn

Incorporated in 1964 in LA.
Foundation type: Community foundation.
Financial data (yr. ended 12/31/12): Assets, $523,407,700 (M); gifts received, $32,742,428; expenditures, $51,659,572; giving activities include $35,351,731 for grants.
Purpose and activities: The Baton Rouge Area Foundation unites human and financial resources to enhance the quality of life in Southern Louisiana.
Fields of interest: Humanities; Arts; Child development, education; Elementary school/education; Secondary school/education; Medical school/education; Nursing school/education; Education; Environment; Health care; Health organizations, association; Disasters, Hurricane Katrina; Children/youth, services; Child development, services; Aging, centers/services; Women, centers/services; Human services; Community/economic development; Religion; Aging; Disabilities, people with; Women; Economically disadvantaged.
Type of support: Capital campaigns; Building/renovation; Equipment; Endowments; Emergency funds; Program development; Seed money; Research; Program-related investments/loans; Scholarships—to individuals; Matching/challenge support; Mission-related investments/loans.
Limitations: Applications accepted. Giving limited to the Baton Rouge, LA, area, including East Baton Rouge, West Baton Rouge, Livingston, Ascension, Iberville, Pointe Coupee, East Feliciana, and West Feliciana parishes. No grants to individuals (except for scholarships), or for continuing support, annual campaigns, deficit financing, fellowships, or operating budgets.
Publications: Application guidelines; Annual report (including application guidelines); Informational brochure; Newsletter.
Application information: Visit foundation web site for online grant application and additional information. Application form required.
Initial approach: Create online grant application account
Copies of proposal: 1
Deadline(s): Varies
Board meeting date(s): May, July, Sept., and Nov.
Final notification: Varies
Officers and Directors:* C. Kris Kirkpatrick,* Chair.; John G. Davies,* C.E.O. and Pres.; John Spain, Exec. V.P.; Suzanne L. Turner,* Secy.; William E. Balhoff, Treas.; Courtney Gustin, Cont.; Edmund J. Giering IV, Genl. Counsel; Annette D. Barton; Mark C. Drennen; Perry J. Franklin; Rose Hudson; Rev. Raymond A. Jetson; Mary Terrell Joseph; Matthew G. McKay; Kevin F. Knobloch; John "Jay" Noland, Jr.; R. Ryland Percy III; Albert D. Sam II; Roland M. Toups; Jeffrey S. Zehnder.
Trustee Bank: JPMorgan Chase Bank, N.A.
Number of staff: 16 full-time professional.
EIN: 726030391
Selected grants: The following grants are a representative sample of this grantmaker's funding activity:
$882,876 to New Schools for Baton Rouge, Baton Rouge, LA, 2013. For distribution.
$833,333 to Catholic Charities of Northwest Florida, Pensacola, FL, 2013. To assist Catholic Charities of Northwest Florida in the Spirit of the South Social Service delivery System.
$658,523 to National Christian Charitable Foundation, Alpharetta, GA, 2013. For fund transfer.
$450,000 to Single Stop USA, New York, NY, 2013. For a regional, multi-state expansion to up to nineteen sites at twelve community colleges/systems in Louisiana, Mississippi, Alabama and Florida.
$400,000 to Gulf Coast Community Foundation, Gulfport, MS, 2013. For Hurricane Isaac Relief to be distributed according to the signed Grant Agreement.
$309,396 to Tulane University, Sponsored Projects Administration, New Orleans, LA, 2013. To assist the Department of Global Environmental Health Sciences at Tulane University's School of Public Health and Tropical Medicine in the Risk and Resilience in Environmental Health.
$278,936 to Nature Conservancy, Baton Rouge, LA, 2013. For Freshwater Assessment.
$150,000 to Rural Life Museum, Friends of the, Baton Rouge, LA, 2013. For Whispers of Change Exhibits Campaign.
$10,000 to Womans Hospital Foundation, Baton Rouge, LA, 2013. For Annual Giving Fund.
$2,000 to KIPP New Orleans, New Orleans, LA, 2013. For KIPP Believe Primary for the Wishlist Registry, the purchase of library books, and other learning tools for the classroom.

3614
Carolyn W. and Charles T. Beaird Family Foundation ✧

(formerly Charles T. Beaird Foundation)
330 Marshall St., Ste. 1112
Shreveport, LA 71101-3015 (318) 221-2823
Contact: Susan Beaird, Pres.
FAX: (318) 221-5993;
E-mail: brandy@beairdfoundation.org; Main URL: http://www.beairdfoundation.org/

Established in 1960 in LA.
Donors: Dr. Charles T. Beaird†; Carolyn W. Beaird†; John B. Beaird; Marjorie Beaird Seawell; Susan Beaird.
Foundation type: Independent foundation.
Financial data (yr. ended 12/31/13): Assets, $23,735,489 (M); expenditures, $1,448,765; qualifying distributions, $1,114,093; giving activities include $1,049,832 for 125 grants (high: $75,000; low: $25).
Purpose and activities: Giving to enable organizations or entities to add opportunity, freedom of action and choice, self-betterment and a climate for change to the lives of residents of the Shreveport, LA, area.
Fields of interest: Humanities; Arts; Employment; Housing/shelter; Human services; Children/youth, services; Women, centers/services; Children; Minorities; Women; Economically disadvantaged.
Type of support: General/operating support; Continuing support; Management development/capacity building; Capital campaigns; Building/renovation; Equipment; Program development; Seed money; Technical assistance; Program evaluation; Mission-related investments/loans.
Limitations: Applications accepted. Giving primarily in the Shreveport-Bosssier City, LA, area. No support for national programs and organizations. No grants to individuals.
Publications: Application guidelines; Financial statement; Grants list.
Application information: Application guidelines available on foundation web site. Application form and proposal must be submitted via the foundation's web site. Application form required.
Initial approach: Not required, but the foundation strongly suggests e-mail, telephone or letter, especially from first-time applicants, prior to filing an application.
Copies of proposal: 1
Deadline(s): Mar. 1 and Sept. 1
Board meeting date(s): Spring, summer, and fall
Final notification: May 15 and Nov. 15

Officers and Directors:* Susan Beaird, Pres.; Leslie M. Darr,* V.P.; Susie Seawell,* Secy.; John B. Beaird, Treas.; Brandy Stroud, Exec. Dir.; Ben McCormick; Jennifer McCormick; David Seawell; Katie Seawell; Marjorie B. Seawell.
Number of staff: 1 full-time professional.
EIN: 726027212
Selected grants: The following grants are a representative sample of this grantmaker's funding activity:
$60,000 to Volunteers for Youth Justice, Shreveport, LA, 2012. For Conflict Diversion Programs for Public School Youngsters.
$15,000 to Catholic Charities of Shreveport, Shreveport, LA, 2012. For funding for a Center to Assist Immigrant Families.
$15,000 to Shreveport Green, Shreveport, LA, 2012. To Expand Education Efforts to Reduce Blight and Slum.
$10,000 to Providence House, Shreveport, LA, 2012. For Program to House Homeless People in Transition.
$10,000 to Shreveport Opera, Shreveport, LA, 2012. For anti-bullying performances in public schools.
$10,000 to Shreveport Regional Arts Council, Shreveport, LA, 2012. For Fabricate Bike Racks for Shreveport Common Areas.
$8,000 to Children and Arthritis, Shreveport, LA, 2012. For Jambalaya Jubilee Summer Program for Families.
$5,000 to Centenary College of Louisiana, Shreveport, LA, 2012. For College-Community Partnership to Improve Immigrants' Living.
$2,700 to Carolina Friends School, Durham, NC, 2012. For Tuition and Salary Assistance.
$100 to Memphis Union Mission, Memphis, TN, 2012. For Primary Care, Disease Prevention and Health Promotion.

3615
Blue Cross and Blue Shield of Louisiana Foundation

(formerly Louisiana Child Caring Foundation, Inc.)
P.O. Box 98029
Baton Rouge, LA 70898-9022 (225) 298-7979
Contact: Christy Oliver Reeves, Exec. Dir.
FAX: (225) 298-3175;
E-mail: foundation@bcbsla.com; Tel. and e-mail for Christy Oliver Reeves: (225) 298-7051, Christy.Reeves@bcbsla.com; tel. and e-mail for The Angel Award: (888) 219-2583, e-mail: angel.award@bcbsla.com; Contact for Challenge for a Healthier Louisiana: Elizabeth Gollub, tel.: (225) 763-0945, e-mail: BCBSChallenge@pbrc.edu; Main URL: http://www.bcbsla.com/web/reddotcm/html/64_205.asp
Angel Award Database: http://ourhomelouisiana.org/signature-programs/angel-award/angel-award-database/
Angel Award Winners video: http://ourhomelouisiana.org/programs/the-angel-award/2011-angel-award-winners/
Challenge for a Healthier Louisiana Video: http://www.youtube.com/watch?feature=player_embedded&v=wwo3aLXJfac
Our Home, Louisiana on Facebook: http://www.facebook.com/ourhomela
Our Home, Louisiana on Twitter: https://twitter.com/#!/ourhomela
Our Home, Lousiana Coalition: A Resource Website for BCBSL and the BCBSL Foundation: http://ourhomelouisiana.org/
RSS Feed: http://ourhomelouisiana.org/feed/

Donor: Blue Cross Blue Shield of Louisiana.
Foundation type: Company-sponsored foundation.
Financial data (yr. ended 12/31/12): Assets, $29,278,325 (M); gifts received, $295,813; expenditures, $7,315,947; qualifying distributions, $7,146,207; giving activities include $6,850,894 for 100 grants (high: $877,500; low: $1,000).
Purpose and activities: The foundation supports programs designed to improve health and education in Louisiana.
Fields of interest: Elementary/secondary education; Education, early childhood education; Education; Medicine/medical care, public education; Hospitals (general); Health care, clinics/centers; Public health; Public health, obesity; Public health, physical fitness; Health care; Nutrition; Children/youth; Aging; Economically disadvantaged.
Type of support: General/operating support; Management development/capacity building; Program development; Faculty/staff development; Research; Employee volunteer services; Sponsorships; Program evaluation; Matching/challenge support.
Limitations: Applications accepted. Giving primarily in areas of company operations in LA. No support for political candidates or organizations, athletes or athletic teams, labor, fraternal, or veterans' organizations, parent-teacher organizations, or religious organizations. No grants to individuals, or for beauty pageants, students raising funds for travel, capital projects or campaigns, or memorials.
Publications: Application guidelines; Informational brochure.
Application information: The foundation generally practices an invitation only process for giving; however letter of inquiries are accepted from organizations aligned with the foundation's priorities. Grants range from $5,000 to $20,000. Organizations receiving support are asked to submit a final report. Application form required.
Initial approach: E-mail letter of inquiry; complete online nomination form for The Angel Award
Deadline(s): None; Apr. 4 for The Angel Award
Officers and Directors:* C. Richard Atkins, D.D.S.*, Chair.; Peggy B. Scott,* Pres.; Kevin McCotter, Secy.-Treas.; Christy Oliver Reeves, Exec. Dir.; Dan Borne; David Carmouche; Jerome "Jerry" Greig; Frances Turner Henry; Sybil H. Morial.
EIN: 721232379
Selected grants: The following grants are a representative sample of this grantmaker's funding activity:
$826,900 to Pennington Biomedical Research Foundation, Baton Rouge, LA, 2012. For Pennington Contract.
$511,084 to BREC Foundation, Baton Rouge, LA, 2012. For Capital Area Pathways Project and Mobile Playground.
$347,368 to YMCA of Northeast Louisiana, Monroe, LA, 2012.
$323,933 to Community Foundation of North Louisiana, Shreveport, LA, 2012. For Healthy Green and Into the Outdoors.
$253,592 to Southwest Louisiana Area Health Education Center, Lafayette, LA, 2012. For Dare to Be Healthy.
$20,000 to Catholic Charities Archdiocese of New Orleans, New Orleans, LA, 2012. For Angel Award.
$20,000 to Common Ground Health Clinic, New Orleans, LA, 2012. For patient assistance program.
$20,000 to Family Service of Greater New Orleans, New Orleans, LA, 2012. For Impact Grant - Children's Mental Health Center.
$20,000 to LifeShare Blood Centers, Shreveport, LA, 2012. For Impact Grant - Rare Cells Preservation and Storage Administered By the John J Moulds Reference Lab and Scientific Support Services at Lifeshare Blood Centers.
$7,500 to Family Service of Greater New Orleans, New Orleans, LA, 2012. For Impact Grant - Connections Count Professional Development.

3616
The Booth-Bricker Fund ✧

826 Union St., Ste. 300
New Orleans, LA 70112-1411 (504) 581-2430
Contact: Gray S. Parker, Chair.; Heather A. Riley, Secy.

Established in 1966 in LA.
Donors: John F. Bricker†; Nina B. Bricker†.
Foundation type: Independent foundation.
Financial data (yr. ended 12/31/13): Assets, $46,123,489 (M); expenditures, $1,939,554; qualifying distributions, $1,710,039; giving activities include $1,595,746 for 67 grants (high: $340,000; low: $50).
Purpose and activities: Giving primarily for the purpose of promoting, developing, and fostering religious, charitable, scientific, literary, and educational programs. Since 2006, the fund's program of charitable distributions has focused exclusively on the reform of public education in New Orleans, LA.
Fields of interest: Visual arts; Museums; Performing arts; Performing arts, theater; Historic preservation/historical societies; Arts; Education, fund raising/fund distribution; Elementary/secondary education; Education, early childhood education; Child development, education; Secondary school/education; Higher education; Theological school/education; Adult education—literacy, basic skills & GED; Libraries/library science; Education, reading; Education; Environment; Hospitals (general); Speech/hearing centers; Health care; Mental health/crisis services; Health organizations, association; Cancer; Biomedicine; Medical research, institute; Cancer research; Crime/law enforcement; Food services; Human services; Youth, services; Child development, services; Family services; Aging, centers/services; Homeless, human services; Catholic agencies & churches; Religion; Aging; Economically disadvantaged; Homeless.
Type of support: Capital campaigns; Building/renovation; Equipment; Endowments; Debt reduction; Professorships; Publication; Scholarship funds; Research; Employee matching gifts; Matching/challenge support.
Limitations: Applications accepted. Giving limited to LA, with priority given to the New Orleans area. No grants to individuals, or for operating or maintenance costs.
Application information: Videotapes or DVDs are not accepted. Application form not required.
Initial approach: Letter
Copies of proposal: 1
Deadline(s): None
Board meeting date(s): Quarterly
Officers and Trustees:* Gray S. Parker,* Chair.; Heather A. Riley, Secy.; Ingrid C. Laffont, Treas.;

Henry N. Kuechler III; Charles B. Mayer; Mary Kay Parker; Nathaniel P. Phillips, Jr.; H. Hunter White, Jr.
EIN: 720818077

3617
Joe W. & Dorothy Dorsett Brown Foundation ✧
c/o The Brown Foundation Center
320 Hammond Hwy., Ste. 500
Metairie, LA 70005-5100
Contact: Beth Buscher
FAX: (504) 834-3441;
E-mail: BethBuscher@thebrownfoundation.org;
Main URL: http://www.thebrownfoundation.org

Established in 1959 in LA.
Donors: Joe W. Brown†; Dorothy Dorsett Brown†.
Foundation type: Independent foundation.
Financial data (yr. ended 12/31/12): Assets, $126,989,563 (M); expenditures, $5,690,604; qualifying distributions, $4,519,367; giving activities include $3,369,968 for 58 grants (high: $300,000; low: $1,000), $2,136 for 1 grant to an individual, $907,618 for 2 foundation-administered programs and $1,015,749 for 25 loans/program-related investments (high: $300,000; low: $141).
Purpose and activities: Giving primarily for science, community benefit, human services, conservation, the environment, the arts, religion, education, and medical and health purposes.
Fields of interest: Education; Environment, natural resources; Hospitals (general); Health care; Food services; Human services; Homeless, human services; Community/economic development; Religion; Homeless.
Type of support: General/operating support; Continuing support; Research; Program-related investments/loans; Matching/challenge support.
Limitations: Applications accepted. Giving limited to southern LA and the New Orleans area, and the Gulf Coast of MS. No support for organizations that are less than 3 years old, or for indirect grants to intermediary institutions, or institutional indirect (overhead) costs, public/charter or private schools grades K-12, or local chapters of national organizations. No grants for equipment, vehicles, videos, computer systems, endowments, building funds, large community-wide capital drives, or multi-year grants, (additional years at the foundation's option for PRIs).
Publications: Application guidelines; Grants list.
Application information: The foundation has discontinued awarding new scholarships to individuals. All applications must be received at least 90 days before funds are required. Application form required.
Initial approach: Submit application form (from foundation web site) via U.S. mail
Copies of proposal: 2
Deadline(s): Between Jan. 1 and Aug. 31
Board meeting date(s): On Fridays mid-monthly
Final notification: 1-2 months
Officers: David Paul Spencer, Pres.; Barbara G. Spencer, V.P.; David B. Spencer, V.P.; Edwin K. Hunter, Secy.; Betty M. Estopinal, Treas.
Directors: Edwin Ford Hunter III; Ronald P. Spencer, M.D.
Number of staff: 4 full-time professional; 2 part-time professional.
EIN: 726027232

3618
The Burden Foundation ✧
4911 Bennington Ave.
Baton Rouge, LA 70808-3153

Established in 1965 in LA.
Foundation type: Independent foundation.
Financial data (yr. ended 12/31/13): Assets, $10,323,009 (M); expenditures, $510,384; qualifying distributions, $449,070; giving activities include $445,000 for 3 grants (high: $348,760; low: $5,000).
Fields of interest: Education; Environment, research; Environment, natural resources; Horticulture/garden clubs; Agriculture; Foundations (community).
Type of support: General/operating support; Building/renovation; Equipment.
Limitations: Applications not accepted. Giving limited to Baton Rouge, LA. No grants to individuals.
Application information: Contributes only to pre-selected organizations.
Board meeting date(s): Apr. and Oct.
Board Members: Annette D. Barton; William E. Bertrand; Nancy Jo Craig; G. Trippe Hawthorne; Leonard L. Kilgore III; Ben Kleinpeter; Lucien P. Laborde, Jr.; Paul W. Murrill; John B. Noland; Christopher L. Odinet; Brandon Parlange; Dorsey Peek; Sue Turner; Ann Wilkinson; Juliet M. Young.
Officers: Robert A. Hawthorne, Pres.; O. Miles Pollard, V.P.; Frances H. Monroe, Secy.; Tom J. Meek, Treas.
Number of staff: None.
EIN: 726030712

3619
The William T. and Ethel Lewis Burton Foundation ✧ ☆
641 W. Prien Lake Rd.
Lake Charles, LA 70601-8315
Contact: William T. Drost, Dir.

Incorporated in 1963 in LA.
Donors: William T. Burton; Wm. T. Burton Industries, Inc.; William B. Lawton Company, L.L.C.; William B. Lawton†; Tower Land Co, LLC.
Foundation type: Independent foundation.
Financial data (yr. ended 05/31/13): Assets, $5,096,508 (M); gifts received, $1,000,000; expenditures, $1,082,817; qualifying distributions, $1,077,311; giving activities include $1,059,033 for 5 grants (high: $1,000,000; low: $164), and $10,000 for 8 grants to individuals (high: $1,250; low: $1,250).
Purpose and activities: Giving primarily for higher education and Protestant churches; giving also in the form of scholarships to Southwest Louisiana High School seniors and members of the McNeese State University, Louisiana football team.
Fields of interest: Higher education; Protestant agencies & churches.
Type of support: General/operating support; Scholarships—to individuals.
Limitations: Applications accepted. Giving primarily in LA. No grants for endowment funds or matching gifts; no loans.
Application information: Application form not required.
Initial approach: Proposal
Deadline(s): None
Directors: Ernest Gerald Conner; Charles Mitchell Drost; William T. Drost; Jack E. Lawton, Jr.; Gus W. Schram III; Roderick Smith.
EIN: 726027957
Selected grants: The following grants are a representative sample of this grantmaker's funding activity:
$100,000 to Tiger Athletic Foundation, Baton Rouge, LA, 2011.
$100,000 to University of Texas M.D. Anderson Cancer Center, Houston, TX, 2011.
$30,000 to McNeese State University, Lake Charles, LA, 2011.
$2,500 to McNeese State University, Lake Charles, LA, 2011.

3620
The Cason Foundation ✧
5129 Hwy. 507
Coushatta, LA 71019

Donor: Edgar F. Cason.
Foundation type: Independent foundation.
Financial data (yr. ended 12/31/13): Assets, $256,118 (M); gifts received, $4,826,000; expenditures, $4,812,425; qualifying distributions, $4,785,413; giving activities include $4,779,807 for 55 grants (high: $1,350,000; low: $577).
Fields of interest: Higher education; Theological school/education; Health organizations; Protestant agencies & churches.
Limitations: Applications not accepted. Giving primarily in LA and VA.
Application information: Contributes only to pre-selected organizations.
Officers and Directors:* Stacy Cason,* C.E.O. and C.F.O.; Flora C. Cason,* Pres.; Edgar F. Cason.
EIN: 274019209

3621
Chambers Charitable Foundation ✧
P.O. Box 61540, Trust Tax Compliance
New Orleans, LA 70161-1540

Established in 2006 in TX.
Donor: Florence Chambers†.
Foundation type: Independent foundation.
Financial data (yr. ended 01/31/14): Assets, $13,804,574 (M); expenditures, $640,855; qualifying distributions, $518,474; giving activities include $460,361 for 5 grants (high: $276,217; low: $46,036).
Purpose and activities: Giving primarily for historical property preservation.
Fields of interest: Museums (art); Historic preservation/historical societies; American Red Cross; Protestant agencies & churches.
Limitations: Applications not accepted. Giving primarily in New Orleans, LA. No grants to individuals.
Application information: Contributes only to pre-selected organizations.
Trustee: Capital One Bank, N.A.
EIN: 202123840
Selected grants: The following grants are a representative sample of this grantmaker's funding activity:
$254,082 to Beaumont Heritage Society, Beaumont, TX, 2011.

3622
Christen Elizabeth Clement Foundation, Inc. ✧
5959 S. Sherwood Forest Blvd.
Baton Rouge, LA 70816-6038 (225) 299-3508
Contact: Michael Pitts

Established in 2003 in LA.
Donor: Amdisys, Inc.
Foundation type: Independent foundation.
Financial data (yr. ended 12/31/13): Assets, $535,796 (M); gifts received, $718,284; expenditures, $869,619; qualifying distributions, $876,890; giving activities include $868,095 for grants.
Fields of interest: Human services.
Application information: Application form required.
Initial approach: Letter
Deadline(s): Monthly
Officers: Scott Ginn, Pres.; Michael D. Lutgring, V.P.; Mark R. Phillips, Treas.
EIN: 200122620

3623
Community Foundation of Acadiana ✧
1035 Camellia Blvd., Ste. 100
Lafayette, LA 70508 (337) 769-4840
Contact: Trish Olivier, Prog. Dir.
FAX: (337) 469-4879; E-mail: info@cfacadiana.org; Main URL: http://www.cfacadiana.org
Facebook: http://www.facebook.com/pages/Lafayette-LA/Community-Foundation-of-Acadiana/58233699334

Established in 2000 in LA.
Foundation type: Community foundation.
Financial data (yr. ended 12/31/12): Assets, $29,784,025 (M); gifts received, $17,909,999; expenditures, $19,424,799; giving activities include $13,003,701 for grants, and $1,082,690 for grants to individuals.
Purpose and activities: The foundation provides leadership in facilitating the charitable and creative giving its donors in an effort to improve the quality of life for the citizens of Acadiana, LA.
Fields of interest: Safety/disasters; Community/economic development.
Type of support: Continuing support; Annual campaigns; Capital campaigns; Building/renovation; Equipment; Endowments; Seed money.
Limitations: Applications accepted. Giving primarily in Acadia, Evangeline, Iberia, Lafayette, St. Martin, St. Mary and Vermilion parishes, LA.
Publications: Annual report; Informational brochure.
Application information: The foundation does not currently have an unrestricted grants procedure as unrestricted funds are limited. Visit foundation web site for Donor-Advised and Corporate Charitable funds grant information and application form. Application form required.
Initial approach: Submit application form
Deadline(s): None
Board meeting date(s): Quarterly
Officers and Directors:* Kevin Moody,* Chair.; Hank Perret,* 1st Vice-Chair.; L.J. Gielen,* 2nd Vice-Chair.; Raymond J. Hebert,* Pres. and C.E.O.; E. Stewart Shea III,* Secy.-Treas.; Eric Guidry, C.O.O.; Ernest P. Breaux; Clive Cloutier; Robert Eddy, Jr.; Wayne Elmore; Al Lippman; Kam Movassaghi, Ph.D.; Alice G. Pecoraro; Jerry Prejean; Duayne Richard; Michael R. Robicheaux; E. Larry Sikes; Gene Sellers; Eddie Soileau; Don Washington.
Number of staff: 4 full-time professional.
EIN: 721493023

3624
The Community Foundation of North Louisiana ✧
(also known as The Community Foundation)
(formerly Community Foundation of Shreveport-Bossier)
401 Edwards St., Ste. 105
Shreveport, LA 71101-5508 (318) 221-0582
Contact: Paula H. Hickman, Exec. Dir.; Finance: Paige Carlisle, Dir., Finance; Marketing, PR, Communications: Jennifer Steadman, Dir., External Rels.
FAX: (318) 221-7463; E-mail: info@cfnla.org; Grant application e-mail: laborde@cfnla.org; Main URL: http://www.cfnla.org
Blog: http://www.cfnla.org/news/blog
Twitter: https://twitter.com/commfoundnla
YouTube: http://www.youtube.com/cfnla

Incorporated in 1961 in Louisiana.
Foundation type: Community foundation.
Financial data (yr. ended 12/31/13): Assets, $93,195,787 (M); gifts received, $2,787,212; expenditures, $5,593,902; giving activities include $4,040,590 for grants.
Purpose and activities: The foundation seeks to promote philanthropy and improve the quality of life in North Louisiana by serving as a permanent and growing resource of expertise and funds. The mission of The Community Foundation is to strengthen the community through philanthropy.
Fields of interest: Arts, single organization support; Arts, formal/general education; Performing arts; Performing arts, dance; Performing arts, theater; Performing arts, theater (musical); Performing arts, orchestras; Performing arts, opera; Arts; Education, research; Education, public education; Education, formal/general education; Elementary/secondary education; Child development, education; Middle schools/education; Elementary school/education; Secondary school/education; Elementary/secondary school reform; Higher education; Higher education, college (community/junior); Higher education, college; Higher education, university; Higher education reform; Adult education—literacy, basic skills & GED; Education, reading; Education, community/cooperative; Education; Environment, natural resources; Environment; Animals/wildlife; Public health; Public health, obesity; Public health, physical fitness; Health care; Mental health/crisis services; Employment, services; Employment, training; Goodwill Industries; Agriculture, community food systems; Nutrition; Housing/shelter; Disasters, Hurricane Katrina; Recreation, community; Youth development, centers/clubs; Boys & girls clubs; Youth development, adult & child programs; American Red Cross; Salvation Army; Volunteers of America; YM/YWCAs & YM/YWHAs; Youth, services; Family services; Aging, centers/services; Homeless, human services; Human services; Economic development; Urban/community development; Nonprofit management; Community/economic development; Foundations (community); Science; Public affairs, citizen participation; Children/youth; Children; Aging; Disabilities, people with; Women; Economically disadvantaged; Homeless.
Type of support: Continuing support; Management development/capacity building; Capital campaigns; Building/renovation; Equipment; Land acquisition; Endowments; Emergency funds; Program development; Conferences/seminars; Seed money; Curriculum development; Scholarship funds; Research; Technical assistance; Employee matching gifts; Matching/challenge support; Mission-related investments/loans.
Limitations: Applications accepted. Giving strictly limited to 501(c)3 organizations in Caddo and Bossier Parishes for the competitive grant process. No support for religious purposes. No grants to individuals, or for debt retirement, general operating expenses, or annual sustaining fund drives.
Publications: Application guidelines; Annual report; Annual report (including application guidelines); Grants list; Informational brochure; Newsletter.
Application information: Visit foundation web site for online application forms and guidelines. All organizations interested in submitting a proposal must send a representative to attend one of the scheduled Grant Overview Sessions prior to submission; reservations are required by calling or e-mailing the foundation. Application form required.
Initial approach: Attend a Grant Applicant Orientation Session
Deadline(s): Sept. 22 for Letter of Intent; Jan. 15 for completed application
Board meeting date(s): Feb., Apr., Aug. and Dec.
Final notification: Apr.
Officers and Directors:* Edward Crawford III,* Chair.; Paula H. Hickman, J.D., Exec. Dir.; Dr. Terry C. Davis,* Secy.; Thomas Murphy,* Treas.; Janie D. Richardson,* Vice-Chair.; Rand Falbaum; Bobby Jelks; Margaret Thompson.
Trustee Banks: JPMorgan Chase Bank, N.A.; Regions Bank.
Number of staff: 3 full-time professional; 2 full-time support; 1 part-time support.
EIN: 726022365

3625
Community Foundation of Southwest Louisiana ✧
(formerly Southwest Louisiana Community Foundation)
1625 Ryan St., Ste. C
P.O. Box 3125
Lake Charles, LA 70602 (337) 491-6688
Contact: Sara Judson, Pres. and C.E.O.
FAX: (337) 491-6710;
E-mail: sjudson@foundationswla.org; Main URL: http://www.foundationswla.org

Established in 2001 in LA.
Foundation type: Community foundation.
Financial data (yr. ended 12/31/12): Assets, $7,456,740 (M); gifts received, $1,135,526; expenditures, $1,982,067; giving activities include $1,530,495 for 26 grants (high: $611,635).
Purpose and activities: The foundation seeks to enhance the quality of life in Southwest Louisiana by becoming a strong and effective catalyst for building philanthropy for present and future generations.
Fields of interest: Education; Human services; Community/economic development.
Publications: IRS Form 990 or 990-PF printed copy available upon request.
Application information:
Deadline(s): Varies

Officers and Directors:* Greg Webb,* Chair.; Tom Sherman,* Vice-Chair.; Sara Judson,* C.E.O. and Pres.; Dan Donald, M.D.*, Secy.; Jonald Walker,* Treas.; Susan Blake; Edwin F. Hunter III; Mary Shaddock Jones; Brent Lumpkin; Jon Manns; Dr. Lehrue Stevens; Mary Leach Werner.
EIN: 721508036

3626
Coughlin-Saunders Foundation, Inc. ✧
2010 Gus Kaplan Dr.
Alexandria, LA 71301-3358 (318) 487-4332
Contact: Ed Crump, Jr., Exec. Dir.
E-mail: csfoundation@kricket.net; Main URL: http://coughlinsaunders.org/

Incorporated in 1950 in LA.
Donors: Anne S. Coughlin†; R.R. Saunders†; F.H. Coughlin†; J.A. Adams†; Carolyn Saunders†.
Foundation type: Independent foundation.
Financial data (yr. ended 11/30/13): Assets, $14,638,894 (M); expenditures, $842,346; qualifying distributions, $753,554; giving activities include $739,128 for 158 grants (high: $80,000; low: $75).
Purpose and activities: Giving primarily for education, particularly to Episcopal, Christian and Roman Catholic schools, as well as to churches; funding also for Baptist churches, and for children, youth and social services.
Fields of interest: Arts; Elementary/secondary education; Education; Human services; Children/youth, services; Christian agencies & churches; Protestant agencies & churches; Catholic agencies & churches.
Type of support: General/operating support; Continuing support; Capital campaigns; Building/renovation; Equipment; Emergency funds; Program development; Professorships; Scholarship funds.
Limitations: Applications accepted. Giving primarily in Alexandria, LA, and the surrounding metropolitan area. No grants to individuals, or for matching gifts.
Publications: Application guidelines; Program policy statement.
Application information: Application form required.
Initial approach: Proposal
Copies of proposal: 1
Deadline(s): Mar. 15
Board meeting date(s): Apr. and Sept.
Final notification: Between Apr. 30 and Oct. 31
Officers: Sally Cockerham, Co-Chair.; Ann Maynard, Co-Chair.; Ed Crump, Jr., Exec. Dir.
Directors: Nell Adams; Scott Brame.
EIN: 726027641
Selected grants: The following grants are a representative sample of this grantmaker's funding activity:
$5,000 to Savannah College of Art and Design, Savannah, GA, 2011. For operations.
$1,000 to Teach for America, New York, NY, 2011. For operations.

3627
John W. & Bertie M. Deming Foundation ✧
3600 Parliament Dr.
Alexandria, LA 71303-3009 (318) 445-5472
Contact: Mamie Sterkx, Dir.

Established in LA.
Donor: Bertie Deming Smith.
Foundation type: Independent foundation.
Financial data (yr. ended 10/31/13): Assets, $11,095,143 (M); expenditures, $443,012; qualifying distributions, $430,735; giving activities include $430,735 for grants.
Purpose and activities: Giving primarily for higher education, as well as for the arts, particularly art museums, and human services.
Fields of interest: Museums (art); Arts; Higher education; Medical research, association; Human services.
Limitations: Applications accepted. Giving primarily in LA. No grants to individuals.
Application information: Application form not required.
Deadline(s): None
Officer: Bertie Deming Smith, Mgr.
Trustees: Brenner Sadler; Mamie Sterkx.
EIN: 726041682

3628
Collins C. Diboll Private Foundation ✧
201 Saint Charles Ave., 50th Fl.
New Orleans, LA 70170-5100 (504) 582-8250
Contact: Donald W. Diboll

Established in 1989 in LA.
Donor: Collins C. Diboll†.
Foundation type: Independent foundation.
Financial data (yr. ended 12/31/13): Assets, $15,364,756 (M); expenditures, $899,334; qualifying distributions, $739,609; giving activities include $668,750 for 21 grants (high: $125,000; low: $2,500).
Purpose and activities: Giving primarily for education and social services.
Fields of interest: Museums (art); Higher education; Education; Health care; Human services; Protestant agencies & churches; Catholic agencies & churches.
Type of support: General/operating support; Capital campaigns; Building/renovation; Endowments.
Limitations: Applications accepted. Giving primarily in LA. No grants to individuals.
Application information: Application form required.
Initial approach: Letter
Deadline(s): None
Officer: Donald W. Diboll, Chair.
Trustees: Herschel L. Abbott, Jr.; David F. Edwards.
EIN: 726126376

3629
The Dore' Family Foundation ✧
120 W. Pujo St., Ste. 300
Lake Charles, LA 70601-4202

Established in 2007 in LA.
Donor: William J. Dore, Sr.
Foundation type: Independent foundation.
Financial data (yr. ended 12/31/13): Assets, $6,841,970 (M); expenditures, $4,766,433; qualifying distributions, $4,718,863; giving activities include $4,715,980 for 15 grants (high: $200,000; low: $2,500).
Fields of interest: Education; Hospitals (general); Human services; Community/economic development; Catholic agencies & churches.
Limitations: Applications accepted. Giving primarily in LA and Alexandria, VA; some funding also in Birmingham, AL and Houston, TX. No grants to individuals.
Application information: Application form required.
Initial approach: Request application form
Deadline(s): None
Officers: William J. Dore', Sr., Pres.; Amy K. Dore' Donner, V.P.; Deborah K. Dore', V.P.; Colette A. Dore' Greene, Secy.; William J. Dore', Jr., Treas.
Director: Fr. Henry Mancuso.
EIN: 261095199

3630
Entergy Charitable Foundation ✧
639 Loyola Ave.
New Orleans, LA 70113-3125 (504) 576-6980
Additional address: P.O. Box 61000, New Orleans, LA 70161, tel.: (504) 576-2674; Main URL: http://www.entergy.com/our_community/ECF_grant_guidelines.aspx

Established in 2000 in AR and LA.
Donor: Entergy Corp.
Foundation type: Company-sponsored foundation.
Financial data (yr. ended 12/31/12): Assets, $1,285,757 (M); gifts received, $2,904,679; expenditures, $3,116,063; qualifying distributions, $3,116,063; giving activities include $3,111,563 for 147+ grants (high: $460,000).
Purpose and activities: The foundation supports programs designed to create and sustain thriving communities. Special emphasis is directed toward programs designed to promote low-income initiatives and solutions; and education and literacy.
Fields of interest: Museums; Education, reading; Education; Environment, energy; Housing/shelter, development; Housing/shelter; Disasters, fire prevention/control; Family services; Human services, financial counseling; Community/economic development, management/technical assistance; United Ways and Federated Giving Programs; Children; Aging; Economically disadvantaged.
Type of support: Scholarship funds; Building/renovation; Program development.
Limitations: Applications accepted. Giving primarily in areas of company operations in AR, LA, MA, MS, NH, NY, TX, and VT, with emphasis on New Orleans. No support for political organizations, religious organizations not of direct benefit to the entire community, or organizations owned or operated by an employee of Entergy. No grants to individuals, or for utility bills, administrative expenses or recurring expenses exceeding 15 percent of the requested amount, capital campaigns, gala events, testimonials, or fundraising meals, advertisements, or uniforms, equipment, or trips for school-related organizations or amateur sports teams; no loans.
Publications: Application guidelines.
Application information: Visit website for contact information for contributions coordinators in each state. Application form required.
Initial approach: Complete online application form
Deadline(s): Feb. 1 and Aug. 1
Board meeting date(s): 3 times per year
Final notification: 3 months
Officers and Directors:* Kim Despeaux, Pres.; Kay Kelley Arnold, V.P.; Leo P. Denault,* Treas.; Renea Conley; Haley R. Fisackerly; John Herron; William Mohl; Gary J. Taylor; Rod K. West.
EIN: 710845366

3631
Eye, Ear, Nose and Throat Foundation ✧
111 Veterans Memorial Blvd., Ste. 702
Metairie, LA 70005-3035
Contact: William F. Finegan, Exec. Dir.
FAX: (504) 828-7192; E-mail: wffeent@aol.com

Established in LA.
Donors: Eye, Ear, Nose and Throat Hospital; Isaac Stauffer Clinic.
Foundation type: Independent foundation.
Financial data (yr. ended 12/31/13): Assets, $76,289,603 (M); expenditures, $3,655,024; qualifying distributions, $3,215,692; giving activities include $3,079,672 for 18 grants (high: $760,822; low: $2,000).
Purpose and activities: Giving for eye and ear care for indigent residents of southeast Louisiana.
Fields of interest: Eye diseases; Ear, nose & throat diseases; Economically disadvantaged.
Limitations: Applications accepted. Giving limited to southeastern LA.
Application information: Application form not required.
Initial approach: Letter
Deadline(s): None
Board meeting date(s): As needed
Officer and Trustees:* William F. Finegan,* Exec. Dir.; Ashley S. Bright; Crichton W. Brown; John D. Charbonnet; Michael D. Charbonnet; R. Foster Duncan; Katherine Gilbert; Charles N. Monsted III; Morgan S. Nalty; Michele Reed; St. Denis J. Villere.
Number of staff: 1 full-time professional; 1 full-time support.
EIN: 720928511

3632
The Ben E. Factor Foundation ✧
106 Wilree Dr.
New Iberia, LA 70563
Application address: c/o Annette F. White, P.O. Box 10555, New Iberia, LA 70562-0555, tel.: (337) 365-3756

Established in 1987 in LA.
Donors: Robert N. White; Annette F. White; Keith White; Mrs. Keith White.
Foundation type: Independent foundation.
Financial data (yr. ended 12/31/13): Assets, $551,387 (M); expenditures, $622,285; qualifying distributions, $614,002; giving activities include $614,002 for 47 grants (high: $240,000; low: $500).
Purpose and activities: Giving primarily to Christian organizations and ministries, as well as to a Baptist school; funding also for health organizations, and social services.
Fields of interest: Elementary/secondary education; Education; Health organizations, association; Human services; Christian agencies & churches; Protestant agencies & churches.
Limitations: Applications accepted. Giving in the U.S., with some emphasis on LA. No grants to individuals.
Application information: Application form required.
Initial approach: Proposal
Deadline(s): None
Officers: Robert N. White, Pres.; Keith White, V.P.; R. Marc White, V.P.; Annette F. White, Secy.
EIN: 721086995

3633
Ruth U. Fertel Foundation ✧
1010 Common St., Ste. 1810
New Orleans, LA 70112-2412

Established in 2002 in LA.
Donor: Ruth U. Fertel Charitable Lead Unitrust.
Foundation type: Independent foundation.
Financial data (yr. ended 12/31/13): Assets, $4,872,300 (M); gifts received, $870,000; expenditures, $518,998; qualifying distributions, $464,000; giving activities include $464,000 for 32 grants (high: $60,000; low: $1,000).
Purpose and activities: Giving primarily for elementary and secondary education, including Catholic and Protestant schools.
Fields of interest: Arts education; Elementary/secondary education; Education.
Limitations: Applications not accepted. Giving primarily in New Orleans, LA. No grants to individuals.
Application information: Contributes only to pre-selected organizations.
Officers and Directors:* Randy Fertel,* Pres.; James E. Ryder, Jr.,* Secy.-Treas.; Robert W. Merrick.
EIN: 710879051
Selected grants: The following grants are a representative sample of this grantmaker's funding activity:
$50,000 to Jesuit High School, New Orleans, LA, 2011.
$30,000 to Good Shepherd Nativity Mission School, New Orleans, LA, 2011.
$25,000 to Saint Michaels Special School, New Orleans, LA, 2011.
$16,000 to Cabrini High School, New Orleans, LA, 2011.
$10,000 to Arts Council of New Orleans, New Orleans, LA, 2011.
$10,000 to Dillard University, New Orleans, LA, 2011.
$10,000 to New Schools for New Orleans, New Orleans, LA, 2011.
$5,000 to Kid Smart Foundation, New Orleans, LA, 2011.
$5,000 to Louisiana Cultural Economy Foundation, New Orleans, LA, 2011.
$5,000 to Louisiana Philharmonic Orchestra, New Orleans, LA, 2011.

3634
The Alta and John Franks Foundation ✧
(formerly The Franks Foundation)
P.O. Box 7625
Shreveport, LA 71137-7625

Established in LA.
Donors: John Franks‡; Alta V. Franks.
Foundation type: Independent foundation.
Financial data (yr. ended 12/31/13): Assets, $23,395,935 (M); gifts received, $9,553,527; expenditures, $580,272; qualifying distributions, $569,815; giving activities include $569,639 for 49 grants (high: $100,000; low: $100).
Purpose and activities: Giving primarily to Baptist and United Methodist churches, and to a science center; funding also for health associations.
Fields of interest: Arts, multipurpose centers/programs; Education; Health organizations, association; Human services; Protestant agencies & churches.
Limitations: Applications not accepted. Giving primarily in LA. No grants to individuals.
Application information: Contributes only to pre-selected organizations.
Officers: Bobby E. Jelks, Pres.; Alta V. Franks, V.P.; Faith N. Gilbert, Secy.
EIN: 237422163
Selected grants: The following grants are a representative sample of this grantmaker's funding activity:
$10,000 to American Cancer Society, Atlanta, GA, 2011.
$5,000 to Nature Conservancy, Arlington, VA, 2011. For unrestricted gift.
$1,000 to Fellowship of Christian Athletes, Kansas City, MO, 2011.

3635
Frazier Foundation, Inc. ✧
419 Homer Rd.
Minden, LA 71055-2933
Application address: P.O. Box 1175, Minden, LA 71058-1175, tel.: (318) 377-0182

Established in 1974 in LA.
Donor: J. Walter Frazier.
Foundation type: Independent foundation.
Financial data (yr. ended 12/31/13): Assets, $8,304,619 (M); expenditures, $1,163,016; qualifying distributions, $992,744; giving activities include $984,550 for 53 grants (high: $67,500; low: $1,000).
Purpose and activities: Support primarily for the Church of Christ, Christian religious organizations, child care, and educational institutions.
Fields of interest: Higher education; Education; Human services; Children/youth, services; Family services; Christian agencies & churches; Protestant agencies & churches.
Limitations: Applications accepted. Giving in the U.S., with emphasis on TX. No grants to individuals, or for endowment funds; no loans.
Publications: Application guidelines.
Application information: Do not fax applications. Application form required.
Initial approach: Letter or proposal, on organization's letterhead
Copies of proposal: 7
Deadline(s): May 15 and Oct. 15
Board meeting date(s): June and Dec.
Final notification: Within 6 months
Officers: James Walter Frazier, Jr., Pres.; Rudith A. Drennan, V.P.; Mikal Frazier, Secy.; A. Don Drennan, Treas.
EIN: 720760891
Selected grants: The following grants are a representative sample of this grantmaker's funding activity:
$13,300 to Church of Christ, Abilene, TX, 2011.

3636
The Ella West Freeman Foundation ✧
6028 Magazine St.
New Orleans, LA 70118-5824 (504) 895-1984
Contact: Louis M. Freeman, Chair.; Catherine Freeman, Exec. Admin.
FAX: (504) 895-1988; E-mail: info@ellawest.org;
Main URL: http://www.ellawest.org
Grants List: http://www.ellawest.org/grants.html

Established in 1941 in LA.

Donors: Richard W. Freeman†; Alfred B. Freeman†.
Foundation type: Independent foundation.
Financial data (yr. ended 12/31/12): Assets, $29,937,008 (M); gifts received, $42,000; expenditures, $1,726,167; qualifying distributions, $1,449,060; giving activities include $1,432,060 for 36+ grants (high: $279,000).
Purpose and activities: Giving primarily for education with an emphasis on private education, arts, both performing and applied, community improvement and governmental oversight, and human service organizations with an emphasis on capital projects for established agencies.
Fields of interest: Arts; Higher education; Human services; Government/public administration.
Type of support: Annual campaigns; Capital campaigns; Building/renovation; Endowments; Program development; Seed money.
Limitations: Applications accepted. Giving primarily in the greater New Orleans, LA, area. No support for organizations supported by community giving campaigns such as the United Way and the Archbishop's Community Appeal. No grants to individuals.
Publications: Application guidelines; Grants list.
Application information: Application form and guidelines available on foundation web site. Application form required.
Initial approach: Proposal summary sheet, which may be sent either via e-mail, fax or surface mail
Copies of proposal: 2
Deadline(s): Jan. 20 or Sept. 1 for proposal summary sheet; Mar. 1 or Oct. 15 for full proposal
Board meeting date(s): Spring and fall
Final notification: Feb. 1 or Sept. 15, via e-mail for proposal summary; after board meetings for full proposal
Officer and Trustees:* Louis M. Freeman,* Chair.; Richard W. Freeman, Jr.; R. West Freeman III; Virginia Rowan; Philip Woollam; Tina Freeman Woollam.
EIN: 726018322
Selected grants: The following grants are a representative sample of this grantmaker's funding activity:
$554,000 to Ochsner Clinic Foundation, New Orleans, LA, 2011. To renovate Ochsner Health System Conference Center, payable over 3.00 years.
$150,000 to New Schools for New Orleans, New Orleans, LA, 2011. For operating support, payable over 2.00 years.
$50,000 to Christ Episcopal School, Covington, LA, 2011. For Phase IV Campus Expansion for Center of Inquiry.
$33,000 to NOCCA Institute, New Orleans, LA, 2011. To develop Academic Studio offering dynamic new academic curriculum.
$25,000 to Louise S. McGehee School, New Orleans, LA, 2011. For Centennial Campaign.
$20,000 to Legacy Donor Foundation, Metairie, LA, 2011. For drivers education video and curriculum on organ, eye and tissue donation.
$5,000 to Start the Adventure in Reading, New Orleans, LA, 2011. For general operating support for one-on-one tutoring for second grade New Orleans public school students.
$5,000 to Tulane University, Center for Public Service, New Orleans, LA, 2011. For general operating support for Children's Reading Program.

3637
German Protestant Orphan Asylum Association Foundation ✧ ☆
(also known as GPOA Foundation)
1441 Canal St., Ste. 211
New Orleans, LA 70112-2714 (504) 895-2361
Contact: Lisa M. Kaichen, Fdn. Mgr.
E-mail: lisa@gpoafoundation.org; Main URL: http://www.gpoafoundation.org/

Parent organization founded in 1855; foundation established in 1979 in LA.
Foundation type: Independent foundation.
Financial data (yr. ended 11/30/13): Assets, $14,448,269 (M); gifts received, $90; expenditures, $666,493; qualifying distributions, $573,321; giving activities include $468,133 for 44 grants (high: $40,000; low: $2,500).
Purpose and activities: Grants only for the benefit and welfare of children and youth in Metro New Orleans, LA.
Fields of interest: Children/youth, services.
Type of support: General/operating support; Program development; Seed money; Matching/challenge support.
Limitations: Giving limited to LA, with emphasis on the New Orleans metropolitan area. No support for programs not focused on children, or for out-of-state organizations (unless request is to serve LA children). No grants to individuals, or for capital campaigns, building or renovation expenses, computers, special events, or traditional scholarships.
Publications: Application guidelines; Annual report; Grants list.
Application information: Full proposals are by invitation only, upon review of concept paper. Applications accepted by mail only. Hand delivery or deliveries which require a signature are not accepted. The foundation will also accept the Southern Grantmakers Common Application Form. Application form required.
Initial approach: Use 1-page concept paper application on foundation web site
Copies of proposal: 12
Deadline(s): Feb. 1, May 1, Aug. 1, and Nov. 1
Board meeting date(s): Jan., Apr., July, and Oct.
Final notification: May 15 (for Feb. 1 deadline), Aug. 15 (for May 1 deadline), Nov. 15 (for Aug. 1 deadline), and Feb. 15 (for Nov. 1 deadline)
Officers and Trustees:* Charles B. Mayer,* Pres.; Camille Jones Strachan,* V.P.; Walter C. Flower III,* Secy.; G. Price Crane,* Treas.; Lisa M. Kaichen, Mgr.; Henry Bodenheimer; Ralph C. Cox, Jr.; Paul Haygood III; Barbara C. MacPhee; Gordon R. Wadge.
Number of staff: 2 part-time professional.
EIN: 720423621

3638
Goldring Family Foundation
524 Metairie Rd.
Metairie, LA 70005-4308 (504) 849-6078
Contact: Trudi Briede, Dir.
FAX: (504) 849-6511; E-mail: trudi@gff1.com

Incorporated in 1955 in LA.
Donors: Magnolia Liquor Co., Inc.; Sazerac Co., Inc.; Great Southern Liquor Co., Inc.; N. Goldring Corp.; and members of the Goldring family.
Foundation type: Independent foundation.
Financial data (yr. ended 11/30/13): Assets, $85,082,259 (M); gifts received, $1,099,500; expenditures, $4,040,442; qualifying distributions, $4,816,790; giving activities include $3,294,432 for 249 grants (high: $333,333; low: $100), and $101,500 for 43 grants to individuals (high: $3,500; low: $1,750).
Purpose and activities: The foundation is rooted in the Jewish tradition and committed to democratic values and social justice, including fairness, diversity and community. The primary areas of interest are arts and culture, economic, development, education, health care, and Jewish causes.
Fields of interest: Arts; Higher education; Education; Health care; Human services; Jewish federated giving programs.
Type of support: General/operating support; Continuing support; Annual campaigns; Capital campaigns; Building/renovation; Equipment; Emergency funds; Program development; Matching/challenge support.
Limitations: Giving primarily in the greater New Orleans, LA region. No support for political purposes.
Application information:
Initial approach: Letter of inquiry
Board meeting date(s): Varies
Officers: William Goldring, Pres.; Jeffrey Goldring, V.P.; Diane Franco, V.P.; Paul Fine, Secy.-Treas.
Number of staff: 1 part-time professional.
EIN: 726022666
Selected grants: The following grants are a representative sample of this grantmaker's funding activity:
$500,000 to Audubon Nature Institute, New Orleans, LA, 2014.
$500,000 to Birthright Israel North America, New York, NY, 2014.
$25,000 to Tulane University, Freeman School of Business, New Orleans, LA, 2012.

3639
Grayson Foundation, Inc. ✧
P.O. Box 1607
Shreveport, LA 71165-1607
Application address: c/o John Dean, 333 Texas St., 15th Fl., Shreveport, LA 71101-3666, tel.: (318) 429-1525

Established in 1973 in LA.
Donors: Grayson Co. of the Southwest, Inc.; Delta Power Equipment Co.; Sam B. Grayson†.
Foundation type: Independent foundation.
Financial data (yr. ended 07/31/13): Assets, $33,294,920 (M); gifts received, $250; expenditures, $1,214,396; qualifying distributions, $1,000,205; giving activities include $991,700 for 17 grants (high: $200,000; low: $100).
Fields of interest: Higher education; Education; Health care; Human services; Philanthropy/voluntarism.
Limitations: Applications accepted. Giving primarily in Shreveport, LA.
Application information: Proposal should include cover letter describing project, amount requested, and timetable for implementation. Proposals should be no longer than 25 pages, not including required attachments. Application form required.
Initial approach: Proposal
Copies of proposal: 1
Deadline(s): Dec. 31 for Jan meeting and June 30 for July meeting
Board meeting date(s): Jan. and July

Officers and Directors: John W. Dean, Pres.; Lisa Axton, Secy.-Treas.; Chris Gabriel; Donald Webb; C. Cody White, Jr.
EIN: 237312000
Selected grants: The following grants are a representative sample of this grantmaker's funding activity:
$60,000 to Volunteers for Youth Justice, Shreveport, LA, 2011.
$50,000 to Sci-Port Discovery Center, Shreveport, LA, 2011.
$27,000 to Providence House, Shreveport, LA, 2011.

3640
The Merice "Boo" Johnson Grigsby Foundation ✧
15635 Airline Hwy.
Baton Rouge, LA 70817-7318 (225) 753-5857
FAX: (225) 751-9777;
E-mail: grants@boogrigsbyfoundation.com; Additional address: P.O. Box 104, Baton Rouge, LA 70821, tel.: (225) 938-7584; Main URL: http://www.boogrigsbyfoundation.com
Grants List: http://www.boogrigsbyfoundation.com/pastgiving.html

Established in 2006 in LA.
Donor: Cajun Constructors, Inc.
Foundation type: Company-sponsored foundation.
Financial data (yr. ended 12/31/12): Assets, $5,145,231 (M); gifts received, $2,132,650; expenditures, $2,547,370; qualifying distributions, $2,506,200; giving activities include $2,506,200 for 40 grants (high: $1,730,000; low: $1,000).
Purpose and activities: The foundation supports organizations involved with arts and humanities, education, conservation and science, medical and health services, human services, and community initiatives.
Fields of interest: Visual arts; Performing arts; Humanities; Arts; Higher education; Education; Environment, natural resources; Environmental education; Environment; Health care; Family services; Human services; Community/economic development; Science.
Type of support: General/operating support; Continuing support; Program development; Scholarship funds; Research.
Limitations: Applications accepted. Giving primarily in Baton Rouge, LA; giving also to national organizations.
Publications: Application guidelines.
Application information: Grants range from $1,000 to $5,000. Application form required.
Initial approach: Complete online application
Deadline(s): Mar. 15, June 15, Sept. 15, and Dec. 15
Board meeting date(s): Quarterly
Directors: L. Lane Grigsby; Todd William Grigsby; Tami Grigsby Moran; Tricia Grigsby Sanchez.
EIN: 208091007

3641
The Helis Foundation ✧
228 St. Charles Ave., Ste. 912
New Orleans, LA 70130-2685 (504) 523-1831
Contact: David A. Kerstein, V.P.

Incorporated in 1955 in LA.
Donors: Adrienne Helis Malvin†; Members of the William G. Helis family.
Foundation type: Independent foundation.
Financial data (yr. ended 12/31/12): Assets, $42,669,501 (M); gifts received, $1,896,787; expenditures, $1,878,909; qualifying distributions, $1,733,013; giving activities include $1,721,580 for 47 grants (high: $200,180; low: $600).
Purpose and activities: Giving primarily for art museums, as well as for health and human services.
Fields of interest: Museums (art); Health organizations, association; Disasters, Hurricane Katrina; Human services; Community/economic development; United Ways and Federated Giving Programs.
Limitations: Applications accepted. Giving primarily in New Orleans, LA.
Application information: Application form required.
Initial approach: Typed letter
Deadline(s): None
Officers: David A. Kerstein, Pres.; Michael F. Schott, V.P. and Treas.; Linda A. Reeg, Secy.
EIN: 726020536

3642
Heymann-Wolf Foundation ✧
228 St. Charles St., Ste. 1141
New Orleans, LA 70130-2667

Incorporated in 1947 in LA.
Donors: Leon Heymann†; Mrs. Leon Heymann†; Leon M. Wolf†; May H. Wolf; Jimmy Heymann; Mrs. Jimmy Heymann; Jonas John Heymann; Krauss Co., Ltd.; Yudelson Foundation.
Foundation type: Independent foundation.
Financial data (yr. ended 12/31/12): Assets, $11,627,428 (M); expenditures, $983,023; qualifying distributions, $735,287; giving activities include $735,287 for grants.
Fields of interest: Performing arts, theater; Arts; Elementary school/education; Higher education; Human services; Jewish federated giving programs; Jewish agencies & synagogues.
Limitations: Applications not accepted. Giving primarily in New Orleans, LA, and New York, NY. No grants to individuals.
Application information: Unsolicited requests for funds not accepted.
Officers: Jerry Heymann, Pres.; Jonas John Heymann, V.P.; Marjorie Heymann, V.P.
EIN: 726019363

3643
Huie-Dellmon Trust ✧
P.O. Box 330
Alexandria, LA 71309-0330 (318) 748-8141
Contact: Richard L. Crowell, Jr., Tr.

Established around 1976.
Foundation type: Independent foundation.
Financial data (yr. ended 12/31/13): Assets, $13,254,128 (M); expenditures, $551,723; qualifying distributions, $452,064; giving activities include $432,110 for 32 grants (high: $69,400; low: $250).
Purpose and activities: Giving primarily to Protestant organizations, as well as for social services, and historic preservation.
Fields of interest: Historic preservation/historical societies; Libraries/library science; Human services; Foundations (private grantmaking); United Ways and Federated Giving Programs; Christian agencies & churches; Protestant agencies & churches.
Type of support: General/operating support; Continuing support; Annual campaigns; Capital campaigns; Building/renovation; Equipment; Endowments; Program development; Professorships; Scholarship funds; Research; Matching/challenge support.
Limitations: Applications accepted. Giving primarily in central LA. No grants to individuals.
Application information: Application form not required.
Initial approach: Proposal
Deadline(s): None
Trustees: Richard L. Crowell, Jr.; Nancy C. Owens.
EIN: 720809684
Selected grants: The following grants are a representative sample of this grantmaker's funding activity:
$50,000 to Louisiana Prison Chapel Foundation, Baton Rouge, LA, 2010.
$50,000 to Saint Frances Cabrini Hospital Foundation of Alexandria, Alexandria, LA, 2010.
$50,000 to Saint Marys Residence, Philadelphia, PA, 2010.
$30,000 to Southern Forest Heritage Museum and Research Center, Longleaf, LA, 2010.
$22,000 to Food Bank of Central Louisiana, Alexandria, LA, 2010.
$20,000 to United Way of Central Louisiana, Alexandria, LA, 2010.
$19,000 to Rapides Parish School Board, Alexandria, LA, 2010.
$16,000 to Volunteers of America, Alexandria, VA, 2011. For operations.
$12,500 to First United Methodist Church, 2010.

3644
Institute of Mental Hygiene of the City of New Orleans ✧ ☆
1055 St. Charles Ave.
New Orleans, LA 70130-3941 (504) 566-1852
Contact: Nancy Freeman, Exec. Dir.; Kris Pottharst, Grants Mgr.
FAX: (504) 566-1853;
E-mail: kpottharst@imhno.org; Additional e-mail: nfreeman@imhno.org; Main URL: http://www.imhno.org

Established in 1937 in LA.
Donors: Samuel Zemurray†; Conrad Hilton Foundation; United Way.
Foundation type: Independent foundation.
Financial data (yr. ended 12/31/12): Assets, $20,532,688 (M); gifts received, $375,000; expenditures, $1,574,098; qualifying distributions, $1,442,277; giving activities include $997,089 for 19 grants (high: $562,000; low: $5,000), and $237,254 for 1 foundation-administered program.
Purpose and activities: Giving to improve mental health for children and their families, in New Orleans, LA.
Fields of interest: Mental health/crisis services; Family services; Children.
Type of support: General/operating support; Continuing support; Program development; Conferences/seminars; Seed money; Research; Technical assistance; Program evaluation; Matching/challenge support.
Limitations: Giving limited to New Orleans, LA. No grants to individuals; or for capital campaigns.
Publications: Application guidelines; Annual report.

Application information: Guidelines for full proposals will be sent to applicants when a full proposal is requested.
Initial approach: Letter of Intent (not exceeding 2 pages), or telephone call prior to letter to discuss project
Deadline(s): See foundation web site for current deadlines
Officers: Bonnie Goldbum, Pres.; J. Storey Charbonnet, V.P.; Bernadette D'Souza, Secy.; Julius E. Kimbrough, Jr., Treas.; Nancy Freeman, Exec. Dir.
Directors: Ayanna Butler; Alan Franco; Geoffrey Nagle; Beverly R. Nichols; Lee Reid; Sarah Newell Usdin; Kyshun Webster, Ph.D.; Carol Wise; and 4 additional directors.
Number of staff: 1 full-time professional; 1 full-time support.
EIN: 720446138

3645
Eugenie and Joseph Jones Family Foundation ✧ ☆
c/o Jones Family Foundation
835 Union St., Ste. 333
New Orleans, LA 70112-1401 (504) 584-1545
Contact: Susan Jones Gundlach, Pres.

Incorporated in 1955 in LA.
Donors: Joseph M. Jones†; Eugenie P. Jones†.
Foundation type: Independent foundation.
Financial data (yr. ended 12/31/13): Assets, $29,565,249 (M); expenditures, $1,242,737; qualifying distributions, $1,034,491; giving activities include $1,008,167 for 51 grants (high: $250,000; low: $200).
Purpose and activities: Primary areas of interest include education, community development, health and human services, and arts and cultural programs.
Fields of interest: Arts; Higher education; Education; Community/economic development; Protestant agencies & churches.
Type of support: General/operating support; Continuing support; Annual campaigns; Capital campaigns; Building/renovation; Equipment; Endowments; Program development; Professorships; Seed money; Fellowships; Scholarship funds; Matching/challenge support.
Limitations: Applications accepted. Giving primarily in LA, especially in the greater New Orleans area. No grants to individuals, or for land acquisition, special projects, research, publications, conferences, start-up or emergency funds, or deficit financing; no loans.
Publications: Application guidelines.
Application information: Application form required.
Initial approach: Contact foundation for application form
Copies of proposal: 1
Deadline(s): None
Officers and Trustees:* Susan Jones Gundlach,* Pres.; Elaine F. Jones, Secy.-Treas.; Sally H. Lapeyre; Miriam H. Lindner; Susan L. Stall; Melissa Steiner.
Number of staff: 4 part-time support.
EIN: 720507534

3646
Keller Family Foundation ✧
c/o Crescent Capital Consulting, LLC
1100 Poydras St., Ste. 1502
New Orleans, LA 70163-1101 (504) 207-8541
Contact: Toni Myers
FAX: (504) 207-8525;
E-mail: info@kellerfamilyfoundation.org; Main URL: http://kellerfamilyfoundation.org/index.html

Established in 1949 in LA.
Donors: Charles Keller, Jr.†; Rosa F. Keller†.
Foundation type: Independent foundation.
Financial data (yr. ended 12/31/13): Assets, $17,021,939 (M); expenditures, $733,315; qualifying distributions, $652,044; giving activities include $645,607 for 2 grants (high: $372,544; low: $273,063).
Purpose and activities: The foundation has interests in education, youth development, human services, and public affairs.
Fields of interest: Arts; Higher education; Education; Human services; Community/economic development; United Ways and Federated Giving Programs.
Type of support: Matching/challenge support; Management development/capacity building; General/operating support; Capital campaigns.
Limitations: Applications accepted. Giving primarily in New Orleans, LA. No grants to individuals, or for tickets or fundraisers.
Publications: Application guidelines; Grants list.
Application information: Application guidelines available on foundation web site. Application form required.
Initial approach: Use online application form on foundation web site
Deadline(s): Feb. 1 for spring meeting, and Sept. 15 for fall meeting
Board meeting date(s): Apr. and Nov.
Officers and Directors:* Mary K. Zervigon,* Pres.; Luis C. Zervigon,* V.P. and Treas.; Caroline K. Loughlin,* Secy.; Thomas K. Loughlin; Andres M. Zervigon.
Number of staff: None.
EIN: 726027426

3647
The Charles Lamar Family Foundation ✧
P.O. Box 66338
Baton Rouge, LA 70896-6338 (225) 924-3527
Contact: Charles Lamar

Established in 2001 in LA.
Donors: Charles W. Lamar, III Trust; Charles W. Lamar III; Charles W. Lamar III Charitable Lead Annuity Trust No. 1.
Foundation type: Independent foundation.
Financial data (yr. ended 12/31/12): Assets, $13,940,721 (M); expenditures, $704,704; qualifying distributions, $690,729; giving activities include $690,729 for grants.
Purpose and activities: The foundation's vision for Baton Rouge is a cadre of stable nonprofit organizations that effect positive change in the community. The foundation seeks to support emerging or maturing and expanding nonprofits with useful missions that are responsive to community challenges and opportunities. Giving is generally limited to those organizations that are located in or near the Baton Rouge, LA, area in the fields of social services, arts and culture, education, animal welfare, and natural and historic conservation.
Fields of interest: Arts; Higher education; Libraries (public); Education; Substance abuse, treatment; Safety/disasters; Recreation; YM/YWCAs & YM/YWHAs; Public affairs.
Limitations: Applications accepted. Giving primarily in Baton Rouge, LA. No grants to individuals.
Application information: Application form required.
Initial approach: Letter
Deadline(s): None
Officers: Charles W. Lamar III, Pres.; Carole E. Lamar, Secy.-Treas.
Director: Allison Lamar Beard.
EIN: 721488497

3648
Libby-Dufour Fund ✧ ☆
P.O. Box 53232
New Orleans, LA 70153-3232
Contact: M. Cleland Powell III, Pres.

Incorporated in 1952 in LA.
Donor: Edith Libby Dufour†.
Foundation type: Independent foundation.
Financial data (yr. ended 12/31/13): Assets, $8,442,238 (M); expenditures, $653,382; qualifying distributions, $546,551; giving activities include $542,100 for 22 grants (high: $50,000; low: $500).
Purpose and activities: Giving primarily for nonprofit organizations, schools, museums, and arts and culture.
Fields of interest: Arts; Education; Human services.
Type of support: Capital campaigns; Building/renovation; Equipment.
Limitations: Applications accepted. Giving limited to the New Orleans, LA, area. No support for churches, political organizations, or public finance programs. No grants to individuals, or for endowment funds or operating budgets.
Application information: The grantmaker accepts the Southern Grantmakers Forum Grant Proposal Summary Sheet. Application form required.
Initial approach: Proposal
Copies of proposal: 1
Deadline(s): None
Board meeting date(s): Quarterly
Officers: M. Cleland Powell III, Pres.; Denis H. McDonald, V.P.; Harry B. Kelleher, Jr., Secy.
Trustees: J. Story Charbonnet; Brian Fitzpatrick; Edward M. Simmons.
EIN: 726027406

3649
Lincoln Health Foundation ✧
1809 Northpointe Ln., Ste. 203
Ruston, LA 71270-3852 (318) 251-3226
Contact: Norman Hanes, C.E.O.
E-mail: nhanes@lincolnhealth.com; Main URL: http://www.lincolnhealth.com/

Established in LA.
Foundation type: Independent foundation.
Financial data (yr. ended 09/30/13): Assets, $27,318,948 (M); gifts received, $159,880; expenditures, $1,840,071; qualifying distributions, $1,594,858; giving activities include $1,516,597 for 17 grants (high: $586,255; low: $926).
Purpose and activities: Giving to improve health care and outcomes for residents of Lincoln Parish, LA.

Fields of interest: Health care, research; Health care, formal/general education; Health care.
Limitations: Giving primarily in Lincoln Parish, LA. No support for disease-specific organizations seeking support for national projects and programs, for-profit organizations, hospitals, religious, fraternal, athletic or veterans groups when primary beneficiaries of such undertakings would be their own members, or for social or political actions programs that advocate a specific point of view. No grants to individuals, or for trips, tours, travel to professional meetings, social events or similar fundraising activities, telethons, or grants awarded for an indeterminate period of time.
Publications: Application guidelines.
Application information: Refer to application guidelines on foundation web site for specific proposal instructions which must be followed, and budget form.
Initial approach: Cover letter on letterhead and proposal (5 pages maximum)
Officers and Board Members:* Ben P. Haley, M.D.*, Chair.; Wilbert Ellis,* Vice-Chair.; Norman Hanes, C.E.O.; James Davison, Secy.-Treas.; John Belton; Sonja Cardwell; Benjamin L. Denny; Allen Herbert, M.D.; Nancy Smith, M.D.; Willie Washington.
EIN: 721335146
Selected grants: The following grants are a representative sample of this grantmaker's funding activity:
$299,934 to Lincoln Parish School Board, Ruston, LA, 2011.
$23,174 to Lincoln Parish School Board, Ruston, LA, 2011.
$16,384 to Lincoln Parish School Board, Ruston, LA, 2011.
$16,019 to Lincoln Parish School Board, Ruston, LA, 2011.

3650
Lorio Foundation ✧
P.O. Box 895
Thibodaux, LA 70302-0895 (985) 449-0380

Established in LA.
Foundation type: Independent foundation.
Financial data (yr. ended 12/31/13): Assets, $25,216,060 (M); expenditures, $1,175,967; qualifying distributions, $1,117,466; giving activities include $1,015,500 for grants.
Purpose and activities: Giving primarily for human services, community development, and Roman Catholic organizations and churches.
Fields of interest: Elementary/secondary education; Animals/wildlife, formal/general education; Animal population control; Housing/shelter, development; Human services; Community/economic development; Protestant agencies & churches; Catholic agencies & churches.
Limitations: Applications accepted. Giving limited to Thibodaux, LA.
Application information: Application form required.
Initial approach: Letter
Deadline(s): None
Officers: Rita Dickie, Mgr.; Ann Hebert, Mgr.; Camille A. Morvant III, Mgr.; Christopher Terracina, Mgr.
EIN: 721318244
Selected grants: The following grants are a representative sample of this grantmaker's funding activity:
$100,000 to Nicholls State University, Thibodaux, LA, 2011.
$25,000 to Saint Vincent de Paul TriParish Community Pharmacy, Houma, LA, 2011.
$15,000 to Saint Charles Elementary School, Thibodaux, LA, 2011.

3651
Louisiana Outside Counsel Health and Ethics Foundation ✧
1419 Ryan St.
Lake Charles, LA 70601-5918

Established in 2004 in LA.
Donor: LA Outside Counsel.
Foundation type: Independent foundation.
Financial data (yr. ended 12/31/13): Assets, $0 (M); gifts received, $750,000; expenditures, $750,000; qualifying distributions, $750,000; giving activities include $750,000 for 9 grants (high: $450,000; low: $3,750).
Fields of interest: Higher education; Law school/education; Legal services; Crime/law enforcement; Human services.
Limitations: Applications not accepted. Giving in LA, primarily in Baton Rouge and New Orleans. No grants to individuals.
Application information: Contributes only to pre-selected organizations.
Officers: Drew Ranier, Pres.; Ken Carter, Secy.; Bob Wright, Treas.
Trustees: Russ Herman; Don Kelly.
EIN: 010550123

3652
The Lupin Foundation ✧
(formerly Physicians New Orleans Foundation)
234 Metairie Rd.
Metairie, LA 70005-4505 (504) 849-0518
Contact: Arnold M. Lupin, Pres.

Incorporated in 1981 in LA.
Foundation type: Independent foundation.
Financial data (yr. ended 12/31/13): Assets, $17,094,016 (M); expenditures, $1,097,733; qualifying distributions, $845,915; giving activities include $597,000 for 73 grants (high: $250,000; low: $500).
Purpose and activities: Giving primarily to Jewish agencies and temples; also support for health associations, education, and the arts.
Fields of interest: Museums; Arts; Higher education; Education; Hospitals (general); Health organizations, association; Medical research, institute; Cancer, leukemia research; Human services; Jewish federated giving programs; Jewish agencies & synagogues; Disabilities, people with.
Limitations: Applications accepted. Giving primarily in LA and NY. No grants to individuals; no loans.
Publications: Application guidelines.
Application information: Application form required.
Initial approach: Proposal
Copies of proposal: 1
Deadline(s): None
Officers and Directors:* Arnold M. Lupin,* Pres.; Samuel Lupin,* V.P.; E. Ralph Lupin,* Secy.-Treas.; Jay Lupin; Lisa R. Lupin; Louis J. Lupin; Michael Lupin; Timothy Lupin; Suzanne Stokar.
Number of staff: 1 full-time support.
EIN: 720940770

3653
Marshall Heritage Foundation ✧
(formerly Marshall Museum & Library)
c/o Dr. S. Cook
320 Hammond Hwy., Ste. 403
Metairie, LA 70005

Established in 1996 in LA.
Donor: JHM Charitable Lead Trust.
Foundation type: Independent foundation.
Financial data (yr. ended 04/30/13): Assets, $15,139,885 (M); expenditures, $7,225,557; qualifying distributions, $6,957,000; giving activities include $6,957,000 for 22 grants (high: $2,100,000; low: $5,000).
Fields of interest: Elementary/secondary education; Higher education; Medical school/education; Cancer; Orthopedics; Children/youth, services; Engineering/technology.
Limitations: Applications not accepted. Giving primarily in LA, NY, and TX. No grants to individuals.
Application information: Contributes only to pre-selected organizations.
Trustees: Dr. Stephen D. Cook; E. Pierce Marshall, Jr.; Elaine T. Marshall; Preston L. Marshall.
EIN: 726163215
Selected grants: The following grants are a representative sample of this grantmaker's funding activity:
$2,000,000 to Baylor University, Waco, TX, 2011. For general support.
$1,000,000 to Court Appointed Special Advocates, Dallas, Dallas, TX, 2011. For general support.
$1,000,000 to Greenhill School, Addison, TX, 2011. For general support.
$552,000 to University of Texas M.D. Anderson Cancer Center, Houston, TX, 2011. For general support.
$500,000 to Americans for Prosperity Foundation, Arlington, VA, 2011. For general support.
$500,000 to Institute for Energy Research, Washington, DC, 2011. For general support.
$500,000 to Mercatus Center, Arlington, VA, 2011. For general support.
$250,000 to Americans for Prosperity Foundation, Arlington, VA, 2010. For general support.
$250,000 to Institute for Energy Research, Washington, DC, 2010. For general support.
$200,000 to Memorial Sloan-Kettering Cancer Center, New York, NY, 2010. For general support.
$200,000 to University of Texas M.D. Anderson Cancer Center, Houston, TX, 2010. For general support.
$100,000 to Committee to Reduce Infection Deaths, New York, NY, 2011. For general support.
$100,000 to Interfaith Housing Coalition, Dallas, TX, 2010. For general support.
$100,000 to Muscular Dystrophy Association, Phoenix, AZ, 2010. For general support.
$50,000 to Baylor University, Waco, TX, 2010. For general support.
$50,000 to Tulane University, New Orleans, LA, 2010. For general support.
$10,000 to Fay School, Houston, TX, 2011. For general support.
$10,000 to Grace School, Houston, TX, 2011. For general support.

3654
Gustaf Westfeldt McIlhenny Family Foundation ✧

601 Poydras St., Ste. 2500
New Orleans, LA 70130-6025 (504) 586-7663
Contact: Edwin R. Rodriguez, Jr., Pres.

Established in 1997 in LA.
Donor: G.W. McIlhenny Charitable Lead Unitrust.
Foundation type: Independent foundation.
Financial data (yr. ended 12/31/12): Assets, $18,058,992 (M); gifts received, $1,045,683; expenditures, $800,029; qualifying distributions, $612,240; giving activities include $546,598 for 82 grants (high: $53,398; low: $286).
Fields of interest: Higher education, university; Education; Hospitals (general); United Ways and Federated Giving Programs; Protestant agencies & churches.
Limitations: Applications accepted. Giving primarily in LA. No grants to individuals.
Application information: Application form required.
Initial approach: Completed application form
Deadline(s): Varies annually, but generally Mar. 30
Officers: Edwin R. Rodriguez, Jr., Pres.; Paul C.P. McIlhenny, Secy.-Treas.
EIN: 721404522
Selected grants: The following grants are a representative sample of this grantmaker's funding activity:
$30,000 to Ozanam Inn, New Orleans, LA, 2012. For Further the Purposes of the Recipient Charity.
$5,000 to Bayou District Foundation, New Orleans, LA, 2012. For Further the Purposes of the Recipient Charity.
$5,000 to Trinity Episcopal School, New Orleans, LA, 2012. For Further Purposes of Recipient Charity.
$2,500 to Louisiana Museum Foundation, New Orleans, LA, 2012. For Further the Purpose of the Recipient Charity.

3655
The James R. Moffett Family Foundation ✧ ☆

1615 Poydras St., 22nd Fl.
New Orleans, LA 70112-1254
Contact: Cynthia M. Molyneux, Exec. Dir.

Established in 1997 in LA.
Donors: James R. Moffett; Louise H. Moffett; Moffett Holdings, LLC.
Foundation type: Independent foundation.
Financial data (yr. ended 09/30/13): Assets, $419,325 (M); gifts received, $428,000; expenditures, $430,237; qualifying distributions, $430,237; giving activities include $428,000 for 97 grants (high: $50,000; low: $500).
Fields of interest: Education; Health organizations, association; Cancer; Children/youth, services; United Ways and Federated Giving Programs; Christian agencies & churches.
Limitations: Applications accepted. Giving primarily in CA, LA, and TX.
Application information: Application form not required.
Initial approach: Letter
Deadline(s): None
Officers: James R. Moffett, Pres.; Louise H. Moffett, V.P.; Crystal L. Moffett-Lourd, Secy.; James R. Moffett, Jr., Treas.; Cynthia M. Molyneux, Exec. Dir.
EIN: 721345770
Selected grants: The following grants are a representative sample of this grantmaker's funding activity:
$34,000 to John Thomas Dye School, Los Angeles, CA, 2011.
$12,500 to New Orleans City Park, New Orleans, LA, 2011.
$7,500 to Catholic Cultural Heritage Center, New Orleans, LA, 2011.
$5,000 to Childrens Hospital, New Orleans, LA, 2011.
$5,000 to Crime Stoppers, Metairie, LA, 2011.
$5,000 to Ducks Unlimited, Ridgeland, MS, 2011.
$5,000 to Libertys Kitchen, New Orleans, LA, 2011.
$5,000 to Project Lazarus, New Orleans, LA, 2011.
$3,000 to American Cancer Society, New Orleans, LA, 2011.
$2,500 to Virginia Rosanne Amato Foundation, New Orleans, LA, 2011.

3656
The Greater New Orleans Foundation ✧

1055 St. Charles Ave., Ste. 100
New Orleans, LA 70130-3981 (504) 598-4663
Contact: Dr. G. Albert Ruesga, C.E.O.
FAX: (504) 598-4676; E-mail: albert@gnof.org; Main URL: http://www.gnof.org
Blog: http://www.gnof.org/our-community/
Facebook: http://www.facebook.com/pages/Greater-New-Orleans-Foundation/200124173059?ref=ts
Philanthropy's Promise: http://www.ncrp.org/philanthropys-promise/who
RSS Feed: http://feeds2.feedburner.com/gnof
Twitter: http://twitter.com/GNOFoundation

Established in 1924 in LA as the Community Chest; became a community foundation in 1983.
Foundation type: Community foundation.
Financial data (yr. ended 12/31/12): Assets, $276,454,560 (M); gifts received, $822,578; expenditures, $23,277,015; giving activities include $19,006,768 for grants.
Purpose and activities: The ultimate goal of the Greater New Orleans Foundation is to create a resilient, sustainable, vibrant community in which individuals and families flourish and in which the special character of the New Orleans region and its people is preserved, celebrated, and given the means to develop. The foundation has a critical role to play in attaining this goal, as community leader and convener; as champion of civil society; and as supporter of effective nonprofit leaders and organizations. By serving as a philanthropic partner to members of the donor community, the foundation helps add meaning and value to the giving of individuals, families and institutions, increasing the effectiveness of their philanthropy and connecting them with the very best nonprofit work in Greater New Orleans and surrounding regions.
Fields of interest: Arts; Education; Environment; Health care; Crime/law enforcement; Housing/shelter; Safety/disasters; Youth development; Human services; Economic development; Community/economic development; Public affairs; Children/youth; Adults, women.
Type of support: General/operating support; Management development/capacity building; Endowments; Emergency funds; Program development; Seed money; Research; Technical assistance; Program evaluation; Matching/challenge support.
Limitations: Applications accepted. Giving limited to southeastern LA, including the greater New Orleans area. No support for religious activities. No grants to individuals, or for annual fund campaigns, capital expenditures, sponsorship of special events, trips, continuing support, endowment funds, equipment, building funds, or deficit financing.
Publications: Annual report; Informational brochure; Newsletter; Program policy statement.
Application information: Each competitive grantmaking fund is governed by different grantmaking priorities, criteria and guidelines. Visit foundation web site for application information per grant type.
Deadline(s): Varies
Board meeting date(s): Quarterly
Final notification: Varies
Officers and Trustees:* Ludovico Feoli, Ph.D.*, Chair.; Cheryl R. Teamer,* Vice-Chair.; Dr. G. Albert Ruesga, C.E.O. and Pres.; Ryan Crespino, V.P., Finance and Admin.; Martha McDermott Landrum, V.P., Mktg. and Comms.; Alice B. Parkerson, V.P., Devel.; Joann Ricci, V.P., Organizational Effectiveness; Leann O. Moses,* Secy.; Robert Bories,* Treas.; Cherie F. Thompson, Cont.; David Barksdale; Mark Blanchard; Robert S. Boh; Christian T. Brown; Robert W. Brown; James J. Buquet III; Daryl G. Byrd; Arnold W. Donald; David Edwards; Monica Edwards; Conrad N. Hilton, III; Pat LeBlanc; Dr. Silas H. Lee III; Walter J. Leger, Jr.; Nancy M. Marsiglia; Monika McKay; R. King Milling; Andree K. Moss; Elizabeth S. Nalty; Anthony Recasner, Ph.D.; Charles L. Rice, Jr.; Edwin "Rod" Rodriguez, Jr.; Ileana Suquet; Dr. Vera Triplett; Madeline D. West; George V. Young; Luis Zervigon.
Number of staff: 13 full-time professional; 1 part-time professional; 3 full-time support.
EIN: 720408921
Selected grants: The following grants are a representative sample of this grantmaker's funding activity:
$592,978 to Southeast Louisiana Legal Services, Hammond, LA, 2011. For New Orleans Title Clearing and Reform Initiative, joint project of SLLS, Pro Bono Project, Lawyers Committee for Civil Rights Under Law and Appleseed.
$375,000 to SEE the Movement Foundation, New Orleans, LA, 2011. For Solar Opportunities for People Everywhere IV project.
$350,000 to Preservation Alliance of New Orleans, Preservation Resource Center of New Orleans, New Orleans, LA, 2011. For PRC's Education and Outreach, Advocacy, Operation Comeback and Rebuilding Together programs.
$328,000 to New Schools for New Orleans, New Orleans, LA, 2011. For Centralized Enrollment System Project Management.
$251,766 to Catholic Social Services of the Diocese of Houma-Thibodaux, Houma, LA, 2011. For Matthew 25 Special Fund for Social Services and Financial Security.
$200,000 to Volunteers of America, Greater New Orleans Chapter, New Orleans, LA, 2011. For the completion of RNDC's (Renaissance Neighborhood Development Corporation) staffing plan to increase RNDC's sustainability through the generation of development fees.
$12,000 to Mary Queen of Vietnam Community Development Corporation, New Orleans, LA, 2011.
$10,000 to University of New Orleans, New Orleans, LA, 2011. For damage assessment of Chandeleur Island seagrasses.

$5,000 to Audubon Charter School, New Orleans, LA, 2011. For 4th, 5th, and 7th grade participation in T.R.E.E.
$5,000 to New Orleans Museum of Art, New Orleans, LA, 2011. For Annual Appeal.

3657
The Noel Foundation, Inc. ✧
1 University Pl.
Shreveport, LA 71115-2399 (318) 798-4161
Contact: Robert Leitz, Pres.

Established in 1973; classified as a private operating foundation in 1990.
Donor: LSUS.
Foundation type: Operating foundation.
Financial data (yr. ended 12/31/12): Assets, $18,278,929 (M); gifts received, $189,762; expenditures, $970,327; qualifying distributions, $739,401; giving activities include $488,432 for 13 grants (high: $200,000; low: $250).
Fields of interest: Higher education.
Type of support: Scholarship funds.
Limitations: Applications accepted. Giving primarily in Shreveport, LA.
Application information: Application form not required.
Initial approach: Proposal
Deadline(s): None
Officers: Robert Leitz, Pres.; Shelby L. Smith, V.P.; Merritt B. Chastain, Jr., Secy.; Gilbert R. Shanley, Jr., Treas.
Trustees: Richard Bremer; Thomas G. Carmody; Kevin L. Cope; Alan D. Gabehart; Wilfred L. Guerin; Vincent Marsala; Pamela Washington.
EIN: 237177629

3658
The Peltier Foundation ✧
101 St. Louis St.
Thibodaux, LA 70301-3027 (985) 447-4033

Established in 1998 in LA.
Donor: Richard Peltier.
Foundation type: Independent foundation.
Financial data (yr. ended 12/31/13): Assets, $18,106,811 (M); expenditures, $1,135,999; qualifying distributions, $901,784; giving activities include $886,500 for 52 grants (high: $125,000; low: $2,000).
Fields of interest: Elementary/secondary education; Human services; Catholic agencies & churches.
Limitations: Applications accepted. Giving primarily in Thibodaux, LA. No grants to individuals.
Application information: Application form required.
Initial approach: Letter
Deadline(s): None
Officers: Dr. James Peltier, Pres.; Sarah Naquin, V.P.; Stephen Peltier, Secy.-Treas.
EIN: 721416778
Selected grants: The following grants are a representative sample of this grantmaker's funding activity:
$20,000 to Archdiocese of New Orleans, New Orleans, LA, 2012. For I Will Give You Shepherds.
$15,000 to Diocese of Houma-Thibodaux, Schriever, LA, 2012. For seminarian's burse for Peltier Foundation.
$15,000 to Nicholls State University, Thibodaux, LA, 2012. For Athletic Department scholarships.

3659
Irene W. & C. B. Pennington Foundation ✧
2237 S. Acadian Thruway, Ste. 705
Baton Rouge, LA 70808-2380 (225) 928-8346
Contact: To Discuss Current or Proposed Projects: Vonnie L. Hawkins, Prog. Off.
FAX: (225) 928-8375;
E-mail: rec@penningtonfamilyfoundation.org; Main URL: http://www.penningtonfamilyfoundation.org

Established in 1982 in LA.
Donors: C.B. Pennington†; Irene W. Pennington†.
Foundation type: Independent foundation.
Financial data (yr. ended 12/31/12): Assets, $7,036,919 (M); expenditures, $9,318,797; qualifying distributions, $6,629,675; giving activities include $6,629,675 for 139 grants (high: $300,000; low: $400).
Purpose and activities: Giving primarily to provide philanthropic support to promote the overall well-being of families and communities.
Fields of interest: Secondary school/education; Medical specialties research; Disasters, preparedness/services; Youth development, centers/clubs; Human services; Youth, services.
Type of support: General/operating support; Capital campaigns; Building/renovation; Program development.
Limitations: Giving limited to communities within or near Baton Rouge, LA. No grants to individuals.
Publications: Application guidelines.
Application information: Paper proposals which have not been invited will not be accepted, considered or returned. Fax or e-mail proposals, or proposals in spiral or ring binders are not accepted. Unsolicited applications are reviewed once per year in a single step process. Proposal guidelines available on foundation web site. Application form required.
Initial approach: Online proposal submission
Copies of proposal: 1
Deadline(s): Aug. 15
Final notification: Dec.
Officers and Trustees:* William E. Hodgkins,* Chair.; Lori Bertman, C.E.O. and Pres.; Richard Blackstone; Paula P. Delabretonne; Claude B. Pennington III; Daryl B. Pennington, Sr.; Daryl B. Pennington, Jr.; Sharon Palmer Pennington.
Number of staff: 2
EIN: 720938097
Selected grants: The following grants are a representative sample of this grantmaker's funding activity:
$300,000 to Knock Knock Childrens Museum, Baton Rouge, LA, 2012. For Capital Campaign.
$250,000 to Baton Rouge Speech and Hearing Foundation, Baton Rouge, LA, 2012. For Campaign for Hope.
$250,000 to East Feliciana Parish Sheriffs Office, Clinton, LA, 2012.
$200,000 to Baton Rouge Area Foundation, Baton Rouge, LA, 2012. For Smash Hits HIV/AIDS Fund.
$200,000 to East Feliciana Emergency Communications Commission, Clinton, LA, 2012. For Emergency Communications Center Project.
$200,000 to YMCA of the Capital Area, Baton Rouge, LA, 2012. For Americana Zachary YMCA.
$150,000 to Baton Rouge Area Foundation, Baton Rouge, LA, 2012. For Pennington Disaster Resiliency Fund.
$100,000 to East Baton Rouge Truancy Assessment, Baton Rouge, LA, 2012. For Truancy Center Startup.
$33,148 to Capital Area Reentry Coalition, Baton Rouge, LA, 2012. For Capital Area ReEntry Coalition Mentoring Program.
$25,000 to Baton Rouge Area Foundation, Baton Rouge, LA, 2012. For Ernest J Gaines Award for Literary Excellence.

3660
Pinhook Foundation, Inc. ✧
200 W. University Ave.
Lafayette, LA 70506-3646

Established in 1999 LA.
Donor: Lucille Donlon Hamner†.
Foundation type: Independent foundation.
Financial data (yr. ended 12/31/13): Assets, $11,061,719 (M); expenditures, $627,664; qualifying distributions, $602,999; giving activities include $602,999 for 32 grants (high: $200,000; low: $100).
Fields of interest: Higher education; Human services; United Ways and Federated Giving Programs; Catholic agencies & churches.
Type of support: General/operating support.
Limitations: Applications not accepted. Giving primarily in Lafayette, LA. No grants to individuals.
Application information: Contributes only to pre-selected organizations.
Officers: Michael G. Hamner, Pres.; Emily H. Hamner, Secy.-Treas.
EIN: 721432054
Selected grants: The following grants are a representative sample of this grantmaker's funding activity:
$26,000 to Boys and Girls Clubs of Acadiana, Lafayette, LA, 2011.

3661
Reily Foundation ✧
640 Magazine St.
New Orleans, LA 70130-3406 (504) 524-6131
Contact: Robert D. Reily, Dir.

Established in 1962.
Donor: Reily Foods Co.
Foundation type: Company-sponsored foundation.
Financial data (yr. ended 12/31/12): Assets, $0 (M); expenditures, $17,985,073; qualifying distributions, $17,876,214; giving activities include $17,874,714 for 34 grants (high: $17,011,815; low: $2,000).
Purpose and activities: The foundation supports community foundations and organizations involved with arts and culture, education, health, human services, and civic affairs.
Fields of interest: Education; Agriculture/food; Human services.
Type of support: General/operating support; Continuing support; Capital campaigns; Building/renovation; Equipment; Program development.
Limitations: Applications not accepted. Giving primarily in the greater New Orleans, LA, area. No support for religious or political organizations. No grants to individuals.
Application information:
Board meeting date(s): Varies
Directors: Robert Aron; Joan M. Coulter; Robert D. Reily; William B. Reily III; Stephen Usdin.
EIN: 726029179

Selected grants: The following grants are a representative sample of this grantmaker's funding activity:
$17,011,615 to Greater New Orleans Foundation, New Orleans, LA, 2012. For liquidating distribution.
$10,000 to Touro Infirmary, New Orleans, LA, 2012. For operating fund.

3662
The Edward L. Rispone Family Foundation ✧
(formerly The Edward L. & Phyllis M. Rispone Family Foundation)
18250 S. Mission Hills Ave.
Baton Rouge, LA 70810-7974

Established in 2000 in LA.
Donors: Edward L. Rispone; Phyllis M. Rispone†.
Foundation type: Independent foundation.
Financial data (yr. ended 12/31/13): Assets, $11,533,844 (M); gifts received, $1,500,000; expenditures, $2,447,642; qualifying distributions, $2,419,590; giving activities include $2,419,590 for 30 grants (high: $1,917,250; low: $100).
Purpose and activities: Giving primarily to Roman Catholic ministries; funding also for education and social services.
Fields of interest: Education; Human services; United Ways and Federated Giving Programs; Catholic agencies & churches.
Limitations: Applications not accepted. Giving primarily in Baton Rouge, LA.
Application information: Unsolicited requests for funds not accepted.
Officers and Directors:* Edward L. Rispone,* Pres.; Lauren Rispone Read,* Secy.; Thad E. Rispone,* Treas.; Dena R. Balart; Skye Lemoine Bray; Benjamin S. Lemoine; Seth A. Lemoine; Kevin J. Rispone; Linda L. Rispone.
EIN: 721474941
Selected grants: The following grants are a representative sample of this grantmaker's funding activity:
$225,000 to Sister Dulce Foundation, Baton Rouge, LA, 2011.
$47,425 to Saint George Catholic Church and School, Baton Rouge, LA, 2010. For general fund.
$35,000 to Saint Joseph Cathedral, Baton Rouge, LA, 2011. For general fund.
$20,250 to Sister Dulce Foundation, Baton Rouge, LA, 2011. For general fund.
$15,000 to Saint George Catholic Church and School, Tuition Assistance Fund, Baton Rouge, LA, 2010. For general fund.
$10,275 to Manresa House of Retreats, Convent, LA, 2011. For general fund.
$10,000 to Redemptorist High School, Baton Rouge, LA, 2011.
$10,000 to United Way, Capital Area, Baton Rouge, LA, 2010. For general fund.
$8,697 to Alliance for School Choice, Washington, DC, 2011. For general fund.
$2,500 to Cross International Catholic Outreach, Boca Raton, FL, 2011. For general fund.
$1,035 to Redemptorist High School, Baton Rouge, LA, 2011. For general fund.
$1,000 to Our Lady of Mercy Catholic Church, Baton Rouge, LA, 2011. For general fund.

3663
The RosaMary Foundation ✧
c/o Crescent Capital Consulting
1100 Poydras St., Ste. 1502
New Orleans, LA 70163-1503 (504) 207-8541
Contact: Toni Myers, Admin.
FAX: (504) 207-8525;
E-mail: Admin@RosaMary.org; Main URL: http://www.rosamary.org

Trust established in 1939 in LA.
Donor: Members of the A.B. Freeman family.
Foundation type: Independent foundation.
Financial data (yr. ended 12/31/12): Assets, $50,532,206 (M); expenditures, $2,850,085; qualifying distributions, $2,245,908; giving activities include $2,224,108 for 55 grants (high: $250,000; low: $1,000).
Purpose and activities: Giving primarily for education, with emphasis on private institutions, human service organizations, arts, both performing and applied, community development activities, and governmental oversight activities. The foundation supports both capital projects and programmatic requests. Capital projects require a history of operating stability and the financial capacity to maintain the new facilities. Capital grants require evidence of broad support from the private sector and are usually made contingent to construct the project.
Fields of interest: Arts; Education; Health care, clinics/centers; Housing/shelter, development; Human services; Community/economic development; Government/public administration.
Type of support: General/operating support; Continuing support; Annual campaigns; Capital campaigns; Building/renovation; Endowments; Program development; Seed money.
Limitations: Applications accepted. Giving primarily in the greater New Orleans, LA, area. No grants to individuals, or for tickets or fundraising events.
Publications: Application guidelines; Grants list.
Application information: Application form and summary sheet available on foundation web site. Application form required.
Initial approach: Proposal, preferably online, otherwise in letter form (no more than 3 pages)
Copies of proposal: 1
Deadline(s): Feb. 1 and Sept. 1
Board meeting date(s): Approximately 2 times a year beginning in spring
Officer and Trustees:* Richard W. Freeman, Jr.,* Chair.; Andrew Wisdom, Secy.; Adelaide Wisdom Benjamin; Edward W. Benjamin; Louis M. Freeman, Jr.; Olivia Woollam; Carlos Zervigon; Luis C. Zervigon; Mary Zervigon.
EIN: 726024696

3664
The Sanford Foundation ✧
P.O. Box 2447
Morgan City, LA 70381-2367
Additional address: c/o The Sanford Foundation, 612 Techeview Dr., Berwick, LA 70342 tel.: (985) 385-9868

Established in 1998 in LA.
Donors: Jodi S. Adams; Burt A. Adams.
Foundation type: Independent foundation.
Financial data (yr. ended 12/31/13): Assets, $0 (M); gifts received, $196,165; expenditures, $2,004,641; qualifying distributions, $1,996,560; giving activities include $1,996,560 for 30 grants (high: $928,886; low: $500).
Fields of interest: Secondary school/education; Higher education; Catholic agencies & churches.
Limitations: Applications accepted. Giving primarily in Morgan City, LA. No grants to individuals.
Application information: Application form required.
Initial approach: Letter
Deadline(s): None
Officers: Jodi S. Adams, Pres.; Burt A. Adams, V.P.
EIN: 721433200

3665
Edward G. Schlieder Educational Foundation ✧
201 St. Charles Ave., 25th Fl., Ste. 2508
New Orleans, LA 70170-1000 (504) 533-5535
Contact: Pierre F. Lapeyre, Consultant

Incorporated in 1945 in LA.
Donor: Edward G. Schlieder†.
Foundation type: Independent foundation.
Financial data (yr. ended 12/31/13): Assets, $80,174,142 (M); expenditures, $4,224,357; qualifying distributions, $3,172,516; giving activities include $3,101,664 for 21 grants (high: $333,333; low: $5,000).
Purpose and activities: Giving limited to educational institutions in Louisiana, particularly to institutions involved in biomedical research.
Fields of interest: Higher education; Education; Biomedicine research.
Type of support: Capital campaigns; Equipment; Research.
Limitations: Applications accepted. Giving limited to LA. No grants to individuals, or for general purposes, endowment funds, scholarships, fellowships, or operating budgets; no loans.
Publications: Annual report.
Application information: Application form not required.
Initial approach: Letter
Copies of proposal: 3
Deadline(s): None
Officers and Directors:* Elizabeth S. Nalty,* Pres.; Thomas D. Westfeldt,* V.P.; John M. Waid,* Secy.; Jill K. Nalty, Treas.; Laura S. Shields.
Number of staff: 1 part-time professional; 1 part-time support.
EIN: 720408974

3666
Scott Foundation, Inc. ✧
P.O. Box 4948
Monroe, LA 71201 (318) 387-4160
Contact: George J. Bershen, Secy.-Treas.

Established in 1992 in LA.
Donors: Betty S. Cummins; Scott Truck & Tractor Co.; Gold Mine Gin, Inc.; Gold Mine Plantation; Jay H. Cummins Farm; Scott Irrigation, LLC; Scott Equipment Co., LLC; Scott Financial Services, LLC.
Foundation type: Independent foundation.
Financial data (yr. ended 07/31/13): Assets, $16,276,358 (M); gifts received, $312,089; expenditures, $973,390; qualifying distributions, $838,341; giving activities include $825,897 for 495 grants (high: $130,000; low: $50).
Purpose and activities: Giving primarily to Christian churches, education, youth organizations, health

care, human services, and civic organizations; funding also for victims of Hurricane Katrina.
Fields of interest: Secondary school/education; Higher education; Health care; Medical research; Disasters, Hurricane Katrina; Recreation; Human services; Youth, services; Community/economic development; Protestant agencies & churches.
Type of support: Scholarship funds.
Limitations: Applications accepted. Giving primarily in northern LA.
Application information: Application form not required.
Initial approach: Proposal
Deadline(s): None
Officers: Betty S. Cummins, Chair.; George J. Bershen, Secy.-Treas.
Trustees: Carrick R. Inabnett; Hugh McDonald; Lyle Miller; Tom Nicholson; Tim Nielsen; Thomas H. Scott, Jr.
EIN: 726027563
Selected grants: The following grants are a representative sample of this grantmaker's funding activity:
$20,000 to United Way of Northeast Louisiana, Monroe, LA, 2011.

3667
Leo W. Seal United Methodist Church Trust ✧ ☆
228 St. Charles Ave. 2nd Fl.
New Orleans, LA 70130

Established in MS.
Foundation type: Independent foundation.
Financial data (yr. ended 12/31/13): Assets, $18,518,510 (M); expenditures, $791,681; qualifying distributions, $654,885; giving activities include $654,885 for 11 grants (high: $185,987; low: $12,574).
Purpose and activities: Giving primarily to United Methodist churches.
Fields of interest: Hospitals (general); Protestant agencies & churches.
Limitations: Applications not accepted. Giving primarily in MS.
Application information: Unsolicited requests for funds not accepted.
Trustee: Whitney Bank.
EIN: 270169216

3668
Stuller Family Foundation ✧
1213 Terrace Hwy.
Broussard, LA 70518-7643 (337) 394-5432
Contact: Scott Brazda, Exec. Dir.
FAX: (337) 262-7713; Main URL: http://www.stullerfoundation.org/

Established in 1995 in LA.
Donor: Matthew G. Stuller, Sr.
Foundation type: Independent foundation.
Financial data (yr. ended 12/31/12): Assets, $47,913,118 (M); gifts received, $3,285,111; expenditures, $2,059,021; qualifying distributions, $1,250,463; giving activities include $1,250,463 for 85 grants (high: $400,000; low: $100).
Purpose and activities: Giving primarily for humanitarian, youth, religion, and education in the Acadiana area.
Fields of interest: Performing arts; Elementary/secondary education; Education; Human services; Foundations (community); Christian agencies & churches; Youth.
Limitations: Applications accepted. Giving limited to Lafayette Parish and its adjacent parishes of Iberia, Vermilion, Acadia, St. Landry and St. Martin in LA. No support for sports teams/events or political candidates/organizations. No grants to individuals.
Publications: Application guidelines.
Application information: Funding request form and specific application information which must be followed available on foundation web site. Application form required.
Initial approach: Proposal
Deadline(s): Mar. 1, Jun. 1, Sept. 1, Dec. 1
Board meeting date(s): Mar. 1, Jun. 1, Sept. 1, and Dec. 1
Officers: Michael G. Dehart, Pres.; Scott Brazda, Exec. Dir.
Board Members: William P. Mills III; CeCe Stuller; Matthew G. Stuller, Sr.
Number of staff: 1 part-time professional; 1 part-time support.
EIN: 721282688

3669
Patrick F. Taylor Foundation ✧
1 Lee Cir.
New Orleans, LA 70130-3931
Contact: Phyllis M. Taylor, Pres.
FAX: (504) 589-0408; Main URL: http://www.pftaylorfoundation.org

Established in 1987 in LA.
Donors: Maj. Gen. L.F. Taylor; Taylor Energy Co.; Patrick F. Taylor.
Foundation type: Independent foundation.
Financial data (yr. ended 12/31/12): Assets, $18,198,077 (M); gifts received, $3,000,000; expenditures, $3,179,051; qualifying distributions, $3,134,144; giving activities include $2,962,444 for 60 grants (high: $1,155,000; low: $100), and $171,700 for grants to individuals.
Purpose and activities: Giving primarily for education, and the arts or humanities. The foundation also offers individual scholarships to graduating Louisiana high school students attending a 4-year Louisiana undergraduate institution, based on financial need and academic performance.
Fields of interest: Arts; Secondary school/education; Higher education; Scholarships/financial aid.
Type of support: General/operating support; Scholarship funds.
Limitations: Giving limited to the Greater New Orleans, LA, Metro Area. No grants to individuals directly.
Publications: Application guidelines.
Application information: Letters of Inquiry sent by U.S. Mail are not accepted. No telephone requests. Specific scholarship information available on foundation web site. Application form required.
Initial approach: Submit Letter of Inquiry through foundation web site
Deadline(s): None (for Letters of Inquiry); July 15 (for scholarships)
Board meeting date(s): Quarterly
Final notification: Within 60 days after receipt of Letter of Inquiry only if the foundation is interested in hearing more about the applicant's project.
Officers and Trustees:* Phyllis M. Taylor, Chair. and Pres.; Amb. Thomas C. Ferguson, V.P.; VADM. Diego E. Hernandez, Secy.; Marvin L. Jacobs,* Treas.; James A. Callier, Exec. Dir.; Morrison C. Bethea; Raymond J. Jeandron, Jr.; Byron A. Leblanc; Dr. James H. Wharton.
EIN: 581686754

3670
William B. Wiener, Jr. Foundation ✧
333 Texas St., Ste. 2290
Shreveport, LA 71101-3681

Established in LA.
Donor: William B. Wiener, Jr.
Foundation type: Independent foundation.
Financial data (yr. ended 02/28/13): Assets, $30,762,807 (M); expenditures, $2,104,172; qualifying distributions, $1,445,399; giving activities include $1,439,000 for 71 grants (high: $405,000; low: $1,000).
Fields of interest: Environment, reform; Environment, government agencies; Animals/wildlife; Health organizations; Human services.
International interests: Israel.
Limitations: Applications not accepted. Giving primarily in LA; some giving also in Washington, DC and New York, NY. No grants to individuals.
Application information: Contributes only to pre-selected organizations.
Officers and Directors:* William B. Wiener, Jr., Pres.; Donald B. Wiener,* V.P. and Secy.; Jeffrey W. Weiss,* Treas.; Peter G. Case; David Rockefeller, Jr.
EIN: 726024398
Selected grants: The following grants are a representative sample of this grantmaker's funding activity:
$10,000 to Interfaith Alliance Foundation, Washington, DC, 2011.

3671
Huey and Angelina Wilson Foundation ✧
3636 S. Sherwood Forest Blvd., Ste. 650
Baton Rouge, LA 70816-5216 (225) 292-1344
FAX: (225) 292-1589; Questions regarding the foundation may be addressed to: Dan Bevan, e-mail: danbevan@hwilson.org or Jan Ross: e-mail: janross@hwilson.org; Main URL: http://www.hawilsonfoundation.org

Established in 1986 in LA.
Donors: Huey J. Wilson‡; Angelina M. Wilson.
Foundation type: Independent foundation.
Financial data (yr. ended 12/31/13): Assets, $56,423,163 (M); expenditures, $3,312,079; qualifying distributions, $3,006,506; giving activities include $2,982,093 for 63 grants (high: $380,000; low: $4,000).
Purpose and activities: Giving primarily for human services, healthcare, education, particularly learning and development from early childhood through high school, and prison release, particularly programs that prepare the incarcerated population for release into society, with interaction in a community church. Of particular interest to the foundation are people who are handicapped, both physically and mentally, those afflicted with disease, disadvantaged youth, the hungry and the homeless. While care for the less fortunate is important to the foundation, the trustees will look particularly favorably on grantees that address the root cause of the misfortune and, where practical or possible, assist their targeted group to become self-sufficient productive contributors to the community.

Fields of interest: Education; Health care; Hemophilia; Offenders/ex-offenders, services; Human services; Children/youth; Youth; Adults; Disabilities, people with; Physically disabled; Mentally disabled; Offenders/ex-offenders; Substance abusers; AIDS, people with; Single parents; Homeless.
Type of support: General/operating support; Continuing support; Management development/capacity building; Capital campaigns; Building/renovation; Equipment; Emergency funds; Program development; Technical assistance; Program evaluation; Matching/challenge support.
Limitations: Applications accepted. Giving limited to the greater Baton Rouge, LA area including the parishes of East and West Baton Rouge, East and West Feliciana, Pointe Coupee, St. Helena, Livingston, Ascension, St. James and Iberville. No grants to individuals, or for endowments, or seed money.
Publications: Application guidelines.
Application information: Complete proposal guidelines available on foundation web site. Application form required.
Initial approach: Online application only (via foundation web site)
Copies of proposal: 1
Deadline(s): 4th Fri. in Feb. and Aug.
Board meeting date(s): 3rd Tue. in Apr. and Oct.
Final notification: May and Nov.
Officer and Trustees:* Daniel J. Bevan,* Pres. and C.F.O.; Renee Graphia Joyal, V.P., Research; Jan Ross, V.P., Grants Admin.; J.H. Campbell, Jr.; Cornelius A. Lewis; Ben R. Miller, Jr.; Donna M. Saurage; Angelina M. Wilson; Denver C. Wilson; Dianne Wilson-Walker.
EIN: 581714586

3672
The Woldenberg Foundation ✧
(formerly Dorothy & Malcolm Woldenberg Foundation)
524 Metairie Rd.
Metairie, LA 70005-4308 (504) 849-6078
Contact: Trudi Briede, Dir.
FAX: (504) 849-6511; E-mail: trudi@gff1.com

Incorporated in 1959 in LA as Woldenberg Charitable and Educational Foundation.
Donors: Malcolm Woldenberg†; Magnolia Liquor Co., Inc.; Sazerac Co., Inc.; Great Southern Liquor Co., Inc.; Duval Spirits, Inc.
Foundation type: Independent foundation.
Financial data (yr. ended 12/31/13): Assets, $36,367,084 (M); expenditures, $2,290,984; qualifying distributions, $2,796,668; giving activities include $1,883,442 for 67 grants (high: $187,500; low: $250), and $85,750 for 38 grants to individuals (high: $3,500; low: $1,750).
Purpose and activities: Giving primarily for arts, education, and to Jewish organizations.
Fields of interest: Museums; Arts; Elementary/secondary education; Charter schools; Elementary/secondary school reform; Human services; Jewish federated giving programs.
International interests: Israel.
Type of support: General/operating support; Continuing support; Capital campaigns; Building/renovation; Equipment; Emergency funds; Program development; Research.
Limitations: Applications not accepted. Giving primarily in the greater New Orleans, LA, area, with special interest in Miami, FL and Israel. No support for political organizations. No grants to individuals (except for employee-related scholarships).
Application information: The foundation is not taking on new grantees. Unsolicited requests for funds not accepted.
Board meeting date(s): Varies
Officers and Trustees:* William Goldring,* Pres.; Minette Brown,* V.P.; Mark Halpern,* V.P.; Robert Steeg,* Secy.; Jeffrey Goldring.
Number of staff: 1 part-time professional.
EIN: 726022665

3673
William C. Woolf Foundation ✧
333 Texas St., SH2069
Shreveport, LA 71101-3666
Contact: Barbara York

Incorporated in 1959 in LA.
Donors: William C. Woolf†; Geraldine H. Woolf†.
Foundation type: Independent foundation.
Financial data (yr. ended 02/28/13): Assets, $10,959,179 (M); expenditures, $674,233; qualifying distributions, $526,400; giving activities include $526,400 for grants.
Purpose and activities: Giving primarily for education, health and human services, and to Christian churches.
Fields of interest: Arts councils; Higher education; Human services; Children/youth, services; Christian agencies & churches.
Type of support: General/operating support; Continuing support; Capital campaigns; Building/renovation; Program development; Research.
Limitations: Applications not accepted. Giving primarily in Shreveport, LA. No grants to individuals.
Application information: Contributes only to pre-selected organizations.
Board meeting date(s): Feb.
Trustees: Willis L. Meadows; C. Lane Sartor; Nicholas Hobson Wheless, Jr.
EIN: 726020630
Selected grants: The following grants are a representative sample of this grantmaker's funding activity:
$101,000 to Shreveport Regional Arts Council, Shreveport, LA, 2011.
$82,000 to Community Renewal International, Shreveport, LA, 2011.
$80,000 to Sci-Port Discovery Center, Shreveport, LA, 2011.
$62,000 to Centenary College of Louisiana, Shreveport, LA, 2011.
$30,000 to Providence House, Shreveport, LA, 2011.
$10,000 to Alliance for Education, Shreveport, LA, 2011.
$5,000 to Southfield School, Shreveport, LA, 2011.
$2,500 to Loyola College Preparatory School, Shreveport, LA, 2011.
$1,000 to United Negro College Fund, Fairfax, VA, 2011.

3674
The H. & B. Young Foundation ✧
(formerly The Morgan City Fund)
P.O. Box 889
Morgan City, LA 70381-0889 (985) 385-0812
Contact: Brenda B. Ayo, Pres.

Incorporated in 1955 in LA.
Donor: Byrnes M. Young†.
Foundation type: Independent foundation.
Financial data (yr. ended 12/31/13): Assets, $16,898,680 (M); expenditures, $1,384,757; qualifying distributions, $1,056,199; giving activities include $796,689 for 30 grants (high: $125,000; low: $1,500).
Purpose and activities: Giving primarily for education and community development.
Fields of interest: Elementary/secondary education; Higher education; Recreation, parks/playgrounds; Human services; Community/economic development; Catholic agencies & churches.
Type of support: General/operating support; Equipment; Grants to individuals.
Limitations: Applications accepted. Giving limited to Morgan City, LA.
Application information:
Initial approach: Letter
Deadline(s): None
Officers: Brenda B. Ayo, Pres.; Phyllis B. Garber, V.P.; Gwen E. Ross, Secy.; Emile A. Wagner III, Treas.
EIN: 726029365

3675
Zemurray Foundation ✧
228 St. Charles Ave., Ste. 1024
New Orleans, LA 70130-2651

Incorporated in 1951 in LA.
Donor: Sarah W. Zemurray.
Foundation type: Independent foundation.
Financial data (yr. ended 12/31/12): Assets, $114,804,554 (M); expenditures, $5,215,365; qualifying distributions, $4,485,616; giving activities include $4,292,666 for 49 grants (high: $750,000; low: $500).
Purpose and activities: Giving primarily for the arts and education.
Fields of interest: Arts; Higher education; Education; Human services; Foundations (private independent).
Limitations: Applications not accepted. Giving primarily in New Orleans, LA, and Cambridge, MA. No grants to individuals.
Application information: Contributes only to pre-selected organizations.
Board meeting date(s): Usually in Nov.
Officers and Trustees:* Ludovico Feoli,* Co-Chair.; Alison Stone,* Co-Chair.; Stephanie Stone Feoli,* V.P.; Haydee T. Stone,* V.P.; Thomas B. Lemann,* Secy.; Kimberley M. Quintana, Treas.
Number of staff: 1 full-time professional; 2 part-time support.
EIN: 720539603

3676
Fred B. and Ruth B. Zigler Foundation ✧
P.O. Box 986
Jennings, LA 70546-0986 (337) 824-2413
FAX: (337) 824-2414; E-mail: frzigler@bellsouth.net; Main URL: http://www.ziglerfoundation.org/

Incorporated in 1956 in LA.
Donors: Fred B. Zigler†; Ruth B. Zigler†.
Foundation type: Independent foundation.
Financial data (yr. ended 12/31/12): Assets, $11,144,258 (M); expenditures, $768,808;

qualifying distributions, $534,591; giving activities include $480,200 for grants.
Purpose and activities: Emphasis on higher and secondary education, including scholarships for Jefferson Davis Parish students, and youth agencies.
Fields of interest: Arts; Secondary school/education; Higher education; Human services; Children/youth, services.
Type of support: General/operating support; Building/renovation; Equipment; Program development; Research; Scholarships—to individuals; Matching/challenge support.
Limitations: Applications accepted. Giving primarily in Jefferson Davis Parish, LA. No grants to individuals (except scholarships for graduates of Jefferson Davis Parish high schools).
Publications: Annual report; IRS Form 990 or 990-PF printed copy available upon request.
Application information: Scholarship application forms available through Jefferson Davis Parish high schools. Application form required.

Initial approach: Letter
Copies of proposal: 1
Board meeting date(s): Bimonthly beginning in Jan.

Officers: Julie G. Berry, Pres.; Marie C. Romero, Secy.-Treas.
Trustees: Paul E. Brummett II; Dale Elmore; John M. Elmore; Richard C. Oustalet; John Pipkin.
Number of staff: 1 full-time professional; 1 part-time professional.
EIN: 726019403

MAINE

3677
Aicher Family Foundation, Inc. ✧
1303 Naples Rd.
Harrison, ME 04040
Contact: Peter Aicher, Pres.
Application address: c/o Kathryn Slawson, 19 Sawmill Rd., Lebanon, NJ 08833-4620, tel.: (908) 832-8994

Established in 1997 in CT.
Donors: Paul J. Aicher†; The Paul J. Aicher Trust.
Foundation type: Independent foundation.
Financial data (yr. ended 12/31/13): Assets, $7,322,760 (M); expenditures, $1,193,085; qualifying distributions, $1,153,687; giving activities include $1,150,000 for 4 grants (high: $550,000; low: $25,000).
Fields of interest: Foundations (private operating).
Limitations: Giving primarily in East Hartford, CT; some giving also in New York, NY.
Application information:
Initial approach: Letter
Deadline(s): None
Officers: Peter Aicher, Pres.; Diana Johnson, V.P.; Kathryn Aicher Slawson, Secy.; Bradford Sparrow, Treas.
EIN: 061398331

3678
Harold Alfond Foundation ✧
c/o Dexter Enterprises
2 Monument Sq.
Portland, ME 04101-4093 (207) 828-7999
Contact: Gregory Powell, Chair.
E-mail: info@haroldalfondfoundation.org; Main URL: http://www.haroldalfondfoundation.org/

Established in 1993 in ME as successor to Harold Alfond Trust.
Donors: Harold Alfond†; Dorothy Alfond†.
Foundation type: Independent foundation.
Financial data (yr. ended 12/31/13): Assets, $727,560,695 (M); expenditures, $32,814,486; qualifying distributions, $28,392,988; giving activities include $27,877,381 for 35 grants (high: $10,334,615; low: $150).
Purpose and activities: Support primarily for higher education, the arts, and health care.
Fields of interest: Arts; Higher education; Hospitals (general); Health care; Health organizations, association; Youth development; Human services; Children/youth, services.
Type of support: Annual campaigns; Capital campaigns; Building/renovation; Endowments; Scholarship funds; Research; Matching/challenge support.
Limitations: Applications accepted. Giving primarily in ME, with emphasis on central ME. No support for religious organizations for religious purposes, for political campaigns or causes, or for legislative lobbying efforts. No grants to individuals, start-up organizations, or for organizations or programs that provide benefits outside the U.S., and no support for private foundations.
Application information: Application form not required.
Initial approach: Online
Copies of proposal: 1
Deadline(s): None
Final notification: 3-6 months
Officer and Trustees:* Gregory Powell,* Chair.; Steven P. Akin; Peter Alfond; Theodore B. Alfond; William Alfond; Peter Lunder; Larry Pugh; Theresa M. Stone.
EIN: 223281672
Selected grants: The following grants are a representative sample of this grantmaker's funding activity:
$10,335,333 to MaineGeneral Medical Center, Augusta, ME, 2012. For new regional hospital.
$3,000,000 to Maine Community College System, Augusta, ME, 2012. For expansion at Kennebec Valley Community College.
$2,516,814 to Alfond Scholarship Foundation, Portland, ME, 2012. For scholarships.
$2,385,000 to Rollins College, Winter Park, FL, 2012. For Alfond Inn at Rollins.
$2,000,000 to University of New England, Biddeford, ME, 2012. For Harold Alfond Forum, athletic facility on the campus of UNE.
$1,670,000 to Colby College, Waterville, ME, 2012. For art museum.
$465,285 to Educare Central Maine, Waterville, ME, 2012. For scholarships.
$310,000 to Waterville Opera House Association, Waterville, ME, 2012. To set building space.
$300,000 to Colby College, Waterville, ME, 2012. For endowment for Athletic Department.
$15,000 to Belgrade Regional Health Center, Belgrade Lakes, ME, 2012. For Annual Fund.

3679
The William and Joan Alfond Foundation ✧
(formerly William L. Alfond Foundation)
c/o Dexter Enterprises, Inc.
2 Monument Sq.
Portland, ME 04101-4093 (207) 828-7999
Contact: Gregory Powell, Secy.

Established in 1986 in NE.
Donors: William Alfond; Joan Alfond; Berkshire Hathaway Inc.
Foundation type: Independent foundation.
Financial data (yr. ended 12/31/12): Assets, $36,951,636 (M); gifts received, $11,999,408; expenditures, $1,288,533; qualifying distributions, $1,103,230; giving activities include $1,103,230 for grants.
Purpose and activities: Giving primarily for higher education, health care and medical research.
Fields of interest: Education; Health care; Community/economic development; Foundations (community); United Ways and Federated Giving Programs.
Type of support: Annual campaigns; Capital campaigns; Endowments; Scholarship funds.
Limitations: Applications accepted. Giving primarily in ME; giving also in MA. No grants to individuals.
Application information: Application form not required.
Initial approach: Letter (no more than 3 pages)
Copies of proposal: 1
Deadline(s): None
Final notification: 3-6 months
Officers and Directors:* William Alfond,* Pres.; Joan Alfond,* V.P. and Treas.; Gregory Powell, Secy.; Justin Alfond; Kenden Alfond; Reis Alfond.
EIN: 010421806
Selected grants: The following grants are a representative sample of this grantmaker's funding activity:
$882,072 to Kennebec Valley Community Action Program, Waterville, ME, 2010. For Educare Construction and Start-Up.
$219,996 to Governor Dummer Academy, Byfield, MA, 2011. For unrestricted support.
$40,000 to Waterville, Town of, Waterville, ME, 2010. For Quarry Road Ski Trail, Phase I.
$30,000 to Maine Centers for Women, Work and Community, Augusta, ME, 2011. For unrestricted support.
$28,900 to Maine School Administrative District No. 46, Dexter, ME, 2010. For Dexter PreK-8 School Gym Debt Service.
$25,000 to Friends of the Belgrade Public Library, Belgrade, ME, 2011. For capital campaign.
$25,000 to Thomas College, Waterville, ME, 2011. For unrestricted support.
$20,790 to Kennebec Valley Community College Foundation, Fairfield, ME, 2011. For childcare program.
$15,000 to Maine Childrens Home for Little Wanderers, Waterville, ME, 2011. For Teen Parenting Program.
$10,000 to Colby College, Waterville, ME, 2011. For Maine Concussion Management Initiative.
$10,000 to Kennebec Valley Consolidated Schools, Waterville, ME, 2011. To resurface track at Waterville High School.
$10,000 to University of Maine Foundation, Orono, ME, 2011. For Ellen Loring Museum Fund.
$5,000 to Caribou Parks and Recreation Foundation, Caribou, ME, 2010.
$4,500 to Carrabassett Valley Academy, Carrabassett Valley, ME, 2010.
$3,200 to University of Maine, Orono, ME, 2010.
$2,500 to Colby College, Waterville, ME, 2010.
$2,000 to Dartmouth College, Hanover, NH, 2010.
$2,000 to Noble and Greenough School, Dedham, MA, 2010.
$1,000 to Eaglebrook School, Deerfield, MA, 2010.

3680
Bangor Savings Bank Foundation ✧
99 Franklin St.
Bangor, ME 04402-0930 (207) 942-5211
E-mail: foundation@bangor.com; Main URL: http://www.bangor.com/
Community Matters More Recipients: http://www.bangor.com/Why-Bangor-Savings/Supporting-Our-Communities/Community-Matters-More.aspx
Grants List: http://www.bangor.com/uploadedFiles/Bangor_com/content/Why_Bangor/Supporting_Our_Communities/FY2011%20to%20FY2012%20Funded%20Proposals.pdf

Established in 1996 in ME.
Donor: Bangor Savings Bank.
Foundation type: Company-sponsored foundation.
Financial data (yr. ended 03/31/14): Assets, $4,659,116 (M); gifts received, $477,000; expenditures, $696,462; qualifying distributions, $662,185; giving activities include $661,410 for 155 grants (high: $40,500; low: $1,000).
Purpose and activities: The foundation supports programs designed to promote culture and arts; education; health and wellness; and social and civic services. Special emphasis is directed toward initiatives designed to increase workforce education levels and address out-migration of youth; increase

regional income levels and economic activity in rural communities; and support Maine entrepreneurs and micro-enterprise businesses whose needs are not met by existing programs.
Fields of interest: Arts; Higher education; Business school/education; Education, services; Education; Public health, physical fitness; Health care; Mental health/crisis services; Employment, services; Employment; Youth, services; Economic development; Rural development; Business/industry; Social entrepreneurship; Community development, small businesses; United Ways and Federated Giving Programs; Economics; Public affairs.
Type of support: Annual campaigns; Capital campaigns; Building/renovation; Equipment; Program development; Matching/challenge support.
Limitations: Applications accepted. Giving limited to areas of company operations in ME. No support for political organizations or candidates, or religious organizations. No grants to individuals, or for annual operating budgets of United Way agencies, conferences or seminars, or endowments.
Publications: Application guidelines; Grants list; Program policy statement.
Application information: Application form required.
Initial approach: Proposal
Copies of proposal: 1
Deadline(s): Jan. 1, Apr. 1, July 1 and Oct. 1
Board meeting date(s): Quarterly
Final notification: 60 to 90 day
Officers: James H. Goff, Chair.; James J. Conlon, Pres.; Yellow Light Breen, V.P., Secy., and Clerk; Bruce G. Nickerson, Treas.
Directors: Kathryn L. Barber; Gena R. Canning; George F. Eaton II, Esq.; Charles E. Hewett, Ph.D.; Richard J. McGoldrick; Martha G. Newman; Scott A. Oxley; William D. Purington; Robert A. Strong; Vincent P. Veroneau.
EIN: 043353896

3681
Cascade Foundation ✧
c/o Daniel Dibner
P.O. Box 913
Rockport, ME 04856-0913

Established in 2006 in MA and ME.
Foundation type: Operating foundation.
Financial data (yr. ended 12/31/11): Assets, $20,177,173 (M); expenditures, $1,430,917; qualifying distributions, $21,188,943; giving activities include $1,057,429 for 68 grants (high: $10,000; low: $85), and $391,567 for foundation-administered programs.
Fields of interest: Environment; Health care; Youth development; Human services; United Ways and Federated Giving Programs.
Limitations: Applications not accepted. Giving in the U.S., with emphasis on ME and NY. No grants to individuals.
Application information: Contributes only to pre-selected organizations.
Officer: Daniel Dibner, Mgr.
Directors: Avalon B. Dibner; Aurora C. Dibner; Bern L. Dibner.
EIN: 204956488

3682
Catalyst for Peace ✧
(formerly The Catalyst Fund)
50 Exchange St., 3rd Fl.
Portland, ME 04101-3308 (207) 775-2616
E-mail: info@catalystforpeace.org; Main URL: http://www.catalystforpeace.org/

Established in ME.
Donors: Elisabeth Hoffman; Alan Lukas; Tides Foundation.
Foundation type: Independent foundation.
Financial data (yr. ended 12/31/11): Assets, $12,709,093 (M); gifts received, $55,715; expenditures, $1,463,149; qualifying distributions, $1,202,702; giving activities include $1,047,791 for 2 grants (high: $1,047,291; low: $500).
Purpose and activities: The foundation identifies and supports community based peacebuilding work around the world.
Fields of interest: Higher education; International peace/security; International human rights; Religion, interfaith issues.
International interests: Africa.
Limitations: Applications not accepted. Giving primarily in ME and VA; some funding also in Sierra Leone.
Application information: Unsolicited requests for funds not accepted.
Officers: Elisabeth Hoffman, Pres.; Seth Johnson, Secy.-Treas.
Directors: Alfred Hoffman, Jr.; Cynthia Sampson.
EIN: 352202654

3683
Cianbro Charitable Foundation ✧ ☆
P.O. Box 1000
Pittsfield, ME 04967-1000 (207) 487-3311
Contact: H. Bonnie Brown, Tr.
Application address: 101 Cianbro Sq., Pittsfield, ME 04967

Established in 1989 in ME.
Donors: Cianbro Corp.; The Cianbro Companies.
Foundation type: Company-sponsored foundation.
Financial data (yr. ended 12/31/13): Assets, $2,889,842 (M); gifts received, $2,001,839; expenditures, $647,519; qualifying distributions, $634,726; giving activities include $632,626 for 29 grants (high: $244,531; low: $500).
Purpose and activities: The foundation supports organizations involved with arts and culture, education, forest conservation, the construction industry, and community development.
Fields of interest: Arts; Education; Environment.
Type of support: Capital campaigns; Program development; Scholarship funds; Employee-related scholarships.
Limitations: Applications accepted. Giving limited to ME. No grants to individuals (except for employee-related scholarships).
Application information: Application form required.
Initial approach: Letter
Deadline(s): None
Board meeting date(s): Quarterly
Trustees: Alan Burton; H. Bonnie Brown; Peter G. Vigue.
EIN: 223020020
Selected grants: The following grants are a representative sample of this grantmaker's funding activity:
$10,000 to Bangor Museum and Center for History, Bangor, ME, 2011.
$10,000 to Gulf of Maine Research Institute, Portland, ME, 2011.
$10,000 to LifeFlight Foundation, Camden, ME, 2011.
$10,000 to Maine Historical Society, Portland, ME, 2011.
$5,000 to Forest Society of Maine, Bangor, ME, 2011.
$5,000 to Maine Central Institute, Pittsfield, ME, 2011.
$5,000 to Maine Discovery Museum, Bangor, ME, 2011.
$5,000 to Maine Historical Society, Portland, ME, 2011.
$5,000 to University of Maine, Orono, ME, 2011.
$1,000 to Nature Conservancy, Brunswick, ME, 2011.

3684
Sam L. Cohen Foundation ✧
50 Foden Rd., Ste. 5
Portland, ME 04106-1718 (207) 871-5600
Contact: Nancy Brain, Exec. Dir.; Stephanie Eglinton, Prog. Off.
FAX: (207) 871-9043;
E-mail: nbrain@samlcohenfoundation.org; Mailing address: P.O. Box 1123, Portland, ME 04104; Main URL: http://www.samlcohenfoundation.org

Re-established in 2005 in ME. Successor to Sam L. Cohen Foundation established in 1983.
Donors: Sam L. Cohen†; Sam L. Cohen Foundation.
Foundation type: Independent foundation.
Financial data (yr. ended 12/31/13): Assets, $41,259,245 (M); expenditures, $2,577,071; qualifying distributions, $2,042,550; giving activities include $1,665,526 for 91 grants (high: $125,000; low: $1,500).
Purpose and activities: The foundation strives to ensure that people have the opportunity to develop their potential and to provide healthy, productive futures for themselves, their families and their communities. It supports nonprofit organizations that benefit individuals living in southern Maine, York and Cumberland counties.
Fields of interest: Arts; Education; Health care; Jewish agencies & synagogues.
Type of support: General/operating support; Management development/capacity building; Program development; Research; Matching/challenge support; Pro bono services - legal; Pro bono services - medical.
Limitations: Applications accepted. Giving primarily in York and Cumberland counties in southern ME. No grants to individuals, or for annual appeals, endowments or for multi-year grants.
Publications: Application guidelines; Grants list.
Application information: Maine Philanthropy Center Common Grant Application Form accepted. See foundation web site for application information and current guidelines.
Deadline(s): See foundation website for current deadlines
Board meeting date(s): May and Nov.
Officers and Directors:* Jerome Goldberg,* Pres.; Jeffrey Nathanson,* Secy.; Edward Simensky,* Treas.; John Shoos, Exec. Dir.; Sherry Broder; Elinor Miller; Kenneth Spirer.
Number of staff: 2 full-time professional; 1 part-time professional.
EIN: 202262822

3685
Sadie and Harry Davis Foundation, Inc. ✧ ☆
135 Sheridan St., No. 303
Portland, ME 04101-2678 (207) 253-1865
Contact: Sharon L. Rosen, Exec. Dir.
E-mail: slrosen@sadieandharrydavis.org; Main URL: http://www.sadieandharrydavis.org

Established in 2007 in NY.
Donor: Sadie Davis†.
Foundation type: Independent foundation.
Financial data (yr. ended 12/31/13): Assets, $17,900,951 (M); expenditures, $717,861; qualifying distributions, $636,958; giving activities include $597,405 for 15 grants (high: $132,523; low: $250).
Purpose and activities: Giving primarily for the advancement of children's health in Maine.
Fields of interest: Health care; Health organizations.
Limitations: Applications accepted. Giving primarily in ME.
Application information: See foundation web site for complete application guidelines.
Officers and Directors:* Andrew Davis Klingenstein,* Pres.; Sally Martell,* Secy.-Treas.; John Klingenstein; Julie Klingenstein; Patricia Davis Klingenstein; Thomas Davis Klingenstein; C. Michael Martell; Nancy Perlman; Nancy Simpkins.
EIN: 203515375

3686
Elliotsville Plantation Inc ✧ ☆
c/o James W. Sewall Company
136 Center St.
P.O. Box 433
Old Town, ME 04468-0433 (207) 370-5813
E-mail: elliotsvilleplantation@gmail.com; Main URL: http://www.keepmebeautiful.org/

Established in 2002 in ME.
Donors: Roxanne Quimby; Burt's Bees, Inc.; Marion McConnell.
Foundation type: Operating foundation.
Financial data (yr. ended 12/31/11): Assets, $129,194,759 (M); expenditures, $2,200,910; qualifying distributions, $10,025,522; giving activities include $569,355 for 8 grants (high: $403,645; low: $1,710), and $7,322,330 for foundation-administered programs.
Fields of interest: Arts; Recreation, parks/playgrounds; Human services.
Limitations: Applications not accepted. Giving primarily in ME. No grants to individuals.
Application information: Contributes only to pre-selected organizations.
Officers and Directors:* Lucas St. Clair,* Pres.; Hannah Quimby,* Secy.; Roxanne Quimby,* Exec. Dir.
EIN: 134223002

3687
Fore River Foundation ✧
P.O. Box 7525
Portland, ME 04112-7525

Established in 1986 in ME.
Donors: Kate Davis P. Quesada; Peter W. Quesada; T. Ricardo Quesada; Kate Davis Baxter; Charlotte Krugh; Bradley Krugh; Kate D. P. Quesada Charitable Lead Trust.
Foundation type: Independent foundation.
Financial data (yr. ended 11/30/13): Assets, $5,395,934 (M); gifts received, $113,647; expenditures, $518,345; qualifying distributions, $496,972; giving activities include $496,422 for 54 grants (high: $85,000; low: $500).
Purpose and activities: Giving primarily for environmental conservation, animal welfare and preservation, and education, particularly secondary education; some funding also for the arts, and social services.
Fields of interest: Historic preservation/historical societies; Elementary/secondary education; Education; Environment, natural resources; Animals/wildlife, preservation/protection; Reproductive health, family planning; Youth development, centers/clubs; Human services.
Type of support: General/operating support.
Limitations: Applications not accepted. Giving primarily in ME. No grants to individuals; no loans or program-related investments.
Application information: Unsolicited requests for funds not accepted.
Officers and Directors:* T. Ricardo Quesada,* Pres.; Peter W. Quesada, V.P. and Treas.; Strand O. Quesada,* V.P.; Dennis C. Keeler, Secy.; Eliza Wright Baxter; Kate Davis Baxter; Anthony C. Quesada; Charlotte R. Quesada; Emily P. Quesada.
EIN: 010421912

3688
Albert B. Glickman Family Foundation ✧
P.O. Box 4569
Portland, ME 04112-4569

Established in 1993 in CA.
Donors: Albert B. Glickman; Judith L. Glickman; David P. Glickman.
Foundation type: Independent foundation.
Financial data (yr. ended 12/31/11): Assets, $14,881,420 (M); gifts received, $40,000; expenditures, $1,043,611; qualifying distributions, $920,935; giving activities include $920,935 for grants.
Purpose and activities: Giving primarily for the arts, medical research, human services, and Jewish agencies and temples.
Fields of interest: Museums (art); Arts; Education; Medical research, institute; Human services; Jewish agencies & synagogues.
Limitations: Applications not accepted. Giving primarily in CA and ME. No grants to individuals.
Application information: Contributes only to pre-selected organizations.
Officers: Richard N. Ellis, Chair.; Albert B. Glickman, Pres.; Judith L. Glickman, Secy.
EIN: 954423553

3689
John T. Gorman Foundation ✧
(formerly JTG Foundation)
1 Canal Plz., Ste. 800
Portland, ME 04101-4083 (207) 518-6784
Contact: Martha E. Greene, Managing Dir.
FAX: (207) 518-6788; E-mail: JTG@brannlaw.com; Application address: c/o Brann & Isaacson, P.O. Box 3070, Lewiston, ME 04243-3070; Main URL: http://www.jtgfoundation.org

Established in 1996 in ME.
Donor: John T. Gorman, Jr.
Foundation type: Independent foundation.
Financial data (yr. ended 12/31/13): Assets, $199,723,215 (M); gifts received, $1,000,000; expenditures, $9,251,264; qualifying distributions, $8,042,377; giving activities include $7,082,551 for 154 grants (high: $310,000; low: $500).
Purpose and activities: Giving primarily to enhance mental health services, improve the care of those suffering from cancer, enhance the lives of the elderly, to provide for the unmet needs of low-income or otherwise disadvantaged children, enhance community services, and to aid under privileged residents of Maine.
Fields of interest: Mental health/crisis services; Cancer; Children, services; Community/economic development; Aging; Economically disadvantaged.
Type of support: Matching/challenge support.
Limitations: Applications accepted. Giving primarily in ME. No grants to individuals.
Application information: Applications should be submitted electronically, via foundation web site. Application form required.
Initial approach: Use online application form on foundation web site
Board meeting date(s): May and Nov.
Officers and Directors: Shawn O. Gorman,* Chair.; Jeffrey J. Gorman,* Vice-Chair.; Tony Cipollone, C.E.O. and Pres.; Weston Bonney, Treas.; Irving Isaacson, Dir. Emeritus; Martha E. Greene; Richard W. Petersen.
Number of staff: 1
EIN: 010498551
Selected grants: The following grants are a representative sample of this grantmaker's funding activity:
$1,000,000 to Preble Street, Portland, ME, 2012. To purchase and renovate Lighthouse Shelter for homeless teens.
$200,000 to Opportunity Alliance, Portland, ME, 2012. To support mental health care needs of individuals in the Greater Portland area.
$200,000 to Wholesome Wave Foundation Charitable Ventures, Bridgeport, CT, 2012. To support a sustainable model for helping Supplemental Nutrition Assistance Program (SNAP) recipients access healthy food through farmers markets.
$190,000 to Maine Equal Justice Partners, Augusta, ME, 2012. To support advocacy organizations working on policy issues facing disadvantaged Maine residents.
$175,000 to Pine Tree Legal Assistance, Portland, ME, 2012. To support several legal services programs for low-income Maine residents.
$150,000 to Sunrise County Economic Council, Machias, ME, 2012. For Community Technology Plan, which provides digital literacy education to residents and businesses in Washington County.
$124,000 to Central Maine Community Health Corporation, Lewiston, ME, 2012. For Healthy Androscoggin, initiative to build the capacity needed to address high lead poisoning rates in children living in downtown Lewiston.
$25,000 to Portland, City of, Portland, ME, 2012. For general operating support for Portland Free Clinic and to develop a long term sustainability plan for the clinic.
$20,000 to Frannie Peabody Center, Portland, ME, 2012. To provide services to people in Maine living with or at risk for HIV/AIDS.
$12,500 to Waldo Community Action Partners, Belfast, ME, 2012. For early education services for

children and their parents from low-income and underserved households.

3690
Hannaford Charitable Foundation ✧
P.O. Box 1000
Portland, ME 04104-5005
Main URL: http://www.hannaford.com/content.jsp?pageName=charitableFoundation&leftNavArea=AboutLeftNav

Established in 1993 in ME.
Donor: Hannaford Bros. Co.
Foundation type: Company-sponsored foundation.
Financial data (yr. ended 12/31/13): Assets, $1,688,881 (M); gifts received, $1,245,000; expenditures, $1,284,261; qualifying distributions, $1,274,261; giving activities include $1,238,700 for grants.
Purpose and activities: The foundation supports organizations involved with arts and culture, education, fisheries, health, human services, marine science, and civic affairs.
Fields of interest: Arts; Higher education; Education; Animals/wildlife, fisheries; Hospitals (general); Health care, clinics/centers; Health care; YM/YWCAs & YM/YWHAs; Children/youth, services; Human services; United Ways and Federated Giving Programs; Marine science; Public affairs.
Type of support: Program development; Capital campaigns; Building/renovation; Employee-related scholarships.
Limitations: Applications accepted. Giving primarily in areas of company operations in MA, ME, NH, NY, and VT. No support for tax-supported organizations or veterans', fraternal, or religious organizations not of direct benefit to the entire community. No grants to individuals (except for employee-related scholarships), or for advertising or general operating support.
Publications: Application guidelines.
Application information: Application form required.
Initial approach: Proposal
Copies of proposal: 10
Deadline(s): 6 to 8 weeks prior to need
Officers: Bob Schools, Pres.; Donna J. Boyce, Secy.; Jim Kacer, Treas.
Directors: Rudy DiPietro; Rick Meyerkopf; Heather Paquette; Mary Wright.
EIN: 010483892
Selected grants: The following grants are a representative sample of this grantmaker's funding activity:
$200,000 to University of New England, Biddeford, ME, 2012.
$197,500 to Scholarship America, Saint Peter, MN, 2012.
$145,000 to United Way of Greater Portland, Portland, ME, 2012.
$101,500 to Maine Medical Center, Portland, ME, 2012.
$100,000 to Foundation for Maines Community Colleges, South Portland, ME, 2012.
$100,000 to Gulf of Maine Research Institute, Portland, ME, 2012.
$100,000 to Spurwink Services, Portland, ME, 2012.
$80,000 to Albany Medical Center Foundation, Albany, NY, 2012.
$50,000 to Wentworth-Douglass Hospital and Health Foundation, Dover, NH, 2012.
$16,500 to United Way of York County, Kennebunk, ME, 2012.

3691
Horizon Foundation, Inc. ✧
1 Monument Way, 2nd Fl.
Portland, ME 04101-4078 (207) 773-5101
E-mail: info@horizonfoundation.org; Main URL: http://www.horizonfoundation.org

Established in 1997 in MA and PA.
Donors: Alexander K. Buck, Sr.; Alexander K. Buck, Jr.; N. Harrison Buck; Alexander K. Buck, 1997 Trust No. 1, Jr.; Alexander K. Buck, 1997 Trust No. 2, Jr.
Foundation type: Independent foundation.
Financial data (yr. ended 06/30/13): Assets, $17,604,234 (M); gifts received, $160,000; expenditures, $857,924; qualifying distributions, $695,499; giving activities include $695,499 for grants.
Purpose and activities: The foundation supports organizations that effect positive change among children, the adults who work with them, and the communities in which they live. The foundation will support programs and organizations that aspire to create and maintain sustainable and livable communities by protecting and conserving land and water resources, educating children and adults about being good stewards of the environment, promoting vibrant, child-oriented arts, teaching respect for and preservation of historic assets, enabling children and adults to lead their communities in thoughtful, creative, and healthy ways, and encouraging service to others. Giving primarily for education in the arts, history, the environment, and leadership training for children; funding also for community services and mentoring.
Fields of interest: Arts education; Historic preservation/historical societies; Education; Environmental education; Leadership development; Children/youth; Adults.
Type of support: Equipment; Program development; Conferences/seminars; Seed money; Curriculum development; Internship funds; Program evaluation; Matching/challenge support.
Limitations: Applications accepted. Giving limited to Fairfield County, CT, Barnstable County, MA, Cumberland, Franklin, Lincoln, and York counties, ME, and Mercer County, NJ. No support for religion, state agencies, mental health agencies, colleges and universities, or public and private schools. No grants to individuals, or for international or foreign affairs, emergency requests, building, capital or endowment funds, or health/mental health.
Publications: Application guidelines; Annual report; Grants list; Informational brochure (including application guidelines).
Application information: Complete application guidelines available on foundation web site. Application form required.
Initial approach: 1-page letter of inquiry; no faxed or e-mailed letters of inquiry or proposals
Copies of proposal: 1
Deadline(s): See foundation web site for latest deadlines; proposals arriving after deadlines will be considered in next awards cycle.
Board meeting date(s): May, July, and Nov.
Officers: Sara L. Buck, Chair. and V.P.; Alexander K. Buck, Jr., Pres.; Nancy B. Buck, V.P.; Anne E. Buck, Secy.; N. Harrison Buck, Treas.
Number of staff: 1 part-time professional.
EIN: 232867116
Selected grants: The following grants are a representative sample of this grantmaker's funding activity:
$20,000 to Barnstable Land Trust, Cotuit, MA, 2013. For Keep Lowell Park Green!.
$20,000 to Maine Natural History Observatory, Gouldsboro, ME, 2013. For Completing the Whole Picture: Documenting the Last Best Places.
$19,800 to Woods Hole Research Center, Falmouth, MA, 2013. For A Cape Cod and the Islands Climate Change and Energy Summit.
$18,000 to Environment Northeast, Rockport, ME, 2013. For Advancing Sustainable Energy in Maine: Education, Awareness and Implementation.
$18,000 to Land Trust Alliance, Litchfield, CT, 2013. For Building Land Trust Excellence in Maine.
$15,000 to Friends of Midcoast Maine, Camden, ME, 2013. For operating support for Smart Growth Technical Assistance Program in Midcoast Maine.
$15,000 to Morris Farm Trust, Wiscasset, ME, 2013. For Project Outreach for Growth.
$14,630 to Maine Organic Farmers and Gardeners Association, Unity, ME, 2013. For Expanding Learning Opportunities for Gardeners and Growers in Southern Maine.
$10,000 to Arts Council of Princeton, Princeton, NJ, 2013. For Youth ArtReach.
$10,000 to Portland Museum of Art, Portland, ME, 2013. For ARTworks: Bringing Children to Art.

3692
Hungarian-American Enterprise Scholarship Fund ✧
c/o CIEE
300 Fore St.
Portland, ME 04101-4110 (207) 553-4194
FAX: (207) 553-5194; E-mail: mivanova@ciee.org; Contact for application, acceptance and pre-departure information and questions: Karoly Kopasz, Andrassy ut 61., I/5, Budapest 1062, Hungary, tel.: (36-1) 413-0018, fax: (36-1) 413-0019, e-mail: info@haesf.org; Contact for Fellowship placement questions and support-related issues: Maggie Ivanova at Portland, ME, address, tel., fax or e-mail; Main URL: http://www.haesf.org

Donor: Hungarian-American Enterprise Fund.
Foundation type: Independent foundation.
Financial data (yr. ended 09/30/13): Assets, $6,015,340 (M); expenditures, $1,459,802; qualifying distributions, $1,459,802; giving activities include $984,356 for 61 grants to individuals (high: $45,938; low: $824), and $1,271,849 for foundation-administered programs.
Purpose and activities: Giving to promote free enterprise and development in Hungary and to continue to strengthen ties between the United States and Hungary by creating opportunities for accomplished Hungarians and those of great promise to gain professional experience in the United States.
Fields of interest: Education; International affairs, goodwill promotion.
Type of support: Scholarships—to individuals; Fellowships.
Application information: Application form required.
Initial approach: Mail
Deadline(s): See foundation web site for current deadlines
Officers and Directors:* Ryan M. Schwarz,* Chair., C.E.O. and Pres.; Charissa Kerr, C.F.O. and

Secy.-Treas.; Hon. Francis Bator; Hon. George D. Gould; Eriberto R. Scocimara; Andras Simonyi.
EIN: 200490204

3693
The Iberdrola USA Foundation, Inc. ✧
(formerly The Energy East Foundation, Inc.)
52 Farm View Dr.
New Gloucester, ME 04260-5100 (207) 688-4341
Contact: Darlene E. Beach, Treas.
E-mail: darlene.beach@iberdrolausa.com; Main URL: http://energyeast.com/AboutIberdrolaUSA/iusafoundation.html

Established in 2001 in DE.
Donors: The Union Water-Power Co.; Central Maine Power Co.; New York State Electric and Gas; Rochester Gas and Electric Corp.
Foundation type: Company-sponsored foundation.
Financial data (yr. ended 12/31/13): Assets, $6,573,381 (M); gifts received, $797,235; expenditures, $1,470,977; qualifying distributions, $1,204,685; giving activities include $1,204,685 for 110 grants (high: $305,000; low: $87).
Purpose and activities: The foundation supports organizations involved with education, health, and community development and the environment. Support is given primarily in areas of company operations.
Fields of interest: Education; Environment; Human services.
Type of support: Emergency funds; Program development; Sponsorships; Matching/challenge support.
Limitations: Applications accepted. Giving primarily in the Northeast, with emphasis on DC, ME, and NY. No support for political, labor, or fraternal organizations, religious organizations, or organizations with overhead expenses exceeding 25 percent of the total operating budget. No grants to individuals, or for capital campaigns or endowments, conferences, or symposia.
Publications: Informational brochure (including application guidelines).
Application information: Application form required.
Initial approach: Proposal
Copies of proposal: 2
Deadline(s): None
Board meeting date(s): Varies
Officers: Robert D. Kump, Pres.; Mark V. Dolan, Secy.; Darlene E. Beach,* Treas.
Number of staff: None.
EIN: 134200689

3694
Stephen and Tabitha King Foundation, Inc. ✧
P.O. Box 855
Bangor, ME 04402-0855 (207) 990-2910
Contact: Stephanie Leonard
FAX: (207) 990-2975; Main URL: http://www.stkfoundation.org

Established in 1986 in ME.
Donor: Stephen E. King.
Foundation type: Independent foundation.
Financial data (yr. ended 12/31/12): Assets, $150,586 (M); gifts received, $1,526,738; expenditures, $2,863,505; qualifying distributions, $2,858,380; giving activities include $2,838,844 for 150 grants (high: $150,000; low: $500).
Purpose and activities: Giving primarily for the arts, education (including libraries), and human services.
Fields of interest: Arts; Higher education; Libraries (public); Education; Health organizations, association; Human services; United Ways and Federated Giving Programs.
Type of support: General/operating support; Capital campaigns; Building/renovation; Equipment; Land acquisition; Endowments; Program development; Seed money; Research; Matching/challenge support.
Limitations: Applications accepted. Giving limited to ME. No support for hospice programs or facilities, animal shelters, hospitals or rehabilitation centers. No grants to individuals, or for fellowships, scholarships, or for travel or sponsorships, student or athletic groups, graduation parties or events, renovations to churches or other religious properties or institutions, or renovations to historical society property unless connected to a library, or for film or video productions, transportation, book or publishing projects, conferences, meetings, exhibits, or workshops, construction of playgrounds; no wheelchair vans; no organizations whose policies encourage discrimination; no academic research, fellowships or publication; no loans.
Publications: Application guidelines.
Application information: Application guideline and form available on foundation web site. Application form required.
Initial approach: Use online application process on foundation web site
Deadline(s): Dec. 31 and June 30. If the deadline falls on the weekend, the foundation will accept applications until the end of the following Monday.
Board meeting date(s): Spring and fall
Final notification: Within 8 weeks of application deadlines
Officers and Directors:* Stephen E. King,* Pres.; Tabitha King,* Secy.; Arthur B. Greene, Treas.; Mark Levenfus.
Number of staff: 1 full-time professional.
EIN: 133364647
Selected grants: The following grants are a representative sample of this grantmaker's funding activity:
$150,000 to American Red Cross, Pine Tree Chapter, Bangor, ME, 2012.
$80,000 to Bangor Public Library, Bangor, ME, 2012.
$50,000 to Acton Ambulance Association, Acton, ME, 2012.
$50,000 to Maine Discovery Museum, Bangor, ME, 2012.
$45,000 to Rockwood Volunteer Fire Department, Rockwood, ME, 2012.
$40,000 to YMCA of Bangor, Bangor, ME, 2012.
$25,000 to York Ambulance, York, ME, 2012.
$20,000 to Stacyville Fire Department, Sherman, ME, 2012.
$15,000 to Searsport District Middle School, Performing Arts Showcase, Searsport, ME, 2012.
$15,000 to Starks Town Library, Starks, ME, 2012.

3695
Emanuel & Pauline A. Lerner Foundation ✧
P.O. Box 10370
Portland, ME 04104-0370 (207) 730-2779
Contact: Eliot R. Cutler, Dir.

Established in 2007 in ME.
Donors: Pauline Lerner Trust; Emanuel R. Lerner Bypass Trust.
Foundation type: Independent foundation.
Financial data (yr. ended 06/30/13): Assets, $6,786,038 (M); expenditures, $1,042,601; qualifying distributions, $804,985; giving activities include $804,985 for grants.
Fields of interest: Education; Civil/human rights.
Type of support: Professorships; Grants to individuals.
Limitations: Applications accepted. Giving primarily in DE and ME.
Application information: Application form required.
Initial approach: Letter
Deadline(s): Jan. 15, Apr. 15 or Oct. 15
Directors: Victoria Bonebakker; Eliot R. Cutler; Melanie Stewart Cutler; William Foster; Susan Ruch; Justin Schair.
EIN: 208797462
Selected grants: The following grants are a representative sample of this grantmaker's funding activity:
$43,000 to Maine Adult Education Association, Greenwood, ME, 2013. For Improving Portland Adult Education Intake Systems for ESOL and Workforce Development Classes for Immigrants/Refugees.
$31,455 to Portland Public Library, Portland, ME, 2013. For Civic Literacy/Civic Engagement Public Event Series.
$30,000 to Maine Farmland Trust, Belfast, ME, 2013. For Community Conversations and Technical Support to Municipalities Focused on Supporting Local Agriculture.
$25,000 to Maine Citizens for Clean Elections, Portland, ME, 2013. For outreach and engagement Program.
$20,000 to Five Rivers Arts Alliance, Brunswick, ME, 2013. For Tedxdirigo Program.
$15,000 to Center for Grieving Children, Portland, ME, 2013. For programs for refugees.
$10,000 to Community Financial Literacy, Portland, ME, 2013. For Financial Literacy Programs for Immigrant/Refugee Community.
$5,000 to York County Community Action Corporation, Sanford, ME, 2013. For Pilot Accel Program to Provide Education on Civic Engagement and Self-Advocacy.

3696
Libra Foundation ✧
3 Canal Plz.
P.O. Box 17516
Portland, ME 04112-8516 (207) 879-6280
Contact: Elizabeth C. Flaherty, Exec. Asst.
FAX: (207) 879-6281; Main URL: http://www.librafoundation.org
Grants List: http://librafoundation.org/grant-lists

Established in 1989 in ME.
Donor: Elizabeth B. Noyce†.
Foundation type: Independent foundation.
Financial data (yr. ended 12/31/12): Assets, $93,721,509 (M); expenditures, $9,732,579; qualifying distributions, $10,540,451; giving activities include $7,755,769 for 45 grants (high:

$4,390,000; low: $1,000), and $1,805,000 for 3 loans/program-related investments.
Purpose and activities: Areas of giving include arts, culture & humanities, education, environment, health, human services, justice, public/society benefit and religion.
Fields of interest: Arts; Education; Animals/wildlife; Health care; Athletics/sports, winter sports; Human services.
Type of support: Building/renovation; Capital campaigns; Continuing support; Curriculum development; Emergency funds; Endowments; Equipment; General/operating support; Land acquisition; Program development; Program-related investments/loans; Research; Seed money; Technical assistance.
Limitations: Applications accepted. Giving limited to ME. No grants to individuals.
Publications: Application guidelines; Annual report; Financial statement; Grants list; Informational brochure (including application guidelines).
Application information: Application form required.
Initial approach: Letter or telephone
Copies of proposal: 1
Deadline(s): Feb. 15, May 15, Aug. 15, and Nov. 15
Board meeting date(s): Mar., June, Sept., and Dec.
Final notification: Within 1 week of board meeting
Officers and Trustees:* Pendred E. Noyce, M.D.*, Chair.; Owen W. Wells,* Vice-Chair.; Craig N. Denekas,* C.E.O. and Pres.; Jere G. Michelson, Exec. V.P. and C.F.O.; Erik K. Hayward, V.P.; William J. Ryan.
Number of staff: 4 full-time professional; 3 full-time support.
EIN: 046626994
Selected grants: The following grants are a representative sample of this grantmaker's funding activity:
$4,390,000 to Pineland Farms, New Gloucester, ME, 2012. To develop, operate and staff Pineland Farms for agricultural promotion, education and research in Maine.
$1,485,715 to Maine Winter Sports Center, Caribou, ME, 2012. For facilities for biathlon and cross-country programs.
$1,035,769 to MaineHealth, Portland, ME, 2012. For Raising Readers Program.
$110,785 to Black Mountain of Maine, Rumford, ME, 2012. For capital improvements.
$100,000 to Foundation for Maines Community Colleges, South Portland, ME, 2012. For campaign.
$100,000 to Thomas College, Waterville, ME, 2012. For construction of school of business and financial center.
$100,000 to United States Biathlon Association, New Gloucester, ME, 2012. For training of biathletes.
$50,000 to Barbara Bush Texas Fund for Family Literacy, Houston, TX, 2012. For Family Reading Literacy in Maine.
$50,000 to Maine Medical Center, Portland, ME, 2012. For Tufts Medical School Program.
$15,000 to Lets Get Ready, Boston, MA, 2012. For college guidance for Maine low-income and minority students.

3697
Lunder Foundation ✧
c/o Kenilworth Inc.
2 Monument Sq., Ste. 530
Portland, ME 04101-4050 (207) 775-7676

Established in 1988 in ME.
Donors: Peter Lunder; Berkshire Hathaway Inc.
Foundation type: Independent foundation.
Financial data (yr. ended 12/31/13): Assets, $21,707,693 (M); expenditures, $1,881,905; qualifying distributions, $1,851,020; giving activities include $1,813,490 for 91 grants (high: $1,753,507; low: $50).
Fields of interest: Arts; Higher education; Health care.
Type of support: Annual campaigns; Capital campaigns; Scholarship funds; Matching/challenge support.
Limitations: Applications accepted. Giving primarily in MA and ME, with emphasis on central ME. No grants to individuals.
Application information: Application form required.
Initial approach: Letter (no more than 3 pages)
Deadline(s): None
Officers and Directors:* Paula Lunder,* Chair.; John B. Emory, Pres.; Peter Lunder,* Treas.; Marjorie L. Goldy; Alan Lunder; Marc Lunder; Steven Lunder.
EIN: 010437556
Selected grants: The following grants are a representative sample of this grantmaker's funding activity:
$1,756,619 to Massachusetts General Hospital, Boston, MA, 2012. For Lunder Building Fund and Dineen Education Fund.
$25,295 to Colby College, Waterville, ME, 2012. For Alumni Fund.

3698
The Maine Community Foundation, Inc. ✧
245 Main St.
Ellsworth, ME 04605-1613 (207) 667-9735
FAX: (207) 667-0447; E-mail: info@mainecf.org; Additional tel.: (877) 700-6800; Portland mailing address: 1 Monument Way, Ste. 200, P.O. Box 7380, Portland, ME 04101, tel.: (207) 761-2440, fax: (207) 773-8832; Main URL: http://www.mainecf.org
E-Newsletter: http://oi.vresp.com/?fid=a9d981ca11
Facebook: http://www.facebook.com/mainecf
LinkedIn: http://www.linkedin.com/companies/maine-community-foundation
Real Time Blog: http://www.mainecf.org/Default.aspx?tabid=541
Vimeo: http://vimeo.com/channels/mainecf
YouTube: http://www.youtube.com/mainecommunityfdn

Incorporated in 1983 in ME.
Foundation type: Community foundation.
Financial data (yr. ended 12/31/12): Assets, $318,658,874 (M); gifts received, $21,853,869; expenditures, $19,795,722; giving activities include $17,832,771 for grants.
Purpose and activities: The foundation promotes active philanthropy by stewarding charitable funds and making effective grants. Primary areas of interest include the arts, child welfare and youth, the disadvantaged, education, health, community development, and sustainable development.
Fields of interest: Humanities; Arts; Education; Environment, natural resources; Environment; Health care; Health organizations, association; Youth development, services; Children/youth, services; Aging, centers/services; Human services; Urban/community development; Nonprofit management; Community/economic development; Leadership development; Economically disadvantaged.
Type of support: Mission-related investments/loans; Management development/capacity building; Land acquisition; Endowments; Program development; Seed money; Technical assistance; Grants to individuals; Scholarships—to individuals; Matching/challenge support.
Limitations: Applications accepted. Giving limited to ME. No support for religious organizations for religious purposes. No grants to individuals (except for scholarship funds), or for equipment, annual campaigns for regular operations, or for capital campaigns.
Publications: Application guidelines; Annual report; Financial statement; Grants list; Informational brochure; Newsletter.
Application information: Visit foundation web site for application form and guidelines. Faxed or e-mailed applications are not accepted. Application form required.
Initial approach: Submit application form and attachments
Copies of proposal: 1
Deadline(s): Feb. 15 for Community Building Prog. (including County Fund Prog.); varies for others
Board meeting date(s): 3 times annually
Final notification: Early June
Officers and Directors:* George T. Shaw,* Chair.; Meredith H. Jones,* C.E.O. and Pres.; James E. Geary, V.P. and C.F.O.; Ellen Pope, V.P. and C.O.O.; Peter Taylor, V.P., Prog. Devel. and Grantmaking Svcs.; Laura Young, V.P., Philanthropy; Tim Smith, Cont.; Peter Rothschild, C.I.O.; Jean M. Deighan; Eileen M.L. Epstein; Sandra Featherman; Andrew Fenniman; Katharine Fullam Harris; Elisabeth C. Heyward; Elizabeth R. Hilpman; Peter F. Lamb; S. Peter Mills III; Elizabeth Neptune; Matthew Polstein; Anna E. Roosevelt; Mary "Polly" Saltonstall; Candace Sanborn; Dighton Spooner; Karen W. Stanley; John Witherspoon; Wendy J. Wolf.
Number of staff: 16 full-time professional; 3 full-time support; 1 part-time support.
EIN: 010391479
Selected grants: The following grants are a representative sample of this grantmaker's funding activity:
$138,670 to Great Pond Mountain Conservation Trust Wildlands Campaign, Orland, ME, 2012. For the To the Summit campaign.
$50,000 to More Than Wheels, Keene, NH, 2012. For expansion of services in Maine for veterans and their families.
$35,000 to Downeast Coastal Conservancy, Machias, ME, 2012. For the Two Rivers Campaign.
$25,000 to University of New England, Biddeford, ME, 2012. For training for the Embedded Mentor/Peer Program to 10% of MENG members.
$22,000 to Association Culturelle et Historique du Mont-Carmel, Lille, ME, 2012. For interior repair and painting of the Musee cultural du Mont-Carmel in Lille, Maine.
$20,000 to Skowhegan School of Painting and Sculpture, New York, NY, 2012. For the organizational assessment.
$3,500 to Maine Historical Society, Portland, ME, 2012. For technology upgrades to support extensive library outreach and training program designed to expand use of the Brown Research Library.
$3,500 to New Beginnings, Lewiston, ME, 2012. To replace the roof to allow for renovation and use of expanded homeless youth Drop-In Center.
$3,000 to Friends of Midcoast Maine, Camden, ME, 2012. To expand the Smart Growth Education

Workshop series to include a new hands-on workshop with Rockland and/or other interested towns on Re-Inhabiting the Commercial Strip.
$875 to Guilford Memorial Library, Guilford, ME, 2012. For one children's program plus supporting books and two adult programs.

3699
Maine Health Access Foundation ✧

150 Capitol St., Ste. 4
Augusta, ME 04330-6858 (207) 620-8266
Contact: Wendy J. Wolf M.D., M.P.H., C.E.O. and Pres.; Barbara A. Leonard M.P.H., V.P., Progs.; Catherine L. Luce MBA, Grants Mgr.
FAX: (207) 620-8269; E-mail: Cluce@mehaf.org; Toll-free tel.: (866) 848-9210; Main URL: http://www.mehaf.org
CEP Study: http://www.mehaf.org/cep-survey-results/
Knowledge Center: http://mehaf.org/resources/
RSS Feed: http://mehaf.org/feeds/news/

Established in 2000 in ME.
Foundation type: Independent foundation.
Financial data (yr. ended 12/31/13): Assets, $124,581,299 (M); gifts received, $6,000; expenditures, $6,253,214; qualifying distributions, $5,477,994; giving activities include $3,417,942 for grants, and $2,060,052 for foundation-administered programs.
Purpose and activities: The foundation's mission is to promote access to quality health care, especially for those who are uninsured and underserved, and to improve the health of everyone in Maine. The foundation uses its human and financial resources to ensure that all people have access to high quality, affordable health care to achieve or preserve better health. The foundation directs its program, grantmaking, and staff resources to advance four strategic priorities in pursuit of its mission. The foundation's priorities are: advancing health system reform, promoting patient-centered care, improving access to quality care, and achieving better health in communities.
Fields of interest: Health care, public policy; Health care.
Type of support: Program-related investments/loans; Management development/capacity building; Equipment; Program development; Conferences/seminars; Research; Technical assistance; Program evaluation.
Limitations: Applications accepted. Giving primarily in ME. No grants to individuals, or for endowments, debt retirement, annual appeals or membership campaigns, fundraising or social events, or public relations campaigns.
Publications: Application guidelines; Annual report; Grants list; Newsletter; Occasional report.
Application information: Online application form required. See foundation web site for application guidelines and procedures, as well as new funding priorities. Application form required.
Initial approach: Phone discussion with program staff
Deadline(s): Varies
Board meeting date(s): 2nd Thurs. Bimonthly
Final notification: Variable depending on type of grant
Officers and Trustees:* Sara Gagne-Holmes, Esq.*, Chair.; Wendy J. Wolf, Pres. and C.E.O.; Constance Sandstrom, M.P.A.*, Vice-Chair.; Nancy Fritz,* Secy.; Anthony Marple,* Treas.; Constance Adler, M.D., FAAFP; John Benoit; Deborah Deatrick, MPH; Roy Hitchings, Jr., FACHE; Frank Johnson; Bruce G. Nickerson, CPA; Catherine Ryder; Lisa Sockabasin, BSN; Ted Sussman; Jeff Wahlstrom; Shirley Weaver, Ph.D.
Number of staff: 7 full-time professional; 3 full-time support.
EIN: 010535144
Selected grants: The following grants are a representative sample of this grantmaker's funding activity:
$100,000 to Maine Primary Care Association, Augusta, ME, 2012. To develop peer-to-peer FQHC mentorship program and direct technical assistance support.
$100,000 to Maine, State of, Augusta, ME, 2012. For MaineCare to develop and implement Medicaid Health Homes program.
$99,984 to Quality Counts, Manchester, ME, 2012. To create sustainable structure and payment system to support community-based, multi-disciplinary primary care-integrated Community Health Teams (CHT).
$99,128 to Maine Health Management Coalition Foundation, Portland, ME, 2012. For organizations transition and peer-to-peer education.
$98,909 to Franklin Memorial Hospital, Farmington, ME, 2012. To implement Franklin CARES, Nurse Navigator pilot program.
$87,500 to Passamaquoddy Tribe of Indian Township, Princeton, ME, 2012. For Waponahki Health Policy Collaboration to provide forum for Maine Tribes.
$55,000 to Consumers for Affordable Health Care Foundation, Augusta, ME, 2012.
$30,137 to Maine Equal Justice Partners, Augusta, ME, 2012. To provide immigrant communities in Maine with information and resources about MaineCare benefits and restrictions, Emergency MaineCare and other public assistance resources.
$5,000 to Maine Community Foundation, Ellsworth, ME, 2012. For Maine Nonprofit Efffectiveness Initiative (NEI) established by Maine Nonprofit Sector Collaboration.
$2,000 to Maine Long Term Care Ombudsman Program, Augusta, ME, 2012. To improve Dementia Care in Nursing Homes Workgroup Conference.

3700
MELMAC Education Foundation ✧

188 Whitten Rd.
Augusta, ME 04330-6021 (207) 622-3066
FAX: (207) 622-3053;
E-mail: info@melmacfoundation.org; Toll free tel.: (866) 622-3066; Main URL: http://www.melmacfoundation.org

Established in 2001 in ME.
Foundation type: Independent foundation.
Financial data (yr. ended 12/31/13): Assets, $41,694,550 (M); expenditures, $1,691,058; qualifying distributions, $1,466,405; giving activities include $1,127,342 for grants, and $217,500 for grants to individuals.
Purpose and activities: Giving primarily for high-quality initiatives that serve the purpose of increasing educational opportunities for people of Maine.
Fields of interest: Secondary school/education; Higher education.
Type of support: Scholarships—to individuals.
Limitations: Applications not accepted. Giving primarily in ME.
Application information: Unsolicited requests for funds not accepted.
Officers and Directors:* Scott MacDonald,* Chair.; Roy Barry,* Vice-Chair.; Pat McNamara,* Secy.; Ron Milliken,* Treas.; Wendy L. Ault, Exec. Dir.; Peggy Crawford; David R. Perkins; Lawrence LaBrie.
EIN: 010390854

3701
The Morton-Kelly Charitable Trust ✧ ☆

c/o Jensen Baird Gardner & Henry
10 Free St.
Box 4510
Portland, ME 04112 (207) 775-7271
Contact: Michael J. Quinlan, Treas., Secy. and Clerk
FAX: (207) 775-7935; E-mail: mquinlan@jbgh.com

Established in 1988 in ME.
Donors: Mildred D. Morton†; Joan M. Kelly†.
Foundation type: Independent foundation.
Financial data (yr. ended 12/31/13): Assets, $16,994,699 (M); gifts received, $11,297,103; expenditures, $726,800; qualifying distributions, $655,684; giving activities include $645,750 for 74 grants (high: $100,000; low: $2,500).
Purpose and activities: Giving primarily for cultural, educational, historical and environmental programs.
Fields of interest: Historic preservation/historical societies; Arts; Education; Environment.
Type of support: General/operating support; Continuing support; Capital campaigns; Building/renovation; Equipment; Land acquisition; Program development; Seed money; Internship funds; Scholarship funds; Research.
Limitations: Applications accepted. Giving limited to ME. No grants for scholarships to individuals directly.
Application information: Applications not accepted prior to July 1 annually. Application form not required.
Initial approach: Letter in duplicate containing information required by the Trust's guidelines (which may be obtained by contacting the Secy. of the Trust)
Copies of proposal: 2
Deadline(s): Oct. 1
Board meeting date(s): Nov.
Final notification: Dec. 31
Officers and Directors:* Merton G. Henry,* Pres.; Michael J. Quinlan,* Secy., Treas., and Clerk; Marilyn A. Lalumiere; Peter Robbins; Dorothy Schwartz.
Number of staff: None.
EIN: 010442078
Selected grants: The following grants are a representative sample of this grantmaker's funding activity:
$10,000 to Canaan Public Library, Canaan, ME, 2012. For construction of new library.
$10,000 to Childrens Museum and Theater of Maine, Portland, ME, 2012. For living animal science exhibit.
$10,000 to Scarborough Land Conservation Trust, Scarborough, ME, 2012. For acquisition of land.
$6,000 to Lincoln County Historical Association, Wiscasset, ME, 2012. For preservation of historical building.
$5,000 to Herring Gut Learning Center, Port Clyde, ME, 2012. For aquaponics greenhouse program.

3702
The Clarence E. Mulford Trust ✧
P.O. Box 290
Fryeburg, ME 04037-0290 (207) 935-2061
Contact: Peter G. Hastings, Tr.

Established in 1950 in ME.
Donor: Clarence E. Mulford‡.
Foundation type: Independent foundation.
Financial data (yr. ended 12/31/13): Assets, $12,133,347 (M); expenditures, $637,340; qualifying distributions, $546,829; giving activities include $479,425 for 29 grants (high: $268,562; low: $500).
Purpose and activities: Giving primarily for education, human services, community organizations, and to Catholic and Protestant churches.
Fields of interest: Education; Human services; Community/economic development; Protestant agencies & churches; Catholic agencies & churches.
Limitations: Applications accepted. Giving primarily in Fryeburg, ME, and neighboring towns. No grants to individuals, or for building or endowment funds, scholarships, fellowships, or matching gifts; no loans.
Application information: Application form required.
Initial approach: Letter
Copies of proposal: 3
Deadline(s): Preferably in June or Dec., no later than Jan. 10 or July 10
Board meeting date(s): Jan. and July
Final notification: Feb. 10 or Aug. 10; positive replies only
Trustees: David R. Hastings III; Peter G. Hastings.
EIN: 010247648

3703
Francis T. and Louise T. Nichols Foundation ✧
P.O. Box 1210
Bangor, ME 04402-1210 (207) 947-0111
Contact: Calvin E. True, Tr.

Established in 1994 in ME.
Donor: Francis T. Nichols‡.
Foundation type: Independent foundation.
Financial data (yr. ended 12/31/13): Assets, $34,387,608 (M); expenditures, $981,924; qualifying distributions, $981,924; giving activities include $854,000 for 45 grants (high: $70,000; low: $500).
Purpose and activities: Giving primarily to education, health care and human services.
Fields of interest: Elementary/secondary education; Hospitals (general); Health care; Disasters, fire prevention/control; Human services; Children/youth, services.
Limitations: Applications accepted. Giving primarily in Hancock County, ME. No grants to individuals.
Application information: Application form required.
Initial approach: Letter
Deadline(s): None
Trustees: William H. Nichols; Susan Thibault; Calvin E. True.
EIN: 010493311
Selected grants: The following grants are a representative sample of this grantmaker's funding activity:
$2,000 to Volunteers of America, Alexandria, VA, 2011.

3704
The Orchard Foundation ✧
P.O. Box 2587
South Portland, ME 04116-2587 (207) 799-0686
Contact: Brigitte L. Kingsbury, Exec. Dir.
E-mail: orchard@maine.rr.com

Established in 1990 in MA.
Donors: Moose Mountain Trust; Leigh Fibers, Inc.; Leigh Fibers Holdings, Inc.
Foundation type: Independent foundation.
Financial data (yr. ended 12/31/13): Assets, $13,059,609 (M); expenditures, $802,055; qualifying distributions, $656,865; giving activities include $610,790 for 73 grants (high: $70,000; low: $100).
Purpose and activities: The foundation supports organizations concerned with the environment and children, youth and families in New York and New England.
Fields of interest: Environment; Children/youth.
Limitations: Applications not accepted. Giving limited to New England and NY.
Application information: Unsolicited requests for funds not accepted.
Officer and Trustees:* Brigitte L. Kingsbury,* Exec. Dir.; Carl P. Lehner; Heidi Lehner.
Number of staff: 1 part-time professional.
EIN: 046660214
Selected grants: The following grants are a representative sample of this grantmaker's funding activity:
$100,000 to Natural Resources Defense Council, New York, NY, 2012. For Hingham Fund.
$60,000 to Massachusetts Institute of Technology, Cambridge, MA, 2012. For Mechanical Engineering Department.
$25,000 to Clean Water Fund, Boston, MA, 2012. For Waste Polices for Reducing Climate Emissions.
$20,000 to Planned Parenthood Hudson Peconic, Hawthorne, NY, 2012. For Strategies for Combating Attacks on PP's Sexuality Education Programs.
$20,000 to Society for the Protection of New Hampshire Forests, Concord, NH, 2012. For The Reasonable Use Project: Northern Pass.
$15,000 to Conservation Law Foundation, Boston, MA, 2012. For New England Clean Water Initiative.
$15,000 to Planned Parenthood League of Massachusetts, Boston, MA, 2012. For Get Real. Comprehensive Sex Education That Works.
$15,000 to Toxics Action Center, Boston, MA, 2012. For Massachusetts Zero Waste Campaign.
$15,000 to Vermont Natural Resources Council, Montpelier, VT, 2012. For Bringing Sound River Science to the People.
$12,000 to Androscoggin River Alliance, Lewiston, ME, 2012. For Holding Maine State Regulators Accountable.

3705
Quimby Family Foundation
P.O. Box 148
Portland, ME 04112-0148
E-mail: info@quimbyfamilyfoundation.org; Main URL: http://www.quimbyfamilyfoundation.org

Established in 2004 in ME.
Donor: Roxanne Quimby.
Foundation type: Independent foundation.
Financial data (yr. ended 12/31/12): Assets, $22,011,252 (M); gifts received, $4,977,292; expenditures, $1,735,268; qualifying distributions, $1,561,915; giving activities include $1,330,382 for 69 grants (high: $50,000; low: $500).
Purpose and activities: The mission of the foundation is to encourage vibrant sustainable Maine communities by promoting health and wellbeing, advancing opportunities for outdoor recreation, protecting and restoring our environment, and supporting local access to the arts for all Maine people. Detailed program information available on foundation web site.
Fields of interest: Arts, multipurpose centers/programs; Arts; Education; Environment, natural resources; Environmental education; Animals/wildlife, preservation/protection; Animals/wildlife.
Type of support: General/operating support.
Limitations: Applications accepted. Giving primarily in ME. No grants to individuals; no multi-year grants.
Publications: Application guidelines; Grants list.
Application information: Full applications will be accepted by invitation only. Application information for invited applicants available on foundation web site. The foundation prefers e-mail correspondence. Complete application guidelines available on foundation web site.
Initial approach: One-page concept letter submitted through foundation web site
Directors: Hannah Quimby; Rachelle Quimby; Roxanne Quimby; Rebecca Rowe; Rebecca Rundquist; Lucas St. Clair.; Yemana St. Clair; Liliane Willens.
EIN: 200041017

3706
Redco Foundation, Inc. ✧
c/o Baker Newman & Noyes
P.O. Box 507
Portland, ME 04112-0507

Established in 2001 in ME.
Donors: Ann Bresnahan; Richard Bresnahan.
Foundation type: Independent foundation.
Financial data (yr. ended 10/31/13): Assets, $3,856,145 (M); gifts received, $217,500; expenditures, $1,112,521; qualifying distributions, $1,093,285; giving activities include $1,093,000 for 5 grants (high: $1,000,000; low: $5,000).
Fields of interest: Education; Health care; Recreation.
Limitations: Applications not accepted. Giving primarily in ME. No grants to individuals.
Application information: Contributes only to pre-selected organizations.
Officers and Directors:* Richard A. Bresnahan,* Pres.; Richard M. Bresnahan,* V.P. and Treas.; James H. Young II,* Secy.; David H. Bresnahan; Elizabeth W. Bresnahan.
EIN: 010546160

3707
The Sandy River Charitable Foundation ✧
349 Voter Hill Rd.
Farmington, ME 04938-6030 (207) 779-1682
FAX: (207) 779-1901;
E-mail: info@srcfoundation.org; Main URL: http://www.srcfoundation.org

Established in 1997 in ME.
Donor: Berry Charitable Trust.
Foundation type: Independent foundation.
Financial data (yr. ended 05/31/13): Assets, $37,972,073 (M); expenditures, $1,099,553;

qualifying distributions, $1,538,528; giving activities include $803,200 for 30 grants (high: $250,000; low: $1,000), and $650,000 for 4 loans/program-related investments (high: $250,000; low: $100,000).
Purpose and activities: Giving primarily to disaster rehabilitation and hunger relief services; funding also for a community foundation in Ellsworth, Maine, and a mountain alliance in Farmington, Maine. Funding is also made for international and rural development, micro financing, and adoption services.
Fields of interest: Environment; Food services; Disasters, preparedness/services; Children, adoption; Family services; International agricultural development; Rural development; Foundations (community).
Type of support: General/operating support; Continuing support; Income development; Management development/capacity building; Building/renovation; Equipment; Program evaluation; Program-related investments/loans; Matching/challenge support.
Limitations: Applications not accepted. Giving on an international and national basis, (particularly Board/staff areas), with a special emphasis on ME. No grants to individuals.
Application information: Unsolicited proposals not accepted.
Board meeting date(s): June and Dec.
Officers: Archie W. Berry, Jr., Pres.; Nathanael W. Berry, V.P. and Secy.; Jon W. Berry, Treas.
Directors: Marla S. Berry; Nan Berry; Suphaporn V. Berry; Lillian Dox.
Number of staff: 1 full-time professional.
EIN: 522029911

3708
Elmina B. Sewall Foundation ✧
15 Maine St., Ste. 230
Freeport, ME 04032-1100 (207) 865-3810
Contact: Jay Espy, Exec. Dir.
FAX: (207) 865-3811;
E-mail: info@sewallfoundation.org; Main URL: http://www.Sewallfoundation.org

Established in 1982 in ME.
Donor: Elmina B. Sewall‡.
Foundation type: Independent foundation.
Financial data (yr. ended 09/30/13): Assets, $183,240,921 (M); expenditures, $10,647,921; qualifying distributions, $9,496,940; giving activities include $8,951,352 for 164 grants (high: $1,085,515; low: $246).
Purpose and activities: The mission of the foundation is to support conservation of the natural environment and the well-being of animals and human beings, primarily in Maine. Through its giving, the foundation seeks to make a significant impact, inspire the generosity of others and empower those who share its vision.
Fields of interest: Environment, plant conservation; Environment; Animal welfare; Animals/wildlife, preservation/protection; Human services; Children/youth, services.
Type of support: General/operating support; Management development/capacity building; Capital campaigns; Program development; Matching/challenge support.
Limitations: Giving primarily in ME, with the exception of a moderate amount of routine annual giving which may take place in other regions. No grants to individuals, or for operating endowments. In general, multi-year projects will not be supported.
Publications: IRS Form 990 or 990-PF printed copy available upon request.
Application information: The foundation now follows a one-step grant application process. To start a new application, visit foundation web site, select the "New Application" tab. Returning applicants will be prompted to enter the appropriate e-mail address and password for their organization. New applicants will be prompted to establish an account and password. Refer to the foundation web site for more detailed information and instructions.
Initial approach: Submit online application
Deadline(s): Jan. 15 for environment and human well-being; June 15 for animal welfare and legacy
Board meeting date(s): Apr., Jul. and Sept.
Final notification: Early June for environment and human well-being; early Oct. for animal welfare and legacy
Officers and Directors:* Margaret Sewall Barbour,* Pres.; Kent W. Wommack,* V.P.; David E. Norris,* Treas.; Jay Espy, Exec. Dir.; Betsy Biemann; William E. Curran; Robert E. McAfee, M.D.; H. Roy Partridge, Jr., Ph.D.; Lisa J. Sockabasin; Carol Wishcamper.
Number of staff: 3 full-time professional.
EIN: 010387404
Selected grants: The following grants are a representative sample of this grantmaker's funding activity:
$1,085,515 to Bank of America Charitable Gift Fund, Providence, RI, 2013. For donor advised fund gift.
$500,000 to Maine Farmland Trust, Belfast, ME, 2013. For Comprehensive Campaign - phase 1.
$500,000 to Penobscot River Restoration Trust, Augusta, ME, 2013. For general purpose.
$450,000 to Maine Coast Heritage Trust, Topsham, ME, 2013. For general purpose.
$300,000 to Preble Street, Portland, ME, 2013. For general purpose.
$200,000 to Cobscook Community Learning Center, Trescott, ME, 2013. For Met Challenge Grant.
$160,000 to Manomet Center for Conservation Sciences, Plymouth, MA, 2013. For FBO Downeast Fisheries Partnership.
$150,000 to Maine Development Foundation, Augusta, ME, 2013. For general purpose.
$35,000 to Wayside Food Programs, Portland, ME, 2013. For Wayside consolidation of operations.
$30,000 to Northern Forest Canoe Trail, Waitsfield, VT, 2013. For general purpose.

3709
Robert and Patricia Switzer Foundation ✧
(formerly Switzer Foundation)
P.O. Box 293
Belfast, ME 04915-0293 (207) 338-5654
Contact: Erin Lloyd, Prog. Off.
E-mail: info@switzernetwork.org; Application e-mail: erin@switzernetwork.org; Main URL: http://www.switzernetwork.org/
Blog: http://www.switzernetwork.org/blogs/opentopics/
Facebook: http://www.facebook.com/SwitzerFoundation
Twitter: http://twitter.com/switzernetwork

Established in 1985 in OH.
Donors: Robert Switzer‡; Patricia Switzer.
Foundation type: Independent foundation.
Financial data (yr. ended 06/30/13): Assets, $18,088,083 (M); expenditures, $969,600; qualifying distributions, $895,225; giving activities include $502,097 for grants.
Purpose and activities: Graduate fellowships awarded for one year to individuals most apt to be leaders in environmental fields. Only awarded to students in CA, and in New England. Grants also to environmental non-profits to hire Switzer Fellow(s) in leadership positions.
Fields of interest: Environment.
Type of support: Mission-related investments/loans; Fellowships.
Limitations: Applications accepted. Giving limited to CA, CT, MA, ME, NH, RI, and VT for fellowship program, leadership grants available on a national basis.
Publications: Application guidelines; Annual report.
Application information: See foundation web site for specific application instructions and requirements. Application form required.
Deadline(s): See foundation web site for deadlines
Board meeting date(s): Varies
Final notification: Varies
Officer and Trustees:* Lissa Widoff,* Exec. Dir.; Adrienne Alvord; Bruce Kahn; Margaret Rubega; Jennifer Sokolove; Elise Switzer; Jessica Switzer; Patricia D. Switzer; Carol Tucker.
Number of staff: 3 full-time professional.
EIN: 341504501

3710
TD Charitable Foundation ✧
(formerly TD Banknorth Charitable Foundation)
P.O. Box 9540
1 Portland Sq.
Portland, ME 04112-9540 (207) 756-6947
Contact: Michael L. Rayder, Jr., Mgr.
E-mail: US-CharitableGiving@TD.com; Main URL: http://www.tdbank.com/community/our_community.html
Housing for Everyone Grant Recipients: http://www.tdbank.com/community/popup_housinggrant_recipients.html

Established in 2002 in ME.
Donors: Carolina First Foundation; Banknorth Group, Inc.; TD Banknorth Inc.; American Savings Bank; Cape Cod Bank and Trust Co.; Interchange Bank; Commerce Bancorp, Inc.
Foundation type: Company-sponsored foundation.
Financial data (yr. ended 12/31/13): Assets, $57,330,161 (M); gifts received, $158; expenditures, $17,408,241; qualifying distributions, $17,158,549; giving activities include $16,680,234 for 1,570 grants (high: $318,000; low: $200).
Purpose and activities: The foundation supports organizations involved with affordable housing; education and financial literacy; and the environment. Special emphasis is directed toward programs designed to support low- to moderate-income individuals by providing services, training, or education that improves the quality of life and provides opportunities for advancement.
Fields of interest: Education, ESL programs; Education, services; Education, reading; Education; Environment, natural resources; Environment, energy; Environment; Food banks; Housing/shelter, development; Housing/shelter, rehabilitation; Housing/shelter; Youth development, adult & child programs; Youth development; Human services,

financial counseling; Human services; Community development, small businesses; Community/economic development; United Ways and Federated Giving Programs; Mathematics; Economically disadvantaged.
Type of support: Management development/capacity building; Annual campaigns; Program development; Employee volunteer services; Sponsorships; Employee matching gifts.
Limitations: Applications accepted. Giving limited to areas of company operations in CT, Washington, DC, DE, FL, MA, MD, ME, NC, NH, NJ, NY, PA, RI, SC, VA, and VT. No support for private foundations, political candidates, lobbying, advocacy, research, or discriminatory organizations, fraternal, labor, or veterans' groups, religious organizations not of direct benefit to the entire community, or athletic teams or social groups. No grants to individuals, or for fundraising events, scholarships, memberships, advertising, annual campaigns, travel or conferences, debt reduction, trips or tours, endowments, or capital campaigns; no general operating support.
Publications: Application guidelines; Corporate giving report; Grants list; Program policy statement.
Application information: Organizations receiving support for the Non-Profit Training Resource Fund are required to provide a certificate of completion or other evidence of the employee's attendance of the training. Support is limited to 1 contribution per organization during any given year. Visit website for application deadlines. Application form required.
Initial approach: Complete online application
Deadline(s): Varies by state; varies but usually July 1 to Aug. 29 for Housing for Everyone Grant Competition; None for Non-Profit Training Resource Fund
Board meeting date(s): Quarterly
Final notification: 2 weeks following committee meeting; Nov. for Housing for Everyone Grant Competition; 2 to 6 weeks for Non-Profit Training Resource Fund
Officers and Directors: Elizabeth K. Warn, Pres.; Mark Crandall, V.P.; Geoffrey Ryan, Secy.; Paul Young, Treas.; Nandita Bakhshi; Greg Braca; Michael Carbone; Fred Graziano; Lisette Lieberman; Scott Mullin; Jeff Nathanson.
EIN: 141864317
Selected grants: The following grants are a representative sample of this grantmaker's funding activity:
$313,900 to United Way of Greater Philadelphia and Southern New Jersey, Camden County Office, Philadelphia, PA, 2012. For United Way Community Campaign.
$150,000 to ACCION East, New York, NY, 2012. For Maine to Miami Microlending and Financial Education Initiative.
$120,000 to New Jersey Citizen Action Education Fund, Newark, NJ, 2012. For 2012 Housing, Community and Economic Development Programs.
$100,000 to College of Charleston Foundation, Charleston, SC, 2012. For 4th Century Initiative.
$100,000 to Peoples Emergency Center, Community Development Corporation, Philadelphia, PA, 2012. For Bigham Place Project.
$50,000 to Salvation Army, A New York Corporation, West Nyack, NY, 2012. For Food Service Program.
$7,500 to Rebuilding Together Broward County, Oakland Park, FL, 2012. For Safe and Healthy Homes Program.
$7,500 to Womens Enterprise Development Center, White Plains, NY, 2012. For 15 Week Entrepreneunal Training and Technical Assistance Program.
$5,000 to Homeless Emergency Project, Clearwater, FL, 2012. For Family Transition.
$5,000 to Jersey Cares, Newark, NJ, 2012. For Environmental Program.

3711
Otto and Fran Walter Foundation, Inc.

(formerly Walter & Lorenz Foundation, Inc.)
c/o The Brick House
7 Oak St.
Boothbay Harbor, ME 04538-1972 (207) 633-7300
Contact: Martha H. Peak, V.P. and Grants Dir.
E-mail: grants@walterfoundation.org; Main URL: http://www.walterfoundation.org/

Established in 1952 in NY.
Donors: Anton Lorenz†; Otto L. Walter†; Fran D. Walter†.
Foundation type: Independent foundation.
Financial data (yr. ended 12/31/13): Assets, $14,733,331 (M); expenditures, $1,069,263; qualifying distributions, $931,242; giving activities include $699,389 for 11 grants (high: $131,500; low: $13,000).
Purpose and activities: Primary areas of interest include education, the arts, the disadvantaged, Holocaust survivorship and international amity.
Fields of interest: Arts; Education; Human services; International affairs, goodwill promotion; Aging; Economically disadvantaged.
Type of support: Seed money; Matching/challenge support.
Limitations: Applications accepted. Giving on a national and international basis. No support for purely religious or ethnic programs, or for programs with political agendas or programs that discriminate; no support for projects with only local impact. No grants or scholarships to individuals, or for annual or capital campaigns.
Application information: Application form not required.
Initial approach: E-mail
Copies of proposal: 1
Deadline(s): None
Board meeting date(s): As necessary
Officers and Directors:* Frank G. Helman,* Pres.; Martha H. Peak,* V.P.; Carl R. Griffin III,* Secy.; Fritz Weinschenk,* Treas.
Number of staff: 3 part-time professional; 1 part-time support.
EIN: 131625529
Selected grants: The following grants are a representative sample of this grantmaker's funding activity:
$60,000 to Mannes College of Music, New York, NY, 2012. To Fund Concerts in Nursing Homes, Senior Centers An.
$30,000 to Brandeis University, Waltham, MA, 2012. For Center for German and European Studies.

MARYLAND

3712
The Abell Foundation, Inc. ✧
111 S. Calvert St., Ste. 2300
Baltimore, MD 21202-6174 (410) 547-1300
Contact: Robert C. Embry, Jr., Pres.
FAX: (410) 539-6579; E-mail: abell@abell.org; Main URL: http://www.abell.org
E-Newsletter: http://www.abell.org/publications/sign.htm
Knowledge Center: http://www.abell.org/publications/pub_library.asp
Twitter: https://twitter.com/abellfoundation

Incorporated in 1953 in MD.
Donors: A.S. Abell Co.; Harry C. Black†; Gary Black, Sr.†; Douglas Koshland.
Foundation type: Independent foundation.
Financial data (yr. ended 12/31/13): Assets, $350,433,538 (M); expenditures, $18,047,752; qualifying distributions, $16,569,976; giving activities include $12,840,154 for 407 grants (high: $5,000,000; low: $285), $244,139 for employee matching gifts, $320,147 for 4 foundation-administered programs and $195,000 for 1 loan/program-related investment.
Purpose and activities: The foundation has seven broad program areas of interest: 1) Community development; 2) Workforce development; 3) Criminal justice and addiction; 4) Education; 5) Health and human services; 6) Conservation and environment; and 7) arts and culture. Within these areas, the foundation invites requests for demonstration projects, feasibility studies, strategic planning, capital improvements, new construction, and equipment, program development and enhancements, research, and program-related investments.
Fields of interest: Arts; Education, research; Education, early childhood education; Child development, education; Elementary school/education; Environment, natural resources; Environment; Reproductive health, family planning; Health care; Substance abuse, services; Crime/violence prevention; Offenders/ex-offenders, services; Employment, services; Employment; Food services; Housing/shelter, development; Youth development, services; Children/youth, services; Family services; Community/economic development; Leadership development; Children/youth; Youth; Adults; Young adults; Minorities; African Americans/Blacks; Hispanics/Latinos; Women; Offenders/ex-offenders; Substance abusers; AIDS, people with; Single parents; Economically disadvantaged; Homeless.
Type of support: General/operating support; Capital campaigns; Building/renovation; Equipment; Land acquisition; Program development; Conferences/seminars; Seed money; Curriculum development; Scholarship funds; Program-related investments/loans; Employee matching gifts; Matching/challenge support.
Limitations: Applications accepted. Giving limited to MD, with emphasis on Baltimore. No support for educational programs at higher education institutions or medical facilities. No grants to individuals, or for scholarships, fellowships, endowments, travel, annual operating expenses, sponsorships, memberships, or deficit financing.
Publications: Application guidelines; Annual report (including application guidelines); Newsletter; Occasional report; Program policy statement; Program policy statement (including application guidelines).
Application information: Should the foundation be interested in the preliminary proposal, the applicant will be asked to submit a formal and detailed application. Downloadable application form is available on the foundation's web site. Association of Baltimore Area Grantmakers Common Grant Application Format accepted. Application form required.
Initial approach: Letter (1-2 pages)
Copies of proposal: 1
Deadline(s): Jan. 1, Mar. 1, May 1, Aug. 1, Sept. 1, and Nov. 1
Board meeting date(s): Bimonthly
Final notification: Within 1 week of board meetings
Officers and Trustees:* Gary Black, Jr.,* Chair.; Robert C. Embry, Jr.,* Pres.; Anne LaFarge Culman, V.P.; Frances Murray Keenan, V.P., Finance; Estelle M. Summerfield, Secy.; Eileen M. O'Rourke, Treas.; Ellen H. Mullan, Cont.; W. Shepherdson Abell; George L. Bunting, Jr.; Robert Garrett; Jacqueline C. Hrabowski; Sally J. Michel.
Number of staff: 9 full-time professional; 4 part-time professional; 4 full-time support.
EIN: 526036106
Selected grants: The following grants are a representative sample of this grantmaker's funding activity:
$450,000 to Center for Urban Families, Baltimore, MD, 2012. For STRIVE Baltimore.
$317,000 to Work First Foundation, New York, NY, 2012. For programming.
$160,000 to Emerging Technology Centers, Baltimore, MD, 2012. For expenses related to Accelerate Baltimore competition, design to provide venture awards to six entrepreneurs and early-stage companies committed to moving to Baltimore.
$150,000 to Environmental Integrity Project, Washington, DC, 2012. For continuing support of Brooklyn/Curtis Bay/Hawkins Point Environmental Justice campaign to identify pollution sources and to reduce pollution affecting underserved communities.

3713
William S. Abell Foundation, Inc. ✧
(formerly Charles S. Abell Foundation, Inc.)
2 Wisconsin Cir., Ste. 890
Chevy Chase, MD 20815-7033 (301) 652-2224
FAX: (301) 652-9173;
E-mail: info@williamsabellfoundation.org; Main URL: http://www.williamsabellfoundation.org
Grants List: http://www.williamsabellfoundation.org/william_s_abell_foundation_grants

Established in 1985 in MD.
Donors: William S. Abell†; Patricia O'Callaghan Abell†.
Foundation type: Independent foundation.
Financial data (yr. ended 12/31/13): Assets, $78,833,375 (M); gifts received, $126,117; expenditures, $6,541,227; qualifying distributions, $5,504,723; giving activities include $4,484,782 for grants.
Purpose and activities: The foundation primarily awards grants quarterly to help the hungry, intellectually disabled, homeless, abused women and children, and to assist at-risk pregnant women in delivering and caring for their infants. Grants typically do not exceed $25,000.
Fields of interest: Performing arts, ballet; Performing arts, theater; Crime/violence prevention, abuse prevention; Crime/violence prevention, child abuse; Food services; Human services; Homeless, human services; Mentally disabled; Women; Homeless.
Type of support: General/operating support; Program development; Matching/challenge support.
Limitations: Applications accepted. Giving primarily in Washington, DC, and five nearby counties in MD, including Montgomery, Prince George's, Charles, Calvert, and St. Mary's counties. No support for organizations performing, sponsoring or referring for abortion; or for national touring companies, even for performances in the Washington, DC, metropolitan area. No grants to individuals, or for capital or endowment campaigns, multi-year grants, grants in consecutive calendar years, or for the construction or improvement of buildings.
Publications: Application guidelines; Grants list.
Application information: Full applications accepted only following approval of letter of intent. Proposal guidelines and forms available on foundation web site. Application form not required.
Initial approach: Telephone foundation prior to submitting application
Copies of proposal: 1
Deadline(s): See foundation web site for current deadlines
Board meeting date(s): Mar., June, Sept., and Dec.
Final notification: 2 weeks after board meeting
Officers and Trustees:* Elaine Abell Nurmi,* Chair.; Anthony F. Abell,* Pres.; Kevin O'C. Abell,* Treas.; Janet Miller, Exec. Dir.; Christopher S. Abell, Sr.; Christopher S. Abell, Jr.; Cindy Work Abell; Gregory T. Abell; Luke Abell; Billy Bednarz; Mike Nolan; Thomas D. Nurmi; Jennifer Nurmi Shoop; Landon Shoop; Elizabeth Sites; Jamie Sites.
Number of staff: 1 full-time professional; 1 part-time professional.
EIN: 521435573

3714
ABMRF/The Foundation for Alcohol Research ✧
(formerly Alcoholic Beverage Medical Research Foundation)
1200-C Agora Dr., No. 310
Bel Air, MD 21014-6849 (410) 821-7066
Contact: Mack C. Mitchell, Jr. M.D., Pres.
FAX: (410) 821-7065; E-mail: info@abmrf.org; Grant Program e-mail: grantinfo@abmrf.org; Main URL: http://www.abmrf.org/
Facebook: http://www.facebook.com/AlcoholResearch?ref=ts
Grants List: http://www.abmrf.org/grants_awarded
LinkedIn: http://www.linkedin.com/company/1137768?trk=NUS_CMPE-updater
Twitter: http://twitter.com/AlcoholResearch

Established in 1982 in MD.
Donors: Beer Institute; Brewers Association of Canada; National Beer Wholesalers Association.
Foundation type: Independent foundation.
Financial data (yr. ended 12/31/13): Assets, $3,853,039 (M); gifts received, $1,883,395; expenditures, $1,975,506; qualifying distributions, $1,951,412; giving activities include $1,392,114

for 64 grants (high: $50,000; low: $10,000), and $1,975,506 for foundation-administered programs.
Purpose and activities: The mission of the foundation is to achieve a better understanding of the effects of alcohol on the health and behavior of individuals; to provide the scientific basis for prevention and treatment of alcohol misuse and alcoholism; to fund innovative, high-quality research; to support promising new investigations; to communicate effectively with the research community and with other interested parties.
Fields of interest: Alcoholism; Medical research.
International interests: Canada.
Type of support: Research.
Limitations: Applications accepted. Giving primarily in the U.S. and Canada. No grants to individuals, or for education projects, public awareness efforts, treatment or referral services, training of pre- and post-doctoral fellows, undergraduates, graduate students, medical students, interns or residents, or for thesis or dissertation research.
Publications: Annual report; Financial statement; Grants list; Informational brochure.
Application information: See foundation web site for application form and guidelines. Application form required.
Initial approach: Use grant application available on foundation web site
Copies of proposal: 1
Deadline(s): See foundation web site for current deadline
Board meeting date(s): Apr. and Nov.
Final notification: Within 2 weeks of board meeting
Officers and Trustees:* Bruce Ambler, M.B.A.*, Chair.; Raymond Anton, Jr., M.D.*, Vice-Chair.; Mack C. Mitchell, Jr., M.D.*, Pres.; Janet L. Hanratty, Cont.; David A. Brenner, M.D.; Thomas A. Collier, M.D.; Ivan Diamond, M.D., Ph.D.; R. Stuart Dickson; Luke Harford; Stephen Hindy; Arthur L. Klatsky; Louis G. Lange, M.D., Ph.D.; Steven W. Leslie, Ph.D.; James G. Martin, Ph.D.; Joseph S. McClain; Craig Purser; Timothy Scully, Jr.; John Sleeman; James Villenueve.
Number of staff: 1 full-time professional; 2 part-time professional; 1 part-time support.
EIN: 521234277
Selected grants: The following grants are a representative sample of this grantmaker's funding activity:
$50,000 to Cleveland Clinic, Cleveland, OH, 2011. For RIP3-mediated necrocytosis and ethanol-induced liver injury.
$50,000 to Hartford Hospital, Hartford, CT, 2011. For alcohol cue reactivity predictor of future alcohol use disorders.
$50,000 to Icahn School of Medicine at Mount Sinai, New York, NY, 2011. For ethanol induction of CYP2A5 and toxicological significance.
$50,000 to Massachusetts General Hospital, Boston, MA, 2011. Toward developing positive and negative reinforcement framework of binge drinking among college students.
$50,000 to San Diego State University, San Diego, CA, 2011. For fetal alcohol effects and vitamin D.
$50,000 to Thomas Jefferson University, Philadelphia, PA, 2011. For alcohol regulates self-renewal and differentiation capacity of embryonic stem cells.
$50,000 to University of Illinois at Chicago, Chicago, IL, 2011. For alcohol effects on visual processing in at-risk social drinkers.
$50,000 to University of Southern California, Keck School of Medicine, Los Angeles, CA, 2011. For notch signaling in synergistic steatohepatitis induced by obesity and alcohol.
$50,000 to University of Tennessee Health Science Center, Memphis, TN, 2011. For alcohol-induced smooth muscle BK current inhibition and followed vasoconstriction is controlled by membrane cholesterol.
$50,000 to University of Washington, Seattle, WA, 2011. For alcohol's impact on academic success of OEF/OIF college students.

3715
Abramson Family Foundation, Inc. ✧
(formerly Abramson Foundation, Inc.)
2000 Tower Oaks Blvd., 9th Fl.
Rockville, MD 20852-4208

Established in 1959 in MD.
Donors: Albert Abramson‡; Gary M. Abramson; Ronald D. Abramson; Dawson Development Co., LLC; Tower Capital, LLC; The Albert Abramson Revocable Trust.
Foundation type: Independent foundation.
Financial data (yr. ended 12/31/12): Assets, $34,216,473 (M); gifts received, $12,974,222; expenditures, $4,221,969; qualifying distributions, $4,137,676; giving activities include $4,137,676 for 108 grants (high: $685,000; low: $100).
Purpose and activities: Primarily giving for the arts, education, health, and for Jewish organizations and temples.
Fields of interest: Museums; Arts; Higher education; Education; Health organizations; Medical research, institute; Cancer research; Human services; Foundations (private grantmaking); Jewish federated giving programs; Jewish agencies & synagogues.
Type of support: General/operating support.
Limitations: Applications not accepted. Giving primarily in the greater Washington, DC, area, including MD; funding also in FL, IA, and NY. No grants to individuals.
Application information: Contributes only to pre-selected organizations.
Officers: Jeffrey Abramson, Pres.; Gary Abramson, V.P.; Ronald Abramson, Secy.-Treas.
EIN: 526039192

3716
Adalman-Goodwin Charitable Foundation Inc. ✧
(formerly Adalman Charitable Foundation, Inc.)
725 Mt. Wilson Ln., Ste. 804
Baltimore, MD 21208-4361 (410) 486-3803
Contact: Hilda P. Goodwin, Pres.
E-mail: hildaperl@comcast.net

Established in 1952.
Foundation type: Independent foundation.
Financial data (yr. ended 12/31/13): Assets, $2,836,377 (M); expenditures, $481,133; qualifying distributions, $455,650; giving activities include $455,650 for 60 grants (high: $125,000; low: $100).
Purpose and activities: Giving primarily for the arts, education, social services, and Jewish organizations.
Fields of interest: Performing arts, orchestras; Performing arts, opera; Arts; Higher education; Medical school/education; Education; Human services; Jewish agencies & synagogues.
Type of support: General/operating support.
Limitations: Applications accepted. Giving primarily in Baltimore, MD. No grants to individuals.
Application information: Application form required.
Initial approach: Proposal
Deadline(s): None
Officers: Hilda P. Goodwin, Pres.; Edward L. Perl, V.P. and Treas.; Lee M. Goodwin, Secy.
EIN: 526045035

3717
The Adams Charitable Foundation, Inc. ✧
11049 Seven Hill Ln.
Potomac, MD 20854-3245

Established in 1996 in MD.
Donor: Richard Adams.
Foundation type: Independent foundation.
Financial data (yr. ended 12/31/13): Assets, $40,751,183 (M); expenditures, $2,382,703; qualifying distributions, $2,371,803; giving activities include $2,152,500 for 7 grants (high: $1,400,000; low: $2,500).
Fields of interest: Museums (art); Education; Foundations (public); Computer science.
Limitations: Applications not accepted. Giving primarily in CA and MD. No grants to individuals.
Application information: Contributes only to pre-selected organizations.
Officers and Directors:* Donnalyn Frey Adams,* Pres.; Allan H. Frey,* V.P.; Richard L. Adams, Jr.,* Secy.-Treas.
EIN: 522002510

3718
Jessie & Hertha Adams Charitable Trust ✧
901 S. Bond St., Ste. 400
Baltimore, MD 21231-3340

Established in 2003 in MD.
Foundation type: Independent foundation.
Financial data (yr. ended 12/31/13): Assets, $18,476,899 (M); expenditures, $951,621; qualifying distributions, $818,987; giving activities include $818,987 for 8 grants (high: $163,797; low: $40,949).
Purpose and activities: Giving primarily for children with disabilities.
Fields of interest: Hospitals (specialty); Human services; Children, services; Child development, services; Protestant agencies & churches; Blind/visually impaired.
Limitations: Applications not accepted. Giving primarily in FL, MD, and NJ. No grants to individuals.
Application information: Unsolicited requests for funds not accepted.
Trustees: Carole S. Brudin; Brown Advisory.
EIN: 256821173

3719
Allegis Group Foundation, Inc. ✧
(formerly Team Aerotek Foundation, Inc.)
7301 Parkway Dr.
Hanover, MD 21076-1159 (410) 579-3509
Contact: Hilary Murray

Established in 1998 in MD.
Donors: Aerotek, Inc.; Allegis Group Holdings, Inc.
Foundation type: Company-sponsored foundation.

Financial data (yr. ended 12/31/13): Assets, $18,643,528 (M); gifts received, $1,796,756; expenditures, $1,221,523; qualifying distributions, $1,154,860; giving activities include $1,152,360 for 280 grants (high: $60,000; low: $75).
Purpose and activities: The foundation supports organizations involved with education, water conservation, cancer, heart disease, recreation, human services, international relief, and Catholicism. Special emphasis is directed toward programs designed to assist underprivileged children.
Fields of interest: Education; Health organizations; Human services.
Type of support: General/operating support; Program development; Scholarship funds; Employee matching gifts.
Limitations: Applications accepted. Giving primarily in areas of company operations in Baltimore, MD.
Application information: Application form required.
Initial approach: Letter
Deadline(s): None
Officers and Directors:* James C. Davis,* Pres.; Neil Mann, V.P. and Treas.; Randall D. Sones, Esq., Secy.; Stephen J. Bisciotti.
EIN: 311608900

3720
The Kathryn Ames Foundation, Inc. ✧
c/o Pierson & Pierson
305 W. Chesapeake Ave., Ste. 308
Towson, MD 21204-4440 (410) 821-3006
Contact: Ms. Lu Pierson, Grant Admin.
FAX: (410) 821-3007;
E-mail: info@kathrynames.org; Main URL: http://www.kathrynames.org/

Established in 1993 in MD.
Donor: Kathryn Ames‡.
Foundation type: Independent foundation.
Financial data (yr. ended 12/31/13): Assets, $8,677,059 (M); expenditures, $778,813; qualifying distributions, $745,574; giving activities include $693,800 for 43 grants (high: $175,000; low: $1,000).
Purpose and activities: Giving primarily to organizations benefiting Israel in social and economic welfare, religious and ethnic pluralism, social justice, and education.
Fields of interest: Education; Economic development; Social sciences; Jewish agencies & synagogues; Religion, interfaith issues; Religion.
International interests: Israel.
Type of support: General/operating support; Building/renovation; Equipment; Program development.
Limitations: Applications accepted. Giving primarily in Washington, DC, and New York, NY. No grants to individuals, or for special events, benefit dinners, advertising, or publications.
Publications: Application guidelines.
Application information: See grantmaker web site for complete application guidelines and form. Application form should only be submitted upon an invitation from the foundation (following receipt and consideration of Letter of Inquiry). Application form required.
Initial approach: Letter of Inquiry (not more than 2 pages, and sent via e-mail or U.S. mail)
Deadline(s): None, for Letters of Inquiry
Board meeting date(s): Quarterly
Officers: W. Michel Pierson, Pres.; Esther E. Saltzman, V.P.; Robert L. Pierson, Secy.-Treas.
EIN: 521828472
Selected grants: The following grants are a representative sample of this grantmaker's funding activity:
$12,500 to New Israel Fund, Washington, DC, 2012. For Pluralism Ethnic.
$10,000 to World Union for Progressive Judaism, New York, NY, 2012. For Pluralism Religious.
$7,500 to New Israel Fund, Washington, DC, 2012. For poverty relief.
$7,500 to New Israel Fund, Washington, DC, 2012. For social welfare.

3721
The Peter and Georgia Angelos Foundation ✧
100 N. Charles St., 22nd Fl.
Baltimore, MD 21201-3805

Established in 1993 in MD.
Donor: Peter G. Angelos.
Foundation type: Independent foundation.
Financial data (yr. ended 09/30/13): Assets, $148,824 (M); expenditures, $3,107,780; qualifying distributions, $3,106,000; giving activities include $3,106,000 for 6 grants (high: $1,000,000; low: $1,000).
Purpose and activities: Giving primarily for the arts, higher education, health associations, social services, federated giving programs, Christian organizations, and Greek Orthodox churches.
Fields of interest: Museums; Arts; Higher education; Medical school/education; Health organizations, association; Human services; Foundations (community); United Ways and Federated Giving Programs; Christian agencies & churches.
Limitations: Applications not accepted. Giving primarily in Baltimore, MD.
Application information: Contributes only to pre-selected organizations.
Officers: Peter G. Angelos, Pres.; John Peter Angelos, V.P.; Louis P. Angelos, V.P.; Georgia K. Angelos, Secy.-Treas.
EIN: 521850984
Selected grants: The following grants are a representative sample of this grantmaker's funding activity:
$250,000 to Johns Hopkins Medicine, Baltimore, MD, 2011.

3722
The Phyllis L. & Leonard J. Attman Foundation Inc. ✧ ☆
20 S. Charles St., Ste. 300
Baltimore, MD 21201-3201

Established in 1990 in MD.
Donors: Leonard J. Attman; Phyllis L. Attman.
Foundation type: Independent foundation.
Financial data (yr. ended 12/31/13): Assets, $12,495 (M); gifts received, $568,600; expenditures, $578,354; qualifying distributions, $535,954; giving activities include $535,954 for 16 grants (high: $151,000; low: $200).
Fields of interest: Secondary school/education; Higher education, university; Education; Health care, research; Jewish agencies & synagogues.
Limitations: Applications not accepted. Giving primarily in Baltimore, MD. No grants to individuals.
Application information: Contributes only to pre-selected organizations.
Officers: Leonard J. Attman, Pres.; Jeffrey Attman, V.P.; Shellye Gilden, V.P.; Phyllis L. Attman, Secy.-Treas.
EIN: 526367308

3723
Ausherman Family Foundation, Inc. ✧ ☆
7420 Hayward Rd., Ste. 203
Frederick, MD 21702-2509 (301) 620-4443
Contact: Joyce Heptner, Exec. Dir.
FAX: (301) 620-4473;
E-mail: info@aushermanfamilyfoundation.org; Main URL: http://www.aushermanfamilyfoundation.org

Established in 2006 in MD.
Donor: Marvin E. Ausherman.
Foundation type: Independent foundation.
Financial data (yr. ended 12/31/12): Assets, $14,271,579 (M); expenditures, $1,030,072; qualifying distributions, $920,199; giving activities include $682,000 for 86 grants (high: $97,250; low: $250).
Fields of interest: Arts; Higher education; Youth development; Human services.
Type of support: General/operating support.
Limitations: Applications accepted. Giving primarily in Frederick County, MD; some limited global funds available. No grants to individuals.
Application information: Application form not required.
Initial approach: Check of foundation web site
Copies of proposal: 1
Deadline(s): Submissions will be reviewed by the Philanthropic committee that meets six times each year.
Board meeting date(s): Quarterly
Officers and Directors:* Marvin E. Ausherman,* Pres. and Treas.; Lisa S. Ausherman,* Secy.; Joyce Heptner, Exec. Dir.
Trustees: Justin E. Ausherman; Kari A. Ausherman; Nicholas A. Branic; J. Brian Gaeng; Renee Lopez; James B. MacGillivray; Joseph S. Welty.
EIN: 204937263

3724
Clayton Baker Trust ✧
2 E. Read St., Ste. 100
Baltimore, MD 21202-2470 (410) 837-3555
Contact: John B. Powell, Jr., Exec. Dir.

Established in 1960 in MD.
Donor: Julia C. Baker‡.
Foundation type: Independent foundation.
Financial data (yr. ended 12/31/12): Assets, $33,460,014 (M); expenditures, $1,819,035; qualifying distributions, $1,655,917; giving activities include $1,634,075 for 73 grants (high: $15,000; low: $5,000).
Purpose and activities: The trust supports organizations in Baltimore, MD, in the areas of education, the environment, and community development.
Fields of interest: Education; Environment.
Type of support: General/operating support; Building/renovation; Program development.
Limitations: Applications accepted. Giving limited to Baltimore, MD. No support for academic or scientific

research, arts and culture, workshops or for specific diseases and disabilities, or local land trusts. No grants to individuals, or for deficit funding, fundraising events, publication or seminars.
Publications: Application guidelines.
Application information: Association of Baltimore Area Grantmakers Common Grant Application Form required. Application information available at http://www.abagmd.org. Application form required.
Initial approach: Letter requesting application form
Copies of proposal: 1
Deadline(s): Apr. 5, Aug. 5, and Dec. 5
Final notification: Within 60 days of deadline
Officer: John B. Powell, Jr., Exec. Dir.
EIN: 526054237
Selected grants: The following grants are a representative sample of this grantmaker's funding activity:
$50,000 to Chesapeake Bay Foundation, Annapolis, MD, 2012. For environment/legal.
$35,000 to Chesapeake Bay Foundation, Annapolis, MD, 2012. For Water Blueprint.
$35,000 to Episcopal Community Services of Maryland, Baltimore, MD, 2012. For Education: Ark Preschool for Homeless Children.
$30,000 to Wye River Upper School, Wye Mills, MD, 2012. For Education: Capital Campaign for New School.
$15,000 to Fund for Educational Excellence, Baltimore, MD, 2012. For Supporting Public Schools of Choice.
$5,000 to Outward Bound Baltimore Chesapeake Bay Center, Baltimore, MD, 2012. For Education - General Support.
$1,000 to Preservation Maryland, Baltimore, MD, 2012. For Restoration and Renovation Fair.

3725
The William G. Baker, Jr. Memorial Fund ✧

2 E. Read St., 9th Fl.
Baltimore, MD 21202-6903 (410) 332-4171
Contact: Melissa Warlow, Exec. Dir.; Aaron Meyers, Philanthropic Svcs. Coord.
FAX: (410) 837-4701; E-mail: mwarlow@bcf.org; Tel. for Melissa Warlow: (410) 332-4172, ext. 150; e-mail for Aaron Meyers: ameyers@bcf.org; Main URL: http://www.bcf.org/BaltimoreCFGrants/GrantProgramDetails/tabid/166/Default.aspx?grid=1

Established in 1964 in MD.
Foundation type: Independent foundation.
Financial data (yr. ended 12/31/12): Assets, $22,113,921 (M); expenditures, $1,175,247; qualifying distributions, $1,086,243; giving activities include $919,000 for 38 grants (high: $215,800; low: $3,000).
Purpose and activities: Giving to support cultural and artistic organizations and programs that enhance Baltimore, MD's, civic participation and economic health. The fund's objectives are to celebrate metropolitan life, spur economic development, improve the quality of life, provide access to cultural opportunities for all, support civic engagement through the arts, and create opportunities for self-expression and reflection.
Fields of interest: Arts, alliance/advocacy; Museums (art); Performing arts; Performing arts centers; Historic preservation/historical societies; Arts.
Type of support: Income development; Management development/capacity building; Equipment; Program development; Seed money; Technical assistance; Consulting services.
Limitations: Applications accepted. Giving limited to 501(c)(3) organizations in the metropolitan Baltimore, MD, area. No support for religious or sectarian purposes. No grants to individuals, or for annual campaigns, event sponsorships, or deficit financing; no loans.
Application information: Specific application guidelines available on foundation web site. Association of Baltimore Area Grantmakers Common Grant Application Form accepted. Grant applicants must complete a Maryland Cultural Data Project data profile and receive a "review complete" status.
Deadline(s): See web site for current deadlines
Board meeting date(s): Mar., May, Sept., and Nov.
Final notification: 2 months
Officer and Governors:* Connie E. Imboden,* Pres.; Louis R. Cestello; Gwen Davidson; Steven G. Ziger.
Trustee: P.N.C. Bank, N.A.
Number of staff: None.
EIN: 526057178
Selected grants: The following grants are a representative sample of this grantmaker's funding activity:
$50,000 to Baltimore Museum of Art, Baltimore, MD, 2012. For FY 13 Operating Expenses.
$50,000 to Baltimore Symphony Orchestra, Baltimore, MD, 2012. For FY 2013 Operations.
$30,000 to Greater Baltimore Cultural Alliance, Baltimore, MD, 2012. For Cy 2012 General Operations.
$25,000 to Baltimore Symphony Orchestra, Baltimore, MD, 2012. For FY 12 Operating Budget.
$20,000 to Baltimore School for the Arts, Baltimore, MD, 2012. For Endowment Campaign Materials.
$20,000 to Greater Baltimore Cultural Alliance, Baltimore, MD, 2012. For C B G a and Cultural Events.
$14,500 to Baltimore Choral Arts Society, Baltimore, MD, 2012. For Upgrade Tech Systems.
$12,000 to Young Audiences of Maryland, Baltimore, MD, 2012. For financial practices audit.

3726
The Baltimore Community Foundation ✧

2 E. Read St., 9th Fl.
Baltimore, MD 21202-6903 (410) 332-4171
Contact: Gigi Wirtz, Dir., Comms.; For grants: Maya Smith, Prog. Asst.
FAX: (410) 837-4701; E-mail: questions@bcf.org; Additional e-mail: msmith@bcf.org; Grant application e-mail: grants@bcf.org; Application address: Anne Ross Knoeller, Baltimore Community Foundation, 2 E. Read St., 9th Fl., Baltimore, MD 21202; Main URL: http://www.bcf.org
E-Newsletter: http://visitor.r20.constantcontact.com/manage/optin?v=00147Jgk4c64VOopn_qbBlkT24m_-OYlaAyq7a8UfMoG9C2hizcNLrD2Q%3D%3D
Facebook: https://www.facebook.com/baltimorecf
Flickr: http://www.flickr.com/photos/36891120@N07/
LinkedIn: http://www.linkedin.com/company/baltimore-community-foundation
Twitter: http://twitter.com/baltcommfdn
YouTube: http://www.youtube.com/user/INVESTinBaltimore

Incorporated in 1972 in MD.
Foundation type: Community foundation.
Financial data (yr. ended 12/31/12): Assets, $148,500,109 (M); gifts received, $25,036,294; expenditures, $44,271,737; giving activities include $20,855,776 for grants.
Purpose and activities: The foundation's mission is to inspire donors to achieve their charitable goals from generation to generation and to improve the quality of life in the Baltimore region through grantmaking, enlightened civic leadership, and strategic investments. BCF's strategic grantmaking focuses on the areas of human services, youth, education, transportation, neighborhoods, diversity, environment, arts and culture, and promoting Baltimore, MD.
Fields of interest: Arts; Adult education—literacy, basic skills & GED; Education; Environment; Human services; Community development, neighborhood development; Transportation; Youth; Aging.
Type of support: Endowments; Income development; Management development/capacity building; Matching/challenge support; Program development; Scholarship funds; Scholarships—to individuals; Seed money; Technical assistance.
Limitations: Applications accepted. Giving primarily in Baltimore City and Baltimore County, MD. No support for religious or sectarian purposes. No grants to individuals (except for scholarships), or for capital campaigns, annual fund campaigns, or event sponsorships.
Publications: Application guidelines; Annual report; Financial statement; Grants list; Informational brochure; Newsletter.
Application information: Visit foundation web site for application guidelines pertaining to specific areas. Applications begin with a brief letter of inquiry; Prog. Officer may request a full proposal upon review of the letter. Application form not required.
Initial approach: Mail or e-mail letter of inquiry (2 pages)
Copies of proposal: 1
Deadline(s): None for letters of inquiry
Board meeting date(s): Mar., June, Sept., and Dec.
Final notification: Within 3 months of proposal deadlines
Officers and Trustees:* Raymond L. Bank,* Chair.; Tedd Alexander III,* Vice-Chair.; Laura L. Gamble,* Vice-Chair. and Treas.; Thomas E. Wilcox,* C.E.O. and Pres.; Amy T. Seto, Exec. V.P. and C.O.O.; Danista Hunte, V.P., Community Investment; Ralph M. Serpe, V.P., Devel.; Juliet A. Eurich,* Secy.; Diane Bell-McKoy; Ellen N. Bernard; Thomas S. Bozzuto; Benjamin S. Carson, Sr., M.D.; Richard W. Cass; Louis R. Cestello; Ronald J. Daniels; Mychelle Y. Farmer, M.D.; Mark R. Fetting; Josh E. Fidler; Sheldon Goldseker; Michael D. Hankin; Ellen M. Heller; Stephon A. Jackson; Harry S. Johnson; Patricia Joseph; Patrick McCarthy; Wes Moore; Michael P. Pinto; Marsha Y. Reeves; Stuart O. Simms; Lenel Srochi-Meyerhoff; Marc B. Terrill; Kenneth L. Thompson; Paul C. Wolman; Steven G. Ziger.
Number of staff: 25 full-time professional; 2 part-time professional; 3 full-time support.
EIN: 237180620
Selected grants: The following grants are a representative sample of this grantmaker's funding activity:
$3,637,317 to East Baltimore Development, Baltimore, MD, 2012. For general support and various projects.

$1,141,550 to Princeton University, Princeton, NJ, 2012. For general support and various projects.
$482,730 to Salvation Army of Baltimore, Baltimore, MD, 2012. For general support and various projects.
$267,050 to Johns Hopkins University, Baltimore, MD, 2012. For general support and various projects.
$253,947 to Baltimore Museum of Art, Baltimore, MD, 2012. For general support and various projects.
$157,673 to Greater Homewood Community Corporation, Baltimore, MD, 2012. For general support and various projects.
$25,000 to Lawrenceville School, Lawrenceville, NJ, 2012. For general support and various projects.
$20,000 to Saint Marys Outreach Center, Baltimore, MD, 2012. For general support and various projects.
$17,835 to Handel Choir of Baltimore, Baltimore, MD, 2012. For general support and various projects.
$17,500 to Banner Neighborhoods Community Corporation, Baltimore, MD, 2012. For general support and various projects.

3727
The Kenneth S. Battye Charitable Trust

P.O. Box 36
Riderwood, MD 21139-0036
E-mail: ksbattyecharitabletrust@yahoo.com

Established in 1992 in MD.
Donors: Kenneth S. Battye†; Susan A. Battye.
Foundation type: Independent foundation.
Financial data (yr. ended 06/30/13): Assets, $49,728,869 (M); gifts received, $3,954,496; expenditures, $2,294,212; qualifying distributions, $1,865,600; giving activities include $1,737,295 for 31 grants (high: $250,000; low: $50).
Fields of interest: Health organizations, association; Food banks; Disasters, preparedness/services; Human services; Homeless.
Type of support: General/operating support.
Limitations: Applications not accepted. Giving primarily in Baltimore, MD. No grants to individuals.
Application information: Contributes only to pre-selected organizations.
Trustees: Audrey B. Drossner; Charlotte B. Floyd; Raymond A. Mason.
EIN: 521748587
Selected grants: The following grants are a representative sample of this grantmaker's funding activity:
$100,500 to Saint Vincent de Paul Society of Baltimore, Baltimore, MD, 2011.
$80,000 to Maryland Food Bank, Baltimore, MD, 2011.
$80,000 to Our Daily Bread, Baltimore, MD, 2011.
$52,500 to SEED School of Maryland, Baltimore, MD, 2011.
$27,000 to Central Scholarship Bureau, Baltimore, MD, 2011.
$25,000 to Paul's Place, Baltimore, MD, 2011.
$20,000 to Franciscan Center, Baltimore, MD, 2011.
$20,000 to House of Ruth Maryland, Baltimore, MD, 2011.
$10,000 to Marian House, Baltimore, MD, 2011.
$3,000 to Samaritan Community, Baltimore, MD, 2011.

3728
Herbert Bearman Foundation ✧

101 W. Mount Royal Ave.
Baltimore, MD 21201-5708 (410) 369-9227
Contact: Mark Bearman, C.O.O.
E-mail: mbearman@comcast.net; Main URL: http://www.herbertbearmanfoundation.org

Established in 2003 in MD.
Foundation type: Independent foundation.
Financial data (yr. ended 12/31/12): Assets, $34,576,659 (M); gifts received, $1,597,040; expenditures, $1,144,668; giving activities include $1,144,668 for 103 grants (high: $150,000; low: $100).
Purpose and activities: Giving to improve the quality of life of members of the Baltimore, south Florida, and Israeli communities.
Fields of interest: Higher education; Education; Health care; Mental health, grief/bereavement counseling; Cystic fibrosis; Breast cancer; Autism; Human services; Jewish federated giving programs; Jewish agencies & synagogues; Aging; Disabilities, people with; Physically disabled; Blind/visually impaired; Substance abusers; Economically disadvantaged; Homeless.
International interests: Israel.
Type of support: Research; Management development/capacity building; Annual campaigns; Equipment; Emergency funds; Program development; Conferences/seminars; Seed money; Technical assistance; Program evaluation; Matching/challenge support.
Limitations: Applications accepted. Giving primarily in south FL, Baltimore, MD, and in Israel. No grants to individuals or for scholarships or capital campaigns.
Application information: Association of Baltimore Area Grantmakers Common Grant Application Format accepted. Application form required.
Initial approach: Letter of inquiry
Copies of proposal: 12
Deadline(s): For letter of inquiry, June 15 and Dec. 15; for full proposal, Feb. 15 and Aug. 15
Board meeting date(s): Apr. and Oct.
Final notification: For letter of inquiry, 2-4 weeks; for full proposal, 1-2 weeks after Apr. and Oct. meetings.
Officers: Sheldon Bearman, Pres. and Treas.; Arlene Bearman, V.P. and Secy.; Mark Bearman, C.O.O.
Number of staff: 1 full-time professional.
EIN: 311602562
Selected grants: The following grants are a representative sample of this grantmaker's funding activity:
$35,000 to Meals on Wheels of Central Maryland, Baltimore, MD, 2012. For Freezer Unit Purchase.
$25,000 to Living Classrooms Foundation, Baltimore, MD, 2012. For Target Investment Zone.
$20,650 to Jewish Museum of Maryland, Baltimore, MD, 2012. For Traveling Chosen Food.
$19,901 to Sheppard and Enoch Pratt Hospital, Baltimore, MD, 2012. For Video Modeling Equipment and Communications Technology.
$15,000 to Baltimore Symphony Orchestra, Baltimore, MD, 2012. For Orchkids Program.
$15,000 to Friends of the Israel Defense Forces, New York, NY, 2012. For Strides Soldier Sponsorship.
$15,000 to KIPP Baltimore, Baltimore, MD, 2012. For Through College Program.
$12,500 to Kennedy Krieger Institute, Baltimore, MD, 2012. For Leap Play Ground.
$10,000 to Concert Artists of Baltimore, Baltimore, MD, 2012. To support of the Lyric Event.
$7,450 to Jewish Community Services, Baltimore, MD, 2012. For Psychological Testing Equipment.

3729
Leo V. Berger Fund ✧ ☆

c/o Sigmund Kassap
3635 Old Ct. Rd., Ste. 309
Baltimore, MD 21208-3907

Established in NY.
Donor: Leo V. Berger†.
Foundation type: Independent foundation.
Financial data (yr. ended 12/31/12): Assets, $8,299,382 (M); expenditures, $446,477; qualifying distributions, $441,418; giving activities include $441,418 for grants.
Purpose and activities: Primarily local giving, with emphasis on Jewish welfare funds, hospitals, health, and education.
Fields of interest: Education; Hospitals (general); Health care; Health organizations; Jewish federated giving programs; Jewish agencies & synagogues.
Limitations: Applications not accepted. Giving primarily in FL, MD, and NY. No grants to individuals.
Application information: Contributes only to pre-selected organizations.
Officers and Directors:* Harvey Schwartz, Esq.*, Pres.; Sigmund Kassap,* V.P.; Harry Kassap; Jason Schwartz.
EIN: 510196887

3730
Berman Charitable Trust ✧

5410 Edson Ln., Ste. 220
Rockville, MD 20852-3195

Established in 1984 in MD.
Donors: I. Wolford Berman; Melvin J. Berman; Gary Berman; Laurie E. Berman; Dennis Berman; Helene Berman Revocable Trust; Helene Berman Trust; B.E. Investments LLC; Brian Berman.
Foundation type: Independent foundation.
Financial data (yr. ended 12/31/13): Assets, $11,000,412 (M); gifts received, $1,190,721; expenditures, $1,281,947; qualifying distributions, $1,251,734; giving activities include $1,251,734 for 299 grants (high: $275,000; low: $20).
Purpose and activities: Giving primarily for Jewish organizations, including welfare funds, temples, and yeshivas.
Fields of interest: Education; Human services; Religion.
Limitations: Applications not accepted. Giving primarily in CA, Washington, DC, MD, and NY. No grants to individuals.
Application information: Contributes only to pre-selected organizations.
Trustees: Dennis Berman; Stephen L. Berman; Vicki Berman; Elyse Vinitsky.
EIN: 942940733

3731
The Dennis Berman Family Foundation Inc. ✧

(formerly The Robin and Dennis Berman Foundation, Inc.)
5410 Edson Ln., Ste. 220
Rockville, MD 20852-3195

Established in 1999 in MD.
Donors: Dennis Berman; Robin Ely Berman; Sylvia Ely Jacobs†; Michael Epstein; Sylvia Ely-Jacobs Trust.
Foundation type: Independent foundation.
Financial data (yr. ended 12/31/13): Assets, $2,964,219 (M); gifts received, $245,000; expenditures, $523,483; qualifying distributions, $481,267; giving activities include $481,267 for 249 grants (high: $58,300; low: $90).
Purpose and activities: Giving primarily to Jewish organizations, temples and schools; some giving for social services.
Fields of interest: Theological school/education; Education; Human services; Foundations (public); Jewish federated giving programs; Jewish agencies & synagogues.
International interests: Israel.
Limitations: Applications not accepted. Giving in the U.S., with emphasis on MD and NY; funding also in Israel, with emphasis on Jerusalem. No grants to individuals.
Application information: Contributes only to pre-selected organizations.
Director: Dennis Berman.
EIN: 311684732

3732
The Bethesda Foundation ✧ ☆

11820 Parklawn Dr., Ste. 404
Rockville, MD 20852-3011

Established in 1986 in MD.
Donor: Sunya Perlmutter Kronstadt†.
Foundation type: Independent foundation.
Financial data (yr. ended 12/31/13): Assets, $9,397,216 (M); expenditures, $455,647; qualifying distributions, $430,293; giving activities include $424,300 for 21 grants (high: $200,000; low: $1,000).
Fields of interest: Performing arts, opera; Education; Jewish agencies & synagogues.
Limitations: Applications not accepted. No grants to individuals.
Application information: Unsolicited requests for funds not accepted.
Directors: Allen R. Kronstadt; Rachel Kronstadt Mann.
EIN: 521495608
Selected grants: The following grants are a representative sample of this grantmaker's funding activity:
$200,000 to University of Pennsylvania, Philadelphia, PA, 2011. For general operating support.
$50,000 to Rollins College, Winter Park, FL, 2011. For general operating support.
$25,000 to Washington Institute for Near East Policy, Washington, DC, 2011. For general operating support.
$10,000 to Jewish Federation, Sarasota-Manatee, Sarasota, FL, 2011. For general operating support.
$5,000 to Global Down Syndrome Foundation, Denver, CO, 2011. For general operating support.
$5,000 to ORT America, New York, NY, 2011. For general operating support.

3733
The Stephen & Renee Bisciotti Foundation, Inc. ✧

c/o Allegis Group Holdings, Inc.
7301 Parkway Dr.
Hanover, MD 21076-1159

Established in 2001 in MD.
Donors: Stephen J. Bisciotti; Renee F. Bisciotti.
Foundation type: Independent foundation.
Financial data (yr. ended 12/31/13): Assets, $3,356,488 (M); expenditures, $1,497,898; qualifying distributions, $1,495,398; giving activities include $1,492,898 for 34 grants (high: $400,000; low: $312).
Purpose and activities: Giving primarily for education, human services, and Roman Catholic organizations.
Fields of interest: Elementary/secondary education; Education; Human services; Catholic agencies & churches.
Limitations: Applications not accepted. Giving primarily in MD. No grants to individuals.
Application information: Contributes only to pre-selected organizations.
Officers: Renee F. Bisciotti, Pres.; Randall D. Sones, Secy.
Director: Stephen J. Bisciotti.
EIN: 522352678

3734
A. T. & Mary H. Blades Foundation ✧

3400 Poplar Neck Rd.
Preston, MD 21655-1309

Established in 1961.
Donors: A.T. Blades†; Mary H. Blades†.
Foundation type: Independent foundation.
Financial data (yr. ended 06/30/13): Assets, $29,824,379 (M); expenditures, $1,639,003; qualifying distributions, $1,421,570; giving activities include $1,420,000 for 55 grants (high: $150,000; low: $3,000).
Purpose and activities: Giving primarily for health, human services and education.
Fields of interest: Education; Hospitals (general); Health organizations, association; Human services; Christian agencies & churches.
Type of support: General/operating support; Continuing support; Annual campaigns; Capital campaigns; Building/renovation; Equipment; Land acquisition; Debt reduction; Emergency funds; Program development; Scholarship funds; Research; Matching/challenge support.
Limitations: Applications accepted. Giving almost exclusively on the eastern shore of MD, with a focus on Caroline, Dorchester, and Talbot counties, some giving also in DE. No support for political organizations. No grants to individuals.
Application information: Application form not required.
Initial approach: Letter
Copies of proposal: 1
Deadline(s): Mar. 1
Board meeting date(s): May
Final notification: Positive responses only
Officers: David Harper, Sr., Pres.; David Harper, Jr., Secy.; Brenda Harper, Treas.
Trustee: Christy Harper.
EIN: 520794020

Selected grants: The following grants are a representative sample of this grantmaker's funding activity:
$20,000 to Johns Hopkins University, School of Nursing, Baltimore, MD, 2013. For scholarship fund.
$15,000 to Country School, Easton, MD, 2013. For African American tuition assistance.
$5,000 to Bethlehem Bible College, New Braunfels, TX, 2013. For 2K school, 3K Shepard society.
$5,000 to Smile Train, Washington, DC, 2013. For Surgeries for children.

3735
The Jacob and Hilda Blaustein Foundation, Inc. ✧

1 South St., Ste. 2900
Baltimore, MD 21202-3334 (410) 347-7201
Contact: Betsy F. Ringel, Exec. Dir.
FAX: (410) 347-7210; E-mail: info@blaufund.org;
Main URL: http://www.blaufund.org/foundations/jacobandhilda_f.html

Incorporated in 1957 in MD.
Donors: Jacob Blaustein†; American Trading and Production Corp.; Barbara B. Hirschhorn; Elizabeth B. Roswell.
Foundation type: Independent foundation.
Financial data (yr. ended 12/31/12): Assets, $113,603,431 (M); gifts received, $1,595,466; expenditures, $8,123,300; qualifying distributions, $7,822,759; giving activities include $7,200,085 for 186 grants (high: $1,200,000; low: $100).
Purpose and activities: The foundation promotes social justice and human rights through its five program areas: Jewish life, strengthening Israeli democracy, health and mental health, educational opportunity, and human rights. The foundation supports organizations that promote systematic change; involve constituents in planning and decision making; encourage volunteer and professional development; and engage in ongoing program evaluation.
Fields of interest: Arts education; Arts; Education, reform; Education, public education; Health care; Mental health, treatment; International human rights; Jewish federated giving programs; Jewish agencies & synagogues.
International interests: Israel.
Type of support: General/operating support; Capital campaigns; Building/renovation; Endowments; Program development; Technical assistance; Program evaluation; Program-related investments/loans; Employee matching gifts; Matching/challenge support.
Limitations: Applications accepted. Giving primarily in MD (no local projects outside Baltimore, MD); giving also in Israel. No support for unaffiliated schools or synagogues. No grants to individuals, or for fundraising events, or direct mail solicitations; no loans (except for program-related investments).
Publications: Application guidelines; Grants list.
Application information: The foundation accepts applications that conform to the Association of Baltimore Area Grantmakers Common Grant Application. Application form not required.
Initial approach: Letter
Copies of proposal: 1
Deadline(s): None
Board meeting date(s): Quarterly
Final notification: 4 to 6 months
Officers and Trustees:* Michael J. Hirschhorn,* Pres.; Barbara B. Hirschhorn, V.P.; Arthur E. Roswell,* V.P.; Elizabeth B. Roswell,* V.P.; Jill R.

Robinson, Secy.; Anne Patterson, Treas.; Betsy F. Ringel, Exec. Dir.
Number of staff: 1 part-time professional.
EIN: 526038382
Selected grants: The following grants are a representative sample of this grantmaker's funding activity:
$2,325,000 to Bizchut, The Israel Human Rights Center for People with Disabilities, Jerusalem, Israel, 2012. For supplemental support for a new data management system.
$1,200,000 to Associated: Jewish Community Federation of Baltimore, Baltimore, MD, 2012. For general support for the annual campaign.
$200,000 to Fund for Global Human Rights, Washington, DC, 2012. For renewed general support to make grants to local and regional human rights groups around the world, payable over 2.00 years.
$150,000 to Negev Institute for Strategies of Peace and Development, Beersheba, Israel, 2012. For general support for activities to promote development in the Bedouin community and positive intergroup relations in the Negev, payable over 2.00 years.
$100,000 to Bend the Arc: A Jewish Partnership for Justice, New York, NY, 2012. For renewed general support.
$100,000 to Kav Mashve, Tel Aviv, Israel, 2012. For renewed support for the Career Training Program for Bedouin high school students in the Negev, payable over 2.00 years.
$100,000 to Young Audiences of Maryland, Baltimore, MD, 2012. For renewed general support of its programming in Baltimore City and support for the Access for All program, payable over 2.00 years.
$75,000 to University of Maryland-Baltimore Foundation, Baltimore, MD, 2012. For renewed support for Maryland Hospitals for a Healthy Environment.
$70,000 to Agenda-The Israeli Center for Strategic Communication, Tel Aviv, Israel, 2012. For renewed general support and for Shutafut-Sharaka, a coalition of coexistence groups working on media portrayal of Arab society, payable over 2.00 years.
$70,000 to Witness, Inc., Brooklyn, NY, 2012. For general support, payable over 2.00 years.
$50,000 to American Jewish Joint Distribution Committee, New York, NY, 2012. For renewed support for the Inter-Agency Task Force on Israeli Arab Issues, payable over 2.00 years.
$50,000 to Union for Reform Judaism, New York, NY, 2012. For renewed support for the Just Congregations Initiative to train Reform Jewish synagogues to address the root causes of economic and social injustice, payable over 2.00 years.
$30,000 to American Visionary Art Museum, Baltimore, MD, 2012. For renewed general support, payable over 2.00 years.
$6,500 to Association of Baltimore Area Grantmakers, Baltimore, MD, 2012. For general support through membership (JB, ER, HH Foundations and Atapco).

3736
The Morton K. and Jane Blaustein Foundation, Inc.
1 South St., Ste. 2900
Baltimore, MD 21202-3334 (410) 347-7201
Contact: Mary Jane Blaustein, Pres.
FAX: (410) 347-7210; E-mail: info@bloufund.org; Main URL: http://www.blaufund.org/foundations/mortonandjane_f.html

Established in 1988 in MD.
Donors: Morton K. Blaustein†; Mary Jane Blaustein; Lord Baltimore Capital Corp.
Foundation type: Independent foundation.
Financial data (yr. ended 12/31/12): Assets, $52,795,115 (M); gifts received, $350,000; expenditures, $3,181,385; qualifying distributions, $2,816,357; giving activities include $2,816,357 for grants.
Purpose and activities: Giving primarily for education, health, human rights, and social justice.
Fields of interest: Education; Health care; Mental health/crisis services; International human rights.
Type of support: General/operating support; Continuing support; Emergency funds; Program development.
Limitations: Applications accepted. Giving primarily in Washington, DC, Baltimore, MD, and New York, NY. No support for fundraising events, direct mail solicitations, or unsolicited proposals for academic, scientific or medical research. No grants or scholarships to individuals, or for fundraising, capital campaigns, annual campaigns, membership campaigns; no loans.
Application information: See foundation web site for program guidelines. Association of Baltimore Area Grantmakers Common Grant Application Form accepted. Application form not required.
Initial approach: Letter
Copies of proposal: 1
Deadline(s): None
Final notification: 4 to 6 months
Officers and Trustees:* Mary Jane Blaustein,* Pres.; Alan Berlow,* V.P.; Jeanne P. Blaustein,* V.P.; Susan B. Blaustein,* V.P.; Peter Bokor,* V.P.; Jill R. Robinson, Secy.; Anne Patterson, Treas.; Betsy Ringel, Exec. Dir.
Number of staff: 1 full-time professional.
EIN: 521607300
Selected grants: The following grants are a representative sample of this grantmaker's funding activity:
$1,000,000 to Johns Hopkins University, Baltimore, MD, 2012. For capital and programmatic support for the JHU School of Nursing, payable over 5.00 years.
$150,000 to Maryland Disability Law Center, Baltimore, MD, 2012. To expand advocacy on behalf of youth with educational or mental disabilities, payable over 2.00 years.
$150,000 to Way Station, Frederick, MD, 2012. For a pilot to coordinate care for low-income people with serious and persistent health and mental health problems, payable over 2.50 years.
$140,000 to Judge David L. Bazelon Center for Mental Health Law, Washington, DC, 2012. For renewed general support, payable over 2.00 years.
$130,000 to Urban Teacher Center, Baltimore, MD, 2012. For renewed general support, payable over 2.00 years.
$100,000 to Doctors Without Borders USA, New York, NY, 2012. For renewed general support, payable over 2.00 years.
$100,000 to LitWorld International, New York, NY, 2012. For renewed general support, payable over 2.00 years.
$75,000 to Coordinated Behavioral Care, New York, NY, 2012. For start-up support to create a coordinated system of health, mental health and supportive services for hard-to-serve, low-income New Yorkers.
$75,000 to Open Society Institute-Baltimore, Baltimore, MD, 2012. For renewed support for a campaign to reduce the number of youth tried as adults and detained pre-trial at the Baltimore City Detention Center.
$50,000 to Committee to Protect Journalists, New York, NY, 2012. For renewed general support, payable over 2.00 years.

3737
The Lois and Irving Blum Foundation ✧
233 E. Redwood St., Ste. 100
Baltimore, MD 21202-3332

Established about 1965 in MD.
Donors: Lois Blum Feinblatt; Irving Blum†; Lois B. Feinblatt Revocable Trust.
Foundation type: Independent foundation.
Financial data (yr. ended 03/31/13): Assets, $17,289,415 (M); gifts received, $644,516; expenditures, $942,693; qualifying distributions, $846,025; giving activities include $846,025 for grants.
Purpose and activities: Giving primarily for a donor-advised fund, Jewish causes, the arts, and human services.
Fields of interest: Arts; Education; Health organizations, association; Human services; United Ways and Federated Giving Programs; Jewish federated giving programs; Philanthropy/voluntarism; Jewish agencies & synagogues.
Type of support: General/operating support.
Limitations: Applications not accepted. Giving primarily in Baltimore, MD and CA. No support for private foundations. No grants to individuals.
Application information: Contributes only to pre-selected organizations.
Officers: Lois B. Feinblatt, Pres.; Lawrence A. Blum, M.D., V.P.; Carolyn P. Blum, M.D., Secy.; Jeffrey D. Blum, M.D., Treas.
EIN: 526057035
Selected grants: The following grants are a representative sample of this grantmaker's funding activity:
$230,000 to Tides Foundation, San Francisco, CA, 2011.
$2,500 to Advocates for Children and Youth, Baltimore, MD, 2011.

3738
Hershel & Esther Boehm Charity Fund ✧ ☆
5919 Winner Ave.
Baltimore, MD 21215-3801
Contact: Howard M. Boehm, Pres.

Established in 1997 in MD.
Donors: Howard M. Boehm; Esther Boehm; Hershel Boehm.
Foundation type: Independent foundation.
Financial data (yr. ended 12/31/13): Assets, $1,149,178 (M); gifts received, $400,000; expenditures, $429,593; qualifying distributions, $429,593; giving activities include $429,593 for 210 grants (high: $51,410; low: $5).
Purpose and activities: Giving primarily for Jewish agencies and temples.
Fields of interest: Education; Human services; Jewish agencies & synagogues.
International interests: Israel.
Limitations: Applications accepted. Giving primarily in Baltimore, MD and New York, NY; giving also in Israel.
Application information: Application form required.

Initial approach: Letter
Deadline(s): None
Officers: Howard M. Boehm, Pres.; Esther Boehm, V.P.; Ronny S. Retter, Secy.
EIN: 522005744
Selected grants: The following grants are a representative sample of this grantmaker's funding activity:
$50,960 to Shearith Hapleita, Baltimore, MD, 2011.
$25,000 to Bais Hamedrash and Mesivta of Baltimore, Baltimore, MD, 2010.
$20,852 to Agudath Israel of Baltimore, Baltimore, MD, 2010.
$15,018 to Ner Israel Rabbinical College, Baltimore, MD, 2011.
$10,300 to Rabbi Chaim Nachman Kowalsky Memorial Ahavas Yisroel Charity Fund, Baltimore, MD, 2010.
$5,350 to Etz Chaim Center for Jewish Studies, Baltimore, MD, 2011.
$3,600 to Bnos Yisroel of Baltimore, Baltimore, MD, 2011.
$2,510 to Agudath Israel of America, New York, NY, 2011.
$2,000 to Project Genesis, Baltimore, MD, 2011.
$1,515 to Agudath Israel of Baltimore, Baltimore, MD, 2011.
$1,200 to Talmudical Yeshiva of Philadelphia, Philadelphia, PA, 2011.
$1,100 to Ohr Yaakov, Jerusalem, Israel, 2011.

3739
The Scott and Patrice Brickman Family Foundation ✧
10721 Red Barn Ln.
Potomac, MD 20854-1956

Established in MD.
Donors: Patrice Brickman; Scott Brickman.
Foundation type: Independent foundation.
Financial data (yr. ended 12/31/13): Assets, $10,028,218 (M); expenditures, $846,706; qualifying distributions, $846,291; giving activities include $846,270 for 66 grants (high: $200,000; low: $100).
Fields of interest: Education; Health organizations; Human services; Social sciences, public policy.
Limitations: Applications not accepted. Giving primarily in MD and Washington, DC. No grants to individuals.
Application information: Unsolicited requests for funds not accepted.
Trustees: Patrice Brickman; Scott Brickman.
EIN: 616356351

3740
Brown Advisory Charitable Foundation Inc. ✧
901 Bond St., Ste. 400
Baltimore, MD 21231-3340 (401) 537-5503
Contact: Irene Alisa Stesch, Secy.

Established in 2009 in MD.
Donors: Brown Advisory LLC; Brown Advisory Securities.
Foundation type: Independent foundation.
Financial data (yr. ended 08/31/13): Assets, $8,803 (M); gifts received, $745,000; expenditures, $739,937; qualifying distributions, $733,630; giving activities include $733,630 for 183 grants (high: $40,000; low: $100).
Fields of interest: Arts; Higher education, university; Education; Human services; United Ways and Federated Giving Programs.
Limitations: Applications accepted. Giving primarily in MD.
Application information: Application form required.
Initial approach: Proposal
Deadline(s): None
Officer: Irene Alisa Stesch, Secy.
EIN: 010912891
Selected grants: The following grants are a representative sample of this grantmaker's funding activity:
$12,500 to Teach for America, New York, NY, 2011.
$10,000 to Outward Bound, Garrison, NY, 2011.
$5,000 to American Cancer Society, Atlanta, GA, 2011.
$5,000 to Chesapeake Bay Foundation, Annapolis, MD, 2011.
$4,500 to National Kidney Foundation, New York, NY, 2011.
$3,700 to Ronald McDonald House Charities, Oak Brook, IL, 2011.
$2,700 to Ronald McDonald House Charities, Oak Brook, IL, 2011.

3741
Alvin I. and Peggy S. Brown Family Charitable Foundation ✧
8180 Wisconsin Ave.
Bethesda, MD 20814-3633

Established about 1963.
Donors: Alvin I. Brown; Peggy S. Brown.
Foundation type: Independent foundation.
Financial data (yr. ended 03/31/14): Assets, $14,320,538 (M); expenditures, $1,048,004; qualifying distributions, $1,048,004; giving activities include $853,084 for 21 grants (high: $400,000; low: $5,000).
Purpose and activities: Giving primarily to Jewish agencies and temples; some giving also for education.
Fields of interest: Museums; Education; Zoos/zoological societies; Health organizations, association; Medical research, institute; Human services; Jewish federated giving programs; Social sciences; Jewish agencies & synagogues.
Limitations: Applications not accepted. Giving on a national basis. No grants to individuals.
Application information: Unsolicited requests for funds not accepted.
Board meeting date(s): Varies
Officers: Peggy S. Brown, Pres.; Barbara Brown, V.P.; Donna Brown, V.P.; Patricia Brown, V.P.
Number of staff: None.
EIN: 526041735
Selected grants: The following grants are a representative sample of this grantmaker's funding activity:
$240,000 to Zoological Society of the Palm Beaches, West Palm Beach, FL, 2011.
$30,000 to Southwestern College, Santa Fe, NM, 2012.
$20,000 to Creativity for Peace, Santa Fe, NM, 2012.
$5,000 to South Florida Science Museum, West Palm Beach, FL, 2012.

3742
The Bunting Family Foundation ✧
c/o Bunting Mgmt. Group
217 International Cir.
Hunt Valley, MD 21030-1332

Established in 1991 in MD.
Donors: George L. Bunting, Jr.; Dorothy W. Bunting; Mary Catherine Bunting; George L. Bunting, Sr.‡; Dorothy W. Bunting Charitable Trust.
Foundation type: Independent foundation.
Financial data (yr. ended 12/31/12): Assets, $42,480,177 (M); gifts received, $4,630,057; expenditures, $1,939,600; qualifying distributions, $1,814,558; giving activities include $1,803,150 for 91 grants (high: $300,000; low: $250).
Purpose and activities: Giving primarily for education, the arts, and human services.
Fields of interest: Arts; Education; Environment; Human services; United Ways and Federated Giving Programs; Catholic agencies & churches.
Limitations: Applications not accepted. Giving primarily in Baltimore, MD. No grants to individuals.
Application information: Contributes only to pre-selected organizations.
Officer: Christopher L. Bunting, Pres. and C.E.O.
Directors: George L. Bunting, Jr.; Jeffrey G. Bunting; Marc G. Bunting; Mary Catherine Bunting; Mary Ellen Bunting.
EIN: 521724988

3743
The Mary Catherine Bunting Foundation, Inc. ✧
c/o Bunting Mgmt. Group
217 International Cir.
Hunt Valley, MD 21030-1332

Established in 1998 in MD.
Donors: Mary Catherine Bunting; Mary Catherine Bunting 2012 Charitable Trust.
Foundation type: Independent foundation.
Financial data (yr. ended 12/31/13): Assets, $10,860,888 (M); gifts received, $2,055,199; expenditures, $1,067,377; qualifying distributions, $1,030,000; giving activities include $1,030,000 for 13 grants (high: $220,000; low: $20,000).
Fields of interest: Higher education; Human services; Catholic agencies & churches.
Limitations: Applications not accepted. Giving primarily in Washington, DC, and Baltimore, MD. No grants to individuals.
Application information: Contributes only to pre-selected organizations.
Officers and Directors:* Mary Catherine Bunting,* Chair.; Eleanor Smith,* Secy.-Treas.; Christopher L. Bunting; Geraldine Fialkowski.
EIN: 522106057
Selected grants: The following grants are a representative sample of this grantmaker's funding activity:
$200,000 to Little Sisters of the Poor, Baltimore, MD, 2011. For general support.
$100,000 to Catholic Relief Services, Baltimore, MD, 2011. For general support.
$40,000 to CARE USA, Atlanta, GA, 2011. For general support.
$40,000 to United States Fund for UNICEF, New York, NY, 2011. For general support.

3744
John Calvin Bible Foundation, Inc. ✧
P.O. Box 268
Jarrettsville, MD 21084-0268

Established in 1998 in MD.
Donors: Robert Henderson; Todd Henderson; Troy Henderson.
Foundation type: Independent foundation.
Financial data (yr. ended 06/30/13): Assets, $2,955,462 (M); gifts received, $1,760,000; expenditures, $596,931; qualifying distributions, $590,500; giving activities include $590,500 for grants.
Purpose and activities: Giving for Christian religious education and churches.
Fields of interest: Theological school/education; Christian agencies & churches.
Limitations: Applications not accepted. Giving primarily in MD, WI and VA. No grants to individuals.
Application information: Unsolicited requests for funds not accepted.
Officers: Robert Henderson, Pres.; Todd Henderson, V.P.; Troy Henderson, Secy.
EIN: 522135959
Selected grants: The following grants are a representative sample of this grantmaker's funding activity:
$5,000 to Baptist Mid-Mission, Cleveland, OH, 2011.

3745
The Annie E. Casey Foundation ✧
701 St. Paul St.
Baltimore, MD 21202-2311 (410) 547-6600
Contact: Satonya C. Fair, Dir., Grants Mgmt.
FAX: (410) 547-6624; E-mail: webmail@aecf.org; E-mail for S.C. Fair: sfair@aecf.org; Main URL: http://www.aecf.org
Casey Places: http://www.aecf.org/CaseyPlaces.aspx
E-Newsletter: http://www.aecf.org/Newsroom/NewsletterSubscribe.aspx
Knowledge Center: http://www.aecf.org/KnowledgeCenter.aspx
Twitter: http://twitter.com/aecfnews

Incorporated in 1948 in CA.
Donors: Annie E. Casey†; James E. "Jim" Casey†; and members of the Casey family.
Foundation type: Independent foundation.
Financial data (yr. ended 12/31/12): Assets, $2,666,068,266 (M); gifts received, $2,063,157; expenditures, $225,437,214; qualifying distributions, $241,888,903; giving activities include $98,475,361 for 996 grants (high: $6,127,523; low: $550), $205,655 for 346 employee matching gifts, $67,544,428 for 135 foundation-administered programs and $28,400,000 for 7 loans/program-related investments (high: $19,000,000; low: $500,000).
Purpose and activities: The primary mission of the foundation is to foster public policies, human service reforms, and community supports that more effectively meet the needs of today's vulnerable children and families. In pursuit of this goal, the foundation makes grants that help states, cities, and communities fashion more innovative, cost-effective responses to these needs.
Fields of interest: Education; Youth development, services; Human services; Children/youth, services; Urban/community development; Public affairs; Children/youth; Children; Adults; African Americans/Blacks; Economically disadvantaged.
Type of support: General/operating support; Management development/capacity building; Program development; Conferences/seminars; Publication; Fellowships; Research; Technical assistance; Consulting services; Program evaluation; Program-related investments/loans; Grants to individuals; Mission-related investments/loans.
Limitations: Applications accepted. Giving on a national basis, with emphasis on the ten sites that consist of the Making Connections initiative, as well as the foundation civic sites in Baltimore, MD, New Haven, CT, and Atlanta, GA. No support for political committees-529s (PACs). No grants to individuals (except for Casey Children and Family Fellowship Program), or for capital projects or medical research.
Publications: Financial statement; Informational brochure; Newsletter; Occasional report.
Application information: The foundation does not often fund unsolicited grant applications. The foundation's approach to grant making focuses on making multi-year, multi-site commitments that enable them to invest in long-term strategies and partnerships that strengthen families and communities. Most grantees are by invitation. Application form not required.
Initial approach: Letter (no more than 3 pages)
Deadline(s): None
Board meeting date(s): 5 times annually
Final notification: Approximately 30 days after receiving letter
Officers and Trustees:* Michael L. Eskew,* Chair.; Patrick McCarthy, C.E.O. and Pres.; Ralph Smith, Sr. V.P.; Kenneth M. Jones II, V.P. and C.F.O.; Stefan Strein, V.P. and C.I.O.; Ryan Chao, V.P., Civic Sites and Community Change; Bob Giloth, V.P., Ctr. for Community and Economic Opportunity; Donna Stark, V.P., Talent Mgmt. and Leadership Devel.; Lisa M. Hamilton, V.P., External Affairs; Teresa Markowitz, V.P., Center for Systems Innovation; Debra Joy Perez, V.P., Research, Evaluation and Learning; Maurice Agresta; Diana M. Bonta; Robert J. Clannin; D. Scott Davis; John Engler; Joseph Moderow; Gabriella E. Morris; Teri Plummer McClure; Lea N. Soupata; Arnold Wellman; Jim Winestock; Sam Zamarripa.
Number of staff: 141 full-time professional; 2 part-time professional; 49 full-time support; 1 part-time support.
EIN: 521951681
Selected grants: The following grants are a representative sample of this grantmaker's funding activity:
$6,400,000 to Case Commons, New York, NY, 2013. For operations of Case Commons, Inc. and development of Casebook, collaborative, family-centered case management system for child welfare, enabling workers serving the most vulnerable families and children to be more effective and efficient via new web-based software tools.
$6,000,000 to Case Commons, New York, NY, 2012. For operations of Case Commons, Inc. and development of Casebook, collaborative, family-centered case management system for child welfare, enabling workers serving the most vulnerable families and children to be more effective and efficient via new web-based software tools.
$2,000,000 to Tides Foundation, San Francisco, CA, 2013. For Campaign for Grade-Level Reading's Enterprise infrastructure and program, policy and site grants.
$1,966,651 to Living Cities: The National Community Development Initiative, New York, NY, 2012. To continue support for cutting-edge community development approaches, innovative financial investment strategies and products, and urban policy advocacy.
$1,100,000 to Center for Working Families, Atlanta, GA, 2013. To connect residents of Neighborhood Planning Unit V (NPU-V) to work supports and public benefits and assist them in obtaining family supporting employment.
$1,000,000 to Tides Foundation, San Francisco, CA, 2012. To provide support for the Campaign for Grade-Level Reading Collective Action Fund.
$925,000 to Jobs for the Future, Boston, MA, 2012. For National Fund for Workforce Solutions.
$596,520 to Center on Budget and Policy Priorities, Washington, DC, 2013. For technical assistance support to state-based organizations to increase the capacity to analyze and respond to emerging state budget and fiscal issues affecting the well-being of disadvantaged families.
$470,000 to Center on Budget and Policy Priorities, Washington, DC, 2012. To support technical assistance to state-based organizations to increase their capacity to analyze and respond to emerging state budget and fiscal issues affecting the well-being of disadvantaged families.
$450,000 to Juvenile Law Center, Philadelphia, PA, 2012. To provide technical assistance to the Juvenile Detention Alternatives Initiative (JDAI) and assist Foundation with related conferences and publications.
$400,000 to Pretrial Justice Institute, Washington, DC, 2013. For technical assistance and training to sites replicating Juvenile Detention Alternatives Initiative (JDAI).
$250,000 to East Baltimore Development, Baltimore, MD, 2013. For core operating support.
$100,000 to MDC, Durham, NC, 2013. To support and expand the adoption of the Center for Working Families approach in community colleges.
$75,000 to Rhode Island Kids Count, Providence, RI, 2012. For KIDS COUNT activities.
$75,000 to Voices for Virginias Children, Richmond, VA, 2013. For KIDS COUNT activities.
$50,000 to Historic East Baltimore Community Action Coalition, Baltimore, MD, 2012. To provide support for creation of East Baltimore Historical Library in the East Baltimore Community School.
$50,000 to Institute of Notre Dame, Baltimore, MD, 2013. For scholarships for eligible young women from East Baltimore.
$50,000 to Louisiana Association of Nonprofit Organizations, Baton Rouge, LA, 2012. To support participation in the State Fiscal Analysis Initiative (SFAI) and on-going analyses of state budget and tax policies affecting low-income children and families.
$50,000 to Providence Plan, Providence, RI, 2013. To support development of Rhode Island state Integrated Data System (IDS). An IDS is one that collects ongoing individual-level data from multiple administrative agencies whether at the city, county or state level. The project will connect local National Neighborhood Indicators Partnership (NNIP) partners, who all work to advance data-driven decision making in their neighborhoods, with organizations and agencies running IDS.
$40,000 to La Union del Pueblo Entero, LUPE, San Juan, TX, 2012. To provide capacity building support for social change.

3746
Eugene B. Casey Foundation ✧
16308 Crabbs Branch Way
Rockville, MD 20855 (301) 948-6500
Contact: Betty Brown Casey, Tr.

Established in 1981 in MD.
Donors: Virginia Casey Visnich Trust; Bernard Corp.
Foundation type: Independent foundation.
Financial data (yr. ended 08/31/13): Assets, $169,892,981 (M); gifts received, $412; expenditures, $7,176,354; qualifying distributions, $5,223,300; giving activities include $5,223,300 for 12 grants (high: $1,010,000; low: $1,000).
Fields of interest: Arts; Botanical gardens; Health care.
Type of support: General/operating support.
Limitations: Applications not accepted. Giving primarily in the greater Washington, DC, area, and MD.
Application information: Generally contributes only to the same pre-selected organizations each year.
Trustee: Betty Brown Casey.
EIN: 526220316
Selected grants: The following grants are a representative sample of this grantmaker's funding activity:
$27,185,332 to Casey Health Institute Foundation, Bethesda, MD, 2012. To establish Alternative Medical Care Center.
$2,079,277 to Casey Health Institute Foundation, Bethesda, MD, 2012. For general operating support.
$1,010,000 to Patrick Henry Memorial Foundation, Brookneal, VA, 2013. For general operating support.
$1,003,555 to Winchester Medical Center, Winchester, VA, 2013. For general operating support.
$1,000,000 to Salvation Army, National Capital Area, Washington, DC, 2013. For Hurricane Sandy Relief.
$1,000,000 to Salvation Army, National Capital Area, Washington, DC, 2013. For Oklahoma Tornado Disaster.
$500,000 to Caring for Others, Fairfax, VA, 2012. For general operating support.
$500,000 to Live and Learn Bethesda, Bethesda, MD, 2013. For general operating support.
$500,000 to Washington National Opera, Washington, DC, 2012. For general operating support.
$500,000 to Washington National Opera, Washington, DC, 2013. For general operating support.
$304,584 to Integrated Medicine Alternatives, Bethesda, MD, 2012. For general operating support.
$150,000 to Olney Children's Ballet Theater, Olney, MD, 2013. For general operating support.
$50,000 to Marine Corps Scholarship Foundation, Alexandria, VA, 2012. For general operating support.
$50,000 to Ronald Reagan Presidential Foundation, Simi Valley, CA, 2012. For general operating support.
$46,745 to W E T A-Greater Washington Educational Telecommunications Association, Arlington, VA, 2013. For general operating support.
$10,000 to Feed the Children, Oklahoma City, OK, 2013. For general operating support.
$10,000 to Learning Ally, Metropolitan Washington Unit, Washington, DC, 2012. For general operating support.
$10,000 to Maryland School for the Blind, Baltimore, MD, 2012. For general operating support.

3747
Ceres Foundation ✧
18606 Reliant Dr.
Gaithersburg, MD 20879-5422
E-mail: ceresmd1@gmail.com; Main URL: http://fdnweb.org/ceres
Grants List: http://fdnweb.org/ceres/foundation-grantees/

Established in 2000 in MD.
Donor: Donald B. Milder.
Foundation type: Independent foundation.
Financial data (yr. ended 12/31/12): Assets, $26,185,976 (M); expenditures, $1,179,158; qualifying distributions, $1,087,485; giving activities include $898,500 for 19 grants (high: $165,000; low: $3,000).
Purpose and activities: The foundation's mission is to provide the catalyst needed to mobilize human energies and talents that lie dormant. The foundation will focus on programs that aim to produce permanent improvements in peoples' lives by means of short-term interventions. The foundation will favor applicants who can best demonstrate a tangible, direct connection between the services their programs provide and the positive shifts that take place in individuals' lives.
Fields of interest: Education; Youth development; Human services; Children/youth, services; Family services; Women, centers/services; Young adults; Crime/abuse victims; Economically disadvantaged; Homeless.
Type of support: General/operating support; Program-related investments/loans.
Limitations: Applications accepted. Giving restricted to the West Coast or the Eastern Seaboard, from Raleigh northward. No support for foreign organizations, programs that serve those with disabilities, injuries, addictions or HIV, programs focused only on particular immigrant, ethnic or religious groups, programs that primarily serve pre-school kids or adults over 30 without children, and youth development programs that are after-school or considered learning centers. No grants to individuals.
Publications: Application guidelines; Program policy statement.
Application information: Full proposals are only accepted via invitation following submission of an application. Application form required.
Initial approach: Send short summary application of 3 - 6 pages following review of application criteria
Copies of proposal: 1
Deadline(s): None
Board meeting date(s): Nov.
Final notification: By Dec.
Officers: Daniel C. Milder, Pres.; Terri L. Milder, Secy.; Donald B. Milder, C.F.O.
EIN: 912170962

3748
Choice Hotels International Foundation ✧
1 Choice Hotels Cir., Ste. 400
Rockville, MD 20850
Contact: Jamie Little
E-mail: jamie_little@choicehotels.com; Main URL: http://www.choicehotels.com/en/responsibility/roomtogive?sid=xBzpH.WEwNOgSY3.10

Established in 1999 in MD.
Donor: Choice Hotels International Services Corp.
Foundation type: Company-sponsored foundation.
Financial data (yr. ended 12/31/13): Assets, $97,478 (M); gifts received, $460,500; expenditures, $488,427; qualifying distributions, $458,829; giving activities include $456,329 for 155 grants (high: $125,000; low: $25).
Purpose and activities: The foundation supports programs designed to provide shelter and food to those in need; enhance educational efforts of schools, workforce entry organizations, and the hospitality industry; and promote the growth and development of tourism.
Fields of interest: Education; Employment; Food services; Housing/shelter; Human services; Economic development, visitors/convention bureau/tourism promotion; Community/economic development; Adults, women.
Type of support: General/operating support; Program development; Scholarship funds; Research; Employee volunteer services; Employee matching gifts; Employee-related scholarships; Scholarships—to individuals.
Limitations: Applications accepted. Giving primarily in areas of company operations in Phoenix, AZ, Grand Junction, CO, Silver Spring, MD, and Minot, ND; giving also to national organizations. No support for religious organizations not of direct benefit to the entire community, lobbying, political, or fraternal organizations, for-profit ventures, or medical- or health-related organizations. No grants to individuals (except for scholarships), or for capital campaigns, endowments, or memorials, golf tournaments, dinners, or events where Choice Hotels International Foundation receives a tangible benefit.
Publications: Application guidelines; Annual report.
Application information: Application form required.
Initial approach: E-mail
Copies of proposal: 1
Deadline(s): None
Board meeting date(s): Rolling
Officers: Stephen Joyce, Pres.; Simone Wu, Secy.; David White, Treas.
EIN: 522184905

3749
Church Home Corporation ✧ ☆
5565 Sterrett Pl., 5th Fl.
Columbia, MD 21044

Established in MD.
Foundation type: Independent foundation.
Financial data (yr. ended 06/30/13): Assets, $10,334,745 (M); gifts received, $9,898; expenditures, $1,149,860; qualifying distributions, $1,112,583; giving activities include $1,112,583 for 1 grant.
Fields of interest: Health care.
Type of support: General/operating support.
Limitations: Applications not accepted. Giving primarily in MD.
Application information: Unsolicited requests for funds not accepted.
Officers and Directors:* Eric Wagner,* Pres.; Susan K. Nelson, V.P. and Treas.; Debora Kuchka Craig, V.P.; Oliver M. Johnson II, Secy.
EIN: 237374724

3750
Clark Charitable Foundation, Inc. ✧
7500 Old Georgetown Rd., 15th Fl.
Bethesda, MD 20814-6133

Incorporated in 1987 in MD.
Donors: A. James Clark; Lawrence C. Nussdorf; Aon Risk Services Co.; J & H Marsh & McLennan; The Clark Endowment; Clark Enterprises, Inc.
Foundation type: Independent foundation.
Financial data (yr. ended 12/31/12): Assets, $73,857,554 (M); gifts received, $2,398,769; expenditures, $4,796,346; qualifying distributions, $4,447,500; giving activities include $4,447,500 for 123 grants (high: $990,000; low: $500).
Purpose and activities: Giving primarily for higher education and programs and services for children and youth; support also for health and hospitals, human services, education, and the arts.
Fields of interest: Arts; Higher education; Education; Hospitals (general); Health care; Human services; Children/youth, services; Catholic agencies & churches.
Type of support: General/operating support.
Limitations: Applications not accepted. Giving limited to the U.S., primarily in Washington, DC, and MD. No support for organizations lacking nonprofit tax-exempt status. No grants to individuals.
Application information: Contributes only to pre-selected organizations.
Officers: A. James Clark, Chair.; Courtney Clark Pastrick, Pres.; Lawrence C. Nussdorf, V.P.
EIN: 521512330

3751
Clark-Winchcole Foundation ✧
3 Bethesda Metro Ctr., Ste. 550
Bethesda, MD 20814-5358 (301) 654-3607
Contact: Vincent C. Burke, III, Pres.

Established in 1964 in DC.
Donors: Dorothy C. Winchcole†; Elizabeth G. Clark†.
Foundation type: Independent foundation.
Financial data (yr. ended 12/31/13): Assets, $125,147,970 (M); expenditures, $6,000,034; qualifying distributions, $4,813,453; giving activities include $4,469,400 for 250 grants (high: $140,000; low: $2,500).
Purpose and activities: Giving primarily for higher education, hospitals and other health agencies, cultural programs, social service and youth agencies, and Protestant and Roman Catholic church support.
Fields of interest: Arts; Higher education; Hospitals (general); Health care; Boys & girls clubs; Human services; Youth, services; Catholic federated giving programs; Protestant agencies & churches; Catholic agencies & churches.
Type of support: General/operating support; Building/renovation.
Limitations: Applications accepted. Giving primarily in the Washington, DC, area. No support for private foundations. No grants to individuals.
Application information: Application form required.
Initial approach: Application
Deadline(s): None
Officers: Vincent C. Burke III, Chair. and Pres.; Grover B. Russell, V.P.; Thomas C. Thompson, Jr., V.P.; Gregory Oyler, Secy.; W. Craig Thompson, Treas.; Steve Ferrigno, Exec. Dir.
EIN: 526058340

3752
Ben & Zelda Cohen Charitable Foundation, Inc. ✧
1233 W. Mount Royal Ave.
Baltimore, MD 21217-4133 (410) 727-4586
Contact: Richard Davidson, Secy.-Treas.

Established in MD.
Donors: Ben Cohen; Zelda G. Cohen†; Ben Cohen Trust.
Foundation type: Independent foundation.
Financial data (yr. ended 02/28/13): Assets, $6,302,382 (M); expenditures, $1,226,071; qualifying distributions, $923,564; giving activities include $898,200 for 16 grants (high: $200,000; low: $1,000).
Purpose and activities: Giving primarily to a children's hospital, as well as for education and Jewish organizations.
Fields of interest: Arts, formal/general education; Higher education; Education; Hospitals (specialty); Jewish federated giving programs; Jewish agencies & synagogues.
Limitations: Applications accepted. Giving primarily in Baltimore, MD. No grants to individuals.
Application information:
Initial approach: Letter
Deadline(s): None
Officers: Rosalee C. Davison, Pres.; Charlotte Cohen Weinberg, V.P.; Richard Davison, Secy.-Treas.
EIN: 526039179
Selected grants: The following grants are a representative sample of this grantmaker's funding activity:
$200,000 to LifeBridge Health, Baltimore, MD, 2011.
$200,000 to Maryland Institute College of Art, Baltimore, MD, 2011.
$50,000 to Enoch Pratt Free Library of Baltimore City, Baltimore, MD, 2011.
$25,000 to National Museum of American Jewish History, Philadelphia, PA, 2011.
$15,000 to Maryland Public Television, Owings Mills, MD, 2011.
$2,500 to Friendship School, Eldersburg, MD, 2011.
$2,500 to Virginia Holocaust Museum, Richmond, VA, 2011.
$1,000 to Jewish Museum of Maryland, Baltimore, MD, 2011.

3753
The Ryna and Melvin Cohen Family Foundation, Inc. ✧
10501 Rhode Island Ave.
Beltsville, MD 20705-2317

Established in 1992 in MD.
Donors: Ryna G. Cohen; Melvin S. Cohen; Mark Cohen; Neil Cohen; Diane Zack.
Foundation type: Independent foundation.
Financial data (yr. ended 12/31/13): Assets, $30,793,922 (M); gifts received, $1,250,000; expenditures, $2,022,190; qualifying distributions, $1,727,751; giving activities include $1,719,188 for 156 grants (high: $300,000; low: $18).
Purpose and activities: Giving primarily for the arts, human services, and Jewish agencies and temples.
Fields of interest: Museums (ethnic/folk arts); Arts; Human services; Jewish federated giving programs; Jewish agencies & synagogues.
Limitations: Applications not accepted. Giving primarily in the Washington, DC, area and MD. No grants to individuals.
Application information: Contributes only to pre-selected organizations.
Officers: Ryna G. Cohen, Pres.; Neil D. Cohen, V.P. and Treas.; Marcy E. Cohen, V.P.; Mark L. Cohen, V.P.; Thea E. Cohen, V.P.; Theresa Cohen, V.P.; Diane C. Zack, V.P.; Howard B. Zack, V.P.
EIN: 521800019
Selected grants: The following grants are a representative sample of this grantmaker's funding activity:
$200,000 to Congregation Kol Shofar, Tiburon, CA, 2011.
$200,000 to Jewish Community Center of Greater Washington, Rockville, MD, 2011.
$50,000 to National Gallery of Art, Washington, DC, 2011.
$10,000 to Neediest Kids, McLean, VA, 2011.

3754
Naomi and Nehemiah Cohen Foundation ✧
P.O. Box 30100
Bethesda, MD 20824-0639 (301) 652-2230
Contact: Alison McWilliams, Exec. Dir.
FAX: (301) 652-2260; E-mail: info@nncf.net; Main URL: http://www.nncf.net

Incorporated in 1959 in DC.
Donors: Emanuel Cohen†; N.M. Cohen†; Naomi Cohen†; Israel Cohen†; Daniel Solomon; Lillian Cohen Solomon†; David Solomon; Stuart Brown; Dr. Diane Solomon Brown.
Foundation type: Independent foundation.
Financial data (yr. ended 12/31/13): Assets, $80,915,949 (M); gifts received, $2,500; expenditures, $4,220,059; qualifying distributions, $3,759,943; giving activities include $3,353,800 for 95 grants (high: $600,000; low: $1,000).
Purpose and activities: The focus of the foundation is on human services, reproductive health care, and civic affairs in Washington, DC, and Jewish-Arab shared society in Israel.
Fields of interest: Environment; Human services; International human rights; Civil liberties, reproductive rights; Civil/human rights; Jewish agencies & synagogues; Minorities; Women; Young adults, female; Economically disadvantaged; Homeless.
International interests: Israel.
Type of support: General/operating support; Annual campaigns; Capital campaigns; Building/renovation; Program evaluation.
Limitations: Giving primarily in Washington, DC, and Israel. No support for private or parochial schools, universities, or for medical research. No grants to individuals.
Publications: Grants list.
Application information: Unsolicited requests for funds not accepted. Current grantees should refer to application guidelines on foundation web site, and may use the Washington Regional Association of Grantmakers' Common Grant Application Format. Proposals sent by e-mail, fax, FedEX or messenger are not accepted.
Deadline(s): Current grantees should refer to foundation web site for deadlines
Board meeting date(s): Quarterly
Officers and Directors:* Dr. Diane Solomon Brown,* Pres.; Daniel Solomon,* V.P.; Jane Solomon,* Secy.; Stuart Brown,* Treas.; Alison McWilliams, Exec. Dir.

Number of staff: 1 full-time professional.
EIN: 201135004

3755
Howard P. Colhoun Family Foundation, Inc. ✧ ☆
14114 Mantua Mill Rd.
Glyndon, MD 21136-4836
Contact: Howard P. Colhoun, Pres.

Established in 1993 in MD; supporting organization of Baltimore Community Foundation, Inc.
Foundation type: Independent foundation.
Financial data (yr. ended 12/31/12): Assets, $19,956,717 (M); gifts received, $501,932; expenditures, $851,282; qualifying distributions, $839,644; giving activities include $818,569 for 95 grants (high: $253,369; low: $500).
Fields of interest: Education; Environment; Animals/wildlife; Community/economic development; Foundations (community).
Type of support: General/operating support.
Limitations: Applications not accepted. Giving primarily to Baltimore, MD.
Application information: Contributes only to pre-selected organizations.
Officer and Directors:* Howard P. Colhoun,* Pres.; Robin Catlin; Alexander H.P. Colhoun.
EIN: 521853373

3756
Commonweal Foundation, Inc. ✧
10770 Columbia Pike, Ste. 150
Silver Spring, MD 20901-4451 (240) 450-0000
Contact: Rozita Green, V.P., Programs
FAX: (240) 450-4115; E-mail: grants@cweal.org; Main URL: http://www.cweal.org

Established in 1968 in Washington, DC.
Donors: Stewart Bainum, Sr.; Roberta Bainum; Jane Bainum; Realty Investment Company, Inc.; Rose-Marie and Jack R. Anderson Foundation.
Foundation type: Operating foundation.
Financial data (yr. ended 06/30/13): Assets, $220,581,715 (M); gifts received, $13,996,769; expenditures, $15,684,057; qualifying distributions, $15,853,223; giving activities include $5,480,108 for 204 grants (high: $1,625,000; low: $20), and $8,656,650 for 2 foundation-administered programs.
Purpose and activities: The foundation's vision is that children living in poverty have the opportunity to break the bonds of their circumstance by gaining access to quality educational opportunities and services, and graduate from high school prepared to enter and succeed in higher education or pursue gainful employment to become contributing members of society.The foundation operates and supports educational programs and projects assisting underserved children and youth. The foundation focuses on primary and secondary education.
Fields of interest: Child development, education; Elementary school/education; Secondary school/education; Human services; Children/youth, services; Child development, services; Minorities.
Type of support: General/operating support; Continuing support; Program development; Seed money; Scholarship funds; Matching/challenge support.
Limitations: Applications accepted. Giving limited to Washington, DC, MD, and northern VA for Community Assistance Grants. No support for political organizations. No grants to individuals, or for endowments or building funds, capital campaigns, special events, lobbying activities, local organizations that raise funds to send to other countries and .
Publications: Application guidelines; Grants list; Program policy statement.
Application information: Organizations with operating budget above 1 million will not be considered for funding. Application form required.
Initial approach: Apply online via foundation web site
Deadline(s): Feb. 1 and Aug. 1 for Community Assistance Grants
Board meeting date(s): June and Dec.
Final notification: 4 to 6 weeks after deadline
Officers and Directors:* Barbara Bainum,* Chair., C.E.O., and Pres.; Stewart Bainum, Sr.,* Vice-Chair.; Christopher Sharkey, V.P. and C.F.O.; Bruce Bainum, Ph.D.; Roberta Bainum; Alexander Froom; Charles A. Ledsinger, Jr.; James MacCutcheon; Scott Renschler.
Number of staff: 11 full-time professional; 4 full-time support.
EIN: 237000192
Selected grants: The following grants are a representative sample of this grantmaker's funding activity:
$1,000 to Adventist Development and Relief Agency International, Silver Spring, MD, 2011.

3757
Community Foundation of Carroll County, Inc. ✧
255 Clifton Blvd. St. 313
Westminster, MD 21157-4690 (410) 876-5505
Contact: Audrey S. Cimino, Exec. Dir.
FAX: (410) 871-9031;
E-mail: acimino@carrollcommunityfoundation.org; Main URL: http://www.carrollcommunityfoundation.org

Established in 1994 in MD.
Foundation type: Community foundation.
Financial data (yr. ended 12/31/13): Assets, $5,658,413 (M); gifts received, $1,435,603; expenditures, $1,588,457; giving activities include $134,656 for 14+ grants (high: $22,756), and $492,912 for 439 grants to individuals.
Purpose and activities: The foundation seeks to maintain and enhance the quality of life in the community of Carroll County through philanthropic means. The foundation will receive, invest, and distribute funds for charitable, cultural, and educational purposes for the benefit of the citizens of Carroll County.
Fields of interest: Historic preservation/historical societies; Arts; Education; Health care; Recreation; Human services.
Limitations: Applications accepted. Giving limited to Carroll County, MD. No support for sectarian religious programs. No grants for to individuals (except for scholarships), or for operational deficits, fundraisers, or debt retirement.
Application information: Visit foundation web site for application form and guidelines. Application form required.
Initial approach: Contact foundation
Officers and Trustees:* Caroline Babylon,* Chair.; Audrey S. Cimino, Exec. Dir.; Gregg Blair; Mel Blizzard; Dean Camlin; Stanley Dill; William Gering; Emily Johnston; Bernie Jones; Donna Lewis; Phil Mullikin; Sue Myers; Tom Rasmussen; Carolyn Scott; Seth Shipley; Jason Stambaugh; Sue Yingling; Pam Zappardino.
EIN: 521865244

3758
The Community Foundation of Frederick County, MD, Inc.
312 E. Church St.
Frederick, MD 21701-5611 (301) 695-7660
Contact: Elizabeth Y. Day, Pres. and C.E.O.
FAX: (301) 695-7775;
E-mail: info@FrederickCountyGives.org; Additional e-mail: donor.services@FrederickCountyGives.org; Main URL: http://FrederickCountyGives.org/
Blog: http://www.frederickcountygives.org/about/blog
Facebook: https://www.facebook.com/CommunityFoundationFredCo
YouTube: https://www.youtube.com/user/CommunityFndFredCo

Established in 1986 in MD.
Foundation type: Community foundation.
Financial data (yr. ended 06/30/14): Assets, $101,356,188 (M); gifts received, $6,154,898; expenditures, $4,826,164; giving activities include $2,185,836 for 208 grants (high: $149,557), and $1,210,244 for 588 grants to individuals.
Purpose and activities: The Community Foundation is dedicated to connecting people who care with causes that matter to enrich the quality of life in Frederick County now and for future generations.
Fields of interest: Historic preservation/historical societies; Arts; Higher education; Education; Environment, pollution control; Health care; Housing/shelter; Youth, services; Aging, centers/services; Human services; Community/economic development; Public affairs; Religion.
Type of support: Capital campaigns; Building/renovation; Emergency funds; Program development; Publication; Seed money; Scholarship funds; Scholarships—to individuals.
Limitations: Applications accepted. Giving limited to Frederick County, MD. No grants for operating costs, annual campaigns, endowments, or multi-year funding.
Publications: Application guidelines; Annual report; Grants list; Newsletter.
Application information: Visit foundation web site for application guidelines. Application form required.
Initial approach: Contact foundation
Copies of proposal: 1
Deadline(s): Aug. 15 for affordable healthcare, housing/homelessness, and school readiness grants, Sept. 15 for arts, agriculture, civic causes, animal welfare, education, youth programs, elder care, and other grants. See website for updated application deadlines
Board meeting date(s): 4th Fri. of each month
Final notification: Sept.-Oct.
Officers and Trustees:* Cynthia S. Palmer,* Chair.; Debra S. Borden, Esq.,* 1st Vice-Chair.; Tod P. Salisbury, Esq.,* 2nd Vice-Chair.; Elizabeth Y. Day,* C.E.O. and Pres.; Gail M. Fitzgerald,* C.F.O.; Joanne R. McCoy,* Secy.; Dale T. Summers,* Treas.; Bill Blakeslee; Colleen Chidester; Lisa Y. Coblentz; Stacey L. Collins; Cornelius Ryan Fay III; Harry

George III; Kevin Hessler, C.P.A.; David L. Hoffman; Dr. Amaris Little; Ted Luck; Mark Mayer; Shabri Moore; Joy Hall Onley; J. Ray Ramsburg III; Garyl L. Rollins; James R. Shoemaker, Esq.; Shirley A. Shores; Daniel K. Tregoning; Barbara K. Walker; C. Matthew Wiley.

Number of staff: 10 full-time professional; 5 full-time support.

EIN: 521488711

3759
Community Foundation of Howard County ✧

(formerly The Columbia Foundation)
10630 Little Patuxent Pkwy.
Century Plaza Ste. 315
Columbia, MD 21044 (410) 730-7840
Contact: Beverley White-Seals, Pres. and C.E.O.; For grants: Tracy Locke-Kitt, Prog. Off.
FAX: (410) 997-6021; E-mail: info@cfhoco.org; Additional e-mail: bwhiteseals@columbiafoundation.org; Grant inquiry e-mail: tlockekitt@cfhoco.org; Main URL: http://www.cfhoco.org/
Facebook: http://www.facebook.com/ColumbiaFoundation
Twitter: https://twitter.com/CFHoCo

Incorporated in 1969 in MD.

Foundation type: Community foundation.

Financial data (yr. ended 12/31/12): Assets, $15,316,463 (M); gifts received, $884,117; expenditures, $1,350,165; giving activities include $648,811 for 40+ grants (high: $58,750), and $42,950 for 28 grants to individuals.

Purpose and activities: The foundation seeks to inspire lifelong giving and connecting people, places and organizations to worthy causes across Howard County.

Fields of interest: Performing arts; Performing arts, music; Historic preservation/historical societies; Arts; Education; Environment; Animals/wildlife; Health care; Housing/shelter, development; Children/youth, services; Family services; Aging, centers/services; Human services; Community/economic development; Youth; Aging; Disabilities, people with; Hispanics/Latinos; Women; Girls; Adults, women; Adults, men; Single parents; Crime/abuse victims; Homeless.

Type of support: General/operating support; Continuing support; Building/renovation; Equipment; Emergency funds; Program development; Conferences/seminars; Curriculum development; Scholarship funds; Technical assistance; Consulting services; Program evaluation; Program-related investments/loans; Scholarships—to individuals; Matching/challenge support.

Limitations: Applications accepted. Giving limited to Howard County, MD. No support for projects of a sectarian religious nature or medical research. No grants to individuals (except for scholarships), or for annual campaigns, deficit financing, capital campaigns, land acquisition, seed money or start-up funding, or general or special endowments.

Publications: Application guidelines; Annual report; Grants list; Informational brochure; Newsletter; Program policy statement.

Application information: Emergency/Urgent Needs grants available throughout the year for requests from $250 - $2,000 for organizations in need of immediate assistance. Visit foundation web site for applications and guidelines per grant type. Application form required.

Initial approach: Submit grant application and attachments
Copies of proposal: 1
Deadline(s): Feb. 27, May 29, and Aug. 31 for mini-grants
Board meeting date(s): 3rd Wed. of each month
Final notification: Mar. 31, June 30, and Sept. 30 for Mini-Grants

Officers and Trustees:* Bruce Harvey,* Chair.; Joe Maranto,* Vice-Chair.; Beverly White-Seals,* C.E.O. and Pres.; Barbara Van Winkle,* Secy.; Lynne Schaefer,* Treas.; Earl Armiger; Edward Berman; Mark D. Biegel; Tara Brummell; Katrina Burton; Thomas G. Coale; Vidia Dhanraj; George Doetsch, Jr.; Nuala Duffy; Brian Eakes; Christopher M. Gable; Rob Goldman; Neil Gordon; Dennis Jankiewicz; Daniel Killiher; Marcia Leonard; Cynthia Lifson, Esq.; Chris Marasco; Spencer Perry; Steven D. Sass, Esq.; Charley C. Sung.

Number of staff: 3 full-time professional; 1 full-time support.

EIN: 520937644

3760
Community Foundation of the Eastern Shore, Inc.

1324 Belmont Ave., Ste. 401
Salisbury, MD 21804 (410) 742-9911
Contact: For grants: Heather Towers, Prog. Off.
FAX: (410) 742-6638; E-mail: cfes@cfes.org; Grant inquiry e-mail: htowers@cfes.org; Main URL: http://www.cfes.org
Facebook: http://www.facebook.com/pages/Community-Foundation-of-the-Eastern-Shore/178920515477
LinkedIn: http://www.linkedin.com/company/2292766
Twitter: http://twitter.com/cfesnonprofit
Vimeo: http://vimeo.com/cfes
YouTube: http://www.youtube.com/user/CFEasternShore
Scholarship inquiry e-mail: bjsummers@cfes.org

Established in 1984 in MD.

Foundation type: Community foundation.

Financial data (yr. ended 06/30/13): Assets, $88,723,926 (M); gifts received, $4,742,431; expenditures, $6,238,774; giving activities include $5,166,559 for 87+ grants (high: $1,090,000), and $256,551 for 69 grants to individuals.

Purpose and activities: The foundation serves the Lower Eastern Shore of Maryland, specifically Somerset County, Wicomico County, and Worcester County. Established in 1984, the foundation is a local philanthropic expert committed to connecting donors with community needs. Gifts to the foundation create permanent endowment funds that steadily grow in value over time and produce income for grants to local charitable nonprofit organizations. The foundation seeks to encourage philanthropy and strengthen our communities.

Fields of interest: Historic preservation/historical societies; Arts; Higher education; Education; Environment; Health care; Human services; Community/economic development; Children/youth; Youth; Women; Girls.

Type of support: Management development/capacity building; Equipment; Emergency funds; Program development; Conferences/seminars; Seed money; Technical assistance; Consulting services; Scholarships—to individuals.

Limitations: Applications accepted. Giving limited to the Lower Eastern Shore of MD, area, encompassing Somerset, Wicomico, and Worcester counties. No support for sectarian religious programs. No grants to individuals (except for scholarships), or for annual campaigns, building campaigns, fundraising campaigns, major capital campaigns, building or endowment funds, continuing support, land acquisition, general operating support, playground equipment, or debt retirement or budget deficits; no program-related investments.

Publications: Application guidelines; Annual report; Financial statement; Informational brochure; Newsletter.

Application information: Visit foundation web site for application form and guidelines per grant type. Application form required.

Initial approach: Letter or telephone
Copies of proposal: 1
Deadline(s): Feb. 1 and Aug. 1 for Community Needs Grant Program; varies for others
Board meeting date(s): Feb., Apr., June, Aug., Oct., and Dec.
Final notification: Apr. and Oct. for Community Needs Grant Program; varies for others

Officers and Directors:* Melody S. Nelson,* Chair.; John J. Allen,* Vice-Chair.; Erica N. Joseph,* Pres.; James R. Thomas, Jr.,* Secy.; David A. Vorhis,* Treas.; David Plotts, Cont.; James W. Almand; John P. Barrett; Todd E. Burbage; Thomas K. Coates; Jane R. Corcoran; Charles G. Goslee; Dr. Carolyn Johnston; Andy Kim; Dwight W. Marshall, Jr.; Kathleen G. McLain; James F. Morris; Susan K. Purnell; Ernest R. Satchell; Greg Tawes; Donald K. Taylor; Lauren C. Taylor; Louis H. Taylor; Michael P. Truitt; Gayle W. Widdowson; Stephanie T. Willey; Julius D. Zant, M.D.

Number of staff: 8 full-time professional.

EIN: 521326014

3761
Community Foundation of Washington County Maryland, Inc. ✧

33 W. Franklin St., Ste. 203
Hagerstown, MD 21740-4863 (301) 745-5210
Contact: Bradley N. Sell, Exec. Dir.
FAX: (301) 791-5752; E-mail: cfwc@cfwcmd.org; Additional e-mail: brads@cfwcmd.org; Main URL: http://www.cfwcmd.org
Facebook: http://www.facebook.com/cfwashingtoncountymd

Established in 1996 in MD.

Foundation type: Community foundation.

Financial data (yr. ended 06/30/13): Assets, $25,213,114 (M); gifts received, $439,329; expenditures, $1,742,840; giving activities include $1,085,240 for 31+ grants (high: $100,000).

Purpose and activities: The foundation's mission includes: 1) serving as a leader, resource, and catalyst to enrich the quality of life in the community; 2) providing a variety of flexible and cost-effective ways for donors to create permanent endowments; 3) providing donor services that allow the foundation to respond to changing community needs and opportunities; 4) making financial gifts to qualified organizations and other community needs; and 5) encouraging philanthropy at all levels.

Fields of interest: Arts; Education; Health care; Boys & girls clubs; YM/YWCAs & YM/YWHAs; Children,

services; Family services; Human services; Economic development, visitors/convention bureau/tourism promotion; United Ways and Federated Giving Programs; Infants/toddlers; Children/youth; Youth; Adults; Aging; Young adults; Disabilities, people with; Physically disabled; Mentally disabled; Minorities; Substance abusers; Single parents; Crime/abuse victims; Economically disadvantaged; Homeless.
Type of support: Program development; Seed money; Scholarship funds.
Limitations: Applications accepted. Giving primarily in Washington County, MD. No support for projects that would ordinarily receive public tax support, sectarian religious programs, or K-12 educational institutions. No grants for annual operating expenses, or for capital campaigns, endowment campaigns, deficit retirement, special fundraising events, or celebration functions.
Publications: Application guidelines; Annual report; Newsletter.
Application information: Visit foundation web site for application and additional information. Application form required.
Initial approach: Complete online application
Deadline(s): Nov. 3
Board meeting date(s): 3rd Thurs. of each month
Final notification: Awards will be made by Mar. 1
Officers and Trustees:* John P. Itell,* Chair.; Mike Day,* Vice-Chair.; Rev. D. Suart Dunnan,* Vice-Chair.; Ted Reeder,* Secy.; Cindy Moore,* Treas.; Bradley N. Sell, Exec. Dir.; Dr. Carol R. Becker; Howard Bowen; Andy Bruns; Rich Daughtridge; Jason Divelbiss; Bob Ernst; Douglas A. Fiery; Mark Fulton; Lou Giustini; John R. Hershey III; Constance G. Manger; Stuart L. Mullendore; Steve P. O'Farrell; Brad Pingrey; Melissa Reabold; Ann Marie Rotz; Elizabeth Schulze; Todd Snook; Mary Helen Strauch; Robin Twigg.
Number of staff: 1 full-time professional; 1 part-time professional; 1 full-time support; 2 part-time support.
EIN: 522001455

3762
Community Trust Foundation ✧
71 Baltimore St.
Cumberland, MD 21502 (301) 876-9172
Contact: For grants: Juli McCoy, Admin.
FAX: (301) 722-0091; E-mail: info@ctfinc.org; Grant application e-mail: ctf@ctfinc.org; Main URL: http://www.ctfinc.org
Facebook: https://www.facebook.com/pages/Community-Trust-Foundation/116858238347691

Established in 2006 in MD.
Foundation type: Community foundation.
Financial data (yr. ended 12/31/12): Assets, $4,100,055 (M); gifts received, $240,792; expenditures, $676,726; giving activities include $630,750 for 6+ grants (high: $206,000).
Purpose and activities: The mission of the foundation is to strengthen the region by working in partnership with donors and community groups.
Fields of interest: Education.
Publications: Application guidelines.
Application information: Visit foundation web site for more information. Application form required.
Copies of proposal: 1
Deadline(s): Feb. 28 and Aug. 31
Officers and Trustees:* Shane Grady,* Pres.; Marion Leonard,* V.P.; Kathy Getty,* Treas.; Dinah Courrier; Jared Fike; William Grant; Kim Hinds; Jonathan Kessler; Fred Learey; Dr. David Moran; Alonzo Naylor; Bartlett Naylor; Todd Pyles; Vic Rezendes; Dr. Wayne Spiggle; R. Terry Stephens; Lonny J. Watro; Jo Wilson.
EIN: 680629840

3763
The Concordia Foundation ✧
c/o PNC Bank
1 E. Pratt St., 10th Fl.
Baltimore, MD 21202-1128
Contact: Pierra Le Gorrec, Tr.
E-mail: wendy.kaczerski@theconcordiafoundation.org; NJ tel.: (609) 924-1254

Established in 1997 in MD.
Donor: John J. Roberts.
Foundation type: Independent foundation.
Financial data (yr. ended 12/31/12): Assets, $19,797,927 (M); expenditures, $1,433,541; qualifying distributions, $1,225,347; giving activities include $1,089,500 for 50 grants (high: $170,000; low: $8,500).
Purpose and activities: Giving primarily for scholarships, preserving the ecosystems of the Eastern Shore of MD and Central NJ, and social service and arts organizations.
Fields of interest: Arts; Education; Environment, natural resources.
Type of support: General/operating support; Capital campaigns; Land acquisition; Program development; Scholarship funds.
Limitations: Applications accepted. Giving primarily in the eastern shore of MD and central NJ, some funding also in NY. No support for religious organizations or for medical research. No grants to individuals, or for matching gifts; no loans.
Publications: Application guidelines.
Application information: Request an application cover sheet and detailed application guidelines via e-mail. Application form required.
Initial approach: Letter with e-mail address
Deadline(s): Aug. 1
Final notification: 2-3 months
Trustees: Pierra LeGorrec; Christopher L. Roberts; John J. Roberts; Rebecca B. Roberts.
Number of staff: 2 full-time professional; 1 part-time support.
EIN: 311486126

3764
Cordish Family Foundation, Inc ✧
601 E. Pratt St., 6th Fl.
Baltimore, MD 21202-3114

Established in MD.
Donor: David S. Cordish.
Foundation type: Independent foundation.
Financial data (yr. ended 12/31/13): Assets, $6,079,643 (M); gifts received, $2,000,000; expenditures, $2,511,825; qualifying distributions, $2,484,141; giving activities include $2,484,072 for 47 grants (high: $1,105,000; low: $100).
Purpose and activities: Giving primarily for Jewish organizations.
Fields of interest: Arts; Higher education; Education; Health organizations; Jewish agencies & synagogues.
Limitations: Applications not accepted. Giving primarily in Washington, DC and Baltimore, MD. No grants to individuals.
Application information: Contributes only to pre-selected organizations.
Officers: David S. Cordish, Pres.; Jonathan A. Cordish, V.P. and Secy.-Treas.
EIN: 263611776

3765
Cornell Douglas Foundation, Inc. ✧ ☆
4701 Sangamore Rd., Ste. 133
Bethesda, MD 20816-2524 (301) 229-3008
FAX: (301) 229-3342; E-mail for Ann Cornell: ann@cornelldouglas.org; e-mail for Holly Cornell: cdf@cornelldouglas.org; Main URL: http://www.cornelldouglas.org/

Established in 2006 in MD.
Donors: Jean Douglas; Ann Cornell; W. Leslie Douglas†; Wallace Genetic Foundation.
Foundation type: Independent foundation.
Financial data (yr. ended 12/31/13): Assets, $12,389,118 (M); expenditures, $640,634; qualifying distributions, $640,363; giving activities include $591,000 for 41 grants (high: $35,000; low: $5,000).
Purpose and activities: The foundation provides small grants to organizations which promote the foundation's vision: advocating for environmental health and justice, encouraging stewardship of the environment, and furthering respect for sustainability of resources.
Fields of interest: Education; Environment, plant conservation.
Application information: Application guidelines available on foundation web site.
Officers and Directors:* Ann Cornell,* Pres.; Elizabeth Sword,* Secy.; George L. Cornell, Jr.,* Treas.; Gillian C. Shinkman, Exec. Dir.; Alex Cornell; Holly Cornell.
EIN: 651287707
Selected grants: The following grants are a representative sample of this grantmaker's funding activity:
$15,000 to Anacostia Watershed Society, Bladensburg, MD, 2012. For Improving Condition of the river.
$15,000 to Virginia Organizing, Charlottesville, VA, 2012. For Environmental Health Sciences.
$10,000 to American Bird Conservancy, The Plains, VA, 2012. For Restriction, cancellation - Harmful Chemicals.
$10,000 to Anacostia Community Museum, Washington, DC, 2012. To support children learning.
$10,000 to Appalachian Voices, Boone, NC, 2012. For Mountain Top Mine Removal.
$10,000 to Rainforest Action Network, San Francisco, CA, 2012. For Stop bank financing for MTR.
$10,000 to Safer Pest Control Project, Chicago, IL, 2012. To reduce Pesticide use - Parks, public places.
$5,000 to Amazon Conservation Team, Arlington, VA, 2012. For Protection of the Amazon in So America.

3766
The Charles Crane Family Foundation, Inc. ✧
c/o DLA Piper Rudnick, LLP
6225 Smith Ave.
Baltimore, MD 21209-3600 (410) 358-0680
Contact: Laurence M. Katz, Pres.
E-mail: lkatz@ubalt.edu; Main URL: http://www.thecranefoundation.org

Established in 1991 in MD.
Donors: Charles Crane‡; Howard S. Brown.
Foundation type: Independent foundation.
Financial data (yr. ended 12/31/13): Assets, $56,222,814 (M); expenditures, $3,872,191; qualifying distributions, $2,993,039; giving activities include $2,892,334 for 57 grants (high: $910,000; low: $500).
Purpose and activities: Giving primarily for education and Jewish organizations.
Fields of interest: Education; Health organizations; Human services; Children/youth, services; Jewish federated giving programs; Jewish agencies & synagogues.
Limitations: Applications accepted. Giving limited to MD, with emphasis on Baltimore. No grants to individuals.
Publications: Application guidelines; Grants list; IRS Form 990 or 990-PF printed copy available upon request.
Application information: The foundation encourages use of the Association of Baltimore Area Grantmakers Common Grant Application Format, which can be downloaded from foundation web site. Application form not required.
Initial approach: Proposal
Copies of proposal: 10
Deadline(s): Oct. 15 for a violence prevention program; Feb. 15 for a Jewish education program
Board meeting date(s): 3 to 4 times per year
Final notification: Within 60 days of application deadline
Officers: Dean Laurence M. Katz, Pres.; Amy Macht, V.P.; Shale D. Stiller, V.P.; Darrell D. Friedman, Secy.; P. McEvoy Cromwell, Treas.
Directors: Hinda Dubin; Benjamin Greenwald.
Number of staff: 1 part-time professional; 2 part-time support.
EIN: 521755504
Selected grants: The following grants are a representative sample of this grantmaker's funding activity:
$915,000 to Center for Jewish Education of Baltimore, Baltimore, MD, 2011.
$250,000 to Day School Council, Baltimore, MD, 2011.
$125,000 to Bet Shemesh Educational Center, Flushing, NY, 2011. For special education services in day schools.
$100,000 to Bet Shemesh Educational Center, Flushing, NY, 2011. For general operating support for day school.
$60,000 to University of Baltimore, Baltimore, MD, 2011.
$50,000 to Central Scholarship Bureau, Baltimore, MD, 2011. For scholarships.
$50,000 to Johns Hopkins University, Baltimore, MD, 2011. For Jewish Studies Program.
$40,000 to Hillel of Greater Baltimore, Baltimore, MD, 2011.
$40,000 to House of Ruth Maryland, Baltimore, MD, 2011.
$38,000 to Teen Court of Baltimore, Baltimore, MD, 2011.
$30,000 to Mercy Medical Center, Baltimore, MD, 2011. For Family Violence Response Program.

3767
The Barbara and George Cromwell Foundation ✧ ☆
P.O. Box 387
Arnold, MD 21012-2153

Donors: Barbara T. Cromwell; The George Cromwell Irrevocable Trust.
Foundation type: Independent foundation.
Financial data (yr. ended 12/31/13): Assets, $50,631 (M); gifts received, $1,176,981; expenditures, $1,374,347; qualifying distributions, $1,359,180; giving activities include $1,162,509 for 15 grants (high: $551,120; low: $1,000).
Fields of interest: Higher education; Education; Health care; Religion.
Limitations: Applications not accepted. Giving primarily in MD.
Application information: Unsolicited requests for funds not accepted.
Trustee: Barbara T. Cromwell.
EIN: 264348468
Selected grants: The following grants are a representative sample of this grantmaker's funding activity:
$50,000 to Anne Arundel Medical Center, Annapolis, MD, 2012. For Joint Center 2012.
$50,000 to Washington College, Chestertown, MD, 2012. For The Washington Fund 2012.
$10,000 to Johns Hopkins Medicine, Baltimore, MD, 2012. For Heart and Vascular Surgery Institute.
$2,500 to Colonial Williamsburg Foundation, Williamsburg, VA, 2012. For Friends of the Collection.

3768
William E. Cross Foundation, Inc. ✧
c/o D. Linton
201 Thomas Johnson Dr.
Frederick, MD 21702 (301) 662-9200
Contact: Donald Linton, Pres. and Dir.

Established in 2004 in MD.
Donors: Cider Barrell, Inc.; William Cross.
Foundation type: Independent foundation.
Financial data (yr. ended 12/31/13): Assets, $16,180,739 (M); expenditures, $878,230; qualifying distributions, $642,000; giving activities include $642,000 for 82 grants (high: $50,000; low: $1,000).
Fields of interest: Education.
Limitations: Applications accepted. Giving primarily in MD.
Application information: Application form required.
Initial approach: Letter
Deadline(s): Dec. 1
Officers and Directors:* Donald C. Linton,* Pres.; Arthur B. Brisker,* V.P.; Hazel Brisker,* Secy.; Rebecca Linton,* Treas.
EIN: 201220528
Selected grants: The following grants are a representative sample of this grantmaker's funding activity:
$10,000 to Salvation Army, Frederick, MD, 2012. For charitable purposes only.

3769
The Cupid Foundation, Inc. ✧
(formerly The KDP Foundation, Inc.)
1010 Hull St., No. 220
Baltimore, MD 21230-5330 (410) 454-6472
Contact: Amy S. Larkin, Exec. Dir.

Established in 2007 in MD.
Donor: Kevin A. Plank.
Foundation type: Independent foundation.
Financial data (yr. ended 12/31/12): Assets, $18,175,405 (M); expenditures, $4,462,638; qualifying distributions, $3,993,376; giving activities include $3,993,376 for grants.
Fields of interest: Education; Medical research, institute; Athletics/sports, school programs; Family services.
Limitations: Applications accepted. Giving primarily in Baltimore and College Park, MD, and Washington, DC.
Application information:
Initial approach: Letter of request
Deadline(s): None
Officer: Amy S. Larkin, Exec. Dir.
Directors: Desiree Jacqueline Plank; Kevin A. Plank; Thomas J. Sippel.
EIN: 261300940
Selected grants: The following grants are a representative sample of this grantmaker's funding activity:
$50,000 to Cal Ripken, Sr. Foundation, Baltimore, MD, 2011.

3770
The Haron Dahan Foundation, Inc. ✧
6225 Smith Ave.
Baltimore, MD 21209-3626
Contact: Haron Dahan, Pres.

Established in 1986 in MD.
Donors: Haron Dahan; Caddie Homes, Inc.; Dahan Homes, Inc.
Foundation type: Independent foundation.
Financial data (yr. ended 12/31/12): Assets, $42,521,041 (M); expenditures, $2,303,293; qualifying distributions, $2,181,977; giving activities include $2,170,280 for 12 grants (high: $1,902,780; low: $500).
Purpose and activities: Giving primarily for Jewish agencies, temples, and education.
Fields of interest: Higher education; Human services; Jewish federated giving programs; Jewish agencies & synagogues.
International interests: Israel.
Limitations: Applications not accepted. Giving in the U.S., primarily in Brooklyn and New York, NY, and MD, with emphasis on Baltimore.
Application information: Contributes only to pre-selected organizations.
Officer: Haron Dahan, Pres.
Number of staff: 1 part-time support.
EIN: 521473704

3771
The Davis Family Foundation, Inc. ✧
c/o Mr. & Mrs. James C. Davis
P.O. Box 468
Hanover, MD 21076-0468 (877) 388-3823

Established in 2002 in MD.

Donors: James C. Davis; Kimberly J. Davis; William Davis; Deborah Davis.
Foundation type: Independent foundation.
Financial data (yr. ended 12/31/12): Assets, $291,542,383 (M); gifts received, $100,000,000; expenditures, $10,214,634; qualifying distributions, $9,831,020; giving activities include $9,821,900 for 48 grants (high: $4,300,000; low: $900).
Purpose and activities: Giving primarily for education, including Roman Catholic education.
Fields of interest: Elementary/secondary education; Higher education; Catholic agencies & churches.
Limitations: Applications not accepted. Giving primarily in Baltimore, MD and PA. No grants to individuals.
Application information: Contributes only to pre-selected organizations.
Officers and Directors:* James C. Davis,* Pres.; Kimberly J. Davis,* V.P. and Secy.-Treas.
EIN: 010751429
Selected grants: The following grants are a representative sample of this grantmaker's funding activity:
$4,300,000 to Vanguard Charitable Endowment Program, Boston, MA, 2012. For general support.
$700,000 to Archdiocese of Baltimore, Baltimore, MD, 2012. For general support.
$520,000 to Malvern Preparatory School, Malvern, PA, 2012. For general support.
$340,000 to Baltimore Jesuit Educational Initiative, Baltimore, MD, 2012. For general support.
$275,000 to McDonogh School, Owings Mills, MD, 2012. For general support.
$250,000 to Vanderbilt University, Nashville, TN, 2012. For general support.
$155,000 to Ashby Ponds, Ashburn, VA, 2012. For general support.
$150,000 to Erickson Foundation, Baltimore, MD, 2012. For general support.
$125,000 to Linden Ponds, Hingham, MA, 2012. For general support.
$35,000 to United States Naval Academy, Annapolis, MD, 2012. For general support.

3772
Cora and John H. Davis Foundation, Inc. ✧

1401 Rockville Pike, Ste. 560
Rockville, MD 20852-1434
Application address: c/o Stuart L. Bindeman, 7101 Wisconsin Ave., Ste. 1203, Bethesda, MD 20814, tel.: (301) 907-7200

Established in 1983 in DC.
Donors: Cora Davis†; John H. Davis†.
Foundation type: Independent foundation.
Financial data (yr. ended 12/31/13): Assets, $11,584,885 (M); expenditures, $567,242; qualifying distributions, $513,674; giving activities include $437,500 for 34 grants (high: $30,000; low: $5,000).
Purpose and activities: Giving primarily for education, youth and social services, hospitals and health associations, and Jewish social service agencies.
Fields of interest: Performing arts; Arts; Secondary school/education; Higher education; Higher education, university; Hospitals (general); Health organizations, association; Boys & girls clubs; Human services; Family services; Jewish agencies & synagogues.
Type of support: General/operating support; Continuing support; Annual campaigns; Capital campaigns; Building/renovation; Equipment; Emergency funds; Scholarship funds; Research.
Limitations: Applications accepted. Giving primarily in the Washington, DC, area, including MD.
Application information: Application form required.
Initial approach: Letter
Copies of proposal: 1
Deadline(s): None
Officers: Stuart L. Bindeman, Pres.; Harold Zirkin, V.P.; Michael F. Glazer, Secy.-Treas.
Number of staff: 3 part-time professional.
EIN: 521282054
Selected grants: The following grants are a representative sample of this grantmaker's funding activity:
$30,000 to Lupus Foundation of America, Washington, DC, 2012. For Lupus Navigation Program.
$25,000 to Family Support Center, Bethesda, MD, 2012. For Prevention Resource Center.
$10,000 to Shady Grove Adventist Hospital, Rockville, MD, 2012. For Medical Equipment - Cardiac/Vascular Center.
$10,000 to So Others Might Eat, Washington, DC, 2012. For feeding the homeless.
$10,000 to Suburban Hospital, Bethesda, MD, 2012. For Heart Center Medical Equipment.
$10,000 to Western Presbyterian Church, Washington, DC, 2012. For Miriam's Kitchen Feeding the Homeless.
$7,500 to ORT America, Bethesda, MD, 2012. For general purposes fund.
$5,000 to American University, Washington, DC, 2012. For Center for Israel Studies.
$5,000 to Fractured Atlas, New York, NY, 2012. For General Operations general purposes Fund.

3773
Richard & Rosalee C. Davison Foundation Inc. ✧

1233 W. Mount Royal Ave.
Baltimore, MD 21217-4133 (410) 727-4586
Contact: Richard Davison, Pres. and Treas.

Established in 1984 in MD.
Donors: Richard Davison; Rosalee C. Davison; CD Associates; Richard Associates; Rosalee Associates; Woodbranch Associates.
Foundation type: Independent foundation.
Financial data (yr. ended 07/31/13): Assets, $1,966,271 (M); gifts received, $94,477; expenditures, $802,570; qualifying distributions, $788,975; giving activities include $788,975 for grants.
Purpose and activities: Giving primarily for education, the arts, and Jewish causes.
Fields of interest: Museums; Higher education; Education; Health care; Human services; Jewish federated giving programs; Jewish agencies & synagogues.
Limitations: Applications accepted. Giving primarily in Baltimore, MD.
Application information: Application form required.
Initial approach: Letter
Deadline(s): None
Officers: Richard Davison, Pres. and Treas.; Rosalee C. Davison, V.P. and Secy.
EIN: 521348965
Selected grants: The following grants are a representative sample of this grantmaker's funding activity:
$90,000 to Walters Art Museum, Baltimore, MD, 2011.
$21,000 to University of Baltimore, Baltimore, MD, 2011.
$10,000 to Baltimore Symphony Orchestra, Baltimore, MD, 2011.
$10,000 to Maryland Institute College of Art, Baltimore, MD, 2011.
$6,000 to Everyman Theater, Baltimore, MD, 2011.
$6,000 to Miami City Ballet, Miami Beach, FL, 2011.

3774
de Beaumont Foundation, Inc. ✧

7501 Wisconsin Ave., Ste. 1310E
Bethesda, MD 20814-6597 (301) 961-5800
Contact: James B. Sprague M.D., Chair.
FAX: (301) 961-5802;
E-mail: info@deBeaumont.org; Main URL: http://www.deBeaumont.org

Established in 1999 in MA.
Donor: Pierre de Beaumont.
Foundation type: Independent foundation.
Financial data (yr. ended 12/31/13): Assets, $188,546,081 (M); gifts received, $62,000,000; expenditures, $5,651,187; qualifying distributions, $4,969,136; giving activities include $4,104,245 for 29 grants (high: $877,949; low: $750).
Purpose and activities: Giving primarily for developing the public health workforce, encouraging health departments to collaborate and implement best practices, and improving information and data management through effective campaigns and innovative technology.
Fields of interest: Public health; Public health, communicable diseases; Public health, epidemiology; Public health, bioterrorism; Health care; Immunology; Disasters, preparedness/services.
Type of support: Conferences/seminars; Curriculum development; Fellowships; General/operating support; Management development/capacity building; Professorships; Program development; Program evaluation; Publication; Research; Scholarship funds; Seed money.
Limitations: Applications not accepted. Giving limited to the U.S. No support for religious or political organizations, or for international programs. No grants to individuals, or for scholarships, endowment funds, cash reserves, capital campaigns, debt, or lobbying.
Publications: Financial statement; Grants list.
Application information: Proposals by invitation only.
Board meeting date(s): Feb., May, Aug., and Oct.
Officers and Directors:* James B. Sprague, M.D.*, Chair. and C.E.O.; Murray Brennan, M.D.*, Vice-Chair.; Leroy Parker, M.D.*, Secy.-Treas.; Ariel C. Moyer, C.O.O.; John M. Auerbach, MBA; Richard M. Burnes, Jr.; Carol H. Massoni; John M. Stevens; Gregory R. Wagner, M.D.
Number of staff: 1 full-time professional.
EIN: 043467074

3775
The Geaton and Joann Decesaris Family Foundation Inc. ✧
(formerly The Decesaris Foundation)
2001 Rosetta Way
Davidsonville, MD 21035-1150

Established in 2001 in DE.
Donors: Geaton A. Decesaris, Jr.; Hovnanian Enterprises, Inc.
Foundation type: Independent foundation.
Financial data (yr. ended 12/31/12): Assets, $13,962,269 (M); expenditures, $686,523; qualifying distributions, $567,000; giving activities include $567,000 for 26 grants (high: $275,000; low: $1,000).
Purpose and activities: Giving primarily for health organizations and hospitals; funding also for Roman Catholic agencies and churches.
Fields of interest: Hospitals (specialty); Health organizations, association; Cancer; Pediatrics; Catholic agencies & churches.
Limitations: Applications not accepted. Giving primarily in Boston, MA and MD. No grants to individuals.
Application information: Contributes only to pre-selected organizations.
Officers: Josephine A. Decesaris, Pres.; Kristen Decesaris, V.P.; Angela Duffy, V.P.; Elizabeth Decesaris, Secy.; JoAnn Decesaris, Treas.
EIN: 522303477

3776
Deerbrook Charitable Trust ✧
(formerly Morningstar Foundation)
c/o Arthur E. Sundstrum, Exec. Dir.
2 Wisconsin Cir., Ste. 700
Chevy Chase, MD 20815-7007
E-mail: art.sundstrom@deerbrooktrust.org; Main URL: http://www.deerbrooktrust.org/

Established in 2004 in FL.
Donor: Hays Clark†.
Foundation type: Independent foundation.
Financial data (yr. ended 12/31/13): Assets, $82,678,848 (M); expenditures, $14,504,622; qualifying distributions, $14,036,273; giving activities include $13,537,138 for 41 grants (high: $5,685,866; low: $150).
Purpose and activities: The trust's mission is to provide individuals of all ages with opportunities for a better education, a stronger family, a healthier life, and a more secure future.
Fields of interest: Elementary/secondary education; Youth development; Human services; Children/youth; Youth; Adults.
Type of support: General/operating support; Continuing support; Management development/capacity building; Capital campaigns; Equipment; Program development; Conferences/seminars; Fellowships; Scholarship funds; Research; Program evaluation; Matching/challenge support.
Limitations: Applications not accepted. Giving primarily on a national basis.
Application information: Unsolicited requests for funds not accepted.
Trustees: Harris Whitlock Clark; Hays Lawrence Clark; Rosamond Clark; John M. Emery; Daniel Hanley; Valerie McNeely.
Number of staff: 1 full-time professional.
EIN: 206257418

Selected grants: The following grants are a representative sample of this grantmaker's funding activity:
$5,685,866 to Baylor Health Care System Foundation, Dallas, TX, 2013. To develop Integrated Geriatric Volunteer Program.
$3,000,000 to Harlem Childrens Zone, New York, NY, 2012. For operating support.
$2,000,000 to Harlem Childrens Zone, New York, NY, 2013. For operating support.
$1,710,505 to Boys and Girls Clubs of America, National Headquarters, Atlanta, GA, 2012. For operating support.
$1,255,942 to American Association of Community Colleges, Washington, DC, 2012. For operating support.
$1,059,000 to Boys and Girls Clubs of America, National Headquarters, Atlanta, GA, 2013. For disaster response and for Advancing Philanthropy Project, which will assist Clubs in boosting their individual giving. This project includes advanced resource development strategies, action learning and leadership principles and will engage teams of board and staff members from 500 organizations.
$1,001,507 to Baylor Health Care System Foundation, Dallas, TX, 2012. For operating support.
$764,043 to National Commission on Teaching and Americas Future, Washington, DC, 2012. For operating support.
$708,996 to Big Brothers Big Sisters Lone Star, Irving, TX, 2012. For operating support.
$431,040 to National Commission on Teaching and Americas Future, Washington, DC, 2013. To replicate Learning Labs.
$418,350 to Boys and Girls Clubs of Annapolis and Anne Arundel County, Annapolis, MD, 2012. For operating support.
$403,350 to Boys and Girls Clubs of Annapolis and Anne Arundel County, Annapolis, MD, 2013. For Junior Staff Program, small-group program that assists Club members ages 13 to 18 in exploring a career in youth or human services, particularly Boys and Girls Club work. Young people prepare for future roles as human services professionals by participating in career development activities, discovering the importance of community service, building customer service skills and completing a Club apprenticeship.
$325,000 to Warrior Gateway, Arlington, VA, 2013. For operating support.
$300,000 to Hobe Sound Bible College, Hobe Sound, FL, 2013. For project support.
$296,927 to National Commission on Teaching and Americas Future, Washington, DC, 2013. For operating support.
$203,182 to Baylor University, Louise Herrington School of Nursing, Waco, TX, 2012. For operating support.
$200,000 to Boys and Girls Club of Martin County, Hobe Sound, FL, 2012. For operating support.
$163,584 to Baylor University, Louise Herrington School of Nursing, Waco, TX, 2013. For Gerontological Nursing Initiative.
$55,000 to Anacostia Community Outreach Center, Washington, DC, 2012. For operating support.
$55,000 to Boys and Girls Club of Chester, Chester, PA, 2013. For Executive Director compensation.

3777
Elsie & Marvin Dekelboum Family Foundation, Inc. ✧
(formerly Elsie & Marvin Dekelboum Foundation, Inc.)
4600 N. Park Ave., Plz. S.
Chevy Chase, MD 20815-7513 (301) 652-8600
Contact: Steven H. Oram, Secy.

Established in 1989 in FL.
Donors: Marvin Dekelboum; Elsie Dekelboum; Marvin Dekelboum Revocable Trust; Elsie Dekelboum Charitable Remainder Trust.
Foundation type: Independent foundation.
Financial data (yr. ended 12/31/13): Assets, $69,804,418 (M); expenditures, $3,395,441; qualifying distributions, $2,828,194; giving activities include $2,803,500 for 54 grants (high: $750,000; low: $400).
Purpose and activities: Giving primarily for health care, medical research and hospitals, including a children's hospitals, and for social services.
Fields of interest: Performing arts centers; Hospitals (general); Hospitals (specialty); Health care; Medical research, institute; Alzheimer's disease research; Human services; Children/youth, services.
Limitations: Applications accepted. Giving primarily in MD and TX; some giving in FL and MN.
Application information: Application form required.
Initial approach: Request application form
Deadline(s): None
Officers: Gail Hartstein, Pres.; Mark Hughes, V.P.; Steven H. Oram, Secy.; Neil S. Kaplan, Treas.
EIN: 650121068

3778
Delaplaine Foundation, Inc. ✧
c/o Great Southern Enterprises, Inc.
244 W. Patrick St.
P.O. Box 3829
Frederick, MD 21701-6945 (301) 662-2753
Contact: Marlene B. Young, Pres.
FAX: (301) 620-1689;
E-mail: info@delaplainefoundation.org; Main URL: http://www.delaplainefoundation.org/

Established in 2001 in MD.
Donors: Edward S. Delaplaine; Elizabeth B. Delaplaine; George B. Delaplaine, Jr.; George B. Delaplaine III; James W. Delaplaine; John F. Delaplaine.
Foundation type: Independent foundation.
Financial data (yr. ended 12/31/13): Assets, $17,462,252 (M); gifts received, $5,000; expenditures, $954,204; qualifying distributions, $763,500; giving activities include $763,500 for 89 grants (high: $127,000; low: $500).
Purpose and activities: Giving primarily for the enrichment of communities and families within Maryland, nearby states, and the District of Columbia, by supporting programs that strengthen the arts and sciences, historical preservation, educational advancement, spiritual enlightenment and physical well-being.
Fields of interest: Historic preservation/historical societies; Arts; Higher education; Health care; Community/economic development; Spirituality.
Type of support: General/operating support; Continuing support; Annual campaigns; Capital campaigns; Endowments; Program development.

Limitations: Applications accepted. Giving primarily in Frederick County, MD, and its surrounding area, including Washington, DC. No grants to individuals.
Publications: Application guidelines; Informational brochure (including application guidelines).
Application information: See foundation web site for complete guidelines and application. Application form required.
Initial approach: Use application form on foundation web site
Copies of proposal: 1
Deadline(s): Nov. 1
Board meeting date(s): 1st Wed. in Nov.
Final notification: 4-6 weeks
Officers and Trustees:* George B. Delaplaine, Jr.,* Chair.; Marlene B. Young,* Pres.; Edward S. Delaplaine II,* V.P.; George B. Delaplaine III,* Secy.; Philip W. Hammond,* Treas.; Bettie Delaplaine; James W. Delaplaine; John P. Delaplaine.
Number of staff: 2 part-time professional.
EIN: 522278038
Selected grants: The following grants are a representative sample of this grantmaker's funding activity:
$25,000 to Mission of Mercy, Frederick, MD, 2012. For Mobile Medical Program.
$20,000 to Frederick Memorial Hospital, Frederick, MD, 2012. For Auxiliary Prenatal Center.
$15,000 to Mental Health Association of Frederick County, Frederick, MD, 2012. For Capital Campaign and Family Service Program.
$6,000 to Community Foundation of Frederick County, Frederick, MD, 2012. For David Marshall Fund/Sharon I. Hooper Memorial Dreams.
$5,000 to Frederick Arts Council, Frederick, MD, 2012. For Yemi's Pillars of Frederick Project/ Inspires Project.
$5,000 to Maryland Historical Society, Baltimore, MD, 2012. For Traveling Trunks and In-Class Museum Tours.
$2,500 to Hospice of Frederick County, Frederick, MD, 2012. For Plan for Living Campaign.
$2,000 to Advocates for Homeless Families, Frederick, MD, 2012. For transitional housing.
$2,000 to Frederick Community Action Agency, Frederick, MD, 2012. For Soup Kitchen and Food Bank.
$1,000 to Washington County Museum of Fine Arts, Hagerstown, MD, 2012. For general operating/ educational programs.

3779
Robert W. Deutsch Foundation ✧ ☆
1122 Kennilworth Dr., Ste. 201
Towson, MD 21204-2143 (443) 275-1144
Contact: Jane Brown, Exec. Dir.
FAX: (410) 321-4882;
E-mail: info@rwdfoundation.org; Main URL: http://www.rwdfoundation.org

Established in 1991 in MD.
Donors: Robert W. Deutsch; RWD Technologies.
Foundation type: Independent foundation.
Financial data (yr. ended 12/31/12): Assets, $96,575,541 (M); gifts received, $13,000,000; expenditures, $4,741,915; qualifying distributions, $4,274,467; giving activities include $3,709,965 for 23 grants (high: $520,000; low: $2,000).
Purpose and activities: The foundation is in the process of reconsidering its mission and goals. It supports innovation broadly.
Fields of interest: General charitable giving.
Type of support: General/operating support; Continuing support; Program development; Seed money; Curriculum development; Fellowships; Internship funds; Research.
Limitations: Applications not accepted. Giving primarily in MD. No support for religious or political organizations.
Application information: Unsolicited requests for funds not accepted.
Officers: Jane Brown, Pres. and Exec. Dir.; Neil Didriksen, C.O.O.
Directors: David Deutsch; Mac Maclure.
Number of staff: 2 full-time professional; 1 full-time support.
EIN: 521758252

3780
J.S. Plank & D.M. DiCarlo Family Foundation, Inc. ✧
100 International Dr., Ste. 21100
Baltimore, MD 21202-4675

Established in 2007 in MD.
Donors: J. Scott Plank; Dana M. DiCarlo.
Foundation type: Independent foundation.
Financial data (yr. ended 12/31/13): Assets, $12,490,378 (M); expenditures, $1,621,606; qualifying distributions, $1,529,883; giving activities include $1,529,883 for 54 grants (high: $460,939; low: $200).
Fields of interest: Education; Health organizations; Human services; Children/youth, services.
Limitations: Applications not accepted. Giving primarily in MD. No grants to individuals.
Application information: Contributes only to pre-selected organizations.
Officers: J. Scott Plank, Pres. and Co.-Treas.; Dana M. DiCarlo, V.P.; Morris L. Garten, Secy.; David A. Goldner, Co-Treas.
EIN: 711040599

3781
The DLA Piper Foundation ✧ ☆
(formerly The Gray Cary Foundation)
6225 Smith Ave.
Baltimore, MD 21209-3600

Established in 2001 in CA.
Donors: Pamela Burke; Gray Cary Ware & Freidenrich; DLA Piper U.S.A. LLP; James Brogan; Cameron Rains; J. Terence O' Malley; Heidi Levine; Frank Burch; Roger Meltzer; Peter Pantaleo; Stacia Kelly; Lee Miller.
Foundation type: Independent foundation.
Financial data (yr. ended 12/31/13): Assets, $321,734 (M); gifts received, $402,750; expenditures, $651,809; qualifying distributions, $650,077; giving activities include $562,698 for 29 grants (high: $60,000; low: $1,250).
Purpose and activities: Giving primarily for legal services and to law centers.
Fields of interest: Education; Legal services; Human services; Children/youth, services; Family services; Civil/human rights; Law/international law; Women; Economically disadvantaged; Homeless.
Limitations: Applications not accepted. Giving primarily in CA, IL, and MA; with giving to Mexico. No grants to individuals.
Application information: Contributes only to pre-selected organizations.
Officers and Directors:* Shale Stiller,* Co-Chair. and Pres.; Lisa Dewey,* Co-Chair. and C.F.O.; Lee I. Miller, Chair.; Lee Sheller; Frank Burch; Allen J. Ginsburg; J. Terence O'Malley; Charles B. Scheeler; Michael Tracy.
EIN: 330967136

3782
The Dresher Foundation, Inc. ✧
4940 Campbell Blvd., Ste. 110
Baltimore, MD 21236-5910 (410) 933-0384
Contact: Robin Platts, Exec. Dir.
FAX: (410) 931-9052;
E-mail: info@dresherfoundation.org; E-mail for Robin Platts: robin@dresherfoundation.org; Main URL: http://www.dresherfoundation.org

Established in 1989 in MD.
Donor: James T. Dresher, Sr.‡.
Foundation type: Independent foundation.
Financial data (yr. ended 12/31/12): Assets, $50,438,383 (M); expenditures, $2,577,261; qualifying distributions, $2,132,622; giving activities include $1,913,260 for 100 grants (high: $205,000; low: $500).
Purpose and activities: Giving primarily for education, including after school programs, and human services, in specific geographic areas.
Fields of interest: Health care; Recreation, camps; Human services; Youth, services; Children/youth; Youth; Disabilities, people with; Mentally disabled; Women; Economically disadvantaged; Homeless.
Type of support: General/operating support; Capital campaigns; Building/renovation; Equipment; Scholarship funds; Technical assistance; Matching/ challenge support.
Limitations: Giving primarily in Baltimore City, eastern Baltimore County, and Harford county in MD. No support for adult literacy, charter or public schools and political organizations, or for national/ local chapters for specific diseases, legal service organizations, or environmental programs. No grants to individuals, or for annual campaigns, legal services, events or conferences, galas or golf tournaments, one-time only events, seminars or workshops.
Publications: Application guidelines; Grants list; Occasional report.
Application information: Funding for educational institutions is pre-selected.
Initial approach: Use online application process via foundation web site
Deadline(s): See foundation web site for current deadlines
Board meeting date(s): See foundation web site for current meeting dates
Officers: Jeffrey M. Dresher, Pres.; Michael Meoli, V.P.; Virginia M. Dresher, Secy.; Joshua Dresher, Treas.; Robin Platts, Exec. Dir.
Trustees: James R. Butcher; Jeanne D. Butcher; Patricia K. Dresher; Anthony J. Meoli; Virginia Meoli; Marcie Michael; James T. Dresher, Jr.; Susan Roarty; Melanie Robinson.
Number of staff: 1 full-time professional.
EIN: 521610465
Selected grants: The following grants are a representative sample of this grantmaker's funding activity:
$15,000 to Young Audiences of Maryland, Baltimore, MD, 2012. For Supporting the Various Charitable and Civic Endeavor.

3783
Dupkin Educational and Charitable Foundation, Inc. ✧
c/o WMS Partners
1 Olympic Pl., 8th Fl.
Towson, MD 21204-4104

Established in 2000 in MD.
Donors: Manuel Dupkin II; Carol N. Dupkin.
Foundation type: Independent foundation.
Financial data (yr. ended 12/31/13): Assets, $34,768,928 (M); expenditures, $1,493,483; qualifying distributions, $1,363,100; giving activities include $1,363,100 for 24 grants (high: $1,310,000; low: $500).
Purpose and activities: Giving primarily to a Jewish federated giving program, as well as for education.
Fields of interest: Elementary/secondary education; Higher education; Education; Human services; Jewish federated giving programs.
Limitations: Applications not accepted. Giving primarily in Baltimore, MD. No grants to individuals.
Application information: Contributes only to pre-selected organizations.
Officers and Trustees:* Manuel Dupkin II,* Pres.; Carol N. Dupkin,* V.P.; Sally P. Thanhouser,* Secy.-Treas.
EIN: 522277075

3784
The Richard Eaton Foundation ✧
(formerly Eaton Foundation, Inc.)
P.O. Box 84176
Gaithersburg, MD 20883-4176

Established in 1952 in MD.
Foundation type: Independent foundation.
Financial data (yr. ended 12/31/13): Assets, $16,522,337 (M); expenditures, $936,568; qualifying distributions, $760,015; giving activities include $672,500 for 53 grants (high: $100,000; low: $5,000).
Fields of interest: Higher education; Education; Youth development, services; Human services; Children/youth, services.
Type of support: General/operating support; Building/renovation; Scholarship funds.
Limitations: Applications not accepted. Giving primarily in Washington, DC, MD, and VA; some giving also in CA and NH. No grants to individuals.
Application information: Contributes only to pre-selected organizations.
Officer and Trustees:* Gerald J. Hroblak,* Chair.; Neil E. Johnson; John V. Pollock; Grover B. Russell.
EIN: 526040787

3785
The Lois & Richard England Family Foundation, Inc. ✧
(formerly The Lois & Richard England Foundation, Inc.)
P.O. Box 34-1077
Bethesda, MD 20827-1077 (301) 657-7737
Contact: Monica Smith, Prog. Asst.
FAX: (301) 657-7738;
E-mail: englandfamilyfdn@verizon.net; E-mail for Monica Smith: monicasmith.eff@verizon.net; Main URL: http://foundationcenter.org/grantmaker/england/

Established in 1990 in MD.
Donors: Richard England†; Lois H. England.
Foundation type: Independent foundation.
Financial data (yr. ended 12/31/12): Assets, $23,913,339 (M); gifts received, $1,545,380; expenditures, $2,589,850; qualifying distributions, $2,400,993; giving activities include $2,175,117 for 52 grants (high: $245,122; low: $2,000).
Purpose and activities: The foundation is committed to the improvement of the lives of children living in underserved communities in Washington, DC. Its current focus is out-of-school programs that provide academic support and/or enrichment during after-school and summer hours. The foundation is currently focused on supporting programs that serve DC youth as they transition from elementary through middle school to high school. In addition, the foundation supports the Jewish community in the following areas: 1) to promote engagement by the Jewish community in Tikkum Olam through improving the situation of underserved populations and people in crisis; 2) to enhance the democratic nature of Israel by promoting economic empowerment and civil rights for all Israelis; 3) to encourage Jews to become active in Jewish culture, synagogue life, and the Jewish community; 4) to combat anti-Semitism by promoting a positive view of Jews and of Israel through education and dialogue; 5) to build coalitions with non-Jews on areas of common concern and to improve intergroup relations; and 6) to participate in the local Jewish community by supporting local organizations which are valued by trustees of the foundation. In Israel, grants are focused on enhancing the democratic nature of Israel by promoting economic empowerment, civil right, religious diversity, and peaceful coexistence between Jews and Arabs.
Fields of interest: Elementary/secondary education; Child development, education; Children/youth, services; Jewish agencies & synagogues; Economically disadvantaged.
International interests: Israel.
Type of support: General/operating support; Continuing support; Annual campaigns; Capital campaigns; Building/renovation; Program development; Publication; Seed money; Program evaluation; Program-related investments/loans; Matching/challenge support.
Limitations: Applications not accepted. Giving primarily in the Washington, DC, area, and Israel. No grants to individuals.
Publications: Grants list.
Application information: Unsolicited requests for funds not accepted. The foundation may request letters of inquiry from organizations working in targeted areas of interest.
Board meeting date(s): May and Nov.
Officers and Board Members:* Catherine S. England,* Chair.; Lois H. England,* V.P.; Rick England,* Treas.; Larry Akman; Nonie Akman; Diana England.
Number of staff: 1 part-time support.
EIN: 521691418

3786
Diana and Michael David Epstein Family Foundation, Inc. ✧
5410 Edson Ln., No. 300
Rockville, MD 20852-3155

Established in 2000 in MD.
Donors: Michael David Epstein; Diana Ely Epstein.
Foundation type: Independent foundation.
Financial data (yr. ended 12/31/13): Assets, $1,136,117 (M); expenditures, $580,756; qualifying distributions, $568,059; giving activities include $568,059 for 49 grants (high: $250,000; low: $100).
Purpose and activities: Giving primarily to Jewish agencies, temples, schools, and federated giving programs.
Fields of interest: Education; Jewish federated giving programs; Jewish agencies & synagogues.
Type of support: General/operating support; Program-related investments/loans.
Limitations: Applications not accepted. Giving primarily in MD, Washington, DC and NY. No grants to individuals.
Application information: Contributes only to pre-selected organizations.
Officers and Directors:* Michael David Epstein,* Pres. and Treas.; Diana Ely Epstein,* V.P. and Secy.; Neil Gurvitch,* V.P.; Samantha Epstein; Jonathan Rubenstein.
EIN: 311684510

3787
Frank M. Ewing Foundation, Inc. ✧
5610 Wisconsin Ave., Ste. PH20C
Chevy Chase, MD 20815-4443
Contact: Judith Ewing, Dir.

Established around 1994 in MD.
Donor: Frank M. Ewing.
Foundation type: Independent foundation.
Financial data (yr. ended 09/30/13): Assets, $8,931,330 (M); gifts received, $1,100; expenditures, $482,647; qualifying distributions, $453,000; giving activities include $453,000 for 42 grants (high: $50,000; low: $1,000).
Purpose and activities: Giving primarily for health and human services; support also for education.
Fields of interest: Elementary/secondary education; Medical care, rehabilitation; Cancer.
Type of support: General/operating support; Continuing support; Annual campaigns; Capital campaigns; Research.
Limitations: Applications accepted. Giving on a national basis. No grants to individuals.
Application information: Application form required.
Initial approach: Letter
Copies of proposal: 1
Deadline(s): None
Board meeting date(s): Oct.
Officers: Frank M. Ewing, Pres.; Frances E. Tennery, V.P. and Treas.; Elizabeth P. Robinson, Secy.; Peggy E. Atherton, Treas.
Director: Judy Ewing.
Number of staff: 2 full-time professional.
EIN: 521902030

3788
The Sherman Fairchild Foundation, Inc. ✧
5454 Wisconsin Ave., Ste. 1205
Chevy Chase, MD 20815-6934 (301) 913-5990
Contact: Bonnie Himmelman, Pres.

Incorporated in 1955 in NY.
Donors: May Fairchild†; Sherman Fairchild†.
Foundation type: Independent foundation.
Financial data (yr. ended 12/31/13): Assets, $671,317,262 (M); expenditures, $36,969,747; qualifying distributions, $30,779,019; giving

activities include $29,645,912 for 83 grants (high: $5,000,000; low: $5,000).
Purpose and activities: Emphasis on higher education and fine arts and cultural institutions; some support for medical research and social welfare.
Fields of interest: Visual arts; Performing arts; Arts; Higher education; Medical research, institute; Human services.
Limitations: Applications not accepted. Giving primarily in CA, Boston, MA, NH, New York, NY and Washington, DC.
Application information: Unsolicited requests for funds not accepted.
Officers and Directors:* Walter F. Burke III,* Chair.; Bonnie Himmelman,* Pres.; Walter Burke,* Treas.; Julie McLean, Cont.; Charles L. Biggs; Bruce M. Dresner; Carol Folt; Dale Knobel; Michele Myers; Charles E. Pierce; James Wright.
Number of staff: 3 full-time professional.
EIN: 131951698
Selected grants: The following grants are a representative sample of this grantmaker's funding activity:
$5,000,000 to Connecticut College, New London, CT, 2012. For Life Science and Computer Science Facility.
$1,666,666 to Metropolitan Museum of Art, New York, NY, 2012. For Strategic Support Grant.
$1,517,654 to University of California, San Francisco, CA, 2012. For Novel Therapeutics for Prion Diseases.
$896,000 to California Institute of Technology, Pasadena, CA, 2012. For Simulation of eXtreme Spacetimes (SXS) Research Programs.
$500,000 to Salvation Army of Greater New York, New York, NY, 2012. For General Operations.
$114,900 to California Institute of Technology, Pasadena, CA, 2012. For Stephen Hawking Visit.
$100,000 to Phillips Collection, Washington, DC, 2012. For Education in Museums Phase II.
$99,900 to Clark University, Worcester, MA, 2012. For SEP Phase XI.
$50,000 to Greenwich Adult Day Care, Cos Cob, CT, 2012. For General Support.
$25,000 to Soft Power Health, Purchase, NY, 2012. For Education, Prevention and Control of Malaria in Uganda.

3789
Felburn Foundation ✧
c/o Robert Philipson & Co.
8601 Georgia Ave., Ste. 1001
Silver Spring, MD 20910-3445

Established in 1978 in VA.
Donors: Phil Felburn†; The Aetna Freight Lines, Inc.
Foundation type: Independent foundation.
Financial data (yr. ended 12/31/12): Assets, $39,406,331 (M); expenditures, $1,829,628; qualifying distributions, $1,267,200; giving activities include $1,267,200 for grants.
Purpose and activities: Giving primarily for natural resources conservation, the environment, and wildlife preservation and protection.
Fields of interest: Higher education; Environment, natural resources; Animals/wildlife, preservation/protection.
Limitations: Applications not accepted. Giving primarily in FL and VA. No grants to individuals.
Application information: Contributes only to pre-selected organizations.
Officers and Directors:* Larry J. White,* Chair. and Pres.; Charles Freeman,* V.P.; Guy Marwick, Secy.-Treas. and Exec. Dir.; B. Kemp Floyd.
EIN: 510234331

3790
Gramma Fisher Foundation ✧
P.O. Box 1647
Easton, MD 21601-8933
Mailing address: c/o Christine F. Hunter, Chair., 6967 Cooke's Hope Dr., Easton, MD 21601, tel.: (410) 822-8450

Incorporated in 1957 in IA.
Donors: J. William Fisher†; William T. Hunter.
Foundation type: Independent foundation.
Financial data (yr. ended 12/31/13): Assets, $28,520,676 (M); expenditures, $1,465,805; qualifying distributions, $1,301,280; giving activities include $1,301,280 for 2+ grants (high: $951,000).
Purpose and activities: Grants mainly for the support and sponsorship of opera.
Fields of interest: Performing arts; Performing arts centers; Performing arts, music; Performing arts, opera.
Limitations: Applications not accepted. Giving in the U.S., primarily in New York, NY. No grants to individuals.
Application information: Unsolicited requests for funds not accepted.
Board meeting date(s): As necessary
Officers: Christine F. Hunter, Chair.; William T. Hunter, Jr., Treas.
EIN: 426068755
Selected grants: The following grants are a representative sample of this grantmaker's funding activity:
$1,154,260 to Metropolitan Opera, New York, NY, 2012. For sustaining grant.

3791
Alice Virginia & David W. Fletcher Foundation ✧
82 W. Washington St.
Hagerstown, MD 21740-4880 (301) 739-6450
Contact: William P. Young, Jr., Exec. Dir.
Main URL: http://www.avdwfletcherfoundation.org/

Established in 1991 in MD.
Donor: Alice Virginia Fletcher†.
Foundation type: Independent foundation.
Financial data (yr. ended 12/31/13): Assets, $19,847,194 (M); gifts received, $785; expenditures, $1,130,298; qualifying distributions, $968,293; giving activities include $903,839 for 26 grants (high: $120,000; low: $4,000).
Purpose and activities: Giving primarily to organizations that benefit the citizens of Washington County, MD.
Fields of interest: Museums (art); Higher education; Libraries (public); Health care; Boys & girls clubs; Foundations (community).
Limitations: Applications accepted. Giving limited to Washington County, MD, with emphasis on Hagerstown. No grants to individuals.
Application information: Application form required.
Initial approach: Letter
Deadline(s): None
Officers: M. Kenneth Long, Jr., Pres.; Hugh J. Breslin III, V.P.; Sandra S. Tillou, Secy.-Treas.; William P. Young, Jr., Exec. Dir.
Directors: Winchester Sherman; Gregory I. Snook.
Number of staff: None.
EIN: 521789319

3792
Sid & Mary Foulger Foundation, Inc. ✧
9600 Blackwell Rd., Ste. 200
Rockville, MD 20850-4315

Established in 1997 in MD.
Donors: Mary Foulger; Sidney W. Foulger; Bryant F. Foulger.
Foundation type: Independent foundation.
Financial data (yr. ended 12/31/13): Assets, $5,489,874 (M); gifts received, $5,744,893; expenditures, $944,153; qualifying distributions, $944,153; giving activities include $283,152 for 29 grants to individuals (high: $140,000; low: $1,300).
Purpose and activities: Giving primarily for higher education assistance.
Fields of interest: Higher education.
Type of support: Scholarships—to individuals.
Limitations: Applications not accepted. Giving primarily in MD and UT.
Application information: Unsolicited requests for funds not accepted.
Directors: Bryant F. Foulger; Clayton F. Foulger; Sidney W. Foulger; Brent K. Pratt.
EIN: 522062781

3793
The Foundation for Adventist Education ✧
1909 Armond Ln.
Silver Spring, MD 20905-3925

Established in 2007 in MD.
Donors: Ernest Edward Zinke; Leonora Anne Zinke; Ann's House of Nuts; Douglas E. Zinke; Christy Zinke; Ernest E. Zinke 2004 Irrevocable Trust.
Foundation type: Independent foundation.
Financial data (yr. ended 12/31/13): Assets, $10,598,950 (M); gifts received, $146,510; expenditures, $913,381; qualifying distributions, $874,783; giving activities include $874,783 for 20 grants (high: $300,000; low: $200).
Fields of interest: Higher education; Theological school/education.
Limitations: Applications not accepted. Giving in the U.S., with some emphasis on CA, MI and TX. No grants to individuals.
Application information: Unsolicited requests for funds not accepted.
Trustees: Ernest Edward Zinke; Leonora Anne Zinke.
EIN: 546771807

3794
The Foundation for Maryland's Future ✧
8171 Maple Lawn Blvd., Ste. 375
Fulton, MD 20759-2531

Established in 1994 in MD.
Donor: Stewart Bainum, Jr.
Foundation type: Independent foundation.
Financial data (yr. ended 12/31/12): Assets, $4,122,723 (M); expenditures, $685,968; qualifying distributions, $668,714; giving activities

include $661,700 for 27 grants (high: $190,000; low: $1,000).
Fields of interest: Arts; Higher education; Education; Health care; Human services.
Type of support: General/operating support; Annual campaigns.
Limitations: Applications not accepted. Giving primarily in Washington, DC, and Baltimore, MD. No grants to individuals.
Application information: Unsolicited requests for funds not accepted.
Trustees: Stewart Bainum, Jr.; Christine A. Shreve.
EIN: 521907725

3795
John Edward Fowler Memorial Foundation ✧
4340 East-West Hwy., Ste. 206
Bethesda, MD 20814-4467 (301) 654-2700
Contact: Richard H. Lee, Pres.
FAX: (301) 654-6700; Main URL: http://fdnweb.org/fowler
Grants List: http://fdnweb.org/fowler/recent-grants/

Incorporated in 1964 in DE.
Donor: Pearl Gunn Fowler†.
Foundation type: Independent foundation.
Financial data (yr. ended 12/31/13): Assets, $36,882,971 (M); expenditures, $1,947,685; qualifying distributions, $1,761,838; giving activities include $1,490,000 for 80 grants (high: $85,000; low: $5,000).
Purpose and activities: Primary areas of interest include the disadvantaged, with emphasis on the homeless, housing, food programs and youth education. Giving primarily to small community service organizations with little public funding, especially for programs that benefit children and youth; support also for social service agencies, literacy programs, and programs that help the elderly maintain their independence.
Fields of interest: Child development, education; Adult education—literacy, basic skills & GED; Education, reading; Food services; Housing/shelter, development; Human services; Children/youth, services; Child development, services; Aging, centers/services; Homeless, human services; Infants/toddlers; Children/youth; Youth; Adults; Aging; Physically disabled; Mentally disabled; Minorities; Economically disadvantaged; Homeless.
Type of support: Continuing support; General/operating support; Building/renovation; Equipment; Consulting services; Matching/challenge support.
Limitations: Applications accepted. Giving limited to the Washington, DC, Beltway area, including suburbs in MD and VA that abut the District of Columbia. No support for agencies principally funded by local, state or federal government sources, national health organizations, or for medical research programs or national organizations. No grants to individuals, or for capital grants (with the exception of long-time grantees); no loans.
Publications: Application guidelines; Grants list; IRS Form 990 or 990-PF printed copy available upon request.
Application information: Washington Grantmakers' Common Grant Application Form accepted, but not required. Application form and application guidelines available on foundation web site.
Initial approach: Telephone call requesting application form and guidelines. Do not send letters of inquiry
Copies of proposal: 1
Deadline(s): None
Board meeting date(s): Periodically
Final notification: Approximately 6 months
Officers and Trustees:* Richard H. Lee,* Pres.; Michael P. Bentzen,* Secy.; Jeffery P. Capron,* Treas.
Number of staff: 1 part-time professional.
EIN: 516019469

3796
France-Merrick Foundation
(formerly The Jacob and Annita France Foundation)
2 Hamill Rd., Ste. 302
Baltimore, MD 21210-1813 (410) 464-2004
Contact: Amy Gross, Exec. Dir.
FAX: (410) 464-2001;
E-mail: info@france-merrickfdn.org; Main URL: http://www.france-merrickfdn.org/

The Jacob and Annita France Foundation was created in 1959. The Robert G. and Anne M. Merrick Foundation was created in 1962. The two foundations were legally merged on June 1,1998, and now operate as the France-Merrick Foundation.
Donors: Robert G. Merrick, Sr.†; Robert G. Merrick, Jr.†; Jacob France†; Annita France†; Anne M. Merrick†.
Foundation type: Independent foundation.
Financial data (yr. ended 05/31/13): Assets, $202,164,610 (M); expenditures, $10,541,668; qualifying distributions, $9,094,945; giving activities include $8,583,357 for 245 grants (high: $250,000; low: $500).
Purpose and activities: Reflecting the interests of its founders, the foundation strives to improve the quality of life in the Greater Baltimore region by focusing its giving in five priority areas: civic & culture, community development, education, health & human welfare, and historic preservation & conservation.
Fields of interest: Historic preservation/historical societies; Arts; Education; Environment; Health care; Human services; Community/economic development.
Type of support: Building/renovation; Capital campaigns; Equipment; Management development/capacity building; Matching/challenge support; Technical assistance.
Limitations: Applications accepted. Giving primarily in Baltimore city, MD, and the five surrounding counties. No grants for operating expenses, sponsorship of fundraising events, symposiums, conferences, or annual giving campaigns.
Publications: Application guidelines.
Application information: Guidelines for applying for a grant are available upon request. The Association of Baltimore Area Grantmakers Common Grant Application Form is also accepted. If request involves new construction or renovation of an existing structure, special attention will be given to the sustainable building practices of the project and if LEED certification is expected. Application form not required.
Initial approach: First submit a letter of inquiry containing brief description of the organization and the project for which funding is sought, total cost of the project and the amount of the request, a timeline over which funding is needed, and overall timeline of the project. Once the letter of inquiry is reviewed the applicant will be notified if they are invited to submit a full proposal.
Copies of proposal: 1
Deadline(s): Letters of intent are accepted through out the year
Board meeting date(s): Five meetings are held annually
Final notification: After a request is considered at a board meeting, the applicant will be notified of a decision within a few days
Officers and Directors:* Walter D. Pinkard, Jr.,* Pres.; Robert G. Merrick III,* V.P.; Robert M. Pinkard,* Secy.; Gregory C. Pinkard,* Treas.; Amy Gross, Exec. Dir.; Freeman A. Hrabowski III; Juliet Eurich.
Number of staff: 2 full-time professional; 3 part-time professional.
EIN: 526072964
Selected grants: The following grants are a representative sample of this grantmaker's funding activity:
$500,000 to University of Maryland-Baltimore Foundation, Baltimore, MD, 2013.
$300,000 to Mount Vernon Place Conservancy, Baltimore, MD, 2013.
$200,000 to Chesapeake Shakespeare Company, Ellicott City, MD, 2013.
$150,000 to Jemicy School, Owings Mills, MD, 2013.
$100,000 to Baltimore Substance Abuse Systems, Baltimore, MD, 2013.
$100,000 to Center for Urban Families, Baltimore, MD, 2013.
$50,000 to Baltimore Community Toolbank, Baltimore, MD, 2013.
$50,000 to Helping Up Mission, Baltimore, MD, 2013.
$50,000 to Ladew Topiary Gardens, Monkton, MD, 2013.
$40,000 to Franciscan Center, Baltimore, MD, 2013.
$40,000 to Northwood Appold Community Academy Charter School, Baltimore, MD, 2013.
$20,000 to Waverly Main Street, Baltimore, MD, 2013.
$15,000 to Project Liberty Ship, Baltimore, MD, 2013.

3797
The Carl M. Freeman Foundation, Inc. ✧
111 Rockville Pike
Rockville, MD 20850-5109
Contact: Patti A. Grimes, Exec. Dir.
E-mail: patti@freemafoundation.org; Telephone for Patti Grimes: (302) 436-3003; Main URL: http://www.carlfreemanfoundation.org/

Established in 1960.
Donors: Joshua M. Freeman†; Carl M. Freeman Charitable Lead Trust; The Freeman Foundation Charitable Lead Annuity Trust.
Foundation type: Independent foundation.
Financial data (yr. ended 12/31/13): Assets, $40,907,701 (M); gifts received, $15,582,361; expenditures, $3,246,484; qualifying distributions, $3,129,314; giving activities include $2,351,575 for 102 grants (high: $1,600,000; low: $100).
Purpose and activities: The foundation commits its time, talent and treasure to facilitate, support, and promote innovative community-based leadership and giving. The foundation seeks to honor our founders' legacies and passions by endorsing

excellence and leveraging resources. Generally, the foundation limits donations to communities where the customers, employees, and vendors of the Carl M. Freeman Companies live and work.
Fields of interest: Performing arts; Performing arts centers; Arts; Education; Human services; Child development, services; Jewish federated giving programs; Jewish agencies & synagogues.
Type of support: General/operating support; Continuing support; Annual campaigns; Equipment; Program development; Technical assistance; Employee matching gifts; Matching/challenge support.
Limitations: Giving in the greater Washington, DC, area, (Delmarva communities), as well as the Eastern Panhandle of WV. No support for religious organizations for religious work. No grants to individuals.
Publications: Application guidelines; Annual report; Grants list.
Application information: Application information and guidelines available on foundation web site. Application form required.
Deadline(s): See foundation web site for current deadlines
Board meeting date(s): Generally on a quarterly basis
Officers and Trustees:* Michelle D. Freeman,* Chair. and Pres.; Stephen B. Huttler,* Secy.; Christine A. Shreve,* Treas.; Patti Grimes, Exec. Dir.
EIN: 526047536
Selected grants: The following grants are a representative sample of this grantmaker's funding activity:
$3,470 to Indian River School District, Selbyville, DE, 2012. For arts and drama.

3798
Dr. and Mrs. James Frenkil Charitable Foundation ✧ ☆

1104 Kenilworth Dr., Ste. 300
Towson, MD 21204-3102
Application address: c/o Carolyn Frenkil, 7205 Park Heights Ave., Baltimore, MD 21208, tel.: (410) 828-4446

Established in 2000 in MD.
Donor: James Frenkil.
Foundation type: Independent foundation.
Financial data (yr. ended 11/30/13): Assets, $10,441,943 (M); expenditures, $635,275; qualifying distributions, $525,000; giving activities include $525,000 for 24 grants (high: $250,000; low: $350).
Fields of interest: Education; Health care; Religion.
Limitations: Applications accepted. Giving primarily in MD.
Application information: Application form required.
Initial approach: Request grant format
Deadline(s): None
Trustees: Carolyn Frenkil; Samuel Handwerger; Francis Hogle; Wilbur Jensen.
EIN: 522312432

3799
Samuel & Zehava Friedman Jewish Learning Exchange Inc. ✧ ☆

18511 Viburnum Way
Olney, MD 20832-3076 (301) 523-1818
Contact: Joseph Friedman, Pres.
E-mail: novograd@comcast.net

Established in 2004 in MD.
Donors: Emanuel J. Friedman; Friedman French Foundation.
Foundation type: Independent foundation.
Financial data (yr. ended 12/31/13): Assets, $49,207 (M); gifts received, $684,350; expenditures, $649,853; qualifying distributions, $649,853; giving activities include $550,759 for 54 grants (high: $112,500; low: $150).
Purpose and activities: Giving primarily to Jewish education programs and schools.
Fields of interest: Elementary/secondary education; Higher education; Scholarships/financial aid; Education; Jewish agencies & synagogues.
Limitations: Applications accepted. Giving primarily in MD and NY.
Application information: Proposals may be e-mailed. Application form required.
Initial approach: Letter requesting application form for scholarships; other applicants should send a letter stating amount requested and purpose of grant
Deadline(s): None
Officers: Joseph Friedman, Pres.; Elisabeth Friedman, Secy.-Treas.
Directors: Daniel Friedman; Michael Friedman.
EIN: 200509400
Selected grants: The following grants are a representative sample of this grantmaker's funding activity:
$8,500 to Yeshiva of Greater Washington, Silver Spring, MD, 2012. For Jewish education scholarship grants.

3800
Fusco Family Foundation, Inc. ✧ ☆

1245 Cherry Tree Ln.
Annapolis, MD 21403-5023

Established in 2001 in MD.
Donors: Jack A. Fusco; Kristin A. Fusco.
Foundation type: Independent foundation.
Financial data (yr. ended 12/31/13): Assets, $4,551,658 (M); expenditures, $1,047,094; qualifying distributions, $1,022,300; giving activities include $1,022,300 for 4 grants (high: $1,014,300; low: $500).
Fields of interest: Higher education, university; Education; Human services; Christian agencies & churches.
Limitations: Applications not accepted. No grants to individuals.
Application information: Contributes only to pre-selected organizations.
Officers: Kristin A. Fusco, Pres. and Treas.; Jack A. Fusco, Secy.
EIN: 522363816
Selected grants: The following grants are a representative sample of this grantmaker's funding activity:
$100,000 to Bates College, Lewiston, ME, 2011.

3801
GEICO Philanthropic Foundation ✧

c/o GEICO Corp.
5260 Western Ave.
Chevy Chase, MD 20815-3701 (301) 986-2750
Contact: Seth M. Ingall, Chair.
Main URL: http://www.geico.com/information/military/service-awards/
Military Service Award Recipients: http://www.geico.com/information/military/award-winners/
Contact for Military Service Awards: Mike Baker, Military Dept., Dir., GEICO, One GEICO Plaza, Washington, DC 20076; tel.: (800) 824-5404, ext. 3906, e-mail: mbaker@geico.com

Established in 1980 in DC.
Donor: Government Employees Insurance Co.
Foundation type: Company-sponsored foundation.
Financial data (yr. ended 12/31/12): Assets, $58,293,306 (M); gifts received, $6,483,521; expenditures, $8,963,658; qualifying distributions, $8,960,704; giving activities include $8,945,704 for 1,536 grants (high: $1,173,032; low: $15), and $15,000 for 6 grants to individuals (high: $2,500; low: $2,500).
Purpose and activities: The foundation supports organizations involved with serious injury rehabilitation, automotive safety, and children's services, and awards grants to federal employees and active members of the military.
Fields of interest: Hospitals (general); Health care, clinics/centers; Medical care, rehabilitation; Health care; Cancer; Breast cancer; Crime/law enforcement; Safety, automotive safety; Boys & girls clubs; Girl scouts; Children, services; United Ways and Federated Giving Programs; Military/veterans' organizations.
Type of support: General/operating support; Sponsorships; Employee matching gifts; Employee-related scholarships; Grants to individuals; Scholarships—to individuals.
Limitations: Applications accepted. Giving primarily in CA, Washington, DC, FL, GA, MD, NY, TX and VA. No support for political organizations or religious organizations not of direct benefit to the entire community. No grants to individuals (except for GEICO Public Service Awards, Military Service Awards, and scholarships).
Application information: Visit website for nomination addresses for Military Service Awards. The foundation primarily supports groups where GEICO associates have significant involvement.
Initial approach: Proposal; contact selected military service channels for Military Service Awards
Deadline(s): None; Oct. 31 for Military Service Awards
Board meeting date(s): Quarterly
Officers and Directors:* Seth M. Ingall, Chair.; Dana K. Proulx,* Pres.; William C. E. Robinson, Secy.; Michael H. Campbell,* Treas.; Stephen C. Parsons; Nancy L. Pierce; Rynthia M. Rost.
Number of staff: 1 full-time professional.
EIN: 521202740
Selected grants: The following grants are a representative sample of this grantmaker's funding activity:
$1,173,032 to Insurance Institute for Highway Safety, Arlington, VA, 2012.
$300,000 to Wounded Warrior Project, Jacksonville, FL, 2012.
$218,610 to Scholarship America, Saint Peter, MN, 2012.
$161,000 to United Way of Central Georgia, Macon, GA, 2012.
$156,398 to Childrens National Medical Center, Washington, DC, 2012.
$70,000 to Dori Slosberg Foundation, Boca Raton, FL, 2012.

$40,000 to American Cancer Society, Virginia Beach, VA, 2012.
$22,000 to United Way of Buffalo and Erie County, Buffalo, NY, 2012.
$3,000 to House of Ruth, Washington, DC, 2012.
$2,184 to George Mason University Foundation, Fairfax, VA, 2012.

3802
Lowell & Harriet Glazer Family Foundation ✧

(formerly Lowell R. Glazer Family Foundation)
9690 Deereco Rd., Ste. 500
Timonium, MD 21093-6900

Established in 1989 in MD.
Donor: Lowell R. Glazer.
Foundation type: Independent foundation.
Financial data (yr. ended 12/31/13): Assets, $1,069,420 (M); gifts received, $331,004; expenditures, $543,673; qualifying distributions, $538,554; giving activities include $530,868 for 74 grants (high: $100,000; low: $36).
Purpose and activities: Giving primarily to Jewish organizations; some funding also for education, health, and social services.
Fields of interest: Higher education; Education; Hospitals (general); Health care; Health organizations, association; Human services; Jewish federated giving programs; Jewish agencies & synagogues.
Limitations: Applications not accepted. Giving primarily in MD. No grants to individuals.
Application information: Contributes only to pre-selected organizations.
Trustees: John P. Abosch; Lowell R. Glazer; Gerald M. Katz.
EIN: 521633239

3803
Morris Goldseker Foundation of Maryland, Inc. ✧

(also known as Goldseker Foundation)
c/o Symphony Center
1040 Park Ave., Ste. 310
Baltimore, MD 21201-5635 (410) 837-5100
Contact: Laurie Latuda Kinkel, Prog. Off.
FAX: (410) 837-7927;
E-mail: laurie@goldsekerfoundation.org; Laurie Latuda Kinkel tel.: (410) 837-6115; Main URL: http://www.goldsekerfoundation.org
Facebook: http://www.facebook.com/pages/Goldseker-Foundation/141220962603871?v=wall
Grants Database: http://www.goldsekerfoundation.org/search_the_grants_database
Twitter: http://twitter.com/GoldsekerFdn

Incorporated in 1973 in MD.
Donor: Morris Goldseker†.
Foundation type: Independent foundation.
Financial data (yr. ended 12/31/12): Assets, $89,855,843 (M); expenditures, $4,657,475; qualifying distributions, $4,175,778; giving activities include $2,941,528 for 92+ grants (high: $261,550).
Purpose and activities: In 2000, the Goldseker Foundation's Board of Trustees and its Selection Committee adopted a two-track approach to grantmaking. This approach designates priority areas that build on existing experience and investments, but it also retains the ability to respond to new ideas and opportunities within the established program areas. The foundation's grantmaking funds will focus on the first-track priority areas. In these areas - community development, regionalism, and the nonprofit sector - the foundation will be a more directly engaged and active partner. The existing grantmaking policies apply to the priority areas. Grants will include a mix of foundation initiatives and projects submitted independently by potential grantees. The second track focuses on the foundation's established program areas: neighborhood development, community affairs, human services, and education.
Fields of interest: Education; Housing/shelter, search services; Human services; Community development, neighborhood development; Public affairs, association.
Type of support: Program development; Seed money; Technical assistance; Consulting services; Program-related investments/loans; Matching/challenge support.
Limitations: Applications accepted. Giving limited to the Baltimore, MD, area. No support for advocacy or political action groups, religious purposes, arts or cultural affairs, specific diseases or disabilities, or for projects normally financed with public funds. No grants to individuals, or for building or endowment funds, deficit financing, annual campaigns, or publications.
Publications: Annual report; Financial statement; Informational brochure (including application guidelines).
Application information: Submit preliminary letter as early as possible before deadlines. See foundation web site for application information, and information on applying for Management Assistance Grants. Association of Baltimore Area Grantmakers Common Grant Application Form accepted. Application form not required.
Initial approach: Letter or telephone inquiry
Copies of proposal: 1
Deadline(s): Feb. 1, May 1, and Sept. 1
Board meeting date(s): Distribution committee meets 3 times a year (Mar., June, and Oct.)
Final notification: Following committee meetings
Officers and Directors:* Sheldon Goldseker,* Chair.; Simon Goldseker,* Vice-Chair.; Matthew D. Gallagher, C.E.O. and Pres; Sheila L. Purkey, V.P., Secy.-Treas. and Cont.; Ana Goldseker; Deby Goldseker; Sharna Goldseker; Susan B. Katzenberg; Howard M. Weiss.
Advisory Selection Committee: Ronald J. Daniels; Marc B. Terrill; David Wilson.
Number of staff: 2 full-time professional; 2 part-time professional; 1 full-time support.
EIN: 520983502

3804
The Goldsmith Family Foundation Inc. ✧

1829 Reisterstown Rd., Ste. 430
Baltimore, MD 21208-7107 (410) 484-9292
Contact: Denise Geiger, Assoc.
FAX: (410) 486-9022; E-mail for Denise Geiger: denise@gffinc.org; tel. for Denise Geiger: (410) 484-9293; Main URL: http://www.goldsmithfamilyfoundation.org/

Established in 1990 in MD.
Foundation type: Independent foundation.
Financial data (yr. ended 09/30/13): Assets, $21,719,911 (M); expenditures, $1,051,936; qualifying distributions, $916,688; giving activities include $758,599 for 86 grants (high: $100,000; low: $250).
Purpose and activities: The foundation is committed to enhancing the lives of Baltimore, MD, area youth by providing enriched educational and cultural opportunities. The foundation considers proposals which include curriculum enhancement, teacher and principal training programs, cultural institutions proving programming for Baltimore City students, tutoring and mentoring programs, after-school programs and summer learning opportunities.
Fields of interest: Arts; Elementary school/education; Higher education; Education; Human services; Youth, services.
Type of support: General/operating support; Scholarship funds.
Limitations: Applications not accepted. Giving primarily in Baltimore, MD. No grants to individuals, or for endowments, building campaigns, deficit financing, publications or events.
Application information: The foundation is currently not accepting proposals from any programs or institutions it has not previously funded. Applicants previously funded by the foundation should visit foundation web site for application information.
Board meeting date(s): Jan., Apr., July and Oct.
Officers and Trustees:* Beth Goldsmith,* Pres.; Alan Berkowitz,* Treas.; Raymond Altman; Adam Goldsmith; H. Josh Goldsmith; Julie Goldsmith Rosenberg.
EIN: 521714353
Selected grants: The following grants are a representative sample of this grantmaker's funding activity:
$50,000 to Teach for America, Baltimore, MD, 2011. For general support.
$30,000 to Middle Grades Partnership, Baltimore, MD, 2011. For general support.
$25,000 to Baltimore Symphony Orchestra, Baltimore, MD, 2011. For general support.
$25,000 to Goucher College, Baltimore, MD, 2011. For general support.
$20,000 to Baltimore School for the Arts, Baltimore, MD, 2011. For general support.
$20,000 to United States Holocaust Memorial Museum, Washington, DC, 2011. For general support.
$15,000 to Baltimore Urban Debate League, Baltimore, MD, 2011. For general support.
$15,000 to Buddy Program, Aspen, CO, 2011. For general support.
$11,068 to Southwest Baltimore Charter School, Baltimore, MD, 2011. For general support.
$10,000 to CenterStage, Baltimore, MD, 2011. For general support.

3805
The Gordon Foundation, Inc. ✧ ☆

8015 Cobble Creek Cir.
Potomac, MD 20854-2732 (301) 983-3774

Donor: Everett J. Gordon.
Foundation type: Independent foundation.
Financial data (yr. ended 12/31/12): Assets, $103 (M); expenditures, $758,580; qualifying distributions, $758,084; giving activities include $758,084 for grants.
Fields of interest: Arts; Health care; Religion.
Type of support: General/operating support.
Application information: Application form not required.

Initial approach: Proposal
Deadline(s): None
Officers: Marian K. Gordon, Pres. and Secy.; Solvin W. Gordon, V.P.
EIN: 526054097
Selected grants: The following grants are a representative sample of this grantmaker's funding activity:
$10,000 to American Society for Technion-Israel Institute of Technology, New York, NY, 2011.
$5,000 to National Jewish Health, Denver, CO, 2011.
$2,250 to Jewish Federation of Greater Washington, Rockville, MD, 2011.

3806
Stephen M. Gorn Family Foundation, Inc. ✧ ☆

124 Slade Ave., Ste. 200
Baltimore, MD 21208-4991

Established in 2006 in MD.
Donor: Stephen M. Gorn.
Foundation type: Independent foundation.
Financial data (yr. ended 12/31/13): Assets, $61,694 (M); gifts received, $750,000; expenditures, $732,644; qualifying distributions, $727,881; giving activities include $727,881 for 2 grants (high: $726,881; low: $1,000).
Fields of interest: Buddhism.
Limitations: Applications not accepted. Giving primarily in MA. No grants to individuals.
Application information: Contributes only to pre-selected organizations.
Officers: Stephen M. Gorn, Pres. and Treas.; James C. Oliver, Secy.
EIN: 208022777
Selected grants: The following grants are a representative sample of this grantmaker's funding activity:
$209,832 to University of Pennsylvania, Philadelphia, PA, 2011.
$15,000 to Vegetarian Resource Group, Baltimore, MD, 2011.

3807
W. R. Grace Foundation Inc. ✧

7500 Grace Dr.
Columbia, MD 21044 (410) 531-4000
Contact: Pamela Wagoner, Chair.

Incorporated in 1996 in FL.
Donors: W.R. Grace & Co.; W. R. Grace.
Foundation type: Company-sponsored foundation.
Financial data (yr. ended 12/31/13): Assets, $422,757 (M); gifts received, $560,000; expenditures, $791,619; qualifying distributions, $768,005; giving activities include $762,236 for 166 grants (high: $86,433; low: $100).
Purpose and activities: The foundation supports organizations involved with arts and culture, the environment, health, youth development, human services, and civic affairs. Special emphasis is directed toward programs designed to address education and basic needs.
Fields of interest: Museums; Arts; Higher education; Education; Environment, natural resources; Environment; Hospitals (general); Health care; Food services; Youth development; Human services; United Ways and Federated Giving Programs; Public affairs.
Type of support: General/operating support; Capital campaigns; Building/renovation; Program development; Scholarship funds; Employee matching gifts.
Limitations: Applications accepted. Giving on a national basis in areas of company operations in the U.S. and in Canada.
Publications: Application guidelines.
Application information: Application form not required.
Initial approach: Proposal
Deadline(s): None
Officers & Directors: Pamela Wagoner,* Chair.; William Dockman, Co-Vice-Chair. and Treas.; Mark A. Shelnitz,* Co-Vice-Chair.; Hudson La Force III,* Co-Vice-Chair.; John A. McFarland, Secy.; Michael Jones, Exec. Dir.
EIN: 650630671
Selected grants: The following grants are a representative sample of this grantmaker's funding activity:
$20,910 to Truist, Atlanta, GA, 2012. For Grants United Way.
$10,000 to National Aquarium in Baltimore, Baltimore, MD, 2012. For grants cultural.
$5,600 to Phoenix Boys Association, Atlanta, GA, 2012. For grants urban-minority-civic.
$5,000 to Duke University, Fuqua School of Business, Durham, NC, 2012. For grants educational.
$5,000 to University of North Carolina, Chapel Hill, NC, 2012. For grants educational.
$2,500 to Rebuilding Together Montgomery County, Gaithersburg, MD, 2012. For Grants Health, Science and Human Services.

3808
Louis H. Gross Foundation, Inc. ✧

c/o B. Waldholtz
P.O. Box 217
Riderwood, MD 21139-0217

Established in 1959 in NY.
Donors: Frank Sutland†; Josephine Sutland†.
Foundation type: Independent foundation.
Financial data (yr. ended 12/31/13): Assets, $12,482,799 (M); gifts received, $1,042,542; expenditures, $1,542,235; qualifying distributions, $1,527,950; giving activities include $1,527,950 for 35 grants (high: $525,000; low: $1,000).
Purpose and activities: Giving primarily for child health, education, and welfare, including pediatric centers and programs for physically or learning disabled youth.
Fields of interest: Hospitals (general); Children/youth, services; Children/youth; Disabilities, people with.
Limitations: Applications not accepted. Giving primarily in Baltimore, MD. No support for political organizations. No grants to individuals.
Application information: Contributes only to pre-selected organizations. Unsolicited requests for funds not accepted.
Board meeting date(s): Annually
Officers and Directors:* Sheila S. Pakula,* Pres.; Baila P. Waldholtz, Secy.; Annette Kessel; Lawrence Pakula; Dale E. Perreault.
Number of staff: None.
EIN: 146018307
Selected grants: The following grants are a representative sample of this grantmaker's funding activity:
$260,000 to Jemicy School, Owings Mills, MD, 2012. For Children with Learning Disabilities.

3809
The Homer and Martha Gudelsky Family Foundation, Inc. ✧

11900 Tech Rd.
Silver Spring, MD 20904-1910 (301) 622-0100
Contact: Medda Gudelsky, V.P.

Incorporated in 1968 in MD.
Donors: Percontee, Inc.; Jonathan Genn; Members of the Gudelsky family.
Foundation type: Independent foundation.
Financial data (yr. ended 12/31/13): Assets, $58,800,599 (M); expenditures, $3,116,413; qualifying distributions, $3,110,000; giving activities include $3,110,000 for 40 grants (high: $600,000; low: $5,000).
Fields of interest: Higher education; Health care; Jewish agencies & synagogues.
Type of support: Annual campaigns; Capital campaigns; Building/renovation; Equipment; Scholarship funds; Research.
Limitations: Applications accepted. Giving primarily in FL and MD. No grants to individuals.
Application information: Application form required.
Initial approach: Letter
Deadline(s): None
Officers: John Gudelsky, Pres.; Medda Gudelsky, V.P.; Rita Regino, V.P.; Holly Stone, V.P.; Jonathan Genn, Secy.; Samuel Yedlin, Treas.
EIN: 520885969

3810
The Hackerman Foundation, Inc. ✧

300 E. Joppa Rd., 8th Fl.
Baltimore, MD 21286-3048

Donor: The Whiting-Turner Construction Company.
Foundation type: Independent foundation.
Financial data (yr. ended 12/31/13): Assets, $521,315 (M); gifts received, $2,678,757; expenditures, $2,404,813; qualifying distributions, $2,404,813; giving activities include $2,404,813 for 77 grants (high: $425,000; low: $100).
Fields of interest: Higher education; Jewish federated giving programs.
Limitations: Applications not accepted. Giving primarily in MD; some funding also in NY. No grants to individuals.
Application information: Contributes only to pre-selected organizations.
Officers: Willard Hackerman, Pres.; Nancy Hackerman, V.P.; Steven Hackerman, V.P.; Lillian Hackerman, Secy.-Treas.
EIN: 521459149

3811
LaVerna Hahn Charitable Trust ✧

7 Saint Paul St., Ste. 1500
Baltimore, MD 21202-1636 (410) 347-8787
Contact: Robert Sloan, Tr.

Established in 1987 in MD.
Foundation type: Independent foundation.
Financial data (yr. ended 11/30/13): Assets, $36,840,092 (M); expenditures, $1,627,201; qualifying distributions, $1,525,899; giving

activities include $1,450,000 for 45 grants (high: $350,000; low: $1,000).
Purpose and activities: Giving primarily for health associations and health care, particularly hospices; funding also for arts and culture, social services, and for education.
Fields of interest: Museums; Performing arts; Arts; Higher education; Education; Health care; Human services; Residential/custodial care, hospices.
Type of support: Capital campaigns; Building/renovation.
Limitations: Applications accepted. Giving primarily in the Baltimore, MD, area, including Hunt Valley. No grants to individuals.
Application information: Application form required.
Initial approach: Letter
Deadline(s): None
Trustee: Robert Sloan.
EIN: 521585047

3812
The Helena Foundation, Inc. ✧
1303 Eva Gude Dr.
Crownsville, MD 21032-2101

Established in 1987 in MD.
Donor: Margaret H. Earl†.
Foundation type: Independent foundation.
Financial data (yr. ended 12/31/13): Assets, $38,905,320 (M); expenditures, $1,592,704; qualifying distributions, $1,586,204; giving activities include $1,584,192 for 26 grants (high: $289,940; low: $3,000).
Purpose and activities: Giving primarily for higher education; some giving also for the environment, the arts, and hospitals.
Fields of interest: Arts; Higher education; Environment, natural resources; Hospitals (general).
Type of support: General/operating support; Capital campaigns; Endowments.
Limitations: Applications not accepted. Giving primarily in MD, with emphasis on Annapolis; some funding also in Boston and Cambridge, MA. No grants to individuals.
Application information: Contributes only to pre-selected organizations.
Officers and Directors:* James A. Earl,* Pres. and Treas.; Sylvia Earl,* V.P. and Secy.
EIN: 521522573

3813
John and Maureen Hendricks Charitable Foundation ✧ ☆
8484 Georgia Ave., Ste. 700
Silver Spring, MD 20910-5619

Established in 2001 in MD.
Donors: John S. Hendricks; Maureen D. Hendricks.
Foundation type: Operating foundation.
Financial data (yr. ended 03/31/13): Assets, $13,416 (M); gifts received, $1,934,240; expenditures, $1,934,400; qualifying distributions, $1,934,304; giving activities include $1,931,454 for 19 grants (high: $451,489; low: $4,550).
Fields of interest: Higher education; Education; Environment; Athletics/sports, soccer; Foundations (community).
Type of support: General/operating support.
Limitations: Applications not accepted. Giving in the U.S., with emphasis on MD and Washington DC; funding also in CO, MT, NJ, NY and VA. No grants to individuals.
Application information: Contributes only to pre-selected organizations.
Trustees: John S. Hendricks; Maureen D. Hendricks; Elizabeth Hendricks North; Eric W. Shaw.
EIN: 137180307
Selected grants: The following grants are a representative sample of this grantmaker's funding activity:
$200,000 to Syracuse University, Syracuse, NY, 2011.
$200,000 to University System of Maryland, Adelphi, MD, 2011.
$69,550 to Montgomery County Community Foundation, Silver Spring, MD, 2011.
$20,000 to Manna Food Center, Gaithersburg, MD, 2011.
$10,000 to Cato Institute, Washington, DC, 2011.
$10,000 to DC SCORES, Washington, DC, 2011.

3814
The Richard A. Henson Foundation, Inc. ✧
P.O. Box 151
Salisbury, MD 21803-0151 (410) 742-7057
Contact: Donna S. Altvater, Exec. Dir.
FAX: (410) 742-4036;
E-mail: dsaltvater@ymail.com; Main URL: http://www.richardhensonfoundation.org

Established in 1989 in MD; funded in 1990.
Donor: Richard A. Henson†.
Foundation type: Independent foundation.
Financial data (yr. ended 12/31/13): Assets, $36,319,004 (M); expenditures, $1,730,509; qualifying distributions, $1,549,681; giving activities include $1,496,177 for 22 grants (high: $260,000; low: $1,000).
Purpose and activities: Giving primarily to enrich the quality of life primarily in (but not exclusively to), the greater Salisbury, MD, area.
Fields of interest: Arts; Higher education; Hospitals (general); Children/youth, services; Foundations (community).
Type of support: Continuing support; Annual campaigns; Capital campaigns; Building/renovation; Equipment; Endowments; Scholarship funds; In-kind gifts; Matching/challenge support.
Limitations: Giving primarily in the Salisbury, MD, area. No support for denominational religious organizations. No grants to individuals.
Publications: Application guidelines; Financial statement; Informational brochure.
Application information: Letters of Inquiry are by invitation only, upon consideration during initial telephone call, or of the e-mail. Application information and guidelines available on foundation web site.
Initial approach: Telephone or e-mail
Copies of proposal: 1
Deadline(s): 2nd Mon. of every month (except Aug. and Dec.) for Letters of Inquiry
Board meeting date(s): 4th Tues. of every month (except Aug. and Dec.)
Final notification: Within 30 days
Officer: Donna S. Altvater, Exec. Dir.
Trustees: Thomas H. Evans; Stephen R. Farrow; Gordon D. Gladden; Victor H. Laws III; Gregory J. Olinde; Jon P. Sherwell; Thomas L. Trice IV.
Number of staff: 1 full-time professional.
EIN: 521642558

3815
Lisa Higgins-Hussman Foundation, Inc. ✧
10215 Tarpley Ct.
Ellicott City, MD 21042-1681
Contact: Lisa Marie Higgins, Pres.

Established in 2006 in MD.
Donor: John P. Hussman.
Foundation type: Independent foundation.
Financial data (yr. ended 06/30/13): Assets, $3,366,206 (M); gifts received, $750,000; expenditures, $619,947; qualifying distributions, $614,750; giving activities include $614,750 for 45 grants (high: $121,500; low: $250).
Purpose and activities: Giving primarily for 1) medical research, particularly efforts to improve scientific knowledge of, and to develop therapies and find cures for conditions such as autism, addiction, alcoholism and neurological disorders, 2) therapeutic care, particularly for hospice care and therapeutic intervention for individuals with debilitating health or neurological disorders, and 3) issues relating to women's health.
Fields of interest: Substance abuse, services; Health organizations; Human services; Children/youth, services; Residential/custodial care, hospices; Mentally disabled; Women.
Limitations: Applications accepted. Giving primarily in MD.
Application information: Application form required.
Initial approach: Proposal
Deadline(s): None
Officers and Directors:* Lisa Marie Higgins,* Pres.; Stacy Loiacono,* V.P. and Treas.; Joseph Loiacono,* Secy.
EIN: 203409415
Selected grants: The following grants are a representative sample of this grantmaker's funding activity:
$113,000 to Organization for Autism Research, Arlington, VA, 2013. To Support Programs and services dedicated to promoting research that helps individuals with autism and their families find much-needed answers to their immediate and urgent questions.
$102,500 to Arc of Howard County, Ellicott City, MD, 2013. To support Programs for children and adults with disabilities.
$50,000 to Angels Place, Southfield, MI, 2013. To support program for adults with developmental disabilities.
$35,000 to Ursuline High School, Youngstown, OH, 2013. For educational Programs at Ursuline High School.
$15,000 to CollegeBound Foundation, Baltimore, MD, 2013. To Support grants for low income, minority students.
$3,000 to Wayne State University, Detroit, MI, 2013. To support student scholarship Programs.

3816
The David and Barbara B. Hirschhorn Foundation, Inc.
c/o AFS
1 South St., Ste. 2900
Baltimore, MD 21202-3334 (410) 347-7201
Contact: Daniel B. Hirschhorn, Pres.
FAX: (410) 347-7210; E-mail: info@blafund.org; Main URL: http://www.blaufund.org/foundations/davidandbarbara_f.html

Established in 1986 in MD.

Donors: Barbara B. Hirschhorn; David Hirschhorn†; Daniel B. Hirschhorn; 3510 LLC.
Foundation type: Independent foundation.
Financial data (yr. ended 12/31/12): Assets, $38,970,237 (M); expenditures, $2,550,903; qualifying distributions, $2,437,811; giving activities include $2,264,446 for 146 grants (high: $116,666; low: $1,000).
Purpose and activities: Giving primarily for Jewish and secular initiatives in the program areas of: education and literacy, summer camping, human services, and intergroup understanding.
Fields of interest: Human services; International relief; Civil rights, race/intergroup relations; Jewish federated giving programs; Jewish agencies & synagogues; Religion, interfaith issues.
Type of support: General/operating support; Annual campaigns; Capital campaigns; Endowments.
Limitations: Applications accepted. Giving primarily in the metropolitan Baltimore, MD, area. No grants to individuals or for fundraisers; no loans.
Publications: Grants list.
Application information: Association of Baltimore Area Grantmakers Common Grant Application Form accepted. Application form not required.
Initial approach: Letter
Copies of proposal: 1
Deadline(s): None
Final notification: 4 to 6 months
Officers and Trustees:* Barbara B. Hirschhorn,* Chair.; Daniel B. Hirschhorn,* Pres.; Michael J. Hirschhorn,* V.P.; Sarah H. Shapiro,* V.P.; Deborah H. Vogelstein,* V.P.; Jill R. Robinson, Secy.; Betsy F. Ringel, Exec. Dir.
EIN: 521489400

3817
Hoffberger Foundation, Inc. ✧
(also known as Hoffberger Family Philanthropies)
101 W. Mount Royal Ave.
Baltimore, MD 21201-5781 (410) 369-9336
FAX: (410) 369-9337; E-mail: info@hoffberger.org; Mailing address: c/o Ann Billingsley, Hoffberger Family Philanthropies, 101 W. Mount Royal Ave., Baltimore, MD 21201-5781; Main URL: http://www.hoffberger.org

Incorporated in 1941 in MD.
Donor: The Hoffberger family.
Foundation type: Independent foundation.
Financial data (yr. ended 12/31/12): Assets, $19,866,619 (M); expenditures, $1,032,980; qualifying distributions, $973,771; giving activities include $832,350 for 52 grants (high: $152,800; low: $250).
Purpose and activities: The foundation's mission is to respond with available resources to unmet needs in the greater Baltimore, Maryland, community, with a significant commitment to the Jewish community. Eligible applications must address one of the following: the academic and social success of Baltimore City middle school students; the prescription medication needs of under-served individuals in the Baltimore, Maryland metropolitan area; the needs of individuals in the Baltimore, Maryland metropolitan area with Alzheimer's or related dementias who are living at home.
Fields of interest: Arts education; Middle schools/education; Pharmacy/prescriptions; Youth development; Aging, centers/services; Youth; Aging; Economically disadvantaged.
Type of support: General/operating support; Program development.
Limitations: Giving in the youth program area is limited to Baltimore, MD. Giving in the health and Jewish Community needs program areas is restricted to the Baltimore, MD metropolitan area. No grants to individuals or for capital projects, fundraising or special events or for direct mail solicitations/campaigns.
Publications: Grants list; Program policy statement.
Application information: Applications are accepted in the Youth and Health program areas only. Grants for Jewish Community needs are made to pre-selected organizations. Unsolicited applications in this program area are not accepted. Online application form required. Applicants must submit 1 hard copy of all application attachments in addition to the online submission. Application guidelines available on foundation website. Applicants must carefully review the website, hoffberger.org, prior to submitting a proposal. They are strongly encouraged to contact staff after reviewing the site to assess whether their project is a good fit for the foundation's giving priorities. Application form required.
Initial approach: Proposal
Deadline(s): Mar. 1
Final notification: June 30
Officers and Directors:* LeRoy E. Hoffberger,* Chair.; Douglas Hoffberger,* Pres.; Lois Halpert, V.P.; Alison Fass,* Secy.; Scott Kursman,* Treas.; Ann Billingsley, Exec. Dir.; Louise Kovens Goodman; Margo Pyes.
Number of staff: 2 part-time professional.
EIN: 520794249
Selected grants: The following grants are a representative sample of this grantmaker's funding activity:
$577,500 to Associated: Jewish Community Federation of Baltimore, Baltimore, MD, 2011. For general operating support for programs in Baltimore and Israel.
$70,000 to Baltimore Montessori, Baltimore, MD, 2011. For staffing of new middle school.
$25,000 to Baltimore Educational Scholarship Trust, Baltimore, MD, 2011. For Middle School Summer Scholars Program.
$25,000 to Boys Hope Girls Hope, Baltimore, MD, 2011. For residential program for youth at-risk of dropping out of school.
$25,000 to Foundation for the Baltimore Leadership School for Young Women, Baltimore, MD, 2011. For STEM teacher training in middle school.
$25,000 to Shepherds Clinic, Baltimore, MD, 2011. For prescription medication for uninsured patients.
$20,000 to Access Art, Baltimore, MD, 2011. For general operating support of after-school arts and media program.
$20,000 to Health Care for the Homeless, Baltimore, MD, 2011. To provide prescription medication for homeless men, women, and children in Baltimore County.
$20,000 to Higher Achievement Program, Baltimore Office, Baltimore, MD, 2011. For After School Academy Achievement Centers for middle school students.
$10,000 to Baltimore Algebra Project, Baltimore, MD, 2011. For Near-Peer Mentors and Leadership Development program serving 8th grade students in Baltimore City Public Schools.

3818
Howard Hughes Medical Institute ✧
c/o Office of Grants and Special Progs.
4000 Jones Bridge Rd.
Chevy Chase, MD 20815-6789 (301) 215-8500
Contact: For general inquiries: Dr. Peter J. Bruns, V.P., Grants and Special Progs.; Dr. William R. Galey, Prog. Dir, Grad. Prog.; Stephen A. Barkanic, Prog. Dir., Undergrad Prog.; Dr. Jill G. Conley, Prog. Dir., International Prog., Precollege Prog., Research Resources Prog.; Dr. Dennis Liu, Prog. Dir., Educational Products
FAX: (301) 215-8888; E-mail: grantswww@hhmi.org; Main URL: http://www.hhmi.org
Facebook: http://www.facebook.com/HowardHughesMed
iTunes: http://itunes.apple.com/us/app/hhmi-bulletin/id411540287?mt=8
News Feed: http://www.hhmi.org/news/rss20.xml
Twitter: http://twitter.com/hhminews
Toll-free tel.: (800) 448-4882

Incorporated in 1953 in DE.
Donor: Howard R. Hughes†.
Financial data (yr. ended 08/31/13): Assets, $19,677,721,527 (M); expenditures, $1,053,985,963; giving activities include $59,924,253 for grants, and $825,610,000 for foundation-administered programs.
Purpose and activities: The purpose of the Institute is promotion of human knowledge within the field of basic sciences (chiefly medical research and education) and the effective application thereof to benefit mankind. The Institute is a medical research organization, not a private foundation, under federal tax codes. Through its Medical Research Program, the Institute's scientists conduct fundamental biomedical research throughout the U.S. in the fields of cell biology, computational biology, genetics, immunology, neuroscience, and structural biology. Through its Office of Grants and Special Programs, the Institute awards grants for education in biology and related sciences, funds research at medical schools, and supports fundamental research abroad. The emphasis of the grants program is graduate, undergraduate, and precollege and public science education. Graduate support is primarily awarded under two programs: 1) Research Training Fellowships for Med. Students. Deadline: early Jan.; 2) HHMI-NIH Research Scholars Program. Deadline: Jan. 10. The Undergraduate Science Education Program, awards grants to colleges and universities for 1) student research and expanding access in the sciences; 2) science equipment and lab renovations; 3) faculty and curriculum development; and 4) outreach programs in the sciences and mathematics with elementary and secondary schools, and with junior/community colleges. The HHMI Professors awards, an Undergraduate Program initiative, supports and empowers accomplished research scientists in transmitting the excitement and values of scientific research to undergraduate education. The Institute continues to monitor trends in science education and science, including public and private support. The Precollege Science Education Program addresses concerns about science literacy in the general population by engaging K-12 students, teachers, and families in science education.
Fields of interest: Secondary school/education; Higher education; Medical school/education; Education; Biomedicine; Medical research, institute; Biology/life sciences; Minorities; Asians/Pacific Islanders; African Americans/Blacks;

Hispanics/Latinos; Native Americans/American Indians.
International interests: Argentina; Australia; Bangladesh; Brazil; Bulgaria; Canada; Chile; Czech Republic; Estonia; France; Germany; Greece; Guinea; Hungary; India; Israel; Lithuania; Mexico; Poland; Russia; Slovakia; South Africa; Switzerland; Taiwan; Uganda; Ukraine; United Kingdom; Uruguay; Venezuela.
Type of support: Building/renovation; Equipment; Program development; Professorships; Curriculum development; Fellowships; Research; Program evaluation; Grants to individuals.
Limitations: Applications accepted. Giving on a national and international basis. Graduate, undergraduate, and pre-college grants are nationwide; grants to foreign scientists made in selected countries. Some graduate fellowships given outside the U.S. Research grants have gone to scientists in Canada and Mexico (1991), Australia, New Zealand, and the United Kingdom (1992), The Baltics, Cent. Europe, and the former Soviet Union (1995), Argentina, Brazil, Canada, Chile, Mexico, and Venezuela (1997), and Australia, Bangladesh, Bulgaria, Czech Republic, Estonia, France, Germany, Greece, Guinea, Hungary, India, Israel, Lithuania, Mexico, Poland, Russia, Slovakia, South Africa, Switzerland, Taiwan, Uganda, Ukraine, United Kingdom, Uruguay, Venezuela (2000). No support for biomedical research in the U.S., except to scientists employed by the Institute; no grants or fellowships except to individuals or institutions competing under established science education programs. No grants for conferences or publications.
Publications: Application guidelines; Annual report; Informational brochure (including application guidelines); Newsletter; Occasional report; Program policy statement.
Application information: Applicants should consult guidelines in program announcements prior to application. Fellowships and grants are awarded on the basis of national or international competitions. Proposals for the Undergraduate Science Education Program and the Precollege Science Education Program are by invitation only. For the HHMI Professors awards, each invited institution may nominate up to two faculty members. In addition to the science education programs, grants are awarded to biomedical scientists in specified countries under the international program. Awards in all programs are based on peer review. Application form required.
Initial approach: Letter, proposal, or application, depending on program
Deadline(s): Oct. for Gilliam Fellowships
Board meeting date(s): Feb., May, Aug., and Nov.
Final notification: Dec. for Gilliam Fellowships
Officers: Robert Tjian, Pres.; Cheryl Moore, Exec. V.P. and C.O.O.; Nitin Kotak, V.P. and C.F.O.; Sean B. Carroll, Ph.D., V.P., Science Education; Heidi E. Henning, V.P. and Genl. Counsel; Mohamoud Jibrell, V.P. Information Tech; Avice A. Meehan, V.P., Comm. and Pub. Affairs; Erin O'Shea, Ph.D., V.P. and Chief Scientific Off.; Gerald M. Rubin, Ph.D., V.P. and Exec. Dir., Janelia Research Campus; Kathy A. Wyszynski, V.P., Human Resources; Landis Zimmerman, V.P. and C.I.O.
Trustees: Kurt L. Schmoke, Esq., Chair.; James A. Baker III, Esq.; Amb. Charlene Barshefsky; Susan Desmond-Hellmann, M.D., M.P.H.; Joseph L. Goldstein, M.D.; Garnett L. Keith; Fred R. Lummis; Sir Paul Nurse; Dame Alison F. Richard, Ph.D.; Clayton S. Rose, Ph.D.; Anne M. Tatlock.
Number of staff: 2479 full-time professional; 64 part-time professional; 484 full-time support; 105 part-time support.
EIN: 590735717

3819
Carol M. Jacobsohn Foundation ✧ ☆
(formerly Carol and Howard Jacobsohn Foundation)
3309 Harness Creek Rd.
Annapolis, MD 21403 (410) 990-9660
Contact: Henry N. Libby, Pres., Secy., and Dir.

Established in IL.
Donors: Howard G. Jacobsohn; Carol M. Jacobsohn; Carol M. Jacobsohn Trust; Henry Libby, Esq.
Foundation type: Independent foundation.
Financial data (yr. ended 12/31/13): Assets, $10,079,030 (M); gifts received, $752,425; expenditures, $662,396; qualifying distributions, $518,355; giving activities include $443,000 for 13 grants (high: $150,000; low: $5,000).
Purpose and activities: The foundation's mission is to improve the quality of life for the general community and/or economically or educationally disadvantaged individuals, particularly women and children. The foundation provides financial support to qualified charitable organizations involved in medical and social outreach programs, education, women's issues, and the visual arts. Wherever possible, the foundation endeavors to combine one or more of these areas with the goal of benefiting economically or educationally disadvantaged persons.
Fields of interest: Arts; Education; Medical research; Women's studies; Children/youth; Youth; African Americans/Blacks; Women; Young adults, female; Single parents; Economically disadvantaged.
Type of support: Scholarships—to individuals; Scholarship funds; Program development; Matching/challenge support; General/operating support; Endowments; Capital campaigns; Building/renovation; Annual campaigns.
Limitations: Applications not accepted. Giving primarily in Annapolis, MD. No grants to individuals (except for scholarships).
Application information: Unsolicited request for funds not accepted.
Officers and Directors:* Henry Libby, Esq.*, Pres. and Secy.; Ellen Libby,* Treas.; John Zarkowski.
Number of staff: 1 full-time professional.
EIN: 366101091
Selected grants: The following grants are a representative sample of this grantmaker's funding activity:
$80,000 to Anne Arundel Medical Center, Annapolis, MD, 2011.
$55,000 to Anne Arundel Community College, Arnold, MD, 2011.
$16,400 to Summit School, Edgewater, MD, 2011.
$10,000 to Annapolis Maritime Museum, Annapolis, MD, 2011.

3820
Jerome Jacobson Foundation ✧
6931 Arlington Rd., Ste. 300
Bethesda, MD 20814-5231 (610) 942-8718
Contact: Louis Rubinfield, Pres.

Established in 1990 in FL.
Donors: Jerome Jacobson; Ruth Crat; Albert Harris Crat; Economic Studies Inc.
Foundation type: Independent foundation.
Financial data (yr. ended 12/31/13): Assets, $9,703,204 (M); gifts received, $320,579; expenditures, $598,809; qualifying distributions, $494,000; giving activities include $494,000 for 14 grants (high: $150,000; low: $1,000).
Fields of interest: Higher education; Hospitals (specialty); Eye research; Jewish federated giving programs.
Limitations: Applications accepted. Giving primarily in Ann Arbor, MI, and New York, NY. No grants to individuals.
Application information: Application form required.
Initial approach: Letter
Deadline(s): None
Officers and Directors:* Louis Rubinfield,* Pres.; Richard Breen,* Secy.-Treas.
EIN: 650167227

3821
The James M. Johnston Trust for Charitable and Educational Purposes ✧
2 Wisconsin Cir., Ste. 870
Chevy Chase, MD 20815-7013 (301) 907-0135

Trust established in 1968 in DC.
Donor: James M. Johnston‡.
Foundation type: Independent foundation.
Financial data (yr. ended 12/31/13): Assets, $86,975,688 (M); expenditures, $4,815,818; qualifying distributions, $3,974,000; giving activities include $3,644,228 for grants.
Purpose and activities: Grants largely to higher and secondary educational institutions located in Washington, DC, and North Carolina. This includes support for scholarships, training of nurses, and faculty salaries.
Fields of interest: Secondary school/education; Higher education; Nursing school/education.
Type of support: Scholarship funds.
Limitations: Applications accepted. Giving primarily in Washington, DC, and NC. No support for private foundations. No grants to individuals.
Application information: Application form required.
Initial approach: Completed application form
Copies of proposal: 1
Deadline(s): Before Oct. 15
Board meeting date(s): Monthly
Final notification: 30 days
Officer: Julie G. Sanders, Exec. Dir.
Trustees: W. Dunbar Gram; Stephen Hayes; Helen Pate.
Number of staff: 1 full-time professional.
EIN: 237019796

3822
The Kahlert Foundation, Inc. ✧ ☆
5848 Pinebrook Farm Rd.
Sykesville, MD 21784-8679
Contact: Greg W. Kahlert, Pres.

Established in 1996 in MD.
Donor: William E. Kahlert.
Foundation type: Independent foundation.
Financial data (yr. ended 06/30/13): Assets, $21,201,972 (M); gifts received, $16,496,636; expenditures, $1,294,372; qualifying distributions, $1,254,000; giving activities include $1,254,000 for 19 grants (high: $1,000,000; low: $1,000).

Fields of interest: Hospitals (general); Human services.
Limitations: Applications not accepted. Giving primarily in MD and VA. No grants to individuals.
Application information: Contributes only to pre-selected organizations.
Officers: Greg W. Kahlert, Pres.; Harold W. Walsh, V.P.; James D. Stone, Secy.; Robert F. Wilson, Treas.
Directors: Roberta Kahlert; Ronald F. Tutrone, Jr.
EIN: 521798711

3823
Grayce B. Kerr Fund, Inc. ✧
117 Bay St.
Easton, MD 21601-2769 (410) 822-6652
Contact: John R. Valliant, C.E.O. and Pres.
FAX: (410) 822-4546; E-mail: office@gbkf.org

Chartered in 1986 in OK; reincorporated in 1993 in MD.
Donors: Grayce B. Kerr Flynn‡; Breene M. Kerr.
Foundation type: Independent foundation.
Financial data (yr. ended 12/31/12): Assets, $31,291,087 (M); expenditures, $1,398,952; qualifying distributions, $1,057,417; giving activities include $615,738 for 24 grants (high: $231,444; low: $100), and $1,052,931 for foundation-administered programs.
Fields of interest: Elementary/secondary education; Higher education; Medical school/education; Human services.
Type of support: Building/renovation; Capital campaigns; Curriculum development; Employee matching gifts; Equipment; Matching/challenge support; Professorships; Program development; Publication; Research.
Limitations: Giving primarily in MD; funding also in MA and ME. No grants to individuals, or for general operating or continuing support.
Publications: Application guidelines.
Application information: Application form required.
Initial approach: Telephone for guidelines
Copies of proposal: 1
Deadline(s): None
Board meeting date(s): As necessary
Final notification: 3 months after final proposal is submitted
Officers: Sheryl V. Kerr, Chair.; John R. Valliant, C.E.O. and Pres.; James S. Maffitt, Secy.-Treas.
Trustees: David A. Yuknat; Marcy Kerr Yuknat.
Number of staff: 1 full-time professional; 1 full-time support.
EIN: 731256124
Selected grants: The following grants are a representative sample of this grantmaker's funding activity:
$400 to Saint Pauls Episcopal Church, Alexandria, VA, 2012. To Be Used in Accordance with the Established Purpose of the Recipient Organization.

3824
The Philip E. and Harriet J. Klein Foundation Inc. ✧
11299 Owings Mills Blvd., Ste. 200
Owings Mills, MD 21117-2903

Established in 1997 in MD.
Donors: Harriet J. Klein; Philip E. Klein; American Technion Society.
Foundation type: Independent foundation.
Financial data (yr. ended 12/31/12): Assets, $14,140,277 (M); expenditures, $629,970; qualifying distributions, $500,400; giving activities include $500,400 for grants.
Purpose and activities: Giving primarily for Jewish organizations.
Fields of interest: Arts; Education; Human services; Jewish agencies & synagogues.
Type of support: General/operating support.
Limitations: Applications not accepted. Giving primarily in MD. No grants to individuals.
Application information: Contributes only to pre-selected organizations.
Officers and Trustees:* Michael F. Klein,* Pres.; Jeffrey F. Klein,* V.P.; Daniel J. Klein,* Secy.-Treas.
EIN: 522046127

3825
The Knapp Foundation, Inc. ✧
P.O. Box O
St. Michaels, MD 21663-0450 (410) 745-5660
Contact: Antoinette P. Vojvoda, Secy.

Incorporated in 1929 in NC.
Donor: Joseph Palmer Knapp‡.
Foundation type: Independent foundation.
Financial data (yr. ended 12/31/13): Assets, $16,720,395 (M); expenditures, $925,444; qualifying distributions, $761,789; giving activities include $419,890 for 26 grants (high: $61,223; low: $1,200).
Purpose and activities: Grants primarily for conservation and preservation of wildlife and wildfowl, and for assistance to college and university libraries in the purchasing of reading materials and equipment to improve education.
Fields of interest: Higher education; Libraries/library science; Animals/wildlife, preservation/protection.
Type of support: Equipment; Matching/challenge support.
Limitations: Applications accepted. Giving limited to the U.S., primarily in the eastern region, including CT, DE, FL, GA, MA, MD, ME, NC, NH, NJ, NY, PA, RI, SC, VA, and VT. No support for foreign projects or for political organizations, religious organizations or local area land trusts. No grants to individuals, or for endowment or building funds, operating budgets, or research.
Application information: Application form not required.
Initial approach: Letter
Copies of proposal: 1
Deadline(s): None
Officers: Ruth M. Capranica, Pres.; Antoinette P. Vojvoda, Secy.; Steven F. Capranica, Treas.
Trustee: Christine Dayton.
Number of staff: 1 part-time professional.
EIN: 136001167
Selected grants: The following grants are a representative sample of this grantmaker's funding activity:
$65,000 to Virginia Living Museum, Newport News, VA, 2012. For Wild and Well Project Equipment.
$50,000 to Tennessee Aquarium, Chattanooga, TN, 2012. For River Otter Exhibit.
$25,000 to Randolph-Macon College, Ashland, VA, 2012. For library furniture acquisition.
$23,940 to McDaniel College, Westminster, MD, 2012. For library equipment acquisition.
$15,000 to Clarkson University, Potsdam, NY, 2012. For volume acquisitions.
$15,000 to Humane Society of Wicomico County, Salisbury, MD, 2012. For supplies.
$10,000 to Goldey-Beacom College, Wilmington, DE, 2012. For library volume acquisitions.
$10,000 to Learning Ally, Princeton, NJ, 2012. For library education materials.
$5,055 to Woodford Cedar Run Wildlife Refuge, Medford, NJ, 2012. For equipment acquisition.

3826
The Marion I. and Henry J. Knott Foundation, Inc. ✧
3904 Hickory Ave.
Baltimore, MD 21211-1834 (410) 235-7068
Contact: Gregory Cantori, Exec. Dir.
FAX: (410) 889-2577;
E-mail: choffman@knottfoundation.org; Main URL: http://www.knottfoundation.org
Grants Database: http://www.knottfoundation.org/past_grants/

Established in 1977 in MD as successor to the first Marion I. and Henry J. Knott Foundation, Inc.
Donors: Marion I. Knott‡; Henry J. Knott, Sr.‡.
Foundation type: Independent foundation.
Financial data (yr. ended 12/31/13): Assets, $57,562,052 (M); expenditures, $3,087,375; qualifying distributions, $2,639,610; giving activities include $2,192,630 for grants, and $30,000 for 1 loan/program-related investment.
Purpose and activities: Giving for Roman Catholic activities and other charitable, cultural, educational, and health and human service organizations. Areas of interest include the fine and performing arts; Roman Catholic and non-sectarian private schools; higher, adult, and vocational education; hospitals and health services, including hospices and programs for the mentally ill; social and family services, including youth, the elderly, the handicapped, and the homeless; and community development and civic affairs.
Fields of interest: Humanities; Arts; Elementary school/education; Secondary school/education; Health care; Human services; Catholic agencies & churches.
Type of support: General/operating support; Management development/capacity building; Capital campaigns; Building/renovation; Equipment; Land acquisition; Endowments; Emergency funds; Program development; Technical assistance; Program evaluation; Program-related investments/loans; Employee matching gifts; Matching/challenge support.
Limitations: Giving limited to Baltimore City and Allegheny, Anne Arundel, Baltimore, Carroll, Frederick, Garrett, Harford, Howard, and Washington counties, MD. No support for public education, public sector agencies, the environment, day care centers, single-disease organizations, pass-through agencies, pro-choice activities or reproductive health programs, or organizations in operation for less than one year. No grants to individuals, or for annual giving, medical research, legal services, endowment funds for the arts or humanities, one-time events, seminars, or workshops, or scholarships.
Publications: Application guidelines; Financial statement; Grants list; Newsletter.
Application information: Unsolicited requests for funds generally not accepted. Applicants who are interested in submitting an initial inquiry must speak with the foundation's Exec. Dir. before doing so. Application guidelines available on foundation web

site and upon request; do not fax or e-mail proposals. Requests for grants must comply with foundation guidelines. If so, the foundation will ask the applicant to submit a 1-page letter of inquiry.; Association of Baltimore Area Grantmakers Common Grant Application Form accepted for those invited to apply. Application form not required.
Initial approach: Letter
Copies of proposal: 2
Deadline(s): See foundation web site for current deadlines
Board meeting date(s): June and Dec.
Final notification: 1 month
Officers and Trustees:* Owen M. Knott, Pres.; Patrick A. Rodgers, V.P.; Margie Riehl, Secy.; David L. Porter,* Treas.; Kelly C. Medinge, Exec. Dir.; Dan Gallagher; Lindsay R. Gallagher; E.B. Harris; Kelly L. Harris; Tom Harris; Erin Knott; Marion I. Knott; Martin G. Knott, Sr.; Martin G. Knott, Jr.; Teresa A. Knott; Brian McDonald; Meghan McDonald; Peter R. McGill; Joanna O. Porter; Laurel Porter; Martin F. Porter; Michael Riehl; Brooke Rodgers; Michael Rodgers; Geralynn D. Smyth; John C. Smyth; Patrick J. Smyth; Peggy Smyth; Jan Steendam; Alice K. Voelkel; Emmett Voelkel.
Number of staff: 3 full-time support.
EIN: 521517876

3827
Lawless Family Foundation ✧
c/o L. Stouffer
18 Loveton Cir.
Sparks, MD 21152-9202

Established in 2002 in MD.
Donor: Robert J. Lawless.
Foundation type: Independent foundation.
Financial data (yr. ended 12/31/13): Assets, $5,699,966 (M); gifts received, $696,000; expenditures, $730,940; qualifying distributions, $720,350; giving activities include $700,000 for 6 grants (high: $200,000; low: $50,000).
Purpose and activities: Giving primarily for Christian organizations providing relief and services to the international community.
Fields of interest: Higher education; Human services; United Ways and Federated Giving Programs; Christian agencies & churches.
Limitations: Applications not accepted. Giving primarily in the Province of Ontario, Canada; funding also in CA, CO and NC. No grants to individuals.
Application information: Contributes only to pre-selected organizations.
Officer: Kristen Miniotas, Exec. Dir.
Trustee: Robert J. Lawless.
EIN: 030486725

3828
Legg Mason Charitable Foundation, Inc. ✧
100 International Dr.
Baltimore, MD 21202-4673 (410) 454-4416
Contact: Kelly Spilman, Mgr., Corp. Citizenship
Main URL: http://www.leggmason.com/about/citizenship/overview.aspx

Donor: Legg Mason, Inc.
Foundation type: Company-sponsored foundation.
Financial data (yr. ended 03/31/13): Assets, $7,310,675 (M); gifts received, $467,967; expenditures, $1,286,759; qualifying distributions, $1,280,503; giving activities include $1,280,503 for 120 grants (high: $125,000; low: $500).
Purpose and activities: The foundation supports organizations involved with arts and culture, the environment, health, human services, and community development. Special emphasis is directed toward programs designed to promote education.
Fields of interest: Arts education; Performing arts, orchestras; Arts; Higher education; Education; Environment, water resources; Environment; Health care, clinics/centers; Health care; Athletics/sports, baseball; Human services; Community/economic development; Foundations (community); United Ways and Federated Giving Programs.
Type of support: General/operating support; Program development.
Limitations: Applications accepted. Giving primarily in areas of company operations in Baltimore, MD.
Publications: Application guidelines.
Application information: Application form not required.
Initial approach: Telephone
Deadline(s): None
Officers: Joseph A. Sullivan, Pres.; Charles J. Daley, Jr., V.P. and Co-Treas.; Peter H. Nachtwey, V.P. and Co-Treas.; Michael McCalister, V.P.; Thomas C. Merchant, Secy.
EIN: 311738146

3829
Legum Foundation, Inc. ✧
1829 Reisterstown Rd.
Baltimore, MD 21208-6320

Donors: Jeffrey Legum; Michael Legum; Harriett Legum; Laurie Legum; Park Circle Motor Co.; Westminster Motor Co.
Foundation type: Independent foundation.
Financial data (yr. ended 12/31/13): Assets, $2,130,543 (M); gifts received, $2,041,483; expenditures, $914,285; qualifying distributions, $907,113; giving activities include $907,113 for 85 grants (high: $500,000; low: $25).
Fields of interest: Museums (art); Higher education, university; Jewish agencies & synagogues.
Limitations: Applications not accepted. Giving primarily in Baltimore, MD.
Application information: Unsolicited requests for funds not accepted.
Trustees: Harriett Legum; Jeffrey Legum; Laurie Legum; Michael Legum.
EIN: 061772390
Selected grants: The following grants are a representative sample of this grantmaker's funding activity:
$5,000 to Chesapeake Bay Foundation, Annapolis, MD, 2011.
$5,000 to Teach for America, New York, NY, 2011.
$1,000 to American Cancer Society, Atlanta, GA, 2011.

3830
The John J. Leidy Foundation, Inc. ✧
305 W. Chesapeake Ave., Ste. 308
Towson, MD 21204-4440 (410) 821-3006
Contact: Robert L. Pierson, Pres.
FAX: (410) 821-3007;
E-mail: info@leidyfoundation.org; Main URL: http://www.leidyfoundation.org

Incorporated in 1957 in MD.
Donor: John J. Leidy‡.
Foundation type: Independent foundation.
Financial data (yr. ended 12/31/13): Assets, $13,729,201 (M); expenditures, $712,389; qualifying distributions, $639,623; giving activities include $569,370 for 91 grants (high: $50,000; low: $1,000).
Purpose and activities: Giving primarily for social and economic welfare, arts and culture, health and human services, education, and for disabled persons.
Fields of interest: Arts; Higher education; Health care; Health organizations, association; Food services; Human services; United Ways and Federated Giving Programs; Jewish federated giving programs; Jewish agencies & synagogues; Disabilities, people with.
Type of support: General/operating support; Building/renovation; Equipment; Program development; Scholarship funds.
Limitations: Applications accepted. Giving primarily in the metropolitan Baltimore, MD, area. No grants to individuals, or for galas, special events, or advertising space in programs.
Publications: Application guidelines.
Application information: E-mailed attachments may be scanned.
Initial approach: Cover letter on organization letterhead, via U.S. mail or e-mail
Copies of proposal: 4
Deadline(s): None
Board meeting date(s): Monthly
Officers: Robert L. Pierson, Pres.; W. Michel Pierson, V.P.; Claire A. Pierson, Secy.-Treas.
EIN: 526034785
Selected grants: The following grants are a representative sample of this grantmaker's funding activity:
$20,000 to Baltimore Symphony Orchestra, Baltimore, MD, 2012. For arts/cultural.
$12,500 to United Way of Central Maryland, Baltimore, MD, 2012. For Community Fund.
$7,500 to Community Law Center, Baltimore, MD, 2012. For legal aid poor.
$7,500 to Maryland Food Bank, Baltimore, MD, 2012. For food pantry.
$5,000 to Waverly Main Street, Baltimore, MD, 2012. For neighborhood improvement.

3831
The Annette M. and Theodore N. Lerner Family Foundation Inc. ✧
2000 Tower Oaks Blvd., 8th Fl.
Rockville, MD 20852-4208

Established in 1986 in MD.
Donors: Edward L. Cohen; Mark D. Lerner; Theodore N. Lerner; Robert K. Tanenbaum; Annette M. Lerner; Debra L. Cohen; Marla L. Tanenbaum.
Foundation type: Independent foundation.
Financial data (yr. ended 12/31/12): Assets, $1,524,036 (M); gifts received, $3,000,000; expenditures, $1,772,461; qualifying distributions, $1,771,896; giving activities include $1,756,282 for 75 grants (high: $350,000; low: $250).
Purpose and activities: Giving for education and to Jewish organizations.
Fields of interest: Arts; Elementary/secondary education; Higher education, university; Human services; Jewish federated giving programs; Jewish agencies & synagogues.
Type of support: General/operating support.

Limitations: Applications not accepted. Giving primarily in Washington, DC, and MD. No grants to individuals.
Application information: Contributes only to pre-selected organizations.
Officers and Directors:* Marla L. Tanenbaum,* Pres.; Mark D. Lerner,* V.P.; Debra L. Cohen,* Secy.; Annette M. Lerner,* Treas.; Theodore N. Lerner.
EIN: 521528436

3832
The Levitt Foundation ✧
(formerly Richard S. Levitt Foundation)
6001 Montrose Rd., Ste. 600
Rockville, MD 20852-4873

Established in 1957 in IA.
Donors: Richard S. Levitt; Members of the Levitt Family.
Foundation type: Independent foundation.
Financial data (yr. ended 12/31/13): Assets, $5,443,618 (M); gifts received, $614,520; expenditures, $1,003,569; qualifying distributions, $969,283; giving activities include $969,283 for 71 grants (high: $185,000; low: $25).
Purpose and activities: Giving primarily for Jewish organizations; support also for the performing arts, as well as for museums and other cultural programs, education, health organizations, and social services.
Fields of interest: Arts, multipurpose centers/programs; Museums; Arts; Higher education; Education; Health organizations, association; Human services; Children/youth, services; Jewish federated giving programs; Jewish agencies & synagogues.
Type of support: Annual campaigns.
Limitations: Applications not accepted. Giving in the U.S., primarily in Washington, DC and Des Moines, IA. No grants to individuals.
Application information: Contributes only to pre-selected organizations.
Officers: Richard S. Levitt, Pres. and Treas.; Mark Levitt, V.P.; Randall Levitt, V.P.; Jeanne Levitt, Secy.
EIN: 426052427
Selected grants: The following grants are a representative sample of this grantmaker's funding activity:
$217,000 to Jewish Federation of Greater Washington, Rockville, MD, 2011.
$150,000 to Israel Project, Washington, DC, 2011.
$123,000 to Walker Art Center, Minneapolis, MN, 2011.
$75,000 to American Israel Education Foundation, Washington, DC, 2011.
$36,200 to Tifereth Israel Synagogue, Des Moines, IA, 2011.
$20,000 to Mayo Foundation, Rochester, MN, 2011.
$19,000 to Jewish Community Foundation, San Diego, CA, 2011.
$16,767 to Des Moines Botanical Center, Des Moines, IA, 2011.
$11,000 to University of Iowa Foundation, Iowa City, IA, 2011.
$5,050 to Des Moines Symphony, Des Moines, IA, 2011.

3833
Life Sciences Research Foundation ✧
3520 San Martin Dr.
Baltimore, MD 21218-2440 (410) 467-2597
Contact: Christine Pratt, Treas.
E-mail: lsrf@ciwemb.edu; Main URL: http://www.lsrf.org
LinkedIn: https://www.linkedin.com/groups?gid=1939524&trk=my_groups-b-grp-v
Application address: Susan DiRenzo, Asst. Dir., Life Sciences Research Foundation, c/o Lewis Thomas Laboratory, Princeton University, Washington Rd., Princeton, NJ 08544, tel.: (609) 258-3551, e-mail: sdirenzo@molbio.princeton.edu

Changed status to a private foundation in 1984 in MD.
Donors: Linda W. Brown; Dept. of Energy, Energy Biosciences Research Division; The Bristol-Myers Squibb Pharmaceutical Research Institute; The Burroughs Wellcome Fund; Merck Research Laboratories; GlaxoSmithKline; Wyeth; Abbott Laboratories; Amgen Inc.; Ellison Medical Foundation; Lilly Research Foundation; Rett Syndrome Research Foundation; Pfizer Inc.; The O'Donnell Foundation; Gilead Sciences, Inc.; Johnson and Johnson; Lilly Research Laboratories; Novartis Corp.
Foundation type: Independent foundation.
Financial data (yr. ended 05/31/13): Assets, $2,272,518 (M); gifts received, $3,318,297; expenditures, $3,332,870; qualifying distributions, $3,332,870; giving activities include $3,204,419 for 59 grants to individuals (high: $56,000; low: $18,666).
Purpose and activities: Three-year fellowships will be awarded on a competitive basis to graduates of medical and graduate schools in the biological sciences holding M.D., Ph.D., D.V.M. or D.D.S. degrees. Awards will be based solely on the quality of the individual applicant's previous accomplishments, and on the merit of the proposal for postdoctoral research. Persons doing a second postdoc are eligible only if they are transferring to a different supervisor's laboratory and embarking on a new project not connected to their previous research. All U.S. citizens are eligible to apply with no geographic restriction on the laboratory of their choice. Foreign applicants will be eligible for study in U.S. laboratories. LSRF fellows must carry out their research at nonprofit institutions. LSRF fellows can change projects, laboratories, and/or institutions during the fellowship as long as the eligibility rules listed here are not violated. A person holding a faculty appointment is not eligible to apply for an LSRF fellowship.
Fields of interest: Graduate/professional education; Medical research, institute; Biology/life sciences.
Type of support: Fellowships; Research.
Limitations: Giving primarily in CA, MA, and MD.
Publications: Application guidelines; Annual report; Financial statement; Grants list; Informational brochure.
Application information: Individuals who have held a Ph.D or M.D. degree for more than 5 years at the time of application are not eligible for a fellowship from the foundation. See foundation web site for specific guidelines. Application form required.
Initial approach: Online
Copies of proposal: 3
Deadline(s): Oct. 1 (for applications); Nov. 1 (for supervisor and reference letters)
Final notification: Mar. to May

Officers and Directors:* Donald D. Brown,* Pres.; Douglas E. Koshland,* V.P.; Christine Pratt, Treas.; James Broach; Thomas Silhavy; Solomon H. Snyder.
Advisory Board of Trustees: Peter Agre; Bruce Alberts; Richard Axel; David Baltimore; Paul Berg; Michael S. Brown; Thomas Cech; James E. Darnell, Jr.; Mark Fishman; Elaine Fuchs; David V. Goeddel; Joseph L. Goldstein; Steven L. McKnight; Ira Mellman; Jasper Rine; Mark B. Roth; William Rutter; Phillip A. Sharp; Shirley M. Tilghman; Robert Tjian; Susan Wessler.
EIN: 521231801

3834
Linehan Family Foundation, Inc. ✧
515 Fairmont Ave., Ste. 400
Towson, MD 21286-8518

Established in 1993 in MD.
Donor: Earl L. Linehan.
Foundation type: Independent foundation.
Financial data (yr. ended 12/31/12): Assets, $4,128,185 (M); gifts received, $1,247,160; expenditures, $596,854; qualifying distributions, $561,978; giving activities include $561,670 for 86 grants (high: $138,900; low: $200).
Fields of interest: Arts; Higher education; Education; Health care, clinics/centers; Health organizations; Human services; United Ways and Federated Giving Programs; Catholic federated giving programs; Catholic agencies & churches.
Type of support: Annual campaigns; Capital campaigns; Building/renovation; Scholarship funds.
Limitations: Applications not accepted. Giving primarily in Baltimore, MD; some funding also in Notre Dame, IN. No grants to individuals.
Application information: Contributes only to pre-selected organizations.
Board meeting date(s): Dec.
Officers: Darielle D. Linehan, Pres.; Earl L. Linehan, Secy.-Treas.
Trustees: Brendan E. Linehan; Charles M. Linehan; John D. Linehan.
EIN: 521853307

3835
The Little Family Foundation, Inc. ✧
201 International Cir., Ste. 400
Hunt Valley, MD 21030-1369

Established in 2004 in MD.
Donors: James Little; Barbara Little.
Foundation type: Independent foundation.
Financial data (yr. ended 12/31/13): Assets, $4,103,825 (M); gifts received, $51,020; expenditures, $687,378; qualifying distributions, $653,700; giving activities include $653,700 for 23 grants (high: $117,000; low: $2,000).
Purpose and activities: Giving primarily for Christian education, agencies, and churches.
Fields of interest: Education; Christian agencies & churches.
Limitations: Applications not accepted. Giving in the U.S., with emphasis on CO, FL, MD, and MO. No grants to individuals.
Application information: Unsolicited requests for funds not accepted.
Directors: Barbara J. Little; James M. Little; Nicole C. Little; Stephanie L. Tarbell.
EIN: 201965919

Selected grants: The following grants are a representative sample of this grantmaker's funding activity:
$120,000 to Fellowship of Christian Athletes, Kansas City, MO, 2012. For fellowship support.
$86,000 to Campus Crusade for Christ International, Orlando, FL, 2012. To Spiritually Guide Individuals.

3836
Lockhart Vaughan Foundation, Inc. ✧

2 E. Read St., Ste. 100
Baltimore, MD 21202-2470 (410) 837-9400
Contact: John B. Powell, Jr., Exec. Dir.

Established in 1990 in MD; funded in 1991.
Donors: The McAshan Foundation, Inc.; Julia C. Baker†.
Foundation type: Independent foundation.
Financial data (yr. ended 12/31/13): Assets, $34,750,811 (M); expenditures, $1,808,128; qualifying distributions, $1,692,268; giving activities include $1,650,740 for 69 grants (high: $65,000; low: $3,000).
Purpose and activities: The foundation directs its giving toward its 4 goals for the city of Baltimore, MD: 1) quality public education; 2) more educational choices; 3) better environment; and 4) vibrant neighborhoods. Giving is for specific strategies.
Fields of interest: Education; Environment.
Type of support: General/operating support; Capital campaigns; Program development.
Limitations: Applications accepted. Giving limited to Baltimore, MD.
Publications: Application guidelines.
Application information: Association of Baltimore Area Grantmakers Common Grant Application Form required. Application information available at http://www.abagmd.org. Application form required.
Initial approach: Letter requesting application form
Copies of proposal: 1
Deadline(s): Feb. 20, June 20, and Oct. 20
Final notification: Within 60 days of deadline
Officer: John B. Powell, Jr., Exec. Dir.
Number of staff: None.
EIN: 521693184
Selected grants: The following grants are a representative sample of this grantmaker's funding activity:
$75,000 to Roland Park Country School, Baltimore, MD, 2012. For Environment: Installation of solar photovoltaic system.
$50,000 to KIPP Baltimore, Baltimore, MD, 2012. For Education: Capital campaign to renovate school building.
$50,000 to Teach for America, Baltimore, MD, 2012. For Education: Recruit, train, and support new teachers in Baltimore public schools.
$40,000 to Blue Water Baltimore, Baltimore, MD, 2012. For Environment: Improve the quality of Baltimore's watersheds.
$30,000 to Baltimore Design School, Baltimore, MD, 2012. For Education: Renovate building to contain Baltimore Design School.
$30,000 to Baltimore Urban Debate League, Baltimore, MD, 2012. For Education: Fostering debating in schools.
$30,000 to SEED School of Maryland, Baltimore, MD, 2012. For Education: Operating expenses for Baltimore SEED boarding school.
$25,000 to Advocates for Children and Youth, Baltimore, MD, 2012. For Community Development: General support of research, education, and advocacy of children's issues.
$20,000 to Central Baltimore Partnership, Baltimore, MD, 2012. For Community Development: To foster growth in Central Baltimore.
$16,000 to Downtown Baltimore Family Alliance, Baltimore, MD, 2012. For Community Development: To encourage young families to remain in downtown Baltimore.

3837
Lockheed Martin Corporation Foundation ✧

(formerly Martin Marietta Corporation Foundation)
c/o Global Community Outreach
6801 Rockledge Dr.
Bethesda, MD 20817-1836 (301) 897-6866
E-mail: community.relations@lmco.com; Main URL: http://www.lockheedmartin.com/us/who-we-are/community.html
Lockheed Martin Educatonal Outreach: http://www.lockheedmartin.com/us/who-we-are/community/education.html
Contact for Lockheed Martin Intl. Scholarships: Ms. Carol Jones, Lockheed Martin Intl. Scholarship Prog., 809 United Nations Plaza, New York, NY 10017-3580, tel.: (212) 984-5386, e-mail: cjones@iie.org

Established in 1955 in MD.
Donors: Martin Marietta Corp.; Lockheed Martin Corp.
Foundation type: Company-sponsored foundation.
Financial data (yr. ended 12/31/13): Assets, $829,992 (M); gifts received, $7,000,000; expenditures, $6,971,743; qualifying distributions, $6,971,743; giving activities include $5,090,601 for 45 grants (high: $2,000,000; low: $2,000), and $1,818,099 for 20 employee matching gifts.
Purpose and activities: The foundation supports programs designed to promote education, including K-16 science, technology, engineering, and math (STEM) education; causes that are important to Lockheed Martin customers and constituents, the U.S. military, and government agencies; and community relations, including partnerships between Lockheed Martin employee volunteers and other civic, cultural, environmental, health, and human services initiatives in the community.
Fields of interest: Arts; Elementary/secondary education; Education; Environment; Health care; Human services; Community/economic development; Mathematics; Engineering/technology; Science; Military/veterans' organizations; Public affairs.
Type of support: Employee volunteer services; General/operating support; Program development; Scholarship funds; Employee matching gifts; Employee-related scholarships.
Limitations: Applications accepted. Giving primarily in areas of company operations, with emphasis on CA, CO, GA, IN, MD, MI, NY, TX, and VA. No support for discriminatory organizations, religious organizations not of direct benefit to the entire community, professional associations, labor or fraternal organizations, social clubs, athletic groups, clubs, or teams, or private K-12 schools. No grants to individuals (except for employee-related scholarships), or for booklet, yearbook, or journal advertising or home-based child care or educational services.
Publications: Application guidelines.
Application information: Contributions to national initiatives and organizations are made from corporate headquarters and contributions to local programs are made by local sites close to the program. Support is limited to 1 contribution per organization during any given year. Application form required.
Initial approach: Complete online eligibility quiz and application
Deadline(s): Rolling
Board meeting date(s): Quarterly
Officer and Trustees:* Regina B. Vasan, Secy.; Patrick M. Dewar; Chris Gregoire; John T. Lucas; Leo S. Mackay; Jennifer M. Whitlow.
Number of staff: 1 full-time professional; 1 full-time support.
EIN: 136161566
Selected grants: The following grants are a representative sample of this grantmaker's funding activity:
$2,000,000 to Project Lead the Way, Indianapolis, IN, 2013. For general support.
$1,710,499 to Public Affairs Support Services, Reston, VA, 2013. For general support.
$1,141,000 to National Merit Scholarship Corporation, Evanston, IL, 2013. For scholarships.
$500,000 to National Geographic Society, Washington, DC, 2013. For general support.
$402,650 to Four-H Council, National, Chevy Chase, MD, 2013. For general support.
$260,000 to Four-H Council, National, Chevy Chase, MD, 2013. For general support.
$198,451 to Girls Incorporated, New York, NY, 2013. For general support.
$100,000 to Great Minds in STEM, Monterey Park, CA, 2013. For general support.
$30,000 to National Center for Advanced Technologies, Arlington, VA, 2013. For general support.
$13,000 to Apple Valley Senior High School, Apple Valley, MN, 2013. For general support.

3838
The Gordon and Marilyn Macklin Foundation Inc. ✧

11200 Rockville Pike, Ste. 415
North Bethesda, MD 20852-3154

Established in 1999 in MD.
Donors: Gordon Macklin; Marilyn Macklin†; Gordon S. Macklin Family Charitable Trust; Marilyn C. Macklin Family Charitable Trust.
Foundation type: Independent foundation.
Financial data (yr. ended 10/31/13): Assets, $25,394,380 (M); gifts received, $1,888,706; expenditures, $1,071,523; qualifying distributions, $966,118; giving activities include $891,546 for 5 grants (high: $480,385; low: $70,000).
Purpose and activities: Giving primarily for Kawasaki Disease and Ataxia research; funding also for a college business institute.
Fields of interest: Business school/education; Medical research, institute.
Limitations: Applications not accepted. Giving primarily in CA and MD; some funding also in MN. No grants to individuals.
Application information: Contributes only to pre-selected organizations.
Officer and Director:* Donald D. Dawn,* Pres.
EIN: 522205133
Selected grants: The following grants are a representative sample of this grantmaker's funding activity:

$230,000 to Montgomery College Foundation, Rockville, MD, 2011.
$150,000 to National Ataxia Foundation, Minneapolis, MN, 2011. For research.
$150,000 to University of California at San Diego, La Jolla, CA, 2011.

3839
Mann-Paller Foundation, Inc. ✧ ☆
5404 Falmouth Rd.
Bethesda, MD 20816-1841

Donors: Alan T. Paller; Marsha Paller.
Foundation type: Independent foundation.
Financial data (yr. ended 09/30/13): Assets, $4,611,941 (M); gifts received, $3,000,000; expenditures, $2,130,687; qualifying distributions, $2,130,000; giving activities include $2,130,000 for 3 grants (high: $2,000,000; low: $10,000).
Fields of interest: Performing arts, dance; Education; Foundations (community).
Limitations: Applications not accepted. Giving in Washington, DC. No grants to individuals.
Application information: Contributes only to pre-selected organizations.
Officers: Marsha Paller, Pres. and Treas.; Channing Paller, V.P.; Alan T. Paller, Secy.
EIN: 521316829
Selected grants: The following grants are a representative sample of this grantmaker's funding activity:
$280,233 to Urban Nation, Washington, DC, 2011.

3840
Marriott Daughters Foundation ✧ ☆
10400 Fernwood Rd., Dept. 901
Bethesda, MD 20817-1102

Foundation type: Independent foundation.
Financial data (yr. ended 10/31/13): Assets, $17,157,918 (M); gifts received, $8,107,881; expenditures, $523,621; qualifying distributions, $451,445; giving activities include $423,000 for 42 grants (high: $85,000; low: $1,000).
Fields of interest: Medical research; Children/youth, services; Human services.
Limitations: Applications not accepted. Giving primarily in MA; with some giving to CA and UT.
Application information: Unsolicited requests for funds not accepted.
Officers and Directors:* Julie Ann Marriott,* Pres.; Nancie Suzuki, Secy.; James A. Poulos, Treas.; Sandra Marriott Bertha; Mary Alice Marriott Hatch; Karen Christine Marriott.
EIN: 452590105

3841
The J. Willard and Alice S. Marriott Foundation ✧
(formerly The J. Willard Marriott Foundation)
10400 Fernwood Rd., Dept. 52/925
Bethesda, MD 20817-1102
Contact: Anne Gunsteens, Exec. Dir.

Established in 1966 in DC.
Donors: J. Willard Marriott†; Alice S. Marriott†; J. Willard Marriott Charitable Annuity Trust.
Foundation type: Independent foundation.
Financial data (yr. ended 12/31/13): Assets, $630,758,193 (M); gifts received, $6,847,789; expenditures, $33,408,199; qualifying distributions, $30,724,962; giving activities include $29,827,002 for 246 grants (high: $5,203,099; low: $1,000).
Purpose and activities: Grants primarily to local, previously supported charities, and a few general scholarship funds.
Fields of interest: Arts; Education; Health care; Human services.
Limitations: Applications not accepted. Giving primarily in Washington, DC. No grants to individuals.
Application information: Contributes only to pre-selected organizations.
Board meeting date(s): Spring and Fall
Officers: Anne Gunsteens, Exec. Dir.; Amanda Farnum, Grants Mgr.; Angela Williams, Finance and Prog. Mgr.
Trustees: J. Willard Marriott, Jr.; Richard E. Marriott; Stephen Marriott.
Number of staff: 3 full-time professional; 3 part-time professional; 1 full-time support.
EIN: 526068678

3842
Nancy Peery Marriott Foundation, Inc. ✧
(also known as NPM Foundation)
10400 Fernwood Rd., Dept. 901-01
Bethesda, MD 20817-1102 (301) 380-1425
Contact: Nancie Suzuki, Fdn. Mgr.
FAX: (301) 380-6993;
E-mail: nancie.suzuki@hosthotels.com
Richard Edwin and Nancy Peery Marriott's Giving Pledge Profile: http://glasspockets.org/philanthropy-in-focus/eye-on-the-giving-pledge/profiles#m

Established in 2002 in MD.
Donor: Nancy Peery Marriott.
Foundation type: Independent foundation.
Financial data (yr. ended 03/31/13): Assets, $19,354,104 (M); expenditures, $752,048; qualifying distributions, $744,180; giving activities include $702,950 for 71 grants (high: $300,000; low: $100).
Fields of interest: Museums; Arts; Higher education.
Limitations: Applications accepted. Giving primarily in the Washington, DC, area. No grants to individuals.
Application information: Application form not required.
Initial approach: Letter
Copies of proposal: 1
Deadline(s): Dec. 31
Board meeting date(s): Jan.
Final notification: 2-3 months
Officers and Directors:* Nancy Peery Marriott,* Pres. and Treas.; Richard E. Marriott,* Exec. V.P.; James A. Poulos, Secy.; Sandra Peery Marriott Bertha; Mary Alice Marriott Hatch; Julie Ann Marriott Keenan; Karen Christine Marriott.
EIN: 522003744
Selected grants: The following grants are a representative sample of this grantmaker's funding activity:
$333,334 to University of Utah, Salt Lake City, UT, 2011.
$15,000 to College Summit, Washington, DC, 2011. For general operations.
$15,000 to Washington Performing Arts Society, Washington, DC, 2011.
$10,000 to American Red Cross of the National Capital Area, Fairfax, VA, 2011. For general operations.
$10,000 to Class Acts Arts, Silver Spring, MD, 2011. For general operations.
$10,000 to DC Youth Orchestra Program, Washington, DC, 2011.
$10,000 to Eclipse Chamber Orchestra, Alexandria, VA, 2011.
$10,000 to Hospice Caring, Gaithersburg, MD, 2011. For general operations.
$5,000 to Chi Omega Foundation, Memphis, TN, 2011. For general operations.
$5,000 to Philharmonic Center for the Arts, Naples, FL, 2011.

3843
Richard E. & Nancy P. Marriott Foundation, Inc. ✧
(also known as REM/NPM Foundation)
10400 Fernwood Rd., Dept. 901
Bethesda, MD 20817-1102 (301) 380-1425
Contact: Nancie Suzuki, Fdn. Mgr.
FAX: (301) 380-6993;
E-mail: nancie.suzuki@hosthotels.com
Richard Edwin and Nancy Peery Marriott's Giving Pledge Profile: http://glasspockets.org/philanthropy-in-focus/eye-on-the-giving-pledge/profiles#m

Established in 1999 in MD.
Donors: Richard E. Marriott; Alice S. Marriott Lifetime Trust; J. Willard Marriott, Jr. Foundation.
Foundation type: Independent foundation.
Financial data (yr. ended 12/31/13): Assets, $38,688,400 (M); expenditures, $1,363,155; qualifying distributions, $1,316,138; giving activities include $1,202,900 for 144 grants (high: $50,000; low: $200).
Fields of interest: Education; Youth development, adult & child programs.
Limitations: Applications accepted. Giving primarily in the Washington, DC metro area. No grants to individuals.
Application information: Application form not required.
Initial approach: Proposal
Copies of proposal: 1
Deadline(s): May 1 and Sept. 30
Board meeting date(s): June and Oct.
Final notification: Two months
Officers and Directors:* Richard E. Marriott,* Pres.; Ralph W. Hardy, Jr.,* Secy.; Nancy P. Marriott,* Treas.
Number of staff: 1 part-time professional.
EIN: 521953832
Selected grants: The following grants are a representative sample of this grantmaker's funding activity:
$1,000 to Boy Scouts of America, Capital Area Council Jeremy E. Pelter, Bethesda, MD, 2012. For general operations.

3844
Maryland Home & Community Care Foundation ✧ ☆
c/o Cavagna
3902 Dance Mill Rd.
Phoenix, MD 21131-2116
Contact: Linda J. Safran, Exec. Dir.

Established in MD.
Foundation type: Independent foundation.
Financial data (yr. ended 06/30/13): Assets, $1,193,182 (M); expenditures, $572,853; qualifying distributions, $550,079; giving activities include $530,000 for 2 grants (high: $265,000; low: $265,000).
Purpose and activities: The foundation is dedicated to improving the quality of life for those in need of health and supportive services at home and in the community, regardless of age, by providing grants to organizations in Maryland.
Fields of interest: Health care, support services; Health care, patient services; Health care, home services; Health care; Residential/custodial care.
Limitations: Applications not accepted. Giving primarily in MD. No grants for general operating costs.
Application information: Contributes only to pre-selected organizations.
Officers: Joseph F. Cavagna, Pres. and Secy.; Jeffrey L. Friedman, Esq., Treas.
Trustees: Esther Bonnet; Lynda Burton, Sc.D.; Neetu Dhawan-Gray; Stanley A. Levi; Kantahyanee Murray; Edyth H. Schoenrich, M.D.
EIN: 521574346
Selected grants: The following grants are a representative sample of this grantmaker's funding activity:
$80,000 to Maintaining Active Citizens, Salisbury, MD, 2012.

3845
Mead Family Foundation ✧
(formerly Gilbert and Jaylee Mead Family Foundation)
c/o International Philanthropy LLC
3 Bethesda Metro Ctr., Ste. 350
Bethesda, MD 20814 (301) 761-4433

Established in 1989 in MD.
Donors: Gilbert D. Mead‡; Jaylee M. Mead; Betsy Mead; Diana Mead-Siohan; Marilyn K. Mead; Stanton Mead; The Jaylee Mead 2008 Charitable Lead Annuity Trust.
Foundation type: Independent foundation.
Financial data (yr. ended 12/31/12): Assets, $18,921,625 (M); gifts received, $1,372,725; expenditures, $1,006,221; qualifying distributions, $915,569; giving activities include $756,500 for 54 grants (high: $30,000; low: $1,000).
Purpose and activities: Giving primarily for academic education (K- 12), arts education (except for performing arts and outreach) and crisis prevention for children and youth, and strengthening families.
Fields of interest: Arts education; Elementary/secondary education; Youth development, services; Family services.
Type of support: General/operating support; Program development.
Limitations: Applications accepted. Giving limited to Washington, DC, MD and NC. No grants to individuals or for capital campaigns, or for third party funding through a fiscal agent.
Publications: Grants list; Informational brochure; IRS Form 990 or 990-PF printed copy available upon request.
Application information: Application form required.
Initial approach: Proposal
Deadline(s): Mar. 15
Officers and Directors:* Elizabeth Mead,* Pres. and Treas.; Diana Mead,* V.P. and Secy.; Rita Berg; Marilyn Mead; Christelle Siohan; Jonathan Staub; Wanda Staub; William Tuegel.
Number of staff: 3 part-time professional.
EIN: 521646030

3846
Morris A. Mechanic Foundation, Inc. ✧ ☆
8418 Smallwood Ct.
Pasadena, MD 21122-2760 (410) 439-0117
Contact: Tina Doyle, Dir.

Established in 1942 in MD.
Donor: Morris A. Mechanic‡.
Foundation type: Independent foundation.
Financial data (yr. ended 12/31/13): Assets, $8,515,583 (M); expenditures, $507,333; qualifying distributions, $450,252; giving activities include $427,000 for 39 grants (high: $100,000; low: $1,000).
Fields of interest: Arts; Education; Health care; Health organizations, association.
Limitations: Applications accepted. Giving primarily in Baltimore, MD. No grants to individuals.
Application information: Maximum grant award will not exceed $50,000. Application form required.
Initial approach: Proposal
Deadline(s): None
Directors: Tina Doyle; Alexandria W. Ducharme; Gerald Kavanaugh; Phyllis Reese.
EIN: 526034753

3847
Merrill Foundation, Inc. ✧
c/o Wilbert H. Sirota
111 S. Calvert St., Ste. 2000
Baltimore, MD 21202-6114
E-mail: whsirota@duanemorris.com

Established in 1986 in MD.
Donors: Philip Merrill‡; Eleanor Merrill; Capital Gazette Communications, Inc.; Washington Magazine, Inc.; Merrill Charitable Lead Trust; Philip Merrill Charitable Lead Trust.
Foundation type: Independent foundation.
Financial data (yr. ended 12/31/12): Assets, $20,752,064 (M); gifts received, $700,000; expenditures, $1,256,541; qualifying distributions, $1,085,340; giving activities include $1,083,815 for 41 grants (high: $425,000; low: $500).
Purpose and activities: Giving primarily for higher education and environmental causes.
Fields of interest: Arts; Higher education; Environment.
Limitations: Applications not accepted. Giving primarily in Washington, DC, MD, and VA. No grants to individuals.
Application information: Contributes only to pre-selected organizations.
Officers: Eleanor Merrill, Chair.; Nancy Merrill, Pres.; Wil Sirota, Secy.
Directors: Douglas Merrill; Catherine Merrill Williams.
EIN: 521490571

3848
The Joseph Meyerhoff Fund, Inc. ✧
1 South St., Ste. 1000
Baltimore, MD 21202-7301
Contact: Terry Rubenstein, V.P. and Secy.
E-mail: info@magnajm.com; Additional contact: Misty Gibson, Grants Admin.; Main URL: http://www.meyerhoffcharitablefunds.org/

Incorporated in 1953 in MD.
Donors: Joseph Meyerhoff‡; Mrs. Joseph Meyerhoff‡; Meyerhoff Charitable Income Trust; Katz Charitable Income Trust; Meyerhoff Charitable Income Trust II; Katz Charitable Income Trust II; Rebecca Meyerhoff Memorial Trusts; The Rebecca Meyerhoff Philanthropic Fund.
Foundation type: Independent foundation.
Financial data (yr. ended 12/31/12): Assets, $70,215,246 (M); expenditures, $3,772,350; qualifying distributions, $3,016,395; giving activities include $2,902,609 for 97 grants (high: $350,000; low: $1,000).
Purpose and activities: Giving primarily to support and encourage cultural and higher educational programs and institutions and to facilitate immigration and absorption of new immigrants into Israel.
Fields of interest: Arts; Higher education; Human services; Jewish federated giving programs; Jewish agencies & synagogues; Immigrants/refugees.
International interests: Israel.
Type of support: General/operating support; Continuing support; Annual campaigns; Capital campaigns; Building/renovation; Equipment; Land acquisition; Endowments; Debt reduction; Emergency funds; Program development; Professorships; Publication; Seed money; Fellowships; Scholarship funds; Research; Matching/challenge support.
Limitations: Applications not accepted. Giving primarily in Baltimore, MD, and New York, NY; some funding also to organizations in Israel. No grants to individuals.
Application information: Contributes only to pre-selected organizations.
Board meeting date(s): May and Oct.
Officer: Jill M. Hieronimus, Pres.; Terry M. Rubenstein, V.P. and Secy.; Joseph Meyerhoff II, V.P. and Treas.; Eleanor Katz, V.P.
Number of staff: 1 part-time professional; 1 part-time support.
EIN: 526035997

3849
The Harvey M. Meyerhoff Fund Inc. ✧
1 South St., Ste. 1000
Baltimore, MD 21202-7301 (410) 727-3200
Contact: Misty Gibson; Terry Rubenstein, V.P. and Treas.
E-mail: info@magnajm.com; Main URL: http://www.meyerhoffcharitablefunds.org/

Established in 1994 in MD.
Donor: Harvey M. Meyerhoff.
Foundation type: Independent foundation.
Financial data (yr. ended 12/31/12): Assets, $10,595,186 (M); expenditures, $604,814; qualifying distributions, $517,473; giving activities include $494,639 for 68 grants (high: $127,000; low: $500).
Purpose and activities: Giving primarily for the arts, education, and health services; support also for Jewish organizations and agencies.
Fields of interest: Performing arts, orchestras; Libraries/library science; Scholarships/financial aid; Health organizations, association; Jewish agencies & synagogues.
International interests: Israel.

Type of support: General/operating support; Continuing support; Annual campaigns; Capital campaigns; Building/renovation; Equipment; Endowments; Emergency funds; Program development; Conferences/seminars; Professorships; Curriculum development; Scholarship funds; Research; Program evaluation; Matching/challenge support.
Limitations: Applications not accepted. Giving primarily in MD. No grants to individuals.
Application information: Unsolicited requests for funds are not accepted. Letters of Inquiry and applications are by invitation only.
Officers: Harvey M. Meyerhoff, Pres.; Lee M. Hendler, V.P. and Secy.; Terry M. Rubenstein, V.P. and Treas.
EIN: 521904818

3850
Middendorf Foundation, Inc. ✧
2 E. Read St., 5th Fl.
Baltimore, MD 21202-2470
Contact: Laura A. Holter, Grants Admin.

Incorporated in 1953 in MD.
Donors: J. William Middendorf, Jr.†; Alice C. Middendorf†.
Foundation type: Independent foundation.
Financial data (yr. ended 03/31/13): Assets, $33,339,838 (M); expenditures, $1,554,255; qualifying distributions, $1,280,490; giving activities include $1,182,300 for 26 grants (high: $200,000; low: $1,000).
Purpose and activities: Giving primarily for higher education, particularly to scholarship funds, and for community and social services.
Fields of interest: Museums (art); Higher education; Education; Environmental education; Human services.
Type of support: General/operating support; Capital campaigns; Building/renovation; Endowments; Professorships; Matching/challenge support.
Limitations: Applications accepted. Giving primarily in MD, with emphasis on Baltimore; some giving also in Charlottesville, VA. No support for political organizations, or for programs. No grants to individuals, or for annual funds.
Application information: Application form not required.
Initial approach: Letter
Copies of proposal: 1
Deadline(s): None
Board meeting date(s): Quarterly (Apr., July, Sept. and Dec.)
Final notification: 2 weeks for acknowledgement, 1 week after trustee meetings for determination
Officers and Trustees:* Craig Lewis,* Pres.; Forrest F. Bramble, Jr., Esq.*, V.P.; Sealy H. Hopkinson,* Secy.; Benjamin F. Lucas II, Esq.*, Treas.; Phillips Hathaway; Linda W. McCleary; Theresa N. Knell.
Number of staff: 2 part-time professional.
EIN: 526048944
Selected grants: The following grants are a representative sample of this grantmaker's funding activity:
$69,800 to Maryland School for the Blind, Baltimore, MD, 2013. For assistive technology.
$12,000 to Blue Water Baltimore, Baltimore, MD, 2013. For H20 Monitoring Equipment.

3851
Mid-Shore Community Foundation, Inc. ✧
102 E. Dover St.
Easton, MD 21601-3002 (410) 820-8175
Contact: W. W. "Buck" Duncan, Pres.; For grants and scholarships: Robbin Hill, Prog. Off.
FAX: (410) 820-8157; E-mail: hpickens@mscf.org; Additional e-mail: wduncan@mscf.org; Grant and scholarship e-mail: rhill@mscf.org; Main URL: http://www.mscf.org
Facebook: http://www.facebook.com/pages/Mid-Shore-Community-Foundation/175044307692

Established in 1992 in MD.
Foundation type: Community foundation.
Financial data (yr. ended 06/30/13): Assets, $46,372,548 (M); gifts received, $4,074,872; expenditures, $2,890,372; giving activities include $1,657,188 for 81+ grants (high: $156,566), and $5,771 for 6 grants to individuals.
Purpose and activities: The foundation connects private resources with public needs to enhance the quality of life for the citizens of Caroline, Dorchester, Kent, Queen Anne's and Talbot counties, MD.
Fields of interest: Arts; Education; Environment; Animals/wildlife; Health care; Youth development; Human services; Community/economic development.
Type of support: General/operating support; Management development/capacity building; Capital campaigns; Building/renovation; Equipment; Land acquisition; Emergency funds; Program development; Seed money; Curriculum development; Scholarship funds; Employee matching gifts; In-kind gifts; Matching/challenge support.
Limitations: Applications accepted. Giving limited to the mid-shore and eastern-shore areas of MD (Caroline, Dorchester, Kent, Queen Anne, and Talbot counties). No support for veterans groups or fraternal organizations. No grants to individuals (except for scholarships), or for fundraisers, conferences, public relations, publications, or for multi-year commitments.
Publications: Application guidelines; Annual report; Financial statement; Informational brochure; Newsletter.
Application information: Visit foundation web site for application form and guidelines. Application form required.
Initial approach: Submit application form and attachments
Copies of proposal: 1
Deadline(s): Apr. 1 and Oct. 1
Board meeting date(s): Mar., June, Sept., and Dec.
Final notification: June 30 and Dec. 30
Officers and Directors:* W. Moorhead Vermilye,* Chair.; John Dillon,* Vice-Chair.; W.W. Duncan,* Pres.; Brett Summers,* Secy.; David Nagel,* Treas.; Heather D. Moore,* C.F.O.; E. Jean Anthony; Joseph M. Anthony; Dick Barker; Scott Beatty; William B. Boyd; Elizabeth Brice; Art Cecil; Mickey Elsberg; Mark Freestate; Wayne Howard; Lynn Knight; Neil Lecompte; John Lewis; Sandy McAllister; John McGinnis; Alice Ryan; Win Trice; Barbara A. Viniar; Hubert Wright.
Number of staff: 2 full-time professional; 1 full-time support.
EIN: 521782373

3852
The Millstream Fund, Inc. ✧
c/o Bond Beebe, P.C.
4600 East-West Hwy., Ste. 900
Bethesda, MD 20814-3423

Established in 1986 in DE.
Donor: Hope Aldrich.
Foundation type: Independent foundation.
Financial data (yr. ended 11/30/13): Assets, $6,381,489 (M); gifts received, $776,000; expenditures, $833,115; qualifying distributions, $790,250; giving activities include $790,250 for 50 grants (high: $125,000; low: $250).
Fields of interest: Arts; Civil liberties, reproductive rights; Foundations (private independent); Foundations (public).
Type of support: General/operating support; Continuing support; Annual campaigns; Capital campaigns.
Limitations: Applications not accepted. Giving in the U.S., with emphasis on CA, Santa Fe, NM and New York, NY. No grants to individuals.
Application information: Unsolicited requests for funds not accepted.
Board meeting date(s): Feb. 1
Officers: Hope Aldrich, Pres.; Phoebe Jane Winthrop, Secy.
EIN: 521472819

3853
The Mirmiran Foundation ✧ ☆
72 Loveton Cir.
Sparks, MD 21152-9202

Established in 2004 in MD.
Donor: Fred Mirmiran.
Foundation type: Independent foundation.
Financial data (yr. ended 12/31/13): Assets, $3,026,312 (M); expenditures, $507,547; qualifying distributions, $475,800; giving activities include $473,300 for 13 grants (high: $200,000; low: $800).
Fields of interest: Higher education, university; Scholarships/financial aid; Health organizations, association; Cancer; Medical research, institute; Human services.
Limitations: Applications not accepted. Giving primarily in MD. No grants to individuals.
Application information: Contributes only to pre-selected organizations.
Trustee: Fred Mirmiran.
EIN: 731710694

3854
The Morningstar Foundation ✧
c/o Gelman, Rosenberg & Freedman
4550 Montgomery Ave., Ste. 650 N.
Bethesda, MD 20814-3250
Contact: Michael C. Gelman, V.P.

Established in 1982 in DC and MD.
Donors: Michael C. Gelman; Susan R. Gelman; Richard Goldman 1997 Charitable Lead Annuity Trust; Susan R. Gelman Charitable Lead Trust; SSR Charitable Lead Annuity Trust 2004; Susan R. Gelman 2001 Trust; Richard and Rhoda Goldman Fund.
Foundation type: Independent foundation.
Financial data (yr. ended 12/31/12): Assets, $235,898,287 (M); gifts received, $136,704,812;

expenditures, $9,208,026; qualifying distributions, $8,144,217; giving activities include $7,306,374 for 134 grants (high: $1,090,040; low: $300).
Fields of interest: Arts; Education; Environment; Human services; International peace/security; Jewish federated giving programs; Jewish agencies & synagogues.
International interests: Israel.
Type of support: General/operating support; Annual campaigns; Capital campaigns.
Limitations: Applications not accepted. Giving primarily in the greater Washington, DC, area and in Israel. No grants to individuals.
Application information: Contributes only to pre-selected organizations. Unsolicited requests for funds not accepted.
Board meeting date(s): Quarterly
Officers: Susan R. Gelman, Pres.; Michael C. Gelman, V.P.; George P. Levendis, Esq., Secy.-Treas.
Number of staff: 1 part-time support.
EIN: 521270464

3855
Jerome S. & Grace H. Murray Foundation ✧
c/o Eileen M. Dillon
P.O. Box 227
Owings, MD 20736-0227 (410) 257-5344
Contact: Kim Harrison, Admin.
FAX: (410) 257-5526;
E-mail: kim@jgmurrayfoundation.org; Main URL: http://www.jgmurrayfoundation.org/

Established in 1980 in FL.
Donors: Grace H. Murray; Jerome S. Murray; Grace Healy Murray Irrevocable Trust.
Foundation type: Independent foundation.
Financial data (yr. ended 12/31/13): Assets, $15,499,994 (M); expenditures, $871,836; qualifying distributions, $711,439; giving activities include $711,439 for 155 grants (high: $97,258; low: $200).
Purpose and activities: Giving primarily for the care, training, and education of people with disabilities, and to those who will provide them with that education and training.
Fields of interest: Education, special; Mental health, association; Health organizations; Human services; Developmentally disabled, centers & services.
Limitations: Applications not accepted. Giving on a national basis.
Publications: Annual report; Grants list; IRS Form 990 or 990-PF printed copy available upon request.
Application information: Unsolicited grant applications not accepted. All applicants for a grant must be sponsored by a Murray lineal descendant 18 and over. See foundation web site for further information and application instructions.
Board meeting date(s): Sept.
Trustees: David Althoff; Eileen M. Dillon; Leo K. Murray; Stanton Murray; Cris White.
Number of staff: 1 full-time professional.
EIN: 521805567

3856
Israel & Mollie Myers Foundation ✧
3635 Old Court Rd., No. 207
Baltimore, MD 21208-3906 (410) 653-0556

Established in 1961.
Donors: Israel Myers‡; Jonathan P. Myers; Herschel L. Langenthal; Judith Lagenthal; Beverly Meyers; Daniel Langenthal; Israel Myers Charitable Lead.
Foundation type: Independent foundation.
Financial data (yr. ended 12/31/12): Assets, $9,718,054 (M); gifts received, $387,207; expenditures, $838,359; qualifying distributions, $649,660; giving activities include $637,125 for 120 grants (high: $170,000; low: $35).
Purpose and activities: Giving primarily for Jewish organizations, including welfare services; support also for education and the arts.
Fields of interest: Arts; Education; Jewish federated giving programs; Jewish agencies & synagogues.
Limitations: Applications accepted. Giving primarily in Baltimore, MD.
Application information: Application form not required.
Initial approach: Proposal
Copies of proposal: 1
Deadline(s): None
Officers: Judith Langenthal, Co-Pres.; Jonathan P. Myers, Co-Pres.; Herschel L. Langenthal, V.P.; Beverly Myers, V.P.; Carol Rogers, Secy.; David Goldner, Treas.
Director: Jeffrey Abarbanel.
EIN: 521314430

3857
NASDAQ OMX Group Educational Foundation, Inc. ✧
(formerly The Nasdaq Stock Marked Educational Foundation, Inc.)
805 King Farm Blvd.
Rockville, MD 20850 (800) 842-0356
E-mail: foundation@nasdaqomx.com; Main URL: http://www.nasdaqomx.com/services/initiatives/educationalfoundation

Established in 1993 in MD and DE.
Donor: The Nasdaq Stock Market, Inc.
Foundation type: Company-sponsored foundation.
Financial data (yr. ended 12/31/12): Assets, $27,463,287 (M); expenditures, $4,679,411; qualifying distributions, $4,309,768; giving activities include $4,309,768 for 41 grants (high: $500,000; low: $7,900).
Purpose and activities: The foundation supports programs designed to promote capital formation, financial markets, and entrepreneurship through education and awards fellowships to individuals for the purpose of conducting independent academic study or research on financial markets.
Fields of interest: Elementary/secondary education; Higher education; Education; Disasters, preparedness/services; Human services, financial counseling; Community/economic development; Economics.
Type of support: Continuing support; Program development; Curriculum development; Fellowships; Research.
Limitations: Applications accepted. Giving primarily in CA, CT, Washington, DC, IN, MD, MN, NY, NC, and TX. No support for discriminatory organizations.
Publications: Application guidelines; Grants list.
Application information: Letters of inquiry should be no longer than one page. Grant seekers may be invited to submit a full proposal at a later date. Ph.D. dissertation fellowships are granted in a set amount of $15,000. Application form not required.
Initial approach: E-mail or mail letter of inquiry
Deadline(s): Feb. 3 and Aug. 1
Final notification: Mar. 1 and Oct. 1
Officers and Directors:* Robert Greifeld,* Chair.; Joan C. Conley, Secy. and Managing Dir.; Peter Strandell, Treas.; Bruce E. Aust; H. Furlong Baldwin; Marc Baum; John J. Lucchese.
EIN: 521864429
Selected grants: The following grants are a representative sample of this grantmaker's funding activity:
$333,000 to Fordham University, Bronx, NY, 2011.
$100,000 to Council on Foreign Relations, New York, NY, 2011.

3858
The Nextgen Foundation Charitable Trust ✧ ☆
10706 Beaver Dam Rd.
Cockeysville, MD 21030-2207

Supporting organization of Amador Land Trust, American Cancer Society, American Endowment Foundation, American Heart Association, American Land Conservancy, American Lung Association of New York, American Pulmonary Medicine Institute, American Red Cross of Gratiot County, American River Conservancy, Anderson Valley Land Trust, Antelope Valley Heritage Foundation, Anza-Borrego Foundation, Aspen Center for Environmental Studies, Associated Jewish Charities of Baltimore, Associated Jewish Community Federation of Baltimore, Atascadero Land Preservation Society, Auburn Park Conservancy, Back County Land Trust, Ballona Lagoon Marine Preserve, Baltimore Community Foundation, Baltimore Museum of Art, Baltimore Symphony Orchestra, Baltimore Urban Leadership Foundation, Bay Area Ridge Trail Council, Billy Graham Evangelistic Association, Biola University, Bowdian College, Boy Scouts of America, Boy Scouts of America Nat'l Council, Boy's Latin School of Maryland, British Schools and Universities Foundation.
Donor: Robert E. Smith.
Foundation type: Independent foundation.
Financial data (yr. ended 03/31/13): Assets, $11,707,147 (M); expenditures, $563,756; qualifying distributions, $505,133; giving activities include $505,133 for 26 grants (high: $262,633; low: $2,500).
Fields of interest: Education.
Limitations: Applications not accepted. Giving limited to MD.
Application information: Contributes only to pre-selected organizations; unsolicited requests for funds not considered or acknowledged.
Officers: Robert E. Smith,* Pres.; Mark D. Knobloch,* V.P.; Melissa W. Smith,* Secy.; Paul O. Wallace,* Treas.
Trustees: Charlotte Lawrence; Ned Lawrence.
EIN: 311480932
Selected grants: The following grants are a representative sample of this grantmaker's funding activity:
$250,000 to Garrison Forest School, Owings Mills, MD, 2011.
$72,000 to Garrison Forest School, Owings Mills, MD, 2011.

3859
The W. O'Neil Foundation ✧
5454 Wisconsin Ave., Ste. 730
Chevy Chase, MD 20815-6924 (301) 656-5848
Contact: Helene O'Neil Shere, Chair., Pres. and Tr.

Incorporated in 1948 in OH.
Donors: William O'Neil†; Grace O'Neil†; John J. O'Neil†; Grace O'Neil Regan; and others.
Foundation type: Independent foundation.
Financial data (yr. ended 12/31/13): Assets, $48,536,213 (M); expenditures, $2,816,578; qualifying distributions, $2,559,622; giving activities include $2,512,300 for 68 grants (high: $500,000; low: $2,000).
Purpose and activities: Grants primarily given to Roman Catholic Church-related organizations for international emergency relief and for programs that bring food, clothing, shelter, basic medical care, and basic education to the poor of the world, preferably through projects that help the poor help themselves toward these goals. International assistance grants are only made to U.S.-based charities.
Fields of interest: Human services; Human services, emergency aid; Homeless, human services; International development; Catholic agencies & churches; Homeless.
Type of support: General/operating support; Equipment; Program development.
Limitations: Applications accepted. Giving primarily in Washington, DC, and New York, NY. No grants to individuals, or for endowment funds, church and school renovations, capital campaigns, administrative overhead, research, conferences, seminars, or matching gifts; no loans.
Publications: Application guidelines.
Application information: If project coincides with the foundation's interests, a proposal will be requested. Application form not required.
Initial approach: Letter of inquiry
Copies of proposal: 1
Deadline(s): None
Board meeting date(s): Feb., Apr., June, and Sept.
Officers and Trustees:* Helene O'Neil Shere,* Chair. and Pres.; Helene Connellan O'Neil,* Vice-Chair. and V.P.; Jane Wieder,* V.P. and Treas.; Ann O'Neil Gradowski,* Secy.; John J. O'Neil, Jr.; Ann Regan; Jane Regan; Mary Regan.
EIN: 346516969
Selected grants: The following grants are a representative sample of this grantmaker's funding activity:
$500,000 to Catholic Relief Services, Baltimore, MD, 2011.
$60,000 to Haitian Health Foundation, Norwich, CT, 2011.
$50,000 to NativityMiguel Network of Schools, Washington, DC, 2011.
$35,000 to Mercy Corps, Portland, OR, 2011.
$30,000 to Bread for the City, Washington, DC, 2011.
$30,000 to DC Central Kitchen, Washington, DC, 2011.
$30,000 to Saint Bernard Project, Chalmette, LA, 2011.
$25,000 to Georgetown Visitation Monastery, Washington, DC, 2011.
$20,000 to Community Council for the Homeless at Friendship Place, Washington, DC, 2011.
$20,000 to Leukemia & Lymphoma Society, Alexandria, VA, 2011.

3860
The Orokawa Foundation, Inc. ✧
c/o Martin J. Eby
1 Olympic Pl., 8th Fl.
Towson, MD 21204-4104

Established in 2005 in MD.
Donors: Bruce Cleland; Isobel Cleland.
Foundation type: Independent foundation.
Financial data (yr. ended 06/30/13): Assets, $57,404,050 (M); expenditures, $3,110,491; qualifying distributions, $2,952,119; giving activities include $2,940,940 for 28 grants (high: $460,000; low: $250).
Purpose and activities: Giving primarily for leukemia and lymphoma research; funding also for a camp for children with life-threatening illnesses, as well as for other health associations, and human services.
Fields of interest: Education; Health organizations, association; Cancer, leukemia research; Human services; Children/youth, services; Foundations (private grantmaking).
Limitations: Applications not accepted. Giving primarily in MD. No grants to individuals.
Application information: Contributes only to pre-selected organizations.
Officers: Bruce Cleland, Pres. and Treas.; Isobel Cleland, V.P. and Secy.
EIN: 201850543
Selected grants: The following grants are a representative sample of this grantmaker's funding activity:
$702,500 to University of Maryland-Baltimore Foundation, Baltimore, MD, 2011. For endowment fund.
$305,000 to Leukemia & Lymphoma Society, Hunt Valley, MD, 2011. For endowment fund.
$250,000 to Chesapeake Bay Foundation, Annapolis, MD, 2011. For endowment fund.
$100,000 to Odyssey School, Stevenson, MD, 2011. For endowment fund.
$100,000 to Saint Ignatius Loyola Academy, Baltimore, MD, 2011. For endowment fund.
$54,000 to Robin Hood Foundation, New York, NY, 2011. For endowment fund.
$50,000 to Community Health Charities of Maryland, Baltimore, MD, 2011. For endowment fund.
$50,000 to Special Olympics, Washington, DC, 2011. For endowment fund.
$25,000 to Baltimore Educational Scholarship Trust, Baltimore, MD, 2011. For endowment fund.
$25,000 to Boys Hope Girls Hope, Baltimore, MD, 2011. For endowment fund.

3861
The Osprey Foundation ✧
1 Olympic Pl., 8th Fl.
Towson, MD 21204-4104

Established in 2002 in MD.
Donors: William C. Clark III; Mrs. William C. Clarke III.
Foundation type: Independent foundation.
Financial data (yr. ended 12/31/12): Assets, $46,629,854 (M); gifts received, $845,000; expenditures, $3,833,993; qualifying distributions, $3,527,464; giving activities include $3,527,464 for 43 grants (high: $307,500; low: $5,000).
Purpose and activities: Giving primarily for health organizations, children, youth and social services, and to Presbyterian organizations.
Fields of interest: Health organizations; Disasters, Hurricane Katrina; Human services; Children/youth, services; Protestant agencies & churches.
Type of support: General/operating support; Scholarship funds.
Limitations: Applications not accepted. Giving in the U.S., with some emphasis on MD, particularly Baltimore. No grants to individuals.
Application information: Contributes only to pre-selected organizations.
Officers: William C. Clarke III, Pres.; Bonnie A. Clarke, Secy.-Treas.
Directors: Jesse Clarke; Steven W. Clarke; Christopher Powell; Meredith Powell; Christopher Wells; Lindsey B. Wells.
EIN: 141862154

3862
Clarence Manger & Audrey Cordero Plitt Trust ✧ ☆
c/o Natalie Stengel
25 S. Charles St., MD2-CS51
Baltimore, MD 21203-1596
Application address: c/o Mary Anne Kirgan, 968 Bellview Rd., McLean, VA 22102, tel.: (410) 244-4630

Established in 1979 in MD.
Donor: Clarence M. Plitt†.
Foundation type: Independent foundation.
Financial data (yr. ended 08/31/13): Assets, $13,229,577 (M); expenditures, $662,390; qualifying distributions, $576,500; giving activities include $451,000 for 1 grant.
Fields of interest: Education.
Type of support: Program-related investments/loans; Matching/challenge support; Student loans—to individuals.
Limitations: Applications accepted. Giving primarily in MA.
Publications: Annual report.
Application information: Application form required.
Initial approach: Letter
Copies of proposal: 2
Deadline(s): May 31
Managers: Mary Anne Kirgan; Robert S. Kirgan.
Trustee: M&T Bank, N.A.
Number of staff: 1 full-time professional.
EIN: 526195778

3863
The John J. Pohanka Family Foundation ✧
1772 Ritchie Station Ct.
Capitol Heights, MD 20743-5065

Established in 1996 in MD.
Donors: John J. Pohanka; Geoffrey P. Pohanka; John J. Pohanka Trust; Susan Schantz Trust.
Foundation type: Independent foundation.
Financial data (yr. ended 12/31/12): Assets, $13,196,127 (M); expenditures, $91,216; qualifying distributions, $652,880; giving activities include $649,880 for 46 grants (high: $200,000; low: $100).
Purpose and activities: Giving primarily for the arts, particularly the opera; funding also for education, health organizations and social services.
Fields of interest: Performing arts, opera; Arts; Higher education; Education; Health organizations; Human services.

Limitations: Applications not accepted. Giving in the U.S., with some emphasis on MD and Washington, DC. No grants to individuals.
Application information: Unsolicited requests for funds not accepted.
Trustees: Steven Parker; Geoffrey Pohanka; John J. Pohanka.
EIN: 566784266

3864
Howard and Geraldine Polinger Family Foundation ✧
(formerly Howard and Geraldine Polinger Foundation)
5530 Wisconsin Ave., Ste. 1000
Chevy Chase, MD 20815-4330
Contact: Lorre Polinger, Pres.
E-mail: info@polingerfoundation.org; Tel./fax: (617) 964-6199; Main URL: http://foundationcenter.org/grantmaker/polinger/

Incorporated in 1968 in MD.
Donors: Howard Polinger†; Geraldine Polinger; Geraldine Polinger Family Trust.
Foundation type: Independent foundation.
Financial data (yr. ended 06/30/13): Assets, $41,414,540 (M); expenditures, $2,105,405; qualifying distributions, $1,919,875; giving activities include $1,626,000 for 58 grants (high: $150,000; low: $1,000).
Purpose and activities: Giving primarily to foster Jewish identity, showcase Jewish arts and culture, build and strengthen Jewish life in emerging communities, specifically the in spurring Jewish identity in Central and Eastern Europe and the Former Soviet Union, combat anti-Semitism, and help people in need. Funding also for the cultivation of the performing arts, and enhancing the well-being of families.
Fields of interest: Performing arts; Youth development; Family services; Jewish federated giving programs; Jewish agencies & synagogues.
International interests: Israel.
Type of support: General/operating support; Continuing support; Program development; Curriculum development; Matching/challenge support.
Limitations: Giving primarily in the Washington, DC, and Montgomery County, MD, area. No grants to individuals. Requests for capital and endowment grants are not normally accepted.
Publications: Grants list; Newsletter.
Application information: Unsolicited applications are not accepted. The foundation prefers to take the initiative to develop projects in conjunction with organizations that are in accord with its mission and funding priorities. Only brief e-mails are accepted if applicant feels their program or project would be a good fit with the foundation's funding priorities.
Initial approach: Brief e-mail
Board meeting date(s): Spring and fall
Officers and Directors:* Lorre Beth Polinger,* Pres.; Arnold Lee Polinger,* V.P., Fin.; Jan Polinger,* V.P., Grants; Erica Pressman, Secy.; David Marc Polinger,* Treas.; Geraldine H. Polinger.
Number of staff: 3 part-time professional.
EIN: 526078041

3865
T. Rowe Price Foundation ✧
(formerly T. Rowe Associates Foundation, Inc.)
100 E. Pratt St.
Baltimore, MD 21202-1008 (410) 345-6673
Contact: Stacy Van Horn, Exec. Dir.
FAX: (410) 345-2848;
E-mail: community_involvement@troweprice.com;
Main URL: http://corporate.troweprice.com/ccw/home/responsibility/tRowePriceFoundation.do

Established in 1981 in MD.
Donors: T. Rowe Price Associates, Inc.; T. Rowe Price Group, Inc.
Foundation type: Company-sponsored foundation.
Financial data (yr. ended 12/31/13): Assets, $67,628,097 (M); gifts received, $10,014,927; expenditures, $6,557,876; qualifying distributions, $6,247,221; giving activities include $6,176,909 for 1,488 grants (high: $1,615,789; low: $25).
Purpose and activities: The foundation supports organizations involved with arts and culture, education, youth development, human services, and community development.
Fields of interest: Museums (art); Arts; Elementary school/education; Secondary school/education; Higher education; Libraries (public); Education; Youth development, business; Family services; Human services, emergency aid; Human services; Community/economic development; United Ways and Federated Giving Programs.
Type of support: General/operating support; Continuing support; Capital campaigns; Program development; Scholarship funds; Employee volunteer services; Employee matching gifts.
Limitations: Applications not accepted. Giving primarily in areas of company operations in Baltimore, MD, area. No support for religious or political organizations, hospitals, healthcare providers, recreational sports leagues, or private foundations. No grants to individuals, or for sports-related fundraisers.
Application information: The foundation generally practices an invitation only process for giving.
Officers and Trustees:* Ann Allston Boyce,* Pres.; Stephen W. Boesel,* V.P.; Barbara J. Burdett,* V.P.; Meredith C. Callahan,* V.P.; Hugh M. Evans III,* V.P.; Jacqueline C. Hrabowski,* V.P.; George A. Roche,* V.P.; William F. Wendler II,* V.P.; Vernon A. Reid, Jr.,* Secy.-Treas.; Stacy Van Horn, Exec. Dir.
Number of staff: 1 full-time professional; 1 full-time support.
EIN: 521231953
Selected grants: The following grants are a representative sample of this grantmaker's funding activity:
$1,092,919 to T. Rowe Price Program for Charitable Giving, Baltimore, MD, 2012.
$140,835 to Teach for America, Baltimore, MD, 2012.
$136,865 to Baltimore Museum of Art, Baltimore, MD, 2012.
$73,049 to American Red Cross of Central Maryland, Central Maryland Chapter, Baltimore, MD, 2012.
$50,000 to Junior Achievement Worldwide, Colorado Springs, CO, 2012.
$21,600 to Charities Aid Foundation America, Alexandria, VA, 2012.
$10,500 to Maryland African American Museum Corporation, Reginald F. Lewis Museum of Maryland African American History and Culture, Baltimore, MD, 2012.
$10,000 to Boys and Girls Club of Harford County, Aberdeen, MD, 2012.
$5,000 to Emmanuel College, Boston, MA, 2012. For Higher Education.
$3,750 to Lower Cape Fear Hospice Foundation, Wilmington, NC, 2012.

3866
John A. Quinn Foundation, Inc. ✧
7711 Brookville Rd.
Chevy Chase, MD 20815-3933
Contact: Robert F. Comstock, Secy.

Established in 1968.
Foundation type: Independent foundation.
Financial data (yr. ended 12/31/13): Assets, $3,113,817 (M); gifts received, $300,000; expenditures, $1,109,557; qualifying distributions, $981,150; giving activities include $981,150 for 13 grants (high: $365,000; low: $2,700).
Purpose and activities: Giving primarily for Roman Catholic education, churches, and social services.
Fields of interest: Secondary school/education; Higher education; Catholic agencies & churches.
Limitations: Applications accepted. Giving primarily in CT, Washington, DC, and MD. No grants to individuals.
Application information:
Initial approach: Letter
Deadline(s): None
Officers: Eileen S. Quinn, Pres.; Robert F. Comstock, Secy.-Treas.
Directors: Lauren L. Bailey; Karen Portlance; George J. Quinn, Jr.; Kathleen M. Quinn; Kimberly B. Shaughnessy; Patricia Testerman.
EIN: 526081612

3867
Rathmann Family Foundation ✧
1290 Bay Dale Dr.
P.O. Box 352
Arnold, MD 21012-0352 (410) 349-2376

Established in 1991 in WA.
Donors: George Rathmann; Joy Rathmann.
Foundation type: Independent foundation.
Financial data (yr. ended 12/31/13): Assets, $47,466,824 (M); expenditures, $2,040,142; qualifying distributions, $1,850,326; giving activities include $1,451,377 for 69 grants (high: $375,000; low: $1,000).
Purpose and activities: The mission (or purpose) of the foundation is to promote and support innovation, development and excellence in science, technology, education and the environment. The foundation funds organizations and programs which apply research, science, technology and education to improving lives and strengthening communities and the nation. The foundation's educational interests extend from elementary through post-secondary years and focus primarily on science, math, technology, the environment, medicine and the arts. Related areas of foundation interest include biotechnology and conservation of the environment and open spaces for low impact use, such as hiking, walking and off-leash recreation.
Fields of interest: Arts; Education; Environment; Health care; Health organizations, association; Children/youth, services; Science, research; Science, public education; Mathematics; Economically disadvantaged.

Type of support: General/operating support; Continuing support; Capital campaigns; Equipment; Endowments; Program development; Conferences/seminars; Seed money; Curriculum development; Fellowships; Internship funds; Scholarship funds; Research; Program evaluation; Program-related investments/loans; Matching/challenge support.
Limitations: Applications not accepted. Giving primarily in the San Francisco Bay Area, CA, Annapolis and Baltimore, MD, the metropolitan Minneapolis-St. Paul, MN, area, and Philadelphia, PA,. No support for private foundations, religious organizations for religious activities, civil rights, social action, or advocacy organizations, fraternal, labor, or veterans' groups, political purposes, or mental health counseling. No grants to individuals, or for fundraising, media events, public relations, propaganda, or annual appeals.
Application information: Mailings will not be accepted or responded to. The foundation will fund only board-initiated or solicited programs and, in selected cases, organizations and programs in which it has previously invested. Unsolicited requests for funds not accepted.
Officers: James Louis Rathmann, Chair.; Margaret Crosby Rathmann, Vice-Chair.; Richard G. Rathmann, Pres.; Alexandra Joy Rathmann-Noonan, V.P.; Sally Rathmann Kadifa, Secy.; Laura Jean Rathmann, Treas.
EIN: 521757445

3868
Rembrandt Foundation, Inc.

(formerly Constellation Energy Group Foundation, Inc.)
c/o Community Partnerships
100 Constellation Way, Ste. 1800
Baltimore, MD 21202-6302
Contact: Ashley Freeman
FAX: (410) 470-4098;
E-mail: exeloncorporatecontributions@exeloncorp.com
E2 Energy to Educate Grants List: http://www.constellation.com/documents/2013_grant_winners.pdf
EcoStar Grants List: http://www.constellation.com/Documents/2012%20Final%20EcoStar%20Awardee%20List.pdf

Established in 1986 in MD.
Donors: Baltimore Gas and Electric Co.; Constellation Energy Group, Inc.
Foundation type: Company-sponsored foundation.
Financial data (yr. ended 12/13/12): Assets, $24,331,164 (M); expenditures, $4,430,747; qualifying distributions, $4,400,438; giving activities include $4,400,438 for grants.
Purpose and activities: The foundation supports organizations involved with education, energy assistance, the environment, and economic growth.
Fields of interest: Higher education; Education; Environment, pollution control; Environment, natural resources; Environment, land resources; Environmental education; Environment; Housing/shelter, development; Recreation, parks/playgrounds; Athletics/sports, golf; Youth development, business; Children/youth, services; Economic development; United Ways and Federated Giving Programs; Mathematics; Engineering/technology; Youth; Economically disadvantaged.
Type of support: Employee volunteer services; General/operating support; Continuing support; Capital campaigns; Building/renovation; Program development; Conferences/seminars; Scholarship funds; Employee matching gifts; Matching/challenge support.
Limitations: Applications not accepted. Giving primarily in areas of company operations, with emphasis on DE, KY, central MD, NJ, NY, PA, TX,. No support for churches not of direct benefit to the entire community, organizations actively opposing Constellation's position on issues, individual schools, or sports teams. No grants to individuals, or for general operating or program development support for United Way agencies, start-up needs, or hospital capital campaigns.
Application information: The foundation is in the process of transitioning into new giving guidelines.
Board meeting date(s): June and Oct.
Officers and Directors:* Mayo A. Shattuck II,* Chair. and Pres.; C. A. Berardesco,* V.P. and Secy.; S. M Ulrich, V.P.; James L. Connaughton.
Number of staff: None.
EIN: 521452037

3869
James S. & Gail P. Riepe Charitable Foundation ✧

P.O. Box 64
Butler, MD 21023-0064

Established in 1986 in MD.
Donor: James S. Riepe.
Foundation type: Independent foundation.
Financial data (yr. ended 12/31/12): Assets, $20,111,728 (M); expenditures, $1,199,215; qualifying distributions, $1,188,515; giving activities include $1,187,365 for 72 grants (high: $479,050; low: $500).
Purpose and activities: Giving primarily for higher education and human services.
Fields of interest: Museums (art); Arts; Higher education; Education; Health organizations, association; Human services.
Type of support: Continuing support; Annual campaigns; Capital campaigns; Building/renovation; Land acquisition; Endowments; Scholarship funds.
Limitations: Applications not accepted. Giving primarily in Baltimore, MD and Philadelphia, PA. No grants to individuals.
Application information: Contributes only to pre-selected organizations.
Trustees: Christina N. Riepe; Gail P. Riepe; James S. Riepe.
EIN: 526287385
Selected grants: The following grants are a representative sample of this grantmaker's funding activity:
$479,050 to University of Pennsylvania, Philadelphia, PA, 2012. For Arthur H Rubenstein Endowed Scholarship Fund.
$100,000 to Baltimore Museum of Art, Baltimore, MD, 2012. For In a New Light Campaign-Contemporary Wing.
$100,000 to University of Pennsylvania, Philadelphia, PA, 2012. For Wharton Annual Giving Fund.
$87,700 to Baltimore Museum of Art, Baltimore, MD, 2012. For In a New Light Campaign-Free Admission.
$25,000 to University of Pennsylvania, Philadelphia, PA, 2012. For Penn Medicine Friends Fund.
$25,000 to University of Pennsylvania, Philadelphia, PA, 2012. For Penn Fund.
$25,000 to University of Pennsylvania, Philadelphia, PA, 2012. For Veterinary Student Scholarship Fund.
$5,000 to University of Pennsylvania, Philadelphia, PA, 2012. For Championship Rings.
$5,000 to University of Pennsylvania, Philadelphia, PA, 2012. For Champions' Club for Football.

3870
The Rock Springs Foundation ✧ ☆

6903 Rockledge Dr., Ste. 214
Bethesda, MD 20817-1863

Established in 1998 in MD.
Donor: Chester Davenport.
Foundation type: Independent foundation.
Financial data (yr. ended 12/31/12): Assets, $260,832 (M); gifts received, $319,608; expenditures, $696,313; qualifying distributions, $587,011; giving activities include $486,350 for 15 grants (high: $85,000; low: $750).
Purpose and activities: Giving primarily for education and civil rights.
Fields of interest: Higher education; Education; Civil/human rights, minorities; Christian agencies & churches; Protestant agencies & churches; African Americans/Blacks.
Limitations: Applications not accepted. Giving primarily in Washington, DC, giving also in GA, MA, MD and VA. No grants to individuals.
Application information: Unsolicited requests for funds not accepted.
Officer: Chester Davenport, Pres.; Siobhan Davenport, Exec. Dir.
EIN: 223624934

3871
Rocking Moon Foundation, Inc. ✧

c/o Ellen Sudow
5630 Wisconsin Ave., Ste. 1201
Chevy Chase, MD 20815

Established in 2002 in DC.
Donors: Joseph R. Higdon; Ellen L. Sudow.
Foundation type: Independent foundation.
Financial data (yr. ended 12/31/13): Assets, $14,065,039 (M); expenditures, $817,336; qualifying distributions, $903,500; giving activities include $803,500 for 20 grants (high: $75,000; low: $10,000).
Fields of interest: Reproductive health, family planning; Civil/human rights, LGBTQ; Children/youth.
Type of support: General/operating support; Program development.
Limitations: Applications not accepted. Giving primarily in New York, NY and Washington, DC. No grants to individuals.
Application information: Contributes only to pre-selected organizations.
Officers and Directors:* Joseph R. Higdon,* Pres.; Ellen L. Sudow,* V.P. and Secy.-Treas.; Robert J. Higdon; Sarah Higdon-Sudow; William J. Higdon-Sudow.
EIN: 050545520
Selected grants: The following grants are a representative sample of this grantmaker's funding activity:
$85,000 to Bailey House, New York, NY, 2012. For General Operating and Sandy Relief.

$50,000 to Advocates for Youth, Washington, DC, 2012. For General Operating and Pilot LGBT Global South Program.
$50,000 to American Civil Liberties Union Foundation, New York, NY, 2012. For LGBT Project 2012.
$50,000 to Family Planning Association of Maine, Augusta, ME, 2012. For Transgender and Teen Programs.
$30,000 to Cystic Fibrosis Foundation, Bethesda, MD, 2012. For Milestones Ii Campaign.

3872
Rollins-Luetkemeyer Foundation, Inc. ✧
(formerly The Rollins-Luetkemeyer Charitable Foundation, Inc.)
1427 Clarkview Rd., Ste. 500
Baltimore, MD 21209-2100 (443) 921-4358
Contact: John A. Luetkemeyer, Jr., Pres.

Established in 1961 in MD.
Donor: J. Mark Shapiro.
Foundation type: Independent foundation.
Financial data (yr. ended 12/31/13): Assets, $69,312,629 (M); gifts received, $2,700,489; expenditures, $3,263,773; qualifying distributions, $3,001,781; giving activities include $2,803,940 for 14 grants (high: $2,366,940; low: $2,000).
Purpose and activities: Giving primarily for building funds for early childhood, elementary and secondary schools; support also for certain health organizations.
Fields of interest: Education, early childhood education; Elementary school/education; Higher education; Education; Health care; Human services.
Type of support: General/operating support; Annual campaigns; Building/renovation.
Limitations: Applications not accepted. Giving primarily in the Baltimore, MD, area. No grants to individuals.
Application information: Contributes only to pre-selected organizations.
Officers and Directors:* John A. Luetkemeyer, Jr.,* Pres.; Richard E. Levine,* V.P. and Secy.; Esther Templeton, Treas.; William B. Dixon, Exec. Dir.; Robert Black III; James C. Davis; Thomas F. Mullan III.
Number of staff: 2 part-time professional.
EIN: 526041536

3873
The Henry and Ruth Blaustein Rosenberg Foundation, Inc.
1 South St., Ste. 2900
Baltimore, MD 21202-3334 (410) 347-7201
Contact: Henry A. Rosenberg, Jr., Pres.
FAX: (410) 347-7210; E-mail: info@blaufund.org; Main URL: http://www.blaufund.org/foundations/henryandruth_f.html

Incorporated in 1959 in MD.
Donors: Ruth Blaustein Rosenberg†; Henry A. Rosenberg, Jr.; Ruth R. Marder; Judith R. Hoffberger; American Trading and Production Corp.; Rosemore, Inc.
Foundation type: Independent foundation.
Financial data (yr. ended 12/31/13): Assets, $28,763,464 (M); expenditures, $1,536,642; qualifying distributions, $1,353,917; giving activities include $1,161,750 for 71 grants (high: $100,000; low: $1,000).
Purpose and activities: The mission of the foundation is to improve the human condition through promoting life-long educational opportunities, research advances and a spectrum of cultural programming.
Fields of interest: Arts; Higher education; Adult education—literacy, basic skills & GED; Education; Health care; Employment, services; Youth development, adult & child programs; Jewish federated giving programs.
Type of support: General/operating support; Annual campaigns; Capital campaigns; Building/renovation; Matching/challenge support.
Limitations: Giving primarily in the greater Baltimore, MD, area. No support for unaffiliated schools. No grants to individuals, or for fundraising events, direct mail solicitations; no loans.
Publications: Application guidelines; Grants list.
Application information: The foundation does not accept unsolicited proposals for health research. Complete application guidelines available on foundation web site; Association of Baltimore Area Grantmakers Common Grant Application Form accepted. Application form not required.
Initial approach: Letter
Copies of proposal: 1
Deadline(s): None
Board meeting date(s): Semiannually
Final notification: 4 to 6 months
Officers and Trustees:* Henry A. Rosenberg, Jr.,* Pres.; Judith R. Hoffberger,* V.P.; Ruth R. Marder,* V.P.; Robert A. Delp, Treas.; Betsy F. Ringel, Exec. Dir.
EIN: 526038384
Selected grants: The following grants are a representative sample of this grantmaker's funding activity:
$5,000 to Your Public Radio Corporation, Baltimore, MD, 2012. For All grants or contributions are made to qualified 501(c)(3) organizations. Purpose of grants or contributions listed above: Unrestricted gift for charitable purposes.

3874
The Dorothy L. & Henry A. Rosenberg, Jr. Foundation, Inc. ✧
1 N. Charles St., 22nd Fl.
Baltimore, MD 21201-3740 (410) 347-7066
Contact: Henry A. Rosenberg, Jr., Pres. and Tr.

Established in 1999 in MD.
Donor: Henry A. Rosenberg, Jr.
Foundation type: Independent foundation.
Financial data (yr. ended 12/31/13): Assets, $2,026,637 (M); gifts received, $1,135,000; expenditures, $1,131,791; qualifying distributions, $1,114,348; giving activities include $1,103,000 for 47 grants (high: $350,000; low: $500).
Fields of interest: Higher education; Education; Boy scouts; Human services; Foundations (private grantmaking); Jewish federated giving programs.
Limitations: Applications accepted. Giving primarily in MD, with emphasis on Baltimore. No grants to individuals.
Application information: Application form required.
Initial approach: Letter
Deadline(s): None
Officers and Trustees:* Henry A. Rosenberg, Jr.,* Pres.; Dorothy L. Rosenberg,* V.P.; Frank B. Rosenberg, Secy.
EIN: 522185213

3875
Ben & Esther Rosenbloom Foundation, Inc. ✧
8 Reservoir Cir., Ste. 202
Baltimore, MD 21208-6398
Contact: Howard Rosenbloom, Exec. Dir.

Established in 1982 in MD.
Donor: Ben Rosenbloom†.
Foundation type: Independent foundation.
Financial data (yr. ended 12/31/12): Assets, $31,852,282 (M); expenditures, $1,741,527; qualifying distributions, $1,470,107; giving activities include $1,142,656 for 55 grants (high: $323,609; low: $25).
Purpose and activities: Giving primarily to higher education, human services, Jewish federated giving programs and Jewish agencies.
Fields of interest: Higher education; Human services; Jewish federated giving programs; Jewish agencies & synagogues.
Limitations: Applications accepted. Giving primarily in Baltimore, MD. No support for disease specific research, advocacy, the environment, or for social work or psychology. No grants to individuals, or for endowments.
Application information: Application form not required.
Initial approach: Proposal
Copies of proposal: 1
Deadline(s): None
Final notification: Positive responses only
Officers and Directors:* Esther Rosenbloom,* Pres.; Robert Rosenbloom,* Secy.; Keith Rosenbloom,* Treas.; Howard Rosenbloom, Exec. Dir.; Michelle G. Rosenbloom, Medical Dir.
Number of staff: 1 full-time professional.
EIN: 521258672

3876
The Elizabeth B. and Arthur E. Roswell Foundation Inc. ✧
c/o AFS
1 South St., Ste. 2900
Baltimore, MD 21202-3334 (410) 347-7201
Contact: Arthur E. Roswell, Pres.

Incorporated in 1986 in MD.
Donor: Elizabeth B. Roswell.
Foundation type: Independent foundation.
Financial data (yr. ended 12/31/13): Assets, $13,190,832 (M); expenditures, $933,086; qualifying distributions, $852,559; giving activities include $801,688 for 84 grants (high: $250,000; low: $500).
Purpose and activities: Giving primarily for basic human needs and the environment.
Fields of interest: Environment, natural resources; Health care; Human services; Family services.
Type of support: General/operating support; Annual campaigns.
Limitations: Applications accepted. Giving primarily in Baltimore, MD, NJ, and southeastern PA. No grants to individuals, or for fundraising or direct mailings; no loans.
Application information: Application form required.
Initial approach: Letter
Deadline(s): None
Officers and Directors:* Elizabeth B. Roswell,* Chair.; Arthur E. Roswell,* Pres.; Barbara S. Roswell,* V.P.; Marjorie B. Roswell,* V.P.; Robert A. Roswell,* V.P.; Judith R. Weinstein,* V.P.; Kenneth

B. Weinstein,* V.P.; Jill R. Robinson, Secy.; Anne A. Patterson, Treas.; David I. Roswell; Michael E. Roswell.
EIN: 521490498

3877
The Rouse Company Foundation, Inc. ✧
2330 W. Joppa Rd, Ste. 165
Lutherville, MD 21093-4612
Contact: Heather D. Crosby, Exec. Dir.

Established in 1963 in MD.
Donor: Smalley Family Foundation.
Foundation type: Independent foundation.
Financial data (yr. ended 12/31/13): Assets, $5,953,272 (M); expenditures, $2,121,587; qualifying distributions, $1,901,057; giving activities include $1,842,778 for 34 grants (high: $300,000; low: $250).
Purpose and activities: The foundation supports organizations involved with fine arts, performing arts, education, affordable housing, and human services. Support is limited to greater Baltimore and Howard County, Maryland.
Fields of interest: Visual arts; Performing arts; Arts; Education; Housing/shelter; Human services.
Type of support: General/operating support; Annual campaigns; Capital campaigns; Building/renovation; Program development.
Limitations: Giving limited to Baltimore City, Baltimore County, and Howard County, MD. No support for religious or political organizations. No grants to individuals, or for endowments, disability- or disease-specific research, publications, promotional campaigns, or predominately government-supported projects.
Application information: Association of Baltimore Area Grantmakers Common Grant Application Format accepted. Application form not required.
Initial approach: Letter or e-mail proposal to foundation
Copies of proposal: 1
Deadline(s): Contact foundation for current deadlines
Board meeting date(s): Quarterly
Officers and Trustees:* Anthony W. Deering,* Chair.; Heather D. Crosby, Exec. Dir.; Gordon H. Glenn; Alton J. Scavo.
EIN: 526056273

3878
Myles D. and J. Faye Sampson Family Foundation ✧
c/o International Philanthropy
3 Bethesda Metro Center, Ste. 350
Bethesda, MD 20814 (301) 761-4433
E-mail for: Rebecka Manglanathan, Grants Mgr.: becka@internationalphilanthropy.com; Main URL: http://thesampsonfoundation.org/
Twitter: http://twitter.com/SampsonFDN

Established in 1993 in PA.
Donors: Myles D. Sampson; J. Faye Sampson; Twila Sampson Foundation; Rimdo Properties Inc.; Toro Development Company.
Foundation type: Independent foundation.
Financial data (yr. ended 12/31/12): Assets, $26,944,785 (M); gifts received, $18,055; expenditures, $1,230,607; qualifying distributions, $756,447; giving activities include $627,500 for 20 grants (high: $500,000; low: $1,000).
Fields of interest: Arts; Higher education; Hospitals (general); Health organizations, association; Youth development, scouting agencies (general); Human services; YM/YWCAs & YM/YWHAs; International development; United Ways and Federated Giving Programs; Protestant agencies & churches.
Limitations: Applications not accepted. Giving primarily in southwestern, PA. No grants to individuals.
Application information: Contributes only to pre-selected organizations.
Officer and Trustees:* Katharine S. McBride,* Secy.; Holli B. Rivera, Exec. Dir.; Kristy Sampson Rodriguez; J. Faye Sampson.
EIN: 256407379
Selected grants: The following grants are a representative sample of this grantmaker's funding activity:
$25,000 to Redstone Presbyterian SeniorCare, Greensburg, PA, 2012. For Promises Kept benevolent care Program.
$5,000 to Family House, Pittsburgh, PA, 2012. For Family Assistance Fund.
$2,500 to Thurston County Food Bank, Olympia, WA, 2012. For School Gardens Program ($1,00).
$1,000 to Grow Pittsburgh, Pittsburgh, PA, 2012. For Computer and Technology Needs.

3879
Herman & Walter Samuelson Foundation, Inc. ✧ ☆
409 Washington Ave., Ste. 900
Towson, MD 21204-4905

Established in MD.
Foundation type: Independent foundation.
Financial data (yr. ended 12/31/13): Assets, $15,578,201 (M); expenditures, $751,871; qualifying distributions, $673,490; giving activities include $655,500 for 15 grants (high: $350,000; low: $1,000).
Fields of interest: Education; Health care; Jewish agencies & synagogues.
Limitations: Applications not accepted. Giving primarily in MD.
Application information: Unsolicited requests for funds not accepted.
Officers: Louis F. Friedman, Pres. and Secy.; Robert Damie, V.P. and Treas.
EIN: 452402050

3880
The William Donald Schaefer Foundation, Inc. ✧
100 Light St., Ste. 1100
Baltimore, MD 21202-1185

Donor: William Donald Schaefer‡.
Foundation type: Independent foundation.
Financial data (yr. ended 12/31/13): Assets, $21,403 (M); gifts received, $152,582; expenditures, $467,779; qualifying distributions, $450,000; giving activities include $450,000 for 1 grant.
Fields of interest: Foundations (community).
Limitations: Applications not accepted. Giving primarily in Baltimore, MD.
Application information: Contributes only to pre-selected organizations.
Officers and Directors:* Lainy LeBow-Sachs,* Pres.; Zelig Robinson,* Secy.-Treas.; Gene Raynor.
EIN: 453847055

3881
William E. Seale Family Foundation ✧
1800 Dreams Landing Way
Annapolis, MD 21401-4489

Established in 2006 in MD.
Donor: William E. Seale.
Foundation type: Independent foundation.
Financial data (yr. ended 12/31/13): Assets, $1,118,188 (M); gifts received, $5,000,000; expenditures, $4,101,947; qualifying distributions, $4,101,000; giving activities include $4,101,000 for 3 grants (high: $4,000,000; low: $1,000).
Fields of interest: Higher education, university.
Limitations: Applications not accepted. Giving primarily in MD. No grants to individuals.
Application information: Unsolicited requests for funds not accepted.
Trustee: William E. Seale.
EIN: 546728997
Selected grants: The following grants are a representative sample of this grantmaker's funding activity:
$1,000,000 to University of Kentucky, Lexington, KY, 2012. For Gatton Building Fund.
$50,000 to University of Kentucky, Lexington, KY, 2012. To support 501(c)(3) organization.

3882
The Shared Earth Foundation ✧
113 Hoffman Ln.
Chestertown, MD 21620-1913 (410) 778-6868
Contact: Caroline D. Gabel, C.E.O. and Pres.
FAX: (410) 778-9050;
E-mail: sharedearth@aol.com; Main URL: http://www.sharedearth.org/

Established in 1999 in MD.
Donor: Caroline D. Gabel.
Foundation type: Independent foundation.
Financial data (yr. ended 03/31/13): Assets, $11,673,774 (M); gifts received, $762,000; expenditures, $696,987; qualifying distributions, $1,501,956; giving activities include $577,600 for 34 grants (high: $104,100; low: $1,000).
Purpose and activities: Support for the environment, biodiversity, the protection and enhancement of the natural habitat, and the protection of wildlife and endangered species.
Fields of interest: Environment, natural resources; Environment, land resources; Environment; Animals/wildlife, preservation/protection; Animals/wildlife, endangered species; Indigenous peoples.
International interests: Chile; Guatemala; Kenya; Malaysia; Mexico; Pakistan; Panama; Papua New Guinea; Peru.
Type of support: General/operating support; Continuing support; Program development; Research; Technical assistance; Matching/challenge support.
Limitations: Applications not accepted. Giving on a national and international basis. No grants to individuals, or for scholarships, fellowships, or financial aid.
Publications: Annual report; Grants list.

Application information: Unsolicited requests for funds not accepted. Applications are by invitation only. See foundation web site for information.
Board meeting date(s): Quarterly
Officer: Caroline D. Gabel, C.E.O. and Pres.
EIN: 522151843
Selected grants: The following grants are a representative sample of this grantmaker's funding activity:
$45,000 to Defenders of Wildlife, Washington, DC, 2011.
$45,000 to Nature Conservancy, Arlington, VA, 2010.
$25,000 to Nature Conservancy, Arlington, VA, 2011.
$25,000 to Rachels Network, Washington, DC, 2010.
$25,000 to Smithsonian Institution, Washington, DC, 2011.
$20,000 to Rachels Network, Washington, DC, 2011.
$20,000 to Woodland Park Zoological Society, Seattle, WA, 2011.
$17,000 to National Aquarium in Baltimore, Baltimore, MD, 2011.
$15,000 to Adkins Arboretum, Ridgely, MD, 2011.
$15,000 to Earth Sangha, Fairfax, VA, 2010.
$15,000 to Eastern Shore Land Conservancy, Queenstown, MD, 2010.
$15,000 to Environmental Film Festival, Washington, DC, 2010.
$15,000 to People for the Ethical Treatment of Animals, Norfolk, VA, 2010.
$15,000 to People for the Ethical Treatment of Animals, Norfolk, VA, 2011.
$15,000 to Worldwatch Institute, Washington, DC, 2010.
$13,340 to Wildlife Conservation Society, Bronx, NY, 2010.
$12,000 to Adkins Arboretum, Ridgely, MD, 2010.
$11,464 to National Aquarium in Baltimore, Baltimore, MD, 2010.
$5,000 to Savannah Science Museum, Savannah, GA, 2011.
$5,000 to Sultana Projects, Chestertown, MD, 2011.

3883
The Thomas B. and Elizabeth M. Sheridan Foundation, Inc. ✧
11350 McCormick Rd., Executive Plz. II, Ste. 704
Hunt Valley, MD 21031-1002 (410) 771-0475
Contact: John B. Sinclair, Pres.

Incorporated in 1962 in MD.
Donors: Thomas B. Sheridan†; Elizabeth M. Sheridan†.
Foundation type: Independent foundation.
Financial data (yr. ended 12/31/13): Assets, $18,111,737 (M); expenditures, $1,085,535; qualifying distributions, $925,506; giving activities include $776,050 for 14 grants (high: $150,000; low: $50).
Purpose and activities: Emphasis on private secondary schools and cultural organizations in the greater Baltimore, MD, area.
Fields of interest: Arts; Secondary school/education.
Type of support: Capital campaigns; Building/renovation; Equipment; Endowments; Program development; Matching/challenge support.
Limitations: Applications accepted. Giving primarily in the greater Baltimore, MD, area. No grants to individuals, or for employee matching gifts; no loans.
Publications: Application guidelines; Program policy statement.
Application information: Application form required.
Initial approach: Letter
Copies of proposal: 1
Deadline(s): None
Board meeting date(s): Mar., June, Sept., and Dec.
Officers: John B. Sinclair, Pres.; Philip D. English, V.P.; Scott A. Wieler, Secy.; Jessica S. Schram, Treas.
Trustees: Anne Lawrence Deering; Mary H. DeKuyper.
Number of staff: 1 full-time professional; 1 part-time support.
EIN: 526075270
Selected grants: The following grants are a representative sample of this grantmaker's funding activity:
$85,000 to Baltimore Symphony Orchestra, Baltimore, MD, 2012. For cultural grants.
$25,000 to Sisters Academy of Baltimore, Baltimore, MD, 2012. For educational grants.

3884
The George L. Shields Foundation, Inc. ✧
c/o Robert M. Reiner
11140 Rockville Pike, Ste. 620
Rockville, MD 20852-3177

Established in 1993 in DC.
Donors: George L. Shields†; George L. Shields Living Trust.
Foundation type: Independent foundation.
Financial data (yr. ended 12/31/13): Assets, $32,252,824 (M); expenditures, $1,998,060; qualifying distributions, $1,481,500; giving activities include $1,481,500 for 103 grants (high: $100,000; low: $1,000).
Fields of interest: Arts; Higher education; Environment; Hospitals (general); Food banks; Human services; Children/youth, services.
Limitations: Applications not accepted. Giving primarily in the metropolitan Washington, DC, area, including MD and VA; giving also in CA, CO, IL, and NY. No grants to individuals.
Application information: Contributes only to pre-selected organizations.
Officers and Directors:* Ann Schein Carlyss,* Pres.; Robert M. Reiner, Secy.-Treas.; Robert Brenengen; Bruce MacDonald; Erma Medgyesy; Carolyn Moore.
EIN: 521851638

3885
Sidgmore Family Foundation ✧ ☆
Persimmon Tree Rd.
Potomac, MD 20854
E-mail: sidgmorefound@aol.com; Although the Foundation is incorporated in the State of Maryland, please address all correspondence, including letters of inquiry and full proposals to: Marian Gelbwaks, Director, 71 Leewater Ave., Massapequa, NY 11758, tel.: (516) 541-2713; Main URL: http://www.sidgmorefoundation.com

Established in 1996 in MD.
Donors: John W. Sidgmore†; Randi Sidgmore.
Foundation type: Independent foundation.
Financial data (yr. ended 12/31/13): Assets, $8,128,011 (M); gifts received, $1,787; expenditures, $650,500; qualifying distributions, $620,441; giving activities include $573,523 for 29 grants (high: $300,000; low: $1,500).
Purpose and activities: The foundation believes that an impoverished environment limits the possibilities for children to develop and thrive. As a consequence, the foundation is particularly interested in funding organizations that: 1) Improve the quality of education and teacher training; 2) Further the advancement of knowledge in the medical fields of hearing, cardiology, and allergies; and 3) Utilize entrepreneurial skills to explore and develop creative, scalable and sustainable solutions to critical social problems.
Fields of interest: Education, single organization support; Ear, nose & throat research; Heart & circulatory research; Allergies research; Medical specialties research; Medical research; Human services, single organization support; Human services; Community/economic development.
Limitations: Applications accepted. Giving on a domestic and international basis. No support for national health organizations, government agencies, or for public advocacy groups. No grants to individuals; multi-year grants are preferred.
Application information: Complete application guidelines available on foundation web site. Application form required.
Initial approach: Letter of inquiry to NY office
Copies of proposal: 2
Director: Marian Gelbwaks.
EIN: 526832168

3886
Gordon V. & Helen C. Smith Foundation ✧
8716 Crider Brook Way
Potomac, MD 20854-4547 (301) 469-8597
Contact: Gordon V. Smith, Pres.

Established in 1986 in MD.
Donors: Gordon V. Smith; Helen C. Smith; Douglas I. Smith; Anne U. Smith; Miller and Smith, Inc.
Foundation type: Independent foundation.
Financial data (yr. ended 12/31/12): Assets, $10,563,326 (M); gifts received, $22,100; expenditures, $2,119,677; qualifying distributions, $1,940,138; giving activities include $1,940,138 for grants.
Purpose and activities: Support primarily for education; also for Christian and health organizations in which family members are currently involved.
Fields of interest: Higher education; Theological school/education; Health organizations; Christian agencies & churches; Protestant agencies & churches.
Type of support: General/operating support; Building/renovation; Scholarship funds.
Limitations: Applications accepted. Giving primarily in the U.S., with some emphasis on MD, MI and VA; funding also in Arusha, Tanzania. No grants to individuals.
Application information: Application form not required.
Deadline(s): None
Officers: Gordon V. Smith, Pres.; Helen C. Smith, V.P.
Directors: Cynthia J. Skarbek; Bruce G. Smith; Douglas I. Smith.
EIN: 521440846

3887
Diana Davis Spencer Foundation ✧
(formerly Kathryn W. Davis Foundation)
3 Bethesda Metro Ctr., Ste. 118
Bethesda, MD 20814-6368 (301) 961-4000
Main URL: http://www.ddsfoundation.org

Donor: Kathryn W. Davis.
Foundation type: Independent foundation.
Financial data (yr. ended 12/31/12): Assets, $649,513,608 (M); expenditures, $2,396,437; qualifying distributions, $2,158,904; giving activities include $1,533,000 for 69 grants (high: $350,000; low: $1,000).
Purpose and activities: Giving to promote entrepreneurship, self-reliance, global understanding, free enterprise, and to enhance the quality of life by supporting the arts, education, health advancements, and preservation of the environment.
Fields of interest: Education; Human services; Children/youth, services; Family services; International democracy & civil society development.
Limitations: Applications not accepted. Giving primarily in DC and VA.
Publications: Annual report.
Application information: Contributes only to pre-selected organizations.
Officers: Diana Davis Spencer, Pres.; Abby Spencer Moffat, V.P. and C.O.O.
Trustees: Harrison Howard; Kimberly F. Lamanna.
EIN: 203672969
Selected grants: The following grants are a representative sample of this grantmaker's funding activity:
$350,000 to Network for Teaching Entrepreneurship, New York, NY, 2012. For NFTE Headquarters ($310,000), NFTE Greater Washington Dc ($30,000), NFTE Programs in New Haven.
$200,000 to Institute of World Politics, Washington, DC, 2012. For $5,000 for Mike Waller's Book Project, $5,000 for Sebastian Gorka's Book Project, and $190,000 Toward.
$80,000 to Wheaton College, Norton, MA, 2012. For Scholarship Support for International Students.
$40,000 to Asia America Initiative, Washington, DC, 2012. For Development for Peace: A Full Spectrum Approach to Citizen Diplomacy.
$30,000 to Best Friends Foundation, Washington, DC, 2012. For Best Friends Foundation and Youth Leadership Foundation After-School Tutoring and Risk Prevention.
$25,000 to Masters School, Dobbs Ferry, NY, 2012. For Global Studies Program.
$15,000 to Babson College, Babson Park, MA, 2012. For the NFTE Endowed Scholarship Fund.
$10,000 to Northeast Harbor Library, Northeast Harbor, ME, 2012. For Northeast Harbor Library ($5,000) and Northeast Harbor Library Scholarship Program ($5,000).
$5,000 to Meridian International Center, Washington, DC, 2012. For International Children's Festival 2012.

3888
Edward St. John Foundation, Inc. ✧
2560 Lord Baltimore Dr.
Baltimore, MD 21244-2666 (410) 788-0100
Contact: Sharon L. Akers, Exec. Dir.
FAX: (410) 788-1873;
E-mail: edwardstjohnfoundation@sjpi.com; Contact for Sharon L. Akers: tel.: (410) 369-1273, e-mail: sakers@sjpi.com; Main URL: http://www.esjfoundation.org/

Donors: Edward A. St. John; St. John Properties, Inc.
Foundation type: Company-sponsored foundation.
Financial data (yr. ended 12/31/12): Assets, $377,794 (M); gifts received, $1,560,600; expenditures, $1,411,733; qualifying distributions, $1,345,614; giving activities include $1,345,614 for 81 grants (high: $1,000,000; low: $35).
Purpose and activities: The foundation provides financial assistance to formal education programs through the high school level. The foundation's mission is based on the strong belief that education has the power to transform lives and strengthen communities.
Fields of interest: Secondary school/education; Higher education; Education; Human services; Community/economic development; Economically disadvantaged.
Type of support: Scholarship funds; General/operating support; Program development.
Publications: Application guidelines.
Application information: The foundation budget allocations are committed through 2014. Proposals are currently not accepted.
Officers and Directors:* Lawrence Maykrantz,* Pres.; Kellay St. John,* V.P.; Jerry Wit,* Secy.; Tina Berzins,* Treas.; Sharon Akers, Exec. Dir.
EIN: 201397204

3889
The John L. Stasiak Private Foundation ✧
c/o M.S. Hellauer
6225 Smith Ave.
Baltimore, MD 21209-3626

Established in 2000 in MD.
Donors: John Stasiak; M. Nelson Barnes & Sons, Inc.
Foundation type: Independent foundation.
Financial data (yr. ended 12/31/13): Assets, $9,343,834 (M); expenditures, $536,456; qualifying distributions, $483,897; giving activities include $458,762 for 21 grants (high: $267,000; low: $200).
Purpose and activities: Giving primarily to a donor advised fund, as well as for education.
Fields of interest: Higher education, college; Foundations (public).
Limitations: Applications not accepted. Giving primarily in MD. No grants to individuals.
Application information: Contributes only to pre-selected organizations.
Trustee: Marianne Schmitt Hellauer.
EIN: 527106974

3890
The Aaron Straus & Lillie Straus Foundation, Inc. ✧
2 E. Read St., Ste. 100
Baltimore, MD 21202-6912 (410) 539-8308
Contact: Jan Rivitz, Exec. Dir.
FAX: (410) 837-7711;
E-mail: info@strausfoundation.org; Main URL: http://www.strausfoundation.org

Established in 1926 in MD.
Foundation type: Independent foundation.
Financial data (yr. ended 12/31/12): Assets, $63,409,106 (M); expenditures, $3,972,585; qualifying distributions, $3,217,012; giving activities include $2,791,230 for 80 grants (high: $600,000; low: $36).
Purpose and activities: Giving primarily for Jewish community services; families, children, and youth; building infrastructure in the non-profit sector; and alternative grantmaking.
Fields of interest: Arts; Education, public policy; Human services; Children, services; Family services; United Ways and Federated Giving Programs; Public policy, research; Jewish agencies & synagogues.
Type of support: General/operating support; Income development; Annual campaigns; Capital campaigns; Building/renovation; Program development; Seed money; Scholarship funds; Technical assistance; Consulting services; Program evaluation.
Limitations: Applications accepted. Giving primarily in Baltimore, MD. No grants to individuals, or for endowments.
Publications: Application guidelines; Informational brochure; Program policy statement (including application guidelines).
Application information: Association of Baltimore Area Grantmakers Common Grant Application Format required. This form is available on the foundation's web site. Unsolicited applications not accepted for Arts and Culture. Application form required.
Initial approach: Proposal
Copies of proposal: 1
Deadline(s): Feb. 1, July 1, and Oct. 1
Final notification: 8-10 weeks
Officers: Jan Rivitz, Pres. and Treas.; Lee E. Coplan, V.P. and Secy.; Terry Underberg, Secy.
Directors: Jane Abraham; Stephen H. Abraham; Charles Baum; Samuel Himmelrich; Susan Leviton.
Number of staff: 1 full-time professional.
EIN: 522040073

3891
Leonard and Helen R. Stulman Charitable Foundation, Inc. ✧
2 E. Read St., 9th Fl.
Baltimore, MD 21202-6903
Contact: Shale D. Stiller, Pres.; Laurie Baker Crosley, Dir., Philanthropic Svcs.; Cathy Brill, Exec. Dir.
E-mail: lcrosley@bcf.org; E-mail for Cathy Brill: cbrill@bcf.org

Established in 1986 in MD.
Donor: Leonard Stulman†.
Foundation type: Independent foundation.
Financial data (yr. ended 12/31/13): Assets, $78,295,041 (M); expenditures, $3,897,647; qualifying distributions, $3,311,678; giving activities include $3,129,095 for 21 grants (high: $1,700,000; low: $17,800).
Purpose and activities: Supports programs in research and treatment for mental illness, aging and health care in MD.
Fields of interest: Mental health, treatment; Mental health, schizophrenia; Mental health, association; Civil/human rights, aging; Gerontology; Children; Adults; Aging; Mentally disabled; Economically disadvantaged.
Type of support: Matching/challenge support; General/operating support.

Limitations: Applications accepted. Giving primarily in Baltimore, MD. No support for organizations that further religious doctrine. No grants to individuals, or for debt retirement, membership campaigns, public primary and secondary education, or conferences/seminars.
Application information: See Web site of Baltimore Community Foundation for application guidelines, procedures, and application deadlines. Association of Baltimore Area Grantmakers Common Grant Application Format accepted. Application form not required.
Initial approach: Letter of inquiry
Copies of proposal: 1
Deadline(s): Rolling
Board meeting date(s): Varies
Final notification: 3 to 6 months
Officers: Shale D. Stiller, Pres.; Frank T. Gray, V.P. and Secy.; Walter D. Pinkard, Jr., Treas.
Number of staff: None.
EIN: 521491609

3892
Sunrise Charitable Foundation Trust ✧
c/o Antoine van Agtmael
7906 Springer Rd.
Bethesda, MD 20817-5547

Established in 1992 in MD.
Donor: Antoine van Agtmael.
Foundation type: Independent foundation.
Financial data (yr. ended 12/31/13): Assets, $40,877,190 (M); expenditures, $2,130,889; qualifying distributions, $2,090,235; giving activities include $2,090,235 for 18 grants (high: $600,000; low: $5,000).
Fields of interest: Media, radio; Performing arts; Elementary/secondary education; Higher education; Scholarships/financial aid; Youth development; Public policy, research; Economically disadvantaged.
Type of support: General/operating support; Scholarship funds; Research.
Limitations: Applications not accepted. Giving primarily in Washington, DC, and MD. No grants to individuals.
Application information: Contributes only to pre-selected organizations.
Trustees: Antoine van Agtmael; Emily van Agtmael.
EIN: 526560157

3893
The Laszlo N. Tauber Family Foundation ✧
6000 Exec. Blvd., Ste. 600
North Bethesda, MD 20852-3818
E-mail: info@tauberfoundation.com; Additional address: 12 Moshe Hess St., Jerusalem, Israel Email: office@tauberfoundation.org.il; Main URL: http://www.tauberfoundation.org/page1/about.html
Grants List: http://www.tauberfoundation.org/page3/grants.html

Established in 2004 in MD.
Donor: Laszlo N. Tauber†.
Foundation type: Independent foundation.
Financial data (yr. ended 12/31/12): Assets, $150,310,339 (M); gifts received, $1,928,435; expenditures, $9,867,971; qualifying distributions, $8,126,884; giving activities include $7,215,780 for 65 grants (high: $67,000; low: $1,000).
Purpose and activities: The foundation is committed to philanthropy in four major areas: education, biomedical research, services to persons with psychosocial and psychiatric disabilities, and social welfare. 1) Educational grants support scholarships and innovative academic programs; 2) biomedical research projects focus on the regulation and organization of complex biological systems; 3) services for persons with psychosocial disabilities include innovative rehabilitation programs and clinical research; 4) social welfare programs encompass a wide array of support for the economically under-privileged. Grants in each area are awarded to institutions of the United States and Israeli affiliates.
Fields of interest: Elementary/secondary education; Mental health/crisis services, research; Mental health, disorders; Medical research; Human services; Jewish agencies & synagogues; Mentally disabled; Economically disadvantaged.
Limitations: Applications not accepted. Giving primarily in Baltimore, MD. No grants to individuals.
Application information: Contributes only to pre-selected organizations.
Officers and Directors:* Ingrid D. Tauber,* Pres.; Alfred I. Tauber,* Secy.-Treas.; Jay Grossman, Cont.
Number of staff: 2 full-time professional.
EIN: 300208793
Selected grants: The following grants are a representative sample of this grantmaker's funding activity:
$867,000 to New Israel Fund, Washington, DC, 2012.
$647,280 to Jewish Family and Childrens Services, San Francisco, CA, 2012.
$515,843 to American Society of the University of Haifa, New York, NY, 2012. For general support.
$376,644 to PEF Israel Endowment Funds, New York, NY, 2012. For general support.
$375,000 to Tipping Point Community, San Francisco, CA, 2012. For general support.
$340,000 to Jewish Community Center of San Francisco, San Francisco, CA, 2012. For general support.
$285,778 to Jewish Community Federation of San Francisco, the Peninsula, Marin and Sonoma Counties, San Francisco, CA, 2012.
$247,811 to Avaloch Farm Music Institute, North Bethesda, MD, 2012. For general support.
$50,000 to University of California, Davis, CA, 2012. For general support.
$25,000 to American Society for Yad Vashem, New York, NY, 2012. For program support.

3894
The Alvin and Fanny Blaustein Thalheimer Foundation, Inc. ✧
6225 Smith Ave., Ste. B100
Baltimore, MD 21209-3633
Contact: Juliet A. Eurich, Exec. Dir.
FAX: (410) 580-9250;
E-mail: info@thalheimerfoundation.org; Main URL: http://www.thalheimerfoundation.org

Incorporated in 1958 in MD.
Donors: American Trading and Production Corp.; Lord Baltimore Capital Corp.
Foundation type: Independent foundation.
Financial data (yr. ended 12/31/12): Assets, $21,488,236 (M); gifts received, $140,000; expenditures, $1,113,571; qualifying distributions, $907,819; giving activities include $897,500 for 53 grants (high: $75,000; low: $1,000).
Purpose and activities: Giving primarily to improve the lives of Baltimore, MD, residents by supporting efforts to improve quality public education, funding workforce development and job opportunity programs, looking for ways to improve the basic needs of Baltimore's most disadvantaged people, and supporting Jewish continuity and community development in Baltimore, Europe and the countries of the former Soviet Union.
Fields of interest: Education; Employment; Human services; Jewish agencies & synagogues.
Type of support: Capital campaigns; Building/renovation; Program development; Conferences/seminars; Curriculum development.
Limitations: Applications accepted. Giving primarily in the Baltimore, MD, metropolitan area; grants in the Jewish Communal Giving program are often in Europe, Russia or countries of the former Soviet Union. No support for No grants for scientific research. No grants to individuals, or for fundraising events, direct mail solicitations, annual giving or membership campaigns, or to finance deficits.
Publications: Application guidelines; Grants list; IRS Form 990 or 990-PF printed copy available upon request.
Application information: Association of Baltimore Area Grantmakers Common Grant Application Format accepted, and can de downloaded from foundation web site. Application will be acknowledged by postcard within 2 weeks. Application form not required.
Initial approach: Letter of inquiry (3-5 pages)
Copies of proposal: 1
Deadline(s): None
Board meeting date(s): Semiannually
Final notification: 3 to 4 months
Officers and Trustees:* Louis B. Thalheimer,* Pres.; Marjorie Thalheimer Coleman,* V.P.; Monica Rovecamp, Secy.; Juliet A. Eurich, Exec. Dir.
EIN: 526038383
Selected grants: The following grants are a representative sample of this grantmaker's funding activity:
$20,000 to Urban Teacher Center, Baltimore, MD, 2012. For general support for Baltimore.
$10,000 to FJC, New York, NY, 2012. For the Slingshot Fund.

3895
Columbus W. Thorn, Jr. Foundation ✧
109 E. Main St.
Elkton, MD 21921 (410) 398-0611

Established in 1971 in MD.
Donor: Columbus W. Thorn†.
Foundation type: Independent foundation.
Financial data (yr. ended 12/31/13): Assets, $22,007,009 (M); gifts received, $690,389; expenditures, $977,323; qualifying distributions, $977,323; giving activities include $722,150 for 137 grants to individuals (high: $6,500; low: $1,500).
Purpose and activities: Awards educational loans to worthy and needy high school graduates of Cecil County, MD.
Fields of interest: Adult/continuing education.
Type of support: Student loans—to individuals.
Limitations: Applications accepted. Giving limited to residents of Cecil County, MD.
Publications: Application guidelines.
Application information: Application form required.

Initial approach: Contact foundation for application form
Deadline(s): None
Trustees: Charles L. Scott; Doris P. Scott.
Number of staff: 1 part-time support.
EIN: 237153983

3896
TKF Foundation ✧
(formerly Open Spaces, Sacred Places)
410 Severn Ave., Ste. 216
Annapolis, MD 21403-2565
Contact: Mary F. Wyatt, Exec. Dir.
FAX: (410) 268-1379;
E-mail: info@Naturesacred.org; Contact for grant programs: Christine Tanabe, Dir., Comm. and Prog. Devel., e-mail: ctanabe@tkffdn.org; Main URL: http://www.tkffdn.org
E-Newsletter: http://www.opensacred.org/connections/stay-connected
Open Spaces Sacred Places: http://www.facebook.com/pages/TKF-Foundation/249821844825
YouTube: http://www.youtube.com/user/TKFOSSP?blend=2&ob=5

Established in 1985 in IA.
Donors: Thomas H. Stoner; Katharine E. Stoner.
Foundation type: Independent foundation.
Financial data (yr. ended 12/31/12): Assets, $9,115,554 (M); gifts received, $523,553; expenditures, $2,026,328; qualifying distributions, $1,309,543; giving activities include $852,011 for 29 grants (high: $84,771; low: $1,200).
Purpose and activities: Giving primarily to provide the opportunity for a deeper human experience by supporting the creation of public greenspaces that offers a temporary place of sanctuary, encourages reflection, provides solace, and engenders peace.
Fields of interest: Arts; Environment, natural resources; Community/economic development.
Type of support: Continuing support; Program development; Seed money; Technical assistance; Matching/challenge support.
Limitations: Applications accepted. Giving limited to Washington, DC, and Annapolis and Baltimore, MD. No grants to individuals or for endowments, debt reduction, ongoing operating costs, special projects or capital campaigns.
Publications: Application guidelines; Annual report; Informational brochure (including application guidelines).
Application information: Association of Baltimore Area Grantmakers Common Grant Application Format and the Washington Regional Association of Grantmakers Common Grant Application Form accepted. Additional application information and application guidelines available on foundation web site. Application form required.
Initial approach: 1-page screening letter
Copies of proposal: 3
Deadline(s): See foundation web site for current deadlines
Board meeting date(s): Bi-annual
Final notification: See foundation web site
Officers and Directors:* Thomas H. Stoner,* Pres. and Treas.; Katharine E. Stoner,* V.P.; Mary F. Wyatt, Secy. and Exec. Dir.; Jack Bloodgood; Chuck Foster; Alden Stoner; Chelle Stoner.
Number of staff: 2 full-time professional; 1 part-time professional; 1 part-time support.
EIN: 421263576
Selected grants: The following grants are a representative sample of this grantmaker's funding activity:
$42,896 to Brooklyn Greenway Initiative, Brooklyn, NY, 2012. For Planning Grant for Nossp - Navel Hospital Cemetery Memorial Landscape.
$27,095 to Parkland College, Champaign, IL, 2012. For Planning Grant for Nossp, Waukegan Area Sacred Spaces.
$20,000 to A Wider Circle, Bethesda, MD, 2012. For Programming Support and Materials to Increase the Impact of the Ossp Healing Garden on the Lives of the Sibley Plaza.
$15,300 to Baltimore Clayworks, Baltimore, MD, 2012. For Completion of Nature Garden Enrichment Plan.
$14,656 to Marian House, Baltimore, MD, 2012. For Additional Plantings, Replacement Trees and Site Furnishings As Well As 2nd Installment of TKF's Commitment to Book Publishing Project.
$12,934 to Village Learning Place, Baltimore, MD, 2012. For Plantings, Improvements and Signage at New Link Bldg..
$10,818 to American Psychological Association, Washington, DC, 2012. For Enhancement Grant.
$9,604 to Newborn Holistic Ministries, Baltimore, MD, 2012. For Street Mural at the Intersection of Presstman St and Pennsylvania Ave.

3897
Town Creek Foundation, Inc. ✧
121 N. West St.
Easton, MD 21601-2709 (410) 763-8171
Contact: Stuart A. Clarke, Exec. Dir.
FAX: (410) 763-8172;
E-mail: info@towncreekfdn.org; Main URL: http://www.towncreekfdn.org

Established in 1981 in MD.
Donor: Edmund A. Stanley, Jr.†.
Foundation type: Independent foundation.
Financial data (yr. ended 12/31/13): Assets, $46,350,512 (M); expenditures, $7,102,104; qualifying distributions, $6,828,328; giving activities include $6,373,500 for 81 grants (high: $300,000; low: $10,000).
Purpose and activities: The foundation supports programs that engage citizens in challenging and reversing the unsustainable use of natural resources and in protecting biological diversity. Strategies supported are grassroots activism, monitoring the enforcement of environmental laws, public policy advocacy, collaborative opportunities, media outreach, and model or demonstration projects fostering sustainable policies and practices. The foundation has restructured its focus to have a more in depth and targeted approach to restoring the Chesapeake Bay and transitioning Maryland to a low carbon economy. In order to attain this mission, the foundation has three programmatic focuses: Chesapeake Bay, Climate Change, and Sustainability.
Fields of interest: Environment, climate change/global warming; Environment, natural resources; Environment.
Type of support: General/operating support; Continuing support; Program development; Seed money; Matching/challenge support.
Limitations: Applications accepted. Giving primarily in the Mid Atlantic region. No support for primary or secondary schools, hospitals, healthcare institutions, or religious organizations. No support for colleges or universities except when some aspect of their work is an integral part of a program supported by the foundation, or for government organizations. No grants to individuals, or for endowment, capital, or building fund campaigns, purchase of land or buildings, research, scholarship programs, conferences, the publication of books or periodicals, or visual or performing arts projects.
Publications: Application guidelines; Grants list.
Application information: All applications must be submitted online, via foundation web site. Full proposals accepted by invitation only. Application guidelines available on foundation web site. Application form required.
Initial approach: Letter of inquiry
Deadline(s): See foundation web site for current deadlines
Board meeting date(s): Spring and summer
Officers and Directors:* Jennifer Stanley,* Pres.; Lisa A. Stanley,* V.P.; Philip E.L. Dietz, Jr.,* Treas.; Stuart A. Clarke, Exec. Dir.; Donald Boesch, Ph.D.; Betsy Taylor.
Number of staff: 3 full-time professional; 1 part-time support.
EIN: 521227030
Selected grants: The following grants are a representative sample of this grantmaker's funding activity:
$200,000 to George Mason University, Fairfax, VA, 2013. To establish Climate Change Communication Coalition in Maryland.
$200,000 to National Wildlife Federation, Annapolis, MD, 2013. For Clean Energy Works for Maryland.
$110,000 to 1000 Friends of Maryland, Baltimore, MD, 2013. For Sustainable Growth for Maryland.
$100,000 to Chesapeake Bay Trust, Annapolis, MD, 2013. For capacity building.
$100,000 to Environmental Integrity Project, Washington, DC, 2013. For Chesapeake Bay Enforcement.
$85,000 to Maryland Pesticide Network, Annapolis, MD, 2013. For Toxic Free Maryland Initiative.
$75,000 to Baltimore Community Foundation, Baltimore, MD, 2013. For Sustainability Leadership in Baltimore and Maryland.
$60,000 to Responsible Purchasing Network, Oakland, CA, 2013. For Chesapeake Bay Sustainable Purchasing Network.
$20,000 to West/Rhode Riverkeeper, Shady Side, MD, 2013. For Riverkeeper Advocacy.
$10,000 to Demos: A Network for Ideas and Action, New York, NY, 2013. To advance genuine progress indicator and other alternative metrics through new convenings.

3898
The Jim and Carol Trawick Foundation ✧
7979 Old Georgetown Rd., 10th Fl.
Bethesda, MD 20814-2429 (301) 654-7030
FAX: (301) 654-7032; Main URL: http://www.trawick.org/
Grants Database: http://www.trawick.org/grants-search

Established in 2005 in MD.
Donors: Carol Trawick; James Trawick; Class Act Arts; Teamup Team of Stars; Howard & Geraldine Polinger Family Foundation; Montgomery County Dept. of Recreation; HSC Health Care Foundation; Casey Family Programs.
Foundation type: Independent foundation.
Financial data (yr. ended 12/31/13): Assets, $7,658,583 (M); gifts received, $103,000;

expenditures, $1,248,791; qualifying distributions, $1,200,430; giving activities include $875,196 for 57 grants (high: $145,000; low: $475).
Purpose and activities: The foundation assists local health and human service and arts nonprofit organizations in Montgomery County, Maryland. Giving also for specific projects that will make a demonstrable impact on the local community by reaching people in need and encouraging and sustaining creative activities.
Fields of interest: Arts; Health care; Human services.
Limitations: Giving limited to Montgomery County, MD. No grants to individuals, or for debt reduction, fundraising, general operating support, capital campaigns, endowment funds, or special events.
Publications: Grants list.
Application information: See foundation web site for full application guidelines and requirements. Applications submitted by fax, e-mail or hand delivery are not accepted.
Officers and Directors:* Carol Trawick,* Pres.; Anne Cantrel, Exec. Dir.; Robby Brewer; Gail Nachman.
EIN: 203932082
Selected grants: The following grants are a representative sample of this grantmaker's funding activity:
$20,000 to Class Acts Arts, Silver Spring, MD, 2012. For My Story Is Our Story Grant.
$20,000 to Imagination Stage, Bethesda, MD, 2012. For Art ability Program.
$17,500 to Interfaith Works, Rockville, MD, 2012. For Project Inform.
$15,000 to A Wider Circle, Bethesda, MD, 2012. For Neighbor to Neighbor Program Expansion.
$12,500 to Sunflower Bakery, Gaithersburg, MD, 2012. For Program Expansion to Accept Additional Trainees.
$10,000 to Manna Food Center, Gaithersburg, MD, 2012. For Smart Snacks Program.
$9,000 to Latin American Youth Center, Washington, DC, 2012. For Inspire Program.
$7,500 to Women Who Care Ministries, Montgomery Village, MD, 2012. For Helping Kids Eat Backpack Program.
$7,500 to Women Who Care Ministries, Montgomery Village, MD, 2012. For Helping Kids Eat Backpack Weekend Food Program.
$5,000 to Art for the People, Takoma Park, MD, 2012. For Art for People at Pre-Release Center.

3899
The David and June Trone Family Foundation ✧ ☆
11417 Skipwith Ln.
Potomac, MD 20854-1640
Contact: David Trone
E-mail: junetrone66@gmail.com

Established in MD.
Donors: David Trone; June Trone.
Foundation type: Independent foundation.
Financial data (yr. ended 06/30/14): Assets, $4,056,133 (M); expenditures, $1,362,380; qualifying distributions, $1,355,000; giving activities include $1,355,000 for 4 grants (high: $1,000,000; low: $75,000).
Fields of interest: Higher education; Jewish agencies & synagogues.
Type of support: Building/renovation.
Limitations: Applications accepted. Giving primarily in Rockville, MD and Greenville, SC.
Application information: Application form not required.
Initial approach: Letter
Deadline(s): None
Trustees: David J. Trone; Julia E. Trone; June S. Trone; Michelle C. Trone; Natalie R. Trone.
EIN: 453564622

3900
The Tzedakah Fund ✧ ☆
c/o Orin Z. Hirschman
6006 Berkeley Ave.
Baltimore, MD 21209-4014

Established in 2003 in MD.
Donors: Orin Z. Hirschman; Hershel Berkowitz; Ettil Berkowitz; Samuel Nebenzahl; Adina Nebenzahl; Aaron Martin.
Foundation type: Independent foundation.
Financial data (yr. ended 12/31/13): Assets, $4,761,277 (M); gifts received, $103,240; expenditures, $566,791; qualifying distributions, $553,625; giving activities include $552,475 for 25 grants (high: $295,795; low: $180).
Fields of interest: Education; Science; Jewish agencies & synagogues.
Limitations: Applications not accepted. No grants to individuals.
Application information: Unsolicited requests for funds not accepted.
Trustees: Esther Hirschman; Orin Z. Hirschman.
EIN: 200386456

3901
Jerrold Van Winter Charitable Foundation ✧
24 Courthouse Sq., No 703
Rockville, MD 20850-2340

Donor: Jerrold A. Van Winter.
Foundation type: Independent foundation.
Financial data (yr. ended 12/31/13): Assets, $191,651 (M); gifts received, $1,100,000; expenditures, $1,041,502; qualifying distributions, $1,041,500; giving activities include $1,041,500 for 7 grants (high: $1,000,000; low: $500).
Fields of interest: Education; Human services; Children/youth, services; Catholic federated giving programs; Catholic agencies & churches.
Limitations: Applications not accepted. Giving primarily in Washington, DC, MD, and Jefferson, WI.
Application information: Contributes only to pre-selected organizations.
Trustee: Jerrold A. Van Winter.
EIN: 207047342

3902
Viragh Family Foundation ✧
c/o Young, Brophy & Duncan, PC
10211 Wincopin Cir., Ste. 450
Columbia, MD 21044-3430

Established in 2000 in MD.
Donors: Albert P. Viragh†; Robert J. Viragh; Mark S. Viragh; Katherine A. Viragh; Jean M. Dahl.
Foundation type: Independent foundation.
Financial data (yr. ended 06/30/13): Assets, $42,985,567 (M); expenditures, $3,446,805; qualifying distributions, $3,004,000; giving activities include $3,004,000 for grants.
Purpose and activities: Giving primarily for education, health, and children, youth and social services.
Fields of interest: Education; Health care; Medical research, institute; Cancer research; Housing/shelter, services; Human services; Children/youth, services; Family services; Economically disadvantaged.
Limitations: Applications not accepted. Giving in the U.S., with emphasis on CA. No grants to individuals.
Application information: Contributes only to pre-selected organizations.
Officers: Mark S. Viragh, Pres.; Roger E. Young, V.P.; Susan B. Rankin, Secy.; Katherine A. Viragh, Treas.
Directors: Jean M. Dahl; Robert J. Viragh; Paula Virgah Williams.
EIN: 522284009

3903
E. C. Wareheim Foundation ✧
c/o M & T Bank, Trust Dept.
25 S. Charles St.
Baltimore, MD 21201-3330
Application address: c/o William L. Mathers, P.O. Box 3444, Virginia Beach, VA 23454-9494, tel.: (804) 582-3166

Established in 1956 in MD.
Donor: Helen Wareheim Trust.
Foundation type: Independent foundation.
Financial data (yr. ended 12/31/13): Assets, $12,844,447 (M); gifts received, $82,471; expenditures, $678,693; qualifying distributions, $603,050; giving activities include $497,000 for 71 grants (high: $20,000; low: $1,000).
Purpose and activities: Giving primarily for children and youth development and services, including youth at risk; support also for education.
Fields of interest: Education; Courts/judicial administration; Legal services; Human services; Children/youth, services.
Limitations: Applications accepted. Giving primarily in VA; some giving also in MD. No grants to individuals.
Application information: Application form not required.
Initial approach: Proposal
Deadline(s): None
Officer: William L. Mathers, Exec. Dir.
Trustee: M&T Trust Co.
EIN: 526033212
Selected grants: The following grants are a representative sample of this grantmaker's funding activity:
$50,000 to Virginia Military Institute Foundation, Lexington, VA, 2011.
$14,000 to Norfolk, City of, Norfolk, VA, 2011.
$10,000 to Advocate Center, Norton, VA, 2011.
$10,000 to American Red Cross of Southeastern Virginia, Norfolk, VA, 2011.
$10,000 to Chesapeake Service Systems, Chesapeake, VA, 2011.
$10,000 to College Bound, Washington, DC, 2011.
$10,000 to Stevenson University, Stevenson, MD, 2011.
$10,000 to Union Mission Ministries, Norfolk, VA, 2011.
$7,000 to Seton Youth Shelters, Virginia Beach, VA, 2011.
$6,000 to Sunrise Center, Richlands, VA, 2011.

3904
The Mathias Washington County Charitable Trust ✧
12019 Bayer Dr.
Smithsburg, MD 21783-2068 (301) 824-2440
Contact: Kenneth W. Graber, Tr.

Established in 2004 in FL.
Donor: Leonard G. Mathias†.
Foundation type: Independent foundation.
Financial data (yr. ended 12/31/13): Assets, $12,192,349 (M); expenditures, $769,058; qualifying distributions, $571,716; giving activities include $571,716 for 27 grants (high: $68,288; low: $2,500).
Purpose and activities: Giving to help the people of Washington County, Maryland, through grants to various nonprofit agencies.
Fields of interest: Museums; Human services; Children, services; Infants/toddlers; Children; Adults; Aging; Disabilities, people with; Mentally disabled; Girls; Boys; Offenders/ex-offenders; Single parents; Crime/abuse victims; Economically disadvantaged; Homeless.
Type of support: General/operating support; Annual campaigns; Capital campaigns; Equipment; Emergency funds; Program development.
Limitations: Applications accepted. Giving limited to Washington County, MD.
Application information:
Initial approach: Letter
Copies of proposal: 1
Deadline(s): None
Final notification: 60 days
Trustee: Kenneth W. Graber.
EIN: 206208889

3905
George Wasserman Family Foundation, Inc. ✧
(formerly George Wasserman Foundation, Inc.)
c/o Grossberg Co.
6500 Rock Spring Dr., Ste. 200
Bethesda, MD 20817-1182
Application address: c/o Aaron Stopak, V.P. and Exec. Dir., 6503 Mountain Branch Ct., Bethesda, MD 20817-5838

Established in 1948.
Donor: George Wasserman†.
Foundation type: Independent foundation.
Financial data (yr. ended 12/31/13): Assets, $9,936,002 (M); expenditures, $598,815; qualifying distributions, $542,637; giving activities include $518,000 for 68 grants (high: $25,000; low: $1,000).
Purpose and activities: Grants primarily to Jewish organizations, as well as for the arts, health and human services.
Fields of interest: Arts; Nursing home/convalescent facility; Health care; Human services; Jewish federated giving programs; Jewish agencies & synagogues.
Type of support: General/operating support; Continuing support; Annual campaigns; Building/renovation; Endowments; Program development; Seed money; Scholarship funds; Research; Technical assistance; Exchange programs.
Limitations: Applications accepted. Giving primarily in Washington, DC, and MD. No grants to individuals.
Application information: Application form required.
Initial approach: Letter
Deadline(s): None
Officers: Carolyn J. Kaplan, Pres.; Aaron Stopak, V.P. and Exec. Dir.; Lisa W. Gill, V.P.
EIN: 526035888
Selected grants: The following grants are a representative sample of this grantmaker's funding activity:
$10,000 to Washington Performing Arts Society, Washington, DC, 2012. For overall charitable purpose of the organization.

3906
The Ellen W. P. Wasserman Foundation ✧
3416 Garrison Farms Rd.
Baltimore, MD 21208-1850 (410) 771-8033
Application address: c/o George W. Cox, 36 S. Charles St., 18th Fl., Baltimore, MD 21201, tel.: (410) 685-5512

Established in 1997 in MD.
Donors: Ellen W.P. Wasserman; Cox, Ferber & Associates, LLC.
Foundation type: Independent foundation.
Financial data (yr. ended 03/31/13): Assets, $19,545,459 (M); gifts received, $499,642; expenditures, $1,086,973; qualifying distributions, $937,801; giving activities include $937,801 for 34 grants (high: $189,652; low: $35).
Purpose and activities: Giving primarily for the arts, education, health, and to Jewish organizations.
Fields of interest: Museums (art); Arts; Education; Health organizations; Jewish federated giving programs; Jewish agencies & synagogues.
Limitations: Applications accepted. Giving primarily in Baltimore, MD. No grants to individuals.
Application information: Application form required.
Initial approach: Letter
Deadline(s): None
Trustee: Ellen W.P. Wasserman.
EIN: 522038129
Selected grants: The following grants are a representative sample of this grantmaker's funding activity:
$153,195 to LifeBridge Health, Baltimore, MD, 2012.

3907
The Joseph and Debra Weinberg Family Foundation Inc. ✧
c/o Katz Abosch
9690 Deereco Rd., Ste. 500
Timonium, MD 21093-6900

Established in 2005 in MD.
Donors: Joseph S. Weinberg; Debra Silberman Weinberg.
Foundation type: Independent foundation.
Financial data (yr. ended 12/31/13): Assets, $2,111,184 (M); gifts received, $2,000,500; expenditures, $470,950; qualifying distributions, $470,450; giving activities include $470,450 for 34 grants (high: $180,000; low: $250).
Fields of interest: Human services; Jewish federated giving programs; Jewish agencies & synagogues.
Limitations: Applications not accepted. Giving primarily in MD and NY. No grants to individuals.
Application information: Contributes only to pre-selected organizations.
Trustees: Debra Silberman Weinberg; Joseph S. Weinberg.
EIN: 203934838

3908
The Harry and Jeanette Weinberg Foundation, Inc.
7 Park Center Ct.
Owings Mills, MD 21117-4200 (410) 654-8500
Contact: Craig Demchak, Dir., Marketing and Communications
For Hawaii operations correspondence: 3660 Waialae Ave., Ste. 400, Honolulu, HI 96816-3260, tel.: (808) 924-1000, fax: (808) 922-3975; Main URL: http://www.hjweinbergfoundation.org
Annual Reports and Grants Summaries: http://hjweinbergfoundation.org/publications/annual-reports/
E-Newsletter: http://hjweinbergfoundation.org/publications/e-newsletters/e-newsletter-sign-up/
Facebook: http://www.facebook.com/pages/The-Harry-and-Jeanette-Weinberg-Foundation-Inc/169299436473114
Get to Know: http://hjweinbergfoundation.org/wp-content/uploads/downloads/2013/12/Get-to-Know.pdf
Grantee Perception Report: http://hjweinbergfoundation.org/publications/what-we-have-learned/
Twitter: https://twitter.com/hjweinbergfdn
YouTube: http://www.youtube.com/user/HJWeinbergFoundation

Incorporated in 1959 in MD.
Donors: Harry Weinberg†; and various companies.
Foundation type: Independent foundation.
Financial data (yr. ended 02/28/14): Assets, $2,127,938,700 (M); expenditures, $117,295,250; qualifying distributions, $101,017,122; giving activities include $96,929,767 for 675 grants (high: $3,000,000; low: $200), and $168,565 for 1 foundation-administered program.
Purpose and activities: Support for programs and direct services (including general operating grants) and capital projects that assist low-income and vulnerable individuals and families primarily located in Maryland, Hawaii, Northeastern Pennsylvania, Israel and the Former Soviet Union.
Fields of interest: Education; Health care; Food services; Housing/shelter; Human services; Aging, centers/services; Aging; Disabilities, people with; Economically disadvantaged.
International interests: Israel; Soviet Union.
Type of support: Program development; Building/renovation; Capital campaigns; Equipment; General/operating support; Matching/challenge support.
Limitations: Applications accepted. Giving nationally, primarily in MD, HI, Northeastern PA, NY, and internationally within Israel and the Former Soviet Union. No support for political organizations, colleges, universities, think tanks, or for arts organizations. No grants to individuals, or for deficit financing, annual giving, publications or for scholarships.
Application information: Unsolicited full proposals will not be accepted. The foundation will invite appropriate proposals following submission of Letter of Inquiry. Guidelines for LOI and invited proposals available on foundation website.

Application form not required. Application form not required.

Initial approach: Complete Letter of Inquiry after reviewing funding guidelines
Copies of proposal: 1
Deadline(s): Rolling basis
Board meeting date(s): Weekly
Final notification: The foundation will confirm receipt of each LOI within 30 days. Within 60 days, the grant application will receive notification either that the LOI was declined or that the applicant is invited to submit a full grant proposal.

Officers and Trustees:* Ellen M. Heller,* Chair.; Rachel Garbow Monroe,* C.E.O. and Pres.; Alvin Awaya,* V.P.; Barry I. Schloss,* Treas.; Kyle McNair, Cont.; Jonathan D. Hook, C.I.O.; Robert T. Kelly, Jr.; Donn Weinberg.
Number of staff: 26
EIN: 526037034
Selected grants: The following grants are a representative sample of this grantmaker's funding activity:
$5,000,000 to Center for Jewish Education of Baltimore, Baltimore, MD, 2013. To support the provision of scholarships for financially disadvantaged students in Jewish Day Schools, payable over 3.00 years.
$3,000,000 to Associated: Jewish Community Federation of Baltimore, Baltimore, MD, 2013. To support the annual campaign of The Associated Jewish Community Federation of Baltimore that funds services for financially disadvantaged individuals and families in Baltimore, payable over 3.00 years.
$1,800,000 to Amigour Asset Management, Tel Aviv, Israel, 2013. To support the construction of an additional 55 housing units at a sheltered housing facility, payable over 3.00 years.
$1,500,000 to West Cecil Health Center, Conowingo, MD, 2013. To support the construction of this Federally Qualified Health Center with the goal of serving more patients with an array of services at one location, payable over 3.00 years.
$1,000,000 to Illinois Housing Development Authority, Chicago, IL, 2013. To support the construction of affordable housing for non-elderly persons with disabilities (rent set at 20% of area median income) - a replication of the Maryland 'Weinberg Deeply Affordable Apartments', payable over 3.00 years.
$750,000 to Job Opportunities Task Force, Baltimore, MD, 2013. To support the general operations of this organization as well as the Baltimore CASH campaign, which together help residents enter employment, increase earnings, and preserve and grow their financial assets, payable over 3.00 years.
$500,000 to Greater Baton Rouge Food Bank, Baton Rouge, LA, 2013. To support the renovation of a larger, safer, and more efficient facility to feed the hungry and transform the hunger relief effort, payable over 3.00 years.
$170,000 to Princeton Center for Leadership Training, Princeton, NJ, 2013. To support the implementation in five City high schools of the Peer Group Connection, an evidence-based high school program that provides a range of support to students as they transition from middle to high school, payable over 3.00 years.
$170,000 to Saint Johns Home Foundation, Rochester, NY, 2013. To support the construction of six Green House homes - smaller, home-like alternatives to nursing facilities - each serving 10 older adults, payable over 3.00 years.
$100,000 to Abilities Network, Towson, MD, 2013. To provide additional support for the All Children Together project serving children with autism who are attending child care or out-of-school programs, payable over 3.00 years.

3909
Thomas Wilson Sanitarium for Children of Baltimore City ✧

P.O. Box 3418
Baltimore, MD 21225-0418 (410) 360-9510
Contact: Kenneth S. Schuberth, Pres.

Trust established in 1879 in MD.
Donor: Thomas Wilson†.
Foundation type: Independent foundation.
Financial data (yr. ended 01/31/13): Assets, $11,747,942 (M); expenditures, $577,422; qualifying distributions, $494,688; giving activities include $494,688 for grants.
Purpose and activities: Giving primarily for hospitals, medical and educational research, and social services, entirely relating to children of Baltimore, MD. Giving also for children's social and medical programs.
Fields of interest: Medical research, institute; Children/youth, services.
Type of support: Equipment; Program development; Seed money; Research.
Limitations: Applications accepted. Giving primarily in Baltimore, MD.
Application information: Application form required.

Initial approach: Letter
Deadline(s): None
Board meeting date(s): May

Officers: Kinloch N. Yellott III, Pres.; Kenneth Schuberth, V.P.; Perry J. Bolton, Secy.-Treas.
Trustees: Lauren Bogue; Susan Dunn; Robert D. Hopkins; Michael J. McCarthy; J. Ronald Walcher, M.D.; Christopher R. West.
Number of staff: 1 part-time support.
EIN: 526044885
Selected grants: The following grants are a representative sample of this grantmaker's funding activity:
$14,600 to Family and Childrens Services of Central Maryland, Baltimore, MD, 2012.

3910
Kathy and Jerry Wood Foundation Inc. ✧

7040 Bembe Beach Rd., Ste. 900, Box 9
Annapolis, MD 21403-3769 (410) 267-5980
FAX: (410) 267-5981;
E-mail: Sallie@kjwfoundation.org; Additional e-mail: Debbie@kjwfoundation.org; Main URL: http://www.kjwfoundation.org/

Established in 2006 in MD.
Donors: Kathryn Wood†; Sallie Hamrick†; Franklin Jerry Wood†.
Foundation type: Independent foundation.
Financial data (yr. ended 12/31/13): Assets, $19,608,495 (M); expenditures, $1,069,394; qualifying distributions, $855,780; giving activities include $757,265 for 9 grants (high: $239,375; low: $30,000).
Purpose and activities: Giving to aid and assist in charitable and educational activities for the moral, mental, intellectual, and physical development of young men and women of the United States. Scholarships are made to students (through their respective colleges or universities) who are U.S. citizens, are in financial need, display exceptional promise, and who have a 2.5 GPA.
Fields of interest: Higher education; Education.
Type of support: Scholarship funds.
Limitations: Applications not accepted. Giving primarily in MD. No grants to individuals directly.
Application information: Contributes only to pre-selected organizations.
Officers: Sallie Hamrick, Pres.; Susan Oyloe, V.P.; David McLoud, Secy.
Director: Debbie Corcoran.
EIN: 841690136
Selected grants: The following grants are a representative sample of this grantmaker's funding activity:
$89,114 to Howard Community College Educational Foundation, Columbia, MD, 2012. For funding for scholarships.

3911
Wright Family Foundation ✧

14626 Thornton Mill Rd.
Sparks, MD 21152-9633 (410) 472-3398
Contact: Mari Beth C. Moulton, Assoc. Exec. Dir. - Baltimore; Secondary Contact: Katherine B. Wright, Exec. Dir.
FAX: (410) 472-3394;
E-mail: mcmoulton@wrightfamilyfdn.org; Additional e-mail: info@wrightfamilyfdn.org; Main URL: http://www.wrightfamilyfdn.org

Established in 2000 in MD.
Donors: Vernon H.C. Wright; Lucy B. Wright.
Foundation type: Independent foundation.
Financial data (yr. ended 12/31/12): Assets, $15,928,565 (M); expenditures, $1,114,152; qualifying distributions, $911,792; giving activities include $911,792 for 79 grants (high: $75,000; low: $250).
Purpose and activities: Giving primarily to organizations and programs that will help achieve the foundation's goals for education that fall within the following areas: in Austin, TX: K-12 education, out-of-school time, and teenage pregnancy; in Baltimore City, MD: early childhood education, K-5 education, and out-of-school time.
Fields of interest: Arts; Elementary/secondary education; Higher education; Youth development, services; Children/youth; Children; Youth; Economically disadvantaged.
Type of support: General/operating support; Program development; Curriculum development; Research; Matching/challenge support.
Limitations: Applications accepted. Giving limited to Baltimore City, MD, and Austin, TX. No support for political organizations. No grants to individuals.
Publications: Application guidelines; Financial statement; Grants list.
Application information: See foundation web site for specific application guidelines. Association of Baltimore Area Grantmakers Common Grant Application Format accepted. Application form required.

Initial approach: Letter of inquiry
Copies of proposal: 1
Deadline(s): None, for Baltimore; Jan. 15 for Austin; Mar. 1 for proposals (if invited)
Board meeting date(s): May, Sept., and Nov.
Final notification: Two weeks after board meeting

Officers: Katherine B. Wright, Exec. Dir., Austin, TX; Mari Beth C. Moulton, Exec. Dir., Baltimore, MD.

Number of staff: 1 full-time professional.
EIN: 522278319

MASSACHUSETTS

3912
The A.M. Fund ✧
400 Atlantic Ave.
Boston, MA 02110-3331

Established in 2001 in MA.
Donors: Arnold S. Hiatt; Fallen Angel Corp.; Autumn Ventures; Stride Rite Charitable Foundation.
Foundation type: Independent foundation.
Financial data (yr. ended 12/31/13): Assets, $2,987,508 (M); gifts received, $833,666; expenditures, $695,420; qualifying distributions, $651,373; giving activities include $504,738 for 42 grants (high: $75,000; low: $250).
Purpose and activities: Giving primarily for secondary and other education, public affairs and human rights organizations, Jewish federated giving programs, and children, youth, and social services.
Fields of interest: Arts; Secondary school/education; Higher education; Education; Human services; Children/youth, services; Civil/human rights; Jewish federated giving programs; Public affairs, research; Public policy, research; Jewish agencies & synagogues.
Limitations: Applications not accepted. Giving primarily in MA, with emphasis on Boston; some giving nationally. No grants to individuals.
Application information: Contributes only to pre-selected organizations.
Trustees: Amy R. Hiatt; Arnold S. Hiatt; Matthew T. Hiatt.
EIN: 046956130

3913
The Aaron Foundation ✧
(formerly The Stop & Shop Charitable Foundation)
10 Possum Rd.
Weston, MA 02493-2318 (781) 899-4445
Contact: Avram J. Goldberg, Tr.

Trust established in 1951 in MA.
Donors: The Stop & Shop Cos., Inc.; The Stop & Shop Supermarket Co.; Avram J. Goldberg.
Foundation type: Independent foundation.
Financial data (yr. ended 12/31/13): Assets, $218,364 (M); expenditures, $2,923,461; qualifying distributions, $2,887,520; giving activities include $2,876,309 for 18 grants (high: $946,451; low: $3,083).
Purpose and activities: Giving primarily for education and to Jewish organizations.
Fields of interest: Higher education; Education; Human services; Youth, services; United Ways and Federated Giving Programs; Jewish federated giving programs; Jewish agencies & synagogues.
Limitations: Applications accepted. Giving primarily in San Francisco, CA, and MA. No grants to individuals.
Application information: Application form required.
Initial approach: Proposal
Copies of proposal: 1
Deadline(s): None
Trustees: Hope R. Edison; Avram J. Goldberg; Carol R. Goldberg; James M. Rabb; Jane M. Rabb; Betty R. Schafer.
Number of staff: 1 full-time professional; 2 full-time support.
EIN: 046039593

3914
Abrams Foundation, Inc. ✧
(formerly The Amy and David Abrams Foundation)
222 Berkeley St.
Boston, MA 02116-3748 (617) 646-6140
Contact: Amy Abrams, Dir.; David C. Abrams, Dir.

Established in 1997 in MA.
Donors: David C. Abrams; Amy Abrams.
Foundation type: Independent foundation.
Financial data (yr. ended 12/31/12): Assets, $58,124,419 (M); gifts received, $5,500,000; expenditures, $3,763,322; qualifying distributions, $3,304,081; giving activities include $3,297,422 for 18 grants (high: $1,000,000; low: $10,000).
Purpose and activities: Giving primarily for the arts, education, health care, and children, youth and social services.
Fields of interest: Arts, formal/general education; Arts; Higher education; Education; Hospitals (general); Health care; Human services; Children/youth, services; Jewish federated giving programs.
Type of support: General/operating support.
Limitations: Applications not accepted. Giving primarily in the Boston, MA, area. No grants to individuals.
Application information: Unsolicited requests for funds not accepted.
Directors: Amy Abrams; David C. Abrams.
EIN: 046856820

3915
Acorn Foundation ✧
1 Chestnut St.
Weston, MA 02493-1525

Established in 1993 in MA.
Donors: Theodore B. Alfond; Berkshire Hathaway Inc.; Theodore B. Alfond Charitable Lead Annuity Trust.
Foundation type: Independent foundation.
Financial data (yr. ended 12/31/13): Assets, $11,601,909 (M); gifts received, $847,607; expenditures, $3,549,079; qualifying distributions, $3,507,556; giving activities include $3,481,674 for 37 grants (high: $2,573,715; low: $25).
Purpose and activities: Giving primarily for museums, education, and human services.
Fields of interest: Museums; Museums (art); Higher education; Education; Human services.
Limitations: Applications not accepted. Giving primarily in MA and ME. No grants to individuals.
Application information: Contributes only to pre-selected organizations.
Trustees: Barbara Alfond; Michael M. Davis.
EIN: 043201916

3916
The C. F. Adams Charitable Trust ✧
c/o Lowell, Blake & Assocs., Inc.
141 Tremont St., Ste. 200
Boston, MA 02111-1209
E-mail: info@cfadamstrust.org; Main URL: http://www.cfadamstrust.org/index.html

Established in 1986 in MA.
Donor: Charles F. Adams†.
Foundation type: Independent foundation.
Financial data (yr. ended 12/11/12): Assets, $16,283,960 (M); gifts received, $498,597; expenditures, $885,305; qualifying distributions, $800,175; giving activities include $761,750 for 25 grants (high: $80,000; low: $750).
Fields of interest: Historic preservation/historical societies; Environment; Human services; Children, services; Community/economic development; United Ways and Federated Giving Programs; Philanthropy/voluntarism.
Type of support: General/operating support; Income development; Management development/capacity building; Program development.
Limitations: Giving primarily in eastern MA and down east ME. No grants to individuals.
Application information: Unsolicited proposals are not accepted. See foundation web site for further information.
Initial approach: Brief letter to Managing Trustee using main e-mail address
Trustees: Beatrice D. Adams; Edward P. Lawrence; James H. Lowell II; Janet C. Taylor.
EIN: 046556188
Selected grants: The following grants are a representative sample of this grantmaker's funding activity:
$80,000 to Center for Public Representation, Northampton, MA, 2012. For Rosie D Legal Advocacy Network.
$75,000 to Washington Hancock Community Agency, Ellsworth, ME, 2012. For Energy Conservation Project.
$65,000 to Downeast Salmon Federation, Columbia Falls, ME, 2012. For operating support and support of downeast.
$50,000 to Children's Hospital Corporation, Boston, MA, 2012. For Children's Mental Health Campaign.
$30,000 to Healthy Acadia, Bar Harbor, ME, 2012. For Downeast Farm to School Initiative.
$22,000 to Downeast Coastal Conservancy, Machias, ME, 2012. For Staff Capacity Building.
$16,000 to Assabet Valley Collaborative, Marlborough, MA, 2012. For Family Success Partnership.
$15,000 to Maine Philanthropy Center, Portland, ME, 2012. For operating and project support.

3917
Frank W. & Carl S. Adams Memorial Fund
(formerly Charles E. & Caroline J. Adams Trust)
c/o US Trust, Bank of America, N.A.
225 Franklin St., 4th Fl., MA1-225-04-02
Boston, MA 02110-2800 (866) 778-6859
Contact: Miki C. Akimoto
E-mail: ma.grantmaking@ustrust.com; Main URL: http://www.bankofamerica.com/grantmaking

Established in 1925 in MA.
Donors: Charles E. Adams†; Caroline J. Adams†.
Foundation type: Independent foundation.
Financial data (yr. ended 05/31/13): Assets, $14,174,292 (M); expenditures, $715,339; qualifying distributions, $637,089; giving activities include $590,000 for 19 grants (high: $147,500; low: $10,000).
Purpose and activities: Giving to support and promote quality educational, human services, and health care programming for underserved populations. Annual gifts are also awarded to the Harvard University Medical School and the

Massachusetts Institute of Technology for student scholarships.
Type of support: General/operating support.
Limitations: Giving primarily in MA. No support for national organizations. No grants to individuals, or for conferences, film production, travel, research projects, or publications; no loans.
Application information: Complete application guidelines available at http://www.bankofamerica.com/grantmaking.
Initial approach: E-mail (Indicate foundation name in subject line)
Deadline(s): See foundation web site for current deadlines
Trustee: Bank of America, N.A.
EIN: 046011995
Selected grants: The following grants are a representative sample of this grantmaker's funding activity:
$50,000 to Boston Foundation, Boston, MA, 2013. For SkillWorks: Partners for a Productive Workforce.
$25,000 to Family Aid Boston, Boston, MA, 2013. For general operations of the organization.
$20,000 to Casa Myrna Vasquez, Boston, MA, 2013. For general operations of the organization.
$20,000 to Harvard University, Cambridge, MA, 2013. For general operations of the organization.
$20,000 to Lawrence CommunityWorks, Lawrence, MA, 2013. For program support for the Lawrence Financial Stability Center.
$20,000 to Partners for Youth with Disabilities, Boston, MA, 2013. For general operations of the organization.
$20,000 to RAW Art Works, Lynn, MA, 2013. For general operations of the organization.
$15,000 to Boston Local Development Corporation, Boston, MA, 2013. For program support for WriteBoston's school-year programs.
$15,000 to Boston Rescue Mission, Boston, MA, 2013. For general operations of the organization.
$15,000 to ROCA, Chelsea, MA, 2013. For High-Risk Young Mothers Project.

3918
Adelson Family Foundation ✧
300 First Ave.
Needham, MA 02494-2736 (781) 972-5950
FAX: (781) 972-5999;
E-mail: questions@adelsonfoundation.org; Main URL: http://www.adelsonfoundation.org/AFF/index.html

Established in 2007.
Donors: Dr. Miriam Adelson; Sheldon G. Adelson.
Foundation type: Independent foundation.
Financial data (yr. ended 12/31/13): Assets, $25,941 (M); gifts received, $53,250,124; expenditures, $53,300,456; qualifying distributions, $53,299,700; giving activities include $52,812,216 for 62 grants (high: $19,026,600; low: $2,500).
Purpose and activities: The primary purpose of the foundation is to strengthen the State of Israel and the Jewish people. The foundation focuses on the following categories: Healthcare, Holocaust and Anti-Semitism awareness, Israel Advocacy and defense, Israel studies, Jewish and Zionist identity and education, media and culture, and welfare.
Fields of interest: Health care; Human services; Jewish agencies & synagogues.
International interests: Israel.
Limitations: Applications not accepted. Giving primarily on a national basis, with some giving in MA and NV. No grants for endowments.
Officer: Michael Bohnen, Pres.
Trustees: Sheldon G. Anderson; Dr. Miriam Adelson.
EIN: 047024330
Selected grants: The following grants are a representative sample of this grantmaker's funding activity:
$32,000,000 to Birthright Israel Foundation, New York, NY, 2012. For general support.
$2,681,997 to American Society for Yad Vashem, New York, NY, 2012. For general support.
$2,000,000 to Jewish Federation of Las Vegas, Las Vegas, NV, 2012. For general support.
$1,400,000 to Combined Jewish Philanthropies of Greater Boston, Boston, MA, 2012. For general support.
$1,000,000 to Fidelity Charitable Gift Fund, Boston, MA, 2012. For general support.
$1,000,000 to Friends of Israel Initiative, Miami, FL, 2012. For general support.
$250,000 to Middle East Media Research Institute, Washington, DC, 2012. For general support.
$100,000 to Friends of the Israel Defense Forces, National/New York Tri-State Region, New York, NY, 2012. For general support.
$100,000 to United States Holocaust Memorial Museum, Washington, DC, 2012. For general support.
$100,000 to Western Wall Heritage Foundation, New York, NY, 2012. For general support.

3919
Dr. Miriam and Sheldon G. Adelson Medical Research Foundation ✧
300 1st Ave.
Needham, MA 02494-2736 (781) 972-5900
Contact: Marissa White
E-mail: info@adelsonfoundation.org; Main URL: http://www.adelsonfoundation.org/amrfphil.html

Established in 2006 in MA.
Donors: Sheldon G. Adelson; Dr. Miriam Adelson.
Foundation type: Independent foundation.
Financial data (yr. ended 12/31/13): Assets, $311,912 (M); gifts received, $24,272,961; expenditures, $25,300,691; qualifying distributions, $25,206,779; giving activities include $23,700,153 for 32 grants (high: $2,942,871; low: $145,080).
Purpose and activities: Giving primarily to foster collaboration in biomedical research in order to accelerate medical innovation and to facilitate commercialization of innovative medical products for the public good. The foundation is designed to encourage a model in which scientists from different institutions (referred to as Collaborating Scientists) come together to identify and conduct a synergetic group of research studies to answer a particular question (each individual study is referred to as a Component Project and the grouping is referred to as a Collaboration). The Collaborating Scientists determine the sequence, timing, scope and direction of the Component Projects, and the foundation provides infrastructure and financial support to foster the Collaborations and to protect and commercialize resulting biomedical innovation. Currently, the foundation is focusing on collaborations in the areas of neurology, oncology, and immunology.
Fields of interest: Cancer research; Brain research; Biomedicine research; Neuroscience research; Medical research.
Limitations: Giving on a national basis.
Application information: Funding for collaborations within program areas only. Application form required.
Initial approach: Letter
Deadline(s): None
Officers: Kenneth H. Fasman, Ph.D., V.P. and C.T.O.; Steven Garfinkel, V.P. and General Counsel.
Trustees: Dr. Miriam Adelson; Sheldon G. Adelson.
EIN: 047023433

3920
The Alchemy Foundation ✧
104 Lakeview Ave.
Cambridge, MA 02138

Established in 2000 in MA.
Donors: Jean I. Montagu; Kyra L. Montagu.
Foundation type: Independent foundation.
Financial data (yr. ended 12/31/13): Assets, $3,152,700 (M); expenditures, $776,776; qualifying distributions, $730,164; giving activities include $730,164 for 227 grants (high: $335,000; low: $50).
Purpose and activities: Giving primarily to international refugee projects in Africa, and health initiatives in Vietnam and internationally.
Fields of interest: Arts; Education; Human services; International migration/refugee issues.
International interests: Africa; Vietnam.
Type of support: Program development.
Limitations: Applications not accepted. Giving on a national basis (with emphasis on MA) and on an international basis (with emphasis on Africa and Vietnam). No grants to individuals, or for capital.
Application information: Contributes only to pre-selected organizations.
Board meeting date(s): Oct.
Trustees: Jean I. Montagu; Kyra L. Montagu.
EIN: 043541830

3921
The George I. Alden Trust ✧
370 Main St., 11th Fl.
Worcester, MA 01608-1779 (508) 459-8005
Contact: Warner S. Fletcher, Chair.
FAX: (508) 459-8305;
E-mail: trustees@aldentrust.org; Main URL: http://www.aldentrust.org
Grants List: http://www.aldentrust.org/grantpledges.html

Trust established in 1912 in MA.
Donor: George I. Alden†.
Foundation type: Independent foundation.
Financial data (yr. ended 12/31/13): Assets, $192,537,442 (M); expenditures, $10,445,440; qualifying distributions, $9,331,388; giving activities include $9,044,638 for grants.
Purpose and activities: The trust is currently focusing on grants to private colleges and universities in PA, NY, NJ and the six New England states with fulltime undergraduate enrollments of 1000 -3000 students. In addition the trust supports YMCAs in Massachusetts and educationally related organizations in the Worcester, MA area.

Fields of interest: Vocational education; Higher education; Higher education, college; Higher education, university; Education.
Type of support: Capital campaigns; Building/renovation; Equipment; Endowments.
Limitations: Applications accepted. Giving limited to NY, NJ, PA and the six New England states. No grants to individuals; no loans.
Publications: Application guidelines; Financial statement; Grants list.
Application information: Applicants are encouraged to contact the trust by telephone, email, or make a visit, prior to submitting an application. Application form not required.
Initial approach: Proposal with cover letter
Copies of proposal: 1
Deadline(s): Feb. 15, May 15, Aug. 15, and Nov. 15
Board meeting date(s): Mar., June, Sept. and Dec.
Final notification: Within a week of grants meeting
Officers and Trustees:* Warner S. Fletcher,* Chair.; Gail T. Randall,* Vice-Chair.; Douglas Q. Meystre,* Clerk; James E. Collins,* Treas.
Number of staff: 4 part-time professional; 2 part-time support.
EIN: 046023784
Selected grants: The following grants are a representative sample of this grantmaker's funding activity:
$1,250,000 to YMCA of Central Massachusetts, Worcester, MA, 2013. For capital support.
$1,000,000 to Worcester Art Museum, Worcester, MA, 2013. For capital support.
$500,000 to College of the Holy Cross, Worcester, MA, 2013. For Alden Excellence Award.
$500,000 to Worcester Academy, Worcester, MA, 2013. For capital support.
$400,000 to Quinsigamond Community College, Worcester, MA, 2013. For equipment.
$300,000 to Worcester County Mechanics Association, Worcester, MA, 2013. For capital support.
$200,000 to Massachusetts Symphony Orchestra, Worcester, MA, 2013. For capital support.
$115,000 to YMCA of Central Massachusetts, Worcester, MA, 2013. For operating support.
$100,000 to Worcester Educational Development Foundation, Worcester, MA, 2013. For operating support.
$33,638 to YMCA of Central Massachusetts, Worcester, MA, 2013. For operating support.

3922
Aloha Foundation ✧
c/o Lourie & Cutler, P.C.
60 State St.
Boston, MA 02109-1800

Established in MA.
Donor: Aloha II Foundation LLC.
Foundation type: Independent foundation.
Financial data (yr. ended 12/31/13): Assets, $13,693,231 (M); gifts received, $937,749; expenditures, $1,331,511; qualifying distributions, $1,275,160; giving activities include $1,275,160 for 13 grants (high: $504,160; low: $25,000).
Fields of interest: Education; Human services.
Limitations: Applications not accepted. Giving primarily in RI and VA.
Application information: Contributes only to pre-selected organizations.
Trustee: Amy B. Naughton.
EIN: 047026648

3923
American Memorial Hospital, Inc. ✧
c/o Fiduciary Trust Co.
P.O. Box 55806
Boston, MA 02205-5806

Foundation type: Independent foundation.
Financial data (yr. ended 06/30/13): Assets, $14,203,685 (M); expenditures, $802,111; qualifying distributions, $727,960; giving activities include $630,710 for 1 grant, and $47,697 for 1 grant to an individual.
Fields of interest: Health care.
Type of support: Fellowships.
Limitations: Applications not accepted. Giving primarily in MA; with some giving in France.
Application information: Unsolicited requests for funds not accepted.
Directors: William B. Beekman; Laurence E. Cranch; Emme Levin Deland; Constance Ellis; Jacques Hugon; Robin Jones; Claude J. Migeon, M.D.; Richard Perry; Dr. Georges Peter; Daniel Pierce; J. Brian Potts; Adrienne M. Scheich; Gerald M. Shea; Hale Sturges; Nancy T. Swift; Alexander Thorndike; Stephen C. Wright.
EIN: 046012766

3924
The AMG Charitable Foundation ✧ ☆
600 Hale St.
Prides Crossing, MA 01965
Main URL: http://www.amg.com/

Donor: Affiliated Managers Group, Inc.
Foundation type: Company-sponsored foundation.
Financial data (yr. ended 12/31/12): Assets, $2,777,207 (M); gifts received, $2,429,500; expenditures, $444,087; qualifying distributions, $442,612; giving activities include $442,612 for 54 grants (high: $25,000; low: $100).
Fields of interest: Arts; Medical research; Human services.
Limitations: Applications not accepted.
Application information: Unsolicited request for funds not accepted.
Officers and Directors:* Sean M. Healey,* Pres.; John Kingston III,* Secy. and Treas.; Jennifer Benson Kelley,* Exec. Dir.
EIN: 364703120

3925
Phyllis Anthony Charitable Trust ✧ ☆
1280 Soldiers Field Rd.
Boston, MA 02135

Donor: Jane Shapiro.
Foundation type: Independent foundation.
Financial data (yr. ended 12/31/13): Assets, $4,933,445 (M); expenditures, $537,954; qualifying distributions, $500,000; giving activities include $500,000 for 1 grant.
Fields of interest: Human services.
Limitations: Applications not accepted. Giving primarily in San Francisco, CA.
Application information: Unsolicited request for funds not accepted.
Trustees: Paula Feldman; Drummond Pike; Jane Shapiro.
EIN: 326175794

3926
Arbella Insurance Group Charitable Foundation, Inc. ✧
(formerly Arbella Charitable Foundation, Inc.)
101 Arch St., Ste. 1860
Boston, MA 02110-1118 (617) 769-3040
Contact: Beverly Tangvik, Dir. of Charitable Giving
E-mail: charitable.foundation@arbella.com; E-mail for BSO Bus Program: bsoschoolbus@arbella.com; Main URL: https://www.arbella.com/arbella-insurance/why-arbella/arbella-insurance-foundation

Established in 2004 in MA.
Donor: Arbella, Inc.
Foundation type: Company-sponsored foundation.
Financial data (yr. ended 12/31/12): Assets, $25,234,330 (M); expenditures, $2,573,403; qualifying distributions, $2,129,451; giving activities include $1,688,270 for 578 grants (high: $314,145; low: $20), and $441,181 for foundation-administered programs.
Purpose and activities: The foundation supports organizations involved with arts and culture, education, breast cancer, hunger, disaster relief, automotive safety, human services, community development, and veterans.
Fields of interest: Museums; Performing arts, orchestras; Arts; Education; Hospitals (general); Breast cancer; Food services; Food banks; Disasters, preparedness/services; Safety, automotive safety; Children/youth, services; Family services; Homeless, human services; Human services; Community/economic development; United Ways and Federated Giving Programs; Military/veterans' organizations.
Type of support: General/operating support; Continuing support; Program development; Scholarship funds; Employee volunteer services; Employee matching gifts.
Limitations: Applications not accepted. Giving primarily in areas of company operations, with emphasis on CT, NH, and MA. No grants to individuals.
Application information: Unsolicited applications are currently not accepted. The foundation is currently working with established partners. Visit website for BSO Bus Program.
Officers and Directors:* John F. Donohue,* Chair. and Pres.; Frances X. Bellotti,* Vice-Chair.; Gail Eagan, Sr. V.P. and Genl. Counsel; Beverly J. Tangvik, Secy. and Dir. of Charitable Giving; Christoper E. Hall, Treas.; Patricia B. Bailey; Thomas S. Carpenter; Anne DeFrancesco; Edmund J. Doherty; J. Robert Dowling; William H. DuMouchel; Andrea Gargiulo; David W. Hattman; Thomas R. Kiley; Jeannette M. Orsino.
EIN: 050613355

3927
The Arzak Foundation ✧
c/o Ropes and Gray LLP
800 Boylston St.
Boston, MA 02199-3600

Established in 2006 in MA.
Donors: L. Dennis Shapiro; Alison I. Shapiro; Rachel T. Shapiro; Zachary Shapiro.
Foundation type: Independent foundation.
Financial data (yr. ended 12/31/13): Assets, $8,642,172 (M); gifts received, $11,077; expenditures, $507,755; qualifying distributions,

$503,184; giving activities include $498,613 for 68 grants (high: $76,000; low: $100).
Purpose and activities: The mission of the foundation is to fund projects related to improving quality of life for all peoples and to foster creative technology-based research and development in support of this goal.
Fields of interest: Arts; Education; Religion.
Limitations: Applications not accepted. Giving primarily in MA. No grants to individuals.
Application information: Unsolicited requests for funds not accepted.
Trustees: L. Dennis Shapiro; Susan R. Shapiro.
EIN: 870760799

3928
The Ashurst Foundation ✧
c/o Elizabeth K. Pozen
9 Arlington St.
Boston, MA 02116-3410

Established in 2004 in MA.
Donor: Robert C. Pozen.
Foundation type: Independent foundation.
Financial data (yr. ended 12/31/13): Assets, $19,526,531 (M); gifts received, $963,464; expenditures, $720,134; qualifying distributions, $637,550; giving activities include $637,550 for 74 grants (high: $100,000; low: $100).
Fields of interest: Higher education; Engineering/technology; Public affairs.
Limitations: Applications not accepted. Giving primarily in Washington, DC, MA, and NY. No grants to individuals.
Application information: Unsolicited requests for funds not accepted.
Trustees: David E. Pozen; Elizabeth K. Pozen; Joanna R. Pozen; Robert C. Pozen.
EIN: 206325176

3929
Association for the Relief of Aged Women of New Bedford ✧
432 County St.
New Bedford, MA 02740-5018

Established in 1866 in MA.
Donor: George D. Barnard Trust.
Foundation type: Operating foundation.
Financial data (yr. ended 03/31/14): Assets, $18,356,039 (M); gifts received, $238; expenditures, $1,039,361; qualifying distributions, $999,006; giving activities include $419,163 for 11 grants (high: $88,562; low: $4,500), and $351,733 for grants to individuals.
Purpose and activities: A private operating foundation; furnishes assistance to and promotes the welfare and relief of elderly women in New Bedford, Dartmouth, Fairhaven, and Acushnet, Massachusetts. Applicants for aid must be 60 years of age or older, have liquid assets of under $5,000, and live alone. Only women who have been residents of the above named towns for at least five years are eligible.
Fields of interest: Health care; Children, services; Family services; Aging; Women; Economically disadvantaged.
Type of support: Grants to individuals.
Limitations: Applications not accepted. Giving limited to residents of New Bedford, Dartmouth, Fairhaven, and Acushnet, MA.
Application information: Unsolicited requests for funds not accepted.
Board meeting date(s): 1st Mon. of each month
Officers and Directors:* Roseanne O'Connell,* Pres.; Elizabeth Brinkerhoff, V.P.; Deborah Brooke, Clerk; Jo-Ann Beaulieu, Treas.; Cheryl Randall-Mach, Exec. Dir.; Shannon Bachman; Diane Breault; Sandra Fogg; Gillian Harris; Nancy Kurtz; Lorraine Mello; Emily Pinheiro; Susan Rothschild; Rosemary Saber; Jean Silver; Barbara Wackowski-Faria; Gretchen Whipple; Lynn Wylde.
EIN: 046056367
Selected grants: The following grants are a representative sample of this grantmaker's funding activity:
$1,258 to Arts Learning, Natick, MA, 2012.

3930
The Robert and Michelle Cooke Atchinson Foundation ✧ ☆
115 Commonwealth Ave., No. 2
Boston, MA 02116

Established in 1998 in MA.
Donors: Robert Atchinson; Michelle Cooke Atchinson.
Foundation type: Independent foundation.
Financial data (yr. ended 12/31/13): Assets, $33,252,889 (M); gifts received, $2,532,232; expenditures, $1,524,963; qualifying distributions, $648,169; giving activities include $644,607 for 12 grants (high: $200,000; low: $5,000).
Purpose and activities: Giving primarily for education, children and youth services, particularly a children's hospital, and for social services.
Type of support: General/operating support.
Limitations: Applications not accepted. Giving primarily in MA. No grants to individuals.
Application information: Unsolicited requests for funds not accepted.
Trustees: Christine J. Atchinson; Daniel S. Atchinson; Katherine M. Atchinson; Michelle Cooke Atchinson; Robert G. Atchinson.
EIN: 046875099

3931
The Ausolus Trust ✧
c/o George P. Beal, The Boston Family Office
88 Broad St., 2nd Fl.
Boston, MA 02110 (617) 624-0800
Contact: George Putnam, Tr.

Established in 1997 in MA.
Donors: George Putnam; Nancy Putnam.
Foundation type: Independent foundation.
Financial data (yr. ended 12/31/13): Assets, $19,909,252 (M); gifts received, $1,000,000; expenditures, $772,699; qualifying distributions, $736,472; giving activities include $707,000 for 58 grants (high: $85,000; low: $1,000).
Purpose and activities: Giving primarily for education, historical societies, the arts, hospitals, and human services.
Fields of interest: Arts; Education; Environment.
Limitations: Applications accepted. Giving primarily in the Boston, MA, area, and ME.
Application information: Application form not required.
Initial approach: Proposal
Deadline(s): Dec. 1
Trustees: George Putnam; Nancy Putnam.
EIN: 043368079

3932
Alice S. Ayling Scholarship Foundation ✧
c/o Richard P. Hamel, Tyler & Reynolds
77 Summer St.
Boston, MA 02110-1006

Established in 1987 in MA.
Donor: Alice S. Ayling.
Foundation type: Independent foundation.
Financial data (yr. ended 12/31/13): Assets, $16,375,373 (M); expenditures, $635,265; qualifying distributions, $558,798; giving activities include $502,500 for 15 grants (high: $47,500; low: $20,000).
Purpose and activities: Giving to colleges and universities which recommend scholarship candidates who are engaged in full-time studies, for assistance at their sole discretion. Strong attention given to scholarships relating to the field of humanities.
Fields of interest: Humanities; Higher education; Scholarships/financial aid.
Type of support: Scholarship funds.
Limitations: Applications not accepted. Giving primarily in MA, ME, NH, and VT. No grants to individuals.
Application information: Unsolicited requests for funds not accepted.
Officer: Geoffrey C. Andrews, Exec. Dir.
Trustees: Richard P. Hamel; Gerald B. O'Grady III.
EIN: 222808952

3933
Paul and Edith Babson Foundation ✧
c/o GMA Foundations
77 Summer St., 8th Fl.
Boston, MA 02110 (617) 391-3088
Contact: Betty Nichols, Prog. Off.; Daniel Roundy, Fdn. Asst.
E-mail: pebabson@gmafoundations.com; Main URL: http://pebabsonfoundation.org/
Grants List: http://pebabsonfoundation.org/grants/

Trust established in 1957 in MA.
Donor: Paul T. Babson‡.
Foundation type: Independent foundation.
Financial data (yr. ended 12/31/12): Assets, $14,739,598 (M); expenditures, $624,446; qualifying distributions, $602,297; giving activities include $586,716 for 107 grants (high: $25,050; low: $1,000).
Purpose and activities: The competitive grant program focuses on providing opportunities for the people of Greater Boston, Massachusetts, through grants in four program areas: entrepreneurship and economic development, culture, education and leadership development, environment and community building, and health and social services.
Fields of interest: Arts; Education; Environment, beautification programs; Youth, services; Economic development; Community development, small businesses.
Type of support: General/operating support; Program development; Scholarship funds.
Limitations: Applications accepted. Giving limited to the greater Boston, MA, area as generally defined by Route 128. Communities touched by Route 128 will

be included. No grants to individuals, or for individual scholarships, conferences, films, fundraising, or donor cultivations.
Publications: Application guidelines; Grants list; Program policy statement.
Application information: Application form required.
Initial approach: Use online application process on foundation web site
Deadline(s): See foundation web site for current deadlines
Board meeting date(s): Late May and early Dec.
Trustees: James A. Babson; Katherine L. Babson; James R. Nichols.
Number of staff: 1 part-time professional; 1 part-time support.
EIN: 046037891
Selected grants: The following grants are a representative sample of this grantmaker's funding activity:
$15,000 to Franklin Park Coalition, Boston, MA, 2012. For Youth Conservation Crew.
$10,000 to Boston Natural Areas Network, Boston, MA, 2012. For Youth Conservation Corps.
$10,000 to Center for Women and Enterprise, Boston, MA, 2012. For entrepreneurship training.
$10,000 to Generations, Inc., Boston, MA, 2012. For Reading Coaches and Classroom Literacy.
$8,000 to Wellesley Scholarship Foundation, Wellesley, MA, 2012. For endowment fund.
$7,000 to Summer Search Boston, Jamaica Plain, MA, 2012. To support Program's Operating Costs.
$5,000 to Arlington Street Church, Boston, MA, 2012. For Rap Program.
$5,000 to Bottom Line, Jamaica Plain, MA, 2012. For Operating Expenses for Boston Office.
$5,000 to Sarvodaya USA, Madison, WI, 2012. For Tsunami Relief Programs.
$5,000 to Sociedad Latina, Roxbury, MA, 2012. For Health Careers for Youth.

3934
The A. W. Baldwin Charitable Foundation, Inc. ✧

(formerly Baldwin Charitable Foundation, Inc.)
c/o Fiduciary Trust Co.
P.O. Box 55806
Boston, MA 02205-5806

Established in 1969 in MA.
Donor: Alfred W. Baldwin.
Foundation type: Independent foundation.
Financial data (yr. ended 12/31/13): Assets, $25,769,941 (M); expenditures, $1,547,009; qualifying distributions, $1,431,718; giving activities include $1,400,000 for 10 grants (high: $500,000; low: $20,000).
Purpose and activities: Giving primarily to hospitals and health organizations, particularly for the blind and visually impaired; funding also for higher education.
Fields of interest: Higher education; Medical school/education; Education; Hospitals (general); Hospitals (specialty); Health organizations; Blind/visually impaired.
Limitations: Applications not accepted. Giving primarily in Boston, MA. No grants to individuals.
Application information: Contributes only to pre-selected organizations.
Officers: Janet D. Wilson, Pres.; Barbara D. Benson, V.P.; Andrew C. Bailey, Esq., Clerk; Elizabeth Graham, Treas.
EIN: 237004131
Selected grants: The following grants are a representative sample of this grantmaker's funding activity:
$50,000 to Learning Ally, Princeton, NJ, 2011. For general purposes.

3935
Lloyd G. Balfour Foundation

c/o US Trust, Bank of America, N.A.
225 Franklin St., 4th Fl.
Boston, MA 02110-2801 (866) 778-6859
Contact: Miki C. Akimoto, Market Dir.
E-mail: ma.grantmaking@ustrust.com; Main URL: https://www.bankofamerica.com/philanthropic/grantmaking.go
Attleboro Scholarship contact: Wendy Holt, Exec. Dir., Attleboro Scholarship Foundation, tel.: 1 (508) 226-4414

Established in 1973 in MA.
Donor: L.G. Balfour†.
Foundation type: Independent foundation.
Financial data (yr. ended 03/31/14): Assets, $114,181,974 (M); expenditures, $6,762,908; qualifying distributions, $4,793,773; giving activities include $4,344,040 for 59 grants (high: $398,000; low: $5,000).
Purpose and activities: Giving primarily for programs that provide access to education, especially those that promote college readiness, access, and success for underserved populations in New England. The foundation's other giving is to favored charities listed in Mr. Balfour's will, and organizations serving the community of Attleboro, Massachusetts, where giving is for general charitable purposes.
Fields of interest: Education.
Type of support: General/operating support; Program development.
Limitations: Giving primarily in New England, with emphasis on Attleboro, MA. No grants to individuals.
Publications: Application guidelines.
Application information: Online application at www.bankofamerica.com/grantmaking.
Initial approach: E-mail
Deadline(s): See foundation web site for current deadlines
Final notification: May/June for Attleboro-based organizations; ongoing for general education requests.
Trustee: Bank of America, N.A.
Number of staff: 5
EIN: 222751372
Selected grants: The following grants are a representative sample of this grantmaker's funding activity:
$398,000 to Attleboro Scholarship Foundation, Attleboro, MA, 2014. For Lloyd G. Balfour Foundation Scholarship Program providing college scholarships to children and grandchildren of former LG Balfour Employees and to the general population of college-bound Attleboro students.
$250,000 to Sigma Chi Foundation, Evanston, IL, 2014. For Balfour Scholars', 'Balfour Leadership Training Workshop', Horizons-'Balfour Participants', Journey-'Balfour Chapter Retreats', and Cornerstone-'Balfour Mentors', payable over 3.00 years.
$200,000 to Attleboro, City of, Attleboro, MA, 2014. For challenge grant to support the Attleboro High School stadium renovation.
$200,000 to Indiana University Foundation, Bloomington, IN, 2014. For Balfour Scholars Program for at-risk students, payable over 4.00 years.
$125,000 to Sturdy Memorial Foundation, Attleboro, MA, 2014. For General operations of the organization, payable over 2.00 years.
$125,000 to Sturdy Memorial Foundation, Attleboro, MA, 2014. For General operations of the organization, payable over 2.00 years.
$120,000 to YMCA of Attleboro, Attleboro, MA, 2014. For Balfour Pool Renovation and Operating Support, payable over 3.00 years.
$75,000 to Congregacion Leon de Juda, Higher Education Resource Center, Boston, MA, 2014. For Passport to College, payable over 2.00 years.
$75,000 to Massachusetts 2020, Boston, MA, 2014. For Expanded Learning Time in Massachusetts and Connecticut.
$50,000 to Arc of Bristol County, Attleboro, MA, 2014. To strengthen adult foster care services for Bristol County seniors and citizens with disabilities, payable over 3.00 years.

3936
J. M. R. Barker Foundation ✧

c/o Ballentine Partners, LLC
230 3rd Ave., 6th Fl.
Waltham, MA 02451-7552 (781) 314-1300
New York, NY fax: (212) 265-6417

Established in 1968 in NY.
Donors: James M. Barker†; Margaret R. Barker†; Robert R. Barker.
Foundation type: Independent foundation.
Financial data (yr. ended 12/31/13): Assets, $71,562,108 (M); expenditures, $3,150,205; qualifying distributions, $2,642,991; giving activities include $2,409,204 for 30 grants (high: $425,000; low: $5,000).
Purpose and activities: Giving primarily for organizations that are well-known to one or more directors, with some emphasis on the areas of education, the environment and cultural programs.
Fields of interest: Arts; Higher education; Education; Environment, natural resources.
Type of support: General/operating support; Continuing support; Annual campaigns; Capital campaigns; Building/renovation; Endowments; Program development; Seed money; Research; Matching/challenge support.
Limitations: Applications accepted. Giving primarily in MA, NH, NY and VA. No grants to individuals, or for scholarships, fellowships, or matching gifts; no loans.
Application information: Application form required.
Initial approach: Proposal
Deadline(s): Nov. 1
Board meeting date(s): June and Dec.
Officers and Directors:* Margaret Barker Clark,* Pres.; James R. Barker,* V.P. and C.I.O.; W.B. Barker,* V.P.; Robert P. Connor,* Treas.; Gregory D. Barker; Kathryn Barker; William S. Barker; John W. Holman, Jr.; Richard D. Kahn; Margaret S. Barker Moore; Troy Y. Murray.
Number of staff: 1 part-time support.
EIN: 136268289
Selected grants: The following grants are a representative sample of this grantmaker's funding activity:
$425,000 to Kimball Union Academy, Meriden, NH, 2012. For Capital Campaign and General Support.
$275,000 to College Forward, Manor, TX, 2012. For It Project.

$117,448 to Rockport Chamber Music Festival, Rockport, MA, 2012. For General Support, Equipment Repair and Loan Interest.
$110,000 to Concerned Citizens of Montauk, Montauk, NY, 2012. For general support and matching grants.
$85,000 to Literacy Coalition of Central Texas, Austin, TX, 2012. For Bookkeeping Help.
$35,000 to Austin Partners in Education, Austin, TX, 2012. For general support of seven special projects.
$25,000 to Cottonwood Gulch Foundation, Albuquerque, NM, 2012. For general support and scholarships.

3937
Barr Foundation ✧
(formerly The Hostetter Foundation)
The Pilot House
Lewis Wharf
Boston, MA 02110 (617) 854-3500
Contact: Kerri Ann Hurley, Grants Mgr.
FAX: (617) 854-3501;
E-mail: info@barrfoundation.org; Main URL: http://www.barrfoundation.org
Grantee Perception Report: http://www.barrfoundation.org/news/barr-foundation-2007-grantee-perception-report/
Knowledge Center: http://www.barrfoundation.org/news/

Established in 1987 in MA.
Donors: Amos B. Hostetter, Jr.; Barbara W. Hostetter.
Foundation type: Independent foundation.
Financial data (yr. ended 12/31/13): Assets, $1,555,580,555 (L); expenditures, $78,640,882; qualifying distributions, $58,571,680; giving activities include $52,102,925 for 356+ grants (high: $4,000,000).
Purpose and activities: The foundation's mission is guided by a vision of a vibrant, just, and sustainable world with hopeful futures for children. Its mission is to support gifted leaders and networked organizations working in Boston and beyond to enhance educational and economic opportunities, to achieve environmental sustainability, and to create rich cultural experiences - all with particular attention to children and families living in poverty.
Fields of interest: Performing arts; Arts; Elementary/secondary education; Education, early childhood education; Elementary school/education; Education, services; Education; Environment, climate change/global warming; Environment, natural resources; Environment, land resources; Environment; Community/economic development; Children/youth; Children; Youth; Young adults; Minorities; Economically disadvantaged.
International interests: Ethiopia; Haiti; India.
Type of support: General/operating support; Management development/capacity building; Annual campaigns; Capital campaigns; Building/renovation; Land acquisition; Endowments; Emergency funds; Program development; Conferences/seminars; Fellowships; Research; Technical assistance; Consulting services; Program evaluation; Matching/challenge support.
Limitations: Giving primarily in the greater Boston, MA, area, and on an international basis in sub-Saharan Africa, Haiti and India. No grants to individuals, or for scholarships, lobbying or elective activity.
Application information: After completing an online inquiry form, staff review and follow up with only selected submissions. Grant applications are by invitation only.
Initial approach: Online inquiry
Board meeting date(s): Quarterly
Officers and Trustee:* Barbara W. Hostetter,* Chair.; James Canales,* Pres.; Amos B. Hostetter, Jr.
Number of staff: 11 full-time professional; 3 full-time support.
EIN: 046579815
Selected grants: The following grants are a representative sample of this grantmaker's funding activity:
$3,000,000 to Fidelity Charitable Gift Fund, Boston, MA, 2012.
$3,000,000 to Isabella Stewart Gardner Museum, Boston, MA, 2012.
$1,000,000 to North Bennet Street School, Boston, MA, 2012.
$760,000 to Childrens Investment Fund, Boston, MA, 2012.
$650,000 to Conservation Law Foundation, Boston, MA, 2012.
$600,000 to Harvard University, John F. Kennedy School of Government, Hauser Center for Nonprofit Organizations, Cambridge, MA, 2012.
$140,000 to Building Educated Leaders for Life Foundation, Dorchester, MA, 2012.
$100,000 to Artists for Humanity, Boston, MA, 2012.
$100,000 to Local Initiatives Support Corporation, Boston, MA, 2012.
$75,000 to Global Philanthropy Partnership, Chicago, IL, 2012.

3938
Adelaide Breed Bayrd Foundation ✧
350 Main St., Ste. 13
Malden, MA 02148-5023 (781) 324-1231
Contact: C. Henry Kezer, Pres.

Incorporated in 1927 in MA.
Donors: Frank A. Bayrd‡; Blanche S. Bayrd‡; Blanche Simpson Bayrd Trust.
Foundation type: Independent foundation.
Financial data (yr. ended 12/31/12): Assets, $2,770,507 (M); gifts received, $640,000; expenditures, $1,065,518; qualifying distributions, $948,785; giving activities include $941,510 for grants.
Purpose and activities: Giving primarily for those activities in which the donors' mother took an active interest. This includes local hospitals, social welfare concerns, libraries, youth-oriented programs, and cultural activities. The foundation does not grant individual scholarships but does fund ten scholarships annually through the Malden High School in MA. All grants must in some manner benefit the citizens of Malden, MA.
Fields of interest: Arts; Higher education; Health care; Health organizations, association; Human services; YM/YWCAs & YM/YWHAs; Children/youth, services; Family services; Community/economic development.
Type of support: Annual campaigns; Capital campaigns; Building/renovation; Equipment; Emergency funds; Program development; Scholarship funds.
Limitations: Applications accepted. Giving limited to the metropolitan Boston, MA, area, with emphasis on Malden. No support for national or out-of-state organizations or the performing arts (except certain educational programs). No grants to individuals (except for scholarships supplementary to the will of Blanche Bayrd), or for matching or challenge grants, demonstration projects, conferences, publications, research or endowment funds; no loans.
Publications: Annual report (including application guidelines).
Application information: AGM Common Proposal Form accepted. Application form not required.
Initial approach: Proposal
Copies of proposal: 1
Deadline(s): Submit proposal before annual meeting on the 2nd Tues. in Feb.
Board meeting date(s): 2nd Tues. in Feb.; special meetings usually held in Apr. or May to consider grant requests
Final notification: Generally in Apr. or May
Officers and Trustees:* C. Henry Kezer,* Pres.; Susan C. Mansur,* Treas.; Richard R. Burns, Jr.; Paul McPheeters; H. Allen Stevens; Robert M. Wallask; Dorothy Whittier.
Number of staff: 1 part-time professional; 1 part-time support.
EIN: 046051258

3939
BCLF Managed Assets Corporation ✧ ☆
56 Warren St., Ste. 300
Boston, MA 02119-3236 (617) 427-8600
Main URL: http://www.bostoncommunitycapital.org
Facebook: https://www.facebook.com/BostonCommunityCapital

Established in MA.
Foundation type: Independent foundation.
Financial data (yr. ended 12/31/12): Assets, $53,925,238 (M); expenditures, $2,251,802; qualifying distributions, $2,251,802; giving activities include $1,250,000 for 2 grants (high: $750,000; low: $500,000), and $1,001,802 for foundation-administered programs.
Purpose and activities: The grantmaker's mission is to create and preserve healthy communities where low-income people live and work. It does this by investing in projects that provide: affordable housing, good jobs, needed goods and services, and new opportunities for people who have been locked out of the economic mainstream.
Fields of interest: Community/economic development.
Limitations: Applications not accepted. Giving primarily in Boston, MA.
Application information: Contributes only to pre-selected organizations.
Officers and Board Members:* Charles Clark,* Chair.; Elyse Cherry,* C.E.O.; Dewitt Jones, Exec. V.P.; Michelle Volpe, Sr. V.P.; James Walsh SJ, Clerk; Sarah C. Lincoln, Treas.; Edward Dugger III; Julie Gould; Maria Maffei; Victor R. Rivera; Mercedes Tompkins.
EIN: 043246547

3940
The Bruce A. & Robert L. Beal Family Foundation ✧ ☆
177 Milk St.
Boston, MA 02109-3410

Donor: Robert L. Beal.
Foundation type: Independent foundation.
Financial data (yr. ended 09/30/13): Assets, $10,519 (M); gifts received, $943,000;

expenditures, $961,319; qualifying distributions, $960,384; giving activities include $960,384 for 22 grants (high: $250,000; low: $100).
Fields of interest: Arts; Higher education; Education; Hospitals (specialty); Health care; Jewish agencies & synagogues; Religion.
Limitations: Applications not accepted. Giving primarily in MA.
Application information: Unsolicited requests for funds not accepted.
Trustees: Bruce A. Beal; Robert L. Beal.
EIN: 222572496

3941
Millicent and Eugene Bell Foundation ✧
c/o Nutter McClennen and Fish LLP
P.O. Box 51400
Boston, MA 02205-1400

Established in MA.
Donor: Millicent Bell.
Foundation type: Independent foundation.
Financial data (yr. ended 12/31/13): Assets, $15,462,293 (M); expenditures, $1,061,215; qualifying distributions, $975,890; giving activities include $938,500 for 13 grants (high: $250,000; low: $8,500).
Fields of interest: Media/communications; Civil/human rights.
Limitations: Applications not accepted. Giving primarily in the Boston, MA, area, and New York, NY; some funding also in San Francisco, CA. No grants to individuals.
Application information: Unsolicited requests for funds not accepted.
Trustees: Millicent Bell; Thomas P. Jalkut.
EIN: 263990463

3942
The Benson Family Charitable Trust ✧
c/o Moriarty & Primack P.C.
1 Monarch Pl., No. 900
Springfield, MA 01144

Donors: Craig R. Benson; Denise A. Benson.
Foundation type: Independent foundation.
Financial data (yr. ended 12/31/13): Assets, $10,724,606 (M); expenditures, $695,815; qualifying distributions, $640,550; giving activities include $640,550 for 11 grants (high: $500,000; low: $550).
Fields of interest: Higher education; Education; Health care; Human services; Children/youth, services; Community/economic development.
Type of support: General/operating support.
Limitations: Applications not accepted. Giving primarily in MA and NH. No grants to individuals.
Application information: Contributes only to pre-selected organizations.
Trustee: Craig R. Benson.
EIN: 225017058

3943
Theodore W. & Evelyn G. Berenson Charitable Foundation ✧
c/o Goulston & Storrs
400 Atlantic Ave., Ste. 401
Boston, MA 02110-3331

Established in 1953 in MA.
Donors: Evelyn G. Berenson; Theodore W. Berenson†; Helaine B. Allen; Theodore S. Berenson.
Foundation type: Independent foundation.
Financial data (yr. ended 11/30/13): Assets, $6,649,995 (M); expenditures, $680,627; qualifying distributions, $572,857; giving activities include $572,857 for 11 grants (high: $192,857; low: $10,000).
Purpose and activities: Giving primarily for higher education, hospitals and health organizations, and to a Jewish federated giving program.
Fields of interest: Education; Health care; Jewish agencies & synagogues.
Limitations: Applications not accepted. No grants to individuals.
Application information: Contributes only to pre-selected organizations.
Trustees: Helaine B. Allen; Theodore S. Berenson; Alan W. Rottenberg; Marvin Sparrow.
EIN: 046068512

3944
The Bergstrom Foundation ✧ ☆
c/o Craig Bergstrom
220 Boylston St., Ste. 1516
Boston, MA 02116-3951

Established in 2000 in MA.
Donors: Gary L. Bergstrom; Joan L. Bergstrom†.
Foundation type: Independent foundation.
Financial data (yr. ended 07/31/13): Assets, $7,368,396 (M); expenditures, $473,294; qualifying distributions, $448,280; giving activities include $447,780 for 10 grants (high: $235,000; low: $2,280).
Fields of interest: Arts; Education; Human services.
Limitations: Applications not accepted. Giving primarily in MA. No grants to individuals.
Application information: Unsolicited requests for funds not accepted.
Trustee: Craig G. Bergstrom.
EIN: 066499658

3945
The Allen H. and Selma W. Berkman Charitable Trust
c/o GMA Foundations
77 Summer St., 8th Fl.
Boston, MA 02110-1006
Contact: Amy Shorey

Established in 1972 in PA.
Donors: Allen H. Berkman†; Selma W. Berkman†.
Foundation type: Independent foundation.
Financial data (yr. ended 10/31/13): Assets, $17,335,266 (M); expenditures, $887,794; qualifying distributions, $819,373; giving activities include $747,000 for 31 grants (high: $200,000; low: $5,000).
Purpose and activities: Giving primarily to promote education, the arts, health and human services, social justice, and Judaism.
Fields of interest: Performing arts; Higher education; Human services; YM/YWCAs & YM/YWHAs; Children/youth, services; Civil/human rights; Jewish federated giving programs; Jewish agencies & synagogues.
Type of support: General/operating support; Capital campaigns; Building/renovation; Endowments; Emergency funds; Program development; Seed money; Fellowships; Scholarship funds; Research; Program-related investments/loans; Matching/challenge support.
Limitations: Applications not accepted. Giving primarily in NY, OH and PA. No support for private foundations. No grants to individuals.
Application information: Unsolicited requests for funds not accepted.
Board meeting date(s): Quarterly
Trustees: Barbara Berkman Ackerman; James S. Berkman; Richard L. Berkman; Helen Berkman Habbert; Susan Berkman Rahm.
EIN: 256144060
Selected grants: The following grants are a representative sample of this grantmaker's funding activity:
$150,000 to Children's Literacy Initiative, Philadelphia, PA, 2011.
$150,000 to Harlem Childrens Zone, New York, NY, 2011.
$100,000 to University of Pennsylvania, Philadelphia, PA, 2011.
$50,000 to American Jewish Committee, New York, NY, 2011.
$50,000 to Freestore/Foodbank, Cincinnati, OH, 2011.
$25,000 to American Jewish Committee, New York, NY, 2011.
$20,000 to Harvard University, Cambridge, MA, 2011.
$10,000 to Pittsburgh Promise Foundation, Pittsburgh, PA, 2011. For scholarship program.
$5,000 to Angels Place, Pittsburgh, PA, 2011. For operating support.
$5,000 to Jewish Family and Childrens Service of Pittsburgh, Pittsburgh, PA, 2011.

3946
Berkshire Bank Foundation, Inc. ✧
(formerly Greater Berkshire Charitable Foundation)
P.O. Box 1308
Pittsfield, MA 01202-1308 (413) 447-1724
Contact: Lori Gazzillo, Exec. Dir.
E-mail: foundation@berkshirebank.com; E-mail for scholarships: scholarshipinfo@berkshirebank.com; Main URL: http://www.berkshirebank.com/about-us/in_the_community/berkshire-bank-foundation
Facebook: http://www.facebook.com/berkshirebank
Grants List: http://www.berkshirebank.com/about_us/in_the_community/berkshire-bank-foundation/foundation-grants-2012

Established in 1996 in MA.
Donor: Berkshire Bank.
Foundation type: Company-sponsored foundation.
Financial data (yr. ended 12/31/13): Assets, $16,096,275 (M); expenditures, $1,525,620; qualifying distributions, $1,389,828; giving activities include $972,077 for 376 grants (high: $15,000; low: $86).
Purpose and activities: The foundation supports organizations involved with arts and culture, environmental education, employment, housing, mentoring, human services, immigrant advocacy, military and veterans, and economically disadvantaged people. Special emphasis is directed toward programs designed to promote education and community economic development.
Fields of interest: Museums; Arts; Education, early childhood education; Higher education; Adult education—literacy, basic skills & GED; Libraries (public); Education; Environmental education;

Employment, services; Housing/shelter, temporary shelter; Housing/shelter, homeless; Housing/shelter, home owners; Housing/shelter; Youth development, adult & child programs; Human services, financial counseling; Human services; Civil/human rights, immigrants; Community development, neighborhood development; Urban/community development; Community/economic development; Military/veterans; Economically disadvantaged.
Type of support: General/operating support; Continuing support; Annual campaigns; Capital campaigns; Program development; Publication; Scholarship funds; Employee volunteer services; Sponsorships; Scholarships—to individuals; Donated equipment.
Limitations: Applications accepted. Giving primarily in areas of company operations in Berkshire County and Pioneer Valley, MA, NY, and southern VT. No support for religious organizations, fraternal, labor, or political organizations, including fraternal orders of police and firefighters, lobbying groups, private foundations, pass-through organizations, or national health organizations. No grants to individuals (except for scholarships), or for golf tournaments, fundraising dinners, annual memberships or annual appeals, endowments, conferences or seminars, camperships, general operating support, or staff costs or internship salaries.
Publications: Application guidelines.
Application information: Small Project Requests are between $1 and $4,999 and Large Project Requests are $5,000 and higher. Support is limited to 1 contribution per organization during any given year. Application form required.
Initial approach: Complete online application form
Copies of proposal: 1
Deadline(s): First of the month for Small Project Requests; Mar. 1, June. 1, Sept. 1, and Nov. 1 for Large Project Requests; Mar. 28 for scholarships
Board meeting date(s): Mar., June, Sept. and Dec.
Final notification: May for scholarships
Officers and Directors:* Michael J. Ferry,* Chair. and Pres.; Catherine B. Miller, Vice-Chair.; Michael P. Daly, V.P.; Lori Gazzillo, Secy. and Exec. Dir.; Robert M. Curley; J. Williar Dunlaevy; Sean A. Gray; Linda A. Johnston; D. Jeffrey Templeton.
EIN: 043365869
Selected grants: The following grants are a representative sample of this grantmaker's funding activity:
$2,500 to Cystic Fibrosis Foundation, Bethesda, MD, 2011.
$2,000 to Boston College, Chestnut Hill, MA, 2011.
$2,000 to University of Rhode Island, Kingston, RI, 2011.
$2,000 to University of Vermont, Burlington, VT, 2011.
$1,000 to Housatonic Valley Association, Cornwall Bridge, CT, 2011.

3947
Berkshire Bank Foundation -Legacy Region, Inc. ✧

(formerly The Legacy Banks Foundation)
P.O. Box 1308
Pittsfield, MA 01201-5114 (413) 447-1724
Contact: Richard M. Sullivan, Pres.
E-mail: plafayette@berkshirebank.com; Application address: Lori Gazzillo, V.P., Community Rels., P.O. Box 1148, Pittsfield, MA 01202-1148; Main URL: http://www.berkshirebank.com/about-us/in_the_community/berkshire-bank-foundation

Established in 2005 in DE and MA.
Donor: Legacy Bank.
Foundation type: Company-sponsored foundation.
Financial data (yr. ended 12/31/13): Assets, $9,703,881 (M); expenditures, $685,618; qualifying distributions, $624,019; giving activities include $558,475 for 102 grants (high: $100,000; low: $30).
Purpose and activities: The foundation supports education and community and economic development projects that enhance opportunities for children and adults in Berkshire County, Massachusetts. Special emphasis is directed toward programs that target disadvantaged communities or populations.
Fields of interest: Education, early childhood education; Education; Community/economic development; Children; Adults; Economically disadvantaged.
Type of support: General/operating support; Program development.
Limitations: Applications accepted. Giving limited to areas of company operations in Berkshire County, MA. No support for religious, political, fraternal, lobbying, national health, or discriminatory organizations, or intermediary organizations that raise and distribute funds in their own name, or private foundations. No grants to individuals, or for golf tournaments, fundraising dinners, annual memberships and appeals, or endowments, or underwriting support for conferences or seminars.
Publications: Application guidelines.
Application information: Support is limited to 1 contribution per organization during any given year. Multi-year funding is not automatic. Application form required.
Initial approach: Complete online application
Deadline(s): Mar. 1, June 1, Sept. 1, and Dec. 1 for requests $5,000 and over
Board meeting date(s): Quarterly
Officers and Directors:* J. Williar Dunlaevy,* Chair. and C.E.O.; Patrick J. Sullivan,* Vice-Chair.; Richard M. Sullivan,* Pres.; Lori Gazzillo, V.P.; Daniel Kinney, V.P.; Heather A. King, Secy.; Dianne M. Supranowicz, Treas.; Lawrence J. Lane; Susan Lombard; Anne W. Pasko; Bruce H. Person; Mary Jo Piretti-Miller.
EIN: 203661535
Selected grants: The following grants are a representative sample of this grantmaker's funding activity:
$50,000 to Barrington Stage Company, Pittsfield, MA, 2011.
$20,000 to Berkshire Community College Foundation, Pittsfield, MA, 2011.
$15,000 to Lenox Library Association, Lenox, MA, 2011.
$15,000 to United Way, Berkshire, Pittsfield, MA, 2011.
$10,000 to Barrington Stage Company, Pittsfield, MA, 2011.
$10,000 to Berkshire Museum, Pittsfield, MA, 2011.
$5,000 to Berkshire South Regional Community Center, Great Barrington, MA, 2011.
$5,000 to Hillcrest Educational Centers, Pittsfield, MA, 2011.
$2,500 to United Way, Berkshire, Pittsfield, MA, 2011.
$1,000 to Salvation Army of Pittsfield, Pittsfield, MA, 2011.

3948
Berkshire Taconic Community Foundation ✧

800 N. Main St.
P.O. Box 400
Sheffield, MA 01257-0400 (413) 229-0370
Contact: Jennifer Dowley, Pres.; For grants: Maeve M. O'Dea, Prog. Dir.
FAX: (413) 229-0329;
E-mail: info@berkshiretaconic.org; Additional tel.: (413) 528-8039; Grant inquiry e-mail: maeve@berkshiretaconic.org; Main URL: http://www.berkshiretaconic.org
Facebook: http://www.facebook.com/berkshiretaconic
Flickr: http://www.flickr.com/photos/berkshiretaconic/
LinkedIn: http://www.linkedin.com/company/berkshire-taconic-community-foundation
RSS Feed: http://feeds.feedburner.com/BTCF-News
YouTube: http://www.youtube.com/user/BerkshireTaconicCF

Established in 1987 in CT.
Foundation type: Community foundation.
Financial data (yr. ended 12/31/13): Assets, $118,503,143 (M); gifts received, $9,833,241; expenditures, $9,749,024; giving activities include $8,319,794 for grants.
Purpose and activities: The Berkshire Taconic Community Foundation builds stronger, more vibrant communities and improves the quality of life for all residents. The foundation primarily provides support for education, the arts, the environment, and health and human services.
Fields of interest: Arts; Education; Environment; Health care; Human services.
Type of support: Management development/capacity building; Building/renovation; Endowments; Emergency funds; Conferences/seminars; Publication; Scholarship funds; Research; Technical assistance; Consulting services; Grants to individuals.
Limitations: Applications accepted. Giving limited to northwest Litchfield County, CT, Berkshire County, MA, and Columbia County and northeast Dutchess County, NY.
Publications: Application guidelines; Annual report; Financial statement; Informational brochure (including application guidelines); Occasional report.
Application information: Visit foundation web site for application forms, deadlines, and specific guidelines per grant type. Application form required.
Initial approach: Create online account on the foundation's application portal
Copies of proposal: 1
Deadline(s): Varies
Board meeting date(s): Quarterly
Final notification: Varies
Officers and Directors:* J. Williar Dunlaevy,* Chair.; Thomas S. Quinn,* Vice-Chair.; Jennifer Dowley, Pres.; Diane Monti-Catania,* Secy.; Peggy Gearity, Cont.; Gloria Gaines Callen,* Treas.; Sheldon Evans; Ann Goodbody; Edward Hoe; Christopher Kennan; Ellen Kennedy; David M. McCarthy; Holly J. Nelson; Robert Windsor Norris; Emilie Mead Pryor; Henry "Pete" Putzel; David Barrett Rich; Sarah Stack; Vera V.J. Weintraub; Carl Whitbeck.
Number of staff: 6 full-time professional; 3 full-time support; 1 part-time support.
EIN: 061254469

3949
Berthiaume Family Foundation, Inc. ✧
18 Buttonwood Dr.
Andover, MA 01810-5880 (508) 478-2000
Contact: Douglas A. Berthiaume, Pres.

Established in 2005 in MA.
Donor: Douglas A. Berthiaume.
Foundation type: Independent foundation.
Financial data (yr. ended 06/30/13): Assets, $12,244,974 (M); expenditures, $2,516,863; qualifying distributions, $2,513,400; giving activities include $2,513,400 for 1 grant.
Purpose and activities: Giving primarily for a children's hospital.
Fields of interest: Hospitals (specialty).
Limitations: Giving primarily in MA.
Application information:
Initial approach: Letter
Deadline(s): None
Officers and Directors:* Douglas A. Berthiaume,* Pres.; Diana M. Berthiaume,* Clerk and Treas.
EIN: 331095606
Selected grants: The following grants are a representative sample of this grantmaker's funding activity:
$3,691,914 to Children's Hospital Corporation, Boston, MA, 2011. For general support.
$2,113,250 to Children's Hospital Corporation, Boston, MA, 2011. For general support.
$901,365 to University of Massachusetts, Amherst, MA, 2011. For general support.

3950
The Beveridge Family Foundation ✧
335 Brookline St.
Needham, MA 02492-3525 (800) 229-9667
Contact: Philip Caswell, Pres.
E-mail: administrator@beveridge.org; Main URL: http://www.beveridge.org

Established in 2001 in MA; absorbed The Frank Stanley Beveridge Foundation in 2008.
Foundation type: Independent foundation.
Financial data (yr. ended 12/31/13): Assets, $57,461,541 (M); gifts received, $100; expenditures, $3,118,971; qualifying distributions, $2,513,315; giving activities include $2,261,840 for 100 grants (high: $832,960; low: $50).
Purpose and activities: The mission of the foundation is to preserve and enhance the quality of life by embracing Frank Stanley Beveridge's philanthropic vision through initiatives in support of programs for youth development, health, education, religion, arts and environment. In addition, the foundation supports the Stanley Park of Westfield.
Fields of interest: Arts; Education; Environment, beautification programs; Environment; Animals/wildlife; Medical care, rehabilitation; Health care; Mental health/crisis services; Health organizations, association; Medical research; Legal services; Crime/law enforcement; Employment; Agriculture/food; Housing/shelter; Safety/disasters; Recreation; Youth development; Human services; Civil/human rights, alliance/advocacy; Civil/human rights; Philanthropy/voluntarism; Science, research; Science; Religion.
Type of support: Annual campaigns; Capital campaigns; Building/renovation; Equipment; Computer technology; Land acquisition; Emergency funds; Program development; Seed money; Research; Consulting services; Program evaluation.
Limitations: Applications accepted. Giving limited to Westfield, MA. No support for international/foreign affairs organizations, or for mutual benefit or membership organizations, foreign organizations, governmental units, private educational institutions, or for federated drives. No grants to individuals, or for awards/competitions, commissioning of new works, conferences and seminars, curriculum development, debt reduction, employee matching gifts, scholarships, endowment funds, exhibitions, faculty and staff development, fellowships, film/video or radio production, foundation-administered programs, general operating support, income development, internships, management development, performances or productions, program-related investments, publications, student aid, or for technical assistance.
Application information: Application form available on foundation web site only. Application form required.
Initial approach: See foundation web site to check if organization pre-qualifies
Copies of proposal: 2
Deadline(s): Feb. 1 and Aug. 1 for online applications; Feb. 15 and Aug. 15 for application materials
Board meeting date(s): Apr. and Oct.
Final notification: May 1 and Nov. 1
Officers and Directors:* Ward Slocum Caswell, Pres.; Philip Caswell, V.P.; Leah Beveridge Richardson, Clerk; Ruth S. DuPont,* Treas.; Christa Palmer Bigue; Alexander L. Caswell; Jonathan Caswell; Jillian L. Hickerson; Elizabeth Stanton Kirkpatrick; Carol A. Leary, Ph.D.; Ian Campbell Palmer; Joseph Beveridge Palmer; Frederick William Stecher; Peter Weston.
EIN: 311698286
Selected grants: The following grants are a representative sample of this grantmaker's funding activity:
$627,960 to Stanley Park of Westfield, Westfield, MA, 2013. For 2013 Gift Run Distribution.
$110,000 to Community Foundation of Western Massachusetts, Springfield, MA, 2013. For $110,000 qualified distribution.
$50,000 to Community Foundation of Western Massachusetts, Springfield, MA, 2013. For Funder Collaborative for Reading Success.
$50,000 to Pioneer Valley Riverfront Club, Springfield, MA, 2013. For Springfield Community Riverfront Activity Center Renovation.
$50,000 to South End Community Center of Springfield, Springfield, MA, 2013. For Before School / After School Program.
$35,000 to New England Public Radio Foundation, Amherst, MA, 2013. For WFCR 50th Anniversary Campaign.
$34,000 to Center for Ecological Technology, Pittsfield, MA, 2013. For Western Massachusetts Go Green Initiative.
$13,000 to Domus, Westfield, MA, 2013. For Westfield Community Education (WCE).
$5,000 to American Red Cross, Westfield, MA, 2013. For 2013 Qualified Discretionary Distributiuon.
$5,000 to Drama Studio, Springfield, MA, 2013. For 2013 Qualified Discretionary Distribution.

3951
Bilezikian Family Foundation, Inc. ✧
231 Willow St.
Yarmouth Port, MA 02675-1744

Established in MA.
Donors: Charles G. Bilezikian; Doreen Bilezikian.
Foundation type: Independent foundation.
Financial data (yr. ended 12/31/12): Assets, $19,735,280 (M); expenditures, $1,092,857; qualifying distributions, $929,094; giving activities include $929,094 for 51 grants (high: $100,000; low: $2,100).
Fields of interest: Education; Environment, water resources; Human services; Children/youth, services.
Limitations: Applications not accepted. Giving primarily in Boston and Cape Cod, MA.
Application information: Contributes only to pre-selected organizations.
Officers and Directors:* Doreen Bilezikian,* Pres.; Gregory C. Bilezikian,* V.P.; Jeffrey D. Bilezikian,* V.P.; Henry L. Murphy, Jr.,* Clerk; Charles G. Bilezikian,* Treas.
EIN: 043504021
Selected grants: The following grants are a representative sample of this grantmaker's funding activity:
$70,000 to Perkins School for the Blind, Watertown, MA, 2012. To support Educational Programs for Individuals with Visual Impairments.
$30,000 to Jewish Community Housing for the Elderly, Brighton, MA, 2012. To support Efforts to Provide Affordable Housing for Low-income Seniors.
$25,000 to Boys and Girls Club of Cape Cod, Mashpee, MA, 2012. To support Local Chapter of Boys and Girls Club.
$25,000 to Charles River Watershed Association, Weston, MA, 2012. For Preservation of the Charles River and Its Watershed.
$20,000 to Armenian Missionary Association of America, Paramus, NJ, 2012. To promote Armenian Missionary Organization's Activities.
$15,000 to Outer Cape Health Services, Wellfleet, MA, 2012. To support Medical Services Provided.
$14,000 to Landmark School, Prides Crossing, MA, 2012. For Programs Aiding Children with Learning Disabilities.
$10,000 to Massachusetts Maritime Academy Foundation, Buzzards Bay, MA, 2012. For the Programs of the Massachusetts Maritime Academy.

3952
Linda Cabot Black Foundation ✧
c/o Cabot-Wellington, LLC
70 Federal St.
Boston, MA 02110-1906

Established in 2002 in MA.
Donor: Linda Cabot Black.
Foundation type: Independent foundation.
Financial data (yr. ended 12/31/12): Assets, $8,367,196 (M); expenditures, $642,228; qualifying distributions, $548,206; giving activities include $536,006 for 22 grants (high: $500,000; low: $1).
Fields of interest: Performing arts, opera; Arts; Education.
Limitations: Applications not accepted. Giving primarily in Boston, MA. No grants to individuals.
Application information: Contributes only to pre-selected organizations.
Trustee: Linda Cabot Black.
EIN: 680532893

3953
Blue Cross Blue Shield of Massachusetts Foundation, Inc. for Expanding Healthcare Access ✧

(formerly Wellchild, the Foundation of Health for Life)
Landmark Ctr.
401 Park Dr.
Boston, MA 02215-3325 (617) 246-3744
Contact: Celeste Reid Lee, Interim Pres.
FAX: (617) 246-3992;
E-mail: info@bluecrossmafoundation.org; Tel. and e-mail for Celeste Reid Lee: (617) 246-8406, celeste.lee@bcbsma.com; Additional contact: Jennifer Lee, Grantmaking Prog. Mgr., Jennifer.Lee@bcbsma.com; E-mail for Massachusetts Institute for Community Health Leadership: mmccorma@hsph.harvard.edu; Main URL: http://www.bcbsmafoundation.org
Grants Database: http://bluecrossmafoundation.org/search-grants
RSS Feed: http://bluecrossmafoundation.org/rss.xml
Contacts for fellowships: Larry Tye, 26 Grant St., Lexington, MA 02420, e-mail: larrytye@aol.com; Anna Gosline, e-mail: Anna.Gosline@bcbsma.com

Established in 2001 in MA; status changed to a private foundation in 2006.
Donors: Blue Cross and Blue Shield of Massachusetts, Inc.; Robert Wood Johnson Foundation; CT Health Foundation; Bingham Betterment Fund; Ottauquechee Health Foundation; Cox Charitable Lead Trust; Tufts.
Foundation type: Company-sponsored foundation.
Financial data (yr. ended 12/31/12): Assets, $103,240,974 (M); gifts received, $6,796,266; expenditures, $7,991,487; qualifying distributions, $7,615,780; giving activities include $3,512,006 for grants.
Purpose and activities: The foundation seeks to expand access to health care by working with public and private organizations to broaden health coverage and reduce barriers to care.
Fields of interest: Health care, research; Health care, public policy; Health care, equal rights; Hospitals (general); Health care, clinics/centers; Public health; Public health, environmental health; Health care, insurance; Health care; Leadership development.
Type of support: Continuing support; Management development/capacity building; Program development; Fellowships; Sponsorships.
Limitations: Applications accepted. Giving primarily in areas of company operations in MA. No grants for events or sponsorships.
Publications: Application guidelines; Grants list; IRS Form 990 or 990-PF printed copy available upon request; Program policy statement.
Application information: Applicants for the Catalyst Fund and the Massachusetts Institute for Community Health Leadership should submit 5 copies of the application. Letters of inquiry should be no longer than 2 pages. Organizations receiving support are asked to submit an interim report and a final report.
Initial approach: Download application and mail for Catalyst Fund and Massachusetts Institute for Community Health Leadership; download application and mail to application address for Health Coverage Fellowship; download letter of inquiry form and mail for Connecting Consumers with Care, Cost and Affordability Grants, and Strengthening the Voice for Access
Deadline(s): Varies for Catalyst Fund, Massachusetts Institute for Community Health Leadership, Connecting Consumers with Care, Strengthening the Voice for Access, and Health Coverage Fellowship; Sept. 7 for Cost and Affordability Grants
Final notification: 6 to 7 weeks for Catalyst Fund
Officers and Directors:* Philip W. Johnston,* Chair.; Robert Meenan, M.D.*, Vice-Chair.; Audrey Shelto, Pres.; Helen Caulton-Harris; Andrew Dreyfus; Barbara Ferrer, Ph.D., MPH; Matt Fishman; Milton Glass; James W. Hunt, Jr.; Rachel Kaprielian; Nick Littlefield; Richard C. Lord; Robert Restuccia; Charlotte S. Yeh, M.D., FACEP.
EIN: 043148824

3954
BOSE Foundation, Inc. ✧

The Mountain, Ste. MS6B1
Framingham, MA 01701-9168 (508) 879-7330

Established in 1987 in MA.
Donor: BOSE Corp.
Foundation type: Company-sponsored foundation.
Financial data (yr. ended 03/31/12): Assets, $0 (M); expenditures, $544,827; qualifying distributions, $544,603; giving activities include $544,603 for 94 grants (high: $185,000; low: $100).
Purpose and activities: The foundation supports organizations involved with music, higher education, health, and housing development and awards research grants to academic institutions in the areas of electric engineering, business, and computer science.
Fields of interest: Education; Human services; Religion.
Limitations: Applications not accepted. Giving limited to MD and MA; giving also to national organizations.
Application information: Contributes only to pre-selected organizations.
Officers and Directors:* Robert Maresca,* Pres.; Mark E. Sullivan, Clerk; Herbert W. Batchelder, Treas.
EIN: 042967717
Selected grants: The following grants are a representative sample of this grantmaker's funding activity:
$70,000 to University of Michigan, Ann Arbor, MI, 2012.
$5,750 to American Cancer Society, Atlanta, GA, 2012.
$1,000 to American Diabetes Association, Alexandria, VA, 2012.

3955
Boston Baptist Social Union ✧

c/o The Organization
179 Green St., Ste. 2
Melrose, MA 02176-1922 (781) 662-6262
Contact: Fred Drauschke, Chair., Comm. on Christian Work
Main URL: http://www.bbsu.org/

Established in 1864.
Foundation type: Independent foundation.
Financial data (yr. ended 03/31/13): Assets, $18,512,775 (M); expenditures, $1,120,066; qualifying distributions, $755,053; giving activities include $718,300 for 21 grants (high: $202,100; low: $500).
Purpose and activities: The foundation's mission is to support worthy Christian ministries in the Boston, MA, area. Its goal is to encourage worthwhile fellowship among Baptist laymen in the Boston area.
Fields of interest: Youth development; Christian agencies & churches; Protestant agencies & churches.
Limitations: Applications accepted. Giving generally limited to the greater Boston, MA area.
Publications: Application guidelines.
Application information: Application form required.
Initial approach: Letter requesting application form, or download form from foundation web site
Deadline(s): Feb. 15
Board meeting date(s): Apr.
Final notification: Apr.
Officers and Directors:* Joe Marcello,* Chair. and Pres.; Christopher Edwards,* V.P.; Richard Wolf,* V.P.; Edwin T. Hobart, Secy.; Gordon L. Abbott, Treas.; Robert Gaffney; Robert Jope; Roger Philbrick; Glenn Randall; Douglas Rogers; Irving Smith; James Stevens; James Thomas.
EIN: 046034977
Selected grants: The following grants are a representative sample of this grantmaker's funding activity:
$25,000 to Emmanuel Gospel Center, Boston, MA, 2011.
$10,000 to City Mission Society of Boston, Boston, MA, 2011.
$10,000 to Trust Project, Boston, MA, 2011. For general support.

3956
Boston Foundation, Inc. ✧

75 Arlington St., 10th Fl.
Boston, MA 02116-3936 (617) 338-1700
Contact: For media: Ted McEnroe, Dir., Public Rels.
FAX: (617) 338-1604; E-mail: info@tbf.org;
Additional e-mails: ted.mcenroe@tbf.org and cld@tbf.org; Main URL: http://www.tbf.org
Blog: http://www.tbf.org/blog
Boston Indicators Project: http://www.bostonindicators.org
E-Newsletter: http://www.tbf.org/UtilityNavigation/NewsPress/Newsletters/NewslettersHome.aspx?id=384
Facebook: http://www.facebook.com/TheBostonFoundation
Flickr: http://www.flickr.com/photos/bostonfoundation/
Google Plus: https://plus.google.com/+TBForg1915/posts
Knowledge Center: http://www.tbf.org/UtilityNavigation/MultimediaLibrary/ReportsListing.aspx?id=354
LinkedIn: http://www.linkedin.com/companies/the-boston-foundation
Pinterest: http://www.pinterest.com/bostonfdn/
Twitter: http://twitter.com/bostonfdn
UStream Video Library: http://www.ustream.tv/channel/tbf-forums
YouTube: http://www.youtube.com/user/TheBostonFoundation

Established in 1915 in MA by agreement and declaration of trust; incorporated in 1917; merged with Victory Supermarkets Charitable Foundation in 2004; merged with The Philanthropic Initiative in 2011.

Foundation type: Community foundation.
Financial data (yr. ended 06/30/13): Assets, $896,216,000 (M); gifts received, $130,482,000; expenditures, $125,049,000; giving activities include $105,365,000 for grants.
Purpose and activities: As Greater Boston's community foundation, the Boston Foundation devotes its resources to building and sustaining a vital, prosperous city and region, where justice and opportunity are extended to everyone.
Fields of interest: Performing arts; Arts; Education, reform; Child development, education; Elementary school/education; Secondary school/education; Charter schools; Elementary/secondary school reform; Higher education; Higher education, college (community/junior); Adult/continuing education; Adult education—literacy, basic skills & GED; Education; Health care, public policy; Public health; Crime/violence prevention, youth; Employment, training; Employment; Agriculture/food, public policy; Nutrition; Housing/shelter, development; Youth development, services; Children/youth, services; Child development, services; Aging, centers/services; Minorities/immigrants, centers/services; Civil/human rights; Economic development; Urban/community development; Community/economic development; Philanthropy/voluntarism, public policy; Leadership development; Youth; Aging; Young adults; Disabilities, people with; Minorities; Women; Immigrants/refugees; Economically disadvantaged; Homeless.
Type of support: Consulting services; Employee matching gifts; General/operating support; Mission-related investments/loans; Program development; Seed money; Technical assistance.
Limitations: Applications accepted. Giving from discretionary funds limited to the greater Boston, MA, area. No support for religious purposes, city or state government agencies or departments, private schools, municipalities, or national or international programs. No grants to individuals, or for scientific or academic research, books or articles, films, radio, or television programs, equipment, travel, endowments, scholarships, fellowships, conferences, or symposia or capital campaigns.
Publications: Application guidelines; Annual report; Financial statement; Grants list; Informational brochure (including application guidelines); Newsletter; Occasional report.
Application information: Submission of online letter of inquiry is first step in application process. The foundation will invite submission of full proposals based on its review of letter of inquiry. Visit the foundation web site for application guidelines. Massachusetts applicants must submit profile in the Giving Common (givingcommon.org). Application form required.

Initial approach: Submit online Letter of Inquiry
Copies of proposal: 1
Deadline(s): Rolling
Board meeting date(s): Mar., June, Sept., and Dec.
Final notification: LOI submissions usually responded to within 8 weeks of submission.

Officers and Board Members:* Michael Keating,* Chair.; Catherine D'Amato,* Vice-Chair.; Paul S. Grogan,* C.E.O. and Pres.; Stephen Chan, Chief of Staff; Kate Guedj, V.P., Philanthropic and Donor Svcs.; Travis McCready, V.P., Prog.; Mary Jo Meisner, V.P., Comms., Community Rels. and Public Affairs; Geeta Pradhan, Assoc. V.P., Progs.; Timothy B. Gassert, Corp. Secy.; Al Van Ranst, C.F.O. and Treas.; George C. Wilson,* C.I.O.; Rosalyn Bonaventure, Cont.; Sandra Edgerley; Michael Eisenson; Grace Fey; Paul Gannon; Paul S. Grogan; Rev. Dr. Gregory Groover; Jackie Jenkins-Scott; Paul A. LaCamera; Paul W. Lee; Claudio Martinez; Linda Mason; Jane Mendillo; Jack R. Meyer; Dr. Myechia Minter-Jordan; Herbert E. Morse; Peter Nessen; Ron O'Hanley; Greg Shell.
Number of staff: 72 full-time professional; 15 full-time support.
EIN: 042104021
Selected grants: The following grants are a representative sample of this grantmaker's funding activity:
$450,000 to English for New Bostonians, Boston, MA, 2011.
$375,000 to Playworks Boston, Boston, MA, 2011.
$240,000 to Perkins School for the Blind, Watertown, MA, 2011.
$225,000 to Family Independence Initiative, Jamaica Plain, MA, 2013.
$225,000 to Pine Street Inn, Boston, MA, 2012.
$200,000 to Action Center for College Educational Services and Scholarships Foundation, Boston, MA, 2013.
$200,000 to Teach Plus, Boston, MA, 2011.
$184,000 to Boston Plan for Excellence in the Public Schools, Boston, MA, 2013.
$150,000 to Hyde Square Task Force, Jamaica Plain, MA, 2013.
$150,000 to Mothers for Justice and Equality, Roxbury, MA, 2012.
$150,000 to Sociedad Latina, Roxbury, MA, 2011.
$50,000 to Mattapan Food and Fitness Coalition, Mattapan, MA, 2013.

3957
Boston Scientific Foundation, Inc. ✧

1 Boston Scientific Pl., MS B2
Natick, MA 01760-1537 (508) 650-8554
Contact: Jacqueline Boas, Fdn Admin.
FAX: (508) 650-8579;
E-mail: bscifoundation@bsci.com; Main URL: http://www.bostonscientific.com/corporate-citizenship/giving/foundation.html
Foundation Fundamentals Video: http://www.bostonscientific.com/templatedata/imports/multimedia/CorporateResponsibility/12-BSC-126-Foundation-Video.mp4

Established in 2001 in MA.
Donors: Boston Scientific Corp.; John Abele; G. David Jang.
Foundation type: Company-sponsored foundation.
Financial data (yr. ended 12/31/12): Assets, $18,355,968 (M); gifts received, $1,476,151; expenditures, $3,515,251; qualifying distributions, $3,489,251; giving activities include $2,989,840 for 143 grants (high: $400,000; low: $2,750), and $178,600 for 90 grants to individuals (high: $2,000; low: $1,000).
Purpose and activities: The foundation supports programs designed to improve the lives of the economically disadvantaged in the areas of health and education.
Fields of interest: Elementary/secondary education; Higher education; Medical school/education; Education; Hospitals (general); Health care, clinics/centers; Health care; Cancer; Breast cancer; Boys & girls clubs; Youth development; YM/YWCAs & YM/YWHAs; Children/youth, services; Human services; Mathematics; Science; Economically disadvantaged; Homeless.
Type of support: Program development; Curriculum development; Fellowships; Employee volunteer services; Employee-related scholarships.
Limitations: Applications accepted. Giving primarily in areas of company operations in Fremont, San Jose, and Valencia, CA, Spencer, IN, Greater Boston, Marlborough, Natick, and Quincy, MA, and Twin Cities, MN. No support for political or religious organizations or discriminatory organizations. No grants to individuals (except for fellowships and employee-related scholarships), or for general operating support, capital campaigns, event-based fundraising or corporate sponsorships.
Publications: Application guidelines; Annual report.
Application information: Visit website for application address. Support is limited to 1 contribution per organization during any given year. Organizations receiving support are asked to submit a year-end report. Application form required.

Initial approach: Complete online application
Copies of proposal: 1
Deadline(s): None
Board meeting date(s): Quarterly
Final notification: 3 to 6 months

Officers and Directors:* Jean P. Lance,* Pres.; Timothy A. Pratt,* Clerk; Robert J. Castagna,* Treas.; Marilee Grant; Wendy Carruthers.
Number of staff: 1 full-time professional.
EIN: 043556844
Selected grants: The following grants are a representative sample of this grantmaker's funding activity:
$40,000 to Greater Minneapolis Crisis Nursery, Golden Valley, MN, 2013. For the Pediatric Assessment and Medical Management (PAMM) program to provide medical care and health assessments to children staying in the overnight residential child care program, many of whom do not receive regular medical attention and who come from uninsured and underinsured households. Crisis Nursery staff work with professional pediatricians from Partners in Pediatrics to diagnose health problems, prescribe and deliver treatment, and inform parents how to care for any medical and health concerns of their child.
$35,000 to Industry Initiatives for Science and Math Education, Santa Clara, CA, 2013. For Revitalizing Bay Area Science Teachers Project that will provide 45 paid science research Fellowships, including at least five health science focused Fellowships, for middle and high school science teachers this summer. IISME's Summer Fellowship Program provides paid summer internships for teachers in industry, universities and research laboratories. The new curriculum that the teachers develop over the summer is linked to national and state science, technology and math teaching standards, and disseminated widely via IISME's Community Website.
$35,000 to North Metro Pediatrics, Coon Rapids, MN, 2013. For the Healthy Beginnings program, which provides affordable and accessible pediatric care for underserved children in the North Metro. Through this program, families gain greater self-sufficiency, confidence, trust in preventive care, and the desire to form lifelong healthy habits.
$35,000 to Riley Childrens Foundation, Indianapolis, IN, 2013. For Camp Riley, which provides youth ages 8 to 18 with disabilities Indiana's only summer camp experience with 24-hour onsite medical staff in a fully accessible environment. Camp Riley is held at Bradford Woods-Indiana University's universally accessible recreational facility in Martinsville, Indiana.

$30,000 to Migizi Communications, Minneapolis, MN, 2013. For Native Academy (NAC), a high school program focusing on science, technology, and math that has developed into a nationally recognized model for Indian student success. The program currently works with 250 students in high school and has a primary goal of increasing the academic performance, graduation rates, and postsecondary enrollment rates of Indian students.
$25,000 to Playworks Silicon Valley, Campbell, CA, 2013.
$20,000 to Joslin Diabetes Center, Boston, MA, 2013. For Joslin's Black Diabetes Initiative (BDI), to enhance the quality of life and health outcomes for blacks living with diabetes - or those at risk for the disease - through research, education, outreach and improved treatment.
$20,000 to Sociedad Latina, Roxbury, MA, 2013. For Health Educators, a youth-led health education and advocacy program.
$15,000 to Project Kindle, Santa Clarita, CA, 2013. For Kindle Ranch Day Camp, educational camp program to support children from mostly low income families who face various disabilities and special needs. The camp program has projects on math, science, music and art.
$15,000 to Urban Ventures Leadership Foundation, Minneapolis, MN, 2013. For the Urban Ventures Learning Lab, which serves urban students from South Minneapolis in grades 1-8 in year-round (5 days a week after school and 4 full days in summer), out-of-school time providing math, science and reading enrichment in a technology-rich environment.

3958
Bresky Foundation ✧
c/o Seaboard Flour, LLC
1320 Centre St., Ste. 200
Newton Centre, MA 02459-2468

Established in KS.
Donor: Helen A. Bresky.
Foundation type: Independent foundation.
Financial data (yr. ended 12/31/13): Assets, $11,991,365 (M); gifts received, $401,000; expenditures, $453,008; qualifying distributions, $448,690; giving activities include $447,500 for 45 grants (high: $115,000; low: $1,000).
Fields of interest: Human services; Community/economic development.
Limitations: Applications not accepted. Giving primarily in MA; with some giving in Congo.
Application information: Unsolicited requests for funds not accepted.
Officers: Steven J. Bresky, Pres. and Treas.; Helen A. Bresky, V.P.; Patricia A. Bresky, V.P.; Paul Squires, Secy.
EIN: 264784817

3959
The Bressler Family Foundation ✧
(formerly The Alan S. Bressler and Lorraine D. Bressler Foundation)
776 Boylston St., Apt. E10D
Boston, MA 02199

Established in 1997 in MA.
Donors: Alan S. Bressler; Lorraine D. Bressler.
Foundation type: Independent foundation.
Financial data (yr. ended 12/31/13): Assets, $6,459,739 (M); gifts received, $692; expenditures, $698,361; qualifying distributions, $611,500; giving activities include $611,500 for 7 grants (high: $257,000; low: $1,000).
Fields of interest: Museums (art); Education.
Limitations: Applications not accepted. Giving primarily in Boston, MA. No grants to individuals.
Application information: Unsolicited requests for funds not accepted.
Trustees: Daryl Bressler; Karen S. Bressler; Lorraine D. Bressler; Nancy Bressler-Starn.
EIN: 046837456

3960
Bristol County Savings Charitable Foundation Inc. ✧
35 Broadway
Taunton, MA 02780-3120 (508) 828-5393
Contact: Michele L. Roberts, Clerk
Application address: 29 Broadway, 2nd Fl., Taunton, MA 02780, tel.: (508) 828-5393

Established in 1996 in MA.
Donors: Bristol County Savings Bank; BCSB Securities Corp Inc.
Foundation type: Company-sponsored foundation.
Financial data (yr. ended 10/31/13): Assets, $7,230,172 (M); gifts received, $300,460; expenditures, $1,328,703; qualifying distributions, $1,275,890; giving activities include $1,275,820 for 158 grants (high: $110,000; low: $110).
Purpose and activities: The foundation supports historical and zoological societies and organizations involved with education, water resources, health, human services, and community economic development.
Fields of interest: Historic preservation/historical societies; Elementary/secondary education; Higher education; Education; Environment, water resources; Zoos/zoological societies; Hospitals (general); Health care; Boys & girls clubs; Boy scouts; YM/YWCAs & YM/YWHAs; Human services; Community/economic development; United Ways and Federated Giving Programs.
Type of support: Building/renovation; Equipment; Program development; Seed money; Scholarship funds; Matching/challenge support.
Limitations: Applications accepted. Giving limited to the greater Attleboro, Berkley, Dartmouth, Dighton, Fall River, Franklin, New Bedford, North Attleborough, Norton, Plainville, Raynham, Rehoboth, Seekonk, Taunton, Westport, and Wrentham, MA, and Pawtucket, RI. No support for religious organizations. No grants for general operating support.
Publications: Application guidelines.
Application information: Organizations receiving support are asked to submit a final report. Application form required.
Initial approach: Contact foundation for application
Deadline(s): Various
Officers: E. Dennis Kelley, Jr., Chair.; Patrick J. Murray, Jr., Pres.; Michele L. Roberts, Clerk; Dennis F. Leahy, Treas.
Trustees: J. Jerome Coogan; Marjorie L. Largey; Russel F. Martorana; Edward P. Pariseau; Louis M. Ricciardi; Frank Teixeira; Carry P. Terry; Suzanne Withers.
EIN: 043332966
Selected grants: The following grants are a representative sample of this grantmaker's funding activity:
$50,000 to Bridgewater State College, Bridgewater, MA, 2011.
$35,000 to Community Care Services, Taunton, MA, 2011.
$27,000 to Pawtucket Foundation, Pawtucket, RI, 2011.
$25,000 to YMCA of Attleboro, Attleboro, MA, 2011.
$20,000 to Southcoast Hospitals Group, New Bedford, MA, 2011.
$18,000 to Boy Scouts of America, Annawon Council, Norton, MA, 2011.
$13,500 to Old Dartmouth Historical Society, New Bedford, MA, 2011.
$10,000 to Highlander Dunn Institute, Providence, RI, 2011.
$7,500 to Attleboro Area Council of Churches, Attleboro, MA, 2011.
$6,600 to Preparatory Rehabilitation for Individual Development and Employment, Taunton, MA, 2011.

3961
The Bromley Charitable Trust ✧
299 Clapboardtree St.
Westwood, MA 02090-2907

Established in 1994 in MA.
Donors: Duncan M. McFarland; Elizabeth M. McFarland; Ellen B. McFarland.
Foundation type: Independent foundation.
Financial data (yr. ended 12/31/13): Assets, $9,489,102 (M); gifts received, $3,203,688; expenditures, $1,853,466; qualifying distributions, $1,785,517; giving activities include $1,781,775 for 46 grants (high: $50,000; low: $100).
Fields of interest: Elementary/secondary education; Environment, natural resources; Health organizations, association; Human services.
Limitations: Applications not accepted. Giving primarily in MA. No grants to individuals.
Application information: Contributes only to pre-selected organizations.
Trustees: Nancy E. Dempze; Duncan M. McFarland; Ellen B. McFarland; William A. Oates, Jr.
EIN: 043237138
Selected grants: The following grants are a representative sample of this grantmaker's funding activity:
$500,000 to New Profit, Boston, MA, 2011. For general support.
$445,000 to Westwood Land Trust, Westwood, MA, 2011. For general support.
$400,000 to Conservacion Patagonica, Sausalito, CA, 2011. For general support.
$250,000 to New England Wild Flower Society, Framingham, MA, 2011. For general support.
$157,809 to Marion Institute, Marion, MA, 2011. For general support.
$115,000 to William Penn Charter School, Philadelphia, PA, 2011. For general support.
$35,000 to Beacon Academy, Boston, MA, 2011. For general support.
$25,000 to Colby College, Waterville, ME, 2011. For general support.
$25,000 to Epiphany School, Dorchester, MA, 2011. For general support.
$25,000 to Peoples Grocery, Oakland, CA, 2011. For general support.

3962
Brookline Community Foundation ✧
40 Webster Pl.
Brookline, MA 02445 (617) 566-4442
Contact: For grants: Jennifer Lemire, Assoc. Dir., Progs. and Grants
FAX: (617) 505-6848;
E-mail: contact@brooklinecommunity.org; Grant application e-mail: jlemire@brooklinecommunity.org; Main URL: http://www.brooklinecommunity.org
Facebook: http://www.facebook.com/pages/Brookline-Community-Foundation/138661852142
Twitter: http://twitter.com/brooklinecomm

Established in 2005 in MA.
Foundation type: Community foundation.
Financial data (yr. ended 12/31/13): Assets, $6,070,581 (M); gifts received, $1,832,398; expenditures, $1,212,659; giving activities include $615,361 for 11+ grants (high: $305,000).
Purpose and activities: The foundation exists to promote a strong, engaged and inclusive community.
Fields of interest: Arts; Education, early childhood education; Student services/organizations; Education; Environment; Employment; Children, day care; Human services; Community/economic development; Public affairs, citizen participation; General charitable giving; Infants/toddlers; Children/youth; Youth; Aging; Economically disadvantaged.
Type of support: Program development.
Limitations: Applications accepted. Giving primarily in Brookline, MA. No grants to individuals, or for travel or research.
Publications: Application guidelines; Annual report; Grants list.
Application information: Applications may be emailed to the foundation; visit web site for application form and guidelines. Application form required.
Initial approach: Telephone
Deadline(s): July 29
Final notification: Mid-Nov.
Officers and Directors:* Frank Steinfield,* Pres.; Julie Marcus,* V.P.; Ashley Mason, Clerk; Jay Lebed,* Treas.; Jenny Amory, Exec Dir.; Carla Benka; Andrew Bernstein; Judy Bullitt; Gerald Davidson; Alexandra Dorf; John F. Hodgman; Sytske Humphrey; Kristen Jilek; Mini Kolluri; Melissa Langa; Michael Lindstrom; Linda Olson Pehlke; Joanne M. Sullivan; David Wood.
EIN: 042103944

3963
Brooks Family Foundation ✧ ☆
(formerly Brooks Family Charitable Foundation)
20 Walnut St., Ste. 318
Wellesley, MA 02481-2104
Contact: Andrew P. Prague

Established in 2001 in MA.
Donors: James E. Brooks; Mary C. Brooks†.
Foundation type: Independent foundation.
Financial data (yr. ended 06/30/13): Assets, $10,128,044 (M); expenditures, $924,297; qualifying distributions, $825,500; giving activities include $825,500 for 94 grants (high: $255,000; low: $1,000).
Fields of interest: Arts; Higher education; Libraries (public); Community/economic development; United Ways and Federated Giving Programs.
Limitations: Applications not accepted. Giving primarily in ME and NY. No grants to individuals.
Application information: Contributes only to pre-selected organizations.
Trustee: Andrew P. Prague.
Advisory Committee: James E. Brooks; Cherie Wendelken.
EIN: 043582018
Selected grants: The following grants are a representative sample of this grantmaker's funding activity:
$50,000 to Harvard University, Cambridge, MA, 2011.

3964
The Byrnes Family Foundation ✧
c/o Sullivan & Worcester LLP, Attn.: Christopher C. Curtis, Esq.
1 Post Office Sq.
Boston, MA 02109-2106

Established in 1984.
Donors: William L. Byrnes; Mary Elizabeth Byrnes; Randall W. Byrnes.
Foundation type: Independent foundation.
Financial data (yr. ended 12/31/13): Assets, $14,563,023 (M); gifts received, $469,886; expenditures, $762,707; qualifying distributions, $735,566; giving activities include $708,420 for 47 grants (high: $140,675; low: $1,000).
Purpose and activities: Giving primarily for education.
Fields of interest: Elementary/secondary education; Education; Human services; Children/youth, services; Christian agencies & churches.
Limitations: Applications not accepted. Giving primarily in MA. No grants to individuals.
Application information: Contributes only to pre-selected organizations.
Trustees: Mary Elizabeth Byrnes; Randall W. Byrnes; William L. Byrnes.
EIN: 222544803
Selected grants: The following grants are a representative sample of this grantmaker's funding activity:
$75,000 to Saint Ann School, Naples, FL, 2011. For general support.
$10,000 to Alzheimers Support Network, Naples, FL, 2011. For general support.
$10,000 to Boys and Girls Club of Collier County, Naples, FL, 2011. For general support.
$10,000 to Boys Town, Boys Town, NE, 2011. For general support.
$10,000 to Humane Society, Naples, Naples, FL, 2011. For general support.
$10,000 to Neighborhood Health Clinic, Naples, FL, 2011. For general support.
$5,000 to Community Foundation of Collier County, Naples, FL, 2011. For general support.
$5,000 to David Lawrence Foundation for Mental Health, Naples, FL, 2011. For general support.
$5,000 to Navy SEAL Foundation, Virginia Beach, VA, 2011. For general support.
$3,000 to McLean Bible Church, Vienna, VA, 2011. For general support.

3965
Cabbadetus Foundation ✧ ☆
c/o Hemenway & Barnes LLP
P.O. Box 961209
Boston, MA 02196-1209
Contact: Michael Elefante, Tr.

Established in 2007 in MA.
Donor: Martha Robes Revocable Trust.
Foundation type: Independent foundation.
Financial data (yr. ended 12/31/13): Assets, $13,697,608 (M); gifts received, $42,000; expenditures, $635,084; qualifying distributions, $548,284; giving activities include $541,000 for 20 grants (high: $160,000; low: $2,000).
Fields of interest: Arts; Education; Human services.
Limitations: Applications not accepted. Giving primarily in ME, NH, VT, and St. John, U.S. Virgin Islands.
Application information: Unsolicited requests for funds not accepted.
Trustees: Michael B. Elefante; Martha S. Robes.
EIN: 266124255

3966
Cabot Corporation Foundation ✧
2 Seaport Ln., Ste. 1300
Boston, MA 02210-2058 (617) 342-6035
Contact: Jane A. Bell, V.P. and Exec. Dir.; Cynthia L. Gullotti, Clerk
E-mail: jane_bell@cabot-corp.com; Additional Contact: Cynthia L. Gullotii, e-mail: Cynthia_Gullotti@cabot-corp.com; Main URL: http://www.cabot-corp.com/About-Cabot/Corporate-Giving

Incorporated in 1953 in MA.
Donor: Cabot Corp.
Foundation type: Company-sponsored foundation.
Financial data (yr. ended 09/30/13): Assets, $47,100 (M); gifts received, $150,000; expenditures, $638,002; qualifying distributions, $637,502; giving activities include $637,502 for 8 grants (high: $495,000; low: $1,500).
Purpose and activities: The foundation supports organizations involved with education, health, human services, community development, science and technology, and civic affairs.
Fields of interest: Elementary/secondary education; Education, early childhood education; Higher education; Education, reading; Education; Health care; Residential/custodial care, hospices; Human services; Community/economic development; United Ways and Federated Giving Programs; Chemistry; Mathematics; Engineering/technology; Computer science; Biology/life sciences; Science.
Type of support: Publication; General/operating support; Continuing support; Capital campaigns; Building/renovation; Equipment; Program development; Scholarship funds.
Limitations: Applications accepted. Giving primarily in Support is given primarily in areas of company operations in Alpharetta, GA, Tuscola, Il, Franklin, and Ville Platte, LA, Billerica, Boston, and Haverhill, MA, Midland, MI, Boyertown, PA, Pampa, and The Woodlands, TX, and in Argentina, Belgium, Brazil, Canada, China, Columbia, Czech Republic, Dubai, France, Germany, India, Indonesia, Italy, Japan, Malaysia, Mexico, Netherlands, Norway, Spain, Switzerland, Venezuela, and Wales. No support for religious organizations not of direct benefit to the entire community, or political or fraternal

organizations. No grants to individuals, or for capital campaigns or endowments, tickets or tables at fundraising events, or advertising.
Publications: Application guidelines; Annual report.
Application information: Application form required.
Initial approach: Download application form and e-mail proposal and application form to foundation
Copies of proposal: 1
Deadline(s): 30 days prior to board meetings
Board meeting date(s): Jan., Apr., July, and Oct.
Officers and Directors:* Patrick M. Prevost,* Pres.; Jane A. Bell,* V.P. and Exec. Dir.; Karen Abrams, Clerk; James P. Kelly,* Treas.; Christina Bramante; Emilie Geslot-Bonnefoy; Carl D. Long; Patrick M. Prevost; Robby D. Sisco.
EIN: 046035227

3967
Cabot Family Charitable Trust ✧

70 Federal St., 7th Fl.
Boston, MA 02110-1906 (617) 226-7505
Contact: Katherine S. McHugh, Exec. Dir.
FAX: (617) 451-1733;
E-mail: kmchugh@cabwel.com; Main URL: http://www.cabwel.com/cabot_family_charitable_trust_v3.htm

Trust established in 1942 in MA.
Donor: Godfrey L. Cabot‡.
Foundation type: Independent foundation.
Financial data (yr. ended 12/31/13): Assets, $44,176,821 (M); expenditures, $2,188,474; qualifying distributions, $2,021,424; giving activities include $1,705,000 for 78 grants (high: $40,000; low: $7,500).
Purpose and activities: Program includes a wide range of organizations and activities important in Boston, MA, as well as nonprofit programs that represent particular family interests.
Fields of interest: Arts; Education; Environment; Health care; Youth development; Human services; Public affairs; Infants/toddlers; Children/youth; Youth.
Type of support: General/operating support; Capital campaigns; Program development.
Limitations: Applications accepted. Giving primarily in Boston, MA. No support for religious institutions for sectarian purposes, or for fraternal organizations. No grants to individuals, or for research, event sponsorship, or matching gifts.
Publications: Application guidelines; Annual report; Annual report (including application guidelines).
Application information: Concept paper format available on foundation web site. Application form required.
Initial approach: Concept letter (3 pages) with Cabot Family Charitable Trust cover sheet
Copies of proposal: 1
Deadline(s): Feb. 1 and Sept. 1
Board meeting date(s): June and Dec.
Final notification: June and Dec.
Officer and Trustees:* John G.L. Cabot,* Chair.; Frank Bradley; Laura Cabot Carrigan; Mary Schneider Enriquez; Greenfield Sluder; Hendrika Sluder.
Number of staff: 1 part-time professional.
EIN: 046036446
Selected grants: The following grants are a representative sample of this grantmaker's funding activity:
$30,000 to Boston Area Rape Crisis Center, Cambridge, MA, 2011. To support work of local organizations to improve lives of Greater Boston youth.
$30,000 to Boston Debate League, Boston, MA, 2011. For Go Deep Initiative to build large debate teams and train teachers to use debate in classroom in Boston's underserved public schools.
$30,000 to CAST, Inc., Wakefield, MA, 2011. To use innovative technology approaches to teaching algebra to struggling students in Boston area schools.
$30,000 to Health Resources in Action, Boston, MA, 2011. For Family Childcare Provider Environmental Health Training Project.
$25,000 to Bostons Higher Ground, Roxbury, MA, 2011. For parenting program to insure newborns in Warren Gardens community have a healthy and supportive environment.
$25,000 to Community Economic Development Assistance Corporation, Boston, MA, 2011. For captial grants program for emergency and repairs to early childhood care and out-of-school time programs.
$25,000 to Family Nurturing Center of Massachusetts, Dorchester, MA, 2011. For ongoing family and child development program in six communities, with special emphasis on Roxbury.
$25,000 to Hull Lifesaving Museum, Hull, MA, 2011. For Maritime Program for DYS-committed African-American and Latino young men.
$25,000 to Roxbury Preparatory Charter School, Roxbury, MA, 2011. For capital campaign for school expansion.
$25,000 to Young Audiences of Massachusetts, Boston, MA, 2011. For Expanding Horizons Through Music, program to address literacy skill building needs of homeless preschool children in Dorchester.

3968
The Virginia Wellington Cabot Foundation ✧

c/o Cabot-Wellington, LLC
70 Federal St., 7th Fl.
Boston, MA 02110-1906 (617) 451-1855, ext. 204
Contact: Joan M. Whelton, Exec. Dir.
FAX: (857) 239-9724; E-mail: Jowhelton@aol.com; Main URL: http://www.cabwel.com/v_w_cabot_foundation.htm

Established in 1992 in MA.
Donors: Thomas D. Cabot, Jr.; Thomas D. Cabot 1986 Conduit Trust; Thomas D. Cabot 1994 Charitable Lead Unitrust; Virginia W. Cabot Revocable Trust; Virginia W. Cabot 1996 Charitable Lead Unitrust.
Foundation type: Independent foundation.
Financial data (yr. ended 12/31/12): Assets, $34,165,591 (M); expenditures, $1,605,221; qualifying distributions, $1,465,142; giving activities include $1,063,801 for 119 grants (high: $60,000; low: $500).
Purpose and activities: The foundation grants program includes a wide range of organizations and activities that represent particular interests of family members.
Fields of interest: Arts; Higher education; Education; Environment; Youth development; Human services; Public affairs.
Type of support: General/operating support; Annual campaigns; Capital campaigns; Building/renovation; Endowments; Program development; Fellowships; Scholarship funds; Matching/challenge support.
Limitations: Giving in the U.S., primarily in MA and ME. No support for religious or political organizations. No grants for one-time events.
Publications: Application guidelines; Grants list.
Application information: Unsolicited applications are generally not accepted. All grant applications are sponsored by family members who initiate the process. Application form required.
Copies of proposal: 1
Deadline(s): Mar. 1, and Sept. 13
Board meeting date(s): Semiannually
Final notification: 1 week after meeting
Officers: Helen C. McCarthy, Chair.; Laura Cabot Carrigan, Secy.; James W. Cabot, Treas.; Joan M. Whelton, Exec. Dir.
Trustees: Linda C. Black; Sophie C. Black; Alexis Cabot; Amiel Cabot; Bradford W. Cabot; Elizabeth C. Cabot; Timothy Eiserle; Carole Ganz; Alexander McCarthy; Peter Myers.
EIN: 046728351

3969
Calderwood Charitable Foundation ✧

c/o Choate Hall & Stewart LLP
P.O. Box 961019
Boston, MA 02196-1019 (617) 248-4760

Established in 1968 in MA.
Donors: Stanford M. Calderwood; Stanford Calderwood Trust.
Foundation type: Independent foundation.
Financial data (yr. ended 12/31/12): Assets, $29,884,768 (M); expenditures, $5,911,812; qualifying distributions, $5,682,814; giving activities include $5,618,978 for 13 grants (high: $2,350,000; low: $1,000).
Purpose and activities: Giving for the performing arts, as well as to an artists' colony; funding also for higher education, and to an academic library.
Fields of interest: Museums (art); Performing arts, theater; Performing arts, orchestras; Performing arts, opera; Higher education; Libraries (academic/research); Hospitals (general).
Limitations: Applications not accepted. Giving primarily in MA, with emphasis on Boston, Chestnut Hill, and Wesley Hills; some funding also in NH, with emphasis on Greenfield and Peterborough. No grants to individuals.
Application information: Contributes only to pre-selected organizations.
Trustees: John M. Cornish; William A. Lowell.
EIN: 046186166
Selected grants: The following grants are a representative sample of this grantmaker's funding activity:
$2,500,000 to Isabella Stewart Gardner Museum, Boston, MA, 2012. For general support.
$1,000,000 to Museum of Fine Arts, Boston, MA, 2012. For general support.
$1,000,000 to New England Conservatory of Music, Boston, MA, 2012. For general support.
$666,667 to Boston Conservatory of Music, Boston, MA, 2012. For general support.
$250,000 to Boston Lyric Opera Company, Boston, MA, 2012. For general support.
$249,317 to Boston Athenaeum, Boston, MA, 2012. For Calderwood Writing Initiative.
$37,138 to University of Massachusetts, Boston, MA, 2012. For general support.
$25,000 to Boston Baroque, Boston, MA, 2012. For general support.

$20,000 to Emerson College, Boston, MA, 2012. For general support.
$15,000 to Boston Athenaeum, Boston, MA, 2012. For general support.

3970
Caldwell Foundation ✧
c/o Robert G. Stewart, PC
3 Heritage Way, Ste. 1
Gloucester, MA 01930-2275

Established in 1999 in MA.
Donors: Alexander L.M. Dingee; Susan J. Gray.
Foundation type: Independent foundation.
Financial data (yr. ended 12/31/12): Assets, $3,209,336 (M); expenditures, $752,550; qualifying distributions, $752,550; giving activities include $735,145 for 14 grants (high: $334,000; low: $5,000).
Fields of interest: Museums; Higher education; Engineering school/education; Human services; YM/YWCAs & YM/YWHAs; Children/youth, services; Jewish agencies & synagogues.
Limitations: Applications not accepted. Giving primarily in MA. No grants to individuals.
Application information: Unsolicited requests for funds not accepted.
Trustees: Alexander L.M. Dingee; Susan J. Gray; Robert G. Stewart.
EIN: 046902006
Selected grants: The following grants are a representative sample of this grantmaker's funding activity:
$37,500 to Pathways for Children, Gloucester, MA, 2011.
$10,000 to Wellspring House, Gloucester, MA, 2011.
$1,000 to Gloucester Stage Company, Gloucester, MA, 2011.

3971
Cambridge Community Foundation ✧
(formerly The Cambridge Foundation)
99 Bishop Allen Dr.
Cambridge, MA 02139-3428 (617) 576-9966
Contact: Robert S. Hurlbut, Jr., Exec. Dir.
FAX: (617) 864-0920; E-mail: info@cambridgecf.org; Additional e-mail: rhurlbut@cambridgecf.org; Main URL: http://www.cambridgecf.org
Facebook: https://www.facebook.com/CambridgeCCF?fref=ts
Twitter: http://twitter.com/cambridgeccf

Established in 1916 in MA by declaration of trust.
Foundation type: Community foundation.
Financial data (yr. ended 06/30/13): Assets, $32,635,156 (M); gifts received, $532,363; expenditures, $1,899,624; giving activities include $1,125,175 for 66+ grants (high: $80,000).
Purpose and activities: The foundation seeks to promote the mental, moral, and physical welfare of the inhabitants of Cambridge, MA (or elsewhere, if specified by the donor), through grants to community agencies, generally for: 1) social services - child welfare and development, emergency aid, employment and job training, legal assistance, and family services; 2) education - elementary and secondary education and ESL/GED programs; 3) health - hospice and home care, mental health and counseling, and substance abuse programs; and 4) housing and shelter - home improvement and repair, housing development, and shelter and transitional housing. Other areas of focus include gender issues, volunteer services, and community and capacity building.
Fields of interest: Arts; Education; Environment; Health care; Mental health/crisis services; Health organizations, association; Housing/shelter, development; Children/youth, services; Human services; Community/economic development; Infants/toddlers; Aging.
Type of support: General/operating support; Emergency funds; Program development; Seed money; Curriculum development; Scholarship funds; Technical assistance.
Limitations: Applications accepted. Giving primarily in Cambridge, MA, except as specified by donors. No support for municipal, state, or federal agencies, or for religious organizations for religious purposes. No grants for individuals, or for research studies, conferences, films, annual dinners or fundraising events, or capital fund drives; no loans.
Publications: Application guidelines; Annual report; Informational brochure; Program policy statement.
Application information: Visit foundation web site for application form and guidelines. Associated Grant Makers Common Proposal Form accepted. Application form required.
Initial approach: Telephone
Copies of proposal: 10
Deadline(s): Apr. 1 and Oct. 1 for General Fund; Jan. 15, Apr. 15, and Oct. 1 for Cambridge/Agassiz/Harvard Community, Culture, and Recreation Fund
Board meeting date(s): Distribution Committee meets in June and Dec.
Final notification: May and Nov.
Officers and Overseers:* Richard A. Harriman,* Pres.; Paul J. Gallagher,* Treas.; Robert S. Hurlbut, Jr., Exec. Dir.; P.J. Blankenhorn; Linda Chin; Frank Duehay; C. Fritz Foley; Melville T. Hodder; Bob Hower; Phil Johnson; Rosemarie Torres Johnson; Lori Lander; Dora Lewin; Martha B. McKenna; Paul Parravano; William M. Polk; Mary H. Power; Dr. Peter B. Randolph; Mina Reddy; Elizabeth Reid; Nan Stone.
Trustees: Bank of America, N.A.; Cambridge Trust Co.
Number of staff: 2 full-time professional.
EIN: 046012492

3972
Cambridge Savings Charitable Foundation Inc. ✧
1374 Massachusetts Ave.
Cambridge, MA 02138-3822
Contact: Jeri Foutter
E-mail: jfoutter@cambridgesavings.com; Main URL: https://www.cambridgesavings.com/community-relations/foundation/

Established in 2003 in MA.
Donor: 1834 Realty Inc.
Foundation type: Company-sponsored foundation.
Financial data (yr. ended 12/31/13): Assets, $625,077 (M); expenditures, $559,312; qualifying distributions, $559,312; giving activities include $486,925 for 62 grants (high: $50,000; low: $1,000), and $64,500 for 26 grants to individuals (high: $2,500; low: $2,000).
Purpose and activities: The foundation supports organizations involved with the arts and culture, education, health, housing, recreation, human services, and youth and awards college scholarships to graduating high school seniors from Acton, Arlington, Bedford, Belmont, Burlington, Cambridge, Concord, Lexington, Lincoln, Medford, Newton, Somerville, Waltham, Watertown, Winchester, and Woburn.
Fields of interest: Arts; Education; Health care; Housing/shelter; Recreation; Human services; Youth.
Type of support: General/operating support; Annual campaigns; Scholarships—to individuals.
Limitations: Applications accepted. Giving primarily in areas of company operations in Acton, Arlington, Bedford, Belmont, Brookline, Burlington, Cambridge, Concord, Lexington, Lincoln, Medford, Newton, Somerville, Waltham, Watertown, Winchester, and Woburn, MA.
Publications: Application guidelines.
Application information: Support is limited to 1 contribution per organization during any given year. Application form required.
Initial approach: E-mail foundation for application form; contact guidance office of participating schools for scholarships
Deadline(s): Jan. 31, Mar. 31, June 30, and Sept. 30
Board meeting date(s): Quarterly
Officers: Wayne Patenaude, Pres. and C.E.O.; Stephen J. Coukos, Exec. V.P., Genl. Counsel, and Clerk; Susan Lapierre, Sr. V.P.
Directors: Anne Adams Cushman; Charlie Lyons; Robert J. Ramsey; Robert P. Reardon; Robert M. Wilson.
EIN: 481307731
Selected grants: The following grants are a representative sample of this grantmaker's funding activity:
$7,500 to University of Massachusetts, Amherst, MA, 2011.
$3,600 to Cooperative Elder Services, Lexington, MA, 2011.
$2,500 to Boston University, Boston, MA, 2011.
$2,500 to University of Miami, Coral Gables, FL, 2011.
$2,500 to University of New Hampshire, Durham, NH, 2011.
$2,500 to University of Rhode Island, Kingston, RI, 2011.

3973
Cape Cod Five Cents Savings Bank Charitable Trust ✧
P.O. Box 10
Orleans, MA 02653-0010
E-mail: jpollock@capecodfive.com; Additional Tel.: (508) 240-0555; Main URL: https://www.capecodfive.com/home/fou/abt
Grants List: http://www.capecodfive.com/home/fou/ann/fou_cont
YouTube: http://www.youtube.com/watch?v=80tRxP7ACDk&feature=player_embedded#at=14

Established in 1998 in MA.
Donor: Cape Cod Five Cents Savings Bank.
Foundation type: Company-sponsored foundation.
Financial data (yr. ended 12/31/13): Assets, $13,570,377 (M); gifts received, $20,000; expenditures, $738,692; qualifying distributions, $677,960; giving activities include $663,750 for 167 grants (high: $55,000; low: $200).
Purpose and activities: The foundation supports programs designed to address health and elder

services; culture and art including historic heritage; human services including economic development; youth education; conservation and the environment.
Fields of interest: Historic preservation/historical societies; Arts; Elementary/secondary education; Education; Environment, natural resources; Environment; Hospitals (general); Health care; Food banks; Children/youth, services; Residential/custodial care, hospices; Aging, centers/services; Human services; Economic development.
Type of support: Continuing support; Capital campaigns; Building/renovation; Equipment; Program development; Sponsorships.
Limitations: Applications accepted. Giving limited to areas of company operations in MA, with emphasis on Cape Cod and the islands. No support for religious organizations. No grants to individuals, or for travel, social functions, athletic events or activities, annual memberships, or appeals.
Publications: Application guidelines; Annual report.
Application information: Application form required.
Initial approach: Download application form and e-mail or mail to foundation
Copies of proposal: 1
Deadline(s): Feb. 17, May 11, July 13, and Sept. 28
Board meeting date(s): Quarterly
Officers: Dorothy A. Savarese, Chair.; David B. Williard, Secy.; Phillip W. Wong, Treas.; Elliott Carr, Exec. Mgr.
EIN: 043423249
Selected grants: The following grants are a representative sample of this grantmaker's funding activity:
$50,000 to Cape Cod Healthcare Foundation, Hyannis, MA, 2011.
$20,000 to Cape Symphony Orchestra, Yarmouth Port, MA, 2011.
$10,000 to Community Health Center of Cape Cod, Mashpee, MA, 2011.
$10,000 to Family Pantry, Harwich, MA, 2010.
$10,000 to Housing Assistance Corporation, Hyannis, MA, 2011.
$7,500 to CapeAbilities, Hyannis, MA, 2011.
$6,600 to Falmouth Housing Corporation, Falmouth, MA, 2011.
$5,000 to Association to Preserve Cape Cod, Barnstable, MA, 2011.
$5,000 to Brewster Conservation Trust, Brewster, MA, 2011.
$5,000 to Homeless Prevention Council, Orleans, MA, 2011.
$4,000 to Harwich Junior Theater, West Harwich, MA, 2011.

3974
The Cape Cod Foundation ✧
(formerly The Community Foundation of Cape Cod)
259 Willow St.
P.O. Box 406
Yarmouthport, MA 02675-1762 (508) 790-3040
Contact: For grants: Kristin O'Malley, Exec. Dir.
FAX: (508) 790-4069;
E-mail: info@capecodfoundation.org; Additional tel.: (800) 947-2322; Grant and scholarship inquiry e-mail: komalley@capecodfoundation.org; Main URL: http://www.capecodfoundation.org
Blog: http://www.capecodfoundation.org/blog/
E-Newsletter: http://www.capecodfoundation.org/index.php?module=FormExpress&func=display_form&form_id=3
Facebook: https://www.facebook.com/pages/The-Cape-Cod-Foundation/155001554539014
Scholarship e-mail: dbryan@capecodfoundation.org

Established in 1989 in MA.
Foundation type: Community foundation.
Financial data (yr. ended 12/31/13): Assets, $48,423,090 (M); gifts received, $4,901,895; expenditures, $3,121,350; giving activities include $2,524,108 for grants.
Purpose and activities: The foundation seeks to improve community life on Cape Cod through philanthropy and grantmaking. One of the ways this mission is accomplished is by developing permanent and flexible endowment funds to help nonprofit organizations respond to the existing and emerging needs of the Cape. Therefore, the foundation's grantmaking program is broad; grants may be made in the areas of health, human services, the environment, education, the arts, and community development.
Fields of interest: Humanities; Arts; Education; Environment; Health care; Youth development, community service clubs; Youth, services; Human services; Economic development; Nonprofit management; Community/economic development; Economically disadvantaged.
Type of support: General/operating support; Continuing support; Management development/capacity building; Annual campaigns; Equipment; Land acquisition; Emergency funds; Conferences/seminars; Seed money; Scholarship funds; Technical assistance; Consulting services; Grants to individuals; Scholarships—to individuals; In-kind gifts; Matching/challenge support; Student loans—to individuals.
Limitations: Applications accepted. Giving limited to Barnstable County, MA. No grants for capital campaigns or improvements, endowment building, or monuments or memorials.
Publications: Application guidelines; Annual report; Financial statement; Informational brochure; Newsletter.
Application information: Visit foundation web site for application and guidelines per grant type. Faxed or e-mailed applications are not accepted. Associated Grant Makers Common Proposal Form accepted. Application form required.
Initial approach: Complete online application
Deadline(s): General Grant requested on a rolling basis; Oct. 1 for Strategic Focus Grants; varies for others
Board meeting date(s): Bimonthly; Grant Review meetings are held semiannually
Final notification: 6 to 8 weeks for General Grants; 2 to 3 months for Strategic Focus Grants; varies for others
Officers and Directors:* Eileen C. Miskell,* Chair. and Pres.; Henry R. Holden,* Vice-Chair.; James T. Hoeck,* Treas.; Kristin O'Malley,* Exec. Dir.; Matthew J. Bresette,* Clerk; Jake F. Brown II; Larry Capodilupo; Elliott Carr; Thomas Evans; Rev. Thomas M. Nelson; Jennifer S.D. Roberts; Myer R. Singer; Sidney H. Snow; Larry R. Thayer; Sheila Vanderhoef.
Number of staff: 4 full-time professional; 1 full-time support; 1 part-time support.
EIN: 510140462

3975
Patrick Carney Foundation ✧
c/o Claremont Mgmt. Co.
1 Lakeshore Ctr.
Bridgewater, MA 02324-1057 (508) 279-4300
Contact: Kathleen Larisa, Exec. Dir.

Established in 1988 in MA.
Donor: Patrick Carney.
Foundation type: Independent foundation.
Financial data (yr. ended 12/31/13): Assets, $10,533,841 (M); gifts received, $5,041,392; expenditures, $1,471,059; qualifying distributions, $1,335,738; giving activities include $1,314,275 for 122 grants (high: $250,000; low: $100).
Purpose and activities: Giving primarily for education, Roman Catholic churches and organizations, and for health organizations and human services.
Fields of interest: Secondary school/education; Higher education; Education; Health organizations, association; Medical research, institute; Human services; Children/youth, services; Catholic agencies & churches.
Type of support: General/operating support; Annual campaigns; Capital campaigns.
Limitations: Applications accepted. Giving primarily in MA, with emphasis on Chestnut Hill, Dartmouth, and New Bedford. No grants to individuals.
Application information: Application form required.
Initial approach: Letter on organization letterhead
Deadline(s): None
Officer: Kathleen Larisa, Exec. Dir.
Trustees: Lillian Carney; Patrick Carney.
EIN: 046614314
Selected grants: The following grants are a representative sample of this grantmaker's funding activity:
$250,000 to Boston College, Chestnut Hill, MA, 2011.
$50,000 to College of New Rochelle, New Rochelle, NY, 2011. For scholarship.
$32,000 to Massachusetts General Hospital, Boston, MA, 2011.
$18,000 to United Way of Greater New Bedford, New Bedford, MA, 2011. For programming.
$10,000 to Diocese of Palm Beach, Palm Beach Gardens, FL, 2011.
$8,000 to Our Sisters School, New Bedford, MA, 2011. For scholarship.
$5,000 to Society of Jesus of New England, Watertown, MA, 2011. For general operations.
$4,000 to Community Boating Center, New Bedford, MA, 2011. For capital improvements.
$2,500 to CapeAbilities, Hyannis, MA, 2011. For general operations.
$1,000 to United Way of Palm Beach County, Boynton Beach, FL, 2011. For general operations.

3976
Ronald G. Casty Family Foundation ✧
830 Boylston St., Ste. 209
Chestnut Hill, MA 02467-2502

Established in 2004 in MA.
Donor: Ronald G. Gasty.
Foundation type: Independent foundation.
Financial data (yr. ended 12/31/13): Assets, $1,340,811 (M); gifts received, $200,000; expenditures, $625,862; qualifying distributions, $599,878; giving activities include $562,660 for 107 grants (high: $60,000; low: $75).

Fields of interest: Arts; Education; Health organizations; Human services; United Ways and Federated Giving Programs; Jewish agencies & synagogues.
Limitations: Applications not accepted. Giving primarily in MA. No grants to individuals.
Application information: Contributes only to pre-selected organizations.
Trustee: Ronald G. Casty.
EIN: 202003598

3977
The Cedar Street Foundation ✧
50 Congress St., Ste. 832
Boston, MA 02109

Established in 2001 in MA.
Donors: M. Dozier Gardner; Margaret B. Gardner.
Foundation type: Independent foundation.
Financial data (yr. ended 12/31/13): Assets, $11,093,351 (M); expenditures, $543,938; qualifying distributions, $519,936; giving activities include $505,500 for 24 grants (high: $50,000; low: $2,500).
Fields of interest: Libraries (public); Education; Environment; Animals/wildlife; Health care; Cancer; Catholic agencies & churches.
Limitations: Applications not accepted. Giving primarily in MA. No grants to individuals.
Application information: Unsolicited requests for funds not accepted.
Trustees: Dozier L. Gardner; Margaret B. Gardner; M. Dozier Gardner; Grace G. Schoelkopf; Diana G. Vogel.
EIN: 043581722

3978
Cedar Tree Foundation ✧
(formerly David H. Smith Foundation)
100 Franklin St., Ste. 704
Boston, MA 02110-1401 (617) 695-6767
FAX: (617) 695-1919;
E-mail: info@cedartreefound.org; E-mail for letters of inquiry: loi@cedartreefound.org; Main URL: http://www.cedartreefound.org
Grants List: http://www.cedartreefound.org/grants.html

Established in 1994 in DE.
Donors: Dr. David H. Smith†; Andrea L. Smith; Rachel A. Smith; Jennifer L. Smith; Andrea L. Smith Charitable Lead Annuity Trust; Jennifer L. Smith Charitable Lead Annuity Trust; Rachel A. Smith Charitable Lead Annuity Trust; Jody Leader Charitable Lead Annuity Trust; Kristen Leader Charitable Lead Annuity Trust.
Foundation type: Independent foundation.
Financial data (yr. ended 12/31/12): Assets, $99,216,905 (M); expenditures, $9,336,826; qualifying distributions, $8,298,656; giving activities include $7,413,291 for 64 grants (high: $1,045,941; low: $1,000).
Purpose and activities: The foundation focuses on the following areas of concern: sustainable agriculture, environmental education, and environmental health. The foundation will give particular consideration to proposals demonstrating strong elements of environmental justice, and conservation.
Fields of interest: Environment, legal rights; Environment, formal/general education; Environment; Agriculture.
Type of support: Program-related investments/loans; General/operating support.
Limitations: Applications accepted. Giving primarily in NY; some giving nationally. No grants to individuals.
Publications: Grants list.
Application information: Unsolicited proposals are not accepted. Application information available on foundation web site. The foundation will review letters of inquiry and request additional information or a proposal if interested. Letters of inquiry are not accepted via fax.
Initial approach: Letter of inquiry (no more than 3 pages), via e-mail to specified LOI address only
Deadline(s): None
Final notification: One month after LOI is reviewed
Officers: Joan M. Smith, Pres.; Andrea L. Smith, V.P.; Jennifer L. Smith, Clerk; Rachel A. Smith, Treas.; Sophia M Kolehmainen, JD, MPH, Exec. Dir.
EIN: 133601934

3979
Irwin Chafetz Family Charitable Trust ✧ ☆
300 1st Ave., Ste. 300
Needham, MA 02494-2736

Established in 1995 in MA.
Donors: Irwin Chafetz; Howard Chafetz; Laurence Chafetz; Chafetz Group LLC.
Foundation type: Independent foundation.
Financial data (yr. ended 12/31/12): Assets, $37,322 (M); gifts received, $1,290,732; expenditures, $1,343,645; qualifying distributions, $1,343,337; giving activities include $1,343,337 for grants.
Purpose and activities: Giving primarily to Jewish causes and to health organizations; funding also for social services.
Fields of interest: Arts; Education; Medical care, community health systems; Health organizations, association; Human services; Children, services; Jewish federated giving programs; Jewish agencies & synagogues.
Limitations: Applications not accepted. Giving primarily in MA, with emphasis on Boston. No grants to individuals.
Application information: Contributes only to pre-selected organizations.
Trustees: Howard Chafetz; Irwin Chafetz; Laurence Chafetz; Roberta Chafetz.
EIN: 043282073

3980
Charlesbank Homes ✧
c/o Bonanno, Savino & Davies, P.C.
105 Chesnut St., Ste. 32
Needham, MA 02492-2520
Application address: c/o Wesley K. Blair, Brookline Bank, P.O. Box 179179, Boston, MA 02117; tel.: (781) 393-2801

Established in 1911.
Donor: Edwin Ginn†.
Foundation type: Independent foundation.
Financial data (yr. ended 04/30/14): Assets, $17,576,768 (M); expenditures, $906,507; qualifying distributions, $864,512; giving activities include $861,942 for 21 grants (high: $70,500; low: $3,900).
Purpose and activities: Emphasis on bricks and mortar projects for low- and moderate-income housing.
Fields of interest: Housing/shelter.
Type of support: Building/renovation.
Limitations: Applications accepted. Giving primarily in the Boston, MA, area. No support for medically oriented housing/shelter. No grants to individuals, or for operating budgets.
Application information: Application form required.
Initial approach: Letter
Deadline(s): None
Board meeting date(s): Quarterly
Officers and Trustees:* Richard H. Sayre,* Pres.; Philip J. Notopoulos,* V.P. and Secy.; Wesley K. Blair,* Treas.; Thomas W. Cornu; Susan K. Keller; Susan F. Kenney; M. Chrysa Long; George Macomber; Charles J. Maneikis, Jr.; Jeanne Pinado; Kathryn Roy; R. Bruce Taylor.
Number of staff: None.
EIN: 042103755
Selected grants: The following grants are a representative sample of this grantmaker's funding activity:
$50,000 to Project Place, Boston, MA, 2012.
$50,000 to Saint Francis House, Boston, MA, 2012.
$50,000 to Saint Francis House, Boston, MA, 2012.
$5,350 to Associated Grant Makers, Boston, MA, 2012.

3981
Child Relief International Foundation ✧
(formerly The Andrew and Bonnie Weiss Foundation)
58 Commonwealth Ave.
Boston, MA 02116-3003 (617) 262-0071
Contact: Andrew M. Weiss, Tr.

Established in 2004 in MA.
Donors: Andrew M. Weiss; Bonnie K. Weiss.
Foundation type: Independent foundation.
Financial data (yr. ended 12/31/13): Assets, $41,166,625 (M); gifts received, $3,152,217; expenditures, $2,448,547; qualifying distributions, $3,176,808; giving activities include $2,076,808 for 21 grants (high: $450,000; low: $5,000).
Fields of interest: Health care; Children, services; Jewish agencies & synagogues.
Limitations: Applications accepted. Giving primarily in MA and NY.
Application information:
Initial approach: Letter
Deadline(s): None
Trustees: Andrew M. Weiss; Bonnie K. Weiss.
EIN: 206391910

3982
China Medical Board, Inc. ✧
(formerly China Medical Board of New York, Inc.)
2 Arrow St.
Cambridge, MA 02138-5102 (617) 979-8000
Additional address: Rm. 402, Tower 2, China Central Pl., No. 79, Jianguo Rd., Chaoyang, Beijing, 10025, tel.: 010-5969-5071/2/3; Main URL: http://www.chinamedicalboard.org

Incorporated in 1928 in NY.
Donor: The Rockefeller Foundation.
Foundation type: Independent foundation.

Financial data (yr. ended 06/30/13): Assets, $214,363,664 (M); gifts received, $205,163; expenditures, $12,138,134; qualifying distributions, $12,011,207; giving activities include $8,702,202 for 62 grants (high: $567,685; low: $6,154), and $651,270 for 3 foundation-administered programs.
Purpose and activities: The foundation works to catalyze new, evidence-based policies and practices that will lead to improved health outcomes; strengthen the development of professional programs that produce competent graduates to meet the demands of the health sector; reduce disparities in access to health services between rural and urban populations; develop innovative approaches to major public health challenges, such as tobacco control; and expand channels that enable health professionals in China and Asia to more deeply engage in global health exchange and development. Southeast Asia remains a focus of the grantmaker's work and grants to institutions in that region reflect the same integrated themes of health policy systems and sciences, medical education, and rural health.
Fields of interest: Medical school/education; Libraries/library science; Nursing care; Health care; Health organizations, association; Medical research, institute.
International interests: Asia; Eastern Asia; Hong Kong; Indonesia; Malaysia; Philippines; Singapore; Southeastern Asia; Taiwan; Thailand.
Type of support: Endowments; Program development; Conferences/seminars; Publication; Fellowships; Scholarship funds; Research; Technical assistance.
Limitations: Applications not accepted. Giving limited to East and Southeast Asia, including the People's Republic of China, Hong Kong, Indonesia, Korea, Malaysia, the Philippines, Singapore, Taiwan, and Thailand. No support for professional or scientific societies, or research institutes not directly under medical school control. No grants to individuals (except for scholarships and fellowships), or for capital projects.
Publications: Annual report.
Application information: Unsolicited requests for funds not accepted.
Board meeting date(s): June and Dec.
Officers and Trustees:* Mary Brown Bullock, Ph.D.*, Chair.; Lincoln C. Chen,* Pres.; Harvey V. Fineberg; Jane E. Henney, M.D.; Fred Z. Hu; Thomas S. Inui, M.D.; Tom G. Kessinger, Ph.D.; Jeffrey P. Koplan; Wendy Harrison O'Neill; Anthony J. Saich; Jeffrey R. Williams; William Y. Yun.
Number of staff: 2 full-time professional; 3 full-time support.
EIN: 131659619
Selected grants: The following grants are a representative sample of this grantmaker's funding activity:
$567,685 to Institute of International Education, New York, NY, 2013. For Extend IIE's Management of CMB Next Generation Fellows and Faculty Development Awards.
$475,600 to Qinghai Normal University, Xining, China, 2012. For integrating Township-Village Rural Health Services in Three Western China Provinces.
$442,114 to London School of Hygiene and Tropical Medicine, London, England, 2013. For Master Degree training at LSHTM in HPSS related subjects for up to 14 individuals from Chinese grantee School.
$397,390 to Ministry of Health of China, Center for Health Statistics and Information, Beijing, China, 2013. To support Health Policy and System Sciences (HPSS) Residency Training Program.
$375,000 to Xian Jiaotong University, Xian, China, 2012. To innovate community nursing practice.
$375,000 to Xian Jiaotong University, Health Science Center, Xian, China, 2013. For Innovating community nursing practice.
$356,148 to Xian Jiaotong University, Health Science Center, Xian, China, 2012. For appraisal of Human Resources Policies for Rural Health in Western China.
$350,000 to Sichuan University, Chengdu, China, 2013. To support Western China Center for Rural Health Development.
$342,550 to Guangxi Medical University, Nanning, China, 2012. For startup support of Western Rural Health Network.
$300,000 to Peking University, Health Science Center, Beijing, China, 2012. For development of Peking University China Center for Health Development Studies.
$285,615 to Fudan University, Shanghai, China, 2012. For Westlake Forum IV and CMB President's Council.
$279,666 to University of Washington, UW Tower, Seattle, WA, 2013. To support Fellowships in Global Health.
$250,000 to Mahidol University, Nakhon Pathom, Thailand, 2012. For Thailand National Initiative in Health Professional Education and Prince Mahidol Award Conference.
$250,000 to Peking Union Medical College, Beijing, China, 2013. For Start-up of PUMC School of Public Health.
$217,280 to Mahidol University, Nakhon Pathom, Thailand, 2012. For CMB Myanmar postgraduate fellowship program.
$137,500 to Cambridge University, Magdalene College, Cambridge, England, 2012. For study on the history of Transnational Health in Southeast Asia.
$137,500 to Cambridge University, Magdalene College, Cambridge, England, 2013. For study on the history of Transnational Health in Southeast Asia.
$124,850 to Shandong University, Jinan City, China, 2012. For capacity-building in health systems.
$105,420 to National Institute of Public Health, Phnom Penh, Cambodia, 2013. For Southeast Asia - Strengthen its Public Health Master Program.
$100,000 to Central South University, Changsha, China, 2013. For Development of Global Health Programs.

3983
The Chirag Foundation ✧ ☆
(formerly The Singhal Foundation)
c/o Anil and Abha Singhal
265 Kimball Rd.
Carlisle, MA 01741-1037

Established in 1999 in MA.
Donors: Anil Singhal; Abha Singhal.
Foundation type: Independent foundation.
Financial data (yr. ended 12/31/13): Assets, $4,936,747 (M); gifts received, $1,000,397; expenditures, $540,898; qualifying distributions, $438,831; giving activities include $438,831 for 8 grants (high: $250,000; low: $1,000).
Fields of interest: Health care; Health organizations; Human services.
Limitations: Applications not accepted. Giving primarily in MA. No grants to individuals.
Application information: Unsolicited requests for funds not accepted.
Trustees: Abha Singhal; Anil Singhal.
EIN: 046902382

3984
The Chorus, Inc. ✧
c/o Rostam
101 Huntington Ave., Ste. 25
Boston, MA 02199-7603

Established in 2007 in MA.
Donor: Farhad A. Ebrahimi.
Foundation type: Independent foundation.
Financial data (yr. ended 11/30/13): Assets, $3,264,953 (M); gifts received, $896,992; expenditures, $3,146,634; qualifying distributions, $2,775,004; giving activities include $2,775,004 for 78 grants (high: $333,000; low: $250).
Fields of interest: Arts; Environment, energy; Environment; Public affairs.
Type of support: General/operating support.
Limitations: Applications not accepted. Giving primarily in CO, CT, Washington, DC and MA. No grants to individuals.
Application information: Contributes only to pre-selected organizations.
Officers and Director:* Farhad A. Ebrahimi, Pres.; Nina Ross,* V.P. and Clerk; Noeleen Little, Treas.
EIN: 208087695
Selected grants: The following grants are a representative sample of this grantmaker's funding activity:
$50,000 to Friends of the Earth, Washington, DC, 2012. For Better Future Project Challenge Grant.
$50,000 to Mountain Association for Community Economic Development, Berea, KY, 2012. For Research/Evaluation.
$2,500 to New Organizing Institute Education Fund, Washington, DC, 2012. For Challenge Grant.

3985
Citizens Programs Corporation ✧
88 Black Falcon Ave., Ste. 342
Center Lobby
Boston, MA 02210-2431 (617) 338-6300
FAX: (617) 542-4487;
E-mail: inform@citizensenergy.com; Toll Free tel. during Oil-Heat Season: (877) 563-4645; Main URL: http://www.citizensenergy.com

Established in MA.
Donor: Citizens Energy Corp.
Foundation type: Independent foundation.
Financial data (yr. ended 06/30/13): Assets, $7,335,074 (M); gifts received, $332,983; expenditures, $54,683,976; qualifying distributions, $48,263,653; giving activities include $42,386,046 for grants.
Purpose and activities: Giving to provide low-income individuals and charitable organizations with lower cost heating oil.
Fields of interest: Human services.
Application information: Application for heating assistance may be made via telephone during the Oil-Heat Season. See web site to find participating states.
Deadline(s): None
Officers: Joseph P. Kennedy II, Chair. and Pres.; Peter F. Smith, C.O.O.; Ernie Panos, C.F.O.
EIN: 043340251

3986
The John Clarke Trust ✧
c/o US Trust, Bank of America, N.A.
225 Franklin St., MA1-225-04-02
Boston, MA 02110-2804
Contact: Emma Greene, Market Dir.; Charles Tickner
E-mail: ma.ri.grantmaking@ustrust.com; Main URL: https://www.bankofamerica.com/philanthropic/grantmaking.go

Established in 1676 in Rhode Island.
Donor: John Clark†.
Foundation type: Independent foundation.
Financial data (yr. ended 12/31/13): Assets, $9,306,975 (M); expenditures, $515,808; qualifying distributions, $489,109; giving activities include $453,514 for 89 grants (high: $20,000; low: $500).
Purpose and activities: Giving primarily for education and to provide relief to people who are economically disadvantaged.
Fields of interest: Higher education; Education; Health care, clinics/centers; Human services; Children/youth, services; Community/economic development.
Type of support: General/operating support; Equipment; Program development; Curriculum development; Scholarship funds; Matching/challenge support.
Limitations: Applications accepted. Giving primarily in The trustees have established a policy of giving preference to organizations located on Aquidneck Island, RI, and within the East Bay area. However, applications from any RI 501(c)(3) are acceptable. The trustees will consider capital grant requests ONLY from Aquidneck Island.
Application information:
Initial approach: Online
Deadline(s): Apr. 1 and Nov. 1
Trustees: William W. Corcoran, Esq.; Barbara N. Watterson; Bank of America, N.A.
EIN: 056006062
Selected grants: The following grants are a representative sample of this grantmaker's funding activity:
$20,000 to Newport Hospital Foundation, Newport, RI, 2011. For five year grant toward renovation and modernization of the pediatric unit.
$12,800 to Community Preparatory School, Providence, RI, 2011. For annual scholarship fund.
$8,000 to Providence Intown Churches Association, Providence, RI, 2011. For the work of our four program areas: daily Food Pantry, Friday evening Community Meal Site for homeless persons, Homeless Outreach Program and SOAR (SSI/SSDI Outreach and Recovery).
$7,500 to Martin Luther King Community Center, Newport, RI, 2011. For the breakfast meal site and Feed a Friend Food Pantry programs.
$5,000 to Boys Clubs and Girls Clubs of Newport County, Newport, RI, 2011. For Hands-on Science Program.
$5,000 to Hope Clinic, Providence, RI, 2011. For operation of Clinica Esperanza/ Hope Clinic at its new location.
$5,000 to Providence Childrens Museum, Providence, RI, 2011. For AmeriCorps Programs - Learning Clubs and Head Start/Good Start.
$5,000 to Providence Community Library, Providence, RI, 2011. For Citywide Extended Learning Program (CELP).
$5,000 to Rhode Island Philharmonic Orchestra and Music School, East Providence, RI, 2011. For Music for Our Schools Education Concerts for school children of Rhode Island.
$5,000 to YMCA of Greater Providence, Providence, RI, 2011. For Neighbors in Need, Providence Youth Services Branch and Chronic Disease Initiatives Programs.

3987
Clipper Ship Foundation, Inc. ✧
c/o GMA Foundations
77 Summer St., 8th Fl.
Boston, MA 02110-1006 (617) 426-7080
Contact: Katy Fyrberg, Fdn. Asst.
FAX: (617) 426-7087;
E-mail: kfyrberg@gmafoundations.com; Tel. for Katy Fyrberg: (617) 391-3094; Main URL: http://clippershipfoundation.org/
Grants List: http://clippershipfoundation.org/previous-grants/

Established in 1979 in MA.
Donor: David Parmely Weatherhead†.
Foundation type: Independent foundation.
Financial data (yr. ended 10/31/13): Assets, $26,372,461 (M); expenditures, $1,722,883; qualifying distributions, $1,630,651; giving activities include $1,519,500 for 129 grants (high: $80,000; low: $3,500).
Purpose and activities: Giving primarily to public charities that serve the sick and poor residents of the Greater Boston, MA, community and the cities of Brockton and Lawrence. Preference is given to organizations devoted to helping: 1) the homeless and under-housed; 2) people in need; 3) children; 4) elders; 5) people with disabilities; 6) new immigrant populations; and 7) low-income communities and neighborhoods. Consideration is also given to emergency disaster situations, worldwide.
Fields of interest: Food services; Food banks; Housing/shelter, development; Disasters, preparedness/services; Human services; Children/youth, services; Aging, centers/services; Minorities/immigrants, centers/services; Homeless, human services; Community/economic development; Public affairs; Aging; Disabilities, people with; Minorities; Homeless.
Type of support: General/operating support; Continuing support; Capital campaigns; Building/renovation; Equipment; Emergency funds; Program development; Technical assistance; Consulting services; Matching/challenge support.
Limitations: Applications accepted. Giving primarily in Brockton, Lawrence, and the greater Boston, MA, area (in cities and towns lying on or within Rte. 128). No support for religion, hospitals, higher education, legal services, or advocacy programs. No grants to individuals, campaigns for endowment funds; for the production of motion pictures, television, video tapes or film strips; for conferences or conventions; for consulting, research, scholarships, fellowships, student loans or travel; for the writing or publishing of books or articles.
Publications: Application guidelines; Annual report (including application guidelines); Grants list; Informational brochure (including application guidelines).
Application information: The foundation prefers that the applying organization's Executive Director register with the foundation as the main contact. Proposals sent by e-mail or U.S. mail will not be accepted. Application form required.
Initial approach: Use online registration and application forms on foundation web site only
Copies of proposal: 1
Deadline(s): See foundation web site for current deadlines
Board meeting date(s): Jan, Apr., July, and Oct.
Final notification: Within 2 months
Officers and Directors:* Benjamin H. Lacy,* Chair.; Kay B. Frishman,* Pres.; Katy Fyrberg,* Clerk; Kathleen O'Connor,* Treas.; Brooks A. Ames; Celia Grant; Donald J. Greene; Brian S. Kelley; Mayra Rodriguez-Howard; Bryan Spence; Christine Swistro.
Number of staff: 1 part-time professional.
EIN: 042687384

3988
Cogan Family Foundation ✧
c/o Choate LLP
P.O. Box 961019
Boston, MA 02196-1019

Established in 2000 in MA.
Donor: John F. Cogan, Jr.
Foundation type: Independent foundation.
Financial data (yr. ended 08/31/13): Assets, $21,310,225 (M); expenditures, $1,197,830; qualifying distributions, $1,010,700; giving activities include $1,010,000 for 94 grants (high: $50,000; low: $2,500).
Purpose and activities: Giving primarily for education and for human services; funding also for the arts.
Fields of interest: Performing arts, orchestras; Arts; Education; Health care; Human services; Children/youth, services; United Ways and Federated Giving Programs.
Limitations: Applications not accepted. Giving primarily in CA, MA, and NY. No grants to individuals.
Application information: Contributes only to pre-selected organizations.
Trustees: Gregory Cogan; John F. Cogan, Jr.; Jonathan Cogan; Peter G. Cogan; Mary Cornille; Pamela Cogan Riddle.
EIN: 046923387
Selected grants: The following grants are a representative sample of this grantmaker's funding activity:
$30,000 to New Israel Fund, Washington, DC, 2011. For general fund.
$30,000 to Ploughshares Fund, San Francisco, CA, 2011. For general fund.
$20,000 to Feeding America, Chicago, IL, 2011. For general fund.
$20,000 to Habitat for Humanity International, Americus, GA, 2011. For general fund.
$20,000 to National Public Radio, Washington, DC, 2011. For general fund.
$10,000 to Ashoka: Innovators for the Public, Arlington, VA, 2011. For general fund.
$10,000 to Reach Out and Read, Boston, MA, 2011. For general fund.
$10,000 to Seeds of Peace, New York, NY, 2011. For general fund.
$5,000 to American Friends Service Committee, Philadelphia, PA, 2011. For general fund.
$4,000 to Summer Search Foundation, San Francisco, CA, 2011. For general fund.

3989
Colombe Foundation ✧
15 Research Dr., Ste. B
Amherst, MA 01002-2776
FAX: (413) 256-0349; E-mail: info@proteusfund.org; Contact for new applicants: Dini Merz, Prog. Dir.: tel.: (203) 439-0076, e-mail: dmerz@proteusfund.org; Contact for current grantees: Beery Adams Jimenez, Grants Mgr., tel.: (413) 256-0349, ext. 12, e-mail: grantsmanager@proteusfund.org; Main URL: http://www.proteusfund.org/programs/colombe-foundation

Established in 1996 in DE.
Donor: Edith W. Allen.
Foundation type: Independent foundation.
Financial data (yr. ended 06/30/13): Assets, $30,293,012 (M); expenditures, $2,482,262; qualifying distributions, $2,052,000; giving activities include $2,052,000 for 26 grants (high: $460,000; low: $7,000).
Purpose and activities: The foundation supports organizations that are: 1) working for the elimination of weapons of mass destruction; 2) advocating for foreign policy that is balanced with diplomacy and prevention rather than dominated by war and aggression; and 3) supporting a shift from wasteful military spending to investments in programs that create real national security, grounded in environmental protection, alternative energy, education and human services. The foundation's current grantmaking priorities are: 1) changing U.S. policy with regards to nuclear weapons disarmament and non-proliferation and complex transformation; 2) shifting the priorities of the military budget; and 3) ending the wars in Afghanistan and Iraq.
Fields of interest: Education, public education; Environment, research; International affairs, information services; International peace/security; Social sciences, public policy; Social sciences, government agencies; Social sciences, formal/general education; Political science.
Limitations: Applications accepted. Giving primarily in Washington, DC. No grants to individuals, or for research, conferences, or films/documentaries.
Publications: Application guidelines; Grants list.
Application information:
Initial approach: Telephone or e-mail to Dina Merz to discuss proposal prior to submitting an application; Current grantees should contact Beery Adams Jimenez for current guidelines
Copies of proposal: 2
Deadline(s): See foundation web site for latest deadlines
Final notification: Spring and fall
Officers: Edith W. Allen, Pres.; Frederick Allen, Secy.
EIN: 137103356
Selected grants: The following grants are a representative sample of this grantmaker's funding activity:
$85,000 to National Priorities Project, Northampton, MA, 2013. For general purposes.

3990
Community Foundation for Nantucket ✧ ☆
P.O. Box 204
Nantucket, MA 02554 (508) 825-9993
Contact: Margaretta Andrews, Exec. Dir.
FAX: (508) 228-4098; E-mail: info@cfnan.org; Main URL: http://www.cfnan.com
Facebook: https://www.facebook.com/CommunityFoundationforNantucket?fref=ts

Established in 2005 in MA.
Foundation type: Community foundation.
Financial data (yr. ended 12/31/13): Assets, $2,850,231 (M); gifts received, $1,497,894; expenditures, $1,061,187; giving activities include $456,177 for 13+ grants (high: $120,695).
Purpose and activities: The foundation seeks to connect people who care with causes that matter by providing simple, powerful and creative ways to give back to the community to help ensue Nantucket's vitality now and forever.
Fields of interest: Arts; Education; Environment; Human services; Community/economic development.
Application information: Visit foundation's web site for application form and guidelines. Application form required.
Initial approach: Submit application form
Copies of proposal: 1
Deadline(s): Oct. 22
Officers and Directors:* Phillip F. Stambaugh,* Pres.; Marsha Egan,* V.P., Comms. and Mktg.; Joe Hale,* V.P., Devel.; Marsha Kotalac,* V.P., Grants and Nonprofits; Melissa Philbrick,* V.P., Governance; Susan Ottison,* Secy.; Victoria McManus,* Treas.; Margaretta Andrews, Exec. Dir.; Jim Bennett; Dr. Bill Frist; Robin L. Harvey; Ellen Hoeffel; Hudson Holland III; Rev. Dr. Gary Klingsporn; Zeldy Lyman; Tom Maggs; Magdalena Padzik; Geoffrey J. Smith; E. Geoffrey Verney.
EIN: 134316755

3991
Community Foundation of Southeastern Massachusetts ✧
30 Cornell St.
New Bedford, MA 02740 (508) 996-8253
Contact: Craig J. Dutra, Pres.
FAX: (508) 996-8254; E-mail: info@cfsema.org; Additional e-mail: cdutra@cfsema.org; Main URL: http://www.cfsema.org
Facebook: http://www.facebook.com/pages/Community-Foundation-of-Southeastern-Massachusetts/323838137171

Established in 1995 in MA.
Foundation type: Community foundation.
Financial data (yr. ended 12/31/13): Assets, $32,186,222 (M); gifts received, $3,483,260; expenditures, $4,465,475; giving activities include $2,402,731 for 63+ grants (high: $199,550), and $186,300 for 109 grants to individuals.
Purpose and activities: The foundation seeks to support programs that improve the quality of life for residents of the 41 towns and cities in Southeastern MA.
Fields of interest: Historic preservation/historical societies; Arts; Child development, education; Education; Environment; Health care; Mental health, treatment; Medical research, institute; Housing/shelter; Disasters, preparedness/services; Children/youth, services; Children, services; Child development, services; Family services; Human services; Economic development; Community/economic development; Leadership development.
Type of support: Technical assistance; General/operating support; Management development/capacity building; Building/renovation; Emergency funds; Program development; Seed money; Scholarship funds.
Limitations: Applications accepted. Giving primarily in southeastern MA.
Publications: Financial statement; Informational brochure; Multi-year report.
Application information: Visit the foundation's web site for more information on current requests for proposals.
Deadline(s): Varies
Board meeting date(s): Monthly
Officers and Directors:* Edward G. Siegal, C.P.A.*, Chair.; Seth Garfield,* Vice-Chair.; Craig J. Dutra,* Pres.; June A. Smith, Esq.*, Clerk; Mary Louise Nunes,* Treas.; Linda Bondenmann, Asst. Clerk; Elizabeth Isherwood, Asst. Treas.; Kim Clark, Dir. Emeritus; Peter C. Bogle, Esq.; Terry Boyle; Peter Bullard; Carl J. Cruz; Matthew J. Downey; Paul C. Downey; Sr. Kathleen Harrington; James S. Hughes; Gerry Kavanaugh; Richard L. Lafrance; Thomas F. Lyons; Deborah A. McLaughlin; Joan Menard; George Oliveira; Eric H. Strand; Leonard W. Sullivan; Dr. Paul Vivino; Dean Robert V. Ward.
Number of staff: 3 full-time professional; 1 full-time support; 1 part-time support.
EIN: 043280353

3992
Community Foundation of Western Massachusetts ✧
1500 Main St., Ste. 2300
P.O. Box 15769
Springfield, MA 01115-1000 (413) 732-2858
Contact: Katie Allan Zobel, C.E.O.; For grants: Sheila Toto, Prog. Off.
FAX: (413) 733-8565;
E-mail: wmass@communityfoundation.org; Additional e-mail: rancrum@communityfoundation.org; Grant information e-mails: stoto@communityfoundation.org and grants@communityfoundation.org; Grant information tel.: (413) 732-2858; Main URL: http://www.communityfoundation.org
LinkedIn: http://www.linkedin.com/companies/community-foundation-of-western-massachusetts
Scholarship e-mail: scholar@communityfoundation.org

Established in 1991 in MA.
Foundation type: Community foundation.
Financial data (yr. ended 03/31/14): Assets, $114,293,627 (M); gifts received, $7,874,113; expenditures, $9,064,965; giving activities include $7,230,039 for 228 grants (high: $510,000).
Purpose and activities: The foundation seeks to enrich the quality of life of the people of Hampden, Hampshire, and Franklin counties in Western Massachusetts by: 1) encouraging philanthropy; 2) developing a permanent, flexible endowment; assessing and responding to emerging and changing needs; 3) serving as a resource, catalyst, and coordinator for charitable activities; and 4) promoting efficiency in the management of charitable funds.
Fields of interest: Performing arts; Historic preservation/historical societies; Arts; Education, fund raising/fund distribution; Adult/continuing education; Adult education—literacy, basic skills & GED; Libraries/library science; Education, reading; Education; Environment, natural resources; Environment; Animals/wildlife, preservation/protection; Hospitals (general); Reproductive health,

family planning; Medical care, rehabilitation; Health care; Substance abuse, services; Health organizations, association; Cancer; Heart & circulatory diseases; AIDS; Crime/violence prevention, youth; Crime/law enforcement; Housing/shelter, development; Safety/disasters; Recreation; Children/youth, services; Aging, centers/services; Women, centers/services; Minorities/immigrants, centers/services; Human services; Civil/human rights; Community/economic development; Voluntarism promotion; Public policy, research; Public affairs; Aging; Disabilities, people with; Minorities; Native Americans/American Indians; Women; Economically disadvantaged; LGBTQ.
Type of support: Continuing support; Management development/capacity building; Capital campaigns; Building/renovation; Equipment; Land acquisition; Program development; Conferences/seminars; Publication; Seed money; Technical assistance; Program evaluation; Scholarships—to individuals; Matching/challenge support; Student loans—to individuals.
Limitations: Applications accepted. Giving limited to western MA, including Franklin County, Hampden County, and Hampshire County. No support for religious purposes, or private education unless broad community needs are served. No grants to individuals directly, or for endowments, fundraising events, tickets for benefits, courtesy advertising, academic or medical research or multi-year funding.
Publications: Application guidelines; Grants list; Informational brochure; Newsletter.
Application information: Visit foundation web site for application cover page, guidelines, and specific deadlines. Faxed or e-mailed applications are not accepted. Application form required.
Initial approach: Attend a Grant Orientation Session
Copies of proposal: 3
Deadline(s): Feb. 23 for Mission Standard Grants
Board meeting date(s): Bimonthly
Final notification: Within 4 months
Officers and Trustees:* Dana R. Barrows,* Chair.; Ralph Tate,* Vice-Chair.; Katie Allen Zobel, C.E.O. and Pres.; Kristin Leutz, V.P., Philanthropic Svcs.; Nancy Reiche, V.P., Progs.; George Arwady; Peter J. Daboul; Kerry Dietz; Dianne Fuller Doherty; Karin George; Dr. Willie Hill, Jr.; Amy Jamrog; Terry Jenoure; George C. Keady III; Ellen Brout Lindsey; Irene Rodriguez Martin; Steven M. Mitus; David Pinsky; Dr. Robert Pura; Elizabeth H. Sillin; Richard B. Steele, Jr.
Number of staff: 4 full-time professional; 3 part-time professional; 5 full-time support.
EIN: 223089640
Selected grants: The following grants are a representative sample of this grantmaker's funding activity:
$303,200 to University of Massachusetts, Amherst, MA, 2012. For scholarships.
$279,814 to Baystate Health Foundation, Springfield, MA, 2012. For general health.
$175,674 to Berkshire Children and Families, Pittsfield, MA, 2012.
$141,000 to West Cummington Congregation Church, Cummington, MA, 2012.
$61,412 to Springfield Symphony Orchestra, Springfield, MA, 2012.
$20,000 to Monson Home for Aged People, Monson, MA, 2012.
$15,183 to Saint John Lutheran Church, Westfield, MA, 2012.
$13,300 to Earthdance Creative Living Project, Plainfield, MA, 2012.
$12,427 to Urban League of Springfield, Springfield, MA, 2012.
$10,750 to Cornell University, Ithaca, NY, 2012.

3993
Conservation, Food and Health Foundation, Inc. ✧

77 Summer St., 8th Fl.
Boston, MA 02110-1006 (617) 391-3092
Contact: Prentice Zinn, Admin.
FAX: (617) 426-7087;
E-mail: pzinn@gmafoundations.com; Main URL: http://cfhfoundation.grantsmanagement08.com/
Grants List: http://cfhfoundation.grantsmanagement08.com/?page_id=8

Established in 1985 in MA.
Foundation type: Independent foundation.
Financial data (yr. ended 12/31/12): Assets, $15,995,635 (M); expenditures, $1,984,147; qualifying distributions, $1,014,616; giving activities include $976,787 for 43 grants (high: $50,000; low: $6,678).
Purpose and activities: The purpose of the foundation is to assist in the conservation of natural resources, the production and distribution of food, and the improvement and promotion of health in the developing world. The foundation is especially interested in supporting projects which lead to the transfer of responsibility to the citizens of developing countries for managing and solving their own problems and for developing the capacity of local organizations. Preference will be given to projects, including research projects, in areas that tend to be under-funded.
Fields of interest: Environment, natural resources; Environment; Animals/wildlife, preservation/protection; Health care; Agriculture; Agriculture/food.
International interests: Developing Countries.
Type of support: Program development; Seed money; Research; Technical assistance.
Limitations: Giving to benefit developing countries. No support for famine, emergency relief, direct delivery of medical care, or for overhead expenses of large institutions. No grants to individuals (except for research efforts sponsored by organizations and institutions), or for building or land purchase, endowments, fundraising activities, scholarships, tuition, and travel grants or general operating support.
Publications: Application guidelines; Grants list.
Application information: Faxed or e-mailed proposals will not be accepted. In order to try to reduce the number of applicants who are turned down for lack of available funds, and to save time loss and expense to the applicants, the foundation has adopted a 2-phase application system, comprised of a short concept application, followed by a limited number of full proposals, at the invitation of the foundation. This system is designed to screen out, at the concept application level, projects which appear unlikely to receive final funding. Application guidelines available on foundation web site. Application form required.
Initial approach: Submit concept application through the online application system on foundation web site
Copies of proposal: 5
Deadline(s): See foundation web site for current deadlines
Board meeting date(s): May and Nov.
Final notification: June 1 and Dec. 1
Officer: Philip M. Fearnside, Pres.
EIN: 222625024

3994
Copeland Family Foundation, Inc. ✧

1183 Randolph Ave.
Milton, MA 02186-5264

Established in 1983 in MA.
Foundation type: Independent foundation.
Financial data (yr. ended 12/31/13): Assets, $40,211,201 (M); expenditures, $2,228,145; qualifying distributions, $1,614,432; giving activities include $1,428,912 for 98 grants (high: $301,575; low: $900).
Purpose and activities: Giving primarily for education, animal welfare, hospitals, health associations, human services, community development, and Christian agencies and churches.
Fields of interest: Education; Animal welfare; Hospitals (general); Health organizations, association; Food services; Human services; Children/youth, services; Community/economic development; Christian agencies & churches.
Limitations: Applications accepted. Giving primarily in MA, with emphasis on Milton.
Application information: Application form required.
Initial approach: Letter
Deadline(s): None
Officers: Martha Verdone, Pres.; Joyce Tobin, Clerk; John Tobin, Treas.
Directors: Mary Gormley; George P. Moran; Raymond G. Pelissier; Richard G. Wells, Jr.
EIN: 222474056

3995
The John and Mary Corcoran Family Foundation ✧

(formerly The 1991 Corcoran Foundation)
100 Grandview Rd., Ste. 207
Braintree, MA 02184-2600

Established in 1991 in MA.
Donor: John M. Corcoran†.
Foundation type: Independent foundation.
Financial data (yr. ended 12/31/13): Assets, $94,207,890 (M); expenditures, $3,936,490; qualifying distributions, $3,237,609; giving activities include $2,982,533 for 15 grants (high: $2,478,123; low: $3,500).
Fields of interest: Elementary/secondary education; Human services; Philanthropy/voluntarism.
Limitations: Applications not accepted. Giving primarily in Boston, MA. No grants to individuals.
Application information: Contributes only to pre-selected organizations.
Trustees: John M. Corcoran, Jr.; Thomas M. Corcoran.
EIN: 046689934

3996
Robert Lloyd Corkin Charitable Foundation ✧
c/o The Entwistle Co.
6 Bigelow St.
Hudson, MA 01749-2697

Established in 1985 in RI.
Donors: John J. Bradley; Howab Trust; Global Securities, Inc.; The Entwistle Company.
Foundation type: Independent foundation.
Financial data (yr. ended 12/31/12): Assets, $23,222,856 (M); expenditures, $1,245,154; qualifying distributions, $1,074,550; giving activities include $1,074,550 for 26 grants (high: $210,000; low: $200).
Purpose and activities: Giving primarily for education, health care, particularly a children's hospital, human services, and to Jewish agencies and temples.
Fields of interest: Education; Hospitals (specialty); Health care; Human services; Jewish agencies & synagogues.
Limitations: Applications not accepted. Giving primarily in MA; funding also in FL. No grants to individuals.
Application information: Contributes only to pre-selected organizations.
Trustees: Dale F. Eck; Marjorie C. Kaplan; Thomas O. Katz; Lee Manning.
Officer: Mary Lou Sullivan, Admin.
EIN: 056022654

3997
The Cosette Charitable Fund ✧
c/o Ropes & Gray, LLP
800 Boylston St.
Boston, MA 02199-3600

Established in 1997 in MA.
Donors: Patti B. Saris; Arthur I. Segel.
Foundation type: Independent foundation.
Financial data (yr. ended 12/31/13): Assets, $11,072,476 (M); gifts received, $2,990,690; expenditures, $6,081,911; qualifying distributions, $6,054,304; giving activities include $6,047,500 for 34 grants (high: $5,000,000; low: $1,000).
Purpose and activities: Giving primarily for Jewish agencies and higher education.
Fields of interest: Performing arts, orchestras; Education, public policy; Higher education; Education; Human services; Jewish federated giving programs; Jewish agencies & synagogues.
Type of support: General/operating support; Management development/capacity building; Program development.
Limitations: Applications not accepted. Giving primarily in the greater Boston, MA, area. No grants to individuals.
Application information: Contributes only to pre-selected organizations.
Trustees: Patti B. Saris; Arthur I. Segel; Robert N. Shapiro.
EIN: 043416880

3998
Josephine and Louise Crane Foundation, Inc. ✧
220 Main St., Ste. 202
P.O. Box 901
Falmouth, MA 02540-2729

Established in 2008 in MA as a result of the merger of the Josephine B. Crane Foundation and Louise Crane Foundation.
Foundation type: Independent foundation.
Financial data (yr. ended 12/31/12): Assets, $69,115,231 (M); expenditures, $3,578,159; qualifying distributions, $3,250,517; giving activities include $3,250,000 for 66 grants (high: $250,000; low: $5,000).
Fields of interest: Arts; Health organizations; Human services; United Ways and Federated Giving Programs.
Limitations: Applications not accepted. Giving primarily in MA, with some emphasis on the Boston area and Pittsfield.
Application information: Contributes only to pre-selected organizations.
Officers and Directors:* Davis Crane Greene,* Pres.; Winnie Crane Mackey,* V.P.; William K. Mackey,* Secy.-Treas.; Amy L. Greene; Josephine B. Greene; Winnie Greene; William T. Mackey.
EIN: 208970284

3999
Crimson Lion Foundation ✧
c/o Jacqueline R. McCoy
31 St. James Ave., Ste. 740
Boston, MA 02116-4186

Established in 2007 in MA.
Donor: Jonathan S. Lavine.
Foundation type: Independent foundation.
Financial data (yr. ended 12/31/12): Assets, $17,892,584 (M); gifts received, $8,298,863; expenditures, $631,681; qualifying distributions, $500,000; giving activities include $500,000 for 2 grants (high: $250,000; low: $250,000).
Purpose and activities: Giving primarily to a children's hospital, and to other youth services; funding also for a venture philanthropy fund.
Fields of interest: Hospitals (specialty); Children/youth, services; Philanthropy/voluntarism.
Limitations: Applications not accepted.
Application information: Unsolicited requests for funds not accepted.
Trustees: Jeanne B. Lavine; Jonathan S. Lavine; Jacqueline R. McCoy.
EIN: 261388142

4000
The Croll Foundation ✧
c/o Goodwin, Proctor, LLP
Exchange Pl.
53 State St
Boston, MA 02109-2881

Established in 1987 in MA.
Donors: David D. Croll; Victoria B. Croll.
Foundation type: Independent foundation.
Financial data (yr. ended 10/31/13): Assets, $18,177,715 (M); expenditures, $2,791,423; qualifying distributions, $2,638,250; giving activities include $2,638,250 for 81 grants (high: $1,000,000; low: $100).
Fields of interest: Museums; Museums (art); Secondary school/education; Higher education; Education; Hospitals (general); Human services.
Type of support: Scholarship funds.
Limitations: Applications not accepted. Giving primarily in MA, with some emphasis on Boston. No grants to individuals.
Application information: Contributes only to pre-selected organizations.
Trustees: David D. Croll; Victoria B. Croll.
EIN: 222946282

4001
The Cross Foundation ✧ ☆
284 Mattison Dr.
Concord, MA 01742-4147

Established in 2000 in MA.
Donors: Robert Lawrence; Connie Lawrence.
Foundation type: Independent foundation.
Financial data (yr. ended 12/31/13): Assets, $4,660,390 (M); expenditures, $729,797; qualifying distributions, $726,647; giving activities include $723,147 for 5 grants (high: $686,807; low: $1,600).
Fields of interest: Education; Youth development; Human services; Religion.
Limitations: Applications not accepted. Giving primarily in MA and MD. No grants to individuals.
Application information: Unsolicited requests for funds not accepted.
Trustees: Kelly Lawrence Anderson; Lars D. Anderson; Connie Lawrence; Robert Lawrence.
EIN: 043526349

4002
The Crotty Family Foundation, Inc. ✧
c/o Battery Global Advisors
1 Marina Park Dr., Ste. 1150
Boston, MA 02210-1880

Established in MA.
Donors: Thomas J. Crotty; Sharolyn K. Crotty.
Foundation type: Independent foundation.
Financial data (yr. ended 12/31/13): Assets, $1,393,177 (M); gifts received, $1,728,605; expenditures, $2,247,553; qualifying distributions, $2,177,820; giving activities include $2,177,820 for 23 grants (high: $1,400,000; low: $25).
Purpose and activities: Giving primarily for education and human services.
Fields of interest: Education; Health organizations; Human services.
Limitations: Applications not accepted. Giving primarily in MA; some funding also in Albuquerque, NM. No grants to individuals.
Application information: Contributes only to pre-selected organizations.
Officers: Thomas J. Crotty, Pres.; Sharolyn K. Crotty, Clerk.
EIN: 830368529

4003
Cummings Foundation, Inc. ✧ ☆
(formerly New Horizons at Choate, Inc.)
200 W. Cummings Park
Woburn, MA 01801-6333
Main URL: http://www.cummingsfoundation.org/
Joyce and WIlliam Cummings' Giving Pledge Profile: http://glasspockets.org/philanthropy-in-focus/eye-on-the-giving-pledge/profiles/cummings

Established in 1986 in MA; In 2002 the foundation changed its name from New Horizons at Choate.
Donors: Joyce M. Cummings; William S. Cummings; Marilyn Morris; James Morris; Cummings Properties

Foundation; W.S. Cummings Realty Trust; J. & M. Forsyth; WSCR LLC; WDKMP LLC; Partners Healthcare System; Woburn Properties LLP; Patricia A. Cu; Jason Z. Morris; Patricia A. Cummings.
Foundation type: Operating foundation.
Financial data (yr. ended 12/31/13): Assets, $1,085,901,102 (M); gifts received, $1,003,853; expenditures, $76,506,699; qualifying distributions, $71,442,133; giving activities include $769,155 for 77 grants (high: $105,000; low: $50), and $70,435,839 for foundation-administered programs.
Fields of interest: Education; Human services; Philanthropy/voluntarism.
Type of support: Scholarships—to individuals; Scholarship funds.
Limitations: Applications not accepted. Giving primarily in MA.
Application information: Unsolicited requests for funds not accepted.
Officers and Trustees:* William S. Cummings,* Pres.; Joel B. Swets, Exec. Dir.; Joseph A. Abate, M.D.; Hon. Margot Botsford; Paul C. Casey; Joyce M. Cummings; Patricia A. Cummings; Carol A. Donovan; Arlan F. Fuller, Jr.; Deborah T. Kochevar; Anthony P. Monaco; Jason A. Morris; Marilyn Cummings Morris; Richard Ockerbloom; Michael H. Pascavage.
EIN: 043073023

4004
Currents of Change, Inc. ✧
(formerly Common Stream)
P.O. Box 300757
Jamaica Plain, MA 02130 (617) 522-6858
E-mail: peter@commonstream.org; Main URL: http://www.commonstream.org
Grants Database: http://commonstream.org/grants

Established in MA.
Foundation type: Independent foundation.
Financial data (yr. ended 12/31/12): Assets, $23,871,344 (M); expenditures, $1,823,621; qualifying distributions, $1,687,653; giving activities include $1,451,000 for 61 grants (high: $60,000; low: $1,000).
Purpose and activities: Giving primarily for the defense of wild areas, environmental and economic justice, youth organizing, and LGBT rights.
Fields of interest: Environment; Human services; LGBTQ.
Limitations: Applications not accepted. Giving primarily in MA and NY. No grants to individuals.
Application information: Contributes only to pre-selected organizations.
Officers: Julia Satti Cosentino, Pres.; Robert D. Webb, Clerk; Mary Ryan, Treas.
EIN: 721556093

4005
Melvin S. Cutler Charitable Foundation ✧ ☆
c/o Greenberg, Rosenblatt, Kull & Bitsoli, P.C.
306 Main St., Ste. 400
Worcester, MA 01615-0034

Established in 1980 in MA.
Donors: Cutler Assocs., Inc.; Melvin S. Cutler.
Foundation type: Independent foundation.
Financial data (yr. ended 07/31/13): Assets, $11,577,277 (M); gifts received, $100; expenditures, $734,133; qualifying distributions, $556,415; giving activities include $556,415 for 418 grants (high: $100,000; low: $50).
Purpose and activities: Giving primarily for education, health organizations, human services, and Jewish organizations.
Fields of interest: Education; Health organizations, association; Human services; Children/youth, services; United Ways and Federated Giving Programs; Jewish federated giving programs; Jewish agencies & synagogues.
Limitations: Applications not accepted. Giving primarily in MA. No grants to individuals.
Application information: Contributes only to pre-selected organizations.
Officer: Barbara Crosbie, Secy.
Trustees: Robert Adler; Douglas Cutler; Elizabeth J. Cutler; Melvin S. Cutler; Frederic Mulligan.
EIN: 042733957
Selected grants: The following grants are a representative sample of this grantmaker's funding activity:
$1,300 to University of Massachusetts Medical School, Worcester, MA, 2011. For general support.
$1,250 to Saint Jude Childrens Research Hospital, Memphis, TN, 2011. For general support.

4006
Theodore H. Cutler Family Charitable Trust ✧ ☆
300 1st Ave., Ste. 300
Needham, MA 02494-2703

Established in 1994 in MA.
Donors: Theodore H. Cutler; Robert Cutler; Joan H. Cutler.
Foundation type: Independent foundation.
Financial data (yr. ended 12/31/12): Assets, $1,054,798 (M); expenditures, $431,866; qualifying distributions, $431,579; giving activities include $431,579 for grants.
Purpose and activities: Giving primarily for the arts, education, health, and Jewish organizations.
Fields of interest: Arts; Education; Human services.
Limitations: Applications not accepted. Giving primarily in the Boston, MA, area.
Application information: Contributes only to pre-selected organizations.
Trustee: Theodore H. Cutler.
EIN: 046773335

4007
The Dalessandro Foundation ✧ ☆
c/o Hemenway & Barnes
P.O. Box 961209
Boston, MA 02196-1209

Donors: Frances C. Dalessandro‡; John J. Dalessandro‡; Trust For Alfie.
Foundation type: Independent foundation.
Financial data (yr. ended 03/31/13): Assets, $9,166,481 (M); gifts received, $1,937; expenditures, $566,814; qualifying distributions, $443,948; giving activities include $437,500 for 11 grants (high: $177,500; low: $5,000).
Fields of interest: Education; Health care; Human services; Foundations (public).
Limitations: Applications not accepted. Giving primarily in NY; funding also in OH.
Application information: Unsolicited requests for funds not accepted.
Trustees: Robert McCann; Walter D. O'Hearn, Jr.; Arthur B. Page; Timothy C. Withers.
EIN: 270210702

4008
Herman Dana Charitable Trust ✧
1340 Centre St., Ste. 101
Newton, MA 02459-2453 (617) 928-1700
Contact: Myer R. Dana, Tr.

Established in 1969 in MA.
Donor: Herman Dana‡.
Foundation type: Independent foundation.
Financial data (yr. ended 12/31/13): Assets, $19,348,153 (M); expenditures, $2,389,527; qualifying distributions, $1,273,394; giving activities include $1,189,496 for 23 grants (high: $154,200; low: $1,380).
Purpose and activities: Grants to participating organizations of the Combined Jewish Philanthropies of greater Boston, MA, for capital purposes or urgent current needs, domestic organizations doing overseas work, and Jewish charitable or educational institutions; support also for organizations and institutions, with the grant to be used for the cost of psychiatric care and counseling of undergraduate students at Harvard University.
Fields of interest: Education; Hospitals (general); Human services; International relief; Jewish federated giving programs; Jewish agencies & synagogues.
Limitations: Applications accepted. Giving primarily in MA; some funding in NY and OK. No grants to individuals.
Application information: Application form not required.
Initial approach: Letter
Copies of proposal: 2
Deadline(s): None
Final notification: 10-15 days
Trustees: Alan G. Dana; Myer R. Dana.
EIN: 046209497
Selected grants: The following grants are a representative sample of this grantmaker's funding activity:
$2,500 to FJC, New York, NY, 2012. For Project Zug.

4009
The Danversbank Charitable Foundation, Inc. ✧
1 Conant St.
Danvers, MA 01923-2902 (978) 739-0211
Contact: Rebecca Skerry, Lead Admin. Asst.
FAX: (978) 739-4998;
E-mail: rebecca.skerry@peoples.com; Main URL: https://www.peoples.com/peoples/Footer/About-People's-United/In-The-Community/Charitable-Giving

Established in 2007 in MA.
Donor: Danversbank.
Foundation type: Company-sponsored foundation.
Financial data (yr. ended 12/31/13): Assets, $14,236,615 (M); expenditures, $582,464; qualifying distributions, $578,464; giving activities include $567,475 for 77 grants (high: $30,000; low: $1,000).
Purpose and activities: The foundation supports nonprofit organizations involved with arts and culture, education, health, affordable housing,

human services, and low and moderate income individuals.
Fields of interest: Arts; Secondary school/ education; Higher education; Libraries (public); Education, services; Education; Health care, clinics/ centers; Speech/hearing centers; Health care; Housing/shelter; YM/YWCAs & YM/YWHAs; Youth, services; Developmentally disabled, centers & services; Human services; Economically disadvantaged.
Type of support: Building/renovation; Scholarship funds; General/operating support; Continuing support; Capital campaigns; Program development.
Limitations: Applications accepted. Giving primarily in areas of company operations in Andover, Beverly, Boston, Boxford, Burlington, Chelsea, Danvers, Hamilton, Ipswich, Lynnfield, Malden, Middleton, Newbury, Newburyport, North Andover, North Reading, Peabody, Reading, Revere, Rowley, Salem, Saugus, Topsfield, Wakefield, Wenham, Wilmington and Woburn, MA. No support for political, religious, labor, or discriminatory organizations, or foundations, or governmental agencies. No grants to individuals, or for operating deficits, conferences or seminars, trips or tours including transportation costs, foundations, or annual appeals.
Publications: Application guidelines; Annual report; IRS Form 990 or 990-PF printed copy available upon request.
Application information: Support is limited to 1 contribution per organization during any given year. Multi-year funding is not automatic. Organizations receiving support are asked to submit a final report. Application form required.

Initial approach: Complete online application
Copies of proposal: 1
Deadline(s): Monthly for Neighborhood Fund; Feb. 1, June. 1, and Oct. 1 for Danversbank Grant Program and Malden Community Fund
Board meeting date(s): Mar., June, and Nov.
Final notification: 30 days after board meetings for Danversbank Grant Program and Malden Community Fund

Officers and Directors:* Kevin T. Bottomley,* Pres.; Thomas Ford,* Clerk; Anthony Petrazzuoli,* Treas.; Ralph Ardiff; Diane C. Brinkley; Timothy Crimmins; John T. Dawley; Matt Hegarty; Eleanor M. Hersey; Richard Larkin; J. Michael O'Brien; John M. Pereira; Diane T. Stringer.
EIN: 260814452
Selected grants: The following grants are a representative sample of this grantmaker's funding activity:
$30,000 to North Shore Medical Center, Salem, MA, 2012. For Best Care, Right Place Capital Campaign toward the Mass General/North Shore Center for Outpatient Care.
$20,000 to North Shore Community College Foundation, Danvers, MA, 2012. For Investing in a Sustainable North Shore.
$15,000 to Montserrat College of Art, Beverly, MA, 2012. For ITP-Website.
$15,000 to YMCA of the North Shore, Beverly, MA, 2012. For Y Financial Assistance Fund.
$10,000 to Career Collaborative, Boston, MA, 2012. For Job Search Course.
$10,000 to Massachusetts Coalition for the Homeless, Lynn, MA, 2012. For TeenCare Initiative.
$7,500 to Plummer Home for Boys, Salem, MA, 2012. For On Point.
$5,000 to Asian American Civic Association, Boston, MA, 2012. For youth employment center.
$5,000 to Horizons for Homeless Children, Roxbury, MA, 2012. For Community Children's Center.
$5,000 to Northeast Health System, Beverly, MA, 2012. For Young Moms Program.

4010
The Davis Family Foundation ✧ ☆

7 Wyndemere Dr.
Southborough, MA 01772-1110

Established in 1999 in MA.
Donor: Robert J. Davis.
Foundation type: Independent foundation.
Financial data (yr. ended 12/31/12): Assets, $1,737,018 (M); gifts received, $1,501,990; expenditures, $550,850; qualifying distributions, $546,020; giving activities include $546,020 for grants.
Fields of interest: Education; Hospitals (general); Food banks; Athletics/sports, baseball; Children, services; Christian agencies & churches.
Limitations: Applications not accepted. Giving primarily in MA. No grants to individuals.
Application information: Unsolicited requests for funds not accepted.
Trustees: Rita M. Davis; Robert J. Davis.
EIN: 046907384

4011
Irene E. and George A. Davis Foundation ✧

1 Monarch Pl., Ste. 1300
Springfield, MA 01144-4011 (413) 734-8336
Contact: Mary E. Walachy, Exec. Dir.
FAX: (413) 734-7845; E-mail: info@davisfdn.org; Additional e-mail (for Mary E. Walachy): mwalachy@davisfdn.org; Main URL: http://www.davisfdn.org
Join E-mail List: http://www.davisfdn.org/matriarch/default.asp

Established in 1970 in MA.
Foundation type: Independent foundation.
Financial data (yr. ended 12/31/13): Assets, $111,740,094 (M); gifts received, $546,506; expenditures, $3,734,707; qualifying distributions, $3,363,300; giving activities include $2,890,156 for 156 grants (high: $400,000; low: $200).
Purpose and activities: The mission of the foundation is to support the development of Hampden County, MA, children, youth and families by insuring that they have the opportunities needed to achieve their full potential. The foundation accomplishes this by: 1) investing in a continuum of services with a particular focus on young children, ages birth through 8, while at the same time, sustaining these early investments through a variety of learning supports and experiences for youth ages 9 through 18; and 2) a holistic approach that encompasses the social, emotional, physical and cognitive needs of children and youth, and supports them within the context of their families.
Fields of interest: Arts; Elementary/secondary education; Education, early childhood education; Health care; Human services; Infants/toddlers; Children/youth; Children; Minorities; Economically disadvantaged.
Type of support: General/operating support; Continuing support; Management development/ capacity building; Annual campaigns; Capital campaigns; Building/renovation; Equipment; Land acquisition; Emergency funds; Program development; Seed money; Technical assistance; Consulting services; Program evaluation; Matching/ challenge support.
Limitations: Applications accepted. Giving generally limited to Hampden County, MA. No support for other private foundations. No grants to individuals, or for scholarships, internships, continuing support of current programs, debt reduction or endowments; no program-related investments or loans.
Publications: Application guidelines.
Application information: All submissions must be done on-line at foundation web site. Application form required.

Initial approach: Online application form
Deadline(s): Feb. 1, May 1, Aug. 1, and Nov. 1 for grants
Board meeting date(s): Mar., June, Sept., and Dec.
Final notification: 2 weeks after board meeting

Officer: Mary E. Walachy, Exec. Dir.
Trustees: John H. Davis; Stephen A. Davis; Jane Davis-Kusek.
Number of staff: 3 full-time professional.
EIN: 263713735

4012
Charles F. De Ganahl Family Foundation ✧ ☆

c/o Rinet Company, LLC
101 Federal St., 14th Fl.
Boston, MA 02110-1859

Established in 2005 in MA.
Foundation type: Independent foundation.
Financial data (yr. ended 12/31/13): Assets, $9,868,121 (M); expenditures, $584,038; qualifying distributions, $505,000; giving activities include $505,000 for 12 grants (high: $150,000; low: $5,000).
Fields of interest: Education; Science; Christian agencies & churches.
Limitations: Applications not accepted. Giving in the U.S., with emphasis on CT, FL, MA, OR and RI. No grants to individuals.
Application information: Contributes only to pre-selected organizations.
Trustees: Frank A. De Ganahl; Patrick B. Maraghy; Rebecca R. Pouliot.
EIN: 206099876

4013
V. Eugene and Rosalie DeFreitas Charitable Foundation ✧ ☆

c/o Eastern Bank & Trust Co.
605 Broadway, LF41
Saugus, MA 01906-3200 (781) 581-4211
Contact: James Rich, Sr. V.P.

Established in 1994 in MA.
Donors: V. Eugene DeFreitas; Rosalie DeFreitas.
Foundation type: Independent foundation.
Financial data (yr. ended 11/30/13): Assets, $10,696,389 (M); expenditures, $557,245; qualifying distributions, $488,693; giving activities include $450,000 for 11 grants (high: $50,000; low: $20,000).
Purpose and activities: Support to colleges and seminaries without regard to religious denomination within the Christian beliefs, for the purpose of teaching and training Christian missionaries. Preference is given to the teaching and training of ministers for foreign missions.

Fields of interest: Elementary/secondary education; Theological school/education; Christian agencies & churches.
Type of support: Endowments.
Limitations: Applications accepted. Giving primarily in Saugus, MA. No grants to individuals.
Application information: Application form required.
Initial approach: Request application form
Deadline(s): None
Board meeting date(s): Nov.
Trustee: Eastern Bank.
EIN: 046714542

4014
Demoulas Foundation ✧
286 Chelmsford St.
Chelmsford, MA 01824-2403 (978) 244-1024
Contact: Arthur T. Demoulas, Tr.

Established in 1964 in MA.
Donors: Demoulas Super Markets, Inc.; Members of the Demoulas family.
Foundation type: Company-sponsored foundation.
Financial data (yr. ended 12/31/13): Assets, $29,687,427 (M); expenditures, $1,583,662; qualifying distributions, $1,551,412; giving activities include $1,504,094 for 131 grants (high: $265,000).
Purpose and activities: The foundation supports hospitals and organizations involved with arts and culture, education, cancer, human services, and religion.
Fields of interest: Higher education; Education; Hospitals (general); Medical care, rehabilitation; Health care; Cancer; Boys & girls clubs; Residential/custodial care, hospices; Human services; Religion.
Type of support: General/operating support; Annual campaigns; Endowments; Program development; Scholarship funds.
Limitations: Applications accepted. Giving primarily in MA.
Application information: Application form required.
Initial approach: Letter
Deadline(s): None
Trustee: Arthur T. Demoulas.
EIN: 042723441
Selected grants: The following grants are a representative sample of this grantmaker's funding activity:
$20,000 to Boston College, Chestnut Hill, MA, 2011.
$10,000 to University of Massachusetts, Lowell, MA, 2011.
$7,500 to United Negro College Fund, Fairfax, VA, 2011.
$2,500 to American Heart Association, Dallas, TX, 2011.

4015
Telemachus A. and Irene Demoulas Foundation ✧
286 Chelmsford St.
Chelmsford, MA 01824-2403 (978) 244-1024
Contact: Arthur T. Demoulas, Tr.

Established in 2001 in MA.
Donors: Telemachus A. Demoulas‡; Irene Demoulas; Arthur T. Demoulas; Frances Demoulas Kettenbach; Glorianne Demoulas Farnham; Caren Demoulas Pasquale.
Foundation type: Independent foundation.
Financial data (yr. ended 12/31/13): Assets, $58,562,282 (M); gifts received, $215,000; expenditures, $3,180,705; qualifying distributions, $3,161,625; giving activities include $3,125,000 for 21 grants (high: $800,000; low: $10,000).
Fields of interest: Higher education; Education; Hospitals (general); Boys & girls clubs; Community/economic development; Orthodox agencies & churches.
Limitations: Applications accepted. Giving primarily in MA. No grants to individuals.
Application information: Application form required.
Initial approach: Letter
Deadline(s): None
Trustees: Arthur T. Demoulas; Irene Demoulas; D. Harold Sullivan.
EIN: 043582759

4016
DentaQuest Foundation ✧
(formerly Oral Health Services Foundation, Inc.)
465 Medford St.
Boston, MA 02129-1454 (617) 886-1700
Contact: Andrea Forscht, Grants and Progs. Assoc.
FAX: (617) 886-1799;
E-mail: andrea.forscht@dentaquestfoundation.org; Additional contact: Mathew Bond, Mgr., Grants and Progs., e-mail: mathew.bond@dentaquestfoundation.org; Main URL: http://www.dentaquestfoundation.org/
Grants Database: http://dentaquestfoundation.org/impact/search
Oral Health Matters: http://oralhealthmatters.blogspot.com/

Established in 2000 in MA.
Donors: Dental Services of Massachusetts Inc.; Delta Dental Plan of Massachusetts.
Foundation type: Company-sponsored foundation.
Financial data (yr. ended 12/31/12): Assets, $85,651,234 (M); gifts received, $25,625,000; expenditures, $12,989,345; qualifying distributions, $12,810,931; giving activities include $9,518,845 for 85 grants (high: $380,000; low: $500).
Purpose and activities: The foundation supports programs designed to improve oral health. Special emphasis is directed toward public policy that improves oral health; increased public and private funding for oral health initiatives; improved delivery of oral health care and prevention; and community engagement on oral health issues.
Fields of interest: Dental school/education; Health care, management/technical assistance; Health care, public policy; Health care, equal rights; Medicine/medical care, public education; Health care, clinics/centers; Dental care; Health care, insurance; Health care; Children/youth, services; Children; Economically disadvantaged.
Type of support: Continuing support; Management development/capacity building; Building/renovation; Equipment; Program development; Technical assistance; Sponsorships.
Limitations: Applications accepted. Giving primarily in areas of company operations, with emphasis on FL, IL, MA, and MD; giving also to national organizations. No support for lobbying organizations. No grants to individuals, or for scholarships, general overhead or indirect costs, capital campaigns, debt reduction, or endowments.
Publications: Application guidelines; Annual report; Grants list; Program policy statement.
Application information: A full proposal may be requested at a later date for Oral Health 2020 and Innovation Fund for Oral Health.
Initial approach: Complete online concept form for Oral Health 2020, Community Response Fund, President Fund, and Innovation Fund for Oral Health
Deadline(s): None
Officers and Directors:* Caswell A. Evans, Jr., DDS, MPH*, Chair.; Michael McPherson, Vice-Chair.; Ralph Fuccillo, MA*, Pres.; Myra Green, Clerk; Scott Frock, Treas.; Alice Huan-mei Chen, MD, MPH; Jamie Collins; Harold D. Cox, MSSW; Fay Donohue; Shephard Goldstein, DMD; Leslie E. Grant, DDS, MSPA; Donald J. Kenney; Linda C. Niessen, DMD, MPH, MPP; Alonzo L. Plough, Ph.D., MPH; Norman A. Tinanoff, DDS; Mary Vallier-Kaplan, MHSA.
EIN: 043265080

4017
Devonshire Foundation ✧
(formerly Devonshire Associates)
c/o Howland Capital Management
75 Federal St., Ste. 1100
Boston, MA 02110-1911

Incorporated in 1949 in MA.
Donors: Melita S. Howland‡; Weston Howland, Jr.; Weston Howland III; Susan H. Power; Melita S. & Weston Howland Trust; Cedar Funding Trust.
Foundation type: Independent foundation.
Financial data (yr. ended 12/31/13): Assets, $47,099,975 (M); gifts received, $90,365; expenditures, $1,102,396; qualifying distributions, $878,693; giving activities include $878,693 for 13 grants (high: $271,000; low: $1,500).
Fields of interest: Higher education; Environment, research; Hospitals (general); Children/youth, services; Philanthropy/voluntarism.
Limitations: Applications not accepted. Giving primarily in MA. No grants to individuals.
Application information: Contributes only to pre-selected organizations.
Officer: Weston Howland III, Pres. and Treas.
Trustee: Charles E. Clapp III.
EIN: 046004808

4018
The Dibner Charitable Trust of Massachusetts ✧
151 Laurel Rd.
Chestnut Hill, MA 02467-2210

Established in 2006 in MA.
Donor: The Dibner Fund, Inc.
Foundation type: Independent foundation.
Financial data (yr. ended 12/31/13): Assets, $22,044,516 (M); expenditures, $1,227,646; qualifying distributions, $1,000,968; giving activities include $966,700 for 31 grants (high: $160,000; low: $1,000).
Fields of interest: Human services.
Limitations: Applications not accepted. No grants to individuals.
Application information: Contributes only to pre-selected organizations.
Trustees: Brent Dibner; Rachel Dibner.
EIN: 205112548

4019
The Dinovi Family Foundation ✧
3 Ravine Rd.
Wellesley, MA 02481

Established in 2003 in MA.
Donors: Anthony J. Dinovi; Deanna L. Dinovi.
Foundation type: Independent foundation.
Financial data (yr. ended 12/31/12): Assets, $5,563,718 (M); gifts received, $4,029,106; expenditures, $913,680; qualifying distributions, $881,250; giving activities include $881,000 for 22 grants (high: $425,000; low: $500).
Purpose and activities: Giving primarily for education, as well as to a children's hospital.
Fields of interest: Elementary/secondary education; Higher education; Hospitals (specialty); Human services.
Limitations: Applications not accepted. Giving primarily in MA. No grants to individuals.
Application information: Contributes only to pre-selected organizations.
Trustees: Anthony J. Dinovi; Deanna L. Dinovi.
EIN: 200011660

4020
The Dintersmith-Hazard Foundation ✧ ☆
c/o Paul McCoy Family
31 St. James Ave., Ste. 740
Boston, MA 02116-4121

Established in 2000 in MA.
Donors: Ted R. Dintersmith; Elizabeth Hazard.
Foundation type: Independent foundation.
Financial data (yr. ended 12/31/13): Assets, $3,287,064 (M); gifts received, $186,498; expenditures, $907,919; qualifying distributions, $844,500; giving activities include $844,500 for 30 grants (high: $200,000; low: $100).
Fields of interest: Higher education; Education; Human services; Foundations (private grantmaking).
Limitations: Applications not accepted. Giving in the U.S., with emphasis on CA, MA, and NY. No grants to individuals.
Application information: Unsolicited requests for funds not accepted.
Trustees: Ted R. Dintersmith; Elizabeth S. Hazard.
EIN: 043538497

4021
The Diomedes Foundation ✧ ☆
c/o John W. Boynton, IV, Firehouse Capital
33 Bradford St.
Concord, MA 01742-2986

Established in MA.
Donors: John W. Boynton IV; Johanna N. Boynton; James E. Gowen II; Judith R. Neilson.
Foundation type: Independent foundation.
Financial data (yr. ended 12/31/13): Assets, $6,774,041 (M); gifts received, $19,562; expenditures, $1,528,828; qualifying distributions, $1,515,154; giving activities include $1,515,154 for 2 grants (high: $1,513,154; low: $2,000).
Fields of interest: Higher education, university.
Limitations: Applications not accepted. Giving primarily in MA.
Application information: Unsolicited requests for funds not accepted.
Trustees: James E. Gowen II; Johanna N. Boynton; John W. Boynton IV.
EIN: 461451480

4022
The Doe Family Foundation ✧
540 Main St., No. 3
Winchester, MA 01890-2940 (781) 729-0951

Donor: Shirley B. Doe Trust 2004.
Foundation type: Independent foundation.
Financial data (yr. ended 12/31/12): Assets, $38,403,482 (M); gifts received, $1,129,863; expenditures, $2,503,214; qualifying distributions, $1,749,173; giving activities include $1,749,173 for grants.
Fields of interest: Education.
Limitations: Giving primarily in NH; some funding also in MA.
Application information:
Initial approach: Letter
Deadline(s): June 1 and Dec. 1
Trustee: Barbara Doe; Charles F. Doe, Jr.; Dana G. Doe; William Doe; Amy Doe Noordzij; Deborah Doe Wamsher.
EIN: 266126856

4023
Richard K. & Nancy L. Donahue Charitable Foundation ✧
52 Belmont Ave.
Lowell, MA 01852-2865
Contact: Nancy L. Donahue, Tr.
E-mail: nldonahue@comcast.net

Established in 1991 in MA.
Donors: Richard K. Donahue; Nancy L. Donahue.
Foundation type: Independent foundation.
Financial data (yr. ended 12/31/13): Assets, $3,390,170 (M); expenditures, $828,934; qualifying distributions, $818,000; giving activities include $818,000 for 30 grants (high: $150,000; low: $1,500).
Purpose and activities: Giving for the arts, education, and human services.
Fields of interest: Museums; Performing arts, theater; Arts; Higher education; Education; Foundations (community).
Type of support: General/operating support; Continuing support; Annual campaigns; Capital campaigns; Endowments; Debt reduction; Professorships; Curriculum development; Scholarship funds; Matching/challenge support.
Limitations: Applications accepted. Giving primarily in the greater Lowell, MA, area. No support for political organizations or lobbying groups. No grants to individuals.
Application information: Application form not required.
Initial approach: Letter
Copies of proposal: 3
Deadline(s): None
Board meeting date(s): Varies
Final notification: 2 weeks
Trustees: David W. Donahue; Nancy L. Donahue; Richard K. Donahue, Jr.
Number of staff: None.
EIN: 043133049

4024
Doran Family Charitable Trust ✧
c/o Hemenway & Barnes LLP
P.O. Box 961209
Boston, MA 02196-1209

Established in 1986 in MA.
Donor: Robert W. Doran.
Foundation type: Independent foundation.
Financial data (yr. ended 12/31/13): Assets, $3,176,373 (M); expenditures, $1,874,485; qualifying distributions, $1,759,255; giving activities include $1,757,500 for 17 grants (high: $250,000; low: $7,500).
Purpose and activities: Giving primarily for the arts, particularly a university's art gallery, as well as for conservation, social services, and animals and wildlife.
Fields of interest: Museums (art); Arts; Education; Environment; Human services.
Limitations: Applications not accepted. Giving primarily in MA. No grants to individuals.
Application information: Contributes only to pre-selected organizations.
Trustees: Evelyn H. Doran; Robert W. Doran.
EIN: 226424850

4025
Duniry Foundation ✧
c/o Choate LLP
P.O. Box 961019
Boston, MA 02196-1019

Established in 1993 in MA.
Donor: William P. Egan.
Foundation type: Independent foundation.
Financial data (yr. ended 09/30/13): Assets, $10,127,331 (M); expenditures, $548,774; qualifying distributions, $478,749; giving activities include $461,400 for 22 grants (high: $125,000; low: $50,000).
Purpose and activities: Giving primarily for higher education, health care, and human services.
Fields of interest: Museums (art); Performing arts, orchestras; Education, public education; Higher education; Education; Hospitals (general); Health care; Boys & girls clubs; Human services; United Ways and Federated Giving Programs; Catholic agencies & churches.
Limitations: Applications not accepted. Giving primarily in CT, MA, and RI. No grants to individuals.
Application information: Contributes only to pre-selected organizations.
Trustees: Charles A. Cheever; William P. Egan.
EIN: 046746970
Selected grants: The following grants are a representative sample of this grantmaker's funding activity:
$25,000 to Fairfield University, Fairfield, CT, 2011. For general support.
$25,000 to Isabella Stewart Gardner Museum, Boston, MA, 2011. For general support.
$21,000 to Saint Sebastians School, Needham, MA, 2011. For general support.
$15,000 to Villanova University, Villanova, PA, 2011. For general support.
$10,000 to Catholic Schools Foundation, Boston, MA, 2011. For general support.
$10,000 to Cystic Fibrosis Foundation, Atlanta, GA, 2011. For general support.
$10,000 to Hope Funds for Cancer Research, Newport, RI, 2011. For general support.

$10,000 to HopeFound, Jamaica Plain, MA, 2011. For general support.
$10,000 to Newport Art Museum and Art Association, Newport, RI, 2011. For general support.
$5,000 to Newport Hospital Foundation, Newport, RI, 2011. For general support.

4026
The Dunkin' Donuts & Baskin-Robbins Community Foundation, Inc. ✧

(formerly Dunkin' Brands Community Foundation)
c/o CSR Dept.
130 Royall St.
2 West A
Canton, MA 02021-1010 (781) 737-3946
Contact: Christine Riley, Dir.
E-mail: foundation@dunkinbrands.com; Main URL: http://www.dunkinbrands.com/Foundation/
Grants List: http://www.dunkinbrands.com/Foundation/page.aspx?section=about&page=grants

Donors: Ashapura, Inc., Inc.; Dunkin Brands Inc.
Foundation type: Company-sponsored foundation.
Financial data (yr. ended 12/31/13): Assets, $3,408,881 (M); gifts received, $2,480,743; expenditures, $1,630,838; qualifying distributions, $802,463; giving activities include $802,463 for 91 grants (high: $100,000; low: $437).
Purpose and activities: The foundation supports programs designed to serve the basic needs of the community. Special emphasis is directed toward programs designed to address food, safety, and children's health.
Fields of interest: Hospitals (general); Health care; Food services; Food banks; Disasters, fire prevention/control; Safety/disasters; Children, services; Human services; Military/veterans' organizations; Children.
Type of support: Scholarship funds; General/operating support.
Limitations: Applications not accepted. Giving primarily in areas of company operations in AZ, CA, Washington, DC, FL, MA, MD, NY, and PA; giving also to national organizations. No support for organizations lacking 501(c)(3) status.
Application information: Contributes only to pre-selected organizations.
Officers and Directors:* Mitch Cohen, Co-Chair.; Karen Raskopf, Co-Chair.; Jeff Miller, Secy.; Jim Damicone, Treas.; Frank Basier; Gary Heckel; Steven Kim; Dominic Laskero; Jon L. Luther; Sheila Patel; Joseph Prazeres; Christine Riley; Dan Saia; Alex Smigelski; Rod Valencia.
EIN: 260593784

4027
Dunn Family Charitable Foundation ✧

c/o AHI
30 Nagog Park, Ste. 210
Acton, MA 01720-3439

Established in 1993 in MA.
Donor: Raymond J. Dunn III.
Foundation type: Independent foundation.
Financial data (yr. ended 10/31/13): Assets, $18,423,329 (M); expenditures, $940,658; qualifying distributions, $929,483; giving activities include $860,359 for 63 grants (high: $226,667; low: $100).
Fields of interest: Education; Human services; Community/economic development.
Limitations: Applications not accepted. Giving primarily in MA. No grants to individuals.
Application information: Contributes only to pre-selected organizations.
Officers and Trustees:* William J. Chase,* Cont.; Raymond J. Dunn III,* Mgr.; Louise Dunn III; Margaret Dunn; Martin Dunn; Peter Dunn; Raymond J. Dunn IV.
EIN: 043251269
Selected grants: The following grants are a representative sample of this grantmaker's funding activity:
$2,000 to Catholic Relief Services, Baltimore, MD, 2011. For unrestricted gift.
$1,000 to Nature Conservancy, Arlington, VA, 2011. For unrestricted gift.
$1,000 to Year Up, Boston, MA, 2011. For unrestricted gift.

4028
The Dusky Foundation ✧

c/o Robert S. Gulick
50 Congress St., Ste. 925
Boston, MA 02109-4075

Established in 1991 in MA.
Donor: J. Linzee Coolidge.
Foundation type: Independent foundation.
Financial data (yr. ended 12/31/13): Assets, $2,409,075 (M); gifts received, $1,487,187; expenditures, $1,223,008; qualifying distributions, $1,190,100; giving activities include $1,190,100 for 34 grants (high: $350,000; low: $2,100).
Fields of interest: Arts; Education; Human services; Foundations (private grantmaking).
Type of support: General/operating support; Continuing support; Capital campaigns; Building/renovation; Equipment.
Limitations: Applications not accepted. Giving primarily in MA. No grants to individuals.
Application information: Contributes only to pre-selected organizations.
Board meeting date(s): Quarterly
Trustees: J. Linzee Coolidge; Robert S. Gulick.
EIN: 043122206
Selected grants: The following grants are a representative sample of this grantmaker's funding activity:
$5,000 to Doctors Without Borders USA, New York, NY, 2012. For Gifts for Unrestricted and various restricted purposes.
$5,000 to Essex County Community Foundation, Danvers, MA, 2012. For Restricted gift to benefit its First Jobs Program.
$3,000 to Marion Institute, Marion, MA, 2012. For Restricted gift to support its Cambodian Living Arts Program.

4029
Eaglemere Foundation, Inc. ✧

60 Edmunds Rd.
Wellesley, MA 02481-2934

Established in 1999 in MA.
Donors: H. Jay Sarles; Marilyn D. Sarles, M.D.
Foundation type: Independent foundation.
Financial data (yr. ended 12/31/13): Assets, $10,153,757 (M); gifts received, $120,000; expenditures, $572,214; qualifying distributions, $503,850; giving activities include $503,850 for 36 grants (high: $105,000; low: $100).
Fields of interest: Education; Environment; Animal welfare; Health care; Human services.
Type of support: General/operating support.
Limitations: Applications not accepted. Giving in the U.S., with emphasis on CA, MA, NH, NY, and RI. No grants to individuals.
Application information: Contributes only to pre-selected organizations.
Officers: Marilyn D. Sarles, M.D., Pres.; H. Jay Sarles, Secy.-Treas.; Daniel G. Sarles, Exec. Dir.
EIN: 043424302
Selected grants: The following grants are a representative sample of this grantmaker's funding activity:
$85,000 to Nature Conservancy, San Francisco, CA, 2011.
$50,000 to Doctors Without Borders USA, New York, NY, 2011.
$50,000 to Oxfam America, Boston, MA, 2011.
$25,000 to Alaska Conservation Foundation, Anchorage, AK, 2011.
$12,500 to Charles River Watershed Association, Weston, MA, 2011.
$5,000 to American Rivers, Washington, DC, 2011.
$2,500 to EcoFlight, Aspen, CO, 2011.
$1,500 to Pet Partners, Bellevue, WA, 2011.
$1,500 to Teton Science Schools, Jackson, WY, 2011.

4030
Eastern Bank Charitable Foundation ✧

195 Market St., EP5-02
Lynn, MA 01901-1508 (781) 598-7530
Contact: Laura Kurzrok, Exec. Dir.
FAX: (781) 596-4445;
E-mail: Foundation@easternbank.com; TDD/TTY tel.: (781) 596-4408; Main URL: https://www.easternbank.com/foundation

Established in 1994 in MA.
Donor: Eastern Bank.
Foundation type: Company-sponsored foundation.
Financial data (yr. ended 12/31/12): Assets, $64,452,431 (M); gifts received, $7,500,000; expenditures, $3,988,909; qualifying distributions, $3,664,104; giving activities include $3,056,419 for 1,528 grants (high: $100,000; low: $50).
Purpose and activities: The foundation supports organizations involved with education, the environment, community health, workforce development, hunger, affordable housing, children and families, human services, civil liberties, and economic revitalization.
Fields of interest: Higher education; Education, services; Education, computer literacy/technology training; Education; Health care, clinics/centers; Health care; Employment, services; Employment, training; Food banks; Nutrition; Housing/shelter; Boys & girls clubs; Youth development; Children, services; Family services; Family services, domestic violence; Human services, financial counseling; Human services; Civil/human rights; Economic development; United Ways and Federated Giving Programs.
Type of support: General/operating support; Annual campaigns; Capital campaigns; Building/renovation; Endowments; Program development; Scholarship funds; Sponsorships; Employee matching gifts.
Limitations: Applications accepted. Giving primarily in areas of company operations in eastern MA.

Publications: Application guidelines; Annual report (including application guidelines).
Application information: Partnership Grants are limited to 1 contribution per organization during any 3-year period. Application form required.
Initial approach: Complete online application
Deadline(s): None for Community Grants and Neighborhood Support; Mar. 1 for Targeted Grants; Mar. 1 and Sept. 1 for Partnership Grants; None for Neighborhood Support
Board meeting date(s): Monthly for Community Grants and Neighborhood Support; Semi-annually for Partnership Grants
Final notification: 60 days for Community Grants and Neighborhood Support; May and Nov. for Partnership Grants
Trustees: Richard C. Bane; Deborah Hill Bornheimer; Paul M. Connolly; Robert A. Glassman; Daryl A. Hellman; Richard E. Holbrook; Deborah C. Jackson; Wendell J. Knox; Stanley J. Lukowski; Peter K. Markell; George A. Massaro; Henry L. Murphy, Jr., Esq.; E. Joel Peterson; John M. Plukas; Roger D. Scoville; Michael B. Sherman.
Number of staff: 1 full-time professional; 2 part-time support.
EIN: 223317340
Selected grants: The following grants are a representative sample of this grantmaker's funding activity:
$100,000 to Salem State College, Salem, MA, 2011.
$10,000 to Adoption and Foster Care Mentoring, Boston, MA, 2011.
$5,000 to Access Program, Elyria, OH, 2011.
$2,500 to A Better Chance Masconomet, Topsfield, MA, 2011.
$2,500 to ACCION East, New York, NY, 2011.
$2,500 to Adopt-A-Student Foundation, Boston, MA, 2011.
$2,500 to Agassiz Village, Lexington, MA, 2011.
$2,000 to Pittsburgh Schweitzer Fellows Program, Pittsburgh, PA, 2011.

4031
The Edgerley Family Foundation ✧
119 Hyslop Rd.
Brookline, MA 02445-5727 (617) 516-2222

Established in 2004 in MA.
Donors: Paul Edgerley; Sandra Edgerley.
Foundation type: Independent foundation.
Financial data (yr. ended 12/31/12): Assets, $47,056,276 (M); gifts received, $40,735,369; expenditures, $9,316,024; qualifying distributions, $9,108,414; giving activities include $9,108,414 for 92 grants (high: $2,000,000; low: $500).
Fields of interest: Higher education; Boys & girls clubs; Human services; United Ways and Federated Giving Programs.
Limitations: Applications not accepted. Giving primarily in MA; some giving also in KS. No grants to individuals.
Application information: Contributes only to pre-selected organizations.
Trustees: Paul Edgerley; Sandra Edgerley.
EIN: 201867709

4032
Egan Family Foundation ✧
116 Flanders Rd., Ste. 3000
Westborough, MA 01581-1072

Established in 1993 in MA.
Donor: Maureen E. Egan.
Foundation type: Independent foundation.
Financial data (yr. ended 12/31/13): Assets, $5,523,355 (M); expenditures, $825,057; qualifying distributions, $741,742; giving activities include $641,000 for 12 grants (high: $330,000; low: $5,000).
Purpose and activities: Giving primarily for health care, education, children and youth services, including a children's hospital, and human services.
Fields of interest: Education; Environment, natural resources; Hospitals (specialty); Health organizations, association; Human services; Children/youth, services.
Limitations: Applications not accepted. Giving primarily in MA; some funding also in FL, NY, and VI. No grants to individuals.
Application information: Contributes only to pre-selected organizations. Unsolicited requests for funds not accepted.
Officer: Catherine E. Walkey, Exec. Dir.
Trustees: Christopher F. Egan; John R. Egan; Michael J. Egan; Maureen E. Petracca.
EIN: 043211653
Selected grants: The following grants are a representative sample of this grantmaker's funding activity:
$50,000 to Duke University, Durham, NC, 2012. For Trinity College Annual Fund.
$12,500 to UMass Memorial Foundation, Shrewsbury, MA, 2012. For AL's Champion Fund.

4033
Elfers Foundation Inc. ✧
c/o Choate LLP
P.O. Box 961019
Boston, MA 02196

Established in 1970 in MA.
Donors: William Elfers†; Harvard College Charitable Lead Trusts.
Foundation type: Independent foundation.
Financial data (yr. ended 11/30/13): Assets, $10,912,992 (M); gifts received, $143,348; expenditures, $686,608; qualifying distributions, $574,246; giving activities include $552,500 for 14 grants (high: $250,000; low: $500).
Purpose and activities: Giving for Christian churches, wildlife conservation, diabetes services and higher education.
Fields of interest: Performing arts, orchestras; Arts; Elementary/secondary education; Higher education; Animal welfare; Hospitals (general); Medical research, institute; Children/youth, services; Christian agencies & churches.
Limitations: Applications not accepted. Giving primarily in MA. No grants to individuals.
Application information: Contributes only to pre-selected organizations.
Officers: William R. Elfers, Pres.; William A. Lowell, Secy.; Deborah B. Elfers, Treas.
Director: Jane Elfers Muther.
EIN: 237090080
Selected grants: The following grants are a representative sample of this grantmaker's funding activity:
$50,000 to Newton-Wellesley Hospital Charitable Foundation, Newton, MA, 2011.
$50,000 to Princeton University, Princeton, NJ, 2011. For Annual Fund.
$25,000 to Boston Symphony Orchestra, Boston, MA, 2011. For general support.
$25,000 to Hotchkiss School, Lakeville, CT, 2011. For Annual Fund.
$25,000 to Saint Andrews Episcopal Church, Wellesley, MA, 2011. For capital campaign.
$20,000 to Boston Symphony Orchestra, Boston, MA, 2011. For Annual Fund.
$20,000 to Winsor School, Boston, MA, 2011. For Annual Fund.
$12,500 to Newton-Wellesley Hospital Charitable Foundation, Newton, MA, 2011. For general support.
$10,000 to Newton-Wellesley Hospital Charitable Foundation, Newton, MA, 2011. For Annual Fund.
$5,000 to American Red Cross, Portsmouth, NH, 2011. For general support.

4034
The Ellison Foundation ✧
c/o Elton Drew
21 King St.
Lynn, MA 01902-2019
Contact: Elton F. Drew, Tr.

Established in 1952 in MA.
Donors: Eben H. Ellison†; William P. Ellison†; Harriet Ellison Rogers†.
Foundation type: Independent foundation.
Financial data (yr. ended 12/31/13): Assets, $79,615,007 (M); expenditures, $5,524,871; qualifying distributions, $4,989,052; giving activities include $4,538,000 for 38 grants (high: $1,000,000; low: $5,000).
Fields of interest: Higher education; Hospitals (general); Health organizations.
Limitations: Applications not accepted. Giving primarily in MA; some giving also in DC. No grants to individuals.
Application information: Contributes only to pre-selected organizations. Generally awards are made to the same organizations year to year, with occasional one-time grants made to organizations solicited by the foundation.
Trustees: Elton F. Drew; Andrew Silverman.
EIN: 046050704

4035
Ruth H. & Warren A. Ellsworth Foundation ✧
370 Main St., 12th Fl., Ste. 1250
Worcester, MA 01608-1723 (508) 459-8000
Contact: Sumner B. Tilton, Jr., Tr.

Trust established in 1964 in MA.
Donor: Ruth H. Ellsworth†.
Foundation type: Independent foundation.
Financial data (yr. ended 12/31/13): Assets, $22,090,221 (M); expenditures, $1,218,959; qualifying distributions, $1,114,020; giving activities include $950,500 for 94 grants (high: $100,000; low: $250).
Purpose and activities: Emphasis on education, social services, and youth agencies.
Fields of interest: Arts; Higher education; Education; Human services; YM/YWCAs & YM/YWHAs; Children/youth, services; United Ways and Federated Giving Programs.
Type of support: General/operating support; Continuing support; Annual campaigns; Building/renovation; Equipment; Land acquisition; Debt reduction; Emergency funds; Seed money.

Limitations: Applications accepted. Giving primarily in the Worcester, MA, area. No grants to individuals, or for endowment funds, scholarships, fellowships, research, publications, conferences, or matching gifts; no loans.
Application information:
Initial approach: Letter
Copies of proposal: 1
Deadline(s): June 1
Board meeting date(s): June and Dec.
Final notification: By Dec. 28
Trustees: Joyce Wetzel Hall; Sumner B. Tilton, Jr.; Mark R. Wetzel; Todd H. Wetzel.
Number of staff: 1 part-time professional.
EIN: 046113491

4036
The Elsevier Foundation ✧
2 Newton Pl., Ste. 350
Newton, MA 02458-1637
Contact: John Regazzi, Chair.
E-mail: foundation@elsevier.com; Application address: 360 Park Ave. S., New York, NY 10010-1710, tel.: (212) 633-3933; Main URL: http://www.elsevierfoundation.org
Facebook: https://www.facebook.com/TheElsevierFoundation
Twitter: https://twitter.com/ELsFoundation
YouTube: http://www.youtube.com/user/ElsevierFoundation

Established in NY.
Donor: Elservier, Inc.
Foundation type: Independent foundation.
Financial data (yr. ended 12/31/12): Assets, $559,337 (M); gifts received, $1,340,160; expenditures, $853,894; qualifying distributions, $853,894; giving activities include $853,894 for grants.
Purpose and activities: The foundation provides grants to institutions around the world, with a focus on support for the world's libraries and for scholars in the early stages of their careers.
Fields of interest: Higher education; Libraries/library science; Education; Health organizations; Human services.
Type of support: General/operating support; Employee matching gifts.
Limitations: Applications accepted. Giving on an international basis. No grants for individuals, nor for basic research, sectarian religious activities or to organizations that lack tax exemption.
Publications: Application guidelines.
Application information:
Initial approach: See foundation web site for guidelines
Officer: David A. Ruth, Exec. Dir.
Directors: YoungSuk "YS" Chi; Dr. Rita Colwell; Paula Kaufman; Dr. Emilie Marcus; Kenneth R. Thompson II; Wu Yishan.
EIN: 431976990

4037
Eos Foundation
537 Main St., Ste. 12
Harwich Port, MA 02646-1894 (508) 430-8130
Contact: Andrea Silbert, Pres.; Kathy Robertson, Opers. and Comms. Coord.
E-mail: info@EosFoundation.org; Additional address: 160 Federal St., 10th Fl., Boston, MA 02110; tel.: (617) 338-2590, ext. 252; Main URL: http://www.eosfoundation.org/
Eos Foundation's Philanthropy's Promise: http://www.ncrp.org/philanthropys-promise/who

Established in 1999 in MA.
Donors: Kenneth S. Nickerson; Katherine A. Deyst.
Foundation type: Independent foundation.
Financial data (yr. ended 06/30/13): Assets, $41,052,675 (M); expenditures, $3,727,533; qualifying distributions, $3,407,826; giving activities include $2,464,561 for 29 grants (high: $487,500; low: $2,500).
Purpose and activities: The foundation seeks an equitable and just society where the basic human needs of all individuals are met, and where children grow up healthy, with opportunities for high quality education and the tools to achieve economic self-sufficiency.
Fields of interest: Education; Human services; Community/economic development; Children.
Limitations: Applications not accepted. Giving primarily in MA, with emphasis on Boston.
Application information: Unsolicited requests for funds not accepted.
Officers: Andrea Silbert, Pres.; Mari Brennan Barrera, V.P.
Trustees: Katherine A. Deyst; Kenneth S. Nickerson.
Number of staff: 4 full-time professional.
EIN: 043494831

4038
Epker-Sinha Foundation ✧
31 Candleberry Ln.
Weston, MA 02493-1901 (617) 526-8992
Contact: Arthur G. Epker III, Tr.

Established in 2000 in MA.
Donors: Arthur G. Epker III; Medha Sinha.
Foundation type: Independent foundation.
Financial data (yr. ended 12/31/13): Assets, $15,552,327 (M); expenditures, $636,958; qualifying distributions, $468,159; giving activities include $467,900 for 16 grants (high: $153,000; low: $150).
Fields of interest: Education; Boys & girls clubs; Human services; United Ways and Federated Giving Programs.
Limitations: Applications accepted. Giving primarily in MA; some giving in AZ. No grants to individuals.
Application information: Application form required.
Initial approach: Letter
Deadline(s): None
Trustees: Arthur G. Epker III; Medha Sinha.
EIN: 043541108
Selected grants: The following grants are a representative sample of this grantmaker's funding activity:
$150,000 to Winsor School, Boston, MA, 2011.
$110,050 to Steppingstone Foundation, Boston, MA, 2011.
$100,000 to University of Michigan, Ann Arbor, MI, 2011.
$2,500 to University of Pennsylvania, Philadelphia, PA, 2011.

4039
Essex County Community Foundation, Inc. ✧
175 Andover St., Ste. 101
Danvers, MA 01923-2833 (978) 777-8876
Contact: David Welbourn, C.E.O. and Pres.; For grants: Julie Bishop, V.P., Grants and Svcs.
FAX: (978) 777-9454; E-mail: info@eccf.org; Grant inquiry e-mail: j.bishop@eccf.org; Grant application e-mail: grantsubmit@eccf.org; Main URL: http://www.eccf.org
Facebook: http://www.facebook.com/ECCFBulletin
Pinterest: http://www.pinterest.com/eccfgives/
Twitter: https://twitter.com/ECCFGives
YouTube: https://www.youtube.com/channel/UCazR-5XIxUdqkvbhaDcjzDg

Established in 1998 in MA.
Foundation type: Community foundation.
Financial data (yr. ended 06/30/14): Assets, $26,451,272 (M); gifts received, $8,928,850; expenditures, $7,647,371; giving activities include $5,565,640 for 115 grants (high: $1,595,178).
Purpose and activities: The mission of the foundation is to connect people, ideas and resources for the common good. The foundation promotes local philanthropy and strengthens the nonprofit organizations of Essex County by: 1) partnering with donors, helping them meet their philanthropic goals by managing donor funds and organization's assets with efficiency, security, expertise and privacy; 2) supporting nonprofit organizations across the county with grants, strategic planning, board development, fundraising, professional training and sustainability; and 3) building collaboration between individuals and organizations to address current issues through programs and collaborative funds.
Fields of interest: Arts; Education; Environment; Youth development; Human services; Children/youth; Youth; Adults; Aging; Young adults; Disabilities, people with; Minorities; Women; Girls; Young adults, female; Offenders/ex-offenders; Economically disadvantaged; Homeless.
Type of support: General/operating support; Management development/capacity building; Capital campaigns; Equipment; Emergency funds; Program development; Seed money; Curriculum development; Scholarship funds; Technical assistance; Consulting services; Program evaluation; Scholarships—to individuals.
Limitations: Applications accepted. Giving limited to Essex County, MA for competitive grantmaking; Donor-Advised funds may grant outside Essex County. No support for sectarian or religious purposes. No grants to individuals (except for scholarships), or for debt or deficit reduction, academic research, feasibility studies, capital campaigns for buildings, land acquisition, or endowment.
Publications: Application guidelines; Annual report; Financial statement; Grants list; Informational brochure; Newsletter.
Application information: Visit foundation web site for application cover sheet and guidelines. Application form required.
Initial approach: Submit online application
Deadline(s): Varies
Board meeting date(s): Usually held monthly, except in Aug.
Final notification: Varies
Officers and Directors:* Jonathan Payson,* Chair.; Robert R. Fanning, Jr., Chair., Finance; Allan Huntley,* Vice-Chair.; Dave Welbourn,* C.E.O. and

Pres.; Jay Caporale,* Exec. V.P. and Dir., Philanthropy; Julie Bishop,* V.P., Grants and Services; Susan Perry, Cont.; Karen Ansara; Mollie Byrnes; Benjamin Chigier; Steven Cohen; Matthew P. Doring; Theresa M. Ellis; Benigno Espaillat; Tracy Abedon Filosa; Susan Gray; Joseph Grimaldi; Joe Knowles; Patricia Maguire Meservey; Michael Prior; Richard Sumberg; Kevin M. Tierney, Sr.
Number of staff: 8 part-time professional; 1 full-time support; 1 part-time support.
EIN: 043407816
Selected grants: The following grants are a representative sample of this grantmaker's funding activity:
$445,000 to One Fund Boston, Boston, MA, 2014.
$394,842 to Issue One, Washington, DC, 2014. For closing fund due to becoming a 501 c3.
$350,000 to Tufts Medical Center, Reid R Sacco AYA Clinic for Cancers and Blood Disease, Boston, MA, 2013. For Reid R Sacco AYA fund and Reid R Sacco Adolescent and Young Adult Clinic.
$250,000 to Montserrat College of Art, Beverly, MA, 2013.
$200,000 to Campaign Legal Center, Washington, DC, 2013. For Judicial Reform Project.
$200,000 to Environmental Defense Fund, Boulder, CO, 2012. For unrestricted.
$130,000 to Boston University, Boston, MA, 2014. For New Dental School Building Project.
$130,000 to Connecticut Childrens Medical Center, Hartford, CT, 2014.
$110,000 to Issue One, Washington, DC, 2013. For general operations.
$100,000 to Environmental Defense Fund, Boulder, CO, 2013. For unrestricted.
$100,000 to Montserrat College of Art, Beverly, MA, 2012. For unrestricted.
$65,000 to Ocean River Institute, Cambridge, MA, 2014. For general operating.
$63,089 to Connecticut Childrens Medical Center, Hartford, CT, 2012. For as specified in the program budget proposal from Director of the AYA (Adolescent and Young Adult) Program at the center.
$62,869 to Issue One, Washington, DC, 2014. For general operations.
$50,000 to Greater Lynn Senior Services, Lynn, MA, 2013. For Safe Passages Consumer Activation Grant.
$50,000 to Issue One, Washington, DC, 2013. For general operations.
$15,000 to Boys and Girls Club of Lawrence, Lawrence, MA, 2012. For Summerfest.
$10,000 to YWCA of Greater Lawrence, Lawrence, MA, 2012. For YWCA Economic Empowerment Program, payable over 3.00 years.
$7,500 to Groundwork Lawrence, Lawrence, MA, 2012. For Lawrence Summer Youth Programs.
$6,000 to Girls Inc. of Greater Haverhill, Haverhill, MA, 2012. For Economic literacy Program.
$5,096 to Fundacja Sendzimira, Warsaw, Poland, 2013. For Warta River Basin in Poland.
$5,000 to Groundwork Lawrence, Lawrence, MA, 2014. For Urban Adventures LPS Summer Enrichment Program.
$5,000 to Windrush Farm Therapeutic Equitation, North Andover, MA, 2013. For Youth at-risk Summer Program.
$4,000 to YMCA, Merrimack Valley, Lawrence, MA, 2014. For Adelante Summer Success.
$3,000 to YMCA of the North Shore, Beverly, MA, 2012. For $1500 Ipswich; $1500 Salem.
$2,500 to Gordon College, Wenham, MA, 2012. For scholarship.
$2,500 to Greater Lawrence Family Health Center, Lawrence, MA, 2014. For Green Team Expansion Summer.
$2,500 to Lawrence General Hospital, Lawrence, MA, 2012. For Annual Campaign.
$2,500 to Raising A Reader Massachusetts, Boston, MA, 2014. For Early Literacy for All: Delivering our Core Program Model in Lawrence.
$2,500 to Saint Michaels College, Colchester, VT, 2013. For unrestricted.

4040
The Evans Family Foundation ✧
31 St. James Ave., No. 740
Boston, MA 02116-4101

Established in 2000 in MA.
Donors: Bruce R. Evans; Bridgitt B. Evans.
Foundation type: Independent foundation.
Financial data (yr. ended 12/31/13): Assets, $2,751,393 (M); gifts received, $500,000; expenditures, $1,522,157; qualifying distributions, $1,492,500; giving activities include $1,492,500 for 24 grants (high: $500,000; low: $2,500).
Fields of interest: Elementary/secondary education; Higher education; Education; Human services.
Type of support: General/operating support; Annual campaigns.
Limitations: Applications not accepted. Giving primarily in MA and TN. No grants to individuals.
Application information: Contributes only to pre-selected organizations.
Trustees: Bridgitt B. Evans; Bruce R. Evans.
EIN: 043523698

4041
Fallon Family Charitable Foundation ✧ ☆
c/o The Fallon Co., LLC
1 Marina Park Dr.
Boston, MA 02210

Established in 2007 in MA.
Donors: The Fallon Co., LLC; Turner Construction Co.
Foundation type: Company-sponsored foundation.
Financial data (yr. ended 12/31/12): Assets, $21,927 (M); gifts received, $1,410,005; expenditures, $1,388,334; qualifying distributions, $1,382,740; giving activities include $671,175 for 7 grants (high: $425,000; low: $175).
Fields of interest: Arts; Education; Human services.
Type of support: Grants to individuals.
Limitations: Applications not accepted.
Application information: Unsolicited requests for funds not accepted.
Trustees: Graceann B. Cirame; Elizabeth J. Fallon; Michael J. Fallon; Susan G. Fallon.
EIN: 207489163

4042
Kelly Family Foundation, Inc. ✧
c/o O'Brien & Associates
10 Kearney Rd., Ste. 305
Needham, MA 02494

Established in MA.
Donors: Sonja Kelly Farmer; Edmund F. Kelly; Deborah M. Kelly.
Foundation type: Independent foundation.
Financial data (yr. ended 12/31/12): Assets, $28,806,319 (M); expenditures, $1,184,914; qualifying distributions, $996,000; giving activities include $996,000 for 18 grants (high: $300,000; low: $1,000).
Purpose and activities: Giving primarily for a children's hospital, as well as for education, and to a library.
Fields of interest: Libraries (public); Education; Hospitals (specialty).
Limitations: Applications not accepted. Giving primarily in MA.
Application information: Unsolicited requests for funds not accepted.
Officers and Directors:* Sonja Kelly Farmer, Pres.; Edmund F. Kelly,* Clerk; Deborah M. Kelly,* Treas.
EIN: 271510984

4043
Charles H. Farnsworth Trust ✧
c/o US Trust, Bank of America, N.A.
225 Franklin St., 4th Fl., MA1-225-04-02
Boston, MA 02110-2804 (866) 778-6859
Contact: Michealle Larkins, V.P.
E-mail: michealle.larkins@ustrust.com; E-mail to discuss application process or for questions: ma.grantmaking@ustrust.com (Foundation name should appear in subject line); Main URL: http://www.bankofamerica.com/grantmaking

Trust established in 1930; became a charitable trust in 1978.
Donor: Charles H. Farnsworth†.
Foundation type: Independent foundation.
Financial data (yr. ended 09/30/13): Assets, $26,940,381 (M); expenditures, $1,394,724; qualifying distributions, $1,235,251; giving activities include $1,139,000 for 26 grants (high: $333,000; low: $2,000).
Purpose and activities: Giving to assist elderly persons to live with dignity and independence. Special focus on services which help prevent premature institutionalization. Grants fostering the development of housing for the elderly are of special interest.
Fields of interest: Housing/shelter, development; Aging, centers/services; Aging.
Type of support: General/operating support; Capital campaigns; Building/renovation; Equipment; Program development; Seed money; Technical assistance.
Limitations: Giving limited to MA. No grants to individuals.
Publications: Application guidelines; Grants list.
Application information: Submit applications online at www.bankofamerica.com/grantmaking.
Initial approach: Proposal online via foundation web site
Deadline(s): See foundation web site for current deadlines
Final notification: See foundation web site
Trustee: Bank of America, N.A.
Number of staff: 2 part-time support.
EIN: 046096075
Selected grants: The following grants are a representative sample of this grantmaker's funding activity:
$333,000 to Greater Boston Chinese Golden Age Center, Boston, MA, 2013. For the construction of the Hong Lok House.
$150,000 to South Cove Manor at Quincy Point Rehabilitation Center, Quincy, MA, 2013. For new 141-bed facility in Quincy for Asian older adults.

$100,000 to Nuestra Comunidad Development Corporation, Roxbury, MA, 2013. For Quincy Commons project.
$75,000 to Kit Clark Senior Services, Dorchester, MA, 2013. For renovation of the lower level and first floor of the headquarters building on Dorchester Avenue.
$70,000 to Assisted Living Center, Salisbury, MA, 2013. For replace worn carpeting and to purchase a generator.
$60,000 to Scandinavian Charitable Society of Greater Boston, West Newton, MA, 2013. For expansion of the dining and common area space.
$50,000 to Rogerson Communities, Boston, MA, 2013. For development and implementation of a database to help better track wellness program outcomes.
$20,000 to HEARTH, Boston, MA, 2013. For Hearth Housing and Outreach programs.
$20,000 to Homeowners Options for Massachusetts Elders, Lowell, MA, 2013. For general operations of the organization.
$10,000 to South Boston Neighborhood House, South Boston, MA, 2013. For Senior Services Program.

4044
The Feigenbaum Foundation, Inc. ✧ ☆
2 South St., Ste. 235
Pittsfield, MA 01201 (413) 499-2880
E-mail: info@feigenbaumfoundation.com; Main URL: http://www.feigenbaumfoundation.org/

Established in 1988 in MA.
Donors: Armand V. Feigenbaum; Donald S. Feigenbaum.
Foundation type: Independent foundation.
Financial data (yr. ended 12/31/13): Assets, $17,469,279 (M); gifts received, $14,681,614; expenditures, $2,459,906; qualifying distributions, $2,404,734; giving activities include $2,213,710 for 21 grants (high: $1,000,000; low: $130).
Purpose and activities: Giving primarily for the arts; funding also for social services, and Jewish temples and federated giving programs.
Fields of interest: Museums; Performing arts centers; Arts; Human services; Jewish federated giving programs; Jewish agencies & synagogues.
Limitations: Applications not accepted. Giving primarily in western MA, particularly in the Berkshires, with emphasis on the Pittsfield area. No grants to individuals.
Application information: Unsolicited requests for funds not accepted.
Directors: Armand V. Feigenbaum; Donald S. Feigenbaum; Bernard E. Riley; Leslie Warren.
Officers: Emil George, Pres.; Richard A. Lombardi, Treas.
EIN: 043000345

4045
Fels Family Foundation ✧
c/o MDW
370 Main St., Ste. 800
Worcester, MA 01608-1741

Established in 2003 in MA.
Donors: Gerald Fels; Marilyn T. Fels.
Foundation type: Independent foundation.
Financial data (yr. ended 12/31/12): Assets, $17,876,631 (M); expenditures, $663,384; qualifying distributions, $639,734; giving activities include $639,484 for 47 grants (high: $200,000; low: $100).
Fields of interest: Education; Animal welfare; Human services; Christian agencies & churches.
Limitations: Applications not accepted. Giving primarily in MA. No grants to individuals.
Application information: Contributes only to pre-selected organizations.
Trustees: Gerald Fels; Marilyn Fels.
EIN: 200477156

4046
Fields Pond Foundation, Inc. ✧
5 Turner St.
P.O. Box 540667
Waltham, MA 02454-0667 (781) 899-9990
FAX: (718) 899-2819; E-mail: info@fieldspond.org; Main URL: http://www.fieldspond.org
Grants List: http://www.fieldspond.org/grants.htm

Established in 1993 in MA.
Foundation type: Independent foundation.
Financial data (yr. ended 12/31/13): Assets, $14,304,205 (M); expenditures, $741,330; qualifying distributions, $693,875; giving activities include $561,191 for 65 grants (high: $25,000; low: $1,000).
Purpose and activities: The foundation provides assistance to nature and land conservation organizations which are community based, and which serve to increase environmental awareness by involving local residents in conservation issues. The foundation makes grants under the following priorities: 1) project grants for trailmaking and other enhancement of public access to conservation lands, rivers, coastlines, and other natural resources; 2) land acquisition for conservation; 3) assistance in the establishment of endowments as a means of funding stewardship of conservation areas; and 4) related education programs and publications. The foundation encourages proposals from municipal government agencies. It may also consider short-term loans to conservation groups for the purpose of acquiring conservation lands. Outside of the primary mission, it will also consider grant requests from other nonprofit organizations that have a demonstrated local impact on precollegiate education.
Fields of interest: Elementary/secondary education; Environment, natural resources; Environment.
Type of support: Capital campaigns; Land acquisition; Endowments; Emergency funds; Seed money; Matching/challenge support.
Limitations: Applications accepted. Giving primarily in New England and New York. No support for sectarian religious activities. No grants to individuals; or for deficit financing, routine operating budgets, or for funding usually supported by public subscription or through national appeals.
Publications: Application guidelines; Grants list.
Application information: AGM Common Proposal Format is accepted. Application form not required.
Initial approach: Telephone or submit a 1-page outline prior to submitting full proposal
Copies of proposal: 1
Deadline(s): None
Board meeting date(s): Bimonthly
Officers and Directors:* Rhoda R. Cohen,* Pres.; Brian H. Rehrig,* V.P. and Treas.; Walter Angoff, V.P. and Secy.; Russell A. Cohen.
Number of staff: 1 part-time professional; 1 part-time support.
EIN: 043196041

4047
Lincoln and Therese Filene Foundation, Inc. ✧
Seaport West
155 Seaport Blvd.
Boston, MA 02210-2604 (617) 439-2498
Contact: Alane Harrington Wallis, Charitable Foundations Mgr.
E-mail: awallis@nutter.com; Main URL: http://www.filenefoundation.org/
Grants List: http://www.filenefoundation.org/current-grant-list-1/

Incorporated in 1937 in MA.
Donor: Lincoln Filene‡.
Foundation type: Independent foundation.
Financial data (yr. ended 12/31/13): Assets, $22,678,918 (M); expenditures, $1,290,503; qualifying distributions, $1,054,769; giving activities include $951,300 for 47 grants (high: $162,500; low: $100).
Purpose and activities: General purposes; grants primarily for civic education, human development and self-sufficiency, music and performing arts education, citizenship, and public education. Funds largely committed to long-term support of existing projects.
Fields of interest: Arts education; Media, television; Arts; Education.
Type of support: Program development.
Limitations: Applications accepted. Giving primarily in the New England area, with emphasis on MA. No support for political groups. No grants to individuals, or for endowment funds, capital campaigns, operating costs, scholarships, fellowships, or religious groups; no loans.
Publications: Application guidelines.
Application information: Funds largely committed. Application guidelines and forms available on foundation web site; AGM Common Proposal Form accepted. Application form required.
Initial approach: Cover letter, Grant Request Cover Sheet and Request for Funding forms via U.S. mail or e-mail
Copies of proposal: 1
Deadline(s): March 1 and Sept. 1
Board meeting date(s): May and Nov.
Final notification: After next semiannual meeting
Officers and Directors:* John J. Robertson,* Pres.; J. Scott Ladd,* V.P.; Peter R. Brown, Secy.-Treas.; Kimberly R. Dietel; Jason D. Hill; Justin C. Hill; David J. Ladd; John D. Ladd; William L. Ladd; Michael E. Mooney.
EIN: 237423946
Selected grants: The following grants are a representative sample of this grantmaker's funding activity:
$10,000 to W G B H Educational Foundation, Boston, MA, 2011.
$1,000 to Juvenile Diabetes Research Foundation International, New York, NY, 2011.

4048
Thomas Austin Finch Foundation ✧
100 Federal St., 37th Fl.
Boston, MA 02110
Application address: c/o Atlantic Trust Co., N.A., 1555 Peachtree St., Ste. 1100, Atlanta, GA 30309

Trust established in 1944 in NC.
Donors: Ernestine L. Finch Mobley‡; Thomas Austin Finch, Jr.‡; Meredith Michener.
Foundation type: Independent foundation.
Financial data (yr. ended 12/31/13): Assets, $10,356,491 (M); expenditures, $494,162; qualifying distributions, $465,746; giving activities include $446,500 for 19 grants (high: $100,000; low: $1,000).
Purpose and activities: Giving primarily for education, health and human services throughout the greater Thomasville, NC, area. Primary consideration is given to projects of a non-recurring nature or to start-up funding of limited duration.
Fields of interest: Elementary/secondary education; Higher education; Human services; Protestant agencies & churches.
Type of support: General/operating support; Continuing support; Annual campaigns; Building/renovation; Equipment; Program development; Seed money; Scholarship funds; Matching/challenge support.
Limitations: Applications accepted. Giving limited to Thomasville, NC; charities located outside the corporate limits of Thomasville will be considered if the grant will primarily benefit Thomasville residents.
Publications: Informational brochure (including application guidelines).
Application information: Application form required.
Initial approach: Proposal and supporting documents
Copies of proposal: 1
Deadline(s): Postmarked by Aug. 15
Board meeting date(s): Fall and spring
Trustee: Atlantic Trust Co., N.A.
EIN: 566037907
Selected grants: The following grants are a representative sample of this grantmaker's funding activity:
$15,000 to Family Service of the Piedmont, Greensboro, NC, 2011.
$15,000 to North Carolina State University, Raleigh, NC, 2010. For scholarship.
$10,000 to Appalachian State University, Boone, NC, 2011. For scholarship.
$10,000 to Campbell University, Buies Creek, NC, 2011. For scholarship.
$10,000 to North Carolina State University, Raleigh, NC, 2011. For scholarships.
$10,000 to Vineyard, The, Westfield, NC, 2011.
$7,500 to Family Services of Davidson County, Lexington, NC, 2011.
$6,100 to Arts United for Davidson County, Lexington, NC, 2010.
$6,000 to His Laboring Few Ministries, Thomasville, NC, 2010.
$6,000 to His Laboring Few Ministries, Thomasville, NC, 2011.
$5,000 to Duke University, Durham, NC, 2011. For scholarship.
$5,000 to Elon University, Elon, NC, 2011. For scholarship.
$5,000 to Wake Forest University, Winston-Salem, NC, 2011. For scholarship.

4049
The Paul and Phyllis Fireman Charitable Foundation ✧
c/o Watermill Ctr.
800 South St., Ste. 610
Waltham, MA 02453-1445 (617) 482-5620
Contact: Ana Jimenez, Grants and Projects Specialist
FAX: (617) 482-5624; E-mail: info@ppffound.org;
Main URL: http://www.ppffound.org

Established in 1985 in MA.
Foundation type: Independent foundation.
Financial data (yr. ended 12/31/12): Assets, $138,768,935 (M); expenditures, $5,176,093; qualifying distributions, $3,751,893; giving activities include $2,900,495 for 37 grants (high: $475,000; low: $250).
Purpose and activities: The foundation dedicates a major share of its resources to ending family homelessness in the Commonwealth and beyond.
Fields of interest: Performing arts centers; Hospitals (general); Housing/shelter, homeless; Human services; Homeless, human services; Jewish agencies & synagogues; Children/youth; Women; Economically disadvantaged; Homeless.
Type of support: General/operating support; Continuing support; Capital campaigns; Emergency funds; Seed money; Program-related investments/loans.
Limitations: Applications not accepted. Giving primarily in MA, with limited funding to Jersey City, NJ. No grants to individuals.
Application information: Unsolicited full proposals not accepted. See foundation web site for updates in this area.
Board meeting date(s): May
Officer: Deborah Fung, Exec. Dir.
Trustees: Paul Fireman; Phyllis Fireman.
EIN: 222677986

4050
The Firstgreen Foundation, Inc. ✧
(formerly Winter Charitable Foundation, Inc.)
175 Highland Ave., No. 1-C
Needham, MA 02494-3034

Foundation type: Independent foundation.
Financial data (yr. ended 12/31/13): Assets, $0 (M); gifts received, $2,000,000; expenditures, $2,737,797; qualifying distributions, $2,663,330; giving activities include $2,663,330 for 8 grants (high: $2,632,830; low: $1,000).
Fields of interest: Human services; Civil liberties, right to life.
Limitations: Applications not accepted. Giving primarily in Boston, MA.
Application information: Contributes only to pre-selected organizations.
Officer: Fergus McCann, Pres.
Directors: Peter J. Mongeau; Michael O'Keefe.
EIN: 203857829

4051
Fish Family Foundation ✧
(formerly The Lawrence K. Fish Charitable Foundation)
75 State St.
Boston, MA 02109-1827
E-mail: fishfamfound@aol.com

Established in 1999 in MA.
Donors: Lawrence K. Fish; Citizens Bank; Members of the Lawrence K. Fish Family.
Foundation type: Independent foundation.
Financial data (yr. ended 06/30/13): Assets, $11,489,166 (M); gifts received, $1,693,244; expenditures, $1,345,577; qualifying distributions, $1,213,187; giving activities include $876,273 for 79 grants (high: $167,814; low: $100), and $66,165 for foundation-administered programs.
Fields of interest: Higher education; Education; Health care; Human services.
Type of support: General/operating support.
Limitations: Applications not accepted. Giving primarily in MA, with emphasis on Boston. No grants to individuals.
Application information: Contributes only to pre-selected organizations.
Officer: Alice Borden, Exec. Dir.
Trustees: Atsuko Toko Fish; Edward Takezo Fish; Emily Fish; Lawrence K. Fish; Leah Okajima Toko Fish; Matias Sacerdote; Thaleia Schlesinger.
Number of staff: 1 part-time support.
EIN: 046905753

4052
Fisher Family Foundation ✧
99 Kirkstall Rd.
Newton, MA 02460-2245

Established in 1999 in MA.
Donors: Ronald Fisher; Lisa Rosenbaum; Fisher Charitable Remainder Trust; Matthew Fisher.
Foundation type: Independent foundation.
Financial data (yr. ended 08/31/13): Assets, $12,285,009 (M); gifts received, $1,055,300; expenditures, $1,094,472; qualifying distributions, $1,050,965; giving activities include $1,045,946 for 8 grants (high: $800,000; low: $100).
Purpose and activities: Giving primarily for Jewish organizations; funding also for education and human services.
Fields of interest: Education; Human services; Jewish federated giving programs; Jewish agencies & synagogues.
Limitations: Applications not accepted. Giving primarily in MA and New York, NY. No grants to individuals.
Application information: Contributes only to pre-selected organizations.
Trustees: Lisa Rosenbaum; Matthew Fisher; Ronald Fisher.
EIN: 046899625
Selected grants: The following grants are a representative sample of this grantmaker's funding activity:
$378,000 to Combined Jewish Philanthropies of Greater Boston, Boston, MA, 2011. For operating support.
$50,000 to Yeshiva University, New York, NY, 2011. For operating support.
$33,000 to Maimonides School, Brookline, MA, 2011. For operating support.
$11,000 to Bais Chana Women International, Brooklyn, NY, 2011. For operating support.
$10,000 to Friends of Ir David, Brooklyn, NY, 2011. For operating support.
$4,000 to Second Step, Newton, MA, 2011. For operating support.
$2,000 to Shalom Bayit, Oakland, CA, 2011. For operating support.
$1,000 to New England Hebrew Academy, Brookline, MA, 2011. For operating support.

4053
The Flatley Foundation ✧
35 Braintree Hill Office Park, Ste. 400
Braintree, MA 02184-8754 (781) 849-5100

Established in 1982 in MA.
Donors: Thomas J. Flatley†; Charlotte E. Flatley.
Foundation type: Independent foundation.
Financial data (yr. ended 12/31/13): Assets, $560,851,531 (M); gifts received, $3,000,000; expenditures, $28,565,625; giving activities include $18,782,610 for 117 grants (high: $10,000,000; low: $1,000), and $6,535,837 for 1 foundation-administered program.
Purpose and activities: Giving primarily for education, health care, and to Roman Catholic organizations.
Fields of interest: Elementary/secondary education; Higher education; Human services; International affairs; Civil liberties, right to life; Catholic agencies & churches.
Limitations: Applications not accepted. Giving primarily in MA, MD, and Bala Cynwyd, PA. No grants to individuals.
Application information: Contributes only to pre-selected organizations.
Trustees: Mary Margaret Darling; Daniel T. Flatley; John J. Flatley.
EIN: 042763837
Selected grants: The following grants are a representative sample of this grantmaker's funding activity:
$10,000,000 to Papal Foundation, Mother Teresa Fund, Bala Cynwyd, PA, 2012. For unrestricted support.
$1,000,000 to Cystic Fibrosis Foundation, Bethesda, MD, 2012. For unrestricted support.
$1,000,000 to NPH USA, Chicago, IL, 2012. For unrestricted support.
$500,000 to AmeriCares, Stamford, CT, 2012. For clinic in El Salvador.
$500,000 to Roman Catholic Archdiocese of Boston, Braintree, MA, 2012. For Regina Cleri Retirement Fund.
$155,000 to My Brothers Keeper, Easton, MA, 2012. For unrestricted support.
$100,000 to Bethany Health Care Center, Framingham, MA, 2012. For unrestricted support.
$30,000 to Elon University, Elon, NC, 2012. For Catholic Campus Ministry.
$20,500 to Compassionate Care ALS, West Falmouth, MA, 2012. For unrestricted support.
$15,000 to Arc of the South Shore, North Weymouth, MA, 2012. For unrestricted support.

4054
The Fletcher Foundation ✧
370 Main St., 12th Fl.
Worcester, MA 01608-1723
Contact: Warner S. Fletcher, Secy.-Treas.

Established in 1981 in MA.
Donor: Paris Fletcher†.
Foundation type: Independent foundation.
Financial data (yr. ended 12/31/12): Assets, $27,296,064 (M); expenditures, $1,539,926; qualifying distributions, $1,389,759; giving activities include $1,317,130 for 74 grants (high: $150,000; low: $4).
Purpose and activities: Giving primarily for education, the arts, community development, and human services.
Fields of interest: Arts; Education; Health care; Human services; Children/youth, services; Community/economic development.
Type of support: Seed money; Land acquisition; Equipment; Capital campaigns; Building/renovation; General/operating support.
Limitations: Applications accepted. Giving limited to Worcester County, MA, with an emphasis on the city of Worcester. No support for religious organizations. No grants to individuals.
Application information: Application form not required.
Initial approach: Letter and telephone
Copies of proposal: 5
Deadline(s): June 1 and Dec. 1
Board meeting date(s): June and Dec.
Final notification: Within 1 month of distribution meeting
Officers and Trustees:* Allen W. Fletcher,* Chair.; Warner S. Fletcher,* Secy.-Treas.; Mary F. Fletcher; Patricia A. Fletcher.
EIN: 046470890

4055
Joseph F. and Clara Ford Foundation ✧
c/o Leslie K. Lerner
77 Pond Ave., Ste. 801
Brookline, MA 02445-7114

Established in 1946 in MA.
Donors: Clara Ford†; Joseph F. Ford†; Charles A. Fortus†.
Foundation type: Independent foundation.
Financial data (yr. ended 07/31/11): Assets, $1,982,333 (M); expenditures, $718,712; qualifying distributions, $660,000; giving activities include $660,000 for 12 grants (high: $298,657; low: $9,219).
Purpose and activities: Giving primarily for higher education, hospitals, and Jewish organizations.
Fields of interest: Higher education; Hospitals (general); Jewish federated giving programs; Jewish agencies & synagogues.
Limitations: Applications not accepted. Giving primarily in MA. No grants to individuals.
Application information: Contributes only to pre-selected organizations.
Trustee: Leslie K. Lerner.
EIN: 046111820
Selected grants: The following grants are a representative sample of this grantmaker's funding activity:
$298,657 to Brandeis University, Waltham, MA, 2011.
$73,742 to Northeastern University, Boston, MA, 2011.
$33,185 to American Society for Technion-Israel Institute of Technology, New York, NY, 2011.
$27,655 to Tufts Medical Center, Boston, MA, 2011.
$22,123 to Hebrew College, Newton Centre, MA, 2011.
$22,123 to Weizmann Institute of Science, Rehovot, Israel, 2011.
$9,219 to Hebrew SeniorLife, Boston, MA, 2011.

4056
The Foundation for MetroWest ✧
(formerly Crossroads Community Foundation, Inc.)
3 Eliot St.
Natick, MA 01760 (508) 647-2260
Contact: Judith G. Salerno, Exec. Dir.
FAX: (508) 647-2288;
E-mail: info@foundationformetrowest.org; Additional e-mail: jsalerno@foundationformetrowest.org; Grant inquiry e-mail: grants@foundationformetrowest.org;
Main URL: http://www.foundationformetrowest.org
Facebook: https://www.facebook.com/FoundationforMetroWest
Instagram: http://instagram.com/foundationformetrowest#
LinkedIn: http://www.linkedin.com/company/foundation-for-metrowest
Twitter: http://twitter.com/ffmw
YouTube: https://www.youtube.com/user/FoundationforMW

Established in 1995 in MA.
Foundation type: Community foundation.
Financial data (yr. ended 12/31/13): Assets, $13,581,824 (M); gifts received, $2,179,758; expenditures, $1,533,059; giving activities include $749,959 for 41+ grants (high: $36,651).
Purpose and activities: The foundation connects philanthropic opportunity with demonstrated need in Metrowest. The foundation promotes philanthropy in the region, helps donors maximize the impact of their local giving, serves as a resource for local nonprofit organizations and enhance the quality of life for all of the community's citizens.
Fields of interest: Arts; Environment; Youth development; Youth, services; Family services; Human services; General charitable giving.
Type of support: General/operating support; Management development/capacity building; Capital campaigns; Building/renovation; Equipment; Endowments; Program development; Conferences/seminars; Publication; Seed money; Curriculum development; Internship funds; Scholarship funds; Technical assistance; Consulting services; Matching/challenge support.
Limitations: Applications accepted. Giving primarily in Acton, Ashland, Boxborough, Concord, Dover, Framingham, Holliston, Hopkinton, Hudson, Lincoln, Marlborough, Maynard, Medfield, Medway, Milford, Millis, Natick, Needham, Sherborn, Southborough, Stow, Sudbury, Waltham, Wayland, Wellesley, Westborough, Weston, and Westwood, MA. No grants to individuals.
Publications: Annual report; Financial statement; Grants list; Informational brochure; Newsletter.
Application information: Visit foundation web site for application and specific guidelines per grant type. Application form required.
Initial approach: Submit online application
Deadline(s): Aug. 15
Board meeting date(s): Quarterly
Final notification: After Dec. 5 for Environment, Fund for Families, and Arts and Culture grants; between Jan. and May for Youth Development grants
Officers and Trustees:* Bob Brack,* Chair.; Garry R. Holmes,* Vice-Chair.; Pamela Lesser,* Secy.; David M. Shuman,* Treas.; Judith G. Salerno, Exec. Dir.; David Bannon; Louis Crosier; Tom Crotty; Susan Elliott; Patty Gannon; Jim Hanrahan; John R. Heerwagen; John J. O'Neil III; Janet Pattillo; Margaret Ramsey; Kyle Schaffer; John Steiger; Andrea Sussman; Robert A. Vigoda; Kenneth Vona.

Number of staff: 4 full-time professional; 3 part-time professional.
EIN: 043266789

4057
Foundation for Research in Cell Biology Cancer and Cardiology ✧ ☆
(formerly Foundation for Research in Cell Biology and Cancer)
c/o Kurt J. Isselbacher
P.O. Box 290088
Charlestown, MA 02129-3502

Established in 1996 in MA as a public charity; re-classified as a independent foundation in 2001.
Donors: Milton Sender; Laune Schwartz; Carmen Family Charitable Foundation; Mrs. John Sullivan; Robert Samuels; The Maurice N. Katz Family Foundation.
Foundation type: Independent foundation.
Financial data (yr. ended 12/31/13): Assets, $68,803,333 (M); gifts received, $2,450; expenditures, $4,572,993; qualifying distributions, $4,433,236; giving activities include $4,382,000 for 3 grants (high: $4,300,000; low: $30,000).
Purpose and activities: Giving primarily to a local hospital; funding also for a marine biological laboratory.
Fields of interest: Medical school/education; Hospitals (general); Marine science.
Limitations: Applications not accepted. Giving primarily in Charlestown, MA.
Application information: Contributes only to pre-selected organizations.
Trustees: Kurt J. Isselbacher, M.D.; Laurel Schwartz; Roy A. Goldberg, M.B.A., Ph.D.; Walter Salmon.
EIN: 042660137

4058
Foundation M ✧
P.O. Box 3219
Andover, MA 01810-0804

Established in 2000 in MA.
Donors: Casper Martin; Martin Foundation, Inc.
Foundation type: Independent foundation.
Financial data (yr. ended 06/30/13): Assets, $12,390,774 (M); expenditures, $629,532; qualifying distributions, $550,000; giving activities include $550,000 for grants.
Fields of interest: Environment; Animals/wildlife, association; Boys & girls clubs; Human services; YM/YWCAs & YM/YWHAs.
Limitations: Applications not accepted. Giving primarily in MA. No grants to individuals.
Application information: Contributes only to pre-selected organizations.
Trustees: Casper Martin; Linda Woolford.
EIN: 043559359
Selected grants: The following grants are a representative sample of this grantmaker's funding activity:
$75,000 to Interfaith Social Services, Quincy, MA, 2013. For Homesafe Program.
$30,000 to Appalachian Mountain Club, Boston, MA, 2013. For Maine Woods Initiative.
$25,000 to Audubon Vermont, Huntington, VT, 2013. For Forest Bird Initiative.
$25,000 to Union of Concerned Scientists, Cambridge, MA, 2013. For Clean Vehicles Program.
$15,000 to National Braille Press, Boston, MA, 2013. For Braille Literacy Programs.
$10,000 to Dismas House of Massachusetts, Worcester, MA, 2013. For Healthy Steps Initiative.
$10,000 to Families First Parenting Programs, Cambridge, MA, 2013. For parenting programs.
$5,000 to Farm Sanctuary, Watkins Glen, NY, 2013. For Compassionate Communities.
$5,000 to Massachusetts Advocates for Children, Boston, MA, 2013. For Autism Special Education Legal Support Center.
$3,000 to Brockton Neighborhood Health Center, Brockton, MA, 2013. For United Voices Program.

4059
Fradian Foundation ✧
c/o Steenhuysen Assoc.
1539 Fall River Ave., Ste. 3
Seekonk, MA 02771-3710

Established in 2007 in DC.
Donor: Diana Martin.
Foundation type: Independent foundation.
Financial data (yr. ended 12/31/13): Assets, $7,069,618 (M); expenditures, $1,409,959; qualifying distributions, $1,350,688; giving activities include $1,310,000 for 24 grants (high: $195,000; low: $20,000).
Fields of interest: Education; Employment; Human services.
Limitations: Applications not accepted. Giving primarily in Washington, DC.
Application information: Contributes only to pre-selected organizations.
Trustees: Sarah Burgess; Diana Martin.
EIN: 208208933

4060
The Frances Fund, Inc. ✧
150 Main St., Ste. 25
Northampton, MA 01060-3131 (413) 582-0082
Contact: Michele Spring-Moore

Established in MA.
Foundation type: Independent foundation.
Financial data (yr. ended 12/31/13): Assets, $18,166,203 (M); expenditures, $3,196,419; qualifying distributions, $3,109,650; giving activities include $2,977,657 for 20 grants (high: $2,517,157; low: $5,000), and $110,000 for 3 loans/program-related investments (high: $50,000; low: $10,000).
Purpose and activities: Giving primarily for food sovereignty, media reform, and community sustainability.
Fields of interest: Agriculture/food; Human services; Foundations (private grantmaking); Social sciences.
Limitations: Giving in the U.S., with emphasis on CA and MA.
Application information:
Initial approach: Letter
Deadline(s): Varies
Officers and Directors:* W. David Rosenmiller,* Pres.; Kimberly Longey,* Secy.-Treas.
EIN: 204211879
Selected grants: The following grants are a representative sample of this grantmaker's funding activity:
$25,000 to Figueroa Corridor Community Land Trust, Los Angeles, CA, 2011. For general support.
$20,000 to Center for Media Justice, Oakland, CA, 2011.

4061
Franklin Square House Foundation ✧
P.O. Box 78037
Belmont, MA 02478 (617) 312-3400
FAX: (617) 484-9252;
E-mail: robertg@franklinsquarehousefoundation.org ; Main URL: http://www.franklinsquarehousefoundation.org

Established in 1902 in MA.
Foundation type: Independent foundation.
Financial data (yr. ended 12/31/13): Assets, $23,930,616 (M); expenditures, $1,110,606; qualifying distributions, $994,431; giving activities include $742,678 for 21 grants (high: $60,000; low: $15,400).
Purpose and activities: The foundation works to provide grants for housing and shelter organizations, primarily in the Boston area, that protect women and preserve families.
Fields of interest: Housing/shelter, services; Family services; Family services, domestic violence; Women.
Limitations: Giving limited to the Boston, MA metropolitan area (applicants must be within the geographical area east of route 495 and/or the location of the project the applicant is applying for must fall within that geographical area). No support for playgrounds, landscaping, or for vehicles. No grants for operating costs, or for classroom materials, supplies or manipulatives, project design or management, or for relocation.
Publications: Application guidelines; Grants list.
Application information: Application forms available on foundation web site. Application form required.
Initial approach: Telephone to Exec. Dir.
Deadline(s): See foundation web site for current deadline
Officers and Directors:* Susan Shelby,* Pres.; George Marsh, Jr.,* V.P.; Vanessa Calderon-Rosado,* Clerk; David Parker,* Treas.; Robert Goldstein, Exec. Dir.; Peter Smith, Board Member Emeritus; Jack Curtin, Board Member Emeritus; Hemmie Chang; Ellen Christie; Cheryl Forte; Janet Frazier; John Hickey; Anita Huggins; Suzanne Kenney; Vincent McCarthy; Jeanne Pinado; Roberta Rubin.
EIN: 042103780
Selected grants: The following grants are a representative sample of this grantmaker's funding activity:
$64,346 to Respond, Somerville, MA, 2012. For Housing - Emergency Shelter.
$50,000 to East End House, Cambridge, MA, 2012. For Childcare - East and House.
$46,500 to Bridge Over Troubled Waters, Boston, MA, 2012. For Housing - Single Parent Home Project.
$37,935 to Just-A-Start, Cambridge, MA, 2012. For Just a Start House, Shelter.
$35,236 to United South End Settlements, Boston, MA, 2012. For early childhood program.
$25,000 to Brockton Day Nursery, Brockton, MA, 2012. For Childcare - Brockton Day Nursery.

4062
Fresh Sound Foundation, Inc. ✧
c/o Tyler Lynch
186 Alewife Brook Pkwy., No. 200
Cambridge, MA 02138-1121

Foundation type: Independent foundation.
Financial data (yr. ended 12/31/12): Assets, $8,732,872 (M); expenditures, $586,830; qualifying distributions, $446,000; giving activities include $446,000 for grants.
Fields of interest: Performing arts; Historic preservation/historical societies; Education; Environment.
Limitations: Applications not accepted. Giving primarily in MA.
Application information: Contributes only to pre-selected organizations.
Trustees: S. Jeffrey Burt; John F. Burt; Laurie Burt.
EIN: 061428363

4063
The George F. and Sybil H. Fuller Foundation ✧
370 Main St., Ste. 660
Worcester, MA 01608-1738 (508) 755-1684
Contact: Mark W. Fuller, Chair.
FAX; (508) 755-2634;
E-mail: MFuller@GSFullerFoundation.org; Main URL: http://www.gsfullerfoundation.org
Grants List: http://www.gsfullerfoundation.org/grants_2009.shtm

Trust established in 1955 in MA.
Donors: George Freeman Fuller†; Sybil H. Fuller.
Foundation type: Independent foundation.
Financial data (yr. ended 12/31/13): Assets, $55,754,146 (M); expenditures, $3,834,164; qualifying distributions, $3,639,500; giving activities include $3,485,506 for 143 grants (high: $200,000; low: $500).
Purpose and activities: The foundation's program interests include: 1) Culture (area museums and arts institutions); 2) Education (area colleges); 3) Health care (hospital and support agencies); 4) Social Services (recreation and youth development); and 5) Religious Institutions.
Fields of interest: Museums; Arts; Higher education; Higher education, university; Health care; Human services.
Type of support: Continuing support; Annual campaigns; Capital campaigns; Building/renovation; Equipment; Land acquisition; Emergency funds; Seed money; Scholarship funds; Research; Matching/challenge support.
Limitations: Applications accepted. Giving primarily in MA, with emphasis on Worcester. No grants to individuals, or for endowments, conferences, seminars, cash reserve management programs, or technical assistance or consulting; no loans.
Publications: Application guidelines; Grants list.
Application information: See foundation web site for additional application requirements. Application form not required.
Initial approach: Letter of inquiry or telephone inquiry
Copies of proposal: 1
Deadline(s): None
Board meeting date(s): Feb., Apr., June, Aug., Oct., and Dec.
Final notification: Bi-monthly
Officers and Trustees:* Mark W. Fuller,* Chair. and Treas.; Joyce I. Fuller,* Vice-Chair.; Diane H. Robbins,* Secy.; Janice L. Fuller; Lincoln E. Fuller; David P. Hallock; Kelsa Zereski.
Number of staff: 1 part-time support.
EIN: 046125606

4064
The Tommy Fuss Fund ✧ ☆
44 Longfellow Rd.
Wellesley, MA 02481-5221
Main URL: http://tommyfussfund.org/

Established in 2007 in MA.
Donors: Rosemary B. Fuss; Daniel J. Fuss; Loomis Sayles Co.
Foundation type: Independent foundation.
Financial data (yr. ended 12/31/13): Assets, $16,069,654 (M); gifts received, $2,602,370; expenditures, $605,342; qualifying distributions, $598,192; giving activities include $594,144 for 2 grants (high: $491,933; low: $102,211).
Fields of interest: Health care.
Limitations: Applications not accepted. Giving primarily in MA.
Application information: Contributes only to pre-selected organizations.
Trustees: Daniel J. Fuss; Rosemary B. Fuss; Christian Mucha.
EIN: 047024674

4065
The Garfield Foundation ✧
89 N. Water St.
New Bedford, MA 02740-6262 (508) 997-3199
Contact: Jennie Curtis, Exec. Dir.
FAX: (508) 997-3122;
E-mail: inquiry@garfieldfoundation.org; E-mail for Collaborative Networks initiative: CN@garfieldfoundation.org; Main URL: http://www.garfieldfoundation.org

Established in 1980.
Foundation type: Independent foundation.
Financial data (yr. ended 11/30/13): Assets, $32,311,678 (M); expenditures, $3,644,793; qualifying distributions, $3,244,267; giving activities include $1,937,500 for 61 grants (high: $350,000; low: $1,000).
Purpose and activities: Giving primarily for projects concerning global warming, biodiversity conservation, sustainable production and consumption, and urban renewal. Across all of its program areas, the foundation favors work that has: 1) a clear path to get at root causes of entrenched problems; 2) supports groups that embrace systems thinking and strategic outcomes in their program designs, and are thoughtful and transparent collaborators; and 3) supports strategies that embolden wide-spread concern for the environment and the role of humans as caretakers of it.
Fields of interest: Environment, toxics; Environment, climate change/global warming; Environment, natural resources; Youth development; Economic development; Community/economic development.
International interests: South America.
Type of support: General/operating support; Income development; Management development/capacity building; Land acquisition; Program development; Research; Technical assistance; Matching/challenge support.
Limitations: Giving primarily in the U.S. No grants to individuals.
Publications: Newsletter.
Application information: Positive replies only. The foundation does not consider unsolicited proposals.
Initial approach: Brief e-mail summarizing the project concept
Officer: Jennie Curtis, Exec. Dir.
Trustees: Michael Baldwin; Ronald Berman; Brian Garfield.
Number of staff: 2 full-time professional; 1 part-time professional.
EIN: 222285358

4066
The Arnold Garrison Foundation ✧ ☆
(formerly Arnold Garrison Charitable Foundation)
c/o Choate, LLP
P.O. Box 961019
Boston, MA 02196-1019

Established in 1993 in MA.
Donor: Arnold Garrison†.
Foundation type: Independent foundation.
Financial data (yr. ended 06/30/13): Assets, $8,316,743 (M); gifts received, $7,791,805; expenditures, $590,789; qualifying distributions, $590,456; giving activities include $590,000 for 9 grants (high: $200,000; low: $1,000).
Fields of interest: Education; Medical research; Youth development.
Type of support: General/operating support.
Limitations: Applications not accepted. Giving primarily in IN, MA, NJ and VA. No grants to individuals.
Application information: Unsolicited requests for funds not accepted.
Trustees: John M. Cornish; Timothy P. Garrison.
EIN: 043216929
Selected grants: The following grants are a representative sample of this grantmaker's funding activity:
$100,000 to University of the Cumberlands, Vineland, NJ, 2013. For general support.
$50,000 to Advanced Medical Research Foundation, Boston, MA, 2013. For general support.
$25,000 to Hillside School, Marlborough, MA, 2013. For general support.
$25,000 to Jackson Historical Society, Jackson, NH, 2013. For general support.
$1,000 to Ethel Walker School, Simsbury, CT, 2013. For general support.
$1,000 to Gow School, South Wales, NY, 2013. For general support.

4067
Genzyme Charitable Foundation, Inc. ✧
500 Kendall St.
Cambridge, MA 02142-1108 (800) 745-447
E-mail: CharitableAccessProgram@genzyme.com; Additional tel.: (617) 768-9009; Main URL: http://www.genzyme.com/Patients/Patient-Support-Services.aspx
Charitable Access Program Website: http://www.cerezyme.com/healthcare/product_services/Charitable%20Access%20Program.aspx

Established as a company-sponsored operating foundation in 1997 in MA.

Donor: Genzyme Corp.
Foundation type: Operating foundation.
Financial data (yr. ended 12/31/13): Assets, $11,036 (M); gifts received, $78,604,357; expenditures, $78,604,357; qualifying distributions, $78,604,357; giving activities include $78,603,357 for grants to individuals.
Purpose and activities: The foundation provides prescription medication to economically disadvantaged individuals lacking prescription drug coverage.
Fields of interest: Health care; Economically disadvantaged.
Type of support: Grants to individuals; Donated products.
Limitations: Applications accepted. Giving on a national basis.
Application information: Application form required.
Initial approach: Telephone foundation for application form
Deadline(s): None
Board meeting date(s): Monthly
Officer and Directors:* David P. Meeker,* Pres.; Caren Arnstein, V.P.; Tracey L. Quarles, Secy.; Marc Esteva,* Treas.; Carlo Incerti.
EIN: 043236375

4068
Edward Payson George Charitable Trust ✧
Charles Street Sta.
P.O. Box 140334
Boston, MA 02114-0334 (617) 306-4917
Contact: Arthur E. Strout, Tr.
E-mail: calaes701@gmail.com

Established in 2001 in ME.
Donor: Edward Payson George Fundind Trust.
Foundation type: Independent foundation.
Financial data (yr. ended 12/31/13): Assets, $5,717,763 (M); expenditures, $845,512; qualifying distributions, $831,588; giving activities include $805,500 for 7 grants (high: $350,000; low: $2,500).
Fields of interest: Education; Medical care, community health systems; Health care; Human services.
Limitations: Applications accepted. Giving primarily in Boston, MA.
Application information: Application form required.
Initial approach: Letter
Deadline(s): None
Trustees: Paul E. Lynch, M.D.; Arthur E. Strout.
EIN: 016162330

4069
Germeshausen Foundation, Inc. ✧
c/o Silver Bridge Advisors
255 State St., 6th Fl.
Boston, MA 02109-2167 (617) 526-6610
Contact: Martin S. Kaplan, Tr.
FAX: (617) 526-5000;
E-mail: trustee@germeshausen.org; Main URL: http://www.germeshausen.org

Established in 1999 in MA.
Foundation type: Independent foundation.
Financial data (yr. ended 12/31/12): Assets, $25,612,811 (M); expenditures, $1,657,084; qualifying distributions, $1,441,871; giving activities include $1,293,590 for 49 grants (high: $225,000; low: $150).
Purpose and activities: Giving primarily for innovative approaches to positive change in youth culture, leadership development for young adults, environmental and ecological values, and imaginative media projects on current issues. In all grants, the foundation seeks to advance the idea of interconnectedness among people, and between people and the environment.
Fields of interest: Environment; Human services; Leadership development; Youth.
Type of support: General/operating support.
Limitations: Applications accepted. Giving on a national basis. No grants to individuals.
Publications: Application guidelines.
Application information: Application form not required.
Initial approach: Letter of inquiry (no more than 2 pages) via e-mail
Copies of proposal: 1
Deadline(s): None
Board meeting date(s): As needed
Officers and Trustees:* Nancy G. Klavans,* Pres.; Martin S. Kaplan,* Secy.-Treas.
EIN: 043485516
Selected grants: The following grants are a representative sample of this grantmaker's funding activity:
$165,000 to Harvard University, John F. Kennedy School of Government, Cambridge, MA, 2012. For Fellows Program in the Women and Public Policy Program.
$37,000 to Chester County Fund for Women and Girls, West Chester, PA, 2012. For Strategic Planning Process.
$10,000 to W G B H Educational Foundation, Boston, MA, 2012. For Annual Fund and Fund for New Programming.

4070
Gerondelis Foundation Inc. ✧
56 Central Ave., Ste. 201
Lynn, MA 01901-1112 (781) 595-3311
Contact: Gregory C. Demakis, Dir.

Established in 1966 in MA.
Foundation type: Independent foundation.
Financial data (yr. ended 12/31/12): Assets, $5,197,420 (M); expenditures, $531,129; qualifying distributions, $509,129; giving activities include $434,100 for 43 grants (high: $68,000; low: $2,000).
Purpose and activities: Giving primarily for higher education and for educational scholarships to students who are of at least one-fourth Greek lineage, reside or attend school in Essex County, MA, rank in the upper 15 percent of their class or have achieved a combined verbal math score of at least 1200 on the SAT I test, and officially be admitted to a 4-year college or university.
Fields of interest: Higher education; Education.
International interests: Greece.
Type of support: Scholarship funds; Scholarships—to individuals.
Limitations: Applications accepted. Giving primarily in MA.
Application information: Application form required.
Initial approach: Proposal
Deadline(s): None
Directors: T. Phillip Comenos; Gregory C. Demakis, Esq.; John N. Demakis; Paul C. Demakis, Esq.; Thomas C. Demakis, Esq.; Thomas L. Demakis; Athas Kourkousis; Nondas Lagonakis; George J. Macropoulous; Christopher Scangas; Russell Smith; Nicholas T. Zervas.
Number of staff: 1 part-time support.
EIN: 046130871

4071
The Edward & Janet Gildea Charitable Foundation ✧
c/o Gilmore Rees & Carlson
70 Walnut St.
Wellesley, MA 02481-2102

Established in 2002 in MA.
Donors: Edward J. Gildea; Janet F. Gildea; Gil-Wal Corp.
Foundation type: Independent foundation.
Financial data (yr. ended 05/31/11): Assets, $0 (M); expenditures, $663,244; qualifying distributions, $612,300; giving activities include $612,300 for 23 grants (high: $151,000; low: $300).
Fields of interest: Higher education, college; Education; Hospitals (specialty); Health care; Liver disorders; Health organizations; Human services; YM/YWCAs & YM/YWHAs; Children/youth, services; Christian agencies & churches.
Limitations: Applications not accepted. Giving primarily in MA. No grants to individuals.
Application information: Contributes only to pre-selected organizations.
Trustees: James Gildea; Ann H. Gildea O'Keefe.
EIN: 562296961
Selected grants: The following grants are a representative sample of this grantmaker's funding activity:
$151,000 to New England Center for Children, Southborough, MA, 2011.
$20,000 to Dana-Farber Cancer Institute, Boston, MA, 2011.
$5,000 to Middlesex Human Service Agency, Waltham, MA, 2011.
$5,000 to Rosies Place, Boston, MA, 2011.
$4,000 to Boston University, Boston, MA, 2011.
$4,000 to College of the Holy Cross, Worcester, MA, 2011.
$3,000 to New York University, New York, NY, 2011.

4072
Glass Charitable Foundation ✧ ☆
55 Old Village Rd.
Sturbridge, MA 01566-1070

Established in 1998 in MA.
Donors: Robert I. Glass; Sandra A. Glass.
Foundation type: Independent foundation.
Financial data (yr. ended 12/31/12): Assets, $7,756,277 (M); gifts received, $2,094,933; expenditures, $565,510; qualifying distributions, $516,000; giving activities include $516,000 for grants.
Fields of interest: Higher education, university; Education.
Limitations: Applications not accepted. Giving primarily in MA. No grants to individuals.
Application information: Unsolicited requests for funds not accepted.
Trustees: Jeffrey D. Glass; Jonathan Glass; Scott L. Glass; Dale St. Lawrence.
EIN: 367255316

Selected grants: The following grants are a representative sample of this grantmaker's funding activity:
$29,000 to Pomfret School, Pomfret, CT, 2011. For general use.
$20,000 to Cooley Dickinson Hospital, Northampton, MA, 2011. For general use.
$20,000 to Northampton Survival Center, Northampton, MA, 2011. For general use.
$20,000 to Smile Train, Washington, DC, 2011. For general use.
$11,000 to Thompson Ecumenical Empowerment Group, North Grosvenordale, CT, 2011. For general use.
$10,000 to Wyndham Land Trust, Pomfret Center, CT, 2011. For general use.
$5,000 to University of Colorado Foundation, Boulder, CO, 2011. For general use.

4073
Jackson and Irene Golden 1989 Charitable Trust ✧
400 Atlantic Ave., Ste. 401
Boston, MA 02110-3333

Established in 1991 in FL.
Donor: Irene L. Golden.
Foundation type: Independent foundation.
Financial data (yr. ended 11/30/13): Assets, $11,037,529 (M); expenditures, $655,779; qualifying distributions, $558,271; giving activities include $526,800 for 31 grants (high: $107,500; low: $1,500).
Fields of interest: Arts; Education; Hospitals (general); Health care, clinics/centers; Health care; Legal services; Human services; Civil/human rights, minorities; Civil liberties, advocacy; United Ways and Federated Giving Programs; Jewish federated giving programs; Jewish agencies & synagogues.
Limitations: Applications not accepted. Giving primarily in Washington, DC, and MA. No grants to individuals.
Application information: Contributes only to pre-selected organizations.
Trustees: Jamie Golden; Robert P. Goldman; Andrew Rothstein; Donald L. Shulman.
EIN: 043150178

4074
Gordon Family Foundation ✧
c/o Michael S. Gordon
126 Brookline Ave.
Boston, MA 02215-3920

Established in 1997 in MA.
Donor: Michael S. Gordon.
Foundation type: Independent foundation.
Financial data (yr. ended 12/31/13): Assets, $34,232,298 (M); expenditures, $3,163,258; qualifying distributions, $3,103,188; giving activities include $3,103,188 for 28 grants (high: $500,000; low: $500).
Purpose and activities: Giving for education and Jewish organizations; funding also for children, youth, and social services.
Fields of interest: Education; Human services; Children/youth, services; Jewish federated giving programs.
Type of support: General/operating support; Scholarship funds.
Limitations: Applications not accepted. Giving primarily in MA. No grants to individuals.
Application information: Contributes only to pre-selected organizations.
Trustees: Christina M. Gordon; Michael S. Gordon.
EIN: 137130595

4075
Gordon Foundation ✧
16B Electronics Ave.
Danvers, MA 01923-1011 (978) 750-6100
Contact: Bernard M. Gordon, Tr.

Established around 1983 in MA.
Donors: Frank B. Gordon; Bernard M. Gordon; Bernard M. Gordon Charitable Remainder Unitrust.
Foundation type: Operating foundation.
Financial data (yr. ended 12/31/13): Assets, $835,402 (M); gifts received, $6,600,000; expenditures, $6,501,541; qualifying distributions, $6,489,333; giving activities include $6,488,833 for 11 grants (high: $1,500,000; low: $7,500).
Fields of interest: Museums (science/technology); Higher education; Engineering school/education; Health organizations, association; Jewish agencies & synagogues.
Limitations: Giving primarily in MA.
Application information: Application form not required.
Initial approach: Proposal
Deadline(s): None
Final notification: Usually within 2 months
Trustees: Bernard M. Gordon; Daniel Lewis Gordon; Sophia Gordon; Robert Stewart.
EIN: 042794647
Selected grants: The following grants are a representative sample of this grantmaker's funding activity:
$1,533,534 to Massachusetts Institute of Technology, Cambridge, MA, 2012. For Engineering Leadership Program.
$1,500,000 to Museum of Science, Boston, MA, 2012. For engineering and technology education.
$1,500,000 to Northeastern University, Boston, MA, 2012. For Leadership Program.
$600,000 to American Society for Technion-Israel Institute of Technology, New England Region, Newton, MA, 2012. For Engineering Leadership Program.
$600,000 to University of California at San Diego, La Jolla, CA, 2012. For Engineering Leadership Program.
$500,000 to Worcester Polytechnic Institute, Worcester, MA, 2012. For Dean of Engineering position.
$300,000 to Citadel Foundation, Charleston, SC, 2012. For unrestricted support.
$10,000 to Yeshiva Achei Tmimim Lubavitz of Springfield, Longmeadow, MA, 2012. For unrestricted support.

4076
Grand Circle Foundation, Inc. ✧
347 Congress St.
Boston, MA 02210-1280 (617) 346-6602
FAX: (617) 346-6030;
E-mail: foundation@grandcirclefoundation.org; Contact for Grand Circle Association Fund: Lianne Hughes, Boston Community Initiative Coord., e-mail: LHughes@grandcirclefoundation.org; Additional tel.: (800) 859-0852;; Main URL: http://www.grandcirclefoundation.org/
E-Newsletter: https://picpacplus.dsgraphics.com/GCF/
Facebook: http://www.facebook.com/pages/Grand-Circle-Foundation/89374752660
Grand Ciricle Associates Fund Recipients: http://www.grandcirclefoundation.org/About-Us/Press-and-Media/Announcing-our-2011-Associates-Fund-Recipients.aspx
Twitter: http://twitter.com/GCFgivesback

Established in 1993 in MA.
Donors: Grand Circle Corp.; Overseas Adventure Travel; Alan E. Lewis; Harriet R. Lewis; Grand Circle Trust; Grand Circle Travel.
Foundation type: Company-sponsored foundation.
Financial data (yr. ended 12/31/13): Assets, $4,264,375 (M); gifts received, $3,181,589; expenditures, $4,598,891; qualifying distributions, $1,786,450; giving activities include $1,786,450 for grants.
Purpose and activities: The foundation supports programs designed to identify and develop gutsy leaders who create social change and economic opportunity; partner with leaders in the villages where Grand Circle members travel, live, and work to create jobs, improve school performance, support small business, and promote the health and safety of citizens; and bring together in dialogue and action Grand Circle associates, travelers, travel partners, and leaders around a shared set of values and goals to create change.
Fields of interest: Arts, cultural/ethnic awareness; Elementary school/education; Education, drop-out prevention; Education, reading; Education; Health care; Employment; Youth development; Human services; Economic development; Rural development; Social entrepreneurship; Community development, small businesses; Aging.
International interests: Africa; Asia; Europe; Italy; Mexico; South America; Thailand; Turkey.
Type of support: Continuing support; Building/renovation; Equipment; Program development; Curriculum development; Employee volunteer services; Employee matching gifts.
Limitations: Applications accepted. Giving primarily in MA, with emphasis on Allston, Dorchester, Mattapan, and Roxbury; some giving in Africa, Asia, Chile, China, Costa Rica, Croatia, Egypt, Europe, Italy, Kenya, Mexico, Namibia, Peru, South America, Tanzania, Thailand, Turkey, and Zimbabwe. No support for discriminatory, political, or religious organizations. No grants to individuals, or for general operating support, administrative costs, salaries, advertising, or dinner table sponsorship.
Publications: Application guidelines; Annual report; Newsletter.
Application information: Proposals should be limited to 2 to 3 pages. Support is limited to 1 contribution per organization during any given year. Organizations receiving support are asked to provide a final report. Application form not required.
Initial approach: E-mail proposal for Grand Circle Associates Fund
Copies of proposal: 1
Deadline(s): Mar. 25 and Oct. 25 for Grand Circle Associates Fund
Board meeting date(s): May, Aug., and Dec.
Officers and Directors:* Alan E. Lewis,* Co-Chair.; Harriet R. Lewis,* Co-Chair.; Martha Prybylo, V.P.
Number of staff: 2 full-time professional.
EIN: 043175434

4077
Grantham Foundation for the Protection of the Environment ✧
(formerly Jeremy and Hannelore Grantham Charitable Trust)
40 Rowes Wharf
Boston, MA 02110-3340 (617) 453-8432
Contact: Jeremy Grantham, Tr.
Main URL: http://www.granthamfoundation.org/

Established in 1997 in MA.
Donors: R. Jeremy Grantham; Eric Oddleifson.
Foundation type: Independent foundation.
Financial data (yr. ended 12/31/13): Assets, $394,136,609 (M); gifts received, $21,600,000; expenditures, $23,408,488; qualifying distributions, $19,032,205; giving activities include $18,911,867 for 62 grants (high: $3,000,000; low: $10,000).
Purpose and activities: To help protect and improve the health of the global environment.
Fields of interest: Education; Environment, legal rights; Environment, natural resources; Environment.
Limitations: Applications not accepted. Giving primarily in MA, VA, and Washington, DC; funding also in London, England. No grants to individuals.
Application information: Contributes only to pre-selected organizations.
Office and Trustees: Ramsay Ravenel, Exec. Dir.; Isable Grantham; Jeremy Grantham; Oliver Grantham; Rupert Grantham.
EIN: 046856456
Selected grants: The following grants are a representative sample of this grantmaker's funding activity:
$3,000,000 to Sierra Club, San Francisco, CA, 2012. For environmental work.
$2,088,108 to Imperial College of London, London, England, 2012. For environmental work.
$2,060,420 to London School of Economics and Political Science, London, England, 2012. For environmental work.
$2,000,000 to Environmental Defense Fund, Washington, DC, 2012. For environmental work.
$1,500,000 to Energy Foundation, San Francisco, CA, 2012. For environmental work.
$800,000 to ClimateWorks Foundation, San Francisco, CA, 2012. For environmental work.
$600,000 to Indian Institute of Science, Bangalore, India, 2012. For environmental work.
$500,000 to Center for Public Integrity, Washington, DC, 2012. For environmental work.
$500,000 to Proyecto Mirador Foundation, Kentfield, CA, 2012. For environmental work.
$100,000 to Environmental League of Massachusetts, Boston, MA, 2012. For environmental work.

4078
Grayson Family Foundation, Inc. ✧
c/o ABS Ventures
950 Winter St., Ste. 2600
Waltham, MA 02451-1488

Established in 1996 in MD.
Donor: Bruns H. Grayson.
Foundation type: Independent foundation.
Financial data (yr. ended 12/31/13): Assets, $13,838,848 (M); gifts received, $929,925; expenditures, $592,440; qualifying distributions, $589,500; giving activities include $589,500 for 35 grants (high: $200,000; low: $500).
Purpose and activities: Giving primarily for education.
Fields of interest: Museums (history); Arts; Elementary/secondary education; Higher education; United Ways and Federated Giving Programs; Christian agencies & churches.
Type of support: General/operating support; Annual campaigns.
Limitations: Applications accepted. Giving primarily in AL, MA, MD, NH, and NY. No grants to individuals.
Application information: Application form required.
Initial approach: Letter
Deadline(s): None
Officers: Bruns H. Grayson, Pres.; Perrin M. Grayson, Secy.-Treas.
Trustee: Lucy P. Grayson.
EIN: 522007478
Selected grants: The following grants are a representative sample of this grantmaker's funding activity:
$100,000 to American Trust for Oxford University, Tuscaloosa, AL, 2011.
$75,000 to Saint Pauls School, Concord, NH, 2011.
$72,775 to Radcliffe College, Cambridge, MA, 2010.
$25,000 to University of Virginia Fund, Charlottesville, VA, 2011.
$20,000 to Teach for America, New York, NY, 2011.
$10,000 to Codman Academy Foundation, Dorchester, MA, 2011.
$10,000 to Rapoport Academy, Waco, TX, 2011.
$5,000 to Young Scholars Charter School, Philadelphia, PA, 2011.
$2,500 to Association of American Rhodes Scholars, Vienna, VA, 2011.
$2,500 to Madeira School, McLean, VA, 2011.
$2,000 to Saint Joseph Notre Dame High School, Alameda, CA, 2011.

4079
Grimshaw-Gudewicz Charitable Foundation ✧
c/o A. Shabshelowitz
263 Walnut St.
Fall River, MA 02720-2426
Application address: c/o Anne Fazendeiro, 173 Auburn St., New Bedford, MA 02740, tel.: (508) 997-2297

Established in 1995 in NH.
Foundation type: Independent foundation.
Financial data (yr. ended 12/31/13): Assets, $30,410,352 (M); expenditures, $1,734,287; qualifying distributions, $1,474,259; giving activities include $1,400,000 for 85 grants (high: $140,000; low: $500).
Purpose and activities: Giving primarily for the arts, and education, particularly education aimed at the enhancement of business and entrepreneurial skills; funding also for health care, and the preservation of local culture. The foundation's trustees also favor organizations that will provide a lasting named memorial whenever possible.
Fields of interest: Arts; Secondary school/education; Higher education; Education; Health organizations, association.
Limitations: Applications accepted. Giving primarily in Bristol County, MA, proximate RI areas, the Peterborough, NH, area and in locations that can affect or benefit the inhabitants of southeastern MA, RI, and NH. No grants to individuals.
Application information: Application form required.
Initial approach: Letter
Deadline(s): None
Trustees: Anne Fazendeiro; Arthur Parker; Andrew Shabshelowitz; Bernard A.G. Taradash.
EIN: 046778721

4080
The Harold Grinspoon Charitable Foundation ✧
67 Hunt St., Ste. 100
Agawam, MA 01001-1913 (413) 276-0700
Contact: Harold Grinspoon, Tr.
FAX: (413) 276-0804; E-mail: info@hgf.org; Main URL: http://www.hgf.org

Established in 1986 in MA.
Donors: Harold Grinspoon; Diane Troderman; Massmutual Financial Group.
Foundation type: Independent foundation.
Financial data (yr. ended 08/31/13): Assets, $8,382,999 (M); gifts received, $955,272; expenditures, $1,012,682; qualifying distributions, $956,794; giving activities include $511,669 for 28 grants (high: $220,000; low: $250), and $179,950 for 241 grants to individuals (high: $4,100; low: $50).
Purpose and activities: Giving primarily to: 1) encourage young people to reach their academic and leadership potential; 2) promote literacy and early childhood education; 3) reward excellence in teaching and education; 4) support entrepreneurship among young people; and 5) promote education and health in Cambodia.
Fields of interest: Arts; Education; Cancer research; Youth development; Human services; Jewish agencies & synagogues; Women.
International interests: Cambodia; Israel.
Type of support: General/operating support; Annual campaigns; Endowments; Program development; Scholarship funds; Program-related investments/loans.
Limitations: Giving primarily in western MA. No grants to individuals (except for research projects), or for scholarships or student aid.
Publications: Annual report; Financial statement; Multi-year report.
Application information: See foundation web site for specific application instructions.
Trustees: Michael Bohnen; David Galper; Rabbi Irving "Yitz" Greenberg; Harold Grinspoon; Winnie Sandler Grinspoon; Jeremy Pava; Lauren Spitz; Diane Troderman; Leigh Weiss.
Number of staff: 2 full-time professional; 2 part-time support.
EIN: 222738277

4081
The Phillip and Elizabeth Gross Family Foundation ✧
c/o Howland Capital Mgmt., Inc.
75 Federal St., Ste. 1100
Boston, MA 02110-1911

Established in 1998 in MA.
Donors: Phillip T. Gross; Elizabeth Cochary Gross.
Foundation type: Independent foundation.
Financial data (yr. ended 12/31/13): Assets, $64,035,874 (M); gifts received, $13,000,000; expenditures, $3,352,509; qualifying distributions, $3,282,970; giving activities include $3,282,970 for 30 grants (high: $900,000; low: $2,500).

Fields of interest: Higher education; Education; Cancer research; Athletics/sports, winter sports; Recreation; Human services; Children/youth, services; Foundations (private independent).
Limitations: Applications not accepted. Giving primarily in MA, with emphasis on Boston and Concord. No grants to individuals.
Application information: Contributes only to pre-selected organizations.
Trustees: Elizabeth Cochary Gross; Phillip T. Gross; Thomas V. Quirk.
EIN: 046878795

4082
The Gruben Charitable Foundation ✧
(formerly The Diana Oehrli Charitable Trust)
c/o J. Robert Casey
400 Atlantic Ave.
Boston, MA 02110-3333

Established in 2007 in MA.
Donor: Diana Oehrli.
Foundation type: Independent foundation.
Financial data (yr. ended 12/31/13): Assets, $13,675,164 (M); expenditures, $592,126; qualifying distributions, $535,968; giving activities include $498,500 for 14 grants (high: $80,000; low: $10,000).
Fields of interest: Education; Environmental education; Animals/wildlife, bird preserves; Recreation, camps; Family services; Women, centers/services.
Limitations: Applications not accepted. Giving primarily in MI, NY and RI.
Application information: Contributes only to pre-selected organizations.
Trustee: J. Robert Casey; Diana Oehrli.
EIN: 261944179

4083
Haley Family Foundation ✧
c/o Steven and Kathleen Haley
148 Linden St., Ste. 303
Wellesley, MA 02482-7970

Established in 1998 in MA.
Donors: Steven Haley; Kathleen Powers Haley; Snows Hill, LLC.
Foundation type: Independent foundation.
Financial data (yr. ended 12/31/13): Assets, $1,591,615 (M); gifts received, $60,000; expenditures, $621,340; qualifying distributions, $558,150; giving activities include $558,115 for 5 grants (high: $447,000; low: $500).
Purpose and activities: Giving primarily for education and youth services.
Fields of interest: Performing arts; Elementary/secondary education; Higher education; Health care; Health organizations; Human services.
Limitations: Applications not accepted. Giving primarily in MA. No grants to individuals.
Application information: Contributes only to pre-selected organizations.
Trustees: Kathleen Powers Haley; Steven Haley.
EIN: 043356222
Selected grants: The following grants are a representative sample of this grantmaker's funding activity:
$320,000 to Brain Science Foundation, Wellesley, MA, 2011. For research.
$58,000 to Brain Science Foundation, Wellesley, MA, 2011. For research.
$10,000 to Camp Harbor View Foundation, Boston, MA, 2011.
$1,000 to Wake Forest University, Winston-Salem, NC, 2011.

4084
Bushrod H. Campbell & Adah F. Hall Charity Fund ✧
c/o Hemenway & Barnes LLP
P.O. Box 961209
Boston, MA 02196-1209
Application address: c/o Arthur B. Page, Esq., Hemenway & Barnes LLP, 60 State St., Boston, MA 02109, tel.: (617) 227-7940

Established in 1956 in MA.
Donors: Bushrod H. Campbell‡; Adah F. Hall‡.
Foundation type: Independent foundation.
Financial data (yr. ended 05/31/13): Assets, $19,810,533 (M); expenditures, $1,108,400; qualifying distributions, $977,852; giving activities include $895,500 for 124 grants (high: $55,000; low: $2,000).
Purpose and activities: Areas of interest include projects that support aid to the elderly, some healthcare programs outside of hospitals/direct care, and reproductive health.
Fields of interest: Reproductive health, family planning; Health organizations, association; Medical research, institute; Aging, centers/services; Aging.
Type of support: General/operating support; Continuing support; Building/renovation; Program development; Seed money; Research.
Limitations: Applications accepted. Giving limited to the greater Boston, MA, area (within Route 128 and Boston); giving on a national basis to organizations dealing with reproductive health. No grants to individuals, or for annual campaigns, emergency funds, deficit financing, land acquisition, publications, or general endowments; no loans.
Publications: Application guidelines; Grants list; Informational brochure.
Application information: Application form required.
Initial approach: Proposal
Copies of proposal: 1
Deadline(s): 1st day of Jan., Apr., Aug., and Oct.
Board meeting date(s): Feb., May, Sept., and Nov.
Trustees: George P. Beal; Nancy B. Gardiner; Arthur B. Page; Curtis Prout, M.D.
Number of staff: 1 part-time professional.
EIN: 046013598
Selected grants: The following grants are a representative sample of this grantmaker's funding activity:
$30,000 to Health Resources in Action, Boston, MA, 2011. For general support.
$17,500 to Boston Partners in Education, Boston, MA, 2011. For general support.
$17,000 to Bridge Fund, Washington, DC, 2011. For general support.
$12,500 to ROCA, Chelsea, MA, 2011. For general support.
$11,000 to Pathfinder International, Watertown, MA, 2011. For general support.
$10,000 to Boston Medical Center, Boston, MA, 2011. For general support.
$8,000 to Cambridge School Volunteers, Cambridge, MA, 2011. For general support.
$8,000 to Heading Home, Charlestown, MA, 2011. For general support.
$7,000 to Boston Area Rape Crisis Center, Cambridge, MA, 2011. For general support.
$6,000 to Somerville-Cambridge Elder Services, Somerville, MA, 2011. For general support.

4085
The Hamilton Company Charitable Foundation ✧
39 Brighton Ave.
Allston, MA 02134-2301 (617) 783-0039
Contact: Jameson Brown, Tr.

Established in 2011 in MA.
Donor: The Harold Brown Charitable lead & Annuity Trust.
Foundation type: Independent foundation.
Financial data (yr. ended 12/31/13): Assets, $12,581,886 (M); gifts received, $5,485,973; expenditures, $667,808; qualifying distributions, $604,300; giving activities include $604,300 for 69 grants (high: $50,000; low: $150).
Fields of interest: Arts; Health care; Housing/shelter.
Limitations: Applications accepted. Giving primarily in MA.
Application information: Application form not required.
Initial approach: Proposal
Deadline(s): None
Trustees: Jameson Brown; Maura Brown; Frederick Lebow; Robert Somma; Carl Valeri.
EIN: 277018900

4086
The Hanover Insurance Group Foundation, Inc. ✧
(formerly Allmerica Financial Charitable Foundation, Inc.)
440 Lincoln St., N100
Worcester, MA 01653-0002 (508) 855-2524
Contact: Jennifer Luisa, Asst. V.P., Community Rels.
E-mail: foundation@hanover.com; Michigan application address: Becky E. Best, Mgr., Corp. Community Rels., Citizens Insurance Co. of America, 808 Highlander Way, HWC340, Howell, MI 48843, tel.: (517) 540-4290, e-mail: bbest@hanover.com; Main URL: http://www.hanover.com/about-foundation.html

Established in 1990 in MA.
Donors: First Allmerica Financial Life Insurance Co.; The Hanover Insurance Co.
Foundation type: Company-sponsored foundation.
Financial data (yr. ended 12/31/13): Assets, $6,520,627 (M); gifts received, $2,600,000; expenditures, $1,874,914; qualifying distributions, $1,874,914; giving activities include $1,821,508 for 426 grants (high: $500,000; low: $50).
Purpose and activities: The foundation supports organizations involved with arts and culture, health, medical research, hunger, housing, human services, and community development. Special emphasis is directed toward programs designed to build world class public education systems; and inspire and empower youth to achieve their full potential.
Fields of interest: Visual arts; Performing arts; Arts; Higher education; Education, reading; Education; Health care; Medical research; Food services; Housing/shelter; Youth development; Aging, centers/services; Homeless, human services;

Human services; Community/economic development; Youth.
Type of support: General/operating support; Building/renovation; Program development; Scholarship funds; Employee volunteer services; Employee-related scholarships; Scholarships—to individuals.
Limitations: Applications accepted. Giving primarily in areas of company operations in the greater Worcester County, MA, area and the Howell and Livingston County, MI, area. No support for private schools, amateur or professional sporting groups, or religious, political, professional, fraternal, or labor organizations. No grants to individuals (except for scholarships), or for national fundraising drives, capital campaigns, or beauty or talent contests.
Publications: Application guidelines; Corporate giving report; Program policy statement.
Application information: Support is limited to 1 contribution per organization during any given year. Organizations receiving support are asked to provide a final report. Application form required.
Initial approach: Download application form and mail to application address
Deadline(s): Jan. 15, Apr. 15, July 15, and Sept. 15
Board meeting date(s): Mar., June, Sept., and Nov.
Officers and Directors:* Jennifer F. Luisa,* Pres.; Charles F. Cronin, Clerk; Celeste J. Nelson, Treas.; Ann K. Tripp, Investment Off.; Maribeth N. Bearfield; Frederick H. Eppinger.
EIN: 043105650
Selected grants: The following grants are a representative sample of this grantmaker's funding activity:
$749,633 to Worcester Center for Performing Arts, Worcester, MA, 2011.
$60,000 to Reading Matters, Boston, MA, 2011.
$55,000 to United Way of Central Massachusetts, Worcester, MA, 2011.
$55,000 to United Way of Central Massachusetts, Worcester, MA, 2011.
$25,000 to YMCA of Central Massachusetts, Worcester, MA, 2011.
$20,000 to Central Massachusetts Housing Alliance, Worcester, MA, 2011.
$13,000 to American Heart Association, Framingham, MA, 2011.
$10,000 to Audubon Society, Massachusetts, Worcester, MA, 2011.
$10,000 to Boys and Girls Club of Worcester, Worcester, MA, 2011.
$5,000 to American Antiquarian Society, Worcester, MA, 2011.

4087
Esmond Harmsworth 1997 Charitable Foundation ✧
535 Boylston St., Ste. 1103
Boston, MA 02116-3768

Established in 1998 in MA.
Donor: Esmond Harmsworth.
Foundation type: Independent foundation.
Financial data (yr. ended 04/30/13): Assets, $6,449 (M); gifts received, $439,833; expenditures, $436,981; qualifying distributions, $435,833; giving activities include $435,833 for grants.
Purpose and activities: Giving primarily for education, AIDS research, gay and lesbian organizations, and social services.
Fields of interest: Education, special; Education; AIDS research; Human services; Civil/human rights, LGBTQ; LGBTQ.
Limitations: Applications not accepted. Giving primarily in MA and NY. No grants to individuals.
Application information: Contributes only to pre-selected organizations.
Trustees: Esmond Harmsworth; James Richardson.
Number of staff: None.
EIN: 046838152

4088
Francis A. & Jacquelyn H. Harrington Foundation ✧
370 Main St., 12th Fl.
Worcester, MA 01608-1723 (508) 798-8621
Contact: Sumner B. Tilton, Jr., Tr.

Established in 1965 in MA.
Donors: Francis A. Harrington†; Jacquelyn H. Harrington†.
Foundation type: Independent foundation.
Financial data (yr. ended 12/31/12): Assets, $10,148,260 (M); expenditures, $1,515,521; qualifying distributions, $1,423,224; giving activities include $1,342,696 for 16 grants (high: $1,000,000; low: $3,000).
Purpose and activities: Giving primarily for arts and culture, education, and health organizations.
Fields of interest: Arts; Elementary/secondary education; Higher education; Health organizations, association; Boys & girls clubs.
Type of support: General/operating support; Capital campaigns; Equipment; Program development.
Limitations: Giving primarily in Worcester, MA. No support for human services. No grants to individuals, or for scholarships; no loans.
Application information: Application form required.
Initial approach: Letter
Copies of proposal: 1
Deadline(s): June 1
Board meeting date(s): June and Dec. 15
Trustees: Francis A. Harrington, Jr.; James H. Harrington; Phyllis Harrington; Sumner B. Tilton, Jr.
Number of staff: 1 part-time professional.
EIN: 046125088

4089
William H. Harris Foundation ✧
19 Windemere Cir.
Braintree, MA 02184-4505

Established in MA.
Donors: William H. Harris, M.D.; Johanna H. Harris.
Foundation type: Independent foundation.
Financial data (yr. ended 12/31/13): Assets, $8,328,873 (M); expenditures, $614,353; qualifying distributions, $467,815; giving activities include $435,565 for 23 grants (high: $250,000; low: $500).
Purpose and activities: Support for higher education, environmental sciences, and medical research, including orthopedic biomechanics and biomaterials research.
Fields of interest: Higher education; Environment, natural resources; Animals/wildlife; Medical research, institute; Medical research; Orthopedics research.
Type of support: Research.
Limitations: Applications not accepted. Giving in the U.S., with some emphasis on PA. No grants to individuals.
Application information: Unsolicited requests for funds not accepted.
Trustees: Johanna H. Harris; William H. Harris, M.D.
EIN: 046197960

4090
The Heartstone Foundation ✧
42 Fisher Ave.
Brookline, MA 02445

Established in 2004 in MA.
Donor: Julie Swartz.
Foundation type: Independent foundation.
Financial data (yr. ended 12/31/13): Assets, $16,926,820 (M); expenditures, $843,346; qualifying distributions, $749,746; giving activities include $743,339 for 3 grants (high: $344,339; low: $199,000).
Fields of interest: Foundations (public); Jewish federated giving programs; Jewish agencies & synagogues.
Limitations: Applications not accepted. No grants to individuals.
Application information: Unsolicited requests for funds not accepted.
Trustee: Julie Swartz.
EIN: 206197750

4091
The Ulf B. and Elizabeth C. Heide Foundation Charitable Trust ✧
c/o Frank P. Conrad
8 Cedar Rd.
Weston, MA 02493-2419

Established in 1991 in MA.
Donor: Ulf B. Heide.
Foundation type: Independent foundation.
Financial data (yr. ended 12/31/13): Assets, $10,339,229 (M); expenditures, $613,587; qualifying distributions, $548,150; giving activities include $548,150 for 32 grants (high: $223,400; low: $50).
Purpose and activities: Giving primarily for the arts, particularly to an art museum; funding also for education and human services.
Fields of interest: Museums (art); Performing arts, orchestras; Higher education; Education; Human services.
Limitations: Applications not accepted. Giving primarily in MA. No grants to individuals.
Application information: Contributes only to pre-selected organizations.
Trustees: Frank P. Conrad; Elizabeth C. Heide; Elizabeth H. Heide; Ulf B. Heide.
EIN: 046665830
Selected grants: The following grants are a representative sample of this grantmaker's funding activity:
$250 to Pleon Yacht Club, Marblehead, MA, 2012. For general charitable.

4092
Andrew David Heitman Foundation ✧ ☆
255 Washington St., Ste. 340
Newton, MA 02458-1634

Established in MA.
Donor: Ann D. Heitman†.
Foundation type: Independent foundation.
Financial data (yr. ended 12/31/12): Assets, $3,753,817 (M); gifts received, $613,794; expenditures, $1,511,568; qualifying distributions, $1,500,000; giving activities include $1,500,000 for 1 grant.
Fields of interest: Hospitals (general).
Limitations: Applications not accepted. Giving primarily in Boston, MA. No grants to individuals.
Application information: Unsolicited requests for funds not accepted.
Officers and Directors:* Stephen P. Koster,* Pres.; Kenneth J. Vacovec,* Clerk and Treas.
EIN: 264503446

4093
The Stephen J. Hendrickson Foundation, Inc. ✧ ☆
1 Charles St. S., PH. 2A
Boston, MA 02116-5460
Contact: S.J. Hendrickson

Established in 1991 in MA.
Donor: Stephen J. Hendrickson.
Foundation type: Independent foundation.
Financial data (yr. ended 06/30/13): Assets, $12,795,875 (M); gifts received, $665,487; expenditures, $725,554; qualifying distributions, $656,823; giving activities include $650,000 for 1 grant.
Purpose and activities: Giving primarily to Christian churches and organizations.
Fields of interest: Religion.
Limitations: Applications not accepted. Giving primarily in Cambridge and Boston, MA; some funding also in the United Kingdom. No grants to individuals.
Application information: Unsolicited requests for funds not accepted.
Officers and Directors:* Stephen J. Hendrickson,* Pres. and Treas.; T. Kirkland Ware III,* Clerk; G. Timothy Johnson, M.D.
EIN: 043140238

4094
Hermann Foundation, Inc. ✧
370 Main St., Ste. 925
Worcester, MA 01608-1797 (508) 756-4657
Contact: Henry Lusardi, Secy.-Treas. and Dir.

Established in 2003 in MA.
Donors: Francoise Hermann†; Francoise Hermann Charitable Remainder Trust 2000.
Foundation type: Independent foundation.
Financial data (yr. ended 12/31/13): Assets, $66,146,245 (M); expenditures, $3,442,309; qualifying distributions, $3,001,333; giving activities include $3,001,333 for 72 grants (high: $133,334; low: $10,000).
Purpose and activities: Giving primarily for health care and medical research, as well as for education, and children, youth, and social services.
Fields of interest: Arts; Higher education; Health care; Medical research, institute; Human services; Children/youth, services.
Limitations: Applications accepted. Giving primarily in MA. No grants to individuals.
Application information: Application form required.
Initial approach: Letter
Deadline(s): None
Officers and Directors:* Maria Starzyk,* Pres.; Henry Lusardi,* Secy.-Treas.; Melissa Dodson; Edward Starzyk.
EIN: 562385301

4095
The Hershey Family Foundation ✧
(formerly Barry J. Hershey Foundation)
c/o Ropes & Gray
800 Boylston St., Ste. 3600
Boston, MA 02199-3600

Established around 1988 in MA.
Donor: Barry J. Hershey.
Foundation type: Independent foundation.
Financial data (yr. ended 12/31/13): Assets, $73,961,371 (M); gifts received, $42,624; expenditures, $4,177,874; qualifying distributions, $4,064,571; giving activities include $4,051,171 for 41 grants (high: $1,165,000; low: $15,000).
Purpose and activities: Giving primarily for the arts, education, health, and human services.
Fields of interest: Performing arts, theater; Arts; Elementary/secondary education; Health care; Food services; Human services; Human services, mind/body enrichment; International affairs; Public affairs, public education.
Limitations: Applications not accepted. Giving primarily in CA and MA. Generally, no grants to individuals.
Application information: Contributes only to pre-selected organizations. Unsolicited requests for funds not accepted.
Trustees: Barry J. Hershey; Connie Hershey.
EIN: 341574366

4096
The Robert F. Higgins Foundation ✧ ☆
c/o JDJ Family Office
2 International Pl.
Boston, MA 02110

Established in 1999 in MA.
Donor: Robert F. Higgins.
Foundation type: Independent foundation.
Financial data (yr. ended 12/31/13): Assets, $7,818,602 (M); expenditures, $860,701; qualifying distributions, $747,928; giving activities include $747,893 for 41 grants (high: $260,000; low: $500).
Fields of interest: Museums; Elementary/secondary education; Business school/education; Hospitals (general); Health care, clinics/centers.
Type of support: General/operating support; Research.
Limitations: Applications not accepted. Giving primarily in MA. No grants to individuals.
Application information: Contributes only to pre-selected organizations.
Trustee: Robert F. Higgins.
EIN: 046906900

4097
High Meadows Foundation ✧
c/o Carl Ferenbach
P.O. Box 171754
Boston, MA 02116
E-mail: info@highmeadowsgroup.org; Main URL: http://www.highmeadowsfoundation.com

Established in 2007 in MA.
Donors: Carl Ferenbach; Judy Ferenbach.
Foundation type: Independent foundation.
Financial data (yr. ended 12/31/12): Assets, $7,534,960 (M); gifts received, $15,462,398; expenditures, $7,967,807; qualifying distributions, $7,912,070; giving activities include $7,912,070 for 29 grants (high: $2,000,000; low: $10,000).
Purpose and activities: Giving primarily to ensure sound environmental stewardship of our planet; for the management and conservation of non-working farm land in northern New England; for the development of a 21st century social contract; and for the preservation and enhancement of the art of the book beyond the content of its pages. Giving also, on a program specific basis, for education and fellowships that are related to the work of the organizations that the foundation supports.
Fields of interest: Higher education; Education; Environment, natural resources.
Limitations: Applications not accepted. Giving primarily in CO and NJ; some funding in MA and NY.
Application information: Contributes only to pre-selected organizations.
Officers and Trustees:* Carl Ferenbach,* Chair.; Lynne Ball, Secy.-Treas.; Jeffrey L. Berenson; Jane Brock-Wilson; Daniel P. Carbonneau; Judy Ferenbach.
EIN: 208521462
Selected grants: The following grants are a representative sample of this grantmaker's funding activity:
$2,000,000 to Environmental Defense Fund, New York, NY, 2012. For continuing support of environmental research.
$800,000 to Princeton University, Princeton, NJ, 2012. For continuing support for High Meadows Preceptorship Fund.
$625,000 to North Bennet Street School, Boston, MA, 2012. For educational programs.
$500,000 to Vermont Community Foundation, Middlebury, VT, 2012. For High Meadows Fund.
$300,000 to Hill School, Pottstown, PA, 2012. For program support.
$300,000 to Princeton University, Princeton, NJ, 2012. For continuing support for High Meadows Preceptors Research Laboratories.
$300,000 to Vermont Community Foundation, Middlebury, VT, 2012. For continuing support for High Meadows Fellows Program.
$250,000 to Harvard University, Cambridge, MA, 2012. For continuing support of Baker Library.
$250,000 to Vermont Community Foundation, Middlebury, VT, 2012. For programs for environment.
$100,000 to Isles, Inc., Trenton, NJ, 2012. For educational programs.

4098
The Highland Street Connection ✧
(doing business as The Highland Street Foundation)
Three Newton Executive Park, Ste. 104
2223 Washington St.
Newton, MA 02462-1417 (617) 969-8900
Contact: Blake Jordan, Exec. Dir.

FAX: (617) 969-8901;
E-mail: info@highlandstreet.org; Main URL: http://www.highlandstreet.org
Facebook: http://www.facebook.com/pages/Highland-Street-Foundation/336718788790
Twitter: http://twitter.com/HighlandStreet

Established in 1989 in MA.
Donor: David J. McGrath, Jr.†.
Foundation type: Independent foundation.
Financial data (yr. ended 12/31/12): Assets, $192,630,472 (M); expenditures, $17,490,689; qualifying distributions, $14,779,218; giving activities include $12,117,467 for 531 grants (high: $2,000,000; low: $250), and $406,666 for loans/program-related investments.
Purpose and activities: The Highland Street Foundation is a family foundation currently awarding grants to nonprofit organizations located predominantly in Massachusetts. The trustees have focused on providing assistance to disadvantaged and underserved children through the funding of programs that support education and mentoring. Grants have also been awarded in the areas of the environment, health care, housing, the arts, and social services.
Fields of interest: Arts; Education; Health care; Youth development; Community/economic development; Religion.
Type of support: General/operating support; Continuing support; Annual campaigns; Capital campaigns; Building/renovation; Endowments; Program development; Scholarship funds; Program-related investments/loans; In-kind gifts; Matching/challenge support.
Limitations: Applications not accepted. Giving primarily in MA. No grants to individuals.
Publications: Grants list.
Application information: Contributes only to pre-selected organizations. Unsolicited proposals are not accepted.
Board meeting date(s): The board meets six times a year
Officers: J. Lawrence Guihan, C.F.O.; Blake Jordan, Exec. Dir.
Trustees: Holly McGrath Bruce; Christopher R. McGrath; David J. McGrath III; JoAnn McGrath; Scott J. McGrath; Sean P. McGrath.
EIN: 043048298
Selected grants: The following grants are a representative sample of this grantmaker's funding activity:
$2,000,000 to Eisenhower Medical Center Foundation, Rancho Mirage, CA, 2012. For healthcare.
$1,000,000 to Alverno College, Milwaukee, WI, 2012. For educational programming.
$250,000 to YMCA of Greater Boston, Boston, MA, 2012. For community.
$149,900 to Friends of the Cultural Center, Palm Desert, CA, 2012. For arts and culture.
$125,000 to Mass Mentoring Partnership, Boston, MA, 2012. For mentoring.
$15,000 to Boys and Girls Club of Newton, Newton, MA, 2012. For youth programming.
$15,000 to Eisenhower Medical Center Foundation, Rancho Mirage, CA, 2012. For healthcare.
$10,000 to Villanova University, Villanova, PA, 2012. For educational programming.
$5,000 to Dress for Success Boston, Boston, MA, 2012. For mentoring.
$5,000 to Palm Springs Art Museum, Palm Springs, CA, 2012. For arts and culture.

4099
Hildreth Stewart Charitable Foundation ✧
c/o Robert J. Hildreth
100 Belvidere St., Ste. 10-E
Boston, MA 02199-7621

Established in 1993 in MA.
Donors: Robert J. Hildreth; IBS, Inc.
Foundation type: Independent foundation.
Financial data (yr. ended 12/31/13): Assets, $15,658,347 (M); gifts received, $2,011,109; expenditures, $950,573; qualifying distributions, $904,221; giving activities include $904,221 for 15 grants (high: $342,071; low: $250).
Fields of interest: Education; Human services; Foundations (private grantmaking).
Limitations: Applications not accepted. Giving primarily in MA. No grants to individuals.
Application information: Contributes only to pre-selected organizations.
Trustees: Diane Hildreth; Robert J. Hildreth.
EIN: 043195994

4100
Charles H. Hood Foundation ✧
95 Berkeley St., Ste. 208
Boston, MA 02116-6230
Contact: Ray Considine, Exec. Dir.
E-mail: glockwood@hria.org; Main URL: http://www.tmfgrants.org/hood

Fund established in 1931; incorporated in 1942 in NH; incorporated in 2000 in MA.
Foundation type: Independent foundation.
Financial data (yr. ended 12/31/13): Assets, $61,293,324 (M); expenditures, $2,847,034; qualifying distributions, $2,640,653; giving activities include $2,417,468 for 18 grants (high: $255,000; low: $52,000).
Purpose and activities: The foundation was incorporated to improve the health and quality of life for children through grant support of New England-based pediatric researchers. Today's research projects encompass many disciplines that accelerate pediatric discoveries while launching the careers of promising junior faculty. The foundation's Child Health Research Awards Program, supports newly independent faculty, provides the opportunity to demonstrate creativity, and assists in the transition to other sources of research funding. Projects must be hypothesis-driven, with relevance to child health.
Fields of interest: Pediatrics research.
Type of support: Research.
Limitations: Giving limited to New England. No grants to individuals, or for building or endowment funds, operating budgets, general support, scholarships, fundraising campaigns, or matching gifts; no loans.
Publications: Application guidelines; Grants list.
Application information: Applicants must be within five years of their first faculty appointment by the start of funding. Only those meeting eligibility requirements may apply. Please see foundation web site for up to date guidelines and current recipients. The foundation does not accept unsolicited applications. Application form not required.
Initial approach: Response to RFA
Deadline(s): See foundation web site for current guidelines
Board meeting date(s): Usually in June and Dec.
Final notification: 8-10 weeks
Officers and Trustees:* Neil Smiley,* Pres. and Treas.; John Parker, Jr.,* V.P. and Clerk; Ray Considine, Exec. Dir.; Jeffrey H. Boutwell, Ph.D.; Barbara Bula.
Number of staff: 3 part-time professional.
EIN: 043507847
Selected grants: The following grants are a representative sample of this grantmaker's funding activity:
$75,000 to Boston Medical Center, Boston, MA, 2012. For Do Basic Unmet Material Needs and Social Safety Nets Influence Child Maltreatment Risk? A Nested Case-Control Study.
$75,000 to Boston University, Boston, MA, 2012. For A Controlled Trail for Telemethods to Expand the Availability of Parent-Child Interaction Therapy for Disruptive Preschoolers.
$75,000 to Brandeis University, Waltham, MA, 2012. For impact of genes and experience on the development of brain circuits.
$75,000 to Massachusetts General Hospital, Boston, MA, 2012. For Prospective Study of Genomic Aberrations during Prenatal Gestation.
$75,000 to Northeastern University, Boston, MA, 2012. For Use of Computer Agent to Promote and Support Breastfeeding.
$75,000 to University of Connecticut, Storrs, CT, 2012. For Vitamin D3 Analogues as Hedgehog Pathway Inhibitors.
$75,000 to University of Massachusetts, Amherst, MA, 2012. To detect and correct errors during cell division.
$75,000 to Yale University, New Haven, CT, 2012. For Molecular Pathogenesis Studies of Childhood Neurological Disorders, Rett and Angelman Syndromes.

4101
The Hopedale Foundation ✧
43 Hope St.
Hopedale, MA 01747-0123
Application address: c/o Vincent J. Arone, Treas., P.O. Box 123, Hopedale, MA 01747, tel.: (508) 473-2871

Trust established in 1946 in MA.
Donors: Thomas H. West†; John D. Gannett†; Richard B. Gannett†; Draper Corp.
Foundation type: Independent foundation.
Financial data (yr. ended 10/31/13): Assets, $10,591,686 (M); expenditures, $481,049; qualifying distributions, $481,049; giving activities include $251,500 for 16 grants (high: $120,000; low: $500), $20,000 for 7 grants to individuals (high: $5,000; low: $2,500), and $148,603 for loans to individuals.
Purpose and activities: Emphasis on area community funds and hospitals; support also for museums and other cultural programs, health agencies, youth services, and higher education; student loans and scholarships are limited to graduates of Hopedale High School in MA. New grants only to organizations having direct impact on the local community.
Fields of interest: Museums; Arts; Education, association; Higher education; Hospitals (general); Health care; Children/youth, services; United Ways and Federated Giving Programs; Social sciences.
Type of support: Scholarships—to individuals; General/operating support; Annual campaigns; Capital campaigns; Student loans—to individuals.

Limitations: Applications accepted. Giving primarily in MA, with emphasis on Hopedale and Milford. No grants for endowment funds.
Application information: Application form not required.
Initial approach: Letter
Copies of proposal: 1
Deadline(s): June 1 for student loans; no set deadline for grants
Board meeting date(s): Feb., June, and Oct.
Officers and Trustees:* William B. Gannett,* Chair.; Peter S. Ellis,* Vice-Chair.; W. Gregory Burrill,* Secy.; Vincent J. Arone,* Treas.; Steven G. Ellis; Alfred H. Sparling, Jr.; Thomas H. West, Jr.
Number of staff: 1 part-time professional.
EIN: 046044779
Selected grants: The following grants are a representative sample of this grantmaker's funding activity:
$10,000 to American Textile History Museum, Lowell, MA, 2011. For general operations.
$7,500 to Boy Scouts of America, Knox Trail Council, Framingham, MA, 2011. For capital campaign.
$2,500 to George Marston Whitin Memorial Community Association, Whitinsville, MA, 2011. For general operations.
$2,500 to Museum of Science, Boston, MA, 2011. For general operations.
$2,500 to New England Aquarium, Boston, MA, 2011. For general operations.
$2,000 to W G B H Educational Foundation, Boston, MA, 2011.

4102
Swanee Hunt Family Foundation ✧
168 Brattle St.
Cambridge, MA 02138-3309
FAX: (617) 995-1982;
E-mail: information@huntalternatives.org; Main URL: http://www.swaneehunt.com/about-swanee/philanthropy/
GiveSmart: http://www.givesmart.org/Stories/Donors/Swanee-Hunt

Established in 1981 in Denver, CO; merged in July 2000 as Swanee Hunt Family Foundation.
Donor: Hon. Swanee Hunt.
Foundation type: Independent foundation.
Financial data (yr. ended 12/31/13): Assets, $44,602,207 (M); expenditures, $6,473,795; qualifying distributions, $6,245,128; giving activities include $5,472,107 for 116 grants, and $1,001,344 for foundation-administered programs.
Purpose and activities: The fund advances innovative and inclusive approaches to social change at the local, national, and global levels.
Fields of interest: Women.
Type of support: Program-related investments/loans; General/operating support; Management development/capacity building; Program development; Conferences/seminars; Seed money.
Limitations: Applications not accepted. Giving on a national and international basis, with interest in areas of conflict, including Colombia, Nepal, Rwanda, Sri Lanka, and Sudan. No grants to individuals.
Publications: Grants list; Informational brochure.
Application information: Contributes only to pre-selected organizations.
Board meeting date(s): Varies, usually spring and fall
Officers and Directors:* Hon. Swanee Hunt,* Chair. and Pres.; Henry Ansbacher,* V.P.; Marva Hammons,* Secy.; Loretta Feehan,* Treas.; Theodore Ansbacher-Hunt; Katherine Archuleta; Tish Emerson; Jane Lute; John Miller; Fern Portnoy; Lillian Shuff; Rodney Shuff; William Snyder.
Number of staff: 25
EIN: 841101901

4103
The Hyams Foundation, Inc. ✧
(formerly Sarah A. Hyams Fund)
50 Federal St., 9th Fl.
Boston, MA 02110-2509 (617) 426-5600
Contact: Elizabeth B. Smith, Exec. Dir.
FAX: (617) 426-5696;
E-mail: info@hyamsfoundation.org; Contact for questions regarding application process: Susan Perry: sperry@hyamsfoundation.org; (617) 426-5600 ext. 307; Main URL: http://www.hyamsfoundation.org
Grantee Stories: http://www.hyamsfoundation.org/documents/CEP_-http://www.hyamsfoundation.org/OurGrantees/GranteeStories.aspx
The Hyams Foundation, Inc.'s Philanthropy's Promise: http://www.ncrp.org/philanthropys-promise/who

Established in 1929 in MA as the Sarah A. Hyams Fund; in 1991 merged with the Godfrey Hyams Trust and adopted current name.
Donors: Godfrey M. Hyams‡; Sarah A. Hyams‡.
Foundation type: Independent foundation.
Financial data (yr. ended 12/31/12): Assets, $134,908,398 (M); expenditures, $8,046,210; qualifying distributions, $6,871,822; giving activities include $5,519,531 for 122 grants (high: $150,000; low: $300), and $416,387 for 4 foundation-administered programs.
Purpose and activities: The mission of the foundation is to increase economic, social justice and power within low-income communities. The foundation believes that investing in strategies that enable low-income people to increase their communities will have the greatest social return in these times. The foundation will carry out its mission by: supporting civic participation by low-income communities; promoting economic development that benefits low-income neighborhoods and their residents; and developing the talents and skills of low-income youth.
Fields of interest: Adult/continuing education; Housing/shelter, development; Human services; Youth, services; Family services; Civil rights, race/intergroup relations; Urban/community development; Community/economic development; Disabilities, people with; Asians/Pacific Islanders; African Americans/Blacks; Hispanics/Latinos; Immigrants/refugees; Economically disadvantaged; LGBTQ.
Type of support: Mission-related investments/loans; General/operating support; Continuing support; Program development; Technical assistance; Program-related investments/loans; Matching/challenge support.
Limitations: Applications accepted. Giving primarily in Boston and Chelsea, MA. No support for municipal, state, or federal agencies; institutions of higher learning for standard educational programs, hospitals and health centers, religious organizations for sectarian religious purposes; support for medical research is being phased out. No grants to individuals, or for endowment funds, capital campaigns, fellowships, publications, conferences, films or videos or curriculum development.
Publications: Application guidelines; Annual report; Grants list; Informational brochure (including application guidelines).
Application information: Application form required.
Initial approach: Use online application system via foundation web site. Applicants who are unsure about whether their organization meets the foundation's funding priorities may send a 2-page letter of interest via e-mail
Copies of proposal: 1
Deadline(s): Mar. 1, Sept. 2, and Dec. 2
Board meeting date(s): Mar., June, and Dec.
Final notification: 3 to 4 months
Officers and Trustees:* Marti Wilson-Taylor,* Chair.; Adam D. Seitchik,* Treas.; Iris Gomez,* Clerk; Elizabeth B. Smith, Exec. Dir.; Wilma H. Davis; Lucas H. Guerra; M. Elena Letona; Penn S. Loh; Karen L. Mapp; Lily Mendez-Morgan; Omar Simmons; Roslyn M. Watson.
Number of staff: 6 full-time professional; 2 full-time support; 1 part-time support.
EIN: 046013680

4104
The Iacocca Family Foundation ✧
(formerly The Iacocca Foundation)
867 Boylston St., 6th Fl.
Boston, MA 02116-2774 (617) 267-7747
Contact: Margaret A. Laurence, Exec. Dir.
FAX: (617) 267-8544;
E-mail: info@iacoccafoundation.org; Main URL: http://www.iacoccafoundation.org

Established in 1984 in MI.
Donor: Lido A. "Lee" Iacocca.
Foundation type: Independent foundation.
Financial data (yr. ended 12/31/13): Assets, $39,741,871 (M); gifts received, $238,531; expenditures, $3,103,318; qualifying distributions, $2,984,875; giving activities include $2,246,955 for 81 grants (high: $500,000; low: $1,000).
Purpose and activities: Giving primarily for innovative and promising type 1 diabetes research programs and projects that will lead to a cure for the disease and alleviate complications caused by it.
Fields of interest: Hospitals (general); Diabetes; Diabetes research; Foundations (private grantmaking).
Type of support: Conferences/seminars; Professorships; Fellowships; Research; Matching/challenge support.
Publications: Application guidelines.
Application information: See foundation web site for full application guidelines and requirements, including downloadable application form. Application form submitted by fax not accepted. Application form required.
Initial approach: Call for proposals via web site or announcement on web site
Copies of proposal: 6
Deadline(s): See foundation web site for application deadline
Board meeting date(s): Fall and spring
Final notification: June 30
Officers and Trustees:* Lido A. "Lee" Iacocca,* Chair.; Kathryn Iacocca Hentz, Pres.; Louis E. Lataif, Secy.; Margaret Laurence, Exec. Dir.; Ken Anderson; Lia Iacocca Assad; Edward Bousa; John Gerace; Desmond Heathwood.

Number of staff: 3 full-time professional.
EIN: 386071154

4105
The Imago Dei Fund ✧
(formerly The Lip Foundation)
c/o Castle Rock Advisors, LCC
200 Clarendon St., 35th Fl.
Boston, MA 02116
E-mail: contact@imagodeifund.org; Main URL: http://www.imagodeifund.org

Established in 2007 in MA.
Donor: Ross M. Jones.
Foundation type: Independent foundation.
Financial data (yr. ended 12/31/12): Assets, $27,105,634 (M); gifts received, $10,610,954; expenditures, $1,482,749; qualifying distributions, $1,431,211; giving activities include $1,252,301 for 56 grants (high: $75,000; low: $1,240), and $69,395 for foundation-administered programs.
Purpose and activities: The foundation's giving is motivated by Christian faith, and supports programs with a holistic emphasis that serve and empower the whole person: body, mind, and spirit.
Fields of interest: Human services; Human services, mind/body enrichment; Christian agencies & churches; Women; Girls.
Limitations: Giving in the U.S., with emphasis on MA. No grants to individuals.
Application information: Applications are by invitation only, upon consideration of initial grant inquiry.
Initial approach: Use grant inquiry form on foundation web site
Deadline(s): See web site for deadlines
Officer: Debra Veth, Exec. Dir.
Trustees: Emily N. Jones; Ross M. Jones.
EIN: 261578446

4106
Inavale Foundation, Inc. ✧
c/o KLR
800 South St., No. 300
Waltham, MA 02453-1478

Established in 1998 in MA.
Donors: Katherine Buffett; William N. Buffett; Susan Kennedy.
Foundation type: Independent foundation.
Financial data (yr. ended 12/31/13): Assets, $17,319,408 (M); gifts received, $311; expenditures, $867,336; qualifying distributions, $715,922; giving activities include $709,025 for 75 grants (high: $80,000; low: $50).
Fields of interest: Arts; Higher education; Education; Health organizations; Human services; Foundations (private grantmaking); Protestant agencies & churches.
Type of support: General/operating support.
Limitations: Applications not accepted. Giving in the U.S., with emphasis on MA. No grants to individuals.
Application information: Contributes only to pre-selected organizations.
Officers and Directors:* William N. Buffett,* Pres.; Susan Kennedy,* Treas.; Thomas M. Buffett; Wendy O. Buffett; Noah E. Buffett-Kennedy.
EIN: 043409789

4107
Informed Medical Decisions Foundation, Inc. ✧
(formerly Foundation for Informed Medical Decisions Foundation)
40 Court St., Ste. 300
Boston, MA 02108-2202 (617) 367-2000
Main URL: http://informedmedicaldecisions.org
Facebook: http://www.facebook.com/imdfoundation?v=app_106171216118819
Google Plus: https://plus.google.com/114164346716236100178/posts
LinkedIn: http://www.linkedin.com/company/informed-medical-decisions-foundation
RSS Feed: http://www.informedmedicaldecisions.org/feed/?cat=15
Scoop.it!: http://www.scoop.it/u/imdfoundation
Slideshare: http://www.slideshare.net/fimdm
Twitter: http://twitter.com/fimdm
YouTube: http://www.youtube.com/user/FIMDM?feature=mhum

Established in MA.
Donor: David Wennberg.
Foundation type: Operating foundation.
Financial data (yr. ended 06/30/13): Assets, $21,059,637 (M); gifts received, $251,937; expenditures, $10,280,431; qualifying distributions, $10,075,788; giving activities include $2,128,106 for 45 grants (high: $157,797; low: $7,500), and $5,401,443 for foundation-administered programs.
Purpose and activities: The foundation is dedicated to assuring that people understand their choices and have the information they need to make sound decisions affecting their health and well-being.
Fields of interest: Higher education; Hospitals (general); Health care.
Limitations: Giving primarily in the U.S., with some emphasis on NH; some funding internationally, particularly in the UK.
Application information:
Initial approach: 1-page Letter of Intent
Deadline(s): Feb. 5 for Letter of Intent; Apr. 1 for full proposals sent by electronic copy
Officers and Directors:* John Billings, J.D.*, Chair.; Michael J. Barry, M.D., Pres.; Leslie Kelly Hall, Sr. V.P., Policy; Benjamin W. Moulton, JD, MPH, Sr. V.P.; Christine M. Fisler,* C.O.O. and C.F.O.; James R. Bell, Ph.D.; Clarence H. Braddock III, M.D., MPH; Archie Clemins; Susan Edgman-Levitan; Ted Epperly, M.D., FAAFP; Jim Everett; Diana Middleton; Margaret E. O'Kane; Ruth Prince; Kristi Saucerman; Richard "Rick" A. Skinner; John "Jack" E. Wennberg, M.D., MPH.
EIN: 020434037

4108
Institution for Savings Charitable Foundation, Inc. ✧
(formerly Institution for Savings in Newburyport & Its Vicinity Charitable Foundation, Inc.)
93 State St.
P.O. Box 510
Newburyport, MA 01950-6618 (978) 462-3106
Contact: Michael J. Jones, Pres. and Tr.
Application address: 2 Depot Sq., Ipswich, MA 01938 tel.: (978) 462-3106
Grants List: https://www.institutionforsavings.com/ifs-grant-recipients.htm

Established in 1997 in MA.
Donors: Institution for Savings; 1820 Security Corp.
Foundation type: Company-sponsored foundation.
Financial data (yr. ended 06/30/14): Assets, $8,844,894 (M); expenditures, $1,042,929; qualifying distributions, $1,037,706; giving activities include $1,035,511 for 147 grants (high: $250,000; low: $200).
Purpose and activities: The foundation supports organizations involved with arts and culture, education, hunger, and human services and awards college scholarships to graduating seniors from Newburyport High School and Triton Regional High School.
Fields of interest: Performing arts; Performing arts, orchestras; Arts; Elementary/secondary education; Higher education; Education; Food services; Boys & girls clubs; American Red Cross; YM/YWCAs & YM/YWHAs; Residential/custodial care, hospices; Aging, centers/services; Human services.
Type of support: General/operating support; Continuing support; Annual campaigns; Capital campaigns; Building/renovation; Program development; Scholarship funds; Sponsorships; Scholarships—to individuals.
Limitations: Applications accepted. Giving limited to Newburyport, MA.
Publications: Application guidelines; Grants list.
Application information: Application form required.
Initial approach: Contact foundation for application form
Deadline(s): None
Board meeting date(s): 3rd Mon. of Mar., June, Sept., and Dec.
Officers and Trustees:* Michael J. Jones,* Pres.; Patricia D. Connelly, Clerk; Stephen P. Cotre, Treas.; James V. Ellard; Freeman J. Condon; Kevin M. Gasiorowski; Donald M. Greenough; Cindy M. Johnson; Peter G. Kelly; Mary E. Larnard; John F. Leary III; Jeremiah T. Lewis; Drew Marc-Aurele; Saira Naseer-Ghiasuddin; Ellen G. Nich; Kimberly A. Rock; Ellen Mackey Rose; Richard J. Silverman; David A. Tibbetts.
EIN: 043353621
Selected grants: The following grants are a representative sample of this grantmaker's funding activity:
$15,000 to Harvard University, Cambridge, MA, 2011.

4109
Island Foundation, Inc. ✧
589 Mill St.
Marion, MA 02738-1553 (508) 748-2809
Contact: Denise Porche, Exec. Dir.
FAX: (508) 748-0991;
E-mail: islandfdn@earthlink.net

Incorporated in 1980 in MA as Ram Island, Inc.; current entity formed in 1986 by merger with Green Island, Inc.
Donor: W. Van Alan Clark, Jr.†.
Foundation type: Independent foundation.
Financial data (yr. ended 12/31/12): Assets, $55,683,827 (M); gifts received, $16,617,724; expenditures, $3,089,165; qualifying distributions, $2,689,000; giving activities include $2,689,000 for 131 grants (high: $750,000; low: $500).
Purpose and activities: Giving primarily for: 1) coastal water protection in New England environmental projects: right whale research, impact of toxins on wildlife research, land use conservation in southeast Massachusetts, and 2)

building the capacity of individuals and neighborhoods in the city of New Bedford, Massachusetts; and 3) alternative education programs.

Fields of interest: Education; Environment, natural resources; Environment; Animals/wildlife, preservation/protection; Economic development; Community/economic development; United Ways and Federated Giving Programs; Marine science; Biology/life sciences; Public policy, research.

Type of support: General/operating support; Capital campaigns; Equipment; Land acquisition; Program development; Curriculum development; Internship funds; Research; Technical assistance; Program-related investments/loans; Exchange programs; Matching/challenge support.

Limitations: Applications accepted. Giving primarily in New Bedford, MA, for economic and community development, MA, ME, and RI for environmental programs. No support for religious organizations for sectarian purposes or political organizations. No grants to individuals.

Publications: Annual report (including application guidelines).

Application information: Full proposals by invitation only. Associated Grantmakers of MA Common Proposal Format accepted; AGM Common Proposal Form accepted. Application form not required.

Initial approach: Telephone or letter (3-5 pages)
Copies of proposal: 1
Deadline(s): Mar. 1, June 1, Sept. 1, and Dec. 1
Board meeting date(s): Annually and as needed

Officers: Hannah Moore, Pres.; Kim Clark, V.P.; Michael Puzo, Clerk; Oliver Moore, Treas.; Denise Porche, Exec. Dir.

Directors: David Clark; Katherine Clark; Stephen Clark; William Clark; Christopher Moore; Michael Moore; Samuel Moore; William Moore; Hannah Nesbeda; Peter Nesbeda; Emily Rice; Christopher Tupper; Helen "Cricket" Tupper; Douglas Watson; Jo-Ann Watson.

Number of staff: 1 full-time professional.

EIN: 042670567

4110
The Jacobson Family Trust Foundation ✧

240 Newbury St., Fl. 2
Boston, MA 02116-2580

Established in 1997 in MA.

Donor: Jonathon Jacobson.

Foundation type: Independent foundation.

Financial data (yr. ended 12/31/12): Assets, $384,311,294 (M); gifts received, $25,000,000; expenditures, $22,299,765; qualifying distributions, $17,490,154; giving activities include $16,499,565 for 117 grants (high: $2,000,000; low: $500).

Fields of interest: Elementary/secondary education; Higher education; Education; Human services; Children/youth, services; Foundations (private grantmaking); Jewish federated giving programs; Jewish agencies & synagogues.

Limitations: Applications not accepted. Giving primarily in MA, with emphasis on the Boston area. No grants to individuals.

Application information: Contributes only to pre-selected organizations.

Officers and Trustees:* Joanna Jacobson,* Pres.; William Foster, Exec. Dir.; Jonathon Jacobson.

EIN: 046836735

Selected grants: The following grants are a representative sample of this grantmaker's funding activity:

$2,000,000 to Birthright Israel Foundation, New York, NY, 2012. For General Purpose.
$2,000,000 to Youth Villages, Memphis, TN, 2012. For Strategic Growth Plan/Multi-Year Pledge.
$1,550,000 to Combined Jewish Philanthropies of Greater Boston, Boston, MA, 2012. For General Purpose.
$1,000,000 to Brandeis University, Waltham, MA, 2012. For Jehuda Reinharz Chair.
$1,000,000 to PEF Israel Endowment Funds, New York, NY, 2012. For Tzohar.
$1,000,000 to Year Up, Boston, MA, 2012. For Year Up's Opportunity Campaign/Multi-Year Pledge.
$391,050 to Strategic Grant Partners, Boston, MA, 2012. For Grants + Operating Expenses.
$325,000 to Israel Promise, Scarsdale, NY, 2012. For the Creative Development Work and General Expenditures.
$25,000 to Catholic Schools Foundation, Boston, MA, 2012. For Inner-City Scholarship Fund.
$25,000 to ROCA, Chelsea, MA, 2012. For General Purpose.

4111
The Janey Fund Charitable Trust ✧

c/o The Philanthropic Initiative
160 Federal St., 8th Fl.
Boston, MA 02110
Contact: Deborah Denhart

Established in 1986 in MA.

Donor: Daniel E. Rothenberg.

Foundation type: Independent foundation.

Financial data (yr. ended 06/30/13): Assets, $4,448,534 (M); gifts received, $3,500,000; expenditures, $4,934,550; qualifying distributions, $4,818,727; giving activities include $4,799,933 for 174 grants (high: $536,433; low: $500).

Purpose and activities: Giving primarily for arts and culture, education, and social services.

Fields of interest: Arts; Higher education; Medical care, rehabilitation; Human services; Community/economic development.

Type of support: General/operating support.

Limitations: Applications not accepted. Giving primarily in MA and NY. No grants to individuals.

Application information: Contributes only to pre-selected organizations.

Trustees: William Buckley; Ann Rothenberg; Daniel E. Rothenberg; Edward Rothenberg; Susan Rothenberg.

EIN: 112836564

4112
Jebediah Foundation ✧

45 School St., 5th Fl.
Boston, MA 02108-3204
Application address: c/o Bingham McCutchen, LLP, Attn.: David L. Silvian, 1 Federal St., Boston, MA 02110-2012, tel.: (617) 951-8424

Established in 1989 in MA.

Donors: Eunice Taylor Vanderhoef†; Robert Amory.

Foundation type: Independent foundation.

Financial data (yr. ended 12/31/13): Assets, $8,216,550 (M); expenditures, $770,335; qualifying distributions, $695,000; giving activities include $661,000 for 101 grants (high: $200,000; low: $100), and $34,000 for 8 grants to individuals (high: $4,250; low: $4,250).

Purpose and activities: Giving primarily for the arts, education, the environment and human services.

Fields of interest: Performing arts; Arts; Higher education; Environment, natural resources; Human services.

Type of support: General/operating support; Building/renovation.

Limitations: Applications accepted. Giving primarily in ME; some funding also in MA. No grants to individuals.

Application information: Application form not required.

Initial approach: Proposal
Deadline(s): None

Trustees: Daniel Amory; Robert Amory; David L. Silvian.

EIN: 222999430

4113
The Gerald R. Jordan Foundation ✧

125 High St., Ste. 801
Boston, MA 02110-2704 (617) 261-9800

Established in 1996 in MA.

Foundation type: Independent foundation.

Financial data (yr. ended 12/31/13): Assets, $36,997,977 (M); expenditures, $5,575,490; qualifying distributions, $5,139,845; giving activities include $5,139,845 for 65 grants (high: $3,000,250; low: $100).

Purpose and activities: Giving primarily for the arts, education, medical care, and children, youth, and social services.

Fields of interest: Museums; Performing arts, orchestras; Historic preservation/historical societies; Higher education; Business school/education; Education; Hospitals (specialty); Health care; Cancer research; Youth development, services; Human services; Children/youth, services; United Ways and Federated Giving Programs.

Type of support: Scholarship funds.

Limitations: Applications not accepted. Giving primarily in MA; giving also in FL. No grants to individuals.

Application information: Contributes only to pre-selected organizations.

Trustee: Darlene L. Jordan; Gerald R. Jordan, Jr.

EIN: 043293081

Selected grants: The following grants are a representative sample of this grantmaker's funding activity:

$3,265,500 to Harvard University, Cambridge, MA, 2011. For general fundraising.
$1,007,500 to Fordham University, Bronx, NY, 2011. For general fundraising.
$5,000 to American Cancer Society, Atlanta, GA, 2011. For general fundraising.

4114
The Josetta Fund ✧

(formerly Martha R. Gerry Townley Foundation)
c/o Burns & Levinson
125 Summer St.
Boston, MA 02110-1634

Established in 1996 in MA.

Donors: Martha R. Gerry Townley; Matha F. Gerry - Martha Farish Gerry Declaration of Trust†.

Foundation type: Independent foundation.

Financial data (yr. ended 12/31/13): Assets, $48,259,963 (M); gifts received, $416,024; expenditures, $2,185,322; qualifying distributions, $1,849,552; giving activities include $1,751,884 for 60 grants (high: $286,884; low: $5,000).
Fields of interest: Education; Animal welfare; Pregnancy centers; Military/veterans' organizations; Religion; Economically disadvantaged.
Type of support: General/operating support.
Limitations: Applications not accepted. Giving primarily in MA, MT, NE, NY, OH, PA and VA. No grants to individuals.
Application information: Contributes only to pre-selected organizations.
Trustees: F. Bradford Townley; Mark A. Nowak; Martha R. Gerry Townley.
EIN: 043340006
Selected grants: The following grants are a representative sample of this grantmaker's funding activity:
$25,000 to Northeast Animal Shelter, Salem, MA, 2012. For Rescue and Adoption Services for Animals.
$25,000 to Truth for Life, Cleveland, OH, 2012. For Religious and Spiritual Education.
$20,000 to Wounded Warrior Project, Jacksonville, FL, 2012. To provide Services for Injured Veterans from 2001 and Beyond.
$15,000 to Petfinder.com Foundation, Tucson, AZ, 2012. To work with Rescue and Animal Welfare Organizations for Adoption.
$5,000 to Literacy Volunteers-Androscoggin, Auburn, ME, 2012. For Educational - for Adults to Acquire Basic Reading, Writing and Math.

4115
JSJN Children's Charitable Trust ✧
(formerly Webster Charitable Trust)
c/o Bain Capital, LLC
200 Clarendon St.
Boston, MA 02116

Established in 1998 in MA.
Donor: Stephen G. Pagliuca.
Foundation type: Independent foundation.
Financial data (yr. ended 09/30/13): Assets, $24,737,079 (M); gifts received, $20,716,101; expenditures, $825,519; qualifying distributions, $796,940; giving activities include $796,940 for 21 grants (high: $300,000; low: $500).
Fields of interest: Education; Boys & girls clubs; Human services; Children/youth, services; Blind/visually impaired.
Limitations: Applications not accepted. Giving primarily in MA, with emphasis on Boston. No grants to individuals.
Application information: Contributes only to pre-selected organizations.
Trustee: Stephen G. Pagliuca.
EIN: 046893292

4116
Kahn Charitable Foundation ✧
(formerly JED Charitable Foundation)
c/o Samet & Company, PC
1330 Boylston St.
Chestnut Hill, MA 02467-2145

Established in 1992 in MA.
Donor: The Jed Trust.
Foundation type: Independent foundation.
Financial data (yr. ended 06/30/13): Assets, $15,009,105 (M); expenditures, $729,935; qualifying distributions, $685,526; giving activities include $685,526 for grants.
Fields of interest: Elementary/secondary education; Higher education, university; Environment, natural resources; Civil/human rights; Jewish federated giving programs.
Limitations: Applications not accepted. Giving primarily in MA. No grants to individuals.
Application information: Contributes only to pre-selected organizations.
Trustees: Joseph Kahn; Atlantic Trust Co.
EIN: 046718867
Selected grants: The following grants are a representative sample of this grantmaker's funding activity:
$200,000 to Shore Country Day School, Beverly, MA, 2011.
$31,000 to New York City Gay and Lesbian Anti-Violence Project, New York, NY, 2011.
$25,000 to American Lung Association, Washington, DC, 2011.
$20,000 to Stoneridge Childrens Montessori School, Beverly, MA, 2011.
$17,000 to Charles River Watershed Association, Weston, MA, 2011.
$17,000 to Needham Community Council, Needham, MA, 2011.
$15,000 to Center for Reproductive Rights, New York, NY, 2011.
$15,000 to Pathfinder International, Watertown, MA, 2011.
$10,000 to Metropolitan Opera, New York, NY, 2011.
$5,000 to Hepatitis B Foundation, Doylestown, PA, 2011.

4117
Karp Family Foundation ✧
c/o New England Development
1 Wells Ave.
Newton, MA 02459-3226

Established in 1994 in MA.
Donor: Stephen R. Karp.
Foundation type: Independent foundation.
Financial data (yr. ended 02/28/14): Assets, $1,057,819 (M); expenditures, $1,458,588; qualifying distributions, $1,449,823; giving activities include $1,448,987 for 70 grants (high: $300,000; low: $250).
Purpose and activities: Giving primarily for education, health organizations, including a children's hospital, human services, and to Jewish organizations.
Fields of interest: Secondary school/education; Higher education; Aquariums; Hospitals (general); Hospitals (specialty); Health organizations; Human services; Jewish federated giving programs; Jewish agencies & synagogues.
Limitations: Applications not accepted. Giving primarily in MA; some funding also in Cape Town, South Africa. No grants to individuals.
Application information: Unsolicited requests for funds not accepted.
Trustees: Jill E. Karp; Stephen R. Karp.
EIN: 043226725
Selected grants: The following grants are a representative sample of this grantmaker's funding activity:
$15,000 to Autism Speaks, New York, NY, 2011.
$5,000 to Special Olympics, Washington, DC, 2011.
$2,000 to Cystic Fibrosis Foundation, Bethesda, MD, 2011.
$1,000 to American Diabetes Association, Alexandria, VA, 2011.

4118
Keane Family Foundation ✧
c/o O'Brien & Assocs.
10 Kearney Rd., Ste. 305
Needham, MA 02494-2544

Established in 1993 in MA.
Donors: John Keane; Marilyn Keane.
Foundation type: Independent foundation.
Financial data (yr. ended 12/31/13): Assets, $24,263,411 (M); expenditures, $1,371,340; qualifying distributions, $1,228,800; giving activities include $1,228,800 for 39 grants (high: $250,000; low: $250).
Purpose and activities: Giving primarily for the arts, particularly art museums, as well as for higher education, a hospital, and social services.
Fields of interest: Media, television; Museums (art); Arts; Higher education; Business school/education; Education; Hospitals (general); Boys & girls clubs; Human services.
Limitations: Applications not accepted. Giving primarily in Boston, MA. No grants to individuals.
Application information: Contributes only to pre-selected organizations. Unsolicited requests for funds not accepted.
Trustees: John F. Keane, Sr.; Marilyn T. Keane.
EIN: 046743248

4119
Heather and Robert Keane Family Foundation Inc. ✧
c/o WTAS LLC
125 High St., 16th Fl.
Boston, MA 02110-2332

Established in 2006 in MA.
Donors: Robert S. Keane; Heather K.L. Keane.
Foundation type: Independent foundation.
Financial data (yr. ended 12/31/13): Assets, $7,242,666 (M); gifts received, $2,093,820; expenditures, $887,611; qualifying distributions, $878,250; giving activities include $878,000 for 5 grants (high: $354,000; low: $100,000).
Fields of interest: Animals/wildlife, preservation/protection; Health organizations; Foundations (community); Christian agencies & churches; Children/youth.
Limitations: Applications not accepted. Giving primarily in Washington, DC, MA, NJ and NY. No grants to individuals.
Application information: Contributes only to pre-selected organizations.
Officers and Directors:* Heather K.L. Keane,* Pres. and Secy.; Robert S. Keane,* Treas.
EIN: 204818414

4120
The Keel Foundation ✧
c/o P. Wilson, Edwards Wildman Palmer LLP
111 Huntington Ave.
Boston, MA 02199-7610 (617) 239-0771
Contact: Diane Gilchrish

Established in 1992 in MA.
Foundation type: Independent foundation.
Financial data (yr. ended 12/31/13): Assets, $4,193,852 (M); expenditures, $529,646; qualifying distributions, $515,537; giving activities include $470,000 for 18 grants (high: $50,000; low: $5,000).
Fields of interest: Higher education; Libraries (public); Health care.
Type of support: General/operating support.
Limitations: Applications accepted. Giving primarily in CT, IL and MA. No support for religious or political organizations. No grants to individuals.
Application information: Application form required.
Initial approach: Request application form
Deadline(s): None
Trustees: Mark M. Christopher; Barbara M. Olsen; James Olsen; Peter A. Wilson.
EIN: 043166698
Selected grants: The following grants are a representative sample of this grantmaker's funding activity:
$25,000 to American Cancer Society, Atlanta, GA, 2011.

4121
The Henry P. Kendall Foundation
c/o Thai Ha-Ngoc, Prog. Assoc.
176 Federal St., 2nd Fl.
Boston, MA 02110-2214 (617) 951-2525
Contact: Andrew W. Kendall, Exec. Dir.
FAX: (617) 951-2556; E-mail: info@kendall.org; Main URL: http://www.kendall.org
Grants List: http://www.kendall.org/grantseekers

Trust established in 1957 in MA.
Donors: Henry Kendall‡; Henry Way Kendall Trust; and members of the Henry P. Kendall family.
Foundation type: Independent foundation.
Financial data (yr. ended 12/31/12): Assets, $79,815,633 (M); expenditures, $4,699,279; qualifying distributions, $4,571,376; giving activities include $3,659,950 for 34 grants (high: $1,600,000; low: $5,000).
Purpose and activities: To create a resilient and healthy food system in New England that increases the production and consumption of local, sustainably produced food.
Fields of interest: Agriculture, community food systems; Agriculture, sustainable programs; Agriculture/food.
Type of support: General/operating support; Program development.
Limitations: Applications not accepted. Giving primarily in New England. No support for specific land parcel preservation. No grants for capital campaigns, or for conference sponsorship.
Publications: Grants list; Program policy statement.
Application information: Unsolicited proposals and inquiries will not be reviewed.
Board meeting date(s): Mar., June, and Nov.
Officer and Trustees:* Andrew W. Kendall,* Exec. Dir.; John P. Kendall; Ken Meyers; Phoebe Winder.
Number of staff: 3 full-time professional; 3 part-time support.
EIN: 046029103

4122
Charles A. King Trust
c/o Bank of America, N.A.
225 Franklin St.
Boston, MA 02110-2801
E-mail: ma.grantmaking@ustrust.com (name of foundation should be indicated in subject line); Main URL: https://www.bankofamerica.com/philanthropic/grantmaking.go

Established in 1938 in MA.
Donor: Charles A. King‡.
Foundation type: Independent foundation.
Financial data (yr. ended 12/31/13): Assets, $22,968,637 (M); expenditures, $1,127,291; qualifying distributions, $1,008,794; giving activities include $876,500 for 13 grants (high: $247,000; low: $23,750).
Purpose and activities: Giving to encourage and support medical and surgical research projects carried on by charitable or educational corporations. Grants are awarded solely for postdoctoral research fellowships.
Fields of interest: Medical research, institute.
Type of support: Fellowships; Research.
Limitations: Applications accepted. Giving limited to MA.
Publications: Application guidelines.
Application information: Fellowships are paid directly to sponsoring institutions. Visit The Medical Foundation's URL: http://www.tmfnet.org/grantmake.html. Application form required.
Initial approach: Telephone
Deadline(s): Dec.
Board meeting date(s): Dec.
Final notification: Apr.
Trustees: Edward M. Dane; Lucy W. West, Esq.; Bank of America, N.A.
EIN: 046012742
Selected grants: The following grants are a representative sample of this grantmaker's funding activity:
$25,500 to Harvard University, Cambridge, MA, 2011. For post-doctoral medical research fellowship.
$25,500 to Harvard University, Cambridge, MA, 2011. For post-doctoral medical research fellowship.
$24,500 to Harvard University, Cambridge, MA, 2011. For post-doctoral medical research fellowship.
$24,500 to Harvard University, Cambridge, MA, 2011. For post-doctoral medical research fellowship.
$24,500 to Harvard University, Cambridge, MA, 2011. For post-doctoral medical research fellowship.
$24,500 to Harvard University, Cambridge, MA, 2011. For post-doctoral medical research fellowship.
$24,500 to Harvard University, Cambridge, MA, 2011. For post-doctoral medical research fellowship.
$24,500 to Harvard University, Cambridge, MA, 2011. For post-doctoral medical research fellowship.
$24,500 to Massachusetts Institute of Technology, School of Humanities, Arts and Social Sciences, Cambridge, MA, 2011. For post-doctoral medical research fellowship.
$24,500 to Massachusetts Institute of Technology, School of Humanities, Arts and Social Sciences, Cambridge, MA, 2011. For post-doctoral medical research fellowship.

4123
Kingsbury Road Charitable Foundation ✧
P.O. Box 140
Mansfield, MA 02048-0140

Established in 1996 in MA.
Donors: Hamilton Osgood‡; G. Grandchamps Charitable Remainder Trust; R.L. Christmas Charitable Remainder Trust.
Foundation type: Independent foundation.
Financial data (yr. ended 12/31/13): Assets, $6,846,932 (M); gifts received, $36,000; expenditures, $567,065; qualifying distributions, $526,206; giving activities include $519,890 for 20 grants (high: $64,890; low: $8,000).
Purpose and activities: Giving primarily for the arts, as well as for education, and human services.
Fields of interest: Performing arts, orchestras; Elementary/secondary education; Education; Human services.
Type of support: General/operating support.
Limitations: Applications not accepted. Giving primarily in the Boston, MA, area. No grants to individuals.
Application information: Unsolicited requests for funds not accepted.
Trustees: Cameron Bright; Sara Hunt Broughel.
EIN: 046820320
Selected grants: The following grants are a representative sample of this grantmaker's funding activity:
$69,000 to Neighborhood House Charter School, Dorchester, MA, 2011.
$32,000 to Crossroads for Kids, Duxbury, MA, 2011.
$32,000 to Dexter School, Brookline, MA, 2011.
$32,000 to Tenacity, Boston, MA, 2011.
$32,000 to Winsor School, Boston, MA, 2011.
$30,000 to Boston Symphony Orchestra, Boston, MA, 2011.
$24,000 to Phillips Academy, Andover, MA, 2011.
$16,000 to Community Music Center of Boston, Boston, MA, 2011.
$16,000 to Handel and Haydn Society, Boston, MA, 2011.
$16,000 to Huntington Theater Company, Boston, MA, 2011.

4124
The Kittredge Foundation ✧ ☆
P.O. Box 52570
Boston, MA 02205-2570

Established in 2000 in MA.
Donors: Michael J. Kittredge; Lisa R. Kittredge.
Foundation type: Independent foundation.
Financial data (yr. ended 04/30/13): Assets, $2,559,301 (M); gifts received, $2,845; expenditures, $690,071; qualifying distributions, $648,533; giving activities include $648,533 for 9 grants (high: $275,000; low: $1,000).
Fields of interest: Education; Hospitals (general); Cancer; Children/youth, services; Religion; Women.
Type of support: General/operating support.
Limitations: Applications not accepted. Giving primarily in MA. No grants to individuals.
Application information: Unsolicited requests for funds not accepted.
Trustees: Lisa R. Kittredge; Michael J. Kittredge.
EIN: 046911444
Selected grants: The following grants are a representative sample of this grantmaker's funding activity:

$250,000 to Brigham and Women's Hospital, Boston, MA, 2011. For general support.
$5,000 to Bement School, Deerfield, MA, 2011. For general support.
$5,000 to YMCA of Greenfield, Greenfield, MA, 2011. For general support.
$1,200 to Greenfield Community College Foundation, Greenfield, MA, 2011. For general support.

4125
The Kiva Foundation ✧
c/o Northstar
1000 Winter St.
P.O. Box 203
Waltham, MA 02451-1436

Established in 1998 in MA.
Donor: Norman C. Payson.
Foundation type: Independent foundation.
Financial data (yr. ended 12/31/13): Assets, $19,480,235 (M); expenditures, $1,428,440; qualifying distributions, $1,273,000; giving activities include $1,273,000 for 9 grants (high: $1,025,000; low: $1,000).
Purpose and activities: Giving primarily for health care; some funding also for a ballet company.
Fields of interest: Performing arts, ballet; Medical school/education; Hospitals (general); Health care.
Limitations: Applications not accepted. No grants to individuals.
Application information: Unsolicited requests for funds not accepted.
Trustees: Robert L. Carson; Melinda B. Payson; Norman C. Payson.
EIN: 043428609

4126
Klarman Family Foundation
(formerly The Seth A. & Beth S. Klarman Foundation)
P.O. Box 171627
Boston, MA 02117-3466 (617) 236-7909
Contact: Kim Philbrick McCabe, Exec. Dir.
E-mail: info@klarmanfoundation.org; Main URL: http://www.klarmanfoundation.org
Beth and Seth Klarman's Giving Pledge Profile: http://glasspockets.org/philanthropy-in-focus/eye-on-the-giving-pledge/profiles#k

Established in 1990 in MA.
Donors: Seth A. Klarman; Beth S. Klarman.
Foundation type: Independent foundation.
Financial data (yr. ended 12/31/12): Assets, $349,476,567 (M); gifts received, $60,000,000; expenditures, $32,715,715; qualifying distributions, $30,655,898; giving activities include $28,526,436 for 161 grants (high: $6,500,000; low: $2,500), and $1,091,667 for 1 loan/program-related investment.
Purpose and activities: Giving primarily for advancing medical and scientific research, with a particular interest in behavioral health; building a vibrant, engaged and inclusive Jewish community that feels connected to and supportive of Israel; and supporting and strengthening the local community, with a current strategic focus on increasing access to music.
Fields of interest: Arts education; Performing arts, music; Education; Hospitals (general); Medical research; Human services; Children/youth, services; Jewish federated giving programs; Science.
Type of support: General/operating support.
Limitations: Applications not accepted. Giving primarily in MA. No support for political organizations. No grants to individuals, or for endowments.
Application information: Proposals by-invitation-only.
Board meeting date(s): Feb., May and Nov.
Trustees: Beth S. Klarman; Seth A. Klarman.
Number of staff: 2 full-time professional; 1 full-time support.
EIN: 043105768
Selected grants: The following grants are a representative sample of this grantmaker's funding activity:
$6,500,000 to Broad Institute, Cambridge, MA, 2012.
$3,597,069 to Health Resources in Action, Boston, MA, 2012.
$1,635,000 to Combined Jewish Philanthropies of Greater Boston, Boston, MA, 2012.
$1,500,000 to Birthright Israel Foundation, New York, NY, 2012.
$1,000,000 to Cornell University, Ithaca, NY, 2012.
$1,000,000 to Facing History and Ourselves National Foundation, Brookline, MA, 2012.
$689,752 to Strategic Grant Partners, Boston, MA, 2012.
$600,000 to Youth Villages, Memphis, TN, 2012.
$586,000 to David Project, Boston, MA, 2012.
$100,000 to Israel on Campus Coalition, Washington, DC, 2012.

4127
Knez Family Charitable Foundation ✧
c/o Castanea Partners
3 Newton Executive Park, Ste. 304
Newton, MA 02462-1433

Established in 2001 in MA.
Donors: Brian J. Knez; Debra Smith Knez.
Foundation type: Independent foundation.
Financial data (yr. ended 11/30/13): Assets, $1,898,499 (M); expenditures, $521,873; qualifying distributions, $519,269; giving activities include $512,000 for grants.
Purpose and activities: Giving primarily for education, social services and medical research.
Fields of interest: Higher education; Education; Medical research, institute; Boys & girls clubs; Human services; Children/youth, services; United Ways and Federated Giving Programs.
Limitations: Applications not accepted. Giving primarily in MA. No grants to individuals.
Application information: Contributes only to pre-selected organizations.
Trustees: Brian J. Knez; Debra Smith Knez.
EIN: 223850785

4128
Robert and Myra Kraft Family Foundation, Inc. ✧
(formerly Robert and Myra Kraft and J. Hiatt Foundation, Inc.)
1 Patriot Pl.
Foxborough, MA 02035-1388 (508) 698-4618
Contact: Robert K. Kraft, Pres.

Incorporated in 1951 in MA.
Donors: Jacob Hiatt; Frances L. Hiatt; Robert K. Kraft; Myra Kraft‡; Estey Charitable Income Trust; Rand-Whitney Packaging Corp.; Kraft Group, LLC.
Foundation type: Independent foundation.
Financial data (yr. ended 12/31/13): Assets, $87,661,797 (M); gifts received, $5,041,889; expenditures, $6,634,531; qualifying distributions, $6,074,017; giving activities include $6,074,017 for 66 grants (high: $1,128,000; low: $275).
Purpose and activities: Giving primarily for higher education and to Jewish organizations.
Fields of interest: Higher education; Jewish federated giving programs; Jewish agencies & synagogues.
Limitations: Applications accepted. Giving primarily in MA and NY.
Application information: Application form required.
Initial approach: Proposal
Deadline(s): None
Officers and Directors:* Robert K. Kraft,* Pres. and Treas.; Joshua M. Kraft,* Clerk; Daniel A. Kraft; Jonathan A. Kraft.
EIN: 046050716

4129
The Krieble Foundation ✧
c/o Greenberg, Rosenblatt, Kull & Bitsoli
306 Main St., No. 400
Worcester, MA 01615-0034

Established in 1979 in CT.
Donors: Robert H. Krieble; Nancy B. Krieble.
Foundation type: Independent foundation.
Financial data (yr. ended 12/31/12): Assets, $17,450,618 (M); expenditures, $746,366; qualifying distributions, $623,800; giving activities include $623,800 for grants.
Fields of interest: Higher education; Education; Social sciences, public policy; Economics.
Type of support: Research.
Limitations: Applications not accepted. Giving in the U.S., with some emphasis on CO and VA; funding also in Montreal, Quebec, Canada. No grants to individuals.
Application information: Unsolicited requests for funds not accepted.
Officers: Frederick B. Krieble, Pres.; Daniel C. Krieble, V.P.; Robert K. Krieble, V.P.
Director: Helen E. Krieble.
EIN: 061011349

4130
Krupp Family Foundation ✧
1 Beacon St., Ste. 1500
Boston, MA 02108-3116
FAX: (617) 556-1472;
E-mail: kruppfamilyfoundation@berkshire-group.com ; Main URL: http://kruppfamilyfoundation.org/

Established in 2005 in MA.
Donor: George Krupp.
Foundation type: Independent foundation.
Financial data (yr. ended 12/31/13): Assets, $3,381,464 (M); expenditures, $503,401; qualifying distributions, $500,000; giving activities include $500,000 for 26 grants (high: $220,000; low: $2,500).
Purpose and activities: The mission of the foundation is to contribute to the common good of the Boston community through efforts that advance the arts, foster cultural expression, and improve,

strengthen, and transform children's futures. In addition, the foundation is dedicated to Jewish continuity, day school education, and local programs that encourage Jewish identity and enrich the lives of disadvantaged Jews in the Boston community.
Fields of interest: Arts; Education; Human services; Jewish agencies & synagogues.
Limitations: Applications not accepted. Giving primarily in the greater Boston, MA metropolitan area.
Application information: Unsolicited requests for funds not accepted.
Trustees: George Krupp; Lizbeth Krupp; Lawrence I. Silverstein.
EIN: 043812871
Selected grants: The following grants are a representative sample of this grantmaker's funding activity:
$25,000 to Boston Arts Academy, Boston, MA, 2011.
$25,000 to RAW Art Works, Lynn, MA, 2011.
$20,000 to Boys and Girls Clubs of Boston, Boston, MA, 2011.
$20,000 to Ronald McDonald House, Boston, Brookline, MA, 2011.
$15,000 to Bridge Over Troubled Waters, Boston, MA, 2011.
$14,000 to Music and Youth Initiative, Boston, MA, 2011.
$13,500 to Food Project, Lincoln, MA, 2011.
$10,000 to Lets Get Ready, New York, NY, 2011.
$10,000 to Project Place, Boston, MA, 2011.

4131
The Krupp Foundation ✧
(formerly The Judith & Douglas Krupp Family Charitable Foundation)
1 Beacon St., Ste. 1500
Boston, MA 02108-3116

Established in 1996 in MA.
Donors: Douglas Krupp; Judith Krupp.
Foundation type: Independent foundation.
Financial data (yr. ended 12/31/13): Assets, $4,381,753 (M); gifts received, $187,500; expenditures, $469,467; qualifying distributions, $468,166; giving activities include $468,166 for 18 grants (high: $125,000; low: $5,000).
Purpose and activities: Giving primarily to Jewish organizations; some funding for theater.
Fields of interest: Performing arts, theater; Civil/human rights, single organization support; Jewish federated giving programs.
Limitations: Applications not accepted. Giving primarily in the Boston, MA, area, and New York, NY. No grants to individuals.
Application information: Contributes only to pre-selected organizations.
Trustees: Douglas Krupp; Judith Krupp; Lawrence I. Silverstein.
EIN: 043294086
Selected grants: The following grants are a representative sample of this grantmaker's funding activity:
$10,000 to Woods Hole Oceanographic Institution, Woods Hole, MA, 2012. To assist the recipient in carrying out its charitable purpose.

4132
Helen & George Ladd Charitable Corporation ✧
c/o Nutter, McClennen, & Fish, LLP
P.O. Box 51400
Boston, MA 02205-1400

Established in 1984 in MA.
Donor: George E. Ladd, Jr. Charitable Trust.
Foundation type: Independent foundation.
Financial data (yr. ended 12/31/13): Assets, $10,835,408 (M); expenditures, $637,943; qualifying distributions, $566,208; giving activities include $546,995 for 75 grants (high: $79,287; low: $50).
Purpose and activities: Giving primarily for education and human services.
Fields of interest: Performing arts, theater; Arts; Higher education; Education; Health organizations, association; Human services; Community/economic development; Public affairs, government agencies.
Limitations: Applications accepted. Giving primarily in ME.
Application information: Application form required.
Initial approach: Letter
Deadline(s): None
Officers and Directors:* Lincoln F. Ladd,* Pres.; Peter R. Brown,* Clerk; David J. Ladd; Robert M. Ladd.
EIN: 042767890

4133
Ladera Foundation ✧ ☆
29 Commonwealth Ave., Ste. 201
Boston, MA 02116-2349 (617) 262-8300
Contact: Mary H. Myers Kauppila, Pres. and Dir.

Donors: Legacy Venture IV, LLC; Milagro de Ladera, L.P.
Foundation type: Independent foundation.
Financial data (yr. ended 12/31/13): Assets, $1,932,422 (M); gifts received, $767,234; expenditures, $596,602; qualifying distributions, $548,261; giving activities include $545,900 for 47 grants (high: $275,000; low: $100).
Fields of interest: Arts; Higher education; Education.
Limitations: Applications accepted. Giving primarily in CA and MA.
Application information: Application form required.
Initial approach: Letter
Deadline(s): None
Officer and Director:* Mary H. Myers Kauppila,* Pres.
EIN: 263877688

4134
G. Barrie Landry Charitable Foundation ✧ ☆
c/o Brown Advisory
99 High St., 10th Fl.
Boston, MA 02110-2320 (617) 717-6383
Contact: Dune Thorne
E-mail: dthorne@brownadvisory.com

Established in MA.
Donor: G. Barrie Landry.
Foundation type: Independent foundation.
Financial data (yr. ended 12/31/13): Assets, $0 (M); gifts received, $1,501,207; expenditures, $1,536,975; qualifying distributions, $1,581,126; giving activities include $1,536,975 for 18 grants (high: $556,400; low: $1,000).
Fields of interest: Health organizations; Human services; Children/youth, services.
Limitations: Applications accepted. Giving primarily in Boston, MA.
Application information: Application form required.
Initial approach: Letter
Deadline(s): None
Trustees: Kimberly Gwinn-Landry; G. Barrie Landry; Jennifer Landry Le.
EIN: 276923170
Selected grants: The following grants are a representative sample of this grantmaker's funding activity:
$25,000 to Share Our Strength, Washington, DC, 2012. For unrestrictive support.
$20,000 to Westover School, Middlebury, CT, 2012. For Girls Match.
$10,000 to Partners in Health, Boston, MA, 2012. For Ansara Event.
$5,000 to Emerald Necklace Conservancy, Boston, MA, 2012. For Justine Mee Liff Fund.
$5,000 to Massachusetts General Hospital, Boston, MA, 2012. For Storybook Ball.
$5,000 to Massachusetts General Hospital, Boston, MA, 2012. For Richard Floor Fund for Brain Tumor Research.

4135
Kevin Landry Charitable Foundation ✧
50 Cole Pkwy., No. 27
Scituate, MA 02066-1337 (781) 545-1112
Contact: Ernest J. Grassey, Dir.

Established in 1986 in MA.
Donor: C. Kevin Landry.
Foundation type: Independent foundation.
Financial data (yr. ended 12/31/12): Assets, $22,233,463 (M); gifts received, $7,558,045; expenditures, $3,477,719; qualifying distributions, $3,477,719; giving activities include $3,477,719 for 44 grants (high: $1,057,994; low: $500).
Purpose and activities: Giving primarily for education.
Fields of interest: Museums (art); Elementary/secondary education; Higher education.
Limitations: Applications accepted. Giving primarily in MA. No grants to individuals.
Application information: Application form required.
Initial approach: Proposal
Deadline(s): None
Directors: Ernest J. Grassey; G. Barrie Landry; C. Kevin Landry; Kimberly Hogan Landry; Jennifer Landry Le.
EIN: 042943405
Selected grants: The following grants are a representative sample of this grantmaker's funding activity:
$36,400 to Middlesex School, Concord, MA, 2012. For educational, historical, civic.
$20,000 to FreedomWorks Foundation, Washington, DC, 2012. For civic, educational, historical.
$20,000 to Tenacre Country Day School, Wellesley, MA, 2012. For civic, educational.
$15,000 to Greenwich Country Day School, Greenwich, CT, 2012. For educational, civic.
$2,000 to Judicial Watch, Washington, DC, 2012. For civic, historical, educational.
$1,000 to Paralyzed Veterans of America, Washington, DC, 2012. For educational, research.

4136
The Landsman Charitable Trust ✧
18 Aspen Rd.
P.O. Box 227
Swampscott, MA 01907-0327

Established in 1994 in MA.
Donor: Emanuel E. Landsman.
Foundation type: Independent foundation.
Financial data (yr. ended 12/31/13): Assets, $12,852,392 (M); gifts received, $3,800; expenditures, $533,178; qualifying distributions, $450,000; giving activities include $450,000 for 1 grant.
Purpose and activities: Giving primarily for higher education and health organizations.
Fields of interest: Higher education; Health organizations, association; Jewish agencies & synagogues.
Limitations: Applications not accepted. Giving primarily in MA. No grants to individuals.
Application information: Contributes only to pre-selected organizations.
Trustees: Samuel Denbo; Emanuel E. Landsman; Sheila E. Landsman; Susan J. Landsman.
EIN: 043236716

4137
Larson Family Foundation ✧
6 Arlington St., Unit 5
Boston, MA 02116-3402 (781) 237-8167
Contact: Jeffrey B. Larson, Tr.; Janet B. Larson, Tr.

Established in 2000 in MA.
Donors: Jeffrey B. Larson; Janet B. Larson.
Foundation type: Independent foundation.
Financial data (yr. ended 12/31/13): Assets, $7,357,600 (M); gifts received, $8,355; expenditures, $593,307; qualifying distributions, $582,570; giving activities include $582,500 for 10 grants (high: $150,000; low: $5,000).
Fields of interest: Higher education; Education; Human services.
Limitations: Applications accepted. Giving primarily in MA and MN. No grants to individuals.
Application information: The foundation generally does not accept unsolicited applications. Application form required.
Initial approach: Contact foundation for application form
Deadline(s): None
Trustees: Janet B. Larson; Jeffrey B. Larson.
EIN: 043533712

4138
Lauring Charitable Foundation ✧
c/o John P. Lauring
23 Brigham Rd.
Worcester, MA 01609-1005

Established in 1997 in MA.
Donors: Claire Lauring; Raymond Lauring.
Foundation type: Independent foundation.
Financial data (yr. ended 12/31/13): Assets, $11,275,662 (M); expenditures, $531,234; qualifying distributions, $528,604; giving activities include $528,034 for 16 grants (high: $138,355; low: $5,000).
Fields of interest: Human services; Catholic agencies & churches.
Type of support: General/operating support.
Limitations: Applications not accepted. Giving primarily in Worcester, MA. No grants to individuals.
Application information: Contributes only to pre-selected organizations.
Trustee: John P. Lauring.
EIN: 043371173

4139
Leaves of Grass Fund ✧
P.O. Box 233
Lincoln, MA 01773-0233
E-mail: leavesofgrassfund@gmail.com

Established in 1987 in MA.
Donor: Community TV Corp.
Foundation type: Independent foundation.
Financial data (yr. ended 12/31/12): Assets, $17,950,124 (M); expenditures, $1,078,153; qualifying distributions, $907,260; giving activities include $893,000 for 52 grants (high: $120,000; low: $500).
Purpose and activities: Giving primarily for higher education, health and medical services, and children, youth, women, and social services.
Fields of interest: Higher education; Education; Hospitals (general); Cancer research; Family services; Philanthropy/voluntarism; Children; Adults; Women; Adults, women; Adults, men.
Limitations: Applications not accepted. Giving primarily in MA and NY. No grants to individuals.
Application information: Contributes only to pre-selected organizations.
Trustees: Eleanor W. Herzog; James Herzog; Noah Herzog; Eve Robbins; Barbara White; Henry S. White; Jared White; Miranda White.
EIN: 222824793

4140
Sherry and Alan Leventhal Family Foundation ✧
c/o Beacon Capital
200 State St., 5th Fl.
Boston, MA 02109-2628

Donor: Alan M. Leventhal.
Foundation type: Independent foundation.
Financial data (yr. ended 08/31/13): Assets, $1,477,163 (M); gifts received, $3,025,605; expenditures, $2,276,545; qualifying distributions, $2,267,369; giving activities include $2,199,869 for 58 grants (high: $1,200,000; low: $250).
Fields of interest: Higher education; Education; Cancer research; Human services.
Limitations: Applications not accepted. Giving primarily in MA, with emphasis on Boston; funding also in New Orleans, LA.
Application information: Unsolicited requests for funds not accepted.
Trustees: Alan M. Leventhal; Sherry M. Leventhal.
EIN: 263358768

4141
Muriel & Norman B. Leventhal Family Foundation Inc. ✧
c/o Beacon Capital
200 State St.
Boston, MA 02109-2605

Established in 1997 in MA.
Donors: Norman B. Leventhal; Leventhal Family Fund.
Foundation type: Independent foundation.
Financial data (yr. ended 12/31/13): Assets, $438,142 (M); gifts received, $750,000; expenditures, $1,115,918; qualifying distributions, $1,110,152; giving activities include $1,019,177 for 57 grants (high: $165,000; low: $200).
Fields of interest: Museums; Performing arts centers; Arts; Higher education; Hospitals (general); United Ways and Federated Giving Programs; Jewish agencies & synagogues.
Limitations: Applications not accepted. Giving primarily in MA. No grants to individuals.
Application information: Unsolicited requests for funds not accepted.
Officers: Norman B. Leventhal, Pres. and Treas.; J. Robert Casey, Clerk.
Directors: Alan M. Leventhal; Mark S. Leventhal; Robert Melzer; Paula L. Sidman.
EIN: 043339819

4142
The Levine Family Charitable Trust ✧ ☆
c/o Cowan, Bolduc, Doherty & Co., LLC
231 Sutton St.
North Andover, MA 01845-1620

Established in 1989 in MA.
Donor: S. Robert Levine.
Foundation type: Independent foundation.
Financial data (yr. ended 12/31/12): Assets, $1,012,675 (M); gifts received, $7,000; expenditures, $518,165; qualifying distributions, $515,375; giving activities include $515,375 for grants.
Purpose and activities: Giving primarily for education and health care.
Fields of interest: Higher education, university; Education; Hospitals (general); Cancer; Human services; Philanthropy/voluntarism.
Limitations: Applications not accepted. Giving primarily in CO, MA, and NH. No grants to individuals.
Application information: Contributes only to pre-selected organizations.
Trustee: S. Robert Levine.
EIN: 043071725
Selected grants: The following grants are a representative sample of this grantmaker's funding activity:
$85,027 to Vail Mountain School, Vail, CO, 2011.
$65,000 to Marthas Vineyard Arena, Vineyard Haven, MA, 2011.
$10,000 to Bancroft School, Worcester, MA, 2011.
$10,000 to Exeter Hospital, Exeter, NH, 2011.
$10,000 to YMCA of Marthas Vineyard, Vineyard Haven, MA, 2011.
$2,500 to FARM Institute, Edgartown, MA, 2011.

4143
Abraham and Marilyn Levovitz Family Foundation Charitable Trust ✧ ☆
19 Brook Rd., No. 201
Needham, MA 02494-2946

Established in MA.
Foundation type: Independent foundation.
Financial data (yr. ended 12/31/13): Assets, $446,867 (M); expenditures, $425,259; qualifying

distributions, $423,410; giving activities include $423,410 for 22 grants (high: $100,000; low: $25).
Fields of interest: Education; Human services; Religion.
Limitations: Applications not accepted. Giving primarily in NY.
Application information: Unsolicited requests for funds not accepted.
Trustee: Marilyn Levovitz.
EIN: 266271759

4144
June Rockwell Levy Foundation, Inc. ✧
20 Oak St.
Beverly Farms, MA 01915-2230
Application address: c/o Jonathan B. Loring, Fiduciary Trust, 175 Federal St., Boston, MA 02110-2289, tel.: (617) 574-3426

Incorporated in 1947 in CT.
Donor: Austin T. Levy†.
Foundation type: Independent foundation.
Financial data (yr. ended 12/31/11): Assets, $23,093,218 (M); expenditures, $1,415,560; qualifying distributions, $1,269,557; giving activities include $1,223,925 for 100 grants (high: $90,000; low: $1,700).
Purpose and activities: Giving primarily for the arts, education, health, and children and social services.
Fields of interest: Arts; Education; Health care; Human services; Children/youth, services; United Ways and Federated Giving Programs.
Type of support: General/operating support; Continuing support; Capital campaigns; Building/renovation; Equipment; Seed money; Scholarship funds; Research.
Limitations: Giving primarily in northern RI. No support for religious purposes. No grants to individuals.
Application information: Application form required.
Initial approach: Letter
Copies of proposal: 1
Deadline(s): None
Board meeting date(s): Starting in Feb., 1st Tues. of every other month
Officers and Trustees:* Jonathan B. Loring,* Pres.; Paul F. Greene,* Secy.; Nancy B. Smith, Treas.; Karen Delponte; Raymond G. Leveille, Jr.; Raymond N. Menard; Robert P. Picard; Thomas H. Quill, Jr.; Dr. H. Denman Scott; Nancy B. Smith.
EIN: 046074284

4145
The Liberty Mutual Foundation, Inc. ✧
175 Berkeley St.
Boston, MA 02116-5066
E-mail: foundation@LibertyMutual.com; Main URL: http://www.libertymutualfoundation.org

Established in 2003 in MA.
Donor: Liberty Mutual Insurance Co.
Foundation type: Company-sponsored foundation.
Financial data (yr. ended 12/31/12): Assets, $43,027,164 (M); gifts received, $28,675,872; expenditures, $10,934,124; qualifying distributions, $10,493,200; giving activities include $10,492,500 for 6,302 grants (high: $250,000; low: $2).
Purpose and activities: The foundation supports organizations involved with arts and culture, education, health, human services, community development, and civic affairs. Special emphasis is directed toward programs designed to serve youth, low-income families and individuals, and people with disabilities.
Fields of interest: Museums; Performing arts, orchestras; Arts; Elementary/secondary education; Elementary school/education; Higher education; Education, services; Education; Health care; Food banks; Safety/disasters; Recreation, camps; Boys & girls clubs; Youth development, adult & child programs; American Red Cross; Salvation Army; Family services; Developmentally disabled, centers & services; Homeless, human services; Human services; Community/economic development; Assistive technology; Leadership development; Public affairs; Youth; Disabilities, people with; Economically disadvantaged; Homeless.
Type of support: General/operating support; Continuing support; Capital campaigns; Program development; Curriculum development; Scholarship funds; Employee volunteer services; Employee matching gifts.
Limitations: Applications accepted. Giving primarily in areas of company operations in MA, with emphasis on Boston. No support for grantmaking foundations, religious organizations not of direct benefit to the entire community, or fraternal, social, or political organizations. No grants to individuals, or for trips, tours, or transportation, debt reduction, conferences, forums, or special events.
Publications: Application guidelines.
Application information: Support is limited to 1 contribution or RFP per organization during any given year. Organizations receiving support are asked to submit a final assessment report. Application form required.
Initial approach: Complete online application form
Deadline(s): None; preferably Mar. 6 for Accessibility and Inclusion RFP; Mar. 31 for the Basic Services Initiative RFP;
Board meeting date(s): Monthly
Final notification: 6 to 8 weeks; May for Basic Services Initiative RFP
Officers and Directors:* David H. Long,* Chair. and C.E.O.; Dexter R. Legg,* V.P. and Secy.; Dennis J. Langwell,* V.P., C.F.O., and Treas.; Christopher C. Mansfield,* V.P. and Genl. Counsel; A. Alexander Fontanes,* V.P. and C.I.O; Melissa M. Macdonnell, V.P.; Gary J. Ostrow, V.P.
EIN: 141893520
Selected grants: The following grants are a representative sample of this grantmaker's funding activity:
$250,000 to American Red Cross National Headquarters, Washington, DC, 2012. For Program Support.
$250,000 to Pine Street Inn, Boston, MA, 2012. For Program Support.
$200,000 to Fund for Catholic Schools, Braintree, MA, 2012. For Program Support.
$125,000 to Rodman Ride for Kids, Foxboro, MA, 2012. For Program Support.
$83,333 to Womens Lunch Place, Boston, MA, 2012. For Capital Funding.
$70,571 to Saint Jude Childrens Research Hospital, Memphis, TN, 2012. For matching contribution.
$50,000 to City Year Boston, Boston, MA, 2012. For Program Support.
$15,000 to Excel Academy Charter School, East Boston, MA, 2012. For Program Support.
$3,380 to Boston Health Care for the Homeless Program, Boston, MA, 2012. For Matching contribution.
$2,860 to Cambridge Family and Childrens Service, Cambridge, MA, 2012. For Matching contribution.

4146
Lincoln Institute of Land Policy ✧
(formerly Lincoln Foundation, Inc.)
113 Brattle St.
Cambridge, MA 02138-3400 (617) 661-3016
FAX: (617) 661-7235; E-mail: help@lincolnist.edu; Phoenix office: c/o Kathryn J. Lincoln, Chair. and C.I.O., and Dione A. Etter, Asst. to the Chair. and Corp. Secy., 11010 N. Tatum Blvd., Ste. D-101, Phoenix, AZ 85028, tel.: (602) 393-4300; Additional tel.: (800) 526-3873, additional fax: (800) 526-3944; Main URL: http://www.lincolninst.edu
Blog: http://www.lincolninst.edu/news/atlincolnhouse.asp
Facebook: https://www.facebook.com/lincolninstituteoflandpolicy
LinkedIn: http://www.linkedin.com/company/1210434
Twitter: http://twitter.com/landpolicy
YouTube: http://www.youtube.com/user/LincolnLandPolicy

Established in 1946 in AZ and MA; Founded as Lincoln Foundation; merged into the Lincoln Institute of Land Policy and adopted current name in 2006.
Foundation type: Operating foundation.
Financial data (yr. ended 06/30/13): Assets, $471,656,024 (M); expenditures, $17,509,698; qualifying distributions, $14,346,101; giving activities include $205,429 for 12 grants (high: $24,000; low: $12,829), $265,750 for 21 grants to individuals (high: $22,200; low: $10,000), and $9,867,508 for foundation-administered programs.
Purpose and activities: The Institute improves the dialogue about urban development, the built environment, and tax policy in the United States and abroad. Through research, training, conferences, demonstration projects, publications, and multi-media, the organization provides non-partisan analysis and evaluation for today's regulatory, planning, and policy decisions.
Fields of interest: Public affairs, research; Public affairs, information services; Public affairs, public education.
International interests: China; Europe; Latin America.
Type of support: Research; Publication; Fellowships.
Limitations: Applications not accepted. Giving on a national and international basis.
Publications: Informational brochure; Newsletter.
Application information: Unsolicited requests for funds not accepted.
Officers and Directors:* Kathryn Lincoln,* Chair. and C.I.O.; George McCarthy,* C.E.O. and Pres.; Dennis W. Robinson, V.P., Finance and Opers., and Treas.; Dione Etter, Secy.; Roy W. Bahl; and 14 additional directors.
EIN: 866021106
Selected grants: The following grants are a representative sample of this grantmaker's funding activity:
$22,642 to Institute for International Urban Development, Cambridge, MA, 2013. For Assessing the Impacts of Climate Change on Land Use La Paz, Bolivia.
$20,000 to Robert Morris University, Moon Township, PA, 2013. For The Pennsylvania Experience Effects of Two-Rate Property Tax.

$14,000 to University of Georgia, Athens, GA, 2013. For Institutional Local Prop Tax-China Rev/Serv-Link/Higher Effect/Pub Choice.
$13,000 to Institute for International Urban Development, Cambridge, MA, 2013. For Measures to Increase Inform Self-Resilience/Climate Change Cent Am.
$12,829 to American Planning Association, Chicago, IL, 2013. For The Impacts of Sea-Level Rise on Economies and Population.

4147
Linde Family Foundation ✧
(formerly Linde Family Charitable Trust)
c/o Eric Riak, Atlantic Trust
100 Federal St.
Boston, MA 02110-1802
Contact: Julia Mott Toulmin, C.E.O. and Pres., Mott Philanthropic

Established in 2000 in MA.
Donors: Edward H. Linde; Joyce G. Linde.
Foundation type: Independent foundation.
Financial data (yr. ended 12/31/12): Assets, $122,484,950 (M); gifts received, $2,006,001; expenditures, $8,356,301; qualifying distributions, $7,798,737; giving activities include $7,125,237 for 130 grants (high: $3,000,000; low: $801).
Purpose and activities: Giving primarily for children's services, education, and the arts.
Fields of interest: Arts; Education; Children/youth, services; Children/youth; Youth.
Type of support: Scholarship funds; General/operating support; Annual campaigns; Capital campaigns; Building/renovation; Endowments; Program development; Curriculum development.
Limitations: Applications not accepted. Giving primarily in MA. No grants to individuals.
Application information: Unsolicited requests for funds not accepted.
Trustees: Carol Croft Linde; Douglas T. Linde; Joyce Linde; Jeffrey N. Packman; Karen Linde Packman.
EIN: 046904949

4148
The Linden Foundation Inc. ✧
c/o GMA Foundations
77 Summer St., 8th Fl.
Boston, MA 02110-1006
Main URL: http://www.lindenfoundation.org

Established in 1996 in NJ.
Donors: Thomas V.A. Kelsey 1968 Revocable Trust; Elizabeth S. Kelsey 1988 Revocable Trust; Thomas V.A. Kelsey.
Foundation type: Independent foundation.
Financial data (yr. ended 12/31/13): Assets, $7,828,364 (M); expenditures, $670,490; qualifying distributions, $631,313; giving activities include $602,500 for 31 grants (high: $40,000; low: $7,000).
Purpose and activities: Giving to organizations that strengthen disadvantaged and homeless families by helping provide them with the skills and support systems they need to become cohesive, internally supportive, and self-sufficient. Preference is given to comprehensive programs that most directly help those in need, involve multiple family members, provide sustained support to the participants, and are administered by community-based organizations.
Fields of interest: Family services; Homeless, human services; Economically disadvantaged; Homeless.
Type of support: General/operating support; Program development; Matching/challenge support.
Limitations: Applications not accepted. Giving in the northern side of the greater Boston, MA, area, with emphasis on communities inside Route 128 and the North Shore to the Gloucester area, as well as in the counties of the Lakes Region and northern NH. No support for public schools, charter schools or universities, or for community organizing or political lobbying efforts. No grants to individuals, or for tickets to artistic performances, computer centers, or operating support for community centers.
Application information: Unsolicited requests for funds not accepted.
Officers: Thomas V.A. Kelsey, Pres. and Treas.; Margen S. Kelsey, Secy.
Directors: Elizabeth S. Kelsey; Suzanne V.A. Kelsey; Lea Dobbs Kelsey; William C. Kelsey; Mark J. Pine; Kenneth V. Siegert.
Number of staff: None.
EIN: 226678640

4149
Ruby W. and Lavon Parker Linn Foundation ✧
c/o Choate, LLP
P.O. Box 961019
Boston, MA 02196-1019

Newly funded in 2001 in MA.
Donors: Ruby W. Linn; Ruby Winslow & Lavon Parker Linn Foundation; Ruby W. Linn Charitable Remainder Unitrust.
Foundation type: Independent foundation.
Financial data (yr. ended 07/31/12): Assets, $34,857,893 (M); gifts received, $30,462,386; expenditures, $827,040; qualifying distributions, $728,251; giving activities include $694,050 for 20 grants (high: $100,000; low: $1,500).
Fields of interest: Museums; Historic preservation/historical societies; Hospitals (general); Diabetes; Aging, centers/services; American studies; Protestant agencies & churches.
Limitations: Applications not accepted. Giving primarily in MA. No grants to individuals.
Application information: Unsolicited requests for funds not accepted.
Trustees: Jo Anne Borek; Scott G. Borek; William A. Lowell.
EIN: 316672883
Selected grants: The following grants are a representative sample of this grantmaker's funding activity:
$25,000 to Beverly School for the Deaf, Beverly, MA, 2011. For general support.
$25,000 to Boys and Girls Club of Stoneham, Stoneham, MA, 2011. For general support.
$25,000 to Massachusetts Historical Society, Boston, MA, 2011. For general support.
$25,000 to Mount Vernon Ladies Association, Mount Vernon, VA, 2011. For general support.
$7,500 to Paul Revere Memorial Association, Boston, MA, 2011. For general support.
$2,000 to American Dietetic Association, Chicago, IL, 2011. For general support.
$1,000 to Exponent Philanthropy, Washington, DC, 2011. For general support.
$1,000 to Media Research Center, Reston, VA, 2011. For general support.

4150
Liswhit Foundation ✧ ☆
200 Lexington St.
Weston, MA 02493-2146
Application address: c/o Charlotte D'Arcy Donaldson, Tr., P.O. Box 215, Weston, MA 02483, tel.: (508) 459-8037

Foundation type: Independent foundation.
Financial data (yr. ended 12/31/13): Assets, $4,926,976 (M); expenditures, $819,256; qualifying distributions, $793,492; giving activities include $787,045 for 14 grants (high: $150,000; low: $4,000).
Fields of interest: Arts; Education; Human services.
Limitations: Applications accepted. Giving primarily in MA.
Application information: Application form required.
Initial approach: Completed application form
Deadline(s): None
Trustee: Charlotte D'Arcy Donaldson.
EIN: 273988759

4151
Lovett/Woodsum Family Charitable Foundation, Inc. ✧
c/o Summit Partners
222 Berkeley St., 18th Fl.
Boston, MA 02116-3755

Established in 1986 in MA.
Donors: Anne R. Lovett; Stephen G. Woodsum.
Foundation type: Independent foundation.
Financial data (yr. ended 11/30/13): Assets, $45,409,580 (M); gifts received, $3,770,903; expenditures, $2,654,294; qualifying distributions, $2,380,905; giving activities include $2,380,905 for 153 grants (high: $300,000; low: $2).
Fields of interest: Museums (children's); Arts; Higher education; Education; Hospitals (general); Health organizations; Boys & girls clubs; Human services; Children/youth, services.
Limitations: Applications not accepted. Giving primarily in CT, MA and NH. No grants to individuals.
Application information: Contributes only to pre-selected organizations.
Officers: Anne R. Lovett, Pres.; David H. Hopfenberg, Clerk; Stephen G. Woodsum, Treas.
EIN: 042944183

4152
Greater Lowell Community Foundation ✧
100 Merrimack St., Ste. 202
Lowell, MA 01852-1723 (978) 970-1600
Contact: Susan Winship, Exec. Dir.
FAX: (978) 970-2444;
E-mail: susan@glcfoundation.org; Main URL: http://www.glcfoundation.org

Established in 1996 in MA.
Donors: Joe Donahue; Richard K. Donahue, Sr.; Human Svcs. Corp.; Lowell Museum Corp.; The Theodore Edson Parker Foundation.
Foundation type: Community foundation.
Financial data (yr. ended 12/31/13): Assets, $27,215,028 (M); gifts received, $2,222,881; expenditures, $2,181,690; giving activities include $1,156,929 for 61+ grants (high: $111,226), and $207,168 for 156 grants to individuals.
Purpose and activities: The foundation seeks to improve the quality of life in the greater Lowell, MA,

area by attracting funds, distributing grants, making loans and striving as a catalyst and leader among funders, agencies and individuals to address identified and emerging community needs.
Fields of interest: Arts; Education; Environment, water pollution; Environment, water resources; Environment; Health care; Human services; Economic development; Community/economic development; Voluntarism promotion.
Type of support: Income development; Management development/capacity building.
Limitations: Applications accepted. Giving limited to the greater Lowell, Nashoba, and Western Merrimack Valley, MA, regions. No support for religious organizations or government agencies. No grants to individuals (except for scholarships), or for continuing support, operating expenses, building funds or endowment funds; no multi-year commitments.
Publications: Application guidelines; Annual report; Financial statement; Grants list.
Application information: Visit foundation web site for application deadlines and guidelines. Full proposals may be submitted by invitation only. Application form required.
Initial approach: E-mail Concept Paper and Cover Sheet
Deadline(s): July 1
Final notification: Aug. 12
Officers and Directors:* Kay Doyle, Ph. D.*, Pres.; Joseph Bartolotta, V.P.; Steven Joncas, Co-V.P.; Annmarie Roark,* Clerk; James C. Shannon III,* Treas.; Brian J. Stafford, C.P.A.*, Asst. Treas.; Susan Winship, Exec. Dir.; Janinne Nocco, Cont.; Jeff Bergart,* C.F.O.; Richard K. Donahue, Sr., Emeritus; George L. Duncan, Emeritus; Luis Pedroso, Emeritus; Susanne Beaton; Brian Chapman; John P. Chemaly; Dorothy Chen-Courtin, Ph.D.; Scott Flagg; Karen Frederick; Glenn Mello; Jacqueline F. Moloney, Ed.D.; Amsi Y. Morales; James D. Nolan; Analise Saab; Timothy M. Sweeney; Lisa Tighe.
EIN: 043401997

4153
The Lowell Institute ✧
c/o Choate, LLP
P.O. Box 961019
Boston, MA 02196-1019

Established in 1836 in MA.
Donor: John Lowell†.
Foundation type: Independent foundation.
Financial data (yr. ended 07/31/13): Assets, $41,016,612 (M); expenditures, $1,724,112; qualifying distributions, $1,516,097; giving activities include $1,465,875 for 23 grants (high: $300,000; low: $2,500).
Fields of interest: Media/communications; Museums; Historic preservation/historical societies; Arts; Higher education.
Type of support: Continuing support; Conferences/seminars; Curriculum development; Scholarship funds; Matching/challenge support.
Limitations: Applications not accepted. Giving primarily in the greater Boston, MA, area. No grants to individuals, or for operating budgets, building or endowment funds; no loans.
Publications: Informational brochure.
Application information: Contributes only to pre-selected organizations.
Trustee: William A. Lowell.
EIN: 042105771

Selected grants: The following grants are a representative sample of this grantmaker's funding activity:
$225,000 to New England Aquarium, Boston, MA, 2013. To support of programs and exhibits.
$103,000 to Harvard University, Extension School, Cambridge, MA, 2013. For programs and lecture.
$35,000 to Boston Symphony Orchestra, Boston, MA, 2013. For Community Chamber Concerts.
$9,000 to Boston University, School of Theology, Boston, MA, 2013. For Lowell Lecture Series.
$2,500 to Massachusetts Historical Society, Boston, MA, 2013. For public lecture.

4154
The Lowndes Foundation, Inc. ✧
c/o Atlantic Trust Co., N.A.
100 Federal St., 37th Fl.
Boston, MA 02110-1802

Established in 1997.
Donors: William Lowndes III; Tindall Corp.; Lowndes III Trust.
Foundation type: Company-sponsored foundation.
Financial data (yr. ended 12/31/13): Assets, $16,149,695 (M); gifts received, $109,457; expenditures, $847,558; qualifying distributions, $677,996; giving activities include $663,200 for 17 grants (high: $150,000; low: $13,000).
Purpose and activities: The foundation supports organizations involved with education, civil liberties, economic development, public policy, and government and public administration.
Fields of interest: Education; Health care; Human services.
Limitations: Applications not accepted. Giving primarily in Washington, DC, Hillside, MI, Irvington-on-Hudson, NY, and Spartanburg, SC. No grants to individuals.
Application information: Contributes only to pre-selected organizations.
Officers and Trustee:* William Lowndes III, Pres. and Treas.; Henrietta M. Lowndes,* Secy.
EIN: 571027898
Selected grants: The following grants are a representative sample of this grantmaker's funding activity:
$150,000 to South Carolina Policy Council, Columbia, SC, 2011.

4155
The Richard K. Lubin Family Foundation ✧
(formerly The Richard K. Lubin Charitable Trust)
776 Boylston St., PH1G
Boston, MA 02199-7853

Established in 1986 in MA.
Donors: Richard K. Lubin; Simon Lubin†.
Foundation type: Independent foundation.
Financial data (yr. ended 12/31/12): Assets, $44,876,409 (M); gifts received, $15,356,127; expenditures, $3,172,596; qualifying distributions, $2,975,450; giving activities include $2,975,450 for 56 grants (high: $911,500; low: $500).
Purpose and activities: Giving primarily for the arts, education, health, social services, and Jewish organizations.
Fields of interest: Museums (art); Arts; Higher education; Hospitals (general); Health organizations, association; Cancer; Human services; Children/youth, services; United Ways and Federated Giving Programs; Jewish agencies & synagogues.
Limitations: Applications not accepted. Giving primarily in MA. No grants to individuals.
Application information: Contributes only to pre-selected organizations.
Trustees: Kate E. Lubin; Nancy K. Lubin; Richard K. Lubin; Emily L. Woods.
EIN: 222773808
Selected grants: The following grants are a representative sample of this grantmaker's funding activity:
$200,000 to Wheaton College, Norton, MA, 2012. For the needs of the organization.

4156
The Lucretia Philanthropic Foundation, Inc. ✧
1 Bridge St., Ste. 200
Newton, MA 02458-1138

Established in 2005 in DE.
Donor: Sarah Lutz.
Foundation type: Independent foundation.
Financial data (yr. ended 12/31/13): Assets, $25,119,275 (M); gifts received, $4,280,737; expenditures, $1,364,287; qualifying distributions, $1,313,200; giving activities include $1,312,000 for 36 grants (high: $200,000; low: $1,000).
Fields of interest: Arts; Education; Human services; Christian agencies & churches.
Limitations: Applications not accepted. Giving in the U.S., with emphasis on New York, NY. No grants to individuals.
Application information: Contributes only to pre-selected organizations.
Officer: Sarah Lutz, Pres. and Secy.-Treas.
EIN: 203964837

4157
The Ludcke Foundation ✧
c/o GMA Foundations
77 Summer St., 8th Fl.
Boston, MA 02110-2224
Contact: Ruth Victorin, Fdn. Asst.
FAX: (617) 426-7087;
E-mail: rvictorin@gmafoundations.com; E-mail and Voice Mail for Gracelaw Simmons, Grants Advisor: gsimmons@gmafoundations.com: (617) 391-3082;
Main URL: http://ludckefoundation.org
RSS Feed: http://ludckefoundation.grantsmanagement08.com/?feed=rss2

Established in 1991 in MA.
Donors: Gipp L. Ludcke; Eleanor R. Ludcke.
Foundation type: Independent foundation.
Financial data (yr. ended 12/31/13): Assets, $41,392,342 (M); expenditures, $2,039,851; qualifying distributions, $1,790,735; giving activities include $1,708,320 for 55 grants (high: $50,000; low: $695).
Purpose and activities: The foundation makes grants in the fields of education, medicine, and human services.
Fields of interest: Education; Health care; Human services; Children/youth; Economically disadvantaged.
Type of support: General/operating support; Continuing support; Capital campaigns; Building/

renovation; Seed money; Research; Matching/challenge support.
Limitations: Giving limited to New England, with preference for Greater Boston and selected eastern MA "Gateway Cities.". No grants to individuals.
Publications: Application guidelines; Annual report; Grants list; Informational brochure; Program policy statement (including application guidelines).
Application information: Only organizations invited by the trustees may apply. The trustees will begin the application process by requesting a concept paper. Applicants whose concept papers have been approved by the trustees will be invited to submit a full proposal. Preliminary Application form required upon invitation.
Initial approach: Telephone call, e-mail, or refer to foundation web site
Deadline(s): Mar. 1 and Sept. 1 (if invited to submit an application)
Board meeting date(s): Apr./May and Nov.
Officer and Trustees:* Douglas R. Smith-Petersen,* Chair.; Daniel S. Cheever; Ruth Ellen Fitch; Constance Huebner; Fiduciary Trust Co.
Number of staff: 1 part-time support.
EIN: 046663582

4158
The Lurie Family Foundation ✧
(formerly Jeffrey Lurie Family Foundation)
c/o Goulston & Storrs
400 Atlantic Ave.
Boston, MA 02110-3331

Established in 2005 in MA.
Donor: Nancy L. Marks.
Foundation type: Independent foundation.
Financial data (yr. ended 06/30/13): Assets, $19,700,580 (M); expenditures, $1,534,722; qualifying distributions, $1,236,884; giving activities include $1,220,338 for 40 grants (high: $400,000; low: $200).
Purpose and activities: Giving primarily for education and health care.
Fields of interest: Arts; Higher education; Education; Hospitals (general); Human services; Children/youth, services.
Limitations: Applications not accepted. Giving primarily in MA and PA. No grants to individuals.
Application information: Contributes only to pre-selected organizations.
Trustees: Richard B. Denning; Joseph M. Leccese; Jeffrey R. Lurie.
EIN: 202741949
Selected grants: The following grants are a representative sample of this grantmaker's funding activity:
$5,000 to Yale University, New Haven, CT, 2011.
$2,000 to Multiple Sclerosis Society, National, New York, NY, 2011.
$1,000 to Learning Ally, Princeton, NJ, 2011.

4159
The Lynch Foundation ✧ ☆
280 Congress St., Ste. 1300
Atlantic Wharf
Boston, MA 02210-1004 (617) 457-2028
Contact: Kathryn Everett, Exec. Dir.
E-mail: victoria@thelynchfoundation.com; Main URL: http://thelynchfoundation.org/
Peter and Carolyn Lynch's Bridgespan Profile: http://www.givesmart.org/Stories/Donors/Peter-and-Carolyn-Lynch

Established in 1988 in MA.
Donors: Carolyn A. Lynch; Peter S. Lynch.
Foundation type: Independent foundation.
Financial data (yr. ended 12/31/12): Assets, $91,915,005 (M); expenditures, $8,363,795; qualifying distributions, $8,233,196; giving activities include $6,807,208 for 86 grants (high: $1,000,000; low: $500).
Purpose and activities: The foundation provides assistance to programs primarily in Massachusetts with an emphasis on education; cultural and historic preservation; healthcare and medical research; and religious and educationl efforts of the Roman Catholic Church.
Fields of interest: Arts; Education; Health care, research; Hospitals (general); Catholic agencies & churches.
Type of support: General/operating support; Capital campaigns; Building/renovation; Endowments; Program development; Scholarship funds; Research; Matching/challenge support.
Limitations: Applications accepted. Giving primarily in Boston, MA. No grants to individuals, or for advertisements, sponsorship of events, or purchase of tables.
Publications: Application guidelines.
Application information: Concept paper submitted through foundation web site. The foundation will respond with either an invitation to submit a full grant application or decline the concept paper. See complete application guidelines on foundation web site.
Initial approach: Concept paper
Copies of proposal: 1
Deadline(s): None
Board meeting date(s): Three times per year
Officers and Trustees:* Carolyn Lynch,* Chair. and Pres.; J. Frederick Bush,* Secy.; Peter S. Lynch,* Treas.; Katie Everett, Exec. Dir.; Nancy R. Coolidge; Richard Spillane; Ralph C. Sweetland, Ph.D.; Marsha Helmstadter.
Number of staff: 2 full-time professional; 1 full-time support.
EIN: 043017940

4160
Maine Timberlands Charitable Trust ✧ ☆
Day Pitney, LLP
1 International Pl.
Boston, MA 02110 (617) 345-4600
Contact: Linda S. Dalby, Tr.

Donor: Barbara Wheatland Recobable Trust.
Foundation type: Independent foundation.
Financial data (yr. ended 12/31/13): Assets, $13,108,590 (M); gifts received, $95,022; expenditures, $1,074,842; qualifying distributions, $987,979; giving activities include $961,565 for 8 grants (high: $300,000; low: $20,000).
Fields of interest: Education; Environment, land resources; Environment.
Limitations: Applications accepted. Giving primarily in MA and ME.
Application information: Application form not required.
Initial approach: Proposal
Deadline(s): None
Trustees: Linda S. Dalby; Timothy A. Ingraham.
EIN: 272377992

4161
Mannion Family Foundation ✧
31 St. James Ave., Ste. 740
Boston, MA 02116-4186

Established in 2000 in MA.
Donors: Martin J. Mannion; Mrs. Martin J. Mannion.
Foundation type: Independent foundation.
Financial data (yr. ended 12/31/13): Assets, $10,169,021 (M); gifts received, $500; expenditures, $730,264; qualifying distributions, $650,000; giving activities include $650,000 for 2 grants (high: $400,000; low: $250,000).
Fields of interest: Arts, multipurpose centers/programs; Education; Philanthropy/voluntarism.
Limitations: Applications not accepted. Giving primarily in the Cambridge and Boston, MA, area. No grants to individuals.
Application information: Unsolicited requests for funds not accepted.
Trustees: Robert G. Bannish; Martin J. Mannion; Tristin L. Mannion.
EIN: 043522053

4162
The Nancy Lurie Marks Family Foundation ✧
(formerly Nancy Lurie Marks Charitable Foundation)
c/o Goulston & Storrs
60 William St., Ste. 110
Wellesley, MA 02481-3810 (781) 237-1311
FAX: (781) 237-0271; Main URL: http://www.nlmfoundation.org/about_nlm.aspx
Multimedia: http://www.nlmfoundation.org/media.htm

Established in 1976 in MA.
Donors: Nancy Lurie Marks; Marian Smith‡.
Foundation type: Independent foundation.
Financial data (yr. ended 10/31/13): Assets, $115,918,996 (M); expenditures, $6,673,979; qualifying distributions, $5,274,662; giving activities include $3,896,312 for 41 grants (high: $672,182; low: $500).
Purpose and activities: Giving primarily to help people with autism lead fulfilling and rewarding lives. The foundation also supports civic, educational, arts and community causes.
Fields of interest: Museums; Arts; Higher education; Hospitals (general); Autism; Medical research, institute; Autism research; Human services; Jewish federated giving programs; Social sciences.
Limitations: Applications not accepted. Giving primarily in Boston, MA. No grants to individuals; no loans or program-related investments.
Application information: Contributes only to pre-selected organizations.
Officers and Trustees:* Nancy L. Marks, Ph.D.*, Chair.; Cathy J. Lurie,* Pres.; Richard B. Denning, C.P.A.*, C.O.O.; Mark D. Balk, Esq.; H. Eric Cushing; Jeffrey R. Lurie, Ph.D.
Director: Clarence Schutt.
EIN: 042607232

4163
Massiah Foundation, Inc. ✧
c/o Deloitte & Touche, Attn.: K. Oates
200 Berkeley St., 9th FL.
Boston, MA 02116-5022 (617) 437-2000
Main URL: http://www.massiah.com

Established in 2000 in MA.
Donors: Fariborz Maseeh; YSA Holdings LLC.
Foundation type: Independent foundation.
Financial data (yr. ended 12/31/13): Assets, $5,279,824 (M); gifts received, $319,600; expenditures, $1,808,553; qualifying distributions, $1,728,501; giving activities include $1,640,541 for 23 grants (high: $700,000; low: $1,000).
Purpose and activities: Giving primarily for education, the arts, hospitals, and human services.
Fields of interest: Arts; Secondary school/education; Higher education; Education; Hospitals (general); Health care; Human services.
Limitations: Applications not accepted. Giving primarily in the greater Boston, MA, area, and CA. No grants to individuals.
Application information: Unsolicited requests for funds not accepted. Applicants may, however fill out a short description of their project on the form available on the foundation web site.
Officer: Fariborz Maseeh, Pres.
EIN: 043536335

4164
Mazar Family Charitable Foundation Trust ✧
c/o The Colony Group
2 Atlantic Ave.
Boston, MA 02110-3918

Established in 1997 in MA.
Donors: Anne Mazar; Brian Mazar.
Foundation type: Independent foundation.
Financial data (yr. ended 12/31/13): Assets, $11,460,956 (M); expenditures, $572,345; qualifying distributions, $545,685; giving activities include $545,685 for 58 grants (high: $300,000; low: $20).
Fields of interest: Environment, natural resources; Health care; Human services; Children/youth, services; International development; United Ways and Federated Giving Programs.
Limitations: Applications not accepted. Giving primarily in MA. No grants to individuals.
Application information: Unsolicited requests for funds not accepted.
Trustees: Anne Mazar; Brian Mazar.
EIN: 043344681
Selected grants: The following grants are a representative sample of this grantmaker's funding activity:
$203,737 to Nature Conservancy, Arlington, VA, 2011.
$5,000 to International Rescue Committee, New York, NY, 2011.
$5,000 to Pathfinder International, Watertown, MA, 2011.
$4,000 to American Indian College Fund, Denver, CO, 2011.
$4,000 to Feeding America, Chicago, IL, 2011.
$4,000 to Habitat for Humanity International, Americus, GA, 2011.
$4,000 to Student Conservation Association, Charlestown, NH, 2011.
$4,000 to Union of Concerned Scientists, Cambridge, MA, 2011.
$3,000 to American Humane Association, Englewood, CO, 2011.

4165
The McCance Foundation ✧
c/o Choate LLP
P.O. Box 961019
Boston, MA 02196-1019
GiveSmart: http://www.givesmart.org/Stories/Donors/HenryMcCance

Established in 1994 in MA.
Donor: Henry F. McCance.
Foundation type: Independent foundation.
Financial data (yr. ended 12/31/12): Assets, $32,191,495 (M); gifts received, $10,398,129; expenditures, $1,604,594; qualifying distributions, $1,388,738; giving activities include $1,380,073 for 65 grants (high: $110,000; low: $29).
Fields of interest: Education; Environment, natural resources; Health organizations; Human services.
Limitations: Applications not accepted. Giving in the U.S., with some emphasis on CT, MA, and NY.
Application information: Contributes only to pre-selected organizations.
Trustees: Keith S. Jennings; Elizabeth McCance; Henry F. McCance; Ellen McCance Pincschmidt.
EIN: 046772532
Selected grants: The following grants are a representative sample of this grantmaker's funding activity:
$60,000 to Ocean Conservancy, Washington, DC, 2012. For Marine Protected Area Program.
$50,000 to Chicago Wilderness Trust, Chicago, IL, 2012. For Metropolitan Greenspace Alliance.
$10,000 to New School of Lancaster, Lancaster, PA, 2012. For 2012-2013 Annual Appeal Match.
$2,500 to Brooklyn Public Library, Brooklyn, NY, 2012. For Friends of the Cortelyou Library.
$2,000 to Save the Children Federation, Fairfield, CT, 2012. For emergency relief.
$2,000 to Yale University, New Haven, CT, 2012. For Yale Sailing Associates.

4166
James S. McDonnell Family Foundation, Inc. ✧
16 Weston Rd.
Lincoln, MA 01773-2002

Established in 2002 in MA.
Donors: James S. McDonnell Charitable Trust A; James S. McDonnell Charitable Trust B.
Foundation type: Independent foundation.
Financial data (yr. ended 12/31/13): Assets, $73,647,613 (M); gifts received, $5,802,692; expenditures, $3,260,702; qualifying distributions, $2,885,537; giving activities include $2,873,000 for 10 grants (high: $1,100,000; low: $10,000).
Purpose and activities: Giving primarily for community development and education.
Fields of interest: Arts; Elementary/secondary education; Higher education; Hospitals (specialty); Urban/community development.
Limitations: Applications not accepted. Giving in the U.S., with emphasis on MO. No grants to individuals.
Application information: Contributes only to pre-selected organizations.
Officers and Directors:* Catherine M. Rogers,* Pres. and Treas.; Katherine H. McDonnell,* Clerk; James S. McDonnell III; John F. McDonnell.
EIN: 364507175
Selected grants: The following grants are a representative sample of this grantmaker's funding activity:
$450,000 to Saint Louis Life Sciences Project, Saint Louis, MO, 2011. For capital campaign.
$26,563 to Sudanese Education Fund, Arlington, MA, 2011. For general support.

4167
The C. Jean & Myles McDonough Charitable Foundation ✧
8 Westwood Dr.
Worcester, MA 01609-1243

Established in 1986 in MA.
Donors: C. Jean McDonough; Myles McDonough; Flexcon Co., Inc.
Foundation type: Company-sponsored foundation.
Financial data (yr. ended 11/30/13): Assets, $1,226,100 (M); expenditures, $1,175,923; qualifying distributions, $1,165,250; giving activities include $1,165,250 for 27 grants (high: $305,000; low: $100).
Purpose and activities: The foundation supports museums and organizations involved with historic preservation, higher education, the environment, and human services.
Fields of interest: Arts; Education; Health organizations.
Limitations: Applications not accepted. Giving primarily in Worcester, MA. No grants to individuals.
Application information: Contributes only to pre-selected organizations.
Trustee: C. Jean McDonough.
EIN: 042947391

4168
Mildred H. McEvoy Foundation ✧
370 Main St., 12th Fl.
Worcester, MA 01608-1779 (508) 459-8000
Contact: Sumner B. Tilton, Jr., Tr.

Trust established in 1963 in MA.
Donor: Mildred H. McEvoy†.
Foundation type: Independent foundation.
Financial data (yr. ended 12/31/13): Assets, $29,199,916 (M); expenditures, $1,427,251; qualifying distributions, $1,307,533; giving activities include $1,108,000 for 62 grants (high: $100,000; low: $500).
Purpose and activities: Giving primarily to health, educational, cultural, and human service organizations based in Worcester, MA, and Boothbay, ME.
Fields of interest: Museums; Historic preservation/historical societies; Higher education; Education; Botanical gardens; Health organizations, association; Human services; YM/YWCAs & YM/YWHAs; Community/economic development.
Limitations: Applications accepted. Giving primarily in Worcester, MA, and the Boothbay Harbor, ME, area. No grants to individuals, or for endowment funds.
Application information: Application form required.
Initial approach: Letter
Copies of proposal: 1

Deadline(s): June 1
Board meeting date(s): During the summer and in Dec.
Trustees: George H. McEvoy; Paul R. Rossley; Sumner B. Tilton, Jr.
Number of staff: 1 part-time professional.
EIN: 046069958
Selected grants: The following grants are a representative sample of this grantmaker's funding activity:
$50,000 to Worcester Academy, Worcester, MA, 2011.
$30,000 to Worcester Center for Performing Arts, Worcester, MA, 2011.
$25,000 to Worcester Center for Performing Arts, Worcester, MA, 2011.
$20,000 to Massachusetts College of Pharmacy and Health Sciences, Worcester, MA, 2011.
$20,000 to Worcester Academy, Worcester, MA, 2011.
$15,000 to Worcester Center for Performing Arts, Worcester, MA, 2011.
$10,000 to Clark University, Worcester, MA, 2011.
$10,000 to Main South Community Development Corporation, Worcester, MA, 2011.
$10,000 to Mechanics Hall, Worcester, MA, 2011.
$10,000 to Rainbow Child Development Center, Worcester, MA, 2011.

4169
McLane/Harper Charitable Foundation Inc. ✧
c/o P. Andrews McLane
200 Clarendon St., 56th Fl.
Boston, MA 02116-5043

Established in 1986 in MA.
Donors: P. Andrews McLane; Linda Harper McLane.
Foundation type: Independent foundation.
Financial data (yr. ended 11/30/13): Assets, $33,116,372 (M); expenditures, $1,886,461; qualifying distributions, $1,838,424; giving activities include $1,838,424 for 11 grants (high: $585,224; low: $10,000).
Fields of interest: Museums (art).
Limitations: Applications not accepted. Giving primarily in MA and NH. No grants to individuals.
Application information: Contributes only to pre-selected organizations.
Officers: P. Andrews McLane, Pres.; David H. Hopfenberg, Clerk; Linda Harper McLane, Treas.
EIN: 042944189
Selected grants: The following grants are a representative sample of this grantmaker's funding activity:
$600,000 to University of Michigan, Ann Arbor, MI, 2011.

4170
The Melville Charitable Trust
11 Beacon St., Ste. 914
Boston, MA 02108-3020 (617) 236-2244
Contact: Aimee Hendrigan
FAX: (617) 307-4590;
E-mail: ahendrigan@melvilletrust.org; Main URL: http://www.melvilletrust.org
Grants List: http://www.melvilletrust.org/grantee-partners/
Melville Charitable Trust's Philanthropy Promise: http://www.ncrp.org/philanthropys-promise/who
Twitter: https://twitter.com/MelvilleTrust

Established in 1987 in NY.
Donor: Dorothy Melville†.
Foundation type: Independent foundation.
Financial data (yr. ended 12/31/13): Assets, $156,847,227 (M); gifts received, $1,003,612; expenditures, $10,757,529; qualifying distributions, $7,489,595; giving activities include $6,206,183 for 59 grants (high: $600,000; low: $250), and $2,490,966 for foundation-administered programs.
Purpose and activities: The trust concentrates its efforts on supporting solutions to prevent and end homelessness. The trust supports service and housing programs in Connecticut that can serve as models throughout the country. The trust also funds educational, research and advocacy initiatives in the state and on the national level.
Fields of interest: Housing/shelter, development; Housing/shelter, services; Homeless, human services; Community development, neighborhood development; Economic development; Homeless.
Type of support: General/operating support; Management development/capacity building; Program development; Conferences/seminars; Publication; Seed money; Research; Technical assistance; Consulting services; Program evaluation; Program-related investments/loans; Matching/challenge support.
Limitations: Applications accepted. Giving primarily in CT. No support for religious organizations for religious purposes. No grants to individuals, for scholarships, budget deficits, or general fundraising drives or events.
Publications: Application guidelines; Grants list; Program policy statement; Program policy statement (including application guidelines).
Application information: See foundation web site. Application form not required.
Initial approach: Concept paper
Copies of proposal: 1
Deadline(s): Rolling
Board meeting date(s): Varies
Final notification: Varies
Officer and Board Members:* Stephen Melville,* Chair.; Aimee Hendrigan, V.P., Progs.; Janice Elliott, Exec. Dir.; Arthur Evans; Shelley Geballe; David Hadden; Robert M. Haggett; Carla Javits; Ruth Melville.
Trustee: Bank of America, N.A.
Number of staff: 2 full-time professional; 2 part-time professional.
EIN: 133415258
Selected grants: The following grants are a representative sample of this grantmaker's funding activity:
$939,789 to Partnership for Strong Communities, Hartford, CT, 2012. To continue to build on the Partnership's core strength of affordable housing policy and advocacy.
$900,000 to Partnership for Strong Communities, Hartford, CT, 2012. For continuing support.
$600,000 to Technical Assistance Collaborative, Boston, MA, 2012. For comprehensive program of technical assistance to implement HUD's Section 811 Supportive Housing for persons with Disabilities Demonstration program.
$600,000 to Technical Assistance Collaborative, Boston, MA, 2012. For a comprehensive program of technical assistance to support the implementation of HUD's Section 811 Supportive Housing for Persons with Disabilities Demonstration program (the Frank Melville Supportive Housing Investment Act) for a second year and to continue TAC's affordable housing, behavioral health, and Medicaid policy, advocacy and technical assistance activities with federal and state government leaders.
$500,000 to National Low Income Housing Coalition and Low Income Housing Information Service, Washington, DC, 2012. For operating support and to implement National Housing Trust Fund.
$300,726 to National Alliance to End Homelessness, Washington, DC, 2012. For continuing support.
$300,000 to National Low Income Housing Coalition and Low Income Housing Information Service, Washington, DC, 2012. For operational support and ongoing strategy development to fund and implement the National Housing Trust Fund.
$300,000 to National Public Radio, Washington, DC, 2012. For the support of programs and activities, including coverage of how the downturn in the nation's economy is affecting families living at or below the poverty line.
$267,275 to Connecticut Voices for Children, New Haven, CT, 2012. For research.
$250,246 to National Alliance on Mental Illness Connecticut, Hartford, CT, 2012. For ongoing support of Keep the Promise Coalition and NAMI's state policy work.
$150,000 to Corporation for Supportive Housing, New York, NY, 2012. For Social Innovative Fund Initiative, national effort to design, pilot and test innovative models that integrate housing with health service in communities across the nation.
$116,500 to Connecticut Coalition to End Homelessness, Hartford, CT, 2012. For Opening Doors CT planning and implementation.
$80,000 to Connecticut News Project, Hartford, CT, 2012. For operation of this nonprofit, non-partisan organization created to reinvigorate news coverage of Connecticut's state government and public policy.
$60,000 to Connecticut Housing Coalition, Wethersfield, CT, 2012. For Opening Doors CT planning and implementation.
$7,500 to Prime Time House, Torrington, CT, 2012. For Educational Opportunity Fund.

4171
Merck Family Fund ✧
95 Eliot St., Ste. 2
Milton, MA 02186-3033 (617) 696-3580
Contact: Jenny Russell, Exec. Dir.
FAX: (617) 696-7262; E-mail: merck@merckff.org; Main URL: http://www.merckff.org

Incorporated in 1954 in NJ.
Donor: Members of the Merck family.
Foundation type: Independent foundation.
Financial data (yr. ended 12/31/12): Assets, $51,239,593 (M); gifts received, $20,500; expenditures, $3,834,461; qualifying distributions, $3,235,058; giving activities include $2,603,533 for 76 grants (high: $150,000; low: $500), and $40,000 for 1 loan/program-related investment.
Purpose and activities: To restore and protect the natural environment, and to strengthen the social fabric and physical landscape of the urban community. Primary areas of interest are: 1) Protecting and restoring vital eastern U.S. ecosystems and promoting sustainable economic practices; and 2) Strengthening the urban community, concentrating on green and open space programs and youth organizing in Boston, MA, Providence, RI, and New York City.

Fields of interest: Environment; Youth development; Children/youth, services; Community development, neighborhood development; Economics; Economically disadvantaged.
Type of support: General/operating support; Continuing support; Land acquisition; Program development; Conferences/seminars; Seed money; Matching/challenge support.
Limitations: Applications accepted. Giving primarily in Boston, MA, New York, NY, and Providence, RI, for Urban Program; the Northern Forest of ME, NH, and VT, southern Appalachia, and SC coastal areas, for Eastern Ecosystems; and nationally for Economics Program. No support for sectarian or religious purposes, for-profit organizations, or for projects intended to support candidates for political office. No grants to individuals, or for endowments, debt reduction, annual fundraising campaigns, capital construction, equipment, land acquisition, or film or video projects; generally no grants for academic research or books.
Publications: Application guidelines; Annual report (including application guidelines); Grants list.
Application information: Full proposals by invitation only upon review of letter of inquiry.
Initial approach: Letter of inquiry via online application system on foundation web site
Copies of proposal: 1
Deadline(s): None for letters of inquiry; deadlines vary annually for full proposals, see foundation web site for current deadlines
Board meeting date(s): Feb., May and Nov.
Final notification: Within 1 week of board decision
Officers and Trustees:* Nat Chamberlin,* Pres.; Eliza Hatch,* V.P.; Elizabeth Merck Lake, Secy.; Wil Merck,* Treas.; Jenny Russell, Exec. Dir.; Katie Chamerlin; Henry Hatch; Ian Hatch; Whitney Hatch; Elliott Merck; Serena Whitridge.
Number of staff: 3 full-time professional.
EIN: 226063382

4172
The John Merck Fund ✧
2 Oliver St., 8th Fl.
Boston, MA 02109-4901 (617) 556-4120
Contact: Ruth G. Hennig, Secy. and Exec. Dir.
FAX: (617) 556-4130; E-mail: info@jmfund.org; Main URL: http://www.jmfund.org
Grants List: http://www.jmfund.org/program.list.php

Established in 1970 in NY as a trust.
Donor: Serena S. Merck‡.
Foundation type: Independent foundation.
Financial data (yr. ended 12/31/13): Assets, $78,359,185 (M); expenditures, $10,726,695; qualifying distributions, $9,966,254; giving activities include $8,810,000 for 121 grants (high: $400,000; low: $1,500).
Purpose and activities: Grants are made in the following areas: for medical research on causes of developmental disabilities in children; to build supply and demand for clear, renewable energy and reduce reliance on coal-fired power plants; to improve the health and vitality of rural communities in Maine, New Hampshire and Vermont by developing a sustainable food systems sector in the region; and to eliminate persistent bio-accumulative toxic chemicals and to encourage comprehensive precaution-based chemicals policy reforms in states to provide both models and upward pressure for eventual reform at the federal level.
Fields of interest: Environment, public policy; Environment, toxics; Environment, climate change/global warming; Environment; Employment, services.
Type of support: Mission-related investments/loans; General/operating support; Program development.
Limitations: Giving on a national basis in the areas of the environment. Generally, no support for large organizations with well-established funding sources. Generally, no grants to individuals, or for endowment or capital fund projects, or for documentary film, photographic or any other artistic projects; generally no general support grants.
Publications: Grants list; Program policy statement.
Application information: The fund does not encourage the submission of unsolicited applications for grants. The fund prefers to request a grant proposal after receiving preliminary written or verbal information about a project. Application form required.
Initial approach: Brief e-mail or letter of inquiry; an e-mail with a letter of inquiry attached is preferable
Deadline(s): Approximately six weeks before quarterly board meetings
Board meeting date(s): Mar., June, Sept., and Dec.
Final notification: Within 2 months
Officers and Trustees:* Ruth G. Hennig, Exec. Dir.; Olivia H. Farr; Robert Gardiner; George Hatch; Whitney Hatch; Roger McFadden; Frederica Perera; William Roberts; Anne Stetson; Serena M. Whitridge.
Number of staff: 3 full-time professional.
EIN: 237082558
Selected grants: The following grants are a representative sample of this grantmaker's funding activity:
$300,000 to Coming Clean, Brattleboro, VT, 2012. To implement a comprehensive platform for reforming federal chemicals policy.
$250,000 to Childrens Hospital Medical Center, Cincinnati, OH, 2012. To conduct a Phase II placebo-controlled proof of concept study of acamprosate in 48 youth with Fragile X Syndrome.
$250,000 to University of California, MIND Institute, Davis, CA, 2012. To evaluate the efficacy of Cogmed, a cognitive training program that enhances working memory and executive function, in individuals with Fragile X Syndrome.
$200,000 to Franklin County Community Development Corporation, Greenfield, MA, 2012. To build a stronger food system by connecting New England farms and food producers to the region's institutions through cross-state collaboration and infrastructure development.
$200,000 to SmartPower, Washington, DC, 2012. To increase adoption of solar power in communities throughout the six New England states, starting in Connecticut, Massachusetts, and Rhode Island.
$160,000 to Washington Toxics Coalition, Seattle, WA, 2012. To protect human health and the environment from the impacts of toxic chemicals through advocacy for model state policy reforms.
$100,000 to Health Care Without Harm, Reston, VA, 2012. To mobilize New England's health care institutions to purchase sustainable, regionally grown food products.
$75,000 to Stanford University, Stanford, CA, 2012. For research on social attention and word learning in typical development and autism spectrum disorders.
$50,000 to Alaska Community Action on Toxics, Anchorage, AK, 2012. To stimulate broad public support for local, national, and international policies that protect the health of Arctic people, wildlife, and the environment from chemical contaminants.
$50,000 to Highfields Institute, Hardwick, VT, 2012. To strengthen the role of composting as a leverage point for food systems development in the Northeast, and to develop communication systems that can better connect composting to other components of the food system.

4173
MetroWest Health Foundation ✧
(formerly MetroWest Community Health Care Foundation, Inc.)
c/o The Meadows Bldg.
161 Worcester Rd., Ste. 202
Framingham, MA 01701-5232 (508) 879-7625
Contact: Martin Cohen, Pres.
FAX: (508) 879-7628; E-mail: info@mwhealth.org; Main URL: http://www.mwhealth.org
Blog: http://www.mwhealth.org/NewsEvents/MWHealthBlog/tabid/248/PostID/15/Default.aspx
E-Newsletter: http://www.mwhealth.org/PublicationsampMedia/Newsletters/tabid/221/Default.aspx
Facebook: http://www.facebook.com/mwhealth
LinkedIn: http://www.linkedin.com/company/2174503?trk=tyah
YouTube: http://www.youtube.com/user/MetroWestCHCF

Established in 1999 in MA; converted from the proceeds of the sale of a non-profit medical center. Serves 25 communities in the MetroWest area of Massachusetts.
Foundation type: Independent foundation.
Financial data (yr. ended 09/30/13): Assets, $99,955,446 (M); gifts received, $352,893; expenditures, $4,690,784; qualifying distributions, $3,725,222; giving activities include $2,418,094 for grants, and $272,944 for foundation-administered programs.
Purpose and activities: The foundation is focused on the health status of the MetroWest area of Massachusetts, its individuals, and its families, through informed and innovative leadership.
Fields of interest: Medicine/medical care, public education; Health care, formal/general education; Medical care, community health systems; Public health; Nursing care; Health care; Children/youth; Adults; Aging; Young adults.
Type of support: Continuing support; Program development; Technical assistance; Scholarships—to individuals.
Limitations: Giving limited to Ashland, Bellingham, Dover, Framingham, Franklin, Holliston, Hopedale, Hopkinton, Hudson, Marlborough, Medfield, Medway, Mendon, Milford, Millis, Natick, Needham, Norfolk, Northborough, Sherborn, Southborough, Sudbury, Wayland, Wellesley, and Westborough, MA.
Publications: Application guidelines; Annual report; Financial statement; Grants list; Newsletter; Occasional report.
Application information: Grant submission guidelines and forms are available on the foundation web site. The foundation usually has 2 grant cycles - fall and spring. Grant guidelines and submission requirements are included with each

announcement. Grant proposals must be submitted online. Application form required.
Initial approach: Organizations must submit a 2-page concept letter via e-mail or mail
Deadline(s): For scholarships: Apr. 15 to May 31 for the academic term following Sept.; Oct. 15 to Nov. 30 for academic term beginning the following Jan.
Board meeting date(s): Last Thurs. of each month
Final notification: 4-6 weeks
Officers and Trustees:* Dana Neshe,* Chair.; Joel Barrera,* Vice-Chair.; Martin D. Cohen, C.E.O. and Pres.; Rosemarie Coelho, Clerk; Adam Rogers,* Treas.; Cynthia Bechtel, Ph.D.; Maria DaSilva; Alan Geller, Esq.; John Krikorian, M.D.; Meyer Levy; Regina Marshall, Esq.; Julie Reed.
Number of staff: 3 full-time professional.
EIN: 042121342

4174
Middlecott Foundation ✧
50 Congress St., Rm. 800
Boston, MA 02109-4034

Established in 1967 in MA.
Donors: Sarah H.C. Ambler; Ames Byrd; Harry F. Byrd; Leverett S. Bryd; Richard E. Byrd III; Eleanor L. Campbell; Eleanor S. Campbell; Levin H. Campbell, Jr.; Emily S. Lewis; Lisa S. Lewis; Lynn Lewis; Deborah S. Pease; Roland F. Pease, Sr.; Roland F. Pease, Jr.; Alice W. Saltonstall; Patrick G. Saltonstall; Timothy Saltonstall; William L. Saltonstall, Jr.‡; and members of the Saltonstall family.
Foundation type: Independent foundation.
Financial data (yr. ended 12/31/13): Assets, $2,728,171 (M); gifts received, $660,893; expenditures, $973,691; qualifying distributions, $913,243; giving activities include $897,714 for 354 grants (high: $200,000; low: $25).
Purpose and activities: Giving primarily for education, arts and culture, health (including hospitals), and human services.
Fields of interest: Museums (art); Historic preservation/historical societies; Arts; Education; Hospitals (general); Health organizations, association; Human services; Children/youth, services.
Limitations: Applications not accepted. Giving on a national basis. No grants to individuals.
Application information: Unsolicited requests for funds not accepted. Giving is donor-driven.
Trustees: George Lewis; G. West Saltonstall; Neil L. Thompson.
Number of staff: 1 part-time support.
EIN: 046155699

4175
George H. & Jane A. Mifflin Memorial Fund ✧
c/o Loring, Wolcott & Coolidge
230 Congress St., 12th Fl.
Boston, MA 02110-2409 (617) 523-6531
Contact: Lawrence Coolidge, Tr.

Established in 1974 in Massachusetts.
Foundation type: Independent foundation.
Financial data (yr. ended 09/30/13): Assets, $36,540,854 (M); expenditures, $1,811,843; qualifying distributions, $1,613,343; giving activities include $1,561,000 for 72 grants (high: $100,000; low: $5,000).
Purpose and activities: Giving primarily for education. Some giving also for human services and environmental conservation.
Fields of interest: Education; Environment, natural resources; Legal services; Human services; Christian agencies & churches; Children/youth; Youth; Minorities; Immigrants/refugees; Economically disadvantaged; Homeless.
Type of support: General/operating support; Capital campaigns; Building/renovation; Land acquisition; Program development; Scholarship funds; Matching/challenge support.
Limitations: Applications accepted. Giving primarily in MA. No grants to individuals.
Application information: Application form not required.
Initial approach: Proposal
Deadline(s): Apr. 15
Trustees: Thomas R. Appleton; David Boit; Lawrence Coolidge.
EIN: 046384983
Selected grants: The following grants are a representative sample of this grantmaker's funding activity:
$100,000 to Conservation Law Foundation, Boston, MA, 2013. For Cashes Ledge Marine National Monument Campaign.
$75,000 to Greater Boston Legal Services, Boston, MA, 2013. For Technology Enhancement Initiative.
$75,000 to Phoenix Charter Academy, Chelsea, MA, 2013. For Network Leadership Program.
$75,000 to Teach for America, Boston, MA, 2013. For Expanding Educational Equity in Massachusetts.
$60,000 to Bottom Line, Jamaica Plain, MA, 2013. For Mass Operations.
$40,000 to Alaska Conservation Foundation, Anchorage, AK, 2013. For Conservation Power Building 2014.
$25,000 to Essex County Greenbelt Association, Essex, MA, 2013. For Norcross Gateway.
$20,000 to Springfield Rescue Mission, Springfield, MA, 2013. For Capital Improvements at 148 Taylor Street.
$15,000 to New England Center for Homeless Veterans, Boston, MA, 2013. For veterans training school.
$10,000 to North Central Charter Essential School, Fitchburg, MA, 2013. For Governance Support Through the High Bar.

4176
The Rebecca and Nathan Milikowsky Family Foundation ✧ ☆
822 Boylston St., Ste. 106
Chestnut Hill, MA 02467-2527 (617) 278-9797
Contact: Nathan Milikowsky, Tr.

Established in 2008 in MA.
Donors: Nathan Milikowsky; The Northern Trust Co. of Delaware.
Foundation type: Independent foundation.
Financial data (yr. ended 06/30/13): Assets, $2,334,658 (M); gifts received, $402,813; expenditures, $672,400; qualifying distributions, $672,228; giving activities include $672,228 for 23 grants (high: $150,000; low: $100).
Fields of interest: Arts; Higher education; Education; Health organizations; Jewish agencies & synagogues; Religion.
Limitations: Applications accepted. Giving primarily in CT, Washington, DC, MA and PA.
Application information: Application form not required.
Initial approach: Proposal
Deadline(s): None
Trustee: Nathan Milikowsky.
EIN: 266711434
Selected grants: The following grants are a representative sample of this grantmaker's funding activity:
$95,000 to American Repertory Theater, Cambridge, MA, 2011.
$40,000 to Shakespeare and Company, Lenox, MA, 2011.
$25,000 to Prostate Cancer Foundation, Santa Monica, CA, 2011.
$22,500 to New York Shakespeare Festival, New York, NY, 2011.
$10,000 to Theater for a New Audience, New York, NY, 2011.
$2,000 to Women in Need, New York, NY, 2011.

4177
Herman and Frieda L. Miller Foundation ✧
c/o GMA Foundations
77 Summer St., Ste. 800
Boston, MA 02110-1006
Contact: Amy Segal Shorey, Admin.
FAX: (617) 426-7087;
E-mail: ashorey@gmafoundations.com; Additional contact: Ruth Victorin, Fdn. Asst., tel.: (617) 391-3101, e-mail: rvictorin@gmafoundations.com; Main URL: http://millerfoundation.grantsmanagement08.com/

Established in 1997 in MA.
Donor: Herman Miller‡.
Foundation type: Independent foundation.
Financial data (yr. ended 11/30/13): Assets, $50,102,606 (M); expenditures, $3,044,136; qualifying distributions, $2,847,952; giving activities include $2,731,000 for 57 grants (high: $130,000; low: $4,000).
Purpose and activities: The foundation supports civic engagement, advocacy, and community organizing in Greater Boston and Eastern Massachusetts. The foundation is also dedicated to improving the infrastructure that supports vibrant urban community life. Key elements toward achieving this goal include: strong civic culture and community empowerment, neighborhood and citywide; development and maintenance of healthy physical settings that facilitate vigorous communities; and access by individuals of all income-levels and backgrounds to employment, housing, education, health care, transportation, and cultural activities.
Fields of interest: Arts; Environment, natural resources; Environment; Human services; Community/economic development.
Type of support: General/operating support; Annual campaigns; Capital campaigns; Building/renovation; Program development; Program evaluation; Matching/challenge support.
Limitations: Applications not accepted. Giving primarily in Boston, MA. No grants to individuals.
Publications: Grants list.
Application information: Unsolicited requests for funds not accepted. Proposals by invitation only. Phone inquires to staff are welcome.
Board meeting date(s): Varies
Trustee: Myron Miller.

Number of staff: 2 part-time professional; 1 part-time support.
EIN: 137131926

4178
Min Charitable Trust ✧
c/o E. Christopher Palmer
30 Colpitts Rd.
Weston, MA 02493-1534

Established in 1996 in MA.
Donors: Ophelia M. Dahl; Felicity Dahl; Lucy Dahl; Tessa Dahl; Theo M.R. Dahl.
Foundation type: Independent foundation.
Financial data (yr. ended 12/31/13): Assets, $38,128 (M); gifts received, $807,616; expenditures, $795,469; qualifying distributions, $785,709; giving activities include $776,848 for 2 grants (high: $414,138; low: $362,710).
Fields of interest: Museums; Children.
International interests: England.
Type of support: General/operating support.
Limitations: Applications not accepted. Giving primarily in Great Missenden, Buckinghamshire, England. No grants to individuals.
Application information: Unsolicited requests for funds not accepted.
Officer: E. Christopher Palmer, Treas.
Trustees: Veronica Teresa Barren; Felicity Ann Dahl; Ophelia M. Dahl; Lisa Frantzis; John Brandan Vaughn-Fowler; Howard Martin Viglio.
EIN: 137070451

4179
Mirowski Family Foundation, Inc. ✧
80 Lyman Rd.
Chestnut Hill, MA 02467

Established in 1997 in MD.
Donors: Anna Mirowski†; Mirowski Family Ventures.
Foundation type: Independent foundation.
Financial data (yr. ended 12/31/13): Assets, $25,485,878 (M); expenditures, $1,275,335; qualifying distributions, $994,083; giving activities include $994,083 for 65 grants (high: $100,000; low: $500).
Fields of interest: Higher education; Medical school/education; Education; Health organizations, association; Human services; Foundations (public); Jewish agencies & synagogues.
Limitations: Applications not accepted. Giving primarily in MA, PA and NY, with some giving in Israel. No grants to individuals.
Application information: Contributes only to pre-selected organizations.
Officers: Ginat W. Mirowski, M.D., Pres.; Ariella M. Rosengard, M.D., Treas.
EIN: 522069951

4180
Michele & David Mittelman Family Foundation ✧
16 Rolling Ln.
Dover, MA 02030-2446

Established in 2005 in MA.
Donors: David Mittelman; Michele Mittelman.
Foundation type: Independent foundation.
Financial data (yr. ended 11/30/13): Assets, $9,385,532 (M); gifts received, $4,169,983; expenditures, $972,500; qualifying distributions, $947,935; giving activities include $756,603 for 17 grants (high: $250,000; low: $500).
Fields of interest: Arts; Elementary/secondary education; Higher education; Hospitals (general); Health care.
Limitations: Applications not accepted. Giving in the U.S., primarily in MA; some funding also in VT. No grants to individuals.
Application information: Contributes only to pre-selected organizations.
Trustees: David Mittelman; Michele Mittelman.
EIN: 206329119
Selected grants: The following grants are a representative sample of this grantmaker's funding activity:
$250,000 to Pan-Massachusetts Challenge, Needham, MA, 2011.
$100,000 to Catalogue for Philanthropy, Watertown, MA, 2011.
$30,000 to Vail Valley Foundation, Avon, CO, 2011.

4181
The Mooney-Reed Charitable Foundation ✧
171 Edmunds Rd.
Wellesley, MA 02481-2209

Established in 2001 in MA.
Donors: Lisa Mooney; James Mooney.
Foundation type: Independent foundation.
Financial data (yr. ended 12/31/13): Assets, $67,451,225 (M); gifts received, $40,001,600; expenditures, $3,060,638; qualifying distributions, $2,894,102; giving activities include $2,856,000 for 18 grants (high: $1,000,000; low: $10,000).
Fields of interest: Scholarships/financial aid; Education; Human services.
Type of support: Scholarship funds.
Limitations: Applications not accepted. Giving primarily in the Boston and Cambridge, MA, area. No grants to individuals.
Application information: Contributes only to pre-selected organizations.
Trustees: James F. Mooney III; Lisa Mooney.
EIN: 046948994

4182
Morgan-Worcester, Inc. ✧
P.O. Box 20193
Worcester, MA 01602
Contact: Gail M. Morgan, Pres. and Treas.

Incorporated in 1953 in MA.
Donor: Morgan Construction Co.
Foundation type: Company-sponsored foundation.
Financial data (yr. ended 09/30/13): Assets, $764,327 (M); gifts received, $98,766; expenditures, $1,029,017; qualifying distributions, $1,013,748; giving activities include $895,500 for 25 grants (high: $500,000; low: $100), and $57,915 for 74 employee matching gifts.
Purpose and activities: The foundation supports organizations involved with arts and culture, education, and human services.
Fields of interest: Education; Human services; Religion.
Limitations: Applications accepted. Giving limited to Worcester County, MA. No support for religious organizations. No grants to individuals, or for endowments, special projects, research, publications, conferences, scholarships, or fellowships; no loans.
Publications: Annual report; Program policy statement.
Application information: Application form required.
Initial approach: Proposal
Copies of proposal: 1
Deadline(s): None
Board meeting date(s): Quarterly
Officers: Gail M. Morgan, Pres. and Treas.; Barrett Morgan, V.P.; Philip R. Morgan, Secy.
EIN: 046111693

4183
The Morningside Foundation ✧
(formerly Morningside-Springfield Foundation, Inc.)
1188 Centre St.
Newton Centre, MA 02459-1556

Established in 1996 in DE and MA.
Donors: Bill Fung; Springfield Financial Asset Mgmt., Inc.; Onyx Holdings, Inc.; Barley, Inc.; Geranium, Inc.; Watercress, Inc.; Stonecorner Corp.; Kadesh Investments Ltd.; Analytic Risk Management; Nabron International, Inc.; ILTS, LLC.
Foundation type: Independent foundation.
Financial data (yr. ended 12/31/12): Assets, $49,491,123 (M); gifts received, $4,050,000; expenditures, $6,024,445; qualifying distributions, $3,069,642; giving activities include $3,069,642 for 14 grants (high: $1,288,942; low: $13,000).
Purpose and activities: Giving primarily to an arts organization, and for Christian churches.
Fields of interest: Arts, cultural/ethnic awareness; Higher education; Cancer; Christian agencies & churches.
Limitations: Applications not accepted. Giving primarily in CA; some funding also in MA and NY. No grants to individuals.
Application information: Contributes only to pre-selected organizations.
Officers: Lisa M. Sambucci, V.P.; Paula E. Turnbull, V.P.
Directors: Gerald Chan; Ronnie Chan.
EIN: 043339572

4184
John C. & Eunice B. Morrison Charitable Foundation ✧
c/o P. Sorgi
6 Beacon St., Ste. 1010
Boston, MA 02108-2537

Established in 1995 in MA.
Donors: Eunice B. Morrison; Eunice B. Morrison Trust; John Bowen Co. Profit Sharing Plan; John C. Morrison Trust.
Foundation type: Independent foundation.
Financial data (yr. ended 12/31/13): Assets, $12,291,759 (M); expenditures, $1,491,137; qualifying distributions, $1,347,189; giving activities include $1,325,000 for 88 grants (high: $450,000; low: $2,500).
Fields of interest: Food banks; Human services; Children/youth, services.
Limitations: Applications not accepted. Giving primarily in MA. No grants to individuals.
Application information: Contributes only to pre-selected organizations.

Trustees: A. Dennis Barbo; Peter Sorgi; James G. Walsh III.
EIN: 043310863
Selected grants: The following grants are a representative sample of this grantmaker's funding activity:
$10,000 to DCF Kids Fund, Boston, MA, 2011. For programs.
$10,000 to Father Bills and MainSpring, Quincy, MA, 2011.
$10,000 to Greater Boston Food Bank, Boston, MA, 2011.
$10,000 to Pine Street Inn, Boston, MA, 2011.
$10,000 to Pure Water for the World, Rutland, VT, 2011. For programs.
$5,000 to Joslin Diabetes Center, Boston, MA, 2011. For research.
$5,000 to Mass Mentoring Partnership, Boston, MA, 2011.
$5,000 to MEDA, Inc., Newton, MA, 2011.
$2,500 to Perkins School for the Blind, Watertown, MA, 2011. For programs.
$2,500 to Year Up, Boston, MA, 2011. For programs.

4185
Edward S. & Winifred G. Moseley Foundation ✧

c/o Seward Mgmt. LP
265 Franklin St., 20th Fl.
Boston, MA 02110-3199

Established in 2007 in MA.
Donors: Edward S. Mosley†; Edward S. Moseley Trust.
Foundation type: Independent foundation.
Financial data (yr. ended 06/30/13): Assets, $18,948,803 (M); expenditures, $970,274; qualifying distributions, $861,000; giving activities include $861,000 for grants.
Fields of interest: Education; Hospitals (general); Human services.
Limitations: Applications not accepted. Giving primarily in MA.
Application information: Contributes only to pre-selected organizations.
Trustees: Christopher T. Barrow; Kay Howe; Robert G. Howe; Roger D. Scoville.
EIN: 743201002
Selected grants: The following grants are a representative sample of this grantmaker's funding activity:
$35,000 to Boys and Girls Club of Lower Merrimack Valley, Salisbury, MA, 2013. For After School Enrichment Program.
$30,000 to Endicott College, Beverly, MA, 2013. For Keys to Degrees: Educating Two Generations Together.
$30,000 to Greater Lawrence Family Health Center, Lawrence, MA, 2013. For Lawrence Family Medical Residency (LFMR).
$25,000 to Esperanza Academy, Lawrence, MA, 2013. For Teacher Salary and Professional Development.
$25,000 to Plummer Home for Boys, Salem, MA, 2013. For Preparedness and Health and Wellness Program.
$15,000 to Lazarus House, Lawrence, MA, 2013. For Campaign for Dignity: Helping the People Served By Lazarus House Ministries.
$15,000 to Phillips Academy, Andover, MA, 2013. For Pals and Abl Summer Programs.
$15,000 to Pingree School, South Hamilton, MA, 2013. For Prep @ Pingree.
$10,000 to Anna Jaques Hospital, Newburyport, MA, 2013. For new power plant.
$10,000 to Essex Art Center, Lawrence, MA, 2013. For Si Se Peude and Community Day Charter School.

4186
MWC Foundation, Inc. ✧

c/o Nutter, McClennen & Fish, LLP
World Trade Ctr. West
155 Seaport Blvd.
Boston, MA 02210-2604
Contact: Thomas P. Jalkut, Clerk

Established in 1988 in MA.
Donor: Barbara Cummings 1987 Revocable Trust.
Foundation type: Independent foundation.
Financial data (yr. ended 12/31/13): Assets, $54,758,905 (M); expenditures, $2,494,026; qualifying distributions, $2,372,093; giving activities include $2,141,900 for 62 grants (high: $315,000; low: $5,000).
Purpose and activities: Giving primarily for social services.
Fields of interest: Environment; Human services; Community/economic development.
Limitations: Applications not accepted. Giving primarily in New England, with emphasis on MA. No grants to individuals.
Application information: Unsolicited requests for funds not accepted.
Officers and Directors:* Thomas P. Jalkut,* Pres.; John A. McBrine, Clerk; Melissa S. McMorrow,* Treas.
EIN: 222914691

4187
The Creighton Narada Foundation ✧

c/o Day, Pitney, LLP
1 International Pl.
Boston, MA 02110-2602

Established in 1994 in MA.
Donors: Albert M. Creighton, Jr.; Creighton Charitable Lead Unitrust.
Foundation type: Independent foundation.
Financial data (yr. ended 12/31/13): Assets, $15,749,336 (M); gifts received, $134,652; expenditures, $628,261; qualifying distributions, $556,918; giving activities include $542,000 for 20 grants (high: $80,000; low: $1,000).
Purpose and activities: Giving primarily for land conservation and social services.
Fields of interest: Museums; Higher education; Environment, natural resources; Environment, land resources; Boys & girls clubs; Human services.
Limitations: Applications not accepted. Giving primarily in MA; some giving also in ME. No grants to individuals.
Application information: Contributes only to pre-selected organizations.
Trustees: Albert M. Creighton, Jr.; Albert M. Creighton III; Hilary H. Creighton; Peter H. Creighton.
EIN: 043243114
Selected grants: The following grants are a representative sample of this grantmaker's funding activity:
$81,500 to Maine Coast Heritage Trust, Topsham, ME, 2012. For social/community.
$25,000 to W G B H Educational Foundation, Boston, MA, 2012. For community/cultural.
$1,000 to Treehouse Foundation, Easthampton, MA, 2012. For community/cultural.

4188
Scott A. Nathan Charitable Trust ✧ ☆

c/o Paul McCoy Family Office Services
31 St. James Ave., Ste. 740
Boston, MA 02116-4186

Established in 1997 in MA.
Donor: Scott A. Nathan.
Foundation type: Independent foundation.
Financial data (yr. ended 12/31/13): Assets, $9,326,997 (M); gifts received, $5,000,000; expenditures, $1,401,701; qualifying distributions, $1,401,666; giving activities include $1,401,666 for 16 grants (high: $500,000; low: $5,000).
Fields of interest: Museums (art); Arts; Environment; Health organizations, association; Public affairs.
Limitations: Applications not accepted. Giving primarily in Washington, D.C. and MA. No grants to individuals.
Application information: Contributes only to pre-selected organizations.
Trustee: Scott A. Nathan.
EIN: 046854624

4189
New Balance Foundation ✧

20 Guest St.
Boston, MA 02135-2040 (617) 783-4000
Contact: Anne M. Davis, Managing Tr.
E-mail: newbalancefoundation@newbalance.com;
Main URL: http://www.newbalancefoundation.org/
New Balance Foundation Video: http://www.newbalancefoundation.org/NewBalance_v8_RT332_FullFrame.wmv

Established in 1981 in MA.
Donor: New Balance Athletic Shoe, Inc.
Foundation type: Company-sponsored foundation.
Financial data (yr. ended 11/20/13): Assets, $124,450,793 (M); gifts received, $1,076,570; expenditures, $6,531,997; qualifying distributions, $6,319,579; giving activities include $6,318,079 for 87 grants (high: $900,000; low: $200).
Purpose and activities: The foundation supports organizations involved with education, the environment, health, nutrition, disaster relief, school athletics, and human services. Special emphasis is directed toward programs designed to promote healthy lifestyles and prevent childhood obesity.
Fields of interest: Education; Environment; Hospitals (general); Public health, obesity; Public health, physical fitness; Health care; Nutrition; Disasters, preparedness/services; Athletics/sports, academies; Family services; Human services; United Ways and Federated Giving Programs; Children; Economically disadvantaged.
Type of support: Research; General/operating support; Continuing support; Scholarship funds; Matching/challenge support.
Limitations: Applications accepted. Giving primarily in Boston and Lawrence, MA and Norridgewock, Norway, and Skowhegan, ME. No support for political parities or discriminatory organizations. No grants to individuals, or for capital campaigns,

fundraising dinners or galas, team sponsorships, sporting events, or film or television underwriting.
Publications: Application guidelines; Financial statement; Grants list; Program policy statement.
Application information: Concept papers should be no longer than 1 page. Proposals should be no longer than 3 pages and existing grant partners should submit 4 copies of that proposal.. Support is limited to 1 contribution per organization during any given year. Organizations receiving support are asked to submit interim reports and a final report. Application form not required.
Initial approach: Concept paper for new grant seekers; proposal for existing grant partners
Deadline(s): Mar. 3 for new grant seekers; Feb. 3 for existing grant partners
Final notification: Apr. 1 for new grant seekers
Trustees: Anne M. Davis; James S. Davis; Paul R. Gauron.
EIN: 046470644
Selected grants: The following grants are a representative sample of this grantmaker's funding activity:
$900,000 to Children's Hospital Corporation, Boston, MA, 2013. For general support.
$650,000 to Playworks, Oakland, CA, 2013. For general support.
$375,000 to ChopChopKids, Watertown, MA, 2013. For general support.
$250,000 to American Red Cross National Headquarters, Washington, DC, 2013. For general support.
$250,000 to Boston College, Chestnut Hill, MA, 2013. For general support.
$204,700 to Boys and Girls Club of Allston-Brighton, West End House, Allston, MA, 2013. For general support.
$78,800 to Barbara Bush Childrens Hospital, Portland, ME, 2013. For general support.
$40,000 to Community Rowing, Brighton, MA, 2013. For general support.
$25,000 to Share Our Strength, Washington, DC, 2013. For general support.
$25,000 to YMCA, Merrimack Valley, Lawrence, MA, 2013. For general support.

4190
New Breeze Foundation ✧
c/o Robert T. Hale, Karen Hale, Jr.
8 Olmstead Dr.
Hingham, MA 02043-2651

Established in 2000 in MA.
Donors: Robert T. Hale, Jr.; Robert Hale, Sr.; Judith Hale; Karen R. Hale; Robert T. Hale, Jr. 2010 Trust.
Foundation type: Independent foundation.
Financial data (yr. ended 12/31/13): Assets, $789,831 (M); gifts received, $764,280; expenditures, $553,241; qualifying distributions, $549,512; giving activities include $548,262 for 26 grants (high: $250,000; low: $50).
Fields of interest: Elementary/secondary education; Education; Hospitals (general); Human services.
Limitations: Applications not accepted. Giving primarily in MA. No grants to individuals.
Application information: Contributes only to pre-selected organizations.
Trustees: Karen R. Hale; Robert T. Hale, Jr.
EIN: 043510635

4191
New Cycle Foundation ✧
c/o Peregrine Financial Corp.
160 State St., 5th Fl.
Boston, MA 02109-2502

Established in 1985 in NY.
Donor: Michael Currier†.
Foundation type: Independent foundation.
Financial data (yr. ended 12/31/13): Assets, $14,916,679 (M); expenditures, $734,043; qualifying distributions, $697,801; giving activities include $679,000 for 6 grants (high: $300,000; low: $2,500).
Fields of interest: Education; Environment; Human services; Foundations (community).
Type of support: Program development.
Limitations: Applications not accepted. Giving primarily in NM; some giving also in CO and NY. No support for religious organizations. No grants to individuals.
Application information: Contributes only to pre-selected organizations.
Officer: Nicholas Noon, Pres.
Trustee: Karin A. Griscom.
Number of staff: 1 part-time professional.
EIN: 133260471
Selected grants: The following grants are a representative sample of this grantmaker's funding activity:
$225,000 to Colorado Conservation Trust, Denver, CO, 2011.
$182,500 to Santa Fe Community Foundation, Santa Fe, NM, 2011.
$15,000 to Western Environmental Law Center, Taos, NM, 2011.

4192
The New England Foundation ✧
c/o Joseph McNay
125 High St., Ste. 1803
Boston, MA 02110-2715 (617) 342-3200

Established in 1986 in MA.
Donors: Joseph C. McNay; Thomas Ebert Bass Irrevocable Trust.
Foundation type: Independent foundation.
Financial data (yr. ended 12/31/13): Assets, $13,047,638 (M); gifts received, $12,642; expenditures, $657,385; qualifying distributions, $515,174; giving activities include $506,700 for 24 grants (high: $123,200; low: $250).
Purpose and activities: Giving primarily for higher education; funding also for the arts and health care.
Fields of interest: Museums; Performing arts; Arts; Higher education; Education; Hospitals (general); Health care; Human services.
Limitations: Applications not accepted. Giving primarily in New England, with emphasis on MA. No grants to individuals.
Application information: Contributes only to pre-selected organizations.
Trustees: Colin McNay; Joseph C. McNay.
EIN: 222757391

4193
The New England Patriots Charitable Foundation, Inc. ✧
1 Patriot Pl.
Foxboro, MA 02035-1388 (508) 384-9292
Contact: Donna Spigarolo
Main URL: http://www.patriots.com/community/volunteerism.html

Established in 1994 in MA.
Donors: New England Patriots LP; Communication Technology Services, LLC; Fidelity Capital; Fidelity Investments.
Foundation type: Company-sponsored foundation.
Financial data (yr. ended 12/31/13): Assets, $3,458,999 (M); gifts received, $3,209,314; expenditures, $3,339,138; qualifying distributions, $3,141,279; giving activities include $3,124,201 for 191 grants (high: $729,931; low: $100).
Purpose and activities: The foundation supports programs designed to foster cultural diversity, education, family services, and health. Special emphasis is directed toward programs designed to serve youth through education, creativity, and development of character.
Fields of interest: Education; Health care; Boys & girls clubs; Youth development; Family services; Civil/human rights, equal rights; Foundations (community); United Ways and Federated Giving Programs; Youth.
Type of support: Employee volunteer services; General/operating support; Continuing support; Building/renovation; Equipment; Program development; Scholarship funds; In-kind gifts.
Limitations: Applications accepted. Giving limited to New England, with some emphasis on MA. No support for religious organizations or for start-up organizations seeking first-time cash grant support. No grants to individuals, or for game tickets or online auctions.
Publications: Application guidelines.
Application information: Application form required.
Initial approach: Email, see website for application form
Deadline(s): 6 weeks prior to need
Officers: Robert K. Kraft, Chair.; Joshua M. Kraft, Treas.
Directors: Daniel A. Kraft; David H. Kraft; Jonathan A. Kraft.
EIN: 043244069
Selected grants: The following grants are a representative sample of this grantmaker's funding activity:
$25,000 to American Ireland Fund, Boston, MA, 2011.
$20,000 to University of Massachusetts, Boston, MA, 2011.
$10,000 to City of Hope, Duarte, CA, 2011.
$5,625 to Scholarship America, Saint Peter, MN, 2011.
$5,000 to University of Notre Dame, Notre Dame, IN, 2011. For scholarship.
$4,000 to Harvard University, Cambridge, MA, 2011. For scholarship.
$3,000 to University of Massachusetts, Boston, MA, 2011.
$3,000 to University of Massachusetts, Amherst, MA, 2011. For scholarship.
$2,500 to Cystic Fibrosis Foundation, Bethesda, MD, 2011.
$2,500 to University of New Hampshire, Durham, NH, 2011. For scholarship.

4194
North Central Massachusetts Community Foundation, Inc. ✧
649 John Fitch Hwy.
Fitchburg, MA 01420-5998 (978) 345-8383
Contact: Philip M. Grzewinski, Pres.; For grants: Maribeth Janssens, Grants Mgr.
FAX: (978) 345-1459; E-mail: info@cfncm.org; Additional e-mail: philg@cfncm.org; Grant inquiry e-mail: maribeth@cfncm.org; Grant inquiry tel.: 978-345-8383; Main URL: http://www.cfncm.org
Facebook: https://www.facebook.com/cfncm
Grants List: http://www.cfncm.org/ReceiveiNonprofitsIndividualsi/GrantsScholarships.aspx
Twitter: https://twitter.com/cfncm

Established in 2000 in MA.
Foundation type: Community foundation.
Financial data (yr. ended 06/30/14): Assets, $37,712,372 (M); gifts received, $1,944,189; expenditures, $3,649,894; giving activities include $3,063,033 for 61+ grants (high: $489,225), and $235,792 for 93 grants to individuals.
Purpose and activities: The foundation aims to provide a means for donors to permanently endow charitable gifts, to increase and stabilize available funding to meet needs and improve the quality of life.
Fields of interest: Arts; Education; Environment; Health care; Human services; Economic development; Community/economic development.
Type of support: General/operating support; Endowments; Scholarship funds.
Limitations: Applications accepted. Giving primarily in north central MA.
Publications: Application guidelines; Annual report; Informational brochure; Newsletter.
Application information: Visit foundation web site for application form and guidelines. Upon review of concept paper, a limited number of applicants will be invited to submit a full proposal. Application form required.
Initial approach: Submit concept paper and cover sheet
Copies of proposal: 9
Deadline(s): Feb. 6 for concept paper; Apr. 11 for full proposal
Final notification: Mid-Nov. for full proposal invitation; Mar. for final notice
Officers and Trustees:* James Garrison,* Chair.; Ted Lapres,* Vice-Chair.; Philip M. Grzewinski,* Pres. and Recording Secy.; Thomas F. Bagley III,* Clerk; Steven L. Stone,* Treas.; Ronald M. Ansin; William E. Aubuchon IV; John B. Barrett; Paul Brown; Richard A. Cella; Jan Cochran; Jay D. Drake; Ashleigh Gelinas; Peter K. Hazel; David Huhtala; David McKeehan; Richard Nobile; C. Deborah Phillips; Allen Rome; Henri L. Sans; Gary Shepherd; Albert Stone.
EIN: 043537449

4195
James W. O'Brien Foundation, Inc. ✧
c/o McInnis Law Offices
807 Turnpike St.
North Andover, MA 01845-6131

Established in MA.
Foundation type: Independent foundation.
Financial data (yr. ended 09/30/13): Assets, $18,176,045 (M); expenditures, $898,162; qualifying distributions, $888,539; giving activities include $653,935 for 35 grants (high: $340,133; low: $100).
Purpose and activities: Giving primarily for secondary and higher education.
Fields of interest: Secondary school/education; Higher education; Scholarships/financial aid; Medical research, institute; Human services.
Limitations: Applications not accepted. Giving primarily in MA.
Application information: Contributes only to pre-selected organizations.
Trustees: Carl Dimaiti; Christopher Hopey; James J. McInnis; Marybeth McInnis; Thomas Strangie.
EIN: 043528495
Selected grants: The following grants are a representative sample of this grantmaker's funding activity:
$83,000 to Lynn English High School, Lynn, MA, 2011. For scholarships.
$30,000 to Girls Inc. of Lynn, Lynn, MA, 2011.
$25,000 to Notre Dame High School, Lawrence, MA, 2011. For capital campaign.
$5,000 to Bishop Guertin High School, Nashua, NH, 2011.
$5,000 to Lazarus House, Lawrence, MA, 2011.
$3,500 to Augustinian Fund, Villanova, PA, 2011.
$2,500 to Central Catholic High School, Lawrence, MA, 2011. For scholarships.
$2,500 to Pike School, Andover, MA, 2011. For scholarships.
$2,000 to Presentation of Mary Academy, Methuen, MA, 2011.

4196
Joseph & Katherine O'Donnell Charitable Trust ✧
c/o Lourie & Cutler, PC
60 State St.
Boston, MA 02109-1801

Established in 1997 in MA.
Donors: Joseph O'Donnell; Katherine O'Donnell; Jon Luther; Centerplate; Hyundai Village of Danvers.
Foundation type: Independent foundation.
Financial data (yr. ended 12/31/13): Assets, $1,287,229 (M); gifts received, $71,282; expenditures, $1,344,608; qualifying distributions, $1,340,575; giving activities include $1,340,575 for 39 grants (high: $500,000; low: $100).
Purpose and activities: Giving primarily for education, including a school for the blind, health, and human services.
Fields of interest: Secondary school/education; Higher education; Business school/education; Education; Hospitals (general); Medical research, institute; Human services.
Limitations: Applications not accepted. Giving primarily in MA. No grants to individuals.
Application information: Contributes only to pre-selected organizations.
Trustee: William Eisen.
EIN: 046828957

4197
One Life Foundation Inc. ✧
10 Bicentennial Dr.
Lexington, MA 02421-7708

Donor: Dr. Suri A. Sastri.
Foundation type: Independent foundation.
Financial data (yr. ended 10/31/13): Assets, $15,501,484 (M); gifts received, $711,378; expenditures, $521,905; qualifying distributions, $464,000; giving activities include $464,000 for 1 grant.
Fields of interest: United Ways and Federated Giving Programs.
Limitations: Applications not accepted. Giving primarily in Cincinnati, OH.
Application information: Contributes only to pre-selected organizations.
Officers and Directors:* Dr. Suri A. Sastri,* Pres. and Secy.; Rakhal Dev Sastri, Treas.; Candace J. Sastri.
EIN: 261524748
Selected grants: The following grants are a representative sample of this grantmaker's funding activity:
$400,000 to Fidelity Charitable Gift Fund, Boston, MA, 2011.

4198
One World Fund ✧ ☆
38 Essex St.
Andover, MA 01810-3761
Application address: c/o Richardf Healy, 1 World Fund, 64R Prospect St., Cambridge, MA 02139

Established in 1990 in MA.
Donor: Josephine L. Murray.
Foundation type: Independent foundation.
Financial data (yr. ended 12/31/13): Assets, $17,463,655 (M); gifts received, $11,024,814; expenditures, $731,363; qualifying distributions, $460,000; giving activities include $460,000 for 23 grants (high: $75,000; low: $2,500).
Fields of interest: Performing arts, dance; Performing arts, theater; Crime/violence prevention; Children, services; International peace/security; Civil rights, race/intergroup relations; United Ways and Federated Giving Programs; Women; Girls.
Limitations: Applications accepted. Giving primarily in CA, MA, MN and NY. No grants to individuals.
Application information: Application form required.
Initial approach: Letter
Deadline(s): None
Trustees: Diana Devegh; Richard Healy.
EIN: 046485766
Selected grants: The following grants are a representative sample of this grantmaker's funding activity:
$30,000 to National People's Action, Chicago, IL, 2012. To strengthen Organization and Develop Grass Roots.
$25,000 to V-Day, San Francisco, CA, 2012. For a Global Movement to Stop Violence Against Women and Girls.
$10,000 to Haitian Health Foundation, Norwich, CT, 2012. To Improve Health and Well-Being of Poor and Sick and with Focus on Women with Children.
$5,000 to Paul Taylor Dance Company, New York, NY, 2012. To promote Artistic Expression Through Dance.
$5,000 to YouthBuild USA, Somerville, MA, 2012. To support Youth and Community Development Fields to Diminish Poverty.

4199
OneWorld Boston, Inc. ✧ ☆
c/o William F. Grant
200 W. Cummings Park
Woburn, MA 01801-6333
Contact: Joel B. Swets, Clerk and Exec. Dir.

Established in MA.
Foundation type: Independent foundation.
Financial data (yr. ended 12/31/13): Assets, $10,924,045 (M); expenditures, $4,821,356; qualifying distributions, $4,821,321; giving activities include $4,821,321 for 125 grants (high: $120,000; low: $20,000).
Fields of interest: Arts; Education; Human services; Children/youth, services.
Limitations: Applications accepted. Giving primarily in the Boston, MA, area.
Application information: Refer to application guidelines on http://www.cummingsfoundation.org/oneworldboston. Application form required.
Officers and Trustees:* William S. Cummings,* Pres.; Patricia A. Cummings,* V.P.; Joel B. Swets, Clerk. and Exec. Dir.; Joyce M. Cummings,* Treas.; Marilyn C. Morris, M.D.
EIN: 800681389

4200
The Linda Hammett & Andrew Ory Charitable Trust ✧ ☆
P.O. Box 6358
Lincoln, MA 01773-6358

Donor: Linda Hammett Ory.
Foundation type: Independent foundation.
Financial data (yr. ended 12/31/13): Assets, $19,551,918 (M); gifts received, $20,973,039; expenditures, $2,259,380; qualifying distributions, $2,193,500; giving activities include $2,193,500 for 9 grants (high: $2,000,000; low: $500).
Fields of interest: Arts; Education; Science.
Type of support: General/operating support.
Limitations: Applications not accepted. Giving primarily in MA.
Application information: Unsolicited requests for funds not accepted.
Trustees: Andrew D. Ory; Linda G. Hammett Ory.
EIN: 387082936

4201
Edith H. Overly Foundation ✧
c/o Choate, LLP
P.O. Box 961019
Boston, MA 02196-1019

Established in 1990 in MA.
Donors: Edith H. Overly; Edith H. Overly Trust.
Foundation type: Independent foundation.
Financial data (yr. ended 12/31/13): Assets, $11,866,636 (M); gifts received, $250,000; expenditures, $739,349; qualifying distributions, $639,819; giving activities include $630,000 for 29 grants (high: $90,000; low: $5,000).
Fields of interest: Arts; Education; Human services.
Limitations: Applications not accepted. Giving primarily in Boston, MA. No grants to individuals.
Application information: Unsolicited requests for funds not accepted.
Trustees: F. Davis Dassori; William A. Lowell; Edith H. Overly.
EIN: 223043340

4202
The Owens Family Foundation ✧
P.O. Box 78
Norwell, MA 02061-0078

Established in 2000 in MA.
Donors: Edward P. Owens; Linda B. Owens.
Foundation type: Independent foundation.
Financial data (yr. ended 12/31/13): Assets, $29,014,449 (M); gifts received, $2,726,028; expenditures, $1,076,000; qualifying distributions, $1,076,000; giving activities include $1,075,000 for 4 grants (high: $750,000; low: $25,000).
Fields of interest: Higher education; Foundations (public).
Limitations: Applications not accepted. Giving primarily in Boston, MA, and Charlottesville, VA. No grants to individuals.
Application information: Contributes only to pre-selected organizations.
Trustees: Edward P. Owens; Linda B. Owens.
EIN: 316652818
Selected grants: The following grants are a representative sample of this grantmaker's funding activity:
$750,000 to University of Virginia, Charlottesville, VA, 2011. For unrestricted contribution.

4203
Palace Head Foundation, Inc. ✧
303 Berkeley St., No. 2
Boston, MA 02116-1553

Established in 2004 in MA.
Donors: Thomas Gill; Joanne Gill.
Foundation type: Independent foundation.
Financial data (yr. ended 03/31/13): Assets, $12,871,055 (M); expenditures, $696,335; qualifying distributions, $607,150; giving activities include $607,150 for grants.
Purpose and activities: Giving primarily for the arts, particularly the opera; funding also for education, and human services.
Fields of interest: Performing arts, opera; Arts; Education; Health care; Human services.
Limitations: Applications not accepted. Giving primarily in Boston and Milton, MA, and ME, with emphasis on Islesboro. No grants to individuals.
Application information: Contributes only to pre-selected organizations.
Officers and Director:* Joanne S. Gill, Pres. and Clerk; Thomas Gill,* Treas.
EIN: 201740632
Selected grants: The following grants are a representative sample of this grantmaker's funding activity:
$500 to Boys and Girls Club of Santa Monica, Santa Monica, CA, 2013. For Community and Charitable.

4204
Thomas Anthony Pappas Charitable Foundation, Inc. ✧
P.O. Box 463
Belmont, MA 02478-0004 (781) 862-2802
Contact: John C. Pappas, Pres. and Treas.
E-mail: TAPCF@aol.com

Incorporated in 1975 in MA.
Donor: Thomas Anthony Pappas†.
Foundation type: Independent foundation.
Financial data (yr. ended 12/31/13): Assets, $14,244,268 (M); expenditures, $1,202,852; qualifying distributions, $911,645; giving activities include $599,300 for 60 grants (high: $100,000; low: $300).
Purpose and activities: Emphasis on higher education, hospitals and health associations, cultural programs, Greek Orthodox church support, religious associations, and youth and social service agencies.
Fields of interest: Arts; Higher education; Education; Hospitals (general); Health care; Health organizations, association; Medical research, institute; Human services; Children/youth, services; Orthodox agencies & churches.
Type of support: Continuing support; Annual campaigns; Building/renovation; Endowments; Professorships; Fellowships; Scholarship funds; Research.
Limitations: Applications accepted. Giving primarily in MA. No grants to individuals.
Publications: Application guidelines; Program policy statement.
Application information: Application form not required.
Initial approach: Letter (not exceeding 3 pages)
Deadline(s): Sept. 30
Board meeting date(s): Mar., June, Sept., Dec., and as required
Officers and Directors:* John Pappas,* Pres. and Treas.; Betsy Pappas Demirjian,* V.P.; Thomas C. Pappas,* V.P.; Sophia Sacher,* V.P.; Donald Young.
Number of staff: 3 full-time professional; 2 part-time professional.
EIN: 510153284
Selected grants: The following grants are a representative sample of this grantmaker's funding activity:
$150,000 to Dana-Farber Cancer Institute, Boston, MA, 2011.
$150,000 to Newton-Wellesley Hospital, Newton, MA, 2011.
$25,000 to Heading Home, Charlestown, MA, 2011.
$25,000 to Perkins School for the Blind, Watertown, MA, 2011.
$11,000 to Massachusetts Society for the Prevention of Cruelty to Animals, Boston, MA, 2011.
$10,000 to Home for Little Wanderers, Boston, MA, 2011.
$10,000 to Isabella Stewart Gardner Museum, Boston, MA, 2011.
$10,000 to Year Up, Boston, MA, 2011.
$7,500 to Black Ministerial Alliance, Roxbury, MA, 2011.
$7,500 to Samaritans, Boston, MA, 2011.

4205
Arthur M. and Martha R. Pappas Foundation ✧
c/o R.N. Lusardi, C.P.A.
271 Main St., Ste. 203
Stoneham, MA 02180-3580

Established in 1988 in MA.
Donors: Arthur M. Pappas; Martha R. Pappas.
Foundation type: Independent foundation.
Financial data (yr. ended 12/31/13): Assets, $11,878,230 (M); gifts received, $200,000; expenditures, $571,425; qualifying distributions,

$565,475; giving activities include $560,425 for 48 grants (high: $251,000; low: $50).
Fields of interest: Arts; Education; Health organizations, association; Human services; Foundations (community).
Limitations: Applications not accepted. Giving primarily in MA. No grants to individuals.
Application information: Unsolicited requests for funds not accepted.
Trustees: Arthur M. Pappas; Martha R. Pappas.
EIN: 222967957

4206
Samuel P. Pardoe Foundation ✧ ☆

c/o Grants Mgmt. Assoc., Inc.
77 Summer St., 8th Fl.
Boston, MA 02110-1006 (617) 391-3088
Contact: Hannah Blaisdell, Admin.
FAX: (617) 426-7087;
E-mail: hblaisdell@gmafoundations.com; Main URL: http://www.pardoefoundation.grantsmanagement08.com
Grants List: http://pardoefoundation.grantsmanagement08.com/?page_id=4

Established in 1989 in DC.
Donors: Samuel P. Pardoe†; Helen P. Pardoe Trust.
Foundation type: Independent foundation.
Financial data (yr. ended 06/30/13): Assets, $11,857,457 (M); expenditures, $550,238; qualifying distributions, $550,238; giving activities include $514,000 for 38 grants (high: $373,500; low: $500).
Purpose and activities: Support primarily for programs that provide educational and economic opportunities for underprivileged persons. Other areas of interest include health and social services, cultural programs, community development activities, education, and land and resource management, with a focus on support for programs related to specific conservation initiatives. The foundation also supports programs that educate New Hampshire residents about conservation and environmental issues. Educational support focuses primarily on programs on a pre-collegiate level, with a special interest in increasing access to educational opportunities, particularly experiential learning. The foundation also supports literacy, tutoring, and arts education programs.
Fields of interest: Education; Environment, land resources; Human services; Children/youth; Economically disadvantaged.
Type of support: Capital campaigns; Building/renovation; Equipment; Program development; Program-related investments/loans.
Limitations: Applications accepted. Giving limited to organizations located within or serving the Lakes Region of NH, with a priority focus on Laconia. No support for religious or sectarian purposes. No grants to individuals, or for operating expenses, endowments, scholarships, deficit financing, advertising, special events, or fundraising activities.
Publications: Application guidelines; Grants list.
Application information: Application form required.
Initial approach: Use online application form on foundation web site
Copies of proposal: 2
Deadline(s): See foundation web site for current deadline
Board meeting date(s): Spring and fall
Officers and Directors:* Charles H. Pardoe II,* Pres.; Prescott Bruce Pardoe,* V.P.; E. Spencer Pardoe Ballou,* Secy.; Charles E. Pardoe,* Treas.; Elizabeth Pardoe Grey.
Number of staff: None.
EIN: 521660757

4207
The Theodore Edson Parker Foundation ✧

c/o GMA Foundations
77 Summer St., 8th Fl.
Boston, MA 02110-1006 (617) 391-3097
Contact: Philip Hall, Admin.; Kirstie David, Prog. Off.
FAX: (617) 426-7087;
E-mail: phall@gmafoundations.com; Main URL: http://parkerfoundation.gmafoundations.com

Incorporated in 1944 in MA.
Donor: Theodore Edson Parker†.
Foundation type: Independent foundation.
Financial data (yr. ended 12/31/13): Assets, $25,511,768 (M); expenditures, $1,372,602; qualifying distributions, $1,163,384; giving activities include $978,449 for 37 grants (high: $140,000; low: $500).
Purpose and activities: The foundation's primary goal is to make effective grants that benefit the city of Lowell, MA, and its residents. Giving for a variety of purposes including social services, cultural programs, community development activities, education, community health needs and urban environmental projects.
Fields of interest: Arts; Education; Environment; Health care; Substance abuse, services; Employment; Housing/shelter, development; Human services; Children/youth, services; Minorities/immigrants, centers/services; Community/economic development; Public affairs; Children/youth; Minorities; Immigrants/refugees; Economically disadvantaged.
Type of support: Conferences/seminars; Capital campaigns; Building/renovation; Equipment; Land acquisition; Program development; Seed money; Research; Consulting services; Program-related investments/loans; Matching/challenge support.
Limitations: Applications accepted. Giving primarily in Lowell, MA. No grants to individuals, or for operating budgets, matching gifts, continuing support, annual campaigns, emergency funds, deficit financing, scholarships, or fellowships.
Publications: Application guidelines; Annual report; Grants list.
Application information: Applicants are limited to 1 application per year. See foundation web site for application guidelines and procedures. Application form not required.
Initial approach: Use online application system on foundation web site
Deadline(s): Jan. 15, May 15, and Sept. 15
Board meeting date(s): Apr. or May; Sept., and Dec.
Final notification: 4 months
Officers and Trustees:* Newell Flather,* Pres.; Andrew C. Bailey,* Secy.-Treas.; Karen H. Carpenter; David Donahue, Jr.; Sophie Theam.
Number of staff: 3 part-time professional.
EIN: 046036092
Selected grants: The following grants are a representative sample of this grantmaker's funding activity:
$100,750 to American Textile History Museum, Lowell, MA, 2012. For Final Support For the Museum's Capital Campaign for Renovations.
$45,000 to New England Quilt Museum, Lowell, MA, 2012. For a Release of Challenge Support to Underwrite a Paid Curator's Position and for Various Activities Celebrating the Museum's 25th Anniversary Year.
$25,000 to Cambodian Mutual Assistance Association of Greater Lowell, Lowell, MA, 2012. To support Key Staffing Positions at the Agency During a Time of Leadership Transition.
$20,000 to Lowell Parks and Conservation Trust, Lowell, MA, 2012. To support of Summer and After-School Environmental Education Programming for Lowell Children.
$15,000 to Appalachian Mountain Club, Boston, MA, 2012. To Expansion of Youth Opportunities Program in Lowell.
$5,000 to Horizons for Homeless Children, Roxbury, MA, 2012. To support Refurbishment of Playspace Programs Serving Children in Lowell.

4208
Patten Family Foundation ✧

665 Simonds Rd.
Williamstown, MA 01267-2105

Established in 2005 in MA.
Donors: National Land Partners, LLC; Inland Management Corp.; American Land Management Corp.; Harry S. Patten.
Foundation type: Independent foundation.
Financial data (yr. ended 12/31/13): Assets, $7,527 (M); gifts received, $831,500; expenditures, $824,659; qualifying distributions, $824,659; giving activities include $824,350 for 18 grants (high: $250,000; low: $1,000).
Fields of interest: Education; Human services.
Limitations: Applications not accepted. Giving primarily in FL and MA. No grants to individuals.
Application information: Unsolicited requests for funds not accepted.
Trustee: Harry S. Patten.
EIN: 202895803

4209
Amelia Peabody Charitable Fund ✧

185 Devonshire Street, Ste. 600
Boston, MA 02110-1414 (617) 451-6178
Contact: Evan C. Page, Exec. Dir.
Main URL: http://www.apcfund.org/

Established in 1974.
Donors: Amelia Peabody†; Eaton Foundation.
Foundation type: Independent foundation.
Financial data (yr. ended 12/31/13): Assets, $165,526,953 (M); gifts received, $87,200; expenditures, $9,005,154; qualifying distributions, $8,129,066; giving activities include $7,647,200 for 74 grants (high: $2,500,000; low: $10,000).
Purpose and activities: Grants primarily in the areas of Health (human and animal), Visual Arts, Land Conservation and Historic Preservation. Support for Social Service and Youth Service organizations limited to Massachusetts.
Fields of interest: Arts, multipurpose centers/programs; Visual arts; Museums; Historical activities; Environment, natural resources; Environment, beautification programs; Animals/wildlife, preservation/protection; Veterinary medicine; Medical care, in-patient care; Health care, support services; Youth development, centers/clubs.
Type of support: Capital campaigns.

Limitations: Applications accepted. Giving primarily in the New England area. No support for tax-supported municipal or government organizations, other private or grantmaking foundations, education or for religious organizations for religious purposes or youth and social services outside MA. No grants to individuals, or for salaries, start-up funds, political lobbying efforts, operating budgets, annual fund drives, scholarships; no unrestricted grants, emergency or immediate funding grants or multi-year funding grants; no events, performances, film/video/radio, theatrical productions, publications, or exhibits or conferences.
Publications: Application guidelines; Grants list.
Application information: Visit the foundation's website for preparing the application. Contact APCF office for a list of last two years of giving. Please note, the foundation does not accept the AGM (Associated Grant Makers) Common Proposal Form. Application form not required.
Deadline(s): Feb. 1 and July 1
Board meeting date(s): More than 15 times annually
Final notification: 10 to 12 weeks from deadline
Officer: Evan C. Page, Exec. Dir.
Trustees: Katherine L. Babson, Jr.; Robert G. Bannish; Caleb Loring III; Margaret H. Morton.
Number of staff: 2 full-time support.
EIN: 237364949

4210
Amelia Peabody Foundation ✧
1 Hollis St., Ste. 215
Wellesley, MA 02482-4677
Contact: Margaret N. St. Clair, Exec. Dir.; Bayard D. Waring, Tr.
E-mail submission to Ms. Smith: jsmith@ameliapeabody.org; Main URL: http://www.ameliapeabody.org

Trust established in 1942 in MA; absorbed a share of the assets of The Eaton Foundation, MA, in 1985.
Donor: Amelia Peabody‡.
Foundation type: Independent foundation.
Financial data (yr. ended 12/31/12): Assets, $160,790,288 (M); expenditures, $9,077,460; qualifying distributions, $7,649,692; giving activities include $6,633,691 for 198 grants (high: $140,000; low: $4,991).
Purpose and activities: The primary mission of the foundation is to increase the number, range and depth of positive learning experiences available to materially disadvantaged young people living in the cities and towns of Massachusetts.
Fields of interest: Child development, education; Education; Health care; Children/youth, services; Youth, services; Child development, services; Children/youth; Children; Youth.
Type of support: General/operating support; Capital campaigns; Building/renovation; Equipment; Program development; Seed money; Matching/challenge support.
Limitations: Applications accepted. Giving limited to MA, with a preference for urban areas and special interests outside of Boston. No support for lobbying organizations. No grants to individuals, or for endowment funds, performances, conferences, research, filmmaking or videos, publications, or fellowships; no loans or program-related investments.
Publications: Application guidelines.
Application information: The Grant Proposal Form available on the foundation's web site is preferred. Application form required.
Initial approach: See web site for full application form
Copies of proposal: 5
Deadline(s): Jan. 21, Apr. 15, July 22 and Oct. 7
Board meeting date(s): Quarterly
Final notification: 8 weeks after deadline
Officers and Trustees:* Margaret N. St. Clair,* Exec. Dir.; Joseph Kelly, C.I.O.; Deborah Carlson; John K. Dineen; Bayard D. Waring; Philip B. Waring.
Number of staff: 6 full-time professional.
EIN: 046036558
Selected grants: The following grants are a representative sample of this grantmaker's funding activity:
$140,000 to YMCA, Old Colony, Central Branch, Brockton, MA, 2012. For the Youth Focus Program.
$136,000 to North Central Charter Essential School Foundation, North Central Charter Essential School, Fitchburg, MA, 2012. For data integration and conditional grant for property purchase - moving expenses, technology, program materials and furniture.
$125,000 to Building Excellent Schools, Boston, MA, 2012. For Massachusetts BES Fellow.
$125,000 to Building Excellent Schools, Boston, MA, 2012. For Massachusetts BES Fellow.
$120,000 to Girls Inc. of Lynn, Lynn, MA, 2012. For Phase 2 of the facility renovation.
$90,000 to Boys and Girls Club, Thomas Chew Memorial, Fall River, MA, 2012. For operations.
$50,000 to Mujeres Unidas Avanzando, Dorchester, MA, 2012. For Adult Basic Education program.
$32,650 to Youth Development Organization, Lawrence, MA, 2012. For programming and operating support.
$30,000 to Paraclete, Inc., South Boston, MA, 2012. For capacity building.
$25,000 to Springfield Day Nursery, Square One, Springfield, MA, 2012. For King Street Children's Center renovation.

4211
The Peabody Foundation, Inc. ✧
c/o Bethany M. Woods LLC
101 Federal St., Ste. 19
Boston, MA 02110-1817
Application address: c/o Judi Mullen, Admin. Dir., 5 Fairbanks Ave., Wellesley, MA 02481; tel.: (508) 728-8780; e-mail: jemullen12@comcast.net

Established in 1894 in MA.
Donors: Kay Manson‡; Emma Fletcher Trust; L.S. Fiske Trust.
Foundation type: Independent foundation.
Financial data (yr. ended 09/30/13): Assets, $20,928,194 (M); gifts received, $11,144; expenditures, $1,162,403; qualifying distributions, $1,061,167; giving activities include $1,045,534 for 23 grants (high: $211,562; low: $6,326).
Purpose and activities: Grants limited to providing care, treatment, rehabilitation, education, and assistance to children with physical disabilities, and to encourage and support medical research in the causes of crippling disease, particularly in children.
Fields of interest: Hospitals (specialty); Medical research, institute; Children/youth, services; Disabilities, people with.
Type of support: Research.
Limitations: Applications accepted. Giving limited to MA, with emphasis on the Boston area. No grants to individuals.
Application information: Application form required.
Initial approach: Request application form
Deadline(s): Feb. 1
Officers and Trustees:* James M. Fitzgibbons,* Pres.; Joseph C. Donnelly, Jr.,* V.P.; Bethany Woods,* Clerk; John E. A. Safford,* Treas.; Harry C. Barr; Catherine B. Damon; Sally D. Hurlbut; Edwin P. Maynard, M.D.; Norman C. Nicholson, Jr.; Jane Otte; Susan W. Paine; Christopher D. Perry; David P. Simmons, M.D.; Sylvia L. Stevens; Joan I. Thorndike; Susannah Barton Tobin; Mary Liz Van Dyck.
EIN: 042104767
Selected grants: The following grants are a representative sample of this grantmaker's funding activity:
$100,000 to Joslin Diabetes Center, Boston, MA, 2011.
$100,000 to Massachusetts General Hospital, Boston, MA, 2011.
$75,000 to Brigham and Women's Hospital, Boston, MA, 2011.
$40,000 to Agassiz Village, Lexington, MA, 2011.
$40,000 to Perkins School for the Blind, Watertown, MA, 2011.
$40,000 to Piers Park Sailing Center, East Boston, MA, 2011.
$32,500 to New England Medical Center, Boston, MA, 2011.
$30,000 to Wheelock Family Theater, Boston, MA, 2011.
$28,200 to Outdoor Explorations, Medford, MA, 2011.
$27,000 to Willie Ross School for the Deaf, Longmeadow, MA, 2011.

4212
Peoples Federal Savings Bank Charitable Foundation ✧ ☆
435 Market St.
Brighton, MA 02135-2715 (617) 254-0707
Contact: Maurice H. Sullivan, Jr., Chair. and C.E.O.
Main URL: http://www.pfsbfoundation.org/

Donor: Peoples Federal Savings Bank Foundation.
Foundation type: Independent foundation.
Financial data (yr. ended 12/31/13): Assets, $9,636,775 (M); expenditures, $463,397; qualifying distributions, $462,221; giving activities include $449,850 for 56 grants (high: $40,000; low: $750).
Fields of interest: Education; Health care; Human services.
Application information: Application form required.
Initial approach: E-mail
Deadline(s): None
Officers and Directors:* Maurice H. Sullivan, Jr., Chair. and C.E.O.; Thomas J. Leetch, Pres. and C.O.O.; James J. Gavin,* Exec. V.P.; Leann Cote,* Secy.; Christopher Lake,* Treas.; Andrea M. Howard.
EIN: 272499279

4213
The Perkin Fund ✧
176 Bay Rd.
P.O. Box 2220
South Hamilton, MA 01982-2232 (978) 468-2266
Contact: Mrs. Winifred P. Gray, Tr.
E-mail: theperkinfund@verizon.net

Established in 1967 in NY.
Donors: Richard S. Perkin†; Gladys T. Perkin†.
Foundation type: Independent foundation.
Financial data (yr. ended 12/31/13): Assets, $27,547,789 (M); expenditures, $1,638,393; qualifying distributions, $1,331,826; giving activities include $1,210,000 for 27 grants (high: $100,000; low: $10,000).
Purpose and activities: Support for established institutions in the fields of astronomy, medicine, and scientific research, as well as limited giving to leading organizations in the arts, education, and social services.
Fields of interest: Humanities; Arts; Education; Medical research; Science, research.
Type of support: Research; General/operating support; Continuing support; Annual campaigns; Capital campaigns; Building/renovation; Equipment; Endowments; Program development; Fellowships; Matching/challenge support.
Limitations: Applications accepted. Giving primarily in CT, MA, and NY. No support for non-U.S. institutions. No grants to individuals; no loans.
Publications: Informational brochure (including application guidelines).
Application information: Application form not required.
Initial approach: Letter
Copies of proposal: 1
Deadline(s): Mar. 15 or Sept. 15
Board meeting date(s): May and Nov.
Final notification: Generally 2-4 weeks
Trustees: Kristina P. Davison; John M. Gray; Matthew E.P. Gray; Winifred P. Gray; Caroline Perkin Los Arcos; Peter W. Oldershaw; Christopher T. Perkin; Nicolas R. Perkin; Richard S. Perkin II; Robert S. Perkin; Thorne L. Perkin; Alexandra T. Wiberg.
Number of staff: 1 part-time professional.
EIN: 136222498

4214
The Perls Foundation ✧
c/o Loring Wolcott Coolidge, Katherine Perls
230 Congress St.
Boston, MA 02110

Established in 1998 in MA.
Donors: Klaus G. Perls; Amelia B. Perls.
Foundation type: Independent foundation.
Financial data (yr. ended 12/31/12): Assets, $18,797,676 (M); expenditures, $1,155,382; qualifying distributions, $628,435; giving activities include $628,435 for grants.
Fields of interest: Environment; Health care; Agriculture/food.
Limitations: Applications not accepted. Giving primarily in CA, Washington, DC, MA, and NY. No grants to individuals.
Application information: Contributes only to pre-selected organizations.
Trustees: Lennart C. Braberg; Katherine M. Perls.
EIN: 046864032

4215
Perpetual Trust for Charitable Giving
c/o US Trust, Bank of America, N.A.
225 Franklin St., 4th Fl.
Boston, MA 02110-2801
Contact: Miki Akimoto, Market Dir.
E-mail regarding application or for questions: ma.grantmaking@ustrust.com (include foundation name in subject line); Main URL: http://www.bankofamerica.com/grantmaking

Established in 1957 in MA.
Foundation type: Independent foundation.
Financial data (yr. ended 12/31/13): Assets, $23,799,915 (M); expenditures, $1,192,194; qualifying distributions, $1,028,928; giving activities include $934,769 for 50 grants (high: $100,000; low: $267).
Purpose and activities: Giving primarily to organizations that support education, health care, and family services.
Fields of interest: Education; Health care; Human services.
Type of support: General/operating support; Program development.
Limitations: Giving limited to MA. No grants to individuals.
Publications: Application guidelines.
Application information: Complete guidelines available on trust website. Application form required.
Initial approach: Proposal with cover sheet
Copies of proposal: 1
Deadline(s): Sept. 1
Board meeting date(s): Nov.
Final notification: Nov. 30
Trustee: Bank of America, N.A.
EIN: 046026301
Selected grants: The following grants are a representative sample of this grantmaker's funding activity:
$100,000 to Boston Foundation, Boston, MA, 2013. For general operations of the organization.
$60,000 to United Way of Massachusetts Bay, Boston, MA, 2013. For Family Fund.
$50,000 to Boston Foundation, Boston, MA, 2013. For StreetSafe Boston.
$40,000 to Forsyth Institute, Cambridge, MA, 2013. For the ForsythKids School Oral Health Program.
$40,000 to Partners HealthCare System, Boston, MA, 2013. For Schwartz Center Rounds Evaluation Project.
$35,000 to Pine Street Inn, Boston, MA, 2013. For Pine Street Inn: Shelter and Support Services to End Homelessness.
$30,000 to Boston Plan for Excellence in the Public Schools Foundation, Boston, MA, 2013. For general operations of the organization.
$30,000 to Dorchester House Multi-Service Center, Dorchester, MA, 2013. To increase capacity of the case management staff.
$20,000 to Boys and Girls Club of Greater Holyoke, Holyoke, MA, 2013. For general operations of the organization.
$15,000 to Full Frame Initiative, Greenfield, MA, 2013. For Greater Boston Full Frame Network.

4216
G. Gorham Peters CBS Trust ✧
(formerly G. Gorham Peters Testementary Trust)
45 School St., 5th Fl.
Boston, MA 02108-3204

Supporting organization of Beth Israel Deaconess Medical Center, Boston Biomedical Research Institute, United Way of Massachusetts Bay, American Red Cross Blood Services, American Red Cross of Massachusetts Bay, Animal Rescue League of Boston, Boston Athenaeum, Boston Medical Library, Brigham Women's Hospital, The Center for Blood Research, The Children's Hospital Medical Center, Cystic Fibrosis Foundation, Dana-Farber Cancer Institute, Faulkner Hospital, Harvard School of Dental Medicine, Judge Baker Children's Center, Massachusetts Eye and Ear Infirmary, Massachusetts General Hospital, Massachusetts Historical Society, Sherrill House, Thompson Island Outward Bound, Wellesley College Students Aid Society, Women's Educational and Industrial Union, and the Home for Little Wanderers.
Foundation type: Independent foundation.
Financial data (yr. ended 04/30/13): Assets, $16,741,153 (M); expenditures, $900,392; qualifying distributions, $800,000; giving activities include $800,000 for 23 grants (high: $90,000; low: $15,000).
Fields of interest: Education; Animals/wildlife; Hospitals (general); Hospitals (specialty); Health organizations; Medical research, institute; Human services; American Red Cross; United Ways and Federated Giving Programs.
Limitations: Applications not accepted. Giving limited to MA, with emphasis on Boston. No grants to individuals.
Application information: Contributes only to pre-selected organizations.
Trustees: Lisa S. Lewis; Theodore E. Ober; Benjamin J. Williams, Jr.
EIN: 046111827
Selected grants: The following grants are a representative sample of this grantmaker's funding activity:
$80,000 to Beth Israel Deaconess Medical Center, Boston, MA, 2011.
$30,000 to Massachusetts Historical Society, Boston, MA, 2011.
$25,000 to Massachusetts Eye and Ear Infirmary, Boston, MA, 2011.
$20,000 to Animal Rescue League of Boston, Boston, MA, 2011.
$20,000 to Boston Athenaeum, Boston, MA, 2011.
$20,000 to Boston Medical Library, Boston, MA, 2011.
$20,000 to Cystic Fibrosis Foundation, Natick, MA, 2011.
$20,000 to Home for Little Wanderers, Boston, MA, 2011.
$20,000 to Immune Disease Institute, Boston, MA, 2011.
$20,000 to Judge Baker Childrens Center, Boston, MA, 2011.

4217
Edwin Phillips Foundation ✧
P.O. Box 610075
Newton Highlands, MA 02461-0075
E-mail: grants@epfgrants.org; Main URL: http://www.edwinphillipsfoundation.org

Donor: Edwin Phillips†.
Foundation type: Independent foundation.
Financial data (yr. ended 12/31/13): Assets, $12,631,901 (M); expenditures, $672,642; qualifying distributions, $554,962; giving activities include $477,120 for grants.

Purpose and activities: Giving strictly limited to help children with disabilities in Plymouth County, MA, only.
Fields of interest: Children/youth, services; Children/youth; Children; Blind/visually impaired; Deaf/hearing impaired; Mentally disabled; Infants/toddlers, female; Infants/toddlers, male.
Limitations: Applications accepted. Giving limited to Plymouth County, MA. No grants to handicapped adults who are over 22 years old.
Publications: Application guidelines.
Application information: Unsolicited requests for funds not accepted from anyone outside of Plymouth County, MA. Application form available on foundation web site. Applications sent by e-mail are not accepted. Application form required.
Initial approach: Proposal or letter
Copies of proposal: 1
Deadline(s): Apr. 1 and Oct. 1
Board meeting date(s): As needed
Final notification: 2 months
Officers and Directors:* Robert E. Galvin,* Chair.; Sandra Sheiber, Exec. Dir.; Kim Bouressa; Melissa DiPanfilo; Wilma Rae Goodhue; Beverly Johnston; Bank of America, N.A.
Number of staff: 1 part-time professional.
EIN: 046025549

4218
Stephen Phillips Memorial Charitable Trust ✧
P.O. Box 870
Salem, MA 01970-0970 (978) 744-2111
Contact: Karen Emery, Scholarship Coord.
FAX: (978) 744-0456; E-mail: staff@spscholars.org; Main URL: http://www.phillips-scholarship.org/
Facebook: https://www.facebook.com/phillipsscholarship
Twitter: https://twitter.com/PhillipsScholar

Established in 1973.
Donor: Bessie Wright Phillips†.
Foundation type: Independent foundation.
Financial data (yr. ended 12/31/12): Assets, $6,956,969 (M); gifts received, $7,565; expenditures, $4,094,662; qualifying distributions, $3,650,991; giving activities include $2,924,200 for grants to individuals.
Purpose and activities: Scholarships for permanent residents of New England states who demonstrate academic excellence, seriousness of purpose, good citizenship and character, a strong work ethic and who meet the foundation's financial-need requirements. Applicants must be an entering or returning student at an accredited undergraduate institution in the United States and must be enrolled full-time (at least 12 hours). Applicants must also be pursuing a bachelor's degree (BA, BS, BFA, BSN, for example) for the first time, have a GPA of 3.0 or higher on a 4.0 scale, be enrolled in a demanding course of study, and demonstrate skilled writing. Students in 1-year or 2-year certificate or associate's degree programs do not qualify. Students in 5-plus year programs ending in a master's degree program or beyond may apply for the first four (undergraduate) years of their programs.
Fields of interest: Education; Economically disadvantaged.
Type of support: Scholarships—to individuals.
Limitations: Applications accepted. Giving limited to all permanent residents of the New England states.
Publications: Application guidelines; Informational brochure (including application guidelines); Newsletter.
Application information: Specific application requirements and forms are available on foundation web site. Application form required.
Initial approach: Use online application process on foundation web site
Deadline(s): See foundation web site for current deadlines
Officer: Barbara Welles Iler, Exec. Dir.
Trustees: Lawrence Coolidge; John H. Finley IV; Dr. Richard F. Gross; Robert M. Randolph.
Number of staff: 2 full-time professional; 1 part-time professional.
EIN: 237235347

4219
Phillips-Green Foundation, Inc. ✧ ☆
c/o Carol Green
P.O. Box 654
Truro, MA 02666-0654

Established in 1986 in IL.
Donors: Lawrence Phillips; Seymour Phillips†; Carol P. Green; Madelyn Phillips†.
Foundation type: Independent foundation.
Financial data (yr. ended 08/31/13): Assets, $739,930 (M); expenditures, $483,862; qualifying distributions, $483,339; giving activities include $470,592 for 57 grants (high: $401,300; low: $150).
Purpose and activities: Giving primarily for medical/nursing schools and education, medical research emphasizing cancer, gun control, domestic violence prevention, human rights on an international basis, women's civil rights including reproductive rights, and Jewish agencies and temples. Also for African Americans, Latinos, aging, women, people with AIDS, and immigrants/refugees.
Fields of interest: Arts; Education; Health care.
Type of support: General/operating support; Annual campaigns; Capital campaigns; Land acquisition; Endowments; Emergency funds; Research; Program-related investments/loans; Matching/challenge support.
Limitations: Applications not accepted. Giving on a national basis. No grants to individuals.
Application information: Unsolicited requests for funds not accepted.
Officers and Directors:* Carol P. Green,* Pres.; Cathy J. Green,* Secy.; Janet A. Green,* Treas.; Douglas M. Green.
Number of staff: 1 part-time support.
EIN: 133334090

4220
The Harold Whitworth Pierce Charitable Trust ✧
c/o Nichols and Pratt
50 Congress St., Ste. 832
Boston, MA 02109-4017 (617) 523-8368
Contact: Betsy Nichols, Prog. Dir.
FAX: (617) 523-8949;
E-mail: piercetrust@nichols-pratt.com; Tel. for Elizabeth Nichols, Prog. Dir.: (617) 523-8368 (Tues. and Thurs.); Main URL: http://www.piercetrust.org

Trust established in 1960 in MA.
Donor: Harold Whitworth Pierce†.
Foundation type: Independent foundation.
Financial data (yr. ended 12/31/13): Assets, $28,204,006 (M); expenditures, $1,469,948; qualifying distributions, $1,342,402; giving activities include $1,257,333 for 41 grants (high: $314,333; low: $1,000).
Purpose and activities: The trust offers grants primarily for projects that will produce long-range benefits through leverage of the trust's resources. Grants are made for specific programs, for seed money, and for capital projects, especially those which can reduce operating costs. Occasional grants are made for operating support. Grants are focused on institutions and programs in the Boston, Massachusetts area.
Fields of interest: Teacher school/education; Education; Environment.
Type of support: General/operating support; Capital campaigns; Building/renovation; Endowments; Seed money; Scholarship funds; Research.
Limitations: Giving primarily in the Boston, MA, area. No grants to individuals, or for scholarships for individuals, fund-raising events, fund-raising training, films, videos, travel, or advocacy.
Publications: Application guidelines; Grants list; IRS Form 990 or 990-PF printed copy available upon request.
Application information: Applicants should submit a concept letter of no more than 2 pages, and the concept letter summary form. Proposals invited from among concept letters. Early submission is strongly encouraged. Late submissions will be held for the next round. Submission of Concept Letters by e-mail is encouraged. Grants are occasionally made for medical research and arts education; unsolicited proposals are not accepted for these areas; AGM Common Proposal Form accepted. Application form not required.
Initial approach: Telephone or e-mail to Betsy Nichols, Prog. Dir. (Telephone calls accepted Tues. and Thurs.)
Copies of proposal: 1
Deadline(s): Mar. 1 and Sept. 30 for preliminary letters; mid-Apr. and early Nov. for invited proposals.
Board meeting date(s): Late May or early June, and late Nov. or early Dec.
Final notification: Approx. June 1 and Dec. 1
Trustees: James R. Nichols; Harold I. Pratt.
EIN: 046019896
Selected grants: The following grants are a representative sample of this grantmaker's funding activity:
$111,559 to Milton Hospital, Milton, MA, 2011.
$85,000 to Boston Teacher Residency, Boston, MA, 2011.
$75,000 to Boston Public Schools, Boston, MA, 2011.
$60,000 to EdVestors, Boston, MA, 2011.
$55,000 to Health Resources in Action, Boston, MA, 2011.
$30,600 to Boston Natural Areas Network, Boston, MA, 2011.
$25,000 to South End Technology Center at Tent City, Boston, MA, 2011.
$25,000 to Steppingstone Foundation, Boston, MA, 2011.
$20,000 to University of Massachusetts Foundation, Boston, MA, 2011.
$15,000 to Hubbard Brook Research Foundation, North Woodstock, NH, 2011.

4221
Play 2 Dream Charitable Foundation ✧
(formerly Kathy's Playground Charitable Foundation)
c/o WTAS LLC
125 High St., 16th Fl.
Boston, MA 02110-2757

Donor: Kathleen Welsh.
Foundation type: Independent foundation.
Financial data (yr. ended 12/31/12): Assets, $4,371,740 (M); expenditures, $750,343; qualifying distributions, $711,694; giving activities include $711,569 for 3 grants (high: $707,569; low: $1,000).
Fields of interest: Education; Zoos/zoological societies; Human services.
Limitations: Applications not accepted. Giving primarily in Boston, MA; some giving also in Chapel Hill, NC.
Application information: Contributes only to pre-selected organizations.
Trustees: Kathleen Welsh; Jeremy Welsh-Loveman; Monica Welsh-Loveman.
EIN: 263791607

4222
The Plymouth Rock Foundation ✧ ☆
695 Atlantic Ave.
Boston, MA 02111-2626

Established in 1993 in MA.
Donors: Plymouth Rock Assurance Corporation; High Point Safety and Management Corp.; Palisades Safety & Insurance Assoc.; SRB Corp.; Bunker Hill Insurance Co.; Pilgrim Insurance Co.; Plymouth Rock Company, Inc.
Foundation type: Independent foundation.
Financial data (yr. ended 12/31/13): Assets, $159,065 (M); gifts received, $160,494; expenditures, $439,057; qualifying distributions, $427,595; giving activities include $427,595 for 382 grants (high: $15,000; low: $20).
Fields of interest: Higher education; Health organizations, association; Human services; Children/youth, services; United Ways and Federated Giving Programs.
Limitations: Applications not accepted. No grants to individuals.
Application information: Contributes only to pre-selected organizations.
Trustees: Paula Gold; Clemence Scouten.
EIN: 046739902
Selected grants: The following grants are a representative sample of this grantmaker's funding activity:
$15,000 to EdVestors, Boston, MA, 2011.
$10,000 to American Red Cross, Des Moines, IA, 2011.
$9,950 to Boston Medical Center, Boston, MA, 2011.
$7,500 to American Cancer Society, Shrewsbury, NJ, 2011.
$5,000 to Ford Hall Forum, Boston, MA, 2011.
$5,000 to IDEAS Boston, Boston, MA, 2011.
$4,400 to United Way of Monmouth County, Farmingdale, NJ, 2011.
$2,500 to Generations, Inc., Boston, MA, 2011.
$2,150 to Sportsmens Tennis Club, Dorchester, MA, 2011.
$1,900 to Greater Boston Food Bank, Boston, MA, 2011.

4223
Pomegranate Foundation ✧ ☆
P.O. Box 590513
Newton Center, MA 02459-0005

Donors: Eitan Milgram; Debra Milgram.
Foundation type: Independent foundation.
Financial data (yr. ended 12/31/13): Assets, $11,591,338 (M); gifts received, $694,771; expenditures, $601,238; qualifying distributions, $593,352; giving activities include $593,352 for 2 grants (high: $450,000; low: $143,352).
Fields of interest: Education; Religion.
Limitations: Applications not accepted.
Application information: Unsolicited requests for funds not accepted.
Trustees: Debra Michelle Milgram; Eitan Milgram.
EIN: 271564392

4224
William J. & Lia G. Poorvu Family Foundation ✧
(formerly William J. & Lia G. Poorvu Foundation)
P.O. Box 380828
Cambridge, MA 02238-0828 (617) 576-1010

Established in 1978.
Donors: William J. Poorvu; Lia G. Poorvu.
Foundation type: Independent foundation.
Financial data (yr. ended 12/31/13): Assets, $88,787,145 (M); gifts received, $11,100,000; expenditures, $4,897,598; qualifying distributions, $4,367,443; giving activities include $4,358,000 for 56 grants (high: $605,000; low: $1,000).
Purpose and activities: Giving primarily for higher education; support also for cultural programs of interest to the Poorvu family.
Fields of interest: Arts; Higher education.
Limitations: Applications not accepted. Giving primarily in MA. No grants to individuals.
Application information: Contributes only to pre-selected organizations. Unsolicited requests for funds not considered.
Trustees: Lia G. Poorvu; William J. Poorvu.
EIN: 042651199

4225
The Popplestone Foundation ✧
c/o Sullivan and Worcester, LLP
1 Post Office Sq.
Boston, MA 02109-2106

Established in 2000 in MA.
Donors: Alan J. Dworsky; Suzanne E. Werber.
Foundation type: Independent foundation.
Financial data (yr. ended 12/31/12): Assets, $48,665,298 (M); expenditures, $2,607,478; qualifying distributions, $2,510,625; giving activities include $2,505,453 for 16 grants (high: $350,000; low: $12,000).
Fields of interest: Performing arts, opera; Performing arts, music (choral); Education; Human services.
Type of support: General/operating support.
Limitations: Applications not accepted. Giving primarily in Washington, DC, MA, and NY. No grants to individuals, or for matching gifts; no loans.
Application information: Contributes only to pre-selected organizations.
Trustees: Alan J. Dworsky; Sally L. Rubin; Suzanne E. Werber.
EIN: 043528004
Selected grants: The following grants are a representative sample of this grantmaker's funding activity:
$300,000 to Environmental Working Group, Washington, DC, 2011. For general use.
$18,000 to Brown University, Providence, RI, 2011. For general use.

4226
The Poss Family Foundation ✧
(formerly The Poss Kapor Familly Foundation)
c/o Dr. Ellen M. Poss
450 Warren St.
Brookline, MA 02445-5907

Established in 1998 in MA.
Donor: Dr. Ellen M. Poss.
Foundation type: Independent foundation.
Financial data (yr. ended 12/31/13): Assets, $14,284,395 (L); gifts received, $292,379; expenditures, $1,278,848; qualifying distributions, $1,169,000; giving activities include $1,169,000 for 10 grants (high: $650,000; low: $5,000).
Fields of interest: Arts; Higher education; Education; Human services.
Type of support: General/operating support; Continuing support; Annual campaigns; Capital campaigns; Professorships; Curriculum development; Matching/challenge support.
Limitations: Applications not accepted. Giving primarily in MA, and New York, NY. No grants to individuals.
Application information: Contributes only to pre-selected organizations. Unsolicited requests for funds will not be acknowledged or returned.
Trustee: Dr. Ellen M. Poss.
EIN: 043412829
Selected grants: The following grants are a representative sample of this grantmaker's funding activity:
$25,000 to Addison Gallery of American Art, Andover, MA, 2012. To Promote Its Charitable Purpose.

4227
Mattina R. Proctor Foundation ✧
c/o Broude & Hochberg, LLP
75 Federal St., Ste. 1300
Boston, MA 02110-1921 (617) 748-5100
Contact: Jeffrey D. Hutchins, Tr.

Established in 1991 in MA.
Donor: Mattina R. Proctor‡.
Foundation type: Independent foundation.
Financial data (yr. ended 12/31/13): Assets, $15,506,404 (M); expenditures, $904,181; qualifying distributions, $764,432; giving activities include $655,000 for 49 grants (high: $75,000; low: $1,000).
Purpose and activities: Giving primarily for health care, medical research, the performing arts, education, and environmental conservation.
Fields of interest: Performing arts, music; Performing arts, opera; Arts; Higher education; Environment, natural resources; Hospitals (specialty); Nursing care; Health care; Pediatrics; Medical research.

Type of support: General/operating support; Annual campaigns; Building/renovation; Equipment; Land acquisition; Research.
Limitations: Applications accepted. Giving primarily in Boston, MA, and ME. No grants to individuals.
Application information: Application form not required.
Initial approach: Proposal letter
Copies of proposal: 1
Deadline(s): None
Board meeting date(s): Varies
Trustees: William I. Hochberg; Jeffrey D. Hutchins.
Number of staff: 1 part-time support.
EIN: 111067014
Selected grants: The following grants are a representative sample of this grantmaker's funding activity:
$75,000 to Mercy Hospital, Portland, ME, 2012. For Diabetes Center Renovations.
$65,000 to University of New England, Portland, ME, 2012. For Dental School.
$25,000 to Maine Medical Center, Portland, ME, 2012. For Childhood Obesity Prevention Program.
$15,000 to Berklee College of Music, Boston, MA, 2012. For Bidmc Music Therapy Practicum.
$15,000 to Maine Humanities Council, Portland, ME, 2012. For Humanities and Healthcare Program.
$15,000 to New England Aquarium, Boston, MA, 2012. For John Prescott Research Laboratory Capital Campaign.
$10,500 to Northeastern University, School of Law, Boston, MA, 2012. For Public Interest Internships in Maine.
$10,000 to Arcadia Players, Northampton, MA, 2012. For 2013 Shakespeare Concerts.
$10,000 to Emmanuel Music, Boston, MA, 2012. For Soloists in La Clemenza Di Tito.
$10,000 to Perkins School for the Blind, Watertown, MA, 2012. For Annual Fund and Internet Radio Station.

4228
Phillip and Susan Ragon Foundation ✧ ☆
P.O. Box 380281
Cambridge, MA 02238-0281

Established in 2003 in MA.
Donors: Phillip T. Ragon; Susan M. Ragon.
Foundation type: Independent foundation.
Financial data (yr. ended 12/31/13): Assets, $713,727 (M); gifts received, $5,500,000; expenditures, $6,650,651; qualifying distributions, $6,646,350; giving activities include $6,644,000 for 16 grants (high: $6,000,000; low: $5,000).
Fields of interest: Higher education; Libraries (academic/research); Education; Health organizations; Human services; Christian agencies & churches.
Limitations: Applications not accepted. Giving primarily in Boston and Cambridge, MA. No grants to individuals.
Application information: Unsolicited requests for funds not accepted.
Trustees: Phillip T. Ragon; Susan M. Ragon.
EIN: 050547000
Selected grants: The following grants are a representative sample of this grantmaker's funding activity:
$20,000 to Massachusetts General Hospital, Boston, MA, 2012. To Carry on Charitable Organization's Activities.

4229
The Rands Foundation ✧
157 Grove St.
Westwood, MA 02090-1027

Established in 2005 in MA.
Donors: Robert D. Rands; Amelia R. Rands.
Foundation type: Independent foundation.
Financial data (yr. ended 12/31/13): Assets, $11,477,548 (M); gifts received, $488,584; expenditures, $453,144; qualifying distributions, $447,248; giving activities include $445,000 for 17 grants (high: $75,000; low: $5,000).
Fields of interest: Higher education, college; Education; Religion.
Limitations: Applications not accepted. Giving primarily in MA. No grants to individuals.
Application information: Contributes only to pre-selected organizations.
Trustees: Amelia R. Rands; Robert D. Rands.
EIN: 870757900
Selected grants: The following grants are a representative sample of this grantmaker's funding activity:
$27,000 to Beacon Academy, Boston, MA, 2011.
$25,000 to Blessed Stephen Bellesini OSA Academy, Lawrence, MA, 2011.
$25,000 to Connecticut College, New London, CT, 2011.
$25,000 to Esperanza Academy, Lawrence, MA, 2011.
$25,000 to Nativity-Boston, Jamaica Plain, MA, 2011.
$25,000 to Our Sisters School, New Bedford, MA, 2011.
$10,000 to MathPOWER, Boston, MA, 2010.
$10,000 to Spark the Wave, Washington, DC, 2011.

4230
Phyllis & Jerome Lyle Rappaport Charitable Foundation ✧
75 State St., 12th Fl.
Boston, MA 02109-1821 (617) 878-7773
E-mail: sjohnson@rappaportfoundation.org; Main URL: http://www.rappaportfoundation.org/

Established in 1996 in FL.
Donors: Jerome Lyle Rappaport; Miguel Arambula.
Foundation type: Independent foundation.
Financial data (yr. ended 09/30/13): Assets, $18,593,138 (M); gifts received, $5,231,716; expenditures, $665,955; qualifying distributions, $590,393; giving activities include $446,600 for 16 grants (high: $200,000; low: $100).
Purpose and activities: The foundation sponsors the work of new and existing leaders to increase the regional capacity for generating effective public policy solutions, breakthroughs for neurologic and mental illnesses, and world class art. Giving has been largely for higher education including fellowships and scholarships, particularly in neuroscience, mental health and Alzheimer's disease, and for museums.
Fields of interest: Arts; Higher education; Education; Environment, natural resources; Hospitals (general); Reproductive health, family planning; Jewish federated giving programs; Jewish agencies & synagogues.
Type of support: General/operating support; Fellowships; Scholarship funds.
Limitations: Giving primarily in the greater Boston, MA, area.
Publications: Informational brochure.
Application information: Application form not required.
Deadline(s): None
Officers: Phyllis Rappaport, Chair.; Stephen P. Johnson, J.D., Exec. Dir.
Board Members: Jonathan Rapaport; Jim Rappaport; Nancy Rappaport, M.D.
Number of staff: 1 full-time professional.
EIN: 311485041

4231
Neil & Anna Rasmussen Foundation ✧
393 Estabrook Rd.
Concord, MA 01742-5604

Established in 1994 in MA.
Donors: Neil Rasmussen; Anna Rasmussen.
Foundation type: Independent foundation.
Financial data (yr. ended 12/31/12): Assets, $40,630,689 (M); gifts received, $200,000; expenditures, $2,042,533; qualifying distributions, $1,657,145; giving activities include $1,652,470 for 39 grants (high: $450,000; low: $1,000).
Purpose and activities: Giving primarily for historical preservation and natural resource conservation; funding also for education, human services, and for a children's hospital.
Fields of interest: Museums; Historic preservation/historical societies; Higher education; Education; Environment, natural resources; Hospitals (specialty); Human services; Children/youth, services.
Limitations: Applications not accepted. Giving primarily in MA, with emphasis on Concord. No grants to individuals.
Application information: Contributes only to pre-selected organizations.
Trustees: Anna Rasmussen; Neil Rasmussen; Susan W. Winter.
EIN: 046771880

4232
Milton and Dorothy Sarnoff Raymond Foundation ✧
P.O. Box 147
Williamstown, MA 01267-0147

Foundation type: Independent foundation.
Financial data (yr. ended 12/31/11): Assets, $12,406,836 (M); expenditures, $638,003; qualifying distributions, $638,003; giving activities include $595,000 for 41 grants (high: $50,000; low: $5,000).
Fields of interest: Arts; Animal welfare; Human services; Jewish agencies & synagogues.
Limitations: Applications not accepted. Giving primarily in MA and NY.
Application information: Contributes only to pre-selected organizations.
Trustees: Catherine L. Burke; Elizabeth L. Hughes; Andrew R. Laitman; Samuel H. Laitman.
EIN: 356803769

4233
Sumner M. Redstone Charitable Foundation ✧
846 University Ave.
Norwood, MA 02062-2631 (781) 461-1600
Contact: Sumner M. Redstone

Application address: 200 Elm St., Dedham, MA 02026

Established in 1986 in MA.
Donors: Sumner M. Redstone; National Amusements, Inc.
Foundation type: Independent foundation.
Financial data (yr. ended 12/31/13): Assets, $6,395,880 (M); gifts received, $10,365,231; expenditures, $10,940,387; qualifying distributions, $10,936,667; giving activities include $10,936,667 for 14+ grants (high: $2,000,000).
Purpose and activities: Giving primarily for health organizations and medical research, particularly for research and patient care advancements in cancer and burn recovery.
Fields of interest: Hospitals (general); Health organizations; Medical research, institute; Cancer research; Human services.
Limitations: Applications accepted. Giving primarily in CA; funding also in MA.
Application information: Application form not required.
Deadline(s): None
Trustee: Sumner M. Redstone.
EIN: 222761621
Selected grants: The following grants are a representative sample of this grantmaker's funding activity:
$2,000,000 to Harvard University, Harvard College, Cambridge, MA, 2013.
$2,000,000 to University of Southern California, Keck School of Medicine, Los Angeles, CA, 2013.
$1,180,000 to Cambodian Childrens Fund, Santa Monica, CA, 2013.
$1,000,000 to American Museum of Movies, Los Angeles, CA, 2013.
$1,000,000 to Sydney D. Holland Foundation, Beverly Hills, CA, 2013.
$750,000 to Global Poverty Project, New York, NY, 2013.
$600,000 to Literacy, Inc., New York, NY, 2013.
$250,000 to UCLA Foundation, Los Angeles, CA, 2013.
$200,000 to Friendly Hand Foundation, Los Angeles, CA, 2013.
$200,000 to Wallis Annenberg Center for the Performing Arts, Beverly Hills, CA, 2013.

4234
The Reebok Foundation ✧
1895 J.W. Foster Blvd.
Canton, MA 02021-1099 (781) 401-5000
FAX: (781) 401-4744;
E-mail: geri.noonan@reebok.com; Main URL: http://www.adidas-group.com/en/sustainability/Community_involvement/Reebok_programmes/default.aspx

Established in 1986 in MA.
Donor: Reebok International Ltd.
Foundation type: Company-sponsored foundation.
Financial data (yr. ended 12/31/13): Assets, $137,888 (M); gifts received, $1,384,994; expenditures, $1,518,737; qualifying distributions, $1,392,922; giving activities include $710,931 for 480 grants (high: $122,692; low: $25).
Purpose and activities: The foundation supports programs designed to serve inner-city youth and provide youth with the tools they need to lead healthy, happy, and active lives.
Fields of interest: Education; Youth, services; Human services; Youth.
Type of support: General/operating support; Program development; Employee matching gifts.
Limitations: Applications accepted. Giving primarily in areas of company operations, with emphasis on the greater Boston, MA area. No grants to individuals, or for seminars or conferences, documentaries or media projects, publications, medical research or other research, or political projects; no product donations; no loans.
Publications: Application guidelines.
Application information: Unsolicited requests from national organizations are not accepted. Associated Grant Makers Common Proposal Form accepted. Application form not required.
Initial approach: Proposal
Copies of proposal: 1
Deadline(s): None
Board meeting date(s): Biannually
Final notification: 4 to 6 weeks
Officers: Ulrich Becker, Pres.; Eric Bodenhofer, V.P. and Secy.; William Holmes, V.P.; John Warren, Treas.; Megan Grimaldi, Exec. Dir.
Number of staff: 1 full-time professional.
EIN: 043073548
Selected grants: The following grants are a representative sample of this grantmaker's funding activity:
$12,800 to DC Treasurer, Washington, DC, 2011.
$5,000 to Peace First, Boston, MA, 2011.
$1,000 to American Liver Foundation, New York, NY, 2011.
$1,000 to Special Olympics Massachusetts, Marlborough, MA, 2011.

4235
The Reeder Foundation ✧
c/o Par Capital Mgmt.
1 International Pl., Ste. 2401
Boston, MA 02110-2633

Established in 2000 in MA.
Donors: Paul A. Reeder III; Paul A. Reeder.
Foundation type: Independent foundation.
Financial data (yr. ended 12/31/13): Assets, $19,352,423 (M); gifts received, $2,100,000; expenditures, $2,396,404; qualifying distributions, $2,254,510; giving activities include $2,254,000 for 12 grants (high: $930,000; low: $10,000).
Fields of interest: Higher education; Education.
Limitations: Applications not accepted. Giving primarily in MA; some giving also in OH. No grants to individuals.
Application information: Contributes only to pre-selected organizations.
Director: Paul A. Reeder III.
EIN: 043542100
Selected grants: The following grants are a representative sample of this grantmaker's funding activity:
$200,000 to Year Up, Boston, MA, 2011.
$150,000 to Teach Plus, Boston, MA, 2011.
$110,000 to Teach for America, Boston, MA, 2011.
$100,000 to Oberlin College, Oberlin, OH, 2011.
$25,000 to Boston Educational Development Foundation, Boston, MA, 2011.
$20,000 to Greenlight Fund, Boston, MA, 2011.

4236
Remillard Family Foundation, Inc. ✧
211 Main St.
Webster, MA 01570-2249 (508) 949-4122
Contact: Arthur J. Remillard, Jr., Pres. and Dir.

Established in 1997 in MA.
Donors: Arthur J. Remillard, Jr.; Gary Peters.
Foundation type: Independent foundation.
Financial data (yr. ended 12/31/13): Assets, $1,904,946 (M); gifts received, $1,000,050; expenditures, $753,466; qualifying distributions, $750,865; giving activities include $749,333 for 6 grants (high: $435,000; low: $16,000).
Fields of interest: Human services; American Red Cross; Salvation Army.
Limitations: Applications accepted. Giving primarily in MA. No grants to individuals.
Application information: Application form required.
Initial approach: Letter
Deadline(s): None
Officers and Directors:* Arthur J. Remillard, Jr.,* Pres.; Arthur J. Remillard III,* Clerk; Regan P. Remillard,* Treas.; Danielle A. Haxton; Robert P. Remillard.
EIN: 043367614

4237
Remondi Family Foundation ✧ ☆
c/o John J. Remondi
300 Boylston St., Ste. 507
Boston, MA 02116-3956

Established in 2006 in MA.
Donors: John J. Remondi; Dorothy A. Remondi.
Foundation type: Independent foundation.
Financial data (yr. ended 12/31/13): Assets, $16,706,634 (M); gifts received, $1,376,857; expenditures, $1,017,393; qualifying distributions, $964,851; giving activities include $927,520 for 25 grants (high: $270,000; low: $500).
Fields of interest: Secondary school/education.
Limitations: Applications not accepted. Giving primarily in MA. No grants to individuals.
Application information: Unsolicited requests for funds not accepted.
Trustees: Diane D. Defalco; Dorothy A. Remondi; John F. Remondi; John J. Remondi; Stephen A. Remondi.
EIN: 208037556

4238
The Christopher Reynolds Foundation, Inc. ✧
77 Summer St., 8th Fl.
Boston, MA 02110-1006 (617) 391-3101
Contact: Carolyn Rau
FAX: (617) 426-7087;
E-mail: crau@gmafoundations.com; Main URL: http://www.creynolds.org

Incorporated in 1952 in NY.
Donors: Libby Holman Reynolds†; Atlantic Philanthropies.
Foundation type: Independent foundation.
Financial data (yr. ended 12/31/13): Assets, $23,825,791 (M); gifts received, $375,000; expenditures, $2,562,004; qualifying distributions, $2,286,396; giving activities include $1,815,892 for 69 grants (high: $180,000; low: $500).

Purpose and activities: In the foundation's first 12 years, it was principally supportive of innovative work toward international peace and disarmament, civil rights, and against racism. Since 1995, the foundation has been steadily increasing its support of work that focuses on: U.S. relations with Cuba, and more recently, it has provided assistance to a limited number of initiatives examining U.S. policy and the U.S. presence in Iraq and possible policy options.
Fields of interest: Human services; International affairs; International studies.
International interests: Cuba; Iraq.
Type of support: Mission-related investments/loans; General/operating support; Continuing support; Conferences/seminars; Technical assistance; Exchange programs.
Limitations: Giving primarily in the U.S., with emphasis on national organizations in Washington, DC, New York, NY, and Arlington, VA. No grants to individuals, or for capital or endowment funds, annual campaigns, emergency funds, deficit financing, scholarships, or matching gifts; no loans.
Publications: Financial statement; Grants list; Multi-year report (including application guidelines).
Application information: Application guidelines and form available on foundation web site. The foundation does not accept full-length proposals that have not been requested by our staff and approved for receipt by the Executive Director. Application form required.
Initial approach: Telephone, or fax or e-mail letter of inquiry, no more than 3 typewritten pages.
Copies of proposal: 6
Deadline(s): Submit proposal preferably 30 days prior to board meeting
Board meeting date(s): Quarterly
Final notification: 1 week
Officers and Directors:* Suzanne Derrer,* Vice-Chair.; John R. Boettiger, Ph.D.*, Pres.; Andrea Panaritis,* Exec. Dir.; Virginia Kahn; Clemens Pietzner.
Number of staff: 1 full-time professional; 1 part-time professional; 1 full-time support.
EIN: 136129401

4239
The Mabel Louise Riley Foundation ✧
(also known as The Riley Foundation)
c/o GMA
77 Summer St., 8th Fl.
Boston, MA 02110-1006 (617) 399-1850
Contact: Nancy A. Saunders, Admin.
FAX: (617) 399-1851;
E-mail: nsaunders@rileyfoundation.com; E-mail for Letters of Inquiry: info@rileyfoundatrion.com; Main URL: http://www.rileyfoundation.com

Established in 1971 in MA as the Mabel Louise Riley Charitable Trust.
Donor: Mabel Louise Riley†.
Foundation type: Independent foundation.
Financial data (yr. ended 12/31/12): Assets, $58,538,112 (M); expenditures, $3,465,470; qualifying distributions, $3,117,909; giving activities include $2,800,682 for 48 grants (high: $100,000; low: $1,292).
Purpose and activities: Giving primarily for 1) education and social services for disadvantaged children and adolescents; 2) preschool reading programs; 3) community development that will benefit low-income and minority neighborhoods, including job development and training, and housing; 4) citywide efforts in Boston and vicinity that promote cultural improvements and the arts; 5) grants that, despite some risk, offer a potential of high impact or significant benefits for a community, (the foundation is especially interested in leveraging its grants by funding new programs that can become self-sufficient or which may serve as a model in other geographic areas); and 6) improvements of race relations and neighborhood safety issues.
Fields of interest: Arts; Education; Employment; Housing/shelter, development; Human services; Children/youth, services; Family services; Minorities/immigrants, centers/services; Community/economic development; Minorities.
Type of support: Capital campaigns; Building/renovation; Equipment; Program development; Seed money; Curriculum development; Technical assistance; Matching/challenge support.
Limitations: Applications accepted. Giving limited to MA, with strong emphasis on Boston's Dudley Street neighborhood. No support for political or sectarian religious purposes, or for national organizations. No grants to individuals, or for operating budgets, continuing support, annual campaigns, emergency funds, deficit financing, research, publications, conferences, professorships, scholarships, travel, internships, exchange programs, fellowships, no loans.
Publications: Application guidelines; Annual report; Grants list.
Application information: Proposals will come at the invitation of the foundation only, following review of Letter of Inquiry. Unsolicited proposals will not be accepted. Associated Grant Makers Common Proposal Form accepted. Application form not required.
Initial approach: Letter of Inquiry, not more than 2 pages (without a cover letter)
Copies of proposal: 1
Deadline(s): None for Letters of Inquiry
Board meeting date(s): Mar., June, Sept., and Dec.
Final notification: 30 days for Letters of Inquiry
Officer: Nancy A. Saunders, Admin.
Trustees: Grace Fey; Robert W. Holmes, Jr.; BNY Mellon.
Number of staff: 1 full-time support.
EIN: 046278857

4240
Roberts Family Foundation ✧
31 St. James Ave., Ste. 740
Boston, MA 02116-4186

Established in 2000 in MA.
Donors: Thomas S. Roberts; Kristen Roberts.
Foundation type: Independent foundation.
Financial data (yr. ended 12/31/13): Assets, $11,940,493 (M); gifts received, $46,000; expenditures, $685,443; qualifying distributions, $576,075; giving activities include $576,075 for 12 grants (high: $525,000; low: $250).
Fields of interest: Elementary/secondary education; Higher education; Education; Human services; Youth, services.
Limitations: Applications not accepted. Giving primarily in MA and NJ. No grants to individuals.
Application information: Contributes only to pre-selected organizations.
Trustees: Robert G. Bannish; Kristen Roberts; Thomas S. Roberts.
EIN: 043522054

4241
Elizabeth Killam Rodgers Trust ✧
c/o Nutter, McClennen & Fish, LLP
P.O. Box 51400
Boston, MA 02205-8982
Application address: c/o Thomas P. Jalkut, Nutter, McClennan and Fish, LLP, Seaport W., 155 Seaport, Blvd., Boston, MA 02110-2604; tel.: (617) 439-2000

Established in 1975 in MA.
Donor: Elizabeth Killam Rodgers†.
Foundation type: Independent foundation.
Financial data (yr. ended 04/30/13): Assets, $451,848 (M); gifts received, $56; expenditures, $1,897,734; qualifying distributions, $1,808,237; giving activities include $1,795,000 for 16 grants (high: $400,000; low: $5,000).
Fields of interest: Higher education; International exchange, students.
Limitations: Giving primarily in MA and CT; funding also in Nova Scotia, Canada. No grants to individuals.
Application information:
Initial approach: Letter
Trustees: Thomas P. Jalkut; John B. Newhall.
EIN: 046385523
Selected grants: The following grants are a representative sample of this grantmaker's funding activity:
$125,000 to University of Calgary, Calgary, Canada, 2011.
$10,000 to McGill University, Montreal, Canada, 2011. For general funds.

4242
Thomas A. Rodgers, Jr. Family Foundation ✧
P.O. Box 2509
Fall River, MA 02722-2509
Application address: 111 Durfee St., Fall River, MA 02722-2126, tel.: (508) 679-6452

Established in 1998 in RI.
Donors: Thomas A. Rodgers, Jr.†; Thomas A. Rodgers III; Christine Fennelly; Geraldine Roos; Maureen Bateman.
Foundation type: Independent foundation.
Financial data (yr. ended 12/31/13): Assets, $30,371,238 (M); gifts received, $27,347; expenditures, $1,736,017; qualifying distributions, $1,533,012; giving activities include $1,409,800 for 58 grants (high: $400,000; low: $1,000).
Purpose and activities: Giving primarily for education and human services.
Fields of interest: Elementary/secondary education; Higher education; Human services; United Ways and Federated Giving Programs; Catholic agencies & churches.
Type of support: General/operating support; Annual campaigns; Building/renovation; Curriculum development.
Limitations: Applications accepted. Giving primarily in Fall River, MA, and RI.
Application information: Application form required.
Initial approach: Letter
Deadline(s): None
Officers: Thomas A. Rodgers III, Pres.; Myron Wilner, Treas.
Director: Robert Stoico.
EIN: 043442439

Selected grants: The following grants are a representative sample of this grantmaker's funding activity:
$300,000 to Salve Regina University, Newport, RI, 2012. For The Acquisition of the Lafarge Windows to Be Placed in the Home of Our Lady of Mercy Chapel at the College.
$60,000 to Bristol Community College, Fall River, MA, 2012. For Writing Computer Labs.
$35,000 to Fall River Historical Society, Fall River, MA, 2012. For operating support, Annual Fund Drive.
$30,000 to Nativity Preparatory School of New Bedford, New Bedford, MA, 2012. For Sponsorships for Two Students and a Teacher and the General Support of the School.
$10,000 to Easter Seals Rhode Island, Wakefield, RI, 2012. For operating support of the Pediatric Outpatient Program.
$1,000 to Save the Bay, Providence, RI, 2012. For Explore the Bay Education Program.

4243
Rogers Family Foundation ✧
c/o GMA Foundations, Attn: Susan Haff
77 Summer St., 8th Fl.
Boston, MA 02110-1006 (617) 426-7080
Contact: Amy Rogers Dittrich, Managing Tr.
FAX: (617) 426-7087;
E-mail: shaff@gmafoundations.com; Main
URL: http://www.rogersfamilyfoundation.com

Established in 1957 in MA.
Donors: Irving E. Rogers†; Martha B. Rogers†; Eagle-Tribune Publishing Co.; Andover Publishing Co.; Rogers Investment Corp.; Consolidated Press, Inc.; Derry Publishing Co.
Foundation type: Independent foundation.
Financial data (yr. ended 12/31/13): Assets, $22,466,180 (M); expenditures, $1,127,751; qualifying distributions, $1,060,986; giving activities include $1,040,229 for 48 grants (high: $200,000; low: $1,000).
Purpose and activities: Giving primarily for education, religion, medicine, and the arts.
Fields of interest: Museums; Secondary school/education; Education; Hospitals (general); Human services; Community/economic development; Christian agencies & churches.
Type of support: Scholarship funds; General/operating support.
Limitations: Applications accepted. Giving limited to Merrimack Valley-North Shore, MA, including Andover, Amesbury, Beverly, Boxford, Byfield, Danvers, Dracut, Essex, Gloucester, Georgetown, Groveland, Haverhill, Ipswich, Lynn, Lynnfield, Lawrence, Marblehead, Manchester, Middleton, Methuen, Merrimac, North Reading, North Andover, Newbury, Newburyport, Peabody, Rockport, Rowley, Swampscott, Salem, South Hamilton, Salisbury, Topsfield, Wenham, and West Newbury; and to Southeastern NH, including Auburn, Atkinson, Chester, Derry, Danville, Exeter, East Kingston, Epping, East Hampstead, Fremont, Hudson, Hampstead, Kingston, Litchfield, Londonderry, Newton, Plaistow, Pelham, Raymond, Stratham, Salem, Sandown, and Windham. No grants to individuals, or for fellowships, or matching gifts; no loans.
Publications: Annual report; Grants list; Program policy statement.
Application information: Application form required.
Initial approach: Online application on foundation web site
Deadline(s): Mar. 1 and Sept. 1
Board meeting date(s): June and Nov.
Final notification: 2 months
Trustees: Amy Rogers Dittrich; T. Tyler Dittrich; Kathryn Doherty; Deborah R. Pratt.
Number of staff: 1 full-time professional.
EIN: 046063152
Selected grants: The following grants are a representative sample of this grantmaker's funding activity:
$75,000 to Home Health VNA, Lawrence, MA, 2012. For Merrimack Valley Hospice House Expansion.
$50,000 to Massachusetts General Hospital, Boston, MA, 2012. For Year 2 of 3.
$30,000 to Colby-Sawyer College, New London, NH, 2012. For Fine and Performing Arts Center.
$20,000 to Central Catholic High School, Lawrence, MA, 2012. For the Montagne Project.
$20,000 to Endicott College, Beverly, MA, 2012. For Keys to Degrees Educating Two Generations.
$20,000 to Essex Art Center, Lawrence, MA, 2012. For After School Arts Program.
$15,000 to YMCA of the North Shore, Beverly, MA, 2012. For the Salem Creative Arts Center.
$10,000 to Esperanza Academy, Lawrence, MA, 2012. For 11th Month Summer Program.
$10,000 to Teach for America, Boston, MA, 2012. To Deepen Impact on Student Achievement.
$10,000 to YWCA of Greater Lawrence, Lawrence, MA, 2012. For YWCA Health Promotion Services.

4244
The Romney Foundation for Children ✧
(formerly The Tyler Charitable Foundation)
c/o Ann D. & W. Mitt Romney
137 Newbury St.
Boston, MA 02116

Established in 1999 in MA.
Donors: Ann D. Romney; W. Mitt Romney; Ann D. Romney Blind Trust.
Foundation type: Independent foundation.
Financial data (yr. ended 12/31/12): Assets, $11,492,322 (M); gifts received, $1,160,171; expenditures, $601,201; qualifying distributions, $534,500; giving activities include $534,500 for 21 grants (high: $200,000; low: $1,000).
Fields of interest: Human services; Christian agencies & churches.
Limitations: Applications accepted. Giving primarily in MA.
Application information: Application form not required.
Initial approach: Proposal
Deadline(s): None
Trustees: Ann D. Romney; W. Mitt Romney.
EIN: 046907315

4245
William Rosenberg Family Foundation, Inc. ✧
265 Nahanton St.
Newton, MA 02459-2900

Established in 1986 in FL.
Donors: Ann Rosenberg; William Rosenberg†.
Foundation type: Independent foundation.
Financial data (yr. ended 12/31/12): Assets, $15,472,680 (M); expenditures, $1,158,314; qualifying distributions, $1,011,911; giving activities include $828,000 for 41 grants (high: $140,000; low: $500).
Fields of interest: Higher education; Education; Hospitals (general); Health organizations, association; Human services; Children/youth, services; Jewish federated giving programs.
Type of support: General/operating support; Continuing support; Capital campaigns; Building/renovation; Equipment; Endowments; Program development; Professorships; Research.
Limitations: Applications not accepted. Giving primarily in CT, FL, MA, and NV; funding also in Toronto, Ontario, Canada. No grants to individuals.
Application information: Contributes only to pre-selected organizations.
Board meeting date(s): 1st week in Dec.
Officers and Trustees:* Ann Rosenberg,* Pres.; Carol Silverstein,* V.P.; Donald Rosenberg,* Co-Treas.; James Rosenberg,* Co-Treas.; Jill Gottlieb; Lauren M. Neill; Jennifer Rosenberg; John Rosenberg; Michael Rosenberg; Robert Rosenberg; Tara-Lynn Boreham Rosenberg; Carolyn Ryan; Michael Ryan.
Number of staff: 1 part-time professional.
EIN: 592675613

4246
Rowland Foundation, Inc. ✧
c/o DiCicco, Gulman & Company, LLP
150 Presidential Way, Ste. 510
Woburn, MA 01801-1121
Application address: c/o JPMorgan Chase Bank, N.A., 270 Park Ave., New York, NY 10017, tel.: (212) 464-1926

Incorporated in 1960 in DE.
Donors: Edwin H. Land†; Helen M. Land.
Foundation type: Independent foundation.
Financial data (yr. ended 11/30/13): Assets, $33,744,727 (M); gifts received, $15,000; expenditures, $977,839; qualifying distributions, $892,222; giving activities include $875,000 for 24 grants (high: $150,000; low: $6,000).
Purpose and activities: Giving primarily for higher education, human services, and children and youth services, including youth arts programs; funding also for other cultural institutions.
Fields of interest: Arts; Higher education; Human services; Children/youth, services; Foundations (private grantmaking).
Type of support: General/operating support; Professorships; Research.
Limitations: Applications accepted. Giving primarily in Boston and Cambridge, MA; some giving also in NH. No grants to individuals, or for capital or endowment funds, or matching gifts; no loans.
Application information: Application form not required.
Initial approach: Proposal
Deadline(s): None
Officers and Trustees:* Edward Smallwood,* Co-Pres. and Treas.; Kate Chertavian,* Co-Pres.; Philip DuBois,* V.P.; Charlotte Houghteling Smallwood,* Secy.; Daniel Drake; Guy Smallwood; Valerie Smallwood.
EIN: 046046756

4247
Adelard A. and Valeda Lea Roy Foundation ✧
1500 Worcester Rd., Apt. F
Framingham, MA 01702-8967
Application address: c/o Nancy Smith, 2676 Wakefield Rd., Wakefield, NH 03872

Established in 1990 in MA.
Donor: Adelard A. Roy†.
Foundation type: Independent foundation.
Financial data (yr. ended 12/31/13): Assets, $9,953,165 (M); expenditures, $727,402; qualifying distributions, $684,911; giving activities include $650,000 for 102 grants (high: $30,000; low: $1,000).
Fields of interest: Arts; Elementary/secondary education; Environment; Health organizations; Human services; Christian agencies & churches.
Type of support: General/operating support; Capital campaigns; Building/renovation.
Limitations: Applications accepted. Giving primarily in MA.
Application information: Application form not required.
Initial approach: Proposal
Deadline(s): Sept. 30
Trustees: Elizabeth M. Fisher; Arthur O. Ricci; Nancy S. Smith.
EIN: 046652923
Selected grants: The following grants are a representative sample of this grantmaker's funding activity:
$15,000 to ALS Family Charitable Foundation, Buzzards Bay, MA, 2011.
$15,000 to Compassionate Care ALS, West Falmouth, MA, 2011.
$15,000 to Epiphany School, Dorchester, MA, 2011.
$15,000 to Journey Forward, Canton, MA, 2011.
$10,000 to Preservation Trust of Vermont, Burlington, VT, 2011.
$10,000 to Share Outreach, Milford, NH, 2011.
$10,000 to Trust for Public Land, Montpelier, VT, 2011.
$5,000 to Breakthrough Greater Boston, Cambridge, MA, 2011.
$5,000 to Keeping Track, Huntington, VT, 2011.
$3,000 to Rogerson Communities, Boston, MA, 2011.

4248
Lawrence J. and Anne Rubenstein Charitable Foundation ✧
c/o Ridgeway PTRS LLC
10 Post Office Sq., No. 960
Boston, MA 02109-4615

Established in 1963 in MA.
Donors: Lawrence J. Rubenstein†; Anne C. Rubenstein†.
Foundation type: Independent foundation.
Financial data (yr. ended 12/31/13): Assets, $20,330,953 (M); expenditures, $961,490; qualifying distributions, $876,186; giving activities include $816,200 for 38 grants (high: $75,000; low: $5,000).
Purpose and activities: Giving primarily for early childhood services and higher education, support also for programs for school preparedness.
Fields of interest: Elementary/secondary education; Children/youth, services; Child development, services; Homeless, human services.
Type of support: General/operating support; Equipment; Emergency funds; Program development; Curriculum development; Scholarship funds.
Limitations: Applications not accepted. Giving primarily in Boston, MA and Philadelphia, PA. No grants to individuals.
Application information: Unsolicited requests for funds not accepted.
Trustees: Joycellen Auritt; Andrew M. Cable; Steven P. Perlmutter.
Number of staff: 1 part-time professional.
EIN: 046087371

4249
Cele H. and William B. Rubin Family Fund, Inc. ✧
32 Monadnock Rd.
Wellesley Hills, MA 02481-1338 (781) 235-1075
Contact: Ellen R. Gordon, Pres.

Incorporated in 1943 in NY.
Donors: Melvin J. Gordon; Ellen R. Gordon; The Sweets Co. of America, Inc.; Joseph Rubin and Sons, Inc.; Tootsie Roll Industries, Inc.
Foundation type: Independent foundation.
Financial data (yr. ended 12/31/13): Assets, $92,168,751 (M); gifts received, $950,000; expenditures, $5,167,230; qualifying distributions, $4,500,255; giving activities include $4,500,255 for 108 grants (high: $1,600,000; low: $30).
Purpose and activities: Giving primarily to a donor advised fund, as well as for colleges and universities.
Fields of interest: Higher education; Education; Health organizations, association; Human services; United Ways and Federated Giving Programs.
Limitations: Applications accepted. Giving primarily in IL, MA, and NY. No grants to individuals.
Application information: Application form not required.
Initial approach: Proposal
Deadline(s): None
Officers: Ellen R. Gordon, Pres.; Melvin J. Gordon, V.P.
EIN: 116026235
Selected grants: The following grants are a representative sample of this grantmaker's funding activity:
$1,618,000 to Bank of America Charitable Gift Fund, Providence, RI, 2011.
$515,000 to University of Chicago Medical Center, Chicago, IL, 2011.
$61,000 to Combined Jewish Philanthropies of Greater Boston, Boston, MA, 2011.
$35,000 to Buckingham Browne and Nichols School, Cambridge, MA, 2011.
$20,000 to Harvard College Fund, Cambridge, MA, 2011.
$15,000 to Brandeis University, Waltham, MA, 2011.
$15,000 to Dartmouth College, Hanover, NH, 2011.
$7,500 to Babson College, Babson Park, MA, 2011.
$7,500 to Boston Womens Health Book Collective, Cambridge, MA, 2011.
$2,000 to United Way of Massachusetts Bay, Boston, MA, 2011.

4250
Ruderman Family Foundation ✧
(formerly Ruderman Family Charitable Foundation)
2150 Washington St.
Newton, MA 02462-1498 (617) 599-9919
Contact: Sharon E. Shapiro, Tr.
Main URL: http://www.rudermanfoundation.org/
Facebook: https://www.facebook.com/RudermanFamilyFoundation
Google Plus: https://plus.google.com/106645418281817434488/about
Twitter: https://twitter.com/RudermanFdn

Established in 1996 in MA.
Donors: Marcia Ruderman; Morton E. Ruderman.
Foundation type: Independent foundation.
Financial data (yr. ended 12/31/12): Assets, $112,043,942 (M); gifts received, $89,628,808; expenditures, $4,084,821; qualifying distributions, $4,043,560; giving activities include $3,448,381 for 52 grants (high: $925,000; low: $118).
Purpose and activities: The foundation supports effective programs, innovative partnerships and a dynamic approach to philanthropy in its core areas of interest: advocating for and advancing the inclusion of people with disabilities throughout the Jewish community; fostering a more nuanced understanding of the American Jewish community among Israeli leaders; and modeling the practice of strategic philanthropy worldwide.
Fields of interest: Education; Jewish federated giving programs; Jewish agencies & synagogues; Disabilities, people with.
Limitations: Applications not accepted. Giving primarily in MA and NY. No grants to individuals.
Application information: Unsolicited requests for funds not accepted.
Officers and Trustees:* Jay Seth Ruderman,* Pres.; Michal Bineth-Horowitz, C.O.O.; Steven P. Rosenthal; Marcia Ruderman; Todd Adam Ruderman; Sharon Ellen Shapiro.
EIN: 043334973

4251
The Michael S. Rudyak Memorial Fund ✧
70 Park St., Apt. 22
Brookline, MA 02446-6300 (617) 784-3478
Contact: Rada Rudyak, Tr.

Donors: Semen Rudyak; Rada Rudyak.
Foundation type: Independent foundation.
Financial data (yr. ended 12/31/13): Assets, $2,627,815 (M); gifts received, $2,169,000; expenditures, $669,068; qualifying distributions, $650,744; giving activities include $580,603 for 3 grants (high: $310,000; low: $300).
Fields of interest: Human services; Jewish agencies & synagogues.
Limitations: Applications accepted. Giving primarily in MA and NY; with giving also in Ukraine and Russia.
Application information:
Initial approach: Letter
Deadline(s): None
Trustees: Rufina Brudnaya; Rada Rudyak; Semen Rudyak.
EIN: 263294531

4252
The Ruettgers Family Charitable Foundation ✧
c/o Atlantic Trust Co., N.A., Attn.: Martina Frangis
100 Federal St., 37th Fl.
Boston, MA 02110-1802

Established in 1997 in MA.
Donor: Michael Ruettgers.
Foundation type: Independent foundation.
Financial data (yr. ended 09/30/13): Assets, $29,609,953 (M); gifts received, $5,004,000; expenditures, $1,947,705; qualifying distributions, $1,776,615; giving activities include $1,763,000 for 19 grants (high: $545,000; low: $5,000).
Fields of interest: Media/communications; Museums (art); Education; Human services.
International interests: Rwanda.
Limitations: Applications not accepted. Giving primarily in MA. No grants to individuals.
Application information: Contributes only pre-selected organizations.
Trustees: Polly Fields; Abagail Ruettgers; Christopher Ruettgers; Maureen Ruettgers; Michael Ruettgers.
EIN: 043340951

4253
Rx Foundation ✧
P.O. Box 23
Hadley, MA 01035-0023
Contact: Jennie Riley

Established in 2002 in MA and DE.
Donor: Serena M. Hatch.
Foundation type: Independent foundation.
Financial data (yr. ended 12/31/13): Assets, $43,216,471 (M); expenditures, $2,168,533; qualifying distributions, $1,832,871; giving activities include $1,818,425 for 11 grants (high: $295,715; low: $20,000).
Purpose and activities: The purpose of the foundation is to fund innovative projects to improve the quality of health care in the United States.
Fields of interest: Health care.
Limitations: Applications not accepted. Giving in the U.S., primarily in Boston, MA. No grants to individuals, or for capital campaigns.
Application information: Contributes only to pre-selected organizations.
Officers and Directors:* George Hatch,* Pres.; Jennie Riley, Secy.-Treas.; Christopher C. Angell; Donald M. Berwick; Atul Gawande; Serena M. Hatch; Whitney Hatch; Howard Hiatt; Matthew H. Liang.
EIN: 810556499
Selected grants: The following grants are a representative sample of this grantmaker's funding activity:
$500,000 to Beth Israel Deaconess Medical Center, Boston, MA, 2012. For Echo Age Project.
$70,763 to Institute for Healthcare Improvement, Cambridge, MA, 2012. For Medical education faculty training.
$62,435 to Boston Medical Center, Boston, MA, 2012. For Grant - Study on MA Healthcare Reform and Access to Care.

4254
Richard Saltonstall Charitable Foundation ✧
c/o Saltonstall & Co., Inc.
50 Congress St., Rm. 800
Boston, MA 02109-4034 (617) 227-8660

Established in 1964 in MA.
Donors: Richard Saltonstall‡; Automatic Data Processing Corp.; Caterpillar Inc.; Chevron Corp.; Church & Dwight Co. Inc.; The Walt Disney Co.; Ecolab Inc.; Exxon Mobil Corp.; General Elec Co.; Intel Corp.; Kimberly Clark Corp.; Market Vectors Gold Miners; Merck & Co. Inc.; Royal Dutch Shell PLC; Vanguard Intermediate Tax Exempt Fund; Wells Fargo & Co.; RFP Sr. 1982 Irrev Trust.
Foundation type: Independent foundation.
Financial data (yr. ended 12/31/13): Assets, $30,284,642 (M); gifts received, $469,470; expenditures, $1,383,341; qualifying distributions, $1,214,718; giving activities include $1,029,500 for 36 grants (high: $150,000; low: $1,000).
Fields of interest: Media/communications; Museums; Performing arts, orchestras; Higher education; Education; Environment, natural resources; Hospitals (general); Alzheimer's disease research; Human services; United Ways and Federated Giving Programs.
Limitations: Applications accepted. Giving primarily in MA, with some emphasis on Boston.
Application information: Application form not required.
Initial approach: Proposal
Deadline(s): Oct. 1
Trustees: Robert A. Lawrence; Mary R. Saltonstall; David S. Willis; Dudley H. Willis; Sally S. Willis.
Number of staff: 1 full-time professional; 1 full-time support.
EIN: 046078934

4255
Samantha, Becky, Mark Foundation ✧
16 Boardman Ave.
Manchester, MA 01944-1406

Established in MA.
Donors: Mark J. Levin; Becky Ruhmann Levin.
Foundation type: Independent foundation.
Financial data (yr. ended 12/31/13): Assets, $10,192,328 (M); gifts received, $998,736; expenditures, $1,079,082; qualifying distributions, $949,625; giving activities include $949,500 for 10 grants (high: $750,000; low: $2,500).
Fields of interest: Health care; Youth development, business; Human services.
Limitations: Applications not accepted. Giving primarily in the Boston, MA, area.
Application information: Contributes only to pre-selected organizations.
Trustees: Becky Ruhmann Levin; Mark J. Levin.
EIN: 263403705
Selected grants: The following grants are a representative sample of this grantmaker's funding activity:
$100,000 to Partners in Health, Boston, MA, 2010. For general support.
$25,000 to Partners in Health, Boston, MA, 2010. For general support.
$18,200 to Personalized Medicine Coalition, Washington, DC, 2011.
$18,200 to Personalized Medicine Coalition, Washington, DC, 2010. For general support.
$10,000 to ReSurge International, Mountain View, CA, 2010. For general support.
$8,000 to Inner-City Scholarship Fund, New York, NY, 2010. For general support.
$5,000 to Buckingham Browne and Nichols School, Cambridge, MA, 2010. For general support.

4256
Santander Bank Foundation ✧
(formerly Sovereign Bank Foundation)
c/o Foundation Mgr.
75 State St., MA1-SST-0407
Boston, MA 02109 (617) 757-3410
Contact: Craig Williams, V.P.
Additional application addresses: DE, MD, NJ, and PA organizations: CRA Div. Mgr., Sovereign Bank, 20-536-CD2, 2 Aldwyn Lane, Villanova, PA 19085, e-mail: MIDAFoundation@sovereignbank.com; CT, MA, NH, and RI organizations: CRA Division Mgr., Sovereign Bank, MA1-MB2-03-06, 2 Morrissey Blvd., Dorchester, MA 02125, e-mail: NEFoundation@sovereignbank.com; Metro-New York, NY organizations: CRA Division Mgr., Sovereign Bank, NY1-6528-LG12, 195 Montague St., Brooklyn, NY 11201, e-mail: NYFoundation@sovereignbank.com; Main URL: https://www.santanderbank.com/us/about/community/grant-application-guidelines

Established in 1989 in PA.
Donor: Sovereign Bank.
Foundation type: Company-sponsored foundation.
Financial data (yr. ended 12/31/13): Assets, $0 (M); gifts received, $1,737,504; expenditures, $1,737,504; qualifying distributions, $1,737,504; giving activities include $1,737,504 for 1 grant.
Purpose and activities: The foundation supports organizations involved with arts and culture, education, health, employment, housing, human services, and community and economic development. Special emphasis is directed toward programs targeting low-and moderate-income individuals and communities.
Fields of interest: Media/communications; Visual arts; Museums; Performing arts; Arts; Education, early childhood education; Child development, education; Libraries (public); Education; Environment; Health care; Employment, training; Housing/shelter, home owners; Housing/shelter, services; Housing/shelter; Children/youth, services; Human services, financial counseling; Human services; Economic development; Community/economic development; Economically disadvantaged.
Type of support: General/operating support; Continuing support; Annual campaigns; Building/renovation; Emergency funds; Program development; Curriculum development; Employee matching gifts; Employee-related scholarships.
Limitations: Applications accepted. Giving primarily in areas of company operations in CT, New Castle, DE, MA, MD, NH, Central and Southern NJ, NY, Mid-Atlantic, PA, and RI. No support for political organizations, or organizations traditionally supported by parents, including Little League, Parent Teacher Organizations, and Scouting. No grants to individuals (except for employee-related scholarships), or for capital campaigns, sectarian or religious purposes, pageants, team sponsorships or sporting events, advertising in programs, bulletins, schedules, maps, yearbooks, book covers, or brochures, trips or tours, or walk-a-thon races or similar fundraising events.

Publications: Application guidelines; Annual report; Program policy statement.
Application information: Proposal narratives should be no longer than 2 pages. Submissions of videos, folders, and plastic covers are not encouraged. Additional information may be requested at a later date. Application form not required.
Initial approach: Download grant proposal cover sheet and e-mail cover sheet and proposal to foundation
Copies of proposal: 1
Deadline(s): Mar. 7, June 6, and Sept. 5
Final notification: Apr. 30, July 31, and Oct. 31
Officers and Directors:* John V. Killen,* Pres.; Sonia L. Alleyne, V.P.; Patricia Rock, V.P.; Joseph E. Schupp, V.P.; Craig M. Williams, V.P.; Cynthia Kelly, Secy.; Jay Bobb, Treas.; Lawrence F. Delp; Patrick Sullivan.
Number of staff: 1 part-time professional; 1 part-time support.
EIN: 232548113

4257
Saquish Foundation ✧
c/o Hunter Associates
75 Federal St., Ste. 2005
Boston, MA 02110-1920

Established in MA.
Donor: Charles M. Werly‡.
Foundation type: Independent foundation.
Financial data (yr. ended 12/31/13): Assets, $21,266,206 (M); expenditures, $929,295; qualifying distributions, $794,895; giving activities include $698,000 for 44 grants (high: $45,000; low: $12,000).
Purpose and activities: Giving for the arts, education, hospitals and health organizations, and human services.
Fields of interest: Arts; Higher education; Education; Environment; Hospitals (general); Health organizations; Human services.
Limitations: Applications not accepted. Giving primarily in MA. No grants to individuals.
Application information: Contributes only to pre-selected organizations.
Trustees: Robyn Borges; Arthur A. Nichols; Horace S. Nichols; John Werly; Scott Werly.
EIN: 046136550

4258
Milton & Dorothy Sarnoff Raymond Foundation ✧
P.O. Box 147
Williamstown, MA 01267

Established in NY.
Foundation type: Independent foundation.
Financial data (yr. ended 12/31/13): Assets, $13,736,690 (M); expenditures, $876,255; qualifying distributions, $876,255; giving activities include $772,500 for 58 grants (high: $200,000; low: $500).
Fields of interest: Arts; Education; Human services.
Limitations: Applications not accepted. Giving primarily in CA, Washington, DC, and MA.
Application information: Unsolicited requests for funds not accepted.
Trustee: Catherine L. Burke; Elizabeth L. Hughes; Andrew R. Laitman; Samuel H. Laitman.
EIN: 356803768
Selected grants: The following grants are a representative sample of this grantmaker's funding activity:
$50,000 to Williams College, Williamstown, MA, 2012. For Shainman Scholarship Fund.

4259
The Michael & Helen Schaffer Foundation ✧
6 Whittier Pl., Ste. 14N
Boston, MA 02114-1422

Established in 2002 in MA.
Foundation type: Operating foundation.
Financial data (yr. ended 07/31/14): Assets, $8,827,840 (M); expenditures, $990,283; qualifying distributions, $959,342; giving activities include $842,864 for 21 grants (high: $400,000; low: $5,000).
Purpose and activities: Giving primarily for human services and medical foundations; funding also for higher education.
Fields of interest: Higher education; Health care; Health organizations; Human services; Foundations (private grantmaking).
Limitations: Applications not accepted. Giving primarily in MA and NY. No grants to individuals.
Application information: Contributes only to pre-selected organizations.
Trustee: Wendy Appel.
EIN: 020534424
Selected grants: The following grants are a representative sample of this grantmaker's funding activity:
$250,000 to Massachusetts Institute of Technology, Cambridge, MA, 2011.
$25,000 to Oxfam America, Boston, MA, 2011.

4260
Schoen Family Foundation ✧
c/o RH&B, Inc.
50 Congress St., Ste. 900
Boston, MA 02109-4022

Established in 2000 in MA.
Donors: Scott A. Schoen; Laurie G. Schoen.
Foundation type: Independent foundation.
Financial data (yr. ended 12/31/12): Assets, $0 (M); gifts received, $844,706; expenditures, $1,106,004; qualifying distributions, $1,099,348; giving activities include $1,093,848 for 8 grants (high: $600,000; low: $4,424).
Purpose and activities: Giving primarily for education, hospitals, and human services, including an organization for homeless children.
Fields of interest: Arts; Higher education; Education; Hospitals (general); Human services; Children/youth, services; Homeless, human services.
Limitations: Applications not accepted. Giving primarily in New Haven, CT and MA, with emphasis on Boston and Dorchester. No grants to individuals.
Application information: Contributes only to pre-selected organizations.
Trustees: Robert G. Bannish; Laurie G. Schoen; Scott A. Schoen.
EIN: 046771174

4261
The Schooner Foundation ✧
(formerly Ryan Family Charitable Foundation)
c/o Schooner Capital LLC
745 Atlantic Ave., Ste. 1100
Boston, MA 02111-2709
E-mail: cryan@schoonercapital.com

Established in 1996 in MA.
Donor: Vincent J. Ryan.
Foundation type: Independent foundation.
Financial data (yr. ended 12/31/12): Assets, $24,776,689 (M); expenditures, $4,332,640; qualifying distributions, $3,598,789; giving activities include $3,422,833 for 90 grants (high: $500,000; low: $250).
Fields of interest: Museums; Arts; Higher education; Education; Environment, natural resources; Health organizations; Human services; International peace/security; International affairs; Foundations (private grantmaking).
Type of support: General/operating support; Income development; Capital campaigns; Endowments; Program development; Professorships; Seed money; Fellowships; Scholarship funds; Consulting services; Matching/challenge support.
Limitations: Applications not accepted. Giving primarily in MA; some funding also in CA, TN, and Washington, DC. No grants to individuals.
Application information: Contributes only to pre-selected organizations.
Officer: Stephen D. Maiocco, Treas.
Trustees: Kimberly R. Dano; Stephanie R. Ditenhafer; Carla E. Meyer; Cynthia A. Ryan; Jennifer Ryan; Nicholas L. Ryan; Vincent J. Ryan.
Number of staff: 1 full-time professional.
EIN: 043347626

4262
Caroline & Sigmund Schott Fund ✧
(formerly Caroline & Sigmund Schott Foundation, Inc.)
c/o Margo Brathwaite
675 Massachusetts Ave., 8th Fl.
Cambridge, MA 02139-3309

Established in 1986 in DE.
Donors: Liselotte J. Leeds; Gerald G. Leeds.
Foundation type: Independent foundation.
Financial data (yr. ended 06/30/13): Assets, $37,564,102 (M); expenditures, $1,920,074; qualifying distributions, $1,526,186; giving activities include $1,341,046 for grants (high: $1,285,000; low: $1,000).
Fields of interest: Education, public education; Education; Human services.
Type of support: General/operating support; Continuing support; Program development; Conferences/seminars; Publication; Research; Technical assistance; Program evaluation.
Limitations: Applications not accepted. Giving primarily in MA, with emphasis on Boston; some funding also in New York, NY. No support for service organizations. No grants to individuals, or for services or service delivery.
Publications: Occasional report.
Application information: Contributes only to pre-selected organizations.
Officers and Board Members:* Greg Jobin-Leeds,* Chair. and Pres.; Liselotte J. Leeds,* Vice-Chair. and Treas.; Maria Jobin-Leeds,* V.P. and Secy.; Gerard G. Leeds,* V.P.

Number of staff: 3 full-time professional; 1 part-time professional; 1 full-time support.
EIN: 112856561
Selected grants: The following grants are a representative sample of this grantmaker's funding activity:
$10,000 to Highlander Research and Education Center, New Market, TN, 2011.
$10,000 to Justice Matters, Oakland, CA, 2011.
$10,000 to North Shore Child and Family Guidance Center, Roslyn Heights, NY, 2011.
$10,000 to Progressive Technology Project, Austin, TX, 2011.
$10,000 to Southern Poverty Law Center, Montgomery, AL, 2011.
$10,000 to Womens Leadership Fund, New York, NY, 2011.
$2,000 to Algebra Project, Cambridge, MA, 2011.
$2,000 to Young Peoples Project, Cambridge, MA, 2011.

4263
William E. Schrafft and Bertha E. Schrafft Charitable Trust ✧
77 Summer St., 8th Fl.
Boston, MA 02110-1006
Contact: Karen Faulkner, Exec. Dir.
E-mail: funding@schrafftcharitable.org; Main URL: http://www.schrafftcharitable.org
Grants List: http://www.schrafftcharitable.org/?page_id=91

Trust established in 1946 in MA.
Donors: William E. Schrafft†; Bertha E. Schrafft†.
Foundation type: Independent foundation.
Financial data (yr. ended 12/31/13): Assets, $36,107,062 (M); expenditures, $2,249,417; qualifying distributions, $1,817,500; giving activities include $1,817,500 for 104 grants (high: $80,000; low: $2,500).
Purpose and activities: Grants primarily for educational programs in the Boston, MA, inner-city area, for minorities and higher and secondary education; support also for community funds, cultural programs, and youth agencies.
Fields of interest: Arts; Elementary school/education; Secondary school/education; Higher education; Children/youth, services; Youth, services; Minorities; Economically disadvantaged.
Type of support: Continuing support; Scholarship funds.
Limitations: Applications accepted. Giving limited to the inner-city Boston, MA, area. No grants to individuals, or for matching gifts, seed money, emergency funds, capital campaigns, or deficit financing; no loans.
Publications: Application guidelines; Grants list.
Application information: Associated Grant Makers Common Proposal Form accepted, which is available through the trust's web site. Application form required.
Initial approach: Proposal
Copies of proposal: 1
Deadline(s): None
Board meeting date(s): About 6 times per year
Final notification: 2 months
Officer: Karen Faulkner, Exec. Dir. and Grants Mgr. Admin.
Trustees: Lavinia B. Chase; Kristen J. McCormack; Arthur H. Parker.
EIN: 046065605

Selected grants: The following grants are a representative sample of this grantmaker's funding activity:
$83,000 to Associated Grant Makers, Boston, MA, 2012. For Summer Fund.
$37,000 to Neighborhood House Charter School, Dorchester, MA, 2012. For Creative Arts Program.
$35,000 to Gordon College, Wenham, MA, 2012. For Clarendon Scholars.
$25,000 to Catholic Schools Foundation, Boston, MA, 2012. For Inner City Scholarship Fund.
$20,000 to New Bedford Whaling Museum, New Bedford, MA, 2012. For Museum Access Boston.
$20,000 to Old Sturbridge Village, Sturbridge, MA, 2012. For Leveling the Playing Field Program.
$20,000 to Trinity Boston Foundation, Boston, MA, 2012. For Trinity Education for Excellence Program.
$20,000 to ZUMIX, East Boston, MA, 2012. For Hands-On Music Education Program.
$18,000 to Artists for Humanity, Boston, MA, 2012. For arts micro-enterprise.
$15,000 to Northeastern University, Boston, MA, 2012. For Balfour Program.

4264
The Gerald & Elaine Schuster Charitable Foundation ✧
c/o Continental Wingate Co.
63 Kendrick St.
Needham, MA 02494-2708 (781) 707-9000
Contact: Gerald Schuster, Tr.; Elaine Schuster, Tr.
Application address: 101 Jungle Rd., Palm Beach, FL 33480, MA tel.: (781) 707-9000

Established in 2005 in MA.
Donors: Elaine Schuster; Gerald Schuster.
Foundation type: Independent foundation.
Financial data (yr. ended 12/31/12): Assets, $265,939 (M); expenditures, $535,671; qualifying distributions, $534,833; giving activities include $534,833 for grants.
Fields of interest: Higher education; Health organizations, association; Jewish federated giving programs; Jewish agencies & synagogues.
Limitations: Applications accepted. Giving primarily in MA.
Application information: Application form not required.
Initial approach: Proposal
Deadline(s): None
Trustees: Elaine Schuster; Gerald Schuster.
EIN: 510518711

4265
Valerie Beth Schwartz Foundation ✧
c/o Spielman Koenigsberg & Parker
P.O. Box 126
Belmont, MA 02478-0002

Established in 2000 in NY.
Donors: Bernard Schwartz; Ida Schwartz; Jonathan Schwartz.
Foundation type: Independent foundation.
Financial data (yr. ended 12/31/13): Assets, $9,494,458 (M); gifts received, $28,250; expenditures, $458,294; qualifying distributions, $437,961; giving activities include $432,175 for 40 grants (high: $80,000; low: $375).
Fields of interest: Arts; Education; Human services; Children/youth, services; Jewish agencies & synagogues.
Limitations: Applications not accepted. No grants to individuals.
Application information: Contributes only to pre-selected organizations.
Trustees: Alexander Schwartz; Jonathan Schwartz.
EIN: 134117395

4266
The SDSC Global Foundation ✧
2 Possum Hollow Rd.
Andover, MA 01810-2446

Established in 2000 in MA.
Donors: Chikong Shue; Susan Shue.
Foundation type: Independent foundation.
Financial data (yr. ended 12/31/12): Assets, $17,629,835 (M); gifts received, $323,180; expenditures, $873,191; qualifying distributions, $730,000; giving activities include $730,000 for grants.
Fields of interest: Foundations (public).
Limitations: Applications not accepted. Giving primarily in NY and OH. No grants to individuals.
Application information: Contributes only to pre-selected organizations.
Trustees: Chikong Shue; Susan Shue.
EIN: 046911403

4267
Carl and Ruth Shapiro Family Foundation ✧
(formerly Carl and Ruth Shapiro Foundation)
75 Park Plz.
Boston, MA 02116-3941 (617) 778-7999
Contact: Jean S. Whitney, Exec. Dir.
FAX: (617) 778-7996;
E-mail: info@shapirofamilyfdn.org; Additional inf. (for Jean S. Whitney) e-mail: jwhitney@shapirofamilyfdn.org; Main URL: http://www.shapirofamilyfdn.org

Established in 1961 in DE as Carl Shapiro Foundation.
Donors: Carl Shapiro; Ruth Shapiro†.
Foundation type: Independent foundation.
Financial data (yr. ended 12/31/13): Assets, $42,447,619 (M); expenditures, $13,954,053; qualifying distributions, $13,790,117; giving activities include $13,424,000 for 72 grants (high: $3,820,000; low: $7,500).
Purpose and activities: Grants primarily for arts and culture, education, health and hospitals, Jewish causes and social welfare in the Greater Boston area.
Fields of interest: Museums; Performing arts, dance; Performing arts, theater; Performing arts, music; Arts; Higher education; Education; Hospitals (general); Cancer research; Medical research; Youth development; Human services; Jewish federated giving programs; Economics; Youth; Young adults; Disabilities, people with; Physically disabled; Immigrants/refugees; Economically disadvantaged.
Type of support: General/operating support; Annual campaigns; Capital campaigns; Building/renovation; Equipment; Program development; Research; Technical assistance.
Limitations: Applications not accepted. Giving primarily in greater Boston, MA. No support for sectarian purposes (except Jewish). No grants to individuals.

Application information: Contributes only to pre-selected organizations.
Board meeting date(s): 3 times per year
Officers and Trustees:* Carl Shapiro,* Chair.; Linda S. Waintrup,* Pres.; Jean S. Whitney, Exec. Dir.; Ellen S. Jaffe.
Number of staff: 1 full-time professional; 1 part-time professional.
EIN: 046135027
Selected grants: The following grants are a representative sample of this grantmaker's funding activity:
$3,560,000 to Brandeis University, Waltham, MA, 2012.
$1,550,000 to Brigham and Women's Hospital, Boston, MA, 2012.
$1,500,000 to Dana-Farber Cancer Institute, Boston, MA, 2012.
$1,200,000 to Museum of Fine Arts, Boston, MA, 2012.
$1,000,000 to Boston Medical Center, Boston, MA, 2012.
$800,000 to Hebrew SeniorLife, Boston, MA, 2012.
$40,000 to EdVestors, Boston, MA, 2012.
$30,000 to Northeastern University, Boston, MA, 2012.
$25,000 to Boston Debate League, Boston, MA, 2012. For After-school Debate League.
$20,000 to Boston Childrens Chorus, Boston, MA, 2012. For Upper Choirs program.
$20,000 to Sociedad Latina, Roxbury, MA, 2012.

4268
Jean S. & Frederic A. Sharf Fund ✧
155 Heath St.
Chestnut Hill, MA 02467-2805

Established in 1965 in MA.
Donors: Frederic A. Sharf; Jean S. Sharf; Evelyn P. Strouse†.
Foundation type: Independent foundation.
Financial data (yr. ended 12/31/13): Assets, $9,515 (M); gifts received, $585,293; expenditures, $578,842; qualifying distributions, $578,842; giving activities include $573,500 for 11 grants (high: $119,000; low: $10,000).
Fields of interest: Museums (art); Education; Hospitals (general); Cancer; Jewish federated giving programs.
Type of support: Annual campaigns; Capital campaigns; Program development; Publication.
Limitations: Applications not accepted. Giving primarily in MA. No grants to individuals.
Application information: Unsolicited requests for funds not accepted.
Trustees: Frederic A. Sharf; Jean S. Sharf.
EIN: 236406343
Selected grants: The following grants are a representative sample of this grantmaker's funding activity:
$65,000 to Norton Museum of Art, West Palm Beach, FL, 2012. For Charitable and Educational Purposes.

4269
Alice Shaver Foundation ✧
P.O. Box 147
Williamstown, MA 01267-0147

Established in 2006 in MA.
Foundation type: Independent foundation.
Financial data (yr. ended 12/31/13): Assets, $15,893,926 (M); expenditures, $994,222; qualifying distributions, $994,222; giving activities include $839,000 for 99 grants (high: $100,000; low: $2,000).
Fields of interest: Arts; Higher education; Health organizations; Human services.
Limitations: Applications not accepted. No grants to individuals.
Application information: Unsolicited requests for funds not accepted.
Trustees: Catherine L. Burke; Elizabeth L. Hughes; Andrew R. Laitman; Samuel H. Laitman.
EIN: 137483764
Selected grants: The following grants are a representative sample of this grantmaker's funding activity:
$50,000 to Williams College, Williamstown, MA, 2012. For Shainman Scholarship.
$50,000 to Williams College, Williamstown, MA, 2012. For Peace Corp Project.
$20,000 to Williams College, Williamstown, MA, 2012. For Dalzell Award.
$15,000 to Williams College, Williamstown, MA, 2012. For dance Program.
$10,000 to Williams College, Williamstown, MA, 2012. For Roosevelt HS Project.
$10,000 to Williams College, Williamstown, MA, 2012. For Urban Scholars.
$3,000 to Berkshire Museum, Pittsfield, MA, 2012. For Photography Project.

4270
Gardiner Howland Shaw Foundation ✧
355 Boylston St.
Boston, MA 02116-3332 (761) 455-8303
Contact: Thomas Coury, Exec. Dir.
FAX: (617) 262-0854;
E-mail: admin@shawfoundation.org; Application tel.: (781) 455-8303; Main URL: http://www.shawfoundation.org

Trust established in 1959 in MA.
Donor: Gardiner Howland Shaw†.
Foundation type: Independent foundation.
Financial data (yr. ended 04/30/13): Assets, $18,649,778 (M); expenditures, $966,384; qualifying distributions, $851,025; giving activities include $621,775 for 55 grants (high: $67,500; low: $750).
Purpose and activities: The study of prevention, correction, and alleviation of crime and delinquency and the rehabilitation of adult and juvenile offenders. The foundation is particularly interested in supporting projects which demonstrate a current awareness of the major issues confronting our criminal justice system, with the following funding priorities: 1) programs which can effectively divert court-involved youth and juvenile offenders from escalating involvement in the criminal justice system; 2) programs which promote the use and acceptance of alternatives to incarceration and intermediate criminal sanctions; 3) innovative and effective approaches to rehabilitation for detained and incarcerated juvenile and adult offenders; 4) methods which improve the administration of justice and the quality of services for individuals appearing before the criminal court; and 5) initiatives which can impact current public policy in the field of criminal justice through education, training and effective advocacy.
Fields of interest: Crime/law enforcement, reform; Crime/violence prevention, youth; Offenders/ex-offenders, rehabilitation; Children/youth; Young adults; Women; Young adults, female; Young adults, male; Offenders/ex-offenders.
Type of support: General/operating support; Continuing support; Program development; Seed money; Technical assistance.
Limitations: Applications accepted. Giving limited to MA. No support for drug or mental health programs or the arts. No grants to individuals, or for capital or building funds, equipment, land acquisition, renovations, endowment funds, scholarships, or fellowships.
Publications: Application guidelines; Annual report (including application guidelines); Grants list; Occasional report; Program policy statement (including application guidelines).
Application information: Associated Grant Makers Common Proposal Form accepted. Application form required.
Initial approach: Letter or telephone
Copies of proposal: 1
Deadline(s): Feb. 1
Board meeting date(s): Feb., May, and Oct. Funding decisions are made in May
Final notification: May 31
Officer: Thomas Coury, Exec. Dir.
Trustees: Peter P. Brown; Theodore E. Ober; Benjamin Williams; Welch & Forbes.
Number of staff: 1 full-time professional; 1 part-time support.
EIN: 046111826
Selected grants: The following grants are a representative sample of this grantmaker's funding activity:
$73,500 to Community Resources for Justice, Boston, MA, 2011.
$35,000 to Citizens for Juvenile Justice, Boston, MA, 2011.
$10,000 to Career Collaborative, Boston, MA, 2011.
$10,000 to Childrens Advocacy Center of Suffolk County, Boston, MA, 2011.
$10,000 to Hull Lifesaving Museum, Hull, MA, 2011.
$10,000 to Massachusetts Law Reform Institute, Boston, MA, 2011.
$8,000 to Penikese Island School, Woods Hole, MA, 2011.
$6,000 to Juvenile Law Center, Philadelphia, PA, 2011.
$5,000 to Freedom Ministries, Boston, MA, 2011.
$2,500 to Rodman Ride for Kids, Foxboro, MA, 2011.

4271
Sheehan Family Foundation ✧
P.O. Box K
Kingston, MA 02364-0510
E-mail: director@sheehanfoundation.org; Main URL: http://www.sheehanfoundation.org/

Established in 1993 in MA.
Donors: Gerald V. Sheehan; Elizabeth Sheehan; Margaret Sheehan; L. Knife & Son, Inc.
Foundation type: Operating foundation.
Financial data (yr. ended 12/31/13): Assets, $3,441,963 (M); expenditures, $550,169; qualifying distributions, $477,200; giving activities include $477,200 for 50 grants (high: $40,000; low: $250).
Purpose and activities: Giving primarily for education, including after school programs, youth development and natural resource protection.

Fields of interest: Education, early childhood education; Education; Environment, natural resources; Youth development.
Type of support: General/operating support; Continuing support; Land acquisition; Conferences/seminars; Curriculum development; Scholarship funds; Technical assistance; Program evaluation; Matching/challenge support.
Limitations: Giving primarily in Barnstable, Dukes, Plymouth and Essex counties, MA; some funding also in Brooklyn, NY and Milwaukee, WI. No grants to individuals.
Publications: Application guidelines; Annual report; Multi-year report.
Application information: See foundation website for complete application guidelines and procedures.
Initial approach: Letter or e-mail
Deadline(s): Rolling basis
Board meeting date(s): Jan., May and Sept.
Officer: Laura Gang, Exec. Dir.
Trustees: Chris Sheehan; John Sheehan; Timothy Sheehan.
EIN: 043197325

4272
Shipley Foundation, Inc. ✧

(formerly The Shipley Family Foundation, Inc.)
c/o Nutter, McClennen & Fish, LLP
P.O. Box 51400
Boston, MA 02205-1400

Established in 1969 in MA.
Donors: Charles R. Shipley, Jr.; Lucia H. Shipley; Richard C. Shipley; Lucia Shipley 1993 Trust.
Foundation type: Independent foundation.
Financial data (yr. ended 12/31/12): Assets, $178,434,583 (M); expenditures, $5,622,171; qualifying distributions, $4,310,256; giving activities include $3,933,333 for 6 grants (high: $2,000,000; low: $50,000).
Fields of interest: Higher education.
Limitations: Applications not accepted. Giving primarily in CO and MA.
Application information: Contributes only to pre-selected organizations.
Officers and Directors:* Richard C. Shipley,* Pres.; Julia S. Cosentino,* Clerk; Thomas P. Jalkut,* Treas.; Karen L. Shipley.
EIN: 237015570
Selected grants: The following grants are a representative sample of this grantmaker's funding activity:
$2,000,000 to Boston University, Boston, MA, 2012. For Beverly A. Brown Professorship.
$1,000,000 to Colorado State University, Fort Collins, CO, 2012. For Shipley University Chair in Comparative Oncology.
$250,000 to Boston University, Boston, MA, 2012. For Shipley Professorship.
$50,000 to Boston University, Boston, MA, 2012. For Shipley Fund for Excellence.

4273
The Sidman Family Foundation, Inc. ✧

c/o Nicholas L. Iacuzio, Beacon Companies
50 Federal St.
Boston, MA 02110-3524

Established in MA.
Donor: Mathew K. Sidman.
Foundation type: Independent foundation.
Financial data (yr. ended 06/30/13): Assets, $10,492,421 (M); gifts received, $3,000,000; expenditures, $982,178; qualifying distributions, $953,748; giving activities include $953,748 for 44 grants (high: $250,718; low: $72).
Fields of interest: Arts; Higher education; Human services; United Ways and Federated Giving Programs; Jewish federated giving programs; Jewish agencies & synagogues.
Limitations: Applications not accepted. Giving primarily in MA and NY.
Application information: Contributes only to pre-selected organizations.
Officers and Directors:* Paula M. Sidman,* Pres.; Mathew K. Sidman, Clerk; Hope Sidman,* Treas.
EIN: 203867727
Selected grants: The following grants are a representative sample of this grantmaker's funding activity:
$213,850 to Combined Jewish Philanthropies of Greater Boston, Boston, MA, 2011. For program services.
$179,483 to New Art Center, Newton, MA, 2011. For program services.

4274
The Sims/Maes Foundation Inc. ✧

c/o Edelstein Co., LLP
160 Federal St.
Boston, MA 02110-1700

Established in 2003 in MA.
Donors: Karl Sims; Patricia Maes.
Foundation type: Independent foundation.
Financial data (yr. ended 12/31/13): Assets, $12,986,979 (M); expenditures, $545,104; qualifying distributions, $542,595; giving activities include $540,625 for 37 grants (high: $420,000; low: $125).
Purpose and activities: Giving primarily to a donor-advised fund, as well as for the arts, environment, education and human services.
Fields of interest: Arts; Education; Environment; Animals/wildlife; Cancer; Human services; United Ways and Federated Giving Programs; Philanthropy/voluntarism.
Limitations: Applications not accepted. No grants to individuals.
Application information: Contributes only to pre-selected organizations.
Officers and Directors:* Karl Sims,* Pres. and Clerk; Patricia Maes,* Treas.; M. Molly Kim.
EIN: 680575207

4275
Richard & Susan Smith 1990 Charitable Trust ✧

(formerly R. & S. Smith Charitable Trust)
c/o Richard A. Smith and Susan F. Smith
One Newton Executive Park, Ste. 104
Newton, MA 02462-1435

Established in 1990 in MA.
Donors: Richard A. Smith; Susan F. Smith.
Foundation type: Independent foundation.
Financial data (yr. ended 12/31/12): Assets, $15,413,973 (M); expenditures, $2,537,742; qualifying distributions, $2,423,500; giving activities include $2,414,800 for 22 grants (high: $2,000,000; low: $500).
Purpose and activities: Giving to a university and a cancer institute.
Fields of interest: Higher education; Cancer; Medical research, institute.
Type of support: Capital campaigns; Building/renovation.
Limitations: Applications not accepted. Giving limited to MA.
Application information: Contributes only to pre-selected organizations.
Trustees: Richard A. Smith; Susan F. Smith.
Number of staff: 1
EIN: 223048829
Selected grants: The following grants are a representative sample of this grantmaker's funding activity:
$2,000,000 to Joslin Diabetes Center, Boston, MA, 2012.
$288,000 to Dana-Farber Cancer Institute, Boston, MA, 2012.
$15,000 to Dana-Farber Cancer Institute, Boston, MA, 2012.
$10,000 to Beth Israel Deaconess Medical Center, Boston, MA, 2012.
$10,000 to Joslin Diabetes Center, Boston, MA, 2012.
$2,500 to Joslin Diabetes Center, Boston, MA, 2012.
$1,000 to Alzheimers Association, Massachusetts/New Hampshire Chapter, Watertown, MA, 2012.

4276
Amy Smith and John G. Berylson Charitable Foundation ✧ ☆

c/o Goulston & Storrs
400 Atlantic Ave.
Boston, MA 02110-3333

Established in 2005 in MA.
Donors: Amy Smith Berylson; John G. Berylson.
Foundation type: Independent foundation.
Financial data (yr. ended 09/30/13): Assets, $8,203,111 (M); gifts received, $2,433,400; expenditures, $1,027,720; qualifying distributions, $972,142; giving activities include $966,340 for 12 grants (high: $583,840; low: $2,000).
Fields of interest: Education.
Limitations: Applications not accepted. Giving primarily in MA. No grants to individuals.
Application information: Unsolicited requests for funds not accepted.
Trustees: Amy Smith Berylson; Elizabeth Berylson; James Berylson; Jennifer Berylson; John G. Berylson.
EIN: 201990804

4277
Richard and Susan Smith Family Foundation ✧

1 Newton Executive Park, Ste. 104
Newton, MA 02462-1435 (857) 404-0700
Contact: Lynne J. Doblin, Exec. Dir.
FAX: (857) 404-0719;
E-mail: info@smithfamilyfoundation.net; Main URL: http://www.smithfamilyfoundation.net

Trust established in 1970 in MA.
Donors: Marian Smith‡; Richard A. Smith; Susan F. Smith.
Foundation type: Independent foundation.

Financial data (yr. ended 04/30/13): Assets, $253,764,175 (M); gifts received, $163,946; expenditures, $15,813,365; qualifying distributions, $13,306,565; giving activities include $11,443,260 for 142 grants (high: $500,000; low: $100).
Purpose and activities: Grants for health, education, and for children and youth; the arts are a secondary field of interest. Of particular interest are organizations providing opportunities for economically disadvantaged populations, especially children and youth. Toward this end, the foundation has directed most of its support toward highly successful operators of non-traditional public schools that are playing an important role in Massachusetts's efforts to eliminate the achievement gap.
Fields of interest: Arts; Education, early childhood education; Elementary school/education; Education; Hospitals (general); Medical research; Children/youth, services; Homeless, human services; Children/youth; Youth; Young adults; Minorities; Economically disadvantaged; Homeless.
Type of support: General/operating support; Management development/capacity building; Annual campaigns; Capital campaigns; Building/renovation; Equipment; Program development; Seed money; Curriculum development; Research; Program evaluation; Matching/challenge support.
Limitations: Applications accepted. Giving primarily in the greater Boston, MA; giving also to agencies that serve the communities of Lawrence, Lowell, Lynn, Brocton, Fall River, and New Bedford, MA. No support for sectarian religious activities, federal, state or municipal agencies or political causes. No grants to individuals, or for deficit financing, or endowment funds.
Publications: Application guidelines; Grants list.
Application information: Applications for all grants, except Small Capital Grants, are by invitation only. Unsolicited applications will not be accepted. See foundation web site for additional application information for the Small Capital Grants program. Application form not required.
Initial approach: Letter
Copies of proposal: 1
Deadline(s): See foundation web site
Board meeting date(s): As needed, 4 or more times per year
Final notification: After board meeting
Officers and Trustees:* Richard A. Smith,* Co-Chair.; Susan F. Smith,* Co-Chair.; Lynne J. Doblin, Exec. Dir.; Amy Smith Berylson; James Berylson; John G. Berylson; Jennifer Berylson Block; Jonathan Block; Elizabeth Berylson Katz; Robert Katz; Andrew Knez; Debra S. Knez; Jessica Knez; Dana W. Smith; Robert A. Smith.
Number of staff: 3 full-time professional; 1 part-time support.
EIN: 237090011
Selected grants: The following grants are a representative sample of this grantmaker's funding activity:
$500,000 to Facing History and Ourselves National Foundation, Brookline, MA, 2013.
$430,000 to Mattapan Community Health Center, Mattapan, MA, 2013.
$365,880 to United Teen Equality Center, Lowell, MA, 2013.
$300,000 to MATCH School Foundation, Match Teacher Residency, Boston, MA, 2013.
$279,607 to Boston Health Care for the Homeless Program, Boston, MA, 2013.
$250,000 to Combined Jewish Philanthropies of Greater Boston, Boston, MA, 2013.
$250,000 to Nurtury, Boston, MA, 2013.
$114,000 to Catholic Charities Archdiocese of Boston, Boston, MA, 2013. For Poverty.
$100,000 to Dana-Farber Cancer Institute, Boston, MA, 2013.
$100,000 to Harvard University, Cambridge, MA, 2013. For Medical.

4278
Cheryl Spencer Memorial Foundation ✧
100 Charles Park Rd.
West Roxbury, MA 02132-4985
Additional address: c/o Aaron Spencer, 69 Farlow Rd., Newton, MA 02458-2457, tel.: (617) 323-9200

Established in 1986 in MA.
Donors: Aaron Spencer; Mark Spencer.
Foundation type: Independent foundation.
Financial data (yr. ended 12/31/13): Assets, $6,268,271 (M); gifts received, $1,000,000; expenditures, $744,656; qualifying distributions, $658,056; giving activities include $658,056 for 28 grants (high: $265,000; low: $250).
Purpose and activities: Giving primarily for Jewish organizations; funding also for education and hospitals, including a children's hospital.
Fields of interest: Higher education; Education; Hospitals (general); Hospitals (specialty); Jewish federated giving programs; Jewish agencies & synagogues.
Limitations: Applications accepted. Giving primarily in MA and New York, NY. No grants to individuals.
Application information: Application form not required.
Initial approach: Proposal
Deadline(s): None
Trustees: Aaron Spencer; Mark Spencer.
EIN: 046360057
Selected grants: The following grants are a representative sample of this grantmaker's funding activity:
$125,000 to Combined Jewish Philanthropies of Greater Boston, Boston, MA, 2011.
$115,000 to American Society of the University of Haifa, New York, NY, 2011.
$20,000 to Maimonides School, Brookline, MA, 2011.
$13,189 to Temple Emanuel, Newton Centre, MA, 2011.
$10,000 to Childrens Hospital League, Boston, MA, 2011.
$5,400 to University of Massachusetts, Amherst, MA, 2011.
$5,000 to Hebrew SeniorLife, Boston, MA, 2011.
$2,000 to Israel Project, Washington, DC, 2011.

4279
Sperling Family Charitable Foundation ✧
4 Moore Rd.
Wayland, MA 01778-1410

Established in 2002 in MA.
Donors: Scott M. Sperling; Laurene M. Sperling.
Foundation type: Independent foundation.
Financial data (yr. ended 06/30/13): Assets, $5,985,502 (M); gifts received, $4,955,899; expenditures, $986,480; qualifying distributions, $973,035; giving activities include $973,000 for 7 grants (high: $370,000; low: $18,000).
Fields of interest: Higher education; Business school/education; Hospitals (general); Jewish federated giving programs; Jewish agencies & synagogues.
Limitations: Applications not accepted. Giving primarily in MA. No grants to individuals.
Application information: Unsolicited requests for funds not accepted.
Trustees: Laurene M. Sperling; Scott M. Sperling.
EIN: 046948423
Selected grants: The following grants are a representative sample of this grantmaker's funding activity:
$100,000 to Building Educated Leaders for Life Foundation, Dorchester, MA, 2011.
$50,000 to New Profit, Boston, MA, 2011.
$5,000 to Anti-Defamation League of Bnai Brith, New York, NY, 2011.

4280
Stephanie H. & David A. Spina Family Foundation ✧
17 Campbell Rd.
Wayland, MA 01778-1001

Established in 2004 in MA.
Donors: Stephanie H. Spina; David A. Spina.
Foundation type: Independent foundation.
Financial data (yr. ended 12/31/13): Assets, $10,176,359 (M); expenditures, $676,289; qualifying distributions, $547,320; giving activities include $545,500 for 28 grants (high: $100,000; low: $500).
Fields of interest: Higher education; Education; Health organizations, association; Human services; Salvation Army; United Ways and Federated Giving Programs; Christian agencies & churches.
Limitations: Applications not accepted. Giving primarily in MA. No grants to individuals.
Application information: Contributes only to pre-selected organizations.
Trustees: David A. Spina; Stephanie H. Spina.
EIN: 202017017
Selected grants: The following grants are a representative sample of this grantmaker's funding activity:
$100,000 to New England Center for Homeless Veterans, Boston, MA, 2012. For Community and Charitable.
$55,000 to American Heart Association, Framingham, MA, 2012. For medical.
$40,000 to Partners in Health, Boston, MA, 2012. For Community and Charitable.
$15,000 to Nativity School of Worcester, Worcester, MA, 2012. For educational.
$5,000 to Planned Parenthood League of Massachusetts, Boston, MA, 2012. For Community and Charitable.
$2,500 to Against the Stream Buddhist Meditation Society, Los Angeles, CA, 2012. For religious.
$1,000 to Sudbury Valley Trustees, Sudbury, MA, 2012. For Community and Charitable.
$500 to New London Barn Playhouse, New London, NH, 2012. For Community and Charitable.

4281
Stamps Family Charitable Foundation, Inc. ✧
c/o Summit Partners
222 Berkeley St., 18th Fl.
Boston, MA 02116-3733

Established in MA.
Donors: Penelope W. Stamps; E. Roe Stamps IV.
Foundation type: Independent foundation.
Financial data (yr. ended 11/30/12): Assets, $82,724,841 (M); gifts received, $788,660; expenditures, $4,846,824; qualifying distributions, $4,687,537; giving activities include $4,537,560 for 72 grants (high: $2,900,000; low: $29), and $35,400 for foundation-administered programs.
Purpose and activities: Giving primarily for the arts and education.
Fields of interest: Arts; Higher education; Education; Health organizations; Human services; Foundations (community).
Limitations: Applications not accepted. Giving primarily in FL, GA, IL and MI. No grants to individuals.
Application information: Contributes only to pre-selected organizations.
Officers: Penelope Stamps, Pres.; David H. Hopfenberg, Clerk; E. Roe Stamps IV, Treas.
EIN: 042943910

4282
Staples Foundation, Inc. ✧
(formerly Staples Foundation for Learning, Inc.)
500 Staples Dr., 4 W.
Framingham, MA 01702-4478 (508) 253-5000
FAX: (508) 253-9600;
E-mail: foundationinfo@staples.com; Main URL: http://www.staplesfoundation.org/
Grants Database: http://www.staplesfoundation.org/grant-recipients-list.php

Established in 2002 in MA.
Donor: Staples, Inc.
Foundation type: Company-sponsored foundation.
Financial data (yr. ended 01/31/13): Assets, $72,967 (M); gifts received, $3,083,000; expenditures, $3,042,400; qualifying distributions, $3,034,200; giving activities include $3,034,200 for 475 grants (high: $600,000; low: $1,000).
Purpose and activities: The foundation supports programs designed to provide education and job skills. Special emphasis is directed toward programs designed to support disadvantaged youth.
Fields of interest: Vocational education; Education, reading; Education; Employment, training; Boys & girls clubs; Youth; Economically disadvantaged.
Type of support: Program development; Curriculum development.
Limitations: Applications not accepted. Giving primarily in CA, CO, GA, MA, NJ, and VA. No support for public schools without 501(c)(3) status, athletic teams, fiscal sponsors, government agencies, substance abuse agencies, discriminatory organizations, international organizations, political organizations, religious organizations not of direct benefit to the entire community, fraternal or veterans' organizations, professional associations, or similar membership groups. No grants to individuals, or for capital campaigns, athletic events, educational loans, travel, conferences or conventions, books, research papers, or articles in professional journals, medical research, or public or commercial broadcasting.
Publications: Annual report; Corporate giving report; Grants list.
Application information: Unsolicited requests for funding are not accepted.
Board meeting date(s): June, Sept., and Jan.
Officers and Directors: John Burke, Pres.; Steve Fund, Exec. V.P.; Erich Rhynhart, Clerk; Laura Granahan, Treas.; Alison Corcoran; Katy Dobbs; Patrick Girard; Gordon Glover; Conor Kearny; Regis Mulot; Neil Ringel; Mary Sagat; Melissa Tetreault.
Number of staff: 2
EIN: 470867951
Selected grants: The following grants are a representative sample of this grantmaker's funding activity:
$1,000,000 to Boys and Girls Clubs of America, Atlanta, GA, 2011.
$25,000 to Boys and Girls Club of Metro West, Marlborough, MA, 2011.
$25,000 to City Year San Jose/Silicon Valley, San Jose, CA, 2011.
$25,000 to Denver Scholarship Foundation, Denver, CO, 2011.
$25,000 to Point Foundation, Los Angeles, CA, 2011.
$20,036 to Rural Alaska Community Action Program, Anchorage, AK, 2011.
$15,000 to Junior Achievement of Central Virginia, Glen Allen, VA, 2011.
$15,000 to Salvation Army, Canton, MA, 2011.
$10,000 to Jewish Family Service of Metrowest, Framingham, MA, 2011.
$10,000 to ProLiteracy Worldwide, Syracuse, NY, 2011.

4283
The Stare Fund ✧
c/o Ropes & Gray
800 Boylston St.
Boston, MA 02199-3600

Established in 1959 in MA.
Donor: Fredrick J. Stare‡.
Foundation type: Independent foundation.
Financial data (yr. ended 11/30/13): Assets, $9,673,557 (M); expenditures, $485,739; qualifying distributions, $445,410; giving activities include $438,967 for 31 grants (high: $68,167; low: $2,000).
Purpose and activities: Giving for health organizations; funding also for the arts and human services.
Fields of interest: Performing arts, orchestras; Arts; Education; Hospitals (general); Health organizations, association; Heart & circulatory research; Human services.
Limitations: Applications not accepted. Giving primarily in IL and MA. No grants to individuals.
Application information: Contributes only to pre-selected organizations.
Trustees: David S. Stare; Fredrick A. Stare; Mary S. Wilkinson.
EIN: 046026648

4284
Starwood Hotels and Resorts Worldwide Foundation, Inc. ✧
(formerly The Sheraton Foundation, Inc.)
155 Federal St., Ste. 700
Boston, MA 02110 (877) 443-4585
Contact: Kristin Meyer, Clerk
E-mail: charitablegiving@starwoodhotels.com; Additional address: 1 Starpoint, Stamford, CT 06902, tel.: (877) 443-4585; Main URL: http://www.starwoodhotels.com/corporate/about/citizenship/foundation.html

Incorporated in 1950 in MA.
Donors: ITT Sheraton Corp.; The Sheraton Corp.; Starwood Hotels & Resorts Worldwide, Inc.
Foundation type: Company-sponsored foundation.
Financial data (yr. ended 12/31/13): Assets, $2,502,376 (M); expenditures, $753,892; qualifying distributions, $703,704; giving activities include $576,811 for 37 grants (high: $53,853; low: $500).
Purpose and activities: The foundation supports organizations involved with education, conservation, workforce development, disaster relief, human services, and community development. Special emphasis is directed toward organizations with a national and international focus.
Fields of interest: Libraries (public); Education, reading; Education; Environment, natural resources; Environment, land resources; Employment, services; Disasters, preparedness/services; Community/economic development; Jewish federated giving programs.
Type of support: General/operating support; Program development; Scholarship funds; Employee volunteer services; Sponsorships; In-kind gifts.
Limitations: Applications accepted. Giving primarily in the CT, Washington, DC, MA, NY, and VA. No grants to individuals, or for endowments, capital campaigns, or research; no matching gifts; no loans.
Publications: Application guidelines.
Application information: The foundation generally practices an invitation-only process for giving, however letters of inquiry are accepted for consideration for future funding. Application form not required.
Initial approach: E-mail letter of inquiry
Deadline(s): None
Board meeting date(s): Monthly
Officers and Director: Sandy Swider, Pres.; Kristin Meyer, Clerk; Nicholas Daddario, Treas.; Kenneth S. Siegel.
Number of staff: 2
EIN: 046039510

4285
State Street Foundation, Inc.
1 Lincoln St
Boston, MA 02111-2900
Contact: Wayne Young, V.P., Global Grants Mgr.
E-mail: wyoung@statestreet.com; E-mail address for international applicants: Europe, Middle East and Africa: statestreet@cafoline.org Asia Pacific: statestreet@give2asia.org; Main URL: http://www.statestreet.com/wps/portal/internet/corporate/home/aboutstatestreet/corporatecitizenship/globalphilanthropy/statestreetfoundation/

Established in 2006 in MA.
Donor: State Street Bank & Trust Co.
Foundation type: Company-sponsored foundation.
Financial data (yr. ended 12/31/13): Assets, $46,353,251 (M); gifts received, $31,318,000; expenditures, $13,722,142; qualifying distributions, $13,718,085; giving activities include $11,072,159 for 328 grants (high: $721,000; low: $500), and $2,566,504 for employee matching gifts.
Purpose and activities: The mission of State Street Foundation's strategic grantmaking program is to contribute to the sustainability of communities where State Street operates, primarily by investing in education and workforce development programs

related to employability for disadvantaged populations.
Fields of interest: Vocational education; Adult/ continuing education; Adult education—literacy, basic skills & GED; Employment, services; Employment, training; Employment; Youth development; Adults; Young adults; Economically disadvantaged.
Type of support: Continuing support; Employee matching gifts; Employee volunteer services; General/operating support; Program development; Sponsorships; Use of facilities.
Limitations: Applications accepted. Giving primarily in areas of company operations in CA, GA, IL, Boston and Quincy, MA, MO, NJ, NY, and PA and in Australia, Austria, Belgium, Canada, Cayman Islands, Europe, France, Germany, India, Ireland, Italy, Japan, Luxembourg, the Middle East, Netherlands, Poland, Qatar, Singapore, South Africa, South Korea, Switzerland, Taiwan, and the United Kingdom. No support for political candidates or organizations, lobbying, labor, or fraternal organizations, or religious organizations not of direct benefit to the entire community. No grants to individuals, or for endowments, political causes or campaigns, sectarian activities for religious organizations, travel, team sponsorships, or sporting events, or medical research or disease specific initiatives.
Publications: Application guidelines; Grants list.
Application information: Applicants may be asked to submit a full grant application. Organizations receiving support are asked to provide a final report. Visit website for nearest community contact information.
Initial approach: Complete online preliminary grant application; e-mail preliminary grant applications for organizations located in the Asia Pacific, Canada, the Cayman Islands, Europe, Middle East, and South Africa
Deadline(s): None for preliminary grant applications
Final notification: 8 weeks for preliminary grant applications
Officers and Directors:* Joseph A. McGrail, Jr., C.O.O.; Michael Scannell, Pres.; Amanda Northrop, V.P.; Simon Zornoza,* Clerk; James J. Malebra,* Treas.; Paul Selian.
EIN: 562615567

4286
Anna B. Stearns Charitable Foundation, Inc. ✧

c/o Fiduciary Trust Co.
P.O. Box 55806
Boston, MA 02205-5806
FAX: (617) 426-7087;
E-mail: kdavid@gmafoundations.com

Established in 1966 in MA.
Donor: Anna B. Stearns†.
Foundation type: Independent foundation.
Financial data (yr. ended 12/31/13): Assets, $15,758,595 (M); expenditures, $735,080; qualifying distributions, $659,830; giving activities include $554,138 for 40 grants (high: $33,000; low: $2,138).
Purpose and activities: The foundation supports projects and organizations that address one or more of the foundation's major interests: 1) to strengthen the education, independence and capabilities of young people, especially girls, and of women and their children; 2) to support the healthy development of girls as the foundation for their adult lives; and 3) to protect and preserve the natural environment.
Fields of interest: Environment; Children/youth, services; Family services; Women, centers/ services; Women; Girls.
Type of support: General/operating support; Continuing support; Program development; Matching/challenge support.
Limitations: Applications not accepted. Giving in the Boston, Cambridge, Somerville, and Chelsea, MA, area. No support for statewide initiatives, or for individual day care programs, crises intervention, family preservation programs, homeless shelters, housing development, medical services, substance abuse, ex-offender programs, or for core educational programs of public, private, parochial or charter schools. No grants for capital campaigns or endowments.
Application information: Unsolicited requests for funds not accepted.
Officers: Kathryn A. Wheeler, Pres.; Katherine L. Babson, Jr., Treas.
Trustees: Leonard Johnson; Katie Smith Milway; Sylvia Simmons; Miren Uriarte.
Number of staff: 2 part-time professional.
EIN: 046144732
Selected grants: The following grants are a representative sample of this grantmaker's funding activity:
$12,500 to Nature Conservancy, Arlington, VA, 2011.

4287
The Steinberg-Lalli Charitable Foundation ✧

P.O. Box 2350
Acton, MA 01720-6350 (978) 263-2989
Contact: Stephen P. Steinberg, Tr.

Established in 2004 in MA.
Donors: Joseph A. Lalli†; Stephen P. Steinberg.
Foundation type: Independent foundation.
Financial data (yr. ended 12/31/13): Assets, $12,390,995 (M); expenditures, $918,031; qualifying distributions, $796,216; giving activities include $796,216 for 16 grants (high: $341,000; low: $1,000).
Fields of interest: Higher education; Education; Health care; Housing/shelter, development; Foundations (public).
Limitations: Applications accepted. Giving primarily in MA.
Application information: Application form required.
Initial approach: Letter
Deadline(s): None
Trustees: Cornelia Steinberg; Randall Steinberg; Stephen P. Steinberg.
EIN: 206184268

4288
The Abbot and Dorothy H. Stevens Foundation ✧

P.O. Box 111
North Andover, MA 01845-0111 (978) 688-7211
Contact: Josh Miner, Exec. Dir.
E-mail: grantprocess@stevensfoundation.com

Trust established in 1953 in MA.
Donor: Abbot Stevens†.
Foundation type: Independent foundation.
Financial data (yr. ended 12/31/13): Assets, $25,309,339 (M); expenditures, $1,541,404; qualifying distributions, $1,305,468; giving activities include $1,305,468 for 89 grants (high: $75,000; low: $100).
Purpose and activities: Giving primarily for the arts, education, conservation, and health and human services.
Fields of interest: Museums; Humanities; Historic preservation/historical societies; Arts; Secondary school/education; Education; Environment, natural resources; Health care; Crime/violence prevention, domestic violence; Youth development; Human services; Children/youth, services; Children/youth; Children; Youth; Adults; Young adults; Disabilities, people with; Physically disabled; Minorities; Hispanics/Latinos; Girls; Immigrants/refugees; Economically disadvantaged.
Type of support: General/operating support; Continuing support; Management development/ capacity building; Capital campaigns; Building/ renovation; Equipment; Endowments; Program development; Technical assistance; Program-related investments/loans; Matching/ challenge support.
Limitations: Applications accepted. Giving limited to MA, with emphasis on the greater Lawrence/ Merrimack Valley area. No support for national organizations, or for state or federal agencies. No grants to individuals, or for annual campaigns, deficit financing, exchange programs, internships, professorships or fellowships.
Publications: Application guidelines; Annual report; IRS Form 990 or 990-PF printed copy available upon request; Program policy statement.
Application information: Associated Grant Makers Common Proposal Form accepted. Application form not required.
Initial approach: Proposal
Copies of proposal: 1
Deadline(s): None
Board meeting date(s): Monthly except in July and Aug.
Final notification: Up to 3 months
Officer and Trustees:* Josh Miner,* Exec. Dir.; Deborah D. Putnam; Christopher W. Rogers.
Number of staff: 1 part-time professional; 1 part-time support.
EIN: 046107991
Selected grants: The following grants are a representative sample of this grantmaker's funding activity:
$50,000 to American Textile History Museum, Lowell, MA, 2012. For operating, split pay 100K 2011 pledge in full.
$30,000 to Groundwork Lawrence, Lawrence, MA, 2012. For new staffing structure and expansion of partnerships.
$25,000 to Christ Church Andover, Andover, MA, 2012. For 2nd on 100K/4 yr. pledged (Nov. 2010) 25K pd. 3/11.
$25,000 to Essex County Community Foundation, Danvers, MA, 2012. For operating-non-profit center/.
$25,000 to Massachusetts 2020, Boston, MA, 2012. For fiscal for Receiver work in Lawrence.
$25,000 to Phillips Academy, Andover, MA, 2012. For Andover Breadloaf Program support.
$20,000 to Andover Village Improvement Society, Andover, MA, 2012. For boost land acquisition fund.
$20,000 to Appalachian Mountain Club, Boston, MA, 2012. For Youth Opportunities Program Lawrence and Lowell.

$15,000 to Endicott College, Beverly, MA, 2012. For Keys to Degrees Program.
$9,000 to Museum of Science, Boston, MA, 2012. For outreach to Lawrence and Lowell visitors.

4289
Nathaniel & Elizabeth P. Stevens Foundation ✧
P.O. Box 111
North Andover, MA 01845-0111 (978) 688-7211
Contact: Joshua L. Miner, Tr.
E-mail: grantprocess@stevensfoundation.com

Trust established in 1943 in MA.
Donor: Nathaniel Stevens†.
Foundation type: Independent foundation.
Financial data (yr. ended 12/31/13): Assets, $19,693,733 (M); expenditures, $1,314,862; qualifying distributions, $1,058,110; giving activities include $1,058,110 for 109 grants (high: $75,000; low: $50).
Fields of interest: Museums (specialized); Humanities; Historic preservation/historical societies; Arts; Secondary school/education; Education; Environment; Health care; Crime/violence prevention, domestic violence; Youth development; Human services; Children/youth, services; Children/youth; Children; Youth; Adults; Young adults; Disabilities, people with; Mentally disabled; Minorities; Hispanics/Latinos; Girls; Young adults, female; Boys; Young adults, male; Immigrants/refugees; Economically disadvantaged.
Type of support: Building/renovation; Capital campaigns; Continuing support; Emergency funds; Endowments; Equipment; General/operating support; Matching/challenge support; Program development; Technical assistance.
Limitations: Applications accepted. Giving limited to MA, with emphasis on the greater Lawrence and Merrimack Valley areas. No support for national organizations, or for state or federal agencies. No grants to individuals, or for deficit financing, exchange programs, internships, lectureships, research, professorships, scholarships, fellowships, or annual campaigns.
Publications: Application guidelines; Program policy statement.
Application information: Associated Grant Makers Common Proposal Form accepted. No more than one application from an agency in the same calendar year is accepted, except for summer youth programs. Application form not required.
Initial approach: Proposal (no more than 5 pages, plus appendices), and a 1-page cover letter summarizing the proposal
Copies of proposal: 1
Deadline(s): None
Board meeting date(s): Monthly except July and Aug.
Final notification: Up to 3 months
Trustees: Joshua L. Miner IV; Deborah D. Putnam; Christopher W. Rogers.
Number of staff: 1 part-time professional; 1 part-time support.
EIN: 042236996
Selected grants: The following grants are a representative sample of this grantmaker's funding activity:
$25,000 to Lazarus House, Lawrence, MA, 2012. For capital campaign-1st pay on 2011 of 125K over 3 yrs.
$18,000 to Jericho Road Project, Concord, MA, 2012. For operating support - Lowell Programming.
$13,000 to YWCA of Greater Lawrence, Lawrence, MA, 2012. For Phase I of air conditioning installation.
$10,000 to Northern Essex Community College, Haverhill, MA, 2012. For Betty Beland endowed scholarship seed.
$9,000 to Coalition for a Better Acre, Lowell, MA, 2012. For foreclosure prevention Program.
$9,000 to Greater Boston Food Bank, Boston, MA, 2012. For Merrimack Valley Food Distribution Program.
$8,000 to CLASS, Lawrence, MA, 2012. For Community Inclusion project.
$6,000 to Lowell Transitional Living Center, Lowell, MA, 2012. For Winter Emergency Bed Program.
$6,000 to Presentation of Mary Academy, Methuen, MA, 2012. For tuition assistance Lawrence students.
$4,500 to Discovery Museums, Acton, MA, 2012. For admissions and outreach to Merrimack Valley.

4290
Stevenson Family Charitable Trust ✧ ☆
31 Fayerweather St.
Cambridge, MA 02138-3329

Established in 1989 in MA.
Donor: Howard H. Stevenson.
Foundation type: Independent foundation.
Financial data (yr. ended 12/31/12): Assets, $6,023,308 (M); gifts received, $20,000; expenditures, $994,845; qualifying distributions, $946,128; giving activities include $946,128 for grants.
Purpose and activities: Giving primarily for education and human services.
Fields of interest: Arts; Elementary/secondary education; Higher education; Education; Environment, natural resources; Hospitals (specialty); Human services.
Limitations: Applications not accepted. Giving primarily in MA. No grants to individuals.
Application information: Contributes only to pre-selected organizations.
Trustees: Fredericka O. Stevenson; Howard H. Stevenson.
EIN: 046629590

4291
The Genevieve McMillan-Reba Stewart Foundation ✧ ☆
17 Walpole St.
Norwood, MA 02062-3318

Established in 2002 in MA.
Donors: Genevieve McMillan; Genevieve McMillan Living Trust.
Foundation type: Independent foundation.
Financial data (yr. ended 12/31/13): Assets, $12,463,191 (M); gifts received, $1,805,850; expenditures, $759,485; qualifying distributions, $610,450; giving activities include $610,450 for 25 grants (high: $62,370; low: $500).
Fields of interest: Arts education; Museums (art).
Limitations: Applications not accepted. Giving primarily in Boston, MA. No grants to individuals.
Application information: Unsolicited requests for funds not accepted.
Trustees: John E. Fedele; Kibebe Gizaw; Catherina LaLanne Gobet; Nancy Murray; Anne-Marie Stein.
EIN: 562293792

4292
Stifler Family Foundation ✧ ☆
100 Codman Rd.
Brookline, MA 02445-7555 (617) 357-9876
Contact: Lawrence T.P. Stifler, Tr.

Established in 2001 in MA.
Donors: Lawrence T.P. Stifler; Mary McFadden; Health Management Resources Corp.
Foundation type: Independent foundation.
Financial data (yr. ended 12/31/13): Assets, $40,964,831 (M); gifts received, $30,000,000; expenditures, $682,564; qualifying distributions, $547,605; giving activities include $547,605 for 81 grants (high: $280,000; low: $200).
Purpose and activities: Giving primarily for environmental conservation and protection.
Fields of interest: Education; Environment; Human services.
Type of support: General/operating support.
Limitations: Applications accepted. Giving primarily in MA and ME. No grants to individuals.
Application information: Application form required.
Initial approach: Letter
Deadline(s): None
Trustees: Mary McFadden; Lawrence T.P. Stifler.
EIN: 106001398

4293
The Stoddard Charitable Trust ✧
370 Main St., 12th Fl.
Worcester, MA 01608-1779 (508) 459-8000
Contact: Warner S. Fletcher, Chair.

Trust established in 1939 in MA.
Donor: Harry G. Stoddard†.
Foundation type: Independent foundation.
Financial data (yr. ended 12/31/12): Assets, $77,952,642 (M); expenditures, $4,533,745; qualifying distributions, $4,110,025; giving activities include $3,905,314 for 110 grants (high: $250,000; low: $5).
Purpose and activities: Giving primarily for education, cultural programs, youth agencies, social services, environmental concerns, and health associations. The trust's primary focus is on support for private nonprofits and on support other than operating support.
Fields of interest: Museums (art); Arts; Higher education; Education; Botanical gardens; Environment; Health organizations, association; Human services; Children/youth, services; Community/economic development.
Type of support: General/operating support; Continuing support; Annual campaigns; Capital campaigns; Building/renovation; Equipment; Land acquisition; Emergency funds; Seed money; Matching/challenge support.
Limitations: Applications accepted. Giving almost exclusively in the Worcester, MA area. No support for religious or political organizations. No grants to individuals.
Application information: Initial approach by telephone is recommended for potential new grant recipients. Application form not required.
Initial approach: Letter
Copies of proposal: 5

Deadline(s): Mar. 1, June 1, Sept. 1, and Dec. 1
Board meeting date(s): Mar., June, Sept., and Dec.
Final notification: Within one month of distribution meeting at which grant request is considered
Officers and Trustees:* Warner S. Fletcher,* Chair.; Valerie S. Loring,* Secy.; Judith S. King,* Treas.; Allen W. Fletcher.
EIN: 046023791

4294
Robert F. Stoico/FIRSTFED Charitable Foundation ✧
P.O. Box 438
Swansea, MA 02777-0438
Contact: Cecilia Viveiros, Exec. Dir.
FAX: (508) 300-2588;
E-mail: Cecilia@stoicofirstfed.org; Main URL: http://www.stoicofirstfed.org

Established in 1997 in MA.
Foundation type: Independent foundation.
Financial data (yr. ended 03/31/13): Assets, $15,346,614 (M); expenditures, $1,027,331; qualifying distributions, $879,472; giving activities include $763,070 for 36 grants (high: $100,000; low: $50).
Purpose and activities: Giving primarily for housing opportunities for: 1) low income or indigent citizens; 2) job development, particularly for low-income, immigrant and student communities; 3) educational programs; 4) arts and cultural programs that benefit the public or the traditionally underserved; and 4) accessible healthcare for all.
Fields of interest: Arts; Education; Health care; Employment, training; Housing/shelter, development; Economically disadvantaged.
Type of support: General/operating support; Continuing support; Annual campaigns; Capital campaigns; Building/renovation; Equipment; Debt reduction; Seed money; Scholarship funds.
Limitations: Applications accepted. Giving primarily in southeastern MA and RI. No support for individual schools or athletic or political organizations, or for fraternal organizations. No grants to individuals.
Publications: Application guidelines; Grants list; Occasional report.
Application information: Application forms available on foundation web site, or e-mail Cecilia Viveiros for form. Application form required.
Initial approach: 1-page letter on organization letterhead (for small grants under $5,001); Refer to guidelines on foundation web site for grants over $5,000. Applications may be sent via U.S. mail or fax
Copies of proposal: 1
Deadline(s): None (for small grants); Feb. 28, May 31, Aug. 31, and Nov. 30 (for large grants)
Board meeting date(s): Twice yearly
Final notification: 8 weeks
Officers and Directors:* Robert F. Stoico,* Chair., C.E.O. and Pres.; Cecilia Viveiros, Exec. Dir.; Peter Panaggio, Treas.
Number of staff: 2 full-time professional; 1 part-time professional.
EIN: 043343529
Selected grants: The following grants are a representative sample of this grantmaker's funding activity:
$75,000 to University of Massachusetts, Amherst, MA, 2012.

4295
James M. Stoneman Charitable Fund ✧
(formerly James and Selma Stoneman Charitable Fund)
c/o Robert J. Morrissey, Tr.
1 International Pl., 32nd Fl.
Boston, MA 02110-2602

Established in 1981 in MA.
Donors: James M. Stoneman; Marjorie R. Zuckerwar; Marjorie Zuckerwar Trust.
Foundation type: Independent foundation.
Financial data (yr. ended 06/30/13): Assets, $39,572,303 (M); gifts received, $11,358; expenditures, $2,799,546; qualifying distributions, $2,354,613; giving activities include $2,354,613 for 19 grants (high: $1,000,000; low: $695).
Purpose and activities: Giving primarily for health associations and hospitals, including a children's hospital; funding also for other children and youth services, and education.
Fields of interest: Education; Hospitals (general); Hospitals (specialty); Health organizations, association; Cancer research; Children/youth, services; Jewish federated giving programs.
Limitations: Applications not accepted. Giving primarily in MA. No grants to individuals.
Application information: Contributes only to pre-selected organizations.
Trustees: Robert J. Morrissey; James M. Stoneman; Thea Stoneman.
EIN: 042741931
Selected grants: The following grants are a representative sample of this grantmaker's funding activity:
$400,000 to Massachusetts General Hospital, Boston, MA, 2011. For general support.
$367,040 to Cape Cod Healthcare Foundation, Hyannis, MA, 2011. For general support.
$250,000 to Children's Hospital Corporation, Boston, MA, 2011. For general support.
$100,000 to Boca Raton Regional Hospital Foundation, Boca Raton, FL, 2011. For general support.
$50,000 to Boston College, Chestnut Hill, MA, 2011. For general support.
$25,000 to Multiple Sclerosis Society, National, New York, NY, 2011. For general support.
$10,000 to Mount Sinai Medical Center Foundation, Miami Beach, FL, 2011. For general support.
$5,000 to YouthBuild USA, Somerville, MA, 2011. For general support.
$1,000 to American Cancer Society, Oklahoma City, OK, 2011. For general support.
$1,000 to Pan-Massachusetts Challenge, Needham, MA, 2011. For general support.

4296
Stoneman Family Foundation ✧
(formerly Anne and David Stoneman Charitable Foundation, Inc.)
c/o Goulstin & Storrs
400 Atlantic Ave.
Boston, MA 02110-3333 (617) 482-1776
Contact: Julia M. Toulmin

Incorporated in 1957 in MA.
Donors: Sidney Stoneman†; Miriam Stoneman†.
Foundation type: Independent foundation.
Financial data (yr. ended 12/31/12): Assets, $114,877,596 (M); expenditures, $7,822,799; qualifying distributions, $6,433,771; giving activities include $5,888,300 for 75 grants (high: $400,000; low: $2,500).
Purpose and activities: Giving to help low-income people achieve independence and economic self-sufficiency, and to improve the well-being of society by promoting economic justice.
Fields of interest: Education; Human services; Social sciences, public policy.
Type of support: General/operating support; Program development; Mission-related investments/loans.
Limitations: Applications not accepted. Giving primarily in Washington, DC, MA, and New York, NY. No grants to individuals.
Application information: Contributes only to pre-selected organizations.
Officers and Directors:* Elizabeth Deknatel,* Co-Chair.; Eric Stein, Co-Chair.; Jane Stein, Treas.; Gabriel Deknatel; Maria Deknatel; Alan Rottenberg; Gerda Stein; David Wood.
Number of staff: None.
EIN: 046047379

4297
Stop & Shop/Giant Family Foundation, Inc. ✧
(formerly The Stop & Shop Family Foundation)
1385 Hancock St.
Quincy, MA 02169-5103

Established in 2002.
Donors: The Stop & Shop Supermarket Co.; The Stop & Shop Supermarket Co. LLC; Ahold Financial Services, LLC.
Foundation type: Company-sponsored foundation.
Financial data (yr. ended 12/31/11): Assets, $7,819,623 (M); gifts received, $1,818; expenditures, $1,697,903; qualifying distributions, $1,280,200; giving activities include $1,280,200 for 27 grants (high: $238,850; low: $500).
Purpose and activities: The foundation supports organizations involved with education, health, hunger, and children.
Fields of interest: Health care; Agriculture/food; Human services.
Limitations: Applications not accepted. Giving primarily in areas of company operations in CT, Washington, DC, MA, NJ, and NY.
Application information: Contributes only to pre-selected organizations.
Officers and Directors:* Carl Schlicker,* Pres.; Thomas Hippler,* Secy.; Patricia King,* Treas.; Jeffrey Martin; Tracy Pawelski; Paula Price; Bhavdeep Singh.
EIN: 043548392

4298
Strategic Grant Partners, Inc. ✧
240 Newbury St., 2nd Fl.
Boston, MA 02116-2580

Established in 2002 in MA.
Donors: James Pallotta; Kimberly Pallotta; Michael Stansky; Jill Stansky; Robert Forlenza; Karen Forlenza; William Helman; Daisy Helman; Martin Mannion; Tristin Mannion; Lourdes Peri Samuels; Maurice Samuels; Klarman Family Foundation; Wade Rubinstein; Jill Block; Phillip and Elizabeth Gross Family Foundation; Jacobson Family Foundation; Josh and Anita Bekenstein Charitable Fund; Frieze Family Foundation; Mannion Family

Foundation; Larson Family Foundation; Robert and Michelle Cooke Foundation; Tishman Family Foundation; Bright Angel Foundation; Abrams Foundation, Inc.; The Edgerley Family Foundation.
Foundation type: Independent foundation.
Financial data (yr. ended 06/30/13): Assets, $152,553 (M); gifts received, $2,138,799; expenditures, $2,678,694; qualifying distributions, $1,966,398; giving activities include $1,966,398 for grants.
Purpose and activities: Giving primarily for education and human services.
Fields of interest: Elementary/secondary education; Higher education; Education; Human services; Children/youth, services; Foundations (public).
Limitations: Applications not accepted. Giving primarily in MA. No grants to individuals.
Application information: Contributes only to pre-selected organizations.
Officers: Joanna Jacobson, Pres. and Managing Dir.; Phill Gross, Treas.; Stephanie Dodson, Clerk; Barbara Sullivan, Mgr.
EIN: 460512638
Selected grants: The following grants are a representative sample of this grantmaker's funding activity:
$635,000 to Centering Healthcare Institute, Boston, MA, 2012. For capacity building and evaluation.
$575,000 to Stand for Children Leadership Center, Boston, MA, 2012. For capacity building.
$488,000 to UP Education Network, Boston, MA, 2013. For start-up support.
$400,000 to Youth Villages, Memphis, TN, 2013. To expand Intercept Services delivery into Massachusetts. Intercept Services is a prevention, early warning system to prevent/treat parent-child programs.
$375,000 to Youth Villages, Memphis, TN, 2012. To expand Intercept Services Delivery in MA.
$350,000 to Edward Brooke Charter School, Roslindale, MA, 2012. For new facility, fundraising and capacity building.
$325,000 to More Than Words, Waltham, MA, 2012. For capacity building.
$307,000 to More Than Wheels, Keene, NH, 2012. For capacity building launch in Massachusetts.
$300,000 to ROCA, Chelsea, MA, 2012. For high-risk youth intervention model in Chelsea, Revere and East Boston.
$288,000 to Harvard University, Cambridge, MA, 2013. For capacity building for EdLab, research, design and development unit at Teachers College, Columbia University in New York.
$240,000 to Boston College, Chestnut Hill, MA, 2012. For capacity building and evaluation of City Connects program.
$200,000 to Summer Search Boston, Jamaica Plain, MA, 2012. To scale up organization and for capacity building.
$150,000 to More Than Wheels, Boston, MA, 2013. For capacity building and to launch in Massachusetts.
$150,000 to Urban Teacher Residency United, Chicago, IL, 2012. For capacity building.
$120,000 to Boston College, Lynch School of Education, Chestnut Hill, MA, 2013. To scale up City Connects (FKA Boston Connects) and conduct capacity building and evaluation. City Connects is a program designed to meet the needs of urban school students, helping hem thrive in school, improving academic performance and narrowing the achievement gap.
$100,000 to Centering Healthcare Institute, Boston, MA, 2013. To evaulate capacity building efforts.
$100,000 to Stand for Children Leadership Center, Boston, MA, 2013. For capacity building.
$70,000 to Raising A Reader Massachusetts, Boston, MA, 2013. To scale RAR-MA.
$50,000 to Edward Brooke Charter School, Roslindale, MA, 2013. To secure new facility, build internalfundraising and for capacity building.

4299
Sudbury Foundation ✧
326 Concord Rd.
Sudbury, MA 01776-1819 (978) 443-0849
Contact: Marilyn Martino, Exec. Dir.
FAX: (978) 579-9536;
E-mail: contact@sudburyfoundation.org; Main URL: http://www.sudburyfoundation.org
Blog: http://www.sudburyfoundation.org/sudbury-foundation-blog/
Twitter: http://twitter.com/SudburyFdn

Trust established in 1952 in MA.
Donors: Esther M. Atkinson‡; Herbert J. Atkinson‡.
Foundation type: Independent foundation.
Financial data (yr. ended 12/31/13): Assets, $32,912,658 (M); expenditures, $1,618,564; qualifying distributions, $1,505,639; giving activities include $844,415 for 39 grants (high: $100,000; low: $4,500), and $291,764 for 57 grants to individuals (high: $8,000; low: $5,000).
Purpose and activities: Scholarships to residents of Sudbury, Lincoln or Boston, MA, who are graduating from Lincoln-Sudbury Regional High School or are dependents of employees of the Town of Sudbury; support also for community building and civic issues, the environment, local social services, and arts and culture.
Fields of interest: Arts; Environment; Human services; Youth, services; Community/economic development.
Type of support: Program evaluation; Management development/capacity building; Consulting services; Program development; Scholarships—to individuals; Matching/challenge support.
Limitations: Applications accepted. Giving primarily in Sudbury, MA, and surrounding towns. No support for sectarian religious activities. No grants to individuals (except for the scholarship program), or for ongoing operating support, deficit financing, general appeals, or graduate study.
Publications: Application guidelines; Financial statement; Informational brochure; Program policy statement.
Application information: Unsolicited requests for funds are not accepted for the Environmental Program. Program and application information and forms are available on foundation web site. Application form required.
Initial approach: Telephone inquiries and concept papers are welcome prior to proposal submission
Copies of proposal: 1
Deadline(s): Feb. 1 for Atkinson Scholarships; Jan. 1, Apr. 1, July 1, and Oct. 1 for The Sudbury Program
Board meeting date(s): Dates available on request
Final notification: 2 months
Officer: Marilyn Martino, Exec. Dir.
Trustees: Susan Iuliano, Chair.; Miner Crary; Richard H. Davison; Jill M. Stansky; Bank of America, N.A.
Number of staff: 1 full-time professional; 1 part-time professional.
EIN: 046037026
Selected grants: The following grants are a representative sample of this grantmaker's funding activity:
$8,870 to Lincoln-Sudbury Regional High School, Sudbury, MA, 2012. For Sudbury.
$7,950 to United Way of Tri-County, Framingham, MA, 2012. For CY and F.

4300
Sudireddy Foundation, Inc. ✧ ☆
15 Cormiers Way
Andover, MA 01810-2879

Donor: Ramakrishna R. Sudireddy.
Foundation type: Independent foundation.
Financial data (yr. ended 11/30/13): Assets, $449,282 (M); gifts received, $1,435,175; expenditures, $1,000,317; qualifying distributions, $1,000,000; giving activities include $1,000,000 for 1 grant.
Fields of interest: Higher education; Theological school/education; Education.
Limitations: Applications not accepted. Giving primarily in Cambridge, MA.
Application information: Unsolicited requests for funds not accepted.
Directors: Ramakrishna R. Sudireddy; Santha K. Sudireddy.
EIN: 463480804

4301
Swartz Foundation ✧
c/o Ropes & Gray LLP
800 Boylston St.
Boston, MA 02199-3600 (617) 951-7000
Contact: Janet C. Taylor, Philanthropic Advisor

Established in 1994 in MA.
Donors: Sidney W. Swartz; Judith W. Swartz.
Foundation type: Independent foundation.
Financial data (yr. ended 12/31/12): Assets, $226,162,423 (M); expenditures, $17,349,933; qualifying distributions, $16,595,213; giving activities include $16,490,905 for 31 grants (high: $9,007,000; low: $500), and $104,308 for foundation-administered programs.
Purpose and activities: Giving primarily to Jewish organizations for medical research, as well as to Jewish temples and federated giving programs; funding also for social services, and education.
Fields of interest: Medical research, institute; Human services; Jewish federated giving programs; Jewish agencies & synagogues; Women.
Type of support: General/operating support; Capital campaigns; Program development.
Limitations: Applications not accepted. Giving primarily in eastern MA, and Palm Beach, FL. No grants to individuals.
Application information: Contributes only to pre-selected organizations.
Trustees: Robert N. Shapiro; Sydney Swartz.
EIN: 043255974
Selected grants: The following grants are a representative sample of this grantmaker's funding activity:
$9,007,000 to Hadassah, The Womens Zionist Organization of America, New York, NY, 2012. For general support.

$5,003,290 to Combined Jewish Philanthropies of Greater Boston, Boston, MA, 2012. For general support.
$1,000,000 to American Israel Education Foundation, Washington, DC, 2012. For general support.
$1,000,000 to Friends of Israel David, Bellmawr, NJ, 2012. For general support.
$100,000 to PEF Israel Endowment Funds, New York, NY, 2012. For general support.
$50,000 to Jewish Federation of South Palm Beach County, Boca Raton, FL, 2012. For general support.
$25,000 to Robin Hood Foundation, New York, NY, 2012. For general support.
$10,000 to Chabad Lubavitch of the North Shore, Swampscott, MA, 2012. For general support.

4302
Sweet Water Trust ✧
1 Short St.
Northampton, MA 01060-2567
Contact: Eve Endicott, Exec Dir.

Established in 1991 in MA.
Donor: Walker G. Buckner, Jr.
Foundation type: Independent foundation.
Financial data (yr. ended 12/31/13): Assets, $28,928,095 (M); expenditures, $1,358,738; qualifying distributions, $984,005; giving activities include $895,000 for 4 grants (high: $460,000; low: $35,000).
Purpose and activities: Support for environmental preservation through its Land Protection Program: Wildlands, Wildwaters - to help purchase land and conservation easements. The trust seeks partners (land trusts, government agencies, businesses and individuals) to work toward the ecological and biotic health of New England by establishing, enlarging, and connecting reserve areas. Grants range from $1,000-$1,000,000 for land acquisition.
Fields of interest: Environment, natural resources; Environment, water resources; Environment, land resources; Animals/wildlife, preservation/protection; Biology/life sciences.
Type of support: Land acquisition; Technical assistance; Matching/challenge support.
Limitations: Giving generally limited to New England and upstate NY; giving also to Canada. No support for projects for the protection of farmland, timberlands, parks, and trails unless they are a small part of a reserve design of a natural area which exceeds 10,000 acres. No grants to individuals, or for operating support or scientific studies (unless tied to qualifying land project that has received approval).
Publications: Application guidelines; Grants list.
Application information: After preliminary contact, grant application is by invitation only. Application form not required.
Copies of proposal: 1
Deadline(s): None
Board meeting date(s): Bi-monthly
Final notification: Varies
Officer: Eve Endicott, Exec. Dir.
Trustee: Walker G. Buckner, Jr.
Number of staff: 1 full-time professional; 1 part-time professional.
EIN: 043118545
Selected grants: The following grants are a representative sample of this grantmaker's funding activity:
$300,000 to Forest Society of Maine, Bangor, ME, 2012. To support of FSM's Work to Protect Forests in Maine As Forever Wild Ecological Reserves.
$150,000 to Penobscot River Restoration Trust, Augusta, ME, 2012. To support of Re-Wilding of the Penobscot River Through Dam Removal and Other Work.
$15,000 to Sierra Club Foundation, San Francisco, CA, 2012. For Maine Woods East-West Highway Campaign.
$12,000 to Appalachian Mountain Club, Boston, MA, 2012. To support T Decommission Roads and Restore Streams and Fish Habitat at Katahdin Iron Works Ecological Reserve Tract.

4303
The Sidney A. Swensrud Foundation ✧
(formerly Sidney A. Swensrud Charitable Trust)
88 Broad St., 2nd Fl.
Boston, MA 02110-3407

Established in 1955 in MA.
Donors: Jeffrey F. Swegler; Leslie R. Swensrud; S. Blake Swensrud II; Anthony S. Swensrud.
Foundation type: Independent foundation.
Financial data (yr. ended 12/31/13): Assets, $19,701,098 (M); expenditures, $1,101,182; qualifying distributions, $920,000; giving activities include $920,000 for 25 grants (high: $250,000; low: $5,000).
Purpose and activities: Giving primarily for higher education, historical preservation, hospitals, including children's hospitals, and public policy, including immigration reform.
Fields of interest: Historic preservation/historical societies; Higher education; Hospitals (specialty); Health care; Human services; Public policy, research; Public affairs; Immigrants/refugees.
Limitations: Applications not accepted. Giving primarily in MA; funding also in Washington, DC. No grants to individuals.
Application information: Unsolicited requests for funds not accepted.
Trustees: Nancy S. Anthony; Dozier Gardner.
EIN: 256050238

4304
Taunton Female Charitable Association ✧ ☆
P.O. Box 704
Raynham Center, MA 02768-0704

Established in 1816 in MA.
Foundation type: Independent foundation.
Financial data (yr. ended 12/31/12): Assets, $14,067 (M); expenditures, $1,345,057; qualifying distributions, $1,325,000; giving activities include $1,325,000 for 12 grants (high: $184,100; low: $10,000).
Fields of interest: Youth development; Human services; Residential/custodial care, hospices.
Limitations: Applications not accepted. Giving primarily in Taunton, MA. No grants to individuals.
Application information: Unsolicited requests for funds not accepted.
Officers: Christine Bisio, Pres.; Karen Ives, Secy.; Michael J. Leahy, Treas.
Directors: Margaret Borden; Nancy Hambly; Virginia Lemaire; Alexandra McNamee.
EIN: 042105743

4305
TBL Charitable Foundation ✧
15 Charlesden Park
Newtonville, MA 02460-2207 (617) 332-0705
Contact: F. Thomson Leighton, Tr.

Established in 2006 in MA.
Donors: F. Thomas Leighton; Ellis Charitable Trust; The February Charitable Trust; Seville Charitable Trust; Solstice Trust.
Foundation type: Independent foundation.
Financial data (yr. ended 12/31/13): Assets, $13,616,921 (M); gifts received, $3,589,670; expenditures, $632,589; qualifying distributions, $551,125; giving activities include $546,000 for 9 grants (high: $250,000; low: $5,000).
Fields of interest: Engineering school/education; Science, formal/general education.
Limitations: Applications accepted. Giving primarily in MA.
Application information: Application form not required.
Initial approach: Proposal
Deadline(s): None
Trustee: F. Thomson Leighton.
EIN: 203982689

4306
Technical Training Foundation ✧
1429 Osgood St.
North Andover, MA 01845-1012 (978) 685-1553
Contact: Ann Nelson

Established in 1985 in MA.
Donors: Ibrahim Hefni; Wensley Hefni.
Foundation type: Independent foundation.
Financial data (yr. ended 08/31/13): Assets, $68,816,812 (M); expenditures, $2,415,695; qualifying distributions, $1,907,294; giving activities include $1,506,513 for 13 grants (high: $400,000; low: $250).
Purpose and activities: Giving primarily for scientific and technical training education.
Fields of interest: Higher education; Engineering/technology.
Limitations: Giving on a national basis.
Application information: Application form required.
Initial approach: Letter
Copies of proposal: 1
Deadline(s): None
Board meeting date(s): As necessary
Officer: Ann Nelson, Cont.
Trustees: Wensley Hefni; Suzanne Wright.
Number of staff: 2 part-time professional.
EIN: 042864138

4307
Thomas Thompson Trust
c/o Rackemann, Sawyer & Brewster
160 Federal St., 15th Fl.
Boston, MA 02110-1700
Contact: Susan T. Monahan, Tr.
FAX: (617) 542-7437;
E-mail: smonahan@rackemann.com; Main URL: http://thomasthompsontrust.org/

Trust established in 1869 in MA.
Donor: Thomas Thompson‡.
Foundation type: Independent foundation.

Financial data (yr. ended 05/31/14): Assets, $15,404,951 (M); expenditures, $691,617; qualifying distributions, $635,240; giving activities include $553,050 for 32 grants (high: $100,000; low: $1,200).
Purpose and activities: The foundation makes grants to charitable organizations whose work and purposes promote health, education or the general social or civic betterment in the stated geographical areas. However, the foundation will continue to place particular emphasis on health care and other social services.
Fields of interest: Arts; Education; Health care; Human services; Children/youth, services; Community/economic development.
Type of support: Capital campaigns; Building/renovation; Equipment; Emergency funds; Program development; Matching/challenge support.
Limitations: Applications accepted. Giving limited to Dutchess County, NY, particularly in Rhinebeck, and in Windham County, VT, primarily in Brattleboro. No grants to individuals (except for designated women), or for operating budgets, continuing support, seed money, deficit financing, endowment funds, scholarships, or fellowships; no loans.
Publications: Application guidelines.
Application information: Grants awarded only to organizations that have been in operation for 3 consecutive years. DVDs or videos are not accepted Applications must be submitted on line at www.cybergrants.com/thompson. Application form available on foundation web site; AGM Common Proposal Form accepted. Application form required.
Initial approach: E-mail to Susan T. Monahan
Copies of proposal: 1
Deadline(s): See foundation web site for current deadlines
Board meeting date(s): Varies, see foundation web site
Trustees: Susan T. Monahan; Maura E. Murphy, Esq.; Michael F. O'Connell.
Number of staff: None.
EIN: 030179429
Selected grants: The following grants are a representative sample of this grantmaker's funding activity:
$75,000 to Northern Dutchess Hospital Foundation, Rhinebeck, NY, 2013. For Burning the Thompson House Mortgage.
$25,000 to Brattleboro Arts Initiative, Brattleboro, VT, 2013. For A Campaign for The Heavens and the Earth.
$25,000 to Brattleboro Retreat, Brattleboro, VT, 2013. For Next 100 Initiative.
$15,000 to Windham Child Care Association, Brattleboro, VT, 2013. For early learning express expansion.
$15,000 to Windham Southeast Supervisory Union, Brattleboro, VT, 2013. For Social Competency Development Curriculum.
$11,600 to Our Place Drop-In Center, Bellows Falls, VT, 2013. For Fundraising and Strategic Plan Development.
$10,000 to Windham Child Care Association, Brattleboro, VT, 2013. For Bookmobile Program transition.
$4,200 to Vermont Independent Media, Brattleboro, VT, 2013. For The Media Mentoring Program.
$3,350 to Vermont Jazz Center, Brattleboro, VT, 2013. For Vermont Jazz Center Community Scholarship Fund.

4308
The TJX Foundation, Inc. ✧
(formerly Zayre Foundation, Inc.)
c/o The TJX Cos., Inc.
770 Cochituate Rd., Rte. 300-1BN
Framingham, MA 01701-4666 (774) 308-3199
Contact: Christine A. Strickland, Mgr.
FAX: (774) 308-5722;
E-mail: TJX_Foundation@TJX.com; Main URL: http://www.tjx.com/corporate_community_foundation.asp

Incorporated in 1966 in MA.
Donors: The TJX Cos., Inc.; Marshalls of MA, Inc.
Foundation type: Company-sponsored foundation.
Financial data (yr. ended 02/01/14): Assets, $39,630,915 (M); gifts received, $8,487,774; expenditures, $11,306,893; qualifying distributions, $10,954,236; giving activities include $10,954,236 for 1,708 grants (high: $500,000; low: $1,000).
Purpose and activities: The foundation supports programs designed to provide basic-need services to disadvantaged women, children, and families. Special emphasis is directed toward programs designed to promote strong families; provide emergency shelter; enhance education and job readiness; and build community ties.
Fields of interest: Vocational education; Adult education—literacy, basic skills & GED; Education, ESL programs; Education; Health care, infants; Reproductive health, prenatal care; Substance abuse, services; Mental health, counseling/support groups; Genetic diseases and disorders; Alzheimer's disease; Medical research; Crime/violence prevention, domestic violence; Food services; Housing/shelter, temporary shelter; Disasters, preparedness/services; Youth development, adult & child programs; Youth development; American Red Cross; Children, adoption; Children, services; Family services; Family services, domestic violence; Residential/custodial care; Residential/custodial care, hospices; Developmentally disabled, centers & services; Independent living, disability; Civil rights, race/intergroup relations; Civil/human rights; Children; Disabilities, people with; Women; AIDS, people with; Economically disadvantaged.
Type of support: General/operating support; Continuing support; Program development.
Limitations: Applications accepted. Giving on a national basis in areas of company operations, with emphasis on MA. No support for political, fraternal, or international organizations. No grants to individuals, or for capital campaigns, cash reserves, computer purchases, conferences, seminars, consultant fees, salaries, conventions, education loans, endowments, fellowships, films, photography, renovation, new construction, publications, public policy research, advocacy, seed money, travel, or transportation.
Publications: Application guidelines; Corporate giving report; Program policy statement.
Application information: Additional information may be requested at a later date. Application form required.
Initial approach: Complete online eligibility quiz and application form
Copies of proposal: 1
Deadline(s): Dec. 15, Mar. 2, and June 29
Board meeting date(s): Week of Mar. 30, June 22, and Oct. 19
Final notification: 4 to 6 weeks following board meeting
Officers and Directors:* Bernard Cammarata,* Chair. and Pres.; Scott Goldenberg,* V.P.; Paul Kangas, V.P.; Carol Meyrowitz, V.P.; Mary B. Reynolds, V.P.; Ann McCauley, Secy.
Number of staff: 3 full-time professional.
EIN: 042399760
Selected grants: The following grants are a representative sample of this grantmaker's funding activity:
$500,000 to Tix for Tots, Saint Paul, MN, 2013.
$333,000 to Alzheimers Association, Atlanta, GA, 2013.
$300,000 to Save the Children Federation, Fairfield, CT, 2013.
$100,000 to Boys and Girls Clubs of America, Atlanta, GA, 2013.
$50,000 to Catholic Schools Foundation, Boston, MA, 2013.
$50,000 to Easter Seals Massachusetts, Boston, MA, 2013.
$25,000 to UNICEF-New England, Cambridge, MA, 2013.
$10,000 to Posse Foundation, New York, NY, 2013.
$5,000 to Kids in Distress, Wilton Manors, FL, 2013.
$5,000 to Leukemia & Lymphoma Society, White Plains, NY, 2013.

4309
Towards Sustainability Foundation ✧
c/o David Olaksen, Eastern Bank
265 Franklin St.
Boston, MA 02110-3120
Application address: Susan K. Syversen, c/o Eastern Bank, 605 Broadway, LF41, Saugus, MA 01906, tel.: (781) 581-4275

Established in 1997 in MA.
Donor: Jeannette W. Renshaw†.
Foundation type: Independent foundation.
Financial data (yr. ended 09/30/13): Assets, $12,980,504 (M); expenditures, $701,604; qualifying distributions, $562,270; giving activities include $562,270 for 28 grants (high: $101,000; low: $5,000).
Purpose and activities: The foundation supports public charities that help promote the efficient use of the earth's natural resources and human capital towards a balanced carrying capacity that can support all living organisms fairly and justly.
Fields of interest: Education; Environment, association; Environment, natural resources; Environment; Reproductive health, family planning; Agriculture/food, research; Agriculture/food, formal/general education.
Limitations: Applications accepted. Giving primarily in Washington, DC, MA, NY, and Philadelphia, PA. No grants to individuals.
Application information: Application form required.
Initial approach: Proposal
Deadline(s): None
Advisory Committee: John R. Dunnell; Susan K. Syversen.
Trustee: Eastern Bank, N.A.
EIN: 043397681
Selected grants: The following grants are a representative sample of this grantmaker's funding activity:
$101,000 to Cornell University, Ithaca, NY, 2013. For Further Domestic and International Organic Farming Research.

$20,000 to American Friends Service Committee, Philadelphia, PA, 2013. For general support of International Programs.
$20,000 to Green America, Washington, DC, 2013. For Climate Action, Fair Trade, and Better Paper.
$20,000 to Oxfam America, Boston, MA, 2013. For Global Programs.
$20,000 to Rainforest Alliance, New York, NY, 2013. For Promotion of Sustainable Forestry Practices in Honduras.
$8,750 to Vamos Adelante Foundation, Miami, FL, 2013. For Secondary School Funding for rural Guatemalan students.

4310
The Charles Irwin Travelli Fund ✧
c/o Tyler & Reynolds
77 Summer St.
Boston, MA 02110-1006
Application address: c/o Geoffrey Andrews, 58 Bowen St., Newton, MA 02159, tel.: (617) 332-0548

Incorporated in 1914 in MA.
Donors: Charles I. Travelli†; Emma R. Travelli†; Emma R. Travelli Trust.
Foundation type: Independent foundation.
Financial data (yr. ended 11/30/13): Assets, $2,208,966 (M); gifts received, $1,104,256; expenditures, $1,194,177; qualifying distributions, $1,152,836; giving activities include $1,116,183 for 17 grants (high: $90,100; low: $10,000).
Purpose and activities: Grants for aid and comfort to the deserving poor; contributes to the support of other Massachusetts charitable corporations or associations, and generally for the doing and carrying on of educational, charitable, benevolent and religious work. Grants largely for higher and other education; minor support also for hospitals and social services.
Fields of interest: Higher education; Education; Human services.
Type of support: Scholarship funds.
Limitations: Applications accepted. Giving limited to the New England area for higher education; grants to other organizations mainly in MA, with emphasis on Boston.
Application information: Scholarship application forms available in financial aid offices at participating educational institutions. Application forms are not required for organizations requesting grants. Application form required.
Initial approach: Proposal
Deadline(s): None, for grants; deadlines for scholarships are related to and integrated with the academic year of participating educational institutions
Board meeting date(s): As required
Officers: Gerald B. O'Grady, III, Pres. and Clerk; Alison E. Andrews, V.P.; Sumner R. Andrews, Jr., Treas.; Geoffrey C. Andrews, Exec. Dir.; Peter J. Franks, Exec. Dir.
Trustees: Michael C. Andrews; Sumner R. Andrews III; Robert L. Wolff, Jr.
Number of staff: 1 part-time professional.
EIN: 042260155

4311
The TripAdvisor Charitable Foundation ✧
(formerly The Trustipadvisor-Expedia Foundation)
141 Needham St.
Newton, MA 02464-1505

Established in DE.
Donor: Expedia, Inc.
Foundation type: Company-sponsored foundation.
Financial data (yr. ended 12/31/12): Assets, $5,996,803 (M); gifts received, $165,339; expenditures, $3,194,719; qualifying distributions, $3,194,719; giving activities include $3,194,699 for 28 grants (high: $1,500,000; low: $10,000).
Fields of interest: Medical research, institute; Disasters, preparedness/services; Human services; Children/youth, services.
Limitations: Applications not accepted. Giving primarily in Washington, DC, and MA; some funding also in CA and NY. No grants to individuals.
Application information: Unsolicited requests for funds not accepted.
Officers and Directors:* Dara Khosrowshahi,* C.E.O.; Stephen Kaufer,* Pres.; Burke F. Norton, Exec. V.P. and Secy.; Seth Kalvert, Sr. V., Genl. Counsel. and Secy.; Julie Bradley,* Sr. V.P., Treas., and C.F.O.; Stuart Haas, Sr. V.P. and Treas.; Tyler Young, V.P., Fin. and Admin.; Michael Adler, C.F.O.; Frances Erskine, V.P.
EIN: 271457299

4312
The Tupancy-Harris Foundation of 1986 ✧
P.O. Box 55806
Boston, MA 02205-5806 (617) 574-3413
Contact: Robert N. Karelitz, V.P., Fiduciary Trust Co.
FAX: (617) 482-2078;
E-mail: karelitz@fiduciary-trust.com; Application address: 175 Federal St., Boston, MA 02110, tel.: (617) 482-5270

Established in 1986 in MA.
Donor: Oswald A. Tupancy†.
Foundation type: Independent foundation.
Financial data (yr. ended 12/31/12): Assets, $26,473,036 (M); expenditures, $1,407,687; qualifying distributions, $1,235,519; giving activities include $1,232,904 for 31 grants (high: $600,000; low: $1,000).
Purpose and activities: Support for the activities of the Nantucket Conservation Foundation and the Nantucket Historical Association.
Fields of interest: Media/communications; Historic preservation/historical societies; Higher education; Environment, natural resources; Hospitals (general); Medical research, institute; Human services; Children/youth, services.
Type of support: Annual campaigns; Capital campaigns; Building/renovation.
Limitations: Applications accepted. Giving limited to Nantucket, MA.
Application information: Application form not required.
Initial approach: Letter or e-mail
Copies of proposal: 1
Deadline(s): None
Trustee: Fiduciary Trust Co.
EIN: 046547989

4313
Two Sisters and a Wife Foundation, Inc. ✧
c/o Sara Whitman
10 Blueberry Cir.
Newton, MA 02462-1437

Donor: Catherine A. Whitman Charitable Remainder Trust.
Foundation type: Independent foundation.
Financial data (yr. ended 06/30/13): Assets, $11,198,018 (M); gifts received, $333,007; expenditures, $686,978; qualifying distributions, $573,000; giving activities include $573,000 for 14 grants (high: $150,000; low: $1,000).
Fields of interest: Arts; Education; Health organizations; LGBTQ.
Limitations: Applications not accepted.
Application information: Unsolicited requests for funds not accepted.
Directors: Jeanine M. Cowen; Sara G. Whitman.
EIN: 264607134

4314
University Industry Research Corp. ✧ ☆
c/o Virtual, Inc.
401 Edgewater Pl., Ste. 600
Wakefield, MA 01880-6200

Donors: Intel Corp.; McAfee Corp.
Foundation type: Independent foundation.
Financial data (yr. ended 12/31/13): Assets, $3,201,327 (M); gifts received, $7,901,342; expenditures, $7,901,342; qualifying distributions, $7,889,780; giving activities include $7,823,500 for 23 grants (high: $1,369,000; low: $35,000).
Fields of interest: Education.
Limitations: Applications not accepted. Giving on a national and international basis, particularly in London, England, and Israel.
Application information: Unsolicited requests for funds not accepted.
Officers and Director:* James Christopher Ramming, Pres.; Erin Richards,* C.F.O.; Mike Witteman, Secy.
EIN: 453967943

4315
The James L. Vincent Foundation ✧
c/o James L. Vincent
7 Audubon Rd.
Weston, MA 02493-1160

Established in 2004 in MA.
Donor: James L. Vincent.
Foundation type: Independent foundation.
Financial data (yr. ended 12/31/12): Assets, $1,729,081 (M); expenditures, $609,853; qualifying distributions, $600,950; giving activities include $600,950 for 10 grants (high: $500,000; low: $100).
Purpose and activities: Giving primarily for higher education; some funding also for the arts.
Fields of interest: Arts; Higher education, university.
Limitations: Giving primarily in NC; some funding in MA.
Trustee: James L. Vincent.
EIN: 412141038

4316
George C. Wadleigh Foundation, Inc. ✧
(formerly George C. Wadleigh Home for Aged Men, Inc.)
P.O. Box 226
Groveland, MA 01834-0226 (978) 374-0115

Established in 1981 in MA.
Donor: George C. Wadleigh†.
Foundation type: Independent foundation.
Financial data (yr. ended 12/31/13): Assets, $15,017,795 (M); expenditures, $707,017; qualifying distributions, $610,025; giving activities include $590,449 for 19 grants (high: $129,712; low: $5,615).
Purpose and activities: Grants primarily to organizations benefiting aged and indigent individuals in the greater Haverhill, MA, area.
Fields of interest: Human services; Aging, centers/services; Aging.
Type of support: Seed money; Equipment; Building/renovation.
Limitations: Applications accepted. Giving primarily in the greater Haverhill, MA, area. No grants to individuals, or for general operating expenses, or research.
Publications: Application guidelines; Informational brochure.
Application information: Application form not required.
Initial approach: Proposal
Copies of proposal: 1
Deadline(s): None
Officers and Directors:* Charles Traver,* Pres.; Thomas Mortimer, V.P.; Peter Carbone,* Clerk; Richard Cammett,* Treas.; Michael Hart; William Kluber; Kara Kosmes; Nancy Rea; Zoe Veasey.
Number of staff: None.
EIN: 042720087

4317
Wagner Family Foundation ✧
c/o Nutter McClennen & Fish, LLP
P.O. Box 51400
Boston, MA 02205-1400

Established in 2003 in MA.
Donors: Charlotte R. Cramer Wagner; Herbert S. Wagner III.
Foundation type: Independent foundation.
Financial data (yr. ended 12/31/13): Assets, $91,779,049 (M); gifts received, $15,000,000; expenditures, $3,416,065; qualifying distributions, $3,265,993; giving activities include $3,224,700 for 34 grants (high: $1,500,000; low: $1,000).
Fields of interest: Elementary/secondary education; Higher education; Hospitals (general); Health care; Human services.
Limitations: Applications not accepted. Giving primarily in MA. No grants to individuals.
Application information: Contributes only to pre-selected organizations.
Trustees: Charlotte R. Cramer Wagner; Herbert S. Wagner III.
EIN: 206079941

4318
The Edward W. Kane & Martha J. Wallace Family Foundation ✧
c/o Edward W. Kane
1437-2 Monument St.
Concord, MA 01742-5309

Established in 1999 in MA.
Donors: Edward W. Kane; Martha J. Wallace.
Foundation type: Independent foundation.
Financial data (yr. ended 12/31/13): Assets, $24,134,812 (M); gifts received, $2,040,339; expenditures, $1,128,247; qualifying distributions, $1,029,385; giving activities include $1,029,385 for 35 grants (high: $680,000; low: $100).
Purpose and activities: Giving primarily for recreation, museums, and education.
Fields of interest: Museums (marine/maritime); Elementary/secondary education; Higher education, university; Athletics/sports, water sports; Recreation; Christian agencies & churches.
Type of support: General/operating support.
Limitations: Applications not accepted. Giving primarily in MA and NH. No grants to individuals.
Application information: Unsolicited requests for funds not accepted.
Trustees: Edward W. Kane; Martha J. Wallace.
EIN: 043466900
Selected grants: The following grants are a representative sample of this grantmaker's funding activity:
$466,868 to University of Pennsylvania, Philadelphia, PA, 2011.
$35,000 to Nashoba Brooks School, Concord, MA, 2011.
$30,750 to Museum of Yachting, Newport, RI, 2011.
$25,000 to Concord Antiquarian Society, Concord, MA, 2011.
$25,000 to New England Wild Flower Society, Framingham, MA, 2011.
$16,800 to Redwood Library and Athenaeum, Newport, RI, 2011.
$5,000 to New Bedford Whaling Museum, New Bedford, MA, 2011.
$5,000 to Newport Historical Society, Newport, RI, 2011.
$5,000 to Preservation Society of Newport County, Newport, RI, 2011.
$2,000 to Concord Land Conservation Trust, Concord, MA, 2011.

4319
The Wang Foundation ✧
c/o Mary Kathleen O'Conbell, Tr., Goodwin Proctor LLP
Exchange Pl.
Boston, MA 02109-2881

Established in 1987 in MA.
Donor: An Wang†.
Foundation type: Independent foundation.
Financial data (yr. ended 12/31/13): Assets, $4,230,226 (M); expenditures, $689,484; qualifying distributions, $640,976; giving activities include $625,900 for 34 grants (high: $140,000; low: $100).
Fields of interest: Education; Hospitals (general); Health care; YM/YWCAs & YM/YWHAs.
Limitations: Applications not accepted. Giving primarily in the greater metropolitan Boston, MA, area; some funding also in Dallas, TX. No grants to individuals.
Application information: Contributes only to pre-selected organizations.
Trustees: Juliette W. Coombs; Mary Kathleen O'Connell, Esq.; Courtney S. Wang; Frederick A. Wang; Lorraine C. Wang.
EIN: 222858458

4320
Stanley W. Watson Foundation ✧
c/o William K. Mackey
P.O. Box 901
Falmouth, MA 02541-0901

Established in 1997 in MA.
Donor: Stanley W. Watson†.
Foundation type: Independent foundation.
Financial data (yr. ended 12/31/13): Assets, $36,661,788 (M); expenditures, $1,895,547; qualifying distributions, $1,610,250; giving activities include $1,610,000 for 26 grants (high: $300,000; low: $3,000).
Purpose and activities: Giving primarily to local charities.
Fields of interest: Education; Health care; Marine science.
Limitations: Applications not accepted. Giving primarily in MA. No grants to individuals.
Application information: Contributes only to pre-selected organizations.
Trustees: William K. Mackey; Frederica W. Valois.
EIN: 223100750

4321
Matthew A. and Susan B. Weatherbie Foundation ✧
c/o Choate LLP
P.O. Box 961019
Boston, MA 02196-1019

Established in 2000 in MA.
Donors: Matthew A. Weatherbie; Susan B. Weatherbie.
Foundation type: Independent foundation.
Financial data (yr. ended 12/31/13): Assets, $2,671,087 (M); gifts received, $500,070; expenditures, $1,403,430; qualifying distributions, $1,397,670; giving activities include $1,396,000 for 19 grants (high: $841,667; low: $1,000).
Fields of interest: Museums (art); Performing arts, music; Higher education.
Type of support: General/operating support.
Limitations: Applications not accepted. Giving primarily in MA and NH. No grants to individuals.
Application information: Contributes only to pre-selected organizations.
Trustees: Matthew A. Weatherbie; Susan B. Weatherbie.
EIN: 043532105
Selected grants: The following grants are a representative sample of this grantmaker's funding activity:
$182,700 to Museum of Fine Arts, Boston, MA, 2011. For general support.
$16,000 to Americans for Oxford, New York, NY, 2011. For general support.
$16,000 to City Year, Boston, MA, 2011. For general support.
$12,000 to Inner-City Scholarship Fund, Boston, MA, 2011. For general support.
$10,000 to Bruce Museum, Greenwich, CT, 2011. For general support.

$4,000 to Montana Land Reliance, Helena, MT, 2011. For general support.
$3,000 to Boston Symphony Orchestra, Boston, MA, 2011. For general support.
$2,500 to Handel and Haydn Society, Boston, MA, 2011. For general support.
$2,000 to Squam Lakes Association, Holderness, NH, 2011. For general support.

4322
Edwin S. Webster Foundation ✧
c/o GMA Foundations
77 Summer St., 8th Fl.
Boston, MA 02110-1006 (617) 391-3087
Contact: Michelle Jenney, Admin.
FAX: (617) 426-7080;
E-mail: mjenney@gmafoundations.com; Duplicate application contact: Alex Hiam, Tr., The Edwin S. Webster Foundation, 24 Chestnut St., Amherst, MA 01002; Main URL: http://websterfoundation.grantsmanagement08.com/

Established in 1948 in MA.
Donor: Edwin S. Webster†.
Foundation type: Independent foundation.
Financial data (yr. ended 12/31/12): Assets, $27,802,778 (M); expenditures, $1,824,074; qualifying distributions, $1,684,287; giving activities include $1,610,000 for 71 grants (high: $75,000; low: $5,000).
Purpose and activities: Giving primarily to organizations that are well known to the foundation's trustees, with emphasis on hospitals, medical research, education, youth agencies, cultural activities, and programs addressing the needs of minorities.
Fields of interest: Arts; Education; Hospitals (general); Medical research, institute; Boys & girls clubs; Human services; Children/youth, services; Minorities/immigrants, centers/services; United Ways and Federated Giving Programs; Minorities.
Type of support: General/operating support; Capital campaigns; Building/renovation; Endowments; Program development; Research.
Limitations: Applications accepted. Giving primarily in the U.S., with emphasis on MA, MD, NH, NY, VA and VT. No grants to individuals, or for emergency funds, deficit financing, publications, or conferences; no loans.
Publications: Application guidelines; Grants list.
Application information: Applications sent by mail should conform generally to the AGM Common Proposal Form. A duplicate of application on paper (whether you apply on paper or electronically) is required and should be sent to Alex Hiam, Tr. Application form not required.
Initial approach: U.S. Mail or electronically
Copies of proposal: 1
Deadline(s): May 1 and Nov. 1
Board meeting date(s): June and Dec.
Trustees: Thomas C. Beck; Henry U. Harris III; Alexander W. Hiam; Suzanne Harte Sears.
Number of staff: 1 part-time professional.
EIN: 046000647
Selected grants: The following grants are a representative sample of this grantmaker's funding activity:
$50,000 to Massachusetts Institute of Technology, Cambridge, MA, 2012. For Co-Lab, Department of Urban Studies and Planning.
$50,000 to Museum of Science, Boston, MA, 2012. For Hall of Life Exhibit Space.
$25,000 to Landmark School, Prides Crossing, MA, 2012. For Construction of the Playing Field.
$20,000 to Massachusetts General Hospital, Boston, MA, 2012. For In-Vitro Fertilization Clinic.
$20,000 to United South End Settlements, Boston, MA, 2012. For General Operational Support at Camp Hale.
$20,000 to Wentworth Institute of Technology, Boston, MA, 2012. For annual fund support.
$15,000 to McLean Hospital, Belmont, MA, 2012. For College Mental Health Program.
$15,000 to Southern Vermont College, Bennington, VT, 2012. For General Operations Support Operational Support.
$10,000 to Boston Medical Center, Boston, MA, 2012. For Spark Program.

4323
Wilderness Point Foundation ✧
c/o Cambridge Associates LLC, Ruta Ruicis
125 High St.
Boston, MA 02110-2103

Established in 2004 in MA.
Donors: James N. Bailey; Roann Costin.
Foundation type: Independent foundation.
Financial data (yr. ended 12/31/13): Assets, $12,179 (M); gifts received, $406,029; expenditures, $687,925; qualifying distributions, $685,335; giving activities include $685,300 for 22 grants (high: $162,000; low: $500).
Fields of interest: Museums; Education; Cancer; Medical research; Human services.
Limitations: Applications not accepted. Giving primarily in MA; funding also in NY. No grants to individuals.
Application information: Contributes only to pre-selected organizations.
Trustees: James N. Bailey; Roann Costin.
EIN: 202061044

4324
The Windover Foundation ✧
c/o Nutter McClennen
155 Seaport Blvd.
Boston, MA 02210-2698
Application address: c/o K&L Gates, Attn.: David W. Lewis, Jr., 1 Lincoln St., Boston, MA 02111-2950, tel.: (617) 261-3100

Established in 1999 in MA.
Donors: Constance B. Fuller; Constance Fuller Marital Trust.
Foundation type: Independent foundation.
Financial data (yr. ended 07/31/13): Assets, $19,152,500 (M); expenditures, $614,539; qualifying distributions, $496,873; giving activities include $456,500 for 8 grants (high: $250,000; low: $1,000).
Fields of interest: Arts; Hospitals (general); Human services.
Limitations: Applications accepted. Giving primarily in MA and ME. No grants to individuals.
Application information: Application form not required.
Initial approach: Proposal
Deadline(s): None
Trustees: Moira H. Fuller; Randolph J. Fuller; Robert G. Fuller, Jr.; Nutter McClennen; K&L Gates.
EIN: 046897800

4325
Louis E. Wolfson Foundation ✧
c/o Gilmore Rees
70 Walnut St.
Wellesley, MA 02481-2104 (781) 431-9788
Contact: Paul Bishop Esq., Tr.

Trust established in 1951 in MA.
Donor: Louis E. Wolfson, M.D.†.
Foundation type: Independent foundation.
Financial data (yr. ended 06/30/13): Assets, $17,254,931 (M); expenditures, $978,313; qualifying distributions, $901,652; giving activities include $850,000 for 3 grants (high: $283,334; low: $283,333).
Purpose and activities: Two-thirds of income is restricted to the support of student aid endowments at the medical schools of Boston University, Harvard University, and Tufts University; remaining grants generally restricted to supporting the education of M.D. degree candidates at medical schools through loan funds administered by the schools.
Fields of interest: Medical school/education.
Limitations: Applications accepted. Giving primarily in Boston, MA. No grants to individuals.
Publications: Application guidelines.
Application information: Application form not required.
Initial approach: Letter
Copies of proposal: 1
Deadline(s): None
Officer: Jules Dienstag, M.D., Chair.
Trustees: Karen Antman, M.D.; Martin Cohne; Albert F. Cullen, Jr.; Henry Klapholz, M.D.; Jack London; Robert Penn.
Number of staff: 1 part-time support.
EIN: 046053295

4326
The Wood Foundation of Chambersburg, PA ✧
1 Brattle Sq., 4th Fl.
Cambridge, MA 02138-3723 (617) 864-1420
Contact: Charles O. Wood III, Tr.

Established in 1989 as successor foundation to the Wood Foundation of Chambersburg, PA.
Foundation type: Independent foundation.
Financial data (yr. ended 12/31/13): Assets, $6,541,646 (M); expenditures, $717,465; qualifying distributions, $641,300; giving activities include $641,300 for 25 grants (high: $155,000; low: $500).
Purpose and activities: Giving primarily for the arts and human services.
Fields of interest: Museums; Arts; Higher education; Human services.
Limitations: Applications accepted. Giving primarily in Chambersburg and Franklin counties, PA.
Application information: Application form not required.
Initial approach: Proposal
Deadline(s): None
Trustees: Emilie W. Robinson; Charles O. Wood III; David S. Wood; Miriam M. Wood.
EIN: 251607838

4327
Greater Worcester Community Foundation, Inc. ✧
370 Main St., Ste. 650
Worcester, MA 01608-1738 (508) 755-0980
Contact: Donor Services: Kelly A. Stimson, Dir., Donor Svcs.; For grants: Pam Kane, Sr. Prog. Off.
FAX: (508) 755-3406;
E-mail: info@greaterworcester.org; Additional e-mail: info@greaterworcester.org; Grant inquiry e-mail: pkane@greaterworcester.org; Main URL: http://www.greaterworcester.org
E-Newsletter: http://www.greaterworcester.org/NewsEvents/SignUpforPublications.aspx
Grants Database: http://www.greaterworcester.org/Nonprofits/RecentGrants.aspx

Incorporated in 1975 in MA.
Foundation type: Community foundation.
Financial data (yr. ended 12/31/13): Assets, $136,666,180 (M); gifts received, $3,714,212; expenditures, $8,560,330; giving activities include $5,418,183 for 548+ grants (high: $437,000; low: $100), and $620,354 for 120 grants to individuals.
Purpose and activities: The foundation's mission is to increase philanthropy and build healthy and vibrant communities throughout Central Massachusetts. The foundation achieves its mission in four primary ways: 1) works with donor on tailored giving programs; 2) invests in local nonprofit organizations through grants and technical support; 3) convenes people and organizations with shared goals to solve problems; and 4) safeguards the assets in its trust.
Fields of interest: Humanities; Arts; Medical school/education; Nursing school/education; Education; Environment; Health care; Health organizations, association; Crime/violence prevention, abuse prevention; Housing/shelter, development; Youth development; Children/youth, services; Family services; Aging, centers/services; Homeless, human services; Human services; Community/economic development; Government/public administration; Public affairs; Children; Youth; Aging; Disabilities, people with; African Americans/Blacks; AIDS, people with; Economically disadvantaged; Homeless.
Type of support: Program development; Seed money; Scholarship funds; Technical assistance; Program evaluation; Scholarships—to individuals.
Limitations: Applications accepted. Giving limited to Worcester County, MA. No grants to individuals (except for designated scholarship funds), or for capital campaigns or endowments.
Publications: Application guidelines; Annual report; Financial statement; Grants list; Newsletter.
Application information: Visit foundation web site for link to online application forms and guidelines. Scholarships are for residents of Worcester County, MA, only. Application form required.
Initial approach: Telephone and create online profile
Copies of proposal: 1
Deadline(s): Mar. 16 and Sept. 15 for discretionary grants; varies for others
Board meeting date(s): Monthly
Final notification: Mar. and Sept. for discretionary grants; varies for others
Officers and Directors:* Gerald "Lee" Gaudette III,* Chair.; Warner S. Fletcher,* Vice-Chair.; Ann T. Lisi,* C.E.O. and Pres.; Christopher O'Keeffe, V.P., Progs.; Carolyn Stempler,* Clerk; Thomas J. Bartholomew,* Treas.; Robert S. Adler; Matilde Castiel; Brian M. Chandley; J. Christopher Collins; Tracy A. Craig; Gerald M. Gates; Timothy M. Jarry; Alison C. Kenary; Patsy A. Lewis; Linda Carre Looft; Monica E. Lowell; Ann K. Molloy; Mary C. Ritter; Scott Rossiter; George A. Tetler, III; Matthew Wally; Charles A. "Chick" Weiss.
Distribution Committee: Gerald Gates,* Chair.; Joanne Calista; Linda C. Looft; Nadia T. McGourthy; Philip Niddrie; Scott Williams.
Number of staff: 7 full-time professional; 2 full-time support; 1 part-time support.
EIN: 042572276

4328
Yawkey Foundation I ✧
(also known as The Thomas A. Yawkey Foundation)
990 Washington St., Ste. 315
Dedham, MA 02026-6704 (781) 329-7470
Contact: Nancy Brodnicki, Prog. Admin.
FAX: (781) 329-8195;
E-mail: ehyman@webershandwick.com; Main URL: http://www.yawkeyfoundation.org

Established in 1976; supporting organization of Tom Yawkey Wildlife Centers, Carolina Department of Natural Resources; Tara Hall Home for Boys; Dana Farber Cancer Institute, Inc.; and Yale University.
Foundation type: Independent foundation.
Financial data (yr. ended 12/31/13): Assets, $66,027,487 (M); expenditures, $3,725,612; qualifying distributions, $3,004,888; giving activities include $2,696,497 for 42 grants (high: $1,053,297; low: $2,000), and $5,225 for 1 foundation-administered program.
Purpose and activities: Yawkey Foundation I was created to support the places and causes that Tom Yawkey loved the most during his lifetime. The foundation primarily supports the work of the Tom Yawkey Wildlife Center in SC.
Fields of interest: Arts; Education; Environment; Animals/wildlife, preservation/protection; Health care; Youth development; Human services.
Limitations: Applications not accepted. Giving primarily in Georgetown County, SC, and New England. Generally, no support for private foundations, legislative lobbying, political campaigns or causes, advocacy groups, public school districts, public schools, fraternal, trade, civic or labor organizations, pass-through or intermediary organizations, religious organizations for sectarian purposes, or for workforce development programs. Generally, no grants to individuals, or for general endowments, operating deficits, debt retirement, general capital campaigns, events, conferences, seminars, group travel, awards, prizes, monuments, feasibility or research studies, or music, video or film production.
Publications: Annual report.
Application information: Unsolicited requests for funds not accepted from organizations not previously funded by the foundation.
Officers and Trustees:* John L. Harrington,* Chair.; James P. Healey, Pres.; Maureen H. Bleday, Secy.; William B. Gutfarb,* Treas.; Eleanor S. Armstrong, Tr. Emerita.
EIN: 132890749
Selected grants: The following grants are a representative sample of this grantmaker's funding activity:
$200,000 to Tara Hall Home for Boys, Georgetown, SC, 2011.
$191,200 to Horry-Georgetown Technical College Foundation, Conway, SC, 2011.
$100,000 to Dana-Farber Cancer Institute, Boston, MA, 2011.
$37,500 to Helping Hands of Georgetown, Georgetown, SC, 2011.
$30,000 to Lowcountry Open Land Trust, Charleston, SC, 2011.
$25,000 to Boys and Girls Clubs of Boston, Boston, MA, 2011.
$25,000 to Friends of Acadia, Bar Harbor, ME, 2011.
$25,000 to New England Wildlife Center, South Weymouth, MA, 2011.
$25,000 to Stonehill College, Easton, MA, 2011.
$12,500 to Georgetown Presbyterian Church, Georgetown, SC, 2011.

4329
Yawkey Foundation II ✧
(also known as The Jean R. Yawkey Foundation)
990 Washington St., Ste. 315
Dedham, MA 02026-6716 (781) 329-7470
Contact: Nancy Keilty-Brodnicki
Main URL: http://www.yawkeyfoundation.org
E-Newsletter: http://www.yawkeyfoundation.org/announcements.html

Established in 1983 in MA.
Donor: Jean R. Yawkey†.
Foundation type: Independent foundation.
Financial data (yr. ended 12/31/13): Assets, $469,619,971 (M); expenditures, $26,413,295; qualifying distributions, $21,537,280; giving activities include $20,227,807 for 169 grants (high: $3,500,000; low: $1,500).
Purpose and activities: The mission of the foundation is to make grants that provide an immediate, significant and positive impact on the quality of life of youth, families and the underserved.
Fields of interest: Arts; Higher education; Adult education—literacy, basic skills & GED; Scholarships/financial aid; Education, services; Education; Environment; Animals/wildlife; Hospitals (general); Health care; Housing/shelter; Recreation; Human services; Children/youth, services; Children/youth; Economically disadvantaged.
Type of support: Scholarship funds.
Limitations: Applications accepted. Giving primarily in MA, with emphasis on the greater metropolitan Boston area. Generally, no support for private foundations, political, fraternal, trade, civic or labor organizations, religious organizations for sectarian purposes, public schools or districts, charter schools, community or economic development corporations or programs, advocacy groups, pass-through or intermediary organizations, or workforce development programs. No grants to individuals. Generally, no grants for operating deficits, retirement of debt, endowments, capital campaigns, events, conferences, seminars, group travel, awards, prizes, monuments, music, video, or film production, feasibility or research studies.
Application information: The foundation is not accepting grant applications from organizations not previously founded by the foundations. The foundation encourages applicants to review grant guidelines on the foundation web site prior to applying for grants. Application form required.
Initial approach: Online grant application form
Deadline(s): Mar. 1 for Arts and Culture, Conservation and Health Care; June 15 for Human Services; Sept. 1 for Education; Nov. 15 for Youth and Amateur Athletics
Final notification: 90-120 days

Officers and Trustees:* John L. Harrington,* Chair.; James P. Healey,* Pres.; William B. Gutfarb,* Treas.; Eleanor S. Armstrong; Charles I. Clough, Jr.; Rev. Ray Hammond; James G. Maguire; Justin P. Morreale; Judy Walden Scarafile.
EIN: 042768239
Selected grants: The following grants are a representative sample of this grantmaker's funding activity:
$3,500,000 to Dana-Farber Cancer Institute, Boston, MA, 2012. For construction.
$3,500,000 to Fund for Catholic Schools, Campaign for Catholic Schools, Braintree, MA, 2012. For renovation and support of an academy serving inner-city students in grades K-8 and a youth center.
$500,000 to Home for Little Wanderers, Boston, MA, 2012. For construction of residential center for children with emotional and behavioral disabilities.
$500,000 to Special Olympics Massachusetts, Marlborough, MA, 2012. For construction of new headquarters and training center.
$400,000 to National Baseball Hall of Fame and Museum, Cooperstown, NY, 2012. For education programs for children and archive project.
$250,000 to Bethel Institute for Social Justice, Boston, MA, 2012. For renovation of Bethel Institute Youth Center.
$50,000 to YMCA of Greater Boston, Boston, MA, 2012. For aquatics program for inner-city children.
$25,000 to Casa Myrna Vasquez, Boston, MA, 2012. For services for victims of domestic violence and their children.
$25,000 to Massachusetts General Hospital, Schwartz Center for Compassionate Healthcare, Boston, MA, 2012. For program to promote compassion in health care.
$25,000 to Ursuline Academy, Dedham, MA, 2012. For scholarship program for disadvantaged students.

4330
Zakat Foundation ✧

c/o GW & Wade, LLC
93 Worcester St.
Wellesley, MA 02481-3609 (781) 239-1188
Contact: Omar Hamoui, Pres.; Omaima Salous, Dir.

Donors: Omar Hamoui; Omaima Salous.
Foundation type: Independent foundation.
Financial data (yr. ended 12/31/13): Assets, $16,259,875 (M); expenditures, $1,981,624; qualifying distributions, $1,714,012; giving activities include $1,714,012 for 7 grants (high: $1,000,000; low: $10,000).
Fields of interest: Elementary/secondary education; Hospitals (general); Islam.
Limitations: Applications accepted. Giving primarily in CA; some giving also in IL and MI.
Application information: Contributes mostly to pre-selected organizations. Application form not required.
Initial approach: Proposal
Deadline(s): None
Officer: Omar Hamoui, Pres.
Director: Omaima Salous.
EIN: 273280120

MICHIGAN

4331
Lynn & Paul Alandt Foundation ✧
1901 Saint Antoine St., 6th Fl.
Detroit, MI 48226-2310 (313) 259-7777
Contact: David M. Hempstead, Secy.

Established in MI.
Donor: Lynn F. Alandt.
Foundation type: Independent foundation.
Financial data (yr. ended 12/31/12): Assets, $9,843,569 (M); expenditures, $637,719; qualifying distributions, $614,692; giving activities include $600,200 for 22 grants (high: $460,000; low: $1,000).
Fields of interest: Education; Health care; Recreation, community.
Limitations: Applications accepted. Giving primarily in MI. No grants to individuals.
Application information: Application form required.
Initial approach: Letter
Deadline(s): None
Officers and Directors:* Lynn F. Alandt,* Pres.; Paul D. Alandt,* V.P.; David M. Hempstead,* Secy.; Rodney P. Wood, Treas.
EIN: 272677218

4332
Albion Community Foundation ✧ ☆
(formerly Albion Civic Foundation)
203 S. Superior St.
P.O. Box 156
Albion, MI 49224 (517) 629-3349
Contact: Elizabeth N. Schultheiss, Exec. Dir.
FAX: (517) 629-8027;
E-mail: foundation@albionfoundation.org; Main URL: http://www.albionfoundation.org

Established in 1968 in MI.
Donor: Thomas T. Lloyd†.
Foundation type: Community foundation.
Financial data (yr. ended 12/31/13): Assets, $5,661,505 (M); gifts received, $2,076,926; expenditures, $1,572,819; giving activities include $828,184 for 8+ grants (high: $508,000).
Purpose and activities: The mission of the foundation is to strengthen the greater Albion area by cultivating community assets to enhance the community's quality of life.
Fields of interest: Arts; Education; Environment; Children/youth, services; Economic development; Community/economic development.
Type of support: Building/renovation; Curriculum development; Equipment; Management development/capacity building; Matching/challenge support; Program development; Publication; Scholarship funds; Seed money; Technical assistance.
Limitations: Applications accepted. Giving limited to greater Albion, MI. No support for religious, fraternal, or service organizations (except for proposed grants that meet a general community need in a non-sectarian, non-exclusive manner). No grants to individuals (except for scholarships), or for general operating support, deficit reduction, endowments, or annual fundraising campaigns.
Publications: Application guidelines; Annual report; Annual report (including application guidelines); Financial statement; Grants list; Informational brochure; Informational brochure (including application guidelines); Newsletter; IRS Form 990 or 990-PF printed copy available upon request.
Application information: Visit foundation web site for application form and guidelines. Application form required.
Initial approach: Submit application
Deadline(s): Varies
Final notification: Within 90 days
Officers and Trustees:* Joyce Spicer,* Pres.; Bernie Konkle, Jr.,* V.P.; Marilyn Hennon,* Secy.; Jeff Bell,* Treas.; Elizabeth N. Schultheiss,* Exec. Dir.; Mandy Dubiel; Robert Dunklin; Tom Pitt; Nancy Roush; John Shedd; Nidia Wolf; Karen Yankie.
Number of staff: 1 full-time professional.
EIN: 237019029

4333
The Alix Foundation ✧
(formerly Jay & Maryanne Alix Foundation)
c/o Jay Alix
151 S. Old Woodward Ave., Ste. 400
Birmingham, MI 48009-6103

Established in 1994 in MI.
Donors: Jay Alix; Maryanne Alix†; Jay Alix Living Trust.
Foundation type: Independent foundation.
Financial data (yr. ended 12/31/12): Assets, $6,555,740 (M); gifts received, $6,001,190; expenditures, $524,590; qualifying distributions, $521,805; giving activities include $518,999 for 5 grants (high: $151,499; low: $20,000).
Purpose and activities: Giving primarily for education, health care and medical research, and to religious organizations.
Fields of interest: Elementary/secondary education; Health care; Medical research, institute; Human services; Religion.
Limitations: Applications not accepted. Giving primarily in MI. No grants to individuals.
Application information: Contributes only to pre-selected organizations.
Officers and Director:* Jay Alix,* Chair.; Robert E. Shields, C.E.O. and Pres.; Arthur J. Kubert, V.P., Secy.-Treas., and C.F.O.
EIN: 383171122

4334
Allegan County Community Foundation ✧
(formerly Allegan County Foundation)
524 Marshall St.
Allegan, MI 49010-1632 (269) 673-8344
Contact: Theresa Bray, Exec. Dir.
FAX: (269) 673-8745;
E-mail: info@alleganfoundation.org; Additional e-mail: theresa@gmail.com; Main URL: http://www.alleganfoundation.org
Twitter: https://twitter.com/ArtsAliveACCF

Established in 1964 in MI.
Donors: Earl Delano†; Chester Ray†; Ethol Stone†.
Foundation type: Community foundation.
Financial data (yr. ended 12/31/13): Assets, $17,924,901 (M); gifts received, $813,015; expenditures, $1,042,900; giving activities include $676,199 for 48+ grants (high: $63,606).
Purpose and activities: The foundation seeks to provide the means for donors to make a lasting impact on Allegan County through the establishment and growth of endowed funds. Giving primarily for education, health and human services.
Fields of interest: Arts; Education; Health care; Recreation; Children/youth, services; Human services; Community development, neighborhood development.
Type of support: Continuing support; Building/renovation; Equipment; Emergency funds; Program development; Curriculum development; Matching/challenge support.
Limitations: Applications accepted. Giving in Allegan County, MI, only. No grants to individuals (except for scholarships).
Publications: Annual report; Financial statement; Grants list.
Application information: Visit foundation web site for application information. Application form required.
Initial approach: Meeting with foundation staff; application available at that time
Copies of proposal: 1
Deadline(s): 1st Fri. in Nov. for TAG grants; 2nd Fri. in Dec. for Legacy grants
Board meeting date(s): Bi-monthly
Final notification: Apr.
Officers and Trustees:* Paula Baker,* Pres.; Rob Marciniak,* V.P.; John Mahan,* Secy.; Steve Angle,* Treas.; Theresa Bray, Exec. Dir.; Cindy Baker; David Balas; Mark Dobias; Lynn Etheridge; Bob Hennip; Brian Marr; Vicki Rosenberg; Jodi White.
Number of staff: 1 full-time professional; 1 full-time support; 1 part-time support.
EIN: 386189947

4335
Allen Foundation, Inc. ✧
P.O. Box 1606
Midland, MI 48641-1606
Contact: Dale Baum, Secy.
FAX: (989) 832-8842;
E-mail: dbaum@allenfoundation.org; Additional e-mail: Lucille@allenfoundation.org; Main URL: http://www.allenfoundation.org/

Established in 1975 in MI.
Foundation type: Independent foundation.
Financial data (yr. ended 12/31/13): Assets, $29,466,076 (M); gifts received, $14,043,445; expenditures, $572,602; qualifying distributions, $507,293; giving activities include $486,348 for 16 grants (high: $81,420; low: $2,000).
Purpose and activities: The foundation focuses on projects that benefit nutritional programs in the areas of education, training and research. A lower priority is given to proposals that help solve immediate or emergency hunger and malnutrition problems.
Fields of interest: Higher education; Hospitals (general); Nutrition.
Limitations: Applications accepted. Giving on a national basis. No grants to individuals.
Publications: Application guidelines; Annual report; Grants list.
Application information: Application forms and latest information available on foundation web site. All applications are to be submitted online. Application form not required.
Initial approach: Take eligibility quiz on foundation web site
Copies of proposal: 1
Deadline(s): Dec. 31

Board meeting date(s): Annually
Final notification: June
Officers and Trustees:* Gail E. Lanphear,* Chair.; Mark Ostahowski, M.D.*, Pres.; William Lauderbach,* V.P., Finance and Treas.; Dale Baum, Ph.D.*, Secy.; William James Allen; Laurie Bouwman; Leslie Hildebrandt, Ph.D.; Ann F. Jay; Charles B. Kendall; Mary M. Neely; Pat Oriel, Ph.D.
Number of staff: 1 part-time support.
EIN: 510152562
Selected grants: The following grants are a representative sample of this grantmaker's funding activity:
$22,369 to INMED Partnerships for Children, Ashburn, VA, 2012. For nutrition.

4336
The Alro Steel Foundation ✧
3100 E. High St.
Jackson, MI 49203-3467

Established in 2004 in MI.
Donors: Li-Cor of Lincoln LLC; Alro Steel Corp.
Foundation type: Company-sponsored foundation.
Financial data (yr. ended 12/31/13): Assets, $14,507,685 (M); gifts received, $6,400,000; expenditures, $1,531,831; qualifying distributions, $1,517,920; giving activities include $1,517,900 for 35 grants (high: $1,500,000; low: $50).
Purpose and activities: The foundation supports orchestras and organizations involved with education, athletics, human services, and community development.
Fields of interest: Performing arts, orchestras; Higher education; Education; Athletics/sports, amateur leagues; Human services; Community/economic development; United Ways and Federated Giving Programs.
Type of support: General/operating support; Building/renovation; Program development; Scholarship funds.
Limitations: Applications not accepted. Giving primarily in MI, with emphasis on Jackson. No grants to individuals.
Application information: Contributes only to pre-selected organizations.
Officers: Carlton L. Glick, Pres.; Alvin L. Glick, V.P. and Secy.; Barry J. Glick, V.P.; Randal L. Glick, Treas.
EIN: 300254220
Selected grants: The following grants are a representative sample of this grantmaker's funding activity:
$2,000,000 to University of Michigan, Ann Arbor, MI, 2012. For Field House Project.

4337
Americana Foundation ✧
28115 Meadowbrook Rd.
Novi, MI 48377-3128 (248) 347-3863
Contact: Marlene J. Fluharty, Exec. Dir.
FAX: (248) 347-3349; E-mail: fluhart5@msu.edu;
Main URL: http://www.americanafoundation.org
Grants List: http://www.americanafoundation.org/grants.asp

Established in 1978 in MI.
Donors: Adolph H. Meyer†; Ida M. Meyer†; Ginger Meyer.
Foundation type: Independent foundation.
Financial data (yr. ended 12/31/13): Assets, $20,456,258 (M); expenditures, $1,143,059; qualifying distributions, $1,019,343; giving activities include $719,786 for 40 grants (high: $50,000; low: $757).
Purpose and activities: Support for education and advocacy programs that address issues of conserving agriculture and natural resources, and the preservation of the American heritage.
Fields of interest: Museums (history); Historic preservation/historical societies; Environment; Agriculture.
Type of support: General/operating support; Building/renovation; Program development; Conferences/seminars; Publication; Internship funds; Technical assistance; Matching/challenge support.
Limitations: Applications accepted. Giving primarily in MI. No support for private foundations or for political purposes. No grants to individuals, or for fundraising events, tables, or scholarships.
Publications: Annual report (including application guidelines); Grants list; Informational brochure (including application guidelines).
Application information: Council of Michigan Foundations Application Form accepted. Application guidelines available on foundation web site. Application form not required.
Initial approach: Letter or telephone
Copies of proposal: 1
Deadline(s): Jan. 10, Apr. 10, July 10, and Oct. 10
Board meeting date(s): Quarterly
Final notification: 3 months
Officers and Trustees:* Robert Janson,* Pres.; Jonathan Thomas,* V.P.; Thomas F. Ranger,* Treas.; Marlene J. Fluharty, Exec. Dir.; Kathryn Bishop Eckert; Kathryn T. Harper; Gary Rentrop.
Number of staff: 1 full-time professional; 1 part-time support.
EIN: 382269431
Selected grants: The following grants are a representative sample of this grantmaker's funding activity:
$70,000 to EARTH University Foundation, Atlanta, GA, 2012. For Memorial for Norm A. Brown.
$54,000 to Detroit Institute of Arts, Detroit, MI, 2012. For Collections Display and Conservation.
$50,000 to Colonial Williamsburg Foundation, Williamsburg, VA, 2012. For Endowment for Curatorial Internship.
$50,000 to EARTH University Foundation, Atlanta, GA, 2012. For Endowed Scholarship for Earth Students.
$50,000 to Michigan State University, East Lansing, MI, 2012. For Maintenance of Tollgate Farm.
$35,000 to Greening of Detroit, Detroit, MI, 2012. For Program support for Urban Agriculture.
$35,000 to Michigan State University, East Lansing, MI, 2012. For Outdoor Education for Youth and Staff.
$35,000 to Wayne State University, Detroit, MI, 2012. To support of Programming, Operating Expenses and Restoration.
$25,000 to Land Information Access Association, Traverse City, MI, 2012. For Strategic Planning and Development.
$20,000 to Detroit Institute of Arts, Detroit, MI, 2012. For conservation and installation.

4338
The Anchor Foundation ✧
3141 N. Lake Shore Dr.
Holland, MI 49424-6020

Established in 1997 in MI.
Donors: Elizabeth I. Huizenga; Herman Kanis; Suzanne Kanis.
Foundation type: Independent foundation.
Financial data (yr. ended 12/31/12): Assets, $1,618,667 (M); expenditures, $452,197; qualifying distributions, $428,500; giving activities include $428,500 for grants.
Purpose and activities: Giving primarily to Christian organizations, education, and ministries.
Fields of interest: Education; Christian agencies & churches.
Limitations: Applications not accepted. Giving in the U.S., with some emphasis on MI. No grants to individuals.
Application information: Unsolicited requests for funds not accepted.
Officers and Directors:* Suzanne Kanis,* Pres.; Herman Kanis,* Mgr.; Michael J. Kanis; Sally J. Morris; April L. Smith.
EIN: 383353871

4339
Frank N. Andersen Foundation ✧
P.O. Box 227
Bridgeport, MI 48722-0225 (989) 772-2361
Contact: Michael Tate

Established in 1955 in MI.
Donor: Frank N. Andersen†.
Foundation type: Independent foundation.
Financial data (yr. ended 12/31/13): Assets, $7,599,528 (M); expenditures, $627,106; qualifying distributions, $557,059; giving activities include $557,059 for 42 grants (high: $200,000; low: $1,000).
Purpose and activities: Giving primarily for education, human services, and to community foundations.
Fields of interest: Higher education; Education; Recreation; Human services; Foundations (community).
Type of support: Capital campaigns; Building/renovation; Equipment; Scholarship funds.
Limitations: Applications accepted. Giving limited to Saginaw and Bay counties, MI. No grants to individuals.
Publications: Annual report.
Application information: Application form required.
Initial approach: Letter requesting application form
Copies of proposal: 1
Deadline(s): None
Board meeting date(s): Quarterly
Officers: Gerald Barber, Pres.; Michael A. Tate, V.P.; Jeffrey W. McNally, Secy.-Treas.
Trustee: Barbara Lincoln.
Number of staff: 3 part-time professional.
EIN: 386062616
Selected grants: The following grants are a representative sample of this grantmaker's funding activity:
$150,000 to Delta College, University Center, MI, 2012. For QVC Studio Renovation.
$25,000 to City Rescue Mission of Saginaw, Saginaw, MI, 2012. For Revitalization Building for Veterans.
$10,000 to Saginaw Community Foundation, Saginaw, MI, 2012. For Update Deindofer Woods Park.
$5,000 to Underground Railroad, Saginaw, MI, 2012. For Update Center.
$1,265 to Read Association of Saginaw County, Saginaw, MI, 2012. To support Reading Center.

4340
Ann Arbor Area Community Foundation ✧
(formerly Ann Arbor Area Foundation)
301 N. Main St., Ste. 300
Ann Arbor, MI 48104-1296 (734) 663-0401
Contact: For grants: Jillian Rosen, Prog. Off.
FAX: (734) 663-3514; E-mail: info@aaacf.org; Grant inquiry e-mail: jrosen@aaacf.org; Main URL: http://www.aaacf.org
Facebook: http://www.facebook.com/pages/Ann-Arbor-Area-Community-Foundation/112856658825507?sk=wall
Flickr: http://www.flickr.com/photos/aaacf
Twitter: http://twitter.com/AAACF
YouTube: https://www.youtube.com/user/ForGoodForEver

Incorporated in 1963 in MI.
Foundation type: Community foundation.
Financial data (yr. ended 12/31/12): Assets, $65,836,192 (M); gifts received, $5,003,084; expenditures, $3,345,449; giving activities include $1,951,305 for 133+ grants.
Purpose and activities: The Ann Arbor Area Community Foundation enriches the quality of life in the region through its knowledgeable leadership, engaged grantmaking, and creative partnerships with donors to make philanthropic investments and build endowment.
Fields of interest: Visual arts; Performing arts; Performing arts, theater; Arts; Higher education; Education; Environment, natural resources; Environment; Health care; Health organizations, association; Crime/violence prevention, domestic violence; Safety/disasters; Children/youth, services; Family services; Aging, centers/services; Homeless, human services; Human services; Economic development; Community/economic development; Public affairs, citizen participation; Public affairs; Aging; African Americans/Blacks; Homeless.
Type of support: Income development; Management development/capacity building; Emergency funds; Program development; Conferences/seminars; Publication; Seed money; Scholarship funds; Research; Matching/challenge support.
Limitations: Applications accepted. Giving limited to Washtenaw County, MI. No support for religious or sectarian purposes. No grants to individuals (except for scholarships), or for construction projects (new building or routine maintenance), re-granting, annual giving campaigns, fundraising events, or computer hardware equipment; no loans.
Publications: Application guidelines; Annual report (including application guidelines); Newsletter; Program policy statement.
Application information: Visit foundation web site for application guidelines per grant type. Applicants must log on to http://www.communitygrants.org to create an online agency profile and complete the Short Community Grants Application. Application form required.
Initial approach: E-mail Program Officer
Deadline(s): Apr. 8 for general grantmaking; varies for others
Board meeting date(s): Jan., Mar., May, June, July, Sept., Oct., and Nov.
Final notification: Early June
Officers and Trustees:* Bhushan Kulkarni,* Chair.; Michelle Crumm,* Vice-Chair.; Cheryl W. Elliott, C.E.O. and Pres.; Neel Hajra, C.O.O.; Jennifer Poteat,* Secy.; Brian P. Campbell,* Treas.; Dr. Rose B. Bellanca; George E. Borel, CPA; Cynthia L. Cattran; Martha Darling; Ann S. Davis; Jeff Hauptman; Robert Laverty; Nancy Margolis; Frederick L. McDonald, II; Jackie Qiu; Paul Schutt; Kevin Thompson; Dr. Levi T. Thompson; Chris Vaughan.
Number of staff: 6 full-time professional; 4 part-time professional; 1 full-time support.
EIN: 386087967
Selected grants: The following grants are a representative sample of this grantmaker's funding activity:
$120,596 to Warm the Children Ann Arbor, Ann Arbor, MI, 2012.
$100,000 to Ann Arbor Skatepark, Friends of the, Ann Arbor, MI, 2012.
$94,790 to Ann Arbor Academy, Ann Arbor, MI, 2012.
$40,000 to University of Michigan, Ann Arbor, MI, 2012. For Reach Out and Read Program.
$21,700 to Michigan Theater Foundation, Ann Arbor, MI, 2012.
$20,000 to Washtenaw Housing Alliance, Ann Arbor, MI, 2012.
$7,047 to Interfaith Hospitality Network of Washtenaw County, Ann Arbor, MI, 2012.
$7,000 to University of Michigan, Ann Arbor, MI, 2012. For Saturday program for native Spanish-speaking students.
$5,000 to Michigan Theater Foundation, Ann Arbor, MI, 2012. For Michigan Theater Cinetopia Festival/Young Professional Outreach and Marketing.

4341
The Eugene Applebaum Family Foundation ✧
39400 Woodward Ave., Ste. 100
Bloomfield Hills, MI 48304-5151

Donors: Pamela Applebaum Wyett; Lisa S. Applebaum; Pamela A. Applebaum; Eugene Applebaum; Eugene Applebaum Charitable Lead Trust.
Foundation type: Independent foundation.
Financial data (yr. ended 11/30/13): Assets, $418,013 (M); gifts received, $3,055,256; expenditures, $2,702,730; qualifying distributions, $2,686,550; giving activities include $2,670,370 for 93 grants (high: $600,000; low: $25) and $2,670 for set-asides.
Purpose and activities: Giving primarily to Jewish organizations, including federated giving programs; support also for education, the arts, and health care.
Fields of interest: Arts; Elementary/secondary education; Higher education; Education; Health care; Jewish federated giving programs; Jewish agencies & synagogues.
Limitations: Applications not accepted. Giving primarily in MI, and New York, NY.
Application information: Unsolicited requests for funds not accepted.
Officers: Eugene Applebaum, Pres.; Marcia Applebaum, V.P.; Lisa S. Applebaum, Secy.; Pamela A. Applebaum, Treas.
EIN: 382782955

4342
Barry Community Foundation ✧
231 S. Bdwy.
Hastings, MI 49058-1835 (269) 945-0526
Contact: Bonnie Hildreth, Pres.
FAX: (269) 945-0826; E-mail: info@barrycf.org; Additional e-mails: bonnie@barrycf.org and grants@barrycf.org; Main URL: http://www.barrycf.org
Facebook: https://www.facebook.com/barrycommunityfoundation
RSS Feed: http://www.barrycf.org/feed/
YouTube: http://www.youtube.com/user/2013BCF?feature=watch

Established in 1996 in MI.
Foundation type: Community foundation.
Financial data (yr. ended 06/30/13): Assets, $22,807,037 (M); gifts received, $3,933,780; expenditures, $1,596,944; giving activities include $816,212 for 15+ grants (high: $360,213), $75,630 for 79 grants to individuals, and $1,350,000 for loans/program-related investments.
Purpose and activities: The mission of the foundation is to develop and manage endowed funds for helping and involving the people of Barry County, MI, to make a positive difference in their lives.
Fields of interest: Arts; Education; Environment, natural resources; Health care; Children/youth, services; Human services; Community development, neighborhood development; Community/economic development.
Type of support: General/operating support; Annual campaigns; Capital campaigns; Building/renovation; Equipment; Endowments; Program development; Conferences/seminars; Seed money; Curriculum development; Scholarship funds; Research; Technical assistance; Consulting services; Program evaluation; Matching/challenge support.
Limitations: Applications accepted. Giving limited to Barry County, MI. No support for private organizations, including churches. No grants to individuals (except for scholarships), or for operating expenses or regularly upgrading equipment.
Publications: Application guidelines; Annual report; Informational brochure; Newsletter.
Application information: The foundation is currently accepting applications for Healthy Communities Grantmaking Program; visit foundation web site for application form and guidelines. Application form required.
Initial approach: Submit application and attachment
Copies of proposal: 10
Deadline(s): Apr. 15 and Oct. 15
Board meeting date(s): 3rd Thurs. monthly
Final notification: Within 8 weeks
Officers and Trustees:* Karen Heath,* Chair.; David Solmes,* Vice-Chair.; Bonnie Hildreth,* Pres. and C.E.O.; Jennifer Richards,* V.P.; Jennifer Haywood,* Secy.; Dave Coleman,* Co-Treas.; Melissa Wallace,* Co-Treas.; Barb Case; Fred Jacobs; Mike McCullough; Deb McKeown; Scott McKeown; Robert Perino; Carl Schoessel; Shauna Swantek; Marcia Szumowski; Jim Toburen.
Number of staff: 1 full-time professional; 3 full-time support; 1 part-time support.
EIN: 383246131

4343
Battle Creek Community Foundation ✧
(formerly Greater Battle Creek Foundation)
1 Riverwalk Ctr.
34 W. Jackson St.
Battle Creek, MI 49017-3505 (269) 962-2181
Contact: Brenda L. Hunt, C.E.O.
FAX: (269) 962-2182;
E-mail: bccf@bccfoundation.org; Main URL: http://www.bccfoundation.org/
E-Newsletter: http://www.bccfoundation.org/newsletter-signup
Facebook: https://www.facebook.com/bccfound
Flickr: http://www.flickr.com/photos/69312701@N06/
Twitter: https://twitter.com/@BCCFound
YouTube: http://www.youtube.com/bccfound

Established in 1974 in MI.
Foundation type: Community foundation.
Financial data (yr. ended 03/31/14): Assets, $114,841,175 (M); gifts received, $3,280,020; expenditures, $8,808,558; giving activities include $6,675,021 for grants.
Purpose and activities: The foundation seeks to promote giving, build endowment, and provide leadership to improve quality of life. Grantmaking for programming in the Battle Creek, MI, area serves the citizens of the community through education, health, human services, arts, public affairs, and community development; scholarships are also available to students residing in the greater Battle Creek area.
Fields of interest: Arts; Child development, education; Adult education—literacy, basic skills & GED; Education, reading; Education; Animal welfare; Hospitals (general); Health care; Health organizations, association; Children/youth, services; Child development, services; Minorities/immigrants, centers/services; Human services; Community/economic development; Public affairs; Youth; Minorities.
Type of support: Research; Film/video/radio; Building/renovation; Equipment; Land acquisition; Emergency funds; Program development; Conferences/seminars; Publication; Seed money; Curriculum development; Scholarship funds; Technical assistance; Program evaluation; Program-related investments/loans; Scholarships—to individuals; Matching/challenge support.
Limitations: Applications accepted. Giving limited to the greater Battle Creek, MI, area. No grants for operating budgets, deficit financing, endowments, or research; no loans (except for program-related investments).
Publications: Application guidelines; Annual report; Biennial report (including application guidelines); Financial statement; Grants list; Informational brochure; Newsletter; Program policy statement.
Application information: Visit foundation web site for grantseeker orientation dates, grant application packets, guidelines per grant type, and specific deadlines. Application form required.
Initial approach: Attend a grantseeker orientation
Copies of proposal: 20
Deadline(s): Varies
Board meeting date(s): Monthly
Final notification: Within 2 months
Officers and Trustees:* Brenda L. Hunt, C.E.O. and Pres.; Annette Chapman, V.P., Grantmaking and Scholarships; Thomas Crothers, V.P., Finance and Investments; Amy Bauman; Susan Baldwin; Rick Baron; Taylor Brown; Deonna F. Estes; Marcus E. Glass; Haley Harris; Dorothy Height; Patrick Horan; Brenda Minter; Kathy Rizor; T.R. Shaw, Jr.; William W. Simonds; C. Glen Walter; Judith Cole Williamson.
Number of staff: 15 full-time professional; 2 part-time professional; 3 full-time support.
EIN: 382045459
Selected grants: The following grants are a representative sample of this grantmaker's funding activity:
$55,000 to Lakeview School District, Battle Creek, MI, 2013. For BCCAN Staff at Lakeview Schools - Pilot Project.
$50,000 to Charitable Union, Battle Creek, MI, 2013. For Phase I - update of software system.
$50,000 to Emily Andrus Home Association of Battle Creek Michigan, Battle Creek, MI, 2013. For the first year of operations for the Women's Life Recovery Program at the Emily Andrus Home.
$40,000 to Kingman Museum, Battle Creek, MI, 2013. For general support.
$34,000 to Binder Park Zoological Society, Battle Creek, MI, 2013. For improvements to zoo pavilions.
$30,000 to Community Inclusive Recreation, Battle Creek, MI, 2013. For general support, organization planning, development, transition planning and execution.
$30,000 to Michigan State University, College of Agriculture and Natural Resources, East Lansing, MI, 2013. For the establishment of the Future Leaders Mentoring Scholarship.
$8,321 to Community Healthcare Connections, Battle Creek, MI, 2013. For The Dentists' Partnership.
$4,741 to Community Action Agency of South Central Michigan, Battle Creek, MI, 2013. For Replace Kitchen Exhaust Hood.
$3,000 to Homer Community School, Homer, MI, 2013. For Mural Restoration.

4344
Bay Area Community Foundation ✧
Pere Marquette Depot
1000 Adams St., Ste. 200
Bay City, MI 48708-5994 (989) 893-4438
Contact: Eileen A. Curtis, C.E.O. and Pres.
FAX: (989) 893-4448;
E-mail: bacfnd@bayfoundation.org; Main URL: http://www.bayfoundation.org
Facebook: http://www.facebook.com/pages/Bay-City-MI/Bay-Area-Community-Foundation/93894481045

Established in 1982 in MI.
Foundation type: Community foundation.
Financial data (yr. ended 12/31/13): Assets, $45,035,286 (M); gifts received, $1,427,973; expenditures, $3,731,924; giving activities include $1,717,806 for grants.
Purpose and activities: The foundation seeks to fulfill a wide array of donors' charitable wishes by building permanent endowment funds and serving as a leader for community improvement through effective grantmaking and collaboration. Priority will be given to projects that focus on charitable, cultural, educational, and environmental areas for Michigan's Bay and Arenac counties.
Fields of interest: Visual arts; Performing arts; Arts; Education; Environment, energy; Environment; Animal welfare; Health care; Alzheimer's disease; Housing/shelter; Recreation; Human services; Community/economic development; Science; Youth; Aging; Mentally disabled.
Type of support: General/operating support; Capital campaigns; Building/renovation; Equipment; Emergency funds; Program development; Seed money; Curriculum development; Internship funds; Scholarship funds; Research; Technical assistance; Matching/challenge support.
Limitations: Applications accepted. Giving limited to Bay and Arenac counties, MI. No support for religious organizations. No grants to individuals (excluding scholarships), or for existing obligations, endowments, or fundraising events.
Publications: Annual report; Financial statement; Grants list; Informational brochure; Newsletter.
Application information: Visit foundation web site for application form and guidelines. Applications sent by fax will not be accepted. Application form required.
Initial approach: Telephone
Deadline(s): Varies
Board meeting date(s): Quarterly
Final notification: Varies
Officers and Trustees:* Mike Hanisko,* Chair.; William Mulders,* Vice-Chair.; Eileen A. Curtis,* C.E.O. and Pres.; Cathy Washabaugh,* Secy.; Amy Rodriguez,* Treas.; William Bowen; Kay Burks; Beth Elliott; Karolyn Goslin; Gregory Grocholski; Debra Lutz; Jeff Mayes; Richard Milster; Dominic Monastiere; Douglas Newcombe; Anne Trahan; Jeff Yantz.
Number of staff: 3 full-time professional; 3 full-time support.
EIN: 382418086

4345
Robert F. Beard Charitable Foundation ✧ ☆
c/o James R. Clark
1704 E. Highland Rd.
Highland, MI 48356-2359

Established in 1994 in MI.
Donors: Robert F. Beard; Robert F. Beard Trust.
Foundation type: Independent foundation.
Financial data (yr. ended 12/31/13): Assets, $12,691,670 (M); gifts received, $1,775,709; expenditures, $624,570; qualifying distributions, $500,000; giving activities include $500,000 for 14 grants (high: $87,500; low: $10,000).
Fields of interest: Human services; Children/youth, services.
Type of support: General/operating support.
Limitations: Applications not accepted. Giving primarily in southeastern MI. No grants to individuals.
Application information: Unsolicited requests for funds not accepted.
Officers and Directors:* James R. Clark,* Pres.; John Beard,* Treas.; Michael Beard; Melissa Chirco; Brian Clark; Garret Clark; Susan Clark; Lauren Ryan.
EIN: 383168934

4346
Mandell L. and Madeleine H. Berman Foundation ✧
(formerly Madeleine and Mandell L. Berman Foundation)
c/o Sarai Brachman Shoup
29100 Northwestern Hwy., Ste. 370
Southfield, MI 48034-1092

Established in 1994 in MI.
Donors: Mandell L. Berman; Madeline Berman.

Foundation type: Independent foundation.
Financial data (yr. ended 12/31/13): Assets, $17,507,980 (M); gifts received, $1,992,066; expenditures, $3,971,880; qualifying distributions, $3,744,357; giving activities include $3,557,415 for 144 grants (high: $600,955; low: $100).
Fields of interest: Jewish agencies & synagogues.
International interests: Israel.
Limitations: Applications not accepted. Giving on a national and international basis, and in the Detroit, MI, area. No grants to individuals.
Application information: Contributes only to pre-selected organizations.
Officer: Mandell L. Berman, Pres.
Trustees: Jonathan Berman; Madeleine Berman; Ann Feld; Janice Friedlander; David Jones.
Number of staff: 2 part-time professional.
EIN: 386644875

4347
Berrien Community Foundation, Inc. ✧

2900 S. State St., Ste. 2E
Saint Joseph, MI 49085-2467 (269) 983-3304
Contact: Lisa Cripps-Downey, Pres.
FAX: (269) 983-4939;
E-mail: bcf@BerrienCommunity.org; Additional e-mail: bcf@BerrienCommunity.org; Main URL: http://www.BerrienCommunity.org
Facebook: https://www.facebook.com/BerrienCommunityFoundation

Incorporated in 1952 in MI.
Foundation type: Community foundation.
Financial data (yr. ended 12/31/13): Assets, $33,229,231 (M); gifts received, $6,653,452; expenditures, $4,340,421; giving activities include $3,831,794 for 115 grants (high: $242,457), and $95,500 for 71 grants to individuals.
Purpose and activities: The mission of the foundation is to promote philanthropy, to build a spirit of community, and to enhance the quality of life in Berrien County through its stewardship of permanently endowed and other funds. The foundation shall accomplish this mission by: 1) building endowments and other funds, and providing a broad range of flexible and cost-effective donor services; 2) investing and managing funds prudently and professionally; 3) making grants to support a broad range of projects and programs that address community needs, with a focus on building a spirit of community/arts and culture, nurturing children, and youth leadership and development; and 4) serving as a facilitative leader, catalyst, and resource for local communities.
Fields of interest: Arts; Child development, education; Education; Housing/shelter; Youth development; Human services; Community/economic development; Children/youth; Youth; Adults; Aging.
Type of support: Program development.
Limitations: Giving primarily in Grants provided in Berrien County, MI only for undesignated and field-of-interest funds; grants in the U.S. for advised and others funds. No support for sectarian religious purposes. No grants to individuals (except for scholarships), or for ongoing operating funds, deficit financing, national fundraising efforts, annual fund drives, or program-related investments.
Publications: Financial statement; Informational brochure (including application guidelines); Occasional report.
Application information: Visit foundation web site for how to start the application process; guidelines and forms are made available by email after staff review of exempt status, Solicitation Registration status, proposed project/program, etc. (see web site for details). 20 copies of application required for youth-oriented projects only, varies for others. Application form required.
Initial approach: E-mail inquiry to bcf@berriencommunity.org
Deadline(s): Varies (see web site)
Board meeting date(s): Oct.
Final notification: 10 to 14 weeks
Officers and Trustees:* Tim Passaro, J.D.*, Chair.; Hillary Bubb,* Vice-Chair.; Lisa Cripps-Downey,* Pres.; Hon. Mabel Mayfield, J.D.*, Secy.; Jeffrey Dorn,* Treas.; Lois Ashbrook; Mary Dunbar; Dr. Robert Harrison, Ph.D.; Brenda Layne; Phil Maki; Lee Reed; Bill Schalk; Larry Schuler.
Number of staff: 2 full-time professional; 1 part-time support.
EIN: 386057160

4348
John & Melissa Besse Foundation ✧ ☆

8 Waterford Ave.
Gladstone, MI 49837-0352
Application address: Gregory D. Besse, P.O. Box 352, Gladstone, MI 49837

Established in 2005 in MI.
Donors: John D. Besse; Melissa Besse†.
Foundation type: Independent foundation.
Financial data (yr. ended 12/31/13): Assets, $10,937,621 (M); gifts received, $9,266,074; expenditures, $2,970,894; qualifying distributions, $2,970,894; giving activities include $2,955,550 for 9 grants (high: $2,500,000; low: $1,000).
Fields of interest: Higher education, college (community/junior); Education; Community/economic development.
Type of support: General/operating support.
Limitations: Applications accepted. Giving primarily in MI.
Application information: Application form required.
Initial approach: Letter
Deadline(s): None
Directors: John D. Besse; Gregory D. Besse.
EIN: 203497950

4349
Besser Foundation ✧

123 N. 2nd Ave., Ste. 3
Alpena, MI 49707-2801 (989) 354-4722
Contact: Gary Dawley, Secy.-Treas and Mgr.

Incorporated in 1944 in MI.
Donors: J.H. Besser†; Besser Co.
Foundation type: Independent foundation.
Financial data (yr. ended 12/31/13): Assets, $19,537,838 (M); expenditures, $1,081,504; qualifying distributions, $1,007,758; giving activities include $951,700 for 31 grants (high: $238,333; low: $300).
Purpose and activities: Grants primarily to local schools and colleges and health and social service agencies; giving also to Africare for projects in underdeveloped nations in Africa. In addition, the foundation partially supports the Jesse Besser Museum, a local historical and art museum.
Fields of interest: Museums; Arts; Education; Human services; Children/youth, services.
Type of support: General/operating support; Continuing support; Capital campaigns; Building/renovation; Matching/challenge support.
Limitations: Applications accepted. Giving limited to the Alpena, MI, area. No support for video projects. No grants to individuals, or for endowment funds, meeting or conference expenses, travel, or research.
Publications: Annual report (including application guidelines).
Application information: Application form required.
Initial approach: Letter
Copies of proposal: 1
Deadline(s): End of 1st month in each calendar quarter
Board meeting date(s): Quarterly beginning in Mar.
Officers: James C. Park, Pres.; Patricia Gardner, V.P.; Gary C. Dawley, Secy.-Treas. and Mgr.
Trustees: Ann Burton; Chris McCoy.
Number of staff: 2 part-time support.
EIN: 386071938

4350
Guido A. & Elizabeth H. Binda Foundation ✧

15 Capital Ave. N.E., Ste. 205
Battle Creek, MI 49017-3557 (269) 968-6171
Contact: Nancy Taber, Exec. Dir.
FAX: (269) 968-5126;
E-mail: grants@bindafoundation.org; E-mail for general information: info@bindafoundation.org; Main URL: http://www.bindafoundation.org

Established in 1977 in MI.
Donor: Guido A. Binda†.
Foundation type: Independent foundation.
Financial data (yr. ended 06/30/13): Assets, $22,463,191 (M); gifts received, $188; expenditures, $1,186,146; qualifying distributions, $1,062,638; giving activities include $939,132 for 69 grants (high: $465,000; low: $90).
Purpose and activities: Giving primarily for education, including health and environmental education, as well as for arts and culture, and human services. Creative educational projects receive the highest consideration.
Fields of interest: Arts; Higher education; Education; Environment, formal/general education; Environment; Health care, formal/general education; Human services.
Type of support: Program development; Seed money; Curriculum development; Scholarship funds.
Limitations: Giving limited to Calhoun County, MI. No grants to individuals, or for endowments, capital campaigns, trips, conferences or summer camps.
Publications: Application guidelines; Occasional report.
Application information: Following a review of the letter of inquiry, the foundation will forward its grant application if the grant request is within the scope of the foundation's mission. Application form required.
Initial approach: Letter of Inquiry (via e-mail or U.S. mail)
Copies of proposal: 11
Deadline(s): None, for letters of inquiry
Board meeting date(s): Jan. and June
Final notification: 10 days
Officers and Trustees:* John H. Hosking,* Pres.; Richard Tsoumas,* V.P.; Nancy Taber, Exec. Dir.; Robert Binda; LaVerne H. Boss; Chris T. Christ; Joel Orosz; Cindy S. Ruble.

Number of staff: 1 part-time support.
EIN: 382184423

4351
Harold & Penny B. Blumenstein Foundation Corporation ✧
32400 Telegraph Rd., Ste. 202
Bingham Farms, MI 48025-2460

Established in 1986 in MI.
Donors: Harold Blumenstein; Penny B. Blumenstein; Richard Blumenstein; Carol Blumenstein.
Foundation type: Independent foundation.
Financial data (yr. ended 12/31/13): Assets, $9,443,864 (M); gifts received, $1,000,000; expenditures, $795,910; qualifying distributions, $786,161; giving activities include $785,581 for 83 grants (high: $257,179; low: $36).
Purpose and activities: Giving primarily for Jewish agencies, federated giving programs, and schools; funding also for the arts, including an orchestra.
Fields of interest: Arts; Education; Health organizations, association; Jewish federated giving programs; Jewish agencies & synagogues.
Limitations: Applications not accepted. Giving primarily in MI; some giving also in NY. No grants to individuals.
Application information: Contributes only to pre-selected organizations.
Officers: Harold Blumenstein, Pres.; Penny B. Blumenstein, V.P. and Secy.; Richard C. Blumenstein, V.P.; Lauren A. Cohen, V.P.; Randall S. Blumenstein, Treas.
EIN: 382710389
Selected grants: The following grants are a representative sample of this grantmaker's funding activity:
$100,168 to American Jewish Joint Distribution Committee, New York, NY, 2011.
$17,500 to Akiva Hebrew Day School-Yeshivat Akiva, Southfield, MI, 2011.

4352
John A. & Marlene L. Boll Foundation ✧
100 Maple Park Blvd., Ste. 118
St. Clair Shores, MI 48081-2253 (586) 777-4770
Main URL: http://bollfoundation.org/

Established in 1986 in MI.
Donors: John A. Boll; Marlene L. Boll.
Foundation type: Independent foundation.
Financial data (yr. ended 12/31/13): Assets, $1,071,659 (M); gifts received, $2,200,000; expenditures, $1,474,404; qualifying distributions, $1,360,981; giving activities include $1,360,981 for 106 grants (high: $250,000; low: $25).
Purpose and activities: Giving educational scholarships to institutions with curriculum based, in part, on Judeo-Christian traditions.
Fields of interest: Arts; Higher education; Scholarships/financial aid; Health care; Human services; YM/YWCAs & YM/YWHAs; Foundations (private grantmaking); Christian agencies & churches; Protestant agencies & churches.
Type of support: General/operating support.
Limitations: Applications accepted. Giving in the U.S., with emphasis on MI. No grants to individuals.
Application information: Letters of recommendation for scholarship candidates are required for further review. Application form not required.
Initial approach: Letter
Deadline(s): None
Directors: John A. Boll; Marlene L. Boll; Kristine B. Mestdagh.
EIN: 382708121
Selected grants: The following grants are a representative sample of this grantmaker's funding activity:
$250,000 to Detroit Institute of Arts, Detroit, MI, 2011.
$250,000 to Ocean Reef Cultural Center, Key Largo, FL, 2011.
$250,000 to Ocean Reef Medical Center Foundation, Key Largo, FL, 2011.
$100,000 to Healthnetwork Foundation, Chagrin Falls, OH, 2011.
$50,000 to Michigan Opera Theater, Detroit, MI, 2011.
$10,000 to Michigan Opera Theater, Detroit, MI, 2011.
$10,000 to Ocean Reef Cultural Center, Key Largo, FL, 2011.
$5,000 to Detroit Institute of Arts, Detroit, MI, 2011.
$2,000 to Detroit Institute of Arts, Detroit, MI, 2011.
$1,200 to Detroit Historical Society, Detroit, MI, 2011.

4353
BorgWarner Foundation ✧
3850 Hamlin Rd.
Auburn Hills, MI 48326-2872

Established in 2001 in IL.
Donor: BorgWarner Inc.
Foundation type: Company-sponsored foundation.
Financial data (yr. ended 12/31/12): Assets, $0 (M); gifts received, $720,974; expenditures, $720,974; qualifying distributions, $720,974; giving activities include $720,974 for 105 grants (high: $575,000; low: $50).
Purpose and activities: The foundation supports organizations involved with education, health, and human services.
Fields of interest: Education; Health care; Human services.
Type of support: General/operating support; Endowments; Scholarship funds.
Limitations: Applications not accepted. Giving primarily in MI. No grants to individuals.
Application information: Unsolicited requests for funds not accepted.
Officers: Laurene H. Horiszny, Pres.; Thomas McGill, Treas.
Director: Jere Drummond.
EIN: 311776016

4354
Bosch Community Fund ✧
3800 Hills Tech Dr.
Farmington Hills, MI 48331

Donor: Robert Bosch LLC.
Foundation type: Independent foundation.
Financial data (yr. ended 12/31/12): Assets, $1,939,172 (M); gifts received, $3,400,000; expenditures, $1,477,989; qualifying distributions, $1,469,670; giving activities include $1,469,670 for 28 grants (high: $250,000; low: $5,000).
Fields of interest: Elementary/secondary education; Higher education; Human services; United Ways and Federated Giving Programs.
Limitations: Applications not accepted. Giving primarily in CA, GA, IL, MI, and PA.
Application information: Contributes only to pre-selected organizations.
Officers: Norman Johnson, Chair.; Maximilian Straub, Vice-Chair.; Kathleen Owsley, Secy.; Lee Manduzzi, Treas.
Trustees: Berend Bracht; Terry Horan; Daniel R. Hyman.
EIN: 454020765

4355
The Hilda E. Bretzlaff Foundation, Inc. ✧
1550 N. Milford Rd., Ste. 101
Milford, MI 48381-1058
Contact: Janelle M. Radtke, V.P.
E-mail: jradtke@hebf.org; Additional e-mail: klindbeck@hebf.org; Main URL: http://www.hebf.org

Established in 1994 in MI.
Donor: Hilda E. Bretzlaff†.
Foundation type: Independent foundation.
Financial data (yr. ended 12/31/13): Assets, $25,077,801 (M); expenditures, $1,593,326; qualifying distributions, $1,299,528; giving activities include $944,600 for 65 grants (high: $60,000; low: $350), and $40,000 for 39 grants to individuals (high: $2,500; low: $1,250).
Purpose and activities: The foundation provides educational grants to assist students in attending educational institutions in the United States or England that promote high educational, moral, and conservative ideals.
Fields of interest: Scholarships/financial aid.
Type of support: Scholarship funds.
Limitations: Applications not accepted. Giving primarily in MI and OH for the benefit of U.S. citizens or individuals in the process of becoming U.S. citizens. No support for schools that are not conservative. No grants to individuals directly.
Application information: Funds administered through educational institutions. Applicants must have and maintain a minimum of 2.0 GPA. The foundation's mission statement indicates that all applicants must be financially needy, moral, conservative, and a credit to America.
Board meeting date(s): Bimonthly
Officers: Gerald W. Radtke, Pres.; Susan J. Vogt, V.P.; Janelle M. Radtke, Secy.-Treas.; Kathleen M. Lindbeck, Mgr.
Number of staff: 4 part-time professional.
EIN: 382619845
Selected grants: The following grants are a representative sample of this grantmaker's funding activity:
$50,000 to Alice Lloyd College, Pippa Passes, KY, 2012. For annual grant - 12 students.
$35,000 to Hillsdale College, Hillsdale, MI, 2012. For Fall grant - A. Vogt scholarship.
$29,000 to Lutheran Special Education Ministries, Detroit, MI, 2012. For Lexia Program.
$25,000 to Ashland University, Ashland, OH, 2012. For spring grant.
$25,000 to Chestnut Hill College, Philadelphia, PA, 2012. For Spring grant - enhanced program.
$25,000 to Chestnut Hill College, Philadelphia, PA, 2012. For enhanced program.

$21,000 to Spring Hill Camps, Evart, MI, 2012. For Urban week day camp program.
$12,500 to Concordia University, Ann Arbor, MI, 2012. For Spring grant - science prof.
$10,000 to Leader Dogs for the Blind, Rochester, MI, 2012. For Fall grant - O and M Program.
$10,000 to Leader Dogs for the Blind, Rochester, MI, 2012. For technology program.

4356
The John and Rosemary Brown Family Foundation ✧
750 Trade Ctr. Way No. 145
Portage, MI 49002-0485

Established in 1997 in MI.
Donors: John W. Brown; Rosemary K. Brown.
Foundation type: Independent foundation.
Financial data (yr. ended 12/31/13): Assets, $26,239,580 (M); gifts received, $502,675; expenditures, $995,535; qualifying distributions, $994,700; giving activities include $990,250 for 45 grants (high: $350,000; low: $1,000).
Purpose and activities: Giving primarily for higher education, economic development, and Christian churches; funding also for health associations, the arts, and children, youth, and social services.
Fields of interest: Arts; Higher education; Education; Health organizations, association; Medical research, institute; Human services; Children/youth, services; Economic development; Community/economic development; United Ways and Federated Giving Programs; Christian agencies & churches.
Limitations: Applications not accepted. Giving primarily in MI, with emphasis on Kalamazoo; funding also in GA, with emphasis on Atlanta. No grants to individuals.
Application information: Contributes only to pre-selected organizations.
Trustees: John W. Brown; Rosemary K. Brown.
EIN: 586343478

4357
Capital Region Community Foundation ✧
330 Marshall St., NO 300
Lansing, MI 48912 (517) 272-2870
Contact: Dennis W. Fliehman, C.E.O.
FAX: (517) 272-2871;
E-mail: dfliehman@crcfoundation.org; Main URL: http://www.crcfoundation.org
Facebook: http://www.facebook.com/givelansing
Flickr: http://www.flickr.com/photos/givelansing
RSS Feed: http://crcfoundation.org/rss/articles/all
Twitter: http://twitter.com/givelansing

Established in 1987 in MI.
Foundation type: Community foundation.
Financial data (yr. ended 12/31/13): Assets, $81,083,450 (M); gifts received, $3,084,128; expenditures, $4,243,505; giving activities include $2,969,486 for 98+ grants (high: $825,000), and $194,910 for 91 grants to individuals.
Purpose and activities: The purpose of the foundation is to build the number and size of permanent endowment funds, income from which is used for grants that meet the charitable needs of Clinton, Eaton, and Ingham counties, MI. The foundation provides support for humanities, education, environment, health care, human services, and public benefit.
Fields of interest: Humanities; Education; Environment; Health care; Children/youth, services; Human services; Community/economic development; Public affairs.
Type of support: Management development/capacity building; General/operating support; Capital campaigns; Building/renovation; Equipment; Program development; Seed money; Technical assistance; Matching/challenge support.
Limitations: Applications accepted. Giving limited to Clinton, Eaton, and Ingham counties, MI. No support for international organizations, religious programs, or sectarian purposes. No grants to individuals (except for scholarships), or for endowment funds, administrative costs of fundraising campaigns, annual meetings, routine operating expenses, or for existing obligations, debts, or liabilities.
Publications: Application guidelines; Annual report; Financial statement; Grants list; Informational brochure.
Application information: To apply for any CRCF grant applicants must use the foundation's online system; visit foundation web site for online application and guidelines. Application form required.
Initial approach: Telephone
Deadline(s): Mar. 3 for grants; Jan. 31 for Youth Fund
Board meeting date(s): Bimonthly
Final notification: Oct. 1 for grants
Officers and Trustees:* Kira Carter-Robertson,* Chair.; Tina Ferland,* Chair.-Elect; Dennis W. Fliehman,* C.E.O. and Pres.; Richard Comstock,* V.P., Finance; Robin Miner-Swartz,* V.P., Mktg. and Comms.; Laurie Robison,* Secy.; Emily L. Matthews, C.O.O.; John Sirrine,* Treas.; Tim Daman; Joe Dewan; Duncan Davidson; Michael Flowers; Bo Garcia; Joan Jackson Johnson, Ph.D.; Michele A. Kirkland; Robert Kolt; Rachel Lewis; Patty Lloyd Barnas; Rachel Michaud; Helen Pratt Mickens; Joe E. Pray; Brian Priester; Jack Roberts; Danielle Robinson; Denise Schroeder; Kate Snyder; James Spaniolo; Marlaine Teahan; Robert L. Trezise, Jr.
Number of staff: 5 full-time professional; 1 part-time professional; 1 full-time support; 1 part-time support.
EIN: 382776652
Selected grants: The following grants are a representative sample of this grantmaker's funding activity:
$15,000 to Care Free Medical, Lansing, MI, 2011. For Pay-It Forward Dental Access Initiative.
$15,000 to Child and Family Services of Michigan, Okemos, MI, 2011. For independent living for teens aging out of foster care.
$15,000 to Clinton County Regional Education Agency, Saint Johns, MI, 2011. For Annie's BIG Nature Lesson for elementary students.
$15,000 to Cristo Rey Community Center, Lansing, MI, 2011. For Prescription Assistance Program.
$15,000 to Eaton Area Senior Center, Charlotte, MI, 2011. For Senior Support Services Lunch Program.
$15,000 to Global Institute of Lansing, Lansing, MI, 2011. For Refugee High School Graduation Program.
$15,000 to Many Hands Foundation, Eaton, MI, 2011. For Weekend Survivor Kits Program.
$14,940 to Lansing Community College Foundation, Lansing, MI, 2011. For From Unemployed to Employed: Building Re-Employment Strategies for the Older Dislocated Workers.
$12,730 to Reach Studio Art Center, Lansing, MI, 2011. For after school art programs.
$8,716 to Williamston Theater, Williamston, MI, 2011. For capital improvement projects.
$8,000 to Volunteers of America of Greater Lansing, Lansing, MI, 2011. For Hotel Emergency Lodging Program.
$6,000 to Bath Charter Township, Clinton County, MI, 2011. For Park Lake Beach Renovation Project to construct handicapp accessible pavillion.
$4,200 to YMCA of Lansing, Lansing, MI, 2011. For Parkwood YMCA Special Adventure Summer Camp and Y-Time Program for children with Down Syndrome and other special needs.

4358
The Carls Foundation ✧
6001 N. Adams Rd., Ste. 215
Bloomfield Hills, MI 48304-1576 (248) 434-5512
Contact: Elizabeth A. Stieg, Exec. Dir.
Main URL: http://www.carlsfdn.org

Established in 1961 in MI.
Donor: William Carls†.
Foundation type: Independent foundation.
Financial data (yr. ended 12/31/12): Assets, $112,282,382 (M); expenditures, $5,990,405; qualifying distributions, $5,411,955; giving activities include $4,826,811 for 45 grants (high: $500,000; low: $11,618).
Purpose and activities: The principal purpose and mission of the foundation is: 1) Children's Welfare including: health care facilities and programs, with special emphasis on the prevention and treatment of hearing impairment, and recreational, educational, and welfare programs especially for children who are disadvantaged for economic and/or health reasons; and 2) Preservation of natural areas, open space and historic buildings and areas having special natural beauty or significance in maintaining America's heritage and historic ideals, through assistance to land trusts and land conservancies and directly related environmental educational programs.
Fields of interest: Historic preservation/historical societies; Education; Environment, natural resources; Hospitals (general); Speech/hearing centers; Health care; Recreation; Children/youth, services.
Type of support: Capital campaigns; Seed money.
Limitations: Applications accepted. Giving primarily in MI. No grants to individuals, or for publications, film, research, endowments, fellowships, travel, conferences, special event sponsorships, playground or athletic facilities, or seminars; no educational loans.
Publications: Annual report; Grants list.
Application information: Letter of inquiry is not required and phone calls are welcome. Use of the CMF Common Grant Application Form is optional and acceptable. Application form not required.
Initial approach: Proposal
Copies of proposal: 1
Board meeting date(s): Jan., May, and Sept.
Final notification: Notification letter sent to all applicants
Officers and Trustees:* Elizabeth A. Stieg,* Pres. and Exec. Dir.; Henry Fleischer,* V.P.; Teresa R. Krieger; Dr. Homer E. Nye; Robert A. Sajdak; Edward C. Stieg.
Advisory Board: Donald A. Delong, Esq.; Bruce M. Fleischer, Ph.D.; Teresa Krieger-Burke, Ph.D.

Number of staff: 1 full-time professional; 1 part-time professional; 1 full-time support.
EIN: 386099935

4359
Cascade Hemophilia Consortium ✧
517 W. William St.
Ann Arbor, MI 48103-4943 (734) 996-3300
E-mail: info@cascadehc.org; Main URL: http://www.cascadehc.org/

Established in 1996 in MI.
Foundation type: Operating foundation.
Financial data (yr. ended 12/31/12): Assets, $16,523,359 (M); expenditures, $4,050,083; qualifying distributions, $34,942,215; giving activities include $2,515,848 for 42 grants (high: $622,134; low: $5,007), and $35,572,151 for foundation-administered programs.
Purpose and activities: Support limited to the medical care and research of hemophilia.
Fields of interest: Hemophilia; Hemophilia research.
Limitations: Applications not accepted. Giving primarily in IN, MI, and OH. No grants to individuals.
Application information: Foundation sends out Requests for Proposals and does not accept unsolicited requests for funds.
Officers: William Berk, M.D., Pres.; William Sparrow, R.N., V.P.; Helen Levenson, J.D., Secy.; Peter Deininger, CPA, MBA, Treas.; Timothy Brent, Exec. Dir.
Directors: Amy Denton; Nancy Duffy, R.N.; Jeffrey Hord, M.D.; Michael McGuire; Gary Priestap, J.D., LLM, MBA; Came Reaume; Lauren Shellenberger, R.N., BSN, JD.
EIN: 383199649

4360
Charboneau Family Foundation ✧
43535 Carla Dr.
Paw Paw, MI 49079-9759

Donors: Kenneth Charboneau; Michael Charboneau; Kent Charboneau.
Foundation type: Independent foundation.
Financial data (yr. ended 12/31/13): Assets, $23,495,500 (M); expenditures, $1,254,131; qualifying distributions, $1,250,000; giving activities include $1,250,000 for 24 grants (high: $225,000; low: $400).
Fields of interest: Education; Human services.
Limitations: Applications not accepted. No grants to individuals.
Application information: Contributes only to pre-selected organizations.
Trustees: Donna Charboneau; Kenneth Charboneau; Kent Charboneau; Michael Charboneau.
EIN: 208080199

4361
Charlevoix County Community Foundation ✧
301 Water St.
P.O. Box 718
East Jordan, MI 49727 (231) 536-2440
Contact: For grants: Maureen Radke, Prog. Off.
FAX: (231) 536-2640; E-mail: info@c3f.org; Grant inquiry e-mail: maureen@c3f.org; Main URL: http://www.c3f.org

Established in 1992 in MI.
Foundation type: Community foundation.
Financial data (yr. ended 12/31/13): Assets, $29,208,915 (M); gifts received, $1,779,744; expenditures, $1,924,146; giving activities include $1,345,020 for 64+ grants (high: $100,000; low: $50), and $139,616 for 147 grants to individuals.
Purpose and activities: The foundation seeks to enhance the quality of life in Charlevoix County, MI, now and for generations to come, by building a permanent charitable endowment from a wide range of donors, addressing needs through grantmaking, and providing leadership on matters of community concern.
Fields of interest: Arts; Higher education; Education; Environment; Health care; Recreation; Children/youth, services; Family services; Human services; Economic development; Community/economic development; Government/public administration; Aging.
Type of support: Endowments; Emergency funds; Program development; Seed money; Scholarship funds; Technical assistance; Consulting services; Scholarships—to individuals.
Limitations: Applications accepted. Giving limited to Charlevoix County, MI. No support for sectarian purposes. No grants to individuals (except for scholarships), or for ongoing organizational operating expenses, office equipment, deficit spending, or fundraising projects; no loans.
Publications: Annual report (including application guidelines); Grants list.
Application information: Visit foundation web site for grant application cover sheet and guidelines. Application form required.
Initial approach: Telephone
Deadline(s): Mar. 1 and Oct. 1
Board meeting date(s): 4th Tues. of the month, 5 times per year
Final notification: May and Dec.
Officers and Trustees:* Valerie Snyder,* Chair.; Chip Hansen, Jr., Pres.; Hugh Conklin; Michelle Cortright; Jim Howell; Fay Keane; John Kempton; David Leusink; Barbara Malpass; Linda Mueller; Don Spencer; Rachel Swiss; Paul Witting; Connie Wojan.
Number of staff: 3 full-time professional; 1 part-time professional.
EIN: 383033739

4362
The Chelsea Health and Wellness Foundation ✧
310 N. Main St., Ste. 203
Chelsea, MI 48118-1291 (734) 433-4599
Contact: Amy Heydlauff, Exec. Dir.
FAX: (734) 433-4598;
E-mail: info@5healthytowns.org; Main URL: http://5healthytowns.org
Facebook: https://www.facebook.com/5healthytowns

Foundation type: Independent foundation.
Financial data (yr. ended 03/31/13): Assets, $40,703,462 (M); gifts received, $13,050; expenditures, $4,516,698; qualifying distributions, $729,945; giving activities include $729,945 for grants.
Fields of interest: Education; Health care; Human services.
Application information: See foundation web site for guidelines. Application form required.
Deadline(s): Varies
Officers: Jeff Hardcastle, Chair.; Larry Cobler, Vice-Chair.; Alison Pollard, Secy.; John R.C. Wheeler, Treas.; Amy Heydlauff, Exec. Dir.
Directors: Patrick J. Conlin, Jr.; Randall T. Forsch; Kenneth Gietzen; Nancy Graebner; Kathleen Griffiths; Diane Howlin; Susan Kheder; James F. Woods.
EIN: 263040367
Selected grants: The following grants are a representative sample of this grantmaker's funding activity:
$440,005 to Chelsea Community Hospital, Chelsea, MI, 2013. For Community Health and Wellness Projects.
$42,600 to Chelsea Community Hospital, Chelsea, MI, 2013. For SRSLY Dexter.
$20,000 to Chelsea Community Hospital, Chelsea, MI, 2013. For SRSLY Chelsea.
$15,750 to Chelsea Community Hospital, Chelsea, MI, 2013. For SRSLY Stockbridge.
$14,400 to Chelsea Community Hospital, Chelsea, MI, 2013. For Farmers Market Health.
$5,000 to Chelsea Community Hospital, Chelsea, MI, 2013. For heart and sole.
$2,000 to Chelsea Community Hospital, Chelsea, MI, 2013. For Manchester Red Barrel.
$2,000 to Chelsea Community Hospital, Chelsea, MI, 2013. For Walking Coordinator.
$1,600 to Chelsea Community Hospital, Chelsea, MI, 2013. For Dexter Red Barrel.

4363
The William Chinnick Charitable Foundation ✧
P.O. Box 1168
Holland, MI 49422-1168

Established in 1992 in FL.
Donor: William C. Swaney.
Foundation type: Independent foundation.
Financial data (yr. ended 12/31/13): Assets, $5,224,907 (M); expenditures, $596,202; qualifying distributions, $585,295; giving activities include $578,954 for 29 grants (high: $246,077; low: $250).
Purpose and activities: Giving primarily to Episcopal churches and schools; funding also for health organizations and human services.
Fields of interest: Education; Health organizations; Human services; Residential/custodial care, hospices; Protestant agencies & churches.
Limitations: Applications not accepted. Giving primarily in FL, ID, IL, MI. No grants to individuals.
Application information: Contributes only to pre-selected organizations.
Officers: William C. Swaney, Pres. and Treas.; Nancy C. Swaney, V.P.; Richard G. Swaney, Secy.
EIN: 650377446
Selected grants: The following grants are a representative sample of this grantmaker's funding activity:
$250 to Bible Reading Fellowship, Winter Park, FL, 2012. For Unrestricted grant to capital fund.

4364
Christ Cares for Kids Foundation ✧
107 Cass St., Rm. H
Traverse City, MI 49684-2602

Donors: Raymond P. Dornbusch; Linda L. Dornbusch.
Foundation type: Independent foundation.
Financial data (yr. ended 01/31/14): Assets, $36,888,285 (M); expenditures, $2,544,122; qualifying distributions, $2,544,122; giving activities include $2,525,000 for 38 grants (high: $720,000; low: $500).
Fields of interest: Education; Human services; Christian agencies & churches.
Limitations: Applications not accepted. Giving primarily in Traverse City, MI.
Application information: Unsolicited requests for funds not accepted.
EIN: 383505507
Selected grants: The following grants are a representative sample of this grantmaker's funding activity:
$833,800 to Friends of the Bridegroom, Kansas City, MO, 2012.
$220,200 to Hope College, Holland, MI, 2012.
$207,000 to International Justice Mission, Arlington, VA, 2012.
$110,000 to Father Fred Foundation, Traverse City, MI, 2012.
$95,000 to Water Missions International, Charleston, SC, 2012.
$51,000 to Traverse City Christian School, Traverse City, MI, 2012.
$26,000 to Good News Media, Traverse City, MI, 2012.
$24,000 to Focus on the Family, Colorado Springs, CO, 2012.
$24,000 to Insight for Living, Frisco, TX, 2012.
$24,000 to Words of Hope, Grand Rapids, MI, 2012.

4365
Christian Evangelical Foundation ✧
3755 36th St. S.E., Ste. 400
Grand Rapids, MI 49512-3143

Established in 1987 in IL.
Donors: John C. Huizenga; Elizabeth I. Huizenga Foundation.
Foundation type: Independent foundation.
Financial data (yr. ended 12/31/13): Assets, $252,383 (M); expenditures, $1,427,924; qualifying distributions, $1,426,700; giving activities include $1,426,700 for 145 grants (high: $125,000; low: $500).
Purpose and activities: Giving primarily to Christian organizations and for Christian education.
Fields of interest: Education; Human services; Christian agencies & churches.
Type of support: General/operating support.
Limitations: Applications not accepted. Giving in the U.S., with emphasis on MI. No grants to individuals.
Application information: Contributes only to pre-selected organizations.
Officers and Directors:* J.C. Huizenga,* Pres. and Mgr.; Jason Pater,* Secy.-Treas.; John R. Grant.
EIN: 363501198
Selected grants: The following grants are a representative sample of this grantmaker's funding activity:
$10,000 to OC International, Colorado Springs, CO, 2012. For ministry.
$5,000 to Christ for the Nations, Dallas, TX, 2012. For Kenya- Christa (Hyde) Muanica.
$5,000 to OC International, Colorado Springs, CO, 2012. For ministry.
$4,000 to Great Commission Ministries, Winter Park, FL, 2012. For ministry.

4366
The Chrysler Foundation ✧
(formerly DaimlerChrysler Corporation Fund)
1000 Chrysler Dr.
CIMS: 485-13-35
Auburn Hills, MI 48326-2766
Contact: Brian G. Glowiak, V.P. and Secy.
FAX: (248) 512-2503; Main URL: http://www.media.chrysler.com/newsroom.do?id=137&mid=202

Incorporated in 1953 in MI.
Donors: Chrysler Corp.; DaimlerChrysler Corp.; Chrysler Group LLC.
Foundation type: Company-sponsored foundation.
Financial data (yr. ended 12/31/13): Assets, $2,764,690 (M); gifts received, $584; expenditures, $2,454,844; qualifying distributions, $2,473,632; giving activities include $2,441,027 for 113 grants (high: $500,000; low: $750).
Purpose and activities: The foundation supports organizations involved with arts and culture, education, workforce development, disaster relief, youth development, human services, diversity, community development, science and technology, and public policy and marketplace issues. Special emphasis is directed toward programs designed to enrich the physical, educational, and cultural needs of local Chrysler Group communities.
Fields of interest: Arts, cultural/ethnic awareness; Arts; Vocational education; Higher education; Business school/education; Engineering school/education; Education; Employment, training; Employment; Disasters, preparedness/services; Safety, automotive safety; Youth development; American Red Cross; Human services; Civil/human rights, equal rights; Economic development; Business/industry; Community/economic development; Engineering/technology; Science; Public policy, research; Infants/toddlers; Children/youth; Children; Youth; Adults; Aging; Young adults; Disabilities, people with; Physically disabled; Blind/visually impaired; Minorities; Asians/Pacific Islanders; African Americans/Blacks; Hispanics/Latinos; Native Americans/American Indians; Indigenous peoples; Women; Infants/toddlers, female; Girls; Young adults, female; Men; Infants/toddlers, male; Boys; Young adults, male; Military/veterans; Single parents; Terminal illness, people with; Economically disadvantaged; Homeless; LGBTQ.
Type of support: General/operating support; Continuing support; Annual campaigns; Building/renovation; Emergency funds; Program development; Curriculum development; Scholarship funds; Cause-related marketing; Employee volunteer services; Sponsorships; Employee matching gifts; Employee-related scholarships.
Limitations: Applications not accepted. Giving primarily in areas of company operations in Yucca, AZ, Irvine, CA, Englewood, CO, Washington, DC, Orlando, FL, Belvidere and Lisle, IL, Indianapolis and Kokomo, IN, Elkridge, MD, Detroit, MI, Syracuse and Tappan, NY, Perrysburg, Toledo, and Twinsburg, OH, Addison, TX, and Kenosha, WI; giving also to regional and national organizations. No support for discriminatory organizations or private or corporate foundations. No grants to individuals (except for employee-related scholarships), or for endowments, general operating support for local United Way agencies, direct health care delivery programs, additions or renovations to real estate, fundraising activities related to individual sponsorship, debt reduction, religious or sectarian programs, or athletic programs involving individual teams; no loans; no vehicle donations; no multi-year pledges.
Application information: The foundation utilizes an invitation only Request For Proposal (RFP) process. Unsolicited requests are not accepted.
Board meeting date(s): As required, usually quarterly
Officers and Trustees:* Joseph "Jody" Trapasso, Pres.; Brian G. Glowiak, V.P. and Secy.; Walter P. Bodden, Jr., V.P. and Treas.; R. J. Elder, Cont.; Fred Diaz; Scott R. Garberding; Scott Kunselman; Nancy A. Rae; Gialberto Ranier.
Number of staff: 2 full-time professional; 1 full-time support.
EIN: 386087371
Selected grants: The following grants are a representative sample of this grantmaker's funding activity:
$195,000 to Howard University, Washington, DC, 2012.
$100,000 to California Latino Legislative Caucus Institute for Public Policy, Los Angeles, CA, 2012.
$100,000 to National Italian American Foundation, Washington, DC, 2012.
$85,000 to Hispanic Scholarship Fund, Gardena, CA, 2012.
$60,000 to Gleaners Community Food Bank, Detroit, MI, 2012.
$50,000 to Michigan Science Center, Detroit, MI, 2012.
$40,000 to Think Detroit PAL, Detroit, MI, 2012.
$37,000 to Inforum Center for Leadership, Detroit, MI, 2012.
$26,000 to Forgotten Harvest, Oak Park, MI, 2012.
$2,250 to Missouri University of Science and Technology, Rolla, MO, 2012.

4367
The Cold Heading Foundation ✧
(formerly DeSeranno Educational Foundation, Inc.)
21777 Hoover Rd.
Warren, MI 48089-2544

Established in 1968 in MI.
Donors: Cold Heading Co.; Ajax Metal Processing, Inc.; Beachlawn Mortgage Co.
Foundation type: Independent foundation.
Financial data (yr. ended 12/31/13): Assets, $26,814,439 (M); expenditures, $1,242,074; qualifying distributions, $1,156,735; giving activities include $993,035 for 36 grants (high: $300,000; low: $500).
Purpose and activities: Giving primarily for education, as well as for health associations, and to Roman Catholic churches and organizations.
Fields of interest: Secondary school/education; Health care; Health organizations, association; Foundations (private grantmaking); Catholic agencies & churches.
Type of support: General/operating support.
Limitations: Applications not accepted. Giving primarily in MI.
Application information: Unsolicited requests for funds not accepted.
Officers: Derek Stevens, Pres.; Elizabeth Stevens, V.P. and Secy.; Gregory Stevens, Treas.
Number of staff: 3 part-time support.
EIN: 237005737

Selected grants: The following grants are a representative sample of this grantmaker's funding activity:
$2,000 to American Cancer Society, Atlanta, GA, 2011.

4368
Comerica Charitable Foundation ✧
c/o Corp. Contribs.
P.O. Box 75000, M.C. 3390
Detroit, MI 48275-0001
Contact: Janice E. Tessier, Pres.
FAX: (313) 222-5555; Application addresses: Florida: Corp. Contribs. Mgr., M.C. 5172, 1675 N. Military Trail, Ste. 600, Boca Raton, FL 33486, Michigan: Corp. Contribs. Mgr., M.C. 3390, P.O. Box 75000, Detroit, MI 48275-0001, Texas: Corp. Contribs. Mgr., M.C. 6503, P.O. Box 650282, Dallas, TX 75265-0282, Western Market: Corp. Contribs. Mgr., M.C. 4805, 333 W. Santa Clara St., San Jose, CA 95113; Tel. for Caroline E. Chambers: (313) 222-3571; Main URL: http://www.comerica.com/about-us/community-involvement/pages/charitable-giving.aspx

Established in 1997 in MI.
Donors: Comerica Bank; Comerica Inc.
Foundation type: Company-sponsored foundation.
Financial data (yr. ended 12/31/12): Assets, $89,523 (M); gifts received, $3,939,586; expenditures, $4,158,864; qualifying distributions, $4,158,864; giving activities include $4,158,864 for 522 grants (high: $468,261; low: $150).
Purpose and activities: The foundation supports organizations involved with education, health, employment, housing, financial literacy, community development, and economically disadvantaged people, and programs designed to promote diversity and inclusion.
Fields of interest: Elementary/secondary education; Business school/education; Adult/continuing education; Education; Health care; Employment, training; Employment; Housing/shelter; Human services, financial counseling; Civil/human rights, equal rights; Business/industry; Community development, small businesses; Community/economic development; Economically disadvantaged.
Type of support: General/operating support; Capital campaigns; Program development; Scholarship funds.
Limitations: Applications accepted. Giving primarily in areas of company operations in AZ, CA, FL, MI, and TX. No support for political parties. No grants to individuals or for capital campaigns; no multi-year requests.
Publications: Application guidelines; Program policy statement.
Application information: Application form not required.
Initial approach: Proposal to application address
Deadline(s): Mar. 15, June 15, Sept 15, and Nov. 15
Final notification: Apr. 15, July 15, Oct. 15, and Dec. 15
Officers and Directors:* Linda D. Forte,* Chair.; Janice M. Tessier,* Pres.; Jon W. Bilstrom,* Exec. V.P.; Nicole V. Gersch, Sr. V.P. and Secy.; Jennifer S. Perry, V.P.; James J. Herzog, Treas.; Caroline E. Chambers.
EIN: 383373052

4369
Community Foundation for Muskegon County ✧
(formerly Muskegon County Community Foundation, Inc.)
425 W. Western Ave., Ste. 200
Muskegon, MI 49440-1101 (231) 722-4538
Contact: Chris Ann McGuigan, C.E.O.; For grants: Janelle Mair, Dir., Grantmaking
FAX: (231) 722-4616; E-mail: info@cffmc.org; Grant inquiry e-mail: jmair@cffmc.org; Grant inquiry tel.: (231) 332-4116; Main URL: http://www.cffmc.org
E-Newsletter: http://www.cffmc.org/e-newsletter
Facebook: http://www.facebook.com/pages/Community-Foundation-for-Muskegon-County/100319078604
Twitter: https://twitter.com/CFFMC
YouTube: http://www.youtube.com/user/cffmc1961?feature=results_right_main

Incorporated in 1961 in MI.
Donors: Alta Daetz‡; Harold Frauenthal‡; Charles Goodnow‡; George Hilt; Jack Hilt; John Hilt; Paul C. Johnson‡; Henry Klooster‡; Ernest Settle‡.
Foundation type: Community foundation.
Financial data (yr. ended 12/31/13): Assets, $146,802,144 (M); gifts received, $10,707,982; expenditures, $11,187,205; giving activities include $8,127,279 for 136+ grants (high: $2,242,563), and $513,166 for 311 grants to individuals.
Purpose and activities: The foundation seeks to build community endowment, effect positive change through grantmaking, and provide leadership on key community issues, all to serve donor's desires to enhance the quality of life for the people of Muskegon County, MI. The foundation presently supports efforts in the areas of arts, education, environment, community development, health and human services as well as youth development issues.
Fields of interest: Arts education; Performing arts, theater; Arts; Scholarships/financial aid; Education; Environment, air pollution; Environment, water pollution; Environment, land resources; Environment; Health care; Health organizations, association; Youth development; Children/youth, services; Human services; Economic development; Urban/community development; Community/economic development; Infants/toddlers; Children.
Type of support: Management development/capacity building; Building/renovation; Emergency funds; Program development; Seed money; Scholarship funds; Research; Consulting services; Program-related investments/loans; Exchange programs; Matching/challenge support.
Limitations: Applications accepted. Giving limited to Muskegon County, MI. No support for sectarian religious programs, or individual schools or districts. No grants to individuals (except for scholarships), or for deficit financing, routine operating expenses, capital equipment, endowment campaigns, special fundraising events, conferences, camps, publications, videos, films, television or radio programs, or for advertising.
Publications: Application guidelines; Annual report (including application guidelines); Financial statement; Grants list; Informational brochure (including application guidelines); Newsletter.
Application information: Visit foundation web site for grant application information.
Initial approach: Register an account with eGrant on the foundation's web site
Deadline(s): Varies
Board meeting date(s): Feb., Apr., June, Aug., Oct., and Dec.
Final notification: 3 months
Officers and Trustees:* John W. Swanson II,* Chair.; Richard W. Peters, M.D.*, Vice-Chair.; Chris Ann McGuigan,* C.E.O. and Pres.; Robert Chapla,* V.P., Devel.; Ann Van Tassel,* V.P., Finance; Susan Meston, Ph.D.*, Treas.; Nancy L. Crandall; Jan Deur; Wes Eklund; Amy Heisser; Charles E. Johnson III; Dick Kamps, M.D.; Kathleen Long; Marvin Nash; Dale K. Nesbary, Ph.D.; Kay Olthoff; Asaline Scott; Michael S. Soimar; Roger Spoelman; Alan D. Steinman, Ph.D.; John M. Sytsema; Kathleen Tyler; James L. Waters.
Trustee Banks: Comerica Bank; Fifth Third Bank; The Huntington National Bank; National City Bank.
Number of staff: 7 full-time professional; 5 full-time support.
EIN: 386114135

4370
Community Foundation for Northeast Michigan ✧
(formerly Northeast Michigan Community Foundation)
100 N. Ripley, Suite F
P.O. Box 495
Alpena, MI 49707-2838 (989) 354-6881
Contact: Barbara Frantz, Exec. Dir.
FAX: (989) 356-3319; E-mail: bfrantz@cfnem.org; Main URL: http://www.cfnem.org
Facebook: http://www.facebook.com/pages/Community-Foundation-for-Northeast-Michigan/211282204045
Twitter: http://twitter.com/CFNEM
Scholarship e-mail: wiesenj@cfnem.org

Incorporated in 1974 in Alpena, MI.
Foundation type: Community foundation.
Financial data (yr. ended 09/30/13): Assets, $28,418,209 (M); gifts received, $1,730,042; expenditures, $1,084,159; giving activities include $518,910 for 562+ grants (high: $10,000; low: $22), and $277,572 for 222 grants to individuals (high: $10,400; low: $250).
Purpose and activities: The foundation seeks to serve the community and to preserve the charitable goals of a wide range of donors now and for generations to come.
Fields of interest: Humanities; Arts; Libraries/library science; Education; Environment; Health care; Health organizations, association; Children/youth, services; Human services; Government/public administration.
Type of support: Equipment; Program development; Conferences/seminars; Seed money; Scholarship funds; Technical assistance; Scholarships—to individuals.
Limitations: Applications accepted. Giving limited to Alcona, Alpena, Montmorency, and Presque Isle counties, MI and through affiliates: Crawford, Cheboygan, Iosco, Ogemaw, and Oscoda counties, MI. No support for religious purposes. No grants to individuals (except for scholarships), or for annual giving campaigns or capital campaigns, normal operating expenses, or multi-year or sustained funding; no loans.
Publications: Application guidelines; Annual report; Financial statement; Grants list; Informational brochure; Newsletter; Program policy statement.
Application information: Visit foundation web site for application forms, guidelines, and deadlines. For grants of $300 or less, organizations should use the

2-page mini-grant application and follow its specific guidelines. Application form required.

Initial approach: Submit application forms and attachments
Copies of proposal: 1
Deadline(s): Generally Feb. 1, Aug. 1, and Nov. 1, but applicants should check our web site to be sure of dates
Board meeting date(s): 2nd Tuesday in March, June, September, and December
Final notification: Within 6 weeks

Officers and Trustees:* Chuck Manning,* Pres.; Esther Ableidinger,* V.P.; Tom Sobeck,* Secy.; Sue Fitzpatrick,* Treas.; Barbara Frantz, Exec. Dir.; Christine Baumgardner; Benjamin Bolser; Kate Bruski; Dave Cook; Brendan Fleishans; Jerry Gosnell; Lora Greene; Kara Grulke; Shanna Johnson; Tony Johnson; Sue Keller; Tim Kuehnlein; Jennifer Lee; John MacMaster; Dave Post; Terri Rondeau; Gina Roose; Carl Woloszyk.
Number of staff: 3 full-time support; 2 part-time support.
EIN: 237384822

4371
Community Foundation for Southeast Michigan ✧

(formerly Community Foundation for Southeastern Michigan)
333 W. Fort St., Ste. 2010
Detroit, MI 48226-3134 (313) 961-6675
Contact: Mariam C. Noland, Pres.
FAX: (313) 961-2886; E-mail: cfsem@cfsem.org; Main URL: http://www.cfsem.org
Facebook: https://www.facebook.com/cfsem
Knowledge Center: http://cfsem.org/initiatives-and-programs
RSS Feed: http://cfsem.org/rss
Twitter: http://twitter.com/cfsem
YouTube: http://www.youtube.com/user/TheCFSEM
Scholarship inquiry e-mail: sfoster@cfsem.org

Established in 1984 in MI.
Foundation type: Community foundation.
Financial data (yr. ended 12/31/13): Assets, $734,226,708 (M); gifts received, $21,594,980; expenditures, $58,566,218; giving activities include $52,560,486 for grants.
Purpose and activities: The foundation exists in perpetuity to enhance the quality of life of the citizens in southeast Michigan. The foundation promotes and facilitates community philanthropy in the seven counties of Wayne, Oakland, Macomb, Monroe, Washtenaw, Livingston and St. Clair, and also help donors invest in organizations they care about nationwide. They are building permanent community capital in the form of endowments that create a base of stable financial support for the region. The foundation does this by: 1) making strategic investments in programs and organizations that benefit the region equipping organizations and the public with knowledge and information that will lead to positive change; 2) building endowment - community capital - to meet the region's needs today and tomorrow; and 3) providing expert assistance to donors and their advisers in their charitable planning.
Fields of interest: Arts; Education; Environment; Health care; Health organizations, association; Youth development, services; Youth, services; Human services; Civil rights, race/intergroup relations; Economic development; Community/economic development; Government/public administration; Leadership development; Public affairs; Economically disadvantaged.
Type of support: Program development; Seed money; Scholarship funds; Technical assistance; Scholarships—to individuals.
Limitations: Applications accepted. Giving primarily to Livingston, Macomb, Monroe, Oakland, St. Clair, Washtenaw, and Wayne counties, MI. No support for sectarian religious programs. No grants to individuals (from unrestricted funds), or for capital projects, endowments, annual campaigns, general operating support, conferences, computers and computer systems, fundraising, annual meetings, buildings, or equipment.
Publications: Application guidelines; Annual report (including application guidelines); Grants list; Informational brochure (including application guidelines); Newsletter.
Application information: There may be separate grantmaking guidelines for targeted grantmaking projects. These guidelines and special application forms are available by contacting the foundation or consulting the foundation's Guidelines for Grantmaking. Visit foundation web site for general grant application guidelines. Application form not required.

Initial approach: Complete online pre-application questionnaire
Deadline(s): Recommended dates of Feb. 15, May 15, Aug. 15, and Nov. 15
Board meeting date(s): Mar., June, Sept., and Dec.
Final notification: 3 months after submission of proposal

Officers and Trustees:* James B. Nicholson,* Chair.; Penny B. Blumenstein,* Vice-Chair.; W. Frank Fountain,* Vice-Chair.; David M. Hempstead,* Vice-Chair.; Mariam C. Noland, Pres.; Katie G. Brisson, V.P., Prog.; Robin D. Ferriby, V.P., Philanthropic Svcs.; Kate French, V.P., Mktg. and Comms.; Karen L. Leppanen, V.P., Finance and Admin.; Mary H. Weiser,* Secy.; Michael T. Monahan,* Treas.; Diane M. Kresnak, Cont., Finance and Admin.; Frederick M. Adams, Jr.; Terence E. Adderley; Margaret Acheson Allesee; Gerard M. Anderson; Michael E. Bannister; Albert M. Berriz; Thomas C. Buhl; Andrew L. Camden; Ahmad Chebbani; Matthew P. Cullen; Paul R. Dimond; Deborah I. Dingell; John M. Erb; David T. Fischer; Phillip W. Fisher; Jenice C. Mitchell Ford; Allan D. Gilmour; Alfred R. Glancy III; Kouhaila G. Hammer; Steven K. Hamp; William M. Hermann; George G. Johnson; Eric B. Larson; David Baker Lewis; John D. Lewis; Henry W. Lim; Dana M. Locniskar; Florine Mark; Jack Martin; Edward J. Miller; Eugene A. Miller; Bruce E. Nyberg; Cynthia J. Pasky; William F. Pickard; Dr. Glenda D. Price; David T. Provost; Jack A. Robinson; Pamela Rodgers; Alan E. Schwartz; William W. Shelden, Jr.; Vivian Day Stroh; Gary Torgow; Reginald M. Turner; Barbara C. Van Dusen; Dale L. Watchowsky; Sean K. Werdlow; Ken Whipple.
Number of staff: 18 full-time professional; 1 part-time support.
EIN: 382530980
Selected grants: The following grants are a representative sample of this grantmaker's funding activity:
$675,000 to College for Creative Studies, Detroit, MI, 2012. For Detroit Creative Corridor Center to provide expanded business acceleration program for creative sector start-up companies.
$400,000 to Arab Community Center for Economic and Social Services, Dearborn, MI, 2012. For Immigrant Entrepreneur Support Centers to provide training and technical assistance to assist underserved immigrant and non-English speaking populations to develop and grow businesses.
$300,000 to Detroit Symphony Orchestra, Detroit, MI, 2012. For Community Engagement Concert Program.
$200,000 to Sphinx Organization, Detroit, MI, 2012. For classical music instruction programs for young people.
$100,000 to Teach for America, Detroit, MI, 2012. To expand program to place high-quality teachers in low-achieving Detroit schools with low-income students.
$50,000 to Adult Well-Being Services, Detroit, MI, 2012. To improve health outcomes of adults with severe mental and co-morbid diet-related illness who live in adult foster care.
$40,000 to Girls on the Run International, Ann Arbor, MI, 2012. To expand curriculum-based, mentored self-esteem running program for girls.
$30,000 to Woodward Avenue Action Association, Royal Oak, MI, 2012. To develop Complete Streets Plan for Woodward Avenue.
$25,000 to VINA Community Dental Center, Brighton, MI, 2012. For Immediate Dental Care Initiative to expand dental services to low-income residents of Livingston County.
$22,285 to First Step-Western Wayne County Project on Domestic Assault, Plymouth, MI, 2012. For program to repair relationships of children and mothers who come from violent home.

4372
Community Foundation of Greater Flint ✧

500 S. Saginaw St.
Flint, MI 48502-1856 (810) 767-8270
Contact: Kathi Horton, Pres.
FAX: (810) 767-0496; E-mail: info@cfgf.org; Additional e-mail: khorton@cfgf.org; Main URL: http://www.cfgf.org

Established in 1988 in MI.
Foundation type: Community foundation.
Financial data (yr. ended 12/31/13): Assets, $163,822,816 (M); gifts received, $1,151,948; expenditures, $6,461,225; giving activities include $4,755,521 for grants.
Purpose and activities: The foundation serves the common good in Genesee County - building a strong community by engaging people in philanthropy and developing the community's permanent endowment - now and for generations to come. The foundation seeks to respond to current or emerging needs in the local area in conservation and the environment, arts and humanities, education, health and human services, and leadership development.
Fields of interest: Humanities; Historic preservation/historical societies; Arts; Education; Environment, natural resources; Environment, beautification programs; Environment; Health care; Youth development, services; Children/youth, services; Human services; Community development, neighborhood development; Leadership development; Children/youth; Women; Girls; Economically disadvantaged.
Type of support: General/operating support; Management development/capacity building; Program development; Seed money; Scholarship

funds; Technical assistance; Program evaluation; Matching/challenge support.
Limitations: Applications accepted. Giving primarily in Genesee County, MI. No support for sectarian religious purposes. No grants to individuals (except for scholarships), or for annual appeals, deficit reduction or routine operating expenses of existing organizations.
Publications: Application guidelines; Annual report; Financial statement; Grants list; Informational brochure; Occasional report; Program policy statement.
Application information: Visit foundation web site for application forms and additional guidelines per grant type. Application form required.
Initial approach: Telephone
Copies of proposal: 3
Deadline(s): None. Once an application is received, the contact person listed on the application cover sheet will be contacted by a Program Officer to discuss a decision-making timeline
Board meeting date(s): Feb., Apr., June, Oct., and Dec.
Officers and Trustees:* Bobby Mukkamala,* Chair.; George D. Wilkinson,* Vice-Chair.; Kathi Horton,* Pres.; Mary Ittigson,* V.P., Finance and Admin.; AnnMarie VanDuyne,* V.P., Philanthropic Svcs.; Nancy J. Hanflik,* Secy.; F. James Cummins,* Treas.; Stephen Arellano; Lauren Chwojnicki; Wanda D. Harden; Timothy Knecht; Sonya LaGore; David E. Lossing; John MacDonald; Heidi McAra; Paityn Miles; Mark Miller; Leanne Panduren; Yeonjung Park; Mark Piper; Ira A. Rutherford; Manal Saab; T. Ardele Shaltz; Lori Tallman; Rafael Turner; Douglas B. Vance; Karen Williams Weaver; Stephen Wilson.
Number of staff: 11 full-time professional; 3 full-time support.
EIN: 382190667

4373
Community Foundation of St. Clair County ✧

516 McMorran Blvd.
Port Huron, MI 48060-3826 (810) 984-4761
Contact: Randy D. Maiers, C.E.O.
FAX: (810) 984-3394;
E-mail: info@stclairfoundation.org; Main URL: http://www.stclairfoundation.org
Facebook: https://www.facebook.com/CommunityFoundationSCC
Pinterest: http://www.pinterest.com/GiveLocalMi/
Twitter: https://twitter.com/@GiveLocalMi

Established in 1944 in MI.
Foundation type: Community foundation.
Financial data (yr. ended 12/31/13): Assets, $47,695,286 (M); gifts received, $6,486,260; expenditures, $2,146,211; giving activities include $1,048,696 for grants.
Purpose and activities: The foundation seeks to serve the charitable needs and enhance the quality of life of the community by: 1) providing a flexible and convenient vehicle for donors having a variety of charitable goals and needs; 2) receiving and investing contributions to build permanent endowments; 3) responding to changing and emerging community needs; 4) serving as a steward for individuals, families, foundations, and organizations entrusting assets to its care; and 5) providing grants to philanthropic organizations, social services, civic concerns, education, arts and culture, recreation and youth.
Fields of interest: Arts; Education; Recreation; Family services; Human services; Economic development; Community/economic development; Youth; Aging.
Type of support: Emergency funds; Management development/capacity building; Building/renovation; Equipment; Program development; Publication; Seed money; Scholarship funds; Technical assistance; Program-related investments/loans; Scholarships—to individuals; Matching/challenge support.
Limitations: Applications accepted. Giving limited to St. Clair County, MI. No support for religious activities. No grants to individuals directly, or for endowments, equipment, annual meetings, conferences, travel expenses, venture capital funds, or film, video, or TV projects, deficit reduction, annual fundraising, capital campaigns, marketing or public relations, general operating expenses, or land use.
Publications: Application guidelines; Annual report; Financial statement; Grants list; Informational brochure; Newsletter.
Application information: Visit foundation web site for application form and guidelines. Application form required.
Initial approach: Contact foundation
Copies of proposal: 1
Deadline(s): Jan. 1, Apr. 1, July 1, and Oct. 1
Board meeting date(s): Quarterly
Final notification: Mar., June, Sept., and Dec.
Officers and Trustees:* Donna Niester,* Chair.; Michael J. Cansfield,* Vice-Chair.; Randy D. Maiers,* Pres. and C.E.O.; Lynn Alexander,* V.P.; Dr. Bassam Nasr,* Secy.; Roy W. Klecha, Jr.,* Treas.; Denise M. Brooks; Rasha Demashkieh; Don Fletcher; William C. Gratopp; Jackie Hanton; Steve L. Hill; Mike Hulewicz; Dr. Randa Jundi-Samman; Gerry Kramer; Jenifer Kusch; Phyllis Ledyard; Dan Lockwood; Michael McCartan; Janal Mossett; Will G. Oldford, Jr.; Donna M. Niester; William G. Oldford, Jr.; Frank Poma; Dr. Sushma Reddy; F. William Schwarz III; Douglas S. Touma; Hale Walker; Mike Wendling; Cathy Wilkinson.
Number of staff: 6 full-time professional.
EIN: 381872132

4374
The Community Foundation of the Holland/Zeeland Area

(formerly Holland Community Foundation, Inc.)
85 E. 8th St., Ste. 110
Holland, MI 49423-3528 (616) 396-6590
Contact: Mike Goorhouse, C.E.O.; Elizabeth Kidd, V.P., Grantmaking
FAX: (616) 396-3573; E-mail: info@cfhz.org; Additional E-mail: mgoorhouse@cfhz.org; Grant inquiry e-mail: ekidd@cfhz.org; Main URL: http://www.cfhz.org
Facebook: https://www.facebook.com/cfohz
LinkedIn: http://www.linkedin.com/in/janetdeyoung
Twitter: http://twitter.com/cfohz

Incorporated in 1951 in MI.
Foundation type: Community foundation.
Financial data (yr. ended 12/31/12): Assets, $48,409,622 (M); gifts received, $8,524,432; expenditures, $5,342,564; giving activities include $3,639,721 for 71+ grants (high: $860,953), $398,186 for 168 grants to individuals, and $750,000 for 2 loans/program-related investments (high: $500,000; low: $250,000).
Purpose and activities: The mission of the foundation is to create lasting positive change. The foundation works to build a permanent community endowment that supports high impact charitable projects, helps donors achieve their charitable goals, and leads and partners in community level initiatives.
Fields of interest: Visual arts, art conservation; Historic preservation/historical societies; Arts; Education; Environment; Health care; Housing/shelter; Recreation; Children/youth, services; Human services; Community/economic development; Children/youth; Aging.
Type of support: Capital campaigns; Building/renovation; Equipment; Emergency funds; Program development; Seed money; Curriculum development; Scholarship funds; Technical assistance; Program evaluation; Employee-related scholarships; In-kind gifts.
Limitations: Applications accepted. Giving limited to the Holland/Zeeland, MI, area and surrounding townships. No support for sectarian religious programs. No grants for endowment funds, operating budgets, expenses for established programs, fundraising drives, capital equipment, conference speakers, salaries, stipends, sabbatical leaves, debt reduction, research, endowments, fellowships, matching gifts, travel or tours, or computers, video equipment, or vehicles; no loans.
Publications: Application guidelines; Annual report; Financial statement; Grants list; Informational brochure; Newsletter; IRS Form 990 or 990-PF printed copy available upon request.
Application information: Visit foundation web site for current application form, guidelines and copies required. Application form required.
Initial approach: Contact Dir. of Grantmaking before preparing and submitting proposal
Copies of proposal: 11
Deadline(s): Jan. 13, May 12, and Sept. 8
Board meeting date(s): Monthly
Final notification: Within 5 weeks of deadline
Officers and Trustees:* Sue Den Herder,* Chair.; Janet DeYoung,* C.E.O. and Pres.; Mike Goorhouse, V.P., Donor Devel.; Juanita Bocanegra,* Secy.; Lori Bush; Eleanor Lopez; Nancy Miller; P. Haans Mulder; Jane Patterson; Judith Smith; Scott Alan Spoelhof.
Number of staff: 6 full-time professional; 1 part-time professional.
EIN: 386095283

4375
Community Foundation of the Upper Peninsula ✧

(formerly Upper Peninsula Community Foundation Alliance)
2420 1st. Ave S., Ste. 101
Escanaba, MI 49829-1309 (906) 789-5972
Contact: Gary LaPlant, Exec. Dir.; Debra Millican, Off. Mgr.
FAX: (906) 786-9124; E-mail: glaplant@cfup.org; Additional e-mail: dmillican@cfup.org; Main URL: http://www.cfup.org

Established in 1994 in MI.
Foundation type: Community foundation.
Financial data (yr. ended 12/31/12): Assets, $22,158,613 (M); gifts received, $2,255,904; expenditures, $2,351,657; giving activities include

$975,006 for 19+ grants (high: $120,186), and $134,971 for 65 grants to individuals.
Purpose and activities: The foundation seeks to enhance the quality of life in the Upper Peninsula of MI. The foundation will provide its own U.P.-wide philanthropy and that of its geographic affiliate members through growth of permanent endowment funds from a wide range of donors, grants, and leadership activities. The CFUP also provides financial, administrative, communication, and other support services to its affiliate members and to other U.P. community foundations.
Fields of interest: Historic preservation/historical societies; Environment; Health care; Human services; Economic development; Infants/toddlers; Children/youth; Children; Youth; Adults.
Type of support: Endowments; Emergency funds; Curriculum development; Continuing support; Conferences/seminars; Capital campaigns; Scholarship funds; Technical assistance; Scholarships—to individuals.
Limitations: Applications accepted. Giving limited to the Upper Peninsula, MI, area, including Chippewa County, Gogebic County, Schoolcraft County, and Alger, Cedarville, Delta, Ontonagon, Paradise, St. Ignace and Watersmeet county areas. No support for religious or sectarian purposes. No grants to individuals (except for scholarships), or for memberships, memorials, endowments, fundraising, social events, exhibits, or deficits in operating budgets or normal operating expenses, construction of buildings, or maintenance.
Publications: Application guidelines; Annual report; Financial statement; Informational brochure; Informational brochure (including application guidelines).
Application information: Visit foundation web site for application form and guidelines. Application form required.
Initial approach: Submit Cover Sheet and attachments
Copies of proposal: 12
Deadline(s): Varies
Board meeting date(s): Feb., Apr., July, and Oct.
Final notification: Generally 1 month
Officers and Trustees:* Mary Bowerman,* Co-Chair.; Matt Smith, Jr.,* Co-Chair.; Will Carne, Sr.,* Co-Vice-Chair.; Bill Inman,* Co-Vice-Chair.; William LeMire III, M.D.*, Secy.; Dr. K. Gerald Marsden,* Treas.; Gary LaPlant, Exec. Dir.; Dr. Kenneth Drenth; Chari Fischer; Margaret LaPonsie; Tom Luckey; Todd Lysinger; Jim North; Velda Sclafani; Jonny Waara; Bonnie Wenick-Kutz; Dean Wood.
Number of staff: 3 full-time professional; 2 part-time professional; 2 part-time support.
EIN: 383227080

4376
Consumers Energy Foundation ✧
(formerly Consumers Power Foundation)
1 Energy Plz., Rm. EP8-210
Jackson, MI 49201-2276 (517) 788-0432
Contact: Carolyn A. Bloodworth, Secy.-Treas.
E-mail: foundation@consumersenergy.com; Main URL: http://www.consumersenergy.com/foundation

Established in 1990 in MI.
Donors: Consumers Power Co.; Consumers Energy Co.
Foundation type: Company-sponsored foundation.
Financial data (yr. ended 12/31/13): Assets, $18,011,688 (M); expenditures, $2,187,991; qualifying distributions, $2,187,991; giving activities include $1,999,073 for 602 grants (high: $100,000; low: $13), and $110,217 for 107 employee matching gifts.
Purpose and activities: The foundation supports programs designed to promote social welfare; Michigan growth and environmental enhancement; education; community and civic development; and culture and the arts.
Fields of interest: Performing arts; Arts; Education, early childhood education; Higher education; Business school/education; Libraries (public); Education; Environment, natural resources; Environment, water resources; Environment, land resources; Environment, energy; Environmental education; Environment; Zoos/zoological societies; Food services; Food banks; Recreation, parks/playgrounds; Boys & girls clubs; Salvation Army; Family services; Family services, domestic violence; Developmentally disabled, centers & services; Homeless, human services; Human services; Community development, neighborhood development; Community development, civic centers; Community/economic development; Foundations (community); United Ways and Federated Giving Programs; Mathematics; Engineering/technology; Science; Economics; Political science; Leadership development.
Type of support: General/operating support; Continuing support; Capital campaigns; Building/renovation; Equipment; Curriculum development; Scholarship funds; Employee volunteer services; Employee matching gifts.
Limitations: Applications accepted. Giving primarily in areas of company operations in MI. No support for discriminatory organizations, United Way supported organizations, political, labor, or veterans' organizations, religious organizations not of direct benefit to the entire community, fraternal orders, or social clubs. No grants to individuals, or for fundraising, endowments, political campaigns, sports tournaments, talent or beauty contests, or debt reduction; no loans for small businesses.
Publications: Annual report; Annual report (including application guidelines); Program policy statement.
Application information: Application form required.
Initial approach: Completed application form
Copies of proposal: 1
Deadline(s): None
Board meeting date(s): Quarterly
Officers and Directors:* John G. Russell,* Chair.; David G. Mengebier,* Pres.; Carolyn A. Bloodworth, Secy.-Treas.; James E. Brunner; John M. Butler; Debra A. Harmon; Nancy A. Popa; Thomas J. Webb; Leeroy Wells, Jr.
Number of staff: 2 full-time professional; 2 full-time support.
EIN: 382935534
Selected grants: The following grants are a representative sample of this grantmaker's funding activity:
$50,000 to Nature Conservancy, Lansing, MI, 2011.
$40,000 to Michigan State University, East Lansing, MI, 2011.
$35,000 to Cranbrook Institute of Science, Bloomfield Hills, MI, 2011.
$25,000 to Community Foundation Alliance of Calhoun County, Homer, MI, 2011.
$25,000 to Michigan State University, College of Engineering, East Lansing, MI, 2011.
$12,500 to Michigan State University, College of Engineering, East Lansing, MI, 2011.
$10,000 to United Way of Manistee County, Manistee, MI, 2011.
$5,000 to Maritime Heritage Alliance, Traverse City, MI, 2011.
$5,000 to Michigan Association of Conservation Districts, East Lansing, MI, 2011.
$5,000 to Michigan Colleges Foundation, Southfield, MI, 2011.

4377
Cook Family Foundation ✧ ☆
312 W. Main St., Ste. 3W
P.O. Box 278
Owosso, MI 48867-0278 (989) 725-1621
Contact: Thomas Cook, Secy.-Treas.

Established in 1979 in MI.
Donors: Donald O. Cook‡; Florence-Etta Cook‡; Donald O. Cook Charitable Trust; Wolverine Sign Works.
Foundation type: Independent foundation.
Financial data (yr. ended 12/31/13): Assets, $11,535,643 (M); expenditures, $684,432; qualifying distributions, $648,479; giving activities include $538,823 for 42 grants (high: $104,779; low: $500).
Purpose and activities: Giving primarily for education and youth programs.
Fields of interest: Education; Environment; Human services.
Type of support: General/operating support; Annual campaigns; Capital campaigns; Building/renovation; Program development; Internship funds; Scholarship funds.
Limitations: Applications accepted. Giving limited to MI, with emphasis on Shiawassee County. No grants to individuals.
Publications: Annual report; Informational brochure.
Application information: Application form required.
Initial approach: Letter
Deadline(s): Annual
Officers: Bruce L. Cook, Pres.; Laurie Caszatt Cook, V.P.; Thomas B. Cook, Secy.-Treas.
Trustees: Jacqueline P. Cook; Paul C. Cook; Anna E. Owens.
Number of staff: 1 part-time professional.
EIN: 382283809

4378
Peter C. and Emajean Cook Foundation ✧
(formerly Cook Charitable Foundation)
2900 Charlevoix Dr. S. E., Ste. 130
Grand Rapids, MI 49546-7049
Main URL: http://www.cookfoundationgr.org/

Established in 1987 in MI.
Donors: Peter C. Cook; Emajean Cook; Peter C. Cook Trust; Thomas H. Claus.
Foundation type: Independent foundation.
Financial data (yr. ended 12/31/13): Assets, $31,189,669 (M); gifts received, $25,455,211; expenditures, $2,726,443; qualifying distributions, $2,646,252; giving activities include $2,646,252 for 108 grants (high: $250,000; low: $52).
Purpose and activities: Giving primarily for education and religious organizations. Some support also for human service organizations, health associations, and arts and cultural organizations.

Fields of interest: Arts; Health organizations, association; Human services; Human services, mind/body enrichment; Christian agencies & churches.
Type of support: General/operating support.
Limitations: Applications not accepted. Giving limited to the Grand Rapids, MI, area. No grants to individuals.
Application information: Contributes only to pre-selected organizations.
Officers and Directors:* Thomas M. Cook,* Chair.; Thomas H. Claus,* Pres.; Robert D. Brower,* Secy.; Carrie L. Boer,* Treas.
EIN: 382752251
Selected grants: The following grants are a representative sample of this grantmaker's funding activity:
$65,000 to Van Andel Institute, Grand Rapids, MI, 2012. For Parkinson's Research.
$50,000 to Grandville Avenue Academy for the Arts, Grand Rapids, MI, 2012. For librarian support.
$50,000 to Grandville Avenue Academy for the Arts, Grand Rapids, MI, 2012. For Program Director Support.
$50,000 to Public Museum of Grand Rapids, Grand Rapids, MI, 2012. For Business Model Study.
$40,000 to Roosevelt Park Neighborhood Association, Grand Rapids, MI, 2012. For salary grant.
$40,000 to Wedgwood Christian Services, Grand Rapids, MI, 2012. For Cook Claus House.
$25,000 to Metro Health Hospital Foundation, Wyoming, MI, 2012. For Heart and Vascular Program.
$15,000 to Guiding Light Mission, Grand Rapids, MI, 2012. For Iron House Support.
$15,000 to YMCA of Greater Grand Rapids, Grand Rapids, MI, 2012. For Swim Program.
$10,000 to Baxter Community Center, Grand Rapids, MI, 2012. For general support and Early Childhood Initiative.

4379
The Rosenzweig Coopersmith Foundation ✧
c/o Robert Van Dongen
333 Bridge N.W., Ste. 1200
Grand Rapids, MI 49504-5367

Established in 1997 in MI.
Donors: Dora Rosenzweig; Leonard Rosenzweig.
Foundation type: Independent foundation.
Financial data (yr. ended 12/31/12): Assets, $9,646,963 (M); expenditures, $731,940; qualifying distributions, $642,138; giving activities include $555,100 for 19 grants (high: $125,000; low: $3,000).
Purpose and activities: Support primarily for Jewish organizations; giving also for universities in Israel.
Fields of interest: Higher education; Jewish federated giving programs; Jewish agencies & synagogues.
International interests: Israel.
Limitations: Applications not accepted. Giving primarily in MI, NY, and in Israel. No grants to individuals.
Application information: Contributes only to pre-selected organizations.
Trustees: Monica Armour; Suzanne Fenster; Harry Rosenzweig; Herschel Rosenzweig; Joseph Rosenzweig.
EIN: 383393545

4380
Cooper-Standard Foundation Inc. ✧ ☆
39550 Orchard Hill Pl.
Novi, MI 48375-5329
E-mail: CSFoundation@cooperstandard.com; Main URL: http://www.cooperstandard.com/about-us/cooper-standard-foundation

Established in 2013 in MI.
Donor: Cooper-Standard Automotive Inc.
Foundation type: Company-sponsored foundation.
Financial data (yr. ended 12/31/13): Assets, $0 (M); gifts received, $680,444; expenditures, $680,444; qualifying distributions, $665,029; giving activities include $665,029 for 65 grants (high: $75,000; low: $500).
Purpose and activities: The foundation supports organizations involved with children, education, health and wellness, and community revitalization.
Fields of interest: Higher education; Education; Health care; Cancer; Heart & circulatory diseases; Crime/violence prevention, abuse prevention; Food services; Children/youth, services; Human services; Community/economic development; Children.
Type of support: Matching/challenge support; General/operating support; Program development; Employee-related scholarships.
Limitations: Applications accepted. Giving primarily in areas of company operations in IN, NC, OH, and Canada, with emphasis on MI. No support for sports teams, private K-12 schools, or other foundation. No grants for dinner fundraising events.
Publications: Application guidelines.
Application information: Personal visits and phone calls are not encouraged. However organizations may be invited to present in-person to the foundation board. Application form required.
Initial approach: E-mail proposal
Deadline(s): None
Board meeting date(s): Mar. and Sept.
Officers and Directors:* Jeffrey S. Edwards,* Pres.; Timothy W. Hefferon,* Secy.; Allen J. Campbell,* Co-Treas.; Glenn Dong, Co-Treas.; Flavia DeVeny; Keith Stephenson.
EIN: 462610373

4381
Cornucopia Family Foundation ✧ ☆
231 W. Fulton St.
Grand Rapids, MI 49503-2668
Application address: c/o Shirley VanHaren, 213 W. Fulton St., Grand Rapids, MI 49503, tel.: (616) 530-5500

Established in 2006 in MI.
Donor: Paulus C. Heule.
Foundation type: Operating foundation.
Financial data (yr. ended 12/31/13): Assets, $2,570,767 (M); gifts received, $90,644; expenditures, $550,236; qualifying distributions, $503,578; giving activities include $503,278 for 21 grants (high: $400,000; low: $150).
Fields of interest: Arts; Education; Human services; Christian agencies & churches.
Limitations: Applications accepted. Giving primarily in MI.
Application information: Application form not required.
Initial approach: Proposal
Deadline(s): None
Directors: Paulus C. Heule; Rosemary L. Heule; Shirley VanHaren.
EIN: 208080952

4382
Peter J. & Constance M. Cracchiolo Foundation ✧
24055 Jefferson Ave., Ste. 200
St. Clair Shores, MI 48080-1514

Established in 1984 in MI.
Donors: Peter J. Cracchiolo; Constance M. Cracchiolo.
Foundation type: Independent foundation.
Financial data (yr. ended 06/30/13): Assets, $14,449,181 (M); gifts received, $398,660; expenditures, $698,742; qualifying distributions, $595,515; giving activities include $595,515 for grants.
Fields of interest: Education; Hospitals (general); Health organizations, association; Human services; Children/youth, services; Catholic agencies & churches.
Type of support: General/operating support.
Limitations: Applications not accepted. Giving primarily in MI. No grants to individuals.
Application information: Contributes only to pre-selected organizations.
Officers: Peter J. Cracchiolo, Pres.; Peter T. Cracchiolo, Secy.-Treas.
Directors: Grace E. Cracchiolo; Phyllis A. Demars; Bernadette P. Lindquist.
EIN: 382561770
Selected grants: The following grants are a representative sample of this grantmaker's funding activity:
$85,000 to Archdiocese of Detroit, Detroit, MI, 2013. For Changing Lives Together Campaign.

4383
Cronin Foundation ✧
203 E. Michigan Ave.
Marshall, MI 49068-1545
Contact: Ronald J. DeGraw, Secy.-Treas. and Dir.

Established in 1990 in MI.
Donors: Elizabeth Cronin†; Mary Virginia Cronin†.
Foundation type: Independent foundation.
Financial data (yr. ended 12/31/13): Assets, $15,349,196 (M); expenditures, $712,639; qualifying distributions, $678,873; giving activities include $678,873 for 21 grants (high: $200,000; low: $571).
Purpose and activities: Giving primarily for educational, social, economic, civic, and cultural needs of the community contained within the Marshall, Michigan, school district.
Fields of interest: Arts; Higher education; Education; Hospitals (general); Human services; Community/economic development.
Type of support: Building/renovation; Equipment; Program development.
Limitations: Applications accepted. Giving limited to Calhoun County, MI, particularly the Marshall School District. No grants to individuals.
Publications: Application guidelines.
Application information: Letter or telephone for guidelines. Application form required.
Initial approach: Proposal
Deadline(s): Mar. 1, June 1, Sept. 1, and Dec. 1
Board meeting date(s): Following application deadlines and as needed
Final notification: Following board meeting
Officers and Directors:* Monica Anderson,* Pres.; Randall Davis, V.P.; Ronald J. DeGraw,* Secy.-Treas.; James Dyer; Mark O'Connell.

Number of staff: 1 part-time professional.
EIN: 382908362
Selected grants: The following grants are a representative sample of this grantmaker's funding activity:
$200,000 to Marshall Public Schools, Marshall, MI, 2012. For Continuation of School Programs.
$150,000 to Oaklawn Hospital, Marshall, MI, 2012. For Building on the Success of 80 years of Caring.
$49,816 to Kellogg Community College, Battle Creek, MI, 2012. For Renovations to the Eastern Academic Center.
$20,000 to Marshall Public Schools, Marshall, MI, 2012. For STEM Project.
$5,000 to American Museum of Magic, Marshall, MI, 2012. For Summer Magic Camp Programs.
$5,000 to Charitable Union, Battle Creek, MI, 2012. For Clothing Drive in Marshall.
$5,000 to Food Bank of South Central Michigan, Battle Creek, MI, 2012. For Installation of new refrigeration box.
$2,445 to Marshall Community Foundation, Marshall, MI, 2012. For tree planting.

4384
Peter D. & Julie F. Cummings Family Foundation ✧

(formerly Peter & Julie Fisher Cummings Foundation)
2 Towne Sq., Ste. 900
Southfield, MI 48076-3761

Established in 2005 in MI.
Donors: Julie Fisher Cummings; Peter D. Cummings; Marjorie S. Fisher; Anthony Fisher Cummings Trust UAD 1.
Foundation type: Independent foundation.
Financial data (yr. ended 12/31/13): Assets, $2,866,005 (M); expenditures, $941,459; qualifying distributions, $909,885; giving activities include $906,500 for 30 grants (high: $203,500; low: $500).
Purpose and activities: Giving primarily for the arts and education.
Fields of interest: Performing arts, orchestras; Arts; Elementary/secondary education.
Type of support: General/operating support.
Limitations: Applications not accepted. Giving primarily in FL, MI, and NY.
Application information: Unsolicited requests for funds not accepted.
Officers: Julie Fisher Cummings, Pres.; Peter D. Cummings, V.P.; Keith L. Cummings, Treas.; Anthony F. Cummings, Co-Secy.; Caroline B. Cummings, Co-Secy.
EIN: 300291756

4385
Dorothy U. Dalton Foundation, Inc. ✧

c/o Greenleaf Trust
211 S. Rose St.
Kalamazoo, MI 49007-4713 (269) 388-9800
Contact: Ronald N. Kilgore, Secy.-Treas.

Incorporated in 1978 in MI as successor to Dorothy U. Dalton Foundation Trust.
Donor: Dorothy U. Dalton†.
Foundation type: Independent foundation.
Financial data (yr. ended 12/31/12): Assets, $31,728,594 (M); expenditures, $2,226,137; qualifying distributions, $1,947,252; giving activities include $1,917,266 for 71 grants (high: $400,000; low: $500).
Purpose and activities: Giving primarily for the arts, human services, and to YMCAs.
Fields of interest: Performing arts; Performing arts, music; Arts; Human services; YM/YWCAs & YM/YWHAs; Youth, services; Foundations (private grantmaking).
Type of support: General/operating support; Continuing support; Capital campaigns; Building/renovation; Equipment; Land acquisition; Debt reduction; Emergency funds; Program development; Seed money; Research; Matching/challenge support.
Limitations: Giving primarily in Kalamazoo County, MI. No support for religious organizations. No grants to individuals, or for annual campaigns, scholarships, fellowships, publications, or conferences; no loans.
Application information: Application form required.
Initial approach: Proposal
Copies of proposal: 5
Deadline(s): Submit proposal preferably in Apr. and Oct.
Board meeting date(s): June, Sept. and Dec.
Final notification: 30 days after board meetings
Officers and Directors:* Howard Kalleward,* V.P.; Ronald N. Kilgore,* Secy.-Treas.; Elizabeth A. Bennett; Sarah A. Johansson; Judy K. Jolliffe.
EIN: 382240062
Selected grants: The following grants are a representative sample of this grantmaker's funding activity:
$400,000 to Western Michigan University Foundation, Kalamazoo, MI, 2012. For College of Fine Arts, Aviation and WMUK-FM Radio.
$100,000 to Kalamazoo Nature Center, Kalamazoo, MI, 2012. For Capital Campaign - No Child Left Inside.
$50,000 to Gryphon Place, Kalamazoo, MI, 2012. For new building campaign.
$50,000 to Pretty Lake Vacation Camp, Mattawan, MI, 2012. For Advancement Campaign.
$40,000 to Kalamazoo College, Kalamazoo, MI, 2012. For Festival Playhouse - Dalton Maintenance Fund.
$35,000 to Kalamazoo Civic Theater, Kalamazoo, MI, 2012. For Development Director.
$30,000 to Ministry with Community, Kalamazoo, MI, 2012. For Drop - in Program.
$25,000 to Kairos Dwelling, Kalamazoo, MI, 2012. For general support 2013.
$20,000 to Kalamazoo Institute of Arts, Kalamazoo, MI, 2012. For Kia Youth Education Programs.
$6,000 to Fontana Chamber Arts, Kalamazoo, MI, 2012. For outreach and educational Programs.

4386
Dana Foundation ✧ ☆

1 Village Center Dr.
Van Buren Township, MI 48111 (419) 887-5141
Contact: Joe Stancati, Secy.
Application address: P.O. Box 1000, Maumee, OH 43537, Tel.: (419) 887-5141

Incorporated in 1956 in OH.
Donors: Dana Corporation; Dana Holding Corporation.
Foundation type: Company-sponsored foundation.
Financial data (yr. ended 03/31/13): Assets, $72,134 (M); gifts received, $200,000; expenditures, $445,299; qualifying distributions, $439,726; giving activities include $363,327 for 52 grants (high: $100,000; low: $500), and $76,399 for employee matching gifts.
Purpose and activities: The foundation supports organizations involved with arts and culture, education, cancer, food distribution, and human services.
Fields of interest: Museums (art); Performing arts, theater; Performing arts, orchestras; Arts; Education; Cancer; Food distribution, meals on wheels; Boys & girls clubs; Youth development, business; American Red Cross; Children/youth, services; Human services; United Ways and Federated Giving Programs.
Type of support: General/operating support; Continuing support; Annual campaigns; Capital campaigns; Building/renovation; Equipment; Emergency funds; Employee matching gifts; Employee-related scholarships.
Limitations: Applications accepted. Giving primarily in areas of company operations in KY and OH. No grants to individuals (except for the Driveshaft Scholarship Fund), or for fellowships; no loans.
Application information: Application form not required.
Initial approach: Proposal
Copies of proposal: 1
Deadline(s): None
Officers and Directors:* Marc Levin,* Pres.; Dave Benson,* V.P.; Joe Stancati,* Secy.; Rick Dyer,* Treas.; Jeffrey Cole; David Nash; Maureen Tackett.
Number of staff: 1 part-time professional.
EIN: 346544909
Selected grants: The following grants are a representative sample of this grantmaker's funding activity:
$50,000 to Toledo Museum of Art, Toledo, OH, 2011.
$50,000 to United Way of Greater Toledo, Toledo, OH, 2011.
$20,000 to Toledo Museum of Art, Toledo, OH, 2011.
$10,000 to Junior Achievement of Northwestern Ohio, Toledo, OH, 2011.
$10,000 to Toledo Symphony, Toledo, OH, 2011.
$4,500 to Coyote Hill Christian Childrens Home, Harrisburg, MO, 2011.
$3,500 to United Fund of Cumberland County, Crossville, TN, 2011.
$3,250 to Genesis House, Cookeville, TN, 2011.
$2,000 to United Way of West Tennessee, Jackson, TN, 2011.
$1,000 to Toledo Day Nursery, Toledo, OH, 2011.

4387
Marvin I. and Betty J. Danto Foundation ✧

1700 Stutz Dr., Ste. 25
Troy, MI 48084-4500

Established in MI.
Donor: Marvin I. Danto Irrevocable Trust.
Foundation type: Independent foundation.
Financial data (yr. ended 12/31/13): Assets, $39,594,387 (M); expenditures, $1,777,318; qualifying distributions, $1,749,622; giving activities include $1,749,622 for 44 grants (high: $316,667; low: $1,000).
Fields of interest: Arts; Higher education; Environment; Health care; Jewish federated giving programs.
Limitations: Applications not accepted. Giving primarily in MI; some funding also in NY.
Application information: Contributes only to pre-selected organizations.

Officers and Trustees:* James H. Danto,* Pres. and Treas.; Joanne F. Danto,* V.P. and Secy.; Gail E. Danto,* V.P.
EIN: 203896742
Selected grants: The following grants are a representative sample of this grantmaker's funding activity:
$166,667 to Jewish Federation of Metropolitan Detroit, Bloomfield Hills, MI, 2011.
$125,000 to American Red Magen David for Israel, Southfield, MI, 2011.
$110,000 to Henry Ford Health System, Detroit, MI, 2011.
$100,000 to University of Michigan, Ann Arbor, MI, 2011.
$60,000 to Detroit Institute of Arts, Detroit, MI, 2011.
$60,000 to Michigan Opera Theater, Detroit, MI, 2011.
$57,500 to American Jewish Joint Distribution Committee, New York, NY, 2011.
$50,000 to American Society for Technion-Israel Institute of Technology, New York, NY, 2011.
$50,000 to JARC, Farmington Hills, MI, 2011.
$50,000 to Jewish Hospice and Chaplaincy Network, West Bloomfield, MI, 2011.

4388
The Dart Foundation ✧
500 Hogsback Rd.
Mason, MI 48854-9547 (517) 244-2190
Contact: Claudia Deschaine, Grants Mgr.
FAX: (517) 244-2631;
E-mail: dartfoundation@dart.biz; Main URL: http://www.dartfoundation.org

Established in 1984 in MI.
Donor: William & Claire Dart Foundation.
Foundation type: Independent foundation.
Financial data (yr. ended 10/31/13): Assets, $612,976 (M); gifts received, $4,500,000; expenditures, $4,446,739; qualifying distributions, $4,446,739; giving activities include $4,376,299 for 176 grants (high: $1,400,000; low: $500), and $57,197 for foundation-administered programs.
Purpose and activities: Giving primarily for education, with emphasis on Science, Technology, Engineering, and Mathematics (STEM); community services, with emphasis on youth programs and basic needs such as food, shelter, clothing, and health services; disaster relief, and to other programs of interest to trustees.
Fields of interest: Higher education; Education; Hospitals (general); Health organizations, association; Alzheimer's disease research; Boys & girls clubs; Human services; Children/youth, services; Engineering/technology; Public affairs; Children/youth; Economically disadvantaged.
Type of support: General/operating support; Continuing support; Annual campaigns; Capital campaigns; Building/renovation; Equipment; Program development; Publication; Curriculum development; Scholarship funds; Research; Matching/challenge support.
Limitations: Applications accepted. Giving primarily in Sarasota, FL, mid-Michigan, and in the immediate vicinities of the following communities: Corona and Lodi, CA; Deerfield Beach and Plant City, FL; Augusta, Conyers, Thomaston, and Lithonia, GA; Twin Falls, ID; North Aurora, Urbana, and some parts of Chicago, IL; Horse Cave and Owensboro, KY; Federalsburg, MD; Quitman, MS; Randleman, NC; Ada, OK; Leola and Lancaster, PA; Dallas and Waxahachie, Texas; and Tumwater, Washington. No grants to individuals.
Publications: Application guidelines; Annual report; Annual report (including application guidelines); Grants list.
Application information: Application guidelines and forms available on foundation web site. Application form required.
Initial approach: Letter, telephone or e-mail
Copies of proposal: 1
Deadline(s): Mar. 15, June 15, Sept. 15, Dec. 15
Final notification: Feb. 1, May 1, Aug. 1, and Nov. 1
Officer: James D. Lammers, V.P. and Secy.
Directors: Ariane L. Dart; Claire T. Dart; Kenneth B. Dart; Robert C. Dart.
Number of staff: 1 full-time professional.
EIN: 382849841

4389
M. E. Davenport Foundation ✧
433 E. Fulton St.
Stewart White Hall
Grand Rapids, MI 49503-5926 (616) 234-6280
Contact: Margaret E. Moceri, Pres.
FAX: (616) 732-1147;
E-mail: info@medavenport.org; Main URL: http://www.medavenport.org

Established in 1986 in MI.
Donors: Robert W. and Margaret D. Sneden Foundation; Margaret Moceri; Gregory Moceri; Kathleen Sneden; Mary Sneden Sullivan; Watson Pierce; Elsie Pierce; Barbara DeMoor.
Foundation type: Independent foundation.
Financial data (yr. ended 09/30/13): Assets, $18,562,008 (M); gifts received, $1,500; expenditures, $997,982; qualifying distributions, $842,963; giving activities include $742,031 for 18 grants (high: $399,643; low: $2,500).
Purpose and activities: Support primarily for private institutions of higher education, and specific social and community needs, usually related to business education, training, employment, and community stability, such as housing.
Fields of interest: Higher education; Employment, training; Youth development, business.
Type of support: Building/renovation; Capital campaigns; Program development; Seed money; Curriculum development.
Limitations: Applications accepted. Giving primarily in Grand Rapids, MI. No support for religious or political agendas. No grants to individuals or for debt retirement or budget deficit remediation, and taxable organizations or activities.
Publications: Application guidelines; Annual report; Financial statement; Grants list; Occasional report.
Application information: Full proposals are by invitation, upon review of initial letter. Application form not required.
Initial approach: Letter (via e-mail preferred)
Copies of proposal: 1
Board meeting date(s): Triennially
Final notification: 4-5 months
Officers and Trustees:* Margaret E. Moceri,* Chair. and Pres.; Gregory C. Moceri, V.P. and Treas.; Mary Sneden Sullivan, Secy.; Donald Maine, Exec. Dir.; Marcia A. Sneden; William Sullivan.
Number of staff: 2 full-time professional.
EIN: 382646809
Selected grants: The following grants are a representative sample of this grantmaker's funding activity:
$432,143 to Davenport University, Grand Rapids, MI, 2011.
$50,000 to Grand Rapids Community College, Grand Rapids, MI, 2011.
$35,000 to Inner City Christian Federation, Grand Rapids, MI, 2011.
$33,300 to Family Promise of Grand Rapids, Grand Rapids, MI, 2011.
$29,028 to Upper Peninsula Childrens Museum, Marquette, MI, 2011.
$28,000 to Neighborhood Ventures, Grand Rapids, MI, 2011.
$12,500 to Christians Opening Opportunities for Learning, Grand Rapids, MI, 2011.
$10,000 to Grand Rapids Opportunities for Women, Grand Rapids, MI, 2011.
$10,000 to Indian Trails Camp, Grand Rapids, MI, 2011.
$10,000 to Literacy Center of West Michigan, Grand Rapids, MI, 2011.

4390
William Davidson Foundation ✧
2 Towne Sq., Ste. 905
Southfield, MI 48076-3726

Established in 2005 in MI.
Donors: William Morse "Bill" Davidson†; William Morse Davidson Grantor Retained Annuity Trust.
Foundation type: Independent foundation.
Financial data (yr. ended 12/31/12): Assets, $449,602,251 (M); gifts received, $101,056,324; expenditures, $43,743,613; qualifying distributions, $43,728,529; giving activities include $42,267,800 for 45 grants (high: $12,500,000; low: $5,000).
Fields of interest: Education; Health care; Jewish federated giving programs.
Limitations: Applications not accepted. Giving primarily in New York, NY; some giving also in MI, OH, PA, and TX. No grants to individuals.
Application information: Contributes only to pre-selected organizations.
Officers and Directors:* Jonathan Aaron,* Pres.; Ethan Davidson,* Treas.; Mary Aaron; Karen Davidson; Oscar Feldman; Ralph Gerson; Eli Saulson.
EIN: 203899187
Selected grants: The following grants are a representative sample of this grantmaker's funding activity:
$5,700,000 to American Committee for the Weizmann Institute of Science, New York, NY, 2011.
$4,000,000 to Jewish Theological Seminary of America, New York, NY, 2011.
$2,250,000 to Jewish Federation of Metropolitan Detroit, Bloomfield Hills, MI, 2011.
$1,830,000 to Schechter Institutes, Philadelphia, PA, 2011. For Jewish studies, classroom building, capital fund and education.
$1,100,000 to Wexner Foundation, New Albany, OH, 2011.
$500,000 to Congregation Shaarey Zedek, Southfield, MI, 2011.
$250,000 to University of Texas Health Science Center, Dallas, TX, 2011.

4391
The John R. & M. Margrite Davis Foundation ✧
49050 Woodward Ave., Ste. 306
Bloomfield Hills, MI 48304-5124
Application address: c/o Raymond C. Cunningham, Jr., 126 Babbs Hollow Rd., Greenville, SC 29607, tel.: (843) 671-1108

Established in 1955 in MI.
Donors: John R. Davis†; M. Margrite Davis.
Foundation type: Independent foundation.
Financial data (yr. ended 12/31/13): Assets, $11,443,571 (M); expenditures, $570,477; qualifying distributions, $535,583; giving activities include $534,000 for 55 grants (high: $100,000; low: $500).
Fields of interest: Higher education; Hospitals (general); Medical research, institute; Human services; Children/youth, services.
Type of support: Continuing support; Annual campaigns; Capital campaigns; Building/renovation; Research.
Limitations: Applications accepted. Giving primarily in MI and SC. No grants to individuals.
Application information: Application form required.
Initial approach: Letter
Copies of proposal: 1
Deadline(s): None
Board meeting date(s): Dec.
Officers and Trustees:* Raymond C. Cunningham, Jr., Pres.; Deborah Sue Cunningham,* Secy.-Treas.; James H. LoPrete; Mary M. Lyneis; Leslie R. Moore.
EIN: 386058593
Selected grants: The following grants are a representative sample of this grantmaker's funding activity:
$2,500 to Boy Scouts of America, Blue Ridge Council, Greenville, SC, 2012. For general charitable.

4392
Dayenu Foundation ✧
169 Monroe Ave. N.W., Ste. 350
Grand Rapids, MI 49503-2632

Established in MI.
Foundation type: Independent foundation.
Financial data (yr. ended 12/31/12): Assets, $14,880,167 (M); expenditures, $1,348,422; qualifying distributions, $1,132,515; giving activities include $1,132,515 for grants.
Fields of interest: Health care; Religion.
Limitations: Applications not accepted. Giving primarily in MI.
Application information: Unsolicited requests for funds not accepted.
Officers: Jonathan Borisch, Pres.; Mary K. Borisch, V.P.; Thomas L. Borisch, Secy.; Matthew A. Borisch, Treas.
Director: David E. Borisch.
EIN: 273008834

4393
Douglas A. & Margaret E. DeCamp Foundation ✧ ☆
3485 W. M-179 Hwy.
Hastings, MI 49058-7646

Established in 2007 in MI.
Donors: Douglas A. DeCamp; Margaret DeCamp; Flexfab Horizons International, Inc.
Foundation type: Independent foundation.
Financial data (yr. ended 12/31/13): Assets, $4,688,344 (M); gifts received, $1,704,900; expenditures, $737,838; qualifying distributions, $718,950; giving activities include $714,000 for 3 grants (high: $600,000; low: $14,000).
Fields of interest: Foundations (community).
Limitations: Applications not accepted. Giving primarily in Hastings, MI.
Application information: Contributes only to pre-selected organizations.
Officers: Douglas A. DeCamp, Pres.; Kent Vana, Secy.; Richard Rathburn, Treas.; James Decamp, Exec. Dir.
Directors: Beverly Osterink; Debra Vanderveen; Kenneth Decamp; Margaret Decamp; Matthew Decamp.
EIN: 208293300
Selected grants: The following grants are a representative sample of this grantmaker's funding activity:
$190,000 to Barry Community Foundation, Hastings, MI, 2012. To support Activities of the Barry County Community Foundation.

4394
Delphi Foundation, Inc. ✧
P.O. Box 5086
Troy, MI 48098-5086
Main URL: http://delphi.com/about/social/delphifoundation

Established in 1998 in MI.
Donors: General Motors Foundation, Inc.; Delphi Automotive Systems Corp.; Delphi Corp.
Foundation type: Company-sponsored foundation.
Financial data (yr. ended 12/31/13): Assets, $17,084,959 (M); expenditures, $1,036,652; qualifying distributions, $967,865; giving activities include $960,240 for 56 grants (high: $100,000; low: $500).
Purpose and activities: The foundation supports organizations involved with science and technology education.
Fields of interest: Elementary/secondary education; Higher education; Education; Science, formal/general education; Engineering/technology; Youth.
Type of support: Program development.
Limitations: Applications not accepted. Giving primarily in areas of company operations in IL, IN, MI, NY, PA, and VA. No support for political, lobbying, or fraternal organizations, private foundations, hospitals, health care institutions, or religious organizations. No grants to individuals, or for endowments, capital campaigns, construction, general operating support, debt reduction, or conferences, workshops, or seminars not directly related to Delphi's business interests.
Publications: IRS Form 990 or 990-PF printed copy available upon request.
Application information: The foundation utilizes an invitation only Request For Proposal (RFP) process. Unsolicited requests are not accepted.
Officers and Trustees:* Eleanor Mascheroni,* Pres.; David Sherbin, Secy.; Brad Spiegal,* Treas.; Alex Biegert; Cheryl Chiuchiarelli; Lindsey Williams.
Number of staff: None.
EIN: 383442971

4395
DENSO North America Foundation ✧
24777 DENSO Dr., MC 4610
Southfield, MI 48086-5047 (248) 372-8238
FAX: (248) 213-2551;
E-mail: DENSOFoundation@denso-diam.com; Additional tel.: (248) 350-7500; Main URL: http://www.densofoundation.org
Disaster Relief Grants: http://densofoundation.org/grants/disaster-relief-grants/
Educational Grants: http://densofoundation.org/grants/educational-grants/

Established in 2001 in MI.
Donor: DENSO International America, Inc.
Foundation type: Company-sponsored foundation.
Financial data (yr. ended 12/31/13): Assets, $12,298,696 (M); gifts received, $1,252,500; expenditures, $665,045; qualifying distributions, $664,220; giving activities include $664,220 for 15 grants (high: $69,100; low: $16,395).
Purpose and activities: The foundation supports programs designed to advance engineering and technology education; and programs designed to promote community development through a skilled and knowledgeable workforce.
Fields of interest: Higher education; Education; Disasters, preparedness/services; American Red Cross; Human services; Engineering/technology.
International interests: Canada; Mexico.
Type of support: Building/renovation; Capital campaigns; Equipment; Program development.
Limitations: Applications not accepted. Giving primarily in CA, MI, MS, OH, and TN, and in Canada and Mexico. No grants to individuals, or for administrative costs, stipends, trips, conferences, or travel expenses.
Publications: Grants list.
Application information: Unsolicited requests are not accepted. Proposals are considered by invitation only.
Board meeting date(s): May and Oct.
Officers and Directors:* Douglas Patton,* Pres.; Robert Townsend, V.P.; Melissa Smith, Secy.; Kim Madaj, Treas.; Mike Brackett; David E. Cole; Karen Cooper-Boyer; Terry Helgeson; Richard Shiozaki.
Agent: DENSO International America, Inc.
Number of staff: 1 full-time professional.
EIN: 383547055

4396
DeRoy Testamentary Foundation ✧
26999 Central Park Blvd., Ste. 160N
Southfield, MI 48076-4174 (248) 827-0920
E-mail: deroyfdtn@aol.com

Established in 1979 in MI.
Donor: Helen L. DeRoy†.
Foundation type: Independent foundation.
Financial data (yr. ended 12/31/13): Assets, $58,050,621 (M); expenditures, $2,740,795; qualifying distributions, $2,183,364; giving activities include $1,789,933 for 83 grants (high: $200,000; low: $1,000).
Purpose and activities: Giving primarily for health, children and social services, and to Jewish organizations.
Fields of interest: Higher education; Health care; Health organizations, association; Human services; Children/youth, services; Family services; Jewish federated giving programs; Jewish agencies & synagogues.

Type of support: General/operating support; Continuing support; Annual campaigns; Building/renovation; Program development; Scholarship funds.
Limitations: Applications accepted. Giving primarily in MI. No grants to individuals.
Application information:
Initial approach: Proposal
Copies of proposal: 1
Deadline(s): None
Board meeting date(s): Monthly
Officers and Trustees:* Julie Rodecker,* Pres.; Marian Keidan Seltzer,* V.P. and Treas.; Gregg D. Watkins,* Secy.
Number of staff: 1 full-time professional; 3 part-time professional; 1 full-time support.
EIN: 382208833
Selected grants: The following grants are a representative sample of this grantmaker's funding activity:
$200,000 to Oakwood Healthcare, Dearborn, MI, 2011.

4397
The Richard C. Devereaux Foundation ✧
39533 Woodward Ave., Ste. 200
Bloomfield Hills, MI 48304-5103

Established in MI.
Donors: Mrs. Richard C. Devereaux; S.W. Smith; Adelyn Devereaux Trust; Leslie C. Devereaux; Curtis J. Mann.
Foundation type: Independent foundation.
Financial data (yr. ended 08/31/13): Assets, $3,255,103 (M); expenditures, $654,202; qualifying distributions, $626,030; giving activities include $626,030 for grants.
Purpose and activities: Giving primarily for education, health organizations, particularly for cancer research, and wildlife preservation; funding also for human services and for a public television station.
Fields of interest: Media, television; Higher education; Animals/wildlife, preservation/protection; Health organizations; Cancer research; Human services.
Type of support: General/operating support.
Limitations: Applications not accepted. Giving primarily in Washington, DC, IL, MI, and VA. No grants to individuals.
Application information: Unsolicited requests for funds not accepted.
Officers: Leslie C. Devereaux, Pres. and Treas.; Sidney W. Smith, Jr., V.P.; Curtis J. Mann, Secy.
EIN: 382638858
Selected grants: The following grants are a representative sample of this grantmaker's funding activity:
$100,000 to Detroit Public TV, Wixom, MI, 2011. For operating support.

4398
Daniel and Pamella DeVos Foundation ✧
P.O. Box 230257
Grand Rapids, MI 49523-0257 (616) 643-4700
Contact: Ginny Vander Hart, Exec. Dir.
FAX: (616) 774-0116;
E-mail: virginiav@rdvcorp.com; Main URL: http://www.dpdevosfoundation.org/

Established in 1992 in MI.
Donors: The Richard and Helen DeVos Foundation; Daniel DeVos; Pamella DeVos.
Foundation type: Independent foundation.
Financial data (yr. ended 12/31/12): Assets, $9,855,552 (M); gifts received, $10,000,000; expenditures, $9,542,786; qualifying distributions, $9,542,169; giving activities include $9,361,000 for 71 grants (high: $1,964,000; low: $500).
Purpose and activities: Giving primarily for the arts, particularly an art museum and for the performing arts; funding also for higher education, health care, including a children's hospital, and for children, youth, and social services.
Fields of interest: Museums (art); Performing arts, ballet; Performing arts, orchestras; Arts; Elementary/secondary education; Higher education; Education; Hospitals (specialty); Health care; Health organizations, association; Human services; Children/youth, services; Public policy, research; Christian agencies & churches.
Type of support: General/operating support; Continuing support; Annual campaigns; Capital campaigns; Building/renovation; Program development; Seed money; Matching/challenge support.
Limitations: Applications accepted. Giving primarily in Grand Rapids, MI. No support for candidates for political office. No grants to individuals, for-profit organizations, operating debt-retirement, endowments, investment opportunities; no loans.
Publications: Application guidelines.
Application information: See foundation web site for detailed information and online application. Application form not required.
Initial approach: Online proposal
Copies of proposal: 1
Deadline(s): None
Board meeting date(s): Quarterly
Final notification: Within three weeks of review
Officers: Daniel G. DeVos, Pres.; Robert H. Schierbeek, Exec. V.P. and Secy-Treas.; Jerry L. Tubergen, Exec. V.P.; Pamella DeVos, V.P.; Jeffery K. Lambert, V.P., Finance and Admin.; Ginny Vander Hart, Exec. Dir.
EIN: 383035976
Selected grants: The following grants are a representative sample of this grantmaker's funding activity:
$1,964,000 to Whitney Museum of American Art, New York, NY, 2012. For general support.
$1,810,000 to Grand Rapids Christian Schools, Grand Rapids, MI, 2012. For general support.
$1,312,500 to Northwood University, Midland, MI, 2012. For general support.
$1,000,000 to Grand Action Foundation, Grand Rapids, MI, 2012. For general support.
$500,000 to George W. Bush Foundation, Dallas, TX, 2012. For general support.
$500,000 to Grand Rapids University Preparatory Association, Grand Rapids, MI, 2012. For general support.
$200,000 to Grand Valley State University, Cook-DeVos Center for Health Sciences, Grand Rapids, MI, 2012. For general support.
$175,000 to Grand Rapids Art Museum, Grand Rapids, MI, 2012. For general support.
$50,000 to National Constitution Center, Philadelphia, PA, 2012. For general support.
$50,000 to Orlando Magic Youth Foundation, Orlando, FL, 2012. For general support.

4399
Douglas & Maria DeVos Foundation ✧
P.O. Box 230257
Grand Rapids, MI 49523-0257 (616) 643-4700
Contact: Ginny Vander Hart, Exec. Dir.
FAX: (616) 774-0116;
E-mail: info@dmdevosfoundation.org; Main URL: http://www.dmdevosfoundation.org/

Established in 1992 in MI.
Donors: Douglas DeVos; Maria DeVos.
Foundation type: Independent foundation.
Financial data (yr. ended 12/31/12): Assets, $110,637,069 (M); gifts received, $27,000,000; expenditures, $24,261,514; qualifying distributions, $23,841,073; giving activities include $21,142,693 for 175 grants (high: $3,731,000; low: $150), and $1,266,460 for 2 foundation-administered programs.
Purpose and activities: The foundation seeks to share the importance of their Christian faith by building holistic and sustainable communities that empower youth and families to prosper physically, intellectually, and spiritually. Foundation focus areas include youth, family and community.
Fields of interest: Health care; Human services; Family services; Community/economic development; Christian agencies & churches; Youth.
Type of support: General/operating support; Capital campaigns; Program development.
Limitations: Applications accepted. Giving primarily in western MI, with a significant focus on the Grand Rapids area. No support for non 501(c)(3) organizations, or for start-up organizations (within 18 months of incorporation), organizations working outside the United States, or for organizations that contradict the stated values of the foundation. No grants or loans to individuals, or for endowments, debt retirement, or for investment opportunities.
Publications: Application guidelines.
Application information: Very few grants are awarded to new organizations with no previous relationship with the trustees. Any grants to new organizations will rarely exceed $5,000. The foundation prefers to receive applications from organizations once every 12 months. In addition, the foundation will not consider second requests from organizations for capital projects. Application form required.
Initial approach: Submit via application form on foundation web site.
Copies of proposal: 1
Deadline(s): None
Board meeting date(s): Quarterly
Final notification: 3-4 months
Officers: Douglas DeVos, Pres.; Jerry L. Tubergen, Exec. V.P.; Maria DeVos, V.P.; Robert H. Schierbeek, Secy.-Treas.; Ginny Vander Hart, Exec. Dir.; Jeffrey K. Lambert.
EIN: 383035972
Selected grants: The following grants are a representative sample of this grantmaker's funding activity:
$3,731,000 to Grand Rapids Christian Schools, Grand Rapids, MI, 2012. For Unrestricted Grant to General Fund.
$2,125,000 to National Constitution Center, Philadelphia, PA, 2012. For Unrestricted Grant to General Fund.
$1,177,000 to LINC Community Revitalization, Grand Rapids, MI, 2012. For Unrestricted Grant to General Fund.

$1,000,000 to Grand Action Foundation, Grand Rapids, MI, 2012. For Unrestricted Grant to General Fund.
$750,000 to American Enterprise Institute for Public Policy Research, Washington, DC, 2012. For Unrestricted Grant to General Fund.
$472,500 to KeyStone Community Church, Ada, MI, 2012. For Unrestricted Grant to General Fund.
$350,000 to First Steps Kent, Grand Rapids, MI, 2012. For Unrestricted Grant to General Fund.
$75,000 to Cornerstone University, Grand Rapids, MI, 2012. For Unrestricted Grant to General Fund.
$37,000 to Vocal Music Workshop, Grand Rapids, MI, 2012. For Unrestricted Grant to General Fund.
$10,000 to Orlando Magic Youth Foundation, Orlando, FL, 2012. For Unrestricted Grant to General Fund.

4400
The Richard and Helen DeVos Foundation ✧

P.O. Box 230257
Grand Rapids, MI 49523-0257 (616) 643-4700
FAX: (616) 774-0116; E-mail: virginiav@rdvcorp.com

Incorporated in 1969 in MI.
Donors: Richard M. DeVos; Helen J. DeVos; Alticor Inc.
Foundation type: Independent foundation.
Financial data (yr. ended 12/31/12): Assets, $281,699 (M); gifts received, $23,199,000; expenditures, $29,869,809; qualifying distributions, $29,887,812; giving activities include $27,771,780 for 125 grants (high: $2,000,000; low: $1,000), and $1,957,811 for 2 foundation-administered programs.
Purpose and activities: The foundation primarily supports the work of religious agencies, churches, and schools in ministry, outreach, and education. Its secondary focus includes social outreach, the arts, public policy, and health care. The foundation focuses its funding in the areas of western Michigan and central Florida.
Fields of interest: Arts; Health care; Social sciences; Public policy, research; Religion.
Type of support: General/operating support; Continuing support; Annual campaigns; Capital campaigns; Building/renovation; Program development; Seed money; Matching/challenge support.
Limitations: Applications not accepted. Giving primarily in central FL and western MI. No grants to individuals.
Application information: Unsolicited requests for funds not accepted.
Board meeting date(s): Every 3 months
Officers and Trustees:* Helen J. DeVos,* Pres.; Jerry L. Tubergen,* C.O.O. and V.P.; Jeffrey K. Lambert, V.P., Finance and Admin.; Robert H. Schierbeek, Exec. V.P. and Secy.-Treas.; Richard DeVos.
EIN: 237066873
Selected grants: The following grants are a representative sample of this grantmaker's funding activity:
$2,000,000 to Donors Trust, Alexandria, VA, 2012. For Unrestricted Grant to General Fund.
$2,000,000 to George W. Bush Foundation, Dallas, TX, 2012. For Unrestricted Grant to General Fund.
$1,500,000 to Grand Valley State University, Grand Rapids, MI, 2012. For Unrestricted Grant to General Fund.
$1,000,000 to Christian Reformed Church in North America Foundation, Grand Rapids, MI, 2012. For Unrestricted Grant to General Fund.
$1,000,000 to Grand Rapids Symphony, Grand Rapids, MI, 2012. For Unrestricted Grant to General Fund.
$1,000,000 to Heritage Foundation, Washington, DC, 2012. For Unrestricted Grant to General Fund.
$500,000 to Michigan State University, Grand Rapids, MI, 2012. For Unrestricted Grant to General Fund.
$50,000 to Madison Square Christian Reformed Church, Grand Rapids, MI, 2012. For Unrestricted Grant to General Fund.
$30,000 to Urban Institute for Contemporary Arts, Grand Rapids, MI, 2012. For Unrestricted Grant to General Fund.
$25,000 to Grand Rapids Initiative for Leaders, Grand Rapids, MI, 2012. For Unrestricted Grant to General Fund.

4401
Oliver Dewey Marcks Foundation ✧

645 Griswold St., Ste. 3180
Detroit, MI 48226-4250

Established in 1960.
Donors: Eula D. Marcks‡; Oliver Dewey Marcks‡.
Foundation type: Independent foundation.
Financial data (yr. ended 12/31/12): Assets, $11,219,135 (M); expenditures, $712,192; qualifying distributions, $552,500; giving activities include $552,500 for grants.
Fields of interest: Arts; Education; Environment, natural resources; Animal welfare; Human services.
Type of support: General/operating support; Program development.
Limitations: Applications not accepted. Giving limited to Detroit, MI, and surrounding communities. No grants to individuals.
Application information: Unsolicited requests for funds not accepted.
Officers and Trustees:* John M. Chase, Jr.,* Pres.; Marian J. Valentine,* Secy.; Michael J. Predhomme,* Treas.
EIN: 386081311

4402
DeWitt Families Conduit Foundation ✧

280 N. River Ave., Ste. B
Holland, MI 49424-2193

Established in 1987 in MI.
Donors: Brian DeWitt; Lisa DeWitt; Dawn Brinks; Kurt Brinks; Deb Koop; J.P. Koop; Donald DeWitt; Minnie DeWitt; Gary D. DeWitt; Joyce DeWitt; Julia M. Morrison; Kathy Muyskens; Chris Muyskens; Keith DeWitt; Mary E. DeWitt; Kelly DeWitt; Kristin DeWitt; Kerri Sue Smits; James Smits; Lisa Vanderkolk; Jon Vanderkolk; Marilyn Norman; Thomas Norman; Marvin G. DeWitt; Jerene L. DeWitt; Merle DeWitt; Sheri DeWitt; Shirley Dedoes; William DeWitt, Jr.; Mary DeWitt; Deb van Heck; Gary & Joyce DeWitt Ltd. Partners; Donald L. DeWitt Trust; Merle J. DeWitt Trust; and members of the DeWitt family.
Foundation type: Independent foundation.
Financial data (yr. ended 12/31/13): Assets, $6,106 (M); gifts received, $642,201; expenditures, $644,144; qualifying distributions, $636,736; giving activities include $632,736 for 114 grants (high: $47,800; low: $150).
Purpose and activities: Giving for Christian churches, religious missionary organizations, and educational institutions.
Fields of interest: Higher education; Human services; Youth, services; Christian agencies & churches.
Limitations: Applications not accepted. Giving primarily in MI. No grants to individuals.
Application information: Contributes only to pre-selected organizations.
Officer: Gary D. DeWitt, Pres.
Directors: Donald L. DeWitt; Keith DeWitt.
EIN: 382761226
Selected grants: The following grants are a representative sample of this grantmaker's funding activity:
$65,945 to Ottawa Reformed Church, West Olive, MI, 2011. For annual support.
$36,000 to Community Reformed Church, Zeeland, MI, 2011. For annual support.
$29,250 to Focus on the Family, Colorado Springs, CO, 2011. For annual support.
$16,000 to Northwestern College, Orange City, IA, 2011. For annual support.
$15,000 to Grand Valley State University, Grand Rapids, MI, 2011. For annual support.
$10,000 to Ridge Point Community Church, Holland, MI, 2011. For annual support.
$10,000 to Salvation Army of Dallas, Dallas, TX, 2011. For annual support.
$8,632 to Bible Study Fellowship, San Antonio, TX, 2011. For annual support.
$6,800 to Campus Crusade for Christ International, Orlando, FL, 2011. For annual support.
$5,000 to Elim Christian Services, Palos Heights, IL, 2011. For annual support.

4403
The Doornink Foundation ✧

111 Lyon St. N.W., Ste. 900
Grand Rapids, MI 49503-2487

Established in 1997 in MI.
Donors: Mary Welch Corl; Robert W. Corl, Jr.; Robert W. Corl III; Mary W. Corl; James M. Corl; Kelli R. Corl.
Foundation type: Independent foundation.
Financial data (yr. ended 12/31/13): Assets, $15,319,473 (M); gifts received, $28,000; expenditures, $693,096; qualifying distributions, $610,972; giving activities include $591,650 for 19 grants (high: $200,000; low: $250).
Fields of interest: Education; Health care; Human services; Children/youth, services; United Ways and Federated Giving Programs.
Type of support: General/operating support; Capital campaigns; Program development.
Limitations: Applications not accepted. Giving primarily in Grand Rapids, MI.
Application information: Contributes only to pre-selected organizations.
Officers and Trustees:* Mary Welch Corl,* Pres.; Robert W. Corl, Jr.,* V.P.; Jeffrey B. Power,* Secy.-Treas.; James M. Corl; Kelli R. Corl; Robert W. Corl III.
EIN: 383386701
Selected grants: The following grants are a representative sample of this grantmaker's funding activity:
$17,500 to Indian Trails Camp, Grand Rapids, MI, 2012. For Installation of new flooring in 8 cabins.

4404
The Dow Chemical Company Foundation ✧
2030 Dow Ctr.
Midland, MI 48674-0001
Contact: R.N. "Bo" Miller, Pres. and Exec. Dir.
FAX: (989) 636-3518; E-mail: bomiller@dow.com; Main URL: http://www.dow.com/company/citizenship/

Established in 1979 in MI.
Donor: The Dow Chemical Co.
Foundation type: Company-sponsored foundation.
Financial data (yr. ended 12/31/13): Assets, $22,714,039 (M); gifts received, $30,000,000; expenditures, $21,514,357; qualifying distributions, $21,503,896; giving activities include $21,503,896 for 1,056 grants (high: $1,417,466; low: $93).
Purpose and activities: The foundation supports organizations involved with community success, science education, and environmental stewardship.
Fields of interest: Elementary/secondary education; Environment; Community/economic development; United Ways and Federated Giving Programs; Chemistry.
Type of support: Equipment; Program development; Seed money; Employee matching gifts; Donated products; In-kind gifts.
Limitations: Applications accepted. Giving on a national and international basis primarily in areas of company operations. No support for political or religious organizations. No grants for travel or administrative costs.
Application information: Application form not required.
Initial approach: Letter of inquiry
Copies of proposal: 1
Deadline(s): None
Board meeting date(s): 4 times per year
Final notification: 2 to 3 months
Officers and Directors:* Dave E. Kepler, Chair.; R.N. "Bo" Miller,* Pres. and Exec. Dir.; Stephen Cifrulak, Secy.; Colleen W. Kay, Treas.; N. Carr; M. Davis; Gregory M. Freiwald; Heinz Haller; A. Sreeram; William H. Weideman.
Number of staff: 1 full-time professional; 7 part-time professional.
EIN: 382314603
Selected grants: The following grants are a representative sample of this grantmaker's funding activity:
$1,400,000 to Nature Conservancy, Arlington, VA, 2012.
$1,251,849 to Habitat for Humanity International, Americus, GA, 2012.
$1,007,500 to National Science Teachers Association, Arlington, VA, 2012.
$544,500 to United Way of Midland County, Midland, MI, 2012.
$35,000 to United Way of Bay County, Bay City, MI, 2012.
$30,000 to Chippewa Nature Center, Midland, MI, 2012.
$29,150 to Rice University, Dept. of Chemical Engineering, Houston, TX, 2012.
$26,000 to Reece Community Living Endeavor, Midland, MI, 2012.
$10,000 to Indiana University-Purdue University Indianapolis, Indianapolis, IN, 2012.

4405
Dow Corning Foundation ✧
c/o Dow Corning Corp.
Coporate Center
P.O. Box 994
Midland, MI 48686-0994
Contact: Kathryn Curtiss Spence, Dir.
E-mail: foundation@dowcorning.com; Main URL: http://www.dowcorning.com/content/about/aboutcomm/dowcorningfoundation.aspx

Established in 1982 in MI.
Donors: Dow Corning Corp.; Hemlock Semiconductor Corp.; Dow Cornínci Toray Co., Ltd.
Foundation type: Company-sponsored foundation.
Financial data (yr. ended 12/31/13): Assets, $30,996,571 (M); gifts received, $98,673; expenditures, $1,392,216; qualifying distributions, $1,262,275; giving activities include $1,262,275 for 22 grants (high: $254,000; low: $2,000).
Purpose and activities: The foundation supports programs designed to increase access to science, technology, engineering and math (STEM) education; improve community vitality; and increase awareness and use of innovative and sustainable technology.
Fields of interest: Museums; Elementary/secondary education; Higher education; Environment, natural resources; Environment; Hospitals (general); Health care; Food services; Recreation, parks/playgrounds; Boy scouts; Youth development, business; Community/economic development; Foundations (community); United Ways and Federated Giving Programs; Science, formal/general education; Mathematics; Engineering/technology.
Type of support: Continuing support; Capital campaigns; Building/renovation; Equipment; Program development; Seed money; Curriculum development; Scholarship funds; Matching/challenge support.
Limitations: Applications accepted. Giving in areas of company operations, with emphasis on Kendallville, IN, Carrollton and Elizabethtown, KY, Bay, Midland, and Saginaw counties, MI, and Greensboro, NC. No support for veterans', political, or religious groups or athletic leagues. No grants to individuals, or for scholarships, conferences, travel costs of groups, dinners, fundraising events, projects normally funded by government taxation, or personal needs; no research or international grants.
Publications: Application guidelines.
Application information: Organizations receiving support are asked to submit annual progress reports and a final report. Application form required.
Initial approach: Complete online application
Deadline(s): STEM grants reviewed in Mar.; Quality-of-life grants reviewed in June; Innovative technology grants reviewed in Sept.; All types of grants reviewed in Dec.
Board meeting date(s): Quarterly
Officers and Trustees:* Christian A. Velasquez,* Chair. and Pres.; Mathew J. Nolan,* Secy.; Ronald G. Thompson,* Treas.; Kathryn Curtiss Spence, Mgr.; Jeanne D. Dodd; Kimberly R. Houston-Philpot; D. Aaron Howald; Robert L. Kain; Thomas H. Lane; Christopher C. Shirk; David R. Soldan.
Number of staff: 1 part-time professional; 1 part-time support.
EIN: 382376485

4406
Herbert H. and Barbara C. Dow Foundation ✧
P.O. Box 393
Frankfort, MI 49635-0393

Incorporated in 1957 in MI.
Donors: Herbert H. Dow†; Barbara C. Dow†; Dow 2005 Charitable Annuity Trust.
Foundation type: Independent foundation.
Financial data (yr. ended 12/31/13): Assets, $20,074,184 (M); expenditures, $996,812; qualifying distributions, $873,106; giving activities include $864,500 for 30 grants (high: $100,000; low: $2,000).
Purpose and activities: Giving primarily for the arts, higher education, health care and Christian ministries and organizations.
Fields of interest: Museums (art); Arts; Higher education; Education; Health care; Human services; Christian agencies & churches.
Type of support: General/operating support; Continuing support; Capital campaigns; Building/renovation; Endowments; Program development; Scholarship funds; Research.
Limitations: Applications not accepted. Giving in the U.S., with emphasis on AZ. No grants to individuals.
Application information: Contributes only to pre-selected organizations.
Board meeting date(s): Annually
Officers and Trustees:* Willard H. Dow II,* Pres.; Dana D. Schuler,* Secy.; Pamela G. Dow,* Treas.
EIN: 386058513
Selected grants: The following grants are a representative sample of this grantmaker's funding activity:
$75,000 to Fellowship of Christian Athletes, Dallas, TX, 2012. For Weekend of Champions.
$75,000 to Hillsdale College, Hillsdale, MI, 2012. For Dow Center Capital Campaign.
$50,000 to Interlochen Center for the Arts, Interlochen, MI, 2012. For Music Complex Building.
$40,000 to Paul Oliver Memorial Hospital Foundation, Frankfort, MI, 2012. For Pomh Hemodialysis Project.
$30,000 to Phoenix Art Museum, Phoenix, AZ, 2012. For art education.
$25,000 to Heritage Foundation, Washington, DC, 2012. For operational funds.
$25,000 to NRA Foundation, Fairfax, VA, 2012. For youth hunter safety education challenge.
$25,000 to Scottsdale Healthcare Foundation, Scottsdale, AZ, 2012. For Clinical Trials Research.
$15,000 to Grand Traverse Regional Community Foundation, Traverse City, MI, 2012. For Grand Traverse YMCA Capital Campaign.

4407
The Herbert H. and Grace A. Dow Foundation ✧
1018 W. Main St.
Midland, MI 48640-4292 (989) 631-3699
Contact: Margaret Ann Riecker, Pres.
FAX: (989) 631-0675;
E-mail: info@hhdowfoundation.org; Grant application e-mail: grants@hhdowfoundation.org; Main URL: http://www.hhdowfoundation.org

Established in 1936 in MI.
Donor: Grace A. Dow†.
Foundation type: Independent foundation.

Financial data (yr. ended 12/31/12): Assets, $406,635,798 (M); gifts received, $5,130; expenditures, $22,601,725; qualifying distributions, $19,948,862; giving activities include $17,728,638 for 188 grants (high: $1,000,000; low: $1,000), and $2,689,240 for 1 foundation-administered program.
Purpose and activities: Support for religious, charitable, scientific, literacy, or educational purposes for the public benefaction of the inhabitants of the city of Midland and of the people of the state of Michigan. Grants largely for education, particularly higher education, community and social services, civic improvement, conservation, scientific research, church support (only in Midland County, MI), and cultural programs; maintains Dow Gardens, a public horticultural garden.
Fields of interest: Arts; Higher education; Libraries/library science; Education; Environment, natural resources; Human services; Community/economic development; Engineering/technology; Science.
Type of support: General/operating support; Building/renovation; Equipment; Endowments; Program development; Seed money; Research; Matching/challenge support.
Limitations: Applications accepted. Giving limited to MI, with emphasis on Midland County. No support for political organizations or sectarian religious organizations or programs, other than churches in Midland County. No grants to individuals, or for travel or conferences; no loans.
Publications: Annual report (including application guidelines); Financial statement; Grants list.
Application information: Application form not required.
Initial approach: Proposal
Copies of proposal: 1
Deadline(s): None
Board meeting date(s): Bimonthly
Final notification: 2 months
Officers and Trustees:* Macauley Whiting, Jr.,* Pres. and Treas.; Michael Lloyd Dow,* V.P.; Margaret E. Thompson,* Secy.; Julie Carol Arbury; Ruth Alden Doan; Alden Lee Hanson; Diane Dow Hullet; Andrew N. Liveris; Bonnie B. Matheson; Suzanna McCuan; Willard Mott; Elias Buchanan Ohrstrom; David Ramaker.
EIN: 381437485
Selected grants: The following grants are a representative sample of this grantmaker's funding activity:
$3,000,000 to Grace A. Dow Memorial Library, Midland, MI, 2012. To fund infrastructure and interior improvements to the Grace A. Dow Memorial Library.
$1,000,000 to Michigan State University, East Lansing, MI, 2012. To create two endowments at MSU that will support one Junior Research Fellow and one Graduate Scholar for each of five years at the MSU Midland Research Institute for Value Chain Creation.
$1,000,000 to Mid-Michigan Regional Health System, Midland, MI, 2012. To increase capacity for MidMichigan Medical Center-Midland as a regional campus of Michigan State University.
$1,000,000 to Mid-Michigan Regional Health System, Midland, MI, 2012. To increase capacity for MidMichigan Medical Center-Midland as a regional campus of Michigan State University.
$1,000,000 to Nature Conservancy, Arlington, VA, 2012. For Great Lakes Project.
$750,000 to Midland Center for the Arts, Midland, MI, 2012. For operations and education outreach.
$250,000 to Northwood University, Midland, MI, 2012. To create a Main Street entryway to its campus, a portion of which would traverse over property owned by Midland Investment properties, LLC, a Michigan limited liability company, of which the Foundation is the sole member.
$100,000 to Grand Traverse Regional Community Foundation, Traverse City, MI, 2012. To help fund the capital campaign to preserve the historic Cathedral Barn and establish a permanent botanic garden.
$60,000 to Chippewa Nature Center, Midland, MI, 2012. For operations for three years beginning with budget.

4408
Alden & Vada Dow Fund ✧ ☆
315 Post St.
Midland, MI 48640-2658

Established in 1960 in MI.
Donors: Alden Dow†; Vada Dow†; Vada B. Dow Charitable Unitrust.
Foundation type: Independent foundation.
Financial data (yr. ended 12/31/13): Assets, $12,676,004 (M); gifts received, $193,014; expenditures, $636,785; qualifying distributions, $571,243; giving activities include $525,300 for 31 grants (high: $100,000; low: $5,000).
Fields of interest: Arts; Health organizations, association; Human services; Community/economic development.
Type of support: General/operating support; Continuing support; Annual campaigns; Capital campaigns; Equipment; Endowments; Conferences/seminars.
Limitations: Applications not accepted. Giving primarily in MI. No grants to individuals.
Application information: Contributes only to pre-selected organizations.
Board meeting date(s): Feb. 15 and Sept. 15
Officers and Trustees:* Michael Lloyd Dow,* Pres.; Diane Hullet,* Secy.; Kendall Mills,* Treas.; Barbara D. Carras; Elizabeth Lewis; Lloyd Mills.
Number of staff: 1 part-time professional.
EIN: 386058512
Selected grants: The following grants are a representative sample of this grantmaker's funding activity:
$25,000 to Windover High School, Midland, MI, 2011.
$20,000 to East Side Soup Kitchen, Saginaw, MI, 2011.
$20,000 to Underground Railroad, Saginaw, MI, 2011.
$15,000 to Eagle Village, Hersey, MI, 2011.
$15,000 to Hidden Harvest, Saginaw, MI, 2011.
$15,000 to Interlochen Arts Academy, Interlochen, MI, 2011.
$10,000 to Bay Area Womens Center, Bay City, MI, 2011.
$10,000 to Chippewa River District Library, Mount Pleasant, MI, 2011.
$10,000 to Safe and Sound Child Advocacy Center, Midland, MI, 2011.
$5,000 to American Red Cross, Midland, MI, 2011.

4409
Vera and Joseph Dresner Foundation ☆
(doing business as Dresner Foundation)
6960 Orchard Lake Rd., Ste. 120
West Bloomfield, MI 48322-4517
248-785-0299
Main URL: http://www.dresnerfoundation.org/

Established in MI.
Donor: Joseph Dresner†.
Foundation type: Independent foundation.
Financial data (yr. ended 12/31/13): Assets, $140,257,669 (M); gifts received, $51,392,447; expenditures, $3,697,053; qualifying distributions, $2,845,155; giving activities include $2,122,300 for 18 grants (high: $1,000,000; low: $1,000).
Purpose and activities: Giving primarily to support health issues, youth programs, the arts and animal welfare.
Fields of interest: Arts; Animal welfare; Health care, research; Youth development.
Limitations: Applications not accepted. Giving primarily in MI.
Application information: Unsolicited requests for funds not accepted.
Officers and Directors:* Kevin Furlong,* C.E.O.; Lori Dresner,* Pres.; Gary Weisman,* V.P.; Mark Cohn,* Secy.
EIN: 205838578

4410
DTE Energy Foundation ✧
(formerly Detroit Edison Foundation)
1 Energy Plz., 1578 WCB
Detroit, MI 48226-1279 (313) 235-9271
Contact: Jennifer Whitteaker, Mgr., Corp. Contribs. and Community Involvement
E-mail: foundation@dteenergy.com; Main URL: https://www2.dteenergy.com/wps/portal/dte/aboutus/community/

Established in 1986 in MI.
Donors: The Detroit Edison Co.; DTE Energy Ventures, Inc.
Foundation type: Company-sponsored foundation.
Financial data (yr. ended 12/31/12): Assets, $65,636,182 (M); gifts received, $21,300,000; expenditures, $9,912,018; qualifying distributions, $9,857,713; giving activities include $9,606,192 for 538 grants (high: $625,000; low: $25).
Purpose and activities: The foundation supports programs designed to promote LEAD initiatives including, leadership, education, environment, achievement, development, and diversity in DTE Energy service territories.
Fields of interest: Arts, cultural/ethnic awareness; Museums (science/technology); Performing arts; Arts; Elementary/secondary education; Higher education; Business school/education; Engineering school/education; Education, services; Education; Environment, natural resources; Environment, energy; Environment, forests; Environmental education; Environment; Employment; Food distribution, meals on wheels; Youth development; American Red Cross; Human services; Civil/human rights, equal rights; Community development, neighborhood development; Urban/community development; Business/industry; Community/economic development; Mathematics; Engineering/technology; Science; Leadership development; Minorities; Women.
Type of support: General/operating support; Continuing support; Capital campaigns; Program

development; Curriculum development; Employee volunteer services; Sponsorships; Employee matching gifts.
Limitations: Applications accepted. Giving primarily in areas of company operations in MI. No support for political parties or organizations, religious organizations not of direct benefit to the entire community, discriminatory organizations, national or international organizations (unless they provide benefits directly to DTE Energy service areas), single purpose health organizations, or hospitals for building or equipment needs. No grants to individuals, or for political activities, student group trips, conferences, or building or equipment needs for hospitals.
Publications: Application guidelines; Program policy statement.
Application information: Telephone calls and video submissions are not encouraged. Organizations receiving support are asked to provide a final report. Application form required.
Initial approach: Download application form and E-mail proposal and application form to foundation
Copies of proposal: 1
Deadline(s): Feb. 3 to Feb. 14; Apr. 21 to May 2; July 21 to Aug. 1; and Oct. 13 to Oct. 25
Board meeting date(s): Quarterly
Final notification: Apr. 17, July 11, Oct. 17, and Jan. 9
Officers and Directors:* Frederick E. Shell, Chair.; Faye Anderson Nelson, Pres.; Karla D. Hall,* V.P. and Secy.; Naif A. Khouri,* Treas.; Joann Chavez; Paul C. Hillegonds; Steven E. Kurmas; Jerry Norcia; Bruce D. Peterson; David Rudd; Larry E. Steward.
Number of staff: 1 full-time professional; 2 full-time support.
EIN: 382708636
Selected grants: The following grants are a representative sample of this grantmaker's funding activity:
$625,000 to City Connect Detroit, Detroit, MI, 2012.
$466,716 to United Way for Southeastern Michigan, Detroit, MI, 2012.
$254,075 to Detroit Symphony Orchestra, Max M Fisher Music Center, Detroit, MI, 2012.
$223,142 to University of Michigan, Office of the President, Ann Arbor, MI, 2012.
$100,000 to American Red Cross, Southeastern Michigan Chapter, Detroit, MI, 2012.
$20,000 to Historical Society of Michigan, Lansing, MI, 2012.
$10,050 to University of Michigan, Office of the Chancellor, Dearborn, MI, 2012.
$10,000 to Detroit Eastside Community Collaborative, Detroit, MI, 2012.
$10,000 to Peoples Community Services of Metropolitan Detroit, Detroit, MI, 2012.
$8,920 to Council on Foundations, Arlington, VA, 2012.

4411
The Duffy Foundation ✧
c/o Miller Canfield
101 N. Main St., 7th Fl.
Ann Arbor, MI 48104-5507
Contact: Erik H. Serr

Established in 1989 in MI.
Donors: Howard S. Holmes; Andrea L. Holmes; Mary B. Holmes.
Foundation type: Independent foundation.
Financial data (yr. ended 12/31/12): Assets, $40,153,486 (M); expenditures, $3,156,668; qualifying distributions, $3,033,000; giving activities include $3,033,000 for grants.
Fields of interest: Arts; Environment, natural resources; Animal welfare; Animals/wildlife, special services; Hospitals (general); Crime/violence prevention, domestic violence; Human services; YM/YWCAs & YM/YWHAs; Children/youth, services.
Limitations: Applications not accepted. Giving primarily in MI, with emphasis on Ann Arbor and Washtenaw County. No grants to individuals.
Application information: Contributes only to pre-selected organizations.
Officers and Directors:* Andrea L. Holmes,* Pres. and Treas.; Christine M. Holmes,* V.P.; Kathryn W. Holmes,* V.P.; Erik Serr, Secy.
EIN: 382908719

4412
Dyer-Ives Foundation ✧ ☆
Waters Bldg.
161 Ottawa Ave. N.W., Ste. 501-H
Grand Rapids, MI 49503-2750 (616) 454-4502
Contact: Linda B. Patterson, Exec. Dir.
FAX: (616) 454-8545; E-mail: info@dyer-ives.org;
Main URL: http://www.dyer-ives.org

Established in 1961 in MI.
Donor: John R. Hunting.
Foundation type: Independent foundation.
Financial data (yr. ended 08/31/13): Assets, $3,831,432 (M); expenditures, $730,905; qualifying distributions, $661,796; giving activities include $448,406 for 34 grants (high: $50,000; low: $100).
Purpose and activities: The foundation acts primarily as a catalyst and stimulator for small innovative projects that encourage a sense of community in educational, social, environmental or cultural fields.
Fields of interest: Humanities; Arts; Education; Environment; Employment; Housing/shelter; Youth development, services; Human services; Community development, neighborhood development.
Type of support: Program development; Publication; Seed money; Curriculum development; Technical assistance; Consulting services.
Limitations: Applications accepted. Giving limited to the central city of Grand Rapids, MI. No grants to individuals, or for building or endowment funds, operating budgets, or scholarship funds.
Publications: Biennial report (including application guidelines); Financial statement; Grants list; Informational brochure (including application guidelines); Multi-year report.
Application information: See foundation web site for complete application guidelines. Application form not required.
Initial approach: Telephone and proposal
Copies of proposal: 1
Deadline(s): None
Board meeting date(s): Monthly
Final notification: After board meetings
Officers: John R. Hunting, Chair.; John D. Hibbard, Jr., Vice-Chair.; Steeve Buckridge, Pres.; R. Malcolm Cumming, Secy.; Susan Cobb, Treas.; Linda B. Patterson, Exec. Dir.
Directors: Rosalynn Bliss; Dotty Clune; Jocelyn Detloff; Julia Guevara; Andy Guy; Paul Haan; Simone Jonaitis; Carl Kelly; Betty Zylstra.
Number of staff: 2 part-time professional.
EIN: 386049657

4413
Earhart Foundation ✧
2200 Green Rd., Ste. H
Ann Arbor, MI 48105-1569 (734) 761-8592
Contact: Ingrid A. Gregg, Pres.

Incorporated in 1929 in MI.
Donor: Harry Boyd Earhart‡.
Foundation type: Independent foundation.
Financial data (yr. ended 12/31/13): Assets, $15,977,580 (M); expenditures, $7,985,144; qualifying distributions, $7,832,519; giving activities include $4,684,397 for 158 grants (high: $150,000; low: $29), and $1,858,609 for 115 grants to individuals (high: $44,800; low: $1,449).
Purpose and activities: H.B. Earhart Fellowships for graduate study awarded through a special nominating process for which direct applications will not be accepted; research fellowships for individual projects in economics, history, philosophy, international affairs, and political science awarded upon direct application to faculty members; grants also to educational and research organizations legally qualified for private foundation support.
Fields of interest: History/archaeology; Philosophy/ethics; Graduate/professional education; Economics; Political science; International studies.
Type of support: Conferences/seminars; Publication; Curriculum development; Fellowships; Research; Grants to individuals; Scholarships—to individuals.
Limitations: Applications accepted. Giving on a national basis. No grants for capital, building, or endowment funds, operating budgets, continuing support, annual campaigns, seed money, emergency funds, deficit financing, or matching gifts; no loans.
Publications: Annual report (including application guidelines).
Application information: Direct applications from candidates or uninvited sponsors for H.B. Earhart Fellowships (for graduate study) are not accepted. Application form not required.
Initial approach: Letter
Copies of proposal: 1
Deadline(s): Proposal should be submitted at least 4 months before beginning of project work period
Board meeting date(s): Monthly except in Aug.
Officers and Trustees:* Dennis L. Bark,* Chair.; John H. Moore,* Vice-Chair.; Ingrid A. Gregg,* Pres.; Montgomery B. Brown, Secy. and Dir., Progs.; Kathleen B. Richeson, Treas.; Thomas J. Bray; Kimberly O. Dennis; Earl H. Heenan III; Ann K. Irish; David B. Kennedy.
Number of staff: 2 full-time professional; 3 full-time support.
EIN: 386008273

4414
C. K. Eddy Family Memorial Fund ✧
c/o Citizens Bank Wealth Mgmt., N.A.
328 S. Saginaw St., M/C 001065
Flint, MI 48502-1926
Application address: c/o Helen James, Trust Off., Citizens Bank Wealth Mgmt., N.A., 101 N. Washington Ave., Saginaw, MI 48607-1207, tel.: (989) 776-7368

Trust established in 1925 in MI.
Donor: Arthur D. Eddy‡.
Foundation type: Independent foundation.
Financial data (yr. ended 06/30/13): Assets, $16,182,714 (M); expenditures, $825,782; qualifying distributions, $808,683; giving activities include $579,300 for 8 grants (high: $250,000; low: $5,000), and $67,000 for 17 loans to individuals (high: $4,000; low: $3,000).
Purpose and activities: Giving primarily for student loans and community programs.
Fields of interest: Arts; Education; Human services; Community/economic development.
Type of support: Equipment; Program development; Student loans—to individuals.
Limitations: Giving limited to Saginaw County, MI, with some emphasis on the city of Saginaw.
Publications: Application guidelines.
Application information: Application form required.
Deadline(s): None for grants; May 1 for student loans
Board meeting date(s): 3rd Wed. of Mar., June, Sept., and Dec.
Trustee: Citizens Bank.
EIN: 386040506
Selected grants: The following grants are a representative sample of this grantmaker's funding activity:
$250,000 to Temple Theater Foundation, Saginaw, MI, 2011.
$80,000 to Saginaw Charter Township, Saginaw, MI, 2011.
$50,000 to Saginaw Community Foundation, Saginaw, MI, 2011.
$50,000 to Saginaw Community Foundation, Saginaw, MI, 2011.
$20,000 to City Rescue Mission of Saginaw, Saginaw, MI, 2011.

4415
Fred A. and Barbara M. Erb Family Foundation ✧
(doing business as Erb Family Foundation)
38710 Woodward Ave., Ste. 210
Bloomfield Hills, MI 48304-5075 (248) 498-2501
Contact: John M. Erb, Pres.; Jodee Fishman Raines, V.P., Progs.
FAX: (248) 644-1517; E-mail: jraines@erbff.org; Main URL: http://www.erbff.org/
Grants List: http://www.erbff.org/recent-grants

Established in 2008 in MI.
Donors: Barbara M. Erb‡; Fred A. Erb‡.
Foundation type: Independent foundation.
Financial data (yr. ended 06/30/13): Assets, $167,382,925 (M); gifts received, $56,160,121; expenditures, $5,938,140; qualifying distributions, $5,293,357; giving activities include $4,931,065 for 69+ grants (high: $908,873), and $195,088 for 42 employee matching gifts.
Purpose and activities: The mission of the foundation is to nurture environmentally healthy and culturally vibrant communities in metropolitan Detroit and support initiatives to restore the Great Lakes Basin.
Fields of interest: Arts; Environment, water resources; Alzheimer's disease research.
Type of support: General/operating support; Management development/capacity building; Program development; Seed money; Matching/challenge support.
Limitations: Applications accepted. Giving primarily in the metropolitan Detroit, MI area (Wayne, Oakland and Macomb counties) though water quality programs will be considered in the watersheds impacting Detroit and the Bayfield area of Ontario. Certain Great Lakes basin-wide efforts will also be considered. No support for religious activities. No grants to individuals, for capital projects, research (unless solicited from the foundation) fundraisers or conferences; no loans.
Publications: Application guidelines; Annual report; Program policy statement.
Application information: Letter of inquiry and application instructions and forms available on foundation web site. Unsolicited applications for Alzheimer's Research and Special Opportunities are not accepted. Proposals in these areas are by invitation only. Application form required.
Initial approach: Letter of inquiry (via foundation web site)
Deadline(s): None
Board meeting date(s): Mar., June, Sept. and Dec.
Final notification: Following board meetings
Officers and Directors:* Ira J. Jaffe,* Chair.; John M. Erb,* Pres.; Jodee Fishman Raines, V.P., Progs.; Patricia D. Smotherman, Secy. and Grants Mgr.; Daryl Larsen, C.F.O.; Susan E. Cooper; Debbie D. Erb; John M. Erb; Chacona W. Johnson; Leslie Erb Liedtke.
Number of staff: 2 full-time professional; 2 part-time professional.
EIN: 205966333
Selected grants: The following grants are a representative sample of this grantmaker's funding activity:
$4,500,000 to University of Michigan, Ann Arbor, MI, 2013. For Great Lakes Water Center.
$255,000 to Huron River Watershed Council, Ann Arbor, MI, 2013. For general operating support.
$240,000 to Huron River Watershed Council, Ann Arbor, MI, 2013. For RiverUp.
$135,000 to Clinton River Watershed Council, Rochester, MI, 2013. For general operating support.
$105,000 to Friends of the Rouge, Dearborn, MI, 2013. For general operating support.
$90,000 to Matrix Theater Company, Detroit, MI, 2013. For Detroit Dreaming.
$50,000 to Friends of Belle Isle, Detroit, MI, 2013. To hire volunteer and membership coordinator.
$45,000 to Friends of the Detroit River, Trenton, MI, 2013. For general operating support.
$45,000 to Southwest Detroit Business Association, Detroit, MI, 2013. For Intersections.

4416
Fabri-Kal Foundation ✧
600 Plastics Pl.
Kalamazoo, MI 49001-4882
Contact: Robert P. Kittredge, Pres.

Established in 1969 in MI.
Donor: Fabri-Kal Corp.
Foundation type: Company-sponsored foundation.
Financial data (yr. ended 12/31/13): Assets, $948 (M); gifts received, $956,220; expenditures, $955,320; qualifying distributions, $955,320; giving activities include $176,430 for 23 grants (high: $38,640; low: $500), and $778,870 for 81 grants to individuals (high: $41,388; low: $58).
Purpose and activities: The foundation supports health clinics and organizations involved with trailways, family planning, human services, and neighborhood development. Special emphasis is directed toward cultural and educational causes.
Fields of interest: Arts; Education; Religion.
Type of support: Employee-related scholarships.
Limitations: Applications accepted. Giving limited to areas of company operations in Kalamazoo, MI, Hazleton, PA, and Greenville, SC.
Publications: Application guidelines; Grants list.
Application information: Application form required.
Initial approach: Letter
Deadline(s): None
Board meeting date(s): May
Officers: Robert P. Kittredge, Pres.; Gary C. Galia, Exec. V.P., Finance; J. Thomas MacFarlane, Secy.
EIN: 237003366
Selected grants: The following grants are a representative sample of this grantmaker's funding activity:
$38,444 to United Way of Greater Hazleton, Hazleton, PA, 2011.
$28,930 to United Way of Greenville County, Greenville, SC, 2011.
$7,500 to Arts Council of Greater Kalamazoo, Kalamazoo, MI, 2011.
$5,000 to YMCA and Outdoor Center, Sherman Lake, Augusta, MI, 2011.
$4,000 to Residential Opportunities, Kalamazoo, MI, 2011.
$2,000 to MRC Industries, Kalamazoo, MI, 2011.
$1,000 to Heritage Community of Kalamazoo, Kalamazoo, MI, 2011.

4417
Family Christian Stores Foundation ✧
5300 Patterson Ave. S.E.
Grand Rapids, MI 49530-0001

Established in 2003 in MI.
Donors: David M. Browne; Cliff Bartow; Beverly Bartow; Family Christian Stores, Inc.; Thomas Nelson Publishers; Zondervan Corp.; Brown Family Agape Foundation; Earl Clifford Bartow; The National Christian Foundation; Julie Martin; Christian Art Gifts, Inc.; John Blend; Steve Biondo; Robert John Pindred; Evergreen Enterprises; Family Christian LLC.
Foundation type: Operating foundation.
Financial data (yr. ended 12/31/13): Assets, $909,944 (M); gifts received, $316,563; expenditures, $950,270; qualifying distributions, $906,412; giving activities include $555,361 for 11 + grants (high: $100,334).
Purpose and activities: Giving primarily for the care of orphans, including adoption assistance.
Fields of interest: Children/youth, services; Children, adoption; Christian agencies & churches.
Limitations: Applications not accepted. Giving primarily in GA, IL, MI and OH. No grants to individuals.
Application information: Contributes only to pre-selected organizations.
Officers: Steve M. Biondo, Pres.; Amy Anderson, Secy.; R. John Pindred, Treas.
Trustees: Earl Clifford Bartow; David M. Browne.
EIN: 383673924
Selected grants: The following grants are a representative sample of this grantmaker's funding activity:
$40,346 to Goshen Valley Foundation, Waleska, GA, 2012. For orphan/foster care.
$33,676 to Pray America, Lansing, MI, 2012. For widow care/outreach.

$25,000 to Bethany Christian Services, Grand Rapids, MI, 2012. For adoption assistance.
$131 to Oaks Indian Mission, Oaks, OK, 2012. To foster Care/Orphan Care.

4418
Dick & Betsy Family DeVos Foundation ✧
P.O. Box 230257
Grand Rapids, MI 49523-0257 (616) 643-4700
Contact: Ginny Vander Hart, Exec. Dir.; Sue Volkers, Grants Mgr.
E-mail: info@dbdvfoundation.org; FAX (for Ginny Vander Hart): (616) 774-0116; E-mail (for Ginny Vander Hart): virginiav@rdvcorp.com; Main URL: http://www.dbdvfoundation.org/

Established in 1989 in MI.
Donors: Dick DeVos; Betsy DeVos; Prince Foundation.
Foundation type: Independent foundation.
Financial data (yr. ended 12/31/12): Assets, $59,920,363 (M); gifts received, $10,000,500; expenditures, $14,660,823; qualifying distributions, $16,722,163; giving activities include $13,758,058 for 153 grants (high: $3,365,000; low: $250), and $350,000 for 1 loan/program-related investment.
Purpose and activities: The foundation seeks to create a legacy of caring and stewardship through its support of projects that build a strong community. To demonstrate this commitment, the foundation concentrates its funding in support of various initiatives that promote a healthier community, with a focus on the arts, health and children's causes.
Fields of interest: Arts; Education; Children/youth, services; Family services; Public policy, research; Christian agencies & churches.
Type of support: Program-related investments/loans; General/operating support; Continuing support; Annual campaigns; Capital campaigns.
Limitations: Applications accepted. Giving primarily in west MI. No grants to individuals.
Publications: Application guidelines.
Application information: See foundation web site for online application process. Application form not required.
Initial approach: Online application
Copies of proposal: 1
Board meeting date(s): Quarterly
Final notification: 4 to 5 months
Officers and Directors:* Richard M. DeVos, Jr.,* Pres.; Robert H. Schierbeek, Exec. V.P. and Secy-Treas.; Jerry L. Tubergen,* Exec. V.P.; Elisabeth DeVos,* V.P.; Jeffrey K. Lambert, V.P., Finance and Admin.; Ginny Vander Hart, Exec. Dir. and Fdn. Dir.
EIN: 382902412
Selected grants: The following grants are a representative sample of this grantmaker's funding activity:
$3,365,000 to West Michigan Aviation Academy, Grand Rapids, MI, 2012. For unrestricted grant to general fund.
$1,145,808 to Urban Institute for Contemporary Arts, Grand Rapids, MI, 2012. For unrestricted grant to general fund.
$1,000,000 to Grand Action Foundation, Grand Rapids, MI, 2012. For unrestricted grant to general fund.
$1,000,000 to Willow Creek Association, South Barrington, IL, 2012. For unrestricted grant to general fund.
$550,000 to Haggai Institute for Advanced Leadership Training, Norcross, GA, 2012. For unrestricted grant to general fund.
$500,000 to George W. Bush Foundation, Dallas, TX, 2012. For unrestricted grant to general fund.
$125,000 to Stephens Children Foundation, Grand Rapids, MI, 2012. For unrestricted grant to general fund.
$50,000 to Grand Rapids Community College Foundation, Grand Rapids, MI, 2012. For unrestricted grant to general fund.
$10,000 to CIVA, Wenham, MA, 2012. For unrestricted grant to general fund.
$10,000 to Orlando Magic Youth Foundation, Orlando, FL, 2012. For unrestricted grant to general fund.

4419
J. Ferrantino Charitable Foundation ✧
126 S. Main St.
Ann Arbor, MI 48104-1903

Donor: Detroit Salt Company, L.C.
Foundation type: Independent foundation.
Financial data (yr. ended 12/31/13): Assets, $11,126,107 (M); expenditures, $527,536; qualifying distributions, $491,886; giving activities include $489,595 for 25 grants (high: $55,000; low: $5,000).
Fields of interest: Housing/shelter; Youth development; Human services.
Limitations: Applications not accepted. Giving primarily in MI.
Application information: Unsolicited requests for funds not accepted.
Officers: Janette Ferrantino, Pres.; Bruce T. Wallace, Secy.; George Borel, Treas.
Directors: Janelle Green; Angela Williams; Elise Williams; Sean Williams.
EIN: 264457061

4420
John E. Fetzer Institute, Inc. ✧
(formerly John E. Fetzer Foundation, Inc.)
9292 West KL Ave.
Kalamazoo, MI 49009-9398
Contact: Thomas F. Beech, C.E.O. and Pres.
FAX: (269) 372-2163; E-mail: info@fetzer.org; Main URL: http://www.fetzer.org
Blog: http://www.fetzer.org/blog
Facebook: http://www.facebook.com/FetzerInstitute
RSS Feed: http://www.fetzer.org/blog/rss
Twitter: http://twitter.com/FetzerInstitute
YouTube: http://www.youtube.com/FetzerInstitute

Established in 1956.
Donors: John E. Fetzer†; John E. Fetzer Memorial Trust; Institute for Research on Unlimited Love; Shinnyo-En Foundation.
Foundation type: Operating foundation.
Financial data (yr. ended 06/30/13): Assets, $462,945,654 (M); gifts received, $2,751,948; expenditures, $29,681,624; qualifying distributions, $25,105,005; giving activities include $950,840 for 32+ grants (high: $290,369), and $5,249,624 for foundation-administered programs.
Purpose and activities: The institute is a nonprofit, private operating foundation with an interest in exploring the relationship between the inner life of mind and spirit and action and service in the world. The institute's mission is to foster awareness of the power of love and forgiveness in the emerging global community through research, education, and service programs.
Fields of interest: Education; Health care; Children/youth, services; Philanthropy/voluntarism; Social sciences, research; Law/international law; Social sciences.
Type of support: Mission-related investments/loans; General/operating support; Program development; Conferences/seminars; Research; Program evaluation; Employee matching gifts; Grants to individuals; Matching/challenge support.
Limitations: Applications not accepted. Giving on a national basis.
Publications: Informational brochure; Newsletter; Occasional report; Program policy statement.
Application information: Contributes only to pre-selected organizations.
Board meeting date(s): Mar., June, and Nov.
Officers and Trustees:* Robert F. Lehman,* Chair.; Janis A. Claflin,* Vice-Chair.; Robert Boisture,* C.E.O. and Pres.; Christina M. Adams, V.P., Finance and Admin.; Timothy J. Jones, V.P., Opers.; Kathleen M. Cavanaugh, Secy.; Bruce F. Fetzer,* Treas.; Bradley S. Miller, Cont.; Carolyn Thompson Brown, Ph.D.; Bruce M. Carlson, M.D., Ph.D.; Lynne W. Twist; Frances E. Vaughan.
Number of staff: 27 full-time professional; 2 part-time professional; 21 full-time support; 8 part-time support.
EIN: 386052788

4421
John E. Fetzer Memorial Trust Fund ✧
c/o Bruce Fetzer, Pres.
1240 W. VW Ave.
Schoolcraft, MI 49087-8744 (269) 679-5334
E-mail: brucefetzer@fetzertrust.org; Main URL: http://www.fetzertrust.org/

Established in 1991 in MI.
Donor: John E. Fetzer Revocable Trust.
Foundation type: Independent foundation.
Financial data (yr. ended 06/30/13): Assets, $91,520,382 (M); expenditures, $5,183,770; qualifying distributions, $4,474,513; giving activities include $3,578,088 for 9+ grants (high: $2,750,000), and $1,199,271 for foundation-administered programs.
Fields of interest: Higher education; Human services, mind/body enrichment; Psychology/behavioral science.
Type of support: General/operating support; Research.
Limitations: Applications not accepted. Giving primarily in Kalamazoo, MI.
Application information: Unsolicited requests for funds not accepted.
Officers: Robert Lehman, Chair.; Bruce Fetzer, C.E.O. and Pres.; Michael Gergely, V.P. and Secy.; Louis Leeburg, Treas.
Trustees: Thomas Beaver; Bruce Carlson, Ph.D.; Frances Vaughan, Ph.D.; Jeremy Waletzky, M.D.; Jan Walleczek, Ph.D.
Number of staff: 1 full-time professional.
EIN: 383010714

4422
Harvey Firestone, Jr. Foundation ✧
2000 Brush St., Ste. 440
Detroit, MI 48226-2251 (313) 961-0500
Contact: Christine Jaggi

Established in 1983 in OH.
Foundation type: Independent foundation.
Financial data (yr. ended 12/31/12): Assets, $15,275,955 (M); expenditures, $4,831,970; qualifying distributions, $4,740,000; giving activities include $4,740,000 for 78 grants (high: $4,100,000; low: $250).
Fields of interest: Museums (specialized); Arts; Education; Health care; Human services.
Type of support: General/operating support.
Limitations: Applications accepted. Giving primarily in CT and MI; giving also in Washington, DC and NY. No grants to individuals.
Application information:
Initial approach: Letter
Deadline(s): None
Trustees: Anne F. Ball; Martha F. Ford.
EIN: 341388254

4423
Max M. and Marjorie S. Fisher Foundation, Inc. ✧
2 Towne Sq., Ste. 920
Southfield, MI 48075-3761 (248) 415-1444
Contact: Douglas Bitonti Stewart, Exec. Dir.; Jennifer Fahnestock, Grants and Opers. Mgr.; Deanna Yow, Exec. Asst.
FAX: (248) 415-1453; E-mail: info@mmfisher.org; Additional e-mail: (for Douglas B. Stewart) dstewart@mmfisher.org; (for Deanna Yow) Dyow@mmfisher.org; (for Cynthia Rowell) crowell@mmfisher.org; (for Jenn Fahnestock) jenn@mmfisher.org; Main URL: http://www.mmfisher.org

Established in 1955 in MI.
Donors: Max M. Fisher†; Marjorie M. Fisher; Martinique Hotel, Inc.
Foundation type: Independent foundation.
Financial data (yr. ended 12/31/12): Assets, $251,151,279 (M); gifts received, $254,955; expenditures, $14,135,800; qualifying distributions, $13,316,391; giving activities include $11,692,958 for 87 grants, and $200,000 for 1 loan/program-related investment.
Purpose and activities: The mission of the foundation is to enrich humanity by strengthening and empowering children and families in need. While remaining flexible in its approach, the foundation gives priority to: providing for the needs of and ensuring the future of the Jewish people, and to respecting its legacy and commitment to the Detroit community. Areas of critical importance include education, arts & culture and health, with particular attention to HIV/AIDS.
Fields of interest: Museums; Performing arts; Arts; Elementary/secondary education; Higher education; Education; Health organizations; Human services; United Ways and Federated Giving Programs; Jewish federated giving programs; Jewish agencies & synagogues; Infants/toddlers; Children/youth; Youth; AIDS, people with; Economically disadvantaged.
International interests: Israel; Zambia.
Type of support: General/operating support; Annual campaigns; Capital campaigns; Endowments; Emergency funds; Conferences/seminars; Seed money; Fellowships; Scholarship funds; Matching/challenge support.
Limitations: Applications not accepted. Giving on an international basis, with emphasis on FL, MI, and NY; and on Israel and Zambia. No grants to individuals.
Application information: Contributes only to pre-selected organizations. At this time the Fisher Foundation is accepting proposals by invitation only.
Officers and Trustees:* Jane F. Sherman,* Chair.; Julie Fisher Cummings,* Vice-Chair.; Marjorie M. Fisher,* Vice-Chair.; Mary D. Fisher,* Vice-Chair.; Phillip William Fisher,* Vice-Chair.; Douglas Bitonti Stewart,* Exec. Dir.; Marjorie S. Fisher.
Number of staff: 4 full-time professional; 1 full-time support.
EIN: 381784340
Selected grants: The following grants are a representative sample of this grantmaker's funding activity:
$5,000,000 to Detroit Symphony Orchestra, Detroit, MI, 2013. For endowment, payable over 3.00 years.
$5,000,000 to Jewish Agency for Israel, New York, NY, 2012. For Kiryat Yearim Youth Aliyah Village, payable over 5.00 years.
$2,500,000 to Ohio State University Foundation, Fisher School of Business, Columbus, OH, 2013. For Max M. Fisher Scholars Fund and the Max M. Fisher Faculty Eminence Award, payable over 5.00 years.
$1,000,000 to Community Foundation for Southeast Michigan, Detroit, MI, 2012. For Marjorie S. Fisher Fund.
$1,000,000 to Community Foundation for Southeast Michigan, Detroit, MI, 2013. For Marjorie S. Fisher Fund.
$1,000,000 to Jewish Federation of Metropolitan Detroit, Bloomfield Hills, MI, 2013. For Annual contribution 2014.
$800,000 to Detroit Symphony Orchestra, Detroit, MI, 2012. For General operations.
$400,000 to Community Foundation for Southeast Michigan, Detroit, MI, 2012. For Fisher-Cummings Family Fund.
$400,000 to Community Foundation for Southeast Michigan, Detroit, MI, 2012. For Marjorie M. Fisher Fund.
$295,000 to Hebrew Free Loan Association, Bloomfield, MI, 2012. For Core loan services and capacity building, payable over 2.00 years.
$274,599 to Development Centers, Detroit, MI, 2012. For Brightmoor Childcare Quality Initiative.
$150,000 to Excellent Schools Detroit, Detroit, MI, 2013. For Early Childhood and Education Continuum Data Infrastructure Development, payable over 2.00 years.
$150,000 to Michigan Opera Theater, Detroit, MI, 2012. To Preserve the Legacy campaign.
$100,000 to Detroit Symphony Orchestra, Detroit, MI, 2013. For Annual operations.
$96,380 to College for Creative Studies, Detroit, MI, 2013. For Brightmoor Neighborhood Arts.
$70,000 to Cultural Alliance of Southeastern Michigan, Detroit, MI, 2013. For CultureSource General Operating Support, payable over 2.00 years.
$65,000 to Michigan Nonprofit Association, Lansing, MI, 2012. For The LEAGUE Michigan.
$20,000 to Community Foundation for Southeast Michigan, Detroit, MI, 2012. For Max M. and Marjorie S. Fisher Foundation Executive Director Fund.
$20,000 to Council of Michigan Foundations, Grand Haven, MI, 2013. For Conference sponsorship with MNA 2013.
$6,500 to Grand Valley State University, Grand Rapids, MI, 2013. For 2013 Johnson Center National Summit on Family Philanthropy.

4424
Ethel and James Flinn Foundation ✧
(formerly Ethel and James Flinn Family Foundation)
333 W. Fort St., Ste. 1950
Detroit, MI 48226-3485 (313) 309-3436
Contact: Andrea M. Cole, C.E.O.
FAX: (313) 309-3441;
E-mail: acole@flinnfoundation.org; Main URL: http://www.flinnfoundation.org/

Established in 1976 in MI as a public foundation; reclassified in 2005 as an independent foundation. Following the founder's passing in 2007, the foundation's assets were increased significantly.
Donors: Ethel W. Flinn†; James H. Flinn, Jr.†.
Foundation type: Independent foundation.
Financial data (yr. ended 12/31/13): Assets, $63,621,257 (M); expenditures, $2,839,271; qualifying distributions, $2,603,482; giving activities include $2,021,516 for 37 grants (high: $100,000; low: $10,000), $30,200 for employee matching gifts, and $161,928 for foundation-administered programs.
Purpose and activities: The foundation is committed to improving the quality of life of children, adolescents, and adults with mental illness by improving the quality, scope, and delivery of mental health services. The foundation uses its resources through research to develop, evaluate, and implement best practice treatment programs delivered in the community.
Fields of interest: Mental health, treatment; Mental health, disorders; Mentally disabled.
Type of support: Program development; Curriculum development; Research; Program evaluation.
Limitations: Applications not accepted. Giving limited to Southeast, MI, (Macomb, Oakland, Washtenaw and Wayne) organizations listed in Trust Agreement. No grants to individuals.
Publications: Annual report; Financial statement; Grants list.
Application information: The foundation has established 2 principal avenues for its grantmaking: competitive grants through a Request for Proposal (RFP) process and grant initiatives where the foundation invites a proposal from a supported organization. See foundation web site for information.
Board meeting date(s): Mar., May, Sept., and Dec.
Officers and Trustees:* Leonard W. Smith, Chair., Treas. and C.I.O.; Duane L. Tarnacki,* Vice-Chair.; Andrea Cole, C.E.O. and Exec. Dir.; Dr. Calmeze H. Dudley, Tr. Emeritus; Hon. Freddie G. Burton, Jr.; Lynn Carpenter; Dr. Linda L. Hryhorczuk; Jack Kresnak; Allen Ledyard; George A. Nicholson III.
Number of staff: 2 full-time professional; 1 full-time support.
EIN: 382143122

4425
William & Lisa Ford Foundation ✧
1901 Saint Antoine St., 6th Fl. at Ford Field
Detroit, MI 48226-2310 (313) 259-7777
Contact: David M. Hempstead, Secy.

Established in 1998 in MI.
Donors: William Clay Ford, Jr.; Lisa V. Ford.
Foundation type: Independent foundation.
Financial data (yr. ended 12/31/12): Assets, $10,642,440 (M); expenditures, $935,119; qualifying distributions, $879,850; giving activities include $879,850 for grants.
Purpose and activities: Giving primarily for children's services and higher education; funding also for human services.
Fields of interest: Museums; Higher education; Education; Environment, land resources; Health care; Human services; Children, services; United Ways and Federated Giving Programs; Buddhism.
Limitations: Giving primarily in MI and NJ. No grants to individuals.
Application information: Application form required.
Initial approach: Letter
Deadline(s): None
Board meeting date(s): As necessary
Officers and Directors: William Clay Ford, Jr.,* Pres.; Lisa V. Ford,* V.P.; David M. Hempstead, Secy.; Rodney P. Wood, Treas.; Eleanor C. Ford.
EIN: 383441138

4426
Benson and Edith Ford Fund ✧
1901 Saint Antoine St., 6th Fl. at Ford Field
Detroit, MI 48226-2310 (313) 259-7777
Contact: David M. Hempstead, Secy.

Incorporated in 1943 in MI as the Hotchkiss Fund.
Donor: Benson Ford†.
Foundation type: Independent foundation.
Financial data (yr. ended 12/31/12): Assets, $28,169,539 (M); expenditures, $2,080,775; qualifying distributions, $1,990,251; giving activities include $1,962,113 for 27 grants (high: $770,000; low: $500).
Purpose and activities: Support for health, human services, education, and arts and culture.
Fields of interest: Arts; Education; Hospitals (general); Youth development, services; Children/youth, services; United Ways and Federated Giving Programs; Jewish agencies & synagogues.
Limitations: Giving primarily in MI, with emphasis on Detroit. No grants to individuals.
Application information: Awards generally limited to charities already favorably known to substantial contributors of the foundation.
Initial approach: Letter
Deadline(s): None
Board meeting date(s): As necessary
Officers and Trustees:* Lynn Ford Alandt,* Pres.; Benson Ford, Jr.,* V.P.; David M. Hempstead,* Secy.; Rodney P. Wood, Treas.
EIN: 386066333

4427
Eleanor and Edsel Ford Fund ✧
c/o David M. Hempstead
1901 Saint Antoine St., 6th Fl. at Ford Field
Detroit, MI 48226-2310

Incorporated in 1944 in MI.
Donor: Eleanor Clay Ford†.
Foundation type: Independent foundation.
Financial data (yr. ended 12/31/12): Assets, $19,499,813 (M); expenditures, $1,541,805; qualifying distributions, $1,410,955; giving activities include $1,400,000 for 6 grants (high: $330,000; low: $40,000).
Purpose and activities: Grants are limited to organizations selected by the trustees from among the charities with which Eleanor Clay Ford was prominently associated during her lifetime.
Fields of interest: Museums; Performing arts; Arts; Elementary/secondary education; Higher education; Medical care, in-patient care; Protestant agencies & churches.
Type of support: General/operating support; Building/renovation; Scholarship funds.
Limitations: Applications not accepted. Giving in MI, with emphasis on Detroit, MI. No grants to individuals.
Application information: Contributes only to pre-selected organizations. Unsolicited requests for funds not considered.
Board meeting date(s): As needed
Officers and Trustees:* William Clay Ford,* Pres.; David M. Hempstead,* Secy.; Rodney P. Wood, Treas.; Martha F. Ford.
EIN: 386066331

4428
William and Martha Ford Fund ✧
1901 Saint Antoine St., 6th Fl. at Ford Field
Detroit, MI 48226-2310 (313) 259-7777
Contact: David M. Hempstead, Secy. and Tr.

Incorporated in 1953 in MI.
Donors: William Clay Ford†; Martha Firestone Ford.
Foundation type: Independent foundation.
Financial data (yr. ended 12/31/13): Assets, $4,528,687 (M); gifts received, $1,370,759; expenditures, $521,810; qualifying distributions, $452,584; giving activities include $440,540 for 64 grants (high: $200,000; low: $100).
Fields of interest: Education; Health care; Human services; United Ways and Federated Giving Programs.
Limitations: Applications accepted. Giving in the U.S., with emphasis on CT and MI. No grants to individuals.
Application information:
Initial approach: Letter
Deadline(s): None
Board meeting date(s): As necessary
Officers and Trustees:* David M. Hempstead,* Secy.; Rodney P. Wood, Treas.; Martha F. Ford.
EIN: 386066335

4429
The Henry Ford II Fund ✧
1901 Saint Antoine St., 6th Fl. at Ford Field
Detroit, MI 48226-2310
Contact: David M. Hempstead, Secy.

Incorporated in 1953 in MI.
Donor: Henry Ford II†.
Foundation type: Independent foundation.
Financial data (yr. ended 12/31/12): Assets, $32,182,855 (M); expenditures, $1,114,199; qualifying distributions, $982,500; giving activities include $982,500 for grants.
Purpose and activities: Giving primarily for higher education.
Fields of interest: Higher education; Education; Health care; Human services.
Limitations: Applications not accepted. Giving primarily in MI, with emphasis on Detroit. No grants to individuals.
Application information: Awards generally limited to charitable organizations already favorably known to, and of interest to, the foundation.
Board meeting date(s): As necessary
Officers and Directors:* Edsel B. Ford II,* Pres.; David M. Hempstead,* Secy.; Rodney P. Wood,* Treas.; Cynthia N. Ford; Henry Ford III.
EIN: 386066332

4430
Ford Motor Company Fund
1 American Rd.
P.O. Box 1899
Dearborn, MI 48126-2798 (888) 313-0102
FAX: (313) 594-7001; E-mail: fordfund@ford.com; Contact for Ford Driving Dreams through Education: David Perez, Devel. Dir., LULAC, tel.: (202) 833-6130, ext. 12, e-mail: DPerez@LULAC.org; E-mail for Belt It Out Contest: FordDSFL@ford.com; Main URL: http://corporate.ford.com/about-ford/community
Blue Oval Scholars Website: https://www.fordscholars.org/
Driving Skills for Life on Facebook: http://www.facebook.com/pages/Ford-Driving-Skills-for-Life/87733201583
Driving Skills for Life on Twitter: http://twitter.com/forddsfl
Driving Skills for Life Website: https://www.drivingskillsforlife.com/
Facebook: http://www.facebook.com/pages/Ford-Motor-Company-Fund/81701977476
Ford Blue Oval Scholars on Facebook: http://www.facebook.com/fordblueovalscholars
Ford Partnership for Advanced Studies on Facebook: http://www.facebook.com/pages/Ford-Partnership-for-Advanced-Studies-Ford-PAS/152239278121235
Ford Partnership for Advanced Studies on Flickr: http://www.flickr.com/photos/fordpas/show/
Ford Partnership for Advanced Studies on YouTube: http://www.youtube.com/fordpas
Ford Partnership for Advanced Studies Website: http://www.fordpas.org/
Ford Partnership of Advanced Studies on Twitter: http://twitter.com/fordngl

Incorporated in 1949 in MI.
Donors: Ford Motor Co.; Ford Motor Credit Co.
Foundation type: Company-sponsored foundation.
Financial data (yr. ended 12/31/12): Assets, $41,832,647 (M); expenditures, $23,588,993; qualifying distributions, $23,603,562; giving activities include $21,970,680 for grants.
Purpose and activities: The fund supports programs designed to promote innovation and education; community development and American heritage and diversity; and auto-related safety education.
Fields of interest: Museums; Performing arts; Performing arts, music; Performing arts, orchestras; Historical activities; Arts; Elementary/secondary education; Charter schools; Higher education; Engineering school/education; Scholarships/financial aid; Education, drop-out prevention; Education; Environment; Food services; Food banks; Safety, automotive safety; Civil/human rights, equal rights; Community/economic development; United Ways and Federated Giving Programs; Minorities; African Americans/Blacks; Hispanics/Latinos.

Type of support: Continuing support; Annual campaigns; Capital campaigns; Building/renovation; Equipment; Emergency funds; Program development; Publication; Curriculum development; Internship funds; Scholarship funds; Employee volunteer services; Sponsorships; Employee matching gifts; Employee-related scholarships; Grants to individuals.
Limitations: Applications accepted. Giving primarily in areas of company operations, with emphasis on southeastern MI; giving also in Phoenix, AZ, San Diego, CA, Miami, FL, Chicago, IL, Detroit, MI, Nashville, TN, and San Antonio, TX. No support for animal-rights, lobbying, political, or fraternal organizations, labor groups, private K-12 schools, profit-making enterprises, religious organizations not of direct benefit to the entire community, species-specific organizations, or sports teams. No grants to individuals (except for scholarships), or for advocacy-directed programs, beauty or talent contests, general operating support, debt reduction, endowments, or sponsorships related to fundraising activities; no loans for small businesses or program-related investments; no vehicle donations.
Publications: Application guidelines; Annual report; Corporate giving report; Newsletter.
Application information: 2015 budget will be determined by mid-February. Grant requests should be submitted by the end of Aug. as the program closes the end of Oct. Application form required.
Initial approach: Complete online application
Deadline(s): None; visit website for Community Challenge grants and scholarship programs
Board meeting date(s): Apr. and Oct.
Final notification: Within 8 weeks
Officers and Trustees:* James G. Vella,* Chair. and Pres.; Neil M. Schloss, V.P. and Secy.; Michael Banister; Steve Biegun; Susan M. Cischke; Alfred B. Ford; Sheila Ford Hamp; David G. Leitch; Martin J. Mulloy; Ziad S. Ojakli.
Number of staff: 11 full-time professional; 10 full-time support.
EIN: 381459376
Selected grants: The following grants are a representative sample of this grantmaker's funding activity:
$2,800,661 to Governors Highway Safety Association, Washington, DC, 2012. For program support.
$1,605,000 to United Way for Southeastern Michigan, Detroit, MI, 2012. For program support.
$1,130,000 to Henry Ford Learning Institute, Dearborn, MI, 2012. For program support.
$400,000 to Henry Ford Estate, Dearborn, MI, 2012. For program support.
$300,000 to Focus: HOPE, Detroit, MI, 2012. For program support.
$50,000 to Detroit Historical Society, Detroit, MI, 2012. For program support.
$30,000 to American Red Cross, Imperial Counties Chapter, San Diego, CA, 2012. For disaster relief.
$25,000 to Matrix Human Services, Detroit, MI, 2012. For program support.
$20,000 to Capital Region Community Foundation, Lansing, MI, 2012. For sponsorship.
$15,000 to Henry Ford Learning Institute, Dearborn, MI, 2012. For scholarships.

4431
Foster Family Foundation ✧ ☆
c/o West Michigan Bank & Trust
120 Cypress St.
Manistee, MI 49660-1753

Established in 1997 in MI.
Donors: Kate Foster; Phyllis L. Foster; Robert C. Foster Trust.
Foundation type: Independent foundation.
Financial data (yr. ended 12/31/13): Assets, $6,865,873 (M); expenditures, $772,881; qualifying distributions, $767,330; giving activities include $750,000 for 1 grant.
Fields of interest: Performing arts, orchestras; Hospitals (general); Christian agencies & churches.
Limitations: Applications not accepted. No grants to individuals.
Application information: Unsolicited requests for funds not accepted.
Trustees: Thomas A. Baither; Phyllis L. Foster; Henry T. Mather.
EIN: 383357234

4432
Foundation for Theological Education in Southeast Asia ✧
119 Oak Valley Dr.
Holland, MI 49424-2729
Main URL: http://www.ftesea.org/

Established in 1934 in NY.
Donors: General Board of Global Ministries; International Ministries ABC; Episcopal Church.
Foundation type: Independent foundation.
Financial data (yr. ended 12/31/13): Assets, $15,814,942 (M); gifts received, $500; expenditures, $686,099; qualifying distributions, $681,617; giving activities include $508,035 for 89 grants (high: $95,000; low: $200).
Purpose and activities: Giving primarily for theological education institutions in Southeast Asia, especially China.
Fields of interest: Theological school/education.
International interests: China.
Type of support: Professorships; Curriculum development.
Limitations: Applications not accepted. Giving primarily in Southeast Asia and China. No grants to individuals.
Application information: Contributes only to pre-selected organizations.
Board meeting date(s): Dec.
Officers: Norman Donkersloot, Treas.; H.S. Wilson, Exec. Dir.
Trustees: Rebecca Asedillo; Ben Chan; Tammy Jackson; Bern Jagunos; Joseph Kaung; Kah-Jin Jeffrey Kuan; Pui Lan Kwok; Peter Ng; Martha Smalley; Scott Sunquist; Mienda Uriate; James Vijayakumar; Ron Wallace; Andrew Yutaka Yamamoto.
Number of staff: 1 full-time professional; 1 part-time support.
EIN: 237362344

4433
Stanley and Judith Frankel Family Foundation ✧ ☆
2301 W. Big Beaver Rd., Ste. 900
Troy, MI 48084-3332

Established in 2000 in MI.
Donors: Stanley Frankel; Judith Frankel.
Foundation type: Independent foundation.
Financial data (yr. ended 02/28/13): Assets, $6,365,155 (M); gifts received, $1,618,094; expenditures, $658,891; qualifying distributions, $624,416; giving activities include $624,416 for 17 grants (high: $282,341; low: $1,000).
Purpose and activities: Giving primarily for Jewish organizations and yeshivas.
Fields of interest: Performing arts, orchestras; Higher education; Education; Jewish federated giving programs; Jewish agencies & synagogues.
Limitations: Applications not accepted. Giving primarily in MI and OK. No grants to individuals.
Application information: Contributes only to pre-selected organizations.
Officers: Stanley Frankel, Pres.; Judith Frankel, V.P.; Arthur Weiss, Secy.
EIN: 383531285
Selected grants: The following grants are a representative sample of this grantmaker's funding activity:
$500,000 to Yeshiva Beth Yehudah, Southfield, MI, 2011.

4434
Samuel and Jean Frankel Fine Arts Foundation ✧
1671 Lochridge Rd.
Bloomfield Hills, MI 48302-0738

Established in 2004 in MI.
Foundation type: Independent foundation.
Financial data (yr. ended 12/31/13): Assets, $29,829,819 (M); expenditures, $1,693,509; qualifying distributions, $1,552,395; giving activities include $1,552,375 for 70 grants (high: $880,000; low: $100).
Purpose and activities: Giving primarily for the arts.
Fields of interest: Arts; Human services; Jewish federated giving programs.
Limitations: Applications not accepted. Giving primarily in Troy, MI.
Application information: Contributes only to pre-selected organizations.
Officers: Stuart Frankel, Pres.; Maxine Frankel, V.P.
EIN: 300095026

4435
Samuel & Jean Frankel Foundation ✧
2301 W. Big Beaver Rd., Ste. 900
Troy, MI 48084-3332 (248) 649-2600

Established in 1970.
Donors: Samuel Frankel; Jean Frankel.
Foundation type: Independent foundation.
Financial data (yr. ended 12/31/12): Assets, $87,649,256 (M); gifts received, $7,001,000; expenditures, $8,722,649; qualifying distributions, $8,398,372; giving activities include $8,398,372 for 12 grants (high: $4,000,000; low: $1,000).
Purpose and activities: Giving primarily for Jewish services, the fine and performing arts, higher education, health organizations, and human services.
Fields of interest: Museums; Performing arts; Education; Health organizations; Youth development, services; Human services; United Ways and Federated Giving Programs; Jewish federated giving programs; Jewish agencies & synagogues.
Limitations: Applications not accepted. Giving primarily in MI. No grants to individuals.
Application information: Contributes only to pre-selected organizations.
Officer: Stanley Frankel, Pres. and Treas.

Trustees: Bruce Frankel; Stuart Frankel; Joelyn Nyman; Arthur Weiss.
EIN: 386088399

4436
The Samuel and Jean Frankel Health and Research Foundation ✧
1004 Brookwood St.
Birmingham, MI 48009-1147

Established in 2004 in MI.
Donors: Bruce Frankel; Jean Frankel.
Foundation type: Independent foundation.
Financial data (yr. ended 12/31/13): Assets, $22,752,459 (M); expenditures, $1,151,585; qualifying distributions, $1,050,000; giving activities include $1,050,000 for 14 grants (high: $275,000; low: $5,000).
Fields of interest: Mental health, depression; Health organizations, association; Children/youth, services; Jewish federated giving programs.
Limitations: Applications not accepted. Giving in MI.
Application information: Contributes only to pre-selected organizations.
Officers and Trustees:* Bruce Frankel,* Pres.; Jo Elyn Nyman, V.P. and Treas.; George Nyman,* Secy.
EIN: 300095044

4437
The Samuel and Jean Frankel Jewish Heritage Foundation ✧
2301 W. Big Beaver Rd., Ste. 900
Troy, MI 48084-3332 (248) 649-2600

Established in 2004 in MI.
Donors: Samuel Frankel†; Jean Frankel.
Foundation type: Independent foundation.
Financial data (yr. ended 12/31/12): Assets, $136,594,022 (M); expenditures, $14,366,366; qualifying distributions, $13,885,203; giving activities include $13,885,203 for 27 grants (high: $6,855,200; low: $1,000).
Fields of interest: Higher education; Theological school/education; Education; Jewish federated giving programs; Jewish agencies & synagogues.
Type of support: Program development; Endowments.
Limitations: Applications not accepted. Giving primarily in MI; giving also in New York, NY and in Israel. No grants to individuals.
Application information: Contributes only to pre-selected organizations.
Officers and Trustees:* Stanley Frankel,* Pres. and Treas.; Judith Frankel,* Secy.
EIN: 300095016

4438
Fremont Area Community Foundation ✧
(formerly The Fremont Area Foundation)
4424 W. 48th St.
P.O. Box B
Fremont, MI 49412-8721 (231) 924-5350
Contact: Carla A. Roberts, Pres. and C.E.O.; For grants: Todd Jacobs, V.P., Community Investment
FAX: (231) 924-5391; E-mail: info@tfacf.org; Additional fax: (231) 924-7637; Additional e-mail: croberts@tfacf.org; Grants inquiry e-mail: grants@tfacf.org or tjacobs@tfacf.org; Main URL: http://www.tfacf.org
Facebook: http://www.facebook.com/pages/Fremont-Area-Community-Foundation/183815588324852
LinkedIn: https://www.linkedin.com/company/fremont-area-community-foundation
Twitter: https://twitter.com/FremontAreaCF
E-mail for scholarship inquiries: rcowles@tfacf.org

Incorporated in 1951 in MI as private foundation; became a community foundation in 1972.
Foundation type: Community foundation.
Financial data (yr. ended 12/31/13): Assets, $226,881,820 (M); gifts received, $1,699,510; expenditures, $10,706,374; giving activities include $7,598,049 for 114+ grants (high: $882,462), and $851,433 for 495 grants to individuals.
Purpose and activities: The foundation has established six broad funding categories: 1) TrueNorth: to sustain operations of this autonomous agency established for the delivery of general social welfare services and educational programs; 2) Community Development: to strengthen the municipal activities of villages, cities, governmental units, and other related organizations; 3) Education: to augment and promote the special projects of schools, libraries, and other organizations for instruction and training, and for scholarships to promote higher education and learning in specialized programs; 4) Arts and Culture: to support activities that promote appreciation of and participation in artistic expression such as music, theater, dance, sculpture, and painting; 5) Human Services: to foster the delivery of services and the operation of programs to help meet basic human needs and to support the provision of rehabilitative services; and 6) Health Care: made to health care providers and other related organizations for activities designed to promote optimal well-being and to provide health-related education. The foundation is also interested in supporting programs that address the particular needs of youth and older (aged) adults.
Fields of interest: Visual arts; Performing arts; Arts; Libraries/library science; Education; Environment; Medical care, rehabilitation; Health care; Substance abuse, services; Health organizations, association; Recreation; Children/youth, services; Family services; Aging, centers/services; Human services; Community/economic development; Government/public administration; Children/youth; Youth; Adults; Aging; Disabilities, people with; Physically disabled; Deaf/hearing impaired; Mentally disabled; Women; Girls; Economically disadvantaged.
Type of support: General/operating support; Continuing support; Management development/capacity building; Capital campaigns; Building/renovation; Equipment; Endowments; Emergency funds; Program development; Conferences/seminars; Seed money; Curriculum development; Scholarship funds; Technical assistance; Consulting services; Program evaluation; Program-related investments/loans; Employee matching gifts; Scholarships—to individuals; Matching/challenge support.
Limitations: Applications accepted. Giving primarily in Newaygo County, MI. No support for religious organizations for religious purposes. No grants to individuals (except for scholarships), or for contingencies, reserves, services which are considered general government or school obligations, or deficit financing.
Publications: Application guidelines; Annual report; Grants list; Informational brochure; Newsletter.
Application information: Visit foundation web site for application, agency profile and grantmaking guidelines. Application form required.
Initial approach: Please call or e-mail
Copies of proposal: 1
Deadline(s): Feb. 1 and Sept. 1 for community grants
Board meeting date(s): Bi-monthly
Final notification: Within 3 months
Officers and Trustees:* Robert Zeldenrust,* Chair.; William Johnson,* Vice-Chair.; Carla Roberts, C.E.O. and Pres.; Todd Jacobs, V.P., Community Investment; Robert Jordan, V.P., Philanthropic Svcs.; Kathy Pope, V.P., Finance; Cathy Kissinger,* Secy.; Richard Dunning,* Treas.; Robert Clouse; Maria Gonzalez; Lindsay Hager; Lola Harmon-Ramsey; Carolyn Hummel; Kent Karnemaat; Mary Rangel; Joseph Roberson; Denise Suttles; Dale Twing; Tom Williams.
Number of staff: 12 full-time professional; 1 part-time professional; 3 full-time support; 3 part-time support.
EIN: 381443367

4439
Twink Frey Charitable Trust ✧
(doing business as Nokomis Foundation)
161 Ottawa Ave. N.W., Ste. 409-A
Grand Rapids, MI 49503-2794 (616) 451-0267
Contact: Mary Alice Williams, Pres.
E-mail: ahagen@nolomisfoundation.org; Main URL: http://www.nokomisfoundation.org

Established in MI.
Foundation type: Independent foundation.
Financial data (yr. ended 12/31/12): Assets, $11,037,859 (M); expenditures, $1,226,070; qualifying distributions, $1,067,738; giving activities include $769,300 for grants.
Fields of interest: Education, public policy; Health care; Human services; Women; Girls.
Limitations: Applications not accepted. Giving primarily in western MI. No support for religious organizations for religious purposes. No grants to individuals; no funding for scholarships, fellowships, medical research, capital requests, endowments or conferences.
Application information: Unsolicited requests for funds not accepted. From time to time, the foundation will send out Requests for Proposals specifically related to its focus areas of women's economic self-sufficiency as well as civic engagement. For questions regarding the grantmaking process, e-mail Anne Hagen, Prog. Dir.
Officers and Trustees:* Twink Frey,* Chair.; Mary Alice Williams, C.E.O. and Pres.; Carroll Velie,* Secy.
EIN: 261131263

4440
Frey Foundation ✧
40 Pearl St. N.W., Ste. 1100
Grand Rapids, MI 49503-3028 (616) 451-0303
Contact: Steve Wilson, Pres.
FAX: (616) 451-8481; E-mail: freyfdn@freyfdn.org; Main URL: http://www.freyfdn.org
Grants List: http://www.freyfdn.org/grants

Established in 1974 in MI; endowed in 1988.

Donors: Edward J. Frey, Sr.†; Frances T. Frey†.
Foundation type: Independent foundation.
Financial data (yr. ended 12/31/12): Assets, $136,566,394 (M); expenditures, $9,739,880; qualifying distributions, $8,612,207; giving activities include $7,400,961 for 213 grants (high: $1,000,000; low: $50).
Purpose and activities: Foundation priorities are: 1) nurturing community arts; 2) community capital projects; 3) enhancing the lives of children and their families; 4) encouraging civic progress; 5) protecting the environment; and 6) strengthening philanthropy.
Fields of interest: Arts; Human services; Children/youth, services; Family services; Community/economic development; Philanthropy/voluntarism.
Type of support: Capital campaigns; Land acquisition; Program development; Seed money; Research; Technical assistance; Employee matching gifts.
Limitations: Applications accepted. Giving primarily in the Grand Rapids, MI, area, as well as Charlevois and Emmet counties. No support for sectarian charitable activity. No grants to individuals, or for endowment funds, debt retirement, general operating expenses, scholarships, conferences, speakers, travel, or to cover routine, current, or emergency expenses.
Publications: Application guidelines; Annual report.
Application information: Application form required for all requests; follow detailed application guidelines on foundation web site. Application form required.
Initial approach: The foundation encourages a pre-proposal meeting with applicants, or telephone, e-mail or letter of inquiry before submitting full application
Copies of proposal: 1
Board meeting date(s): Feb., May, Aug., and Nov.
Officers and Trustees:* David G. Frey,* Chair.; John M. Frey,* Vice-Chair.; Steve Wilson, Pres.; Edward J. Frey, Jr.,* Secy.-Treas.; Mary Caroline "Twink" Frey, Tr. Emeritus; Mary E. Frey Bennett; William O. Frey; Sarah R. Frey Rose; Eleonora H. Frey Zagel.
Number of staff: 5 full-time professional; 1 full-time support.
EIN: 237094777

4441
G. II Charities ✧

c/o Ken Cregel
55 Campau Ave. NW, Ste. 501
Grand Rapids, MI 49503-2609 (616) 363-9209
Contact: Ken Kregel

Established in MI.
Donor: Gordon Food Service Inc.
Foundation type: Independent foundation.
Financial data (yr. ended 12/31/12): Assets, $11,224,208 (M); gifts received, $4,500,000; expenditures, $4,584,751; qualifying distributions, $4,584,385; giving activities include $4,584,385 for 58 grants (high: $1,000,000; low: $6,000).
Purpose and activities: Giving limited to Christian organizations and limited to effective evangelization activities emphasizing proclamation, church planting, discipleship, and leadership development.
Fields of interest: Christian agencies & churches.
Limitations: Giving primarily in MI.
Application information:
Initial approach: Letter
Deadline(s): None
Officers: Ronald K. Williams, Pres.; James D. Gordon, V.P.; John M. Gordon, Jr., Secy.-Treas.
EIN: 900098975
Selected grants: The following grants are a representative sample of this grantmaker's funding activity:
$1,000,000 to Wycliffe Seed Company, Arlington, TX, 2012.
$550,000 to Overseas Council International, Indianapolis, IN, 2012.
$311,000 to Josiah Venture, Wheaton, IL, 2012.
$150,000 to Near East Initiatives, New Albany, OH, 2012.
$99,000 to Youth for Christ USA, Englewood, CO, 2012.
$75,000 to Military Community Youth Ministries, Colorado Springs, CO, 2012.
$54,000 to Kids Hope USA, Zeeland, MI, 2012.
$50,000 to Thornston Educational Fund, Glendora, CA, 2012.
$50,000 to Word for the World, USA, Colorado Springs, CO, 2012.
$42,000 to Leadership Development International, Newnan, GA, 2012.

4442
General Motors Foundation, Inc. ✧

(also known as GM Foundation)
300 Renaissance Ctr., M.C. 482-C27-D76
Detroit, MI 48265-3000
Contact: Ann Kihn
E-mail: ann.kihn@gm.com; Main URL: http://www.gm.com/company/aboutGM/gm_foundation.html

Incorporated in 1976 in MI.
Donor: General Motors Corp.
Foundation type: Company-sponsored foundation.
Financial data (yr. ended 12/31/12): Assets, $123,104,236 (M); expenditures, $30,010,295; qualifying distributions, $28,562,336; giving activities include $27,627,768 for 421 grants (high: $8,502,185; low: $200).
Purpose and activities: The foundation supports programs designed to promote education; health and human services; environment and energy; and community development.
Fields of interest: Museums; Performing arts, orchestras; Arts; Education, early childhood education; Secondary school/education; Higher education; Engineering school/education; Education; Environment, natural resources; Environment, energy; Environmental education; Environment; Health care; Cancer research; Heart & circulatory research; Diabetes research; Medical research; Food services; Food banks; Housing/shelter, development; Disasters, preparedness/services; Safety, automotive safety; American Red Cross; Children/youth, services; Human services; Civil/human rights; Community development, civic centers; Business/industry; Community/economic development; United Ways and Federated Giving Programs; Mathematics; Engineering/technology; Science; Military/veterans' organizations.
Type of support: General/operating support; Continuing support; Annual campaigns; Equipment; Emergency funds; Program development; Scholarship funds; Research; Employee volunteer services; Sponsorships; Employee matching gifts; Matching/challenge support.
Limitations: Applications accepted. Giving primarily in areas of company operations, with emphasis on MI. No support for discriminatory organizations, religious organizations, or political parties or candidates. No grants to individuals (except for the Buick Scholarship Program), or for capital campaigns, endowments, general operating support for U.S. hospitals or health care institutions, conferences, workshops, or seminars not directly related to GM's business interests; no vehicle donations.
Publications: Application guidelines; Annual report (including application guidelines); Corporate giving report; Informational brochure; Program policy statement.
Application information: Multi-year requests are not encouraged. Additional information may be requested at a later date. Application form required.
Initial approach: Complete online eligibility quiz and application form; complete online application for Buick Scholarship Program
Deadline(s): None; Feb. 28 for Buick Scholarship Program
Board meeting date(s): Quarterly
Final notification: 4 to 8 weeks
Officers and Directors:* Selim Bingol,* Chair.; Mark L. Reuss,* Vice-Chair.; Vivian R. Pickard, Pres.; Lori Wingerter, V.P.; Kevin W. Cobb, Secy.; Mary E. Williams, Treas.; John P. Moylan, C.F.O.; Daniel Amman; Lori Arpin; Jim Davlin; Susan E. Docherty; Robert E. Ferguson; Stephen J. Girsky; Christopher J. Perry; Michael J. Robinson; John F. Smith; Diane D. Tremblay; Janice K. Uhlig; Edward T. Welburn, Jr.
Number of staff: 3 full-time professional; 2 full-time support.
EIN: 382132136
Selected grants: The following grants are a representative sample of this grantmaker's funding activity:
$8,502,185 to Scholarship America, Saint Peter, MN, 2012. For scholarships.
$5,425,000 to United Way for Southeastern Michigan, Detroit, MI, 2012. For local education initiatives.
$1,700,000 to Safe Kids Worldwide, Washington, DC, 2012. For General Support.
$500,000 to Michigan Science Center, Detroit, MI, 2012. For General Support.
$321,429 to SAE International, Warrendale, PA, 2012. For General Support.
$100,000 to Cornell University, Ithaca, NY, 2012. For General Support.
$50,000 to Detroit Historical Society, Detroit, MI, 2012. For General Support.
$50,000 to MATHCOUNTS Foundation, Alexandria, VA, 2012. For General Support.

4443
The Gerber Foundation

(formerly The Gerber Companies Foundation and The Gerber Baby Food Fund)
4747 W. 48th St., Ste. 153
Fremont, MI 49412-8119 (231) 924-3175
Contact: Catherine A. Obits, Prog. Mgr.
FAX: (231) 924-7906; E-mail: tgf@ncresa.org; Additional e-mail (Catherine A. Obits): cobits@ncresa.org; Main URL: http://www.gerberfoundation.org

Incorporated in 1952 in MI with funds from Gerber Products Co.
Foundation type: Independent foundation.
Financial data (yr. ended 12/31/13): Assets, $74,314,600 (M); expenditures, $4,116,500; qualifying distributions, $3,733,300; giving activities include $3,076,343 for grants, $302,018

for 70 grants to individuals (high: $9,200; low: $2,300), and $132,939 for 300 employee matching gifts.
Purpose and activities: The foundation seeks to enhance the quality of life for infants and children by focusing on their nutrition, care, and development.
Fields of interest: Health care, infants; Health organizations, research; Pediatrics; Pediatrics research; Nutrition; Science, research; Infants/toddlers; Children.
Type of support: Research; Scholarships—to individuals.
Limitations: Applications accepted. Giving on a national basis. No support for national child welfare or international based programs. No grants or loans to individuals (except for scholarships), or for capital campaigns or operating support.
Publications: Application guidelines; Annual report (including application guidelines); Grants list; Program policy statement.
Application information: The foundation prefers that applications be submitted only after receiving approval of a letter of inquiry. Application guidelines are available on foundation web site. All materials should be submitted on CD along with the 7 hard copies. Application form required.
Initial approach: Proposal, of no more than 15 pages
Copies of proposal: 7
Deadline(s): Feb. 15 and Aug. 15; June 1 and Dec. 1 for letter of inquiry
Board meeting date(s): Feb., May, Aug., Nov.
Final notification: May and Nov.
Officers and Trustees:* Barbara J. Ivens,* Pres.; Fernando Flores-New,* V.P.; Tracy A. Baker,* Secy.; Stan M. VanderRoest,* Treas.; William L. Bush, M.D.; Michael G. Ebert; Raymond J. Hutchinson, M.D.; Jane M. Jeannero; David C. Joslin; Carolyn R. Morby; Nancy Nevin-Folino; Steven W. Poole; Randy Puff; Robert Schumacher, M.D.
Number of staff: 1 full-time professional; 1 part-time support.
EIN: 386068090
Selected grants: The following grants are a representative sample of this grantmaker's funding activity:
$300,000 to Massachusetts General Hospital, Boston, MA, 2013. For study on early risk factors for gastrointestinal mucosal food allergies as part of Pediatric Nutrition Program, payable over 3.00 years.
$299,764 to State University of New York Upstate Medical University, Syracuse, NY, 2012. For study on blood-based biomarkers for early autism as part of Pediatric Health Program, payable over 3.00 years.
$299,379 to Childrens Hospital Medical Center, Cincinnati, OH, 2013. For study on procalcitonin and risk stratification in pediatric pneumonia as part of Pediatric Nutrition Program, payable over 3.00 years.
$299,193 to Vanderbilt University, Nashville, TN, 2013. For study on impact of a multi-interventional nutrition program on the outcomes of newborns requiring surgery for congenital heart disease as part of Pediatric Nutrition Program, payable over 3.00 years.
$298,996 to Albert Einstein College of Medicine of Yeshiva University, Bronx, NY, 2012. For study on early L-Carnitine supplementation and neurodevelopmental outcomes as part of Pediatric Nutrition Program, payable over 2.00 years.
$295,082 to Franciscan Saint Francis Health, Indianapolis, IN, 2013. For study entitled, Does Pesticide Exposure in Pregnancy Cause Fetal DNA Imprinting as part of Pediatric Nutrition Program, payable over 2.00 years.
$294,888 to University of California, San Francisco, CA, 2013. For study entitled, Patent Ductus Arteriosus: Trial of Conservative vs. Early Enteral Treatment as part of Pediatric Health Program, payable over 3.00 years.
$291,420 to University of Massachusetts, Worcester, MA, 2012. For longitudinal assessment of thyroid function in infants with Down Syndrome as part of Pediatric Nutrition Program, payable over 3.00 years.
$290,600 to Johns Hopkins University, Baltimore, MD, 2013. For study on molecular point-of-care diagnosis of early onset neonatal sepsis as part of Pediatric Health Program, payable over 2.00 years.
$289,194 to Children's Hospital Corporation, Boston, MA, 2012. For study on toddler development and aluminum concentrations as part of Pediatric Nutrition Program, payable over 3.00 years.
$264,000 to Brigham and Women's Hospital, Boston, MA, 2013. For study on growth velocity, caloric intake and nutritional outcomes after continuous exposure to mother's voice as part of Pediatric Nutrition Program, payable over 3.00 years.
$223,088 to University of Colorado Hospital, Aurora, CO, 2013. For study on contribution of the airway microbiome to chronic lung disease in premature infants as part of Pediatric Health Program, payable over 2.00 years.
$173,495 to Childrens Hospital Medical Center, Cincinnati, OH, 2013. For study on intestinal motility and gastroschisis as part of Pediatric Health Program, payable over 3.00 years.
$144,110 to University of California, San Francisco, CA, 2012. For study on cholesterol and fatty acids on developmental outcomes as part of Pediatric Nutrition Program, payable over 3.00 years.
$138,314 to University of Michigan, Ann Arbor, MI, 2013. To evaluate effects of prenatal exposure to non-essential heavy metals on hearing as part of Pediatric Nutrition Program, payable over 2.00 years.
$50,000 to White Cloud Community Library, White Cloud, MI, 2012. For capital campaign for new library.
$14,700 to Grant Area District Library, Grant, MI, 2012. For 60th Anniversary Grant.
$14,700 to Hesperia Community Library, Hesperia, MI, 2012. For 60th Anniversary Grant.
$14,700 to Newaygo Area District Library, Newaygo, MI, 2012. For 60th Anniversary Grant.
$7,000 to Croton Township Library, Newaygo, MI, 2012. For 60th Anniversary Grant.

4444
The Rollin M. Gerstacker Foundation ✧

P.O. Box 1945
Midland, MI 48641-1945 (989) 631-6097
Contact: E.N. Brandt, V.P.
FAX: (989) 832-8842; Main URL: http://www.gerstackerfoundation.org/

Incorporated in 1957 in MI.
Donors: Eda U. Gerstacker‡; Carl A. Gerstacker‡.
Foundation type: Independent foundation.
Financial data (yr. ended 12/31/13): Assets, $180,352,949 (M); expenditures, $10,134,617; qualifying distributions, $9,572,302; giving activities include $9,226,794 for 161 grants (high: $1,000,000; low: $1,000).
Purpose and activities: Giving to assist community projects, with emphasis on the aged and the youth; grants also for higher education, health care, medical research, and hospitals.
Fields of interest: Higher education; Hospitals (general); Health care; Mental health/crisis services; Health organizations, association; Human services; Children/youth, services; Aging, centers/services; Government/public administration; Aging.
Type of support: General/operating support; Continuing support; Annual campaigns; Capital campaigns; Building/renovation; Equipment; Land acquisition; Endowments; Emergency funds; Seed money; Research; Matching/challenge support.
Limitations: Applications accepted. Giving primarily in Midland County, MI; giving also in OH. No grants to individuals, or for scholarships or fellowships; no loans.
Publications: Annual report.
Application information: Application form not required.
Initial approach: Letter
Copies of proposal: 1
Deadline(s): Prior to Apr. 1, Aug. 1, and Nov. 1
Board meeting date(s): May, Sept., and Dec.
Final notification: 1 month
Officers and Trustees:* Gail E. Lanphear,* Chair.; Lisa J. Gerstacker,* Pres.; E.N. Brandt,* V.P. and Secy.; Alan W. Ott,* V.P. and Treas.; William D. Schuette,* V.P.; Alexio R. Baum; Frank E. Gerace; Paula A. Liveris; Thomas L. Ludington; Paul F. Oreffice; William S. Stavropoulos.
EIN: 386060276
Selected grants: The following grants are a representative sample of this grantmaker's funding activity:
$700,000 to Meridian Public Schools, Sanford, MI, 2012. For 21st Century Learning Project.
$500,000 to Alma College, Alma, MI, 2012. For Eddy Music Center Renovation Project.
$500,000 to MidMichigan Medical Center Midland, Midland, MI, 2012. For Medical Education Facility and Program.
$500,000 to Nature Conservancy, Arlington, VA, 2012. For Great Lakes Project.
$100,000 to West Midland Family Center, Shepherd, MI, 2012. For General Fund.
$65,000 to Starry Night, Lake Isabella, MI, 2012. For Billable Autism Insurance Program.
$30,000 to Prairie View A & M University, Prairie View, TX, 2012. For General Fund.
$26,000 to Michigans Children, Lansing, MI, 2012. For General Fund.
$21,000 to Chippewa Watershed Conservancy, Mount Pleasant, MI, 2012. For Hall's Lake Project.
$10,000 to Midland Symphony Orchestra, Midland, MI, 2012. For General Fund.

4445
Irving S. Gilmore Foundation ✧

136 E. Michigan Ave., Ste. 900
Kalamazoo, MI 49007-3915 (269) 342-6411
Contact: Richard M. Hughey, Jr., Exec. V.P. and C.E.O.
FAX: (269) 342-6465; Main URL: http://www.isgilmore.org

Established in 1972 in MI.
Donor: Irving S. Gilmore‡.
Foundation type: Independent foundation.

Financial data (yr. ended 12/31/13): Assets, $260,838,595 (M); expenditures, $11,338,100; qualifying distributions, $9,832,481; giving activities include $8,857,132 for 166 grants (high: $1,000,000; low: $850), and $25,802 for employee matching gifts.
Purpose and activities: The mission of the foundation is to support and enrich the cultural, social, and economic life of the greater Kalamazoo, MI, area. The priorities of the foundation are: 1) arts, culture, and humanities; 2) human services; 3) education and youth activities; 4) community development; and 5) health and well-being.
Fields of interest: Performing arts; Arts; Education; Health care; Youth development; Human services; Community/economic development.
Type of support: General/operating support; Continuing support; Annual campaigns; Capital campaigns; Building/renovation; Equipment; Land acquisition; Debt reduction; Emergency funds; Program development; Conferences/seminars; Publication; Seed money; Scholarship funds; Technical assistance; Consulting services; Program evaluation; Employee matching gifts; Matching/challenge support.
Limitations: Applications accepted. Giving primarily in the greater Kalamazoo, MI, area. No support for political organizations. No grants to individuals.
Publications: Application guidelines; Annual report.
Application information: Organizations that are first time foundation applicants or have not received foundation funding since 2007 must contact the foundation at least four weeks prior to an applicable submission deadline. Please refer to foundation web site for further guidelines and deadlines. Application form not required.
Initial approach: Single, unbound proposal including cover letter; narrative, limited to 6 numbered pages, at least 12-point font
Copies of proposal: 1
Deadline(s): Jan. 10, Mar. 1, May 2, July 1, Sept. 1 and Nov. 1
Board meeting date(s): Jan., Mar., May, July, Sept., and Nov.
Final notification: Acknowledgement letter within 2 weeks
Officers and Trustees:* Richard M. Hughey, Jr., C.E.O. and Exec. V.P.; Floyd L. Parks,* Pres.; Judith H. Moore,* 1st V.P.; Janice C. Elliott, V.P., Admin.; Robert M. Beam,* Secy.; Charles D. Wattles,* Treas.; Russell L. Gabier, Tr. Emeritus; Howard D. Kalleward,* Tr. Emeritus; Ronald N. Kilgore.
Number of staff: 3 full-time professional; 2 full-time support.
EIN: 237236057
Selected grants: The following grants are a representative sample of this grantmaker's funding activity:
$1,000,000 to Irving S. Gilmore International Keyboard Festival, Kalamazoo, MI, 2013. For operational support.
$625,000 to Kalamazoo Regional Educational Service Agency, Kalamazoo, MI, 2013. For EFA operational support.
$489,981 to Western Michigan University Foundation, Kalamazoo, MI, 2013. For Legacy Collections Facility.
$350,000 to Southwest Michigan First Corporation, Kalamazoo, MI, 2013. For operational support.
$300,000 to Ministry with Community, Kalamazoo, MI, 2013. For capital campaign.
$100,000 to Communities in Schools of Kalamazoo, Kalamazoo, MI, 2013. For program support.
$50,000 to Comstock Community Center, Comstock, MI, 2013. For bilingual preschool program.
$30,000 to Arts Council of Greater Kalamazoo, Kalamazoo, MI, 2013. For programming support.
$25,000 to Council of Michigan Foundations, Grand Haven, MI, 2013. For Office of Urban and Metro Initiatives-Kalamazoo Office.
$20,000 to Disability Network Southwest Michigan, Kalamazoo, MI, 2013. For independent living program.

4446
Grand Haven Area Community Foundation, Inc. ✧

1 S. Harbor Dr.
Grand Haven, MI 49417-1385 (616) 842-6378
Contact: Holly Johnson, Pres.; For grants: Beth Larson, Dir., Grants and Nonprofit Svcs.
FAX: (616) 842-9518; E-mail: lgrevel@ghacf.org; Grant application E-mail: blarsen@ghacf.org; Main URL: http://www.ghacf.org
Facebook: http://www.facebook.com/pages/Grand-Haven-Area-Community-Foundation/416194020318
Scholarship e-mail: bpost@ghacf.org

Incorporated in 1971 in MI.
Foundation type: Community foundation.
Financial data (yr. ended 12/31/13): Assets, $78,677,937 (M); gifts received, $3,145,598; expenditures, $3,945,689; giving activities include $2,964,172 for 117+ grants (high: $427,087), and $290,867 for 204 grants to individuals.
Purpose and activities: The foundation seeks to improve and enhance the quality of life in the Tri-Cities area by: 1) serving as a leader, catalyst and resource for philanthropy; 2) building and holding a permanent and growing endowment for the community's changing needs and opportunities; 3) striving for community improvement through strategic grantmaking in such fields as the arts, education, health, the environment, youth, social services and other human needs; and 4) providing a flexible and cost-effective way for donors to improve their community now and in the future.
Fields of interest: Arts; Vocational education, post-secondary; Business school/education; Education; Environment; Health care; Crime/law enforcement; Human services; Community/economic development; Mathematics.
Type of support: Capital campaigns; Equipment; Land acquisition; Program development; Seed money; Scholarship funds; Scholarships—to individuals; Matching/challenge support.
Limitations: Applications accepted. Giving primarily in the MI Tri-Cities area. No support for profit-making organizations or religious programs that serve, or appear to serve, specific religious denominations. No grants to individuals (except for scholarships), or for annual campaigns, emergency or deficit financing, operating costs or ongoing operating support, fundraising events, or endowments.
Publications: Application guidelines; Annual report (including application guidelines); Financial statement; Informational brochure (including application guidelines); Newsletter; Program policy statement.
Application information: Visit foundation web site for more information. Application form required.
Initial approach: Contact foundation
Deadline(s): Jan. 10, Apr. 4, June 27, and Oct. 10
Board meeting date(s): Distribution committee meets quarterly: Jan., Apr., July, and Oct.; board meetings are usually 2 weeks following the distribution committee meeting
Final notification: 1 week after board meeting
Officers and Trustees:* Timothy Parker,* Chair.; Lana Jacobson,* Vice-Chair.; Holly Johnson,* Pres.; Sheila Steffel,* Secy.; Steven Moreland,* Treas.; Tammy Bailey; Kennard Creason; Edward Hanenburg; Randy Hansen; Sandy Huber; Mark Kleist; Monica Verplank.
Number of staff: 4 full-time professional.
EIN: 237108776

4447
Grand Rapids Community Foundation

(formerly The Grand Rapids Foundation)
185 Oakes Street SW
Grand Rapids, MI 49503-4219 (616) 454-1751
Contact: Diana R. Sieger, Pres.; For grant inquiries: Shavon Doyle, Grants Admin.
FAX: (616) 454-6455;
E-mail: grfound@grfoundation.org; Grant inquiry tel.: (616) 454-1751, ext. 111; Main URL: http://www.grfoundation.org
E-Newsletter: http://www.grfoundation.org/enews
Facebook: http://www.facebook.com/GRCommFound
Podcasts: http://feeds.feedburner.com/grfoundation/gigr
President's Page: http://www.grfoundation.org/president
Twitter: http://twitter.com/GRCommFound
Vimeo: http://vimeo.com/channels/grcommfound
Scholarship contact: Ruth Bishop, tel.: (616) 454-1751, ext. 103, e-mail: rbishop@grfoundation.org

Established in 1922 in MI by resolution and declaration of trust; Incorporated 1989.
Foundation type: Community foundation.
Financial data (yr. ended 06/30/14): Assets, $322,783,752 (M); gifts received, $16,776,942; expenditures, $16,160,956; giving activities include $9,574,054 for 223+ grants (high: $510,000), and $1,099,400 for 642 grants to individuals.
Purpose and activities: The Community Foundation seeks to build and manage the community's permanent endowment and lead the community to strengthen the lives of its people. Grants are awarded to expand impact in Grand Rapids and surrounding communities. Leadership goals areas are academic achievement, economic prosperity, healthy ecosystems, healthy people, social enrichment and vibrant neighborhoods.
Fields of interest: Performing arts; Performing arts, theater; Arts; Higher education; Education, reading; Education; Environment; Health organizations, association; Employment; Housing/shelter, development; Youth development, services; Family services; Minorities/immigrants, centers/services; Human services; Civil/human rights, immigrants; Civil/human rights, minorities; Civil/human rights, disabled; Civil/human rights, women; Civil/human rights, aging; Civil/human rights, LGBTQ; Civil rights, race/intergroup relations; Civil liberties, reproductive rights; Community/economic development; Infants/toddlers; Children/youth; Children; Youth; Adults; Aging; Young adults; Disabilities, people with; Blind/visually impaired; Deaf/hearing impaired; Minorities; Asians/Pacific Islanders; African Americans/Blacks; Hispanics/

Latinos; Native Americans/American Indians; Indigenous peoples; Women; Girls; Adults, women; Men; Boys; Adults, men; Single parents; Crime/abuse victims; Immigrants/refugees; Economically disadvantaged; Homeless; LGBTQ; Gay men; Bisexual.

Type of support: Capital campaigns; Building/renovation; Land acquisition; Program development; Seed money; Technical assistance; Program-related investments/loans; Employee matching gifts; Employee-related scholarships; Scholarships—to individuals.

Limitations: Applications accepted. Giving limited to Greater Grand Rapids, MI area. No support for religious programs, hospitals, child care centers, or nursing homes/retirement facilities. No grants to individuals (except for scholarships), or for continued operating support, annual campaigns, travel expenses, medical or scholarly research, deficit financing, endowment funds, computers, vehicles, films, videos, or conferences; no student loans; no venture capital for competitive profit-making activities.

Publications: Annual report; Informational brochure; Newsletter.

Application information: Visit foundation web site for online applications and guidelines per grant type. The foundation will request a full proposal based on the pre-application for the Fund for Community Good. Application form required.

Initial approach: Submit online pre-application (reviewed every 2 weeks) for Fund for Community Good

Deadline(s): Varies

Board meeting date(s): 6 times a year (bimonthly)

Final notification: 30 days

Officers and Trustees:* Wayman P. Britt,* Chair.; Paul Keep,* Vice-Chair.; Diana R. Sieger, Pres.; Lynne Black, V.P., Finance and Admin.; Roberta F. King, V.P., Public Rels. and Mktg.; Marcia Rapp, V.P., Progs.; Kevin Harmelink, Cont.; Laurie F. Beard; Eva Aguirre Cooper; Carol J. Karr; Christina Keller; Arend Lubbers; Michael Rosloniec; Robert W. Roth; E. Miles Wilson.

Number of staff: 15 full-time professional; 9 full-time support.

EIN: 382877959

Selected grants: The following grants are a representative sample of this grantmaker's funding activity:

$500,000 to Grand Action Foundation, Grand Rapids, MI, 2011. For Grand Rapids Downtown Market.

$400,000 to Dwelling Place of Grand Rapids, Grand Rapids, MI, 2012. For Heckner Block Revitalization.

$400,000 to Grand Rapids Public Schools, Grand Rapids, MI, 2013. For Challenge Scholars: Year Three.

$350,000 to Grand Valley State University, Grand Rapids, MI, 2011. For Community Research Institute.

$253,825 to Friends of Grand Rapids Parks, Grand Rapids, MI, 2011. For Grand Rapids Tree Urban Inventory.

$232,155 to Bank of America Charitable Gift Fund, Providence, RI, 2013. For Closing Fund.

$170,000 to Community Rebuilders, Grand Rapids, MI, 2013. For Housing Resource Specialist-collective impact.

$150,000 to Cherry Street Health Services, Grand Rapids, MI, 2013. For increasing Access to Healthcare in Wyoming.

$150,000 to Kent County Health Department, Grand Rapids, MI, 2012. For Kent County Dental Clinic.

$150,000 to West Michigan Sports Commission, Grand Rapids, MI, 2011. For construction of youth baseball and softball community fields.

$125,000 to First Steps Kent, Grand Rapids, MI, 2011. For sustaining Children's Healthcare Access Program.

$100,000 to Goodwill Industries of Greater Grand Rapids, Grandville, MI, 2011. For Kent County Recycling Transitional Work Project.

$100,000 to Goodwill Industries of Greater Grand Rapids, Grandville, MI, 2013. For Year Two: Kent County Recycling Transitional Work Project.

$100,000 to Urban Institute for Contemporary Arts, Grand Rapids, MI, 2013. For general support.

$75,000 to Arbor Circle Corporation, Grand Rapids, MI, 2013. For Arbor Circle P21! Early Impact.

$60,670 to Christians Opening Opportunities for Learning, Project Cool, Grand Rapids, MI, 2013. For Project COOL Youth Employment Program.

$4,536 to Association for the Blind and Visually Impaired, Grand Rapids, MI, 2013. For Business Planning.

$2,500 to Grand Rapids Student Advancement Foundation, Grand Rapids, MI, 2013. To support of Mindshare.

4448
Grand Traverse Regional Community Foundation ✧

250 E. Front St., Ste. 310
Traverse City, MI 49684-2552 (231) 935-4066
Contact: Phil Ellis, Exec. Dir.; For grants: Gina Limbocker, Grantmaking and Prog. Assoc.
FAX: (231) 941-0021; E-mail: info@gtrcf.org; Grant application e-mail: glimbocker@gtrcf.org; Main URL: http://www.gtrcf.org
Facebook: https://www.facebook.com/grandtraverseregionalcommunityfoundation

Established in 1992 in MI.

Foundation type: Community foundation.

Financial data (yr. ended 12/31/13): Assets, $52,104,808 (M); gifts received, $3,478,253; expenditures, $8,009,074; giving activities include $7,252,608 for 283+ grants (high: $834,446; low: $25), and $141,784 for 166 grants to individuals.

Purpose and activities: The foundation seeks to enhance the quality of life and facilitate philanthropy in Antrim, Benzie, Grand Traverse, Kalkaska, and Leelanau counties, MI.

Fields of interest: Arts; Education; Environment; Community/economic development; Youth.

Type of support: Building/renovation; Equipment; Endowments; Program development; Seed money; Curriculum development; Scholarship funds; Technical assistance; Scholarships—to individuals; Matching/challenge support.

Limitations: Applications accepted. Giving limited to the counties of Antrim, Benzie, Grand Traverse, Kalkaska, and Leelanau, MI. No grants for routine training or professional conferences, annual events, budget shortfalls, or payroll or other general operating expenses.

Publications: Annual report; Informational brochure; Newsletter.

Application information: Visit foundation Web site for application information. Application form required.

Initial approach: Submit application

Copies of proposal: 1

Deadline(s): Mar. 31 for Spring Grant and Oct. 1 for Fall Grant.

Board meeting date(s): Quarterly

Officers and Directors:* Susan Cogswell,* Chair.; Virginia Mouch,* Vice-Chair.; Blake Brooks,* Secy.; Bud Cline,* Treas.; Phil Ellis, Exec. Dir.; Ed Arbut; Truman Bicum; Sara Brubaker; Amy Burk; Dale Claudepierre; Doug Cook; Gail Dall'Olmo; Matt Davis; Jack Findlay; Rich Hannan; Jon Hawley; Penny Hill; Gary Hoensheid; Wesley Jacobs; Sherrie Jones; Dick Kennedy; Larry Miller; Kerry Nelson; Rex O'Connor; Roger Perry; Pam Prairie; Steve Rawlings; Bob Robbins; Neal Ronquist; Janet Sieting; Gregg Smith; Bill Stege; Ryan Sterkenburg; Troy Stobert; Tom Wiltse; Jeff Wonacott.

Number of staff: 3 full-time professional; 2 part-time support.

EIN: 383056434

Selected grants: The following grants are a representative sample of this grantmaker's funding activity:

$234,844 to Crystal Lake Arts Center, Frankfort, MI, 2011. For capital campaign for contractor's construction costs.

$180,000 to Suttons Bay Township, Suttons Bay, MI, 2011. For capital campaign for construction costs.

$80,224 to Old Town Playhouse, Traverse City, MI, 2011. For annual distribution for operating support.

$75,000 to Paul Oliver Memorial Hospital, Frankfort, MI, 2011. For dialysis equipment.

$70,000 to Habitat for Humanity, Grand Traverse Region, Traverse City, MI, 2011. For Kingsley Home Project.

$48,528 to Central Lake District Library, Central Lake, MI, 2011. For general operating support.

$43,418 to Leelanau Community Cultural Center, Leland, MI, 2011. For building funds.

$20,198 to YMCA of Grand Traverse Bay, Traverse City, MI, 2011. For capital campaign.

$15,628 to YMCA of Grand Traverse Bay, Traverse City, MI, 2011. For capital campaign.

$12,500 to Northwestern Michigan College Foundation, Traverse City, MI, 2011. For Hagerty Center capital campaign.

4449
Granger Foundation ✧

P.O. Box 22187
Lansing, MI 48909-7185 (517) 393-1670
Contact: Eva Lee
E-mail: elee@grangerconstruction.com; Main URL: http://www.grangerfoundation.org/

Established in 1978.

Donors: Granger Associates, Inc.; Granger Construction Co.; and members of the Granger family.

Foundation type: Independent foundation.

Financial data (yr. ended 12/31/12): Assets, $10,213,570 (M); gifts received, $795,600; expenditures, $988,932; qualifying distributions, $948,821; giving activities include $948,821 for 71 grants (high: $67,146; low: $100).

Purpose and activities: The foundation's primary mission is to support Christ-centered activities. It also supports efforts that enhance the lives of youth in the community.

Fields of interest: Health care; Youth development; Human services; YM/YWCAs & YM/YWHAs; Christian agencies & churches; Youth.

Type of support: Annual campaigns; Capital campaigns.

Limitations: Applications accepted. Giving primarily in the greater Lansing and the Tri-County (Ingham, Eaton and Clinton counties), MI, areas. No support for capital funds or improvements for churches or public schools. No grants to individuals, or for endowments, fundraising, social events, conferences, or exhibits.
Publications: Application guidelines; Annual report; Program policy statement.
Application information: Form letters and lengthy proposals are not accepted. Application form required.
Initial approach: Completed Request for Funding form that is available on foundation web site
Copies of proposal: 4
Deadline(s): Apr. 15 and Oct. 15
Board meeting date(s): Semiannually
Trustees: Alton L. Granger; Donna Granger; Janice Granger; Jerry P. Granger; Lynne Granger; Ronald K. Granger.
EIN: 382251879
Selected grants: The following grants are a representative sample of this grantmaker's funding activity:
$30,000 to Mission India, Grand Rapids, MI, 2012. For Adult Literacy in Ne India Pledge.
$25,000 to New Tribes Mission, Sanford, FL, 2012. For Ministry Support for Dorr and Nancy Granger.
$15,100 to Fellowship of Christian Athletes, Jenison, MI, 2012. For Fca Huddles/Drug Free/ Coaches Ministry.
$15,000 to Cristo Rey Community Center, Lansing, MI, 2012. For prescription assistance Program.
$15,000 to Foundation for Traditional Values, Lansing, MI, 2012. For SSI/Greatest Story Never Told.
$15,000 to Impression 5 Science Center, Lansing, MI, 2012. For Interpretive Programs Officer.
$15,000 to Junior Achievement of Mid Michigan, Lansing, MI, 2012. For Economic Gardening Project.
$15,000 to Sunny Crest Youth Ranch, Sunfield, MI, 2012. For Rock the Ranch.
$12,000 to Giving Tree Farm, Lansing, MI, 2012. For Respite Care Adoptive Families.
$6,000 to Michigan State University, East Lansing, MI, 2012. For Granger Endowment at Wharton.

4450
Granger III Foundation Inc. ✧

P.O. Box 27185
Lansing, MI 48909-7185
Contact: Todd J. Granger, Secy.
Application address: 16980 Wood Rd., Lansing, MI 48906-1044, tel.: (517) 372-2800

Established in 2000 in OH.
Donors: Granger Electric Co.; Granger Energy; Granger Associates, Inc.; Granger Holdings, LLC; Granger Energy of Decatur, LLC; Granger Energy of Honeybrook, LLC; Granger Meadows, LLC; Granger Holdings II LLC.
Foundation type: Independent foundation.
Financial data (yr. ended 12/31/13): Assets, $5,958,221 (M); gifts received, $1,670,000; expenditures, $917,786; qualifying distributions, $907,930; giving activities include $907,930 for 28 grants (high: $125,000; low: $1,000).
Purpose and activities: Giving primarily for a Christian school as well as for other Christian organizations; funding also for human services, education, volunteer organizations, and YMCAs.
Fields of interest: Theological school/education; Human services; YM/YWCAs & YM/YWHAs; Philanthropy/voluntarism; Christian agencies & churches.
Limitations: Applications accepted. Giving primarily in the Lansing, MI, area. No grants to individuals.
Application information: Application form required.
Initial approach: Letter
Deadline(s): None
Officers: Thomas D. Hofman, Pres.; Ray A. Easton, V.P.; Todd J. Granger, Secy.; Keith L. Granger, Treas.
Directors: Randy J. Russ; Joel M. Zylstra.
EIN: 383555568

4451
Great Lakes Capital Fund Nonprofit Housing Corporation ✧

(formerly Michigan Capital Fund for Non-Profit Housing Corporation)
1000 S. Washington Ave., Ste. 200
Lansing, MI 48910-1647
Main URL: http://www.capfund.net/
Facebook: https://www.facebook.com/Greatlakescapfund
Google Plus: https://plus.google.com/116783011127817898294/videos
LinkedIn: http://www.linkedin.com/company/great-lakes-capital-fund
Twitter: https://twitter.com/GLCapFund/
YouTube: https://www.youtube.com/user/GLCapFund

Foundation type: Operating foundation.
Financial data (yr. ended 12/31/12): Assets, $30,076,000 (M); expenditures, $12,675,000; qualifying distributions, $21,836,213; giving activities include $989,510 for 32 grants (high: $500,000; low: $50).
Purpose and activities: Giving primarily for the delivery of quality, affordable housing to the poor and underprivileged, the promotion of efforts to facilitate self-sufficiency and upward mobility of very-low and low-income households, and the preservation of social welfare through efforts to facilitate the construction and development of housing for very low-, low- and moderate-income households in a manner directed to eliminate prejudice and discrimination, lessen neighborhood tensions, and combat the deterioration of communities throughout Michigan.
Fields of interest: Housing/shelter; Economically disadvantaged.
Limitations: Applications not accepted. Giving primarily in MI.
Application information: Unsolicited requests for funds not accepted.
Officers and Directors:* Wendell Johns,* Chair.; Mark McDaniel, Pres. and C.E.O.; Michael Taylor,* Secy.-Treas.; James Logue III, C.O.O.; Christopher Cox, C.F.O.; Jennifer Everhart, Exec. V.P.; Ricky Laber, Exec. V.P.; Catherine A. Cawthon; Derrick C. Collins; Christine Hobbs; William C. Perkins; Rob Rossiter; James Stretz; Donald F. Tucker; Paul J. Weaver.
EIN: 383126310

4452
Greenville Area Community Foundation ✧

(formerly Greenville Area Foundation)
101 N. Lafayette St.
Greenville, MI 48838-1853 (616) 754-2640
Contact: Alison Barberi, C.E.O.; For grants: Amy O'Brien, Dir., Grants and Comms.
E-mail: alison@gacfmi.org; Grant inquiry e-mail: amy@gacfmi.org; Main URL: http://www.gacfmi.org
Facebook: http://www.facebook.com/pages/Greenville-Area-Community-Foundation/156967467647838

Established in 1989 in MI.
Foundation type: Community foundation.
Financial data (yr. ended 12/31/13): Assets, $25,702,554 (M); gifts received, $643,091; expenditures, $1,400,719; giving activities include $845,998 for 20+ grants (high: $186,352), and $142,250 for grants to individuals.
Purpose and activities: The foundation seeks to enhance the quality of life in the Greenville area. To do this it will attract and hold permanent endowment funds from a wide range of donors, it will manage these funds to assure safety and growth, it will make grants directed to the community's cultural, educational, social, environmental, recreational, and health related concerns and it will function as a community leader and catalyst.
Fields of interest: Arts; Adult education—literacy, basic skills & GED; Education; Environment; Health care; Recreation; Children/youth, services; Community/economic development; Government/ public administration.
Type of support: General/operating support; Management development/capacity building; Capital campaigns; Building/renovation; Equipment; Endowments; Emergency funds; Program development; Publication; Seed money; Curriculum development; Scholarship funds; Program evaluation; Matching/challenge support.
Limitations: Applications accepted. Giving limited to Montcalm County, MI. No support for sectarian religious programs. No grants for general operating support, annual fundraising drives, or endowments or debt reduction.
Publications: Application guidelines; Annual report; Financial statement; Grants list; Informational brochure; Informational brochure (including application guidelines); Newsletter.
Application information: Visit foundation web site for grant information. The Spring Grant Cycle is for programs and projects with a strong educational component only and the grant if awarded is payable over the next school year. The Fall Grant Cycle includes general programs and projects that fall within the identified needs of area youth, and health-related programs. Application form required.
Initial approach: Telephone
Copies of proposal: 16
Deadline(s): Spring and Fall
Board meeting date(s): Jan., Apr., June, Sept., Oct., and Nov.
Final notification: Dec. and Apr.
Officers and Directors:* Dr. Peter Blinkilde,* Chair.; Charlotte Lothian,* Vice-Chair.; Alison Barberi,* C.E.O. and Pres.; Eric Januzelli,* Secy.-Treas.; Byron Cook,* Chair. Emeritus; Lemont Renterghem,* Chair. Emeritus; Susan Ayres; Keane Blazczynski; Dick Ellafrits; Bill Ham; Doug Hinken; John Kerschen; Dr. Charles McNinch; John O'Donald, D.D.S.; Fran Schuleit; Corey Smith; Phil Tower.
Number of staff: 1 full-time professional; 2 part-time professional.
EIN: 382899657

4453
The Grosfeld Foundation ✧

2290 First National Bldg.
Detroit, MI 48226-3583

Established in 1984 in MI.
Donors: James Grosfeld; Nancy Grosfeld; Multivest.
Foundation type: Independent foundation.
Financial data (yr. ended 11/30/13): Assets, $5,545,050 (M); gifts received, $7,946,350; expenditures, $4,424,570; qualifying distributions, $4,420,570; giving activities include $4,418,015 for 90 grants (high: $1,405,000; low: $350).
Fields of interest: Arts; Education; Human services; Jewish federated giving programs; Jewish agencies & synagogues.
Limitations: Applications not accepted. Giving primarily in MI. No grants to individuals.
Application information: Contributes only to pre-selected organizations.
Officers: James Grosfeld, Pres. and Treas.; Nancy Grosfeld, V.P. and Secy.
EIN: 382575307

4454
Guardian Industries Educational Foundation ✧
2300 Harmon Rd.
Auburn Hills, MI 48326-1714 (615) 627-3833

Established in 1986 in DE and MI.
Donor: Guardian Industries Corp.
Foundation type: Company-sponsored foundation.
Financial data (yr. ended 12/31/13): Assets, $69,085 (M); gifts received, $655,596; expenditures, $668,032; qualifying distributions, $668,032; giving activities include $624,000 for 156 grants to individuals (high: $6,000; low: $2,000).
Purpose and activities: The foundation awards college scholarships to children of full-time employees of Guardian Industries and its subsidiaries. The scholarship program is administered by Educational Testing Service.
Limitations: Applications accepted. Giving primarily in areas of company operations. No loans or program-related investments.
Application information: Application form required.
Initial approach: Completed Application form
Deadline(s): Dec. 31
Officers: Ronald Vaupel,* Pres.; Katherine Castillo, V.P.; Todd Roeser, Secy.; Laurent Hendrickx, Treas.
Director: Douglas Girdler.
EIN: 382707035

4455
Charles Stewart Harding Foundation ✧
c/o MFO Mgmt. Co.
111 E. Court St., Ste. 3D
Flint, MI 48502-1649 (810) 767-0136
Contact: Timothy C. Sanford

Established in 1963 in MI.
Donors: C.S. Harding Mott†; C.S. Harding Mott II†; Claire Mott White.
Foundation type: Independent foundation.
Financial data (yr. ended 06/30/13): Assets, $12,508,186 (M); expenditures, $628,024; qualifying distributions, $570,770; giving activities include $565,000 for 11 grants (high: $250,000; low: $1,000).
Purpose and activities: Giving primarily for the arts.
Fields of interest: Performing arts, music; Arts; Human services.
Type of support: General/operating support; Continuing support; Annual campaigns; Scholarship funds.
Limitations: Applications accepted. Giving primarily in Flint, MI. No grants to individuals.
Application information: Application form not required.
Initial approach: Letter
Copies of proposal: 1
Deadline(s): None
Board meeting date(s): Usually Apr.
Officers and Trustees:* Claire Mott White,* Pres.; William S. White,* V.P. and Treas.; C. Edward White, Jr., Secy.; Tiffany W. Lovett; Paula M. Turrentine; Ridgway H. White.
Number of staff: None.
EIN: 386081208

4456
Helppie Family Charitable Foundation ✧
P.O. Box 607
Bloomfield Hills, MI 48303-0607 (248) 386-8300
Contact: Richard D. Helppie, Jr., Pres.

Established in 1997 in MI.
Donors: Richard Helppie; Richard D. Helppie Trust.
Foundation type: Independent foundation.
Financial data (yr. ended 12/31/12): Assets, $2,958,686 (M); expenditures, $491,062; qualifying distributions, $463,990; giving activities include $462,490 for 59 grants (high: $130,000; low: $100).
Purpose and activities: Giving for organizations involved with the disadvantaged, medically impaired children, community improvement, and education.
Fields of interest: Elementary/secondary education; Hospitals (specialty); Health organizations; Human services; Children, services; Community/economic development; Protestant agencies & churches; Economically disadvantaged.
Limitations: Giving primarily in MI. No support for private foundations. No grants to individuals.
Application information:
Initial approach: Letter
Deadline(s): None
Officers and Directors:* Richard D. Helppie, Jr.,* Pres.; Leslie S. Helppie,* V.P.; Susan M. Synor,* Secy.-Treas.
EIN: 383374687
Selected grants: The following grants are a representative sample of this grantmaker's funding activity:
$66,550 to Lutheran Church of the Redeemer, Birmingham, MI, 2012. For Religious, Church Gift Fund.
$4,000 to Hospice of Michigan, Detroit, MI, 2012. For Health Care Assistance for People with a Terminal Illness.
$2,000 to University of Hawaii Foundation, Honolulu, HI, 2012. For assistance for the University of Hawaii and Its Students.
$500 to Autism Speaks, New York, NY, 2012. For child health advocacy.
$500 to Equest Center for Therapeutic Riding, Rockford, MI, 2012. For Equine-Based Therapy to Physically and Mentally Challenged Individuals.
$500 to Racquet Up Detroit, Detroit, MI, 2012. For Detroit Youth Through Squash and Fitness Instruction and Academic Tutoring.
$300 to Forgotten Harvest, Oak Park, MI, 2012. To Relieve Hunger in the Detroit Metropolitan Community.
$300 to Gleaners Community Food Bank, Detroit, MI, 2012. For Fight Against Hunger.
$200 to Susan G. Komen for the Cure, Dallas, TX, 2012. For general fund support.
$100 to March of Dimes Foundation, White Plains, NY, 2012. To support and Research for the Health of Babies.

4457
Here to Help Foundation ✧ ☆
P.O. Box 480
Royal Oak, MI 48068-0480
Contact: Bob Schwartz, Pres.
FAX: (248) 534-1490;
E-mail: info@heretohelpfoundation.org; Main URL: http://www.heretohelpfoundation.org

Established in 2007 in MI.
Donors: Ilene Schwartz; Leonard Schwartz.
Foundation type: Independent foundation.
Financial data (yr. ended 12/31/13): Assets, $2,116,920 (M); gifts received, $100,740; expenditures, $489,239; qualifying distributions, $465,145; giving activities include $452,271 for 375 grants to individuals (high: $2,500; low: $7).
Purpose and activities: Grant awards are based on a one-time basis to individuals who have encountered a crisis and need assistance in moving forward and being independent.
Fields of interest: Disasters, preparedness/services; Economically disadvantaged.
Type of support: Grants to individuals.
Limitations: Applications accepted. Giving to benefit residents of southeastern MI, specifically the counties of Wayne and Oakland. No grants for scholarships or tuition, student loans, summer camps, property tax bills, funeral expenses, medical and dental expenses, wheelchair-associated expenses and wheelchair ramps, driver responsibility fees, or for major home repairs.
Publications: Application guidelines.
Application information: See foundation web site for full application guidelines and requirements. Application form required.
Initial approach: Completion of online application form from a qualified advocate, including social workers, employees at charitable organizations, members of the clergy, or DHS, JET and Michigan Works employees
Deadline(s): None
Officers: Robin Schwartz, C.E.O.; Robert Schwartz, Pres.; Adam Schwartz, V.P.; Ilene Schwartz, Treas.; Citibank, N.A.
EIN: 208057969

4458
Heritage Mark Foundation ✧
P.O. Box 980
East Lansing, MI 48826-0980

Established in 1968 in MI.
Donors: David R. Foote; Frederick C. Foote; Shirley A. Foote; Kenneth J. Foote; Marnie Foote; Steven M. Foote; Lynne Foote; Cheryl F. Groenendyke; Arthur C. Litton II; Theresa M. Foote; First National Bancshares, Inc.; 1889 Bancorp, Inc.; Renaissance Charitable Foundation, Inc.; Barbara Shingleton Trust; S.M. Foote Trust Co. 1.
Foundation type: Independent foundation.
Financial data (yr. ended 12/31/13): Assets, $18,349,101 (M); gifts received, $1,146,549;

expenditures, $2,594,602; qualifying distributions, $2,506,086; giving activities include $2,505,301 for 84 grants (high: $504,000; low: $400).
Purpose and activities: Giving primarily for Christian agencies and churches, with emphasis on evangelism, and for education.
Fields of interest: Education, research; Higher education; Health care, single organization support; Human services; Economics; Public policy, research; Christian agencies & churches.
Limitations: Applications not accepted. Giving primarily in MA, MI, NM, NJ, NY and OH. No grants to individuals.
Application information: Contributes only to pre-selected organizations.
Officers: Shirley A. Foote, Chair.; Cheryl F. Groenendyke, Pres.; Frederick C. Foote, V.P.; Barbara Shingleton, V.P.; Amy A. Payne, Secy.-Treas.
Trustees: David R. Foote; Kenneth J. Foote; Steven M. Foote; Susan L. Foote; Rhonda F. Judy.
EIN: 237017100

4459
Herrick Foundation ✧
First National Bldg.
660 Woodward Ave., Ste. 2290
Detroit, MI 48226-3506 (313) 465-7733
Contact: Todd W. Herrick, Pres.

Incorporated in 1949 in MI.
Donors: Ray W. Herrick†; Hazel M. Herrick†.
Foundation type: Independent foundation.
Financial data (yr. ended 09/30/13): Assets, $158,089,052 (M); expenditures, $7,541,884; qualifying distributions, $6,463,327; giving activities include $5,958,606 for 30 grants (high: $1,000,000; low: $3,610).
Purpose and activities: Emphasis on higher education, including research grants, scholarship programs (made through college and postgraduate educational institutions, not individual scholarships), and capital funding; grants also for church support, youth, health and welfare agencies, hospitals, and libraries.
Fields of interest: Secondary school/education; Higher education; Hospitals (general); Health care; Cancer; Human services; Children/youth, services.
Type of support: General/operating support; Continuing support; Annual campaigns; Capital campaigns; Building/renovation; Equipment; Land acquisition; Endowments; Emergency funds; Program development; Professorships; Curriculum development; Scholarship funds; Research; Matching/challenge support.
Limitations: Applications accepted. Giving primarily in MI. No support for international organizations, or for domestic organizations for international programs. No grants to individuals.
Publications: Application guidelines.
Application information: Application form not required.
Initial approach: 1- to -3 page grant proposal letter
Copies of proposal: 1
Deadline(s): None
Board meeting date(s): Monthly
Final notification: By letter
Officers and Trustees:* Todd W. Herrick,* Chair., Pres. and Treas.; Kent B. Herrick,* V.P. and Exec. Dir.; Michael A. Indenbaum,* Secy.
Number of staff: 1 part-time support.
EIN: 386041517

Selected grants: The following grants are a representative sample of this grantmaker's funding activity:
$1,000,000 to Henry Ford Health System, Detroit, MI, 2012. For Neuro-Oncologic Research and Advancements.
$1,000,000 to Heritage Foundation, Washington, DC, 2012. For Political Climate Change Campaign.
$500,000 to AOPA Foundation, Frederick, MD, 2012. Toward improving general aviation safety, preserving general aviation airports, growing the pilot population, CFI academy feasibility study, learning to Fly Days and Flying Clubs.
$500,000 to Gloucester Institute, Richmond, VA, 2012. For repairs, renovation and maintenance of house, dormitories and conference rooms at Robert R. Moton Conference Center in Gloucester, VA.
$500,000 to Michigan State University, East Lansing, MI, 2012. For Michigan State University Anaerobic Digestion Research and Education Center.
$401,442 to Barbara Ann Karmanos Cancer Institute, Detroit, MI, 2012. For Scientific Research Programs.
$342,769 to University of Michigan, School of Education, Ann Arbor, MI, 2012. For Aim High-Language and Literacy Processing Program to develop model program for education of students with Asperger's Syndrome, Autism Spectrum Disorders, and Non-Verbal Learning Disorders.
$250,000 to University of Michigan, Ann Arbor, MI, 2012. For Food Allergy Center's Food Allergy Database Project.
$200,000 to Conservation Fund, Shepherdstown, WV, 2012. To conduct research to Identify the cost and Effectiveness of Three Technologies to Remove Nitrate Nitrogen from Effluents of Land-Based Closed Containment Systems.
$150,000 to Aquaculture Research Corporation, Tecumseh, MI, 2012. For general support.

4460
The Stephen L. Hickman Family Foundation ✧
2711 E. Maumee St.
Adrian, MI 49221-3534 (517) 263-5055
Contact: Sally D. Hickman, V.P. and Treas.

Established in 1997 in MI.
Donors: Sally D. Hickman; Stephen L. Hickman.
Foundation type: Independent foundation.
Financial data (yr. ended 12/31/12): Assets, $3,379,179 (M); expenditures, $452,283; qualifying distributions, $426,004; giving activities include $426,004 for grants.
Purpose and activities: Giving primarily for youth services, education and for health and human services.
Fields of interest: Arts; Education; Environment; Hospitals (general); Health care; Cancer research; Boys & girls clubs; Human services; YM/YWCAs & YM/YWHAs; Children/youth, services.
Type of support: Capital campaigns; Endowments; Scholarship funds.
Limitations: Applications accepted. Giving primarily in Adrian and Lenawee County, MI. No grants to individuals.
Application information: Application form required.
Initial approach: Letter
Deadline(s): Oct. 1
Officers: Tracy L. Hickman, Pres.; Sally D. Hickman, V.P. and Treas.; Stephanie L. Hickman-Boyse, Secy.
Trustee: Stephen L. Hickman.
EIN: 383349206

4461
Hillsdale County Community Foundation ✧
2 S. Howell St.
P.O. Box 276
Hillsdale, MI 49242-0276 (517) 439-5101
Contact: Sharon E. Bisher, Exec. Dir.
FAX: (517) 439-5109; E-mail: info@abouthccf.org; Additional e-mail: s.bisher@abouthccf.org; Main URL: http://www.abouthccf.org
Facebook: https://www.facebook.com/pages/Hillsdale-County-Community-Foundation/105456042855711

Established in 1991 in MI.
Foundation type: Community foundation.
Financial data (yr. ended 09/30/13): Assets, $13,068,166 (M); gifts received, $1,010,426; expenditures, $965,989; giving activities include $428,698 for 19+ grants (high: $140,925), and $171,401 for grants to individuals.
Purpose and activities: The foundation receives and administers funds for artistic, charitable, educational, and scientific purposes in a manner that both promotes the spirit of philanthropy and meets the needs of the people of Hillsdale County, MI.
Fields of interest: Visual arts; Performing arts; Performing arts, theater; Arts; Education, association; Education, early childhood education; Child development, education; Elementary school/education; Higher education; Libraries/library science; Education; Environment, natural resources; Environment; Animal welfare; Hospitals (general); Health care; Health organizations, association; Crime/violence prevention, youth; Crime/law enforcement; Employment; Food services; Recreation; Youth development, services; Children/youth, services; Child development, services; Family services; Residential/custodial care, hospices; Aging, centers/services; Human services; Community/economic development; Voluntarism promotion; Biology/life sciences; Economics; Leadership development; Public affairs; Aging; Economically disadvantaged.
Type of support: Scholarships—to individuals; Conferences/seminars; Publication; Seed money; Scholarship funds; In-kind gifts; Matching/challenge support.
Limitations: Applications accepted. Giving limited to Hillsdale County, MI. No support for religious or sectarian purposes. No grants to individuals (except for scholarships), or for administrative costs, new building campaigns, routine maintenance, remodeling, or capital campaigns; no loans.
Publications: Application guidelines; Annual report; Financial statement; Informational brochure (including application guidelines); Newsletter.
Application information: Visit foundation web site for application form and guidelines. Application form required.
Initial approach: Telephone or in person
Copies of proposal: 1
Deadline(s): May 1 and Nov. 1 for general grants; Apr. 1 and Nov. 1 for Kellogg YOUTH grants; and Mar. 1 for scholarships
Board meeting date(s): 1st Tues. of the month
Final notification: Within 2 months
Officers and Trustees:* David Pope,* Pres.; Jeff Lantis,* V.P.; Michelle Bianchi,* Secy.; John Barrett,* Treas.; Sharon E. Bisher, Exec. Dir.; Clint

Barrett; Branden Bisher; Pat Dillon; Jeremiah Hodshire; Les Hutchinson; Tim Raker; Don Sanderson; Bambi Somerlott; Shawn Vondra; Jason Wade; Jim Whitehill; Jay Williams.
Number of staff: 1 full-time professional; 2 part-time professional.
EIN: 383001297

4462
Hough Family Foundation ✧
32907 Bingham Ln.
Bingham Farms, MI 48025-2419
Contact: David Hough, Secy.

Established in 2007 in IL.
Donor: Richard T. Hough†.
Foundation type: Independent foundation.
Financial data (yr. ended 12/31/13): Assets, $14,747,553 (M); gifts received, $175; expenditures, $1,076,435; qualifying distributions, $1,000,684; giving activities include $965,000 for 5 grants (high: $400,000; low: $25,000).
Fields of interest: Human services.
Limitations: Applications not accepted.
Application information: Contributes only to pre-selected organizations.
Officers: William Hough, Pres.; Clyde Folley, V.P.; David R. Hough, Secy.; Pat McHenry, Treas.
Trustees: Janet Folley; Bonnie Hough.
EIN: 260176778

4463
Hudson-Webber Foundation ✧
333 W. Fort St., Ste. 1310
Detroit, MI 48226-3149
Contact: Katy Locker, V.P., Programs
FAX: (313) 963-2818; Main URL: http://www.hudson-webber.org
Grants List: http://www.hudson-webber.org/giving/past-grants

Incorporated in 1943 in MI; on Jan. 1, 1984 absorbed the Richard H. and Eloise Jenks Webber Charitable Fund, Inc., and the Eloise and Richard Webber Foundation.
Donors: Eloise Webber†; Richard Webber†; The J.L. Hudson Co.; Mary Webber Parker; and members of the Webber family.
Foundation type: Independent foundation.
Financial data (yr. ended 12/31/13): Assets, $174,906,493 (M); gifts received, $1,000,062; expenditures, $9,834,448; qualifying distributions, $8,825,501; giving activities include $7,298,194 for 80 grants (high: $900,000; low: $500), $419,209 for 101 employee matching gifts, and $91,604 for foundation-administered programs.
Purpose and activities: The foundation concentrates efforts and resources in Detroit, Michigan, and in support of projects within four missions: 1) physical revitalization; 2) economic development; 3) enhancement of major art and cultural institutions; and 4) safe communities. The foundation also provides charitable assistance to qualified J. L. Hudson Co. employees or ex-employees needing help in overcoming personal crises and misfortunes.
Fields of interest: Arts; Crime/violence prevention; Urban/community development.
Type of support: General/operating support; Continuing support; Annual campaigns; Capital campaigns; Building/renovation; Program development; Seed money; Consulting services; Program evaluation; Employee matching gifts; Matching/challenge support.
Limitations: Applications accepted. Giving primarily in the city of Detroit, MI. No support for educational institutions or neighborhood organizations (except for projects that fall within current program missions). No grants to individuals (except for J.L. Hudson Co. employees and their families), or for emergency funds, deficit financing, endowment funds, scholarships, fellowships, publications, conferences, fundraising, social events, or exhibits; no loans.
Publications: Application guidelines; Financial statement; Grants list.
Application information: See foundation's web site for additional application information. Application form not required.
Initial approach: Letter of request or proposal
Copies of proposal: 1
Deadline(s): Rolling
Board meeting date(s): May, Aug. and Dec.
Final notification: 1 week after board decision
Officers and Trustees:* Jennifer Hudson Parke,* Chair.; David O. Egner,* C.E.O. and Pres.; Amanda Van Dusen,* Secy.; David E. Meador,* Treas.; Julie Ermler, Dir., Finance and Admin.; Toby Barlow; Matthew P. Cullen; Stephen R. D'Arcy; W. Frank Fountain; Gilbert Hudson; Joseph L. Hudson, Jr.; Joseph L. Hudson IV; Reginald M. Turner, Jr.; Jean Hudson Witmer.
Number of staff: 4 full-time professional; 1 full-time support; 2 part-time support.
EIN: 386052131

4464
The Hurst Foundation ✧
675 Robinson Rd.
Jackson, MI 49203-1155 (517) 841-4886

Trust established in 1955 in MI.
Donors: Peter F. Hurst†; Elizabeth S. Hurst†.
Foundation type: Independent foundation.
Financial data (yr. ended 12/31/12): Assets, $9,437,506 (M); expenditures, $469,568; qualifying distributions, $459,000; giving activities include $459,000 for grants.
Fields of interest: Arts; Secondary school/education; Higher education; Human services; Youth, services; Community/economic development; Protestant agencies & churches.
Type of support: General/operating support; Building/renovation; Equipment; Program development; Seed money.
Limitations: Applications accepted. Giving primarily in Jackson County, MI. No grants to individuals, or for endowment funds, scholarships, fellowships, or matching gifts; no loans.
Application information: Application form required.
Initial approach: Letter
Copies of proposal: 2
Deadline(s): Oct. 1
Board meeting date(s): Dec. and as necessary
Officer: Anthony P. Hurst, Pres.
Directors: Charles Kuntzleman; Carey R. Lefere.
EIN: 386089457

4465
Bill and Bea Idema Foundation ✧
(formerly Wren Foundation)
P.O. Box 3636
Grand Rapids, MI 49501-3636
Application address: c/o Fifth Third Bank, Attn.: Joyce Versluis, 111 Lyon St. NW, MD: RMOBGG, Grand Rapids, MI 49503; tel.: (616) 653-5552

Established in 1986 in MI.
Donors: Beatrice A. Idema; William W. Idema†.
Foundation type: Independent foundation.
Financial data (yr. ended 12/31/13): Assets, $16,954,705 (M); expenditures, $1,632,744; qualifying distributions, $1,453,942; giving activities include $1,450,000 for 2 grants (high: $750,000; low: $700,000).
Purpose and activities: The Bill and Bea Idema Foundation focuses its grants primarily on funding special projects or programs in the Grand Rapids, Michigan area that are consistent with its mission: The Bill and Bea Idema Foundation exists to give expression to our traditional Christian values by supporting schools, organizations and community programs that help children and families.
Fields of interest: Zoos/zoological societies; Human services.
Type of support: General/operating support; Capital campaigns; Building/renovation; Program development; Seed money; Scholarship funds.
Limitations: Applications accepted. Giving primarily in the Grand Rapids, MI, area.
Application information:
Initial approach: Letter
Copies of proposal: 1
Deadline(s): June and Dec.
Board meeting date(s): July and Dec.
Officers: Beatrice A. Idema, Pres.; Joyce Versluis, V.P.; Jeff Power, Secy.; Lisa Sharp, Treas.
Trustee: P. Craig Welch, Jr.
EIN: 382653272
Selected grants: The following grants are a representative sample of this grantmaker's funding activity:
$30,000 to Gildas Club Grand Rapids, Grand Rapids, MI, 2011.
$5,000 to Steepletown Neighborhood Services, Grand Rapids, MI, 2011.

4466
The Isabel Foundation ✧
111 E. Court St., Ste. 3D
Flint, MI 48502-1649 (810) 767-0136
Contact: Frederick S. Kirkpatrick
FAX: (810) 767-1207; Main URL: http://www.isabel.org

Established in 1988 in MI.
Foundation type: Independent foundation.
Financial data (yr. ended 06/30/13): Assets, $62,269,675 (M); expenditures, $3,112,441; qualifying distributions, $2,769,948; giving activities include $2,664,900 for 62 grants (high: $250,000; low: $2,500).
Purpose and activities: Funding primarily for organizations dedicated to supporting or contributing to the cause of Christian Science; support also for the arts, education, and convalescent facilities.
Fields of interest: Arts; Higher education; Nursing home/convalescent facility; Recreation, camps.

Type of support: General/operating support; Continuing support; Annual campaigns; Capital campaigns; Building/renovation; Equipment; Program development.
Limitations: Applications accepted. Giving in the U.S., including but not limited to CA, CO, FL, MA, ME, MI, MO, NY, OH, PA, TX, and WA. No support for Christian Science branch churches. No grants to individuals.
Publications: Application guidelines.
Application information: Application form not required.
Initial approach: Letter of introduction (in triplicate)
Deadline(s): Mar. 1 (except for pledged or matching grants)
Final notification: Grants are primarily made in June
Officers and Trustees:* Claire Mott White,* Pres.; William S. White,* V.P.; Tiffany W. Lovett; Ridgeway H. White.
Number of staff: 2 part-time professional.
EIN: 382853004

4467
Jackson Community Foundation ✧
(formerly The Jackson County Community Foundation)
1 Jackson Sq.
100 East Michigan Ave., Ste. 308
Jackson, MI 49201-1406 (517) 787-1321
Contact: For grants: Dana Ashlock, Grant and Scholarship Coord.
FAX: (517) 787-4333; E-mail: jcf@jacksoncf.org; Grant inquiry e-mail: dashlock@jacksoncf.org; Main URL: http://www.jacksoncf.org/

Incorporated in 1948 in MI.
Foundation type: Community foundation.
Financial data (yr. ended 12/31/13): Assets, $21,860,163 (M); gifts received, $871,540; expenditures, $1,388,862; giving activities include $636,292 for 25+ grants (high: $54,069), and $159,500 for 62 grants to individuals.
Purpose and activities: The foundation seeks to improve the quality of life for the residents of Jackson County, MI.
Fields of interest: Humanities; Historic preservation/historical societies; Arts; Adult education—literacy, basic skills & GED; Education, reading; Education; Environment; Health care; Substance abuse, services; Recreation; Children/youth, services; Human services; Economic development; Community/economic development.
Type of support: Building/renovation; Capital campaigns; Consulting services; Equipment; General/operating support; Land acquisition; Matching/challenge support; Program development; Program evaluation; Scholarships—to individuals; Seed money; Technical assistance.
Limitations: Applications accepted. Giving limited to Jackson County, MI. No support for religious activities. No grants to individuals (except for scholarships), or for endowment funds, debt retirement, fellowships, publications, or conferences.
Publications: Application guidelines; Annual report (including application guidelines); Grants list; Newsletter.
Application information: Visit foundation web site for application forms, guidelines, and specific deadlines. Application form required.
Initial approach: Telephone, e-mail, or letter
Deadline(s): Varies
Board meeting date(s): Jan., Mar., May, July, Sept., and Nov.
Officers and Trustees:* Hendrik Schuur,* Chair.; Monica M. Moser,* C.E.O. and Pres.; John Butterfield; Anne E. Campau; Karen A. Chaprnka; Rick Davies; Tom Draper; Travis Fojtasek; Michael Funkhouser; H. Ronald Griffith; John Gruel; Jim Miller; Phil Moilanen; Kevin Oxley; Randy Purvis; Sarah Richmond; Cynthia A. Rider, D.M.D.; Jon Robinson; Jim Serino.
Number of staff: 2 full-time professional; 2 full-time support; 2 part-time support.
EIN: 386070739
Selected grants: The following grants are a representative sample of this grantmaker's funding activity:
$25,000 to Catholic Charities of Jackson, Jackson, MI, 2012. For Jackson County Child Advocacy Center.
$25,000 to Jackson Public Schools, Jackson, MS, 2012. For Hurst Planetarium Full Dome Immersive Theater Project.
$25,000 to United Way of Jackson County, Jackson, MI, 2012. For Energizing Education: A Cradle-to-College/Career Pipeline.
$20,000 to Legal Services of South Central Michigan, Ann Arbor, MI, 2012. For homeless prevention.
$15,000 to Allegiance Health, Jackson, MI, 2012. To enhance breastfeeding within our community.
$14,800 to Nonprofit Network, Jackson, MI, 2012. To build cultural competency within nonprofit organizations.
$10,000 to Jackson County Parks, Jackson, MI, 2012. For Inter City Trail Connector.
$7,340 to Spring Arbor University, Spring Arbor, MI, 2012. For Center for Autism Spectrum Enrichment (CASE).
$5,000 to Jackson Symphony Association, Jackson, TN, 2012. For History and Music in a Note Shell, A Community Music Tour.
$5,000 to United Way of Jackson County, Jackson, MI, 2012. For startup support.

4468
The Lloyd and Mabel Johnson Foundation ✧
10315 Grand River, Ste. 301
Brighton, MI 48116-9586

Established in 1990 in FL.
Donors: Lloyd R. Johnson‡; Mabel K. Johnson.
Foundation type: Independent foundation.
Financial data (yr. ended 09/30/13): Assets, $56,998,609 (M); expenditures, $2,820,459; qualifying distributions, $2,555,300; giving activities include $2,262,806 for 47 grants (high: $260,000; low: $695).
Purpose and activities: Giving primarily to Christian faith-based organizations.
Fields of interest: Higher education; Environment, land resources; Health care; American Red Cross; Christian agencies & churches; Children/youth; Children; Disabilities, people with; Physically disabled; Military/veterans; Economically disadvantaged.
Type of support: General/operating support; Building/renovation; Land acquisition; Debt reduction; Program development; Scholarship funds.
Limitations: Applications not accepted. Giving primarily in MI, with emphasis on southeast MI. No grants to individuals.
Publications: Financial statement; Grants list.
Application information: Contributes only to pre-selected organizations.
Board meeting date(s): 4 times per year, varies as to dates
Officer: Gordon H. Kummer, Pres.
Director: Linda Kummer.
Trustees: Catherine Kalman; Anna Miller; Daniel Miller; Karen Townsley.
Number of staff: 2 full-time professional; 1 part-time professional.
EIN: 593009032
Selected grants: The following grants are a representative sample of this grantmaker's funding activity:
$165,000 to Kids Hope USA, Zeeland, MI, 2011. For operations.

4469
The Ronda E. Stryker and William D. Johnston Foundation ✧
211 S. Rose St.
Kalamazoo, MI 49007-4713 (269) 388-9800
Contact: Lisa Thomas, Exec. Dir.
FAX: (269) 553-7248;
E-mail: info@strykerjohnstonfoundation.org; Main URL: http://www.strykerjohnstonfoundation.org/

Established in 1995 in MI.
Donors: Ronda E. Stryker; William Johnston.
Foundation type: Independent foundation.
Financial data (yr. ended 12/31/13): Assets, $3,035,479 (M); gifts received, $2,058,390; expenditures, $2,159,351; qualifying distributions, $2,103,570; giving activities include $2,082,997 for 23 grants (high: $1,000,000; low: $1,000).
Purpose and activities: The foundation focuses its grant making on organizations that demonstrate the ability to making substantial and unique progress in the following areas: the elimination of racism; empowerment of the disenfranchised; elimination of poverty; compensatory education; support of non-traditional women students; minority student education in sciences, math, and finance; elimination of sexism; elimination of discrimination on the basis of gender and sexual orientation; affordable housing initiatives; Kalamazoo based support of economic development; and enhancement support for Kalamazoo area public school programs.
Fields of interest: Arts; Higher education; Education; Human services; YM/YWCAs & YM/YWHAs; Community/economic development; Foundations (community).
Limitations: Applications accepted. Giving primarily in Kalamazoo, MI. No grants to individuals.
Application information: See web site for additional application policies. Application form not required.
Initial approach: Download application form
Copies of proposal: 5
Deadline(s): Usually Mar. 1, June 1, Sept. 1, and Dec. 1
Board meeting date(s): Quarterly, typically in Jan., Apr., July, and Oct.
Final notification: Within fourteen days of board meeting
Officers and Trustees:* Ronda E. Stryker,* Pres.; William D. Johnston,* Secy.-Treas.; Lisa Thomas,

Exec. Dir.; Anne E. Johnston; Megan M. Johnston; Michael B. Johnston.
EIN: 383224966
Selected grants: The following grants are a representative sample of this grantmaker's funding activity:
$1,000,000 to University of Northern Colorado Foundation, Greeley, CO, 2013. For general support.
$225,000 to Kalamazoo College, Kalamazoo, MI, 2013. For general support.
$200,000 to Pathfinder International, Watertown, MA, 2013. For general support.
$150,000 to Gilmore Car Museum, Hickory Corners, MI, 2013. For general support.
$150,000 to Southwest Michigan First Corporation, Kalamazoo, MI, 2013. For general support.
$60,000 to Kalamazoo County Ready 4S, Kalamazoo, MI, 2013. For general support.
$11,400 to Kalamazoo Civic Theater, Kalamazoo, MI, 2013. For general support.
$10,000 to Kalamazoo Symphony Orchestra, Kalamazoo, MI, 2013. For general support.

4470
Jubilee Foundation ✧
(formerly Herman Miller Design Foundation)
P.O. Box 75000
Detroit, MI 48275-3462

Established in 1994 in MI.
Donor: Herman Miller Inc.
Foundation type: Company-sponsored foundation.
Financial data (yr. ended 05/31/14): Assets, $2,915,619 (M); gifts received, $401,824; expenditures, $2,114,645; qualifying distributions, $2,110,050; giving activities include $2,110,050 for 203 grants (high: $180,000; low: $250).
Purpose and activities: The foundation supports community foundations and organizations involved with arts and culture, education, the environment, hunger, human services, international affairs, Christianity, neighborhood development, and economically disadvantaged people.
Fields of interest: Arts; Elementary/secondary education; Higher education; Theological school/education; Education; Environment, natural resources; Environment, water resources; Environment; Health care; Food services; Developmentally disabled, centers & services; Human services; International relief; International affairs; Community development, neighborhood development; Foundations (community); Christian agencies & churches; Economically disadvantaged.
Type of support: Scholarship funds; General/operating support.
Limitations: Applications not accepted. Giving primarily in CA, GA, and VA, with emphasis on MI. No grants to individuals.
Application information: Contributes only to pre-selected organizations.
Officers: Michael A. Volkema, Pres.; James E. Christenson, Secy.; James R. Kackley, Treas.
Directors: Mary Vermeer Andringa; Douglas D. French; Brian C. Walker.
EIN: 383003821

4471
The D. Dan and Betty Kahn Foundation ✧ ☆
(formerly Kahn Family Foundation)
8655 E. Eight Mile Rd.
Warren, MI 48089-3019
Contact: David D. Kahn, Pres.

Established in 1986 in MI.
Donor: David D. Kahn.
Foundation type: Independent foundation.
Financial data (yr. ended 03/31/13): Assets, $121,182,613 (M); gifts received, $119,696,065; expenditures, $2,399,431; qualifying distributions, $2,367,578; giving activities include $2,337,000 for 8 grants (high: $1,430,000; low: $1,000).
Purpose and activities: Giving primarily for higher education as well as for Jewish organizations and Jewish federated giving programs; some funding for children and social services.
Fields of interest: Higher education; Education; Human services; Children/youth, services; Jewish federated giving programs; Jewish agencies & synagogues.
Type of support: General/operating support; Building/renovation; Scholarship funds.
Limitations: Applications not accepted. Giving primarily in MI and NY. No grants to individuals.
Application information: Contributes only to pre-selected organizations.
Officers and Trustees:* Lawrence A. Wolfe,* Pres.; Patrice Aaron,* V.P.; Arthur Weiss, Secy.-Treas.
EIN: 382712361

4472
Kalamazoo Community Foundation ✧
(formerly Kalamazoo Foundation)
402 E. Michigan Ave.
Kalamazoo, MI 49007-3888 (269) 381-4416
Contact: For grants: Kari Benjamin, Community Investment Asst.
FAX: (269) 381-3146; E-mail: info@kalfound.org; Main URL: http://www.kalfound.org
Facebook: https://www.facebook.com/kalfound
LinkedIn: http://www.linkedin.com/company/kalfound
Twitter: http://twitter.com/kalfound

Established in 1925; incorporated in 1930 in MI.
Foundation type: Community foundation.
Financial data (yr. ended 12/31/13): Assets, $434,375,359 (M); gifts received, $47,550,262; expenditures, $19,209,274; giving activities include $15,191,135 for grants.
Purpose and activities: The foundation is dedicated to enhancing the spirit of the community and quality of life in the greater Kalamazoo area through its stewardship of permanently endowed funds. Primary areas of giving include: 1) economic development; 2) early childhood learning and school readiness; 3) youth development; and 4) individuals and families. Grants largely for capital purposes and innovative programs.
Fields of interest: Education; Environment; Health care; Employment; Housing/shelter, development; Youth development; Family services; Economic development; Community/economic development.
Type of support: General/operating support; Equipment; Emergency funds; Program development; Seed money; Scholarship funds; Technical assistance; Program-related investments/loans; Employee matching gifts; Scholarships—to individuals; Matching/challenge support; Mission-related investments/loans.
Limitations: Applications accepted. Giving generally limited to Kalamazoo County, MI. No support for for-profit business development projects. No grants to individuals (except for scholarships), or for private land purchases, private home purchases, or endowment funds.
Publications: Application guidelines; Annual report; Financial statement; Grants list; Informational brochure; Informational brochure (including application guidelines); Newsletter; Quarterly report.
Application information: Visit foundation web site for more information and online application. Application form required.
Initial approach: Submit Letter of Inquiry
Copies of proposal: 1
Deadline(s): Mar. 10, Sept. 3, and Dec. 4 for Letters of Inquiry for requests over $10,000
Board meeting date(s): Jan., Mar., May, June, July, Sept., Nov., and Dec.
Final notification: 10 weeks
Officers and Trustees:* Si Johnson,* Chair.; Frank Sardone,* Vice-Chair.; Carrie Pickett-Erway, C.E.O. and Pres.; Joanna Donnelly Dales, V.P., Donor Rels.; Susan Springgate, V.P., Finance and Admin.; Suprotik Stotz-Ghosh, V.P., Community Investment; Karen Racette, Cont.; James Escamilla; Barbara L. James; Amy Upjohn; Hon. Carolyn H. Williams; Dr. Eileen B. Wilson-Oyelaran.
Custodian Bank: PNC Bank, N.A.
Number of staff: 17 full-time professional; 3 part-time professional; 3 full-time support; 3 part-time support.
EIN: 383333202
Selected grants: The following grants are a representative sample of this grantmaker's funding activity:
$436,273 to Kalamazoo Public Schools, Kalamazoo, MI, 2012.
$400,000 to Michigan Commission for the Blind, Training Center, Kalamazoo, MI, 2012.
$250,000 to United Way, Greater Kalamazoo, Kalamazoo, MI, 2012.
$180,000 to Local Initiatives Support Corporation, Kalamazoo, MI, 2012.
$125,000 to Community Homeworks, Kalamazoo, MI, 2012.
$100,000 to University of Michigan Hospitals and Health System, Depression Center, Ann Arbor, MI, 2012.
$5,000 to Housing Resources, Kalamazoo, MI, 2012.
$5,000 to United Way, Greater Kalamazoo, Kalamazoo, MI, 2012.
$3,500 to Comstock Community Center, Comstock, MI, 2012.
$2,500 to Western Michigan University Foundation, Kalamazoo, MI, 2012.

4473
Kellogg Company 25-Year Employees Fund, Inc. ✧
c/o Kellogg Co.
1 Kellogg Sq.
P.O. Box 3599
Battle Creek, MI 49016-3599 (269) 961-2000
Contact: Timothy S. Knowlton, Co-Pres.

Established in 1944 in MI.
Donor: W.K. Kellogg†.
Foundation type: Company-sponsored foundation.

Financial data (yr. ended 12/31/12): Assets, $64,524,389 (M); expenditures, $3,929,759; qualifying distributions, $3,898,492; giving activities include $2,400,000 for 1 grant, and $1,219,544 for 165 grants to individuals (high: $36,529; low: $189).
Purpose and activities: The fund supports retiree associations and awards grants for living and medical expenses to current and former 25-year employees and the dependents of 25-year employees of Kellogg.
Fields of interest: Zoos/zoological societies; Food banks; Community/economic development; United Ways and Federated Giving Programs; Economically disadvantaged.
International interests: Australia; Canada; Mexico; United Kingdom.
Type of support: Emergency funds; Grants to individuals.
Limitations: Applications not accepted. Giving primarily in areas of company operations, with emphasis on Battle Creek, MI; giving also in Australia, Canada, England, Mexico, and the United Kingdom. No grants to individuals (except for employee-related funds).
Application information: Applicants must be employees or dependents of employees at Kellogg or a Kellogg subsidiary for at least 25 years.
Board meeting date(s): Jan., Apr., July, and Oct.
Officers and Directors:* Margaret Bath, Co-Pres.; Timothy S. Knowlton,* Co-Pres.; Ed Rector, V.P.; Linda Fields, Secy.; Joel Vanderkooi, Treas.; Jodi Gibson, Exec. Dir.; Ronald L. Dissinger; Gustavo Fernandez; Sammie Long.
Number of staff: 1 full-time support.
EIN: 386039770

4474
W. K. Kellogg Foundation

1 Michigan Ave. E.
Battle Creek, MI 49017-4005 (269) 968-1611
Main URL: http://www.wkkf.org
America Healing: https://www.facebook.com/americahealing
Blog: http://blog.wkkf.org
Facebook: https://www.facebook.com/WKKelloggFoundation
Food & Community: https://www.facebook.com/foodandcommunity
GR8by8 - For Education and Learning
Grantees: http://www.facebook.com/GR8by8
Grants Database: http://www.wkkf.org/grants
Knowledge Center: http://www.racialequityresourceguide.org/index.cfm
Knowledge Center: http://www.wkkf.org/resource-directory
RSS Feed: http://www.wkkf.org/shared/syndication/rss/news-and-media-rss
Twitter: http://www.twitter.com/WK_Kellogg_Fdn
W.K. Kellogg Foundation's Philanthropy Promise: http://www.ncrp.org/philanthropys-promise/who
YouTube: http://www.youtube.com/KelloggFoundation
Fellowship application URL: http://www.wkkf.org/leadership

Incorporated in 1930 in MI.
Donors: W.K. Kellogg†; W.K. Kellogg Foundation Trust; Carrie Staines Kellogg Trust.
Foundation type: Independent foundation.
Financial data (yr. ended 08/31/14): Assets, $8,621,183,526 (M); expenditures, $387,923,060; qualifying distributions, $294,891,874; giving activities include $294,891,874 for grants.
Purpose and activities: The W.K. Kellogg Foundation supports children, families, and communities as they strengthen and create conditions that propel vulnerable children to achieve success as individuals and as contributors to the larger community and society. The foundation's work is carried out by partners and programs that help it achieve its three organizational goals and embody its commitments to community and civic engagement, and to racial equity. The three goals are: 1) Educated kids: Success by third grade. Increase the number of children who are reading-and-math proficient by third grade; 2) Healthy Kids: Healthy birth weight and optimal development. Increase the number of children born at a healthy birth weight and who receive the care and healthy food they need for optimal development; and 3) Secure Families: Children and families at 200 percent above poverty. Increase the number of children and families living at least 200 percent above the poverty level.
Fields of interest: Education, early childhood education; Elementary school/education; Secondary school/education; Education; Health care, reform; Health care; Health organizations, association; Agriculture; Agriculture/food; Youth development, services; Youth, services; Minorities/immigrants, centers/services; Community development, neighborhood development; Rural development; Community/economic development; Voluntarism promotion; Leadership development; Infants/toddlers; Children/youth; Children; Youth; Minorities; Asians/Pacific Islanders; African Americans/Blacks; Hispanics/Latinos; Native Americans/American Indians; Indigenous peoples; Single parents; Immigrants/refugees; Economically disadvantaged.
International interests: Brazil; Haiti; Mexico; Southern Africa.
Type of support: Fellowships; General/operating support; Program development; Seed money; Technical assistance; Program evaluation; Program-related investments/loans; Employee matching gifts; Matching/challenge support; Mission-related investments/loans.
Limitations: Applications accepted. Giving primarily in the U.S., with emphases on Michigan, Mississippi, New Mexico and New Orleans, LA, funding also for programs in Mexico, Haiti, northeastern Brazil and southern Africa. No support for religious purposes or for capital facilities. No grants to individuals (except for fellowship), or for scholarships, endowment funds, development campaigns, films, equipment, publications, conferences, or radio and television programs unless they are an integral part of a project already being funded; no grants for operating budgets.
Publications: Annual report; Financial statement; Grants list.
Application information: The foundation requires all proposals to be submitted online via its website. No funds directly to individuals. Funding is limited to the United States (with priority funding in Michigan, Mississippi, New Mexico and New Orleans), two micro-regions in southern Mexico and two micro-regions in Haiti. Unsolicited proposals are not currently being accepted for the southern Africa and northeastern Brazil. In general, it does not provide funding for operational phases of established programs, capital requests (which includes the construction, purchase, renovation, and/or furnishing of facilities), equipment, conferences and workshops, scholarships or tuition assistance, films, television and/or radio programs, endowments, development campaigns, or research/studies unless they are an integral part of a larger program budget being considered for funding. Application form required.
Initial approach: Online submission is required. For additional questions, contact the Central Proposal Processing office at (269) 969-2329
Copies of proposal: 1
Deadline(s): None
Board meeting date(s): Monthly
Final notification: 45 days
Officers and Trustees:* Bobby Moser,* Chair.; La June Montgomery-Tabron, C.E.O. and Pres.; Linh C. Nguyen, C.O.O.; Ross Comstock, V.P., Technology and Information Systems; Donald G. Williamson, V.P., Finance and Treas.; Joel R. Wittenberg, V.P. and C.I.O.; Gail C. Christopher, V.P., Policy and Sr. Advisor; Joanne K. Krell, V.P., Comms.; Dianna Langenburg, V.P., Talent and HR; James E. McHale, V.P., Prog. Strategy; Carla D. Thompson, V.P., Prog. Strategy; Joseph Scantlebur, V.P., Prog. Strategy; Cindy Smith, V.P., Integrated Services; Alandra Washington, V.P., Quality and Organizational Effectiveness; Barbara Ferrer, Chief Strategy Off.; Kathryn A. Kreckle, General Counsel and Corp. Secy.; Celeste A. Clark; Roderick D. Gillum; Fred P. Keller; Hanmin Liu; Cynthia H. Milligan; Ramon Murguia; Joseph M. Stewart; Richard M. Tsoumas.
Number of staff: 126 full-time professional; 60 full-time support.
EIN: 381359264
Selected grants: The following grants are a representative sample of this grantmaker's funding activity:
$4,000,000 to Education Achievement Authority of Michigan, Detroit, MI, 2013. To improve the college, career and work readiness of the lowest performing schools in Michigan by developing a statewide system that transforms low performing schools into stable, financially responsible public schools, payable over 3.00 years.
$3,850,000 to Public Health Solutions, New York, NY, 2013. To support the momentum to leverage procurement through regional food labs and a national procurement strategy to benefit vulnerable children participating in free or reduced lunch programs, payable over 4.00 years.
$3,150,000 to HealthConnect One, Chicago, IL, 2013. To expand community-based doula and breastfeeding peer counselor programs in four sites, including Michigan and New Mexico, and build the field through expanding national networks, payable over 5.00 years.
$2,804,241 to Baoba-Fund for Racial Equity, Recife, Brazil, 2013. To propel the Baoba Fund to self-sustainability by consolidating the Fund's institutional and operational planning and increasing staff performance and achievements, payable over 3.75 years.
$2,000,000 to Battle Creek Unlimited, Battle Creek, MI, 2013. To enable the organization to achieve its mission of facilitating regional wealth creation through human, economic and community development by providing general operating support, payable over 2.00 years.
$1,800,000 to Los Alamos National Laboratory Foundation, Espanola, NM, 2013. To meet the needs of first-time New Mexican families in McKinley and San Juan counties by establishing the First Born Program as a unique parent education and home visiting program, payable over 3.00 years.

$200,000 to Harvard University, Cambridge, MA, 2013. To support and strengthen community-based efforts to address the early roots of racial/ethnic disparities in health, payable over 3.00 years.
$200,000 to Womens Foundation for a Greater Memphis, Memphis, TN, 2013. To strengthen two-generation approaches and improve early childhood education for mixed-income public housing families, by developing a multi-sector early childhood education framework.
$150,000 to STEPS Coalition, Biloxi, MS, 2013. To improve achievement of young males of color through increased family economic security, wrap-around case management, solutions-focused need assessments, health policy advocacy and racial healing activities, payable over 2.00 years.
$100,000 to Mississippians Engaged in Greener Agriculture, Shelby, MS, 2013. To inform youth on proper planting and harvesting practices, promote healthy food preparation and consumption and introduce economic development opportunities for farmers through educational mentoring/outreach program.

4475
Kellogg's Corporate Citizenship Fund ✧
1 Kellogg Sq.
Battle Creek, MI 49016-3599 (269) 961-2867
Contact: Linda Fields, Secy.
E-mail: linda.fields@kelloggs.com; Additional e-mail: corporateresponsibility@kellogg.com; Main URL: http://crr.kelloggcompany.com/en_US/corporate-responsibility/community.html

Established in 1994 in MI.
Donor: Kellogg Co.
Foundation type: Company-sponsored foundation.
Financial data (yr. ended 12/31/13): Assets, $24,344,057 (M); gifts received, $401,374; expenditures, $8,898,261; qualifying distributions, $8,873,938; giving activities include $7,320,180 for 440 grants (high: $1,050,000; low: $100), and $401,374 for grants to individuals.
Purpose and activities: The fund supports food banks and community foundations and organizations involved with arts and culture, education, fitness and health, hunger, nutrition, athletics, and human services.
Fields of interest: Arts; Elementary/secondary education; Higher education; Education; Public health, obesity; Public health, physical fitness; Health care; Food services; Food banks; Nutrition; Disasters, preparedness/services; Athletics/sports, amateur leagues; Athletics/sports, water sports; American Red Cross; YM/YWCAs & YM/YWHAs; Children/youth, services; Human services; Foundations (community); United Ways and Federated Giving Programs.
Type of support: General/operating support; Building/renovation; Program development; Scholarship funds; Research; Technical assistance; Employee volunteer services; Employee matching gifts.
Limitations: Applications not accepted. Giving primarily in areas of company operations in CA, Washington, DC, IL, PA, and TX, with emphasis on Battle Creek, MI; some giving also in Australia, Canada, and the United Kingdom.
Application information: The foundation practices an invitation only process for giving.
Officers and Directors:* Kris Charles, Pres.; Gary H. Pilnick, V.P.; Linda Fields, Secy.; Janice L. Perkins,* Treas.; Jodi Bosley,* Exec. Dir.; Brigette Schmidt Gwyn; Paul Norman; Doug Vandevelde; Mark Wagner.
EIN: 383167772
Selected grants: The following grants are a representative sample of this grantmaker's funding activity:
$3,565,572 to Truist, Chicago, IL, 2012.
$3,398,057 to Truist, Chicago, IL, 2013.
$1,050,000 to Community Foundation for Greater Manchester, Manchester, England, 2013.
$495,000 to Resource Foundation, New York, NY, 2012.
$400,000 to Resource Foundation, New York, NY, 2013.
$350,000 to Action for Healthy Kids, Chicago, IL, 2012.
$336,000 to ASA, Loughborough, England, 2012.
$300,000 to Healthy Weight Commitment Foundation, Washington, DC, 2012. For Nutrition research.
$275,000 to Action for Healthy Kids, Chicago, IL, 2013.
$275,000 to Action for Healthy Kids, Chicago, IL, 2013.
$254,500 to Global FoodBanking Network, Chicago, IL, 2012.
$250,000 to American Red Cross National Headquarters, Washington, DC, 2012. For disaster relief.
$250,000 to Share Our Strength, Washington, DC, 2013.
$200,000 to Food Research and Action Center, Washington, DC, 2013.
$110,000 to Global FoodBanking Network, Chicago, IL, 2013.
$100,000 to CARE, Washington, DC, 2013. For disaster relief.
$50,000 to Food Research and Action Center, Washington, DC, 2013.
$50,000 to United Way of Quinte, Belleville, Canada, 2012.
$20,000 to Bentonville Youth Baseball, Bentonville, AR, 2012.

4476
Edward M. & Henrietta M. Knabusch Charitable Trust 2 ✧
c/o Monroe Bank Trust
102 E. Front St.
Monroe, MI 48161-2162 (734) 242-2068
Contact: Andrew M. Weisenburger

Established in 1995 in MI.
Donor: Edward M. Knabusch Marital Trust.
Foundation type: Independent foundation.
Financial data (yr. ended 12/31/13): Assets, $6,570,774 (M); expenditures, $563,954; qualifying distributions, $537,866; giving activities include $525,000 for 25 grants (high: $50,000; low: $2,500).
Fields of interest: Health care; Human services.
Limitations: Applications accepted. Giving primarily in Monroe, MI. No grants to individuals.
Application information: Application form not required.
Initial approach: Proposal
Deadline(s): None
Trustees: Charles T. Knabusch, Jr.; John F. Weaver; Gregory D. White.
EIN: 386643328
Selected grants: The following grants are a representative sample of this grantmaker's funding activity:
$8,000 to Boy Scouts of America, Ann Arbor, MI, 2011.

4477
James A. and Faith Knight Foundation ✧
180 Little Lake Dr., Ste. 6B
Ann Arbor, MI 48103-6219 (734) 769-5653
Contact: Carol Knight-Drain, Pres. and Treas.
FAX: (734) 769-8383;
E-mail: info@knightfoundationmi.org; E-mail for Carol Knight-Drain: carol@KnightFoundationMI.org; Main URL: http://www.knightfoundationmi.org

Established in 1999 in MI.
Donor: James A. Knight Trust.
Foundation type: Independent foundation.
Financial data (yr. ended 12/31/12): Assets, $14,517,201 (M); expenditures, $881,054; qualifying distributions, $753,099; giving activities include $702,516 for 36 grants (high: $44,000; low: $7,500).
Purpose and activities: Primarily serving Jackson and Washtenaw counties, Michigan, the foundation is dedicated to improving communities by providing grant support to qualified nonprofit organizations including, but not limited to, those that address the needs of women and girls, animals and the natural world, and internal capacity. Giving primarily for human services, including a neighborhood center, women's organizations, and family services; support also for nonprofit management, the United Way, housing, the arts, education, and environmental conservation.
Fields of interest: Arts; Adult education—literacy, basic skills & GED; Environment, natural resources; Housing/shelter, development; Human services; Family services; Women, centers/services; Nonprofit management; Women; Girls; Young adults, female.
Type of support: Building/renovation; Capital campaigns; Debt reduction; General/operating support; Management development/capacity building; Program development.
Limitations: Applications accepted. Giving limited to MI, with emphasis on Jackson and Washtenaw counties. No support for religious or political organizations. No grants to individuals, or for conferences or special events, or for annual campaigns.
Publications: Application guidelines; Grants list; Occasional report; Program policy statement.
Application information: All applicants are encouraged to submit applications online using the Community Grants online system at http://www.communitygrants.org. If applicant does not have access to a computer, applicant can mail application (three copies plus one copy of attachments). Complete application guidelines available on foundation web site. Application form required.
Initial approach: Online application
Copies of proposal: 3
Deadline(s): See foundation web site for current deadlines
Board meeting date(s): 10 times per year
Officers: Carol Knight-Drain, Pres. and Treas.; Scott Drain, Secy.
Directors: Christopher Ballard.
Number of staff: 1 part-time professional; 1 part-time support.
EIN: 383465904

Selected grants: The following grants are a representative sample of this grantmaker's funding activity:
$44,000 to Humane Society of Huron Valley, Ann Arbor, MI, 2012. To Cultivate Compassion and Respect Toward Living Beings By Giving Children the Knowledge and Tools Needed to Make Choices That Foster a Humane Life for All.
$40,000 to Peace Neighborhood Center, Ann Arbor, MI, 2012. For Supportive Services to the Women and Young Girls of the Population It Serves.
$30,000 to Washtenaw Housing Alliance, Ann Arbor, MI, 2012. To Move the Implementation of the Next Phase of the Blueprint to End Homelessness.
$28,700 to Stewardship Network, Ann Arbor, MI, 2012. To Develop and Implement New Capacity Building Services to Conserve the Diversity Ecosystems and Educate Citizens About the Importance of Ecological Communities.
$25,000 to 826 Michigan, Ann Arbor, MI, 2012. To Fund Increased Staff and Develop Strongest Possible Tutorial Programs for Students and Local Schools in Need.
$25,000 to Girls Group, Ann Arbor, MI, 2012. To Ensure Sustainability of Program By Having a Paid Part-Time Program Director and Paid Full- Time Education Director.
$25,000 to Nonprofit Network, Jackson, MI, 2012. For Building Cultural Competency Within Nonprofit Organizations.
$20,000 to Michigan Shakespeare Festival, Jackson, MI, 2012. For the Operating Expenses to Improve Effectiveness, Audience and Marketing Development While Increasing Funding.
$18,955 to Jackson Friendly Home, Jackson, MI, 2012. For and Install Security System to Monitor Building for the Safety Or Residents, Staff, Visitors and Stakeholders.
$18,860 to Center for Family Health, Jackson, MI, 2012. To Assist in Funding a New Multi-Faceted Model of Group Care for Their Pregnant Patients.

4478
The Korth Family Foundation, Inc. ✧ ☆

P.O. Box 468
Ada, MI 49301-0468

Established in 1997 in FL.
Donors: James E. Korth; Valerie Korth.
Foundation type: Independent foundation.
Financial data (yr. ended 12/31/13): Assets, $5,942,122 (M); expenditures, $563,717; qualifying distributions, $552,141; giving activities include $552,141 for 16 grants (high: $365,337; low: $1,304).
Fields of interest: Higher education; Environment, land resources; Animal welfare; Human services; Religion.
Limitations: Applications not accepted. Giving primarily in FL. No grants to individuals.
Application information: Unsolicited requests for funds not accepted.
Officers and Directors:* Thomas Korth,* Pres.; Valerie Korth,* V.P. and Secy.; Colleen Korth; James Korth; Paul Korth; Robin Korth.
EIN: 650737345
Selected grants: The following grants are a representative sample of this grantmaker's funding activity:
$10,000 to Island Dolphin Care, Key Largo, FL, 2012. For General Contribution to Charity.

4479
The Kresge Foundation ✧

3215 W. Big Beaver Rd.
Troy, MI 48084-2818 (248) 643-9630
Contact: Rip Rapson, C.E.O. and Pres.
FAX: (248) 643-0588; E-mail: info@kresge.org; Main URL: http://kresge.org/
E-Newsletter: http://kresge.org/subscribe?quicktabs_1=0#quicktabs-1
Facebook: http://www.facebook.com/TheKresgeFoundation
Grantee Perception Survey: http://www.kresge.org/sites/default/files/Kresge%202011%20Grantee%20Perception%20Report%20FINAL%2020120305.pdf
Grants Database: http://maps.foundationcenter.org/grantmakers/index.php?gmkey=KRES002
Knowledge Center: http://www.kresge.org/library
Kresge Blog: http://www.kresge.org/kresge-blog
RSS Feed: http://kresge.org/subscribe?quicktabs_1=0#quicktabs-1
Twitter: https://twitter.com/kresgefdn
YouTube: http://www.youtube.com/user/TheKresgeFoundation

Incorporated in 1924 in MI.
Donor: Sebastian S. Kresge†.
Foundation type: Independent foundation.
Financial data (yr. ended 12/31/13): Assets, $3,543,405,167 (M); expenditures, $167,102,337; qualifying distributions, $162,742,127; giving activities include $128,241,663 for 598 grants (high: $6,000,000; low: $5,000), $1,942,164 for 760 employee matching gifts, and $15,946,298 for 10 loans/program-related investments (high: $5,000,000; low: $400,000).
Purpose and activities: The foundation seeks to strengthen nonprofit organizations by catalyzing their growth, connecting them to their stake holders, and challenging greater support through grants. The foundation believes that strong, sustainable, high capacity organizations are positioned to achieve their missions and strengthen communities. Grants are awarded to nonprofit organizations operating in the fields of education, health and long-term care, human services, arts and humanities, public affairs, and science, nature, and the environment.
Fields of interest: Arts, artist's services; Arts; Higher education; Environment, public policy; Environment, government agencies; Environment, natural resources; Environment, energy; Environment; Health care; Human services; Community/economic development; Public policy, research; Economically disadvantaged.
Type of support: Employee matching gifts; General/operating support; Program development; Program-related investments/loans; Research; Technical assistance.
Limitations: Applications accepted. Giving on a national basis with emphasis on Detroit, MI, as well as some international funding. No support for religious organizations, (unless applicant is operated by a religious organization and it serves secular needs and has financial and governing autonomy separate from the parent organization with space formally dedicated to its programs) private foundations, or elementary and secondary schools (unless they predominantly serve individuals with physical and/or developmental disabilities). No grants to individuals, or for debt retirement, projects that are already substantially completed, minor equipment purchases, or for constructing buildings for worship services.
Publications: Annual report; Financial statement; Grants list; Informational brochure.
Application information: See foundation web site for more application information for each program. Application procedures vary for each foundation program area. See foundation web site for information on its Social Investment Practice. Application form required.
Initial approach: Online submission of proposal. Some grant opportunities are by invitation only.
Copies of proposal: 1
Deadline(s): Announced when grant opportunities open
Board meeting date(s): Mar., June, Sept. and Dec.
Final notification: Generally within 10 to 12 weeks of the submission date
Officers and Trustees:* Elaine D. Rosen,* Chair.; Rip Rapson,* C.E.O. and Pres.; Amy B. Coleman, V.P. and C.F.O.; Robert J. Manilla, V.P. and C.I.O.; Sheryl Madden, Cont.; James L. Bildner; Lee C. Bollinger; Phillip L. Clay; Steven K. Hamp; Paul C. Hillegonds; Irene Y. Hirano; Cynthia L. Kresge; Maria Otero; Nancy M. Schlichting.
Number of staff: 23 full-time professional.
EIN: 381359217
Selected grants: The following grants are a representative sample of this grantmaker's funding activity:
$5,000,000 to Community Foundation for Southeast Michigan, Detroit, MI, 2013. For The New Economy Initiative, payable over 4.00 years.
$5,000,000 to Nonprofit Finance Fund, ArtPlace, New York, NY, 2013. For ArtPlace America Funder Collaborative, payable over 2.00 years.
$2,250,000 to Nemours Foundation, Nemours Health and Prevention Services, Jacksonville, FL, 2013. For project, Accelerating Population Health Innovation for Families and Communities, payable over 3.00 years.
$1,500,000 to Community Foundation for Southeast Michigan, Detroit, MI, 2013. For Detroit Early Childhood Innovation Fund, payable over 3.00 years.
$900,000 to Institute for Sustainable Communities, Montpelier, VT, 2013. To advance and accelerate urban climate and sustainability solutions in the United States, payable over 2.00 years.
$300,000 to Lawrence Technological University, Southfield, MI, 2013. For Detroit Center for Design + Technology, payable over 2.00 years.
$250,000 to Innovation Network for Communities, Tamworth, NH, 2013. For Carbon Neutral City Network.
$250,000 to MDRC, New York, NY, 2013. For Aid Like a Paycheck, program to help low-income college students achieve academic success. ALAP is based on the idea that after tuition and fees have been paid to the college, disburse remaining financial aid to students every other week, like a paycheck, rather than in one or two lump sums., payable over 1.50 years.
$213,000 to Detroit Economic Growth Association, Detroit, MI, 2013. For Detroit Blight Authority.
$180,000 to University of Southern California, Los Angeles, CA, 2013. To translate health impacts of ports and goods movement, payable over 2.00 years.

4480
The Lachimi Foundation ✧
3270 W. Big Beaver Rd.
Troy, MI 48084-2901

Established in 1998 in MI.
Donors: Madhava G. Reddy; HTC Global Services Inc.
Foundation type: Independent foundation.
Financial data (yr. ended 12/31/13): Assets, $10,119,798 (M); gifts received, $4,300,000; expenditures, $3,044,839; qualifying distributions, $3,000,000; giving activities include $3,000,000 for 1 grant.
Purpose and activities: Giving primarily for the education and enhancement of knowledge and spirituality.
Fields of interest: Human services, mind/body enrichment; Spirituality.
Limitations: Applications not accepted. Giving primarily in Chennai, India; some giving also in MI. No grants to individuals.
Application information: Contributes only to pre-selected organizations.
Officer: Madhava G. Reddy, Pres.
Directors: Narasimhachary Mudumby; Sobha Reddy.
EIN: 383429963

4481
La-Z-Boy Foundation ✧
(formerly La-Z-Boy Chair Foundation)
1284 N. Telegraph Rd.
Monroe, MI 48162-3390 (734) 242-1444
Contact: Donald E. Blohm, Admin.

Incorporated in 1953 in MI.
Donors: La-Z-Boy Chair Co.; La-Z-Boy Inc.; E. M. Knabusch†; Edwin J. Shoemaker†; H. F. Gertz†.
Foundation type: Company-sponsored foundation.
Financial data (yr. ended 12/31/12): Assets, $20,031,134 (M); expenditures, $1,167,493; qualifying distributions, $1,058,850; giving activities include $1,043,450 for 98 grants (high: $125,000; low: $1,500).
Purpose and activities: The foundation supports organizations involved with education, health, human services, and government and public administration. Support is given primarily in areas of company operations.
Fields of interest: Education; Health care; Human services; United Ways and Federated Giving Programs; Government/public administration.
Type of support: General/operating support; Building/renovation.
Limitations: Applications accepted. Giving primarily in areas of company operations in Siloam Springs, AR, Redlands, CA, Monroe, MI, Neosho, MO, Newton and Saltillo, MS, Hudson, Lenoir, and Taylorsville, NC, Dayton and New Tazewell, TN. No support for religious or political organizations. No grants to individuals, or for travel or conferences, or start-up needs; no loans.
Publications: Application guidelines; Annual report (including application guidelines).
Application information: Application form not required.
Initial approach: Proposal
Copies of proposal: 1
Deadline(s): Mar. 1, June 1, Sept. 1, and Dec. 1
Board meeting date(s): Mar., June, Sept., and Dec.
Officers: June E. Knabush-Taylor, Pres.; Marvin J. Bauman, Secy.; Donald E. Blohm, Admin.
Number of staff: 1 part-time support.
EIN: 386087673
Selected grants: The following grants are a representative sample of this grantmaker's funding activity:
$50,000 to United Way, Rhea County, Dayton, TN, 2012.
$45,000 to American Red Cross, Monroe, MI, 2012.
$45,000 to United Way of Monroe County, Monroe, MI, 2012.
$35,000 to Neosho United Fund, Neosho, MO, 2012.
$30,000 to Salvation Army of Monroe, Monroe, MI, 2012.
$25,000 to Newton United Givers Fund, Newton, MS, 2012.
$25,000 to United Way of Northeast Mississippi, Tupelo, MS, 2012.

4482
Lear Corporation Charitable Foundation ✧
21557 Telegraph Rd.
Southfield, MI 48033-4248

Established in 2003 in MI.
Donor: Lear Corp.
Foundation type: Company-sponsored foundation.
Financial data (yr. ended 12/31/13): Assets, $8,801,098 (M); gifts received, $4,500,000; expenditures, $2,259,574; qualifying distributions, $2,252,901; giving activities include $2,252,901 for 16 grants (high: $570,726; low: $7,500).
Purpose and activities: The foundation supports organizations involved with arts and culture, education, youth development, and human services.
Fields of interest: Museums (science/technology); Performing arts, orchestras; Arts; Higher education; Education; Boy scouts; Girl scouts; Human services; United Ways and Federated Giving Programs.
Type of support: Scholarship funds; General/operating support; Program development.
Limitations: Applications not accepted. Giving primarily in MI, with emphasis on Detroit.
Application information: Contributes only to pre-selected organizations.
Officers: Mathew J. Simoncini, Pres.; William P. McLaughlin, V.P.; Dave Mullin, V.P.; Mel Stephens, V.P.; Terrence B. Larkin, Secy.; Shari L. Burgess, Treas.
EIN: 200302085

4483
The Legion Foundation ✧
1750 S. Telegraph Rd., Ste. 301
Bloomfield Hills, MI 48302-0179 (248) 253-1100
Contact: James E. Mulvoy Esq., Pres.
FAX: (248) 253-1142;
E-mail: mulvoy@thelegionfoundation.org; Main URL: http://www.thelegionfoundation.org/Pages/default.aspx

Established in 1997 in MI.
Donors: The Thewes Trust; The TT Trust; The Thewes Charitable Annuity Lead Trust.
Foundation type: Independent foundation.
Financial data (yr. ended 12/31/12): Assets, $9,574,084 (M); expenditures, $1,364,119; qualifying distributions, $1,121,124; giving activities include $1,121,124 for grants.
Purpose and activities: Giving for 1) the development and administration of religious, educational, and/or charitable programs to foster and promote public awareness and adoption of the moral and ethical principles of Christian religions, with special emphasis on supporting the Roman Catholic Church and its members; 2) the distribution of financial support to qualified individuals to promote their physical and spiritual development in order to facilitate and encourage the study and maintenance of their Christian faith in the secular world, with preference given to Roman Catholics for such purposes; and 3) the distribution of financial support to other qualifying organizations engaged in similar work.
Fields of interest: Education; Christian agencies & churches; Catholic agencies & churches.
Type of support: General/operating support; Scholarships—to individuals.
Application information: Application forms available on foundation web site. Scholarships will be paid directly to the educational institution. Application form required.
Initial approach: Send application form via U.S. mail or fax
Deadline(s): None, for grants; June 30 for scholarships
Officers: James E. Mulvoy, Pres.; Maree R. Mulvoy, V.P.; William C. Hanson, Secy.
EIN: 383330588

4484
Leighton-Oare Foundation, Inc. ✧
1999 Morris Ave.
Niles, MI 49120-8620
Contact: Nancy O. Butler, Pres.
E-mail: robrown@butlerfamilyent.com

Incorporated in 1955 in IN.
Donors: Mary Morris Leighton; Judd C. Leighton.
Foundation type: Independent foundation.
Financial data (yr. ended 12/31/13): Assets, $21,947,731 (M); expenditures, $1,376,623; qualifying distributions, $1,322,894; giving activities include $1,269,800 for 84 grants (high: $420,000; low: $225).
Fields of interest: Performing arts; Historic preservation/historical societies; Arts; Higher education; Law school/education; Health care, fund raising/fund distribution; Health care, clinics/centers; Goodwill Industries; Athletics/sports, equestrianism.
Type of support: Matching/challenge support; Annual campaigns; General/operating support; Continuing support; Building/renovation; Endowments.
Limitations: Applications accepted. Giving primarily in IN and MI; selected interest in FL and VA. No grants to individuals.
Application information: Application form not required.
Initial approach: Letter
Copies of proposal: 1
Deadline(s): None
Board meeting date(s): Jan., Apr., July, and Oct.
Final notification: 90 to 120 days
Officers and Directors:* Nancy O. Butler,* Pres.; Ernest M. Oare,* V.P.; Carol F. Oare,* Secy.; Kevin J. Butler,* Treas.; Joseph E. Kernan.
EIN: 356034243

Selected grants: The following grants are a representative sample of this grantmaker's funding activity:
$420,000 to University of Notre Dame, Notre Dame, IN, 2012. For Stayer Center.
$10,000 to Michigan Gateway Community Foundation, Buchanan, MI, 2012. For Niles Fund.
$5,250 to Converse College, Spartanburg, SC, 2012. For Capital Project/Pell Dorm.
$5,000 to Western Michigan University Foundation, Kalamazoo, MI, 2012. For Fort St Joseph.

4485
Lenawee Community Foundation ✧
(formerly Tecumseh Community Fund Foundation)
603 N. Evans St.
P.O. Box 142
Tecumseh, MI 49286-1166 (517) 423-1729
Contact: Suann D. Hammersmith, C.E.O.
FAX: (517) 424-6579;
E-mail: shammersmith@ubat.com; Main URL: http://www.lenaweecommunityfoundation.com/
Blog: http://volunteerlenawee.wordpress.com/
Facebook: https://www.facebook.com/LenaweeCommunityFoundation
YouTube: http://www.youtube.com/lenaweefoundation

Established in 1961 in MI.
Foundation type: Community foundation.
Financial data (yr. ended 09/30/13): Assets, $19,487,789 (M); gifts received, $901,517; expenditures, $2,970,839; giving activities include $2,605,398 for 11+ grants (high: $40,000), and $74,564 for grants to individuals.
Purpose and activities: The mission of the foundation is to enhance the quality of life of the citizens of Lenawee County, Michigan by: 1) identifying and addressing current and anticipated community needs; and 2) raising, managing, and distributing funds for charitable purposes in the areas of civic, cultural, health, education, and social services with an emphasis on permanent endowments.
Fields of interest: Arts; Education; Health organizations, association; Human services; Community/economic development; Youth.
Type of support: Program development; General/operating support; Capital campaigns; Building/renovation; Management development/capacity building; Equipment; Endowments; Conferences/seminars; Scholarship funds; Employee-related scholarships.
Limitations: Applications accepted. Giving limited for the benefit of Lenawee County, MI. No support for religious purposes. No grants to individuals (except for scholarships), or for fundraising.
Publications: Application guidelines; Annual report (including application guidelines); Grants list; Informational brochure; Newsletter.
Application information: Visit foundation web site for application guidelines. Application form required.
Initial approach: Inquiry by telephone or e-mail
Copies of proposal: 1
Deadline(s): Varies
Board meeting date(s): Bimonthly, 4th Thurs. of the month
Final notification: Varies
Officers and Directors:* Charles H. Gross,* Co-Chair.; Bob Vogel,* Co-Chair.; David S. Hickman, Chair. Emeritus; Suann D. Hammersmith,* C.E.O. and Pres.; Scott Hill,* Secy.; Jim Kapnick,* Treas.; Laura Bell; Michele Buku; Alison Carpenter; Charlotte Coberley; Carlton Cook; Frank Dick; Jack Patterson; Kris Schmidt; Amy Stamats.
Number of staff: 2 full-time professional; 2 part-time professional.
EIN: 386095474

4486
The Leppien Foundation ✧
815 N. State St.
Alma, MI 48801-1155

Established in 1987 in MI.
Donors: Cleo M. Leppien; John C. Leppien; Garr Tool Co.
Foundation type: Independent foundation.
Financial data (yr. ended 12/31/13): Assets, $4,055,231 (M); gifts received, $1,750,000; expenditures, $2,706,530; qualifying distributions, $2,705,000; giving activities include $2,705,000 for 16 grants (high: $2,000,000; low: $5,000).
Purpose and activities: Giving primarily to Christian organizations, particularly an organization which provides assistance to impoverished children.
Fields of interest: Higher education; Children/youth, services; Christian agencies & churches.
Limitations: Applications not accepted. Giving primarily in CO and MI. No grants to individuals.
Application information: Contributes only to pre-selected organizations.
Officers: John C. Leppien, Pres.; Jeffrey C. Leppien, V.P.; Stephanie E. Leppien, V.P.; Cleo M. Leppien, Secy.-Treas.
EIN: 382692343

4487
Edward C. and Linda Dresner Levy Foundation ✧
(formerly Julie & Edward Levy, Jr. Foundation)
9300 Dix Ave.
Dearborn, MI 48120-1528

Established in 1973 in MI.
Donors: Carol Levy; Ellen Levy; Edward C. Levy, Jr.; Edward C. Levy, Co.; The Charitable Lead Trust.
Foundation type: Independent foundation.
Financial data (yr. ended 09/30/13): Assets, $7,161,806 (M); gifts received, $300,069; expenditures, $1,466,132; qualifying distributions, $1,385,281; giving activities include $1,381,831 for 34 grants (high: $325,250; low: $250).
Purpose and activities: Giving primarily for Jewish organizations, primarily health care, particularly to a cancer center, as well as for education.
Fields of interest: Higher education; Hospitals (specialty); Health care; Health organizations, association; Cancer research; International exchange, students; Jewish federated giving programs; Jewish agencies & synagogues.
Limitations: Applications not accepted. Giving primarily in MI, with emphasis on Detroit; some giving also in Washington, DC. No grants to individuals.
Application information: Contributes only to pre-selected organizations.
Officer: Edward C. Levy, Jr., Pres.
Directors: Patrick Duerr; Linda Dresner Levy.
EIN: 386091368
Selected grants: The following grants are a representative sample of this grantmaker's funding activity:
$66,000 to Michigan State University, East Lansing, MI, 2011.
$50,000 to Detroit Symphony Orchestra, Detroit, MI, 2011.
$50,000 to Southwest Solutions, Detroit, MI, 2011.
$20,200 to Yad Ezra, Berkley, MI, 2011.
$15,000 to Food Bank Council of Michigan, Lansing, MI, 2011.
$13,000 to Cornerstone Schools Association, Detroit, MI, 2011.
$12,500 to New Urban Learning, Detroit, MI, 2011.
$12,000 to Middle East Media Research Institute, Washington, DC, 2011.
$10,000 to Heritage Foundation, Washington, DC, 2011.
$5,000 to Society for Research in Child Development, Ann Arbor, MI, 2011.

4488
The Lewis Family Trust ✧
(formerly Peter D. and Dorothy S. Brown Charitable Trust)
401 S. Old Woodward Ave., Ste. 311
Birmingham, MI 48009-6612

Established in 1987 in FL.
Donors: Peter D. Brown; Dorothy S. Brown; A. Bart Lewis; Susan Lewis.
Foundation type: Independent foundation.
Financial data (yr. ended 12/31/13): Assets, $14,979,593 (M); expenditures, $752,572; qualifying distributions, $579,554; giving activities include $517,054 for 10 grants (high: $215,100; low: $5,000).
Fields of interest: Jewish federated giving programs; Jewish agencies & synagogues.
Limitations: Applications not accepted. Giving primarily in MI; some funding also in FL. No grants to individuals.
Application information: Contributes only to pre-selected organizations.
Trustees: A. Bart Lewis; Susan Lewis.
EIN: 386517224
Selected grants: The following grants are a representative sample of this grantmaker's funding activity:
$210,000 to Jewish Hospice and Chaplaincy Network, West Bloomfield, MI, 2011.

4489
The Mackey Foundation ✧
(formerly The Harvey and Elizabeth Mackey Foundation)
3181 Tri-Park Dr.
Grand Blanc, MI 48439-7088

Established in 1993 in MI.
Donors: Bruce B. Mackey†; Robert B. Mackey.
Foundation type: Independent foundation.
Financial data (yr. ended 12/31/13): Assets, $8,802,139 (M); gifts received, $700,000; expenditures, $4,187,700; qualifying distributions, $4,140,725; giving activities include $2,069,500 for 28 grants (high: $300,000; low: $7,000).
Fields of interest: Food banks; Housing/shelter, homeless; Boys & girls clubs; Human services; Protestant agencies & churches; Catholic agencies & churches; Economically disadvantaged.
Limitations: Applications not accepted. Giving primarily in Flint, MI. No grants to individuals.

Application information: Contributes only to pre-selected organizations.
Officers: Marilyn Johnson, Pres.; Robert B. Mackey, Secy.-Treas.
Trustee: Stanley D. Mackey.
EIN: 383134945
Selected grants: The following grants are a representative sample of this grantmaker's funding activity:
$200,000 to Catholic Charities of Shiawassee and Genesee Counties, Flint, MI, 2011.
$100,000 to Community Foundation of Greater Flint, Flint, MI, 2011.

4490
Manat Foundation ✧
186 E. Main St., Ste. 300
Northville, MI 48167-2676

Established in 1986 in MI.
Donors: Manuel Charach; Natalie Charach; Jeffrey Charach; Michael Berman; Sherrill Berman.
Foundation type: Independent foundation.
Financial data (yr. ended 07/31/13): Assets, $5,696,391 (M); gifts received, $501,000; expenditures, $441,815; qualifying distributions, $426,860; giving activities include $426,860 for 21 grants (high: $200,000; low: $250).
Purpose and activities: Giving primarily for health associations, particularly for cancer, and to Jewish organizations; funding also for children, youth and social services.
Fields of interest: Health organizations, association; Human services; Children/youth, services; Jewish federated giving programs; Jewish agencies & synagogues.
Limitations: Applications not accepted. Giving primarily in NY. No grants to individuals.
Application information: Unsolicited requests for funds not accepted.
Officers: Manuel Charach, Mgr.; Natalie Charach, Mgr.
Trustees: Michael P. Berman; Joel Shulman.
EIN: 382710511
Selected grants: The following grants are a representative sample of this grantmaker's funding activity:
$45,500 to American Friends of Magen David Adom, New York, NY, 2012.

4491
Alex and Marie Manoogian Foundation ✧
21001 Van Born Rd.
Taylor, MI 48180-1340 (313) 274-7400

Incorporated in 1942 in MI.
Donors: Alex Manoogian‡; Marie Manoogian.
Foundation type: Independent foundation.
Financial data (yr. ended 12/31/13): Assets, $50,499,900 (M); expenditures, $3,935,241; qualifying distributions, $4,267,806; giving activities include $2,616,227 for 15 grants (high: $1,500,000; low: $1,500).
Purpose and activities: Giving primarily to the arts, including a museum.
Fields of interest: Arts; Higher education; Human services; Minorities/immigrants, centers/services; Religion.
Type of support: General/operating support; Continuing support; Building/renovation; Equipment; Endowments; Emergency funds; Seed money; Fellowships; Scholarship funds; Research; Matching/challenge support.
Limitations: Applications not accepted. Giving primarily in MI. No grants to individuals or for annual campaigns, deficit financing, land acquisition, publications, or conferences or seminars.
Application information: Contributes only to pre-selected organizations.
Board meeting date(s): Twice per year
Officers and Directors:* Richard A. Manoogian,* Pres.; Eugene A. Gargaro, Jr.,* Secy.
EIN: 386089952
Selected grants: The following grants are a representative sample of this grantmaker's funding activity:
$2,500,000 to Detroit Institute of Arts, Detroit, MI, 2012. For operating support.
$422,000 to Armenian Apostolic Society, Southfield, MI, 2012. For operating support.
$250,000 to Armenian General Benevolent Union, New York, NY, 2012. For operating support.
$250,000 to Michigan Science Center, Detroit, MI, 2012. For operating support.
$54,760 to Saint John Armenian Church, Southfield, MI, 2012. For operating support.
$25,000 to Armenian General Benevolent Union of America, West Bloomfield, MI, 2012. For operating support.

4492
Richard & Jane Manoogian Foundation ✧
21001 Van Born Rd.
Taylor, MI 48180-1300

Established in 1984 in MI.
Donors: Alex Manoogian‡; Marie Manoogian.
Foundation type: Independent foundation.
Financial data (yr. ended 06/30/14): Assets, $127,889,149 (M); expenditures, $6,046,477; qualifying distributions, $11,974,057; giving activities include $3,567,203 for 79 grants (high: $1,000,000; low: $60).
Purpose and activities: Giving primarily for the arts, with emphasis on an art museum; funding also for education, health care, human services, community development, and federated giving programs.
Fields of interest: Museums; Performing arts; Performing arts, orchestras; Historic preservation/historical societies; Arts; Higher education; Education; Environment, natural resources; Health organizations, association; Human services; Children/youth, services; Community/economic development; Foundations (private grantmaking); Foundations (community); United Ways and Federated Giving Programs.
Type of support: General/operating support.
Limitations: Applications not accepted. Giving primarily in MI. No grants to individuals.
Application information: Contributes only to pre-selected organizations.
Officers: Richard A. Manoogian, Pres. and Treas.; Eugene A. Gargaro, Jr., Secy.
Director: Jane C. Manoogian.
EIN: 382531814
Selected grants: The following grants are a representative sample of this grantmaker's funding activity:
$2,000,000 to Yale Art Gallery, New Haven, CT, 2012. For operating support.
$500,000 to Museum of Contemporary Art Detroit, Detroit, MI, 2012. For building renovations.
$200,000 to College for Creative Studies, Detroit, MI, 2012. For operating support.
$150,000 to White Barn Project, Petaluma, CA, 2012. For operating support.
$117,875 to Detroit Institute of Arts, Detroit, MI, 2012. For operating support.
$110,000 to Henry Ford Health System, Detroit, MI, 2012. For operating support.
$100,000 to Barbara Ann Karmanos Cancer Institute, Detroit, MI, 2012. For operating support.
$100,000 to Savannah College of Art and Design, Savannah, GA, 2012. For operating support.
$50,000 to Michigan State University, East Lansing, MI, 2012. For operating support.
$26,145 to Mackinac Associates, Mackinaw City, MI, 2012. For operating support.

4493
Manoogian Simone Foundation ✧
(formerly Louise Manoogian Simone Foundation)
21001 Van Born Rd.
Taylor, MI 48180-1340

Established in 1962 in MI.
Donors: Alex Manoogian‡; Marie Manoogian; Masco Corp.
Foundation type: Independent foundation.
Financial data (yr. ended 12/31/13): Assets, $112,860,601 (M); expenditures, $7,206,013; qualifying distributions, $7,111,304; giving activities include $7,109,000 for 12 grants (high: $5,000,000; low: $8,000).
Purpose and activities: Giving primarily to Armenian organizations, as well as for other human service organizations.
Fields of interest: Human services.
International interests: Armenia.
Limitations: Applications not accepted. Giving primarily in CA and NY; some funding in MI. No grants to individuals.
Application information: Contributes only to pre-selected organizations.
Officers and Directors:* Louise M. Simone,* Pres.; David Simone,* V.P.; Christine M. Simone, Secy.-Treas.; Mark Simone.
EIN: 381799107

4494
Edward & Helen Mardigian Foundation ✧
c/o Comerica Bank
P.O. Box 75000, MC 3318
Detroit, MI 48275-3318
Application address: c/o Edward Mardigian, Jr., 39400 Woodward Ave., Ste. 225, Bloomfield Hills, MI 48304, tel.: (248) 647-0077

Incorporated in 1955 in MI.
Donors: Edward S. Mardigian‡; Helen Mardigian; Arman Mardigian‡.
Foundation type: Independent foundation.
Financial data (yr. ended 12/31/12): Assets, $38,631,591 (M); gifts received, $22,545,047; expenditures, $8,268,386; qualifying distributions, $7,897,276; giving activities include $7,824,900 for 32 grants (high: $3,735,000; low: $400).
Purpose and activities: Giving primarily for Armenian organizations and churches in the U.S.; funding also for children, youth and social services, and health associations.
Fields of interest: Arts; Higher education; Zoos/zoological societies; Health organizations, association; Human services; Children/youth, services; Christian agencies & churches.

Limitations: Applications accepted. Giving primarily in MI; some funding nationally. No grants to individuals.
Application information: Application form not required.
Initial approach: Letter
Deadline(s): None
Officers: Edward S. Mardigian, Pres.; Janet M. Mardigian, V.P.; Grant Mardigian, Secy.; Matthew Mardigian, Treas.
Director: Robert D. Mardigian.
EIN: 386048886

4495
Marquette County Community Foundation ✧ ☆
(formerly Marquette Community Foundation)
401 E. Fair Ave.
P.O. Box 37
Marquette, MI 49855-2951 (906) 226-7666
Contact: Gail Anthony, C.O.O.
FAX: (906) 226-2104; E-mail: mcf@chartermi.net; Main URL: http://www.mqt-cf.org
Facebook: https://www.facebook.com/mqtccf?ref=search&sid=219708050.3543819631..1

Established in 1988 in MI.
Foundation type: Community foundation.
Financial data (yr. ended 12/31/13): Assets, $13,248,036 (M); gifts received, $650,740; expenditures, $1,085,179; giving activities include $803,213 for 8+ grants (high: $358,500), and $41,682 for 49 grants to individuals.
Purpose and activities: The foundation supports organizations involved with the arts, education, health, human services, and other projects and programs that enhance life.
Fields of interest: Arts; Education; Health care; Health organizations, association; Recreation; Children/youth, services; Human services.
Type of support: Film/video/radio; Technical assistance; Consulting services; Capital campaigns; Building/renovation; Equipment; Program development; Seed money; Scholarship funds; Scholarships—to individuals.
Limitations: Applications accepted. Giving limited to Marquette County, MI. No support for religious programs that promote their particular religion.
Publications: Application guidelines; Annual report; Financial statement; Informational brochure; Newsletter; Program policy statement; Program policy statement (including application guidelines).
Application information: Visit foundation web site for application form and guidelines. Application form required.
Initial approach: Create online profile
Deadline(s): Apr. 1 and Oct. 3
Board meeting date(s): Six times annually
Final notification: Within one week of board meeting
Officers and Trustees:* Jack Lenten,* Chair.; Tom Baldini,* Vice-Chair.; Maura Davenport,* Secy.; Tom Humphrey,* Treas.; Pam Benton; Stu Bradley; Brad Canale; Mark Canale; Robert Cowell; Anne Giroux; James Hewitt; Don Mourand; Nancy Wiseman Seminoff; Fred Taccolini; Tom Vear; Karl Weber.
Number of staff: 2 full-time professional.
EIN: 382826563

4496
Marshall Community Foundation ✧
(formerly Marshall Civic Foundation)
614 Homer Rd.
Marshall, MI 49068-1966 (269) 781-2273
Contact: Sherry Anderson, Exec. Dir.
FAX: (269) 781-9747; E-mail: info@marshallcf.org; Main URL: http://www.marshallcf.org

Established in 1970 in MI.
Foundation type: Community foundation.
Financial data (yr. ended 09/30/13): Assets, $11,745,464 (M); gifts received, $475,446; expenditures, $890,298; giving activities include $732,796 for grants to individuals.
Purpose and activities: The foundation's mission is to help make the Marshall area an even better place to live, work, and raise a family. This is done by attracting permanently endowed funds from a wide range of donors serving as a conduit for special projects and distributing of grants in support of innovative programs, while always being mindful to carry out the intention of the donors.
Fields of interest: Arts; Education; Environment; Health care; Health organizations, association; Youth, services; Human services; Community/economic development; Youth; Aging.
Type of support: General/operating support; Building/renovation; Equipment; Program development; Conferences/seminars; Seed money; Curriculum development; Scholarship funds; Technical assistance; Scholarships—to individuals; Matching/challenge support.
Limitations: Applications accepted. Giving limited to Calhoun County, MI. No support for religious or sectarian purposes. No grants to individuals (except for scholarships), or for annual fundraising drives or capital campaigns, endowments or debt reductions, or normal operating expenses (except for start-up purposes and/or special needs).
Publications: Application guidelines; Annual report; Informational brochure.
Application information: Visit foundation web site for application forms and guidelines. Application form required.
Initial approach: Submit application form and attachments
Deadline(s): Jan. 1 , Apr. 1, July 1, and Oct. 1
Board meeting date(s): Quarterly
Final notification: Within 2 months
Officers and Trustees:* Charles B. Cook,* Pres.; Mark F. Stuart,* V.P.; Jennifer Caplis,* Secy.; Frank E. Boley,* Treas.; Sherry Anderson, Exec. Dir.; Mary Jo Byrne; Dr. Randy Davis; Sandra J. Dobbins; Thomas F. Franke; Pastor Richard Gerten; Dr. Lynne M. Haley; Michael E. Kinter; Dr. Jay Larson; Darlene Neidlinger; James A. Pardoe; Ron Smith; Tom Tarkiewicz; Wendee Woods.
Number of staff: 1 part-time professional; 1 part-time support.
EIN: 237011281

4497
Masco Corporation Foundation ✧
(formerly Masco Corporation Charitable Trust)
c/o Corp. Affairs
21001 Van Born Rd.
Taylor, MI 48180-1340 (313) 274-7400
Contact: Melonie B. Colaianne, Pres.
FAX: (313) 792-6262; Main URL: http://masco.com/corporate-responsibility/masco-foundation/

Trust established in 1952 in MI.
Donor: Masco Corp.
Foundation type: Company-sponsored foundation.
Financial data (yr. ended 12/31/12): Assets, $12,182,077 (M); gifts received, $3,000,000; expenditures, $3,087,118; qualifying distributions, $2,994,027; giving activities include $2,817,690 for 71 grants (high: $375,000; low: $300).
Purpose and activities: The foundation supports organizations involved with arts and culture, the environment, affordable housing, human services, civic affairs, economically disadvantaged, and military and veteran's.
Fields of interest: Performing arts; Arts; Environment; Food services; Housing/shelter, development; Housing/shelter; Homeless, human services; Human services; Military/veterans' organizations; Public affairs; Economically disadvantaged.
Type of support: General/operating support; Annual campaigns; Capital campaigns; Building/renovation; Employee matching gifts.
Limitations: Applications accepted. Giving primarily in areas of company operations, with emphasis on the greater Detroit, MI, area. No support for discriminatory organizations, political organizations or candidates, lobbying organizations, athletic clubs, religious organizations not of direct benefit to the entire community, or organizations benefiting few people. No grants to individuals, or for debt reduction, endowments, sports programs or events or school extracurricular activities, or conferences, travel, seminars, or film or video projects; no loans.
Publications: Application guidelines; Occasional report.
Application information: A full proposal may be requested after inquiry. The Council of Michigan Foundations Common Grant Application form is also accepted. Application form not required.
Initial approach: Letter of inquiry or telephone
Copies of proposal: 1
Deadline(s): None
Board meeting date(s): Spring and fall
Final notification: Within 6 weeks following receipt of proposal
Officers and Directors: Sharon Rothwell,* Chair.; Melonie B. Colaianne, Pres.; Eugene A. Gargaro, Jr., Secy.; Richard A. Manoogian; Timothy J. Wadhams.
Trustee: Comerica Bank.
Number of staff: 2 part-time professional; 2 part-time support.
EIN: 386043605
Selected grants: The following grants are a representative sample of this grantmaker's funding activity:
$1,363,532 to Detroit Institute of Arts, Detroit, MI, 2011.
$175,000 to Detroit Symphony Orchestra, Detroit, MI, 2011.
$175,000 to Edison Institute, Dearborn, MI, 2011.
$150,000 to Fisher House Foundation, Rockville, MD, 2011.
$125,000 to ArtServe Michigan, Wixom, MI, 2011.
$100,000 to Michigan Opera Theater, Detroit, MI, 2011.
$80,000 to Habitat for Humanity, Detroit, Detroit, MI, 2011.
$50,000 to Cranbrook Educational Community, Bloomfield Hills, MI, 2011.
$50,000 to Michigan State University, East Lansing, MI, 2011.
$25,000 to Sphinx Organization, Detroit, MI, 2011.

4498
McGregor Fund ✧
333 W. Fort St., Ste. 2090
Detroit, MI 48226-3134 (313) 963-3495
Contact: C. David Campbell, Pres.
FAX: (313) 963-3512;
E-mail: info@mcgregorfund.org; Main URL: http://www.mcgregorfund.org

Incorporated in 1925 in MI.
Donors: Tracy W. McGregor†; Katherine W. McGregor†.
Foundation type: Independent foundation.
Financial data (yr. ended 06/30/13): Assets, $164,329,580 (M); expenditures, $7,251,104; qualifying distributions, $5,822,884; giving activities include $4,638,800 for 63 grants (high: $300,000; low: $300), and $275,323 for 87 employee matching gifts.
Purpose and activities: A private foundation organized to relieve misfortune and improve the well-being of people. The foundation provides grants to support activities in human services, education, health care, arts and culture, and public benefit.
Fields of interest: Arts; Higher education; Education; Medical care, in-patient care; Health organizations, association; Human services; Youth, services; Homeless.
Type of support: General/operating support; Continuing support; Capital campaigns; Building/renovation; Equipment; Program development; Seed money; Employee matching gifts.
Limitations: Applications accepted. Giving primarily in the metropolitan Detroit, MI, area, including Wayne, Oakland, and Macomb counties. No support for disease-specific organizations (or their local affiliates). No grants to individuals, or for scholarships directly, fellowships, travel, workshops, seminars, special events, film or video projects, or conferences; no loans.
Publications: Application guidelines; Annual report (including application guidelines); Grants list.
Application information: Grantmaking guidelines and application procedures are available on the foundation's Web site. Potential applicants are encouraged to contact the foundation to discuss proposed projects before submitting a proposal. Organizations are limited to submitting one grant application per year. Application form not required.
Initial approach: Cover letter and proposal
Copies of proposal: 1
Deadline(s): Applicants are encouraged to submit proposals at least 3 months in advance of board meetings
Board meeting date(s): Mar., June, Sept., and Dec.
Final notification: 90 to 120 days
Officers and Trustees:* James B. Nicholson,* Chair.; Denise J. Lewis,* Vice-Chair.; Norah M. O'Brien, C.F.O.; Kate Levin Markel, C.O.O.; William W. Shelden, Jr.,* Treas.; Dave Bing, Tr. Emeritus; Ira J. Jaffe, Tr. Emeritus; Eugene A. Miller, Tr. Emeritus; Bruce W. Steinhauer, M.D.*, Tr. Emeritus; Peter P. Thurber, Tr. Emeritus; Gerard M. Anderson; Cynthia N. Ford; Reuben A. Munday; Richard L. Rogers; Susan Schooley, M.D.
Number of staff: 4 full-time professional; 1 full-time support.
EIN: 380808800
Selected grants: The following grants are a representative sample of this grantmaker's funding activity:
$500,000 to Neighborhood Service Organization, Detroit, MI, 2012. For the development and start-up operation of the Bell Building.
$350,000 to Forgotten Harvest, Oak Park, MI, 2012. For the Integrated Capacity Expansion.
$300,000 to Detroit Institute of Arts, Detroit, MI, 2012. For general operations.
$300,000 to Detroit Symphony Orchestra, Detroit, MI, 2012. For general operations.
$300,000 to Michigan Future, Ann Arbor, MI, 2012. For the Metro Detroit High School Accelerator Project.
$260,000 to Turning Point, Mount Clemens, MI, 2012. For $325,000 for the capital campaign to build a new emergency shelter and $120,000 for general operations.
$100,000 to Greening of Detroit, Detroit, MI, 2012. For the expansion of its urban agriculture work.
$75,000 to Arab Community Center for Economic and Social Services, Dearborn, MI, 2012. For annual operations of the Emergency Services Department.
$60,000 to Sphinx Organization, Detroit, MI, 2012. For Detroit-area educational programs for youth.
$15,000 to Detroit Public Schools Foundation, Detroit, MI, 2012. For Mumford High School.

4499
The Meijer Foundation ✧
c/o Michael R. Julien
2929 Walker Ave. NW
Grand Rapids, MI 49544-6402
E-mail for Mike Julien: Mikejulien@meijer.com

Established in 1990 in MI.
Donors: Frederik G.H. Meijer†; Meijer, Inc.; Lena Meijer.
Foundation type: Independent foundation.
Financial data (yr. ended 12/31/12): Assets, $122,745,620 (M); gifts received, $57,607,438; expenditures, $28,131,411; qualifying distributions, $26,950,236; giving activities include $26,889,018 for 113 grants (high: $7,500,000; low: $326).
Purpose and activities: Giving primarily to a horticultural society, and to a charitable trust; funding also for community foundations and an art museum. The foundation administers a donor-advised fund.
Fields of interest: Museums (art); Botanical gardens; Horticulture/garden clubs; Foundations (community).
Type of support: Program-related investments/loans.
Limitations: Applications not accepted. Giving primarily in Grand Rapids, MI. No grants to individuals.
Application information: Contributes only to pre-selected organizations.
Trustees: Douglas F. Meijer; Hendrik G. Meijer; Mark D. Meijer.
EIN: 386575227
Selected grants: The following grants are a representative sample of this grantmaker's funding activity:
$7,500,000 to Grand Rapids Community Foundation, Grand Rapids, MI, 2012. For Fred and Lena Meijer Scholarship Fund.
$2,000,000 to West Michigan Horticultural Society, Frederik Meijer Gardens and Sculpture Park, Grand Rapids, MI, 2012. For Japanese Garden.
$1,000,000 to Grand Valley University Foundation, Allendale, MI, 2012. For Grand Valley State University Honors College.
$1,000,000 to Spectrum Health Foundation, Grand Rapids, MI, 2012. For Frederik Meijer Heart and Vascular Institute.
$976,350 to Kent County Parks Foundation, Grand Rapids, MI, 2012. For Fred Meijer Millennium Park Trail Project.
$250,000 to University of Michigan, Ann Arbor, MI, 2012. For curatorship for Michigan Historical Collection.
$50,000 to West Michigan Horticultural Society, Frederik Meijer Gardens and Sculpture Park, Grand Rapids, MI, 2012. For exhibition.
$25,183 to West Michigan Trails and Greenways Coalition, Comstock Park, MI, 2012. For Fred Meijer Berry Junction Trail.
$25,000 to Marine Corps Scholarship Foundation, Alexandria, VA, 2012. For Dakota Meyer Challenge, fundraising effort to "honor marines by educating their children".
$20,000 to West Michigan Horticultural Society, Frederik Meijer Gardens and Sculpture Park, Grand Rapids, MI, 2012. For R&D for sculpture and exhibitions.

4500
Orville D. & Ruth A. Merillat Foundation ✧
1800 W. U.S. Hwy. 223
Adrian, MI 49221-8479

Established in 1983 in MI.
Donors: Orville D. Merillat†; Ruth A. Merillat.
Foundation type: Independent foundation.
Financial data (yr. ended 02/28/13): Assets, $54,867,982 (M); expenditures, $3,629,535; qualifying distributions, $3,464,490; giving activities include $3,449,550 for 66 grants (high: $200,000; low: $600).
Purpose and activities: Support primarily for churches and religious welfare.
Fields of interest: Elementary/secondary education; Human services; Religious federated giving programs; Christian agencies & churches.
Type of support: General/operating support; Building/renovation; Equipment.
Limitations: Applications not accepted. Giving primarily in MI. No grants to individuals.
Application information: Contributes only to pre-selected organizations.
Officers and Directors:* Ruth A. Merillat,* Pres. and Secy.; Richard D. Merillat,* V.P.; John D. Thurman, Treas.; Tricia L.M. McGuire.
EIN: 382476813

4501
Micah 6:8 Foundation ✧
P.O. Box 451
Zeeland, MI 49464-0451

Established in 2006 in MI.
Donors: Michael Mulder; Kimberly Mulder.
Foundation type: Independent foundation.
Financial data (yr. ended 12/31/13): Assets, $4,413,302 (M); gifts received, $2,731,502; expenditures, $1,240,641; qualifying distributions, $1,230,252; giving activities include $1,229,097 for 22 grants (high: $294,597; low: $5,000).
Fields of interest: Theological school/education; Boys & girls clubs; Human services; Children/youth, services; Christian agencies & churches.
Limitations: Applications not accepted. Giving primarily in MI. No grants to individuals.

Application information: Contributes only to pre-selected organizations.
Trustees: Jennifer Mesler; Kimberly Mulder; Michael Mulder.
EIN: 205900630
Selected grants: The following grants are a representative sample of this grantmaker's funding activity:
$200,150 to World Relief, Baltimore, MD, 2011.
$100,000 to Partners Worldwide, Grand Rapids, MI, 2011.
$100,000 to Water Missions International, Charleston, SC, 2011.
$50,000 to FamilyLife, Little Rock, AR, 2011.
$50,000 to International Justice Mission, Arlington, VA, 2011.
$50,000 to Kids Hope USA, Zeeland, MI, 2011.
$50,000 to Lakeshore Pregnancy Center, Holland, MI, 2011.
$50,000 to Other Way Ministries, Grand Rapids, MI, 2011.
$40,000 to Jubilee Ministries, Holland, MI, 2011.
$10,000 to Holland Rescue Mission, Holland, MI, 2011.

4502
Midland Area Community Foundation ✧
(formerly Midland Foundation)
76 Ashman Cir.
Midland, MI 48640 (989) 839-9661
Contact: For grants: Nancy Money, Prog. Off.
FAX: (989) 839-9907;
E-mail: info@midlandfoundation.org; Additional tel.: (800) 906-9661; Grant application e-mail: nmoney@midlandfoundation.org; Main URL: http://www.midlandfoundation.org
Facebook: http://www.facebook.com/pages/Midland-MI/Midland-Area-Community-Foundation/56875302551
Pinterest: http://www.pinterest.com/midlandfdn/
Twitter: https://twitter.com/MidlandFDN
YouTube: http://www.youtube.com/user/MidlandAreaCommFound

Established in 1973 in MI.
Foundation type: Community foundation.
Financial data (yr. ended 12/31/13): Assets, $85,584,180 (M); gifts received, $3,985,074; expenditures, $5,254,672; giving activities include $3,474,663 for 89+ grants (high: $703,000), and $420,165 for grants to individuals.
Purpose and activities: The foundation strengthens the community by providing leadership, fostering collaboration on local needs and issues, and encouraging a legacy of giving through grants, scholarships and events.
Fields of interest: Humanities; Arts; Adult/continuing education; Education; Environment, energy; Environment; Health care; Recreation; Youth, services; Human services; Economic development; Community/economic development; Infants/toddlers; Children/youth; Children; Youth; Adults; Aging; Young adults; Disabilities, people with; Physically disabled; Deaf/hearing impaired; Mentally disabled; Minorities; African Americans/Blacks; Women; Infants/toddlers, female; Girls; Adults, women; Young adults, female; Men; Infants/toddlers, male; Adults, men; Young adults, male; Military/veterans; Substance abusers; Single parents; Crime/abuse victims; Terminal illness, people with; Economically disadvantaged; Homeless.
Type of support: Building/renovation; Equipment; Seed money; Scholarship funds; Technical assistance; Consulting services; Matching/challenge support.
Limitations: Applications accepted. Giving primarily in full support services to Midland and Gladwin counties, MI, and also Clare County through affiliate. No support for sectarian religious programs, basic governmental services, or basic educational functions. No grants for operating budgets, continuing support, annual campaigns or fundraising, normal office equipment, deficit financing, or endowment funds.
Publications: Application guidelines; Annual report; Grants list; Informational brochure; Newsletter.
Application information: Visit foundation web site for application guidelines. Application form required.
Initial approach: Telephone Prog. Off. to discuss project
Copies of proposal: 3
Deadline(s): Jan. 15, Apr. 15, July 15, and Oct. 15
Board meeting date(s): 4th Mon. of every month
Final notification: Early in Mar., June, Sept., and Dec.
Officers and Trustees:* Elizabeth Lumbert,* Chair.; Angela Hine,* Vice-Chair.; Sharon Mortensen,* C.E.O. and Pres.; Kevin Gay,* Treas.; Sam Howard; Cal Ieuter; Liz Kapla; Kevin Kendrick; Craig McDonald; Dave Ramaker; Mike Rush; Duncan Stuart; Beth Swift; Kay Wagner; Kim White.
Number of staff: 4 full-time professional; 1 part-time professional; 2 full-time support.
EIN: 382023395

4503
Miller Foundation ✧
310 WahWahTaySee Way
Battle Creek, MI 49015-4065 (269) 964-3542
Main URL: http://www.themillerfoundation.org/

Incorporated in 1963 in MI.
Donors: Louise B. Miller†; Robert B. Miller†.
Foundation type: Independent foundation.
Financial data (yr. ended 12/31/13): Assets, $28,395,180 (M); expenditures, $1,174,351; qualifying distributions, $1,071,771; giving activities include $752,583 for 92 grants (high: $208,000; low: $67).
Purpose and activities: Giving mainly to improve the quality of life in the Battle Creek, MI, community area by supporting local organizations and government agencies that provide for economic development, neighborhood improvement, improving educational outcomes for youth, and eliminating barriers to employment for all in Battle Creek, MI, and the surrounding area.
Fields of interest: Arts; Adult/continuing education; Human services; Children/youth, services; Community development, neighborhood development; Economic development.
Type of support: General/operating support; Management development/capacity building; Annual campaigns; Capital campaigns; Building/renovation; Equipment; Emergency funds; Program development; Seed money; Scholarship funds; Consulting services; Program-related investments/loans; Employee matching gifts; Matching/challenge support.
Limitations: Applications accepted. Giving limited to the greater Battle Creek, MI, area. No support for religious or political organizations. No grants to individuals, or for endowments.
Publications: Application guidelines; Annual report; Annual report (including application guidelines).
Application information: Application form required.
Initial approach: Letter
Deadline(s): Jan. 1, Mar. 1, May 1, July 1, Sept. 1, and Nov. 1
Board meeting date(s): Jan., Mar., May, July, Sept., and Nov.
Officers: Greg Dotson, Chair.; Arthur W. Angood, Vice-Chair.; Allen L. Miller, Secy.; Rance Leaders, Treas.
Trustees: Barbara L. Comai; John Gallagher; Paul R. Ohm; Gloria J. Robertson.
Number of staff: 1 full-time professional; 1 part-time support.
EIN: 386064925
Selected grants: The following grants are a representative sample of this grantmaker's funding activity:
$20,000 to Charitable Union, Battle Creek, MI, 2012. For Clothing for Families.
$10,000 to Robert B. Miller College, Battle Creek, MI, 2012. For Children's Literature and Theatre.
$6,553 to Robert B. Miller College, Battle Creek, MI, 2012. For legal.
$2,000 to Robert B. Miller College, Battle Creek, MI, 2012. For College Endowment Fund.
$2,000 to Robert B. Miller College, Battle Creek, MI, 2012. For 50/50 Scholarship/Endowment.
$1,198 to Calhoun Christian School, Battle Creek, MI, 2012. For field trip.
$250 to Robert B. Miller College, Battle Creek, MI, 2012. For college endowment.
$150 to First Congregational Church, Battle Creek, MI, 2012. For Sunday Afternoon Live.

4504
Howard Miller Foundation ✧
860 E. Main Ave.
Zeeland, MI 49464-0301

Established in 1976 in MI.
Donors: Howard Miller Clock Co.; Herman Furniture Co.
Foundation type: Independent foundation.
Financial data (yr. ended 12/31/13): Assets, $17,856,787 (M); gifts received, $95,000; expenditures, $808,198; qualifying distributions, $755,130; giving activities include $728,000 for 47 grants (high: $113,500; low: $3,000), and $25,000 for 10 grants to individuals (high: $2,500; low: $2,500).
Purpose and activities: Giving primarily for education, Christian missionary work, the arts, health, and human services; also awards college scholarships to children of Howard Miller Clock Co. employees for undergraduate education.
Fields of interest: Arts; Higher education; Education; Health care; Mental health/crisis services; Human services; Christian agencies & churches.
Type of support: General/operating support; Scholarships—to individuals.
Limitations: Applications not accepted. Giving primarily in MI.
Application information: Unsolicited requests for funds not accepted.
Officers: Philip D. Miller, Pres.; Jack H. Miller, V.P.; Howard J. Miller, Secy.-Treas.
EIN: 382137226

4505
Molinello Family Foundation ✧
P.O. Box 721067
Berkley, MI 48072-0067 (248) 544-2775
Contact: Earl C. Bossenberry, Pres.

Established in 2000 in MI.
Donors: Richard Molinello Revocable Trust; John Molinello Revocable Trust.
Foundation type: Independent foundation.
Financial data (yr. ended 12/31/13): Assets, $21,531,421 (M); expenditures, $987,252; qualifying distributions, $860,000; giving activities include $860,000 for 30 grants (high: $60,000; low: $10,000).
Fields of interest: Health care; Medical research, institute; Human services; Salvation Army; Christian agencies & churches; Blind/visually impaired; Economically disadvantaged.
Limitations: Applications accepted. Giving primarily in MI.
Application information: Application form required.
Initial approach: Letter
Deadline(s): None
Officers: Earl C. Bossenberry, Pres.; Rita Morelli, V.P.; Michele A. Morelli, Secy.
EIN: 383494266
Selected grants: The following grants are a representative sample of this grantmaker's funding activity:
$60,000 to Capuchin Soup Kitchen, Detroit, MI, 2012. For assistance to indigent persons.
$60,000 to Leader Dogs for the Blind, Rochester, MI, 2012. For assistance to blind persons.

4506
Dorothy D. and Joseph A. Moller Foundation ✧
33 E. College St.
Hillsdale, MI 49242-1205 (517) 607-2239

Established in 1987 in AZ.
Donors: Dorothy D. Moller†; Joseph A. Moller†.
Foundation type: Independent foundation.
Financial data (yr. ended 12/31/12): Assets, $194,920,419 (M); expenditures, $11,820,269; qualifying distributions, $9,690,426; giving activities include $9,600,000 for 25 grants (high: $2,552,000; low: $24,000).
Fields of interest: Media/communications; Higher education; Education; Animal welfare; Legal services, public interest law; Public affairs, research; Public affairs, formal/general education; Public affairs, political organizations.
Limitations: Applications not accepted. Giving primarily in AZ, CO, MI, NM, and OK; some giving also in the U.K. No grants to individuals.
Application information: Contributes only to pre-selected organizations.
Trustee: Hillsdale College Independence Foundation.
EIN: 746355685
Selected grants: The following grants are a representative sample of this grantmaker's funding activity:
$2,552,000 to Daystar Foundation, Oklahoma City, OK, 2012. For general support.
$2,552,000 to Hillsdale College, Hillsdale, MI, 2012. For general support.
$2,552,000 to United States Air Force Academy Association of Graduates, Colorado Springs, CO, 2012. For general support.
$504,000 to 390th Memorial Museum Foundation, Tucson, AZ, 2012. For general support.
$144,000 to Arizona Animal Welfare League, Phoenix, AZ, 2012. For general support.
$144,000 to Arizona Zoological Society, Phoenix Zoo, Phoenix, AZ, 2012. For general support.
$144,000 to Humane Society of Southern Arizona, Tucson, AZ, 2012. For general support.
$144,000 to Humane Society, Arizona, Phoenix, AZ, 2012. For general support.
$48,000 to Santa Fe Animal Shelter and Humane Society, Santa Fe, NM, 2012. For general support.
$24,000 to 390th Bomb Group Memorial Fund Association, Parham, England, 2012. For general support.

4507
Monroe-Brown Foundation ✧
7950 Moorsbridge Rd., Ste. 300
Portage, MI 49024-4420
E-mail: jbaker@monroebrown.org; Main URL: http://www.monroebrown.org/

Incorporated in 1983 in MI.
Donors: Albertine M. Brown†; Robert J. Brown†; Robert M. Brown; Gail B. Kasdorf; Jane B. Todd; Robert J. Brown Charitable Lead Trust.
Foundation type: Independent foundation.
Financial data (yr. ended 12/31/13): Assets, $20,384,794 (M); gifts received, $216,508; expenditures, $871,650; qualifying distributions, $759,916; giving activities include $675,855 for 26 grants (high: $361,936; low: $100).
Purpose and activities: The mission of the foundation is twofold: to provide support for higher education in the State of Michigan, and to advance economic development in the Kalamazoo community through programs designed to encourage the retention and employment of local scholars.
Fields of interest: Arts; Higher education; Education; Human services; Urban/community development; Foundations (community).
Type of support: Annual campaigns; Capital campaigns; Building/renovation; Program development; Matching/challenge support.
Limitations: Applications not accepted. Giving primarily in the Kalamazoo, MI area. No grants to individuals.
Application information: Unsolicited requests for funds not accepted.
Officers and Trustees:* Robert M. Brown,* Pres.; Gail B. Kasdorf,* V.P.; Jane B. Todd,* Treas.; Frederick O. Brown; Robert M. Brown, Jr.; Albert John Todd IV; John C. Wattles.
Number of staff: 1 full-time professional.
EIN: 382513263
Selected grants: The following grants are a representative sample of this grantmaker's funding activity:
$7,700 to Kalamazoo College, Kalamazoo, MI, 2011. For scholarships.

4508
The Morey Foundation ✧
P.O. Box 374
Winn, MI 48896-0374
Application address: c/o Lon Morey, Pres., P.O. Box 1000, Winn, MI 48896-1000, tel.: (989) 866-2381

Established in 1990 in MI.
Donor: Norval Morey.
Foundation type: Independent foundation.
Financial data (yr. ended 12/31/13): Assets, $34,398,435 (M); gifts received, $217; expenditures, $2,441,138; qualifying distributions, $1,964,898; giving activities include $1,841,819 for 48 grants (high: $300,000; low: $159).
Purpose and activities: Scholarships are limited to students of Central Michigan University.
Fields of interest: Museums; Higher education; Education; Hospitals (general); Human services; Foundations (community); Public policy, research.
Type of support: Scholarship funds.
Limitations: Giving primarily in MI, with emphasis on Mount Pleasant. No grants to individuals directly.
Application information: Application form required for scholarship requests.
Initial approach: Letter
Deadline(s): Mar. 15 for scholarships; none for grants
Officers and Trustees:* Lon Morey,* Pres.; Krista Morey,* V.P.; Terra Lynn Boone,* V.P.; Ellen E. Crane, Secy.; Larry H. Noch, Treas.
EIN: 382965346
Selected grants: The following grants are a representative sample of this grantmaker's funding activity:
$5,125 to Shepherd Public Schools, Shepherd, MI, 2012. For talent show.
$1,000 to Northwood University, Midland, MI, 2012. For golf tournament fundraiser.

4509
The Mosaic Foundation of R. & P. Heydon ✧
324 E. Washington St.
Ann Arbor, MI 48107

Established in 1990 in MI.
Donors: Kenneth F. Montgomery; Peter N. Heydon; Henrietta M. Heydon.
Foundation type: Independent foundation.
Financial data (yr. ended 12/31/12): Assets, $2,392,843 (M); gifts received, $100,000; expenditures, $882,616; qualifying distributions, $801,810; giving activities include $801,810 for 165 grants (high: $130,000; low: $100).
Purpose and activities: Giving primarily for the arts and education.
Fields of interest: Media, radio; Museums; Performing arts; Arts; Elementary/secondary education; Higher education; Environment; Animals/wildlife; Human services.
Type of support: Program-related investments/loans; General/operating support.
Limitations: Applications not accepted. Giving primarily in FL, MI and NY. No grants to individuals.
Application information: Unsolicited requests for funds not accepted.
Directors: James R. Beuche; Henrietta M. Heydon; Peter N. Heydon; Tommy York.
EIN: 382910797

4510
Charles Stewart Mott Foundation ✧
Mott Foundation Bldg.
503 S. Saginaw St., Ste. 1200
Flint, MI 48502-1851 (810) 238-5651
FAX: (810) 766-1753; E-mail: info@mott.org; Main URL: http://www.mott.org/
E-Newsletter: http://www.mott.org/about/thefoundation/newslettersubscribe.aspx
Facebook: http://www.facebook.com/mottfoundation
Grants Database: http://www.mott.org/about/searchgrants.aspx
Program News Feeds: http://feeds.feedburner.com/mott/news/General
RSS Grants Feed: http://feeds.feedburner.com/mott/grant/General
Twitter: http://www.twitter.com/mottfoundation
YouTube: http://www.youtube.com/csmottfoundation

Incorporated in 1926 in MI.
Donors: Charles Stewart Mott†; and members of the Mott family.
Foundation type: Independent foundation.
Financial data (yr. ended 12/31/13): Assets, $2,587,788,238 (M); expenditures, $144,385,858; qualifying distributions, $130,409,685; giving activities include $114,442,289 for 1,169 grants (high: $3,200,000; low: $150), and $1,456,819 for 21 foundation-administered programs.
Purpose and activities: To support efforts that promote a just, equitable and sustainable society with the primary focus on civil society, the environment, the area of Flint, MI and poverty. The foundation makes grants for a variety of purposes within these program areas including: philanthropy and voluntarism; assisting emerging civil societies in Central/Eastern Europe, Russia and South Africa; conservation of fresh water ecosystems in North America; reform of international finance and trade; improving the outcomes for children, youth and families at risk of persistent poverty; education and neighborhood and economic development. The foundation also makes grants to strengthen the capacity of local institutions in its home community of Flint, MI.
Fields of interest: Education; Environment, pollution control; Environment, natural resources; Employment, services; Human services; Children, services; Child development, services; Family services, parent education; Civil rights, race/intergroup relations; Economic development; Urban/community development; Rural development; Community/economic development; Voluntarism promotion; Leadership development; Children/youth; Young adults; Minorities; Economically disadvantaged.
International interests: Eastern Europe; Latin America; Russia; South Africa; Ukraine.
Type of support: General/operating support; Continuing support; Management development/capacity building; Program development; Conferences/seminars; Seed money; Technical assistance; Program evaluation; Program-related investments/loans; Employee matching gifts; Matching/challenge support.
Limitations: Applications accepted. Giving nationally and to emerging countries in Central and Eastern Europe, Russia, and South Africa. No support for religious activities or programs serving specific religious groups or denominations. Faith based organizations may submit inquiries if the project falls within the foundation's guidelines and serves a broad segment of the population. No grants to individuals or for capital development (with the exception of the Flint area and legacy institutions). Grants for research, project replication or endowments are rarely funded unless these activities grow out of work the foundation already supports. No support for local projects, except in the Flint area, unless they are part of a Mott-planned national demonstration or network of grants. Film and video projects, books, scholarships, and fellowships are rarely funded; no loans.
Publications: Annual report (including application guidelines); Financial statement; Occasional report.
Application information: Full proposals by invitation only. Application form not required.
Initial approach: Online letter of inquiry
Deadline(s): None; grants are determined by Aug. 31 of any given year
Board meeting date(s): Mar., June, Sept., and Dec.
Final notification: 60-90 days
Officers and Trustees:* William S. White,* Chair. and C.E.O.; Frederick S. Kirkpatrick,* Vice-Chair.; Ridgway H. White, Pres.; Jay C. Flaherty, V.P. and C.I.O.; Neal R. Hegarty, V.P., Progs.; Phillip H. Peters, V.P., Admin. Group and Secy.-Treas.; Gavin T. Clabaugh, V.P., Inf. Svcs.; Kathryn A. Thomas, V.P., Comms.; Douglas X. Patino, Tr. Emeritus; A. Marshall Acuff, Jr.; Lizabeth Ardisana; Tiffany W. Lovett; Webb F. Martin; Olivia P. Maynard; John Morning; Maryanne Mott; Charlie Nelms; William H. Piper; Marise M.M. Stewart.
Number of staff: 54 full-time professional; 1 part-time professional; 24 full-time support.
EIN: 381211227
Selected grants: The following grants are a representative sample of this grantmaker's funding activity:
$4,506,740 to Kettering University, Flint, MI, 2012. To support key initiatives at Kettering University which includes increasing enrollment, launching a branding and marketing campaign, contributing to the economic revitalization of Flint and the region and increasing alumni support and participation.
$2,000,000 to Foundation for the Uptown Reinvestment Corporation, Flint, MI, 2012. For Uptown Reinvestment Corporation's downtown revitalization efforts. Grant will be used to purchase the Flint Journal properties which will house the Michigan State University medical education and Masters of Public Health program. The remaining property will be used for other charitable purposes.
$1,550,000 to Flint Cultural Center Corporation, Flint, MI, 2012. For operating support so that Center may offer quality entertainment locally; provide educational programming for area students around the arts, science, and history; expand outreach efforts to underserved populations; and for campus maintenance at Whiting Auditorium, Sloan Museum, and Longway Planetarium on the Center campus.
$1,500,000 to Flint Institute of Arts, Flint, MI, 2013. For operating support to enable the art institute to present new exhibits that inspire and stimulate patrons, provide educational programming to area students, offer art classes to people of all ages, and maintain its facilities.
$1,200,000 to Afterschool Alliance, Washington, DC, 2013. For general support to continue efforts to ensure that children and youth, particularly those in underserved populations, will have access to afterschool opportunities that inspire learning and achievement in school and in life. The grantee will continue to: 1) serve as information source on afterschool programs and resources; 2) be effective voice in its efforts to expand quality afterschool programs; 3) encourage the development of local, state, and national afterschool constituencies and systems; and 4) communicate the positive impact of afterschool programs on children, families, and communities. The grantee will work with the 41 statewide afterschool networks as a member of the national Afterschool Technical Assistance Collaborative.
$950,000 to Center on Budget and Policy Priorities, Washington, DC, 2013. For ongoing support State Fiscal and Low-Income Initiatives Project. The overall goals of this project are to promote federal and state fiscal responsibility, so that adequate resources are available to meet critical needs, and to protect and strengthen low-income programs that reduce poverty and expand opportunity. Mott funding will support the grantee's continued work promoting policy initiatives, such as the Earned Income Tax Credit, which helps increase the incomes of low-income working families. To accomplish these goals, the grantee will: monitor changes to the social safety net; prepare strategy papers and analyses of fiscal policies; facilitate networking at the state and local level for low-income advocates; and provide strategic and technical assistance to state and local policymakers, program administrators, and nonprofit organizations working on issues affecting low-income families, payable over 3.00 years.
$850,000 to Prima Civitas Foundation, East Lansing, MI, 2013. For general support to continue to implement a strategic plan focused on promoting international trade; attracting international businesses; and recruiting, retaining, and developing a 21st century workforce. Through the Flint Area Reinvestment Office, a program of Prima Civitas, the grantee will continue to maintain a strong focus on the Greater Flint region.
$600,000 to Academy for the Development of Philanthropy in Poland, Akademia Rozwoju Filantropii W Polsce, Warsaw, Poland, 2013. For regranting work to strengthen community foundation development in the Czech Republic, Hungary, Poland, and Slovakia (the Visegrad countries) with tailor-made grantmaking and technical assistance programs, networking and learning opportunities. In addition, Grantee will strengthen the Visegrad networks and associations of community foundations, payable over 3.00 years.
$576,200 to Flint Community Schools, Flint, MI, 2013. To support newly formed Brownell Holmes STEM (Science, Technology, Engineering and Math) pod. A STEM facilitator will help develop and implement STEM curriculum, coordinate teacher and staff professional development, and work with community partners who can bring specialized STEM experiences to students. The STEM facilitator will coordinate the purchase of supplies critical to a STEM curriculum, including tablet computers, science and engineering kits and laboratory equipment and will host engaging events for families and community partners to help create a sense of ownership of the STEM pod within the neighborhood.
$500,000 to Center of Socio-Environmental Studies, Salvador, Brazil, 2013. For re-granting toward South America Small Grants Program. This grant renewal will support the small grants program in South America to build capacity in local communities impacted by large-scale energy and infrastructure projects, which are funded by international and national financial institutions, including the Brazilian Development Bank, payable over 2.00 years.

$500,000 to Mozaik Community Development Foundation, Sarajevo, Bosnia and Herzegovina, 2012. To strengthen the financial sustainability of the Grantee. As part of its long-term financial sustainability strategy, the Grantee will launch endowment-building program designed to raise support over the next five years. To match the contribution from the Mott Foundation, the grantee will target support from individuals, corporate donors, and other donor agencies operating in Bosnia. Additionally, during the grant period the Grantee will contribute to the endowment a portion of the revenue from two social enterprises it owns in Bosnia, payable over 5.00 years.
$500,000 to Workshop for Civic Initiatives Foundation, Sofia, Bulgaria, 2012. To strengthen the financial sustainability through tailored capacity-building and funding programs. To this end, the Workshop will run endowment building program to raise money to match the support provided by the Mott Foundation and increase its total endowment by the end of 2015. Through this process, the grantee will strengthen its overall fundraising strategies and capacities and access new sources of funding, payable over 4.00 years.
$400,000 to Bank Information Center, Washington, DC, 2012. For general support for work to provide information and capacity-building services, networking and coalition-building expertise and advocacy support to partners around the world, payable over 2.00 years.
$400,000 to Insight Center for Community Economic Development, Oakland, CA, 2013. For National Network of Sector Partners, the national trade association for sector employment intermediaries and other interested parties, to continue improving employment opportunities for low-income families and communities, payable over 2.00 years.
$200,000 to Harlem Childrens Zone, New York, NY, 2013. For general support to enable HCZ to continue to provide system of supports to reach more children, open a new K-12 Promise Academy Charter School, continue a longitudinal study that documents the success of participants in Harlem Children's Zone core programs, and assist more than 50 communities participating in the federally supported Promise Neighborhoods Initiative.
$131,000 to EduGuide, Lansing, MI, 2012. For GEAR UP (Gaining Early Awareness and Readiness for Undergraduate Programs) Michigan Project. EduGuide has established a web-based platform that provides online mentoring to low-income and first-generation college students in Flint, MI which helps them navigate the secondary and post-secondary educational systems. From the platform, EduGuide offers a host of online resources for children, parents, and professionals to establish developmental goals, recognize academic and social hurdles and strategies to assist a child to reach and complete post-secondary education.
$125,000 to Greater Flint Health Coalition, Flint, MI, 2012. Toward implementation of Flint Healthcare Employment Opportunities Project. Purpose of initiative is to create sustainable employment and promote career advancement for low-income Flint and Genesee County residents by working with health industry employers to restructure hiring, retention and promotional practices for healthcare employees.
$120,000 to Institute for Conservation Leadership, Takoma Park, MD, 2013. To provide a range of intensive capacity building support services to organizations and coalitions addressing high priority freshwater restoration and protection issues in the Great Lakes region as part of Freshwater Leadership Initiative.

4511
Ruth Mott Foundation ✧

111 E. Court St., Ste. 3C
Flint, MI 48502-1649 (810) 233-0170
Contact: Dolores Ennis, Secy.
FAX: (810) 233-7022;
E-mail: ruthmott@ruthmott.org; Main URL: http://www.ruthmottfoundation.org

Established in 1989 in MI.
Donor: Ruth R. Mott†.
Foundation type: Independent foundation.
Financial data (yr. ended 12/31/12): Assets, $208,154,161 (M); gifts received, $61,685; expenditures, $11,528,471; qualifying distributions, $9,894,598; giving activities include $6,148,440 for 131 grants (high: $500,000; low: $112), and $1,965,242 for 4 foundation-administered programs.
Purpose and activities: The foundation's mission is to advocate, stimulate, and support community vitality. Its commitment is to base the foundation in its home community of Flint, Michigan.
Fields of interest: Arts, cultural/ethnic awareness; Arts; Youth development; Children/youth, services; Community/economic development.
Type of support: Technical assistance; Program evaluation; Program development; Matching/challenge support; Management development/capacity building; General/operating support; Continuing support.
Limitations: Applications accepted. Giving primarily in Genesee County and Flint, MI. No grants to individual scholarships or fellowships, or for capital projects, major equipment, land purchases, deficit financing, endowments, or renovations; no loans.
Publications: Annual report; Annual report (including application guidelines); Grants list; Informational brochure (including application guidelines); Multi-year report; Program policy statement.
Application information: See foundation web site for grant guidelines, and more information. Application form not required.
Initial approach: Phone call
Deadline(s): See web site for annual deadlines
Board meeting date(s): Mar., June, and Nov.
Officers and Trustees:* Maryanne Mott,* Chair.; Harriet Kenworthy,* Vice-Chair.; Handy Lindsey, Jr., Pres.; Dolores Ennis, Secy.; Joseph R. Robinson, Treas.; Maria Jordan, Dir., Finance; Gloria Coles; Cris Doby; Lawrence E. Moon; Melissa Patterson; Robert Pestronk.
Number of staff: None.
EIN: 382876435
Selected grants: The following grants are a representative sample of this grantmaker's funding activity:
$460,098 to United Way of Genesee County, Flint, MI, 2013. For Keep Genesee County Beautiful - General Project Support.
$237,500 to Crim Fitness Foundation, Flint, MI, 2013. For CrimFit Youth Program.
$161,841 to Flint Institute of Music, Flint, MI, 2013. For Outreach.
$143,860 to YMCA, Flint, Flint, MI, 2013. For Safe Places.
$130,000 to Foundation for Mott Community College, Flint, MI, 2013. For Beecher Scholarship Incentive Program (BSIP) - Pre College Programming.
$129,381 to Crim Fitness Foundation, Flint, MI, 2013. For Safe and Active Genesee for Everyone (SAGE).
$118,750 to United Way of Genesee County, Flint, MI, 2013. For Building Excellence Sustainability and Trust (BEST) Non-Profit Capacity Building 2013.
$80,660 to Genesee Conservation District, Flint, MI, 2013. For Flint Forestry Project.
$73,400 to YOUR Center, Flint, MI, 2013. For YOUR Blessed Health.
$24,638 to VSA Arts of Michigan, Detroit, MI, 2013. For artsJAM Flint 2013.

4512
Mount Pleasant Area Community Foundation ✧ ☆

(formerly Mount Pleasant Community Foundation)
306 S. Univ.
P.O. Box 1283
Mount Pleasant, MI 48804-1283 (989) 773-7322
Contact: Amanda Schafer, Exec. Dir.
FAX: (989) 773-1517; E-mail: info@mpacf.org; Main URL: http://www.mpacf.org
Facebook: http://www.facebook.com/MPACF
YouTube: http://www.youtube.com/user/mpareacf

Established in 1990 in MI.
Foundation type: Community foundation.
Financial data (yr. ended 12/31/13): Assets, $1,426,471 (M); gifts received, $462,900; expenditures, $876,684; giving activities include $399,510 for 4+ grants (high: $137,500), and $63,390 for grants to individuals.
Purpose and activities: The foundation seeks to enhance the quality of life for all citizens of Isabella County, both current and future generations, by holding and attracting permanent, endowed funds from a wide range of donors, addressing needs through grant making, and providing leadership on key community issues.
Fields of interest: Arts; Education, research; Education; Environment; Health care; Recreation; Youth development; Human services; Community development, neighborhood development; Children/youth; Children; Aging; Women; Girls; Adults, women.
Type of support: Consulting services; Management development/capacity building; Building/renovation; Equipment; Land acquisition; Endowments; Emergency funds; Program development; Conferences/seminars; Film/video/radio; Publication; Seed money; Curriculum development; Scholarship funds; Research; Technical assistance; Program evaluation; Scholarships—to individuals; Matching/challenge support; Student loans—to individuals.
Limitations: Applications accepted. Giving limited to Isabella County, MI. No support for the promotion of religious organizations. No grants to individuals (except for scholarships), or for annual operating expenses including salaries, ongoing program support, debt reduction, and travel for groups such as school classes, clubs or sports teams.
Publications: Application guidelines; Annual report; Financial statement; Grants list; Informational brochure; Newsletter; IRS Form 990 or 990-PF printed copy available upon request.
Application information: Visit foundation web site for specific deadline dates, application and guidelines. Incomplete, late and/or faxed proposals will not be accepted. Application form required.
Initial approach: Contact foundation staff

Copies of proposal: 1
Deadline(s): Jan. 29, May 28, and Sept. 24 for general grants; Mar. for scholarships
Board meeting date(s): Bimonthly
Final notification: Within 2 weeks of board meeting

Officers and Trustees:* Bob Long,* Pres.; Steve Pung,* V.P.; Al Kaufmann,* Secy.; Terrie Zitzelsberger,* Treas.; Amanda Schafer, Exec. Dir.; Jay Anders; Jill Bourland; Bill Chilman; Shirley Martin Decker; Dan Eversole; Cheryl Gaudard; Joanne Golden; Dyke Heinze; Shelly Hinck; Chuck Hubscher; Dave Keilitz; Lon Morey; Mary Ann O'Neil; Lynn Pohl; Laura Richards; Donald Schuster; Harold Stegman; Jan Strickler; Thomas Sullivan; Robert L. Wheeler.
Number of staff: 1 full-time professional; 1 full-time support; 1 part-time support.
EIN: 382951873

4513
MSJ Foundation ✧ ☆

c/o Molly Nawrocki, Michael Jandernoa
171 Monroe Ave. N.W., Ste. 410
Grand Rapids, MI 49503

Established in 1992 in MI.
Donors: Michael J. Jandernoa; Susan M. Jandernoa; Susan M. Jandernnoa Trust.
Foundation type: Independent foundation.
Financial data (yr. ended 12/31/13): Assets, $42,224,035 (M); gifts received, $17,031,840; expenditures, $1,775,258; qualifying distributions, $1,753,980; giving activities include $1,753,980 for 30 grants (high: $797,349; low: $2,497).
Fields of interest: Secondary school/education; Higher education; Medical school/education; YM/YWCAs & YM/YWHAs; United Ways and Federated Giving Programs.
Limitations: Applications not accepted. Giving primarily in East Lansing and Grand Rapids, MI. No grants to individuals.
Application information: Unsolicited requests for funds not accepted.
Officers and Directors:* Michael J. Jandernoa,* Pres.; Susan M. Jandernoa,* V.P. and Treas.; Carl Jandernoa,* Secy.
EIN: 383083625
Selected grants: The following grants are a representative sample of this grantmaker's funding activity:
$50,048 to Michigan State University, East Lansing, MI, 2011.
$50,048 to Van Andel Institute, Grand Rapids, MI, 2011.

4514
Larry and Karen Mulder Foundation ✧

P.O. Box 451
Zeeland, MI 49464-0451

Established in 2006 in MI.
Donors: Larry Mulder; Karen Mulder; Michael Mulder; Kimberly Mulder.
Foundation type: Independent foundation.
Financial data (yr. ended 12/31/13): Assets, $4,355,906 (M); gifts received, $4,028,181; expenditures, $862,526; qualifying distributions, $851,138; giving activities include $837,761 for 77 grants (high: $150,000; low: $200).
Fields of interest: Theological school/education; Education; Boys & girls clubs; Human services; Christian agencies & churches; Protestant agencies & churches.
Limitations: Applications not accepted. Giving primarily in MI, with some emphasis on Holland. No grants to individuals.
Application information: Contributes only to pre-selected organizations.
Trustees: Jennifer Mesler; Karen Mulder; Larry Mulder.
EIN: 205853542
Selected grants: The following grants are a representative sample of this grantmaker's funding activity:
$145,000 to Saint Johns Home, Grand Rapids, MI, 2011. For unrestricted grant to general fund.
$139,965 to Western Theological Seminary, Holland, MI, 2011. For unrestricted grant to general fund.
$35,000 to Reformed Church in America, Grand Rapids, MI, 2011. For unrestricted grant to general fund.
$20,000 to Jubilee Ministries, Holland, MI, 2011. For unrestricted grant to general fund.
$15,000 to Geneva Camp and Retreat Center, Holland, MI, 2011. For unrestricted grant to general fund.
$5,000 to Smile Train, New York, NY, 2011. For unrestricted grant to general fund.
$4,000 to Center for Women in Transition, Holland, MI, 2011. For unrestricted grant to general fund.
$1,000 to Community Action House, Holland, MI, 2011. For unrestricted grant to general fund.

4515
David & Carol Myers Foundation ✧ ☆

(formerly David G. & Carol P. Myers Charitable Foundation)
c/o Carol P. Myers
109 W. 12th St.
Holland, MI 49423-3214

Established in 1989 in MI.
Donors: David G. Myers; Carol P. Myers.
Foundation type: Independent foundation.
Financial data (yr. ended 12/31/13): Assets, $35,985,478 (M); expenditures, $2,455,662; qualifying distributions, $1,920,876; giving activities include $1,913,514 for 56 grants (high: $250,000; low: $420).
Fields of interest: Higher education; Theological school/education; Human services; International affairs; Community/economic development; Christian agencies & churches.
Limitations: Applications not accepted. Giving in the U.S., with emphasis on MI; some funding also in Scotland. No grants to individuals.
Application information: Contributes only to pre-selected organizations.
Board meeting date(s): Spring
Officers: Carol P. Myers, Pres.; David G. Myers, V.P.
Director: Scott Kling.
EIN: 382884733

4516
Oleson Foundation ✧

P.O. Box 904
Traverse City, MI 49685-0904
Contact: Kathryn L. Huschke, Exec. Dir.
E-mail: kathy@olesonfoundation.org; Main URL: http://www.olesonfoundation.org

Established in 1959 in MI.
Donors: Don Oleson; Gerald Oleson; Gerald W. Oleson‡; Frances M. Oleson‡.
Foundation type: Independent foundation.
Financial data (yr. ended 12/31/13): Assets, $15,656,287 (M); gifts received, $1,000,758; expenditures, $1,588,379; qualifying distributions, $1,033,909; giving activities include $982,646 for 86 grants (high: $150,000; low: $500).
Purpose and activities: The foundation's mission is to help people help themselves achieve the greatest good for the greatest number efficiently over a broad range of social and environmental interests.
Fields of interest: Historic preservation/historical societies; Elementary/secondary education; Higher education; Environment; Health care; Youth development, centers/clubs; Human services; United Ways and Federated Giving Programs; Christian agencies & churches.
Type of support: General/operating support; Continuing support; Annual campaigns; Capital campaigns; Building/renovation; Equipment; Land acquisition; Curriculum development; Technical assistance; Matching/challenge support.
Limitations: Applications accepted. Giving limited to the Lower Peninsula region in northwestern MI, mainly the counties of Benzie, Emmet, Grand Traverse, and Manistee. No grants to individuals, or for endowments or scholarships.
Application information: Application form required.
Initial approach: Use forms on foundation web site
Copies of proposal: 1
Deadline(s): Apr. 1
Board meeting date(s): June
Final notification: Usually in mid-June

Officers and Directors:* Donald W. Oleson,* Pres.; Gerald E. Oleson,* V.P.; Richard Ford,* Secy.-Treas.; Kathryn Wise Huschke, Exec. Dir.; John Tobin.
Number of staff: 1 part-time professional.
EIN: 386083080
Selected grants: The following grants are a representative sample of this grantmaker's funding activity:
$100,000 to Munson Healthcare Regional Foundation, Traverse City, MI, 2012. For Year 1 and 2 of Five Year Commitment.
$38,300 to Northwestern Michigan College Foundation, Traverse City, MI, 2012. For grant for Special Projects.
$35,000 to Grand Traverse Regional Land Conservancy, Traverse City, MI, 2012. For grant for Maple Bay, Stewardship, Farmability.
$30,000 to Alliance for Economic Success, Manistee, MI, 2012. For grant for Recreation Opportunities at 4 Sites.
$30,000 to Leelanau Conservancy, Leland, MI, 2012. For grant for Clay Cliffs Acquisition.
$25,000 to Grand Traverse Regional Land Conservancy, Traverse City, MI, 2012. For Year End Grant for Operations.
$20,000 to Father Fred Foundation, Traverse City, MI, 2012. For matching grant for Fall Food Drive.
$10,000 to Interlochen Center for the Arts, Interlochen, MI, 2012. For grant for Ceramics Studio.
$10,000 to Northwestern Michigan College Foundation, Traverse City, MI, 2012. For grant for Equipment for Water Resources Lab.
$5,000 to Good Samaritan Family Services, Ellsworth, MI, 2012. For emergency fuel needs.

4517
Elsa U. Pardee Foundation ✧
P.O. Box 2767
Midland, MI 48641-2767
Contact: James A. Kendall, Secy.
E-mail: kmcdonald@pardeefoundation.org; Main URL: http://www.pardeefoundation.org

Incorporated in 1944 in MI.
Donor: Elsa U. Pardee‡.
Foundation type: Independent foundation.
Financial data (yr. ended 12/31/13): Assets, $90,109,613 (M); expenditures, $5,475,237; qualifying distributions, $5,043,156; giving activities include $4,970,989 for 20 grants (high: $1,800,000; low: $9,700).
Purpose and activities: Giving primarily to support: 1) research programs directed toward discovering new approaches for cancer treatment and cure; and 2) financial support for cancer treatment.
Fields of interest: Cancer; Medical research, institute; Cancer research.
Type of support: Research.
Limitations: Applications accepted. Giving on a national basis. No grants to individuals, or for capital campaigns, building, or endowment funds, equipment (except when used in a specific project), scholarships, fellowships, general purposes, matching gifts, or fundraising campaigns; no loans.
Publications: Application guidelines; Annual report.
Application information: Application form not required.
Initial approach: Use online application on foundation web site
Deadline(s): See foundation web site for deadline information
Board meeting date(s): 3 times per year
Final notification: 4 to 6 months
Officers and Trustees:* Gail E. Lanphear,* Pres.; Lisa J. Gerstacker,* V.P.; Mary M. Neely, Secy.; Alan W. Ott,* Treas.; W. James Allen; Laurie G. Bouwman; William C. Lauderbach; William D. Schuette; Michael Woolhiser.
Number of staff: 1 part-time support.
EIN: 386065799
Selected grants: The following grants are a representative sample of this grantmaker's funding activity:
$157,461 to University of Illinois at Chicago, Chicago, IL, 2012. For study of determining therapeutic value of targeting breast tumor kinase PTK6 in breast cancer.
$155,214 to University of California, Berkeley, CA, 2012. For study of potential application of irreversible electroporation (IRE) in treatment of pancreatic cancer.
$141,049 to University of California, Berkeley, CA, 2012. For study of novel roles of microRNA let-7C in prostate cancer.
$131,050 to Yale University, New Haven, CT, 2012. For study of novel apoptosis inducing therapy targeted to mitochrondria in cancer cells.
$125,000 to Pennsylvania State University, University Park, PA, 2012. For the study of development of novel thiobarbituric acid analogs for lung cancer.
$125,000 to University of Nebraska-Lincoln, Lincoln, NE, 2012. For study of hpaf1 in drug resistance of ovarian cancer stem cells.
$124,858 to Johns Hopkins University, Baltimore, MD, 2012. For study of in vitro and in vivo characterization of miR-675 in esophageal squamous cell carcinomas.
$123,949 to University of Michigan, Ann Arbor, MI, 2012. For tumor growth and metastasis in human ovarian cancer.
$122,627 to University of California, Berkeley, CA, 2012. For study of roles of autophagy in promoting treatment resistance in giloblastoma.
$117,399 to University of South Florida, Tampa, FL, 2012. For study of novel proteasome inhibitors as potential anti-cancer agents.
$100,000 to University of Iowa, Iowa City, IA, 2012. For study of multifunctional RNA-based therapy for advanced cancers of the breast.
$100,000 to University of Michigan, Ann Arbor, MI, 2012. For medical oncology fellowship training program.
$95,025 to Henry Ford Health System, Detroit, MI, 2012. For study of CDDO-Me novel triterpenoid for treatment of pancreatic cancer.
$94,023 to University of Nebraska-Lincoln, Lincoln, NE, 2012. For study of direct protein kinase activity sensors for interrogating clinically relevant signaling pathways.
$81,385 to University of Cincinnati, Cincinnati, OH, 2012. For study of targeting tumor-associated fibroblasts as therapeutic strategy in melanoma.

4518
Suzanne Upjohn Delano Parish Foundation ✧
(formerly Suzanne D. Parish Foundation)
211 S. Rose St.
Kalamazoo, MI 49007-4713
Contact: Ronald N. Kilgore, V.P.

Established in MI.
Donors: Suzanne U.D. Parish; Suzanne U.D. Parish Irrevocable Trust.
Foundation type: Independent foundation.
Financial data (yr. ended 12/31/12): Assets, $3,914,994 (M); gifts received, $36,819,900; expenditures, $37,770,942; qualifying distributions, $37,735,717; giving activities include $37,725,000 for 7 grants (high: $35,000,000; low: $10,000).
Purpose and activities: Support primarily to an aviation history museum.
Fields of interest: Museums (history); Space/aviation.
Type of support: General/operating support.
Limitations: Applications not accepted. Giving primarily in Portage and Kalamazoo, MI. No grants to individuals; no loans.
Application information: Contributes only to pre-selected organizations.
Officers and Directors:* Katharine P. Miller,* Pres.; P. William Parish,* V.P.; Preston L. Parish,* V.P.; Ronald N. Kilgore,* Secy.-Treas.
EIN: 382484268

4519
Penske Foundation, Inc. ✧ ☆
2555 Telegraph Rd
Bloomfield Hills, MI 48302-0954

Donors: Kathryn H. Penske; Lawrence N. Bluth.
Foundation type: Independent foundation.
Financial data (yr. ended 12/31/13): Assets, $3,202,428 (M); gifts received, $2,461,000; expenditures, $2,464,289; qualifying distributions, $2,462,600; giving activities include $2,461,000 for 10 grants (high: $1,000,000; low: $10,000).
Fields of interest: Museums (specialized); Education.
Limitations: Applications not accepted.
Application information: Contributes only to pre-selected organizations.
Officers: Kathryn H. Penske, Pres.; Lawrence N. Bluth, Secy.; Mary Lou Pernicano, Treas.
Directors: Blair Penske Hall; Gregory W. Penske; Jay C. Penske; Mark H. Penske; Roger S. Penske, Jr.
EIN: 274648290

4520
Joe D. Pentecost Foundation ✧
1651 W. Lake Lansing Rd., Ste. 300
East Lansing, MI 48823-6337

Established in 2002 in MI.
Donor: Joe D. Pentecost‡.
Foundation type: Independent foundation.
Financial data (yr. ended 12/31/12): Assets, $19,998,469 (M); expenditures, $1,056,853; qualifying distributions, $833,518; giving activities include $741,274 for 21 grants (high: $540,774; low: $1,000).
Purpose and activities: The foundation focuses on youth and education.
Fields of interest: Higher education; Higher education, university; Protestant agencies & churches; Children/youth; Children; Substance abusers.
Type of support: Annual campaigns; Program development; Building/renovation; Endowments.
Limitations: Applications not accepted. Giving primarily in Ingham, Eaton and Clinton counties, MI. No support for political organizations. No grants to individuals.
Application information: Unsolicited requests for funds not accepted.
Board meeting date(s): Varies
Directors: Gary Hurand; Vic Loomis; Calvin C. Lutz; Robert J. Phipps; Rita F. Stoskopf.
EIN: 352178154
Selected grants: The following grants are a representative sample of this grantmaker's funding activity:
$540,774 to Michigan State University, East Lansing, MI, 2012. For Endowed Scholarship, Building Renovations.

4521
Perrigo Company Charitable Foundation ✧
515 Eastern Ave.
Allegan, MI 49010-9070
E-mail: perrigofoundation@perrigo.com; Main URL: http://www.perrigo.com/

Established in 2000 in MI.
Donor: Perrigo Co.
Foundation type: Company-sponsored foundation.
Financial data (yr. ended 06/30/13): Assets, $902,408 (M); gifts received, $1,758,550; expenditures, $1,777,004; qualifying distributions, $1,731,620; giving activities include $1,185,597 for 174+ grants (high: $75,000).
Purpose and activities: The foundation supports organizations involved with arts and culture, education, health, substance abuse prevention, cancer, and human services.
Fields of interest: Arts; Higher education; Education; Hospitals (general); Health care; Substance abuse, prevention; Cancer; Boy scouts;

Girl scouts; American Red Cross; Developmentally disabled, centers & services; Homeless, human services; Human services; United Ways and Federated Giving Programs.
Type of support: Scholarship funds; General/operating support; Building/renovation; Program development.
Limitations: Applications accepted. Giving primarily in areas of company operations in MI. No grants to individuals.
Application information: Application form required.
Initial approach: Online application form
Deadline(s): None
Officers and Directors:* Joseph C. Papa,* Pres.; Judy L. Brown,* Exec. V.P.; John T. Hendrickson,* Exec. V.P.; Scott R. Rush, V.P.; Todd W. Kingma,* Secy.; Ronald L. Winowiecki, Treas.; Michael R. Stewart.
EIN: 383553518
Selected grants: The following grants are a representative sample of this grantmaker's funding activity:
$18,800 to Safeway Foundation, Pleasanton, CA, 2011. For charitable activities.
$15,000 to Borgess Foundation, Kalamazoo, MI, 2011. For charitable activities.
$15,000 to Center for Women in Transition, Holland, MI, 2011. For charitable activities.
$15,000 to Hope College, Holland, MI, 2011.
$15,000 to Kids Food Basket, Grand Rapids, MI, 2011. For charitable activities.
$10,000 to Business Leaders for Michigan, Detroit, MI, 2011. For charitable activities.
$10,000 to International Aid, Spring Lake, MI, 2011. For charitable activities.
$5,000 to American Cancer Society, Grand Rapids, MI, 2011. For charitable activities.
$5,000 to Bethany Christian Services, Grand Rapids, MI, 2011. For charitable activities.
$3,000 to Otsego Public Schools Foundation, Otsego, MI, 2011.

4522
Petoskey-Harbor Springs Area Community Foundation ✧

616 Petoskey St., Ste. 203
Petoskey, MI 49770-2779 (231) 348-5820
Contact: David L. Jones, Exec. Dir.; For grants: Sara Ward, Prog. Off.
FAX: (231) 348-5883; E-mail: info@phsacf.org; Additional e-mails: djones@phsacf.org, lwendland@phsacf.org and sward@phsacf.org; Main URL: http://www.phsacf.org
Facebook: https://www.facebook.com/PetoskeyHarborSpringsAreaCommunityFoundation
Application inquiry e-mail: sward@phsacf.org

Established in 1991 in MI.
Foundation type: Community foundation.
Financial data (yr. ended 03/31/14): Assets, $34,375,158 (M); gifts received, $902,563; expenditures, $1,713,439; giving activities include $1,276,711 for 57+ grants (high: $123,334), and $28,500 for 50 grants to individuals.
Purpose and activities: The foundation's to improve the quality of life for all people in Emmet County, by: 1) connecting donors with community needs; 2) building a permanent source of charitable funds to serve our area; 3) addressing a broad range of community issues through innovative grantmaking; 4) championing philanthropy and active citizenship.
Fields of interest: Historic preservation/historical societies; Arts; Higher education; Education; Environment; Health care; Agriculture/food; Recreation; Youth development; Human services; Economic development; Community/economic development.
Type of support: Building/renovation; Equipment; Program development; Seed money; Scholarship funds; Technical assistance; Scholarships—to individuals; Matching/challenge support.
Limitations: Applications accepted. Giving limited to Emmet County, MI. No support for sectarian religious purposes. No grants to individuals (except for scholarships), or for endowments, debt reduction, annual fundraising drives, operational phases of established programs, conferences, travel, or scholarly research; no loans.
Publications: Application guidelines; Annual report; Financial statement; Grants list; Informational brochure.
Application information: Potential applicants must contact the foundation prior to submitting an application to discuss their project. Visit foundation web site for application information. Application form required.
Initial approach: Telephone
Copies of proposal: 30
Deadline(s): Mar. 2 and Oct. 1
Board meeting date(s): Monthly
Final notification: Approx. 2 months
Officers and Directors:* Charles H. Gano,* Pres.; Lisa G. Blanchard,* V.P.; Mike Eberhart,* Secy.; Todd Winnell,* Treas.; David L. Jones, Exec. Dir.; Robert W. Charlton; J. Wilfred Cwikiel; Jennifer E. Deegan; Kathy Erber; Michael J. FitzSimons; James W. Ford; Ann K. Irish; Hon. Charles W. Johnson; Kelsey L. Nuorala; Jill O'Neill; B. Thomas Smith.
Number of staff: 3 full-time professional; 1 part-time professional.
EIN: 383032185

4523
The Pokagon Fund, Inc. ✧

821 E. Buffalo St.
New Buffalo, MI 49117-1522 (269) 469-9322
Contact: Mary L. Dunbar, Exec. Dir.
E-mail: info@pokagonfund.org; E-mail address for applications: grants@pokagonfund.org; Main URL: http://www.pokagonfund.org/
Facebook: http://www.facebook.com/pages/the-pokagon-fund/123810620966970
Grants List: http://www.pokagonfund.org/Grants.asp
E-mail address for scholarships: scholarships@pokagonfund.org

Established in 2007 in MI.
Donor: Four Winds Casino Resort.
Foundation type: Company-sponsored foundation.
Financial data (yr. ended 06/30/13): Assets, $8,859,236 (M); gifts received, $2,376,667; expenditures, $3,774,758; qualifying distributions, $3,726,854; giving activities include $3,455,074 for 190 grants (high: $500,000; low: $450).
Purpose and activities: The fund supports programs designed to enhance the lives of residents in the New Buffalo, Michigan, region and the communities where the Pokagon Band of Potawatomi Indians own land. Special emphasis is directed toward arts and culture, education, the environment, health, recreation, and human services.
Fields of interest: Performing arts; Arts; Libraries (public); Education, reading; Education; Environment, recycling; Environment, land resources; Environment; Health care; Food services; Food banks; Recreation, camps; Recreation, parks/playgrounds; Recreation, fairs/festivals; Recreation; Residential/custodial care, hospices; Human services; Community/economic development; Native Americans/American Indians.
Type of support: General/operating support; Continuing support; Management development/capacity building; Building/renovation; Equipment; Land acquisition; Emergency funds; Program development; Conferences/seminars; Film/video/radio; Curriculum development; Scholarship funds; Research; Consulting services; Program-related investments/loans; Scholarships—to individuals; Matching/challenge support.
Limitations: Applications accepted. Giving in primarily in New Buffalo, MI, region, including the townships of Chikaming, Grand Beach, Michiana, and Three Oaks; some giving also in South Bend, IN, and Dowagia and Hartford MI. No support for political candidates, political advocacy, or religious organizations not of direct benefit to the entire community. No grants to individuals (except for scholarships), or for endowments.
Publications: Application guidelines; Annual report (including application guidelines); Grants list; IRS Form 990 or 990-PF printed copy available upon request.
Application information: The foundation supports municipalities, nonprofit organizations, and charities in areas where the Pokagon Band of Potawatomi Indians are located, and other organizations. An application form is available for each type of organization. Application form required.
Initial approach: Complete online application
Deadline(s): 90 days prior to need; Mar. 19 for high school scholarships; Mar. 31 for adult scholarships
Board meeting date(s): Second Thurs. of each month
Final notification: Within 90 days; May for scholarships
Officers and Directors:* Roger Radar,* Chair.; Robert Carpenter,* Vice-Chair; Viki Gudas,* Secy.; Robert Gow, Treas.; Mary L. Dunbar, Exec. Dir.; Ryan Fellows; Marie Manley.
Number of staff: 1 full-time professional; 1 full-time support.
EIN: 300130499

4524
Ralph L. and Winifred E. Polk Foundation ✧

260 E. Brown St., Ste. 340
Birmingham, MI 48009-6234

Incorporated in 1962 in MI.
Donors: Ralph L. Polk†; Winifred E. Polk; Stephen R. Polk.
Foundation type: Independent foundation.
Financial data (yr. ended 12/31/13): Assets, $16,142,360 (M); gifts received, $12,279,010; expenditures, $12,904,336; qualifying distributions, $12,835,055; giving activities include $12,827,510 for 66 grants (high: $11,000,000; low: $2,500).
Purpose and activities: Giving primarily for education and youth programs.
Fields of interest: Media, television; Arts; Education; Environment, natural resources; Zoos/zoological societies; Human services; Children/youth, services; Christian agencies & churches.
Type of support: General/operating support; Capital campaigns.

Limitations: Applications not accepted. Giving primarily in MI, with some emphasis on Detroit. No grants to individuals.
Application information: Contributes only to pre-selected organizations.
Officers: Stephen R. Polk, Pres. and Treas.; Ann S. Hoerle, Secy.
Directors: Kathy Polk Osborne; Julie A. Polk; Susan P. Scyphers.
EIN: 386080075

4525
Edgar and Elsa Prince Foundation ✧
(formerly Prince Foundation)
190 River Ave., Ste. 300
Holland, MI 49423-2825

Established in 1977.
Donors: Edgar D. Prince†; Elsa D. Prince; Prince Corp.; Elsa D. Prince Living Trust; Prince Charitable Remainder Unitrust.
Foundation type: Independent foundation.
Financial data (yr. ended 06/30/13): Assets, $34,973,049 (M); gifts received, $18,999,889; expenditures, $4,929,604; qualifying distributions, $4,748,470; giving activities include $4,740,000 for 146 grants (high: $700,000; low: $1,000).
Purpose and activities: Giving to Christian organizations, churches, and schools and community activities.
Fields of interest: Elementary/secondary education; Health organizations, association; Family services; Aging, centers/services; Community development, neighborhood development; Christian agencies & churches; Aging.
Type of support: General/operating support.
Limitations: Applications not accepted. Giving primarily in MI. No grants to individuals.
Application information: Contributes only to pre-selected organizations.
Officers: Elsa D. Prince Brokehuizen, Pres.; Elisabeth DeVos, V.P.; Eileen Ellens, V.P.; Erik D. Prince, V.P.; Emilie Wierda, V.P.; Robert Haveman, Secy.-Treas.
EIN: 382190330
Selected grants: The following grants are a representative sample of this grantmaker's funding activity:
$750,000 to Focus on the Family, Colorado Springs, CO, 2012.
$702,000 to Family Research Council, Washington, DC, 2012.
$600,000 to Haggai Institute for Advanced Leadership Training, Norcross, GA, 2012.
$275,000 to Media Research Center, Reston, VA, 2012.
$202,000 to Ridge Point Community Church, Holland, MI, 2012.
$195,000 to Holland Christian Schools, Holland, MI, 2012.
$15,000 to Promise Keepers, Denver, CO, 2012.
$15,000 to Resthaven Patrons, Holland, MI, 2012.
$10,000 to Rehoboth Christian School, Rehoboth, NM, 2012.
$5,000 to Eagle Forum Education and Legal Defense Fund, Alton, IL, 2012.

4526
The Ravitz Foundation ✧
514 S. Rose St.
Kalamazoo, MI 49007-5212

Established in 2001 in MI.
Donors: Edward Ravitz†; The Edward Ravitz Revocable Living Trust.
Foundation type: Independent foundation.
Financial data (yr. ended 12/31/13): Assets, $40,127,452 (M); expenditures, $2,359,360; qualifying distributions, $2,046,429; giving activities include $1,917,800 for 44 grants (high: $260,000; low: $750).
Purpose and activities: Giving primarily for higher education, particularly medical school education, and for medical research.
Fields of interest: Higher education; Medical school/education; Health care; Medical research, institute; Jewish agencies & synagogues.
Type of support: Professorships; Seed money; Matching/challenge support; Endowments.
Limitations: Applications not accepted. Giving primarily in MI; some funding also in New York, NY. No grants to individuals.
Publications: Annual report.
Application information: Contributes only to pre-selected organizations.
Board meeting date(s): June and Nov.
Officers: Burton R. Shifman, Pres.; Bruce Gelbaugh, V.P. and Treas.
Directors: Jonathan Aaron; Lawrence Handler; Arnold Shifman; Jerry Speedy.
Number of staff: 2 part-time professional.
EIN: 383508943
Selected grants: The following grants are a representative sample of this grantmaker's funding activity:
$200,000 to Western Michigan University Foundation, Kalamazoo, MI, 2012. For Edward Ravitz Memorial Scholarship in Construction Engineering.
$167,000 to University of Michigan, Ann Arbor, MI, 2012. For Depression Center.
$125,000 to University of Michigan, Ann Arbor, MI, 2012. For Mott's Children's Hospital.
$100,000 to Jewish Federation of Metropolitan Detroit, Bloomfield Hills, MI, 2012. For Small Communities Initiative.
$5,000 to Congregation Beth Shalom, Oak Park, MI, 2012. For Sanctuary Fund.
$5,000 to Jewish Federation of Metropolitan Detroit, Bloomfield Hills, MI, 2012. For L Simon Archives.
$5,000 to University of Michigan, Ann Arbor, MI, 2012. For Richard D. Swartz, M.D. Collegiate Professorship.
$2,500 to University of Michigan, Ann Arbor, MI, 2012. For Craniofacial Anomalies Program-Research.

4527
RNR Foundation, Inc. ✧ ☆
2212 Old Falls Dr.
Ann Arbor, MI 48103

Established in 1994 in FL.
Donor: Rhoda Newberry Reed.
Foundation type: Independent foundation.
Financial data (yr. ended 07/31/13): Assets, $5,973,807 (M); expenditures, $729,852; qualifying distributions, $661,314; giving activities include $574,779 for 9 grants (high: $208,668; low: $290).
Purpose and activities: Giving primarily for education, human services, community foundations, and health care programs, particularly a foundation's clinical nurse program.
Fields of interest: Higher education; Health care; Human services; Foundations (public); Foundations (community); Leadership development.
Limitations: Applications not accepted. Giving primarily in FL and MI. No grants to individuals.
Application information: Contributes only to pre-selected organizations.
Officers: David Lord, Pres.; Charles Lord, V.P.; Edith Lord-Wolff, Secy.; Richard Lord, Treas.
Director: Heather Lord.
EIN: 650539370

4528
The Rodney Fund ✧
19100 W. Eight Mile Rd.
Southfield, MI 48075-5792
Contact: James M. Rodney, Dir.

Established in 1992 in MI.
Donors: James M. Rodney; Leign Rodney; Clare Rodney.
Foundation type: Independent foundation.
Financial data (yr. ended 12/31/13): Assets, $8,554,373 (M); gifts received, $659,000; expenditures, $846,106; qualifying distributions, $810,621; giving activities include $810,621 for 44 grants (high: $70,000; low: $500).
Purpose and activities: Giving primarily for public affairs institutes and centers. The fund supports libertarian principles: limited government, private property, free markets, individual liberty, free trade, and rule by law, as established by the U.S. Constitution.
Fields of interest: Education, research; Higher education; Education; Employment, public policy; Human services; United Ways and Federated Giving Programs; Social sciences; Public affairs.
Limitations: Applications accepted. Giving on a national basis.
Application information: Application form required.
Initial approach: Letter
Deadline(s): None
Directors: Lawrence Reed; James M. Rodney; Leigh Rodney; Steven Thomas.
EIN: 383030437
Selected grants: The following grants are a representative sample of this grantmaker's funding activity:
$198,483 to Free To Choose Network, Erie, PA, 2011. For general funding.
$130,000 to Mackinac Center for Public Policy, Midland, MI, 2011. For general funding.
$123,500 to Foundation for Economic Education, Irvington, NY, 2011. For general funding.
$20,000 to Action Institute NC, Charlotte, NC, 2011. For general funding.

4529
Rordor Foundation ✧
c/o Robert O. Roskam
P.O. Box 202
Grand Rapids, MI 49501-0202

Established in 1983 in MI.
Donors: Donald O. Roskam; Robert O. Roskam; Harold Zeigler Chrysler; Don Roskam†; Bakers Food; Roskam Baking Co.
Foundation type: Independent foundation.
Financial data (yr. ended 12/31/12): Assets, $106,170 (M); gifts received, $225,540; expenditures, $1,330,655; qualifying distributions,

$1,330,345; giving activities include $1,330,345 for 7 grants (high: $10,000; low: $1,500).
Purpose and activities: Giving primarily for health; support also for education, Christian organizations, and human services.
Fields of interest: Higher education; Medical care, community health systems; Hospitals (specialty); Health organizations; Human services; Christian agencies & churches; Children/youth.
Limitations: Applications not accepted. Giving limited to Grand Rapids, MI. No grants to individuals.
Application information: Contributes only to pre-selected organizations.
Officer: Robert O. Roskam, Pres.
EIN: 382500050

4530
Saddle Foundation ✧
101 N. Main St., 7th Fl.
Ann Arbor, MI 48104-1400

Established in 1997 in MI.
Donor: Kathryn W. Holmes.
Foundation type: Independent foundation.
Financial data (yr. ended 12/31/13): Assets, $12,953,313 (M); gifts received, $55,526; expenditures, $722,369; qualifying distributions, $664,680; giving activities include $660,000 for 10 grants (high: $100,000; low: $45,000).
Purpose and activities: Giving primarily for education, human services, wildlife conservation, and to a YMCA.
Fields of interest: Museums; Higher education; Animals/wildlife, preservation/protection; Human services; YM/YWCAs & YM/YWHAs; Residential/custodial care, hospices.
Limitations: Applications not accepted. Giving primarily in MI; funding also in CA and NY. No grants to individuals.
Application information: Contributes only to pre-selected organizations.
Officers and Directors:* Kathryn W. Holmes,* Pres. and Secy.-Treas.; Howard S. Holmes,* V.P.; Howard S. Holmes II,* V.P.; Erik H. Serr.
EIN: 383347262
Selected grants: The following grants are a representative sample of this grantmaker's funding activity:
$90,000 to Wildlife Conservation Society, Bronx, NY, 2011.
$90,000 to YMCA of San Francisco, San Francisco, CA, 2011.
$75,000 to Ann Arbor Hands-On Museum, Ann Arbor, MI, 2011.
$75,000 to Arbor Hospice Foundation, Ann Arbor, MI, 2011.
$60,000 to Wildlife Conservation Society, Bronx, NY, 2011.
$50,000 to Eles Place, Lansing, MI, 2011.
$50,000 to University Musical Society, Ann Arbor, MI, 2011.
$40,000 to YMCA of San Francisco, San Francisco, CA, 2011.
$33,000 to University of Michigan, Ann Arbor, MI, 2011.

4531
Sage Foundation ✧
P.O. Box 1919
Brighton, MI 48116-5719 (810) 227-7660
Contact: Melissa Sage Fadim, Pres. and Tr.

Incorporated in 1954 in MI.
Donors: Charles F. Sage†; Effa L. Sage†.
Foundation type: Independent foundation.
Financial data (yr. ended 12/31/13): Assets, $57,612,262 (M); expenditures, $3,456,983; qualifying distributions, $3,170,518; giving activities include $2,948,310 for 109 grants (high: $265,000; low: $2,500).
Purpose and activities: Giving primarily for the arts, education, health organizations, social services, and Roman Catholic churches and agencies.
Fields of interest: Arts; Higher education; Education; Health organizations, association; Human services; Catholic agencies & churches.
Type of support: General/operating support; Continuing support; Annual campaigns; Capital campaigns; Building/renovation; Equipment; Endowments; Program development; Scholarship funds; Research; Matching/challenge support.
Limitations: Applications accepted. Giving primarily in IL and MI.
Application information: Application form required.
Initial approach: Letter
Copies of proposal: 1
Deadline(s): None
Board meeting date(s): Quarterly
Final notification: 12 weeks
Officers and Trustees:* Melissa Sage Fadim,* Pres.; James E. Van Doren,* V.P.; Anne Sage Price.
Number of staff: 1 part-time professional.
EIN: 386041518
Selected grants: The following grants are a representative sample of this grantmaker's funding activity:
$200,000 to Adrian College, Adrian, MI, 2012. For Downs Hall Renovation and Restoration.
$75,000 to Siena Heights University, Adrian, MI, 2012. For general, charitable and educational-University Center.
$50,000 to Kartemquin Educational Films, Chicago, IL, 2012. For general, charitable and educational-Mormon Movie.
$38,340 to Art Institute of Chicago, Chicago, IL, 2012. For School of the Art Institute of Chicago-Scholarships.
$25,000 to Art Institute of Chicago, Chicago, IL, 2012. For general, charitable and educational-School of the Art Institute, gene Siskel Film Center.
$25,000 to Kartemquin Educational Films, Chicago, IL, 2012. For general, charitable and educational-Prisoner of Her Past film.
$15,000 to Adrian College, Adrian, MI, 2012. For general, charitable and educational-Kartemquin Education Films presentation.
$15,000 to Grant Park Orchestral Association, Chicago, IL, 2012. For general, charitable and educational-June, 2012 Divertimento.

4532
Saginaw Community Foundation ✧
1 Tuscola, Ste. 100
Saginaw, MI 48607-1282 (989) 755-0545
Contact: Renee S. Johnston, C.E.O.
FAX: (989) 755-6524;
E-mail: info@saginawfoundation.org; Main
URL: http://www.saginawfoundation.org
Facebook: http://www.facebook.com/pages/Saginaw-MI/Saginaw-Community-Foundation/59408999148
Flickr: https://www.flickr.com/photos/scfoundation/
LinkedIn: http://www.linkedin.com/company/saginaw-community-foundation
Pinterest: http://www.pinterest.com/scfoundation/
Twitter: http://twitter.com/SCFoundation
YouTube: http://www.youtube.com/user/saginawcomfoundation

Incorporated in 1984 in MI.
Foundation type: Community foundation.
Financial data (yr. ended 12/31/13): Assets, $48,410,402 (M); gifts received, $3,152,323; expenditures, $4,224,215; giving activities include $1,296,901 for 63+ grants (high: $145,157), and $409,346 for 492 grants to individuals.
Purpose and activities: Support for projects not currently being served by existing community resources and for projects providing leverage for generating other funds and community resources.
Fields of interest: Arts; Education; Environment; Health care; Recreation; Family services; Human services; Economic development; Community/economic development; General charitable giving; Youth; Aging.
Type of support: Building/renovation; Equipment; Emergency funds; Program development; Publication; Seed money; Scholarship funds; Technical assistance; Scholarships—to individuals; Matching/challenge support.
Limitations: Applications accepted. Giving limited to Saginaw County, MI. No support for churches or sectarian religious programs. No grants to individuals (except for designated scholarship funds), or for operating budgets, endowment campaigns, debt reduction, travel, or basic municipal or educational services; generally no multi-year grants.
Publications: Application guidelines; Annual report (including application guidelines); Newsletter; Occasional report.
Application information: Visit foundation web site for application cover form and guidelines. Application form required.
Initial approach: Telephone
Copies of proposal: 1
Deadline(s): Feb. 1, May 1, Aug. 1 and Nov. 1
Board meeting date(s): Monthly
Final notification: 2 months after deadline
Officers and Directors:* David J. Abbs,* Chair.; Heidi A. Bolger,* Vice-Chair.; Renee Johnston,* C.E.O. and Pres.; Smallwood Holoman,* Secy.; Frederick C. Gardner,* Treas.; Bridget Smith,* Asst. Treas.; Andre Buckley; Paul Chaffee; Desmon Daniel, Ph.D.; James Fabiano II; Victor Gomez; Todd Gregory; Dr. Carlton Jenkins; Shari Kennett; Dr. John Kosanovich; Trish Luplow; Leslie Orozco; Francine Rifkin; Cheri Sammis; Kari Shaheen; John Shelton; Richard Syrek; Laura Yockey.
Number of staff: 4 full-time professional; 2 full-time support.
EIN: 382474297

4533
The A. Paul and Carol C. Schaap Foundation ✧
P.O. Box 75000, MC 3302
Detroit, MI 48275
Application address: c/o Comerica Bank, 500 Woodward Ave., 21st Fl., Detroit, MI 48226
tel: (313) 222-3304

Established in MI.
Donors: A. Paul Schaap; Carol C. Schaap.

Foundation type: Independent foundation.
Financial data (yr. ended 12/31/13): Assets, $5,075,748 (M); expenditures, $1,017,145; qualifying distributions, $956,401; giving activities include $955,065 for 21 grants (high: $255,000; low: $5,000).
Purpose and activities: Giving primarily for higher education, including a Presbyterian seminary.
Fields of interest: Media, radio; Higher education; Theological school/education.
Limitations: Applications accepted. Giving primarily in MI; some funding also in KY.
Application information: Application form not required.
Initial approach: Letter
Deadline(s): None
Trustee: Comerica Bank.
EIN: 207097647
Selected grants: The following grants are a representative sample of this grantmaker's funding activity:
$50,000 to Hope College, Holland, MI, 2012. For Annual Contribution - Bio-Chem and Chemistry Research.
$20,000 to Wayne State University, Detroit, MI, 2012. For Annual Contribution - WSU Math Corp Pledge.
$10,000 to Hope College, Holland, MI, 2012. For Presidential Scholarship Program.
$10,000 to Wayne State University, School of Medicine, Detroit, MI, 2012. For Richard J. Mazurek Medical Education.
$5,000 to Wayne State University, Detroit, MI, 2012. For Robert and Sandra Thomas Endowed Scholarship.

4534
The Schalon Foundation ✧ ☆
4418 Tanglewood Trail
St. Joseph, MI 49085-9686
Application address: c/o Susan Schalon, 5694 Forest Glen Dr., Ada, MI 49301, tel.: (616) 318-9555

Established in 1997 in MI.
Donors: Edward I. Schalon‡; Marcella J. Schalon.
Foundation type: Independent foundation.
Financial data (yr. ended 12/31/13): Assets, $5,091,170 (M); expenditures, $760,299; qualifying distributions, $732,500; giving activities include $732,500 for 33 grants (high: $500,000; low: $500).
Fields of interest: Performing arts, orchestras; Performing arts, opera; Arts; Human services.
Type of support: Building/renovation.
Limitations: Applications accepted. Giving primarily in MI, with emphasis on St. Joseph. No grants to individuals.
Application information: Application form required.
Initial approach: Letter
Deadline(s): Dec. 1
Officers and Directors:* Marcella J. Schalon,* Pres.; Susan K. Schalon,* Secy.; Scott Schalon,* Treas.
EIN: 383341098

4535
Sebastian Foundation ✧
c/o Linda Jones
3333 Evergreen Dr. N.E., Ste. 110
Grand Rapids, MI 49525-9493 (616) 361-1996
Contact: David S. Sebastian, Pres. and Dir.

Established in 1980 in MI.
Donors: Audrey M. Sebastian; James R. Sebastian.
Foundation type: Independent foundation.
Financial data (yr. ended 08/31/13): Assets, $9,771,185 (M); expenditures, $1,395,437; qualifying distributions, $1,289,304; giving activities include $1,131,650 for 70 grants (high: $85,000; low: $500).
Purpose and activities: Supports human services and public benefit organizations, education, and the arts.
Fields of interest: Arts; Education; Human services; Foundations (private grantmaking).
Limitations: Applications accepted. Giving primarily in the Grand Rapids, MI, area. No support for religious programs. No grants to individuals.
Application information:
Initial approach: Proposal
Copies of proposal: 1
Deadline(s): None
Officers and Directors:* David S. Sebastian,* Pres.; John O. Sebastian,* Secy.-Treas.; Linda Jones.
Number of staff: 2 full-time support.
EIN: 382340219
Selected grants: The following grants are a representative sample of this grantmaker's funding activity:
$150,000 to Kent, County of, Grand Rapids, MI, 2011. To support annual fund.

4536
Secchia Family Foundation ✧
(formerly Peter F. Secchia Foundation)
220 Lyon Square., N.W., Ste. 510
Grand Rapids, MI 49503-2210

Established in 1985 in MI.
Donors: Peter F. Secchia; SIBSCO, LLC.
Foundation type: Independent foundation.
Financial data (yr. ended 12/31/13): Assets, $15,023,482 (M); gifts received, $500,000; expenditures, $820,221; qualifying distributions, $765,321; giving activities include $713,700 for 70 grants (high: $150,000; low: $100).
Purpose and activities: Giving for education, health associations, youth programs, and religion.
Fields of interest: Higher education; Education; Hospitals (specialty); Health organizations, association; Children/youth, services; Catholic agencies & churches.
Type of support: Building/renovation; Equipment; Scholarship funds.
Limitations: Applications not accepted. Giving primarily in MI. No grants to individuals.
Application information: Contributes only to pre-selected organizations.
Officers: Peter F. Secchia, Pres.; James A. Ens, Secy.; Mark A. Schut, Treas.
EIN: 382641093

4537
Elizabeth, Allan & Warren Shelden Fund ✧
17152 Kercheval St.
Grosse Pointe Farms, MI 48230-1661 (313) 881-2282
Contact: William W. Shelden, Jr., Pres.

Incorporated in 1937 in MI.
Donors: Elizabeth Warren Shelden‡; Allan Shelden III‡; W. Warren Shelden‡.
Foundation type: Independent foundation.
Financial data (yr. ended 12/31/12): Assets, $34,057,447 (M); expenditures, $1,547,516; qualifying distributions, $1,530,369; giving activities include $1,529,000 for 55 grants (high: $130,000; low: $1,000).
Purpose and activities: Giving primarily for the arts, education, and health care.
Fields of interest: Arts; Education; Environment, natural resources; Hospitals (general); Health care; Human services; United Ways and Federated Giving Programs.
Type of support: General/operating support; Continuing support; Annual campaigns; Capital campaigns; Building/renovation; Equipment; Endowments; Research.
Limitations: Giving primarily in the metropolitan Detroit, MI, area. No grants to individuals, or for scholarships, fellowships, or matching gifts; no loans.
Publications: Annual report.
Application information: Application form not required.
Initial approach: Proposal
Copies of proposal: 1
Deadline(s): None
Board meeting date(s): Nov. or Dec.
Final notification: Positive replies only
Officers and Trustees:* William W. Shelden, Jr.,* Pres. and Treas.; David M. Hempstead,* Secy.; Sally S. Sheldon.
Number of staff: 1 part-time professional; 1 part-time support.
EIN: 386052198

4538
The Shepherds Hand ✧
4943 Birchcrest Dr.
Oscoda, MI 48750-9750
Contact: Richard A. Porter, Pres.

Foundation type: Independent foundation.
Financial data (yr. ended 12/31/13): Assets, $11,039,830 (M); expenditures, $601,119; qualifying distributions, $511,630; giving activities include $464,360 for 98 grants (high: $20,000; low: $250).
Fields of interest: Youth development; Human services; Religion.
Limitations: Applications accepted. Giving primarily in FL, IL, and MI.
Application information: Application form required.
Initial approach: Proposal
Deadline(s): None
Officers: Richard A. Porter, Pres.; Sharon Porter, Secy.-Treas.
Trustee: Richard Porter, Jr.
EIN: 382092191

4539
Edwin J. & Ruth M. Shoemaker Foundation ✧
840 W. Long Lake Rd., Ste. 200
Troy, MI 48098-6358 (231) 943-4717
Contact: Robert L. Shoemaker, Pres.
Application address: 9130 Hunter Ln., Traverse City, MI 49684, tel.: (231) 943-4717

Established in 1998 in MI.
Donors: Edwin J. Shoemaker†; Dale Shoemaker.
Foundation type: Independent foundation.
Financial data (yr. ended 12/31/13): Assets, $17,799,073 (M); expenditures, $734,245; qualifying distributions, $684,873; giving activities include $644,500 for 20 grants (high: $150,000; low: $2,500).
Purpose and activities: The foundation supports organizations that pursue and further the tenets of the Christian faith.
Fields of interest: Health care; Human services; Civil/human rights.
Limitations: Applications accepted. Giving in the U.S. primarily in MI; some funding also in North TX. No grants to individuals.
Application information: Application form required.
Initial approach: Letter
Deadline(s): None
Officers and Directors:* Robert L. Shoemaker,* Pres.; Dale A. Shoemaker,* V.P.; Mary Kaye Johnston,* Secy.-Treas.; David S. Johnston; Rocque E. Lipford; Eric C. Shoemaker.
EIN: 383137832
Selected grants: The following grants are a representative sample of this grantmaker's funding activity:
$25,000 to University of Michigan, Ann Arbor, MI, 2011. For general support.

4540
Bill and Vi Sigmund Foundation ✧
P.O. Box 1128
Jackson, MI 49204-1128 (517) 784-5464
Contact: Carolyn M. Pratt, Secy.
E-mail: sigmundfoundation@sbcglobal.net; Main URL: http://www.sigmundfoundation.org

Established in 2002 in MI.
Foundation type: Independent foundation.
Financial data (yr. ended 12/31/12): Assets, $10,287,234 (M); expenditures, $648,514; qualifying distributions, $591,193; giving activities include $250,300 for grants, and $337,125 for grants to individuals.
Purpose and activities: Scholarships primarily awarded to students majoring in the medical and aviation fields who are residents of Jackson or Lenawee County, Michigan; have been acceptance to an accredited college or university; have proof of financial need; have a cumulative grade point average of 2.5 or higher; and who have completed the Free Application for Federal Student Aid (FAFSA).
Fields of interest: Salvation Army; United Ways and Federated Giving Programs.
Type of support: Scholarships—to individuals.
Limitations: Applications accepted. Giving limited to Jackson and Lenawee Counties, MI.
Publications: Application guidelines; Grants list.
Application information: Letter of intent and application form available on foundation web site.
Initial approach: For grants submit a letter of intent; for scholarships submit an application
Deadline(s): See foundation web site for current deadlines
Officers and Directors:* Ralph L. Bodman, Pres.; Carolyn M. Pratt, Secy.; Charles C. McClafferty,* Treas.; Kenneth A. Dillon; John Macchia; Kent Mauer.
EIN: 300002491

4541
Silverwing Foundation ✧
660 Ada Dr., Ste. 301
Ada, MI 49301-9153 (616) 957-5823
Contact: James Rosloniec, Treas.

Established in CA and MI.
Donors: Jay and Betty Van Andel Foundation; Jay Van Andel Trust; RDV Foundation.
Foundation type: Independent foundation.
Financial data (yr. ended 12/31/12): Assets, $58,946,805 (M); expenditures, $16,026,667; qualifying distributions, $12,512,585; giving activities include $12,512,585 for 45 grants (high: $2,523,750; low: $1,000).
Fields of interest: Human services; Christian agencies & churches.
Type of support: General/operating support; Capital campaigns; Seed money.
Limitations: Giving in the U.S., with emphasis on MI, particularly Grand Rapids, as well as CA and TX.
Application information:
Initial approach: Letter of reference
Deadline(s): None
Officers: Nan Van Andel, Pres.; James Rosloniec, Treas.
EIN: 202110480

4542
Skilling and Andrews Foundation ✧
c/o Ann Skilling Andrews
11720 E. Shore Dr.
Whitmore Lake, MI 48189-9104

Established in 1996 in MI.
Donors: Hazel D. Skilling†; Hugh H. Skilling Trust.
Foundation type: Independent foundation.
Financial data (yr. ended 12/31/13): Assets, $0 (M); expenditures, $504,909; qualifying distributions, $503,850; giving activities include $503,850 for 15 grants (high: $300,000; low: $50).
Purpose and activities: The foundation's primary interest is in working with charter school authorizers, and in research on charter schools and authorizers; some support also for conservation. The foundation is helping to fund a research center at the Central Michigan University Center for Charter Schools.
Fields of interest: Elementary/secondary education; Charter schools; Environment, natural resources.
Limitations: Applications not accepted. Giving primarily in the central U.S. No grants to individuals.
Application information: Contributes only to pre-selected organizations.
Board meeting date(s): First week of Aug.
Officers and Trustees:* Ann Skilling Andrews,* Pres. and Treas.; Kenneth Andrews,* V.P.; Steven Andrews,* Secy.
EIN: 383335356
Selected grants: The following grants are a representative sample of this grantmaker's funding activity:
$1,000 to Lake Champlain Committee, Burlington, VT, 2012. For environmental work.

4543
The Skillman Foundation ✧
100 Talon Centre Dr., Ste. 100
Detroit, MI 48207-4266 (313) 393-1185
Contact: Suzanne Moran, Grants Mgr.
FAX: (313) 393-1187;
E-mail: mailbox@skillman.org; Main URL: http://www.skillman.org
A Rose for Detroit Blog: http://skillman.org/Knowledge-Center/A-Rose-for-Detroit-Blog
E-Newsletter: http://skillman.org/Knowledge-Center/E-newsletters
Facebook: http://www.facebook.com/pages/The-Skillman-Foundation/83980402909
Grants Database: http://www.skillman.org/Knowledge-Center/Grants-Map
Pinterest: http://www.pinterest.com/skillmanfound/
Skillman's Instagram: http://instagram.com/skillmanfoundation
The Skillman Foundation's Philanthropy Promise: http://www.ncrp.org/philanthropys-promise/who
Twitter: http://twitter.com/skillmanfound
YouTube: http://www.youtube.com/skillmanfoundation

Incorporated in 1960 in MI.
Donor: Rose P. Skillman†.
Foundation type: Independent foundation.
Financial data (yr. ended 12/31/13): Assets, $470,151,665 (M); expenditures, $25,436,014; qualifying distributions, $22,486,535; giving activities include $16,229,201 for 217 grants (high: $750,000; low: $475), $580,958 for 196 employee matching gifts, and $250,000 for 1 loan/program-related investment.
Purpose and activities: The foundation is a resource for improving the lives of children in metropolitan Detroit, MI. Children in disadvantaged situations are of special concern. The foundation applies its resources to foster positive relationships between children and adults, support high quality learning opportunities and strengthen healthy, safe and supportive homes and communities.
Fields of interest: Visual arts; Performing arts; Arts; Education, early childhood education; Child development, education; Education, reading; Education; Health care; Substance abuse, services; Crime/violence prevention, youth; Food services; Recreation; Human services; Children/youth, services; Child development, services; Family services; Homeless, human services; Children/youth; Children; Youth; Economically disadvantaged; Homeless.
Type of support: Continuing support; General/operating support; Program development; Program-related investments/loans; Employee matching gifts.
Limitations: Applications accepted. Giving primarily in metropolitan Detroit, with emphasis on six neighborhoods in the city of Detroit. No support for long-term projects not being aided by other sources, sectarian religious activities, political lobbying or legislative activities, or new organizations which do not have an operational and financial history. The foundation does not make grants to organizations

that had public support and revenues of less than $100,000 for the preceding year. No grants to individuals, or for endowment funds, annual campaigns, purchase, construct or renovate facilities, basic research or deficit financing.
Publications: Application guidelines; Annual report; Informational brochure (including application guidelines); Newsletter; Occasional report; Program policy statement.
Application information: Complete online Grant Inquiry for new applicants. Previous grantees should contact their program officer before starting application process. Application form required.
Initial approach: Online application process
Deadline(s): For new inquiries, 2 months prior to trustee meeting date
Board meeting date(s): March, June, Sept. and Dec.
Final notification: 6 weeks after board meeting
Officers and Trustees:* Lizabeth Ardisana,* Chair.; Herman B. Gray, M.D.*, Vice-Chair.; Tonya Allen, C.E.O. and Pres.; Danielle Olekszyk, V.P., Opers. and C.F.O.; Kristen McDonald, V.P., Programs; Chris Uhl, V.P., Social Innovation; David Baker Lewis; Stephen E. Ewing; Denise Ilitch; Mary L. Kramer; Amyre Makupson; Eddie R. Munson; Jerry Norcia.
Number of staff: 20 full-time professional; 5 full-time support.
EIN: 381675780
Selected grants: The following grants are a representative sample of this grantmaker's funding activity:
$850,000 to University of Michigan, Ann Arbor, MI, 2012. To continue to support technical assistance to effectively implement the Foundation's Good Neighborhoods (GN) work in six targeted communities of Detroit.
$800,000 to Michigan State University, East Lansing, MI, 2013. To continue to support the Good Schools Resource Center-Detroit (GSRC) in partnership with Michigan State University. The GSRC will serve as a critical partner to deliver on the Foundations education strategy of building capacity.
$750,000 to Michigan State University, East Lansing, MI, 2012. To fund the expansion and operations of the Good Schools Resource Center - Detroit. The Center will continue to serve as the hub for the Good Neighborhoods School Improvement Strategy.
$500,000 to Education Achievement Authority of Michigan, Detroit, MI, 2012. For the operations of the Education Achievement Authority of Michigan, a statewide recovery district established to transform the lowest-performing five percent of schools in Michigan.
$500,000 to Education Trust, Washington, DC, 2013. To build on the Foundation's efforts to improve the quality of Michigan's education system by supporting a leading statewide education reform organization in its efforts to provide advocacy and data to policymakers, educators and citizens, payable over 2.00 years.
$420,000 to Prevention Network, East Lansing, MI, 2012. For continued implementation of the neighborhood small grants program for community-based, resident-driven projects in Brightmoor, Chadsey Condon, Cody Rouge, Northend Central, Osborn and Southwest Detroit Neighborhoods.
$396,000 to IFF, Chicago, IL, 2013. To support the launch of the IFF (Illinois Finance Fund) in Detroit to provide real estate development and financing to charter schools, early childhood development centers, and other nonprofits in the six Skillman target neighborhoods, payable over 3.00 years.
$302,000 to Southwest Solutions, Detroit, MI, 2013. For The Vista Partnership which seeks to address the conditions of long-term disinvestment and wide-scale blight in the project area by placing residents at the center of planning and implementation, and as drivers of change in their neighborhood.
$300,000 to Black Family Development, Detroit, MI, 2013. To support the planning and implementation of a comprehensive community engagement strategy to address community safety in the Cody Rouge, Osborn and Southwest Detroit Neighborhoods.
$300,000 to Don Bosco Hall, Detroit, MI, 2013. To continue to provide implementation funds to support the expansion, centralization and coordination of a high-quality youth development system in Cody Rouge and Brightmoor.
$300,000 to Southwest Counseling Solutions, Detroit, MI, 2012. For implementation funds to support the expansion, centralization and coordination of high-quality youth development activities in the Chadsey Condon and Southwest Detroit neighborhoods.
$185,000 to Detroit Hispanic Development Corporation, Detroit, MI, 2012. To continue support for Hispanic-led agencies and fundraising that collectively serve, advocate for, and represent the interests of the Detroit Latino community in Southwest Detroit and Chadsey Condon neighborhoods.
$175,000 to Southwest Detroit Business Association, Detroit, MI, 2012. To continue to provide operational support and staff to Southwest Detroit Neighborhoods Congress of Communities (CoC), a resident-stakeholder partnership, to conduct planning and advocacy to improve the conditions for children.
$173,000 to Institute for Research and Reform in Education, Toms River, NJ, 2013. For continued support for a comprehensive evaluation and performance measurement system, designed to provide timely, credible information for monitoring progress, making course corrections, and assessing the results of the Foundation's investments.
$125,000 to Prevention Network, East Lansing, MI, 2013. To support the continuation and expansion of a small grants program that provides up to $1,000 for community-based, resident driven projects that target boys of color.
$120,000 to Clark Park Coalition, Detroit, MI, 2013. To support the Southwest Detroit Positive Youth Development Initiative, which promotes high school graduation rates, advances youth public safety around the Park, and builds youth leadership and neighborhood community services.
$110,000 to Michigan Nonprofit Association, Lansing, MI, 2013. To create online dashboard that can be used to provide accurate and easily accessible parcel data for community planning, foreclosure prevention and blight removal in Brightmoor.
$100,000 to Big Brothers Big Sisters of Metropolitan Detroit, Detroit, MI, 2012. To engage a group of African-American and Latino boys residing in the Cody Rouge community in positive mentoring relationships.
$90,000 to Michigan College Access Network, Lansing, MI, 2012. For the expansion of the National College Advising Corps in the Good Neighborhood Schools, a nationally recognized program that returns recent college graduates to their home communities as college advisor at neighborhood high schools.
$85,000 to Urban Neighborhood Initiatives, Detroit, MI, 2012. To continue to support the capacity of a community-based organization in Southwest Detroit to coordinate and increase participation in high-quality youth programming and secure external funding to support revitalization.

4544
Spartan Stores Foundation ✧ ☆
850 76th St., GR761225
P.O. Box 8700
Grand Rapids, MI 49518-8700

Established in 2007 in MI.
Donor: Spartan Stores Inc.
Foundation type: Company-sponsored foundation.
Financial data (yr. ended 12/31/13): Assets, $750,006 (M); gifts received, $1,931,763; expenditures, $848,320; qualifying distributions, $759,287; giving activities include $759,287 for 38 grants (high: $300,000; low: $100).
Purpose and activities: The foundation supports organizations involved with education, health, cancer, hunger, youth development, and human services.
Fields of interest: Higher education; Education, reading; Education; Hospitals (general); Health care; Cancer; Food services; Youth development; Salvation Army; YM/YWCAs & YM/YWHAs; Children, services; Human services; United Ways and Federated Giving Programs.
Type of support: Annual campaigns; General/operating support; Building/renovation.
Limitations: Applications not accepted. Giving primarily in Grand Rapids, MI. No grants to individuals.
Application information: Contributes only to pre-selected organizations.
Officers: Dennis Eidson, Pres.; Meredith Gremel, V.P.; Alex J. DeYounker, Secy.; David M. Staples, Treas.
EIN: 208767495

4545
John and Judy Spoelhof Foundation ✧
151 Central Ave., Ste. 200
Holland, MI 49423-2831

Established in 1984 in MI.
Donors: John Spoelhof; Judy Spoelhof; Prince Holding Corp.; JJS Partnership.
Foundation type: Independent foundation.
Financial data (yr. ended 12/31/13): Assets, $21,678,096 (M); expenditures, $2,081,558; qualifying distributions, $1,856,350; giving activities include $1,846,900 for 93 grants (high: $750,000; low: $250).
Purpose and activities: Giving primarily for Christian organizations and churches, education, health organizations, and social services.
Fields of interest: Elementary/secondary education; Human services; Christian agencies & churches.
Type of support: General/operating support; Building/renovation.
Limitations: Applications not accepted. Giving primarily in MI, with emphasis on Holland. No grants to individuals.

Application information: Contributes only to pre-selected organizations.
Officers: John Spoelhof, Pres.; Judith Spoelhof, Secy.
Trustee: Scott Spoelhof.
EIN: 382492821

4546
Mary G. Stange Charitable Trust ✧
201 W. Big Beaver Rd., Ste. 500
Troy, MI 48084-4160

Established in 1999 in MI.
Donor: Mary G. Stange Trust.
Foundation type: Independent foundation.
Financial data (yr. ended 12/31/13): Assets, $13,440,971 (M); expenditures, $683,201; qualifying distributions, $576,266; giving activities include $514,500 for 12 grants (high: $200,000; low: $1,000).
Purpose and activities: Giving primarily for higher education.
Fields of interest: Higher education; Human services.
Limitations: Applications not accepted. Giving primarily in MI; some giving also in NC. No grants to individuals.
Application information: Contributes only to pre-selected organizations.
Trustee: David C. Stone.
EIN: 386739773

4547
Steelcase Foundation ✧
P.O. Box 1967, GH-4E
Grand Rapids, MI 49501-1967
Contact: Phyllis Gebben, Donations Coord.
FAX: (616) 475-2200;
E-mail: pgebben@steelcase.com; Main URL: http://www.steelcase.com/en/company/who/steelcase-foundation/pages/steelcasefoundation.aspx
Grants List: http://www.steelcase.com/en/Company/Who/Steelcase-Foundation/Documents/2014%20Second%20Quarter%20Grant%20Awards.pdf

Established in 1951 in MI.
Donor: Steelcase Inc.
Foundation type: Company-sponsored foundation.
Financial data (yr. ended 11/30/13): Assets, $97,773,053 (M); gifts received, $516,100; expenditures, $5,509,752; qualifying distributions, $4,037,425; giving activities include $3,531,757 for 59 grants (high: $400,000; low: $176), and $485,668 for 824 employee matching gifts.
Purpose and activities: The foundation supports organizations involved with arts and culture, education, the environment, health, human services, and community development. Special emphasis is directed toward programs designed to assist youth, the elderly, people with disabilities, and economically disadvantaged people.
Fields of interest: Arts; Education, early childhood education; Libraries (public); Education; Environment; Health care; Homeless, human services; Human services; Economic development; Community/economic development; Youth; Aging; Disabilities, people with; Economically disadvantaged.
Type of support: General/operating support; Management development/capacity building; Capital campaigns; Building/renovation; Equipment; Program development; Seed money; Scholarship funds; Employee matching gifts; Employee-related scholarships.
Limitations: Applications accepted. Giving limited to areas of company operations, with emphasis on Athens, AL and Grand Rapids, MI. No support for churches or religious organizations not of direct benefit to the entire community, or discriminatory organizations. No grants to individuals (except for employee-related scholarships), or for endowments or conferences or seminars.
Publications: Application guidelines; Annual report; Grants list.
Application information: Letters of inquiry should be submitted using organization letterhead. A full proposal may be requested at a later date. Support is limited to 1 contribution per organization during any given year. Application form required.
Initial approach: Letter of inquiry for application form
Copies of proposal: 1
Deadline(s): Quarterly
Board meeting date(s): Quarterly
Final notification: At least 90 days
Officers and Trustees:* Kate Pew Wolters,* Chair.; Julie Ridenour, Pres.; James P. Hackett; Mary Anne Hunting; Elizabeth Welch Lykins; Mary Goodwillie Nelson; Craig Niemann; Robert C. Pew III.
Number of staff: 1 full-time professional; 1 full-time support.
EIN: 386050470

4548
Stonisch Foundation ✧
371 Lake Shore Rd.
Grosse Point Farms, MI 48236-3048

Established in 1961 in MI.
Donor: Helen Stonisch.
Foundation type: Independent foundation.
Financial data (yr. ended 12/31/13): Assets, $15,778,093 (M); expenditures, $1,117,873; qualifying distributions, $766,000; giving activities include $766,000 for 34 grants (high: $100,000; low: $500).
Fields of interest: Higher education; Health care; Human services; Christian agencies & churches; Catholic agencies & churches.
Type of support: Research.
Limitations: Applications not accepted. Giving primarily in MI.
Application information: Contributes only to pre-selected organizations.
Board meeting date(s): Nov.
Officers: Gail Riggs, Pres.; Glorie Stonisch, V.P.; Mary Sue Stonisch, Secy.
EIN: 386088638
Selected grants: The following grants are a representative sample of this grantmaker's funding activity:
$120,000 to Rochester General Hospital, Rochester, NY, 2011. For research.
$115,000 to Hillsdale College, Hillsdale, MI, 2011.
$10,000 to Albion College, Albion, MI, 2011.

4549
The Charles J. Strosacker Foundation ✧
812 W. Main St.
P.O. Box 471
Midland, MI 48640-0471 (989) 832-0066
Contact: Marian L. Cimbalik, Tr.

Incorporated in 1957 in MI.
Donors: Charles J. Strosacker†; Ula G. Shaffer Administration Trust.
Foundation type: Independent foundation.
Financial data (yr. ended 12/31/13): Assets, $65,328,800 (M); expenditures, $2,904,889; qualifying distributions, $2,632,874; giving activities include $2,509,556 for 116 grants (high: $250,000; low: $25).
Purpose and activities: Giving to assist and benefit political subdivisions of the state of Michigan, educational organizations, and social services.
Fields of interest: Higher education; Human services; Community/economic development; Foundations (community); United Ways and Federated Giving Programs.
Type of support: Continuing support; Building/renovation; Equipment; Endowments; Program development; Seed money; Research.
Limitations: Applications accepted. Giving primarily in MI, with emphasis on Midland County. No grants to individuals, or for matching gifts; no loans.
Publications: Annual report (including application guidelines).
Application information: Application form not required.
Initial approach: Letter
Copies of proposal: 1
Deadline(s): None
Board meeting date(s): May, Aug., and Nov.
Officers and Trustees:* David J. Arnold,* Chair.; Bobbie N. Arnold, C.E.O. and Pres.; Richard M. Reynolds, Exec. V.P.; Donna T. Morris,* Secy.; James L. Borin, Treas.; Lawrence Burks, Tr. Emeritus; Ralph A. Cole, Tr. Emeritus; Richard Hazleton, Tr. Emeritus; Kimberlee K. Baczewski; John N. Bartos; Stephanie A. Burns; Marian L. Cimbalik; David H. Dunn; Carolyn Thrune Durand; Charles J. Thrune; Charlie C. Thrune-Lundquist.
Number of staff: 1 part-time support.
EIN: 386062787

4550
Sturgis Area Community Foundation ✧
(formerly Sturgis Foundation)
310 N. Franks Ave.
Sturgis, MI 49091-1259 (269) 659-8508
Contact: LeeAnn McConnell, Chair.
FAX: (269) 659-4539;
E-mail: sacf@sturgisfoundation.org; Main URL: http://www.sturgisfoundation.org

Established in 1962 in MI.
Foundation type: Community foundation.
Financial data (yr. ended 03/31/14): Assets, $23,368,984 (M); gifts received, $380,381; expenditures, $1,143,603; giving activities include $753,738 for 20+ grants (high: $87,020), and $97,271 for 97 grants to individuals.
Purpose and activities: The foundation seeks to provide benefits to area community charitable organizations.
Fields of interest: Arts; Education; Animals/wildlife; Health care; Recreation; Human services; Community/economic development; Children/youth; Children; Youth; Young adults; Disabilities,

people with; Mentally disabled; Women; Substance abusers; Crime/abuse victims; Economically disadvantaged; Homeless.
Type of support: General/operating support; Capital campaigns; Building/renovation; Equipment; Endowments; Program development; Scholarship funds; Consulting services; Scholarships—to individuals; Matching/challenge support; Student loans—to individuals.
Limitations: Applications accepted. Giving limited to the Sturgis, MI, area. No support for religious organizations. No grants to individuals (except for scholarships), or for existing obligations or debts, fundraising events, or new business loans.
Publications: Application guidelines; Annual report; Financial statement; Grants list; Informational brochure; Informational brochure (including application guidelines); Newsletter.
Application information: Visit foundation web site application form and guidelines. Application form required.
Initial approach: Telephone or e-mail
Copies of proposal: 10
Deadline(s): Oct. 15
Board meeting date(s): Monthly
Final notification: 6 weeks
Officers and Trustees:* LeeAnn McConnell,* Chair.; Ruth Perry,* Vice-Chair.; Ray Sterling,* Secy.; Mary Dresser, Co-Dir.; John Wiedlea, Co-Dir.; Warren English; Michael Frost; Theo Omo; John Svendsen.
Number of staff: 1 full-time professional; 1 part-time support.
EIN: 383649922

4551
Tarakji Foundation ✧
26300 Telegraph Rd., 2nd Fl.
Southfield, MI 48033-2436

Established in 1999.
Donor: N. Tarakji.
Foundation type: Independent foundation.
Financial data (yr. ended 12/31/11): Assets, $3,669,047 (M); gifts received, $660,000; expenditures, $659,394; qualifying distributions, $648,760; giving activities include $648,760 for 14 grants (high: $563,960; low: $100).
Fields of interest: Islam.
Limitations: Applications not accepted. Giving primarily in MI. No grants to individuals.
Application information: Contributes only to pre-selected organizations.
Officers: Nael Tarakji, Pres.; Lama Tarakji, V.P.; Bilal Tarakji, Secy.
EIN: 383478158

4552
The A. Alfred Taubman Foundation ✧
(formerly A. Alfred Taubman Foundation II)
200 E. Long Lake Rd., Ste. 180
Bloomfield Hills, MI 48304-2336 (248) 258-6800
Contact: Kevin Molloy

Established in 2009 in MI as successor to A. Alfred Taubman Foundation, which was established in 1979.
Donors: A. Alfred Taubman; A. Alfred Taubman Restated Rev. Trust.
Foundation type: Independent foundation.
Financial data (yr. ended 07/31/13): Assets, $1,035 (M); gifts received, $570,048; expenditures, $569,066; qualifying distributions, $569,066; giving activities include $561,330 for 139 grants (high: $100,000; low: $50).
Fields of interest: United Ways and Federated Giving Programs; Jewish federated giving programs; Jewish agencies & synagogues.
Limitations: Applications accepted. Giving primarily in MI and NY.
Application information: Application form required.
Initial approach: Letter
Deadline(s): None
Officers and Director:* A. Alfred Taubman,* Chair. and Treas.; Gayle Taubman Kalisman, Pres.; William S. Taubman, V.P.; Jeffrey H. Miro, Secy.
EIN: 271366308
Selected grants: The following grants are a representative sample of this grantmaker's funding activity:
$20,000 to American Jewish Committee, New York, NY, 2011.
$10,000 to Community Foundation for Southeast Michigan, Detroit, MI, 2011.
$10,000 to Congregation Shaarey Zedek, Southfield, MI, 2011.
$5,000 to Child Mind Institute, New York, NY, 2011.
$5,000 to University of Michigan, Ann Arbor, MI, 2011.
$2,000 to American Diabetes Association, Alexandria, VA, 2011.
$2,000 to American Diabetes Association, Alexandria, VA, 2011.
$1,000 to Coleman A. Young Foundation, Detroit, MI, 2011.
$1,000 to Federation of Protestant Welfare Agencies, New York, NY, 2010. For general operating fund.
$1,000 to National Organization for Women Foundation, Washington, DC, 2011.
$1,000 to Park Avenue Synagogue, New York, NY, 2011.

4553
The Taubman Foundation ✧
200 E. Long Lake Rd., Ste. 180
Bloomfield Hills, MI 48304-2336 (248) 258-6800
Contact: Kevin Molloy

Donors: Robert S. Taubman; William S. Taubman; Gayle T. Kalisman; A. Alfred Taubman Restated Rev. Trust.
Foundation type: Independent foundation.
Financial data (yr. ended 01/31/14): Assets, $157 (M); gifts received, $850,079; expenditures, $850,128; qualifying distributions, $849,705; giving activities include $849,705 for 21 grants (high: $166,142; low: $7,500).
Fields of interest: Museums (art); Higher education; Education; Hospitals (general); Human services; Jewish agencies & synagogues.
Limitations: Applications accepted. Giving primarily in FL, MD, MI, and New York, NY.
Application information: Application form not required.
Initial approach: Letter
Deadline(s): None
Officers: A. Alfred Taubman, Chair.; Gayle T. Kalisman, Pres.; William S. Taubman, V.P.; Jeffrey H. Miro, Secy.; Robert S. Taubman, Treas.
EIN: 271366438

4554
Thewes Family Foundation ✧ ☆
355 S. Old Woodward Ave., Ste. 200
Birmingham, MI 48009-6260

Established in MI.
Donor: Beverly A. Thewes.
Foundation type: Independent foundation.
Financial data (yr. ended 12/31/13): Assets, $275,003 (M); gifts received, $1,484,125; expenditures, $1,467,899; qualifying distributions, $1,457,000; giving activities include $1,457,000 for 15 grants (high: $1,000,000; low: $500).
Fields of interest: Health organizations; Human services; Catholic agencies & churches.
Limitations: Applications not accepted. Giving primarily in MI.
Application information: Unsolicited requests for funds not accepted.
Officers and Directors:* Beverly A. Thewes,* Pres.; George V. Cassar, Jr.,* V.P. and Secy.; Leonard J. Gayeski,* V.P. and Treas.
EIN: 453660252

4555
Thompson Educational Foundation ✧
P.O. Box 6349
Plymouth, MI 48170-0353

Established in 2002 in MI.
Donors: Ellen A. Thompson; Robert M. Thompson.
Foundation type: Independent foundation.
Financial data (yr. ended 12/31/13): Assets, $107,912,883 (M); expenditures, $6,685,057; qualifying distributions, $15,657,569; giving activities include $1,075,283 for 3 grants (high: $801,066; low: $22,184).
Fields of interest: Education.
Type of support: General/operating support; Program-related investments/loans.
Limitations: Applications not accepted. Giving primarily in MI. No grants to individuals.
Application information: Contributes only to pre-selected organizations.
Officers and Trustees:* Robert M. Thompson,* Chair. and Pres.; Ellen A. Thompson,* V.P.; Joseph G. Horonzy,* Secy.-Treas.
EIN: 300107259
Selected grants: The following grants are a representative sample of this grantmaker's funding activity:
$98,409 to New Urban Learning, Detroit, MI, 2012. For Management of Charter School Operations.

4556
Thompson Foundation ✧
(formerly Thompson-McCully Foundation)
c/o Bridget Makridakis
P.O. Box 6349
Plymouth, MI 48170-0353
FAX: (734) 453-6475;
E-mail: cebejer@thompsonfdn.org; Main
URL: http://www.thompsonfdn.org

Established in 1999 in MI.
Donors: Robert M. Thompson; Ellen Anne Thompson.
Foundation type: Independent foundation.
Financial data (yr. ended 12/31/13): Assets, $46,222,660 (M); expenditures, $1,314,927; qualifying distributions, $1,296,674; giving

activities include $1,271,613 for 17 grants (high: $616,114; low: $250).
Fields of interest: Education.
Type of support: Program development; Scholarship funds.
Limitations: Applications not accepted. Giving primarily in the metropolitan Detroit, MI, area. No grants to individuals.
Application information: Unsolicited requests for funds not accepted.
Board meeting date(s): Feb., Apr., June, Aug., Oct., Dec.
Officers and Trustees:* Robert M. Thompson,* Pres.; Ellen Anne Thompson,* V.P.; Edward M. Parks,* Secy.-Treas.; Joseph G. Horonzy.
Number of staff: 1 full-time professional.
EIN: 383452577
Selected grants: The following grants are a representative sample of this grantmaker's funding activity:
$666,873 to Bowling Green State University, Bowling Green, OH, 2012. To increase Thompson Scholars to a total of 50 students in the President's Leadership Academy.
$80,000 to Wayne State University, Detroit, MI, 2012. For Math Corps student scholarships.
$70,628 to University of Michigan, Ann Arbor, MI, 2012. For Project Healthy Schools 3 Year Grant 2010-11 School Year 2011-12 School Year 2012-13 School Year.
$60,800 to Grand Valley State University, Allendale, MI, 2012. For Thompson Foundation UPA Award.
$50,000 to University of Michigan, Ann Arbor, MI, 2012. For Unrestricted Gift to U of M Cardiovascular Center Project Year 1 of 1 (2012) (previous grant number 07-036).
$10,000 to Salvation Army, Plymouth, MI, 2012. For Summer Day Camp 2012.
$850 to Loyola High School, Detroit, MI, 2012. For EAP 2012 - 2013 Scholarship.
$250 to Detroit Cristo Rey High School, Detroit, MI, 2012. For EAP 2011-2012 Scholarship.
$250 to Detroit Cristo Rey High School, Detroit, MI, 2012. For EAP 2012-2013 Scholarship.

4557
The Harry A. and Margaret D. Towsley Foundation ✧
240 W. Main St., Ste. 2400
P.O. Box 349
Midland, MI 48640-5191 (989) 837-1100
Contact: Lynn T. White, Pres.

Incorporated in 1959 in MI.
Donors: Margaret D. Towsley‡; Margaret Ann Riecker.
Foundation type: Independent foundation.
Financial data (yr. ended 12/31/13): Assets, $58,504,091 (M); expenditures, $1,542,426; qualifying distributions, $1,519,580; giving activities include $1,456,200 for 28 grants (high: $200,000; low: $6,000).
Purpose and activities: Support for medical and preschool education, social services, and continuing education and research in the health sciences.
Fields of interest: Arts; Education, early childhood education; Higher education; Medical school/education; Education; Medical research, institute; Human services.
Type of support: General/operating support; Continuing support; Annual campaigns; Capital campaigns; Building/renovation; Endowments; Program development; Professorships; Seed money; Research; Employee matching gifts; Matching/challenge support.
Limitations: Applications accepted. Giving primarily in MI. No grants to individuals, or for travel, scholarships, fellowships, conferences, books, publications, films, tapes, audio-visual, or other communication media; no loans.
Publications: Annual report (including application guidelines).
Application information: Environmental Impact Statement is required for all capital projects. Application form not required.
Initial approach: Proposal
Copies of proposal: 2
Deadline(s): Mar. 31
Final notification: 60 to 90 days
Officers and Trustees:* Margaret Ann Riecker,* Chair.; Lynn T. White,* Pres.; Judith D. Rumelhart,* V.P.; Mary Ivers, Treas.; C. Wendell Dunbar; David Winston Inglish; Douglas Inglish; Jennifer R. Poteat-Flores; Steven Towsley Riecker; Sharon Rothwell; Margaret E. Thompson, M.D.
Number of staff: 1 part-time support.
EIN: 386091798
Selected grants: The following grants are a representative sample of this grantmaker's funding activity:
$78,480 to University of Michigan, School of Music, Ann Arbor, MI, 2012. To support of the Program.
$6,000 to Munson Healthcare Regional Foundation, Traverse City, MI, 2012. To support of the Program.

4558
Thomas J. and Erma J. Tracy Family Foundation ✧
(formerly The Thomas J. Tracy Family Foundation)
c/o Rosenberger Law Group PLLC
4111 Andover Rd., Ste. 100W
Bloomfield Hills, MI 48302-1911

Established in 1998 in MI.
Donors: Thomas J. Tracy; Emmet and Frances Tracy Fund; Tracy Industries, Inc.; Thomas J. Tracy, Sr. Survivor's Trust.
Foundation type: Independent foundation.
Financial data (yr. ended 12/31/13): Assets, $981,613 (M); gifts received, $750,000; expenditures, $836,097; qualifying distributions, $823,210; giving activities include $823,210 for 35 grants (high: $75,000; low: $5,000).
Fields of interest: Higher education; Hospitals (general); Catholic agencies & churches.
Limitations: Applications not accepted. Giving primarily in CA. No grants to individuals.
Application information: Contributes only to pre-selected organizations.
Officers: Erma Jean Tracy, Pres. and Treas.; Cynthia Tracy, V.P.; David M. Rosenberger, Secy.
Trustee: Katherine McCanna.
EIN: 383390017

4559
Jerry L. & Marcia D. Tubergen Foundation ✧
P.O. Box 230257
Grand Rapids, MI 49523-0257 (616) 643-4700
Contact: Ginny Vander Hart, Exec. Dir.

Established in 1996 in MI.
Donors: Jerry L. Tubergen; Helen J. DeVos; Marcia D. Tubergen; Charitable Trust No. 2.
Foundation type: Independent foundation.
Financial data (yr. ended 12/31/12): Assets, $31,886,959 (M); expenditures, $2,599,075; qualifying distributions, $2,528,658; giving activities include $2,527,700 for 51 grants (high: $1,000,000; low: $250).
Purpose and activities: Giving primarily for Christian-based programs and services, as well as to a heart science center.
Fields of interest: Arts; Education; Heart & circulatory research; Human services; Children/youth, services; Christian agencies & churches.
Type of support: General/operating support; Annual campaigns; Capital campaigns.
Limitations: Applications not accepted. Giving primarily in the U.S., with emphasis on western MI; giving also England. No grants to individuals.
Application information: Contributes only to pre-selected organizations.
Officers: Jerry L. Tubergen, Pres. and Treas.; Marcia D. Tubergen, V.P and Secy.; Robert H. Schierbeek, V.P.
EIN: 383297265

4560
Tuktawa Foundation ✧
4812 Willow Ln.
Orchard Lake, MI 48324-3073
Contact: Charles J. Andrews, Pres.

Established in 1998 in MI.
Donor: Delphine J. Andrews.
Foundation type: Independent foundation.
Financial data (yr. ended 12/31/12): Assets, $8,693,556 (M); expenditures, $494,953; qualifying distributions, $421,289; giving activities include $420,631 for 43 grants (high: $100,000; low: $1,000).
Fields of interest: Historic preservation/historical societies; Higher education; Animals/wildlife; Hospitals (general); Youth development; Human services.
Type of support: General/operating support.
Limitations: Applications accepted. Giving in the U.S., primarily in MI.
Application information: Application form not required.
Deadline(s): None
Officers: Charles J. Andrews, Pres.; Adelaide Ford, Secy.-Treas.
Directors: Christopher C. Andrews; Tracey Andrews; Carolyn Ford Kowles; Jennifer Andrews Moilanen; Joanna Ford Virgne.
EIN: 383393453

4561
Jane Smith Turner Foundation, Inc. ✧
500 Woodward Ave., Ste. 2500
Detroit, MI 48226-5499

Established in 1994 in MI.
Foundation type: Independent foundation.
Financial data (yr. ended 12/31/13): Assets, $12,254,047 (M); expenditures, $594,705; qualifying distributions, $510,981; giving activities include $491,500 for 52 grants (high: $35,000; low: $2,500).
Fields of interest: Arts; Education; Environment, natural resources; Animals/wildlife, preservation/

protection; Health organizations, association; Children/youth, services; Protestant agencies & churches.
Limitations: Applications not accepted. Giving primarily in GA; some funding also in FL. No grants to individuals.
Application information: Contributes only to pre-selected organizations.
Officers and Directors:* Jane Smith Turner,* Pres. and Secy.; David W. Laughlin,* Treas.; Sarah Jean Turner Garlington; Laura Turner Seydel; Reed Beauregard Turner; Rhett Lee Turner; Robert E. Turner IV; John Wilson.
EIN: 383199326
Selected grants: The following grants are a representative sample of this grantmaker's funding activity:
$50,000 to High Museum of Art, Atlanta, GA, 2011.
$25,000 to Captain Planet Foundation, Atlanta, GA, 2011.
$25,000 to Georgia Public Broadcasting, Atlanta, GA, 2011.
$25,000 to Sayre School, Lexington, KY, 2011.
$20,000 to Florida Blood Services Foundation, Saint Petersburg, FL, 2011.
$15,000 to Conservation Fund, Arlington, VA, 2011.
$10,000 to Childrens Healthcare of Atlanta Foundation, Atlanta, GA, 2011.
$10,000 to Peregrine Fund, Boise, ID, 2011.
$5,000 to Oglethorpe University, Atlanta, GA, 2011.
$5,000 to Wilderness Society, Bozeman, MT, 2011.

4562
Tuscola County Community Foundation ✧ ☆
317 S. State St.
P.O. Box 534
Caro, MI 48723-0534
Contact: Ken Micklash, Exec. Dir.
E-mail: tccf534@centurytel.net; Tel/fax: (989) 673-8223; Main URL: http://www.tuscolacountycommunityfoundation.org

Established in 1997 in MI.
Foundation type: Community foundation.
Financial data (yr. ended 12/31/13): Assets, $9,784,651 (M); gifts received, $217,591; expenditures, $605,992; giving activities include $274,273 for 12+ grants (high: $22,900), and $146,550 for grants to individuals.
Purpose and activities: The foundation is to make Tuscola County a better place to live by maintaining a permanent philanthropic endowment base which will assist and fund a variety of efforts, turning needs and dreams into realities.
Fields of interest: Education; Recreation; Youth development; Human services; Children/youth; Children; Youth; Adults; Aging; Substance abusers; Economically disadvantaged; Homeless.
Type of support: Building/renovation; Equipment; Emergency funds; Program development; Seed money; Curriculum development; Scholarship funds; Matching/challenge support.
Limitations: Applications accepted. Giving limited to Tuscola County, MI. No support for sectarian religious programs. No grants for operating budgets, previously incurred debt, endowment campaigns, or fundraising activities.
Publications: Application guidelines; Annual report; Financial statement; Grants list; Informational brochure; Newsletter.
Application information: Visit foundation web site for application form and guidelines. Application form required.
Initial approach: Letter or telephone
Copies of proposal: 6
Deadline(s): Mar. 1 and Oct. 1
Board meeting date(s): 4th Thurs., quarterly
Final notification: 3 months
Officers and Trustees:* Rick Zimmer,* Pres.; Randy Stec,* V.P.; Janet Thane,* Secy.; Ann Marie Ball,* Treas.; Ken Micklash,* Exec. Dir.; Kurt Bender; Gary Crews; Pat Curtis; Denise Harrington; Tim Lyons; Amy Peters; Luther Stewart; Robert Worth.
Number of staff: 1 part-time professional.
EIN: 383351315

4563
Two Seven Oh, Inc. ✧
P.O. Box 1725
Birmingham, MI 48012-1725

Established in 2006 in MI.
Donor: Lynn Moran.
Foundation type: Independent foundation.
Financial data (yr. ended 12/31/13): Assets, $15,864,555 (M); expenditures, $986,771; qualifying distributions, $934,459; giving activities include $860,800 for 409 grants (high: $51,500; low: $100).
Fields of interest: Animal welfare; Housing/shelter; Catholic agencies & churches.
Limitations: Applications not accepted. Giving primarily in MI. No grants to individuals.
Application information: Contributes only to pre-selected organizations.
Officer: Lynn Moran, Pres. and Secy.-Treas.
Trustees: Amanda Ann Moran; Katherine Lynn Moran; Madison Dianne Moran.
EIN: 205576623
Selected grants: The following grants are a representative sample of this grantmaker's funding activity:
$2,500 to Recycling for Newaygo County, Fremont, MI, 2012. For General Operating Budget/Purchase of Microchips.

4564
Harold and Grace Upjohn Foundation ✧
211 S. Rose St.
Kalamazoo, MI 49007
Application address: c/o Floyd L. Parks, Harold and Grace Upjohn Foundation, 136 E. Michigan Ave., 9th Fl., Ste. B, Kalamazoo, MI 49007

Incorporated in 1958 in MI.
Donors: Grace G. Upjohn†; Edwin Meader†; Mary Meader Irrevocable Trust; Edwin Meader Revocable Trust.
Foundation type: Independent foundation.
Financial data (yr. ended 10/31/13): Assets, $19,752,129 (M); gifts received, $244,750; expenditures, $1,104,741; qualifying distributions, $1,005,349; giving activities include $986,000 for 68 grants (high: $40,000; low: $2,500).
Purpose and activities: Grants primarily to promote scientific research for the alleviation of human suffering; to care for the sick, aged, and helpless whose private resources are inadequate; to conduct research for and otherwise assist in the improvement of living, moral and working conditions; to promote the spread of education and to provide scholarships for deserving young men and women; to promote and aid in the mental, moral, intellectual and physical improvement, assistance and relief of the poor, indigent or deserving inhabitants of the U.S., regardless of race, color or creed.
Fields of interest: Arts; Higher education; Environment; Family services; Aging, centers/services; Community development, neighborhood development; Christian agencies & churches.
Type of support: Program development; Seed money; Scholarship funds; Research.
Limitations: Applications accepted. Giving limited to greater Kalamazoo, MI. No grants to individuals, or for operating budgets or annual campaigns.
Publications: Application guidelines; Annual report.
Application information: Application form required.
Initial approach: Contact foundation
Copies of proposal: 6
Deadline(s): None
Board meeting date(s): Spring and fall
Officers: Timothy Light, Pres.; Florence Upjohn Orosz, V.P.; Floyd L. Parks, Secy.-Treas.
Trustees: Janet J. Deal-Koestner; Randall W. Eberts.
EIN: 386052963

4565
Frederick S. Upton Foundation ✧
100 Ridgeway St.
St. Joseph, MI 49085-1047 (269) 982-1905
Contact: Stephen E. Upton, Chair.
FAX: (269) 982-0323;
E-mail: uptonfoundation@comcast.net

Trust established in 1954 in IL.
Donor: Frederick S. Upton†.
Foundation type: Independent foundation.
Financial data (yr. ended 12/31/13): Assets, $43,198,215 (M); expenditures, $2,085,869; qualifying distributions, $1,708,281; giving activities include $1,638,441 for 73 grants (high: $592,862; low: $200).
Type of support: General/operating support; Management development/capacity building; Annual campaigns; Capital campaigns; Building/renovation; Equipment; Program development; Seed money; Research.
Limitations: Applications accepted. Giving primarily in MI and SC.
Publications: Application guidelines.
Application information: Application form required.
Initial approach: Letter or telephone
Copies of proposal: 5
Deadline(s): Mar. 15, June 15, and Oct. 15
Board meeting date(s): Varies
Final notification: All applicants will be notified
Officers and Trustees:* Stephen E. Upton,* Chair.; Sylvia Upton Wood,* Secy.; Elizabeth Bartels; Priscilla Upton Byrns; Tom Fowler; Betsy Stover; Margaret Trumbull; Carrié Vill; JPMorgan Chase Bank, N.A.
Number of staff: 1 part-time professional.
EIN: 366013317
Selected grants: The following grants are a representative sample of this grantmaker's funding activity:
$50,000 to Boys and Girls Club of Benton Harbor, Benton Harbor, MI, 2012. For the construction of a new building and renovation of the teen center.
$50,000 to Cornerstone Alliance, Benton Harbor, MI, 2012. For the mission of Cornerstone Alliance.
$25,000 to Interlochen Center for the Arts, Interlochen, MI, 2012. For summer camp

scholarships for Berrien County students of color through partnership with Boys and Girls Club.
$25,000 to Western Michigan University, Kalamazoo, MI, 2012. For the Upton Graduate Fellowship Program with the Heritage Center for three years.
$20,000 to Starkey Hearing Foundation, Eden Prairie, MN, 2012. To fund the Hearing Angels Mission.
$20,000 to Starkey Hearing Foundation, Eden Prairie, MN, 2012. For hearing missions around the world.
$15,000 to Westminster Presbyterian Church, Grand Rapids, MI, 2012. For equipment for the Change the Climate, Change the World Program.
$10,000 to Boy Scouts of America, Southwest Michigan Council, Kalamazoo, MI, 2012. For the building of a long house at Camp Rota-Kiwan.
$5,000 to Upton Trio, Camden, SC, 2012. For the Chamber Music Program in schools.
$2,000 to University of Michigan, Ross School of Business, Ann Arbor, MI, 2012. For the University of Michigan Men's Rugby Club No. 312092.

4566
David and Carol Van Andel Foundation ✧
3133 Orchard Vista Dr. S.E.
Grand Rapids, MI 49546-7033
Contact: Mark J. Bugge, Secy.

Established in 2005 in MI.
Donors: Jay and Betty Van Andel Foundation; Jay Van Andel Trust.
Foundation type: Independent foundation.
Financial data (yr. ended 12/31/12): Assets, $70,705,598 (M); expenditures, $10,098,026; qualifying distributions, $3,982,038; giving activities include $3,695,036 for 80 grants (high: $1,000,000; low: $100).
Purpose and activities: Giving primarily for Christian religious activities, including higher and secondary education; support also for museums and performing arts groups.
Fields of interest: Museums; Performing arts; Secondary school/education; Higher education; Christian agencies & churches.
Type of support: General/operating support.
Limitations: Applications accepted. Giving primarily in Grand Rapids, MI.
Application information:
Initial approach: Letter
Deadline(s): None
Officer: Mark J. Bugge, Secy.
Trustee: David Van Andel.
Number of staff: 1 full-time professional; 1 full-time support.
EIN: 202110420

4567
Steve Van Andel Foundation
(formerly Steve & Cindy Van Andel Foundation)
P.O. Box 172
Ada, MI 49301-0172 (616) 787-6554
Contact: Deb Rushlo

Established in 2005 in MI.
Donor: Jay and Betty Van Andel Foundation.
Foundation type: Independent foundation.
Financial data (yr. ended 12/31/12): Assets, $70,977,688 (M); expenditures, $11,185,791; qualifying distributions, $4,606,543; giving activities include $4,606,543 for 61 grants (high: $1,500,000; low: $25).
Fields of interest: Hospitals (general); Youth development; Human services; Children/youth, services; Community/economic development; Public policy, research; Children/youth; Aging; Adults, women; Economically disadvantaged; Homeless.
Type of support: General/operating support; Annual campaigns; Capital campaigns; Program development; Scholarship funds.
Limitations: Applications accepted. Giving primarily in MI, with some emphasis on Grand Rapids.
Application information:
Initial approach: Letter of request
Deadline(s): None
Number of staff: 1 full-time support.
EIN: 202110604

4568
Van Andel Fund, Inc. ✧
3133 Orchard Vista Dr. S.E.
Grand Rapids, MI 49546-7033
Contact: Mark J. Bugge, Secy.-Treas.
E-mail: mark.bugge@vaegr.com

Established in 2007 in MI.
Donor: Jan and Betty Van Andel Foundation.
Foundation type: Independent foundation.
Financial data (yr. ended 12/31/12): Assets, $209,465,467 (M); expenditures, $4,822,323; qualifying distributions, $3,023,858; giving activities include $3,000,000 for 1 grant.
Fields of interest: Museums (specialized).
Limitations: Giving primarily in Grand Rapids, MI.
Application information:
Initial approach: Letter of reference
Deadline(s): None
Officers: David Van Andel, Pres.; Mark Bugge, Secy.-Treas.
Director: Linda Wasserman.
EIN: 208446997
Selected grants: The following grants are a representative sample of this grantmaker's funding activity:
$3,000,000 to George W. Bush Foundation, Dallas, TX, 2012.

4569
Van Elslander Family Foundation ✧
6500 E. Fourteen Mile Rd.
Warren, MI 48092-1281

Established in 1993 in MI.
Donors: Archie A. Van Elslander; Comfort Mattress, Inc.; Art Van Furniture, Inc.
Foundation type: Independent foundation.
Financial data (yr. ended 12/31/13): Assets, $1,184,512 (M); gifts received, $1,200,000; expenditures, $1,204,407; qualifying distributions, $1,202,126; giving activities include $1,201,500 for 3 grants (high: $1,000,000; low: $1,500).
Fields of interest: Health care; Human services; Catholic agencies & churches.
Limitations: Applications not accepted. Giving primarily in MI, with emphasis on Detroit. No grants to individuals.
Application information: Contributes only to pre-selected organizations.
Officers: Archie A. Van Elslander, Pres.; Kenneth Van Elslander, V.P.; Mary Ann Van Elslander, Secy.; Debra A. Van Elslander, Treas.
EIN: 383144274

4570
Van Kampen Boyer Molinari Charitable Foundation ✧
5440 Farr Rd.
Fruitport, MI 49415-9751 (231) 865-6000
Contact: Joan M. Mack

Donor: Kimberly Van Kampen Boyer.
Foundation type: Independent foundation.
Financial data (yr. ended 12/31/12): Assets, $2,682,590 (M); gifts received, $1,000,000; expenditures, $942,770; qualifying distributions, $749,557; giving activities include $749,557 for 21 grants (high: $125,000; low: $1,267).
Fields of interest: Arts; Education; Hospitals (specialty); Cancer; Health organizations; Athletics/sports, equestrianism; Human services; Children/youth, services; Children/youth.
Limitations: Applications accepted. Giving primarily in MI; funding also in FL, KY, NY, and OH.
Application information: Application form required.
Deadline(s): None
Officers and Directors:* Kimberly Van Kampen Boyer,* Pres.; Frederic Jacques Boyer,* Secy.; Michael William Molinari.
EIN: 201190854
Selected grants: The following grants are a representative sample of this grantmaker's funding activity:
$18,159 to Sister Cities International, Washington, DC, 2012. For Cultural and Educational Programs.
$17,622 to Muskegon Museum of Art, Muskegon, MI, 2012. For art museum programs.

4571
Andrew and Gladys Van Noord Foundation ✧ ☆
P.O. Box 3230
Grand Rapids, MI 49501-3230

Donors: Andrew Van Noord; Gladys Van Noord.
Foundation type: Independent foundation.
Financial data (yr. ended 12/31/13): Assets, $15,682,535 (M); gifts received, $7,910,877; expenditures, $583,873; qualifying distributions, $553,040; giving activities include $545,000 for 9 grants (high: $200,000; low: $3,000).
Fields of interest: Human services; Public affairs; Christian agencies & churches.
Limitations: Applications not accepted.
Application information: Unsolicited requests for funds not accepted.
Officers: Gladys Van Noord, Pres.; Robert Van Dongen, V.P. and Treas.; Geralyn Pasi, Secy.
EIN: 274255801

4572
VanderWeide Family Foundation ✧
(formerly Robert & Cheri VanderWeide Foundation)
P.O. Box 230257
Grand Rapids, MI 49523-0257 (616) 643-4700
Contact: Ginny Vander Hart, Exec. Dir.; Sue Volkers, Fdn. Admin.
FAX: (616) 774-0116;
E-mail: info@vw-foundation.org; E-mail:

virginiav@rdvcorp.com (for G. Vander Hart) or SueV@rdvcorp.com (for S. Volkers); Main URL: http://www.vw-foundation.org

Established in 1992 in MI.
Donor: Suzanne DeVos Vanderweide.
Foundation type: Independent foundation.
Financial data (yr. ended 12/31/12): Assets, $42,646,642 (M); gifts received, $11,000,000; expenditures, $9,897,851; qualifying distributions, $9,709,665; giving activities include $9,379,650 for 93 grants (high: $3,810,900; low: $250).
Purpose and activities: The foundation seeks to create a legacy of caring and stewardship through their support of projects that build community and improve the quality of people's lives. To carry out this commitment, it focuses on organizations, projects, or programs that demonstrate Christian charity to meet both the spiritual and physical needs of people, which strengthen the bond of families and communities, and bring opportunity to disadvantaged persons. Giving primarily for Christian churches; giving also for education and human services.
Fields of interest: Education; Medical specialties; Human services; Youth, services; Family services; Community/economic development; United Ways and Federated Giving Programs; Christian agencies & churches; Protestant agencies & churches.
Type of support: General/operating support; Continuing support; Annual campaigns; Capital campaigns; Building/renovation; Program development; Matching/challenge support.
Limitations: Applications accepted. Giving primarily in western MI. No support for for-profit organizations or candidates for political office. No grants to individuals, loans, operating debt-retirement, or endowments.
Publications: Application guidelines.
Application information: Tapes, DVD's CD's, brochures or bound proposals are not accepted. Application form not required.
Initial approach: On-line application
Copies of proposal: 1
Deadline(s): 3 weeks prior to review
Board meeting date(s): 3 times annually
Final notification: 3 to 5 months
Officers and Trustees:* Suzanne C. Devos Vanderweide,* Pres.; Robert H. Schierbeek,* Exec. V.P. and Secy.-Treas.; Jerry L. Tubergen,* Exec. V.P.; Jeffrey Lambert,* V.P., Finance; Douglas L. Devos; Hannah J. Vanderweide; Katelyn S. Vanderweide.
Number of staff: 3 full-time professional.
EIN: 383035978
Selected grants: The following grants are a representative sample of this grantmaker's funding activity:
$3,810,900 to Grand Rapids Christian Schools, Grand Rapids, MI, 2012. For unrestricted support of general fund.
$1,000,000 to Grand Action Foundation, Grand Rapids, MI, 2012. For unrestricted support of general fund.
$500,000 to George W. Bush Foundation, Dallas, TX, 2012. For unrestricted support of general fund.
$431,000 to Wake Forest University, Winston-Salem, NC, 2012. For unrestricted support of general fund.
$375,000 to Aquinas College, Grand Rapids, MI, 2012. For unrestricted support of general fund.
$227,500 to Grand Rapids Student Advancement Foundation, Grand Rapids, MI, 2012. For unrestricted support of general fund.
$89,000 to Orlando Magic Youth Foundation, Orlando, FL, 2012. For unrestricted support of general fund.
$75,000 to Potters House, Grand Rapids, MI, 2012. For unrestricted support of general fund.
$25,000 to United Way, Heart of West Michigan, Grand Rapids, MI, 2012. For unrestricted support of general fund.
$15,000 to Grand Rapids Community Foundation, Grand Rapids, MI, 2012. For unrestricted support of general fund.

4573
Vaughan Foundation ✧
c/o Miller Canfield, Erik H. Serr
101 N. Main St., 7th Fl.
Ann Arbor, MI 48104-5507

Established in 1997 in MI.
Donors: Christine M. Holmes; Christine Holms Trust.
Foundation type: Independent foundation.
Financial data (yr. ended 12/31/13): Assets, $17,140,707 (M); gifts received, $228,988; expenditures, $941,439; qualifying distributions, $921,000; giving activities include $921,000 for 34 grants (high: $100,000; low: $2,000).
Purpose and activities: Funding primarily for arts and culture, human services, and animal welfare.
Fields of interest: Arts; Animal welfare; Human services.
Limitations: Applications not accepted. Giving primarily in MI. No grants to individuals.
Application information: Contributes only to pre-selected organizations.
Officers and Directors:* Christine Holmes,* Pres. and Treas.; Erik E. Serr, Secy.; Jeanne N. Draper; Erik H. Serr.
EIN: 383355160

4574
Ted & Jane Von Voigtlander Foundation ✧
109 W. Clinton St.
Howell, MI 48843-1565

Established in 2007 in MI.
Foundation type: Independent foundation.
Financial data (yr. ended 12/31/12): Assets, $36,588,545 (M); expenditures, $3,692,458; qualifying distributions, $3,242,800; giving activities include $3,242,800 for grants.
Fields of interest: Health organizations; Human services; Residential/custodial care, hospices; United Ways and Federated Giving Programs.
Type of support: General/operating support.
Limitations: Applications not accepted. Giving primarily in MI. No grants to individuals.
Application information: Contributes only to pre-selected organizations.
Officers and Directors:* C. Gwen Haggerty-Bearden,* Pres.; Steven W. Bearden,* V.P.; Mary T. Cole, Secy.; Peter Bowen, Treas.; Jacquelin A. Moody; Jeffrey P. Von Voigtlander.
EIN: 205003935
Selected grants: The following grants are a representative sample of this grantmaker's funding activity:
$150,000 to United Way, Livingston County, Brighton, MI, 2011.
$15,000 to Livingston Arts Council, Howell, MI, 2011.
$10,000 to Humane Society of Livingston County, Howell, MI, 2011.
$10,000 to Make-A-Wish Foundation of Michigan, Brighton, MI, 2011.
$5,000 to Livingston Area Council Against Spouse Abuse, Howell, MI, 2011.

4575
Shaw and Betty Walker Foundation ✧
(formerly Shaw Walker Foundation)
c/o Stephanie L. Geoghan
P.O. Box 5100
North Muskegon, MI 49445-5100 (231) 744-5294

Established in 1993 in MI.
Donors: Shaw Walker, Jr.; Betty Walker; Bruce Walker.
Foundation type: Independent foundation.
Financial data (yr. ended 12/31/13): Assets, $20,294,278 (M); gifts received, $50,000; expenditures, $1,430,672; qualifying distributions, $1,195,671; giving activities include $1,170,000 for 37 grants (high: $150,000; low: $5,000).
Purpose and activities: Giving primarily for education, research, and environmental advocacy.
Fields of interest: Arts; Education; Health organizations; Civil/human rights; Foundations (public).
Type of support: General/operating support; Continuing support; Annual campaigns; Scholarship funds; Research; In-kind gifts.
Limitations: Applications accepted. Giving primarily in MI and VA. No grants to individuals.
Application information: Application form not required.
Initial approach: Proposal
Deadline(s): None
Officers and Directors:* Shaw Walker, Jr.,* Pres. and Treas.; Betty Walker,* V.P.; Stephanie Geoghan, Secy.; Bruce Walker, Treas.; Fred Guenther.
Number of staff: 1 part-time professional.
EIN: 383125893
Selected grants: The following grants are a representative sample of this grantmaker's funding activity:
$100,000 to NRA Foundation, Fairfax, VA, 2011.

4576
The Alvin and Edith Wasserman Family Foundation ✧ ☆
39400 Woodward Ave., Ste. 101
Bloomfield Hills, MI 48304-5151

Established in 1997 in MI.
Donors: Alvin Wasserman; Edith L. Wasserman‡.
Foundation type: Independent foundation.
Financial data (yr. ended 12/31/13): Assets, $909,278 (M); gifts received, $1,645,913; expenditures, $1,815,276; qualifying distributions, $1,806,590; giving activities include $1,805,825 for 11 grants (high: $209,052; low: $2,000), and $1,361,273 for 18 in-kind gifts.
Purpose and activities: Giving primary for education.
Fields of interest: Zoos/zoological societies; Animals/wildlife; Human services; Community/economic development; Foundations (community).
Limitations: Applications not accepted. Giving primarily in MI. No grants to individuals.

Application information: Unsolicited requests for funds not accepted.
Officers: Linda Wasserman Aviv, Pres. and Treas.; Gary L. Wasserman, V.P.; Rodger D. Wasserman, Secy.
EIN: 383343567

4577
Weatherwax Foundation ✧
145 S. Jackson St.
Jackson, MI 49201-1283 (517) 787-2117
Contact: Maria M. Dotterweich, Exec. Dir.
E-mail: wwfnd@sbcglobal.net

Established in 1981 in MI.
Donor: K.A. Weatherwax Trust I†.
Foundation type: Independent foundation.
Financial data (yr. ended 09/30/13): Assets, $10,040,398 (M); expenditures, $1,841,162; qualifying distributions, $1,632,258; giving activities include $1,632,258 for grants.
Purpose and activities: Support primarily for arts and culture, education, and civic and social programs.
Fields of interest: Arts education; Performing arts; Performing arts, orchestras; Arts; Higher education; Human services; United Ways and Federated Giving Programs.
Type of support: General/operating support; Annual campaigns; Capital campaigns; Building/renovation; Equipment; Emergency funds; Conferences/seminars; Curriculum development; Technical assistance; Consulting services; Program evaluation; Matching/challenge support.
Limitations: Giving limited to Hillsdale, Lenawee, and Jackson counties, MI. No grants to individuals, or for computer purchases.
Publications: Application guidelines; Grants list.
Application information: Application form required.
Initial approach: Proposal (not to exceed 2 pages)
Copies of proposal: 3
Deadline(s): None
Board meeting date(s): Monthly
Final notification: Acknowledgement within 60 days
Officer: Maria Miceli Dotterweich, Exec. Dir.
Trustees: Lawrence Bullen; Comerica Bank.
Number of staff: 1 part-time professional.
EIN: 386439807
Selected grants: The following grants are a representative sample of this grantmaker's funding activity:
$250,000 to Allegiance Health, Jackson, MI, 2011.
$200,000 to Hillsdale College, Hillsdale, MI, 2011.
$35,000 to Saint Lukes Clinic, Jackson, MI, 2011.
$25,000 to Goodwill Industries of Southeastern Michigan, Adrian, MI, 2011. For operations.

4578
The Wayne and Joan Webber Foundation ✧
c/o Richard Gibbs
44710 Morley Dr.
Clinton Township, MI 48036-1357

Established in 1998 in MI.
Donors: Joan Webber; Wayne Webber; Hanson Aggregates West, Inc.; Southern Crushed Concrete, Inc.
Foundation type: Independent foundation.
Financial data (yr. ended 12/31/12): Assets, $43,642,024 (M); expenditures, $2,530,256; qualifying distributions, $2,207,075; giving activities include $2,141,639 for 23 grants (high: $500,000; low: $2,332).
Fields of interest: Arts, formal/general education; Education; Hospitals (general); Human services.
Type of support: Capital campaigns.
Limitations: Applications not accepted. Giving primarily in MI. No grants to individuals.
Application information: Contributes only to pre-selected organizations.
Officers and Directors:* Cynthia Helisek, Pres.; Joan Webber,* Secy.; Wayne Webber,* Treas.; David Stone.
EIN: 383390733

4579
The Wege Foundation ✧
P.O. Box 6388
Grand Rapids, MI 49516-6388 (616) 957-0480
Contact: Jody Price, C.F.O.
E-mail for Jody Price: jprice@wegefoundation.org;
Main URL: http://www.wegefoundation.com/
YouTube: https://www.youtube.com/user/wegefoundation

Established on July 13, 1967 in MI.
Donor: Peter M. Wege.
Foundation type: Independent foundation.
Financial data (yr. ended 12/31/12): Assets, $84,647,413 (M); gifts received, $84,647,413; expenditures, $12,971,072; qualifying distributions, $12,171,450; giving activities include $11,372,480 for 541 grants (high: $200,000; low: $5,000).
Purpose and activities: Giving primarily to the environment, education, arts and culture, community service and health care.
Fields of interest: Museums; Performing arts; Elementary/secondary education; Higher education; Environment, natural resources; Hospitals (general); Human services; Children/youth, services; Community/economic development.
Type of support: Scholarship funds; General/operating support; Annual campaigns; Capital campaigns; Building/renovation; Equipment; Endowments; Program development; Curriculum development; Matching/challenge support.
Limitations: Applications accepted. Giving primarily in greater Kent County, MI, with emphasis on the Grand Rapids area. No grants to individuals.
Publications: Application guidelines; Annual report.
Application information: See foundation's web site for online grant application and eligibility quiz. Application form required.
Initial approach: Online grant application
Copies of proposal: 1
Deadline(s): Spring and fall. Check web site for dates
Board meeting date(s): Apr. 15
Officers and Directors:* Peter M. Wege,* Chair.; Ellen Satterlee,* C.E.O. and Treas.; Peter M. Wege II,* Pres.; Terri McCarthy, V.P., Progs; Jonathan M. Wege,* V.P.; W. Michael Van Haren,* Secy.; Jody Price, C.F.O.; Mary Goodwillie Nelson; Christopher M. Wege; Diana Wege.
Number of staff: 3 full-time professional.
EIN: 386124363
Selected grants: The following grants are a representative sample of this grantmaker's funding activity:
$250,000 to Catholic Secondary Schools, Grand Rapids, MI, 2012. For Capital and E.
$200,000 to Diocese of Grand Rapids, Grand Rapids, MI, 2012. To support the Cathedral Square project.
$200,000 to Diocese of Grand Rapids, Grand Rapids, MI, 2012. To support the Cathedral Square project.
$187,500 to Grand Rapids Art Museum, Grand Rapids, MI, 2012. For Unrestricted support.
$125,000 to John Ball Zoological Society, Grand Rapids, MI, 2012. For Restore the Roar.
$112,500 to National Parks Conservation Association, Washington, DC, 2012. To support Healing Our Water Great Lakes coalition.
$36,250 to Great Lakes Fishery Trust, Lansing, MI, 2012.
$31,250 to Grand Rapids University Preparatory Association, Grand Rapids, MI, 2012. To support UPrep Capital campaign.
$25,000 to Environmental Grantmakers Association, New York, NY, 2012. For General Support.
$25,000 to Grand Rapids Symphony, Grand Rapids, MI, 2012. For Endowment.

4580
Weingartz Family Foundation ✧
P.O. Box 182008
Shelby Township, MI 48318-2008

Established in 2004 in MI.
Donors: Power Equipment Distributors, Inc.; Weingartz Supply Co.
Foundation type: Company-sponsored foundation.
Financial data (yr. ended 12/31/13): Assets, $3,588,398 (M); gifts received, $975,000; expenditures, $877,765; qualifying distributions, $889,765; giving activities include $887,775 for 14 grants (high: $265,036; low: $5,000).
Purpose and activities: The foundation supports organizations involved with hunger, human services, international relief, and religion.
Fields of interest: Agriculture/food; Safety/disasters; Religion.
Type of support: General/operating support.
Limitations: Applications not accepted. Giving primarily in Washington, DC, MI, and NY. No grants to individuals.
Application information: Contributes only to pre-selected organizations.
Officers and Directors:* Raymond Weingartz,* Pres.; Marie Weingartz,* V.P.; Edward Radtke,* Secy.; Daniel Weingartz,* Treas.; Beverly Devriendt; Angela Malburg; Donald Malburg; Catherine Radtke; Amy Weingartz; Debbie Weingartz; Kenneth Weingartz; Kris Weingartz; Peggy Weingartz; Ronald Weingartz; Thomas Weingartz.
EIN: 201516609
Selected grants: The following grants are a representative sample of this grantmaker's funding activity:
$146,788 to Food for the Poor, Coconut Creek, FL, 2011.
$132,627 to Catholic Relief Services, Baltimore, MD, 2011.

4581
Henry E. and Consuelo S. Wenger Foundation, Inc. ✧
8916 Gale Rd.
White Lake, MI 48386-1409

Incorporated in 1959 in MI.
Donor: Consuelo S. Wenger.
Foundation type: Independent foundation.
Financial data (yr. ended 12/31/13): Assets, $21,127,761 (M); expenditures, $970,122; qualifying distributions, $945,358; giving activities include $941,722 for 87 grants (high: $140,000; low: $100).
Fields of interest: Arts; Elementary/secondary education; Higher education; Education.
Limitations: Applications not accepted. Giving primarily in MA, MI, NY, and RI. No grants to individuals.
Application information: Contributes only to pre-selected organizations.
Officer: Diane Wenger Wilson, Pres.
Directors: Caprice W. Baun; Camille W. Broadbent; Consuelo D. Peirrepont; Charles L. Wilson III.
EIN: 386077419
Selected grants: The following grants are a representative sample of this grantmaker's funding activity:
$135,000 to Americans for Oxford, New York, NY, 2012. For Junior research fellowship in American History, Education.
$100,000 to Brown University, Providence, RI, 2012. For educational academic enrichment.
$60,000 to Georgetown University, Washington, DC, 2012. For annual fund education.
$50,000 to American University, Washington, DC, 2012. For Educational Support Women in Law and Domestic Violence.
$25,000 to Conservation Resource Alliance, Traverse City, MI, 2012. For Natural Resource conservation and restoration in Northwest MI.
$25,000 to Society of the Four Arts, Palm Beach, FL, 2012. For cultural promotion of the four arts.
$10,000 to Dartmouth College, Hanover, NH, 2012. For Educational the 06 Fellowship Fund.
$10,000 to Greenwich Land Trust, Cos Cob, CT, 2012. To preserve and protect wildlife habitat.
$9,755 to Detroit Institute of Arts, Detroit, MI, 2012. For cultural education promotion of art.
$2,915 to New York City Ballet, New York, NY, 2012. For cultural promotion of ballet.

4582
The Samuel L. Westerman Foundation ✧
40950 Woodward Ave., Ste. 306
Bloomfield Hills, MI 48304-5124
Application address: Ruth R. LoPrete, 4739 N. Pennsylvania St., Indianpolis, IN 46205, tel.: (248) 835-3002

Established in 1971 in MI.
Donor: Samuel L. Westerman‡.
Foundation type: Independent foundation.
Financial data (yr. ended 12/31/13): Assets, $8,695,939 (M); expenditures, $483,153; qualifying distributions, $528,020; giving activities include $528,020 for grants.
Purpose and activities: Giving primarily for education, youth services and religious programs.
Fields of interest: Performing arts, music; Arts; Higher education; Education; Hospitals (general); Health care; Health organizations, association; Human services; Children/youth, services; Religion.
Type of support: General/operating support; Continuing support; Endowments; Program development; Scholarship funds; Research.
Limitations: Applications accepted. Giving primarily in MI. No grants to individuals.
Application information: Application form required.
Initial approach: Letter
Copies of proposal: 1
Deadline(s): None
Officers: James H. LoPrete, Pres.; Martha M. Muir, V.P. and Treas.; Kent G. LoPrete, V.P.; Cameron K. Muir, V.P.; Mary M. Lyneis, Secy.
Trustees: Ruth R. Loprete; Gordon J. Muir.
EIN: 237108795
Selected grants: The following grants are a representative sample of this grantmaker's funding activity:
$2,000 to Adrian Dominican Sisters, Adrian, MI, 2012. For gen. charitable.
$2,000 to Leadership Institute, Arlington, VA, 2012. For educational research.
$1,000 to Boy Scouts of America, Clinton Valley Council, Waterford, MI, 2012. For programs for youth.
$1,000 to Boy Scouts of America, Detroit Area Council, Detroit, MI, 2012. For programs for youth.

4583
Whirlpool Foundation ✧
2000 N. M-63, MD 3106
Benton Harbor, MI 49022 (269) 923-5580
Contact: Candice Garman, Communty Rels. Mgr.
FAX: (269) 925-0154;
E-mail: whirlpool_foundation@whirlpool.com; Tel. for Candice Garman: (269) 923-5584; Main URL: http://www.whirlpoolcorp.com/responsibility/building_communities/whirlpool_foundation.aspx

Incorporated in 1951 in MI.
Donor: Whirlpool Corp.
Foundation type: Company-sponsored foundation.
Financial data (yr. ended 12/31/12): Assets, $587,136 (M); gifts received, $14,555,000; expenditures, $14,143,109; qualifying distributions, $14,143,108; giving activities include $13,804,448 for 325 grants (high: $2,000,000; low: $50).
Purpose and activities: The foundation supports programs designed to promote lifelong learning, quality family life, and cultural diversity; and partnerships and collaborations designed to address community issues.
Fields of interest: Arts, cultural/ethnic awareness; Arts; Elementary/secondary education; Higher education; Business school/education; Education; Disasters, preparedness/services; Boys & girls clubs; Youth development, business; American Red Cross; YM/YWCAs & YM/YWHAs; Family services; Human services; Community/economic development; United Ways and Federated Giving Programs.
Type of support: General/operating support; Continuing support; Program development; Scholarship funds; Research; Employee volunteer services; Employee matching gifts; Employee-related scholarships; Matching/challenge support.
Limitations: Applications not accepted. Giving primarily in areas of company operations, with emphasis on Benton Harbor, MI. No support for social, labor, veterans', alumni, or fraternal organizations, athletic associations, or national groups whose local chapters have already received funding. No grants to individuals (except for employee-related scholarships), or for conferences or seminars, political causes, capital campaigns or endowments, sporting events, goodwill advertisements for fundraising benefits or program books, tickets for testimonials or similar benefit events, or general operating support for United Way agencies.
Application information: The foundation is not accepting new requests for grantmaking at this time.
Board meeting date(s): Quarterly
Officers and Trustees:* D. Jeffrey Noel,* Pres.; David A. Binkley, V.P.; John F. Geddes, Secy.-Treas.; Larry Range, Legal Counsel; Jim Keppler; Deb O'Connor.
Number of staff: 1 full-time professional; 1 full-time support.
EIN: 386077342
Selected grants: The following grants are a representative sample of this grantmaker's funding activity:
$2,000,000 to Renaissance Development Nonprofit Housing Corporation, Detroit, MI, 2012.
$1,600,000 to Renaissance Development Nonprofit Housing Corporation, Detroit, MI, 2012.
$1,500,000 to Renaissance Development Nonprofit Housing Corporation, Detroit, MI, 2012.
$1,075,000 to Renaissance Development Nonprofit Housing Corporation, Detroit, MI, 2012.
$886,026 to United Way of Southwest Michigan, Saint Joseph, MI, 2012.
$800,000 to Renaissance Development Nonprofit Housing Corporation, Detroit, MI, 2012.
$500,000 to Cornerstone Alliance, Benton Harbor, MI, 2012.
$500,000 to Cornerstone Alliance, Benton Harbor, MI, 2012.
$187,224 to United Way of Sandusky County, Fremont, OH, 2012.
$68,770 to United Way, Darke County, Greenville, OH, 2012.

4584
The Whiting Foundation ✧
718 Harrison St.
Flint, MI 48502-1614

Incorporated in 1940 in MI.
Donor: Members of the Johnson family.
Foundation type: Independent foundation.
Financial data (yr. ended 06/30/13): Assets, $10,466,184 (M); expenditures, $573,434; qualifying distributions, $473,500; giving activities include $473,500 for grants.
Purpose and activities: Giving primarily for cultural activities, and for basic needs for people who are underprivileged.
Fields of interest: Historic preservation/historical societies; Arts; Education; Cancer; Medical research, institute; Housing/shelter, development; Children/youth, services; Community/economic development; United Ways and Federated Giving Programs.
Type of support: General/operating support; Program development.
Limitations: Applications not accepted. Giving primarily in the Genesee County, MI, area, including the city of Flint.
Application information: Unsolicited requests for funds not accepted.
Officers: Donald E. Johnson, Jr., Pres.; John T. Lindholm, Secy.-Treas.

Trustee: Mary Alice J. Heaton.
EIN: 386056693
Selected grants: The following grants are a representative sample of this grantmaker's funding activity:
$25,000 to Flint Cultural Center Corporation, Flint, MI, 2013. For See Note 2 Carpet.
$15,000 to Flint Institute of Music, Flint, MI, 2013. For See Note 2 Classical Concert Series.
$15,000 to Hurley Foundation, Flint, MI, 2013. For See Note 2 Burn Unit Special Heating Units.
$10,000 to Cancer Research Institute, New York, NY, 2013. For See Note 2 National Headquarters Research Programs.
$7,500 to Christ Enrichment Center, Flint, MI, 2013. For See Note 2 Building Improvements.
$7,500 to Flint Institute of Music, Flint, MI, 2013. For See Note 2 Music in the Parks.
$5,000 to Christ Enrichment Center, Flint, MI, 2013. For See Note 2 After School Programs.
$5,000 to Flint Institute of Music, Flint, MI, 2013. For See Note 2 Flint Youth Theatre.
$5,000 to Flint Institute of Music, Flint, MI, 2013. For See Note 2 Nutcracker.
$5,000 to Priority Children, Flint, MI, 2013. For Note 2: Unless otherwise stated all of the gifts were given for the general purposes of the recipient in each case, without limitation.

4585
Harvey Randall Wickes Foundation ✧
Plaza N., Ste. 472
4800 Fashion Sq. Blvd.
Saginaw, MI 48604-2677 (989) 799-1850
Contact: Hugo E. Braun, Jr., Pres.
FAX: (989) 799-3327; E-mail: hrwickes@att.net

Incorporated in 1945 in MI.
Donors: Harvey Randall Wickes†; members of the Wickes family.
Foundation type: Independent foundation.
Financial data (yr. ended 12/31/13): Assets, $44,124,116 (M); expenditures, $2,061,489; qualifying distributions, $1,876,311; giving activities include $1,779,264 for 61 grants (high: $400,000; low: $750).
Purpose and activities: Giving primarily for civic affairs groups, parks and recreation agencies; support also for a library, youth and social services, hospitals, and cultural programs, for the betterment of Saginaw County, MI.
Fields of interest: Arts; Libraries/library science; Education; Hospitals (general); Recreation; Human services; Children/youth, services.
Type of support: Annual campaigns; Building/renovation; Equipment; Seed money.
Limitations: Applications accepted. Giving limited to the Saginaw, MI, area. No support for government where support is forth coming from tax dollars. No grants to individuals, or for endowments, travel, conferences, or film or video projects; no loans.
Publications: Application guidelines; Financial statement.
Application information: Application form not required.
Initial approach: Letter followed by proposal
Copies of proposal: 1
Deadline(s): Submit proposal 2 weeks prior to meeting
Board meeting date(s): Mar., June, Sept. and Dec.
Final notification: 2 weeks following board meeting

Officers and Trustees:* Hugo E. Braun, Jr.,* Pres.; Craig W. Horn,* V.P.; Michele Pavlicek,* Secy.; Mary Lou Case,* Treas.; Ellen Crane; Peter Ewend; Wlliam A. Hendrick; Richard Heuschele; Richard Katz.
Number of staff: 1 part-time professional; 1 part-time support.
EIN: 386061470

4586
Williams Family Foundation ✧
(formerly Koinonia Foundation)
80 Ottawa Ave., N.W., Ste. 101
Grand Rapids, MI 49503

Established in 2004 in MI.
Donors: United Methodist Church; Dale L. Williams, M.D.
Foundation type: Independent foundation.
Financial data (yr. ended 12/31/12): Assets, $729,221 (M); expenditures, $700,427; qualifying distributions, $697,947; giving activities include $691,600 for 3 grants (high: $663,000; low: $3,600).
Purpose and activities: Giving primarily for medical and educational supplies for Rwanda.
Fields of interest: Family services; International development; International relief.
International interests: Rwanda.
Type of support: Equipment.
Limitations: Applications not accepted. Giving primarily in MI. No grants to individuals.
Application information: Contributes only to pre-selected organizations.
Officers: Dale L. Williams, Pres.; Christel G. Williams, Secy.; Dale F. Williams, Treas.
Directors: Andrew K. Williams; Peter H. Williams; Susan B. Williams.
EIN: 201025162

4587
Willmas Charitable Trust ✧
P.O. Box 75000
Detroit, MI 48275-3302

Established in 2007 in MI.
Foundation type: Independent foundation.
Financial data (yr. ended 06/30/13): Assets, $11,292,871 (M); expenditures, $760,234; qualifying distributions, $642,851; giving activities include $566,459 for 12 grants (high: $275,209; low: $4,000).
Fields of interest: Education; Nursing care; Health care; Foundations (community); Protestant agencies & churches; Catholic agencies & churches.
Limitations: Applications not accepted. Giving primarily in CA.
Application information: Contributes only to pre-selected organizations.
Trustees: Donald Schultz; Royale Vadakin; Comerica Bank.
EIN: 326042143
Selected grants: The following grants are a representative sample of this grantmaker's funding activity:
$10,000 to Happy Trails Childrens Foundation, Apple Valley, CA, 2011.

4588
Ralph C. Wilson Foundation ✧
63 Kercheval Ave., Ste. 200
Grosse Pointe Farms, MI 48236-3652

Established around 1954.
Donor: Ralph C. Wilson, Jr.†.
Foundation type: Independent foundation.
Financial data (yr. ended 10/31/13): Assets, $4,793,356 (M); gifts received, $4,000,000; expenditures, $1,614,247; qualifying distributions, $1,614,247; giving activities include $1,612,900 for 44 grants (high: $550,000; low: $100).
Purpose and activities: Giving primarily for education, health associations, and social services.
Fields of interest: Museums (sports/hobby); Higher education; Education; Hospitals (general); Health organizations; Human services; Children/youth, services; Residential/custodial care, hospices.
Type of support: General/operating support.
Limitations: Applications not accepted. Giving primarily in MI, NY, and OH. No grants to individuals.
Application information: Contributes only to pre-selected organizations.
Officers and Trustees:* Mary M. Owen, Secy.; Jeffrey C. Littmann,* Treas.; Eugene Driker; Mary M. Wilson.
EIN: 386091638
Selected grants: The following grants are a representative sample of this grantmaker's funding activity:
$100,000 to Hospice Buffalo, Cheektowaga, NY, 2011. For general support.
$100,000 to University at Buffalo Foundation, Buffalo, NY, 2011. For general support.

4589
Matilda R. Wilson Fund ✧
1901 Saint Antoine St., 6th Fl. (Ford Field)
Detroit, MI 48226-2310
Contact: David P. Larsen, Secy.
FAX: (313) 393-7579;
E-mail: roosterveen@bodmanlaw.com

Incorporated in 1944 in MI.
Donors: Matilda R. Wilson†; Alfred G. Wilson†.
Foundation type: Independent foundation.
Financial data (yr. ended 12/31/12): Assets, $22,713,748 (M); expenditures, $2,692,594; qualifying distributions, $2,460,729; giving activities include $2,257,764 for 28 grants (high: $500,000; low: $7,500).
Purpose and activities: Support for the arts, youth agencies, higher education, and social services.
Fields of interest: Arts; Higher education; Hospitals (general); Human services; Youth, services.
Type of support: General/operating support; Building/renovation; Equipment; Endowments; Program development; Scholarship funds; Research; Matching/challenge support.
Limitations: Applications accepted. Giving primarily in southeast MI. No grants to individuals; no loans.
Application information: Application form not required.
Initial approach: Letter
Copies of proposal: 1
Deadline(s): None
Board meeting date(s): Jan., Apr., and Sept.
Final notification: At the Jan., Apr., and Sept. board meetings

Officers and Trustees:* David M. Hempstead,* Pres.; David P. Larsen,* Secy.; David B. Stephens,* Treas.
EIN: 386087665

4590
Jean & Lewis Wolff Family Foundation ✧ ☆
c/o Comerica Bank
P.O. Box 75000, MC 7874
Detroit, MI 48275-7874
Application address: c/o Keith Wolff, V.P., 11828 La Grange Ave., Ste. 200, Los Angeles, CA 90025, tel.: (650) 461-6016

Established in 1998 in CA.
Donors: Jean Wolff; Lewis Wolff.
Foundation type: Independent foundation.
Financial data (yr. ended 05/31/13): Assets, $410,121 (M); expenditures, $1,079,600; qualifying distributions, $1,075,904; giving activities include $1,063,419 for 23 grants (high: $1,004,609; low: $200).
Fields of interest: Education; Health care; Human services.
Limitations: Applications accepted. Giving primarily in CA, with some emphasis on the Los Angeles area. No grants to individuals.
Application information: Application form not required.
Initial approach: Letter
Deadline(s): None
Officers: Lewis Wolff, Pres.; Jean Wolff, V.P.; Kevin Wolff, V.P.; Kari Wolff Goldstein, Secy.; Keith Wolff, Treas.
EIN: 954679221

4591
Wolohan Family Foundation ✧
5291 Colony Dr. N., Ste. 1
Saginaw, MI 48638

Established in 1986 in MI.
Donors: Richard V. Wolohan; Angela M. Wolohan; James L. Wolohan; Christine M. Wolohan; Sharon Wolohan; Mary Kay Ness; Michael Wolohan; Patricia Kremin.
Foundation type: Independent foundation.
Financial data (yr. ended 12/31/13): Assets, $26,849,427 (M); gifts received, $21,000; expenditures, $1,324,836; qualifying distributions, $1,028,497; giving activities include $1,025,200 for 43 grants (high: $150,000; low: $500).
Fields of interest: Higher education; Human services; Children/youth, services; Catholic agencies & churches.
Limitations: Applications not accepted. Giving primarily in MI, with emphasis on Saginaw County. No grants to individuals.
Application information: Unsolicited requests for funds not accepted.
Officers: Christine M. Wolohan, Pres.; James L. Wolohan, V.P.; Michael J. Wolohan, V.P.; Sharon L. Wolohan, Secy.; Teri Hull, Treas.
Directors: Patricia A. Kremin; Sharon McGrann; Mary K. Ness; Richard Niederstat; Richard P. Wolohan.
EIN: 382700797

4592
Kate and Richard Wolters Foundation ✧
2260 Cascade Springs Dr. S.E.
Grand Rapids, MI 49546-7410 (616) 949-0716
Contact: Kate P. Wolters, Pres. and Secy.-Treas.

Established in 1997 in MI.
Donors: Kate Pew Wolters; Richard Wolters†; Robert C. Pew; Marabeth Spencer.
Foundation type: Independent foundation.
Financial data (yr. ended 12/31/13): Assets, $32,393,467 (M); gifts received, $25,066,279; expenditures, $1,363,488; qualifying distributions, $1,322,075; giving activities include $1,317,000 for 28 grants (high: $250,000; low: $2,000).
Purpose and activities: Giving primarily for arts and culture, higher education, health organizations, and human services.
Fields of interest: Museums (art); Arts; Higher education; Health organizations; Human services; Children/youth, services.
Type of support: General/operating support; Capital campaigns; Endowments; Program development.
Limitations: Applications accepted. Giving primarily in Grand Rapids, MI.
Application information: Application form required.
Initial approach: Letter
Deadline(s): None
Officer and Trustees:* Kate Pew Wolters,* Pres. and Secy.-Treas.; John Pew; Jeffrey B. Power.
EIN: 383384598

4593
Wolverine World Wide Foundation ✧
c/o Wolverine World Wide, Inc.
9341 Courtland Dr. N.E.
Rockford, MI 49351-0001 (616) 866-5500
Contact: Christi Cowdin, V.P.
Main URL: http://www.wolverineworldwide.com/about-us/causes/

Established in MI.
Donor: Wolverine World Wide.
Foundation type: Company-sponsored foundation.
Financial data (yr. ended 12/31/12): Assets, $4,460,003 (M); gifts received, $791,517; expenditures, $802,513; qualifying distributions, $770,059; giving activities include $770,059 for 168 grants (high: $117,000; low: $50).
Purpose and activities: The foundation supports organizations involved with arts and culture, education, the environment, cancer, muscular dystrophy, diabetes, housing development, youth and family services, and urban development.
Fields of interest: Museums; Performing arts, orchestras; Arts; Higher education; Medical school/education; Education; Environment, natural resources; Environment, land resources; Environment; Cancer; Muscular dystrophy; Diabetes; Housing/shelter, development; Youth development, business; YM/YWCAs & YM/YWHAs; Children/youth, services; Family services; Urban/community development; United Ways and Federated Giving Programs.
Type of support: General/operating support; Scholarship funds; Employee matching gifts.
Limitations: Applications accepted. Giving primarily in areas of company operations in MI.
Application information: Application form not required.
Initial approach: Proposal
Deadline(s): None
Officers and Trustees:* Blake W. Krueger,* Pres.; Christi L. Cowdin, V.P.; Kenneth A. Grady,* Secy.; Donald T. Grimes,* Treas.; James D. Zwiers.
EIN: 320140361

4594
World Heritage Foundation ✧
2675 W. Jefferson Ave.
Trenton, MI 48183-3284 (734) 675-2200
Contact: Waltraud E. Prechter, Chair.

Established in 1985 in MI.
Donors: Heinz C. Prechter†; Thomas Denomme; Waltraud E. Prechter; Heinz C. Prechter Charitable Lead Trust.
Foundation type: Independent foundation.
Financial data (yr. ended 12/31/13): Assets, $8,911,712 (M); gifts received, $316,012; expenditures, $628,961; qualifying distributions, $546,745; giving activities include $528,500 for 90 grants (high: $125,000; low: $100).
Purpose and activities: Giving primarily for education and medical research; funding also for social services and children's services, including a children's hospital.
Fields of interest: Higher education; Hospitals (specialty); Health care; Mental health, disorders; Health organizations, association; Medical research, institute; Human services; Children/youth, services.
Type of support: General/operating support; Capital campaigns; Program development; Professorships.
Limitations: Applications accepted. Giving primarily in Ann Arbor and Detroit, MI; some giving also in Washington, DC. No grants to individuals.
Publications: Informational brochure (including application guidelines).
Application information: Application form required.
Initial approach: Letter
Deadline(s): None
Officers: Waltraud Prechter, Pres.; Paul Prechter, V.P.; Stephanie Prechter, Treas.
Director: J. Patrick Howe.
EIN: 382640416
Selected grants: The following grants are a representative sample of this grantmaker's funding activity:
$100,000 to Georgetown University, Washington, DC, 2012. For Prechter Professorship.
$20,000 to Oakwood Healthcare System Foundation, Dearborn, MI, 2012. For 2nd draw of 5 ($100,000 pledge).
$12,500 to Covenant House Michigan, Detroit, MI, 2012. For 1st draw on $50,000 pledge.
$10,000 to College for Creative Studies, Detroit, MI, 2012. For 9th draw on $100,000 pledge.
$10,000 to College for Creative Studies, Detroit, MI, 2012. For CCS Annual Fund.
$2,500 to College for Creative Studies, Detroit, MI, 2012. For 2011 Wine Auction.
$1,500 to College for Creative Studies, Detroit, MI, 2012. For May 11, 2012 Student Exhibition Donation.
$1,000 to Wayne State University, Law School, Detroit, MI, 2012. For In Honor of Damon J Keith.
$250 to Covenant House Michigan, Detroit, MI, 2012. For Calling All Angels.
$250 to Henry Ford Health System, Detroit, MI, 2012. For Josephine Ford Cancer Center.

4595
Zatkoff Family Foundation ✧ ☆
23230 Industrial Park Dr.
Farmington Hills, MI 48335-2850

Established in 2000 in MI.
Donor: Roger Zatkoff Co.
Foundation type: Company-sponsored foundation.
Financial data (yr. ended 12/31/13): Assets, $23,008,050 (M); gifts received, $7,000,000; expenditures, $494,839; qualifying distributions, $482,099; giving activities include $482,099 for 20 grants (high: $447,849; low: $100).
Purpose and activities: The foundation supports organizations involved with education, health, and Christianity.
Fields of interest: Higher education; Education; Health care; Mental health/crisis services; United Ways and Federated Giving Programs; Christian agencies & churches.
Limitations: Applications not accepted. Giving limited to MI. No grants to individuals.
Application information: Unsolicited requests for funds not accepted.
Officer: Gary Zatkoff, Pres.
EIN: 383574982

MINNESOTA

4596
1988 Irrevocable Cochrane Memorial Trust ✧
c/o Trust Tax Services
P.O. Box 64713
Saint Paul, MN 55164-0713
Application address: c/o Darcy Frederickson, 101 E. 5th St., St. Paul, MN 55101, tel.: (651) 466-8708

Established in 1989 in MN.
Foundation type: Independent foundation.
Financial data (yr. ended 12/31/13): Assets, $11,001,204 (M); expenditures, $677,440; qualifying distributions, $622,452; giving activities include $615,000 for 15 grants (high: $60,000; low: $10,000).
Fields of interest: Environment, natural resources; Human services; Catholic agencies & churches.
Type of support: General/operating support.
Limitations: Applications accepted. Giving primarily in the Washington, DC, area, including MD. No grants to individuals.
Application information: Application form required.
Initial approach: Letter
Deadline(s): None
Trustees: Mary McGahey Dwan; U.S. Bank, N.A.
EIN: 416309348

4597
3M Foundation ✧
(also known as Minnesota Mining and Manufacturing Foundation)
3M Ctr., Bldg., 225-01-S-23
St. Paul, MN 55144-1000 (651) 733-0144
Contact: Cynthia F. Kleven, Secy.
FAX: (651) 737-3061; E-mail: cfkleven@mmm.com; Main URL: http://www.3Mgives.com
3M Gives: http://link.brightcove.com/services/player/bcpid1235504375001?bckey=AQ~~,AAABHqwikGk~,7S9Nw1m3fNFTwq93UrKqo40g7IQeb2jv&bctid=3166526528001

Incorporated in 1953 in MN.
Donors: Minnesota Mining and Manufacturing Co.; 3M Co.
Foundation type: Company-sponsored foundation.
Financial data (yr. ended 12/31/13): Assets, $17,562,084 (M); gifts received, $15,000,000; expenditures, $21,354,512; qualifying distributions, $21,207,718; giving activities include $21,207,718 for 1,526 grants (high: $1,150,000; low: $13).
Purpose and activities: The foundation supports programs designed to improve lives through education; community; and the environment.
Fields of interest: Arts, cultural/ethnic awareness; Museums (science/technology); Performing arts, orchestras; Arts; Elementary/secondary education; Education, early childhood education; Higher education; Business school/education; Engineering school/education; Education, services; Education; Environment, climate change/global warming; Environment, natural resources; Environmental education; Environment; Disasters, preparedness/services; United Ways and Federated Giving Programs; Science, formal/general education; Mathematics; Engineering/technology; Science; Children/youth; Minorities; Women; Economically disadvantaged.
Type of support: General/operating support; Capital campaigns; Program development; Curriculum development; Scholarship funds; Employee volunteer services; Employee matching gifts; In-kind gifts.
Limitations: Applications accepted. Giving on a national basis in areas of company operations. No support for religious, fraternal, social, or veterans' organizations, disease-specific organizations, government agencies, hospitals, clinics, or nursing homes, treatment centers or hospices, or individual K-12 schools. No grants to individuals, or for capital endowments, advocacy or lobbying efforts, conferences, seminars, or workshops, publications, film or video production, fundraising, testimonial, athletic or special events, playground or athletic equipment, non-3M equipment, travel, or scholarship funds; no loans or investments.
Publications: Application guidelines; Annual report; Grants list; Program policy statement.
Application information: Most grants are by-invitation-only. Application form required.
Initial approach: Complete online prescreening assessment
Copies of proposal: 1
Deadline(s): None
Board meeting date(s): June and Dec.
Officers: Ian F. Hardgrove, Pres.; Kimberly F. Price, V.P.; Cynthia F. Kleven, Secy.; S. D. Krohn, Treas.
Number of staff: 6 full-time professional; 3 full-time support.
EIN: 416038262
Selected grants: The following grants are a representative sample of this grantmaker's funding activity:
$3,817,552 to Kids in Need Foundation, Dayton, OH, 2013. For Network of Resource Centers.
$2,191,662 to Good360, Alexandria, VA, 2013. For 3M Supplies4Nonprofit Organizations.
$1,874,094 to National Association for the Exchange of Industrial Resources, Galesburg, IL, 2012. To provide blank business card stock to qualified health and human services organizations.
$1,699,332 to Good360, Alexandria, VA, 2012. To support 2 projects of Good 360, 3M Supplies4Nonprofit Organizations and Sales Force4Kids.
$1,623,667 to National Association for the Exchange of Industrial Resources, Galesburg, IL, 2012. To distribute office products to qualified schools.
$1,000,000 to Arts Partnership, Saint Paul, MN, 2013. For the Arts Partnership Campaign.
$1,000,000 to University of Minnesota Foundation, Minneapolis, MN, 2012. For Physics Nano Technology Building.
$667,390 to Project HOPE - The People-to-People Health Foundation, Millwood, VA, 2013. For Yearly Product Request.
$603,625 to US FIRST, Manchester, NH, 2013. For Sponsorship of the Hood for the August Nascar Race.
$550,000 to Minnesota Childrens Museum, Saint Paul, MN, 2012. For Play it Forward capital expansion and renovation project.
$32,322 to University of Minnesota Foundation, Minneapolis, MN, 2012. For in-kind product donation to University of Minnesota Department of Physics and Nanotechnology.
$15,000 to University of Minnesota Foundation, Minneapolis, MN, 2013. For Mutilfunctional Catalytic Systems.
$5,164 to Saint Paul Public Schools, Independent School District No. 625, Saint Paul, MN, 2012. For Stuff for Schools.
$5,000 to Austin Community Foundation for the Capital Area, Austin, TX, 2012. For Central Texas Excellence in Writing Scholarships.
$5,000 to Saint Ambrose University, Davenport, IA, 2013. For Math and Science Student Scholarships.
$4,035 to United Way, Greater Twin Cities, Minneapolis, MN, 2013. For Marketing Materials.
$3,250 to Childrens Inn at NIH, Bethesda, MD, 2013. For Sponsorship for a Winnter Affair.
$3,000 to Austin Theater Alliance, Austin, TX, 2012. For Paramount and State Theatres Education and Outreach Program.
$2,622 to Minnesota Museum of American Art, Saint Paul, MN, 2013. For Mmaa Project Space.
$2,500 to Marthas Vineyard Hospital, Oak Bluffs, MA, 2012. For Sponsorship of the 25th Anniversary of the Sullivan Run/Walk.

4598
A Better Place, Inc. ✧
c/o Clearwater Equity Group, Inc.
2764 W. Lake of the Isles Pkwy.
Minneapolis, MN 55416

Established in 1999 in MN.
Donors: Stephen R. Sefton; Claudia Sefton; Clearwater Equity Group, Inc.
Foundation type: Independent foundation.
Financial data (yr. ended 12/31/13): Assets, $17,397,471 (M); gifts received, $11,644; expenditures, $1,732,429; qualifying distributions, $1,475,822; giving activities include $1,470,000 for 32 grants (high: $300,000; low: $500).
Purpose and activities: Giving primarily for education and human services; funding also for Catholic organizations.
Fields of interest: Higher education; Education; Human services; Catholic agencies & churches.
Limitations: Applications not accepted. Giving primarily in MN; funding also in IN. No grants to individuals.
Application information: Contributes only to pre-selected organizations.
Officers: Stephen R. Sefton, Pres.; William L. Dietz, C.F.O.
Directors: Brian Sefton; Maureen Sefton.
EIN: 411955000

4599
AHS Foundation ✧
90 S. 7th St., Ste. 5300
Minneapolis, MN 55402-4120
Contact: Thomas Wright, Secy.-Treas.

Established in 1968 in MN.
Donors: Arthur H. Schubert†; Leland Schubert; Helen D. Schubert†.
Foundation type: Independent foundation.
Financial data (yr. ended 06/30/13): Assets, $9,313,107 (M); expenditures, $562,560; qualifying distributions, $509,938; giving activities include $473,000 for grants.
Purpose and activities: Support for the relief of poverty and the advancement of education, religion, and community issues.

Fields of interest: Performing arts; Arts; Education; Human services; United Ways and Federated Giving Programs; Christian agencies & churches; Protestant agencies & churches; Catholic agencies & churches.
Type of support: General/operating support; Capital campaigns; Building/renovation; Endowments; Program development.
Limitations: Applications accepted. Giving primarily in CA, HI, MN, NJ, and OH. No grants to individuals; no loans.
Application information: Application form required.
Initial approach: Letter
Copies of proposal: 1
Deadline(s): None
Board meeting date(s): July
Final notification: 1 to 3 months
Officers: Leland W. Schubert, Pres.; John Dwan Schubert, 1st V.P.; Gage A. Schubert, 2nd V.P.; Thomas Wright, Secy.-Treas.
EIN: 410944654

4600
Alliss Educational Foundation ✧

(formerly Charles and Ellora Alliss Educational Foundation)
c/o U.S. Bank, N.A.
P.O. Box 64713
St. Paul, MN 55164-0713
Application address: c/o Sarah Godfrey, 101 E. 5th St., St. Paul, MN 55101; tel.: (651) 466-8710

Trust established in 1958 in MN.
Donors: Charles C. Alliss†; Ellora Martha Alliss†.
Foundation type: Independent foundation.
Financial data (yr. ended 12/31/13): Assets, $104,237,525 (M); expenditures, $5,591,451; qualifying distributions, $4,961,844; giving activities include $4,773,381 for 65 grants (high: $668,145; low: $2,061).
Purpose and activities: Giving to further the education of young people by granting scholarships, fellowships, gifts, and awards; grants made in lump sums solely to institutions. Support of undergraduate aid programs administered by the grantee institutions and including the period of postgraduate study.
Fields of interest: Secondary school/education; Higher education; Higher education, college; Higher education, university; Graduate/professional education.
Type of support: Scholarship funds.
Limitations: Applications accepted. Giving limited to MN educational institutions for scholarship programs for secondary, higher and postgraduate study. No grants to individuals directly.
Application information: Application form not required.
Initial approach: Letter
Copies of proposal: 1
Deadline(s): None
Board meeting date(s): Mar., June, Sept., and Dec.
Final notification: 3 months
Officer: Becky Roloff, C.E.O.
Trustees: Nina M. Archabal; Anita Pampusch; Edward Stringer; Frederick T. Weyerhaeuser; U.S. Bank, N.A.
EIN: 416011054

4601
Andersen Corporate Foundation

(formerly The Bayport Foundation of Andersen Corporation)
White Pine Bldg.
342 5th Ave. N., Ste. 200
Bayport, MN 55003-1201 (651) 275-4450
Contact: Chloette Haley, Prog. Off.
FAX: (651) 439-9480;
E-mail: andersencorpfdn@srinc.biz; Additional tel.: (651) 439-1557; Main URL: http://www.andersencorporation.com/corporate-responsibility/community-involvement/andersen-corporate-foundation/

Incorporated in 1941 in MN.
Donor: Andersen Corp.
Foundation type: Company-sponsored foundation.
Financial data (yr. ended 11/30/13): Assets, $43,349,719 (M); gifts received, $100; expenditures, $2,252,377; qualifying distributions, $2,085,785; giving activities include $1,914,400 for 151 grants (high: $100,000; low: $1,500).
Purpose and activities: The foundation supports programs designed to provide community, social, and support services to better people's lives and strengthen communities. Special emphasis is directed toward programs designed to promote affordable housing; health and safety; education and youth development; human services; and civic support.
Fields of interest: Media/communications; Visual arts; Museums; Performing arts; Performing arts, music; Arts; Elementary/secondary education; Education, services; Education; Environment, natural resources; Hospitals (general); Public health; Health care; Substance abuse, prevention; Mental health/crisis services; Employment, services; Housing/shelter, temporary shelter; Housing/shelter, owner/renter issues; Housing/shelter; Disasters, preparedness/services; Safety/disasters; Recreation; Aging, centers/services; Minorities/immigrants, centers/services; Independent living, disability; Human services; Mathematics; Engineering/technology; Science; Children/youth; Aging; Disabilities, people with; Economically disadvantaged.
International interests: Canada.
Type of support: General/operating support; Annual campaigns; Capital campaigns; Building/renovation; Emergency funds; Program development.
Limitations: Applications accepted. Giving primarily in areas of company operations in Des Moines and Dubuque, IA, East Metro, MN, North Brunswick, NJ; Luray and Page County, VA, Dunn County, Menomonie, and St. Croix Valley, WI, and to national organizations; some giving also in Huron, London, Middlesex, and Perth, Ontario Province, Canada. No support for national research organizations. No grants to individuals, or for endowments, or the purchase of Andersen products.
Publications: Application guidelines; IRS Form 990 or 990-PF printed copy available upon request.
Application information: Call foundation before sending request. Visit foundation Web site for application address and guidelines. Application form required.
Initial approach: Download application form and mail proposal and application form to nearest application address
Copies of proposal: 1
Deadline(s): Oct. 15, Feb. 15, and June 15
Board meeting date(s): Mar., July, and Nov.
Final notification: 10 working days
Officers and Directors: Keith D. Olson, Pres.; Susan Roeder, V.P., Grants Admin., and Secy.; Phil Donaldson, Treas.; Laurie Bauer; Jay Lund; Jerry Redmond.
Number of staff: 1 full-time professional; 1 full-time support.
EIN: 416020912
Selected grants: The following grants are a representative sample of this grantmaker's funding activity:
$50,000 to Regions Hospital, Saint Paul, MN, 2012. For campaign to transform mental health.
$40,000 to Partnership Plan for Stillwater Area Schools, Stillwater, MN, 2012. For Math and Science Partnership Plan Programs.
$30,000 to Habitat for Humanity, Saint Croix Valley, River Falls, WI, 2012. For Eco Village project.
$20,000 to Canvas Health, Oakdale, MN, 2012. For Integrative Health Initiative.
$10,000 to Junior Achievement of the Upper Midwest, Maplewood, MN, 2012. For JA BizTown and STEM program.
$8,000 to Operation Help, Hudson, WI, 2012. For general operating support.
$2,500 to Bridge to Hope, Menomonie, WI, 2012. For general operating support.

4602
Fred C. and Katherine B. Andersen Foundation ✧

(formerly Andersen Foundation)
P.O. Box 80
Bayport, MN 55003-0080
Contact: Mary Gillstrom, V.P., Secy. and Dir.

Incorporated in 1959 in MN.
Donor: Fred C. Andersen†.
Foundation type: Independent foundation.
Financial data (yr. ended 12/31/13): Assets, $410,054,291 (M); expenditures, $21,389,351; qualifying distributions, $20,573,762; giving activities include $20,439,713 for 203 grants (high: $3,000,000; low: $1,000).
Purpose and activities: Focuses on higher education institutions that do not accept state or federal funding, youth, elderly and health programs in local areas.
Fields of interest: Arts; Higher education; Hospitals (general); Health care; Youth development; Aging, centers/services.
Type of support: General/operating support; Capital campaigns; Program development.
Limitations: Applications accepted. Giving on a national basis for higher education, locally in MN and western WI for all other areas. No support for federally funded colleges, universities, or endowment programs. No grants to individuals.
Application information: Proposals must be received in the foundation's office, not postmarked, on or before deadline date. Must include original copy of proposal among the six required. Application form required.
Initial approach: Letter
Copies of proposal: 6
Deadline(s): Mar. 11, July 15, and Oct. 14
Board meeting date(s): Apr., Aug., and Nov.
Final notification: Varies
Officers and Directors:* Jerold W. Wulf,* Pres.; Mary Gillstrom,* V.P. and Secy.; Gregory L. Benson,* V.P. and Treas.; Peter J. Clements; David L. Croft; George O. Hoel; John D. Piepel.

Number of staff: 1 part-time professional.
EIN: 416020920
Selected grants: The following grants are a representative sample of this grantmaker's funding activity:
$4,000,000 to Saint Paul Foundation, Saint Paul, MN, 2012. For program support.
$3,000,000 to Minnesota Medical Foundation, Minneapolis, MN, 2012. For program support.
$1,650,000 to Mayo Foundation, Rochester, MN, 2012. For program support.
$265,000 to American Red Cross, Saint Croix Valley Chapter, Bayport, MN, 2012. For program support.
$175,000 to Alice Lloyd College, Caney Creek Community Center, Pippa Passes, KY, 2012. For unrestricted general support.
$175,000 to Asbury University, Wilmore, KY, 2012. For unrestricted general support.
$175,000 to Grove City College, Grove City, PA, 2012. For unrestricted general support.
$100,000 to Regions Hospital Foundation, Saint Paul, MN, 2012. For program support.
$45,000 to United Way of Washington County-East, Stillwater, MN, 2012. For program support.
$20,000 to Amery Area Senior Citizens, Amery, WI, 2012. For program support.

4603
Hugh J. Andersen Foundation ✧
342 5th Ave. N., Ste. 200
White Pine Bldg.
Bayport, MN 55003-1201 (651) 275-4489
Contact: Bradley Kruse, Prog. Dir.
FAX: (651) 439-9480; E-mail: hjafdn@srinc.biz; Main URL: https://www.srinc.biz/foundations/hugh-j-andersen-foundation/

Established in 1962.
Donors: Hugh J. Andersen†; Jane K. Andersen†; Katherine B. Andersen†.
Foundation type: Independent foundation.
Financial data (yr. ended 02/28/14): Assets, $58,561,595; expenditures, $2,767,685; qualifying distributions, $2,696,529; giving activities include $2,434,929 for 212 grants (high: $75,000; low: $500).
Purpose and activities: The foundation's mission is to give back to the community through focused efforts that foster inclusiveness, promote equality, and lead to increased human independence, self-sufficiency, and dignity. Emphasis on women and children's programs, community education and social issues, and general community health and medical services, including AIDS services.
Fields of interest: Humanities; Arts; Health care; Human services; Children/youth, services; Family services; Women; Economically disadvantaged; Homeless.
Type of support: General/operating support; Continuing support; Annual campaigns; Capital campaigns; Building/renovation; Program development.
Limitations: Applications accepted. Giving primarily in St. Croix Valley-Washington County, MN, and Pierce, Polk, and St. Croix counties, WI, with a secondary interest in St. Paul, MN. No support for private foundations or schools, political or religious organizations, athletic teams, child care centers, civic action groups, business or economics education, or immigration and refugee issues and programming. No grants to individuals, or for fundraising dinners and events, travel, curriculum development, independent media productions, debt relief, scholarships, or fellowships; no loans.
Publications: Annual report (including application guidelines); IRS Form 990 or 990-PF printed copy available upon request.
Application information: Accepts Minnesota Common Grant Application Form (without modification) along with required grant proposal checklist and request cover sheet. Proposals should be unbound, preferably double-sided, and limited to 10-pages (exclusive of attachments). Mass appeals or generic solicitations not considered. Faxed or e-mailed applications will not be considered, nor will the inclusion of videotapes, CDs or DVDs. Application form required.
Initial approach: Letter or telephone requesting guidelines, requirements and cover sheet. Application cover forms can also be downloaded from foundation web site
Copies of proposal: 1
Deadline(s): Mar. 15, June 15, Aug. 15 and Nov. 15
Board meeting date(s): Feb., June, Sept. and Dec.
Final notification: 4 weeks after board meeting
Officers and Trustees:* Sarah J. Andersen,* Pres.; Christine E. Andersen, V.P.; Lisa W. Copeland,* V.P.; Stephen S. Wolfson,* V.P.; William H. Rubenstein,* Secy.-Treas.
EIN: 416020914
Selected grants: The following grants are a representative sample of this grantmaker's funding activity:
$100,000 to Hudson Hospital Foundation, Hudson, WI, 2012. For Cancer Center of Western Wisconsin.
$47,000 to Girl Scouts of the U.S.A., Minnesota and Wisconsin River Valleys Council, Saint Paul, MN, 2012. For general operating support.
$20,000 to Valley Outreach, Stillwater, MN, 2012. For capital support.
$10,000 to Saint Croix Art Barn, Osceola, WI, 2012. For general operating support.
$9,000 to Regions Hospital Foundation, Saint Paul, MN, 2012. For HIV/AIDS medication program.

4604
L. & N. Andreas Foundation ✧
(formerly Cayman Conand Foundation)
c/o Andreas Office
P.O. Box 3584
Mankato, MN 56002-3584

Established in MN.
Donors: Lowell W. Andreas†; Andreas Lee.
Foundation type: Independent foundation.
Financial data (yr. ended 11/30/13): Assets, $37,146,442 (M); gifts received, $1,397; expenditures, $2,086,259; qualifying distributions, $2,002,050; giving activities include $2,002,050 for 117 grants (high: $217,500; low: $1,000).
Fields of interest: Higher education; Human services; Foundations (community); Christian agencies & churches; Protestant agencies & churches.
Limitations: Applications not accepted. Giving primarily in MN. No grants to individuals.
Application information: Contributes only to pre-selected organizations.
Officers: Andreas Lee, Pres. and Secy.; David Andreas, V.P. and Treas.
Trustees: Cayman Campbell; Jason Lee.
EIN: 363382956

4605
The Andreas Foundation ✧
c/o Andreas Office
P.O. Box 3584
Mankato, MN 56002-3584

Incorporated in 1945 in IA.
Donors: D.O. Andreas; Michael Andreas.
Foundation type: Independent foundation.
Financial data (yr. ended 11/30/13): Assets, $98,977,392 (M); expenditures, $3,795,050; qualifying distributions, $3,688,207; giving activities include $3,688,207 for 148 grants (high: $410,000; low: $100).
Purpose and activities: Giving primarily for education, hospitals, children and social services, Roman Catholic churches and organizations, and to Christian organizations.
Fields of interest: Higher education; Education; Hospitals (general); Human services; Children/youth, services; Foundations (private grantmaking); Christian agencies & churches; Catholic agencies & churches.
Limitations: Applications not accepted. Giving primarily in FL and IL; some giving also in Washington, DC and MD. No grants to individuals.
Application information: Contributes only to pre-selected organizations.
Officers and Trustees:* Michael D. Andreas,* Pres. and Treas.; Terry Andreas,* V.P.; Sandra McMurtrie,* V.P.; Dean Wuebker, Secy.; D.O. Andreas.
EIN: 416017057

4606
The Annexstad Family Foundation ✧
5516 Merritt Cir.
Edina, MN 55436-2026
Application address: c/o Annexstad Family Foundation, W9429 Peterson Dr., Iron Mountain, MI 49801, tel.: (906) 776-1952

Established in 2000 in MN.
Donors: Albert T. Annexstad; Catherine C. Annexstad; A. Daniel Lewis; Bonita Lewis; Federated Mutual Insurance; J-C Press; Anthony Vineyards; Annestad Family; Federated Foundation; Dan Lewis; Bonnie Lewis.
Foundation type: Independent foundation.
Financial data (yr. ended 12/31/13): Assets, $22,939,510 (M); gifts received, $4,163,216; expenditures, $2,007,832; qualifying distributions, $1,871,203; giving activities include $728,330 for 18 grants (high: $300,000; low: $351), and $988,945 for 115 grants to individuals (high: $25,000; low: $2,182).
Purpose and activities: Scholarships to U.S. citizens who are part of Big Brothers/Big Sisters for at least 18 months, who maintain a 2.75 GPA or higher, and who have achieved at least national average on ACT/SAT.
Fields of interest: Higher education.
Limitations: Applications accepted. Giving in the U.S., with some emphasis on MN. No grants to individuals (directly).
Application information: Application form required.
Initial approach: Contact local Big Brothers/Big Sisters chapter to obtain application packet
Deadline(s): None
Officers: Albert T. Annexstad, Pres.; Catherine C. Annexstad, V.P.; Tom Annexstad, V.P.; Patti Marinovich, Secy.-Treas.; Dick Sherwood, Exec. Dir.

Trustees: Kaci Annexstad; Shane Annexstad; Mackenzi Marinovich; Morgan Marinovich.
EIN: 411975043

4607
Athwin Foundation ✧
5200 Willson Rd., Ste. 307
Minneapolis, MN 55424-1344 (952) 915-6165
Contact: Jim Storm

Trust established in 1956 in MN.
Donors: Atherton Bean†; Winifred W. Bean†.
Foundation type: Independent foundation.
Financial data (yr. ended 12/31/13): Assets, $7,455,123 (M); expenditures, $900,052; qualifying distributions, $849,575; giving activities include $758,175 for 73 grants (high: $250,000; low: $1,000).
Purpose and activities: Giving primarily for arts and humanities, education, human services, environmental enhancement, and organizational capacity building.
Fields of interest: Visual arts; Performing arts; Arts; Education; Crime/law enforcement; Human services; Children/youth, services; Religion.
Type of support: General/operating support; Management development/capacity building; Capital campaigns; Program development.
Limitations: Applications accepted. Giving primarily in MN. No grants to individuals, or for scholarships or fellowships; no loans.
Publications: Application guidelines.
Application information: Application form required.
Initial approach: Letter
Copies of proposal: 1
Deadline(s): Mar. 1 and Oct. 1
Board meeting date(s): Biannually
Trustees: Bruce W. Bean; Glen Bean; Mary F. Bean.
Number of staff: None.
EIN: 416021773

4608
Bakken Family WRC Foundation ✧
90 S. 7th St., Ste. 5300
Minneapolis, MN 55402-4120

Established in 1995 in MN.
Donor: Constance L. Bakken.
Foundation type: Independent foundation.
Financial data (yr. ended 12/31/13): Assets, $20,971,542 (M); expenditures, $905,562; qualifying distributions, $785,494; giving activities include $764,750 for 33 grants (high: $155,000; low: $1,000).
Purpose and activities: The foundation's primary interests are education, social services, humanities, and the arts in Minnesota. Applications are also accepted from individuals pursuing college or graduate school degrees or considering a religious career, and are in need of scholarship, fellowship, or loan assistance; fine arts and performing arts will also be considered.
Fields of interest: Education; Hospitals (general); Human services; Protestant agencies & churches.
Type of support: General/operating support; Scholarships—to individuals.
Limitations: Applications not accepted.
Application information: Contributes only to pre-selected organizations.
Board meeting date(s): Apr., Aug., and Nov.
Directors: Bradley E. Bakken; Constance L. Bakken; Jeffrey Bakken; Pamela C. Petersmeyer; Wendy K. Watson.
EIN: 411796283
Selected grants: The following grants are a representative sample of this grantmaker's funding activity:
$10,000 to Kinship of Greater Minneapolis, Minneapolis, MN, 2011. For general support.

4609
The Beim Foundation ✧
318 W. 48th St.
Minneapolis, MN 55419-5418 (612) 825-1404
E-mail: beimfoundation@earthlink.net; Main URL: http://www.beimfoundation.org
Grants List: http://www.beimfoundation.org/recent-grants.asp

Incorporated in 1947 in MN.
Donors: N.C. Beim†; Raymond N. Beim†.
Foundation type: Independent foundation.
Financial data (yr. ended 12/31/12): Assets, $11,153,303 (M); expenditures, $569,801; qualifying distributions, $541,724; giving activities include $455,000 for 49 grants (high: $20,000; low: $500).
Purpose and activities: Primary areas of interest are arts, education, environment, and human services.
Fields of interest: Arts; Education; Environment, natural resources; Environment; Human services; Children/youth; Youth; Adults; Aging; Disabilities, people with; Mentally disabled.
Type of support: Equipment; Program development.
Limitations: Applications accepted. Giving primarily in MN; some giving also in selected communities outside of MN. No support for private foundations, or for political or religious organizations or international organizations. No grants to individuals, or for deficit financing memberships, endowments, subscriptions, tickets, conferences, fundraisers, or annual campaigns, multi-year support, capital campaigns or for general operating support; no grants for building or equipment, except for equipment qualifying under small arts capital grants; no loans.
Publications: Application guidelines.
Application information: Complete application policies and guidelines available on foundation web site. Application form required.
Initial approach: See foundation web site
Copies of proposal: 1
Deadline(s): See foundation web site for current deadlines
Board meeting date(s): Board meeting dates available on foundation web site
Final notification: See foundation web site
Officers: Carol Nulsen, Pres.; Patricia Arnold, Treas.
Directors: Jim McKim; David Nulsen; Julie Packard; Barbara Peters; Jack Stephenson; Allison Villani.
Number of staff: None.
EIN: 416022529
Selected grants: The following grants are a representative sample of this grantmaker's funding activity:
$20,000 to City Year Seattle/King County, Seattle, WA, 2012. For the Whole School Whole Child Program.
$16,500 to Montana State University Foundation, Bozeman, MT, 2012. For Montana Shakespeare in the Parks 2013 MONTANA SHAKES! tour.
$15,000 to Coyote Central, Seattle, WA, 2012. For the Hit the Streets Program.
$15,000 to Hopa Mountain, Bozeman, MT, 2012. For $10,000 support for the Youth Leadership Program and $5,000 support for the Indigenous Scholars of Promise Program.
$15,000 to Minnesota Center for Book Arts, Minneapolis, MN, 2012. To support of Art Camps for Youth.
$15,000 to Palos Verdes Art Center, Rolling Hills Estates, CA, 2012. For Art At Your Fingertips.
$13,500 to Western Sustainability Exchange, Livingston, MT, 2012. For the Youth Entrepreneur Stewardship Program.
$13,000 to Southern Maine Agency on Aging, Scarborough, ME, 2012. For Money Minders.
$10,000 to Kalamazoo Institute of Arts, Kalamazoo, MI, 2012. For the Children and Teen Arts Program.
$10,000 to Phinney Neighborhood Association, Seattle, WA, 2012. For PNA Village.

4610
Agnes M. Bendorf Charitable Trust ✧ ☆
c/o Trust Tax Services
P.O. Box 64713
Saint Paul, MN 55164-0713

Established in MN.
Foundation type: Independent foundation.
Financial data (yr. ended 11/30/13): Assets, $0 (M); expenditures, $670,328; qualifying distributions, $667,964; giving activities include $667,078 for 2 grants (high: $657,078; low: $10,000).
Fields of interest: Philanthropy/voluntarism; Religion.
Limitations: Applications not accepted. Giving primarily in MN.
Application information: Unsolicited requests for funds not accepted.
Trustee: U.S. Bank, N.A.
EIN: 416490149

4611
Bentson Foundation ✧
315 Lake St. E., No. 302
Wayzata, MN 55391-1700 (952) 923-1040
Contact: Judi Dutcher

Established in 1956 in MN.
Foundation type: Independent foundation.
Financial data (yr. ended 06/30/14): Assets, $104,882,747 (M); expenditures, $5,132,158; qualifying distributions, $4,146,748; giving activities include $4,146,748 for 33 grants.
Fields of interest: Higher education, university; Hospitals (general); Jewish agencies & synagogues.
Limitations: Applications accepted. Giving primarily in MN. No grants to individuals.
Application information: Application form not required.
Initial approach: Proposal
Deadline(s): None
Officers: Laurie Bentson Kauth, Pres.; George Reilly, Secy.; Mark S. Niblick, Treas.; Judi Dutcher, Exec. Dir.
Board Member: Lowell Stortz.
EIN: 416020204
Selected grants: The following grants are a representative sample of this grantmaker's funding activity:
$6,650,000 to University of Minnesota, Minneapolis, MN, 2012. For general support.

$1,000,000 to Walker Art Center, Minneapolis, MN, 2012. For general support.
$30,000 to New York University, New York, NY, 2012. For general support.
$25,000 to Museum of Russian Art, Minneapolis, MN, 2012. For general support.
$25,000 to University of Wisconsin Foundation, Madison, WI, 2012. For general support.
$10,000 to University of California, Oakland, CA, 2012. For general support.

4612
Best Buy Foundation ✧
(formerly Best Buy Children's Foundation)
7601 Penn Ave. S.
Richfield, MN 55423-3645 (866) 625-4350
FAX: (612) 292-4001;
E-mail: bestbuygrants@easymatch.com; Additional e-mail and tel.: communityrelations@bestbuy.com, (612) 291-6108; Main URL: http://www.bby.com/community-relations/

Established in 1994 in MN.
Donor: Best Buy Co., Inc.
Foundation type: Company-sponsored foundation.
Financial data (yr. ended 03/02/13): Assets, $52,912 (M); gifts received, $8,804,089; expenditures, $9,936,715; qualifying distributions, $8,067,994; giving activities include $7,742,839 for 602 grants (high: $1,100,000; low: $950).
Purpose and activities: The foundation supports programs designed to provide teens with opportunities to develop technology skills that inspire future education and careers.
Fields of interest: Media/communications; Media, film/video; Interactive games; Mobile media; Elementary/secondary education; Education; Disasters, preparedness/services; Boys & girls clubs; Human services; United Ways and Federated Giving Programs; Engineering/technology; Leadership development; Youth; Economically disadvantaged.
Type of support: General/operating support; Continuing support; Capital campaigns; Program development; Curriculum development; Scholarship funds.
Limitations: Applications accepted. Giving limited to areas of company operations, with emphasis on the Twin Cities, MN area. No support for fraternal organizations or social clubs, units of government or quasi-governmental agencies, labor or lobbying organizations, for-profit organizations, religious organizations not of direct benefit to the entire community, or athletic teams. No grants to individuals or for political campaigns, general operating support, endowments, travel, national ceremonies, memorials, fundraising dinners, testimonials, conferences, or similar events, health, medical, therapeutic programs, or living subsidies, athletic events, or multi-year requests; no product donations.
Publications: Application guidelines; Grants list; Program policy statement.
Application information: Capital requests are limited to the Twin Cities, MN, area organizations that have previously received funding from the foundation. Support is limited to 1 contribution per organization during any given year. Organizations receiving support are asked to provide a final report. Multi-year funding is not automatic. Application form required.
Initial approach: Complete online eligibility quiz and application form
Copies of proposal: 1
Deadline(s): June 2 to June 27 for Community Grants; Feb. 1, May 1, Aug. 1, and Nov. 1 for National Program and Twin Cities Fund; Feb. 1 for Twin Cities capital grants
Board meeting date(s): Annually
Final notification: Sept. 15 for Community Grants
Officers and Trustees:* Susan S. Hoff,* Chair.; Todd Hartman, Secy.; Lisa Erickson, Treas.; Matt Furman; Hubert Joly; Dean Kimberly; Scott Moore; Susan Bass Roberts; Raymond Slivia.
Number of staff: 1 full-time professional.
EIN: 411784382
Selected grants: The following grants are a representative sample of this grantmaker's funding activity:
$1,100,000 to Scholarship America, Minneapolis, MN, 2013. For National Partnership Grants.
$488,000 to Museum of Science, Boston, MA, 2013. For National Partnership Grants. For Teen Tech Center.
$312,000 to Museum of Science, Boston, MA, 2013. For National Partnership Grants.
$300,000 to MOUSE, New York, NY, 2013. For National Partnership Grants.
$150,000 to Boys and Girls Clubs of America, National Headquarters, Atlanta, GA, 2013. For National Partnership Grants.
$100,000 to Urban League, National, New York, NY, 2013. For National Partnership Grants.
$6,000 to Park City Performances, Park City, UT, 2013. For Community Partnership Grant.
$5,000 to Boys and Girls Club of Bastrop, Bastrop, TX, 2013. For Community Partnership Grant.
$5,000 to KIPP Minnesota, Minneapolis, MN, 2013. For Twin City Metro Hometown Grants.
$5,000 to Phyllis Wheatley Community Center, Minneapolis, MN, 2013. For Twin City Metro Hometown Grants.

4613
Bethel University Foundation Pooled Common Fund ✧ ☆
(formerly Bethel College and Seminary Pooled Common Fund)
3900 Bethel Dr.
St. Paul, MN 55112-6902

Established in MN.
Donors: Warren Magnuson; Wayland Jensen; Randal S. Monson; Lori Monson; Ethel Nelson†.
Foundation type: Independent foundation.
Financial data (yr. ended 12/31/13): Assets, $1,884,647 (M); gifts received, $1,026,913; expenditures, $1,004,451; qualifying distributions, $1,092,125; giving activities include $1,001,360 for 19 grants (high: $505,851; low: $749).
Fields of interest: Higher education; Education; Human services; Religion.
Type of support: General/operating support.
Limitations: Applications not accepted. Giving in the U.S., with some emphasis on MN. No grants to individuals.
Application information: Unsolicited requests for funds not accepted.
Officers and Director:* Donald Benson,* Chair.; Randal Monson, Secy.; Alan Bergstrom, Treas.; Angella J. Hjelle, Exec. Dir.
EIN: 411815788
Selected grants: The following grants are a representative sample of this grantmaker's funding activity:
$25,967 to Bethel University, Saint Paul, MN, 2011. For general fund.

4614
Better Way Foundation, Inc. ✧
(formerly Alpha Omega Foundation, Inc.)
10350 Bren Rd. West
Minnetonka, MN 55343-9014 (952) 656-4597
E-mail: info@betterwayfoundation.org; Main URL: http://betterwayfoundation.org/

Established around 1994 in FL.
Donors: North Star Ventures; Arbeit Investment, LP; Arbeit & Co.; Opus Corp.
Foundation type: Company-sponsored foundation.
Financial data (yr. ended 12/31/12): Assets, $32,958,633 (M); expenditures, $1,592,994; qualifying distributions, $1,564,979; giving activities include $1,293,656 for 29 grants (high: $175,000; low: $5,000).
Purpose and activities: The foundation supports programs designed to provide holistic and cost-effective development opportunities to young children and families. Special emphasis is directed toward programs designed to improve early childhood outcomes.
Fields of interest: Education, early childhood education; Higher education; Health care; Nutrition; Family services; Human services; United Ways and Federated Giving Programs; Catholic agencies & churches; Children; Economically disadvantaged.
Type of support: General/operating support; Continuing support; Capital campaigns; Program development; Scholarship funds; Research.
Limitations: Applications accepted. Giving primarily in CA, IN, MN, WA, and Tanzania. No grants to individuals.
Publications: Application guidelines.
Application information: Unsolicited full proposals are not accepted. Organizations interested in presenting an idea for funding must submit a brief letter of inquiry. Application form not required.
Initial approach: Complete online letter of inquiry
Deadline(s): None
Officers and Directors:* Matthew G. Rauenhorst,* Chair. and Pres.; Amy R. Goldman,* V.P.; Sophie Kelley, V.P.; Mary Pickard, V.P.; Fr. Kevin McDonough,* Secy.; Judy Mahoney,* Treas.; Kristin Grubb, Tax Off.; Anne Mahony; Louise Myers; Gia Rauenhorst; Steve Cashin.
EIN: 411795984

4615
The Beverly Foundation ✧
(formerly The Beverly Deikel Foundation)
1660 Hwy. 100 S., Ste. 230
Minneapolis, MN 55416-1557 (952) 545-3000
Contact: Beverly Deikel, Pres. and Treas.

Established in 1999 in MN.
Donor: Beverly Deikel.
Foundation type: Independent foundation.
Financial data (yr. ended 12/31/13): Assets, $31,197,404 (M); expenditures, $1,772,471; qualifying distributions, $1,426,044; giving activities include $1,374,915 for 70 grants (high: $226,000; low: $4).
Fields of interest: Education; Environment; Human services; Children/youth, services; Jewish federated giving programs.

Type of support: General/operating support; Management development/capacity building; Capital campaigns; Building/renovation; Emergency funds; Program development; Consulting services; Program evaluation.
Limitations: Applications accepted. Giving primarily in the Minneapolis-St. Paul, MN, area. No grants to individuals.
Application information: Application form required.
Initial approach: Letter
Copies of proposal: 1
Deadline(s): None
Officers: Beverly Deikel, Pres. and Treas.; Ronald Fingerhut, Secy.
Number of staff: 1 part-time professional; 1 part-time support.
EIN: 411958161

4616
F. R. Bigelow Foundation ✧
55 E. 5th St., Ste. 600
St. Paul, MN 55101-1797 (651) 224-5463
Contact: Carleen K. Rhodes, Secy.
FAX: (651) 224-8123; E-mail: inbox@frbigelow.org; Toll Free tel.: (800) 875-6167; Main URL: http://www.frbigelow.org
Grants List: http://www.frbigelow.org/what_we_fund/

Trust established in 1934; incorporated in 1946 in MN.
Donor: Frederick Russell Bigelow†.
Foundation type: Independent foundation.
Financial data (yr. ended 12/31/12): Assets, $136,196,899 (M); gifts received, $26,569; expenditures, $7,221,053; qualifying distributions, $61,385,527; giving activities include $6,038,433 for 161 grants (high: $275,000; low: $50).
Purpose and activities: Established as a trust to promote the well-being of mankind and to support the civic, educational, religious, and other needs of the community.
Fields of interest: Humanities; Arts; Education, early childhood education; Child development, education; Elementary school/education; Secondary school/education; Higher education; Adult education—literacy, basic skills & GED; Education, reading; Housing/shelter, development; Human services; Child development, services; Economic development; Minorities; Economically disadvantaged.
Type of support: Capital campaigns; Building/renovation; Equipment; Program development; Seed money; Matching/challenge support.
Limitations: Applications accepted. Giving limited to the Greater St. Paul, MN, metropolitan area, which includes; Ramsey, Washington, and Dakota counties, with a particular emphasis on serving people who live and work in the city of St. Paul. No support for sectarian religious programs. No grants to individuals, or for annual operating expenses, medical research, or ongoing, open-ended needs.
Publications: Application guidelines; Grants list.
Application information: Application requirements are included in the foundation's application guidelines available on the foundation's web site. Application form required.
Initial approach: Letter of inquiry (no more than 3 pgs.) or full application
Copies of proposal: 1
Deadline(s): Approximately 3 1/2 months prior to board meetings
Board meeting date(s): Apr., Aug., and Nov.
Final notification: 4 to 5 months
Officers and Trustees:* Dr. Richard B. Heydinger,* Chair.; Peter F. Jackson, Vice-Chair.; Carleen K. Rhodes, Secy.; Heidi Gesell, Treas.; William L. Collins; Terry Devitt; Mari Oyanagi Eggum; Glenn E. Johnson; Judith Kishel; Gloria Perez; Susan J. Sands; Terri Thao; Paul Williams.
Number of staff: None.
EIN: 510232651
Selected grants: The following grants are a representative sample of this grantmaker's funding activity:
$225,000 to Center for Victims of Torture, Minneapolis, MN, 2012. For primary care clinic partnership.
$30,000 to Accountability Minnesota, Saint Paul, MN, 2012. For financial services messaging and continued infrastructure building.
$25,000 to District Councils Collaborative of Saint Paul and Minneapolis, Saint Paul, MN, 2012. For Last Mile to Green Line Project.
$25,000 to Latino Economic Development Center, Minneapolis, MN, 2012. Toward East Metro Latino Academy Teocalli Tequiotl OIC (TTOIC), business development and employment training center for low-income Latinos.
$20,000 to Housing Preservation Project, Saint Paul, MN, 2012. For East Metro Housing Equity Project.

4617
Charles K. Blandin Foundation ✧
(formerly The Blandin Foundation)
100 N. Pokegama Ave.
Grand Rapids, MN 55744-2739 (218) 326-0523
Contact: James Hoolihan, Pres.
FAX: (218) 327-1949;
E-mail: info@blandinfoundation.org; Additional tel.: (877) 882-2257; Main URL: http://www.blandinfoundation.org
Blandin on Broadband Blog: http://blandinonbroadband.wordpress.com/
Charles K. Blandin Foundation's Philanthropy Promise: http://www.ncrp.org/philanthropys-promise/who
E-Newsletter: http://www.blandinfoundation.org/news/
Multimedia: http://www.blandinfoundation.org/resources/videos.php
Twitter: https://twitter.com/blandinfound
Vital Forests, Vital Communities Blog: http://vfvc.wordpress.com

Incorporated in 1941 in MN.
Donor: Charles K. Blandin†.
Foundation type: Independent foundation.
Financial data (yr. ended 12/31/13): Assets, $449,897,821 (M); expenditures, $19,809,858; qualifying distributions, $12,429,008; giving activities include $11,633,225 for grants, $795,783 for grants to individuals, and $4,966,321 for foundation-administered programs.
Purpose and activities: Giving primarily in four areas for rural MN: 1) Community leadership; 2) Economic opportunity; 3) Life-long learning; and 4) Diversity.
Fields of interest: Higher education; Education; Economic development; Rural development; Community/economic development; Leadership development.
Type of support: General/operating support; Continuing support; Program development; Seed money; Scholarship funds; Technical assistance; Program-related investments/loans; Employee matching gifts; Scholarships—to individuals; Matching/challenge support.
Limitations: Applications accepted. Giving limited to rural areas of MN; scholarships limited to graduates of an Itasca County, Hill City, or Remer, Blackduck, Northome, MN, high school, Northern Lights Community School, and Chief Bug-O-Nay-Ge-Shig Schools in MN. No support for religious activities, camping and athletic programs, or urban projects. No grants to individuals (except for Blandin Educational Awards), for operating budgets, annual campaigns, deficit financing, government services, capital funds (outside home community), endowments, publications, travel, medical research, films or videos, conferences, or seminars (outside of those sponsored by the foundation and related to its grantmaking).
Publications: Financial statement; Informational brochure (including application guidelines).
Application information: Scholarship applicants should call or write to the foundation for deadlines and other information. Foundation will accept the Minnesota Common Grant Application Form available on the foundation's web site. Application form not required.
Initial approach: Online grant inquiry form or call to meet a staff member
Copies of proposal: 1
Deadline(s): Major grants: Mar. 15, June 15, Sept. 15, and Dec. 15. Quick Response, Rural Quick Start and Itasca County Area: None. Blandin Broadband Community: Apr. and June
Board meeting date(s): Mar., June, Sept. and Dec.
Officers and Trustees:* Mike Johnson, Chair.; Kathleen Annette, C.E.O. and Pres.; Wade Fauth, V.P. and Dir., Grants; Marian Barcus; Timothy Bonner, M.D.; Yvonne Cheek; Kandace Creel Falcon, Ph.D.; Kris Ferraro; James Hoolihan; Martin Jennings; Heidi Korstad; William D. Maki; Brian D. McInnes; Brian Nicklason; Liwanag Ojala; Bonnie Besse Rietz; Bruce Stender.
Number of staff: 14 full-time professional; 17 full-time support; 1 part-time support.
EIN: 416038619

4618
Blue Cross and Blue Shield of Minnesota Foundation, Inc. ✧
1750 Yankee Doodle Rd., N159
Eagan, MN 55122-1613 (651) 662-3950
FAX: (651) 662-4266;
E-mail: foundation@bluecrossmn.com; Additional address: P.O. Box 64560, St. Paul, MN 55164-0560; Additional tel.: (866) 812-1593; Contact for Growing Up Healthy: Jocelyn Ancheta, Prog. Off., tel.: (651) 662-2894, e-mail: Jocelyn_L_Ancheta@bluecrossmn.com; Contact for Public Libraries for Health and Building Health Equity Together: Stacey Millett, Sr. Prog. Off, tel.: (651) 662-1019, e-mail: Stacey_D_Millett@bluecrossmn.com; Main URL: http://www.bcbsmnfoundation.org
Grants Database: http://www.bcbsmnfoundation.org/pages-grants-tier3-Grantees?oid=9228
News Releases: http://www.bcbsmnfoundation.org/feed.cfm?oid=10209
Perspectives: http://www.bcbsmnfoundation.org/feed.cfm?oid=10208

Publications & DVDs: http://www.bcbsmnfoundation.org/feed.cfm?oid=10212

Established in 1986 in MN.
Donors: Blue Cross and Blue Shield of Minnesota; American Healthways; HMO Minnesota.
Foundation type: Company-sponsored foundation.
Financial data (yr. ended 12/31/12): Assets, $65,401,618 (M); expenditures, $4,858,119; qualifying distributions, $4,443,412; giving activities include $3,069,477 for 71 grants (high: $500,000; low: $3,000).
Purpose and activities: The foundation supports programs designed to improve community conditions that have an impact on the health of children and families. Special emphasis is directed toward health and early childhood development; health and housing; health and social connectedness; health and the environment; and healthier Minnesota communities.
Fields of interest: Child development, education; Libraries (public); Education; Environment, toxics; Environment; Health care, equal rights; Health care, clinics/centers; Public health; Public health, environmental health; Health care; Mental health/crisis services; Employment; Nutrition; Housing/shelter; Safety/disasters; Family services; Human services; Community/economic development; Children; Minorities; African Americans/Blacks; Native Americans/American Indians; Immigrants/refugees; Economically disadvantaged.
Type of support: Continuing support; Management development/capacity building; Program development; Technical assistance.
Limitations: Applications accepted. Giving limited to MN; giving also to statewide and regional organizations. No support for athletic organizations or groups. No grants to individuals, or for lobbying, political, or fraternal activities, legal services, sports events, religious activities, clinical quality improvement activities, biomedical research, capital campaigns, endowments or travel, fundraising events, or development campaigns, debt reduction, the payment of services or benefits reimbursable from other sources, the supplanting of funds already secured for budgeted staff and/or services, or long-term support; no loans.
Publications: Application guidelines; Annual report; Corporate giving report; Grants list; Informational brochure; Newsletter; Occasional report.
Application information: Support is limited to 1 contribution per organization during any given year. Site visits may be requested for Building Health Equity Together. Application form not required.
Initial approach: Telephone foundation; mail letter of inquiry to foundation; proposal for Public Libraries for Health; complete online application for Building Health Equity Together
Deadline(s): Visit website for deadlines; July 20 for Public Libraries for Health; Aug. 27 to Sept. 28 for Building Health Equity Together
Board meeting date(s): Feb., May, Aug., and Nov.
Final notification: Sept. for Public Libraries for Health; Mid-Dec. for Building Health Equity Together
Officers and Directors: Pamela A. Wheelock,* Chair.; Kathy Gaalswyk,* Vice-Chair.; Marsha Shotley,* Pres.; Denise Bergevin, V.P.; John Orner, V.P.; Nancy Nelson,* Secy.-Treas.; Carolyn Link, Exec. Dir.; Colleen Connors; Frank Fernandez; Shirley Hughes; Jan K. Malcolm; Deborah Meehan.
Number of staff: 6 full-time professional.
EIN: 363525653

4619
The Douglass Brandenborg Family Foundation ✧
920 Shady Ln. E.
Wayzata, MN 55391-1930

Established in 1999 in MN.
Donors: John Brandenborg; Laurie Douglass Brandenborg.
Foundation type: Independent foundation.
Financial data (yr. ended 12/31/12): Assets, $40,501,663 (M); expenditures, $2,127,841; qualifying distributions, $2,030,000; giving activities include $2,030,000 for 9 grants (high: $1,750,000; low: $5,000).
Purpose and activities: Giving primarily to a donor-advised fund, as well as for education, and to health organizations.
Fields of interest: Higher education; Education; Health organizations, association; Foundations (public).
Limitations: Applications not accepted. Giving primarily in CA and MN. No grants to individuals.
Application information: Contributes only to pre-selected organizations.
Officers and Directors:* John Brandenborg,* Pres.; Laurie Douglass Brandenborg,* Secy.
EIN: 411958170

4620
Otto Bremer Foundation ✧
445 Minnesota St., Ste. 2250
St. Paul, MN 55101-2107 (651) 227-8036
Contact: Danielle Cheslog, Grants Mgr.; Kari Suzuki, Dir., Opers.
FAX: (651) 312-3665; E-mail: obf@ottobremer.org; Additional tel.: (888) 291-1123; Main URL: http://www.ottobremer.org
Blog: http://www.ottobremer.org/news/ottoblog
Grants Database: http://www.ottobremer.org/recipients.php
Twitter: https://twitter.com/OttoBremer

Trust established in 1944 in MN.
Donor: Otto Bremer‡.
Foundation type: Independent foundation.
Financial data (yr. ended 12/31/13): Assets, $898,842,764 (M); expenditures, $43,336,945; qualifying distributions, $43,521,495; giving activities include $38,321,048 for 855 grants (high: $333,333; low: $2,500), and $1,000,000 for 1 loan/program-related investment.
Purpose and activities: The mission of the foundation is to assist people in achieving full economic, civic and social participation in and for the betterment of their communities.
Fields of interest: Child development, education; Higher education; Libraries (public); Reproductive health, family planning; Health care; Mental health/crisis services; Health organizations, association; Crime/violence prevention, youth; Crime/violence prevention, domestic violence; Legal services; Nutrition; Housing/shelter, development; Youth development, citizenship; Human services; Children/youth, services; Child development, services; Residential/custodial care, hospices; Women, centers/services; Minorities/immigrants, centers/services; Homeless, human services; Civil/human rights, immigrants; Civil/human rights, minorities; Civil/human rights, disabled; Civil/human rights, women; Civil/human rights, aging; Civil/human rights, LGBTQ; Civil rights, race/intergroup relations; Civil/human rights; Rural development; Community/economic development; Voluntarism promotion; Public affairs, citizen participation; Infants/toddlers; Children/youth; Children; Youth; Adults; Aging; Young adults; Disabilities, people with; Physically disabled; Blind/visually impaired; Deaf/hearing impaired; Mentally disabled; Minorities; Asians/Pacific Islanders; African Americans/Blacks; Hispanics/Latinos; Native Americans/American Indians; Indigenous peoples; Women; Infants/toddlers, female; Girls; Adults, women; Young adults, female; Men; Infants/toddlers, male; Boys; Adults, men; Young adults, male; Offenders/ex-offenders; Substance abusers; AIDS, people with; Single parents; Crime/abuse victims; Terminal illness, people with; Immigrants/refugees; Economically disadvantaged; Homeless; Migrant workers; LGBTQ.
Type of support: General/operating support; Continuing support; Management development/capacity building; Capital campaigns; Building/renovation; Equipment; Emergency funds; Program development; Conferences/seminars; Seed money; Curriculum development; Internship funds; Technical assistance; Program evaluation; Program-related investments/loans; Matching/challenge support.
Limitations: Applications accepted. Giving limited to organizations whose beneficiaries are residents of MN, ND and WI with preference given to those in regions served by Bremer Banks. No support for economic development, or historic preservation, museums and interpretive centers, sporting activities. No grants to individuals, or for endowment funds, medical research, professorships, annual fund drives, benefit events, camps, or artistic or media projects.
Publications: Annual report (including application guidelines); Grants list; Informational brochure (including application guidelines).
Application information: Foundation staff may seek additional information through telephone conversations or in-person site visits. Following a preliminary screening process, complete applications are considered by the foundation's trustees at six annual grantmaking meetings.Previous foundation grant recipients should review the foundation's one-grant-at-a-time policy before submitting an application.See web site for application form. Application form not required.
Initial approach: Online
Copies of proposal: 1
Deadline(s): Sept. 25, Jan. 7, Apr. 8 and July 8
Board meeting date(s): Monthly
Final notification: One week after each grantmaking meeting
Officers and Trustees:* Charlotte S. Johnson,* Co-C.E.O.; S. Brian Lipschultz,* Co-C.E.O.; Daniel C. Reardon,* Co-C.E.O.
Number of staff: 11 full-time professional; 1 part-time professional.
EIN: 416019050

4621
Bush Foundation ✧
101 5th St. East, Ste. 2400
St. Paul, MN 55101-1898 (651) 227-0891
Contact: Kelly M. Kleppe, Dir., Prog. Opers.
FAX: (651) 297-6485;
E-mail: info@bushfoundation.org; Main URL: http://www.bushfoundation.org
Courageous Leadership Blog: http://www.bushfoundation.org/blog

Facebook: http://www.facebook.com/bushfoundation
Knowledge Center: http://www.bushfoundation.org/about/resources/reports-publications
LinkedIn: http://www.linkedin.com/company/644935?trk=tyah
Twitter: http://twitter.com/bushfoundation

Incorporated in 1953 in MN.
Donors: Archibald Granville Bush†; Edyth Bassler Bush†.
Foundation type: Independent foundation.
Financial data (yr. ended 12/31/13): Assets, $888,876,731 (M); gifts received, $1,000; expenditures, $43,190,277; qualifying distributions, $38,192,468; giving activities include $26,506,749 for 170 grants (high: $1,031,700; low: $500), and $2,102,266 for grants to individuals.
Purpose and activities: The foundation is a catalyst for the courageous leadership necessary to create sustainable solutions to tough public problems and ensure community vitality.
Fields of interest: Education; Leadership development; General charitable giving; Native Americans/American Indians.
Type of support: Program development; Fellowships.
Limitations: Applications accepted. Giving primarily in MN, ND, SD and the 23 federally recognized native nations that share the same geography.
Publications: Annual report; Financial statement; Informational brochure; Occasional report.
Application information: See foundation web site for complete application policies for each program. Application form required.

Deadline(s): For fellowships the deadline varies but is multiple times each year. For other programs the date varies. See web site for current dates

Board meeting date(s): Feb., May, Aug. and Nov.

Officers and Directors:* Pamela Moret,* Chair.; Wendy M. Nelson,* Vice-Chair.; Jennifer Ford Reedy, Pres.; Allison Barmann, V.P., Strategy and Learning; Lars Leafblad, V.P., Leadership and Engagement; Gregory H. Keane, C.F.O.; Jennifer Alstad; Anthony Heredia; Curtis W. Johnson; Eric J. Jolly; Robert J. Jones; Jan K. Malcolm; Tim Mathern; Peter H. Pennekamp; Michael Solberg; Dee Thomas; Irving Weiser; Tracey Zephier.
Number of staff: 26 full-time professional; 3 part-time professional; 6 full-time support; 2 part-time support.
EIN: 416017815
Selected grants: The following grants are a representative sample of this grantmaker's funding activity:
$3,000,000 to Management Assistance Program for Nonprofits, Saint Paul, MN, 2013. To create digital and physical convening platform, where leaders build connections, share stories and grow ideas to help our communities innovate and inspire, payable over 3.00 years.
$1,542,700 to Red Lake Band of Chippewa Indians, Redlake, MN, 2012. For constitutional reform outreach, education and meetings, payable over 2.00 years.
$1,000,000 to Arts Partnership, Saint Paul, MN, 2013. Toward Arts Partnership Building Campaign in honor of Bush Foundation's 60th Anniversary, payable over 1.25 years.
$916,920 to Family Health International, Washington Office, Washington, DC, 2012. For technical support for the Bush Foundation School Leadership Initiative.
$900,000 to GTS Educational Events, Saint Paul, MN, 2012. For Bush Fellowships for elected and government officials with policy-making authority, payable over 2.75 years.
$600,000 to Intermedia Arts of Minnesota, Minneapolis, MN, 2012. For continued funding for Creative Community Leadership Institute to allow the program to build its work and implement evaluation and learning, payable over 3.00 years.
$586,831 to Family Health International, Washington Office, Washington, DC, 2013. For technical support and coaching for institution partners for Bush Foundation Teacher Preparation and Effectiveness Initiative.
$568,261 to Family Health International, Washington Office, Washington, DC, 2013. For technical support and coaching for institution partners for the Bush Foundations Teacher Preparation and Effectiveness Initiative 2013.
$500,000 to Community Violence Intervention Center, Grand Forks, ND, 2013. To advance charitable mission, in recognition of winning a Bush Prize for Community Innovation, payable over 3.00 years.
$500,000 to North Dakota Community Foundation, Bismarck, ND, 2012. For Bush Foundation donor advised, non-permanent fund at the North Dakota Community Foundation, payable over 8.00 years.
$300,000 to Northern Clay Center, Minneapolis, MN, 2012. For Bush funding will be used for general operating support through the Regional Arts Development Program II (RADP II), payable over 3.00 years.
$204,000 to Saint Paul Foundation, Saint Paul, MN, 2012. For the Forever Saint Paul Challenge to support community engagement opportunities across Minnesota.
$200,000 to Fargo-Moorhead Coalition for Homeless Persons, Fargo, ND, 2013. To support CARES (Coordinated Assessment and Referral Effectiveness System), which works to more efficiently and effectively assess, shelter and house persons who are experiencing or at risk of homelessness in the Fargo-Moorhead area.
$180,000 to Northland Foundation, Duluth, MN, 2012. For expansion and replication of intergenerational collaborations that enhance the vitality of towns and promote the well-being of participants of all ages, payable over 3.00 years.
$120,000 to Immigrant Development Center, Moorhead, MN, 2012. To build leadership capacity among low-income immigrant population residing in the Fargo-Moorhead area, payable over 1.25 years.
$110,000 to Sioux Falls Area Community Foundation, Sioux Falls, SD, 2012. For media campaign to strengthen philanthropy in South Dakota.
$100,000 to Dakota Resources, Renner, SD, 2012. For Dakota Rising Team-Based Community Leadership pilot.
$100,000 to Fargo-Moorhead Area Foundation, Fargo, ND, 2012. For media campaign to increase philanthropic contributions in North Dakota.
$100,000 to Springboard for the Arts, Saint Paul, MN, 2013. For Artist Organizers: a pilot program to mobilize artists around community challenges.
$100,000 to United Way, Greater Twin Cities, Minneapolis, MN, 2012. For start-up funding for Twin Cities Strive, a model focused on identifying measurable goals to raise student achievement, publically reporting on progress and using data driven improvement processes to target resources and gauge progress.
$75,000 to South Dakota Community Foundation, Pierre, SD, 2013. To administer a Community Innovation Small Grants Program that supports community problem-solving in South Dakota.
$52,260 to William Mitchell College of Law, Saint Paul, MN, 2013. For a symposium for tribal leaders on Tribal Citizenship.
$50,000 to Black Hills Area Community Foundation, Black Hills Knowledge Network, Rapid City, SD, 2012. For website enhancement and training materials to increase access to and usage of data indicators. Network connects people to ideas and local information to strengthen the community.
$50,000 to MinnCAN, Minneapolis, MN, 2012. To contribute to the support for educational achievement public policy.
$50,000 to Minnesota Council of Churches, Minneapolis, MN, 2012. To convene multiple Respectful Dialogue conversations about the Minnesota Marriage Amendment with trained facilitators in Minnesota congregations.
$50,000 to Saint Paul Foundation, Saint Paul, MN, 2012. For general operating support for Itasca Project, employer-led alliance that seeks to address regional economic issues that affect competitiveness and quality of life in the Twin Cities region. In particular, the nonpartisan group is concerned with addressing socioeconomic disparities.
$50,000 to Southwest Initiative Foundation, Hutchinson, MN, 2012. For Southwest Initiative Foundation Community-Based Leadership Network.
$25,000 to Minnesota E-Democracy, E-Democracy.org, Minneapolis, MN, 2012. For building online engagement networks with Twin Cities Neighbors Forums - BeNeighbors.
$18,400 to Minneapolis College of Art and Design, Minneapolis, MN, 2012. For The Rural Arts Initiative - summer fellowships in two rural innovation sites for InCommons.

4622
Patrick and Aimee Butler Family Foundation ✧

2356 University Ave. W., Ste. 420
St. Paul, MN 55114-3801 (651) 222-2565
Contact: Kerrie Blevins, Dir.
E-mail: kerrieb@butlerfamilyfoundation.org; E-mail for assistance with application problems: bffinfo@visi.com; Main URL: http://www.butlerfamilyfoundation.org
Grants Database: http://www.butlerfamilyfund.org/grantees.php

Incorporated in 1951 in MN.
Donors: Patrick Butler†; Aimee Mott Butler†; Kate Butler Peterson†.
Foundation type: Independent foundation.
Financial data (yr. ended 12/31/13): Assets, $102,688,735 (M); gifts received, $131,482; expenditures, $4,809,824; qualifying distributions, $4,415,465; giving activities include $4,089,405 for 118 grants (high: $500,000; low: $2,500).
Purpose and activities: Giving primarily for the arts and humanities, the environment, human services and philanthropy and non-profit management.
Fields of interest: Arts; Environment; Substance abuse, services; Housing/shelter, development; Human services; Family services; Women, centers/services; Philanthropy/voluntarism.

Type of support: General/operating support; Continuing support; Annual campaigns; Program development; Consulting services.
Limitations: Applications accepted. Giving primarily in the St. Paul and Minneapolis, MN, area. No support for criminal justice, secondary and elementary education, health or hospitals, employment or vocational programs, theater or dance programs, or economic education. No grants to individuals, or for medical research, films or videos, capital funds, endowment funds or events; no loans.
Publications: Application guidelines; Annual report (including application guidelines); Grants list.
Application information: Application process available on foundation web site. Application form required.
Initial approach: See foundation web site for guidelines
Deadline(s): May 15 (for Arts and Environment applications)
Board meeting date(s): Oct.
Final notification: July 15 (status notification for Arts and Environment applications)
Officers and Trustees:* John K. Butler,* Pres.; Patrick Butler, Jr.,* V.P.; Catherine C. Butler,* Secy.; Peter M. Butler,* Treas.; Brigid M. Butler; Patricia M. Butler; Paul S. Butler; Sandra K. Butler; Suzanne A. LeFevour; Melanie Martinez; Temple Peterson.
Director: Kerrie Blevins.
Number of staff: 2 part-time professional; 1 part-time support.
EIN: 416009902

4623
Buuck Family Foundation ✧
90 S. 7th St., Ste. 5300
Minneapolis, MN 55402-4120

Established in 1995 in MN.
Donors: Gail P. Buuck; Robert E. Buuck.
Foundation type: Independent foundation.
Financial data (yr. ended 12/31/13): Assets, $16,032,437 (M); gifts received, $305,500; expenditures, $733,765; qualifying distributions, $568,310; giving activities include $545,835 for 60 + grants (high: $65,000).
Fields of interest: Arts; Education; Environment; Community/economic development.
Type of support: General/operating support; Continuing support; Annual campaigns; Land acquisition; Fellowships; Scholarship funds; Research.
Limitations: Applications not accepted. Giving primarily in MN and AZ. No support for religious or political organizations. No grants to individuals.
Application information: Unsolicited requests for funds not accepted.
Officers: Robert E. Buuck, Pres.; David A. Buuck, V.P. and Secy.; Gail P. Buuck, V.P. and Treas.; John R. Buuck, V.P.; Katherine E. Fratzke, V.P.
Number of staff: 1 part-time support.
EIN: 411796911

4624
C C Criss Hattie B Munroe Foundation ✧
c/o Trust Tax Svcs.
P.O. Box 64713
St. Paul, MN 55164-0713

Foundation type: Independent foundation.
Financial data (yr. ended 12/31/13): Assets, $14,829,947 (M); expenditures, $925,327; qualifying distributions, $814,184; giving activities include $792,355 for 1 grant.
Fields of interest: Human services.
Limitations: Applications not accepted. Giving primarily in Omaha, NE.
Application information: Contributes only to pre-selected organizations.
Trustee: US Bank, N.A.
EIN: 476170400

4625
The Cade Foundation ✧ ☆
4200 County Rd. 42 W.
Savage, MN 55378-2611

Established in 1986 in WI.
Donors: Molly F. Cade; Joe Cade.
Foundation type: Independent foundation.
Financial data (yr. ended 12/31/13): Assets, $2,443,344 (M); expenditures, $1,656,902; qualifying distributions, $1,625,812; giving activities include $1,625,812 for 4 grants (high: $809,315; low: $2,500).
Fields of interest: Elementary/secondary education; Education; Cancer research; Catholic agencies & churches.
Type of support: General/operating support; Scholarship funds.
Limitations: Applications not accepted.
Application information: Unsolicited requests for funds not accepted.
Trustees: Brian Cade; Joseph Cade; Julie Nelson.
EIN: 391570749

4626
Campbell Foundation ✧
90 S. 7th St., Ste. 5100
Minneapolis, MN 55402-4168

Established in 2000 in MN.
Donors: James R. Campbell; Carmen Campbell.
Foundation type: Independent foundation.
Financial data (yr. ended 12/31/13): Assets, $11,522,939 (M); expenditures, $1,059,269; qualifying distributions, $999,014; giving activities include $988,040 for 56 grants (high: $117,500; low: $500).
Fields of interest: Education; Hospitals (general); Health organizations, association; Human services; Christian agencies & churches.
Limitations: Applications not accepted. Giving primarily in MN. No grants to individuals.
Application information: Unsolicited requests for funds not accepted.
Officers and Directors:* Carmen D. Campbell,* Pres.; James R. Campbell,* V.P.; Peter I. Campbell,* V.P.; Kathryn A. Campbell,* V.P.; Laurie Rivard, Secy.-Treas.
EIN: 411988560

4627
Margaret A. Cargill Foundation ✧
6889 Rowland Rd.
Eden Prairie, MN 55344-3380
E-mail: info@macfoundation.org; E-mail for restricted grants program: grantinfo@macfoundation.org; Main URL: http://macphilanthropies.org/macfoundation/
GiveSmart: http://www.givesmart.org/Stories/Donors/Christy-Morse

Established in 2006 in MN.
Donor: Margaret A. Cargill†.
Foundation type: Independent foundation.
Financial data (yr. ended 12/31/13): Assets, $3,094,112,687 (M); expenditures, $69,896,121; qualifying distributions, $50,558,552; giving activities include $38,269,750 for 226 grants (high: $3,000,000; low: $50).
Purpose and activities: The purpose of the foundation is to provide meaningful assistance and support to society, the arts, environment, and all living things.
Fields of interest: Arts; Environment; Animals/wildlife; Health care; Human services; Family services; Native Americans/American Indians.
Limitations: Applications not accepted. No grants to individuals.
Application information: Unsolicited requests for funds not accepted.
Officers and Trustees:* Christine M. Morse,* Chair. and C.E.O.; Paul B. Busch,* Pres.; Terrence R. Meersman, V.P., Prog(s).; Naomi Horsager, C.F.O. and Treas.; Shawn Wischmeier, C.I.O.
Number of staff: 75
EIN: 205434405
Selected grants: The following grants are a representative sample of this grantmaker's funding activity:
$3,000,000 to Smithsonian Institution, Washington, DC, 2012. For national museum of natural history capital project-science education center.
$3,000,000 to World Wildlife Fund, Washington, DC, 2012. For protecting the Sunda-Banda seascape region.
$2,500,000 to Catholic Relief Services, Baltimore, MD, 2012. For response, recovery and resilience in east and south Asia, Latin American and the Caribbean.
$2,000,000 to CommonBond Communities, Saint Paul, MN, 2012. For open 4000 doors campaign housing investment fund.
$1,068,312 to Tides Canada Foundation, Vancouver, Canada, 2012. For Taku and BC coast capacity for conservation program.
$600,000 to Courage Center, Minneapolis, MN, 2012. For health care home: maturity and sustainability.
$30,000 to Haitian Project, Providence, RI, 2012. For enhancing the quality of life for children through educational scholarships.
$20,000 to Lutheran World Relief, Baltimore, MD, 2012. For operations support.
$20,000 to Marine Conservation Biology Institute, Seattle, WA, 2012. For operations support.
$20,000 to National Guild for Community Arts Education, New York, NY, 2012. For operations support.

4628
The Cargill Foundation ✧
P.O. Box 5626
Minneapolis, MN 55440-5626 (952) 742-4311
Contact: Stacy Smida, Grants Mgr.
FAX: (952) 742-7224;
E-mail: stacy_smida@cargill.com; Application address: c/o Mark Murphy, P.O. Box 5650, Minneapolis, MN 55440-5632, tel.: (952)

742-4311; e-mail for Tola Oyewole: tola_oyewale@cargill.com; Main URL: http://www.cargill.com/corporate-responsibility/community-engagement/charitable-giving/headquarters-giving/index.jsp

Incorporated in 1952 in MN.
Donors: Agualia Foundation; Cargill, Inc.; Cargill Charitable Trust.
Foundation type: Company-sponsored foundation.
Financial data (yr. ended 12/31/12): Assets, $126,499,928 (M); expenditures, $10,145,933; qualifying distributions, $9,480,679; giving activities include $9,480,679 for 75 grants (high: $1,200,000; low: $6,000).
Purpose and activities: The foundation supports programs designed to educate socio-economically disadvantaged children and eliminate barriers to their educational success.
Fields of interest: Museums (science/technology); Performing arts, orchestras; Arts; Elementary/secondary education; Education, early childhood education; Higher education; Education, services; Education; Learning disorders; YM/YWCAs & YM/YWHAs; Developmentally disabled, centers & services; United Ways and Federated Giving Programs; Children; Youth; Economically disadvantaged.
Type of support: General/operating support; Continuing support; Capital campaigns; Program development; Curriculum development.
Limitations: Applications accepted. Giving primarily in Minneapolis and its northern and western suburbs with emphasis on Brooklyn Center, Brooklyn Park, Crystal, Eden Prairie, Edina, Golden Valley, Hopkins, Minnetonka, New Hope, Plymouth, Robbinsdale, and St. Louis Park, MN. No support for religious organizations not of direct benefit to the entire community, or for individual schools, or organizations that serve mental or dental needs of children. No grants to individuals, or for athletic scholarships, memberships in civic organizations or trade associations, fundraising events, tickets or campaigns, endowments, recognition or testimonial events, public service or political campaigns, lobbying activities, conferences, travel, programs serving adults (including domestic violence), youth employment, summer, or juvenile justice programs, or programs that serve children whose parents are incarcerated or have serious medical problems.
Publications: Application guidelines; Program policy statement.
Application information: Organizations requesting Education support are asked to contact Cargill Foundation staff for more information. Education program support is given primarily by invitation rather than through applications. Video and audio submissions are not encouraged.
Initial approach: Contact foundation
Deadline(s): None for Education
Board meeting date(s): Mar., June, Sept., and Dec.
Final notification: Within 4 weeks
Officers: Robbin S. Johnson, Pres.; Terri D. Barreiro, V.P.; Marsha MacMilan, V.P.; Marianne Short, V.P.; Scott Portnoy, Secy.; Mark Murphy, Exec. Dir.
Number of staff: 2 full-time professional; 1 full-time support.
EIN: 416020221

4629
Carlson Family Foundation ✧
(formerly The Curtis L. Carlson Family Foundation)
550 Tonkawa Rd.
Long Lake, MN 55356-9724 (952) 404-5605
Contact: C. David Nelson, Exec. Dir.
FAX: (952) 404-5051; Contact for C. David Nelson: tel.: (952) 404-5636, fax: (952) 358-2405, e-mail: david.nelson@carlson.com; Additional contact: Joanie Weis, Grants Mgr., tel.: (952) 404-5605, fax: (952) 358-2405, e-mail: jweis@carlson.com; Main URL: http://www.clcfamilyfoundation.com
Grants List: http://www.clcfamilyfoundation.com/recent_grants.asp

Incorporated in 1959 in MN, originally as The Curtis L. Carlson Foundation.
Donors: Curtis L. Carlson†; Arleen M. Carlson†; Glen D. Nelson; Marilyn C. Nelson; Arleen M. Carlson 2000 BCG Charitable Annuity Trust; Arleen M. Carlson 2000 MCN Charitable Annuity Trust; Carlson Companies, Inc.
Foundation type: Company-sponsored foundation.
Financial data (yr. ended 12/31/12): Assets, $198,501,922 (M); gifts received, $5,714; expenditures, $7,437,038; qualifying distributions, $6,609,945; giving activities include $5,750,603 for 282 grants (high: $400,000; low: $40).
Purpose and activities: The foundation supports organizations involved with education, at-risk children and youth, and youth mentoring.
Fields of interest: Secondary school/education; Higher education; Education; Youth development, adult & child programs; Big Brothers/Big Sisters; American Red Cross; Children/youth, services; Human services; Children/youth.
Type of support: General/operating support; Management development/capacity building; Annual campaigns; Program development; Matching/challenge support.
Limitations: Applications accepted. Giving primarily in the Twin Cities, MN metropolitan area. No support for political activities or causes. No grants to individuals, (including scholarships), or for endowment funds, dinners, benefits, conferences, travel, athletic events, or endowments.
Publications: Application guidelines; Grants list.
Application information: A site visit and additional information may be requested. Applicants for youth mentoring grants are required to complete the Mentoring Partnership of Minnesota's Quality Mentoring Assessment Path (QMAP) before an application can be submitted. Organizations receiving support are asked to submit a Minnesota Common Grant Report Form. Application form required.
Initial approach: Complete online application
Deadline(s): Jan. 1, Apr. 1, and July 1
Board meeting date(s): Apr., July, and Oct.
Final notification: Following a board meeting
Officers and Trustees:* Barbara Carlson Gage,* Chair. and Pres.; Marilyn Carlson Nelson,* Vice-Chair.; Diana L. Nelson, V.P.; Rick Carlson Gage, Treas.; C. David Nelson, Exec. Dir.; Geoffrey Carlson Gage; Scott Carlson Gage; Wendy M. Nelson.
EIN: 416028973

4630
Carolyn Foundation
818 W. 46th St., Ste. 203
Minneapolis, MN 55402-3402 (612) 596-3266
FAX: (612) 339-1951;
E-mail: grant.application@carolynfoundation.org; Contacts for application questions: Becky Erdahl, Exec. Dir., tel.: (612) 596-3279; e-mail: berdahl@carolynfoundation.org, or Kristen Cullen, Admin., tel.: (612) 596-3266, e-mail Kcullen@carolynfoundation.org; Main URL: http://www.carolynfoundation.org
Grants Database: http://www.carolynfoundation.org/index.asp?page_seq=1

Trust established in 1964 in MN.
Donor: Carolyn McKnight Christian†.
Foundation type: Independent foundation.
Financial data (yr. ended 12/31/13): Assets, $39,875,609 (M); expenditures, $1,765,445; qualifying distributions, $1,532,621; giving activities include $1,168,095 for 154 grants (high: $40,000; low: $100).
Purpose and activities: The foundation's vision is to improve the lives of children/families, communities and the environment through the involvement of successive generations of the family of Carolyn McKnight Christian. The foundation's mission is to support programs and initiatives that effect positive change now and into the future.
Fields of interest: Arts; Environment; Youth development; Children/youth; Youth; Economically disadvantaged.
Type of support: General/operating support; Program development.
Limitations: Applications accepted. Giving limited to New Haven, CT, and Minneapolis, MN, excluding suburbs. No support for political or veterans' groups, fraternal societies, umbrella organizations, or religious organizations for religious purposes. No grants to individuals, or for endowment funds, annual fund drives, conferences, seminars, fund raisers, events, deficit funding, costs of litigation, or continuing support; no loans.
Publications: Application guidelines; Annual report; Grants list.
Application information: Visit foundation web site for updated application guidelines, download of application and cover sheet forms, and procedures. Application form required.
Initial approach: Check foundation web site (online application required)
Copies of proposal: 1
Deadline(s): Feb. 1 and Aug. 1
Board meeting date(s): June and Dec.
Final notification: June and Dec.
Officers and Trustees:* Brewster Crosby,* Chair.; Andrew Crosby,* Vice-Chair.; Rebecca L. Erdahl,* Secy. and Exec. Dir.; Christopher M. Dobson, Treas.; Guido Calabresi; Claire Crosby; Lesley Crosby; Mike Crosby; Teri Crosby; Dale Crosby-Newman; Charles C. Dobson; Megan Dobson; Michael Dobson; Mancy Jolliffe; Caroline Walker.
Number of staff: 1 full-time professional; 1 part-time support.
EIN: 416044416
Selected grants: The following grants are a representative sample of this grantmaker's funding activity:
$27,250 to Toxics Action Center, Boston, MA, 2012. For Focus Area: Responsive Neighborhood Assistance Program.

$25,000 to Achievement First, New Haven, CT, 2012. For Focus Area: Children and Youth Achievement First's New Haven School.
$25,000 to Athletes Committed to Educating Students, Minneapolis, MN, 2012. For Focus Area: Middle School Youth general operating expenses.
$25,000 to Dakota Rural Action, Brookings, SD, 2012. For Focus Area: Responsive Community Energy Development Committee.
$25,000 to Hiawatha Academies, Minneapolis, MN, 2012. For Focus Area: Middle School Youth Expansion of Adelante College Prep Middle School.
$25,000 to Iowa Environmental Council, Des Moines, IA, 2012. For Focus Area: Responsive Moving Iowa toward a clean energy economy by increasing utility energy efficiency savings goals.
$25,000 to Project SUCCESS, Minneapolis, MN, 2012. For Focus Area: Middle School Youth support to sustain and grow Program in Olson Middle School in North Minneapolis.
$20,130 to American Rivers, Washington, DC, 2012. For Focus Area: Responsive advancing a water management and ecosystem conservation plan in the Yakima River Basin.
$20,000 to YMCA of the Greater Twin Cities, Minneapolis, MN, 2012. For Focus Area: Middle School Youth YMCA Beacons.
$13,000 to Division of Indian Work, Minneapolis, MN, 2012. For Focus Area: Middle School Youth the American Indian Math Project.

4631
Central Minnesota Community Foundation ✧

101 S. 7th Ave., Ste. 100
Saint Cloud, MN 56301 (320) 253-4380
Contact: Steven R. Joul, Pres.; For grants: Susan Lorenz, Dir., Community Progs.
FAX: (320) 240-9215;
E-mail: info@communitygiving.org; Toll-free tel.: (877) 253-4380; Grant inquiry e-mail: Slorenz@communitygiving.org; Main URL: http://www.communitygiving.org

Established in 1985 in MN.
Foundation type: Community foundation.
Financial data (yr. ended 06/30/13): Assets, $83,633,831 (M); gifts received, $5,616,592; expenditures, $7,803,358; giving activities include $6,164,299 for 170+ grants (high: $189,753), and $186,095 for 61 grants to individuals.
Purpose and activities: The foundation seeks to engage people, connect resources, and build community. The foundation fulfills this mission by making grants to support key issues in Central Minnesota by: 1) encouraging individuals, families and businesses to partner with us to fulfill their charitable and financial goals; 2) convening people to work on community problems; 3) honoring individuals for improving the community; and 4) connecting people and resources to build a better community.
Fields of interest: Arts; Education; Environment; Health care; Youth development, services; Family services; Human services; Public affairs.
Type of support: Building/renovation; Equipment; Program development; Conferences/seminars; Seed money; Scholarship funds; Technical assistance; Scholarships—to individuals.
Limitations: Applications accepted. Giving primarily in Benton, Sherburne, and Stearns counties, MN. No support for religious organizations for direct activities, or for fraternal organizations, societies, or orders. No grants to individuals (except for designated scholarship funds), or for medical research, general operating expenses, national fundraising, telephone solicitations, travel, capital campaigns, endowments, or debt retirement or deficit financing.
Publications: Application guidelines; Annual report; Informational brochure; Newsletter.
Application information: Visit foundation web site for application guidelines and deadlines per grant type. Application form required.
Initial approach: Complete online application
Deadline(s): Varies
Board meeting date(s): 3rd Thurs. in Jan., Mar., May, July, Sept., and Nov.
Final notification: 2 months after deadline date
Officers and Directors:* Pete Hill,* Chair.; Dennis Gregory,* Vice-Chair.; Steven R. Joul,* Pres.; Mimi Bitzan,* Secy.; Colette Carlson,* Treas.; Fred Bursch; Keith Finstad; Karlo Goerges; Steve Linder; Maryanne Mahowald; Devinder Malhotra; Gary Marsden; Michelle Meyer; Brian Myres; Michael Noonan; Joyce Schlough; Brad Wheelock.
Number of staff: 6 full-time professional; 3 full-time support; 1 part-time support.
EIN: 363412544

4632
The Ceres Trust ✧

c/o Anne Haddad, Prog. Dir.
204 7th St. W., No. 114
Northfield, MN 55057-2419
E-mail: info@cerestrust.org; Main URL: http://www.cerestrust.org

Established in WI.
Foundation type: Independent foundation.
Financial data (yr. ended 12/31/12): Assets, $19,741,283 (M); expenditures, $4,285,370; qualifying distributions, $4,197,537; giving activities include $3,801,449 for 26 grants (high: $550,000; low: $6,625).
Purpose and activities: Giving to provide grants that support research in organic agriculture at universities and to graduate students; education to create careers in the production and processing of certified organic food; programs to eliminate pesticide exposure and GMO contamination; and efforts to preserve crop biodiversity and public access to seeds.
Fields of interest: Environment, forests; Environment, plant conservation; Agriculture, sustainable programs.
Limitations: Applications not accepted. Giving primarily in the upper Midwest and in HI.
Application information: Contributes only to pre-selected organizations.
Trustees: Judith A. Kern; Kent Whealy.
EIN: 205768077

4633
Charlson Foundation ✧

5275 Edina Industrial Blvd., Ste. 111
Edina, MN 55439-2902 (952) 938-6968
E-mail: charlson@usinternet.com

Established in 1977 in MN.
Donor: Lynn L. Charlson.
Foundation type: Independent foundation.
Financial data (yr. ended 12/31/13): Assets, $11,623,981 (M); expenditures, $792,081; qualifying distributions, $694,372; giving activities include $676,500 for 41 grants (high: $40,000; low: $1,000).
Purpose and activities: Giving primarily for children, youth and families. Priority is given to requests for programs that do a superior job helping individuals overcome multiple obstacles by providing an integrated, wrap-around array of services, as well as programs that focus on prevention and long term solutions, have made provisions for measurable outcomes, can demonstrate past success, and that generally serve low income people.
Fields of interest: Children/youth, services; Family services; Economically disadvantaged.
Type of support: General/operating support; Annual campaigns; Capital campaigns; Matching/challenge support.
Limitations: Applications accepted. Giving limited to the Twin Cities area of Minneapolis and St. Paul, MN. No support for organizations that use fiscal agents. No grants to individuals, or for scholarships, chemical dependency treatment, endowments, the arts, annual appeals, fundraisers, special events or memberships.
Publications: Application guidelines.
Application information: Full proposals are by invitation only. Unsolicited proposals will not be considered. There is a $10,000 limit for first-time requests. The foundation encourages applicants who are applying for renewal grants to use the Minnesota Common Report Form, which can be found at URL: http://www.mcf.org. If you are not invited to submit a full proposal, the foundation asks that you wait 3 years before submitting another letter of intent. The foundation accepts the Minnesota Council on Foundations' Common Grant Proposal form. Application form required.
Initial approach: 2-page letter of intent
Copies of proposal: 1
Deadline(s): Mar. 1 and Aug. 1 for letters of intent; Apr. 1 and Sept. 1 for renewal grant proposals
Board meeting date(s): Apr. and Oct.
Final notification: Within 3 months of deadlines
Officers: Karen K. McElrath, Pres.; Leslie H. Stiles, Secy.-Treas.
Directors: Kim Herzog; Mary L. Rippy.
EIN: 411313302
Selected grants: The following grants are a representative sample of this grantmaker's funding activity:
$25,000 to YouthLink, Minneapolis, MN, 2012. For general operating support.
$20,000 to YouthZone, Glenwood Springs, CO, 2012. For Restorative Justice Program.
$17,500 to Dunwoody College of Technology, Minneapolis, MN, 2012. For Youth Career Awareness Program.
$5,000 to KIPP Minnesota, Minneapolis, MN, 2012. For KIPP Stand Academy.
$3,043 to Oasis for Youth, Bloomington, MN, 2012. For In-kind Fundraising Expenses.
$1,675 to Minnesota Council on Foundations, Minneapolis, MN, 2012. For go's (general operating support).

4634
Cherbec Advancement Foundation ✧

30 E. 7th St., Ste. 2000
St. Paul, MN 55101-4930 (651) 228-0935

Established in 1997 in MN.
Donors: Robert M. Weyerhaeuser; CAW 1966 Trust; CAW 1968 Trust; CAW 1969 Trust C; CAW 1972

Trust; CAW Charitable Unitrust; CHAW 2012 Charitable Trust; RMW 2012 Charitable Trust.
Foundation type: Independent foundation.
Financial data (yr. ended 12/31/13): Assets, $2,489,791 (M); gifts received, $1,509,236; expenditures, $578,106; qualifying distributions, $958,908; giving activities include $958,908 for 51 grants (high: $126,000; low: $1,000).
Purpose and activities: Giving primarily for education, human services, museums, community and private grantmaking foundations, including a foundation for research in immuno endocrine neurological disorders.
Fields of interest: Museums; Education; Neuroscience research; Human services; Foundations (private grantmaking); Foundations (community).
Limitations: Applications not accepted. Giving primarily in MA and MN; support also in NC and PA.
Application information: Unsolicited requests for funds not accepted.
Board meeting date(s): 2 times per year
Officers and Directors:* Robert M. Weyerhaeuser,* Pres.; Joseph S. Micallef, Secy.-Treas.; Elizabeth W. Bentinck-Smith; Carrie W. Farmer; Charles A. Weyerhaeuser; Henry G. Weyerhaeuser.
EIN: 411906601

4635
W. G. Christianson Foundation ✧
c/o Warren G. Christianson
730 2nd Ave. S., No. 1300
Minneapolis, MN 55402-2416

Established in 1992 in MN.
Donor: Warren G. Christianson.
Foundation type: Independent foundation.
Financial data (yr. ended 12/31/13): Assets, $8,935,118 (M); expenditures, $1,161,593; qualifying distributions, $1,096,275; giving activities include $1,078,750 for 63 grants (high: $100,000; low: $50).
Purpose and activities: Giving primarily to Roman Catholic churches and organizations.
Fields of interest: Health organizations, association; Human services; Children/youth, services; Civil liberties, right to life; Christian agencies & churches; Catholic agencies & churches.
Type of support: General/operating support; Building/renovation; Scholarship funds.
Limitations: Applications not accepted. Giving primarily in MN; some funding nationally, particularly in CA. No grants to individuals.
Application information: Contributes only to pre-selected organizations.
Officers: Warren G. Christianson, Pres.; Theresa L. Christianson, Secy.
EIN: 411743109

4636
CHS Foundation ✧
5500 Cenex Dr.
Inver Grove Heights, MN 55077-1733 (800) 814-0506
Contact: William J. Nelson, Pres.
FAX: (651) 355-5073;
E-mail: info@chsfoundation.org; Main URL: http://www.chsfoundation.org
Contact for scholarships: Jennifer Thatcher, Mgr., tel.: (800) 814-0506 ext. 3

Trust established in 1947 in MN.
Donors: Farmers Union Central Exchange, Inc.; CENEX, Inc.; Cenex Harvest States Cooperatives; CHS Inc.
Foundation type: Company-sponsored foundation.
Financial data (yr. ended 12/31/12): Assets, $33,914,988 (M); gifts received, $4,540,238; expenditures, $3,284,739; qualifying distributions, $3,207,890; giving activities include $2,506,183 for grants.
Purpose and activities: The foundation supports organizations involved with education, agriculture, safety, youth development, rural development, and leadership development. Special emphasis is directed toward programs that invest in the future of rural America, agriculture, and cooperative business.
Fields of interest: Higher education; Education, community/cooperative; Education; Agriculture; Disasters, preparedness/services; Youth development, agriculture; Youth development; American Red Cross; Rural development; Leadership development; Children/youth; Youth; Adults; Young adults.
Type of support: General/operating support; Annual campaigns; Program development; Conferences/seminars; Seed money; Curriculum development; Scholarship funds; Research; Use of facilities; Sponsorships; Program evaluation; Scholarships—to individuals.
Limitations: Applications accepted. Giving on a national basis, primarily in areas of company operations in CO, IA, ID, IL, IN, KS, MI, MN, MO, MT, NE, ND, OH, OK, OR, SD, TX, UT, WA, WI, and WY. No support for religious or political organizations. No grants for building projects, debt reduction, community development, or program related loans.
Publications: Application guidelines; Informational brochure; Program policy statement.
Application information: Application form required.
Initial approach: Complete online application form
Deadline(s): None; Apr. 1 for High School Scholarships and Two-Year Scholarships; Sept. 30 for Cooperative Education Grants Program
Board meeting date(s): Monthly
Final notification: 30 to 90 days; Dec. for Cooperative Education Grants Program
Officer and Trustees:* Michael Toelle,* Chair.; Robert Bass,* Vice-Chair.; William J. Nelson, Pres.; Jerry Hasnedl,* Secy.-Treas.; Bruce Anderson; Donald Anthony; Dave Bielenberg; C.J. Blew; Dennis Carlson; Curt Eischens; Steve Fritel; David Kayser; Randy Knecht; Greg Kruger; Michael Mulcahey; Richard Owen; Steve Riegel; Dan Schurr.
Number of staff: 1 part-time professional; 2 part-time support.
EIN: 416025858

4637
Michael V. & Ann C. Ciresi Foundation ✧ ☆
222 2nd St. SE, Ste. 1601
Minneapolis, MN 55414-5182

Established in 1998 in MN.
Donors: Michael V. Ciresi; Ann C. Ciresi.
Foundation type: Independent foundation.
Financial data (yr. ended 12/31/13): Assets, $3,141,094 (M); gifts received, $4,030,000; expenditures, $948,000; qualifying distributions, $948,000; giving activities include $948,000 for 42 grants (high: $550,000; low: $1,000).
Purpose and activities: Giving primarily for higher education.
Fields of interest: Media, radio; Arts; Higher education; Education; Human services; Catholic federated giving programs; Catholic agencies & churches.
Limitations: Applications not accepted. Giving primarily in Minneapolis and St. Paul, MN. No grants to individuals.
Application information: Contributes only to pre-selected organizations.
Directors: Steve A. Brand; Ann C. Ciresi; Michael V. Ciresi.
EIN: 411926735

4638
Cloverfields Foundation ✧
c/o Dean Barr, Dorsey & Whitney, LLP
50 S. 6th St., Ste. 1500
Minneapolis, MN 55402-1498

Established in 2004 in MN.
Donors: Stephen J. Hemsley; Barbara K. Hemsley.
Foundation type: Independent foundation.
Financial data (yr. ended 12/31/12): Assets, $18,964,846 (M); gifts received, $495,000; expenditures, $2,750,725; qualifying distributions, $2,619,806; giving activities include $2,619,806 for 24 grants (high: $750,000; low: $500).
Purpose and activities: Giving primarily for Roman Catholic organizations and churches, as well as to an interfaith organization; funding also for education, and children and youth services, including a children's theater.
Fields of interest: Elementary/secondary education; Higher education; Education; Children/youth, services; Foundations (public); Catholic agencies & churches; Religion, interfaith issues.
Limitations: Applications not accepted. Giving primarily in Minneapolis and St. Paul, MN. No grants to individuals.
Application information: Contributes only to pre-selected organizations.
Officers and Directors:* Stephen J. Hemsley,* Pres. and Treas.; Barbara K. Hemsley,* Secy.; Matthew S. Hemsley.
EIN: 201919362

4639
Cox Family Fund ✧
c/o Philip S. Sherburne
1920 S. 1st St., Ste. 403
Minneapolis, MN 55454-1096

Incorporated in 1986 in MN.
Donors: David C. Cox; Vicki B. Cox.
Foundation type: Independent foundation.
Financial data (yr. ended 12/31/12): Assets, $3,768,203 (M); gifts received, $81,264; expenditures, $496,845; qualifying distributions, $481,000; giving activities include $481,000 for grants.
Purpose and activities: Giving for arts and culture, education and the environment.
Fields of interest: Arts; Education; Environment; Human services.
Limitations: Applications not accepted. Giving primarily in CA; some giving also in MN. No grants to individuals.
Application information: Contributes only to pre-selected organizations.

Officers: David C. Cox, Pres. and Treas.; Vicki B. Cox, V.P. and Secy.
Director: Philip S. Sherburne.
EIN: 411570849

4640
Dr. C.C. and Mabel L. Criss Memorial Foundation ✧
(also known as Criss Memorial Foundation)
c/o U.S. Bank, N.A.
P.O. Box 64713, Trust Tax Svcs.
St. Paul, MN 55164-0713

Trust established in 1978 in NE.
Donors: C.C. Criss, M.D.†; Mabel L. Criss†.
Foundation type: Independent foundation.
Financial data (yr. ended 02/28/13): Assets, $28,563,483 (M); expenditures, $1,902,404; qualifying distributions, $1,663,122; giving activities include $1,539,527 for 37 grants (high: $820,000; low: $3,000).
Purpose and activities: Giving primarily for the arts, education, children and youth services, including a children's hospital, and social services.
Fields of interest: Arts; Elementary/secondary education; Higher education; Education; Hospitals (specialty); Human services; Children/youth, services.
Limitations: Applications not accepted. Giving primarily in Omaha, NE. No grants to individuals.
Application information: Contributes only to pre-selected organizations.
Board meeting date(s): Monthly
Trustees: M. Philip Crummer; Andrew Davis; Donna Turner; John J. Vinardi; U.S. Bank, N.A.
EIN: 470601105
Selected grants: The following grants are a representative sample of this grantmaker's funding activity:
$110,000 to Creighton University, Omaha, NE, 2013. For construction costs.
$30,000 to Hospice House, Omaha, NE, 2013. To upgrade facilities.
$30,000 to Siena Francis House, Omaha, NE, 2013. For meal Program Support.
$12,500 to Omaha Symphony Association, Omaha, NE, 2013. For choral program.
$10,000 to Northstar Foundation, Omaha, NE, 2013. For Outward Bound Program.
$7,815 to National Arbor Day Foundation, Lincoln, NE, 2013. To support Nature Explore Series.
$7,500 to Joslyn Art Museum, Omaha, NE, 2013. To support Joslyn Lectures.
$5,000 to Bellevue University Foundation, Bellevue, NE, 2013. To support 2012 Signature Series Lecture.
$5,000 to Heartland Hope Mission, Omaha, NE, 2013. For Homelessness and Hunger Prevention.
$3,000 to Volunteers Assisting Seniors, Omaha, NE, 2013. For Volunteer Auditor Program.

4641
Cummins Family Foundation ✧
2 Carlson Pkwy., Ste. 375
Plymouth, MN 55447-4446

Established in 1998 in MN.
Donors: Robert Cummins; Joan Cummins.
Foundation type: Independent foundation.
Financial data (yr. ended 09/30/13): Assets, $30,815,064 (M); gifts received, $3,400,000; expenditures, $1,265,368; qualifying distributions, $1,251,920; giving activities include $1,250,000 for 1 grant.
Purpose and activities: Giving primarily for Roman Catholic education.
Fields of interest: Elementary/secondary education.
Limitations: Applications not accepted. Giving primarily in MN. No grants to individuals.
Application information: Contributes only to pre-selected organizations.
Officers: Robert Cummins, Pres.; Joan M. Cummins, Treas.
EIN: 411920226
Selected grants: The following grants are a representative sample of this grantmaker's funding activity:
$1,200,000 to Archdiocese of Saint Paul and Minneapolis, Saint Paul, MN, 2011. For general operations.
$1,100,000 to Providence Academy, Plymouth, MN, 2011. For general operations.

4642
Edwin W. and Catherine M. Davis Foundation ✧
30 E. 7th St., Ste. 2000
Saint Paul, MN 55101-4930 (651) 228-0935
Contact: Bette D. Moorman, Pres.

Incorporated in 1956 in MN.
Donors: Samuel S. Davis†; Edwin W. Davis†; Frederick W. Davis†; Bette D. Moorman.
Foundation type: Independent foundation.
Financial data (yr. ended 12/31/13): Assets, $24,814,491 (M); expenditures, $1,161,307; qualifying distributions, $1,094,583; giving activities include $1,030,000 for 48 grants (high: $140,000; low: $1,000).
Purpose and activities: The foundation is concerned with the amelioration of social problems and increasing the opportunities available to disadvantaged people, with particular interest in the fields of education, social welfare, mental health, the arts, and environmental problems. Educational grants primarily for colleges and universities.
Fields of interest: Arts; Higher education; Environment, natural resources; Botanical gardens; Human services; Children/youth, services.
Type of support: General/operating support; Continuing support; Annual campaigns; Scholarship funds.
Limitations: Applications accepted. Giving in the U.S., with emphasis on CA and MN. No grants to individuals, or for emergency funds, capital outlay, building funds or equipment, or endowments; no loans.
Publications: Annual report (including application guidelines).
Application information: Application form required.
Initial approach: Proposal
Copies of proposal: 1
Deadline(s): None
Officers and Directors:* Bette D. Moorman,* Pres.; Lisa M. Fremont,* V.P.; Joel F.C. Davis,* Secy.; John L. Davis,* Treas.
EIN: 416012064

4643
Edward Dayton Family Fund ✧
80 S. 8th St., 1800 IDS Ctr., Ste. 1800
Minneapolis, MN 55402-4523

Established in 1998 in MN.
Foundation type: Independent foundation.
Financial data (yr. ended 12/31/12): Assets, $2,166,371 (M); expenditures, $598,853; qualifying distributions, $565,500; giving activities include $565,500 for grants.
Fields of interest: Education; Environment, natural resources; Zoos/zoological societies; Health care; United Ways and Federated Giving Programs.
Limitations: Applications not accepted. Giving primarily in FL and MN. No grants to individuals.
Application information: Contributes only to pre-selected organizations.
Officers: Edward N. Dayton, Pres.; Sherry Ann Dayton, Secy.-Treas.
Director: Risa Boegel.
EIN: 522390636

4644
Deluxe Corporation Foundation ✧
(formerly Deluxe Check Printers Foundation)
3680 Victoria St. N.
Shoreview, MN 55126-2966 (651) 483-7111
Contact: Jennifer A. Anderson, Dir., Foundations & Community Affairs
E-mail: Jenny.Anderson@deluxe.com; Application contact for organizations outside of MN: Pamela Bridger, Foundation and Community Affairs Admin., tel.: (651) 787-5124, e-mail: pam.bridger@deluxe.com; Main URL: http://www.deluxe.com/dlxab/deluxe-foundation.jsp
Grants List: http://www.deluxe.com/miscfiles/pdf/deluxe-foundation-grant-recipients.pdf

Incorporated in 1952 in MN.
Donor: Deluxe Corp.
Foundation type: Company-sponsored foundation.
Financial data (yr. ended 12/31/13): Assets, $27,449,789 (M); expenditures, $2,384,061; qualifying distributions, $2,311,048; giving activities include $1,886,166 for 267 grants (high: $158,000; low: $48), and $224,143 for 396 employee matching gifts.
Purpose and activities: The foundation supports programs designed to invest in tomorrow through education; address transitional and youth services; and promote community enrichment through the arts. Special emphasis is directed toward partnerships to help people, businesses, and communities grow.
Fields of interest: Museums (art); Performing arts; Business school/education; Education, services; Education, reading; Mental health/crisis services; Food services; Boys & girls clubs; Youth development, adult & child programs; YM/YWCAs & YM/YWHAs; Human services, financial counseling; Human services; Community development, small businesses; United Ways and Federated Giving Programs; Youth; Economically disadvantaged.
Type of support: General/operating support; Continuing support; Annual campaigns; Capital campaigns; Building/renovation; Equipment; Emergency funds; Program development; Employee volunteer services; Employee matching gifts.
Limitations: Applications accepted. Giving on a national basis in areas of company operations, with emphasis on MN; giving also to national organizations. No support for national, religious,

health, political, or lobbying organizations, fraternal organizations, start-up organizations, civic organizations, or organizations supported by government sources. No grants to individuals, or for event sponsorships, conferences, fundraisers, advertising, research projects, travel, athletic events, start-up needs, or long-term housing; no loans.
Publications: Application guidelines; Grants list.
Application information: Application form not required.
Initial approach: Complete online letter of inquiry for first-time applicants in MN; complete online application for previous grantees in MN; e-mail letter of inquiry to application address for organizations located outside of MN
Copies of proposal: 1
Deadline(s): Feb. 1 to Mar. 15 for Arts organizations in MN; Apr. 1 to June 30 for Economic Empowerment organizations in MN; Aug. 1 and Oct. 1 for Crisis organizations in MN; Apr. 1 to Oct. 1 for organizations located outside of MN
Board meeting date(s): Feb.
Final notification: 3 months
Officers and Directors:* Lee J. Schramm,* Pres.; Jennifer A. Anderson,* V.P. and Secy.; Amanda K. Brinkman; Julie M. Loosbruck; Edward A. Merritt; Terry D. Peterson; Anthony C. Scarfone.
Number of staff: 1 full-time professional; 1 full-time support.
EIN: 416034786

4645
George Deziel Family Foundation, Inc. ✧ ☆
2112 Holy Name Dr.
Wayzata, MN 55391-9647

Established in 2001 in MN.
Donors: George H. Deziel Trust; George H. Deziel Charitable Lead Trust.
Foundation type: Independent foundation.
Financial data (yr. ended 09/30/13): Assets, $0 (M); gifts received, $13,633; expenditures, $1,545,988; qualifying distributions, $1,540,206; giving activities include $1,539,079 for 4 grants (high: $554,068; low: $76,955).
Fields of interest: Education; Crime/law enforcement; Christian agencies & churches; Religion.
Limitations: Applications not accepted. Giving primarily in Washington, DC, MN and VA. No grants to individuals.
Application information: Unsolicited requests for funds not accepted.
Directors: Annette Deziel; Regina Magnuson; Susan Sween.
EIN: 412000257

4646
Donaldson Foundation ✧
P.O. Box 1299, MS 104
Minneapolis, MN 55440-1299 (952) 887-3043
Main URL: http://www.donaldson.com/

Established in 1966 in MN.
Donor: Donaldson Co., Inc.
Foundation type: Company-sponsored foundation.
Financial data (yr. ended 07/31/13): Assets, $2,693,806 (M); gifts received, $200,000; expenditures, $1,146,370; qualifying distributions, $1,143,870; giving activities include $1,143,870 for grants.
Purpose and activities: The foundation supports organizations involved with education.
Fields of interest: Education; United Ways and Federated Giving Programs.
Type of support: Continuing support; Annual campaigns; Capital campaigns; Building/renovation; Scholarship funds; Employee matching gifts; Employee-related scholarships.
Limitations: Applications accepted. Giving on a national basis in areas of company operations. No support for religious organizations. No grants to individuals (except for employee-related scholarships).
Application information: Application form required.
Initial approach: Letter
Copies of proposal: 1
Deadline(s): None
Officers: Lillian Perez, Pres.; Shen Weber, Secy.; Mike Dwyer, Treas.
Directors: Peter Lucas; Catherine Luebke; Grace Ngunu; Rod Radosevich; Robert Van Nelson; Paul Way.
EIN: 416052950

4647
Dorea Foundation ✧
P.O. Box 5628
Minneapolis, MN 55440-5628

Established in 1991 in MN.
Donor: Members of the Keinath family.
Foundation type: Independent foundation.
Financial data (yr. ended 12/31/12): Assets, $8,033,921 (M); expenditures, $1,435,071; qualifying distributions, $1,371,232; giving activities include $1,370,000 for 14 grants (high: $250,000; low: $25,000).
Fields of interest: Christian agencies & churches.
Limitations: Applications not accepted. Giving primarily in MO; funding also in GA and IA. No grants to individuals.
Application information: Contributes only to pre-selected organizations.
Officers: Warren G. Keinath, Jr., Pres.; Pauline M. Keinath, V.P.; Steven A. Hornig, Secy.; Robert J. Theiler, Treas.
EIN: 411703735

4648
Driscoll Foundation ✧
30 E. 7th St., Ste. 2000
St. Paul, MN 55101-4930 (651) 228-0935
Contact: Elizabeth D. Hlavka, Pres. and Dir.

Incorporated in 1962 in MN.
Donors: W. John Driscoll Revocable Trust; and members of the Driscoll family.
Foundation type: Independent foundation.
Financial data (yr. ended 02/28/13): Assets, $27,761,718 (M); expenditures, $1,272,304; qualifying distributions, $1,236,734; giving activities include $1,199,000 for 94 grants (high: $300,000; low: $1,000).
Fields of interest: Arts education; Arts; Higher education; Education; Hospitals (general); Human services; United Ways and Federated Giving Programs; Protestant agencies & churches.
Type of support: General/operating support; Capital campaigns.
Limitations: Applications accepted. Giving primarily in the metropolitan areas of St. Paul-Minneapolis, MN, and San Francisco, CA. No grants to individuals, or for scholarships, conferences, travel, publications, or films.
Publications: Annual report (including application guidelines).
Application information: Application form not required.
Initial approach: Letter
Copies of proposal: 1
Deadline(s): None
Board meeting date(s): Annually and as required
Final notification: 3 to 4 weeks
Officers and Directors:* Elizabeth D. Hlavka,* Pres.; Jeff R. Tolzin, Secy.-Treas.; Elizabeth S. Driscoll; John B. Driscoll; Margaret L. Driscoll; William L. Driscoll.
EIN: 416012065
Selected grants: The following grants are a representative sample of this grantmaker's funding activity:
$426,824 to House of Hope Presbyterian Church, Saint Paul, MN, 2011. For operating support.
$25,000 to Tabor Academy, Marion, MA, 2011. For operating support.
$15,000 to Denver Health and Hospitals Foundation, Denver, CO, 2011. For operating support.
$10,000 to Minneapolis Society of Fine Arts, Minneapolis, MN, 2011. For operating support.
$10,000 to Palo Alto Players, Palo Alto, CA, 2011. For operating support.
$10,000 to Peninsula Open Space Trust, Palo Alto, CA, 2011. For operating support.
$10,000 to Stanford University, Stanford, CA, 2011. For operating support.
$10,000 to Tacoma Art Museum, Tacoma, WA, 2011. For operating support.
$5,000 to Smuin Ballet, San Francisco, CA, 2011. For operating support.
$3,000 to Stanford University, Stanford, CA, 2011. For operating support.

4649
Duluth Superior Area Community Foundation ✧
Zeitgeist Arts Building
222 E. Superior St., Ste. 302
Duluth, MN 55802 (218) 726-0232
Contact: Holly C. Sampson, Pres.
FAX: (218) 726-0257;
E-mail: info@dsacommunityfoundation.com; Grant application e-mail: grantsinfo@dsacommunityfoundation.com; Main URL: http://www.dsacommunityfoundation.com
Facebook: http://www.facebook.com/pages/Duluth-Superior-Area-Community-Foundation/128701853838939
Scholarship application e-mail: dhammer@dsacommunityfoundation.com

Established in 1982 in MN.
Foundation type: Community foundation.
Financial data (yr. ended 12/31/13): Assets, $58,697,197 (M); gifts received, $2,875,286; expenditures, $3,271,237; giving activities include $1,858,252 for 65+ grants (high: $261,000), and $283,769 for 141 grants to individuals.
Purpose and activities: The foundation supports a wide variety of activities in five interest areas: Arts, Community and Economic Development, Education, Environment, and Human Services.

Fields of interest: Visual arts; Performing arts; Performing arts, music; Arts; Child development, education; Higher education; Education; Environment; Animal welfare; Crime/violence prevention; Employment; Food services; Housing/shelter, development; Children/youth, services; Child development, services; Family services; Homeless, human services; Human services; International affairs, goodwill promotion; International peace/security; Civil rights, race/intergroup relations; Economic development; Community/economic development; Government/public administration; Disabilities, people with; Minorities; Native Americans/American Indians; Women; Economically disadvantaged; Homeless.
Type of support: General/operating support; Emergency funds; Program development; Film/video/radio; Publication; Seed money; Curriculum development; Scholarship funds; Research; Technical assistance; Consulting services; Program evaluation; Scholarships—to individuals.
Limitations: Applications accepted. Giving primarily in Ashland, Bayfield and Douglas counties, WI, and Atkin, Carlton, Cook, Itasca, Koochiching, Lake, and St. Louis counties in northeastern MN. No support for religious organizations for religious activities. No grants to individuals (except for scholarships initiated or managed by the foundation), or for capital or annual campaigns, endowments, debt retirement, medical research, fundraising, continuing support, deficit financing, land acquisition, tickets for benefits, telephone solicitations, or for grants beyond single funding cycle; no loans.
Publications: Application guidelines; Annual report; Grants list; Informational brochure (including application guidelines); Newsletter.
Application information: Based on the outcome of the online inquiry, an organization may be encouraged to submit a full proposal. Visit foundation web site for application forms and guidelines. Application form required.
Initial approach: E-mail
Deadline(s): Apr. 1 and Oct. 1 for Community Opportunity Fund grants; varies for others
Board meeting date(s): Monthly
Final notification: 60 to 90 days
Officers and Board Members:* Claudia Scott Welty,* Chair.; Amy Kuronen,* Vice-Chair.; Holly C. Sampson, Pres.; Howard T. Klatzky,* Secy.; Philip D. Rolle,* Treas.; Ryan Boman; Jennifer L. Carey; Marlene David; Bethany M. Owen; Branden Robinson; Arend J. Sandbulte; Mia Thibodeau; Renee Wachter; Tony Yung; Jim Zastrow.
Number of staff: 8 full-time professional; 1 full-time support.
EIN: 411429402

4650
The Eagle Foundation ✧
8357 100th St. W.
Bloomington, MN 55438-1971 (952) 938-4811
Contact: Philip F. Fandrei, Pres. and Treas.

Established in 2006 in MN.
Donors: Mark D. Hanson; Auto Mark Inc.; Cornerstone Auto.
Foundation type: Independent foundation.
Financial data (yr. ended 12/31/13): Assets, $15,679,307 (M); gifts received, $535,000; expenditures, $1,692,276; qualifying distributions, $1,642,759; giving activities include $1,642,759 for 94 grants (high: $505,000; low: $1,175).
Fields of interest: Higher education.
Limitations: Applications accepted. Giving primarily in MN. No grants to individuals.
Application information: Application form required.
Initial approach: Proposal
Deadline(s): None
Officers and Directors:* Philip F. Fandrei,* Pres. and Treas.; Mark D. Hanson,* V.P. and Secy.; Kari M. Hanson,* V.P.
EIN: 208070601

4651
Ecolab Foundation ✧
(also known as Ecolab Industry Foundation)
370 Wabasha St. N.
St. Paul, MN 55102-1323 (651) 225-3427
Contact: Kris J. Taylor, V.P.
FAX: (651) 225-3193;
E-mail: ecolabfoundation@ecolab.com; Additional tel.: (651) 293-2259; Main URL: http://www.ecolab.com/our-story/our-company/community-involvement
Facebook: https://www.facebook.com/EcolabFoundation
Flickr: http://www.flickr.com/photos/ecolabfoundation/
Twitter: https://twitter.com/EcolabFdn
YouTube: http://www.youtube.com/ecolabfoundation

Established in 1982 in MN.
Donor: Ecolab Inc.
Foundation type: Company-sponsored foundation.
Financial data (yr. ended 12/31/12): Assets, $11,538,974 (M); gifts received, $10,939,499; expenditures, $5,094,052; qualifying distributions, $5,094,052; giving activities include $4,228,776 for 852 grants (high: $290,000; low: $50).
Purpose and activities: The foundation supports programs designed to promote youth development and serve at-risk youth through education; address poverty, affordable housing, work readiness, crisis assistance, and hunger relief through civic and community development; support hands-on environmental learning; and promote arts education for children and youth.
Fields of interest: Arts education; Arts; Elementary/secondary education; Higher education; Education; Environment, natural resources; Environmental education; Environment; Employment, services; Employment; Food services; Food banks; Housing/shelter; Youth development; Children/youth, services; Community/economic development; United Ways and Federated Giving Programs; Youth; Economically disadvantaged.
Type of support: General/operating support; Emergency funds; Program development; Curriculum development; Employee matching gifts; Grants to individuals.
Limitations: Applications accepted. Giving primarily in areas of company operations in City of Industry, CA, McDonough, GA, Elk Grove Village, Joliet, and Naperville, IL, Huntington, IN, Garyville, LA, Columbus, MS, Greensboro, NC, Fort Worth, Fresno, Irving, Garland, and Sugarland, TX, Beloit, WI, and Martinsburg, WV, with emphasis on St. Paul, MN. No support for sectarian or denominational religious organizations not of direct benefit to the entire community, political or lobbying organizations, or disease-specific or health related organizations. No grants to individuals (except for Visions for Learning), or for industry, trade, or professional association memberships, sports or athletic programs or facilities, or fundraising events or sponsorships; no loans or program-related investments.
Publications: Application guidelines.
Application information:
Initial approach: Call or e-mail foundation for organizations located outside of St. Paul, MN; complete online application form for organizations located in St. Paul, MN; e-mail foundation for Visions for Learning
Deadline(s): Varies for organizations located outside of St. Paul, MN; Dec. 1 for organizations in St. Paul, MN; Spring for Visions for Learning
Board meeting date(s): Quarterly
Officers and Directors:* Michael J. Monahan,* Pres.; Kris J. Taylor,* V.P.; David F. Duvick, Secy.; Ching-Meng Chew, Treas.; Douglas M. Baker, Jr.
Number of staff: 2 full-time professional.
EIN: 411372157

4652
Edelstein Family Foundation ✧
c/o Bubuque Bank & Trust Co., MN Bank
7701 France Ave. S.
Edina, MN 55435-5288

Established in 1954 in MN.
Donors: Ruth Easton Revocable Trust; David Edelstein†; Sparkle Sugar Corp.
Foundation type: Independent foundation.
Financial data (yr. ended 12/31/13): Assets, $39,660,858 (M); expenditures, $1,959,810; qualifying distributions, $1,638,722; giving activities include $1,484,808 for 13 grants (high: $224,964; low: $5,000).
Fields of interest: Performing arts, theater; Secondary school/education; Higher education; Education; Health care; Jewish federated giving programs; Jewish agencies & synagogues.
Limitations: Applications not accepted. Giving primarily in St. Paul and Minneapolis, MN; some giving also in MA and NY. No grants to individuals, or for loans or program-related investments.
Application information: Contributes only to pre-selected organizations.
Trustees: Thomas A. Keller III; US Bank, N.A.
EIN: 416013675
Selected grants: The following grants are a representative sample of this grantmaker's funding activity:
$80,512 to University of Minnesota, Sociology Department, Minneapolis, MN, 2012. For general operating support.

4653
Edwards Memorial Trust ✧
c/o Trust Tax Services
P.O. Box 64713
St. Paul, MN 55164-0713

Established in 1961 in MN.
Donor: Ray Edwards†.
Foundation type: Independent foundation.
Financial data (yr. ended 12/31/13): Assets, $20,605,539 (M); expenditures, $1,066,506; qualifying distributions, $911,063; giving activities include $881,000 for 33 grants (high: $100,000; low: $5,000).
Purpose and activities: Emphasis on public hospitals, including the maintaining of free beds;

some support for social services and health agencies, including those benefiting the handicapped.
Fields of interest: Hospitals (general); Health care; Mental health/crisis services; Human services; Disabilities, people with.
Type of support: General/operating support; Capital campaigns; Program development.
Limitations: Applications not accepted. Giving limited to the benefit of the East Metro St. Paul, area, and in the counties of Ramsey, Washington, and Dakota, MN. No grants to individuals, or for endowments, research, film and video production or travel.
Application information: Unsolicited requests for funds not accepted.
Trustee: U.S. Bank, N.A.
EIN: 416011292
Selected grants: The following grants are a representative sample of this grantmaker's funding activity:
$50,000 to Presbyterian Homes Foundation, Roseville, MN, 2012. For grant award - 3rd of 4 Yearly Installments Consortium at Carondelet Village.
$25,000 to Tubman, Minneapolis, MN, 2012. For grant award - Clinical Services Division.
$15,000 to Northeast Residence, Little Canada, MN, 2012. For Grant Award General Operations.
$5,000 to Minnesota AIDS Project, Minneapolis, MN, 2012. For grant award - General Operations.

4654
The Engdahl Family Foundation ✧
c/o Nancy Graser
17991 70th Pl. N.
Maple Grove, MN 55311-3031

Established in 2006 in MN.
Donor: Marion E. Engdahl.
Foundation type: Independent foundation.
Financial data (yr. ended 12/31/13): Assets, $10,969,179 (M); expenditures, $1,285,321; qualifying distributions, $1,277,575; giving activities include $1,277,575 for 9 grants (high: $1,000,000; low: $8,000).
Fields of interest: Medical research, institute; Human services; Children/youth, services; Christian agencies & churches; Economically disadvantaged.
Limitations: Applications not accepted. Giving primarily in Minneapolis and St. Paul, MN and Boone, NC. No grants to individuals.
Application information: Contributes only to pre-selected organizations.
Directors: Brian E. Engdahl; David R. Engdahl; Marion E. Engdahl; Nancy M. Graser.
EIN: 205257180

4655
Evert Foundation ✧
c/o John Nelson
200 S. 6th St., Ste. 4000
Minneapolis, MN 55402-1431

Established in 2005 in MN.
Donors: Ann McCabe; Lindsay McCabe.
Foundation type: Independent foundation.
Financial data (yr. ended 12/31/12): Assets, $4,194,894 (M); gifts received, $1,002,779; expenditures, $1,294,093; qualifying distributions, $1,285,000; giving activities include $1,285,000 for 7 grants (high: $1,220,000; low: $5,000).
Fields of interest: Arts, ethics; Performing arts, theater; Education; Human services; Salvation Army; Human services, emergency aid; Military/veterans' organizations; Christian agencies & churches.
Limitations: Applications not accepted. No grants to individuals.
Application information: Unsolicited requests for funds not accepted.
Trustees: Ann L. McCabe; Lindsay E. McCabe.
EIN: 416543299

4656
Mike & Linda Fiterman Family Foundation ✧
(formerly The Jack and Bessie Fiterman Foundation)
5500 Wayzata Blvd., Ste. 1015
Minneapolis, MN 55416 (763) 971-1904
Contact: Linda Fiterman, Treas.

Established in 1966 in MN.
Donors: Fidelity Products Co.; Liberty Carton Co.; Safco Products Co.; Shamrock Industries, Inc.; FLS Properties; B&B Lease Co.; Liberty Diversified Industries Inc.
Foundation type: Company-sponsored foundation.
Financial data (yr. ended 05/31/14): Assets, $15,175,351 (M); gifts received, $1,600,000; expenditures, $940,411; qualifying distributions, $833,503; giving activities include $833,478 for 176 grants (high: $216,500; low: $500).
Purpose and activities: The foundation supports hospitals and clinics and organizations involved with education, employment, housing development, human services, and religion.
Fields of interest: Education, early childhood education; Elementary school/education; Education; Hospitals (general); Health care, clinics/centers; Health care; Employment, services; Housing/shelter, development; YM/YWCAs & YM/YWHAs; Children/youth, services; Family services; Developmentally disabled, centers & services; Human services; Catholic agencies & churches; Jewish agencies & synagogues; Religion.
Type of support: General/operating support.
Limitations: Applications accepted. Giving primarily in MN. No support for lobbying or advocacy groups. No grants to individuals.
Application information: Application form required.
Initial approach: Contact foundation for application form
Deadline(s): None
Officers: Michael Fiterman, Pres.; David Lenzen, Secy.; Linda Fiterman, Treas.
EIN: 416058465
Selected grants: The following grants are a representative sample of this grantmaker's funding activity:
$400 to We Win Institute, Minneapolis, MN, 2013. For public support.

4657
Foundation for Educational Research and Development ✧
2800 N. Niagra Ln.
Plymouth, MN 55447-4834

Established in 1997 in MN.
Donor: Irvin R. Kessler.
Foundation type: Independent foundation.
Financial data (yr. ended 12/31/13): Assets, $11,918,411 (M); gifts received, $315,000; expenditures, $1,335,443; qualifying distributions, $1,333,443; giving activities include $1,331,418 for 10 grants (high: $500,000; low: $5,000).
Fields of interest: Museums (science/technology); Education; Hospitals (specialty); Health care; Health organizations, association; Human services; United Ways and Federated Giving Programs; Jewish federated giving programs; Jewish agencies & synagogues; Children.
Type of support: General/operating support.
Limitations: Applications not accepted. Giving primarily in MN. No grants to individuals.
Application information: Contributes only to pre-selected organizations.
Officers and Directors:* Irvin R. Kessler,* C.E.O. and Pres.; Barbara Anderson,* V.P.
EIN: 411876141

4658
Frey Foundation ✧
5000 Wells Fargo Ctr.
90 S. 7th St.
Minneapolis, MN 55402-3903 (612) 359-6215
Contact: Jo Ann Gruesner
FAX: (612) 359-6210;
E-mail: joann@freyfoundationmn.org; Main URL: http://freyfoundationmn.org/

Established in 1988 in MN.
Foundation type: Independent foundation.
Financial data (yr. ended 06/30/13): Assets, $25,641,993 (M); expenditures, $1,427,897; qualifying distributions, $1,235,628; giving activities include $960,229 for 43 grants (high: $150,000; low: $100).
Purpose and activities: The foundation strives to be a catalyst in strengthening its community through effective, direct giving which promotes self-sufficiency and stimulates creative change, resulting in an improved quality of life for all.
Fields of interest: Education, early childhood education; Higher education; Housing/shelter, development; Housing/shelter; Human services; Children/youth; Homeless.
Type of support: General/operating support; Annual campaigns; Program development; Matching/challenge support.
Limitations: Applications accepted. Giving primarily in the Minneapolis-St. Paul, MN, area and in Naples, FL. No support for political organizations. No grants to individuals, including scholarships and tuition assistance, or for endowments.
Publications: Annual report; Grants list; Program policy statement.
Application information: See foundation web site for application information and form. Full applications will be accepted by invitation only. All letters of inquiry, applications and evaluations must be e-mailed. The foundation requests that materials not be sent via USPS. Application form required.
Initial approach: Letter of inquiry (no more than 2 pages) via e-mail, and in word format (not in .pdf), to Jo Ann Gruesner, Exec. Asst.
Copies of proposal: 1
Deadline(s): See foundation web site for deadlines
Board meeting date(s): June, Sept., and Dec.
Final notification: 3 days following board meetings
Officers and Directors:* Eugene U. Frey,* Chair.; Mary F. Frey,* Vice-Chair.; James R. Frey,* C.E.O.

and Pres.; Carol F. Wolfe,* V.P. and Prog. Mgr.; Flor Frey; John J. Frey; Mary W. Frey; Peter J. Frey; Jane E. Letourneau; Andrew Wilson; Sarah F. Wilson; Andrew Frey Wolfe; Daniel T. Wolfe; Molly Frey Wolfe.
Number of staff: 1 full-time professional; 2 part-time professional.
EIN: 363588505

4659
H.B. Fuller Company Foundation ✧ ☆
P.O. Box 64683
St. Paul, MN 55164-0683
E-mail: hbfullerfoundation@hbfuller.com; Main URL: http://www.hbfuller.com/north-america/about-us/community-responsibility

Established in 1986 in MN.
Donor: H.B. Fuller Co.
Foundation type: Company-sponsored foundation.
Financial data (yr. ended 11/30/13): Assets, $1,660,425 (M); gifts received, $50; expenditures, $822,960; qualifying distributions, $817,877; giving activities include $808,514 for 155 grants (high: $75,249; low: $35).
Purpose and activities: The foundation supports youth education initiatives in areas of science, technology, engineering, and math (STEM); and programs designed to promote leadership development for youth.
Fields of interest: Arts; Elementary/secondary education; Education; Health care; Disasters, preparedness/services; Youth development; Children/youth, services; Human services; Mathematics; Engineering/technology; Science; Leadership development; Youth.
Type of support: General/operating support; Annual campaigns; Building/renovation; Equipment; Program development; Employee matching gifts; Matching/challenge support.
Limitations: Applications accepted. Giving primarily in areas of company operations in Roseville, CA, Covington, GA, Aurora and Palatine, IL, Paducah, KY, St. Paul, MN, and Vancouver, WA, and China. No support for religious, fraternal, or veterans' organizations, political or lobbying organizations, national organizations, or disease-specific organizations. No grants to individuals, or for capital campaigns, endowments, travel, basic or applied research, advertising, fundraising events or sponsorships, or general support of educational institutions.
Publications: Application guidelines; Corporate giving report.
Application information: Proposals should be no longer than five pages. Funding decisions are made by Community Affairs Councils at each facility location. The Minnesota Common Grant Application Form is accepted. Applications from organizations located outside of the U.S. are by invitation only. Application form required.
Initial approach: Download application form and e-mail, fax, or mail proposal and application form to foundation
Deadline(s): Postmarked by Mar. 31 and Aug. 31
Officers and Directors:* Richard Kastner,* Pres.; Joel Hedberg, V.P.; Rachel Hart, Secy.; Jodie Monson, Treas.; Kimberlee Sinclair, Exec. Dir.; Traci Jensen; Jim Owens; Wes Oren; Nathan Weaver; Jeff Wroblewski.
EIN: 363500811
Selected grants: The following grants are a representative sample of this grantmaker's funding activity:
$12,477 to Organization for Tropical Studies, Durham, NC, 2011.
$10,000 to Saint Catherine University, Saint Paul, MN, 2011.
$10,000 to University of Saint Thomas, Saint Paul, MN, 2011.
$5,000 to College Possible, Saint Paul, MN, 2011.
$1,050 to University of Saint Thomas, Saint Paul, MN, 2011.
$1,000 to University of Massachusetts, Amherst, MA, 2011.

4660
The Gallagher Foundation ✧
c/o Gerald R. Gallagher
3890 Wells Fargo Ctr.
90 S. 7th St.
Minneapolis, MN 55402-3903
Main URL: http://www.gallagherfoundation.org/

Established in 2001 in MN.
Donors: Ellen M. Gallagher; Gerald R. Gallagher; Michael Moore; John Fangman.
Foundation type: Independent foundation.
Financial data (yr. ended 12/31/12): Assets, $5,544,283 (M); gifts received, $521,606; expenditures, $810,113; qualifying distributions, $781,044; giving activities include $629,007 for 102 grants (high: $14,500; low: $183).
Fields of interest: Scholarships/financial aid.
Type of support: Scholarships—to individuals.
Limitations: Applications not accepted. Giving primarily in Cape Town, South Africa, with some giving in Mexico and Turkey.
Application information: Unsolicited requests for funds not accepted.
Officers and Directors:* Gerald R. Gallagher,* Pres.; Ellen M. Gallagher,* V.P.; Gerald P. Gallagher.
EIN: 412019884

4661
General Mills Foundation ✧
1 General Mills Blvd.
MS CC-01
Minneapolis, MN 55426-1347
Contact: Ellen Luger, Exec. Dir.
FAX: (763) 764-4114;
E-mail: CommunityActionQA@genmills.com; Application address: P.O. Box 1113, Minneapolis, MN 55440; Main URL: http://www.genmills.com/en/Responsibility/Community_Engagement.aspx
Champions for Healthy Kids Recipients: http://www.genmills.com/Home/Responsibility/Community_Engagement/Grants/Champions_for_healthy_kids/2011_recipients.aspx
Communities of Color Recipients: http://content.generalmills.com/Home/Responsibility/community_engagement/Grants/Twin%20Cities_area/Communities_of_color/grant_recipients_2012.aspx
Facebook: http://www.facebook.com/GeneralMillsGives
General Mills Foundation's Philanthropy Promise: http://www.ncrp.org/philanthropys-promise/who
Grants Database: http://content.generalmills.com/Responsibility/Community_Engagement/Grants/Grantees.aspx?cat={4020A4F2-C35C-40DD-9CE4-2374486831E7}
Philanthropy's Promise: http://www.ncrp.org/philanthropys-promise/who

Incorporated in 1954 in MN.
Donor: General Mills, Inc.
Foundation type: Company-sponsored foundation.
Financial data (yr. ended 05/31/13): Assets, $110,841,484 (M); gifts received, $25,100,000; expenditures, $27,259,015; qualifying distributions, $27,259,015; giving activities include $24,789,661 for 706 grants, and $2,108,664 for employee matching gifts.
Purpose and activities: The foundation supports programs designed to support hunger and nutrition wellness; education; and arts and culture.
Fields of interest: Performing arts; Arts; Elementary/secondary education; Education; Public health, physical fitness; Food services; Food banks; Nutrition; Disasters, preparedness/services; YM/YWCAs & YM/YWHAs; Family services; Human services; United Ways and Federated Giving Programs; Children/youth; Adults; Minorities; Economically disadvantaged.
Type of support: Capital campaigns; Employee matching gifts; Employee volunteer services; Employee-related scholarships; General/operating support; Program development; Scholarship funds.
Limitations: Applications accepted. Giving primarily in areas of major company operations and headquarters of Twin Cities, MN area; giving also in CA, GA, IA, IL, IN, MA, MD, MI, MO, MT, NJ, NM, NY, OH, TN, WA, and WI for the Community Action Councils Program. No support for discriminatory organizations, religious, political, social, labor, veterans', alumni, or fraternal organizations, disease-specific organizations, or athletic associations. No grants to individuals (except for employee scholarships), or for endowments, annual appeals, federated campaigns, fund drives, recreational or sporting events, healthcare, research, advertising, political causes, travel, emergency funding, debt reduction or operating deficits, conferences, seminars or workshops, publications, film, or television, sponsorships, special events, or fundraisers; no loans.
Publications: Application guidelines; Corporate report; Corporate giving report; Financial statement; Grants list.
Application information: Applications for Community Action Council grants are available by invitation only. A full proposal may be requested at a later date for Twin Cities grants. E-mail letter of inquiry to foundation for capital requests. Telephone calls and personal visits are not encouraged. Organizations receiving support may be asked to submit an evaluation report. Application form required.
Initial approach: Complete online letter of inquiry for Twin Cities grants; complete online application for Celebrating Communities of Color
Deadline(s): None for Twin Cities grants; Dec. See website for Celebrating Communities of Color annual information
Board meeting date(s): Ongoing
Final notification: Varies depending on program, see website for additional information per program
Officers and Trustees:* Kendall J. Powell,* Chair.; Kimberly A. Nelson,* Pres.; Ellen Goldberg Luger, V.P., Secy., and Exec. Dir.; Marie Pillai, Treas.; Marc Belton; John R. Church; Michael L. Davis; Peter C. Erickson; Ian R. Friendly; Donal Leo Mulligan; Shawn O'Grady; Christopher O'Leary; Roderick A. Palmore.

Number of staff: 7 full-time professional; 2 full-time support.
EIN: 416018495
Selected grants: The following grants are a representative sample of this grantmaker's funding activity:
$1,000,000 to Second Harvest Heartland, Saint Paul, MN, 2013. For Hunger-Free Minnesota.
$125,000 to Minnesota Orchestral Association, Minneapolis, MN, 2013. For operating support.
$50,000 to Achieve Minneapolis, Minneapolis, MN, 2013. For Community Engagement Program.
$35,000 to Jeremiah Program, Minneapolis, MN, 2013. For operating support.
$25,000 to Interfaith Outreach and Community Partners, Plymouth, MN, 2013. For operating support.
$10,000 to Volunteers of America of Minnesota, Edina, MN, 2013. For Experience Corps.

4662
George Family Foundation ✧
1818 Oliver Ave. S.
Minneapolis, MN 55405-2208 (612) 377-3356
FAX: (612) 233-2194; Letter of Inquiry contact: Robin Barker, e-mail: robin@georgefamilyfoundation.org; contact for George Family Foundation Catalyst Initiative: Dawn Johnson: dawn@georgefamilyfoundation.org; Main URL: http://www.georgefamilyfoundation.org

Established in 1992 in MN.
Donors: Penny Pilgram George; William W. George.
Foundation type: Independent foundation.
Financial data (yr. ended 12/31/13): Assets, $63,066,055 (M); gifts received, $1,429,994; expenditures, $6,191,271; qualifying distributions, $5,700,576; giving activities include $4,981,587 for 126 grants (high: $500,000; low: $500).
Purpose and activities: The foundation's current focus is integrated health and healing (programs and initiatives that advance an integrated, patient-centered approach to health, healing and well being), authentic leadership (programs that are developing future leaders who are authentic, values-based and empowering of the leadership of others), and community.
Fields of interest: Health organizations, association; Leadership development.
Type of support: General/operating support; Continuing support; Program development.
Limitations: Giving primarily in the Twin Cities area of MN. No support for fraternal or veterans organizations, school athletic programs, or for disease-specific organizations. No grants to individuals, or for endowments, capital campaigns, memberships, debt reduction, fundraisers, special events, courtesy, goodwill or public service advertisements, re-granting, or for operating expenses.
Publications: Annual report.
Application information:
Initial approach: E-mail Letter of Inquiry after reviewing application requirements on foundation web site
Officers: Penny Pilgram George, Pres.; William W. George, V.P.; Gayle M. Ober, Exec. Dir.
Directors: Jeffrey Pilgram George; Jonathan R. George.
EIN: 411730855
Selected grants: The following grants are a representative sample of this grantmaker's funding activity:
$109,321 to Harvard University, Cambridge, MA, 2011. For scholarships.

4663
Gesner-Johnson Foundation ✧
c/o Wells Fargo Bank MN, N.A.
90 S. 7th St., N9305-530
Minneapolis, MN 55402-2308 (612) 343-6453

Established in 1997 in MN.
Donors: Lloyd P. Johnson; Rosalind G. Johnson‡; L. Johnson Charitable Lead Annuity Trust; Marcia Johnson; Paul Johnson; Russell Johnson; L. Johnson Irrevocable Trust; Lloyd Johnson‡.
Foundation type: Independent foundation.
Financial data (yr. ended 12/31/13): Assets, $16,104,081 (M); expenditures, $697,056; qualifying distributions, $619,359; giving activities include $593,983 for 25 grants (high: $50,000; low: $2,000).
Purpose and activities: Each grant is intended to create a significant difference in the receiving organization, with funds designated for specific projects that will have a lasting impact on the community served.
Fields of interest: Education; Health care; Protestant agencies & churches.
Type of support: Building/renovation; Equipment.
Limitations: Applications accepted. Giving to Phoenix, AZ, Los Angeles, CA, and Seattle, WA. No grants for general operating expense.
Application information: Application form required.
Initial approach: Letter
Deadline(s): None
Officers: Russell Johnson, Pres.; Paul C. Johnson, Secy.; Marcia Campbell, Treas.
Number of staff: None.
EIN: 411890875

4664
GHR Foundation ☆
10350 Bren Rd. W.
Minnetonka, MN 55343-9002 (952) 656-4806
E-mail: info@ghrfoundation.org; Main URL: http://ghrfoundation.org/

Established in 2011 in MN.
Foundation type: Independent foundation.
Financial data (yr. ended 12/31/12): Assets, $294,168,291 (M); expenditures, $20,803,750; qualifying distributions, $15,396,369; giving activities include $14,024,205 for 89 grants (high: $1,000,000; low: $1,000).
Fields of interest: Elementary school/education; Higher education; Education; Health organizations; Human services; Catholic agencies & churches; Religion.
Limitations: Applications not accepted. Giving primarily in MD, MN and WI. No grants to individuals.
Application information: Contributes only to pre-selected organizations.
Officers and Directors:* Amy R. Goldman,* Chair. and Exec. Dir.; Luz Campa, Vice-Chair. and Secy.; Mark Rauenhorst,* Vice-Chair. and Treas.; Peter Karoff; Cardinal Theodore McCarrick; Gerald Rauenhorst; Joseph J. Rauenhorst; Matt Rauenhorst; Tim Welsch.
EIN: 453996122
Selected grants: The following grants are a representative sample of this grantmaker's funding activity:
$1,000,000 to Marquette University, Milwaukee, WI, 2011. For Discovery Energy Lab.
$1,000,000 to Mayo Clinic, Rochester, MN, 2011. For Alzheimer's Research.
$1,000,000 to Papal Foundation, Bala Cynwyd, PA, 2011. For various projects.
$1,000,000 to University of Saint Thomas, Opus College of Business, Saint Paul, MN, 2011. For Association to Advance Collegiate Schools of Business (AACSB) Accreditation and Ethics and Excellence Initiative.
$900,000 to Marquette University, Milwaukee, WI, 2011. For Transform the College of Engineering.
$624,055 to Catholic Relief Services, Baltimore, MD, 2011. For Emergency Preparedness and Capacity Building.
$525,000 to Carondelet Village, Saint Paul, MN, 2011. For Carondelet Circle - Alzheimer's Disease support.
$130,000 to Dominican Sisters of Saint Mary of the Springs, Columbus, OH, 2011. For Partnership with Nigerian Indigenous Congregation Project support to partner with a Dominican congregation in Nigeria to provide intensive training and development to enable the African congregation to develop leadership and sustainability to support ministries to the poor in area of Muslim majority.
$75,000 to Missionary Society Salesian Sisters, North Haledon, NJ, 2011. For formation training support for women currently enrolled in the Salesian Sisters formation program.
$50,000 to Apostles of the Sacred Heart of Jesus, Hamden, CT, 2011. For Sacred Heart Learning Center.

4665
Gostomski Family Foundation ✧
1666 Valley View Dr.
Winona, MN 55987-6222

Established in 2003 in MN.
Donors: Joette Gostomski; Michael Gostomski.
Foundation type: Independent foundation.
Financial data (yr. ended 05/31/13): Assets, $3,609,833 (M); expenditures, $896,139; qualifying distributions, $844,828; giving activities include $823,332 for 11 grants (high: $300,000; low: $10,000).
Fields of interest: Higher education, university; Youth development; Human services.
Limitations: Applications not accepted. Giving primarily in MN and WI. No grants to individuals.
Application information: Contributes only to pre-selected organizations.
Trustees: Joette Gostomski; Michael Gostomski.
EIN: 206075013

4666
The Graco Foundation ✧
P.O. Boxc 1441
Minneapolis, MN 55440-1441 (612) 623-6000
Contact: Kristi Lee
Main URL: http://www.graco.com/us/en/about-graco/foundation.html

Incorporated in 1956 in MN.
Donor: Graco Inc.
Foundation type: Company-sponsored foundation.
Financial data (yr. ended 12/31/13): Assets, $10,457,482 (M); gifts received, $1,750,000; expenditures, $1,041,710; qualifying distributions,

$1,037,887; giving activities include $964,085 for 177 grants (high: $100,000; low: $500).
Purpose and activities: The foundation helps organizations serve community needs by expanding or enhancing services to clients, with some emphasis on capital projects and technology needs. Special emphasis is directed toward organizations with a proven track record of enabling self-sufficiency and programs that promote education, workforce development, and youth development. Support is given primarily in areas of company operations, with emphasis on Minnesota.
Fields of interest: Education, early childhood education; Education; Employment, services; Employment; Youth development; Human services; Business/industry; United Ways and Federated Giving Programs; Children/youth; Adults; Minorities.
Type of support: Management development/capacity building; Capital campaigns; Building/renovation; Equipment; Program development; Scholarship funds; Technical assistance; Employee volunteer services; Employee matching gifts; Employee-related scholarships.
Limitations: Applications not accepted. Giving primarily in areas of company operations, with emphasis on MN, including the northern and northeastern communities in Minneapolis, as well as North Canton, OH and Sioux Falls, SD. No support for political, religious, or fraternal organizations. No grants to individuals (except for employee-related scholarships), or for start-up needs, emergency needs, debt reduction, land acquisition, endowments, publications, fundraising, travel, conferences, or national or local campaigns for disease research; no loans or product donations.
Application information: The foundation is not currently accepting new applications.
Board meeting date(s): June
Officers: Patrick J. McHale, Pres.; Kristi Lee, Secy.; Janel W. French, Treas.
Directors: David Alhers; Joe Daniski; Karen Park Gallivan; Karl A. Hurston; Chad L. Hellwig; Eric Hesse; David Lowe.
Number of staff: 1 full-time professional.
EIN: 416023537
Selected grants: The following grants are a representative sample of this grantmaker's funding activity:
$22,500 to Dunwoody College of Technology, Minneapolis, MN, 2012. For operating/scholarship fund.
$1,000 to League of Minnesota Human Rights Commissions, Robbinsdale, MN, 2012. For Dollars for Doers Program.

4667
Grand Rapids Area Community Foundation ✧
350 N.W. First Ave., Ste. E
Grand Rapids, MN 55744-2756 (218) 999-9100
Contact: Chris Fulton, Exec. Dir.; For grants: Sarah Copeland, Dir., Grants and Progs.
FAX: (218) 999-7430; E-mail: info@gracf.org; Grant application e-mail: sarah.copeland@gracf.org; Main URL: http://www.gracf.org
Facebook: https://www.facebook.com/pages/Grand-Rapids-Area-Community-Foundation/103029313097109
Google Plus: https://plus.google.com/+GracfOrg/videos
Twitter: https://twitter.com/GRACFfoundation
YouTube: http://www.youtube.com/channel/UCqxaUK9t3qMjZRxsFmMCS7Q

Established in 1994 in MN.
Donors: Blandin Foundation; Itasca Medical Center Foundation; Larry Latterell.
Foundation type: Community foundation.
Financial data (yr. ended 12/31/13): Assets, $15,974,466 (M); gifts received, $2,066,990; expenditures, $1,603,999; giving activities include $1,093,050 for 7+ grants (high: $50,000).
Purpose and activities: The foundation seeks to provide individuals and organizations opportunities to invest in their community to improve the quality of life.
Fields of interest: Humanities; Arts; Education; Environment; Health care; Recreation; Family services; Community/economic development.
Type of support: Endowments; Emergency funds; Conferences/seminars; Curriculum development; Technical assistance; Scholarships—to individuals.
Limitations: Applications accepted. Giving in the greater Itasca County, MN, area. No support for religious groups for religious purposes. No grants to individuals (except for scholarships), or for fundraising events or activities, communications including video tapes, brochures, and advertising, building campaigns, travel or conferences.
Publications: Application guidelines; Annual report (including application guidelines); Financial statement; Informational brochure; Newsletter; IRS Form 990 or 990-PF printed copy available upon request.
Application information: Visit foundation web site for online grant applications and guidelines. Application form required.
Initial approach: Letter of Inquiry
Copies of proposal: 1
Deadline(s): Sept. 15
Board meeting date(s): 1st Tues. of alternate months
Final notification: 1 month
Officers and Directors:* Mark White,* Chair.; Daryl Erdman,* Chair.-Elect.; Mike Lentz,* Vice-Chair.; Kelly Kirwin,* Secy.; Steve Burggraf,* Treas.; Chris Fulton, Exec. Dir.; Edwin A. Anderson, M.D.; Dennis Anderson; Keith Anderson; Derek Bostyancic; Megan Christianson; Chris Deadrick; Skip Drake; Mary Jo Gibbons; Mary Ives; Rhett Johnson; Tina Kane; Cynthia Margo; Sonja Merrild; Mike Olson; Cyrus White.
Number of staff: 3 full-time professional; 1 full-time support.
EIN: 411761590

4668
The Greystone Foundation ✧
730 2nd Ave. S., Ste. 1300
Minneapolis, MN 55402-2475 (612) 752-1772

Established in 1948 in MN.
Donor: Members of the Paul A. Brooks family.
Foundation type: Independent foundation.
Financial data (yr. ended 12/31/12): Assets, $10,933,722 (M); gifts received, $371,195; expenditures, $1,319,565; qualifying distributions, $1,120,512; giving activities include $1,089,725 for 300 grants (high: $50,000; low: $250).
Purpose and activities: Giving for health and medical research, community funds, private secondary and higher education, and arts and cultural programs.
Fields of interest: Arts; Secondary school/education; Higher education; Hospitals (general); Health care; Medical research, institute; Human services; United Ways and Federated Giving Programs.
Type of support: General/operating support; Continuing support; Annual campaigns; Building/renovation; Equipment; Land acquisition; Emergency funds; Program development; Conferences/seminars; Publication; Seed money; Research.
Limitations: Applications not accepted. Giving primarily in MN, with emphasis on the Twin Cities. No grants to individuals, or for endowment funds, matching gifts, scholarships, or fellowships; no loans.
Application information: Unsolicited requests for funds not accepted.
Board meeting date(s): As required
Trustees: Julie Hara; Katherine M. Leighton.
EIN: 416027765

4669
Mary Livingston Griggs and Mary Griggs Burke Foundation ✧
2221 Ford Pkwy., Ste. 204
St. Paul, MN 55116-3857 (651) 227-2649
Contact: Marvin Pertzik, Secy.-Treas.
FAX: (651) 602-2670;
E-mail: pkarasov@mchlaw.com

Established in 1966 in MN.
Donor: Mary L. Griggs‡.
Foundation type: Independent foundation.
Financial data (yr. ended 06/30/14): Assets, $32,333,981 (M); expenditures, $1,268,267; qualifying distributions, $1,230,157; giving activities include $1,181,453 for grants.
Purpose and activities: Giving primarily for arts and culture, and for higher education.
Fields of interest: Museums (art); Arts; Higher education; Human services; Foundations (private grantmaking).
Type of support: General/operating support; Continuing support; Annual campaigns; Capital campaigns; Building/renovation; Endowments; Scholarship funds; Matching/challenge support.
Limitations: Giving primarily in St. Paul, MN as well as in Minneapolis, and New York, NY. No grants to individuals.
Application information: Application form not required.
Initial approach: Letter
Copies of proposal: 1
Deadline(s): None
Board meeting date(s): Semiannually
Final notification: 10 days to 3 months
Officers and Directors:* Gale Lansing Davis,* Pres.; Eleanor Briggs, V.P.; Marvin Pertzik,* Secy.-Treas.
EIN: 416052355
Selected grants: The following grants are a representative sample of this grantmaker's funding activity:
$200,000 to Sarah Lawrence College, Bronxville, NY, 2011.
$10,000 to Northwest Wisconsin Concentrated Employment Program, Ashland, WI, 2011.

4670
Hageman Foundation of Hope ✧
2019 Westridge Ct.
Buffalo, MN 55313-1994

Established in 2004 in MN.
Donors: Robert Hageman; Colleen Hageman; Michael Hageman; Stacy Hageman; J&B Group, Inc.
Foundation type: Independent foundation.
Financial data (yr. ended 12/31/13): Assets, $1,014,299 (M); gifts received, $412,803; expenditures, $871,006; qualifying distributions, $858,018; giving activities include $828,130 for 14 grants (high: $701,000; low: $500).
Purpose and activities: Giving primarily to a Christian school.
Fields of interest: Elementary/secondary education; Food banks; Human services.
Limitations: Applications not accepted. Giving primarily in MN. No grants to individuals.
Application information: Contributes only to pre-selected organizations.
Officers and Directors:* Robert Hageman,* Pres.; Lori Cassady,* Secy.-Treas.; Colleen Hageman; Michael Hageman.
EIN: 201700412
Selected grants: The following grants are a representative sample of this grantmaker's funding activity:
$3,000 to Sharing and Caring Hands, Minneapolis, MN, 2011.

4671
E. W. Hallett Charitable Trust ✧
P.O. Box 64713, Trust Tax Svcs.
St. Paul, MN 55164-0713
Application address: U.S. Bank, N.A., Att.: Sarah Godfrey, 101 E. 5th St., 14th Fl., St. Paul, MN 55101, tel.: (651) 466-8710

Established in 1984 in MN.
Foundation type: Independent foundation.
Financial data (yr. ended 11/30/13): Assets, $14,130,785 (M); expenditures, $646,879; qualifying distributions, $538,916; giving activities include $430,746 for 16 grants (high: $165,952; low: $2,000).
Fields of interest: Libraries/library science; Education; Human services; Community/economic development.
Limitations: Applications accepted. Giving primarily in the Cuyuna Range (Crosby, Ironton, Deerwood, etc.) MN, area. No support for religious functions. No grants to individuals.
Application information: The foundation uses the Minnesota Common Grant Application Form. Application form required.
Initial approach: Letter
Copies of proposal: 1
Deadline(s): None
Trustees: Tom Jensen; Desiree Parker; Paul Schliesman; Kirk Springsted; U.S. Bank, N.A.
Number of staff: 1 part-time professional.
EIN: 416261160
Selected grants: The following grants are a representative sample of this grantmaker's funding activity:
$200,000 to Presbyterian Homes and Services, Roseville, MN, 2011. For capital support.
$15,000 to Kinship Partners, Brainerd, MN, 2011. For program support.
$12,000 to Bridges of Hope, Brainerd, MN, 2011. For general support.
$10,000 to Lakes Area Interfaith Caregivers, Baxter, MN, 2011. For operating support.
$3,000 to Kinship of Aitkin County, Aitkin, MN, 2011. For general support.

4672
Hardenbergh Foundation ✧
(formerly St. Croix Foundation)
5959 Centerville Rd., Ste. 260
North Oaks, MN 55127-6813 (651) 653-4956
Contact: Jeffrey T. Peterson, Exec. Dir.
E-mail: jeff.peterson@hardenberghfdn.org

Established in 1950 in MN.
Donors: Ianthe B. Hardenbergh†; I. Hardenbergh Charitable Annuity Trust; Gabrielle Hardenbergh.
Foundation type: Independent foundation.
Financial data (yr. ended 12/31/13): Assets, $84,153,430 (M); expenditures, $4,128,873; qualifying distributions, $3,615,650; giving activities include $3,416,500 for 117 grants (high: $400,000; low: $2,000).
Purpose and activities: Giving for health organizations and hospitals, cultural programs, social service and youth agencies, and education; support also for churches.
Fields of interest: Arts; Education; Hospitals (general); Health care; Health organizations, association; Human services; Youth, services.
Type of support: General/operating support; Continuing support; Annual campaigns; Capital campaigns; Building/renovation; Equipment; Program development; Matching/challenge support.
Limitations: Applications accepted. Giving limited to the St. Croix River Valley, Washington and Ramsey Counties, MN.
Application information: Common Grant Application Form accepted for full grant proposal. Application form not required.
Initial approach: Letter or telephone
Copies of proposal: 1
Deadline(s): Oct. 15
Board meeting date(s): Dec. 1
Final notification: 6 weeks
Officers and Directors:* Jeffrey T. Peterson,* Pres. and Exec. Dir.; Gerald C. Bren,* V.P.; John G. Couchman,* V.P.; Jon A. Theobald,* Secy.-Treas.
Number of staff: 1 full-time professional.
EIN: 416011826
Selected grants: The following grants are a representative sample of this grantmaker's funding activity:
$650,000 to Merrick Community Services, Saint Paul, MN, 2012.
$100,000 to Carondelet Village, Saint Paul, MN, 2012.
$30,000 to FamilyMeans, Stillwater, MN, 2012.
$20,000 to College Possible, Saint Paul, MN, 2012.
$20,000 to Minnesota Independent School Fund, Saint Paul, MN, 2012.
$10,000 to People Incorporated, Saint Paul, MN, 2012.
$5,000 to Little Brothers - Friends of the Elderly, Minneapolis, MN, 2012.
$5,000 to Saint Paul Foundation, Saint Paul, MN, 2012. For Community Sharing Fund.

4673
Hersey Foundation ✧ ☆
408 Saint Peter St., Rm. 434
St. Paul, MN 55102-1119

Established about 1968 in MN.
Donor: William Hamm, Jr.†.
Foundation type: Independent foundation.
Financial data (yr. ended 12/31/13): Assets, $11,272,736 (M); gifts received, $1,000; expenditures, $509,357; qualifying distributions, $506,156; giving activities include $476,666 for 9 grants (high: $266,666; low: $25,000).
Purpose and activities: Giving primarily for higher education, human services and community development.
Fields of interest: Historic preservation/historical societies; Higher education; Children/youth, services; Community/economic development; Public affairs; Christian agencies & churches.
Limitations: Applications not accepted. Giving primarily in FL, MN and NY. No grants to individuals.
Application information: Contributes only to pre-selected organizations.
Officers and Directors: Edward H. Hamm, Jr.,* Pres.; Edward H. Hamm,* V.P. and Treas.; Dean E. Busch,* Secy.
EIN: 237001771
Selected grants: The following grants are a representative sample of this grantmaker's funding activity:
$25,000 to Oglala Lakota College, Kyle, SD, 2012. For general fund-educational purposes.
$25,000 to Pro-Choice Resources, Minneapolis, MN, 2012. For general fund-community projects.

4674
Hiawatha Education Foundation ✧
c/o Hawkins Ash CPAs
975 34th Ave. N.W., Ste. 301
Rochester, MN 55901-6795
Contact: Robert Kierlin
Application address: c/o Robert Kierlin, 2001 Theurer Blvd., Winona, MN 55987-1500, tel.: (507) 453-8765

Established in 1987 in MN.
Donor: Robert A. Kierlin.
Foundation type: Independent foundation.
Financial data (yr. ended 12/31/13): Assets, $25,355,196 (M); gifts received, $5,136,140; expenditures, $1,130,456; qualifying distributions, $1,128,550; giving activities include $1,128,550 for 23 grants (high: $351,000; low: $1,000).
Purpose and activities: Giving primarily for public and private tax-exempt Minnesota schools that are considering new/expanded pre-school Montessori programs, particularly for at-risk children.
Fields of interest: Education, early childhood education.
Type of support: General/operating support; Scholarships—to individuals.
Limitations: Applications accepted. Giving limited to MN.
Publications: Annual report.
Application information: Awards are limited to non-profit educational organizations or other charitable organizations that use the awards for educational purposes. Application form required.
Initial approach: Letter
Copies of proposal: 1
Deadline(s): None
Final notification: July 31
Officer: Robert A. Kierlin,* Pres.
Directors: Monique N. Duncan; Phillip Duncan; Lara Kierlin.

Number of staff: 1 full-time professional; 1 part-time professional.
EIN: 363537959

4675
Holmes CSM Family Foundation ✧
500 Washington Ave. S., Ste. 3000
Minneapolis, MN 55415-1151

Established in 1997 in MN.
Donors: Gary S. Holmes; Mary L. Holmes.
Foundation type: Independent foundation.
Financial data (yr. ended 12/31/13): Assets, $14,551,224 (M); expenditures, $666,929; qualifying distributions, $644,787; giving activities include $642,250 for 2 grants (high: $542,250; low: $100,000).
Fields of interest: Higher education.
Type of support: General/operating support.
Limitations: Applications not accepted. No grants to individuals.
Application information: Contributes only to pre-selected organizations.
Officers and Directors:* Gary S. Holmes,* Chair. and Pres.; Eugene M. Bowar,* V.P.; Chesley Foster, Secy.-Treas.; Robert Dann; C. William Franke; Curt Petersen.
EIN: 931220868

4676
Hormel Foods Corporation Charitable Trust ✧
1 Hormel Pl.
Austin, MN 55912-3673
E-mail: rjsmith@hormel.com; Main URL: http://www.hormelfoods.com/responsibility/default.aspx

Established in 2003 in MN.
Donor: Hormel Foods Corp.
Foundation type: Company-sponsored foundation.
Financial data (yr. ended 12/31/13): Assets, $1,230,994 (M); gifts received, $1,000,000; expenditures, $1,372,498; qualifying distributions, $1,372,125; giving activities include $1,372,125 for 406 grants (high: $200,000; low: $25).
Purpose and activities: The foundation supports programs designed to promote education; hunger; and quality of life.
Fields of interest: Elementary/secondary education; Higher education; Education; Health care, clinics/centers; Food services; Food banks; Disasters, preparedness/services; Human services; United Ways and Federated Giving Programs.
Type of support: General/operating support; Continuing support; Annual campaigns; Building/renovation; Program development; Scholarship funds; Sponsorships; Employee matching gifts; Employee-related scholarships; Donated products; In-kind gifts.
Limitations: Applications accepted. Giving primarily in areas of company operations, with emphasis on IA, MN, NE, and WI. No support for political campaigns. No grants to individuals or families.
Publications: Application guidelines.
Application information:
Initial approach: Proposal
Deadline(s): None
Board meeting date(s): Quarterly
Officers and Directors:* David P. Juhlke,* Pres.; Steven G. Binder,* Secy.; Roland G. Gentzler, Treas.; Julie H. Craven; Jody H. Feragen.
EIN: 010761416
Selected grants: The following grants are a representative sample of this grantmaker's funding activity:
$130,000 to Feeding America, Chicago, IL, 2012. For hunger relief.

4677
HRK Foundation ✧
(formerly The MAHADH Foundation)
345 Saint Peter St., Ste. 1200
St. Paul, MN 55102-1216
Contact: Kathleen Fluegel, Fdn. Dir.
FAX: (651) 298-0551;
E-mail: Info@HRKFoundation.org; Toll-free tel.: (866) 342-5475; Main URL: http://www.hrkfoundation.org

Established in 1962 in MN.
Donors: Mary Andersen Hulings†; Albert D. Hulings†; Fred C. Andersen†; Katherine B. Andersen†; Katherine D. Rice; Katherine D.R. Hayes; Julia L. Hynnek; Frederick C. Kaemmer; Martha H. Kaemmer; Mary E. Rice; Mary H. Rice.
Foundation type: Independent foundation.
Financial data (yr. ended 12/31/12): Assets, $24,886,174 (M); gifts received, $999,146; expenditures, $2,464,679; qualifying distributions, $2,071,199; giving activities include $1,672,166 for 270 grants (high: $100,234; low: $250), and $21,300 for 10 employee matching gifts.
Purpose and activities: HRK Foundation s defined by quiet leadership and philanthropy. The Board seeks to improve the fabric of our society by promoting healthy families and healthy communities. It supports all families, both traditional and non-traditional.
Fields of interest: Arts, single organization support; Arts, formal/general education; Arts, cultural/ethnic awareness; Child development, education; Education; Reproductive health, sexuality education; Health care, patient services; Health care; AIDS; Children/youth, services; Family services; Community/economic development; AIDS, people with.
Type of support: General/operating support; Continuing support; Annual campaigns; Program development; Employee matching gifts; Matching/challenge support.
Limitations: Applications accepted. Giving primarily in MN, with emphasis on the metropolitan Twin Cities and St. Croix Valley areas, and in Ashland and Bayfield counties, WI. No grants to individuals, or for scholarships, fellowships or capital requests.
Publications: Application guidelines.
Application information: Application form required.
Deadline(s): See foundation web site for current deadlines
Board meeting date(s): Generally May., and Nov.
Officer and Directors:* Julia L. Kaemmer,* Chair.; Arthur W. Kaemmer, M.D.*, Vice-Chair.; Kathleen Fluegel, Exec. Dir.; James D. Hayes; Katherine D.R. Hayes; Frederick C. Kaemmer; Martha H. Kaemmer; Daniel Priebe; Mary H. Rice; Molly E. Rice; Katherine R. Tilney.
Number of staff: 1 full-time professional; 2 part-time professional.
EIN: 416020911

4678
The Hubbard Broadcasting Foundation ✧
(formerly The Hubbard Foundation)
3415 University Ave.
St. Paul, MN 55114-1019 (651) 642-4305
Contact: Kathryn Hubbard Rominski, Exec. Dir.

Incorporated in 1958 in MN.
Donors: Hubbard Broadcasting, Inc.; KSTP, Inc.; Stanley E. Hubbard†.
Foundation type: Company-sponsored foundation.
Financial data (yr. ended 12/31/13): Assets, $29,543,434 (M); expenditures, $1,713,575; qualifying distributions, $1,669,680; giving activities include $1,669,680 for 316 grants (high: $50,000; low: $500).
Purpose and activities: The foundation supports zoos and organizations involved with arts and culture, education, health, skin disorders, hockey, human services, and leadership development.
Fields of interest: Media, print publishing; Museums; Performing arts, theater; Performing arts, orchestras; Arts; Elementary/secondary education; Education, early childhood education; Higher education; Education; Zoos/zoological societies; Hospitals (general); Health care, clinics/centers; Health care; Skin disorders; Athletics/sports, winter sports; Children/youth, services; Human services; Leadership development.
Type of support: General/operating support; Capital campaigns.
Limitations: Applications accepted. Giving primarily in MN. No grants to individuals.
Application information: Application form required.
Initial approach: Proposal
Deadline(s): Prior to end of calendar year
Officers and Directors:* Stanley S. Hubbard,* Pres.; Karen H. Hubbard,* V.P.; Tom Newberry, Secy-Treas.; Kathryn Hubbard Rominski,* Exec. Dir.; Robert W. Hubbard; Stanley E. Hubbard; Virginia H. Morris.
EIN: 416022291
Selected grants: The following grants are a representative sample of this grantmaker's funding activity:
$5,000 to Hamline University, School of Law, Saint Paul, MN, 2012. For operating contributions.

4679
Initiative Foundation ✧
(formerly Central Minnesota Initiative Fund)
405 1st St., S.E.
Little Falls, MN 56345-3007 (320) 632-9255
Contact: Kathy Gaalswyk, Pres.
FAX: (320) 632-9258; E-mail: info@ifound.org; Additional tel: (877) 632-9255; Grant inquiry e-mail: grants@ifound.org; Additional e-mail: kgaalswyk@ifound.org; Main URL: http://www.ifound.org
Facebook: http://www.facebook.com/ifound
KeyNOTES Blog: http://ifoundmn.blogspot.com/
LinkedIn: http://www.linkedin.com/groups?gid=1928428&trk=hb_side_g
Twitter: http://twitter.com/ifoundmn
YouTube: http://www.youtube.com/user/initiativefoundation

Established in 1986 in MN.
Foundation type: Community foundation.
Financial data (yr. ended 12/31/13): Assets, $60,796,062 (M); gifts received, $4,618,008; expenditures, $5,743,004; giving activities include

$2,550,915 for 78+ grants (high: $796,988), and $258,212 for 90 grants to individuals.
Purpose and activities: The foundation awards grants and loans, pools resources, and creates partnerships to enhance the quality of life only in the 14-county area of central Minnesota. Focus is on activities that support resilient businesses, thriving communities, effective organizations and local philanthropy.
Fields of interest: Environment, water pollution; Children/youth, services; Family services; Human services; Civil rights, race/intergroup relations; Community development, public/private ventures; Economic development; Nonprofit management; Community/economic development.
Type of support: General/operating support; Program development; Seed money; Technical assistance; Program-related investments/loans; Scholarships—to individuals; Matching/challenge support.
Limitations: Applications accepted. Giving limited to Benton, Cass, Chisago, Crow Wing, Isanti, Kanabec, Mille Lacs, Morrison, Pine, Sherburne, Stearns, Todd, Wadena, and Wright counties, MN. No support for religious programs. No grants to individuals (except for scholarships) or for continuing support, endowments, capital expenses, curriculum development, or video production.
Publications: Application guidelines; Annual report; Grants list; Informational brochure; Program policy statement; Quarterly report.
Application information: Visit foundation website for application information. Contact Don Hickman, VP for Community and Economic Development, for information concerning the foundation's business financing programs. Application form required.

Initial approach: Complete online Letter of Inquiry for general grants
Deadline(s): Feb. 28, May 9, Sept. 5, and Nov. 21 for full proposals
Board meeting date(s): Mar., June, Sept., and Dec.
Final notification: Within 45 days

Officers and Directors:* Linda Eich DesJardins,* Chair.; Larry Korf,* Vice-Chair.; Kathy Gaalswyk,* Pres.; Don Hickman,* V.P., Community and Economic Devel.; Linda Holliday,* V.P., Organization Devel.; Eric Stommes, V.P., External Rels.; Lynn Bushinger,* Treas. and C.F.O.; John E. Babcock; John J. Babcock; Mayuli Bales; Rick Bauerly; Charles Black Lance; Reggie Clow; Pat Gorham; Lee Hanson; Dan Meyer; Dr. Earl Potter; Steve Shurts; Traci Tapani; Wayne Wolden.
Number of staff: 13 full-time professional; 1 part-time professional; 8 full-time support.
EIN: 363451562

4680
The Jennings Family Foundation, Inc. ✧ ☆

(formerly The Prophet Corporation Foundation)
c/o National Christian Foundation
730 2nd St. S., Ste. 415
Minneapolis, MN 55402 (612) 288-2292

Donors: The Prophet Corp.; Joel Jennings; Mary Lee Jennings; Genesis Apparel, Inc.; Gopher Sport.
Foundation type: Company-sponsored foundation.
Financial data (yr. ended 12/31/13): Assets, $7,671,344 (M); gifts received, $200,000; expenditures, $828,091; qualifying distributions, $763,297; giving activities include $751,600 for 22 grants (high: $250,500; low: $2,500).
Purpose and activities: The foundation supports hospitals and organizations involved with Alzheimer's disease, hunger, housing development, human services, Christianity, and economically disadvantaged people.
Fields of interest: Health care; Health organizations; Human services.
Type of support: General/operating support.
Limitations: Applications accepted. Giving primarily in Minneapolis and Owatonna, MN.
Application information: Application form not required.

Initial approach: Proposal
Deadline(s): None

Officer: Joel Jennings, Pres.
Director: Mary Lee Jennings.
EIN: 411765206
Selected grants: The following grants are a representative sample of this grantmaker's funding activity:
$24,020 to Fellowship of Christian Athletes, Kansas City, MO, 2012. For gifts and sponsorships.
$20,000 to Minnesota Medical Foundation, Minneapolis, MN, 2012. For Gamble Professorship Fund.

4681
Jerome Foundation ✧

400 Sibley St., Ste. 125
St. Paul, MN 55101-1928 (651) 224-9431
Contact: Cynthia A. Gehrig, Pres.
FAX: (651) 224-3439; E-mail: info@jeromefdn.org; Toll-free tel.: (800) 995-3766 (MN and New York City only); Main URL: http://www.jeromefdn.org

Incorporated in 1964 in MN.
Donor: J. Jerome Hill†.
Foundation type: Independent foundation.
Financial data (yr. ended 04/30/14): Assets, $94,556,666 (M); gifts received, $35,000; expenditures, $4,684,568; qualifying distributions, $4,425,069; giving activities include $3,106,040 for 102+ grants (high: $216,000), $491,220 for 65 grants to individuals (high: $30,000; low: $950), and $3,213,390 for 4 foundation-administered programs.
Purpose and activities: The foundation seeks to contribute to a dynamic and evolving culture by supporting the creation, development, and production of new works by emerging artists. Foundation programs include: dance, film/video/new media, literature, multidisciplinary, music, theater and the visual arts.
Fields of interest: Media, film/video; Visual arts; Performing arts; Performing arts, dance; Performing arts, theater; Performing arts, music; Literature; Arts.
Type of support: Film/video/radio; General/operating support; Continuing support; Program development; Publication; Seed money; Fellowships; Research; Technical assistance; Program-related investments/loans; Grants to individuals.
Limitations: Applications accepted. Giving limited to MN and the 5 boroughs of New York City, NY. No support for educational programs in the arts and humanities. No grants to individuals (except for Film and Video program, and Travel and Study Grant program) or for undergraduate or graduate student research projects, capital or endowment funds, equipment, scholarships, or matching gifts.
Publications: Application guidelines; Financial statement; Grants list; Informational brochure (including application guidelines).
Application information: Applicants may request funding only for expenses associated with supporting emerging New York, NY or MN-based artists. The foundation accepts applications from arts organizations and artist groups using fiscal sponsors. Minnesota Council on Foundations Common Grant Application Form accepted. Application form required.

Initial approach: See foundation website
Copies of proposal: 1
Deadline(s): See foundation website
Board meeting date(s): 4 times per year
Final notification: 4 to 5 months

Officers and Directors:* Charles Zelle,* Chair.; Calogero Salvo, Vice-Chair.; Cynthia A. Gehrig, Pres.; Barbara H. McLanahan,* Secy.; Gary Nan Tie, Treas.; Philip Bither; Carlyle Brown; Patricia Hampl; Elizabeth Streb.
Number of staff: 3 full-time professional; 3 full-time support.
EIN: 416035163
Selected grants: The following grants are a representative sample of this grantmaker's funding activity:
$154,460 to Minnesota Historical Society, Saint Paul, MN, 2013. For Jerome Hill Papers Collection.
$130,000 to Northern Lights.mn, Minneapolis, MN, 2013. For Art(ists) on the Verge Fellowship Program.
$100,000 to American Composers Forum, Saint Paul, MN, 2013. For Jerome Fund for New Music and The Minnesota Emerging Composer Awards Program.
$90,000 to Playwrights Center, Minneapolis, MN, 2013. For Many Voices Fellowship Program.
$68,000 to Forecast Public Artworks, Saint Paul, MN, 2013. For Artist Services Grant Program.
$52,000 to Loft Literary Center, Minneapolis, MN, 2013. For Mentor Series.
$40,000 to Franklin Furnace Archive, Brooklyn, NY, 2013. For Franklin Furnace Fund.
$40,000 to New Dramatists, New York, NY, 2013. For Playwrights Lab and Composer-Librettist Studio.
$40,000 to Open Channels New York, New York, NY, 2013. For Mondo Cane Commissioning Program and Artist-In-Residence Program.
$20,000 to Haleakala, New York, NY, 2013. For Emerging Artists' Commissions.

4682
The George F. Jewett Foundation ✧ ☆

c/o FCI
30 E. 7th St., Ste. 2000
St. Paul, MN 55101-4930

Established in 2010 in CA.
Donor: George F. Jewett, Jr.†.
Foundation type: Independent foundation.
Financial data (yr. ended 12/31/13): Assets, $26,936,736 (M); expenditures, $1,302,539; qualifying distributions, $1,201,243; giving activities include $1,076,000 for 49 grants (high: $60,000; low: $5,000).
Fields of interest: Arts; Education; Human services; Foundations (community).
Limitations: Applications not accepted.
Application information: Contributes only to pre-selected organizations.

Officers and Directors:* George F. Jewett III,* Pres.; Betsy Jewett,* C.F.O. and Secy.; Richard T. Gill; Brenda C. Jewett; Lucille M. Jewett.
EIN: 273409281

4683
Lloyd K. Johnson Foundation ✧
130 W. Superior St., Ste. 710
Duluth, MN 55802-4035 (218) 726-9000
Contact: Joan Gardner-Goodno, Exec. Dir.
FAX: (218) 726-9002;
E-mail: jgardner@lloydkjohnsonfoundation.org; Main URL: http://www.lloydkjohnsonfoundation.org/

Established in 1975 in MN.
Donor: Lloyd K. Johnson.
Foundation type: Independent foundation.
Financial data (yr. ended 12/31/12): Assets, $19,999,830 (M); gifts received, $150; expenditures, $1,133,046; qualifying distributions, $1,036,960; giving activities include $911,157 for 71 grants (high: $60,000; low: $20).
Purpose and activities: Support for: 1) Arts and Culture, primarily activities that contribute to the creation and development of a healthy and vibrant arts community including new and traditional forms of the visual, performing, and interdisciplinary arts; 2) Community and Economic Development causes that enhance the economic and social well-being of all residents, and to support opportunities for economic self-sufficiency, particularly for low-income individuals and families; 3) Educational activities that contribute to the development and advancement of quality educational and training opportunities, and promote opportunities for life-long learning; 4) Environmental projects that support educational programs that promote respect for the natural environment, and encourage efforts to maintain quality air, water and land resources for future generations; and 5) Social Welfare programs that support the health and well-being of all members of the community, and support activities that promote healthy youth development.
Fields of interest: Arts; Education; Environment; Human services; Economic development; Community/economic development.
Type of support: General/operating support; Building/renovation; Program development.
Limitations: Applications accepted. Giving limited to organizations benefiting residents within Cook, Lake, and southern St. Louis counties, MN, including the communities of Duluth, Hermantown, and Proctor. No support for political organizations. No grants to individuals, or for endowments, debt reduction, loans or research.
Publications: Application guidelines; Annual report; Grants list.
Application information: Letters of Intent and full proposals are by invitation only. Application form required.
Initial approach: Telephone or e-mail to determine if the project is consistent with the foundation's goals and interests
Deadline(s): None for letter of intent. For grant application: Jan. 15, Apr. 15, July 15 and Oct. 15
Board meeting date(s): Mar., June, Sept., and Dec.
Final notification: Within 2 months after submittal
Officers and Directors:* Mark Smithson,* C.E.O. and Pres.; Bill Hansen, V.P.; Scott Harrison, C.F.O. and Treas.; Joan Gardner-Goodno, Exec. Dir.; Darryl E. Coons; Ruth Ann Eaton; Heidi Johnson; Susan Michels.
Number of staff: 1 full-time professional.
EIN: 510180842
Selected grants: The following grants are a representative sample of this grantmaker's funding activity:
$30,000 to Cook County Higher Education, Grand Marais, MN, 2012. For Academic Warrior Project.
$25,000 to Arrowhead Regional Corrections, Duluth, MN, 2012. For Juvenile Detention Alternatives Init.
$25,000 to Program for Aid to Victims of Sexual Assault, Duluth, MN, 2012. For Trafficking Awareness Program.
$20,000 to Men as Peacemakers, Duluth, MN, 2012. For Duluth Champion's Initiative.
$15,000 to Community Action Duluth, Duluth, MN, 2012. For Circles @ Work/Getting Ahead Program.
$11,580 to Hartley Nature Center, Duluth, MN, 2012. For extension to classroom.
$10,000 to Community Action Duluth, Duluth, MN, 2012. For Seeds of Success Operating Support.
$10,000 to Nature Conservancy, Minneapolis, MN, 2012. For sustainability project.
$10,000 to Safe Haven Shelter for Battered Women, Duluth, MN, 2012. For organization rebranding.
$5,860 to Duluth Library Foundation, Duluth, MN, 2012. For outdoor furniture.

4684
The Jostens Foundation, Inc. ✧
3601 Minnesota Dr., Ste. 400
Minneapolis, MN 55435-5281 (952) 830-3235
Contact: Veronica Sanderson, Secy.
E-mail: foundation@jostens.com; Main URL: http://www.jostens.com/misc/aboutus/about_jostens_cp_involvement.html

Established in 1976 in MN.
Donor: Jostens, Inc.
Foundation type: Company-sponsored foundation.
Financial data (yr. ended 12/31/13): Assets, $184,840 (M); gifts received, $500,000; expenditures, $436,103; qualifying distributions, $436,103; giving activities include $391,858 for 313 grants (high: $25,000; low: $25), and $30,000 for 13 grants to individuals (high: $5,000; low: $2,500).
Purpose and activities: The foundation supports organizations involved with education and youth development.
Fields of interest: Elementary/secondary education; Higher education; Education, drop-out prevention; Education, reading; Education; Youth development.
Type of support: General/operating support; Program development; Employee matching gifts; Employee-related scholarships.
Limitations: Applications accepted. Giving in areas of company operations, with emphasis on MN. No support for schools, school districts, or school foundations, organizations involved with highly political or controversial issues, churches or religious groups, or fraternal, veterans', or professional organizations. No grants to individuals (except for employee-related scholarships), or for personal needs, political campaigns or political lobbying activities, benefit fundraising events or tickets to fundraisers, recognition or testimonial events, disease-specific fundraising campaigns, athletic scholarships or activities, advertising, endowments, or capital campaigns.
Publications: Application guidelines; Informational brochure (including application guidelines); Program policy statement.
Application information: Requests may be submitted using the Minnesota Common Grant Form. Application form required.
Initial approach: Proposal
Copies of proposal: 1
Deadline(s): Feb. 22, May 24, Aug. 23, and Nov. 22.
Board meeting date(s): Quarterly
Final notification: Within 1 month of board meetings
Officers and Directors:* Charley Nelson, Pres.; Veronica Sanderson, Secy.; Randall Wilson, Treas.; Tricia Bishop; Sheri Hank; Aaron Kjolhaug; Marin Koentopf; Lindsey Robertson; Natalie Stute.
EIN: 411280587
Selected grants: The following grants are a representative sample of this grantmaker's funding activity:
$10,000 to 360 Communities, Burnsville, MN, 2012. For funding for Partners for Success Program which works with preschool-12th grade students who are struggling in school, and their families to create a home environment that encourages learning Family Support Workers work with students, parents, and teachers.
$10,000 to Centro Campesino, Owatonna, MN, 2012. For funding for the Latino College Access Program - initiative that provides personalized information, assistance, guidance and education to Latino students and their parents in southern Minnesota The goal is increase the number of Latino students going to.
$10,000 to Life House, Duluth, MN, 2012. For Funding would help at risk and homeless youth achieve success in school, work and life Program helps disadvantaged students improve graduation rates and prepare for college.
$7,500 to Phyllis Wheatley Community Center, Minneapolis, MN, 2012. For Funding to support academic achievement Program, which provides literacy tutoring and parent academy in order close the achievement gap for students at Bethune Community School and Lucy Craft Laney School in North Minneapolis.
$5,000 to Bolder Options, Minneapolis, MN, 2012. To support Youth Mentoring Program focusing on the needs of low-income and/or at risk youth, ages 10-14, with Locations in Minneapolis, St Paul and Rochester, MN B O is physically active, academic tutoring, goal setting, healthy lifestyles and volunteerism in comm.
$5,000 to Topeka Youth Project, Topeka, KS, 2012. For Funds for the jobs for Young Adults Program job readiness/Life Skills workshops for 16-20 year olds offered monthly with 90% gaining unsubsidized employment Emphasis on poverty/low income youth.
$5,000 to Way to Grow, Minneapolis, MN, 2012. For Funding will support the early childhood and elementary learning Program for at risk children and families in Minneapolis Targeted population served Low income families with children from birth up to 3rd grade, including expectant parents.
$5,000 to YouthCARE, Minneapolis, MN, 2012. For funding for Styling Science , technology, engineering and math (STEM) Program This is a primary component of our very successful Young Women's Mentoring Program The grant would be used to help

cover the basis associated with providing STEM learn.
$2,500 to Tubman, Minneapolis, MN, 2012. For Funding to support violence prevention education and community engagement training Pop served Youth ages 13-18.
$50 to American Cancer Society, Oakland, CA, 2012. For employee matching.

4685
K.A.H.R. Foundation ✧
4305 Trillum Way
Minnetrista, MN 55364-7708
Contact: Kerri Bawek, Secy.

Established in 2005 in MN.
Donor: Jeannine Rivet.
Foundation type: Independent foundation.
Financial data (yr. ended 12/31/13): Assets, $39,786,325 (M); expenditures, $1,839,121; qualifying distributions, $1,718,661; giving activities include $1,521,063 for 18 grants (high: $300,000; low: $10,000).
Fields of interest: Education; Health care; Military/veterans.
Limitations: Applications not accepted. Giving primarily in MN. No grants to individuals.
Application information: Unsolicited requests for funds not accepted.
Officers: Jeannine M. Rivet, Pres.; Warren Herreid II, V.P. and Treas.; Kerri Bawek, Secy.; Jadi Gray; Nikki Herreid Ness.
EIN: 432093439

4686
Margaret H. and James E. Kelley Foundation, Inc. ✧
408 Saint Peter St., Ste. 425
St. Paul, MN 55102-1187 (651) 222-7463
Contact: Timothy J. Dwyer, Treas. and Dir.
E-mail: timdwyer@visi.com

Established in 1960 in MN.
Donors: Cynthia Kelley O'Neill Children's Trust; M.H. Kelley Grandchildren Trust.
Foundation type: Independent foundation.
Financial data (yr. ended 11/30/13): Assets, $18,591,749 (M); expenditures, $947,294; qualifying distributions, $850,000; giving activities include $850,000 for grants.
Purpose and activities: Giving primarily for human rights, medical disciplines, family planning and social services; support also for higher education and a community fund.
Fields of interest: Arts; Law school/education; Hospitals (specialty); Reproductive health, family planning; Health care; Human services; Children/youth, services; International affairs; Civil liberties, advocacy; United Ways and Federated Giving Programs; Disabilities, people with.
Type of support: General/operating support; Continuing support; Annual campaigns; Capital campaigns; Equipment; Program development; Professorships; Scholarship funds.
Limitations: Applications accepted. Giving primarily in MN; some funding nationally. No grants to individuals.
Publications: Annual report (including application guidelines); Grants list.
Application information: Application form required.
Initial approach: Request application form
Copies of proposal: 1
Deadline(s): Oct. 1
Board meeting date(s): Varies
Officers and Directors:* Kelley McC. O'Neill,* Pres.; Hampton K. O'Neill,* V.P.; Timothy J. Dwyer,* Treas.; Cindy Wolf O'Neill; Sher M. O'Neill.
Number of staff: 2 part-time professional.
EIN: 416017973
Selected grants: The following grants are a representative sample of this grantmaker's funding activity:
$100,000 to Hamm Memorial Psychiatric Clinic, Saint Paul, MN, 2011.
$35,000 to William Mitchell College of Law, Saint Paul, MN, 2011.
$25,000 to NRA Foundation, Fairfax, VA, 2011.
$20,000 to Minnesota Medical Foundation, Minneapolis, MN, 2011.
$15,000 to Habitat for Humanity, Twin Cities, Saint Paul, MN, 2011.
$15,000 to Park Square Theater, Saint Paul, MN, 2011.
$10,000 to Cato Institute, Washington, DC, 2011.
$10,000 to International Rescue Committee, New York, NY, 2011.
$10,000 to United Way of Natrona County, Casper, WY, 2011.
$10,000 to YMCA, Winona Family, Winona, MN, 2011.

4687
Peter J. King Family Foundation ✧
3001 Broadway St. N.E., Ste. 665
Minneapolis, MN 55413-2297 (612) 884-0270
FAX: (612) 884-0241;
E-mail: info@pjkingfamilyfoundation.org; Main URL: http://www.pjkingfamilyfoundation.org/

Established in 1985 in MN.
Donor: Peter J. King‡.
Foundation type: Independent foundation.
Financial data (yr. ended 11/30/13): Assets, $83,268,884 (M); expenditures, $2,478,129; qualifying distributions, $1,779,718; giving activities include $1,321,273 for 20 grants (high: $400,000; low: $1,000).
Purpose and activities: The foundation's focus is to provide brick-and-mortar facilities to local communities and organizations whose activities are dedicated to the improvement of children's health, education and welfare and the family environment.
Fields of interest: Elementary/secondary education; Education, early childhood education; Hospitals (general); Medical care, outpatient care; Health care, support services; Health care, EMS; Youth development, centers/clubs; Youth development, adult & child programs; Children/youth, services; Family services.
Type of support: General/operating support; Capital campaigns; Building/renovation; Equipment; Land acquisition; Matching/challenge support.
Limitations: Applications accepted. Giving primarily in the Twin Cities, MN metropolitan area; some giving also in Tanzania. No grants for programming needs.
Application information: See foundation web site for complete application guidelines. Application form required.
Officers and Directors:* Russell S. King,* Pres.; Stephen D. Higgins,* Secy.; James C. Teal; James A. Weichert.
EIN: 261600569

4688
Kopp Family Foundation ✧
(formerly Caring and Sharing Foundation, Inc.)
8400 Normandale Lake Blvd., Ste. 1450
Bloomington, MN 55437-3837 (952) 841-0438
Contact: Lindsey Lang, Admin.
FAX: (952) 841-0411;
E-mail: foundation@koppinvestments.com

Established in 1986 in MN.
Donors: LeRoy Kopp; Barbara Kopp.
Foundation type: Independent foundation.
Financial data (yr. ended 12/31/13): Assets, $13,762,473 (M); expenditures, $1,800,425; qualifying distributions, $9,401,352; giving activities include $1,325,632 for grants.
Purpose and activities: Giving primarily for education and human services.
Fields of interest: Elementary/secondary education; Human services; Children/youth, services; Catholic agencies & churches; Disabilities, people with.
Type of support: General/operating support; Annual campaigns; Capital campaigns; Emergency funds; Scholarship funds; Matching/challenge support.
Limitations: Giving primarily in MN. No grants to individuals.
Publications: Annual report (including application guidelines).
Application information: The foundation accepts the Minnesota Common Grant Application Form. Application form required.
Initial approach: Letter of inquiry from a new organization
Copies of proposal: 1
Deadline(s): None
Board meeting date(s): Every other month
Final notification: Within 2 months
Directors: Barbara Kopp; Kristin Kopp; LeRoy Kopp.
Number of staff: 1 full-time professional.
EIN: 363485918
Selected grants: The following grants are a representative sample of this grantmaker's funding activity:
$25,000 to Normandale Community College Foundation, Bloomington, MN, 2012. For Toast of the Town.
$7,500 to North Hennepin Community College Foundation, Brooklyn Park, MN, 2012. For additional scholarships.
$5,000 to City of Lakes Community Land Trust, Minneapolis, MN, 2012. For affordable housing.
$4,000 to MacPhail Center for Music, Minneapolis, MN, 2012. For Pathways to Performance.
$3,500 to Simpson Housing Services, Minneapolis, MN, 2012. For Women's Housing Partnership.
$3,000 to Catholic Eldercare, Minneapolis, MN, 2012. For affordable housing for low income seniors.
$3,000 to Friendship Ventures, Annandale, MN, 2012. For program scholarships.
$2,000 to Canvas Health, Oakdale, MN, 2012. For Community call center.
$2,000 to Episcopal Community Services, Minneapolis, MN, 2012. For Supportive Housing Program.
$1,000 to Yinghua Academy, Minneapolis, MN, 2012. For Rak.

4689
Ida C. Koran Trust ✧
c/o Ecolab Inc.
370 Wabasha St. N.
St. Paul, MN 55102-1323 (651) 293-2392
FAX: (651) 452-0485;
E-mail: Sue@idakorantrust.org; Main URL: http://idakoran.com/

Established around 1992.
Donor: Ida Koran†.
Foundation type: Independent foundation.
Financial data (yr. ended 12/31/13): Assets, $45,065,176 (M); expenditures, $1,990,996; qualifying distributions, $2,157,254; giving activities include $1,510,137 for grants to individuals, and $417,147 for loans to individuals.
Purpose and activities: Academic assistance to dependents of Ecolab employees, and hardship grants and loans to employees of Ecolab, Inc., MN.
Fields of interest: Education; Human services, emergency aid.
Type of support: General/operating support; Scholarship funds; Grants to individuals.
Limitations: Giving primarily in MN.
Publications: Application guidelines.
Application information: Only Ecolab, Inc., employees are eligible for grant awards. See foundation web site for guidelines.
Trustees: Diana D. Lewis; Stanley Osborn; U.S. Bank, N.A.
EIN: 416124022

4690
Jerome and Marlyce Koskovich Foundation ✧ ☆
3321 County Rd., 15 S.W.
Byron, MN 55920-6403 (507) 286-9209
Contact: Jerome Koskovich, Dir.

Established in 2005 in MN.
Donors: Jerome Koskovich; Marlyce Koskovich.
Foundation type: Independent foundation.
Financial data (yr. ended 06/30/13): Assets, $3,215,854 (M); expenditures, $590,582; qualifying distributions, $587,500; giving activities include $587,500 for 18 grants (high: $100,000; low: $2,500).
Purpose and activities: Giving primarily to Baptist churches and organizations.
Fields of interest: Education; Human services; Protestant agencies & churches.
Limitations: Applications accepted. Giving primarily in MN and MT.
Application information:
Initial approach: Proposal
Deadline(s): None
Directors: Jerome Koskovich; Marlyce Koskovich.
EIN: 202051209
Selected grants: The following grants are a representative sample of this grantmaker's funding activity:
$100,000 to Baptist College of Ministry, Menomonee Falls, WI, 2011.
$40,000 to Yellowstone Baptist College, Billings, MT, 2011. For general support.
$24,000 to Ironwood Springs Christian Ranch, Stewartville, MN, 2011.
$3,500 to Christian Veterinary Mission, Seattle, WA, 2011.

4691
Land O'Lakes Foundation ✧
P.O. Box 64150
St. Paul, MN 55164-0150
Contact: Lydia Botham, Exec. Dir.
E-mail: mlatkins-sakry@landolakes.com; Contact for California Regions Grant Prog., Mid-Atlantic Grants Prog., and John Brandt Scholarship Program: LandOLakesFoundation@LandOLakes.com; Additional contact: Martha Atkins-Sakry, Exec. Asst., tel.: (651) 375-2470; Main URL: http://www.foundation.landolakes.com/

Established in 1996 in MN.
Donor: Land O'Lakes, Inc.
Foundation type: Company-sponsored foundation.
Financial data (yr. ended 12/31/12): Assets, $10,546,206 (M); gifts received, $2,885,503; expenditures, $3,134,989; qualifying distributions, $3,066,955; giving activities include $2,848,785 for 1,400 grants (high: $25,000; low: $125).
Purpose and activities: The foundation supports organizations involved with arts and culture, education, human services, civic improvements, and youth and awards graduate scholarships to graduate students studying the dairy sciences. Special emphasis is directed toward programs designed to alleviate rural hunger.
Fields of interest: Media, film/video; Media, television; Visual arts; Performing arts; Literature; Arts; Elementary/secondary education; Higher education; Libraries (public); Education; Environment, water resources; Environment, land resources; Environment, plant conservation; Hospitals (general); Agriculture, sustainable programs; Food services; Food banks; Nutrition; Agriculture/food; Disasters, fire prevention/control; Recreation, parks/playgrounds; Youth development, agriculture; Youth development; Human services; Rural development; Community/economic development; United Ways and Federated Giving Programs; Leadership development; Public affairs; Youth; Native Americans/American Indians.
Type of support: Building/renovation; Capital campaigns; Employee matching gifts; Employee volunteer services; Equipment; General/operating support; Matching/challenge support; Scholarships—to individuals; Seed money.
Limitations: Applications accepted. Giving on a national basis in areas of company operations in AR, CA, IA, ID, IL, IN, KS, MD, MI, MN, MS, MO, ND, NE, OH, OR, PA, SD, TX, WA, and WI; giving also to statewide, regional, and national organizations. No support for lobbying or political organizations, religious organizations not of direct benefit to the entire community, or veterans', fraternal, or labor organizations. No grants to individuals (except for scholarships), or for fundraising events, dinners, or benefits, advertising, higher education capital campaigns or endowments, travel, racing or sports sponsorships, or disease or medical research or treatment.
Publications: Application guidelines; Annual report; Grants list; Informational brochure (including application guidelines); IRS Form 990 or 990-PF printed copy available upon request.
Application information: Application form required.
Initial approach: Complete online application for Community Grants Program; contact a Land O'Lakes dairy farmer or unit delegate for application form for California Regions Grants and Mid-Atlantic Grants; download application and mail for John Memorial Scholarships
Copies of proposal: 1
Deadline(s): May 1 for Education, July 1 for Hunger, and Oct. 2 for all other proposals for the Community Grants Program; None for California Regions Grants and Mid-Atlantic Grants; May 2 for John Brandt Memorial Scholarships
Board meeting date(s): Feb., June, Aug., and Dec.
Final notification: 2 to 4 weeks for California Regions Grants and Mid-Atlantic Grants
Officers and Directors:* Jim Hager,* Chair.; Tom Wakefield, Vice-Chair.; Nancy Breyfogle,* Treas.; Lydia Botham,* Exec. Dir.; Tanya Dowda; John Ellenberger; Pete Janzen; Stephen Mancebo; Ronnie Mohr; Doug Reimer.
Number of staff: 1 full-time professional; 1 full-time support.
EIN: 411864977

4692
David & Janis Larson Foundation ✧
581 N. Stream Rd.
Wayzata, MN 55391

Established in MN.
Donors: David M. Larson; Janis Larson.
Foundation type: Independent foundation.
Financial data (yr. ended 12/31/13): Assets, $21,735,744 (M); gifts received, $2,265; expenditures, $1,131,787; qualifying distributions, $1,119,627; giving activities include $1,106,050 for 6 grants (high: $812,000; low: $20,000).
Fields of interest: Historic preservation/historical societies; Children/youth, services; Family services; Community development, civic centers.
Limitations: Applications not accepted. No grants to individuals.
Application information: Contributes only to pre-selected organizations.
Officers and Directors:* David M. Larson,* Pres.; Janis L. Larson,* Secy.
EIN: 411957525
Selected grants: The following grants are a representative sample of this grantmaker's funding activity:
$1,234,500 to University of Minnesota Foundation, Minneapolis, MN, 2012. For Larson Scholars, College of Liberal Arts, and Football Program in the Department Of.

4693
The Legacy of Angels ✧
104 10th Ave. S.E.
Waseca, MN 56093-3122 (507) 833-8144
Contact: Paul Rosenau, Co-Chair.; Susan Rosenau, Co-Chair.

Donors: Paul Rosenau; Susan Rosenau.
Foundation type: Independent foundation.
Financial data (yr. ended 12/31/13): Assets, $35,951,608 (M); gifts received, $100,075; expenditures, $1,575,287; qualifying distributions, $1,486,630; giving activities include $1,475,013 for 9 grants (high: $300,004; low: $7,503).
Purpose and activities: Giving primarily for childhood diseases and for newborn screening for disease, particularly Krabbe's and cystic fibrosis.
Fields of interest: Hospitals (general); Hospitals (specialty); Health care; Pediatrics; Pediatrics research; Medical research.

Limitations: Applications accepted. Giving primarily in Pittsburgh, PA; some giving also in Philadelphia, PA and in Madison and Milwaukee, WI.
Application information: Application form required.
Initial approach: Letter
Deadline(s): None
Officers: Paul Rosenau, Co-Chair. and Co-Treas.; Susan Rosenau, Co-Chair.; Stacy Pike, Co-Secy.; Brett Rosenau, Co-Secy.; Heather Techmeier, Co-Treas.
Board Member: Dale Deraad.
EIN: 263070514
Selected grants: The following grants are a representative sample of this grantmaker's funding activity:
$193,373 to Thomas Jefferson University, Philadelphia, PA, 2012. For Research to Better Treat Krabbe's Disease.
$99,597 to Medical College of Wisconsin, Milwaukee, WI, 2012. For Research for Quality Improvement in Cystic Fibrosis Newborn Screening.

4694
The Leonard Street and Deinard Foundation ✧
c/o Steven Brandl
150 S. 5th St., Ste. 2300
Minneapolis, MN 55402-4223
Main URL: http://www.leonard.com/about/foundation
RSS Feed: http://www.leonard.com/rss/newspubs.xml

Established in 1982 in MN.
Donor: Shareholders of Leonard Street and Deinard.
Foundation type: Company-sponsored foundation.
Financial data (yr. ended 12/31/13): Assets, $101,984 (M); gifts received, $401,592; expenditures, $458,377; qualifying distributions, $457,522; giving activities include $456,600 for 118 grants (high: $60,000; low: $100).
Purpose and activities: Support for major community institutions and legal organizations providing legal aid.
Fields of interest: Arts; Legal services; Crime/law enforcement; Community/economic development.
Type of support: General/operating support; Annual campaigns; Program-related investments/loans.
Limitations: Applications not accepted. Giving primarily in DC, MN, ND, SD, and WI. No support for clubs, or government agencies, personal charities, political campaigns, religious or fraternal organizations, athletic groups, or schools. No grants to individuals, or for fundraisers, or competitions.
Application information: Contributes only to pre-selected organizations.
Directors: Tim Pabst; Barbara Portwood; Tom Sanders; Michael Taylor.
Number of staff: None.
EIN: 411446976
Selected grants: The following grants are a representative sample of this grantmaker's funding activity:
$60,000 to United Way, Greater Twin Cities, Minneapolis, MN, 2011.
$33,500 to Legal Aid Society of Minneapolis, Minneapolis, MN, 2011.
$15,000 to Guthrie Theater, Minneapolis, MN, 2011.
$10,000 to Saint Paul Chamber Orchestra Society, Saint Paul, MN, 2011.
$9,500 to Minnesota Justice Foundation, Minneapolis, MN, 2011.
$6,500 to Southern Minnesota Regional Legal Services, Saint Paul, MN, 2011.
$3,000 to Walker Art Center, Minneapolis, MN, 2011.

4695
Steven C. Leuthold Family Foundation ✧
33 S. 6th St., Ste. 4600
Minneapolis, MN 55402-3718 (612) 332-1567
Contact: Steven C. Leuthold, Dir.
E-mail: cshultz2186@aol.com

Established in 1990 in MN.
Donors: Steven C. Leuthold; Russell Leuthold.
Foundation type: Independent foundation.
Financial data (yr. ended 12/31/13): Assets, $41,534,065 (M); gifts received, $4,071,058; expenditures, $5,327,845; qualifying distributions, $5,198,571; giving activities include $5,000,000 for 167 grants (high: $2,500,000; low: $1,000).
Purpose and activities: Giving primarily for education, health organizations, nature conservation, animal welfare, and children and social services.
Fields of interest: Environment, natural resources; Environment; Animal welfare; Animals/wildlife; Health organizations, association; Human services; Children/youth, services.
Limitations: Giving primarily in ID, MN, ME, IA, and AZ for regional charities. No support for religious or political organizations. No grants to individuals.
Application information:
Initial approach: E-mail
Deadline(s): None
Board meeting date(s): Varies
Directors: Dr. Linda Leuthold Donerkiel; Kurt Leuthold; Michael Leuthold; Russell Leuthold; Steven C. Leuthold.
Number of staff: 1 part-time support.
EIN: 411680986
Selected grants: The following grants are a representative sample of this grantmaker's funding activity:
$11,000 to Boys and Girls Clubs of Tucson, Tucson, AZ, 2011.

4696
Richard Coyle Lilly Foundation ✧
c/o Trust Tax Services
P.O. Box 64713
St. Paul, MN 55164-0713
Application address: c/o Peter Kenefick, 101 E. 5th St., St. Paul, MN 55101, tel.: (651) 466-8213

Incorporated in 1941 in MN.
Donor: Richard C. Lilly†.
Foundation type: Independent foundation.
Financial data (yr. ended 12/31/13): Assets, $20,078,602 (M); expenditures, $1,163,273; qualifying distributions, $974,935; giving activities include $931,500 for 54 grants (high: $315,000; low: $1,000).
Purpose and activities: Emphasis on higher and environmental education, culture, youth, and social services.
Fields of interest: Arts; Higher education; Environment, natural resources; Environment; Human services; Children/youth, services.
Type of support: General/operating support; Continuing support; Annual campaigns; Building/renovation; Equipment; Land acquisition; Endowments; Program development; Publication; Seed money; Research; Matching/challenge support.
Limitations: Applications accepted. Giving primarily in St. Paul, MN. No grants to individuals, or for fellowships or scholarships; no loans.
Application information: Application form required.
Initial approach: Letter
Deadline(s): None
Board meeting date(s): Dec.
Officers: David M. Lilly, Pres.; Susanne Lilly Hutcheşon, V.P.; David M. Lilly, Jr., V.P.; Peter R. Kenefick, Secy.; Bruce A. Lilly, Treas.
EIN: 416038717
Selected grants: The following grants are a representative sample of this grantmaker's funding activity:
$152,500 to Planned Parenthood of Minnesota, North Dakota, South Dakota, Minneapolis, MN, 2011. For general support.
$50,000 to Metropolitan State University Foundation, Saint Paul, MN, 2011. For general support.
$40,000 to K T C A/K T C I Twin Cities Public Television, Saint Paul, MN, 2011. For general support.
$40,000 to Saint Paul Academy and Summit School, Saint Paul, MN, 2011. For general support.
$34,000 to Ordway Center for the Performing Arts, Saint Paul, MN, 2011. For general support.
$15,000 to Family Partnership, Minneapolis, MN, 2011. For general support.
$10,500 to Dartmouth College, Hanover, NH, 2011. For general support.
$7,500 to Minnesota Opera, Minneapolis, MN, 2011. For general support.
$5,000 to YWCA of Saint Paul, Saint Paul, MN, 2011. For general support.
$1,000 to Nantucket Cottage Hospital, Nantucket, MA, 2011. For general support.

4697
Lored Foundation ✧ ☆
200 S. 6th St., No. 4000
Minneapolis, MN 55402-1431

Established in 1998 in MN.
Donors: Anne B. Zink; Phillip L. Zink.
Foundation type: Independent foundation.
Financial data (yr. ended 12/31/13): Assets, $6,420,687 (M); expenditures, $610,108; qualifying distributions, $561,000; giving activities include $561,000 for 3 grants (high: $450,000; low: $36,000).
Fields of interest: Recreation; Human services.
Limitations: Applications not accepted. No grants to individuals.
Application information: Contributes only to pre-selected organizations.
Officers and Directors:* Anne B. Zink,* Pres.; Phillip L. Zink,* Secy.
EIN: 411924853

4698
The Luther Family Foundation ✧
3701 Alabama Ave. S.
St. Louis Park, MN 55416-5156 (952) 258-8800
Contact: Charles David Luther, Tr.

Established in 1994 in MN.
Donors: Charles David Luther; Rudy Dan Luther; Bloomington Acura; Luther Family Ford; Rudy Luther Toyota; Luther Nissan Kia; Barb Hilbert.
Foundation type: Independent foundation.
Financial data (yr. ended 12/31/13): Assets, $9,551,096 (M); gifts received, $300,000; expenditures, $563,172; qualifying distributions, $505,207; giving activities include $503,520 for 33 grants (high: $90,000; low: $1,000).
Fields of interest: Health organizations; Autism; Human services; Christian agencies & churches.
Limitations: Applications accepted. Giving primarily in MN.
Application information: Application form required.
Initial approach: Proposal
Deadline(s): None
Trustees: Barb Hilbert; Charles David Luther; Rudy Dan Luther.
EIN: 411798367

4699
Maas Foundation ✧ ☆
4910 Lincoln Dr.
Edina, MN 55436-1071

Established in 1986 in SD.
Donor: George E. Maas.
Foundation type: Independent foundation.
Financial data (yr. ended 12/31/13): Assets, $6,492,248 (M); expenditures, $433,334; qualifying distributions, $433,334; giving activities include $433,334 for 11 grants (high: $200,000; low: $5,000).
Fields of interest: Higher education; Hospitals (general); Health care; Human services; Catholic agencies & churches.
Type of support: Annual campaigns; Building/renovation; Scholarship funds.
Limitations: Applications not accepted. Giving primarily in IN and MN. No grants to individuals.
Application information: Unsolicited requests for funds not accepted.
Officer and Trustees:* George E. Maas,* Pres.; Thomas K. Berg; Patricia A. Maas.
EIN: 460393558
Selected grants: The following grants are a representative sample of this grantmaker's funding activity:
$25,000 to Academy of Holy Angels, Richfield, MN, 2012. For building fund.

4700
W. Duncan and Nivin MacMillan Foundation ✧ ☆
P.O. Box 5628
Minneapolis, MN 55440-5628

Established in MN.
Donors: Steven A. Hornig; Roger S. Wherry; W. Duncan MacMillan†; Lucy Stitzer.
Foundation type: Independent foundation.
Financial data (yr. ended 12/31/13): Assets, $26,471,303 (M); gifts received, $511,500; expenditures, $1,340,000; qualifying distributions, $1,048,850; giving activities include $1,026,775 for 50 grants (high: $250,000; low: $50).
Fields of interest: Arts; Education; Environment; Hospitals (general).
Limitations: Applications not accepted. Giving primarily in FL and MN.
Application information: Unsolicited requests for funds not accepted.
Officers: Nivin S. Macmillian, Pres.; Steven A. Hornig, Secy.-Treas.
Director: Michella L. Johnson.
EIN: 262162073
Selected grants: The following grants are a representative sample of this grantmaker's funding activity:
$2,000 to Episcopal High School, Bellaire, TX, 2012. For Andrew H. H. Kaufman Scholarship Endowment.

4701
Manitou Fund ✧
c/o Space Center Inc.
2501 Rosegate
St. Paul, MN 55113-2717 (651) 604-4200
Contact: Michael A. Urbanos, Secy. and Tr.

Established in 1966 in MN.
Donors: Donald G. McNeely; Space Center, Inc.
Foundation type: Independent foundation.
Financial data (yr. ended 12/31/13): Assets, $29,782,634 (M); gifts received, $3,000,000; expenditures, $3,003,344; qualifying distributions, $3,001,385; giving activities include $3,000,000 for 1 grant.
Fields of interest: Historic preservation/historical societies; Arts; Education; Human services; Foundations (public); Catholic agencies & churches.
Limitations: Applications accepted. Giving primarily in CA and MN. No grants to individuals.
Application information: Application form required.
Initial approach: Letter
Deadline(s): None
Officers and Trustees:* Mike Urbanos,* Secy.; Paul Puerzer, Treas.; Chas Arend; Cheryl Granlund; Gregory McNeely; Kevin McNeely; Nora McNeely.
EIN: 416055113

4702
Marbrook Foundation ✧
730 2nd Ave. S., Ste. 1300
Minneapolis, MN 55402-2475 (612) 752-1783
Contact: Julie Hara, Exec. Dir.
FAX: (612) 752-1780;
E-mail: jhara@marbrookfoundation.org; Main URL: http://marbrookfoundation.org
Grants Database: http://marbrookfoundation.org/2013-grants/

Established in 1948 in MN.
Donors: Edward Brooks†; Markell C. Brooks†.
Foundation type: Independent foundation.
Financial data (yr. ended 12/31/12): Assets, $14,551,370 (M); expenditures, $954,030; qualifying distributions, $700,000; giving activities include $700,000 for grants.
Purpose and activities: Primary areas of interest include organizations that create equal opportunities for immigrants and refugees in the Twin Cities metropolitan area. Focuses include: 1) Equal opportunity and empowerment; 2) Environmental justice and advocacy for immigrants; 3) Expanding access to healthy food; 4) Academic success for children of immigrants; 5) English language instruction; 6) Cultural preservation for new Americans; 7) Integrating a "mind-body-spirit" approach to the well being of immigrants; and 8) Arts projects that highlight cultural awareness or address social issues of immigrants.
Fields of interest: Arts, cultural/ethnic awareness; Visual arts; Museums; Performing arts; Performing arts, theater; Historic preservation/historical societies; Arts; Elementary school/education; Education; Environment, natural resources; Environment; Employment; Housing/shelter; Human services; Children/youth, services; Community/economic development; Spirituality; Immigrants/refugees.
Type of support: Annual campaigns; Building/renovation; Capital campaigns; Continuing support; Endowments; Equipment; General/operating support; Land acquisition; Matching/challenge support; Professorships; Program development; Research; Scholarship funds.
Limitations: Applications accepted. Giving limited to the Minneapolis-St. Paul, MN, area. No support for political purposes, or for start-up organizations, programs for the elderly, domestic abuse programs, disease-related organizations, homeless shelters, food shelves, or programs servicing the mentally or physically disabled. No grants to individuals, or for early-childhood education, legal services, conferences or events.
Publications: Annual report (including application guidelines); Financial statement; Grants list.
Application information: Complete application guidelines available on foundation web site. Application form required.
Initial approach: Online application on foundation web site
Copies of proposal: 1
Deadline(s): See foundation web site for current deadlines
Board meeting date(s): June and Dec.
Officer: Julie S. Hara, Exec. Dir.
Trustees: Conley Brooks; Conley Brooks, Jr.; Markell C. Brooks; Stephen B. Brooks; Markell Kiefer; Katherine M. Leighton; Julie B. Zelle.
Number of staff: 1 part-time professional.
EIN: 416019899

4703
Mardag Foundation ✧
101 5th St., E., Ste. 2400
St. Paul, MN 55101-1800 (651) 224-5463
Contact: John G. Couchman, Admin. Dir.
FAX: (651) 224-8123; E-mail: inbox@mardag.org; Toll free tel.: (800) 875-6167; Main URL: http://www.mardag.org

Established in 1969 in MN.
Donor: Agnes E. Ober†.
Foundation type: Independent foundation.
Financial data (yr. ended 12/31/12): Assets, $50,824,355 (M); expenditures, $2,722,474; qualifying distributions, $2,371,769; giving activities include $2,087,992 for 110 grants (high: $75,000; low: $3,000).
Purpose and activities: The foundation is committed to making grants to nonprofit organizations that improve the quality of life in Minnesota for children, seniors, and other at-risk populations and also for programs in education and the arts.

Fields of interest: Arts; Child development, education; Elementary school/education; Adult education—literacy, basic skills & GED; Education, reading; Education; Youth development; Human services; Children/youth, services; Child development, services; Aging, centers/services; Aging; Minorities.
Type of support: Capital campaigns; Building/renovation; Equipment; Program development; Seed money; Matching/challenge support.
Limitations: Applications accepted. Giving primarily in the east metropolitan area of Ramsey, Washington, and Dakota counties, MN, and greater MN. No support for programs serving Minneapolis, MN, and the surrounding west metropolitan area. No support for ongoing annual operating expenses, sectarian religious programs, medical research, federated campaigns, conservation or environmental programs, or for programs serving the physically, developmentally or mentally disabled. No grants or scholarships to individuals, or for events and conferences, capital campaigns of private secondary schools, or capital and endowment campaigns of private colleges and universities.
Publications: Application guidelines; Annual report; Financial statement; Grants list; Program policy statement.
Application information: Application requirements are included in the foundation's guidelines, which are available on the foundation web site. Application form required.

Initial approach: 2- to 3- page letter of inquiry or full proposal
Copies of proposal: 1
Deadline(s): Dec. 31 for Apr. meeting, May 1 for Aug. meeting, and Aug. 1 for Nov. meeting
Board meeting date(s): Apr., Aug., and Nov.
Final notification: 4-5 months

Officers and Directors:* Timothy M. Ober,* Pres.; Gretchen D. Davidson,* V.P.; Phyllis Rawls Goff,* Secy.; Richard B. Ober,* Treas.; Janice K. Angell; Robert Davidson; Cornelia Ober Eberhart; Samuel Eberhart; Pat Medure; Gayle M. Ober; Hon. Wilhelmina Wright.
EIN: 411698990

4704
Martin and Brown Foundation ✧
P.O. Box 46286
Plymouth, MN 55446-0286

Established in 2001 in MN.
Donors: Jennifer L. Martin; The Martin Foundation.
Foundation type: Independent foundation.
Financial data (yr. ended 06/30/13): Assets, $11,478,422 (M); expenditures, $621,900; qualifying distributions, $527,500; giving activities include $527,500 for grants.
Purpose and activities: Giving primarily for women's interests, particularly organizations related to health and reproductive rights; giving also for the arts, including journalism and a museum.
Fields of interest: Media, journalism; Museums (art); Arts; Education; Environment; Health care, clinics/centers; Civil liberties, reproductive rights; Women.
Type of support: General/operating support; Continuing support; Annual campaigns; Capital campaigns; Building/renovation; Endowments; Program development; Professorships; Matching/challenge support.
Limitations: Applications not accepted. Giving primarily in Minneapolis, MN. No grants to individuals.
Application information: Unsolicited requests for funds not accepted.
Officers: Jennifer L. Martin, Pres. and Secy.; Tamara M. Brown, V.P.; Ariana M. Brown, Treas.
Directors: Gabrial Brown; Isaac Brown.
EIN: 411997225
Selected grants: The following grants are a representative sample of this grantmaker's funding activity:
$18,000 to Columbia University, School of Journalism, New York, NY, 2013. For general support.
$12,000 to Minnesota Landscape Arboretum, Chaska, MN, 2013. For general support/directorship fund.

4705
McCarthy-Bjorklund Foundation ✧
345 St. Peter St., Rm. 2020
St. Paul, MN 55102-1221

Established in 1994 in MN.
Donor: Alexandra O. Bjorklund.
Foundation type: Independent foundation.
Financial data (yr. ended 12/31/13): Assets, $27,074,181 (M); expenditures, $1,024,920; qualifying distributions, $988,200; giving activities include $988,200 for 98 grants (high: $100,000; low: $1,000).
Purpose and activities: Giving primarily for the arts, education, and human services.
Fields of interest: Museums; Arts; Education; Environment, natural resources; Human services.
Type of support: General/operating support.
Limitations: Applications not accepted. Giving primarily in MN, with emphasis on St. Paul. No grants to individuals.
Application information: Contributes only to pre-selected organizations.
Officers: Alexandra O. Bjorklund, Pres.; Thomas O. McCarthy, Secy.; Edwin J. McCarthy, Treas.
Director: Kathryn M. Parsons.
EIN: 411794941

4706
McGlynn Family Foundation ✧ ☆
P.O. Box 680
Wayzata, MN 55391

Established in 1994 in MN.
Donors: Burton J. McGlynn; Patricia J. McGlynn.
Foundation type: Independent foundation.
Financial data (yr. ended 12/31/13): Assets, $13,783,468 (M); expenditures, $733,835; qualifying distributions, $666,188; giving activities include $655,000 for 35 grants (high: $102,000; low: $1,000).
Fields of interest: Higher education; Human services; United Ways and Federated Giving Programs; Catholic agencies & churches.
Type of support: General/operating support.
Limitations: Applications not accepted. Giving primarily in MN. No grants to individuals.
Application information: Contributes only to pre-selected organizations.
Directors: Daniel J. McGlynn; Michael J. McGlynn; Thomas P. McGlynn; Molly McGlynn Varley.
EIN: 411784157
Selected grants: The following grants are a representative sample of this grantmaker's funding activity:
$20,000 to Minnehaha Academy, Minneapolis, MN, 2011.
$20,000 to Saint Johns University, Collegeville, MN, 2011.
$19,000 to United Way, Greater Twin Cities, Minneapolis, MN, 2011.
$18,000 to United Way, Greater Twin Cities, Minneapolis, MN, 2010.
$10,000 to Breck School, Minneapolis, MN, 2011.
$10,000 to United Way, Greater Twin Cities, Minneapolis, MN, 2010.
$10,000 to United Way, Greater Twin Cities, Minneapolis, MN, 2010.
$10,000 to Wallin Education Partners, Minneapolis, MN, 2011.
$10,000 to Young Life, Saint Louis Park, MN, 2010.
$7,600 to United Way, Greater Twin Cities, Minneapolis, MN, 2010.
$5,000 to Basilica of Saint Mary, Minneapolis, MN, 2011.
$5,000 to Be The Match Foundation, Minneapolis, MN, 2010.
$5,000 to Grove City College, Grove City, PA, 2010.
$5,000 to Saint Johns University, Collegeville, MN, 2011.
$5,000 to United Way, Greater Twin Cities, Minneapolis, MN, 2010.
$4,000 to Mayo Clinic, Rochester, MN, 2010.
$2,500 to Church of the Ascension, Minneapolis, MN, 2011.
$2,500 to College of Saint Benedict, Saint Joseph, MN, 2010.

4707
The William W. and Nadine M. McGuire Family Foundation ✧
(formerly The William W. McGuire and Nadine M. McGuire Family Foundation)
c/o Dorsey & Whitney, LLP, Attn.: D. Barr
50 S. 6th St., Ste. 1500
Minneapolis, MN 55402-1498 (952) 936-1219

Established in 1996 in MN.
Donors: Dr. William W. McGuire; Nadine M. McGuire.
Foundation type: Independent foundation.
Financial data (yr. ended 12/31/12): Assets, $2,098,672 (M); expenditures, $3,340,862; qualifying distributions, $3,096,250; giving activities include $3,096,250 for grants.
Fields of interest: Arts, multipurpose centers/programs; Arts; Medical research, institute.
Limitations: Applications not accepted. Giving primarily in Minneapolis, MN. No grants to individuals.
Application information: Contributes only to pre-selected organizations.
Officers and Directors:* Nadine M. McGuire,* Pres.; Dr. William W. McGuire,* Secy.-Treas.
EIN: 411861103

4708
The McKnight Endowment Fund for Neuroscience ✧
710 2nd St. S., Ste. 400
Minneapolis, MN 55401-2290 (612) 333-4220
FAX: (612) 332-3833; E-mail: emaler@mcknight.org;
Main URL: http://www.mcknight.org/neuroscience

Established in 1987 in MN.
Donor: The McKnight Foundation.
Foundation type: Operating foundation.
Financial data (yr. ended 12/31/13): Assets, $16,423 (M); gifts received, $3,661,200; expenditures, $3,652,814; qualifying distributions, $3,652,814; giving activities include $3,150,000 for 37 grants to individuals (high: $100,000; low: $25,000), and $256,424 for foundation-administered programs.
Purpose and activities: Awards grants for neuroscience research, especially as it pertains to memory and to a clearer understanding of diseases affecting memory and its biological substrates.
Fields of interest: Medical research, institute; Neuroscience research.
Type of support: Research.
Limitations: Applications accepted. Giving limited to U.S. citizens or permanent residents.
Publications: Application guidelines; Financial statement.
Application information: Application form required.
Initial approach: Letter or telephone for application forms and guidelines; materials for Scholar Awards available in Sept. annually
Deadline(s): See foundation web site for current deadlines
Board meeting date(s): Apr.
Final notification: See foundation web site
Officers and Directors:* Thomas M. Jessell, Ph.D.*, Pres.; Huda Yahya Zoghbi, M.D.*, V.P.; Patricia S. Binger; Allison J. Doupe, M.D., Ph.D.; Michael Ehlers, M.D., Ph.D.; David Julius, Ph.D.; Anthony Movshon, Ph.D.; Carla J. Shatz, Ph.D.; Wendy Suzuki, Ph.D.; David Tank; Kate Wolford.
EIN: 411563321

4709
The McKnight Foundation

710 S. 2nd St., Ste. 400
Minneapolis, MN 55401-2290 (612) 333-4220
Contact: Kate Wolford, Pres.
FAX: (612) 332-3833; E-mail: info@mcknight.org; Main URL: http://www.mcknight.org
Blog: http://blog.mcknight.org/
E-Newsletter: http://visitor.constantcontact.com/manage/optin/ea?v=001mBomMP0GdY8UKXJsN5z3Cw%3D%3D
Facebook: http://www.facebook.com/pages/McKnight-Foundation/131199140270392
Grantee Perception Report: http://www.mcknight.org/resource-library/grant-programs/general-information/grantee-perception-report
Grants Database: http://www.mcknight.org/grantsprograms/findagrantee.aspx
Knowledge Center: http://www.mcknight.org/resource-library
McKnight Foundation's Philanthropy Promise: http://www.ncrp.org/philanthropys-promise/who
RSS Feed: http://www.mcknight.org/rss
State of the Artist: http://www.stateoftheartist.org/
Twitter: https://twitter.com/McKnightFdn

Incorporated in 1953 in MN.
Donors: William L. McKnight‡; Maude L. McKnight‡; Virginia M. Binger‡; James H. Binger‡.
Foundation type: Independent foundation.
Financial data (yr. ended 12/31/13): Assets, $2,239,101,229 (M); gifts received, $23,174,603; expenditures, $117,530,113; qualifying distributions, $97,760,202; giving activities include $86,500,529 for 742 grants (high: $9,986,300; low: $1,000), $97,700 for 212 employee matching gifts, and $426,371 for 4 foundation-administered programs.
Purpose and activities: The grant maker seeks to improve the quality of life for present and future generations. Through grant making, coalition-building, and encouragement of strategic policy reform, it uses its resources to attend, unite, and empower those it serves.
Fields of interest: Arts; Environment, energy; Environment; Neuroscience; Housing/shelter, development; Youth development; Children/youth, services; Child development, services; Community/economic development; Transportation; Children/youth; Economically disadvantaged.
International interests: Cambodia; Laos; Tanzania; Uganda; Vietnam.
Type of support: Mission-related investments/loans; General/operating support; Capital campaigns; Building/renovation; Equipment; Program development; Fellowships; Technical assistance; Program evaluation; Program-related investments/loans; Employee matching gifts; Matching/challenge support.
Limitations: Applications accepted. Giving limited to organizations in MN, especially the seven-county Twin Cities, MN, area, except for programs in the environment which are made mainly in the 10 states bordering the Mississippi River and in the Twin Cities region, international aid, or research. No support for religious organizations for religious purposes, or for medical health or health-related services, including those for chemical dependency, services for seniors or people with disabilities. No grants to individuals (except for the Virginia McKnight Binger Awards in Human Service and the McKnight Distinguished Artist Award.), or for basic research in academic disciplines (except for defined programs in crop research and neuroscience) endowment funds, scholarships, fellowships, national fundraising campaigns, ticket sales, travel or conferences.
Publications: Application guidelines; Annual report; Financial statement; Grants list; Informational brochure; Newsletter; Occasional report.
Application information: The foundation will e-mail to decline requests or to provide additional instructions for submitting a full proposal online. Application form not required.
Initial approach: Online grant application
Deadline(s): Jan. 15, Apr. 15, July 15, and Oct. 15 for arts, and region and communities; Feb. 1, May 1, Aug. 1, Nov. 1 for Mississippi River. See foundation web site for additional program deadlines
Board meeting date(s): Feb., May, Aug., Nov.
Final notification: 5 months
Officers and Directors:* Ted Staryk,* Chair.; Kate Wolford, Pres.; Richard J. Scott, V.P., Finance and Compliance, and Secy.; Richard D. McFarland,* Treas.; Anne Binger; Erika L. Binger; Meghan Binger Brown; Robert Bruininks; David Crasby; Phyllis Goff; Bill Gregg; Debby Landesman; Perry Moriearty; Robert J. Struyk.
Number of staff: 21 full-time professional; 1 part-time professional; 15 full-time support; 1 part-time support.
EIN: 410754835

4710
The McNeely Foundation ✧

444 Pine St.
St. Paul, MN 55101-2453 (651) 228-4503
Contact: Karen M. Reynolds
FAX: (651) 228-4506;
E-mail: kreynolds@mcneelyfoundation.org; Main URL: http://www.mcneelyfoundation.org

Established in 1981 in MN.
Donor: Family and private contributors.
Foundation type: Independent foundation.
Financial data (yr. ended 12/31/13): Assets, $25,863,381 (M); expenditures, $1,018,223; qualifying distributions, $1,006,651; giving activities include $956,993 for 121 grants (high: $75,000; low: $50).
Purpose and activities: Support for economics and business education; grants also for selected community projects, environmental programs and for arts education. Specific interest in funding projects that benefit the St. Paul, MN area, especially the East Side neighborhoods. The foundation commits resources to benefit the local community resulting in increased family and/or individual self-sufficiency, opportunities for community and individual enrichment, and the improved vibrancy and effectiveness of organizations in working with under-served populations or serving targeted needs. In doing its work, the foundation prefers to act as a catalyst for creative approaches to individual and community issues, to leverage other resources through partnerships and the sharing of resources, and to evaluate the results of its grantmaking. The foundation makes grants in the areas of education, human services, the environment, the arts and community betterment, and has a special interest in funding projects that benefit the Saint Paul community, especially East Side neighborhoods.
Fields of interest: Arts education; Education; Environment; Human services; Children/youth, services; Community/economic development; Economically disadvantaged.
Type of support: Matching/challenge support; Employee-related scholarships; Continuing support; Program development; Employee matching gifts.
Limitations: Applications accepted. Giving primarily in the Minneapolis-St. Paul Metro area, especially in East Side St. Paul neighborhoods.
Publications: Application guidelines; Grants list.
Application information: Application guidelines available on foundation web site. Application form required.
Initial approach: Proposal
Copies of proposal: 1
Deadline(s): Mar. 1, June 1, and Dec. 1
Board meeting date(s): Quarterly
Final notification: Average time is 180 days
Officer and Directors:* Shannon McNeely Whitaker,* Chair.; Armar A. Archbold; W.E. Barsness; Ted Madden; Greg McNeely; Irene E. McNeely; Kevin McNeely; Nicholas McNeely.
Number of staff: 1 part-time professional; 1 part-time support.
EIN: 411392221
Selected grants: The following grants are a representative sample of this grantmaker's funding activity:
$20,000 to East Side Prosperity Campaign, MN, 2012.
$20,000 to Latino Economic Development Center, Minneapolis, MN, 2012.

$20,000 to Minnesota Sinfonia, Minneapolis, MN, 2012. For Music in Schools and East Side Saint Paul Concerts.
$20,000 to Urban Roots, Saint Paul, MN, 2012.
$15,000 to Lift Community Development Corporation, Saint Paul, MN, 2012.
$15,000 to Lower Phalen Creek Project, Saint Paul, MN, 2012.
$15,000 to Merrick Community Services, Saint Paul, MN, 2012.
$15,000 to Opportunity Neighborhood Development Corporation, Saint Paul, MN, 2012.

4711
McVay Foundation ✧

14820 Highway 7, Ste. 200
Minnetonka, MN 55345-3630

Established in 1984 in MN.
Donors: M.D. McVay‡; Mary McVay.
Foundation type: Independent foundation.
Financial data (yr. ended 12/31/13): Assets, $14,353,433 (M); expenditures, $655,648; qualifying distributions, $591,015; giving activities include $583,750 for 75 grants (high: $200,000; low: $200).
Purpose and activities: Giving primarily for the arts, education, Christian organizations, and social services.
Fields of interest: Performing arts; Arts; Higher education; Theological school/education; Education; Human services; Christian agencies & churches.
Type of support: General/operating support; Capital campaigns; Scholarship funds.
Limitations: Applications not accepted. Giving primarily in MN and the Midwest. No grants to individuals.
Application information: Unsolicited requests for funds not accepted.
Officers: Mary McVay, Pres.; Marcelle McVay, V.P. and Secy.; Danita Greene, Treas.
Directors: Sara McVay; T. Todd McVay.
EIN: 363311833

4712
The Medtronic Foundation ✧

710 Medtronic Pkwy., LC110
Minneapolis, MN 55432-5604 (763) 505-2639
Contact: Deb Anderson, Grants Admin.
FAX: (763) 505-2648;
E-mail: medtronicfoundation@medtronic.com; Additional tel.: (800) 328-2518; Contact for PatientLink and Strengthening Health Systems in Africa, Europe, Middle East, and South America: Luc Girad, Medtronic Fdn., Medtronic Europe, Route du Molliau 31, Case postale, CH-1131 Tolochenaz, Switzerland, tel.: +41 21 802 7574, e-mail: foundation.emea@medtronic.com; E-mail for Global Heroes: mtcm.globalheroes@medtronic.com; Main URL: http://philanthropy.medtronic.com/index.htm
Grants List: http://www.medtronic.com/foundation/grants/search-grants.html
HeartRescue Project on Twitter: http://twitter.com/HeartRescue
Medtronic "What We Care About" Video: http://www.medtronic.com/foundation/video//video-what_we_care_about.html
Medtronic "Where We Focus" Video: http://www.medtronic.com/foundation/video/video-where_we_focus.html
Medtronic "Who We Are" Video: http://www.medtronic.com/foundation/video/video-who_we_are.html
Medtronic Global Heroes on Facebook: http://www.facebook.com/pages/Medtronic-Global-Heroes/54011966662

Established in 1979 in MN.
Donor: Medtronic, Inc.
Foundation type: Company-sponsored foundation.
Financial data (yr. ended 04/30/13): Assets, $640,143 (M); gifts received, $6,185,804; expenditures, $28,327,376; qualifying distributions, $27,950,971; giving activities include $22,557,653 for grants, and $1,550,464 for employee matching gifts.
Purpose and activities: The foundation supports programs designed to promote health, with a focus on heath systems in developing countries, chronic disease, patient advocacy and support, and sudden cardiac arrest; education, including primary and secondary science, math, and engineering initiatives and education reform; and community, through local human services and arts initiatives and disaster relief efforts providing short- and long-term help.
Fields of interest: Arts, cultural/ethnic awareness; Media, radio; Museums (science/technology); Arts; Education, reform; Elementary/secondary education; Elementary school/education; Higher education; Teacher school/education; Education; Medical care, community health systems; Hospitals (general); Health care, emergency transport services; Health care, EMS; Public health; Health care, patient services; Health care; Cancer; Heart & circulatory diseases; Lung diseases; Diabetes; Disasters, preparedness/services; Human services; United Ways and Federated Giving Programs; Science, formal/general education; Mathematics; Engineering/technology; Science; Public affairs; Youth; Minorities; Women; Economically disadvantaged.
International interests: Australia; Austria; Belgium; Brazil; Canada; China; Czech Republic; Denmark; France; Germany; India; Ireland; Italy; Japan; Mexico; Netherlands; Poland; Portugal; Russia; South Africa; Spain; Sweden; Switzerland; United Kingdom.
Type of support: Fellowships; Continuing support; Management development/capacity building; Annual campaigns; Program development; Conferences/seminars; Publication; Seed money; Curriculum development; Scholarship funds; Employee volunteer services; Sponsorships; Employee matching gifts; Donated products.
Limitations: Applications not accepted. Giving primarily in areas of company operations, with emphasis on Maricopa County and Tempe, AZ, Santa Clarita, San Fernando, and Simi Valley regions, western Los Angeles, and Orange, Santa Barbara, Sonoma, Sunnyvale, and Ventura counties, CA, Denver metro area and Louisville, CO, Jacksonville, FL, Kosciusko County, IN, Beverly, Danvers, Middleton, North Shore, Peabody, and Salem, MA, Minneapolis, St. Paul, and Twin Cities-Seven County metro, MN, area, Humacao, Juncos, and Villalba, PR, Memphis, TN, Fort Worth and San Antonio, TX, and King and Snohomish County, WA, and in Africa, Australia, Austria, Belgium, Brazil, Canada, Czech Republic, Shanghai, China, Denmark, Europe, France, Germany, Hungary, India, Ireland, Italy, Japan, Mexico, Netherlands, Poland, Russia, South Africa, Spain, Switzerland, and the United Kingdom. No support for lobbying, political, or fraternal organizations, fiscal agents, religious groups not of direct benefit to the entire community, or private foundations. No grants individuals, or for scholarships, Continuing Medical Education (CME) grants, capital campaigns, fundraising events or activities, social events, goodwill advertising, general operating support, general support for educational institutions, long-term counseling or personal development, endowments, automatic external defibrillators (AEDs) purchases, or research.
Publications: Corporate giving report; Financial statement; Grants list; Program policy statement.
Application information: The foundation currently has an invitation only process for giving.
Board meeting date(s): Quarterly
Officers and Directors:* Gary L. Ellis,* Chair.; H. James Dallas, Vice-Chair.; Jacob A. Gayle, Ph.D., V.P. and Exec. Dir.; Kristin L. Gorsuch; Stephen N. Oesterle, M.D.; Chris J. O'Connell; Herb F. Riband; Tony B. Semedo; David M. Steinhaus, M.D.; Caroline Stockdale; Tom M. Tefft.
Number of staff: 3 full-time professional; 2 part-time professional; 1 full-time support; 1 part-time support.
EIN: 411306950
Selected grants: The following grants are a representative sample of this grantmaker's funding activity:
$2,203,289 to United Way, Greater Twin Cities, Minneapolis, MN, 2013. For matching grant for Employee Campaign.
$1,000,000 to Teach for America, New York, NY, 2013. For Teach for America Math And Science Initiative, Teach For America—Twin Cities, Memphis, and Jacksonville.
$544,646 to Scholarship America, One Scholarship Way, Saint Peter, MN, 2013. For Medtronic Family Scholarships.
$500,000 to University of Washington, Harborview Medical Center CPEC, Seattle, WA, 2013. For HeartRescue Flagship Premier Partner Program.
$435,000 to Partners in Health, Boston, MA, 2013. For NCD Synergies Initiative.
$50,000 to American Chronic Pain Association, Rocklin, CA, 2013. For Growing Pains.
$50,000 to Hypertrophic Cardiomyopathy Association, Hibernia, NJ, 2013. For Roots and Wings.
$29,277 to United Way of Tarrant County, Fort Worth, TX, 2013. For matching grant for Employee Campaign.
$15,000 to Childrens Bureau, Porter-Leath Children's Center, Memphis, TN, 2013. For Porter-Leath Pre-School /Head Start Expansion.
$10,300 to Horn Lake High School, Horn Lake, MS, 2013. For FIRST robotics competition.

4713
Kendrick B. Melrose Family Foundation ✧

319 Barry Ave. S., Ste. 200
Wayzata, MN 55391

Established in 1997 in MN.
Donor: Kendrick B. Melrose.
Foundation type: Independent foundation.
Financial data (yr. ended 12/31/13): Assets, $10,928,725 (M); expenditures, $2,403,725; qualifying distributions, $2,301,400; giving activities include $2,297,375 for 12 grants (high: $1,500,000; low: $100).

Fields of interest: Performing arts, theater; Arts; Higher education; Foundations (private grantmaking).
Type of support: General/operating support; Annual campaigns; Capital campaigns.
Limitations: Applications not accepted. Giving in the U.S., with emphasis on MN. No grants to individuals.
Application information: Contributes only to pre-selected organizations.
Directors: Kendra L. Melrose; Kendrick B. Melrose; Robert A. Melrose; Velia E. Melrose.
EIN: 411894134
Selected grants: The following grants are a representative sample of this grantmaker's funding activity:
$60,000 to Animal Humane Society, Golden Valley, MN, 2012. For Whisker Whirl: Fund a Need.
$50,000 to Center for Faithwalk Leadership, Augusta, GA, 2012. For Lead Like Jesus.
$27,333 to Princeton Prospect Foundation, Princeton, NJ, 2012. For Tiger Inn Class of 62.
$7,000 to Guthrie Theater, Minneapolis, MN, 2012. For World Stage.
$2,200 to Farm Sanctuary, Watkins Glen, NY, 2012. For mower upgrade.

4714
The Minneapolis Foundation ✧

800 IDS Ctr.
80 S. Eighth St.
Minneapolis, MN 55402-2100 (612) 672-3878
Contact: For grants: Andrea Porter, Grants Admin.
FAX: (612) 672-3846;
E-mail: e-mail@mplsfoundation.org; Grants application request e-mail: grants@mplsfoundation.org; Main URL: http://www.MinneapolisFoundation.org
Additional URL: http://www.mplsfoundation.org
At The Table Blog: http://atthetable.minneapolisfoundation.org/
At The Table Blog Feed: http://atthetable.minneapolisfoundation.org/feed/
Facebook: http://www.facebook.com/MinneapolisFoundation
The Minneapolis Foundation's Philanthropy Promise: http://www.ncrp.org/philanthropys-promise/who
Twitter: http://twitter.com/mplsfoundation

Incorporated in 1915 in MN.
Foundation type: Community foundation.
Financial data (yr. ended 03/31/13): Assets, $631,073,506 (M); gifts received, $38,204,009; expenditures, $59,859,761; giving activities include $52,591,314 for grants.
Purpose and activities: The foundation believes that the well-being of each citizen is connected to that of every other and that the vitality of any community is determined by the quality of those relationships. With this principle in mind, the foundation's purpose is to join with others to strengthen the community, in measurable and sustainable ways, for the benefit of all citizens, especially those who are disadvantaged. The foundation is committed to being an effective resource developer and a responsible steward of those resources, an active grantmaker and convener addressing crucial community needs, and a constructive catalyst, changing systems to serve people better.
Fields of interest: Arts; Education, early childhood education; Child development, education; Education; Health care; Crime/violence prevention, domestic violence; Housing/shelter; Disasters, Hurricane Katrina; Children/youth, services; Child development, services; Family services; Women, centers/services; Human services; International development; Civil/human rights, immigrants; Civil/human rights, minorities; Civil/human rights, disabled; Civil/human rights, women; Civil/human rights, aging; Civil rights, race/intergroup relations; Civil/human rights; Economic development; Community/economic development; Public policy, research; Aging; Disabilities, people with; Minorities; Asians/Pacific Islanders; African Americans/Blacks; Hispanics/Latinos; Native Americans/American Indians; Immigrants/refugees; Economically disadvantaged; Homeless.
Type of support: General/operating support; Continuing support; Capital campaigns; Equipment; Program development; Seed money; Technical assistance; Program-related investments/loans.
Limitations: Applications accepted. Giving limited to MN, with emphasis on organizations in the Twin Cities metropolitan region. No support for national campaigns, direct religious activities, veterans' or fraternal organizations, or organizations within umbrella organizations. No grants to individuals, or for annual campaigns, capital support, deficit financing, building or endowment funds, emergency/safety net services, production of housing units, conferences, purchase or repair of vehicles, direct fundraising efforts, or memberships.
Publications: Application guidelines; Annual report; Annual report (including application guidelines); Financial statement; Grants list; Informational brochure; Newsletter.
Application information: Visit foundation web site for online application and guidelines. Application form required.
Initial approach: Submit Letter of Inquiry
Deadline(s): Aug. 8 for Letter of Inquiry; Sept. 22 for full proposals
Board meeting date(s): Committee meets 4 times a year
Final notification: Dec. 17
Officers and Trustees:* Lowell Stortz,* Chair.; Norman Rickeman,* Vice-Chair.; Sandy L. Vargas,* C.E.O. and Pres.; Jean Adams,* C.O.O. and C.F.O.; Beth Halloran, Sr. V.P., Advancement; Luz Maria Frias, V.P., Community Impact; Teresa Morrow, V.P., External Rels. and Mktg.; William M. Sternberg, V.P., Philanthropic Svcs.; Archie Givens, Jr.,* Secy.; Jane Wyatt,* Treas.; Tim Baylor; Maureen Bazinet Beck; Ann Burns; Jan Conlin; Terrance R. Dolan; Robert Fullerton; J. Andrew Herring; Suzanne Koepplinger; Nekima Levy-Pounds, Esq.; Todd J. Lifson; David C. Mortenson; Patty Murphy; Gloria Perez; Brian J. Pietsch; Gretchen Piper; Steven Rothschild; Catherine Shreves; Nancy Siska; Phil Smith; David Sternberg; John Sullivan; Ellen Valde; Sven Wehrwein; Ben Whitney.
Trustee Banks: U.S. Bank, N.A.; Wells Fargo Bank Minnesota, N.A.
Number of staff: 26 full-time professional; 2 part-time professional; 13 full-time support; 1 part-time support.
EIN: 416029402
Selected grants: The following grants are a representative sample of this grantmaker's funding activity:
$5,000,000 to Smith College, Wurtele Center for Work and Life, Northampton, MA, 2013. For endowment for facility that gives students skills and habits-of-mind they need to thrive at Smith and beyond. Programs help students to deepen their knowledge of themselves, as well as to explore their personal capacities.
$5,000,000 to Walker Art Center, Minneapolis, MN, 2013. For capital campaign.
$5,000,000 to Walker Art Center, Minneapolis, MN, 2013. For capital campaign.
$877,490 to Raymond James Charitable Endowment Fund, Saint Petersburg, FL, 2013. For donor advised fund.
$500,000 to Saint Olaf College, Northfield, MN, 2013. For The Harry C. Piper Center for Vocation and Career.
$250,000 to Wayzata Community Church, Wayzata, MN, 2013. For entry renovation handicap accessibility and Parables Ministry special needs families.
$5,000 to PGA Tour Charities, Ponte Vedra Beach, FL, 2013. For general operating support on behalf of the Austin Mutual Foundation.
$2,500 to Edina Education Fund, Edina, MN, 2013. For general operating support.
$2,383 to Tenderfoot Transmitting, Salida, CO, 2013. For general operating support.
$2,000 to Amherst H. Wilder Foundation, Saint Paul, MN, 2013. For general operating support ($1000) and Shannon Leadership Institute ($1000).

4715
Minnesota Community Foundation ✧

(formerly Minnesota Foundation)
101 Fifth St., Ste. 2400
St. Paul, MN 55101-1800 (651) 224-5463
Contact: Carleen K. Rhodes, C.E.O.
FAX: (651) 224-8123; E-mail: info@mnpartners.org; Additional tel.: (800) 875-6167; Main URL: http://www.mncommunityfoundation.org
Facebook: https://www.facebook.com/mnpartners
Twitter: http://twitter.com/mnpartnerstweet
YouTube: http://www.youtube.com/mnpartnersvideo

Incorporated in 1949 in MN; in 1984 became an affiliated organization of The Saint Paul Foundation.
Foundation type: Community foundation.
Financial data (yr. ended 12/31/13): Assets, $241,367,658 (M); gifts received, $11,164,905; expenditures, $12,501,224; giving activities include $9,648,864 for grants.
Purpose and activities: The foundation seeks to assist individuals, organizations and communities statewide in developing local charitable trusts. Grants are made from these funds according to the recommendations and interests of donors and advisory boards.
Fields of interest: Humanities; Environment; Animal welfare; Health care; Youth development, services; Human services; Rural development; Community/economic development; United Ways and Federated Giving Programs; Leadership development.
Type of support: Program development; Matching/challenge support; Equipment; Capital campaigns; Building/renovation; Annual campaigns; General/operating support; Continuing support; Endowments; Scholarships—to individuals.
Limitations: Giving limited to MN.
Publications: Financial statement; Grants list; Informational brochure; Newsletter.
Application information: Visit foundation web site for scholarship application information.
Board meeting date(s): Quarterly or as required
Officers and Trustees:* Mark L. Wilson,* Chair.; Mary K. Brainerd,* Vice-Chair.; Carleen K. Rhodes, C.E.O. and Pres.; Suzanne Kelly, Chief of Staff; Ann

Mulholland, V.P., Grants and Prog.; Jack Pohl, V.P., Investments; Christine Searson, V.P., Finance and Opers.; Jeremy Wells, V.P., Philanthropic Svcs.; Claire Chang, Assoc. V.P., Grants and Prog.; Christine Elias, Assoc. V.P., Philanthropic Svcs.; Melissa Pelland, Cont.; Rassoul Dastmozd; Donald Day; John DeClue; Jacqueline Dorsey; Mary Frey; Steven Fritze; Tom Grossman; May Kao Hang; Christopher M. Hilger; Cynthia L. Lesher; Nancy E. Lindahl; Manuel M. Lopez; Gerald O'Brien II; Kathleen Schmidlkofer; Paul L. Snyder; Timothy Welsh; Pamela Wheelock.
EIN: 410832480
Selected grants: The following grants are a representative sample of this grantmaker's funding activity:
$1,342,025 to Warroad Memorial Arena Association, Warroad, MN, 2012. For the New Lobby Project.
$1,051,648 to Fidelity Charitable Gift Fund, Boston, MA, 2012. For the St. Angelo Family Charitable Fund.
$975,781 to Minnesota Public Radio, Saint Paul, MN, 2012. For multiple grants for multiple purposes.
$823,643 to Dollars for Scholars, Saint Louis Park, Saint Louis Park, MN, 2012. For multiple grants for multiple purposes.
$326,446 to Amherst H. Wilder Foundation, Saint Paul, MN, 2012. For multiple grants for multiple purposes.
$322,407 to Saint Johns Lutheran Home, Albert Lea, MN, 2012. For multiple grants for multiple purposes.
$250,000 to Lowell Lundstrom Ministries, Sisseton, SD, 2012. For multiple grants for multiple purposes.
$56,918 to Bank of America Charitable Gift Fund, Providence, RI, 2012. For multiple grants for multiple purposes.
$21,600 to Childrens Theater Company and School, Minneapolis, MN, 2012. For multiple grants for multiple purposes.
$12,013 to Wayzata Public Schools, Wayzata, MN, 2012. For multiple grants for multiple purposes.

4716
Minnesota Power Foundation ✧
30 W. Superior St.
Duluth, MN 55802-2191
Contact: Peggy Hanson, Secy.
E-mail: mhanson@mnpower.com; Main URL: http://www.mnpowerfoundation.org/

Established in 2006 in MN.
Donor: ALLETE, Inc.
Foundation type: Company-sponsored foundation.
Financial data (yr. ended 12/31/13): Assets, $460,301 (M); expenditures, $779,032; qualifying distributions, $778,483; giving activities include $767,353 for 139 grants (high: $50,000).
Purpose and activities: The foundation supports programs designed to improve the quality of life in communities where Minnesota Power conducts business through education, the environment, community services, youth development, arts and culture, and health and human services. Special emphasis is directed toward programs designed to promote K-12 and post-secondary education; human services; arts and culture; and the preservation of natural resources.
Fields of interest: Arts; Elementary/secondary education; Vocational education; Higher education; Education; Environment, natural resources; Environment; Health care; Food services; Youth development; Human services; Community/economic development; Foundations (community); United Ways and Federated Giving Programs; Engineering/technology.
Type of support: General/operating support; Annual campaigns; Capital campaigns; Building/renovation; Equipment; Program development; Scholarship funds; Sponsorships; Scholarships—to individuals; Matching/challenge support.
Limitations: Applications accepted. Giving primarily in areas of company operations in MN and ND. No grants to individuals (except for scholarships) or for travel.
Publications: Application guidelines.
Application information: Application form required.
Initial approach: Proposal
Deadline(s): None
Board meeting date(s): Feb., May, Aug., and Nov.
Officers and Directors: Alan R. Hodnik, Pres.; David J. McMillan, V.P.; Peggy Hanson, Secy.; Laura Schauer, Treas.; Patrick A. Mullen; Michael A. Perala; Joshua J. Skelton; Todd Simmons; Daniel L. Tonder.
EIN: 562560595
Selected grants: The following grants are a representative sample of this grantmaker's funding activity:
$125,000 to University of Wisconsin-Superior, Superior, WI, 2010.
$100,000 to Center Against Sexual and Domestic Abuse, Superior, WI, 2011.
$50,000 to Duluth-Superior Area Community Foundation, Duluth, MN, 2011.
$50,000 to Duluth-Superior Area Community Foundation, Duluth, MN, 2011.
$43,160 to United Way of Greater Duluth, Duluth, MN, 2011.
$43,160 to United Way of Greater Duluth, Duluth, MN, 2011.
$43,160 to United Way of Greater Duluth, Duluth, MN, 2011.
$30,000 to Miller-Dwan Foundation, Duluth, MN, 2011.
$30,000 to Science Museum of Minnesota, Saint Paul, MN, 2011.
$14,975 to United Way, Morrison County, Little Falls, MN, 2011.
$3,600 to Science Museum of Minnesota, Saint Paul, MN, 2011.

4717
Wildey H. Mitchell Family Foundation ✧
c/o Wells Fargo Bank Trust Tax
222 W. Superior St., Ste. 200
Duluth, MN 55802-1939

Established in 1979 in MN.
Donors: Wildey H. Mitchell†; Margaret Mitchell†.
Foundation type: Independent foundation.
Financial data (yr. ended 12/31/13): Assets, $7,069,272 (M); expenditures, $550,723; qualifying distributions, $505,134; giving activities include $494,500 for 45 grants (high: $60,000; low: $1,000).
Purpose and activities: Giving primarily for the arts, education, and children, youth and social services.
Fields of interest: Arts; Education; Health organizations, association; Boys & girls clubs; Human services; Children/youth, services; United Ways and Federated Giving Programs.
Limitations: Applications not accepted. Giving primarily in Duluth, MN. No grants to individuals.
Application information: Contributes only to pre-selected organizations.
Directors: Michael S. Altman; Don Carlson; Robert J. Zallar.
EIN: 416222997
Selected grants: The following grants are a representative sample of this grantmaker's funding activity:
$15,000 to College of Saint Scholastica, Duluth, MN, 2011.
$5,000 to University of Minnesota, Duluth, MN, 2011.

4718
Mithun Family Foundation ✧
900 E. Wayzata Blvd., Ste. 130
Wayzata, MN 55391-1895

Established in 1986 in MN.
Donors: Robert O. Mithun, Sr.; Doris B. Mithun; Doris Mithun Trust; Mithun Enterprises, Inc.
Foundation type: Independent foundation.
Financial data (yr. ended 12/31/12): Assets, $48,340,453 (M); expenditures, $2,720,547; qualifying distributions, $2,366,667; giving activities include $2,366,667 for 47 grants (high: $250,000; low: $250).
Purpose and activities: Giving primarily for the arts, education, and human services.
Fields of interest: Education; Health care; Human services; Family services; Girls.
Limitations: Applications not accepted. Giving primarily in Santa Barbara, CA, Danbury, CT, and MN. No grants to individuals.
Application information: Contributes only to pre-selected organizations.
Directors: John C. Mithun; Lewis M. Mithun; Raymond O. Mithun, Jr.
EIN: 363495071

4719
Jane N. Mooty Foundation Trust ✧ ☆
P.O. Box 24628
Edina, MN 55424-0628

Established in 1998 in MN.
Donor: Jane N. Mooty.
Foundation type: Independent foundation.
Financial data (yr. ended 12/31/13): Assets, $9,085,672 (M); expenditures, $473,584; qualifying distributions, $456,250; giving activities include $456,250 for 34 grants (high: $80,000; low: $500).
Fields of interest: Media/communications; Higher education, university; Boys clubs; YM/YWCAs & YM/YWHAs; Children, services; Christian agencies & churches.
Limitations: Applications not accepted. Giving primarily in MN. No grants to individuals.
Application information: Contributes only to pre-selected organizations.
Trustees: Barbara L. Glaser; Kenneth C. Glaser.
EIN: 411687108
Selected grants: The following grants are a representative sample of this grantmaker's funding activity:
$50,000 to Scottsdale Healthcare Foundation, Scottsdale, AZ, 2012. For community medical care.

$45,000 to Community Foundation for the Greater Capital Region, Albany, NY, 2012. For community/land preservation fund.
$40,000 to Rio Verde Community Church, Rio Verde, AZ, 2012. For music ministries.
$5,000 to Adirondack Community Trust, Lake Placid, NY, 2012. For internships.
$5,000 to Foundation for Blind Children, Phoenix, AZ, 2012. For Services for blind children.

4720
John W. Mooty Foundation Trust ✧ ☆
80 S. 8th St., 500 IDS Ctr.
Minneapolis, MN 55402-2100 (612) 632-3333
Contact: Bruce W. Mooty, Tr.
E-mail: bruce_mooty@gpmlaw.com

Established in 1998 in MN.
Donor: John W. Mooty.
Foundation type: Independent foundation.
Financial data (yr. ended 12/31/13): Assets, $12,023,025 (M); expenditures, $553,708; qualifying distributions, $553,558; giving activities include $553,558 for 22 grants (high: $470,458; low: $300).
Fields of interest: Higher education; Higher education, university; Law school/education; YM/YWCAs & YM/YWHAs; Community/economic development; United Ways and Federated Giving Programs; Christian agencies & churches.
Limitations: Applications accepted. Giving primarily in MN. No grants to individuals.
Application information: Application form not required.
Deadline(s): None
Trustees: Bruce W. Mooty; Charles W. Mooty; David N. Mooty.
EIN: 411686710
Selected grants: The following grants are a representative sample of this grantmaker's funding activity:
$500 to University of Minnesota Alumni Association, Minneapolis, MN, 2012. For educational services.

4721
The Mortenson Family Foundation ✧
700 Meadow Ln. N.
Minneapolis, MN 55422-4899

Established in 1999 in MN.
Donors: M.A. Mortenson Co.; Alice D. Mortenson; Mauritz A. Mortenson, Jr.
Foundation type: Company-sponsored foundation.
Financial data (yr. ended 12/31/12): Assets, $36,890,671 (M); gifts received, $2,546,485; expenditures, $1,538,045; qualifying distributions, $1,137,500; giving activities include $1,137,500 for grants.
Purpose and activities: The foundation supports organizations involved with education, hunger, youth development, human services, religion, and economically disadvantaged people.
Fields of interest: Education; Environment; Youth development.
International interests: Bangladesh; Cambodia; Ghana; Guatemala; Honduras; Laos; Liberia; Malawi; Mozambique; Nicaragua; Senegal; Sierra Leone; Tanzania; Zambia.
Type of support: General/operating support; Program development.
Limitations: Applications not accepted. Giving primarily in MN, and in Bangladesh, Cambodia, Ghana, Guatemala, Honduras, Laos, Liberia, Malawi, Mozambique, Nicaragua, Senegal, Sierra Leone, Tanzania, and Zambia. No support for political, religious, or proselytizing organizations. No grants to individuals, or for sponsorships or events.
Application information: Contributes only to pre-selected organizations.
Officers: Alice D. Mortenson, Chair. and Pres.; Mauritz A. Mortenson, Jr., V.P.; Mark A. Mortenson, Secy.; Randy Jenson, Treas.; Donna Dalton, Exec. Dir.
Directors: David C. Mortenson; Christopher D. Mortenson; Mathias H. Mortenson.
Number of staff: 1 full-time professional.
EIN: 411958621

4722
Mosaic Company Foundation ✧
3033 Campus Dr., Rm. E490
Plymouth, MN 55441-2655 (763) 577-2700
FAX: (763) 559-2860;
E-mail: community.relations@mosaicco.com; Toll free tel.: (800) 918-8270; Main URL: http://www.mosaicco.com/sustainability/givingmap/index.htm
RSS Feed: http://www.mosaicco.com/2650.htm?subcat=ALL

Established in 2009 in MN.
Donor: The Mosaic Company.
Foundation type: Company-sponsored foundation.
Financial data (yr. ended 05/31/13): Assets, $3,065,396 (M); gifts received, $7,001,125; expenditures, $8,331,844; qualifying distributions, $8,326,483; giving activities include $8,326,009 for 74 grants.
Purpose and activities: The foundation supports programs designed to address food; water; and local community investments.
Fields of interest: Education; Environment, natural resources; Environment, water resources; Environment; Agriculture; Agriculture, community food systems; Agriculture, farmlands; Food services; Nutrition; Disasters, preparedness/services; Human services; Community/economic development; Public affairs.
Type of support: General/operating support; Continuing support; Capital campaigns; Program development; Employee volunteer services; Sponsorships; Donated products; In-kind gifts.
Limitations: Applications accepted. Giving primarily in areas of company operations in FL, LA, MN, Argentina, Brazil, Canada, Chile, China, and India; giving also to national organizations. No support for political, private membership, or faith-based organizations not of direct benefit of the entire community. No grants to individuals, or for endowments, public policy, grassroots organizing, advocacy, or electoral campaigns, residential recycling, energy development including dams or renewable energy, or sewage improvement projects in developed countries.
Publications: Application guidelines.
Application information: Minnesota applicants are encouraged to visit website for additional application guidelines.
Initial approach: Complete online application; e-mail letter of inquiry for international organizations
Deadline(s): Sept. 30, Dec. 20, Apr. 4, and June 27
Final notification: Jan. 28, Apr. 18. Aug. 1, and Oct. 24
Officers and Directors: Mark E. Kaplan, Pres.; Richard L. Mack, Secy.; Lawrence Stranghoener, Treas.; Christopher Lambe, Exec. Dir.; Gary Bo Davis; Richard Mclellan; Todd Madden; James Joc O'Rourke; Walt Precourt.
EIN: 270304734
Selected grants: The following grants are a representative sample of this grantmaker's funding activity:
$3,200,000 to Conservation Foundation of the Gulf Coast, Osprey, FL, 2013. For Robinson Preserve Expansion.
$250,000 to Brazil Foundation, New York, NY, 2013. For Mosaic Institute.
$106,000 to Freshwater Society, Excelsior, MN, 2013. For Minnesota Farm Wise.
$100,000 to American Farmland Trust, Washington, DC, 2013. For Improving Water Quality in the Ohio River Basin.
$100,000 to Florida Association of Food Banks, Fort Myers, FL, 2013. For Farmers Feeding Florida.
$73,690 to All Faiths Food Bank, Sarasota, FL, 2013. For Desoto County Hope Against Hunger.
$50,000 to Emergency Foodshelf Network, New Hope, MN, 2013. For Baskets of Hope.
$50,000 to University of Minnesota Foundation, Minneapolis, MN, 2013. For Mosaic Co Professorship for Excellence in Corporate Responsibility.
$25,000 to United Way for South Louisiana, Houma, LA, 2013. For Disaster Relief - Hurricane Isaac.
$50 to United Way of Elgin, South Elgin, IL, 2013. For United Way Campaign Match.

4723
Kevin J. Mossier Foundation ✧
7201 Ohms Ln., Ste. 100
Edina, MN 55439-2148

Established in 1998 in MN.
Donor: Kevin J. Mossier.
Foundation type: Independent foundation.
Financial data (yr. ended 12/31/13): Assets, $1,489,168 (M); expenditures, $1,643,667; qualifying distributions, $1,527,000; giving activities include $1,527,000 for 27 grants (high: $250,000; low: $2,500).
Fields of interest: International human rights; Foundations (public); LGBTQ.
Limitations: Applications not accepted. Giving primarily in Washington, DC, MA, MN and New York, NY; some funding nationally. No grants to individuals.
Application information: Contributes only to pre-selected organizations.
Trustees: Steve Brandwein; Larry Bye; Helen Dehner; Donald S. Ofstedal; Charlie Rounds.
EIN: 411863691

4724
The Laura Jane Musser Fund ✧
(formerly The Musser Fund)
c/o Trust Tax Services
P.O. Box 64713
St. Paul, MN 55164-0713 (612) 303-3208
Contact: Mary Karen Lynn-Klimenko, Grants Prog. Mgr.

FAX: (612) 822-8587;
E-mail: ljmusserfund@earthlink.net; Application address: c/o U.S. Bank, N.A., Att.: Sally Godfrey, 800 Nicollet Mall, Minneapolis, MN 55402, tel.: (612) 303-3208; Main URL: http://www.musserfund.org/

Established in 1990 in MN.
Donor: Laura J. Musser†.
Foundation type: Independent foundation.
Financial data (yr. ended 12/31/13): Assets, $20,280,054 (M); expenditures, $1,129,032; qualifying distributions, $932,259; giving activities include $705,924 for 97 grants (high: $35,000; low: $250).
Purpose and activities: Primary areas of interest include community-based approaches to solving environmental problems, smaller participatory arts programs, securing intercultural harmony and developing leadership in rural communities.
Fields of interest: Arts; Environment; Civil rights, race/intergroup relations; Rural development.
Type of support: Program development; Seed money.
Limitations: Applications accepted. Giving primarily in CO and MN.
Publications: Application guidelines; Grants list; Program policy statement.
Application information: See foundation web site for complete application guidelines. Application form required.
Initial approach: Letter
Copies of proposal: 1
Deadline(s): None
Directors: Lisa Walker Duke; Joseph S. Micallef; Ivy Parish; Robert Strasburg; James Kahea Taylor; Jane Taylor; Drew Walker; Timothy Walker.
Trustee: U.S. Bank, N.A.
Number of staff: None.
EIN: 416334475

4725
George W. Neilson Foundation ✧
P.O. Box 692
Bemidji, MN 56619-0692 (218) 444-4963
Contact: Suzanne Liapis, Secy.
E-mail: sueliapis@excite.com; Main URL: http://www.gwnf.org

Trust established in 1962 in MN.
Donors: George W. Neilson†; Catherine Neilson Cram†.
Foundation type: Independent foundation.
Financial data (yr. ended 12/31/13): Assets, $32,409,544 (M); expenditures, $1,749,125; qualifying distributions, $1,518,193; giving activities include $1,434,406 for 34 grants (high: $250,000; low: $552).
Purpose and activities: Emphasis on matching funds for community needs, leadership, and rural and economic development in the Bemidji, MN, area.
Fields of interest: Arts; Human services; Children/youth, services; Community/economic development.
Type of support: Building/renovation; Equipment; Program development; Matching/challenge support.
Limitations: Applications accepted. Giving primarily in the Bemidji, MN, area. No support for religious activities or governmental services. No grants to individuals, or for endowment funds, scholarships, fellowships, or basic research.
Publications: Application guidelines; Grants list; Informational brochure (including application guidelines).
Application information: Accepts MN Common Grant Application Form; questions answered via telephone Wednesdays 12:30pm-4:30pm. Application form required.
Initial approach: Letter (1-2 pages)
Copies of proposal: 5
Deadline(s): 1st Wed. of each month
Board meeting date(s): 3rd Tues. of each month
Final notification: 1 week following board meeting
Officers and Trustees:* Paul Welle,* Chair.; Marcus Wiechmann, Vice-Chair.; Suzanne Liapis,* Secy.; James Naylor,* Treas.
Number of staff: 1 part-time support.
EIN: 416022186

4726
The Nelson Family Foundation ✧
c/o Tonkawa Inc.
550 Tonkowa Rd.
Long Lake, MN 55356-9724 (952) 404-5636
Contact: C. David Nelson, Secy.

Established in 1997 in MN.
Donors: Glen D. Nelson; Marilyn C. Nelson; Arleen M. Carlson.
Foundation type: Independent foundation.
Financial data (yr. ended 12/31/13): Assets, $485,262 (M); gifts received, $338,074; expenditures, $1,122,085; qualifying distributions, $1,120,521; giving activities include $1,119,508 for 6 grants (high: $502,599; low: $1,217).
Fields of interest: Performing arts, orchestras; Higher education.
Type of support: General/operating support; Annual campaigns; Capital campaigns; Scholarship funds.
Limitations: Applications accepted. Giving primarily in Minneapolis, MN; funding also in Cambridge, MA.
Application information: Application form required.
Initial approach: Proposal, including 3-year budget history
Deadline(s): Mar. 1, for June grants and Sept. 1, for Dec. grants
Officers: Glen D. Nelson, Pres. and C.E.O.; Marilyn C. Nelson, V.P., Treas. and C.F.O.; C. David Nelson, Secy.
Directors: Diana L. Nelson; Wendy M. Nelson.
EIN: 411876884

4727
NFC Foundation ✧
c/o Nash Finch Co.
7600 France Ave. S.
Edina, MN 55435-5924 (952) 844-1201
Contact: Brian Numanville, Chair.
E-mail: NFCFoundation@NashFinch.com; Main URL: http://www.nfcfoundation.org/
Facebook: http://www.facebook.com/pages/NFC-Foundation/197762547845
Funding Recipients: http://www.nfcfoundation.org/fund.htm
NFC Foundation Video: http://www.loavesandfishesmn.org/nf_foundation_video.html

Established in 1997 in MN.
Donors: Nash Finch Co.; General Mills, Inc.
Foundation type: Company-sponsored foundation.
Financial data (yr. ended 12/31/12): Assets, $1,291,705 (M); gifts received, $1,002,814; expenditures, $802,536; qualifying distributions, $802,536; giving activities include $690,449 for 51 grants (high: $32,115; low: $44).
Purpose and activities: The foundation supports programs designed to address hunger and shelter.
Fields of interest: Education, reading; Food services; Food banks; Nutrition; Housing/shelter, homeless; Athletics/sports, Special Olympics; Children/youth, services; Family services; Family services, domestic violence; Homeless, human services; Economically disadvantaged.
Type of support: General/operating support; Program development; Scholarship funds; Employee volunteer services; Donated products.
Limitations: Applications accepted. Giving primarily in areas of company operations in MN. No grants to individuals.
Publications: Application guidelines; Grants list.
Application information: Application form required.
Initial approach: Download application form and mail to foundation
Deadline(s): None
Officers and Directors:* Brian Numanville,* Chair.; Michael Campbell,* Secy.; Robert B. Dimond,* Treas.; Alec C. Covington; Paula Docken; Kathleen M. Mahoney; Gary Spinazzo.
EIN: 411878919
Selected grants: The following grants are a representative sample of this grantmaker's funding activity:
$28,300 to Fisher House Foundation, Rockville, MD, 2011.
$25,535 to Loaves and Fishes Too, Minneapolis, MN, 2011.
$21,190 to Neighborhood House, Saint Paul, MN, 2011.
$21,000 to Dakota Woodlands, Eagan, MN, 2011.
$20,700 to Theresa Living Center, Saint Paul, MN, 2011.
$20,000 to Casa de Esperanza, Saint Paul, MN, 2011.
$20,000 to Catholic Charities of the Archdiocese of Saint Paul and Minneapolis, Minneapolis, MN, 2011.
$5,728 to Great Plains Food Bank, Fargo, ND, 2011.
$5,000 to Valley Rescue Mission, Columbus, GA, 2011.
$5,000 to West Ohio Food Bank, Lima, OH, 2011.

4728
Nicholson Family Foundation ✧
(formerly Richard H. and Nancy B. Nicholson Foundation)
6 W. 5th St., Ste. 200
St. Paul, MN 55102-1490
FAX: (651) 290-0719; E-mail: krj@draftco.net

Established in 1986 in MN.
Donors: Richard H. Nicholson; Nancy B. Nicholson; David O. Nicholson; Ford J. Nicholson; Todd S. Nicholson.
Foundation type: Independent foundation.
Financial data (yr. ended 06/30/13): Assets, $11,890,258 (M); gifts received, $403,082; expenditures, $1,246,149; qualifying distributions, $1,113,093; giving activities include $1,113,093 for grants.
Purpose and activities: Giving primarily for the arts, education, health, and human services.
Fields of interest: Historic preservation/historical societies; Arts; Higher education; Education;

Environment, natural resources; Health organizations, association; Human services; Christian agencies & churches.
Limitations: Applications not accepted. Giving primarily in MN. No grants to individuals.
Application information: Contributes only to pre-selected organizations. Unsolicited requests for funds not accepted.
Officers: Richard H. Nicholson, Pres.; David O. Nicholson, V.P.; Ford J. Nicholson, Secy.; Todd S. Nicholson, Treas.
Number of staff: 1 part-time professional.
EIN: 411572346
Selected grants: The following grants are a representative sample of this grantmaker's funding activity:
$5,300 to Afton Historical Society Press, Afton, MN, 2011. For general operations.
$2,500 to Adler Graduate School, Richfield, MN, 2011. For general operations.

4729
Northwest Area Foundation ✧
60 Plato Blvd. E., Ste. 400
St. Paul, MN 55107-1832 (651) 224-9635
FAX: (651) 225-7701; E-mail: info@nwaf.org; E-mail for grant inquiries: grants@nwaf.org; Main URL: http://www.nwaf.org
Facebook: http://www.facebook.com/pages/Northwest-Area-Foundation/394883336881
Grants Database: http://www.nwaf.org/Content/Grantsearch
Knowledge Center: http://www.grassrootsandgroundwork.org/
Lessons Learned From a Decade of Philanthropy: http://www.nwaf.org/content/Lessons
LinkedIn: http://www.linkedin.com/companies/northwest-area-foundation?trk=fc_badge
Northwest Area Foundation's Philanthropy Promise: http://www.ncrp.org/philanthropys-promise/who
Twitter: http://twitter.com/NWAFound

Incorporated in 1934 in MN as Lexington Foundation; name changed to Louis W. and Maud Hill Family Foundation in 1950; present name adopted 1975.
Donors: Louis W. Hill, Sr.†; Maud Hill†.
Foundation type: Independent foundation.
Financial data (yr. ended 12/31/13): Assets, $456,739,996 (M); expenditures, $25,372,353; qualifying distributions, $20,188,864; giving activities include $13,508,204 for 169 grants (high: $1,000,000; low: $250), and $4,424,273 for foundation-administered programs.
Purpose and activities: The mission of the foundation is to support the efforts by the people, organizations and communities in the eight state region, (MN, IA, SD, ND, MT, ID, WA, and OR), to reduce poverty and achieve sustainable prosperity. By funding the work of proven and promising organizations, the foundation will focus on three outcomes: Increased assets and wealth among people with low incomes; Increased capacity and leadership to reduce poverty; and Improved public policy solutions to reduce poverty.
Fields of interest: Community/economic development; African Americans/Blacks; Hispanics/Latinos; Native Americans/American Indians; Indigenous peoples; Immigrants/refugees; Economically disadvantaged.
Type of support: General/operating support; Management development/capacity building; Program development; Conferences/seminars; Technical assistance; Program-related investments/loans; Employee matching gifts.
Limitations: Applications not accepted. Giving limited to IA, ID, MN, MT, ND, OR, SD, and WA. No grants to individuals, or for lobbying activities.
Publications: Annual report; Financial statement; Grants list; Informational brochure; Occasional report; Program policy statement.
Application information: The foundation does not accept unsolicited proposals. The foundation will support the work of proven or promising organizations working towards reducing poverty and increasing prosperity for low income people.
Board meeting date(s): Feb., May, Aug. and Nov.
Officers and Directors:* Rev. Kevin M. McDonough,* Chair.; Sally Pederson,* Vice-Chair.; Kevin F. Walker, C.E.O. and Pres.; Millie Acamovic, V.P., Fin. and Admin., and C.F.O.; Gary Cunningham, V.P., Progs.; Terrence Glarner, Tr.; Rodney W. Jordan, Tr.; Nicholas Slade, Tr.; M. Lorena Gonzalez; Louis Fors Hill; Linda L. Hoeschler; Hyeok Kim; Jim Laducer; Elsie Meeks; Natalie Camacho Mendoza; Lynda Bourque Moss; William Thorndike, Jr.; Sarah Vogel; Nicholas Walrod.
Number of staff: 22 full-time professional; 6 part-time professional; 1 part-time support.
EIN: 410719221
Selected grants: The following grants are a representative sample of this grantmaker's funding activity:
$1,500,000 to Seventh Generation Fund for Indian Development, Arcata, CA, 2013. For Reservation-Based Nonprofit Capacity-Building Grant Pilot.
$1,000,000 to First Peoples Fund, Rapid City, SD, 2013. For Native Arts Economy-Building Pilot Project, payable over 3.00 years.
$500,000 to First Nations Development Institute, Longmont, CO, 2013. For Informing Strategies for Change: A Survey of Northwest Regional Native American Assets, payable over 2.00 years.
$500,000 to Headwaters Foundation for Justice, Minneapolis, MN, 2013. For African American Leadership Forum Regional.
$500,000 to Hopa Mountain, Bozeman, MT, 2013. For Strengthening the Circle, a Native Nonprofit Leadership Program, payable over 3.00 years.
$200,000 to OneAmerica, Seattle, WA, 2013. For Washington New Americans Financial Literacy Project, payable over 2.00 years.
$150,000 to A Minnesota Without Poverty, Minneapolis, MN, 2013. For Connecting to End Poverty.
$25,000 to Asian Americans/Pacific Islanders in Philanthropy, San Francisco, CA, 2013. For Coalition of Asian American Leaders.
$10,000 to Native American Youth and Family Center, Portland, OR, 2013. For CCC Planning and participation in Twin Cities Replication Efforts.
$7,700 to American Indian Institute, Bozeman, MT, 2013. For sponsorship for Weaving Webs of Women's Wisdom.

4730
Northwest Minnesota Foundation (NWMF) ✧
201 3rd St. N.W.
Bemidji, MN 56601 (218) 759-2057
Contact: For grants: Nate Dorr, Grants Off.
FAX: (218) 759-2328; E-mail: info@nwmf.org; Additional tel. for MN residents: (800) 659-7859; Grant request e-mail: nated@nwmf.org; Main URL: http://www.nwmf.org

Established in 1986 in MN.
Donors: The McKnight Foundation; The Bremer Foundation; Blandin Foundation.
Foundation type: Community foundation.
Financial data (yr. ended 06/30/13): Assets, $53,461,348 (M); gifts received, $4,303,938; expenditures, $4,409,928; giving activities include $1,524,246 for 50+ grants (high: $55,740), and $172,882 for 141 grants to individuals.
Purpose and activities: The foundation invests resources, creates opportunities, and promotes philanthropy to make the region a better place to live and work.
Fields of interest: Arts; Education; Environment, natural resources; Environment; Health care; Housing/shelter; Recreation; Youth development; Economic development; Community development, small businesses; Infants/toddlers; Children/youth; Youth; Aging; Economically disadvantaged.
Type of support: In-kind gifts; Management development/capacity building; Emergency funds; Program development; Conferences/seminars; Seed money; Scholarship funds; Research; Technical assistance; Consulting services; Program evaluation; Program-related investments/loans; Scholarships—to individuals; Matching/challenge support; Loans—to individuals.
Limitations: Applications accepted. Giving limited to Beltrami, Clearwater, Hubbard, Kittson, Lake of the Woods, Mahnomen, Marshall, Norman, Pennington, Polk, Red Lake, and Roseau counties, MN. No support for religious activities. No grants to individuals (except for scholarships), businesses, or for capital campaigns, major equipment purchases, annual campaigns, endowments, building construction, past operating deficits, publicity or advertising, or general/operating expenses.
Publications: Application guidelines; Annual report; Grants list; Informational brochure; Newsletter.
Application information: Online application process beginning July 1. The foundation strongly encourages all potential applicants to contact the foundation's staff before sending a pre-proposal. To be considered for grant funding, a pre-proposal must be submitted on the foundation's pre-proposal application form; if a project is determined to be eligible, a full application is invited. Visit foundation Web site for pre-proposal form and guidelines. Application form required.
Initial approach: Telephone inquiry preferred
Copies of proposal: 2
Deadline(s): None for pre-proposal
Board meeting date(s): 3rd Fri. of each month
Final notification: 3 weeks for full proposal determination
Officers and Directors:* Bob Hager,* Chair.; Pete Haddeland,* Vice-Chair.; Nancy Vyskocil,* Pres.; Marty Sieve,* V.P., Progs.; Faye Auchenpaugh,* Secy.; Judy Roy,* Treas.; Tom Anderson; Kristin Eggerlirg; Cathy Forgit; Jody Horntvedt; Jon Linnell; Leah Pigatti; Jon Quistgaard; Edie Ramstad.
Number of staff: 13 full-time professional; 2 part-time professional; 4 full-time support.
EIN: 411556013
Selected grants: The following grants are a representative sample of this grantmaker's funding activity:
$25,000 to Adult Day Services, Bemidji, MN, 2012. For health and quality assistance implementation.

$25,000 to Blackduck, City of, Blackduck, MN, 2012. For Community Coordinator.
$25,000 to Northwest Regional Sustainable Development Partnership, Saint Paul, MN, 2012. For social science assess of conservation practices.
$25,000 to Northwest Service Cooperative, Thief River Falls, MN, 2012. For secondary school reform pilot project.
$25,000 to University of Minnesota, Crookston, MN, 2012. For college and career prep pilot project.
$24,639 to Bemidji State University, Bemidji, MN, 2012. For Direct Digital Manufacturing Plan.
$22,975 to Park Rapids Community Development Corporation, MN, 2012. For Upper Mississippi Arts Planning.
$21,000 to Mississippi Headwaters Area Dental Health Center, Bemidji, MN, 2012. For oral health prevention expansion.
$19,000 to Agricultural Utilization Research Institute, Crookston, MN, 2012. For Biomass gasifier pilot.
$15,000 to Park Rapids Living at Home/Block Nurse Program, Park Rapids, MN, 2012. For geriatric care management.
$15,000 to Village of Hope, Salisbury, MD, 2012. For trauma related services.
$10,000 to Northwest Community Action, Badger, MN, 2012. For Karlstad disaster assistance.
$7,500 to Oslo, City of, MN, 2012. For comprehensive plan.
$5,000 to Roseau, City Of, Roseau, MN, 2012. For housing study.

4731
Opus Foundation ✧
10350 Bren Rd. W., Tax Dept.
Minnetonka, MN 55343-9014
Main URL: http://www.opus-group.com/AboutUs/Community

Established in 2000 in MN.
Donors: Opus Corp.; Opus, LLC; North Star Ventures.
Foundation type: Company-sponsored foundation.
Financial data (yr. ended 12/31/12): Assets, $70,001,407 (M); expenditures, $3,385,850; qualifying distributions, $3,280,478; giving activities include $3,041,035 for 104 grants (high: $1,000,000; low: $100).
Purpose and activities: The foundation supports programs designed to enhance school readiness for pre-school aged children through early childhood education; achieve healthy social and academic development of school-aged youth through youth development; position and prepare individuals for better futures through workforce development; increase the vitality of struggling neighborhoods or communities through community revitalization; and respond to emergency needs resulting from economically challenging times.
Fields of interest: Education, early childhood education; Higher education; Education; Employment, training; Employment; Housing/shelter; Boys & girls clubs; Youth development; Human services; Community development, neighborhood development; Community/economic development; United Ways and Federated Giving Programs.
Type of support: General/operating support; Annual campaigns; Capital campaigns; Building/renovation; Endowments; Program development; Scholarship funds; Sponsorships.
Limitations: Applications not accepted. Giving limited to AZ, FL, and MN. No grants to individuals.
Application information: Contributes only to pre-selected organizations.
Officers and Directors:* Mark H. Rauenhorst,* Chair. and Pres.; Kate Seng, V.P.; Becky Finnigan, Secy.-Treas.; Kristen Grubb, Tax Off.; John Albers; Tim Murnane; Mark Murphy; Joe Rauenhorst; Thomas Shaver.
EIN: 411983284
Selected grants: The following grants are a representative sample of this grantmaker's funding activity:
$55,200 to Link Unlimited, Chicago, IL, 2012. For Opus Scholars.
$53,600 to Aspire of Illinois, Westchester, IL, 2012. For Aspire and the Belle Center of Chicago Merger.
$50,000 to Washburn Center for Children, Minneapolis, MN, 2012. For School-Based Mental Health Services.
$30,000 to Catholic Charities of the Archdiocese of Chicago, Chicago, IL, 2012. For veterans employment program.
$30,000 to Interfaith Outreach and Community Partners, Plymouth, MN, 2012. For Employment Services Program.
$25,000 to Rebuilding Together Metro Chicago, Chicago, IL, 2012. For Safe at Home Modifications Program.
$24,000 to Notre Dame Middle School, Milwaukee, WI, 2012. For Laptop Initiative Project.
$21,390 to Child Saving Institute, Omaha, NE, 2012. For Creative Curriculum System for Preschool Project.
$5,000 to Sacred Heart House of Denver, Denver, CO, 2012. For homeless mothers and single women.
$5,000 to School on Wheels, Indianapolis, IN, 2012. For school supplies.

4732
Ordean Foundation ✧
501 Ordean Bldg.
Duluth, MN 55802-4725
Contact: Stephen A. Mangan, Exec. Dir.

Incorporated in 1933 in MN.
Donors: Albert L. Ordean†; Louise Ordean†.
Foundation type: Independent foundation.
Financial data (yr. ended 12/31/13): Assets, $38,854,749 (M); expenditures, $2,257,694; qualifying distributions, $1,821,379; giving activities include $1,420,228 for 45+ grants (high: $200,000).
Purpose and activities: Giving primarily for the food, clothing, shelter, physical and mental health care of economically disadvantaged Duluthians, and for the treatment, care, and rehabilitation of persons who are chronically or temporarily mentally ill, or whose physical capacity is impaired either by injury, illness, birth defects, age, alcoholism or similar causes; funding also for youth guidance programs designed to avoid and prevent delinquency from lawful and healthful pursuits by young citizens.
Fields of interest: Education; Medical care, rehabilitation; Health care; Substance abuse, services; Mental health/crisis services; Alcoholism; Crime/violence prevention, youth; Food services; Housing/shelter; Human services; YM/YWCAs & YM/YWHAs; Children/youth, services; Family services; Homeless, human services; Aging; Disabilities, people with; Economically disadvantaged.
Type of support: General/operating support; Continuing support; Program development; Scholarship funds; Program-related investments/loans; Matching/challenge support.
Limitations: Applications accepted. Giving limited to Duluth and contiguous cities and townships in St. Louis County, MN. No support for direct religious purposes, or for political campaigns or lobbying activities. No grants to individuals (directly), or for endowment funds, travel, conferences, seminars or workshops, telephone solicitations, benefits, dinners, research, including biomedical research, deficit financing, national fundraising campaigns, or to supplant government funding.
Application information: Accepts Minnesota Common Grant Application Form. Scholarship applications are available at the financial aid office of the College of St. Scholastica and Lake Superior College.
Board meeting date(s): 2nd Tues. of each month
Officers and Directors:* Lonnie Swartz,* Pres.; Ann Niedringhaus,* V.P.; Benjamin Stromberg,* Secy.; Mary Beth Santori, Treas.; Stephen A. Mangan, Exec. Dir.; Marge Bray; Carl Crawford; Tom Patnoe; Jim Vizanko; Chuck Walt.
Number of staff: 2 full-time professional; 1 part-time support.
EIN: 410711611

4733
Dr. William James And Winifred Joyce O'Rourke Family Charitable Trust ✧ ☆
9450 Old Cedar Ave. S.
Bloomington, MN 55425-2418

Established in WI.
Foundation type: Independent foundation.
Financial data (yr. ended 12/31/13): Assets, $408,512 (M); expenditures, $2,031,536; qualifying distributions, $2,000,000; giving activities include $2,000,000 for 3 grants (high: $1,000,000; low: $69,448).
Fields of interest: Secondary school/education; Higher education.
Limitations: Applications not accepted. Giving primarily in Madison, WI.
Application information: Unsolicited requests for funds not accepted.
Trustees: Kathleen Losardo; Colleen O'Rourke; Patrick O'Rourke; Sean O'Rourke; Timothy O'Rourke.
EIN: 461529496

4734
I. A. O'Shaughnessy Foundation, Inc. ✧
2001 Killebrew Dr., No. 120
Bloomington, MN 55425-1865 (952) 698-0959
Contact: Timothy J. O'Shaughnessy, Pres.
FAX: (952) 698-0958;
E-mail: iaoshaughnessyfdn@tds.net; Main URL: http://www.iaoshaughnessyfdn.org

Incorporated in 1941 in MN.
Donors: I.A. O'Shaughnessy†; John F. O'Shaughnessy†; Globe Oil and Refining Companies; Lario Oil and Gas Co.
Foundation type: Independent foundation.
Financial data (yr. ended 12/31/12): Assets, $82,087,832 (M); gifts received, $200,000; expenditures, $4,267,203; qualifying distributions,

$3,927,090; giving activities include $3,588,529 for 74 grants (high: $500,000; low: $695).
Purpose and activities: The foundation's current interest is the support of high quality education that prepares students in disadvantaged communities for educational and life success. The foundation funds organizations that: provide support networks, remove impediments to student success, are broadly supported by the community, and have a record of demonstrated success. The foundation is especially interested in funding endeavors that are broad in scope, widespread in influence, high-impact, innovative, and replicable models.
Fields of interest: Elementary/secondary education; Education, early childhood education; Elementary school/education; Children/youth; Children; Youth; Young adults; Minorities; Girls; Young adults, female; Boys; Young adults, male; Economically disadvantaged.
Type of support: General/operating support; Continuing support; Annual campaigns; Capital campaigns; Endowments; Program development; Curriculum development; Scholarship funds; Research; Matching/challenge support.
Limitations: Applications not accepted. Giving limited to the U.S., with emphasis on areas where foundation directors live. No support for religious missions or individual parishes, or for national fundraising organizations, or political organizations. No grants to individuals, or for operational dependence, lobbying, or capital campaign gifts exceeding twenty percent of the campaign goal; no loans.
Publications: Grants list; Program policy statement.
Application information: Letters of inquiry are not being accepted at this time. See foundation web site for updates in this area.
Board meeting date(s): Varies
Officers and Directors:* John F. O'Shaughnessy, Jr.,* Pres.; Eileen A. O'Shaughnessy,* V.P. and Secy.; Teresa O'Shaugnessy Duggan, V.P.; Charles Lyman, V.P.; Chevonne E. O'Shaughnessy,* V.P.; Daniel J. O'Shaughnessy, V.P.; Karen J. O'Shaughnessy, V.P.; Terence P. O'Shaughnessy, V.P.; Michele O'Shaughnessy Traeger,* V.P.; Kathryn Lyman Wysong,* V.P.; Michael F. Sullivan, Treas.
Number of staff: 1 part-time support.
EIN: 416011524

4735
Oswald Family Foundation ✧
(formerly Oswald Charitable Foundation)
7400 Metro Blvd., Ste. 475
Edina, MN 55439-2380
E-mail: scwilkes@adventuresingiving.com

Established in 1986 in MN.
Donor: Charles W. Oswald.
Foundation type: Independent foundation.
Financial data (yr. ended 12/31/12): Assets, $17,793,366 (M); expenditures, $822,184; qualifying distributions, $784,159; giving activities include $694,000 for 79 grants (high: $40,000; low: $1,000).
Purpose and activities: Giving primarily for the arts, education, children, youth and social services, international economic and community development, leadership, and social entrepreneurship.
Fields of interest: Arts; Education; Mental health/crisis services; Human services; Children/youth, services; International affairs; Community/economic development.
International interests: Africa; Bolivia; Kenya; Mexico; Peru; Tanzania; Uganda.
Type of support: General/operating support; Continuing support; Management development/capacity building; Program development; Seed money; Program-related investments/loans; Exchange programs; Matching/challenge support.
Limitations: Applications not accepted. Giving primarily in Minneapolis, MN, Troy, OH, Boston, MA, and San Diego, CA. No support for religious organizations. No grants to individuals.
Application information: Contributes only to pre-selected organizations, but will respond to inquiry by letter, telephone or e-mail.
Board meeting date(s): Nov.
Officers and Directors:* Julie Oswald,* Pres.; David C. Oswald,* Treas.; Charles W. Oswald; Kathleen Oswald; Sara Oswald; Thomas Oswald; Carolyn Workman.
EIN: 363486546

4736
Pagel Foundation ✧ ☆
(formerly Jack W. Pagel Foundation)
2940 Gale Rd.
Wayzata, MN 55391-2626 (507) 475-2084
Contact: Jack Pagel, Pres.

Established in 1986 in MN.
Donors: Jack W. Pagel; Vivian Gruber.
Foundation type: Independent foundation.
Financial data (yr. ended 12/31/12): Assets, $3,811,129 (M); gifts received, $775,000; expenditures, $781,394; qualifying distributions, $693,592; giving activities include $693,592 for grants.
Fields of interest: Education; Recreation, camps; Human services; Christian agencies & churches.
Limitations: Applications accepted. Giving primarily in FL and MN. No grants to individuals.
Application information: Application form not required.
Initial approach: Letter
Deadline(s): None
Officer: Jack Pagel, Pres.
EIN: 363575392

4737
The Patch Foundation ✧
3201 Rankin Rd.
Minneapolis, MN 55418-2505 (612) 781-7677
Contact: Carolyn P. Sample, Pres.

Established in 1997 in MN.
Donors: Earl Patch†; Carolyn Sample.
Foundation type: Independent foundation.
Financial data (yr. ended 12/31/13): Assets, $8,370,146 (M); expenditures, $628,350; qualifying distributions, $622,900; giving activities include $622,000 for 41 grants (high: $100,000; low: $1,000).
Purpose and activities: In awarding grants, the foundation gives preference to Christian charitable organizations in MN. Medical foundations and education receive prime consideration.
Fields of interest: Higher education; Health care, association; Health care; Human services; Salvation Army; Christian agencies & churches.
Limitations: Applications accepted. Giving primarily in MN. No support for political groups or causes, the arts, or any group whose goals are contrary to Christian principles.
Application information: Application form required.
Board meeting date(s): Jan.
Officer: Carolyn P. Sample, Pres.
Directors: Ernest Lindstrom; William C. Peterson.
EIN: 411873951

4738
Patterson Foundation ✧
(formerly Patterson Dental Foundation)
1031 Mendota Heights Rd.
St. Paul, MN 55120-1419 (651) 686-1929
Contact: Admin.
E-mail: information@pattersonfoundation.net; Main URL: http://www.pattersonfoundation.net

Established in 2003 in MN.
Donor: Several individuals associated with Patterson Cos.
Foundation type: Independent foundation.
Financial data (yr. ended 12/31/12): Assets, $16,890,021 (M); gifts received, $84,261; expenditures, $981,875; qualifying distributions, $846,393; giving activities include $796,755 for 28 grants (high: $210,000; low: $5,000).
Purpose and activities: The foundation provides resources to programs and to nonprofit organizations in the areas of oral health, animal health, and occupational and physical rehabilitation. The foundation also supports educational programs, and programs for youth and for the economically disadvantaged. It also provides educational scholarships for dependents of Patterson Dental Co. employees. Within oral health, animal health, and occupational and physical rehabilitation, the foundation is focuses on services to those most in need. In addition the foundation seeks to increase the number of underrepresented people in these fields. There is very strong preference for one-time projects or start-up costs, or programs involving as volunteers a number of professionals or students in dentistry, veterinary medicine, occupational or physical rehabilitation.
Fields of interest: Museums (specialized); Higher education; Higher education, college (community/junior); Graduate/professional education; Dental school/education; Animals/wildlife, volunteer services; Veterinary medicine; Animals/wildlife, training; Dental care; Medical care, rehabilitation; Physical therapy; Athletics/sports, Special Olympics.
Type of support: Employee-related scholarships; Capital campaigns; Continuing support; Program development; Seed money.
Limitations: Applications accepted. Giving in North America with emphasis on the United States. No support for religious, political or advocacy organizations. No grants for purchase of products sold by Patterson Companies, or for film/video productions, fundraising events, conferences or seminars; no funding of direct costs of treatment or therapies.
Publications: Application guidelines; Grants list; Informational brochure (including application guidelines).
Application information: Scholarships to dependents of Patterson Companies employees paid through Scholarship America. Contact the foundation office for current due dates and decision dates. Application form required.

Initial approach: Letter of inquiry (e-mail accepted)
Copies of proposal: 2
Deadline(s): At least 6 weeks prior to board meetings
Board meeting date(s): 4 times per year
Final notification: Within 30 days of decision

Officers: Gary D. Johnson, Pres.; Robert C. Clifford, V.P.; Matthew L. Levitt, Secy.; R. Stephen Armstrong, Treas.; Michelle Mennicke, Mgr.
Directors: Scott P. Anderson; Jeffrey B. Baker; Ronald E. Ezerski; Raymond D. (Tad) Godsil III; Pam Hemmen; George Henriques; David G. Misiak; Todd W. Mueller; James W. Wiltz.
EIN: 743076772
Selected grants: The following grants are a representative sample of this grantmaker's funding activity:
$212,250 to Scholarship America, Minneapolis, MN, 2011. For scholarships for dependents of Patterson employees.
$60,000 to Dental Lifeline Network, Denver, CO, 2011. To expand Donated Dental Services for people with disabilities.
$56,000 to National Childrens Oral Health Foundation, Charlotte, NC, 2011. To expand Tomorrow's SMILES and Students United for America's Toothfairy.
$52,055 to Oral Health America, Chicago, IL, 2011. To start school-based dental care in 2 communities and identify 1 new site.
$37,750 to Americas Dentists Care Foundation Missions of Mercy, Wichita, KS, 2011. To assist in starting 12 new Missions of Mercy programs and a new forklift.
$20,000 to Childrens Dental Center, Inglewood, CA, 2011. For over 100 dental and hygiene students serving children.
$15,000 to Loma Linda University, Loma Linda, CA, 2011. For scholarships for 3 Hispanic dental hygiene students.
$12,000 to Texas A & M Foundation, College Station, TX, 2011. For partial funding for minority fellow to become faculty member.
$10,000 to Iowa Dental Foundation, Johnston, IA, 2011. For volunteers to provide free dental care at event for hundreds.
$4,000 to Saint Catherine University, Saint Paul, MN, 2011. For OT students pilot handwriting program with low-income preschoolers.

4739
The Pentair Foundation ✧
5500 Wayzata Blvd., Ste. 800
Golden Valley, MN 55416-1261 (763) 545-1730
Contact: Susan Carter, Fdn. Mgr.
FAX: (763) 656-5404; Main URL: http://www.pentair.com/about-us/corporate-social-responsibility/team-pentair

Established in 1998 in MN.
Donor: Pentair, Inc.
Foundation type: Company-sponsored foundation.
Financial data (yr. ended 12/31/13): Assets, $3,725,813 (M); gifts received, $5,355,996; expenditures, $5,457,788; qualifying distributions, $5,456,233; giving activities include $4,839,083 for 252 grants (high: $350,000; low: $1,000), and $178,383 for 119 employee matching gifts.
Purpose and activities: The foundation supports programs designed to promote education, sustainability in water and energy, and workforce readiness.
Fields of interest: Arts, cultural/ethnic awareness; Arts education; Elementary/secondary education; Vocational education; Higher education; Education; Environment, water resources; Environment, energy; Public health, clean water supply; Employment, services; Employment, training; Employment; American Red Cross; Youth, services; Family services; Community/economic development; United Ways and Federated Giving Programs; Mathematics; Engineering/technology; Science; Economically disadvantaged.
Type of support: General/operating support; Program development; Scholarship funds; Employee matching gifts.
Limitations: Giving primarily in areas of company operations in Moorpark, CA, Hanover Park and North Aurora, IL, Kansas City, KS, Mt. Sterling, KY, Anoka, Minneapolis/St. Paul, and New Brighton, MN, Sanford, NC, Ashland and Chardon, OH, Warwick, RI, Radford, VA, Brookfield and Delavan, WI and Colon, Honduras. No support for political, lobbying, or fraternal organizations, religious groups for religious purposes, athletic or sports-related organizations, or non 501 (c)(3) organizations or those operating under a fiscal agent. No grants to individuals, or for scholarships, medical research, fundraising events, sponsorships, or advertising, travel or tour expenses, conferences, seminars, workshops, or symposiums.
Publications: Application guidelines.
Application information: The foundation is currently conducting a strategic program and awards grants only to current or past grant recipients. Application form not required.
Initial approach: Complete online application
Deadline(s): June 30 for current or past grant recipients
Board meeting date(s): Feb. and Aug.

Officers and Directors:* Michael G. Meyer, Pres. and Treas.; Michael Conklin,* Secy.; Amy Skoczlas Cole, Exec. Dir.; Todd R. Gleason; Randall J. Hogan; Frederick S. Koury; Angela D. Lageson; John L. Stauch.
Number of staff: 1 full-time professional.
EIN: 411890149

4740
Edward J. & Leslye Phillips Family Foundation ✧
100 University Ave. S.E.
Minneapolis, MN 55414-2101

Established in 2004 in MN.
Donors: Edward J. Phillips; Leslye F.M. Phillips; Edward J. Phillips Charitable Lead Annuity Trust.
Foundation type: Independent foundation.
Financial data (yr. ended 12/31/12): Assets, $26,870,920 (M); gifts received, $250,000; expenditures, $1,502,968; qualifying distributions, $1,391,006; giving activities include $1,377,918 for 22 grants (high: $500,000; low: $250).
Purpose and activities: Giving primarily for education, medical research, and children and youth services, particularly a children's hospital.
Fields of interest: Education; Hospitals (specialty); Human services; Children/youth, services.
Limitations: Applications not accepted. Giving primarily in MN and NY. No grants to individuals.
Application information: Contributes only to pre-selected organizations.
Officers: Dean Phillips, Pres. and Secy.; Typer Phillips, V.P.
EIN: 202041201

4741
The Jay and Rose Phillips Family Foundation of Minnesota
615 1st Ave. N.E., Ste. 330
Minneapolis, MN 55413-2640 (612) 623-1654
E-mail: info@phillipsfamilymn.org; Main URL: http://phillipsfamilymn.org/
Twitter: https://twitter.com/JayRosePhillips

Established in 2011 in MN.
Foundation type: Independent foundation.
Financial data (yr. ended 12/31/13): Assets, $70,383,181 (M); expenditures, $4,122,638; qualifying distributions, $3,641,979; giving activities include $3,027,746 for 161 grants (high: $200,000; low: $41), and $57,606 for foundation-administered programs.
Purpose and activities: Giving to address the unmet human and social needs of individuals, families, and communities that have the least access to resources.
Fields of interest: Elementary/secondary school reform; Vocational education; Education; Employment, vocational rehabilitation; Housing/shelter, alliance/advocacy; Housing/shelter, search services; Human services; Family services; Civil/human rights, immigrants; Civil/human rights, minorities; Civil/human rights, LGBTQ; Civil liberties, reproductive rights; Transportation; Jewish agencies & synagogues; Disabilities, people with; Minorities; Asians/Pacific Islanders; African Americans/Blacks; Hispanics/Latinos; Native Americans/American Indians; Women; AIDS, people with; Immigrants/refugees; Economically disadvantaged; Homeless; LGBTQ.
Type of support: General/operating support; Management development/capacity building; Program development; Curriculum development; Consulting services; Program evaluation.
Limitations: Giving primarily in the Twin Cities metropolitan, MN, area. No support for political campaigns or lobbying efforts to influence legislation. No grants to individuals.
Publications: Annual report.
Application information: Check foundation web site for updates on application information.
Initial approach: Telephone call or online Letter of Inquiry

Officers: Dean Phillips,* Co-Chair. and Treas.; Jeanne Phillips,* Co-Chair.; Patrick J. Troska, Exec. Dir.
Trustees: Walter Harris; Karin Philips; Tyler Phillips.
EIN: 274196509
Selected grants: The following grants are a representative sample of this grantmaker's funding activity:
$200,000 to Minneapolis Jewish Federation, Minnetonka, MN, 2012. For Annual Campaign.
$200,000 to Minneapolis Jewish Federation, Minnetonka, MN, 2013. For Annual Campaign.
$150,000 to Saint Paul Foundation, Saint Paul, MN, 2013. For Twin Cities Workforce Innovation Network.
$140,000 to Nexus Community Partners, Saint Paul, MN, 2013. For work to build community-based power.
$125,000 to Minnesota Private College Fund, Saint Paul, MN, 2012. For Phillips Scholars Program.
$124,400 to Minnesota Private College Fund, Saint Paul, MN, 2013. For Phillips Scholars.
$90,000 to International Institute of Minnesota, Saint Paul, MN, 2012. For Sector Employment Initiative- Year 2.

$75,000 to Transit for Livable Communities, Saint Paul, MN, 2013. To provide transit access to underserved communities.
$60,000 to Family Housing Fund, Minneapolis, MN, 2012. For Supportive Housing Central Referral System.
$50,000 to Family Housing Fund, Minneapolis, MN, 2013. For Metro Access To Supportive Housing (MATSH).
$50,000 to Jewish Family Service of Los Angeles, Los Angeles, CA, 2012. For 1st year on a 5 year $250,000 pledge for the endowment campaign.
$50,000 to Jewish Family Service of Los Angeles, Los Angeles, CA, 2013. For Endowment Campaign.
$50,000 to Northside Achievement Zone, Minneapolis, MN, 2012. For Northside Achievement Zone.
$50,000 to Planned Parenthood of Minnesota, North Dakota, South Dakota, Saint Paul, MN, 2012. For capital support.
$45,000 to Opportunities Industrialization Center, Summit Academy, Minneapolis, MN, 2012. For Sector Employment Initiative- Year 2.
$30,000 to Equality Minnesota, Project 515 Education Campaign, Minneapolis, MN, 2012. For business outreach for equality.
$30,000 to Genesys Works, Saint Paul, MN, 2013. For Pipeline Expansion Project.
$30,000 to Minnesota Housing Partnership, Saint Paul, MN, 2013. For Federal Housing Policy Advocacy.
$25,000 to Educators for Excellence, New York, NY, 2013. For general operating support.
$10,000 to Courage Center, Minneapolis, MN, 2012. For general operating support.

4742
The Pine River Foundation ✧ ☆

601 Carlson Pkwy., Ste. 330
Minnetonka, MN 55305-7703

Donors: Pine River Domestic Management L.P.; Steve Kuhn.
Foundation type: Independent foundation.
Financial data (yr. ended 12/31/13): Assets, $216,235 (M); gifts received, $821,212; expenditures, $604,977; qualifying distributions, $604,977; giving activities include $604,473 for 46 grants (high: $100,000; low: $250).
Fields of interest: Education; Health organizations; Human services; Women.
Type of support: General/operating support.
Limitations: Applications not accepted. Giving primarily in New York, NY.
Application information: Unsolicited requests for funds not accepted.
Officers and Directors:* Brendan McAllister,* Pres.; Ben Hawn, V.P. and Secy.; Pam Opland, Treas.; Richard Knight; Tom Siering.
EIN: 463366714

4743
Piper Jaffray Foundation ✧ ☆

(formerly U.S. Bancorp Piper Jaffray Companies Foundation)
800 Nicollet Mall, J09SFA
Minneapolis, MN 55402-7000 (612) 303-8202
Main URL: http://www.piperjaffray.com/

Established in 1993 in MN.
Donor: Piper Jaffray Cos. Inc.
Foundation type: Company-sponsored foundation.
Financial data (yr. ended 12/31/13): Assets, $707,379 (M); gifts received, $954,050; expenditures, $826,153; qualifying distributions, $826,073; giving activities include $826,073 for 120 grants (high: $152,756; low: $20).
Purpose and activities: The foundation supports organizations involved with arts and culture, economic education, community development, and civic engagement.
Fields of interest: Arts; Health care; Human services.
Type of support: General/operating support; Capital campaigns; Program development; Employee matching gifts.
Limitations: Applications accepted. Giving limited to areas of company operations in CA, Denver, CO, Chicago, IL, Kansas City, KS, Boston, MA, Minneapolis and St. Paul, MN, St. Louis, MO, New York, NY, Portland, OR, and Seattle, WA. No support for religious, political, veterans', or fraternal groups, teams, organizations receiving primary funding from the United Way, or newly formed nonprofit organizations. No grants to individuals, or for groups seeking support for planning, personal needs, or travel, public service or political campaigns, athletic or pageant scholarships, publications, audio-visual pieces, or debt reduction.
Publications: Application guidelines.
Application information: Application form required.
Initial approach: See website for application form
Copies of proposal: 1
Deadline(s): Jan.1 through Mar. 15
Board meeting date(s): 2nd qtr.
Officers and Directors:* Debra L. Schoneman,* Pres. and C.F.O.; John W. Geelan, Secy.; Timothy L. Carter, Treas.; Christopher D. Crawshaw; Andrew S. Duff; Frank E. Fairman; Patrick E. Gray; Matthew S. Hemsley; Thomas P. Schnettler.
Number of staff: 2 full-time professional; 1 full-time support.
EIN: 411734808

4744
Poepl Family Foundation ✧

c/o John F. Poepl
P.O. Box 28
Vermillion, MN 55085-0028

Established in 1997 in MN.
Donors: John F. Poepl; Mary Pat Poepl.
Foundation type: Independent foundation.
Financial data (yr. ended 12/31/13): Assets, $716,518 (M); gifts received, $1,300,000; expenditures, $744,576; qualifying distributions, $744,200; giving activities include $744,200 for 9 grants (high: $605,500; low: $1,000).
Fields of interest: Education; Human services; Catholic agencies & churches.
Limitations: Applications not accepted. Giving primarily in MN; some funding also in OH. No grants to individuals.
Application information: Contributes only to pre-selected organizations.
Directors: John F. Poepl; Mary Pat Poepl; James Reissner.
EIN: 411894854

4745
Carl and Eloise Pohlad Family Foundation ✧

60 S. 6th St., Ste. 3900
Minneapolis, MN 55402-4439
Contact: Misha Dashevsky, Grants Mgr.
E-mail: info@pohladfamilygiving.org; Main URL: http://www.pohladfamilygiving.org

Established in 1993 in MN.
Donors: Carl R. Pohlad†; Eloise O. Pohlad†; BP Corp.; Marquette Bancshares, Inc.
Foundation type: Independent foundation.
Financial data (yr. ended 12/31/12): Assets, $109,586,767 (M); gifts received, $6,161,732; expenditures, $11,077,099; qualifying distributions, $10,962,924; giving activities include $9,905,927 for 477 grants (high: $1,000,000; low: $25), $293,109 for 3 foundation-administered programs and $560,000 for 2 loans/program-related investments (high: $410,000; low: $150,000).
Purpose and activities: The mission of the foundation is to improve the quality of life in the Minneapolis-St. Paul region by supporting organizations and leading initiatives that address important issues and needs.
Fields of interest: Arts; Employment; Housing/shelter; Youth development; Human services; Children/youth; Youth; Young adults; Economically disadvantaged.
Type of support: Program-related investments/loans; General/operating support; Capital campaigns; Scholarship funds; Employee matching gifts; Matching/challenge support.
Limitations: Applications accepted. Giving primarily in the Minneapolis and St. Paul, MN, metro region. No support for religious or political organizations. No grants to individuals.
Publications: Application guidelines; Grants list; Multi-year report.
Application information: Applications for public grants are considered only in response to open online applications or an invitation to apply.Requests for private grants come directly from family members. Applications submitted directly to the foundation for private grants will not be considered.
Initial approach: Online
Deadline(s): Varies
Final notification: 2-6 months
Officers and Directors:* William M. Pohlad,* Pres.; Marina Munoz Lyon,* V.P.; Pamela E. Omann,* Secy.-Treas.; James O. Pohlad; Robert C. Pohlad.
Number of staff: 2 full-time professional; 3 full-time support.
EIN: 411768558
Selected grants: The following grants are a representative sample of this grantmaker's funding activity:
$1,000,000 to Breck School, Minneapolis, MN, 2012. For project support.
$1,000,000 to Urban Homeworks, Minneapolis, MN, 2012. For project support.
$500,000 to Basilica Landmark, Minneapolis, MN, 2012. For capital support.
$500,000 to Cal Ripken, Sr. Foundation, Baltimore, MD, 2012. For project support.
$500,000 to Foundation of Childrens Hospitals and Clinics of Minnesota, Roseville, MN, 2012. For capital support.
$130,000 to Lakeview Ranch Innovative Dementia Care Foundation, Darwin, MN, 2012. For general operating support.

$25,000 to People Serving People, Minneapolis, MN, 2012. For general operating support.
$11,040 to Neighborhood Involvement Program, Minneapolis, MN, 2012. For program support.
$10,000 to Bright Water Montessori School, Minneapolis, MN, 2012. For project support.
$10,000 to Twin Cities Film Fest, Minneapolis, MN, 2012. For program support.

4746
The Polaris Foundation ✧
2100 Hwy. 55
Medina, MN 55340-9770
Main URL: http://www.polaris.com/en-us/company/2012/polaris-foundation.aspx

Established in 1996 in MN.
Donor: Polaris Industries Inc.
Foundation type: Company-sponsored foundation.
Financial data (yr. ended 12/31/13): Assets, $275,163 (M); gifts received, $437,778; expenditures, $880,463; qualifying distributions, $880,463; giving activities include $879,428 for 72 grants (high: $525,965; low: $25).
Purpose and activities: The foundation supports programs designed to promote youth; the environment; and community development.
Fields of interest: Arts; Health care; Recreation.
Type of support: General/operating support; Program development; In-kind gifts.
Limitations: Applications accepted. Giving primarily in areas of company operations in Spirit Lake, IA, Roseau and Wyoming, MN, Vermillion, SD, Osceola, WI, and Winnipeg, Canada. No support for public charities or foundations, political, fraternal, or veterans' organizations, for-profit organizations, state agencies, religious organizations not of direct benefit to the entire community, international or foreign based organizations, social service organizations, or discriminatory organizations. No grants to individuals, or for research projects, discretionary or emergency funds, capital campaigns, or courtesy advertising.
Publications: Application guidelines; Program policy statement.
Application information: Application form required.
Initial approach: Contact foundation for application form
Deadline(s): None
Officers and Directors:* Stacy L. Bogart,* Pres.; Paul Moe, V.P. and Treas.; Jennifer Carbert, Secy.; Michael W. Malone; Bennett J. Morgan; James P. Williams; Scott W. Wine.
EIN: 411828276
Selected grants: The following grants are a representative sample of this grantmaker's funding activity:
$256,919 to United Way, Greater Twin Cities, Minneapolis, MN, 2011.

4747
Prospect Creek Foundation ✧
4900 IDS Ctr.
80 S. 8th St.
Minneapolis, MN 55402-2100 (612) 672-9603
Contact: Martha C. Atwater, Dir.

Established in 1993 in MN.
Donor: H. Brewster Atwater, Jr.
Foundation type: Independent foundation.
Financial data (yr. ended 12/31/13): Assets, $52,204,019 (M); gifts received, $1,200,000; expenditures, $2,984,504; qualifying distributions, $2,827,196; giving activities include $2,789,781 for 107 grants (high: $696,001; low: $250).
Fields of interest: Performing arts; Performing arts, theater; Arts; Higher education; Education; Hospitals (general); Reproductive health, family planning; Health organizations, association; Medical research, institute; Human services; United Ways and Federated Giving Programs.
Limitations: Applications accepted. Giving primarily in CA and MN. No grants to individuals.
Application information: Application form required.
Initial approach: Letter
Copies of proposal: 1
Deadline(s): None
Directors: H. Brewster Atwater, Jr.; Martha Clark Atwater; Elizabeth Atwater Connolly.
EIN: 411736420

4748
RBC Foundation USA ✧
(formerly RBC Dain Rauscher Foundation)
60 S. 6th St., M.S. P20
Minneapolis, MN 55402-4422 (612) 371-2936
Contact: Julie Allen, Mgr.
FAX: (612) 371-7933;
E-mail: fndapplications@rbc.com; Additional tel.: (612) 371-2218; Main URL: http://www.rbcwm-usa.com/community/cid-275952.html

Incorporated in 1960 in MN.
Donors: Dain Rauscher Inc.; RBC Dain Rauscher Corp.; RBC Capital Markets Corp.
Foundation type: Company-sponsored foundation.
Financial data (yr. ended 10/31/13): Assets, $312,203 (M); gifts received, $2,088,192; expenditures, $2,398,698; qualifying distributions, $2,398,698; giving activities include $2,398,698 for grants.
Purpose and activities: The foundation supports organizations involved with arts and culture, human services, and civic affairs. Special emphasis is directed toward programs designed to promote education and health.
Fields of interest: Arts, cultural/ethnic awareness; Visual arts; Performing arts, music; Arts; Elementary/secondary education; Adult education—literacy, basic skills & GED; Education, services; Education, reading; Education; Health care; Mental health/crisis services, public education; Mental health, treatment; Mental health, disorders; Mental health, depression; Mental health/crisis services; Employment, training; Food services; Youth development, adult & child programs; Youth development; Family services; Human services, financial counseling; Human services; Community/economic development; Public affairs, citizen participation; Public affairs; Children; Youth; Economically disadvantaged.
Type of support: Program development; General/operating support; Continuing support; Annual campaigns; Employee volunteer services; Employee matching gifts.
Limitations: Applications accepted. Giving on a national basis in areas of company operations, with emphasis on the Twin Cities, MN, metropolitan area. No support for religious, political, fraternal, or veterans' organizations, athletic teams, or hospitals, nursing homes, hospices, or daycare facilities; generally no start-up organizations. No grants to individuals, or for sponsorships, fundraising events, athletic events or scholarships, travel, academic, medical, or scientific research, recreational or athletic programs, audio or video recording projects, literary or media art projects, artist enrichment programs, medical, health, mental health, or disease-specific or disease-related services, senior citizen programs, or developmental disabilities or disorders, including deafness and blindness, non-K-12 educational programs, environmental education programs, programs limited to special needs students, or childcare or day care programs; generally no capital or endowment campaigns or multi-year commitments.
Publications: Application guidelines; Program policy statement.
Application information: Letters of inquiry for organizations located in the Twin Cities, MN, area should be submitted if the applying organization did not receive funding from the RBC Foundation last year. Support is limited to 1 contribution per organization during any given year. Application form required.
Initial approach: Complete online letter of inquiry for new applicants located in Twin Cities, MN; complete online application form for returning grantees located in Twin Cities, MN; complete online application form for organizations located outside of the Twin Cities, MN metropolitan area
Deadline(s): Jan. 17 and June 13 for new applicants located in Twin Cities, MN; Jan. 31 and June 27 for returning grantees located in Twin Cities, MN; Feb. 18 and July 18 for organizations located outside of Twin Cities, MN, metropolitan area
Board meeting date(s): Feb., Mar., Aug., and Sept.
Final notification: Within 90 days
Directors: Martha Baumbach; John Taft; Mary Zimmer.
Number of staff: 1 full-time professional; 1 full-time support.
EIN: 416030639

4749
Red Wing Shoe Company Foundation ✧
314 Main St.
Red Wing, MN 55066-2300
Contact: Kellie Steiner, Tr.
E-mail: kellie.steiner@redwingshoe.com

Incorporated in 1955 in MN.
Donor: Red Wing Shoe Co., Inc.
Foundation type: Company-sponsored foundation.
Financial data (yr. ended 12/31/13): Assets, $387,723 (M); gifts received, $850,000; expenditures, $641,021; qualifying distributions, $641,021; giving activities include $574,900 for 40 grants (high: $127,500; low: $500), and $59,976 for 208 employee matching gifts.
Purpose and activities: The foundation supports organizations involved with arts and culture, education, environmental education, human services, and community development.
Fields of interest: Arts; Environment; Human services.
Limitations: Applications accepted. Giving primarily in the Danville, KY, Red Wing, MN, and Potosi, MO, areas. No grants to individuals.
Publications: Annual report.
Application information: Application form required.
Initial approach: Letter
Deadline(s): None
Officer: William J. Sweasy, Chair.

Directors: Suzanne Blue; Kellie Steiner; Carol Sweasay.
EIN: 416020177
Selected grants: The following grants are a representative sample of this grantmaker's funding activity:
$127,000 to Environmental Learning Center, Vero Beach, FL, 2011.
$127,000 to Environmental Learning Center, Vero Beach, FL, 2011.

4750
Regis Foundation ✧
7201 Metro Blvd.
Minneapolis, MN 55439-2103 (952) 947-7777
Contact: Eric Bakken, Secy.
Main URL: http://www.regiscorp.com/

Established in 1981 in MN.
Donors: Regis Corp.; Regis, Inc.
Foundation type: Company-sponsored foundation.
Financial data (yr. ended 06/30/13): Assets, $248,078 (M); gifts received, $16,437; expenditures, $512,768; qualifying distributions, $512,768; giving activities include $511,728 for 6 grants (high: $155,000; low: $10,000).
Purpose and activities: The foundation supports organizations involved with arts and culture, education, human services, and Judaism.
Fields of interest: Arts; Elementary/secondary education; Higher education; Libraries (public); Education; Human services; United Ways and Federated Giving Programs; Jewish federated giving programs; Jewish agencies & synagogues.
Type of support: Annual campaigns; Capital campaigns; General/operating support; Building/renovation; Scholarship funds.
Limitations: Applications accepted. Giving primarily in the Minneapolis, MN, area.
Application information: Application form required.
Initial approach: Letter
Deadline(s): None
Officers: Dan Hanrahan, Pres.; Eric A. Bakken, Secy.; Steven Spiegel, Treas.
EIN: 411410790
Selected grants: The following grants are a representative sample of this grantmaker's funding activity:
$150,000 to Minneapolis Jewish Federation, Minnetonka, MN, 2011. For general contribution.
$105,000 to Minneapolis Society of Fine Arts, Minneapolis, MN, 2011.
$100,000 to Enactus, Springfield, MO, 2011. For general contribution.
$71,500 to Walker Art Center, Minneapolis, MN, 2011.
$50,000 to United Way, Greater Twin Cities, Minneapolis, MN, 2011. For general contribution.
$15,000 to Ordway Center for the Performing Arts, Saint Paul, MN, 2011. For general contribution.
$10,000 to American Jewish Committee, Chicago, IL, 2011. For general contribution.
$5,000 to Japanese American National Museum, Los Angeles, CA, 2011. For general contribution.
$3,000 to Harvard University, Cambridge, MA, 2011. For general contribution.
$3,000 to University of Pennsylvania, Philadelphia, PA, 2011. For general contribution.

4751
Robert & Helen Remick Charitable Foundation ✧
P. O. Box 123
Lakefield, MN 56150-0123

Established in 1998 in MN.
Donor: Robert Remick‡.
Foundation type: Independent foundation.
Financial data (yr. ended 12/31/13): Assets, $11,702,011 (M); expenditures, $677,743; qualifying distributions, $575,012; giving activities include $551,524 for 36 grants (high: $49,629; low: $500).
Fields of interest: Arts; Education; Environment; Youth development; Human services; Foundations (community).
Type of support: Equipment; Donated land.
Limitations: Applications not accepted. Giving primarily in MN, with emphasis on Windom. No grants to individuals.
Application information: Contributes only to pre-selected organizations.
Trustees: Howard C. Davis; Lynel Rae Nelson; John D. Remick; Cheryl Holthe Rients.
EIN: 411950527
Selected grants: The following grants are a representative sample of this grantmaker's funding activity:
$42,500 to Southwest Initiative Foundation, Hutchinson, MN, 2012. For General Endowment, Early Childhood and Ag.
$1,000 to Freedom Farm, Waverly, MN, 2012. For equine therapy programs.

4752
Margaret Rivers Fund ✧
P.O. Box 197
Stillwater, MN 55082-0197
Contact: Lawrence Severson, Pres.

Incorporated in 1948 in MN.
Donor: Robert E. Slaughter‡.
Foundation type: Independent foundation.
Financial data (yr. ended 12/31/13): Assets, $29,902,281 (M); expenditures, $1,915,573; qualifying distributions, $1,837,381; giving activities include $1,759,224 for 143 grants (high: $100,000; low: $500).
Purpose and activities: Grants primarily for hospitals, church support, youth agencies, aid to the handicapped, and care of the aged; support also for cultural programs and conservation.
Fields of interest: Arts; Environment, natural resources; Hospitals (general); Youth, services; Aging, centers/services; Christian agencies & churches; Children; Aging; Disabilities, people with.
Type of support: General/operating support.
Limitations: Applications accepted. Giving primarily in the St. Croix Valley, area, MN. No grants to individuals.
Application information: Application form not required.
Initial approach: Letter
Copies of proposal: 1
Deadline(s): None
Board meeting date(s): Monthly
Final notification: 30-60 days
Officers and Directors:* Lawrence Severson,* Pres. and Secy.; Jean Berry, V.P. and Treas.; Robert G. Briggs; David F. Pohl.
EIN: 416017102

Selected grants: The following grants are a representative sample of this grantmaker's funding activity:
$30,000 to Courage Center, Minneapolis, MN, 2011.
$17,500 to Young Life, Colorado Springs, CO, 2011.
$7,500 to Leukemia & Lymphoma Society, White Plains, NY, 2011.
$5,000 to American Lung Association, New York, NY, 2011.
$3,000 to American Composers Forum, Saint Paul, MN, 2011.
$2,500 to American Cancer Society, Atlanta, GA, 2011.
$2,000 to National Jewish Health, Denver, CO, 2011.
$1,500 to Nature Conservancy, Arlington, VA, 2011.

4753
Robina Foundation ✧
4900 IDS Ctr.
80 S. 8th St.
Minneapolis, MN 55402-2100
Contact: Penny Hunt, Exec. Dir.
E-mail: info@robinafoundation.org; Main URL: http://www.robinafoundation.org

Established in 2004.
Donor: James H. Binger‡.
Foundation type: Independent foundation.
Financial data (yr. ended 12/31/13): Assets, $92,836,555 (M); gifts received, $21,001,000; expenditures, $13,991,986; qualifying distributions, $13,537,791; giving activities include $13,152,126 for 9 grants (high: $4,245,492; low: $250,000).
Purpose and activities: The foundation seeks to positively impact critical social issues by encouraging innovation and financially supporting transformative projects of its four industrial partners. These partners, selected by the foundation's founder, James H. Binger, are: Abbott Northwestern Hospital, Minneapolis, MN; The Council on Foreign Relations, New York, NY; University of Minnesota Law School, Minneapolis, MN; and Yale University, New Haven, CT.
Fields of interest: Education; Environment, natural resources; Animals/wildlife, preservation/protection; Hospitals (general).
Limitations: Applications not accepted. Giving primarily in MN; some giving nationally. No grants to individuals.
Application information: Contributes only to pre-selected organizations.
Board meeting date(s): 4 times per year
Officers and Directors:* Kathleen Blatz, Chair.; Steven A. Schroeder, M.D.*, Vice-Chair.; Susan Berresford, Secy.; Stephen R. Lewis, Jr., Treas.; Penny Hunt, Exec. Dir.; Gordon M. Aamoth, M.D.; H. Peter Karoff; Marianne D. Short.
Number of staff: 2 part-time professional.
EIN: 201163610
Selected grants: The following grants are a representative sample of this grantmaker's funding activity:
$18,000,000 to Yale University, School of Drama, New Haven, CT, 2012. To endow Binger Center for New Theater.
$2,356,696 to Abbott Northwestern Hospital, Minneapolis, MN, 2012. For LifeCourse, (formerly Late Life Supportive Care), initiative to create a sustainable model of systematic care to improve the

experience of patients, their families, and caregivers.
$2,046,627 to Council on Foreign Relations, New York, NY, 2012. For Phase II of International Institutions and Global Governance (IIGG) Program.
$1,000,000 to Yale University, School of Law, New Haven, CT, 2012. For Phase II of Robina Foundation Human Rights Fellowship Initiative.
$377,034 to Council on Foreign Relations, New York, NY, 2012. For Diversity Initiative in Foreign Policy.
$276,805 to Council on Foreign Relations, New York, NY, 2012. For Online Video Project.

4754
Robins, Kaplan, Miller & Ciresi Foundation ✧

800 LaSalle Ave.
2800 LaSalle Plaza
Minneapolis, MN 55402
Main URL: http://www.rkmc.com/firm/community/foundations
Grants List: http://www.rkmc.com/private_foundation.htm

Established in 1993 in MN.
Donor: Robins, Kaplan, Miller & Ciresi L.L.P.
Foundation type: Company-sponsored foundation.
Financial data (yr. ended 08/31/13): Assets, $94,666 (M); gifts received, $1,246,288; expenditures, $1,255,176; qualifying distributions, $1,124,187; giving activities include $1,124,187 for 251 grants (high: $51,296; low: $50).
Purpose and activities: The foundation supports organizations involved with arts and culture, education, health, crime and law enforcement, athletics, and human services.
Fields of interest: Media/communications; Performing arts; Arts; Higher education; Law school/education; Education; Hospitals (general); Health care, clinics/centers; Health care; Legal services; Crime/law enforcement; Athletics/sports, Special Olympics; YM/YWCAs & YM/YWHAs; Children, services; Human services; United Ways and Federated Giving Programs.
Type of support: General/operating support; Program development; Scholarship funds; Sponsorships.
Limitations: Applications accepted. Giving primarily in areas of company operations, with emphasis on Minneapolis and St. Paul, MN. No grants to individuals.
Application information: Application form not required.
Initial approach: Proposal
Deadline(s): None
Officer and Trustees:* Martin R. Lueck,* Chair.; David W. Beehler; Maria R. Butler; James V. Chin; Jan M. Conlin; Christopher W. Madel; Steven A. Schumeister; Ronald J. Schutz; Roman M. Silberfeld.
EIN: 411735325
Selected grants: The following grants are a representative sample of this grantmaker's funding activity:
$750 to University of Minnesota, Law School - T.O.R, Minneapolis, MN, 2013.

4755
Rochester Area Foundation ✧

400 S. Broadway, Ste. 300
Rochester, MN 55904 (507) 282-0203
Contact: JoAnn Stomer, Pres.; For grants: Ann Fahy-Gust, Grants and Donors Mgr.
FAX: (507) 282-4938;
E-mail: raf-info@rochesterarea.org; Grant application e-mail: ann@rochesterarea.org; Main URL: http://www.rochesterarea.org
Facebook: https://www.facebook.com/pages/Rochester-Area-Foundation/132787263554048
LinkedIn: http://www.linkedin.com/groups/Rochester-Area-Foundation-4844420
Twitter: http://twitter.com/rochesterarea
YouTube: http://www.youtube.com/user/RochAreaFoundation

Established in 1944 in MN by resolution of corporation.
Foundation type: Community foundation.
Financial data (yr. ended 12/31/13): Assets, $39,734,471 (M); gifts received, $1,839,590; expenditures, $2,290,330; giving activities include $1,106,587 for grants.
Purpose and activities: The foundation is dedicated to using its resources to improve the quality of life, promote greater equality of opportunities, and to develop effective methods to assist those in need in the greater Rochester area. The foundation makes grants in the fields of arts and culture, community development, education, human services and recreation.
Fields of interest: Arts; Child development, education; Higher education; Education; Environment; Health care; Housing/shelter, development; Recreation; Child development, services; Family services; Aging, centers/services; Minorities/immigrants, centers/services; Human services; Civil/human rights; Community/economic development; Voluntarism promotion; Government/public administration; Public affairs; Children; Youth; Adults; Aging; Disabilities, people with; Mentally disabled; Minorities.
Type of support: Management development/capacity building; Building/renovation; Emergency funds; Seed money; Technical assistance; Consulting services; Matching/challenge support.
Limitations: Applications accepted. Giving limited to the greater Rochester, MN, area. No support for religious organizations for sectarian purposes. No grants to individuals (except for scholarships), or for endowment funds, annual campaigns, operating budgets, continuing support, land acquisition, deficit financing, fellowships, or research.
Publications: Application guidelines; Annual report; Informational brochure (including application guidelines); Newsletter.
Application information: Visit foundation web site for application forms and guidelines. If the foundation's Board of Trustees approves the applicant's pre-application for a grant, they will be notified and asked to submit a full application. Application form required.
Initial approach: Submit pre-application form
Deadline(s): Jan. 1 and Aug. 1 for pre-application form; Feb. 15 and July 15 for full application
Board meeting date(s): Jan., Feb., Apr., May, Aug., Sept., Oct., Nov., and Dec.
Final notification: Mid Jan. and mid June for pre-application determination; mid Mar. and mid Aug. for grants
Officers and Trustees:* Wendy Shannon,* Vice-Chair.; Dr. Hugh Smith,* Co-Pres.; JoAnn Stormer,* Co-Pres.; Barbara Porter,* Secy.; Tom Wente,* Treas.; Jane Campion, Emeritus; John Benike; Paul Gorman; Leigh Johnson; Denise Kelly; Greg Layton; Walt Ling; Jean Locke; Joe Powers; Jose Rivas; Mark Utz; Karel Weigel; Vivien Williams.
Number of staff: 6 full-time professional.
EIN: 416017740
Selected grants: The following grants are a representative sample of this grantmaker's funding activity:
$25,000 to Salvation Army of Rochester, Rochester, MN, 2011. To remodel Community Center Kitchen.
$20,000 to Intercultural Mutual Assistance Association, Rochester, MN, 2011. To create sustainability for Community Health Workers in Rochester serving foreign born residents.
$15,000 to Accessible Space, Saint Paul, MN, 2011. For automatic door openers.
$10,000 to Breaking Free, Saint Paul, MN, 2011. For services.
$8,000 to Wing House, Rochester, MN, 2011. For renovations of women's handicap bathroom, shower and dressing room facilities.
$7,500 to FamilyMeans, Stillwater, MN, 2011. For budget and credit counseling for Olmsted County residents.
$5,000 to Minnesota Assistance Council for Veterans, Saint Paul, MN, 2011. For outreach and direct program to homeless and at-risk veterans in Rochester and surrounding communities.
$5,000 to Mixed Blood Theater Company, Minneapolis, MN, 2011. For Educational Touring Program.
$2,500 to Community Food Response, Rochester, MN, 2011. To provide food.
$2,500 to Youth Commission of Olmsted County, 2011. For Tix 4 Kids program.

4756
The Sabes Family Foundation ✧

(formerly The Moe and Esther Sabes Family Foundation)
c/o Steven Sabes
220 S. 6th St., Ste. 1200
Minneapolis, MN 55402-4512

Established in 1991 in MN.
Donors: Moe Sabes; Esther Sabes; Robert Sabes; Janet Sabes; Steven Sabes; Amy Sabes; Jon Sabes.
Foundation type: Independent foundation.
Financial data (yr. ended 12/31/13): Assets, $46,251,927 (M); gifts received, $30,000; expenditures, $3,387,446; qualifying distributions, $2,010,191; giving activities include $1,881,743 for 50 grants (high: $661,755; low: $200).
Purpose and activities: Giving primarily for higher education, health organizations, children and social services, and Jewish organizations.
Fields of interest: Arts; Higher education; Health organizations, association; Cancer research; Human services; Children/youth, services; Foundations (private grantmaking); Jewish federated giving programs; Jewish agencies & synagogues.
Limitations: Applications not accepted. Giving primarily in NV; some funding also in MN. No grants to individuals.
Application information: Contributes only to pre-selected organizations.
Trustees: Robert Sabes; Steven Sabes.
EIN: 411699714

4757
The Saint Paul Foundation ✧
101 Fifth St. E., Ste. 2400
St. Paul, MN 55101 (651) 224-5463
Contact: Carleen K. Rhodes, C.E.O.
FAX: (651) 224-8123;
E-mail: inbox@saintpaulfoundation.org; Additional tel.: (800) 875-6167; Additional e-mail: ckr@saintpaulfoundation.org; Main URL: http://saintpaulfoundation.org
Facebook: https://www.facebook.com/mnpartners
Grants Database: http://www.saintpaulfoundation.org/what_we_fund/
LinkedIn: http://www.linkedin.com/companies/the-saint-paul-foundation
The Saint Paul Foundation's Philanthropy Promise: http://www.ncrp.org/philanthropys-promise/who
Twitter: http://twitter.com/mnpartnerstweet
YouTube: http://www.youtube.com/mnpartnersvideo

Established in 1940 in MN by adoption of a plan; incorporated in 1964.
Foundation type: Community foundation.
Financial data (yr. ended 12/31/13): Assets, $790,446,947 (M); gifts received, $44,550,701; expenditures, $73,157,114; giving activities include $53,814,642 for 771+ grants (high: $7,444,000), and $937,696 for 1,611 grants to individuals.
Purpose and activities: The foundation actively serves the people of St. Paul, Minnesota, and the surrounding communities by building permanent charitable capital, making philanthropic grants, and providing services that contribute to the health and vitality of the community. This is done by working with donors to achieve their philanthropic goals; managing responsibly the foundation's assets; encouraging and participating in community initiatives and partnerships; broadening the base of effective leadership in the community; building awareness of the role of philanthropy in meeting the needs of the community; and providing services to other charitable organizations. The foundation pays special attention to helping achieve the following outcomes through its grants from unrestricted funds: an anti-racist community, economic development for disadvantaged people and communities, strong families that provide healthy beginnings for children and youth, and quality education for all.
Fields of interest: Humanities; Arts; Elementary/secondary education; Education, early childhood education; Higher education; Adult education—literacy, basic skills & GED; Education, reading; Education; Health care; Health organizations, association; Children/youth, services; Minorities/immigrants, centers/services; Human services; Civil rights, race/intergroup relations; Community development, neighborhood development; Economic development; Community/economic development; Minorities.
Type of support: Capital campaigns; Building/renovation; Equipment; Program development; Seed money; Technical assistance; Matching/challenge support.
Limitations: Applications accepted. Giving limited to Dakota, Ramsey, and Washington counties in the metropolitan St. Paul, MN, area. No support for sectarian religious programs (except from designated funds). No grants to individuals (except from designated funds), or for ongoing annual operating budgets, agency endowment funds, and programs located outside the East Metro area.
Publications: Application guidelines; Financial statement; Grants list; Newsletter.
Application information: Visit foundation web site for application form and guidelines. Application form required.
Initial approach: Submit letter of inquiry (no more than 3 pages) or application
Copies of proposal: 1
Deadline(s): Approximately 3 1/2 months before next board meeting
Board meeting date(s): Apr., Aug., and Nov.
Final notification: Within 4 to 5 months
Officers and Directors:* Mark L. Wilson,* Chair.; Mary K. Brainerd,* Vice-Chair.; Carleen K. Rhodes, C.E.O. and Pres.; Ann Mullholland, V.P., Grants and Prog.; Jack Pohl, V.P., Investments; Christine Searson, V.P., Finance and Opers.; Jeremy Wells, V.P., Philanthropic Svcs.; Melissa Pelland, Cont.; Rassoul Dastmozd; Donald R. Day; John M. DeClue; Jacqueline A. Dorsey; Mary W. Frey; Steve Fritze; Thomas Grossman; MaryKao L. Hang; Christopher M. Hilger; Cynthia Lesher; Nancy E. Lindahl; Manuel Mariano Lopez; E. Gerald O'Brien II; Kathleen Schmidlkofer; Paul L. Snyder; Tim Welsh; Pam Wheelock.
Corporate Trustees: American National Bank; Bank of America, N.A.; U.S. Bank, N.A.; U.S. Trust; Wells Fargo Bank Minnesota, N.A.
Number of staff: 39 full-time professional; 1 part-time professional; 20 full-time support; 4 part-time support.
EIN: 416031510
Selected grants: The following grants are a representative sample of this grantmaker's funding activity:
$250,000 to Trust for Public Land, Minneapolis, MN, 2012. For Frogtown Park and Farm.
$75,000 to Bedlam Theater, Minneapolis, MN, 2012.
$25,000 to ServeMinnesota, Minneapolis, MN, 2012. For Minnesota Math Corps.
$15,000 to African American Registry, Minneapolis, MN, 2012. For African American Male School.
$10,000 to Camphor Memorial United Methodist Church, Saint Paul, MN, 2012. For Camphor Fiscally Fit Center.
$10,000 to McDonough Organization with Respect and Equality for People, Saint Paul, MN, 2012. For mental health program.

4758
Carl and Verna Schmidt Foundation ✧
P.O. Box 638
Rochester, MN 55903-0638
Contact: Alan C. Anderson, Tr.; Kay Caskey

Established in 1958 in MN.
Donors: Carl Schmidt‡; Verna Schmidt‡.
Foundation type: Independent foundation.
Financial data (yr. ended 12/31/13): Assets, $30,132,348 (M); expenditures, $1,819,529; qualifying distributions, $1,355,914; giving activities include $1,271,509 for 127 grants (high: $90,000; low: $500).
Purpose and activities: Giving primarily for public libraries, health associations, including a children's hospital, volunteer fire departments and human services; funding also for the arts, natural resource conservation, and animals and wildlife.
Fields of interest: Historic preservation/historical societies; Arts; Libraries (public); Environment, natural resources; Animals/wildlife; Hospitals (specialty); Health organizations, association; Housing/shelter, development; Disasters, fire prevention/control; Human services; Children, services.
Limitations: Applications accepted. Giving primarily in MN. No grants to individuals.
Application information: Telephone applications not accepted. Application form required.
Initial approach: Letter only
Copies of proposal: 1
Deadline(s): None
Board meeting date(s): Monthly
Final notification: 1 month from receipt of application
Trustees: Alan C. Anderson; Jonathan S. Anderson.
Number of staff: 1 part-time professional.
EIN: 237423942
Selected grants: The following grants are a representative sample of this grantmaker's funding activity:
$59,615 to Saint Peter Public Library, Saint Peter, MN, 2012. For Literary Library Materials.
$50,000 to Minnesota Waterfowl Association, Hopkins, MN, 2012. For Conservation Restore outlet channel.
$40,000 to Boys and Girls Club of Rochester, Rochester, MN, 2012. For Community Capital Campaign to build The Place.
$25,000 to Ability Building Center, Rochester, MN, 2012. For Community Replace roof.
$20,000 to Brown County Historical Society, New Ulm, MN, 2012. For Historical Exhibit of the 150th U.S. Dakota War of 1862.
$15,000 to Shriners Hospitals for Children, Minneapolis, MN, 2012. For Medical Pediatric specialty care.
$10,000 to Friends of the Minnesota Valley, Bloomington, MN, 2012. For Conservation Wetland restoration project.
$10,000 to Rochester Art Center, Rochester, MN, 2012. For Community Exhibit by Miguel Calderon.
$7,500 to Lifetrack Resources, Saint Paul, MN, 2012. For Medical Hearing Program - Guide by Your Side.
$6,250 to Preservation Alliance of Minnesota, Saint Paul, MN, 2012. For Historical Quarterly magazine.

4759
Schoeneckers Foundation ✧ ☆
P.O. Box 1610
Minneapolis, MN 55440-1610

Established in 1979 in MN.
Donor: Schoeneckers, Inc.
Foundation type: Company-sponsored foundation.
Financial data (yr. ended 09/30/13): Assets, $100,075 (M); gifts received, $601,500; expenditures, $801,525; qualifying distributions, $801,525; giving activities include $800,000 for 1 grant.
Purpose and activities: The foundation supports the University of St. Thomas in St. Paul, Minnesota.
Fields of interest: Education.
Limitations: Applications not accepted. Giving primarily in St. Paul, MN. No grants to individuals.
Application information: Contributes only to a pre-selected organization.
Officer: Guy L. Schoenecker, Pres.
Directors: Barbara Schoenecker; David Schoenecker; Larry Schoenecker.
EIN: 411369001

Selected grants: The following grants are a representative sample of this grantmaker's funding activity:
$600,000 to University of Saint Thomas, Saint Paul, MN, 2011.

4760
Richard M. Schulze Family Foundation ✧
3033 Excelsior Blvd., Ste. 525
Minneapolis, MN 55416-3375 (952) 324-8910
FAX: (952) 324-8982; Main URL: http://www.schulzefamilyfoundation.org/

Established in 2004 in MN.
Donor: Richard M. Schulze.
Foundation type: Independent foundation.
Financial data (yr. ended 12/31/12): Assets, $29,547,422 (M); gifts received, $7,172,930; expenditures, $3,572,303; qualifying distributions, $3,221,911; giving activities include $3,221,911 for 14 grants (high: $2,000,000; low: $695).
Purpose and activities: Giving primarily for: 1) education, particularly to organizations that offer Kindergarten through 5th grade programs that focus on reading, writing, math and science, as well as tutoring and after-school support programs; 2) human services, particularly to organizations which provide food, meals, temporary housing/shelter and services to families and children to assist them back to self-sufficiency; 3) agencies that assist adults and their families with initial transitional needs when dealing with a new medical challenge; and 4) organizations that provide educational camps for children ages 5-11.
Fields of interest: Elementary/secondary education; Health organizations; Recreation, camps; Human services; Children/youth, services.
Limitations: Giving primarily in Dakota, Hennepin and Ramsey counties in MN. No support for the arts.
Publications: Application guidelines; Grants list.
Application information: If invited after staff review of LOI, submit full application through online application portal. Complete application guidelines available of foundation web site.
Initial approach: Submit Letter of Inquiry via online application portal on foundation web site
Deadline(s): See foundation web site for current deadlines
Officer: Mark Dienhart, C.E.O. and Pres.
Directors: Kevin Bergman; Robert Bruininks; Maureen Schulze; Richard M. Schulze; Allen Lenzmeier; Nancy JS Tellor; Ann Winblad.
EIN: 200752440
Selected grants: The following grants are a representative sample of this grantmaker's funding activity:
$2,000,000 to Mayo Clinic, Rochester, MN, 2012. For cancer research.
$750,000 to Minnesota Medical Foundation, Minneapolis, MN, 2012. For research on Type 1 Diabetes.
$287,953 to Amherst H. Wilder Foundation, Saint Paul, MN, 2012. For education programs.
$18,263 to Saint Paul Public Schools Foundation, Saint Paul, MN, 2012. For general support.
$10,000 to Companies to Classrooms, Bloomington, MN, 2012. For financial assistance.
$3,000 to Musella Foundation for Brain Tumor Reseach and Information, Hewlett, NY, 2012. For research.

4761
Securian Foundation ✧
Minnesota Mutual Bldg.
400 Robert St. N
St. Paul, MN 55101-2098 (651) 665-3501
Contact: Lori J. Koutsky, Mgr.
Main URL: http://www.securian.com

Established in 1988 in MN.
Donors: Minnesota Life Insurance Co.; Securian Holding Co.
Foundation type: Company-sponsored foundation.
Financial data (yr. ended 12/31/13): Assets, $39,719,398 (M); gifts received, $1,468,526; expenditures, $1,733,478; qualifying distributions, $1,661,156; giving activities include $1,594,699 for 98 grants (high: $395,000; low: $100).
Purpose and activities: The foundation supports organizations involved with arts and culture, education, employment, youth development, human services, community economic development, and economically disadvantaged people.
Fields of interest: Arts; Higher education; Education; Health care; Employment, services; Employment, training; Employment; Youth development; Human services; Economic development; Business/industry; Community/economic development; United Ways and Federated Giving Programs; Mathematics; Economics; Public affairs; Economically disadvantaged.
Type of support: General/operating support; Annual campaigns; Capital campaigns; Program development; Technical assistance; Employee volunteer services; Employee matching gifts.
Limitations: Applications accepted. Giving primarily in areas of company operations, with emphasis on MN; giving also to national organizations. No support for political, lobbying, fraternal, or international organizations, athletic, recreation, or sports-related organizations, religious organizations not of direct benefit to the entire community, or public or private K-12 schools. No grants to individuals, or for scholarships, start-up funds for new organizations, endowments, benefits, sponsorships, fundraising events, advertising, conferences, seminars, workshops, symposiums, trips, or tours.
Publications: Application guidelines; Grants list; Informational brochure; IRS Form 990 or 990-PF printed copy available upon request; Program policy statement.
Application information: Proposals should be no longer than 7 pages. Proposals may be submitted using the Minnesota Common Grant Application Form. Application form required.
Initial approach: Letter
Copies of proposal: 1
Deadline(s): None
Officers: Robert L. Senkler, Pres.; Kathleen Pinkett, V.P.; Gary Christensen, Secy.; David LePlavy, Treas.
Number of staff: 1 part-time professional; 1 part-time support.
EIN: 363608619

4762
Shiebler Family Foundation ✧ ☆
12219 Wood Lake Dr., Ste. 200
Burnsville, MN 55337-1526
Contact: William Perron, Tr.

Established in 1999 in MN.
Donors: William Shiebler; Joanne Shiebler; Bruce Classon.
Foundation type: Operating foundation.
Financial data (yr. ended 12/31/13): Assets, $752,666 (M); gifts received, $299,643; expenditures, $602,932; qualifying distributions, $592,610; giving activities include $592,610 for 26 grants (high: $200,000; low: $50).
Purpose and activities: Giving primarily for education, human services, the arts, and to a ski association.
Fields of interest: Arts; Higher education; Education; Animal welfare; Athletics/sports, winter sports; Human services.
Limitations: Applications accepted. Giving primarily in UT. No grants to individuals.
Application information: Application form not required.
Initial approach: Letter
Deadline(s): Prior to Dec.1
Trustees: William Perron; Christina Shiebler; Jason Shiebler; Joanne Shiebler; William Shiebler.
EIN: 411960074
Selected grants: The following grants are a representative sample of this grantmaker's funding activity:
$148,650 to USAA Foundation, Inc., San Antonio, TX, 2011.

4763
Sieben Foundation, Inc. ✧
10350 Bren Rd. W.
Minnetonka, MN 55343-9014

Established in 1988 in MN.
Donor: Opus U.S. Corp.
Foundation type: Independent foundation.
Financial data (yr. ended 12/31/12): Assets, $19,514,855 (M); expenditures, $946,808; qualifying distributions, $940,763; giving activities include $801,825 for 29 grants (high: $302,787; low: $2,000).
Purpose and activities: Giving primarily for Roman Catholic education and for human services.
Fields of interest: Elementary school/education; Higher education; Human services; Catholic federated giving programs; Catholic agencies & churches.
Type of support: General/operating support; Program evaluation.
Limitations: Applications not accepted. Giving primarily in MN; some giving nationally. No grants to individuals.
Application information: Contributes only to pre-selected organizations.
Officers and Directors:* Philip Goldman,* Pres.; Mary Pickard, V.P.; Jeff Rauenhorst,* V.P.; Fr. Bill Lies, CSC*, Secy.; Joe Mahoney,* Treas.; Sr. Gemma Doll; Judy Mahoney; Sr. Margaret Ormond, OP; Kristine W. Rauenhorst.
EIN: 363608625
Selected grants: The following grants are a representative sample of this grantmaker's funding activity:
$49,496 to Creighton University, Omaha, NE, 2012. For Sieben Mission Schools Network Annual Meeting 2013 and the ongoing Network Building Project.
$17,547 to Creighton University, Omaha, NE, 2012. For Professional Development Initiative - Phase 1.
$10,000 to National Outdoor Leadership School, Lander, WY, 2012. For NOLS Campaign.

4764
The Eugene C. and Gail V. Sit Foundation ✧ ☆
80 S. 8th St., Ste. 3300
Minneapolis, MN 55402-4130

Established in 1986 in MN.
Donor: Eugene C. Sit.
Foundation type: Independent foundation.
Financial data (yr. ended 11/30/13): Assets, $9,266,415 (M); expenditures, $493,424; qualifying distributions, $490,000; giving activities include $490,000 for 6 grants (high: $464,300; low: $1,200).
Purpose and activities: Giving primarily to a military appreciation fund; funding also for the arts, education, and social services.
Fields of interest: Arts; Higher education; Human services; Military/veterans' organizations.
Limitations: Applications not accepted. Giving primarily in MN. No grants to individuals.
Application information: Contributes only to pre-selected organizations.
Officer: Ronald D. Sit, Secy.
EIN: 411572465

4765
Sit Investment Associates Foundation ✧
3300 IDS Ctr.
80 S. 8th St.
Minneapolis, MN 55402-2100

Established in 1984.
Donor: Sit Investment Associates, Inc.
Foundation type: Company-sponsored foundation.
Financial data (yr. ended 12/31/13): Assets, $33,150,295 (M); gifts received, $1,728,676; expenditures, $1,472,934; qualifying distributions, $1,452,430; giving activities include $1,452,430 for 120 grants (high: $323,500; low: $200).
Purpose and activities: The foundation supports organizations involved with arts and culture, education, cancer, hunger, human services, international affairs, and military and veterans.
Fields of interest: Performing arts; Performing arts, orchestras; Historic preservation/historical societies; Arts; Higher education; Education; Cancer; Food services; Food banks; Boy scouts; Salvation Army; Children/youth, services; Homeless, human services; Human services; International affairs, goodwill promotion; United Ways and Federated Giving Programs; Military/veterans' organizations.
Type of support: Annual campaigns; General/operating support.
Limitations: Applications not accepted. Giving primarily in MN; giving also to national organizations. No grants to individuals.
Application information: Contributes only to pre-selected organizations.
Officer: Paul E. Rasmussen, Secy.
Director: Debra A. Sit.
EIN: 411468021
Selected grants: The following grants are a representative sample of this grantmaker's funding activity:
$200,000 to Minnesota Medical Foundation, Minneapolis, MN, 2011.
$125,000 to Federated Insurance Foundation, Owatonna, MN, 2011.
$100,000 to Macalester College, Saint Paul, MN, 2011.

4766
Slaggie Family Foundation ✧
111 Market St., Ste. 3B
Winona, MN 55987-5532 (507) 474-9150

Established in 1997 in MN.
Donors: Steve Slaggie; Nipper NCLA Trust No. 1.
Foundation type: Independent foundation.
Financial data (yr. ended 12/31/13): Assets, $27,162,951 (M); gifts received, $1,821,040; expenditures, $1,694,728; qualifying distributions, $1,458,791; giving activities include $1,444,537 for 69 grants (high: $850,000; low: $250).
Purpose and activities: Giving primarily for education, human services, and religion.
Fields of interest: Museums; Historic preservation/historical societies; Secondary school/education; Higher education; Human services; Family services; Foundations (private independent); Catholic agencies & churches.
Type of support: Capital campaigns; Debt reduction; Scholarship funds; Matching/challenge support.
Limitations: Applications accepted. Giving primarily in MN, with some emphasis on Winona. No grants to individuals.
Application information: Application form required.
Initial approach: E-mail or telephone
Copies of proposal: 1
Deadline(s): None
Officers: Stephen M. Slaggie, Pres.; Michael J. Slaggie, V.P.; Barbara J. Slaggie, Secy.; Matthew S. Slaggie, Treas.
Trustees: Gregory T. Poulos; Sara J. Slaggie Poulos; Michelle M. Schlehuber; Thomas M. Schlehuber; Amanda Slaggie; Lindsay Slaggie.
EIN: 411878894

4767
Smikis Foundation ✧
Parkdale Plz., Ste. 426
1660 Hwy. 100 S.
St. Louis Park, MN 55416-1533 (952) 512-1165
Contact: Lucy B. Hartwell, Dir.

Established in 1993 in MN.
Donors: Charitable Lead Annuity Trust 2; Charitable Lead Annuity Trust 1; Lucy B. Hartwell.
Foundation type: Independent foundation.
Financial data (yr. ended 12/31/13): Assets, $17,433,991 (M); gifts received, $519,358; expenditures, $899,955; qualifying distributions, $689,525; giving activities include $689,500 for 33 grants (high: $100,000; low: $1,000).
Fields of interest: Education; Environment; Housing/shelter, services; Youth development, services; Community development, neighborhood development.
Type of support: General/operating support; Capital campaigns; Program development; Seed money; Scholarship funds.
Limitations: Applications accepted. Giving limited to MN, with emphasis on Minneapolis. No grants to individuals, or for membership drives.
Application information: Application form required.
Initial approach: Proposal
Deadline(s): None
Board meeting date(s): Monthly
Director: Lucy B. Hartwell.
EIN: 411742700

4768
Southwest Initiative Foundation ✧
(formerly Southwest Minnesota Foundation)
15 3rd Ave. N.W.
Hutchinson, MN 55350-1643 (320) 587-4848
FAX: (320) 587-3838;
E-mail: info@swifoundation.org; Toll-free tel.: (800) 594-9480; Main URL: http://www.swifoundation.org
Facebook: https://www.facebook.com/SouthwestInitiativeFoundation
RSS Feed: http://feeds.feedburner.com/swif
Twitter: https://twitter.com/mn_core
YouTube: https://www.youtube.com/user/SWIFoundation

Established in 1986 in MN.
Foundation type: Community foundation.
Financial data (yr. ended 06/30/13): Assets, $70,726,527 (M); gifts received, $4,135,439; expenditures, $4,784,400; giving activities include $1,420,672 for 41+ grants (high: $165,000).
Purpose and activities: The mission of the foundation is to be a catalyst, facilitating opportunities for economic and social growth by developing and challenging leaders to build on the assets of southwestern Minnesota.
Fields of interest: Youth development; Economic development; Community/economic development; Philanthropy/voluntarism; Children/youth; Aging.
Type of support: Program development; Conferences/seminars; Technical assistance; Program-related investments/loans; Loans—to individuals.
Limitations: Applications accepted. Giving limited to Big Stone, Chippewa, Cottonwood, Jackson, Kandiyohi, Lac Qui Parle, Lincoln, Lyon, McLeod, Meeker, Murray, Nobles, Pipestone, Redwood, Renville, Rock, Swift, and Yellow Medicine counties, MN. No support for for-profit businesses (except loans), or for arts programs. No grants to individuals, or for capital expenses, video production, fundraising, past operating debts or ongoing, open-ended grants.
Publications: Application guidelines; Annual report; Grants list; Informational brochure (including application guidelines); Newsletter.
Application information: Only those organizations with successful pre-application questionnaires will be invited by the foundation to submit a full proposal. Application form required.
Initial approach: Online pre-application questionnaire
Copies of proposal: 1
Deadline(s): Rolling
Board meeting date(s): Every other month
Officers and Trustees:* Rob Saunders,* Chair.; Robert Thurston,* Vice-Chair.; Sherry Ristau,* Pres. and C.E.O.; Tim Connell,* Secy.; Janice Nelson,* Treas.; Marcy Costello; Jim Keul; Patricia Loehr-Dols; Jan Lundebrek; Mary Maertens; William McCormack; Greg Raymo; Bob Taubert.
Number of staff: 16 full-time professional; 1 part-time professional; 5 full-time support; 1 part-time support.
EIN: 411555592

4769
St. Agnes Catholic Education Foundation ✧ ☆
7040 Willow Creek Rd.
Eden Prairie, MN 55344-3224

Established in 2007 in MN.
Donor: Mary Jo Feltl.
Foundation type: Independent foundation.
Financial data (yr. ended 12/31/13): Assets, $2,214,247 (M); gifts received, $390,586; expenditures, $456,465; qualifying distributions, $451,966; giving activities include $449,525 for 8 grants (high: $243,500; low: $943).
Fields of interest: Education.
Type of support: General/operating support.
Limitations: Applications not accepted. Giving primarily in MN. No grants to individuals.
Application information: Contributes only to pre-selected organizations.
Officer: Mary Jo Feltl, Pres. and Secy.-Treas.
EIN: 260229866
Selected grants: The following grants are a representative sample of this grantmaker's funding activity:
$243,500 to Saint Agnes High School, Saint Paul, MN, 2013. For general support.
$50,000 to Academy of Holy Angels, Richfield, MN, 2013. For general support.
$50,000 to Blessed Trinity Catholic School, Richfield, MN, 2013. For general support.
$28,967 to Saint Agnes High School, Saint Paul, MN, 2013. For property expenses paid on behalf of donee.
$16,115 to University of Saint Thomas, Minneapolis, MN, 2013. For tuition.
$10,000 to Saint Anne's Catholic School, Le Sueur, MN, 2013. For general support.
$5,350 to North Hennepin Community College, Brooklyn Park, MN, 2012. For tuition support.

4770
St. Jude Medical Foundation ✧
1 St. Jude Medical Dr.
St. Paul, MN 55117-1761 (651) 756-2157
FAX: (877) 291-7569;
E-mail: info@sjmfoundation.com; Main URL: http://www.sjmfoundation.com/

Established in 1997 in MN.
Donor: St. Jude Medical, Inc.
Foundation type: Company-sponsored foundation.
Financial data (yr. ended 12/31/12): Assets, $492,722 (M); gifts received, $3,225,000; expenditures, $3,137,088; qualifying distributions, $3,135,362; giving activities include $3,133,887 for 74 grants (high: $600,000; low: $2,500).
Purpose and activities: The foundation supports organizations involved with arts and culture, K-12 education, health, disaster relief, human services, community development, science, and civic affairs. Special emphasis is directed toward programs designed to improve awareness and treatment of cardiac and chronic pain conditions.
Fields of interest: Arts; Elementary/secondary education; Health care; Health organizations, public education; Heart & circulatory diseases; Health organizations; Surgery; Disasters, preparedness/services; Human services; Community/economic development; Mathematics; Engineering/technology; Science; Public affairs.
Type of support: General/operating support; Continuing support; Conferences/seminars; Seed money; Fellowships; Research; Sponsorships; Employee matching gifts.
Limitations: Applications accepted. Giving on a national basis, with some emphasis on CA, Washington, DC, MA, and MN. No grants to individuals.
Publications: Application guidelines; Program policy statement.
Application information: Applications for community outreach, research study, and mission trips are also accepted. Organizations receiving general operating support are asked to submit narrative and financial progress reports near the end of each one-year grant period. Application form required.
Initial approach: Complete online application
Copies of proposal: 1
Deadline(s): 60 days prior to need
Officers and Directors:* Rachel Ellingson,* Pres.; John C. Heinmiller,* V.P.; Daniel J. Starks, V.P.; Donald Zurbay,* V.P.; Pamela S. Krop,* Secy.; Robert Frenz,* Treas.
EIN: 411868372

4771
Elaine F. Stepanek Foundation Agency ✧
P.O. Box 64713
Saint Paul, MN 55164-0713
Application address: c/o U.S. Bank, N.A., 101 E. 5th St., 14th Fl., St. Paul, MN 55101-1860; tel.: (651) 466-8724

Established in 2006 in MN.
Donors: Elaine F. Stepanek‡; Elaine Stepanek Revocable Trust.
Foundation type: Independent foundation.
Financial data (yr. ended 12/31/13): Assets, $39,890,629 (M); expenditures, $1,573,901; qualifying distributions, $1,338,184; giving activities include $1,275,469 for 11 grants (high: $400,000; low: $40,000).
Fields of interest: Arts; Education; Cancer; Human services.
Limitations: Applications accepted. Giving primarily in Santa Barbara, CA; some giving also in Owatonna, MN.
Application information: Application form not required.
Initial approach: Letter
Deadline(s): None
Officers: Anna F. Laynor, Pres.; Daniel H. Gainey, V.P.; John R. Wicks, V.P.
EIN: 205632706

4772
The Stevens Square Foundation ✧
318 W. 48th St.
Minneapolis, MN 55419-5418 (612) 825-1368
FAX: (612) 822-8587;
E-mail: ssgfoundation@earthlink.net; Main URL: http://www.thestevenssquarefoundation.org

Established in 1979 in MN.
Foundation type: Independent foundation.
Financial data (yr. ended 12/31/13): Assets, $12,124,469 (M); expenditures, $571,497; qualifying distributions, $522,538; giving activities include $451,825 for 36 grants (high: $25,000; low: $900).
Purpose and activities: The foundation will continue its funding efforts on programs for seniors, particularly programs that are existing and enable seniors to remain in their own homes.
Fields of interest: Food distribution, meals on wheels; Aging, centers/services; Aging.
Type of support: General/operating support; Program development.
Limitations: Applications accepted. Giving limited to the Twin Cities, MN, 7-county metropolitan area (including the Anoka, Carver, Dakota, Hennepin, Ramsey, Scott and Washington). No support for political organizations or candidates, fraternal societies, or orders. No grants to individuals, or for endowments, major capital building projects, religious purposes or funding deficits.
Publications: Application guidelines; Grants list.
Application information: See foundation web site for complete application guidelines. Application form required.
Initial approach: Proposal and application cover form which can be downloaded from foundation web site
Copies of proposal: 2
Deadline(s): See foundation web site for current deadline
Officers and Directors:* Kate Bryant,* Pres.; Margit Berg,* V.P., Grants; Katherine Campbell,* V.P., Nominations; Courtney Grimsrud,* V.P., Education; Cheryl Newell,* V.P., Fin. and Investment; Susan Byrne,* Secy.; Blyth Brookman; Patricia Davis; Mimi Rae; Heather Williamson; and 24 additional directors.
EIN: 411380920
Selected grants: The following grants are a representative sample of this grantmaker's funding activity:
$25,000 to Legal Aid Society of Minneapolis, Minneapolis, MN, 2012. For Program support - Senior Law Project.
$10,000 to CAPI USA, Minneapolis, MN, 2012. For Program support - Hmong Elder and Caregiver Program.
$10,000 to Community Thread, Stillwater, MN, 2012. For Program support - Chore Services Initiative.
$6,000 to Tubman, Minneapolis, MN, 2012. For Program support - Senior Resource Workshops.

4773
Stone Pier Foundation ✧
1800 IDS Ctr.
80 S. 8th St., Ste. 1800
Minneapolis, MN 55402-2127

Established in 1998 in MN.
Donor: Robert J. Dayton.
Foundation type: Independent foundation.
Financial data (yr. ended 12/31/12): Assets, $5,806,709 (M); expenditures, $758,480; qualifying distributions, $679,000; giving activities include $679,000 for grants.
Fields of interest: Arts, multipurpose centers/programs; Arts; Education; Environment, natural resources; Hospitals (general); Children/youth, services; United Ways and Federated Giving Programs; Protestant agencies & churches.
Limitations: Applications not accepted. Giving primarily in MN, with emphasis on Minneapolis; some funding nationally. No grants to individuals.
Application information: Contributes only to pre-selected organizations.
Officers: Robert J. Dayton, Pres.; Joan L. Dayton, V.P.; Megan M. Dayton, Secy.-Treas.
Directors: Ann C. Dayton; James G. Dayton; Mae F. Dayton; Scott N. Dayton; Tobin J. Dayton.
EIN: 522390637

4774
Sundet Foundation ✧
7556 Washington Ave. S.
Eden Prairie, MN 55344-3705

Established in 1980 in MN.
Donors: Leland N. Sundet; Louise C. Sundet; Mary, Inc.; MDSC; Goodall; Fountain Industries; Leland N. Sundet.
Foundation type: Independent foundation.
Financial data (yr. ended 12/31/13): Assets, $12,122,334 (M); gifts received, $226,239; expenditures, $870,226; qualifying distributions, $837,523; giving activities include $828,429 for 155 grants (high: $139,825; low: $200).
Purpose and activities: Giving primarily for education, and for Christian organizations and Lutheran churches; funding also children, youth and social services.
Fields of interest: Vocational education; Higher education; Education; Human services; Children/youth, services; Foundations (private grantmaking); Christian agencies & churches.
Type of support: General/operating support.
Limitations: Applications not accepted. Giving primarily in MN. No grants to individuals directly.
Application information: Contributes only to pre-selected organizations.
Officers and Directors:* Leland N. Sundet,* Pres.; Louise C. Sundet,* V.P. and Secy.; Carol Sundet-Meeker,* V.P. and Treas.
EIN: 411378654
Selected grants: The following grants are a representative sample of this grantmaker's funding activity:
$25,000 to Courage Center, Minneapolis, MN, 2011.
$2,000 to Focus on the Family, Colorado Springs, CO, 2011.
$1,500 to Search Ministries, Ellicott City, MD, 2011.
$1,250 to Mayo Clinic, Rochester, MN, 2011.
$1,000 to Young Life, Colorado Springs, CO, 2011.

4775
SUPERVALU Foundation ✧
P.O. Box 990
Minneapolis, MN 55440-0990
Contact: Sherry Smith, Sr. V.P. and Co-Treas.
Main URL: http://www.supervalu.com/responsibility/community.html

Established in 1993 in MN.
Donors: General Mills; SUPERVALU INC.
Foundation type: Company-sponsored foundation.
Financial data (yr. ended 02/28/14): Assets, $2,884,750 (M); gifts received, $715,470; expenditures, $512,595; qualifying distributions, $512,595; giving activities include $503,959 for 84 grants (high: $124,665; low: $25).
Purpose and activities: The foundation supports programs designed to promote hunger relief; dietary health and nutrition; and environmental stewardship.
Fields of interest: Environment, natural resources; Environment; Health care; Diabetes; Food services; Food banks; Nutrition.
Type of support: Sponsorships; General/operating support; Program development; Scholarship funds; Employee matching gifts.
Limitations: Applications accepted. Giving primarily in areas of company operations in MN. No support for United Way-supported organizations (over 30 percent of budget) or veterans', fraternal, or labor organizations, or religious organizations. No grants to individuals, or for third-party requests, conferences, seminars, or travel, advertising, emergency relief, fundraising, travel or academic research, parties, ceremonies, or memorials, lobbying or political initiatives, school field trips, or workforce readiness programs.
Publications: Application guidelines.
Application information: Application form required.
Initial approach: Complete online application
Deadline(s): None
Board meeting date(s): Quarterly
Final notification: Within 90 days
Officers and Directors: John F. Boyd, V.P. and Treas.; Liz Pham,* Secy.; Mary Vander Leest.
EIN: 411752955
Selected grants: The following grants are a representative sample of this grantmaker's funding activity:
$30,000 to Minnesota Project, Saint Paul, MN, 2012.
$15,000 to American Heart Association, Dallas, TX, 2012.
$15,000 to Nature Conservancy, Arlington, VA, 2012.
$15,000 to Urban League of Los Angeles, Los Angeles, CA, 2012.
$12,500 to American Heart Association, Dallas, TX, 2012.
$5,000 to Washburn Center for Children, Minneapolis, MN, 2012.

4776
Target Foundation ✧
(formerly Dayton Hudson Foundation)
c/o Community Rels.
1000 Nicollet Mall, TPN1144
Minneapolis, MN 55403-2467 (800) 388-6740
Contact: Jeanne Kavanaugh, Sr. Specialist
FAX: (612) 696-4706;
E-mail: community.relations@target.com; Main URL: https://corporate.target.com/corporate-responsibility/grants

Incorporated in 1918 in MN.
Donors: Dayton Hudson Corp.; Target Corp.
Foundation type: Company-sponsored foundation.
Financial data (yr. ended 02/02/13): Assets, $17,200,751 (M); gifts received, $4,750,000; expenditures, $9,714,803; qualifying distributions, $9,699,006; giving activities include $9,690,000 for 174 grants (high: $1,225,000; low: $5,000).
Purpose and activities: The foundation supports programs designed to promote arts and culture accessibility; and provide for basic needs of individuals and families at risk. Support is limited to the Minneapolis/St. Paul, Minnesota 7-county metropolitan area.
Fields of interest: Museums; Arts; Food services; Housing/shelter; Salvation Army; Family services; Human services; Community/economic development; United Ways and Federated Giving Programs.
Type of support: General/operating support.
Limitations: Applications accepted. Giving limited to the Minneapolis/St. Paul, MN 7-county metropolitan area. No support for religious organizations not of direct benefit to the entire community; generally, no support for health organizations. No grants to individuals, or for endowments, national ceremonies, memorials, conferences, fundraising dinners, testimonials, or similar events, recreation, therapeutic programs, or living subsidies.
Publications: Application guidelines; Annual report; Grants list; Program policy statement.
Application information: Applicants are required to register through the Minnesota Cultural Data Project. Application form required.
Initial approach: Complete online application
Deadline(s): Jan 1. to Feb. 1 for Arts; Apr. 1 to May 1 for Social Services
Board meeting date(s): Varies
Final notification: June 30 for Arts; Sept. 30 for Social Services
Officers and Trustees:* Gregg W. Steinhafel,* Chair.; Laysha Ward,* Pres.; Timothy R. Baer,* Secy.; John J. Mulligan, Treas.; John D. Griffith; Beth M. Jacob; Jodeen A. Kozlak; Terrance J. Scully; Kathee Tesjia.
Number of staff: 1 full-time professional.
EIN: 416017088
Selected grants: The following grants are a representative sample of this grantmaker's funding activity:
$1,225,000 to United Way, Greater Twin Cities, Minneapolis, MN, 2013. For general operating support, 2012 Campaign.
$275,000 to Catholic Charities of the Archdiocese of Saint Paul and Minneapolis, Minneapolis, MN, 2013. For general operating support.
$250,000 to Minnesota Orchestral Association, Minneapolis, MN, 2013. For general operating support.
$225,000 to Second Harvest Heartland, Saint Paul, MN, 2013. For general operating support.
$200,000 to People Serving People, Minneapolis, MN, 2013. For general operating support.
$50,000 to Minnesota Home Ownership Center, Saint Paul, MN, 2013. For general operating support and framework.
$40,000 to Hunger Solutions Minnesota, Saint Paul, MN, 2013. For Food Shelf capacity building program.
$35,000 to Neighborhood House, Saint Paul, MN, 2013. For Basic Needs Program.
$27,000 to Charities Review Council of Minnesota, Saint Paul, MN, 2013. For general operations and Campaign for Growth.
$25,000 to Minnesota Museum of American Art, Saint Paul, MN, 2013. For general operating support.

4777
Glen A. Taylor Foundation ✧
1725 Roe Crest Dr.
North Mankato, MN 56003-1807 (507) 625-2828
Contact: Glen Taylor, Tr.

Established in 1992 in MN.
Donors: Taylor Corp.; Glen A. Taylor Charitable Trust; Tol-O-Matic; Creative Banner Assemblies; MMSDC; Franz Altpeter; Lariat Co.
Foundation type: Independent foundation.
Financial data (yr. ended 12/31/13): Assets, $639,705 (M); expenditures, $572,370; qualifying distributions, $572,370; giving activities include $571,500 for 5 grants (high: $300,000; low: $15,000).
Purpose and activities: Giving primarily for higher education, and to a foundation which promotes hearing health awareness.

Fields of interest: Higher education; Education; Health organizations; Human services; Foundations (private grantmaking).
Limitations: Applications accepted. Giving primarily in MN, with emphasis on Mankato.
Application information: Application form required.
Initial approach: Proposal
Deadline(s): None
Trustees: Robert Anderson; William Kozitza; Larry Lorenzen; Bradley Schreier; Debra Taylor; Glen Taylor; Jean Taylor; Larry Taylor.
EIN: 411737411

4778
TCF Foundation ✧
(also known as TCF Bank Foundation)
150 Lake St. W., Mail Code: LSW-01-F
Wayzata, MN 55391-1693
Contact: Denise Peterson, Community Affairs Off.
FAX: (952) 745-2775; E-mail: dpete@tcfbank.com;
Main URL: http://www.tcfbank.com/About/about_community_relations.jsp

Established in 1989 in MN.
Donors: TCF National Bank Minnesota; TCF National Bank; TCF Financial Corp.
Foundation type: Company-sponsored foundation.
Financial data (yr. ended 12/31/13): Assets, $18,693 (M); gifts received, $1,350,000; expenditures, $1,421,342; qualifying distributions, $1,421,342; giving activities include $976,440 for 245 grants (high: $100,000; low: $100), and $444,902 for 658 employee matching gifts.
Purpose and activities: TCF Foundation's mission is to promote philanthropic efforts in its major market areas and to develop both a community and public affairs awareness which will project the Corporation's commitment to preserve and improve the quality of life of those in the communities they serve. Support is limited to areas of company operations and only to nonprofit organizations where there are TCF employees actively involved.
Fields of interest: Arts; Education; Housing/shelter; Youth development; Human services, financial counseling; Human services; Community/economic development; Economically disadvantaged.
Type of support: Employee matching gifts; General/operating support; Program development.
Limitations: Applications not accepted. Giving is limited to the communities in which there are TCF offices: Phoenix, AZ, Denver, CO, greater Chicago, IL, northwest IN, MI, MN, Sioux Falls, SD, and southeastern WI, including the greater Milwaukee area. No support for lobbying organizations. No grants to individuals, or for international grantmaking.
Application information: The foundation accepts full proposals by invitation only. Only nonprofit organizations where there are TCF employees actively involved are considered.
Board meeting date(s): Quarterly
Officers and Directors: William A. Cooper,* Chair.; Barbara E. Shaw,* Vice-Chair.; Thomas F. Jasper,* Treas.; Mark L. Jeter; Jason E. Korstange; James J. Urbanek.
Number of staff: 1 full-time professional.
EIN: 411659826
Selected grants: The following grants are a representative sample of this grantmaker's funding activity:
$1,000 to University of Chicago, Charter School Woodlawn Campus, Chicago, IL, 2012. For Retail Branch Funds.

4779
TEAM Foundation ✧ ☆
105 Park Ave. N.W.
Bagley, MN 56621-9558 (218) 694-3550
Contact: Tricia Young, Treas.
E-mail: teamfoundation@team-ind.com; Main URL: http://www.team-foundation.org/

Established in 2003 in MN.
Donors: TEAM Industries, Inc.; Okuma America Corporation; Toyoda Machinety USA; Ch Robinson Company; Interdyn BMI.
Foundation type: Company-sponsored foundation.
Financial data (yr. ended 12/31/13): Assets, $293,417 (M); gifts received, $547,505; expenditures, $723,841; qualifying distributions, $723,841; giving activities include $661,982 for 23 grants (high: $150,000; low: $1,000).
Purpose and activities: The foundation supports programs designed to promote education; health; and community.
Fields of interest: Elementary/secondary education; Education, early childhood education; Education, reading; Education; Hospitals (general); Health care; Food services; Nutrition; Children, services; Residential/custodial care, hospices; Aging, centers/services; Human services; Community/economic development; Mathematics; Engineering/technology; Youth; Aging.
Type of support: Continuing support; Building/renovation; Endowments; Equipment; General/operating support; Program development; Sponsorships.
Limitations: Applications accepted. Giving primarily in areas of company operations in MN.
Publications: Application guidelines; Program policy statement.
Application information: Application form required.
Initial approach: Download application form and mail to foundation
Deadline(s): None
Officers: Debra Matthews, Pres.; Steve Kast, V.P.; Sara Gordon, Secy.; Tricia Young, Treas.
Director: Beatrice Ricke.
EIN: 061696861
Selected grants: The following grants are a representative sample of this grantmaker's funding activity:
$22,000 to Northwest Minnesota Foundation, Bemidji, MN, 2011.
$1,000 to American Cancer Society, Atlanta, GA, 2011.

4780
The Toro Foundation ✧
8111 Lyndale Ave. S.
Bloomington, MN 55420-1196 (952) 887-8870
Contact: Judson McNeil, Pres. and Dir.

Established in 1988 in MN.
Donor: The Toro Co.
Foundation type: Company-sponsored foundation.
Financial data (yr. ended 12/31/13): Assets, $3,719,518 (M); gifts received, $566,997; expenditures, $1,103,278; qualifying distributions, $1,072,294; giving activities include $976,907 for 110 grants (high: $480,031; low: $300), and $92,248 for 194 employee matching gifts.
Purpose and activities: The foundation supports organizations involved with arts and culture, education, the environment, health, human services, and civic affairs. Special emphasis is directed toward programs designed to promote turf maintenance, water management, and agronomy.
Fields of interest: Education; Human services; Religion.
International interests: Australia; Mexico.
Limitations: Applications accepted. Giving primarily in areas of company operations in El Cajon and Riverside, CA, Minneapolis and Windom, MN, Beatrice, NE, El Paso, TX, Tomah and western WI, and in Australia and Mexico. No support for political or religious organizations. No grants for capital campaigns.
Publications: Application guidelines; Corporate giving report.
Application information: Application form required.
Initial approach: Contact foundation via mail for application form
Deadline(s): None
Board meeting date(s): Quarterly
Officers and Directors:* Judson McNeil,* Pres.; Nancy McGrath, Secy.; Thomas Larson,* Treas.; Amy Dahl; Timothy P. Dordell; Michael D. Drazen; Blake Grams; Michael J. Hoffman; Renee Peterson; Peter M. Ramstad.
Number of staff: 1 part-time professional; 1 full-time support; 1 part-time support.
EIN: 363593618
Selected grants: The following grants are a representative sample of this grantmaker's funding activity:
$413,543 to United Way, Greater Twin Cities, Minneapolis, MN, 2011.
$1,740 to United Way of Abilene, Abilene, TX, 2011.

4781
Total Depth Foundation ✧ ☆
315 Manitoba Ave., Ste. 200
Wayzata, MN 55391 (612) 766-8805
Contact: Ryan Gilbertson, Pres.

Established in MN.
Donors: Ryan Gilbertson; Michael Reger; Holden Gibertson.
Foundation type: Independent foundation.
Financial data (yr. ended 12/31/12): Assets, $3,112,049 (M); gifts received, $4,446,250; expenditures, $679,442; qualifying distributions, $655,000; giving activities include $655,000 for grants.
Fields of interest: Cancer; Children.
Limitations: Applications accepted. Giving primarily in CO, FL and MN.
Application information: Application form required.
Initial approach: Proposal
Deadline(s): None
Officers: Ryan Gilbertson, Pres.; Michael Reger, Secy.-Treas.
Directors: James Randall Reger; James Russell Reger; Kellie E. Tasto.
EIN: 271110988

4782
Tozer Foundation, Inc. ✧
1213 1/2 5th Ave. S.
Stillwater, MN 55082-5813 (651) 439-1530
FAX: (651) 430-2112;
E-mail: info@TozerFoundation.com; Main URL: http://www.tozerfoundation.com

Incorporated in 1946 in MN.
Donor: David Tozer‡.

Foundation type: Independent foundation.
Financial data (yr. ended 10/31/13): Assets, $26,367,912 (M); gifts received, $6,500; expenditures, $1,401,025; qualifying distributions, $1,207,428; giving activities include $1,070,979 for 200 grants (high: $118,000; low: $500).
Purpose and activities: Giving primarily for scholarships to graduating high school students who are residents of Kanabec, Pine, or Washington counties in MN.
Fields of interest: Higher education; Education.
Type of support: General/operating support; Continuing support; Annual campaigns; Capital campaigns; Building/renovation.
Limitations: Giving primarily in the St. Paul and Stillwater, MN, areas; scholarships limited to residents of Kanabec, Pine, and Washington counties, MN.
Publications: Application guidelines.
Application information: Application guidelines and form available on foundation web site. Candidates must apply for scholarships through selected high schools. Candidates must be residents of Washington, Pine or Kanabec County, MN. Checks are sent directly to the schools. Application form required.
Initial approach: Use application process on foundation web site
Copies of proposal: 1
Deadline(s): Mar. 1
Board meeting date(s): May and Oct.
Final notification: Immediately after board meeting
Officers and Directors:* Greg Benson,* Pres.; David Wettergren, V.P.; Alan Bernick; Tracy Galowitz; Orville Johnson; Gretchen M. Stein, Ph.D.; Jon A. Theobald; John F. Thoreen.
EIN: 416011518

4783
Travelers Foundation ✧

385 Washington St., MC514D
St. Paul, MN 55102-1396 (651) 310-7757
Contact: Marlene Ibsen, Pres. and C.E.O.
FAX: (651) 310-2327;
E-mail: lcolanin@travelers.com; Additional contacts: Michael Newman, V.P., Travelers Foundation, tel.: (651) 310-7263; Tara N. Spain, V.P., Travelers Foundation, tel.:(860) 277-7015; and Lisa Colaninno, Opers. Mgr., tel.: (860) 277-3761; Main URL: http://www.travelers.com/corporate-info/about/community/foundation.aspx

Established in 1998 in MN.
Donors: The St. Paul Companies, Inc.; The St. Paul Travelers Companies, Inc.; The Travelers Companies, Inc.
Foundation type: Company-sponsored foundation.
Financial data (yr. ended 12/31/13): Assets, $160,892 (M); gifts received, $8,033,472; expenditures, $8,015,297; qualifying distributions, $8,015,297; giving activities include $8,006,130 for 199 grants (high: $700,000; low: $500).
Purpose and activities: The foundation supports organizations involved with arts and culture, education, employment, housing, youth, community development, leadership development, and economically disadvantaged people.
Fields of interest: Arts, cultural/ethnic awareness; Arts education; Arts; Education, reform; Elementary/secondary education; Higher education; Teacher school/education; Education; Employment, training; Employment; Housing/shelter; Youth, services; Community development, neighborhood development; Community development, small businesses; Community/economic development; Leadership development; Minorities; Economically disadvantaged.
Type of support: General/operating support; Capital campaigns; Program development; Scholarship funds; Employee volunteer services; Sponsorships; Employee matching gifts.
Limitations: Applications accepted. Giving primarily in areas of significant company operations, with emphasis on Hartford, CT and St. Paul, MN; limited giving to national organizations. No support for discriminatory organizations, sectarian religious organizations, political, lobbying, or fraternal organizations, health or disease-specific organizations, or hospitals or other health services organizations generally supported by third-party reimbursement mechanisms, or environmental programs. No grants to individuals, or for scholarships, benefits, fund-raisers, walk-a-thons, telethons, galas or other revenue generating events, advertising, medical research, medical equipment, hospital capital or operating funds, replacement of government funding, human services such as counseling, chemical abuse treatment or family programs, or special events.
Publications: Application guidelines; Corporate giving report; Program policy statement.
Application information: A full proposal may be requested at a later date. Application form required.
Initial approach: Complete online pre-application
Deadline(s): 3 weeks before 1/16, 4/10, and 9/11
Board meeting date(s): Quarterly
Officers and Directors:* Andy F. Bessette,* Chair.; Marlene M. Ibsen,* C.E.O and Pres.; Michael Newman, V.P.; Tara N. Spain, V.P.; Wendy Skjerven, Corp. Secy.; Jay S. Benet,* C.F.O. and Treas.; Lisa Caputo; John P. Clifford, Jr.; Ron James; Michael F. Klein; Brian MacLean; Doreen Spadorcia; Kenneth F. Spence III; Joan K. Woodword.
Number of staff: None.
EIN: 411924256
Selected grants: The following grants are a representative sample of this grantmaker's funding activity:
$700,000 to Saint Paul Public Schools, ISD 625, Saint Paul, MN, 2013. For special project support for aligned AVID/Leadership Development program to foster dynamic school leadership and high student achievement.
$500,000 to United Way of Central and Northeastern Connecticut, Hartford, CT, 2013. For operating support, including our corporate contribution to the United Way Community Campaign and the short-fall amount from the 2012 Travelers Hartford-Area Employee Giving Campaign.
$340,000 to Habitat for Humanity International, Operational Headquarters, Americus, GA, 2013. For program support to help revitalize communities through funding homes for families in need while engaging employees in team building through volunteerism in up to 38 Travelers field markets.
$130,000 to Boys and Girls Clubs of Hartford, Hartford, CT, 2013. For project support for after-school program at Asian Studies Academy at Bellizzi and operating support at four Main Club sites in collaboration with Joe Young Studios.
$100,000 to Common Ground Communities, Community Solutions, New York, NY, 2013. For project support for Healthy Northeast Initiative, Restoration of the Swift Factory.
$85,000 to Ordway Center for the Performing Arts, Saint Paul, MN, 2013. For operating support for programs that make the arts accessible to young people from low-income communities.
$25,000 to Rebuilding Together Hartford, Hartford, CT, 2013. For project support for the organization's Emergency Home Repair initiative.
$25,000 to Trinity College, Hartford, CT, 2013. For project support for Dream Camp at Trinity College.
$15,000 to Central Connecticut State University, New Britain, CT, 2013. For project support to help CCSU conserve, and move to the state capital, the Forlorn Soldier statue.
$15,000 to YMCA of Metropolitan Hartford, Hartford, CT, 2013. For program support for Y Achievers program, academic enrichment and mentoring initiative.

4784
U.S. Bancorp Foundation, Inc. ✧

U.S. Bank BC-MN-H21B
800 Nicollet Mall
Minneapolis, MN 55402 (612) 303-4000
Contact: James D. Rhodes, Grants Mgr.
FAX: (612) 303-0787;
E-mail: USBancorp@Easymatch.com; Additional address: U.S. Bank Foundation, Grant Prog., P.O. Box 8857, Princeton, NJ 08543-8857, tel.: (866) 243-6925; Main URL: http://www.usbank.com/cgi_w/cfm/about/community_relations/charit_giving.cfm
Grants List: http://www.usbank.com/community/charitable-giving.html

Established in 1979.
Donors: First Bank System, Inc.; U.S. Bancorp; U.S. Bank, N.A.
Foundation type: Company-sponsored foundation.
Financial data (yr. ended 12/31/12): Assets, $38,459,360 (M); gifts received, $24,000,000; expenditures, $23,977,140; qualifying distributions, $23,739,696; giving activities include $23,292,965 for grants.
Purpose and activities: The foundation supports organizations involved with arts and culture, economic opportunity (see website for definition), education, and United Way. Special emphasis is directed toward programs designed to improve the educational and economic opportunities of low- and moderate-income individuals and families; and enhance the cultural and artistic lives of communities.
Fields of interest: Arts, multipurpose centers/programs; Arts education; Museums; Performing arts; Historic preservation/historical societies; Arts; Elementary/secondary education; Higher education; Education; Employment, training; Employment; Housing/shelter, development; Housing/shelter, rehabilitation; Housing/shelter, home owners; Housing/shelter; Youth development, adult & child programs; Youth development; Human services, financial counseling; Economic development; Community development, small businesses; Community/economic development; United Ways and Federated Giving Programs; Children/youth; Children; Youth; Adults; Young adults; Economically disadvantaged.
Type of support: General/operating support; Capital campaigns; Program development; Scholarship funds; Employee matching gifts; In-kind gifts.
Limitations: Applications accepted. Giving primarily in AR, AZ, CA, CO, IA, ID, IL, IN, KS, KY, MN, MO, MT, ND, NE, NM, NV, OH, OR, SD, TN, UT, WA, WI,

and WY. No support for fraternal organizations, merchant associations, or 501(c)(4) or (6) organizations, 509(a)(3) supporting organizations, pass-through organizations or private foundations, religious organizations, political organizations or lobbying organizations, or sponsorships. No grants to individuals, or for fundraising events or sponsorships, travel, endowments, debt reduction, or chamber memberships or programs.
Publications: Application guidelines; Annual report; Corporate report; Grants list.
Application information: Unsolicited applications accepted from organizations located in communities served by U.S. Bank. Visit website for state charitable giving contacts and various application deadlines. Application form required.
Initial approach: Complete online application
Deadline(s): Deadlines vary by state; Check website for deadlines for local area; Feb. 1 for Arts and Culture, Apr. 1 for Economic Opportunity, and July 1 for Education for organizations located in Twin Cities, Minnesota
Board meeting date(s): 5 times per year
Officers and Directors:* Deborah M. Burke,* Chair. and Pres.; James L. Chosy,* Secy.; Andrew Cecere,* Treas.; Jennie P. Carlson; Richard K. Davis; Terrance Dolan; John Elmore; Elliot Jaffee; Barry Martin; Richard Payne; Kent Stone; Jeffry H. von Gillern.
EIN: 411359579
Selected grants: The following grants are a representative sample of this grantmaker's funding activity:
$850,000 to United Way, Greater Twin Cities, Minneapolis, MN, 2012. For general operating support.
$200,000 to Minnesota Orchestral Association, Minneapolis, MN, 2012. For general operating support.
$150,000 to Junior Achievement of Greater Saint Louis, Chesterfield, MO, 2012. For general operating support.
$150,000 to Saint Louis University, Saint Louis, MO, 2012. For general operating support.
$100,000 to American Red Cross, Twin Cities Chapter, Minneapolis, MN, 2012. For general operating support.
$100,000 to Local Initiatives Support Corporation, New York, NY, 2012. For general operating support.
$60,000 to Sioux Empire Housing Partnership, Sioux Falls, SD, 2012. For general operating support.
$5,000 to United Way, Shelby County, United Way of Shelby County, Sidney, OH, 2012. For general operating support.
$3,000 to No Limits Theater Group, No Limits for Deaf Children, Culver City, CA, 2012. For general operating support.
$2,500 to Log Cabin Literary Center, Boise, ID, 2012. For general operating support.

4785
United Health Foundation ✧

9900 Bren Rd. E., MN008-W150
Minnetonka, MN 55343-9664
Contact: Shelly Espinosa, Dir., Community Affairs
FAX: (952) 936-1675;
E-mail: unitedhealthfoundationinfo@uhc.com; Main URL: http://www.unitedhealthfoundation.org
RSS Feed: http://www.unitedhealthfoundation.org/News/RSS.aspx

Established in 1999 in MN.
Donors: United Healthcare Services, Inc.; UnitedHealth Group Inc.; Accenture, LLP; Pacificare Health Systems Foundation; Homecall Hospice.
Foundation type: Company-sponsored foundation.
Financial data (yr. ended 12/31/11): Assets, $67,405,508 (M); gifts received, $1,838,301; expenditures, $11,316,000; qualifying distributions, $11,536,806; giving activities include $9,838,607 for 62 grants (high: $1,375,000; low: $5,000), and $8,217,903 for 4 foundation-administered programs.
Purpose and activities: The foundation supports programs designed to create healthier communities; expand access to healthcare services; nurture the future health workforce; and improve medical outcomes.
Fields of interest: Medical school/education; Health care, clinics/centers; Health care, patient services; Health care; Economically disadvantaged.
Type of support: Continuing support; Program development; Publication; Scholarship funds; Technical assistance.
Limitations: Applications not accepted. Giving on a national basis in areas of company operations, with emphasis on Washington, DC, FL, MN, and NY. No support for private foundations, fiscal agents, political candidates, athletic associations, or religious organizations not of direct benefit to the entire community. No grants to individuals, or for scholarships (except for the Diverse Scholar Program), general operating support, capital campaigns, building or renovation, equipment (unless related to a request for project support), endowments, fundraising events, development campaigns, political causes, lobbying efforts, recreational or sporting events, basic or biomedical research, or travel.
Publications: Annual report; Corporate giving report.
Application information: The foundation is currently not accepting unsolicited requests.
Officers and Directors:* James R. Campbell,* Chair.; Kate Rubin, Pres.; Jeanette Pfotenhauer, Secy.; Robert Oberrender, Treas.; Cory Alexander; Tina Brown-Stevenson; Kate Erickson; Thomas Paul; Marianne Short; Andrew Slavitt; David Wichmann.
Number of staff: None.
EIN: 411941615
Selected grants: The following grants are a representative sample of this grantmaker's funding activity:
$1,000,000 to University of Minnesota Foundation, Minneapolis, MN, 2012. For Healthy Communities Innovation Center.
$500,000 to United Network for Organ Sharing, Richmond, VA, 2012. For Automation of the OPTN/UNOS Kidney Paired Donation Program.
$500,000 to Unity Health Care, Washington, DC, 2012. For Centers of Excellence.
$250,000 to Distance Learning Center, Philadelphia, PA, 2012. For STEMPREP Project.
$250,000 to University of Miami, Coral Gables, FL, 2012. For Centers of Excellence.
$250,000 to University of Miami, Coral Gables, FL, 2012. For Centers of Excellence.
$236,309 to Campaign for Tobacco-Free Kids, Washington, DC, 2012. For Youth By Youth Initiative.
$236,309 to Campaign for Tobacco-Free Kids, Washington, DC, 2012. For Youth By Youth Initiative.
$50,000 to American Joint Replacement Registry, Rosemont, IL, 2012. For operating support.
$50,000 to Hispanic Association of Colleges and Universities, San Antonio, TX, 2012. For partner in the Latino Health Scholars as part of the Foundations Diverse Scholarship Initiative.

4786
The Valspar Foundation ✧

P.O. Box 1461
Minneapolis, MN 55440-1461
Contact: Susan Carter
Main URL: http://www.valsparglobal.com/corp/about/valspar_foundation.jsp

Established in 1979.
Donor: The Valspar Corp.
Foundation type: Company-sponsored foundation.
Financial data (yr. ended 09/30/13): Assets, $77,069 (M); gifts received, $550,000; expenditures, $1,001,928; qualifying distributions, $1,001,777; giving activities include $1,001,777 for 180 grants (high: $325,000; low: $20).
Purpose and activities: The foundation supports organizations involved with arts and culture, education, health, housing, poison prevention, human services, and community development.
Fields of interest: Media, radio; Museums (science/technology); Performing arts, orchestras; Arts; Education; Health care; Housing/shelter, development; Housing/shelter; Safety, poisons; American Red Cross; YM/YWCAs & YM/YWHAs; Children/youth, services; Family services; Human services; Community/economic development; United Ways and Federated Giving Programs; Economically disadvantaged.
Type of support: Annual campaigns; General/operating support; Building/renovation; Program development; Sponsorships; Employee matching gifts; Employee-related scholarships; In-kind gifts.
Limitations: Applications accepted. Giving limited to areas of company operations, with emphasis on the Twin Cities, MN, metropolitan area. No support for religious, ethnic, fraternal, labor, or veterans' organizations.
Application information: Application form required.
Initial approach: Request application form
Deadline(s): Oct. 1
Officer: Rolf Engh, Chair.
Directors: C.A. Arnold; Anthony L. Blaine; H.C. Heckes; G.E. Hendrickson.
Number of staff: 1 full-time professional; 1 part-time support.
EIN: 411363847

4787
Frank W. Veden Charitable Trust ✧

c/o Trust Tax Services
P.O. Box 64713
St. Paul, MN 55164-0713

Established in 1997 in MN.
Donor: Frank Veden Trust.
Foundation type: Independent foundation.
Financial data (yr. ended 12/31/13): Assets, $11,205,356 (M); expenditures, $592,155; qualifying distributions, $515,778; giving activities include $473,339 for 11 grants (high: $150,000; low: $2,000).
Purpose and activities: Giving primarily for education and human services.
Fields of interest: Higher education; Education; Human services; Community/economic development; United Ways and Federated Giving Programs.

Limitations: Applications not accepted. Giving primarily in MN, with emphasis on Fergus Falls. No grants to individuals.
Application information: Contributes only to pre-selected organizations.
Trustees: Kenneth Broin; Ruth Reister; U.S. Bank, N.A.
EIN: 416432193

4788
Sid and Carol Verdoorn Family Foundation ✧
c/o Jeff Verdoorn
9011 Sutton Dr.
Eden Prairie, MN 55347-5358

Established in 1999 in MN.
Donors: Carol Verdoorn; Daryl R. Verdoorn; Jeff Verdoorn.
Foundation type: Independent foundation.
Financial data (yr. ended 12/31/12): Assets, $39,358,831 (M); expenditures, $589,557; qualifying distributions, $5,549,290; giving activities include $500,000 for 7 grants (high: $250,000; low: $5,000).
Fields of interest: Education; Christian agencies & churches.
Limitations: Applications not accepted. Giving primarily in MN. No grants to individuals.
Application information: Contributes only to pre-selected organizations.
Officers: Daryl Verdoorn, Chair.; Carol Verdoorn, Pres. and Secy.; Jay Verdoorn, V.P.; Jeff Verdoorn, Treas.
EIN: 411926065

4789
Veritas Foundation ✧
c/o Wipeli LLP
7601 France Ave. S., Ste. 400
Edina, MN 55435-5969
Main URL: http://veritas-foundation.org/

Established in 2005 in MN.
Donors: Peter S. Karle; Patricia J. Karle.
Foundation type: Independent foundation.
Financial data (yr. ended 12/31/13): Assets, $8,562,163 (M); gifts received, $15,000; expenditures, $810,751; qualifying distributions, $989,335; giving activities include $776,786 for 15 grants (high: $343,718; low: $3,600).
Fields of interest: Media/communications; Christian agencies & churches.
Type of support: General/operating support.
Limitations: Applications not accepted. Giving primarily in MN. No grants to individuals.
Application information: Contributes only to pre-selected organizations.
Officers: Patricia J. Karle, Pres.; Kristine E. Isaac, Secy.; Peter S. Karle, Treas.
EIN: 202522960

4790
W.M. Foundation ✧
1800 IDS Ctr., Rm. 1800
80 S. 8th St.
Minneapolis, MN 55402-4523

Established in MN.
Donors: Wallace C. Dayton; Mary Lee Dayton.
Foundation type: Independent foundation.
Financial data (yr. ended 12/31/12): Assets, $18,577,137 (M); expenditures, $1,473,925; qualifying distributions, $1,255,430; giving activities include $1,240,500 for grants.
Purpose and activities: Giving primarily for the environment.
Fields of interest: Environment, natural resources; Animals/wildlife, preservation/protection.
Limitations: Applications not accepted. Giving primarily in MA, and the Minneapolis-St. Paul, MN, area; funding also in Arlington, VA. No grants to individuals.
Application information: Contributes only to pre-selected organizations.
Officers: Ellen D. Grace, Co-Chair.; Katherine D. Nielsen, Co-Chair.; James M. Karges, Secy.
Directors: Sally D. Clement; Mary L. Dayton; Elizabeth D. Dovydenas.
EIN: 416080486

4791
Wallestad Foundation ✧
730 Second Ave. S., Ste. 415
Minneapolis, MN 55402 (612) 288-2233
Contact: Jay L. Bennett

Established in 1986 in MN.
Donors: Phadoris Wallestad†; Cary Humphries; Jay L. Bennett; Stan Geyer; Bev Geyer; Fluoroware, Inc.; Entegris, Inc.; Youthworks!; Harvest Foundation.
Foundation type: Independent foundation.
Financial data (yr. ended 12/31/12): Assets, $7,414,187 (M); expenditures, $705,084; qualifying distributions, $1,405,867; giving activities include $496,959 for 8 grants (high: $300,000; low: $2,000).
Purpose and activities: Giving primarily to Christian agencies and churches.
Fields of interest: Human services; Children/youth, services; Family services; Religious federated giving programs; Christian agencies & churches.
Type of support: Program-related investments/loans; Employee matching gifts.
Limitations: Applications accepted. Giving primarily in the Minneapolis, MN area.
Application information: Application form required.
Initial approach: Letter
Deadline(s): None
Officers: Jay L. Bennett, Chair.; Andy Bennett, Pres.; Sandra Byzewski, Secy.
EIN: 363485265

4792
Wallin Education Partners ✧
(formerly Northstar Partners Scholarship Fund)
5200 Willson Rd., Ste. 209
Minneapolis, MN 55424-1343 (952) 345-1920
FAX: (952) 345-1930;
E-mail: wallin.staff@wallinpartners.org; Additional e-mail: info@wallinpartners.org; Main URL: http://www.wallinfoundation.org
Facebook: https://www.facebook.com/wallin.education.partners
Wallin Education Partners Alumni Assoc.: http://www.linkedin.com/groups?gid=4038198

Established in 2007 in MN.
Donors: Winston R. Wallin; Maxine H. Wallin; Ron Cornwell; Joan Cornwell; Marilyn Erickson; James C. Hayes; Carol Pfleiderer; Peter Pierce; Janice Pierce; Ardes Johnson; St. Paul Foundation; Medtronic Foundation; Alpha Kappa Psi Scholarship Foundation; Wallin Foundation; Simpson Family Charitable Foundation; Junior League; Tom and Mary McCary Foundation.
Foundation type: Operating foundation.
Financial data (yr. ended 06/30/13): Assets, $0 (M); gifts received, $2,664,390; expenditures, $2,687,900; qualifying distributions, $2,684,900; giving activities include $1,830,681 for grants to individuals.
Fields of interest: Higher education, university.
Type of support: Scholarships—to individuals.
Limitations: Giving primarily in MN. No grants to.
Application information:
Initial approach: Use online application form for scholarships
Officers and Directors:* Tom Holman,* Chair.; Bradford W. Wallin, Vice-Chair.; Charles M. Denny, Jr., Treas.; Susan Basil King, Exec. Dir.; Joan Cornwell; Stephen R. Lewis, Jr.; Brian C. Rosenberg; Sandra L. Vargas; Maxine H. Wallin.
EIN: 208505156

4793
Wallin Foundation ✧
5200 Wilson Rd., Ste. 207
Minneapolis, MN 55424-1343
FAX: (612) 338-0570;
E-mail: paula.deziel@wallinfoundation.org

Established in 1986 in MN.
Donors: Maxine H. Wallin; Winston R. Wallin.
Foundation type: Independent foundation.
Financial data (yr. ended 12/31/12): Assets, $13,908,174 (M); gifts received, $197,494; expenditures, $1,564,976; qualifying distributions, $1,473,429; giving activities include $1,442,892 for 58 grants (high: $500,000; low: $250).
Fields of interest: Higher education; Education.
Limitations: Applications not accepted. Giving primarily in MN. No grants to individuals.
Application information: Contributes only to pre-selected organizations.
Board meeting date(s): Quarterly
Officer: Bradford W. Wallin, Mgr.
Trustee: Maxine H. Wallin.
Number of staff: 2 full-time professional; 2 part-time professional.
EIN: 416283068

4794
The Wasie Foundation ✧
230 Manitoba Ave. S.
Wayzata, MN 55391-1612 (952) 955-8500
Main URL: http://www.wasie.org/

Incorporated in 1966 in MN as the Wasie Educational Foundation.
Donors: Donald A. Wasie†; Stanley L. Wasie†; Marie F. Wasie†.
Foundation type: Independent foundation.
Financial data (yr. ended 12/31/12): Assets, $25,623,926 (M); expenditures, $2,738,116; qualifying distributions, $2,189,231; giving activities include $847,233 for 29 grants (high: $150,000; low: $1,441).
Purpose and activities: To provide education for students of Polish ancestry. This is done through endowed scholarship programs at specific private colleges and universities in Minnesota. The Wasie

family also had a strong desire to help people living with schizophrenia, arthritis, and cancer as well as to help children living with chronic illness, disabling conditions, or terminal illness. Serving these populations is done by providing grant support to non-profit organizations that work with these particular conditions.
Fields of interest: Health care; Mental health, schizophrenia; Cancer; Arthritis; Health organizations; Arthritis research.
Type of support: Building/renovation; Capital campaigns; Equipment; General/operating support; Income development; Matching/challenge support; Research; Technical assistance.
Limitations: Applications accepted. Giving primarily in Washington, DC, Broward, Palm Beach, and Miami-Dade counties FL, and the Twin Cities, MN. No support for non-501(c)(3) organizations. No funding for advocacy or for cancer research. No grants to individuals; no loans.
Publications: Application guidelines.
Application information: Application form required.
Initial approach: Proposal
Copies of proposal: 1
Deadline(s): None
Board meeting date(s): Quarterly and as required
Officers and Directors:* Gregg D. Sjoquist,* Pres.; Regina C. Bergeron,* V.P. and Treas.; Linda M. Cooke,* Secy.
Number of staff: 4 full-time professional.
EIN: 410911636

4795
WCA Foundation ✧
(formerly Woman's Christian Association)
10249 Yellow Circle Dr., Ste. 101
Minnetonka, MN 55343-9111 (952) 932-9032
Contact: Susan Carter, Exec. Dir.
FAX: (952) 932-9036; Main URL: http://www.wcafoundation.org

Established in 1866 in MN.
Donors: Minneapolis Foundation; John Windhorst, Jr.; Peter Windhorst.
Foundation type: Independent foundation.
Financial data (yr. ended 12/31/13): Assets, $18,717,226 (M); gifts received, $12,749; expenditures, $1,044,397; qualifying distributions, $800,475; giving activities include $588,680 for 43 grants (high: $50,000; low: $1,000).
Purpose and activities: Primary area of interest is in programs helping women achieve or sustain self-sufficiency and general human services. Grants also may be awarded for (but are not limited to) battered women's programs, subsidized housing programs, programs for homeless persons, recovery programs, day care subsidies, children's and youth programs, scholarships for education or jobs training, and programs for immigrants.
Fields of interest: Education; Employment, training; Employment, retraining; Human services; Children/youth, services; Family services; Aging, centers/services; Women.
Type of support: General/operating support; Capital campaigns; Building/renovation; Emergency funds; Program development; Scholarship funds; Program evaluation.
Limitations: Applications accepted. Giving limited to MN. No support for private foundations, political or veterans' organizations, religious organizations for religious purposes, national medical associations, pro-life/pro-choice programs, organizations which require employees to raise some or all of their own salaries in individual fundraising, or organizations affiliated with the foundation. No grants to individuals, or for annual fund drives, medical research, costs of litigation or previously incurred deficits, or multi-year awards.
Publications: Application guidelines; Grants list.
Application information: See foundation website for complete application guidelines. Application form required.
Initial approach: Telephone Exec. Dir. between 9:00am and 4:00pm on weekdays to request application form
Copies of proposal: 1
Deadline(s): May 1 and Nov. 1
Board meeting date(s): 1st Fri. of each month
Officers: Patricia Scott, Pres.; Dot Lilja, 1st V.P.; Barbara Horton, 2nd V.P.; Barbara Lyons, 3rd V.P.; Joanne Lieske, Secy.; Barbara Rose, Treas.; Susan Carter, Exec. Dir.; Sarah Karon, Chair., Dunwoody Dept.; Gail Emerson, Chair., Paige Dept.; Norma Cox, Chair., Pillsbury Dept.; Molly Cox, Dir., Pillsbury Dept.; Sally Knutzen, Dir., Dunwoody Dept.; Hope Thornberg, Dir., Paige Dept.
Number of staff: 1 full-time professional; 1 full-time support.
EIN: 410694712
Selected grants: The following grants are a representative sample of this grantmaker's funding activity:
$20,000 to Homeward Bound, Plymouth, MN, 2012. For Full range of services for profoundly disabled persons. Grant for scholarships for staff seeking advancement in the field of long-term care.
$15,000 to Ampersand Families, Minneapolis, MN, 2012. For Recruits and supports permanent adoptive families for youth aging out of foster care.
$15,000 to House of Charity, Minneapolis, MN, 2012. For The Co-Occurring Women's Program provides housing and supportive services for women who have been dually diagnosed with chemical dependency and mental illness.
$15,000 to Micrograints, Minneapolis, MN, 2012. For Makes $1,000 grants to individuals who have approved plans to attain self-sufficiency.
$15,000 to YouthCARE, Minneapolis, MN, 2012. For Styling Science Program is designed to use female teen mentors to help develop interest in STEM subjects in younger girls.
$15,000 to YouthLink, Minneapolis, MN, 2012. For Sisters Program helps youth 16 to 21 at risk for sexual exploitation.
$13,000 to Centro Cultural Chicano, Minneapolis, MN, 2012. For Multi-service organization service Chicano-Latino community. Capital grant for equipment for Siembra day care Program.
$13,000 to Dunwoody College of Technology, Minneapolis, MN, 2012. For Scholarships for women attending school plus support for Kate L. Dunwoody Emergency Fund which makes one-time grants to help women with unexpected financial crises.
$12,000 to Illusion Theater and School, Minneapolis, MN, 2012. For a play written and produced by teens and performed at high schools about avoiding pregnancy and risky behaviors.
$12,000 to North Metro Pediatrics, Coon Rapids, MN, 2012. For Pediatric primary care clinic for un- and under-insured families.

4796
J.A. Wedum Foundation ✧
2615 University Ave. S.E.
Minneapolis, MN 55414-3207
Contact: Jay J. Portz, Pres.
FAX: (612) 789-4044; E-mail: jayportz@wedum.org; Main URL: http://www.wedum.org
Grants List: http://www.wedumfoundation.org/wedum_grant.html

Established in 1959 in MN.
Donors: Maynard C. Wedum‡; John A. Wedum‡.
Foundation type: Independent foundation.
Financial data (yr. ended 12/31/13): Assets, $165,271,855 (M); gifts received, $502,216; expenditures, $31,768,211; qualifying distributions, $1,438,131; giving activities include $1,438,131 for 85 grants (high: $510,000; low: $50).
Purpose and activities: The mission of the foundation is to develop and utilize the resources of the foundation to help organizations and individuals change and improve people's lives in the spirit of stewardship and generosity exemplified by John A. Wedum, the grandfather, and carried forward by John A. Wedum, the grandson. The vision of the foundation is to provide needed housing for communities, invest its assets to increase the capital available for its mission, expend its income to change and improve the lives of people in a very efficient manner, giving priority to the support of education, and be recognized as an organization that seeks excellence in whatever it chooses to do.
Fields of interest: Higher education, university; Education; Human services.
Type of support: Continuing support; Seed money; Scholarship funds; Matching/challenge support.
Limitations: Applications not accepted. Giving primarily in MN; funding also in ID, ND, and WI.
Publications: Annual report; Informational brochure.
Application information: Unsolicited requests for funds will not be accepted.
Board meeting date(s): Apr. and Sept.
Officers and Board Members:* Frank Starke,* Chair.; Jay J. Portz, Pres.; Dawn Downs; Dana Wedum Kennelly; David Kjos; Joseph A. Rusche; Gary Slette; Dayton Soby; Dale Vesledahl.
Number of staff: 2 full-time professional.
EIN: 416025661
Selected grants: The following grants are a representative sample of this grantmaker's funding activity:
$5,000 to Knute Nelson, Alexandria, MN, 2012. For assistance to aging.

4797
Donald Weesner Charitable Trust ✧
c/o Trust Tax Services
P.O. Box 64713
St. Paul, MN 55164-0713

Established in 2000 in MN.
Foundation type: Independent foundation.
Financial data (yr. ended 12/31/13): Assets, $13,305,460 (M); expenditures, $704,061; qualifying distributions, $598,610; giving activities include $559,842 for 21 grants (high: $93,722; low: $6,000).
Purpose and activities: The foundation was established to promote the founder's lifelong commitment to preserving the Minnesota communities' natural ecosystems and historical legacy. It supports charitable organizations that

preserve our natural environment and educate the public about the need for protection of our environmental resources. Well-established non-profit organizations with a long track record of successful environmental and wildlife preservation education programs will be given priority. The foundation has limited funds to support community groups.
Fields of interest: Museums (science/technology); Arts; Environment, natural resources; Zoos/zoological societies; Human services; United Ways and Federated Giving Programs.
Limitations: Applications not accepted. Giving primarily in MN. No grants to individuals or for debt reduction, travel expenses or for general operating support.
Application information: Unsolicited requests for funds not accepted.
Trustee: U.S. Bank, N.A.
EIN: 416463406

4798
Weiser Family Foundation ✧ ☆
600 S. 2nd St., Ste. 703
Minneapolis, MN 55401-2175

Established in 2000 in MN.
Donors: Irving Weiser; Marjorie Weiser.
Foundation type: Independent foundation.
Financial data (yr. ended 12/31/12): Assets, $6,235,270 (M); expenditures, $680,477; qualifying distributions, $644,275; giving activities include $640,750 for 26 grants (high: $320,000; low: $600).
Purpose and activities: Giving primarily for the arts and human services.
Fields of interest: Arts; Human services; Jewish agencies & synagogues.
Limitations: Applications not accepted. Giving primarily in Minneapolis, MN; funding also in NY. No grants to individuals.
Application information: Unsolicited requests for funds not accepted.
Officers: Irving Weiser, Pres.; Marjorie Weiser, Secy.
Directors: Dana Weiser; Jennifer Weiser.
EIN: 411987618

4799
WEM Foundation ✧
P.O. Box 5628
Minneapolis, MN 55440-9300
Contact: James Hield, Pres.

Established in 1988 in MN.
Donors: Whitney MacMillan, Jr.; W. MacMillan 1989 Trust; W. MacMillan, Jr. 2003 Charitable Annuity Trust; W. MacMillan, Jr. 2005 Charitable Annuity Trust; W. MacMillan, Jr. Family '74 Trust; W. MacMillan, Jr. Charitable Annuity Trust.
Foundation type: Independent foundation.
Financial data (yr. ended 12/31/12): Assets, $272,726,501 (M); gifts received, $9,799,311; expenditures, $9,191,999; qualifying distributions, $8,961,132; giving activities include $8,900,050 for 109 grants (high: $2,075,000; low: $100).
Purpose and activities: Giving primarily for arts and cultural programs, education, health care and international affairs.
Fields of interest: Museums; Arts; Education; Hospitals (general); Health care; International affairs, public policy.
Limitations: Applications not accepted. Giving primarily in FL and MN. No grants to individuals.
Application information: Contributes only to pre-selected organizations.
Officers and Directors:* Whitney MacMillan,* Chair.; Elizabeth S. MacMillan,* Vice-Chair. and Secy.; James Hield,* Pres.; Harriet S. Norgren.
Number of staff: 1 full-time professional.
EIN: 411604640
Selected grants: The following grants are a representative sample of this grantmaker's funding activity:
$2,075,000 to National Museum of American History, Washington, DC, 2012.
$1,625,000 to Smithsonian American Art Museum, Washington, DC, 2012.
$1,035,000 to Minnesota Historical Society, Saint Paul, MN, 2012.
$1,015,000 to National Museum of Natural History, Washington, DC, 2012.
$500,000 to Yale University, New Haven, CT, 2012.
$300,000 to University of Minnesota Foundation, Minneapolis, MN, 2012. For research.
$250,000 to Learning Alliance, Vero Beach, FL, 2012.
$200,000 to Dartmouth College, Hanover, NH, 2011. For Dealt Scholarship.
$200,000 to Dartmouth College, Hanover, NH, 2012.
$50,000 to Risen Christ Catholic School, Minneapolis, MN, 2012.
$25,000 to Old Vero Beach Ice Age Sites Committee, Vero Beach, FL, 2012.
$25,000 to University of Maryland-College Park, College Park, MD, 2011. For National History Day.
$15,000 to United Way of Indian River County, Vero Beach, FL, 2011.
$10,000 to Blake School, Hopkins, MN, 2011.

4800
West Central Initiative
(formerly West Central Minnesota Initiative Fund)
P.O. Box 318
Fergus Falls, MN 56538-0318 (218) 739-2239
Contact: Nancy Straw, Pres.; Sandra King, V.P., Opers.
FAX: (218) 739-5381; E-mail: wci@wcif.org; Additional tel.: (800) 735-2239 (MN only).; Main URL: http://www.wcif.org
Facebook: https://www.facebook.com/westcentralinitiative
LinkedIn: https://www.linkedin.com/company/west-central-initiative
Twitter: http://twitter.com/WCIMinn
Vimeo: http://vimeo.com/wciminn

Established in 1986 in MN.
Foundation type: Community foundation.
Financial data (yr. ended 06/30/14): Assets, $61,106,541 (M); gifts received, $4,973,553; expenditures, $5,721,898; giving activities include $3,368,786 for 72+ grants (high: $772,149), and $67,220 for 14 grants to individuals.
Purpose and activities: The fund seeks to improve the region's economic and social viability by expanding quality employment opportunities, addressing shortages of skilled labor, strengthening families, addressing critical regional needs, and developing leadership capacity within local communities.
Fields of interest: Education; Employment, training; Employment; Youth development, services; Children/youth, services; Family services; Economic development; Nonprofit management; Community/economic development; Leadership development.
Type of support: Mission-related investments/loans; Income development; Program development; Seed money; Curriculum development; Scholarship funds; Research; Technical assistance; Program-related investments/loans.
Limitations: Applications accepted. Giving limited to Becker, Clay, Douglas, Grant, Otter Tail, Pope, Stevens, Traverse, and Wilkin counties, MN. No support for religious activities, sports or recreational programs, arts, historical or cultural activities, or groups without physical presence in region. No grants to individuals.
Publications: Application guidelines; Annual report; Financial statement; Grants list; Informational brochure; Newsletter.
Application information: Visit foundation web site for application form and guidelines per grant type. Application form required.
Initial approach: Telephone
Copies of proposal: 1
Deadline(s): Generally at least 6 weeks prior to planned commencement of project for grants exceeding $5,000; at least 3 weeks for grants less than $5,000
Board meeting date(s): Monthly
Final notification: 4 to 6 weeks for grants over $5,000; 2 to 3 weeks for less
Officers and Directors:* David Nelson,* Chair.; Nancy Straw,* Pres.; Kim Embretson,* V.P., Fund Devel.; Sandy King,* V.P., Opers.; Dale Umlauf,* V.P., Business Devel.; Warrenn Anderson; Jerry Arneson; Jessica Boyer; Amy Coley; Sue Dieter; Dan Ellison; Cheri Johnson; John MacFarlene; Melissa Persing; Dean Simpson; Merle Wagner; Rebecca Worner.
Number of staff: 12 full-time professional; 1 part-time professional; 2 full-time support; 3 part-time support.
EIN: 363453471
Selected grants: The following grants are a representative sample of this grantmaker's funding activity:
$24,800 to Rural Minnesota Concentrated Employment Program, Detroit Lakes, MN, 2013. For Foundational Skills for Future Success.
$11,200 to Enterprise Minnesota, Minneapolis, MN, 2013. For Training Within Industry Job Instruction Training at Donnelly Custom Manufacturing.
$7,500 to Enterprise Minnesota, Minneapolis, MN, 2013. For Sync Flow Training at Alderon Industries.
$5,000 to Ashby, City of, Ashby, MN, 2013. For Grow Grant County Action Plan.
$5,000 to Immigrant Development Center, Moorhead, MN, 2013. For Entrepreneurial Business Development.
$5,000 to West Central Minnesota Communities Action, Elbow Lake, MN, 2013. For Free Tax Preparation for Family Economic Success.
$5,000 to White Earth Child Care Program, White Earth, MN, 2013. For White Earth Early Childhood Initiative.
$3,900 to Enterprise Minnesota, Minneapolis, MN, 2013. For Science of Plastic Injection Molding.
$3,000 to Morris Area Chamber of Commerce, Morris, MN, 2013. For Leadership Stevens County.

4801
Westcliff Foundation ✧
730 2nd Ave. S., Ste. 1300
Minneapolis, MN 55402-2416

Established in 2003 in MN.
Donors: Markell Brooks; Markell B. Krafchuk.
Foundation type: Independent foundation.
Financial data (yr. ended 12/31/13): Assets, $23,054 (M); gifts received, $445,000; expenditures, $482,170; qualifying distributions, $482,132; giving activities include $477,500 for 12 grants (high: $305,000; low: $2,500).
Fields of interest: Arts; Human services; Civil/human rights, public policy; Foundations (private grantmaking).
Limitations: Applications not accepted. Giving primarily in CA and CO; some giving also in MN.
Application information: Contributes only to pre-selected organizations.
Officers and Director:* Markell B. Krafchuk,* Pres.; John Hinck, Secy.; Katherine Leighton, Treas.
EIN: 411999931

4802
Weyerhaeuser Family Foundation ✧
(formerly Weyerhaeuser Foundation)
30 7th St. E., Ste. 2000
St. Paul, MN 55101-4930 (303) 993-5385
Contact: Peter Konrad Ed.D., C.P.A.
E-mail: pkonrad@konradconsulting.com; Main URL: http://www.wfamilyfoundation.org

Incorporated in 1950 in MN.
Donors: Bette D. Moorman; Stanley R. Day, Jr.; Dana L. Day; George H. Weyerhaeuser; Mrs. George H. Weyerhauser; Lucy R. Jones; Jane Weyerhaeuser-Johnson; Hayley M. Reiter; Kyle W. Reiter; Leilee Weyerhaeuser; Elizabeth Bentinck-Smith; Cody N. Reiter; Carol R. Caruthers; Cherbec Advancement Foundation; Rosenberry Charitable Term Trust; Wendy Weyerhaeuser; Ian Weyehaeuser; Lucy Rosenberry Jones Charitable Tust; Robert M. Weyerhaeuser; Stan Day; Vivian W. Day; John Stroh III.
Foundation type: Independent foundation.
Financial data (yr. ended 12/31/12): Assets, $23,090,394 (M); gifts received, $207,141; expenditures, $1,160,720; qualifying distributions, $1,106,931; giving activities include $900,014 for 36 grants (high: $75,000; low: $1,000).
Purpose and activities: The foundation supports programs of national and international significance that promote the welfare of human and natural resources.
Fields of interest: Environment, natural resources; Environment; Health care; Mental health, treatment; Children, services; International development; International peace/security.
Type of support: Program development; Seed money.
Limitations: Applications accepted. Giving for international programs only through U.S.-based organizations. No support for elementary or secondary education, or for books or media projects, unless the project is connected to other areas of foundation interest. No grants to individuals, or for building or endowment funds, annual campaigns, operating budgets, equipment, land acquisitions or trades, research, scholarships, fellowships, travel, or matching gifts; no loans.
Publications: Application guidelines; Annual report (including application guidelines); Grants list.
Application information: See foundation web site for specific application guidelines for each program, as well as application cover sheets. Application form required.
Initial approach: Letter
Copies of proposal: 1
Deadline(s): See foundation web site for the current deadline for each program
Board meeting date(s): Program committee meets annually in early summer to review proposals; board usually meets in June and Nov.
Officers and Trustees:* Frederick W. Titcomb,* Pres.; John B. Driscoll,* V.P.; Blaine Gaustad, Secy.; Peter E. Heymann,* Treas.; John L. Davis; Melissa M. Davis; Lucie C. Greer; Anne W. Henderson; Rebecca Martin; Kristin Rasmussen; Kyle W. Reiter; Amy W. Stried; Daniel L. Titcomb; John W. Titcomb, Jr.; W. Drew Weyerhaeuser; Ian Weyerhaeuser.
Number of staff: 1 part-time professional.
EIN: 416012062

4803
The Frederick and Margaret L. Weyerhaeuser Foundation ✧
30 E. 7th St., Ste. 2000
St. Paul, MN 55101-4930
E-mail: dlc@fidcouns.org

Incorporated in 1963 in MN.
Donors: Margaret Weyerhaeuser Harmon‡; Frederick T. Weyerhaeuser; Ginnie Weyerhaeuser; C.L. Weyerhaeuser Trust; Margaret W. Harmon Charitable Fund Unitrust.
Foundation type: Independent foundation.
Financial data (yr. ended 06/30/13): Assets, $20,720,368 (M); gifts received, $160,002; expenditures, $901,592; qualifying distributions, $843,311; giving activities include $785,000 for 84 grants (high: $30,000; low: $1,000).
Purpose and activities: The foundation supports programs in the areas of adolescent mental health, youth conservation education, service learning, and innovative teaching techniques which reflect the interests of the founders' grandchildren.
Fields of interest: Higher education; Environment; Hospitals (specialty); Mental health/crisis services, public education; Youth development, adult & child programs; Human services.
Limitations: Applications not accepted. Giving limited to the U.S., with some emphasis on MN. No support for public schools, or to organizations located outside the U.S. No grants to individuals, or for capital funding, equipment, general operating support, endowments, research, or for travel.
Application information: Contributes only to pre-selected organizations.
Officers and Directors:* Catherine W. Morley,* Pres.; Amy W. Streid,* V.P. and Secy.; Ellen R. Middleton,* Treas.; Julia L.W. Heidmann; Daniel J. Weyerhaeuser; Anne E. Zaccaro.
EIN: 416029036
Selected grants: The following grants are a representative sample of this grantmaker's funding activity:
$87,500 to Inver Hills Community College Foundation, Inver Grove Heights, MN, 2013. For nursing scholarship.
$30,000 to Hazelden Foundation, Center City, MN, 2013. For youth initiative capital campaign.
$25,000 to Dakota County Technical College Foundation, Rosemount, MN, 2013. For Peggy Rasmussen King Memorial Scholarship.
$23,000 to San Francisco Zoological Society, San Francisco, CA, 2013. For sculpture garden.
$10,000 to New England Forestry Foundation, Littleton, MA, 2013. For General operating support and Timber Stabilization Fund.
$10,000 to San Francisco Zoological Society, San Francisco, CA, 2013. For program intern project.
$10,000 to South Puget Sound Community College Foundation, Olympia, WA, 2013. For Gold Level Scholarship.
$7,500 to Shady Hill School, Cambridge, MA, 2013. For Class of 2013 gift.
$5,000 to Baylor School, Chattanooga, TN, 2013. For Bill Cushman Speaker Series.
$5,000 to Harris Center for Conservation Education, Hancock, NH, 2013. For Meade Cadot Land Protection Fund.

4804
Weyerhaeuser/Day Foundation ✧
30 E. 7th St., Ste. 2000
Saint Paul, MN 55101-4930 (651) 228-0935
Contact: Vivian W. Day, Pres. and Dir.

Established in 1995 in MN.
Donors: Lynn Weyerhaeuser Day‡; Stanley R. Day.
Foundation type: Independent foundation.
Financial data (yr. ended 12/31/13): Assets, $11,066,062 (M); expenditures, $530,059; qualifying distributions, $501,137; giving activities include $475,000 for 15 grants (high: $265,000; low: $5,000).
Fields of interest: Elementary/secondary education; Environment, natural resources; Transportation.
Type of support: General/operating support; Annual campaigns; Endowments.
Limitations: Applications accepted. Giving primarily in Chicago, IL, and MI, with some emphasis on Detroit.
Application information: Application form required.
Initial approach: Letter
Deadline(s): None
Officers and Directors:* Vivian W. Day,* Pres.; Lincoln W. Day,* V.P.; Stanley R. Day, Jr.,* Secy.; Frederick K.W. Day,* Treas.
EIN: 411815686

4805
Whiteside Scholarship Fund Trust ✧
(formerly Robert B. and Sophia Whiteside Scholarship Fund)
c/o U.S. Bank, N.A., Trust Tax Svcs.
P.O. Box 64713
St. Paul, MN 55164-0713

Established in 1976.
Foundation type: Independent foundation.
Financial data (yr. ended 12/31/13): Assets, $4,084,586 (M); expenditures, $751,234; qualifying distributions, $594,164; giving activities include $552,000 for 37 grants to individuals (high: $141,000; low: $3,000).
Purpose and activities: Giving for undergraduate scholarships, limited to individuals from the top ten percent of graduating classes of Duluth, MN, high schools. The trust works directly with the guidance offices at each of the local area high schools.
Fields of interest: Higher education.
Type of support: Scholarships—to individuals.
Limitations: Applications accepted. Giving limited to residents of Duluth, MN.
Application information: Applications must be submitted to local high school counselors. Direct contact with the trust by individual student

applicants is not accepted. Application form required.
Initial approach: Contact foundation
Deadline(s): Fall of senior year
Trustee: U.S. Bank, N.A.
Number of staff: 1
EIN: 411288761

4806
Winona Community Foundation ✧
(formerly Greater Winona Area Community Foundation)
51 E. 4th St., Ste. 314
Winona, MN 55987-6203 (507) 454-6511
Contact: Jeni Arnold, Exec. Dir.
FAX: (507) 454-0441; E-mail: adminwcf@hbci.com; Grant inquiry e-mail: jarnold@hbci.com; Grant inquiry tel.: (507) 454-6511; Main URL: http://www.winonacommunityfoundation.com
Facebook: https://www.facebook.com/adminwcf1
Twitter: http://twitter.com/wcfpres

Established in 1987 in MN.
Foundation type: Community foundation.
Financial data (yr. ended 12/31/13): Assets, $12,667,099 (M); gifts received, $1,495,701; expenditures, $1,874,412; giving activities include $1,329,420 for 44+ grants (high: $232,768).
Purpose and activities: The foundation improves the quality of life in the Winona area by: 1) educating the public about the practice of philanthropy and its benefits both to donors and to the community; 2) connecting people with charitable intent and resources with organizations and causes that can advance the public good; 3) gathering, preserving, and stewarding philanthropic resources; 4) collaborating with other charitable organizations; 5) serving as a catalyst for selected community initiatives; 6) making grants to projects and causes that address both the needs; and the 7) opportunities present in the community.
Fields of interest: Arts, multipurpose centers/programs; Arts; Elementary/secondary education; Education; Environment; Health care; Recreation; Human services; Public affairs.
Type of support: General/operating support; Continuing support; Management development/capacity building; Annual campaigns; Equipment; Emergency funds; Program development; Conferences/seminars; Technical assistance; Program evaluation; Scholarships—to individuals; Matching/challenge support.
Limitations: Applications accepted. Giving primarily in Winona, MN, and its surrounding community. No support for religious programs or fraternal organizations, societies, or order. No grants to individuals (except for scholarships), or for capital campaigns, endowments, debt retirements or debt financing, tickets for benefits, telephone solicitations, fundraising drives or activities, or travel; no loans.
Publications: Application guidelines; Annual report; Grants list; Informational brochure (including application guidelines); Newsletter.
Application information: Visit foundation web site for application guidelines. Applicants must call foundation staff to review projects prior to submission of any materials. Application form required.
Initial approach: Telephone
Copies of proposal: 1
Deadline(s): None
Board meeting date(s): 4th Tues. of each month
Officers and Directors:* Judy Davis,* Chair.; Shelley Milek,* Secy.; Gary Watts,* Treas.; Jeni Arnold, Exec. Dir.; Diane Amundson; Sandra Burke; Vicki Decker; Susan Eddy; Fred Fletcher; Joan Greshik; Andrea Herczeg; Ann Lavine; Tedd Morgan; Kelley Olson; Ryan Ping; Tom Wynn.
Number of staff: 1 full-time professional; 3 part-time professional; 1 part-time support.
EIN: 363500853

4807
WSDC Foundation ✧
P.O. Box 5628
Minneapolis, MN 55440-5628

Established in 2006 in MN and MO.
Donors: Pauline Macmillan Keinath; Pauline Macmillan Keinath 1969 Trust; David S. Keinath Family 1974 Trust.
Foundation type: Independent foundation.
Financial data (yr. ended 12/31/12): Assets, $1,001,912 (M); gifts received, $2,028,000; expenditures, $1,698,025; qualifying distributions, $1,698,025; giving activities include $1,689,725 for 24 grants (high: $528,000; low: $10,725).
Fields of interest: Education; Medical research, institute; Human services; Deaf/hearing impaired.
Limitations: Applications not accepted. Giving primarily in MO. No grants to individuals.
Application information: Contributes only to pre-selected organizations.
Officers: Robert J. Theiler, Pres.; Heather A. Dorsey, Secy.-Treas.
Directors: David S. Keinath; Steven W. Keinath; Warren C. Keinath; Carolyn K. Rayner.
EIN: 205444923

4808
Xcel Energy Foundation ✧
414 Nicollet Mall
Minneapolis, MN 55401-1927
Contact: James R. Garness, Sr. Fdn. Rep., MN
FAX: (612) 215-4522;
E-mail: foundation@xcelenergy.com; Additional e-mail contacts: Monique Lovato, Dir., Corporate Giving and Xcel Energy Fdn. CO, monique.l.lovato@xcelenergy.com; Jeanne Fox, Grants Contact, MI and WI, jean.fox@xcelenergy.com; Judith Paukert, Community Rels.. Mgr., ND and SD, judith.n.paukert@xcelenergy.com; Kathy Aas, Community Rels. Mgr., Minot, ND, kathleen.a.aas@xcelenergy; Terry Price, Sr. Fdn.. Rep., TX and NM, terry.price@xcelenergy.com; Eric Pauli, Community Rels.. Mgr., SD, eric.pauli@xcelenergy.com; Main URL: http://www.xcelenergy.com/About_Us/Community/Corporate_Giving
Arts and Culture Grantee List: http://www.xcelenergy.com/staticfiles/xe/Corporate/Corporate%20PDFs/2013_Art_and_Culture.pdf
Economic Sustainabililty Grantee List: http://www.xcelenergy.com/staticfiles/xe/Corporate/Corporate%20PDFs/2013_Economic_Sustainability.pdf
Education Grantee List: http://www.xcelenergy.com/staticfiles/xe/Corporate/Corporate%20PDFs/2013_Education.pdf
Environment Grantee List: http://www.xcelenergy.com/staticfiles/xe/Corporate/Corporate%20PDFs/2013_Environment.pdf

Established in 2001.
Donor: Xcel Energy Inc.
Foundation type: Company-sponsored foundation.
Financial data (yr. ended 12/31/12): Assets, $13,549,039 (M); gifts received, $18,123,702; expenditures, $7,535,935; qualifying distributions, $7,532,606; giving activities include $7,436,826 for 753 grants.
Purpose and activities: The foundation supports programs designed to improve science, technology, engineering, economics and math education; improve and enhance the natural environment; help individuals achieve economic self-sufficiency; and provide access to arts and culture.
Fields of interest: Arts, equal rights; Arts education; Visual arts; Performing arts; Performing arts, music; Arts; Elementary/secondary education; Scholarships/financial aid; Education, services; Education; Environment, alliance/advocacy; Environment, public education; Environment, natural resources; Environment, water resources; Environment, land resources; Environment, energy; Environment, beautification programs; Environmental education; Environment; Animals/wildlife; Employment, training; Employment, retraining; Employment; Disasters, preparedness/services; Boy scouts; Economic development; Business/industry; Community/economic development; United Ways and Federated Giving Programs; Science, formal/general education; Mathematics; Engineering/technology; Science; Economically disadvantaged.
Type of support: General/operating support; Program development; Curriculum development; Employee volunteer services; Employee matching gifts.
Limitations: Applications accepted. Giving limited to areas of company operations in CO, MI, MN, ND, NM, SD, TX, and WI. No support for national organizations, government agencies, religious, political, veterans', or fraternal organizations not of direct benefit to the entire community or disease-specific organizations. No grants to individuals, or for research programs, endowments, capital campaigns, energy efficiency projects or improvements, athletics or sports, or benefits or fundraising; no multi-year commitments.
Publications: Application guidelines; Grants list; Informational brochure; Program policy statement.
Application information: The foundation is currently not accepting new partners for organizations located in CO and MN, but check website for periodic announcements. Organizations receiving support are asked to submit a final report. Application form required.
Initial approach: Complete online eligibility quiz
Deadline(s): Mar. 10 and May 9 for organizations in CO and MN; Mar. 3 for organizations in NM and TX; Mar. 3 for Education and Environment focus areas for organizations in ND, SD, and WI; and May 9 for Arts and Culture and Economic Sustainability focus areas for organizations in ND, SD, and WI
Final notification: Early June and Aug.
Officers and Directors:* Benjamin G.S. Fowke III,* Chair. and Pres.; Roy Palmer,* Secy.; George E. Tyson II,* Treas.; David L. Eves; David T. Hudson; Marvin McDaniel; David Sparby; Mark E. Stoering.
EIN: 412007734

4809
Youth Hope Foundation ✧
c/o Gray Plant Mooty
500 IDS Ctr.
80 S. 8th St.
Minneapolis, MN 55402-2100

Donors: John Candela; Youth Hope Enterprises, LLC.

Foundation type: Independent foundation.
Financial data (yr. ended 12/31/12): Assets, \$22,394 (M); gifts received, \$643,000; expenditures, \$664,870; qualifying distributions, \$664,870; giving activities include \$589,374 for 7 grants (high: \$190,910; low: \$30,000).
Fields of interest: Education; Children, services; International relief; Children; Youth.

Limitations: Applications not accepted. Giving primarily in the Netherlands, as well as CA, MN, and NY.
Application information: Contributes only to pre-selected organizations.
Trustees: John Candela; Douglas M. Cravens; Frank Minton; Gary R. Yakes.
EIN: 611509889

MISSISSIPPI

4810
The Armstrong Foundation ✧
(formerly The Texas Educational Association)
P.O. Box 2299
Natchez, MS 39121-2299
Contact: Thomas K. Armstrong, Pres.
FAX: (601) 442-4716; E-mail: tka@natchez.net; Additional contact: Laura J. Harrison, Secy., P.O. Box 470338, Fort Worth, TX 76147

Incorporated in 1949 in TX.
Donor: George W. Armstrong, Sr.‡.
Foundation type: Independent foundation.
Financial data (yr. ended 12/31/13): Assets, $26,022,411 (M); expenditures, $1,348,793; qualifying distributions, $1,094,213; giving activities include $982,702 for 97 grants (high: $150,000; low: $100).
Purpose and activities: Giving to support educational undertakings through financial assistance to schools, colleges, universities, and other educational mediums advocating the perpetuation of constitutional government. Grants only for educational programs on American ideals and traditional values; support for free market and free enterprise educational programs.
Fields of interest: Education, research; Business/industry; Economics; Government/public administration.
Type of support: General/operating support; Continuing support; Program development; Conferences/seminars; Publication; Research.
Limitations: Applications accepted. Giving on a national basis. No grants to individuals, or for capital or endowment funds; no loans.
Publications: Application guidelines.
Application information: Application form not required.
Initial approach: Proposal
Copies of proposal: 1
Deadline(s): None
Board meeting date(s): Mar., June, Sept., and Dec.
Final notification: 2 months
Officers and Directors:* Thomas K. Armstrong,* Pres.; Allen L. Armstrong,* V.P. and Treas.; Thomas K. Armstrong, Jr.,* V.P.; J. Hatcher James III,* V.P.; Laura J. Harrison,* Secy.
Number of staff: 1 part-time professional; 1 full-time support; 1 part-time support.
EIN: 756003209

4811
Asbury Foundation of Hattiesburg, Inc. ✧
P.O. Box 17797
Hattiesburg, MS 39404-7797 (601) 296-3555
Contact: William K. Ray, C.E.O.
Main URL: http://www.asburyfoundationofhattiesburg.com/

Established in 1989; converted from the sales of Wesley Health System.
Foundation type: Independent foundation.
Financial data (yr. ended 12/31/13): Assets, $36,800,911 (M); expenditures, $2,599,151; qualifying distributions, $2,277,519; giving activities include $2,024,728 for 12 grants (high: $500,000; low: $5,000).
Purpose and activities: The foundation provides support in areas of education and health to other non-profit organizations to improve the quality of life.
Fields of interest: Higher education; Health care; Youth development.
Limitations: Applications accepted. Giving limited to Covington, Forrest, Jefferson Davis, Jones, Lamar, Marion, Pearl River and Perry counties in MS. No grants to individuals.
Application information: Application form required.
Initial approach: Submit a bound application
Deadline(s): Mar, 31, May 31, Aug. 31, and Oct. 31
Officer and Board Members:* William K. Ray,* C.E.O.; Raymond Dearman; Glenn Galey; Rev. Keith Hagenson; George Komp III; Harry McArthur; Doris Miller; Carey Revels.
EIN: 640692161

4812
BancorpSouth Foundation ✧ ☆
P.O. Box 789
Tupelo, MS 38802-0789 (662) 680-2000
Contact: Cathy S. Freeman

Established in 1999 in MS.
Donor: BancorpSouth, Inc.
Foundation type: Company-sponsored foundation.
Financial data (yr. ended 12/31/13): Assets, $2,405,978 (M); expenditures, $857,966; qualifying distributions, $834,575; giving activities include $834,575 for 46 grants (high: $200,000; low: $1,000).
Purpose and activities: The foundation supports organizations involved with orchestras, secondary and higher education, legal aid, housing, youth development, and human services.
Fields of interest: Education; Youth development; Human services.
Type of support: General/operating support.
Application information: Application form required.
Initial approach: Letter
Deadline(s): Based on Quarterly
Trustee: Bancorpsouth Bank.
EIN: 646217237

4813
BBB Foundation ✧
P.O. Box 8670
Columbus, MS 39705-0012 (662) 328-8176
Contact: Greg Rader, Pres.

Established in 2005 in MS.
Donor: Greg C. Rader.
Foundation type: Independent foundation.
Financial data (yr. ended 10/31/13): Assets, $339,119 (M); gifts received, $985,000; expenditures, $1,238,114; qualifying distributions, $1,238,080; giving activities include $1,238,080 for 70 grants (high: $277,000; low: $50).
Fields of interest: Education; Human services; Protestant agencies & churches.
Limitations: Applications accepted. Giving primarily in MS. No grants to individuals.
Application information: Application form not required.
Initial approach: Proposal
Deadline(s): None
Officer: Gregory C. Rader, Pres.
Directors: Welissa W. Rader; Henry Stephen Wise.
EIN: 202042606
Selected grants: The following grants are a representative sample of this grantmaker's funding activity:
$10,000 to Lifeline Childrens Services, Birmingham, AL, 2011.

4814
Biloxi Regional Medical Center, Inc. ✧ ☆
P.O. Box 128
Biloxi, MS 39533-0128
Main URL: http://www.biloxiregional.net/

Established in 2003 in MS.
Foundation type: Operating foundation.
Financial data (yr. ended 09/30/13): Assets, $15,940,673 (M); expenditures, $867,409; qualifying distributions, $866,880; giving activities include $866,880 for 9 grants (high: $366,900; low: $1,800).
Fields of interest: Nursing school/education; Education; Hospitals (general); Health organizations.
Limitations: Applications not accepted. Giving primarily in MS. No grants to individuals.
Application information: Contributes only to pre-selected organizations.
Officers: Robert B. Briscoe, Chair.; Andy Carpenter, Vice-Chair.
Directors: Erroll Bradley; Larry Drawdy; Ann LaRosa; John McKee, M.D.; Alfred McNair, M.D.; Jeffrey O'Keefe; Edward Shumski, M.D.; Argile Smith.
EIN: 640657989
Selected grants: The following grants are a representative sample of this grantmaker's funding activity:
$20,000 to Loaves and Fishes, Biloxi, MS, 2011.
$14,095 to Mississippi Gulf Coast Community College, Gulfport, MS, 2011.
$12,600 to University of Southern Mississippi Foundation, Hattiesburg, MS, 2011.
$9,000 to University of South Alabama, Mobile, AL, 2011.

4815
Blue Cross & Blue Shield of Mississippi Foundation ✧
3545 Lakeland Dr.
Flowood, MS 39232-8839 (601) 664-4281
Contact: Sheila Grogan, Exec. Dir.
FAX: (601) 952-8344;
E-mail: foundation@bcbsms.com; Additional tel.: (601) 664-4525; Application address: P.O. Box 1043, Jackson, MS 39215-1043; E-mail for Healthy Hometown Award: healthyhometown@bcbsms.com; Main URL: http://www.healthiermississippi.org
Healthy Hometown Winners: http://www.healthiermississippi.org/index.php?id=14

Donor: Blue Cross and Blue Shield of Mississippi.
Foundation type: Company-sponsored foundation.
Financial data (yr. ended 12/31/12): Assets, $59,981,759 (M); expenditures, $3,382,554; qualifying distributions, $3,274,371; giving activities include $2,988,682 for 56 grants (high: $406,827; low: $11,488).
Purpose and activities: The foundation supports programs designed to improve the health and wellness of Mississippians; and promote preventive health as a solution for the heath care crisis. Special

emphasis is directed toward programs designed to promote children's health and wellness; community health initiatives; and healthy lifestyles and choices.
Fields of interest: Public health; Public health, obesity; Public health, physical fitness; Health care; Nutrition; Recreation; Children.
Type of support: General/operating support; Continuing support; Building/renovation; Equipment; Program development; Curriculum development; Sponsorships.
Limitations: Applications accepted. Giving limited to areas of company operations in MS. No support for discriminatory organizations, denominational or religious organizations, political caucuses or candidates, hospitals, college alumni associations, or high school or college sports teams. No support for individuals, or for political campaigns, special occasion or commemorative advertising, journals, or dinner programs (unless part of overall sponsorship effort), hospital building funds, or high school or college sports events.
Publications: Application guidelines; Annual report; Financial statement; Grants list.
Application information: Letter of inquiry should not exceed 3 pages. Additional information may be requested at a later date. A site visit may be requested for Healthy Hometown Award. Organizations receiving support are asked to provide a final report. Application form required.
Initial approach: Complete online letter of inquiry or mail letter of inquiry to foundation; download application form and mail to foundation for Healthy Hometown Award
Copies of proposal: 1
Deadline(s): None; Apr. 1 for Healthy Hometown Award
Final notification: Within 6 weeks
Officers and Directors:* John L. Sewell,* Chair.; Thomas C. Fenter, M.D.*, Vice-Chair.; Jeffery T. Leber,* Pres.; Scott T. Williamson,* Secy.; Douglas R. Garrett,* Treas.; Sheila Grogan, Exec. Dir.; J. Edward Hill; Harry M. Walker.
EIN: 200471034
Selected grants: The following grants are a representative sample of this grantmaker's funding activity:
$286,270 to Pearl River Community College, Poplarville, MS, 2011.
$250,000 to Health Care Foundation of North Mississippi, Tupelo, MS, 2011.
$101,217 to Regional Rehabilitation Center, Tupelo, MS, 2011.
$24,967 to Lawhon Elementary School, Tupelo, MS, 2011.
$24,967 to North Bay Elementary School, Bay Saint Louis, MS, 2011.
$24,967 to Pecan Park Elementary School, Ocean Springs, MS, 2011.
$24,967 to Pierce Street Elementary School, Tupelo, MS, 2011.
$24,967 to Pillow Academy, Greenwood, MS, 2011.
$10,000 to Project Fit America, Boyes Hot Springs, CA, 2011.

4816
The Bower Foundation, Inc. ✧
(formerly Kidney Care, Inc.)
578 Highland Colony Pkwy., Ste. 120
Ridgeland, MS 39157-8779 (601) 607-3163
FAX: (601) 607-3164;
E-mail: info@bowerfoundation.org; Additional e-mail (for grant concept submissions): atravis@bowerfoundation.org; Main URL: http://www.bowerfoundation.org

Established in 1972 in MS.
Foundation type: Independent foundation.
Financial data (yr. ended 12/31/13): Assets, $94,620,475 (M); expenditures, $4,512,874; qualifying distributions, $4,059,683; giving activities include $3,601,323 for 15+ grants.
Purpose and activities: The foundation is committed to the promotion of fundamental improvements in the health status of all Mississippians through the creation, expansion, and support of quality healthcare initiatives. The goals of the foundation are: 1) Access to health care: All children and adults should have reasonable access to health care services so that all citizens have the opportunity to live healthy and productive lives. 2) Health Care Services: To promote health, prevent disease, and reduce health risks among children, young adults, and the underserved. 3) Health Policy and Education: To support approaches that match the needs of the underserved with existing public and private providers. 4) End Stage Renal Disease: To improve the quality of life for patients with End Stage Renal Disease.
Fields of interest: Health care; Kidney diseases.
Limitations: Applications accepted. Giving primarily in Jackson, MS. No grants to individuals.
Publications: Grants list.
Application information: Application guidelines and form available on foundation web site. Nearly all the foundation's grantmaking activities are pro-active. A small percentage of grants develop from grant concepts submitted by prospective grantees. The grant concept can be mailed, faxed, or e-mailed to the foundation.
Initial approach: Grant concept proposal (no more than 2 pages)
Deadline(s): None
Final notification: Within 4 to 6 months
Officers and Directors:* Anne Travis,* C.E.O. and V.P.; John Bower, M.D.*, Pres.; James F. Dorris,* Secy.-Treas.; Ralph Didlake, M.D.; Kathy Ellis; Alan Hull, M.D.; Walter Neely, Ph.D.; William S. Painter; Dana Shires, M.D.
Number of staff: 2 full-time professional.
EIN: 640540635

4817
C Spire Wireless Foundation ✧
1018 Highland Colony Pkwy., Ste. 360
Ridgeland, MS 39157-2068 (601) 355-1522
Contact: Elizabeth C. Byrd, Exec. Dir.
Main URL: http://www.cspire.com/company_info/about/programs/foundation.jsp

Established in 2005 in MS.
Donors: James H. Creekmore; Wade Creekmore; Brightpoint North America, LP; Meredith Creekmore; V. Hugo Meena, Jr.; Beth Byrd; Sidney Crews; Cellular South, Inc.
Foundation type: Company-sponsored foundation.
Financial data (yr. ended 12/31/13): Assets, $117,631 (M); gifts received, $603,500; expenditures, $594,907; qualifying distributions, $594,907; giving activities include $541,200 for 60 grants (high: $100,000; low: $300).
Purpose and activities: The foundation supports programs designed to improve quality of life in markets where C Spire Wireless operates and organizations involved with academics, athletics, heath, wellness, safety, and civic affairs. Special emphasis is directed toward programs designed to improve opportunities for education in Mississippi.
Fields of interest: Museums; Secondary school/education; Higher education; Education; Health care; Disasters, preparedness/services; Safety/disasters; Athletics/sports, amateur leagues; Human services; Public affairs; Christian agencies & churches.
Type of support: Endowments; General/operating support; Annual campaigns; Program development; Scholarship funds; Sponsorships.
Limitations: Applications accepted. Giving primarily in areas of company operations in AL, FL, MS, and TN. No support for political candidates or groups, amateur sports teams, or religious organizations. No grants to individuals, or for administrative expenses, capital campaigns, or purchase of uniforms or trips for school-related organizations; no loans.
Publications: Application guidelines.
Application information: Application form required.
Initial approach: Request application form
Deadline(s): None
Officers: Hu Meena, Pres.; Wesley Goings, V.P.; Meredith Creekmore, Secy.-Treas.; Beth C. Byrd, Exec. Dir.
Director: Jim Richmond.
EIN: 203426826

4818
The Chisholm Foundation ✧
544 Central Ave.
P.O. Box 2766
Laurel, MS 39440-3955 (601) 426-3378
FAX: (601) 649-2264;
E-mail: info@chisholmfoundation.org; Main URL: http://www.chisholmfoundation.org

Established in 1960 in MS.
Donors: A.F. Chisholm‡; Margaret A. Chisholm Charitable Trust.
Foundation type: Independent foundation.
Financial data (yr. ended 12/31/12): Assets, $25,431,931 (M); gifts received, $789,800; expenditures, $2,276,241; qualifying distributions, $2,082,935; giving activities include $1,884,625 for 141 grants (high: $135,000; low: $250).
Purpose and activities: Giving primarily for higher and regular education; funding also for the arts, health, and human services.
Fields of interest: Museums; Performing arts, theater; Arts; Elementary/secondary education; Higher education; Education; Health organizations, association; Medical research, institute; Alzheimer's disease research; Human services.
Type of support: General/operating support; Endowments; Program development; Matching/challenge support.
Limitations: Giving primarily in MS, New York, NY, and WA. No grants to individuals.
Publications: Application guidelines.
Application information: Application form not required.
Initial approach: Proposal
Officers and Trustees:* John L. Lindsey,* Pres.; Alexander C. Lindsey,* Secy.; Nathan E. Saint-Amand, Treas.; Julia V. Lindsey; Lynn M. Lindsey; Alexander Saint-Amand; Cynthia C. Saint-Amand; Elisabeth Saint-Amand.
EIN: 646014272

4819
The Community Foundation, Inc. ✧ ☆
P.O. Box 13328
Jackson, MS 39236-3328

Incorporated in 1963 in MS.
Donor: W.K. Paine.
Foundation type: Independent foundation.
Financial data (yr. ended 12/31/13): Assets, $48,214,961 (M); expenditures, $5,506,153; qualifying distributions, $5,067,391; giving activities include $5,060,000 for 13 grants (high: $1,000,000; low: $10,000).
Purpose and activities: Giving primarily for education, human services, and to a Baptist church.
Fields of interest: Family services; Protestant agencies & churches.
Type of support: General/operating support.
Limitations: Applications not accepted. Giving primarily in MS; funding also in Colorado Springs, CO, and Washington, DC. No grants to individuals.
Application information: Unsolicited requests for funds not accepted.
Officers: W.K. Paine, Pres. and Treas.; Robert H. Paine, Secy.
EIN: 237033813

4820
Community Foundation of Greater Jackson ✧
(formerly Greater Jackson Foundation)
525 E. Capitol St., Ste. 5B
Jackson, MS 39201-2702 (601) 974-6044
Contact: Jane Alexander, C.E.O.
FAX: (601) 974-6045; E-mail: info@cfgj.com; Main URL: http://www.cfgreaterjackson.org
Facebook: https://www.facebook.com/communityfoundationofgreaterjackson

Established in 1994 in MS.
Foundation type: Community foundation.
Financial data (yr. ended 03/31/13): Assets, $33,102,122 (M); gifts received, $4,939,151; expenditures, $2,647,670; giving activities include $1,958,243 for 74 grants (high: $151,436), and $47,300 for 138 grants to individuals.
Purpose and activities: The foundation helps charitable donors establish permanent giving funds that reflect individual philanthropic interests while also making a long term, positive impact on the community. Giving for the arts, education, health, families/children, environment, and community building.
Fields of interest: Museums; Performing arts; Arts; Elementary/secondary education; Higher education; Environment; Health organizations, association; Disasters, Hurricane Katrina; Youth development; Children/youth, services; Family services; Human services; Community development, neighborhood development.
Type of support: General/operating support; Continuing support; Annual campaigns; Capital campaigns; Building/renovation; Endowments; Program development; Conferences/seminars; Professorships; Curriculum development; Scholarship funds; Scholarships—to individuals; Matching/challenge support.
Limitations: Applications accepted. Giving primarily in Hinds, Madison, and Rankin counties, MS. No support for religious activities.
Publications: Application guidelines; Annual report; Financial statement; Informational brochure; Newsletter; Occasional report.
Application information: Visit foundation web site for online application form and guidelines. Application form required.
Initial approach: Submit Project/Concept Outline
Copies of proposal: 1
Deadline(s): Quarterly
Board meeting date(s): Feb., May, Aug., and Nov.
Final notification: 90 days
Officers and Trustees:* Luther Ott,* Chair.; Jane Alexander,* C.E.O. and Pres.; Jackie Bailey,* C.O.O.; Amanda Alexander; Hogan Allen; Tommy Darnell; Janet Harris; Jane Hiatt; Jamie Houston; Jan Lewis; Paul McNeill; Mike McRee; Hibbett Neel; Chuck Nicholson; Worth Thomas; Lee Unger; Judy Wiener; Dudley Wooley; Wirt Yerger, Jr.
Number of staff: 5 full-time professional; 1 full-time support.
EIN: 640845750

4821
Community Foundation of Northwest Mississippi ✧
315 Losher St.
Hernando, MS 38632-2124 (662) 449-5002
Contact: Tom Pittman, Pres.; For grants: Peggy Linton, Community Devel. Dir.
FAX: (662) 449-5006;
E-mail: tompittman@cfnm.org; Grant application e-mail: plinton@cfnm.org; Main URL: http://www.cfnm.org
Facebook: https://www.facebook.com/CFNM315
RSS Feed: http://cfnm.org/feed/
Twitter: https://twitter.com/CFNM_2002
YouTube: http://www.youtube.com/cfnm2002

Established in 2002 in MS.
Foundation type: Community foundation.
Financial data (yr. ended 12/31/12): Assets, $13,774,906 (M); gifts received, $4,970,594; expenditures, $2,995,354; giving activities include $848,500 for 29 grants (high: $56,000).
Purpose and activities: The mission of the foundation is to impact its communities by connecting people who care with causes that matter; priorities include education, health care and young people. Its current strategies to address these issues are initiatives in pre-kindergarten education, prevention of childhood obesity and place-based education.
Fields of interest: Education, early childhood education; Education; Environment; Public health; Health care; Nutrition; Children/youth; Children; Youth; Adults; Aging; Young adults; Minorities; African Americans/Blacks; Hispanics/Latinos; Native Americans/American Indians; Women; Girls; Adults, women; Young adults, female; Men; Boys; Adults, men; Young adults, male; Military/veterans; Single parents; Economically disadvantaged.
Type of support: Matching/challenge support; Management development/capacity building; Endowments; General/operating support; Continuing support; Program development; Scholarship funds.
Limitations: Applications accepted. Giving limited to the northwest MS: Bolivar, Coahoma, DeSoto, Marshall, Panola, Quitman, Sunflower, Tallahatchie, Tate and Tunica counties. No support for organizations lacking 501(c)(3) status, or for exclusively religious purposes. No grants to individuals (except for scholarships).
Publications: Application guidelines; Annual report; Financial statement; Grants list; Informational brochure; Newsletter.
Application information: Visit foundation web site for application form, guidelines, and requirements. Application form required.
Initial approach: Submit application form and attachments
Copies of proposal: 1
Deadline(s): Nov. 1, Feb. 1, May 1, and Aug. 1
Board meeting date(s): Mar., May, Aug. and Nov.
Final notification: Within 4 months
Officers and Directors:* Steve Beene,* Chair.; Josephine Rhymes,* Vice-Chair.; Tom Pittman,* Pres. and C.E.O.; Scott Burnham Hollis,* Secy.; Mackey Moore,* Treas.; Joe Azar; Bob Bowen; Charles Burnett III; Scott Coopwood; Kevin Doddridge; Betty Jo Dulaney; Dr. Ishmell Edwards; Joan Ferguson; Dr. Eleanor Gill; Tom Gresham; Lucy Janoush; Pete Johnson; Manuel Killebrew; Campbell Melton; Frank Mitchener; Rev. Bartholomew Orr.
Number of staff: 5 full-time professional; 1 part-time professional; 2 full-time support.
EIN: 943421724
Selected grants: The following grants are a representative sample of this grantmaker's funding activity:
$30,000 to DeSoto County Schools, Hernando, MS, 2012. For Youth Leadership Council.
$27,000 to AW Bouchillon Planning Institute, 2012. For health symposium.
$26,500 to Northwest Mississippi Community College Foundation, Senatobia, MS, 2012. For nursing scholarships.
$20,964 to Jonestown Family Center for Education and Wellness, Jonestown, MS, 2012. For pre-school program.
$20,964 to Teach for America, Oxford, MS, 2012.
$10,000 to Quitman County Development Organization, Marks, MS, 2012. For youth financial literacy.
$8,200 to First Regional Library, Hernando, MS, 2012. For Mobile Library Words on Wheels.
$6,745 to Strawberry Plains Audubon Center, Holly Springs, MS, 2012. For youth environmental education program.
$5,000 to Byhalia, Town of, MS, 2012. To increase physical activity facilities.
$5,000 to Friends of Olive Branch, Olive Branch, MS, 2012. To establish Farmers Market.

4822
CREATE Foundation ✧
(formerly Create Christian Research Education Action Technical Enterprise, Inc.)
213 W. Main St.
Tupelo, MS 38802-3941 (662) 844-8989
Contact: Michael K. Clayborne, Pres.
FAX: (662) 844-8149;
E-mail: info@createfoundation.com; Mailing address: P.O. Box 1053, Tupelo, MS 38802-1053; E-Mail for Michael K. Clayborne: mike@createfoundation.com; Main URL: http://www.createfoundation.com

Established in 1972 in MS.
Foundation type: Community foundation.
Financial data (yr. ended 12/31/13): Assets, $76,299,063 (M); gifts received, $10,272,616; expenditures, $6,578,783; giving activities include

$4,829,620 for grants, and $178,771 for 186 grants to individuals.
Purpose and activities: The foundation acts as a catalyst for positive change by supporting projects that will improve the quality of life for all citizens of northeast Mississippi, and by helping individuals and groups achieve their goals of providing financial support to meaningful projects; grantmaking priorities are in the areas of community development, human development, and education.
Fields of interest: Education; Human services; Youth, services; Community/economic development.
Type of support: Endowments; Program development; Seed money; Scholarship funds; Grants to individuals.
Limitations: Applications accepted. Giving primarily in Alcorn, Benton, Calhoun, Chickasaw, Clay, Itawamba, Lafayette, Lee, Marshall, Monroe, Oktibbeha, Pontotoc, Prentiss, Tippah, Tishomingo, and Union counties, MS. No support for for-profit organizations. No grants for general operating support or building projects.
Publications: Application guidelines; Annual report; Informational brochure; Newsletter.
Application information: Visit foundation website for application information. Application form required.
Initial approach: Submit letter of request
Copies of proposal: 12
Deadline(s): None
Officers and Directors:* Bobby P. Martin,* Chair.; Michael K. Clayborne,* Pres.; Lewis Whitfield, Sr. V.P.; Juanita Floyd, V.P., Finance and Admin.; Dr. David Beckley; Grace Clark; John Creekmore; Dr. Ornelia Cummings; Clay Foster; Hassell H. Franklin; Betsey Hamilton; Bobby Harper; Octavious Ivy; Dr. Gloria Kellum; Larry Kirk; Randy Long; Robin Y. McCormick; Buddy Montgomery; Aubrey Patterson; Greg Pirkle; Eddie Prather; Jack Reed, Sr.; Cathy Robertson; Ronny Rowland; David Rumbarger; Sean Suggs; Milton Sundbeck; Tommy Tomlinson; Mitch Waycaster; H.L. "Sandy" Williams, Jr.
Number of staff: 3 full-time professional; 1 part-time professional; 1 full-time support.
EIN: 237248582

4823
Delta Research Foundation ✧
P.O. Box 257
Stoneville, MS 38776-0257

Foundation type: Independent foundation.
Financial data (yr. ended 12/31/13): Assets, $1,829,931 (M); gifts received, $963,706; expenditures, $1,060,056; qualifying distributions, $868,314; giving activities include $868,314 for 9 grants (high: $494,494; low: $2,500).
Fields of interest: Education.
Limitations: Applications not accepted. Giving primarily in MS.
Application information: Unsolicited requests for funds not accepted.
Officers: Dan Branton, Chair.; Chip Morgan, Secy.; Jimmy Dick Carter, Chair. Emeritus.
Directors: Bowen Flowers; Dr. Steve Martin; Frank Mitchener; Travis Satterfield; Mike Sturdivant, Jr.
EIN: 646025124

4824
Ergon Foundation, Inc. ✧
P.O. Drawer 1639
Jackson, MS 39215-1639

Established in 1980.
Donors: Diversified Technology, Inc.; Ergon Exploration, Inc.; Ergon Nonwovens, Inc.; Ergon Refining, Inc.; Ergon, Inc.; Magnolia Marine Transport Co.; Ergon Asphalt & Emulsions, Inc.; Ergon-West Virginia, Inc.; Leslie B. Lampton.
Foundation type: Company-sponsored foundation.
Financial data (yr. ended 06/30/13): Assets, $54,028,957 (M); gifts received, $19,240,000; expenditures, $1,269,956; qualifying distributions, $663,345; giving activities include $656,400 for 38 grants (high: $50,000; low: $1,400).
Purpose and activities: The foundation supports organizations involved with education, health, cancer, human services, and Christianity.
Fields of interest: Elementary/secondary education; Education, special; Higher education; Theological school/education; Health sciences school/education; Education; Hospitals (general); Health care; Cancer; Salvation Army; Children/youth, services; Family services; Residential/custodial care, group home; Homeless, human services; Human services; Christian agencies & churches.
Type of support: General/operating support; Annual campaigns.
Limitations: Applications not accepted. Giving primarily in MS. No grants to individuals.
Application information: Contributes only to pre-selected organizations.
Officers and Directors:* Leslie B. Lampton,* Pres.; Dorothy Lee Lampton,* V.P.; Lee C. Lampton,* V.P.; Leslie B. Lampton III, V.P.; Robert H. Lampton,* V.P.; William W. Lampton,* V.P.; Kathryn W. Stone,* Secy.-Treas.
EIN: 640656341

4825
Feild Co-Operative Association Inc. ✧
4400 Old Canton Rd., Ste. 170
Jackson, MS 39211-5982 (601) 713-2312
Contact: Cindy May, Secy.
FAX: (601) 713-2314; Application address: P.O. Box 5054, Jackson, MS 39296

Incorporated in 1919 in TN.
Donor: Sons of the late Dr. and Mrs. Monfort Jones.
Foundation type: Independent foundation.
Financial data (yr. ended 12/31/12): Assets, $19,180,701 (M); expenditures, $868,467; qualifying distributions, $770,767; giving activities include $220,200 for 46 grants (high: $20,000; low: $500), and $352,000 for loans to individuals.
Purpose and activities: Awards interest-bearing student loans to residents of MS, who are juniors or seniors in college, graduate and professional students, or students in special fields; some grants to local hospitals and social service agencies.
Fields of interest: Museums; Performing arts; Arts; Higher education; Education; Hospitals (specialty); Health organizations; Human services; Children/youth, services; Christian agencies & churches.
Type of support: General/operating support; Student loans—to individuals.
Limitations: Applications accepted. Giving primarily in MS. No grants for building or endowment funds, operating budgets, or for special projects.
Publications: Application guidelines; Informational brochure.
Application information: Application guidelines for student loans are available online. Students must be enrolled on a full-time basis in order to qualify for loans. Application form required.
Initial approach: Call to schedule an interview prior to receiving an application for student loans
Copies of proposal: 1
Deadline(s): 6 to 8 weeks before a semester begins for student loans
Board meeting date(s): Annually
Officers: Cindy S. May, Secy.; Suzanne Neely, Treas.
Directors: Amanda Link Greenlee; John Henry Jackson; B. Bryan Jones III; B. Bryan Jones IV; William M. Link, Jr.; Betty R. May; Hobson C. McGehee, Jr.; Hobson C. McGehee III; Cynthia J. Thompson.
Number of staff: 3
EIN: 640155700

4826
The Gertrude C. Ford Foundation, Inc. ✧
P.O. Box 13100
Jackson, MS 39236-3100
Application address: c/o Anthony T. Papa, Mgr., Lefleur Bluffs Tower, Ste. 410, Jackson, MS 39211, tel.: (601) 713-2300

Established in 1997 in MS.
Foundation type: Independent foundation.
Financial data (yr. ended 12/31/13): Assets, $56,382,534 (M); expenditures, $3,136,263; qualifying distributions, $2,780,621; giving activities include $2,620,150 for 75 grants (high: $250,000; low: $500).
Purpose and activities: Giving primarily for higher education, and children and youth services, including a children's museum; funding also for health organizations and human services.
Fields of interest: Museums (children's); Arts; Higher education; Education; Health organizations, association; Children/youth, services.
Type of support: Annual campaigns.
Limitations: Applications accepted. Giving primarily in MS, with emphasis on Jackson.
Application information: Application form required.
Initial approach: Letter
Deadline(s): None
Board meeting date(s): Tues. weekly
Managers: Leon E. Lewis, Jr.; Anthony T. Papa; Cheryle M. Sims.
EIN: 640804548

4827
Foundation for the Mid South ✧
134 E. Amite St.
Jackson, MS 39201-2101 (601) 355-8167
Contact: For grants: Denise Ellis, Grants and Technology Mgr.
FAX: (601) 355-6499;
E-mail: bdellis@fndmidsouth.org; Grant Inquiry Form e-mail: concept@fndmidsouth.org; Main URL: http://www.fndmidsouth.org
Facebook: http://www.facebook.com/pages/Foundation-for-the-Mid-South/103086276414874
Flickr: http://www.flickr.com/photos/midsouth/
Foundation for the Mid-South's Philanthropy Promise: http://www.ncrp.org/philanthropys-promise/who

Established in 1989 in MS.
Foundation type: Community foundation.
Financial data (yr. ended 12/31/13): Assets, $16,054,437 (M); gifts received, $716,977; expenditures, $2,546,311; giving activities include $818,438 for 12+ grants (high: $45,000).
Purpose and activities: The foundation invests in people and strategies that build philanthropy and promote racial, social, and economic equity in Arkansas, Louisiana, and Mississippi. Priority areas include health and wellness, education, wealth building, and community development.
Fields of interest: Education, early childhood education; Education; Health care; Disasters, Hurricane Katrina; Youth development, services; Children/youth, services; Family services; Minorities/immigrants, centers/services; Economic development; Community/economic development; Leadership development; Religion; Children/youth; Aging; Minorities; African Americans/Blacks.
Type of support: Technical assistance; General/operating support; Continuing support; Management development/capacity building; Program development; Conferences/seminars; Curriculum development; Consulting services; Matching/challenge support.
Limitations: Applications accepted. Giving limited to AR, LA, and MS. No grants to individuals, or to make grants for personal needs or business assistance. No grants for ongoing general operating expenses or existing deficits, endowments, capital costs including construction, renovation, or equipment, or international programs.
Publications: Application guidelines; Annual report; Financial statement; Grants list; Informational brochure (including application guidelines); Multi-year report; Newsletter; Occasional report.
Application information: Visit foundation web site for Grant Inquiry Form application guidelines. Application form required.
Initial approach: E-mail Grant Inquiry Form
Copies of proposal: 1
Deadline(s): None
Board meeting date(s): Feb., May, Aug., and Nov.
Final notification: Within 6 weeks for full proposal invitation; Generally within 3 months for grant determination
Officers and Directors:* Paul E. Davis,* Chair.; Kay Kelly Arnold,* Vice-Chair.; Ivye L. Allen,* Pres.; Hon. Robert Jackson,* Secy.; Patrick C. Moore,* Treas.; Bill Bynum; C. Chad Causey; Diana Lewis; Ted Kendall III; Ed Lupberger; Carla Martin; Victor McTeer; Sip B. Mouden; James Rutherford; Don Munro; Hon. William Winter.
Number of staff: 7 full-time professional; 3 full-time support.
EIN: 721151070
Selected grants: The following grants are a representative sample of this grantmaker's funding activity:
$150,000 to Jobs for Mississippi Graduates, Jackson, MS, 2013.
$150,000 to Mississippi Hospital Association Health, Research and Education Foundation, Madison, MS, 2012.
$150,000 to We2Gether Creating Change, Drew, MS, 2013.
$100,000 to New Leaders for New Schools, Greater New Orleans Office, New Orleans, LA, 2012. To support efforts to raise student achievement; improve test scores; and increase graduation rates.
$60,000 to NOVA Workforce Institute of Northeast Louisiana, Monroe, LA, 2012.
$51,500 to United Way of the Capital Area, Jackson, MS, 2012.
$50,000 to Center for Family Life, Jackson, MS, 2012.
$50,000 to Local Initiatives Support Corporation, Greenville, MS, 2013.
$50,000 to Mississippi Action for Community Education, Greenville, MS, 2013.
$50,000 to Phoenix Youth and Family Services, Crossett, AR, 2012.
$30,000 to Mississippi Valley State University, Itta Bena, MS, 2012.
$25,200 to Bicycle Advocacy Group of Mississippi, Jackson, MS, 2012. To support the Bicycle Friendly Mississippi initiative to improve access to health resources.
$25,000 to Womens Fund of Mississippi, Jackson, MS, 2013.
$24,000 to Children and Family First, Canton, MS, 2012.
$10,000 to Hopkins Street Revitalization Association, New Iberia, LA, 2013.
$10,000 to Itta Bena, City of, Itta Bena, MS, 2013.
$10,000 to Little Rock, City of, Little Rock, AR, 2012.
$7,000 to Clarendon, City of, Clarendon, AR, 2013.
$6,000 to Dumas, City of, Dumas, AR, 2013.
$5,000 to Vidalia, City of, Vidalia, LA, 2013.

4828
Gilmore Sanitarium, Inc. ✧
(also known as Gilmore Sanitarium, Inc.)
(formerly Gilmore Foundation, Inc.)
P.O. Box 459
Amory, MS 38821-0459 (662) 257-2395
Main URL: http://www.gilmorefoundation.org
E-Newsletter: http://gilmorefoundation.org/wordpress/?cat=8
Grants List: http://gilmorefoundation.org/wordpress/?cat=4

Foundation type: Independent foundation.
Financial data (yr. ended 05/31/13): Assets, $18,242,838 (M); gifts received, $2,910; expenditures, $3,298,045; qualifying distributions, $2,934,704; giving activities include $2,278,774 for 9 grants (high: $1,920,330; low: $6,000).
Purpose and activities: Giving primarily for education, health, community development and other initiatives that improve the quality of life in the Monroe County and Northeast Mississippi area.
Fields of interest: Education; Human services.
Limitations: Applications not accepted. Giving limited to Monroe and Chickasaw counties in MS. No grants to individuals.
Publications: Newsletter; IRS Form 990 or 990-PF printed copy available upon request.
Application information: Unsolicited proposals are not accepted.
Officers and Directors: C. Herman Hester,* Chair.; William T. "Skip" Miles,* Vice-Chair.; Ivan O. "Buddy" Bryant, Jr.,* Secy.; Danny J. Spreitler, Exec. Dir.; Larry W. Clark; Robert J. Cole, M.D.; John Creekmore; Gary Franks; Douglas "Pete" Patterson; Phillip E. Roberts.
EIN: 640331636

4829
Greater Pinebelt Community Foundation ✧
1507 Hardy St., Ste. 208
Hattiesburg, MS 39401 (601) 583-6180
Contact: Theresa Erickson, Exec. Dir.
FAX: (601) 583-6188;
E-mail: contact@pinebeltfoundation.org; Main URL: http://www.pinebeltfoundation.org
Facebook: https://www.facebook.com/PineBeltFoundation
Twitter: https://twitter.com/PinebeltCF/

Established in 1997 in MS.
Foundation type: Community foundation.
Financial data (yr. ended 12/31/13): Assets, $17,033,661 (M); gifts received, $1,611,924; expenditures, $1,157,663; giving activities include $846,976 for 41+ grants (high: $50,378).
Purpose and activities: The mission of the foundation is to build better communities through philanthropy.
Fields of interest: Historic preservation/historical societies; Safety/disasters; Community/economic development.
Limitations: Giving primarily in the Pine Belt, MS area.
Officers and Directors:* Iris Easterling,* Pres.; David Fortenberry,* V.P.; Paul Laughlin,* Secy.; Richard Topp,* Treas.; Theresa Erickson, Exec. Dir.; Alex Agnew; Mike Axton; Terri Bell; Jeff Bowman; David Burckel; Robert Cornett; Jonathan Duhon; Fran Ginn; Dr. Frances Karnes; Edward J. "Ed" Langton; Michelle Mabry; Joshua Mars; Morgan McCarty; Annie McMillian; Holt McMullan; Hayden Mitchell; Kris Powell; Dr. Steve Ramp; Jim Raspberry; Bonnie Warren; Lance Williams.
EIN: 721390352

4830
Gulf Coast Community Foundation ✧
11975 Seaway Rd., Ste. B-150
Gulfport, MS 39503 (228) 897-4841
Contact: Rodger Wilder, Pres.
FAX: (228) 897-4843; E-mail: rwilder@mgccf.org; Main URL: http://www.mgccf.org
LinkedIn: http://www.linkedin.com/groups?homeNewMember=&gid=2654681&trk=
Philanthropy's Promise: http://www.ncrp.org/philanthropys-promise/who
Twitter: http://twitter.com/gccf

Established in 1989 in MS.
Foundation type: Community foundation.
Financial data (yr. ended 06/30/13): Assets, $19,624,158 (M); gifts received, $6,168,957; expenditures, $6,693,684; giving activities include $5,578,923 for 37+ grants (high: $2,679,728), and $164,750 for 511 grants to individuals.
Purpose and activities: The foundation is a public charity dedicated to the progressive development of worthy causes, providing donor services, and promoting and providing leadership in response to changing community needs. The foundation is a vehicle for charitable giving through which individuals, families, corporations, nonprofit organizations and private foundations can meet charitable objectives in the fields of education, arts and culture, historic preservation, neighborhood enrichment, and health and human services.
Fields of interest: Historic preservation/historical societies; Arts; Education; Health care; Disasters, Hurricane Katrina; Human services; Community/economic development; Infants/toddlers; Children/

youth; Children; Adults; Young adults; Disabilities, people with; Mentally disabled; Minorities; Men; Economically disadvantaged.
Type of support: General/operating support; Continuing support; Scholarship funds; Technical assistance; Matching/challenge support.
Limitations: Applications accepted. Giving limited to George, Hancock, Harrison, Jackson, Pearl River, and Stone counties, MS. No support for religious organizations or for religious purposes. No grants to individuals (except for scholarships), or for capital or operating endowment drives.
Publications: Application guidelines; Annual report; Financial statement; Informational brochure; Newsletter; Occasional report.
Application information: Visit foundation web site for application forms, guidelines, and specific deadlines. Application form required.
Initial approach: Complete Letter of Intent
Copies of proposal: 9
Deadline(s): Varies
Board meeting date(s): Monthly
Final notification: Varies
Officers and Directors:* Dorothy Shaw,* Chair.; Dr. Kaizad Tamboli,* Chair.-Elect; Roger Wilder, Pres.; Raymond Brown,* Secy.; Cindy Shaw,* Treas.; Wynn Alexander; Ron Barnes; John Baxter; Mike Bruffey; Greg Cronin; George Cullinan; Jane Dennis; Henry Dick; Trent Favre; Angie Juzang; Bill McDonough; H. Gordon Myrick; Robert F. Neal; Virginia Shanteau Newton; Donald Perkins; Joy Phillips; Rufus Smith; Genl. Joe Spraggins; Stan Tiner; David Treutel, Jr.; Susan Walker; Linda Watts; Tom Wicks; H. Rodger Wilder.
Number of staff: 2 full-time professional; 1 part-time professional.
EIN: 570908490
Selected grants: The following grants are a representative sample of this grantmaker's funding activity:
$1,554,106 to International Relief and Development, Arlington, VA, 2012. For general support.
$656,817 to Hope Community Development Agency, Biloxi, MS, 2012. For general support.
$353,487 to Hancock Housing Resource Center, Waveland, MS, 2012. For general support.
$334,442 to CLIMB Community Development Corporation, Gulfport, MS, 2012. For general support of YouthBuild Gulf Coast.
$250,000 to Mississippi Center for Justice, Jackson, MS, 2012. For general support.
$240,500 to Coastal Family Health Center, Biloxi, MS, 2012. For general support.
$234,171 to Memorial Hospital at Gulfport Foundation, Gulfport, MS, 2012. For general support.
$218,920 to Saint Vincent de Paul Community Pharmacy, Biloxi, MS, 2012. For general support.
$200,000 to Asian Americans for Change, Ocean Springs, MS, 2012. For general support.
$200,000 to Mercy Housing and Human Development, Gulfport, MS, 2012. For general support.

4831
Phil Hardin Foundation ✧
2750 N. Park Dr.
Meridian, MS 39305-2687 (601) 483-4282
Contact: Rebecca Combs-Dulaney, C.E.O.
FAX: (601) 483-5665; E-mail: info@philhardin.org; Main URL: http://www.philhardin.org

Incorporated in 1964 in MS.
Donors: Philip Bernard Hardin†; Hardin's Bakeries Corp.
Foundation type: Independent foundation.
Financial data (yr. ended 12/31/13): Assets, $50,466,624 (M); expenditures, $2,363,313; qualifying distributions, $2,120,622; giving activities include $1,733,100 for 32 grants (high: $300,000; low: $500).
Purpose and activities: Giving primarily for early childhood education, community-based initiatives in Meridian and Lauderdale County in MS, and emergent opportunities where the foundation can be proactive and flexible.
Fields of interest: Education, association; Education, research; Education, early childhood education; Higher education; Education; Community/economic development; Children; Minorities.
Type of support: Equipment; Endowments; Program development; Conferences/seminars; Professorships; Publication; Curriculum development; Fellowships; Internship funds; Research; Program evaluation; Matching/challenge support.
Limitations: Applications accepted. Giving primarily in MS; support also to out-of-state organizations for programs and projects benefiting Mississippians.
Publications: Application guidelines; Grants list; Informational brochure (including application guidelines); Program policy statement.
Application information: The student loan program has been phased out. Application guidelines and form available on foundation web site. The foundation prefers that proposals not be stapled or bound. Videotapes, or faxed or e-mailed proposals are not accepted. Priority is given to proposals solicited by the foundation. Application form required.
Initial approach: Use application process on foundation web site
Deadline(s): None
Board meeting date(s): As required, usually at least every other month
Final notification: 3 months
Officers and Directors:* Rebecca Combs-Dulaney, C.E.O.; Robert F. Ward,* Pres.; Robert B. Deen, Jr.,* Sr. V.P.; Ronnie L. Walton,* Secy.; Stephen O. Moore,* Treas.; Joe S. Covington, M.D.; Marty Davidson; Jim McGinnis.
Number of staff: 1 full-time professional; 1 full-time support.
EIN: 646024940
Selected grants: The following grants are a representative sample of this grantmaker's funding activity:
$1,065,000 to Meridian Public School District, Meridian, MS, 2011. For monetary incentives to attract and retain teachers and leaders.
$200,000 to Boys and Girls Club of East Mississippi, Meridian, MS, 2011. For Project Learn.
$117,000 to Mississippi Museum of Natural Science, Jackson, MS, 2011. For initiative to link childhood obesity and science education.
$114,000 to United Way of East Mississippi and West Alabama, Meridian, MS, 2011. For Imagination Library.
$100,000 to Lauren Rogers Museum of Art, Laurel, MS, 2011. For ArtReach Endowment.
$100,000 to Magnolia Speech School for the Deaf, Jackson, MS, 2011. For Listening and Spoken Language Intervention for children 0-5.
$18,000 to Sunflower County Freedom Project, Sunflower, MS, 2011. For Freedom Project Saturday School Program.

4832
The Robert M. Hearin Foundation ✧
P.O. Box 16505
Jackson, MS 39236-6505
Contact: Daisy S. Blackwell, Tr.

Established in 1965 in MS.
Donors: Robert M. Hearin, Sr.; Bay Street Corp.; Yazoo Investment Corp.
Foundation type: Independent foundation.
Financial data (yr. ended 11/30/13): Assets, $45,351,436 (M); expenditures, $1,548,421; qualifying distributions, $1,227,720; giving activities include $1,150,000 for 8 grants (high: $300,000; low: $50,000).
Purpose and activities: Giving to 4-year colleges and graduate schools located in the state of Mississippi, and to other charities.
Fields of interest: Higher education; Law school/education; Hospitals (general).
Limitations: Applications accepted. Giving primarily in MS. No grants to individuals.
Application information: Application form required.
Initial approach: Letter
Deadline(s): None
Trustees: Daisy S. Blackwell; Robert M. Hearin, Jr.; Matthew L. Holleman III; E.E. Laird, Jr.; Laurie H. McRee; Alan W. Perry.
EIN: 646027443

4833
The Luckyday Foundation ✧
1020 Highland Colony Parkway, Ste. 804
Ridgeland, MS 39157-2128 (601) 354-5869
Contact: Holmes S. Adams, Chair.

Established in 1978 in MS.
Donor: Frank R. Day†.
Foundation type: Independent foundation.
Financial data (yr. ended 12/31/12): Assets, $95,810,379 (M); expenditures, $5,674,927; qualifying distributions, $5,297,834; giving activities include $5,159,118 for 10 grants (high: $3,216,500; low: $125).
Purpose and activities: Giving primarily to educational institutions, churches, and organizations to benefit sick and needy people.
Fields of interest: Higher education; Youth development; Protestant agencies & churches.
Limitations: Applications accepted. Giving primarily in MS, with emphasis on Jackson. No grants to individuals.
Application information: Application form required.
Initial approach: Letter
Copies of proposal: 1
Deadline(s): None
Final notification: Usually within 3 months
Officer and Managers:* Holmes S. Adams,* Chair.; Patricia G. Smith, Exec. Dir.; Barbara Arnold Day; Roger P. Friou; Jerry Host; Jamie G. Houston III; S. Griffin Norquist, Jr.
Number of staff: 1 full-time professional.
EIN: 640617746
Selected grants: The following grants are a representative sample of this grantmaker's funding activity:

$1,500,000 to University of Mississippi Foundation, Oxford, MS, 2012. For Luckyday Success Scholarship Program.
$1,337,500 to University of Mississippi Foundation, Oxford, MS, 2012. For Luckyday Success Scholarship Program.
$800,000 to University of Southern Mississippi, Hattiesburg, MS, 2012. For Luckyday Citizenship Scholars Program.
$750,000 to University of Southern Mississippi Foundation, Hattiesburg, MS, 2012. For Luckyday Citizenship Scholars Program.
$211,315 to University of Southern Mississippi Foundation, Hattiesburg, MS, 2012. For administrative, salaries and program.
$115,000 to University of Mississippi Foundation, Oxford, MS, 2012. For Luckyday University Scholarship Program.
$115,000 to University of Mississippi Foundation, Oxford, MS, 2012. For Luckyday University Scholarship Program.
$84,000 to University of Mississippi Foundation, Oxford, MS, 2012. For Luckyday Merit Scholarship Program.
$65,053 to University of Southern Mississippi Foundation, Hattiesburg, MS, 2012. For administrative, salaries and program.
$45,000 to University of Mississippi Foundation, Oxford, MS, 2012. For Luckyday Merit Scholarship Program.

4834
Maddox Foundation ✧ ☆
180 W. Commerce St.
Hernando, MS 38632-2202
FAX: (662) 449-3698;
E-mail: staff@maddoxfoundation.org; Contact for questions regarding the grantmaking process or to submit a 1-page inquiry: Glenda Gurley, e-mail: glenda@maddoxfoundation.org; Main URL: http://www.maddoxfoundation.org
Facebook: https://www.facebook.com/MaddoxFoundation

Established in 1968 in TN.
Donors: Margaret Maddox Trust; Dan Maddox†; Margaret H. Maddox†; Margaret Energy, Inc.
Foundation type: Independent foundation.
Financial data (yr. ended 12/31/13): Assets, $42,505,560 (M); expenditures, $3,033,381; qualifying distributions, $2,421,304; giving activities include $1,682,750 for 5 grants (high: $880,000; low: $1,250), and $120,948 for foundation-administered programs.
Purpose and activities: The grantmaker serves as a catalyst for building strong and viable communities that meet the needs of their citizens through collaborative action and service. The foundation believes that successful communities must engage a diverse mix of human, social and economic assets in the process of defining and addressing community needs. It encourages collaborative efforts that engage a wide range of public, corporate, private and other nonprofit partners as investors and service providers. Priority is given to investments that leverage additional support from other sources, and that serve as a channel for long-term strategic change in organizations and communities to better meet local needs. This includes supporting efforts to increase philanthropy in the region through the establishment and support of community foundations.
Fields of interest: Education; Environment; Health care; Human services; Religion.
Type of support: General/operating support; Capital campaigns; Building/renovation; Equipment; Land acquisition; Endowments; Program development; Conferences/seminars; Seed money; Scholarship funds; Technical assistance; Matching/challenge support.
Limitations: Giving primarily in northwest MS; the foundation also makes grants from the Maddox Advised Fund in the Community Foundation of Middle Tennessee in Nashville. No support for organizations in the greater Nashville, TN, area, or in Memphis or west TN, unless their work has a direct impact in Northwest MS. No grants to individuals, and generally no grants for annual campaigns or appeals, awards/prizes/competitions, start-up or expansion of businesses or other economic development ventures, debt reduction, emergency funds, loans or lines of credit, publications, public relations services, research, or travel to conferences or events.
Publications: Informational brochure; IRS Form 990 or 990-PF printed copy available upon request.
Application information: Unsolicited proposals or requests for funds not accepted. Proposals are by invitation only. Organizations and programs located outside of the Northwest MS region should contact the foundation directly. The foundation encourages organizations that directly serve Memphis and other west TN counties in the Memphis metropolitan area to contact the Community Foundation of Greater Memphis and the United Way of the Mid-South for support. See foundation web site for additional information.
Initial approach: 1-single page inquiry only via e-mail, U.S. mail or fax
Deadline(s): None, but submitting a 1-page inquiry at least 3 months before funding if needed is advised
Board meeting date(s): Varies; meets as needed
Officers and Board Member:* Robin Grindstaff Costa,* Pres.; Michael C. Ward, V.P.; Paul T. Morris, Secy.; Carol Ayers; Karen S. Carter; Lanier Hurdle.
Number of staff: 6 full-time professional; 2 full-time support.
EIN: 640917900

4835
McLean Foundation ✧
c/o Sheila Brooks
330 Church St.
Columbia, MS 39429-2726

Established in 1990 in MS.
Donors: E.D. McLean, Jr.†; Mrs. E.D. McLean; Justina McLean.
Foundation type: Independent foundation.
Financial data (yr. ended 12/31/13): Assets, $7,363,502 (M); gifts received, $50,000; expenditures, $586,720; qualifying distributions, $540,000; giving activities include $540,000 for 12 grants (high: $125,000; low: $10,000).
Fields of interest: Arts; Environment; Cancer research; Human services.
Type of support: Annual campaigns; Research.
Limitations: Applications not accepted. Giving primarily in CO, TN, and VA. No grants to individuals.
Publications: Annual report.
Application information: Contributes only to pre-selected organizations. Unsolicited requests for funds not accepted.
Trustees: Justina W. McLean; Justina McLean; William E. Walker III.
EIN: 581889403

4836
Selby and Richard McRae Foundation, Inc. ✧
(formerly McRae Foundation)
P.O. Box 20080
Jackson, MS 39289-0080

Established in 1965 in MS.
Donors: Richard D. McRae, Sr.; Richard D. McRae Charitable Lead Annuity Trust.
Foundation type: Independent foundation.
Financial data (yr. ended 01/31/13): Assets, $24,114,058 (M); gifts received, $993,556; expenditures, $2,262,541; qualifying distributions, $1,514,359; giving activities include $1,499,277 for 72 grants (high: $250,000; low: $500).
Purpose and activities: Grants primarily for social services, religion, and education; some support for cultural programs.
Fields of interest: Education; Human services; Christian agencies & churches.
Type of support: Continuing support; Annual campaigns; Capital campaigns; Scholarship funds.
Limitations: Applications not accepted. Giving primarily in MS. No grants to individuals.
Application information: Unsolicited requests for funds not accepted.
Officers: Richard D. McRae, Sr., Pres.; Richard D. McRae, Jr., V.P.; Susan McRae Shanor, Secy.; Vaughan W. McRae, Treas.
Number of staff: None.
EIN: 646026795

4837
Mississippi Common Fund Trust ✧
c/o Maggie Abernathy, Memory House
P.O. Box 249
University, MS 38677-0249 (662) 915-1581

Established in 1996 in MS.
Donors: James L. Barksdale; Sally M. Barksdale†; Robert Seymour; R. Faser Triplett; Jane C. Thomas.
Foundation type: Independent foundation.
Financial data (yr. ended 06/30/13): Assets, $453,664 (M); gifts received, $9,224,034; expenditures, $10,745,072; qualifying distributions, $10,742,251; giving activities include $10,742,251 for 10 grants (high: $6,929,267; low: $50,000).
Purpose and activities: Giving primarily for education and human services.
Fields of interest: Higher education; Education; Human services; Protestant agencies & churches.
Limitations: Applications not accepted. Giving primarily in MS. No grants to individuals.
Application information: Contributes only to pre-selected organizations.
Officers: Wendell W. Weakley, Sr., C.E.O. and Pres.; Sandra M. Guest, V.P. and Secy.; Maggie E. Abernathy, Treas.
Trustee: The University of Mississippi Foundation.
Number of staff: 7
EIN: 640875827
Selected grants: The following grants are a representative sample of this grantmaker's funding activity:

$6,929,267 to University of Mississippi Foundation, Oxford, MS, 2013. For program support and scholarships.
$1,092,984 to University of Mississippi Medical Center, Jackson, MS, 2013. For program support and scholarships.
$1,000,000 to Americas Promise - The Alliance for Youth, Washington, DC, 2013. For program support.
$500,000 to Mayo Clinic, President's Initiative, Rochester, MN, 2013. For health care research.
$350,000 to Mississippi Childrens Museum, Jackson, MS, 2013. For general support.
$300,000 to Millsaps College, Jackson, MS, 2013. For International Sponsored Scholarship Program and program support.
$250,000 to Boys and Girls Clubs of the Gulf Coast, Gulfport, MS, 2013. For local community programs.
$200,000 to Tougaloo College, Tougaloo, MS, 2013. For program support and scholarships.
$70,000 to DonorsChoose.org, New York, NY, 2013. For general support.
$50,000 to Community Foundation of Northwest Mississippi, Hernando, MS, 2013. For general support.

4838
Mississippi Hospital Association Health Research and Educational Foundation ✧
(formerly Mississippi Hospital Association Educational Foundation)
P.O. Box 1909
Madison, MS 39130-1909 (800) 289-8884
Contact: Marcella McKay Ph.D., C.E.O. and Pres.
E-mail: mmckay@mhanet.org; Main URL: http://www.mhanet.org/MHANet/MemberServices/MHA_Foundation/MHANet/Foundation/FoundationHome.aspx

Established in 1931 in MS.
Donors: Mississippi State Dept. of Health; Mississippi Development Authority; Mississippi Board of Nursing; Hinds County Workforce Investment Network; U.S. Dept. of Health & Human Services; U.S. Dept of Labor; Robert Wood Johnson Foundation; Kellogg Foundation; Bower Foundation; Foundation for the Mid South.
Foundation type: Independent foundation.
Financial data (yr. ended 06/30/13): Assets, $3,085,387 (M); gifts received, $2,553,404; expenditures, $2,813,532; qualifying distributions, $2,122,038; giving activities include $812,642 for grants, and $1,309,496 for foundation-administered programs.
Fields of interest: Hospitals (general); Public health, bioterrorism.
Type of support: Equipment; Scholarship funds.
Limitations: Applications not accepted. Giving primarily in MS.
Application information: Unsolicited requests for funds not accepted.
Officers: Elizabeth Mahaffey, Chair.; Marcella McKay, Ph.D., C.E.O. and Pres.
Board Members: Sam W. Cameron; James G. Chastain; Edward L. Foster; Richard Hilton; Tonya Moore; Hank Wheeler.
EIN: 237068714

4839
Mississippi Power Foundation Inc. ✧
P.O. Box 4079
Gulfport, MS 39502-4079 (228) 865-5925
Contact: Rodger Meizinger, Exec. Dir.

Established in 1997 in MS.
Donors: Mississippi Power Co.; Mississippi Power Education Fdn.
Foundation type: Company-sponsored foundation.
Financial data (yr. ended 12/31/13): Assets, $19,077,615 (M); expenditures, $1,166,316; qualifying distributions, $905,895; giving activities include $757,175 for 186 grants (high: $54,080; low: $100).
Purpose and activities: The foundation supports organizations involved with arts and culture, education, the environment, health, cancer, heart disease, housing, youth development, human services, and community development.
Fields of interest: Museums; Museums (art); Arts; Higher education; Education; Environment, natural resources; Environment, water resources; Environment, beautification programs; Environment; Health care; Cancer; Heart & circulatory diseases; Housing/shelter, repairs; Housing/shelter; Youth development, centers/clubs; American Red Cross; Children/youth, services; Human services; Nonprofit management; Community/economic development; United Ways and Federated Giving Programs.
Type of support: General/operating support; Continuing support; Annual campaigns; Capital campaigns; Building/renovation; Program development; Scholarship funds; Employee matching gifts.
Limitations: Applications accepted. Giving primarily in MS. No support for lobbying or legislative organizations. No grants to individuals, or for voter registration drives, electric appliance purchases, athletic field lighting installation, or any activity that provides a tangible economic benefit to Mississippi Power Company.
Application information: Application form required.
Initial approach: Request application form
Deadline(s): None
Officers: John Atherton, Pres.; Cindy Webb, Secy.; Moses Feagin, Treas.; Rodger Meinziger, Co-Exec. Dir.; Rebecca Montgomery, Co-Exec. Dir.
Board Members: Jeff Franklin; Ed Holland; John Huggins; Christy Irig; Cindy Shaw; Billy Thornton.
EIN: 721370746

4840
Edwin E. and Ruby C. Morgan Foundation Inc. ✧
254A Katherine Dr.
Flowood, MS 39232-8801

Established in 1983 in MS.
Donors: Edwin E. Morgan; Ruby C. Morgan†; R. Miller Reid.
Foundation type: Independent foundation.
Financial data (yr. ended 12/31/13): Assets, $21,288,662 (M); expenditures, $1,105,483; qualifying distributions, $894,966; giving activities include $680,000 for 27 grants (high: $75,000; low: $3,000).
Purpose and activities: Giving primarily for animal rescue organizations, community and civic organizations, and human services.
Fields of interest: Animal welfare; Food services; Human services; Salvation Army.
Limitations: Applications not accepted. Giving limited to CA and MS. No grants to individuals.
Application information: Contributes only to pre-selected organizations.
Officers and Directors:* R. Miller Reid,* Pres. and Treas.; Miller David Reid,* V.P. and Secy.; Philip L. Colson; G.E. Morgan; Karen M. Morgan.
EIN: 640667872

4841
Oakwood Foundation Charitable Trust ✧
P.O. Box 4200
Tupelo, MS 38803-4200

Established in 1995 in MS.
Donors: Elizabeth Renee Grisham; John R. Grisham, Jr.; Bennington Press, LLC; Belfry Holdings, Inc.
Foundation type: Independent foundation.
Financial data (yr. ended 12/31/12): Assets, $8,761,811 (M); gifts received, $6,875,000; expenditures, $3,930,440; qualifying distributions, $3,928,000; giving activities include $3,928,000 for grants.
Purpose and activities: Giving primarily for Baptist organizations, private foundations and a hospital.
Fields of interest: Education; Hospitals (general); Health care; Housing/shelter, development; Human services; Foundations (private grantmaking); Christian agencies & churches.
Limitations: Applications not accepted. Giving primarily in MS, NJ, and VA.
Application information: Unsolicited requests for funds not accepted.
Officer: Robert E. McDade, Fin. Mgr.
Trustees: Elizabeth Renee Grisham; John R. Grisham.
EIN: 640858879

4842
The Pruet Foundation ✧ ☆
217 W. Capitol St.
Jackson, MS 39201-2004

Established in 1991 in AR.
Donor: Chesley Pruet.
Foundation type: Independent foundation.
Financial data (yr. ended 12/31/13): Assets, $8,208,720 (M); expenditures, $479,917; qualifying distributions, $438,012; giving activities include $438,012 for 11 grants (high: $100,000; low: $2,350).
Fields of interest: Education; Cancer; Protestant agencies & churches.
Limitations: Applications not accepted. Giving primarily in AR and MS. No grants to individuals.
Application information: Unsolicited requests for funds not accepted.
Officers: Paula James, Pres. and Treas.; Ann Calhoon, V.P. and Secy.
EIN: 710710627

4843
Regions Foundation ✧
(formerly AmSouth Foundation)
P.O. Box 23100
Jackson, MS 39225-3100

Incorporated in 1962 in MS.
Donors: Deposit Guaranty National Bank; First American National Bank.

Foundation type: Company-sponsored foundation.
Financial data (yr. ended 12/31/12): Assets, $11,059,847 (M); expenditures, $833,923; qualifying distributions, $753,084; giving activities include $740,000 for 21 grants (high: $100,000; low: $5,000).
Purpose and activities: The foundation supports hospitals and organizations involved with arts and culture, education, youth development, human services, and Christianity.
Fields of interest: Arts; Education; Youth development.
Type of support: General/operating support; Annual campaigns; Capital campaigns; Scholarship funds; Program-related investments/loans; Employee matching gifts.
Limitations: Applications not accepted. Giving limited to MS. No grants to individuals.
Application information: Contributes only to pre-selected organizations.
Officers and Directors:* Charles L. Irby, Chair.; James W. Hood, Vice-Chair. and Pres.; Debbie Purvis, Secy.; Richard D. McRae, Jr., Treas.; Sharon S. Greener; William R. James; James L. Moore; W.R. Newman III; E.B. Robinson, Jr.; Ronnie Smith.
EIN: 646026793

4844
The Riley Foundation ✧
4518 Poplar Springs Dr.
Meridian, MS 39305-2616 (601) 481-1430
Contact: Becky G. Farley, Exec. Dir.
FAX: (601) 481-1434;
E-mail: info@rileyfoundation.org; Main URL: http://www.rileyfoundation.org

Established in 1998 in MS.
Foundation type: Independent foundation.
Financial data (yr. ended 12/31/13): Assets, $65,425,347 (M); expenditures, $1,931,860; qualifying distributions, $1,541,371; giving activities include $975,107 for 35 grants (high: $500,319; low: $250).
Purpose and activities: The foundation's purpose is to make grants to charitable and governmental organizations for charitable purposes, and to provide financial resources and assistance for community-wide projects and programs in health care, education, and the betterment of cultural, environmental, and economic conditions for the people of Meridian and Lauderdale County, MS.
Fields of interest: Arts; Education; Health care; Human services; Economic development; Community/economic development; Foundations (public); United Ways and Federated Giving Programs.
Type of support: General/operating support; Continuing support; Building/renovation; Equipment; Endowments; Seed money; Scholarship funds; Technical assistance; Consulting services; Program evaluation; Matching/challenge support.
Limitations: Applications accepted. Giving limited to Lauderdale County, MS. No support for private foundations or political activities. No grants for individuals; or for advertising or sponsorships.
Publications: Application guidelines; Grants list.
Application information: E-mailed or faxed grant applications will not be accepted, and incomplete applications will be returned. Application guidelines and forms available on foundation web site. Application form required.
Copies of proposal: 1
Deadline(s): By noon on Feb. 15, May 15, Aug. 15, and Nov. 15
Board meeting date(s): Jan., Apr., July and Oct.
Final notification: 2 weeks after board meeting
Officers and Directors:* R.B. Deen, Jr.,* Chair. and Pres.; Malcolm Portera, Ph.D., V.P. and Secy.; Marty Davidson, V.P. and Treas.; Becky G. Farley, Exec. Dir.; Edwin E. Downer; Tommy E. Dulaney; Manny Mitchell; Christine Riley; Gail W. Riley; Mary Ann Riley; Richard F. Riley, Jr.
Number of staff: 3 full-time professional.
EIN: 640707746

4845
Risen Son Foundation, Inc. ✧ ☆
1801 Crane Ridge Dr.
Jackson, MS 39216-4902
Application address: c/o Paul Laughlin, 4476 Main St., Ste. 106, Amherst, NY 14226, tel.: (716) 839-1292

Donor: David A. Rich, Sr.
Foundation type: Independent foundation.
Financial data (yr. ended 12/31/11): Assets, $4,385,057 (M); gifts received, $1,553,000; expenditures, $641,102; qualifying distributions, $545,064; giving activities include $480,975 for 26 grants (high: $135,700; low: $500).
Fields of interest: Arts; Youth development; Human services.
Type of support: General/operating support.
Limitations: Applications accepted. Giving primarily in MS.
Application information: Application form not required.
Initial approach: Proposal
Deadline(s): None
Officers: David A. Rich, Sr., Pres.; Grace E. Rich, V.P. and Secy.; David A. Rich, Jr., Treas.
EIN: 204446969

4846
The Algernon Sydney Sullivan Foundation ✧
P.O. Box 1113
1109 Van Buren
Oxford, MS 38655-1113 (662) 236-6335
Contact: Allan E. Strand, Pres.
FAX: (662) 281-8353;
E-mail: admin@sullivanfdn.org; Main URL: http://www.sullivanfdn.org
Facebook: https://www.facebook.com/pages/Sullivan-Foundation-Service-Social-Entrerpeneurship-Program/155744524468715
Twitter: https://twitter.com/sullivanfdn

Incorporated in 1930 in NY.
Donors: Mrs. Algernon Sydney Sullivan†; George Hammond Sullivan†; Zilph P. Devereaux†; Charles Watson†.
Foundation type: Independent foundation.
Financial data (yr. ended 06/30/13): Assets, $15,076,648 (M); expenditures, $887,615; qualifying distributions, $765,358; giving activities include $445,859 for 32 grants (high: $30,730; low: $1,500).
Purpose and activities: Grants primarily to colleges and universities for scholarship funds.
Fields of interest: Higher education.
Type of support: General/operating support; Endowments; Scholarship funds.
Limitations: Applications not accepted. Giving primarily in the Appalachian region of the southeastern U.S. No grants to individuals, or for capital construction.
Application information: Contributes only to pre-selected organizations.
Board meeting date(s): May and Nov.
Officers and Directors:* Stephan L. McDavid,* Pres.; Randolph V. Merrick, M.D.*, V.P.; Darla J. Wilkinson, Esq.*, Secy.; John C. Hardy, Treas.
Trustees: John Clayton Crouch; Thomas S. Rankin; Peter Rooney; Elizabeth H. Verner; Perry Wilson.
Number of staff: 1 part-time professional; 1 part-time support.
EIN: 136084596

4847
Van Devender Family Foundation ✧ ☆
(formerly Van Devender Foundation)
c/o William Van Devender
P.O. Box 5327
Jackson, MS 39296-5327

Established in 2002 in MI.
Donors: William J. Van Devender; Mollie M. Van Devender.
Foundation type: Operating foundation.
Financial data (yr. ended 09/30/13): Assets, $3,275 (M); gifts received, $432,560; expenditures, $431,202; qualifying distributions, $430,354; giving activities include $429,508 for 61 grants (high: $121,500; low: $40).
Fields of interest: Education; Youth development; Religion.
Limitations: Applications not accepted. Giving primarily in MS. No grants to individuals.
Application information: Contributes only to pre-selected organizations.
Trustees: Mollie M. Van Devender; William J. Van Devender.
EIN: 311480644

4848
Vicksburg Medical Foundation ✧
(formerly Vicksburg Hospital Medical Foundation)
P.O. Box 1578
Vicksburg, MS 39181-1578 (601) 636-5514
Contact: Howell N. Gage, Chair.

Established in 1956 in MS.
Foundation type: Independent foundation.
Financial data (yr. ended 12/31/13): Assets, $12,219,841 (M); expenditures, $639,661; qualifying distributions, $564,014; giving activities include $547,500 for 12 grants (high: $125,000; low: $2,500).
Purpose and activities: Giving primarily for higher education scholarships.
Fields of interest: Higher education.
Type of support: Endowments; Scholarship funds.
Limitations: Applications accepted. Giving primarily in MS. No grants to individuals.
Application information: Application form required.
Initial approach: Proposal
Deadline(s): None
Officers: Howell N. Gage, Chair.; Robert K. Purks, Vice-Chair.; Philip B. Watson, Jr., Secy.-Treas.
Trustees: Dr. Susan Chiarito; Robert Morrison III; Gordon Sluis.

Number of staff: 1 part-time professional; 1 part-time support.
EIN: 646025312

4849
Walker Foundation ✧

(formerly W. E. Walker Foundation)
c/o Belinda Styres
1020 Highland Colony Pkwy., Ste. 802
Ridgeland, MS 39157-8880 (601) 939-3003
Contact: Marcie Skelton, Dir.
FAX: (601) 939-4433;
E-mail: mskelton@walkercos.com

Established in 1972 in MS.
Donors: Gloria Walker; W.E. Walker, Jr.‡; Walker Lands; The Walker Cos.; His Way Homes.
Foundation type: Independent foundation.
Financial data (yr. ended 12/31/12): Assets, $11,397,384 (M); gifts received, $350,000; expenditures, $941,385; qualifying distributions, $608,150; giving activities include $608,150 for 30 grants (high: $115,300; low: $100).
Purpose and activities: Giving primarily for education, conservation, the arts and human services.
Fields of interest: Museums (art); Arts; Education; Environment; Animals/wildlife, bird preserves; Human services; Children/youth, services; Foundations (private independent); Christian agencies & churches.
Type of support: General/operating support; Annual campaigns; Capital campaigns.
Limitations: Applications accepted. Giving primarily in MS, with emphasis on Jackson. Generally no grants for deficit reduction, operating budgets, endowment programs, personnel costs, welfare agencies, physical plant construction, or individual scholarships.
Publications: Annual report; Occasional report.
Application information: Application form required.
Initial approach: Proposal
Copies of proposal: 1
Deadline(s): None
Board meeting date(s): As needed
Officer: Belinda Styres, Secy.
Trustees: Merry Dougherty; Andrew Mallison; Katie McBrayer; Gloria Walker; W.E. Walker III.
Director: Marcie Skelton.
Number of staff: 1 part-time professional.
EIN: 237279902

MISSOURI

4850
The Albrecht Family Charitable Foundation ✧
9761 Clayton Rd.
St. Louis, MO 63124-1503 (314) 692-4242
Contact: Barry D. Albrecht, Dir.
E-mail: info@albrechtfoundation.org; Main URL: http://www.albrechtfoundation.org

Established in 2007 in MO.
Foundation type: Independent foundation.
Financial data (yr. ended 12/31/13): Assets, $693,153 (M); gifts received, $756,430; expenditures, $1,221,358; qualifying distributions, $1,211,333; giving activities include $1,163,333 for 37 grants (high: $333,333; low: $1,000).
Purpose and activities: Giving primarily for education, health, and children and social services.
Fields of interest: Higher education; Education; Health organizations; Human services; Children/youth, services; Community/economic development; United Ways and Federated Giving Programs.
Limitations: Giving primarily in St. Louis, MO. No support for organizations without a direct connection to the St. Louis, MO, area. No grants for films and travel, or for capital campaigns, annual appeals; no loans.
Publications: Application guidelines.
Application information: The foundation does not accept applications in Nov. or Dec. Any questions about the foundation or proposal submission, please e-mail.
Initial approach: Proposal via U.S. mail
Deadline(s): Mar. 31 for spring; June 30 for summer; and Sept. 30 for fall
Trustees and Director:* Barry D. Albrecht,* Managing Tr.; Anne O'C. Albrecht; Douglas A. Albrecht.
EIN: 207509796
Selected grants: The following grants are a representative sample of this grantmaker's funding activity:
$50,000 to John Burroughs School, Saint Louis, MO, 2012. For Planning for Burroughs installment No. 4/5.
$10,000 to University of Southern California, Department of History, Los Angeles, CA, 2012. For unrestricted use.
$2,000 to University of Southern California, Los Angeles, CA, 2012. For History Department.
$2,000 to Washington University, Saint Louis, MO, 2012. For Department of English.

4851
Ameren Corporation Charitable Trust ✧
(formerly Union Electric Company Charitable Trust)
c/o Corp. Contribs., Ameren
P.O. Box 66149, M.C. 100
St. Louis, MO 63166-6149
Contact: Brian K. Leonard, Dir., Business and Community Affairs
FAX: (314) 554-2888;
E-mail: bleonard@ameren.com; Application address for organizations located in IL: Corp. Contribs., Ameren, 300 Liberty St., Peoria, IL 61602-1404, tel.: (877) 426-3736, ext. 75001; tel.: (314) 554-6441; e-mail: CommunityRelations@ameren.com; Main URL: http://www.ameren.com/community-members/corporate-charitable-trust

Trust established in 1944 in MO.
Donors: Union Electric Co.; Ameren Corp.
Foundation type: Company-sponsored foundation.
Financial data (yr. ended 12/31/13): Assets, $4,639,068 (M); gifts received, $4,000,000; expenditures, $4,899,611; qualifying distributions, $4,886,905; giving activities include $4,876,824 for 167 grants (high: $1,330,000; low: $15).
Purpose and activities: The trust supports organizations involved with arts and culture, human services, and civic affairs. Special emphasis is directed toward organizations involved with education, the environment, youth, and senior citizens.
Fields of interest: Arts; Higher education; Education; Environment, energy; Hospitals (general); Youth development, business; Salvation Army; Youth, services; Human services; United Ways and Federated Giving Programs; Public affairs; Aging.
Type of support: Sponsorships; In-kind gifts; Donated land; Donated equipment; Annual campaigns; Building/renovation; Capital campaigns; Continuing support; Emergency funds; Employee matching gifts; Equipment; General/operating support; Matching/challenge support; Program development; Scholarship funds.
Limitations: Applications accepted. Giving limited to areas of company operations in IL and MO. No support for political organizations or candidates or religious, fraternal, veterans', social, or similar organizations. No grants to individuals; no electric or natural gas service donations.
Publications: Application guidelines; Annual report; Corporate giving report (including application guidelines).
Application information: Application requests under $5,000 require a cover letter and IRS determination letter; requests over $5,000 require additional information. Application form required.
Initial approach: Download application form and mail to foundation for organizations located in MO; download application form and mail to application address for organizations located in IL
Copies of proposal: 1
Deadline(s): None
Board meeting date(s): 2 or 3 times per month
Final notification: 4 to 6 weeks
Trustee: Bank of America, N.A.
Number of staff: 2 full-time professional; 1 full-time support.
EIN: 436022693
Selected grants: The following grants are a representative sample of this grantmaker's funding activity:
$1,304,100 to United Way of Greater Saint Louis, Saint Louis, MO, 2012. For operating support.
$270,000 to Energy Assistance Foundation, Decatur, IL, 2012. For Warm Neighbors Program.
$100,000 to BioSTL, Saint Louis, MO, 2012. For operating support.
$100,000 to University of Missouri, College of Business Administration, Saint Louis, MO, 2012. For capital campaign.
$80,000 to Arts and Education Council, Saint Louis, MO, 2012. For annual campaign.
$50,000 to Ronald McDonald House Charities of Metro Saint Louis, Saint Louis, MO, 2012. For capital campaign.
$50,000 to Urban League of Metropolitan Saint Louis, Saint Louis, MO, 2012. For outreach center.
$30,000 to World Bird Sanctuary, Valley Park, MO, 2012. For Summer Education Program.
$15,000 to American Red Cross, Saint Louis Chapter, Saint Louis, MO, 2012. For Harrisburg, IL Relief.
$10,000 to Opera Theater of Saint Louis, Saint Louis, MO, 2012. For season support.

4852
American Century Investments Foundation ✧
(formerly American Century Companies Foundation)
4500 Main St.
P.O. Box 418210
Kansas City, MO 64141 (816) 340-7046
Contact: Kristin Raven

Established in 2000 in MO.
Donor: American Century Co., Inc.
Foundation type: Company-sponsored foundation.
Financial data (yr. ended 12/31/13): Assets, $3,735,626 (M); gifts received, $1,000,000; expenditures, $1,220,000; qualifying distributions, $1,200,000; giving activities include $1,200,000 for 1 grant.
Purpose and activities: The foundation supports programs designed to provide innovative opportunities that are sustainable and inspire growth in communities. Special emphasis is directed toward health and human service organizations designed to provide direct services to individuals.
Fields of interest: Hospitals (general); Health care, patient services; Health care; Children/youth, services; Family services, domestic violence; Human services; Community/economic development; Foundations (community); United Ways and Federated Giving Programs; Economically disadvantaged.
Type of support: General/operating support; Program development; Employee volunteer services; Employee matching gifts.
Limitations: Applications accepted. Giving primarily in areas of company operations in Mountain View, CA, Kansas City, MO, and New York, NY. No support for religious organizations not of direct benefit to the entire community, social, labor, veterans', alumni, or fraternal organizations, athletic teams, or political candidates. No grants to individuals, or for special events, capital campaigns, recreational sporting events, political causes or legislative lobbying efforts, debt reduction, travel, or conferences.
Publications: Application guidelines.
Application information: Application form required.
Initial approach: Proposal
Deadline(s): None
Board meeting date(s): Semi-annually
Final notification: 8 weeks
Officers and Directors:* Mark Gilstrap,* Pres.; Charles Etherington,* V.P. and Secy.; Jami Waggoner,* Treas.
EIN: 431881225
Selected grants: The following grants are a representative sample of this grantmaker's funding activity:
$1,450,000 to Greater Kansas City Community Foundation, Kansas City, MO, 2011. For operating expenses.

4853
Anheuser-Busch Foundation
c/o Anheuser-Busch Cos., Inc.
1 Busch Pl.
St. Louis, MO 63118-1849 (314) 577-2000
Main URL: http://anheuser-busch.com/index.php/our-responsibility/

Established in 1975 in MO.
Donor: Anheuser-Busch Cos., Inc.
Foundation type: Company-sponsored foundation.
Financial data (yr. ended 12/31/13): Assets, $42,623,837 (M); expenditures, $10,893,775; qualifying distributions, $10,195,992; giving activities include $9,943,682 for 297 grants (high: $2,011,000; low: $100).
Purpose and activities: The foundation supports programs designed to promote disaster relief and preparedness; increase access to and completion of higher education; raise consciousness and action for water conservation and recycling; and increase the quality of life through homeownership and entrepreneurship.
Fields of interest: Higher education; Scholarships/financial aid; Education; Environment, recycling; Environment, natural resources; Environment, water resources; Environmental education; Housing/shelter, development; Housing/shelter; Disasters, preparedness/services; American Red Cross; Human services; Economic development; Community/economic development; United Ways and Federated Giving Programs; Military/veterans' organizations; Minorities; African Americans/Blacks; Hispanics/Latinos; Economically disadvantaged.
Type of support: General/operating support; Continuing support; Building/renovation; Program development; Scholarship funds; Employee volunteer services; Employee matching gifts; Matching/challenge support.
Limitations: Applications not accepted. Giving primarily in areas of company operations, with emphasis on Fairfield, Los Angeles, and San Diego, CA, Fort Collins, CO, Jacksonville, Orlando, and Tampa, FL, Cartersville, GA, St. Louis, MO, Merrimack, NH, Newark, NJ, Baldwinsville, NY, Columbus, OH, Houston and San Antonio, TX, and Williamsburg, VA. No support for discriminatory, political, fraternal, social, or religious organizations, legislators, athletic organizations or teams, charter schools, pre-schools, elementary, middle, or high schools, or hospitals or healthcare-related organizations. No grants to individuals, or for political campaigns, annual or capital campaigns, conferences or seminars, travel or organized field trips, family reunions, general operating support for United Way agencies, or endowments; no multi-year commitments.
Application information: The foundation is moving to an invitation-only process for giving.
Board meeting date(s): Approximately every 3 months
Trustees: David Peacock; Gary L. Rutledge; James Villeneuve; U.S. Bank, N.A.
EIN: 510168084
Selected grants: The following grants are a representative sample of this grantmaker's funding activity:
$2,000,000 to United Way of Greater Saint Louis, Saint Louis, MO, 2012.
$1,000,000 to Commission on Presidential Debates, Washington, DC, 2012.
$1,000,000 to World Trade Center Memorial Foundation, New York, NY, 2012.
$600,000 to Saint Louis University, Saint Louis, MO, 2012.
$335,000 to American Red Cross, Saint Louis Chapter, Saint Louis, MO, 2012.
$100,000 to Mexican American Legal Defense and Educational Fund, Los Angeles, CA, 2012.
$50,000 to United Way of Central Ohio, Columbus, OH, 2012.
$50,000 to Urban League, National, New York, NY, 2012.
$25,000 to Drumthwacket Foundation, Princeton, NJ, 2012.
$10,000 to Cardinal Hayes High School, Bronx, NY, 2012.

4854
Apex Oil Company Charitable Foundation ✧
8235 Forsyth Blvd., Ste. 400
Clayton, MO 63105-1621 (314) 889-9600
Contact: Chandra N. Niemann, Treas.

Established in 2002 in MO.
Donors: Apex Oil Co., Inc.; Edgington Oil Co.
Foundation type: Company-sponsored foundation.
Financial data (yr. ended 12/31/13): Assets, $9,860,457 (M); gifts received, $2,500,000; expenditures, $2,526,390; qualifying distributions, $2,455,750; giving activities include $2,455,750 for 45 grants (high: $1,000,000; low: $100).
Purpose and activities: The foundation supports organizations involved with historic preservation, performing arts, education, health, mental health, and human services.
Fields of interest: Performing arts; Historic preservation/historical societies; Secondary school/education; Higher education; Scholarships/financial aid; Education; Hospitals (general); Health care, clinics/centers; Health care; Mental health/crisis services; Children/youth, services; Human services.
Type of support: General/operating support; Capital campaigns; Building/renovation; Program development; Scholarship funds.
Limitations: Applications accepted. Giving primarily in Washington, DC, New York, NY, LA, and St. Louis, MO.
Application information: Application form required.
Initial approach: Letter
Deadline(s): None
Officers and Directors:* Paul A. Novelly,* Pres.; Karon M. Burns, Secy.; Chandra N. Nieman,* Treas.; Paul A. Novelly II.
EIN: 710914470

4855
Arch Coal Foundation ✧ ☆
1 Cityplace Dr., Ste. 300
St. Louis, MO 63141
Teacher Achievement Awards Grants List: http://www.archcoal.com/community/teacherawards.aspx

Established in 2006 in MO.
Donor: Donald H. Bernstein.
Foundation type: Company-sponsored foundation.
Financial data (yr. ended 12/31/13): Assets, $1,393,414 (M); expenditures, $1,174,647; qualifying distributions, $1,165,374; giving activities include $983,475 for 78 grants (high: $300,000; low: $500).
Purpose and activities: The foundation supports organizations involved with arts and culture, education, and the environment; awards grants to K-12 classroom teachers in recognition of outstanding achievement; and awards grants to K-12 classroom teachers to invent and test innovative teaching ideas in the classroom.
Fields of interest: Museums (art); Performing arts, theater; Arts; Elementary/secondary education; Higher education; Environment, natural resources; Environment.
Type of support: Continuing support; Capital campaigns; General/operating support; Sponsorships; Employee-related scholarships; Grants to individuals.
Limitations: Applications accepted. Giving primarily in areas of company operations in CO, IL, KY, MO, UT, WV, and WY.
Publications: Application guidelines; Grants list.
Application information: Application form required.
Initial approach: Proposal
Deadline(s): None
Officers and Directors:* Deck S. Slone,* Pres.; James E. Florczak, V.P., Finance; Jon Ploetz,* Secy.; John W. Lorson; R. Gregory Schaefer; John D. Snider.
EIN: 203980901
Selected grants: The following grants are a representative sample of this grantmaker's funding activity:
$1,600 to Campbell County Healthcare Foundation, Gillette, WY, 2012. For school playground.

4856
Arthur & Helen Baer Charitable Foundation ✧ ☆
c/o UHY Advisors MO, Inc.
15 Sunnen Dr., Ste. 100
St. Louis, MO 63143-3819

Established in 1984 in MO.
Donor: Helen K. Baer†.
Foundation type: Independent foundation.
Financial data (yr. ended 12/31/13): Assets, $9,330,187 (M); expenditures, $616,807; qualifying distributions, $459,402; giving activities include $429,215 for 20 grants (high: $50,000; low: $1,000).
Fields of interest: Arts; Education; Health organizations.
Type of support: Building/renovation; Equipment; Program development; Scholarship funds; Program-related investments/loans.
Limitations: Applications not accepted. Giving primarily in St. Louis, MO. No grants to individuals.
Application information: Contributes only to pre-selected organizations.
Officers: Patrick E. Stark, Pres.; Philip N. Chilton, Secy.
EIN: 431353474

4857
Sidney R. Baer, Jr. Foundation ✧
c/o U.S. Bank, N.A., The Private Client Reserve
10 N. Hanley Rd.
Clayton, MO 63105-3426
Contact: Carol A. Eaves
Main URL: http://www.baerfoundation.org

Established in 1999 in MA.
Donor: Sidney R. Baer, Jr. Trust.

Foundation type: Independent foundation.
Financial data (yr. ended 06/30/13): Assets, $42,325,652 (M); expenditures, $3,305,212; qualifying distributions, $2,364,843; giving activities include $2,220,810 for 31 grants (high: $171,000; low: $2,750).
Purpose and activities: The primary focus of the foundation relates to depression and schizophrenia. Funding is provided to organizations for the care and rehabilitation of the victims of these maladies; formal education for the victims, their families, and the public; and research related to the cause, alleviation, and prevention of these conditions.
Fields of interest: Mental health, association.
Type of support: Program development; Research.
Limitations: Giving primarily in NY, Boston, MA and St. Louis, MO. No support for mental retardation, physical disability, drugs or alcohol addiction programs, medical researchers, or autism. No grants to individuals, or for current operating funds, annual fund raising drives, endowments, international activities or foreign charitable institutions.
Publications: Application guidelines.
Application information: See foundation web site for application guidelines and download of application form. Application form required.
Initial approach: Letter of intent
Copies of proposal: 3
Deadline(s): See foundation web site for deadlines
Board meeting date(s): June and Oct.
Trustees: George B. Handran; U.S. Bank, N.A.
EIN: 436829338

4858
The Ballmann Family Private Foundation ✧
c/o U.S. Bank, N.A.
P.O. Box 387
St. Louis, MO 63166-0387
Contact: For Scholarship Awards: Angela Pearson

Established in 1993 in MO.
Foundation type: Independent foundation.
Financial data (yr. ended 05/31/13): Assets, $29,001,154 (M); expenditures, $1,565,533; qualifying distributions, $1,452,320; giving activities include $1,341,137 for 42 grants (high: $101,250; low: $612).
Purpose and activities: Giving for education, children, youth, and social services, and health care, particularly a children's hospital. Scholarships are awarded 1 time to female high school graduates from the St. Louis, MO, metropolitan area.
Fields of interest: Higher education; Nursing school/education; Education; Animal welfare; Hospitals (specialty); Health care; Food distribution, meals on wheels; Human services; Salvation Army; Children/youth, services; Residential/custodial care.
Type of support: Scholarships—to individuals.
Limitations: Giving primarily in St. Louis, MO; scholarship awards limited to St. Louis, MO. No grants to individuals (except for designated scholarships).
Application information: Applications accepted for scholarship program only.
Initial approach: Letter
Trustee: U.S. Bank, N.A.
EIN: 436466750
Selected grants: The following grants are a representative sample of this grantmaker's funding activity:
$93,750 to Good Samaritan Home, Saint Louis, MO, 2011.
$62,500 to Childrens Home Society of Missouri, Saint Louis, MO, 2011.
$62,500 to Humane Society of Missouri, Saint Louis, MO, 2011.
$62,500 to Missouri Council of the Blind, Saint Louis, MO, 2011.
$62,500 to Ranken Technical College, Saint Louis, MO, 2011.
$62,500 to Saint Louis College of Pharmacy, Saint Louis, MO, 2011.
$37,500 to Barnes-Jewish Hospital Foundation, Saint Louis, MO, 2011.
$25,000 to Epworth Childrens Home, Saint Louis, MO, 2011.
$25,000 to Independence Center, Saint Louis, MO, 2011.
$7,500 to Truman State University, Kirksville, MO, 2011.

4859
The Bellwether Foundation, Inc. ✧
231 S. Bemiston Ave., Ste. 925
St. Louis, MO 63105-1991
E-mail: info@bellwetherstl.org; Main URL: http://www.bellwetherstl.org

Established in 1985 in MO.
Donors: Robert B. Smith†; Nancy M. Smith†; Wallace H. Smith†; Nancy Morrill Smith Revocable Trust; Robert Brookings Smith Marital Trust; Nancy M. Smith Charitable Remainder Unitrust; Smith Joint Charitable Remainder Unitrust.
Foundation type: Independent foundation.
Financial data (yr. ended 12/31/13): Assets, $76,819,761 (M); expenditures, $4,290,866; qualifying distributions, $3,810,077; giving activities include $3,627,100 for 32 grants (high: $1,500,000; low: $500).
Purpose and activities: Primarily supports projects which anticipate the future in the areas of the arts, computer science, education, finance, health care, medicine, and the social sciences, including research in any of these areas.
Fields of interest: Arts; Education; Environment, natural resources; Botanical gardens; Medical research, institute.
Type of support: Management development/capacity building; Program development; Research.
Limitations: Applications accepted. Giving primarily in St. Louis, MO. No grants to individuals.
Application information: Application form required.
Initial approach: Use form on foundation web site
Deadline(s): Preliminary grant inquires are accepted between Feb. 1 and June 30
Officers: Robert B. Smith III, Chair.; Virginia V. Smith, Pres. and Secy.
Trustees: Sally Duffield; Robert B. Smith II; John J. Wolfe.
Number of staff: 2 full-time support.
EIN: 222635309
Selected grants: The following grants are a representative sample of this grantmaker's funding activity:
$1,624,850 to Missouri Botanical Garden, Saint Louis, MO, 2012.
$906,500 to Saint Louis Zoo, Saint Louis, MO, 2012.
$500,000 to Donald Danforth Plant Science Center, Saint Louis, MO, 2012.
$100,000 to City Academy, Saint Louis, MO, 2012.
$100,000 to Marian Middle School, Saint Louis, MO, 2012.
$60,000 to Sheldon Arts Foundation, Saint Louis, MO, 2012.
$25,000 to De La Salle Middle School, Saint Louis, MO, 2012.
$25,000 to Rainbow Village, Saint Louis, MO, 2012.
$20,000 to Saint Louis Childrens Hospital, Saint Louis, MO, 2012.
$15,000 to Boys and Girls Club, Herbert Hoover, Saint Louis, MO, 2012.

4860
The Stephen F. and Camilla T. Brauer Charitable Trust ✧
424 S. Woodsmill Rd., Rm. 325
Chesterfield, MO 63017-3479

Established in 1997 in MO.
Donor: Stephen F. Brauer.
Foundation type: Independent foundation.
Financial data (yr. ended 12/31/13): Assets, $118,200 (M); gifts received, $3,092,895; expenditures, $3,090,562; qualifying distributions, $3,049,152; giving activities include $3,049,152 for 105 grants (high: $1,150,100; low: $50).
Purpose and activities: Giving for the arts and education.
Fields of interest: Museums (art); Arts; Higher education; Education; Environment; Zoos/zoological societies; Health organizations, association; Human services; Children/youth, services; United Ways and Federated Giving Programs.
Limitations: Applications not accepted. Giving primarily in St. Louis, MO. No grants to individuals.
Application information: Contributes only to pre-selected organizations.
Board meeting date(s): No set dates
Trustees: Camilla Brauer; Stephen F. Brauer.
EIN: 311534822
Selected grants: The following grants are a representative sample of this grantmaker's funding activity:
$1,175,170 to Washington University, Saint Louis, MO, 2011.
$131,058 to United Way of Greater Saint Louis, Saint Louis, MO, 2011. For general purposes.
$50,000 to George W. Bush Foundation, Dallas, TX, 2011. For general purposes.
$10,000 to Teach for America, Saint Louis, MO, 2011. For general purposes.
$5,000 to Logos School, Saint Louis, MO, 2011. For general purposes.
$3,000 to Characterplus, Saint Louis, MO, 2011. For general purposes.
$2,250 to Saint Louis Mercantile Library, Saint Louis, MO, 2011. For general purposes.
$2,000 to Library Foundation for the Benefit of Saint Louis Public Library, Saint Louis, MO, 2011. For general purposes.
$1,000 to John Burroughs School, Saint Louis, MO, 2011. For general purposes.
$1,000 to Today and Tomorrow Educational Foundation, Saint Louis, MO, 2011. For general purposes.

4861
Marion I. Breen Charitable Foundation ✧
1 N. Brentwood Blvd.
Saint Louis, MO 63105-3925

Established in 2007 in MO.
Donor: Marion I. Breen.
Foundation type: Independent foundation.
Financial data (yr. ended 12/31/13): Assets, $12,078,775 (M); expenditures, $678,616; qualifying distributions, $678,616; giving activities include $635,572 for 3 grants (high: $540,572; low: $45,000).
Purpose and activities: Giving primarily for higher education and Lutheran agencies and churches.
Fields of interest: Higher education; Theological school/education; Protestant agencies & churches.
Limitations: Applications not accepted. Giving primarily in Selma, AL. No grants to individuals.
Application information: Contributes only to pre-selected organizations.
Trustees: Kathleen Helge; Leonard J. Pranschke.
EIN: 260640175

4862
Dana Brown Charitable Trust ✧
c/o U.S. Bank, N.A., Pvt. Client Reserve
10 N. Hanley Rd.
Clayton, MO 63105-3426
Contact: Daniel L. Watt
Additional e-mail for application information: kimberly.livingston@usbank.com

Established in 1994 in MO.
Donor: Dana Brown.
Foundation type: Independent foundation.
Financial data (yr. ended 06/30/13): Assets, $67,962,319 (M); expenditures, $4,512,005; qualifying distributions, $3,557,354; giving activities include $3,437,250 for 102 grants (high: $500,000; low: $2,800).
Purpose and activities: The primary purpose of the trust is to provide for the health, education and welfare of underprivileged and economically disadvantaged children in the St. Louis, Missouri metropolitan area.
Fields of interest: Education; Animal welfare; Animals/wildlife; Hospitals (general); Human services; Children/youth, services; Children/youth; Children; Economically disadvantaged.
Type of support: General/operating support; Annual campaigns; Capital campaigns; Building/renovation; Matching/challenge support.
Limitations: Applications accepted. Giving exclusively in the metropolitan St. Louis, MO, area. No grants to individuals or for feasibility studies.
Publications: Application guidelines; Program policy statement; Program policy statement (including application guidelines).
Application information: Application form required.
Initial approach: Application only
Copies of proposal: 10
Deadline(s): Feb. 15, May 15, Aug. 15, and Nov. 15
Board meeting date(s): Mar., June, Sept. and Dec.
Trustees: Lela G. Rice; U.S. Bank, N.A.
EIN: 436531876
Selected grants: The following grants are a representative sample of this grantmaker's funding activity:
$500,000 to Saint Louis Childrens Hospital Foundation, Saint Louis, MO, 2011.
$500,000 to Saint Louis Zoo Foundation, Saint Louis, MO, 2011.
$250,000 to Cardinal Glennon Childrens Hospital Foundation, Saint Louis, MO, 2011.
$250,000 to Saint Louis Science Center Foundation, Saint Louis, MO, 2011.
$200,000 to Library Foundation for the Benefit of Saint Louis Public Library, Saint Louis, MO, 2011.
$153,500 to Saint Louis Regional Public Media, Saint Louis, MO, 2011.
$100,000 to Humane Society of Missouri, Saint Louis, MO, 2011.
$50,000 to BackStoppers, Saint Louis, MO, 2011.
$50,000 to Lutheran Elementary School Association, Saint Louis, MO, 2011.
$50,000 to Saint Johns Mercy Health System, Saint Louis, MO, 2011.
$50,000 to Special Education Foundation, Ballwin, MO, 2011.

4863
The Brunner Foundation ✧
c/o Larry Legrand
540 Maryville Centre Dr., Ste. 105
St. Louis, MO 63141-5829

Established in 2005 in MO.
Donors: Janell S. Brunner; John G. Brunner.
Foundation type: Independent foundation.
Financial data (yr. ended 12/31/13): Assets, $4,182,982 (M); gifts received, $2,894; expenditures, $490,784; qualifying distributions, $474,397; giving activities include $473,222 for 3 grants (high: $460,722; low: $2,500).
Fields of interest: Human services.
Limitations: Applications not accepted. Giving primarily in AR, MO, TN, and TX. No grants to individuals.
Application information: Contributes only to pre-selected organizations.
Trustees: Janell S. Brunner; John G. Brunner.
EIN: 206768914
Selected grants: The following grants are a representative sample of this grantmaker's funding activity:
$1,000 to Autism Speaks, Princeton, NJ, 2011.

4864
G. A., Jr. and Kathryn M. Buder Charitable Foundation ✧
c/o Scott E. Hunt
7700 Forsyth Blvd., Ste. 1800
Saint Louis, MO 63105-1807

Established in 1991 in MO.
Donor: Kathryn M. Buder.
Foundation type: Independent foundation.
Financial data (yr. ended 12/31/13): Assets, $17,284,934 (M); expenditures, $1,094,981; qualifying distributions, $938,562; giving activities include $918,254 for 13 grants (high: $750,000; low: $3,000).
Fields of interest: Education; Animals/wildlife.
Type of support: Scholarship funds.
Limitations: Applications not accepted. Giving primarily in MO. No grants to individuals.
Application information: Unsolicited requests for funds not accepted.
Trustees: Marshall O. Buder; Theodore A. Buder; Robert Dorhauer; Amy Locklear Hertel; Theresa B. Howe; Scott E. Hunt; Shanti K. Khinduka.
EIN: 431582356
Selected grants: The following grants are a representative sample of this grantmaker's funding activity:
$7,000 to Manhattan School of Music, New York, NY, 2012. For charitable educational.

4865
Bunge North America Foundation ✧
(formerly Bunge Corporation Foundation)
11720 Borman Dr.
St. Louis, MO 63146-4129 (314) 292-2300
Contact: Geralyn F. Hayes

Established in 1993 in MO.
Donor: Bunge North America, Inc.
Foundation type: Company-sponsored foundation.
Financial data (yr. ended 12/31/12): Assets, $14,426 (M); gifts received, $750,000; expenditures, $755,707; qualifying distributions, $755,707; giving activities include $145,007 for 165 grants (high: $25,000; low: $20), and $610,700 for 30 employee matching gifts.
Purpose and activities: The foundation supports organizations involved with arts and culture, education, the environment, and community development.
Fields of interest: Arts; Education.
Type of support: General/operating support; Program development; Sponsorships; Employee matching gifts.
Limitations: Applications accepted. Giving primarily in areas of company operations, with emphasis on KS, MA, MO, and NY. No grants to individuals.
Application information: Application form required.
Initial approach: Letter
Deadline(s): None
Officers and Directors:* Soren Schroder,* Pres.; Todd A. Bastean,* V.P.; Geralyn F. Hayes,* V.P.; David G. Kabbes, Secy.; Aaron L. Elliot, Treas.; John P. Sabourin, Cont.
EIN: 431617648
Selected grants: The following grants are a representative sample of this grantmaker's funding activity:
$200,450 to Progressive Agriculture Foundation, Kansas City, MO, 2011.
$104,500 to Future Farmers of America, Houston, TX, 2011.
$20,000 to United Way of Greater Saint Louis, Saint Louis, MO, 2011.
$3,000 to University of Missouri, Saint Louis, MO, 2011.

4866
Burns & McDonnell Foundation ✧
9400 Ward Pkwy.
Kansas City, MO 64114-3319 (816) 333-9400
Contact: Melissa Lavin-Hickey, Community Rels. Dir.
FAX: (816) 822-3516;
E-mail: mlavin@burnsmcd.com; Tel. for Melissa Lavin-Hickey: (816) 822-3024; Main URL: http://www.burnsmcd.com/Company/Community-Involvement-co
Battle of the Brains on Facebook: http://www.facebook.com/BattleoftheBrainsKC
Battle of the Brains on Twitter: https://twitter.com/#!/botbkc

Established in 1987 in MO.
Donor: Burns & McDonnell, Inc.
Foundation type: Company-sponsored foundation.
Financial data (yr. ended 12/31/13): Assets, $24,023,165 (M); gifts received, $2,500,000; expenditures, $892,399; qualifying distributions, $879,299; giving activities include $879,299 for 140 grants (high: $76,000; low: $250).
Purpose and activities: The foundation supports organizations involved with arts and culture, environmental practices, and human services. Special emphasis is directed toward science, technology, engineering, and math education.
Fields of interest: Museums (science/technology); Performing arts; Performing arts, theater; Historic preservation/historical societies; Arts; Elementary/secondary education; Higher education; Engineering school/education; Education; Environment; Children/youth, services; Human services; Foundations (community); United Ways and Federated Giving Programs; Mathematics; Engineering/technology; Science.
Type of support: General/operating support; Annual campaigns; Endowments; Program development.
Limitations: Applications accepted. Giving primarily in areas of company operations in Kansas City, MO. No support for religious or political organizations.
Application information: Application form not required.
Initial approach: Proposal
Deadline(s): None
Officers and Directors:* Gregory M. Graves,* Chair. and Pres.; Dennis W. Scott, V.P; G. William Quatman, Secy.; Mark H. Taylor,* Treas.; Donald F. Greenwood; Raymond J. Kowalik; John E. Nobles; Walter C. Womack; David G. Yeamans.
EIN: 431448871

4867
August A. Busch III Charitable Trust ✧
P.O. Box 16550
Clayton, MO 63105-6550 (314) 746-7266
Contact: David J. Krauss
E-mail: david.krauss@commercebank.com

Established in 1986 in MO.
Donor: August A. Busch III.
Foundation type: Independent foundation.
Financial data (yr. ended 12/31/13): Assets, $1,993,680 (M); gifts received, $3,026,508; expenditures, $1,796,476; qualifying distributions, $1,765,078; giving activities include $1,765,078 for 66 grants (high: $250,000; low: $500).
Fields of interest: Education; Animal welfare; Human services; American Red Cross; Children/youth, services; Space/aviation; Catholic agencies & churches.
Limitations: Applications accepted. Giving primarily in FL and MO, with emphasis on St. Louis. No grants to individuals.
Application information: Application form not required.
Initial approach: Proposal
Deadline(s): None
Officer: Virginia M. Busch, Mgr.
Trustee: August A. Busch III.
EIN: 431435400
Selected grants: The following grants are a representative sample of this grantmaker's funding activity:
$50,000 to Experimental Aircraft Association, Oshkosh, WI, 2011. For general support.
$25,000 to Paralyzed Veterans of America, Washington, DC, 2011. For general support.
$20,000 to Fauna and Flora International, Cambridge, England, 2011. For general support.
$10,450 to Ducks Unlimited, Memphis, TN, 2011. For general support.
$8,000 to World Wildlife Fund, Washington, DC, 2011. For general support.
$5,000 to University of Missouri, Columbia, MO, 2011. For general support.

4868
E. Kemper and Anna Curry Carter Community Memorial Trust ✧
(formerly Carter Community Memorial Trust)
c/o UMB Bank, N.A.
P.O. Box 415044, M/S 1020307
Kansas City, MO 64141-6692
Application address: Jan Leonard, P.O. Box 41962, Kansas City, MO 64106, Tel: (816) 860-1933

Established in 1993 in MO.
Foundation type: Independent foundation.
Financial data (yr. ended 12/31/13): Assets, $14,264,124 (M); expenditures, $656,239; qualifying distributions, $596,726; giving activities include $547,004 for 25 grants (high: $135,000; low: $2,500).
Purpose and activities: Giving primarily for higher education and agriculture; funding also for the arts and human services.
Fields of interest: Arts; Education; Agriculture; Human services.
Limitations: Applications accepted. Giving limited to KS and MO, with emphasis on the Kansas City area.
Application information: Application form not required.
Initial approach: Proposal
Deadline(s): None
Trustee: UMB Bank, N.A.
EIN: 436483356
Selected grants: The following grants are a representative sample of this grantmaker's funding activity:
$125,000 to Kemper Museum of Contemporary Art and Design, Kansas City, MO, 2011.

4869
Jim Casey Youth Opportunities Initiative, Inc. ✧
222 S. Central Ave., Ste. 305
St. Louis, MO 63105-3509 (314) 863-7000
FAX: (314) 863-7003; Main URL: http://www.jimcaseyyouth.org
E-Newsletter: http://www.jimcaseyyouth.org/newsletter-eupdates-initiative
Facebook: https://www.facebook.com/JimCaseyYouthOpportunitiesInitiative
Knowledge Center: http://www.jimcaseyyouth.org/knowledge-center
Twitter: http://twitter.com/jimcaseyyouth

Established in 2001 in DE.
Donors: Casey Family Grants Program; The Annie E. Casey Foundation.
Foundation type: Independent foundation.
Financial data (yr. ended 12/31/13): Assets, $7,332,332 (M); gifts received, $10,709,704; expenditures, $13,211,804; qualifying distributions, $13,102,675; giving activities include $2,834,992 for 28 grants (high: $312,338; low: $10,000), and $10,337,683 for foundation-administered programs.
Purpose and activities: The mission of the Jim Casey Youth Opportunities Initiative is to help youth in foster care make successful transitions to adulthood. It brings together the people and resources needed for youth to make the connections they need to education, employment, health care, housing, and supportive personal and community relationships.
Fields of interest: Higher education; Human services; Children, foster care.
Limitations: Applications not accepted. Giving primarily in San Diego, CA, Front Range and Denver, CO, Hartford, Bridgeport, New Haven, and Waterbury, CT, Tampa, FL, Atlanta, GA, IN, Des Moines, IA, ME, Detroit and ten northern counties, MI, Omaha, NE, RI, and Nashville, TN. No grants to individuals.
Application information: Contributes only to pre-selected organizations.
Officers and Trustees:* Patrick McCarthy,* Chair.; Sharon L. McDaniel-Lowe, Ph.D.*, Secy.; Lisa Hamilton,* Treas.; Leonard Burton, C.O.O.; Jim Hoke, C.F.O.; Gary Stangler,* Exec. Dir.; William C. Bell; Brenda Donald; Joseph R. Moderow; David Sanders.
Number of staff: 12 full-time professional.
EIN: 233081243
Selected grants: The following grants are a representative sample of this grantmaker's funding activity:
$180,000 to Family Empowerment Institute, Detroit, MI, 2012. To foster Youth Initiatives.

4870
The Centene Charitable Foundation ✧
7700 Forsyth Blvd., Ste. 800
St. Louis, MO 63105-1837 (314) 505-6992
E-mail: CCF@centene.com; Main URL: http://www.centene.com/about-us/responsible-enterprise/charitablefoundation/

Established in 2005 in MO.
Donor: Centene Management Company, LLC.
Foundation type: Company-sponsored foundation.
Financial data (yr. ended 05/31/13): Assets, $1,771,957 (M); gifts received, $6,234,500; expenditures, $6,456,343; qualifying distributions, $6,452,999; giving activities include $6,449,753 for 226 grants (high: $500,000; low: $200).
Purpose and activities: The foundation supports programs designed to help individuals in need, with emphasis on families and children.
Fields of interest: Media, radio; Museums; Performing arts; Performing arts centers; Performing arts, ballet; Performing arts, orchestras; Arts; Secondary school/education; Higher education; Libraries (public); Education; Hospitals (general); Health care; Athletics/sports, amateur leagues; Boys & girls clubs; Boy scouts; Children, services; Family services; Developmentally disabled, centers & services; Human services; Community/economic development; United Ways and Federated Giving Programs; Children; Minorities; African Americans/Blacks.
Type of support: General/operating support; Continuing support; Annual campaigns; Capital campaigns; Building/renovation; Endowments; Program development; Scholarship funds; Sponsorships.
Limitations: Applications accepted. Giving primarily in areas of company operations, with emphasis on

St. Louis, MO. No support for political, religious, or similar groups. No grants to individuals.
Publications: Application guidelines.
Application information: Application form required.
Initial approach: Complete online application
Deadline(s): 6 months prior to need
Final notification: 1 month
Officers: Michael F. Neidorff, Pres.; Keith H. Williamson, Secy.; William N. Scheffel, Treas.
EIN: 201298192
Selected grants: The following grants are a representative sample of this grantmaker's funding activity:
$497,180 to John F. Kennedy Center for the Performing Arts, Washington, DC, 2011.
$100,000 to State of Saint Louis Foundation, Saint Louis, MO, 2011. For general fund.
$100,000 to Urban League, National, New York, NY, 2011.
$86,468 to Boys and Girls Club, Mathews-Dickey, Saint Louis, MO, 2011.
$50,000 to Provident, Inc., Saint Louis, MO, 2011. For general fund.
$48,500 to Manhattan School of Music, New York, NY, 2011.
$48,000 to National Marfan Foundation, Port Washington, NY, 2011.
$40,000 to Wisconsin Womens Health Foundation, Madison, WI, 2011. For general fund.
$26,975 to American Liver Foundation, Saint Louis, MO, 2011.
$25,000 to Saint Louis Sports Foundation, Saint Louis, MO, 2011. For general fund.

4871
Commerce Bancshares Foundation ✧
(formerly The Commerce Foundation)
922 Walnut, Ste. 200
Kansas City, MO 64106-1809 (816) 234-2577
Contact: Elizabeth Radtke II, V.P., Treas. and Dir.

Incorporated in 1952 in MO.
Donor: Commerce Bancshares.
Foundation type: Company-sponsored foundation.
Financial data (yr. ended 12/31/13): Assets, $493,833 (M); gifts received, $1,453,530; expenditures, $1,523,423; qualifying distributions, $1,502,557; giving activities include $1,492,222 for 768 grants (high: $63,199; low: $50).
Purpose and activities: The foundation supports organizations involved with arts and culture, education, health, human services, and civic affairs.
Fields of interest: Arts; Higher education; Education; Health care; American Red Cross; YM/YWCAs & YM/YWHAs; Human services; United Ways and Federated Giving Programs; Public affairs.
Type of support: General/operating support; Continuing support; Annual campaigns; Capital campaigns; Building/renovation; Equipment; Emergency funds; Program development; Conferences/seminars; Professorships; Seed money; Curriculum development; Scholarship funds; Employee volunteer services.
Limitations: Applications accepted. Giving primarily in areas of company operations in Kansas City and St. Louis, MO. No support for private foundations or non-501(c)(3) organizations. No grants to individuals, or for loans or matching gifts.
Application information: Application form required.
Initial approach: Proposal
Deadline(s): None
Board meeting date(s): As required
Officers and Directors:* Jonathan M. Kemper, Pres.; Edward J. Reardon II, V.P. and Treas.; Elizabeth Radtke,* V.P.; James L. Swarts, Secy.; Kevin G. Barth; David W. Kemper.
EIN: 446012453
Selected grants: The following grants are a representative sample of this grantmaker's funding activity:
$4,000 to True/False Film Festival, Columbia, MO, 2012. For art.
$2,500 to Boy Scouts of America, W. D. Boyce Council, Peoria, IL, 2012. For Hum.
$2,000 to Susan B. Allen Memorial Hospital, El Dorado, KS, 2012. For Hea.
$1,500 to Boy Scouts of America, Great Rivers Council, Columbia, MO, 2012. For Hum.
$1,500 to Boy Scouts of America, W. D. Boyce Council, Peoria, IL, 2012. For Hum.
$1,350 to Wichita State University Foundation, Wichita, KS, 2012. For education.
$1,250 to Boy Scouts of America, Ozark Trails Council, Springfield, MO, 2012. For Hum.
$1,000 to Boy Scouts of America, Ozark Trails Council, Springfield, MO, 2012. For Hum.
$600 to Boy Scouts of America, Indian Nations Council, Tulsa, OK, 2012. For Hum.
$500 to Tulsa Historical Society, Tulsa, OK, 2012. For Civ.

4872
Community Foundation of the Ozarks ✧
(formerly Community Foundation, Inc.)
425 E. Trafficway
Springfield, MO 65806-1121 (417) 864-6199
Contact: Bridget Dierks, Dir., Nonprofit Svcs.
FAX: (417) 864-8344;
E-mail: mlemmon@cfozarks.org; Mailing address: P.O. Box 8960, Springfield, MO, 65801; Additional tel.: (888) 266-6815; Main URL: http://www.cfozarks.org
Facebook: http://www.facebook.com/pages/Community-Foundation-of-the-Ozarks/131151120248309?ref=ts
RSS Feed: http://www.cfozarks.org/feed/
Twitter: http://twitter.com/cfozarks
Vimeo: http://vimeo.com/cfozarks

Incorporated in 1973 in MO.
Foundation type: Community foundation.
Financial data (yr. ended 06/30/13): Assets, $225,287,783 (M); gifts received, $37,633,336; expenditures, $26,736,890; giving activities include $22,331,261 for grants.
Purpose and activities: The mission of the foundation is to enhance the quality of life in our region through resource development, community grantmaking, collaboration, and public leadership.
Fields of interest: Arts; Education; Environment; Health care; Children, services; Human services; Civil/human rights; Community/economic development; Aging.
Type of support: General/operating support; Continuing support; Management development/capacity building; Annual campaigns; Capital campaigns; Building/renovation; Equipment; Endowments; Emergency funds; Program development; Conferences/seminars; Seed money; Curriculum development; Scholarship funds; Research; Technical assistance; Consulting services; Program evaluation; Program-related investments/loans; Matching/challenge support; Mission-related investments/loans.
Limitations: Applications accepted. Giving limited to southern MO.
Publications: Application guidelines; Annual report (including application guidelines); Financial statement; Informational brochure; Newsletter.
Application information: Visit foundation web site for online application form and guidelines. Application form required.
Initial approach: Submit online grant application
Deadline(s): Varies. See foundation website for deadline information
Board meeting date(s): 6 times per year
Final notification: Within 1 month
Officers and Directors:* Richard Cavender,* Chair.; Stephanie Stenger Montgomery,* Vice-Chair.; Brian Fogle,* C.E.O. and Pres.; Julie Leeth, Exec. V.P.; Michael Chatman, Sr. V.P., Philanthropy; Louise Whall Knauer, Sr. V.P., Comms. and Mktg.; Jami S. Peebles,* Secy.; Susanne Gray, C.F.O.; Roger D. Shaw, Jr.,* Treas.; Dr. Gloria Galanes, Chair.-Emeritus; Margie Berry; Chris Craig; Rob Foster; Judith Gonzales; Brian Hammons; Mitch Holmes; Randy Howard; Bill Lee; Jared Lightle; Karen Miller; Mark Nelson; Ron Penney; Gary Powell; Sandra Thomason; Jean Twitty; Robin Walker; Rosalie O'Reilly Wooten.
Number of staff: 16 full-time professional; 3 full-time support.
EIN: 237290968
Selected grants: The following grants are a representative sample of this grantmaker's funding activity:
$158,879 to Tornadoes 2011 - Multiple Recipients, 2011.
$17,307 to Kinsey Volunteer Fire Department, Bloomsdale, MO, 2011. For turnout gear and mutual aid equipment.
$16,000 to Halfway R-III School District, Half Way, MO, 2011. For Back Snacks for students in need.
$15,000 to Family Violence Center, Springfield, MO, 2011. To restore lost funding to continue supporting women and children domestic violence survivors.
$15,000 to Ozarks Food Harvest, Springfield, MO, 2011. For Weekend Backpack Program, which serves about 1,000 kids a week at 30 schools.
$15,000 to Ronald McDonald House Charities of the Ozarks, Springfield, MO, 2011. For basic supplies for The Tooth Truck.
$15,000 to YMCA, Ozarks Regional, Springfield, MO, 2011. To augment the Strong Kids Financial Aid Program, which provides after-school Prime Time services.
$6,698 to Sainte Genevieve County Health Department, Sainte Genevieve, MO, 2011. For home medical waste disposal program.
$5,000 to YMCA, Ozarks Regional, Springfield, MO, 2011. For Monett YMCA branch.
$2,500 to Joplin School District R-VIII, Joplin, MO, 2011. For Bright Futures program.

4873
Concorde Foundation ✧
8737 Del Vista Dr.
Crestwood, MO 63126-1923

Donors: Harry L. Schroeder; Donna L. Schroeder.
Foundation type: Independent foundation.
Financial data (yr. ended 12/31/13): Assets, $476,879 (M); gifts received, $154,639; expenditures, $499,286; qualifying distributions, $490,000; giving activities include $490,000 for 6 grants (high: $420,000; low: $3,000).

Fields of interest: Housing/shelter; Christian agencies & churches; Religion.
Type of support: General/operating support.
Limitations: Applications not accepted. Giving primarily in MO.
Application information: Unsolicited requests for funds not accepted.
Officers and Directors:* Donna L. Schroeder,* Pres. and Treas.; Harry L. Schroeder,* V.P. and Secy.; Gary L. Breneman.
EIN: 262989824

4874
Cox Foundation, Inc. ✧
c/o The St. Louis Trust Co.
7701 Forysth Blvd., Ste. 1100
Clayton, MO 63105-1823

Established in 1970.
Donors: William C. Cox, Jr.; Martha Cox.
Foundation type: Independent foundation.
Financial data (yr. ended 12/31/13): Assets, $29,483,808 (M); expenditures, $1,226,803; qualifying distributions, $1,044,857; giving activities include $1,035,750 for 47 grants (high: $166,500; low: $500).
Purpose and activities: Giving primarily for education, conservation, and human services.
Fields of interest: Museums; Arts; Secondary school/education; Environment, natural resources; Environment; Hospitals (general); Medical research, institute.
Type of support: General/operating support; Continuing support; Annual campaigns; Capital campaigns; Land acquisition; Program development; Research.
Limitations: Applications not accepted. Giving primarily in FL and MA. No grants to individuals.
Application information: Contributes only to pre-selected organizations.
Board meeting date(s): Dec.
Officers: Martha W. Cox,* Pres.; Ann Cox Bartram, Treas.; Heidi Cox, Clerk.
Directors: Martha Farrell; Elizabeth K. Goldenberg; John M. Jennings.
EIN: 237068786
Selected grants: The following grants are a representative sample of this grantmaker's funding activity:
$150,000 to Sankaty Head Foundation, Siasconset, MA, 2012. For General Fund and Scholarship Fund and Lighthouse.
$5,650 to Nantucket Historical Association, Nantucket, MA, 2012. For Antiques Show and Annual Fund.
$2,000 to Nantucket Atheneum, Nantucket, MA, 2012. For 1847 Society.

4875
E. L. Craig Foundation ✧ ☆
P.O. Box 1404
Joplin, MO 64802-1404

Incorporated in 1960 in MO.
Donors: Ethelmae Humphreys; David Humphreys; Tamko Asphalt Products, Inc.; Royal Brand Roofing, Inc.; Ethelmae Humphreys Revocable Trust; Ethelmae C. Humphreys.
Foundation type: Independent foundation.
Financial data (yr. ended 12/31/13): Assets, $10,414,871 (M); gifts received, $2,250,000; expenditures, $2,478,904; qualifying distributions, $2,456,602; giving activities include $2,456,000 for 31 grants (high: $400,000; low: $1,000).
Fields of interest: Education, research; Health organizations; Social sciences, public policy.
Limitations: Applications not accepted. Giving in the U.S., with emphasis on Washington, DC, and Arlington, VA. No grants to individuals, or for publicly funded groups.
Application information: Contributes only to pre-selected organizations.
Officers: Ethelmae C. Humphreys, Pres.; Sarah Humphreys Atkins, V.P.; David C. Humphreys, Secy.-Treas.
Directors: Paul S. Atkins; Debra G. Humphreys.
EIN: 446015127
Selected grants: The following grants are a representative sample of this grantmaker's funding activity:
$8,000,000 to Thomas Jefferson Independent Day School, Joplin, MO, 2011. For building project.

4876
Cloud L. Cray Foundation ✧
c/o Thomas M. Cray
800 W. 47th St., Ste. 711
Kansas City, MO 64112-1249

Established in 1967 in MO.
Donor: Cloud L. Cray†.
Foundation type: Independent foundation.
Financial data (yr. ended 12/31/13): Assets, $8,695,376 (M); expenditures, $622,680; qualifying distributions, $520,402; giving activities include $448,820 for 24 grants (high: $212,500; low: $110).
Purpose and activities: Giving primarily for economic education.
Fields of interest: Higher education; Economics.
Type of support: General/operating support; Continuing support; Annual campaigns; Program development; Professorships.
Limitations: Applications not accepted. Giving primarily in KS and MO. No grants to individuals.
Application information: Contributes only to pre-selected organizations.
Trustee: Thomas M. Cray.
EIN: 436077249

4877
Lee H. Cruse Trust ✧
7777 Bonhomme Ave., Ste. 2001
St. Louis, MO 63105-1946

Established in 2005 in MO.
Donor: Lee H. Cruse Trust.
Foundation type: Independent foundation.
Financial data (yr. ended 12/31/13): Assets, $36,054,198 (M); expenditures, $2,179,047; qualifying distributions, $1,972,250; giving activities include $1,851,500 for 27 grants (high: $500,000; low: $10,000).
Fields of interest: Education; Human services; American Red Cross; Children/youth, services; Homeless, human services.
Limitations: Applications not accepted. Giving primarily in Springfield, MO.
Application information: Contributes only to pre-selected organizations.
Trustees: Don Ryan; Steven R. Wilhelm; William T. Woolsey.
EIN: 766188736
Selected grants: The following grants are a representative sample of this grantmaker's funding activity:
$150,000 to American Red Cross, Springfield, MO, 2012. For disaster recovery.
$25,000 to Community Foundation of the Ozarks, Springfield, MO, 2012. For Community Response Grants.

4878
Deer Creek Foundation ✧
720 Olive St., Ste. 1975
St. Louis, MO 63101-2307 (314) 241-3228
Contact: Mary Stake Hawker, Dir.

Established in 1964 in MO.
Donors: Aaron Fischer†; Teresa M. Fischer†.
Foundation type: Independent foundation.
Financial data (yr. ended 12/31/12): Assets, $36,370,686 (M); expenditures, $2,247,433; qualifying distributions, $1,804,144; giving activities include $1,494,678 for 26+ grants (high: $200,000).
Purpose and activities: Support primarily for programs that preserve and advance our democratic system and government accountability, with civil liberties and civil rights protection provided by the Constitution and the Bill of Rights, and to promote education about democracy; grants primarily to 'action programs' with promise of making a significant national or regional impact; some preference to projects in Missouri.
Fields of interest: Visual arts, sculpture; Environment, climate change/global warming; Environment; Civil rights, race/intergroup relations; Civil liberties, advocacy; Civil liberties, reproductive rights; Public affairs, citizen participation.
Type of support: Program development; Seed money.
Limitations: Applications accepted. Giving on a national basis, with some emphasis on MO. No grants to individuals, or for building or endowment funds, equipment, or operating budgets.
Publications: Informational brochure.
Application information: Letter of inquiry should contain items specified in grantmaker's brochure. See programs for additional information for each area. Application form not required.
Initial approach: Letter of inquiry
Deadline(s): None
Board meeting date(s): Apr. and Sept.
Officer and Trustees:* M. Peter Fischer,* Pres.; Martha C. Fischer; Matthew A. Fischer; Michael P. Fischer.
Director: Mary Stake Hawker.
Number of staff: 1 full-time professional; 1 full-time support; 1 part-time support.
EIN: 436052774
Selected grants: The following grants are a representative sample of this grantmaker's funding activity:
$150,000 to Common Cause Education Fund, Washington, DC, 2012. To educate and activate the American people about the threat to our democracy posed by unprecedented corporate political influence unleashed by the U.S. Supreme Court's Citizens United decision and the need for a constitutional amendment to reverse U.S. Supreme Court decision.

$150,000 to Constitutional Accountability Center, Washington, DC, 2012. For scholarship, litigation and public education demonstrating that the U.S. Constitution dictates progressive outcomes and exposing common misconceptions about our founding document.
$150,000 to Public Citizen Foundation, Washington, DC, 2012. To educate and activate the American people about the threat to our democracy posed by unprecedented corporate political influence unleashed by the U.S. Supreme Court's 2010 Citizens United decision and the need for a constitutional amendment to reverse.
$100,000 to Center for Progressive Reform, Washington, DC, 2012. For research, public and policymaker education and administrative agency advocacy conducted by this national network of progressive scholar-experts who aim to preserve and strengthen federal regulatory and other legal protections for public health.
$50,000 to Committee to Bridge the Gap, Ben Lomond, CA, 2012. For monitoring, public education, community organizing, administrative advocacy, and litigation aimed at ensuring responsible government radiation protection standards, the safe operation of U.S. nuclear facilities and handling of nuclear materials.
$35,000 to League of Women Voters of Wisconsin Education Fund, Madison, WI, 2012. For legal defense of the injunction secured by the League to stop implementation of Wisconsin's strict voter ID requirements, which effectively disenfranchise large numbers of the poor, elderly, and students.
$25,000 to Center for the Future of Arizona, Phoenix, AZ, 2012. For the final year of a five-year special grant to the Center's Beat the Odds Institute which attempts to ensure that Latino-intensive, low-income schools succeed in improving student achievement despite daunting odds against success.
$25,000 to Crag Law Center, Portland, OR, 2012. For legal services, public education and community organizing assistance to organizations working to protect key natural resources from the damaging environmental impacts of proposed new coal exports through the Columbia River and corporate use of public waters.
$25,000 to Electronic Privacy Information Center, Washington, DC, 2012. For EPIC's Open Government Project's policy research, public education, litigation and administrative advocacy aimed at protecting individual privacy and other civil liberties in the face of array of threats, including privacy threat.
$25,000 to Nuclear Information and Resource Service, Takoma Park, MD, 2012. For public and policymaker education, community organizing and administrative agency advocacy seeking expansion of the approximately 10-mile Emergency Planning Zone around U.S. commercial nuclear reactor sites.

4879
The Dierberg Foundation ✧
c/o Tax Dept. - Mail Code 019
600 James S. McDonnell Blvd.
Hazelwood, MO 63042-2302

Established in 2003 in MO.
Donor: First Banks, Inc.
Foundation type: Company-sponsored foundation.
Financial data (yr. ended 12/31/13): Assets, $12,252,587 (M); expenditures, $435,251; qualifying distributions, $435,000; giving activities include $435,000 for 17 grants (high: $282,000; low: $500).
Purpose and activities: The foundation supports museums and hospitals and organizations involved with historic preservation, higher education, human services, and Catholicism.
Fields of interest: Museums; Historic preservation/historical societies; Higher education; Hospitals (general); Boys & girls clubs; Human services; United Ways and Federated Giving Programs; Catholic agencies & churches.
Type of support: General/operating support; Annual campaigns; Building/renovation.
Limitations: Applications not accepted. Giving primarily in St. Louis, MO.
Application information: Contributes only to pre-selected organizations.
Trustees: Ellen Dierberg; James F. Dierberg; James F. Dierberg II; Mary W. Dierberg; Michael J. Dierberg.
EIN: 436897690
Selected grants: The following grants are a representative sample of this grantmaker's funding activity:
$10,000 to CRUDEM Foundation, Ludlow, MA, 2012. For annual fundraiser for hospital.

4880
The Richard W. & Phyllis B. Duesenberg Foundation ✧
P.O. Box 11356
Clayton, MO 63105-0156
Application address: c/o Richard W. Duesenberg, 1 Indian Creek Ln., St. Louis, MO 63131, tel.: (314) 746-3601

Established in 1989 in MO.
Donors: Richard W. Duesenberg; Phyllis B. Duesenberg.
Foundation type: Independent foundation.
Financial data (yr. ended 12/31/13): Assets, $16,883,912 (M); expenditures, $1,726,097; qualifying distributions, $1,672,629; giving activities include $1,660,873 for 5 grants (high: $1,506,873; low: $5,000).
Purpose and activities: Giving generally limited to Lutheran musical and educational programs; funding also for a Lutheran seminary.
Fields of interest: Performing arts; Higher education; Education; Protestant agencies & churches.
Limitations: Applications accepted. Giving primarily in MO. No grants to individuals.
Application information: Application form not required.
Initial approach: Proposal
Deadline(s): None
Trustees: Phyllis B. Duesenberg; Richard W. Duesenberg.
EIN: 431526439

4881
Caleb C. and Julia W. Dula Educational and Charitable Foundation ✧
c/o Todd Snyder
7800 Forsyth Blvd., Ste. 600
Clayton, MO 63105-3311
Contact: James F. Mauze

Established in 1995 in MO.
Foundation type: Independent foundation.
Financial data (yr. ended 12/31/13): Assets, $41,778,893 (M); expenditures, $2,155,164; qualifying distributions, $1,711,794; giving activities include $1,600,000 for 115 grants (high: $50,000; low: $2,500).
Purpose and activities: Grants to charities which the Dulas supported during their lifetime, with emphasis on education, hospitals, including children's hospitals, social service agencies, and cultural programs.
Fields of interest: Performing arts; Arts; Elementary/secondary education; Education; Hospitals (general); Hospitals (specialty); Health organizations; Human services; Children/youth, services; Residential/custodial care, hospices.
Type of support: General/operating support.
Limitations: Giving primarily in MO, with emphasis on St. Louis. No grants to individuals.
Application information:
Initial approach: Letter
Deadline(s): Apr. 1 and Oct. 1
Trustees: Margaret W. Kobusch; Letitia W. Scott; Orrin Sage Wightmen IV; Sage Wightman; Susan K. Werner.
EIN: 431716767

4882
Dunn Family Foundation ✧ ☆
1001 Locust St.
Kansas City, MO 64106-1904
Contact: Robert P. Dunn, Pres.

Established in 1981 in MO.
Donors: William H. Dunn, Sr.; Terrence P. Dunn; J.E. Dunn Construction; Steven D. Dunn; Terry Dunn; Robert P. Dunn.
Foundation type: Independent foundation.
Financial data (yr. ended 06/30/13): Assets, $2,542,649 (M); gifts received, $753,669; expenditures, $478,605; qualifying distributions, $442,362; giving activities include $442,362 for 152 grants (high: $100,000; low: $75).
Fields of interest: Education; Health care; Human services; Community/economic development; Religion; Youth; Aging; Disabilities, people with; Minorities.
Type of support: Debt reduction; General/operating support; Building/renovation; Equipment.
Limitations: Applications accepted. Giving within a 75-mile radius of the greater metropolitan Kansas City, MO, area. No support for the visual or performing arts. No grants to individuals, or for research, endowments, travel, conferences, or telethons.
Application information: Application form required.
Initial approach: Letter
Deadline(s): None
Board meeting date(s): Quarterly
Officers and Directors:* William H. Dunn, Sr.,* Chair.; Robert P. Dunn,* Pres.; Kevin A. Dunn,* V.P. and Treas.; Terrence P. Dunn,* V.P.; William H. Dunn, Jr.,* V.P.; Stephen D. Dunn.
EIN: 431244010
Selected grants: The following grants are a representative sample of this grantmaker's funding activity:
$5,000 to NAACP, Baltimore, MD, 2011.
$2,000 to Local Initiatives Support Corporation, New York, NY, 2011.
$1,000 to American Lung Association, New York, NY, 2011.
$1,000 to General Council of the Assemblies of God, Springfield, MO, 2011.

$1,000 to Society of Saint Andrew, Big Island, VA, 2011.

4883
Harry Edison Foundation ✧
220 N. 4th St., Ste. A
St. Louis, MO 63102-1905 (314) 331-6504
Contact: Bernard A. Edison, Pres.

Incorporated in 1949 in IL.
Donor: Harry Edison†.
Foundation type: Independent foundation.
Financial data (yr. ended 12/31/13): Assets, $16,462,861 (M); expenditures, $817,395; qualifying distributions, $577,704; giving activities include $555,200 for 42 grants (high: $130,000; low: $100).
Fields of interest: Education; Hospitals (general); Medical research, institute; Human services; Jewish federated giving programs.
Type of support: Annual campaigns; Capital campaigns; Building/renovation; Professorships; Scholarship funds; Research.
Limitations: Applications accepted. Giving primarily in St. Louis, MO. No grants to individuals.
Application information: Application form required.
Initial approach: Proposal
Deadline(s): None
Board meeting date(s): As required
Officers: Bernard Edison, Pres.; Julian Edison, V.P. and Secy.; Peter Edison, V.P.; Andrew E. Newman, V.P.; Eric P. Newman, V.P.
Number of staff: 2
EIN: 436027017
Selected grants: The following grants are a representative sample of this grantmaker's funding activity:
$500 to Washington University, School of Medicine, Saint Louis, MO, 2012. For Dr. I. Jerome Flance Pulmonary Endowment Fund.

4884
Julian I. & Hope R. Edison Foundation, Inc. ✧
8 Saint Andrews Dr.
St. Louis, MO 63124-1622

Established in 1959.
Donors: Julian I. Edison; Hope R. Edison.
Foundation type: Independent foundation.
Financial data (yr. ended 09/30/13): Assets, $15,408,541 (M); gifts received, $465,326; expenditures, $552,438; qualifying distributions, $533,442; giving activities include $530,406 for grants.
Purpose and activities: Giving primarily for the arts, particularly to art museums, as well as for education, Jewish organizations, and health and human services.
Fields of interest: Museums (art); Arts; Higher education; Libraries (public); Education; Health organizations, association; Human services; Jewish federated giving programs; Jewish agencies & synagogues.
Limitations: Applications not accepted. Giving primarily in St. Louis, MO and New York, NY. No grants to individuals.
Application information: Contributes only to pre-selected organizations.
Officers: Julian I. Edison, Pres.; Hope R. Edison, V.P.; Evelyn E. Newman, Secy.
EIN: 436027034

4885
Emerson Charitable Trust ✧
8000 W. Florissant Ave.
P.O. Box 4100
St. Louis, MO 63136-8506
Contact: Patrick Sly, Exec. V.P.
Main URL: http://www.emerson.com/en-US/about_emerson/company_overview/pages/emerson_charitable_trust.aspx

Established in 1944 in MO as Emerson Electric Manufacturing Company Charitable Trust; current name adopted in 1981.
Donors: Emerson Electric Co.; Daniel Industries, Inc.; Astec America Inc.; Emerson Ventures.
Foundation type: Company-sponsored foundation.
Financial data (yr. ended 09/30/13): Assets, $20,857,698 (M); gifts received, $32,630,000; expenditures, $29,088,666; qualifying distributions, $29,063,228; giving activities include $29,059,957 for 2,483 grants (high: $1,400,000; low: $25).
Purpose and activities: The foundation supports programs designed to improve and enrich lives; foster volunteerism; promote education; and provide services to those in need.
Fields of interest: Media/communications; Museums; Performing arts; Arts; Elementary/secondary education; Higher education; Libraries (public); Education; Zoos/zoological societies; Hospitals (general); Health care; Crime/violence prevention; Employment, training; Employment; Housing/shelter; Disasters, preparedness/services; Recreation, parks/playgrounds; Youth development, adult & child programs; Youth development; American Red Cross; Salvation Army; Family services; Residential/custodial care, hospices; Human services; United Ways and Federated Giving Programs; Public affairs; Youth.
Type of support: General/operating support; Program development; Employee volunteer services; Sponsorships; Employee matching gifts; Employee-related scholarships.
Limitations: Applications not accepted. Giving primarily on a national basis areas of company operations, with emphasis on St. Louis, MO.
Publications: Corporate giving report.
Trustees: Emerson Electric Co.; The Northern Trust Co.
EIN: 526200123
Selected grants: The following grants are a representative sample of this grantmaker's funding activity:
$1,400,000 to United Way of Greater Saint Louis, Saint Louis, MO, 2012. For General Support.
$660,000 to Washington University, Saint Louis, MO, 2012. For General Support.
$500,000 to Mercy Health Foundation Saint Louis, Saint Louis, MO, 2012. For General Support.
$500,000 to Saint Louis Science Center Foundation, Saint Louis, MO, 2012. For General Support.
$437,500 to Boy Scouts of America, Saint Louis, MO, 2012. For General Support.
$200,000 to OASIS Institute, Saint Louis, MO, 2012. For General Support.
$20,000 to Craft Alliance, Saint Louis, MO, 2012. For General Support.
$20,000 to United Way of Greater Houston, Houston, TX, 2012. For General Support.
$11,000 to Midview Local School District, Grafton, OH, 2012. For General Support.
$10,000 to Better Family Life, Saint Louis, MO, 2012. For General Support.

4886
Engelhardt Family Foundation ✧
901 Kent Rd.
St. Louis, MO 63124-1661

Established in 2005 in MO.
Donors: Irl Engelhardt; Sue Engelhardt.
Foundation type: Independent foundation.
Financial data (yr. ended 12/31/13): Assets, $3,980,891 (M); gifts received, $1,003,668; expenditures, $604,003; qualifying distributions, $505,200; giving activities include $505,200 for 40 grants (high: $126,000; low: $100).
Purpose and activities: Giving primarily for arts programs, education, and youth and social services.
Fields of interest: Arts; Education; Human services; Children/youth, services.
Limitations: Applications not accepted. Giving primarily in St. Louis, MO; some funding also in Pinckneyville, IL. No grants to individuals.
Application information: Unsolicited requests for funds not accepted.
Trustees: Irl Engelhardt; Sue Engelhardt.
Director: Erin Engelhardt.
EIN: 436926810
Selected grants: The following grants are a representative sample of this grantmaker's funding activity:
$750 to Neighborhood Farmers Market Alliance, Seattle, WA, 2012. For Farmers and Food Banks.

4887
Enterprise Holdings Foundation ✧
(formerly Enterprise Rent-A-Car Foundation)
600 Corporate Park Dr.
St. Louis, MO 63105-4204 (314) 512-5000
Contact: Jo Ann Taylor Kindle, Pres.
FAX: (314) 512-4754; E-mail: foundation@ehi.com; Main URL: http://www.enterpriseholdings.com/about-us/corporate-citizenship/

Established in 1982 in MO.
Donors: Enterprise Holdings, Inc.; Enterprise Rent-A-Car Co.; Jack C. Taylor.
Foundation type: Company-sponsored foundation.
Financial data (yr. ended 07/31/13): Assets, $208,789,368 (M); gifts received, $42,994,405; expenditures, $22,170,961; qualifying distributions, $21,854,614; giving activities include $21,854,614 for grants.
Purpose and activities: The foundation supports organizations with which employees, family members of employees, and established customers of Enterprise Rent-A-Car are involved, and organizations involved with education, reforestation, disaster relief, minorities, and economically disadvantaged people.
Fields of interest: Higher education; Environment, land resources; Environment, forests; Employment, training; Disasters, preparedness/services; United Ways and Federated Giving Programs; General charitable giving; Minorities; Economically disadvantaged.
International interests: Canada; United Kingdom.

Type of support: General/operating support; Capital campaigns; Building/renovation; Equipment; Emergency funds; Program development; Scholarship funds; Research.
Limitations: Applications accepted. Giving on a national basis in areas of company operations, with emphasis on CA, MO, NE, TX, Canada, and the United Kingdom. No support for religious, political, or labor organizations, or sports teams. No grants to individuals, or for ongoing operating support, salary costs, debt reduction, sponsorships, tuition, fees, memberships, dues, tickets, subscriptions, telethons, or beauty pageants; no vehicle or rental donations.
Publications: Application guidelines.
Application information: The foundation primarily accepts requests for donations from Enterprise Holdings employees. Unsolicited requests are also accepted from employees and their spouses, and established customers of Enterprise Rent-A-Car on behalf of nonprofit organizations with which there is an established connection. Support is limited to 1 contribution per organization during any given year. Annual reports, videos, DVDs, CD's and other extraneous materials are not encouraged. The average amount for a first-time request is usually up to $1,500. Grants range from $2,500 to $5,000. Application form not required.
Initial approach: Complete online application for customers/employees
Copies of proposal: 1
Deadline(s): Nov. 1, Feb. 1, and Aug. 1
Board meeting date(s): Oct. 14., Feb. 5, Apr. 30
Final notification: 3 to 4 weeks following board meetings
Officers and Directors:* Jo Ann Taylor Kindle,* Pres.; Rick A. Short,* V.P. and Treas.; Carolyn Kindle, V.P. and Exec. Dir.; Matthew G. Darrah,* V.P.; James Mann; Jack C. Taylor.
EIN: 431262762
Selected grants: The following grants are a representative sample of this grantmaker's funding activity:
$2,000,000 to University of Missouri, Columbia, MO, 2013. For endowment.
$1,000,000 to American Red Cross National Headquarters, Washington, DC, 2013. For Disaster Relief 2012 Superstorm Hurricane Sandy.
$1,000,000 to National Arbor Day Foundation, Lincoln, NE, 2013. For 50 Year Commitment of $1 million per year.
$1,000,000 to Saint Louis University, Saint Louis, MO, 2013. For Habitat for Neighborhood Business (HNB).
$1,000,000 to Urban League, National, New York, NY, 2013. For Whitney M Young Jr Center for Urban Leadership.
$754,108 to United Way of Greater Saint Louis, Saint Louis, MO, 2013. For campaign.
$5,461 to United Way Capital Area, Austin, TX, 2013. For Fleet United Way for Greater Austin.
$2,500 to Legacy Ladies, Calabasas, CA, 2013. For Annual assistance with their Adopt a School Program.
$2,500 to Palm Beach Atlantic University, West Palm Beach, FL, 2013. For Palm Beach Atlantic University Distinguished Artists Series November 2013 April 2014.
$2,000 to Catholic Charities of Los Angeles, Los Angeles, CA, 2013. For Project Achieve-Long Beach.

4888
Express Scripts Foundation ✧
1 Express Way
St. Louis, MO 63121-1824
E-mail: ExpressScriptsCares@easymatch.com; Main URL: http://www.express-scripts.com/aboutus/citizenship/corp_giving.shtml

Established in 2002 in MO.
Donor: Express Scripts, Inc.
Foundation type: Company-sponsored foundation.
Financial data (yr. ended 12/31/12): Assets, $23,426,666 (M); gifts received, $7,140,389; expenditures, $1,697,616; qualifying distributions, $1,562,981; giving activities include $1,511,354 for 53 grants (high: $200,000; low: $500), and $51,627 for 3 employee matching gifts.
Purpose and activities: The foundation supports programs designed to provide access to health and medical services for those in need; educate underserved youth to prepare them for success; provide services to U.S. military troops and their families; strengthen communities by aiding youth and families in need; and support education programs designed to prepare students for careers in pharmacy.
Fields of interest: Arts; Elementary/secondary education; Higher education; Medical school/education; Education, reading; Education; Medicine/medical care, public education; Pharmacy/prescriptions; Public health; Health care, insurance; Health care, patient services; Health care; Children/youth, services; Children, services; Family services; Mathematics; Science; Military/veterans' organizations; Children; Military/veterans.
Type of support: General/operating support; Continuing support; Capital campaigns; Program development; Employee matching gifts.
Limitations: Applications accepted. Giving primarily in areas of company operations, with emphasis on St. Louis, MO. No support for discriminatory organizations, political candidates or organizations, social clubs, or athletic teams. No grants to individuals, or for political causes or campaigns, fundraising activities, benefits, charitable dinners, galas, or endowments or capital campaigns.
Publications: Application guidelines; Annual report; Program policy statement.
Application information: Support is limited to 1 contribution per organization during any given year. Multi-year funding is not automatic. Organizations receiving support are asked to provide status reports and a final report. Application form required.
Initial approach: Complete online application form
Deadline(s): None
Officers and Directors:* James E. McCleod, Ph.D., Chair. and Pres.; Larry Zarin,* V.P.; Martin P. Akins, Secy.; Matt Harper, Treas.; Susan Schlichter, Exec. Dir.; Chip Casteel; Mimi Hirshberg; Susan Lang.
Number of staff: 1 part-time support.
EIN: 020566229

4889
The Farber Foundation ✧
100 S. Wood St.
Neosho, MO 64850-1819 (417) 451-1040
Contact: Rudolph E. Farber, Mgr.

Established in 1997 in MO.
Donor: Rudolph E. Farber.
Foundation type: Independent foundation.
Financial data (yr. ended 12/31/13): Assets, $5,207,406 (M); gifts received, $506,724; expenditures, $1,684,539; qualifying distributions, $1,675,204; giving activities include $1,647,200 for 32 grants (high: $1,000,000; low: $250).
Fields of interest: Higher education; Health care, patient services; Human services; YM/YWCAs & YM/YWHAs.
Type of support: Program-related investments/loans; General/operating support.
Limitations: Applications accepted. Giving limited to Jasper, McDonald, and Newton counties, MO.
Application information: Application form required.
Initial approach: Letter
Copies of proposal: 1
Deadline(s): None
Officer: Rudolph E. Farber, Mgr.
EIN: 431763102

4890
William Pablo Feraldo Memorial Fund ✧ ☆
c/o U.S. Bank, N.A.
P.O. Box 387
St. Louis, MO 63166-0387
Contact: Angela Pearson

Established in MO.
Foundation type: Independent foundation.
Financial data (yr. ended 12/31/13): Assets, $14,198,524 (M); expenditures, $934,124; qualifying distributions, $776,304; giving activities include $752,500 for 3 grants (high: $331,000; low: $90,500).
Purpose and activities: Scholarship funds for male applicants who have graduated or will graduate from an accredited secondary school.
Fields of interest: Higher education.
Type of support: Scholarship funds.
Limitations: Giving primarily in MO; some giving also in MN.
Application information: Application forms are available at the high school counselors' offices in the metropolitan St. Louis, MO, area, and through the financial aid offices of St. Louis Univ. and Washington Univ. Application form required.
Deadline(s): Feb. 1
Final notification: Apr. 1
Trustee: U.S. Bank, N.A.
EIN: 436019398
Selected grants: The following grants are a representative sample of this grantmaker's funding activity:
$200,000 to Saint Louis University, Saint Louis, MO, 2011.
$200,000 to Washington University, Saint Louis, MO, 2011.

4891
The John and Alison Ferring Family Foundation ✧
c/o Wagner Industrial Park
105 Bolte Ln.
St. Clair, MO 63077-3219

Established in 2001 in MO.
Donors: John H. Ferring IV; Alison N. Ferring.
Foundation type: Independent foundation.
Financial data (yr. ended 12/31/13): Assets, $7,251,523 (M); expenditures, $1,474,446; qualifying distributions, $1,418,630; giving activities include $1,418,630 for 40 grants (high: $259,650; low: $500).

Fields of interest: Museums (art); Arts; Libraries (public); Education; Recreation, parks/playgrounds; Children, services.
Limitations: Applications not accepted. Giving primarily in St. Louis, MO. No grants to individuals.
Application information: Contributes only to pre-selected organizations.
Board meeting date(s): Jan.
Trustees: Alison N. Ferring; John H. Ferring IV.
EIN: 431944616

4892
Fox Family Foundation ✧
7701 Forsyth Blvd., Ste. 600
St. Louis, MO 63105-1875 (314) 889-0890
Contact: Cheri Fox, Exec. Dir.
FAX: (314) 727-7314; E-mail: fff@harbourgroup.com

Established in 1986 in MO.
Donors: Marilyn Fox; Sam Fox.
Foundation type: Independent foundation.
Financial data (yr. ended 12/31/12): Assets, $26,847,178 (M); gifts received, $100,000; expenditures, $3,242,665; qualifying distributions, $3,018,855; giving activities include $2,903,240 for 224 grants (high: $1,000,000; low: $100).
Purpose and activities: Giving primarily for projects which meet basic human needs, including food, shelter, basic adult education, job training, early childhood education for the poor, and independence for those dependent on others. In Israel, the foundation supports projects which address the issues of environmental protection, violence in Israeli society, and the full integration of the Ethiopian community.
Fields of interest: Arts; Education, early childhood education; Adult education—literacy, basic skills & GED; Employment, training; Housing/shelter; Human services; Jewish agencies & synagogues; Economically disadvantaged; Homeless.
International interests: Israel.
Type of support: Program development; Seed money; Matching/challenge support.
Limitations: Applications accepted. Giving primarily in St. Louis, MO. No grants to individuals, or for annual campaigns, endowment funds, deficit financing, or operating expenses.
Publications: Application guidelines.
Application information: Application form required.
Initial approach: Letter requesting application form
Copies of proposal: 2
Deadline(s): Contact foundation for annual deadlines
Board meeting date(s): Biannually
Final notification: 3 months for preliminary applications; 6 months for formal applications if accepted for review
Officers and Directors:* Sam Fox,* Chair.; Marilyn Fox,* Vice-Chair.; Cheri Fox, Exec. Dir.; Gregory Fox; Jeffrey Fox; Steven Fox; Pamela Fox-Claman.
Number of staff: 1 full-time professional; 1 part-time support.
EIN: 431456258

4893
The Francis Family Foundation ✧
(formerly The Francis Families Foundation)
800 W. 47th St., Ste. 717
Kansas City, MO 64112-1249 (816) 531-0077
Contact: Jim Koeneman, Exec. Dir.; Lyn Knox, Prog. Off.
FAX: (816) 531-8810;
E-mail: webmaster@francisfoundation.org; Main URL: http://www.francisfoundation.org/
Application address for fellowship program only: Thomas R. Martin, M.D., Dir., Parker B. Francis Fellowship Prog., 8427 SE 35th St., Mercer Island, WA 98040; tel.: (206) 764-2219;
E-mail: trmartin@u.washington.edu; URL: http://www.francisfellowships.org

Established in 1989 in MO from the merger of the Parker B. Francis Foundation (established in 1951 in MO) and the Parker B. Francis III Foundation (established in 1962 in MO).
Donors: Parker B. Francis†; Mary B. Francis†; Parker B. Francis III†.
Foundation type: Independent foundation.
Financial data (yr. ended 12/31/13): Assets, $115,869,763 (M); expenditures, $6,955,371; qualifying distributions, $6,468,203; giving activities include $5,724,160 for 311 grants (high: $750,000; low: $100).
Purpose and activities: Giving primarily to fund post-doctoral fellowships in pulmonary research in North America, and in the metropolitan Kansas City area, to support lifelong learning, especially in early care and education; and to support arts and culture with a focus on excellence and access.
Fields of interest: Arts; Education; Medical research, institute.
Type of support: General/operating support; Continuing support; Program development; Fellowships.
Limitations: Applications accepted. Giving limited to a 60-mile radius of Kansas City, MO, for educational and arts and cultural institutions, and to the U.S. and Canada for pulmonary fellowships.
Publications: Application guidelines; Informational brochure (including application guidelines).
Application information: Open Application for Lifelong Learning is currently suspended for new applicants. Applications are to be submitted by invitation only. Please visit the foundation web site for additional information and most current application requirements. Application form required for pulmonary fellowship program. Pulmonary research fellowships are granted to U.S and Canada universities and for nonprofit research institutions. Funding for the pulmonary research area of interest within the foundation's strategic plan is directed through the Parker B. Francis Fellowship Program, a North American post-doctoral program in pulmonary research. For more information, visit the Fellowship Program's Web site at http:///www.http://www.francisfellowships.org. Application form required.
Initial approach: Online application (Small Arts Grant Program)
Deadline(s): See foundation web site for current deadlines
Board meeting date(s): Jan., Mar., May, Sept. and Nov.
Final notification: Lifelong Learning: May; Arts & Culture: Nov.; Fellowships: Feb.
Officers and Directors:* David V. Francis,* Chair.; J. Scott Francis,* Vice-Chair.; Jim Koeneman, Secy. and Exec. Dir.; Charles Schellhorn,* Treas.; Ann Francis Barhoum; Gregory Glore; Mary Lou Jaramillo; David Oliver; Susan Stanton; Katie Wendel.
Number of staff: 4 full-time professional.
EIN: 431492132
Selected grants: The following grants are a representative sample of this grantmaker's funding activity:
$539,413 to Francis Institute for Child and Youth Development, Kansas City, MO, 2012. For Francis Resource Center and FICYD Director.
$175,000 to Partnership for Regional Educational Preparation, Kansas City, MO, 2012. For general operating support.
$156,000 to Columbia University Medical Center, New York, NY, 2012. For Fellow and Mentor, payable over 3.00 years.
$156,000 to Dartmouth Medical School, Hanover, NH, 2012. For Fellow and Mentor, payable over 3.00 years.
$156,000 to Mayo Clinic, Rochester, MN, 2012. For Fellow and Mentor, payable over 3.00 years.
$156,000 to University of Chicago, Chicago, IL, 2012. For Fellow and Mentor, payable over 3.00 years.
$156,000 to Wake Forest University, Winston-Salem, NC, 2012. For Fellow and Mentor, payable over 3.00 years.
$100,000 to Conservatory of Music of Kansas City, Kansas City, MO, 2012. For Leadership/Innovation/Sustainability Funds for Musical Bridges Program of the UMKC Conservatory of Music and Dance.
$92,387 to Greater Kansas City Community Foundation, Kansas City, MO, 2012. For Arts and Culture fund for 2013 grantmaking.
$20,000 to Coterie Theater, Kansas City, MO, 2012. For general operating support.

4894
Gateway Foundation ✧
720 Olive St., Ste. 1977
St. Louis, MO 63101-2307 (314) 241-3337
Contact: Christy B. Fox, Admin.
FAX: (314) 241-3559;
E-mail: info@gateway-foundation.org; Main URL: http://www.gateway-foundation.org

Established in 1986 in MO under the EIN of 431420333; reincorporated in 2004 under the current EIN.
Donor: Deer Creek Foundation.
Foundation type: Independent foundation.
Financial data (yr. ended 12/31/13): Assets, $55,749,838 (M); gifts received, $45,009; expenditures, $1,861,582; qualifying distributions, $1,424,093; giving activities include $1,072,415 for 6 grants (high: $865,106; low: $1,006), and $23,000 for 1 loan/program-related investment.
Purpose and activities: Support for the arts and cultural projects and, on occasion, related educational activities. Priority given to acquisition, creation, or improvement of items of a physical, durable nature. Focus on enhancing the physical environment in the St. Louis, Missouri, metropolitan area.
Fields of interest: Visual arts; Visual arts, architecture; Museums; Performing arts; Arts; Recreation, parks/playgrounds; Recreation; Urban/community development.
Type of support: Building/renovation; Equipment; Technical assistance; Matching/challenge support.
Limitations: Applications accepted. Giving limited to the metropolitan St. Louis, MO, area. Generally no

support for programmatic operating expenses or for endowments.
Publications: Application guidelines; Grants list; Informational brochure.
Application information: The foundation does not consider grant presentations. Written application is required. See foundation Web site for application guidelines, programs and procedures. Application form not required.
Initial approach: Telephone
Copies of proposal: 1
Deadline(s): Feb. 1, May 1, Aug. 1 and Nov. 1
Board meeting date(s): Quarterly
Final notification: Mar., Jun., Sept., Dec.
Officers and Directors:* M. Peter Fischer,* Pres.; James D. Burke,* V.P.; Susan R. Rava,* Secy.-Treas.; Martha Fischer; Matthew G. Fischer; Michael P. Fischer; Christy B. Fox; Paul Ha; David Mesker; Gyo Obata; Susan Philpott.
Number of staff: 1 full-time professional; 1 full-time support; 1 part-time support.
EIN: 206294706

4895
Alvin Goldfarb Foundation ✧
6349 Clayton Rd.
St. Louis, MO 63117-1808

Established in 1992 in MO.
Donors: Alvin Goldfarb†; Alvin Goldfarb Trust.
Foundation type: Independent foundation.
Financial data (yr. ended 12/31/12): Assets, $208,600,856 (M); gifts received, $65,912,598; expenditures, $7,027,653; qualifying distributions, $5,955,857; giving activities include $5,726,795 for 10 grants (high: $3,355,000; low: $42,777).
Fields of interest: Education; Human services; Children/youth, services; Family services.
Limitations: Applications not accepted. Giving primarily in St. Louis, MO. No grants to individuals.
Application information: Contributes only to pre-selected organizations.
Manager: Jean M. Cody, C.P.A.
Trustee: Robert Goldfarb.
Number of staff: 1 part-time professional.
EIN: 431621937

4896
The Goppert Foundation ✧
10401 Holmes Rd., Ste. 222
Kansas City, MO 64131-3498 (816) 942-7595
Contact: Autumn Y. Markley, V.P.

Incorporated in 1958 in MO.
Donor: Clarence H. Goppert†.
Foundation type: Independent foundation.
Financial data (yr. ended 10/31/13): Assets, $40,243,986 (M); expenditures, $2,039,116; qualifying distributions, $1,876,893; giving activities include $1,759,300 for 32 grants (high: $150,000; low: $10,000).
Purpose and activities: Giving primarily for medical facilities, civic centers and projects, and education.
Fields of interest: Higher education; Education; Hospitals (general); Human services; Youth, services; Youth; Minorities; Economically disadvantaged.
Type of support: Capital campaigns; Building/renovation; Equipment; Endowments; Scholarship funds; Matching/challenge support.
Limitations: Applications accepted. Giving primarily in eastern KS and western MO. No grants to individuals.
Application information: Application form not required.
Initial approach: Typewritten Letter
Copies of proposal: 1
Deadline(s): None
Board meeting date(s): Quarterly
Final notification: None
Officers and Directors:* Richard D. Goppert,* Chair. and Pres.; Thomas A. Goppert,* Vice-Chair. and Secy.-Treas.; M. Charles Kellogg,* V.P.; Autumn Y. Markley,* V.P.; Billy Campbell; Carolyn Kellogg.
EIN: 446013933

4897
Arvin Gottlieb Charitable Foundation ✧
c/o UMB Bank, N.A.
P.O. Box 419692 M/S 1020307
Kansas City, MO 64141-6692 (816) 860-1933
Contact: Jan B. Leonard

Established in 1990 in MO.
Foundation type: Independent foundation.
Financial data (yr. ended 12/31/12): Assets, $34,274,645 (M); expenditures, $2,018,812; qualifying distributions, $1,768,760; giving activities include $1,711,000 for 53 grants (high: $200,000; low: $1,000).
Purpose and activities: Giving primarily to arts and cultural programs, education, human services, housing development, and Jewish agencies.
Fields of interest: Museums; Arts; Higher education; Medical school/education; Education; Hospitals (general); Health organizations; Human services; Jewish federated giving programs; Jewish agencies & synagogues.
Limitations: Giving primarily in Kansas City, MO.
Application information:
Initial approach: Typewritten letter
Deadline(s): None
Trustees: Peter Brown; Barton J. Cohen; UMB Bank, N.A.
EIN: 436380792

4898
Graybar Foundation ✧ ✫
34 N. Meramec Ave.
Clayton, MO 63105-3844
Contact: Mathew W. Geekie, Secy. and Dir.
Application address: P.O. Box 7231, St. Louis, MO 63177

Established in 1984 in MO.
Donor: Graybar Electric Company, Inc.
Foundation type: Company-sponsored foundation.
Financial data (yr. ended 11/30/13): Assets, $5,005,170 (M); gifts received, $1,437,483; expenditures, $477,144; qualifying distributions, $477,144; giving activities include $472,798 for 68 grants (high: $100,000; low: $350).
Purpose and activities: The foundation supports zoos and festivals and organizations involved with arts and culture, youth development, human services, and public policy.
Fields of interest: Performing arts, orchestras; Arts; Zoos/zoological societies; Recreation, fairs/festivals; Boy scouts; Girl scouts; Youth development; Salvation Army; YM/YWCAs & YM/YWHAs; Children/youth, services; Residential/custodial care; Human services; Community/economic development, public policy; United Ways and Federated Giving Programs.
Type of support: General/operating support; Continuing support; Employee matching gifts.
Limitations: Applications accepted. Giving primarily in St. Louis, MO.
Application information: Application form required.
Initial approach: Letter
Copies of proposal: 1
Deadline(s): None
Officers and Directors:* Kathleen M. Mazzerella,* Pres.; S. M. Stone,* V.P.; J. N. Reed, V.P.; Mathew W. Geekie,* Secy.; R. R. Harwood,* Treas.; Lawrence R. Giglio; Beverly L. Propst.
EIN: 431301419

4899
Preston M. Green Charitable Foundation ✧
c/o Commerce Bank
P.O. Box 11356
Clayton, MO 63105-0156 (314) 746-7436
Contact: Dorothy Evers

Established in 2003 in MO.
Foundation type: Independent foundation.
Financial data (yr. ended 07/31/13): Assets, $17,171,248 (M); expenditures, $1,108,443; qualifying distributions, $1,000,000; giving activities include $1,000,000 for grants.
Fields of interest: Higher education.
Type of support: Building/renovation.
Limitations: Applications accepted. Giving primarily in the St. Louis, MO, area. No grants to individuals.
Application information: Application form required.
Initial approach: Letter
Deadline(s): None
Directors: Nancy Green; Stephan A. Green, Jr.
Trustee: Commerce Trust Co.
EIN: 436911130

4900
Allen P. & Josephine B. Green Foundation ✧
c/o Greater Kansas City Community Foundation
1055 Broadway, Ste. 130
Kansas City, MO 64105-1595 (816) 627-3420
Contact: Matthew Fuller, Mgr., Community Investment, Greater Kansas City Community Foundation
FAX: (816) 268-3420;
E-mail: greenfoundation@gkccf.org; Main URL: http://www.greenfdn.org

Trust established in 1941 in MO.
Donors: Allen P. Green†; Josephine B. Green†.
Foundation type: Independent foundation.
Financial data (yr. ended 12/31/12): Assets, $10,748,762 (M); expenditures, $612,946; qualifying distributions, $518,885; giving activities include $485,000 for 43 grants (high: $25,000; low: $1,000), and $20,000 for 4 grants to individuals (high: $5,000; low: $5,000).
Purpose and activities: Giving primarily for human service programs providing direct services to people in need, youth development programs, innovative developmental and educational programs for children, health and hospitals (with the exception of research projects), and religious institutions with an emphasis on projects that support community

churches and the provision of social services. Each year the foundation also offers a $7,500 scholarship, renewable for three years, to a graduating senior of Mexico High School in Missouri.
Fields of interest: Education; Hospitals (general); Health care; Youth development; Human services; Religion; Children.
Type of support: Building/renovation; Equipment; Land acquisition; Endowments; Emergency funds; Program development; Conferences/seminars; Seed money; Curriculum development; Scholarship funds; Matching/challenge support.
Limitations: Applications accepted. Giving limited to central and eastern MO. No support for political organizations, programs located outside of the U.S., or to a charity that is not publicly supported. No grants to individuals, or for operating budgets, social causes or social activism, or lobbying; no loans.
Publications: Application guidelines; Annual report (including application guidelines); Grants list.
Application information: Scholarship application forms are available on Sept. 15 at Mexico High School. Application form required.
Initial approach: Use application form on foundation web site only
Copies of proposal: 1
Deadline(s): See foundation web site for current deadlines for grants; Jan. 15 for scholarships
Officers: Laura White Erdel, Pres.; Franklin E.W. Staley, V.P.; Carl D. Fuemmeler, Secy.-Treas.
Directors: A.D. Bond III; Christopher S. Bond; Nancy A. Ekern; Walter G. Staley III; Larry D. Webber; Nancy G. White; John F. Wood; Robert A. Wood.
Number of staff: 1 part-time support.
EIN: 436030135
Selected grants: The following grants are a representative sample of this grantmaker's funding activity:
$10,000 to Presser Hall Restoration Society, Mexico, MO, 2012. For general Program support for Program basis only.
$9,000 to Job Point, Columbia, MO, 2012. For Computer Network Upgrade.
$5,000 to Conservation Federation of Missouri, Jefferson City, MO, 2012. For Missouri Share The Harvest Program.
$1,000 to Audrain County Area Literacy Council, Mexico, MO, 2012. For Audrain County Area Literacy Council.

4901
Margaret Blanke Grigg Foundation ✧
c/o William H. Hobson
8909 Ladue Rd.
St. Louis, MO 63124

Established around 1995 in MO.
Donor: Margaret B. Grigg.
Foundation type: Independent foundation.
Financial data (yr. ended 12/31/13): Assets, $9,868,901 (M); expenditures, $671,644; qualifying distributions, $666,873; giving activities include $579,500 for 21 grants (high: $100,000; low: $1,500).
Fields of interest: Performing arts; Performing arts, orchestras; Arts.
Limitations: Applications not accepted. Giving primarily in St. Louis, MO. No grants to individuals.
Application information: Contributes only to pre-selected organizations.
Officers and Directors:* William H. Hobson,* Pres.; Charles R. Grigg,* V.P.; Kaatri Grigg,* V.P.; Harry H. Langenberg II,* V.P.; Thomas E. Venker, Jr.,* Secy.-Treas.
EIN: 431699657
Selected grants: The following grants are a representative sample of this grantmaker's funding activity:
$100,000 to Saint Louis Symphony Orchestra, Saint Louis, MO, 2011.

4902
The H & R Block Foundation ✧
1 H&R Block Way
Kansas City, MO 64105-1905 (816) 854-4361
Contact: David P. Miles, Pres.
FAX: (816) 854-8025;
E-mail: foundation@hrblock.com; Additional contacts: David P. Miles, Pres., tel.: (816) 854-4372, e-mail: davmiles@hrblock.com; Carey Wilkerson Looney, V.P. and Secy., tel.: (816) 854-4373, e-mail: cwilkerson@hrblock.com; Robert Bloch, Prog. Off., tel.: (816) 854-4360, e-mail: rbloch@hrblock.com; Hillary Beuschel, Prog. Off., tel.: (816) 854-4361, e-mail: hillary.beuschel@hrblock.com; Jack Nachman, Prog. Asst., tel.: (816) 854-4363, e-mail: jnachman@hrblock.com; Main URL: http://www.blockfoundation.org
Grants List: http://www.blockfoundation.org/downloads/2011_Payments_by_Category.pdf

Incorporated in 1974 in MO.
Donors: H&R Block, Inc.; HRB Management, Inc.
Foundation type: Company-sponsored foundation.
Financial data (yr. ended 12/31/12): Assets, $59,809,580 (M); gifts received, $655,029; expenditures, $2,150,536; qualifying distributions, $1,930,600; giving activities include $1,640,169 for 191 grants (high: $100,000; low: $100).
Purpose and activities: The foundation supports organizations involved with arts and culture, education, health, mental health, housing, youth development, human services, community development, and economically disadvantaged people.
Fields of interest: Arts; Education, early childhood education; Adult education—literacy, basic skills & GED; Education; Health care; Mental health/crisis services; Housing/shelter; Youth development; Human services; Economic development; Urban/community development; Community/economic development; Economically disadvantaged.
Type of support: General/operating support; Continuing support; Annual campaigns; Capital campaigns; Building/renovation; Equipment; Emergency funds; Program development; Scholarship funds; Employee volunteer services; Employee matching gifts; Employee-related scholarships; Matching/challenge support.
Limitations: Applications accepted. Giving primarily in Johnson and Wyandotte, KS, and Clay, Jackson, Kansas City, and Platte, MO. No support for discriminatory organizations, businesses, or disease-specific organizations. No grants to individuals (except for employee-related scholarships), or for publications, travel, conferences, telethons, dinners, advertising, fundraising, animal-related causes, sports programs, or historic preservation projects.
Publications: Application guidelines; Grants list; Program policy statement.
Application information: Proposals should be no longer than 5 to 6 pages. Application form required.
Initial approach: Download application form and mail proposal and application form to foundation
Copies of proposal: 1
Board meeting date(s): Quarterly
Final notification: 10 weeks following deadlines
Officers and Directors:* Henry W. Bloch,* Chair. and Treas.; Frank L. Salizzoni,* Vice-Chair.; David P. Miles, Pres.; Carey Wilkenson Looney, V.P. and Secy.; William A. Hall; Edward T. Matheny, Jr.; Morton I. Sosland.
Number of staff: 3 full-time professional; 1 part-time professional.
EIN: 237378232

4903
The Hagan Scholarship Foundation ✧ ☆
P.O. Box 1225
Columbia, MO 65205-1225 (573) 875-2020
Contact: Dan Hagan, Tr.
E-mail: scholarships@hsfmo.org; Main URL: http://haganscholarships.org
Grants Database: http://haganscholarships.org/recipients.php

Established in MO.
Donors: Dan Hagan; The Hagan Endowment Foundation; The Hagan Trust.
Foundation type: Independent foundation.
Financial data (yr. ended 12/31/13): Assets, $173,079,976 (M); gifts received, $27,459,426; expenditures, $1,276,074; qualifying distributions, $11,727,257; giving activities include $736,091 for grants.
Fields of interest: Education.
Limitations: Applications accepted. Giving primarily in MO.
Application information:
Initial approach: Use forms on foundation web site
Deadline(s): Nov.15
Trustee: Dan Hagan.
EIN: 686260880

4904
The Hagan Trust ✧ ☆
P.O. Box 1225
Columbia, MO 65205-1225

Donor: Dan Hagan.
Foundation type: Independent foundation.
Financial data (yr. ended 12/31/13): Assets, $175,958,076 (M); expenditures, $4,126,742; qualifying distributions, $637,607; giving activities include $552,476 for 7 grants (high: $462,476; low: $5,000).
Fields of interest: Education; Animals/wildlife; Food banks; Agriculture/food.
Limitations: Applications not accepted. Giving primarily in MO.
Application information: Unsolicited requests for funds not accepted.
Trustee: Dan Hagan.
EIN: 456159017
Selected grants: The following grants are a representative sample of this grantmaker's funding activity:
$10,000 to Child Abuse and Neglect Emergency Shelter, Columbia, MO, 2010.
$10,000 to Humane Society, Central Missouri, Columbia, MO, 2011.

$10,000 to Humane Society, Central Missouri, Columbia, MO, 2010.
$10,000 to State Historical Society of Missouri, Columbia, MO, 2010.
$5,000 to State Historical Society of Missouri, Columbia, MO, 2011.

4905
Hall Family Foundation
P.O. Box 419580, Dept. 323
Kansas City, MO 64141-6580 (816) 274-8516
FAX: (816) 274-8547; Main URL: http://www.hallfamilyfoundation.org

Hallmark Educational Foundation incorporated in 1943 in MO; Hallmark Educational Foundation of KS incorporated in 1954 in KS; combined funds formerly known as Hallmark Educational Foundations; current name adopted due to absorption of Hall Family Foundation of Kansas in 1993.
Donors: Hallmark Cards, Inc.; Joyce C. Hall‡; E.A. Hall‡; R.B. Hall‡.
Foundation type: Independent foundation.
Financial data (yr. ended 12/31/13): Assets, $880,600,000 (M); expenditures, $42,152,716; qualifying distributions, $38,152,716; giving activities include $38,152,716 for 117 grants (high: $5,450,000; low: $8,500).
Purpose and activities: The foundation is dedicated to enhancing the quality of human life. Programs that enrich the community, help people and promote excellence are considered to be of prime importance. The foundation views its primary function as that of a catalyst. It seeks to be responsive to programs that are innovative, yet strive to create permanent solutions to community needs in the Greater Kansas City area.
Fields of interest: Performing arts; Arts; Education, early childhood education; Child development, education; Elementary school/education; Secondary school/education; Higher education; Education; Housing/shelter, development; Human services; Youth, services; Child development, services; Family services; Minorities/immigrants, centers/services; Homeless, human services; Urban/community development; Community/economic development.
Type of support: General/operating support; Capital campaigns; Building/renovation; Equipment; Land acquisition; Emergency funds; Program development; Technical assistance; Program evaluation; Program-related investments/loans; Employee-related scholarships.
Limitations: Applications accepted. Giving limited to greater Kansas City, MO. No support for international or religious organizations or for political purposes. No grants to individuals (except for employee-related scholarships), or for travel, operating deficits, conferences, scholarly research, or fundraising campaigns or event promotion such as telethons, or for endowments.
Publications: Annual report; Grants list; Informational brochure (including application guidelines).
Application information: Scholarships are for the children and close relatives of Hallmark Cards employees only. Only eligible applicants should apply. Application form not required.
Initial approach: Letter
Copies of proposal: 1
Deadline(s): 6 weeks before board meetings
Board meeting date(s): Mar., June, Sept., and Dec.
Final notification: 6 to 8 weeks
Officers and Directors:* Donald J. Hall,* Chair.; William A. Hall, Pres.; John A. MacDonald, V.P. and Treas.; Jeanne Bates, V.P.; Tracy McFerrin Foster, V.P. and Secy.; Richard C. Green; Robert E. Hemenway; Irvine O. Hockaday, Jr.; Robert A. Kipp; Sandra A.J. Lawrence; Margaret Hall Pence; Morton I. Sosland; David A. Warm.
EIN: 446006291
Selected grants: The following grants are a representative sample of this grantmaker's funding activity:
$5,562,851 to Kansas City Area Life Sciences Institute, Kansas City, MO, 2012.
$3,000,000 to Nelson Gallery Foundation, Kansas City, MO, 2012.
$2,000,000 to Truman Medical Center Charitable Foundation, Kansas City, MO, 2012.
$1,500,000 to Salvation Army of Kansas City, Kansas City, KS, 2012.
$175,000 to Kansas City Care Clinic, Kansas City, MO, 2012.
$150,000 to Kansas City Area Life Sciences Institute, Kansas City, MO, 2012.
$119,756 to Leading Educators, Kansas City, MO, 2012.
$50,000 to Triality, Pleasant Valley, MO, 2012.
$40,000 to Young Audiences, Kansas City, Kansas City, MO, 2012.

4906
Hallmark Corporate Foundation ✧
P.O. Box 419580, M.D. 323
Kansas City, MO 64141-6580
Contact: Carol Hallquist, Pres.; Cora Storbeck
E-mail: contributions@hallmark.com; Main URL: http://corporate.hallmark.com/Corporate-Citizenship/Community-Involvement

Established in 1983 in MO.
Donors: Hallmark Cards, Inc.; Crayola, LLC.
Foundation type: Company-sponsored foundation.
Financial data (yr. ended 12/31/13): Assets, $161,174 (M); gifts received, $1,169,544; expenditures, $1,818,670; qualifying distributions, $1,818,454; giving activities include $1,717,880 for 207 grants (high: $275,750; low: $25), and $100,523 for 130 employee matching gifts.
Purpose and activities: The foundation supports programs designed to address the needs of children and families; promote arts and culture; address human service infrastructure and civic assets; and support the military.
Fields of interest: Performing arts; Performing arts, theater; Performing arts, orchestras; Arts; Child development, education; Education; Hospitals (general); Children/youth, services; Family services; Human services; Urban/community development; United Ways and Federated Giving Programs; Military/veterans' organizations; Public affairs.
Type of support: General/operating support; Continuing support; Capital campaigns; Building/renovation; Equipment; Program development; Technical assistance; Employee volunteer services; Program evaluation; Employee matching gifts.
Limitations: Applications accepted. Giving limited to areas of company operations in Columbus, GA, Metamora, IL, Lawrence, Leavenworth, and Topeka, KS, Liberty and the Kansas City, MO, area, and Center, TX. No support for religious, fraternal, political, international, or veterans' organizations, athletic or labor groups, social clubs, or disease-specific organizations. No grants to individuals, or for scholarships, endowments, debt reduction, travel, conferences, sponsorships, scholarly or health-related research, advertising, mass media campaigns, or fundraising; no furniture, machines, computers, or other equipment donations.
Publications: Application guidelines; Informational brochure (including application guidelines).
Application information: Support is limited to 1 contribution per organization during any given year. Additional information may be requested at a later date. A personal or telephone interview or site visit may be requested. Application form required.
Initial approach: Complete online application form
Copies of proposal: 1
Deadline(s): None
Board meeting date(s): Periodic
Final notification: Up to 6 weeks
Officers and Directors:* Donald J. Hall, Jr., Chair.; Carol Hallquist, Pres.; Cora Storbeck, V.P.; Albert P. Mauro, Jr., Secy.; Terri R. Maybee, Treas.; Stephen D. Doyal; David E. Hall.
Number of staff: 3 full-time professional; 1 full-time support.
EIN: 431303258
Selected grants: The following grants are a representative sample of this grantmaker's funding activity:
$11,260,000 to United Way of Greater Kansas City, Kansas City, MO, 2011. For annual campaign.
$183,400 to Kansas City Symphony, Kansas City, MO, 2011. For general support.
$120,700 to Kansas City Repertory Theater, Kansas City, MO, 2011. For general support.
$115,000 to Kansas City Area Development Council, Kansas City, MO, 2011.
$100,000 to Nelson Gallery Foundation, Kansas City, MO, 2011.
$98,800 to Kansas City Ballet Association, Kansas City, MO, 2011. For general support.
$89,000 to Chamber of Commerce of Greater Kansas City, Kansas City, MO, 2011.
$79,200 to Lyric Opera of Kansas City, Kansas City, MO, 2011.
$67,000 to Civil Council of Greater Kansas City, 2011.
$65,000 to Childrens Mercy Hospital, Kansas City, MO, 2011.
$65,000 to Kansas City Art Institute, Kansas City, MO, 2011.

4907
John Q. Hammons Foundation, Inc. ✧
300 John Q. Hammons Pkwy., Ste. 900
Springfield, MO 65806-2550 (417) 864-4300
Contact: Jacqueline Dowdy, Pres.

Established in 1990 in MO.
Foundation type: Independent foundation.
Financial data (yr. ended 12/31/13): Assets, $117,722 (M); gifts received, $2,505,491; expenditures, $2,720,556; qualifying distributions, $2,720,556; giving activities include $825,691 for 50 grants (high: $88,164; low: $1,000).
Purpose and activities: Giving primarily for children, youth and social services.
Fields of interest: Boys & girls clubs; Human services; Foundations (private grantmaking).
Limitations: Applications accepted. Giving primarily in southwest MO, with emphasis on Springfield. No grants to individuals.

Application information: Application form required.
Initial approach: Typed letter, not exceeding 4 pages
Deadline(s): None
Final notification: Usually within 2 months
Officers: Jacqueline Dowdy, Pres.; Greggory Groves, V.P.; Christopher Smith, Secy.-Treas.
EIN: 431521852
Selected grants: The following grants are a representative sample of this grantmaker's funding activity:
$23,312 to Boys and Girls Clubs of Springfield, Springfield, MO, 2011.

4908
Hauck Charitable Foundation ✧
999 Executive Pkwy., Ste. 202
St. Louis, MO 63141-6336
Contact: John C. Hauck, Pres. and Dir.

Established in 1987 in MO.
Donors: John M. Hauck; Steven J. Hauck; Ellen Hauck Smith; John C. Hauck; Carolyn Gold; Kathleen H. Alexander; TSI Holding Co.; John M. Hauck Marital Trust.
Foundation type: Independent foundation.
Financial data (yr. ended 12/31/13): Assets, $37,809,198 (M); expenditures, $1,834,496; qualifying distributions, $1,800,235; giving activities include $1,800,235 for 30 grants (high: $456,000; low: $500).
Purpose and activities: Giving primarily for education and human services.
Fields of interest: Arts; Education; Human services; Children/youth, services; United Ways and Federated Giving Programs.
Limitations: Applications accepted. Giving primarily in St. Louis, MO. No grants to individuals.
Application information: Application form required.
Initial approach: Letter by mail or fax
Deadline(s): None
Officers and Directors:* John C. Hauck,* Pres.; Deborah Hauck,* V.P; Annette Eckerle, Secy.-Treas.; Kathleen H. Alexander; Carolyn Gold; David P. Hauck; Ellen Hauck; Steven J. Hauck.
EIN: 431467676
Selected grants: The following grants are a representative sample of this grantmaker's funding activity:
$1,000 to Muscular Dystrophy Association, Houston, TX, 2012. For 2010 Stride and Ride.

4909
Hecker Family Foundation ✧ ☆
c/o The St. Louis Trust Co.
7701 Forsyth Blvd., No. 1100
St. Louis, MO 63166-1823 (314) 727-4600
Contact: Voula Francis

Established in 2006 in MO.
Donors: Harvard K. Hecker†; Patricia G. Hecker.
Foundation type: Independent foundation.
Financial data (yr. ended 10/31/13): Assets, $19,981 (M); gifts received, $490,080; expenditures, $5,454,789; qualifying distributions, $5,418,146; giving activities include $5,411,604 for 6 grants (high: $4,848,158; low: $300).
Fields of interest: Performing arts, orchestras; Performing arts, opera; Education; Aquariums; Human services.
Limitations: Applications accepted. Giving primarily in MO and SC.
Application information: Application form required.
Initial approach: Contact foundation for application form
Deadline(s): Contact foundation for deadline
Trustees: Bruce G. Hecker; Patricia G. Hecker; The St. Louis Trust Company; U.S. Bank, N.A.
EIN: 205854888
Selected grants: The following grants are a representative sample of this grantmaker's funding activity:
$20,000 to Saint Louis Symphony Orchestra, Saint Louis, MO, 2011.
$20,000 to Saint Louis Zoo, Saint Louis, MO, 2011.
$20,000 to South Carolina Aquarium, Charleston, SC, 2011.
$5,500 to Nature Conservancy, Saint Louis, MO, 2011.
$5,000 to Pitzer College, Claremont, CA, 2011.
$5,000 to World Neighbors, Oklahoma City, OK, 2011.
$5,000 to World Wildlife Fund, Washington, DC, 2011.
$4,250 to Saint Peters Episcopal Church, Saint Louis, MO, 2011.
$2,500 to Sheldon Arts Foundation, Saint Louis, MO, 2011.
$2,000 to Planned Parenthood Federation of America, New York, NY, 2011.

4910
The Holekamp Foundation ✧
c/o William F. Holekamp
7733 Forsyth Blvd., Ste. 1375
St. Louis, MO 63105-1834

Established in 1998 in MO.
Donors: Kerry L. Holekamp; William F. Holekamp.
Foundation type: Independent foundation.
Financial data (yr. ended 12/31/12): Assets, $3,768,027 (M); gifts received, $1,994,231; expenditures, $1,538,807; qualifying distributions, $1,503,812; giving activities include $1,502,000 for 35 grants (high: $385,000; low: $100).
Purpose and activities: Giving primarily for education, hospitals, including children's hospitals, and for human services.
Fields of interest: Elementary/secondary education; Higher education; Education; Hospitals (general); Hospitals (specialty); Human services; Children/youth, services.
Limitations: Applications not accepted. Giving primarily in St. Louis, MO; some funding also in Hanover, NH, Philadelphia, PA, and Lexington, VA. No grants to individuals.
Application information: Contributes only to pre-selected organizations.
Managers: Kerry L. Holekamp; William F. Holekamp.
EIN: 436800541

4911
The Hulston Family Foundation ✧ ☆
P.O. Box 10226
Kansas City, MO 64171-0226

Established in 1997 in MO.
Donor: John K. Hulston.
Foundation type: Independent foundation.
Financial data (yr. ended 12/31/13): Assets, $14,097,619 (M); gifts received, $1,317,000; expenditures, $614,504.
Purpose and activities: Giving to health care associations and secondary and higher education.
Fields of interest: Higher education; Law school/education; Health care; Cancer; Salvation Army; United Ways and Federated Giving Programs.
Limitations: Applications not accepted. No grants to individuals.
Application information: Contributes only to pre-selected organizations.
Officers: John L. Hulston, Pres.; Lorrie Hulston Carvin, Secy.
Trustees: John Patrick Hulston; Joseph Fred Hulston; Lucia C. Hulston.
EIN: 431781350

4912
Lewis H. Humphreys Charitable Trust ✧
c/o US Trust, Philanthropic Solutions
1200 Main St., 14th Fl.
P.O. Box 219119
Kansas City, MO 64121-9119
Contact: James Mueth, V.P.
E-mail: james.mueth@ustrust.com; E-mail to discuss application process or for questions about the foundation: mo.grantmaking@ustrust.com (Foundation name should be indicated in subject line); Main URL: http://www.bankofamerica.com/grantmaking

Established in 2004 in KS and MO.
Donor: Lewis H. Humphreys†.
Foundation type: Independent foundation.
Financial data (yr. ended 09/30/13): Assets, $97,630,924 (M); expenditures, $4,511,953; qualifying distributions, $3,906,724; giving activities include $3,822,300 for 35 grants (high: $392,000; low: $5,000).
Purpose and activities: Giving to support and promote quality educational, cultural, human services, and health care programming for underserved and disadvantaged populations.
Fields of interest: Higher education; Human services; Children/youth, services; Foundations (private grantmaking); Protestant agencies & churches; Aging; Economically disadvantaged.
Type of support: Scholarship funds.
Limitations: Applications accepted. Giving primarily in Osage and Coffey counties, KS.
Application information: Application form required.
Initial approach: Use application form on the trust's web site
Copies of proposal: 2
Deadline(s): Between Aug. 1 and Sept. 30
Final notification: Nov. 30
Trustee: Bank of America, N.A.
EIN: 597276551
Selected grants: The following grants are a representative sample of this grantmaker's funding activity:
$50,000 to American Red Cross, Topeka, KS, 2011. For the Kansas Capital Area Chapter as unrestricted contribution.
$50,000 to Boy Scouts of America, Jayhawk Area Council, Topeka, KS, 2011. For Jayhawk Area Council to assist with rebuilding of Camp Rangers Home at Falley Scout Reservation.
$50,000 to Corner House, Emporia, KS, 2011. For Mother Child Project.
$50,000 to Land Institute, Salina, KS, 2011. For unrestricted contribution.

$50,000 to Railroad Heritage, Topeka, KS, 2011. For the Great Overland Station, unrestricted contribution.
$36,350 to Inman Senior Citizens, Inman, KS, 2011. For Inman Senior Center to assist with renovation of facility.
$27,220 to Boys and Girls Club of Topeka, Topeka, KS, 2011. To establish learning center in Adams location.
$25,000 to AARP Foundation, Washington, DC, 2011. To assist with technology purchase.
$25,000 to Stormont-Vail Foundation, Topeka, KS, 2011. For unrestricted contribution.
$15,000 to Meals on Wheels, Topeka, KS, 2011. To assist with rural delivery program.

4913
J. P. Humphreys Foundation ✧
P.O. Box 1404
Joplin, MO 64802-1404

Established in 1981 in MO.
Donors: Ethelmae Craig Humphreys; J.P. Humphreys†.
Foundation type: Independent foundation.
Financial data (yr. ended 12/31/13): Assets, $17,463,357 (M); gifts received, $1,250,000; expenditures, $2,034,518; qualifying distributions, $1,948,602; giving activities include $1,948,000 for 56 grants (high: $250,000; low: $500).
Purpose and activities: Giving for higher education and economic and social science research.
Fields of interest: Higher education; Education; Boy scouts; Civil/human rights; Social sciences, public policy; Economics; Public policy, research.
Limitations: Applications not accepted. Giving in the U.S., with some emphasis on Washington, DC, KS, NY, PA, and VA. No grants to individuals.
Application information: Unsolicited requests for funds not accepted.
Officers: Ethelmae C. Humphreys, Pres.; Sarah Humphreys Atkins, V.P.; David C. Humphreys, Secy.-Treas.
Directors: Paul S. Atkins; Debra G. Humphreys.
EIN: 431244445
Selected grants: The following grants are a representative sample of this grantmaker's funding activity:
$2,500 to Boy Scouts of America, Black Warrior Council, Tuscaloosa, AL, 2013. For general administration.

4914
Interco Charitable Trust ✧
7701 Forsyth Blvd., Ste. 1000
Saint Louis, MO 63015 (314) 696-2217
Contact: Michael R. Loynd, Admin.

Trust established in 1944 in MO.
Donor: Furniture Brands International, Inc.
Foundation type: Company-sponsored foundation.
Financial data (yr. ended 12/31/13): Assets, $40,870,918 (M); expenditures, $2,079,477; qualifying distributions, $1,606,617; giving activities include $1,417,128 for 75 grants (high: $100,000; low: $500).
Purpose and activities: The foundation supports organizations involved with arts and culture, education, health, youth development, human services, science, and religion. Support is given primarily in the greater St. Louis, Missouri, area.
Fields of interest: Museums (art); Arts; Higher education; Education; Health care; Boys & girls clubs; Youth development; American Red Cross; Youth, services; Homeless, human services; Human services; United Ways and Federated Giving Programs; Science; Religion.
Type of support: General/operating support; Continuing support; Scholarship funds.
Limitations: Applications accepted. Giving primarily in St. Louis, MO. No grants to individuals.
Publications: Application guidelines; Annual report.
Application information: Application form required.
Initial approach: Letter
Deadline(s): None
Officer: Michael R. Loynd, Admin.
Trustees: Donald E. Lasater; Richard B. Loynd; Robert H. Quenon; Ralph Scozzafava.
Number of staff: 1 full-time professional.
EIN: 311593436

4915
The Diane and Thomas Jacobsen Foundation ✧
P.O. Box 387
St. Louis, MO 63166-0387
Application address: c/o Diane E. Jacobsen, 830 A1A N., Ste. 13, P.O. Box 411, Ponte Vedra, FL 32082, tel.: (314) 418-8007

Established in 1997.
Donor: Diane E. Jacobsen.
Foundation type: Independent foundation.
Financial data (yr. ended 12/31/13): Assets, $2,689,823 (M); gifts received, $30; expenditures, $893,769; qualifying distributions, $877,476; giving activities include $850,659 for 11 grants (high: $807,025; low: $100).
Fields of interest: Museums (art); Higher education; International affairs, foreign policy.
Limitations: Applications accepted. Giving primarily in FL, MO and NY. No grants to individuals.
Application information: Application form required.
Initial approach: Letter
Deadline(s): None
Trustee: Diane E. Jacobsen.
EIN: 436777274
Selected grants: The following grants are a representative sample of this grantmaker's funding activity:
$63,733 to Metropolitan Museum of Art, New York, NY, 2011.
$18,000 to Cummer Museum of Art and Gardens, Jacksonville, FL, 2011.
$16,000 to Christ Episcopal Church, Ponte Vedra Beach, FL, 2011.
$5,000 to New-York Historical Society, New York, NY, 2011.
$2,000 to Whitney Museum of American Art, New York, NY, 2011.
$1,000 to Amon Carter Museum of Western Art, Fort Worth, TX, 2011.
$1,000 to International Arts and Artists, Washington, DC, 2011.
$1,000 to Saint Louis Art Museum, Saint Louis, MO, 2011.

4916
Dennis M. Jones Family Foundation ✧
(formerly Dennis & Judith Jones Charitable Foundation Trust)
1700 S. Warson Rd.
St. Louis, MO 63124-1146 (314) 889-1100
Contact: Dennis M. Jones, Tr.
E-mail: dennis.jones@deuxsources.com

Established in 1998 in MO.
Donor: Dennis M. Jones.
Foundation type: Independent foundation.
Financial data (yr. ended 12/31/13): Assets, $50,173,978 (M); gifts received, $5,750; expenditures, $2,904,616; qualifying distributions, $2,486,000; giving activities include $2,486,000 for 23 grants (high: $500,000; low: $1,000).
Purpose and activities: Giving primarily for education and social services.
Fields of interest: Higher education; Education; Human services; Youth, services; Children/youth; Military/veterans; Economically disadvantaged.
Type of support: Scholarship funds.
Limitations: Applications accepted. Giving primarily in MO, with emphasis on St. Louis. No grants to individuals.
Publications: Annual report.
Application information: Application form required.
Initial approach: Letter on organization's letterhead
Copies of proposal: 1
Deadline(s): None
Board meeting date(s): Periodic
Trustees: J. Denise Franz; Dennis M. Jones; Dennis M. Jones, Jr.; Judith A. Jones.
EIN: 436786094
Selected grants: The following grants are a representative sample of this grantmaker's funding activity:
$154,800 to Junior Achievement of Greater Saint Louis, Chesterfield, MO, 2011.
$150,000 to Saint Patrick Center, Saint Louis, MO, 2011.

4917
Mary Ranken Jordan and Ettie A. Jordan Charitable Foundation ✧
c/o U.S. Bank, N.A.
P.O. Box 387
St. Louis, MO 63166-0387
Contact: Angela L. Pearson
Application address: c/o Fred E. Arnold, Advisory Committee, 1 U.S. Bank Plz., Ste. 3400, St. Louis, MO 63101, tel.: (314) 552-6000; e-mail: farnold@thompsoncoburn.com

Foundation established in 1957 in MO.
Donors: Mary Ranken Jordan†; Ettie A. Jordan†.
Foundation type: Independent foundation.
Financial data (yr. ended 12/31/13): Assets, $23,465,948 (M); expenditures, $1,182,185; qualifying distributions, $1,025,536; giving activities include $977,332 for grants.
Purpose and activities: Giving limited to Missouri charitable and eleemosynary institutions, with emphasis on the arts, including a symphony orchestra, education, and children's health and welfare, including a pediatric rehabilitation center.
Fields of interest: Performing arts, orchestras; Arts; Higher education; Education; Botanical gardens; Children/youth, services; Family services; Children.

Type of support: General/operating support; Continuing support; Capital campaigns; Building/renovation; Endowments.
Limitations: Applications accepted. Giving limited to MO, with emphasis on the St. Louis area. No grants to individuals.
Application information: Application form not required.
Initial approach: Letter
Copies of proposal: 3
Deadline(s): Dec. 31
Board meeting date(s): Late Spring
Advisory Board: Fred E. Arnold; W. Stanley Walch; David Wells.
Trustee: U.S. Bank, N.A.
EIN: 436020554
Selected grants: The following grants are a representative sample of this grantmaker's funding activity:
$100,000 to Saint Louis Art Museum, Saint Louis, MO, 2011.
$90,000 to Saint Louis Symphony Orchestra, Saint Louis, MO, 2011.
$66,666 to Saint Louis Zoo Foundation, Saint Louis, MO, 2011.
$60,000 to Washington University, Saint Louis, MO, 2011.
$50,000 to K W M U Saint Louis Public Radio, Saint Louis, MO, 2011.
$50,000 to Ranken Jordan Home for Convalescent Crippled Children, Maryland Heights, MO, 2011.
$50,000 to Saint Louis Regional Public Media, Saint Louis, MO, 2011.

4918
The JSM Charitable Trust ✧
1034 S. Brentwood Blvd., Ste. 1860
St. Louis, MO 63117-1229 (314) 862-1040
Contact: Jeffrey McDonnell, Tr.

Established in 1997.
Donors: James S. McDonnell III; Jeffrey M. McDonnell; John F. McDonnell; William D. James; Alicia S. McDonnell; Marcella M. Stevens; Katherine M. Pipoli; James S. McDonnell Foundation.
Foundation type: Independent foundation.
Financial data (yr. ended 12/31/13): Assets, $202 (M); gifts received, $22,660,310; expenditures, $22,663,930; qualifying distributions, $22,663,930; giving activities include $22,663,930 for 18 grants (high: $769,541; low: $8,090).
Purpose and activities: Giving primarily for higher education, civic and community, and cultural organizations.
Fields of interest: Arts; Higher education; Civil/human rights; Community/economic development; Science, research.
Type of support: Research; Program development; Professorships; Matching/challenge support; Endowments; Capital campaigns; Building/renovation; Annual campaigns.
Limitations: Applications not accepted. Giving primarily in St. Louis, MO, with some giving in NJ. No support for religious or political organizations. No grants to individuals.
Application information: Contributes only to pre-selected organizations.
Board meeting date(s): 3 times per year
Trustees: James S. McDonnell III; Jeffrey M. McDonnell.
EIN: 431769438

Selected grants: The following grants are a representative sample of this grantmaker's funding activity:
$8,016,205 to Washington University, Saint Louis, MO, 2013. For matching grant for McDonnell Fund for Academic Excellence.
$4,636,842 to Mary Institute and Saint Louis Country Day School, Saint Louis, MO, 2013. For matching grant for facility construction.
$4,271,024 to Mary Institute and Saint Louis Country Day School, Saint Louis, MO, 2012. For capital campaign.
$3,857,066 to Princeton University, Princeton, NJ, 2012. For facility construction.
$3,699,777 to Princeton University, Princeton, NJ, 2013. For matching grant to establish Center for Systems Neuroscience.
$3,276,460 to Washington University, Saint Louis, MO, 2012. For McDonnell Fund for Academic Excellence.
$1,852,256 to Donald Danforth Plant Science Center, Saint Louis, MO, 2012. For endowment campaign.
$1,766,487 to Donald Danforth Plant Science Center, Saint Louis, MO, 2013. For matching grant to endow McDonnell International Programs.
$1,588,431 to Washington University, Saint Louis, MO, 2012. For McDonnell International Scholars Academy.
$1,583,343 to Washington University, Saint Louis, MO, 2013. For matching grant for McDonnell International Scholars Academy.
$984,347 to Saint Louis Zoo, Saint Louis, MO, 2012. For capital campaign.
$769,541 to Missouri History Museum, Saint Louis, MO, 2013. For general support.
$496,336 to Municipal Theater Association of Saint Louis, Saint Louis, MO, 2013. For matching grant for endowment.
$150,272 to Saint Louis Regional Public Media, Nine Network of Public Media, Saint Louis, MO, 2013. For matching grant for American Graduate: Let's Make It Happen, a public media initiative to address the dropout crisis in 35 states.
$130,590 to Community School Association, Saint Louis, MO, 2013. For matching grant for capital campaign.
$100,000 to Community School Association, Saint Louis, MO, 2012. For renovations.
$29,000 to Saint Louis Beacon, Saint Louis, MO, 2013. For matching grant to provide financial stability for new entity when it merges with Saint Louis Public Radio.
$19,708 to John Burroughs School, Saint Louis, MO, 2012. For capital campaign.
$10,000 to City Academy, Saint Louis, MO, 2012. To provide iPads for science and mathematics classes.
$6,173 to Mary Institute and Saint Louis Country Day School, Saint Louis, MO, 2012. For 25th Class Reunion.

4919
The Henry A. Jubel Foundation ✧ ☆
3668 S. Geyer Rd., Ste. 210
Saint Louis, MO 63127-1232 (314) 620-2548
Contact: Melissa A. Markwort, Tr.

Established in MO.
Donors: Donald A. Jubel; Spartan Light Metal Products, Inc.
Foundation type: Independent foundation.

Financial data (yr. ended 12/31/13): Assets, $210,288 (M); gifts received, $1,550,000; expenditures, $1,366,175; qualifying distributions, $1,357,500; giving activities include $1,357,500 for 4 grants (high: $1,250,000; low: $2,500).
Fields of interest: Engineering school/education; Education; Religion.
Type of support: Building/renovation.
Limitations: Applications accepted. Giving primarily in MO.
Application information: Application form required.
Initial approach: Request application form
Deadline(s): None
Trustees: Donald A. Jubel; Melissa A. Markwort; Patrick E. Stark.
EIN: 453551627

4920
Greater Kansas City Community Foundation ✧
(formerly The Greater Kansas City Community Foundation and Affiliated Trusts)
1055 Broadway, Ste. 130
Kansas City, MO 64105-1595 (816) 842-0944
Contact: Deborah L. Wilkerson, C.E.O.
FAX: (816) 842-8079;
E-mail: info@growyourgiving.org; Tel. for Donor Svcs. Ctr.: (816) 842-7444; Main URL: http://www.growyourgiving.org/
Blog: http://www.givingbetter.org/giving-blog
Facebook: http://www.facebook.com/pages/Greater-Kansas-City-Community-Foundation/10259751361
Google Plus: https://plus.google.com/118114070082770989796/posts
LinkedIn: http://www.linkedin.com/companies/greater-kansas-city-community-foundation
Pinterest: http://www.pinterest.com/gkccf/
Twitter: http://twitter.com/gkccf
YouTube: http://www.youtube.com/user/GivingBetter
Tel. for scholarship info.: (816) 842-7444, e-mail inquiries: scholarship@gkccf.org

Established in 1978 in MO.
Foundation type: Community foundation.
Financial data (yr. ended 12/31/13): Assets, $2,151,222,919 (M); gifts received, $433,191,147; expenditures, $236,817,754; giving activities include $234,274,371 for grants.
Purpose and activities: The foundation seeks to improve the quality of life in Greater Kansas City by increasing charitable giving, connecting donors to the needs in the community they care about, and providing leadership on critical community issues.
Fields of interest: Arts; Health care; Children/youth, services; Family services; Civil rights, race/intergroup relations; Urban/community development; Community/economic development; Biology/life sciences.
Type of support: General/operating support; Continuing support; Capital campaigns; Building/renovation; Endowments; Emergency funds; Program development; Seed money; Curriculum development; Scholarship funds; Research; Technical assistance; Program-related investments/loans; Employee matching gifts; Employee-related scholarships; Scholarships—to individuals; Matching/challenge support.
Limitations: Applications accepted. Giving primarily in the bi-state greater Kansas City region. No grants

to individuals (except through scholarship funds), or for deficit financing.
Publications: Annual report; Financial statement; Informational brochure; Newsletter.
Application information: Visit foundation web site for application guidelines per grant type. Application form required.
Deadline(s): Varies
Board meeting date(s): Mar., June, Sept., and Dec.
Final notification: Varies
Officers and Directors:* Robert D. Regnier,* Chair.; Dr. Jim Hinson,* Vice-Chair.; Debbie Wilkerson, C.E.O. and Pres.; Julie Barry, V.P., Finance; Brenda Chumley, Sr. V.P., Donor Rels. and Opers.; Katie Gray, Sr. V.P., Finance and Foundation Svcs.; Denise St. Omer, V.P., Community Investment; Debbie Starke, V.P., Donor Rels.; Deryl W. Wynn,* Secy.; Corey Ziegler, Corp. Counsel; Kate Ferrell Banks; William S. Berkley; Michael J. Brown; Diane Y. Canaday; William H. Coughlin; William C. Gautreaux; Hon. Jon R. Gray; Kenneth V. Hager; Joseph F. Reardon; Nelson Sabetes, M.D.; Kay A. Saunders; Jeannine Strandjord; Brenda Tinnen.
Number of staff: 38 full-time professional; 3 part-time professional; 6 full-time support; 1 part-time support.
EIN: 431152398
Selected grants: The following grants are a representative sample of this grantmaker's funding activity:
$17,661,943 to Kauffman Center for the Performing Arts, Kansas City, MO, 2012.
$4,690,651 to Childrens Center for the Visually Impaired, Kansas City, MO, 2012.
$3,922,389 to Philanthropic Ventures Foundation, Oakland, CA, 2012.
$2,150,000 to Food and Water Watch, Washington, DC, 2012.
$1,575,000 to University of Missouri Law School Foundation, Columbia, MO, 2012.
$1,010,969 to Truman Medical Centers, Kansas City, MO, 2012.
$1,000,000 to Saint Ann Catholic Church, Prairie Village, KS, 2012.
$3,700 to Grand Teton Music Festival, Wilson, WY, 2012.
$2,500 to Ronald McDonald House Charities of Kansas City, Kansas City, MO, 2012.
$2,500 to Westminster College, Fulton, MO, 2012.

4921
Ewing Marion Kauffman Foundation ✧

4801 Rockhill Rd.
Kansas City, MO 64110-2046 (816) 932-1000
Contact: Barbara Pruitt, Dir., Comms.
FAX: (816) 932-1100; E-mail: info@kauffman.org; Main URL: http://www.kauffman.org
E-Newsletter: http://www.kauffman.org/stay-connected
Entrepreneurship.Org: http://www.entrepreneurship.org
Facebook: http://www.facebook.com/kauffmanfdn
Grants Database: http://www.kauffman.org/grants/grants-list
Kauffman Foundation's Small Business America Blog on Huffington Post: http://www.huffingtonpost.com/tag/ewing-kauffman-foundation
Multimedia: http://www.kauffman.org/KauffmanMultimedia.aspx
Twitter: http://www.twitter.com/kauffmanfdn

Established in 1966 in MO.
Donor: Ewing M. Kauffman‡.
Foundation type: Independent foundation.
Financial data (yr. ended 12/31/13): Assets, $2,125,039,000 (M); expenditures, $146,982,000; qualifying distributions, $17,666,000; giving activities include $17,666,000 for grants.
Purpose and activities: The foundation's mission is to help individuals attain economic independence by advancing educational achievement and entrepreneurial success, consistent with the aspirations of its founder Ewing Marion Kauffman. To fulfill the mission, the foundation: 1) Identifies opportunities where application of the foundation's people, ideas, and capital can benefit society in significant and measurable ways; 2) Develops innovative, research-based programs leading to practical, sustainable solutions that are widely accepted and implemented; 3) Treats the Kansas City region as a program incubator where feasible, in which new approaches can be tried and tested before being disseminated nationally; and 4) Partners with others to leverage its resources and capabilities while avoiding the creation of dependency.
Fields of interest: Education, public policy; Elementary/secondary education; Education, services; Education; Community development, business promotion; Community development, small businesses; Science; Mathematics.
Type of support: General/operating support; Emergency funds; Program development; Conferences/seminars; Curriculum development; Fellowships; Research; Program evaluation; Program-related investments/loans; Employee matching gifts; Matching/challenge support.
Limitations: Applications accepted. Giving limited to the U.S., with emphasis on the bi-state metropolitan Kansas City area (KS/MO) for K-12 education initiatives focused on math and science. No support for international programs, political, social, fraternal, or arts organizations, and capital campaigns or construction projects. No grants for fund endowments, or for special events.
Publications: Application guidelines; Annual report; Financial statement; Grants list; Newsletter.
Application information: To receive a copy of the foundation's Guidelines for Grantseekers brochure, visit foundation's web site or send a request via e-mail or by mail. Application form not required.
Initial approach: Letter of inquiry, less than 3 pages
Deadline(s): None
Board meeting date(s): Mar., June, Sept., and Dec.
Final notification: As soon as possible
Officers and Trustees:* Janice Kreamer,* Chair.; Wendy Guillies, Acting Pres. and C.E.O. and V.P., Comm.; Dane Stangler, V.P., Research and Policy; Thom Ruhe, V.P., Entrepreneurship; Aaron North, V.P., Education; Kristin Bechard, Cont.; Mary McLean, C.I.O.; John E. Tyler III, Genl. Counsel; Julia Irene Kauffman; Barbara Mowry; Benno C. Schmidt, Jr.; Michael Schultz; John Sherman; Michael Stolper; Jeannine Strandjord.
Number of staff: 48 full-time professional; 4 part-time professional; 35 full-time support; 1 part-time support.
EIN: 436064859
Selected grants: The following grants are a representative sample of this grantmaker's funding activity:
$1,100,000 to Greater Kansas City Community Foundation, Kansas City, MO, 2012. For Kauffman Foundation match of associate and trustee contributions.
$330,000 to Silicon Valley Community Foundation, Mountain View, CA, 2012. To support the CODE: 2040 fellows program, which provides minority engineers with immersion experience in Silicon Valley, setting them up for success in their own ventures, and paving the way for increased minority entrepreneurship nationwide, payable over 1.50 years.
$250,000 to Teach for America, New York, NY, 2012. To support the launch of innovative new ventures that address the root causes of educational inequity, payable over 1.75 years.
$200,000 to Harvard University, Berkman Center for Internet and Society, Cambridge, MA, 2012. To support Phase 2 of the Berkman Center for Internet and Society's Law Lab project, payable over 2.00 years.
$180,000 to Urban Institute, Washington, DC, 2012. To support the production and dissemination of research that is central to understanding the role of tax policy and its effect on innovation and entrepreneurial activity in the United States, payable over 2.00 years.
$54,984 to Duke University, Pratt School of Engineering, Durham, NC, 2012. To support research to address immigrant entrepreneurship trends in the United States with a sample of companies started between 1996 - 2010.
$20,000 to Ascension Catholic School, Overland Park, KS, 2012. For general operating support.
$10,000 to Jewish Federation of Greater Kansas City, Overland Park, KS, 2012. For General operating support.
$10,000 to Negro Leagues Baseball Museum, Kansas City, MO, 2012. For general support for programming in effort to maximize the heightened interest in the museum created by the 2012 All-Star Game.

4922
Muriel McBrien Kauffman Foundation ✧

4801 Rockhill Rd.
Kansas City, MO 64110-2046
Contact: Julia Irene Kauffman, Chair.
FAX: (816) 932-1287; E-mail: info@mmkf.org; Main URL: http://www.MMKF.org

Established in 1987 in MO.
Donor: Muriel McBrien Kauffman‡.
Foundation type: Independent foundation.
Financial data (yr. ended 12/31/12): Assets, $248,168,189 (M); expenditures, $28,584,110; qualifying distributions, $27,629,214; giving activities include $25,954,355 for 207 grants (high: $6,100,000; low: $300), and $29,250 for 11 employee matching gifts.
Purpose and activities: The mission of the foundation is to support the visual and performing arts.
Fields of interest: Performing arts, dance; Performing arts, music; Arts.
Type of support: General/operating support; Management development/capacity building; Capital campaigns; Endowments; Program development; Employee matching gifts; Matching/challenge support.
Limitations: Applications accepted. Giving primarily in the bi-state metropolitan Kansas City, area. No

support for religious or political organizations. No loans or program-related investments.
Publications: Application guidelines.
Application information: Application form not required.
Initial approach: Proposal
Copies of proposal: 1
Deadline(s): None
Board meeting date(s): Quarterly
Final notification: 1-2 months
Officers and Directors:* Julia Irene Kauffman,* Chair. and C.E.O.; David Lady,* C.O.O. and Pres.; Sharon L. Blickensderfer, V.P., Finance; George P. Jandl; Cara Z. Newell; Julia Power Weld.
Number of staff: 3 full-time professional; 1 part-time professional; 1 full-time support; 2 part-time support.
EIN: 431460787
Selected grants: The following grants are a representative sample of this grantmaker's funding activity:
$6,100,000 to Kauffman Center for the Performing Arts, Kansas City, MO, 2012.
$5,000,000 to Kauffman Center for the Performing Arts, Kansas City, MO, 2012.
$3,000,000 to Kauffman Center for the Performing Arts, Kansas City, MO, 2012.
$1,698,375 to Kauffman Center for the Performing Arts, Kansas City, MO, 2012.
$1,698,375 to Kauffman Center for the Performing Arts, Kansas City, MO, 2012.
$850,000 to Kansas City Symphony, Kansas City, MO, 2012. For annual operating support.
$676,000 to Kansas City Ballet Association, Kansas City, MO, 2012. For operating support.
$500,000 to Kansas City Ballet Association, Kansas City, MO, 2012. For capital campaign.
$500,000 to Kansas City Ballet Association, Kansas City, MO, 2012. For capital campaign.
$25,000 to Youth Symphony Association of Kansas City, Mission, KS, 2012. For general operating support of its educational programs.

4923
R. C. Kemper Charitable Trust ✧
c/o UMB Bank, N.A.
P.O. Box 415044, M/S 1020307
Kansas City, MO 64141-5044

Established in 1953 in MO.
Donor: R. Crosby Kemper, Sr.‡.
Foundation type: Independent foundation.
Financial data (yr. ended 12/31/13): Assets, $38,980,178 (M); expenditures, $1,486,557; qualifying distributions, $1,409,055; giving activities include $1,343,010 for 27 grants (high: $705,250; low: $1,000).
Purpose and activities: Giving primarily for education and the arts.
Fields of interest: Museums (art); Arts; Higher education; Education.
Type of support: General/operating support.
Limitations: Applications not accepted. Giving primarily in MO. No grants to individuals.
Application information: Contributes only to pre-selected organizations.
Trustees: Sheila Kemper Dietrich; John Mariner Kemper; R. Crosby Kemper, Jr.; UMB Bank, N.A.
EIN: 446010318
Selected grants: The following grants are a representative sample of this grantmaker's funding activity:
$886,834 to Kemper Museum of Contemporary Art and Design, Kansas City, MO, 2011.
$50,000 to Phillips Academy, Andover, MA, 2011. For general support.
$25,000 to Addison Gallery of American Art, Andover, MA, 2011.

4924
William T. Kemper Charitable Trust ✧
c/o UMB Bank, N.A.
P.O. Box 415044, M/S 1020307
Kansas City, MO 64141-5044

Established in 1989 in MO.
Foundation type: Independent foundation.
Financial data (yr. ended 12/31/13): Assets, $60,725,956 (M); expenditures, $2,836,949; qualifying distributions, $2,675,199; giving activities include $2,556,927 for 15 grants (high: $1,979,927; low: $1,000).
Purpose and activities: Giving primarily for the arts and education.
Fields of interest: Museums; Arts; Education; Agriculture/food, formal/general education; Foundations (private grantmaking).
Limitations: Applications not accepted. Giving primarily in Kansas City, MO. No grants to individuals.
Application information: Contributes only to pre-selected organizations.
Trustees: R. Crosby Kemper; UMB Bank, N.A.
EIN: 436362480
Selected grants: The following grants are a representative sample of this grantmaker's funding activity:
$2,443,102 to Kemper Museum of Contemporary Art and Design, Kansas City, MO, 2011. For general support.
$147,000 to Phillips Academy, Andover, MA, 2011. For general support.

4925
Enid and Crosby Kemper Foundation ✧
c/o UMB Bank, N.A.
P.O. Box 415044, M/S1020307
Kansas City, MO 64141-6692

Established in 1972 in MO.
Donors: Enid J. Kemper; R. Crosby Kemper, Sr.‡.
Foundation type: Independent foundation.
Financial data (yr. ended 12/31/13): Assets, $52,784,733 (M); expenditures, $2,507,144; qualifying distributions, $2,334,843; giving activities include $2,216,785 for 36 grants (high: $987,285; low: $2,000).
Purpose and activities: Giving primarily for the arts, education, and human services.
Fields of interest: Museums (art); Performing arts, orchestras; Arts; Education; Human services.
Type of support: General/operating support.
Limitations: Applications not accepted. Giving primarily in CO and MO. No support for medical institutions. No grants to individuals, or for capital funds.
Application information: Contributes only to pre-selected organizations.
Board meeting date(s): Quarterly and as needed
Trustees: Alexander C. Kemper; Mary S. Kemper; R. Crosby Kemper, Jr.; UMB Bank, N.A.
EIN: 237279896

4926
William T. Kemper Foundation ✧
c/o Commerce Bank
118 W. 47th St.
Kansas City, MO 64112-1692 (816) 234-2568
Application address: Exec. Dir., c/o Commerce Bank, Tr., 922 Walnut St., Ste. 200, Kansas City, MO 64106-1809, tel.: (816) 234-2112

Established in 1989 in MO.
Donors: William T. Kemper‡; William T. Kemper Revocable Trust.
Foundation type: Independent foundation.
Financial data (yr. ended 10/31/13): Assets, $279,011,459 (M); gifts received, $200,629; expenditures, $12,806,963; qualifying distributions, $11,972,928; giving activities include $11,547,724 for 221 grants (high: $1,666,666; low: $500).
Purpose and activities: Giving primarily for education, health, human services, civic improvements and the arts.
Fields of interest: Arts; Education; Health care; Human services; Community/economic development.
Type of support: General/operating support; Continuing support; Annual campaigns; Capital campaigns; Building/renovation; Equipment; Program development; Conferences/seminars; Publication; Seed money; Curriculum development; Research; Technical assistance.
Limitations: Applications accepted. Giving primarily in the Midwest with emphasis on MO and surrounding areas. No support for private foundations or for politically partisan purposes. No grants to individuals, or for tickets for dinners, benefits, exhibits, sports and other event activities, advertisements, endowment funds, or fundraising activities.
Publications: Informational brochure (including application guidelines).
Application information: Guidelines available upon request. Application form not required.
Initial approach: Proposal with proof of nonprofit status
Copies of proposal: 1
Deadline(s): 3 weeks before board meetings
Board meeting date(s): Quarterly
Final notification: 2 - 4 months
Officer: Beth Radtke, Exec. Dir.
Trustees: Jonathan M. Kemper, Member, Contribs. Comm.; Commerce Bank, N.A.
Contributions Committee: Laura Kemper Fields; Julie Kemper Foyer; David W. Kemper.
EIN: 436345116
Selected grants: The following grants are a representative sample of this grantmaker's funding activity:
$1,666,666 to CityArchRiver 2015 Foundation, Saint Louis, MO, 2013.
$1,000,000 to Donald Danforth Plant Science Center, Saint Louis, MO, 2013.
$1,000,000 to Kansas City Symphony, Kansas City, MO, 2013.
$500,000 to Childrens Mercy Hospital, Kansas City, MO, 2013.
$250,000 to Kansas City Art Institute, Kansas City, MO, 2013.
$150,000 to Drumm Foundation, Independence, MO, 2013.
$27,500 to Bradley University, Peoria, IL, 2013.
$25,000 to OASIS Institute, Saint Louis Oasis, Saint Louis, MO, 2013.

$25,000 to Urban Strategies, Saint Louis, MO, 2013.
$20,000 to Friends of Chamber Music, Kansas City, MO, 2013.

4927
David Woods Kemper Memorial Foundation ✧
922 Walnut St., Ste. 200
Kansas City, MO 64106-1809

Incorporated in 1946 in MO.
Donor: James M. Kemper, Jr.
Foundation type: Independent foundation.
Financial data (yr. ended 12/31/13): Assets, $8,855,493 (M); expenditures, $790,254; qualifying distributions, $781,818; giving activities include $657,250 for 37 grants (high: $100,000; low: $500).
Purpose and activities: Giving primarily for arts organizations, education, health, social services, and children and youth services, including a children's hospital.
Fields of interest: Museums; Arts; Higher education; Education; Hospitals (specialty); Health care; Human services; Children/youth, services.
Limitations: Applications not accepted. Giving primarily in Kansas City, MO. No grants to individuals.
Application information: Contributes only to pre-selected organizations.
Officers: James M. Kemper, Jr., Pres.; David W. Kemper, V.P.; Laura Kemper Fields, Secy.-Treas.
Directors: Jonathan M. Kemper; Julie Ann Kemper.
Number of staff: 3
EIN: 446012535

4928
The Theodore A. Kienstra Foundation ✧ ☆
c/o Theodore A. Kienstra, Jr
755 S. New Ballas Rd., Ste. 150
Saint Louis, MO 63141-8797

Established in MO.
Donors: Theodore A. Kienstra, Sr.; Theodore A. Kienstra, Jr.; Tony Soukenik; H. Diekemper Trust.
Foundation type: Independent foundation.
Financial data (yr. ended 12/31/13): Assets, $6,968,470 (M); gifts received, $111,800; expenditures, $505,408; qualifying distributions, $481,460; giving activities include $480,700 for 68 grants (high: $180,000; low: $250).
Fields of interest: Elementary school/education; Catholic agencies & churches.
Limitations: Applications not accepted. Giving primarily in MO. No grants to individuals.
Application information: Unsolicited requests for funds not accepted.
Officers: Theodore A. Kienstra, Jr., Pres.; Daniel Bruns, V.P.; Anthony J. Soukenik, Secy.; Patrick Wessels, Treas.
Board Members: Christina L. Kienstra; Faith Kienstra; Genevieve Casagrande; Kathleen Bruns; Kimberly McDonough.
EIN: 431727300

4929
Bill and Amy Koman Family Foundation ✧ ☆
7733 Forsyth Blvd., Ste. 1375
St. Louis, MO 63105-1834

Established in 2010 in MO.
Donor: William J. Koman.
Foundation type: Independent foundation.
Financial data (yr. ended 12/31/12): Assets, $571,691 (M); expenditures, $810,613; qualifying distributions, $796,600; giving activities include $796,600 for grants.
Fields of interest: Health care; Health organizations; Medical research.
Limitations: Applications not accepted. Giving primarily in St. Louis, MO.
Application information: Unsolicited requests for funds not accepted.
Officers: Amy M. Koman, Mgr.; William J. Koman, Mgr.
Trustee: Paul L. Vogel.
EIN: 276982384

4930
Thomas A. Kooyumjian Family Trust ✧
c/o Tony Kooyumjian
277 Schindler Rd.
Augusta, MO 63332

Established in 1996 in IL.
Donor: Thomas A. Kooyumjian.
Foundation type: Independent foundation.
Financial data (yr. ended 12/31/13): Assets, $9,753,620 (M); expenditures, $537,027; qualifying distributions, $457,897; giving activities include $454,535 for 7 grants (high: $116,000; low: $16,700).
Fields of interest: Performing arts, orchestras; Historic preservation/historical societies; Education, fund raising/fund distribution; Higher education, university; Economic development.
Type of support: Endowments.
Limitations: Applications not accepted. Giving primarily in Chicago, IL, MA and MO. No grants to individuals.
Application information: Contributes only to pre-selected organizations.
Officers: Tony Kooyumjian, Pres.; Thomas A. Kooyumjian, Treas.
EIN: 363406582
Selected grants: The following grants are a representative sample of this grantmaker's funding activity:
$75,000 to Armenia Tree Project, Watertown, MA, 2011.
$70,000 to University of Missouri, Columbia, MO, 2011.
$30,000 to California State University, Fresno, CA, 2011.
$23,000 to University of Chicago, Chicago, IL, 2011.
$8,500 to Armenian General Benevolent Union, New York, NY, 2011.
$5,500 to California State University, Fresno, CA, 2011.

4931
The Laclede Group Foundation ✧
(formerly Laclede Gas Charitable Trust)
720 Olive St., Ste. 1306
St. Louis, MO 63101-2338
Main URL: http://www.thelacledegroup.com/aboutthelacledegroup/foundation/

Established in 1966 in MO.
Donor: Laclede Gas Co.
Foundation type: Company-sponsored foundation.
Financial data (yr. ended 09/30/13): Assets, $7,188,343 (M); gifts received, $2,000,000; expenditures, $669,793; qualifying distributions, $657,411; giving activities include $635,293 for 21 grants (high: $410,320; low: $325), and $22,118 for 40 employee matching gifts.
Purpose and activities: The foundation supports the United Way; community enrichment programs designed to support educational, diversity, and inclusion efforts and cultural institutions; and sustainability initiatives designed to protect and preserve community's environmental and natural resources.
Fields of interest: Arts; Education; Environment, natural resources; Environment; Health care; Human services; United Ways and Federated Giving Programs.
Type of support: General/operating support; Continuing support; Annual campaigns; Building/renovation; Equipment; Program development; Employee matching gifts.
Limitations: Applications accepted. Giving primarily in areas of company operations in St. Louis, MO. No support for political, labor, fraternal, or religious organizations, civic clubs, K-8 schools, or school-affiliated clubs. No grants to individuals, or for family services, advertising, school-affiliated events, sports, athletic events, or athletic programs, travel related events, student trips or tours, development or production of books, films, videos, or television programs, endowments, or memorial campaigns.
Application information: The Missouri Common Grant Application is also accepted. Support is limited to 1 contribution per organization during any given year. Application form required.
Initial approach: Complete online eligibility quiz and application
Copies of proposal: 1
Deadline(s): None
Board meeting date(s): Quarterly
Officers and Trustees:* Mary Caola Kullman,* Chair. and Pres.; Micheal R. Spotanski,* V.P.; P.S. Kramer, Secy.; Lynn D. Rawlings, Treas.; Scott E. Jaskowiak; Steven L. Lindsey.
EIN: 436068197
Selected grants: The following grants are a representative sample of this grantmaker's funding activity:
$45,000 to Saint Louis Science Center, Saint Louis, MO, 2011.
$40,000 to Saint Louis Zoo, Saint Louis, MO, 2011.
$20,000 to Barnes-Jewish Hospital Foundation, Saint Louis, MO, 2011.
$20,000 to Magic House, Saint Louis, MO, 2011.
$20,000 to Teach for America, Saint Louis, MO, 2011.
$20,000 to YMCA of Greater Saint Louis, Saint Louis, MO, 2011.
$15,000 to Webster University, Saint Louis, MO, 2011.
$10,000 to Boy Scouts of America, Saint Louis, MO, 2011.

$10,000 to Characterplus, Saint Louis, MO, 2011.
$10,000 to Ranken Technical College, Saint Louis, MO, 2011.

4932
Frank S. and Julia M. Ladner Family Foundation ✧
P.O. Box 220399
Kirkwood, MO 63122-0399

Established in 1993 in KY.
Donors: Frank S. Ladner; Julia M. Ladner.
Foundation type: Independent foundation.
Financial data (yr. ended 12/31/13): Assets, $13,098,036 (M); gifts received, $62,823; expenditures, $946,574; qualifying distributions, $929,944; giving activities include $851,848 for 92 grants (high: $180,948; low: $400).
Purpose and activities: Giving primarily for education, and to Roman Catholic organizations and schools; funding also for social services.
Fields of interest: Education; Human services; Catholic agencies & churches.
Limitations: Applications not accepted. Giving primarily in IL, IN and MN; some funding also in MO and OK. No grants to individuals.
Application information: Contributes only to pre-selected organizations.
Officers: Frank S. Ladner, Pres.; Mary F.L. Bauer, Secy.
Directors: Ann Marie Ladner; Julia M. Ladner; Margaret M. Ladner; Thomas M. Ladner; William P. Ladner.
EIN: 611248781
Selected grants: The following grants are a representative sample of this grantmaker's funding activity:
$23,000 to Nature Conservancy, Arlington, VA, 2011.
$10,000 to Archdiocese of Saint Louis, Saint Louis, MO, 2011.
$8,000 to Common Cause, Washington, DC, 2011.
$8,000 to Common Cause, Washington, DC, 2011.
$7,000 to Covenant House, New York, NY, 2011.
$5,000 to Special Olympics, Washington, DC, 2011.
$4,000 to League of Women Voters of the United States, Washington, DC, 2011.

4933
Laurie Foundation for the Performing Arts, Inc. ✧ ☆
302 Campusview Dr., Ste. 108
Columbia, MO 65201-7507

Donor: Nancy W. Laurie.
Foundation type: Independent foundation.
Financial data (yr. ended 12/31/12): Assets, $352,985 (M); gifts received, $2,474,781; expenditures, $5,848,995; qualifying distributions, $5,021,237; giving activities include $1,680,450 for 8 grants (high: $1,640,795; low: $175), and $4,981,584 for 2 foundation-administered programs.
Purpose and activities: Giving primarily for human services, and for a ballet company.
Fields of interest: Performing arts, ballet; Human services.
Limitations: Applications not accepted. Giving primarily in Columbia, MO.
Application information: Unsolicited requests for funds not accepted.
Officers and Directors:* Nancy W. Laurie,* Pres.; Richard C. Thomas,* Secy.-Treas.; Gregory B. Mudd, Exec. Dir.; Paige Laurie Dubbert; Brent P. Karasiuk.
EIN: 273493939

4934
The Lay Family Foundation ✧
(formerly Sister Mary Louis Foundation)
c/o Tod Moses, C.P.A.
10135 Manchester Rd., Ste. 206
St. Louis, MO 63122-1558

Established in 1989 in MO.
Donors: Henry A. Lay‡; Antonia Investments, Ltd.
Foundation type: Independent foundation.
Financial data (yr. ended 12/31/12): Assets, $16,452,921 (M); expenditures, $1,048,876; qualifying distributions, $965,518; giving activities include $965,518 for grants.
Purpose and activities: Giving primarily for Roman Catholic education, particularly to an organization that provides scholarships to low-income children; some funding for higher education, the arts, including a sculpture park, and for children and youth services.
Fields of interest: Visual arts, sculpture; Elementary/secondary education; Higher education; Scholarships/financial aid; Education; Children/youth, services; Catholic agencies & churches.
Type of support: General/operating support; Endowments; Scholarship funds.
Limitations: Applications not accepted. Giving primarily in St. Louis, MO. No grants to individuals.
Application information: Contributes only to pre-selected organizations.
Officers: John E. Dooling, Jr., Chair.; Charles B. Luber, C.E.O.; Louis J. Garr, Jr., Pres.
EIN: 431510405
Selected grants: The following grants are a representative sample of this grantmaker's funding activity:
$1,212,219 to Today and Tomorrow Educational Foundation, Saint Louis, MO, 2010. For scholarship fund.
$226,261 to West Kentucky Community and Technical College, Paducah, KY, 2010.
$183,498 to Northeastern Illinois University, Chicago, IL, 2010.
$121,000 to Saint Josephs Academy, Saint Louis, MO, 2011. For general support.
$16,000 to Saint Louis University, Saint Louis, MO, 2011. For general support.
$9,600 to University of Connecticut Foundation, Storrs, CT, 2010.
$6,400 to University of Connecticut Foundation, Storrs, CT, 2011.
$5,641 to Block Yeshiva High School, Saint Louis, MO, 2011. For scholarship fund.

4935
Jean, Jack, and Mildred Lemons Charitable Trust ✧ ☆
P.O. Box 387
St. Louis, MO 63166-0387

Established in 1987 in MO.
Foundation type: Independent foundation.
Financial data (yr. ended 06/30/13): Assets, $7,743,946 (M); expenditures, $808,431; qualifying distributions, $730,013; giving activities include $726,556 for 71 grants (high: $40,000; low: $2,000).
Purpose and activities: Giving primarily for education, health, and children, youth and social services.
Fields of interest: Education; Health care; Health organizations, association; Human services; Children/youth, services; Foundations (private grantmaking).
Limitations: Applications not accepted. Giving primarily in MO, with emphasis on Joplin.
Application information: Unsolicited requests for funds not accepted.
Trustee: U.S. Bank, N.A.
EIN: 436328116
Selected grants: The following grants are a representative sample of this grantmaker's funding activity:
$30,000 to American Red Cross, Joplin, MO, 2011.
$30,000 to Community Health Clinic of Joplin, Joplin, MO, 2011.
$26,500 to Salvation Army of Joplin, Joplin, MO, 2011.
$18,000 to YMCA, Joplin Family, Joplin, MO, 2011.
$13,000 to Humane Society of Joplin, Joplin, MO, 2011.
$13,000 to Joplin Historical and Mineral Museum, Joplin, MO, 2011.
$10,000 to United Way of Southwest Missouri and Southeast Kansas, Joplin, MO, 2011.
$8,400 to Ozark Christian College, Joplin, MO, 2011.
$6,000 to Bridge Ministries, Joplin, MO, 2011.
$5,500 to Joplin Area Catholic Schools, Joplin, MO, 2011.

4936
David B. Lichtenstein Foundation ✧
(formerly Lichtenstein Foundation)
1400 Forum Blvd., Ste. 38
Columbia, MO 65203-1997 (573) 445-9176
Contact: Davida Layer, Chair.

Established in 1947 in MO.
Donors: David B. Lichtenstein, Jr.; Doris Lichtenstein.
Foundation type: Independent foundation.
Financial data (yr. ended 12/31/13): Assets, $12,110,402 (M); expenditures, $900,990; qualifying distributions, $754,795; giving activities include $754,795 for 7 grants (high: $412,500; low: $1,000).
Fields of interest: Performing arts, opera; Botanical gardens; Zoos/zoological societies.
Type of support: Annual campaigns; Capital campaigns; Equipment; Matching/challenge support.
Limitations: Applications accepted. Giving primarily in MO. No support for for-profit organizations or organizations that contribute funds to a national organization.
Application information: Application form not required.
Initial approach: Proposal
Deadline(s): None
Officers: Davida Layer, Chair.; Randy Layer, Vice-Chair.; Gail Abernathy, Secy.; Connie Popejoy, Treas.
Trustee: Kevin Popejoy.
EIN: 436033786

4937
Jacob L. & Ella C. Loose Foundation ✧
1055 Broadway, Ste. 130
Kansas City, MO 64105-1595

Trust established in 1945 in MO.
Donors: Jacob L. Loose†; Ella C. Loose†; Ella C. Loose Trust; Jacob L. Loose Trust.
Foundation type: Independent foundation.
Financial data (yr. ended 12/31/12): Assets, $0 (M); gifts received, $537,000; expenditures, $537,000; qualifying distributions, $537,000; giving activities include $537,000 for 1 grant.
Purpose and activities: The foundation's mission is to help the poor and needy children and families of Jackson County and/or Kansas City, Missouri.
Fields of interest: Health care; Children/youth, services; Family services; Economically disadvantaged.
Type of support: Program development; Technical assistance.
Limitations: Applications not accepted. Giving limited to Kansas City and Jackson County, MO. No support for programs that support adult mental health. No grants to individuals, or for scholarships, debt reduction, capital expenditures, endowment campaigns, or annual appeals or fund raising drives, events, membership contributions and conference expenses.
Application information: Unsolicited requests for funds not accepted.
Officers: Jeanne Sosland, Pres.; Bill Lyons, V.P.; Marny Sherman, Secy.; Mark Foster, Treas.
Directors: Dianne Cleaver; Randall Ferguson; David Francis; Daniel Fromm; Jean Green; Jean McDonnell; Kevin Pavicic; Carlos Salazar; Susan Stanton.
EIN: 436050347

4938
Stanley and Lucy Lopata Foundation ✧
c/o Lopata, Flegel & Co., LLP
600 Mason Ridge Ctr. Dr., Ste. 100
St. Louis, MO 63141-8572

Established in 1968.
Donors: Stanley Lopata†; Lucy Lopata; Lopata Charitable Lead Trust No. 1; Lopata Charitable Lead Trust No. 4.
Foundation type: Independent foundation.
Financial data (yr. ended 12/31/13): Assets, $11,020,768 (M); gifts received, $122,375; expenditures, $501,710; qualifying distributions, $450,500; giving activities include $445,575 for 77 grants (high: $50,200; low: $50).
Fields of interest: Museums (art); Arts; Higher education; Education; Botanical gardens; Health organizations, association; Human services; United Ways and Federated Giving Programs; Jewish agencies & synagogues.
Type of support: General/operating support; Annual campaigns; Capital campaigns; Endowments; Emergency funds; Program development.
Limitations: Applications not accepted. Giving primarily in St. Louis, MO. No grants to individuals.
Application information: Contributes only to pre-selected organizations.
Trustees: James R. Lopata; Lucy Lopata; Roger Lopata; Steven Lopata.
EIN: 436099972

4939
Joseph J. Mayer Education Trust ✧
c/o Hawthorn Bank
132 E. High St.
Jefferson City, MO 65101-2930

Established in MO.
Foundation type: Independent foundation.
Financial data (yr. ended 12/31/13): Assets, $12,168,383 (M); expenditures, $573,523; qualifying distributions, $507,225; giving activities include $505,225 for 4 grants (high: $333,406; low: $4,445).
Fields of interest: Education.
Type of support: Scholarship funds.
Limitations: Applications not accepted. Giving primarily in Jefferson City and Sikeston, MO.
Application information: Contributes only to pre-selected organizations.
Trustee: Hawthorn Bank.
EIN: 436738915
Selected grants: The following grants are a representative sample of this grantmaker's funding activity:
$339,181 to Jefferson City Public Schools, Jefferson City, MO, 2012. For Financial Assistance to Schools to Grant Scholarship.

4940
McDonnell Foundation, Inc. ✧
4909 Sunset Dr.
Kansas City, MO 64112-2309

Established in 1986 in MO.
Donors: Thomas A. McDonnell; Jean McDonnell; Thomas A. McDonnell Trust.
Foundation type: Independent foundation.
Financial data (yr. ended 12/31/13): Assets, $47,253,054 (M); gifts received, $3,336,599; expenditures, $1,992,028; qualifying distributions, $1,977,327; giving activities include $1,949,935 for 89 grants (high: $300,000; low: $60).
Purpose and activities: Giving primarily for education, the arts, and human services.
Fields of interest: Arts; Secondary school/education; Higher education; Education; Health organizations, association; Human services; Catholic agencies & churches.
Limitations: Applications not accepted. Giving primarily in KS and Kansas City, MO. No grants to individuals.
Application information: Contributes only to pre-selected organizations.
Officer and Directors:* Jean McDonnell,* Pres.; Kerry Barrett; Mary C. Fielder; Thomas A. McDonnell.
EIN: 431439173
Selected grants: The following grants are a representative sample of this grantmaker's funding activity:
$500,000 to Saint Teresas Academy, Kansas City, MO, 2011.
$100,000 to DeLaSalle Education Center, Kansas City, MO, 2011.
$46,875 to Bishop Miege High School, Shawnee Mission, KS, 2011.
$40,000 to Operation Breakthrough, Kansas City, MO, 2011.
$31,250 to Bishop Miege High School, Shawnee Mission, KS, 2011.
$10,000 to Operation Breakthrough, Kansas City, MO, 2011.
$10,000 to Rose Brooks Center, Kansas City, MO, 2011.
$10,000 to Vail Valley Foundation, Avon, CO, 2010.
$5,000 to Bishop Miege High School, Shawnee Mission, KS, 2011.
$1,000 to Boys Town, Boys Town, NE, 2011.
$1,000 to Hudson Guild, New York, NY, 2011.

4941
James S. McDonnell Foundation ✧
(also known as JSMF)
1034 S. Brentwood Blvd., Ste. 1850
St. Louis, MO 63117-1229 (314) 721-1532
Contact: Susan M. Fitzpatrick, Pres.
FAX: (314) 721-7421; E-mail: info@jsmf.org; Additional e-mail: help@jsmf.org; Main URL: http://www.jsmf.org
E-Newsletter: http://www.jsmf.org/about/mailinglist.htm
Facebook: http://www.facebook.com/JSMFoundation
Grants Database: http://www.jsmf.org/grants/search.php
Twitter: http://twitter.com/jsmf

Established in MO.
Foundation type: Independent foundation.
Financial data (yr. ended 12/31/13): Assets, $506,185,338 (M); expenditures, $32,678,774; qualifying distributions, $28,291,772; giving activities include $27,804,075 for 126 grants (high: $4,584,000; low: $30,817).
Purpose and activities: JSMF believes that private philanthropic support for science is most effective when it invests in the acquisition of new knowledge and in the responsible application of knowledge for solving the real world problems. The 21st Century Science Initiative, the foundation's revised program and funding strategy, will award two types of grants in three program areas. The three program areas are Mathematical & Complex Systems Approaches for Brain Cancer Research, Studying Complex Systems, and Understanding Human Cognition. Projects supported through the 21st Century Science Initiative are expected to meet highly selective intellectual standards.
Fields of interest: Cancer research; Brain research; Medical research; Science, research; Science.
Type of support: Research.
Limitations: Applications accepted. Giving on a local, national and international basis. No support for religious, educational or political organizations. No grants to individuals or for ongoing operational support for university-based centers, programs or institutes, no support for tuition, stipends, scholarships, underwriting or sponsoring of charitable functions, or museum exhibitions, expenses tied to projects whose explicit goal is the publication of a work, or expenses tied to the establishment or day-to-day running of a journal or small press.
Publications: Financial statement; Grants list; Program policy statement.
Application information: See foundation's web site for application information, all proposals must be electronically submitted. Institutions sponsoring an application on behalf of a particular principal investigator to JSMF programs (Research Awards, Collaborative Activity Awards) can only submit one application every 3 years on behalf of the named principal investigator. Application form not required.
Initial approach: Letter of inquiry for collaborative activity awards
Copies of proposal: 1

Deadline(s): Early to mid-Mar. for research awards; no deadline for letters of inquiry for collaborative activity awards
Board meeting date(s): Varies
Final notification: Varies depending on submission date
Officers and Directors:* Susan M. Fitzpatrick, Ph.D., Pres.; James S. McDonnell III,* Secy.; John F. McDonnell,* Treas.; Jeanne M. Champer; Holly M. James; Alicia S. McDonnell; Jeffrey M. McDonnall; Marcella M. Stevens.
Number of staff: 2 full-time professional; 2 full-time support.
EIN: 542074788
Selected grants: The following grants are a representative sample of this grantmaker's funding activity:
$4,328,562 to JSM Charitable Trust, Saint Louis, MO, 2012. For Operating Fund Transfers to JSMCT.
$3,531,173 to JSM Charitable Trust, Saint Louis, MO, 2012. For Operating Fund Transfers to JSMCT.
$1,428,220 to Washington University, Saint Louis, MO, 2012. For research project, Applying Cognitive Psychology to Enhance Educational Practice: II.
$150,000 to New York University, New York, NY, 2012. For research project, Dissecting learning: Combining experimental and computational approaches.
$150,000 to Stanford University, Stanford, CA, 2012. For research project, Mental representations of abstract domains.
$100,000 to Massachusetts Institute of Technology, Cambridge, MA, 2012. For Postdoctoral Fellow's salary, fringe benefits and research plan.

4942
The McGee Foundation ✧
c/o Bernard J. Duffy, III
2001 Walnut St.
Kansas City, MO 64108-1811
Application address: c/o Whitney Hosty, 1055 Broadway, Ste. 130, Kansas City, MO 64105, tel.: (816) 627-3441

Incorporated in 1951 in MO.
Donors: Joseph J. McGee†; Mrs. Joseph J. McGee†; Frank McGee†; Mrs. Frank McGee†; Louis B. McGee†; Old American Insurance Co.; Thomas McGee and Sons; Joseph J. McGee, Jr.†; Julie McGee; David McGee; Simon McGee.
Foundation type: Independent foundation.
Financial data (yr. ended 12/31/13): Assets, $14,984,649 (M); expenditures, $732,303; qualifying distributions, $709,525; giving activities include $678,234 for 29 grants (high: $50,000; low: $4,905).
Purpose and activities: The foundation uses its funds primarily for education, health, charitable, and religious agencies and institutions operated, supervised or controlled by or in connection with the Roman Catholic Church. This includes any Roman Catholic non-profit organization which qualifies for exemption from federal income tax under Section 501(c)(3) of the Internal Revenue Code to the United States Catholic Conference by virtue of its listing in the current official Catholic Directory.
Fields of interest: Education; Health care; Human services.
Type of support: Capital campaigns; Equipment; Debt reduction.
Limitations: Applications accepted. Giving limited to the greater bi-state Kansas City area. No support for arts and cultural activities, or for charter schools, civic organizations, economic or neighborhood development, individual churches or diocesan schools, information/referral programs, local affiliates of national disease organizations, regranting organizations, historic preservation or for public schools or taxpayer supported institutions. No grants to individuals, or for annual campaigns, charitable advertising, compensation for specific positions, scholarly research, conferences and seminars, endowments, fund raisers, or for multi-year grants and United appeals.
Publications: Application guidelines.
Application information: Application form required.
Initial approach: 1 or 2-page letter
Copies of proposal: 1
Deadline(s): None
Officers and Directors:* Simon P. McGee, Pres.; Sheila M. Lillis,* Secy.; Bernard J. Duffy III, Treas.; Virginia L. Coppinger; John R. McGee; Molly McGee; Thomas R. McGee, Jr.; Clyde F. Wendel.
Number of staff: None.
EIN: 446006285
Selected grants: The following grants are a representative sample of this grantmaker's funding activity:
$25,000 to Truman Medical Center Charitable Foundation, Kansas City, MO, 2012. For facility upgrade.

4943
MFA Foundation ✧
201 Ray Young Dr.
Columbia, MO 65201-3568 (573) 876-5458
Contact: Larna Lavelle, Secy.-Treas.

Established in 1958 in MO.
Donors: Robert O. Wurmb; MFA Inc.; MFA Oil Co.
Foundation type: Company-sponsored foundation.
Financial data (yr. ended 06/30/13): Assets, $15,210,054 (M); gifts received, $119,280; expenditures, $853,804; qualifying distributions, $853,804; giving activities include $640,332 for 328 grants to individuals (high: $2,000; low: $210).
Purpose and activities: The foundation supports programs designed to provide educational opportunity for youth and awards college scholarships to high school seniors.
Fields of interest: Higher education; Education; Agriculture; Youth development, agriculture; Youth development.
Type of support: General/operating support; Scholarship funds; Scholarships—to individuals.
Limitations: Applications accepted. Giving primarily in areas of company operations, with emphasis on MO.
Publications: Application guidelines; Informational brochure.
Application information: Application form required.
Initial approach: Completed Application form
Deadline(s): Mar. 15
Board meeting date(s): June and Nov.
Officers and Trustees:* Bill Streeter,* Pres.; Jerry Taylor,* V.P.; Larna Lavelle, Secy.-Treas.; Ken Caspall; Bill Coen; Don Copenhaver; Larry Fick; J. Brian Griffith; John Percival; Phil Perkins; Janice Schuerman; Ernie Verslues.
EIN: 436026877
Selected grants: The following grants are a representative sample of this grantmaker's funding activity:
$5,000 to Columbia College, Columbia, MO, 2011.
$5,000 to Drury University, Springfield, MO, 2011.
$5,000 to Four-H Foundation, Missouri, Columbia, MO, 2011.
$5,000 to Missouri Young Farmers Association, Jefferson City, MO, 2011.
$4,000 to Job Point, Columbia, MO, 2011.
$2,500 to College of the Ozarks, Point Lookout, MO, 2011.
$1,500 to Great Circle, Saint James, MO, 2011.
$1,500 to Missouri Girls Town Foundation, Kingdom City, MO, 2011.
$1,000 to Alzheimers Association, Columbia, MO, 2011.
$1,000 to Missouri Lions Eye Research Foundation, Columbia, MO, 2011.

4944
Millstone Foundation ✧ ☆
7733 Forsyth Blvd., No. 1525
St. Louis, MO 63105-1867
Application address: c/o Robert D. Millstone, 7701 Forsyth Blvd., Ste. 925, St. Louis, MO 63105, tel.: (314) 721-1932

Incorporated in 1955 in MO.
Donors: I.E. Millstone; Goldie G. Millstone†.
Foundation type: Independent foundation.
Financial data (yr. ended 05/31/13): Assets, $7,750,609 (M); expenditures, $570,896; qualifying distributions, $514,049; giving activities include $498,742 for 62 grants (high: $78,232; low: $250).
Purpose and activities: Giving primarily for higher education and to Jewish organizations.
Fields of interest: Higher education; Education; Hospitals (specialty); Human services; Jewish federated giving programs; Jewish agencies & synagogues.
International interests: Israel.
Type of support: General/operating support; Continuing support; Annual campaigns; Emergency funds; Scholarship funds; Research.
Limitations: Applications accepted. Giving primarily in St. Louis, MO. No grants to individuals; no loans.
Application information: Application form required.
Initial approach: Letter
Copies of proposal: 1
Deadline(s): None
Officer and Directors:* Robert D. Millstone,* Pres.; Colleen Millstone.
Number of staff: 2 part-time professional.
EIN: 436027373
Selected grants: The following grants are a representative sample of this grantmaker's funding activity:
$100,000 to Washington University, Saint Louis, MO, 2011.
$19,500 to Jewish Federation of Saint Louis, Saint Louis, MO, 2011.
$13,232 to Barnes-Jewish Hospital, Saint Louis, MO, 2011.
$11,600 to University of Missouri, Saint Louis, MO, 2011.
$7,000 to Cystic Fibrosis Foundation, Saint Ann, MO, 2011.
$5,000 to Memory Care Home Solutions, Saint Louis, MO, 2011.
$2,500 to Fontbonne University, Saint Louis, MO, 2011.
$2,500 to University of Vermont, Burlington, VT, 2011.
$2,000 to Thomas Jefferson School, Saint Louis, MO, 2011.

$1,250 to Miriam Foundation, Saint Louis, MO, 2011.

4945
Monsanto Fund ✧
800 N. Lindbergh Blvd.
St. Louis, MO 63167-7843 (314) 694-4391
Contact: Deborah J. Patterson, Pres.
FAX: (314) 694-7658;
E-mail: monsanto.fund@monsanto.com; Additional tel.: (314) 694-1000, fax: (314) 694-1001; Contact for America's Farmers Grow Communities and America's Farmers Grow Rural Education: Eileen Jensen, 914 Spruce St., St. Louis, MO 63102, tel.: (877) 267-3332; Main URL: http://www.monsantofund.org/
America's Farmers Campaign on Facebook: http://www.facebook.com/AmericasFarmers
America's Farmers Campaign on Twitter: https://twitter.com/americasfarmers
America's Farmers: Grow Communities Winners: http://www.americasfarmers.com/recognition-programs/grow-communities-2014-winners/
America's Farmers: Grow Rural Education Winners: http://www.americasfarmers.com/recognition-programs/grow-rural-education-2013-winners/

Incorporated in 1964 in MO as successor to the Monsanto Charitable Trust.
Donor: Monsanto Co.
Foundation type: Company-sponsored foundation.
Financial data (yr. ended 12/31/13): Assets, $14,466,836 (M); gifts received, $14,450,000; expenditures, $22,138,072; qualifying distributions, $22,106,265; giving activities include $20,004,683 for 2,916 grants (high: $900,000; low: $250), and $1,761,596 for 6,803 employee matching gifts.
Purpose and activities: The fund supports programs designed to strengthen farming communities and the communities where Monsanto employees live and work. Special emphasis is directed toward programs designed to improve education in farming communities, including schools, libraries, science centers, farmer training, and academic initiatives that enrich school programming; and meet critical needs in communities through food security, sanitation, access to clean water, public safety, and various other local needs.
Fields of interest: Arts education; Visual arts; Performing arts; Literature; Arts; Elementary/secondary education; Libraries (public); Education; Environment, pollution control; Environment, water pollution; Botanical/horticulture/landscape services; Environment; Public health, clean water supply; Public health, sanitation; Agriculture/food, research; Agriculture/food, public education; Agriculture; Agriculture, farmlands; Agriculture, farm bureaus/granges; Food services; Nutrition; Disasters, fire prevention/control; Safety, education; Safety/disasters; Youth development, agriculture; Human services; Science, formal/general education; Mathematics; Science; Public affairs; Children; Youth; Economically disadvantaged.
Type of support: General/operating support; Continuing support; Equipment; Program development; Conferences/seminars; Seed money; Curriculum development; Research; Program evaluation; Employee matching gifts; Matching/challenge support.
Limitations: Applications accepted. Giving on a national and international basis primarily in areas of company operations in GA, IA, ID, IL, and LA, with emphasis on the greater St. Louis, MO, area. Giving outside the U.S. in Canada, Mexico, the United Kingdom, and Africa, including Malawi, Burkina Faso, Kenya, South Africa, and Uganda, Asia, including China, India, Indonesia, Philippines, and Thailand, and South America including Argentina, Brazil, Chile, Columbia, Guatemala, Honduras, Paraguay, and Uruguay. No support for start-up organizations, fraternal, labor, or veterans' organizations not of direct benefit to the entire community, religious, politically partisan, or similar organizations, or discriminatory organizations. No grants to individuals, or for debt reduction, benefits, dinners, or advertisements, endowments, marketing, or projects in which Monsanto Company has a financial interest or could derive a financial benefit through cash or rights to intellectual property; no donations of printers, computer software, copiers, scanners, or computers.
Publications: Application guidelines; Annual report; Grants list; Program policy statement.
Application information: Support is limited to 1 contribution per organization during any given year. Organizations receiving support are asked to submit a mid-year report and a final report. A site visit may be requested for Kids Garden Fresh Program. All applicants are welcome to attend a grant information session at Monsanto headquarters. Session dates are available on Monsanto's website.
Initial approach: Complete online application; complete online nomination for America's Farmers: Grow Rural Education
Deadline(s): Feb. 28 and Aug. 31 for Math & Science Education K-12 and Access to Arts; Feb. 28 for US Site Grants; Feb. 28 and Aug. 31 for international organizations; Apr. 21 for America's Farmers: Grow Rural Education; June 1 for Kids Garden Fresh Program; and Nov. 30 for America's Farmers: Grow Communities
Board meeting date(s): Twice per year
Final notification: July for Kids Garden Fresh Program
Officers and Directors:* Derek K. Rapp,* Chair.; Deborah J. Patterson,* Pres.; Sonya Meyers Davis, Secy.; Thomas D. Hartley, Treas.; Michael J. Frank; Janet M. Holloway; Jesus Madrazo; Nicole M. Ringenberg; Michael K. Stern.
Number of staff: 1 full-time professional; 1 part-time professional; 2 full-time support.
EIN: 436044736
Selected grants: The following grants are a representative sample of this grantmaker's funding activity:
$844,484 to United Way of Greater Saint Louis, Saint Louis, MO, 2012. For 2011 Campaign Contribution.
$500,000 to Washington University, Saint Louis, MO, 2012. For Extension of Mysci grant for 1 year from July 1, 2011 thru June 30, 2012.
$473,000 to Washington University, Institute for School Partnership, Saint Louis, MO, 2012. For MySci Plus.
$169,200 to Africa Educational Trust, London, England, 2012. For Administration of Canada's Farmers Grow Communities Grants.
$160,000 to Saint Louis Symphony Orchestra, Saint Louis, MO, 2012. For 2012-13 IN UNISON Church Program and IN UNISON Chorus.
$132,000 to Gateway Greening, Saint Louis, MO, 2012. For GGI to partner with Monsanto to provide a co-branded education model called Kids Garden Fresh that would focus on garden-based learning opportunities in urban areas in St Louis region.
$20,000 to Farm Share, Homestead, FL, 2012. For Farm Share Food Recovery and Distribution Program.
$10,000 to Greece Central School District, Rochester, NY, 2012. For Navigation to College and Career Readiness.
$10,000 to Wishek 19, Wishek, ND, 2012. For STEM Education in the Classroom.
$2,600 to United Way, White County, Monticello, IN, 2012. For United Way Seed 2012.

4946
Judge C. F. Moulton Christmas Poor Fund ✧ ☆
c/o Commerce Bank
118 W. 47th St.
Kansas City, MO 64112-1601

Established in 2008 in MO.
Foundation type: Independent foundation.
Financial data (yr. ended 03/31/13): Assets, $8,881,834 (M); expenditures, $560,861; qualifying distributions, $450,298; giving activities include $425,000 for 37 grants (high: $43,250; low: $2,500).
Fields of interest: Human services; Christian agencies & churches.
Limitations: Applications not accepted. Giving primarily in MO.
Application information: Unsolicited requests for funds not accepted.
Trustee: Commerce Bank, N.A.
EIN: 436936927
Selected grants: The following grants are a representative sample of this grantmaker's funding activity:
$30,000 to Community Services League, Independence, MO, 2011.
$25,000 to Metropolitan Lutheran Ministry, Kansas City, MO, 2011.
$20,000 to City Union Mission, Kansas City, MO, 2011.
$20,000 to Episcopal Community Services, Kansas City, MO, 2011.
$20,000 to Operation Breakthrough, Kansas City, MO, 2011.
$20,000 to Raytown Emergency Assistance Program, Raytown, MO, 2011.
$15,000 to Kansas City Rescue Mission, Kansas City, MO, 2011.
$15,000 to Phoenix Family Housing Corporation, Kansas City, MO, 2011.
$10,000 to Benilde Hall, Kansas City, MO, 2011.
$5,000 to Save Foundation, Kansas City, MO, 2011.

4947
Musgrave Foundation ✧
1 Corporate Ctr.
1949 E. Sunshine, Ste. 1-130
Springfield, MO 65804-1601 (417) 841-4698
FAX: (417) 882-2529;
E-mail: contact@musgravefoundation.org;
Application address: c/o Jerry L. Redfern, Mgr., Musgrave Foundation, P.O. Box 10327, Springfield, MO 65808; Main URL: http://www.musgravefoundation.org

Established in 1983 in MO.
Donor: Jeannette Musgrave.
Foundation type: Independent foundation.
Financial data (yr. ended 06/30/13): Assets, $15,029,153 (M); expenditures, $1,062,719; qualifying distributions, $834,236; giving activities include $677,017 for 54 grants (high: $138,500; low: $500).
Purpose and activities: Giving primarily for arts and community betterment, healthcare and education, and children and senior services.
Fields of interest: Arts; Higher education; Nursing school/education; Nursing care; Boys & girls clubs; Boy scouts; Human services; Salvation Army; Children/youth, services; Community/economic development; Christian agencies & churches; Economically disadvantaged.
Type of support: General/operating support; Continuing support; Annual campaigns; Capital campaigns; Building/renovation; Equipment; Program development; Scholarship funds; Matching/challenge support.
Limitations: Applications accepted. Giving limited to Green County, MO, and to other counties that share a border with Greene. No grants to individuals.
Application information: Application form required.
Initial approach: Use online application form on foundation web site; alternatively, applications may be downloaded from web site and submitted via U.S. Mail
Deadline(s): Mar. 1 and Aug. 1
Officers: Charles Fuller, Chair.; Jerry L. Redfern, Mgr.
Directors: Rob Baird; Junior Cline; Dr. Peggy Riggs; Thomas L. Slaight.
Trustee: U.S. Bank, N.A.
Number of staff: 1 part-time professional.
EIN: 431304514
Selected grants: The following grants are a representative sample of this grantmaker's funding activity:
$41,000 to Ozarks Technical Community College, Springfield, MO, 2011. For general operations.
$34,500 to Council of Churches of the Ozarks, Springfield, MO, 2011. For general operations.
$33,000 to Drury University, Springfield, MO, 2011. For general operations.
$31,000 to Community Foundation of the Ozarks, Springfield, MO, 2011.
$20,000 to American Red Cross, Springfield, MO, 2011. For general operations.
$20,000 to Springfield Regional Arts Council, Springfield, MO, 2011.
$19,000 to Springfield Community Center, Springfield, MO, 2011. For general operations.
$12,000 to Convoy of Hope, Springfield, MO, 2011. For general operations.
$6,500 to Kitchen, Inc., Springfield, MO, 2011. For general operations.
$4,000 to Newborns in Need, Pfafftown, NC, 2011. For general operations.

4948
Nestle Purina PetCare Trust Fund ✧
(formerly Ralston Purina Trust Fund)
c/o Nestle Purina PetCare Community Affairs
Checkerboard Sq., 1C
St. Louis, MO 63164-0001
Contact: Kasey Bergh, Mgr., Community Affairs
E-mail: CommunityAffairs@purina.nestle.com; Main URL: http://www.nestlepurina.com/CommunityInv_Index.aspx

Trust established in 1951 in MO.
Donors: Ralston Purina Co.; Nestle Purina PetCare Co.
Foundation type: Company-sponsored foundation.
Financial data (yr. ended 12/31/13): Assets, $17,958,040 (M); expenditures, $916,569; qualifying distributions, $812,075; giving activities include $811,575 for 13 grants (high: $560,000; low: $4,450).
Purpose and activities: The foundation supports organizations involved with animal welfare and the education and wellbeing of disadvantaged youth.
Fields of interest: Education, services; Education; Animal welfare; Animals/wildlife, preservation/protection; Animals/wildlife, special services; Animals/wildlife, training; Disasters, preparedness/services; Boys & girls clubs; Youth development; United Ways and Federated Giving Programs; Youth; Economically disadvantaged.
Type of support: General/operating support; Continuing support; Annual campaigns; Capital campaigns; Building/renovation; Equipment; Program development; Sponsorships.
Limitations: Applications accepted. Giving primarily in manufacturing operations in Flagstaff, AZ, Maricopa, CA, Denver, CO, Atlanta, GA, Clinton, Davenport, and Fort Dodge, IA, Bloomfield, Cape Girardeau, Springfield, and St. Joseph, MO, Crete, NE, Dunkirk, NY, Zanesville, OH, Oklahoma City, OK, Allentown and Mechanicsburg, PA, King William, VA, Hager City and Jefferson, WI, and Weirton, WV, with emphasis on the greater St. Louis area. No support for veterans' or fraternal organizations not of direct benefit to the entire community. No grants to individuals, or for religious or politically partisan purposes, investment funds, tickets for dinners, benefits, exhibits, conferences, sports events, or other short-term activities, advertisements, debt reduction, or post-event support; no loans.
Publications: Application guidelines.
Application information: Application form required.
Initial approach: Complete online application
Deadline(s): None
Board meeting date(s): Quarterly
Final notification: 60 to 90 days
Trustees: Stephen Degnan; Susan Denigan; Rock A. Foster.
Number of staff: 1 part-time professional; 1 part-time support.
EIN: 431209652

4949
Miller Nichols Charitable Foundation ✧
411 Nichols Rd., Ste. 237
Kansas City, MO 64112-2015

Established in 1960.
Donor: Miller Nichols†.
Foundation type: Independent foundation.
Financial data (yr. ended 12/31/13): Assets, $14,329,583 (M); expenditures, $1,197,213; qualifying distributions, $1,118,400; giving activities include $1,069,404 for 74+ grants.
Purpose and activities: Giving primarily for hospitals, federated giving programs, and arts and cultural programs.
Fields of interest: Museums; Performing arts centers; Performing arts, theater; Performing arts, orchestras; Hospitals (general); United Ways and Federated Giving Programs.
Limitations: Applications not accepted. Giving primarily in Kansas City, MO. No grants to individuals.
Application information: Contributes only to pre-selected organizations.
Officers and Directors:* Kay Nichols Callison, Pres. and Treas.; Mark Callison,* V.P.; Jeannette Nichols, V.P.; Kenneth I. Fligg, Jr., Secy.; Terrence P. Dunn.
EIN: 431567351

4950
Oppenstein Brothers Foundation ✧
922 Walnut St., Ste. 200
Kansas City, MO 64106-1809 (816) 234-2577
Contact: Beth Radtke, Prog. Off.

Established in 1975 in MO.
Donor: Michael Oppenstein†.
Foundation type: Independent foundation.
Financial data (yr. ended 03/31/13): Assets, $34,209,031 (M); expenditures, $1,641,778; qualifying distributions, $1,474,764; giving activities include $1,412,000 for 105 grants (high: $100,000; low: $2,000).
Fields of interest: Performing arts; Arts; Education; Health care; Human services; Children/youth, services; Jewish federated giving programs.
Type of support: General/operating support; Capital campaigns; Building/renovation; Equipment; Emergency funds; Program development; Seed money; Curriculum development; Technical assistance.
Limitations: Applications accepted. Giving primarily in Kansas City, MO and Kansas City, KS. No grants to individuals, or for annual campaigns, building funds or expansion.
Publications: Informational brochure (including application guidelines); Multi-year report.
Application information: Application guidelines available on request. Application form not required.
Initial approach: Telephone or letter
Copies of proposal: 1
Deadline(s): 3 weeks prior to board meetings
Board meeting date(s): Every other month
Final notification: 2 to 4 months
Disbursement Committee: Warren W. Weaver, Chair.; Mary Bloch; Laura Kemper Fields; Roger T. Hurwitz; Estelle Sosland.
Trustee: Commerce Bank, N.A.
EIN: 436203035
Selected grants: The following grants are a representative sample of this grantmaker's funding activity:
$300,000 to Kauffman Center for the Performing Arts, Kansas City, MO, 2011.
$100,000 to Jewish Federation of Greater Kansas City, Overland Park, KS, 2011.
$50,000 to Saint Lukes Hospital of Kansas City, Kansas City, MO, 2011.
$50,000 to Saint Lukes Hospital of Kansas City, Kansas City, MO, 2011.
$25,000 to Child Advocacy Services Center, Kansas City, MO, 2011.
$25,000 to Horizon Academy, Roeland Park, KS, 2011.
$12,500 to Avila University, Kansas City, MO, 2011.
$10,000 to Health Partnership of Johnson County, Overland Park, KS, 2011.
$10,000 to Shepherds Center, Kansas City, MO, 2011.
$7,500 to Unicorn Theater, Kansas City, MO, 2011.

4951
Orscheln Industries Foundation Inc. ✧
P.O. Box 280
Moberly, MO 65270-0280 (660) 263-4900
Contact: R. Brent Bradshaw

Established in 1968 in MO.
Donors: ADEO, LLC; AGAO, LLC; Orscheln Co.
Foundation type: Company-sponsored foundation.
Financial data (yr. ended 09/30/13): Assets, $19,945,237 (M); expenditures, $928,376; qualifying distributions, $815,426; giving activities include $815,426 for 141+ grants (high: $105,500).
Purpose and activities: The foundation supports organizations involved with performing arts, theater, education, health, Alzheimer's disease, human services, and Catholicism and awards college scholarships.
Fields of interest: Performing arts; Performing arts, theater; Secondary school/education; Higher education; Education; Health care; Alzheimer's disease; YM/YWCAs & YM/YWHAs; Children/youth, services; Developmentally disabled, centers & services; Homeless, human services; Human services; United Ways and Federated Giving Programs; Catholic agencies & churches.
Type of support: General/operating support; Continuing support; Annual campaigns; Building/renovation; Scholarship funds; Employee-related scholarships; Scholarships—to individuals.
Limitations: Applications accepted. Giving primarily in MO.
Publications: Application guidelines.
Application information: Graduating high school seniors from the Cairo, Higbee, Madison, Moberly and Westran schoolsshall be eligible to apply. Application form required.
Initial approach: Completed application form
Deadline(s): Apr. 1
Officers and Directors:* William L. Orscheln,* Chair., Exec. V.P., and Treas.; Donald W. Orscheln, Pres.; James L. O'Loughlin,* Sr. V.P., Genl. Counsel, Secy., and Exec. Dir.; Barbara A. Westhues, Sr. V.P., Finance; Robert J. Orscheln,* Exec. V.P.
EIN: 237115623
Selected grants: The following grants are a representative sample of this grantmaker's funding activity:
$200,000 to YMCA, Randolph Area, Moberly, MO, 2011.
$114,640 to Diocese of Jefferson City, Jefferson City, MO, 2011.
$46,026 to United Way of Randolph County, Moberly, MO, 2011.
$37,500 to Moberly Area Community College, Moberly, MO, 2011. For scholarships.
$15,000 to Carroll College, Helena, MT, 2011.
$13,640 to Alzheimers Association, Columbia, MO, 2011.
$12,500 to Arrow Rock Lyceum Theater, Arrow Rock, MO, 2011.
$10,000 to Safe Passage, Moberly, MO, 2011.
$5,000 to Avila University, Kansas City, MO, 2011.
$5,000 to Saint Louis Roman Catholic Theological Seminary, Saint Louis, MO, 2011.

4952
Pershing Charitable Trust ✧
801 S. Skinker Blvd., Apt. 17B
St. Louis, MO 63105-3265
Contact: Mary Langenberg, Tr.

Established in 1968 in MO.
Donors: Oliver M. Langenberg; Mary B. Langenberg; Oliver M. Langenberg Trust.
Foundation type: Independent foundation.
Financial data (yr. ended 09/30/13): Assets, $39,494,684 (M); gifts received, $31,284,611; expenditures, $1,471,142; qualifying distributions, $1,392,475; giving activities include $1,371,100 for 116 grants (high: $100,000; low: $100).
Purpose and activities: Giving primarily for education, and human services.
Fields of interest: Performing arts, theater; Higher education; Education; Human services; Foundations (private operating); Christian agencies & churches.
Type of support: General/operating support; Annual campaigns; Capital campaigns; Emergency funds; Program development; Seed money; Curriculum development; Scholarship funds; Research; Scholarships—to individuals.
Limitations: Applications accepted. Giving primarily in St. Louis, MO.
Application information: Application form required.
Initial approach: Letter
Copies of proposal: 1
Deadline(s): None
Trustees: Mary B. Langenberg; Marian Mehan; William L. Polk, Jr.
EIN: 436103545

4953
Pershing Place Foundation ✧ ☆
c/o William Jochens, Greensfelder, Hemker & Gale PC
10 S. Broadway., Ste. 2000
Saint Louis, MO 63102-1712

Established in 1998 in MO.
Donor: John D. Weil.
Foundation type: Independent foundation.
Financial data (yr. ended 12/31/13): Assets, $9,421,374 (M); expenditures, $483,944; qualifying distributions, $448,690; giving activities include $448,690 for 20 grants (high: $181,900; low: $150).
Fields of interest: Museums (art); Performing arts, theater; Arts; Elementary/secondary education; Education, special; Higher education, college; Environment, natural resources; Human services; United Ways and Federated Giving Programs; Jewish agencies & synagogues.
Limitations: Applications not accepted. Giving primarily in St. Louis, MO. No grants to individuals.
Application information: Contributes only to pre-selected organizations.
Director: William Jochens.
Trustees: Joseph D. Lehrer; Anna Elizabeth C. Weil; John D. Weil.
EIN: 436795985

4954
Pettus Foundation ✧
(formerly James T. Pettus, Jr. Foundation)
c/o Finch Assocs.
1175 Mill Crossing Dr., No. 100
Creve Coeur, MO 63141-6192 (314) 605-6430
Contact: James A. Finch III, Managing Tr.
E-mail: jimfinch@finchassociates.net

Established in 1960 in MO.
Donor: James T. Pettus Jr.†.
Foundation type: Independent foundation.
Financial data (yr. ended 12/31/13): Assets, $20,285,388 (M); expenditures, $1,210,728; qualifying distributions, $981,509; giving activities include $927,000 for 94 grants (high: $100,000; low: $1,500).
Purpose and activities: Giving primarily for children at risk, and training and support for under or unemployed people.
Fields of interest: Child development, education; Education; Employment; Human services; Children/youth, services; Child development, services; Children; Disabilities, people with.
Type of support: General/operating support; Continuing support; Scholarship funds.
Limitations: Applications accepted. Giving primarily in HI and St. Louis, MO. No grants for capital campaigns.
Application information: Rarely funds new applicants; all new applications limited to HI, and St. Louis, MO. Application form not required.
Initial approach: Letter
Copies of proposal: 2
Deadline(s): None
Final notification: Within 90 days
Trustees: James A. Finch III, Managing Tr.; Lisa Hamilton; The Northern Trust Co.
Number of staff: 1 part-time professional.
EIN: 436029569

4955
Ed & H. Pillsbury Foundation ✧
10411 Clayton Rd., Ste. 100
St. Louis, MO 63131-2928

Established in 1995 in MO.
Foundation type: Independent foundation.
Financial data (yr. ended 12/31/13): Assets, $19,778,973 (M); expenditures, $837,712; qualifying distributions, $803,877; giving activities include $792,650 for grants.
Fields of interest: Arts; Higher education; Health care; Human services; Christian agencies & churches; Buddhism.
Type of support: General/operating support; Continuing support; Emergency funds; Matching/challenge support.
Limitations: Applications not accepted. Giving primarily in MO. No grants to individuals.
Application information: Unsolicited requests for funds not accepted.
Board meeting date(s): Jan.
Officers: John Pillsbury, Pres.; Ruth Pillsbury, V.P.; Mary Wainwright, V.P.; Douglas Copeland, Secy.; Nancy Pillsbury, Treas.
EIN: 431699917
Selected grants: The following grants are a representative sample of this grantmaker's funding activity:
$5,000 to Washington University, School of Music, Saint Louis, MO, 2012. For educational.

4956
Harriet Pillsbury Foundation ✧
(formerly William Pillsbury Foundation)
10411 Clayton Rd., No. 100
St. Louis, MO 63131-2911

Established in MO in 1995.
Foundation type: Independent foundation.
Financial data (yr. ended 12/31/11): Assets, $0 (M); expenditures, $467,406; qualifying

distributions, $449,908; giving activities include $443,149 for 42 grants (high: $50,000; low: $5).
Purpose and activities: Giving primarily for higher education and to Protestant churches, particularly Baptist churches; some funding for human services.
Fields of interest: Higher education; Health organizations, association; Human services; Protestant agencies & churches.
Type of support: General/operating support; Continuing support; Capital campaigns; Building/renovation; Program development.
Limitations: Applications not accepted. Giving primarily in MO. No grants to individuals.
Application information: Contributes only to pre-selected organizations.
Board meeting date(s): Jan.
Officers: John Pillsbury, Pres.; Ruth Pillsbury, V.P.; Mary Pillsbury-Wainwright, V.P.; Douglas Copeland, Secy.; Nancy Pillsbury, Treas.
Director: Donald Wainwright.
EIN: 431699919

4957
Robert W. Plaster Foundation, Inc. ✧
2100 Evergreen Pkwy.
Lebanon, MO 65536-7379 (417) 533-3007
Contact: Dolly Plaster Clement, Exec. Dir.
Main URL: http://robertwplasterfoundation.org/

Established in 1983 in MO.
Donors: Robert W. Plaster; Robert W. Plaster Trust.
Foundation type: Independent foundation.
Financial data (yr. ended 11/30/13): Assets, $70,284,006 (M); gifts received, $400,000; expenditures, $3,024,649; qualifying distributions, $2,891,256; giving activities include $2,795,000 for 7 grants (high: $1,200,000; low: $20,000).
Fields of interest: Higher education; Education; Protestant agencies & churches.
Type of support: General/operating support.
Limitations: Applications not accepted. Giving primarily in MO and VA. No grants to individuals.
Application information: Contributes only to pre-selected organizations.
Officer and Directors:* Stephen R. Plaster,* Pres.; Larry Weis,* Secy.-Treas.; Dolly Plaster Clement, Exec. Dir.; Peter DeSilva; Mary M. Posner.
EIN: 431369856

4958
Herman T. & Phenie R. Pott Foundation ✧
c/o U.S. Bank, N.A.
10 N. Hanley Rd., Mail Loc: SL-MO-CTCS
Clayton, MO 63105-3426
Contact: Kimberly Livingston
Main URL: http://www.pottfoundation.org

Trust established in 1963 in MO.
Foundation type: Independent foundation.
Financial data (yr. ended 12/31/13): Assets, $28,205,713 (M); expenditures, $1,510,601; qualifying distributions, $1,309,577; giving activities include $1,278,000 for 123 grants (high: $85,000; low: $1,000).
Purpose and activities: Giving primarily for children's organizations, education, health, and human services in the St. Louis, MO, metropolitan area.
Fields of interest: Education; Health care; Mental health/crisis services; Human services; Children/youth, services; Family services; Homeless, human services; United Ways and Federated Giving Programs.
Type of support: General/operating support; Continuing support; Annual campaigns; Scholarship funds.
Limitations: Giving primarily in the metropolitan St. Louis, MO, area. No grants to individuals.
Publications: Application guidelines.
Application information: The foundation generally does not accept unsolicited requests for funds. Refer to foundation web site for guidelines, information, and the grant application. Application form required.
Copies of proposal: 1
Deadline(s): Apr. 1
Board meeting date(s): Spring
Advisory Committee: Kristine E. Collins; Roy T. Collins; Thomas R. Corbet; Tom Doherty; John F. Fechter; Mary Jane King; Richard D. Rogers.
Number of staff: 1 part-time professional.
EIN: 436041541

4959
The Ceil & Michael E. Pulitzer Foundation, Inc. ✧
(formerly The Michael E. Pulitzer Foundation, Inc.)
c/o James V. Maloney
P.O. Box 23368
St. Louis, MO 63156-3368

Established in 1993 in MO.
Donors: Michael E. Pulitzer; Ceil Pulitzer.
Foundation type: Independent foundation.
Financial data (yr. ended 12/31/13): Assets, $2,401,874 (M); gifts received, $50; expenditures, $1,382,222; qualifying distributions, $1,370,641; giving activities include $1,339,700 for 10 grants (high: $805,220; low: $2,000).
Purpose and activities: Giving primarily for higher education; funding also for museums and human services.
Fields of interest: Museums; Higher education; Human services.
Limitations: Applications accepted. Giving primarily in CA; some funding also in NY.
Application information:
Initial approach: Letter
Deadline(s): None
Officers: Michael E. Pulitzer, Pres.; James V. Maloney, V.P. and Secy.; Christina H. Eisenbeis, V.P.; Marian Mehan, V.P.; Ceil Pulitzer, V.P.
EIN: 431659437
Selected grants: The following grants are a representative sample of this grantmaker's funding activity:
$15,000 to Metropolitan Museum of Art, New York, NY, 2012. For Educational Programming Support Touch Tour.

4960
Ravarino Family Foundation ✧
5 W. Geyer Ln.
St. Louis, MO 63131-3325

Established in 2003.
Donors: Helen Ravarino; Mirella Ravarino.
Foundation type: Independent foundation.
Financial data (yr. ended 12/31/13): Assets, $9,019,114 (M); expenditures, $649,418; qualifying distributions, $536,231; giving activities include $528,736 for 38 grants (high: $265,248; low: $250).
Fields of interest: Higher education; Catholic agencies & churches.
Limitations: Applications not accepted. Giving primarily in MO; funding also in Glen Ellyn, IL. No grants to individuals.
Application information: Contributes only to pre-selected organizations.
Officer: Mirella Ravarino, Chair.
EIN: 436898544

4961
J.B. Reynolds Foundation ✧
P.O. Box 219139
Kansas City, MO 64121-9139

Incorporated in 1961 in MO.
Donors: Walter Edwin Bixby, Sr.; Pearl G. Reynolds†.
Foundation type: Independent foundation.
Financial data (yr. ended 12/31/13): Assets, $15,425,371 (M); expenditures, $833,649; qualifying distributions, $820,000; giving activities include $820,000 for 74 grants (high: $50,000; low: $1,000).
Purpose and activities: Giving primarily for the arts, education, and for health and human services.
Fields of interest: Performing arts; Education; Health organizations, association; Medical research, institute; Youth development; Human services; Children/youth, services.
Type of support: General/operating support; Continuing support; Annual campaigns; Capital campaigns; Building/renovation; Equipment; Land acquisition; Endowments; Emergency funds; Publication; Research.
Limitations: Applications not accepted. Giving primarily within a 150-mile radius of Kansas City, MO. No grants to individuals.
Application information: Contributes only to pre-selected organizations.
Officers and Directors:* R. Philip Bixby,* Pres. and Treas.; Lee M. Vogel,* V.P.; Walter E. Bixby III,* Secy.
EIN: 446014359

4962
Elmer C. Rhoden Charitable Foundation ✧
c/o Husch Blackwell Sanders LLP
4801 Main St., Ste. 1000
Kansas City, MO 64112-2551
Contact: Christine DeMarea

Established in 1986 in MO and KS.
Foundation type: Independent foundation.
Financial data (yr. ended 07/31/13): Assets, $10,699,008 (M); expenditures, $618,262; qualifying distributions, $566,951; giving activities include $540,000 for 16 grants (high: $200,000; low: $5,000).
Purpose and activities: Giving primarily for the benefit of women and children.
Fields of interest: Higher education; Education; Health care; Human services; Children/youth, services; Protestant agencies & churches.
Type of support: General/operating support; Building/renovation; Equipment; Program development; Conferences/seminars.
Limitations: Applications accepted. Giving primarily in the Kansas City, MO, metropolitan area. No grants to individuals.

Application information: Application form required.
Initial approach: Proposal
Deadline(s): None
Directors: Lois D. Lacy; Bruce Longenecker; Janet R. Longenecker.
EIN: 431337876
Selected grants: The following grants are a representative sample of this grantmaker's funding activity:
$200,000 to Village Presbyterian Church, Prairie Village, KS, 2011.
$40,000 to University of Kansas, Lawrence, KS, 2011.
$20,000 to Angel Charity for Children, Tucson, AZ, 2011.

4963
Joseph H. & Florence A. Roblee Foundation ✧

P.O. Box 191255
St. Louis, MO 63119-7255 (314) 963-7713
Contact: Kathy Doellefeld-Clancy, Exec. Dir.
FAX: (314) 963-7716;
E-mail: grantapplication@robleefoundation.org; Address for FL organizations to submit their 3 additional application copies: 5003 S.W. 71st Pl., Miami, FL 33155; Main URL: http://www.robleefoundation.org
Grants List: http://www.robleefoundation.org/past.php

Trust established in 1971 in MO.
Donors: Louise Roblee McCarthy‡; Florence Roblee Trust.
Foundation type: Independent foundation.
Financial data (yr. ended 12/31/12): Assets, $16,832,727 (M); expenditures, $943,326; qualifying distributions, $855,127; giving activities include $712,900 for 72 grants (high: $25,000; low: $500).
Purpose and activities: The foundation awards grants to enable organizations to promote change by addressing significant social issues in order to improve the quality of life and help fulfill the potential of individuals. The foundation arises out of a Christian framework, and values ecumenical endeavors. The foundation particularly supports programs which work to break down cultural, racial, and ethnic barriers. Organizations and churches are encouraged to collaborate in achieving positive change through advocacy, prevention, and systemic improvements.
Fields of interest: Education, reform; Teacher school/education; Substance abuse, prevention; Crime/violence prevention; Crime/violence prevention, domestic violence; Housing/shelter; Youth development, citizenship; Children/youth, services; Youth, pregnancy prevention; Family services; Women, centers/services; Civil rights, race/intergroup relations; Civil liberties, reproductive rights; Public affairs, citizen participation; Women; Economically disadvantaged; Homeless.
Type of support: Technical assistance.
Limitations: Applications accepted. Giving limited to the greater bi-state St. Louis region, and Miami/Dade, FL. No grants to individuals, or for annual campaigns; no loans.
Publications: Application guidelines.
Application information: Organizations in FL should submit their 3 additional application copies to the foundation's Miami, FL address. Proposals submitted by fax are not accepted. Application forms and specific submission requirements available on foundation web site. Application form required.
Initial approach: Cover letter, proposal summary and application form
Copies of proposal: 3
Deadline(s): Jan. 15 and June 15
Officers: Jeffrey Allen Von Arx, Pres.; Kathy Doellefeld-Clancy, Exec. Dir.
Trustees: Carol M. Duhme; Carol Von Arx; Bank of America, N.A.
Board Members: David W. Duhme; Jeremy Duhme; Sally Welker McAdam; Eugenie Ross McCarthy; Juliana Allen McCarthy; Roblee McCarthy, Jr.; Jeanne R. Radley; Robyn Ann Von Arx; Lisa Welker.
Number of staff: 1 full-time professional.
EIN: 436109579

4964
Rosewood Foundation ✧

c/o Central Trust & Investment Co.
7733 Forsyth Blvd., Ste. 900
Clayton, MO 63105-1882
Contact: Roy Blair

Established in 1988 in MO.
Donor: Katie Rose McClendon Revocable Trust.
Foundation type: Independent foundation.
Financial data (yr. ended 06/30/13): Assets, $8,064,688 (M); expenditures, $1,965,322; qualifying distributions, $1,918,500; giving activities include $1,918,500 for grants.
Purpose and activities: Giving primarily to Baptist, Christian, and United Methodist churches and organizations, as well as for social services, health associations, and children and youth services, including a children's hospital.
Fields of interest: Education; Hospitals (specialty); Health organizations; Human services; YM/YWCAs & YM/YWHAs; Children/youth, services; Christian agencies & churches; Protestant agencies & churches.
Type of support: General/operating support.
Limitations: Giving on a national basis, with emphasis on the Southeastern United States. No grants to individuals.
Application information: Application form not required.
Initial approach: Letter
Copies of proposal: 1
Deadline(s): None
Board meeting date(s): Apr.
Trustee: Central Trust & Investment Co.
EIN: 436348906
Selected grants: The following grants are a representative sample of this grantmaker's funding activity:
$80,000 to Gideons International, Nashville, TN, 2011. For general charitable purpose.
$55,000 to Billy Graham Evangelistic Association, Charlotte, NC, 2011. For general charitable purpose.
$55,000 to Samaritans Purse, Boone, NC, 2011. For general charitable purpose.
$25,000 to Asbury Theological Seminary, Wilmore, KY, 2011. For general charitable purpose.
$15,000 to Youth-Reach Houston, Houston, TX, 2011. For general charitable purpose.
$12,000 to Feed the Children, Oklahoma City, OK, 2011. For general charitable purpose.
$10,000 to Guiding Eyes for the Blind, Yorktown Heights, NY, 2011. For general charitable purpose.
$10,000 to Leukemia & Lymphoma Society, White Plains, NY, 2011. For general charitable purpose.

4965
The Saigh Foundation ✧

7777 Bonhomme Ave., Ste. 2007
St. Louis, MO 63105-1911 (314) 862-3055
Contact: JoAnn Hejna, Exec. Dir.
FAX: (314) 862-9288;
E-mail: saigh@thesaighfoundation.org; Main URL: http://www.thesaighfoundation.org/

Established in 1998 in NY.
Donor: Fred M. Saigh‡.
Foundation type: Independent foundation.
Financial data (yr. ended 03/31/13): Assets, $65,517,148 (M); expenditures, $3,307,382; qualifying distributions, $2,823,821; giving activities include $2,298,383 for 92 grants (high: $380,000; low: $2,500).
Purpose and activities: Supports funding for St. Louis, Missouri metropolitan, area organizations benefiting children and youth in the areas of education and health care.
Fields of interest: Education; Health care; Children/youth, services; Children/youth; Children; Youth; Physically disabled; Minorities; Girls; Boys.
Type of support: Endowments; Program development; Scholarship funds; Research; Matching/challenge support.
Limitations: Applications accepted. Giving limited to St. Louis, MO. No grants for capital campaigns, annual appeals, dinner functions, fundraising events, or for films and travel; no loans.
Application information: Proposals may be submitted by mail or fax. Missouri Common Grant Application accepted. Application form required.
Initial approach: Letter
Copies of proposal: 1
Deadline(s): Jan, 15, Apr. 15, July 15, and Oct. 15
Board meeting date(s): Jan., Apr., July, and Oct.
Final notification: 2 days after quarterly meeting
Officer and Trustees:* JoAnn Hejna,* Exec. Dir.; Heidi Veron; Franklin F. Wallis; Fiduciary Trust Co. Int'l.
Number of staff: 2 full-time professional.
EIN: 516511117
Selected grants: The following grants are a representative sample of this grantmaker's funding activity:
$247,500 to Missouri Botanical Garden, Saint Louis, MO, 2012.
$247,500 to Saint Louis Zoo, Saint Louis, MO, 2012.
$160,000 to Washington University, Saint Louis, MO, 2012.
$75,000 to Forest Park Forever, Saint Louis, MO, 2012.
$50,000 to Scholarship Foundation of Saint Louis, Saint Louis, MO, 2012.
$50,000 to Special Education Foundation, Ballwin, MO, 2012.
$20,000 to Opera Theater of Saint Louis, Saint Louis, MO, 2012.
$15,000 to Saint Louis Crisis Nursery, Saint Louis, MO, 2012.
$12,500 to University of Missouri, Saint Louis, MO, 2012.
$10,000 to Lift for Life Gym, Saint Louis, MO, 2012.

4966
Greater Saint Louis Community Foundation ✧
(formerly St. Louis Community Foundation)
319 N. 4th St., Ste. 300
Saint Louis, MO 63102-1906 (314) 588-8200
FAX: (314) 588-8088; E-mail: info@stlouisgives.org;
Main URL: http://www.stlouisgives.org
Scholarship inquiry e-mail:
amurphy@stlouisgives.org

Established in 1915 in MO.
Foundation type: Community foundation.
Financial data (yr. ended 03/31/13): Assets, $219,377,679 (M); gifts received, $48,931,374; expenditures, $35,980,434; giving activities include $33,338,981 for grants.
Purpose and activities: The foundation seeks to improve the quality of life in the greater St. Louis metropolitan area by facilitating the philanthropy of individuals, families and businesses in, but not limited to, the areas of arts and culture, community building, education, environment, health, and human services.
Fields of interest: Arts; Education; Environment; Health care; Human services; Nonprofit management; Community/economic development; Philanthropy/voluntarism; Government/public administration; Infants/toddlers; Children/youth; Children; Adults; Aging; Young adults; Disabilities, people with; Physically disabled; Blind/visually impaired; Deaf/hearing impaired; Mentally disabled; Minorities; African Americans/Blacks; Hispanics/Latinos; Native Americans/American Indians; Women; Adults, women; Adults, men; Military/veterans; AIDS, people with; Single parents; Crime/abuse victims; Terminal illness, people with; Economically disadvantaged; Homeless; LGBTQ.
Type of support: General/operating support; Management development/capacity building; Program development; Seed money; Scholarship funds; Technical assistance; Consulting services; Program-related investments/loans; Matching/challenge support.
Limitations: Applications accepted. Giving primarily in the metropolitan St. Louis, MO, area, including IL. No grants to individuals (except through scholarship funds), or for deficit financing, or endowment or building funds, camperships, annual appeals, memberships, computers (unless presented as a necessary component of larger program or objective) or travel for bands, sports teams, classes, etc.; grants for operating expenses only during an organization's start-up.
Publications: Informational brochure.
Application information: Contact foundation for specific guidelines and special grant initiative guidelines. Application form required.
Initial approach: Letter of inquiry
Deadline(s): Applications accepted throughout the year. Deadlines and application criteria for special grant initiatives vary depending on grant program or individual fund specifications
Board meeting date(s): Mar., June, Sept., and Dec.
Final notification: Within 2 weeks of board meetings
Officers and Directors:* Laurna C. Godwin,* Chair.; Donald Poling,* Vice-Chair.; Amelia A.J. Bond, C.E.O. and Pres.; Dwight D. Canning, V.P. and C.F.O.; Stephen J. Rafferty,* Secy.; Mara "Mitch" Meyers,* Treas.; Matthew J. Madsen, Counsel; Jo Ann H. Arnold; Christopher S. Bond; M. Darnetta Clinkscale; Thomas R. Collins; L.B. Eckelkamp, Jr.; John C. Fort; Frank J. Guyol III; Bruce B. Holland; Dennis J. Jacknewitz; Kathryn L. Kiefer; Kimball R. McMullin; Winthrop B. Reed III; Richard A. Sauget; James M. Snowden, Jr.; Susan P. Sullivan; Rebecca S. Weaver.
Trustee Banks: Commerce Bank, N.A.; A.G. Edwards Trust Co.; The Guaranty Trust Co. of Missouri; U.S. Bank, N.A.; Merrill Lynch Trust Co.; Bank of America, N.A.; Regions Bank.
Number of staff: 7 full-time professional; 2 full-time support.
EIN: 436023126

4967
Sander Foundation ✧
524 High Hampton Rd.
St. Louis, MO 63124-1014
Contact: Derick L. Driemeyer, Tr.

Established in 2005 in MO.
Donors: Derick L. Driemeyer Trust; Derick L. Driemeyer.
Foundation type: Independent foundation.
Financial data (yr. ended 12/31/13): Assets, $3,835,408 (M); expenditures, $523,931; qualifying distributions, $521,366; giving activities include $521,366 for 121 grants (high: $75,000; low: $25).
Purpose and activities: Giving to organizations that assist challenged children, support selected education, or protect and improve our natural world environment. In addition, support is given to organizations that support wounded warriors. The foundation prefers to give to smaller organizations where the contribution can make a difference.
Fields of interest: Education; Environment; Children/youth, services; Children/youth; Military/veterans; Economically disadvantaged.
Type of support: General/operating support; Land acquisition; Endowments; Matching/challenge support.
Limitations: Applications accepted. Giving primarily in MO. No support for political organizations. No grants to individuals.
Application information: Application form required.
Initial approach: Letter
Copies of proposal: 1
Deadline(s): Varies
Trustees: Derick L. Driemeyer; Sally M. Driemeyer.
Number of staff: None.
EIN: 202007940
Selected grants: The following grants are a representative sample of this grantmaker's funding activity:
$250,000 to Danforth Museum, Framingham, MA, 2011.
$150,000 to Danforth Museum, Framingham, MA, 2011.
$100,000 to Danforth Museum, Framingham, MA, 2011.

4968
A. J. Schwartze Community Foundation ✧
111 E. Miller St.
Jefferson City, MO 65101-2915 (573) 634-1224
Contact: Michael W. Prenger

Established in 1976 in MO.
Donor: A.J. Schwartze.
Foundation type: Independent foundation.
Financial data (yr. ended 11/30/13): Assets, $44,693,080 (M); gifts received, $4,180; expenditures, $2,247,037; qualifying distributions, $2,038,247; giving activities include $2,013,620 for 97 grants (high: $151,938; low: $500).
Fields of interest: Elementary/secondary education; Disasters, fire prevention/control; Community/economic development; Catholic agencies & churches; Fraternal societies.
Type of support: General/operating support.
Limitations: Applications accepted. Giving primarily in Osage County, MO. No grants to individuals.
Application information: Application form required.
Initial approach: Letter
Deadline(s): Feb.
Board meeting date(s): Mar.
Officer and Distribution Committee:* Charles Schwartze,* Chair.; Gary Boes; Kathy Robertson; Emil Schwartz; Fred Wieberg; Julie Wieberg.
Trustee: Central Trust Bank.
EIN: 431092255

4969
The Shaughnessy Family Foundation ✧
c/o Joseph F. Shaughnessy
6767 Southwest Ave.
St. Louis, MO 63143-2623

Established in 1995 in MO.
Donors: BSI Constructors, Inc.; BSI Redevelopment Corp.
Foundation type: Independent foundation.
Financial data (yr. ended 12/31/13): Assets, $2,387,686 (M); gifts received, $150,000; expenditures, $545,757; qualifying distributions, $544,500; giving activities include $544,500 for 61 grants (high: $100,000; low: $500).
Purpose and activities: Giving primarily for education and human services.
Fields of interest: Arts; Education; Human services; Christian agencies & churches.
Limitations: Applications not accepted. Giving primarily in St. Louis, MO. No grants to individuals.
Application information: Contributes only to pre-selected organizations.
Board meeting date(s): Dec.
Officers and Trustees:* Joseph F. Shaughnessy,* Chair.; Rosemary E. Shaughnessy, Vice-Chair.; Anne S. Carlson; Aurzella S. Harlan; Ellen S. Martin; Daniel G. Shaughnessy; James A. Shaughnessy; Paul J. Shaughnessy.
Number of staff: None.
EIN: 436648962

4970
Arch W. Shaw Foundation ✧
(also known as William W. Shaw)
HC 3, Box 60B
Birch Tree, MO 65438-9304 (417) 764-3701
Contact: William W. Shaw, Tr.

Trust established in 1949 in IL.
Donor: Arch W. Shaw‡.
Foundation type: Independent foundation.
Financial data (yr. ended 12/31/13): Assets, $18,326,088 (M); expenditures, $807,604; qualifying distributions, $800,038; giving activities include $800,000 for 112 grants (high: $59,000; low: $500).
Fields of interest: Museums; Arts; Higher education; Education; Hospitals (general); Health

care; Medical research, institute; Human services; Residential/custodial care, hospices.
Type of support: General/operating support; Continuing support; Annual campaigns; Capital campaigns; Building/renovation; Equipment; Endowments; Emergency funds; Program development; Seed money; Scholarship funds; Research.
Limitations: Applications accepted. Giving primarily in IL, MA, MO, NY, and WI. No support for private foundations. No grants to individuals.
Publications: Financial statement.
Application information: Application form required.
Initial approach: Letter
Copies of proposal: 1
Deadline(s): None
Board meeting date(s): Dec.
Trustees: Arch W. Shaw II; Bruce P. Shaw; Roger D. Shaw, Jr.; William W. Shaw.
EIN: 366055262

4971
Shelter Insurance Foundation ✧
1817 W. Broadway
Columbia, MO 65218-0001 (573) 214-4324
Contact: Joe L. Moseley, V.P. and Secy.

Established in 1981 in MO.
Donor: Shelter Mutual Insurance Co.
Foundation type: Company-sponsored foundation.
Financial data (yr. ended 12/31/13): Assets, $13,375,538 (M); gifts received, $17,743; expenditures, $654,863; qualifying distributions, $650,590; giving activities include $83,821 for 48 + grants (high: $12,500; low: $30), and $566,769 for grants to individuals.
Purpose and activities: The foundation supports hospitals, parks, and organizations involved with education, breast cancer, Alzheimer's disease, child welfare, human services, and Christianity, and awards grants and scholarships to individuals.
Fields of interest: Education; Health organizations; Human services.
Type of support: General/operating support; Scholarship funds; Employee matching gifts; Employee-related scholarships; Grants to individuals; Scholarships—to individuals.
Limitations: Applications accepted. Giving primarily in areas of company operations in AR, CO, IA, IL, IN, KS, KY, LA, MO, MS, NE, NV, OK, and TN.
Application information: Application form required.
Initial approach: Letter
Deadline(s): None
Officers and Directors:* Rick L. Means,* Pres.; Joe L. Moseley,* V.P. and Secy.; S. Daniel Clapp,* Treas.; Paul J. LaRose; Teresa Magruder; Madison M. Moore; Randa Rawins.
EIN: 431224155
Selected grants: The following grants are a representative sample of this grantmaker's funding activity:
$2,500 to University of Missouri, School of Law, Columbia, MO, 2012. For education.
$1,500 to University of Missouri, Sinclair School of Nursing, Columbia, MO, 2012. For education.

4972
The Sherman Family Foundation ✧
c/o Mary N. Sherman
5306 Sunset Dr.
Kansas City, MO 64112

Established in 2006 in MO.
Donors: John Sherman; Mary Sherman.
Foundation type: Independent foundation.
Financial data (yr. ended 12/31/13): Assets, $20,019,468 (M); gifts received, $9,967,679; expenditures, $501,182; qualifying distributions, $458,333; giving activities include $458,333 for 2 grants (high: $333,333; low: $125,000).
Fields of interest: Scholarships/financial aid; Education.
Limitations: Applications not accepted. Giving primarily in Kansas, MO. No grants to individuals.
Application information: Contributes only to pre-selected organizations.
Directors: John Sherman; Mary Sherman; Amy Van Houten.
EIN: 205667031

4973
Mildred, Herbert and Julian Simon Foundation ✧
1727 Locust St.
St. Louis, MO 63103 (314) 241-1716
Contact: Charles Baron, Chair., Steering Comm.; Martin M. Rosen, Exec. Dir.
FAX: (314) 241-1588;
E-mail: mrosen@mersgoodwill.org

Established in 1993 in MO.
Donors: Herbert Simon†; Julian Simon†; Mildred Simon†.
Foundation type: Independent foundation.
Financial data (yr. ended 09/30/13): Assets, $13,668,645 (M); expenditures, $717,997; qualifying distributions, $648,569; giving activities include $522,372 for 22 grants (high: $180,372; low: $1,000).
Purpose and activities: The foundation is interested in developing projects which will have a significant impact on the St. Louis, Missouri area. It seeks concept papers concerning programs that will meet unique specific community needs and seeks the appropriate organizations to best implement them. The primary focus includes but is not limited to programs which enhance the quality of life of senior citizens and children, with primary consideration given to the needs of the St. Louis Jewish community.
Fields of interest: Elementary/secondary education; Higher education; Employment, services; Neighborhood centers; Children, services; Jewish agencies & synagogues; Children/youth; Youth; Aging; Disabilities, people with.
International interests: Israel; Middle East.
Type of support: Program development; Seed money; Scholarship funds.
Limitations: Applications accepted. Giving primarily in St. Louis, MO. No grants to individuals or for capital campaigns.
Application information: Concepts preferred to grant applications. Application form not required.
Initial approach: Letter/concept paper
Copies of proposal: 1
Deadline(s): None
Board meeting date(s): Monthly
Final notification: 1-6 months
Officers and Steering Committee:* Charles B. Baron,* Chair.; Lewis Chartock,* Vice-Chair.; Martin M. Rosen,* Exec. Dir.; Lucy Lopata; Joan M. Newman.
Trustee: U.S. Bank, N.A.
Number of staff: 1 part-time professional; 1 part-time support.
EIN: 436498119

4974
Ralph L. Smith Foundation ✧
P.O. Box 415044 M/S 1020307
Kansas City, MO 64141-6692 (816) 860-1933
Contact: Jan B. Leonard

Trust established in 1952 in MO.
Donors: Harriet T. Smith†; Ralph L. Smith†.
Foundation type: Independent foundation.
Financial data (yr. ended 12/31/13): Assets, $15,247,925 (M); expenditures, $700,947; qualifying distributions, $612,654; giving activities include $590,000 for 42 grants (high: $165,000; low: $500).
Purpose and activities: Giving primarily for education, health care, including ALS organizations, and human services.
Fields of interest: Arts; Higher education; Education; Environment, natural resources; Health care; Human services; Women, centers/services; Community development, neighborhood development; Foundations (community).
Limitations: Applications accepted. Giving primarily in CA, KS, and MO. No grants to individuals.
Application information: Applications for grants will not be acknowledged. Application form required.
Initial approach: Telephone first to determine what attachments to accompany initial letter (maximum 3 pages)
Copies of proposal: 1
Deadline(s): None
Board meeting date(s): Quarterly
Final notification: 2 months
Managers: Suzanne D. Birkans; Neil T. Douthat; Paul N. Douthat; Elizabeth Smith; Neil T. Smith.
Trustee: UMB Bank, N.A.
EIN: 446008508

4975
Vivian & Hymie J. Sosland Charitable Trust ✧
P.O. Box 30067
Kansas City, MO 64112-0667

Established in 2007 in MO.
Donor: Vivan J. Sosland Revocable Trust.
Foundation type: Independent foundation.
Financial data (yr. ended 12/31/13): Assets, $13,966,939 (M); expenditures, $791,948; qualifying distributions, $676,684; giving activities include $637,000 for 60 grants (high: $100,000; low: $1,000).
Fields of interest: Arts; Human services; Children/youth, services; Jewish federated giving programs; Jewish agencies & synagogues.
Limitations: Applications not accepted. Giving primarily in Kansas City, MO.
Application information: Contributes only to pre-selected organizations.
Trustees: Marcia A. Rhodes; Leslie A. Small; Deborah Sosland-Edelman.
EIN: 416551808

4976
Vivian and Hymie J. Sosland Charitable Trust ✧
P.O. Box 30067
Kansas City, MO 64112-0667

Foundation type: Independent foundation.
Financial data (yr. ended 12/31/13): Assets, $13,966,939 (M); expenditures, $791,948; qualifying distributions, $676,684; giving activities include $637,000 for 60 grants (high: $100,000; low: $1,000).
Fields of interest: Education; Agriculture/food; Jewish federated giving programs; Christian agencies & churches.
Limitations: Applications not accepted. Giving primarily in Kansas City, MO.
Application information: Contributes only to pre-selected organizations.
Trustees: Marcia A. Rhodes; Leslie A. Small; Deborah Sosland-Edelman.
EIN: 207457935

4977
The Sosland Foundation ✧
4800 Main St., Ste. 100
Kansas City, MO 64112-2504
Contact: Debbie Sosland-Edelman Ph.D., Exec. Dir.
E-mail: debbie@sosland.com; Main URL: http://www.soslandfoundation.org

Incorporated in 1955 in MO.
Donors: Hymie J. Sosland Trust B; Members of the Sosland family.
Foundation type: Independent foundation.
Financial data (yr. ended 12/31/12): Assets, $55,813,131 (M); expenditures, $3,367,130; qualifying distributions, $2,923,502; giving activities include $2,708,689 for 125 grants (high: $400,000; low: $100).
Purpose and activities: Giving to Jewish and social welfare funds, higher and secondary education, the arts, and health organizations.
Fields of interest: Performing arts; Performing arts, theater; Performing arts, music; Arts; Secondary school/education; Higher education; Health care; Health organizations, association; Human services; Jewish federated giving programs; Government/public administration; Jewish agencies & synagogues.
Type of support: Fellowships; Professorships; General/operating support; Continuing support; Annual campaigns; Capital campaigns; Building/renovation; Equipment; Endowments; Program development; Curriculum development; Scholarship funds; Research; Program evaluation; Employee matching gifts.
Limitations: Applications accepted. Giving primarily in the metropolitan bi-state Kansas City area. No grants to individuals, or for publications or conferences.
Publications: Application guidelines.
Application information: The foundation is currently not accepting new grant applications. See web site for grant guidelines.
Board meeting date(s): Mar., June, Sept., and Dec.
Officers and Directors:* Neil N. Sosland,* Chair.; Morton I. Sosland, Vice-Chair.; Charles S. Sosland, Secy.; L. Joshua Sosland,* Treas.; Deborah Sosland-Edelman, Ph.D., Exec. Dir.; Blanche E. Sosland; David N. Sosland; Estelle G. Sosland; Meyer J. Sosland.
Number of staff: 2 part-time professional; 2 part-time support.
EIN: 446007129

4978
Victor E. Speas Foundation ✧
c/o U.S. Trust
1200 Main St., 14th Fl.
P.O. Box 219119
Kansas City, MO 64121-9119 (816) 292-4300
Contact: Spence Heddens, Sr. V.P.
E-mail: Spence.heddens@ustrust.com; E-mail to discuss application process or for questions about the foundation: mo.grantmaking@ustrust.com (Foundation name should be indicated in subject line); Main URL: http://www.bankofamerica.com/grantmaking

Trust established in 1947 in MO.
Donors: Effie E. Speas†; Victor E. Speas†; Speas Co.; Alice J. Speas Unitrust.
Foundation type: Independent foundation.
Financial data (yr. ended 12/31/13): Assets, $39,277,696 (M); expenditures, $1,933,709; qualifying distributions, $1,605,465; giving activities include $1,464,505 for 42 grants (high: $115,000; low: $5,000).
Purpose and activities: Giving restricted to improving the quality of health care in the Kansas City, MO, area. Support mainly for medically-related higher education, including loans for medical students at the University of Missouri at Kansas City, and for a school for dentistry; funding also for preventive health care, and medical research; grants also for agencies serving the healthcare needs of the elderly, youth, and the handicapped.
Fields of interest: Medical school/education; Health care; Health organizations; Human services; Children/youth, services; Economically disadvantaged.
Type of support: General/operating support; Capital campaigns; Building/renovation; Equipment; Emergency funds; Program development; Seed money; Research; Matching/challenge support; Student loans—to individuals.
Limitations: Giving limited to Kansas City, MO. No grants for endowment funds, capital support, or scholarships; no loans (except to medical students at the University of Missouri at Kansas City).
Publications: Application guidelines.
Application information: Application form available online. Application form required.
Copies of proposal: 2
Deadline(s): Rolling
Trustee: Bank of America, N.A.
Number of staff: 1 full-time professional.
EIN: 446008340
Selected grants: The following grants are a representative sample of this grantmaker's funding activity:
$100,000 to Childrens Mercy Hospital, Kansas City, MO, 2011. For drug discovery and repurposing program in collaboration with University of Kansas Cancer Center and its quest for NCI designation.
$75,000 to Cornerstones of Care, Kansas City, MO, 2011. For ancillary therapy services.
$50,000 to DeLaSalle Education Center, Kansas City, MO, 2011. For capital campaign.
$50,000 to Metropolitan Community Colleges Foundation, Kansas City, MO, 2011. For medical equipment for the Health Science Institute training facility.
$50,000 to William Jewell College, Liberty, MO, 2011. For the purchase of human-patient simulators for the nursing program.
$40,000 to First Call Alcohol/Drug Prevention and Recovery, Kansas City, MO, 2011. For Community CareLink, the electronic health information exchange.
$30,000 to Kansas City Care Clinic, Kansas City, MO, 2011. For underwriting support for staff nurse practitioner salaries in the general medicine program.
$30,000 to Mattie Rhodes Center, Kansas City, MO, 2011. For capital improvements at Northeast KCMO facility.
$25,000 to Saint Lukes Hospital Foundation, Kansas City, MO, 2011. For Cabot operations.
$25,000 to Shepherds Center, Kansas City, MO, 2011. For Coming of Age: Kansas City.

4979
John W. and Effie E. Speas Memorial Trust ✧
c/o US Trust
1200 Main St., 14th Fl.
Kansas City, MO 64121-9119 (816) 292-4300
Contact: Spence Heddens, Sr. V.P.
E-mail: spence.heddins@ustrust.com; Main URL: https://www.bankofamerica.com/philanthropic/grantmaking.go

Trust established in 1943 in MO.
Donors: Effie E. Speas†; Victor E. Speas†; Speas Co.
Foundation type: Independent foundation.
Financial data (yr. ended 12/31/13): Assets, $38,456,166 (M); expenditures, $1,981,704; qualifying distributions, $1,672,302; giving activities include $1,547,666 for 38 grants (high: $200,000; low: $2,500).
Purpose and activities: Giving to support and promote quality educational, cultural, human services, and health care programming.
Fields of interest: Education; Hospitals (general); Health care; Human services.
Type of support: General/operating support; Equipment; Program development; Seed money; Research.
Limitations: Applications accepted. Giving limited to organizations that serve the residents of the Greater Kansas City Metropolitan area.
Application information: Application guidelines and form available on foundation web site. Application form required.
Initial approach: Online application
Copies of proposal: 2
Deadline(s): Rolling
Trustee: Bank of America, N.A.
Number of staff: 1 full-time professional.
EIN: 446008249
Selected grants: The following grants are a representative sample of this grantmaker's funding activity:
$60,000 to Kauffman Center for the Performing Arts, Kansas City, MO, 2011. For capital support.
$50,000 to Friends of the Library in Kansas City Kansas, Kansas City, KS, 2011. For the capital campaign for the Kansas City, KS Public Library/USD500 project in Argentine.
$50,000 to Kansas University Endowment Association, Lawrence, KS, 2011. For underwriting support for KU Cancer Centers hematology/oncology professorship in its quest for NCI designation-year 2.

$50,000 to Teach for America, Kansas City, MO, 2011.
$40,000 to Don Bosco Community Center, Kansas City, MO, 2011. For youth development and transitional funding.
$30,000 to Higher M-Pact, Kansas City, MO, 2011. For operational support to hire a full-time development director.
$25,000 to Catholic Charities of Northeast Kansas, Overland Park, KS, 2011. For emergency assistance and housing programs in metro Kansas City.
$25,000 to Operation Breakthrough, Kansas City, MO, 2011. For mental health programming for children.
$25,000 to PE4life Foundation, Kansas City, MO, 2011. For operating support for the metropolitan Kansas City school expansion.
$25,000 to Support Kansas City, Mission, KS, 2011. For operating support.

4980
Richard J. Stern Foundation for the Arts ✧
c/o Commerce Bank, N.A.
118 W. 47th St.
Kansas City, MO 64112-9969
Application address: c/o Beth Ratke, Commerce Bank, N.A., 922 Walnut St., Ste. 200, Kansas City, MO 64106-1809, tel.: (816) 234-2577

Established in 1986 in MO.
Donor: Richard J. Stern‡.
Foundation type: Independent foundation.
Financial data (yr. ended 06/30/13): Assets, $49,248,612 (M); expenditures, $2,573,974; qualifying distributions, $2,172,892; giving activities include $2,172,892 for grants.
Purpose and activities: Giving only to organizations engaged in supporting the arts in the 5-county, metropolitan Kansas City, MO, area, including the performing arts and art education.
Fields of interest: Performing arts; Performing arts, music; Arts.
Type of support: General/operating support; Continuing support; Capital campaigns; Building/renovation; Equipment; Emergency funds; Program development.
Limitations: Applications accepted. Giving limited to the 5-county, metropolitan Kansas City, MO, area only. No support for private foundations. No grants to individuals.
Publications: Informational brochure (including application guidelines).
Application information: Application form not required.
Initial approach: Letter
Copies of proposal: 1
Deadline(s): None
Board meeting date(s): Quarterly
Final notification: 2-4 months
Contributions Committee: Michael D. Fields, Chair.; Jonathan M. Kemper; John A. Ovel.
Trustee: Commerce Bank, N.A.
EIN: 436313811
Selected grants: The following grants are a representative sample of this grantmaker's funding activity:
$100,000 to William Jewell College, Liberty, MO, 2011.
$100,000 to William Jewell College, Liberty, MO, 2011.
$10,000 to University of Missouri, College of Arts and Sciences, Kansas City, MO, 2011.

4981
Steward Family Foundation ✧ ☆
2200 W. Port Plaza Dr., Ste. 203
St. Louis, MO 63146-3211

Established in MO.
Donors: David L. Steward; Thelma E. Steward.
Foundation type: Independent foundation.
Financial data (yr. ended 12/31/13): Assets, $91,066 (M); gifts received, $1,814,373; expenditures, $1,722,526; qualifying distributions, $1,722,513; giving activities include $1,705,288 for 64 grants (high: $340,714; low: $1,000).
Fields of interest: Arts; Human services; Christian agencies & churches.
Limitations: Applications not accepted. Giving primarily in St. Louis, MO.
Application information: Unsolicited requests for funds not accepted.
Trustees: David L. Steward; Thelma E. Steward.
EIN: 461802424

4982
Stupp Bros. Bridge & Iron Company Foundation ✧
3800 Weber Rd.
St. Louis, MO 63125-1160

Trust established about 1952 in MO.
Donors: Stupp Bros. Bridge & Iron Co.; Stupp Bridge Co.
Foundation type: Company-sponsored foundation.
Financial data (yr. ended 10/31/13): Assets, $9,460,826 (M); expenditures, $610,732; qualifying distributions, $505,000; giving activities include $505,000 for 177 grants (high: $42,500; low: $100).
Purpose and activities: The foundation supports organizations involved with education, health, children and youth, business, and religion.
Fields of interest: Education; Human services; Religion.
Type of support: General/operating support; Annual campaigns; Program development; Scholarship funds.
Limitations: Applications not accepted. Giving primarily in St. Louis, MO.
Application information: Unsolicited requests for funds not accepted.
Trustees: John P. Stupp, Jr.; Robert P. Stupp.
EIN: 237412437
Selected grants: The following grants are a representative sample of this grantmaker's funding activity:
$12,000 to University of Arizona Foundation, Tucson, AZ, 2011.
$5,000 to Duke University, Durham, NC, 2011.
$5,000 to Lehigh University, Bethlehem, PA, 2011.
$1,000 to United Negro College Fund, Fairfax, VA, 2011.
$1,000 to University of Colorado Foundation, Boulder, CO, 2011.

4983
Norman J. Stupp Foundation ✧
P.O. Box 11356
Clayton, MO 63105-0156
FAX: (314) 746-3907;
E-mail: susan.muse@commercebank.com;
Application address: c/o Cindy Lewis, Commerce Trust Co., 8000 Forsyth Blvd., Clayton, MO 63105 (314) 746-7322

Established in 1952 in MO.
Donor: Norman J. Stupp‡.
Foundation type: Independent foundation.
Financial data (yr. ended 06/30/13): Assets, $19,565,899 (M); expenditures, $1,082,210; qualifying distributions, $906,217; giving activities include $906,217 for grants.
Purpose and activities: The foundation focus is within three categories: Strengthening the Region; Building Strong Communities and Neighborhoods; and Helping Youth Succeed. The mission is to enhance the lives of residents in the metropolitan St. Louis, Missouri area.
Fields of interest: Arts; Education; Housing/shelter; Youth development; Human services; Children/youth, services; Community/economic development.
Type of support: Capital campaigns; Building/renovation; Equipment; Program development; Research; Technical assistance; Matching/challenge support.
Limitations: Applications accepted. Giving primarily in the metropolitan St. Louis, MO, area. No grants to individuals; no sponsorships.
Publications: Application guidelines.
Application information: Application form required.
Initial approach: Letter
Copies of proposal: 1
Deadline(s): Mar 1 and Sept. 1
Trustee: Commerce Bank, N.A.
EIN: 436027433
Selected grants: The following grants are a representative sample of this grantmaker's funding activity:
$7,000 to Jefferson County Rescue Mission, Pevely, MO, 2013. For Hum.

4984
Everett D. and Geneva V. Sugarbaker Foundation ✧ ☆
2113 W. Main St.
Jefferson City, MO 65109-0912
Contact: Connie C. Moore, Treas.
Application address: 228 Papin Ave., Webster Grove, MO 63119-3716 tel.: (314) 231-2573

Established in 1997 in MO.
Donors: Geneva V. Sugarbaker; Everett V. Sugarbaker‡.
Foundation type: Independent foundation.
Financial data (yr. ended 12/31/13): Assets, $8,249,136 (M); expenditures, $480,605; qualifying distributions, $427,000; giving activities include $427,000 for 37 grants (high: $72,500; low: $1,500).
Fields of interest: Education; Christian agencies & churches; Religion.
Limitations: Applications accepted. Giving primarily in IL and TN. No grants to individuals.
Application information: Application form required.
Initial approach: Proposal
Deadline(s): Sept. 30
Officers: David J. Sugarbaker, Pres.; Evangeline Tolley, V.P.; Paul Sugarbaker, Secy.; Connie Moore, Treas.
Trustees: Elizabeth I. Akre; Katie Caliguri; Charles W. Digges IV; Rena Pedersen; Geneva V. Sugarbaker; Stephen P. Sugarbaker.
EIN: 431785474

4985
SunEdison Foundation ✧ ☆
(formerly MEMC Foundation)
501 Pearl Dr.
P.O. Box 8
St. Peters, MO 63376-0090

Established in 2007 in MO.
Donor: MEMC Electronic Materials, Inc.
Foundation type: Company-sponsored foundation.
Financial data (yr. ended 12/31/13): Assets, $2,818,279 (M); expenditures, $1,494,877; qualifying distributions, $1,481,866; giving activities include $1,481,866 for 7 grants (high: $1,350,000; low: $5,000).
Purpose and activities: The foundation supports science museums and organizations involved with cancer, multiple sclerosis, disaster relief, children and youth, and residential care.
Fields of interest: Museums (science/technology); Cancer; Cancer, leukemia; Multiple sclerosis; Disasters, preparedness/services; Children/youth, services; Residential/custodial care.
Type of support: Sponsorships; General/operating support.
Limitations: Applications not accepted. Giving primarily in St. Louis, MO; giving also to national organizations. No grants to individuals.
Application information: Unsolicited requests for funds not accepted.
Officers: Steve Edens, Chair. and Pres.; Martin Truong, Secy.; Brian Wuebbels, Treas.
EIN: 208722904

4986
Sunnen Foundation ✧
7910 Manchester Ave.
St. Louis, MO 63143-2712
Contact: Kurt J. Kallaus, Pres.

Incorporated in 1953 in MO.
Donors: Joseph Sunnen†; Helen Sly; Sunnen Products Co.
Foundation type: Independent foundation.
Financial data (yr. ended 12/31/13): Assets, $14,334,320 (M); gifts received, $20,000; expenditures, $543,437; qualifying distributions, $426,851; giving activities include $421,160 for 15 grants (high: $107,850; low: $700).
Purpose and activities: Specific goal-oriented projects for protection of reproductive and First Amendment rights, educational opportunities for the economically or physically disadvantaged and for youth and family services.
Fields of interest: Child development, education; Reproductive health, family planning; Children/youth, services; Child development, services; Family services; Civil liberties, reproductive rights; Children/youth; Disabilities, people with; Economically disadvantaged.
Type of support: Capital campaigns; Program development; Matching/challenge support.
Limitations: Applications accepted. Giving primarily in MO, with emphasis on the metropolitan St. Louis area. No support for educational institutions, environmental organizations, hospitals or medical charities, the arts or private day care centers. Generally no support for charities with broad-based public appeal, or religious bodies. No grants to individuals, or for scholarships, general operating costs, or research projects.
Publications: Informational brochure (including application guidelines).
Application information: Proposals submitted in notebooks, binders or plastic folders are not accepted. Application form not required.
Initial approach: Proposal, not to exceed 10 pages
Copies of proposal: 5
Deadline(s): Proposal due June or July; final deadline is Aug. 1
Board meeting date(s): Generally in Dec.
Final notification: Jan.
Officers and Directors:* Kurt J. Kallaus,* Pres.; Matthew S. Kreider,* V.P.; Ruth Cardinale,* Secy.; Susan S. Brasel,* Treas.; Helen S. Sly.
EIN: 436029156
Selected grants: The following grants are a representative sample of this grantmaker's funding activity:
$170,000 to Planned Parenthood of the Saint Louis Region, Saint Louis, MO, 2012.
$112,000 to YMCA of the Ozarks, Potosi, MO, 2012.
$50,000 to Planned Parenthood of Alabama, Birmingham, AL, 2012.
$25,000 to Operation Food Search, Saint Louis, MO, 2012.
$10,000 to Faith Aloud, Saint Louis, MO, 2012.

4987
The Crawford Taylor Foundation ✧
600 Corporate Park Dr.
Clayton, MO 63105-4204 (314) 512-4283
Contact: Jo Ann Kindle, Pres.
FAX: (314) 512-4754;
E-mail: info@crawfordtaylorfoundation.org; Main URL: http://www.crawfordtaylorfoundation.org

Established in 1997 in MO.
Donor: Jack C. Taylor.
Foundation type: Independent foundation.
Financial data (yr. ended 12/31/13): Assets, $555,372,193 (M); gifts received, $1,054,175; expenditures, $18,370,168; qualifying distributions, $17,552,000; giving activities include $17,552,000 for 76 grants (high: $1,000,000; low: $1,000).
Purpose and activities: Support primarily for charitable and educational organizations.
Fields of interest: Environment; Animals/wildlife; Community/economic development; Youth; Women.
Limitations: Applications accepted. Giving primarily in St. Louis, MO. No support for political parties or candidates, or private foundations, religious organizations promoting specific doctrines, international organizations, sports teams, talent or beauty contests, or for media productions and for-profit ventures. No grants to individuals or for fundraising for individuals' sponsorships or support for conferences ; no multi-year grants.
Application information: Application guidelines and deadlines available on foundation web site. Application form required.
Initial approach: Proposal or via foundation web site
Deadline(s): See foundation web site
Board meeting date(s): Apr. 1, Aug. 1 and Nov. 1
Final notification: Within 3 months of application
Officers and Directors:* Jack C. Taylor,* Chair.; Jo Ann Kindle,* Pres.; Andrew C. Taylor,* V.P.; Carolyn Kindle, Secy.; James Manu, Treas.
Number of staff: 1 part-time professional; 2 part-time support.
EIN: 431790817
Selected grants: The following grants are a representative sample of this grantmaker's funding activity:
$25,000,000 to Forest Park Forever, Saint Louis, MO, 2012.
$10,000,000 to CityArchRiver 2015 Foundation, Saint Louis, MO, 2012.
$25,000 to Greater Saint Louis Honor Flight, Chesterfield, MO, 2012.

4988
Charles H. Taylor Memorial Trust ✧
2407 N. Woodbine Rd.
St. Joseph, MO 64506-3700 (816) 364-4900
Contact: W. Scott Hinde, Tr.

Established in MO.
Foundation type: Independent foundation.
Financial data (yr. ended 06/30/12): Assets, $24,813 (M); expenditures, $753,991; qualifying distributions, $748,802; giving activities include $748,802 for 37 grants (high: $687,597; low: $200).
Fields of interest: Arts; Health care; Human services; YM/YWCAs & YM/YWHAs; Youth, services; Foundations (community).
Limitations: Applications accepted. Giving primarily in the St. Joseph, MO, area. No grants to individuals.
Application information: Application form not required.
Initial approach: Letter
Deadline(s): None
Trustees: W. Scott Hinde; James Roth.
EIN: 436118395

4989
Ten Talents Foundation ✧
(formerly Larry D. Vander Maten Charitable Foundation)
11701 Borman Dr., Ste. 315
St. Louis, MO 63146-4194

Established in 1995 in MO.
Donors: Larry D. Vander Maten; HSM Management Services, Inc.; LVM Limited Partnership; Westcom Investment, LLC.
Foundation type: Independent foundation.
Financial data (yr. ended 12/31/12): Assets, $24,821,293 (M); gifts received, $4,861,123; expenditures, $1,167,309; qualifying distributions, $1,069,635; giving activities include $1,042,600 for 17 grants (high: $501,000; low: $1,000).
Fields of interest: Human services; Christian agencies & churches.
Type of support: General/operating support.
Limitations: Applications not accepted. Giving primarily in Longwood, FL, and IL; some funding also in TX. No grants to individuals.
Application information: Contributes only to pre-selected organizations.
Officer: Paul T. Thonnard, Exec. Dir.
Trustee: Larry D. Vander Maten.
EIN: 431719896

4990
The Ten-Ten Foundation ✧
120 Main St., Ste. 3500
Kansas City, MO 64105-2163 (816) 474-3200
Contact: Beth K. Smith, Pres.
E-mail: bethksmith@kc.rr.com

Established in 1964 in MO.
Donors: Beth K. Smith Charitable Lead Annuity Trust; Beth K. Smith Charitable Lead Unitrust.
Foundation type: Independent foundation.
Financial data (yr. ended 12/31/12): Assets, $5,549,036 (M); gifts received, $313,027; expenditures, $993,018; qualifying distributions, $947,581; giving activities include $926,550 for 47 grants (high: $300,000; low: $100).
Fields of interest: Performing arts; Arts; Higher education; Health care; Legal services; Women, centers/services; United Ways and Federated Giving Programs; Jewish agencies & synagogues.
Limitations: Applications accepted. Giving primarily in Kansas City, MO. No grants to individuals.
Application information: Application form not required.
Initial approach: Proposal
Deadline(s): None
Officers and Directors:* Beth K. Smith,* Pres.; Sarah Malino,* V.P.; Deborah M. Smith,* V.P.; James D. Smith,* V.P.; Judith E. Smith,* V.P.; B. John Readey III, Secy.; Joseph L. Hiersteiner, Treas.
EIN: 436055675

4991
The Tilles Fund ✧

(formerly Rosalie Tilles Nonsectarian Charity Fund)
c/o U.S. Bank, N.A
The Private Client Reserve, Attn.: Carol Eaves, Mail Loc: SL-MO-CTCS
10 N. Hanley Rd.
Clayton, MO 63105-3426 (314) 505-8204
Contact: Garth Silvey, V.P.
Application information: Carol Eaves, tel.: (314) 418-8391; Main URL: http://www.thetillesfund.org

Trust established in 1926 in MO.
Donor: Cap Andrew Tilles†.
Foundation type: Independent foundation.
Financial data (yr. ended 06/30/13): Assets, $12,930,390 (M); expenditures, $586,763; qualifying distributions, $504,756; giving activities include $148,400 for 15 grants (high: $15,000; low: $400), and $341,783 for grants to individuals.
Purpose and activities: Giving primarily for scholarship awards for recent high school graduates who are residents of the City or County of St. Louis, Missouri, to attend any Missouri university or college; funding also available for St. Louis area organizations for a one-year period that provide services for the special needs of children with physical and/or mental disabilities.
Fields of interest: Higher education; Scholarships/financial aid; Health organizations; Human services; Children/youth, services.
Type of support: Scholarship funds.
Limitations: Applications accepted. Giving limited to the city of St. Louis and St. Louis County, MO. No support for political causes and candidates, or for-profit entities. No grants to individuals directly, or for operating costs, fundraising dinners, courtesy advertising or other benefits and endowment projects.
Publications: Application guidelines.
Application information: The foundation generally does not accept unsolicited applications, and is not currently accepting new scholar applications. See foundation web site for additional information. Application form not required.
Initial approach: 1-page concept paper
Copies of proposal: 7
Deadline(s): Aug. 15th for grants; May 1 for scholarships
Board meeting date(s): Monthly
Trustees: Rabbi Mark L. Shook; Richard W. Braun; Paul P. Weil; Archdiocese of St. Louis; U.S. Bank, N.A.
Number of staff: 1 part-time professional; 1 part-time support.
EIN: 436020833
Selected grants: The following grants are a representative sample of this grantmaker's funding activity:
$20,000 to American Red Cross, Saint Louis, MO, 2011.
$10,000 to Asthma and Allergy Foundation of America, Saint Louis, MO, 2011.
$10,000 to Boys and Girls Town of Missouri, Saint Louis, MO, 2011.
$10,000 to Delta Gamma Center for Children with Visual Impairments, Saint Louis, MO, 2011.
$10,000 to Life Skills, Ballwin, MO, 2011.
$10,000 to Lutheran Association for Special Education, Saint Louis, MO, 2011.
$10,000 to Provident, Inc., Saint Louis, MO, 2011.
$10,000 to Stages Saint Louis, Chesterfield, MO, 2011.

4992
Ruth D. and Wylie Todd Charitable Foundation ✧

307 Cabin Grove Ln.
St. Louis, MO 63141-8171
Contact: Anna Polizzi-Keller, Tr.

Donors: Ruth Davis Todd Established Foundation; Oratory of St. Augustine and St. Gregory.
Foundation type: Independent foundation.
Financial data (yr. ended 12/31/13): Assets, $431,934 (M); gifts received, $250,000; expenditures, $440,256; qualifying distributions, $436,197; giving activities include $436,197 for 13 grants (high: $109,650; low: $9,682).
Fields of interest: Crime/law enforcement; Agriculture/food; Public affairs; Catholic agencies & churches.
Limitations: Applications not accepted. Giving primarily in St. Louis, MO; some giving also in Alton, IL.
Application information: Contributes only to pre-selected organizations.
Trustees: Fr. Gregory Morhman; Anna Polizzi-Keller.
EIN: 263273942

4993
Towle Family Foundation ✧

1610 Des Peres Rd., Ste. 250
St. Louis, MO 63131-1814

Established in 1998 in MO.
Donors: J. Ellwood Towle; Patience E. Toele†; Robin D. Towle.
Foundation type: Independent foundation.
Financial data (yr. ended 09/30/13): Assets, $16,427,669 (M); gifts received, $155,841; expenditures, $586,855; qualifying distributions, $489,311; giving activities include $489,311 for 11 grants (high: $75,000; low: $11,311).
Fields of interest: Education; Recreation, camps; Human services.
Limitations: Applications not accepted. Giving primarily in MO. No grants to individuals.
Application information: Contributes only to pre-selected organizations.
Officers: J. Ellwood Towle, Pres.; Christopher D. Towle, Secy.-Treas.
EIN: 431800405
Selected grants: The following grants are a representative sample of this grantmaker's funding activity:
$55,000 to Camps Newfound Owatonna, Harrison, ME, 2011. For endowment fund.
$30,000 to Washington University, Saint Louis, MO, 2011.
$25,000 to Peace Haven Association, Saint Louis, MO, 2011. For endowment fund.
$18,000 to City Academy, Saint Louis, MO, 2011. For endowment fund.

4994
Trio Foundation of St. Louis ✧

(formerly Trio Foundation)
8029 Forsyth Blvd., No. 201
St. Louis, MO 63105-1723 (314) 725-3040
Contact: Wendy Jaffe, Exec. Dir.
FAX: (314) 725-2603; E-mail: trio@triostl.org; Main URL: http://www.triostl.org/

Established in 1990 in MO.
Donor: Dorothy Moog.
Foundation type: Independent foundation.
Financial data (yr. ended 12/31/13): Assets, $29,155,218 (M); expenditures, $1,478,421; qualifying distributions, $1,145,437; giving activities include $998,000 for 109 grants (high: $30,000; low: $1,000).
Purpose and activities: Giving primarily for arts and culture (particularly programs that increase the capacity of small and mid-sized organizations, or are especially unique and innovative); children and youth development; education (particularly programs that improve education among urban populations); the environment; health and human services (particularly programs that serve economically disadvantaged people, directly serve individuals with health issues, serve people with physical and/or developmental disabilities, and empower women); and Jewish community support.
Fields of interest: Arts; Education; Environment; Youth development; Human services; Jewish agencies & synagogues; Children/youth; Disabilities, people with; Women; Economically disadvantaged.
Type of support: General/operating support; Capital campaigns; Building/renovation; Program development.
Limitations: Applications accepted. Giving primarily in St. Louis, MO. No grants to individuals, or for medical/science research; generally not interested in supporting the production of videos, CD-ROMs, conferences, seminars, feasibility studies, the development of strategic plans, or for the purchase of computer hardware or software.
Publications: Application guidelines; Grants list.
Application information: Application form required.
Initial approach: Use proposal process on foundation web site
Deadline(s): See foundation web site for current deadlines
Officers and Directors:* James R. Moog,* Pres.; Terri Mason, V.P. and Secy.; Mary Moog, Treas.; Wendy Jaffe, Exec. Dir.; Donna L. Moog; Thomas H. Moog; Lee Nussbaum.
Number of staff: 1 part-time professional.
EIN: 431553538

Selected grants: The following grants are a representative sample of this grantmaker's funding activity:
$15,000 to CARE, Chicago, IL, 2012. For Power Within.
$10,000 to Big Brothers Big Sisters of Southwestern Illinois, Belleville, IL, 2012. For Community Based Mentoring.
$10,000 to University of Miami, Department of Neurology, Miami, FL, 2012. For Department of Neurology Grand Rounds Education Program.

4995
Robert J. Trulaske, Jr. Family Foundation ✧
7700 Forsyth Blvd., Ste. 1220
St. Louis, MO 63105-1819

Established in MO.
Donors: R.J. Trulaske, Sr. & G.M. Trulaske Charitable Trust No. 1; GMT Interim Trust.
Foundation type: Independent foundation.
Financial data (yr. ended 12/31/13): Assets, $23,030,209 (M); gifts received, $5,621,155; expenditures, $632,066; qualifying distributions, $531,408; giving activities include $465,447 for 13 grants (high: $120,000; low: $4,000).
Fields of interest: Environment, natural resources; Human services.
Limitations: Applications not accepted. Giving primarily in MO.
Application information: Unsolicited requests for funds not accepted.
Officers: Jeanne Trulaske Dalba, Pres.; Michael Newmark, Secy.; Meghan Trulaske Miers, Treas.
Trustees: John Bechtold; Stephen Kincaid; Jay Sarver; Jerome Thomasson; Sarah Trulaske.
EIN: 203825944
Selected grants: The following grants are a representative sample of this grantmaker's funding activity:
$29,500 to Missouri Botanical Garden, Saint Louis, MO, 2011.
$20,500 to Campbell House Museum, Saint Louis, MO, 2011. To support operations.
$20,000 to Leelanau Conservancy, Leland, MI, 2011.
$13,200 to Friends of Buford Park and Mount Pisgah, Eugene, OR, 2011.
$10,000 to Library Foundation for the Benefit of Saint Louis Public Library, Saint Louis, MO, 2011. To support operations.
$3,000 to Forest Park Forever, Saint Louis, MO, 2011. To support operations.
$1,500 to Cascades Raptor Center, Eugene, OR, 2011. To support operations.
$1,500 to Ducks Unlimited, Memphis, TN, 2011. To support operations.
$1,500 to National Wild Turkey Federation, Edgefield, SC, 2011. To support operations.
$1,000 to Gateway Greening, Saint Louis, MO, 2011. To support operations.

4996
Truman Heartland Community Foundation ✧
(formerly Independence Community Foundation)
4200 Little Blue Parkway, Ste. 340
Independence, MO 64057-8303 (816) 836-8189
Contact: Elizabeth A. McClure, Dir., Progs. and Rels.
FAX: (816) 836-8898; E-mail: hanson@thcf.org; Additional e-mail: mcclure@thcf.org; Main URL: http://www.thcf.org

Incorporated in 1982 in MO; received assets converted from merger of Independence Community Foundation with Independence Regional Health Center Foundation in 1994.
Foundation type: Community foundation.
Financial data (yr. ended 12/31/12): Assets, $27,875,910 (M); gifts received, $2,610,153; expenditures, $5,176,573; giving activities include $4,139,059 for 143+ grants (high: $289,694), and $189,441 for 173 grants to individuals.
Purpose and activities: The mission of the Truman Heartland Community Foundation is to improve area communities by promoting and serving private giving for the public good. The foundation primarily provides support for arts, culture, and historic preservation, building stronger neighborhoods, education, fostering a sense of community spirit, health needs for the community, leadership development for youth and adults, programs for seniors, positive youth development, transportation and violence prevention.
Fields of interest: Historic preservation/historical societies; Arts; Adult/continuing education; Education; Health care; Crime/violence prevention; Employment, training; Housing/shelter, development; Youth development; Children/youth, services; Family services, domestic violence; Aging, centers/services; Human services; Community/economic development; Transportation; Leadership development; Aging.
Type of support: General/operating support; Continuing support; Program development; Seed money; Scholarship funds; In-kind gifts; Matching/challenge support.
Limitations: Applications accepted. Giving limited to suburban Jackson County, MO. No grants to individuals (except for scholarships).
Publications: Application guidelines; Annual report; Informational brochure; Newsletter.
Application information: Visit foundation web site for application forms and guidelines. Organizations whose letters of interest show the greatest potential for serving or strengthening the community will be invited to submit full applications. Application form required.
Initial approach: Letter of interest
Deadline(s): First Thurs. in Apr. for letter of interest; fourth Thursday in May for full proposal
Board meeting date(s): Quarterly
Final notification: Mid-May for full proposal invitation; early October for funding decisions
Officers and Directors:* Martha Cockerell,* Chair.; Judy Forrester,* Vice-Chair.; Phillip J. Hanson,* C.E.O. and Pres.; Joy Hobick,* Secy.; Rick Kreher,* Treas.; Beverly J. Powell,* C.F.O.; Paul Broome; Cindy Cavanah; Brad Constance; William C. Esry; Randall Ferguson; Ron Finke; Eleanor Frasier; Chuck Foudree; Helen Hatridge; Darrel Hensely; Robert Hepting; David Jeter; Cliff Jones; Barbara Koirtyohann; Steve Krueger; Dr. Allan Markley; Tracey Mershon; Melanie Moentmann; Jim Pryde; Charlie Shields; Dr. Barbara Thompson; Brenda West; David Williams; Sharon Williams.
Number of staff: 2 full-time professional; 2 full-time support; 1 part-time support.
EIN: 431482136

4997
The Lesley A. Waldheim Charitable Foundation ✧
600 Washington Ave., Ste. 2500
St. Louis, MO 63101-1311
Contact: Marian V. Mehan, Tr.

Established in 2002 in MO.
Donor: Lesley A. Waldheim.
Foundation type: Independent foundation.
Financial data (yr. ended 12/31/13): Assets, $26,202,489 (M); expenditures, $1,468,014; qualifying distributions, $1,183,000; giving activities include $1,183,000 for 14 grants (high: $228,000; low: $15,000).
Fields of interest: Performing arts, theater; Food banks; Boys & girls clubs; Human services.
Limitations: Applications accepted. Giving primarily in St. Louis, MO.
Application information: Application form not required.
Initial approach: Proposal
Deadline(s): None
Trustees: Marian V. Mehan; Lesley A. Waldheim.
EIN: 436886268
Selected grants: The following grants are a representative sample of this grantmaker's funding activity:
$200,000 to Washington University, Medical School, Saint Louis, MO, 2012. For Prevention of Child.

4998
Louis L. & Adelaide C. Ward Foundation ✧
(formerly Ward Foundation)
4900 Oak St.
Kansas City, MO 64112-0480

Established in 1966 in MO.
Donors: Adelaide C. Ward; and members of the Ward Family.
Foundation type: Independent foundation.
Financial data (yr. ended 12/31/13): Assets, $40,190,683 (M); expenditures, $2,102,256; qualifying distributions, $2,061,000; giving activities include $2,056,000 for 27 grants (high: $800,000; low: $1,000).
Fields of interest: Higher education; Recreation, parks/playgrounds; Human services; Salvation Army.
Type of support: Annual campaigns; Capital campaigns; Endowments.
Limitations: Applications not accepted. Giving primarily in Kansas City, MO. No grants to individuals.
Application information: Unsolicited requests for funds not accepted.
Officers: Scott H. Ward, Chair.; Adelaide C. Ward, Pres. and Treas.; Thomas S. Ward, Secy.
EIN: 436064548
Selected grants: The following grants are a representative sample of this grantmaker's funding activity:
$850,000 to Kansas University Endowment Association, Lawrence, KS, 2011. For general charitable purpose.
$150,000 to Harvesters-The Community Food Network, Kansas City, MO, 2011.

4999
Frank K. Webb Charitable Trust ✧ ☆
P.O. Box 66916
St. Louis, MO 63166-6916

Foundation type: Independent foundation.
Financial data (yr. ended 12/31/13): Assets, $11,362,548 (M); expenditures, $638,197; qualifying distributions, $508,950; giving activities include $508,000 for 12 grants (high: $120,000; low: $1,000).
Fields of interest: Youth development; Human services; Protestant agencies & churches.
Limitations: Applications not accepted.
Application information: Unsolicited requests for funds not accepted.
Trustees: Edward Jones Trust Co.; William Dietel; Martha Webb.
EIN: 276146743

5000
James L. & Nellie M. Westlake Scholarship Fund ✧
c/o U.S. Bank, N.A.
P.O. Box 387
St. Louis, MO 63166-0387
Main URL: http://sms.scholarshipamerica.org/westlake/

Established in 1981 in MO.
Donors: James L. Westlake†; Nellie M. Westlake.
Foundation type: Independent foundation.
Financial data (yr. ended 06/30/13): Assets, $20,930,963 (M); gifts received, $5,000; expenditures, $1,069,280; qualifying distributions, $964,319; giving activities include $878,381 for grants to individuals.
Purpose and activities: Awards scholarships to graduates of Missouri high schools, based on need and scholastic achievement, for higher education scholarships. Applicants must be enrolled in full-time undergraduate study for the entire upcoming academic year at an accredited 4-year college or university, or have completed 1 or 2 full years at a Missouri community college with sufficient credits to transfer to an accredited 4-year college or university at the sophomore or junior level. Applicants must also demonstrate limited financial resources with a family adjusted gross income of $50,000 or less, and an expected family contribution toward college of $7,000 or less, and have at least a cumulative GPA of 2.5 on a 4.0 scale, except community college applicants with 1-year transferable credits who must have 2.25 or higher on a 4.0 scale.
Fields of interest: Young adults.
Type of support: Scholarships—to individuals.
Limitations: Giving limited to high school graduates who are residents of MO. No loans or program-related investments.
Publications: Application guidelines.
Application information: Application form available on program web site. Application form required.
Deadline(s): See program web site for current deadline
Trustee: U.S. Bank, N.A.
EIN: 436248269

5001
Whitaker Foundation ✧
(also known as Lyndon C. and Mae M. Whitaker Charitable Foundation)
308 N. 21st St., Ste. 400
St. Louis, MO 63103-1642 (314) 241-4352
Contact: Christy E. Gray, Exec. Dir.
FAX: (314) 241-4381;
E-mail: cgray@thewhitakerfoundation.org; Additional e-mail: info@thewhitakerfoundation.org; Main URL: http://www.thewhitakerfoundation.org

Trust established in 1975 in MO.
Donor: Mae M. Whitaker†.
Foundation type: Independent foundation.
Financial data (yr. ended 04/30/13): Assets, $26,181,495 (M); expenditures, $1,378,065; qualifying distributions, $1,193,683; giving activities include $948,786 for 21 grants (high: $141,086; low: $6,000).
Purpose and activities: Giving primarily to strengthen arts organizations and local park preservation and use.
Fields of interest: Arts; Recreation, parks/playgrounds.
Type of support: Capital campaigns; Building/renovation; Program development.
Limitations: Applications accepted. Giving in the metropolitan St. Louis, MO, area, particularly within 50 miles of the Arch. No grants to individuals, or for galas, tournaments, or other social events.
Publications: Application guidelines; Annual report; Grants list.
Application information: Paper letters and proposals are no longer accepted. Full proposals are by invitation only, after review of Letter of Inquiry. Application form required.
Initial approach: Letter of Inquiry via online application process through foundation web site
Copies of proposal: 1
Deadline(s): For Letters of Inquiry: Feb. 1, Aug. 1, and Nov. 1; For invited proposals: Mar. 1, Sept. 1 and Dec. 1
Board meeting date(s): Jan., Apr., July and Oct.
Final notification: Jan., Apr., and Oct.
Officer: Christy E. Gray, Exec. Dir.
Trustees: Arnold Donald; Barbara Eagleton; Dr. Gerald Early; Shaun Hayes; Kiku Obata.
Number of staff: 1 full-time professional; 1 part-time support.
EIN: 510173109
Selected grants: The following grants are a representative sample of this grantmaker's funding activity:
$250,000 to Saint Louis Symphony Orchestra, Saint Louis, MO, 2011.
$170,000 to Opera Theater of Saint Louis, Saint Louis, MO, 2011.
$100,000 to Laumeier Sculpture Park, Saint Louis, MO, 2011.
$100,000 to Missouri Botanical Garden, Saint Louis, MO, 2011.
$74,575 to Grace Hill Settlement House, Saint Louis, MO, 2011.
$70,000 to Contemporary Art Museum Saint Louis, Saint Louis, MO, 2011.
$60,000 to Shakespeare Festival Saint Louis, Saint Louis, MO, 2011.
$40,000 to Dance Saint Louis, Saint Louis, MO, 2011.
$30,000 to Gateway Greening, Saint Louis, MO, 2011.
$30,000 to Metro Theater Company, Saint Louis, MO, 2011.

5002
World Wide Technology Foundation ✧
60 Weldon Pkwy.
St. Louis, MO 63043-3202

Donor: World Wide Technology Holding Co. Inc.
Foundation type: Independent foundation.
Financial data (yr. ended 12/31/13): Assets, $944,642 (M); gifts received, $2,664,633; expenditures, $2,998,738; qualifying distributions, $2,997,570; giving activities include $2,938,698 for 196 grants (high: $285,000; low: $50).
Fields of interest: Arts; Education; Health care; Health organizations, association; Human services; Catholic agencies & churches.
Limitations: Applications not accepted. Giving primarily in St. Louis, MO.
Application information: Contributes only to pre-selected organizations.
Officers and Directors:* Joseph G. Koenig, Pres.; Ann Marr,* Secy.; Thomas W. Strunk, Treas.; James P. Kavanaugh; David L. Steward.
EIN: 263571211

5003
Kearney Wornall Charitable Foundation ✧
(formerly Kearney Wornall Charitable Trust & Foundation)
c/o UMB Bank, N.A.
P.O. Box 415044 M/S 1020307
Kansas City, MO 64141-6692

Established in 1954 in MO.
Donor: Kearney Wornall†.
Foundation type: Independent foundation.
Financial data (yr. ended 12/31/13): Assets, $13,994,878 (M); expenditures, $756,801; qualifying distributions, $686,457; giving activities include $636,000 for 11 grants (high: $250,000; low: $1,000).
Fields of interest: Museums; Performing arts, ballet; Performing arts, orchestras; Arts; Agriculture/food, formal/general education; Human services.
Type of support: General/operating support.
Limitations: Applications not accepted. Giving primarily in the Kansas City, MO, area. No grants to individuals.
Application information: Contributes only to pre-selected organizations.
Trustees: Paul L. Skahan; UMB Bank, N.A.
EIN: 446013874
Selected grants: The following grants are a representative sample of this grantmaker's funding activity:
$346,000 to Agriculture Future of America, Kansas City, MO, 2011. For general support.
$110,000 to Kansas City Symphony Foundation, Kansas City, MO, 2011. For general support.

MONTANA

5004
Charles M. Bair Memorial Trust ✧
c/o U.S. Bank, N.A.
P.O. Box 30678
Billings, MT 59115-0001
FAX: (406) 657-8034;
E-mail: penny.doak@usbank.com; Main URL: http://www.charlesmbairtrusts.org/scholarship.html

Established in 1978 in MT.
Donors: Marguerite B. Lamb†; Bair Ranch Foundation.
Foundation type: Independent foundation.
Financial data (yr. ended 01/31/14): Assets, $10,030,679 (M); gifts received, $1,000,000; expenditures, $1,079,087; qualifying distributions, $1,040,969; giving activities include $500,000 for 5 grants (high: $300,000; low: $25,000), and $507,619 for grants to individuals.
Purpose and activities: The trust's purpose is to fund scholarships for high school graduates who have lived and attended school in Meagher County or Wheatland County, Montana.
Fields of interest: Higher education; Hospitals (general); Protestant agencies & churches.
Type of support: General/operating support; Scholarships—to individuals.
Limitations: Giving scholarships to students from Yellowstone, Meagher, and Wheatland counties, MT. The foundation also gives to five charities that are named in its documents.
Publications: Application guidelines.
Application information: See foundation web site for current application guidelines which must be followed. Application form required.
Trustee: U.S. Bank, N.A.
EIN: 810370774

5005
The Bair Ranch Foundation ✧
c/o Anderson Zurmuehlen & Company, P.C.
P.O. Box 20435
Billings, MT 59104-0435

Established in 1998 in MT.
Foundation type: Independent foundation.
Financial data (yr. ended 12/31/13): Assets, $90,415,416 (M); expenditures, $4,496,941; qualifying distributions, $2,434,182; giving activities include $2,090,457 for 5 grants (high: $1,000,000; low: $16,557).
Purpose and activities: The foundation was created for the purpose of owning and operating a working ranch that will be used for scientific research, experimentation, and educational programs to be conducted in conjunction with local universities.
Fields of interest: Higher education; Science.
Limitations: Applications not accepted. Giving limited to experimentation on a ranch in Meagher County, MT. No grants to individuals.
Application information: Contributes only to pre-selected organizations.
Officers: Wayne Hirsch, Pres.; Bill Davies, V.P.; Bill Gottwals, Secy.-Treas.
EIN: 810108184

5006
Central Montana Foundation ✧ ☆
224 W. Main, Ste. 403
P.O. Box 334
Lewistown, MT 59457
Contact: Mike Zacher, Pres.
E-mail: cmtfoundation@midrivers.com; Main URL: http://www.centralmontanafoundation.com/

Established in 1985; a regional affiliate of the Montana Community Foundation.
Foundation type: Community foundation.
Financial data (yr. ended 12/31/13): Assets, $19,446,216 (M); gifts received, $1,119,877; expenditures, $1,983,528; giving activities include $1,678,840 for 32+ grants (high: $912,733), and $199,875 for 85 grants to individuals.
Purpose and activities: The foundation promotes the health and improvement of residents in central Montana, and works to improve the quality of life in the area.
Fields of interest: Education; Health care; Human services; Community/economic development.
Type of support: Scholarships—to individuals.
Limitations: Applications accepted. Giving limited to central MT.
Application information:
Initial approach: Email
Deadline(s): Apr. 1 for major grants. Minor grants are due the 10th of the month to be considered in the month the application is received
Board meeting date(s): Fourth Tuesday of the month
Officers and Directors: Carrie Mantooth, Exec. Dir.; Jason Butcher; Beth Putnam; Josh Webber; Jennifer Weeden; Sandra Westhodd; Mike Zacher, Pres.; Dean Comes, V.P.; Robyn Bakkedahl, Secy.-Treas.; Sonny Comes; Doug Flament; Carl Seilstad.
EIN: 810425314

5007
Cross Charitable Foundation, Inc. ✧
3805 Valley Commons Dr., Ste. 7
Bozeman, MT 59718-6510
Contact: John R. Clark, Treas.
Additional address: P.O. Box 1789, West Yellowstone, MT 59758, tel. (406) 585-3393; Main URL: http://crosscharitablefoundation.org/

Established in WY.
Donors: C. Walker Cross; C. Walker Cross Living Trust.
Foundation type: Independent foundation.
Financial data (yr. ended 12/31/13): Assets, $27,530,529 (M); gifts received, $1,200,000; expenditures, $1,270,658; qualifying distributions, $1,270,658; giving activities include $1,002,400 for 48 grants (high: $35,000; low: $5,000).
Fields of interest: Environment; Animals/wildlife.
Limitations: Applications accepted. Giving in the U.S., with some emphasis on MT and UT. No grants to individuals.
Application information: Application form required.
Initial approach: Use online application process on foundation web site
Deadline(s): Aug. 1
Final notification: Nov. 1
Officers: Charles Folland, Pres.; Rex Child, V.P.; Carol H. Gonnella, Secy.; John R. Clark, Treas.
EIN: 830331707

5008
O. P. and W. E. Edwards Foundation, Inc. ✧
c/o Jo Ann Eder
P.O. Box 2445
Red Lodge, MT 59068-2445 (406) 446-1077
Contact: Amy Moore, Foundation Mgr.
FAX: (406) 446-1363;
E-mail: info@opweedwards.org; E-mail address of Amy Moore, Foundation Mgr., for specific grant questions: amoore@opweedwards.org; Main URL: http://opweedwards.org
Grants List: http://opweedwards.org/Grants_List.html

Incorporated in 1962 in NY.
Donors: William E. Edwards†; J.N. Edwards†; Harriet E. Gamper; David E. Gamper†; Jo Ann Eder.
Foundation type: Independent foundation.
Financial data (yr. ended 08/31/13): Assets, $34,130,144 (M); gifts received, $1,701,000; expenditures, $2,998,781; qualifying distributions, $2,423,698; giving activities include $2,380,472 for 85 grants (high: $169,600; low: $1,000).
Purpose and activities: Major interest in programs helping economically disadvantaged young people become able to survive and thrive on their own, with preference to smaller, comprehensive programs that are integral parts of their communities' networks of services.
Fields of interest: Visual arts; Performing arts; Education; Youth development; Human services; Children/youth, services; Family services; Community/economic development; Astronomy; Infants/toddlers; Children/youth; Youth; Young adults; Native Americans/American Indians; Indigenous peoples; Economically disadvantaged.
Type of support: General/operating support; Continuing support; Management development/capacity building; Emergency funds; Program development; Seed money; Scholarship funds; Program-related investments/loans; Matching/challenge support.
Limitations: Giving primarily in MT, NY, and VT; limited funding in, ND, Minneapolis, MN, OR, SD, and the Northwest. No grants to individuals, or for capital grants.
Publications: Application guidelines; Grants list; IRS Form 990 or 990-PF printed copy available upon request.
Application information: Unsolicited full proposals not considered. The foundation requests proposals from organizations about which the trustees are personally and directly knowledgeable. See foundation web site for details. Application form required.
Initial approach: See foundation web site for instructions and guidelines
Board meeting date(s): As required
Officers and Trustees:* Jo Ann Eder,* Pres.; Gisela Gamper,* V.P.; Mark D. Eder,* Secy.; Yogeeta Gamper,* Treas.; Jessica Dunbar; Christopher E. Gamper; Harriet E. Gamper.
Number of staff: 1 part-time support.
EIN: 136100965
Selected grants: The following grants are a representative sample of this grantmaker's funding activity:
$177,000 to United Methodist Church of Leipsic, Leipsic, OH, 2012. For grant of which $118,000 - 10% thereof to be paid to the Defiance District Office of the United Methodist Church to be used toward college scholarships for pre-ministerial students, 5% thereof to the Caring and Sharing Group, and the

balance to be distributed in such Christian Mission projects as the Outreach Committee, and $59,000 for Church's Christian Education and Music Programs.
$150,000 to Hopa Mountain, Bozeman, MT, 2012. For Strengthening the Circle.
$140,000 to Vermont Community Foundation, Middlebury, VT, 2012. For Edwards Foundation Preschool Scholarships.
$118,000 to Life Enriching Communities Foundation, Loveland, OH, 2012. For Benevolent Care Fund for health care residents requiring financial assistance.
$118,000 to Wesley Services Organization, Cincinnati, OH, 2012. To improve the lives of so many seniors and disabled in the Cincinnati area with your wide range of programs.
$60,000 to Center for Creative Education, Kingston, NY, 2012. For after-school arts programs for at-risk and low-income children and youth in Kingston, NY.
$55,000 to Boys and Girls Club of the Northern Cheyenne Nation, Lame Deer, MT, 2012. For general support.
$55,000 to Boys and Girls Club of the Northern Cheyenne Nation, Lame Deer, MT, 2012. For Directions Native American Scholarships.
$50,000 to Vermont Community Foundation, Middlebury, VT, 2012. For Vermont Community Foundation Birth to Three.
$40,000 to Southside Family Nurturing Center, Minneapolis, MN, 2012. For general operating support.
$35,000 to Vermont Community Foundation, Middlebury, VT, 2012. For Vermont Community Preschool Collaborative.
$30,000 to Farmworker Housing Development Corporation, Woodburn, OR, 2012. For educational programs for farmworker children and youth.
$25,000 to Big Brothers Big Sisters of Lake County and the Flathead Reservation, Ronan, MT, 2012. For Native American Mentoring Project.
$25,000 to Hopa Mountain, Bozeman, MT, 2012. To implement Indigenous Scholars of Promise Program.
$25,000 to Hopa Mountain, Bozeman, MT, 2012. For program support.
$25,000 to Vermont Community Loan Fund, Montpelier, VT, 2012. For Project SUCCESS.
$20,000 to Flagship Program, Missoula, MT, 2012. For The Flagship Program at Lowell Elementary School.
$20,000 to Friends of Green Chimneys, Brewster, NY, 2012. For Green Chimneys Promise Program.
$20,000 to Manaia, Livingston, MT, 2012. For general support.
$20,000 to Thrive, Inc., Bozeman, MT, 2012. For Partnership Project Child Care Scholarships.
$15,000 to Center for Creative Education, Kingston, NY, 2012. For David Hykes - Harmonic Presence.

5009
First Interstate BancSystem Foundation, Inc. ✧
401 N. 31st St., Ste. 700
Billings, MT 59101-1285 (406) 255-5393
Contact: Kelly Bruggeman
E-mail: foundation@fib.com; Main URL: https://www.firstinterstatebank.com/company/commitment/foundation/
Grants Database: https://www.firstinterstatebank.com/company/commitment/foundation/grant_awards.php
RSS Feed: http://www.firstinterstatebank.com/rss/foundation.php

Established in 1990 in MT.
Donors: First Interstate Bank of Commerce; Wells Fargo Bank, N.A.; First Interstate Bank.
Foundation type: Company-sponsored foundation.
Financial data (yr. ended 12/31/13): Assets, $2,498,061 (M); gifts received, $1,558,000; expenditures, $1,155,710; qualifying distributions, $1,146,817; giving activities include $1,116,782 for grants.
Purpose and activities: The foundation supports organizations involved with arts and culture, education, health, hunger, housing, human services, community development, leadership development, and economically disadvantaged people. Support is given primarily in areas of company operations.
Fields of interest: Arts; Secondary school/education; Higher education; Education; Health care; Food services; Housing/shelter; Human services; Community development, neighborhood development; Economic development; Community/economic development; Leadership development; Economically disadvantaged.
Type of support: Capital campaigns; Building/renovation; Equipment; Program development; Scholarship funds; Employee volunteer services; Employee matching gifts; Matching/challenge support.
Limitations: Applications accepted. Giving primarily in areas of company operations in MT, western SD, and WY. No support for lobbying or political organizations, sectarian or religious organizations not of direct benefit to the entire community, or discriminatory organizations. No grants to individuals, or for endowments, or general operating support for established organizations.
Publications: Application guidelines; Grants list; Program policy statement.
Application information: Application form required.
Initial approach: Download application and mail to nearest branch location
Deadline(s): None
Board meeting date(s): Quarterly
Officer and Directors:* Randy Scott,* Chair. and Pres.; Kelly Bruggeman, Exec. Dir.; Ka Alberts; Sara Flitner; Ed Garding; Charles Heyneman; Susan Humble; Mike Huston; Donovan McComb; Shawn Rost; James Scott; Lynette Scott; Risa Scott; Thomas Scott; Steve Wheeler.
Trustee: First Interstate Bank.
Number of staff: 3 full-time professional.
EIN: 810465899
Selected grants: The following grants are a representative sample of this grantmaker's funding activity:
$728 to United Way of Yellowstone County, Billings, MT, 2012. For 3rd Quarter VM 2012.
$708 to Senior Center of Jackson Hole, Jackson, WY, 2012. For 4th quarter vm 2011.
$360 to Montana Food Bank Network, Missoula, MT, 2012. For NFN2012VM.
$170 to Boy Scouts of America, Black Hills Area Council, Rapid City, SD, 2012. For program support.
$100 to Youth Homes, Missoula, MT, 2012. For NFN2012GM.

5010
Gianforte Family Charitable Trust ✧
c/o Susan Gianforte
1320 Manley Rd.
Bozeman, MT 59715-8779

Established in 2004 in MT.
Donors: Greg Gianforte; Susan Gianforte.
Foundation type: Independent foundation.
Financial data (yr. ended 12/31/12): Assets, $129,456,006 (M); expenditures, $7,463,267; qualifying distributions, $6,992,168; giving activities include $6,992,168 for 78 grants (high: $2,002,500; low: $100).
Fields of interest: Education; Human services; Children/youth, services; Family services; Christian agencies & churches.
Limitations: Applications not accepted. Giving primarily in MT, with emphasis on Bozeman. No grants to individuals.
Application information: Contributes only to pre-selected organizations.
Trustees: Greg Gianforte; Richard Gianforte; Susan Gianforte.
EIN: 306089834

5011
Gilhousen Family Foundation
599 High Tower Rd.
Bozeman, MT 59718-8163 (406) 600-6816
Contact: Patti A. Guptill, Admin.
FAX: (406) 586-2518;
E-mail: foundation.admin@gilhousen.net; Tel. for Patti A. Guptill: (503) 643-4183

Established in 1999 in MT.
Donors: Klein Gilhousen; Karen Gilhousen; Patricia Guptill; Roy Guptill; Gilhousen Investments, LP.
Foundation type: Independent foundation.
Financial data (yr. ended 12/31/13): Assets, $2,486,642 (M); gifts received, $600; expenditures, $2,540,835; qualifying distributions, $2,459,093; giving activities include $2,378,418 for 87 grants (high: $250,000; low: $100), and $4,578 for 1 loan/program-related investment.
Purpose and activities: Giving to support spiritual life, education, community-based projects, and cultural programs in and around Bozeman, Montana. On the broader level, funding for projects that allow people to more actively participate in society through access to spiritual development, education, and health care.
Fields of interest: Arts; Education; Health care; Human services; Children/youth, services; Christian agencies & churches.
Type of support: General/operating support; Program-related investments/loans.
Limitations: Applications accepted. Giving primarily in Gallatin County, MT. No grants to individuals.
Application information: Applications only accepted from MT organizations. Contributions outside of MT go to pre-selected organizations. Certified mail not accepted. Application form not required.
Initial approach: 1-page letter of inquiry
Copies of proposal: 1
Deadline(s): Mar. 31, June 30, Sept. 30, and Dec. 31
Board meeting date(s): Jan., Apr., July and Oct.
Final notification: 2-4 months
Officers and Director:* Klein Gilhousen, Pres.; Karen M. Gilhousen, V.P.; Patricia A. Guptill,* Admin.

Number of staff: 1 part-time professional.
EIN: 742938609
Selected grants: The following grants are a representative sample of this grantmaker's funding activity:
$250,000 to Montana Center for Horsemanship, Dillon, MT, 2012. To build new Equestrian Center at Montana Western.
$249,529 to Rock Youth Center, Bozeman, MT, 2012. For salaries and operations for Youth Center.
$165,000 to Yellowstone Theological Institute, Bozeman, MT, 2012. For start-up funds for development of theological institute. Grant made through Belgrade Community Church.
$125,000 to Intermountain Children's Home, Helena, MT, 2012. For unreimbursed expenses for resident traumatized children.
$100,000 to Bozeman Deaconess Foundation for Gifting, Bozeman, MT, 2012. For expanded emergency services.
$100,000 to Family Promise of Gallatin Valley, Bozeman, MT, 2012. For shelter for homeless families (two years of grant funds).
$100,000 to Thrive, Inc., Bozeman, MT, 2012. For operating support for various programs surrounding children and families.
$42,500 to Young Life of Montana, Belgrade, MT, 2012. For Christian youth programs.
$39,271 to Eagle Mount Bozeman, Bozeman, MT, 2012. For Adventure Days summer programming.
$25,000 to Montana Shakespeare in the Parks, Bozeman, MT, 2012. For general support for summer touring Shakespearean theater group.

5012
Jane S. Heman Foundation, Inc. ✧ ☆
401 Dearborn Ave.
Missoula, MT 59801-8032 (406) 549-3195
Contact: John Dayries, Pres.

Established in 1999 in MT.
Donor: Jane S. Heman†.
Foundation type: Independent foundation.
Financial data (yr. ended 12/31/13): Assets, $12,808,024 (M); expenditures, $624,651; qualifying distributions, $574,012; giving activities include $554,813 for 17 grants (high: $100,000; low: $10,000).
Fields of interest: Education.
Limitations: Applications accepted. Giving primarily in MT. No grants to individuals.
Application information: Application form not required.
Initial approach: Proposal
Deadline(s): None
Officers: John Dayries, Pres.; Carol Capp, V.P.; Robert A. Thomas, Secy.-Treas.
EIN: 810526846

5013
Montana Community Foundation ✧
1 N. Last Chance Gulch, Ste. 1
Helena, MT 59624-1145 (406) 443-8313
FAX: (406) 442-0482; E-mail: info@mtcf.org; Mailing address: P.O. box 1145, Helena, MT 59624-1145; Main URL: http://www.mtcf.org
Facebook: http://www.facebook.com/pages/Montana-Community-Foundation/187434094625353

Incorporated in 1988 in MT.
Foundation type: Community foundation.
Financial data (yr. ended 06/30/13): Assets, $65,095,733 (M); gifts received, $2,719,454; expenditures, $4,995,197; giving activities include $2,479,697 for 123+ grants (high: $107,377).
Purpose and activities: The foundation seeks to cultivate a culture of giving so Montana communities can flourish.
Fields of interest: Arts; Education; Environment, natural resources; Human services; Economic development; Minorities; Native Americans/American Indians; Girls; Adults, women; Young adults, female; LGBTQ.
Type of support: Continuing support; Emergency funds; Employee-related scholarships; Scholarships—to individuals.
Limitations: Applications accepted. Giving limited to MT. No support for religious purposes. No grants for annual or capital campaigns, endowment funds, or generally for debt retirement.
Publications: Annual report; Financial statement; Newsletter.
Application information: Visit foundation web site for Application Cover Sheet and application guidelines. Application form required.
Initial approach: Submit Application Cover Sheet with proposal
Board meeting date(s): 3 times per year
Officers and Directors:* Dan Clark,* Chair.; Brian Patrick,* Vice-Chair.; Mary Rutherford,* C.E.O.; Mary Craigle,* Secy.; Dale Woolhiser,* Treas.; Emily Kovarik,* C.F.O.; Jeff Bretherton; Mike Gustafson; Stacey Mueller; Cynthia R. Woods.
Number of staff: 5 full-time professional; 2 full-time support; 1 part-time support.
EIN: 810450150

5014
Oro y Plata Foundation ✧
P.O. Box 1079
Kalispell, MT 59903-1079
Contact: Jean Agather, Mgr.; Bruce Ennis

Established in 2002 in MT.
Donors: Bruce Ennis; Margaret Davis.
Foundation type: Independent foundation.
Financial data (yr. ended 12/31/13): Assets, $8,098,128 (M); expenditures, $742,667; qualifying distributions, $697,295; giving activities include $622,665 for 57 grants (high: $40,000; low: $1,000).
Purpose and activities: The mission of the foundation is to support selected, effective Montana-based programs that are dedicated to helping people in need of assistance and to enlarge their competencies.
Fields of interest: Arts; Education; Health organizations; Legal services; Crime/law enforcement; Agriculture/food; Housing/shelter; Human services; Children/youth, services; Infants/toddlers; Children/youth; Children; Youth; Adults; Aging; Young adults; Disabilities, people with; Physically disabled; Mentally disabled; Minorities; Native Americans/American Indians; Indigenous peoples; Women; Girls; Men; Crime/abuse victims; Economically disadvantaged; Homeless.
Type of support: General/operating support; Management development/capacity building.
Limitations: Applications not accepted. Giving primarily in MT. No grants to individuals.
Application information: Contributes only to pre-selected organizations.
Officers: Bruce Ennis, Pres. and Treas.; Margaret Davis, V.P.; L.W. Petersen, Secy.; Jean Agather, Mgr.
Number of staff: 1 part-time professional.
EIN: 460512750

5015
The Scoob Trust Foundation ✧
P.O. Box 97
Alder, MT 59710

Donors: Susan Kelly; Brian Kelly; Kelly Charitable Lead Annuity Trust.
Foundation type: Independent foundation.
Financial data (yr. ended 12/31/13): Assets, $3,425,572 (M); gifts received, $823,242; expenditures, $760,166; qualifying distributions, $702,500; giving activities include $702,500 for 60 grants (high: $37,500; low: $1,000).
Fields of interest: Performing arts, music; Education; Environment; Foundations (community); Military/veterans' organizations.
Limitations: Applications not accepted. Giving primarily in CA and Washington, DC. No grants to individuals.
Application information: Contributes only to pre-selected organizations.
Directors: Brian Kelly; Susan Kelly; Gay Weake; Jaci Wilkins.
EIN: 206790446
Selected grants: The following grants are a representative sample of this grantmaker's funding activity:
$5,000 to Wildlife Waystation, Sylmar, CA, 2012. To support of selected public charities.

5016
Town Pump Charitable Foundation ✧
P.O. Box 6000
Butte, MT 59702-6000
Application address: c/o Karen Kelly, 600 S. Main St., Butte, MT 59701

Established in 1999 in MT.
Donors: Tom Kenneally; MaryAnn Keneally; Town Pump of Ennis, Inc.; U-Pump, Inc.; Capitol Town Pump, Inc.; Town Pump of Northwest Missoula, Inc.; Town Pump of Rocker, Inc.; Belgrade Town Pump, Inc.; Dillon Casino, Inc.; Great Falls Lounge Corp.; Silver Bow Lounge Corp.; Cascade Lounge Corp.; Kalispell Lounge Corp.; Bonner Town Pump & Casino, Inc.; Town Pump of Townsend, Inc.; Missoula Casino, Inc.; Three Forks Casino, Inc.; Thompson Falls Casino, Inc.; Big Timber Convenience Store & Casino, Inc.; Park Casino, Inc.; Whitehall Casino, Inc.; Western Catering Services, Inc.; Sidney Casino, Inc.; Laurel Casino, Inc.; Colestrip Casino, Inc.
Foundation type: Independent foundation.
Financial data (yr. ended 12/31/12): Assets, $18,389,559 (M); gifts received, $2,000,000; expenditures, $919,994; qualifying distributions, $917,808; giving activities include $909,900 for 378 grants (high: $100,000; low: $150).
Fields of interest: Historic preservation/historical societies; Education; Food banks; Housing/shelter; Athletics/sports, Special Olympics; Human services; YM/YWCAs & YM/YWHAs; Youth, services.
Limitations: Applications accepted. Giving primarily in MT.

Application information: Application form required.
Initial approach: Letter
Deadline(s): None
Officers and Directors:* Thomas F. Kenneally,* Pres.; Mary Ann Kenneally,* V.P.; Thomas P. Kenneally,* V.P.; Maureen E. Kenneally,* Secy.-Treas.; Daniel J. Kenneally; James M. Kenneally; Kevin J. Kenneally; Michael E. Kenneally.
EIN: 810523786
Selected grants: The following grants are a representative sample of this grantmaker's funding activity:
$1,000 to American Foundation for Suicide Prevention, New York, NY, 2012. For Billings MT Out of the Darkness Walk.

5017
Treacy Company ✧
(also known as Treacy Foundation)
P.O. Box 1479
Helena, MT 59624-1479 (406) 443-3549
Contact: Kimmy Skiftun, Exec. Dir.
FAX: (406) 443-6183;
E-mail: kimmy@treacyfoundation.org; Main URL: http://www.treacyfoundation.org/

Established in 1947.
Donors: Treacy Co.; James O'Connell.
Foundation type: Independent foundation.
Financial data (yr. ended 12/31/12): Assets, $37,358,279 (M); expenditures, $1,616,774; qualifying distributions, $1,243,733; giving activities include $1,033,555 for 61 grants (high: $128,625; low: $200), and $125,000 for grants to individuals.
Purpose and activities: Giving primarily for human services and education, including scholarship awards to college freshmen or sophomores who reside in Idaho, Montana, and North Dakota.
Fields of interest: Higher education; Health care; Human services; Protestant agencies & churches.
Type of support: Continuing support; Scholarship funds.
Limitations: Applications accepted. Giving primarily in MT. No support for political organizations, candidates and campaigns, or for private operating and non-operating foundations. No grants to individuals (directly), or for operating expenses, salaries, travel, or meals; no loans.
Publications: Application guidelines; Annual report.
Application information: Applications must be typed or electronically produced. Application form required.
Initial approach: Use application form on foundation web site
Deadline(s): See foundation web site and application form for current deadlines
Board meeting date(s): Between July 1 and July 15
Final notification: Grants submitted for $10,000 or less will be given a response within 30 days
Officers: Don Campbell, Chair.; Kelly O'Connell, Secy.-Treas.; Tom McCarvel, Vice-Chair.; Kimmy Skiftun, Exec. Dir.
Trustee: Mike Cooney; Theresa Ortega.
Number of staff: 1 full-time support.
EIN: 810270257
Selected grants: The following grants are a representative sample of this grantmaker's funding activity:
$120,000 to Carroll College, Helena, MT, 2012. To assist with facility improvements.
$38,500 to Special K Ranch, Columbus, MT, 2012. For funding for new building.
$26,500 to Rialto Community Theater, Deer Lodge, MT, 2012. To assist with funding of capital campaign.
$25,000 to Yellowstone Foundation, Bozeman, MT, 2012. To assist with funding for photo project.
$10,000 to Museum of the Rockies, Bozeman, MT, 2012. For funding for purchase of displays.
$7,500 to Gallatin Historical Society, Bozeman, MT, 2012. To provide assistance with facility repairs.
$7,000 to Jefferson Elementary School, Helena, MT, 2012. For funding for purchase of art supplies.
$6,500 to Helena Education Foundation, Helena, MT, 2012. To assist with books purchase.
$2,500 to Rocky Mountain Development Council, Helena, MT, 2012. For funding for purchase of supplies.
$2,500 to Salish Kootenai College, Pablo, MT, 2012. For higher education scholarships.

5018
Dennis & Phyllis Washington Foundation, Inc. ✧
(formerly Dennis R. Washington Foundation, Inc.)
P.O. Box 16630
Missoula, MT 59808-6630 (406) 523-1300
Contact: Mike Halligan, Exec. Dir.
Main URL: http://www.dpwfoundation.org/
Dennis R. Washington Achievement Recipients: http://www.dpwfoundation.org/?page_id=1146%22http://
Facebook: http://www.facebook.com/pages/The-Dennis-and-Phyllis-Washington-Foundation/205084757814?ref=search&sid=23500478.2362658217..1
Horatio Alger Recipients: http://dpwfoundation.org/?page_id=504

Established in 1988 in MT.
Donors: Dennis & Phyllis Washington; Washington Corporations; Montana Rail Link, Inc.; Montana Resources, L.L.P; Dennis Washington; Phyllis J. Washington; Modern Machinery, Inc.
Foundation type: Company-sponsored foundation.
Financial data (yr. ended 12/31/12): Assets, $499,978,077 (M); gifts received, $58,100,115; expenditures, $5,299,198; qualifying distributions, $4,060,966; giving activities include $3,759,769 for grants.
Purpose and activities: The foundation supports organizations involved with arts and culture, education, health, human services, and community services, and awards college scholarships and fellowships. Special emphasis is directed toward programs designed to provide a direct service to economically and socially disadvantaged youth and their families, at-risk or troubled youth, and individuals with special needs.
Fields of interest: Performing arts, theater; Performing arts, music; Arts; Education, early childhood education; Higher education; Scholarships/financial aid; Education, services; Education; Dental care; Health care; Food banks; Recreation, parks/playgrounds; Athletics/sports, Special Olympics; Youth development; Human services; Community/economic development; Infants/toddlers; Children/youth; Children; Youth; Disabilities, people with; Physically disabled; Native Americans/American Indians; Economically disadvantaged; Homeless.
Type of support: Continuing support; Annual campaigns; Building/renovation; Program development; Fellowships; Scholarship funds; Employee-related scholarships; Scholarships—to individuals; Matching/challenge support.
Limitations: Applications accepted. Giving primarily in areas of company operations, with emphasis on MT. No support for discriminatory organizations, sectarian or religious organizations not of direct benefit to the entire community, veterans' or fraternal organizations not of direct benefit to the entire community, private or public foundations, or political action or legislative advocacy groups. No grants to individuals (except for scholarships), or for debt reduction, general operating support, travel expenses or trips, endowments, sponsorships including auctions, dinners, tickets, advertising, or annual fundraising events, curriculum development for educational institutions, or motor vehicle or other transportation equipment purchases; generally, no grants for capital campaigns; no loans.
Publications: Application guidelines; Program policy statement.
Application information: Organizations receiving support are asked to submit a post-grant evaluation. An interview may be required for graduate level scholarships. Application form required.
Initial approach: Complete online application form
Deadline(s): None; Jan. 15 to Apr. 1 for Dennis R. Washington Achievement Scholarship; Apr. 15 for Horatio Alger Montana Undergraduate Scholarship Program (apply directly to Horatio Alger Association via their website)
Board meeting date(s): Quarterly
Final notification: 90 days
Officers and Directors:* Phyllis J. Washington,* Chair.; Lawrence R. Simkins, Pres.; Mike Halligan, Exec. Dir.; William H. Brodsky; Rolin Erickson; Brian T. Sheridan.
Number of staff: 1 full-time professional.
EIN: 363606913
Selected grants: The following grants are a representative sample of this grantmaker's funding activity:
$1,000,000 to Projecthandup, Westlake, TX, 2012. For the Gatehouse Project.
$150,000 to Montana, State of, Office of Public Instruction, Helena, MT, 2012. For Graduation Matters Program.
$109,569 to Young Life, Missoula, MT, 2012. For WA Family Ranch Creekside Project.
$100,000 to David Foster Foundation, Santa Monica, CA, 2012. For general support.
$100,000 to Mainstreet Uptown Butte, Butte, MT, 2012. For MT Folk Festival Challenge Grant.
$25,000 to Special Olympics Montana, Great Falls, MT, 2012. For Annual Events Grant.
$20,000 to YMCA, Missoula Family, Missoula, MT, 2012. For Active 6 Program.
$10,000 to Boys and Girls Club of Missoula County, Missoula, MT, 2012. For Afterschool Program.
$10,000 to Lewistown Art Center, Lewistown, MT, 2012. For Art Education Classes.
$5,000 to Montana Rescue Mission, Billings, MT, 2012. For Reach Out Grant.

5019
Whitefish Community Foundation ✧
214 2nd St. W.
P.O. Box 1060
Whitefish, MT 59937 (406) 863-1781
Contact: Linda Engh-Grady, Exec. Dir.
FAX: (406) 863-2628;
E-mail: info@whitefishcommunityfoundation.org;

Main URL: http://www.whitefishcommunityfoundation.org
Facebook: http://www.facebook.com/pages/Whitefish-MT/Whitefish-Community-Foundation/192411305234

Established in 2000 in MT.
Foundation type: Community foundation.
Financial data (yr. ended 12/31/13): Assets, $10,554,400 (M); gifts received, $4,947,114; expenditures, $3,809,433; giving activities include $3,571,729 for 35+ grants (high: $1,767,850).
Purpose and activities: The mission of the Whitefish Community Foundation is to enrich the quality of life in the Whitefish area by fostering philanthropy, building endowments, and helping donors and nonprofits benefit the local community.
Fields of interest: Arts; Education; Environment; Animals/wildlife; Health care; Recreation; Human services.
Type of support: General/operating support; Management development/capacity building; Capital campaigns; Building/renovation; Equipment; Endowments; Emergency funds; Program development; Film/video/radio; Publication; Scholarship funds; Research; Technical assistance; Matching/challenge support.
Limitations: Applications accepted. Giving primarily in Flathead County, MT. No support for organizations or institutions operated primarily by religious organizations, or medical research. No grants to individuals, or for conduit organizations.
Publications: Application guidelines; Annual report; Financial statement; Grants list; Informational brochure; Multi-year report; Newsletter.
Application information: Visit foundation web site for application form and guidelines. Faxed or e-mailed applications are not accepted. Application form required.

Initial approach: Submit application form
Copies of proposal: 10
Deadline(s): May 30
Board meeting date(s): Jan., Apr., July and Oct.
Final notification: Nov.

Officers and Executive Committee: David Dittman,* Pres.; Jay Latimer,* Secy.-Treas.; Linda Engh-Grady, Exec. Dir.; Carol Atkinson; Judah Gersh; Doug Reed; Ardyce Whisler.
Board Members: Lin Akey; Betsy Bayne; Michael Jenson; James Kenyon III; John Kramer; Lori Miller; Tom Quinn; Karen Rosenberg; Jamie Shennan; Kristin Tabor; Kelly Talsma; Kenneth Wessels; John Witt.
Number of staff: 1 full-time professional; 1 part-time support.
EIN: 810533002

NEBRASKA

5020
Ethel S. Abbott Charitable Foundation ✧
P.O. Box 81407
Lincoln, NE 68501-1407 (402) 435-4369
Contact: Del Lienemann Sr., Pres.
FAX: (402) 435-4371;
E-mail: info@abbottfoundation.org; Main
URL: http://www.abbottfoundation.org

Established in 1989 in NE.
Donors: Ethel S. Abbott†; Ruth Cummings Trust.
Foundation type: Independent foundation.
Financial data (yr. ended 09/30/13): Assets, $23,534,698 (M); expenditures, $838,075; qualifying distributions, $837,321; giving activities include $575,754 for grants (high: $500,000; low: $200).
Purpose and activities: Giving for arts and culture, education, hospitals and human services.
Fields of interest: Arts; Higher education; Education; Hospitals (general); Human services; Foundations (private grantmaking).
Limitations: Giving primarily in Lincoln, NE, and the surrounding 50 mile radius, Omaha, NE, and the surrounding 50 mile radius up to the Missouri River and Western, NE, which is defined as all parts of the state in the Mountain Time Zone. No grants to individuals.
Publications: Application guidelines; Grants list.
Application information: Application guidelines and form available on foundation web site. Failure to properly fill out the application form will result in automatic denial of grant request. Application form required.
Initial approach: Submit application form which can be downloaded from foundation web site, or telephone or write for form
Deadline(s): Within 90 days after contacting the Fdn. Mgr.
Officers: Del Lienemann, Sr., C.E.O. and Pres.; Denise Lienemann Scholz, 1st V.P. and Secy.; Daniel Lienemann, 2nd V.P.; Del Lienemann, Jr., Treas.
Trustee: Dorothy Pflug.
EIN: 237265876
Selected grants: The following grants are a representative sample of this grantmaker's funding activity:
$100,000 to Omaha Zoo Foundation, Omaha, NE, 2011.
$100,000 to University of Nebraska Foundation, Lincoln, NE, 2011.
$100,000 to University of Nebraska Foundation, Lincoln, NE, 2011.
$75,000 to Heritage Services, Omaha, NE, 2011.
$30,000 to TeamMates Mentoring Program, Lincoln, NE, 2011.
$20,000 to Bellevue University, Bellevue, NE, 2011.
$10,000 to University of Nebraska Foundation, Lincoln, NE, 2011. For student scholarships.
$5,000 to Special Olympics Nebraska, Omaha, NE, 2011.
$2,000 to Grant County Historical Society, Hyannis, NE, 2011.
$2,000 to Hastings College, Hastings, NE, 2011. For student scholarships.

5021
Abel Foundation ✧
1815 Y. St.
P.O. Box 80268
Lincoln, NE 68501-0268
Contact: J. Ross McCown, V.P. and Secy.
FAX: (402) 434-1799;
E-mail: rossm@nebcoinc.com; Additional e-mail: nebcoinfo@nebconic.com; Main URL: http://www.abelfoundation.org/
Grants List: http://www.abelfoundation.org/beneficiaries.htm

Trust established in 1951.
Donors: Constructors, Inc.; NEBCO, Inc.; Alice V. Abel.
Foundation type: Company-sponsored foundation.
Financial data (yr. ended 12/31/13): Assets, $14,187,880 (M); gifts received, $1,957,000; expenditures, $559,543; qualifying distributions, $532,249; giving activities include $532,249 for 74 grants (high: $32,500; low: $100).
Purpose and activities: The foundation supports organizations involved with arts and culture, education, the environment, endangered species, human services, and community development.
Fields of interest: Performing arts; Humanities; Arts; Higher education; Education; Environment, natural resources; Environment; Animals/wildlife, endangered species; YM/YWCAs & YM/YWHAs; Human services; Community/economic development; United Ways and Federated Giving Programs.
Type of support: General/operating support; Capital campaigns; Building/renovation; Program development.
Limitations: Applications accepted. Giving limited to areas of company operations in NE, with emphasis on Lincoln and Lancaster County. No support for businesses, private foundations, or religious organizations. No grants to individuals, or for endowments, travel, or membership fees.
Publications: Application guidelines; Grants list.
Application information: The Lincoln/Lancaster County Grantmakers Common Application Form is accepted. Application form required.
Initial approach: Download application form and mail to foundation
Copies of proposal: 1
Deadline(s): Mar. 15, July 15, and Oct. 31
Board meeting date(s): May, Aug., and Dec.
Final notification: Mid-May, mid-Sept., and mid-Jan
Officers and Directors: James P. Abel, Pres.; J. Ross McCown, V.P. and Secy.; Shannon Doering, V.P. and Treas.; Elizabeth N. Abel; John C. Abel; Mary C. Abel.
Number of staff: None.
EIN: 476041771

5022
Acklie Charitable Foundation ✧
P.O. Box 81228
Lincoln, NE 68501-1228
Contact: Duane W. Acklie, Pres.

Established in 1989 in NE.
Donors: Duane W. Acklie; Phyllis A. Acklie; Irene Acklie†.
Foundation type: Independent foundation.
Financial data (yr. ended 12/31/13): Assets, $13,770,914 (M); gifts received, $292,716; expenditures, $665,929; qualifying distributions, $620,640; giving activities include $618,953 for 133 grants (high: $340,000; low: $15).
Purpose and activities: Giving primarily for health, youth programs, and federated giving programs.
Fields of interest: Education; Human services; Protestant agencies & churches; Catholic agencies & churches.
Type of support: General/operating support; Scholarship funds; Matching/challenge support.
Limitations: Applications accepted. Giving primarily in NE. No support for religious or political organizations.
Application information: Application form required.
Initial approach: Completed application form
Copies of proposal: 1
Deadline(s): None
Board meeting date(s): Third week of Dec.
Officers: Duane W. Acklie, Pres.; Phyllis A. Acklie, Secy.; Holly Acklie Ostergard, Treas.
Number of staff: 1 part-time support.
EIN: 363662965

5023
Ameritas Charitable Foundation ✧
(formerly BLN Charitable Foundation)
5900 O St.
Lincoln, NE 68510-2234 (402) 325-4234
Contact: Sue Wilkinson, Secy. and Cont.

Established in 1985 in NE.
Donor: Ameritas Life Insurance Corp.
Foundation type: Company-sponsored foundation.
Financial data (yr. ended 12/31/13): Assets, $9,456,982 (M); expenditures, $425,963; qualifying distributions, $419,662; giving activities include $419,662 for 52 grants (high: $100,000; low: $500).
Purpose and activities: The foundation has primary interest in education programs, but will consider civic, cultural, and health and welfare requests.
Fields of interest: Museums (children's); Arts; Secondary school/education; Higher education; Education; Animal welfare; Hospitals (general); Health care; Crime/violence prevention, child abuse; Boy scouts; YM/YWCAs & YM/YWHAs; Children, services; Family services; Human services.
Type of support: General/operating support; Continuing support; Annual campaigns; Capital campaigns; Equipment; Program development; Scholarship funds; Sponsorships.
Limitations: Applications accepted. Giving primarily in Lincoln, NE. No support for organizations that utilize a major portion of their budget for administration and solicitation. No grants to individuals.
Publications: Application guidelines.
Application information: Application form required.
Initial approach: Proposal
Deadline(s): Apr. 1 and Nov. 1
Board meeting date(s): May and Dec.
Officers and Directors:* James P. Abel,* Pres.; Sue Wilkinson, Secy. and Cont.; William W. Lester,* Treas.; JoAnn M. Martin.
Number of staff: None.
EIN: 363428705
Selected grants: The following grants are a representative sample of this grantmaker's funding activity:
$800,000 to University of Nebraska Foundation, Lincoln, NE, 2012. For R and D Corridor Fund.

$100,000 to University of Nebraska Foundation, Lincoln, NE, 2012. For Ameritas Actuarial Faculty Fellowship Fund.
$25,000 to University of Nebraska Foundation, Lincoln, NE, 2012. For Centennial Mall Development.
$15,000 to Nebraska Wesleyan University, Lincoln, NE, 2012. For Archway Fund - Scholarship Support.
$10,000 to Nebraska Wesleyan University, Lincoln, NE, 2012. For Faculty Fellowship Fund.
$5,000 to Lincoln Literacy Council, Lincoln, NE, 2012. For English Language and Literacy Academy.
$5,000 to University of Nebraska Foundation, Lincoln, NE, 2012. For Former USDA Ag Secretaries Artwork Fund.

5024
Paul Beer Trust ✧
c/o Wells Fargo Bank, N.A., Trust Tax Dept.
1919 Douglas St., 2nd Fl., MACN8000-027
Omaha, NE 68102-1317

Supporting organization of Rensselaer Polytechnic Institute, YMCA, St. Paul's Episcopal Church, Iowa Methodist Health Foundation, Iowa Lutheran Hospital Foundation, Drake University, and Iowa Episcopate Fund.
Foundation type: Independent foundation.
Financial data (yr. ended 12/31/13): Assets, $14,028,582 (M); expenditures, $723,895; qualifying distributions, $643,680; giving activities include $617,124 for 7 grants (high: $299,562; low: $2,000).
Fields of interest: Education; Health care; Protestant agencies & churches.
Limitations: Applications not accepted. Giving primarily to Des Moines, IA; funding also in Troy, NY.
Application information: Contributes only to pre-selected organizations.
Trustee: Wells Fargo Bank, N.A.
EIN: 426215149

5025
John K. & Lynne D. Boyer Foundation ✧ ☆
(formerly Margre & Charles Durham Foundation III)
500 Energy Plz.
409 S. 17th St.
Omaha, NE 68102-2603

Established in 2000 in NE; Dec. 2008 absorbed assets of the Durham Foundation.
Donors: Charles W. Durham Trust; Charles W. Durham Trust II.
Foundation type: Independent foundation.
Financial data (yr. ended 12/31/13): Assets, $22,455,374 (M); gifts received, $500,000; expenditures, $812,403; qualifying distributions, $667,450; giving activities include $667,450 for 80 grants (high: $100,000; low: $500).
Fields of interest: Environment, natural resources; Environment, beautification programs; Arthritis; Housing/shelter, development; Boy scouts.
Type of support: General/operating support.
Limitations: Applications not accepted. Giving primarily in NE. No grants to individuals.
Application information: Contributes only to pre-selected organizations.
Officer: Lynne D. Boyer, Pres.
Directors: David Boyer; Michael Boyer.
EIN: 470830373

Selected grants: The following grants are a representative sample of this grantmaker's funding activity:
$7,500 to Camp Fire USA, Kansas City, MO, 2011.
$1,000 to Camp Fire USA, Kansas City, MO, 2011.

5026
Thomas D. Buckley Trust ✧
P.O. Box 647
Chappell, NE 69129-0647 (308) 874-2929
Contact: Connie Loos

Established about 1980 in NE.
Donor: Thomas D. Buckley†.
Foundation type: Independent foundation.
Financial data (yr. ended 05/31/13): Assets, $10,178,858 (M); expenditures, $662,252; qualifying distributions, $434,508; giving activities include $434,508 for grants.
Purpose and activities: Giving primarily for social services, particularly a child daycare center, health care, and community development, including community programs, and to Lutheran, Roman Catholic, and United Methodist churches; funding also for scholarship programs.
Fields of interest: Elementary/secondary education; Education; Hospitals (general); Health care; Human services; Children/youth, services; Children, day care; Community/economic development; Protestant agencies & churches; Catholic agencies & churches.
Type of support: Matching/challenge support; General/operating support; Continuing support; Capital campaigns; Building/renovation; Equipment; Emergency funds; Seed money; Scholarship funds.
Publications: Application guidelines; Annual report.
Application information: Application form required.
Initial approach: Letter requesting application form
Copies of proposal: 1
Deadline(s): None
Board meeting date(s): 2nd Wed. of each month
Trustees: Bill M. Hughes; D. Francis Kripal; Dwight E. Smith.
Number of staff: 1 full-time support.
EIN: 476121041
Selected grants: The following grants are a representative sample of this grantmaker's funding activity:
$20,000 to University of Nebraska Foundation, Lincoln, NE, 2013. For High Plains Ag Lab.
$10,000 to Regional West Medical Center, Scottsbluff, NE, 2013. For radio system.
$10,000 to Sedgwick County Health Center, Julesburg, CO, 2013. For mammography unit.
$5,000 to Farm and Ranch Museum, Gering, NE, 2013. For Building expansion project.
$500 to Nebraska Community Foundation, Lincoln, NE, 2013. For Nebraska LEAD Program.

5027
Buffett Early Childhood Fund ✧
3555 Farnam St.
Omaha, NE 68131-3302
Main URL: http://www.buffettearlychildhoodfund.org/

Established in 2005 in NE.
Donors: Susan A. Buffett Foundation; Novo Foundation; The Sherwood Foundation.
Foundation type: Independent foundation.
Financial data (yr. ended 12/31/13): Assets, $14,565,830 (M); gifts received, $30,104,734; expenditures, $19,992,468; qualifying distributions, $19,962,244; giving activities include $18,357,885 for 37 grants (high: $3,090,622; low: $1,000).
Purpose and activities: Support for education.
Fields of interest: Education, early childhood education; Child development, education; Education; United Ways and Federated Giving Programs.
Limitations: Applications not accepted. Giving primarily in Washington, DC, Chicago, IL, and Lincoln and Omaha, NE.
Application information: Contibutes only to pre-selected organizations.
Officers: Jessie Rasmussen, Pres.; Michael Burke, V.P.
Director: Susan Buffett.
EIN: 201768874
Selected grants: The following grants are a representative sample of this grantmaker's funding activity:
$3,583,333 to Winnebago Tribe of Nebraska, Educare of Winnebago, Winnebago, NE, 2012. For capital campaign.
$3,006,803 to Alliance for Early Success, Leawood, KS, 2012. For general operating support.
$2,615,387 to Nebraska Children and Families Foundation, Lincoln, NE, 2012. For Sixpence Early Learning.
$2,529,800 to Ounce of Prevention Fund, Chicago, IL, 2012. For Educare Learning Network.
$2,006,166 to Ounce of Prevention Fund, Chicago, IL, 2012. For Educare National TA.
$1,008,480 to Ounce of Prevention Fund, Chicago, IL, 2012. For First Five Years Fund.
$902,178 to Frank Porter Graham Child Development Center, Chapel Hill, NC, 2012. For National Evaluation for BLN implementation study.
$700,000 to Educare of Omaha, Omaha, NE, 2012. For operating support.
$550,000 to Next Door Foundation, Milwaukee, WI, 2012. For scholarships and operating support.
$377,049 to Erikson Institute, Chicago, IL, 2012. For distance learning and general support.

5028
The Susan Thompson Buffett Foundation ✧
(formerly The Buffett Foundation)
222 Kiewit Plz.
Omaha, NE 68131-3302
Contact: Allen Greenberg, Pres.
E-mail: scholarships@stbfoundation.org; Main URL: http://www.buffettscholarships.org
Warren Buffett's Giving Pledge Profile: http://glasspockets.org/philanthropy-in-focus/eye-on-the-giving-pledge/profiles/buffett
Tel. for scholarship information: (402) 943-1383

Incorporated in 1964 in NE. In 2006, Warren Buffett pledged almost $3 billion worth of his Berkshire-Hathaway, Inc. stock to the foundation to be paid out over time. As a result, the Susan Thompson Buffett Foundation's assets and annual giving have risen sharply.
Donors: Warren E. Buffett; Susan T. Buffett†.
Foundation type: Independent foundation.
Financial data (yr. ended 12/31/13): Assets, $2,731,731,558 (M); gifts received, $204,231,344; expenditures, $458,175,436;

qualifying distributions, $457,585,033; giving activities include $424,935,535 for 289 grants (high: $45,954,954; low: $1,000), and $25,384,253 for grants to individuals.
Purpose and activities: Grants primarily for family planning programs, and scholarships to residents of Nebraska attending Nebraska public colleges or universities.
Fields of interest: Reproductive health, family planning; Civil liberties, reproductive rights.
Type of support: General/operating support; Scholarships—to individuals.
Limitations: Applications accepted. Giving on a national and international basis; scholarships awarded only to residents in NE. No grant to individuals (except for Teacher Awards and scholarships).
Application information: Unsolicited requests for grants not accepted. The foundation accepts scholarship applications. The foundation only responds to questions about scholarships and awards. Please see the foundation's web site for additional details.
Initial approach: Application form required for scholarship program only
Deadline(s): Feb. 1 for scholarships
Officers and Directors:* Susan A. Buffett,* Chair. and Treas.; Allen Greenberg, Pres.; Melissa How, Secy.; Peter A. Buffett; Allison Cowan; Geoffrey Cowan; Carol Loomis; Patti Matson.
Number of staff: 9 full-time professional; 3 full-time support.
EIN: 476032365
Selected grants: The following grants are a representative sample of this grantmaker's funding activity:
$39,892,246 to Population Services International, Washington, DC, 2012. For Project Support.
$20,774,355 to National Abortion Federation, Washington, DC, 2012. For project support.
$15,883,751 to DKT International, Washington, DC, 2012. For Project Support.
$6,981,740 to Nuclear Threat Initiative, Washington, DC, 2012. For Project Support.
$3,840,942 to University of Nebraska-Lincoln, Lincoln, NE, 2012. For Scholarships.
$2,927,948 to CARE USA, Atlanta, GA, 2012. For Project Support.
$2,202,156 to National Womens Law Center, Washington, DC, 2012. For Project Support.
$750,469 to Catholics for a Free Choice, Washington, DC, 2012. For Project Support.
$498,079 to National Family Planning and Reproductive Health Association, Washington, DC, 2012. For Project Support.
$182,000 to University of California at San Diego, La Jolla, CA, 2012. For Project Support.

5029
ConAgra Foods Feeding Children Better Foundation ✧

1 ConAgra Dr.
Omaha, NE 68102-5001
Contact: Candy Becker, Fdn. Coord.
FAX: (402) 595-4595;
E-mail: foundation@conagrafoods.com; Main URL: http://www.nourishkidstoday.org

Established in 1999 in NE.
Donors: ConAgra, Inc.; ConAgra Foods, Inc.
Foundation type: Company-sponsored foundation.
Financial data (yr. ended 05/31/13): Assets, $3,136,118 (M); expenditures, $5,701,710; qualifying distributions, $5,701,710; giving activities include $5,694,797 for 51 grants (high: $2,088,000; low: $2,500).
Purpose and activities: The foundation, under the umbrella of Nourish Today, Flourish Tomorrow, supports programs designed to provide solutions for child hunger and nutrition education. Special emphasis is directed toward programs designed to help children in need.
Fields of interest: Health organizations, research; Health organizations, public education; Agriculture/food, public policy; Agriculture/food, public education; Food services; Food banks; Food services, congregate meals; Nutrition; Agriculture/food; Youth development, agriculture; Children/youth, services.
Type of support: Program development; Research; Technical assistance; Program evaluation; In-kind gifts.
Limitations: Applications not accepted. Giving primarily in Washington, DC, and Chicago, IL; giving also to national organizations. No support for religious organizations not of direct benefit to the entire community, fraternal, social, labor, veteran, or alumni organizations, exclusive membership clubs, professional and amateur sports organizations and teams, terrorist organizations or those not compliant with the USA Patriot Act, athletic events and programs, capital campaigns (unless solicited at the funder's discretion), or memorial campaigns. No grants to individuals, or for fundraising, travel, or advertising.
Application information: Contributes only to pre-selected organizations.
Officers: Christopher P. Kircher, Chair.; Kori E. Reed, Pres.; Colleen Batcheler, Secy.; Robert G. Wise, Treas.
EIN: 470824577
Selected grants: The following grants are a representative sample of this grantmaker's funding activity:
$47,384 to University of Idaho Foundation, Moscow, ID, 2013. For nutrition education.

5030
ConAgra Foods Foundation ✧

(formerly The ConAgra Foundation, Inc.)
1 ConAgra Dr.
Omaha, NE 68102-5001
Contact: Candy Becker, Fdn. Coord.
FAX: (402) 595-4595;
E-mail: foundation@conagrafoods.com; Main URL: http://www.nourishkidstoday.org
Cooking Matters on Facebook: http://www.facebook.com/cookingmatters.national
Cooking Matters on Flickr: http://www.flickr.com/photos/share_our_strength/collections/72157618116628821/
Cooking Matters on Twitter: http://twitter.com/cookingmatters
Facebook: http://www.facebook.com/conagrafoodsfoundation
Hungry 2 Help Blog: http://www.hungry2help.org/
Hungry 2 Help RSS Feed: http://www.hungry2help.org/rss

Established in 1977.
Donors: ConAgra, Inc.; ConAgra Foods, Inc.; Barbara Rodkin; Gary M. Rodkin.
Foundation type: Company-sponsored foundation.
Financial data (yr. ended 05/31/13): Assets, $14,153,036 (M); gifts received, $7,657,410; expenditures, $3,150,710; qualifying distributions, $3,150,170; giving activities include $2,790,436 for 76 grants (high: $800,000; low: $250).
Purpose and activities: The foundation supports programs designed to provide solutions for child hunger and nutrition education. Special emphasis is directed toward programs designed to help children in need.
Fields of interest: Public health, physical fitness; Health organizations, research; Health organizations, public education; Agriculture/food, public policy; Agriculture/food, public education; Food services; Food banks; Food services, congregate meals; Nutrition; Agriculture/food; Youth development, agriculture; Children.
Type of support: Management development/capacity building; Program development; Research; Employee matching gifts; Employee-related scholarships; Donated products; In-kind gifts.
Limitations: Applications accepted. Giving on a national basis in areas of company operations, with emphasis on AR, AZ, CA, CO, FL, GA, ID, IL, IN, LA, MA, MI, MS, NE, OH, OR, PA, TN, TX, and WA. No support for religious organizations not of direct benefit to the entire community, fraternal, social, labor, veteran, or alumni organizations, exclusive membership clubs, professional or amateur sports organizations or teams, political organizations, terrorist organizations or those not compliant with the USA Patriot Act, or elementary or secondary schools. No grants to individuals (except for scholarships), or for fundraising or testimonial events or dinners, travel or tours, advertising, endowments, capital campaigns (unless solicited at the funders discretion), memorial campaigns, conferences, seminars, workshops, symposia, or publication of proceedings, radio or television programming underwriting, emergency needs, or athletic events; no loans or debt reduction.
Publications: Application guidelines; Program policy statement.
Application information: A full proposal may be requested at a later date for Community Impact Grants. Organizations receiving support are asked to submit interim reports and a final report. National partnerships are solicited only at the discretion of ConAgra Foods staff. Application form required.
Initial approach: Complete online eligibility survey and letter of intent for Community Impact Grants
Deadline(s): Jan. 7 to Jan 28 for Community Impact Grants
Officers: Christopher P. Kircher, Chair.; Kori E. Reed, Pres.; Colleen R. Batcheler, Secy.; Robert G. Wise, Treas.
Number of staff: 2 full-time professional.
EIN: 362899320
Selected grants: The following grants are a representative sample of this grantmaker's funding activity:
$800,000 to Donors Trust, Omaha, NE, 2013.
$500,000 to American Red Cross, Heartland Chapter, Omaha, NE, 2012. For disaster and humanitarian relief.
$500,000 to American Red Cross, Heartland Chapter, Omaha, NE, 2013. For disaster and humanitarian relief.
$400,000 to Donors Trust, Omaha, NE, 2012.
$303,750 to Scholarship America, Saint Peter, MN, 2013.
$292,000 to Scholarship America, Saint Peter, MN, 2012.
$264,800 to United Way of the Midlands, Omaha, NE, 2013.

$256,800 to United Way of the Midlands, Omaha, NE, 2012.
$200,000 to Summer Splash, Omaha, NE, 2013.
$150,000 to Akshaya Patra Foundation USA, Stoneham, MA, 2013.
$113,235 to JK Group, Plainsboro, NJ, 2012.
$100,000 to Food Research and Action Center, Washington, DC, 2013.
$81,206 to JK Group, Plainsboro, NJ, 2013.
$25,000 to Macon County Ministries, Macon, MO, 2012.
$25,000 to Main Street Mission, Russellville, AR, 2012.
$25,000 to Second Harvest Food Bank of the Inland Northwest, Spokane, WA, 2012.
$20,000 to Food Bank of Lincoln, Lincoln, NE, 2012.
$15,000 to Heart Ministry Center, Omaha, NE, 2013.
$15,000 to Kids Food Basket, Grand Rapids, MI, 2013.
$15,000 to United Way of Metropolitan Chicago, Chicago, IL, 2012.

5031
Cooper Foundation ✧
870 Wells Fargo Ctr.
1248 O St.
Lincoln, NE 68508-1493 (402) 476-7571
Contact: E. Arthur Thompson, Pres.; Victoria Kovar, Sr. Prog. Off.
FAX: (402) 476-2356;
E-mail: info@cooperfoundation.org; Main URL: http://www.cooperfoundation.org/
Facebook: https://www.facebook.com/CooperFoundation
Grants List: http://cooperfoundation.org/2013-grants-approved

Incorporated in 1934 in NE.
Donor: Joseph H. Cooper†.
Foundation type: Independent foundation.
Financial data (yr. ended 12/31/13): Assets, $24,458,351 (M); gifts received, $100; expenditures, $1,040,916; qualifying distributions, $959,171; giving activities include $606,491 for 69 grants (high: $40,000; low: $100).
Purpose and activities: The mission of the foundation is to support strong, sustainable organizations, innovative ideas, and ventures of significant promise in Nebraska.
Fields of interest: Humanities; Arts; Education; Environment; Human services.
Type of support: Advocacy; General/operating support; Management development/capacity building; Program development.
Limitations: Giving limited to NE, with emphasis on Lincoln and Lancaster County. No support for religious, health or political purposes, private foundations, or for businesses. No grants to individuals, or for multi-year grants, memberships, travel, or endowment funds.
Publications: Application guidelines; Financial statement; Grants list; Occasional report.
Application information: If the foundation is interested in the proposal, it will request that an inquiry be submitted via its online application website. Unsolicited applications are not accepted. See foundation web site for complete application guidelines and procedures. Application form required.
Initial approach: Contact foundation in person, or via telephone, letter or e-mail to discuss proposal
Copies of proposal: 1
Deadline(s): Jan. 15, Apr. 1, Aug. 1, and Oct. 1
Board meeting date(s): Quarterly
Final notification: 2 months
Officers and Trustees:* Jack D. Campbell,* Chair.; Robert Nefsky,* Vice-Chair.; E. Arthur Thompson,* Pres.; Victoria Kovar,* Corp. Secy.; Brad Korell,* Treas.; Richard Knudsen, Genl. Counsel; Linda Crump; Jane Renner Hood; Kim Robak; Richard J. Vierk; Norton Warner.
Number of staff: 2 full-time professional; 1 part-time professional.
EIN: 470401230
Selected grants: The following grants are a representative sample of this grantmaker's funding activity:
$29,840 to Nebraska Art Association, Lincoln, NE, 2012. For phase one of Initiative for Digitization and Educational Access.
$20,000 to Asian Community and Cultural Center, Lincoln, NE, 2012. For general operating support.
$20,000 to Audubon Nebraska, Denton, NE, 2012. For conservation and education programs.
$20,000 to Food Bank of Lincoln, Lincoln, NE, 2012. For BackPack Program.
$20,000 to Jewish Federation of Omaha, Omaha, NE, 2012. For part-time administrative and marketing assistant positions.
$20,000 to NET Foundation for Television, Lincoln, NE, 2012. For Platte River Basin Time-Lapse Project.
$15,000 to Lincoln-Lancaster County Child Advocacy Center, Lincoln, NE, 2012. For general operating support.
$15,000 to TeamMates Mentoring Program, Lincoln, NE, 2012. For general operating support-challenge grant.
$14,000 to University of Nebraska-Lincoln, Center for Great Plains Studies, Lincoln, NE, 2012. For School Consolidation in the Great Plains: Efficiencies, Change, and Community Identity Symposium.
$10,000 to Houses of Hope of Nebraska, Lincoln, NE, 2012. For NABHO development of Medicaid funding plan.
$10,000 to Nebraska Shakespeare Festival, Omaha, NE, 2012. For 2012 Educational Fall Tour of Julius Caesar.
$7,500 to Girl Scouts of the U.S.A., Lincoln, NE, 2012. For Outreach troops at Clinton and Elliott elementary schools.

5032
Ron and Carol Cope Foundation ✧
22033 Central Ave.
P.O. Box 1775
Kearney, NE 68848 (308) 237-4571
Contact: William Oldfather, Tr.

Established in 1990 in NE.
Donor: Carol I. Cope.
Foundation type: Independent foundation.
Financial data (yr. ended 12/31/13): Assets, $13,445,835 (M); expenditures, $623,317; qualifying distributions, $556,219; giving activities include $554,435 for 18 grants (high: $176,135; low: $1,500).
Fields of interest: Arts; Education; Human services.
Type of support: Capital campaigns; Building/renovation.
Limitations: Applications not accepted. Giving limited to Buffalo County, NE, with emphasis on Kearney. No grants to individuals.
Application information: Contributes only to pre-selected organizations.
Board meeting date(s): Quarterly
Trustees: Larry Jepson; Sherry Morrow; Alan Oldfather; William Oldfather.
EIN: 363693227

5033
Robert B. Daugherty Foundation ✧
1 Valmont Plz., Ste. 202
Omaha, NE 68154-5301 (402) 933-4663
Contact: Kimberly Yungtum, Chief Grants Off.
FAX: (402) 933-4248;
E-mail: grants@daughertyfdn.org; Main URL: http://www.daughertyfdn.org

Established in NE.
Donor: Robert B. Daugherty.
Foundation type: Independent foundation.
Financial data (yr. ended 12/31/13): Assets, $773,059,646 (M); expenditures, $36,957,300; qualifying distributions, $32,229,019; giving activities include $31,092,742 for 69 grants (high: $8,630,000; low: $2,000).
Purpose and activities: The foundation provides grants to organizations that conduct religious, charitable, scientific, cultural or education activities exclusively.
Fields of interest: Education; Science; Religion.
Type of support: Matching/challenge support.
Limitations: Applications accepted. Giving primarily in NE, with emphasis on the greater Omaha area. Generally, no support for religious organizations for religious purposes or to international organizations that do not have a qualified domestic representative. Generally, no grants to individuals or for endowments or other discretionary funding pools, dinners, balls, and other events.
Publications: Application guidelines.
Application information: Application guidelines available on foundation web site.
Initial approach: Online application
Deadline(s): None
Final notification: Response via e-mail to the submitting organization confirming receipt of the preliminary grant application
Officers and Trustees:* John K. Wilson, Exec. Dir.; Rebecca J. Nadgwick, Cont. and Grants Mgr.; Mogens Bay; F. Joe Daugherty; J. Timothy Daugherty; Robert Daugherty III; Ken Stinson.
EIN: 363766006
Selected grants: The following grants are a representative sample of this grantmaker's funding activity:
$5,000,000 to Omaha Botanical Center, Omaha, NE, 2012. For capital support.
$5,000,000 to Omaha Zoo Foundation, Omaha, NE, 2012. For capital support.
$3,477,271 to University of Nebraska Foundation, Lincoln, NE, 2012. For program support.
$2,000,000 to University of Nebraska Foundation, Omaha, NE, 2012. For capital support.
$864,000 to Joslyn Art Museum Foundation, Omaha, NE, 2012. For program support and capital support.
$800,000 to Boys Town, Boys Town, NE, 2012. For capital support.
$150,000 to Opera Omaha, Omaha, NE, 2012. For program support.

$110,000 to Lutheran Family Services of Nebraska, Omaha, NE, 2012. For program support.
$80,000 to Wayne State University Foundation, Detroit, MI, 2012. For capital support.
$25,000 to Groundwater Foundation, Lincoln, NE, 2012. For program support.

5034
Henry A. Davis Foundation ✧
P.O. Box 7566
Omaha, NE 68107-0566

Donor: Henry A. Davis.
Foundation type: Independent foundation.
Financial data (yr. ended 12/31/13): Assets, $4,314,883 (M); gifts received, $2,003,820; expenditures, $1,308,662; qualifying distributions, $1,307,623; giving activities include $1,307,623 for 24 grants (high: $750,000; low: $50).
Fields of interest: Arts; Education; Crime/violence prevention, child abuse; Children/youth, services.
Limitations: Applications not accepted. Giving primarily in Omaha, NE.
Application information: Contributes only to pre-selected organizations.
Officer: Henry A. Davis, Secy.
EIN: 263740254

5035
Dillon Foundation ✧
P.O. Box 6368
Lincoln, NE 68506-0368 (402) 937-9818
Contact: Joseph Kerrigan, Pres. and Treas.
E-mail: dillonfdn@aol.com

Established in 1997 in NE.
Donor: Donald F. Dillon.
Foundation type: Independent foundation.
Financial data (yr. ended 12/31/13): Assets, $38,778,483 (M); expenditures, $1,577,955; qualifying distributions, $1,432,640; giving activities include $1,432,640 for 84 grants (high: $100,000; low: $1,000).
Fields of interest: Education; Human services; Catholic agencies & churches.
Limitations: Applications accepted. Giving primarily in NE, with emphasis on Lincoln. No grants to individuals.
Application information: Application form required.
Initial approach: Letter or e-mail requesting application form
Deadline(s): None
Officers and Directors:* Joseph Kerrigan, Pres. and Treas.; Patrick J. Kerrigan,* V.P. and Secy.; Donald F. Dillon; David B. Policky.
EIN: 911805591
Selected grants: The following grants are a representative sample of this grantmaker's funding activity:
$100,000 to University of Nebraska Foundation, Lincoln, NE, 2011. For program.
$50,000 to Lincoln Parks and Recreation Foundation, Lincoln, NE, 2011. For capital improvements.
$50,000 to Saint Thomas Aquinas Church, Lincoln, NE, 2011. For capital improvements.
$45,000 to Tabitha, Lincoln, NE, 2011. For program.
$35,000 to Friendship Home of Lincoln, Lincoln, NE, 2011. For program.
$25,000 to Girl Scouts of the U.S.A., Lincoln, NE, 2011. For capital improvements.
$20,000 to Audubon Nebraska, Denton, NE, 2011. For program.
$20,000 to Food Bank of Lincoln, Lincoln, NE, 2011. For program.
$15,000 to Lincoln Symphony Orchestra, Lincoln, NE, 2011. For program.
$10,000 to Project Kindle, Lincoln, NE, 2011. For program.

5036
Rupert Dunklau Foundation, Inc. ✧
P.O. Box 22990
Lincoln, NE 68542-2990 (402) 328-0370
Contact: Lloyd Probasco, Exec. Dir.
FAX: (402) 420-4904;
E-mail: dunklaufoundation@windstream.net

Established in 1968 in NE.
Donors: Rupert Dunklau; Ruth Dunklau†.
Foundation type: Independent foundation.
Financial data (yr. ended 12/31/13): Assets, $28,352,257 (M); expenditures, $1,214,549; qualifying distributions, $1,113,413; giving activities include $1,113,413 for 37 grants (high: $100,000; low: $10,000).
Purpose and activities: In this constantly changing world, the foundation exists to glorify God and serve His gracious will by providing financial resources for the varied ministries related to the Lutheran tradition, especially the Lutheran Church-Missouri Synod, and to consider appropriate projects that promote the welfare of mankind.
Fields of interest: Higher education; Family services; Foundations (private grantmaking); Protestant agencies & churches; Children/youth; Adults; Aging; Physically disabled; Blind/visually impaired; Minorities; African Americans/Blacks; Native Americans/American Indians; Women; Substance abusers; Single parents; Economically disadvantaged; Homeless.
Type of support: Income development; Equipment; Curriculum development; Continuing support; Annual campaigns; Capital campaigns; Building/renovation; Conferences/seminars; Scholarship funds; Matching/challenge support.
Limitations: Applications accepted. Giving primarily in NE; giving nationally for Lutheran colleges and universities that are part of LCMS. No support for organizations supporting abortion. No grants to individuals.
Publications: Application guidelines; Informational brochure (including application guidelines).
Application information: Application form required.
Initial approach: Letter or e-mail requesting grant inquiry form
Copies of proposal: 5
Deadline(s): Mar. 31 and Aug. 30
Board meeting date(s): Twice per year
Final notification: Within 30 days for application acknowledgement; response within 30 days following meeting
Officers: Rupert Dunklau, Pres.; Del Toebben, V.P.; Larry R. Larson, Treas.; Donald Levenhagen, Secy.; Lloyd Probasco, Exec. Dir.
Directors: Alan Harre; Larry Shepard.
Number of staff: 1 full-time support.
EIN: 476059030

5037
Eagle Foundation ✧
1475 Road 105
Sidney, NE 69162-4236

Established in 1993 in NE.
Donor: James W. Cabela.
Foundation type: Independent foundation.
Financial data (yr. ended 12/31/13): Assets, $83,853,352 (M); expenditures, $4,844,707; qualifying distributions, $4,343,521; giving activities include $4,330,000 for 21 grants (high: $650,000; low: $25,000).
Purpose and activities: Giving primarily to Roman Catholic agencies and churches.
Fields of interest: Health care; Human services; Catholic agencies & churches.
Type of support: General/operating support.
Limitations: Applications not accepted. Giving primarily in FL, MA, NE, and NY. No grants to individuals.
Application information: Contributes only to pre-selected organizations.
Officers and Directors:* James W. Cabela,* Pres. and Treas.; Gerald E. Matzke,* Secy.; Michael R. McCarthy.
EIN: 470773892

5038
Debby Durham Family Foundation ✧ ☆
(formerly Margre & Charles Durham Foundation IV)
c/o Hancock & Dana, PC
12829 W. Dodge Rd., Ste. 100
Omaha, NE 68154

Established in 2000 in NE; Dec. 2008 absorbed assets of the Durham Foundation.
Donors: Charles Durham Charitable Lead Annuity Trust; Charles W. Durham Revocable Trust; Durham Resources.
Foundation type: Independent foundation.
Financial data (yr. ended 12/31/13): Assets, $23,707,648 (M); gifts received, $226,250; expenditures, $1,007,923; qualifying distributions, $871,061; giving activities include $871,061 for 38 grants (high: $600,000; low: $500).
Fields of interest: Arts; Higher education; Education; Human services; Christian agencies & churches.
Limitations: Applications not accepted. Giving primarily in NE. No grants to individuals.
Application information: Unsolicited requests for funds not accepted.
Officers and Directors:* Debra A. Durham,* Pres.; Molly Crook,* V.P.; Michael D. Jones, Secy.; Matthew C. Milligan,* Treas.
EIN: 470830372

5039
Fremont Area Community Foundation ✧
1005 E. 23rd St., Ste. 2
P.O. Box 182
Fremont, NE 68025-4932 (402) 721-4252
Contact: Melissa Diers, Exec. Dir.
FAX: (402) 816-4102;
E-mail: info@facfoundation.org; Main URL: http://www.facfoundation.org
Blog: http://www.facfoundation.wordpress.com
Facebook: http://www.facebook.com/FremontAreaCommunityFoundation

Established in 1980 in NE.
Foundation type: Community foundation.
Financial data (yr. ended 06/30/13): Assets, $13,351,468 (M); gifts received, $1,900,124; expenditures, $1,630,834; giving activities include $1,234,067 for 26+ grants (high: $139,960).
Purpose and activities: The foundation seeks to improve the quality of life by connecting donor interests with community needs. Grantmaking primarily for social services, health and recreation, education, arts and culture, and civic purposes.
Fields of interest: Arts; Education; Health care; Recreation; Human services; Government/public administration.
Type of support: Annual campaigns; Management development/capacity building; Capital campaigns; Building/renovation; Equipment; Endowments; Program development; Seed money; Scholarships—to individuals; In-kind gifts; Matching/challenge support.
Limitations: Applications accepted. Giving primarily in the Fremont and Dodge County, NE, area. Some limited grantmaking in Burt, Colfax, Douglas, Cuming, Saunders and Washington counties in NE. No support for religious organizations for religious purposes. No grants to individuals (except for designated scholarship funds).
Publications: Application guidelines; Annual report; Informational brochure (including application guidelines); Newsletter.
Application information: Visit foundation web site for application form and guidelines. Application form required.
Initial approach: Contact foundation
Copies of proposal: 1
Deadline(s): Jan. 3, Apr. 1, July 1, and Oct. 1; May 16 for field-of-interest grants
Board meeting date(s): Monthly; grant committee meets quarterly
Final notification: Within 2 months
Officers and Directors:* Dick Hendriksen,* Pres.; Russ Peterson,* V.P.; Chris Leech,* Secy.-Treas.; Melissa Diers,* Exec. Dir.; Dolores Bang; Mary Buller; Barbara Christensen; Cindy Coffman; Larry Flamme; Todd Hansen; Dr. Greg Haskins; Bob Hillis; Cyndy Koerber; Martin Koopman; Ron Kortan; Cheryl Lamme; Sheila Monke; Gaylord Mussman; Steve Navarrette; Dale Olson; Cathy Seager; Joe Sajevic; Toni Vering; Marvin G. Welstead; and 3 additional directors.
Number of staff: 2 full-time professional; 1 part-time support.
EIN: 470629642
Selected grants: The following grants are a representative sample of this grantmaker's funding activity:
$40,000 to Midland University, Fremont, NE, 2011. For student transition, athletic and facilities equipment.
$15,000 to Fremont, City of, Fremont, NE, 2011. For community branding initiative.
$8,841 to Care Corps, Fremont, NE, 2011. To purchase commercial washer and dryer.
$8,500 to Heartland Equine Therapeutic Riding Academy, Valley, NE, 2011. For volunteer coordinator.
$5,000 to Arlington Public Schools, 2011. For resurfacing of community trail.
$5,000 to Legal Aid of Nebraska, Omaha, NE, 2011. For legal services for victims of domestic violence.
$5,000 to Lutheran Family Services, Fremont, NE, 2011. For Center for Healthy Families.
$4,269 to Dodge County Head Start, 2011. For early learning computers.
$4,000 to Logan View Athletic Boosters, 2011. For new score board.
$1,000 to Washington Elementary School, 2011. For learning garden.

5040
Monte L. and Lisa R. Froehlich Family Foundation ✧ ☆
129 N. 10th St., Ste. 107
Lincoln, NE 68508-1510

Established in 2004 in NE.
Donors: Monte L. Froehlich; Lisa R. Froelich; U.S. Property; The Grand Manse Events & Lodging; 5800 Building, LLC; 6000 Fulton, LLC; FW Townhouse, LLC.
Foundation type: Independent foundation.
Financial data (yr. ended 12/31/13): Assets, $47,552 (M); gifts received, $113,500; expenditures, $516,648; qualifying distributions, $473,207; giving activities include $469,466 for 19 grants (high: $387,735; low: $50).
Fields of interest: Arts; Education; Religion.
Limitations: Applications not accepted. Giving primarily in AZ and GA. No grants to individuals.
Application information: Unsolicited requests for funds not accepted.
Directors: Lisa R. Froehlich; Monte L. Froehlich.
EIN: 202025465
Selected grants: The following grants are a representative sample of this grantmaker's funding activity:
$387,735 to National Christian Charitable Foundation, Alpharetta, GA, 2013. To further the programs of the organization.
$59,492 to Alliance Defending Freedom, Scottsdale, AZ, 2013. To further the programs of the organization.
$6,925 to Willow Creek Church Association, Barrington, IL, 2013. To further the programs of the organization.
$5,481 to Lincoln Berean Church, Lincoln, NE, 2013. To further the programs of the organization.
$1,250 to Lincoln Arts Council, Lincoln, NE, 2013. To further the programs of the organization.
$1,202 to Lincoln Rotary Club No. 14 Foundation, Lincoln, NE, 2013. To further the programs of the organization.
$300 to Young Life, Colorado Springs, CO, 2012. To further the programs of the organization.

5041
Gardner Foundation ✧
307 Main St.
Wakefield, NE 68784-6026
Contact: Board of Trustees
Application address: P.O. Box 390, Wakefield, NE 68784, tel.: (402) 287-2538

Established in 1990 in NE.
Donors: David J. Gardner; Kirk N. Gardner; Leslie A. Bebee.
Foundation type: Independent foundation.
Financial data (yr. ended 12/31/13): Assets, $28,090,639 (M); expenditures, $1,701,747; qualifying distributions, $1,271,732; giving activities include $1,271,732 for 27 grants (high: $200,000; low: $1,000).
Purpose and activities: Giving primarily for education and the arts.
Fields of interest: Performing arts, theater; Performing arts, orchestras; Education, fund raising/fund distribution; Higher education; Hospitals (general).
Type of support: Capital campaigns; Building/renovation; Equipment; Endowments; Seed money.
Limitations: Applications accepted. Giving primarily in NE, with emphasis on the 75-mile radius of Wakefield, NE. No support for private, non-operating foundations. No grants to individuals.
Publications: Program policy statement.
Application information: Application form required.
Initial approach: Letter
Copies of proposal: 1
Deadline(s): 90 days before board meeting
Board meeting date(s): Quarterly
Final notification: 90 days
Officers: Jeanne M. Gardner, Pres. and Treas.; Leslie A. Bebee, V.P. and Secy.
Trustees: David J. Gardner; Kirk N. Gardner.
Number of staff: 1 full-time professional; 1 full-time support.
EIN: 363705723
Selected grants: The following grants are a representative sample of this grantmaker's funding activity:
$238,945 to Wayne State College Foundation, Wayne, NE, 2012.
$185,750 to Wakefield Fire and Rescue Department, Wakefield, NE, 2012.
$111,150 to Wakefield, City of, Wakefield, NE, 2012.
$75,000 to Wakefield Health Care Center, Wakefield, NE, 2012.
$45,000 to Little Red Hen Theater, Wakefield, NE, 2012.
$28,000 to Emerson Senior Center, 2012.
$16,545 to Wakefield Legion Post 81, 2012.
$12,600 to Dakota K 9 Foundation, 2012.
$10,000 to Goodwill Industries, 2012.
$5,000 to Nebraska Educational Television Network, Lincoln, NE, 2012.

5042
Gaughan Family Foundation ✧
(formerly Jackie & Bertie Gaughan Foundation)
617 N. 90th St.
Omaha, NE 68114-2821

Established in 1997 in NV.
Donor: John D. Gaughan.
Foundation type: Independent foundation.
Financial data (yr. ended 12/31/13): Assets, $14,773,984 (M); expenditures, $753,611; qualifying distributions, $590,000; giving activities include $590,000 for 13 grants (high: $400,000; low: $5,000).
Fields of interest: Secondary school/education.
Limitations: Applications not accepted. Giving primarily in Omaha, NE and Las Vegas, NV. No grants to individuals.
Application information: Contributes only to pre-selected organizations.
Officer: Michael J. Gaughan, Pres. and Secy.-Treas.
EIN: 860873950

5043
J. Wesley Graham Trust ✧
c/o Wells Fargo Bank, N.A. (MAC N8000-0027)
1919 Douglas St., 2nd Fl.
Omaha, NE 68102-1317

Foundation type: Independent foundation.
Financial data (yr. ended 12/31/13): Assets, $15,137,493 (M); expenditures, $1,107,828; qualifying distributions, $623,668; giving activities include $600,000 for 2 grants (high: $599,000; low: $1,000).
Fields of interest: Salvation Army.
Limitations: Applications not accepted. Giving primarily in MN.
Application information: Contributes only to pre-selected organizations.
Trustee: Wells Fargo Bank, N.A.
EIN: 426315781
Selected grants: The following grants are a representative sample of this grantmaker's funding activity:
$540,000 to Salvation Army, Northern Division, Roseville, MN, 2011.

5044
Grand Island Community Foundation, Inc. ✧

1811 W. 2nd St., Ste. 480
Grand Island, NE 68803 (308) 381-7767
Contact: Tammy Morris M.S., C.E.O.
FAX: (308) 384-4069; E-mail: info@gicf.org; Main URL: http://www.gicf.org

Established in 1960 in NE.
Foundation type: Community foundation.
Financial data (yr. ended 12/31/12): Assets, $7,077,774 (M); gifts received, $636,374; expenditures, $763,287; giving activities include $499,132 for 66 grants to individuals.
Purpose and activities: The foundation is a community endowment established to accept charitable contributions in order to preserve and enhance the quality of life in Central Nebraska and to assist donors in realizing their charitable goals.
Fields of interest: Arts; Libraries/library science; Education; Health care; Youth development; Human services; Economic development; Community/economic development; United Ways and Federated Giving Programs; Government/public administration; Public affairs; Children/youth; Youth.
Type of support: Scholarships—to individuals; General/operating support; Emergency funds; Program development; Scholarship funds; Matching/challenge support.
Limitations: Applications accepted. Giving limited to Hall County, NE. No support for religious purposes. No grants to individuals (except for scholarships), or for endowments, capital campaigns, or annual fund drives.
Publications: Application guidelines; Annual report; Annual report (including application guidelines); Financial statement; Grants list; Informational brochure; Informational brochure (including application guidelines); Newsletter; Occasional report.
Application information: Visit foundation web site for application form and guidelines. Faxed or e-mailed applications are not accepted. Application form required.
Initial approach: Submit application
Copies of proposal: 8
Deadline(s): May 1 and Nov. 1
Board meeting date(s): Every other month
Officers and Directors:* Ellen Hornady,* Chair.; Kris Nolan Brown,* Chair.-Elect; Tammy Morris, M.S.*, C.E.O.; Tom Gdowski,* Treas.; Meta Armstrong; Roger Bullington; Doug Fargo; Ken Gnandt; Harry Hoch; Mike Kneale; Marcy Luth; Jodi Maruska; Mike Schuster; Judy Smith; Lisa Thayer; Tim Wojcik.
Number of staff: 1 full-time professional.
EIN: 476032570

5045
Hamilton Community Foundation, Inc. ✧

1216 L St.
P.O. Box 283
Aurora, NE 68818-2016 (402) 694-3200
Contact: Sidney L. Widga, Treas.
FAX: (402) 694-6160; E-mail: hcf@hamilton.net; Additional e-mail: swidga@hamilton.net; Main URL: http://hcfne.org/
Facebook: http://www.facebook.com/pages/Hamilton-Community-Foundation/129841327056963

Incorporated in 1965 in NE.
Foundation type: Community foundation.
Financial data (yr. ended 12/31/13): Assets, $13,834,973 (M); gifts received, $1,129,703; expenditures, $809,296; giving activities include $470,126 for 72+ grants (high: $74,188), and $216,850 for 106 grants to individuals.
Purpose and activities: The foundation seeks to meet local community needs for all manner of civic, charitable, educational, cultural, health, recreational, and humanitarian purposes.
Fields of interest: Arts; Higher education; Education; Health care; Recreation; Human services; Community/economic development; Christian agencies & churches; Aging.
Type of support: Scholarships—to individuals; Equipment; Scholarship funds.
Limitations: Applications accepted. Giving limited to Hamilton County, NE. No grants for operating expenses, deficit financing, or fund demonstration.
Publications: Annual report.
Application information:
Initial approach: Letter
Copies of proposal: 21
Deadline(s): Jan. 15, Apr. 15, July 15, and Oct. 15
Board meeting date(s): Quarterly and as necessary
Final notification: 2 weeks
Officers and Directors:* Sidney L. Widga,* Secy.-Treas.; Karen Bamesberger; Colleen Barger; Becky Goertzen; Jerry Hinrichs; Dean Klute; Carolyn Kuehner; Tina Larson; Dave Long; Sherri Miller; Gary Ross; Kim Schaffert; Marcia Spiehs; Margo Stenson; Deb Vanderheiden.
EIN: 476038289

5046
Hastings Community Foundation, Inc. ✧ ☆

800 W. 3rd St. Ste. 232
Hastings, NE 68901 (402) 462-5152
Contact: Susan Poppe, Office Mgr.; Stephanie Bliss, Admin. Asst.
FAX: (402) 462-5171; E-mail: hcf@inebraska.com; Mailing address: P.O. Box 703, Hastings, NE 68902-0703; Main URL: http://www.hastingscommunityfoundation.org/
Facebook: https://www.facebook.com/pages/Hastings-Community-Foundation/111765092220534

Established in 1987 in NE.
Foundation type: Community foundation.
Financial data (yr. ended 12/31/13): Assets, $9,147,189 (M); gifts received, $756,687; expenditures, $1,044,778; giving activities include $936,086 for 42+ grants (high: $247,500), and $37,991 for 23 grants to individuals.
Purpose and activities: The foundation works to perpetuate and enrich the quality of life in Hastings and the surrounding area through the prudent investment and management of philanthropic donations it does this by: 1) receiving and managing funds to build a permanent unrestricted endowment for the needs of Hastings and the surrounding area. It uses these resources wisely and efficiently to respond to emerging and changing needs and to sustain existing organizations and institutions, through grants for education, arts and culture, health, social services, economic development, and civic affairs; 2) providing a flexible vehicle for donors with varied philanthropic desires. In doing so the Foundation serves as a steward for individuals, families, foundations and organizations which entrust assets to its care; and 3) acting as a leader for the local philanthropic community, identifying and exploring important needs and concerns, addressing serious problems, and shaping effective responses.
Fields of interest: Humanities; Historic preservation/historical societies; Arts; Elementary school/education; Higher education; Scholarships/financial aid; Education; Health care; Disasters, fire prevention/control; Recreation; Children/youth, services; Human services; Economic development; Community/economic development.
Type of support: Continuing support; Building/renovation; Equipment; Endowments; Program development; Conferences/seminars; Seed money; Scholarship funds; Consulting services; In-kind gifts; Matching/challenge support.
Limitations: Applications accepted. Giving primarily in Hastings, NE, and the surrounding area. No support for religious organizations for religious purposes. No grants for operating expenses, endowments, fellowships, capital campaigns, or medical or scientific research.
Publications: Application guidelines; Annual report; Grants list; Informational brochure; Informational brochure (including application guidelines); Newsletter; Occasional report.
Application information: Occasionally makes additional grants in the fall if funds are available. Application form required.
Initial approach: Telephone to request an application
Copies of proposal: 2
Deadline(s): Dec. 31
Board meeting date(s): 3rd Tues. of each month
Final notification: Feb. 27
Officers and Directors:* D. Charles Shoemaker,* Pres.; Martha Boyd,* V.P.; John Quirk,* V.P.; Charles Hastings,* Secy.; Marilyn Nielsen,* Treas.; Gary Anderson; Lafe Anderson; Paula Beirow; John Crowley; Jim Guthmann; Cheryl Lockwood; Gayle McClure; Dean Moors; Michael Nevrivy; John C. Osborne; Beth Robertson; Hauli Sabatka; James Thom; Michael A. Walenz.
Number of staff: 1 full-time support; 1 part-time support.
EIN: 363569968

5047
The Hawks Foundation ✧
14302 FNB Pkwy.
Omaha, NE 68154-5212 (402) 691-9500
Contact: Rhonda Hawks, Tr.

Established in 1994 in NE.
Donors: Tom Hawks; Don Carter; Linda Carter; Kenny Trout; Lisa Trout; Howard Hawks; Rhonda Hawks; McCarthy Group, Inc.; NHH Enterprises; H.T. Ardinger and Sons; Hillwood Enterprises; Greater Richardson Anesthesia.
Foundation type: Independent foundation.
Financial data (yr. ended 12/31/13): Assets, $99,132,144 (M); gifts received, $278,995; expenditures, $3,657,150; qualifying distributions, $2,891,557; giving activities include $2,756,203 for 178 grants (high: $290,000; low: $73).
Purpose and activities: Giving primarily for higher education and to Lutheran churches and organizations; funding also for health associations, children, youth and social services, the arts, and Christian organizations and churches. Scholarships to individuals who are enrolled as full-time students, who demonstrate financial need, and who maintain at least a 2.8 cumulative GPA.
Fields of interest: Arts; Higher education; Education; Health organizations, association; Youth development; Human services; Children/youth, services; Family services; Christian agencies & churches; Protestant agencies & churches.
Type of support: Program-related investments/loans; Scholarships—to individuals.
Limitations: Giving primarily in Omaha, NE.
Application information: Application form required for scholarships. Forms maybe obtained from foundation office.
Initial approach: Letter
Deadline(s): None
Trustees: Heather L. Hawks; Howard L. Hawks; Neal H. Hawks; Rhonda A. Hawks; Troy T. Hawks.
EIN: 476194021

5048
The Charles and Mary Heider Family Foundation ✧
9409 Westchester Ln.
Omaha, NE 68114-3841

Established in 1998 in NE.
Donor: Charles F. Heider.
Foundation type: Independent foundation.
Financial data (yr. ended 12/31/13): Assets, $9,076,987 (M); expenditures, $743,266; qualifying distributions, $697,950; giving activities include $697,950 for 53 grants (high: $140,500; low: $500).
Fields of interest: Education; Human services; Catholic agencies & churches.
Limitations: Applications not accepted. Giving primarily in Omaha, NE. No grants to individuals.
Application information: Contributes only to pre-selected organizations.
Officers: Charles F. Heider, Pres. and Treas.; Mary C. Heider, V.P. and Secy.
Directors: Mark J. Heider; Scott C. Heider.
EIN: 470810266
Selected grants: The following grants are a representative sample of this grantmaker's funding activity:
$25,000 to Big Brothers Big Sisters of the Midlands, Omaha, NE, 2011.
$25,000 to Child Saving Institute, Omaha, NE, 2011.
$25,000 to United Way of the Midlands, Omaha, NE, 2011.
$24,000 to Creighton Preparatory School, Omaha, NE, 2011.
$18,500 to Creighton University, Omaha, NE, 2011.
$17,000 to Jesuit Academy, Omaha, NE, 2011.
$14,500 to Boys and Girls Clubs of the Midlands, Omaha, NE, 2011.
$10,000 to Boy Scouts of America, Omaha, NE, 2011.
$10,000 to Saint Augustine Indian Mission, Winnebago, NE, 2011.
$10,000 to Seeds of Hope Charitable Trust, Denver, CO, 2011.

5049
Hirschfeld Family Foundation, Inc. ✧
3606 4th Ave.
Kearney, NE 68847-2828 (308) 234-5579
Contact: Dan Hirschfeld

Established in 1992 in NE.
Donor: Daniel J. Hirschfeld.
Foundation type: Independent foundation.
Financial data (yr. ended 08/31/13): Assets, $167,606,170 (M); expenditures, $7,438,841; qualifying distributions, $6,437,491; giving activities include $6,437,491 for 28 grants (high: $2,000,000; low: $3,000).
Purpose and activities: Giving primarily for education and for human services.
Fields of interest: Museums; Elementary/secondary education; Higher education; Hospitals (general); Human services; YM/YWCAs & YM/YWHAs; Aging, centers/services.
Type of support: General/operating support; Capital campaigns; Building/renovation; Equipment; Land acquisition; Emergency funds; Program development; Professorships; Seed money; Curriculum development; Scholarship funds; Matching/challenge support.
Limitations: Applications accepted. Giving primarily in NE. No grants to individuals.
Application information: Application form required.
Initial approach: Letter requesting application form
Copies of proposal: 1
Deadline(s): None
Board meeting date(s): As needed
Final notification: 1 month
Officers and Director:* Daniel J. Hirschfeld,* Pres. and Treas.; Benjamin G. Hirschfeld, V.P.; David J. Hirschfeld, V.P.; Letitia A. Spencer, V.P.; Monya A. Hirschfeld,* Secy.
EIN: 470762188
Selected grants: The following grants are a representative sample of this grantmaker's funding activity:
$1,000,000 to Mayo Clinic, Rochester, MN, 2011.
$800,000 to York College, York, NE, 2011.
$170,000 to University of Nebraska Foundation, Lincoln, NE, 2011.
$125,000 to Crossroads Center, Hastings, NE, 2011.
$125,000 to Hastings College, Hastings, NE, 2011.
$100,000 to YMCA, Kearney Family, Kearney, NE, 2011.
$20,000 to Kearney Catholic High School Foundation, Kearney, NE, 2011.
$20,000 to Madonna Foundation, Homewood, IL, 2011.
$20,000 to Madonna School, Omaha, NE, 2011.
$10,000 to Childrens Hospital and Medical Center Foundation, Omaha, NE, 2011.

5050
Gilbert M. and Martha H. Hitchcock Foundation ✧
209 S. 19th St., Ste. 151
Omaha, NE 68102-1711 (402) 345-0043
Contact: Neely Kountze, Pres. and Tr.

Incorporated in 1943 in NE.
Donor: Martha H. Hitchcock‡.
Foundation type: Independent foundation.
Financial data (yr. ended 12/31/13): Assets, $16,738,735 (M); expenditures, $918,684; qualifying distributions, $822,100; giving activities include $822,100 for 52 grants (high: $85,100; low: $1,000).
Purpose and activities: Support for private education; support also for the arts and social service agencies; sponsors scholarship program for Omaha World-Herald newspaper carriers.
Fields of interest: Museums; Arts; Higher education; Education; Animal welfare; Human services.
Type of support: General/operating support; Capital campaigns; Building/renovation; Endowments; Scholarship funds; Matching/challenge support.
Limitations: Applications accepted. Giving limited to western IA, and to NE. No grants to individuals directly.
Publications: Application guidelines.
Application information: Application form required.
Initial approach: Letter
Copies of proposal: 8
Deadline(s): Nov. 30
Board meeting date(s): Annually
Officers and Trustees:* Neely Kountze,* Pres.; Mary L. Kountze,* V.P.; John Q. Bachman,* Secy.; John W. Webster,* Treas.; W. Russell Bowie III; Elizabeth Mallory Kountze; Tower Kountze; James E. Landen.
EIN: 476025723

5051
The Holland Foundation ✧
1501 S. 80th St.
Omaha, NE 68124-1423
Contact: Richard D. Holland, Pres.

Established in 1996 in NE.
Donors: Marilyn M. Holland; Richard D. Holland.
Foundation type: Independent foundation.
Financial data (yr. ended 12/31/13): Assets, $137,267,832 (M); gifts received, $4,500,000; expenditures, $18,367,608; qualifying distributions, $18,221,128; giving activities include $18,221,128 for 95 grants (high: $4,261,138; low: $500).
Purpose and activities: Giving primarily for the arts, education and human services.
Fields of interest: Performing arts; Performing arts, orchestras; Arts; Education; Human services.
Limitations: Applications accepted. Giving primarily in NE. No grants to individuals.
Application information:
Initial approach: Proposal
Deadline(s): None
Officers: Richard D. Holland, Pres.; Thomas R. Pansing, Secy.

Directors: Gerald Hoberman; Mary A. Holland; Barbara H. Kral; Wallace R. Weitz; Kathryn A. Weitz White.
Number of staff: 1 part-time support.
EIN: 470804949
Selected grants: The following grants are a representative sample of this grantmaker's funding activity:
$4,261,138 to Omaha Symphony, Omaha, NE, 2013. For operating support.
$2,677,500 to University of Nebraska Foundation, Lincoln Office, Lincoln, NE, 2013. For operating support.
$1,495,000 to Building Bright Futures, Omaha, NE, 2012. For operating support and program support.
$1,027,959 to Partnership for Our Kids, Omaha, NE, 2013. For operating support.
$1,000,000 to Northstar Foundation, Omaha, NE, 2013. For operating support.
$1,000,000 to Planned Parenthood of the Heartland, Omaha, NE, 2013. For operating support.
$900,000 to Partnership for Our Kids, Omaha, NE, 2012. For operating support.
$850,000 to Avenue Scholars Foundation, Omaha, NE, 2012. For operating support.
$772,500 to Building Bright Futures, Omaha, NE, 2013. For operating support and program support.
$553,750 to Omaha Performing Arts Society, Omaha, NE, 2012. For operating support.
$501,080 to Opera Omaha, Omaha, NE, 2012. For operating support.
$374,365 to Omaha Symphony, Omaha, NE, 2012. For operating support.
$227,500 to Joslyn Art Museum, Omaha, NE, 2012. For operating support.
$100,000 to Creighton Preparatory School, Omaha, NE, 2013. For operating support.
$100,000 to Nebraska Methodist Hospital Foundation, Omaha, NE, 2013. For operating support.
$50,000 to Bemis Center for Contemporary Arts, Omaha, NE, 2012. For operating support.
$50,000 to Urban League of Nebraska, Omaha, NE, 2013. For operating support.
$35,000 to University of Nebraska Foundation, Omaha Office, Omaha, NE, 2012. For operating support.
$31,000 to Film Streams, Omaha, NE, 2013. For operating support.
$25,000 to Lena Pope Home, Fort Worth, TX, 2012. For operating support.

5052
Holthus Foundation ✧ ☆
529 Lincoln Ave.
York, NE 68467-2944 (402) 363-7409
Contact: C.G. Holthus, Dir.

Established in 2001 in NE.
Donors: Cornerstone Bank, N.A.; Tom Holthus; Marcy Holthus; C.G. Holthus; Kristie Holthus; Kendell Holthus; Beth Godbout.
Foundation type: Company-sponsored foundation.
Financial data (yr. ended 12/31/13): Assets, $3,086,608 (M); gifts received, $381,000; expenditures, $1,432,474; qualifying distributions, $1,429,343; giving activities include $1,429,343 for 2 grants (high: $1,424,343; low: $5,000).
Purpose and activities: The foundation supports nonprofit organizations in Nebraska, with emphasis on Boone and York counties.
Fields of interest: Health care; Housing/shelter.
Type of support: General/operating support.
Limitations: Applications accepted. Giving primarily in Boone and York counties, NE.
Application information: Application form required.
Initial approach: Letter
Deadline(s): None
Directors: Kristie Holoch; C.G. Holthus; Virginia Holthus.
EIN: 470807361

5053
Theodore F. and Claire M. Hubbard Family Foundation ✧
32018 E. Lake Park Dr.
South Bend, NE 68058-4320

Established in 1995 in NE.
Donors: Anne M. Hubbard; Claire M. Hubbard; Claire M. Hubbard Charitable Lead Trust.
Foundation type: Independent foundation.
Financial data (yr. ended 11/30/13): Assets, $23,256,273 (M); gifts received, $1,503,785; expenditures, $3,664,014; qualifying distributions, $3,664,014; giving activities include $3,334,493 for 4 grants (high: $2,710,999; low: $15,000).
Purpose and activities: Giving primarily to a foundation that supports a zoo; some funding also for education and human services.
Fields of interest: Higher education; Education; Zoos/zoological societies; Hospitals (general); Human services.
Limitations: Applications not accepted. Giving primarily in Omaha, NE. No grants to individuals.
Application information: Contributes only to pre-selected organizations.
Officers and Directors:* Theodore F. Hubbard, Jr.,* Pres.; Colleen Hubbard,* V.P.; T. Geoffrey Lieben,* Secy.
EIN: 476205113

5054
Claire M. Hubbard Foundation ✧
4532 S. 163rd St.
Omaha, NE 68135

Established in 2005 in NE.
Donors: Anne M. Hubbard; Claire M. Hubbard; Theodore F. Hubbard, Jr.; Claire M. Hubbard Charitable Lead Trust.
Foundation type: Independent foundation.
Financial data (yr. ended 11/30/13): Assets, $28,614,564 (M); gifts received, $1,506,796; expenditures, $878,136; qualifying distributions, $878,136; giving activities include $640,029 for 17 grants (high: $257,174; low: $200).
Purpose and activities: Giving primarily for the arts, education, and human services.
Fields of interest: Environment; Animals/wildlife.
Limitations: Applications not accepted. Giving primarily in Omaha, NE; some giving also in Philadelphia, PA. No grants to individuals.
Application information: Contributes only to pre-selected organizations.
Officers and Directors:* Anne M. Hubbard,* Pres.; Marcia Blum,* V.P.; T. Geoffrey Lieben,* Secy.
EIN: 202364902

5055
Kearney Area Community Foundation ✧
412 W. 48th St., Ste. 12
Kearney, NE 68845 (308) 237-3114
Contact: Judi Sickler, Exec. Dir.
FAX: (308) 237-9845;
E-mail: kacf@kearneyfoundation.org; Mailing address: P.O. Box 1694, Kearney, NE 68848; Additional e-mail: judi@kearneyfoundation.org; Main URL: http://www.kearneyfoundation.org
Facebook: http://www.facebook.com/pages/Kearney-Area-Community-Foundation/118780074843224

Established in 1995 in NE.
Foundation type: Community foundation.
Financial data (yr. ended 12/31/13): Assets, $10,886,008 (M); gifts received, $3,765,191; expenditures, $2,922,538; giving activities include $488,932 for 1+ grant (high: $70,000), and $46,801 for grants to individuals.
Purpose and activities: The foundation exists to enhance the quality of life in the Kearney area by promoting the spirit of charitable giving and effectively responding to the community's needs.
Fields of interest: Visual arts; Museums; Performing arts; Arts; Libraries/library science; Education; Horticulture/garden clubs; Hospitals (general); Health care; Mental health/crisis services; Disasters, Hurricane Katrina; Recreation; Human services; Economic development; Community/economic development; Children; Adults; Aging.
Type of support: Building/renovation; Equipment; Emergency funds; Seed money; Scholarships—to individuals; Matching/challenge support.
Limitations: Applications accepted. Giving limited to Kearney and surrounding area. No support for religious activities (unless non-denominational and serving a broad segment of the population) or private or parochial schools (unless serving a broad segment of the population), as well as other private organizations. No grants to individuals (except for scholarships), or for annual fund drives, galas, or other special-event fundraising activities, capital campaigns/renovation projects, debt reduction, dissertations or student/faculty research projects, endowment funds, indirect/administrative costs, fellowships, travel, tours or trips; no loans.
Publications: Application guidelines; Grants list.
Application information: Visit foundation web site for application form and guidelines. Faxed or e-mailed applications are not accepted. Application form required.
Initial approach: Telephone
Copies of proposal: 9
Deadline(s): Feb. 1 and Aug. 1
Officers and Directors:* Susan Bigg,* Chair.; Mike Tye,* Vice-Chair.; Marsha Fairbanks,* Secy.; Roxanne Bascom,* Treas.; Judi Sickler, Exec. Dir.; John Bancroft, M.D.; Dottie Bowman; Rachelle Bryant; Corliss Dixon; Ron Eckloff; Bob Huddleston; Teresa Ibach; Michaela Lewis; Tom McCarty; Sherry Morrow; Dirk Nickel; Bill Ross; Greg Shea; Lori Smith.
EIN: 470786586

5056
Kiewit Companies Foundation ✧
Kiewit Plz.
3555 Farnam St.
Omaha, NE 68131-3302 (402) 342-2052
Contact: Michael L. Faust, Fdn. Admin.

FAX: (402) 943-1302;
E-mail: mike.faust@kiewit.com

Established in 1963 in NE.
Donors: Peter Kiewit Sons', Inc.; Wytana, Inc.; Big Horn Coal Co.; Kiewit Construction Group Inc.; Kiewit Diversified Group Inc.; Peter Kiewit & Sons Co.
Foundation type: Company-sponsored foundation.
Financial data (yr. ended 12/31/12): Assets, $13,081,252 (M); gifts received, $5,000,000; expenditures, $3,896,175; qualifying distributions, $3,854,527; giving activities include $3,844,889 for 211 grants (high: $500,000; low: $100).
Purpose and activities: The foundation supports organizations involved with arts and culture, higher education, youth development, human services, and community development. Special emphasis is directed toward nonprofits engaged in improving the quality of life in communities where there is a significant corporate presence.
Fields of interest: Arts; Higher education; Youth development; Human services; Community/economic development.
Type of support: General/operating support; Annual campaigns; Capital campaigns; Building/renovation; Scholarship funds.
Limitations: Applications accepted. Giving primarily in areas of company operations, with emphasis on Omaha, NE. No support for elementary or secondary schools or individual churches or similar religious groups. No grants to individuals, or for endowments.
Publications: Annual report (including application guidelines).
Application information: Application form not required.

Initial approach: Letter of inquiry
Copies of proposal: 1
Deadline(s): None
Board meeting date(s): As needed
Final notification: 1 to 3 months

Trustee: U.S. Bank, N.A.
Number of staff: None.
EIN: 476029996
Selected grants: The following grants are a representative sample of this grantmaker's funding activity:
$100,000 to Childrens Hospital and Medical Center, Omaha, NE, 2011. For Specialty Pediatric Center.
$100,000 to Omaha Community Playhouse, Omaha, NE, 2011. For information technology upgrade.
$50,000 to Durham Museum, Omaha, NE, 2011. For Abraham Lincoln exhibit.
$50,000 to Iowa State University Foundation, Ames, IA, 2011. For Student Services Center renovation project.
$50,000 to Joslyn Art Museum, Omaha, NE, 2011. For Treasury Joslyn Exhibit.
$50,000 to Omaha Symphony Association, Omaha, NE, 2011. For youth education program.
$20,000 to Arizona State University Foundation for a New American University, Tempe, AZ, 2011. For highway curriculum fund.
$10,000 to Brownell-Talbot School, Omaha, NE, 2011. For Discovery Summer Camp.
$10,000 to Skirball Cultural Center, Los Angeles, CA, 2011. For program support.
$5,000 to Prevent Cancer Foundation, Alexandria, VA, 2011. For cancer screening at state fair.

5057
Peter Kiewit Foundation ✧

1125 S. 103rd St., Ste. 500
Omaha, NE 68124-6022 (402) 344-7890
Contact: Lyn Wallin Ziegenbein, Exec. Dir.
FAX: (402) 344-8099; Main URL: http://www.peterkiewitfoundation.org/

Established in 1975 in NE.
Donor: Peter Kiewit†.
Foundation type: Independent foundation.
Financial data (yr. ended 06/30/13): Assets, $397,287,545 (M); gifts received, $346,312; expenditures, $14,845,364; qualifying distributions, $13,709,786; giving activities include $9,806,688 for 136 grants (high: $1,000,000; low: $472), $1,088,750 for grants to individuals, $275,762 for 2 foundation-administered programs and $952,259 for 1 loan/program-related investment.
Purpose and activities: Giving primarily for cultural programs, including the arts, civic affairs, community development, higher and other education, health and social service agencies, and youth programs. Contributions almost always made as challenge or matching grants.
Fields of interest: Arts; Higher education; Education; Human services; Youth, services; Community development, neighborhood development; Rural development; Community/economic development.
Type of support: General/operating support; Capital campaigns; Building/renovation; Equipment; Land acquisition; Program development; Seed money; Program-related investments/loans; Matching/challenge support.
Limitations: Applications accepted. Giving limited to Rancho Mirage, CA, western IA (within 100 miles of Omaha), NE, and Sheridan, WY. No support for elementary or secondary schools (public or private), churches, or religious groups. No grants to individuals directly or for endowment funds or annual campaigns.
Publications: Application guidelines; Annual report; Informational brochure (including application guidelines).
Application information: All applicants are required to submit the standard Peter Kiewit Foundation application form and required attachments. The form and instructions must be requested from the foundation office. Application form required.

Initial approach: Letter or telephone
Copies of proposal: 4
Deadline(s): Jan. 15, Apr. 15, July 15, and Oct. 15 for grants
Board meeting date(s): Mar., June, Sept., and Dec.
Final notification: Within quarter submitted

Officers and Trustees:* John W. Hancock,* Chair.; Jane E. Miller,* Vice-Chair.; Jeff Ziegenbein, Exec. Dir.; Mogens C. Bay; Michael L. Gallagher; G. Richard Russell; U.S. Bank, N.A.
Number of staff: 4 full-time professional; 2 full-time support.
EIN: 476098282
Selected grants: The following grants are a representative sample of this grantmaker's funding activity:
$2,200,000 to Omaha, City of, Omaha, NE, 2012. For Baseball Stadium.
$1,500,000 to Creighton University, Omaha, NE, 2012. For Capital project.
$1,000,000 to Omaha Zoo Foundation, Omaha, NE, 2012. For Capital improvements.
$1,000,000 to Omaha Zoo Foundation, Omaha, NE, 2013. For Capital support.
$600,000 to University of Nebraska Foundation, Lincoln, NE, 2013. For Capital.
$494,589 to United Way of the Midlands, Omaha, NE, 2013. For campaign support.
$350,000 to Habitat for Humanity of Omaha, Omaha, NE, 2013. For Capital.
$315,021 to Omaha, City of, Omaha, NE, 2013. For South Omaha Trail project.
$255,000 to Bemis Center for Contemporary Arts, Omaha, NE, 2012. For Capital improvements.
$250,000 to Rose Blumkin Performing Arts Center Foundation, Omaha, NE, 2013. For Program support.
$102,650 to Uta Halee Girls Village, Omaha, NE, 2012. For Program support.
$100,000 to Crisis Center for Domestic Abuse and Sexual Assault, Fremont, NE, 2013. For Capital.
$100,000 to Humane Society, Nebraska, Omaha, NE, 2012. For Program support.
$100,000 to Humane Society, Nebraska, Omaha, NE, 2013. For Program support.
$45,000 to Nebraska Methodist College of Nursing and Allied Health, Omaha, NE, 2012. For Legacy Scholarship.
$30,000 to Nebraska Wesleyan University, Lincoln, NE, 2013. For Legacy Scholarship Program.
$25,000 to Joslyn Castle Trust, Omaha, NE, 2012. For Program support.
$22,750 to Imperial Community Foundation, Imperial, NE, 2012. For Rural Emergency Grant. Funds will be used to provide food, utility assistance and housing assistance, including emergency clothing and household supplies.
$16,250 to Radio Talking Book Service, Omaha, NE, 2013. For Equipment.
$15,000 to Walnut, City of, Walnut, IA, 2012. For improvements to the park.

5058
Kim Foundation ✧

c/o Larry J. Courtnage
13609 California St., Ste. 500
Omaha, NE 68154-5245
E-mail: info@thekimfoundation.org; Main URL: http://www.thekimfoundation.org/
Blog: http://blog.thekimfoundation.org/
E-Newsletter: http://www.thekimfoundation.org/html/mh_happenings/newsletter.html
Facebook: http://www.facebook.com/pages/The-Kim-Foundation-Advocating-for-Mental-Health-Services/120739160051

Established in 2000 in NE.
Donors: Larry J. Courtnage; C&A Industries, Inc.; United Way of The Midlands.
Foundation type: Independent foundation.
Financial data (yr. ended 12/31/12): Assets, $4,398,343 (M); gifts received, $230,844; expenditures, $556,765; qualifying distributions, $538,039; giving activities include $475,500 for 17 grants (high: $300,000; low: $1,000).
Purpose and activities: Giving primarily to organizations that assist individuals with mental health difficulties.
Fields of interest: Mental health/crisis services; Health organizations; Human services; Children/youth, services.
Limitations: Applications not accepted. Giving primarily in NE.
Application information: Unsolicited requests for funds not accepted.

Officers: Larry J. Courtnage, Pres.; Kathleen A. Courtnage, V.P. and Secy.; Vicki F. Witkovski, Treas.
EIN: 470837377

5059
Richard P. Kimmel and Laurine Kimmel Charitable Foundation, Inc. ✧

8555 Executive Woods Dr., Ste. 600
Lincoln, NE 68512-9305 (402) 475-1797
Contact: Ernest L. Weyeneth, Pres.
FAX: (402) 475-3236;
E-mail: info@KimmelFoundation.org; Main
URL: http://www.kimmelfoundation.org

Established in 1988.
Foundation type: Independent foundation.
Financial data (yr. ended 12/31/12): Assets, $22,094,931 (M); expenditures, $8,431,819; qualifying distributions, $8,073,311; giving activities include $7,614,013 for 19 grants (high: $5,100,000; low: $500).
Purpose and activities: Giving primarily for: 1) Education, particularly programs of broad impact in art, agriculture and business, 2) The Arts, including the improvement of art education, appreciation and exhibition, 3) Agriculture, notably the teaching and study of significant changes that have broad effects on agricultural practices, with emphasis on horticulture, 4) Human Services, including broad community improvements that emphasize partnerships among agencies and stakeholders, eliminate duplication, and improve the awareness of human services, and 5) Humanities, with priority given to improvements in the teaching of the humanities including increased accessibility to underserved audiences. The foundation places emphasis on interdisciplinary approaches, application of new research and organizational collaboration. The foundation also supports ideas that provide leadership in a field, encourage matching grants of equal or greater size, and contribute substantially to an organization's mission and service to its constituents.
Fields of interest: Arts education; Museums (history); Humanities; Higher education; Business school/education; Horticulture/garden clubs; Agriculture/food, public education; Human services; Community development, neighborhood development.
Type of support: Capital campaigns; Fellowships; Scholarship funds; Matching/challenge support.
Limitations: Giving primarily in IA and NE, with emphasis on Nebraska City and Otoe County. No support for religious purposes, or for economic or industrial development. No grants to individuals, or for voter registration drives, travel, or testing public safety; no loans.
Publications: Application guidelines; Biennial report; Financial statement.
Application information: Application guidelines available on foundation web site. Inquires should be made well before the beginning of a project. Application form required.
Initial approach: Letter of inquiry
Copies of proposal: 1
Deadline(s): Mar. 31, June 30, Sept. 30, and Dec. 31
Board meeting date(s): Quarterly
Officers and Directors:* Ernest L. Weyeneth, Pres. and Treas.; Len Weyeneth,* V.P.; Patricia Holmes,* Secy.; William J. Carroll; Tyler Crownover.
Number of staff: 1 full-time professional; 1 full-time support; 1 part-time support.
EIN: 363617581

5060
The Kind World Foundation ✧

1125 S. 103rd St., Ste. 425
Omaha, NE 68124-6025 (402) 697-8000
Contact: Patty Killgore

Established in 1991 in SD.
Donor: Norman W. Waitt, Jr.
Foundation type: Independent foundation.
Financial data (yr. ended 12/31/12): Assets, $13,748,285 (M); expenditures, $2,201,608; qualifying distributions, $2,102,426; giving activities include $1,721,722 for 74 grants (high: $750,000; low: $300).
Purpose and activities: Giving primarily for the arts, particularly a performing arts center, education, and human services.
Fields of interest: Performing arts centers; Arts; Higher education; Education; Environment, natural resources; Children/youth, services; Family services; International relief; Foundations (community).
Type of support: General/operating support; Continuing support; Annual campaigns; Capital campaigns; Building/renovation; Equipment; Land acquisition; Endowments; Program development; Scholarship funds; Research; Consulting services; Matching/challenge support.
Limitations: Applications accepted. Giving primarily in Santa Barbara, CA, Sioux City, IA, and nationally for overseas relief programs and projects.
Application information: Application form required.
Initial approach: Letter
Deadline(s): None
Officer: Lee Lysne, Exec. Dir.
Director: Norman W. Waitt, Jr.
Number of staff: 1 full-time professional; 1 part-time professional; 1 part-time support.
EIN: 363776553

5061
Lauritzen Foundation ✧ ☆

525 First National Ctr.
Omaha, NE 68102-1500

Established in 1973 in NE.
Donor: John R. Lauritzen Marital Trust.
Foundation type: Independent foundation.
Financial data (yr. ended 12/31/13): Assets, $75,373,475 (M); gifts received, $68,151,990; expenditures, $2,205,030; qualifying distributions, $2,061,203; giving activities include $2,057,500 for 17 grants (high: $1,587,500; low: $2,000).
Fields of interest: Performing arts, theater; Arts; Higher education; Health care; United Ways and Federated Giving Programs; Protestant agencies & churches.
Limitations: Applications not accepted. Giving primarily in NE. No grants to individuals.
Application information: Unsolicited requests for funds not accepted.
Officers: Bruce R. Lauritzen, Pres.; Blair L. Gogel, V.P.; Margret L. Dodge, Secy.; Clarkson D. Lauritzen, Treas.
EIN: 237352686

5062
Lexington Community Foundation ✧ ☆

607 N. Washington St.
P.O. Box 422
Lexington, NE 68850-1915 (308) 324-6704
Contact: Jacqueline Berke, Exec. Dir.
E-mail: lexfoundation@windstream.net; Main
URL: http://www.lexfoundation.org
Facebook: http://www.facebook.com/pages/Lexington-Community-Foundation/133425550027265
Twitter: https://twitter.com/lexfoundation

Established in 1982 in NE.
Foundation type: Community foundation.
Financial data (yr. ended 12/31/13): Assets, $9,324,243 (M); gifts received, $2,177,674; expenditures, $1,125,576; giving activities include $679,160 for 64+ grants (high: $262,357), and $46,815 for 63 grants to individuals.
Purpose and activities: The foundation seeks to encourage and strengthen philanthropy in order to provide a permanent source of funding for opportunities to improve the quality of life, strengthen the sense of community, and benefit future generations in Lexington, NE.
Fields of interest: Arts; Education; Health care; Recreation, camps; Recreation; Children/youth, services; Human services; Community development, neighborhood development; Community/economic development.
Type of support: Capital campaigns; Building/renovation; Equipment; Program development; Seed money; Technical assistance; Scholarships—to individuals; Matching/challenge support.
Limitations: Applications accepted. Giving limited to the Lexington, NE, area. No support for religious activities (unless non-denominational and serving a brand segment of the population). No grants to individuals directly, or for operational expenses, debt servicing, trips, tours, camps, or endowment funds.
Publications: Application guidelines; Annual report; Financial statement; Grants list; Informational brochure; Newsletter; Program policy statement.
Application information: Visit foundation web site for application form and guidelines. Application form required.
Initial approach: Contact foundation
Copies of proposal: 1
Deadline(s): None
Board meeting date(s): 4th Mon. in Jan., Mar., May, July, Sept., and Nov.
Final notification: 1 to 2 months
Officers and Directors:* Amy Biehl-Owens,* Pres.; Tom Fagot,* V.P.; Bill Stewart,* Secy.-Treas.; Jacqueline Berke, Exec. Dir.; Rob Anderson; Audrey Beck-Racek; Dean Brand; Stephanie Buell; Dan Clark; Jill Denker; David Fairbanks; Tom Feltes; Wes Lubberstedt; Patty Mandelko; Barry McFarland; Tod McKeone; Linda Miller; Larry Reynolds; Curt Rickertson; Tempie Roberts; Mark Sarratt; Steve Smith; Dave Stenberg; Rusty Sutton; Gail Wightman; John Wightman.
Number of staff: 1 full-time professional; 1 part-time support.
EIN: 470794760

5063
Lincoln Community Foundation, Inc. ✧
(formerly Lincoln Foundation, Inc.)
215 Centennial Mall S., Ste. 100
Lincoln, NE 68508-1813 (402) 474-2345
Contact: For grants: Sarah Peetz, V.P., Community Outreach
FAX: (402) 476-8523; E-mail: lcf@lcf.org; Main URL: http://www.lcf.org
Facebook: https://www.facebook.com/LincolnCommunityFoundation
Twitter: http://twitter.com/Linc_Comm_Fdn

Incorporated in 1955 in NE.
Foundation type: Community foundation.
Financial data (yr. ended 12/31/13): Assets, $72,780,529 (M); gifts received, $21,554,709; expenditures, $7,680,290; giving activities include $5,404,377 for grants.
Purpose and activities: The foundation seeks to enrich the quality of life in the greater Lincoln, NE, area by responding to emerging and changing needs and sustaining existing organizations and institutions through grants for education, arts and culture, health, social services, economic development, and civic affairs in Lincoln/Lancaster County, NE. Primary areas of interest include family issues, children's issues, older adults, environmental enhancement, higher education, and basic needs.
Fields of interest: Arts, cultural/ethnic awareness; Museums (marine/maritime); Arts; Child development, education; Higher education; Environment; Animals/wildlife; Health care; Youth development; Child development, services; Family services; Aging, centers/services; Human services; Economic development; Public affairs; Aging.
Type of support: General/operating support; Management development/capacity building; Capital campaigns; Building/renovation; Equipment; Land acquisition; Emergency funds; Program development; Seed money; Scholarship funds; Research; Technical assistance; Consulting services; Program evaluation; Employee matching gifts; Matching/challenge support.
Limitations: Applications accepted. Giving limited to the Lincoln-Lancaster County, NE, area. No support for religious purposes. No grants to individuals (except for scholarships), or for endowments, large capital expenditures, budget deficits, or projects with long future commitments.
Publications: Application guidelines; Annual report; Financial statement; Grants list; Informational brochure (including application guidelines); Newsletter; Program policy statement.
Application information: Visit foundation web site for application forms and guidelines. Letters of inquiry will be reviewed and those receiving approval will be notified and asked to submit a full application. Application form required.
Initial approach: Telephone
Deadline(s): May 1 and Nov. 3 for letter of inquiry; June 2 and Dec. 5 for full application
Board meeting date(s): 3rd Thurs. of Feb., May, Aug., and Nov.
Final notification: Full application within 3 months of deadline
Officers and Directors:* Rich Vierk,* Chair.; Cathy Lang,* Vice-Chair.; Barbara Bartle,* Pres.; Chip DeBuse,* V.P., Devel.; Pam Hunzeker,* V.P., Mktg.; Scott Lawson,* V.P., Finance; Paula Metcalf,* V.P., Gift Planning and General Counsel; Sarah Peetz,* V.P., Community Outreach; Bill Mueller,* Secy.; Bill Cintani,* Treas.; Rich Bailey; Christi Ball; John Bergmeyer; Bob Caldwell; John Dittman; Juan Franco; Randy Haas; Dave Landis; Diane Mendenhall; William Olson; Deb Schorr; Mark Whitehead; Nancy Wiederspan; Sue Wilkinson; Hank Woods; and 9 additional directors.
Number of staff: 5 full-time professional; 5 full-time support; 1 part-time support.
EIN: 470458128

5064
Linder Family Foundation ✧
527 N. Elmwood Rd.
Omaha, NE 68132-2604 (402) 391-1065
Contact: James Linder, Pres. and Secy.

Established in 2000 in NE.
Donor: James Linder.
Foundation type: Independent foundation.
Financial data (yr. ended 12/31/13): Assets, $1,562,330 (M); gifts received, $500,000; expenditures, $523,246; qualifying distributions, $509,616; giving activities include $509,616 for 29 grants (high: $214,400; low: $100).
Fields of interest: Arts, multipurpose centers/programs; Higher education, university; United Ways and Federated Giving Programs.
Type of support: General/operating support.
Limitations: Applications accepted. Giving primarily in NE. No grants to individuals.
Application information: Application form required.
Initial approach: Letter
Deadline(s): None
Officer: James Linder, Pres. and Secy.
EIN: 470837337

5065
The Lozier Foundation ✧
c/o Barbara Molck
6336 Pershing Dr.
Omaha, NE 68110-1100 (402) 457-8160
Contact: Robert Braun, Jr., Exec. Dir.; Tre Brashear
E-mail for Robert Braun Jr.: bob.braun@lozier.biz. E-mail for Tre Brashear: tre.brashear@lozier

Established in 1986 in WA.
Donors: Allan Lozier; Dianne S. Lozier.
Foundation type: Independent foundation.
Financial data (yr. ended 12/31/13): Assets, $355,523,166 (M); gifts received, $12,750,811; expenditures, $20,140,025; qualifying distributions, $17,627,106; giving activities include $17,514,453 for 186 grants (high: $8,700,000; low: $250), and $91,250 for 37 grants to individuals (high: $2,500; low: $1,250).
Purpose and activities: Grants are made primarily for higher education, domestic violence prevention, human and youth services, women centers, homeless, minorities, and the economically disadvantaged.
Fields of interest: Higher education; Crime/violence prevention, domestic violence; Human services; Youth, services; Women, centers/services; Homeless, human services; Minorities; Women; Girls; Economically disadvantaged; Homeless.
Type of support: General/operating support; Continuing support; Annual campaigns; Capital campaigns; Building/renovation; Employee matching gifts; Matching/challenge support.
Limitations: Applications not accepted. Giving limited to the immediate Omaha, NE, area, with an emphasis on the inner city. No support for the arts. No grants to individuals (except for scholarships), and, generally, no grants for endowments.
Application information: Unsolicited requests for funds not accepted.
Board meeting date(s): Six times a year, in odd months.
Officer and Trustees: Robert Braun, Jr., Exec. Dir.; Vickey Kleinsmith; Allan Lozier; Dianne Lozier; Sandy Lozier; Susan Lozier.
EIN: 943027928
Selected grants: The following grants are a representative sample of this grantmaker's funding activity:
$2,000,000 to College of Saint Mary, Omaha, NE, 2012. For Remodel of Walsh Hall to provide for new medical teaching labs and classrooms, payable over 3.00 years.
$2,000,000 to Heartland Family Service, Omaha, NE, 2012. For Capital Campaign for Family Works and the former St. Richards campus, payable over 4.00 years.
$1,394,900 to Building Bright Futures, Omaha, NE, 2012. For 2013 general operating support plus contracted programs.
$1,019,350 to Omaha Schools Foundation, Omaha, NE, 2012. For OPS Summer Phonics Program with the balance going to UNO for their Career Ladder in Reading Program, payable over 2.00 years.
$1,000,000 to Childrens Respite Care Center, Omaha, NE, 2012. For capital campaign, payable over 3.00 years.
$425,000 to Habitat for Humanity of Omaha, Omaha, NE, 2012. For Capital Campaign, payable over 2.00 years.
$250,000 to Rebuilding Together Omaha, Omaha, NE, 2012. For Roof Replacement Program, payable over 4.00 years.
$50,000 to Family Housing Advisory Services, Omaha, NE, 2012. For 2012 General Operating Support.
$25,000 to Boys and Girls Clubs of the Midlands, Omaha, NE, 2012. For 2012 general operating support plus $25,000 to help start a reading program.
$16,800 to Catholic Charities of the Archdiocese of Omaha, Omaha, NE, 2012. For general operating support for The Shelter and the Latina Resource Center.

5066
Mapes Charitable Trust ✧ ☆
c/o Wells Fargo Bank Iowa, N.A.
1919 Douglas St., 2nd Fl., MAC N8000-0027
Omaha, NE 68102-1317

Established in 1996 in IA.
Donor: Mapes Charitable Trust.
Foundation type: Independent foundation.
Financial data (yr. ended 12/31/13): Assets, $7,366,084 (M); expenditures, $539,798; qualifying distributions, $451,560; giving activities include $430,000 for 9 grants (high: $125,000; low: $10,000).
Purpose and activities: Giving for education, as well as orphaned and injured wildlife.
Fields of interest: Higher education; Animal welfare; Animals/wildlife, preservation/protection; Protestant agencies & churches.
Limitations: Applications not accepted. Giving primarily in IA. No grants to individuals.
Application information: Contributes only to pre-selected organizations.

Trustees: Irving Stone; Wells Fargo Bank Iowa, N.A.
EIN: 426543426

5067
Merrick Foundation, Inc. ✧
1532 17th Ave.
P.O. Box 206
Central City, NE 68826 (308) 946-3707
Contact: Chuck Griffith, Exec. Dir.; Michelle Carroll, Acct.
E-mail: merrickfoundation@gmail.com; Main URL: http://www.merrick-foundation.org

Established in 1960 in NE.
Foundation type: Community foundation.
Financial data (yr. ended 10/31/13): Assets, $15,359,069 (M); gifts received, $215,835; expenditures, $745,733; giving activities include $370,411 for 7+ grants (high: $45,000), and $112,590 for 152 grants to individuals.
Purpose and activities: The foundation seeks to contribute to the growth of the quality of life in Merrick County by directing charitable funds to achieve the maximum benefits for the community's residents.
Fields of interest: Arts; Education; Environment; Health care; Recreation; Human services; Community/economic development; Public affairs; Children; Adults; Young adults; Disabilities, people with.
Type of support: Capital campaigns; Endowments; Scholarships—to individuals.
Limitations: Applications accepted. Giving limited to Merrick County, NE. No support for religious purposes. No grants to individuals (except for scholarships).
Publications: Annual report; Financial statement.
Application information: Visit foundation web site for application form and guidelines. Application form required.
Initial approach: Submit application form and attachments
Copies of proposal: 6
Deadline(s): 1st Mon. of every month, except Dec.
Board meeting date(s): 4th Mon. of every month, except Dec.
Final notification: Within 1 month
Officers and Board Members:* Sean Wagner,* Pres.; Chuck Griffith,* Exec. Dir.; Dave Beck; Teri Beck; Kim Benner; Brian Buhlke; Lori Cave; Adam Clarke; Ed Dexter; Kathy Dubas; Bob Eversoll; Michelle Kohl; Carol Quandt; Randy Rinkol; Robb Schnitzler; D. Jay Wolfe.
Number of staff: 2 full-time professional; 1 part-time professional; 1 part-time support.
EIN: 476024770

5068
Mid-Nebraska Community Foundation, Inc. ✧
120 N. Dewey
P.O. Box 1321
North Platte, NE 69101 (308) 534-3315
Contact: Eric Seacrest, Exec. Dir.
FAX: (308) 534-6117; E-mail: mncf@hamilton.net; Main URL: http://www.midnebraskafoundation.org

Established in 1978 in NE.
Foundation type: Community foundation.
Financial data (yr. ended 05/31/13): Assets, $22,346,610 (M); gifts received, $1,124,238; expenditures, $1,274,789; giving activities include $823,197 for 17 grants (high: $175,021), and $185,912 for 127 grants to individuals.
Purpose and activities: The foundation seeks to enhance the quality of life in the mid-Nebraska area by providing a vehicle for the pooling of financial resources and wisely managing those resources to allow the making of grants for present and future charitable purposes. The foundation is interested in supporting innovative solutions to community problems, including collaborative efforts.
Fields of interest: Arts; Elementary/secondary education; Education; Environment; Health care; Human services; Community/economic development.
Type of support: Scholarships—to individuals; Capital campaigns; Building/renovation; Equipment; Land acquisition; Program development; Conferences/seminars; Seed money; Curriculum development.
Limitations: Applications accepted. Giving primarily limited to Custer, Dawson, Frontier, Hayes, Keith, Lincoln, Logan, McPherson and Perkins counties, NE. No support for religious organizations for religious activities, or for-profit organizations. No grants to individuals (except through designated scholarship funds), or for current operating budgets or deficit financing.
Publications: Application guidelines; Annual report; Financial statement; Informational brochure; Occasional report.
Application information: Visit foundation web site for application information. Scholarship applications generally available only through area school counselors, except for non-traditional students or for college students from the North Platte area. Application form required.
Initial approach: 1-page letter of inquiry or telephone for grants; complete current application form for scholarships
Copies of proposal: 1
Deadline(s): Jan. 15, Apr. 15, July 15, and Oct. 15
Board meeting date(s): Quarterly
Final notification: Approx. 45 days after deadline
Officers and Directors:* Bob Spady,* Pres.; John A. Patterson,* V.P.; J. Patrick Keenan,* Secy.-Treas.; Eric Seacrest, Exec. Dir.; Gary D. Byrne; Olivia Conrad; Alan J. Erickson; Jo Anne Grady; Dr. Todd E. Hlavaty; Mary Lynn Horst; Don Kilgore; Connie Klemm; Jim McClymont; Cynthia D. Norman; Sam Perry, M.D.; Brenda Robinson; Charlene Schneider; Betty Sones; Jean States; Larry Stobbs; Mary Thompson; Glenn Van Velson; Dorothy Wycoff; and 2 additional directors.
Number of staff: 1 full-time professional; 2 full-time support.
EIN: 470604965

5069
Moglia Family Foundation ✧
1302 N. 138th St.
Omaha, NE 68154-5102

Established in 2007 in NE.
Donor: Joseph Moglia.
Foundation type: Independent foundation.
Financial data (yr. ended 03/31/13): Assets, $49,027,530 (M); gifts received, $6,876,491; expenditures, $1,973,195; qualifying distributions, $1,965,140; giving activities include $1,940,640 for 191 grants (high: $200,000; low: $100).
Purpose and activities: Giving primarily for education and health organizations.
Fields of interest: Elementary/secondary education; Higher education; Education; Health organizations, association; Children/youth, services; Foundations (private grantmaking).
Limitations: Applications not accepted. Giving primarily in IL and NE.
Application information: Contributes only to pre-selected organizations.
Trustee: Joseph Moglia.
EIN: 356766677
Selected grants: The following grants are a representative sample of this grantmaker's funding activity:
$250,000 to Creighton University, Omaha, NE, 2011.
$100,000 to Archmere Academy, Claymont, DE, 2011.
$100,000 to Chicago Hope Academy, Chicago, IL, 2011.
$25,000 to Big Brothers Big Sisters of Greater Kansas City, Kansas City, MO, 2011.
$25,000 to Big Brothers Big Sisters of the Midlands, Omaha, NE, 2011.
$20,000 to Donors Trust, Omaha, NE, 2011.
$15,000 to Omaha Community Foundation, Omaha, NE, 2011.
$10,000 to TeamMates Mentoring Program, Lincoln, NE, 2011.
$10,000 to United Way of the Midlands, Omaha, NE, 2011.
$5,000 to University of Nebraska Foundation, Lincoln, NE, 2011.

5070
G. Robert Muchemore Foundation ✧
c/o First National Bank of Omaha
1620 Dodge St.
Omaha, NE 68197-1081

Established in 1998 in NE.
Donor: Agnes B. Muchemore†.
Foundation type: Independent foundation.
Financial data (yr. ended 12/31/13): Assets, $14,230,722 (M); expenditures, $630,853; qualifying distributions, $578,444; giving activities include $572,619 for 4 grants (high: $271,428; low: $21,500).
Purpose and activities: Giving primarily to universities for scholarship funds.
Fields of interest: Higher education; Scholarships/financial aid; Boys & girls clubs.
Type of support: Scholarship funds.
Limitations: Applications not accepted. Giving primarily in Omaha, NE; some funding also in Ames, IA. No grants to individuals.
Application information: Contributes only to pre-selected organizations.
Officers: Harold Kosowsky, Pres.; John Maginn, V.P.; Kathy Callahan, Secy.-Treas.
Director: J. Terry MacNamara.
EIN: 911781660
Selected grants: The following grants are a representative sample of this grantmaker's funding activity:
$196,002 to University of Nebraska Foundation, Omaha, NE, 2011. For scholarships.
$38,834 to Iowa State University Foundation, Ames, IA, 2011. For scholarships.

5071
Mutual of Omaha Foundation ✧
Mutual of Omaha Plz.
Omaha, NE 68175-0002 (866) 663-5665
Contact: Christine Johnson, Pres. and Secy.
E-mail: mutualofomaha.foundation@mutualofomaha.com; Main URL: http://www.mutualofomahafoundation.org
Facebook: http://www.facebook.com/mutualofomahafoundation?ref=ts
Grants List: http://www.mutualofomahafoundation.org/documents/2014_year_end.pdf
Twitter: https://twitter.com/MutualFdn

Established in 2005.
Donor: Mutual of Omaha Insurance Co.
Foundation type: Company-sponsored foundation.
Financial data (yr. ended 12/31/13): Assets, $65,180,294 (M); gifts received, $16,500,000; expenditures, $3,416,694; qualifying distributions, $3,402,674; giving activities include $3,402,674 for 128 grants (high: $327,329; low: $25).
Purpose and activities: The foundation supports programs designed to break the cycle of poverty. Special emphasis is directed toward programs designed to prevent and end homelessness; increase self-sufficiency; increase educational achievement; and prevent and end violence.
Fields of interest: Education, early childhood education; Secondary school/education; Education, drop-out prevention; Education; Mental health/crisis services; Crime/violence prevention, youth; Food services; Food banks; Children, services; Family services; Family services, domestic violence; Human services, financial counseling; Homeless, human services; Human services; United Ways and Federated Giving Programs.
Type of support: General/operating support; Capital campaigns; Building/renovation; Emergency funds; Program development; Employee volunteer services; Employee matching gifts; In-kind gifts; Matching/challenge support.
Limitations: Applications accepted. Giving primarily in areas of company operations in Council Bluffs, IA and Omaha, NE. No support for religious or sectarian organizations, social clubs, fraternal organizations, or political organizations or candidates. No grants to individuals, or for tickets and tables, endowment funds, travel, team sponsorships or athletic scholarships, civic or commemorative advertising, festivals, monuments or memorials.
Publications: Application guidelines; Grants list; Informational brochure.
Application information: Applicants are encouraged to apply early. Support is limited to 1 contribution per organization during any given year. Organizations receiving support are asked to submit a final report. Application form required.
Initial approach: Complete online application
Deadline(s): See website for deadline
Board meeting date(s): Quarterly
Final notification: Up to 90 days
Officers and Directors:* Christine D. Johnson,* Pres. and Secy.; Richard A. Witt,* V.P.; Laura Fender,* Treas.; Richard C. Anderi; Michelle Lebens; Jeffrey R. Schmid; Dana Washington.
EIN: 202176636

5072
Nelnet Foundation ✧
121 S. 13th St., Ste. 201
Lincoln, NE 68508-1911 (402) 458-3024
Main URL: http://www.nelnet.com/GiveBack/

Established in 2005 in NE.
Donor: Nelnet, Inc.
Foundation type: Company-sponsored foundation.
Financial data (yr. ended 12/31/13): Assets, $8,879,492 (M); gifts received, $2,041,760; expenditures, $1,617,548; qualifying distributions, $1,573,816; giving activities include $1,570,813 for 186 grants (high: $500,002; low: $60).
Purpose and activities: The foundation supports programs designed to expand educational possibilities for youth and adults and awards college scholarships to high school seniors.
Fields of interest: Secondary school/education; Higher education; Scholarships/financial aid; Education; Youth development, business; American Red Cross; United Ways and Federated Giving Programs; Youth.
Type of support: Scholarship funds; General/operating support; Annual campaigns; Employee matching gifts; Employee-related scholarships; Scholarships—to individuals.
Limitations: Applications accepted. Giving on a national basis in areas of company operations, with emphasis on NE.
Publications: Application guidelines.
Application information: Application form required.
Initial approach: Contact foundation for application form
Deadline(s): None
Officers: Ben Kiser, Pres.; Edward P. Martinez, Secy.; Jim Kruger, V.P. and Treas.
Directors: James P. Abel; Steve Butterfield; William Cintani; Michael S. Dunlap; Kathy Farrell; Terry J. Heimes; Thomas E. Henning; Jeff Noordhoek; Kimberly Rath; Michael D. Reardon.
EIN: 202202134
Selected grants: The following grants are a representative sample of this grantmaker's funding activity:
$25,000 to Imagine America Foundation, Washington, DC, 2012. For The provide scholarships for higher education.

5073
Donald E. Nielsen Foundation, Inc. ✧ ☆
P.O. Box 62
Oakland, NE 68045-0062
Application address: c/o Clarence E. Mock, Pres., 307 N. Oakland Ave., Oakland, NE 68045, tel.: (402) 372-5166

Established in 2005.
Donors: Donald Nielsen; Robert Prinz; Ulrich Cattle, Inc.; Donald E. Nielsen Revocable Trust.
Foundation type: Independent foundation.
Financial data (yr. ended 08/31/13): Assets, $15,641,804 (M); gifts received, $431,238; expenditures, $676,987; qualifying distributions, $558,674; giving activities include $558,674 for 17 grants (high: $125,000; low: $500).
Fields of interest: Crime/law enforcement; Recreation, centers.
Limitations: Applications accepted. Giving primarily in NE.
Application information:
Initial approach: Contact foundation Pres.
Deadline(s): None
Officers and Directors:* Clarence E. Mock,* Pres.; Sara A. Neilson,* V.P.; Harold L. Baldwin,* Secy.-Treas.
EIN: 202629290

5074
Omaha Community Foundation ✧
302 S. 36th St., Ste. 100
Omaha, NE 68131-3845 (402) 342-3458
Contact: Sara Boyd, C.E.O.
FAX: (402) 342-3582;
E-mail: info@omahafoundation.org; Additional tel.: (800) 794-3458; additional e-mail: sarah@omahafoundation.org; Main URL: http://www.omahafoundation.org
Facebook: https://www.facebook.com/omahafoundation
LinkedIn: http://www.linkedin.com/companies/omaha-community-foundation
Program Connect: http://omahafoundation.org/contact/program-connect/
Twitter: https://twitter.com/#!/omahafoundation

Established in 1982 in NE.
Foundation type: Community foundation.
Financial data (yr. ended 12/31/12): Assets, $654,375,931 (M); gifts received, $61,062,211; expenditures, $89,072,273; giving activities include $75,638,463 for grants.
Purpose and activities: The foundation seeks to build enduring charitable partnerships that make the community better. Support primarily for cultural programs, education, neighborhood development, civic affairs, health, and social services, and programs for women.
Fields of interest: Arts; Education; Health care; Health organizations, association; Children/youth, services; Human services; Community/economic development; Government/public administration; General charitable giving; Youth; African Americans/Blacks; Hispanics/Latinos.
Type of support: General/operating support; Continuing support; Management development/capacity building; Building/renovation; Equipment; Emergency funds; Program development; Conferences/seminars; Publication; Seed money; Scholarship funds; Technical assistance; Matching/challenge support.
Limitations: Applications accepted. Giving primarily in the metropolitan Omaha, NE, area including southwest IA. No support for the direct support of religious activities. No grants to individuals, or for new small businesses established for personal gain or profit, annual fund drives, capital campaigns, deficit or endowment.
Publications: Application guidelines; Annual report; Grants list; Informational brochure; Newsletter; Occasional report; Quarterly report.
Application information: Visit foundation web site for application form and guidelines. Handwritten grant applications are not accepted; training sessions on filling out OCF's online application are held approximately 3-6 weeks before upcoming deadlines. Application form required.
Initial approach: Contact foundation
Copies of proposal: 1
Deadline(s): Mar. 1 and Sept. 1
Board meeting date(s): Mar., June, Sept., and Dec.
Final notification: May and Nov.
Officers and Directors:* Todd D. Simon,* Chair.; Constance M. Ryan,* Vice-Chair.; Sara Boyd, C.E.O. and Pres.; Mark Weber,* Secy.; Melisa Sunde,

C.F.O.; Mary S. Jones,* Treas.; Robert D. Bates; Steve Baumert; Mike Cassling; Cristina Castro-Matukewicz; Tim L. Clark; Patrick J. Corrigan; Jeff Gordman; Jennifer Hamann; Carey Hamilton; Sharon R. Kresha; Janet Melchior-Kopp; Thomas K. Nichting; Thomas R. Pansing, Jr.; John A. Scott; Jeffrey L. Snyder; Thomas H. Warren, Sr.; Katie Weitz.
Number of staff: 9 full-time professional; 7 full-time support.
EIN: 470645958
Selected grants: The following grants are a representative sample of this grantmaker's funding activity:
$21,550,000 to University of Nebraska Foundation, Omaha, NE, 2012.
$7,245,729 to University of Nebraska Foundation, Omaha, NE, 2012.
$4,600,000 to Creighton University, Omaha, NE, 2012.
$500,000 to Joslyn Art Museum, Omaha, NE, 2012.
$500,000 to Omaha Church Center, Omaha, NE, 2012.
$300,000 to Building Bright Futures, Omaha, NE, 2012.
$250,000 to KANEKO, Omaha, NE, 2012.
$3,000 to Brownville Concert Series, Auburn, NE, 2012.
$2,500 to Salvation Army of Omaha, Omaha, NE, 2012.
$2,100 to Malvern Public Library, Friends of, Malvern, IA, 2012.

5075
Phelps County Community Foundation, Inc. ✧

504 4th Ave.
Holdrege, NE 68949 (308) 995-6847
Contact: Vickie Klein, Exec. Dir.
FAX: (308) 995-2146;
E-mail: vlpccf@phelpsfoundation.org; Main URL: http://www.phelpsfoundation.org
Facebook: https://www.facebook.com/pages/Phelps-County-Community-Foundation/248896181849368
Twitter: https://twitter.com/TheFoundation37
E-mail for L. Chapman: lcpccf@phelpsfoundation.org

Incorporated in 1976 in NE.
Foundation type: Community foundation.
Financial data (yr. ended 06/30/13): Assets, $13,843,311 (M); gifts received, $1,239,331; expenditures, $1,017,991; giving activities include $602,221 for 71+ grants (high: $70,414), and $175,359 for 82 grants to individuals.
Purpose and activities: The foundation seeks to encourage and provide opportunities for charitable giving, to manage and distribute the funds in a responsible manner, and to enhance the quality of life for the people of Phelps County, NE.
Fields of interest: Performing arts; Arts; Education; Health care; Recreation; Youth, services; Human services; Community/economic development.
Type of support: General/operating support; Continuing support; Building/renovation; Equipment; Emergency funds; Program development; Publication; Seed money; Scholarship funds; Matching/challenge support.
Limitations: Applications accepted. Giving limited to the Phelps County, NE, area. No support for religious organizations for religious purposes. No grants to individuals (except for scholarships), or for annual campaigns, deficit financing, land acquisition, endowments, program support, research, demonstration projects, travel, or conferences and seminars.
Publications: Application guidelines; Financial statement; Grants list; Informational brochure; Newsletter.
Application information: Visit foundation web site for application information. Applicants are encouraged to meet with the Exec. Dir. prior to submission of application. Application form required.
Initial approach: Letter or telephone
Copies of proposal: 8
Deadline(s): Apr. 1 and Oct. 1; Feb. 18 for scholarships
Board meeting date(s): 1st Thurs. of each month
Final notification: May and Nov.
Officers and Directors:* Sandy Kraus,* Pres.; Chris Erickson,* V.P.; Nancy Ecklun,* Secy.; Scott Latter,* Treas.; Vickie Klein, Exec. Dir.; Jeff Cox, Counsel; Kyle Anderson; Jeff Buettner; Sue Gustafson; Tim Gustafson; Beverly Hansen; Nancy Morse; Sue Waller; Vicki Westcott.
Number of staff: 1 full-time professional; 2 full-time support.
EIN: 510189077
Selected grants: The following grants are a representative sample of this grantmaker's funding activity:
$77,000 to Give 2 Grow, NE, 2012.
$21,700 to Funk School Community Center, Funk, NE, 2012. To replace boiler with furnace.
$20,000 to Bertrand Community School, Bertrand, NE, 2012. For concession and handicap restroom project.
$20,000 to Bertrand, Village of, Emergency Unit, Bertrand, NE, 2012.
$20,000 to Loomis Public Schools, Loomis, NE, 2012. For technology project.
$17,500 to Holdrege Memorial Homes, Holdrege, NE, 2012. For library renovations and upgrade.
$6,650 to Tassel Performing Arts Center, Holdrege, NE, 2012. For live theater project.

5076
Edward & Lida Robinson Charitable Trust ✧

P.O. Box 241021
Omaha, NE 68124-5021

Established in 1995 in NE.
Foundation type: Independent foundation.
Financial data (yr. ended 12/31/13): Assets, $50,595,191 (M); expenditures, $559,510; qualifying distributions, $549,924; giving activities include $538,750 for 88 grants (high: $125,000; low: $48).
Purpose and activities: Giving primarily for education, and health and human services.
Fields of interest: Higher education; Education; Health organizations; Human services; Children/youth, services.
Limitations: Applications not accepted. Giving primarily in NE, with emphasis on Omaha. No grants to individuals.
Application information: Contributes only to pre-selected organizations.
Trustees: Sherry Rathbun; James Roubal.
EIN: 470767603

5077
Rogers Foundation ✧

1311 M St., Ste. A
Lincoln, NE 68508-2539 (402) 477-3725
Contact: Rex A. Marquart, Pres.

Established in 1954 in NE.
Donor: Richard H. Rogers†.
Foundation type: Independent foundation.
Financial data (yr. ended 12/31/13): Assets, $11,230,180 (M); expenditures, $600,914; qualifying distributions, $561,669; giving activities include $544,609 for 59 grants (high: $30,000; low: $9).
Purpose and activities: Giving primarily for programs that fulfill immediate and practical needs of the community.
Fields of interest: Performing arts; Health organizations, association; Food banks; Human services; Children/youth, services.
Limitations: Applications accepted. Giving primarily in Lincoln and Lancaster County, NE.
Publications: Application guidelines.
Application information: Application form required.
Initial approach: Proposal
Deadline(s): None
Officers: Rex Marquart, Pres. and Treas.; Kuulei M. Marquart, V.P. and Secy.; Mary Kay Jones, V.P.
EIN: 476026897
Selected grants: The following grants are a representative sample of this grantmaker's funding activity:
$25,000 to Bright Lights, Lincoln, NE, 2011.
$25,000 to University of Nebraska Foundation, Lincoln, NE, 2011.
$20,000 to Food Bank of Lincoln, Lincoln, NE, 2011.
$20,000 to Madonna Foundation, Lincoln, NE, 2011.
$20,000 to Tabitha Foundation, Lincoln, NE, 2011.
$15,000 to Alzheimers Association, Lincoln, NE, 2011.
$15,000 to American Red Cross, Lincoln, NE, 2011.
$15,000 to Lincoln Symphony Orchestra, Lincoln, NE, 2011.
$10,000 to Good Neighbor Community Center, Lincoln, NE, 2011.
$8,000 to Lincoln Municipal Band Association, Lincoln, NE, 2011.

5078
The Ryan Foundation ✧

P.O. Box 45625
Omaha, NE 68145-0625
Contact: Wayne L. Ryan, Dir.

Established in 1990 in NE.
Donors: Wayne L. Ryan; Eileen Ryan.
Foundation type: Independent foundation.
Financial data (yr. ended 12/31/13): Assets, $2,510,483 (M); gifts received, $2,500,000; expenditures, $1,960,230; qualifying distributions, $1,957,000; giving activities include $1,957,000 for 32 grants (high: $1,800,000; low: $100).
Fields of interest: Higher education; Education; Human services; Catholic agencies & churches.
Limitations: Applications accepted. Giving primarily in NE.
Application information: Application form required.
Initial approach: Proposal
Deadline(s): None

Directors: Carol Ryan; Constance Ryan; Stacy Ryan; Steve Ryan; Tim Ryan; Wayne L. Ryan.
EIN: 363755606

5079
Phillip and Terri Schrager Foundation ✧
(formerly Phillip Schrager Foundation)
4405 S. 96th St.
Omaha, NE 68127-1283

Established in 1972 in NE.
Donors: Phillip G. Schrager; Terri Schrager; The Pacesetter Corp.
Foundation type: Independent foundation.
Financial data (yr. ended 12/31/13): Assets, $9,937,510 (M); expenditures, $1,811,587; qualifying distributions, $1,759,215; giving activities include $1,759,215 for 54 grants (high: $1,550,000; low: $70).
Fields of interest: Higher education; Education; Jewish federated giving programs; Jewish agencies & synagogues.
Limitations: Applications not accepted. Giving primarily in Omaha, NE. No grants to individuals.
Application information: Contributes only to pre-selected organizations.
Officers and Directors:* Terri L. Schrager, Pres.; Jeffrey Schrager, V.P.; Angela Goldman,* Secy.; Harley Schrager,* Treas.; Janet Farber, Exec. Dir.; Jack Schrager; Richard A. Schrager; Timothy Schrager.
EIN: 237184025
Selected grants: The following grants are a representative sample of this grantmaker's funding activity:
$10,000 to United Way of the Midlands, Omaha, NE, 2012. For exempt charitable purposes.

5080
Scoular Foundation ✧
2027 Dodge St., Ste. 300
Omaha, NE 68102-1229
Main URL: http://www.scoular.com/about/community-involvement/

Established in 1967 in NE.
Donor: The Scoular Co.
Foundation type: Company-sponsored foundation.
Financial data (yr. ended 05/31/14): Assets, $594 (M); gifts received, $677,991; expenditures, $678,232; qualifying distributions, $678,232; giving activities include $678,232 for 146 grants (high: $76,650; low: $100).
Purpose and activities: The foundation supports organizations involved with arts and culture, education, public health, and children and youth.
Fields of interest: Museums (art); Performing arts, theater; Arts; Secondary school/education; Higher education; Education; Health care, clinics/centers; Public health; Boy scouts; American Red Cross; Salvation Army; Children/youth, services.
Type of support: General/operating support; Annual campaigns; Capital campaigns; Building/renovation; Equipment; Program development; Scholarship funds; Sponsorships; Matching/challenge support.
Limitations: Applications not accepted. Giving limited to areas of company operations in IA, KS, MN, MO, Omaha, NE, and SC. No grants to individuals.
Application information: Unsolicited requests for funds not accepted.
Trustees: Roger L. Barber; David M. Faith; Marshall E. Faith.
EIN: 363323189
Selected grants: The following grants are a representative sample of this grantmaker's funding activity:
$81,250 to Hope Center, Omaha, NE, 2011.
$46,431 to United Way of the Midlands, Omaha, NE, 2011.
$21,525 to Habitat for Humanity of Omaha, Omaha, NE, 2011.
$20,000 to Boy Scouts of America, Omaha, NE, 2011.
$18,750 to Salina Community Theater, Salina, KS, 2011.
$10,000 to Bellevue University, Bellevue, NE, 2011.
$10,000 to Hidaya Foundation, Santa Clara, CA, 2011.
$10,000 to Project Interfaith, Omaha, NE, 2011.
$6,000 to Emerging Terrain, Omaha, NE, 2011.
$5,650 to American Heart Association, Omaha, NE, 2011.

5081
The Sherwood Foundation ✧
(formerly The Susan A. Buffett Foundation)
3555 Farnam St.
Omaha, NE 68131-3302 (402) 341-1717
FAX: (402) 341-0972;
E-mail: info@sherwoodfoundation.org; For information regarding human service, social justice or national initiatives contact Kristin Williams, e-mail: kristin@sherwoodfoundation.org; For information regarding primary educational initiatives contact Katie Weitz White, e-mail: katie@sherwoodfoundation.org; For information regarding secondary education initiatives contact Jerry Bexten, e-mail: jerry@sherwoodfoundation.org; Main URL: http://www.sherwoodfoundation.org/

Established in 1999 in NE.
Donor: Warren E. Buffett.
Foundation type: Independent foundation.
Financial data (yr. ended 12/31/13): Assets, $184,904,318 (M); gifts received, $140,552,021; expenditures, $105,409,887; qualifying distributions, $105,044,614; giving activities include $101,964,342 for 420 grants (high: $15,101,100; low: $150).
Purpose and activities: The foundation is committed to improving child and family welfare through community investments in the following areas: public education, human services and social justice.
Fields of interest: Performing arts, theater; Arts; Higher education, college; Girls clubs; Human services; Children/youth, services; United Ways and Federated Giving Programs.
Type of support: General/operating support.
Limitations: Applications accepted. Giving primarily in Omaha, NE. No support for political candidates, campaigns or organizations, or for organizations that discriminate in hiring staff and/or providing services on the basis of race, religion, gender, sexual orientation, age or disability; no support for organizations that are not established and current 501c (3) organizations. No grants to individuals.
Publications: Application guidelines.
Application information: Organizations may apply for more than one category of funding. If you are an employee of the Omaha Public Schools, you must attach a letter of approval from the District before submitting an application. Please see foundation's web site for additional information and application requirements.
Initial approach: Online application
Deadline(s): Feb. 15th for Operating Grants; Aug. 15th for Program/Project Grants and Capital Grants;
Final notification: E-mail notification within 90 days of the deadline
Officers and Directors:* Susan A. Buffett,* Chair.; Richard Putnam, Secy. and Legal Counsel; Howard Buffett; Wallace Weitz; Roberta Wilhelm.
Number of staff: 1 full-time professional; 1 part-time professional; 2 part-time support.
EIN: 470824755
Selected grants: The following grants are a representative sample of this grantmaker's funding activity:
$5,025,888 to Buffett Early Childhood Fund, Omaha, NE, 2012. For operating support.
$5,007,900 to Buffett Early Childhood Fund, Omaha, NE, 2012. For operating support.
$3,032,210 to Jim Casey Youth Opportunities Initiative, Saint Louis, MO, 2012. For operating support.
$2,044,664 to Minnesota Humanities Center, Saint Paul, MN, 2012. For Omaha Public Schools Cultural Proficiency Project.
$2,008,704 to Omaha Theater Company for Young People, Omaha, NE, 2012. For Capital Campaign.
$986,812 to Omaha Schools Foundation, Omaha, NE, 2012. For OPS Library Services.
$50,000 to Omaha Public Library Foundation, Omaha, NE, 2012. For additional funding.
$40,000 to Lutheran Family Services of Nebraska, Omaha, NE, 2012. For operating support.
$25,000 to Womens Fund of Greater Omaha, Omaha, NE, 2012. For Excellence Award.
$20,000 to Omaha Symphony Association, Omaha, NE, 2012. For operating support.

5082
The Todd and Betiana Simon Foundation ✧
11030 O St.
Omaha, NE 68137-2346

Established in 2004 in NE.
Donor: Omaha Steaks International, Inc.
Foundation type: Company-sponsored foundation.
Financial data (yr. ended 12/31/13): Assets, $2,963,376 (M); gifts received, $6,000; expenditures, $668,100; qualifying distributions, $644,629; giving activities include $644,629 for 57 grants (high: $198,000; low: $70).
Purpose and activities: The foundation supports organizations involved with arts and culture, education, family planning, and youth services.
Fields of interest: Arts; Health care; Religion.
Limitations: Applications not accepted. Giving primarily in Omaha, NE; some giving in CA and NY. No grants to individuals.
Application information: Contributes only to pre-selected organizations.
Officers: Todd D. Simon, Pres. and Treas.; Joanna French, V.P.; Barbara Goldstein, Secy.
EIN: 470820673
Selected grants: The following grants are a representative sample of this grantmaker's funding activity:

$198,000 to United States Artists, Los Angeles, CA, 2012. To provide Support for Artists.
$37,500 to Big Brothers Big Sisters of the Midlands, Omaha, NE, 2012. To provide Support of Helping Children Reach Full Potential.
$30,000 to Film Streams, Omaha, NE, 2012. To support Film As Art Exhibitions.
$30,000 to Planned Parenthood of the Heartland, Omaha, NE, 2012. For Reproductive Health Care and Sexual Education.
$25,000 to Bemis Center for Contemporary Arts, Omaha, NE, 2012. To support Artists-In-Residence Program.
$21,000 to Omaha Conservatory of Music, Omaha, NE, 2012. To support Musical Development Programs for Youth.
$10,450 to Partnership for Our Kids, Omaha, NE, 2012. For Fund Career Exploration Academy for South Omaha.
$10,000 to Omaha Community Playhouse, Omaha, NE, 2012. To underwrite 21 and Over Alternative Programming.
$6,020 to Boys and Girls Clubs of the Midlands, Omaha, NE, 2012. To support Youth Development Programs.
$5,000 to Alliance of Artists Communities, Providence, RI, 2012. To provide Support for Artists Communities.

5083
Slosburg Family Charitable Trust ✧

10040 Regency Cir., Ste. 200
Omaha, NE 68114-3734 (402) 391-7900
Contact: D. David Slosburg, Tr.

Established in 1996 in NE.
Donors: Richard H. Slosburg; D. David Slosburg; Jacob Slosburg; Rachel Slosburg Kramer; Elliot Street Investments, Ltd.
Foundation type: Independent foundation.
Financial data (yr. ended 12/31/13): Assets, $1,537,793 (M); gifts received, $846,096; expenditures, $2,899,211; qualifying distributions, $2,871,113; giving activities include $2,870,462 for 84 grants (high: $789,911; low: $50).
Purpose and activities: Giving for Jewish agencies, medical and health agencies, art and higher education.
Fields of interest: Arts; Higher education; Health care; Health organizations, association; Community/economic development; Foundations (private grantmaking); Jewish federated giving programs; Jewish agencies & synagogues.
Limitations: Applications accepted. Giving primarily in NE; some giving in PA.
Application information: Application form required.
Initial approach: Letter
Deadline(s): None
Trustees: D. David Slosburg; Richard H. Slosburg.
EIN: 470798965
Selected grants: The following grants are a representative sample of this grantmaker's funding activity:
$375,000 to University of Pennsylvania, Philadelphia, PA, 2011.
$275,898 to Omaha Symphony Association, Omaha, NE, 2011.
$125,000 to Omaha Performing Arts Center, Omaha, NE, 2011.
$100,000 to Behavioral Health Support Foundation, Omaha, NE, 2011.

5084
Sokolof Grandchildren Charitable Foundation ✧

9740 Brentwood Rd.
Omaha, NE 68114-4925
Application address: c/o Mark Javitch, 1800 Washington St., Apt. 716, San Francisco, CA 94109, tel.: (402) 393-3893

Established in 2005 in NE.
Donor: Phil Sokolof†.
Foundation type: Independent foundation.
Financial data (yr. ended 12/31/13): Assets, $10,738,178 (M); expenditures, $544,022; qualifying distributions, $486,762; giving activities include $477,000 for 37 grants (high: $50,000; low: $500).
Fields of interest: Higher education; Human services; Jewish federated giving programs.
Application information: Application form required.
Initial approach: Letter
Deadline(s): None
Trustees: Jennifer Javitch; Mark Javitch; Rachel Javitch.
EIN: 206423564
Selected grants: The following grants are a representative sample of this grantmaker's funding activity:
$20,000 to Birthright Israel Foundation, New York, NY, 2011. For general support.
$20,000 to Jewish Federation of Omaha, Omaha, NE, 2011.
$20,000 to Project Harmony, Omaha, NE, 2011.
$15,000 to Omaha Public Library Foundation, Omaha, NE, 2011.
$10,000 to Family Housing Advisory Services, Omaha, NE, 2011.
$10,000 to Film Streams, Omaha, NE, 2011.
$10,000 to Northstar Foundation, Omaha, NE, 2011.
$10,000 to Omaha Small Business Network, Omaha, NE, 2011.
$5,000 to Planned Parenthood of the Heartland, Des Moines, IA, 2011.
$4,000 to Project Interfaith, Omaha, NE, 2011.

5085
St. Anthony Foundation ✧

P.O. Box 83246
Lincoln, NE 68501-3246

Established in 2004 in NE.
Donors: Jeffrey Schumacher; Laura Schumacher.
Foundation type: Independent foundation.
Financial data (yr. ended 12/31/13): Assets, $22,820,598 (M); expenditures, $1,340,868; qualifying distributions, $1,210,547; giving activities include $1,202,900 for 46 grants (high: $419,000; low: $250).
Fields of interest: Education, single organization support; Secondary school/education; Catholic agencies & churches.
Limitations: Applications not accepted. Giving primarily in NE. No grants to individuals.
Application information: Contributes only to pre-selected organizations.
Officers and Directors:* Jeffrey Schumacher,* Pres. and Secy.-Treas.; Laura Schumacher,* V.P.; Laura Provorse.
EIN: 202055887
Selected grants: The following grants are a representative sample of this grantmaker's funding activity:
$101,000 to Nebraska Wesleyan University, Lincoln, NE, 2012. For contribution to an Educational Organization.
$10,000 to TeamMates Mentoring Program, Lincoln, NE, 2012. For contribution to Charitable Organization.
$4,000 to Fellowship of Christian Athletes, Kansas City, MO, 2012. For contribution to a Religious Organization.
$3,600 to University of Nebraska Foundation, Lincoln, NE, 2012. For contribution to Charitable Organization.
$2,000 to Bright Lights, Lincoln, NE, 2012. For contribution to Educational Organization.
$1,000 to Cato Institute, Washington, DC, 2012. For contribution to a Charitable Organization.

5086
Robert Herman Storz Foundation ✧ ☆

10050 Regency Cir., Ste. 101
Omaha, NE 68114-3721
Contact: Herbert A. Engdagl, Tr.

Established in 1957.
Donor: Robert Herman Storz†.
Foundation type: Independent foundation.
Financial data (yr. ended 12/31/13): Assets, $5,168,127 (M); expenditures, $479,336; qualifying distributions, $442,800; giving activities include $429,519 for 31 grants (high: $75,000; low: $1,000).
Fields of interest: Arts; Human services.
Type of support: Annual campaigns; Capital campaigns; Building/renovation; Matching/challenge support.
Limitations: Applications accepted. Giving primarily in the Omaha, NE, area. No support for political organizations. No grants to individuals.
Application information: Application form not required.
Initial approach: Letter
Copies of proposal: 1
Deadline(s): May 1, Sept. 1, Dec. 1
Board meeting date(s): 2nd Mon. in May, Sept., and Dec.
Trustees: Susan Storz Butler; Herbert A. Engdahl; Diane Higgins; Robert S. Howard.
Number of staff: 1 full-time professional.
EIN: 476025980
Selected grants: The following grants are a representative sample of this grantmaker's funding activity:
$80,000 to Joslyn Art Museum, Omaha, NE, 2011.
$37,012 to University of Nebraska Foundation, Lincoln, NE, 2011.
$25,000 to All Saints Episcopal Church, Omaha, NE, 2011.
$25,000 to Bellevue University Foundation, Bellevue, NE, 2011.
$25,000 to Strategic Air and Space Museum, Ashland, NE, 2011.
$15,000 to Childrens Hospital and Medical Center Foundation, Omaha, NE, 2011.
$15,000 to Hospice House, Omaha, NE, 2011.
$10,000 to Humane Society, Nebraska, Omaha, NE, 2011.
$8,000 to Boy Scouts of America, Omaha, NE, 2011.
$5,000 to Womens Center for Advancement, Omaha, NE, 2011.

5087
Gretchen Swanson Family Foundation, Inc. ✧
4935 Battlefield Dr.
Omaha, NE 68152-1556
Application address: Laura Bucholz, HCR 63, Box 17, Saratoga, WY 82331

Established in 1960.
Donors: Frederick S. Bucholz; Kurt S. Bucholz; Gretchen Swanson Velde†.
Foundation type: Independent foundation.
Financial data (yr. ended 12/31/13): Assets, $22,668,831 (M); expenditures, $1,032,967; qualifying distributions, $918,273; giving activities include $910,900 for 27 grants (high: $100,000; low: $100).
Purpose and activities: Giving primarily for a community center; some funding also for a museum, and social services for disaster relief.
Fields of interest: Museums (art); Arts; Higher education; Environment; Human services.
Limitations: Applications accepted. Giving primarily in CO and WY.
Application information: Application form not required.
Initial approach: Proposal
Deadline(s): None
Trustee: Provident Trust Company.
EIN: 476024650
Selected grants: The following grants are a representative sample of this grantmaker's funding activity:
$100,000 to Platte Valley Community Center, Saratoga, WY, 2011.
$100,000 to Texas Christian University, Fort Worth, TX, 2011.
$100,000 to University of Virginia, Charlottesville, VA, 2011.
$100,000 to Woodberry Forest School, Woodberry Forest, VA, 2011.
$60,000 to Buffalo Bill Historical Center, Cody, WY, 2011.
$50,000 to Colorado State University, Fort Collins, CO, 2011.
$50,000 to Corbett Medical Foundation, Saratoga, WY, 2011.
$50,000 to Mountain States Legal Foundation, Lakewood, CO, 2011.
$50,000 to University of Wyoming, Laramie, WY, 2011.
$15,000 to University of Texas M.D. Anderson Cancer Center, Houston, TX, 2011.

5088
Carl and Caroline Swanson Foundation, Inc. ✧
4935 Battlefield Dr.
Omaha, NE 68152-1556
Contact: Frederick S. Bucholz, Pres.

Trust established in 1945; incorporated in 1953 in NE.
Donors: Kurt S. Bucholz; Frederick S. Bucholz; Gretchen Swanson Velde†; members of the Carl A. Swanson family.
Foundation type: Independent foundation.
Financial data (yr. ended 12/31/13): Assets, $22,948,591 (M); expenditures, $1,091,757; qualifying distributions, $971,296; giving activities include $903,500 for 8 grants (high: $350,000; low: $10,000).
Fields of interest: Higher education; Environment, land resources; Environmental education; Animals/wildlife; Health care; Agriculture, farmlands; Athletics/sports, equestrianism; Human services.
Type of support: General/operating support.
Limitations: Applications accepted. Giving primarily in CO, NE, and TX. No grants to individuals.
Application information: Application form not required.
Initial approach: Proposal
Deadline(s): None
Board meeting date(s): Quarterly
Trustee: Provident Trust Company.
EIN: 476024644
Selected grants: The following grants are a representative sample of this grantmaker's funding activity:
$270,000 to Colorado State University Foundation, Fort Collins, CO, 2011.
$170,000 to American Quarter Horse Foundation, Amarillo, TX, 2011.
$50,000 to Breckenridge Outdoor Education Center, Breckenridge, CO, 2011.

5089
LeRoy, Jean Thom and T-L Foundation ✧
P.O. Box 1047
Hastings, NE 68902-1047 (402) 462-4128
Contact: James L. Thom, V.P., Finance

Established in 1994 in NE.
Donors: LeRoy W. Thom; James Thom; David Thom; Michael Thom; Elizabeth Peshek; T-L Irrigation Co.; Thomas Thom.
Foundation type: Independent foundation.
Financial data (yr. ended 12/31/13): Assets, $32,578,066 (M); gifts received, $5,172,650; expenditures, $1,944,964; qualifying distributions, $1,886,450; giving activities include $1,886,450 for 106 grants (high: $230,000; low: $300).
Purpose and activities: Giving for religious and educational institutions.
Fields of interest: Higher education; Religion.
Limitations: Applications accepted. Giving limited to NE.
Application information: Application form not required.
Initial approach: Proposal
Deadline(s): None
Officers and Directors: LeRoy W. Thom, Pres.; James L. Thom, V.P., Finance; Jean E. Thom, Secy.; David H. Fisher,* Genl. Counsel; Thomas A. Thom; David W. Thom; Robert Lubken.
EIN: 470776789

5090
Union Pacific Foundation ✧
1400 Douglas St., Stop 1560
Omaha, NE 68179-1001 (402) 544-5600
Contact: Darlynn Myers, Dir.
FAX: (402) 501-2291; E-mail: upf@up.com; Main URL: http://www.up.com/aboutup/community/foundation/index.htm
RSS Feed: http://www.uprr.com/newsinfo/releases/news_rss.cfm?category=community

Incorporated in 1959 in UT.
Donor: Union Pacific Corp.
Foundation type: Company-sponsored foundation.
Financial data (yr. ended 12/31/12): Assets, $1,462,836 (M); gifts received, $6,780,000; expenditures, $5,774,931; qualifying distributions, $5,641,507; giving activities include $5,641,507 for 910 grants (high: $360,000; low: $500).
Purpose and activities: The foundation supports zoos and aquariums and organizations involved with arts and culture, education, the environment, health, human services, community development, and civic affairs.
Fields of interest: Media, television; Media, radio; Museums; Museums (science/technology); Historic preservation/historical societies; Education, public education; Libraries (public); Education, services; Education; Botanical gardens; Environment; Zoos/zoological societies; Aquariums; Hospitals (general); Health care; Boys & girls clubs; Children, services; Human services; Community/economic development; Public affairs.
Type of support: General/operating support; Continuing support; Management development/capacity building; Capital campaigns; Building/renovation; Equipment; Program development.
Limitations: Applications accepted. Giving on a national basis in areas of company operations, with emphasis on AR, AZ, CA, CO, IA, ID, IL, KS, LA, MN, MO, MT, NE, NM, NV, OK, OR, TX, UT, WA, WI, and WY. No support for pass-through organizations, political or lobbying organizations, religious organizations not of direct benefit to the entire community, fraternal or veterans' organizations, local affiliates of national health and disease-specific organizations, animal rights organizations, elementary or secondary schools, volunteer fire departments or other emergency response organizations, labor organizations, or organizations whose programs are national or international in scope. No grants to individuals, or for debt reduction, salaries, athletic programs or events, conventions, conferences, or seminars, sponsorship of dinners, benefits or other special events, fellowships or research; no railroad equipment donations; no loans.
Publications: Application guidelines; Program policy statement.
Application information: A full application may be requested at a later date. Support is limited to 1 contribution per organization during any given year. The foundation does not provide leadership gifts or support requests for which it is asked to be the sole funder. Application form required.
Initial approach: Complete online Stage One preliminary application
Deadline(s): May 1 to Aug. 15 for Stage One and Stage Two applications
Board meeting date(s): Late Jan.
Final notification: 2 business days for Stage One; Feb. for Stage Two
Officers and Trustees:* John J. Koraleski,* Chair.; Robert W. Turner,* Pres.; C. R. Eisele, Sr. V.P., Strategic Planning and Admin.; Robert M. Knight, Jr.,* V.P., Finance; P. J. O'Malley, V.P., Taxes; Barbara W. Schaefer,* Secy.; J. Michael Hemmer,* Genl. Counsel; S. A. Oiness, Treas.; Jeffrey P. Totusek, Cont.
Number of staff: 1 full-time professional.
EIN: 136406825
Selected grants: The following grants are a representative sample of this grantmaker's funding activity:
$360,000 to Durham Museum, Omaha, NE, 2012.
$315,000 to United Way of the Midlands, Omaha, NE, 2012.
$100,000 to Dona Ana Branch Community College, Las Cruces, NM, 2012.

$25,000 to Belvidere, Village of, Belvidere, NE, 2012.
$25,000 to YMCA, Grand Island, Grand Island, NE, 2012.
$20,000 to Boys and Girls Club of the Los Angeles Harbor, San Pedro, CA, 2012.
$5,000 to Assistance League of Riverside, Riverside, CA, 2012. For Health/Human Services.
$5,000 to Stuhr Museum Foundation, Grand Island, NE, 2012. For Community/Civic.
$5,000 to University Foundation at Sacramento State, Sacramento, CA, 2012.
$3,000 to United Way of Central Iowa, Des Moines, IA, 2012. For Health/Human Services.

5091
Vetter Foundation ✧
c/o Jack Vetter
20220 Harney St.
Elkhorn, NE 68022-2063
Main URL: http://www.vetterhealthservices.com/vetter-foundation/

Established in NE.
Donors: Vetter Holding, Inc; Heritage Partners; Vetter Leasing Services.
Foundation type: Independent foundation.
Financial data (yr. ended 06/30/13): Assets, $2,249,440 (M); gifts received, $606,864; expenditures, $683,428; qualifying distributions, $528,066; giving activities include $528,066 for 27 + grants (high: $95,900), and $630,621 for foundation-administered programs.
Fields of interest: Environment, water resources; Human services; Protestant agencies & churches.
Limitations: Applications not accepted. No grants to individuals.
Application information: Contributes only to pre-selected organizations.
Officers: Jack D. Vetter, Pres.; Eldora D. Vetter, V.P.
Directors: Vicki Cates; Denith D. Vetter; Todd Vetter.
EIN: 470762483

5092
Weitz Family Foundation ✧
110 N. 92nd St.
Omaha, NE 68114-3903
Contact: Wallace R. Weitz, Pres. and Treas.

Established in 1999 in NE.
Donors: Wallace R. Weitz; Barbara V. Weitz; Roger Weitz.
Foundation type: Independent foundation.
Financial data (yr. ended 08/31/13): Assets, $49,116,157 (M); gifts received, $500; expenditures, $6,718,725; qualifying distributions, $6,718,173; giving activities include $6,718,173 for 82 grants (high: $2,011,673; low: $250).
Purpose and activities: Giving primarily for higher education, the arts, federated giving programs, and children, youth, family and social services.
Fields of interest: Media, radio; Performing arts; Arts; Education; Housing/shelter, development; Housing/shelter; Human services; Community/economic development; Children/youth; Girls; Economically disadvantaged.
Type of support: General/operating support; Continuing support; Professorships; Seed money; Research.
Limitations: Applications not accepted. Giving primarily in Chicago, IL, and Omaha, NE. No support for religious organizations or anti-choice organizations.
Application information: Unsolicited requests for funds not accepted.
Board meeting date(s): Apr. and Oct.
Officers: Wallace R. Weitz, Pres. and Treas.; Barbara V. Weitz, V.P. and Secy.
Directors: Andrew S. Weitz; Kate Noble Weitz; Meredith Weitz; Roger T. Weitz; Kathryn W. White.
Number of staff: 1 part-time support.
EIN: 470834133

5093
The Weller Foundation, Inc. ✧ ☆
P.O. Box 636
Atkinson, NE 68713-0636 (402) 925-2803

Incorporated in 1979 in NE.
Donors: E.C. Weller†; Frances W. Weller†.
Foundation type: Independent foundation.
Financial data (yr. ended 10/31/13): Assets, $8,616,201 (M); expenditures, $680,139; qualifying distributions, $576,817; giving activities include $539,425 for 163 grants to individuals (high: $6,800; low: $1,500).
Purpose and activities: Scholarships for students attending one of the technical community colleges in Nebraska or pursuing other vocational education, such as nursing.
Fields of interest: Vocational education; Nursing care.
Type of support: Scholarships—to individuals.
Limitations: Applications accepted. Giving limited to NE, with primary consideration for residents of Boyd, Brown, Garfield, Holt, Keya Paha, and Rock counties. No grants for scholarships for education toward a bachelor's degree.
Publications: Application guidelines.
Application information: Application form required.
Initial approach: Completed Application form
Deadline(s): For renewal applicants: June 1 for the fall semester and Nov. 1 for the spring semester. For new applicants: Apr. 1 for the fall semester and Nov. 1 for the spring semester
Final notification: Within 30 days of the deadlines
Officers: Dick Bilstein, Pres.; Bryan Rentschler, V.P.; Clark Gotschall, Secy.-Treas.
Directors: Clayton Goeke; Jean Fleming; Robert Randall; Barb Shane.
Number of staff: 1 full-time support.
EIN: 470611350

5094
CL Werner Foundation ✧
14301 FNB Pkwy., Ste. 115
Omaha, NE 68154-5299

Donor: Clarence L. Werner.
Foundation type: Independent foundation.
Financial data (yr. ended 12/31/13): Assets, $26,564,723 (M); expenditures, $4,113,065; qualifying distributions, $4,088,019; giving activities include $4,042,599 for 23 grants (high: $1,698,552; low: $1,500).
Fields of interest: Education; Hospitals (general); Boys & girls clubs; Human services; Children/youth, services; Protestant agencies & churches; Catholic agencies & churches.
Limitations: Applications not accepted. Giving primarily in NE and SD.
Application information: Contributes only to pre-selected organizations.
Officers and Board Members:* Gail M. Werner-Robertson,* Chair.; Mary R. Werner, Pres.; Stefanie K. Christensen, Secy.-Treas.; Adrienne Werner.
EIN: 263839487

5095
Paul, John, Anton & Doris Wirth Foundation Inc. ✧
P.O. Box 9
Nebraska City, NE 68410-0009 (402) 263-4085

Established around 1985 in NE.
Donors: Paul Wirth; John Wirth; Anton Wirth; Doris Wirth; Lutz & Co., PC.
Foundation type: Independent foundation.
Financial data (yr. ended 12/31/13): Assets, $19,028,511 (M); expenditures, $806,708; qualifying distributions, $797,697; giving activities include $797,697 for 24 grants (high: $525,000; low: $500).
Purpose and activities: Giving primarily for education, including Roman Catholic schools.
Fields of interest: Education; Human services; Family services; Community/economic development; Catholic agencies & churches.
Type of support: General/operating support; Building/renovation.
Limitations: Applications accepted. Giving limited to Nebraska City and Otoe County, NE. No grants to individuals.
Application information: Application form required.
Initial approach: Letter
Deadline(s): None
Officers: Arlene Easter, Pres.; Duane Smith, V.P.; Nancy Lutz, Secy.; Gail Lutz, Treas.
Directors: Bruce Madsen; Jacqueline Smith; Don Wittler.
EIN: 470662109

5096
Woods Charitable Fund, Inc. ✧
1248 O St., Ste. 1130
Lincoln, NE 68508-1409 (402) 436-5971
Contact: Tom Woods, Exec. Dir.; Joan Stolle, Opers. Mgr.
E-mail: info@woodscharitable.org; Additional e-mails: twoods@woodscharitable.org (Tom Woods); azmarly@woodscharitable.org (Angie Zmarly); jstolle@woodscharitable.org (Joan Stolle);ksteinauersmith@woodscharitable.org (Kathy Steinauer Smith); Main URL: http://www.woodscharitable.org
E-Newsletter: http://woodscharitable.org/news/
Facebook: https://www.facebook.com/pages/Woods-Charitable-Fund-Inc/168904933137312
Grants List: http://woodscharitable.org/recent-grants/
Philanthropy In/Sight Grants Map: http://maps.foundationcenter.org/?account=woods

Incorporated in 1941 in NE.
Donors: Frank H. Woods†; Nelle C. Woods†; Frank H. Woods, Jr.†; Thomas C. Woods, Jr.†; Henry C. Woods†; Sahara Coal Co., Inc.
Foundation type: Independent foundation.
Financial data (yr. ended 12/31/13): Assets, $33,553,457 (M); expenditures, $2,028,998; qualifying distributions, $1,712,947; giving

activities include $1,165,500 for 53 grants (high: $60,000; low: $4,500), and $40,000 for 1 loan/program-related investment.
Purpose and activities: Giving to improve the quality of life in Lincoln, Nebraska, by expanding prosperity and justice, advancing diverse and balanced participation of community residents, and stimulating creativity and ingenuity.
Fields of interest: Visual arts; Performing arts; Humanities; Arts; Elementary school/education; Education; Crime/violence prevention, domestic violence; Housing/shelter, development; Human services; Children/youth, services; Family services; Community/economic development; Children/youth; Children; Aging; Disabilities, people with; Minorities; Asians/Pacific Islanders; African Americans/Blacks; Hispanics/Latinos; Native Americans/American Indians; Women; Adults, women; Adults, men; Crime/abuse victims; Immigrants/refugees; Economically disadvantaged; Homeless.
Type of support: General/operating support; Program development; Seed money; Technical assistance; Consulting services; Program evaluation; Program-related investments/loans; Matching/challenge support.
Limitations: Applications accepted. Giving primarily in Lincoln, NE. No support for religious activities, recreational programs, healthcare programs, and individual school programs, or for college or university programs that do not involve students and/or faculty in projects of benefit to the Lincoln, NE, area, or for environmental programs, recreational programs, individual school programs, or healthcare programs or residential care and medical clinics. No grants to individuals, or for endowments, scholarships, fellowships, fundraising benefits or for program advertising.
Publications: Application guidelines; Annual report; Financial statement; Grants list; Informational brochure; Newsletter.
Application information: Applications submitted only through on-line application. No hard copies required or accepted. If a full proposal is requested, please use the link to the Woods on-line application system. The proposal itself should not exceed 10 pages. Application form required.
Initial approach: Prior to submitting application, grantseekers must contact the fund (phone, e-mail or letter of intent) to determine eligibility
Copies of proposal: 1
Deadline(s): Mar. 15, July. 15 and Nov. 15 for full proposals only
Board meeting date(s): Mar., June, and Nov.
Final notification: 1 week after board meeting
Officers and Directors:* Donna W. Woods,* Chair.; Kathleen Rutledge,* Vice-Chair.; Thomas C. Woods IV, Pres. and Secy.; Hank Woods,* Treas.; Ernesto Castillo; Carl Eskridge; Nelle Woods Jamison; Orville Jones III; Michael J. Tavlin.
Number of staff: 3 full-time professional; 1 part-time professional.
EIN: 476032847
Selected grants: The following grants are a representative sample of this grantmaker's funding activity:
$200,000 to Friends of Woods Tennis, Lincoln, NE, 2013. For capital campaign, Taking the Game to The Community.
$150,000 to Lincoln Parks and Recreation Foundation, Lincoln, NE, 2013. For Civic Plaza.
$100,000 to Nebraska Art Association, Lincoln, NE, 2013. For renovations to Sheldon Sculpture Garden.
$100,000 to NeighborWorks Lincoln, Lincoln, NE, 2012. For Capital Campaign.
$100,000 to Woods Hall Craft Shop, La Pointe, WI, 2013. For gallery addition.
$60,000 to Educare of Lincoln, Lincoln, NE, 2013. For Family Engagement Specialists.
$59,000 to Lincoln-Lancaster County Human Services Federation, Lincoln, NE, 2012. For CSI Reorganization Project.
$50,000 to Family Violence Council, Lincoln, NE, 2013. For Keepers of the Flame, outreach and services project for ethnic and minority populations.
$50,000 to Legal Aid of Nebraska, Omaha, NE, 2013. To provide access to Justice Self-Help Center of Lincoln.
$45,000 to Lincoln Literacy Council, Lincoln, NE, 2012. For New Beginnings Project.
$40,000 to Nebraska Appleseed Center for Law in the Public Interest, Lincoln, NE, 2012. For Health Reform Implementation Project.
$37,500 to Food Bank of Lincoln, Lincoln, NE, 2012. For bilingual Supplemental Nutrition Assistance Program (SNAP) Outreach Coordinator/Leader.
$30,000 to Flatwater Shakespeare Company, Lincoln, NE, 2012. For Twelfth Night Parks Tour.
$30,000 to Legal Aid of Nebraska, Omaha, NE, 2012. For Mobile Justice Center of Lancaster County.
$25,000 to Common Cause Nebraska Education Fund, Lincoln, NE, 2013. For general operating support.
$25,000 to El Centro de las Americas, Lincoln, NE, 2013. For operating support.
$20,000 to Girl Scouts of the U.S.A., Homestead Council, Lincoln, NE, 2012. For Girl Scout Outreach Program.
$20,000 to Malone Community Center, Lincoln, NE, 2012. For General Operating Support Continuation Grant.
$20,000 to Nebraska Lawyers Foundation, Lincoln, NE, 2012. For The Volunteer Lawyers Project/Self-Help Desk.
$15,000 to Lux Center for the Arts, Lincoln, NE, 2013. To build capacity for LUX Art Education Programs for the community.

5097
J. A. Woollam Foundation ✧
c/o D.R. Stogsdill
233 S. 13th St., Ste. 1900
Lincoln, NE 68508-2095

Established in 2001 in NE.
Donors: John A. Woollam; John A. Woollam Co., Inc.
Foundation type: Operating foundation.
Financial data (yr. ended 12/31/11): Assets, $22,129,372 (M); gifts received, $6,876,650; expenditures, $3,697,821; qualifying distributions, $5,354,255; giving activities include $3,489,311 for 58 grants (high: $799,000; low: $100), and $4,150,897 for foundation-administered programs.
Fields of interest: Higher education; Environment, natural resources; Foundations (community).
Limitations: Applications not accepted. Giving in the U.S., with emphasis on MI and VA. No grants to individuals.
Application information: Contributes only to pre-selected organizations.
Trustee: John A. Woollam.
EIN: 470812219
Selected grants: The following grants are a representative sample of this grantmaker's funding activity:
$20,000 to Yellow Dog Watershed Preserve, Big Bay, MI, 2011.

5098
York Community Foundation ✧
603 N. Lincoln Ave.
York, NE 68467-4240 (402) 362-5531
Contact: Donna Bitner, Exec. Dir.
E-mail: ycf@yorkchamber.net; Main URL: http://www.yorkcommunityfoundation.org/index.html

Established in 1984 in NE.
Foundation type: Community foundation.
Financial data (yr. ended 09/30/13): Assets, $7,050,617 (M); gifts received, $2,181,318; expenditures, $526,083; giving activities include $294,793 for 5+ grants (high: $95,341), $146,950 for 66 grants to individuals, and $6,624,320 for loans/program-related investments.
Purpose and activities: The foundation seeks to utilize charitable funds to strengthen and improve the community for the benefit of all its citizens.
Fields of interest: Arts; Education; Health care; Health organizations; Recreation; Human services; Children/youth, services; Human services; Community/economic development; Religion; Economically disadvantaged.
Type of support: Program development; Scholarships—to individuals.
Limitations: Applications accepted. Giving limited to the York, NE, area. No support for religious purposes. No grants to individuals (except for scholarships), or for operating expenses, annual fund drives, endowment funds, or travel.
Application information: Visit foundation web site for application form and guidelines. Application form required.
Initial approach: Submit application form
Deadline(s): None
Officers and Directors:* Kristie Holoch,* Pres.; Charles W. Harris,* V.P.; Donna Bitner, Exec. Dir.; Charles W. Campbell; Gordon B. Fillman; Richard Hankel; C.G. Holthus; Lawrence R. Kopsa; Garold Leggott; Donna Loschen; Judi Nordlund; Katie North; Kent Rauert; Sally Ruben; Cheryl Thomas-Miller.
EIN: 363324526

NEVADA

5099
Dr. Miriam & Sheldon G. Adelson Charitable Trust ✧
410 South Rampart Blvd., Ste. 440
Las Vegas, NV 89145-5749

Established in 1994 in NV.
Donors: Dr. Miriam Adelson; Sheldon G. Adelson.
Foundation type: Operating foundation.
Financial data (yr. ended 12/31/13): Assets, $335,679,305 (M); gifts received, $55,214,397; expenditures, $80,817,094; qualifying distributions, $80,817,094; giving activities include $80,729,814 for 5 grants (high: $52,911,552; low: $9,951).
Fields of interest: Substance abuse, treatment; Medical research; Human services; Foundations (private grantmaking).
Type of support: General/operating support.
Limitations: Applications not accepted. Giving primarily in MA and NV.
Application information: Unsolicited requests for funds not accepted.
Trustees: Dr. Miriam Adelson; Sheldon G. Adelson.
EIN: 886063073

5100
AJA Charitable Fund ✧
3605 Town Center Dr., Ste. A
Las Vegas, NV 89135-3017

Established in 2004 in NV.
Donor: Andrew J. Astrachan.
Foundation type: Independent foundation.
Financial data (yr. ended 09/30/13): Assets, $14,316,280 (M); gifts received, $2,516,829; expenditures, $547,895; qualifying distributions, $484,044; giving activities include $477,550 for 25 grants (high: $210,000; low: $250).
Fields of interest: Elementary/secondary education; Higher education; Medical research, institute; Human services; Children, services.
Limitations: Applications not accepted. Giving in the U.S., with emphasis on CA, CT and NY. No grants to individuals.
Application information: Contributes only to pre-selected organizations.
Officers: Andrew J. Astrachan, Pres.; Cathy Hunter Daniels, Secy.
EIN: 202054545

5101
The Bennett Family Foundation ✧
6650 Via Austi Pkwy., Ste. 150
Las Vegas, NV 89119-3551 (702) 631-5161
Contact: Diana L. Bennett, Dir.

Donor: Diana Bennett.
Foundation type: Independent foundation.
Financial data (yr. ended 12/31/13): Assets, $4,309 (M); gifts received, $1,430,580; expenditures, $1,438,750; qualifying distributions, $1,437,730; giving activities include $1,342,900 for 21 grants (high: $250,000; low: $900).
Fields of interest: Performing arts centers; Education; Food banks; Nutrition; Children/youth, services.
Type of support: General/operating support.
Limitations: Applications accepted. Giving primarily in Las Vegas, NV.
Application information: Application form required.
Initial approach: Letter
Deadline(s): Jan. and July
Directors: Diana L. Bennett; Michael Kern; Henry Lichtenberger; Marlee Palermo.
EIN: 262785614
Selected grants: The following grants are a representative sample of this grantmaker's funding activity:
$200,000 to Three Square, Las Vegas, NV, 2012. For Backpack for Kids and Childhood Nutrition Programs.
$55,970 to Child Focus, Las Vegas, NV, 2012. For Share Discovery Program Which Teaches Personal Growth and Independent Living Skills to Separated Siblings in Foster Care.
$38,000 to Three Square, Las Vegas, NV, 2012. For Backpack for Kids, Senior Share, and Food Bank/Food Rescue Programs.
$25,000 to Casa De Luz, Las Vegas, NV, 2012. For women's shelter.
$25,000 to Three Square, Las Vegas, NV, 2012. For Dish Las Vegas 2012, Three Squares Annual Benefit Event.
$10,000 to Child Focus, Las Vegas, NV, 2012. For Diamond Sponsorship Mothers Dea Tea 2012.
$7,200 to Child Focus, Las Vegas, NV, 2012. For Camper Memberships for Camp to Belong 2012.

5102
Berner Educational Trust No. 2 ✧
P.O. Box 5940
Stateline, NV 89449-5940 (775) 588-6676
E-mail: info@bernerscholarship.org

Established in NV.
Foundation type: Independent foundation.
Financial data (yr. ended 12/31/13): Assets, $20,092,336 (M); expenditures, $2,083,662; qualifying distributions, $1,586,563; giving activities include $1,446,485 for 81 grants to individuals (high: $52,550; low: $806).
Purpose and activities: Scholarship awards for post-high school education, to students who have graduated with a G.P.A. of 3.0 or better (2.75 if current college/trade school student), from high schools in northern Nevada.
Fields of interest: Higher education.
Type of support: Scholarships—to individuals.
Limitations: Applications accepted. Giving limited to residents of northern NV, who have either graduated or are graduating seniors from high schools in Carson City, Churchill, Douglas, Elko, Eureka, Humboldt, Lander, Lyon, Mineral, Pershing, Storey, Washoe and White Pine counties.
Application information: Application form required.
Initial approach: Contact foundation
Deadline(s): Mar. 31
Trustees: Ron Alling, Esq.; Neil Spellman.
EIN: 201799697

5103
The Bretzlaff Foundation, Inc. ✧
4795 Caughlin Pkwy., Ste. 100
Reno, NV 89519-0994 (775) 333-0300
Contact: Michael J. Melarkey, Secy.

Established in 1988 in NV.
Donors: Hazel C. Van Allen; Hazel Van Allen Marital Trust.
Foundation type: Independent foundation.
Financial data (yr. ended 06/30/13): Assets, $17,114,482 (M); expenditures, $772,398; qualifying distributions, $565,420; giving activities include $565,420 for grants.
Purpose and activities: Giving primarily for higher education, youth, the arts, health care, and the environment.
Fields of interest: Museums; Arts; Higher education; Environment; Health care; Human services; Youth, services; Community/economic development; Foundations (private grantmaking).
Type of support: General/operating support; Building/renovation; Equipment; Endowments; Scholarship funds.
Limitations: Applications accepted. Giving primarily in Honolulu, HI and Reno, NV. No grants to individuals.
Application information:
Initial approach: Letter
Board meeting date(s): Apr., July, and Oct.
Officers and Directors:* Michael J. Melarkey, Pres.; Dick Gilbert, Secy.; G. Dan Morgan.
EIN: 880241424
Selected grants: The following grants are a representative sample of this grantmaker's funding activity:
$60,000 to University of San Francisco, School of Law, San Francisco, CA, 2013. For scholarship endowment.
$51,250 to Nevada Museum of Art, Reno, NV, 2013. For Exhibits and Fundraising Event.
$10,000 to Artown, Reno, NV, 2013. For Summer Festival 2013.
$10,000 to Reno Chamber Orchestra, Reno, NV, 2013. For concerto competition/concert.
$5,000 to Assistance League of Reno-Sparks, Reno, NV, 2013. For Operation School Bell.
$2,500 to Reno High School, Reno, NV, 2013. For We the People Program.

5104
Val A. Browning Foundation ✧
c/o Whittier Trust Co.
100 W. Liberty St., Ste. 890
Reno, NV 89501-1954

Established in 1975 in UT.
Donor: Val A. Browning.
Foundation type: Independent foundation.
Financial data (yr. ended 12/31/13): Assets, $30,254,641 (M); expenditures, $1,323,916; qualifying distributions, $1,134,065; giving activities include $1,047,040 for 39 grants (high: $143,697; low: $1,000).
Purpose and activities: Giving primarily for education and the arts.
Fields of interest: Arts; Higher education; Education; Human services.
Type of support: Continuing support; Annual campaigns; Capital campaigns; Building/renovation; Endowments; Program development.

Limitations: Applications not accepted. Giving primarily in UT; some funding also in ID, WA, and England.
Application information: Unsolicited requests for funds not accepted.
Officer: Pegine Grayson, Secy.
Directors: Bruce W. Browning; Christopher Browning; John Browning; Carol Browning Dumke; Edmund Dumke; Amelia Jones; Judith Ann Browning Jones.
EIN: 876167851
Selected grants: The following grants are a representative sample of this grantmaker's funding activity:
$50,000 to Animal Shelter of Wood River Valley, Hailey, ID, 2012. For Spay - Neuter/Valerie A. Dumke Fund.
$25,000 to Treatment Advocacy Center, Arlington, VA, 2012. For The Torrey Action Fund.
$25,000 to West Sound Academy, Poulsbo, WA, 2012. For International Baccalaureate Program.
$20,000 to Tracy Aviary, Friends of, Salt Lake City, UT, 2012. For new education van.
$10,000 to Cambridge in America, New York, NY, 2012. For Magdalene College - General Operating Support.
$10,000 to Charities Aid Foundation America, Alexandria, VA, 2012. For Great Bustard Group - Operating Support.
$10,000 to Charities Aid Foundation America, Alexandria, VA, 2012. For Gunmakers Charitable Trust - Support of Apprentices.
$10,000 to Friends of Arches and Canyonlands Parks, Moab, UT, 2012. For The Bates Wilson Legacy Fund -Environmental Stewardship Preservation and.

5105
Carol Franc Buck Foundation ✧
(formerly Carol Buck Sells Foundation)
P.O. Drawer 6085
Incline Village, NV 89450-6085 (775) 831-6366
Contact: Marti Winslow, Admin. Asst.

Incorporated in 1979 in NV.
Donor: Carol B. Sells.
Foundation type: Independent foundation.
Financial data (yr. ended 11/30/13): Assets, $13,023,981 (M); expenditures, $1,136,293; qualifying distributions, $1,072,311; giving activities include $935,000 for 11 grants (high: $400,000; low: $5,000).
Purpose and activities: Support for visual and performing arts, especially music, and for education in the arts.
Fields of interest: Performing arts; Performing arts, ballet; Performing arts, music; Performing arts, orchestras; Performing arts, opera; Arts.
Type of support: General/operating support; Continuing support; Equipment; Program development; Matching/challenge support.
Limitations: Giving primarily in the western U.S. No grants to individuals, or for emergency funds, deficit financing, capital campaigns, renovations, scholarships, fellowships, research, publications, or conferences; no loans.
Publications: Application guidelines; Annual report.
Application information: Unsolicited requests for funds are generally not accepted. Application form not required.
Initial approach: Written proposal
Copies of proposal: 1
Deadline(s): Mar. 15, for summer funding requests; Sept. 15, final date for accepting funding requests during the fiscal year
Board meeting date(s): Jan., Apr., July, and Oct.
Final notification: 3 months
Trustees: Carol Franc Buck; Christian P. Erdman; Helen J. O'Hanlon.
Number of staff: 1 full-time professional; 1 part-time support.
EIN: 880163505

5106
Caesars Foundation ✧
(formerly The Harrah's Foundation)
1 Caesars Palace Dr.
Las Vegas, NV 89109-8969 (702) 880-4728
Contact: Torben Cohrs, Treas.
FAX: (702) 407-6520;
E-mail: caesarsfoundation@caesars.com; Main URL: http://www.caesarsfoundation.com/
Facebook: https://www.facebook.com/CaesarsFoundation
YouTube: https://www.youtube.com/channel/UCCHa6zB7mDMWbTntZw6mlRw

Established in 2002 in NV.
Donors: Caesars Entertainment Operating Company, Inc.; Harrah's Operating Co., Inc.
Foundation type: Company-sponsored foundation.
Financial data (yr. ended 12/31/13): Assets, $1,422,279 (M); gifts received, $4,106,392; expenditures, $4,017,188; qualifying distributions, $3,824,337; giving activities include $3,695,588 for 113 grants (high: $300,000; low: $10).
Purpose and activities: The foundation supports programs designed to help older individuals live longer, healthier, and more fulfilling lives; promote a more sustainable world through environmental and educational initiatives; and improve the quality of life in communities where Caesars operates.
Fields of interest: Higher education; Environment, natural resources; Environment, land resources; Environment; Hospitals (general); Health care, clinics/centers; Health care, patient services; Health care; Mental health/crisis services; Alzheimer's disease; Food services; Food distribution, meals on wheels; Nutrition; Disasters, preparedness/services; American Red Cross; Youth, services; Human services, mind/body enrichment; Aging, centers/services; Developmentally disabled, centers & services; Human services; Public affairs; Aging.
Type of support: General/operating support; Continuing support; Capital campaigns; Building/renovation; Program development; Scholarship funds; Research; Employee volunteer services; Sponsorships.
Limitations: Applications accepted. Giving primarily in areas of company operations in AZ, CA, IA, IL, IN, LA, MO, MS, NC, NJ, Las Vegas and Reno, NV, and PA. No grants to individuals; no in-kind gifts.
Publications: Application guidelines; Informational brochure.
Application information: The foundation generally funds programs and projects of $10,000 or more. Application form required.
Initial approach: Complete online application
Deadline(s): None
Board meeting date(s): Quarterly
Officers and Trustees:* Janet Beronio,* Chair.; Jan Jones Blackhurst,* Vice-Chair.; Scott Weigand,* Secy.; Torben Cohrs, Treas.; Thom Reilly, Exec. Dir.; Thomas M. Jenkin; Fred Keeton; Dan Nita; John Payne; Diane Wilfong.
EIN: 743050638

5107
The Castleman Family Foundation ✧
917 Tahoe Blvd., Ste. 200
Incline Village, NV 89451-9422

Established in 2006 in Connecticut and Nevada.
Donor: Peter M. Castleman.
Foundation type: Independent foundation.
Financial data (yr. ended 12/31/12): Assets, $8,984,405 (M); expenditures, $480,710; qualifying distributions, $444,363; giving activities include $433,122 for 19 grants (high: $100,000; low: $2).
Fields of interest: Animal welfare; Health care, clinics/centers.
Limitations: Applications not accepted. Giving primarily in AZ. No grants to individuals.
Application information: Contributes only to pre-selected organizations.
Trustees: Peter M. Castleman; Sloane C. Castleman; Daniel J. O'Brien.
EIN: 205393405

5108
Community Foundation of Western Nevada ✧
1885 S. Arlington Ave., Ste. 103
Reno, NV 89509-3370 (775) 333-5499
Contact: Margaret Stewart, Comms. Dir.
FAX: (775) 333-5487; E-mail: info@cfwnv.org; Additional e-mail: mstewart@cfwnv.org; Main URL: http://www.cfwnv.org
Facebook: http://www.facebook.com/nevadafund
Google Plus: https://plus.google.com/+CommunityFoundationofWesternNevadaReno/about?hl=en-US

Established in 1998 in NV.
Foundation type: Community foundation.
Financial data (yr. ended 12/31/13): Assets, $71,702,545 (M); gifts received, $8,152,812; expenditures, $7,894,364; giving activities include $6,174,532 for 182+ grants (high: $472,359), and $514,842 for 58 grants to individuals.
Purpose and activities: The foundation seeks to strengthen the community through philanthropy and leadership by connecting people who care with causes that matter.
Fields of interest: Arts; Higher education; Education; Environment; Health care; Human services; Community/economic development; United Ways and Federated Giving Programs.
Type of support: General/operating support; Management development/capacity building; Program development; Scholarship funds; Scholarships—to individuals.
Limitations: Applications accepted. Giving primarily in Carson City, Reno, Sparks, and rural western NV. No support for religious purposes (unless from a donor-advised or organizational endowment fund) or for for-profit educational institutions. No grants to individuals (except scholarships), or for tickets for benefits, capital outlay or capital campaigns, debt retirement, or endowment.
Publications: Application guidelines; Annual report; Financial statement; Informational brochure; Newsletter.

Application information: The foundation maintains a grant application process for grants disbursed from Partnership Grant Program; all other grants are specifically disbursed on the advisement of donors. Visit foundation web site for more information. Application form required.

Initial approach: Submit letter of intent
Deadline(s): Varies
Board meeting date(s): Quarterly

Officers and Trustees:* Linda Smith,* Chair.; Butch Anderson,* Vice-Chair.; Christopher Askin, C.E.O. and Pres.; Tom Hall,* Secy.; Jim Pfrommer,* Treas.; Melissa Tschanz, Cont.; Sallie B. Armstrong; Kathie Bartlett; Seth Berry; Rebecca Dickson; Nora James; Brian Kennedy; Diana Kern; Cary Lurie; Janice Rude-Willson; Jennifer A. Satre; Norma Webster.
Advisory Board: Kim Becker; Greg Bower; Barbara Drake; David Geddes; Matthew Gray; Gail Humphreys; Klaus Grimm; Craig King; Dong-Joon "DJ" Lee; Lance McKenzie; Teresa Mentzer; Doug Nelson; Susanne Pennington; Alicia Reban; Beth Schuler; John Solari; Lilli Trinchero; Jim Webster.
Number of staff: 5 full-time professional; 1 part-time professional.
EIN: 880370179

5109
The William E. Connor Foundation ✧

990 S. Rock Blvd., Ste. F
Reno, NV 89502-4149

Established in 2007 in NV.
Donors: William E. Connor & Assoc. Ltd., Ltd.; William E. Connor.
Foundation type: Independent foundation.
Financial data (yr. ended 12/31/13): Assets, $758,580 (M); gifts received, $1,306,000; expenditures, $538,611; qualifying distributions, $651,522; giving activities include $651,522 for 24 grants (high: $250,000; low: $471).
Fields of interest: Higher education; Education.
Limitations: Applications not accepted. Giving primarily in CA; some funding also in MA. No grants to individuals.
Application information: Contributes only to pre-selected organizations.
Officers: Susan L. Skidmore, Pres.; James E. Gagnon, Secy.; Terri L. Darling, Treas.
Director: William E. Connor II.
EIN: 320176090

5110
The E.L. Cord Foundation ✧

320 W. Liberty St.
Reno, NV 89501-2012
Contact: Joseph S. Bradley, Tr.
E-mail: elcordfoundation@sbcglobal.net

Established in 1962 in NV.
Donor: E.L. Cord†.
Foundation type: Independent foundation.
Financial data (yr. ended 12/31/13): Assets, $67,947,609 (M); expenditures, $5,207,175; qualifying distributions, $4,055,760; giving activities include $3,978,250 for 171 grants (high: $200,000; low: $1,000).
Purpose and activities: Support primarily for secondary and higher education, including colleges and universities, social services and youth organizations, and for cultural organizations.
Fields of interest: Secondary school/education; Higher education; Human services; Youth, services.
Type of support: General/operating support; Building/renovation; Equipment; Emergency funds; Program development; Scholarship funds; Research; Matching/challenge support.
Limitations: Applications accepted. Giving primarily in northern NV and the rural counties of NV. No support for religious organizations for sectarian purposes. No grants to individuals, or for continuing support.
Publications: Application guidelines; Informational brochure.
Application information: All grants are restricted to and are to be used only for the purposes set forth in the respective grant proposals. Administrative fees, grant writer fees and other indirect costs shall not be included in grant proposals. Application form not required.

Initial approach: Write for brochure
Copies of proposal: 1
Board meeting date(s): Monthly (if schedules permit)
Final notification: 1 week after board meeting

Trustees: Bill Bradley; Joseph S. Bradley; Robert L. Sims.
Number of staff: 1 full-time professional; 1 part-time professional.
EIN: 366072793

5111
Cordelia Corp. ✧

990 N. Sierra St.
Reno, NV 89503-3719

Established in 1994 in NV.
Donors: Mary A. Bing; R.D. Burch.
Foundation type: Independent foundation.
Financial data (yr. ended 05/31/13): Assets, $55,988,018 (M); expenditures, $3,686,998; qualifying distributions, $3,564,596; giving activities include $3,540,000 for 12 grants (high: $1,590,000; low: $5,000).
Fields of interest: Performing arts; Higher education; Education; Foundations (private grantmaking).
Limitations: Applications not accepted. Giving in the U.S., with emphasis on New Haven, CT and New York, NY. No grants to individuals.
Application information: Contributes only to pre-selected organizations.
Officers: Mary A. Bing, Pres.; William Stinehart, Jr., Secy.; Douglas Ellis, Treas.
EIN: 880326514
Selected grants: The following grants are a representative sample of this grantmaker's funding activity:
$1,000,000 to Nonprofit Finance Fund, New York, NY, 2013. For Artplace Initiative.
$500,000 to Yale University, New Haven, CT, 2013. For Dean's Fund for Visiting Artists and Exhibitions.

5112
Crescere Foundation ✧

c/o Beverly L. Ozmun
2625 N. Green Valley Pkwy., Ste. 115
Henderson, NV 89014

Established in 1997 in NV.
Donors: Beverly O. Hamman; Stephen R. Hamman; Beverly L. Ozmun.
Foundation type: Independent foundation.
Financial data (yr. ended 12/31/13): Assets, $1,697,926 (M); gifts received, $500,000; expenditures, $629,196; qualifying distributions, $621,030; giving activities include $620,000 for 9 grants (high: $300,000; low: $10,000).
Fields of interest: Human services; Salvation Army; Children/youth, services; Christian agencies & churches.
Limitations: Applications not accepted. Giving in the U.S., with emphasis on Henderson and Las Vegas, NV. No grants to individuals.
Application information: Contributes only to pre-selected organizations.
Officer: Beverly L. Ozmun, Pres.
EIN: 860877267
Selected grants: The following grants are a representative sample of this grantmaker's funding activity:
$100,000 to Fellowship of Christian Athletes, Henderson, NV, 2012. For Fellowship of Christian Athletes.
$50,000 to Young Life, Henderson, NV, 2012. For Young Life Las Vegas.

5113
Crystal Family Foundation ✧

P.O. Box 12367
Reno, NV 89510-2367

Established in 1994 in CO, NJ and NV.
Donor: Norman S. Crystal†.
Foundation type: Independent foundation.
Financial data (yr. ended 12/31/13): Assets, $23,786,741 (M); expenditures, $1,161,725; qualifying distributions, $1,104,849; giving activities include $1,003,425 for 74 grants (high: $175,000; low: $125).
Fields of interest: Human services; Jewish federated giving programs.
Type of support: General/operating support.
Limitations: Applications not accepted. Giving in the U.S., with some emphasis on Washington, DC, and NY. No grants to individuals.
Application information: Contributes only to pre-selected organizations.
Officer and Trustee:* Steven B. Crystal,* Pres.
EIN: 860852945

5114
Davidson Institute for Talent Development ✧

9665 Gateway Dr., Ste. B
Reno, NV 89521-8997
E-mail: info@davidsongiften.org; Main URL: http://www.davidsongifted.org
E-Newsletter: http://news.ditd.org/signup/eNews_SignUp.html
Facebook: http://www.facebook.com/pages/Davidson-Institute-for-Talent-Development/107118226318
Twitter: http://twitter.com/DavidsonGifted
YouTube: http://www.youtube.com/user/DavidsonAcademyNV

Established in NV.
Donors: Donna Buchholz; Janice Davidson; Robert Davidson; San Francisco Foundation; William G. Mcgowan Charitable Fund; Tse Ying Foundation.
Foundation type: Operating foundation.

Financial data (yr. ended 06/30/13): Assets, $3,226,843 (M); gifts received, $4,375,538; expenditures, $4,947,634; qualifying distributions, $4,336,257; giving activities include $10,000 for 1 grant, $477,470 for 105 grants to individuals (high: $45,000; low: $20), and $3,799,609 for 4 foundation-administered programs.
Purpose and activities: Giving for the education of gifted young people.
Fields of interest: Education, gifted students; Scholarships/financial aid.
Publications: Application guidelines; Annual report; Informational brochure.
Application information: Faxed or e-mailed applications are not accepted. Application information and form available on foundation web site. Application form required.
Initial approach: Completed application form
Deadline(s): 14th of each month by 5:00pm
Officers and Board Members: Janice Davidson,* Pres.; Robert Davidson,* V.P.; Travis Rabe,* V.P.; Mark Herron,* Secy.-Treas.; Katie Graham,* Dir., Summer Institute; Colleen Harsin, Dir., Svcs.
EIN: 880427864
Selected grants: The following grants are a representative sample of this grantmaker's funding activity:
$10,000 to Reno Philharmonic Association, Reno, NV, 2013. For the Reno Philharmonic.

5115
The Frank M. Doyle Foundation, Inc. ✧
3495 Lakeside Dr., No. 34
Reno, NV 89509-4841 (775) 829-1972
FAX: (775) 829-1974;
E-mail: FMDFoundation@aol.com; Main URL: http://www.frankmdoyle.org

Established in 1996 in CA and NV.
Donors: Gertrude R. Doyle; Shirley Freedland; Steve Inch; Tara Inch; F. Patrick Doyle; Molly K.D. Glen.
Foundation type: Operating foundation.
Financial data (yr. ended 08/31/13): Assets, $69,711,491 (M); expenditures, $4,259,601; qualifying distributions, $3,703,863; giving activities include $2,383,173 for 24 grants (high: $350,000; low: $3,500), and $1,043,757 for 409 grants to individuals (high: $10,000; low: $67).
Purpose and activities: Scholarships to high school graduates of the Huntington Beach Union High School District and Huntington Beach Adult High School in CA; as well as students and graduates of community colleges in Coastline, Cypress, Fullerton, Golden West, Irvine Valley, Orange Coast, Saddleback, Santa Ana, or Santiago Canyon, CA. Scholarships also to students and graduates of the Washoe County School District or Washoe Adult High School in NV. Some funding also for human services.
Fields of interest: Higher education; Human services.
Type of support: Scholarships—to individuals.
Limitations: Giving primarily in CA; funding also in NV.
Publications: Application guidelines.
Application information: Cover letters must be formatted and labeled in the particular order that appears in the "Guidelines for New Grants" section (under "Grants" tab) of the foundation web site. Application form required.
Initial approach: Cover letter
Copies of proposal: 1
Deadline(s): May 1 (for grants); Mar. 1 (for scholarships)
Board meeting date(s): Late Apr., late Sept., and as necessary throughout the year
Final notification: Mid-Nov
Officers and Directors:* F. Patrick Doyle,* Pres.; Doug Doyle,* V.P.; Molly Brown,* Secy.; Molly K.D. Glen,* Treas.; Nancy Doyle; Lauren Gunstone; Kathleen MacKinnon; Dan O'Hanlon; Mary Reed Roberts.
Number of staff: 2 part-time professional.
EIN: 880372802

5116
EBV Foundation ✧
38 Grand Corniche Dr.
Henderson, NV 89011-2004
E-mail: dani@ebvfoundation.org; Main URL: http://www.ebvfoundation.org

Established in NV.
Donors: Theodore Lachowicz; Cheryl Lachowicz; Cantor Fitzgerald; Bruce Carusi; Sue Carusi; Tom Foley; Kevin Coyne.
Foundation type: Independent foundation.
Financial data (yr. ended 12/31/12): Assets, $331,739 (M); gifts received, $78,378; expenditures, $593,931; qualifying distributions, $553,150; giving activities include $553,150 for 2 grants (high: $500,000; low: $53,150).
Purpose and activities: Giving primarily to participating veterans to assist in the development of their business plans.
Fields of interest: Social entrepreneurship; Military/veterans.
Limitations: Applications not accepted. Giving primarily in Syracuse, NY; some funding also in Henderson, NV.
Application information: Unsolicited requests for funds not accepted.
Officer: Theodore Lachowicz, Pres.
Board Members: George Bodine; Hon. John C. Cherundolo; Thomas C. Colella; Thomas Foley; Richard L. Haydon; Mark Larsen.
EIN: 263844672
Selected grants: The following grants are a representative sample of this grantmaker's funding activity:
$500,000 to Syracuse University, Syracuse, NY, 2012. To help fund the educational EBV Programs.

5117
Engelstad Family Foundation ✧
851 S. Rampart Blvd., Ste. 150
Las Vegas, NV 89145-4882 (702) 732-7102

Established in 2002 in NV.
Donors: Richard A. Clyne; Ralph Engelstad; Ralph and Betty Engelstad Trust.
Foundation type: Independent foundation.
Financial data (yr. ended 12/31/12): Assets, $728,328,702 (M); expenditures, $30,737,849; qualifying distributions, $26,338,086; giving activities include $26,338,086 for 100+ grants (high: $3,000,000).
Purpose and activities: Giving primarily to Roman Catholic schools, organizations and churches; funding also for children, youth and social services.
Fields of interest: Education; Human services; Children/youth, services; Catholic agencies & churches.
Limitations: Applications not accepted. Giving primarily in NV, with emphasis on Las Vegas. No grants to individuals.
Application information: Contributes only to pre-selected organizations.
Officers and Trustees:* Betty Engelstad,* Pres.; Kris McGarry,* V.P.; Jeffrey Cooper,* Treas.
EIN: 806008137
Selected grants: The following grants are a representative sample of this grantmaker's funding activity:
$5,000,000 to Nevada Cancer Institute, Las Vegas, NV, 2012. For program support.
$3,000,000 to Andre Agassi Foundation for Education, Las Vegas, NV, 2012. For program support.
$2,710,000 to University of Nevada at Las Vegas Foundation, Las Vegas, NV, 2012. For program support.
$2,000,000 to Smith Center for the Performing Arts, Las Vegas, NV, 2012. For program support.
$2,000,000 to University of North Dakota Foundation, Grand Forks, ND, 2012. For program support.
$1,000,000 to Metro Sports Foundation, Fargo, ND, 2012. For program support.
$1,000,000 to Opportunity Village, Las Vegas, NV, 2012. For program support.
$35,000 to United Service Organization Las Vegas Center, Las Vegas, NV, 2012. For program support.
$30,000 to Nevada Community Learning Centers, North Las Vegas, NV, 2012. For program support.
$30,000 to Ohr-OKeefe Museum of Art, Biloxi, MS, 2012. For program support.

5118
The Fairweather Foundation ✧
(formerly The Hall Family Foundation)
1726 Cedarwood Dr.
Minden, NV 89423-4726
Contact: Joanne Hall, Secy.-Treas.

Established in 1983 in NV.
Donors: Joanne Hall; Arthur E. Hall.
Foundation type: Independent foundation.
Financial data (yr. ended 12/31/13): Assets, $30,490,396 (M); expenditures, $1,997,979; qualifying distributions, $1,856,712; giving activities include $1,839,436 for 9 grants (high: $1,104,439; low: $1,000).
Purpose and activities: Giving primarily for higher education, conservation of wilderness areas, cancer research and a facility that provides temporary lodging for families of cancer patients on a cost-free basis, and a child welfare organization; support also for health, including medical education, and the biological sciences, and nursing.
Fields of interest: Performing arts; Performing arts, music; Arts; Higher education; Education; Environment, natural resources; Environment; Hospitals (general); Reproductive health, family planning; Speech/hearing centers; Nursing care; Health care; Substance abuse, services; Health organizations, association; Cancer; Heart & circulatory diseases; AIDS; Alcoholism; Biomedicine; Medical research, institute; Cancer research; Heart & circulatory research; AIDS research; Human services; Children/youth, services; Aging, centers/services; Biology/life sciences; Aging; Disabilities, people with; Economically disadvantaged.
Type of support: General/operating support; Continuing support; Capital campaigns; Building/

renovation; Emergency funds; Research; Matching/challenge support.
Limitations: Applications not accepted. Giving primarily in CA, NV, and VA. No grants to individuals.
Application information: Contributes only to pre-selected organizations.
Board meeting date(s): Fall
Officers and Directors:* Arthur E. Hall,* C.E.O.; Joanne Hall,* Pres. and Secy.-Treas.
Number of staff: None.
EIN: 880193741

5119
Findlay Education Foundation ✧ ☆
c/o Tyler Corder
310 N. Gibson
Henderson, NV 89014-6702

Established in 2006 in NV.
Donors: Findlay Cadillac; Clifford J. Findlay; Greg Heinrich; River City Petrolium; Findlay Shack Properties LLC; Findlay Management Group; Al Clise; South Point Hotel Casino; William Boyd.
Foundation type: Independent foundation.
Financial data (yr. ended 12/31/13): Assets, $28,003 (M); gifts received, $413,300; expenditures, $424,000; qualifying distributions, $424,000; giving activities include $424,000 for 1 grant.
Fields of interest: Higher education.
Limitations: Applications not accepted. Giving primarily in NV.
Application information: Unsolicited requests for funds not accepted.
Officers and Trustees:* Clifford J. Findlay,* Pres. and Treas.; Tyler Corder, Secy.; Bruce Becker; Jeffrey L. Burr.
EIN: 205109148

5120
Gabelli Foundation, Inc. ✧
165 W. Liberty St.
Reno, NV 89501-1955

Established in 1985 in NV.
Donors: Mario J. Gabelli; Gabelli Group Capital Partners, Inc.
Foundation type: Independent foundation.
Financial data (yr. ended 03/31/13): Assets, $67,304,661 (M); gifts received, $8,114,546; expenditures, $2,500,635; qualifying distributions, $2,221,106; giving activities include $2,159,000 for 46 grants (high: $1,000,000; low: $1,000).
Purpose and activities: Giving primarily for education, and youth and social services.
Fields of interest: Elementary/secondary education; Higher education; Business school/education; Education; Human services; Children/youth, services; Christian agencies & churches.
Type of support: General/operating support; Building/renovation.
Limitations: Applications not accepted. Giving in the U.S., with emphasis on MA and NY. No grants to individuals.
Application information: Contributes only to pre-selected organizations.
Officers: Mario J. Gabelli, Chair.; Elisa Gabelli Wilson, Pres.
Trustees: Marc J. Gabelli; Matthew R. Gabelli; Michael Gabelli; Mary Mazzolla.
EIN: 942975159

5121
Mark & Carolyn Guidry Foundation ✧ ☆
2654 W. Horizon Ridge Pkwy., No. B588
Henderson, NV 89052-2803

Established in 1994 in WA.
Donors: Carolyn Guidry†; Mark Guidry.
Foundation type: Independent foundation.
Financial data (yr. ended 12/31/13): Assets, $6,338,334 (M); gifts received, $2,050; expenditures, $984,330; qualifying distributions, $977,000; giving activities include $977,000 for 28 grants (high: $805,000; low: $1,000).
Purpose and activities: Giving primarily for higher education, particularly education in engineering and veterinary medicine.
Fields of interest: Museums; Elementary/secondary education; Higher education; Engineering school/education; Education; Veterinary medicine.
Limitations: Applications not accepted. Giving primarily in CA, LA and WA. No grants to individuals.
Application information: Contributes only to pre-selected organizations.
Officer: Mark Guidry, Mgr.
EIN: 943185161

5122
The Thelma B. & Thomas P. Hart Foundation ✧
4795 Coughlin Pkwy., Ste. 100
Reno, NV 89519-0994 (775) 333-0300
Contact: Mark W. Knobel, Tr.

Established in 1998 in NV.
Donors: Thomas Hart; Thelma Hart; The Hart Survivors Trust; The Hart Marital Trust.
Foundation type: Independent foundation.
Financial data (yr. ended 12/31/13): Assets, $31,645,863 (M); expenditures, $1,984,919; qualifying distributions, $1,683,955; giving activities include $1,524,250 for 68 grants (high: $200,000; low: $1,000).
Purpose and activities: Giving primarily for education, children's programs, service animal programs, health, and community-based programs.
Fields of interest: Education; Health care; Children, services; Community/economic development.
Limitations: Applications accepted. Giving primarily in northern CA, northern NV, and HI. No grants to individuals.
Application information: Application form required.
Initial approach: Letter
Deadline(s): None per se but recommended by June of each year
Trustees: Craig Karrasch; Mark Knobel.
EIN: 860881550
Selected grants: The following grants are a representative sample of this grantmaker's funding activity:
$50,000 to Boys and Girls Club of Truckee Meadows, Reno, NV, 2012. For Capital Campaign/Foster Drive.
$35,000 to Nevada Museum of Art, Reno, NV, 2012. For School Tour Program.
$25,000 to Canine Companions for Independence, Santa Rosa, CA, 2012. For Team Training Support.
$25,000 to Keep Memory Alive, Las Vegas, NV, 2012. For event/operational support.
$20,000 to Lake Tahoe Shakespeare Festival, Incline Village, NV, 2012. For technical equipment.
$15,000 to Boys and Girls Club of Truckee Meadows, Reno, NV, 2012. For sponsorship/fundraising event.
$15,000 to Washoe Legal Services, Reno, NV, 2012. For child advocacy program.
$10,000 to Artown, Reno, NV, 2012. For Summer Festival.
$10,000 to Boy Scouts of America, Nevada Area Council, Reno, NV, 2012. For operational support.
$10,000 to Solace Tree, Reno, NV, 2012. For printing costs.

5123
Robert Z. Hawkins Foundation ✧
1 E. Liberty St., Ste. 509
Reno, NV 89501-2117 (775) 786-1105

Established in 1980 in NV.
Donors: Kathryn Ackley Hawkins Trust; Robert Z. Hawkins†.
Foundation type: Independent foundation.
Financial data (yr. ended 12/31/13): Assets, $24,182,061 (M); expenditures, $1,192,053; qualifying distributions, $1,145,051; giving activities include $1,014,600 for 107 grants (high: $130,000; low: $1,000).
Fields of interest: Arts; Education; Animal welfare; Health care; Human services; Children/youth, services.
Type of support: General/operating support; Building/renovation; Equipment; Program development; Scholarship funds; Matching/challenge support.
Limitations: Applications accepted. Giving limited to northern NV. No grants to individuals.
Application information: Application form required.
Initial approach: Proposal
Deadline(s): None
Officer: William H. Wallace, Chair.; Carolyn K. Bernard, Vice-Chair.
Trustees: Bill A. Ligon, Jr.; C. David Russell; Prince A. Hawkins.
Number of staff: 1 full-time support; 1 part-time support.
EIN: 880162645
Selected grants: The following grants are a representative sample of this grantmaker's funding activity:
$25,000 to Artown, Reno, NV, 2012. For grant to support Monday Night Series.
$20,000 to Catholic Charities of Northern Nevada, Reno, NV, 2012. For assistance Programs - Xmas grant.
$20,000 to Food Bank of Northern Nevada, McCarran, NV, 2012. For Christmas Grant.
$20,000 to Nevada Humanities Committee, Reno, NV, 2012. For Chautauqua festival at the Hawkins Amphitheater.
$20,000 to Reno Philharmonic Association, Reno, NV, 2012. For grant for general support and education Programs.
$20,000 to Tahoe Truckee Community Foundation, Truckee, CA, 2012. For grant to fund the Community House project located in Kings Beach.
$10,000 to Casa de Vida, Reno, NV, 2012. For holiday grant.
$10,000 to Food Bank of Northern Nevada, McCarran, NV, 2012. For additional holiday grant.
$10,000 to Special Recreation Services, Reno, NV, 2012. For Summer Session camp support.
$5,000 to Nevada Museum of Art, Reno, NV, 2012. For grant to support 2012-13 School Tour Program.

5124
Roxie and Azad Joseph Foundation ✧
2890 Outlook Dr.
Reno, NV 89509-3953 (775) 825-2134
Contact: Robert Sims, Tr.
Additional application addresses: c/o Michael Melarkey, 4795 Caughlin Pkwy., Ste. 100, Reno, NV 89509, and c/o Vicki Puliz, 1180 Mile Circle Dr., Reno, NV 89511

Established in 2005 in NV.
Donors: Azad McIver Trust; Roxie Archie Trust.
Foundation type: Independent foundation.
Financial data (yr. ended 04/30/13): Assets, $9,872,212 (M); expenditures, $715,746; qualifying distributions, $569,162; giving activities include $553,000 for 39 grants (high: $25,000; low: $3,000).
Fields of interest: Higher education, university; Hospitals (general); Orthodox agencies & churches.
Limitations: Applications accepted. Giving primarily in CA and NV.
Application information: Application form required.
Initial approach: Letter
Deadline(s): None
Trustees: Michael Melarkey; Vicki Puliz; Robert L. Sims.
EIN: 202388760
Selected grants: The following grants are a representative sample of this grantmaker's funding activity:
$50,000 to Nevada Discovery Museum, Reno, NV, 2011. For general purpose.
$25,000 to Tahoe Truckee Community Foundation, Truckee, CA, 2011. For general purpose.
$20,000 to Armenian Community School of Fresno, Clovis, CA, 2011.
$15,000 to Food Bank of Northern Nevada, McCarran, NV, 2011.
$10,000 to Artown, Reno, NV, 2011. For general purpose.
$10,000 to K N P B Channel 5 Public Broadcasting, Reno, NV, 2011.
$10,000 to National Judicial College, Reno, NV, 2011.
$10,000 to Northern Nevada Youth Golf Foundation, Reno, NV, 2011.
$5,000 to Childrens Cabinet-A Child and Family Resource, Reno, NV, 2011. For general purpose.
$5,000 to Veterans Guest House, Reno, NV, 2011. For general purpose.

5125
The Eleanor Kagi Foundation ✧ ☆
(formerly The Bennett Foundation)
2964 Via Della Amore
Henderson, NV 89052-4028 (702) 260-4593
Contact: Kimberly Rick, Pres.

Established in 1994 in NV.
Donors: Lynn M. Bennett; William G. Bennett.
Foundation type: Independent foundation.
Financial data (yr. ended 12/31/12): Assets, $11,344,707 (M); expenditures, $719,548; qualifying distributions, $518,675; giving activities include $518,675 for grants.
Purpose and activities: Giving primarily for animal welfare; some funding also to an institute for women's research.
Fields of interest: Animals/wildlife; Mental health/crisis services.
Limitations: Applications accepted. Giving primarily in Las Vegas, NV.
Application information: The letter of inquiry should contain a brief statement of the applicant's need for funds and enough factual information to enable the staff to determine whether or not the application falls within the foundation's areas of preferred interest or warrants consideration as a special project. Application form required.
Initial approach: Letter of inquiry
Deadline(s): None
Officers and Directors:* Kimberly Rick,* Pres.; John R. Mackall,* Secy.; Bryan J. Dziedziak,* Treas.
EIN: 943189650

5126
Robert S. & Dorothy J. Keyser Foundation ✧
4795 Caughlin Pkwy., Ste. 100
Reno, NV 89519-0994 (775) 333-0300
Contact: Michael J. Melarkey, Tr.

Established in 1996 in NV.
Donor: The Charlene King Trust.
Foundation type: Independent foundation.
Financial data (yr. ended 12/31/13): Assets, $17,925,397 (M); expenditures, $1,050,202; qualifying distributions, $887,665; giving activities include $825,300 for 31 grants (high: $100,000; low: $2,500).
Purpose and activities: Giving primarily for programs that can be shown to benefit children.
Fields of interest: Museums; Elementary school/education; Higher education; Hospitals (general); Human services; Children/youth, services; Foundations (private grantmaking).
Limitations: Applications accepted. Giving primarily in Las Vegas and Reno, NV. No grants to individuals.
Application information: Application form not required.
Initial approach: Request application form
Deadline(s): None
Trustees: Timothy Cashman; Michael J. Melarkey; G. Blake Smith.
EIN: 880346537

5127
Theodore and Doris Lee Family Foundation ✧ ☆
3271 S. Highland Dr., Ste. 704
Las Vegas, NV 89109-1051

Established in NV.
Donors: Doris S. Lee; Theodore B. Lee; Lee Charitable Lead Trust.
Foundation type: Independent foundation.
Financial data (yr. ended 12/31/13): Assets, $1,159,192 (M); gifts received, $635,000; expenditures, $1,065,100; qualifying distributions, $1,065,100; giving activities include $1,065,100 for 52 grants (high: $400,000; low: $100).
Fields of interest: Arts; Law school/education; Health organizations; Human services.
Limitations: Applications not accepted. Giving primarily in CA and NV.
Application information: Unsolicited requests for funds not accepted.
Officers: Theodore B. Lee, Pres.; Doris S. Lee, Treas.
Directors: Ernest T.H. Lee; Gregory T.H. Lee.
EIN: 272531820

Selected grants: The following grants are a representative sample of this grantmaker's funding activity:
$75,000 to Nevada Ballet Theater, Las Vegas, NV, 2012. For general operations.

5128
Lied Foundation Trust ✧
3907 W. Charleston Blvd.
Las Vegas, NV 89102-1620 (702) 878-1559
Contact: Christina M. Hixson, Tr.

Established in 1972 in NE.
Donor: Ernst F. Lied†.
Foundation type: Independent foundation.
Financial data (yr. ended 12/31/13): Assets, $11,483,466 (M); expenditures, $1,542,234; qualifying distributions, $1,259,620; giving activities include $1,134,000 for 10 grants (high: $300,000; low: $10,000).
Fields of interest: Arts; Higher education; Higher education, university; Animal welfare; Agriculture/food; Youth development, services; Children/youth, services; Catholic federated giving programs.
Limitations: Applications accepted. Giving primarily in NE, and Las Vegas, NV.
Application information: Application form not required.
Initial approach: Letter
Deadline(s): None
Trustee: Christina M. Hixson.
EIN: 237282946

5129
Mallory Foundation ✧
c/o Riley Beckett
130 Cogorno Way
Carson City, NV 89703-5414

Established in 1991 in NV.
Donor: Jean L. Mallory.
Foundation type: Independent foundation.
Financial data (yr. ended 12/31/13): Assets, $13,961,162 (M); expenditures, $887,990; qualifying distributions, $597,877; giving activities include $517,000 for 6 grants (high: $190,000; low: $20,000).
Fields of interest: Arts, multipurpose centers/programs; Higher education; Hospitals (general); Human services; Children/youth, services.
Type of support: Program development; Scholarship funds.
Limitations: Applications not accepted. Giving primarily in NV; giving also in MA and MI. No grants to individuals.
Application information: Contributes only to pre-selected organizations.
Officers: Riley Beckett, Chair.; Ellen Shock, Secy.; Tom Cook, Treas.
EIN: 880272695

5130
Brenden Mann Foundation ✧
4321 W. Flamingo Rd.
Las Vegas, NV 89103-3903

Established in 2006 in NV.
Donor: Ted and Roberta Mann Foundation.
Foundation type: Independent foundation.

Financial data (yr. ended 12/31/12): Assets, $20,427,343 (M); expenditures, $718,674; qualifying distributions, $618,133; giving activities include $528,686 for 48 grants (high: $100,000; low: $1,000).
Fields of interest: Media, film/video; Education; Boys & girls clubs; Jewish agencies & synagogues; Children; Women; Men.
Limitations: Applications not accepted. Giving primarily in CA, MA and NV. No grants to individuals.
Application information: Unsolicited requests for funds not accepted.
Officer and Director:* John Brenden,* Pres.
EIN: 113789260

5131
Charles N. Mathewson Foundation ✧
4795 Caughlin Pkwy., Ste. 100
Reno, NV 89519-0994
Application address: c/o Charles N. Mathewson, Pres., P.O. Box 6448, Reno, NV 89513-6448, tel.: (775) 348-1844

Established in 1993 in NV.
Donor: Charles N. Mathewson.
Foundation type: Independent foundation.
Financial data (yr. ended 12/31/13): Assets, $25,015,505 (M); gifts received, $2,457,195; expenditures, $1,967,947; qualifying distributions, $1,967,947; giving activities include $1,948,631 for 36 grants (high: $515,000; low: $120).
Purpose and activities: Giving primarily for the arts, education, medical research, and children, youth, and social services.
Fields of interest: Media, film/video; Arts; Secondary school/education; Higher education; Education; Health organizations, association; Brain research; Youth development; Human services; Children/youth, services; Foundations (private grantmaking).
Limitations: Applications accepted. Giving primarily in CA and NV.
Application information: Application form required.
Initial approach: Proposal
Deadline(s): None
Officers and Executive Advisory Committee: Charles N. Mathewson,* Pres. and Secy.; Curtis N. Mathewson,* V.P.; Raymond Zimmerman, Treas.; Paulina G. Mathewson; Robert A. Mathewson.
EIN: 943179777

5132
Wilbur May Foundation ✧
c/o Suellen Fulstone
6100 Neil Rd., Ste. 555
Reno, NV 89511-1159

Established in 1992 as successor to the Wilbur D. May Foundation.
Donor: Wilbur May†.
Foundation type: Independent foundation.
Financial data (yr. ended 05/31/13): Assets, $48,427,732 (M); expenditures, $2,599,241; qualifying distributions, $2,214,550; giving activities include $2,214,550 for 40 grants (high: $300,000; low: $860).
Fields of interest: Higher education; Education; Health organizations, association; Recreation, parks/playgrounds; Human services; Children/youth, services.
Limitations: Applications not accepted. Giving primarily in CA and NV. No grants to individuals.
Application information: Contributes only to pre-selected organizations.
Officers: Anita May Rosenstein, Chair. and Pres.; Amanda May Stefan, Vice-Chair. and V.P.; Dorothy Duffy May, V.P. and Secy.; Dixie May, V.P. and Treas.; Kathy May Fritz, V.P.; Suellen Fulstone, Esq., V.P.; Alysia May, V.P.; Brian Rosenstein, V.P.
EIN: 943126741

5133
The M-K LINK Foundation ✧
c/o Stephen Haberkorn
P.O. Box 80270
Las Vegas, NV 89180-0270

Established in 1997 in AZ.
Donor: MK-LINK Investments LP.
Foundation type: Independent foundation.
Financial data (yr. ended 05/31/13): Assets, $4,636,635 (M); expenditures, $985,060; qualifying distributions, $904,515; giving activities include $900,770 for 23 grants (high: $175,000; low: $1,000).
Fields of interest: Education; Jewish agencies & synagogues.
Limitations: Applications not accepted. Giving primarily in CA and NV. No grants to individuals.
Application information: Contributes only to pre-selected organizations.
Officers and Directors:* Stephen Haberkorn,* Pres.; Matthew Haberkorn, V.P.; Vicki Haberkorn Abeles,* Secy.
EIN: 860870822
Selected grants: The following grants are a representative sample of this grantmaker's funding activity:
$6,300,000 to Temple Sinai Las Vegas, Las Vegas, NV, 2012. For general support.
$275,000 to Temple Beth Israel, Phoenix, AZ, 2012. For general support.
$175,000 to Jewish Federation of Las Vegas, Las Vegas, NV, 2013. For general support.
$130,000 to Young Israel of Phoenix, Phoenix, AZ, 2012. For general support.
$110,000 to Congregation Beth Israel, Scottsdale, AZ, 2013. For general support.
$94,151 to Temple Sinai Las Vegas, Las Vegas, NV, 2013. For general support.
$80,000 to Chabad of Contra Costa, Walnut Creek, CA, 2012. For general support.
$70,000 to Chabad of Contra Costa, Walnut Creek, CA, 2013. For general support.
$70,000 to Young Israel of Phoenix, Phoenix, AZ, 2013. For general support.
$68,439 to Dr. Miriam and Sheldon G. Adelson Educational Institute, Adelson Educational Campus, Las Vegas, NV, 2013. For general support.
$67,680 to Saint Jude Childrens Research Hospital, Memphis, TN, 2013. For general support.
$50,000 to Stanford University, Stanford, CA, 2013. For general support of medical research.
$25,000 to Case Western Reserve University, School of Medicine, Cleveland, OH, 2013. For general support.
$25,000 to Chelseas Hope Lafora Children Research Fund, Danville, CA, 2013. For general support.
$10,000 to Midbar Kodesh Temple, Henderson, NV, 2012. For general support.
$10,000 to Mountain View Presbyterian Church, Scottsdale, AZ, 2012. For general support.

5134
Nevada Community Foundation, Inc. ✧
1635 Village Center Circle, Ste. 160
Las Vegas, NV 89134 (702) 892-2326
Contact: Gian Brosco, Pres.
FAX: (702) 892-8580; E-mail: info@nevadacf.org;
Main URL: http://www.nevadacf.org
E-Newsletter: http://www.nevadacf.org/eNewsSignup.aspx
Facebook: https://www.facebook.com/NevadaCommunityFoundation
Twitter: https://twitter.com/nvcommunityfdtn

Established in 1988 in NV.
Foundation type: Community foundation.
Financial data (yr. ended 06/30/13): Assets, $32,595,639 (M); gifts received, $2,798,297; expenditures, $3,002,857; giving activities include $1,836,069 for 58+ grants (high: $355,000).
Purpose and activities: The foundation is committed to improving the lives of southern Nevadans today and for future generations by matching acts of caring to the many needs in the community.
Fields of interest: Arts; Adult/continuing education; Adult education—literacy, basic skills & GED; Education, reading; Education; Environment; Animal welfare; Medical care, rehabilitation; Health care; Substance abuse, services; Mental health/crisis services; Health organizations, association; Cancer; Heart & circulatory diseases; AIDS; Cancer research; Heart & circulatory research; AIDS research; Food services; Youth development, citizenship; Children/youth, services; Family services; Aging, centers/services; Women, centers/services; Minorities/immigrants, centers/services; Homeless, human services; Human services; Economic development; Community/economic development; United Ways and Federated Giving Programs; Government/public administration; Public affairs, citizen participation; Children/youth; Aging; Disabilities, people with; Blind/visually impaired; Minorities; Women; Economically disadvantaged; Homeless.
Type of support: Consulting services; General/operating support; Capital campaigns; Equipment; Emergency funds; Program development; Conferences/seminars; Publication; Seed money; Scholarship funds; Technical assistance; Matching/challenge support.
Limitations: Applications accepted. Giving limited to NV, with an overwhelming emphasis on the southern communities around greater Las Vegas.
Publications: Application guidelines; Annual report; Financial statement; Grants list.
Application information: Visit the foundation's web site for more information on grant programs. Application form required.
Board meeting date(s): Quarterly
Officers and Directors:* Maureen Schafer,* Chair.; Michael Threet,* Vice-Chair.; Gian Brosco, Esq.,* Pres.; Joselyn Cousins,* Secy.; Geraldine Tomich,* Treas.; Daniel Anderson; Larry Carter; Candace Johnson; Duncan Lee; Michael Morrissey; Charles Silvestri.
Number of staff: 3 full-time professional; 1 part-time professional; 3 full-time support; 1 part-time support.
EIN: 880241420

5135
Nova Foundation, Inc. ✧ ☆
316 California Ave., Ste. 448
Reno, NV 89509-1650

Established in 2007 in NV.
Donors: 2003 Dynamic Irrevocable Trust; Investment Capital Tech, LLC; Skip Viragh Foundation.
Foundation type: Independent foundation.
Financial data (yr. ended 06/30/13): Assets, $308,909 (M); gifts received, $500,000; expenditures, $533,922; qualifying distributions, $525,000; giving activities include $525,000 for 2 grants (high: $500,000; low: $25,000).
Purpose and activities: Giving primarily for cancer research, particularly for pancreatic cancer serum biomarker study.
Fields of interest: Cancer; Cancer research.
Limitations: Applications not accepted. Giving primarily in Baltimore, MD, and New York, NY.
Application information: Unsolicited requests for funds not accepted.
Officers: Mark S. Viragh, Pres.; Katherine A. Viragh, V.P.; Roger E. Young, V.P.
EIN: 020807885

5136
NV Energy Charitable Foundation ✧
(formerly NV Energy Foundation)
P.O. Box 10100
Reno, NV 89520-3150 (775) 834-5642
Contact: Mary Simmons, Secy.
E-mail: Communitynorth@nvenergy.com; Application address for Southern Nevada: Admin., NV Energy Fdn., P.O. Box 98910, Las Vegas, NV 89151-0001, tel.: (702) 402-5741, e-mail: Communitysouth@nvenergy.com; Main URL: http://www.nvenergy.com/community/funding/sprfoundation/
Application address for Southern Nevada: NV Energy, Powerful Partnership Scholarship - M/S 15, P.O. Box 98910, Las Vegas, NV 89151; Northern Nevada: NV Energy, Powerful Partnership Scholarship, Community Foundation of Western Nevada, 1885 South Arlington Ave., Ste. 103, Reno, NV 89509

Established in 1987 in NV.
Donors: Sierra Pacific Resources; NV Energy, Inc.
Foundation type: Company-sponsored foundation.
Financial data (yr. ended 12/31/12): Assets, $6,886,115 (M); gifts received, $3,000,000; expenditures, $4,027,816; qualifying distributions, $4,027,600; giving activities include $4,027,600 for 205 grants (high: $300,000; low: $250).
Purpose and activities: The foundation supports programs designed to promote arts and culture; education; the environment; youth; and health and human services.
Fields of interest: Arts, cultural/ethnic awareness; Arts; Higher education; Education; Environment, recycling; Environment, natural resources; Environment, energy; Environment; Animals/wildlife; Health care; Recreation, parks/playgrounds; Youth development; Youth, services; Human services; United Ways and Federated Giving Programs.
Type of support: General/operating support; Continuing support; Annual campaigns; Capital campaigns; Program development; Scholarship funds; Employee volunteer services; Sponsorships; Employee matching gifts; Scholarships—to individuals; Matching/challenge support.
Limitations: Applications accepted. Giving limited to areas of company operations in northeastern CA and northeastern NV. No support for religious organizations, foundations, political or partisan organizations, or sports leagues. No grants to individuals (except for scholarships), or for tickets for contests, raffles, or other activities with prizes; film, television, or video productions, advertising, debt reduction, sporting events or tournaments, trips or tours, talent or beauty contests, or conferences.
Publications: Application guidelines; Informational brochure (including application guidelines); Program policy statement.
Application information: Multi-year funding is not automatic. An application form is required for scholarships. Applications are not accepted by e-mail, fax, or telephone.
Initial approach: Proposal; download application form and mail to application address for scholarships
Copies of proposal: 1
Deadline(s): None; Mar. 1 for Powerful Partnerships High School Scholarships
Board meeting date(s): Bi-monthly
Final notification: 2 months; Apr. 30 for Powerful Partnerships High School Scholarships
Officers and Directors:* Michael W. Yackira,* Pres.; Mary Simmons, Secy.; Jonathan Halkyard, Treas.; Dimek Samil; Tony Sanchez.
Number of staff: 1 part-time professional; 1 part-time support.
EIN: 880244735
Selected grants: The following grants are a representative sample of this grantmaker's funding activity:
$500,000 to United Way of Southern Nevada, Las Vegas, NV, 2011.
$250,000 to University of Nevada, Reno, NV, 2011.
$200,000 to Nevada Cancer Institute, Las Vegas, NV, 2011.
$200,000 to Nevada Cancer Institute, Las Vegas, NV, 2011.
$200,000 to Smith Center for the Performing Arts, Las Vegas, NV, 2011.
$55,000 to Opportunity Village, Las Vegas, NV, 2011.
$20,000 to Nevada Museum of Art, Reno, NV, 2011.
$20,000 to Washoe County School District Educational Foundation, Reno, NV, 2011.
$15,000 to United Way of Southern Nevada, Las Vegas, NV, 2011.
$10,000 to Nathan Adelson Hospice Foundation, Las Vegas, NV, 2011.

5137
Michael A. O'Bannon Foundation ✧
2275 E. Desert Inn Rd.
Las Vegas, NV 89169-3216

Established in 1995 in NV.
Foundation type: Independent foundation.
Financial data (yr. ended 12/31/13): Assets, $11,710,982 (M); expenditures, $584,462; qualifying distributions, $516,319; giving activities include $446,767 for 15 grants (high: $221,767; low: $3,000).
Purpose and activities: Giving primarily for medical research, and for children and youth services.
Fields of interest: Animals/wildlife; Cancer research; Medical research; Human services; Children/youth, services; Family services.
Limitations: Applications not accepted. Giving primarily in AZ and NV. No grants to individuals.
Application information: Contributes only to pre-selected organizations.
Officer and Trustees:* Kay F. Alchu,* Mgr.; Ryan Lawrence; Mark McElroy; Victoria Willson.
EIN: 943216555
Selected grants: The following grants are a representative sample of this grantmaker's funding activity:
$5,000 to Best Friends Animal Society, Kanab, UT, 2012. For animal protection and care.
$5,000 to Omaha Schools Foundation, Omaha, NE, 2012. For education of children.
$5,000 to Siena Francis House, Omaha, NE, 2012. For Homeless; shelter and food.

5138
Parasol Tahoe Community Foundation ✧
(formerly Parasol Community Foundation, Inc.)
948 Incline Way
Incline Village, NV 89451 (775) 298-0100
Contact: Megan Weiss, Dir., Progs. and Svcs.
FAX: (775) 298-0099; E-mail: info@parasol.org; Main URL: http://www.parasol.org
Facebook: http://www.facebook.com/pages/Parasol-Tahoe-Community-Foundation/117062444912
Twitter: https://twitter.com/ptcf

Established in 1996 in NV.
Foundation type: Community foundation.
Financial data (yr. ended 06/30/13): Assets, $54,124,976 (M); gifts received, $11,639,269; expenditures, $8,114,806; giving activities include $6,463,772 for 80+ grants (high: $200,300).
Purpose and activities: The Parasol Tahoe Community Foundation envisions a region known for engaged community. As Tahoe's largest community foundation, they are committed to improving the quality of life throughout the Lake Tahoe basin and empowering donors in meeting their charitable passions. The foundation seeks to serve as a catalyst for a new nonprofit model that will better serve the community.
Fields of interest: Arts; Education; Environment; Human services; Community/economic development.
Type of support: Seed money; Scholarship funds; Matching/challenge support; Capital campaigns; General/operating support; Annual campaigns; Endowments; In-kind gifts.
Limitations: Applications accepted. Giving limited to the Lake Tahoe region of CA and NV.
Publications: Application guidelines; Annual report; Financial statement; Grants list; Newsletter.
Application information: Visit foundation web site application form and guidelines. Application form required.
Initial approach: Submit application form
Copies of proposal: 1
Deadline(s): Early Nov.
Board meeting date(s): Quarterly
Final notification: 4-6 weeks
Officers and Directors:* David Hardie,* Chair.; Dean Meiling,* Co-Vice Chair.; Bridge Stuart,* Co-Vice Chair.; Claudia Anderson,* C.E.O.; George Ashley,* Treas.; Deborah Hackett, C.F.O.; Ron Alling; Wayne Cameron; Colleen Chapman; Robert Holman; Mary Jurkonis; Aimee LaFayette; Aaron Moore; Janet Pahl; Bill Watson.

Number of staff: 6 full-time professional; 1 part-time professional.
EIN: 880362053

5139
William N. Pennington Foundation ✧
P.O. Box 7290
Reno, NV 89510-7290 (775) 333-9100
Contact: Kent Green

Established in 1989 in NV.
Donors: William N. Pennington; William N. Pennington Separate Property Trust; William N. Pennington Charitable Remainder Unitrust; The William N. Pennington 1998 Charitable Trust; The William N. Pennington 1999 Charitable Trust; William N. Pennington 2003 Charitable Remainder Unitrust; The Pennington 2008 Charitable Remainder Trust; William N. Pennington 2010 Charitable Remainder Trust.
Foundation type: Independent foundation.
Financial data (yr. ended 12/31/13): Assets, $103,717,833 (M); gifts received, $16,720,884; expenditures, $4,931,812; qualifying distributions, $4,028,627; giving activities include $3,841,591 for 31 grants (high: $1,500,000; low: $3,000).
Purpose and activities: Giving limited to education, community services, health, and medical research. The foundation also has interest in supporting community and health services for children and the elderly, as well providing financial aid to students in colleges and universities.
Fields of interest: Higher education; Scholarships/financial aid; Health care; Cancer; Medical research, institute; Human services; Children/youth, services.
Type of support: General/operating support; Continuing support; Building/renovation; Equipment; Scholarship funds.
Limitations: Applications accepted. Giving primarily in northern NV, with emphasis on the Reno/Sparks area. No grants to individuals, arts or cultural programs, religious institutions or endowments.
Publications: Financial statement.
Application information: Application form required.
Initial approach: Proposal
Copies of proposal: 1
Deadline(s): None
Trustees: Richard P. Banis; Donald L. Carano; John Mackall; Fred Scarpello.
EIN: 943096845
Selected grants: The following grants are a representative sample of this grantmaker's funding activity:
$150,000 to Saint Marys Foundation, Reno, NV, 2011.
$125,000 to Renown Health Foundation, Reno, NV, 2011.
$40,000 to Boys and Girls Club of Truckee Meadows, Reno, NV, 2011.
$35,000 to Assistance League of Reno-Sparks, Reno, NV, 2011.
$30,000 to University of Nevada Reno Foundation, Reno, NV, 2011.
$28,750 to University of Nevada Reno Foundation, Reno, NV, 2011.
$5,000 to House Calls, Fernley, NV, 2011.
$2,000 to United Blood Services, Reno, NV, 2011.

5140
Wayne L. Prim Foundation ✧
P.O. Box 12219
Zephyr Cove, NV 89448-4219 (775) 588-7300
Contact: Wayne L. Prim, Tr.

Established in 1990 in NV.
Donors: Wayne L. Prim; Prim Ventures, Inc.
Foundation type: Independent foundation.
Financial data (yr. ended 12/31/13): Assets, $24,186,373 (M); expenditures, $1,230,285; qualifying distributions, $1,228,633; giving activities include $1,228,500 for 34 grants (high: $574,350; low: $200).
Purpose and activities: Giving primarily for education.
Fields of interest: Museums (art); Performing arts, theater; Education; Crime/violence prevention, youth; Crime/violence prevention, abuse prevention; Human services.
Limitations: Applications accepted. Giving primarily in CA and NV. No grants to individuals.
Application information: Application form not required.
Initial approach: Letter
Deadline(s): None
Trustees: Wayne L. Prim; Wayne L. Prim, Jr.; Stuart R. Sagan.
EIN: 880265893
Selected grants: The following grants are a representative sample of this grantmaker's funding activity:
$711,000 to Parasol Tahoe Community Foundation, Incline Village, NV, 2012. For Funds for Programs to Promote Non-Profit Collaboration and Philanthropy.
$340,375 to Sierra Nevada College, Incline Village, NV, 2012. For Funds for the Sierra Nevada College Scholarship Program.
$100,000 to Nevada Museum of Art, Reno, NV, 2012. For funding for Art Programs and Exhibitions.
$15,000 to Lake Tahoe School, Incline Village, NV, 2012. To support Technology Initiative - Providing Tools Needed for Children to Be Successful Citizens Of.
$9,430 to Palm Springs Art Museum, Palm Springs, CA, 2012. For Funds to Promote Enjoyment and Appreciation of the Art.
$1,200 to Lake Tahoe Shakespeare Festival, Incline Village, NV, 2012. To educate Future Generations on the Importance of Including Theater, Music and Art in Their.

5141
Prometheus Foundation ✧
P.O. Box 1157
Crystal Bay, NV 89402-1157

Established in NV.
Donor: Carl B. Barney.
Foundation type: Independent foundation.
Financial data (yr. ended 12/31/12): Assets, $14,479,097 (M); expenditures, $4,140,593; qualifying distributions, $3,938,000; giving activities include $3,938,000 for 2 grants (high: $3,582,000; low: $356,000).
Fields of interest: Literature; Education.
Limitations: Applications not accepted. Giving primarily in CA; some giving also in VA. No grants to individuals.
Application information: Contributes only to pre-selected organizations.
Officer: Carl B. Barney, Pres.
EIN: 271456655
Selected grants: The following grants are a representative sample of this grantmaker's funding activity:
$3,321,500 to Ayn Rand Institute, Irvine, CA, 2011.

5142
The Nell J. Redfield Foundation ✧
(formerly The NJR Foundation)
P.O. Box 61
Reno, NV 89504-0061 (775) 323-1373
Contact: Gerald C. Smith, V.P. and Secy.
E-mail: redfieldfoundation@yahoo.com

Foundation type: Independent foundation.
Financial data (yr. ended 12/31/13): Assets, $86,500,541 (M); expenditures, $6,169,291; qualifying distributions, $5,654,557; giving activities include $5,404,338 for 93 grants (high: $500,000; low: $298).
Purpose and activities: Giving only for the advancement of health care, medical research, care of handicapped children and the aged, education, and religion.
Limitations: Applications accepted. Giving primarily in Reno, NV.
Publications: Application guidelines; Annual report.
Application information: Application form required.
Initial approach: Letter
Deadline(s): 15 days before quarterly meetings
Board meeting date(s): Mar., June, Sept., and Dec.
Officers and Directors:* Helen Jeane Jones,* Pres.; Gerald C. Smith,* V.P., Secy., and Mgr.; Kenneth G. Walker,* V.P. and Treas.
EIN: 271017158

5143
Donald W. Reynolds Foundation ✧
1701 Village Center Cir.
Las Vegas, NV 89134-6303 (702) 804-6000
Contact: Karina Mayer, Grants Manager
FAX: (702) 804-6099;
E-mail: generalquestions@dwrf.org; Main URL: http://www.dwreynolds.org

Established in 1954 in NV.
Donor: Donald W. Reynolds†.
Foundation type: Independent foundation.
Financial data (yr. ended 12/31/13): Assets, $175,552,668 (M); expenditures, $62,988,267; qualifying distributions, $62,363,024; giving activities include $58,832,495 for 82 grants (high: $14,879,743; low: $200), and $107,436 for 22 employee matching gifts.
Purpose and activities: The foundation seeks to honor the memory of its benefactor, for whom it is named, by filling unmet needs and attempting to gain an immediate, transformational impact in four principal areas of interest: 1) Meeting the greatest needs of communities in Arkansas, Nevada and Oklahoma, primarily through improved facilities for their outstanding local nonprofit organizations; 2) Accelerating the fight against atherosclerosis and atherosclerotic heart disease through cutting-edge, translational research; 3) Improving the quality of life of America's growing elderly population through better training of physicians in geriatrics; and 4) Enhancing the quality and integrity of journalism, focusing particularly on better training of journalists who serve smaller communities and on business journalism. The foundation remains open to

consideration of special opportunities in other areas that are consistent with its broad goals. In pursuing its goals, the foundation is committed to the support of nonprofit organizations and institutions that demonstrate sound financial management, efficient operation, program integrity and an entrepreneurial spirit.
Fields of interest: Higher education; Health care; Medical research, institute; Human services; Public affairs.
Type of support: Building/renovation; Equipment; Program development; Research; Employee matching gifts.
Limitations: Applications accepted. Giving primarily in AR, NV, and OK for capital and planning grants. Giving nationally for cardiovascular clinic research and geriatrics training of physicians, and business journalism. No support for elementary or secondary education, or religious institutions or hospitals. No grants to individuals, or for continuing support, program or operating support, or endowment funds.
Publications: Financial statement; Grants list.
Application information: Request guidelines before submitting proposal or visit the foundation's web site. Proposals sent by fax or e-mail not considered. Applicants are encouraged to discuss projects/ requests with foundation staff by telephone or in writing. Application form not required.
Initial approach: Letter (1-2 pages)
Deadline(s): Varies by program, contact the foundation or visit foundation web site
Board meeting date(s): Apr. and Oct.
Officers and Trustees:* Fred W. Smith,* Chair.; Wes Smith,* Vice-Chair.; Steven L. Anderson,* Pres.; Lynn Mosier, Exec. V.P. and C.F.O.; Neal R. Pendergraft; Jonathan Smith, O.D.
Number of staff: 11 full-time professional; 2 full-time support; 1 part-time support.
EIN: 716053383

5144
Abraham & Sonia Rochlin Foundation ✧
3690 Grant Dr., Ste. I-2
Reno, NV 89509-5360

Established in 1969 in CA.
Donors: Abraham Rochlin†; Sonia Rochlin; Heidemarie Rochlin; Heidemarie Rochlin Trust.
Foundation type: Independent foundation.
Financial data (yr. ended 12/31/12): Assets, $46,232,372 (M); expenditures, $2,354,793; qualifying distributions, $2,249,018; giving activities include $2,150,145 for 25 grants (high: $896,500; low: $46).
Purpose and activities: Grants primarily for Jewish organizations, including welfare funds and higher educational institutions.
Fields of interest: Higher education; Human services; Jewish federated giving programs; Jewish agencies & synagogues.
Limitations: Applications not accepted. Giving primarily in CA, NV, and NY. No grants to individuals.
Publications: Annual report.
Application information: Contributes only to pre-selected organizations.
Officers: Heidemarie Rochlin, Pres.; Joseph Schonwald, V.P.
EIN: 941696244
Selected grants: The following grants are a representative sample of this grantmaker's funding activity:
$20,000 to Central Fund of Israel, New York, NY, 2012. For organizational mission.

5145
The Ruvo Family Foundation ✧
8400 S. Jones Blvd.
Las Vegas, NV 89139
Application address: c/o Camille Ruvo, 24 Sawgrass Ct., Las Vegas, NV 89113

Established in 2002 in NV.
Donors: Larry Ruvo; Camille Ruvo.
Foundation type: Independent foundation.
Financial data (yr. ended 12/31/13): Assets, $3,249,738 (M); gifts received, $994,630; expenditures, $614,810; qualifying distributions, $613,950; giving activities include $611,300 for 70 grants (high: $262,700; low: $25).
Purpose and activities: Giving primarily for health organizations and medical research, particularly an institute specializing in Alzheimer's, Parkinson's, Huntington's, ALS, and memory disorders; funding also for Roman Catholic churches, education, and organizations, the arts, and children, youth, and social services.
Fields of interest: Performing arts centers; Education; Brain disorders; Medical research, institute; Cancer research; Human services; Children/youth, services; Catholic federated giving programs; Catholic agencies & churches; Children/ youth; Economically disadvantaged.
Application information: Application form required.
Initial approach: Letter
Deadline(s): None
Director: Camille Ruvo.
EIN: 731688102

5146
Safe Endowment Fund, Inc. ✧
P.O. Box 10100
Reno, NV 89520

Established in NV.
Foundation type: Independent foundation.
Financial data (yr. ended 07/31/11): Assets, $0 (M); expenditures, $644,842; qualifying distributions, $644,500; giving activities include $643,750 for 1 grant.
Fields of interest: Human services.
Limitations: Applications not accepted. Giving primarily in Reno, NV. No grants to individuals.
Application information: Unsolicited requests for funds not accepted.
Officers: Robert Jones, Pres.; Linda Ellsworth, Secy.; Karen C. Ross, Treas.
Directors: Bruce Bullock; Carol Marin; Cloyd Phillips.
EIN: 860845648

5147
The Sawyer Family Foundation ✧
2654 W. Horizon Ridge Pkwy., Ste. B-5
P.O. Box 176
Henderson, NV 89052-2858 (702) 796-9991
Contact: Gail L. Sawyer, Pres.

Established in 2004 in NV.
Donor: Gail L. Sawyer.
Foundation type: Independent foundation.
Financial data (yr. ended 12/31/13): Assets, $2,225,866 (M); gifts received, $1,050,000; expenditures, $1,505,588; qualifying distributions, $1,470,100; giving activities include $1,470,100 for 8 grants (high: $400,000; low: $5,000).
Fields of interest: Education; Health care; Human services.
Limitations: Applications accepted. Giving primarily in NV, with emphasis on Las Vegas.
Application information: Application form not required.
Initial approach: Proposal
Deadline(s): None
Officers: Gail L. Sawyer, Pres.; Jack R. Hanifan, Secy.-Treas.
EIN: 680559353
Selected grants: The following grants are a representative sample of this grantmaker's funding activity:
$100,000 to Nathan Adelson Hospice, Las Vegas, NV, 2012. For End of Life Care.

5148
The David and Linda Shaheen Foundation, Inc. ✧
P.O. Box 973
Crystal Bay, NV 89402-0973
Contact: David M. Shaheen, Chair.
E-mail: s@eatyourpeas.org; Main URL: http:// www.eatyourpeas.org

Established in 2001 in NV.
Donors: David M. Shaheen; Linda F. Shaheen.
Foundation type: Operating foundation.
Financial data (yr. ended 12/31/12): Assets, $8,205,558 (M); expenditures, $526,860; qualifying distributions, $491,700; giving activities include $491,700 for 16 grants (high: $236,200; low: $1,000).
Purpose and activities: Education is the centerpiece of the foundation, with a concentration on three areas: breast cancer prevention and research, AIDS prevention, and higher education for inner city youth.
Fields of interest: Scholarships/financial aid; Breast cancer; AIDS; Breast cancer research; Youth; Economically disadvantaged.
Limitations: Applications accepted. Giving primarily in CA and GA. No grants to individuals.
Application information: Application information available on foundation web site.
Initial approach: E-mail
Deadline(s): None
Officer: David Shaheen, C.E.O. and Pres.
EIN: 582489866
Selected grants: The following grants are a representative sample of this grantmaker's funding activity:
$236,200 to A Place Called Home, Los Angeles, CA, 2012. To advance Education for at risk children of South Central Los Angeles.
$35,000 to Los Angeles Philharmonic, Los Angeles, CA, 2012. For Music Education in Public Schools.
$10,000 to Piedmont Hospital, Atlanta, GA, 2012. For Breast Health services and prescription drugs for indigent.
$7,000 to Homeboy Industries, Los Angeles, CA, 2012. For Fund Programs to educated and job train gang involved youth.
$5,000 to Dalton Education Foundation, Dalton, GA, 2012. For Help School System provide services cut by state budget.
$5,000 to InsideOut Writers, Los Angeles, CA, 2012. For Writing education for incarcerated youth.
$1,000 to Forward Stride, Beaverton, OR, 2012. To provide Equine therapy for handicap individuals.

5149
Southwest Gas Corporation Foundation ✧
5241 Spring Mountain Rd.
P.O. Box 98510
Las Vegas, NV 89193-8510 (702) 876-7247
Contact: Suzanne Farinas

Established in 1985 in NV.
Donor: Southwest Gas Corp.
Foundation type: Company-sponsored foundation.
Financial data (yr. ended 12/31/13): Assets, $2,145,857 (M); gifts received, $643,231; expenditures, $599,952; qualifying distributions, $665,534; giving activities include $629,534 for 384 grants (high: $50,000; low: $25), and $36,000 for 24 grants to individuals (high: $1,500; low: $1,500).
Purpose and activities: The foundation supports organizations involved with arts and culture, education, the environment, health, and human services.
Fields of interest: Arts; Education; Environment.
Limitations: Applications accepted. Giving limited to areas of company operations in AZ, San Bernardino County, CA, and NV. No support for churches, religious or discriminatory organizations, athletic teams, or hospitals. No grants to individuals, or for endowments, trips, or tours.
Publications: Application guidelines; Informational brochure (including application guidelines).
Application information: Application form required.
Initial approach: Completed application form
Copies of proposal: 1
Deadline(s): None
Board meeting date(s): As needed
Trustees: Roy R. Centrella; Karen Haller; Jeffrey W. Shaw.
Number of staff: None.
EIN: 942988564

5150
Thomas Spiegel Family Foundation ✧
(formerly Columbia Charitable Foundation)
9101 Alta Dr., Ste. 107
Las Vegas, NV 89145-8501

Established in 2004 in CA as the result of a reorganization of the Columbia Charitable Foundation.
Foundation type: Independent foundation.
Financial data (yr. ended 12/31/12): Assets, $42,056,085 (M); expenditures, $4,782,037; qualifying distributions, $3,699,874; giving activities include $3,222,764 for 8 grants (high: $1,600,000; low: $1,000).
Fields of interest: Health care; Jewish federated giving programs; Jewish agencies & synagogues.
Limitations: Applications not accepted. Giving primarily in Las Vegas, NV. No grants to individuals.
Application information: Contributes only to pre-selected organizations.
Officer and Directors:* Thomas Spiegel, C.F.O.; Charles V. Roven; Helene Spiegel.
EIN: 331050281

5151
Elbridge and Debra Stuart Family Foundation ✧
P.O. Box 8340
Incline Village, NV 89452-8340

Foundation type: Independent foundation.
Financial data (yr. ended 12/31/12): Assets, $46,775,379 (M); expenditures, $904,148; qualifying distributions, $687,672; giving activities include $687,672 for grants.
Fields of interest: Education; Recreation, camps.
Limitations: Applications not accepted. Giving primarily in WA.
Application information: Unsolicited requests for funds not accepted.
Directors: Debra E. Stuart; Elbridge H. Stuart.
EIN: 264492027

5152
The Richard Tam Foundation ✧
8535 Edna Ave., Ste. 120
Las Vegas, NV 89117-4430

Established in NV.
Donor: Richard Tam‡.
Foundation type: Independent foundation.
Financial data (yr. ended 06/30/13): Assets, $17,310,023 (M); gifts received, $628,740; expenditures, $1,195,056; qualifying distributions, $1,053,320; giving activities include $1,053,320 for grants.
Purpose and activities: Giving primarily for education.
Fields of interest: Elementary/secondary education; Human services.
Type of support: General/operating support.
Limitations: Applications not accepted. Giving primarily in MI; funding also in Las Vegas, NV. No grants to individuals.
Application information: Contributes only to pre-selected organizations.
Officers: Judith L. Sargent, Pres.; R. Ian Ross, Exec. Dir.
EIN: 880241216
Selected grants: The following grants are a representative sample of this grantmaker's funding activity:
$100,000 to I Have A Dream Foundation, Las Vegas, NV, 2013. For Education for at -Risk Youth.
$25,000 to Autism Research Institute, San Diego, CA, 2013. For ARI Is Dedicated to Developing a Standard of Care for Individuals with Autism Spectrum Disorders and Their Families.
$20,000 to Tragedy Assistance Program for Survivors, Washington, DC, 2013. To Provide Care and Support for Families and Friends Grieving the Loss of a Member of the Armed Forces.

5153
Cyrus Tang Foundation ✧
(formerly Tang Family Foundation)
8960 Spanish Ridge Ave.
Las Vegas, NV 89148-1302 (702) 734-3700
Contact: Stella Liang, Treas.
FAX: (702) 734-6766;
E-mail: tang@tangfoundation.org; Main URL: http://www.tangfoundation.org
Photo Gallieries: http://www.tangfoundation.org/index.php?option=com_content&view=article&id=51&Itemid=97&site=CTF&sub=7

Established in 1996 in NV.
Donors: Cyrus Tang; Tang Industries, Inc.
Foundation type: Independent foundation.
Financial data (yr. ended 12/31/12): Assets, $229,395,891 (M); gifts received, $2,190,010; expenditures, $10,066,869; qualifying distributions, $9,901,184; giving activities include $9,526,333 for grants.
Purpose and activities: Giving primarily to improve the quality of life in disadvantaged communities of China, through effective investments in education and public health, and by fostering community spirit.
Fields of interest: Higher education; Scholarships/financial aid; Education; Human services.
International interests: China.
Type of support: Building/renovation; Scholarship funds; Matching/challenge support.
Limitations: Applications not accepted. Giving primarily in China. No grants to individuals.
Application information: Contributes only to pre-selected organizations. Applications are by invitation only, and are also accepted in Chinese (traditional or simplified).
Officers and Directors:* Cyrus Tang,* Pres.; Patrick Liang,* V.P.; Vytas Ambutas, Secy.; Stella Liang,* Treas.
Number of staff: 3 full-time professional.
EIN: 880361180

5154
Tusher Family Foundation ✧
c/o Sierra Corporate Svcs.
100 W. Liberty St., 10th Fl.
Reno, NV 89501-1962

Established in 2005 in NV.
Donors: Thomas W. Tusher; Pauline B. Tusher.
Foundation type: Independent foundation.
Financial data (yr. ended 12/31/13): Assets, $17,139,453 (M); gifts received, $550,412; expenditures, $556,545; qualifying distributions, $460,000; giving activities include $460,000 for 3 grants (high: $250,000; low: $10,000).
Fields of interest: Higher education, university; Environment; Animals/wildlife; Science.
Limitations: Applications not accepted. Giving primarily in CA and Washington, DC. No grants to individuals.
Application information: Contributes only to pre-selected organizations.
Officers and Trustees:* Thomas W. Tusher,* Pres.; Pauline B. Tusher,* V.P.; Gregory Malcolm Tusher,* Secy.-Treas.
EIN: 760777686
Selected grants: The following grants are a representative sample of this grantmaker's funding activity:
$210,000 to California Academy of Sciences, San Francisco, CA, 2011.
$110,000 to World Wildlife Fund, Washington, DC, 2011.
$100,000 to University of California, Berkeley, CA, 2011.

5155
Jack Van Sickle Foundation ✧
646 Humboldt St.
Reno, NV 89509-1606

Established in 2005 in NV.
Donors: Jack Van Sickle Trust; Hettie Van Sickle Trust.
Foundation type: Independent foundation.

Financial data (yr. ended 12/31/13): Assets, $11,836,090 (M); expenditures, $740,102; qualifying distributions, $538,482; giving activities include $538,482 for 32 grants (high: $145,000; low: $500).
Fields of interest: Education; Boys & girls clubs; Children/youth, services.
Limitations: Applications not accepted. Giving primarily in Reno, NV. No grants to individuals.
Application information: Contributes only to pre-selected organizations.
Officer: David Pringle, Pres. and Secy.-Treas.
Trustees: Leo Bergin; Mark Knobel.
EIN: 201292268

5156
The Skip Viragh Foundation, Inc. ✧
316 California Ave., Ste. 448
Reno, NV 89509-1650 (775) 323-2125

Established in 2007 in NV.
Donor: Rydex NV, Inc.
Foundation type: Independent foundation.
Financial data (yr. ended 06/30/13): Assets, $316,308,420 (M); expenditures, $19,124,301; qualifying distributions, $16,349,105; giving activities include $16,136,450 for 36 grants (high: $4,759,450; low: $10,000).
Fields of interest: Higher education; Health care, clinics/centers; Housing/shelter, development; Housing/shelter, homeless.
Type of support: Scholarship funds.
Limitations: Applications not accepted. Giving primarily in AL and MD.
Application information: Contributes only to pre-selected organizations.
Officers: Mark S. Viragh, Pres.; Roger E. Young, V.P.; Katherine A. Viragh, Secy.
EIN: 208044292
Selected grants: The following grants are a representative sample of this grantmaker's funding activity:
$2,754,500 to Lung Cancer Alliance, Washington, DC, 2012.
$1,900,000 to Fidelity Charitable Gift Fund, Boston, MA, 2012.
$977,086 to Habitat for Humanity, Sandtown, Baltimore, MD, 2012.
$847,599 to University of Texas M.D. Anderson Cancer Center, Houston, TX, 2012. For pancreatic cancer research.
$500,000 to Nova Foundation, Reno, NV, 2012. For Johns Hopkins pancreatic cancer research.
$500,000 to Saint Marys Foundation, San Francisco, CA, 2012. For outreach programs for underserved, state-of-the-art technology, wellness and prevention programs for children, seniors and families.
$500,000 to Step 2, Reno, NV, 2012. For capital campaign.
$450,000 to International Cooperating Ministries, Hampton, VA, 2012. For orphanage construction.
$430,000 to Salvation Army of Reno, Reno, NV, 2012. To repair facility and provide Christmas food baskets and toys.
$25,000 to Samaritan Women, Owings Mills, MD, 2012.

5157
Terry Lee Wells Foundation ✧ ☆
P.O. Box 70806
Reno, NV 89570-0806 (775) 322-7733
E-mail: info@terryleewellsfoundation.org; Main URL: http://www.terryleewellsfoundation.org
Grants List: http://www.terryleewellsfoundation.org/awards_12.php

Established in 1999 in NV.
Donor: Terry Lee Wells†.
Foundation type: Independent foundation.
Financial data (yr. ended 12/31/12): Assets, $4,800,790 (M); expenditures, $946,219; qualifying distributions, $814,600; giving activities include $814,600 for grants.
Purpose and activities: Giving to improve the quality of life in northern Nevada by exposing the underprivileged to arts, cultural, economic, and educational opportunities, with a focus on women and children. The foundation also has an interest in addressing the medical needs of northern Nevadans with an emphasis on diabetes.
Fields of interest: Arts; Education; Health care; Diabetes; Human services; Children/youth, services; Adults, women; Economically disadvantaged.
Limitations: Giving to organizations located in any county in NV, except Clark County. No grants to individuals, or for endowments or venture capital.
Publications: Application guidelines; Grants list.
Application information: Application guidelines and form available on foundation web site. Application form required.
Initial approach: 2-4 page narrative
Deadline(s): See application form for current deadline
Board meeting date(s): Between May 1 and June 12, and between Sept. 1 and Oct. 12
Officers and Directors:* Dawn E. Wells,* Chair. and Pres.; Eloise Esser,* V.P.; Sherrie Cartinella,* Secy.; Charlotte McConnell,* Treas. and Exec. Dir.; Lynn Atcheson.
EIN: 880431758

5158
White Horse Youth Ranch ✧ ☆
3515 E. Russell Rd., Ste. 205
Las Vegas, NV 89120-2918

Established in 2006.
Donors: Amy Meyer; Paul E. & Helen S. Meyer Foundation.
Foundation type: Operating foundation.
Financial data (yr. ended 09/30/12): Assets, $990,351 (M); gifts received, $14,306; expenditures, $3,335,185; qualifying distributions, $3,293,176; giving activities include $2,898,208 for 1 grant.
Purpose and activities: Giving primarily for a riding program for disadvantaged and at risk youth.
Fields of interest: Youth development.
Limitations: Applications not accepted. Giving primarily in Las Vegas, NV.
Application information: Unsolicited requests for funds not accepted.
Officers: Amy Meyer, Pres.; Laurie Howard-Malm, V.P.; Peggy Paulin, Secy.; Cynthia McNeal, Treas.
Directors: Jan Craddock; Adrian Leon.
EIN: 205682991

5159
E. L. Wiegand Foundation ✧
Wiegand Ctr.
165 W. Liberty St., Ste. 200
Reno, NV 89501-2902
Contact: Kristen A. Avansino, Pres. and Exec. Dir.

Established in 1982 in NV.
Donors: Ann K. Wiegand†; Edwin L. Wiegand†.
Foundation type: Independent foundation.
Financial data (yr. ended 10/31/13): Assets, $130,496,411 (M); expenditures, $5,846,142; qualifying distributions, $4,262,559; giving activities include $2,638,589 for 40 grants (high: $470,507; low: $1,000), and $723,152 for 1 foundation-administered program.
Purpose and activities: The foundation makes grants primarily to develop and strengthen programs and projects: at educational institutions in the academic areas of science, business, fine arts, law, and medicine; and at health institutions in the areas of heart, eye, and cancer surgery, treatment and research, with priority given to programs and projects that benefit children. Emphasis on Roman Catholic institutions, including Catholic education.
Fields of interest: Visual arts; Museums; Performing arts; Performing arts, theater; Performing arts, music; Arts; Elementary school/education; Secondary school/education; Higher education; Business school/education; Law school/education; Medical school/education; Heart & circulatory diseases; Medical research, institute; Cancer research; Eye research; Heart & circulatory research; Chemistry; Physics; Biology/life sciences; Public affairs.
Type of support: Building/renovation; Equipment; Program development; Research.
Limitations: Applications accepted. Giving primarily in NV and adjoining western states, including AZ, ID, MT, OR, UT and WA; public affairs grants given primarily in Washington, DC, and New York, NY. No support for organizations receiving significant support from the United Way or public tax funds; organizations with beneficiaries of their own choosing; or federal, state, or local government agencies or institutions. No grants to individuals, or for endowment funds, fundraising campaigns, debt reductions, emergency funding, film or media presentations, or operating funds; no loans.
Application information: The foundation is only able to review a small percentage of the proposals it receives. Rejection of a proposal may be due to a number of factors and no adverse inference as to the quality of the proposal or the applicant should be construed from such rejection. Application form required.
Initial approach: Letter of inquiry with precise description of request. If proposal complies with staff review, a numbered Application for Grant form shall be forwarded to the applicant
Copies of proposal: 1
Deadline(s): None
Board meeting date(s): 2 to 4 times per year, typically in Feb., June, and Oct.
Final notification: Within 15 days of meeting at which application is reviewed
Officers and Trustees:* Raymond C. Avansino, Jr.,* Chair.; Kristen A. Avansino, Pres. and Exec. Dir.; Jim Carrico, Exec. V.P. and Treas.; Frank J. Fahrenkopf, Jr.; Harvey C. Fruehauf, Jr.; Mario J. Gabelli.
Number of staff: 2 full-time professional; 2 part-time professional; 2 part-time support.
EIN: 942839372

5160
World Education Foundation ✧
(formerly Vinod Gupta Family Foundation)
9017 Greenboro Ln.
Las Vegas, NV 89134

Established in CA.
Donors: Vinod Gupta Charitable Remainder Trust; Vidya Srinivasan; Vinod Gupta Revocable Trust; Mark and Anne Hansen Foundation; Benjamin Gupta Revocable Trust; Benjamin Gupta 2001 Trrevocable Trust.
Foundation type: Independent foundation.
Financial data (yr. ended 12/31/13): Assets, $3,222,156 (M); gifts received, $2,291,348; expenditures, $2,883,677; qualifying distributions, $2,748,168; giving activities include $2,748,168 for 11 grants (high: $1,000,000; low: $114).
Fields of interest: Education; Foundations (private grantmaking); Hinduism.
Limitations: Applications not accepted. Giving primarily in India; giving also in Washington, DC, and NH.
Application information: Contributes only to pre-selected organizations.
Trustees: Alexander A. Gupta; Jess Gupta; Vinod Gupta; Gary A. Hatfield; Paul E. Nietzel.
EIN: 200634413

5161
Severin Wunderman Family Foundation ✧
1645 Village Center Cir., Ste. 60
Las Vegas, NV 89134-6332

Donor: SWAT.
Foundation type: Independent foundation.
Financial data (yr. ended 12/31/13): Assets, $61,835 (M); expenditures, $2,563,597; qualifying distributions, $2,150,000; giving activities include $2,150,000 for grants.
Fields of interest: Foundations (private grantmaking).
Limitations: Applications not accepted.
Application information: Unsolicited requests for funds not accepted.
Officers: Richard E. Tomlin, Jr., Pres.; Andy Bui, C.F.O. and Secy.
Directors: Raphaelle Cassens; Deborah Wunderman; Michael Wunderman; Nathan Wunderman.
EIN: 800558916

NEW HAMPSHIRE

5162
Alexander Eastman Foundation ✧
75 S. Main St., Unit 7, PMB 250
Concord, NH 03301-4828
Contact: Grants and Admin. Mgr.: Amy Lockwood, Prog. Off.
E-mail: alockwood@alexandereastman.org; Tel. for grant application inquiries: 1-(888) 228-1821, ext. 80; tel. for scholarship application inquiries: 1-(888) 228-1821, ext. 81; Main URL: http://www.alexandereastman.org
Grants List: http://www.alexandereastman.org/04pgrants.html

Established in 1983 in NH.
Donor: Leon P. Widger Trust.
Foundation type: Independent foundation.
Financial data (yr. ended 09/30/13): Assets, $11,822,480 (M); gifts received, $76,441; expenditures, $663,475; qualifying distributions, $605,060; giving activities include $507,559 for 14 grants (high: $235,000; low: $5,000), and $23,700 for 12 grants to individuals (high: $2,500; low: $500).
Purpose and activities: Awards grants to improve the quality and availability of health care and to promote good health and well-being for residents of the Derry, Londonderry, Windham, Chester, Hampstead, and Sandown, NH, area; giving also includes scholarship assistance for area residents working in the health care field.
Fields of interest: Education; Health care; Mental health/crisis services; Agriculture/food; Human services; Family services.
Type of support: Seed money; General/operating support; Continuing support; Capital campaigns; Building/renovation; Equipment; Program development; Conferences/seminars; Scholarship funds; Technical assistance; Consulting services; Program evaluation; Scholarships—to individuals.
Limitations: Applications accepted. Giving limited to organizations serving residents of Derry, Londonderry, Windham, Chester, Hampstead and Sandown, NH. No grants to individuals (except for designated scholarship funds); no grants for basic costs that should be covered in municipal budgets.
Publications: Application guidelines; Annual report.
Application information: Online application required; application guidelines and form available on foundation web site. Application form required.
Initial approach: 1st-time applicants: telephone; all other applicants, online-line via foundation web site
Copies of proposal: 1
Deadline(s): Apr. 1 and Oct. 1
Board meeting date(s): May and Nov.
Final notification: May and Nov.
Officers and Trustees:* John Patrick Ahern,* Chair.; William Lonergan,* Vice-Chair.; Cindy Gray,* Secy.; Michael Buckley,* Treas.; Sharyn Findlay; Angela Kouroyen; Angela Loring; Bob McDonald; Earle Rosse; Rebecca Rutter; Larry VanDeventer; Dr. Wayne White.
Number of staff: 2 part-time professional.
EIN: 020222124

5163
Barrette Family Fund ✧ ☆
P.O. Box 5254
Hanover, NH 03755-5254

Established in 2002 in NH as a supporting organization of New Hampshire Charitable Foundation; status changed to a private non-operating foundation in 2007.
Donor: Raymond Barrette.
Foundation type: Independent foundation.
Financial data (yr. ended 12/31/13): Assets, $3,217,400 (M); expenditures, $621,280; qualifying distributions, $614,605; giving activities include $614,605 for 25 grants (high: $160,000; low: $250).
Fields of interest: Performing arts, theater; Foundations (community).
Limitations: Applications not accepted. Giving primarily in NH and VT.
Application information: Contributes only to pre-selected organizations.
Officer: Cynthia Barrette, Pres.
Directors: David R. Barrette; Julie A. Barrette; Kaitlyn S. Barrette; Raymond Barrette.
EIN: 043732711

5164
Norwin S. and Elizabeth N. Bean Foundation ✧
40 Stark St.
Manchester, NH 03101-1979 (603) 493-7257
E-mail: kcook@beanfoundation.org; Main URL: http://www.beanfoundation.org

Trust established in 1967 in NH; later became an affiliated trust of the New Hampshire Charitable Foundation, of which it is now independent.
Donors: Norwin S. Bean†; Elizabeth N. Bean†.
Foundation type: Independent foundation.
Financial data (yr. ended 12/31/13): Assets, $13,037,184 (M); expenditures, $676,846; qualifying distributions, $616,515; giving activities include $507,483 for 35 grants (high: $40,000; low: $2,000).
Purpose and activities: Giving primarily for human services, including low-income housing programs and youth; support also for education, health associations, the arts, the environment, and the public benefit.
Fields of interest: Arts; Education; Environment; Health care; Health organizations, association; Housing/shelter, development; Human services; Youth, services.
Type of support: General/operating support; Capital campaigns; Building/renovation; Equipment; Program development; Conferences/seminars; Seed money; Consulting services; Program evaluation; Matching/challenge support.
Limitations: Applications accepted. Giving limited to Amherst and Manchester, NH. No support for religious or political organizations. No grants to individuals, or for scholarships, fellowships, or deficit financing.
Publications: Application guidelines; Annual report (including application guidelines); Informational brochure (including application guidelines).
Application information: See foundation web site for application guidelines. Application form required.
Copies of proposal: 2
Board meeting date(s): Feb., Apr., June, Sept. and Dec.
Final notification: 2-3 months
Trustees: John F. Dinkel, Jr.; Thomas J. Donovan; William H. Dunlap; William G. Steele, Jr.; Cathryn E. Vaughn; Michael Whitney.
Number of staff: 1 part-time professional.
EIN: 026013381

5165
The Butler Foundation ✧
(formerly Neslab Charitable Foundation)
c/o Charter Trust Co.
90 N. Main St.
Concord, NH 03301-4915 (603) 224-1350

Established in 1985 in NH.
Donors: Clara W. Butler Trust; Thomas Butler Trust.
Foundation type: Independent foundation.
Financial data (yr. ended 12/31/13): Assets, $9,584,485 (M); expenditures, $580,646; qualifying distributions, $570,948; giving activities include $464,140 for 23 grants (high: $100,000; low: $2,100).
Purpose and activities: Giving primarily for environmental conservation; scholarship awards to children of employees of NES Labs.
Fields of interest: Arts; Higher education; Environment, natural resources; Animals/wildlife; Community/economic development.
International interests: Ecuador.
Type of support: General/operating support; Program development; Research; Scholarships—to individuals.
Limitations: Applications accepted. Giving primarily in NH and WI.
Application information: Application form required.
Initial approach: Proposal for Scholarships; Letter for others
Deadline(s): None
Officer and Trustees:* Cynthia Wentworth,* Exec. Dir.; Steven Albrecht; Bonnie B. Bunning; Barbara Butler; Clara W. Butler; Marjorie W. Butler; F. Graham McSwiney, Esq.
EIN: 222701588

5166
The Jack and Dorothy Byrne Foundation, Inc. ✧
c/o Robert E. Snyder
80 S. Main St., Ste. 202
Hanover, NH 03755-2053
Application address: c/o Dorothy Byrne, Pres., 3 Laramie Rd., P.O. Box 599, Etna, NH 03755

Established in 1999 in DE; On Nov. 30, 2007 the foundation absorbed the assets of The Byrne Foundation, Inc.
Donors: Dorothy Byrne; John J. Byrne†.
Foundation type: Independent foundation.
Financial data (yr. ended 12/31/13): Assets, $40,768,342 (M); gifts received, $42,194,187; expenditures, $7,719,533; qualifying distributions, $7,681,994; giving activities include $7,635,799 for 551 grants (high: $500,000; low: $300).
Fields of interest: Higher education, college (community/junior); Cancer research; Philanthropy/voluntarism.
Type of support: General/operating support.

Limitations: Applications accepted. Giving primarily in the upper valley of NH and VT. No grants to individuals.
Application information: No telephone calls.
Initial approach: Letter
Deadline(s): None
Officers and Directors:* Dorothy M. Byrne,* Pres.; Robert E. Snyder,* Secy.-Treas.
EIN: 030363118

5167
Cogswell Benevolent Trust ✧
1001 Elm St.
Manchester, NH 03101-1828 (603) 622-4013

Trust established in 1929 in NH.
Donor: Leander A. Cogswell‡.
Foundation type: Independent foundation.
Financial data (yr. ended 12/31/13): Assets, $34,393,769 (M); expenditures, $1,782,034; qualifying distributions, $1,496,503; giving activities include $1,425,543 for 115 grants (high: $75,000; low: $1,000).
Purpose and activities: Giving primarily for social services, children and youth services, health care and the arts.
Fields of interest: Arts; Education; Health care; Human services; YM/YWCAs & YM/YWHAs; Children/youth, services.
Limitations: Giving primarily in NH, with some emphasis on Manchester. No grants to individuals, or for endowment funds, operating budgets, or deficit financing.
Application information: The foundation no longer gives scholarships or loans to individuals; scholarship funds have been donated to the New Hampshire Charitable Foundation Student Aid Program. Application form required.
Initial approach: Proposal
Copies of proposal: 1
Deadline(s): None
Board meeting date(s): Usually monthly and as required
Final notification: 30 days
Trustees: Charles Goodwin; Peter Kachavos; Mark Northridge.
Number of staff: 1 part-time support.
EIN: 020235690

5168
The DEKA Foundation ✧ ☆
340 Commercial St.
Manchester, NH 03101-1121

Donors: Dean Kamen; HHD, LLC.
Foundation type: Independent foundation.
Financial data (yr. ended 05/31/13): Assets, $10,268,358 (M); gifts received, $5,000,000; expenditures, $1,047,416; qualifying distributions, $1,025,000; giving activities include $1,025,000 for 2 grants (high: $1,000,000; low: $25,000).
Fields of interest: Science; Children.
Limitations: Applications not accepted. Giving primarily in NH and NY.
Application information: Unsolicited requests for funds not accepted.
Directors: Stephen Hazard; Dean Kamen; Maureen Toohey; Robert Tuttle.
EIN: 271188399
Selected grants: The following grants are a representative sample of this grantmaker's funding activity:
$25,000 to Salk Institute for Biological Studies, La Jolla, CA, 2013. To assist the Salk Institute in their efforts to make scientific discoveries that will improve various medical treatments.

5169
Endowment for Health, Inc.
1 Pillsbury St., Ste. 301
Concord, NH 03301-3556 (603) 228-2448
FAX: (603) 228-1304;
E-mail: info@endowmentforhealth.org; Application e-mail: applications@endowmentforhealth.org; Main URL: http://www.endowmentforhealth.org
Endowment for Health's Philanthropy Promise: http://www.ncrp.org/philanthropys-promise/who
E-Newsletter: http://www.endowmentforhealth.org/join-our-mailing-list.aspx
Facebook: http://www.facebook.com/pages/Endowment-for-Health/214040860747
Twitter: http://twitter.com/EndowmentHealth

Established in 1999 in NH; converted from Blue Cross/Blue Shield.
Foundation type: Independent foundation.
Financial data (yr. ended 09/30/13): Assets, $82,180,630 (M); expenditures, $3,476,218; qualifying distributions, $3,273,618; giving activities include $1,966,912 for 55 grants (high: $200,000; low: $1,000).
Purpose and activities: The mission of the endowment is to improve the health and reduce the burden of illness of the people of New Hampshire. Giving for oral health, and reducing social-cultural, geographic, and economic barriers to receiving health care.
Fields of interest: Dental care; Health care; Social sciences, public policy.
Type of support: Emergency funds; Program development; Conferences/seminars; Research; Technical assistance.
Limitations: Applications accepted. Giving primarily limited to NH. No support for biomedical research organizations, or for out of state projects. No grants for capital campaigns, lobbying efforts, expensed already incurred, fundraisers, or ongoing expenses.
Publications: Application guidelines; Annual report; Annual report (including application guidelines); Financial statement; Grants list; Informational brochure (including application guidelines); Newsletter; Program policy statement.
Application information: Application form available on foundation web site. Application form required.
Initial approach: Telephone or visit foundation web site
Deadline(s): See web site for current deadlines
Board meeting date(s): Quarterly
Officers and Directors:* Sandra Pelletier, Chair.; Margaret Franckhauser, Vice-Chair.; Steven Rowe, Pres.; Yvonne Goldsberry,* Secy.; Marshall Rowe,* Treas.; Eddie Edwards; Orville Fitch; Randy Foose; Jody Hoffer Gittell; Stephen F. Lawlor; Kathleen Murphy; Ann Peters; Cindy Rosenwald; Adrienne Rupp; Jackie Sparks; John Wallace.
Number of staff: 5 full-time professional; 3 part-time professional; 1 full-time support.
EIN: 020512290
Selected grants: The following grants are a representative sample of this grantmaker's funding activity:
$218,688 to Health Strategies of New Hampshire, Concord, NH, 2012. To improve the health and health care system of New Hampshire, especially for the vulnerable and underserved through health reform strategies especially public policy.
$200,000 to Health Strategies of New Hampshire, Concord, NH, 2013. To improve the health care system of NH especially for the vulnerable and underserved by evaluating Medicaid Managed Care and identifying areas for improvement.
$150,000 to New Hampshire Voices for Health, Concord, NH, 2012. To enhance public policy and health advocacy in New Hampshire by building operational and management capacity.
$142,968 to New Hampshire Legal Assistance, Manchester, NH, 2013. For New Hampshire Legal Assistance Youth Law Project, to ensure delinquent and CHINS youth receive the mental health, educational and other services they need by providing civil legal services in collaboration with courts, juvenile services officers, public defenders, mental health providers, schools and other key organizations serving children and youth.
$107,526 to University of New Hampshire, Durham, NH, 2013. To implement RENEW model in community mental health centers, which provides high-quality transition services for youth with emotional and behavioral challenges.
$65,507 to University of New Hampshire, Durham, NH, 2012. To implement core competencies of personnel working in children's behavioral health in New Hampshire, which will improve the outcomes for children, youth and their families who need behavioral health services and supports, by continuously assessing and improving the competencies of the child-serving behavioral health workforce and thereby improving the quality, consistency and efficiency of the service delivery system.
$65,000 to Planned Parenthood of Northern New England, New Hampshire Grassroots and Public Affairs Office, Concord, NH, 2012. For work of New Hampshire Public Policy Program which will maximize opportunities for women's health care and safety-net family planning services and ensure these issues are represented in state health policy planning and rulemaking by enhancing public affairs capacity and increasing community engagement and leadership.
$53,830 to Cooperative Alliance for Seacoast Transportation, Dover, NH, 2013. To improve regional transportation services for people in Strafford and Eastern Rockingham Counties by coordinating transportation services offered by COAST.
$50,000 to Foundation for Healthy Communities, Concord, NH, 2012. To implement Healthy Eating/Active Living (HEAL) Plan.
$50,000 to New Hampshire Charitable Foundation, Concord, NH, 2012. To improve the quality of life outcomes (physical, mental and social well-being) for low-income and vulnerable residents of New Hampshire by enhancing the range of advocacy resources which support the work of the New Hampshire health and human service nonprofit sector.
$50,000 to New Hampshire Fiscal Policy Institute, Concord, NH, 2013. For general operating support.
$50,000 to Tri-County Community Action Program, Berlin, NH, 2013. To ensure the Tri-County CAP Agency is sustained by working with the Special Trustee appointed by the NH Charitable Trust Unit and others.

$47,301 to Foundation for Healthy Communities, Concord, NH, 2013. For NHRx Connects Pharmacy for the Medication Bridge Program, to improve access to pharmacy assistance for uninsured or underinsured individuals by extending the unused medication program statewide and by forming a new entity that will manage and sustain the program into the future.
$46,119 to Community Bridges, Concord, NH, 2013. To improve early childhood mental health support and services for NH's young children (age birth to six) and their families by creating and implementing a state early childhood mental health competency system for NH professionals serving this population and by collaborating with NH Early Childhood Advisory Council on systems building.
$36,765 to New Hampshire Psychological Association Educational Foundation, Concord, NH, 2012. For Psychology Internship Consortium, initiative to increase doctoral level internship opportunities in New Hampshire, which will assure a high quality workforce that meets the mental health needs of New Hampshire residents with a special emphasis on children and underserved populations by increasing the number of doctoral level internship opportunities in the state.
$26,802 to Endowment for Health, New Hampshire Nursing Diveristy Pipeline Project, Concord, NH, 2012. To expand diversity within the nursing workforce and nursing education in New Hampshire by promoting awareness of the nursing profession among youth from diverse cultures and supporting underrepresented populations to earn a Master's Degree in nursing and join the nursing faculty in New Hampshire.
$25,000 to NAMI New Hampshire, Concord, NH, 2012. To ensure quality advocacy, knowledge development and nonprofit capacity building for the mental health system which supports New Hampshire children and their families by sustaining the general operations of key related New Hampshire nonprofits.
$25,000 to NAMI New Hampshire, Concord, NH, 2013. For general operating support.
$25,000 to New Hampshire Legal Assistance, Manchester, NH, 2013. For general operating support.
$14,240 to Health Strategies of New Hampshire, New Hampshire Children's Behavioral Health Collaborative, Concord, NH, 2012. To improve mental health of New Hampshire children and their families by convening a Children's Mental Health Collaborative of diverse interests, establishing a baseline of knowledge among participants, developing a statewide, comprehensive, strategic plan and broadly disseminating it.

5170
Fidelity Foundation ✧

11 Keewaydin Dr., Ste. 100
Salem, NH 03079-2999
E-mail: info@FidelityFoundation.org; Main
URL: http://www.fidelityfoundation.org

Trust established in 1965 in MA.
Donors: FMR Corp.; Fidelity Ventures Ltd.; FMR Capital; The Colt, Inc.
Foundation type: Company-sponsored foundation.
Financial data (yr. ended 12/31/12): Assets, $336,020,153 (M); expenditures, $20,768,333; qualifying distributions, $19,164,045; giving activities include $17,460,333 for grants.
Purpose and activities: The foundation supports organizations involved with arts and culture, education, health, human services, and community development. Special emphasis is directed toward programs designed to strengthen long-term effectiveness of nonprofit institutions.
Fields of interest: Arts; Education; Health care; Human services; Community/economic development.
International interests: Canada.
Type of support: Faculty/staff development; Management development/capacity building; Capital campaigns; Building/renovation; Equipment; Program development; Conferences/seminars; Publication; Curriculum development; Technical assistance; Consulting services; Employee matching gifts; Matching/challenge support.
Limitations: Applications accepted. Giving primarily in areas of company operations in the Northeast and Middle Atlantic, with emphasis on Jacksonville, FL, New York, NY, Cincinnati, OH, RI, Dallas, Fort Worth and northern TX, Salt Lake City, UT, and Toronto, Canada; giving also to regional and national organizations. No support for start-up, sectarian, or civic organizations, public school systems, or disease-specific organizations. No grants to individuals, or for general operating support, sponsorships, scholarships, galas or benefits, corporate memberships, or video or film projects.
Publications: Application guidelines.
Application information: Grants are generally made to organizations with operating budgets of $500,000 or more. Letters of inquiry should be no longer than 3 pages. A full proposal may be requested at later date. A site visit may be requested. Organizations receiving support are asked submit a six-month progress report and a final report. Application form required.
Initial approach: E-mail letter of inquiry
Deadline(s): None
Final notification: 4 to 6 months
Officers and Trustees:* Anne-Marie Soulliere,* Pres.; Desiree Caldwell, C.O.O.; Paul Kuenstner, V.P.; Tom Lewis, V.P.; Mary Sullivan, Cont.; Abigail P. Johnson; Edward C. Johnson III; Edward C. Johnson IV; Ross E. Sherbrooke.
Number of staff: 4 full-time professional; 3 full-time support.
EIN: 046131201
Selected grants: The following grants are a representative sample of this grantmaker's funding activity:
$5,450,000 to Peabody Essex Museum, Salem, MA, 2012. For Endowment.
$1,000,000 to Conservation International, Arlington, VA, 2012. For Program Development.
$750,000 to National Arts Strategies, Alexandria, VA, 2012. For Program Support.
$500,000 to Berklee College of Music, Boston, MA, 2012. For Program Support.
$250,000 to Denver Museum of Nature and Science, Denver, CO, 2012. For Construction.
$250,000 to MacDowell Colony, Peterborough, NH, 2012. For Endowment.
$250,000 to Rhode Island School of Design, Providence, RI, 2012. For Construction.
$100,000 to League of New Hampshire Craftsmen Foundation, Concord, NH, 2012. For Building Acquisition.
$100,000 to Pennsylvania Horticultural Society, Philadelphia, PA, 2012. For Consulting.
$2,450 to University of Texas, Austin, TX, 2012. For Operating Support.

5171
Foundation for Seacoast Health ✧

100 Campus Dr., Ste. 1
Portsmouth, NH 03801-5892 (603) 422-8200
Contact: Debra S. Grabowski, Exec. Dir.
FAX: (603) 422-8207;
E-mail: ffsh@communitycampus.org; Main
URL: http://www.ffsh.org
Facebook: https://www.facebook.com/pages/Foundation-for-Seacoast-Health/431317490236981

Incorporated in 1984 in NH as the Portsmouth Hospital Foundation; converted from the proceeds of the sale of Portsmouth Hospital to Hospital Corporation of America. Name changed in 1986 to Foundation for Seacoast Health.
Foundation type: Independent foundation.
Financial data (yr. ended 12/31/13): Assets, $45,008,431 (M); gifts received, $26,533; expenditures, $2,566,954; qualifying distributions, $1,790,202; giving activities include $693,185 for 10 grants (high: $325,850; low: $500), and $9,500 for 6 grants to individuals (high: $3,500; low: $500).
Purpose and activities: The foundation invests its resources to improve the health and well being of Seacoast citizens. Funding particularly for affordable mental health services, preventative and restorative dental services, affordable child care and after school care, affordable primary medical care, and coordination and dissemination of health information related to identified priority needs.
Fields of interest: Health care, infants; Public health, obesity; Mental health/crisis services; Health organizations; Medical research; Aging, centers/services; Children/youth; Youth; Adults; Disabilities, people with; Physically disabled; Crime/abuse victims; Economically disadvantaged; Homeless; LGBTQ.
Type of support: General/operating support; Technical assistance; Scholarships—to individuals.
Limitations: Applications not accepted. Giving limited to Kittery, Eliot, and York, ME and Portsmouth, Rye, New Castle, Greenland, Newington, and North Hampton, NH. No support for political activities. No grants to individuals (except through the foundation scholarship program), bricks and mortar, deficit financing, travel, lodging, or conferences.
Publications: Annual report; Financial statement; Newsletter.
Application information: The foundation is not considering new grant initiatives at this time.
Board meeting date(s): 3rd Tues. of Jan., Feb., Mar., May, Aug., Sept., Oct., and Nov.; annual meeting, 3rd Tues. in Apr.
Officers and Trustees:* Daniel C. Hoefle,* Chair.; Timothy J. Connors,* Vice-Chair.; Nancy L. Cutter, Secy.; Timothy Driscoll,* Treas.; Debra S. Grabowski, Exec. Dir.; Patricia A. Barbour; Richard Chace, M.D.; Jameson French; John Hebert; Ann Hodsdon; Peter Loughlin; John Lyons; Archie McGowan, M.D.; Neal Ouellett; Amy Schwart; Sharon R. Weston.
Number of staff: 1 full-time professional; 1 part-time professional; 6 full-time support; 2 part-time support.
EIN: 020386319

5172
The Fuller Foundation, Inc. ✧
P.O. Box 479
Rye Beach, NH 03871-0479 (603) 964-6998
Contact: John T. Bottomley, Exec. Dir.; Sandi Scagliotti, Prog. Assoc.
FAX: (603) 964-8901; E-mail: ATfuller@aol.com; Main URL: http://www.fullerfoundation.org

Incorporated in 1938 in MA.
Donor: Alvan T. Fuller, Sr.‡.
Foundation type: Independent foundation.
Financial data (yr. ended 12/31/12): Assets, $13,044,053 (M); expenditures, $834,049; qualifying distributions, $668,524; giving activities include $554,817 for grants.
Purpose and activities: The purpose of the foundation is to support non-profit agencies which improve the quality of life for people, animals, and the environment. The foundation also funds the Fuller Foundation of New Hampshire, which supports horticultural and educational programs for the public at Fuller Gardens.
Fields of interest: Arts education; Museums; Performing arts; Arts; Education; Environment, natural resources; Animals/wildlife, preservation/protection; Substance abuse, services; Youth development.
Type of support: General/operating support; Continuing support; Land acquisition; Emergency funds; Program development; Seed money; Scholarship funds; Matching/challenge support.
Limitations: Applications accepted. Giving primarily in the greater Boston, MA, area (inside Rte. 128), and the immediate seacoast area of NH. There are no geographic limitations for grants for endangered species. No grants to individuals or for capital projects, or conferences; no loans.
Publications: Application guidelines.
Application information: Contact foundation for current guidelines; Faxed or e-mailed requests not accepted. Associated Grant Makers Common Proposal Form accepted, and can be downloaded via foundation web site. Application form required.
Initial approach: Proposal or telephone call
Copies of proposal: 1
Deadline(s): Jan. 15 and June 15
Board meeting date(s): May and Oct.
Final notification: 30 to 60 days
Officers and Trustees:* James D. Henderson II,* Pres.; Peter D. Fuller, Jr.,* Treas.; John T. Bottomley,* Clerk and Exec. Dir.; Miranda Fuller Bocko; Peter Fuller; Peter S. Langley; Corey Fuller MacDonald; Melinda Fuller vanden Heuvel.
Number of staff: 1 full-time professional; 1 part-time support.
EIN: 042241130

5173
Adelle Gifford Residuary Trust ✧
P.O. Box 477
Concord, NH 03302-0477

Supporting organization of Albany Medical College, Benedictine Hospital, Felician Sisters, and Roman Catholic Bishop of Manchester.
Foundation type: Independent foundation.
Financial data (yr. ended 11/30/13): Assets, $14,040,048 (M); expenditures, $935,371; qualifying distributions, $802,100; giving activities include $802,100 for 4 grants (high: $200,525; low: $200,525).
Fields of interest: Medical school/education; Hospitals (general); Catholic agencies & churches.
Limitations: Applications not accepted. Giving limited to CT, NH, and NY. No grants to individuals.
Application information: Contributes only to pre-selected organizations; unsolicited requests for funds not considered or acknowledged.
Trustees: Harold C. Hansen, Esq.; TD Bank, N.A.
EIN: 026046966

5174
Thomas W. Haas Foundation ✧
(formerly RNAV Foundation)
P.O. Box 21948
Portsmouth, NH 03802-1948

Established in NH.
Donors: Thomas W. Haas; Otto Haas 1956 Trust; Phoebe W. Haas 1961 Trust; 1955 TWH Trust.
Foundation type: Independent foundation.
Financial data (yr. ended 06/30/13): Assets, $38,596,653 (M); gifts received, $14,663,453; expenditures, $7,698,814; qualifying distributions, $7,230,133; giving activities include $6,673,500 for 56 grants (high: $3,000,000; low: $2,500).
Fields of interest: Education; Environment; Animals/wildlife; Human services; Foundations (community).
Limitations: Applications not accepted. Giving primarily in Portsmouth, NH; some funding also in the Boston, MA, area. No grants to individuals.
Application information: Contributes only to pre-selected organizations.
Officers: Thomas W. Haas, Pres. and Treas.; Benjamin F. Gayman, Secy.
EIN: 264036968

5175
HNH Foundation, Inc. ✧
49 S. Main St., Ste. 204
Concord, NH 03301-4872 (603) 229-3260
Contact: Patti Baum
FAX: (603) 229-3259;
E-mail: info@hnhfoundation.org; Letter of Inquiry e-mail: application@hnhfoundation.org (Include "LOI" in subject line, and organization's name and contact in body of e-mail); Main URL: http://www.hnhfoundation.org

Established in 1997 in NH, as a result of the merger of the Matthew Thornton Health Plan and Blue Cross/Blue Shield of New Hampshire.
Donor: Matthew Thornton, Inc.
Foundation type: Independent foundation.
Financial data (yr. ended 12/31/13): Assets, $23,517,579 (M); expenditures, $1,366,459; qualifying distributions, $1,175,208; giving activities include $593,984 for 25 grants (high: $177,319; low: $900).
Purpose and activities: Giving primarily to: 1) increase the number of New Hampshire children who have access to health and dental insurance coverage, with a priority on children through age 18; 2) promote preventive oral health care for children through age five and pregnant women, with a priority focus on Coos County, NH; and 3) prevent childhood obesity with a focus on children through age 5.
Fields of interest: Dental care; Public health, obesity; Health care, insurance; Health care; Children/youth, services; Children.
Type of support: General/operating support; Program development; Program-related investments/loans; Matching/challenge support.
Limitations: Applications accepted. Giving limited to NH. No support for sectarian or religious programs. No grants to individuals, or for capital campaigns or expenditures, fundraisers, or bricks and mortar.
Publications: Application guidelines; Annual report; Financial statement; Grants list.
Application information: If the applying organization requires a fiscal sponsor to accept and spend grant funds, the Letter of Inquiry must be submitted by the sponsoring organization,. Application form required.
Initial approach: Letter of Inquiry (not to exceed 2 pages, submitted via e-mail, and in .pdf format)
Copies of proposal: 1
Deadline(s): See foundation web site for current deadlines
Officers and Directors:* Martha McLeod,* Chair.; Sandi Van Scoyoc, Pres.; Dr. Steven Paris,* Secy.; Keith R. Ballingall, Treas.; Tyler Brannen; Marc Cullerot; Elaine Van Dyke; Sandra Mann; Shannon Mills.
Number of staff: 2 full-time professional; 1 part-time professional.
EIN: 020497577
Selected grants: The following grants are a representative sample of this grantmaker's funding activity:
$217,347 to Foundation for Healthy Communities, Concord, NH, 2012. For general support for the NH Healthy Eating Active Living (Heal) Campaign.
$55,000 to Foundation for Healthy Communities, Concord, NH, 2012. To Conduct a Statewide Random-Sample Screening and Analysis of NH 3rd Grade Oral Health and Body Mass.
$22,442 to Lakes Region Partnership for Public Health, Laconia, NH, 2012. For Early Sprouts Implementation and Training.
$15,000 to North Country Health Consortium, Littleton, NH, 2012. For Dental Restorative Services to Un and Underinsured Children.
$10,000 to Coos County Family Health Services, Berlin, NH, 2012. For Oral Restorative Care Services to Un-Or Underinsured Children.
$8,100 to Coos County Family Health Services, Berlin, NH, 2012. For Preventative Dental Care to 170 Wic Enrolled Children in Coos County.
$900 to Southwestern Community Services, Keene, NH, 2012. For Garden Related Expenses and to Update the Early Sprouts Curriculum in the Head Start Program.

5176
Hank and Lynn Hopeman Foundation, Inc. ✧
P.O. Box 2626
New London, NH 03257-2626

Foundation type: Independent foundation.
Financial data (yr. ended 12/31/13): Assets, $20,410,215 (M); expenditures, $1,087,734; qualifying distributions, $1,008,989; giving activities include $1,004,200 for 12 grants (high: $395,000; low: $1,300).
Fields of interest: Higher education; Health care; Catholic federated giving programs; Protestant agencies & churches.
Limitations: Applications not accepted. Giving primarily in NC, NH, and PA.
Application information: Contributes only to pre-selected organizations.

Officers: Henry W. Hopeman, Pres. and Treas.; Lynn G. Hopeman, V.P. and Secy.
EIN: 261834362
Selected grants: The following grants are a representative sample of this grantmaker's funding activity:
$10,000 to Grove City College, Grove City, PA, 2012. For Full Circle.
$10,000 to Lake Sunapee Protective Association, Sunapee, NH, 2012. For Land and Lake Conservation.

5177
Samuel P. Hunt Foundation ✧
555 Canal St., Ste. 710
Manchester, NH 03101-1517 (603) 622-4052
Contact: Douglas A. McIninch, Tr.
E-mail: fdtn555@aol.com

Trust established in 1951 in NH.
Donor: Samuel P. Hunt†.
Foundation type: Independent foundation.
Financial data (yr. ended 12/31/13): Assets, $11,792,006 (M); expenditures, $648,875; qualifying distributions, $470,871; giving activities include $443,306 for 31 grants (high: $75,000; low: $1,000).
Fields of interest: Arts; Education; Health care; Human services; Children/youth, services; Christian agencies & churches.
Type of support: General/operating support; Continuing support; Management development/capacity building; Annual campaigns; Capital campaigns; Building/renovation; Equipment; Land acquisition; Emergency funds; Program development; Conferences/seminars; Film/video/radio; Publication; Seed money; Research; Matching/challenge support.
Limitations: Applications accepted. Giving limited to NH. No support for public schools. No grants to individuals; no loans.
Publications: Application guidelines.
Application information: Application form required.
Initial approach: Completed application form
Copies of proposal: 3
Deadline(s): Mar. 15 and Sept. 15
Trustees: Douglas A. McIninch; James C. Tyrie.
Number of staff: 1 part-time support.
EIN: 026004471
Selected grants: The following grants are a representative sample of this grantmaker's funding activity:
$25,000 to Derryfield School, Manchester, NH, 2012. For digital project room.
$25,000 to Spaulding Youth Center Foundation, Northfield, NH, 2012. For Capital campaign for new facility.
$15,000 to Currier Museum of Art, Manchester, NH, 2012. For Development of multimedia tour.
$7,500 to Appalachian Mountain Club, Boston, MA, 2012. For Old Bridle Path Trail.
$6,500 to Webster House, Manchester, NH, 2012. For Emergency beds and care for youth.
$5,000 to CATCH Neighborhood Housing, Concord, NH, 2012. For Removal of lead paint.
$2,000 to Unitarian Universalist Church of Manchester, Manchester, NH, 2012. For Restoration of Estey Opus organ.
$1,700 to Sunset Hill Educational Institute, South Sutton, NH, 2012. For Wheelchair Health in Motion Program.

5178
Edward C. Johnson Fund ✧
11 Keewaydin Dr., Ste. 100
Salem, NH 03079-2999
Contact: Anne-Marie Soulliere, Pres.

Trust established in 1964 in MA.
Donors: Edward C. Johnson II†; Edward C. Johnson III; Abigail P. Johnson; Edward C. Johnson IV; Elizabeth L. Johnson; Abel Partners; FMR Corp.
Foundation type: Independent foundation.
Financial data (yr. ended 12/31/13): Assets, $300,564,418 (M); gifts received, $6,847,000; expenditures, $85,473,372; qualifying distributions, $83,910,534; giving activities include $82,350,200 for 112 grants (high: $16,819,341; low: $500), and $202,199 for foundation-administered programs.
Purpose and activities: Emphasis on museums, historical societies, medical institutions, and some youth programs. Support also for the visual arts, historic preservation, higher education, elementary and secondary schools, and environmental organizations.
Fields of interest: Visual arts; Museums; Performing arts; Historic preservation/historical societies; Arts; Environment; Health care; Medical research, institute; Youth, services.
Type of support: Capital campaigns; Building/renovation; Endowments; Program development; Research.
Limitations: Applications not accepted. Giving limited to the greater Boston, MA, area. No grants to individuals, or for scholarships.
Application information: Unsolicited requests for funds not accepted.
Board meeting date(s): June and Dec.
Officers and Directors:* Edward C. Johnson III,* Chair.; Anne-Marie Soulliere, Pres.; Desiree Caldwell, V.P.; Melanie S. Sommer, Secy.; Rupal M. Poltack, Treas.; Abigail P. Johnson; Edward C. Johnson IV; Elizabeth L. Johnson.
EIN: 046108344
Selected grants: The following grants are a representative sample of this grantmaker's funding activity:
$12,102,650 to Brookfield Arts Foundation, Boston, MA, 2012. For art acquisition.
$7,353,975 to Brookfield Arts Foundation, Boston, MA, 2012. For art acquisition.
$5,750,000 to Brookfield Arts Foundation, Boston, MA, 2012. For art acquisition.
$5,750,000 to Brookfield Arts Foundation, Boston, MA, 2012. For art acquisition.
$2,103,680 to Brookfield Arts Foundation, Boston, MA, 2012. For art acquisition.
$1,650,000 to Hebron Academy, Hebron, ME, 2012. For debt reduction.
$1,000,000 to Park School, Brookline, MA, 2012. For program support.
$280,499 to Brookfield Arts Foundation, Boston, MA, 2012. For art acquisition.
$50,000 to Shady Hill School, Cambridge, MA, 2012. For annual support.
$25,000 to Centerville Public Library Association, Centerville, MA, 2012. For memorials.

5179
Agnes M. Lindsay Trust ✧
660 Chestnut St.
Manchester, NH 03104-3550 (603) 669-1366
Contact: Susan E. Bouchard, Admin. Dir.
FAX: (603) 665-8114;
E-mail: admin@lindsaytrust.org; Toll-free tel.: (866) 669-1366; Letter of Inquiry e-mail: proposals@lindsaytrust.org; Main URL: http://www.Lindsaytrust.org
Grants List: http://www.lindsaytrust.org/Grants-Awarded.html

Trust established in 1939 in NH.
Donor: Agnes M. Lindsay†.
Foundation type: Independent foundation.
Financial data (yr. ended 12/31/13): Assets, $25,168,058 (M); expenditures, $982,961; qualifying distributions, $684,369; giving activities include $476,934 for 178 grants (high: $15,000; low: $1,000).
Purpose and activities: Support for health and welfare, including services for the blind, deaf and learning disabled, the elderly, children's hospitals, children's homes, youth organizations, youth/family services and summer camperships/summer enrichment programs. The trust also supports colleges, universities, and private secondary schools through scholarship funds administered by the educational institutions to deserving students from rural communities.
Fields of interest: Higher education; Education; Health care; Human services; Children/youth, services; Infants/toddlers; Children/youth; Children; Youth; Young adults; Disabilities, people with; Physically disabled; Blind/visually impaired; Deaf/hearing impaired; Mentally disabled; Minorities; Asians/Pacific Islanders; African Americans/Blacks; Hispanics/Latinos; Native Americans/American Indians; Adults, women; Adults, men; Substance abusers; AIDS, people with; Crime/abuse victims; Immigrants/refugees; Economically disadvantaged; Homeless.
Type of support: Capital campaigns; Building/renovation; Equipment; Program development; Scholarship funds; Matching/challenge support.
Limitations: Applications accepted. Giving limited to MA, ME, NH, and VT. No support for private foundations, organizations lacking 501(c)(3) status, public entities, libraries, museums, municipalities, or sectarian organizations. No grants to individuals, or for endowments; generally no grants for general operating funds. Capital grants are not awarded to educational institutions.
Publications: Application guidelines; Annual report; Grants list.
Application information: Application form required.
Initial approach: Letter of Inquiry via e-mail
Copies of proposal: 1
Deadline(s): None
Board meeting date(s): Monthly
Trustees: Michael S. DeLucia; Ernest E. Dion; Alan G. Lampert.
Number of staff: 1 full-time professional.
EIN: 026004971
Selected grants: The following grants are a representative sample of this grantmaker's funding activity:
$5,000 to Child and Family Services of New Hampshire, Manchester, NH, 2012. For Annual Scholarship Grant for the Robert L. Chiesa At-Risk Youth Memorial Scholarship.
$4,000 to University of New England, Portland, ME, 2012. For annual scholarship grant - physician's assistant.
$4,000 to Urban College of Boston, Boston, MA, 2012. For Annual Scholarship Grant - To benefit needy students from urban Greater Boston.

$2,500 to Center for New Americans, Northampton, MA, 2012. For state-of-the-art laptop computers that will allow increase in students time distance learning.
$2,500 to Manchester Community Health Center, Manchester, NH, 2012. For Capacity building expansion/start-up for a new location.
$2,500 to Railroad Street Youth Project, Great Barrington, MA, 2012. For technology to upgrade RAM memory capabilities, purchase a new server, and upgrade to Windows 7 and labor for IT professional.
$2,500 to School on Wheels of Massachusetts, Brockton, MA, 2012. For 4 iPads and educational apps for use in one-on-one tutoring sessions with students.
$2,000 to Montshire Museum of Science, Norwich, VT, 2012. For Camperships 2012 - for children ages 4 through 8th grade.
$2,000 to New Hampshire Teen Institute, Nashua, NH, 2012. For Camperships 2012 - Summer Leadership Program, a dynamic residential week of leadership development, self-discovery, and social connection that brings 100 diverse high school students from across NH together through experiential workshops.
$2,000 to Thompson Island Outward Bound Education Center, Boston, MA, 2012. For Campership 2012 - To provide adventurous and challenging experiential learning Programs that inspire character development, compassion, community service, environmental responsibility and academic achievement.

5180
Roy M. Malool Family Foundation ✧ ☆

c/o Roymal, Inc.
P.O. Box 658
Newport, NH 03773-0658 (603) 863-2410

Established in 1997 in ME.
Donor: Roy M. Malool.
Foundation type: Independent foundation.
Financial data (yr. ended 06/30/13): Assets, $208,702 (M); gifts received, $125,915; expenditures, $811,197; qualifying distributions, $808,838; giving activities include $808,838 for 7 grants (high: $645,948; low: $250).
Fields of interest: Human services; Foundations (community).
Type of support: General/operating support.
Limitations: Applications not accepted. Giving primarily in Newport, NH. No grants to individuals.
Application information: Contributes only to pre-selected organizations.
Trustees: George A. Dorr III; Larry Huot; Roy M. Malool; Susannah M. Malool; Laura Stocker.
EIN: 020498236
Selected grants: The following grants are a representative sample of this grantmaker's funding activity:
$5,500 to New London Hospital, New London, NH, 2011.

5181
The Mosaic Fund ✧

c/o Colin Cabot
7097 Sanborn Rd.
Loudon, NH 03307-1618

Established in 1994 in NY.
Donors: Clattesad Trust; Clapttrap Trust; Clatpag Trust; Clatscatt Trust; Clattaur Trust; Clattecam Trust.
Foundation type: Independent foundation.
Financial data (yr. ended 12/31/13): Assets, $21,616 (M); gifts received, $98,220; expenditures, $2,003,812; qualifying distributions, $2,003,812; giving activities include $1,997,744 for 12 grants (high: $1,659,469; low: $275).
Purpose and activities: Giving primarily for environmental conservation and protection, including urban parks and gardens; funding also for a therapeutic equestrian center, and some support also for secondary education and the arts.
Fields of interest: Arts; Elementary/secondary education; Environment, natural resources; Environment; Athletics/sports, equestrianism; Foundations (private grantmaking).
Limitations: Applications not accepted. Giving primarily in NY. No grants to individuals.
Application information: Contributes only to pre-selected organizations.
Trustees: F. Colin Cabot; Katherine R. Steiner.
EIN: 137045257

5182
New Hampshire Charitable Foundation ✧

37 Pleasant St.
Concord, NH 03301-4005 (603) 225-6641
Contact: Kate Merrow, V.P., Community Impact
FAX: (603) 225-1700; E-mail: info@nhcf.org; NHCF-Piscataqua Region application address: 446 Market St., Portsmouth, NH 03801; NHCF-Upper Valley Region application address: P.O. Box 995, Hanover, NH 03755-2700; Scholarship inquiry e-mail: jb@nhcf.org; Main URL: http://www.nhcf.org
E-Newsletter: http://www.nhcf.org/Page.aspx?pid=392
Facebook: http://www.facebook.com/nhcfoundation
Flickr: http://www.flickr.com/photos/nhcf/sets/
Twitter: http://twitter.com/nhcfoundation
YouTube: http://www.youtube.com/user/NHCFoundation

Incorporated in 1962 in NH.
Foundation type: Community foundation.
Financial data (yr. ended 12/31/13): Assets, $608,878,722 (M); gifts received, $51,331,692; expenditures, $39,058,751; giving activities include $24,825,209 for 531+ grants (high: $816,779), and $5,388,240 for 1,555 grants to individuals.
Purpose and activities: The foundation seeks to strengthen communities and inspire greater giving by: 1) investing charitable assets for today and tomorrow; 2) connecting donors with effective organizations, ideas and people; and 3) leading and collaborating on important public issues.
Fields of interest: Arts; Education; Environment; Health care; Human services; Philanthropy/voluntarism.
Type of support: General/operating support; Income development; Management development/capacity building; Program development; Seed money; Fellowships; Scholarship funds; Technical assistance; Consulting services; Program-related investments/loans; Scholarships—to individuals; Student loans—to individuals; Mission-related investments/loans.
Limitations: Applications accepted. Giving in the Lakes, Manchester, Monadnock, Nashua, North Country, Piscataqua, and Upper Valley regions in NH. No support for sectarian or religious purposes. No grants to individuals (except for student aid and special awards); generally no grants for building funds, endowments, deficit financing, capital campaigns for acquisition of land or renovations to facilities, purchase of major equipment, academic research, travel, or to replace public funding or for purposes which are a public responsibility.
Publications: Application guidelines; Annual report; Financial statement; Grants list; Informational brochure; Informational brochure (including application guidelines); Newsletter; Program policy statement.
Application information: Deadlines are statewide, except for Manchester Region. Visit foundation web site for application coversheet and additional application guidelines. Application form required.
Initial approach: Telephone
Copies of proposal: 1
Deadline(s): Varies
Board meeting date(s): Jan., Mar., Apr., May, June, Sept., Nov. and Dec.
Final notification: 6 to 12 weeks
Officers and Directors:* Eric Herr,* Chair.; Peter Bergh,* Vice-Chair.; Richard Ober, C.E.O. and Pres.; Shari Landry, V.P., Philanthropy; Katherine B. Merrow, V.P., Prog.; Michael J. Wilson, C.F.O. and V.P., Finance; Anu Mullikin,* Secy.; Richard W. Couch,* Treas.; Rebecca Carr, Cont.; Paula Marie Buley; Cynthia "Mil" Duncan; Dr. Ross Gittell; Donnalee Lozeau; Catherine P. McDowell; Matthew Pierson; Joseph Reilly; Sherry Young.
Number of staff: 30 full-time professional; 1 part-time professional; 14 full-time support; 3 part-time support.
EIN: 026005625
Selected grants: The following grants are a representative sample of this grantmaker's funding activity:
$167,337 to North Country Health Consortium, Littleton, NH, 2013. To implement North Country Regional Prevention Network's Regional Strategy Plan.
$75,000 to Northern Forest Center, Concord, NH, 2013. To implement Sustainable Economy Initiative in four state Northern Forest Region.
$70,000 to Peterborough, Town of, Peterborough, NH, 2013. To continue revitalizing Community Center with addition of full kitchen facility.
$46,000 to New Hampshire Center for Nonprofits, Concord, NH, 2013. For advocacy.
$40,000 to Child and Family Services of New Hampshire, Manchester, NH, 2013. For mobile mental healthcare and ready access to services or referrals for homeless youth.
$30,000 to Nashua Regional Planning Commission, Nashua, NH, 2013. For HUD-supported Sustainable Communities Program.
$25,000 to Housing Action New Hampshire, Manchester, NH, 2013. To build alliances for low income housing and homelessness advocacy.
$25,000 to Massachusetts Immigrant and Refugee Advocacy Coalition, Boston, MA, 2013. For Welcoming New Hampshire Program.
$20,000 to Currier Museum of Art, Manchester, NH, 2013. To research, draft, and publish online illustrated essays on 100 objects from collection.
$20,000 to Winchester Learning Center, Winchester, NH, 2013. To provide safe and developmentally positive Night Care to children from 4pm to 12am.

5183
Robert & Joyce Oberkotter Family Foundation ✧
P.O. Box 45
Newport, NH 03773-0045 (603) 863-8088

Established in 2002 in NH.
Donor: Joyce Oberkotter.
Foundation type: Independent foundation.
Financial data (yr. ended 06/30/13): Assets, $9,972,780 (M); expenditures, $476,268; qualifying distributions, $447,000; giving activities include $447,000 for grants.
Purpose and activities: Scholarship awards to graduating seniors of Fall Mountain Regional High School, Kearsarge High School, Kimball Union Academy, Lebanon High School, Mascoma Valley Regional High School, Mount Royal Academy, Newport High School, The Oliverian School, Stevens High School, Claremont, New Hampshire, Mid-Vermont Christian School, or Windsor High School, Vermont.
Fields of interest: Higher education.
Type of support: Scholarships—to individuals.
Limitations: Applications accepted. Giving limited to residents of NH and VT.
Application information: Application form required.
Initial approach: Essay
Deadline(s): Feb. 12
Officers: Caryl McDevitt, Pres.; Anu Millikin, Secy.; Robert J. McDevitt, Treas.
EIN: 820577634

5184
The Panjandrum Foundation ✧
c/o C&S Wholesale Grocers, Inc.
7 Corporate Dr.
Keene, NH 03431-5042
Contact: William Hamlin, Treas.
E-mail: info@panjandrum.org; Main URL: http://www.panjandrum.org
Grants List: http://www.panjandrum.org/pages/past.htm

Established in 1999 in NH.
Donors: Richard B. Cohen; Janet L. Cohen.
Foundation type: Independent foundation.
Financial data (yr. ended 12/31/12): Assets, $3,723,526 (M); gifts received, $300,000; expenditures, $1,518,263; qualifying distributions, $1,510,332; giving activities include $1,508,475 for 4 grants (high: $800,000; low: $15,000).
Purpose and activities: The foundation provides funding to charitable organizations in New Hampshire that are committed to protecting the environment, ending human rights abuses, and supporting women's issues.
Fields of interest: Environment; Civil/human rights; Women.
Type of support: General/operating support; Land acquisition; Program development.
Limitations: Applications not accepted. Giving primarily in NH. No support for religious organizations, or for national health organizations, or organizations with less than 2 years of direct service experience. No grants to individuals, or for multi-year requests, capital requests, endowment drives, mass mailing appeals, sponsorship requests, scholarships, travel expenses or deficit reduction; no loans.
Application information: Unsolicited requests for funds not accepted.
Board meeting date(s): Late spring, late fall
Trustees: Janet L. Cohen; Jill R. Cohen; Perry L. Cohen; Rachel F. Cohen; Richard B. Cohen.
EIN: 036069606

5185
The Penates Foundation
1 Liberty Ln. E., Ste. 100
Hampton, NH 03842-1809 (603) 926-2369
Contact: Michele M. Cogan, V.P.

Established in 1984 in NH.
Donors: Paul M. Montrone; Sandra G. Montrone; Prestolite Wire Corp.; Latona Associates Inc.; Chatam, Inc.; Winthrop, Inc.; The Oxford League, Inc.; Fisher Scientific.
Foundation type: Independent foundation.
Financial data (yr. ended 06/30/13): Assets, $11,088,457 (M); gifts received, $8,000; expenditures, $1,239,956; qualifying distributions, $1,153,291; giving activities include $1,116,750 for 69 grants (high: $165,000; low: $250).
Purpose and activities: Giving primarily for the arts, education, medical research, and human services.
Fields of interest: Performing arts centers; Performing arts, opera; Arts; Higher education; Business school/education; Education; Human services; Residential/custodial care, hospices; Christian agencies & churches.
Type of support: Continuing support; Annual campaigns; Capital campaigns; Building/renovation; Land acquisition; Emergency funds; Scholarship funds.
Limitations: Giving primarily in MA, NH, and NY. No grants to individuals.
Application information: Application form not required.
Initial approach: Letter
Copies of proposal: 1
Deadline(s): None
Officers and Directors:* Sandra G. Montrone,* Pres.; Michele M. Cogan,* V.P. and Secy.-Treas.; Kevin Clark; Anthony DiNovi; Matthew Friel; Angelo Montrone; Jerome Montrone; Paul M. Montrone; Fred Seigel.
EIN: 222536075

5186
Putnam Foundation ✧
20 Central Sq., 2nd Fl.
P.O. Box 323
Keene, NH 03431-3795 (603) 352-2448
Contact: James Putnam, Tr.

Trust established in 1952 in NH.
Donors: David F. Putnam‡; Rosamond Putnam‡; Louisa Putnam; Frederick A. Putnam; Thomas P. Putnam; Rosamond Delori; David F. Putnam, Jr.
Foundation type: Independent foundation.
Financial data (yr. ended 10/31/13): Assets, $34,718,478 (M); expenditures, $1,517,433; qualifying distributions, $1,209,322; giving activities include $1,209,322 for 124 grants (high: $100,000; low: $250).
Purpose and activities: The foundation's mandate and purpose are to provide funds on a regional basis in New Hampshire, and, in particular, the Monadnock Region for historic preservation, cultural enhancement, and ecological maintenance.
Fields of interest: Historic preservation/historical societies; Arts; Education; Environment; Children/youth, services; Government/public administration.
Type of support: General/operating support; Capital campaigns; Endowments; Program-related investments/loans; Mission-related investments/loans.
Limitations: Giving limited to NH. No grants to individuals or for scholarships.
Publications: Application guidelines.
Application information: Application form not required.
Initial approach: Letter
Copies of proposal: 1
Deadline(s): None
Board meeting date(s): Monthly
Trustees: James A. Putnam; Thomas P. Putnam.
EIN: 026011388

5187
Walter S. Quinlan Foundation ✧ ☆
c/o Robert A. Zock & Co., Inc.
98 Birch Hill Rd.
Warner, NH 03278-6401

Established in 1959 in MA.
Foundation type: Independent foundation.
Financial data (yr. ended 12/31/13): Assets, $12,505,273 (M); expenditures, $476,160; qualifying distributions, $459,000; giving activities include $459,000 for 23 grants (high: $200,000; low: $1,000).
Purpose and activities: Giving for education, Christian organizations, and the arts.
Fields of interest: Arts; Higher education; Education; Christian agencies & churches.
Type of support: General/operating support.
Limitations: Applications not accepted. Giving primarily in MA.
Application information: Unsolicited requests for funds not accepted.
Trustees: Jean Marie Doin; Andrew P. Hellmuth; John S. Hellmuth; Mary Ann Hellmuth; Robert L. Hellmuth; Thomas P. Loftis; Maureen Casey Rollins.
EIN: 046030253
Selected grants: The following grants are a representative sample of this grantmaker's funding activity:
$20,000 to Community Mercy Foundation, Springfield, OH, 2012. For general support.

5188
The Schleyer Foundation ✧
P.O. Box 222
Rye Beach, NH 03871-0222 (732) 295-1000
Contact: William T. Schleyer, Tr.

Established in 2002 in NH.
Donor: William T. Schleyer.
Foundation type: Independent foundation.
Financial data (yr. ended 12/31/12): Assets, $11,054,257 (M); gifts received, $214,605; expenditures, $676,838; qualifying distributions, $600,121; giving activities include $595,046 for 23 grants (high: $200,000; low: $100).
Fields of interest: Higher education; Education; Human services; Foundations (private grantmaking).
Limitations: Applications accepted. Giving primarily in ME, NH and PA. No grants to individuals.
Application information: Application form required.

Initial approach: Proposal
Deadline(s): None
Trustees: William T. Schleyer; Mary Zygala.
EIN: 056132358

5189
The Trust Family Foundation ✧
1 Stiles Rd., Ste. 202
Salem, NH 03079-4844 (603) 898-2002
Contact: Peter Lee, Fdn. Admin.

Established in 1986 in NH.
Donors: Diane Trust; Martin Trust.
Foundation type: Independent foundation.
Financial data (yr. ended 12/31/13): Assets, $25,629,231 (M); gifts received, $4,999,419; expenditures, $1,463,083; qualifying distributions, $1,262,939; giving activities include $1,187,863 for 24 grants (high: $303,600; low: $500).
Purpose and activities: Giving primarily for the arts, education, medical technology, and Jewish philanthropies.
Fields of interest: Visual arts; Performing arts; Humanities; Arts; Education; Medical research, institute; Jewish agencies & synagogues.
Type of support: Program development.
Limitations: Applications accepted. Giving primarily in New England, with emphasis on MA and NH. No grants to individuals, including scholarships, or for capital campaigns, operating budgets, or endowments.
Publications: Annual report (including application guidelines).
Application information: Application form required.
Initial approach: Proposal
Copies of proposal: 4
Deadline(s): None
Officer: Peter Lee, Fdn. Admin.
Trustees: David Trust; Diane Trust; Laura Trust; Martin Trust.
Number of staff: None.
EIN: 026070843

NEW JERSEY

5190
Alcatel-Lucent Foundation ✧
(formerly Lucent Technologies Foundation)
600 Mountain Ave.
Murray Hill, NJ 07974-2008
Contact: Bishalakhi Ghosh, Exec. Dir.
E-mail: foundation@alcatel-lucent.com; E-mail for Bishalakhi Ghosh: bishalakhi.ghosh@alcatel-lucent.com; Main URL: http://www2.alcatel-lucent.com/foundation/index.php
ConnectEd on Facebook: https://www.facebook.com/ALFConnectEd
Facebook: http://www.facebook.com/AlcatelLucentFoundation
Flickr: https://www.flickr.com/photos/alcatel_lucent_foundation/

Established in 1996.
Donors: Lucent Technologies Inc.; Alcatel-Lucent.
Foundation type: Company-sponsored foundation.
Financial data (yr. ended 12/31/12): Assets, $3,554,752 (M); gifts received, $3,000,000; expenditures, $3,508,868; qualifying distributions, $3,498,868; giving activities include $3,343,300 for 22+ grants (high: $1,057,900).
Purpose and activities: The foundation supports programs designed to promote digital inclusion and sustainability with a focus on underserved communities that enable youth and young women to access education and life skills training.
Fields of interest: Elementary/secondary education; Vocational education; Higher education; Education, e-learning; Education; Employment, training; Disasters, preparedness/services; Youth development, adult & child programs; Big Brothers/Big Sisters; Girl scouts; Youth development, business; Youth development; Youth; Young adults, female; Economically disadvantaged.
Type of support: General/operating support; Continuing support; Program development; Employee volunteer services.
Limitations: Applications not accepted. Giving primarily in areas of company operations, with emphasis on CA, NJ, and NY; giving also to international and national organizations.
Application information: Unsolicited applications are not accepted. Projects must be submitted by employees and supported by senior management.
Board meeting date(s): Bi-annually
Officers and Trustees:* Janet G. Davidson,* Chair.; Barbara Landmann, Vice-Chair.; Sandra D. Motley, V.P.; Alex Yip, Secy. and Legal Counsel; Richard Campbell, Treas.; Elisabeth Eude, Exec. Dir.; Frederic Chapelard; Christine Diamente; Radwa Hafez; Marco Malfavon; William Reese; Theodore Sizer.
EIN: 223480423

5191
Rita Allen Foundation, Inc. ✧
92 Nassau St., 3rd Fl.
Princeton, NJ 08542-4530 (609) 683-8010
Contact: Elizabeth G. Christopherson, C.E.O. and Pres.
FAX: (609) 683-8025; E-mail: info@ritaallen.org; Main URL: http://www.ritaallen.org
Blog: http://www.ritaallenfoundation.org/investing-in-innovation.htm
E-Newsletter: http://www.ritaallenfoundation.org/index.htm

Incorporated in 1953 in NY.
Donor: Rita Allen Cassel†.
Foundation type: Independent foundation.
Financial data (yr. ended 12/31/12): Assets, $147,522,548 (M); gifts received, $1,836; expenditures, $7,644,660; qualifying distributions, $7,131,007; giving activities include $5,823,826 for 101 grants (high: $250,000; low: $450), and $80,985 for 1 foundation-administered program.
Purpose and activities: The foundation invests in transformative ideas in their earliest stages to leverage their growth and promote breakthrough solutions to significant problems. The foundation's areas of active interest include investing in young leaders in the sciences and social innovation, promoting civil literacy, and building stronger communities. The foundation recognizes that it must be flexible enough to respond to unique challenges, ideas and projects that lie beyond its original program areas.
Fields of interest: Humanities; Arts; Higher education; Health care; Medical research, institute; Agriculture/food; Youth development; Civil/human rights, advocacy; Community/economic development; Jewish federated giving programs; Biology/life sciences; Children/youth; Children; Youth; Adults; Young adults; Minorities; Asians/Pacific Islanders; African Americans/Blacks; Hispanics/Latinos; Native Americans/American Indians; Women; Girls; Adults, women; Young adults, female; Men; Boys; Adults, men; Young adults, male; Economically disadvantaged.
Type of support: Continuing support; Management development/capacity building; Endowments; Emergency funds; Program development; Conferences/seminars; Seed money; Curriculum development; Fellowships; Scholarship funds; Research; Consulting services; Program evaluation.
Limitations: Applications not accepted. Giving on a national basis. No grants to individuals (except university research scientists), or for building funds.
Publications: Annual report; Financial statement; Grants list.
Application information: Unsolicited requests for funds not accepted.
Board meeting date(s): Quarterly and as required
Officers and Directors:* William F. Gadsden,* Chair.; Elizabeth G. Christopherson,* C.E.O. and Pres.; Henry H. Hitch,* Secy.-Treas.; Moore Gates, Jr., Dir. Emeritus; Aristides Georgantas, Dir. Emeritus; Robert E. Campbell, Dir. Emeritus; Jon Cummings; Robbert Dijkgraaf, Ph.D.; Landon Y. Jones; Hon. Thomas H. Kean; Sivan Nemovicher; Geneva Overholser; Sam S.H. Wang, Ph. D.
Number of staff: 2 full-time professional; 1 full-time support; 1 part-time support.
EIN: 136116429
Selected grants: The following grants are a representative sample of this grantmaker's funding activity:
$325,000 to Ashoka: Innovators for the Public, Arlington, VA, 2013. For Feedback Labs Project.
$300,000 to Rockefeller University, New York, NY, 2012. For Rita Allen Foundation Scholars Program.
$300,000 to Rockefeller University, New York, NY, 2013. For Rita Allen Foundation Scholars Program.
$300,000 to Salk Institute for Biological Studies, La Jolla, CA, 2012. For Rita Allen Foundation Scholars Program.
$300,000 to Salk Institute for Biological Studies, La Jolla, CA, 2013. For Rita Allen Foundation Scholars Program.
$250,000 to Pew Charitable Trusts, Philadelphia, PA, 2013. For Voting Information Project.
$250,000 to Public Radio International, Minneapolis, MN, 2012. For Immigrant Lives.
$220,000 to Harvard University, Cambridge, MA, 2012. For Rita Allen Foundation Scholars Program.
$220,000 to Harvard University, Cambridge, MA, 2013. For Rita Allen Foundation Scholars Program.
$200,000 to Center for Responsive Politics, Washington, DC, 2012. For 501c4 data project.
$200,000 to PopTech, Camden Office, Camden, ME, 2012. For Science and Social Innovation Fellows.
$150,000 to Code for America Labs, San Francisco, CA, 2013. For 2013/14 fellowship program.
$150,000 to MAPLight.org, Berkeley, CA, 2013. For Voter's Edge Project, payable over 1.50 years.
$150,000 to Public Radio International, Minneapolis, MN, 2013. For Immigrant Lives.
$110,000 to KnowledgeWorks Foundation, Cincinnati, OH, 2012. For knowledge sharing time bank project.
$100,000 to University of California, Berkeley, CA, 2012. For Rita Allen Foundation Scholars Program.
$100,000 to University of Texas Southwestern Medical Center, Dallas, TX, 2013. For Rita Allen Foundation Scholars Program.
$50,000 to Center for Public Integrity, Washington, DC, 2012. For State Accountability Project.
$50,000 to Media Impact Funders, Philadelphia, PA, 2013. For Media Taxonomy Website Redesign and Impact Metrics Work.
$50,000 to PopTech, Camden Office, Camden, ME, 2012. For PeaceTXT.

5192
The Antz Foundation ✧
P.O. Box 1501, NJ2-130-03-31
Pennington, NJ 08534-0671

Established in 1989 in NY.
Donor: John A. Thain.
Foundation type: Independent foundation.
Financial data (yr. ended 01/31/14): Assets, $522,923 (M); expenditures, $7,278,857; qualifying distributions, $7,263,018; giving activities include $7,255,993 for 12 grants (high: $4,957,143; low: $500).
Fields of interest: Higher education; Botanical gardens; Hospitals (general); Human services.
Type of support: General/operating support.
Limitations: Applications not accepted. Giving primarily in NY; some funding also in MA. No grants to individuals, or scholarships; no loans.
Application information: Contributes only to pre-selected organizations.
Trustees: Carmen M. Thain; John Thain.
EIN: 133536523
Selected grants: The following grants are a representative sample of this grantmaker's funding activity:
$1,057,142 to New York Botanical Garden, Bronx, NY, 2012.
$100,000 to MIT Museum, Cambridge, MA, 2012.

5193
Appaloosa Management Charitable Foundation, Inc. ✧ ☆
51 John F. Kennedy Pkwy., Ste. 250
Short Hills, NJ 07078-2704

Donor: Appaloosa Management, L.P.
Foundation type: Independent foundation.
Financial data (yr. ended 12/31/13): Assets, $7,955,000 (M); gifts received, $20,000,000; expenditures, $12,045,000; qualifying distributions, $12,045,000; giving activities include $12,045,000 for 1 grant.
Fields of interest: Foundations (private grantmaking).
Limitations: Applications not accepted. Giving primarily in Short Hills, NJ.
Application information: Unsolicited requests for funds not accepted.
Officers: David A. Tepper, Pres.; Jeffrey Kaplan, V.P.; Kenneth Maiman, Secy.; Lawrence Rogers, Treas.
EIN: 464011140

5194
ARCH Foundation ✧
100 Bayer Blvd.
Whippany, NJ 07981-1544 (862) 404-4022
Contact: Donald Nerz, Treas.
E-mail: donald.nerz@bayer.com; Additional application addresses: P.O. Box 220908, Charlotte, NC 29222-0908, tel.: (877) 393-9071, Fax: (877) 229-1421; Main URL: http://www.archfoundation.com/

Established in 2001 in NJ; status changed to company-sponsored operating foundation in 2005.
Donors: Berlex Laboratories, Inc.; Berlex Inc.; Bayer Healthcare Pharmaceuticals Inc.; Bauer USA Foundation.
Foundation type: Operating foundation.
Financial data (yr. ended 12/31/13): Assets, $145,711 (M); gifts received, $12,399,600; expenditures, $12,268,445; qualifying distributions, $12,268,445; giving activities include $11,370,600 for grants to individuals.
Purpose and activities: The foundation provides the birth control medication Mirena to economically disadvantaged women who live below the federal poverty level and have no insurance coverage.
Fields of interest: Health care; Women; Economically disadvantaged.
Type of support: Grants to individuals; Donated products.
Limitations: Applications accepted. Giving on a national basis.
Publications: Application guidelines.
Application information: Applications must be completed in part by a healthcare provider. Application form required.
Initial approach: Download application form and fax or mail to application address
Deadline(s): None
Officers and Trustees:* Edio Zampaglione, Chair.; Paul Bedard, Pres.; David Weinstock, Secy.; Donald Nerz, Treas.; David Grimes, M.D.; Anita Nelson, M.D.; Ruth Merkatz; Sandy Oliver; Mary Pendergast; Jim Sailer.
EIN: 221231236

5195
The David R. and Patricia D. Atkinson Foundation ✧
100 Overlook Ctr., 2nd Fl.
Princeton, NJ 08540-7814

Established in 2000 in NJ.
Donors: David R. Atkinson; Patricia D. Atkinson.
Foundation type: Independent foundation.
Financial data (yr. ended 08/31/13): Assets, $31,723,416 (M); gifts received, $1,200,000; expenditures, $1,487,065; qualifying distributions, $1,426,000; giving activities include $1,426,000 for 67 grants (high: $250,000; low: $1,500).
Purpose and activities: Giving primarily for health associations and human services, including services for people who are blind; funding also for children and youth services.
Fields of interest: Education; Health organizations, association; Alzheimer's disease research; Human services; Salvation Army; Children/youth, services; Blind/visually impaired.
Limitations: Applications not accepted. Giving primarily in NJ; some funding nationally, particularly in NY and PA. No grants to individuals.
Application information: Contributes only to pre-selected organizations.
Trustees: David R. Atkinson; Patricia D. Atkinson; Paul D. Atkinson; Steven R. Atkinson.
EIN: 223753685
Selected grants: The following grants are a representative sample of this grantmaker's funding activity:
$50,000 to Doctors Without Borders USA, New York, NY, 2011. For general support.
$35,000 to Salvation Army National Headquarters, Alexandria, VA, 2011. For general support.

5196
The Atlantic Foundation ✧
14 Fairgrounds Rd., Ste. A
Hamilton, NJ 08619-3447 (609) 689-1040
Contact: Michael Unger, Chief Admin. Officer; Craig Ingwer, Cont.

Incorporated in 1963 in NJ.
Donors: J. Seward Johnson†; The J. Seward Johnson 1963 Charitable Trust; Johnson Art and Education Foundation.
Foundation type: Independent foundation.
Financial data (yr. ended 12/31/13): Assets, $73,009,423 (M); gifts received, $8,510,056; expenditures, $8,445,844; qualifying distributions, $7,377,935; giving activities include $6,221,000 for 6 grants (high: $4,550,000; low: $3,500), and $487,853 for foundation-administered programs.
Fields of interest: Arts, public policy; Arts, single organization support; Visual arts; Visual arts, sculpture; Arts; Education, single organization support; Science, single organization support; Public affairs, research.
Type of support: Program development; Matching/challenge support; Management development/capacity building; General/operating support; Building/renovation.
Limitations: Applications not accepted. Giving primarily in Mercer County, NJ and Fort Pierce, FL; some funding also in Washington, DC and in New York, NY. No grants to individuals.
Application information: Contributes only to pre-selected organizations.
Officers and Directors:* J. Seward Johnson, Jr.,* C.E.O.; John S. Johnson III, Secy.; Michael H. Greenleaf, Treas.; Craig Ingwer, Cont.; Lakshman Achuthan; Robert Campbell; Garrett M. Heher; Carrie Rossip Malcolm.
EIN: 226054882

5197
Atran Foundation, Inc. ✧
155 N. Dean St., 3rd Fl.
Englewood, NJ 07631-2532 (201) 569-9677
Contact: Diane Fischer, Pres.

Incorporated in 1945 in NY.
Donor: Frank Z. Atran†.
Foundation type: Independent foundation.
Financial data (yr. ended 11/30/13): Assets, $23,714,820 (M); expenditures, $1,032,143; qualifying distributions, $1,010,772; giving activities include $699,920 for 27 grants (high: $120,000; low: $1,500).
Purpose and activities: Support for research relating to labor and labor relations, art, science, literature, economics, and sociology; support of publications furthering these purposes; and endowment for chairs of learning in these fields.
Fields of interest: Arts; Higher education; Medical school/education; Employment, labor unions/organizations; Jewish federated giving programs.
Type of support: General/operating support; Continuing support; Annual campaigns; Endowments; Program development; Conferences/seminars; Professorships; Publication; Scholarship funds; Research; Exchange programs.
Limitations: Giving primarily in New York, NY. No grants to individuals.
Publications: Application guidelines.
Application information: Application form not required.
Initial approach: Proposal
Copies of proposal: 1
Deadline(s): Sept. 30
Board meeting date(s): Between Nov. and Feb. and as required
Final notification: Positive references only
Officers and Trustees:* Diane Fischer,* Pres.; Sam Norich,* Treas.
Number of staff: 1 full-time professional; 1 part-time support.
EIN: 135566548
Selected grants: The following grants are a representative sample of this grantmaker's funding activity:
$120,000 to YIVO Institute for Jewish Research, New York, NY, 2013. To support General Operating.

5198
Bacchetta Foundation ✧ ☆
c/o Princeton Family Office
2 Princess Rd., Ste. 2H
Lawrenceville, NJ 08540-7638

Donors: Monroe Milstein; Andrew Milstein.
Foundation type: Independent foundation.
Financial data (yr. ended 12/31/13): Assets, $40,873,819 (M); expenditures, $1,759,298; qualifying distributions, $1,665,833; giving activities include $1,665,833 for 4 grants (high: $1,500,000; low: $18,000).
Fields of interest: Education; Human services; Jewish federated giving programs; Religion.
Type of support: General/operating support.

Limitations: Applications not accepted. Giving primarily in New York, NY.
Application information: Unsolicited requests for funds not accepted.
Directors: Andrew Milstein; Carol Milstein.
EIN: 452554800

5199
The Endre A. Balazs Foundation ✧
725 River Rd., Ste. 205
Edgewater, NJ 07020-3180

Established in 2000 in NJ.
Foundation type: Independent foundation.
Financial data (yr. ended 12/31/13): Assets, $5,076,065 (M); expenditures, $1,170,341; qualifying distributions, $1,091,667; giving activities include $1,091,667 for 5 grants (high: $915,000; low: $20,000).
Fields of interest: Performing arts, opera; Higher education; Civil liberties, reproductive rights; Biology/life sciences.
Limitations: Applications not accepted. Giving primarily in NJ and NY.
Application information: Unsolicited requests for funds not accepted.
Trustees: Endre A. Balazs; Eric R. Fox; Janet L. Denlinger.
EIN: 316638795

5200
Banbury Fund, Inc. ✧
c/o Withumsmith & Brown, CPAs
331 Newman Springs Rd., Ste. 125
Red Bank, NJ 07701-6765

Incorporated in 1946 in NY.
Donors: Marie H. Robertson‡; Charles S. Robertson‡.
Foundation type: Independent foundation.
Financial data (yr. ended 12/31/13): Assets, $25,528,723 (M); expenditures, $660,837; qualifying distributions, $514,133; giving activities include $462,850 for 36 grants (high: $137,500; low: $200).
Purpose and activities: Primary areas of interest include higher and other education, health and medical research, the environment, and marine research and conservation programs.
Fields of interest: Higher education; Education; Environment; Health care; Medical research, institute; Cancer research; Human services; Marine science; Engineering/technology; Biology/life sciences; Science.
Type of support: General/operating support; Continuing support; Annual campaigns; Capital campaigns; Building/renovation; Equipment; Endowments; Debt reduction; Emergency funds; Seed money; Research.
Limitations: Applications not accepted. Giving primarily in CA and NY; funding also in CO, CT, FL, SC and VA. No grants to individuals.
Application information: Contributes only to pre-selected organizations.
Officers: Victoria Linnartz, Pres.; Diana McKibben, Secy.; Andrew McKibben, Treas.
Board Members: Katherine R. Ernst; Robert J. Ernst; Anne R. Meier; Walter C. Meier; Geoffrey S. Robertson; Julia Robertson; William S. Robertson.
Number of staff: 4 part-time professional.
EIN: 136062463

5201
Swain Barber Foundation ✧ ☆
c/o RR LLP
P.O. Box 730
Point Pleasant, NJ 08742-0730
Application address: c/o Peter W. Grousbeck, Tr., P.O. Box 29129, Los Angeles, CA 90029, tel.: (323) 655-1144, e-mail: swainbarber@gmail.com

Donor: Grousbeck Family Foundation.
Foundation type: Independent foundation.
Financial data (yr. ended 11/30/13): Assets, $43,046,469 (M); expenditures, $2,370,135; qualifying distributions, $2,156,501; giving activities include $2,156,501 for 24 grants (high: $550,000; low: $21).
Fields of interest: Education; International affairs; Community/economic development.
Limitations: Applications accepted. Giving primarily in CA; funding also in New York, NY.
Application information: Application form not required.
Initial approach: Proposal
Deadline(s): None
Trustees: Brie Cameron Grousbeck; Peter Walker Grousbeck.
EIN: 306284989

5202
C. R. Bard Foundation, Inc. ✧
730 Central Ave.
Murray Hill, NJ 07974-1139
Contact: Linda Hrevnack, Mgr., Community Affairs and Contribs.
FAX: (908) 277-8098; Main URL: http://www.crbard.com/Community_Outreach/C__R__Bard_Foundation,_Inc_.html

Established in 1987 in NY.
Donor: C.R. Bard, Inc.
Foundation type: Company-sponsored foundation.
Financial data (yr. ended 12/31/12): Assets, $744,663 (M); gifts received, $2,548,000; expenditures, $2,558,565; qualifying distributions, $2,558,299; giving activities include $2,524,458 for 170 grants (high: $100,000; low: $360).
Purpose and activities: The foundation supports organizations involved with education, health, and human services. Special emphasis is directed toward programs designed to promote urology, oncology, vascular, and surgical medicine.
Fields of interest: Education; Health care; Medical specialties; Human services; United Ways and Federated Giving Programs.
Type of support: Employee matching gifts; General/operating support; Program development; Scholarship funds; Sponsorships.
Limitations: Applications accepted. Giving primarily in areas of company operations. No support for private foundations, political parties, fraternal, religious, or sectarian groups, or veterans' organizations. No grants to individuals, or for events that provide a non-charitable benefit to C.R. Bard, or capital campaigns.
Publications: Application guidelines.
Application information: Additional information may be requested at a later date. Site visits may also be encouraged and scheduled before grant awards are made. Application form required.
Initial approach: Complete online application
Copies of proposal: 2
Deadline(s): None
Board meeting date(s): Quarterly

Officers: Timothy M. Ring, Pres.; Scott T. Lowry, V.P. and Treas.; John H. Weiland, V.P.; Bronwen K. Kelly, Secy.
EIN: 222840708
Selected grants: The following grants are a representative sample of this grantmaker's funding activity:
$100,000 to Institute for Health Technology Studies, Washington, DC, 2012. For research grants.
$10,000 to New York University, School of Medicine, New York, NY, 2012. For research grants.
$10,000 to Paper Mill Playhouse, Millburn, NJ, 2012. For culture, arts and humanities.
$5,712 to United Way of Salt Lake, Salt Lake City, UT, 2012. For Federated Giving Programs for Employee Campaigns.
$5,000 to University of Utah, David Eccles School of Business, Salt Lake City, UT, 2012. For education.

5203
Barer Family Foundation Inc. ✧ ☆
c/o Sol J. Barer
2 Barer Ln.
Mendham, NJ 07945-2205

Established in 2005 in NJ.
Donors: Sol J. Barer; Meri I. Barer.
Foundation type: Independent foundation.
Financial data (yr. ended 12/31/13): Assets, $152,073 (M); expenditures, $1,030,651; qualifying distributions, $1,030,651; giving activities include $1,030,651 for 8 grants (high: $508,106; low: $25,285).
Fields of interest: Higher education, college; Medical research; Neuroscience research; Foundations (public).
Limitations: Applications not accepted. Giving primarily in NY and NJ. No grants to individuals.
Application information: Unsolicited requests for funds not accepted.
Officers and Trustees:* Sol J. Barer,* Pres. and Treas.; Meri I. Barer,* Secy.; Lori Ingber; Ilyssa Maisano; Jennifer Zairi.
EIN: 203972085

5204
The Elizabeth and Barets O. Benjamin Charitable Foundation, Inc. ✧
c/o Lasser
217 Metzger Dr., Ste. 217
West Orange, NJ 07052-6620

Established in 1995 in NJ.
Donors: Elizabeth Benjamin; Mary R. Lasser.
Foundation type: Independent foundation.
Financial data (yr. ended 12/31/13): Assets, $11,802,702 (M); expenditures, $682,251; qualifying distributions, $594,311; giving activities include $550,000 for 15 grants (high: $85,000; low: $10,000).
Fields of interest: Health organizations, association; Cancer.
Limitations: Applications not accepted. Giving primarily in NJ and NY. No grants to individuals.
Application information: Contributes only to pre-selected organizations.

Officers and Trustee:* Mary R. Lasser,* Pres.; Peter Lasser, V.P. and Treas.; Andrew Stamelman, Esq., Secy.
EIN: 223390586

5205
Sol & Margaret Berger Foundation ✧
140 Hepburn Rd.
Clifton, NJ 07012-2231

Established in 1962 in NY.
Donor: Sol Berger.
Foundation type: Independent foundation.
Financial data (yr. ended 04/30/13): Assets, $17,027,336 (M); expenditures, $737,965; qualifying distributions, $707,533; giving activities include $630,914 for 59 grants (high: $275,000; low: $90).
Purpose and activities: Giving primarily for health, particularly cancer research, education, and human services.
Fields of interest: Arts; Education; Health care.
Type of support: Scholarship funds.
Limitations: Applications not accepted. Giving primarily in NJ and NY. No grants to individuals.
Application information: Unsolicited requests for funds not accepted.
Board meeting date(s): Mar.
Trustees: Sandye Aidner; Renee Berger.
EIN: 136118516
Selected grants: The following grants are a representative sample of this grantmaker's funding activity:
$75,000 to Columbia University, New York, NY, 2011.
$7,000 to Indiana University, Bloomington, IN, 2011.
$6,500 to New York City Ballet, New York, NY, 2011.

5206
The Russell Berrie Foundation ✧
300 Frank W. Burr Blvd., Bldg. East, 7th Fl.
Teaneck, NJ 07666-6704 (201) 928-1880
Contact: Ruth Salzman, C. E. O
E-mail: inquiry@rbfdtn.org; Main URL: http://www.russellberriefoundation.org
E-Newsletter: http://www.russellberriefoundation.org/getinvolved-enewsletter.php

Established in 1985 in NJ.
Donor: Russell Berrie†.
Foundation type: Independent foundation.
Financial data (yr. ended 12/31/12): Assets, $215,018,834 (M); gifts received, $77,180; expenditures, $21,536,292; qualifying distributions, $20,617,146; giving activities include $18,359,047 for 118 grants (high: $5,160,000; low: $750), and $173,888 for 12 grants to individuals (high: $35,000; low: $5,000).
Purpose and activities: The foundation as created to express the values and passions of Russell Berrie through social investments in innovative ideas designed to: 1) Promote the continuity and enrichment of Jewish communal life; 2) Support advances in medicine focusing on diabetes and humanism in medicine; 3) Fostering the spirit of religious understanding and pluralism; 4) Recognizing individuals who have made a significant difference to the lives of others; 5) Elevating the profession of sales; and 6) Raising the awareness of terrorism and promoting its prevention.
Fields of interest: Arts; Higher education; Hospitals (general); Health care, clinics/centers; Medical research; Human services; Science, research; Engineering/technology; Jewish agencies & synagogues; Religion, interfaith issues.
Type of support: General/operating support; Continuing support; Management development/capacity building; Emergency funds; Program development; Fellowships; Research; Matching/challenge support.
Limitations: Applications not accepted. Giving primarily in northern NJ, New York City, Israel, and Italy.
Application information: Unsolicited requests for funds not accepted.
Officers and Trustees:* Ruth Salzman, C.E.O. and Exec. Dir.; Angelica Berrie,* Pres.; Scott Berrie,* V.P.; Myron Rosner,* Secy.; Adam Hirsch, C.F.O.; Stephen Seiden,* Treas.; Ilan Kaufthal; Norman Seiden.
Number of staff: 8 full-time professional.
EIN: 222620908
Selected grants: The following grants are a representative sample of this grantmaker's funding activity:
$5,160,000 to Columbia University, New York, NY, 2012.
$1,360,889 to Jewish Federation of Northern New Jersey, Paramus, NJ, 2012.
$1,238,386 to Institute of International Education, New York, NY, 2012.
$1,100,000 to Nefesh B'Nefesh - Jewish Souls United, Paramus, NJ, 2012.
$1,000,000 to New York-Presbyterian Hospital, New York, NY, 2012.
$50,000 to New Israel Fund, Washington, DC, 2012.
$50,000 to Philanthropic Initiative, Boston, MA, 2012.
$35,000 to Riverview School, East Sandwich, MA, 2012.
$20,000 to Brotherhood Synagogue, New York, NY, 2012.
$10,000 to American Friends of Assaf Harofeh Medical Center, Rocky Mountain Chapter, Los Angeles, CA, 2012.

5207
Bolger Foundation ✧
79 Chestnut St.
Ridgewood, NJ 07450-2533

Established in 1964.
Donor: David F. Bolger.
Foundation type: Independent foundation.
Financial data (yr. ended 12/31/13): Assets, $9,070,281 (L); gifts received, $2,764,672; expenditures, $1,747,073; qualifying distributions, $1,732,081; giving activities include $1,666,583 for 16 grants (high: $500,000; low: $834).
Purpose and activities: Giving primarily for education, health care organizations, and human services, and Christian organizations and Protestant churches.
Fields of interest: Higher education; Education; Health care; Human services; Children/youth, services; Community/economic development; Christian agencies & churches; Protestant agencies & churches.
Type of support: General/operating support.
Limitations: Applications not accepted. Giving primarily in FL and NJ. No grants to individuals.
Application information: Contributes only to pre-selected organizations.
Officers and Trustees:* Thomas Wells,* C.E.O.; David F. Bolger,* Pres.; James T. Bolger,* Treas.; John G. Bolger; Bettina M. Daly.
EIN: 237418090
Selected grants: The following grants are a representative sample of this grantmaker's funding activity:
$1,610,953 to Valley Hospital Foundation, Ridgewood, NJ, 2012.
$325,456 to Midland Park, Borough of, Midland Park, NJ, 2012.
$260,000 to University of Maine 4-H Camp and Learning Center at Bryant Pond, Bryant Pond Oxford County Fund, Bryant Pond, ME, 2012.
$65,200 to Cerebral Palsy Center of Bergen County, Children's Therapy Center, Fair Lawn, NJ, 2012.
$55,000 to Wells Mountain Foundation, Bristol, VT, 2012.
$25,000 to InStride Therapy, Nokomis, FL, 2012.
$23,140 to Womans Club of Ridgewood, Ridgewood, NJ, 2012.
$17,110 to Lester Stable, Ridgewood, NJ, 2012.
$10,200 to YMCA of Ridgewood, Ridgewood, NJ, 2012.

5208
The Corella & Bertram F. Bonner Foundation, Inc. ✧
10 Mercer St.
Princeton, NJ 08540-6808 (609) 924-6663
Contact: Robert Hackett, Pres.
FAX: (609) 683-4626; E-mail: info@bonner.org; Main URL: http://www.bonner.org
Bonner Network Blog: http://bonnernetwork.wordpress.com
Bonner Network Wiki: http://bonnernetwork.pbworks.com/
LinkedIn: http://www.linkedin.com/groups?mostPopular=&gid=86257
Slideshare: http://www.slideshare.net/BonnerFoundation/slideshows
Twitter: http://twitter.com/bonnernetwork
YouTube: http://www.youtube.com/user/BonnerNetwork

Established in 1981 in NJ; reactivated in 1989.
Donors: Bertram F. Bonner†; Corella A. Bonner†.
Foundation type: Independent foundation.
Financial data (yr. ended 06/30/13): Assets, $40,080,407 (M); gifts received, $85; expenditures, $6,613,536; qualifying distributions, $5,719,490; giving activities include $5,610,494 for 51 grants (high: $2,500,000; low: $1,250), and $108,996 for foundation-administered programs.
Purpose and activities: Through sustained partnerships with colleges and congregations, the foundation seeks to improve the lives of individuals and communities by helping meet the basic needs of nutrition and educational opportunity. Support primarily for higher education institutions and local anti-poverty and anti-hunger organizations.
Fields of interest: Higher education; Education; Food services; Christian agencies & churches; Religion; Minorities.
Type of support: Continuing support.
Limitations: Applications not accepted. Giving primarily in NJ. No grants to individuals or for capital

improvements, endowments, operating budgets, building funds, or renovations.
Publications: Informational brochure.
Application information: Unsolicited requests for funding not accepted. See foundation web site for further information.
Board meeting date(s): Mar., June, Sept., and Dec.
Officers and Trustees:* Kenneth F. Kunzman,* Chair.; Robert Hackett, Pres.; Ariane Hoy, V.P., Prog. and Resource Devel.; William Bush; Carol Clarke; Charles C. Goodfellow; Rev. Dr. John Kuykendall.
Number of staff: 1 full-time professional.
EIN: 222316452
Selected grants: The following grants are a representative sample of this grantmaker's funding activity:
$2,500,000 to Carson-Newman College, Jefferson City, TN, 2013. To endow Bonner Scholars Program.
$1,500,000 to Stetson University, DeLand, FL, 2013. To endow Bonner Scholars Program.
$250,000 to Allegheny College, Meadville, PA, 2013. To endow Bonner Scholars Program.
$250,000 to Centre College of Kentucky, Danville, KY, 2013. To endow Bonner Scholars Program.
$75,000 to College of New Jersey, Ewing, NJ, 2013. For Crisis Ministry Grant, which provide foods for the hungry while encouraging congregations to build community relationships and strengthen their outreach programs. The program's focus is on funding the purchase of food for anti-hunger initiatives that are supported by congregations with the involvement of their clergy, are actively involved in addressing the underlying causes of their clients' hunger and are located in economically and socially disadvantaged communities of the United States.
$46,250 to Stetson University, DeLand, FL, 2013. For Bonner Scholars Grant.
$40,000 to Nassau Presbyterian Church, Princeton, NJ, 2013. For Crisis Ministry Grant, which provide foods for the hungry while encouraging congregations to build community relationships and strengthen their outreach programs. The program's focus is on funding the purchase of food for anti-hunger initiatives that are supported by congregations with the involvement of their clergy, are actively involved in addressing the underlying causes of their clients' hunger and are located in economically and socially disadvantaged communities of the United States.
$40,000 to Princeton Outreach Projects, Crisis Ministry of Princeton and Trenton, Princeton, NJ, 2013. For Crisis Ministry Grant, which provide foods for the hungry while encouraging congregations to build community relationships and strengthen their outreach programs. The program's focus is on funding the purchase of food for anti-hunger initiatives that are supported by congregations with the involvement of their clergy, are actively involved in addressing the underlying causes of their clients' hunger and are located in economically and socially disadvantaged communities of the United States.
$25,000 to Habitat for Humanity, Trenton Area, Trenton, NJ, 2013. For Crisis Ministry Grant, which provide foods for the hungry while encouraging congregations to build community relationships and strengthen their outreach programs. The program's focus is on funding the purchase of food for anti-hunger initiatives that are supported by congregations with the involvement of their clergy, are actively involved in addressing the underlying causes of their clients' hunger and are located in economically and socially disadvantaged communities of the United States.
$25,000 to Rider University, Lawrenceville, NJ, 2013. For Crisis Ministry Grant, which provide foods for the hungry while encouraging congregations to build community relationships and strengthen their outreach programs. The program's focus is on funding the purchase of food for anti-hunger initiatives that are supported by congregations with the involvement of their clergy, are actively involved in addressing the underlying causes of their clients' hunger and are located in economically and socially disadvantaged communities of the United States.

5209
Mary Owen Borden Memorial Foundation ✧
4 Blackpoint Horseshoe
Rumson, NJ 07760-1929 (732) 741-4645
Contact: Quincy A.S. McKean III, Exec. Dir.
FAX: (732) 741-2542; E-mail: qmckean@aol.com; Main URL: http://fdnweb.org/borden

Incorporated in 1934 in NJ.
Donors: Bertram H. Borden‡; Victory Memorial Park Foundation.
Foundation type: Independent foundation.
Financial data (yr. ended 12/31/12): Assets, $12,732,468 (M); expenditures, $796,582; qualifying distributions, $691,653; giving activities include $630,710 for 59 grants (high: $62,500; low: $1,000).
Purpose and activities: The foundation's special focus will be on programs in New Jersey's Mercer and Monmouth counties, addressing the needs of economically disadvantaged youth and their families. This will include health, family planning, education, counseling, child care, substance abuse, and delinquency. Other areas of interest include affordable housing, conservation and the environment, and the arts.
Fields of interest: Arts; Education, early childhood education; Child development, education; Education; Environment, natural resources; Environment; Reproductive health, family planning; Health care; Substance abuse, services; Mental health/crisis services; Health organizations, association; Alcoholism; Crime/violence prevention, youth; Housing/shelter, development; Human services; Children/youth, services; Child development, services; Family services; Women, centers/services; Homeless, human services; Women; Economically disadvantaged; Homeless.
Type of support: General/operating support; Continuing support; Capital campaigns; Building/renovation; Equipment; Program development; Seed money; Matching/challenge support.
Limitations: Applications accepted. Giving limited to Monmouth and Mercer counties, NJ. No grants for scholarships, fellowships, or multi-year grants.
Publications: Application guidelines; Annual report (including application guidelines).
Application information: The foundation only accepts applications from its current grantees. No applications from new applicants will be accepted. Application form required.
Initial approach: Proposal
Deadline(s): None
Board meeting date(s): June and Dec.
Officers: Linda B. McKean, Pres.; Jerri L. Morrison, V.P.; Julie B. Kennedy,* Secy.; Quincy A.S. McKean III, Exec. Dir.
Trustees: Paul McEvily; Vincent Myers.
Number of staff: 1 part-time professional.
EIN: 136137137

5210
Borgenicht Foundation, Inc. ✧
392 Fairview Ave.
Long Valley, NJ 07853-3259

Donor: Borgenicht Char. Rem. Unitrust.
Foundation type: Independent foundation.
Financial data (yr. ended 03/31/13): Assets, $10,116,503 (M); gifts received, $5,025,218; expenditures, $601,455; qualifying distributions, $540,500; giving activities include $540,500 for grants.
Fields of interest: Higher education; Education; Human services; International affairs, goodwill promotion.
Limitations: Applications not accepted. No grants to individuals.
Application information: Contributes only to pre-selected organizations.
Trustees: Jan Schwartz Baden; David Bennett; Frances Bordenicht; Yoel Borgenicht; Berta Kerr; James H. Knox.
EIN: 200051444
Selected grants: The following grants are a representative sample of this grantmaker's funding activity:
$90,625 to Abraham Fund Initiatives, New York, NY, 2012.
$25,000 to Swain School, Allentown, PA, 2012.
$20,000 to Delaware Center for the Contemporary Arts, Wilmington, DE, 2012.
$20,000 to Triton Museum of Art, Santa Clara, CA, 2012.
$15,000 to Public Allies Delaware, Wilmington, DE, 2012.
$14,000 to Goucher College, Baltimore, MD, 2012.
$10,000 to Hiddush, Freedom of Religion for Israel, New York, NY, 2012.
$10,000 to Military Religious Freedom Foundation, Albuquerque, NM, 2012.
$10,000 to YMCA of Delaware, Wilmington, DE, 2012.
$1,000 to Silicon Valley Conference for Community and Justice, San Jose, CA, 2012.

5211
The Nicholas J. and Anna K. Bouras Foundation, Inc. ✧
25 De Forest Ave.
Summit, NJ 07901-2140 (908) 918-9400

Established in 1998 in NJ.
Donors: Nicholas J. Bouras; United Steel Deck, Inc.
Foundation type: Independent foundation.
Financial data (yr. ended 12/31/13): Assets, $48,244,964 (M); expenditures, $5,789,344; qualifying distributions, $5,425,546; giving activities include $5,340,757 for 44 grants (high: $2,379,757; low: $5,000).
Purpose and activities: Giving primarily to Greek Orthodox agencies and churches, and to human service organizations which support Greek people.
Fields of interest: Human services; Orthodox agencies & churches.
Limitations: Applications not accepted. Giving in the U.S., with emphasis on NJ and New York, NY. No grants to individuals.
Application information: Contributes only to pre-selected organizations.
Officers and Trustees:* Nicholas J. Bouras,* Pres.; Andrew J. Stamelman,* Secy.; William S. Crane,* Treas.; B. Theodore Bozonelis.
EIN: 223591803

Selected grants: The following grants are a representative sample of this grantmaker's funding activity:
$1,386,751 to Greek Orthodox Archdiocese of America, New York, NY, 2012.
$922,300 to Saint Annas Greek Orthodox Church, Flemington, NJ, 2012.
$759,000 to Greek American Rehabilitation and Care Centrer, Wheeling, IL, 2012. For care of elderly Greek Americans.
$700,000 to Citadel Foundation, Charleston, SC, 2012.
$250,000 to Greek Orthodox Ladies Philoptochos Society, New York, NY, 2012. For support of GOA women.
$250,000 to Overlook Hospital Foundation, Summit, NJ, 2012.
$100,000 to Hellenicare, Chicago, IL, 2012. For Medical Relief Fund.
$20,000 to StreetLight Mission, Elizabeth, NJ, 2012. For support of inner-city homeless.
$18,000 to Union Catholic High School, Scotch Plains, NJ, 2012.
$15,000 to Holy Trinity Greek Orthodox Church, Westfield, NJ, 2012.

5212
The Boye Foundation, Inc. ✧
575 Curran Pl.
Franklin Lakes, NJ 07417-2410

Established in 2000 in NJ.
Donor: William E. Boye, Jr.†.
Foundation type: Independent foundation.
Financial data (yr. ended 12/31/13): Assets, $23,320,383 (M); expenditures, $1,341,567; qualifying distributions, $1,276,469; giving activities include $1,273,000 for 44 grants (high: $150,000; low: $1,000).
Fields of interest: Arts; Health care; Human services; YM/YWCAs & YM/YWHAs.
Limitations: Applications not accepted. Giving primarily in NJ; some funding also in MD. No grants to individuals.
Application information: Contributes only to pre-selected organizations.
Officers: Nancy R. Boye, Pres. and Treas.; Melinda L. Boye-Nolan, V.P.; Robert R. Boye, Secy.
Trustees: Brett A. Boye; Robert B. Boye; William D. Boye.
EIN: 223769157
Selected grants: The following grants are a representative sample of this grantmaker's funding activity:
$60,000 to University of Arizona, Tucson, AZ, 2011.
$50,000 to New York-New Jersey Trail Conference, Mahwah, NJ, 2011.
$10,000 to Explora Science Center and Childrens Museum of Albuquerque, Albuquerque, NM, 2011.

5213
Bridge Street Foundation, Inc. ✧ ☆
55 Bridge St.
Lambertville, NJ 08530-2115
Main URL: http://bridgestreetfoundation.org/

Established in NJ.
Donor: Kevin Daugherty.
Foundation type: Independent foundation.
Financial data (yr. ended 12/31/13): Assets, $1,229,569 (M); expenditures, $2,037,542; qualifying distributions, $2,032,847; giving activities include $1,879,923 for 2 grants (high: $1,571,872; low: $308,051).
Fields of interest: Performing arts; Performing arts, theater.
Limitations: Applications not accepted. Giving primarily in Lambertville, NJ.
Application information: Unsolicited requests for funds not accepted.
Officers and Directors:* Kevin Daugherty,* Chair. and Treas.; Sherri Daugherty,* Secy.
EIN: 454035843

5214
Broadridge Foundation ✧
c/o Broadridge Financial Solutions, Inc.
2 Journal Square Plz.
Jersey City, NJ 07306-4001 (201) 714-3505
Contact: Adam Amsterdam

Donor: Broadridge Financial Solutions, Inc.
Foundation type: Independent foundation.
Financial data (yr. ended 03/31/13): Assets, $1,071,429 (M); gifts received, $1,002,020; expenditures, $545,217; qualifying distributions, $545,217; giving activities include $545,217 for grants.
Fields of interest: Higher education; Education; Health organizations, association; Medical research, institute; Human services; Children/youth, services.
Application information:
Initial approach: Letter
Officers and Directors:* John Hogan,* Chair.; Adam Amsterdam,* Secy.; Dan Sheldon,* Treas.
EIN: 262870487
Selected grants: The following grants are a representative sample of this grantmaker's funding activity:
$15,000 to Alzheimers Association, New York City Chapter, New York, NY, 2011.
$10,000 to Museum of the City of New York, New York, NY, 2011.
$5,000 to New Jersey Performing Arts Center, Newark, NJ, 2011.
$2,500 to Autism Speaks, Los Angeles, CA, 2011.
$1,500 to Florida State University Foundation, Tallahassee, FL, 2011.
$1,050 to Network for Good, Washington, DC, 2011.
$1,000 to Adoptions Together, Baltimore, MD, 2011.
$1,000 to Boy Scouts of America, Alameda, CA, 2011.
$1,000 to Entertainment Industry Foundation, Los Angeles, CA, 2011.
$1,000 to World Vision, Federal Way, WA, 2011.

5215
The Brothers Ashkenazi Foundation, Inc. ✧
759 Shrewsbury Ave.
Long Branch, NJ 07740-5027 (732) 574-9000
Contact: Ezra E. Ashkenazi, Tr.

Donors: Isaac Ashkenazi; Ezra E. Ashkenazi; Ronald Ashkenazi; David E. Ashkenazi.
Foundation type: Independent foundation.
Financial data (yr. ended 02/28/13): Assets, $8,611,333 (M); expenditures, $618,391; qualifying distributions, $605,943; giving activities include $605,943 for 1,059 grants (high: $400,000; low: $52).
Purpose and activities: Giving primarily to Jewish agencies, temples, and schools.
Fields of interest: Education; Jewish agencies & synagogues.
Application information: Application form not required.
Initial approach: Letter
Deadline(s): None
Trustees: Ezra E. Ashkenazi; Isaac Ashkenazi; Ronald Ashkenazi.
EIN: 223469592

5216
Fred J. Brotherton Charitable Foundation
(formerly Fred J. Brotherton Foundation, Inc.)
1141 Greenwood Lake Tpke., Ste. C-6
Ringwood, NJ 07456-1433 (973) 728-6100
Contact: Maribeth A. Ligus, Admin. Dir.
E-mail: brothertonfoundation@yahoo.com; Main URL: http://foundationcenter.org/grantmaker/brotherton/

Established in 1995.
Donor: Fred J. Brotherton†.
Foundation type: Independent foundation.
Financial data (yr. ended 09/30/13): Assets, $14,151,379 (M); expenditures, $850,733; qualifying distributions, $691,029; giving activities include $651,255 for 38 grants (high: $50,000; low: $725).
Purpose and activities: The foundation's major areas of interest are: 1) Educational programs and/or institutions (primarily schools and colleges), with emphasis on, but not limited to, educational programs providing assistance to the needy or disabled; 2) Religion-based programs and/or institutions, with an emphasis on, but not limited to, providing assistance to the needy or disabled, or to benefit a local church in a capital program; 3) Historic Preservation programs and/or institutions (including societies); and 4) Medical and/or Scientific programs and/or their affiliated institutions.
Fields of interest: Historic preservation/historical societies; Education; Medical research; Human services; Children/youth, services; Science, research; Religion.
Type of support: Capital campaigns; Equipment; Endowments; Program development; Conferences/seminars; Seed money; Internship funds; Scholarship funds; Research; Matching/challenge support.
Limitations: Applications accepted. Giving primarily in NJ and NY. No support for environmental programs, or for legal aid programs, advocacy groups, senior citizens programs, soup kitchens or food banks, or for well-endowed institutions or non 501c(3) organizations. No grants to individuals, or for conferences, or for day care programs, documentaries, films or videos, loans, moving expenses, polls or surveys, or for deficit financing.
Publications: IRS Form 990 or 990-PF printed copy available upon request.
Application information: When an organization receives an invitation to submit a full grant proposal, then the full grant proposal guidelines will be provided.
Initial approach: Letter of Inquiry (2 to 3 pages)
Copies of proposal: 4
Deadline(s): None for letter of inquiry; June 1 and Dec. 1 for full grant proposals

Board meeting date(s): Feb. and Aug.
Final notification: Aug. (June 1 cycle); Feb. (Dec. 1 cycle)
Trustees: Wayne A. Brotherton; William P. Brotherton, M.D.
Board of Advisors: Emily Brotherton; John Carrick; Steve Doty; Gary Jannarone; Robert H. Neth, Jr.; William Rahal; Nancy Shade.
Number of staff: 1 part-time professional.
EIN: 650774706
Selected grants: The following grants are a representative sample of this grantmaker's funding activity:
$30,000 to Boy Scouts of America, Northern New Jersey Council, Oakland, NJ, 2012.
$25,000 to Concerts of Prayer, Long Island City, NY, 2012.
$25,000 to New City Kids Church, Jersey City, NJ, 2012.
$25,000 to Orleans Athletic Association, Orleans, MA, 2012.
$25,000 to Urbana Theological Seminary, Champaign, IL, 2012. For endowment.
$15,000 to Childrens Aid and Family Services, Paramus, NJ, 2012.
$15,000 to Leukemia & Lymphoma Society, New York, NY, 2012.
$15,000 to Paper Mill Playhouse, Millburn, NJ, 2012.
$15,000 to Rutgers University Foundation, New Brunswick, NJ, 2012. For endowment.
$15,000 to Wistar Institute of Anatomy and Biology, Philadelphia, PA, 2012.
$13,000 to Ramapo-Bergen Animal Refuge, Oakland, NJ, 2012.
$12,000 to Snow Library, Friends of the, Orleans, MA, 2012. For endowment.
$10,000 to Kula for Karma, Franklin Lakes, NJ, 2012.
$8,284 to Hole in the Wall Gang Fund, New Haven, CT, 2012.
$7,000 to Ocean Grove Camp Meeting Association, Ocean Grove, NJ, 2012.
$6,468 to Passaic County Historical Society, Paterson, NJ, 2012. For endowment.

5217
The W. Dale Brougher Foundation, Inc. ✧
P.O. Box 1501, NJ2-130-03-31
Pennington, NJ 08534-1501

Established in 1986 in MD.
Donors: W. Dale Brougher; W. Dale Brougher Trust.
Foundation type: Independent foundation.
Financial data (yr. ended 12/31/13): Assets, $80,212,849 (M); expenditures, $3,390,156; qualifying distributions, $3,049,808; giving activities include $2,747,948 for 59 grants (high: $333,333; low: $200).
Fields of interest: Arts; Education; Animal welfare; Human services; YM/YWCAs & YM/YWHAs; Family services; United Ways and Federated Giving Programs; Christian agencies & churches.
Limitations: Applications not accepted. Giving primarily in PA; funding also in FL. No grants to individuals.
Application information: Contributes only to pre-selected organizations.
Officers: Robert E. Bossert, Pres.; Nancy Brougher, V.P.
Director: Sonya L. Eicholtz.
EIN: 521499358

5218
The Robert & Marion Schamann Brozowski Foundation, Inc. ✧
355 E. Linden Ave.
Linden, NJ 07036-2421 (908) 862-4990
Contact: Edmund Faulkner, V.P.

Established in 1999 in NJ.
Donor: Marion S. Brozowski†.
Foundation type: Independent foundation.
Financial data (yr. ended 12/31/13): Assets, $9,292,623 (M); gifts received, $55,007; expenditures, $503,750; qualifying distributions, $483,721; giving activities include $460,000 for 31 grants (high: $40,000; low: $3,500).
Fields of interest: Animal welfare; Cancer; Human services; Residential/custodial care, hospices.
Type of support: General/operating support.
Limitations: Applications accepted. Giving primarily in NJ.
Application information: Application form not required.
Initial approach: Proposal
Deadline(s): None
Officers: James Koslovski, Pres.; Edmund Faulkner, V.P.; Veronica Daniel, Secy.; Robert R. Stanicki, Treas.
EIN: 223613766
Selected grants: The following grants are a representative sample of this grantmaker's funding activity:
$25,000 to Franciscan Charities, Keyport, NJ, 2012. For general charitable contributions.

5219
Emil Buehler Perpetual Trust ✧
c/o Boyle & Co., PA
113 Johnson Ave.
Hackensack, NJ 07601-4825
Application address: c/o Gale Sykes, Grants Admin., Wells Fargo Private Bank, 190 River Rd., 2nd Fl., Summit, NJ 07901-1444; Main URL: https://www.wellsfargo.com/privatefoundationgrants/buehler

Established in 1984 in NJ.
Donor: Emil Buehler†.
Foundation type: Independent foundation.
Financial data (yr. ended 11/30/13): Assets, $64,594,620 (M); expenditures, $6,410,212; qualifying distributions, $3,282,515; giving activities include $2,691,197 for 10 grants (high: $531,197; low: $50,000).
Purpose and activities: Giving limited to the research, development, improvement, and promotion of aviation science and technology.
Fields of interest: Museums (science/technology); Higher education; Space/aviation; Engineering/technology; Science.
Type of support: Building/renovation; Equipment; Internship funds; Research; Matching/challenge support.
Limitations: Applications accepted. Giving primarily in southern FL and NJ.
Publications: Informational brochure (including application guidelines).
Application information: See foundation website for complete application guidelines. Application form required.
Initial approach: Letter requesting application form
Copies of proposal: 1
Deadline(s): Feb. 1, May 1, Aug. 1, and Nov. 1
Board meeting date(s): Mar., June., Sept., and Dec.
Trustees: Robert D. Boyle; George Weaver; Wells Fargo Bank, N.A.
EIN: 226395303
Selected grants: The following grants are a representative sample of this grantmaker's funding activity:
$666,667 to Bergen Community College Foundation, Paramus, NJ, 2011.
$600,000 to Hackensack University Medical Center, Hackensack, NJ, 2011.
$231,198 to Broward College, Fort Lauderdale, FL, 2011.
$26,500 to Broward College, Fort Lauderdale, FL, 2011.

5220
The Bunbury Company, Inc. ✧
2 Railroad Pl.
Hopewell, NJ 08525-1818 (609) 333-8800
Contact: Samuel W. Lambert III, Treas.
FAX: (609) 333-8900;
E-mail: grants@bunburycompany.org; Main URL: http://www.bunburycompany.org

Incorporated in 1952 in NY.
Donor: Dean Mathey†.
Foundation type: Independent foundation.
Financial data (yr. ended 12/31/12): Assets, $20,939,930 (M); expenditures, $1,286,122; qualifying distributions, $1,193,767; giving activities include $1,014,500 for 158 grants (high: $50,000; low: $100).
Purpose and activities: Giving primarily for education, environmental conservation, community building and social services, and the arts.
Fields of interest: Arts; Education; Environment; Youth development; Children/youth, services; Family services.
Type of support: Building/renovation; General/operating support; Capital campaigns; Program development; Matching/challenge support.
Limitations: Giving limited to NJ, with emphasis on Mercer County, as well as Burlington, Camden, Hunterdon, Middlesex, Monmouth, Ocean, and Somerset counties. No support for organizations outside of Mercer county with multiple chapters. No support for sporting activities, outings or events; fraternal or religious organizations, including affiliated schools; summer camps or day care facilities, unless part of a comprehensive aftercare program; nor for specific cultural performances. No grants to individuals, including scholarships and individual fellowships. No support for endowment campaigns, building funds, publications, or surveys.
Publications: Application guidelines; Annual report; Financial statement; Grants list.
Application information: Please follow submission requirements as outlined in guidelines. Application guidelines and forms available on foundation Web site. Faxed or e-mailed applications are not accepted. Application form required.
Initial approach: Use electronic application process on foundation web site
Deadline(s): Varies; see foundation web site for current deadlines
Board meeting date(s): Jan., May, July, and Oct.
Final notification: Within 10 weeks of submission deadline
Officers and Directors:* Jamie Kyte Sapoch,* Pres.; Robert M. Olmsted,* V.P.; Jeffrey Smith,* Secy.;

William H. Bruett,* Treas.; Elizabeth A. Bankowski; Frederic Boswell; William A. Gilbert; Samuel W. Lambert III; Edward J. Zuccaro.
Number of staff: 1 full-time professional; 8 part-time professional.
EIN: 136066172

5221
C Funding ✧
c/o David Fishel
348 Jones Rd.
Englewood, NJ 07631-4412

Established in 2000 in NJ.
Donors: David Fishel; Capital Investors LLC; Liquidity Solutions Inc.
Foundation type: Independent foundation.
Financial data (yr. ended 12/31/13): Assets, $1,584,626 (M); gifts received, $1,318,000; expenditures, $1,004,856; qualifying distributions, $1,004,788; giving activities include $1,004,788 for 146 grants (high: $115,000; low: $18).
Purpose and activities: Giving primarily to Jewish agencies and temples.
Fields of interest: Education; Human services; Jewish agencies & synagogues.
Limitations: Applications not accepted. No grants to individuals.
Application information: Contributes only to pre-selected organizations.
Trustee: David Fishel.
EIN: 223769647
Selected grants: The following grants are a representative sample of this grantmaker's funding activity:
$200,000 to Central Fund of Israel, New York, NY, 2011.
$200,000 to Migdal Ohr, Miami Beach, FL, 2011.

5222
Cabin Road Foundation ✧ ☆
c/o RR, LLP
P.O. Box 730
Pt. Pleasant, NJ 08742-0730
Application address: c/o Anne G. Matta, 2995 Woodside Rd., Ste. 400, Woodside, CA 94602; tel.: (650) 454-4731;
e-mail: osobuccochile@gmail.com

Established in CA.
Donor: Grousbeck Family Foundation.
Foundation type: Independent foundation.
Financial data (yr. ended 11/30/13): Assets, $43,164,026 (M); expenditures, $2,532,642; qualifying distributions, $2,319,008; giving activities include $2,319,008 for 11 grants (high: $724,148; low: $22).
Fields of interest: Secondary school/education; Higher education; Education; Housing/shelter; Human services.
Limitations: Applications accepted. Giving primarily in CA.
Application information: Application form not required.
Initial approach: Contact foundation
Deadline(s): None
Trustees: Anne Grousbeck Matta; Horacio Matta Velasco.
EIN: 306284988

5223
Campbell Soup Foundation ✧
(formerly Campbell Soup Fund)
1 Campbell Pl.
Camden, NJ 08103-1799 (856) 342-4800
Contact: Wendy Milanese, Secy.
E-mail: community_relations@campbellsoup.com; Main URL: http://
www.campbellsoupcompany.com/about-campbell/corporate-responsibility/campbell-soup-foundation

Incorporated in 1953 in NJ.
Donor: Campbell Soup Co.
Foundation type: Company-sponsored foundation.
Financial data (yr. ended 06/30/13): Assets, $23,579,012 (M); gifts received, $2,000,000; expenditures, $1,831,469; qualifying distributions, $1,673,322; giving activities include $1,673,322 for 278 grants (high: $250,000; low: $100).
Purpose and activities: The foundation supports programs designed to promote community wellbeing; youth empowerment; and economic sustainability initiatives to develop healthy communities.
Fields of interest: Arts; Higher education; Education; Health care; Food services; Nutrition; Recreation, camps; Recreation; Boys & girls clubs; Youth development; Children/youth, services; Human services; Economic development; Community/economic development; United Ways and Federated Giving Programs.
Type of support: Capital campaigns; General/operating support; Building/renovation; Equipment; Program development; Employee volunteer services; Employee matching gifts; Employee-related scholarships; Matching/challenge support.
Limitations: Applications accepted. Giving primarily in areas of company operations in Bakersfield, Davis, Dixon, Emeryville, and Stockton, CA, Bloomfield and Norwalk, CT, Lakeland, FL, Downers Grove, IL, Maxton, NC, New Brunswick and South Plainfield, NJ, Napoleon and Willard, OH, Denver and Downingtown, PA, Paris, TX, Richmond, UT, Everett, WA, and Milwaukee, WI, with emphasis on Camden, NJ. No support for religious organizations not of direct benefit to the entire community, political organizations, or units of government. No grants to individuals (except for employee-related scholarships), or for events or sponsorships; no product donations.
Publications: Application guidelines.
Application information: Letters of intent are accepted during the first week of each grant cycle. Proposals may be requested at a later date. Support is limited to 1 contribution per organization during any given year. Priority is given to applicants who have established an ongoing relationship with the local Campbell or Pepperidge Farm operating facility. Application form not required.
Initial approach: Complete online letter of intent; contact local Campbell or Pepperidge Farm facility for organizations located outside of Camden, NJ
Copies of proposal: 1
Deadline(s): Jan. 1 to Apr. 30 and Sept. 1 to Nov. 30
Board meeting date(s): As required
Final notification: Up to 3 months
Officers and Trustees:* Dave Stangis,* Pres.; Wendy A. Milanese, Secy.; Ashok Madhaven, Treas.; Anthony P. DiSilvestro, Cont.; Mark Cacciatore; Richard Landers; Karen J. Lewis; Joe Spagnoletti; Steve White.
Number of staff: 1 part-time professional; 1 part-time support.
EIN: 216019196

5224
Cape Branch Foundation ✧
P.O. Box 86
Oldwick, NJ 08858-0086

Established in 1964 in NJ.
Foundation type: Independent foundation.
Financial data (yr. ended 12/31/12): Assets, $9,418,824 (M); expenditures, $6,691,339; qualifying distributions, $6,568,860; giving activities include $6,558,147 for 13 grants (high: $4,000,000).
Purpose and activities: Giving primarily for education, conservation, and the arts.
Fields of interest: Arts; Education; Environment, natural resources.
Type of support: General/operating support; Building/renovation; Land acquisition; Scholarship funds; Research.
Limitations: Applications accepted. Giving primarily in NJ; some funding also in NY. No grants to individuals.
Application information: Application form not required.
Initial approach: Brief letter
Deadline(s): None
Board meeting date(s): Annually
Directors: Gretchen W. Johnson; James L. Johnson.
Trustees: Gordon O. Danser; Scarlet S. Johnson Jarrell; Juliana L. Johnson Merton; Christopher Dirk Wittenborn.
EIN: 226054886

5225
Tina and Richard V. Carolan Foundation ✧
88 E. Main St., Ste. 507
Mendham, NJ 07945-1832

Established in 1990 in NJ.
Donors: Richard V. Carolan; Tina Carolan; Kimberly Carolan - Faga.
Foundation type: Independent foundation.
Financial data (yr. ended 11/30/13): Assets, $12,681,067 (M); expenditures, $590,921; qualifying distributions, $537,555; giving activities include $480,000 for 15 grants (high: $100,000; low: $2,000).
Purpose and activities: Giving primarily for medical research and education and to Armenian churches and organizations.
Fields of interest: Elementary/secondary education; Medical school/education; Medical research, institute; Christian agencies & churches.
Type of support: Equipment; Emergency funds; Program development; Research; Matching/challenge support.
Limitations: Applications accepted. Giving primarily in CA, GA, NJ, and NY. No grants to individuals.
Application information: Application form required.
Initial approach: Letter
Deadline(s): None
Officers: Tina Carolan, Pres.; Kimberly M. Carolan-Faga, V.P. and Secy.; Richard C. Carolan, V.P. and Treas.
EIN: 223085237

5226
Catholic Human Services Foundation ✧
P.O. Box 673
Pittstown, NJ 08867-0673 (908) 730-6883
Contact: Maggie Hackett, Grant Prog. Off.
E-mail: chsfoundation@embargmail.com; Main URL: http://www.catholichumanservicesfoundation.org/

Foundation type: Independent foundation.
Financial data (yr. ended 12/31/12): Assets, $12,328,081 (M); expenditures, $897,838; qualifying distributions, $798,990; giving activities include $581,190 for 67 grants (high: $15,000; low: $1,100).
Purpose and activities: Giving primarily to Catholic organizations that provide health and human services, including hospitals, medical research facilities, innovative educational programs and specialized programs for the disabled. Grants are primarily for supplies and equipment.
Fields of interest: Education; Hospitals (general); Health organizations; Housing/shelter; Human services; Religion.
Limitations: Applications accepted. Giving primarily in DE, NJ, and PA. No support for supporting organization having a 509(a)(3) status, non-U.S. based organizations, or to the same organization or project on an ongoing basis. No grants to individuals, or for scholarships, endowments, fellowships, salaries, administrative expenses, matching funds, taxes or shipping and handling charges, demonstration projects or capital campaigns.
Publications: Application guidelines; Grants list.
Application information: Application form required.
Initial approach: Letter of inquiry on organization letterhead
Deadline(s): None
Board meeting date(s): Mar., June, Sept., and Dec.
Officers and Directors:* R. Kevin Hackett,* C.E.O. and Pres.; Maggie Hackett, V.P. and Secy.; Ray Burns; John DeGraaf; Darin Petro.
EIN: 262967521
Selected grants: The following grants are a representative sample of this grantmaker's funding activity:
$15,000 to Meals on Wheels of Northampton County, Bethlehem, PA, 2012. For funding for Door Replacement for Program Supporting the Independent Living of Seniors By Providing Meals and Support Services.
$14,980 to Princeton Healthcare System Foundation, Princeton, NJ, 2012. For funding for Oncology Patient Navigation System for This Comprehensive Community Health System.
$14,937 to Make-A-Wish Foundation of New Jersey, Monroe Township, NJ, 2012. For Purchase Technology Equipment for Program That Grants Wishes to Children with Life-Threatening Medical Conditions.
$12,000 to Metropolitan Area Neighborhood Nutrition Alliance, Philadelphia, PA, 2012. For Purchase Food and Packaging Materials for Program Delivering Meals to Those at Risk from Life-Threatening Illnesses.
$10,977 to Inn Dwelling, Philadelphia, PA, 2012. For funding for Equipment for Program Providing Educational Opportunities for Inner-city Students with Above Average Potential.
$10,233 to 180 Turning Lives Around, Hazlet, NJ, 2012. For Purchase Computer Equipment for Agency Working to End Domestic Violence, Sexual Assault and Child Abuse in Monmouth Co.
$10,000 to Multiple Sclerosis Association of America, Cherry Hill, NJ, 2012. For funding for Safety Equipment for Program Serving Those Affected By Multiple Sclerosis.
$10,000 to Saint Peter's University, Jersey City, NJ, 2012. For funding for Medical Research Equipment in the Fields of Regenerative Medicine and Drug Development.
$9,332 to Christian Brothers Conference, Washington, DC, 2012. For funding for Supplies for Child Rescue Program, Vocational Training Center and High School in Nyeri, Kenya.
$5,621 to IHM Center for Literacy and GED Programs, Philadelphia, PA, 2012. For funding for Supplies for Center Teaching Language Skills to the Multi-Ethnic, Non-English Speaking Immigrant Population.

5227
Charles Foundation, Inc. ✧
c/o Robert C. Rooke
668 Spring Valley Rd.
Morristown, NJ 07960-6466

Established in 1994 in NJ.
Donors: Robert C. Rooke; Robert L. Rooke†.
Foundation type: Independent foundation.
Financial data (yr. ended 12/31/13): Assets, $40,234,212 (M); expenditures, $2,124,728; qualifying distributions, $2,106,055; giving activities include $2,094,900 for 52 grants (high: $516,000; low: $400).
Purpose and activities: Giving for education and health care.
Fields of interest: Higher education; Education; Hospitals (general).
Type of support: Capital campaigns; Building/renovation; Equipment; Land acquisition; Endowments; Scholarship funds.
Limitations: Applications not accepted. Giving primarily in NH and NJ. No grants to individuals.
Application information: Contributes only to pre-selected organizations.
Board meeting date(s): Varies
Officers and Directors:* Robert C. Rooke,* Pres. and Treas.; Natalie D. Rooke,* V.P.; Robert C. Rooke, Jr.,* Secy.
Number of staff: None.
EIN: 223292066

5228
CHDI Foundation, Inc. ✧ ☆
(formerly CHDI, Inc.)
c/o Tax Exempt Group, Ken Slutsky
65 Livingston Ave.
Roseland, NJ 07068-1725

Established in 2004 in NJ.
Donors: Triplet Investments Co., LLC; HDSA; Milstein Foundation; Lotsa LLC; JSY Foundation Inc.; Kurtz Foundation Inc.; Aqua Funding LLC; VBS Holdings LLC.
Foundation type: Independent foundation.
Financial data (yr. ended 10/31/13): Assets, $46,428,010 (M); gifts received, $150,018,130; expenditures, $153,812,439; qualifying distributions, $153,805,388; giving activities include $538,314 for 2 grants (high: $513,314; low: $25,000).
Purpose and activities: The foundation performs neurodegenerative research as well as holds conferences and workshops.
Fields of interest: Education.
Limitations: Applications not accepted. Giving in the U.S., with emphasis on Rochester, NY.
Application information: Unsolicited requests for funds not accepted.
Officers: Kenneth J. Slutsky, Co-Pres. and Treas.; Robi Blumenstein, Co-Pres.; Allen Levithan, V.P. and Secy.; John L. Berger, V.P.
EIN: 731683871

5229
The Chubb Foundation ✧
15 Mountain View Rd.
Warren, NJ 07059-6711
Scholarship address: c/o R & R Consultants, Attn.: Roger Lehecka, P.O. Box 250861, Columbia University Station, New York, NY 10025

Established in 1953 in NJ.
Donor: Hendon Chubb†.
Foundation type: Company-sponsored foundation.
Financial data (yr. ended 12/31/13): Assets, $23,321,620 (M); expenditures, $915,130; qualifying distributions, $904,667; giving activities include $854,000 for 311 grants to individuals (high: $6,000; low: $500).
Purpose and activities: Giving primarily for employee-related academic scholarships for undergraduate studies.
Fields of interest: Scholarships/financial aid; Education; Young adults.
Type of support: Employee-related scholarships.
Limitations: Applications accepted. Giving limited to Chubb Group employees and dependents worldwide.
Application information: Application information available from all branches and affiliated companies. Application form required.
Initial approach: See Website
Deadline(s): Dec. 31 for return of formal application; Feb. 24 for financial statement; Mar. 1 for Secondary School Report
Board meeting date(s): Apr. or May
Officers and Trustees:* Tommie Ann Gibney,* Chair.; Paul R. Geyer,* Co-Pres.; Beverly Luehs,* Co-Pres.; Kathleen B. Travinsky, Secy.; Tammie Vosburg,* Treas.; Nicolas D. Constan; Mark D. Wrigley.
EIN: 226058567

5230
David R. Clare & Margaret C. Clare Foundation ✧
c/o Porzio Bromberg & Newman
100 Southgate Pkwy.
P.O. Box 1997
Morristown, NJ 07962-1997

Established in 1991 in FL.
Donor: David R. Clare.
Foundation type: Independent foundation.
Financial data (yr. ended 10/31/13): Assets, $16,839,704 (M); expenditures, $613,639; qualifying distributions, $600,601; giving activities include $591,089 for 32 grants (high: $206,089; low: $500).

Purpose and activities: Giving primarily for education, children, youth and social services, and to Roman Catholic churches and schools.
Fields of interest: Elementary/secondary education; Higher education; Education; Human services; Children/youth, services; Catholic agencies & churches.
Type of support: Building/renovation; Conferences/seminars; Consulting services; Employee matching gifts; In-kind gifts; Matching/challenge support.
Limitations: Applications not accepted. No grants to individuals.
Application information: Contributes only to pre-selected organizations.
Trustees: Christopher E. Clare; David R. Clare.
EIN: 650300004
Selected grants: The following grants are a representative sample of this grantmaker's funding activity:
$200,435 to Medical University of South Carolina, Charleston, SC, 2011. For general support.

5231
Kenneth Cole Productions Foundation ✧
400 Plaza Dr., 3rd Fl.
Secaucus, NJ 07094-3605 (212) 265-1500
Contact: Charlynn Walker
Application address: 601 W. 50th St., New York, NY 10019, tel.: (212) 265-1500

Donor: Kenneth Cole Productions, Inc.
Foundation type: Company-sponsored foundation.
Financial data (yr. ended 12/28/13): Assets, $197,198 (M); gifts received, $189,687; expenditures, $495,719; qualifying distributions, $495,482; giving activities include $495,482 for 69 grants (high: $60,000; low: $6).
Purpose and activities: The foundation supports organizations involved with arts and culture, HIV/AIDS research, youth development, the fashion industry, and Judaism.
Fields of interest: Media, print publishing; Museums (art); Performing arts centers; Arts; AIDS; AIDS research; Legal services; Girl scouts; Business/industry; Jewish agencies & synagogues.
Type of support: General/operating support.
Limitations: Applications accepted. Giving primarily in New York, NY.
Application information: Generally contributes only to pre-selected organizations. Application form not required.
Initial approach: Proposal
Deadline(s): None
Directors: Kenneth D. Cole; Michael F. Colosi; David P. Edelman; Dieter C. Pasewaldt.
EIN: 562283049
Selected grants: The following grants are a representative sample of this grantmaker's funding activity:
$10,000 to Challenged Athletes Foundation, San Diego, CA, 2012. For general funds of organization.

5232
Community Foundation of New Jersey ✧
35 Knox Hill Rd.
P.O. Box 338
Morristown, NJ 07963-0338 (973) 267-5533
Contact: Hans Dekker, C.E.O.
FAX: (973) 267-2903; E-mail: info@cfnj.org; Additional Tel: (800) 659-5533; Additional e-mail: hdekker@cfnj.org; Main URL: http://www.cfnj.org Twitter: http://twitter.com/givingnj

Incorporated in 1979 in NJ.
Foundation type: Community foundation.
Financial data (yr. ended 12/31/12): Assets, $229,753,768 (M); gifts received, $32,367,610; expenditures, $33,211,860; giving activities include $28,395,393 for grants.
Purpose and activities: The foundation promotes and champions the betterment of New Jersey and the quality of life for its citizens by helping donors to fulfill their philanthropic goals.
Fields of interest: Arts; Education; Environment; Youth development, services; Family services; Human services; Urban/community development; Community/economic development; Leadership development; Public affairs; Economically disadvantaged.
Type of support: Program development; Scholarship funds; Program-related investments/loans.
Limitations: Applications accepted. Giving on a national basis for the benefit of NJ. No grants to individuals (except for scholarships), or for continuing support or deficit financing.
Publications: Annual report; Financial statement; Informational brochure; Newsletter; IRS Form 990 or 990-PF printed copy available upon request.
Application information: Visit foundation web site for scholarship information. The foundation does not accept unsolicited grant proposals.
Initial approach: 1 page letter
Deadline(s): None
Board meeting date(s): 4 times per year
Officers and Trustees:* Peter S. Reinhart,* Chair.; Hans Dekker,* C.E.O. and Pres.; Faith A. Krueger, C.O.O.; Robert J. Vogel,* Secy.; Susan I. Soldivieri, C.P.A., C.F.O.; Michael S. Maglio,* Treas.; Mark C. Alexander; Dale Robinson Anglin; Bernard S. Berkowitz; E. Michael Caulfield; James H. Caulfield; Grant M. Gille; Benedict M. Kohl; Kenneth Collins MacKenzie; Helen Mazarakis; Margaret V. Prentice; Frederick K. Schoenbrodt II; Wendy Supron; Thomas M. Uhlman; Richard P. Urfer; Robert J. Vogel.
Number of staff: 9 full-time professional; 3 full-time support; 2 part-time support.
EIN: 222281783
Selected grants: The following grants are a representative sample of this grantmaker's funding activity:
$740,000 to Community Food Bank of New Jersey, Hillside, NJ, 2012. For general operating support.
$725,000 to From Houses to Homes-Guatemala, Mount Tabor, NJ, 2012. For general operating support.
$650,000 to Foundation for Morristown Medical Center, Morristown, NJ, 2012. For capital campaign and general operating support.
$480,830 to Jewish Renaissance Medical Center, Perth Amboy, NJ, 2012. To develop mobile and permanent sites in Newark improving access to healthcare for residents.
$400,000 to Seton Hall University, South Orange, NJ, 2012. For Whitehead School of Diplomacy and International Relations.
$154,175 to Holy Spirit High School, Absecon, NJ, 2012. For scholarships.
$100,000 to Covenant House New Jersey, Newark, NJ, 2012. For general operating support.
$50,000 to Planned Parenthood of Greater Northern New Jersey, Morristown, NJ, 2012. For general operating support and EASE Campaign.
$20,000 to Clean Ocean Action, Highlands, NJ, 2012. To support Hurricane Sandy Relief.

5233
The Leon and Toby Cooperman Family Foundation ✧
(formerly Leon & Toby Cooperman Foundation)
c/o Gittelman & Co., PC
P.O. Box 2369
Clifton, NJ 07015-2369 (973) 778-8885
Contact: Leon Cooperman, Tr.
Leon and Toby Cooperman's Giving Pledge Profile: http://glasspockets.org/philanthropy-in-focus/eye-on-the-giving-pledge/profiles/cooperman

Established in 1981 in NJ.
Donors: Leon G. Cooperman; Toby F. Cooperman; D. Gideon Cohen.
Foundation type: Independent foundation.
Financial data (yr. ended 01/31/14): Assets, $296,329,153 (M); gifts received, $48,608,150; expenditures, $20,740,611; qualifying distributions, $13,356,434; giving activities include $13,356,434 for 150 grants (high: $3,000,000; low: $100).
Purpose and activities: Giving primarily for the arts, particularly a performing arts center, as well as for education, health organizations and medical research, human services, and to Jewish organizations.
Fields of interest: Performing arts centers; Arts; Higher education; Business school/education; Education; Health organizations, association; Medical research, institute; Cancer research; Human services; Foundations (community); Jewish federated giving programs; Jewish agencies & synagogues.
Type of support: General/operating support.
Limitations: Applications accepted. Giving primarily in NJ and New York, NY. No grants to individuals.
Application information:
Initial approach: Letter
Deadline(s): None
Trustees: Jodi Cooperman; Leon G. Cooperman; Michael S. Cooperman; Toby F. Cooperman; Wayne M. Cooperman.
EIN: 133102941
Selected grants: The following grants are a representative sample of this grantmaker's funding activity:
$2,479,879 to Jewish Community Foundation of MetroWest, Whippany, NJ, 2012.
$1,000,000 to Columbia University, Business School, New York, NY, 2012.
$1,000,000 to Newark Community Foundation, Morristown, NJ, 2012.
$500,000 to Jewish Community Foundation of MetroWest, Whippany, NJ, 2012.
$500,000 to Jewish Community Foundation of MetroWest, Whippany, NJ, 2012.
$250,000 to Robin Hood Foundation, New York, NY, 2012.
$249,750 to Hunter College Foundation, New York, NY, 2012.
$25,000 to Columbia University, Business School, New York, NY, 2012.
$25,000 to New Jersey Heroes, Mendham, NJ, 2012.
$11,000 to Columbia University, New York, NY, 2012.

5234
The Cowles Charitable Trust ✧
P.O. Box 219
Rumson, NJ 07760-0219 (732) 936-9826
Contact: Mary Croft, Treas.

Trust established in 1948 in NY.
Donor: Gardner Cowles†.
Foundation type: Independent foundation.
Financial data (yr. ended 12/31/12): Assets, $20,098,086 (M); expenditures, $1,274,467; qualifying distributions, $1,100,815; giving activities include $1,003,250 for 170 grants (high: $23,250; low: $500).
Fields of interest: Museums; Performing arts; Arts; Education; Hospitals (general); Health care; Health organizations, association; Human services; Protestant agencies & churches.
Type of support: General/operating support; Continuing support; Annual campaigns; Capital campaigns; Building/renovation; Equipment; Endowments; Emergency funds; Program development; Professorships; Seed money; Matching/challenge support.
Limitations: Applications accepted. Giving primarily along the Eastern Seaboard, with emphasis on FL and NY. No grants to individuals; no loans.
Publications: Application guidelines; Annual report.
Application information: Applications from any organizations submitted more than once every 12 months not considered. Telephone inquiries are not considered. Proposals must be sent by USPS First Class or Priority Mail. Application form required.
Initial approach: Letter requesting proposal cover sheet and guidelines
Copies of proposal: 8
Deadline(s): Dec. 1, Mar. 1, June 1, and Sept. 1
Board meeting date(s): Jan., Apr., July, and Oct.
Final notification: Within 2 weeks of board meeting
Officers and Trustees:* Gardner Cowles III,* Pres.; Mary Croft, Treas.; Charles Cowles; Jan S. Cowles; Lois Cowles Harrison; Lois Eleanor Harrison; Kate Cowles Nichols; Virginia Cowles Schroth.
Number of staff: 1 full-time professional.
EIN: 136090295

5235
Crane Fund for Widows & Children ✧
140 Sylvan Ave., Ste. 4
Englewood Cliffs, NJ 07632
E-mail: cfwc@craneco.com; Main URL: http://www.craneco.com/Category/34/Crane-Fund-for-Widows-and-Children.html

Established in 1914 in IL.
Foundation type: Company-sponsored foundation.
Financial data (yr. ended 12/31/13): Assets, $41,962 (M); expenditures, $1,581,385; qualifying distributions, $1,536,468; giving activities include $1,406,400 for 268 grants (high: $60,000; low: $1,000).
Purpose and activities: The foundation provides assistance to the needy through education, health, and human services.
Fields of interest: Elementary/secondary education; Higher education; Education; Hospitals (general); Health care, patient services; Health care; Cancer; Cancer, leukemia; Boys & girls clubs; Family services; Residential/custodial care, hospices; Human services; United Ways and Federated Giving Programs; Economically disadvantaged.
Type of support: Continuing support; Annual campaigns; Program development; Scholarship funds.
Limitations: Applications not accepted. Giving primarily in the U.S.; some giving also in Canada and the U.K. No grants to individuals.
Application information: Unsolicited requests for funds not accepted.
Trustees: A.I. duPont; E.M. Kopczick; A.L. Krawitt; R. A. Maue.
EIN: 366116543

5236
J. Fletcher Creamer Foundation ✧ ☆
101 E. Broadway
Hackensack, NJ 07601-6851 (201) 488-9800
Contact: J. Fletcher Creamer, Tr.

Established in 1980 in NJ.
Donor: J. Fletcher Creamer & Son, Inc.
Foundation type: Company-sponsored foundation.
Financial data (yr. ended 12/31/13): Assets, $2,866,726 (M); gifts received, $1,700,000; expenditures, $482,689; qualifying distributions, $479,107; giving activities include $478,082 for 146 grants (high: $186,500; low: $100).
Purpose and activities: The foundation supports organizations involved with performing arts, education, health, and human services.
Fields of interest: Performing arts; Performing arts centers; Higher education; Education; Hospitals (general); Health care, clinics/centers; Health care; Human services.
Type of support: Scholarship funds; Program development; Sponsorships; Continuing support; General/operating support.
Limitations: Applications accepted. Giving primarily in NJ. No grants to individuals.
Application information:
Initial approach: Proposal
Deadline(s): None
Trustees: Dale A. Creamer; J. Fletcher Creamer; J. Fletcher Creamer, Jr.
EIN: 222335557
Selected grants: The following grants are a representative sample of this grantmaker's funding activity:
$400 to Boy Scouts of America, Dayton, NJ, 2012. For Boy Scouts.
$300 to Shelter Our Sisters, Hackensack, NJ, 2012. For victims of domestic violence.

5237
Danellie Foundation ✧
P.O. Box 375/376
Marlton, NJ 08053-0375 (856) 273-6057
Contact: Nancy L. Dinsmore, Exec. Dir.
FAX: (856) 273-6977;
E-mail: danelliefoundation1@verizon.net

Established in 1988 in NJ.
Donor: Daniel L. Cheney.
Foundation type: Independent foundation.
Financial data (yr. ended 12/31/13): Assets, $1,304,887 (M); gifts received, $1,041,752; expenditures, $1,489,403; qualifying distributions, $1,467,540; giving activities include $1,386,630 for 61 grants (high: $100,000; low: $1,000).
Purpose and activities: Primary areas of interest include services for the financially disadvantaged, including housing and social services.
Fields of interest: Education; AIDS; Employment, training; Housing/shelter, development; Human services; Children/youth, services; Residential/custodial care, hospices; Homeless, human services; International relief; Community/economic development; Christian agencies & churches; Children/youth; Children; Youth; Adults; Aging; Young adults; Disabilities, people with; Mentally disabled; Offenders/ex-offenders; Substance abusers; AIDS, people with; Single parents; Economically disadvantaged; Homeless.
International interests: Guatemala; Haiti.
Type of support: General/operating support; Continuing support; Capital campaigns; Building/renovation; Program development; Sponsorships.
Limitations: Giving primarily in southern NJ (including Mercer and portions of Monmouth counties), and Baltimore, MD. No support for political organizations or professional sports, libraries or museums. No grants to individuals, or for endowments or radio and television.
Publications: Application guidelines.
Application information: The foundation is not accepting new applicants at this time. Applications are only being accepted from organizations which have received grants from the foundation in the past. Contact foundation for application guidelines. New York/New Jersey Area Common Application Form and New York/New Jersey Common Report Form accepted. Application form required.
Initial approach: Letter of inquiry/telephone
Copies of proposal: 2
Deadline(s): 3 weeks prior to meetings
Board meeting date(s): Varies
Final notification: 2 weeks after board meeting
Officers and Trustees:* Daniel L. Cheney,* Pres.; Eleanora L. Cheney,* Secy.-Treas.; Nancy L. Dinsmore,* Exec. Dir.; Julia Carleton; Richard D. Dinsmore; Keith A. Walter; Patricia E. Walter.
Number of staff: 1 part-time professional.
EIN: 222935245
Selected grants: The following grants are a representative sample of this grantmaker's funding activity:
$10,000 to YMCA Camp Ockanickon, Medford, NJ, 2012. To Fund the Recipient's Operating Budget.
$5,000 to Boy Scouts of America, Central Nj, Dayton, NJ, 2012. To Fund the Recipient's Operating Budget.

5238
D'Angelo Foundation ✧
731 Alexander Rd.
Princeton Plz., Bldg. 2
Princeton, NJ 08540-6345

Established in 1997 in NY and DE.
Donors: Peter P. D'Angelo; Margaret A. D'Angelo.
Foundation type: Independent foundation.
Financial data (yr. ended 12/31/13): Assets, $17,746,417 (M); gifts received, $3,058,228; expenditures, $1,686,008; qualifying distributions, $1,640,000; giving activities include $1,640,000 for 23 grants (high: $525,000; low: $5,000).
Purpose and activities: Giving primarily for education and human services, particularly for services for those who are economically disadvantaged.
Fields of interest: Higher education; Education; Hospitals (general); Human services; Children/youth, services; Economically disadvantaged.

Limitations: Applications not accepted. Giving primarily in the metropolitan New York, NY, area, including Long Island. No grants to individuals.
Application information: Contributes only to pre-selected organizations.
Officers and Directors:* Margaret A. D'Angelo,* Pres.; Peter P. D'Angelo,* Secy.-Treas.
EIN: 223555150

5239
Anthony and Christie De Nicola Foundation ✧

214 Green Ridge Rd.
Franklin Lakes, NJ 07417-2010
Contact: Anthony J. De Nicola, Dir.

Established in 2000 in NJ.
Donors: Anthony J. De Nicola; Christie De Nicola.
Foundation type: Independent foundation.
Financial data (yr. ended 11/30/13): Assets, $11,604,953 (M); gifts received, $676,172; expenditures, $1,160,415; qualifying distributions, $1,100,000; giving activities include $1,100,000 for 2 grants (high: $1,000,000; low: $100,000).
Fields of interest: Education; Human services; Foundations (public); Catholic federated giving programs.
Limitations: Applications accepted. Giving primarily in NJ.
Application information: Application form required.
Initial approach: Letter
Deadline(s): None
Trustees: Anthony J. De Nicola; Christie B. De Nicola.
EIN: 316647684
Selected grants: The following grants are a representative sample of this grantmaker's funding activity:
$50,000 to Posse Foundation, New York, NY, 2011.

5240
The Barbara Delano Foundation, Inc. ✧

(formerly The Barbara Gauntlett Foundation, Inc.)
c/o BNY Mellon, N.A.
26 Central Ave.
Cranford, NJ 07016-2103 (908) 477-6261
Contact: Charles Goodfellow
E-mail: bdfoundation@usa.net

Established in 1985 in NY.
Donor: Barbara Gauntlett†.
Foundation type: Independent foundation.
Financial data (yr. ended 12/31/12): Assets, $9,239,774 (M); expenditures, $3,664,833; qualifying distributions, $3,602,533; giving activities include $3,574,400 for 1 grant.
Fields of interest: Environment, natural resources; Environment, forests; Animals/wildlife, preservation/protection; Animals/wildlife, endangered species.
Type of support: Equipment; Land acquisition; Emergency funds; Program development; Matching/challenge support.
Limitations: Giving primarily in Washington, DC. No support for private foundations. No grants to individuals, or for research, film projects, conferences, administrative costs, large equipment purchases, for-profit organizations, wildlife sanctuaries, rescue centers or hospitals, or projects not specifically dedicated to wildlife conservation.
Application information: Proposals only considered after letter of request. Application form not required.
Initial approach: Letter, fax or e-mail inquiry of no more than 2 pages
Copies of proposal: 1
Deadline(s): None
Board meeting date(s): Nov., Dec.
Final notification: Notification only if grant is awarded
Officers and Directors:* Suwanna Gauntlett,* Pres.; Christopher C. Angell,* Secy.; Charles C. Goodfellow III,* Treas.; Neal P. Myerberg.
Number of staff: 1 full-time professional; 1 part-time professional.
EIN: 115238046

5241
Robert and Joan Dircks Foundation, Inc. ✧

(formerly Joan M. Dircks Foundation, Inc.)
P.O. Box 6
Mountain Lakes, NJ 07046-0006
Contact: Carolyn Dircks Van Riper, Pres.
E-mail: grants@dircksfoundation.org; PA tel.: (610) 925-3713; MA tel.: (978) 449-0072; Main URL: http://www.dircksfoundation.org

Established in 1991 in NJ.
Donor: Robert J. Dircks†.
Foundation type: Independent foundation.
Financial data (yr. ended 12/31/13): Assets, $10,947,636 (M); gifts received, $291,065; expenditures, $590,611; qualifying distributions, $510,393; giving activities include $464,500 for 65 grants (high: $20,000; low: $1,000; average: $1,000–$15,000).
Purpose and activities: The mission is to support small non-profit organizations that enrich and improve the quality of life for individuals primarily located in NJ. The focus is to encourage innovative programs and projects that benefit and improve the lives of children and individuals who are physically, mentally, or economically disadvantaged.
Fields of interest: Education; Health care; Human services, volunteer services; Human services; Children/youth, services.
Type of support: Management development/capacity building; Program development; Publication; Curriculum development; Scholarship funds; Research; Technical assistance; Program evaluation.
Limitations: Applications accepted. Giving primarily in NJ. No support for environmental or cultural organizations, or for programs of national or international scope. No grants to individuals, or for capital or annual campaigns, endowments, operating budgets, deficit/debt reduction, or for housing projects; no loans.
Publications: Application guidelines.
Application information: Application form and guidelines available on foundation web site. Application form required.
Initial approach: Online
Copies of proposal: 1
Deadline(s): None
Board meeting date(s): 5 times per year
Final notification: Via e-mail
Officer and Trustees:* Carolyn Dircks Van Riper,* Pres.; Robert E. Dircks; Thomas C. Dircks; William C. Dircks; Joan Dirks Walsh.
Number of staff: 1 part-time professional.
EIN: 223135737
Selected grants: The following grants are a representative sample of this grantmaker's funding activity:
$15,000 to Happiness is Camping, Bronx, NY, 2012. Toward 2012 Summer Camp's Direct Medical Services.
$15,000 to Kelly Anne Dolan Memorial Fund, Ambler, PA, 2012. Toward the Bright Lights and Single Parents project.
$10,000 to CASA Project, Worcester, MA, 2012. Toward volunteer recruitment and training.
$10,000 to Emmanuel Cancer Foundation, Scotch Plains, NJ, 2012. Toward the Depression Intervention component of the Family Services Program.
$10,000 to Saint Barnabas High School, Bronx, NY, 2012. Toward the Sr Georgette Dircks Scholarship Fund.
$7,500 to Cornerstone Family Programs, Morristown, NJ, 2012. Toward the Early Childhood Mental Health Intervention Program.
$5,000 to Cancer Hope Network, Chester, NJ, 2012. Toward partial funding of a Patient Service Coordinator for one year.
$5,000 to Loyola University Maryland, Baltimore, MD, 2012. Toward the current-use Dircks Family Men's Lacrosse Scholarship.
$5,000 to Main Street Counseling Center, West Orange, NJ, 2012. Toward the School-Based Counseling Program.
$2,500 to Leader Dogs for the Blind, Rochester, MI, 2012. Toward the Leader Dogs' dog training Program.

5242
Dirshu International, Inc. ✧

212 2nd St., Ste. 404B
Lakewood, NJ 08701-3424
Contact: Ahron Gobioff, Tr.

Established in 2008 in NJ.
Donor: David Hofstedter Foundation.
Foundation type: Independent foundation.
Financial data (yr. ended 01/31/13): Assets, $69,567 (M); gifts received, $2,793,496; expenditures, $2,742,102; qualifying distributions, $1,562,366; giving activities include $149,945 for 34 grants (high: $19,200; low: $50), and $1,029,791 for grants to individuals.
Purpose and activities: Giving primarily for Jewish education.
Fields of interest: Religion, formal/general education; Jewish agencies & synagogues.
Limitations: Applications not accepted. Giving primarily in Lakewood, NJ.
Application information: Unsolicited requests for funds not accepted.
Trustees: Elimelech Brailofsky; Adam Enock; Ahron Gobioff; Avrohom Steinharter.
EIN: 261870154

5243
Geraldine R. Dodge Foundation, Inc. ✧

14 Maple Ave., Ste. 400
Morristown, NJ 07960-5451 (973) 540-8442
Contact: Christopher J. Daggett, C.E.O. and Pres.
FAX: (973) 540-1211; E-mail: info@grdodge.org;
Main URL: http://www.grdodge.org
Blog: http://blog.grdodge.org/
Facebook: http://www.facebook.com/pages/Geraldine-R-Dodge-Foundation/165852012675#

Geraldine R. Dodge Foundation Staff: https://twitter.com/grdodge/dodge-staff-on-twitter/members
Grantee Perception Report: http://blog.grdodge.org/2008/11/06/grantee-perception-survey-results/
Grants List: http://www.grdodge.org/apply/search-grants/
Twitter: http://www.twitter.com/grdodge

Incorporated in 1974 in NJ.
Donor: Geraldine R. Dodge†.
Foundation type: Independent foundation.
Financial data (yr. ended 12/31/12): Assets, $262,211,732 (M); gifts received, $44,809; expenditures, $14,802,662; qualifying distributions, $11,802,431; giving activities include $10,386,000 for 241 grants (high: $375,000; low: $750), $14,431 for 41 employee matching gifts, and $1,402,000 for 12 foundation-administered programs.
Purpose and activities: The foundation seeks to work to foster a more creative and sustainable New Jersey. Proposals are invited from organizations that: 1) Enhance the cultural richness of the community in which they reside and contribute to New Jersey's creative economy; 2) Provide transformational, experiential educational opportunities both inside and outside of the classroom for young people who have limited access to educational excellence; 3) Promote healthy ecosystems and sustainable communities in New Jersey; and 4) Use traditional and new media to educate the public about issues in the foundation's areas of interest and to promote new paradigms towards a creative, sustainable New Jersey.
Fields of interest: Media/communications; Visual arts; Museums; Performing arts; Performing arts, dance; Performing arts, theater; Performing arts, music; Arts; Elementary school/education; Secondary school/education; Education; Environment, natural resources; Environment; Leadership development; Children/youth; Children; Youth; Adults, women; Economically disadvantaged; Homeless.
Type of support: General/operating support; Continuing support; Management development/capacity building; Program development; Curriculum development; Technical assistance; Program evaluation; Employee matching gifts; Matching/challenge support.
Limitations: Giving primarily in NJ, with support for the arts limited to NJ, and support for other local projects limited to the Morristown area; some giving to national organizations for projects in NJ. No support for religious, higher education, health, or conduit organizations. No grants to individuals, for capital projects, equipment purchases, indirect costs, endowment funds, deficit financing, or scholarships.
Publications: Application guidelines; Biennial report; Grants list.
Application information: Full proposals accepted by invitation only following letter of inquiry. Applications accepted online. Visit foundation web site for guidelines and information. Application form required.
Initial approach: Online letter of inquiry
Copies of proposal: 1
Deadline(s): Letter of inquiry: Feb. 1, Aug. 1 and Nov. 1. Proposal: Mar. 4, Aug. 30 and Dec. 3
Board meeting date(s): Mar., June, and Nov.
Officers and Trustees:* Christopher J. Elliman,* Chair.; Preston D. Pinkett III,* Vice-Chair.; Christopher J. Daggett, C.E.O. and Pres.; Cynthia Sherwood Evans, C.F.O.; Betsy S. Michel,* Treas.; Robert M.B. Baldwin, Chair. Emeritus; Kate Adams; Elizabeth A. Duffy; Rose Harvey; Thomas J. Healey; Carlos Hernandez; Robert LeBuhn; Barbara F. Moran; Clement A. Price, Ph.D.; James W. Stevens.
Number of staff: 5 full-time professional; 5 full-time support; 1 part-time support.
EIN: 237406010
Selected grants: The following grants are a representative sample of this grantmaker's funding activity:
$375,000 to Woodrow Wilson National Fellowship Foundation, Princeton, NJ, 2012. For the Woodrow Wilson New Jersey Teaching Fellowship.
$375,000 to Woodrow Wilson National Fellowship Foundation, Princeton, NJ, 2013. To improve teacher preparation programs and recruit STEM teachers for high-need schools.
$300,000 to Sustainable Jersey, Ewing, NJ, 2012. For general operating support for the municipal government certification program.
$300,000 to Sustainable Jersey, Ewing, NJ, 2013. For general operating support for Sustainable Jersey's municipal certification program and the creation of the new schools program.
$200,000 to W F M U Radio, Jersey City, NJ, 2013. For project support of WFMU's Audience Engine, a new content management tool for media publishers working in radio, television and journalism.
$150,000 to Stony Brook-Millstone Watershed Association, Pennington, NJ, 2012. To support the Watershed Institute work to protect and restore New Jersey's watersheds.
$125,000 to Montclair State University, Montclair, NJ, 2012. For the New Jersey Digital Media Initiative.
$125,000 to Newark Museum, Newark, NJ, 2012. For general operating support of the Museum's exhibition and education initiatives.
$125,000 to Shakespeare Theater of New Jersey, Florham Park, NJ, 2012. For general operating support of The Shakespeare Theatre of New Jersey's 50th Anniversary Season in 2012.
$125,000 to Shakespeare Theater of New Jersey, Florham Park, NJ, 2013. For general operating support for The Shakespeare Theatre of New Jersey's 2013 season of artistic and education programs.
$125,000 to William Paterson University of New Jersey, Wayne, NJ, 2013. For creativity professors-in-residence in three Paterson schools charged with increasing student achievement and engagement through arts integration.
$120,000 to New Jersey Conservation Foundation, Far Hills, NJ, 2013. For general operating support for efforts to preserve New Jersey's land and natural resources through land acquisition, stewardship, public policy and conservation assistance and partnerships.
$75,000 to Education Law Center, Newark, NJ, 2013. For general operating support ELC's efforts on behalf of disadvantaged public school children for equal access to a high quality education.
$50,000 to Camden City Garden Club, Camden, NJ, 2012. For general operating support for community gardening and greening efforts, urban agriculture programs, and the Access to Better Food Program.
$50,000 to Newark Trust for Education, Newark, NJ, 2012. For general operating support to remove obstacles to school reform through resource alignment, community empowerment, and accountability.
$42,000 to Rutgers, The State University of New Jersey, Graduate School of Education, New Brunswick, NJ, 2013. For a year-long teacher professional development program that will improve teacher effectiveness by integrating Arts and STEM pedagogical practices.
$40,000 to GreenFaith, Highland Park, NJ, 2013. To analyze, enhance and scale up the Water Shield program and water conservation efforts among New Jersey's faith communities.
$35,000 to City Without Walls, Newark, NJ, 2013. For general operating support of the gallery and education and community programming.
$30,000 to Dance-New Jersey, Fanwood, NJ, 2012. For general operating support of programs and services that address the needs of the state's dance community.

5244
The Christina and Robert Dow Foundation ✧
2719 Main St.
Lawrenceville, NJ 08648-1014

Donors: Christina Seix Dow; Robert S. Dow; Christina Seix Dow 2011 Trust.
Foundation type: Independent foundation.
Financial data (yr. ended 11/30/13): Assets, $137,178,871 (M); gifts received, $3,743,255; expenditures, $3,346,180; qualifying distributions, $3,301,500; giving activities include $3,301,500 for 13 grants (high: $2,000,000; low: $500).
Fields of interest: Elementary school/education; Human services; Children/youth, services.
Limitations: Applications not accepted. Giving primarily in Trenton, NJ and in Jenkintown, PA.
Application information: Contributes only to pre-selected organizations.
Trustees: Christina Seix Dow; Robert S. Dow.
EIN: 136879648

5245
Dunbar Family Foundation Dima ✧
P.O. Box 1501, NJ2-130-03-31
Pennington, NJ 08534-1501

Established in 2004 in AL.
Donors: Bruce C. Dunbar; Ida D. Dunbar.
Foundation type: Independent foundation.
Financial data (yr. ended 12/31/13): Assets, $12,559,713 (M); gifts received, $340,650; expenditures, $596,104; qualifying distributions, $507,496; giving activities include $461,712 for 17 grants (high: $100,000; low: $10,000).
Fields of interest: Higher education; Human services; Christian agencies & churches; Protestant agencies & churches.
Limitations: Applications not accepted. Giving primarily in AL. No grants to individuals.
Application information: Contributes only to pre-selected organizations.
Trustees: Bruce C. Dunbar; Ida D. Dunbar.
EIN: 201932272
Selected grants: The following grants are a representative sample of this grantmaker's funding activity:
$25,000 to United Way of Central Alabama, Birmingham, AL, 2011.
$20,000 to Church Resource Ministries, Anaheim, CA, 2011.
$10,000 to Fixed Point Foundation, Birmingham, AL, 2011.

$10,000 to Hope International, Lancaster, PA, 2011.
$10,000 to Reformed University Fellowship, Lawrenceville, GA, 2011.
$10,000 to Restoration Academy, Fairfield, AL, 2011.
$10,000 to Virginia Athletics Foundation, Charlottesville, VA, 2011.

5246
John and Jennifer Eckerson Family Foundation ✧ ☆
c/o Untracht Early
325 Columbia Tpke., Ste. 202
Florham Park, NJ 07932-1212

Established in NY.
Donor: John Eckerson.
Foundation type: Independent foundation.
Financial data (yr. ended 12/31/13): Assets, $3,396,860 (M); gifts received, $4,000,000; expenditures, $603,140; qualifying distributions, $603,140; giving activities include $603,000 for 13 grants (high: $500,000; low: $1,000).
Fields of interest: Elementary/secondary education; Human services.
Limitations: Applications not accepted. Giving in the U.S., with emphasis on CT, NY, and VA.
Application information: Unsolicited requests for funds not accepted.
Trustee: John Eckerson.
EIN: 466921946

5247
The Sidney & Mildred Edelstein Foundation ✧
(formerly The Sidney M. Edelstein Foundation)
c/o J. Grossman
57 Troy Dr.
Short Hills, NJ 07078-1365

Established in 1986 in NY.
Donors: Sidney M. Edelstein‡; Mildred Edelstein‡.
Foundation type: Independent foundation.
Financial data (yr. ended 12/31/13): Assets, $6,370,735 (M); expenditures, $582,414; qualifying distributions, $563,250; giving activities include $562,500 for 8 grants (high: $400,000; low: $1,000).
Purpose and activities: Giving primarily for higher education and Jewish agencies and temples.
Fields of interest: Higher education; Jewish agencies & synagogues.
Limitations: Applications not accepted. Giving primarily in New York, NY. No grants to individuals.
Application information: Contributes only to pre-selected organizations.
Directors: Richard Finkelstein; Jeffrey Grossman; Roy Jacobs; Harvey Reich.
EIN: 133347784
Selected grants: The following grants are a representative sample of this grantmaker's funding activity:
$275,000 to American Friends of the Hebrew University, New York, NY, 2011.
$75,000 to American Committee for Shenkar College in Israel, New York, NY, 2011.
$71,000 to Chemical Heritage Foundation, Philadelphia, PA, 2011.
$6,500 to Joseph Kushner Hebrew Academy, Livingston, NJ, 2011.
$6,000 to Hospice by the Sea, Boca Raton, FL, 2011.
$2,500 to Friends of the Israel Defense Forces, New York, NY, 2011.
$2,500 to Rabbinical College of America, Morristown, NJ, 2011.
$1,000 to National Marfan Foundation, Port Washington, NY, 2011.

5248
Charles Edison Fund ✧
1 Riverfront Plz., 4th Fl.
Newark, NJ 07102 (973) 648-0500
Contact: John P. Keegan, Pres.
FAX: (973) 648-0400;
E-mail: info@charlesedisonfund.org; Main URL: http://www.charlesedisonfund.org

Incorporated in 1948 in DE.
Donors: Charles Edison‡; and others.
Foundation type: Independent foundation.
Financial data (yr. ended 12/31/12): Assets, $21,315,310 (M); gifts received, $510; expenditures, $2,716,331; qualifying distributions, $2,313,390; giving activities include $1,166,291 for 20 grants (high: $450,000; low: $250), and $292,324 for foundation-administered programs.
Purpose and activities: Grants largely for historic preservation, with emphasis on the homes of Thomas Alva Edison, and for education, medical research, and hospitals. Support also for foundation-sponsored exhibits at over 80 museums throughout the U.S., for science education teaching kits in over 60,000 classrooms, and for cassette re-recording of antique phonograph records for schools and museums.
Fields of interest: Museums; Historic preservation/historical societies; Arts; Education; Hospitals (general); Medical research; Engineering/technology; Science.
Type of support: General/operating support; Continuing support; Equipment; Program development; Seed money; Research.
Limitations: Applications accepted. Giving on a national basis. No grants to individuals; no loans.
Publications: Informational brochure (including application guidelines).
Application information: Application form not required.
Initial approach: Letter or proposal on letterhead
Copies of proposal: 1
Deadline(s): None
Board meeting date(s): Feb. or Mar., and June and Dec.
Officers and Trustees:* John P. Keegan,* Chair., Pres., and Treas.; Thomas J. Ungerland,* Exec. V.P.; Alberta Ench, Secy.; Edward L. Allman; Jennifer Gonring; James E. Howe; George Q. Keegan; Wade Knowles; John M. O'Shea; John N. Schullinger, M.D.; J. Thomas Smoot, Jr.
Number of staff: 7 full-time professional.
EIN: 221514861

5249
Eisai USA Foundation, Inc. ✧
100 Tice Blvd.
Woodcliff Lake, NJ 07677-8404

Established in 2008 in NJ.
Donor: Easi, Inc.
Foundation type: Independent foundation.
Financial data (yr. ended 03/31/13): Assets, $6,063,098 (M); gifts received, $3,000,000; expenditures, $1,526,716; qualifying distributions, $1,526,550; giving activities include $1,526,550 for 46 grants (high: $920,000; low: $300).
Fields of interest: Higher education; Health organizations, association; Human services; American Red Cross.
Limitations: Applications not accepted. Giving in the U.S., with emphasis on MA and NJ.
Application information: Unsolicited requests for funds not accepted.
Officers: Lonnell Coats, Pres.; Hideo Dan, Exec. V.P. and Secy.; Kenneth Klauser, Treas.
EIN: 770711011

5250
Mitzi & Warren Eisenberg Family Foundation, Inc. ✧
c/o Rockdale Capital
650 Liberty Ave.
Union, NJ 07083-8130

Established in 1992 in NJ.
Donors: Warren Eisenberg; Bed Bath & Beyond, Inc.
Foundation type: Independent foundation.
Financial data (yr. ended 06/30/13): Assets, $94,299,595 (M); expenditures, $4,390,434; qualifying distributions, $4,359,783; giving activities include $4,349,090 for 155 grants (high: $1,300,000; low: $20).
Purpose and activities: Giving primarily to Jewish organizations and temples; giving also for the arts, medical research, and human services.
Fields of interest: Arts; Environment; Medical research, institute; Human services; Jewish agencies & synagogues.
Limitations: Applications not accepted. Giving primarily in NJ and NY. No grants to individuals.
Application information: Contributes only to pre-selected organizations.
Officers: Warren Eisenberg, Pres.; Maxine Eisenberg, Secy.; Ronald Eisenberg, Treas.
EIN: 521798583

5251
The Eisenreich Family Foundation ✧
c/o David Sussman, Avery Eisenreich
35 Journal Sq., Ste. 1103
Jersey City, NJ 07306-4007

Established in 1997 in NY.
Donors: Avery Eisenreich; Joel Eisenreich; Toby Eisenreich; Mark Elliot Freund; David Sussman; Mizari Charity Fund; Commercial Security Mortgage Credit, Inc.; SCHI.
Foundation type: Independent foundation.
Financial data (yr. ended 12/31/12): Assets, $44,852,360 (M); gifts received, $48,500; expenditures, $2,616,417; qualifying distributions, $2,341,020; giving activities include $2,338,195 for 21 grants (high: $2,200,000; low: $330).
Purpose and activities: Funding primarily for Jewish agencies and temples; some support also for yeshivas.
Fields of interest: Elementary/secondary education; Jewish agencies & synagogues.
Limitations: Applications not accepted. Giving primarily in New York, NY. No grants to individuals.
Application information: Contributes only to pre-selected organizations.

EIN: 137118478

5252
The Elias Foundation ✧
P.O. Box 1501, NJ2-130-03-31
Pennington, NJ 08534-1501 (914) 449-6782
FAX: (914) 449-6783;
E-mail: info@eliasfoundation.org; E-mail for questions regarding grantmaking: pwithers@eliasfoundation.org; Main URL: http://www.eliasfoundation.org
Grants List: http://www.eliasfoundation.org/recent_grants/grantees.htm

Established in 1999 in DE.
Donors: Jacqueline Mann; James E. Mann.
Foundation type: Independent foundation.
Financial data (yr. ended 12/31/12): Assets, $6,572,507 (M); gifts received, $1,077,713; expenditures, $824,316; qualifying distributions, $694,510; giving activities include $509,900 for 50 grants (high: $30,000; low: $100).
Purpose and activities: The foundation seeks to promote a more equitable and progressive society by supporting projects that mobilize community leadership and create networks for community change. The foundation values the pursuit of economic equity and social justice, self-directed change led by the experience and wisdom of local communities, community advocacy as a fundamental strategy for progressive action, and community leaders as catalysts, guiding and inspiring future generations.
Fields of interest: Civil/human rights, advocacy; Civil/human rights, minorities; Civil/human rights; Community/economic development; Economically disadvantaged.
Type of support: General/operating support; Management development/capacity building; Research.
Limitations: Applications accepted. Giving primarily in Westchester County, NY. No grants to individuals.
Publications: Application guidelines; Grants list.
Application information: Full proposals will be accepted only following approval of Letter of Intent. Unsolicited full proposals will not be accepted. Guidelines available on foundation Web site.
Initial approach: Letter of Intent
Deadline(s): None
Officers: Jacqueline Mann, Pres.; Alison Mann, V.P.; Anastasia Mann, V.P.; James E. Mann, Secy.; Eldar Shafir, Treas.
EIN: 134092287

5253
Elizabethtown Healthcare Foundation ✧ ☆
P.O. Box 259
Elizabeth, NJ 07207-0259 (908) 994-8065
Contact: David A. Fletcher, Pres.
E-mail: dfletcher@trinitas.org

Established in 2002 in NJ.
Foundation type: Independent foundation.
Financial data (yr. ended 12/31/13): Assets, $11,553,927 (M); expenditures, $739,755; qualifying distributions, $815,445; giving activities include $739,000 for 18 grants (high: $150,000; low: $15,000).
Purpose and activities: Giving to strengthen existing and/or seed innovative initiatives that address health care and related needs in Elizabeth, NJ, and surrounding communities. Funding priorities include services for women and children, and mental health.
Fields of interest: Health care.
Type of support: Program evaluation; Equipment; Program development; Seed money; Curriculum development.
Limitations: Applications accepted. Giving limited to Elizabeth, NJ, and surrounding communities. No support for lobbying activities or religious activities. No grants to individuals, or for budget deficits or general operating expenses, endowments, lending, research, annual appeals, fundraising dinners or journals, scholarships, attendance at workshops, or for conferences.
Publications: Application guidelines.
Application information: Application form required.
Initial approach: Proposal
Copies of proposal: 2
Deadline(s): Apr. 10 or Oct. 10
Board meeting date(s): May and Nov.
Officers: Mortimer Gershman, Chair.; Richard Width, Esq., Vice-Chair.; David A. Fletcher, Pres.; Alice A. Holzapfel, Secy.; David Gibbons, Treas.
Directors: John R. Blasi, Esq.; Richard Mackessey, M.D.; Victor Richel; Laurie Westra.
Number of staff: 1 part-time professional.
EIN: 222473474
Selected grants: The following grants are a representative sample of this grantmaker's funding activity:
$175,000 to Trinitas Health Foundation, Elizabeth, NJ, 2011.
$75,000 to Trinitas Health Foundation, Elizabeth, NJ, 2011.
$20,000 to Trinitas Health Foundation, Elizabeth, NJ, 2011.
$10,000 to American Heart Association, Dallas, TX, 2011.
$4,500 to National Kidney Foundation, New York, NY, 2011.

5254
The Charles Evans Foundation ✧
116 Village Blvd., Ste. 200
Princeton, NJ 08540-5700 (609) 951-2208

Established in 1988 in NY as successor to the Charles Evans Foundation, Inc.
Donor: Charles Evans‡.
Foundation type: Independent foundation.
Financial data (yr. ended 12/31/12): Assets, $3,523,295 (M); gifts received, $4,389,089; expenditures, $17,136,653; qualifying distributions, $16,938,559; giving activities include $16,735,810 for 185 grants (high: $1,757,690; low: $500).
Fields of interest: Media, film/video; Education; Health organizations, association; Prostate cancer; Alzheimer's disease; Legal services; Legal services, public interest law; Human services; Jewish agencies & synagogues.
Limitations: Applications not accepted. Giving primarily in New York, NY. No grants to individuals.
Application information: Contributes only to pre-selected organizations.
Officer and Trustees:* Linda J. Munson,* Pres.; Henry M. Buhl; Bonnie L. Pfeifer Evans; Charles Evans, Jr.; Joel M. Pashcow; Alice Shure.
EIN: 136914974
Selected grants: The following grants are a representative sample of this grantmaker's funding activity:
$1,757,690 to Association of Charles Evans Housing Foundation, New York, NY, 2012.
$1,750,000 to Alzheimers Drug Discovery Foundation, New York, NY, 2012.
$1,150,000 to Employed Again, Plainsboro, NJ, 2012.
$1,011,000 to Venezuelan American Endowment for the Arts, New York, NY, 2012.
$800,000 to Adrienne Jules Foundation, Los Angeles, CA, 2012.
$597,900 to Association of Community Employment Programs for the Homeless, New York, NY, 2012.
$250,000 to New York University, New York, NY, 2012.
$30,000 to Nancy Davis Foundation for Multiple Sclerosis, Los Angeles, CA, 2012.
$25,000 to New York-Presbyterian Hospital, New York, NY, 2012.
$15,000 to Little Flower Children and Family Services of New York, Brooklyn, NY, 2012.

5255
The Fairbanks Family Foundation ✧
319 Lenox Ave.
Westfield, NJ 07090-2137 (908) 789-7310
Contact: Steven J. Giacona

Established in 2000 in FL.
Donors: Richard M. Fairbanks III; Shannon A. Fairbanks; Fairbanks Charitable Lead Unitrust.
Foundation type: Independent foundation.
Financial data (yr. ended 12/31/12): Assets, $2,841,853 (M); expenditures, $1,210,345; qualifying distributions, $1,139,235; giving activities include $1,139,235 for 13+ grants (high: $700,000).
Fields of interest: Arts; Education; Human services; International affairs, goodwill promotion.
Limitations: Giving primarily in Washington, DC.
Application information:
Initial approach: Letter or proposal (1-2 pages)
Deadline(s): None
Trustees: Jonathan B. Fairbanks; Richard M. Fairbanks III; Shannon A. Fairbanks; Woods A. Fairbanks.
EIN: 582583288
Selected grants: The following grants are a representative sample of this grantmaker's funding activity:
$375,000 to Layalina Productions, Washington, DC, 2012. To Promote the Exempt Purpose of the Recipient.
$25,000 to Fresh Arts Coalition, Houston, TX, 2012. To Promote the Exempt Purpose of the Recipient 0.
$1,000 to Columbia University, Law School, New York, NY, 2012. To Promote the Exempt Purpose of the Recipient.
$1,000 to Parkinsons Action Network, Washington, DC, 2012. To Promote the Exempt Purpose of the Recipient.

5256
Falcon Foundation, Inc. ✧
400 W. Main St.
Wyckoff, NJ 07481-1420

Foundation type: Independent foundation.
Financial data (yr. ended 12/31/13): Assets, $21,253,600 (M); expenditures, $1,398,247; qualifying distributions, $1,352,513; giving

activities include $1,352,188 for 39 grants (high: $222,500; low: $500).
Fields of interest: Education; Animals/wildlife; Human services.
Limitations: Applications not accepted.
Application information: Unsolicited requests for funds not accepted.
Officers and Trustees:* James Leitner,* Chair. and Pres.; Janice Brennan,* Secy.-Treas.; Walter Leitner.
EIN: 271262865

5257
Torcivia Family Foundation ✧ ☆
328 Newman Springs Rd.
Red Bank, NJ 07701-5654

Established in 1987 in NJ.
Donors: Benedict J. Torcivia, Sr.; Benedict J. Torcivia, Jr.; Joseph Torcivia.
Foundation type: Independent foundation.
Financial data (yr. ended 02/28/13): Assets, $2,138,632 (M); gifts received, $2,052,050; expenditures, $720,136; qualifying distributions, $717,218; giving activities include $715,800 for 15 grants (high: $525,000; low: $300).
Purpose and activities: Giving primarily for education and hospitals.
Fields of interest: Elementary/secondary education; Higher education; Scholarships/financial aid; Hospitals (general); Foundations (public); Catholic agencies & churches.
Limitations: Applications not accepted. Giving primarily in NJ, with some giving in PA and WA. No grants to individuals.
Application information: Contributes only to pre-selected organizations.
Officers: Benedict J. Torcivia, Jr., Co-Pres. and Secy.; Joseph Torcivia, Co-Pres. and Treas.
EIN: 521571994

5258
M.W. Family Foundation Inc. ✧
1155 Bloomfield Ave.
Clifton, NJ 07012-2308

Established in NY.
Donor: Mark Weisz.
Foundation type: Independent foundation.
Financial data (yr. ended 12/31/12): Assets, $1,095 (M); gifts received, $457,850; expenditures, $708,040; qualifying distributions, $702,150; giving activities include $702,150 for grants.
Fields of interest: Education; Jewish agencies & synagogues.
Limitations: Applications not accepted. Giving primarily in NY, with emphasis on Brooklyn.
Application information: Unsolicited requests for funds not accepted.
Officers: Mark Weisz, Pres.; Michael Konig, V.P.; Steven Krausman, Secy.-Treas.
EIN: 272374133

5259
Fenwick Foundation ✧ ☆
(formerly Phoenix Family Foundation)
P.O. Box 1501, NJ-2-130-03-31
Pennington, NJ 08534-1501

Established in 1999 in NC.
Donors: Anne Phoenix; Anne and Julius Phoenix Charitable Trust; Anne and Julius Phoenix Charitable Lead Unitrust; Anne and Julius Phoenix Charitable Lead Unitrust No. 2.
Foundation type: Independent foundation.
Financial data (yr. ended 04/30/13): Assets, $6,128,867 (M); gifts received, $165,679; expenditures, $739,937; qualifying distributions, $709,504; giving activities include $508,015 for 97 grants (high: $25,000; low: $300).
Purpose and activities: Giving primarily for the arts, education, and children, youth, and social services.
Fields of interest: Arts; Education; Human services; Children/youth, services.
Limitations: Applications not accepted. Giving primarily in CA and NC. No grants to individuals.
Application information: Contributes only to pre-selected organizations.
Officers: Frank L. Phoenix, Pres.; James E. Phoenix, Secy.; J. Stuart Phoenix, Treas.
Trustees: Joy Phoenix; Kaola Phoenix; Tricia Phoenix.
EIN: 562150323
Selected grants: The following grants are a representative sample of this grantmaker's funding activity:
$25,000 to North Carolina Museum of Art, Raleigh, NC, 2011.
$25,000 to North Carolina Museum of Art Foundation, Raleigh, NC, 2011.
$23,000 to Blue Mountain Center of Meditation, Tomales, CA, 2011.
$22,500 to Peace College, Raleigh, NC, 2011.
$17,250 to Carolina Ballet, Raleigh, NC, 2011.
$15,000 to Dominican University of California, San Rafael, CA, 2011.
$10,000 to Mary Baldwin College, Staunton, VA, 2011.
$7,000 to YMCA, Chapel Hill-Carrboro, Chapel Hill, NC, 2011.
$6,500 to Ritter Center, San Rafael, CA, 2011.
$5,000 to Mountain Play Association, Mill Valley, CA, 2011.

5260
Roger S. Firestone Foundation ✧
P.O. Box 1501, NJ2-130-03-31
Pennington, NJ 08534-1501

Established in 1983 in OH.
Foundation type: Independent foundation.
Financial data (yr. ended 12/31/13): Assets, $12,797,209 (M); gifts received, $15; expenditures, $633,796; qualifying distributions, $554,542; giving activities include $500,726 for 38 grants (high: $55,000; low: $1,000).
Fields of interest: Arts; Education; Hospitals (specialty); Health care; Human services; Children/youth, services.
Type of support: General/operating support; Continuing support; Annual campaigns; Capital campaigns.
Limitations: Applications not accepted. Giving primarily in AZ and CA. No grants to individuals, including scholarships.
Application information: Unsolicited requests for funds not accepted.
Officers and Trustees:* John D. Firestone,* Chair.; Gay F. Wray,* Pres.; Susan F. Semegen,* Secy.; Lisa F. Firestone,* Treas.; Lucy D. Firestone; Mary C. Firestone; Nicholas Firestone; Sarah Catherine Firestone; Timothy F. Wray.
EIN: 341388255

5261
Fish Foundation, Inc. ✧
P.O. Box 929
Plainsboro, NJ 08536-0929 (609) 275-0011
Contact: Rev. Dr. Kathy J. Nelson, Pres.
FAX: (609) 275-1114;
E-mail: knelson@fishfoundationinc.com; Additional e-mail: drkjnelson@comcast.net; Main URL: http://www.fishfoundationinc.org

Established in 2006 in NJ.
Donor: Dorothy Hanle.
Foundation type: Independent foundation.
Financial data (yr. ended 12/31/13): Assets, $86,873 (M); gifts received, $700,000; expenditures, $714,857; qualifying distributions, $554,644; giving activities include $438,906 for 21 grants (high: $39,534; low: $2,000).
Purpose and activities: The foundation seeks to address aspects of well-being for mental, physical and spiritual health.
Fields of interest: Education; Health care; Religion.
Limitations: Applications accepted. Giving on a national and international basis. No grants to individuals.
Application information:
Initial approach: Letter with applicable materials
Copies of proposal: 1
Deadline(s): Floating
Board meeting date(s): As often as needed
Officers: Dorothy B. Hanle, Chair.; Rev. Dr. Kathy J. Nelson, Pres.; Judith A. Cashmore, V.P., Education.
Number of staff: 1 full-time professional; 1 part-time professional.
EIN: 204813479
Selected grants: The following grants are a representative sample of this grantmaker's funding activity:
$50,000 to Berea College, Berea, KY, 2012. For Learning Programs and Scholarships.
$35,167 to Free Wheelchair Mission, Irvine, CA, 2012. For Wheelchairs for Vietnam.
$25,000 to Wounded Warrior Project, Jacksonville, FL, 2012. For Wounded Warrior Retreats.

5262
Focus Autism, Inc. ✧
776 Mountain Blvd., Ste. 202
Watchung, NJ 07069-6269
E-mail: info@focusautisminc.org; Main URL: http://www.focusautisminc.org/
Facebook: https://www.facebook.com/focusautisminc
Twitter: https://twitter.com/FocusAutismInc
YouTube: http://www.youtube.com/watch?v=n8MnzXv3E8E

Established in NJ.
Donors: Barry Segal; Bas Properties, LLC.
Foundation type: Independent foundation.
Financial data (yr. ended 12/31/12): Assets, $7,053,404 (M); gifts received, $2,836,421; expenditures, $1,062,480; qualifying distributions, $738,100; giving activities include $738,100 for grants.
Purpose and activities: The foundation is dedicated to providing information to the public that exposes

the cause or causes of the autism epidemic and the rise of chronic illnesses in general, focusing specifically on the role of vaccinations.
Fields of interest: Autism; Medical research, institute; Autism research.
Limitations: Applications not accepted.
Application information: Unsolicited requests for funds not accepted.
Officers and Directors:* Barry Segal, Pres.; Martin Segal,* V.P.; Richard Segal,* Secy.; Tracey Dupree, Exec. Dir.; Lisa Green; Brian Hooker; David Lewis, Ph.D.; Dolly Segal.
EIN: 273400299

5263
Fortune Education Foundation, Inc. ✧
20 Carbon Pl.
Jersey City, NJ 07305-1125
Application address: c/o Frances Wong, Dir., 14 Thoreau Dr., South Easton, MA 02375, tel.: (401) 330-0360

Donors: Norman Ng; Fortune Metal Group Inc. of Rhode Island; Fortune Plastic Mental Inc.
Foundation type: Independent foundation.
Financial data (yr. ended 12/31/13): Assets, $695,203 (M); gifts received, $1,065,000; expenditures, $1,272,873; qualifying distributions, $1,266,500; giving activities include $1,150,000 for 1 grant, and $116,500 for 10 grants to individuals (high: $20,000; low: $6,000).
Fields of interest: Higher education; Hospitals (general).
Limitations: Applications accepted. Giving primarily in MA.
Application information: Application form not required.
Initial approach: Proposal
Deadline(s): None
Directors: Chuck Man Ng; John Ng; Norman Ng; Frances Wong.
EIN: 261564290

5264
The Fournier Family Foundation ✧
c/o Pennant Capital Mgmt., LLC
1 DeForest Ave., No. 200
Summit, NJ 07901-2188

Established in 2004 in NJ.
Donor: Alan P. Fournier.
Foundation type: Independent foundation.
Financial data (yr. ended 12/31/13): Assets, $10,297,249 (M); gifts received, $3,059,722; expenditures, $3,681,440; qualifying distributions, $3,660,600; giving activities include $3,660,600 for 37 grants (high: $1,000,000; low: $100).
Fields of interest: Education; Health organizations, association; Human services.
Limitations: Applications not accepted. Giving primarily in CA, MA, MI, NJ, and NY. No grants to individuals.
Application information: Contributes only to pre-selected organizations.
Officers: Alan P. Fournier, Pres.; H. Norman Bott, V.P.; Jennifer L. Fournier, Secy.-Treas.
EIN: 202015176

5265
Frankel Family Foundation, Inc. ✧
c/o Keith Frankel
8 Henderson Dr.
West Caldwell, NJ 07006-6608

Established in NJ.
Donors: Keith Frankel; Keith Frankel 2007 Investment Trust.
Foundation type: Independent foundation.
Financial data (yr. ended 12/31/13): Assets, $1,017,059 (M); gifts received, $1,427,099; expenditures, $742,455; qualifying distributions, $740,886; giving activities include $739,326 for 12 grants (high: $500,000; low: $9,326).
Fields of interest: Health organizations; Residential/custodial care; Jewish agencies & synagogues.
Limitations: Applications not accepted.
Application information: Contributes only to pre-selected organizations.
Officers: Keith Frankel, Pres.; Edward Frankel, Secy.; Scott Yagoda, Treas.
EIN: 203326897
Selected grants: The following grants are a representative sample of this grantmaker's funding activity:
$412,000 to Tikva Childrens Home, New York, NY, 2011. For general fund.

5266
Samuel J. & Connie M. Frankino Charitable Foundation ✧
c/o Preziosi Nicholson & Assoc. PA
1101 Wheaton Ave., Ste. 100
Millville, NJ 08332-2003 (856) 794-8400
Contact: Connie M. Frankino, Tr.

Established in 1988 in OH.
Donors: Connie M. Frankino; Samuel J. Frankino.
Foundation type: Independent foundation.
Financial data (yr. ended 03/31/13): Assets, $27,889,306 (M); expenditures, $2,478,314; qualifying distributions, $2,161,763; giving activities include $2,060,093 for 10 grants (high: $10,000; low: $1,000).
Purpose and activities: Giving primarily for education, children, youth and social services, and to health care organizations.
Fields of interest: Arts; Elementary/secondary education; Higher education; Education; Hospitals (specialty); Health care; Health organizations, association; Cancer research; Eye research; Human services; Children/youth, services; Family services; Foundations (private grantmaking); Catholic agencies & churches.
Type of support: General/operating support; Building/renovation; Research.
Limitations: Giving primarily in FL, MO, and OH. No grants to individuals.
Application information: Application form not required.
Initial approach: Letter
Deadline(s): Jan. 1
Trustee: Connie M. Frankino.
EIN: 341577766
Selected grants: The following grants are a representative sample of this grantmaker's funding activity:
$5,000 to Food for the Poor, Coconut Creek, FL, 2012.
$5,000 to Lambda Legal Defense and Education Fund, New York, NY, 2012.
$5,000 to Northwood University, Midland, MI, 2012.
$3,000 to University of Miami, Coral Gables, FL, 2012.
$1,250 to Easter Seals, Chicago, IL, 2012.
$1,000 to Leukemia & Lymphoma Society, White Plains, NY, 2012.

5267
The Sam J. Frankino Foundation ✧
1101 Wheaton Ave., Ste. 100
Millville, NJ 08332-2003
Application address: c/o Lorraine Dodero, P.O. Box 127, Rome, OH 44085, tel.: (440) 498-5100

Donors: William Dodero; Lorraine Dodero.
Foundation type: Independent foundation.
Financial data (yr. ended 12/31/13): Assets, $61,468,508 (M); gifts received, $310,000; expenditures, $3,398,090; qualifying distributions, $3,151,270; giving activities include $3,019,049 for 50 grants (high: $400,000; low: $100).
Fields of interest: Elementary/secondary education; Hospitals (general); Health organizations, association; American Red Cross.
Limitations: Applications accepted. Giving primarily in Cleveland, OH.
Application information: Application form required.
Initial approach: Request application form
Deadline(s): None
Trustee: Lorraine Dodero.
EIN: 205380431

5268
Friedman Family Charitable Trust ✧
c/o Philip Friedman
33 Vanderbilt Ave.
Livingston, NJ 07039-6120

Established in 2003 in NJ.
Donors: Philip Friedman; Rosa Friedman.
Foundation type: Independent foundation.
Financial data (yr. ended 10/31/13): Assets, $745,414 (M); gifts received, $1,052,778; expenditures, $812,760; qualifying distributions, $788,848; giving activities include $785,985 for 15 grants (high: $301,360; low: $36).
Purpose and activities: Giving primarily for Jewish culture, religion, and education.
Fields of interest: Arts; Higher education; Business school/education; Education; Human services; Family services; Jewish agencies & synagogues.
Limitations: Applications not accepted. Giving primarily in NJ and NY.
Application information: Unsolicited requests for funds not accepted.
Trustees: Philip Friedman; Rosa Friedman.
EIN: 137385556
Selected grants: The following grants are a representative sample of this grantmaker's funding activity:
$250,000 to Yeshiva University, New York, NY, 2011.
$18,000 to American Friends of Brothers Aid, Monsey, NY, 2011.
$5,000 to Bris Avrohom, Hillside, NJ, 2011.
$1,800 to Great Neck Synagogue, Great Neck, NY, 2011.

5269
Paul & Maxine Frohring Foundation, Inc. ✧
P.O. Box 1501, NJ2-130-03-31
Pennington, NJ 08534-1501 (609) 274-6968

Established in 1958 in OH.
Donors: Paul R. Frohring†; Maxine A. Frohring†; Paula Frohring.
Foundation type: Independent foundation.
Financial data (yr. ended 12/31/13): Assets, $53,905,661 (M); gifts received, $10,557,101; expenditures, $2,561,730; qualifying distributions, $2,260,411; giving activities include $2,161,000 for 12 grants (high: $600,000; low: $1,000).
Fields of interest: Higher education; Environment; Human services.
Type of support: General/operating support; Building/renovation; Equipment; Scholarship funds.
Limitations: Giving primarily in MD and OH. No grants to individuals; no loans or program-related investments.
Application information:
Initial approach: Proposal
Deadline(s): None
Officer and Trustees:* Paula Frohring Kushlan,* Pres.; Jeffrey La Riche,* V.P.; William W. Falsgraf,* Secy.; Kritsin Kushlan; Philip Kushlan; Adele Wick.
EIN: 346513729
Selected grants: The following grants are a representative sample of this grantmaker's funding activity:
$400,000 to Hiram College, Hiram, OH, 2011.
$200,000 to Lighthouse, Cleveland, OH, 2011.
$100,000 to Western Reserve Land Conservancy, Moreland Hills, OH, 2011.

5270
The Fund for New Jersey ✧
1 Palmer Sq., Ste. 303
Princeton, NJ 08542-3718 (609) 356-0421
Contact: Lucy Vandenberg, Sr. Prog. Off.; Kiki Jamieson, Pres.
E-mail: lmandell@fundfornj.org; Main URL: http://www.fundfornj.org

Incorporated in 1969 in NJ as successor to The Florence Murray Wallace Fund established in 1958.
Donors: Charles F. Wallace†; and members of his family.
Foundation type: Independent foundation.
Financial data (yr. ended 12/31/13): Assets, $56,888,903 (M); expenditures, $3,188,561; qualifying distributions, $2,946,175; giving activities include $2,144,750 for 48 grants (high: $125,000; low: $1,000), and $230,000 for 5 employee matching gifts.
Purpose and activities: The foundation works to improve the quality of public policy decision-making on the most significant issues affecting the people of NJ and the region. The foundation's grantmaking advances systemic and sustainable solutions to public problems through the work of policy, advocacy, analysis and organizing.
Fields of interest: Education; Environment, land resources; Environment; AIDS; Housing/shelter, development; Minorities/immigrants, centers/services; Community/economic development; Public policy, research; Government/public administration; Public affairs; Infants/toddlers; Children/youth; Youth; Adults; Young adults; Minorities; African Americans/Blacks; Hispanics/Latinos; Women; Men; Offenders/ex-offenders; Substance abusers; AIDS, people with; Economically disadvantaged; Migrant workers.
Type of support: General/operating support; Continuing support; Management development/capacity building; Program development; Conferences/seminars; Publication; Seed money; Research; Technical assistance; Matching/challenge support.
Limitations: Applications accepted. Giving primarily in NJ or to regional programs that benefit NJ. No support for day care centers, drug treatment programs, health care delivery, or arts programs. No grants to individuals, or for capital projects, equipment, scholarships.
Publications: Annual report (including application guidelines); Financial statement; Grants list; Occasional report.
Application information: Application form not required.
Initial approach: Letter of Inquiry
Copies of proposal: 1
Deadline(s): 8 weeks prior to board meeting
Board meeting date(s): Mar., June, Sept., and Dec.
Final notification: 2 weeks after board meeting
Officers and Trustees:* Lawrence S. Lustberg,* Co-Chair.; Gary D. Rose,* Co-Chair.; Candace McKee Ashmun,* Vice-Chair.; Beth Kiyoko Jamieson, Pres.; Brendan Thomas Byrne, Jr.*, Treas.; Jane W. Thorne, Tr. Emeritus; Dr. Henry A. Coleman; John W. Cornwall, M.D.; Hon. Dickinson R. Debevoise; Linda Dennery; Hon. James Florio; Hon. John J. Gibbons; Leonard Lieberman; Edward Lloyd; Hon. Deborah T. Poritz; Richard W. Roper; Richard L. Wright.
Number of staff: 2 full-time professional; 1 full-time support.
EIN: 221895028

5271
The Lois E. & Neil J. Gagnon Foundation Inc. ✧
P.O. Box 691
Bernardsville, NJ 07924-0691

Established in 1994 in NJ.
Donors: Neil J. Gagnon; Lois E. Gagnon.
Foundation type: Independent foundation.
Financial data (yr. ended 11/30/13): Assets, $20,147,566 (L); gifts received, $208,410; expenditures, $948,082; qualifying distributions, $856,600; giving activities include $856,350 for 25 grants (high: $278,000; low: $500).
Purpose and activities: Giving primarily for higher education, health organizations, and YMCAs.
Fields of interest: Higher education; Education; Hospitals (general); Health organizations, association; Human services; YM/YWCAs & YM/YWHAs.
Limitations: Applications not accepted. Giving primarily in NJ. No grants to individuals.
Application information: Contributes only to pre-selected organizations.
Officers: Neil J. Gagnon, Pres.; Lois E. Gagnon, Secy.
Director: Brian Gagnon.
EIN: 521868735

5272
Galanta Foundation, Inc. ✧
c/o Royal Wine Corp.
63 Lefante Ln.
Bayonne, NJ 07002-5024

Established in 2003 in NY.
Donor: Royal Wine Corp.
Foundation type: Company-sponsored foundation.
Financial data (yr. ended 12/31/13): Assets, $182,260 (M); gifts received, $500,000; expenditures, $583,650; qualifying distributions, $583,550; giving activities include $583,550 for 34 grants (high: $105,000; low: $500).
Purpose and activities: The foundation supports organizations involved with Judaism.
Fields of interest: Human services; Religion.
Type of support: General/operating support.
Limitations: Applications not accepted. Giving limited to Brooklyn, Monsey, and Spring Valley, NY. No grants to individuals.
Application information: Contributes only to pre-selected organizations.
Officers and Directors:* Davic Herzog,* Pres.; Judith Buchler, V.P.; Eli Herzog, V.P.; Gary Herzog, V.P.; Herman Herzog, V.P.; Joseph Herzog, V.P.; Michael Herzog,* V.P.; Michael B. Herzog, V.P.; Mordechai Herzog, V.P.; Morris Herzog, V.P.; Nathan Herzog,* V.P.; Phillip Herzog, V.P.; Robert Herzog, V.P.; Aaron Herzog,* Secy.-Treas.
EIN: 030533223
Selected grants: The following grants are a representative sample of this grantmaker's funding activity:
$10,000 to Congregation Ahavas Tzdokah V Chesed, Brooklyn, NY, 2011.
$5,000 to American Friends of Kesher, Brooklyn, NY, 2011.
$5,000 to American Friends of Kesher, Brooklyn, NY, 2011.
$2,250 to Chesed Avraham, Brooklyn, NY, 2011.

5273
Gem Foundation, Inc. ✧
130 Stevens Ln.
Far Hills, NJ 07931-2323

Established in 2007 in NJ.
Donor: Putnam L. Crafts, Jr.
Foundation type: Independent foundation.
Financial data (yr. ended 12/31/13): Assets, $2,923,838 (M); gifts received, $1,868,200; expenditures, $1,251,411; qualifying distributions, $1,218,854; giving activities include $1,213,631 for 12 grants (high: $300,000; low: $20,000).
Fields of interest: Education; Foundations (community).
Limitations: Applications not accepted. Giving primarily in CO, NJ, and NY. No grants to individuals.
Application information: Contributes only to pre-selected organizations.
Officers and Directors:* Putnam L. Crafts, Jr.,* Pres. and Treas.; Marcia Zweig,* V.P.; Patricia Callan Crafts,* Secy.; Martha S. Sproule.
EIN: 208856858
Selected grants: The following grants are a representative sample of this grantmaker's funding activity:
$300,000 to Charter Fund, Broomfield, CO, 2011.

5274
Jacob and Miriam Ghermezian Foundation ✧
1 Meadowlands Plz., 6th Fl.
East Rutherford, NJ 07073

Donors: First International LLC; Triple Five VIII, LLC; Moac Mall Holdings LLC; Syd Ghermezian.
Foundation type: Independent foundation.
Financial data (yr. ended 12/31/13): Assets, -$31,444 (M); gifts received, $3,402,000; expenditures, $3,405,191; qualifying distributions, $3,403,284; giving activities include $3,395,129 for 394 grants (high: $308,000; low: $50).
Purpose and activities: Giving primarily to Jewish agencies and temples and for Jewish education.
Fields of interest: Education; Jewish agencies & synagogues.
Limitations: Applications not accepted. Giving primarily in NY.
Application information: Contributes only to pre-selected organizations.
Officer: Syd Ghermezian, Pres.
EIN: 800592321
Selected grants: The following grants are a representative sample of this grantmaker's funding activity:
$5,000 to Yeshiva Mikdash Melech, Brooklyn, NY, 2012. For Educational and religious activities.

5275
GHH Foundation, Inc. ✧
401 Cooper Landing Rd., Ste. C-12
Cherry Hill, NJ 08002-2538

Established in 2001 in NJ.
Foundation type: Independent foundation.
Financial data (yr. ended 12/31/13): Assets, $1,770,330 (M); expenditures, $489,483; qualifying distributions, $467,717; giving activities include $457,000 for 4 grants (high: $322,000; low: $10,000).
Fields of interest: Residential/custodial care, hospices; Residential/custodial care, senior continuing care; Aging, centers/services; Christian agencies & churches; Aging.
Limitations: Applications not accepted. Giving on a national basis. No support for political organizations.
Application information: Unsolicited requests for funds not accepted.
Board meeting date(s): 2nd Thurs. in Apr. and Oct.
Officers: Alexander J. Higgins, M.D., Pres.; Jack Coleman, V.P.; Robert Rexon, Secy.; David Curran, Treas.
Trustees: T. Edgar Chambers; J. Wilbur Coleman.
EIN: 210735044

5276
Gibson Family Foundation ✧ ☆
3 Royal Oak Dr.
Far Hills, NJ 07931-2569

Established in 2008 in NY.
Donor: Peter Gibson.
Foundation type: Independent foundation.
Financial data (yr. ended 06/30/13): Assets, $73,753 (M); gifts received, $535,064; expenditures, $467,958; qualifying distributions, $457,400; giving activities include $457,400 for 7 grants (high: $150,000; low: $1,000).
Fields of interest: Higher education; Boys & girls clubs; Human services.
Type of support: General/operating support.
Limitations: Applications not accepted. Giving primarily in NJ.
Application information: Unsolicited requests for funds not accepted.
Directors: Dana Gibson; Peter Gibson.
EIN: 261316921
Selected grants: The following grants are a representative sample of this grantmaker's funding activity:
$20,000 to Long Island University, Brookville, NY, 2011.
$2,000 to Market Street Mission, Morristown, NJ, 2011.

5277
Gibson Family Foundation, Inc. ✧
58 Lyons Pl.
Basking Ridge, NJ 07920-1914

Established in 1993 in NJ.
Donor: James G. Gibson.
Foundation type: Independent foundation.
Financial data (yr. ended 12/31/13): Assets, $22,091 (M); gifts received, $625,000; expenditures, $701,816; qualifying distributions, $698,735; giving activities include $698,735 for 15 grants (high: $300,000; low: $2,500).
Fields of interest: Higher education; Environment, natural resources; Human services; YM/YWCAs & YM/YWHAs.
Limitations: Applications not accepted. Giving primarily in NJ; some funding also in Knoxville, TN. No grants to individuals.
Application information: Contributes only to pre-selected organizations.
Officers and Trustees:* James G. Gibson,* Pres.; Jill R. Gibson,* Secy.
EIN: 223197727
Selected grants: The following grants are a representative sample of this grantmaker's funding activity:
$160,000 to University of Tennessee, Knoxville, TN, 2011.
$148,560 to YMCA, Somerset Hills, Basking Ridge, NJ, 2011.
$100,000 to Rutgers University Foundation, New Brunswick, NJ, 2011.
$50,000 to Trust for Public Land, Morristown, NJ, 2011.
$30,000 to Audubon Society, New Jersey, Bernardsville, NJ, 2011.
$25,000 to Adult Day Center of Somerset County, Bridgewater, NJ, 2011.
$25,000 to Raritan Valley Community College, Branchburg, NJ, 2011.
$20,000 to Wilderness Society, Washington, DC, 2011.
$10,000 to American Red Cross, Princeton, NJ, 2011.
$2,500 to Briteside Adult Day Centers, Flemington, NJ, 2011.

5278
Give Something Back Foundation, Inc. ✧
c/o Untracht Early LLC
325 Columbia Tpke., Ste. 202
Florham Park, NJ 07932

Established in 2006 in NJ.
Donors: Jill A. Carr; Carr Holdings LLC; The Robert O. Carr 2001 Charitable Remainder Unitrust.
Foundation type: Independent foundation.
Financial data (yr. ended 12/31/13): Assets, $1,306,224 (M); gifts received, $3,750,000; expenditures, $3,724,097; qualifying distributions, $3,720,214; giving activities include $3,257,267 for 26+ grants (high: $894,446; low: $2,110), and $38,006 for 1 grant to an individual.
Fields of interest: Secondary school/education; Education; Community development, business promotion.
Type of support: Scholarship funds.
Limitations: Applications not accepted. Giving primarily in IL and NJ.
Application information: Unsolicited requests for funds not accepted.
Officers and Trustees:* Steven J. Cardamone, Secy. and Exec. Dir.; Tracey B. Early,* Treas.; Judy Fox.
EIN: 204257149
Selected grants: The following grants are a representative sample of this grantmaker's funding activity:
$43,683 to Northern Illinois University, DeKalb, IL, 2011. For scholarships.
$27,615 to University of Missouri, Columbia, MO, 2011. For scholarships.
$23,028 to University of Iowa, Iowa City, IA, 2011. For scholarships.
$21,971 to University of Pittsburgh, Pittsburgh, PA, 2011. For scholarships.
$21,811 to Loyola University of Chicago, Chicago, IL, 2011. For scholarships.
$19,645 to Bradley University, Peoria, IL, 2011. For scholarships.
$19,143 to University of Illinois at Chicago, Chicago, IL, 2011. For scholarships.
$16,398 to Lewis University, Romeoville, IL, 2011. For scholarships.
$11,464 to Carroll College, Helena, MT, 2011. For scholarships.
$11,421 to DePaul University, Chicago, IL, 2011. For scholarships.

5279
Arthur M. Goldberg and Veronica Goldberg Foundation, Inc. ✧
(formerly Arthur M. Goldberg Foundation, Inc.)
20 Post Kennel Rd.
Far Hills, NJ 07931-2407

Established in 1986 in NJ.
Foundation type: Independent foundation.
Financial data (yr. ended 12/31/13): Assets, $7,569,043 (M); expenditures, $658,289; qualifying distributions, $550,374; giving activities include $528,700 for 25 grants (high: $250,000; low: $100).
Fields of interest: Arts; Higher education; Law school/education; Human services.
Type of support: General/operating support; Annual campaigns; Research.
Limitations: Applications not accepted. No grants to individuals.
Application information: Contributes only to pre-selected organizations.
Officers: Veronica Goldberg, Pres. and Secy.; Richard B. Neff, Treas.
Directors: Michael Goldberg; Wendy Pew; Jody Seibert.
EIN: 222779193

Selected grants: The following grants are a representative sample of this grantmaker's funding activity:
$350,000 to Villanova University, School of Law, Villanova, PA, 2012. For Fund for Villanova Law.
$32,000 to Boston College, Chestnut Hill, MA, 2012. For Arthur M Goldberg Memorial Scholarship Fund.
$15,000 to Duke University, Durham, NC, 2012. For Arthur M. Goldberg Scholarship Endowment Fund.

5280
Golden Family Foundation ✧
c/o David G. Miller and Assoc., LLC.
127 Main St., Ste. A.
Chatham, NJ 07928-2404
Contact: Sibyl R. Golden, Pres.

Incorporated in 1952 in NY.
Donors: William T. Golden†; Sibyl L. Golden†.
Foundation type: Independent foundation.
Financial data (yr. ended 12/31/12): Assets, $37,409,571 (M); expenditures, $2,018,630; qualifying distributions, $1,711,678; giving activities include $1,710,928 for 113 grants (high: $250,000; low: $100).
Purpose and activities: Support for a broad range of programs in higher education, science, public affairs, and cultural areas.
Fields of interest: Museums (natural history); Arts; Higher education; Engineering/technology; Science; Public policy, research.
Type of support: General/operating support; Annual campaigns; Capital campaigns; Building/renovation; Program-related investments/loans; Matching/challenge support.
Limitations: Applications not accepted. Giving primarily in NY. No grants to individuals.
Application information: Contributes only to pre-selected organizations.
Board meeting date(s): Jan. and as required
Officers and Directors:* Sibyl R. Golden,* Pres.; Helene L. Kaplan,* Secy.; Ralph E. Hansmann,* Treas.; Pamela P. Golden, M.D.
EIN: 237423802

5281
E. J. Grassmann Trust ✧
P.O. Box 4470
Warren, NJ 07059-0470 (908) 753-2440
Contact: William V. Engel, Exec. Dir.

Trust established in 1979 in NJ.
Donor: Edward J. Grassmann†.
Foundation type: Independent foundation.
Financial data (yr. ended 12/31/13): Assets, $31,465,818 (M); expenditures, $1,744,480; qualifying distributions, $1,638,660; giving activities include $1,595,700 for 159 grants (high: $70,000; low: $2,500).
Purpose and activities: Grants for educational institutions, local hospitals and health organizations, organizations engaged in ecological endeavors, and social welfare organizations, particularly those helping children. Preference given to organizations with low administration costs, and which show efforts to achieve a broad funding base.
Fields of interest: Historic preservation/historical societies; Arts; Elementary/secondary education; Higher education; Education; Environment, natural resources; Environment; Hospitals (general); Health care; Health organizations, association; Human services; YM/YWCAs & YM/YWHAs; Children/youth, services; Catholic agencies & churches.
Type of support: Capital campaigns; Building/renovation; Equipment; Land acquisition; Endowments.
Limitations: Giving primarily in GA, particularly middle GA, and in NJ, with emphasis on Union County. No grants to individuals, or for operating expenses, current scholarship funds, conferences, or workshops.
Publications: Application guidelines.
Application information: Application form not required.
Initial approach: Letter, no more than 4 pages
Copies of proposal: 1
Deadline(s): Apr. 20 and Oct. 15
Board meeting date(s): May or June and Nov.
Final notification: After May or June meeting by July 31; after Nov. meeting by Dec. 31
Officer and Trustees:* William V. Engel, Esq.*, Exec. Dir.; Hunter W. Corbin; Robert S. Devlin; Suzanne B. Engel; Anita Spivey.
Number of staff: 1 part-time professional; 2 part-time support.
EIN: 226326539
Selected grants: The following grants are a representative sample of this grantmaker's funding activity:
$8,600 to Jersey Animal Coalition, South Orange, NJ, 2011.

5282
The Grove Foundation Inc. ✧
(formerly Frommer Family Foundation, Inc.)
919 Green Grove Rd.
Neptune, NJ 07753

Established in 2001 in NJ.
Donors: Jacob Frommer; Mordechai Shon.
Foundation type: Independent foundation.
Financial data (yr. ended 12/31/12): Assets, $8,099,405 (M); gifts received, $420,000; expenditures, $507,204; qualifying distributions, $503,489; giving activities include $502,840 for 73 grants (high: $158,000; low: $300).
Fields of interest: Jewish agencies & synagogues.
Limitations: Applications not accepted. Giving primarily in Lakewood, NJ; some funding also in NY. No grants to individuals.
Application information: Unsolicited requests for funds not accepted.
Trustees: Jacob Frommer; Sara M. Frommer; Mordechai Shon.
EIN: 260000488

5283
The Frank J. Guarini Foundation, Inc. ✧
c/o Mandel, Fekete & Bloom, C.P.A.s
30 Montgomery St., Ste. 685
Jersey City, NJ 07302-3829

Established in 1999 in NJ.
Donor: Frank J. Guarini.
Foundation type: Independent foundation.
Financial data (yr. ended 12/31/13): Assets, $3,322,796 (M); gifts received, $199,066; expenditures, $558,640; qualifying distributions, $520,285; giving activities include $520,285 for 29 grants (high: $400,000; low: $200).
Purpose and activities: Giving primarily for higher education, the arts, health organizations, and to Italian-American causes.
Fields of interest: Museums; Higher education; Health care; Health organizations, association.
Limitations: Applications not accepted. Giving primarily in NJ and NY; some funding also in Rome, Italy. No grants to individuals.
Application information: Contributes only to pre-selected organizations.
Officers: Frank J. Guarini, Pres.; Caroline M. Mangin, V.P.; Frank L. Fekete, Secy.-Treas.
Trustees: Marie L. Garibaldi; Peter G. Mangin; Carol M. Maurer.
EIN: 223677856
Selected grants: The following grants are a representative sample of this grantmaker's funding activity:
$1,000 to Society for Research in Child Development, Ann Arbor, MI, 2011.

5284
Gulton Foundation Inc. ✧
c/o Raia, Bredefeld and Assocs., PC
163 Washington Valley Rd., Ste. 103
Warren, NJ 07059-7181

Incorporated in 1961 in NY.
Donors: Leslie K. Gulton†; Marian G. Malcolm; Edith Gulton.
Foundation type: Independent foundation.
Financial data (yr. ended 10/31/13): Assets, $6,141,208 (M); expenditures, $585,712; qualifying distributions, $544,500; giving activities include $544,500 for grants.
Purpose and activities: Giving primarily for higher education and the arts, particularly to museums as well as to a public television station; funding also for health associations and human services.
Fields of interest: Media/communications; Museums (art); Arts; Higher education; Health organizations, association; Human services; Foundations (private grantmaking).
Limitations: Applications not accepted. Giving primarily in GA and NY. No grants to individuals.
Application information: Contributes only to pre-selected organizations.
Officers: Marian G. Malcolm, Pres.; Daniel Malcolm, V.P.; John Malcolm, Secy.
EIN: 136105207
Selected grants: The following grants are a representative sample of this grantmaker's funding activity:
$100,000 to Metropolitan Museum of Art, New York, NY, 2011. For general operations.

5285
The Gordon and Llura Gund Foundation ✧
14 Nassau St.
Princeton, NJ 08542-0449

Established in 1989 in NJ.
Donors: Gordon Gund; Llura Gund.
Foundation type: Independent foundation.
Financial data (yr. ended 12/31/13): Assets, $95,018,392 (M); expenditures, $2,702,901; qualifying distributions, $2,350,296; giving activities include $2,350,296 for 138 grants (high: $387,504; low: $100).
Purpose and activities: Giving primarily to organizations fighting blindness and to services for

people who are blind; funding also for arts and culture, education, health associations and medical research, youth development, human services, and federated giving programs.
Fields of interest: Arts; Education; Health care; Health organizations, association; Eye diseases; Medical research, institute; Youth development, services; Human services; Foundations (community); United Ways and Federated Giving Programs.
Limitations: Applications not accepted. Giving primarily in Washington, DC, MA, MD, NJ, and NY. No grants to individuals.
Application information: Contributes only to pre-selected organizations.
Trustees: Gordon Gund; Llura A. Gund.
EIN: 222987293
Selected grants: The following grants are a representative sample of this grantmaker's funding activity:
$5,977,400 to Foundation Fighting Blindness, Baltimore, MD, 2012.
$2,110,008 to Foundation Fighting Blindness, Baltimore, MD, 2012.
$919,600 to Autism Speaks, New York, NY, 2012.
$528,310 to Foundation Fighting Blindness, Baltimore, MD, 2012.
$499,912 to Earthjustice, San Francisco, CA, 2012.
$249,160 to Nantucket Conservation Foundation, Nantucket, MA, 2012.
$100,003 to Harvard University, Cambridge, MA, 2012. For eye study.
$76,252 to Autism Speaks, New York, NY, 2012.
$30,000 to FasterCures, Washington, DC, 2012.
$15,000 to Alliance to Protect Nantucket Sound, Hyannis, MA, 2012.

5286
The Gurwin Family Foundation, Inc. ✧ ☆
(formerly Joseph and Rosalind Gurwin Foundation, Inc.)
5 Coventry Rd.
Livingston, NJ 07039-5105

Established in 1998 in FL.
Donor: Joseph Gurwin.
Foundation type: Independent foundation.
Financial data (yr. ended 12/31/13): Assets, $16,238,384 (M); expenditures, $717,578; qualifying distributions, $612,850; giving activities include $612,850 for 24 grants (high: $129,500; low: $100).
Fields of interest: Jewish federated giving programs.
Limitations: Applications not accepted. Giving primarily in FL and NY. No grants to individuals.
Application information: Contributes only to pre-selected organizations.
Officers: Eric Gurwin, Pres.; Laura Flug, Secy.
EIN: 311596951

5287
Raymond and Sharon Haber Foundation, Inc. ✧
c/o Fleet Street
18 Engelhard Ave.
Avenel, NJ 07001-2217

Established in 2005 in NY.
Donors: Raymond Haber; Sharon Haber; Syudio Ray, LLC.
Foundation type: Independent foundation.
Financial data (yr. ended 12/31/13): Assets, $13,967 (M); gifts received, $1,250,000; expenditures, $1,214,538; qualifying distributions, $1,214,538; giving activities include $1,212,012 for 163+ grants (high: $172,588).
Purpose and activities: Giving primarily to Jewish agencies, temples, and schools.
Fields of interest: Education; Jewish agencies & synagogues.
Limitations: Applications not accepted. Giving primarily in Deal, NJ and Brooklyn, NY. No grants to individuals.
Application information: Contributes only to pre-selected organizations.
Officers: Raymond Haber, Pres.; Sharon Haber, V.P.; Howard Gutterman, Secy.
EIN: 202059762

5288
Hahn Family Foundation, Inc. ✧
1313 Hastings St.
Teaneck, NJ 07666-2103 (305) 652-9306
Contact: Barry J. Hahn, Dir.
E-mail: hahnfamilyfoundation@yahoo.com

Established in 1997 in FL.
Donors: Elliot Hahn; Lillian Hahn.
Foundation type: Independent foundation.
Financial data (yr. ended 12/31/12): Assets, $12,686,475 (M); expenditures, $745,606; qualifying distributions, $686,623; giving activities include $686,623 for grants.
Fields of interest: Human services; Jewish agencies & synagogues.
Limitations: Applications accepted. Giving primarily in FL and NY.
Application information: Application form required.
Initial approach: E-mail
Deadline(s): None
Directors: Barry Hahn; Helen Helfman.
EIN: 650757808

5289
The Haines Family Foundation, Inc. ✧
c/o Holy Haines
2187 River Rd.
Egg Harbor, NJ 08215 (609) 335-2317
Contact: Holly Haines, Treas.
E-mail: hhaines@hainesfamilyfoundation.org

Established in 1995 in NJ.
Donors: Haines & Haines, Inc.; Pine Island Cranberry Co., Inc.; William S. Haines†; William S. Haines, Jr.
Foundation type: Company-sponsored foundation.
Financial data (yr. ended 12/31/13): Assets, $10,630,632 (M); gifts received, $50,000; expenditures, $529,315; qualifying distributions, $480,500; giving activities include $480,500 for 9 grants (high: $120,000; low: $500).
Purpose and activities: The foundation supports the Burlington County Institute of Technology in Burlington, New Jersey.
Fields of interest: Education; Human services; Religion.
Limitations: Applications accepted. Giving limited to NJ. No grants to individuals.
Application information: Application form required.
Initial approach: Letter or Proposal
Copies of proposal: 1
Deadline(s): Sep. 30th
Officers: Holly Haines, Pres. and Treas.; William S. Haines, Jr., V.P.; Joanne Martin, Secy.
EIN: 223412616
Selected grants: The following grants are a representative sample of this grantmaker's funding activity:
$150,000 to YMCA Camp Ockanickon, Medford, NJ, 2011.

5290
Arie and Eva Halpern Family Foundation ✧
c/o Henry Stein
580 Ashwood Rd.
Springfield, NJ 07081-2527

Established in 1986 in NJ.
Donors: Arie Halpern†; Eva Halpern†; Shelley Paradis; Bella Savran; Nanette Brenner.
Foundation type: Independent foundation.
Financial data (yr. ended 12/31/13): Assets, $13,782,028 (M); gifts received, $550,000; expenditures, $662,453; qualifying distributions, $637,400; giving activities include $637,400 for 80 grants (high: $50,000; low: $1,000).
Purpose and activities: Giving primarily to Jewish agencies, as well as for Jewish education.
Fields of interest: Education; Jewish federated giving programs; Jewish agencies & synagogues.
Limitations: Applications not accepted. No grants to individuals.
Application information: Contributes only to pre-selected organizations.
Trustees: Nanette Brenner; Shelley Paradis; Bella Savran; Ben Stein; Henry Stein.
EIN: 222764210

5291
Hansen Foundation, Inc. ✧ ☆
523 S. Liepziq Ave.
P.O. Box 1020
Cologne, NJ 08213-0001
Main URL: https://www.hansenfoundationnj.org/
Facebook: https://www.facebook.com/HansenFoundationNJ?ref=hl
Twitter: https://twitter.com/HansenFoundNJ

Established in 1999 in NJ.
Donors: Ole Hansen and Sons, Inc.; Todd Michael; Levine Staller; Christopher Scarborough; The James and Barbara Summers Foundation.
Foundation type: Independent foundation.
Financial data (yr. ended 12/31/12): Assets, $595,130 (M); gifts received, $22,132; expenditures, $2,009,032; qualifying distributions, $1,867,679; giving activities include $1,555,934 for 1 grant, and $311,745 for foundation-administered programs.
Fields of interest: Substance abuse, services.
Limitations: Applications not accepted. Giving primarily in NJ. No grants to individuals.
Application information: Unsolicited requests for funds not accepted.
Officers: Roger B. Hansen, Chair. and Secy.; Jennifer Hansen, Pres.; Edwina Hansen, V.P.; Michael Lentz, Treas.
Trustee: Erika Hansen Weich.
EIN: 311667973

5292
Alex and Laura Hanson CGF, Inc. ✧
1 Moorehead Dr.
Pennington, NJ 08534-1700

Established in 2001 in NJ.
Donor: Alexander D. Hanson.
Foundation type: Independent foundation.
Financial data (yr. ended 09/30/13): Assets, $3,985,441 (M); gifts received, $2,200,000; expenditures, $465,801; qualifying distributions, $465,000; giving activities include $465,000 for 9 grants (high: $235,000; low: $3,000).
Purpose and activities: Giving primarily for education, including higher.
Fields of interest: Higher education; Education; Environment; Human services.
Limitations: Applications not accepted. Giving primarily in CT, NJ, and NY. No grants to individuals.
Application information: Contributes only to pre-selected organizations.
Trustees: Abigail Hanson; Alexander D. Hanson; Eliza F. Hanson; Laura F. Hanson.
EIN: 223834524
Selected grants: The following grants are a representative sample of this grantmaker's funding activity:
$210,000 to Cornell University, Ithaca, NY, 2011.
$100,000 to Columbia University, New York, NY, 2011.
$47,000 to Hotchkiss School, Lakeville, CT, 2011.
$30,000 to D and R Greenway Land Trust, Princeton, NJ, 2011.
$10,000 to Princeton Day School, Princeton, NJ, 2011.
$10,000 to Stony Brook-Millstone Watershed Association, Pennington, NJ, 2011.
$5,000 to Trinity Counseling Service, Princeton, NJ, 2011.

5293
Harbourton Foundation ✧
47 Hulfish St., Ste. 305
Princeton, NJ 08542-3706
Contact: Amy H. Regan, V.P.

Established in 1982 in NJ.
Donor: James S. Regan.
Foundation type: Independent foundation.
Financial data (yr. ended 06/30/13): Assets, $21,639,458 (M); expenditures, $690,188; qualifying distributions, $669,142; giving activities include $491,460 for 31 grants (high: $100,000; low: $1,000).
Purpose and activities: Giving primarily for educational organizations, an international human rights organization, and children and youth services.
Fields of interest: Arts; Education, association; Environment, natural resources; Health organizations; Human services; Children/youth, services; Homeless, human services; International human rights.
Type of support: General/operating support; Capital campaigns; Program development; Technical assistance.
Limitations: Applications not accepted. Giving primarily in NJ, NY and Washington D.C. No grants to individuals.
Application information: Contributes only to pre-selected organizations.
Officers: Amy H. Regan, Pres.; Catherine H. Regan Lawliss, V.P. and Secy.; James S. Regan III, V.P. and Treas.; James S. Regan, V.P.; Patrick H. Regan, V.P.
EIN: 222436112
Selected grants: The following grants are a representative sample of this grantmaker's funding activity:
$125,000 to Centurion Ministries, Princeton, NJ, 2011.
$92,500 to American Ballet Theater, New York, NY, 2011.
$60,000 to Young Scholars Institute, Trenton, NJ, 2011.
$55,000 to HomeFront, Lawrenceville, NJ, 2011.
$33,215 to Isles, Inc., Trenton, NJ, 2011.
$25,000 to Institute for Justice, Arlington, VA, 2011.
$20,000 to Learning Ally, Princeton, NJ, 2011.
$20,000 to Rock Brook School Foundation, Skillman, NJ, 2011.
$15,000 to Inspiring Kids, Norwich, VT, 2011.
$10,000 to Passage Theater Company, Trenton, NJ, 2011.

5294
The Robinson Harris Foundation, Inc. ✧
71 Valley St., No. 303
South Orange, NJ 07079-2835

Established in 2003 in NJ.
Donors: Malcolm Ari Robinson; Tamara Leona Robinson.
Foundation type: Independent foundation.
Financial data (yr. ended 12/31/12): Assets, $13,433,800 (M); expenditures, $1,103,677; qualifying distributions, $1,033,632; giving activities include $1,028,602 for 11 grants (high: $449,376; low: $10,000).
Fields of interest: Scholarships/financial aid; Education; African Americans/Blacks.
Limitations: Applications not accepted. Giving primarily in NJ, NY, and VA. No grants to individuals.
Application information: Contributes only to pre-selected organizations.
Trustees: M. Bruce Robinson; Malcolm Ari Robinson.
EIN: 200518403

5295
Hawthorne Charitable Foundation ✧
c/o Essex Equity
70 S. Orange Ave., Ste. 105
Livingston, NJ 07039-4916 (908) 988-1090
FAX: (888) 253-4969;
E-mail: Fax@EssexEquity.com; Main URL: http://hawthornecharitablefoundation.org/

Donor: Basil Maher.
Foundation type: Independent foundation.
Financial data (yr. ended 12/31/13): Assets, $8,697,302 (M); expenditures, $602,335; qualifying distributions, $602,335; giving activities include $597,500 for 5 grants (high: $432,500; low: $5,000).
Fields of interest: Arts; Youth development; Human services.
Limitations: Applications not accepted. Giving primarily in NJ.
Application information: Unsolicited requests for funds not accepted.
Officers and Directors:* Basil Maher,* Chair. and Treas.; Miriam Duffy Maher,* Pres.; Scott Schley,* Secy. and Genl. Counsel.
EIN: 271447633
Selected grants: The following grants are a representative sample of this grantmaker's funding activity:
$70,000 to Montclair Art Museum, Montclair, NJ, 2012. For The grant was to be used for art education and enhancing the ability of the museum to serve low and moderate income families from disadvantaged areas.
$25,000 to Newark Museum Association, Newark, NJ, 2012. For The grant was a general Unrestricted grant to be used in the furtherance of exempt purposes of the recipient with the exception that re-grant of the funds was prohibited.

5296
The Healthcare Foundation of New Jersey
(formerly NBI Healthcare Foundation, Inc.)
60 E. Willow St. 2nd Fl.
Millburn, NJ 07041-1438 (973) 921-1210
Contact: Marsha Atkind, Exec. Dir.
FAX: (973) 921-1274; E-mail: info@HFNJ.org; Main URL: http://www.hfnj.org/
Grants List: http://www.hfnj.org/index.php?option=com_content&view=article&id=66&Itemid=71

Established in 1996 in NJ; an independent grantmaking organization converted from the sale of the assets of the Newark Beth Israel Medical Center to the Saint Barnabas Healthcare System.
Foundation type: Independent foundation.
Financial data (yr. ended 12/31/12): Assets, $151,235,753 (M); expenditures, $8,101,793; qualifying distributions, $7,259,681; giving activities include $6,392,473 for 160 grants (high: $500,000; low: $500).
Purpose and activities: The foundation's grantmaking is focused on: 1) Serving the healthcare needs of the vulnerable populations of greater Newark, NJ; 2) Serving the healthcare needs of the MetroWest Jewish community of northern New Jersey; and 3) Applied clinical research and medical education that could positively impact the foundation's targeted communities. The foundation has an interest in innovative health-related programs for vulnerable communities and medically underserved populations, and supports efforts to improve humanism in medicine, especially programs that support compassion and cultural sensitivity in direct patient care.
Fields of interest: Medical school/education; Health care, equal rights; Hospitals (specialty); Public health; Public health, obesity; Public health, physical fitness; Palliative care; Health care; Substance abuse, services; Substance abuse, treatment; Mental health/crisis services; Cancer; AIDS; Autism; Diabetes; Geriatrics; Health organizations; Crime/violence prevention, domestic violence; Human services; Family services; Aging, centers/services; Jewish agencies & synagogues; Infants/toddlers; Children; Youth; Adults; African Americans/Blacks; Hispanics/Latinos; Military/veterans; AIDS, people with; Immigrants/refugees; Economically disadvantaged.
Type of support: Seed money; Program development; Building/renovation; Equipment.
Limitations: Applications accepted. Giving primarily in the greater Newark, NJ area and the Jewish community of MetroWest, NJ, including Essex,

Morris, and Union counties. No grants to individuals, or for deficit retirement, ongoing general operating expenses, endowments, general capacity building, or fundraising campaigns.
Publications: Application guidelines; Annual report (including application guidelines); Grants list.
Application information: Grant proposals should be submitted using the NY/NJ Common Application Form. See foundation's web site for downloadable form. Different applications for proposals for initial funding and for grant renewals are required. See foundation web site for details. Application form required.
Initial approach: Online application process
Copies of proposal: 1
Deadline(s): Rolling basis- see foundation web site for most current deadlines
Board meeting date(s): Mar., June, Sept., and Dec.
Final notification: 4 months
Officers and Trustees:* Lester Z. Lieberman,* Chair.; Beth Levithan, Ph.D.*, 1st Vice-Chair.; Lester M. Bornstein, MPH*, Vice-Chair.; Michael D. Francis,* Vice-Chair.; Amy Reisen Freundlich, Esq., Vice-Chair.; John H. Reichman, Esq.*, Secy.; Stefano Musolino, Jr., CPA, C.F.O.; Ellen R. Wagenberg, MBA*, Treas.; Marsha Atkind, Exec. Dir.; Gary O. Aidekman; Gary Beinhaker; Philip M. Berman; Jay Blumenfeld; Stephan Gross, Esq.; Mimi Heyman; Kenneth Jaffe; Steven R. Kamen, Esq.; Nancy Kridel, CPA; Lionel M. Levey; Jerome S. Lieb; Carol P. Marcus; Natalie Peck; Adam Perlman, M.D.; Selma Rosen; Donald B. Rosenthal; Amy Schechner; Stephanie Sherman; Bruce Shoulson, Esq.; Marvin Wertheimer, C.P.A.
Number of staff: 6 full-time professional.
EIN: 223451664
Selected grants: The following grants are a representative sample of this grantmaker's funding activity:
$422,433 to Newark Beth Israel Medical Center Foundation, Newark, NJ, 2011. To implement a cardiothoracic surgery program at Children's Hospital of NJ.
$176,385 to Statewide Parent Advocacy Network, Newark, NJ, 2011. For pilot initiative to provide child psychiatrist consultation with primary care providers for Essex County children suspected of having emotional/mental health disabilities.
$162,736 to Essex County Family Justice Center, Newark, NJ, 2011. To continue to provide crisis intervention and counseling to victims of domestic violence.
$154,823 to Smith Center for Infectious Diseases and Urban Health, East Orange, NJ, 2011. To extend HIV treatment focus to include other infectious diseases such as hepatitis, TB and sexually transmitted diseases to further reach the needs of people of Greater Newark.
$150,000 to Center for Autism, Newark, NJ, 2011. To continue operational and professional framework for the start of the North Ward Center for Autism which will offer array of services for individuals and families in the Greater Newark area living with autism spectrum disorder and other developmental disorders.
$145,500 to Jewish Family Service of Metrowest, Florham Park, NJ, 2011. To better identify and treat children's exposure to domestic violence in the urban and suburban areas of Essex County.
$135,000 to University of Medicine and Dentistry of New Jersey Foundation, New Brunswick, NJ, 2011. To accomplish a Community Health Worker Training program which will result in measured decline n Emergency Dept. utilization and employment of the Community Health Workers who participate in the program.
$114,379 to Jewish Family Service of Metrowest, Florham Park, NJ, 2011. To continue to support MetroWest Community Housecalls as integrated and seamless approach to the provision of social work and healthcare services for frail, homebound older adults who are either without caregivers or who have minimal involvement with their caregivers.
$100,000 to Hetrick-Martin Institute, New York, NY, 2011. For continuing support of Safety, Wellness and Educational After School Programs.
$75,000 to Congregation Ahavas Sholom, Newark, NJ, 2011. To fund the development of a holistic community wellness resource which includes edible garden accompanied by a nutritional and obesity teaching curriculum.
$50,000 to Chabad Jewish Center of Southeastern Morris County, Madison, NJ, 2011. To launch expanded program toward enhancing the quality of life for Morris County seniors.
$50,000 to Kindersmile Foundation, Upper Montclair, NJ, 2011. To increase oral care access and oral care education to underserved children in Essex County.

5297
Heart Institute of Southern New Jersey ✧
1400 E. Rte. 70
Cherry Hill, NJ 08034-2230

Established in 1999 in NJ.
Foundation type: Independent foundation.
Financial data (yr. ended 06/30/13): Assets, $9,345,403 (M); expenditures, $823,349; qualifying distributions, $448,250; giving activities include $448,250 for grants.
Fields of interest: Medical research, association; Heart & circulatory research.
Limitations: Applications not accepted. Giving primarily in PA. No grants to individuals.
Application information: Contributes only to pre-selected organizations.
Officers and Board Members:* Harvey L. Waxman, M.D.*, Pres. and Treas.; William J. Untereker, M.D.*, V.P.; Michael Sheerin.
EIN: 222574758
Selected grants: The following grants are a representative sample of this grantmaker's funding activity:
$20,000 to Shore Memorial Health Foundation, Somers Point, NJ, 2013. To support Cardiology Research, Education and Patient C.
$3,000 to Cherry Hill Education Foundation, Cherry Hill, NJ, 2013. To support Education of Public School Children of Township of Cherry Hill.

5298
Hess Foundation, Inc. ✧
4 Becker Farm Road
Roseland, NJ 07068-1600

Incorporated in 1954 in DE.
Donor: Leon Hess‡.
Foundation type: Independent foundation.
Financial data (yr. ended 11/30/13): Assets, $807,050,408 (M); gifts received, $32,321,166; expenditures, $31,897,921; qualifying distributions, $29,717,467; giving activities include $29,281,120 for 170 grants (high: $3,544,880; low: $500).
Purpose and activities: Emphasis on higher education and the arts; grants also for hospitals, synagogues, and human services.
Fields of interest: Performing arts; Higher education; Hospitals (general); Human services; Jewish agencies & synagogues.
Limitations: Applications not accepted. Giving primarily in NJ and NY. No grants to individuals.
Application information: Contributes only to pre-selected organizations.
Board meeting date(s): As required
Officers and Directors:* John B. Hess,* Pres.; Marlene Hess,* V.P.; Constance Hess Williams,* V.P.; Thomas H. Kean,* Secy.; Eugene W. Goodwillie, Jr.,* Treas.
Number of staff: 1 full-time professional.
EIN: 221713046
Selected grants: The following grants are a representative sample of this grantmaker's funding activity:
$5,000,000 to Mount Sinai Medical Center, New York, NY, 2012. For unrestricted support.
$4,045,000 to Harvard University, Cambridge, MA, 2012. For unrestricted support.
$2,637,000 to Museum of Modern Art, New York, NY, 2012. For unrestricted support.
$1,600,000 to Deerfield Academy, Deerfield, MA, 2012. For unrestricted support.
$1,378,000 to Philadelphia Museum of Art, Philadelphia, PA, 2012. For unrestricted support.
$1,253,265 to Whitney Museum of American Art, New York, NY, 2012. For unrestricted support.
$100,000 to College of Physicians of Philadelphia, Philadelphia, PA, 2012. For unrestricted support.
$25,000 to Central Harlem Initiative for Learning and Development, Saint Aloysius School, New York, NY, 2012. For unrestricted support.
$25,000 to International Medical Corps, Los Angeles, CA, 2012. For unrestricted support.
$25,000 to Metropolitan Museum of Art, New York, NY, 2012. For unrestricted support.

5299
Hickory Foundation ✧
P.O. Box 281
Lambertville, NJ 08530-0281

Established in 1997 in NY.
Donors: Virginia Manheimer; Mary V. Chromiak‡; Virginia James; Emerick Chromiak Testamentary Trust.
Foundation type: Independent foundation.
Financial data (yr. ended 12/31/13): Assets, $35,309,231 (M); expenditures, $1,677,608; qualifying distributions, $1,671,864; giving activities include $1,666,934 for 60 grants (high: $250,000; low: $1,000).
Purpose and activities: Giving primarily for education, federated giving programs, and public affairs.
Fields of interest: Media/communications; Education; Human services; Civil/human rights, association; United Ways and Federated Giving Programs; Social sciences, public policy; Public affairs.
Limitations: Applications not accepted. Giving primarily in NY.
Application information: Contributes only to pre-selected organizations.
Officer: Virginia James, Pres.
EIN: 223472805

5300
The Charles & Marjorie Holloway Foundation Inc. ✧
c/o FGP, CPAs
106 Prospect St., 3rd Fl.
Ridgewood, NJ 07450-4433

Established in NJ.
Foundation type: Independent foundation.
Financial data (yr. ended 12/31/13): Assets, $18,007,290 (M); expenditures, $906,402; qualifying distributions, $896,063; giving activities include $896,063 for 11 grants (high: $150,000; low: $37,000).
Fields of interest: Education; Hospitals (specialty); Medical research, institute.
Limitations: Applications not accepted. Giving primarily in NJ and New York, NY.
Application information: Contributes only to pre-selected organizations.
Officers and Trustees:* Pierre Casimir-Lambert,* Co-Pres. and Co-Treas.; Ian MacCallum, Co-Pres. and Co-Treas.; Charles Casimir-Lambert,* V.P.; Veronique Casimir-Lambert Batrus,* Secy.
EIN: 223048105

5301
Holman Foundation, Inc. ✧ ☆
c/o Danser & Associates, LLC
5 Independence Way, Ste. 320
Princeton, NJ 08540-6627

Established in 1991 in NJ.
Donors: Wayne J. Holman III; Holman 1993 Charitable Remainder Unitrust.
Foundation type: Independent foundation.
Financial data (yr. ended 12/31/13): Assets, $13,061,776 (M); gifts received, $310,000; expenditures, $543,894; qualifying distributions, $487,548; giving activities include $444,500 for 19 grants (high: $50,000; low: $10,000).
Fields of interest: Philanthropy/voluntarism; Economics; Public affairs, research; Public policy, research.
Limitations: Applications not accepted. Giving primarily in Washington, DC and VA, with some giving in MT. No grants to individuals.
Application information: Contributes only to pre-selected organizations.
Officers and Trustees:* Wayne J. Holman III,* Pres.; John Vonkannon,* Secy.-Treas.; Eugene Meyer; Stephen Moore; Lee Liberman Otis.
EIN: 223127387
Selected grants: The following grants are a representative sample of this grantmaker's funding activity:
$50,000 to Cato Institute, Washington, DC, 2011. For general purpose.
$50,000 to Heritage Foundation, Washington, DC, 2011. For general purpose.
$25,000 to Ethics and Public Policy Center, Washington, DC, 2011. For general purpose.
$22,500 to Center for Equal Opportunity, Falls Church, VA, 2011. For general purpose.
$20,000 to American Family Business Foundation, Washington, DC, 2011. For general purpose.
$20,000 to Donors Trust, Alexandria, VA, 2011. For general purpose.
$20,000 to Intercollegiate Studies Institute, Wilmington, DE, 2011. For general purpose.
$10,000 to Bill of Rights Institute, Arlington, VA, 2011. For general purpose.
$10,000 to Council for National Policy, Washington, DC, 2011. For general purpose.

5302
D. Holmes Family Foundation, Inc. ✧
P.O. Box 1501, NJ2-130-03-31
Pennington, NJ 08534-1501

Established in 2004 in NJ.
Donors: Stephen Holmes; Bonnie Holmes.
Foundation type: Independent foundation.
Financial data (yr. ended 12/31/13): Assets, $6,225,286 (M); gifts received, $2,889,475; expenditures, $702,882; qualifying distributions, $622,663; giving activities include $610,000 for 5 grants (high: $200,000; low: $10,000).
Fields of interest: Higher education, university; Education; Hospitals (general); Boys & girls clubs; Girl scouts; Human services; Christian agencies & churches.
Type of support: General/operating support.
Limitations: Applications not accepted. Giving primarily in NJ. No grants to individuals.
Application information: Contributes only to pre-selected organizations.
Officers: Stephen P. Holmes, Pres.; Bonnie L. Holmes, V.P. and Secy.
EIN: 383709254
Selected grants: The following grants are a representative sample of this grantmaker's funding activity:
$200,000 to Chilton Memorial Hospital, Pompton Plains, NJ, 2011.

5303
Honickman Charitable Fund ✧
8275 Rte. 130
Pennsauken, NJ 08110-1435

Established in 1998 in PA.
Donors: Pepsi-Cola & National Brand Beverages, Ltd.; Harold Honickman; Lynne Honickman.
Foundation type: Independent foundation.
Financial data (yr. ended 12/31/12): Assets, $1,012,887 (M); gifts received, $1,107,762; expenditures, $611,965; qualifying distributions, $611,950; giving activities include $611,950 for 12 grants (high: $250,000; low: $100).
Purpose and activities: The foundation supports organizations involved with arts and culture, education, and breast cancer.
Fields of interest: Visual arts; Museums; Performing arts centers; Historic preservation/historical societies; Arts; Higher education; Education; Breast cancer; American Red Cross.
Type of support: General/operating support.
Limitations: Applications not accepted. Giving limited to PA. No grants to individuals.
Application information: Unsolicited requests for funds not accepted.
Trustees: Harold Honickman; Jeffrey Honickman; Walter Wilkinson.
EIN: 256612575
Selected grants: The following grants are a representative sample of this grantmaker's funding activity:
$130,000 to Thomas Jefferson University, Philadelphia, PA, 2011.
$35,000 to Community College of Philadelphia, Philadelphia, PA, 2011.
$12,500 to National Museum of American Jewish History, Philadelphia, PA, 2011.

5304
The Hope Foundation ✧
P.O. Box 408
Midland Park, NJ 07432-0408 (212) 308-4411
Contact: Andrew Grumet

Established in 2001 in NJ.
Donors: KEA Motor Car Corp.; Constance E. Bartichek.
Foundation type: Independent foundation.
Financial data (yr. ended 12/31/13): Assets, $1,739,948 (M); gifts received, $500,000; expenditures, $495,653; qualifying distributions, $495,000; giving activities include $495,000 for 11 grants (high: $100,000; low: $5,000).
Fields of interest: Cancer research; Children, services; Christian agencies & churches.
Limitations: Applications accepted. Giving primarily in FL, GA, NJ, and TN. No grants to individuals.
Application information: Application form required.
Initial approach: Proposal
Deadline(s): None
Trustees: Constance E. Bartichek; John J. Bartichek; Jennifer E. Tyler; Whitney A. Wilkinson.
EIN: 223808603
Selected grants: The following grants are a representative sample of this grantmaker's funding activity:
$50,000 to Samaritans Purse, Boone, NC, 2011.
$50,000 to World Vision, Federal Way, WA, 2011.

5305
Horizon Charitable Foundation, Inc. ✧
(doing business as The Horizon Foundation for New Jersey)
3 Penn Plz. E., PP-M2H
Newark, NJ 07105-2258
Contact: Michele L. Berry, Grants Coord.
E-mail: foundation_info@horizonblue.com;
Additional contact: Filomena Machleder, Prog. Off., tel.: (973) 466-8945, e-mail: filomena_machleder@horizonblue.com; Main URL: http://www.horizon-bcbsnj.com/foundation
Healthy U on Facebook: http://www.facebook.com/pages/Healthy-U/109310708427
Healthy U Video: http://www.horizon-bcbsnj.com/foundation/healthyu/Video.html?WT.svl=leftnav

Established in 2003 in NJ.
Donors: Horizon Healthcare Services, Inc.; Parners Investing in Nursing's Future.
Foundation type: Company-sponsored foundation.
Financial data (yr. ended 12/31/12): Assets, $54,029,798 (M); gifts received, $49,000; expenditures, $5,630,937; qualifying distributions, $4,937,763; giving activities include $4,737,030 for 117 grants (high: $455,158; low: $7,500), and $200,733 for employee matching gifts.
Purpose and activities: The foundation supports programs designed to promote health, well-being, and quality of life in New Jersey communities. Special emphasis is directed toward health prevention, education, and program support for chronic diseases; and building vibrant communities through arts and cultural programs.
Fields of interest: Arts, cultural/ethnic awareness; Arts education; Performing arts; Arts; Education; Health care, information services; Health care,

clinics/centers; Public health; Public health, obesity; Public health, physical fitness; Health care; Mental health, depression; Mental health/crisis services; Cancer; Heart & circulatory diseases; Diabetes; Nutrition; YM/YWCAs & YM/YWHAs; Children, services; Children; Aging.
Type of support: General/operating support; Continuing support; Program development; Curriculum development; Research; Technical assistance; Employee volunteer services; Sponsorships; Employee matching gifts.
Limitations: Applications accepted. Giving limited to areas of company operations in NJ. No support for hospitals or hospital foundations or political organizations or candidates. No grants to individuals, or for capital campaigns, endowments, or political causes or campaigns.
Publications: Application guidelines; Program policy statement.
Application information: General operating support is only available for art projects. Support is limited to 1 contribution per organization during any given year. Multi-year funding is not automatic. Organizations receiving support are asked to submit a final report. Application form required.
Initial approach: Complete online application form
Copies of proposal: 1
Deadline(s): Jan. 8, Apr. 2, July 16, and Oct. 8
Board meeting date(s): Mar. 18, June 10, Sept. 23, and Dec. 16
Final notification: 90 days
Officers and Directors:* Robert A. Marino,* Pres.; Kevin P. Conlin, V.P.; Linda A. Willet, Secy.; David R. Huber, Treas.; Jonathan R. Pearson, Exec. Dir.
Number of staff: None.
EIN: 200252405

5306
Hirair and Anna Hovnanian Foundation, Inc. ✧
4000 Rte. 66, 4th Fl.
Tinton Falls, NJ 07753-7308 (732) 922-6100
Contact: Hirair Hovnanian, Chair.

Established in 1986 in FL.
Donors: Hirair Hovnanian; Anna Hovnanian.
Foundation type: Independent foundation.
Financial data (yr. ended 12/31/12): Assets, $62,078,934 (M); gifts received, $6,775,000; expenditures, $2,641,204; qualifying distributions, $1,968,652; giving activities include $1,635,389 for 67 grants (high: $343,333; low: $200), and $50,000 for 25 grants to individuals (high: $2,000; low: $2,000).
Purpose and activities: Giving primarily for Armenian culture and education.
Fields of interest: Arts, cultural/ethnic awareness; Higher education; Education; Health organizations; International affairs.
International interests: Armenia.
Limitations: Giving primarily in NJ and Washington, DC; some funding also in Armenia.
Application information:
Initial approach: Letter on organization letterhead
Deadline(s): None
Officers: Hirair Hovnanian, Chair.; Anna Hovnanian, Pres.; Edele Hovnanian, V.P. and Treas.; Armen Hovnanian, V.P.; Leela Hovnanian, V.P.; Siran Sahakian, V.P.; Tanya Hovnanian-Baghdassarian, Secy.
EIN: 592714390

Selected grants: The following grants are a representative sample of this grantmaker's funding activity:
$20,000 to Georgetown University, Washington, DC, 2012. For Used for the Organizations Exempt Purpose.

5307
The Kevork and Sirwart Hovnanian Foundation ✧
110 W. Front St.
Red Bank, NJ 07701-1139

Established in 2002.
Donors: Sirwart K. Hovnanian; Kevork S. Hovnanian†.
Foundation type: Independent foundation.
Financial data (yr. ended 12/31/13): Assets, $2,183,487 (M); expenditures, $2,636,976; qualifying distributions, $2,579,655; giving activities include $2,579,655 for 8 grants (high: $1,750,000; low: $105).
Purpose and activities: Giving primarily for health and hospitals; some funding also for Armenian causes, particularly Armenian churches.
Fields of interest: Hospitals (general); Health care; Christian agencies & churches.
Limitations: Applications not accepted. Giving primarily in NJ; funding also in NY. No grants to individuals.
Application information: Unsolicited requests for funds not accepted.
Trustees: Esto K. Barry; Ara K. Hovnanian; Sirwart K. Hovnanian; Lucy K. Kalian; Sossie K. Najarian; Nadia K. Rodriguez.
EIN: 050562489

5308
Hugin Family Foundation Inc. ✧
19 Essex Rd.
Summit, NJ 07901-2801

Established in 2001 in NJ.
Donor: Robert J. Hugin.
Foundation type: Independent foundation.
Financial data (yr. ended 12/31/13): Assets, $8,029,381 (M); gifts received, $6,140,210; expenditures, $2,273,329; qualifying distributions, $2,273,329; giving activities include $2,238,174 for 27 grants (high: $514,395; low: $100).
Purpose and activities: Giving primarily for higher and other education.
Fields of interest: Higher education; Education; Hospitals (general); Human services.
Limitations: Applications not accepted. No grants to individuals.
Application information: Contributes only to pre-selected organizations.
Officers: Robert J. Hugin, Pres. and Treas.; Kathleen M. Hugin, Secy.
Director: James R. Swenson.
EIN: 030374762
Selected grants: The following grants are a representative sample of this grantmaker's funding activity:
$300,720 to High Mountain Institute, Leadville, CO, 2012. For any general purposes of the recipient org.

5309
Hummingbird Foundation, Inc. ✧ ☆
c/o David R. Hummel
120 Partree Rd.
Cherry Hill, NJ 08003-2112

Established in 2005 in NJ.
Donor: David R. Hummel.
Foundation type: Independent foundation.
Financial data (yr. ended 02/28/13): Assets, $10,386,441 (M); gifts received, $588,544; expenditures, $504,717; qualifying distributions, $460,000; giving activities include $460,000 for 8 grants (high: $106,000; low: $10,000).
Fields of interest: Arts; Hospitals (general); Arthritis; Medical research, institute; Food banks; Human services; Children, services.
Type of support: Research.
Limitations: Applications not accepted. Giving primarily in NJ and PA.
Application information: Contributes only to pre-selected organizations.
Officers: David R. Hummel, Pres.; Jane Hummel, V.P.
Trustees: John Blasi; Chad Hummel; Todd Hummel; Richard Vestal.
EIN: 593797192
Selected grants: The following grants are a representative sample of this grantmaker's funding activity:
$53,200 to Community Food Bank of New Jersey, Hillside, NJ, 2011.
$40,000 to Big Brothers Big Sisters of New York City, New York, NY, 2011.
$30,000 to Cathedral Kitchen, Camden, NJ, 2011.

5310
The Hyde and Watson Foundation
31-F Mountain Blvd.
Warren, NJ 07059-5617 (908) 753-3700
FAX: (908) 753-0004;
E-mail: info@hydeandwatson.org; Main URL: http://fdnweb.org/hydeandwatson
Grants List: http://fdnweb.org/hydeandwatson/grant-summary/

The Lillia Babbitt Hyde Foundation incorporated in 1924 in NY; The John Jay and Eliza Jane Watson Foundation incorporated in 1949; consolidation of two foundations into Hyde and Watson Foundation in 1983.
Donors: Lillia Babbitt Hyde†; Eliza Jane Watson†.
Foundation type: Independent foundation.
Financial data (yr. ended 12/31/13): Assets, $109,543,399 (M); expenditures, $5,849,375; qualifying distributions, $5,345,577; giving activities include $4,585,500 for 438 grants (high: $125,000; low: $3,000).
Purpose and activities: Support for capital projects such as hard costs related to construction or purchase of new facilities, building renovations and improvements, purchase of capital equipment and furnishings, one-time capital needs, support to limited medical research. Broad fields include health, education, religion, social services, arts, and humanities.
Fields of interest: Performing arts; Humanities; Arts; Education, early childhood education; Child development, education; Elementary school/education; Secondary school/education; Medical school/education; Education; Environment, natural resources; Environment; Hospitals (general); Medical care, rehabilitation; Health care; Substance

abuse, services; Mental health/crisis services; Health organizations, association; Cancer; Human services; Children/youth, services; Child development, services; Family services; Aging, centers/services; Minorities/immigrants, centers/services; Homeless, human services; Religion; Infants/toddlers; Children/youth; Children; Youth; Adults; Young adults; Disabilities, people with; Physically disabled; Blind/visually impaired; Deaf/hearing impaired; Mentally disabled; Minorities; African Americans/Blacks; Hispanics/Latinos; Women; Girls; Men; Boys; Substance abusers; AIDS, people with; Crime/abuse victims; Immigrants/refugees; Economically disadvantaged; Homeless; LGBTQ.
Type of support: Capital campaigns; Building/renovation; Equipment; Land acquisition; Debt reduction; Research; Matching/challenge support.
Limitations: Applications accepted. Giving is focused in the five boroughs of New York, NY, and primarily Essex, Union and Morris counties in NJ. No support for projects outside the United States, or for political organizations. No grants to individuals, or for endowments, operating support, benefit fundraisers, annual fund appeals, scholarships, or from fiscal agents.
Publications: Application guidelines; Annual report (including application guidelines); Financial statement; Grants list.
Application information: Due to the large volume of appeals received, it may be impossible to answer all of them; however, every effort will be made to respond. Inquiries by e-mail are not accepted. Supplemental information may be required if proposal is considered by grants committee. The foundation also accepts the New York/New Jersey Area Common Application Form but prefers its own application procedure. See foundation web site for complete application guidelines, instructions, and form. Application form required.
Initial approach: Letter with grant application form, which is available by fax or at the foundation's web site, and attachments
Copies of proposal: 1
Deadline(s): No later than Feb. 15 and Sept. 15
Board meeting date(s): Apr./May and Nov./Dec.
Final notification: After grant or board meeting or preliminary review
Officers and Directors:* Hunter W. Corbin,* Chair.; William V. Engel,* Pres.; Brunilda Moriarty, Exec. V.P.; Robert W. Parsons, Jr.,* Secy.; Thomas W. Berry,* Treas.; H. Corbin Day, Dir. Emeritus; Roger B. Parsons, Dir. Emeritus; Elizabeth R. Curry; Hans Dekker; John W. Holman, Jr.; John W. Holman III; Thomas H. MacCowatt; Anita V. Spivey; Kate B. Wood.
Number of staff: 4 full-time professional; 2 part-time professional.
EIN: 222425725
Selected grants: The following grants are a representative sample of this grantmaker's funding activity:
$150,000 to Shakespeare Theater of New Jersey, Florham Park, NJ, 2012. For hard costs related to purchase of a facility in Florham Park, NJ.
$25,000 to Girl Scouts of the U.S.A., Montclair, NJ, 2012. For hard costs related to facility renovations and improvements.
$20,000 to New York Hall of Science, Corona, NY, 2012. For purchase of specialized equipment.
$20,000 to Saint Vincent Academy, Newark, NJ, 2012. For purchase of computer equipment and software.
$15,600 to Primary Care Development Corporation, New York, NY, 2012. For purchase of computer equipment.
$10,000 to Boys and Girls Club, Madison Square, New York, NY, 2012. For purchase of computer equipment.
$10,000 to Civic Builders, New York, NY, 2012. For hard costs related to facility renovations, and purchase of equipment and furnishings.
$10,000 to New Jersey Conservation Foundation, Far Hills, NJ, 2012. For purchase of equipment and software.
$10,000 to Sanctuary for Families, New York, NY, 2012. For purchase of office furnishings.
$9,700 to Brooklyn Bureau of Community Service, Brooklyn, NY, 2012. For purchase of computer equipment.

5311
The IDT Charitable Foundation ✧
520 Broad St.
Newark, NJ 07102-3121
Contact: Sidney Mehl

Established as a company-sponsored operating foundation in 2001.
Donor: IDT Corp.
Foundation type: Operating foundation.
Financial data (yr. ended 12/31/13): Assets, $1,600,488 (M); gifts received, $1,358,000; expenditures, $1,838,175; qualifying distributions, $1,794,124; giving activities include $1,794,124 for 367 grants (high: $750,000).
Purpose and activities: The foundation supports organizations involved with education, health, cancer, human services, international relief, and Judaism.
Fields of interest: Elementary/secondary education; Higher education; Theological school/education; Libraries (public); Education; Hospitals (general); Health care; Cancer; Children/youth, services; Human services; International relief; Jewish federated giving programs; Jewish agencies & synagogues.
International interests: Israel.
Type of support: Employee matching gifts; General/operating support; Scholarship funds; Sponsorships; Program-related investments/loans.
Limitations: Applications not accepted. Giving on a national basis in areas of company operations, with emphasis on NJ, NY, and Israel. No grants to individuals.
Application information: Contributes only to pre-selected organizations.
Officers and Directors:* Howard Millendorf,* Pres.; Blake Reiser,* Treas.; Moshe Kaganoff.
EIN: 364450442

5312
IGH Charitable Foundation, Inc. ✧ ☆
4 Fox Run
Randolph, NJ 07869-4568

Established in 2005 in NJ.
Donors: Deborah A. MacArthur; Thomas C. MacArthur.
Foundation type: Independent foundation.
Financial data (yr. ended 12/31/13): Assets, $0 (M); gifts received, $78,000; expenditures, $572,893; qualifying distributions, $499,144; giving activities include $478,500 for 28 grants (high: $115,000; low: $2,500).
Fields of interest: Human services; Christian agencies & churches.
Limitations: Applications not accepted. Giving primarily in NJ. No grants to individuals.
Application information: Unsolicited requests for funds not accepted.
Officers: Deborah A. MacArthur, Pres.; Thomas C. MacArthur, V.P.
Director: Isabella Cavaco.
EIN: 202931753

5313
Indian Trail Charitable Foundation, Inc. ✧
c/o Konner, Harbus and Schwartz, P.C.
80 E. Rte. 4, Ste. 408
Paramus, NJ 07652-2620 (201) 556-1311

Established in 1986 in DE.
Donors: Edna Askwith; Patricia Kenner; Bertram J. Askwith; Kathy Franklin; Lisa Franklin; Max Franklin; Dennis Askwith; Keri Tours Inc.; Campus Travel, Inc.
Foundation type: Independent foundation.
Financial data (yr. ended 11/30/13): Assets, $23,188,656 (M); gifts received, $3,202,678; expenditures, $1,603,715; qualifying distributions, $1,598,189; giving activities include $1,598,189 for 75 grants (high: $375,000; low: $100).
Fields of interest: Higher education; Education; Health organizations, association; Human services; Jewish agencies & synagogues.
Limitations: Applications not accepted. Giving primarily in MI, New York, NY, and Pittsburgh, PA.
Application information: Contributes only to pre-selected organizations.
Trustees: Bertram J. Askwith; Patricia Askwith Kenner.
EIN: 222769941

5314
Ingersoll-Rand Charitable Foundation ✧
1 Centennial Ave.
Piscataway, NJ 08854-3921
Contact: Misty Zelent
Main URL: http://company.ingersollrand.com/ircorp/en/discover-us/our-company/community-relations/ingersoll-rand-foundation.html

Established in 2004 in DE.
Donor: Ingersoll-Rand Co.
Foundation type: Company-sponsored foundation.
Financial data (yr. ended 12/31/12): Assets, $592,010 (M); gifts received, $3,000,000; expenditures, $3,007,471; qualifying distributions, $2,969,306; giving activities include $1,172,092 for grants, and $1,761,214 for employee matching gifts.
Purpose and activities: The foundation supports food banks and organizations involved with education, health, cancer research, housing development, disaster relief, and human services.
Fields of interest: Elementary/secondary education; Higher education; Scholarships/financial aid; Education; Health care; Cancer; Cancer research; Food banks; Housing/shelter, development; Disasters, preparedness/services; Girl scouts; American Red Cross; YM/YWCAs & YM/YWHAs; Human services; United Ways and Federated Giving Programs.

Type of support: General/operating support; Program development; Scholarship funds; Employee volunteer services; Employee matching gifts.
Limitations: Applications accepted. Giving primarily in MO, NC and NJ; giving also to national organizations. No equipment donations.
Application information: Application form not required.
Initial approach: Letter of inquiry
Deadline(s): None
Officers and Directors:* Michael Lamach, Pres.; Marcia Avedon,* V.P.; Robert L. Katz, V.P.; Barbara A. Santoro,* Secy.; David S. Kuhl, Treas.
EIN: 202045897
Selected grants: The following grants are a representative sample of this grantmaker's funding activity:
$222,000 to Girl Scouts of the U.S.A., Abilene, TX, 2011.
$147,516 to National Merit Scholarship Corporation, Evanston, IL, 2011.
$41,875 to Ada Jenkins Families and Careers Development Center, Davidson, NC, 2011.

5315
The Integra Foundation, Inc. ✧
311 Enterprise Dr.
Plainsboro, NJ 08536-3344 (949) 855-7165
Contact: Linda Littlejohns, Pres. and Exec. Dir.
FAX: (949) 595-8703;
E-mail: linda.littlejohns@integralife.com; Application address: 2 Goodyear #A, Irvine, CA 92618; Main URL: http://www.integra-foundation.org
Grants List: http://www.integra-foundation.org/gh.asp

Established in 2002 in NJ.
Donor: Integra LifeSciences Corp.
Foundation type: Company-sponsored foundation.
Financial data (yr. ended 12/31/13): Assets, $300,520 (M); gifts received, $562,500; expenditures, $682,078; qualifying distributions, $682,053; giving activities include $682,053 for 67 grants (high: $50,000; low: $250).
Purpose and activities: The foundation supports programs designed to advance innovative medical and health care research and education, primarily in the areas of neurosurgery, reconstructive surgery, and general surgery, to improve the outcome and quality of life for patients and their communities.
Fields of interest: Medical school/education; Hospitals (general); Health care, clinics/centers; Health care; Neuroscience research; Medical research; Surgery research.
Type of support: Sponsorships; Conferences/seminars; Equipment; Scholarship funds; General/operating support; Program development.
Limitations: Applications accepted. Giving primarily in areas of company operations. No support for political, fraternal, social, veterans', or religious organizations. No grants to individuals, or for programs that directly support marketing or sales objectives of Integra LifeSciences.
Publications: Application guidelines; Grants list; Newsletter.
Application information: Application form required.
Initial approach: Download application form and mail or fax to foundation
Copies of proposal: 1
Deadline(s): None
Board meeting date(s): Feb., May, Aug., and Nov.
Officers and Trustees: Linda Littlejohns, Pres. and Exec. Dir.; Simon Archibald, V.P.; JoAnne Harla, V.P.; Karen March, V.P.; Nora Brennan, Treas.; Stuart Essig; Jack Henneman; Judith O'Grady.
Number of staff: 1 part-time professional.
EIN: 522388679

5316
The International Foundation
1700 Rte. 23N., Ste. 300
Wayne, NJ 07470-7537
Contact: Kathy Gaiser
E-mail: info@intlfoundation.org; Main URL: http://www.intlfoundation.org

Incorporated in 1948 in DE.
Foundation type: Independent foundation.
Financial data (yr. ended 12/31/12): Assets, $23,199,362 (M); expenditures, $1,265,083; qualifying distributions, $1,052,732; giving activities include $764,700 for grants.
Purpose and activities: The foundation has supported world-wide development since its founding in 1948. The foundation recognizes the importance of emerging economies and the developmental challenges they face. It supports projects that promote sustainable development in: 1) agriculture: research and production; 2) health: medical, nutrition, and water; 3) education: formal at all levels research; 4) social development: cultural, economic, community, and entrepreneurial activity, and some aid to refugees, and grants for population planning are given; and 5) the environment.
Fields of interest: Education; Environment, natural resources; Health care; Health organizations; Agriculture; Human services; Economic development; Urban/community development; Rural development.
Limitations: Applications not accepted. Giving primarily in Grants limited to U.S.-based 501(c)(3) organizations that design, implement and directly supervise the overseas development program only. No support for overseas adoption, religious organizations, non-profit organizations significantly funded or reimbursed by the U.S. Government, projects in which a U.S.-based organization's (NGO) programs are implemented by an overseas organization that is not a 501 (c)(3) and in which the grant seeker does not have a major management and oversight role. No grants to individuals, or for endowment funds, operating budgets, capital improvements or construction projects, emergency or disaster aid, service delivery projects, scholarships, fellowships, matching gifts, video productions, or conferences; no loans.
Publications: IRS Form 990 or 990-PF printed copy available upon request.
Application information: The foundation is currently not accepting applications. Check foundation web site periodically for updates.
Board meeting date(s): Jan., Apr., July, and Oct.
Officers and Trustees:* William McCormack, M.D.*, Grants Chair.; Frank Madden,* Pres.; John D. Carrico,* Secy.-Treas.; Gary Dicovitsky,* Investment Chair.; Letitia K. Butler; Edward A. Holmes, Ph.D; Douglas Walker.
Number of staff: 1 full-time professional.
EIN: 131962255
Selected grants: The following grants are a representative sample of this grantmaker's funding activity:
$15,000 to African Services Committee, New York, NY, 2013.
$15,000 to EcoLogic Development Fund, Cambridge, MA, 2013.
$15,000 to Lotus Outreach, Aptos, CA, 2013. For anti-trafficking program in Cambodia.
$15,000 to One Acre Fund, Washington DC Office, Highland Park, IL, 2013.
$15,000 to Quaker Bolivia Education Fund, East Concord, NY, 2013. For education.
$15,000 to Stanford University, School of Education, Stanford, CA, 2012. For Stanford Mobile Inquiry-based Learning Environment (SMILE) for education development in Tanzania.
$12,000 to Grassroots International, Boston, MA, 2013. For agriculture development in Brazil.
$11,500 to International Action, Washington, DC, 2012. For clean water program.
$10,000 to Brackett Foundation, Hamilton, NY, 2012. For education.
$10,000 to Corps Africa, Washington, DC, 2013. To train young community leaders in Ethiopia.
$10,000 to Namaste Foundation, San Francisco, CA, 2013. For micro-lending program in Guatemala.

5317
Investors Foundation, Inc. ✧
(formerly Investors Savings Bank Charitable Foundation)
101 John F. Kennedy Pkwy.
Short Hills, NJ 07078-2716
E-mail: rodger@herrigelbolan.com; Main URL: http://www.isbnj.com/home/community/foundation

Established in 2005 in DE.
Donor: Investors Savings Bank.
Foundation type: Company-sponsored foundation.
Financial data (yr. ended 06/30/13): Assets, $30,767,073 (M); gifts received, $1,400,000; expenditures, $941,724; qualifying distributions, $935,849; giving activities include $863,108 for 181 grants (high: $25,000; low: $500).
Purpose and activities: The foundation supports organizations involved with arts and culture, education, health, affordable housing, youth development, and human services. Support is limited to areas of company operations.
Fields of interest: Arts; Education; Health care; Housing/shelter; Youth development; Human services.
Type of support: General/operating support; Continuing support; Capital campaigns; Equipment; Program development; Seed money; Scholarship funds; Matching/challenge support.
Limitations: Applications accepted. Giving limited to areas of company operations in NJ. No support for political organizations. No grants to individuals.
Publications: Application guidelines.
Application information: Application form required.
Initial approach: Letter
Copies of proposal: 1
Deadline(s): 2 months prior to month of board meetings
Board meeting date(s): Sept., Dec., Mar., and June
Officers and Directors:* Robert M. Cahshill,* Chair.; Kevin Cummings,* Pres.; Rodger K. Herrigel,* Exec. Dir.; Vincent D. Manahan III; Ada Melendez; Rose Sigler; William A. Tansey III.
Number of staff: 1 part-time professional; 1 part-time support.
EIN: 203743857

Selected grants: The following grants are a representative sample of this grantmaker's funding activity:
$5,000 to American Heart Association, Dallas, TX, 2011. For general support.
$5,000 to Garden Conservancy, Cold Spring, NY, 2011. For general support.
$1,000 to United Negro College Fund, Fairfax, VA, 2011. For general support.

5318
The Isdell Family Foundation ✧
c/o Hamel Assocs., Inc.
615 W. Mt. Pleasant Ave.
Livingston, NJ 07039-1620

Established in 2005 in NJ.
Donor: E. Nivelle Isdell.
Foundation type: Independent foundation.
Financial data (yr. ended 12/31/13): Assets, $15,627,756 (M); gifts received, $9,500,000; expenditures, $2,062,726; qualifying distributions, $2,052,898; giving activities include $2,052,898 for 20 grants (high: $1,558,200; low: $1,000).
Fields of interest: Museums (natural history); Arts; Environment; Animal welfare.
Limitations: Applications not accepted. Giving primarily in GA. No grants to individuals.
Application information: Contributes only to pre-selected organizations.
Trustees: Pamela Anne Isdell; Cara Anne Isdell Lee.
EIN: 206759053
Selected grants: The following grants are a representative sample of this grantmaker's funding activity:
$3,500 to High Museum of Art, Atlanta, GA, 2012. For Unrestricted use by recipient in its charitable endeavor.

5319
Isermann Family Foundation, Inc. ✧
c/o Gene R. Korf, Esq.
89 Headquarters Plz. N. Tower, 14th Fl.
Morristown, NJ 07960

Established in 1985 in NJ.
Donor: Howard Isermann.
Foundation type: Independent foundation.
Financial data (yr. ended 12/31/13): Assets, $10,760,434 (M); gifts received, $150,000; expenditures, $571,962; qualifying distributions, $536,603; giving activities include $516,000 for 27 grants (high: $100,000; low: $2,500).
Fields of interest: Arts; Human services; Jewish federated giving programs; Jewish agencies & synagogues.
Type of support: General/operating support; Capital campaigns; Scholarship funds.
Limitations: Applications not accepted. Giving primarily in FL, NJ, and NY. No grants to individuals.
Application information: Contributes only to pre-selected organizations.
Officers: Howard Isermann, Pres. and Treas.; Betty Isermann, V.P.; Carol Isermann, V.P.; Gene R. Korf, Secy.
EIN: 222615361

5320
The Jaffe Family Foundation ✧
c/o Elliot S. Jaffe
933 Macarthur Blvd.
Mahwah, NJ 07430

Established in 1986 in NY.
Donors: Elliot Jaffe; Roslyn Jaffe; The Jaffe Family Limited Partnership.
Foundation type: Independent foundation.
Financial data (yr. ended 12/31/13): Assets, $72,630,128 (M); expenditures, $2,958,191; qualifying distributions, $2,717,788; giving activities include $2,658,699 for 324 grants (high: $300,000; low: $40).
Purpose and activities: Giving primarily for the arts, higher education, Jewish support organizations, medical research, and children, and social services.
Fields of interest: Museums; Performing arts; Arts; Higher education; Education; Health organizations, association; Medical research, institute; Human services; Children/youth, services; Jewish federated giving programs; Jewish agencies & synagogues.
Limitations: Applications not accepted. Giving primarily in CT, Washington, DC, MA, and NY. No grants to individuals.
Application information: Unsolicited requests for funds not accepted.
Officer: Elliot S. Jaffe, Pres.
Directors: David R. Jaffe; Elise P. Jaffe; Richard E. Jaffe; Roslyn Jaffe.
EIN: 222827692

5321
Roger James Charitable Foundation ✧
P.O. Box 1501, NJ2-130-03-31
Pennington, NJ 08534-1501

Donor: Roger James.
Foundation type: Independent foundation.
Financial data (yr. ended 11/30/13): Assets, $9,935,333 (M); expenditures, $564,686; qualifying distributions, $522,411; giving activities include $472,708 for 5 grants (high: $94,542; low: $94,541).
Fields of interest: Animal welfare.
Limitations: Applications not accepted. Giving primarily in OR, UT, and WA.
Application information: Contributes only to pre-selected organizations.
Trustee: Merrill Lynch Trust Company.
EIN: 261586251
Selected grants: The following grants are a representative sample of this grantmaker's funding activity:
$91,358 to Best Friends Animal Society, Kanab, UT, 2011.
$91,358 to Cat Adoption Team, Sherwood, OR, 2011.
$91,358 to Feral Cat Coalition of Oregon, Portland, OR, 2011.

5322
The James Family Charitable Foundation ✧
c/o Cappiccille
615 W. Mount Pleasant Ave.
Livingston, NJ 07039-1620

Established in 1994 in DE and NY.
Donors: Amabel B. James; Hamilton E. James.
Foundation type: Independent foundation.
Financial data (yr. ended 12/31/12): Assets, $73,953,718 (M); gifts received, $20,000,000; expenditures, $1,620,710; qualifying distributions, $1,469,570; giving activities include $1,469,570 for 74 grants (high: $249,000; low: $100).
Purpose and activities: Giving primarily for the arts, education, environmental conservation, and health organizations.
Fields of interest: Performing arts; Historic preservation/historical societies; Arts; Secondary school/education; Higher education; Education; Environment, natural resources; Animals/wildlife, preservation/protection; Health organizations; Christian agencies & churches.
Limitations: Applications not accepted. Giving primarily in NY. No grants to individuals.
Application information: Contributes only to pre-selected organizations.
Officers: Hamilton E. James, Pres. and Treas.; Amabel B. James, V.P. and Secy.
EIN: 137051493

5323
The JM Foundation ✧
116 Village Blvd., Ste. 200
Princeton, NJ 08540-5700 (609) 951-2283
Contact: Carl Helstrom, Exec. Dir.
FAX: (609) 951-2281; Main URL: http://fdnweb.org/jm
Grants List: http://fdnweb.org/jm/grants/year/2013/category/grants-awarded/

Incorporated in 1924 in NY.
Donors: Jeremiah Milbank†; Katharine S. Milbank†.
Foundation type: Independent foundation.
Financial data (yr. ended 12/31/13): Assets, $25,732,932 (M); expenditures, $1,606,734; qualifying distributions, $1,257,691; giving activities include $910,500 for 26 grants (high: $100,000; low: $3,000), $80,450 for employee matching gifts, and $43,414 for foundation-administered programs.
Purpose and activities: The foundation has a strong interest in educational activities which strengthen America's pluralistic system of free markets, entrepreneurship, and private enterprise. The foundation's current priorities include: supporting education and research that fosters market-based policy solutions, especially at state think tanks; developing state and national organizations that promote free enterprise, entrepreneurship, and private initiative; and identifying and educating young leaders.
Fields of interest: Children/youth, services; Public policy, research; Children/youth; Adults.
Type of support: Management development/capacity building; Program development; Publication; Fellowships; Internship funds; Research; Employee matching gifts; Matching/challenge support.
Limitations: Applications accepted. Giving on a national basis. No support for the arts, government agencies, public schools, or international activities. No grants to individuals, or for operating expenses, annual fundraising campaigns, equipment, or endowment funds; no loans.
Publications: Application guidelines.
Application information: See foundation web site for guidelines. Faxes, e-mails or overnight mail requests not accepted. Application form not required.

Initial approach: Summary letter accompanied by proposal
Copies of proposal: 1
Deadline(s): No firm deadlines. Proposals processed as received. Grant decisions made at board meetings in May and Oct
Board meeting date(s): May and Oct
Final notification: Usually in writing within 30 working days

Officers and Directors:* Jeremiah Milbank III,* Pres.; Jeremiah M. Bogert, V.P.; Peter C. Morse, Secy.; William Lee Hanley, Jr.,* Treas.; Carl Helstrom, Exec. Dir.; Chris Olander, Exec. Dir. Emeritus; Mary Caslin Ross.
Number of staff: 1 full-time professional; 1 part-time professional; 1 part-time support.
EIN: 136068340

5324
JMP Foundation Inc. ✧
c/o Toni Novak
11 Clifton Ave.
Merchantville, NJ 08109-2601

Established in 2005 in NJ.
Donors: Joseph Papa; Marylee M. Pratnicki.
Foundation type: Independent foundation.
Financial data (yr. ended 12/31/13): Assets, $10,388,497 (M); expenditures, $639,128; qualifying distributions, $595,604; giving activities include $553,600 for 33 grants (high: $100,000; low: $2,000).
Fields of interest: Higher education; Animal welfare; Human services; Foundations (community).
Limitations: Applications not accepted. Giving primarily in NJ, NY, PA, and VI. No grants to individuals.
Application information: Contributes only to pre-selected organizations.
Officers and Directors:* Joseph Papa,* C.E.O.; Juliana Drinane,* V.P.; Christine A. Papa,* V.P.; Marylee M. Pratnicki,* Secy.
EIN: 203462159

5325
The Jockey Hollow Foundation, Inc. ✧
P.O. Box 462
Bernardsville, NJ 07924-0462 (908) 901-0007
Contact: Betsy S. Michel, Tr.

Incorporated in 1960 in NJ.
Donors: Carl Shirley†; Mrs. Carl Shirley.
Foundation type: Independent foundation.
Financial data (yr. ended 03/31/14): Assets, $16,059,538 (M); expenditures, $812,887; qualifying distributions, $694,525; giving activities include $694,525 for 109 grants (high: $35,000; low: $725).
Fields of interest: Performing arts; Historic preservation/historical societies; Education; Environment; Hospitals (general); Health care; Human services.
Limitations: Giving primarily in Nantucket, MA, NJ, with emphasis on Morristown and Newark, New York, NY, and in Islesboro, ME. No grants to individuals.
Application information: Application form not required.
Initial approach: Proposal
Copies of proposal: 1
Deadline(s): None

Trustees: Betsy S. Michel; Clifford F. Michel; Jason L. Michel; Katherine B. Michel.
EIN: 221724138
Selected grants: The following grants are a representative sample of this grantmaker's funding activity:
$30,000 to Natural Resources Defense Council, New York, NY, 2011.
$28,500 to Peck School, Morristown, NJ, 2011.
$20,000 to GlassRoots, Newark, NJ, 2011.
$15,000 to Matheny School and Hospital, Peapack, NJ, 2011.
$8,000 to Black Student Fund, Washington, DC, 2011.
$8,000 to Nantucket Cottage Hospital, Nantucket, MA, 2011.
$8,000 to Wounded Warrior Project, Jacksonville, FL, 2011.
$5,000 to Homeless Solutions, Morristown, NJ, 2011.
$5,000 to New Jersey Performing Arts Center, Newark, NJ, 2011.
$5,000 to Outward Bound Center for Peacebuilding, Long Island City, NY, 2011.

5326
Johnson & Johnson Family of Companies Foundation ✧
(also known as Johnson & Johnson Family of Companies Contribution Fund)
c/o Janine Connell
1 Johnson & Johnson Plz., WH-2112
New Brunswick, NJ 08933-0001
Main URL: http://www.jnj.com/connect/caring/

Incorporated in 1953 in NJ.
Donor: Johnson & Johnson.
Foundation type: Company-sponsored foundation.
Financial data (yr. ended 12/31/13): Assets, $40,950,880 (M); gifts received, $127,100,000; expenditures, $46,445,669; qualifying distributions, $46,445,669; giving activities include $34,558,066 for 467 grants (high: $1,173,000; low: $50), and $11,236,091 for 24,824 employee matching gifts.
Purpose and activities: The foundation supports programs designed to improve the lives of women and children; prevent disease in vulnerable populations; and strengthen the healthcare workplace.
Fields of interest: Arts; Education, early childhood education; Higher education; Education; Hospitals (general); Health care, clinics/centers; Health care, infants; Reproductive health, prenatal care; Health care; Genetic diseases and disorders; Cancer; AIDS; Pediatrics; Food services; American Red Cross; Children, services; Human services; International development; International relief; International affairs, U.N.; International migration/refugee issues; International affairs; United Ways and Federated Giving Programs; Philanthropy/voluntarism; Children; Women; Economically disadvantaged.
Type of support: General/operating support; Continuing support; Annual campaigns; Program development; Scholarship funds; Employee matching gifts.
Limitations: Applications not accepted. Giving on a national basis in areas of company operations; giving also to national and international organizations. No support for fraternal, political, religious, or athletic organizations. No grants to individuals, or for debt reduction, trips, tours, capital campaigns or endowments, or publications; no loans.
Publications: Corporate giving report.
Application information: Contributes only to pre-selected organizations.
Board meeting date(s): Mar., June, Sept., and Dec.

Officers: Michael. E. Sneed, Pres.; Sharon Kathryn Dagostino, V.P.; Elizabeth R. Forminard, Secy.; John A. Papa, Treas.
EIN: 226062811
Selected grants: The following grants are a representative sample of this grantmaker's funding activity:
$2,000,000 to mothers2mothers International, Los Angeles, CA, 2012.
$1,173,000 to Dartmouth College, Hanover, NH, 2012.
$1,000,000 to Americans for UNFPA, New York, NY, 2012.
$916,196 to Task Force for Global Health, Decatur, GA, 2012.
$533,500 to AIDS United, Washington, DC, 2012.
$500,000 to International Rescue Committee, New York, NY, 2012.
$50,000 to Harvard University, Cambridge, MA, 2012.
$39,578 to CDC Foundation, Atlanta, GA, 2012.
$30,000 to Give2Asia, San Francisco, CA, 2012.
$25,000 to Boomer Esiason Foundation, New York, NY, 2012.

5327
Johnson & Johnson Patient Assistance Foundation, Inc. ✧
(formerly Janssen Ortho Patient Assistance Foundation, Inc.)
1 Johnson & Johnson Plz.
New Brunswick, NJ 08933-0001
Contact: Denise Sitarikev, V.P.
FAX: (888) 526-5168; E-mail: dsitarik@jnj.com; Application address: Patient Assistance Program, P.O. Box 221857, Charlotte, NC 28222-1857; Additional tel.: (866) 317-2775, (800) 652-6227; Main URL: http://www.jjpaf.org/

Established as a company-sponsored operating foundation in 1997 in NJ.
Donors: Janssen Pharmaceutica Inc.; Johnson & Johnson; Ortho Biotech Inc.; Ortho-McNeil Pharmaceutical, Inc.; Vistakon Pharmaceutical; Pricara; Ortho Womens Health & Urology; Neurogena; DePuy Mitek, Inc.; Therakos, Inc.
Foundation type: Operating foundation.
Financial data (yr. ended 12/31/12): Assets, $69,921,484 (M); gifts received, $645,062,590; expenditures, $628,527,654; qualifying distributions, $611,680,261; giving activities include $611,680,261 for 152,000 grants to individuals.
Purpose and activities: The foundation provides pharmaceutical products to needy persons who lack prescription drug coverage.
Fields of interest: Health care; Economically disadvantaged.
Type of support: Donated products.
Limitations: Applications accepted. Giving on a national basis, including U.S. territories and the Virgin Islands. No support for religious or political organizations.
Publications: Application guidelines; Informational brochure.

Application information: Application must be completed and signed, and accompanied by proof of income and a HIPAA release form signed by the patient. Applicants may receive free medicines for up to one year. Application form required.

Initial approach: Complete online eligibility quiz and fax or mail application or apply via phone
Deadline(s): None
Board meeting date(s): Third Thursday of each month
Final notification: Within 24 business hours, expedited same day approval possible if needed

Officers and Directors:* Sharon D'Agostino,* Pres.; Denise Sitarik,* V.P.; Michael McCully,* Secy.; Michael Hepburn,* Treas.; Judith Fernandez; Margaret Forrestel; Robert Inserra; Gwendolyn Miley; Greg Panico; Louise Weingrod.
Number of staff: 5 full-time professional; 1 full-time support.
EIN: 311520982

5328
Johnson Art and Education Foundation ✧
14 Fairgrounds Rd., Ste. A
Hamilton, NJ 08619-3447 (609) 689-1040
Contact: Michael Unger, C.A.O.; Craig Ingwer, Cont.

Established in 2001 in NJ.
Foundation type: Independent foundation.
Financial data (yr. ended 12/31/13): Assets, $78,000,764 (M); gifts received, $6,554,000; expenditures, $6,995,793; qualifying distributions, $21,633,636; giving activities include $2,426,000 for 4 grants (high: $1,900,000; low: $25,000).
Purpose and activities: The foundation was created in 2001 to make grants to charitable organizations to further the charitable interests of its founder, J. Seward Johnson, Jr. Currently the strategic focus of support is for organizations that promote greater public appreciation and knowledge of the arts and culture. Priority is given to support for The Sculpture Foundation, Inc. and Grounds For Sculpture, Inc. The foundation operates by making grants to charitable organizations, and by owning, developing and maintaining property for the benefit of Grounds For Sculpture, a public charity, for its exempt purpose.
Fields of interest: Arts, management/technical assistance; Arts, formal/general education.
Type of support: General/operating support; Income development; Building/renovation; Equipment; Program development; Matching/challenge support.
Limitations: Applications not accepted. Giving primarily in NY and NJ. No grants to individuals.
Application information: Contributes only to pre-selected organizations.

Board meeting date(s): May and Nov.

Officers and Trustees:* J. Seward Johnson, Jr.,* Chair.; J.S. Johnson III,* Vice-Chair.; Michael H. Greenleaf,* Treas.; Lakshman Achuthan; Robert Campbell; Garrett M. Heher; Charles Jefford; Carrie Rossip Malcolm.
Number of staff: 3 full-time professional; 4 full-time support.
EIN: 223808507
Selected grants: The following grants are a representative sample of this grantmaker's funding activity:
$3,000,600 to Atlantic Foundation, Hamilton, NJ, 2011. For temporarily restricted fund.
$3,000,000 to Sculpture Foundation, Hamilton, NJ, 2011. For general operating support.
$2,106,000 to Grounds for Sculpture, Hamilton, NJ, 2012. For general operating support.
$1,789,990 to Grounds for Sculpture, Hamilton, NJ, 2011. For general operating support and capacity building.
$1,000,000 to Sculpture Foundation, Hamilton, NJ, 2012. For general operating support.
$502,000 to Eyebeam Atelier, New York, NY, 2011. For general operating support.
$380,000 to Eyebeam Atelier, New York, NY, 2012. For general operating support.
$60,000 to International Sculpture Center, Hamilton, NJ, 2011. For general operating support.
$50,000 to International Sculpture Center, Hamilton, NJ, 2012. For general operating support.
$10,000 to Art Education for the Blind, New York, NY, 2011. For program support.

5329
The Robert Wood Johnson Foundation
College Rd. E. and Rte. 1
P.O. Box 2316
Princeton, NJ 08543-2316 (877) 843-7953
E-mail: mail@rwjf.org; Main URL: http://www.rwjf.org
Culture of Health Blog: http://www.rwjf.org/en/blogs/culture-of-health.html
David C. Colby, V.P., Research & Evaluation on Twitter: https://twitter.com/DavidCColby
Facebook: http://www.facebook.com/RobertWoodJohnsonFoundation
Flickr: http://www.flickr.com/photos/rwjf
GiveSmart: http://www.givesmart.org/Stories/Donors/Risa-Lavizzo-Mourey
Grants Database: http://www.rwjf.org/en/grants.html#q/maptype/grants/ll/37.91,-96.38/z/4
Human Capital Blog: http://blog.rwjf.org/humancapital/
Knowledge Center: http://www.rwjf.org/pr
NewPublicHealth Blog: http://blog.rwjf.org/publichealth/
Pioneering Ideas Blog: http://www.rwjf.org/en/blogs/pioneering-ideas.html
Risa Lavizzo-Mourey, C.E.O. and Pres. on Twitter: https://twitter.com/risalavizzo
Robert Wood Johnson Foundation's Philanthropy Promise: http://www.ncrp.org/philanthropys-promise/who
RSS Directory: http://www.rwjf.org/global/rss.jsp
The Robert Wood Johnson Foundation Staff: https://twitter.com/RWJF/rwjf-staff-4
Twitter: http://www.twitter.com/rwjf
Twitter: http://twitter.com/RWJF
YouTube: http://youtube.com/rwjfvideo

Incorporated in 1936 in NJ; became a national philanthropy in 1972.
Donor: Robert Wood Johnson‡.
Foundation type: Independent foundation.
Financial data (yr. ended 12/31/13): Assets, $10,173,403,442 (M); gifts received, $1,418; expenditures, $519,562,775; qualifying distributions, $447,151,675; giving activities include $337,561,658 for 2,839 grants (high: $7,029,911; low: $125), $47,387,717 for foundation-administered programs and $7,603,787 for 4 loans/program-related investments (high: $4,545,454; low: $375,000).
Purpose and activities: The foundation's mission is to improve the health and health care of all Americans. Its efforts focus on fostering environments that promote health and on improving how health care in America is delivered and paid for, and how well it does for patients and their families.
Fields of interest: Child development, education; Medical school/education; Hospitals (general); Public health; Public health, obesity; Public health, physical fitness; Public health, environmental health; Health care, insurance; Health care, cost containment; Palliative care; Nursing care; Health care; Substance abuse, services; Mental health, smoking; Mental health, disorders; Mental health/crisis services; Crime/violence prevention; Children/youth, services; Child development, services; Family services; Aging, centers/services; Homeless, human services; Voluntarism promotion; Leadership development; Children/youth; Aging; Disabilities, people with; Minorities; Native Americans/American Indians; Homeless.
Type of support: Employee matching gifts; Matching/challenge support; Program development; Program evaluation; Program-related investments/loans; Research; Seed money; Technical assistance.
Limitations: Applications accepted. Giving primarily in the U.S. No support for political organizations, international activities, programs or institutions concerned solely with specific chronic conditions or basic biomedical research. No grants to individuals, or for ongoing general operating expenses, endowment funds, capital costs, including construction, renovation, or equipment, or research on unapproved drug therapies or devices, end-of-life care, long-term care or for physical activity for adults age 50 or older.
Publications: Application guidelines; Annual report (including application guidelines); Financial statement; Grants list.
Application information: The foundation awards most grants through calls for proposals connected with its areas of focus. It accepts unsolicited proposals for projects that suggest new and creative approaches to solving health and health care problems. RWJF will continue to accept unsolicited proposals for the Pioneer Portfolio. Pioneer welcomes proposals for unsolicited grants at any time and issues awards throughout the year. There are no deadlines. Check web site for Open Calls for Proposals. Application form required.

Initial approach: Electronic brief proposal
Deadline(s): None
Board meeting date(s): Quarterly
Final notification: 6 to 12 months

Officers and Trustees:* Roger S. Fine,* Chair.; Risa Lavizzo-Mourey, M.D.*, C.E.O. and Pres.; Robin E. Mockenhaupt, Chief of Staff; James S. Marks, Exec. V.P.; John R. Lumpkin, M.D., Sr. V.P. and Dir., Health Care Group; David C. Colby, Ph.D., V.P., Research and Evaluation; Katherine Hatton, V.P., Secy., and Genl. Counsel; Charles "Robin" Hogen, V.P., Communications; David L. Waldman, V.P., Human Resources and Admin.; Albert O. Shar, Ph.D., V.P., Inf. Tech.; Brian S. O'Neil, C.I.O.; Peggi Einhorn, C.F.O. and Treas.; William Roell, Cont.; Linda Burnes Bolton; Allan S. Bufferd; Brenda S. Davis; Charles D. Ellis, Ph.D., M.B.A; William H. Frist, M.D.; Kathryn S. Fuller; Patricia A. Gabow, M.D.; Thomas M. Gorrie, Ph.D; Joann Heffernan Heisen; Jeffrey P. Koplan; Ralph S. Larsen; Robert Litterman; Willard D. Nielsen; Peter R. Orszag; A. Eugene Washington, M.D., M.Sc.; Phyllis M. Wise.
Number of staff: 134 full-time professional; 8 part-time professional; 86 full-time support; 3 part-time support.
EIN: 226029397

Selected grants: The following grants are a representative sample of this grantmaker's funding activity:
$12,500,000 to Rutgers, The State University of New Jersey, New Brunswick, NJ, 2013. To help facilitate Rutgers University-University of Medicine and Dentistry of New Jersey integration currently under way, payable over 2.00 years.
$10,458,985 to George Washington University, Washington, DC, 2013. For technical assistance and direction for Robert Wood Johnson Foundation's Aligning Forces for Quality: Regional Market Project, national program designed to help communities across the country improve the quality of health care for patients with chronic conditions such as diabetes, asthma, depression and heart disease.
$10,000,000 to Enroll America, Washington, DC, 2013. To match contributions to Enroll America in order to build the organization's capacity to enroll uninsured Americans in new coverage options under the Affordable Care Act (ACA).
$9,607,858 to American Heart Association, Dallas, TX, 2013. To build and support infrastructure that will advance policies to address root causes of the childhood obesity epidemic, payable over 1.25 years.
$7,360,551 to Pennsylvania State University, Office of Health Policy and Administration, University Park, PA, 2013. To provide grants and technical assistance to community coalitions to work toward high-quality, patient-centered and equitable care as part of evaluation of Aligning Forces for Quality: Regional Market Project, national program designed to help communities across the country improve the quality of health care for patients with chronic conditions such as diabetes, asthma, depression and heart disease, payable over 3.50 years.
$1,650,000 to New Teacher Center, Santa Cruz, CA, 2013. To embed more content on social and emotional learning in NTC's curricula, payable over 2.00 years.
$999,790 to Association of American Medical Colleges, Washington, DC, 2013. For technical assistance and direction for Robert Wood Johnson's Summer Medical and Dental Education Program, six-week academic enrichment program for undergraduate college students from minority groups, rural areas and economically disadvantaged backgrounds who are interested in pursuing careers in medicine or dentistry focusing on African-American, Hispanic/Latino and Native American students.
$500,000 to Community Coalition for Substance Abuse Prevention and Treatment, Los Angeles, CA, 2013. To expand community-driven solutions to the dropout crisis and school-to-prison pipeline affecting young males of color in South Los Angeles. To replicate at Dorsey High a set of interventions that have been effective at helping students of color succeed in Fremont schools, including: comprehensive mental wellness programming, career academy, and dropout prevention program. Invest in Community Coalition's community-driven school reform model, which is rooted in the concepts of youth leadership, parent engagement, and cross-sector collaborations. Also, support evaluation efforts to assess health, social, and education program outcomes for young men of color.
$315,000 to University of Washington, Seattle, WA, 2013. For Summer Medical and Dental Education Program, six-week academic enrichment program for undergraduate college students from minority groups, rural areas and economically disadvantaged backgrounds who are interested in pursuing careers in medicine or dentistry focusing on African-American, Hispanic/Latino and Native American students.
$199,007 to Loyola Marymount University, Los Angeles, CA, 2013. To build state and national momentum to reverse the epidemic of childhood obesity through strategic investment in those communities most affected.

5330
The Kaplen Foundation ✧
c/o Margaret R. Kaplen
P.O. Box 792
Tenafly, NJ 07670-0792 (201) 227-0722

Established about 1963.
Donor: Wilson R. Kaplen.
Foundation type: Independent foundation.
Financial data (yr. ended 07/31/13): Assets, $49,761,714 (M); expenditures, $6,766,801; qualifying distributions, $6,175,835; giving activities include $5,829,020 for 112 grants (high: $678,650; low: $50).
Purpose and activities: Giving primarily for hospitals and health associations and cultural organizations, including the performing arts.
Fields of interest: Higher education; Education; Hospitals (general); Health organizations, association; Human services; Jewish agencies & synagogues.
Limitations: Applications not accepted. Giving primarily in NJ and NY. No grants to individuals.
Application information: Contributes only to pre-selected organizations.
Board meeting date(s): Quarterly
Officers and Trustees:* Wilson R. Kaplan,* Pres.; Margaret R. Kaplen,* Mgr.; Alexander Kaplen; Lawrence Kaplen; Andrew V. Schnurr, Jr.; Nancy Sutherland.
Number of staff: 1 part-time support.
EIN: 226048152
Selected grants: The following grants are a representative sample of this grantmaker's funding activity:
$1,028,000 to Jewish Community Center on the Palisades, Tenafly, NJ, 2012.
$948,400 to Englewood Hospital and Medical Center Foundation, Englewood, NJ, 2012.
$535,000 to W N Y C Foundation, New York, NY, 2012.
$410,000 to PEN American Center, New York, NY, 2012.
$370,000 to Philharmonic-Symphony Society of New York, New York, NY, 2012.
$300,000 to Roundabout Theater Company, New York, NY, 2012.
$230,000 to Play Company, New York, NY, 2012.
$212,500 to Seton Hall University, South Orange, NJ, 2012.
$101,000 to Jewish Home at Rockleigh, Rockleigh, NJ, 2012.
$50,100 to Arnold P. Gold Foundation, Englewood Cliffs, NJ, 2012.

5331
Karma Foundation ✧
140 Arreton Rd.
Princeton, NJ 08540-1429 (609) 924-5939
Contact: Dina Karmazin Elkins, Exec. Dir.
FAX: (609) 924-2714;
E-mail: info@karmafoundation.org; Main URL: http://www.karmafoundation.org/

Established in 1996 in NJ.
Donors: Sharon Karmazin; Sharon Karmazin Trust; Sharon Karmazin Charitable Lead Annuity Trust.
Foundation type: Independent foundation.
Financial data (yr. ended 12/31/12): Assets, $7,023,492 (M); gifts received, $148,346; expenditures, $1,301,576; qualifying distributions, $1,205,432; giving activities include $1,085,262 for 135+ grants (high: $62,750).
Purpose and activities: Giving primarily for arts and culture, health and human services, autism, education, literacy, public libraries in NJ, and the enrichment of Jewish life.
Fields of interest: Arts; Education; Health care; Autism; Human services; Jewish agencies & synagogues; Children; Youth; Disabilities, people with; Mentally disabled; Economically disadvantaged; Homeless.
Type of support: General/operating support; Annual campaigns; Capital campaigns; Building/renovation; Equipment; Emergency funds; Program development; Seed money; Scholarship funds; Research; Technical assistance; Program evaluation.
Limitations: Giving primarily in NJ, with emphasis on Middlesex and Union counties; funding also in Mercer and Somerset counties. No support for charter schools, political candidates or lobbying activity. No grants to individuals, or for travel expenses, advertising, fundraising or litigation; no loans.
Publications: Application guidelines.
Application information: Full proposals are by invitation only, upon review of Letter of Inquiry. See foundation web site for specific application instructions. Application form not required.
Initial approach: Use Letter of Inquiry form on foundation web site. The foundation suggests applicant telephone to discuss project before letter is sent
Deadline(s): None
Board meeting date(s): Monthly
Final notification: Between 2-4 weeks for letters of inquiry
Officers: Sharon Karmazin, Pres.; Craig Karmazin, Secy.; Dina Karmazin Elkins, Treas. and Exec. Dir.
Number of staff: 1 full-time professional.
EIN: 223478433

5332
Katz Foundation ✧
c/o Drew Katz
905 N. Kings Hwy.
Cherry Hill, NJ 08034-1514

Established in 1994 in NJ.
Donors: Lewis Katz†; Drew Katz; Melissa Silver; Elkay Holdings, LP.
Foundation type: Independent foundation.
Financial data (yr. ended 12/31/13): Assets, $198,296 (M); gifts received, $5,000; expenditures, $530,421; qualifying distributions, $525,736; giving activities include $525,736 for 21 grants (high: $250,000; low: $1,650).
Purpose and activities: Giving primarily for higher and other education, health organizations, children, youth, and social services.
Fields of interest: Higher education; Education; Health organizations, association; Boys & girls

clubs; Human services; Children/youth, services; Jewish agencies & synagogues.
Limitations: Applications not accepted. Giving primarily in NJ, NY, and PA; some funding nationally. No grants to individuals.
Application information: Contributes only to pre-selected organizations.
Director: Lewis Katz.
EIN: 223336393

5333
M. D. Katz Foundation, Inc. ✧
300 E. Linden Ave.
Englewood, NJ 07631-3719

Established in 1960 in NY.
Donors: Monique C. Katz; Mordecai D. Katz; Michael D. Katz.
Foundation type: Independent foundation.
Financial data (yr. ended 07/31/13): Assets, $60,693,043 (M); gifts received, $90,000; expenditures, $2,535,860; qualifying distributions, $2,409,682; giving activities include $2,143,829 for 58 grants (high: $1,003,980; low: $5).
Purpose and activities: Support for higher education and Jewish organizations, including welfare funds, religious associations, and yeshivas.
Fields of interest: Elementary/secondary education; Higher education; Human services; Jewish federated giving programs; Jewish agencies & synagogues.
Limitations: Applications not accepted. Giving primarily in NJ and NY. No grants to individuals.
Application information: Contributes only to pre-selected organizations.
Officers: Mordecai D. Katz, Pres. and Treas.; Monique C. Katz, V.P. and Secy.; Michael D. Katz, V.P.
EIN: 116035541
Selected grants: The following grants are a representative sample of this grantmaker's funding activity:
$180 to Otsar Family Services, Brooklyn, NY, 2013. For 3. Contributions to Public Charitable Institutions for general purposes.
$36 to Massachusetts Institute of Technology, Cambridge, MA, 2013. For 1. Contributions to Public Educational Institutions for general purposes.

5334
The Fritz and Adelaide Kauffmann Foundation Inc. ✧
6 Oxford Pl.
Cresskill, NJ 07626-1625 (212) 269-8628
Contact: Bernard Turner, Treas.

Established in 1999 in NJ.
Donors: Fritz Kauffman†; Adelaide Kauffman†.
Foundation type: Independent foundation.
Financial data (yr. ended 06/30/13): Assets, $9,908,856 (M); expenditures, $1,448,524; qualifying distributions, $1,345,000; giving activities include $1,345,000 for 49 grants (high: $280,000; low: $5,000).
Purpose and activities: Giving primarily to hospitals and for medical research.
Fields of interest: Higher education; Hospitals (general); Hospitals (specialty); Health organizations, association; Cancer research; Human services; Children/youth, services; Jewish federated giving programs.
Limitations: Applications accepted. Giving primarily in NJ and NY. No grants to individuals.
Application information: Application form required.
Initial approach: Letter
Deadline(s): None
Officers: Elliot M. Hershberg, Pres.; Theodore N. Mirvis, Secy.; Bernard Turner, Treas.
EIN: 223689518
Selected grants: The following grants are a representative sample of this grantmaker's funding activity:
$50,000 to Partnership for Public Service, Washington, DC, 2011.
$25,000 to Hole in the Wall Gang Fund, New Haven, CT, 2011.
$20,000 to Greenwich Hospital, Greenwich, CT, 2011.
$15,000 to Hole in the Wall Gang Fund, New Haven, CT, 2011.
$10,000 to Columbia University, New York, NY, 2011.
$10,000 to Hole in the Wall Gang Fund, New Haven, CT, 2011.
$10,000 to Jerusalem Foundation, New York, NY, 2011.
$10,000 to Johns Hopkins University, Baltimore, MD, 2011.
$10,000 to Mount Sinai Hospital, New York, NY, 2011.
$10,000 to United States Holocaust Memorial Museum, Washington, DC, 2011.

5335
Brian & Joelle Kelly Family Foundation ✧
225 Hwy. 35, Ste. 102C
Red Bank, NJ 07701-5933

Established in 2007 in NJ.
Donors: Brian G. Kelly; Joelle S. Kelly.
Foundation type: Independent foundation.
Financial data (yr. ended 12/31/13): Assets, $26,100,621 (M); gifts received, $4,000,000; expenditures, $1,122,018; qualifying distributions, $1,092,522; giving activities include $1,047,335 for 61 grants (high: $50,500; low: $10).
Fields of interest: Education; Diabetes; Human services; Catholic agencies & churches.
Limitations: Applications not accepted. Giving primarily in New York, NY.
Application information: Unsolicited requests for funds not accepted.
Trustees: Brian G. Kelly; Joelle S. Kelly.
EIN: 266139249
Selected grants: The following grants are a representative sample of this grantmaker's funding activity:
$485,000 to Juvenile Diabetes Research Foundation International, New York, NY, 2011.
$100,000 to Marymount School, New York, NY, 2011.

5336
The Kemmerer Family Foundation, Inc. ✧
323 Main St.
Chatham, NJ 07928-2229

Established in 2000 in DE.
Foundation type: Independent foundation.
Financial data (yr. ended 12/31/13): Assets, $46,826,728 (M); expenditures, $2,242,710; qualifying distributions, $2,145,000; giving activities include $2,125,000 for 33 grants (high: $500,000; low: $10,000).
Fields of interest: Education; Environment, natural resources; Human services; Children/youth, services; Foundations (community).
Limitations: Applications not accepted. Giving in the U.S., with emphasis on ID, NJ and WY. No grants to individuals.
Application information: Contributes only to pre-selected organizations.
Officers: John L. Kemmerer III, Pres.; Peter F. Nejes, Secy.-Treas.
EIN: 223706044
Selected grants: The following grants are a representative sample of this grantmaker's funding activity:
$200,000 to Grand Teton National Park Foundation, Jackson, WY, 2011.
$100,000 to Community Foundation of Jackson Hole, Jackson, WY, 2011.
$100,000 to Kemmerer Library Harding Township, New Vernon, NJ, 2011.

5337
Quentin J. Kennedy Foundation Inc. ✧
22 Old Smith Rd.
Tenafly, NJ 07670-2227

Established in 1986 in NJ.
Donor: Quentin J. Kennedy.
Foundation type: Independent foundation.
Financial data (yr. ended 12/31/13): Assets, $14,811,310 (M); expenditures, $679,176; qualifying distributions, $530,225; giving activities include $530,225 for 38 grants (high: $60,000; low: $1,000).
Purpose and activities: Giving primarily for higher education and human services; funding also for a medical center.
Fields of interest: Higher education; Hospitals (general); Human services.
Limitations: Applications not accepted. Giving primarily in NJ and NY. No grants to individuals.
Application information: Contributes only to pre-selected organizations.
Officers: Quentin J. Kennedy, Pres. and Treas.; Mary E. Kennedy, V.P.; Quentin J. Kennedy, Jr., Secy.
EIN: 222653050

5338
The William A. Kerr Foundation ✧
P.O. Box 1501, NJ2-130-03-31
Pennington, NJ 08534-1501

Established in 1998 in WA.
Foundation type: Independent foundation.
Financial data (yr. ended 12/31/13): Assets, $17,971,660 (M); expenditures, $721,983; qualifying distributions, $656,926; giving activities include $480,000 for 51 grants (high: $50,000; low: $550).
Purpose and activities: Support primarily for the arts, education, and to Jewish synagogues.
Fields of interest: Museums (specialized); Arts; Higher education; Environment, natural resources; Foundations (community); Jewish agencies & synagogues.
Type of support: General/operating support.
Limitations: Applications not accepted. Giving primarily in Walnut Creek, CA, and St. Louis, MO. No grants to individuals.

Application information: Contributes only to pre-selected organizations.
Trustees: John H.K. Sweet; William R. Sweet.
EIN: 431770857

5339
F. M. Kirby Foundation, Inc. ✧
17 DeHart St.
P.O. Box 151
Morristown, NJ 07963-0151 (973) 538-4800
Contact: For application procedure questions: William H. Byrnes, Jr., V.P., Grants
FAX: (973) 538-4801; Main URL: http://fdnweb.org/kirby

Incorporated in 1931 in DE.
Donors: F.M. Kirby†; Allan P. Kirby, Sr.†; F.M. Kirby II†.
Foundation type: Independent foundation.
Financial data (yr. ended 12/31/13): Assets, $441,611,886 (M); expenditures, $23,639,874; qualifying distributions, $20,913,526; giving activities include $20,404,834 for 262 grants (high: $1,050,000; low: $2,000).
Purpose and activities: Support for community programs, the arts, historic preservation, social services, conservation, public policy and education organizations, and family planning. Grants are generally limited to organizations associated with the personal interests of present or former family members. Requests to support churches, hospitals, schools and colleges, other than ones attended by or used by members of the family, are not likely to receive favorable consideration.
Fields of interest: Performing arts; Historic preservation/historical societies; Arts; Environment, natural resources; Biomedicine; Medical research, institute; Cancer research; AIDS research; Recreation; Youth development, services; Youth, services; Economics; Public policy, research; Government/public administration; Leadership development; Children/youth; Youth; Aging; Deaf/hearing impaired; Military/veterans; Offenders/ex-offenders; Substance abusers; AIDS, people with; Economically disadvantaged.
Type of support: General/operating support; Continuing support; Annual campaigns; Capital campaigns; Building/renovation; Equipment; Land acquisition; Endowments; Emergency funds; Program development; Conferences/seminars; Research.
Limitations: Applications accepted. Giving primarily in the Raleigh/Durham, NC, area, the Morris County, NJ, area, and eastern PA. Generally no support for churches, hospitals, schools and colleges, other than ones attended by or used by members of the family. No grants to individuals, or for fundraising benefits, dinners, theater, or sporting events; no loans or pledges.
Publications: Informational brochure (including application guidelines).
Application information: Solicitations for grants must contain certain basic information about the applicant, be signed by an official of the applicant and be addressed to the F. M. Kirby Foundation. Unsolicited requests should be in the form of a letter of inquiry. No solicitations by telephone, fax or E-mail are accepted. Application form not required.
Initial approach: Letter of inquiry after checking solicitation guidelines
Copies of proposal: 1
Deadline(s): Proposals received throughout the year; requests received after Oct. 31 are held over to the following year
Board meeting date(s): Three times per year
Final notification: Monthly for positive responses and declinations
Officers and Directors:* S. Dillard Kirby,* Pres. and Dir.; William H. Byrnes, Jr., V.P., Grants; Jefferson W. Kirby,* V.P. and Dir.; Frank N. Barra, Secy.-Treas.; Alice Kirby Horton, Asst. Secy. and Dir.; Wilson M. Compton, M.D. M.P.E., Dir.; Walker D. Kirby, Dir.; Sandra Brown Sherman, Dir.; Laura H. Virkler, Dir.
Number of staff: 6 full-time support.
EIN: 516017929
Selected grants: The following grants are a representative sample of this grantmaker's funding activity:
$850,000 to Wyoming Seminary, Kingston, PA, 2012. Toward the creation and construction of the Allan P. and Marian Sutherland Kirby Center for Creative Arts plus part of $6,000,000 payable between 2010 and 2014.
$770,000 to Lawrenceville School, Lawrenceville, NJ, 2012. For the Kirby Science Center Endowment Fund- $250,000; for Kirby House Endowment Fund- $150,000; toward Kirby Reserved for Future Decisions Fund- $350,000; Class of '38- $20,000.
$637,500 to American Red Cross National Headquarters, Washington, DC, 2012. For National Headquarters -$500,000; Northern New Jersey Chapter- $90,000; for Colonial Crossroads Chapter- $22,500; and Wyoming Valley Chapter $25,000.
$530,000 to Duke University, Fuqua School of Business, Durham, NC, 2012. For Annual Fund-$30,000 and Reserved for Future Decision Fund-$500,000.
$500,000 to Wake Forest University, Winston-Salem, NC, 2012. To name and endow the FM Kirby Foundation Chair of Leadership Development within the Office of Personal and Career Development (OPCD).
$422,500 to Alzheimers Association National Headquarters, Chicago, IL, 2012. For Alzheimer's basic science research through the National Office- $400,000 and for Northern Jersey programs through the Greater New Jersey Chapter- $22,500.
$400,000 to Memorial Sloan-Kettering Cancer Center, New York, NY, 2012. Toward renewed support of the F.M. Kirby Foundation Brain Tumor Research Fund.
$350,000 to Planned Parenthood of Greater Northern New Jersey, Morristown, NJ, 2012. For Central and Greater Northern New Jersey affiliate- $110,000; Central North Carolina Affiliate- $40,000; Northeast and Mid-Penn affiliate- $30,000; Federation of America- $150,000; NexGen Software- $20,000.
$125,000 to Foundation for AIDS Research, AMFAR AIDS Research Foundation, New York, NY, 2012. For Krim Fellows Program.
$25,000 to Cooper-Hewitt Museum, The Smithsonians National Museum of Design, New York, NY, 2012. For general operating support.

5340
A. P. Kirby, Jr. Foundation Inc. ✧
14 E. Main St.
P.O. Box 90
Mendham, NJ 07945-1505

Established in 1988 in NJ.
Donors: Allan P. Kirby, Jr.; Allan Kirby 2010 Trust.
Foundation type: Independent foundation.
Financial data (yr. ended 12/31/13): Assets, $17,850,106 (M); gifts received, $18,971; expenditures, $2,322,533; qualifying distributions, $2,243,258; giving activities include $2,240,000 for 85 grants (high: $275,000; low: $1,000).
Purpose and activities: Giving primarily to support public policy, free enterprise, entrepreneurship, historical preservation, medical research, and education.
Fields of interest: Historical activities; Arts; Libraries (public); Education; Medical research, institute; Human services; United Ways and Federated Giving Programs; Public affairs.
Limitations: Applications not accepted. Giving primarily in NJ and PA; funding also in Washington, DC, and VA. No grants to individuals.
Application information: Contributes only to pre-selected organizations.
Officers: Allan P. Kirby, Jr., Chair.; Milan S. Kirby, Pres.; Coray S. Kirby, Secy.; Slater B. Kirby, Treas.
Trustee: Carl O. Helstrom.
EIN: 222922817

5341
John C. Kish Foundation ✧
(also known as Kish Foundation)
c/o Merrill Lynch Bank & Trust Co.
P.O. Box 1501, NJ2-130-03-31
Pennington, NJ 08534-0671

Donors: John C. Kish; Joan Kish.
Foundation type: Independent foundation.
Financial data (yr. ended 11/30/13): Assets, $33,078,065 (M); gifts received, $3,206,233; expenditures, $1,273,237; qualifying distributions, $1,212,721; giving activities include $1,091,091 for 47 grants (high: $238,697; low: $1,000).
Fields of interest: Education; Animal welfare; Health organizations; Boys & girls clubs; Human services; Christian agencies & churches; Protestant agencies & churches.
Limitations: Applications not accepted. Giving primarily in Henderson and Las Vegas, NV, and Washington, DC. No grants to individuals.
Application information: Contributes only to pre-selected organizations.
Principals: H. Matthew Frazier; Joan Kish; Frank Plevo.
EIN: 731688377
Selected grants: The following grants are a representative sample of this grantmaker's funding activity:
$210,000 to Human Rights Campaign, Washington, DC, 2011.
$96,744 to University of Nevada at Las Vegas Foundation, Las Vegas, NV, 2011.
$79,000 to Animal Foundation, Las Vegas, NV, 2011.
$17,500 to Saint Rose Dominican Hospital, Henderson, NV, 2011.
$15,000 to Bishop Gorman High School, Las Vegas, NV, 2011.
$11,500 to Golden Rainbow, Las Vegas, NV, 2011.
$10,000 to Adopt-A-Native Elder, Park City, UT, 2011.
$5,000 to Humane Society, Nevada, Reno, NV, 2011.
$2,000 to Spread the Word Nevada, Henderson, NV, 2011.

5342
The Charles and Lynne Klatskin Family Charitable Trust ✧ ☆
400 Hollister Rd.
Teterboro, NJ 07608-1147

Established in NJ.
Donor: Charles Klatskin.
Foundation type: Independent foundation.
Financial data (yr. ended 06/30/13): Assets, $1,839,290 (M); gifts received, $250,000; expenditures, $1,166,752; qualifying distributions, $1,164,532; giving activities include $1,164,532 for 26 grants (high: $900,000; low: $250).
Fields of interest: Education; Human services; Jewish agencies & synagogues.
Limitations: Applications not accepted. Giving primarily in NJ and NY. No grants to individuals.
Application information: Unsolicited requests for funds not accepted.
Trustees: Charles Klatskin; Deborah Klatskin; Lynne Klatskin; Samuel Klatskin.
EIN: 226831861

5343
Thomas D. Klingenstein Fund ✧
c/o E. M. Davidoff
P.O. Box 835
Dayton, NJ 08810-0835

Established in 2004 in NJ.
Donors: Thomas D. Klingenstein; John Klingenstein.
Foundation type: Independent foundation.
Financial data (yr. ended 12/31/12): Assets, $25,242,544 (M); expenditures, $1,145,340; qualifying distributions, $1,079,660; giving activities include $1,079,660 for 26 grants (high: $500,000; low: $1,000).
Fields of interest: Higher education; Education; Environment, water resources; Human services; Public policy, research.
Limitations: Applications not accepted. Giving primarily in CA, ME, NY and PA. No grants to individuals.
Application information: Contributes only to pre-selected organizations.
Officers: Thomas D. Klingenstein, Pres. and Treas.; Andrew D. Klingenstein, Secy.
EIN: 201450695

5344
The Knowles Charitable Foundation a New Jersey Nonprofit Corporation ✧
425 E. Linden St.
Moorestown, NJ 08057-3017

Established in NJ.
Donor: C. Harry Knowles.
Foundation type: Independent foundation.
Financial data (yr. ended 12/31/13): Assets, $793,356 (M); expenditures, $2,704,863; qualifying distributions, $2,702,871; giving activities include $2,700,794 for 3 grants (high: $1,500,000; low: $2,500).
Fields of interest: Education; Foundations (private grantmaking).
Limitations: Applications not accepted. Giving primarily in NJ.
Application information: Contributes only to pre-selected organizations.
Trustees: C. Harry Knowles; Janet H. Knowles.
EIN: 205446261

5345
Janet H. and C. Harry Knowles Foundation, Inc. ✧
(also known as Knowles Science Teaching Foundation (KSTF))
1000 N. Church St.
Moorestown, NJ 08057-1764 (856) 608-0001
FAX: (856) 608-0008; E-mail: info@kstf.org; Main URL: http://www.kstf.org
Facebook: http://www.facebook.com/KnowlesScienceTeachingFoundation
Twitter: http://twitter.com/TheKSTF

Established in NJ in 1999.
Donors: Janet H. Knowles; C. Harry Knowles; Paul Kuerbis.
Foundation type: Operating foundation.
Financial data (yr. ended 05/31/13): Assets, $70,321,523 (M); gifts received, $1,171,391; expenditures, $6,892,284; qualifying distributions, $6,716,167; giving activities include $161,013 for 16 grants (high: $24,000; low: $75), and $1,146,849 for grants to individuals.
Purpose and activities: Giving to increase the number of high quality high school science and mathematics teachers in the United States, and to raise the status of the teaching profession.
Fields of interest: Secondary school/education; Higher education; Teacher school/education; Education; Science; Mathematics; Young adults.
Type of support: Continuing support; Conferences/seminars; Fellowships; Research; Grants to individuals; Scholarships—to individuals.
Limitations: Applications not accepted. Giving limited to the U.S. No support for religious or political organizations, schools or school districts, or university programs. No grants for second career or advanced degrees in any discipline other than education.
Publications: Annual report; Informational brochure; Occasional report.
Application information: Unsolicited requests for funds not accepted.
Board meeting date(s): Three times a year
Officers and Trustees:* C. Harry Knowles,* Chair.; Edward Viner, M.D.*, Vice-Chair.; William Rulon-Miller,* Pres. and Treas.; Janet H. Knowles,* Secy.; Dr. Nicole Gillespie,* Exec. Dir.; Paul Kuerbis, Ph.D.; Scott McVay; Lawrence Tint; Dr. Suzanne M. Wilson.
Number of staff: 9 full-time professional; 1 part-time professional; 5 full-time support; 1 part-time support.
EIN: 010485964

5346
The Leo Koguan Foundation ✧
c/o SHI International Corp.
290 Davidson Ave.
Somerset, NJ 08873-4145

Established in 2002 in NJ.
Donor: Leo Koguan.
Foundation type: Independent foundation.
Financial data (yr. ended 12/31/13): Assets, $1,932,471 (M); gifts received, $4,000,000; expenditures, $4,870,591; qualifying distributions, $4,869,236; giving activities include $4,868,456 for 5 grants (high: $1,747,530; low: $25,000).
Fields of interest: Arts, cultural/ethnic awareness; Higher education, university.
Limitations: Applications not accepted. Giving primarily in CA, CT, and FL. No grants to individuals.
Application information: Contributes only to pre-selected organizations.
Trustees: Leo Koguan; Fred Teng.
EIN: 320065960
Selected grants: The following grants are a representative sample of this grantmaker's funding activity:
$2,328,000 to Chiao Tung University Alumni Foundation of America, Fort Myers, FL, 2012. For unrestricted support.
$1,396,537 to Tsinghua Education Foundation North America, West Covina, CA, 2012. For unrestricted support.
$1,250,000 to Fudan University Education Development Foundation, New Haven, CT, 2012. For unrestricted support.
$1,107,167 to Peking University Education Foundation USA, Millbrae, CA, 2012. For unrestricted support.

5347
Kolatch Family Foundation ✧
910 Sylvan Ave., Ste. 130
Englewood Cliffs, NJ 07632-3306

Established in 1996 in NJ.
Donor: Jonathan L. Kolatch.
Foundation type: Independent foundation.
Financial data (yr. ended 10/31/13): Assets, $30,419,983 (M); gifts received, $11,164,757; expenditures, $558,139; qualifying distributions, $525,639; giving activities include $519,843 for 41 grants (high: $250,000; low: $100).
Fields of interest: Education; Human services; Jewish agencies & synagogues.
Limitations: Applications not accepted. Giving primarily in MA, NJ, NY, and Washington, D.C. No grants to individuals.
Application information: Unsolicited requests for funds not accepted.
Trustees: Jonathan L. Kolatch; Mindy S. Kolatch.
EIN: 133918276
Selected grants: The following grants are a representative sample of this grantmaker's funding activity:
$250,000 to New York University, New York, NY, 2011.
$100,000 to New York University, New York, NY, 2011.
$100,000 to Ramaz School, New York, NY, 2011.
$50,000 to Chabad Serving NYU, New York, NY, 2011.
$40,000 to East Hill Synagogue, Englewood, NJ, 2011.
$36,000 to Jewish Federation of Northern New Jersey, Paramus, NJ, 2011.
$25,000 to Yeshiva University, New York, NY, 2011.
$3,600 to Etzion Foundation, Teaneck, NJ, 2011.
$1,000 to Community Chest of Englewood, Englewood, NJ, 2011.
$1,000 to Yeshiva University, New York, NY, 2011.

5348
The Kovner Foundation ✧
Princeton Plz., Bldg. 2
731 Alexander Rd.
Princeton, NJ 08540-5236 (609) 919-7600

Established in 1986.
Donor: Bruce S. Kovner.
Foundation type: Independent foundation.
Financial data (yr. ended 12/31/13): Assets, $203,862,496 (M); gifts received, $73,230,810; expenditures, $11,503,664; qualifying distributions, $10,014,321; giving activities include $10,014,321 for 18 grants (high: $2,500,000; low: $50,000).
Purpose and activities: Giving primarily for education.
Fields of interest: Arts; Higher education; Education; Public policy, research.
Limitations: Applications not accepted. Giving primarily in Washington, DC New York, NY. No grants to individuals.
Application information: Contributes only to pre-selected organizations.
Officers and Directors:* Bruce S. Kovner,* Pres.; Suzanne F. Kovner, V.P.; Scott B. Bernstein, Secy.; Peter P. D'Angelo,* Treas.; Karen Cross, Cont.; Frank Wohl.
EIN: 223468030
Selected grants: The following grants are a representative sample of this grantmaker's funding activity:
$3,300,000 to American Enterprise Institute for Public Policy Research, Washington, DC, 2012.
$2,500,000 to Lincoln Center for the Performing Arts, New York, NY, 2012.
$1,000,000 to Success Charter Network, New York, NY, 2012.
$542,363 to American Associates of the Royal National Theater, New York, NY, 2012.
$500,000 to New World Symphony, Miami Beach, FL, 2012.
$400,000 to Juilliard School, New York, NY, 2012.
$390,800 to Royal Shakespeare Company, Stratford-upon-Avon, England, 2012.
$250,000 to Alliance for School Choice, Washington, DC, 2012.
$250,000 to Foundation for Excellence in Education, Tallahassee, FL, 2012.
$200,000 to Foundation for Education Reform and Accountability, Clifton Park, NY, 2012.

5349
The KPMG Foundation ✧
(formerly The KPMG Peat Marwick Foundation)
3 Chestnut Ridge Rd.
Montvale, NJ 07645-0435 (201) 307-7932
Contact: Tara Perino, Dir.
FAX: (201) 624-7763;
E-mail: us-kpmgfoundation@kpmg.com; E-mail for Tara Perino: tperino@kpmg.com; Main URL: http://www.kpmgfoundation.org
Application address for Minority Accounting Doctoral Scholarships: KPMG Foundation, Doctoral Scholarship Prog., c/o Joanne Berry

Trust established in 1968 in NY.
Donor: KPMG LLP.
Foundation type: Company-sponsored foundation.
Financial data (yr. ended 06/30/13): Assets, $4,649,348 (M); gifts received, $7,553,145; expenditures, $8,670,021; qualifying distributions, $8,657,870; giving activities include $3,480,868 for 57+ grants, $455,000 for 46 grants to individuals (high: $10,000; low: $5,000), and $4,695,777 for 492 employee matching gifts.
Purpose and activities: The foundation supports organizations involved with business education and volunteerism and awards graduate scholarships to minority doctoral accounting students.
Fields of interest: Secondary school/education; Higher education; Business school/education; Education, reading; Youth development, business; Human services, financial counseling; Business/industry; Community development, business promotion; Philanthropy/voluntarism; Minorities; African Americans/Blacks; Hispanics/Latinos; Native Americans/American Indians.
Type of support: Continuing support; Program development; Conferences/seminars; Professorships; Curriculum development; Scholarship funds; Sponsorships; Employee matching gifts; Scholarships—to individuals.
Limitations: Applications accepted. Giving primarily in CA, Washington, DC, FL, NJ, NY, and RI.
Publications: Application guidelines; Annual report; Grants list.
Application information: Unsolicited applications for general grants not accepted. Application form required.
Initial approach: Download application form and mail to foundation for scholarships
Deadline(s): May 1 for scholarships
Board meeting date(s): May
Officers and Trustees:* Jose R. Rodriguez,* Chair.; Bernard J. Milano,* Pres.; Theresa Ahlstrom; Kelli J. Brooks; Robert P. Fisher; Laurel A. Hammer; Kathy A.H. Hannan; Laura J. Hay; Tammy Y. Hunter; Paul J. Knopp; Milford W. McGuirt; Bruce N. Pfau; Rebecca P. Sproul; French Taylor.
Number of staff: 3 full-time professional; 6 full-time support.
EIN: 136262199
Selected grants: The following grants are a representative sample of this grantmaker's funding activity:
$664,000 to PhD Project, Montvale, NJ, 2013.
$500,000 to Junior Achievement, 2013.
$283,000 to Alcohol and Drug Services, High Point, NC, 2013.
$250,000 to National Abortion Federation, Washington, DC, 2013.
$69,852 to American Accounting Association, Sarasota, FL, 2013. For Association dues.
$69,625 to Beta Alpha Psi, New York, NY, 2013.
$50,000 to Diversified Search, LLC/STEM Connector, Philadelphia, PA, 2013.
$30,500 to American Accounting Association, Sarasota, FL, 2013.
$20,000 to American Accounting Association, Sarasota, FL, 2013.
$20,000 to North Carolina A & T State University, Greensboro, NC, 2013.

5350
Kresa Family Foundation ✧
P.O. Box 1501, NJ2-130-03-31
Pennington, NJ 08534-1501

Established in 2005 in NJ.
Donors: Kent Kresa; Joyce Kresa.
Foundation type: Independent foundation.
Financial data (yr. ended 12/31/12): Assets, $5,324,476 (M); expenditures, $522,119; qualifying distributions, $482,081; giving activities include $443,700 for 9 grants (high: $218,000; low: $1,000).
Fields of interest: Performing arts, orchestras; Education; Medical research; Human services; American Red Cross; Children/youth, services; United Ways and Federated Giving Programs.
Limitations: Applications not accepted. Giving primarily in CA. No grants to individuals.
Application information: Contributes only to pre-selected organizations.
Officers: Kent Kresa, Pres.; Kiren Kresa-Reahl, M.D., Secy.
EIN: 202890253
Selected grants: The following grants are a representative sample of this grantmaker's funding activity:
$50,000 to United Friends of the Children, Los Angeles, CA, 2011.
$10,000 to UCLA Foundation, Los Angeles, CA, 2011.
$5,000 to Harmony Project, Los Angeles, CA, 2011.
$5,000 to Los Angeles Master Chorale, Los Angeles, CA, 2011.

5351
Charles and Seryl Kushner Charitable Foundation ✧
18 Columbia Tpke.
Florham Park, NJ 07932-2266 (973) 822-0050

Donors: Charles Kushner; Seryl Kushner; G. Gellert.
Foundation type: Independent foundation.
Financial data (yr. ended 12/31/12): Assets, $43,103 (M); gifts received, $3,886,000; expenditures, $3,877,015; qualifying distributions, $3,875,130; giving activities include $3,875,130 for 140 grants (high: $387,500; low: $500).
Purpose and activities: Giving primarily to Jewish organizations; funding also for higher education.
Fields of interest: Elementary/secondary education; Higher education; Jewish federated giving programs; Jewish agencies & synagogues.
Limitations: Applications not accepted. Giving primarily in NJ and NY. No grants to individuals.
Application information: Contributes only to pre-selected organizations.
Officer: Mark Pasquerella, Cont.
Directors: Charles Kushner; Jared Kushner; Josh Kushner; Seryl Kushner; Nicole Meyer; Dara Orbach.
EIN: 223422337

5352
The L.A.W. Foundation, Inc. ✧
200 Central Ave.
Mountainside, NJ 07092-1926

Established in 1990 in NJ.
Donors: Leonard A. Wilf; Judith Wilf‡; Jenna Wilf Charitable Lead Trust; Judith Wilf Charitable Lead Trust; Harley Ryan Wilf Charitable Lead Trust; Harrison Wilf Charitable Lead Trust; Alex H. Wilf Charitable Lead Trust; Halle Wilf Charitable Trust; Halle Wilf Charitable Trust II.
Foundation type: Independent foundation.
Financial data (yr. ended 12/31/12): Assets, $117,250,381 (M); gifts received, $9,589,678; expenditures, $4,852,998; qualifying distributions, $4,670,500; giving activities include $4,670,500 for 62 grants (high: $500,000; low: $800).

Purpose and activities: Giving primarily for a law school and Jewish organizations; support also for the arts, education, and human services.
Fields of interest: Arts; Higher education; Law school/education; Education; Human services; Jewish federated giving programs; Jewish agencies & synagogues.
Limitations: Applications not accepted. Giving primarily in New York, NY. No grants to individuals.
Application information: Contributes only to pre-selected organizations.
Officers and Trustees:* Leonard A. Wilf,* Pres.; Orin Wilf,* V.P.; Beth Wilf,* Secy.; Zygmunt Wilf.
EIN: 223074635

5353
L.F.H. Foundation Family Trust ✧
233 Rock Rd., PMB 133
Glen Rock, NJ 07452-1708

Established in 1997 in NJ.
Donors: Patrick D. Duff; Mary Duff.
Foundation type: Independent foundation.
Financial data (yr. ended 12/31/13): Assets, $8,461,641 (M); gifts received, $203,229; expenditures, $459,700; qualifying distributions, $455,789; giving activities include $453,000 for 24 grants (high: $110,000; low: $500).
Purpose and activities: Giving primarily for education, health, human services, community development, and Roman Catholic organizations and churches.
Fields of interest: Historic preservation/historical societies; Arts; Higher education, university; Education; Health organizations, association; Cancer; Human services; Children, services; Community/economic development; United Ways and Federated Giving Programs; Catholic agencies & churches.
Limitations: Applications not accepted. Giving primarily in NJ and New York, NY. No grants to individuals.
Application information: Contributes only to pre-selected organizations.
Trustees: Mary Duff; Patrick D. Duff.
EIN: 226727578

5354
Lackner Family Foundation ✧ ☆
2107 Aqueduct Ln.
Cherry Hill, NJ 08002-1932 (856) 216-2008
Contact: David Lackner, Dir.

Established in 1999 in PA.
Donor: David Lackner.
Foundation type: Independent foundation.
Financial data (yr. ended 08/31/13): Assets, $73,983 (M); gifts received, $873,662; expenditures, $897,482; qualifying distributions, $862,869; giving activities include $862,869 for 5 grants (high: $500,000; low: $319).
Fields of interest: Human services; Jewish agencies & synagogues.
Limitations: Applications accepted. Giving primarily in Brooklyn, NY. No grants to individuals.
Application information: Contributes mostly to pre-selected organizations.
Initial approach: Letter
Deadline(s): None
Director: David Lackner.
EIN: 137153253

5355
The Large Foundation ✧
171 Main St.
Flemington, NJ 08822-1607
Contact: C. Gregory Watts, Pres.

Incorporated in 1957 in NJ.
Donors: George K. Large†; Edwin J.S. Anderson†; and members of the Large family.
Foundation type: Independent foundation.
Financial data (yr. ended 12/31/13): Assets, $10,381,133 (M); gifts received, $164,109; expenditures, $558,474; qualifying distributions, $532,770; giving activities include $507,250 for 61 grants (high: $60,000; low: $350).
Fields of interest: Education; Health care; Human services; YM/YWCAs & YM/YWHAs.
Limitations: Applications accepted. Giving primarily in Hunterdon County, NJ. No grants to individuals.
Application information: Application form required.
Initial approach: Letter
Deadline(s): Usually by Aug.
Board meeting date(s): Oct.
Officers: C. Gregory Watts, Pres.; Cheryl Copeland, V.P.; Richard L. Tice, Secy.
EIN: 226049246

5356
John C. Lasko Foundation ✧
P.O. Box 1501, NJ2-130-03-31
Pennington, NJ 08534-1501
Contact: Clint Blair

Established in 1998 MI. Reincorporated in 2010 under a new IRS EI number.
Donors: John C. Lasko†; Republic Die & Tool Co.
Foundation type: Independent foundation.
Financial data (yr. ended 12/31/13): Assets, $117,940,113 (M); expenditures, $5,772,444; qualifying distributions, $5,371,992; giving activities include $4,915,000 for 21 grants (high: $550,000; low: $35,000).
Fields of interest: Protestant agencies & churches.
Type of support: Scholarships—to individuals.
Limitations: Applications not accepted. Giving in the U.S., with some emphasis on MI.
Application information: Unsolicited requests for funds not accepted.
Trustees: Sean H. Cook; Merrill Lynch Trust Co.
EIN: 276173297
Selected grants: The following grants are a representative sample of this grantmaker's funding activity:
$500,000 to Crossway Church of Lancaster, Millersville, PA, 2013. For Crossway Church Meeting House.
$465,000 to Legacy United Methodist Church, Bismarck, ND, 2013. For construction of new church facility.
$300,000 to Community Baptist Church of Huron Township, Trenton, MI, 2013. For purchase and renovation of Ministry Center (church building).
$300,000 to Eden Baptist Church, Burnsville, MN, 2013. For construction of worship space.
$261,000 to New Covenant Community Church, Homer Glen, IL, 2013. For Construction of new facility.
$250,000 to Community Baptist Church of Huron Township, Trenton, MI, 2013. For purchase and renovation of Ministry Center (church building).
$225,000 to Bethlehem Baptist Church, Hampden, MA, 2013. For We Are His Body Building Project.
$200,000 to 242 Community Church, Howell, MI, 2013. For 2|42 Community Church - Brighton Campus.
$200,000 to Calvary Baptist Church, New Philadelphia, OH, 2013. For construction of worship space.
$125,000 to Faith Assembly of God Church, Joplin, MO, 2013. For Rising from the Rubble.

5357
Blanche & Irving Laurie Foundation, Inc. ✧
P.O. Box 53
Roseland, NJ 07068-5788
Contact: Gene R. Korf, Exec. Dir.

Established in 1983 in NJ.
Donor: Irving Laurie†.
Foundation type: Independent foundation.
Financial data (yr. ended 09/30/13): Assets, $56,576,069 (M); expenditures, $4,564,030; qualifying distributions, $3,984,584; giving activities include $3,748,730 for 106 grants (high: $200,000; low: $500).
Purpose and activities: Support for Jewish social services, secondary schools, and cultural organizations; the arts, particularly for theater; also for medical and health centers.
Fields of interest: Performing arts, theater; Arts; Children/youth, services; Aging, centers/services; Jewish agencies & synagogues.
Type of support: Capital campaigns; Building/renovation; Equipment; Program development.
Limitations: Applications accepted. Giving primarily in NJ. No support for medical research.
Publications: Application guidelines; Informational brochure (including application guidelines).
Application information: Application form not required.
Initial approach: Proposal
Copies of proposal: 7
Deadline(s): None
Board meeting date(s): Quarterly
Final notification: 3-4 months
Officers and Trustees:* Laura Baron, Pres.; Gene R. Korf,* Exec. Dir.; Scott Korf; Richard A. Patt, M.D.; Harvey S. Rich; Robert Zagoren, M.D.
Number of staff: None.
EIN: 222489725

5358
Lenzmeier Family Foundation ✧
P.O. Box 1501, NJ2-130-03-31
Pennington, NJ 08534-1501

Established in 2003 in MN.
Donors: Allen Lenzmeier; Kathleen Lenzmeier.
Foundation type: Independent foundation.
Financial data (yr. ended 12/31/13): Assets, $22,458,673 (M); gifts received, $790,000; expenditures, $891,310; qualifying distributions, $810,003; giving activities include $758,000 for 12 grants (high: $160,000; low: $20,000).
Fields of interest: Performing arts, theater; Education; Boys & girls clubs; Human services.
Limitations: Applications not accepted. Giving primarily in MN. No grants to individuals.
Application information: Unsolicited requests for funds not accepted.
Officers: Allen Lenzmeier, Pres.; Kathleen Lenzmeier, Secy.-Treas.
EIN: 200472176

Selected grants: The following grants are a representative sample of this grantmaker's funding activity:
$105,000 to Boys and Girls Clubs of the Twin Cities, Minneapolis, MN, 2011.
$100,000 to Guthrie Theater, Minneapolis, MN, 2011.
$100,000 to K T C A/K T C I Twin Cities Public Television, Saint Paul, MN, 2011.
$50,000 to Open Arms of Minnesota, Minneapolis, MN, 2011.
$50,000 to United Way, Greater Twin Cities, Minneapolis, MN, 2011.
$30,000 to PACER Center, Minneapolis, MN, 2011.

5359
The Philip & Janice Levin Foundation ✧
975 U.S. Hwy. 22 W.
North Plainfield, NJ 07060-3624 (908) 755-2401

Incorporated in 1963 in NJ.
Donors: Janice H. Levin†; Philip J. Levin†; Adam Corp.
Foundation type: Independent foundation.
Financial data (yr. ended 08/31/13): Assets, $31,161,460 (M); expenditures, $1,436,630; qualifying distributions, $2,465,890; giving activities include $2,465,890 for 31 grants (high: $375,000; low: $2,000).
Purpose and activities: Giving primarily for the arts and higher education.
Fields of interest: Museums (art); Arts; Higher education; Human services.
Limitations: Applications accepted. Giving primarily in NJ and New York, NY. No grants to individuals.
Application information: Application form not required.
Initial approach: Letter only
Deadline(s): None
Officers: Adam Levin, Pres.; William A. Farber, V.P.; Matthew K. Harding, V.P.; Arielle Tepper Madover, V.P.; Maureen Mooney, Secy.; Timothy G. Decola, Treas.
EIN: 226075837

5360
Michael J. and Patricia Levitt Family Charitable Foundation, Inc. ✧
3 E. Stow Rd., Ste. 100
P.O. Box 994
Marlton, NJ 08053-3188
Contact: Michael J. Levitt, Chair., Pres., and Treas.; Patricia Levitt, Exec. V.P. and Secy.; Andrew J. Bocchino, V.P.; Paul Chan, Tr.

Donors: Michael J. Levitt; Lee A. Levine; Asher & Co., Ltd.; Frank Monastero; Mary E. Mcafee; Marybeth Monastero.
Foundation type: Independent foundation.
Financial data (yr. ended 12/31/12): Assets, $29,945 (M); gifts received, $480,600; expenditures, $492,314; qualifying distributions, $492,314; giving activities include $468,420 for 87 grants (high: $50,000; low: $1,000).
Purpose and activities: Giving primarily for education and animal welfare. The foundation will also grant scholarships for college tuition to residents of low- and mid-income communities, whose names appear on the most recent owner's certification or compliance with HUD's tenant eligibility and rent procedures form. Residents must have a minimum of a C or 2.0 GPA at the high school or college level. All scholarships are paid directly to the college or university, and will be applied toward the payment of tuition expenses for 1-year.
Fields of interest: Elementary/secondary education; Higher education; Animal welfare; Human services.
Limitations: Applications accepted. Giving in the U.S., with emphasis on NJ and PA. No grants to individuals directly.
Application information: Scholarship applications must include: 1) official high school transcripts, 2) proof of acceptance to an undergraduate college or university, 3) three 1-page character references, including at least 1 reference from a teacher, and 4) an essay or presentation focusing on the resident's expected field of study. Application form required.
Initial approach: Proposal
Deadline(s): None
Officers: Michael J. Levitt, Chair., Pres., and Treas.; Patricia Levitt, Exec. V.P. and Secy.; Andrew J. Bocchino, V.P.
Trustee: Paul Chan.
EIN: 208140755
Selected grants: The following grants are a representative sample of this grantmaker's funding activity:
$100,000 to Best Friends Animal Society, Kanab, UT, 2011.
$50,150 to University of Pennsylvania, Philadelphia, PA, 2011.
$20,000 to University of Delaware, Newark, DE, 2011.
$15,000 to James Madison University, Harrisonburg, VA, 2011.
$13,500 to New York University, New York, NY, 2011.
$11,000 to Arcadia University, Glenside, PA, 2011.
$10,000 to Philadelphia Animal Welfare Society, Philadelphia, PA, 2011.
$5,000 to Friends of Camden Animal Shelter, Lindenwold, NJ, 2011.
$5,000 to Humane Society of Dorchester County, Cambridge, MD, 2011.
$3,000 to Bradley University, Peoria, IL, 2011.

5361
Mortimer Levitt Foundation, Inc. ✧
c/o Levitt Properties
106 Quarry Rd., Ste. A
Hamburg, NJ 07419-1341 (973) 823-1140
Contact: Kathy Eberly, Treas.

Established in 1966 in NY.
Donors: Mortimer Levitt†; The Custom Shops; Farmers Branch.
Foundation type: Independent foundation.
Financial data (yr. ended 02/28/11): Assets, $45,698,803 (M); expenditures, $4,753,509; qualifying distributions, $2,162,219; giving activities include $1,979,192 for 439 grants (high: $75,000; low: $40).
Purpose and activities: Giving primarily for the arts; funding also for health organizations and human services.
Fields of interest: Museums; Performing arts; Arts; Higher education; Health organizations, association; Human services; Children/youth, services; Community/economic development; Foundations (community); Jewish federated giving programs.
Limitations: Giving primarily in New York, NY. No grants to individuals.
Application information:
Initial approach: Letter
Deadline(s): None
Officers: AnneMarie Levitt, Pres.; Elizabeth Levitt-Hirsch, V.P.; Malcolm Chaifetz, Secy. and Gen. Counsel; Kathy Eberly, Treas.
EIN: 136204678

5362
Lewis Family Trust ✧
c/o Larry Levy
80 Broadway
Elmwood Park, NJ 07407-3044

Established in 2001 in NJ.
Donor: Lillian Lewis†.
Foundation type: Independent foundation.
Financial data (yr. ended 12/31/13): Assets, $13,827,096 (M); expenditures, $852,219; qualifying distributions, $691,000; giving activities include $691,000 for 27 grants (high: $100,000; low: $1,000).
Fields of interest: Jewish federated giving programs; Jewish agencies & synagogues.
Limitations: Applications not accepted. Giving primarily in NJ and NY. No grants to individuals.
Application information: Contributes only to pre-selected organizations.
Trustee: Larry Levy.
EIN: 226885462
Selected grants: The following grants are a representative sample of this grantmaker's funding activity:
$25,000 to Central Synagogue, New York, NY, 2012. For Contribution Given to Preselected Organizations.
$2,000 to Sharsheret, Teaneck, NJ, 2012. For Contributions Given to Preselected Organizations.

5363
LifeCare Foundation Inc. ✧
4242 Rte. 1
Monmouth Junction, NJ 08852-9801 (732) 274-1000
Contact: Jemo Kang, Dir.

Established in 1999 in NJ.
Donors: Jemo Kang; Walter Kang; Roger Kang; Monica Kang; Princeton Biomeditech Corporation.
Foundation type: Independent foundation.
Financial data (yr. ended 12/31/13): Assets, $11,455,713 (M); gifts received, $300,000; expenditures, $854,081; qualifying distributions, $531,625; giving activities include $530,000 for 16 grants (high: $180,000; low: $5,000).
Purpose and activities: Scholarship awards to graduating students of the Princeton, NJ, school system.
Fields of interest: Higher education; Health care, single organization support.
Type of support: Scholarships—to individuals.
Limitations: Applications accepted. Giving primarily in NJ.
Application information: Application form required.
Initial approach: Letter
Deadline(s): None
Directors: Jemo Kang; Monica Kang; Roger Kang; Walter Kang.
EIN: 223625576

5364
The Lipman Family Foundation, Inc. ✧
(formerly Howard and Jean Lipman Foundation, Inc.)
c/o Boyle
103 Cedar Village Blvd.
Ocean, NJ 07712-8726
Contact: Beverly S. Lipman, Pres.

Established in 1959 in NY.
Donors: Howard W. Lipman‡; Jean Lipman‡.
Foundation type: Independent foundation.
Financial data (yr. ended 06/30/13): Assets, $17,670,375 (M); expenditures, $621,281; qualifying distributions, $510,240; giving activities include $499,250 for 44 grants (high: $240,000; low: $500).
Purpose and activities: Giving primarily for art museums, scientific research, educational institutions, and conservation organizations.
Fields of interest: Museums; Arts; Higher education; Environment, natural resources; Health care.
Type of support: Endowments; Seed money; Matching/challenge support.
Limitations: Applications not accepted. Giving primarily in CA and NY. No grants to individuals.
Application information: Contributes only to pre-selected organizations.
Officers and Directors:* Beverly S. Lipman,* Pres.; Roger A. Goldman, V.P. and Treas.; Peter W. Lipman,* V.P.; Timothy E. Lipman,* V.P.; Lester A. Greenberg,* Secy.; Benjamin H. Lipman.
EIN: 136066963
Selected grants: The following grants are a representative sample of this grantmaker's funding activity:
$7,000,000 to Artworks, Trenton, NJ, 2011. For annual support.
$240,000 to San Jose Museum of Art, San Jose, CA, 2011. For annual support.
$120,000 to San Jose Museum of Art, San Jose, CA, 2011. For annual support.
$25,000 to Geological Society of America Foundation, Boulder, CO, 2011. For annual support.
$25,000 to New Mexico Bureau of Geology and Mineral Resources, Socorro, NM, 2011. For annual support.
$10,000 to Doctors for Global Health, Atlanta, GA, 2011. For annual support.
$10,000 to Fordham University, Bronx, NY, 2011. For annual support.
$10,000 to Storm King Art Center, Mountainville, NY, 2011. For annual support.
$10,000 to Whitney Museum of American Art, New York, NY, 2011. For Smith exhibition.
$10,000 to Whitney Museum of American Art, New York, NY, 2011. For annual support.

5365
Edward and Mary Lord Foundation ✧ ☆
P.O. Box 1501, NJ2-130-03-31
Pennington, NJ 08534-1501

Established in CT.
Donors: Edward P. Lord Revocable Living Trust; Mary Lord‡.
Foundation type: Independent foundation.
Financial data (yr. ended 10/31/13): Assets, $19,219,351 (M); expenditures, $785,923; qualifying distributions, $689,088; giving activities include $548,125 for 16 grants (high: $233,000; low: $1,500).
Fields of interest: Education; Human services; Family services.
Limitations: Applications not accepted. Giving primarily in Norwich, CT.
Application information: Unsolicited requests for funds not accepted.
Trustees: Jeffrey Lord; Kathryn Lord-Richard; Joel Suisman.
EIN: 270785866

5366
The David & Sondra Mack Family Foundation, Inc. ✧
2115 Linwood Ave., Ste. 110
Fort Lee, NJ 07024-5022

Established in 1998.
Donor: David Mack.
Foundation type: Independent foundation.
Financial data (yr. ended 12/31/12): Assets, $17,663,226 (M); gifts received, $7,500,000; expenditures, $3,873,634; qualifying distributions, $3,873,615; giving activities include $3,873,615 for 260 grants (high: $1,000,000; low: $100).
Purpose and activities: Giving primarily for higher education and to health organizations; some funding also for the arts, social services and Jewish organizations.
Fields of interest: Arts; Higher education; Health organizations, association; Human services; Jewish agencies & synagogues.
Limitations: Applications not accepted. Giving primarily in NY, with emphasis on the metropolitan New York, area, including Long Island and Westchester. No grants to individuals.
Application information: Contributes only to pre-selected organizations.
Trustee: David Mack.
EIN: 223632663
Selected grants: The following grants are a representative sample of this grantmaker's funding activity:
$5,000 to Brandeis University, Waltham, MA, 2012. For replacement.

5367
The William & Phyllis Mack Family Foundation, Inc. ✧
2115 Linwood Ave., Ste. 110
Fort Lee, NJ 07024-5022

Established in 1997 in NJ.
Donor: William Mack.
Foundation type: Independent foundation.
Financial data (yr. ended 12/31/13): Assets, $10,136,544 (M); gifts received, $6,176,310; expenditures, $6,363,034; qualifying distributions, $6,355,308; giving activities include $6,355,308 for 86 grants (high: $3,000,000; low: $300).
Purpose and activities: Giving primarily to museums, as well as for hospitals, education, and Jewish organizations.
Fields of interest: Museums; Higher education; Hospitals (general); Human services; Jewish federated giving programs; Jewish agencies & synagogues.
Limitations: Applications not accepted. Giving primarily in NY. No grants to individuals.
Application information: Contributes only to pre-selected organizations.
Trustees: Phyllis Mack; Richard Mack; Stephen Mack; William Mack.
EIN: 223512719

5368
Maher Charitable Foundation ✧ ☆
(formerly M. Brian and Sandra Maher Charitable Foundation)
c/o Essex Equity
70 S. Orange Ave., Ste. 105
Livingston, NJ 07039-4916
Main URL: http://www.mahercharitablefoundation.org/

Donor: M. Brian Maher.
Foundation type: Independent foundation.
Financial data (yr. ended 12/31/13): Assets, $107,051 (M); expenditures, $596,766; qualifying distributions, $596,766; giving activities include $525,000 for 2 grants (high: $500,000; low: $25,000).
Fields of interest: Recreation, parks/playgrounds; Catholic federated giving programs.
Limitations: Applications not accepted. Giving primarily in NJ and NY.
Application information: Unsolicited requests for funds not accepted.
Officers and Directors:* M. Brian Maher,* Chair. and Treas.; Sandra Maher,* Pres.; Scott Schley,* Secy. and Genl. Counsel.
EIN: 271447747

5369
Marcon Foundation, Inc. ✧
79 Chestnut St., Ste. 101
Ridgewood, NJ 07450-2533 (201) 447-0185
Contact: W.J. Haggerty, Asst. Treas.

Established in 2003 in NJ.
Donors: Fred R. Marcon; Natalie Marcon.
Foundation type: Independent foundation.
Financial data (yr. ended 12/31/13): Assets, $251,996 (M); expenditures, $1,348,284; qualifying distributions, $1,289,538; giving activities include $1,195,000 for 54 grants (high: $150,000; low: $5,000).
Fields of interest: Health care; Human services; Catholic agencies & churches.
Limitations: Giving primarily in FL and IL. No grants to individuals.
Application information:
Initial approach: Letter
Deadline(s): None
Officers: Fred R. Marcon, Pres.; Alison Conti, Exec. Dir.
EIN: 571167051

5370
The Mario Family Foundation ✧
P.O. Box 445
Chatham, NJ 07928
Contact: Christopher Mario, Dir.

Established in 2005. Successor foundation of the Ernest and Mildred Martha Mario Foundation.
Donors: Dr. Ernest Mario; Mildred Martha Mario.
Foundation type: Independent foundation.
Financial data (yr. ended 12/31/13): Assets, $29,522,345 (M); gifts received, $39,107; expenditures, $1,446,679; qualifying distributions,

$1,366,294; giving activities include $1,354,900 for 17 grants (high: $500,000; low: $5,000).
Fields of interest: Higher education; Education; Human services.
Limitations: Applications not accepted. Giving primarily in NC and NJ; some support also in RI.
Application information: Unsolicited requests for funds not accepted.
Directors: Christopher B. Mario; Ernest Mario; Gregory G. Mario; Jeremy K. Mario; Mildred M. Mario.
EIN: 201400656

5371
Marsh Family Foundation ✧ ☆
P.O. Box 1501, NJ2-130-03-31
Pennington, NJ 08534-1501

Established in MO.
Donor: Themla Stanley†.
Foundation type: Independent foundation.
Financial data (yr. ended 12/31/13): Assets, $1,211,415 (M); gifts received, $61,960; expenditures, $544,118; qualifying distributions, $528,568; giving activities include $510,000 for 2 grants (high: $500,000; low: $10,000).
Fields of interest: Foundations (community).
Limitations: Applications not accepted. Giving primarily in MO. No grants to individuals.
Application information: Unsolicited requests for funds not accepted.
Trustee: Merrill Lynch.
EIN: 275154810

5372
Nicholas Martini Foundation ✧
50 Walnut St.
P.O. Box 29
Newark, NJ 07101-0419
NY tel.: (212) 571-2300

Established in 1986 in NJ.
Donor: Nicholas Martini†.
Foundation type: Independent foundation.
Financial data (yr. ended 12/31/12): Assets, $12,710,956 (M); expenditures, $702,175; qualifying distributions, $598,674; giving activities include $487,249 for 75 grants (high: $105,000; low: $300).
Purpose and activities: Giving primarily for programs in the fields of youth and education, public health and welfare, community development, and arts and humanities programs.
Fields of interest: Arts; Secondary school/education; Higher education; Health care; Health organizations, association; Youth development, services; Human services; Children/youth, services.
Type of support: General/operating support; Matching/challenge support.
Limitations: Giving primarily in Bergen, Essex, and Passaic counties, NJ. No grants to individuals.
Publications: Application guidelines; Annual report.
Application information: Application form required.
Initial approach: Letter requesting application form on organization letterhead; phone requests not accepted
Copies of proposal: 1
Deadline(s): Varies
Board meeting date(s): Varies; 2 to 3 meetings per year
Final notification: Varies
Officer and Trustees:* William J. Martini,* Pres.; Peter Garino; Gail A. Hansen; Fannie Rosta; Marie Salanitri.
Number of staff: 1 part-time professional.
EIN: 222756049

5373
Martinson Family Foundation, Inc. ✧
1009 Lenox Dr., Ste. 4
Lawrenceville, NJ 08648-2321

Established in 1999 in NJ.
Donor: John H. Martinson.
Foundation type: Independent foundation.
Financial data (yr. ended 11/30/13): Assets, $4,524,698 (M); gifts received, $998,274; expenditures, $1,139,919; qualifying distributions, $1,021,476; giving activities include $1,019,497 for 9 grants (high: $326,000; low: $25,000).
Fields of interest: Higher education; Education.
Limitations: Applications not accepted. Giving in the U.S., with emphasis on NJ. No grants to individuals.
Application information: Contributes only to pre-selected organizations.
Officer and Trustees:* John H. Martinson,* Chair. and Treas.; Ross T. Martinson.
EIN: 223695793
Selected grants: The following grants are a representative sample of this grantmaker's funding activity:
$200,000 to United States Air Force Academy, Colorado Springs, CO, 2011.
$169,000 to Saint Peter's University, Jersey City, NJ, 2011.
$150,000 to Rowan University, Glassboro, NJ, 2011.
$110,000 to Rider University, Lawrenceville, NJ, 2011.
$100,000 to Purdue Foundation, West Lafayette, IN, 2011.
$27,000 to United States Air Force Academy, Colorado Springs, CO, 2011.

5374
William M. Matthews Trust ✧
31 Glendale Dr.
Freehold, NJ 07728-1357

Donor: C. Thomas Barkalow.
Foundation type: Independent foundation.
Financial data (yr. ended 12/31/13): Assets, $820,042 (M); expenditures, $1,031,838; qualifying distributions, $1,000,000; giving activities include $1,000,000 for 1 grant.
Fields of interest: Health care.
Limitations: Applications not accepted. Giving primarily in Red Bank, NJ.
Application information: Contributes only to pre-selected organizations.
Trustee: C. Thomas Barkalow.
EIN: 276412070

5375
Helen and William Mazer Foundation ✧
P.O. Box 542
Berkeley Heights, NJ 07922-0542
Contact: Leonard Berkowitz, Treas.

Established in 1999 in DE.
Foundation type: Independent foundation.
Financial data (yr. ended 09/30/13): Assets, $15,839,567 (M); expenditures, $814,352; qualifying distributions, $681,620; giving activities include $666,858 for 116 grants (high: $50,000; low: $200).
Fields of interest: Arts; Education; Environment; Health organizations, association; Community/economic development.
Limitations: Applications not accepted. No grants to individuals.
Application information: Unsolicited requests for funds not accepted.
Board meeting date(s): As needed
Officers and Directors:* Linda Berkowitz,* Pres.; Steven Bercu,* Secy.; Leonard Berkowitz,* Treas.; Alan Berkowitz; David Berkowitz.
EIN: 020511160
Selected grants: The following grants are a representative sample of this grantmaker's funding activity:
$35,000 to Rockefeller University, New York, NY, 2011.
$35,000 to Ubuntu Education Fund, New York, NY, 2011.
$25,000 to Trust for Public Land, Morristown, NJ, 2011.
$20,000 to Brandeis University, Waltham, MA, 2011.
$17,000 to Innocence Project, New York, NY, 2011.
$5,000 to New York Times Neediest Cases Fund, New York, NY, 2011.
$3,500 to National Mentoring Partnership, Alexandria, VA, 2011.
$3,500 to W N Y C Radio, New York, NY, 2011.
$3,000 to Congregation Bnai Israel, Bridgeport, CT, 2011.
$2,500 to Trinitas Health Foundation, Elizabeth, NJ, 2011.

5376
The Curtis W. McGraw Foundation ✧
c/o Drinker, Biddle & Reath, LLP
P.O. Box 627
Princeton, NJ 08542-0627 (609) 716-6511
Contact: Samuel W. Lambert III, Secy.-Treas.

Established in 1964 in NJ.
Donor: Elizabeth McGraw Webster.
Foundation type: Independent foundation.
Financial data (yr. ended 12/31/13): Assets, $26,226,894 (M); expenditures, $1,374,994; qualifying distributions, $1,132,817; giving activities include $1,121,730 for 132 grants (high: $100,000; low: $1,000).
Purpose and activities: Support primarily for hospitals, mental health, AIDS research, elementary and other educational institutions, the arts, social services, and churches. Grants usually made to charities which are of interest to the officers.
Fields of interest: Performing arts; Arts; Elementary school/education; Education; Environment, natural resources; Environment; Hospitals (general); Substance abuse, services; Mental health/crisis services; AIDS; AIDS research; Human services; Religion.
Type of support: General/operating support; Continuing support; Annual campaigns.
Limitations: Applications accepted. Giving limited to the Vail, CO, Sun Valley, ID, and Princeton, NJ, areas. No grants to individuals, or for endowment funds, research, scholarships, fellowships, or matching gifts; no loans.
Publications: Annual report.

Application information: Application form not required.
Initial approach: Letter
Copies of proposal: 1
Deadline(s): Oct. 15
Board meeting date(s): Nov. or Dec., and as required
Final notification: By Dec. 31
Officers and Trustees:* Elizabeth McGraw Webster,* Chair.; Curtis M. Webster,* Pres.; Lisette S. Edmond,* V.P.; Mariana S. Paen,* V.P.; Theo M. Webster,* V.P.; Samuel W. Lambert III,* Secy.-Treas.
EIN: 221761678

5377
The MCJ Amelior Foundation ✧
(formerly The MCJ Foundation)
310 South St., 4th Fl.
Morristown, NJ 07960-7301 (973) 540-1946
Contact: Suzanne M. Spero, Exec. Dir.
GiveSmart: http://www.givesmart.org/Stories/Donors/Ray-Chambers

Established in 1983 in NJ.
Donors: Raymond G. Chambers; Kurt T. Borowsky; Harding Service, LLC.
Foundation type: Independent foundation.
Financial data (yr. ended 12/31/12): Assets, $112,506,314 (M); gifts received, $39,110; expenditures, $8,112,312; qualifying distributions, $8,105,715; giving activities include $6,333,685 for 413 grants (high: $600,000; low: $20).
Purpose and activities: Giving primarily for mentoring and youth initiatives.
Fields of interest: Education, early childhood education; Child development, education; Elementary school/education; Education; Health organizations, association; Crime/violence prevention, gun control; Crime/violence prevention, domestic violence; Human services; Children/youth, services; Youth, pregnancy prevention; Child development, services; Community/economic development; United Ways and Federated Giving Programs; Disabilities, people with; Minorities; Women; AIDS, people with; Economically disadvantaged; Homeless.
Type of support: General/operating support; Seed money; Technical assistance; Matching/challenge support.
Limitations: Applications not accepted. Giving primarily in NJ and NY.
Application information: Contributes only to pre-selected organizations.
Officers and Directors:* Christine Chambers Gilfillan,* Pres.; Donald R. Smith, Secy.; Anthony J. Romano, Treas.; Suzanne M. Spero,* Exec. Dir.; Barbara B. Coleman.
Number of staff: 2 full-time professional; 1 full-time support.
EIN: 222497895
Selected grants: The following grants are a representative sample of this grantmaker's funding activity:
$600,000 to Foundation for Morristown Medical Center, Morristown, NJ, 2012. For general operating support.
$397,121 to Malaria No More, New York, NY, 2012. For general operating support.
$250,000 to Better World Fund, Washington, DC, 2012. For general operating support.
$176,700 to Newark Alliance, Newark, NJ, 2012. For general operating support.
$150,000 to Seton Hall University, South Orange, NJ, 2012. For general operating support.
$138,750 to New Jersey Performing Arts Center, Newark, NJ, 2012. For general operating support.
$125,000 to Malaria No More, New York, NY, 2012. For general operating support.
$110,000 to Rockefeller Philanthropy Advisors, New York, NY, 2012. For general operating support.
$100,000 to National Mentoring Partnership, Boston, MA, 2012. For general operating support.
$5,000 to Newark Public Library, Newark, NJ, 2012. For general operating support.

5378
McMullen Family Foundation ✧
53 Undercliff Rd.
Montclair, NJ 07042-1738
Contact: Linda M. Drasheff, Secy.
FAX: (973) 744-4428;
E-mail: lindamdrasheff@aol.com

Established in 1993 in NY.
Donor: John J. McMullen, Sr.‡.
Foundation type: Independent foundation.
Financial data (yr. ended 05/31/13): Assets, $30,040,173 (M); expenditures, $949,023; qualifying distributions, $709,250; giving activities include $643,500 for 26 grants (high: $200,000; low: $1,000).
Purpose and activities: Giving primarily for higher education; funding also for human services.
Fields of interest: Museums (art); Elementary/secondary education; Higher education; Human services; Foundations (private grantmaking).
International interests: Ireland.
Type of support: General/operating support; Continuing support; Capital campaigns; Endowments; Professorships; Fellowships; Scholarship funds; Exchange programs.
Limitations: Applications not accepted. Giving primarily in NJ, with emphasis on Montclair. No grants to individuals.
Publications: Annual report.
Application information: Contributes only to pre-selected organizations.
Officers: Catherine McMullen, Pres.; John J. McMullen, Jr., V.P.; Linda M. Drasheff, Secy.; Peter McMullen, Treas.; Ilia Scriven, Exec. Dir.
Directors: James Blake; Patrick Gilmartin; Catherine McMullen; Jacqueline McMullen; John J. McMullen, Jr.; Peter McMullen.
Number of staff: 1 part-time professional; 1 part-time support.
EIN: 133721747
Selected grants: The following grants are a representative sample of this grantmaker's funding activity:
$15,000 to Childrens Tumor Foundation, New York, NY, 2011. For general purposes.

5379
The Merck Company Foundation ✧
1 Merck Dr.
P.O. Box 100
Whitehouse Station, NJ 08889-3400 (908) 423-1000
Contact: Brian Grill, Exec. V.P.
FAX: (908) 423-1987;
E-mail: OCP_TMCFSupport@Merck.com; Additional tel.: (908) 423-1000; Contact for Neighbor of Choice Program in New Jersey: Doreen Robert, e-mail: doreen_robert@merck.com; Additional e-mail: corporate_responsibility@merck.com; Main URL: http://www.merckresponsibility.com/giving-at-merck/foundation/
Grants List: http://www.merckresponsibility.com/wp-content/uploads/2014/07/3Q14-Transparency-Report.pdf?e82295
Merck Grants Managment Website: https://www.mercksupport.com/
RSS Feed: http://www.merck.com/rss/corporate_responsibility.xml

Incorporated in 1957 in NJ.
Donor: Merck & Co., Inc.
Foundation type: Company-sponsored foundation.
Financial data (yr. ended 12/31/13): Assets, $172,067,130 (M); expenditures, $44,227,356; qualifying distributions, $43,984,916; giving activities include $27,588,827 for 205+ grants (high: $6,000,000), and $14,234,573 for employee matching gifts.
Purpose and activities: The foundation supports programs designed to promote health, education, and community. Special emphasis is directed toward programs designed to improve healthcare quality and capacity; increase access to care for underserved populations in select disease areas of global need; enhance the quality of STEM education at the graduate and post-graduate level; advance woman and minorities in the sciences; advance women and minorities in the science; and programs that share Merck innovation and Merck employee expertise to address critical health and social issues in communities where Merck has a presence.
Fields of interest: Arts; Education, early childhood education; Higher education; Education, services; Education; Environment; Animal welfare; Health care, public policy; Health care, equal rights; Medical care, community health systems; Health care, clinics/centers; Public health; Health care; Asthma; AIDS; Diabetes; Biomedicine; Pediatrics; Health organizations; Medical research; Food services; Food banks; Food distribution, meals on wheels; Nutrition; Disasters, preparedness/services; American Red Cross; Children, services; Family services; Aging, centers/services; Human services; Community/economic development; Science, formal/general education; Mathematics; Engineering/technology; Science; Minorities; African Americans/Blacks; Hispanics/Latinos; Women; Economically disadvantaged.
Type of support: Continuing support; Management development/capacity building; Building/renovation; Program development; Conferences/seminars; Seed money; Curriculum development; Fellowships; Internship funds; Scholarship funds; Research; Employee volunteer services; Employee matching gifts.
Limitations: Applications not accepted. Giving on a national and international basis in areas of company operations, with emphasis on CA, Washington, DC, DE, IL, MA, MD, NC, NE, NJ, NY, PA, TN, TX, VA, and WY, and in Africa, China, and Puerto Rico. No support for political organizations, fraternal, labor, or veterans' organizations, religious organizations not of direct benefit to the entire community, or discriminatory organizations. No grants to individuals, or for capital campaigns, endowments, basic or clinical research projects including epidemiological studies, clinical trials, or other pharmaceutical studies, direct medical care including medical screening or testing, or the purchase of medicines, vaccines, or devices, meetings, conferences, symposia or workshops that

do not have or are not associated with long-term program objectives, unrestricted general operating support, or fundraising events including concerts, sporting events, annual appeals, membership drives, benefit dinners, or galas unrelated the strategic priorities of the Merck Company Foundation.
Publications: Application guidelines; Corporate giving report; Program policy statement.
Application information: Unsolicited applications are currently not accepted. Merck typically initiates specific requests for charitable contributions and donations.
Board meeting date(s): Semiannually and as required
Officers and Trustees:* Miriam M. Graddick-Wier,* Chair.; Geralyn S. Ritter,* Pres.; Brian Grill, Exec. V.P.; Robert B. McCovern, V.P., Tax; Leslie M. Hardy, V.P.; Jon Filderman, Secy.; Mark E. McDonough, Treas.
EIN: 226028476
Selected grants: The following grants are a representative sample of this grantmaker's funding activity:
$4,223,342 to Merck Childhood Asthma Network, Washington, DC, 2012. To enhance the quality of life for children with asthma and their families, and to reduce the burden of the disease on them and society.
$3,500,000 to African Comprehensive HIV/AIDS Partnerships, White House Station, NJ, 2012. To support and enhance Botswana's response to the HIV/AIDS epidemic through a comprehensive approach that includes HIV/AIDS prevention, treatment, care and support and impact mitigation.
$3,390,905 to Merck Institute for Science Education, Rahway, NJ, 2012. To improve science education from K-12th grade through teacher and program development.
$1,250,000 to CARE USA, Atlanta, GA, 2012. For Join My Village India.
$1,000,000 to BroadReach Institute for Training and Education, Arlington, VA, 2012. To implement Management and Leadership Academy (MLA) in Zambia.
$1,000,000 to Childrens Inn at NIH, Bethesda, MD, 2012. For general support.
$216,510 to PYXERA Global, Washington, DC, 2012. For Richard T. Clark Fellowship Program.
$125,000 to Community Education Group, Washington, DC, 2012. For project, The Road to AIDS.
$50,000 to Eagles Charitable Foundation, Philadelphia, PA, 2012. For Eagles Eye Mobile, which offers children in the Philadelphia area free eye exams and eyeglasses to children and their familie.
$25,000 to George Mason University Foundation, Fairfax, VA, 2012. For Virginia Initiative for Science Teaching and Achievement (VISTA), initiative to innovate science education in Virginia and beyond by promoting hands-on, problem based learning that empowers teachers and engages students.

5380
Merck Institute for Science Education, Inc. ✧

P.O. Box 100, WS2F-96
Whitehouse Station, NJ 08889-0100
Contact: Carlo Parravano, Exec. Dir.
E-mail: contactus@mise.org; Additional address: P.O. Box 2000 RY60-215, Rahway, NJ 07065, tel.: (732) 594-3443; fax: (732) 594-3977; Main URL: http://www.merckresponsibility.com/giving-at-merck/education/
Grants List: http://www.mise.org/secure/approach/grants.html
Merck Corporate Responsibility Education Website: http://www.merckresponsibility.com/giving-at-merck/education/

Established in 1992 in NJ.
Donors: Merck & Co., Inc.; Merck Foundation.
Foundation type: Company-sponsored foundation.
Financial data (yr. ended 12/31/13): Assets, $0 (M); gifts received, $1,479,080; expenditures, $1,479,080; qualifying distributions, $1,479,080; giving activities include $117,325 for 4 grants (high: $41,175; low: $12,750).
Purpose and activities: The institute supports programs designed to improve science education; raise levels of science performance in students grades K-12; and provide professional development for teachers and administrators to enhance their knowledge and skills.
Fields of interest: Education, fund raising/fund distribution; Elementary/secondary education; Higher education; Teacher school/education; Science, formal/general education; Mathematics; Engineering/technology; Science.
Type of support: General/operating support; Management development/capacity building; Program development; Conferences/seminars; Publication; Curriculum development; Fellowships; Internship funds; Research; Scholarships—to individuals.
Limitations: Applications not accepted. Giving limited to NJ and PA.
Application information: Unsolicited grant requests are not accepted. Applicants for the UNCF/Merck Science Initiative should contact the United Negro College Fund. Giving from the MISE is phasing down.
Officers: Geralyn S. Ritter, Pres.; Carlo Parravano, Exec. V.P.; Brian Grill, V.P.
EIN: 223208944

5381
Merck Patient Assistance Program, Inc. ✧

1 Merck Dr.
P.O. Box 100, Ste. WSF-96
Whitehouse Station, NJ 08889-0100 (800) 727-5400
Application address: P.O. Box 690, Horsham, PA 19044; Main URL: http://www.merckresponsibility.com/giving-at-merck/product-donations/
RSS Feed: http://www.merck.com/rss/corporate_responsibility.xml

Established as a company-sponsored operating foundation in 2001 in New Jersey.
Donors: Merck & Co., Inc.; Merck Sharp & Dohme Corp.
Foundation type: Operating foundation.
Financial data (yr. ended 12/31/13): Assets, $11,124,231 (M); gifts received, $686,800,564; expenditures, $686,800,564; qualifying distributions, $686,800,564; giving activities include $686,800,564 for grants to individuals.
Purpose and activities: The foundation provides Merck medication to economically disadvantaged individuals lacking prescription drug coverage when a physician has determined that a Merck product may be appropriate.
Fields of interest: Economically disadvantaged.
Type of support: Grants to individuals; Donated products.
Limitations: Applications accepted. Giving on a national basis and in Guam, Puerto Rico, the U.S. Virgin Islands, and U.S. Territories.
Publications: Application guidelines.
Application information: Application forms must be signed by a physician and include prescription information. Application form required.
Initial approach: Download enrollment form and mail to foundation
Deadline(s): None
Officers: Patrick Magri, Pres.; Patrick Davish, Exec. V.P.; Robert B. McGovern, V.P., Tax; David L. Foberg, Secy.; Susan L. Cimmino, Treas.
EIN: 010575520

5382
Richard D. & Lynette S. Merillat Private Foundation ✧

c/o Merrill Lynch Trust Co. FSB
P.O. Box 1525
Pennington, NJ 08534-0686
Application address: c/o Richard D. Merillat, Pres. and Tr., 1800 West US 223, Adrian, MI 49221

Established in 1993 in MI.
Donors: Richard D. Merillat; Lynette S. Merillat.
Foundation type: Independent foundation.
Financial data (yr. ended 06/30/13): Assets, $15,167,953 (M); expenditures, $851,829; qualifying distributions, $778,580; giving activities include $775,000 for 14 grants (high: $320,000; low: $5,000).
Purpose and activities: Grants primarily to organizations promoting Christian values.
Fields of interest: Higher education; Human services; Family services; Christian agencies & churches.
Limitations: Applications accepted. Giving primarily in Adrian MI, and the surrounding communities. No grants to individuals.
Application information: Application form required.
Initial approach: Letter
Deadline(s): None
Officers and Trustees:* Richard D. Merillat,* Pres.; Lynette S. Merillat,* Secy.; John Thurman.
EIN: 383148627
Selected grants: The following grants are a representative sample of this grantmaker's funding activity:
$5,000 to RBC Ministries, Grand Rapids, MI, 2013. For operational. support.

5383
Messner Foundation, Inc. ✧

1 Meadow Pond Ln.
Ocean View, NJ 08230 (609) 653-1500
Contact: Harold Messner, Tr.

Established in 2007 in NJ.
Donors: Elaine Messner; Harold Messner.
Foundation type: Independent foundation.
Financial data (yr. ended 12/31/13): Assets, $9,316,774 (M); gifts received, $100,000; expenditures, $698,923; qualifying distributions, $645,179; giving activities include $639,746 for 49 grants (high: $205,000; low: $500).
Fields of interest: Human services; Christian agencies & churches; Children/youth.

Limitations: Applications accepted. Giving primarily in NJ.
Application information: Application form required.
Initial approach: Letter
Deadline(s): None
Trustees: Brenda Cacossa; Leslie Kohler; Elaine Messner; Harold Messner; Laura Messner.
EIN: 260581765
Selected grants: The following grants are a representative sample of this grantmaker's funding activity:
$10,000 to University of Pennsylvania, Philadelphia, PA, 2012. To support cause.

5384
Milano Foundation, Inc. ✧ ☆
c/o Robert J. DiQuollo
One Giralda Farms, Ste. 130
Madison, NJ 07940-1027

Established in 1967.
Donors: Robert J. Milano; Sidonia Milano Charitable Lead Trust.
Foundation type: Independent foundation.
Financial data (yr. ended 12/31/13): Assets, $2,196,383 (M); gifts received, $105,000; expenditures, $460,348; qualifying distributions, $444,325; giving activities include $437,025 for 26 grants (high: $112,500; low: $1,500).
Fields of interest: Arts; Higher education; Education; Health care; Children/youth, services; Jewish agencies & synagogues.
Limitations: Applications not accepted. Giving primarily in CA, NJ and NY. No grants to individuals.
Application information: Contributes only to pre-selected organizations.
Officers and Trustee: Robert J. DiQuollo, Pres.; Colleen Betzler,* V.P.
EIN: 132620691
Selected grants: The following grants are a representative sample of this grantmaker's funding activity:
$50,800 to Los Angeles County High School for the Arts Foundation, Los Angeles, CA, 2011.
$50,000 to Saint Benedicts Preparatory School, Newark, NJ, 2011.
$30,000 to Fidelity Charitable Gift Fund, Boston, MA, 2011.
$10,000 to Collegiate School, New York, NY, 2011.
$10,000 to K C R W Foundation, Santa Monica, CA, 2011.
$10,000 to San Francisco State University, San Francisco, CA, 2011.
$6,000 to Delbarton School, Morristown, NJ, 2011.
$2,500 to Partnership in Philanthropy, Chatham, NJ, 2011.
$1,500 to Rutgers University Foundation, New Brunswick, NJ, 2011.
$1,500 to Villanova University, Villanova, PA, 2011.

5385
Milbank Foundation
(formerly Milbank Foundation for Rehabilitation)
116 Village Blvd., Ste. 200
Princeton, NJ 08540-5700 (609) 951-2283
Contact: Carl Helstrom, Exec. Dir.
FAX: (609) 951-2281; Main URL: http://fdnweb.org/milbank
Grants List: http://fdnweb.org/milbank/grants/year/2013/category/grants-awarded/

Established in 1995 in NY; converted through an affiliation between the ICD International Center for the Disabled and the New York Hospital-Cornell Medical Center Network.
Foundation type: Independent foundation.
Financial data (yr. ended 12/31/13): Assets, $30,429,056 (M); expenditures, $2,446,540; qualifying distributions, $2,109,196; giving activities include $1,797,500 for 36 grants (high: $250,000; low: $5,000), and $50,700 for employee matching gifts.
Purpose and activities: The foundation's mission is to integrate people with disabilities into all aspects of American life. Current priorities include, but are not limited to: consumer-focused initiatives that enable people with disabilities to lead fulfilling, independent lives; innovative policy research and education on market-based approaches to health care and rehabilitation; improving and expanding quality health services, especially palliative care, and education and training of allied health and rehabilitation professionals.
Fields of interest: Health care, public policy; Medical care, rehabilitation; Palliative care; Health care; Disabilities, people with.
Type of support: Program development; Conferences/seminars; Publication; Fellowships; Research; Employee matching gifts.
Limitations: Applications accepted. Giving limited to the U.S., with some emphasis on New York, NY. No support for government agencies. No grants to individuals, or for general operating funds, annual appeals, dinners or events, capital campaigns, building funds, direct mailings, solicitations, equipment, music, theater, or campaigns. Usually, the foundation does not make multi-year grants.
Publications: Annual report (including application guidelines); Grants list.
Application information: See web site for guidelines and limitations. Inquiries and proposals are to be sent by regular mail only. Unless requested, please do not send by fax, e-mail, or overnight mail. Application form not required.
Initial approach: Letter or proposal
Copies of proposal: 1
Deadline(s): Proposals processed as received. Grant decisions made at Board Meetings.
Board meeting date(s): May and Oct.
Final notification: Within 1 month of application
Officers and Directors:* Jeremiah M. Bogert,* Chair. and Secy.; Jeremiah Milbank III,* Pres. and Treas.; Carl Helstrom,* Exec. Dir.; Chris Olander, Exec. Dir. Emeritus; Jeremiah M. Bogert, Jr.; Rev. Terence L. Elsberry; Ezra K. Zilkha.
Number of staff: None.
EIN: 115125050

5386
Mohler Family Foundation ✧
P.O. Box 1501, NJ2-130-03-31
Pennington, NJ 08534-1501

Established in 1998 in MO.
Donors: Marguerite Mohler Trust; Dennison Mohler QTIP.
Foundation type: Independent foundation.
Financial data (yr. ended 12/31/13): Assets, $15,790,473 (M); gifts received, $96; expenditures, $725,086; qualifying distributions, $693,671; giving activities include $660,355 for 12 grants (high: $184,117; low: $4,104).
Fields of interest: Elementary/secondary education; Higher education; Catholic agencies & churches.
Limitations: Applications not accepted. Giving primarily in MI. No grants to individuals.
Application information: Contributes only to pre-selected organizations.
Trustee: Merrill Lynch Trust Co.
EIN: 436782973
Selected grants: The following grants are a representative sample of this grantmaker's funding activity:
$171,440 to Aquinas College, Grand Rapids, MI, 2011.
$136,324 to Saint Marys Catholic Church, Spring Lake, MI, 2011.
$3,825 to Guest House, Lake Orion, MI, 2011.
$3,825 to Saint Johns Home, Grand Rapids, MI, 2011.
$3,756 to Catholic Social Services, Grand Rapids, MI, 2011.
$3,756 to Diocese of Grand Rapids, Grand Rapids, MI, 2011.

5387
The Mosakowski Family Charitable Foundation ✧
(formerly Mosakowski Family Foundation)
P.O. Box 1501, NJ2-130-03-31
Pennington, NJ 08534-1501

Established in 2004 in MA.
Donors: William S. Mosakowski; Jane Rossetti Mosakowski.
Foundation type: Independent foundation.
Financial data (yr. ended 12/31/13): Assets, $29,551,748 (M); gifts received, $4,089,113; expenditures, $1,127,833; qualifying distributions, $954,643; giving activities include $881,000 for 9 grants (high: $250,000; low: $5,000).
Fields of interest: Elementary/secondary education; Higher education; Human services; Catholic agencies & churches.
Limitations: Applications not accepted. Giving primarily in MA. No grants to individuals.
Application information: Contributes only to pre-selected organizations.
Trustee: Jane Rossetti Mosakowski; William S. Mosakowski.
EIN: 202052977

5388
Mushett Family Foundation, Inc. ✧
c/o PGB Trusts & Investments
P.O. Box 7037
Bedminster, NJ 07921-7037

Established in 1998 in NJ.
Donors: Charles Mushett†; The Mushett Estate.
Foundation type: Independent foundation.
Financial data (yr. ended 05/31/13): Assets, $11,722,703 (M); expenditures, $645,491; qualifying distributions, $521,692; giving activities include $441,300 for 18 grants (high: $150,000; low: $2,800).
Purpose and activities: Giving primarily for higher education, human services, health care, including a cancer hospital, animal and wildlife preservation, and environmental conservation.
Fields of interest: Higher education; Environment; Animals/wildlife, preservation/protection;

Hospitals (specialty); Health care; Health organizations, association; Cancer research; Human services.
Limitations: Applications not accepted. Giving primarily in NJ and NY. No grants to individuals.
Application information: Unsolicited requests for funds not accepted.
Officers and Trustees:* Henry J. Daaleman, Pres. and Treas.; Mark Daaleman,* V.P. and Secy.; James Morgan, M.D.; Sr. Mary Eleanor Thornton.
EIN: 223614593
Selected grants: The following grants are a representative sample of this grantmaker's funding activity:
$12,500 to Doctors Without Borders USA, New York, NY, 2012.

5389
New Jersey Natural Gas Company Charity Inc. ✧
1415 Wyckoff Rd.
P.O. Box 1464
Wall, NJ 07719-3940
Contact: Tom Hayes
Main URL: http://www.njresources.com/

Established in NJ.
Foundation type: Independent foundation.
Financial data (yr. ended 09/30/13): Assets, $3,582,449 (M); expenditures, $1,394,175; qualifying distributions, $1,394,175; giving activities include $1,375,485 for 528 grants (high: $420,000; low: $50).
Purpose and activities: Giving primarily to help improve the health, education, advancement and quality of community life in central and northern New Jersey.
Fields of interest: Education; Health organizations; Safety/disasters.
Type of support: In-kind gifts.
Limitations: Applications accepted. Giving primarily in central and northern NJ.
Application information: Application form not required.
Initial approach: Proposal
Deadline(s): None
Officers and Trustees:* Laurence M. Downes,* Chair. and Pres.; Mariellen Dugan,* Sr. V.P. and Genl. Counsel; Glenn C. Lockwood,* Exec. V.P., C.F.O. and Treas.; Kathleen T. Ellis,* Exec. V.P.; Rhonda M. Figueroa,* Corp. Secy.; Thomas F. Hayes.
EIN: 223828939

5390
Newark Charter School Fund, Inc. ✧
60 Park Pl., 17th Fl.
Newark, NJ 07102-5511 (973) 733-2285
FAX: (973) 733-9555; E-mail: info@ncsfund.org;
Main URL: http://ncsfund.org
Facebook: https://www.facebook.com/ncsfund
RSS Feed: http://ncsfund.org/whats-happening/rss
Twitter: https://twitter.com/NCSFund

Established in NJ and DE.
Donors: Doris and Donald Fisher Fund; Bill & Melinda Gates Foundation; Laurene Powell Jobs; Robertson Foundation; Walton Family Foundation.
Foundation type: Operating foundation.
Financial data (yr. ended 12/31/12): Assets, $3,357,948 (M); gifts received, $2,814,492; expenditures, $2,971,992; qualifying distributions, $2,971,592; giving activities include $808,672 for 7 grants (high: $213,300; low: $50,000).
Purpose and activities: NCSF makes grants to charter schools and to nonprofit organizations that support charter schools.
Fields of interest: Elementary/secondary education; Charter schools.
Limitations: Applications not accepted. Giving primarily in NJ, NY and MA. No grants to individuals.
Application information: Unsolicited requests for funds not accepted. The fund works closely with local nonprofit organizations, charter schools, foundations and stakeholders of various kinds to identity and develop grant prospects.
Officers and Directors:* Mashea Ashton,* C.E.O. and Secy.; Nicole Butler, V.P., Advocacy and Collaboration; Aileen Philbrick, V.P., Quality Schools; Jim Blew; Phoebe Boyer; Chris Nelson.
EIN: 262224940
Selected grants: The following grants are a representative sample of this grantmaker's funding activity:
$150,000 to Education Reform Now, New York, NY, 2012. For One Year Grant for Advocacy for Academic Year 2010-2011.
$145,372 to Robert Treat Academy Charter School, Newark, NJ, 2012. For the Launch and Expansion of Robert Treat Academy - Central.

5391
The Charlotte W. Newcombe Foundation ✧
35 Park Pl.
Princeton, NJ 08542-6918 (609) 924-7022
Contact: Thomas N. Wilfrid Ph.D., Exec. Dir.
FAX: (609) 252-1773;
E-mail: twilfrid@newcombefoundation.org;
Additional e-mail: info@newcombefoundation.org;
Main URL: http://www.newcombefoundation.org

Trust established in 1979 in PA.
Donor: Charlotte W. Newcombe†.
Foundation type: Independent foundation.
Financial data (yr. ended 12/31/12): Assets, $47,794,700 (M); expenditures, $2,712,532; qualifying distributions, $2,361,526; giving activities include $2,119,725 for 47 grants (high: $743,060; low: $195), and $2,361,526 for foundation-administered programs.
Purpose and activities: Supporting students in pursuit of degrees in higher education.
Fields of interest: Humanities; Higher education; Adult/continuing education; Disabilities, people with; Adults, women; Economically disadvantaged.
Type of support: Endowments; Fellowships; Internship funds; Scholarship funds; Matching/challenge support.
Limitations: Giving for scholarship programs for mature women and students with disabilities is limited to colleges and universities in DE, MD, NJ, PA, Washington, DC, and New York, NY. No grants or scholarships to individuals directly, or for staffing, program development, postdoctoral fellowships, or building funds; scholarships to institutions only; no loans.
Publications: Informational brochure; Program policy statement.
Application information: The foundation accepts inquiries from accredited institutions of higher education within New York City, New Jersey, Pennsylvania, Delaware, Maryland and the District of Columbia. Formal applications are accepted only at the foundation's invitation following institutional inquiry. Application form not required.
Initial approach: Inquire with foundation
Deadline(s): For Newcombe Fellowships: Nov. 15. No deadline for institutional inquiries re scholarship grants.
Board meeting date(s): Feb., Apr., June, Oct., and Dec.
Officer and Trustees:* Thomas N. Wilfrid, Exec. Dir.; Robert M. Adams; Dale Robinson Anglin; Elizabeth T. Frank; Louise U. Johnson; J. Barton Luedeke.
Number of staff: 1 full-time professional; 3 part-time professional.
EIN: 232120614
Selected grants: The following grants are a representative sample of this grantmaker's funding activity:
$743,060 to Woodrow Wilson National Fellowship Foundation, Princeton, NJ, 2012. For Newcombe Doctoral Dissertation Fellowships.
$100,000 to Misericordia University, Dallas, PA, 2012. For Newcombe Scholarships for Mature Women Students, payable over 5.00 years.
$75,000 to Pennsylvania State University, University Park, PA, 2012. For Newcombe Scholarships for Students with Disabilities, payable over 5.00 years.
$50,000 to Gwynedd-Mercy University, Gwynedd Valley, PA, 2012. For Newcombe Scholarships for Mature Women Students, payable over 5.00 years.
$47,000 to Bloomfield College, Bloomfield, NJ, 2012. For Newcombe Scholarships for Mature Women Students.
$47,000 to Bloomfield College, Bloomfield, NJ, 2013. For Newcombe Scholarships for Mature Women Students.
$47,000 to La Salle University, Philadelphia, PA, 2012. For Newcombe Scholarships for Mature Women Students.
$46,000 to Gwynedd-Mercy University, Gwynedd Valley, PA, 2013. For Newcombe Scholarships for Mature Women Students.
$46,000 to Hunter College of the City University of New York, New York, NY, 2012. For Newcombe Scholarships for Mature Women Students.
$45,000 to Pennsylvania State University, University Park, PA, 2012. For Newcombe Scholarships for Students with Disabilities.
$42,000 to Kean University, Union, NJ, 2012. For Newcombe Scholarships for Mature Women Students at Kean University.
$42,000 to Kean University, Union, NJ, 2013. For Newcombe Scholarships for Mature Women Students.
$40,008 to Hunter College of the City University of New York, New York, NY, 2013. For Newcombe Scholarships for Mature Women Students.
$34,000 to University of Scranton, Scranton, PA, 2012. For Newcombe Scholarships for Mature Women Students.
$34,000 to University of Scranton, Scranton, PA, 2013. For Newcombe Scholarships for Mature Women Students.

5392
The Nicolais Foundation, Inc. ✧
40 Lake Rd.
Green Pond, NJ 07435-1206

Established in 1994.
Donors: Michael A. Nicolais; Margaret Nicolais.

Foundation type: Independent foundation.
Financial data (yr. ended 03/31/11): Assets, $0 (M); expenditures, $3,087,076; qualifying distributions, $3,086,824; giving activities include $3,086,824 for 1 grant.
Fields of interest: Elementary/secondary education; Libraries (public); Environment, natural resources; Girl scouts; Protestant agencies & churches.
Limitations: Applications not accepted. Giving primarily in CT, NJ, NY, and TX. No grants to individuals.
Application information: Unsolicited requests for funds not accepted.
Officers: Michael A. Nicolais, Pres.; Margaret M. Nicolais, V.P.
EIN: 223269467

5393
Novartis Patient Assistance Foundation, Inc. ✧
1 Health Plz.
USEH 701-441
East Hanover, NJ 07936-1080 (800) 277-2254
Application address: P.O. Box 66531, St. Louis, MO 63166-6556; fax: (866) 470-1750; Main URL: http://www.pharma.us.novartis.com/about-us/our-patient-caregiver-resources/index.shtml
NPC Patient Assistance Web Portal: https://www.npcpapportal.com/

Established in 2008 in NJ.
Donor: Novartis Pharmaceuticals Corp.
Foundation type: Company-sponsored foundation.
Financial data (yr. ended 12/31/12): Assets, $31,616,576 (M); gifts received, $467,999,604; expenditures, $459,661,136; qualifying distributions, $459,661,136; giving activities include $452,745,445 for grants to individuals.
Purpose and activities: The foundation provides medication assistance to patients experiencing financial hardship who have no third party insurance coverage.
Fields of interest: Economically disadvantaged.
Type of support: Donated products; In-kind gifts.
Limitations: Applications accepted. Giving on a national basis.
Publications: Application guidelines.
Application information: Faxed applications must be sent from a physician's office. Application address varies per medication requested. Application form required.
Initial approach: Telephone, complete online application, or download application form and fax or mail to application address
Copies of proposal: 1
Deadline(s): None
Officers and Directors:* Kevin Rigby,* Pres.; Joe Visaggio,* V.P.; Rhoda Crichlow, Secy.; Marc Lewis, Treas.; Alissa Jaffenagler; Barry Rosenfeld.
EIN: 262502555

5394
OceanFirst Foundation ✧
(formerly Ocean Federal Foundation)
1415 Hooper Ave., Ste. 304
Toms River, NJ 08753-2800 (732) 341-4676
Contact: Katherine B. Durante, Secy. and Exec. Dir.
FAX: (732) 473-9641;
E-mail: kdurante@oceanfirstfdn.org; Additional e-mail: info@oceanfirstfdn.org; Main URL: http://www.oceanfirstfdn.org
Facebook: http://www.facebook.com/pages/OceanFirst-Foundation/170318316430830?rf=162030737160252

Established in 1996 in NJ.
Donors: Ocean Financial Corp.; OceanFirst Financial Corp.; Ocean Federal Savings Bank; OceanFirst Bank.
Foundation type: Company-sponsored foundation.
Financial data (yr. ended 12/31/13): Assets, $20,643,612 (M); expenditures, $1,189,802; qualifying distributions, $1,173,927; giving activities include $852,838 for 233 grants (high: $50,000; low: $100), and $17,900 for 17 employee matching gifts.
Purpose and activities: The foundation supports programs designed to promote health and wellness, housing, quality of life, and youth development and education.
Fields of interest: Museums; Performing arts, theater; Performing arts, music; Arts; Libraries (school); Education; Environment, water resources; Environment; Health care, equal rights; Health care; Mental health, counseling/support groups; Mental health/crisis services; Employment, training; Food banks; Housing/shelter, homeless; Housing/shelter; Youth development, adult & child programs; Youth development; Children/youth, services; Family services, domestic violence; Aging, centers/services; Homeless, human services; Human services; Children/youth; Disabilities, people with; Economically disadvantaged.
Type of support: General/operating support; Continuing support; Annual campaigns; Capital campaigns; Building/renovation; Equipment; Emergency funds; Program development; Scholarship funds; Sponsorships; Employee matching gifts; Matching/challenge support.
Limitations: Applications accepted. Giving primarily in areas of company operations in Monroe Township, southern and western Monmouth County, and Ocean County, NJ. No support for religious congregations, political candidates or organizations, lobbying organizations or sports teams. No grants to individuals, or for research or political causes or campaigns, or personnel expenses.
Publications: Application guidelines; IRS Form 990 or 990-PF printed copy available upon request; Program policy statement.
Application information: Major Grants are grants greater than $5,000 and applicants must address an OceanFirst Foundation priority area. Organizations receiving Major Grants are asked to provide a final report. Application form required.
Initial approach: Telephone foundation and complete online application form for Arts & Cultural Grants, Good Neighbor Grants, Home Runs for Heroes Grants, and Major Grants
Copies of proposal: 1
Deadline(s): Varies; 2 months prior to need for Good Neighbor Grants
Board meeting date(s): Quarterly
Officers and Directors:* John R. Garbarino,* Chair. and Pres.; Katherine B. Durante,* Secy. and Exec. Dir.; Michael J. Fitzpatrick, Treas.; Joseph J. Burke; Angelo Catania; John W. Chadwick; Anthony J. DiCroce; Anita M. Kneeley; Msgr. Casimir H. Ladzinski; Amy W. Lotano; Donald E. McLaughlin; Samuel T. Melillo; Diane F. Rhine; James T. Snyder; Mark G. Solow; John E. Walsh; David C. Wintrode; David W. Wolfe.
Number of staff: 1 full-time professional; 1 part-time support.
EIN: 223465454

5395
The Sandler O'Neill Assistance Foundation ✧
10 Town Sq.
Chatham, NJ 07928-2566

Donors: Douglas MacKenzie; Thomas J. Stanton III; Tom Dundon; Cornerstone CSO.
Foundation type: Independent foundation.
Financial data (yr. ended 12/31/13): Assets, $12,305,697 (M); gifts received, $11,000; expenditures, $1,127,459; qualifying distributions, $1,096,201; giving activities include $1,090,259 for 21 grants to individuals (high: $85,963; low: $12,445).
Purpose and activities: Giving to students for tuition, room, and board.
Fields of interest: Disasters, 9/11/01.
Limitations: Applications not accepted. Giving primarily in NJ; some giving also in CT, FL, and NY.
Application information: Unsolicited requests for funds not accepted.
Officers: Andrew J. Armstrong, Jr., Pres.; Timothy H. Neher, Secy.; Charles H. Witmer, Treas.
EIN: 061631340

5396
The Orange Orphan Society ✧
11 Glenside Rd.
South Orange, NJ 07079-1601
Contact: Rebecca Linn, Pres.
E-mail: jareemha@aol.com

Established in 1855 in NJ.
Foundation type: Independent foundation.
Financial data (yr. ended 12/31/13): Assets, $12,411,972 (M); expenditures, $696,671; qualifying distributions, $620,500; giving activities include $620,500 for 28 grants (high: $80,000; low: $1,000).
Purpose and activities: Giving primarily to agencies that benefit needy residents of the Oranges and Maplewood, NJ, who are under 19 years of age.
Fields of interest: Education; Youth development, scouting agencies (general); Human services; YM/YWCAs & YM/YWHAs; Children/youth, services; Family services; Infants/toddlers; Children; Youth; Economically disadvantaged; Homeless.
Type of support: General/operating support; Capital campaigns; Equipment; Program development; Scholarship funds.
Limitations: Applications accepted. Giving limited to Maplewood and the Oranges, NJ, area in Essex County. No support for religious institutions. No grants to individuals.
Publications: Application guidelines.
Application information: Application form required.
Initial approach: The foundation prefers applicants use the Cover Sheet of the NY/NJ Area Common Grant Application Form, and it is preferred that the remainder of the application be in the Common Grant Application format, or the applicant's own format if necessary. E-mailed applications are accepted
Copies of proposal: 1
Deadline(s): Jan. 15 of the grant year

Board meeting date(s): Jan., Apr., and Nov.
Final notification: Open
Officers and Trustees:* Rebecca Linn,* Pres.; Byron Yake,* V.P.; Barbara B. Murray,* Secy.; Paula Stuart,* Treas.; Irene Jones Cates; Betty Debnaun; Nancy Hamilton; Mary Hogan; Penny Joseph; Cindy Lamy; Marilyn Neibart; Curtis Pew; Joseph Riopel; Edith Ries.
EIN: 221711513

5397
Henry and Carolyn Sue Orenstein Foundation, Inc. ✧
c/o Henry Orenstein
35 Smull Ave.
Caldwell, NJ 07006-5011

Established in 1986 in NJ.
Donors: Carolyn Sue Orenstein; Henry Orenstein.
Foundation type: Independent foundation.
Financial data (yr. ended 12/31/12): Assets, $4,472,919 (M); expenditures, $889,299; qualifying distributions, $887,669; giving activities include $887,669 for 13 grants (high: $800,250; low: $100).
Purpose and activities: Grants primarily for Jewish organizations, educational activities, and for medical research.
Fields of interest: Education; Medical research, institute; Human services; Jewish agencies & synagogues.
Type of support: Grants to individuals.
Limitations: Applications not accepted. Giving primarily in New York, NY.
Application information: Unsolicited requests for funds not accepted.
Trustees: Carolyn Sue Orenstein; Dr. Frederick Orenstein; Henry Orenstein.
EIN: 222806030

5398
OritaniBank Charitable Foundation ✧
(formerly Oritani Savings Bank Charitable Foundation)
370 Pascack Rd.
Township of Washington, NJ 07676 (201) 664-5400
Contact: Rosanne Buscemi, Corresponding Secy.
Application address: P.O. Box 1329, Township of Washington, NJ 07675; Main URL: http://www.oritani.com/cms/content.asp?contentid=591

Established in 2006 in NJ.
Foundation type: Independent foundation.
Financial data (yr. ended 12/31/13): Assets, $17,962,605 (M); expenditures, $941,503; qualifying distributions, $931,905; giving activities include $915,418 for 168 grants (high: $203,907; low: $97).
Purpose and activities: Giving primarily for education, health and human services, youth, and affordable housing.
Fields of interest: Education; Health care; Housing/shelter; Human services; Children/youth, services.
Limitations: Applications accepted. Giving primarily in NJ. No support for political or religious organizations, or activities for sectarian purposes.
Application information: Application form required.
Initial approach: Letter
Deadline(s): None
Officers and Directors:* Kevin J. Lynch,* Pres.; John M. Fields, Jr., Exec. V.P. and Treas.; Michael Debernardi, Exec. V.P.; Thomas G. Guinan, Exec. V.P.; Ann Marie Jetton, Sr. V.P. and C.A.O.; Leonard Carlucci, Sr. V.P.; David Garcia, Sr. V.P.; Louis Manderino, Sr. V.P.; Anne Morradian, Sr. V.P.; Giacchino "Jack" Anastasi, V.P.; Robert J. Barbarino, V.P.; Christopher Canlas, V.P.; Christopher Carola, V.P.; Paul M. Cordero, V.P.; Veronica DeLuise, V.P.; Joseph J. Laquidara, V.P.; Bing Luh, V.P.; Emanuele Minardi, V.P.; John Pagano, V.P.; Michael Sandberg, V.P.; Daniel Schapira, V.P.; Paul Skinner, V.P.; Kelly Valasquez, V.P.; Philip M. Wyks, Secy.; James L. Doyle, Jr.; Robert S. Hekemian, Jr.; John J. Skelly, Jr.; James M. Vandervalk.
EIN: 205692529
Selected grants: The following grants are a representative sample of this grantmaker's funding activity:
$24,784 to Eva's Village, Paterson, NJ, 2012. For donation general support.

5399
Oster Family Foundation, Inc. ✧ ☆
429 Sylvan Ave.
Englewood Cliffs, NJ 07632-2703

Established in 1992 in NJ.
Donors: Miriam Oster†; Commercial Realty; Oster Realty; Bernard Oster, Inc.; ABA Realty; Interstate Realty; Oster Finance; Oster Properties LLP.
Foundation type: Operating foundation.
Financial data (yr. ended 04/30/13): Assets, $6,859,274 (M); expenditures, $494,424; qualifying distributions, $482,321; giving activities include $482,321 for 38 grants (high: $150,000; low: $500).
Purpose and activities: Giving for Jewish organizations, including to a museum of Jewish heritage.
Fields of interest: Museums (specialized); Education; Health organizations; Human services; Jewish federated giving programs; Jewish agencies & synagogues.
Limitations: Applications not accepted. Giving primarily in NJ and NY. No grants to individuals.
Application information: Contributes only to pre-selected organizations.
Officers: Ann Oster, Pres.; Avi Oster, V.P.; Dan Oster, V.P.
EIN: 223188305

5400
Alfiero and Lucia Palestroni Foundation, Inc. ✧
333 Sylvan Ave.
Englewood Cliffs, NJ 07632-2724 (201) 568-8000
Contact: Kristine Sayrafe, Exec. Dir.

Established in NJ.
Donor: Alfiero Palestroni†.
Foundation type: Independent foundation.
Financial data (yr. ended 12/31/13): Assets, $26,529,594 (M); expenditures, $989,214; qualifying distributions, $812,546; giving activities include $606,591 for 22 grants (high: $250,000; low: $1,000).
Fields of interest: Higher education; Education; Hospitals (general); Human services.
Limitations: Applications accepted. Giving primarily in NJ. No grants to individuals.
Application information: Application form required.
Initial approach: Letter on applying organization's letterhead
Deadline(s): None
Officers: Lucia Palestroni, Pres.; Kristine Sayrafe, Exec. Dir.
Trustees: Frank Huttle III; Karen Lloyd; Debbie Sena.
EIN: 223452466
Selected grants: The following grants are a representative sample of this grantmaker's funding activity:
$250,000 to Seton Hall University, South Orange, NJ, 2011. For general support.
$52,000 to Valerie Fund, Maplewood, NJ, 2011. For general support.
$36,000 to Cerebral Palsy Center of Bergen County, Fair Lawn, NJ, 2011. For general support.
$16,000 to Adler Aphasia Center, Maywood, NJ, 2011. For general support.
$3,500 to Englewood Hospital and Medical Center Foundation, Englewood, NJ, 2011. For general support.
$2,500 to Community Chest of Englewood, Englewood, NJ, 2011. For general support.
$2,000 to Project Literacy of Bergen County, Hackensack, NJ, 2011. For general support.

5401
Parker Family Foundation ✧
P.O. Box 1501, NJ2-130-03-31
Pennington, NJ 08534-1501

Established in 2000 in MA.
Donors: Faith K. Parker; Glenn P. Parker.
Foundation type: Independent foundation.
Financial data (yr. ended 07/31/13): Assets, $10,327,226 (M); expenditures, $654,589; qualifying distributions, $607,814; giving activities include $577,600 for 10 grants (high: $102,600; low: $20,000).
Fields of interest: Museums; Arts; Education; Human services.
Limitations: Applications not accepted. Giving primarily in MA.
Application information: Unsolicited requests for funds not accepted.
Trustees: Faith K. Parker; Glenn P. Parker.
EIN: 043542674

5402
E. & H. Parnes Foundation Inc. ✧
P.O. Box 703
Edison, NJ 08818-0703

Established in 1971 in NY.
Donors: Emanuel Parnes; Herschel Parnes; Harvard Partners; FBE Limited.
Foundation type: Independent foundation.
Financial data (yr. ended 06/30/13): Assets, $2,901,509 (M); gifts received, $78,380; expenditures, $3,209,880; qualifying distributions, $3,198,159; giving activities include $3,198,159 for grants.
Purpose and activities: Funding primarily for Jewish agencies, temples, yeshivas, and seminaries.
Fields of interest: Elementary/secondary education; Jewish agencies & synagogues.
Limitations: Applications not accepted. Giving primarily in NY. No grants to individuals.

Application information: Unsolicited requests for funds not accepted.
Officers: Emanuel Parnes, Mgr.; Herschel Parnes, Mgr.
EIN: 237237932

5403
Pascale/Sykes Foundation, Inc. ✧
316 Broad St.
Red Bank, NJ 07701-2154 (732) 747-2807
Contact: Frances P. Sykes, Pres.
FAX: (732) 747-2691;
E-mail: generalmailbox@pascalesykesfoundation.com; Vineland, NJ address: 80 S. Main Rd., Ste. 114, Vineland, NJ 08360, tel.: (856) 213-5068, fax: (856) 457-7098; Main URL: http://www.pascalesykesfoundation.com
Facebook: https://www.facebook.com/pascalesykes
Twitter: https://twitter.com/PascaleSykes

Established in 1992 in NJ.
Donor: Frances P. Sykes.
Foundation type: Independent foundation.
Financial data (yr. ended 12/31/13): Assets, $47,445,519 (M); gifts received, $3,184,444; expenditures, $3,957,303; qualifying distributions, $3,535,980; giving activities include $2,800,706 for 19 grants (high: $288,405; low: $22,500).
Purpose and activities: Support given to innovative, flexible, holistic, long-range umbrella programs targeting working low-income families that promote the independence, well-being, and the integrity of the entire family unit, with emphasis on projects using integrated services and interagency linkages; the foundation also encourages programs with volunteers, neighborhood workers, interagency cooperation and marriage strengthening.
Fields of interest: Health care; Human services; Family services; Community development, neighborhood development; Economically disadvantaged.
Type of support: Management development/capacity building; Income development; Conferences/seminars; Continuing support; Emergency funds; Program development; Seed money; Research; Consulting services; Program evaluation; Program-related investments/loans; Matching/challenge support.
Limitations: Giving limited to NJ and parts of New York, NY, that are within the Red Bank, NJ, vicinity. No support for churches. No grants to individuals.
Publications: Annual report; Grants list; Informational brochure; Program policy statement.
Application information: Site visit and preliminary evaluation of project required before proposal will be considered; telephone to set date for site visits. Application form required.
Initial approach: Telephone call between Sept. 1 and May 15 for possible consideration of a project in May
Copies of proposal: 7
Board meeting date(s): Jan. and May
Final notification: 30 days
Officers and Trustees:* Frances P. Sykes,* Pres.; Elaine Bradford,* Secy.; Colleen Maguire, Treas. and Exec. Dir.; Debra French; James Gallagher; Michael Jeary; Jeanie F. Lazerov.
Number of staff: 1 part-time support.
EIN: 223161324

5404
Perrin Foundation Inc. ✧
14 Green Valley Dr.
Green Brook, NJ 08812-2036
Additional address: c/o Scott Thomson, 1335 Sterling Dr., York, PA 17404, tel.: (717) 505-8553

Established in 1928 in NY.
Donor: Mary Ricks†.
Foundation type: Independent foundation.
Financial data (yr. ended 12/31/13): Assets, $14,678,631 (M); expenditures, $941,351; qualifying distributions, $753,550; giving activities include $753,550 for 32 grants (high: $217,375; low: $1,400).
Purpose and activities: Giving limited to Christian organizations, including churches, nursing homes, missionary programs, and schools.
Fields of interest: Elementary/secondary education; Residential/custodial care, senior continuing care; Christian agencies & churches; Religion.
Type of support: Curriculum development; Continuing support; Building/renovation; General/operating support.
Limitations: Applications accepted. Giving primarily in the U.S. and to U.S.-originating missionaries. No support for political organizations. No grants to individuals.
Application information: Application form not required.
Initial approach: Proposal
Deadline(s): None
Board meeting date(s): May
Officers: Robert Dadd, Pres.; Robert Q. Bennett, V.P.; David C. Wohlgemuth, Secy.; R. Scott Thomson, Treas.
Directors: George MacKenzie; Daniel J. Mearns; Fred Schwertfeger; Robert Sullivan.
EIN: 226049335

5405
Gustavus and Louise Pfeiffer Research Foundation ☆
P.O. Box 765
Short Hills, NJ 07078-0765 (973) 376-0986
FAX: (973) 376-0987;
E-mail: pfeiffer.research.foundation@gmail.com; Main URL: http://www.pfeifferfoundation.org

Incorporated in 1942 in NY.
Donors: Gustavus A. Pfeiffer†; Louise F. Pfeiffer†.
Foundation type: Independent foundation.
Financial data (yr. ended 12/31/13): Assets, $26,568,174 (M); expenditures, $840,343; qualifying distributions, $767,270; giving activities include $621,857 for 8 grants (high: $100,000; low: $71,857).
Purpose and activities: The Foundation supports graduate medical scholarship programs and university medical/pharmacy related research projects.
Fields of interest: Medical school/education; Eye research; Ear, nose & throat research; Geriatrics research; Pediatrics research; Medical research; Nutrition.
Limitations: Giving limited to the U.S. No support for national fundraising organizations or publicly financed projects, or for projects involving vivisection or other experiments on animal subjects (excluding insects). No grants to individuals, or for dissertations, tuitions and fees for PhD or Masters programs or individual scholarship requests, or for building or endowment funds; overhead, supplies, equipment, travel, conferences, exhibits, seminars, lectures, workshops, surveys or general purposes, delivery of healthcare services, sabbatical leave, indirect costs, general programs of biomedical research, and projects which are more appropriate for support by other sources, such as pharmaceutical companies for commercial applications of existing products.
Application information: The foundation considers grant applications by invitation only. No other applications will be considered, except institutions with a current grant outstanding may apply for a renewal under the prior application process. Principal investigators with questions must go through their institution's office of sponsored research, which, in turn, will contact the foundation Secretary via email or phone. The foundation does not work directly with principal investigators. If invited, all formal applications must be mailed to the P.O. Box and received by the deadline. Note that courier services do not deliver to the U.S. Post Office. Electronic submissions will not be accepted.
Board meeting date(s): Apr. and Oct.
Officers: Kim Alvarez, Pres. and C.E.O.; H. Robert Herold II, V.P.; Matthew Mayro Keeney, Treas.
Directors: Matthew G. Herold, Jr.; Anne Herold Keeney; Sarah S. P. McCarthy; Patricia Herold Nagle.
Number of staff: None.
EIN: 136086299

5406
Howard Phipps Foundation ✧
c/o Bessemer Trust Co., N.A.
100 Woodbridge Ctr. Dr.
Woodbridge, NJ 07095-0983

Established in 1967 in NJ.
Donor: Harriet Phipps†.
Foundation type: Independent foundation.
Financial data (yr. ended 06/30/13): Assets, $3,275,946 (M); expenditures, $445,895; qualifying distributions, $429,500; giving activities include $429,500 for grants.
Fields of interest: Museums (natural history); Higher education; Environment, natural resources; Animals/wildlife, preservation/protection; Girl scouts; Human services; Community/economic development.
Limitations: Applications not accepted. Giving primarily in NY. No grants to individuals.
Application information: Contributes only to pre-selected organizations.
Trustees: Howard Phipps, Jr.; Anne P. Sidamon-Eristoff; Bessemer Trust Co., N.A.
EIN: 226095226

5407
Claudio and Penny Pincus Foundation ✧ ☆
133 Blackburn Dr.
Summit, NJ 07901-2301

Established in 2007 in NJ.
Donors: Claudio Pincus; Penny Pincus.
Foundation type: Independent foundation.
Financial data (yr. ended 12/31/12): Assets, $8,121,477 (M); expenditures, $471,424; qualifying distributions, $447,250; giving activities include $447,250 for grants.

Fields of interest: Arts; Religion.
Limitations: Applications not accepted. No grants to individuals.
Application information: Unsolicited requests for funds not accepted.
Officers: Claudio Pincus, Pres.; Aaron Pincus, V.P.; Daniel Pincus, V.P.; Penny Pincus, Secy.-Treas.
EIN: 261446530

5408
Winifred M. & George P. Pitkin Foundation Inc. ✧ ☆
900 Main St.
Hackensack, NJ 07601-4908 (201) 342-0167
Contact: Frances Hoffman, Tr.

Established in 1991 in NJ.
Donors: George M. Pitkin‡; Winifred M. Pitkin Inc.
Foundation type: Independent foundation.
Financial data (yr. ended 05/31/13): Assets, $13,638,742 (M); expenditures, $891,627; qualifying distributions, $549,600; giving activities include $450,000 for 3 grants (high: $150,000; low: $150,000).
Purpose and activities: The foundation was created for the benefit of persons desiring to further their education by attending college, and who are in need of assistance because of financial difficulties, or mental or physical disability. The foundation presently also donates to qualified charities in the fields of medicine and higher education.
Fields of interest: Higher education; Foundations (community).
Type of support: General/operating support; Capital campaigns; Equipment; Program development; Professorships.
Limitations: Applications accepted. Giving primarily in NJ.
Publications: Annual report; Financial statement.
Application information: Application form required.
Initial approach: Proposal
Copies of proposal: 2
Deadline(s): None
Board meeting date(s): Quarterly
Trustees: Joseph L. Basralian; Frances Hoffman.
Number of staff: 1 full-time support.
EIN: 223119444
Selected grants: The following grants are a representative sample of this grantmaker's funding activity:
$300,000 to Columbia University, New York, NY, 2011.

5409
Hellen I. Plummer Charitable Foundation, Inc. ✧
P.O. Box 1501, NJ2-130-03-31
Pennington, NJ 08534-1501

Established in 1997 in DE.
Donors: Hellen Ingram Plummer‡; Beatrice P. Potts Trust.
Foundation type: Independent foundation.
Financial data (yr. ended 12/31/13): Assets, $15,343,142 (M); expenditures, $924,316; qualifying distributions, $797,917; giving activities include $742,960 for 25 grants (high: $150,865; low: $6,820).
Fields of interest: Arts; Elementary/secondary education; Human services; Christian agencies & churches.
Type of support: General/operating support.
Limitations: Applications not accepted. Giving primarily in GA, with emphasis on the Atlanta area, and MA; giving also in AL, CT, FL, and NY. No grants to individuals.
Application information: Unsolicited requests for funds not accepted.
Trustees: William C. Crawford; Jere W. Goldsmith; Thomas J. Lombardi; Mark E. Magowan; Amy Merrill.
EIN: 223365605

5410
Point Gammon Foundation ✧
c/o Paseornek & Stimola CPAs PC
140 Rte. 17 N., Ste. 206
Paramus, NJ 07652-2822

Established in 1994 in DE.
Donor: Jane C. Carroll.
Foundation type: Independent foundation.
Financial data (yr. ended 12/31/13): Assets, $14,310,994 (M); expenditures, $1,040,084; qualifying distributions, $1,023,062; giving activities include $1,023,062 for 36 grants (high: $209,000; low: $500).
Purpose and activities: Giving primarily for the arts, education, and human services.
Fields of interest: Arts, formal/general education; Museums (art); Performing arts; Performing arts, ballet; Higher education; Hospitals (general); Human services; Protestant agencies & churches.
Limitations: Applications not accepted. Giving primarily in New York, NY; funding also in MA and RI.
Application information: Unsolicited requests for funds not accepted.
Directors: Jane C. Carroll; Jonathan C. Clay.
EIN: 134049057

5411
Princeton Area Community Foundation, Inc. ✧
(formerly The Princeton Area Foundation, Inc.)
15 Princess Rd.
Lawrenceville, NJ 08648-2301 (609) 219-1800
Contact: Nancy W. Kieling, Pres.
FAX: (609) 219-1850; E-mail: info@pacf.org; Main URL: http://www.pacf.org
Blog: http://pacf.org/about/blog/
E-Newsletter: http://visitor.r20.constantcontact.com/manage/optin/ea?v=001M6t4uPDAuUosqZXG2NXM7cpTZ_vgysF174H7fKucHoUtXly0HvbPuW4kCl4tp8_q
Twitter: https://twitter.com/princetonareacf

Established in 1991 in NJ.
Foundation type: Community foundation.
Financial data (yr. ended 12/31/13): Assets, $98,639,543 (M); gifts received, $8,652,927; expenditures, $9,354,740; giving activities include $7,491,913 for 203+ grants (high: $440,600), and $201,102 for 58 grants to individuals.
Purpose and activities: The foundation seeks to promote philanthropy across central New Jersey by managing charitable funds created by members of the community, providing competitive discretionary grants to nonprofits, and by making advised grants to nonprofits after consultation with individuals or groups of donors. The foundation also serves as a convener and catalyst, leveraging new funds, and creating partnerships to enable residents to solve community problems.
Fields of interest: Education; Health care; Substance abuse, services; Minorities/immigrants, centers/services; Human services; Community/economic development; Minorities; Economically disadvantaged.
Type of support: Scholarships—to individuals; General/operating support; Continuing support; Emergency funds; Program development; Seed money; Curriculum development; Scholarship funds; Technical assistance.
Limitations: Applications accepted. Giving limited to Mercer County, NJ and surrounding communities in Hunterdon, Somerset, Middlesex, Monmouth and Burlington counties. No support for fraternal and religious activities. No grants for building renovations and new facility construction, capital and endowment campaigns and projects, fundraising appeals and events, field trips (unless part of a larger educational effort), sports activities (unless part of a larger educational effort), or sponsorship of events (sponsorships are occasionally made as part of the foundation's marketing efforts, and solely at the foundation's initiation).
Publications: Application guidelines; Annual report; Grants list; Informational brochure; Newsletter.
Application information: Visit foundation web site for application forms and information. The foundation recommends attending a grant information session before applying for a grant. Application form required.
Initial approach: Submit application form and attachments
Copies of proposal: 1
Deadline(s): Varies
Board meeting date(s): Quarterly
Final notification: 3 months
Officers and Trustees:* David R. Scott,* Chair.; John S. Watson, Jr.,* Vice-Chair.; Carol P. Herring,* Vice-Chair.; Nancy W. Kieling,* Pres.; Michelle Cash,* V.P., Grants and Progs.; Elizabeth B. Wagner,* V.P., Devel.; Anne LaBate,* Secy.; Laura J. Longman, C.F.O.; Gordon Danser,* Treas. and Chair., Audit Comm.; William P. Burks, M.D.*, Chair., Asset Building Comm.; Andrew K. Golden,* Chair., Investment Comm.; Samuel W. Lambert III,* Chair., Grants Comm.; John D. Wallace,* Chair., Audit Comm.; Richard Bilotti; Anthony "Skip" Cimino; Sonia Delgado; Liz Erickson; Patricia U. Herst; Eleanor Horne; Meredith C. Moore; Jeffrey F. Perlman; Patrick L. Ryan; Carolyn Sanderson; Lisa Skeete Tatum; Thomas P. Weidner.
Number of staff: 4 full-time professional; 2 full-time support.
EIN: 521746234

5412
Princeton Regional Chamber of Commerce Foundation, Inc. ✧ ☆
(formerly The Free Enterprise Foundation, Inc.)
182 Nassau St., Ste. 301
Princeton, NJ 08542-7000 (609) 924-1776
E-mail: info@princetonchamber.org; Main URL: http://princetonchamberfoundation.org/

Established in 1995 in NJ.
Donors: Princeton University; Bristol Meyers Squibb.
Foundation type: Independent foundation.
Financial data (yr. ended 07/31/13): Assets, $97,899 (M); gifts received, $3,650; expenditures,

$540,343; qualifying distributions, $501,847; giving activities include $500,000 for 1 grant.
Purpose and activities: The foundation exists to effectively focus the skills and resources of the greater Princeton business community on the critical civic, educational, scientific, cultural and economic development interests of the region it serves. The foundation serves: 1) non-profit and local government boards, committees, councils, and commissions who are in need of a diverse, skilled, knowledgeable and passionate pool of community leaders; and 2) established and emerging business, academic, non-profit, and local government leaders throughout the greater Princeton region.
Fields of interest: Community/economic development; Foundations (community).
Limitations: Applications accepted. Giving primarily in NJ.
Application information: Application information and forms available on foundation web site. Application form required.
Deadline(s): None
Officers and Directors:* Patrick Ryan,* Chair.; Kristin Appelget,* Pres.; Peter Crowley,* Secy.; Roxanne L. Globis, Treas.; Peter Dawson; Maria A. Del Cristo; Deborah J. Frazier; Anna Lustenberg; Lori Rabon; Patrick Ryan; Hillary Spivak; Melissa Tenzer; John P. Thurber.
EIN: 223413287

5413
The Providence Charitable Foundation, Inc. ✧
c/o Schiff Foods
994 Riverview Dr.
Totowa, NJ 07512-1129 (973) 237-1990
Contact: David Deutscher, Tr.

Established in 1999 in NY.
Donor: Schiff Food Products Co.
Foundation type: Independent foundation.
Financial data (yr. ended 11/30/13): Assets, $4,273,587 (M); gifts received, $750,000; expenditures, $728,850; qualifying distributions, $700,596; giving activities include $700,596 for grants.
Fields of interest: Jewish agencies & synagogues.
Limitations: Applications accepted. Giving primarily in NJ.
Application information: Application form required.
Initial approach: Letter
Deadline(s): None
Trustee: David Deutscher.
EIN: 134037405

5414
The Provident Bank Foundation ✧
239 Washington St., Ste. 401
Jersey City, NJ 07302 (201) 499-0883
Main URL: http://www.providentnjfoundation.org

Established in 2003 in NJ.
Donor: Provident Financial Services, Inc.
Foundation type: Company-sponsored foundation.
Financial data (yr. ended 12/31/13): Assets, $23,748,440 (M); expenditures, $1,425,550; qualifying distributions, $1,340,148; giving activities include $1,044,173 for 215 grants (high: $100,000; low: $500).
Purpose and activities: The foundation supports programs designed to promote family and youth services; community enrichment; education; and health and human services.
Fields of interest: Arts education; Museums; Arts; Elementary/secondary education; Adult/continuing education; Libraries (public); Education, services; Education; Hospitals (general); Health care; Mental health/crisis services; Employment, services; Food services; Food banks; Housing/shelter; Recreation; Youth development, centers/clubs; Youth development, adult & child programs; Youth, services; Human services, financial counseling; Residential/custodial care, hospices; Homeless, human services; Human services; Public affairs.
Type of support: Curriculum development; Research; General/operating support; Continuing support; Management development/capacity building; Capital campaigns; Building/renovation; Equipment; Program development; Seed money; Scholarship funds; Matching/challenge support.
Limitations: Applications accepted. Giving is limited to areas of company operations in NJ, with emphasis on Bergen, Essex, Hudson, Mercer, Middlesex, Monmouth, Morris, Ocean, Passaic, Somerset, and Union counties. No support for political organizations or religious organizations not of direct benefit to the entire community, or for pass-through organizations.
Publications: Application guidelines; Annual report.
Application information: Application form required.
Initial approach: Completed application form
Copies of proposal: 1
Deadline(s): Jan. 1, Apr. 1, July 1, and Oct. 1
Board meeting date(s): Jan., Apr., July, and Oct.
Officers and Directors:* Carlos M. Hernandez, Chair.; Christopher P. Martin,* Pres.; John F. Kuntz, Secy.; George Dailey, Jr., Treas.; Jane Kurek, Exec. Dir.; Katharine Laud; Karen McMullen.
Number of staff: 1 part-time professional.
EIN: 043739441

5415
The Prudential Foundation ✧
751 Broad St., 15th Fl.
Prudential Plz.
Newark, NJ 07102-3777 (973) 802-4070
Contact: Lata Reddy, V.P., Corp. Social Responsibility
E-mail: community.resources@prudential.com; Main URL: http://www.prudential.com/view/page/public/12182

Incorporated in 1977 in NJ.
Donors: The Prudential Insurance Co. of America; Prudential Equity Group, LLC.
Foundation type: Company-sponsored foundation.
Financial data (yr. ended 12/31/12): Assets, $107,236,777 (M); gifts received, $30,066,825; expenditures, $27,422,063; qualifying distributions, $33,074,610; giving activities include $20,191,025 for 858 grants (high: $1,000,000; low: $250), $221,294 for 558 grants to individuals, $6,447,539 for 11,209 employee matching gifts, and $5,864,502 for 3 loans/program-related investments.
Purpose and activities: The foundation supports organizations involved with education; economic development; and arts and culture.
Fields of interest: Arts education; Arts; Education, reform; Education; Employment, services; Community development, neighborhood development; Economic development; Community development, small businesses; Leadership development; Youth; Economically disadvantaged.
International interests: Brazil; India; Japan; Mexico; North Korea; South Korea; Taiwan.
Type of support: General/operating support; Management development/capacity building; Capital campaigns; Emergency funds; Program development; Seed money; Technical assistance; Program-related investments/loans; Employee matching gifts; Mission-related investments/loans.
Limitations: Applications accepted. Giving primarily in areas of company operations, with emphasis on Phoenix, AZ, Los Angeles, CA, Hartford, CT, Jacksonville, FL, Dubuque, IA, Chicago, IL, New Orleans, LA, Minneapolis, MN, Newark, NJ, New York, NY, Philadelphia and Scranton, PA, and in Brazil, India, Japan, Korea, Mexico, and Taiwan; giving also to national organizations. No support for discriminatory organizations or labor, religious, fraternal, or athletic organizations, or single-disease health groups. No grants to individuals or for goodwill advertising.
Publications: Application guidelines; Annual report (including application guidelines).
Application information: The foundation accepts the New York/ New Jersey Area Common Application Form and the New York/ New Jersey Common Report Form. Additional information may be requested at a later date. Video submissions are not encouraged. Application form required.
Initial approach: Complete online application
Deadline(s): None
Board meeting date(s): Feb., June, and Oct.
Final notification: Within 60 days
Officers and Trustees:* Sharon C. Taylor,* Chair.; Lata N. Reddy, Pres.; Shane Harris, V.P. and Secy.; James W. McCarthy, Treas.; Brian Cloonan, Cont.; Gilbert F. Casellas; Constance J. Horner; Barbara G. Koster; John R. Strangfeld, Jr.
Number of staff: 5 full-time professional; 4 full-time support.
EIN: 222175290
Selected grants: The following grants are a representative sample of this grantmaker's funding activity:
$3,000,000 to New Jersey Symphony Orchestra, Newark, NJ, 2013. For comprehensive campaign to grow endowment and to provide world class orchestral performances across the state.
$2,400,000 to Architecture for Humanity, San Francisco, CA, 2013. To establish a one-stop business support center, as part of the disaster management process in Japan, to help develop small and medium enterprises in the Tohoku area.
$1,850,000 to Washington Center for Internships and Academic Seminars, Washington, DC, 2013. To continue and expand Prudential Foundation Global Citizens program, international exchange and experiential education program targeting high achieving college students from India, Japan, Korea and Taiwan.
$1,325,000 to YouthBuild USA, Somerville, MA, 2013. To establish two affiliates in Brazil and expand program in Mexico.
$1,000,000 to Community Foundation of New Jersey, Morristown, NJ, 2013. For Newark Strong Healthy Communities Initiative, which supports integrated strategies around preventive healthcare, housing, public spaces, fresh food, and local employment to help end the negative cycle of poverty and to help citizens pursue economic advancement and educational achievement. The Initiative is a collaboration of cross sector partners focused on creating lasting change for Newark's youth and families by improving the health of Newark neighborhoods and its children.

$1,000,000 to Trust for Public Land, Newark, NJ, 2013. For efforts to create public parks that help to revitalize local economies, improve public health and strengthen urban neighborhoods in Newark, NJ and Bridgeport, CT.
$200,000 to La Casa de Don Pedro, Newark, NJ, 2012. For capacity building and general operating support.
$165,000 to United States Fund for UNICEF, New York, NY, 2013. For earthquake relief efforts in China.
$150,000 to United Way of Central and Northeastern Connecticut, Hartford, CT, 2013. For Workforce Solutions Collaborative of Metro Hartford, a funders' collaborative and network of public/private organizations committed to facilitating career advancement opportunities for low income workers in Hartford.
$75,000 to BoardSource, Washington, DC, 2012. For Prudential Leadership Awards for Exceptional Nonprofit Boards.
$50,000 to Citizen Schools New Jersey, Newark, NJ, 2012. For Managing Challenging Behavior.
$50,000 to Saint Benedicts Preparatory School, Newark, NJ, 2013. To strengthen capacity to continue delivering a rigorous educational experience for young men in Newark.
$50,000 to Save the Children Federation, Fairfield, CT, 2012. For Disaster Relief Payments - Hurricane Sandy.
$45,000 to Newark School of the Arts, Newark, NJ, 2013. To develop new strategic plan.
$40,000 to ArtPride New Jersey Foundation, Burlington, NJ, 2012. For Arts/Business Partnership.
$15,000 to Commission on Economic Opportunity of Luzerne County, Wilkes Barre, PA, 2012. For CEO/Weinberg NE Regional Food Bank.

5416
PSEG Foundation, Inc. ✧

(formerly Public Service Electric and Gas Company Foundation, Inc.)
80 Park Plz., 10C
Newark, NJ 07102-4109 (973) 430-7842
Contact: Marion C. O'Neill, Mgr., Corp. Contribs.
FAX: (973) 297-1480;
E-mail: marion.oneill@pseg.com; Additional tel.: (973) 430-5874; e-mail: corporatecitizenship@pseg.com; Main URL: https://www.pseg.com/info/community/new_site/giving.jsp

Established in 1991 in NJ.
Donors: Public Service Electric and Gas Co.; Public Service Enterprise Group, Inc.
Foundation type: Company-sponsored foundation.
Financial data (yr. ended 12/31/13): Assets, $25,742,682 (M); expenditures, $6,512,992; qualifying distributions, $6,512,992; giving activities include $6,512,992 for grants.
Purpose and activities: The foundation supports organizations involved with sustainable neighborhoods; STEM education; safety and disaster preparedness and response; and PSEG employee engagement and volunteerism.
Fields of interest: Elementary/secondary education; Higher education; Education, services; Environment, climate change/global warming; Environment, natural resources; Environment, energy; Environmental education; Health care; Disasters, preparedness/services; Youth development; Economic development; Urban/community development; Community/economic development; Science, formal/general education; Mathematics; Engineering/technology; Science.
Type of support: Management development/capacity building; Continuing support; Program development; Employee volunteer services; Use of facilities; Employee matching gifts.
Limitations: Applications accepted. Giving primarily in areas where PSEG does business. No support for religious or political organizations, discriminatory organizations, lobbying organizations, athletic, labor, or fraternal groups, or disease-specific organizations. No grants to individuals, or for political causes or campaigns, or endowments.
Publications: Application guidelines; Corporate report; Newsletter (including application guidelines).
Application information: Multi-year funding is not automatic. Application form required.
Initial approach: Complete online application form
Deadline(s): Jan. 1 to Oct. 31 for general funding; June 2 to Aug. 1 for Neighborhood Partner Program; July 7 to Aug. 15 for Science SPARK Partners Program
Board meeting date(s): 3 times per year
Final notification: 6 months
Officers and Trustees:* Richard T. Thigpen,* Chair. and C.E.O.; Ellen Lambert,* Pres.; Courtney M. McCormick, Secy.; Derek M. DiRisio, Cont.; Caroline Dorsa; Anne. E. Hoskins; Bradford D. Huntin; Gwen Kell; Robert C. Krueger; Ralph A. LaRossa; William Levis; Tamara L. Linde; Randall E. Mehrberg; Clifford Pardo; Benjamin Zoe.
Number of staff: 7 full-time professional.
EIN: 223125880
Selected grants: The following grants are a representative sample of this grantmaker's funding activity:
$500,000 to Childrens Specialized Hospital, Mountainside, NJ, 2012.
$285,000 to Rutgers, The State University of New Jersey, Newark, NJ, 2012.
$275,000 to Sustainable Jersey, Ewing, NJ, 2012.
$200,000 to New Jersey Performing Arts Center, Newark, NJ, 2012.
$200,000 to Newark Museum, Newark, NJ, 2012.
$135,000 to Boys and Girls Clubs in New Jersey, Clifton, NJ, 2012.
$133,000 to Montclair State University, Sustainablility Institute, Montclair, NJ, 2012.
$100,000 to Cooper University Hospital, Camden, NJ, 2012.
$80,000 to Foundation for New Jersey Public Broadcasting, Trenton, NJ, 2012.
$60,000 to Saint Peter's University, Jersey City, NJ, 2012.
$50,000 to Cooper's Ferry Partnership, Camden, NJ, 2012.

5417
Puffin Foundation, Ltd. ✧

20 Puffin Way
Teaneck, NJ 07666-4167
Contact: Gladys Miller-Rosenstein, Exec. Dir.
Main URL: http://www.puffinfoundation.org

Established in 1985 in NY.
Donors: Perry Rosenstein; Brighton-Best Socket Screw Manufacturing, Inc.
Foundation type: Independent foundation.
Financial data (yr. ended 12/31/12): Assets, $12,466,688 (M); gifts received, $1,000,694; expenditures, $2,614,568; qualifying distributions, $2,346,428; giving activities include $1,253,826 for grants, and $668,220 for 339 grants to individuals.
Purpose and activities: The foundation make grants that encourage emerging artists whose works might have difficulty being aired due to their genre and/or social philosophy. Current areas of interest are video/film, fine arts, dance, and public interest.
Fields of interest: Media, film/video; Performing arts, dance; Arts.
Type of support: Publication; Seed money; Fellowships; Grants to individuals.
Limitations: Applications accepted. Giving on a national basis. No support for religious organizations. No grants for travel, general living expenses, continuing education, or publications.
Publications: Application guidelines.
Application information:
Initial approach: Send a S.A.S.E. (#10 business letter sized envelope) to request application form
Deadline(s): See foundation web site for current deadline
Board meeting date(s): Annually
Officers and Directors:* Perry Rosenstein,* Pres.; Gladys Miller-Rosenstein, Exec. Dir; Carl Rosenstein; Neal Rosenstein.
Number of staff: 6
EIN: 133155489

5418
R. & R. Family Foundation, Inc. ✧

1070 U.S. Hwy. 46
Ledgewood, NJ 07852-9735 (973) 927-8300

Established in 2008 in NJ.
Donors: Dominick V. Romano; Mrs. Dominick V. Romano; Ronetco Supermarkets Inc.
Foundation type: Independent foundation.
Financial data (yr. ended 05/31/13): Assets, $3,074,264 (M); expenditures, $661,558; qualifying distributions, $644,000; giving activities include $644,000 for 11 grants (high: $290,000; low: $1,500).
Fields of interest: Elementary/secondary education; Education; Health care; Christian agencies & churches.
Limitations: Applications accepted. Giving primarily in NJ.
Application information: Application form not required.
Initial approach: Letter
Deadline(s): None
Officers and Trustees:* Dominick V. Romano,* Pres.; Dominick J. Romano,* V.P.; Kathryn P. Romano,* Secy.; David P. Romano,* Treas.; Nina A. Romano.
EIN: 320217970
Selected grants: The following grants are a representative sample of this grantmaker's funding activity:
$100,000 to Blair Academy, Blairstown, NJ, 2011.
$100,000 to SCARC, Augusta, NJ, 2011.
$70,000 to Hilltop Country Day School, Sparta, NJ, 2011.

5419
Ramapo Trust ✧
c/o The Brookdale Foundation Group
300 Frank W. Burr Blvd., Ste. 13
Teaneck, NJ 07666-6703 (201) 836-4602
Contact: For inquiry by mail:: Stephen L. Schwartz, Tr.; For telephone inquiries: Nora O'Brien
FAX: (201) 836-4342;
E-mail: vcb@brookdalefoundation.org; Main URL: http://www.brookdalefoundation.org/

Trust established in 1973 in NY.
Donors: Henry L. Schwartz†; Montebello Trust.
Foundation type: Independent foundation.
Financial data (yr. ended 06/30/13): Assets, $69,803,097 (M); expenditures, $4,148,859; qualifying distributions, $3,595,392; giving activities include $2,684,503 for 45 grants (high: $2,000,000; low: $953).
Purpose and activities: Giving for gerontological and geriatric research and innovative services; support also for health, higher and other education.
Fields of interest: Higher education; Medical school/education; Health care; Health organizations, association; Medical research, institute; Human services; Aging, centers/services; Jewish agencies & synagogues; Aging.
Type of support: Program development; Conferences/seminars; Seed money; Research; Matching/challenge support.
Limitations: Applications not accepted. Giving on a national basis. No grants to individuals, or for capital or building campaigns, operating budgets, continuing support, annual campaigns, media or the arts, or deficit financing; no loans.
Application information: Contributes only to pre-selected organizations.
Board meeting date(s): Quarterly
Trustees: Arthur Norman Field; Karen Schwartz Hart; Stephen L. Schwartz; Rebecca Shaffer; Mary Ann Van Clief.
Number of staff: 3 full-time professional; 2 part-time support.
EIN: 136594279

5420
The Reeves Foundation, Inc. ✧
115 Summit Ave.
Summit, NJ 07901-2899

Established in 1988 as successor foundation to The Reeves Brothers Foundation, Inc.
Donor: John E. Reeves, Jr.
Foundation type: Independent foundation.
Financial data (yr. ended 06/30/13): Assets, $24,796,463 (M); gifts received, $55,571; expenditures, $1,607,808; qualifying distributions, $1,253,946; giving activities include $969,027 for 12 grants (high: $250,000; low: $3,000).
Fields of interest: Higher education; Youth development, scouting agencies (general).
Type of support: Capital campaigns.
Limitations: Applications not accepted. Giving primarily in NC, NJ, and NY. No grants to individuals.
Application information: Contributes only to pre-selected organizations. Unsolicited requests for funds not considered or acknowledged.
Board meeting date(s): Quarterly
Officers: J.E. Reeves, Jr., Pres. and Treas.; Caroline Strong, V.P. and Secy.
Directors: Jane R. Mahelis; John E. Reeves III; Katherine Mercer Reeves; Daphne Wagner.
Number of staff: 1 full-time professional; 2 full-time support.
EIN: 581792933

5421
Renewable Foundation, Inc. ✧
c/o Ken Slutsky, Tax Exempt Inst. Group-Lowenstein Sandler
65 Livingston Ave.
Roseland, NJ 07068-1725

Established in 2005 in NJ.
Foundation type: Independent foundation.
Financial data (yr. ended 11/30/13): Assets, $28,096,696 (M); expenditures, $1,550,000; qualifying distributions, $1,550,000; giving activities include $1,550,000 for 1 grant.
Fields of interest: Jewish federated giving programs.
Limitations: Applications not accepted. Giving primarily in New York, NY. No grants to individuals.
Application information: Contributes only to pre-selected organizations.
Officers: Kenneth J. Slutsky, Pres. and Treas.; Allen Levithan, V.P. and Secy.; John L. Berger, V.P.
EIN: 861135859

5422
Nora Roberts Foundation ✧
P.O. Box 1501, NJ2-130-03-31
Pennington, NJ 08534-1501

Established in 1999 in MD.
Donors: Nora Roberts; Eleanor Wilder Trust; Nora Roberts Charitable Lead Annuity Trust I; Nora Roberts Charitable Lead Annuity Trust II; Jason Aufdem-Brinke; Jennifer Wilson; Dianne Eff; Harvey Friedman; John Arguelles; Lora McGraw; Regina King; Joseph Danis.
Foundation type: Independent foundation.
Financial data (yr. ended 07/31/13): Assets, $54,723,331 (M); gifts received, $4,210,385; expenditures, $2,679,127; qualifying distributions, $2,205,713; giving activities include $1,608,545 for 106 grants (high: $110,000; low: $500).
Purpose and activities: Giving primarily for the arts, education, health organizations, and human services.
Fields of interest: Performing arts, theater; Arts; Higher education; Adult education—literacy, basic skills & GED; Education; Health organizations, association; Human services.
Type of support: General/operating support.
Limitations: Applications not accepted. Giving in the U.S., with emphasis on MD; some emphasis also on NY and WV. No grants to individuals.
Application information: Contributes only to pre-selected organizations.
Trustees: Daniel N. Aufdem-Brinke; Jason M. Aufdem-Brinke; Kathryn Pong; Charlotte Ryan.
EIN: 522189081
Selected grants: The following grants are a representative sample of this grantmaker's funding activity:
$50,000 to Habitat for Humanity International, Americus, GA, 2011.

5423
The Norman and Bettina Roberts Foundation, Inc. ✧
277 Fairfield Rd., No. 300
Fairfield, NJ 07004-1942

Established in 1992 in NY.
Donors: Norman Roberts†; Bettina Roberts†.
Foundation type: Independent foundation.
Financial data (yr. ended 12/31/12): Assets, $26,340,308 (M); expenditures, $1,710,937; qualifying distributions, $1,710,937; giving activities include $1,491,250 for grants.
Purpose and activities: Giving for human services and education.
Fields of interest: Education; Youth development; Human services; Jewish federated giving programs; Christian agencies & churches; Catholic agencies & churches; Jewish agencies & synagogues.
Type of support: General/operating support; Continuing support; Emergency funds; Matching/challenge support.
Limitations: Applications not accepted. Giving primarily in NJ and NY; some funding also in NC. No grants to individuals, or for administrative expenses.
Application information: Contributes only to pre-selected organizations.
Board meeting date(s): Various
Officers: Lawrence Magid, Pres.; David McIntee, Treas.; Joseph R. Canciglia, Secy.
EIN: 133702467
Selected grants: The following grants are a representative sample of this grantmaker's funding activity:
$34,000 to Chabad of Port Washington, Port Washington, NY, 2012. For children's playground.
$25,000 to American Friends of Shalva, New York, NY, 2012. For Programs for physically Challenged.
$10,000 to Art Education for the Blind, New York, NY, 2012. For assistance to blind.
$10,000 to Lighthouse International, New York, NY, 2012. For Comprehensive Music Program for Young People (Blind).
$5,000 to Manhattan Jewish Experience, New York, NY, 2012. For religious education programs.
$2,750 to Housing for New Hope, Durham, NC, 2012. For emergency assistance.
$2,500 to Freedom House Foundation, Glen Gardner, NJ, 2012. For substance abuse rehabilitation Programs.
$1,000 to Alamance Community College Foundation, Graham, NC, 2012. For Ivan Burger Memorial Scholarship.
$750 to Communities of Faith for Housing, Hoboken, NJ, 2012. For Food Pantry and homeless assistance.
$500 to KidZNotes, Durham, NC, 2012. For Inner City Children's music Program.

5424
Robertson Foundation for Government Inc. ✧ ☆
c/o WithumSmith Brown, CPAs
331 Newman Springs Rd., Ste. 125
Red Bank, NJ 07701-6765

Established in 2006 in DE.
Foundation type: Independent foundation.
Financial data (yr. ended 12/31/13): Assets, $11,317,994 (M); gifts received, $6,462,500; expenditures, $1,858,875; qualifying distributions,

$1,491,884; giving activities include $850,398 for 9 grants (high: $206,250; low: $1,000).
Fields of interest: Education.
Type of support: Building/renovation.
Limitations: Applications not accepted. Giving primarily in CA, MD, MA, NY and TX.
Application information: Unsolicited request for funds not accepted.
Officers: Robert Halligan, Chair.; Katherine R. Ernst, Pres.; Geoffrey S. Robertson, Secy.; John H. Linnartz, Treas.; Timothy Kemper, Exec. Dir.
Board Members: Robert Ernest; Charles R. Meier.
EIN: 204630877

5425
The Rose Foundation ✧
P.O. Box 359
Elmwood Park, NJ 07407-0359

Established in 1990 in NJ.
Donors: Martin J. Wygod; Emily Wygod; Max Wygod; WebMD Health Corp.; Sync Inc.
Foundation type: Independent foundation.
Financial data (yr. ended 11/30/12): Assets, $2,774,955 (M); gifts received, $20,000; expenditures, $1,188,413; qualifying distributions, $1,165,134; giving activities include $1,057,658 for 34 grants (high: $500,000; low: $177).
Fields of interest: Arts; Education; Health care; Health organizations, association; Medical research, institute; Boys & girls clubs; Children/youth, services.
Limitations: Applications not accepted. Giving primarily in CA and NC. No grants to individuals.
Publications: Occasional report.
Application information: Contributes only to pre-selected organizations.
Officers: Pamela Wygod, Pres.; Frank J. Failla, Jr., V.P.; Charles A. Mele, V.P.; Martin J. Wygod, Secy.-Treas.
Director: Dixie Newman.
Trustee: Emily Wygod.
Number of staff: 2 part-time professional.
EIN: 223088744

5426
Daryl & Steven Roth Foundation ✧
c/o Interstate Properties
210 E. State Rte. 4
Paramus, NJ 07652-5108

Established in 1994 in NJ.
Donor: Steven Roth.
Foundation type: Independent foundation.
Financial data (yr. ended 12/31/13): Assets, $663,539 (M); gifts received, $900,000; expenditures, $755,239; qualifying distributions, $755,012; giving activities include $755,012 for 83 grants (high: $100,000; low: $250).
Purpose and activities: Giving primarily for Jewish agencies and temples, Jewish federated giving programs, education, the arts, and health and human services.
Fields of interest: Performing arts; Performing arts, theater; Arts; Elementary/secondary education; Higher education; Theological school/education; Education; Health care; Health organizations, association; Youth development; Human services; Jewish federated giving programs; Jewish agencies & synagogues.
Limitations: Applications not accepted. Giving primarily in NJ and NY. No grants to individuals.
Application information: Contributes only to pre-selected organizations.
Trustee: Steven Roth.
EIN: 223339611

5427
Henry M. Rowan Family Foundation, Inc. ✧
P.O. Box 157
Rancocas, NJ 08073-0157
Application address: c/o Henry M. Rowan, Pres., 10 Indel Ave., Rancocas, NJ 08073

Established in 1999 in NJ.
Donor: Henry M. Rowan.
Foundation type: Independent foundation.
Financial data (yr. ended 12/31/13): Assets, $214,900,561 (M); gifts received, $30,196,522; expenditures, $7,485,867; qualifying distributions, $6,878,000; giving activities include $6,878,000 for 45 grants (high: $1,500,000; low: $5,000).
Fields of interest: Scholarships/financial aid; Education; Environment; Human services.
Limitations: Applications accepted. Giving primarily in NJ and NY.
Application information: Application form not required.
Initial approach: Letter
Deadline(s): None
Officers and Directors:* Henry M. Rowan,* Pres.; Virginia Rowan Smith,* V.P.; Manning J. Smith III,* Secy.-Treas.; Gilbert A. Gehin-Scott; Eleanor Rowan.
EIN: 223655770

5428
Steven and Beverly Rubenstein Charitable Foundation, Inc. ✧
101 E. Main St.
Little Falls, NJ 07424-5608

Established in 2003 in NJ.
Donor: Steven Rubenstein.
Foundation type: Independent foundation.
Financial data (yr. ended 12/31/13): Assets, $29,266,738 (M); expenditures, $2,136,907; qualifying distributions, $1,959,559; giving activities include $1,959,559 for 48 grants (high: $1,000,000; low: $500).
Fields of interest: Elementary/secondary education; Higher education, university; Science, research; Jewish agencies & synagogues.
Type of support: General/operating support.
Limitations: Applications not accepted. Giving primarily in NJ, with emphasis on Gladstone, New York, NY, and Burlington, VT. No grants to individuals.
Application information: Contributes only to pre-selected organizations.
Trustees: Barry Mandelbaum; Andrew Rubenstein; Beverly Rubenstein.
EIN: 200223308

5429
Ruesch Family Foundation, Inc. ✧
P.O. Box 1501, NJ2-130-03-31
Pennington, NJ 08534-1501

Established in 2004 in MD.
Donor: Jeanette Weaver Ruesch.
Foundation type: Independent foundation.
Financial data (yr. ended 12/31/13): Assets, $15,351,307 (M); expenditures, $1,527,013; qualifying distributions, $1,445,713; giving activities include $1,402,500 for 12 grants (high: $1,000,000; low: $2,500).
Fields of interest: Secondary school/education; Higher education; Education; Catholic agencies & churches.
Limitations: Applications not accepted. Giving primarily in the greater Washington, DC, area, including portions of MD. No grants to individuals.
Application information: Contributes only to pre-selected organizations.
Officers: Jeanette Weaver Ruesch, Chair. and Pres.; Matthew Ruesch, Secy.-Treas.
EIN: 201851598
Selected grants: The following grants are a representative sample of this grantmaker's funding activity:
$605,000 to Georgetown University Medical Center, Washington, DC, 2011.
$60,000 to National Rehabilitation Hospital, Washington, DC, 2011.
$50,000 to Gonzaga College High School, Washington, DC, 2011.
$10,000 to Center for American Progress, Washington, DC, 2011.
$10,000 to Providence Health Foundation, Washington, DC, 2011.
$5,000 to Sibley Memorial Hospital Foundation, Washington, DC, 2011.

5430
The Fred C. Rummel Foundation ✧
101 JFK Pkwy.
Short Hills, NJ 07078-2708
Application address: c/o Annemarie Puleio, Exec. Dir., 316 Lenox Ave., Ste. 2C Westfield, NJ 07090; tel.: (908) 317-8600

Established in 1997 in NJ.
Foundation type: Independent foundation.
Financial data (yr. ended 12/31/13): Assets, $11,156,169 (M); expenditures, $558,124; qualifying distributions, $521,827; giving activities include $482,300 for 84 grants (high: $25,000; low: $500).
Purpose and activities: Grant support for children, elderly, human services, and health programs.
Fields of interest: Education; Health organizations, association; Youth development; Human services.
Limitations: Applications accepted. Giving primarily in NJ. No grants for operating capital.
Publications: Application guidelines.
Application information: Application form required.
Initial approach: Contact foundation
Copies of proposal: 5
Deadline(s): None
Trustees: Patricia Burch Byers; Robert W. Cockren; Bank of America, N.A.
Number of staff: 1 part-time professional.
EIN: 226703253
Selected grants: The following grants are a representative sample of this grantmaker's funding activity:
$5,000 to Adler Aphasia Center, Maywood, NJ, 2011.

5431
The RuthMarc Foundation, Inc. ✧ ☆
37 Hageman Ln.
Princeton, NJ 08540-7547

Established in 2000 in NJ and DE.
Donor: Andrew M. Okun.
Foundation type: Independent foundation.
Financial data (yr. ended 03/31/13): Assets, $2,493,698 (M); gifts received, $100,626; expenditures, $430,424; qualifying distributions, $429,000; giving activities include $429,000 for 21 grants (high: $60,000; low: $1,000).
Fields of interest: Higher education; Legal services, public interest law; Public policy, research.
Limitations: Applications not accepted. Giving primarily in Washington, DC, MA and NJ. No grants to individuals.
Application information: Contributes only to pre-selected organizations.
Officers: Andrew M. Okun, Pres. and Treas.; Laurie R. Okun, V.P. and Secy.
EIN: 061580750
Selected grants: The following grants are a representative sample of this grantmaker's funding activity:
$45,000 to Princeton University, Princeton, NJ, 2011.
$30,000 to New Jersey SEEDS, Newark, NJ, 2011.
$25,000 to University of Pennsylvania, Philadelphia, PA, 2011.
$20,000 to Cato Institute, Washington, DC, 2011.
$20,000 to Massachusetts Institute of Technology, Cambridge, MA, 2011.
$20,000 to Reason Foundation, Los Angeles, CA, 2011.
$12,000 to Drug Policy Alliance, New York, NY, 2011.
$5,000 to Harvey Mudd College, Claremont, CA, 2011.
$5,000 to Princeton Junior School, Princeton, NJ, 2011.
$2,500 to Centurion Ministries, Princeton, NJ, 2011.

5432
The Charles and Brenda Saka Family Foundation ✧
c/o Charles Saka
195 Carter Dr.
Edison, NJ 08817-2068

Established in 2001 in NJ.
Donor: Sakar International Inc.
Foundation type: Company-sponsored foundation.
Financial data (yr. ended 12/31/13): Assets, $1,396,546 (M); gifts received, $1,344,930; expenditures, $729,471; qualifying distributions, $728,810; giving activities include $728,810 for 198 grants (high: $150,000; low: $100).
Purpose and activities: The foundation supports organizations involved with education, children and youth, and Judaism.
Fields of interest: Education; Agriculture/food; Religion.
Type of support: General/operating support.
Limitations: Applications not accepted.
Application information: Contributes only to pre-selected organizations.
Trustees: Charles Saka; Jeffrey Saka; Raymond Saka; Sammy Saka.
EIN: 316650219

5433
The Samaritan Project Inc. ✧
c/o Pauline Lascano
209 Ridgewood Ave.
Glen Ridge, NJ 07028-1216

Established in 2000 in NY.
Donors: Daniel R. Lascano; Pauline P. Melfi; Pauline Lascano.
Foundation type: Independent foundation.
Financial data (yr. ended 12/31/13): Assets, $21,848,486 (M); gifts received, $1,500,000; expenditures, $1,124,430; qualifying distributions, $1,097,210; giving activities include $1,090,000 for 22 grants (high: $175,000; low: $10,000).
Fields of interest: Human services; Christian agencies & churches.
Limitations: Applications not accepted. Giving primarily in CA, CO, NJ, and NY.
Application information: Contributes only to pre-selected organizations.
Officers and Director:* Pauline Lascano, Pres.; Diana M. Lascano,* V.P.
Board Members: Christopher Lascano; Daniel Lascano; Jeffrey Lascano.
EIN: 134107424

5434
Marvin Samson Foundation ✧
P.O. Box 2730
Cherry Hill, NJ 08034-0236

Established in 2003 in NJ.
Donors: Marvin Samson; Marvin Samson Charitable Lead Annuity Trust.
Foundation type: Independent foundation.
Financial data (yr. ended 12/31/13): Assets, $1,940,311 (M); gifts received, $686,287; expenditures, $579,818; qualifying distributions, $560,050; giving activities include $556,875 for 28 grants (high: $200,000; low: $25).
Fields of interest: Education; Jewish agencies & synagogues.
Limitations: Applications not accepted. Giving primarily in NJ and PA. No grants to individuals.
Application information: Contributes only to pre-selected organizations.
Officer: Marvin Samson, Fdn. Mgr.
EIN: 226943216
Selected grants: The following grants are a representative sample of this grantmaker's funding activity:
$125 to National Constitution Center, Philadelphia, PA, 2012. For Payment for Activities.

5435
George H. and Estelle M. Sands Foundation ✧
c/o Jeffrey H. Sands, Tr.
902 Carnegie Ctr., Ste. 400
Princeton, NJ 08540-6530

Established in 1996 in NJ.
Donors: George H. Sands; Estelle M. Sands†; General Land Abstract Co. Inc.
Foundation type: Independent foundation.
Financial data (yr. ended 12/31/13): Assets, $49,428,956 (M); gifts received, $2,075,000; expenditures, $1,962,717; qualifying distributions, $1,670,951; giving activities include $1,670,950 for 19 grants (high: $1,000,000; low: $200).
Fields of interest: Arts councils; Libraries (public); Education; Health care; Human services.
Limitations: Applications not accepted. Giving primarily in Princeton, NJ. No grants to individuals.
Application information: Contributes only to pre-selected organizations.
Trustees: Deborah Sands Gartenberg; Elizabeth Sands; Jeffrey H. Sands.
EIN: 223483828

5436
Sandy Hill Foundation ✧
330 South St., Ste. 4
Morristown, NJ 07960-7391

Incorporated in 1985 in NJ.
Donors: Frank E. Walsh, Jr.; Mary D. Walsh; Frank E. Walsh.
Foundation type: Independent foundation.
Financial data (yr. ended 12/31/13): Assets, $39,118,611 (M); gifts received, $35,427; expenditures, $2,084,403; qualifying distributions, $1,987,378; giving activities include $1,980,248 for 76 grants (high: $1,150,000; low: $250).
Purpose and activities: Giving primarily for a community foundation; funding also for education, particularly higher education, as well as for health organizations and human services.
Fields of interest: Higher education; Education; Health care; Health organizations, association; Human services; Foundations (community); Catholic agencies & churches.
Limitations: Applications not accepted. Giving primarily in FL, NJ, and NY; some funding also in PA. No grants to individuals.
Application information: Unsolicited requests for funds not considered or acknowledged.
Officers and Director:* Frank E. Walsh, Jr.,* Chair.; Joseph Walsh, Pres.; Meghan Walsh Cioffi, V.P.; Robert F. Cioffi, V.P.; Frank E. Walsh III, V.P.; Karen R. Walsh, V.P.; Mary D. Walsh, V.P.; Jeffrey R. Walsh, Secy.-Treas.
EIN: 222668774

5437
Sanofi Foundation for North America ✧
(formerly Sanofi-aventis Patient Assistance Foundation)
55 Corporate Dr.
Bridgewater, NJ 08807-2855 (888) 847-4877
FAX: (888) 847-1797; E-mail: nacsr@sanofi.com; Application address: P.O. Box 222138, Charlotte, NC 28222-2138; Main URL: http://www.sanofifoundation-northamerica.org/
Sanofi Patient Connection Enrollment Form: https://www.visitspconline.com/

Established in 1992.
Donors: Marion Merrell Dow Inc.; Hoechst Marion Roussel, Inc.; Aventis Pharmaceuticals Inc.; Sanofi-Aventis US, LLC; Genzyme Corp.
Foundation type: Company-sponsored foundation.
Financial data (yr. ended 12/31/12): Assets, $2,559,174 (M); gifts received, $286,483,724; expenditures, $284,044,399; qualifying distributions, $284,044,399; giving activities include $3,559,363 for grants, and $280,485,036 for grants to individuals.
Purpose and activities: The foundation provides medication for patients whose incomes are below the federal poverty level and who are not eligible for

any third-party medication payments, and supports nonprofit organizations involved with health, human services, education, the environment, and civic and community issues.
Fields of interest: Elementary/secondary education; Higher education; Education; Environment, natural resources; Environment, energy; Environment; Health care; Pediatrics; Youth, services; Family services; Human services; Business/industry; Community/economic development; Economically disadvantaged.
Type of support: General/operating support; Grants to individuals; Donated products.
Limitations: Applications accepted. Giving on a national basis.
Publications: Application guidelines.
Application information: The foundation practices an invitation only process for general grants to organizations. Application form required.
Initial approach: Download enrollment form or contact foundation for application information
Deadline(s): None
Officers and Directors:* John Spinnato,* Pres.; Peter Lalli, V.P.; George Pompetzki, V.P.; Sabrina Spitaletta, V.P.; Martin Travers, Secy.; Edgar Grass, Treas.; Bernard Armoury; Marc Bonnefoi; Damian Braga; Gregory Irace; David Meeker; Anne Whitaker; Tom Zerzan.
EIN: 431614543

5438
Sansom Foundation Inc. ✧
P.O. Box 2777
Oak Ridge, NJ 07438-2777

Established in 1958 in NY.
Donor: Ira D. Glackens†.
Foundation type: Independent foundation.
Financial data (yr. ended 12/31/12): Assets, $18,434,042 (M); expenditures, $1,066,611; qualifying distributions, $675,000; giving activities include $675,000 for grants.
Purpose and activities: Giving primarily for art museums; funding also for human services.
Fields of interest: Museums (art); AIDS; Human services.
Type of support: General/operating support; Program-related investments/loans.
Limitations: Applications not accepted. Giving primarily in FL, with emphasis on Ft. Lauderdale, Notre Dame, IN and NY. No grants to individuals.
Application information: Contributes only to pre-selected organizations.
Officers and Director: Frank Buscaglia, Pres. and Treas.; Jorge H. Santis,* V.P.; Edward M. DePaoli, Secy.; Lawrence B. Thompson.
EIN: 136136127

5439
The Leroy Schecter Foundation, Inc. ✧
(formerly The Schecter Family Foundation, Inc.)
55 Passaic Ave.
Kearny, NJ 07032-1103

Established in 2002 in NJ.
Donor: Leroy Schechter.
Foundation type: Independent foundation.
Financial data (yr. ended 12/31/13): Assets, $3,797,651 (M); gifts received, $1,000,000; expenditures, $1,649,646; qualifying distributions, $1,571,189; giving activities include $1,571,189 for 15 grants (high: $1,000,000; low: $1,800).
Purpose and activities: Giving primarily for education, health organizations, social services, and Jewish organizations.
Fields of interest: Higher education; Health organizations, association; Cancer; Human services; Foundations (private grantmaking); Jewish federated giving programs; Jewish agencies & synagogues.
Limitations: Applications not accepted. Giving primarily in FL, MA, and NY.
Application information: Contributes only to pre-selected organizations.
Officers and Trustees:* Leroy Schecter,* Chair.; Ottavia McLaughlin,* V.P. and Secy-Treas.
EIN: 300134495
Selected grants: The following grants are a representative sample of this grantmaker's funding activity:
$2,700,000 to Friends of the Israel Defense Forces, New York, NY, 2011. For general operating support.
$1,000,000 to Icahn School of Medicine at Mount Sinai, New York, NY, 2011. For general operating support.
$800,000 to Eva's Village, Paterson, NJ, 2011. For general operating support.
$500,000 to University of Miami, Coral Gables, FL, 2011. For general operating support.
$300,000 to Dana-Farber Cancer Institute, Boston, MA, 2011. For general operating support.
$50,000 to Blue Card, New York, NY, 2011. For general operating support.
$25,000 to American Friends of Beit Issie Shapiro, New York, NY, 2011. For general operating support.
$25,000 to Saint Jude Childrens Research Hospital, Memphis, TN, 2011. For general operating support.

5440
Schmidt Family Foundation ✧
P.O. Box 1501, NJ2-130-03-31
Pennington, NJ 08534-1501

Established in 2007 in NJ.
Donors: Linda Schmidt; Ralph Schmidt.
Foundation type: Independent foundation.
Financial data (yr. ended 12/31/13): Assets, $2,218,782 (M); gifts received, $1,067,700; expenditures, $446,100; qualifying distributions, $434,364; giving activities include $428,018 for 32 grants (high: $50,000; low: $1,000).
Fields of interest: Education; Human services.
Type of support: General/operating support.
Limitations: Applications not accepted. Giving primarily in TX.
Application information: Unsolicited requests for funds not accepted.
Trustees: Linda Schmidt; Ralph Schmidt; Ryan Schmidt.
EIN: 260742462
Selected grants: The following grants are a representative sample of this grantmaker's funding activity:
$33,000 to Old Spanish Missions, San Antonio, TX, 2011.
$10,000 to Loretto Academy, El Paso, TX, 2011.
$1,000 to Bridges to Life, Houston, TX, 2011.
$1,000 to Centro Santa Catalina, El Paso, TX, 2011.

5441
The Schumann Fund for New Jersey, Inc. ✧
21 Van Vleck St.
Montclair, NJ 07042-2373 (973) 509-9883
Contact: Barbara Reisman, Exec. Dir.
Main URL: http://foundationcenter.org/grantmaker/schumann/

Established in 1988 in NJ.
Donors: Florence Schumann†; John Schumann†; Florence and John Schumann Foundation.
Foundation type: Independent foundation.
Financial data (yr. ended 12/31/13): Assets, $27,025,807 (M); expenditures, $2,130,693; qualifying distributions, $1,768,380; giving activities include $1,375,300 for 84 grants (high: $50,000; low: $500).
Purpose and activities: Support primarily for 1) early childhood development; 2) environmental protection; 3) school innovation; and 4) local activities directed at solving community problems within Essex County.
Fields of interest: Education, early childhood education; Education; Environment; Human services; Children/youth, services; Public affairs; Infants/toddlers; Children/youth; Children.
Type of support: General/operating support; Continuing support; Program development; Seed money.
Limitations: Applications accepted. Giving limited to NJ, with emphasis on Essex County. No support for arts programs. No grants to individuals, or for capital campaigns, annual giving, or endowments.
Publications: Application guidelines; Annual report; Financial statement; Grants list.
Application information: The foundation accepts the New York/ New Jersey Area Common Application Form and the New York/ New Jersey Common Report Form. Program guidelines available on foundation web site. Application form not required.
Initial approach: Proposal
Copies of proposal: 1
Deadline(s): Jan. 15, Apr. 15, July 15, and Oct. 15
Board meeting date(s): Mar., June, Sept., and Dec.
Final notification: 4 to 8 weeks
Officers and Trustees:* Leonard S. Coleman,* Chair.; Anthony Cicatiello,* Vice-Chair.; Roger Pratt,* Secy.-Treas.; Barbara Reisman, Exec. Dir.; Aubin Z. Ames; Barbara Bell Coleman; Christopher J. Daggett; Martha Bonsal Day; Kenneth Zimmerman.
Number of staff: 2 full-time professional.
EIN: 521556076
Selected grants: The following grants are a representative sample of this grantmaker's funding activity:
$50,000 to Advocates for Children of New Jersey, Newark, NJ, 2012. For ACNJ's early learning agenda.
$50,000 to Advocates for Children of New Jersey, Newark, NJ, 2012. For ACNJ's Right From the Start early education initiative.
$50,000 to Education Law Center, Newark, NJ, 2012. For ELC's Secondary Reform Project.
$50,000 to Woodrow Wilson National Fellowship Foundation, Princeton, NJ, 2012. For Woodrow Wilson New Jersey Science Technology Mathematics Teaching Fellowship.
$45,000 to Paterson Education Foundation, Paterson, NJ, 2012. For PEF's Graduating Every Paterson Child initiative.
$25,000 to Newark Trust for Education, Newark, NJ, 2012. For a pool of funds for the Newark Funders

Collaborative to be used to support 11 model schools that are being mucbated by Newark Public Schools.
$25,000 to Public Interest Projects, New York, NY, 2012. For PIP's Communities for Public Education Reform (CPER) that is working to build a network of community leaders and advocates for equitable school reform.
$20,000 to Council of New Jersey Grantmakers, Trenton, NJ, 2012. For the Council's Newark philanthropic liaison.
$20,000 to Greater Newark Conservancy, Newark, NJ, 2012. For education programming.
$12,500 to Camden City Garden Club, Camden, NJ, 2012. For the Camden Children's Garden's educational Programs.

5442
Alvin & Dorothy Schwartz Foundation ✧

c/o Friedman LLP
100 Eagle Rock Ave., Ste. 200
East Hanover, NJ 07936-3149

Established in 1966 in NY.
Donors: Alvin Schwartz; Amy Speilman; Thomas Schwartz; Jane Stein; Alvin Schwartz Charitable Lead Unitrust.
Foundation type: Independent foundation.
Financial data (yr. ended 12/31/11): Assets, $4,504,415 (M); gifts received, $914,583; expenditures, $901,735; qualifying distributions, $859,353; giving activities include $859,103 for 27 grants (high: $360,000; low: $100).
Purpose and activities: Giving primarily to Jewish agencies, temples, and federated giving programs; funding also for medical research, including juvenile diabetes.
Fields of interest: Hospitals (general); Medical research, institute; Diabetes research; Jewish federated giving programs; Jewish agencies & synagogues.
Limitations: Applications not accepted. Giving primarily in the greater metropolitan New York, NY, area; some support also in CA. No support for private foundations. No grants to individuals.
Application information: Contributes only to pre-selected organizations.
Officers and Directors:* Amy Spielman,* Pres.; Thomas Schwartz,* Secy.-Treas.
EIN: 116112410

5443
The Schwartz Foundation, Inc. ✧

(formerly The Bernard Schwartz and Robert Schwartz Foundation)
c/o Robert Schwartz
821 E. Gate Dr.
Mount Laurel, NJ 08054-1208

Established in 1983 in PA.
Donors: Bernard Schwartz‡; Robert S. Schwartz.
Foundation type: Independent foundation.
Financial data (yr. ended 08/31/13): Assets, $24,522,419 (M); gifts received, $300,000; expenditures, $1,497,936; qualifying distributions, $1,439,467; giving activities include $1,432,367 for 33 grants (high: $500,000; low: $250).
Purpose and activities: Giving primarily for Jewish organizations; funding also for education, and human services.
Fields of interest: Education; Human services; Jewish federated giving programs; Jewish agencies & synagogues.
Limitations: Applications not accepted. Giving primarily in NJ and Philadelphia, PA. No grants to individuals.
Application information: Contributes only to pre-selected organizations.
Officer: Robert Schwartz, Chair.
Directors: Lois Schwartz; Michael Schwartz.
EIN: 232267403

5444
Schwarz Foundation ✧

200 Central Ave., Ste. 102
Mountainside, NJ 07092-1691

Established in 1982 in NJ.
Donors: Steven Schwarz; Henryk Schwarz; Brooklawn Gardens Inc.; East Rock Village, Inc.; Hensyn, Inc.; Greenwood Gardens, Inc.; Oakwood Homes, Inc.; Woodcliff, Inc.
Foundation type: Company-sponsored foundation.
Financial data (yr. ended 06/30/14): Assets, $31,790,276 (M); gifts received, $2,240,000; expenditures, $1,773,025; qualifying distributions, $1,771,000; giving activities include $1,771,000 for 25 grants (high: $1,125,000; low: $1,000).
Purpose and activities: The foundation supports hospitals and organizations involved with children and youth, family services, and Judaism.
Fields of interest: Hospitals (general); Children/youth, services; Family services; Jewish federated giving programs; Jewish agencies & synagogues.
Type of support: General/operating support.
Limitations: Applications not accepted. Giving primarily in NY; some funding in MA. No grants to individuals.
Application information: Contributes only to pre-selected organizations.
Officers: Steven Schwarz, Pres.; Henryk Schwarz, Secy.
EIN: 222430208
Selected grants: The following grants are a representative sample of this grantmaker's funding activity:
$640,000 to PEF Israel Endowment Funds, New York, NY, 2011.
$200,000 to Beth Israel Deaconess Medical Center, Boston, MA, 2011.
$20,000 to American Society for Yad Vashem, New York, NY, 2011.
$10,000 to Harlem Childrens Zone, New York, NY, 2011.
$5,000 to Anti-Defamation League Foundation, New York, NY, 2011.
$2,500 to Simon Wiesenthal Center, New York, NY, 2011.

5445
Gay D. & William F. Scott Family Foundation ✧

P.O. Box 1501, NJ2-130-03-31
Pennington, NJ 08534-1501

Established in 2006 in NJ.
Donors: Gay Scott; William Scott.
Foundation type: Independent foundation.
Financial data (yr. ended 10/31/13): Assets, $3,492,082 (M); expenditures, $489,097; qualifying distributions, $470,033; giving activities include $451,925 for 35 grants (high: $78,500; low: $500).
Fields of interest: Arts; Higher education, university; Boy scouts; Human services; Family services; Jewish agencies & synagogues.
Type of support: General/operating support.
Limitations: Applications not accepted. Giving primarily in TX. No grants to individuals.
Application information: Contributes only to pre-selected organizations.
Officers: William Scott, Pres.; James Scott, V.P.; William Scott II, V.P.; Gay Scott, Secy.-Treas.
EIN: 203797595

5446
Segal Family Foundation

776 Mountain Blvd., Ste. 202
Watchung, NJ 07069-6269 (908) 279-7881
E-mail: info@segalfamilyfoundation.org; Main URL: http://www.segalfamilyfoundation.org
Blog: http://www.segalfamilyfoundation.org/category/blog/
Facebook: https://www.facebook.com/pages/Segal-Family-Foundation/120479467995531
Twitter: https://www.twitter.com/SegalFoundation
YouTube: https://www.youtube.com/user/SegalFamilyAfrica

Established in 2004 in NJ.
Donors: Barry Segal; Sydney Siegel‡; William Siegel‡; Martin Segal; Siegel Family Foundation; Retail Apparel Service Corp.
Foundation type: Independent foundation.
Financial data (yr. ended 12/31/12): Assets, $118,487,479 (M); gifts received, $5,378,946; expenditures, $7,499,003; qualifying distributions, $6,743,022; giving activities include $5,978,913 for 148 grants (high: $244,000; low: $2,500).
Purpose and activities: The foundation is led by a small team with a proactive, informed approach to development. It is most interested in innovative programming delivering reproductive health, food security, and youth engagement. The majority of its partners work in East Africa. However, it also supports projects elsewhere in Sub-Saharan Africa when it discovers a strong leader and a compelling project. The foundation's giving is directed to grassroots organizations with innovative approaches to holistic community development and innovative strategies for service delivery. It believes that change happens through collaboration and it tries to broker connections by facilitating on-the-ground linkages among its partners. The foundation also prioritizes organizations that it can grow with, learn from, and support for many years. At times, it will engage other funders to learn, share, and work together on areas of common interest. In an effort to support its partners through the inevitable ups and downs of grassroots work, the foundation facilitates holistic support in the form of U.S. and Africa-based events, workshops, and resources that offer a platform for networking, thought sharing, and professional development.
Fields of interest: Education, alliance/advocacy; Education, formal/general education; Vocational education, post-secondary; Reproductive health; Reproductive health, family planning; Health care; Agriculture; Housing/shelter, development; Youth development, alliance/advocacy; Human services; Rural development.
International interests: Africa; Burundi; Congo, Democratic Republic of the; Kenya; Malawi;

Rwanda; Sub-Saharan Africa; Tanzania; Uganda; Zambia.
Type of support: General/operating support.
Limitations: Applications accepted. Giving primarily in NY to organizations that provide aid in sub-Saharan Africa, with emphasis on east Africa; some giving nationally and in Sub-Saharan Africa. Because the foundation is interested in sustainable, long-term development, it avoids areas where conflict threatens the day to day security of households. No support for organizations that only provide temporary solutions to the root causes of poverty or for organizations that do not have a reproductive health policy. No grants to individuals.
Publications: Newsletter.
Application information: Application guidelines available at http://www.segalfamilyfoundation.org/request-a-grant/ Application form available at online grants portal: http://bit.ly/SNmvEM. Application form required.
Initial approach: Letter (no more than 2 pages)
Deadline(s): Rolling
Final notification: 2-6 weeks
Officers and Directors:* Barry Segal,* Pres.; Andy Bryant, Exec. Dir.; Martin Segal,* Managing Dir.; Barbara Bush; Macdella Cooper; Dolly Segal; Richard Segal; Larry Seruma; Janis Simon.
EIN: 562446941

5447
George & Helen Segal Foundation ✧
136 Davidson's Mill Rd.
North Brunswick, NJ 08902-4747
Contact: Susan Kutliroff, Secy.-Treas.
FAX: (732) 821-5877;
E-mail: segalfoundation@comcast.net; Application address for New Jersey Photographers: 357 Shawn Pl., North Brunswick, NJ 08902; Main URL: http://www.segalfoundation.org

Established in 2000 in NJ.
Donor: George Segal†.
Foundation type: Independent foundation.
Financial data (yr. ended 06/30/13): Assets, $19,085,822 (M); expenditures, $1,861,862; qualifying distributions, $1,294,900; giving activities include $1,294,900 for 6 grants (high: $450,000; low: $6,000).
Purpose and activities: Giving to exhibit and display the works of George Segal, and to award grants to artists for the pursuit of their artistic endeavors. Grants also to NJ photographers who are over the age of 21, and who are not students.
Fields of interest: Visual arts, photography; Museums (art).
Type of support: Grants to individuals.
Limitations: Giving primarily in NJ; funding for photographers is limited to NJ.
Publications: Grants list; Informational brochure.
Application information: The foundation has postponed its grant cycle. Check foundation web site for updates in this matter.
Board meeting date(s): Monthly
Officers: Helen Segal, Pres.; Rena Segal, V.P.; Susan Kutliroff, Secy.-Treas.
Number of staff: 2 full-time professional.
EIN: 223744151
Selected grants: The following grants are a representative sample of this grantmaker's funding activity:
$850,000 to Solomon R. Guggenheim Museum, New York, NY, 2011.

5448
Norman and Barbara Seiden Foundation ✧
1095 Cranbury S. River Rd., Ste. 18
Jamesburg, NJ 08831-3411

Established in 1973 in NJ.
Donors: Norman Seiden; Barbara Seiden; Mark Seiden.
Foundation type: Independent foundation.
Financial data (yr. ended 12/31/12): Assets, $4,503,457 (M); gifts received, $470,432; expenditures, $707,479; qualifying distributions, $672,325; giving activities include $667,265 for 58 grants (high: $301,800; low: $50).
Purpose and activities: Giving primarily for Jewish organizations, as well as for the arts, health organizations and human services.
Fields of interest: Museums; Arts; Health organizations, association; Human services; Jewish federated giving programs; Jewish agencies & synagogues.
Limitations: Applications not accepted. Giving primarily in NJ and NY. No grants to individuals.
Application information: Contributes only to pre-selected organizations.
Officers and Trustees:* Norman Seiden,* Pres. and Treas.; Barbara Seiden,* V.P.; Mark Seiden,* V.P.; Stephen Seiden,* Secy.; Mildred Graye; Charles Klatskin; Pearl Seiden.
EIN: 237351938

5449
SFF Foundation ✧
911 E. County Line Rd., Ste. 204
Lakewood, NJ 08701-2069

Donor: Cam-Elm Co. LLC.
Foundation type: Independent foundation.
Financial data (yr. ended 12/31/13): Assets, $15,592,540 (M); expenditures, $1,033,389; qualifying distributions, $1,027,000; giving activities include $1,027,000 for 81 grants (high: $38,000; low: $10,000).
Fields of interest: Jewish federated giving programs; Jewish agencies & synagogues.
Limitations: Applications not accepted. Giving primarily in NY; some funding also in NJ.
Application information: Contributes only to pre-selected organizations.
Trustees: Avi Schron; Eli Schron; Mark Schron.
EIN: 208522594

5450
The Shen Family Foundation ✧
c/o Cappiccille & Co.
615 W. Mt. Pleasant Ave.
Livingston, NJ 07039-1620

Established around 1994 in NY.
Donors: Theodore P. Shen; The Shen Family 2003 Charitable Lead Trust.
Foundation type: Independent foundation.
Financial data (yr. ended 12/31/12): Assets, $17,235,171 (M); gifts received, $355,000; expenditures, $2,007,939; qualifying distributions, $1,817,235; giving activities include $1,817,235 for 20 grants (high: $900,000; low: $500).
Purpose and activities: Giving primarily for the arts, particularly theater, and for higher education; funding also for a cancer hospital.
Fields of interest: Performing arts centers; Performing arts, theater; Arts; Higher education; Hospitals (specialty); Cancer.
Limitations: Applications not accepted. Giving primarily in the metropolitan New York, NY, area. No grants to individuals.
Application information: Contributes only to pre-selected organizations.
Trustees: Carla Shen; Theodore P. Shen.
EIN: 226627837

5451
Shepherd Foundation ✧
106 Prospect St., 3rd Fl.
Ridgewood, NJ 07450-4433

Established in 1988 in NJ.
Donor: Charles V. Schaefer, Jr.
Foundation type: Independent foundation.
Financial data (yr. ended 12/31/13): Assets, $23,494,546 (M); expenditures, $1,447,757; qualifying distributions, $1,053,350; giving activities include $1,053,350 for 71 grants (high: $200,000; low: $100).
Fields of interest: Performing arts; Higher education; Health care; Human services.
Limitations: Applications not accepted. Giving primarily in NJ; some funding nationally, particularly in New York, NY. No grants to individuals.
Application information: Contributes only to pre-selected organizations.
Trustees: George Bovenizer; Lynn S. Bovenizer; Richard B. Passen; Carol Schaefer; Charles V. Schaefer III; Charles V. Schaefer IV.
EIN: 226460210
Selected grants: The following grants are a representative sample of this grantmaker's funding activity:
$200,000 to Hackensack University Medical Center Foundation, Hackensack, NJ, 2011.
$200,000 to Jupiter Medical Center Foundation, Jupiter, FL, 2011.
$150,000 to Lehigh University, Bethlehem, PA, 2011.

5452
Dr. Howard and Brenda Sheridan Family Foundation ✧ ☆
P.O. Box 1501, NJ2-130-03-31
Pennington, NJ 08534-1501

Donors: Howard Sheridan; Brenda Sheridan.
Foundation type: Independent foundation.
Financial data (yr. ended 12/31/13): Assets, $2,583,237 (M); gifts received, $3,000,000; expenditures, $511,800; qualifying distributions, $507,610; giving activities include $505,000 for 12 grants (high: $225,000; low: $5,000).
Fields of interest: Higher education, university; Education; Animals/wildlife; Health care.
Type of support: General/operating support.
Limitations: Applications not accepted. Giving primarily in FL and LA.
Application information: Unsolicited requests for funds not accepted.
Trustees: Brenda Sheridan; Howard Sheridan.
EIN: 466879829

5453
The Gerald B. Shreiber Foundation ✧
6000 Central Hwy.
Pennsauken, NJ 08109-4607

Established in 1999 in NJ.
Donor: Gerald B. Shreiber.
Foundation type: Independent foundation.
Financial data (yr. ended 11/30/13): Assets, $20,917,600 (M); gifts received, $1,755,335; expenditures, $777,517; qualifying distributions, $749,656; giving activities include $747,264 for 122 grants (high: $300,000; low: $100).
Fields of interest: Performing arts, theater (musical); Higher education; Hospitals (general).
Limitations: Applications not accepted. Giving primarily in DC, NJ, and PA. No grants to individuals.
Application information: Contributes only to pre-selected organizations.
Trustees: A. Fred Ruttenberg, Esq.; Gerald B. Shreiber.
EIN: 226868479

5454
Siemens Foundation ✧
170 Wood Ave. S.
Iselin, NJ 08830-2704 (877) 822-5233
FAX: (732) 590-1252;
E-mail: foundation.us@siemens.com; Main URL: http://www.siemens-foundation.org
Facebook: http://www.facebook.com/SiemensFoundation
Siemens STEM Academy on Facebook: http://www.facebook.com/pages/Siemens-STEM-Academy/268535066939?ref=nf
Siemens STEM Academy on Twitter: http://twitter.com/SiemensSTEMAcad
Siemens We Can Change the World Challenge: http://www.facebook.com/WeCanChange
Twitter: http://twitter.com/sfoundation
YouTube: http://www.youtube.com/siemensfoundation

Established in 1998 in NY.
Donor: Siemens Corp.
Foundation type: Company-sponsored foundation.
Financial data (yr. ended 09/30/13): Assets, $58,339,837 (M); gifts received, $6,093,618; expenditures, $7,624,391; qualifying distributions, $7,856,293; giving activities include $1,688,098 for 14+ grants (high: $420,812).
Purpose and activities: The foundation supports programs designed to enhance math and science education.
Fields of interest: Secondary school/education; Higher education; Teacher school/education; Education; Environment; Science, formal/general education; Chemistry; Mathematics; Physics; Engineering/technology; Computer science; Science; Children/youth; Minorities.
Type of support: General/operating support; Scholarship funds; Employee-related scholarships; Scholarships—to individuals.
Limitations: Applications accepted. Giving primarily in GA, IL, NV, TX, and VA; giving on a national basis for Seimens Competition in Math, Science.
Publications: Application guidelines; Program policy statement.
Application information:
Initial approach: Complete online application for Siemens Competition in Math, Science, and Technology and Siemens STARs and Institute; complete online registration for Siemens We Can Change the World Challenge
Copies of proposal: 1
Deadline(s): Oct. 1 for Siemens Competition in Math, Science, and Technology; Feb. 9 for Siemens STARs and Institute; Aug. 24 to Mar. 15 for Siemens We Can Change the World Challenge
Officers and Directors:* Thomas N. McCausland,* Chair.; James Whaley,* Vice-Chair.; David D. Etzwiler, C.E.O.; Jeniffer Harper-Taylor, Pres.; Daryl Dulaney; Judy Marks; Michael Panigel; Michael Reitermann; Gergory Sorensen; Eric A. Spiegel; Klaus P. Stegeman; Randy H. Zwirn.
EIN: 522136074
Selected grants: The following grants are a representative sample of this grantmaker's funding activity:
$35,000 to University of Texas, Austin, TX, 2011.
$20,000 to University of Washington, Seattle, WA, 2011.

5455
Sierra Foundation Inc. ✧ ☆
(formerly S. T. Grim Foundation)
33 Witherspoon St., 3rd Fl.
Princeton, NJ 08542-3207

Established in 1994 in NJ.
Donors: Andrew J. Schechtel; C. Fred Taylor; Sierra Enterprises Group LLC; RAC Funding LLC C/O Ken Slutsky Tax Exempt Inst Grp.
Foundation type: Independent foundation.
Financial data (yr. ended 10/31/13): Assets, $18,107,911 (M); gifts received, $91,525; expenditures, $1,141,225; qualifying distributions, $1,141,200; giving activities include $1,141,200 for 2 grants (high: $1,001,200; low: $140,000).
Fields of interest: Education; Jewish agencies & synagogues; Religion.
Limitations: Applications not accepted. Giving primarily in Princeton, NJ; some giving also in New York, NY. No grants to individuals.
Application information: Unsolicited requests for funds not accepted.
Trustees: Martin J. Deitchman; Andrew J. Shechtel; Raquel Shechtel.
EIN: 223331554
Selected grants: The following grants are a representative sample of this grantmaker's funding activity:
$5,000 to Foundation Fighting Blindness, Princeton, NJ, 2011.
$1,200 to Jewish Funders Network, New York, NY, 2011.

5456
The Rosanne H. Silbermann Foundation, Inc. ✧
c/o M. Steven Silbermann
23 Camelot Dr.
Livingston, NJ 07039-5126

Established in 1997 in NJ.
Donor: Rosanne H. Silbermann†.
Foundation type: Independent foundation.
Financial data (yr. ended 12/31/13): Assets, $10,658,849 (M); gifts received, $1,712,530; expenditures, $480,399; qualifying distributions, $480,000; giving activities include $470,000 for 5 grants (high: $265,000; low: $2,500).
Fields of interest: Medical school/education; Hospitals (specialty); Medical research, institute.
Type of support: Continuing support; Research; Grants to individuals.
Limitations: Applications not accepted. Giving primarily in NJ and NY.
Application information: Unsolicited requests for funds not accepted.
Officers: Karen S. Silbermann, Pres.; S. David Silbermann, V.P.; Julie A. Silbermann, Secy.; M. Steven Silbermann, Treas.
EIN: 223578791
Selected grants: The following grants are a representative sample of this grantmaker's funding activity:
$150,000 to Memorial Sloan-Kettering Cancer Center, New York, NY, 2012. For geriatric psychiatry Program.

5457
The Silver Family Foundation, Inc. ✧
105 Grove St., Ste. 5
Montclair, NJ 07042-4053

Established in 2005 in NJ.
Donors: Robert H. Silver; Rhonda A. Silver; David L. Zoll; Justin P. Silver.
Foundation type: Independent foundation.
Financial data (yr. ended 12/31/13): Assets, $205,279 (M); gifts received, $438,527; expenditures, $447,796; qualifying distributions, $447,646; giving activities include $447,634 for 89 grants (high: $100,000; low: $60).
Fields of interest: Education; Health organizations, association; Human services; YM/YWCAs & YM/YWHAs; Jewish agencies & synagogues.
Limitations: Applications not accepted. Giving primarily in NJ and NY. No grants to individuals.
Application information: Contributes only to pre-selected organizations.
Officers: Robert H. Silver, Pres.; Justin P. Silver, V.P.; Rhonda A. Silver, Secy.-Treas.
EIN: 861150491

5458
Silver Mountain Foundation for the Arts ✧
c/o William E. Simon & Sons, Inc., LLC
310 South St.
P.O. Box 1913
Morristown, NJ 07962-1913 (973) 898-0290
Contact: Donald Gummer, Tr.; M.S. Gummer, Tr.

Established in 1983.
Donors: Donald Gummer; M.S. Gummer.
Foundation type: Independent foundation.
Financial data (yr. ended 12/31/13): Assets, $12,468,344 (M); gifts received, $2,000,000; expenditures, $1,234,231; qualifying distributions, $1,100,440; giving activities include $1,100,440 for 78 grants (high: $335,000; low: $15).
Purpose and activities: Giving primarily for the arts, education, health care, and human services.
Fields of interest: Arts; Higher education; Education; Health care; Human services.
Limitations: Applications accepted. Giving primarily in CT and NY. No loans or program-related investments.
Application information: Application form required.
Initial approach: Letter
Deadline(s): None

Trustees: Donald Gummer; M.S. Gummer.
EIN: 133157286
Selected grants: The following grants are a representative sample of this grantmaker's funding activity:
$200,000 to National Womens History Museum, Alexandria, VA, 2011.
$25,000 to Massachusetts Museum of Contemporary Art Foundation, North Adams, MA, 2011.
$25,000 to Vassar College, Poughkeepsie, NY, 2011.
$25,000 to Vassar College, Poughkeepsie, NY, 2011.
$20,000 to Partners in Health, Boston, MA, 2011.
$10,000 to Columbia University Medical Center, New York, NY, 2011.
$10,000 to Equality Now, New York, NY, 2011.
$10,000 to Kageno Worldwide, New York, NY, 2011.
$5,000 to Museum of Fine Arts, Boston, MA, 2011.
$5,000 to Women for Women International, Washington, DC, 2011.

5459
Kenneth and Claudia Silverman Family Foundation ✧
788 Morris Tpke.
Short Hills, NJ 07078-2637
Application address: c/o Kenneth Silverman, Tr., P.O. Box 825, Short Hills, NJ 07078, tel.: (973) 765-0100

Established in 1999 in NJ.
Donors: Kenneth Silverman; Claudia Silverman; Silver Line Building Products Corp.
Foundation type: Independent foundation.
Financial data (yr. ended 12/31/13): Assets, $11,870,627 (M); expenditures, $1,032,089; qualifying distributions, $857,114; giving activities include $857,114 for 38 grants (high: $250,000; low: $14).
Fields of interest: Higher education; Health organizations; Human services.
Application information: Application form required.
Initial approach: Letter
Deadline(s): None
Officer and Trustees:* Brittany Silverman,* Mgr.; Claudia Silverman; Kenneth Silverman.
EIN: 226831069

5460
The Cynthia L. & William E. Simon, Jr. Foundation ✧
310 South St.
P.O. Box 1913
Morristown, NJ 07962-1913
Application address: William E. Simon Jr., c/o William E. Simon & Sons, 11100 Santa Monica Blvd., Ste. 1910, Los Angeles, CA 90025-3335

Established in 1994 in NJ.
Donors: William E. Simon, Jr.; William E. Simon Foundation, Inc.; U.S. Dept. of Education - Carol M. White Physical Ed. Program; Cynthia L. Simon.
Foundation type: Independent foundation.
Financial data (yr. ended 12/31/13): Assets, $65,131 (M); gifts received, $565,250; expenditures, $539,797; qualifying distributions, $536,650; giving activities include $536,650 for 56 grants (high: $400,000; low: $100).
Purpose and activities: Giving primarily for education, particularly high schools; funding also for children, youth and social services, and health care.
Fields of interest: Secondary school/education; Education; Health care; Human services; YM/YWCAs & YM/YWHAs; Children/youth, services; United Ways and Federated Giving Programs.
Limitations: Applications accepted. Giving primarily in CA and MA.
Application information: Application form required.
Initial approach: Letter
Deadline(s): None
Officer and Trustees:* Cynthia L. Simon,* Pres.; William E. Simon, Jr.
EIN: 133799555
Selected grants: The following grants are a representative sample of this grantmaker's funding activity:
$50,000 to UCLA Foundation, Los Angeles, CA, 2011.
$40,000 to Saint Johns Health Center, Santa Monica, CA, 2011.
$25,000 to Calvary Christian School, Pacific Palisades, CA, 2011.
$20,000 to Team Prime Time, Los Angeles, CA, 2011.
$9,600 to UCLA Foundation, Los Angeles, CA, 2011.
$5,000 to AmeriCares, Stamford, CT, 2011.
$5,000 to Oaks Christian School, Westlake Village, CA, 2011.
$3,000 to Christopher and Dana Reeve Foundation, Short Hills, NJ, 2011.
$3,000 to Dorot, New York, NY, 2011.
$2,500 to Promises Foundation, Los Angeles, CA, 2011.

5461
George Graham and Elizabeth Galloway Smith Foundation, Inc. ✧
P.O. Box 202
Hopewell, NJ 08525 (609) 466-2210
Contact: Ellen S. Morehouse, Pres. and Secy.

Established in 1960.
Donors: Elizabeth G. Smith‡; Beatrice Erlin‡; George G. Smith‡; Elizabeth G. Smith Charitable Lead Unitrust.
Foundation type: Independent foundation.
Financial data (yr. ended 05/31/13): Assets, $7,963,600 (M); gifts received, $125; expenditures, $453,305; qualifying distributions, $435,730; giving activities include $432,500 for 21 grants (high: $75,000; low: $2,500).
Purpose and activities: Funding primarily for an arts center and other music and arts organizations; funding also for education and human services.
Fields of interest: Museums (science/technology); Performing arts centers; Performing arts, orchestras; Higher education; Education; Human services; United Ways and Federated Giving Programs.
Type of support: Building/renovation; Equipment; Program development.
Limitations: Applications accepted. Giving primarily in western NY, with emphasis on Buffalo and Orchard Park. No grants to individuals.
Application information: Application form required.
Initial approach: Letter
Deadline(s): June 15 for requests above $1,000; none for requests below that amount
Board meeting date(s): July
Officers: Ellen S. Morehouse, Pres. and Secy.; George G. Smith III, V.P. and Treas.
Directors: C. Schuyler Morehouse; Janet Smith.
EIN: 166031530
Selected grants: The following grants are a representative sample of this grantmaker's funding activity:
$15,000 to Mendelssohn Club, Philadelphia, PA, 2011.
$10,000 to Buffalo Society of Natural Sciences, Buffalo, NY, 2011. For operating expenses.
$10,000 to Roycroft Campus Corporation, East Aurora, NY, 2011.
$9,065 to Buffalo Society of Natural Sciences, Buffalo, NY, 2011.
$8,000 to Irish Classical Theater, Buffalo, NY, 2011.
$8,000 to Roswell Park Cancer Institute, Buffalo, NY, 2011.
$8,000 to Shakespeare in Delaware Park, Buffalo, NY, 2011.
$7,000 to Niagara Frontier Radio Reading Service, Buffalo, NY, 2011.
$5,000 to Camphill Soltane, Glenmoore, PA, 2011.

5462
The Harold B. and Dorothy A. Snyder Foundation ✧ ☆
331 Newman Springs Rd., Bldg. 1, No. 143
Red Bank, NJ 07701-5688
Application address: P.O. Box 671, Moorestown, NJ 08057-0671; Main URL: http://www.snyderfoundation.com/.
E-Newsletter: http://snyderfoundation.com/page.php?id=10

Established in 1971 in NJ as a trust; incorporated in 1981 in NJ.
Donor: Harold B. Snyder, Sr.‡.
Foundation type: Independent foundation.
Financial data (yr. ended 09/30/13): Assets, $10,190,604 (M); expenditures, $1,080,591; qualifying distributions, $595,844; giving activities include $457,000 for 7 grants (high: $385,000; low: $500).
Purpose and activities: Support for programs in Union County, NJ, and scholarships to either residents of Union County, NJ, or applicants attending a college or university in Union County, who are high school or college graduates with a cumulative GPA of 3.2 or above, or who are an undergraduate in their junior or senior year, pursuing a degree in nursing, special education, or construction management, or a graduate pursuing a degree/vocation in the ministry an accredited educational institution.
Fields of interest: Medical care, rehabilitation; Nursing care; Heart & circulatory diseases; Cancer research; Recreation, community; Human services.
Type of support: Capital campaigns; Building/renovation; Equipment; Seed money; Matching/challenge support.
Limitations: Giving primarily in the Union County, NJ, area. No support for colleges. No grants to individuals directly.
Application information: Application form required.
Initial approach: See foundation web site for application guidelines and forms
Officers: Laura Stammel, Chair.; Joseph A. Vallone III, C.E.O. and Exec. Dir.; J. Vernon Whittenburg, Secy.; Phyllis Johnson Snyder, Treas.
Trustees: Melvin Cook; Arline S. Cortese; Shannon Cortese.

Number of staff: 1 full-time professional; 1 part-time support.
EIN: 222316043
Selected grants: The following grants are a representative sample of this grantmaker's funding activity:
$24,500 to Seton Hall University, South Orange, NJ, 2011.
$8,000 to Kean University Foundation, Union, NJ, 2011.

5463
South Jersey Charitable Foundation ✧ ☆
(formerly South Jersey Savings Charitable Foundation)
601 White Horse Rd.
Voorhees, NJ 08043-2493

Established in 1999 in DE.
Donor: South Jersey Financial Corp., Inc.
Foundation type: Independent foundation.
Financial data (yr. ended 12/31/13): Assets, $6,171,151 (M); expenditures, $474,310; qualifying distributions, $458,725; giving activities include $445,000 for 17 grants (high: $100,000; low: $10,000).
Purpose and activities: To support organizations that contribute to the quality of life in Camden and Gloucester counties, NJ.
Fields of interest: Human services; Community/economic development.
Type of support: General/operating support; Continuing support; Capital campaigns; Building/renovation; Equipment; Program development; Seed money.
Limitations: Applications not accepted. Giving primarily in NJ.
Application information: Unsolicited requests for funds not accepted.
Officers: Richard W. Culbertson, Jr., Pres.; John V. Field, Secy.; Ronald L. Woods, Treas.
Trustees: G. Harold Hozey; Richard G. Mohrfeld.
Number of staff: None.
EIN: 223643575

5464
ST2 Foundation, Inc. ✧
33 Witherspoon St., 3rd Fl.
Princeton, NJ 08542-3209

Established in 2000 in NJ.
Donor: Sierra Enterprises Group LLC.
Foundation type: Independent foundation.
Financial data (yr. ended 11/30/13): Assets, $22,048,629 (M); expenditures, $1,203,025; qualifying distributions, $1,203,000; giving activities include $1,203,000 for 2 grants (high: $1,185,000; low: $18,000).
Fields of interest: Jewish federated giving programs.
Limitations: Applications not accepted. Giving primarily in New York, NY. No grants to individuals.
Application information: Contributes only to pre-selected organizations.
Trustees: Martin J. Deitchman; Andrew J. Shechtel; Raquel Shechtel.
EIN: 223766419

5465
Stadler Family Charitable Foundation, Inc. ✧
307 Freemans Ln.
Franklin Lakes, NJ 07417-1052

Donors: Christopher Stadler; Loretta Stadler.
Foundation type: Independent foundation.
Financial data (yr. ended 12/31/13): Assets, $3,040,470 (M); gifts received, $2,000,653; expenditures, $1,346,408; qualifying distributions, $1,329,153; giving activities include $1,322,500 for 37 grants (high: $500,000; low: $2).
Fields of interest: Education; Animal welfare; Animals/wildlife, preservation/protection; Cancer research; Human services.
Limitations: Applications not accepted.
Application information: Unsolicited requests for funds not accepted.
Officers and Trustees:* Christopher J. Stadler,* Pres. and Secy.; Loretta M. Stadler, Treas.; Gabrielle Stadler.
EIN: 452470819

5466
Marisa & Richard Stadtmauer Family Foundation, Inc. ✧
26 Columbia Tpke.
Florham Park, NJ 07932-2213 (973) 822-0220
Contact: Marisa Stadtmauer, V.P.

Established in 1999 in NJ.
Donor: Richard Stadtmauer.
Foundation type: Independent foundation.
Financial data (yr. ended 11/30/13): Assets, $6,013,500 (M); expenditures, $1,107,715; qualifying distributions, $1,105,187; giving activities include $1,105,187 for 77 grants (high: $201,500; low: $36).
Purpose and activities: Giving primarily to Jewish agencies, temples, and schools.
Fields of interest: Education; Jewish federated giving programs; Jewish agencies & synagogues.
Limitations: Applications accepted. Giving primarily in NJ and NY.
Application information: Application form required.
Initial approach: Letter
Deadline(s): None
Officers: Richard Stadtmauer, Pres.; Marisa Stadtmauer, V.P.
EIN: 223645402

5467
The David S. and Sylvia Steiner Charitable Trust ✧
75 Eisenhower Pkwy.
Roseland, NJ 07068-1697 (973) 228-5800
Contact: David S. Steiner, Tr.

Established in 1986 in NJ.
Donors: David S. Steiner; Sylvia Steiner; Syliva Steiner 1999 Trust.
Foundation type: Independent foundation.
Financial data (yr. ended 12/31/13): Assets, $337,719 (M); gifts received, $603,270; expenditures, $855,551; qualifying distributions, $825,513; giving activities include $817,991 for grants.
Fields of interest: Performing arts, theater; Higher education; Jewish agencies & synagogues.
Limitations: Applications accepted. Giving primarily in NJ and New York, NY. No grants to individuals.
Application information:
Initial approach: Letter
Deadline(s): None
Trustees: David S. Steiner; Sylvia Steiner.
EIN: 226423709
Selected grants: The following grants are a representative sample of this grantmaker's funding activity:
$575,465 to Jewish Community Center of Metrowest, West Orange, NJ, 2011.
$277,686 to Carnegie Mellon University, Pittsburgh, PA, 2011.
$150,000 to American Israel Education Foundation, Washington, DC, 2011.
$55,446 to National Yiddish Book Center, Amherst, MA, 2011.
$47,500 to Actors Fund of America, New York, NY, 2011.
$25,050 to American Jewish Committee, New York, NY, 2011.
$25,000 to New Jersey Performing Arts Center, Newark, NJ, 2011.
$23,225 to New York Stage and Film, New York, NY, 2011.
$13,122 to Congregation Bnai Jeshurun, Short Hills, NJ, 2011.
$6,000 to Friars Foundation, New York, NY, 2011.

5468
The Stern Family Foundation ✧
4A Cedarbrook Dr.
Cranbury, NJ 08512-3507 (609) 655-5400
Contact: A. Joseph Stern

Established in 1983 in NJ.
Donors: A. Joseph Stern; Eli Stern; Frieda Stern; Feldberg Family Foundation; Cedar Brook 2005 L.P.; Cedar Brook 5 Corporate Center L.P.; Cedar Brook 3 Corporate Center L.P.
Foundation type: Independent foundation.
Financial data (yr. ended 12/31/13): Assets, $7,048 (M); gifts received, $540,312; expenditures, $539,700; qualifying distributions, $539,700; giving activities include $539,700 for 38 grants (high: $170,500; low: $100).
Purpose and activities: Giving primarily to Jewish agencies, temples, and schools.
Fields of interest: Elementary/secondary education; Jewish federated giving programs; Jewish agencies & synagogues.
Application information: Application form required.
Initial approach: Letter
Deadline(s): None
Trustees: A. Joseph Stern; Rochelle Stern.
EIN: 222495169

5469
The Zahava and Moshael J. Straus Family Foundation ✧
707 Palisade Ave., 3rd Fl.
Englewood Cliffs, NJ 07632-3042

Established in 1996 in NJ.
Donors: Moshael J. Straus; Zahava Straus.
Foundation type: Independent foundation.
Financial data (yr. ended 09/30/13): Assets, $1,155,246 (M); gifts received, $750,000; expenditures, $1,018,814; qualifying distributions,

$1,011,567; giving activities include $1,009,000 for 10 grants (high: $550,000; low: $1,000).
Purpose and activities: Giving primarily to Jewish higher education, and to Jewish agencies and temples.
Fields of interest: Higher education; Health care; Religion.
Limitations: Applications not accepted. Giving primarily in NJ and NY. No grants to individuals.
Application information: Unsolicited requests for funds not accepted.
Officers and Director:* Moshael J. Straus,* Pres.; Zahava Straus, V.P.; Daniel E. Straus, Secy.-Treas.
EIN: 133913229
Selected grants: The following grants are a representative sample of this grantmaker's funding activity:
$500,000 to Yeshiva University, New York, NY, 2011.
$25,000 to New York University, New York, NY, 2011.

5470
Judith and Howard Strauss Foundation ✧
9 Broadmoor Dr.
Rumson, NJ 07760-1202
Contact: Howard E. Strauss, Pres.

Established in 1989 in DE.
Donor: Howard E. Strauss.
Foundation type: Independent foundation.
Financial data (yr. ended 06/30/13): Assets, $1,405,210 (M); expenditures, $704,948; qualifying distributions, $695,285; giving activities include $695,285 for grants.
Purpose and activities: Giving primarily for animal welfare, health care, health associations, and community development.
Fields of interest: Education; Animal welfare; Hospitals (general); Health care; Health organizations, association; Human services; Community/economic development; Jewish federated giving programs.
Limitations: Applications accepted. Giving primarily in FL, NJ, and NY. No grants to individuals.
Application information: Application form required.
Initial approach: Letter
Deadline(s): None
Officers: Howard E. Strauss, Pres.; Judith Strauss, V.P.
EIN: 222987092
Selected grants: The following grants are a representative sample of this grantmaker's funding activity:
$5,000 to Fund for Animals, New York, NY, 2011.
$5,000 to Humane Society of the United States, Washington, DC, 2011.
$5,000 to National Wildlife Federation, Reston, VA, 2011.
$5,000 to National Wildlife Federation, Reston, VA, 2011.
$3,000 to World Wildlife Fund, Washington, DC, 2011.

5471
Subaru of America Foundation, Inc. ✧
P.O. Box 6000
Cherry Hill, NJ 08034-6000 (856) 488-5099
Contact: Sandra Capell, Mgr.
FAX: (856) 488-3300;
E-mail: foundation@subaru.com; Main URL: http://www.subaru.com/company/soa-foundation/index.html
Grants List: http://www.subaru.com/content/downloads/pdf/soafoundation/2013_Spring_Grant_List.pdf
Subaru Scholars Grant List: http://www.subaru.com/content/downloads/pdf/soafoundation/SubaruScholars.pdf

Established in 1984 in NJ.
Donor: Subaru of America, Inc.
Foundation type: Company-sponsored foundation.
Financial data (yr. ended 03/31/14): Assets, $4,078,655 (M); gifts received, $1,200,000; expenditures, $533,288; qualifying distributions, $530,563; giving activities include $468,226 for 73 grants (high: $54,735; low: $100), and $62,337 for 189 employee matching gifts.
Purpose and activities: The foundation supports programs designed to promote youth-based environmental stewardship and enhance the academic learning experience for youth.
Fields of interest: Elementary/secondary education; Teacher school/education; Education, services; Education, reading; Education; Environment, natural resources; Environmental education; Environment; Human services; Science, formal/general education; Mathematics; Science; Children/youth.
Type of support: General/operating support; Continuing support; Program development; Employee matching gifts; Employee-related scholarships.
Limitations: Applications accepted. Giving limited to areas of company operations in Phoenix, AZ, Los Angeles, San Diego, and San Francisco, CA, Denver, CO, Washington, DC, Orlando, FL, Atlanta, GA, Chicago and Itasca, IL, Prince, Georges, Frederick, Howard Counties, MD, Minneapolis, MN, Burlington, Camden, and Westhampton, NJ, Columbus, OH, Portland, OR, Philadelphia, PA, Dallas, TX, Fairfax, Loudon, and Prince William Counties, VA, and Seattle, WA. No support for veterans', fraternal, or labor organizations, government agencies, churches, religious, or sectarian organizations, public or private schools, charter schools, or school districts, social, membership, or other organizations not of direct benefit to the entire community, political organizations or candidates, discriminatory organizations, or national organizations. No grants to individuals (except for employee-related scholarships), or for advertising, sponsorships of special events, table purchases, athletic campaigns, capital campaigns, or political campaigns; no vehicle donations.
Publications: Application guidelines; Grants list.
Application information: E-mail communications are strongly encouraged and preferred. Support is limited to 1 contribution per organization during any given year. Application form required.
Initial approach: Complete online questionnaire and download application form and e-mail to foundation
Deadline(s): Feb. 15 and Aug. 15 for Partnership Grants
Board meeting date(s): Twice per year
Final notification: June and Dec. for Partnership Grants
Officers: Thomas J. Doll, Pres.; Sheila Galluci-Davis, Secy.; Daniel J. Dalton, Treas.
Trustees: Richard L. Crosse; Kozo Kanashiro.
EIN: 222531774

5472
The Sudler Foundation ✧
(formerly The Samuel and Claire Sudler Charitable Trust)
245 Green Village Rd.
P.O. Box 39
Chatham, NJ 07928-0039 (973) 257-0700
Contact: Peter D. Sudler, Tr.

Established in 1986 in NJ.
Donors: Samuel Sudler†; Claire E. Sudler; Claire Sudler 2003 Trust; Allan Engler Charitable Remainder Unitrust; Claire Sudler 2003 Trust.
Foundation type: Independent foundation.
Financial data (yr. ended 12/31/13): Assets, $3,720,508 (M); gifts received, $1,164,215; expenditures, $474,288; qualifying distributions, $452,830; giving activities include $447,800 for 31 grants (high: $300,000; low: $200).
Purpose and activities: Giving primarily for higher education and Jewish organizations.
Fields of interest: Higher education; Law school/education; Health organizations, association; Human services; Jewish federated giving programs; Jewish agencies & synagogues.
Type of support: Continuing support; Annual campaigns; Building/renovation; Equipment; Emergency funds; Research.
Limitations: Applications accepted. Giving primarily in NJ and NY. No support for private foundations. No grants to individuals; or for administrative expenses.
Application information: Application form required.
Initial approach: Letter
Copies of proposal: 1
Deadline(s): None
Trustee: Peter Sudler.
EIN: 226423710
Selected grants: The following grants are a representative sample of this grantmaker's funding activity:
$300,000 to New York University, School of Law, New York, NY, 2011.
$25,000 to Opportunity Project, Millburn, NJ, 2011.
$25,000 to Vermont Law School, South Royalton, VT, 2011.
$13,000 to Breast Cancer Research Foundation, New York, NY, 2011.
$10,000 to New York University, New York, NY, 2011.
$5,000 to Jupiter Medical Center Foundation, Jupiter, FL, 2011.
$5,000 to Lexington Institute, Arlington, VA, 2011.
$2,000 to Charity: Water, New York, NY, 2011.
$1,000 to Friends of Ofanim, Wynnewood, PA, 2011.
$1,000 to Newark Boys Chorus School, Newark, NJ, 2011.

5473
The Summit Area Public Foundation ✧
P.O. Box 867
Summit, NJ 07902-0867 (908) 277-1422
Contact: Barbara Bunting, Treas.
FAX: (908) 277-3042; E-mail: info@sapfnj.org; Grant inquiry e-mail: grants@sapfnj.org; Main URL: http://www.sapfnj.org

Established in 1972 in NJ.
Foundation type: Community foundation.
Financial data (yr. ended 12/31/13): Assets, $15,592,222 (M); gifts received, $217,443; expenditures, $799,819; giving activities include

$711,627 for 185+ grants (high: $46,000; low: $23).
Purpose and activities: The Summit Area Public Foundation fosters area-wide philanthropy by identifying local needs and offering donors flexible ways to make a difference in the lives of their neighbors.
Fields of interest: Arts; Education; Health care; Cancer research; Children, services; Community/economic development; Children/youth; Aging; Disabilities, people with.
Type of support: Building/renovation; Equipment; Emergency funds; Program development; Conferences/seminars; Seed money; Scholarship funds; Research; Technical assistance; Matching/challenge support.
Limitations: Applications accepted. Giving limited to the Summit, NJ, area. No support for religious organizations. No grants to individuals (except for scholarships), or for normal annual operating budgets, capital campaigns, or endowments.
Publications: Application guidelines; Grants list; Informational brochure.
Application information: Visit web site for additional application information. Application form required.
Initial approach: Letter
Copies of proposal: 10
Deadline(s): Feb. 15 and Sept. 15
Board meeting date(s): Quarterly
Final notification: June and Dec.
Officers and Trustees:* John W. Cooper,* Pres.; David Dietze,* V.P.; Lyle Brehm,* Secy.; Barbara E. Bunting,* Treas.; Linda B. Hander,* Asst. Treas.; Celine Benet; Sandy Bloom; Reagan Burkholder; Eugene Fox; Jordan Glatt; Baxter Graham; Cary Hardy; Esther Harper; David Hartman; Julie Keenan; Sandra R. Lizza; Frank Macioce; Joanne McDonough; Henry M. Ogden; Mort O'Shea; Gregory Sachs, M.D.
EIN: 221948007
Selected grants: The following grants are a representative sample of this grantmaker's funding activity:
$71,191 to Connection for Women and Families, Summit, NJ, 2011. For special needs, senior and ESL programs and to purchase cardiac fitness equipment.
$35,000 to SAGE Eldercare, Summit, NJ, 2011. For planning and guidance program.
$35,000 to Summit Speech School, New Providence, NJ, 2011. For parent/infant program for children from birth to 3 years.
$25,362 to Our House Foundation, Murray Hill, NJ, 2011. For renovations to provide handicap access to New Providence group home and to purchase new furniture in New Providence and Summit homes.
$25,000 to Arc Kohler School, Mountainside, NJ, 2011. To provide music and art therapy to students once per week.
$25,000 to Berkeley Heights Rescue Squad, Berkeley Heights, NJ, 2011. To purchase Hi-Visibility jackets and liners.
$25,000 to Boys and Girls Clubs of Union County, Union, NJ, 2011. For PROJECT LEARN educational enhancement.
$25,000 to Planned Parenthood of Greater Northern New Jersey, Morristown, NJ, 2011. For bi-lingual community educator.
$20,000 to American Red Cross, Summit, NJ, 2011. For electrical and kitchen upgrades.
$20,000 to Reeves-Reed Arboretum, Summit, NJ, 2011. For Eco-Corps, experiential learning initiative for high school students, recovery and restoration of grounds after December 2011 ice storm.

5474
Sunup Foundation, Inc. ✧
c/o CohnReznick LLP
27 Christopher Way
Eatontown, NJ 07724-3329
Application address: c/o Edward C. Taylor, Dir., 288 Western Way, Princeton, NJ 08540; tel: (609) 924-3483

Established in 1999 in NJ.
Donors: Edward C. Taylor; Virginia C. Taylor.
Foundation type: Operating foundation.
Financial data (yr. ended 12/31/12): Assets, $4,096,441 (M); gifts received, $5,624,414; expenditures, $4,241,173; qualifying distributions, $4,212,271; giving activities include $4,210,000 for 15 grants (high: $3,000,000; low: $5,000).
Fields of interest: Education; Environment; Community/economic development.
Type of support: General/operating support; Equipment.
Limitations: Applications accepted. Giving primarily in Trenton, NJ; some giving also in VT. No support for private foundations. No grants to individuals.
Application information:
Initial approach: Letter
Deadline(s): None
Officers: Edward C. Taylor, Pres.; Virginia C. Taylor, Treas.
Directors: Richard Spielman; Susan Spielman; Connie Taylor; Edward N. Taylor.
EIN: 223693832

5475
Sy Syms Foundation ✧
1 Bridge Plz. N., Ste. 275
Fort Lee, NJ 07024-7586

Established in 1985 in NJ.
Donor: Sy Syms†.
Foundation type: Independent foundation.
Financial data (yr. ended 04/30/13): Assets, $40,826,374 (M); expenditures, $1,933,251; qualifying distributions, $1,656,608; giving activities include $1,636,880 for 45 grants (high: $150,000; low: $5,000).
Purpose and activities: Giving primarily for media, Jewish welfare and other Jewish organizations; grants also for higher education and the arts.
Fields of interest: Media, television; Arts; Higher education; Education; Health organizations, association; Human services; Jewish federated giving programs; Jewish agencies & synagogues.
International interests: Israel.
Type of support: General/operating support; Scholarship funds.
Limitations: Applications not accepted. Giving primarily in the U.S., with emphasis on NY. No grants to individuals.
Application information: Contributes only to pre-selected organizations.
Officers and Trustees:* Marcy Syms Merns,* Pres.; Mark Freiberg,* Treas.; Lynn Tamarkin Syms; Robert Syms.
EIN: 222617727
Selected grants: The following grants are a representative sample of this grantmaker's funding activity:
$150,000 to Beit Knesset Ashkenaz, Modiin, Israel, 2011.

5476
The Marion & Norman Tanzman Charitable Foundation ✧
(formerly The Norman Tanzman Charitable Foundation)
10 Woodbridge Center Dr., Ste. 405
Woodbridge, NJ 07095-1152

Established in 1996 in NJ.
Donor: Norman Tanzman†.
Foundation type: Independent foundation.
Financial data (yr. ended 12/31/13): Assets, $22,516,386 (M); expenditures, $1,282,166; qualifying distributions, $1,136,500; giving activities include $1,136,500 for 49 grants (high: $300,000; low: $1,000).
Purpose and activities: Giving primarily for health and medical services and for Jewish organizations.
Fields of interest: Higher education, university; Hospitals (general); Health care; Cerebral palsy; Cancer; Aging, centers/services; Jewish federated giving programs; Jewish agencies & synagogues.
Type of support: General/operating support.
Limitations: Applications not accepted. Giving primarily in NJ. No grants to individuals.
Application information: Contributes only to pre-selected organizations.
Trustees: Janice Barshad; Dru Kleinfeld; Sanders Kleinfeld; Jefferies Shein; Barbara Sousa; Roy H. Tanzman; Jennifer Turner.
EIN: 223506061

5477
The Henry and Marilyn Taub Foundation ✧
300 Frank W. Burr Blvd., 7th Fl.
Teaneck, NJ 07666-6703 (201) 287-2500

Established in 1967 in DE.
Donors: Henry Taub†; Marilyn Taub; Endowment Foundation of UJA Federation of Bergen County & North Hudson; Henry Taub Revocable Trust.
Foundation type: Independent foundation.
Financial data (yr. ended 12/31/13): Assets, $171,679,489 (M); expenditures, $8,441,678; qualifying distributions, $7,412,337; giving activities include $6,705,338 for 188 grants (high: $1,175,750; low: $100).
Purpose and activities: Grants largely for Jewish welfare funds; some support for higher and other education, social service and youth agencies, and hospitals.
Fields of interest: Higher education; Education; Hospitals (general); Human services; Children/youth, services; Jewish federated giving programs; Jewish agencies & synagogues.
Limitations: Applications not accepted. Giving primarily in NJ and NY. No grants to individuals.
Application information: Contributes only to pre-selected organizations.
Officers and Directors:* Steven Taub,* Chair. and Pres.; Judith Gold,* V.P. and Secy.; Ira Taub,* V.P. and Treas.; Barbara Lawrence, Exec. Dir.; Marilyn Taub.
EIN: 226100525
Selected grants: The following grants are a representative sample of this grantmaker's funding activity:
$1,500,000 to Jewish Community Center on the Palisades, Tenafly, NJ, 2012.
$750,000 to American Society for Technion-Israel Institute of Technology, New York, NY, 2012.

$500,000 to Columbia University, College - Taub Institute for Alzheimer's Disease, New York, NY, 2012.
$500,000 to Columbia University, College - Taub Institute for Research, New York, NY, 2012.
$250,000 to Jewish Federation of Northern New Jersey, Paramus, NJ, 2012.
$120,000 to Jewish Federation of Northern New Jersey, Paramus, NJ, 2012.
$50,000 to Meadowlands Transportation Brokerage Corp, Wood Ridge, NJ, 2012.
$30,000 to Dwight-Englewood School, Englewood, NJ, 2012.
$20,000 to Childrens Day Nursery and Family Services, Passaic, NJ, 2012.
$1,000 to Amyotrophic Lateral Sclerosis Association, New York, NY, 2012.

5478
Joseph & Arlene Taub Foundation ✧
(formerly Rotary Club of Woodbridge/ Perth Amboy)
c/o Wiss & Co., LLP
354 Eisenhower Pkwy.
Livingston, NJ 07039-1022

Established in 1968 in DE.
Donors: Joseph Taub; Sylvia Gorelick†; Sandra Taub†; Arlene Taub; Rick Pitino Foundation.
Foundation type: Independent foundation.
Financial data (yr. ended 12/31/13): Assets, $17,723,282 (M); expenditures, $1,440,089; qualifying distributions, $1,327,106; giving activities include $1,301,580 for 35+ grants (high: $633,333).
Fields of interest: Education; Health care; Health organizations; Medical research.
Type of support: General/operating support; Endowments.
Limitations: Applications not accepted. Giving primarily in NJ, and New York, NY; some funding also in Washington, DC. No grants to individuals.
Application information: Contributes only to pre-selected organizations.
Officers and Directors:* Joseph Taub,* Pres.; Arlene Taub,* Treas.
EIN: 226104545

5479
Tavitian Foundation Inc. ✧
c/o Syncsort Inc.
50 Tice Blvd.
Woodcliff Lake, NJ 07677-7654

Established in 1995 in NJ.
Donor: Assadour Tavitian.
Foundation type: Independent foundation.
Financial data (yr. ended 12/31/12): Assets, $28,390,498 (M); expenditures, $2,785,184; qualifying distributions, $2,644,994; giving activities include $2,514,800 for 51 grants (high: $1,395,113; low: $100).
Purpose and activities: Giving primarily for higher education, including scholarships, with a preference given to persons of Armenian and Eastern European descent; some support also for the arts.
Fields of interest: Arts; Higher education.
Type of support: Program development; Scholarship funds; Research; Scholarships—to individuals.
Limitations: Applications not accepted. Giving primarily in MA and NY.
Application information: Foundation approaches potential awardees through contact with professors who recommend a recipient.
Officers: Assadour Tavitian, Pres.; Joyce Barsam, V.P.; David Oifer, Secy.
EIN: 521939275

5480
The David Tepper Charitable Foundation, Inc. ✧
9 Stonehenge Terr., No. 250B
Livingston, NJ 07039

Established in 1996 in NJ.
Donor: David A. Tepper.
Foundation type: Independent foundation.
Financial data (yr. ended 11/30/13): Assets, $162,433,034 (M); expenditures, $5,903,420; qualifying distributions, $5,900,020; giving activities include $5,887,720 for 41 grants (high: $943,170; low: $5,000).
Fields of interest: Higher education; Health organizations, association; Food banks; Human services; Jewish agencies & synagogues.
Type of support: General/operating support.
Limitations: Applications not accepted. Giving primarily in NJ, NY, and PA; funding also in Chicago, IL. No grants to individuals.
Application information: Contributes only to pre-selected organizations.
Officer: David A. Tepper, Pres.
EIN: 223500313
Selected grants: The following grants are a representative sample of this grantmaker's funding activity:
$1,200,115 to Feeding America, Chicago, IL, 2011. For general support.
$785,828 to Robin Hood Foundation, New York, NY, 2011. For general support.
$500,000 to Community Food Bank of New Jersey, Hillside, NJ, 2011. For general support.
$400,000 to United Jewish Communities of MetroWest, Whippany, NJ, 2011. For general support.
$350,000 to Greater Pittsburgh Community Food Bank, Duquesne, PA, 2011. For general support.
$200,000 to Teach for America, New York, NY, 2011. For general support.
$200,000 to University of Pittsburgh, Pittsburgh, PA, 2011. For general support.
$125,000 to CARE, New York, NY, 2011. For general support.
$100,000 to Washington Institute for Near East Policy, Washington, DC, 2011. For general support.
$50,000 to Saint Anthony High School, Jersey City, NJ, 2011. For general support.

5481
Touchpoint Foundation ✧ ☆
(formerly Labuda Family Foundation)
P.O. Box 1501, NJ2-130-03-31
Pennington, NJ 08534-1501
Application address: c/o Cindy Labuda, 600 Jay St., Los Altos, CA 84022, tel.: (650) 559-7407

Established in 1999 in CA.
Donors: David S. Labuda; Cindy A. Labuda.
Foundation type: Independent foundation.
Financial data (yr. ended 06/30/13): Assets, $2,657,377 (M); expenditures, $858,076; qualifying distributions, $829,322; giving activities include $809,800 for 23 grants (high: $712,500; low: $1,500).
Purpose and activities: Giving to health, social and independent-living services for seniors in northern California and social services for residents of San Mateo, California's rural coastal communities.
Fields of interest: Education; Health care; Human services.
Type of support: General/operating support.
Limitations: Applications accepted. Giving primarily in northern CA.
Publications: Application guidelines.
Application information: Application form required.
Initial approach: Letter
Copies of proposal: 1
Deadline(s): None
Board meeting date(s): July, Oct., Jan., Apr.
Officers: Cindy A. Labuda, C.E.O. and Pres.; David S. Labuda, V.P.
EIN: 943339119
Selected grants: The following grants are a representative sample of this grantmaker's funding activity:
$17,500 to Senior Coastsiders, Half Moon Bay, CA, 2011.
$15,000 to Bernal Heights Neighborhood Center, San Francisco, CA, 2011.
$12,500 to Coastside Adult Day Health Center, Half Moon Bay, CA, 2011.
$5,500 to Senior Gleaners, Sacramento, CA, 2011.
$5,000 to Alameda Hospital Foundation, Alameda, CA, 2011.
$5,000 to Meals on Wheels of San Francisco, San Francisco, CA, 2011.
$5,000 to Senior Housing Solutions, Milpitas, CA, 2011.
$4,000 to Institute on Aging, San Francisco, CA, 2011.
$2,000 to Legal Assistance for Seniors, Oakland, CA, 2011.
$1,500 to K Q E D, San Francisco, CA, 2011.

5482
The Turner Construction Company Foundation ✧
3 Paragon Dr.
Montvale, NJ 07645

Established in 1980 in NY.
Donors: Turner Construction Co.; Garner USA LP; Sauer Group Inc.; All Brite Electric; Ann MacDonald; Ducci Electrical Contractors; Joe Capasso Mason Enterprises; M. Frank Higgins; Manafort Brothers, Inc.; Massey's Glass; RJB Contracting; SG Milazzo; Belway Electrical; Eastern Excavation; Speer Mechanical; Limbach Company LLC; Anderson Aluminum Corp.; Runyon Erectors, Inc.; Turner Construction Co.; Bruner; Charles Steitz; Janet Steitz; Kazmer Tile & Stone, Inc.; Flooring Resources Corp.; Acco Engineered Systems; Collins Electrical Company Inc.; Turner for Employees/Guests.
Foundation type: Company-sponsored foundation.
Financial data (yr. ended 12/31/13): Assets, $788,011 (M); gifts received, $1,705,097; expenditures, $1,947,922; qualifying distributions, $1,909,282; giving activities include $986,699 for 104 grants (high: $100,000; low: $500).
Purpose and activities: The foundation supports organizations involved with education, health, heart disease, cancer research, children and youth, domestic violence, and international relief.
Fields of interest: Health care; Health organizations; Human services.

Type of support: General/operating support; Program development; Scholarship funds.
Limitations: Applications not accepted. Giving primarily in FL and IL. No grants to individuals.
Application information: Contributes only to pre-selected organizations.
Officers: Peter J. Davoren, Chair. and Pres.; Karen Gould, Sr. V.P., C.F.O. and Treas.; Michael Murphy, Secy.
EIN: 133072570

5483
Turrell Fund ✧
21 Van Vleck St.
Montclair, NJ 07042-2358 (973) 783-9358
Contact: Curtland E. Fields, Pres., C.E.O. and Secy.
FAX: (973) 783-9283; E-mail: turrell@turrellfund.org; Application Contact: Jeneanne Kautzmann, Grants, Mgr.; e-mail: application@turrellfund.org; Main URL: http://www.turrellfund.org

Incorporated in 1935 in NJ.
Donors: Herbert Turrell†; Margaret Turrell†.
Foundation type: Independent foundation.
Financial data (yr. ended 12/31/13): Assets, $119,188,821 (M); expenditures, $5,624,389; qualifying distributions, $5,120,312; giving activities include $3,833,993 for 188 grants (high: $610,000; low: $500).
Purpose and activities: Grants to organizations dedicated to service or care of children and youth under 12 years of age, with emphasis on the needy, and the disadvantaged; funding also for advocacy and policy involvement.
Fields of interest: Education, early childhood education; Education; Human services; Children/youth, services; Children/youth; Children; Economically disadvantaged.
Type of support: General/operating support; Continuing support; Capital campaigns; Building/renovation; Equipment; Program development; Seed money; Scholarship funds; Matching/challenge support.
Limitations: Applications accepted. Giving limited to Essex, Union, Hudson and Passaic counties, NJ, and VT. No support for lobbying activity, most hospital work, or health delivery services; generally no support for cultural activities. No grants to individuals, or for endowment funds, conferences indirect costs, or research; no loans.
Publications: Application guidelines; Annual report (including application guidelines); Financial statement; Grants list.
Application information: No proposals are to be faxed or sent by e-mail. Organizations applying to the fund for the first time should submit written travel instructions (or a map) along with the proposal in order to facilitate a possible site visit. Online grant transmission only (see foundation web site for guidelines and application). Application form not required.
Initial approach: All applications and proposals must be submitted online
Copies of proposal: 1
Deadline(s): Jan. 1-Feb. 1 (for spring grant cycle), and July 1- Aug. 1 (for fall grant cycle)
Board meeting date(s): May and Nov.
Final notification: Late June and Dec.
Officers and Trustees:* S. Lawrence Prendergast,* Chair.; Curtland E. Fields,* C.E.O., Pres. and Secy.; Sonya Woloshyn, V.P. and Treas.; Robert E. Angelica; Elizabeth W. Christie; William S. Gannon; Matthew Melmed; Julia A. Miller; Rev. Dr. John P. Mitchell; John Morning; Mark Sustic.
Advisor: Stewart F. Campbell.
Number of staff: 3 full-time professional; 2 full-time support; 1 part-time support.
EIN: 221551936
Selected grants: The following grants are a representative sample of this grantmaker's funding activity:
$610,000 to Vermont Community Foundation, Middlebury, VT, 2013. For Vermont's Birth to Three Program (395,000), Vermont Community Preschool Collaborative (75,000), Communications and campaign support for Vermont's Birth to Three Program (25,000), President's grant for staff support for assisting with the application for Race to the Top Early Learning Grant (10,000), President's grant for a grant writer for the PA campaign for the Early Care and Education Fund (7,500), President's grant for Technical Assistance for the Early Care and Education Fund (10,000), President's grant for the Governor's Summit for the Early Care and Education Fund (10,000), President's grant for pre-campaign planning for the Early Care and Education Fund (2,500), Grant for staff support for a grant writer for Vermont's Race to the Top Early Learning Challenge Grant (25,000) President's grant for the Governor' Early Childhood Summit (5,000), President's grants for continuing support for staff for the Vermont Community Preschool Collaborative (10,000 + 10,000), Grant for the Hart Research Project (25,000).
$140,000 to Gray Charter School, Newark, NJ, 2013. For the Gray Charter School Capital Campaign (130,000), President's grant for camperships for Gray Charter School students (10,000).
$126,000 to Advocates for Children of New Jersey, Newark, NJ, 2013. For initiatives for infant and toddler care (125,000), Trustee grant for program support (1,000).
$100,000 to North Ward Center, Newark, NJ, 2013. For Robert Treat Academy expansion through the creation of Robinson/Marshall Schools.
$100,000 to TEAM Academy, Newark, NJ, 2013. For expansion in Newark.
$96,500 to New Jersey Symphony Orchestra, Newark, NJ, 2013. For trustee grant for program support (7,500), Preschool and early strings programs (85,000), Trustee grant for program support for young children (1,000), President's grant in support of joint Turrell/NJSO reception (3,000).
$18,000 to Saint Dominic Academy, Jersey City, NJ, 2013. For financial aid.
$16,000 to Vivian Beaumont Theater, New York, NY, 2013. For trustee grant for the Lincoln Center Theater education program (15,000), Trustee grant for the Open Stages program for public schools (1,000).
$12,000 to Kids Corporation II, Newark, NJ, 2013. For afterschool and summer enrichment programs.
$8,000 to Educational Arts Team, Jersey City, NJ, 2013. For family Literacy Project for very young children (7,000), Trustee grant (1,000).

5484
Unilever United States Foundation, Inc. ✧
c/o Unilever United States, Inc.
800 Sylvan Ave.
Englewood Cliffs, NJ 07632-3113 (201) 894-2450
Contact: Greg Postian, Asst. V.P.
Additional contact: Philip Cohen, tel.: (201) 894-2236; Main URL: http://www.unileverusa.com/aboutus/foundation/

Incorporated in 1952 in NY.
Donors: Unilever United States, Inc.; Lever Bros. Co.; Van den Bergh Foods Co.; Unilever Research.
Foundation type: Company-sponsored foundation.
Financial data (yr. ended 12/31/13): Assets, $764,917 (M); gifts received, $2,130,782; expenditures, $1,904,905; qualifying distributions, $1,904,905; giving activities include $1,898,440 for 521 grants (high: $798,262; low: $13).
Purpose and activities: The foundation supports programs designed to promote healthier lifestyles for families and children with a focus on good nutrition, active healthy lifestyles, self-esteem, and hunger relief; and environmental issues with a focus on climate change, water conservation, waste and packaging, and environmental preservation.
Fields of interest: Education; Environment, waste management; Environment, climate change/global warming; Environment, natural resources; Environment, water resources; Environment; Public health, physical fitness; Food services; Food banks; Nutrition; Children/youth, services; Human services; Community/economic development.
Type of support: General/operating support; Program development; Scholarship funds; Employee matching gifts; Employee-related scholarships.
Limitations: Applications accepted. Giving primarily in areas of company operations, with emphasis on Washington, DC, IL, NJ, and NY. No support for religious, labor, political, or veterans' organizations. No grants to individuals (except for employee-related scholarships), or for goodwill advertising, fundraising events or testimonial dinners, or capital campaigns; no loans.
Publications: Application guidelines.
Application information: Application form not required.
Initial approach: Proposal
Copies of proposal: 1
Deadline(s): None
Board meeting date(s): May, Oct., and Dec.
Final notification: 1 month following board meetings
Officers and Directors:* Jonathan Atwood,* Pres.; Sharon Rossi,* V.P.; David A. Schwartz, V.P.; Lauren Beck, Secy.; Henry Schirmer,* Treas.
Number of staff: 1 part-time professional.
EIN: 136122117
Selected grants: The following grants are a representative sample of this grantmaker's funding activity:
$125 to New York University, School of Business Leonard N Stern School of, New York, NY, 2012. For general operating funds.
$125 to New York University, School of Business Leonard N Stern School of, New York, NY, 2012. For general operating funds.
$50 to University of Chicago, Graduate School of Business, Chicago, IL, 2012. For general operating funds.

5485
Union Foundation ✧
P.O. Box 4470
Warren, NJ 07059-0470 (908) 753-2440
Contact: William V. Engel, Pres.

Incorporated in 1951 in NJ.
Donor: Edward J. Grassmann†.

Foundation type: Independent foundation.
Financial data (yr. ended 11/30/13): Assets, $14,918,927 (M); expenditures, $807,281; qualifying distributions, $795,355; giving activities include $723,200 for 85 grants (high: $35,000; low: $1,020).
Purpose and activities: Grants to local hospitals and health organizations, organizations engaged in ecological endeavors, educational institutions, especially privately supported ones, organizations that help the needy, particularly children, and historic preservation, animal welfare, and religious organizations. Preference given to organizations with low administrative expenses that show efforts to encourage individuals to help themselves, and which make efforts to achieve a broad base of funding.
Fields of interest: Arts; Elementary/secondary education; Higher education; Education; Environment; Hospitals (general); Health organizations; Human services; YM/YWCAs & YM/YWHAs; Children/youth, services; Catholic agencies & churches.
Type of support: Capital campaigns; Building/renovation; Equipment; Land acquisition; Endowments.
Limitations: Giving primarily in Union County, NJ. No grants to individuals, or for operating budgets.
Publications: Application guidelines.
Application information: Application form not required.
Initial approach: Proposal in letter form (no more than 4 pages)
Copies of proposal: 1
Deadline(s): Oct. 1
Board meeting date(s): Nov.
Final notification: Nov.
Officers: William V. Engel, Pres.; Edward S. Atwater IV, V.P.; Suzanne B. Engel, V.P.; Thomas H. Campbell, Treas.
Trustee: Abby O'Neill.
Number of staff: 1 part-time professional; 2 part-time support.
EIN: 226046454
Selected grants: The following grants are a representative sample of this grantmaker's funding activity:
$6,000 to Linden Animal Shelter, Friends of, Linden, NJ, 2011.

5486
United Water Foundation, Inc. ✧
200 Old Hook Rd.
Harrington Park, NJ 07640 (877) 900-3401
Contact: Sonja Clark, Exec. Dir.

Established in NJ.
Donor: United Water.
Foundation type: Independent foundation.
Financial data (yr. ended 12/31/13): Assets, $233,941 (M); gifts received, $650,000; expenditures, $549,836; qualifying distributions, $545,804; giving activities include $531,626 for 31 grants (high: $120,886; low: $1,000).
Fields of interest: Education; Environment; Health care; Human services.
Limitations: Applications accepted. No support for athletic teams, fraternal or veterans organizations, volunteer firefighters or similar groups, religious and political organizations, or projects from which United Water would benefit. No grants to individuals, or for advertising, corporate tables for charitable events, or for endowments funds.
Application information: Application form required.
Initial approach: Letter
Deadline(s): None
Officers and Board Members: Robert J. Iacullo, Chair. and Pres.; Patricia Derrico, V.P.; Rich Henning,* V.P.; Danielle Capozzoli, Secy.; Mike Algranati, Treas.; Sonja Clark, Exec. Dir.; Erika Berlinghoff; Thomas P. Brown; Bruce Harper; Nadine Leslie; Janet Sharma; David Stanton; Charlie Wall; Marie Waugh.
EIN: 270274498

5487
The Vanech Family Foundation ✧
c/o Denise E. Vanech
67 Park Pl. E.
Morristown, NJ 07960-7105

Established in 2002 in NJ.
Donors: Dean N. Vanech; Denise Vanech.
Foundation type: Independent foundation.
Financial data (yr. ended 12/31/13): Assets, $3,982,549 (M); gifts received, $2,500,000; expenditures, $502,297; qualifying distributions, $491,200; giving activities include $487,500 for 8 grants (high: $250,000; low: $2,500).
Fields of interest: Performing arts; Education; Human services; Economically disadvantaged.
Limitations: Applications not accepted. Giving primarily in NJ and NY, with some giving nationally. No grants to individuals.
Application information: Contributes only to pre-selected organizations.
Trustees: Dean N. Vanech; Denise Vanech.
EIN: 611435014
Selected grants: The following grants are a representative sample of this grantmaker's funding activity:
$275,000 to Pingry School, Martinsville, NJ, 2011. For general support.
$10,000 to Cornerstone Family Programs, Morristown, NJ, 2011. For general support.

5488
The Emet V'Emunah Foundation, Inc. ✧
c/o Sam Sasson
200 Parker Ave.
Deal, NJ 07723-1430

Established in 2001 in NJ.
Donors: Sam N. Sasson; Samantha Sasson; Extra Sportswear, Inc.; Royal Blue Jeans; Sutton Warehousing.
Foundation type: Independent foundation.
Financial data (yr. ended 12/31/11): Assets, $93,088 (M); gifts received, $600,000; expenditures, $507,649; qualifying distributions, $506,611; giving activities include $506,611 for 17 + grants (high: $279,294).
Purpose and activities: Giving primarily to Jewish agencies, temples, and schools.
Fields of interest: Elementary/secondary education; Jewish agencies & synagogues.
Limitations: Applications not accepted. Giving primarily in Deal, NJ. No grants to individuals.
Application information: Contributes only to pre-selected organizations.
Trustees: Albert Sasson; Sam N. Sasson; Samantha Sasson.
EIN: 311814428

5489
Verizon Foundation ✧
(formerly Bell Atlantic Foundation)
1 Verizon Way, VC34W539B
Basking Ridge, NJ 07920-1025
FAX: (908) 630-2660; Contact for Verizon Foundation Progs.: Binta Vann-Joseph, Dir. of Mktg. Strategy, e-mail: binta.d.vann-joseph@verizon.com; Susan Sullivan, Dir., Domestic Violence Prevention, e-mail: dvp@verizonfoundation.org; Justina Nixon-Saintil, Dir., Education, e-mail: support@thinikfinity.org; Anthony Llompart, Dir., Healthcare, e-mail: healthcare@verizonfoundation.org; Main URL: http://www.verizon.com/about/verizon-foundation/
Facebook: http://www.facebook.com/VerizonFoundation
Responsibility Blog: http://forums.verizon.com/t5/Verizon-In-Your-Community-Blog/bg-p/ResidentialBlog2
RSS Feed: http://www.verizonfoundation.org/rss/feed
Twitter: https://twitter.com/verizongiving
YouTube: http://www.youtube.com/user/VerizonCSRVideos

Established in 1985 in NY.
Donors: NYNEX Corp.; Bell Atlantic Corp.; Verizon Communications Inc.
Foundation type: Company-sponsored foundation.
Financial data (yr. ended 12/31/12): Assets, $98,050,530 (M); expenditures, $54,973,480; qualifying distributions, $53,975,067; giving activities include $43,374,615 for 21,689 grants (high: $1,832,831; low: $25).
Purpose and activities: The foundation supports programs designed to use technology to solve critical social issues in the areas of education, healthcare, and energy management.
Fields of interest: Arts; Elementary/secondary education; Higher education; Libraries (public); Education, services; Education, reading; Education, e-learning; Education; Environment, energy; Environmental education; Environment; Health care, information services; Hospitals (general); Health care, clinics/centers; Public health; Public health, obesity; Health care; Asthma; Diabetes; Pediatrics; Crime/violence prevention, domestic violence; Crime/law enforcement; Children/youth, services; Family services, parent education; Family services, domestic violence; Community/economic development; Mathematics; Engineering/technology; Computer science; Science; Public affairs; Children; Aging; Disabilities, people with; Women; Economically disadvantaged.
Type of support: General/operating support; Building/renovation; Equipment; Program development; Curriculum development; Scholarship funds; Technical assistance; Employee volunteer services; Sponsorships; Employee matching gifts; Employee-related scholarships.
Limitations: Applications accepted. Giving on a national basis, with emphasis on CA, Washington DC, MN, NJ, and NY. No support for private charities or foundations, religious organizations not of direct benefit to the entire community, religious organizations duplicating the work of other organizations in the same community, political candidates or organizations, discriminatory organizations, or lobbying organizations. No grants to individuals (except for employee-related scholarships), or for political causes or campaigns, endowments or capital campaigns, film, music,

television, video, or media production or broadcast underwriting, research studies (unless related to projects already being supported by Verizon), sports sponsorships, performing arts tours, or association memberships, or field trips for secondary or elementary schools; no product donations.
Publications: Application guidelines; Corporate giving report; Financial statement; Informational brochure (including application guidelines); IRS Form 990 or 990-PF printed copy available upon request; Program policy statement.
Application information: Applications are currently considered on an invitation-only basis. However, prospective applicants are welcome to contact a Community Relations Manager in their state to determine eligibility. The average grant ranges from $5,000 to $10,000. Support is limited to 1 contribution per organization during any given year for 3 years in length. Organizations receiving support are asked to submit impact reports and a final report.
Board meeting date(s): Annually
Officers and Directors: Randal S. Milch, Vice-Chair. and Secy.; Rose Stuckey Kirk, Pres.; Ken Chan Sin, V.P. and Treas.; Michael W. Morrell, V.P. and Cont.; Nicholas G. Botticelli, C.I.O.; Lowell C. McAdam; Francis J. Shammo.
Number of staff: 8 full-time professional.
EIN: 133319048
Selected grants: The following grants are a representative sample of this grantmaker's funding activity:
$1,823,811 to Scholarship America, Saint Peter, MN, 2012.
$1,023,322 to American Red Cross National Headquarters, Washington, DC, 2012. For Disaster Relief Fund.
$547,000 to National Endowment for the Humanities, Washington, DC, 2012. For Edsitement.
$514,337 to Classic Pearls, Birmingham, AL, 2012. For Getting Stronger Program.
$450,000 to National Association of Community Health Centers, Bethesda, MD, 2012.
$50,000 to American Red Cross National Headquarters, Washington, DC, 2012. For Disaster Relief Fund.
$12,000 to Rush-Copley Foundation, Aurora, IL, 2012.
$10,000 to Jacob Burns Film Center, Pleasantville, NY, 2012.
$10,000 to Womens Resource Center for the Grand Traverse Area, Traverse City, MI, 2012.
$2,500 to College of William and Mary Foundation, Williamsburg, VA, 2012.

5490
Victoria Foundation, Inc. ✧
31 Mulberry St., 5th Fl.
Newark, NJ 07102-5202 (973) 792-9200
Contact: Irene Cooper-Basch, Exec. Off.
FAX: (973) 792-1300;
E-mail: info@victoriafoundation.org; Main URL: http://www.victoriafoundation.org

Incorporated in 1924 in NJ.
Donor: Hendon Chubb†.
Foundation type: Independent foundation.
Financial data (yr. ended 12/31/13): Assets, $242,123,778 (M); gifts received, $550; expenditures, $13,166,047; qualifying distributions, $12,433,244; giving activities include $11,145,231 for 205 grants (high: $500,000; low: $5,000).
Purpose and activities: Within Newark, NJ, grants primarily for urban activities and education programs, including early childhood and elementary education; support also for urban problems, leadership development, youth agencies, and certain statewide environmental projects.
Fields of interest: Arts education; Education, early childhood education; Elementary school/education; Education; Environment; Crime/violence prevention, youth; Housing/shelter, development; Youth development, services; Human services; Children/youth, services; Civil/human rights, minorities; Urban/community development; Community/economic development; Leadership development; Public affairs; Children/youth; Children; Minorities; African Americans/Blacks; Hispanics/Latinos; Economically disadvantaged.
Type of support: General/operating support; Continuing support; Management development/capacity building; Capital campaigns; Building/renovation; Land acquisition; Emergency funds; Program development; Seed money; Scholarship funds; Technical assistance; Consulting services; Matching/challenge support.
Limitations: Applications accepted. Giving limited to greater Newark, NJ; environmental grants limited to NJ. No grants to individuals.
Publications: Application guidelines; Annual report; Grants list.
Application information: Request application guidelines or visit the foundation's web site for application information. The foundation accepts the New York/ New Jersey Area Common Application Form. Application form required.
Initial approach: Proposal or 2-page letter of introduction
Copies of proposal: 1
Deadline(s): For current grantees, submit proposal prior to Jan. 15. For new grantees, submit proposal prior to Feb. 1; Feb. 1 for schools only; Sept. 8 for summer camps and summer programs only
Board meeting date(s): June and Dec.
Final notification: Within 3 weeks after board meeting if accepted
Officers and Trustees:* Kevin Shanley,* Pres. and Treas.; Margaret H. Parker,* V.P.; Irene Cooper-Basch, Exec. Off. and Secy.; Frank Alvarez; Charles M. Chapin III; Percy Chubb III; Sally Chubb; Robert C. Holmes; Robert L. Johnson; Gordon A. Millspaugh, Jr.; Franklin E. Parker IV; John F. Parker; Sarah Chubb Sauvayre; Grizel Ubarry; Gay M. Wingens; A. Zachary Yamba.
Number of staff: 5 full-time professional; 3 full-time support.
EIN: 221554541
Selected grants: The following grants are a representative sample of this grantmaker's funding activity:
$400,000 to New Community Corporation, Newark, NJ, 2012. For Development Department, Workforce Development Training and Operations, and Youth Services, Information Technology.
$315,000 to New Jersey Performing Arts Center, Newark, NJ, 2012. For administration of NJPACs Arts Education Department, to increase participation in the Artist-in-Residency programs and Arts Training initiatives, and to support In-School Residency programs.
$235,000 to United Way of Essex and West Hudson, Newark, NJ, 2012. For Summer Expansion Initiative, Johns Hopkins, Future Scholars, RU Ready, and WEB.
$200,000 to Ironbound Community Corporation, Newark, NJ, 2012. For general operating support and for development of a Family Empowerment Institute.
$175,000 to Trust for Public Land, Mid-Atlantic Regional Office, New York, NY, 2012. For Parks for People.
$75,000 to Clean Water Fund, Long Branch, NJ, 2012. To partner with ICC to achieve the following programs: Sustainable Newark, Healthy Ports and Kids Clean Air Zones and Green Jobs, payable over 1.50 years.
$40,000 to All Stars Project of New Jersey, Newark, NJ, 2012. For capital support for the build-out of the Scott Flamm Center for Afterschool Development and continued support for the Development School for Youth and UX leadership and development programs.
$37,500 to Audubon Society, New Jersey, Bernardsville, NJ, 2012. For funding for Opening space in the Urban and Built Environment and the Changing the Landscape-White Tailed Deer components of the land conservation work, payable over 1.50 years.
$35,000 to Sharron Miller's Academy for the Performing Arts, Montclair, NJ, 2012. For two year grant to support the continuation and expansion of SMAPAs artist-in-residence partnership at Newark Quitman Street Community School, payable over 2.00 years.
$25,000 to AIDS Resource Foundation for Children, Newark, NJ, 2012. For Academy Street Firehouse youth program.

5491
The Wagner Family Foundation, Inc. ✧
c/o Untracht Early
325 Columbia Tpke., Ste. 202
Florham Park, NJ 07932-1212

Established in 1997 in NY.
Donors: Leon Wagner; Marsha Wagner.
Foundation type: Independent foundation.
Financial data (yr. ended 09/30/13): Assets, $1,018,680 (M); expenditures, $1,457,235; qualifying distributions, $1,403,104; giving activities include $1,386,929 for 177 grants (high: $200,000; low: $36).
Purpose and activities: Giving primarily to Jewish organizations.
Fields of interest: Elementary/secondary education; Higher education; Hospitals (general); Health care; Health organizations, association; Medical research, institute; Cancer research; Human services; United Ways and Federated Giving Programs; Jewish federated giving programs; Jewish agencies & synagogues.
Limitations: Applications not accepted. Giving primarily in CA and NY. No grants to individuals.
Application information: Contributes only to pre-selected organizations.
Officers: Leon Wagner, Pres.; Harry Wagner, V.P. and Secy.
EIN: 133980685

5492
Vance Wall Foundation, Inc. ✧
c/o Carol Wall
160 Lloyd Rd.
Montclair, NJ 07042-1730

Established in 1990 in NJ.
Donors: Terence D. Wall; Carol V. Wall; Terry D. Wall.
Foundation type: Independent foundation.
Financial data (yr. ended 12/31/12): Assets, $31,231,387 (M); expenditures, $3,004,738; qualifying distributions, $2,787,319; giving activities include $2,787,186 for 21 grants (high: $1,320,000; low: $1,000).
Fields of interest: Museums (art); Education; Cancer; Breast cancer; Human services.
Limitations: Applications not accepted. Giving in the U.S., with some emphasis on NJ. No grants to individuals.
Application information: Contributes only to pre-selected organizations.
Trustees: Carol Vance Wall; Douglas V. Wall; Terry D. Wall.
EIN: 521739419
Selected grants: The following grants are a representative sample of this grantmaker's funding activity:
$200,000 to Metropolitan Museum of Art, New York, NY, 2012. For American Wing Challenge Grant Fund.
$26,000 to Storm King Art Center, Mountainville, NY, 2012. For Mark di Suverd Exhibition/ Unrestricted.
$1,000 to Jazz House Kids, Montclair, NJ, 2012. For John J. Calr Scholarship Fund.

5493
Wallerstein Foundation for Geriatric Life Improvement ✧
200 Executive Dr., Ste. 100
West Orange, NJ 07052-3303 (973) 731-2500
FAX: (973) 731-0163; E-mail: mjwpaesq@aol.com

Established in 1956 in NJ.
Donor: Julian W. Wallerstein†.
Foundation type: Independent foundation.
Financial data (yr. ended 06/30/14): Assets, $11,925,664 (M); expenditures, $1,020,895; qualifying distributions, $522,230; giving activities include $522,230 for 106 grants (high: $45,000; low: $50).
Purpose and activities: Grants primarily for health, and human service organizations for the aged.
Fields of interest: Health care; Health organizations, association; Aging, centers/services; Aging; Blind/visually impaired; Mentally disabled.
Type of support: Program development; Seed money.
Limitations: Applications accepted. Giving primarily in NJ and NY. No grants to individuals.
Application information: Application form required.
Initial approach: Simple 3-page letter
Copies of proposal: 1
Officer: Melvin J. Wallerstein, Pres.
Directors: Lesley W. Bunn; Mitchell B. Wallerstein; Rita Wallerstein; Debra W. Williams.
Number of staff: 1 part-time professional; 3 part-time support.
EIN: 223052726

5494
Johanette Wallerstein Institute ✧
Llewellyn Park
1 Elm Court Way
West Orange, NJ 07052-4927 (973) 731-1394
Contact: Bernard Wallerstein, Pres.
E-mail: bwallerstein@comcast.net

Established in 1967 in NJ.
Donors: Julian Wallerstein†; Jane Wallerstein; Bernard Wallerstein.
Foundation type: Independent foundation.
Financial data (yr. ended 06/30/13): Assets, $11,519,593 (M); gifts received, $382,341; expenditures, $771,404; qualifying distributions, $761,154; giving activities include $692,330 for 50 grants (high: $175,000; low: $500).
Purpose and activities: Primary interests are the environment, with emphasis on global warming and water conservation.
Fields of interest: Environment.
Type of support: Annual campaigns; Building/ renovation; Publication; Seed money; Research; Program evaluation; Matching/challenge support.
Limitations: Applications accepted. Giving primarily in northern NJ. No support for political organizations. No grants for endowment campaigns.
Publications: Informational brochure (including application guidelines); Program policy statement.
Application information: Application form not required.
Initial approach: Letter
Copies of proposal: 4
Deadline(s): None
Board meeting date(s): July
Final notification: Varies
Officers and Trustee:* Bernard Wallerstein,* Pres.; Jane Wallerstein, V.P. and Secy.; Peggy Kontz, V.P.
EIN: 226042908

5495
The Charles B. Wang International Foundation ✧
(formerly The Sagamore Hill Supporting Organization, Inc.)
c/o Robert Bell
250 Pehle Ave., No. 404
Saddle Brook, NJ 07663-5803 (201) 368-7880

Established in 1999 in NJ; supporting organization of Alliance for Lupus Foundation, Charles B. Wang Community Health Center, Chinatown Health Clinic Foundation, Jay's World Cancer Foundation, Memorial Day School, The Smile Train, and St. Francis Hospital Foundation.
Foundation type: Independent foundation.
Financial data (yr. ended 07/27/12): Assets, $9,426,509 (M); expenditures, $688,378; qualifying distributions, $598,179; giving activities include $488,894 for 16 grants (high: $125,000; low: $2,500).
Fields of interest: Higher education; Education; Health care; Human services; Children/youth, services.
Limitations: Applications not accepted. Giving primarily in the metropolitan New York, NY, area; funding also in China. No grants to individuals.
Application information: Contributes only to pre-selected organizations.
Officer and Director:* Robert T. Bell,* Pres.
EIN: 113486100

5496
WebMD Health Foundation, Inc. ✧
(formerly WebMD Charitable Fund)
c/o Katherine Crow, Tr.
P.O. Box 359
Elmwood Park, NJ 07407-0359

Established in 1991 in NJ.
Donors: Martin J. Wygod; Crocker Nevin; James Manning; Per Lofberg.
Foundation type: Independent foundation.
Financial data (yr. ended 04/30/13): Assets, $203,257 (M); expenditures, $2,639,660; qualifying distributions, $2,607,072; giving activities include $2,358,572 for 18 grants (high: $1,666,667; low: $750).
Purpose and activities: Giving primarily to health services and health care related to prescription drugs. The foundation focuses on projects that provide assistance to the elderly and others who cannot otherwise secure medical care and prescription drugs; assist in the fight against drug abuse; encourage the development of geriatric drug utilization research; help specific disease and health categories, such as AIDS and prenatal care; and foster pharmacy education and professionalism.
Fields of interest: Higher education; Medical school/education; Pharmacy/prescriptions; Health care; Health organizations, association; Medical research, institute; Human services; Children/ youth, services.
Limitations: Applications not accepted. Giving primarily in CA, NJ, and NY. No support for religious or fraternal organizations. No grants to individuals, or for basic research or endowments.
Application information: Unsolicited requests for funds not accepted.
Board meeting date(s): Apr. and Oct.
Officers and Trustees:* James Manning,* Pres.; Charles A. Mele, V.P. and Secy.; Frank J. Failla, Jr., V.P.; Paul C. Suthern,* V.P.; Pamela Wygod,* V.P.; Dixie Newman, Exec. Dir.; Pamela Fishman; Lawrence Lahr; Martin Raynes; Jeffrey Sachs, D.D.S.; Martin J. Wygod.
Number of staff: 2 part-time professional.
EIN: 223114859

5497
Weitzman Family Foundation ✧ ☆
P.O. Box 1501, NJ2-130-03-31
Pennington, NJ 08534-1501

Donor: Stuart Weitzman.
Foundation type: Independent foundation.
Financial data (yr. ended 12/31/13): Assets, $24,904,999 (M); expenditures, $2,205,285; qualifying distributions, $2,121,662; giving activities include $2,076,000 for 3 grants (high: $2,000,000; low: $1,000).
Fields of interest: Education; Health care; Recreation.
Type of support: General/operating support.
Limitations: Applications not accepted. Giving primarily in CT.
Application information: Unsolicited requests for funds not accepted.
Trustee: Stuart Weitzman.
EIN: 466477200

5498
The Werdiger Family Foundation ✧
60 Walnut Ave., Ste. 100
Clark, NJ 07066-1635 (732) 382-3100
Contact: Jonah Blumenfrucht, Secy.-Treas.

Established in 1989 in NY.
Donors: Solomon Werdiger; Outerstuff, Ltd.
Foundation type: Independent foundation.
Financial data (yr. ended 11/30/13): Assets, $28,438,180 (M); gifts received, $2,500,000; expenditures, $1,612,707; qualifying distributions, $1,344,502; giving activities include $1,318,960 for 300 grants (high: $100,000; low: $72).
Purpose and activities: Giving primarily to Jewish agencies, temples, and schools.
Fields of interest: Elementary/secondary education; Jewish agencies & synagogues.
Application information: Application form required.
Initial approach: Letter
Deadline(s): None
Officers: Solomon Werdiger, Pres.; Esther Werdiger, V.P.; Jonah Blumenfrucht, Secy.-Treas.
EIN: 133505439

5499
Josh & Judy Weston Family Foundation ✧
217 Christopher St.
Montclair, NJ 07042-4205 (973) 974-5828
Contact: Josh S. Weston, Pres.

Established in 1992 in NJ.
Donor: Josh S. Weston.
Foundation type: Operating foundation.
Financial data (yr. ended 12/31/13): Assets, $4,241,000 (M); gifts received, $730,096; expenditures, $2,475,000; qualifying distributions, $2,475,000; giving activities include $2,453,000 for 70 grants (high: $105,000).
Purpose and activities: Giving primarily for arts and culture, education, including Jewish education, and social services.
Fields of interest: Museums; Arts; Higher education; Education; Human services.
Type of support: Emergency funds; Program development.
Limitations: Applications accepted. Giving primarily in NJ and New York, NY. No grants to individuals.
Application information:
Initial approach: Letter
Deadline(s): None
Officers: Josh S. Weston, Pres.; Eric Weston, V.P.; Judy Weston, V.P.; Ron Weston, V.P.
EIN: 521798616
Selected grants: The following grants are a representative sample of this grantmaker's funding activity:
$25,000 to Yeshiva University, New York, NY, 2011.
$22,500 to Teach for America, New York, NY, 2011.
$15,000 to American Littoral Society, Highlands, NJ, 2011.

5500
Wicks Chapin Inc ✧
855 Centennial Ave.
Piscataway, NJ 08855

Established in 1985 in NJ.
Donors: Edward J. Foley III; Joan Foley‡; John C. Foley; Foley Inc.; E.J. Foley Inc.
Foundation type: Independent foundation.
Financial data (yr. ended 12/31/12): Assets, $2,597,615 (M); gifts received, $200,000; expenditures, $512,225; qualifying distributions, $491,217; giving activities include $476,850 for 27 grants (high: $72,500; low: $250).
Fields of interest: Elementary/secondary education; Health care; Medical research, institute; Human services; Family services.
Limitations: Applications not accepted. Giving primarily in NJ. No grants to individuals.
Application information: Contributes only to pre-selected organizations.
Officers and Trustees:* Edward J. Foley III,* Co-Pres.; John C. Foley,* Co-Pres.
EIN: 222691706

5501
The Wight Foundation, Inc. ✧ ☆
550 Broad St., Ste. 717
Newark, NJ 07102-4516 (973) 824-1195
Contact: Rhonda Aususte, Exec. Dir.
FAX: (973) 824-1199;
E-mail: Wightfoundation@wightfoundation.org;
E-mail for Rhonda Auguste, Exec. Dir.:
rauguste@wightfoundation.org; Main URL: http://www.wightfoundation.org

Incorporated in 1986 in NJ.
Donor: Russell Wight, Jr.
Foundation type: Independent foundation.
Financial data (yr. ended 12/31/12): Assets, $13,976,551 (M); expenditures, $1,554,601; qualifying distributions, $1,511,860; giving activities include $147,240 for grants, and $395,921 for grants to individuals.
Purpose and activities: Scholarship awards to seventh-grade students, primarily economically disadvantaged, who attend school in the greater Newark, New Jersey, area.
Fields of interest: Education.
Type of support: General/operating support; Scholarships—to individuals.
Limitations: Applications accepted. Giving limited to the greater Newark, NJ, area.
Publications: Informational brochure (including application guidelines); Newsletter.
Application information: Application guidelines and form available on foundation web site. Application form required.
Initial approach: Complete preliminary application form
Deadline(s): See foundation web site for application deadlines
Board meeting date(s): Bimonthly
Officers and Trustees:* Russell Wight, Jr.,* Pres.; Rhonda Auguste, Exec. Dir.; Bruce Byrne; Yvonne Goyins; Shakirah Miller; Christopher Miller; Alfred Woods.
Number of staff: 1 full-time professional; 2 full-time support.
EIN: 222743349

5502
Wilf Family Foundation ✧
820 Morris Tpke.
Short Hills, NJ 07078-2624
Contact: Joseph Wilf, Tr.

Established in 1964.
Donors: Joseph Wilf; Leonard Wilf; Harry Wilf‡.
Foundation type: Independent foundation.
Financial data (yr. ended 10/31/13): Assets, $115,780,969 (M); gifts received, $3,860,000; expenditures, $8,012,779; qualifying distributions, $7,760,095; giving activities include $7,660,095 for 133 grants (high: $2,000,000; low: $250), and $100,000 for 1 loan/program-related investment.
Purpose and activities: Grants for Jewish welfare funds, including educational programs, and temple support; giving also for educational institutions and health organizations.
Fields of interest: Higher education; Education; Hospitals (general); Health organizations, association; Human services; Jewish federated giving programs; Jewish agencies & synagogues.
Type of support: Annual campaigns; Capital campaigns; Building/renovation; Endowments; Scholarship funds.
Limitations: Applications not accepted. Giving primarily in NJ and NY.
Publications: Annual report.
Application information: Unsolicited requests for funds not considered.
Officers and Trustees:* Joseph Wilf,* Chair.; Leonard Wilf,* Pres.; Zygmunt Wilf,* V.P.; Mark Wilf,* Secy.; Orin Wilf,* Treas.; Elizabeth Wilf; Jason Wilf; Jeffrey Wilf; Jonathan Wilf.
EIN: 226075840
Selected grants: The following grants are a representative sample of this grantmaker's funding activity:
$2,000,000 to New York University, New York, NY, 2012. For unrestricted support.
$2,000,000 to New York University, New York, NY, 2013. For unrestricted support.
$1,139,600 to American Society for Yad Vashem, New York, NY, 2013. For unrestricted support.
$1,000,000 to University of Pennsylvania, Philadelphia, PA, 2013. For unrestricted support.
$936,000 to New York-Presbyterian Hospital, New York, NY, 2012. For unrestricted support.
$900,000 to New York-Presbyterian Hospital, New York, NY, 2013. For unrestricted support.
$851,250 to Jewish Federation of Central New Jersey, Scotch Plains, NJ, 2012. For unrestricted support.
$325,180 to American Society for Yad Vashem, New York, NY, 2012. For unrestricted support.
$293,000 to United Jewish Communities of MetroWest, Whippany, NJ, 2013. For unrestricted support.
$261,000 to UJA-Federation of New York, New York, NY, 2012. For unrestricted support.
$250,000 to Newark Academy, Livingston, NJ, 2012. For unrestricted support.
$250,000 to Newark Academy, Livingston, NJ, 2013. For unrestricted support.
$200,000 to United Way of Greater Union County, Elizabeth, NJ, 2013. For unrestricted support.
$100,000 to American Committee for Shaare Zedek Hospital in Jerusalem, National/Northeast Region, New York, NY, 2012. For unrestricted support.
$100,000 to Jewish Museum, New York, NY, 2013. For unrestricted support.
$72,300 to Jewish Educational Center, Elizabeth, NJ, 2012. For unrestricted support.
$52,000 to Yeshiva University, New York, NY, 2013. For unrestricted support.
$50,000 to United Jewish Communities of MetroWest, Whippany, NJ, 2012. For unrestricted support.
$35,000 to Lincoln Center for the Performing Arts, New York, NY, 2012. For unrestricted support.
$35,000 to Lincoln Center for the Performing Arts, New York, NY, 2013. For unrestricted support.

5503
Z. S. & M. Wilf Foundation, Inc. ✧
(formerly Z & M Foundation, Inc.)
200 Central Ave., Ste. 102
Mountainside, NJ 07092-1961

Established in 1997 in NJ.
Donors: Mark Wilf; Zygmunt Wilf; Joseph Wilf.
Foundation type: Independent foundation.
Financial data (yr. ended 12/31/12): Assets, $113,875,824 (M); gifts received, $5,204,787; expenditures, $4,299,443; qualifying distributions, $4,219,847; giving activities include $4,219,847 for 30 grants (high: $1,250,000; low: $1,000).
Purpose and activities: Giving primarily for Jewish agencies and temples, and Jewish federated giving programs; funding also for education and health associations.
Fields of interest: Higher education; Education; Health care; Health organizations, association; Human services; Jewish federated giving programs; Jewish agencies & synagogues.
Limitations: Applications not accepted. Giving primarily in NJ and NY. No grants to individuals.
Application information: Contributes only to pre-selected organizations.
Trustees: Elizabeth Wilf; Jason Wilf; Jeffrey Wilf; Jonathan Wilf; Joseph Wilf; Leonard Wilf; Mark Wilf; Zygmunt Wilf.
EIN: 223553441
Selected grants: The following grants are a representative sample of this grantmaker's funding activity:
$1,010,000 to Princeton University, Princeton, NJ, 2011. For general support.
$1,000,000 to Yeshiva University, New York, NY, 2011. For general support.
$850,000 to Jewish Federation of Central New Jersey, Scotch Plains, NJ, 2011. For general support.
$530,000 to Pingry School, Martinsville, NJ, 2011. For general support.
$520,000 to New York University, New York, NY, 2011. For general support.
$250,000 to Newark Academy, Livingston, NJ, 2011. For general support.
$44,081 to United Jewish Communities of MetroWest, Whippany, NJ, 2011. For general support.
$11,800 to American Friends of Melitz, Baltimore, MD, 2011. For general support.

5504
Zygmunt & Audrey Wilf Foundation ✧
200 Central Ave., Ste. 102
Mountainside, NJ 07092-2807

Established in 1986 in NJ.
Donors: Zygmunt Wilf; Audrey Wilf; Joseph Wilf; Zygmunt Wilf Charitable Trust.
Foundation type: Independent foundation.
Financial data (yr. ended 12/31/13): Assets, $18,442,426 (M); gifts received, $1,700,000; expenditures, $816,673; qualifying distributions, $805,550; giving activities include $805,550 for 36 grants (high: $160,000; low: $250).
Purpose and activities: Giving primarily for higher education, as well as for Jewish organizations.
Fields of interest: Arts, multipurpose centers/programs; Higher education; Human services; Jewish agencies & synagogues.
Type of support: General/operating support.
Limitations: Applications not accepted. Giving primarily in NJ and NY. No grants to individuals.
Application information: Contributes only to pre-selected organizations.
Trustees: Audrey Wilf; Mark Wilf; Zygmunt Wilf.
EIN: 222747584

5505
The Willits Foundation ✧
730 Central Ave.
Murray Hill, NJ 07974-1139

Incorporated in 1963 in NJ.
Donors: Harris L. Willits‡; John H. Evans; members of the Willits family.
Foundation type: Independent foundation.
Financial data (yr. ended 11/30/13): Assets, $22,231,412 (M); expenditures, $1,006,548; qualifying distributions, $900,708; giving activities include $876,014 for 41 grants (high: $176,007; low: $500).
Purpose and activities: Emphasis on grants to higher educational institutions for scholarships for the children of employees of C.R. Bard, Inc. only; some support for hospitals and social service agencies.
Fields of interest: Higher education; Hospitals (general).
Type of support: General/operating support; Scholarships—to individuals.
Limitations: Applications not accepted. Giving primarily in FL and NJ. No grants to individuals (except for scholarships).
Application information: Unsolicited requests for funds not accepted.
Board meeting date(s): Mar. and as required
Officer: John Evans, Chair.
Number of staff: None.
EIN: 226063106

5506
Wishes By Wyndham Foundation ✧ ☆
(formerly Wyndham Worldwide Charitable Foundation)
22 Sylvan Way
Parsippany, NJ 07054-3801

Donor: Wyndham Worldwide Corp.
Foundation type: Independent foundation.
Financial data (yr. ended 12/31/13): Assets, $2,919,709 (M); gifts received, $750,000; expenditures, $1,593,000; qualifying distributions, $1,593,000; giving activities include $1,592,616 for 65 grants (high: $239,250; low: $50).
Fields of interest: Medical research; Recreation, camps; Athletics/sports, golf; Child development, services; Family services; Human services.
Limitations: Applications not accepted. Giving primarily in CA, CT, IN and NC.
Application information: Unsolicited requests for funds not accepted.
Officers: Scott G. McLester, Exec. V.P. and Corp. Secy.; Thomas J. Edwards, Jr., Exec. V.P. and Treas.; Mary R. Falvey, Exec. V.P.; Gregory Thomas Geppel, Sr. V.P.; Nicola Rossi, Sr. V.P.; Steve Meetre, Group V.P.; Alyson Johnson, V.P., Mktg. and Comm.
Directors: Terence P. Conley; Stephen P. Holmes; John M. Osborne.
EIN: 261466294
Selected grants: The following grants are a representative sample of this grantmaker's funding activity:
$200,000 to Piedmont Triad Charitable Foundation, Greensboro, NC, 2012. For Donation made out of Wyndham Championship Charity is dedicated to running a premier PGA Tour event in North Carolina's Piedmont Triad, promoting the Piedmont Triad to the world as attractive place to live and work.
$25,000 to American Junior Golf Association, Braselton, GA, 2012. For Sponsorship of the 2012 Wyndham Cup event Organization supports the growth and development of young men and women who aspire to earn college golf scholarships through competitive junior golf.
$25,000 to Breast Cancer Research Foundation, New York, NY, 2012. For Contribution in support of the Annual Gala held to promote public awareness of breast cancer and self-examinations.
$25,000 to New Bridge Services, Pequannock, NJ, 2012. For Charity dedicated to helping people find balance in their lives by providing affordable and innovative behavioral health and education Programs.
$25,000 to Petty Family Foundation, Randleman, NC, 2012. For Premium sponsorship of annual R Petty Charity Golf Classic.
$20,000 to Music City Bowl, Nashville, TN, 2012. For Donation to support the annual charity cup golf tournament.
$10,000 to Breast Cancer Research Foundation, New York, NY, 2012. For Donation to a symposium and awards luncheon on 10/30/12.
$1,000 to Alliance for Lupus Research, New York, NY, 2012. For Sponsorship of May 12, 2012 Walk to Cure Lupus.

5507
Yin-Shun Foundation ✧ ☆
67 Lawrence Rd.
Lafayette, NJ 07848-3018
Main URL: http://yinshun.org/

Established in 1996 in NJ.
Donors: Eva Lin; Ray Jui Chuang Chung; Tai Hwa Yen.
Foundation type: Independent foundation.
Financial data (yr. ended 12/31/12): Assets, $9,404,501 (M); gifts received, $24,538; expenditures, $739,257; qualifying distributions, $586,862; giving activities include $521,406 for 8 grants (high: $301,456; low: $1,700).
Fields of interest: Education; Human services; Buddhism; Religion.
Type of support: Continuing support.
Limitations: Applications not accepted. Giving primarily in Lafayette, NJ and Taiwan. No grants to individuals.
Application information: Unsolicited requests for funds not accepted.
Officers and Trustees:* Ven Bhikkhu Bodhi,* Chair.; Juichang Chuang,* Secy.; Hueyling Wu,* Treas.; Kent Chen; Wan-Ju Chen; Ven T. Chueng; Tsuku Lee.
EIN: 223458312

5508
The Avi Yosef Foundation, Inc. ✧
140 Chadwick Rd.
Teaneck, NJ 07666-4206 (201) 836-3613
Contact: Mark Karasick, Pres.

Established in 2000 in NJ.
Donor: Mark Karasick.
Foundation type: Independent foundation.
Financial data (yr. ended 12/31/13): Assets, $126,830 (M); gifts received, $663,500; expenditures, $1,063,062; qualifying distributions, $1,063,062; giving activities include $1,060,682 for 40 grants (high: $200,000; low: $5,000).
Purpose and activities: Giving primarily to Jewish agencies, temples, and schools.
Fields of interest: Elementary/secondary education; Jewish federated giving programs; Jewish agencies & synagogues.
Limitations: Applications not accepted. No grants to individuals.
Application information: Contributes only to pre-selected organizations.
Officer: Mark Karasick, Pres.
EIN: 223772451

5509
Zucker Foundation ✧ ☆
c/o KRS CPAS LLC
80 Rte. 4 E., Ste, 370
Paramus, NJ 07652

Established in 2007 in DE.
Donor: Uzi Zucker.
Foundation type: Independent foundation.
Financial data (yr. ended 12/31/13): Assets, $4,825,953 (M); expenditures, $1,259,922; qualifying distributions, $1,250,000; giving activities include $1,250,000 for 1 grant.
Fields of interest: Jewish federated giving programs.
Limitations: Applications not accepted. Giving primarily in New York, NY. No grants to individuals.
Application information: Contributes only to pre-selected organizations.
Officer: David Warmflash, Secy.
Directors: Adam Zucker; Jonathan Zucker; Uzi Zucker.
EIN: 261562646

5510
Zurs Foundation, Inc. ✧ ☆
c/o Porzio, Bromberg and Newman PC
100 Southgate Pkwy.
P.O. Box 1997
Morristown, NJ 07962-1997

Established in 1997 in NJ.
Donor: William D. Dearstyne.
Foundation type: Independent foundation.
Financial data (yr. ended 11/30/13): Assets, $1,246,301 (M); expenditures, $856,050; qualifying distributions, $849,447; giving activities include $837,800 for 12 grants (high: $520,000; low: $500).
Fields of interest: Arts; Education; Human services.
Limitations: Applications not accepted. Giving primarily in PA; giving also in NY. No grants to individuals.
Application information: Contributes only to pre-selected organizations.
Officers and Trustees:* William D. Dearstyne, Pres.; Elizabeth T. Dearstyne,* Secy.-Treas.; Katharine B. Dearstyne; Marjorie Farquhar; Elizabeth D. Geletka.
EIN: 311486893
Selected grants: The following grants are a representative sample of this grantmaker's funding activity:
$7,500 to American Camp Association, Martinsville, IN, 2011.

NEW MEXICO

5511
Albuquerque Community Foundation ✧
624 Tijeras Ave., NW
Albuquerque, NM 87102 (505) 883-6240
Contact: For grants: Nancy Johnson, Prog. Dir.
FAX: (505) 883-3629;
E-mail: foundation@albuquerquefoundation.org;
Mailing address: P.O. Box 25266, Albuquerque, NM 87125-5266; Additional e-mail: njohnson@albuquerquefoundation.org; Main URL: http://www.albuquerquefoundation.org
E-Newsletter: http://visitor.constantcontact.com/manage/optin?v=001EZ1xV5UTY8v4rVPDf6-vAY-_jw1XHvIL
Facebook: http://www.facebook.com/pages/Albuquerque-Community-Foundation/172927816931?ref=ts
Twitter: http://twitter.com/abqfoundation

Established in 1981 in NM.
Foundation type: Community foundation.
Financial data (yr. ended 12/31/12): Assets, $58,483,813 (M); gifts received, $4,523,537; expenditures, $4,336,610; giving activities include $2,896,420 for 161+ grants (high: $800,000), and $131,996 for 126 grants to individuals.
Purpose and activities: The foundation's mission is to build, invest and manage endowment funds to enhance the quality of the community through informed strategic grantmaking.
Fields of interest: Historic preservation/historical societies; Arts; Education; Environment, natural resources; Environment; Health care; Children/youth, services; Human services; Children/youth.
Type of support: Continuing support; General/operating support; Program development; Scholarship funds; Scholarships—to individuals.
Limitations: Applications accepted. Giving primarily in the greater Albuquerque, NM, area. No support for religious purposes, private foundations, or for grantmaking organizations. Generally, no grants to individuals (except for scholarship funds), or for debt retirement, annual campaigns, capital campaigns, fundraising events, endowments, conferences or symposia, emergency funding or interest or tax payments; no multi-year grants.
Publications: Annual report (including application guidelines); Financial statement; Grants list; Newsletter.
Application information: Visit foundation web site for application guidelines. Faxed applications are not accepted. Application form not required.
Initial approach: Letter of Intent
Copies of proposal: 8
Deadline(s): Changes annually
Board meeting date(s): Quarterly
Final notification: 1 to 2 months
Officers and Trustees:* Kevin Yearout,* Chair.; Jennifer S. Thomas,* Chair.-Elect.; R. Randall Royster, Esq.,* Pres. and C.E.O.; Glenn Fellows,* Secy.; Julie Weaks Gutierrez,* Treas.; Carl M. Alongi; Karen Bard; Julie Bowdich; William E. Ebel; Terri Giron-Gordon; Mark Gorham; Ted Jorgensen; Steven Keene; William Lang; Kenneth C. Leach; Steve Maestas; Bev McMillan; Marcus Mims, CPA; Diane Harrison Ogawa; Deborah Peacock; Kathleen Raskob; Ron J. Rivera; Jerrald J. Roehl; Chester French Stewart; Peter Touche.
Number of staff: 4 full-time professional; 2 part-time professional; 1 full-time support; 1 part-time support.
EIN: 850295444
Selected grants: The following grants are a representative sample of this grantmaker's funding activity:
$60,000 to New Mexico Philharmonic, Albuquerque, NM, 2012. For season including performances, audience outreach and educational programs.
$11,500 to Storehouse, Albuquerque, NM, 2012. For Food Rescue Network provides free food five days per week all year to the hungry who self-select groceries for their families.
$11,000 to New Mexico Child Advocacy Network, Albuquerque, NM, 2012. For leadership training and recruitment of volunteers for Building Futures and Foundation program matching trained adult mentors with young people aging out of foster care.
$10,000 to Albuquerque Health Care for the Homeless, Albuquerque, NM, 2012. To provide Primary Care Dental services for men, women and children without home through comprehensive treatment, preventive and restorative dental care, regardless of ability to pay.
$10,000 to Bosque School, Albuquerque, NM, 2012. For Bosque Ecosystem Monitoring Program (BEMP), collaborative project involving nearly 7,000 K-12 students from nearly 40 schools in long-term ecological and scientific research work.
$10,000 to VSA Arts of New Mexico, Albuquerque, NM, 2012. For Arts Adventures Program, arts-based Respite Program for youth with autism and their families.
$9,000 to New Mexico Foundation for Dental Health Research and Education, Albuquerque, NM, 2012. For Donated Dental Services providing access to life changing major dental care free of charge to elderly and disabled people who otherwise cannot afford this care.
$7,000 to Hawks Aloft, Albuquerque, NM, 2012. For Living with the Landscape program for two Title 1 elementary schools including single visit programs, field trips and conservation projects.
$5,000 to Acupuncturists Without Borders, Albuquerque, NM, 2012. For Albuquerque Female Veterans Clinic, first community acupuncture clinic in the nation dedicated exclusively to provide services for women veterans, active duty soldiers and reservists.
$5,000 to Animal Humane Association of New Mexico, Albuquerque, NM, 2012. Fof Senior Pet Owner Veterinary Fund assists senior citizens who cannot afford to pay for vital health services for their companion pets.

5512
Albuquerque Public Library ✧ ☆
c/o Richard A. Freedman
500 Marquette Ave. N.W., Ste. 650
Albuquerque, NM 87102-5341

Established in NM.
Foundation type: Independent foundation.
Financial data (yr. ended 12/31/13): Assets, $9,607,470 (M); expenditures, $1,155,652; qualifying distributions, $1,155,652; giving activities include $971,594 for 1 grant.
Fields of interest: Libraries (public).
Limitations: Applications not accepted. Giving primarily in Albuquerque, NM.
Application information: Unsolicited requests for funds not accepted.
Trustee: Thomas D. Walker.
EIN: 456252449

5513
Jonathan & Kathleen Altman Foundation ✧
c/o Avalon Trust
125 Lincoln Ave., Ste. 301
Santa Fe, NM 87501-2060

Established in 2000 in NM.
Donors: Jonathan Altman; Kathleen Altman; Bartos & Altman, CLT.
Foundation type: Independent foundation.
Financial data (yr. ended 12/31/12): Assets, $10,583,348 (M); gifts received, $1,916,327; expenditures, $724,963; qualifying distributions, $660,997; giving activities include $610,406 for 55 grants (high: $70,000; low: $6).
Fields of interest: Libraries (public); Education; Environment; Health care; Human services; United Ways and Federated Giving Programs; Jewish federated giving programs; Buddhism.
Limitations: Applications not accepted. Giving primarily in CA, IL, NM, and NY. No grants to individuals.
Application information: Contributes only to pre-selected organizations.
Directors: Jonathan Altman; Rafael Altman.
EIN: 850470898

5514
Angelica Foundation ✧ ☆
1688 Cerro Gordo
Santa Fe, NM 87501-6175

Established in 1994 in CA.
Donors: Ruben and Elizabeth Ransing Trust; The Keller Group Investment; Sigrid Rausing Trust; Open Society Institute.
Foundation type: Independent foundation.
Financial data (yr. ended 12/31/12): Assets, $3,669,448 (M); gifts received, $430,748; expenditures, $839,971; qualifying distributions, $440,500; giving activities include $440,500 for grants.
Purpose and activities: Giving primarily to support progressive organizations working for democratic change, environmental sustainability, and social justice.
Fields of interest: Environment; Human services; International human rights; Foundations (public).
International interests: Latin America; Mexico.
Type of support: Annual campaigns.
Limitations: Applications not accepted. No support for public education, political organizations, or programs promoting religious doctrines. No grants to individuals, or for academic scholarships, conferences, or fundraising events.
Publications: Annual report.
Application information: Contributes only to pre-selected organizations.
Officers and Directors:* Suzanne D. Gollin,* Pres.; James D. Gollin,* Secy.-Treas.; Christopher Brown; Nancy Harris Campbell; Nina Royal; Gladys Schmidt.
Number of staff: 1 part-time professional; 2 part-time support.
EIN: 330632647

5515
Aurora Foundation ✧
551 W. Cordova Rd.
PMB 710
Santa Fe, NM 87505-1825
Application address: c/o Jeffrey Bronfman, 1000 Cordova Pl., PMB 710, Santa Fe, NM 87505, tel.: (505) 988-5924

Established in 1993 in TX and NM.
Donor: Jeffrey Bronfman Living Trust.
Foundation type: Operating foundation.
Financial data (yr. ended 09/30/13): Assets, $704,964 (M); gifts received, $741,208; expenditures, $1,030,180; qualifying distributions, $908,982; giving activities include $869,744 for 27 grants (high: $564,989; low: $500).
Purpose and activities: Giving for projects that embody strategic efforts for the preservation and protection of planetary ecosystems (i.e. the environment), as well as efforts that secure the perpetuation and practice of indigenous cultures and ancient religious, spiritual and ceremonial traditions (e.g. certain Native American cultures and their religious traditions.).
Fields of interest: Education; Environment.
International interests: Central America; South America.
Limitations: Applications accepted. Giving primarily in NM; some funding also in CA, HI and NY.
Application information:
Initial approach: Proposal
Deadline(s): None
Officers: Jeffrey Bronfman, Pres. and Treas.; Duncan E. Osborne, Secy.
Director: Irvin F. Diamond.
EIN: 742660772
Selected grants: The following grants are a representative sample of this grantmaker's funding activity:
$5,000 to Earth Care, Santa Fe, NM, 2011.
$3,000 to Amazon Conservation Team, Arlington, VA, 2011.
$3,000 to Amazon Conservation Team, Arlington, VA, 2010.
$2,500 to Earth Care, Santa Fe, NM, 2010.
$2,000 to Southwest Learning Centers, Albuquerque, NM, 2011.
$1,000 to Maui Tomorrow Foundation, Wailuku, HI, 2011.
$1,000 to Truthout, Sacramento, CA, 2011.

5516
Brindle Foundation ✧
P.O. Box 31696
Santa Fe, NM 87594-1696 (505) 986-3983
Contact: Kim Straus, Mgr.
FAX: (505) 986-3983;
E-mail: info@brindlefoundation.org; Main URL: http://www.brindlefoundation.org

Established in 2002 in DE.
Donor: Martha Healy.
Foundation type: Independent foundation.
Financial data (yr. ended 12/31/13): Assets, $19,955,971 (M); gifts received, $1,837,954; expenditures, $1,119,708; qualifying distributions, $941,530; giving activities include $875,542 for 51 grants (high: $75,054; low: $50).
Purpose and activities: Giving primarily for early childhood development and literacy serving children from pre-birth to 3 years and their families in New Mexico.
Fields of interest: Arts; Environment, legal rights; Environment, formal/general education; Animal welfare; Family services; Infants/toddlers; Children.
Type of support: General/operating support; Management development/capacity building; Program development; Technical assistance; Matching/challenge support.
Limitations: Applications not accepted. Giving primarily in NM. No grants to individuals.
Application information: Contributes only to pre-selected organizations. Unsolicited requests for funds not accepted.
Board meeting date(s): Annually
Officers: Nancy Healy Schwanfelder, Pres.; Kevin Schwanfelder, V.P.; Craig Schwanfelder, Secy.-Treas.; Kim Straus, Mgr.
Number of staff: 1 full-time professional.
EIN: 030466957
Selected grants: The following grants are a representative sample of this grantmaker's funding activity:
$50,000 to Santa Fe Public Schools, Santa Fe, NM, 2012. For Adelante and Teen Parent Programs.
$25,034 to La Familia Medical Center, Santa Fe, NM, 2012. For Prenatal services and pediatrics.
$25,034 to Las Cumbres Community Services, Espanola, NM, 2012. For Community Infant Program.
$25,034 to New Vistas, Santa Fe, NM, 2012. For early childhood and early intervention services.
$25,034 to Presbyterian Medical Services Foundation, Santa Fe, NM, 2012. For Head Start and Early Head Start Programs in Santa Fe County.
$23,000 to New Mexico Association for the Education of Young Children, Albuquerque, NM, 2012. For T.E.A C H scholarships in Santa Fe County and early childhood Incentives Program.
$20,261 to Museum of New Mexico Foundation, Santa Fe, NM, 2012. For Annual Fund for Education and History Museum education Program.
$20,036 to Santa Fe Community Foundation, Santa Fe, NM, 2012. For Brindle Donor Advised Fund.
$20,036 to United Way of Santa Fe County, Santa Fe, NM, 2012. For First Born Program.
$10,039 to Weber State University, Ogden, UT, 2012. For archive project of Utah Construction/Utah International materials.

5517
Chase Foundation ✧
510 Texas Ave.
Artesia, NM 88210-2041 (575) 746-4610
Contact: Richard Price, Exec. Dir.
E-mail: richardprice@chasefoundation.com; Additional e-mail: info@chasefoundation.com; Additional Contact: Ginny Bush, Assoc. Dir., e-mail: GinnyBush@chasefoundation.com; Main URL: http://www.chasefoundation.com
Facebook: http://www.facebook.com/chasefoundation
Grants List: http://www.chasefoundation.com/index.php/grants-11/historical-funding
Scholarship Recipients: http://www.chasefoundation.com/index.php/scholarships-12/past-recipients/2013

Established in 2006 in NM.
Donors: Gerene Furguson; Mack C. Chase; Marilyn Y. Chase; Chase Oil Co.
Foundation type: Company-sponsored foundation.
Financial data (yr. ended 12/31/13): Assets, $45,511,982 (M); gifts received, $100,907; expenditures, $2,677,927; qualifying distributions, $2,439,146; giving activities include $2,152,038 for 85 grants (high: $486,050; low: $200).
Purpose and activities: The foundation supports organizations involved with pre-school through 12th grade education, higher education, substance abuse, domestic violence, community development, charity infrastructure, youth development, and emergency and critical human services.
Fields of interest: Elementary/secondary education; Higher education; Substance abuse, services; Crime/violence prevention, domestic violence; Youth development; Human services; Community/economic development; Philanthropy/voluntarism.
Type of support: General/operating support; Building/renovation; Program development; Scholarship funds; Employee-related scholarships; Scholarships—to individuals.
Limitations: Applications accepted. Giving primarily in southeastern NM; some giving also in west TX. No support for political or lobbying organizations or international organizations,. No grants to individuals (except for scholarships), or for general operating expenses of established programs, interests or programs detrimental to the oil and gas industry, ticketed events, or projects that do not have sustainability for a 5 year period; no loans.
Publications: Application guidelines; Grants list.
Application information: Application form required.
Initial approach: Compete online application
Deadline(s): 4 weeks prior to quarterly board meeting; Apr. 24 for scholarships for graduating AHS students; June 9 for scholarships for 5th year college seniors
Board meeting date(s): 2nd Tues. of Mar., June, Sept., and Dec.
Officer and Directors: Richard Price,* Exec. Dir.; Deb Chase; Karla Chase; Mack C. Chase; Marilyn Y. Chase; Richard Chase; Robert Chase; Gerene Dianne Chase Ferguson; Johnny Knorr.
Advisor: Brad Bartek.
Trustee: JPMorgan Chase Bank, N.A.
EIN: 367466258

5518
The Delle Foundation ✧ ☆
c/o LANB
1200 Trinity Dr.
Los Alamos, NM 87544-3286

Established in 2004 in NM.
Donors: George A. Cowan; Helen Dunham Cowan; Cowan Trust.
Foundation type: Independent foundation.
Financial data (yr. ended 12/31/13): Assets, $7,920,065 (M); gifts received, $3,965,022; expenditures, $1,221,801; qualifying distributions, $1,200,200; giving activities include $1,200,200 for 13 grants (high: $655,000; low: $1,000).
Purpose and activities: Giving primarily to promote early development and supporting research.
Fields of interest: Human services; Science, research.
Type of support: General/operating support; Research; Scholarships—to individuals; Matching/challenge support.
Limitations: Applications not accepted. Giving primarily in NM. No grants to individuals directly.
Publications: Annual report.
Application information: Unsolicited requests for funds not accepted.
Board meeting date(s): Quarterly

Officers: Jeffrey F. Howell, Pres.; William C. Enloe, V.P.; Susan Seestrom, Secy.-Treas.
Directors: Dan Castillo; Christine Chandler.
Number of staff: None.
EIN: 201247630

5519
The Frost Foundation, Ltd. ✧
511 Armijo St., Ste. A
Santa Fe, NM 87501-2899 (505) 986-0208
Contact: Mary Amelia Whited-Howell, Pres.
E-mail: info@frostfound.org; Louisiana grant request fax: (505) 986-0430; Main URL: http://www.frostfound.org

Incorporated in 1959 in LA.
Donor: Virginia C. Frost†.
Foundation type: Independent foundation.
Financial data (yr. ended 12/31/12): Assets, $27,933,056 (M); expenditures, $2,220,527; qualifying distributions, $1,820,036; giving activities include $1,568,768 for 86+ grants (high: $505,000).
Purpose and activities: Focus on the following areas: 1) Social service and humanitarian needs including, but not limited to, violence in the streets, domestic violence, child abuse, specific public health issues such as alcohol and drug abuse, homelessness, and problems of the elderly; 2) Environment - consideration given to programs in research, education, and action to conserve and protect the environment for the well-being and safety of plants, animals, and human beings; and 3) Education - focus on new, innovative, creative, practical programs to address students' and society's needs today, and which recognize our changing sociological structure and concerns.
Fields of interest: Higher education; Business school/education; Education; Environment, natural resources; Environment; Animal welfare; Health care; Substance abuse, services; Mental health/crisis services; Health organizations, association; AIDS; AIDS research; Food services; Human services; Children/youth, services; Family services; Residential/custodial care, hospices; Aging, centers/services; Women, centers/services; Minorities/immigrants, centers/services; Homeless, human services; Aging; Minorities; Native Americans/American Indians; Women; Homeless.
Type of support: Continuing support; Capital campaigns; Equipment; Program development; Conferences/seminars; Publication; Seed money; Curriculum development; Fellowships; Technical assistance; Matching/challenge support.
Limitations: Giving primarily in LA and NM. No support for animal experimentation. No grants to individuals, or for building funds, sponsorships for special events, endowment funds, medical research, or scholarships; no loans.
Publications: Application guidelines; Biennial report.
Application information: Full proposals are by invitation, upon review of initial letter. Faxed submissions are not accepted. Application form not required.
Initial approach: 1-page letter
Copies of proposal: 4
Deadline(s): Dec. 1, for consideration at Mar. meeting, and June 1, for consideration at Sept. meeting
Board meeting date(s): Mar. and Sept.
Final notification: 7 to 10 days
Officers and Directors:* Mary Amelia Whited-Howell,* Pres.; Philip B. Howell,* Exec. V.P.; Taylor Frost Moore,* Secy.-Treas.; Ann Rogers Gerber; John A. LeVan.
Number of staff: 1 full-time professional; 1 part-time professional; 1 full-time support.
EIN: 720520342
Selected grants: The following grants are a representative sample of this grantmaker's funding activity:
$25,000 to LSU Foundation, Baton Rouge, LA, 2012. For Poverty Center Initiative Program.
$10,000 to Assistance Dogs of the West, Santa Fe, NM, 2012. For Student Trainer Program.
$10,000 to Food for Santa Fe, Santa Fe, NM, 2012. For Feeding the Hungry of Santa Fe Program.
$10,000 to La Familia Medical Center, Santa Fe, NM, 2012. For Family Health and Fitness Program.
$10,000 to Outside In, Santa Fe, NM, 2012. For Youth with Promise Project.
$10,000 to Southwest Creations Collaborative, Albuquerque, NM, 2012. For Buena Fe Expansion Project.
$10,000 to Think New Mexico, Santa Fe, NM, 2012. For 2010 initiatives program.
$5,000 to Canones Early Childhood Center, Canones, NM, 2012. For Project Literary Outreach.
$5,000 to Site Santa Fe, Santa Fe, NM, 2012. For Visual Thinking.

5520
Frederick Hammersley Foundation ✧ ☆
P.O. Box 56548
Albuquerque, NM 87187-6548

Established in NM.
Donor: Frederick H. Hammersley†.
Foundation type: Independent foundation.
Financial data (yr. ended 12/31/13): Assets, $14,389,600 (M); gifts received, $100; expenditures, $1,812,254; qualifying distributions, $1,725,560; giving activities include $1,543,655 for 10 grants (high: $424,410; low: $13,500).
Fields of interest: Museums (art).
Limitations: Applications not accepted. Giving primarily in CA and NM. No grants to individuals.
Application information: Unsolicited requests for funds not accepted.
Officers: Kathleen A. Shields, Pres. and Exec. Dir.; Marge Devon, V.P.
Director: Joe Traugott.
EIN: 264790167

5521
The Melville Hankins Family Foundation Inc. ✧ ☆
P.O. Box 23731
Santa Fe, NM 87502-3731

Established in 2007 in NM.
Donors: Mari Alyce Hankins; Mari Alyce Hankins Living Trust.
Foundation type: Independent foundation.
Financial data (yr. ended 12/31/12): Assets, $13,944,473 (M); gifts received, $10,000; expenditures, $1,211,386; qualifying distributions, $718,808; giving activities include $670,940 for 14 grants (high: $200,400; low: $25,000).
Fields of interest: Performing arts; Arts; Education; Animal welfare.
Limitations: Applications not accepted. Giving primarily in Santa Fe, NM.
Application information: Unsolicited requests for funds not accepted.
Officers: Cameron McCluskey, Pres.; Kenneth Bateman, Secy.; Kevon Zehner, Treas.; George E. Watson, Exec. Dir.
EIN: 260707823
Selected grants: The following grants are a representative sample of this grantmaker's funding activity:
$120,250 to Aspen Santa Fe Ballet, Aspen, CO, 2012. For Offset of Audit Expense and Support of Folklorico Program.
$45,000 to Assistance Dogs of the West, Santa Fe, NM, 2012. For ongoing training.
$30,000 to Lensic Performing Arts Center, Santa Fe, NM, 2012. For Technical Theater Internship Program.
$25,000 to Santa Fe Partners in Education, Santa Fe, NM, 2012. For Art Works at Nava Elementary School.
$20,000 to Santa Fe Girls School, Santa Fe, NM, 2012. For Sixth Grade Shop, Math, History, and Art Project.

5522
Healy Foundation ✧
c/o Edmund Healy
P.O. Box 760
Taos, NM 87571-0760

Established in 2002 in NM.
Donors: Martha Ann Healy†; M.A. Healy Family Foundation, Inc.
Foundation type: Independent foundation.
Financial data (yr. ended 12/31/13): Assets, $22,002,072 (M); gifts received, $835,917; expenditures, $995,842; qualifying distributions, $807,050; giving activities include $807,050 for 33 grants (high: $100,000; low: $2,500).
Fields of interest: Education; Environment, water resources.
Limitations: Applications not accepted. Giving primarily in NM; some funding also in FL and MD. No grants to individuals.
Application information: Unsolicited requests for funds not accepted.
Advisors: Edmund Healy; Wilmington Trust Co.
EIN: 030466977

5523
R.D. & Joan Dale Hubbard Foundation ✧
103 Sierra Blanca Dr.
P.O. Box 2498
Ruidoso, NM 88345
Contact: Robert Donaldson, Exec. Dir.

Established in 1986 in CA as the R. Dee Hubbard Foundation, reincorporated in 1989 in TX.
Donors: R.D. Hubbard; ZIA Partners LLP.
Foundation type: Independent foundation.
Financial data (yr. ended 12/31/12): Assets, $32,859,939 (M); expenditures, $1,658,628; qualifying distributions, $1,321,603; giving activities include $1,104,141 for 98 grants (high: $70,000; low: $500).
Purpose and activities: Giving primarily for education, children, youth, and social services, and health organizations, particularly to hospitals.

Fields of interest: Museums; Higher education; Education; Hospitals (general); Hospitals (specialty); Health organizations, association; Human services; Children/youth, services.
Type of support: Annual campaigns; Building/renovation; Endowments; Professorships; Scholarship funds; Scholarships—to individuals; Matching/challenge support.
Limitations: Applications accepted. Giving primarily in CA, KS, NM, and TX. No grants to individuals (except from designated scholarship funds).
Publications: Application guidelines; Annual report; Program policy statement.
Application information: Application form required.
Initial approach: Letter
Copies of proposal: 1
Deadline(s): None
Board meeting date(s): Varies
Officers and Directors:* R.D. Hubbard,* Pres.; Joan Dale Hubbard,* V.P.; Edward A. Burger,* Secy.-Treas.; Robert P. Donaldson, Exec. Dir.
Number of staff: 1 full-time professional; 1 part-time support.
EIN: 752266308

5524
Johns Family Foundation ✧
(formerly La Vida Foundation)
1311 Tijeras Ave. N.W.
Albuquerque, NM 87102-2882
Contact: Virgil Dugan, Admin.
E-mail: vdugan@tijeras.org

Established in 1985 in NM.
Donors: Kenneth E. Johns; Cynthia Johns; Julie Johns Taylor; Jeffrey Johns.
Foundation type: Independent foundation.
Financial data (yr. ended 10/31/13): Assets, $12,429,367 (M); expenditures, $627,010; qualifying distributions, $577,601; giving activities include $573,499 for 23 grants (high: $195,578; low: $150).
Purpose and activities: Giving for communications and Christian organizations.
Fields of interest: Media/communications; Christian agencies & churches; Protestant agencies & churches.
Type of support: Program development; Matching/challenge support.
Limitations: Applications not accepted. Giving on a national and international basis. No support for political organizations, or to programs antithetical to Christian values. No grants to individuals.
Application information: Contributes only to pre-selected organizations. Unsolicited requests for funds not accepted.
Officers and Directors:* Kenneth E. Johns, Chair. and Pres.; Cynthia Johns,* V.P.; Don Miller, Secy.-Treas.; Jeffrey Johns; Julie J. Johns.
Number of staff: None.
EIN: 850348850

5525
The Karakin Foundation ✧
c/o Atkinson & Co.
P.O. Box 26867
Albuquerque, NM 87125-6867

Established in 1997 in TX.
Donors: Joseph B. Matthews; Julia Jones Matthews; Dodge Jones Foundation.
Foundation type: Independent foundation.
Financial data (yr. ended 12/31/12): Assets, $71,047,174 (M); gifts received, $8,278,668; expenditures, $4,247,628; qualifying distributions, $3,165,880; giving activities include $3,165,880 for 30 grants (high: $500,000; low: $6,000).
Fields of interest: Children/youth, services; International affairs, equal rights.
Limitations: Applications not accepted. Giving primarily in TX; support also in FL, NY and VA. No grants to individuals.
Application information: Contributes only to pre-selected organizations.
Officers: Joseph B. Matthews, Pres.; Leroy Bolt, V.P. and Treas.; David L. Buhrmann, Secy.
EIN: 752692023
Selected grants: The following grants are a representative sample of this grantmaker's funding activity:
$175,000 to ARCA, Albuquerque, NM, 2012. For Helping Individuals with Developmental Disabilities.
$150,000 to Montclair State University Foundation, Montclair, NJ, 2012. For Prism Program.
$100,000 to Admiral Nimitz Foundation, Fredericksburg, TX, 2012. For National Museum of the Pacific War Renovation.
$100,000 to Smile Train, New York, NY, 2012. For Cleft Care for the World's Poorest and Vulnerable Children.
$60,000 to Volunteers of America, Durango, CO, 2012. For Safe House and Community Shelter.
$50,000 to Partners Asia, Seattle, WA, 2012. For education initiative project.
$40,000 to Montclair State University Foundation, Montclair, NJ, 2012. For foster care program.
$30,000 to All Hands Volunteers, Mattapoisett, MA, 2012. For Relief Project in New Jersey and New York in wake of Hurricane Sandy.

5526
Lannan Foundation ✧
313 Read St.
Santa Fe, NM 87501-2628 (505) 986-8160
Contact: Ruth Simms, Cont.
FAX: (505) 986-8195; E-mail: info@lannan.org; Additional contact information (for Ruth Simms): Fax: (505) 954-5143, e-mail: ruth@lannan.org; Main URL: http://www.lannan.org
E-Newsletter: http://www.lannan.org/about/subscribe/
Facebook: http://www.facebook.com/lannanfoundation
Flickr: http://www.flickr.com/photos/lannan/
iTunes: http://itunes.apple.com/us/podcast/lannan-podcasts/id129140044
Podcasts: http://podcast.lannan.org/
Vimeo: http://vimeo.com/user3101443
YouTube: http://www.youtube.com/lannanfoundation

Established in 1960 in IL.
Donors: J. Patrick Lannan†; James Turrell; Thomas Joshua Cooper; Jean-Luc Telliez; Mylene Birembaut; Sebastio Salgado; Chuck Close.
Foundation type: Independent foundation.
Financial data (yr. ended 12/31/13): Assets, $223,074,452 (M); gifts received, $230,000; expenditures, $28,708,514; qualifying distributions, $27,877,881; giving activities include $21,849,898 for 199 grants (high: $15,075,000; low: $200), $677,500 for 12 grants to individuals (high: $149,000; low: $1,000), and $825,260 for 4 foundation-administered programs.
Purpose and activities: The foundation is a family foundation dedicated to cultural freedom, diversity and creativity through projects which support exceptional contemporary artists and writers, as well as inspired Native activists in rural indigenous communities. The foundation recognizes the profound and often unquantifiable value of the creative process and is willing to take risks and make substantial investments in ambitious and experimental thinking. Believing that globalization threatens all cultures and ecosystems, the foundation is particularly interested in projects that encourage freedom of inquiry, imagination, and expression. The foundation supports this mission with long-term special projects requiring multi-year commitments of funding and technical assistance in the areas of contemporary visual art, literature, indigenous communities, and issues of cultural freedom.
Fields of interest: Visual arts; Museums; Literature; Historic preservation/historical societies; Arts; Native Americans/American Indians.
Type of support: General/operating support; Building/renovation; Equipment; Land acquisition; Endowments; Publication; Fellowships; Technical assistance; Program-related investments/loans; Employee matching gifts; Grants to individuals; In-kind gifts; Matching/challenge support.
Limitations: Applications accepted. Giving on a national basis. No grants to individuals (except for Lannan Literary Awards and certain fellowships in the Literary and Cultural Freedom program areas).
Application information: If a letter of inquiry is of interest to the foundation, program staff will then contact selected organizations with an invitation to apply for funding by writing a full proposal. Funding in each program is highly competitive, however. Please be aware that the foundation rarely awards funding for unsolicited requests. Letters of inquiry submitted via fax or E-mail are not accepted.
Initial approach: Letter of inquiry
Board meeting date(s): Three times per year
Officers and Directors:* J. Patrick Lannan,* Pres.; Frank C. Lawler,* V.P. and Dir., Opers.; Ruth Simms, Cont.; Marian P. Day; Sharon A. Ferrill; Karen Hetherington; William E. Johnston; John R. Lannan; Lawrence P. Lannan, Jr.; Mary M. Plauche; David Ungerledes, SJ.
Number of staff: 1 part-time support.
EIN: 366062451
Selected grants: The following grants are a representative sample of this grantmaker's funding activity:
$250,000 to Northwest Indian College, Bellingham, WA, 2012. For Native Studies Program.
$197,000 to InterTribal Sinkyone Wilderness Council, Ukiah, CA, 2012. For general operating support.
$178,980 to Georgetown University, Lannan Center for Poetics and Social Practice, Washington, DC, 2012. For program support.
$175,000 to Dia Center for the Arts, New York, NY, 2012. For donated art objects.
$150,000 to American Civil Liberties Union of New Mexico Foundation, Albuquerque, NM, 2012. For general operating support.
$100,000 to Red Cloud Indian School, Pine Ridge, SD, 2012. For scholarships.
$50,000 to Boa Editions, Rochester, NY, 2012. For challenge grant and to publish Lucille Clifton Collected Poems.
$40,000 to Red Bay Stronghold Foundation, West Palm Beach, FL, 2012. For general operating support to manage Okeechobee County Land.

$30,000 to Santa Fe Indian School, Santa Fe, NM, 2012. For library and media center.
$27,900 to Somos Un Pueblo Unido, Santa Fe, NM, 2012. For general operating support.

5527
Max and Anna Levinson Foundation ✧
P.O. Box 6309
Santa Fe, NM 87502-6309 (505) 995-8802
Contact: Charlotte Levinson, Pres.
FAX: (505) 995-8982;
E-mail: info@levinsonfoundation.org; Main URL: http://www.levinsonfoundation.org

Incorporated in 1956 in DE.
Donors: Max Levinson†; Carl A. Levinson.
Foundation type: Independent foundation.
Financial data (yr. ended 05/31/13): Assets, $15,768,418 (M); expenditures, $1,135,538; qualifying distributions, $1,035,776; giving activities include $778,300 for grants.
Purpose and activities: Funding is allocated among three categories: 1) Environment - including preservation of ecosystems and biological diversity, alternative energy and efficiency; toxins, alternative agriculture, environmental restoration, natural resource conservation, and sustainable communities; 2) Social - including urban and rural community economic development, multiculturalism, human rights, youth leadership and empowerment, conflict resolution, and aid to survivors of violence, and health care; and 3) Jewish/Israel - including Jewish culture and spirituality, history and education, eastern and world Jewry, the Israeli peace movement, and social and environmental issues in Israel. Whatever the specific area of interest, the foundation encourages projects which are concerned with promoting community, social justice, a healthy environment and a sustainable economy, either by developing alternatives to the status quo or by responsibly modifying existing systems, institutions, conditions, and attitudes which block promising innovation. Support for large organizations given a lower priority.
Fields of interest: Environment; International human rights; Jewish agencies & synagogues.
International interests: Israel.
Type of support: General/operating support; Equipment; Program development; Conferences/seminars; Publication; Seed money.
Limitations: Giving on a national basis. No support for projects of primary local community significance. No grants for capital or endowment funds, building programs, travel, expansion of existing services, matching gifts, scholarships, or fellowships; no loans.
Publications: Grants list.
Application information: Full proposals are accepted by invitation only. However, letter of inquiry may be submitted in format provided on foundation web site.
Board meeting date(s): Varies
Officers: Charlotte Levinson, Pres.; Robin Beck, V.P.; Carol Doroshow, Secy.; Kris Murphey, Secy.; Rachel Krich, Treas.
Directors: Peter Gabel; Ed Levinson; Gordon Levinson; Julian Levinson; Suntara Loba.
Number of staff: 1 full-time professional.
EIN: 236282844

5528
J. F Maddox Foundation ✧
P.O. Box 2588
Hobbs, NM 88241-2588 (575) 393-6338
Contact: Robert J. Reid, Secy. and Exec. Dir.
E-mail: bobreid@jfmaddox.org; Main URL: http://www.jfmaddox.org/
Physical address and address for Scholarship applications: 220 W. Broadway St., Ste. 200, Hobbs, NM 88240

Established in 1963 in NM.
Donors: J.F Maddox†; Mabel S. Maddox†.
Foundation type: Independent foundation.
Financial data (yr. ended 12/31/12): Assets, $245,058,304 (M); expenditures, $15,582,079; qualifying distributions, $12,123,562; giving activities include $8,465,690 for 266 grants (high: $2,887,390; low: $100), $197,006 for 26 grants to individuals (high: $46,833; low: $75), $366,172 for 4 foundation-administered programs and $1,521,985 for 2 loans/program-related investments (high: $1,468,684; low: $53,301).
Purpose and activities: The mission of the J.F Maddox Foundation is to significantly improve the quality of life in southeastern New Mexico by investing in education, community development, and other social programs. The foundation particularly supports initiatives driven by innovative leadership, designed for substantial impact, and committed to lasting value.
Fields of interest: Performing arts; Elementary/secondary school reform; Higher education; Education; Environment, beautification programs; Substance abuse, services; Youth development; Human services; Children/youth, services; Aging, centers/services; Economic development; Aging.
Type of support: Research; General/operating support; Capital campaigns; Building/renovation; Equipment; Land acquisition; Program development; Seed money; Curriculum development; Program-related investments/loans; Scholarships—to individuals; Matching/challenge support.
Limitations: Applications accepted. Giving primarily in Lea County, NM; scholarships limited to Lea County, NM, residents. No support for private foundations or political organizations. No grants to individuals (except for scholarships), or for endowment funds.
Publications: Grants list.
Application information: Application form required for scholarships. Refer to foundation web site for full application guidelines and requirements. Application form not required.
Initial approach: Letter; telephone for recommended proposal outline
Copies of proposal: 1
Deadline(s): For scholarships: June 30
Board meeting date(s): Quarterly
Final notification: Varies
Officers and Directors:* Don Maddox,* Pres.; James M. Maddox,* Exec. V.P.; Kerri Frizzell, V.P, Fin. and C.F.O.; Jennifer Grassham, V.P., Grants; Dennis M. Holmberg, V.P., Special Projects; Robert J. Reid, Exec. Dir.; Elaine Agather; Paul Campbell; Benjamin W. Maddox; Catherine M. Maddox; John L. Maddox; Thomas M. Maddox; Sue Maddox; Susan Maddox; Ann M. Utterback.
Number of staff: 6 full-time professional; 3 full-time support.
EIN: 756023767

5529
McCune Charitable Foundation ✧
(formerly Marshall L. & Perrine D. McCune Charitable Foundation)
345 E. Alameda St.
Santa Fe, NM 87501-2229 (505) 983-8300
Contact: Wendy Lewis, Assoc. Dir.
FAX: (505) 983-7887;
E-mail: mccune@nmmccune.org; Main URL: http://www.nmmccune.org

Established in 1992 in NM.
Donors: Perrine Dixon McCune†; Marshall L. McCune†.
Foundation type: Independent foundation.
Financial data (yr. ended 12/31/12): Assets, $125,763,190 (M); expenditures, $7,243,883; qualifying distributions, $6,687,934; giving activities include $5,297,887 for 350 grants (high: $100,000; low: $500).
Purpose and activities: The mission of the foundation is to memorialize its benefactors through grants which enrich the cultural life, health, education, environment, and spiritual life of the citizens of New Mexico. The Foundation supports philanthropic programs which are responsive, flexible, and may be proven effective at aiding the people of New Mexico to reach their full human and spiritual potential. Primary areas of interest include the arts, education, youth, health, social services and environment.
Fields of interest: Visual arts; Museums; Performing arts; Performing arts, dance; Performing arts, theater; Performing arts, music; History/archaeology; Historic preservation/historical societies; Arts; Education, early childhood education; Child development, education; Elementary school/education; Secondary school/education; Vocational education; Higher education; Adult/continuing education; Adult education—literacy, basic skills & GED; Libraries/library science; Education, reading; Education; Environment, natural resources; Environment; Animal welfare; Animals/wildlife, preservation/protection; Hospitals (general); Reproductive health, family planning; Medical care, rehabilitation; Health care; Substance abuse, services; Mental health/crisis services; Health organizations, association; Cancer; Heart & circulatory diseases; AIDS; Alcoholism; Crime/violence prevention, youth; Crime/law enforcement; Employment; Agriculture; Food services; Nutrition; Housing/shelter, development; Youth development, services; Youth development, citizenship; Human services; Children/youth, services; Child development, services; Family services; Residential/custodial care, hospices; Aging, centers/services; Women, centers/services; Minorities/immigrants, centers/services; Homeless, human services; Rural development; Community/economic development; United Ways and Federated Giving Programs; Public affairs, citizen participation; Leadership development; Public affairs; Aging; Disabilities, people with; Minorities; Native Americans/American Indians; Women; Economically disadvantaged; Homeless; LGBTQ.
Type of support: General/operating support; Continuing support; Annual campaigns; Building/renovation; Equipment; Emergency funds; Program development; Conferences/seminars; Seed money; Scholarship funds; Technical assistance; Program-related investments/loans; Matching/challenge support.

Limitations: Applications accepted. Giving limited to NM. No grants to individuals, or for endowments, research, operating or capital expenses, voter registration drives, or to cover deficits.
Publications: Application guidelines; Biennial report.
Application information: Please check foundation web site for updates. Application form not required.
Initial approach: Online application only
Copies of proposal: 1
Deadline(s): See foundation web site for current deadlines
Board meeting date(s): Changes annually
Final notification: Changes annually
Officers and Directors:* Sarah McCune Losinger,* Chair.; Wendy Lewis, Exec. Dir.; Aaron Cathey; David L. Edwards; David M. Edwards; James M. Edwards; John M. Edwards; John R. Losinger; Amy Sparks.
Number of staff: 1 full-time professional; 5 full-time support.
EIN: 850429439

5530
The New Mexico Community Foundation ✧

502 W. Cordova, Ste. 1
Santa Fe, NM 87505 (505) 820-6860
FAX: (505) 820-7860; E-mail: info@nmcf.org;
Additional address: 2015 Mountain Rd., NW, Albuquerque, NM 87104, tel.: (505) 821-6735;
Main URL: http://www.nmcf.org
Facebook: https://www.facebook.com/pages/New-Mexico-Community-Foundation-NMCF/182905491758440
Philanthropy's Promise: http://www.ncrp.org/philanthropys-promise/who
Twitter: https://twitter.com/NMCF_Thrives
Scholarship inquiry e-mail: pdoane@nmcf.org

Incorporated in 1983 in NM.
Foundation type: Community foundation.
Financial data (yr. ended 12/31/12): Assets, $24,256,952 (M); gifts received, $4,973,967; expenditures, $6,312,277; giving activities include $4,436,498 for 103+ grants (high: $50,000).
Purpose and activities: Giving primarily to build community resources and relationships, with special emphasis on rural communities, and issues important to communities such as water, kids, health, families, elderly, education, hardship, and livelihoods.
Fields of interest: Education; Health care; Health organizations, association; AIDS; Child development, services; Family services; Rural development; Aging; Native Americans/American Indians.
Type of support: General/operating support; Continuing support; Annual campaigns; Endowments; Program development; Conferences/seminars; Publication; Seed money; Internship funds; Scholarship funds; Technical assistance; In-kind gifts; Matching/challenge support.
Limitations: Applications accepted. Giving limited to NM, with emphasis on rural communities. No support for religious purposes or the United Way or other federated giving organizations. No grants for endowment funds.
Publications: Annual report; Newsletter; Occasional report.
Application information: Unsolicited requests for funds not accepted. Visit foundation web site to submit a General Information Organization Profile Form. Based on the form, the foundation's staff will attempt to identify possible funding resources in your area of service; if funding becomes available, foundation staff will contact you.
Board meeting date(s): Quarterly
Officers and Directors:* Sandy Kiser,* Chair.; Barbara Poley,* Vice-Chair.; Jenny Parks,* C.E.O. and Pres.; Ted Olin Harrison,* Secy.; Carla Melendez, C.F.O.; Bruce Bleakman,* Treas.; Paula Blacher; Peter Brill; Thomas M. Hnasko; Howell Palmer; Regis Pecos; Robert Otto Valdez.
Number of staff: 6 full-time professional; 2 part-time professional.
EIN: 850311210

5531
Waite and Genevieve Phillips Foundation ✧ ☆

P.O. Box 5726
Santa Fe, NM 87502-5726

Established in 1986 in NM.
Donors: Genevieve Phillips; Waite and Genevieve Phillips Charitable Trust.
Foundation type: Independent foundation.
Financial data (yr. ended 05/31/13): Assets, $11,958,440 (M); expenditures, $699,602; qualifying distributions, $568,324; giving activities include $481,100 for 38 grants (high: $165,300; low: $300).
Fields of interest: Museums (art); Arts; Education; Hospitals (general); Health care; Health organizations, association; Human services; Children/youth, services; United Ways and Federated Giving Programs.
Limitations: Applications not accepted. Giving primarily in NM, OK, and TX. No grants to individuals.
Application information: Unsolicited requests for funds not accepted.
Officers: Julie Phillips Puckett, Chair. and Pres.; Connie J. Wootton, Sr. V.P. and Secy.-Treas.; Douglas Clay Holcomb, V.P.; Tom Coker; Lela Phillips Puckett.
EIN: 850335071

5532
PNM Resources Foundation, Inc. ✧

(formerly PNM Foundation, Inc.)
Alvarado Sq., M.S. 0410
Albuquerque, NM 87158-1410 (505) 241-2872
Contact: Diane Harrison Ogawa, Exec. Dir.
Contact for PNM Energy Exploration Grants and Reduce Your Use Grants: Jaci Bertand, tel.: (505) 241-2864,
e-mail: jaci.bertand@pnmresources.com; Main URL: http://www.pnm.com/foundation/home.htm
Energy Exploration Grant Recipients: http://www.pnm.com/foundation/energy_explore_2011.htm
Facebook: http://www.facebook.com/PNMResourcesFoundation
Reduce Your Use Grant Process Webinar Presentation: http://www.pnm.com/foundation/docs/reduce_your_use_webinar_022912.pdf
Reduce Your Use Grant Recipients: http://www.pnm.com/foundation/reduce_use_recipients_2011.htm

Incorporated in 1983 in NM.
Donors: Public Service Co. of New Mexico; PNM Resources, Inc.
Foundation type: Company-sponsored foundation.
Financial data (yr. ended 12/31/13): Assets, $15,049,233 (M); expenditures, $892,825; qualifying distributions, $848,675; giving activities include $837,552 for 512 grants (high: $100,000; low: $25).
Purpose and activities: The foundation supports programs designed to promote education, environmental awareness and education, and economic vitality.
Fields of interest: Arts; Elementary/secondary education; Middle schools/education; Charter schools; Education, services; Education, reading; Education; Environment, natural resources; Environment, energy; Environmental education; Environment; Food services; Food banks; Aging, centers/services; Human services; Economic development.
Type of support: General/operating support; Building/renovation; Equipment; Program development; Employee volunteer services; Employee matching gifts.
Limitations: Applications accepted. Giving primarily in NM and TX. No support for discriminatory organizations, sectarian or religious organizations, veterans', labor, or political organizations, fraternal, athletic, or social clubs, or municipalities. No grants to individuals, or for testimonial dinners, fundraising events, or advertising, debt reduction, special events, annual events, or one-time only events, endowments, capital campaigns, administrative or overhead costs, documentaries or film production, or programs or projects that duplicate existing services and/or programs.
Publications: Application guidelines; Grants list; Program policy statement.
Application information: Support is limited to 1 contribution per organization during any given year. Organizations receiving support are asked to submit a final report. Application form required.
Initial approach: Complete online application form
Deadline(s): Apr. 23 for PNM Reduce Your Use Grants
Board meeting date(s): 3 times per year
Officers and Trustees: Shirley Ragin, Pres.; Maureen Gannon, V.P.; Jeff Mechenbier, Secy.-Treas.; Diane Harrison Ogawa, Exec. Dir.; Patrick Apodaca; Kevin Judice; Valerie Smith; Neal Walker; Sayuri Yamada.
Number of staff: 1 full-time professional; 1 full-time support.
EIN: 850309005

5533
Santa Fe Community Foundation ✧

501 Halona St.
Santa Fe, NM 87505 (505) 988-9715
Contact: Brian T. Byrnes, C.E.O. and Pres.; Donor-Advised Funds and Grants Contact: Christa Coggins, V.P., Community Philanthropy
FAX: (505) 988-1829;
E-mail: foundation@santafecf.org; Mailing address: P.O. Box 1827, Sante Fe, NM 87504-1827;
Workshop registration e-mail: workshops@santafecf.org; Main URL: http://www.santafecf.org
Facebook: http://www.facebook.com/pages/Santa-Fe-Community-Foundation/108633257617
Santa Fe Community Foundation's Philanthropy Promise: http://ncrp.org/philanthropys-promise/who
Twitter: https://twitter.com/SantaFeCForg

YouTube: http://www.youtube.com/SantaFeCommFound

Incorporated in 1981 in NM.
Foundation type: Community foundation.
Financial data (yr. ended 12/31/12): Assets, $57,212,049 (M); gifts received, $22,330,673; expenditures, $6,325,123; giving activities include $3,916,552 for 149+ grants (high: $137,763).
Purpose and activities: The foundation improves the quality of life for people in Santa Fe and Northern New Mexico, now and for future generations, by: 1) building and managing endowment funds in order to award grants; 2) helping nonprofits operate more effectively; 3) convening area residents to discuss issues of critical importance to the community; and 4) providing leadership for key community initiatives.
Fields of interest: Arts education; Visual arts; Performing arts; Performing arts, music; Humanities; Arts; Education, public education; Child development, education; Elementary school/education; Adult education—literacy, basic skills & GED; Education, drop-out prevention; Education; Environment, natural resources; Environment; Animals/wildlife, preservation/protection; Health care; Substance abuse, prevention; Mental health/crisis services; Health organizations, association; Cancer; AIDS; Alcoholism; Crime/violence prevention, domestic violence; Food services; Housing/shelter; Children/youth, services; Child development, services; Family services, domestic violence; Family services, adolescent parents; Aging, centers/services; Homeless, human services; Human services; Civil/human rights, immigrants; Civil/human rights, minorities; Civil/human rights, disabled; Civil/human rights, women; Civil/human rights, aging; Civil/human rights, LGBTQ; Civil rights, race/intergroup relations; Community development, citizen coalitions; Economic development; Nonprofit management; Community/economic development; Science; Public affairs, citizen participation; Public affairs; Aging; Disabilities, people with; Minorities; Asians/Pacific Islanders; African Americans/Blacks; Hispanics/Latinos; Native Americans/American Indians; Women; AIDS, people with; Immigrants/refugees; Economically disadvantaged; Homeless; LGBTQ.
Type of support: General/operating support; Continuing support; Management development/capacity building; Annual campaigns; Emergency funds; Program development; Publication; Seed money; Scholarship funds; Technical assistance; Matching/challenge support.
Limitations: Applications accepted. Giving limited to northern NM counties, including Los Alamos, Mora, Rio Arriba, San Miguel, Santa Fe and Taos. No support for religious purposes. No grants for capital campaigns, endowments, or technical assistance grants for travel, conferences, start-up costs, or staff salaries or functions.
Publications: Annual report; Informational brochure (including application guidelines); Newsletter.
Application information: Visit foundation web site for online application and guidelines. Free pre-proposal workshops are offered to assist perspective applicants with information on proposal guidelines and the application/grant process for the foundation's grant cycles; telephone or e-mail to register. Faxed proposals are not accepted. Application form required.
Initial approach: Complete online application
Copies of proposal: 1
Deadline(s): Mar. 3 for Spring Grants Cycle covering Economic Opportunity, Education and Environment; Aug. 26 for Fall Grants Cycle covering Arts, Animal Welfare, Health and Human Services
Board meeting date(s): Bimonthly
Final notification: June 29 and Nov. 15
Officers and Directors:* Hervey A. Juris,* Chair.; Suzanne Ortega Cisneros,* Vice-Chair.; Brian Byrnes, C.E.O. and Pres.; Christa Coggins, V.P., Community Philanthropy; Sarah Sawtell, V.P., Finance and Opers.; Thomas Bustamante; Lisa Enfield; Steve Gaber; Bud Hamilton; Barry Herskowitz; Peggy Hubbard; Dottie Indyke; Jerry G. Jones; Stephanie Kiger; Jennifer Kimball; Sheila Ortega McLaughlin; Beth Moise; Richard Moore; Michael Namingha; Susan Priem; Elizabeth Rice; Kenneth Romero; Patricia Rosenberg.
Number of staff: 7 full-time professional; 7 full-time support.
EIN: 850303044

5534
Eugene V. & Clare E. Thaw Charitable Trust ✧
P.O. Box 2422
Santa Fe, NM 87504-2422

Established in 1981 in NY as a private operating foundation; status changed to an independent grantmaking foundation in 1994 in NM.
Donors: Eugene Victor Thaw; Clare Eddy Thaw.
Foundation type: Independent foundation.
Financial data (yr. ended 12/31/13): Assets, $11,840,099 (M); expenditures, $2,810,353; qualifying distributions, $2,475,853; giving activities include $2,412,900 for 9 grants (high: $800,000; low: $10,000).
Purpose and activities: Support for the arts, ecology and the environment, and animal rights and protection. The trust prefers to make challenge grants that are conditional on recipients matching the funds in an agreed-upon proportion.
Fields of interest: Arts; Environment; Animal welfare.
International interests: Russia; United Kingdom.
Type of support: Program development; Conferences/seminars; Publication; Seed money; Research; Technical assistance; Matching/challenge support.
Limitations: Applications not accepted. Giving on a national basis. No support for political or religious organizations. No grants to individuals or for operating support.
Publications: Biennial report.
Application information: Contributes only to pre-selected organizations.
Board meeting date(s): Fall
Officers and Directors:* Eugene Victor Thaw,* Pres.; Kathleen Flanagan, V.P. and Exec. Dir.; Sherry Thompson Miller, Exec. Dir.; Patricia Tang; Clare Eddy Thaw.
Number of staff: 2 full-time professional.
EIN: 133081491

5535
Thornburg Foundation ✧
(formerly Garrett Thornburg Foundation)
2300 N. Ridgetop Rd.
Santa Fe, NM 87506-8361

Established in 1998 in NM.
Donor: Garrett Thornburg.
Foundation type: Independent foundation.
Financial data (yr. ended 12/31/12): Assets, $77,191,517 (M); gifts received, $41,006,224; expenditures, $1,800,295; qualifying distributions, $1,688,245; giving activities include $1,526,029 for 45 grants (high: $466,699; low: $1,000).
Fields of interest: Arts; Education; Human services.
Type of support: General/operating support; Continuing support; Program development.
Limitations: Applications not accepted. Giving primarily in NM. No support for political or religious organizations, animal rights, or large scale medical programs. No grants to individuals, or for debt retirement or endowment campaigns.
Application information: Contributes only to pre-selected organizations.
Officers: Garrett H. Thornburg, Pres.; Catherine Oppenheimer, V.P.; Carolyn M. Dobbs, Secy.-Treas.; Suzanne Barker Kalangis, Exec. Dir.
Directors: Alon Kasha; Alissa Oppenheimer; Lloyd J. Thornburg.
Number of staff: 1 part-time professional.
EIN: 850457010

5536
Toan-O'Brien Foundation ✧ ☆
c/o Barrett Toan & Paula O'Brien
463 Camino Manzano
Santa Fe, NM 87505-2833

Established in NM.
Donors: Paula O'Brien; Barrett Toan.
Foundation type: Independent foundation.
Financial data (yr. ended 12/31/13): Assets, $11,319,100 (M); gifts received, $3,085; expenditures, $873,045; qualifying distributions, $856,250; giving activities include $856,250 for 22 grants (high: $168,500; low: $500).
Fields of interest: Arts; Education; Environment, natural resources.
Limitations: Applications not accepted. Giving primarily in St. Louis, MO.
Application information: Unsolicited requests for funds not accepted.
Trustees: Paula O'Brien; Barrett Toan.
EIN: 204464256
Selected grants: The following grants are a representative sample of this grantmaker's funding activity:
$25,000 to Site Santa Fe, Santa Fe, NM, 2012. For art fund.

5537
S. P. & Estelle Yates Family Foundation ✧
101 S. 4th St., Ste. B
Artesia, NM 88210-2177
Main URL: http://www.yatesfamilyfoundation.org

Established in 1995 in NM.
Donors: S.P. Yates; Estelle H. Yates; S.P. Yates Trust.
Foundation type: Independent foundation.
Financial data (yr. ended 12/31/13): Assets, $11,690,252 (M); expenditures, $716,488; qualifying distributions, $635,493; giving activities include $627,471 for 18 grants (high: $198,805; low: $1,000).
Fields of interest: Arts; Human services.
Type of support: General/operating support; Equipment.

Limitations: Applications not accepted. Giving primarily in NM, with emphasis on Artesia. No grants to individuals.
Application information: Contributes only to pre-selected organizations.
Officers: Mary Beth Yates, Pres.; Mary Yates Davis, V.P.; Estelle H. Yates, V.P.; Peyton Yates, V.P.; Pamela J. Horner, Treas.
Directors: Peyton Davis; Jennifer Peterson; Kelsy Yates.
EIN: 850434556

5538
The Estelle H. Yates Foundation ✧ ☆
P.O. Box 1020
Artesia, NM 88211-1020
Application address: c/o Estelle H. Yates, Tr., P.O. Box 1344, Artesia, NM 88211-1344, tel.: (575) 748-1471

Established in 2009 in NM.
Donor: Estelle H. Yates.
Foundation type: Independent foundation.
Financial data (yr. ended 12/31/12): Assets, $4,222,932 (M); expenditures, $1,705,270; qualifying distributions, $1,687,573; giving activities include $1,687,573 for grants.
Fields of interest: Education.
Application information: Application form not required.
Initial approach: Proposal
Deadline(s): None
Trustees: Peyton Yates Davis; Estelle H. Yates; Richard Martin Yates; St. Clair Peyton Yates, Jr.
EIN: 276185888

NEW YORK

5539
291 Foundation ✧
c/o Nancy L. Wender
291 Church St.
New York, NY 10013-2403

Established in 2001 in NY.
Donor: Nancy L. Wender.
Foundation type: Independent foundation.
Financial data (yr. ended 10/31/13): Assets, $2,442,430 (M); gifts received, $50,000; expenditures, $700,607; qualifying distributions, $681,983; giving activities include $678,843 for 45 grants (high: $125,000; low: $350).
Purpose and activities: Giving primarily to an art curatorial fund, as well as for human services.
Fields of interest: Arts, single organization support; Arts; Human services.
Limitations: Applications not accepted. Giving primarily in CT and NY. No grants to individuals.
Application information: Contributes only to pre-selected organizations.
Trustee: Nancy L. Wender.
EIN: 137298760
Selected grants: The following grants are a representative sample of this grantmaker's funding activity:
$2,500 to Food Bank for New York City, New York, NY, 2011.
$1,500 to Planned Parenthood of New York City, New York, NY, 2011.
$1,000 to Human Rights First, New York, NY, 2011.

5540
The 2A Foundation, Inc. ✧
c/o Anchin
1375 Broadway, 21st Fl.
New York, NY 10018-7032

Established in NY.
Donor: Alexander Morcos.
Foundation type: Independent foundation.
Financial data (yr. ended 12/31/13): Assets, $36,362,786 (M); expenditures, $1,778,746; qualifying distributions, $1,640,838; giving activities include $1,640,000 for 19 grants (high: $400,000; low: $5,000).
Fields of interest: Media, radio; Higher education; Animals/wildlife.
Limitations: Applications not accepted. Giving primarily in MA and UT.
Application information: Unsolicited requests for funds not accepted.
Directors: Stephen McInerney; Alexander Morcos; Amanda Morcos.
EIN: 270846607

5541
The 5 51 5 Foundation, Inc. ✧
755 Park Ave., Apt 12B
New York, NY 10021-4283

Established in 2007 in NY.
Donor: David C. Hodgson.
Foundation type: Independent foundation.
Financial data (yr. ended 12/31/12): Assets, $196,890 (M); gifts received, $1,502,752; expenditures, $1,368,873; qualifying distributions, $1,352,575; giving activities include $1,352,500 for 11 grants (high: $1,000,000; low: $500).
Fields of interest: Higher education; Education.
Limitations: Applications not accepted. Giving primarily in CA, MD, NH, NY, and OH.
Application information: Contributes only to pre-selected organizations.
Officers: Laurie B. Hodgson, Pres.; Richard Gold, Secy.; David C. Hodgson, Treas.
EIN: 208844111

5542
A Kinder World Foundation ✧ ☆
954 Lexington Ave., No. 325
New York, NY 10021-5013
Contact: Kathy Savesky, Advisor

Established in 2004 in MA.
Donors: David B. Swartz; Diana Castellanos Swartz; Robert Wurm.
Foundation type: Independent foundation.
Financial data (yr. ended 12/31/13): Assets, $12,076,493 (M); expenditures, $537,419; qualifying distributions, $496,564; giving activities include $450,091 for 5 grants (high: $100,000; low: $31,000), and $46,473 for 1 foundation-administered program.
Purpose and activities: Giving primarily for animal/wildlife protection and preservation.
Fields of interest: Animals/wildlife; Youth development, services; Human services; Children/youth, services; Jewish agencies & synagogues.
Limitations: Applications not accepted. Giving primarily in LA, ME, and NY. No grants to individuals.
Application information: Contributes only to pre-selected organizations.
Trustees: Robert N. Shapiro; David B. Swartz; Diana Castellanos Swartz.
EIN: 206197902

5543
The A M Foundation ✧
(formerly Usher and Miriam Meisels Family Foundation)
290 Hewes St.
Brooklyn, NY 11211-8109 (718) 624-6008
Contact: Arthur Meisels, Tr.

Established in 2002 in NY.
Donors: Arthur Meisels; Miriam Meisels; Agnes Meisels; Martin Meisels; Pearl Meisels; Shifra Meisels; Agnes Herman; Pearl Stark; Esther Mendlovics; The Arthur and Miriam Meisels Family Trust.
Foundation type: Independent foundation.
Financial data (yr. ended 03/31/13): Assets, $5,621,598 (M); gifts received, $725,410; expenditures, $636,513; qualifying distributions, $603,312; giving activities include $603,312 for 146 grants (high: $120,000; low: $18).
Purpose and activities: Giving primarily for Jewish education, and to Jewish temples and social services organizations.
Fields of interest: Education; Human services; Jewish agencies & synagogues.
Type of support: General/operating support.
Limitations: Applications accepted. Giving primarily in NY. No grants to individuals.
Application information: Application form required.
Initial approach: Letter
Deadline(s): None
Trustees: Arthur Meisels; Martin Meisels; Miriam Meisels.
EIN: 030463941

5544
Joseph & Sophia Abeles Foundation ✧
18 Ponds Ln.
Purchase, NY 10577-1712

Established in 1960 in NY.
Donors: Joseph C. Abeles†; Sophia Abeles†.
Foundation type: Independent foundation.
Financial data (yr. ended 12/31/13): Assets, $20,917,796 (M); expenditures, $1,144,824; qualifying distributions, $959,503; giving activities include $910,700 for 56 grants (high: $100,000; low: $1,000).
Purpose and activities: Giving to support local educational arts activities and humanitarian institutions.
Fields of interest: Museums (art); Performing arts; Higher education; Hospitals (general); Human services; Children; Youth; Young adults.
Type of support: General/operating support; Annual campaigns; Endowments; Emergency funds; Program development.
Limitations: Applications not accepted. Giving primarily in New York and Westchester County, NY. No support for political organizations. No grants to individuals.
Application information: Contributes only to pre-selected organizations.
Board meeting date(s): Dec.
Officers: Lucille Werlinich, Pres.; Barbara Abeles, V.P.; Greg Werlinich, Treas.
Number of staff: 2 part-time professional; 1 part-time support.
EIN: 136259577

5545
The Alexander Abraham Foundation ✧ ☆
232 E. 62nd St.
New York, NY 10065-8201
E-mail: info@abrahamfoundation.org; Main URL: http://abrahamfoundation.org/cms/
Facebook: https://www.facebook.com/AbrahamFoundation
Twitter: http://twitter.com/aabrahamfound

Established in 2002 in DE.
Donors: Nancy Abraham; Tiger Conservation Fund.
Foundation type: Independent foundation.
Financial data (yr. ended 11/30/13): Assets, $203,723 (M); gifts received, $574,265; expenditures, $549,459; qualifying distributions, $539,334; giving activities include $457,481 for 50 grants (high: $73,000; low: $39).
Purpose and activities: The foundation is dedicated to conserving the environment and to defending indigenous wildlife with an emphasis on protection of endangered species.
Fields of interest: Animal welfare; Animals/wildlife; Human services.
Limitations: Applications accepted. Giving primarily in Africa and Asia.

Application information: Contributes only to invited organizations upon review of preliminary application form from foundation web site.

Initial approach: Fill out preliminary form from foundation web site if organization is appropriate match for funding

Officers and Director:* Nancy Abraham,* Pres.; Eleonor Content, Exec. Dir.

EIN: 300139596

5546
Louis and Anne Abrons Foundation, Inc. ✧

437 Madison Ave.
New York, NY 10022-7001 (212) 756-3376
Contact: Richard Abrons, Pres.

Incorporated in 1950 in NY.
Donors: Anne S. Abrons†; Louis Abrons†.
Foundation type: Independent foundation.
Financial data (yr. ended 12/31/13): Assets, $86,209,692 (M); expenditures, $4,513,427; qualifying distributions, $4,006,040; giving activities include $3,831,100 for 163 grants (high: $300,000; low: $1,000).
Purpose and activities: Giving primarily to social welfare agencies, Jewish charities, major New York, NY, institutions, civic improvement programs, education, and environmental and cultural projects.
Fields of interest: Museums; Arts; Libraries/library science; Education; Environment; Hospitals (general); Reproductive health, family planning; Legal services; Employment; Human services; Children/youth, services; Family services; Aging, centers/services; Minorities/immigrants, centers/services; Community/economic development; Jewish agencies & synagogues; Children/youth; Children; Adults; Aging; African Americans/Blacks; Offenders/ex-offenders; Economically disadvantaged; Homeless.
International interests: Israel.
Type of support: General/operating support; Continuing support; Annual campaigns; Capital campaigns; Building/renovation; Program development; Scholarship funds; Research; Technical assistance; Consulting services.
Limitations: Applications not accepted. Giving primarily in the metropolitan New York, NY, area. No grants to individuals.
Application information: Contributes only to pre-selected organizations. Telephone calls not accepted. Unsolicited applications not considered or acknowledged.

Board meeting date(s): Feb., June, and Oct.

Officers and Directors:* Richard Abrons,* Pres.; Rita Aranow,* V.P.; Anne S. Abrons,* Secy.-Treas.; Adam Abrons; Alix Abrons; Eleanor Abrons; Henry Abrons; John Abrons; Leslie Abrons; Peter Abrons; Judith Aranow; Stephanie DeChristina; Vicki Feiner; Jennifer Schwartz.
EIN: 136061329

5547
The Abstraction Fund ✧

c/o Eisneramper LLP, Joel Zbar
750 3rd Ave.
New York, NY 10017

Established in 2006 in NY.
Donor: William Rosenwald Family Fund.
Foundation type: Independent foundation.
Financial data (yr. ended 12/31/12): Assets, $8,013,058 (M); gifts received, $2,654,334; expenditures, $2,154,881; qualifying distributions, $2,046,666; giving activities include $1,982,930 for 141 grants (high: $250,000; low: $200).
Fields of interest: International affairs, public policy; International affairs, foreign policy; Jewish federated giving programs; Jewish agencies & synagogues.
Limitations: Applications not accepted. Giving primarily in Washington, DC, Baltimore, MD, New York, NY, and Philadelphia, PA. No grants to individuals.
Application information: Unsolicited requests for funds not accepted.
Officers: Nina Rosenwald, Pres. and Treas.; Georgette Gelbard, Secy.
Director: Joel Zbar.
EIN: 205327719

5548
ACE Foundation Inc. ✧

1650 49th St.
Brooklyn, NY 11204-1133

Established in 1994 in NY.
Donor: Aaron Elbogen.
Foundation type: Independent foundation.
Financial data (yr. ended 10/31/13): Assets, $17,563,427 (M); expenditures, $904,507; qualifying distributions, $897,220.
Purpose and activities: Giving primarily to Jewish agencies, temples, and schools.
Fields of interest: Elementary/secondary education; Theological school/education; Jewish agencies & synagogues.
Limitations: Applications not accepted. No grants to individuals.
Application information: Contributes only to pre-selected organizations.
Officers: Aaron Elbogen, Pres.; Chaya Elbogen, V.P.
EIN: 113237003

5549
The Achelis Foundation ✧

767 3rd Ave., 4th Fl.
New York, NY 10017-9029 (212) 644-0322
Contact: John B. Krieger, Secy. and Exec. Dir.; Carmel Mazzola, Bookkeeper; Vicki Puluso, Admin. Asst.
FAX: (212) 759-6510;
E-mail: main@achelis-bodman-fnds.org; Main URL: http://www.achelis-bodman-fnds.org
Grants List: http://www.achelis-bodman-fnds.org/grants.html

Incorporated in 1940 in NY.
Donor: Elisabeth Achelis†.
Foundation type: Independent foundation.
Financial data (yr. ended 12/31/12): Assets, $36,714,169 (M); expenditures, $1,748,695; qualifying distributions, $1,540,003; giving activities include $1,400,000 for 55 grants (high: $125,000; low: $2,500).
Purpose and activities: Giving for some social services includes child welfare and disconnected youth, the disabled, substance abusers, ex-offenders and veterans. Education giving includes a preference for K-12 school reform, school choice, and charter schools rather than nonprofits that provide direct services in public schools. The foundation also makes grants to large arts and cultural institutions in New York City. Other interests include voluntarism, entrepreneurship, employment, strengthening the two-parent family, marriage, fatherhood (and father absence), programs that promote self-help and self-reliance, faith-based programs, and prevention and early intervention. The foundation prefers programs that emphasize measurable participant outcomes and program results, innovations and new cost-saving approaches, consumer choice, and parental involvement.
Fields of interest: Humanities; Education, reform; Medical care, rehabilitation; Health care, cost containment; Substance abuse, prevention; Alcoholism; Medical research, institute; Crime/violence prevention, youth; Offenders/ex-offenders, prison alternatives; Employment; Children/youth, services; Family services; International relief; Public policy, research; Welfare policy/reform; Religion; Children/youth; Youth; Disabilities, people with; Physically disabled; Military/veterans; Offenders/ex-offenders; Substance abusers; Economically disadvantaged.
Type of support: General/operating support; Equipment; Program development; Conferences/seminars; Publication; Seed money; Curriculum development; Scholarship funds; Research; Technical assistance; Program evaluation; Matching/challenge support.
Limitations: Applications accepted. Giving primarily in the New York, NY, area. Generally, no support for political organizations, small art, dance, music, or theater groups, national health or mental health organizations, housing, international projects, government agencies, public schools (except charter schools), or nonprofit programs and services significantly funded or wholly reimbursed by the government. No grants to individuals, or for annual appeals, dinner functions, fundraising events, capital campaigns, deficit financing, or film or travel; no loans.
Publications: Financial statement; Grants list.
Application information: Do not send CDs, DVDs, discs or tapes, or proposals through the internet unless requested; see foundation web site for application guidelines and procedures. New York/New Jersey Area Common Grant Application Form accepted. Application form not required.

Initial approach: Letter or short proposal
Copies of proposal: 1
Deadline(s): None
Board meeting date(s): Usually in May, Sept., and Dec.
Final notification: 5 to 6 weeks

Officers and Trustees:* John N. Irwin III,* Chair. and C.E.O.; Russell P. Pennoyer,* Pres.; Peter Frelinghuysen,* V.P.; Mary S. Phipps,* V.P.; John B. Krieger, Secy. and Exec. Dir.; Horace I. Crary, Jr.,* Treas.; Hon. Walter J.P. Curley; Leslie Lenkowsky; Tatiana Pouschine.
Number of staff: 1 full-time professional; 2 part-time support.
EIN: 136022018
Selected grants: The following grants are a representative sample of this grantmaker's funding activity:
$80,000 to Cancer Research Institute, New York, NY, 2012. For Cancer Vaccine Collaborative, payable over 2.25 years.
$75,000 to Christodora, New York, NY, 2013. For general operating support, payable over 1.25 years.
$50,000 to Achievement First, New York Office, Brooklyn, NY, 2012. For Achievement First Brownsville Middle School.

$50,000 to Classroom, Inc., New York, NY, 2013. To expand programs into middle schools in the Roman Catholic Diocese of Brooklyn, payable over 1.50 years.
$50,000 to Launch Expeditionary Learning Charter School, Brooklyn, NY, 2012. For first-year expenses.
$50,000 to Lending Education Assistance Program, Brooklyn Workforce Innovations, Brooklyn, NY, 2013. For workforce development programs, payable over 1.50 years.
$50,000 to New York Landmarks Conservancy, New York, NY, 2013. For Sacred Sites program, payable over 1.50 years.
$50,000 to Opportunities for a Better Tomorrow, Brooklyn, NY, 2013. For Youth Education and Job Training Program at Y Roads Center in Jamaica, Queens, NY, payable over 1.25 years.
$50,000 to Per Scholas, Bronx, NY, 2013. For Brooklyn IT Ready program, payable over 1.50 years.
$40,000 to Spence-Chapin Services to Families and Children, New York, NY, 2013. For A Special Adoption Program focusing on disabled children ages 0-2, payable over 1.50 years.
$30,000 to Presbyterian Senior Services, New York, NY, 2012. For Strengthening Grandparent-led Families program, payable over 1.25 years.
$25,000 to Bronx River Alliance, Bronx, NY, 2013. For general operating support, payable over 1.25 years.
$25,000 to Brooklyn Historical Society, Brooklyn, NY, 2013. For general operating support, payable over 1.50 years.
$25,000 to Catholic Big Sisters and Big Brothers, New York, NY, 2013. For general operating support, payable over 1.50 years.
$25,000 to City Harvest, New York, NY, 2012. For general operating support.
$25,000 to Jewish Museum, New York, NY, 2012. For Crossing Borders: Medieval Manuscripts from the Bodleian Library exhibition, payable over 1.50 years.
$25,000 to Teach for America, New York, NY, 2012. For general operating support, payable over 1.25 years.
$25,000 to Visions Services for the Blind and Visually Impaired, New York, NY, 2012. For Financial Education and Workforce Development Program, payable over 1.50 years.
$15,000 to Magnum Cultural Foundation, New York, NY, 2012. For Legacy Program.
$15,000 to West Side Campaign Against Hunger, New York, NY, 2012. For general operating support.

5550
Acquavella Family Foundation ✧
18 E. 79th St.
New York, NY 10075-0106

Established in 1997 in NY.
Donors: William R. Acquavella; H. Anthony Ittleson; Donna Jo Acquavella; Edythe C. Acquavella Charitable Lead Trust.
Foundation type: Independent foundation.
Financial data (yr. ended 12/31/13): Assets, $3,213,909 (M); gifts received, $898,107; expenditures, $769,352; qualifying distributions, $764,679; giving activities include $762,562 for 15 grants (high: $314,062; low: $5,000).
Purpose and activities: Giving primarily for the arts; some giving for animal welfare.
Fields of interest: Museums (art); Arts; Libraries (special); Veterinary medicine, hospital; Human services; Children/youth, services.
Limitations: Applications not accepted. Giving primarily in NY. No grants to individuals.
Application information: Contributes only to pre-selected organizations.
Trustees: Donna Jo Acquavella; William R. Acquavella.
EIN: 137140356
Selected grants: The following grants are a representative sample of this grantmaker's funding activity:
$25,000 to University of Virginia, School of Architecture Campbell Hall, Charlottesville, VA, 2012. For unrestricted charitable purpose.
$10,000 to Virginia Athletics Foundation, Charlottesville, VA, 2012. For unrestricted charitable purpose.

5551
The AD Philanthropic Fund, Inc. ✧ ☆
(formerly Huntington Hartford Family Fund Inc.)
c/o Eaton & Van Winkle
3 Park Ave., 16th Fl.
New York, NY 10016-5902

Established in NY.
Donor: Huntington Hartford Trust.
Foundation type: Independent foundation.
Financial data (yr. ended 12/31/13): Assets, $9,715,317 (M); expenditures, $527,845; qualifying distributions, $469,688; giving activities include $444,000 for 30 grants (high: $56,000; low: $3,000).
Fields of interest: Education; Health care; Human services.
Limitations: Applications not accepted. No grants to individuals.
Application information: Unsolicited requests for funds not accepted.
Officers: Arthur A. Lane, Pres.; Richard J. Carter, Jr., V.P.; Jane F. Lane, Secy.; Alexandra Carter, Treas.
EIN: 136092857
Selected grants: The following grants are a representative sample of this grantmaker's funding activity:
$15,000 to Columbia University, Law School, New York, NY, 2012. For unrestricted.

5552
H.T., M.T. and H.T. Adams Town Memorial Fund ✧ ☆
Church Street Sta.
P.O. Box 1297
New York, NY 10008

Foundation type: Independent foundation.
Financial data (yr. ended 11/30/13): Assets, $15,157,448 (M); expenditures, $995,906; qualifying distributions, $906,352; giving activities include $833,032 for 5 grants (high: $484,332; low: $3,000).
Fields of interest: Historic preservation/historical societies; Arts; Education; Human services.
Limitations: Applications not accepted. Giving primarily in CT.
Application information: Unsolicited requests for funds not accepted.
Trustee: Deutsche Bank Trust Co.
EIN: 274249393

5553
The Adar Foundation ✧
156 W. 56th St., Ste. 1701
New York, NY 10019-3877

Established in 2005 in NY.
Donors: Shvat Charitable Lead Trust; The Laurie Pinck Charitable Trust; New Springville Jewish Center.
Foundation type: Independent foundation.
Financial data (yr. ended 12/31/13): Assets, $6,252,683 (M); gifts received, $2,558,806; expenditures, $2,484,717; qualifying distributions, $2,483,706; giving activities include $2,438,726 for 49 grants (high: $407,000; low: $500).
Purpose and activities: Giving primarily to Jewish agencies, temples, and schools.
Fields of interest: Elementary/secondary education; Theological school/education; Jewish federated giving programs; Jewish agencies & synagogues.
Limitations: Applications not accepted. Giving primarily in MD and NY.
Application information: Contributes only to pre-selected organizations.
Officers: Laurie Pinck, Pres.; Menachem Pinck, V.P.; Lyudmila Koyenova, Secy.; David Camhi, Treas.
EIN: 206607160
Selected grants: The following grants are a representative sample of this grantmaker's funding activity:
$207,475 to Bnos Yisroel of Baltimore, Baltimore, MD, 2012. For Educational Institute.
$1,300 to Yeshiva Karlin Stolin, Brooklyn, NY, 2012. For Charitable Institute.

5554
Ethel & Philip Adelman Charitable Foundation, Inc. ✧ ☆
860 United Nations Plz., Ste. 25/26C
New York, NY 10017-1810

Established in 1996 in NY.
Donors: Philip Adelman†; Ethel Adelman†.
Foundation type: Independent foundation.
Financial data (yr. ended 12/31/13): Assets, $3,862,396 (M); expenditures, $733,574; qualifying distributions, $643,674; giving activities include $560,360 for 75 grants (high: $170,800; low: $100).
Fields of interest: Arts; Higher education; Hospitals (specialty); Human services; Jewish federated giving programs; Jewish agencies & synagogues.
Type of support: General/operating support.
Limitations: Applications not accepted. Giving primarily in NY. No grants to individuals.
Application information: Contributes only to pre-selected organizations.
Directors: Seymour Flug; Robert B. Kay.
EIN: 133917004
Selected grants: The following grants are a representative sample of this grantmaker's funding activity:
$102,000 to Hospital for Special Surgery, New York, NY, 2012. To Help Make State of the Art Facilities Available to the Public.
$25,000 to Seeds of Peace, New York, NY, 2012. For The Empower Young Persons in Regions of Conflict to Advance Coexistence and Reconciliation.
$20,000 to Haverford College, Haverford, PA, 2012. For a Liberal Arts Education While Instilling Dignity, Tolerance, and Respect Among Its Students.

$5,000 to Brearley School, New York, NY, 2012. To Develop Intellectual Energy, Exuberance, and Character in Children.
$5,000 to Cornell University, Ithaca, NY, 2012. To Form a Living and Learning Community.
$5,000 to Ethical Culture Fieldston School, New York, NY, 2012. To Challenge Students and Help Develop Their Ethical Sensibilities.
$3,200 to Metropolitan Museum of Art, New York, NY, 2012. For Programs and Services to Visitors of the Museum.
$3,000 to Fairleigh Dickinson University, Teaneck, NJ, 2012. For Training Equipment and Classroom Materials to the Students.
$2,600 to Metropolitan Opera, New York, NY, 2012. For Access to the Opera to the Public.
$1,500 to Playwrights Horizons, New York, NY, 2012. For the Development of Contemporary American Playwrights, Composers and Lyricists.

5555
Adelson Family Foundation ✧
P.O. Box 820
Katonah, NY 10536-0820

Established in 2000 in NY.
Donors: Andrew Adelson; Nancy Adelson.
Foundation type: Independent foundation.
Financial data (yr. ended 12/31/13): Assets, $8,410,252 (M); gifts received, $4,200; expenditures, $1,044,100; qualifying distributions, $1,030,213; giving activities include $1,027,000 for 23 grants (high: $500,000; low: $500).
Fields of interest: Arts; Higher education; Education; Human services; International migration/refugee issues; Jewish federated giving programs; Public affairs, ethics; Jewish agencies & synagogues; Women.
Limitations: Applications not accepted. Giving primarily in NJ and NY. No grants to individuals.
Application information: Contributes only to pre-selected organizations.
Trustees: Andrew Adelson; Nancy Adelson.
EIN: 223769645
Selected grants: The following grants are a representative sample of this grantmaker's funding activity:
$500,000 to Grassroots Business Partners, Washington, DC, 2011.
$333,000 to Grassroots Business Partners, Washington, DC, 2010.
$150,000 to Hastings Center, Garrison, NY, 2010.
$100,000 to Jewish Community Center on the Palisades, Tenafly, NJ, 2010.
$2,500 to Disabled American Veterans, Cold Spring, KY, 2011.

5556
Adirondack Foundation ✧
(formerly Adirondack Community Trust)
2284 Saranac Ave.
P.O. Box 288
Lake Placid, NY 12946 (518) 523-9904
Contact: Cali Brooks, Exec. Dir.; For grants: Andrea Grout, Prog. Off.
FAX: (518) 523-9905;
E-mail: info@generousact.org; Grant inquiry e-mail: andrea@generousact.org; Main URL: http://www.generousact.org
Facebook: http://www.facebook.com/pages/Adirondack-Community-Trust/215603083110

Established in 1997 in NY.
Foundation type: Community foundation.
Financial data (yr. ended 06/30/14): Assets, $40,124,660 (M); gifts received, $3,912,279; expenditures, $2,690,095; giving activities include $1,980,463 for 62+ grants (high: $317,200), and $76,750 for 24 grants to individuals.
Purpose and activities: The foundation seeks to unite donors' charitable interests with the needs of the Adirondack region by: 1) building a permanent and flexible endowment that can respond to the most pressing current, and future, needs of the region; 2) working with donors and their advisors to design named endowments that meet the unique and individual charitable objectives of the donor; 3) administering a creative program of grantmaking to give maximum benefit to charitable needs within the area and carry out the wishes of donors; 4) being a prudent manager and faithful steward of philanthropic assets; 5) and being a leader and catalyst focusing attention on the needs of the region.
Fields of interest: Historic preservation/historical societies; Arts; Libraries/library science; Education; Environment; Animal welfare; Health care; Recreation; Children/youth, services; Human services; Community/economic development.
Type of support: General/operating support; Continuing support; Annual campaigns; Capital campaigns; Building/renovation; Land acquisition; Endowments; Program development; Publication; Seed money; Curriculum development; Scholarship funds; Technical assistance; Scholarships—to individuals; Matching/challenge support.
Limitations: Applications accepted. Giving limited to the Adirondack region of NY.
Publications: Annual report; Financial statement; Grants list; Informational brochure; Newsletter.
Application information: Visit foundation web site for application information.
Initial approach: Create online profile
Deadline(s): Varies
Board meeting date(s): Jan., May, July, and Oct.
Officers and Trustees:* John Ernst,* Chair.; Nancy Keet,* Vice-Chair.; David Mason,* Vice-Chair.; Susan Waters,* Secy.; David Heidecorn,* Treas.; Cali Brooks, Exec. Dir.; John Fritzinger; Barbara Linell Glaser; Jerry Hayes; Cathy Johnston; Rich Kroes; Nancy Monette; Peter Paine; Joe Shaw; Joseph Steiniger; Dick Strowger; Holly Wolff; Cecil Wray.
Number of staff: 2 full-time professional; 1 part-time professional.
EIN: 161535724
Selected grants: The following grants are a representative sample of this grantmaker's funding activity:
$200,000 to Bruce L. Crary Foundation, Elizabethtown, NY, 2013. For wire transfer for scholarships and operation.
$180,000 to Bruce L. Crary Foundation, Elizabethtown, NY, 2012. For scholarships and operations.
$60,000 to National Sports Academy, Lake Placid, NY, 2013. For Emergency Operating Distribution.
$50,000 to Keene Volunteer Fire Department, Keene, NY, 2012. To assist with acquisition of a new site for the Keene Fire Department, which was destroyed in Irene flood.
$50,000 to North Country Society for the Prevention of Cruelty to Animals, Elizabethtown, NY, 2013. For North Country SPCA Capital Campaign for new shelter.
$46,600 to Lake Placid Center for the Arts, Lake Placid, NY, 2013. For annual distribution from endowment.
$36,700 to Lake Placid Center for the Arts, Lake Placid, NY, 2012. For annual distribution from the fund.
$36,000 to Points of Light Foundation, New York, NY, 2013. For general support for generationOn.
$32,000 to NatureServe, Arlington, VA, 2013. For Gift ($30K) to be matched for the annual fund, plus $2K for a Larry Morse internship.
$30,000 to Adirondack Land Trust/Nature Conservancy, Keene Valley, NY, 2012. For Heart of the Adirondacks Campaign.
$28,365 to North Country Society for the Prevention of Cruelty to Animals, Elizabethtown, NY, 2012. For Capital Campaign.
$28,000 to Lake Placid Central School District, Lake Placid, NY, 2013. For Nash Williams/Founding Families Scholarships.
$21,000 to Lake Placid Central School District, Lake Placid, NY, 2012. For Nash Williams Founding Families Scholarships.
$18,900 to Infant Jesus of Prague, Tupper Lake, NY, 2013. For bi-annual distribution for grantmaking from IJP Inc.
$15,500 to Infant Jesus of Prague, Tupper Lake, NY, 2012. For biannual distribution for further grants from IJPF.
$10,000 to Mountain Meadows, Keene Valley, NY, 2012. To assist with building repairs and lost inventory due to Irene flooding.
$1,000 to Burlington City Arts Foundation, Burlington, VT, 2012. For general support.
$1,000 to Northern Forest Center, Concord, NH, 2013. For general support.
$1,000 to Pendragon, Saranac Lake, NY, 2013. For general operations.
$1,000 to Wilderness Society, Washington, DC, 2012. For general support.

5557
Jack Adjmi Family Foundation, Inc. ✧
463 7th Ave., 4th Fl.
New York, NY 10018-7604 (212) 790-5700
Contact: Eric Adjmi, Dir.

Established in 1983 in NY.
Donors: Eric Adjmi; Jack Adjmi†; Mark Adjmi; Ronald Adjmi; Joey Dewk; Kim Dabah; Rachel Adjmi; Solomon Dabah; Elliott Mahana; Joy Mahana; Beluga, Inc.; Consolidated Childrens Apparel; IFG Corp.; Popsicle Playwear, Ltd.; Blue School; Congregation Z.Y.C.; Klatskin Assocs.; Adjmi Dwek Foundation.
Foundation type: Independent foundation.
Financial data (yr. ended 11/30/13): Assets, $170,240 (M); gifts received, $3,750,608; expenditures, $3,772,360; qualifying distributions, $3,769,863; giving activities include $3,769,863 for 663 grants (high: $676,000; low: $18).
Purpose and activities: Giving primarily to Jewish temples and Jewish medical and human services organizations; giving also for Jewish education.
Fields of interest: Elementary/secondary education; Human services; Jewish federated giving programs; Jewish agencies & synagogues.
Limitations: Giving primarily in NY. No grants to individuals.
Application information: Application form not required.
Initial approach: Proposal
Deadline(s): None

Directors: Eric Adjmi; Rachel Adjmi.
EIN: 133202295

5558
The Amin and Lillian Adjmi Foundation ✧
(formerly Lillian Adjmi Foundation)
1412 Broadway, 3rd Fl.
New York, NY 10018-9228

Established in 1999 in NY.
Donors: Harry Adjmi; Elliot Sutton; Laurie Sutton; One Step Up; Moses Michael Fallas; Joseph Feldman; Howard Klaus.
Foundation type: Independent foundation.
Financial data (yr. ended 07/31/13): Assets, $12,337 (M); gifts received, $557,300; expenditures, $714,939; qualifying distributions, $706,167; giving activities include $705,245 for 176 grants (high: $68,000; low: $100).
Purpose and activities: Giving primarily for Jewish education, temples, and organizations.
Fields of interest: Education; Human services; Jewish agencies & synagogues.
Limitations: Applications not accepted. Giving primarily in NY. No grants to individuals.
Application information: Contributes only to pre-selected organizations.
Trustee: Harry Adjmi.
EIN: 061532888
Selected grants: The following grants are a representative sample of this grantmaker's funding activity:
$10,000 to Israel Cancer Research Fund, New York, NY, 2011. For operating expenses.

5559
The Adjmi-Dwek Family Foundation, Inc. ✧
463 7th Ave., 4th Fl.
New York, NY 10018-4502 (212) 239-8615
Contact: Joseph Dwek, Dir.

Established in 1994 in NY.
Donors: Joseph Dwek; Sister Sister, Inc.; Sports Products of America LLC.
Foundation type: Independent foundation.
Financial data (yr. ended 12/31/13): Assets, $2,101 (M); gifts received, $825,623; expenditures, $828,048; qualifying distributions, $828,048; giving activities include $822,934 for 438 grants (high: $53,800; low: $101).
Purpose and activities: Support primarily for Jewish agencies, temples, and schools.
Fields of interest: Jewish agencies & synagogues.
Limitations: Applications accepted. Giving primarily in NY and NJ; some giving internationally.
Application information: Application form required.
Initial approach: Letter
Deadline(s): None
Directors: Joseph Dwek; Terry Dwek.
EIN: 133782816

5560
Aequus Institute ✧ ☆
P.O. Box 3485
Elmira, NY 14905-0485 (800) 441-1963
Contact: Nancy Padilla

Established in 1990 in CA as successor to Aequus Institute.
Foundation type: Independent foundation.
Financial data (yr. ended 12/31/13): Assets, $2,605,470 (M); expenditures, $1,167,557; qualifying distributions, $1,112,471; giving activities include $985,000 for 38 grants (high: $150,000; low: $1,000).
Purpose and activities: Giving to promote the teaching of Mary Baker Eddy and the Christian Science Church, and the free market economic system.
Fields of interest: Economics; Political science; Public policy, research; Government/public administration.
Type of support: General/operating support.
Limitations: Applications accepted. Giving primarily in CA; some giving in other states as well. No grants to individuals.
Publications: Informational brochure (including application guidelines).
Application information: Application form required.
Initial approach: Letter
Deadline(s): None
Officers and Directors:* Patrick Parker,* Pres.; David Keyston,* V.P.; Edwin Feulner, Jr., Ph.D.*, Secy.; Larry P. Arnn, Ph.D.*, Exec. Dir.
Number of staff: 2
EIN: 521620982
Selected grants: The following grants are a representative sample of this grantmaker's funding activity:
$50,000 to Hillsdale College, Hillsdale, MI, 2012. For Kirby Center Programs.
$40,000 to Mont Pelerin Society, Alexandria, VA, 2012. For Hayek Essay Contest.
$10,000 to Intercollegiate Studies Institute, Wilmington, DE, 2012. For Leadership for America's Future Campaign.
$2,500 to Philadelphia Society, Jerome, MI, 2012. For General Operations, Meeting Expenses.
$2,500 to Principia College, Elsah, IL, 2012. For general operations, research.
$1,000 to Foundation for Research on Economics and the Environment, Bozeman, MT, 2012. For religious leader's programs.

5561
The Afognak Fund ✧
c/o WithumSmith+Brown, PC
1411 Broadway, 9th Fl.
New York, NY 10018-3496

Established in 1998 in MA.
Donor: Anne Symchych.
Foundation type: Independent foundation.
Financial data (yr. ended 12/31/13): Assets, $24,864,615 (M); gifts received, $200,000; expenditures, $1,016,697; qualifying distributions, $987,339; giving activities include $978,283 for 31 grants (high: $75,783; low: $7,500).
Fields of interest: Arts; Environment, natural resources; Science, formal/general education.
Limitations: Applications not accepted. No grants to individuals.
Application information: Contributes only to pre-selected organizations.
Trustees: Elizabeth King; Margaret Murphy; Anne Symchych; Catherine Symchych; Christine Symchych; Stephen Symchych.
EIN: 061521981
Selected grants: The following grants are a representative sample of this grantmaker's funding activity:
$120,000 to World Wildlife Fund, Washington, DC, 2011.
$75,000 to Seacology, Berkeley, CA, 2011.
$67,237 to Little Traverse Conservancy, Harbor Springs, MI, 2011.
$60,000 to Center for Puppetry Arts, Atlanta, GA, 2011.
$50,000 to Coalition for Buzzards Bay, New Bedford, MA, 2011.
$45,000 to First Book, Washington, DC, 2011.
$40,000 to Boston Landmarks Orchestra, Boston, MA, 2011.
$40,000 to Paul Revere Memorial Association, Boston, MA, 2011.
$30,000 to Blessings in a Backpack, Louisville, KY, 2011.
$25,000 to Coastal Studies for Girls, Freeport, ME, 2011.

5562
AHBA, Inc. ✧
c/o Hertz, Herson & Co., LLP
477 Madison Ave., 10th Fl.
New York, NY 10022-5802

Established in 1998 in DE and NY.
Donors: Bella Wexner Charitable Remainder Unitrust; Susan Wexner Revocable Trust.
Foundation type: Independent foundation.
Financial data (yr. ended 03/31/13): Assets, $43,621,128 (M); expenditures, $1,966,103; qualifying distributions, $1,888,630; giving activities include $1,885,002 for 5 grants (high: $1,500,000; low: $2).
Fields of interest: Education; Hospitals (general); Children, services; Jewish federated giving programs; Jewish agencies & synagogues.
Limitations: Applications not accepted. Giving primarily in New York, NY, and Israel. No grants to individuals.
Application information: Contributes only to pre-selected organizations.
Officer and Directors:* Susan R. Wexner,* Pres. and Secy.-Treas.; Saul G. Agus; Raymond Kanner; Gregg H. Levy, Esq.; Michael S. Oberman, Esq.; Mark W. Saks, Esq.; Walter Stern.
EIN: 133997367
Selected grants: The following grants are a representative sample of this grantmaker's funding activity:
$40,000 to American Friends of MaTaN, Levittown, PA, 2011.
$22,500 to PEF Israel Endowment Funds, New York, NY, 2011.
$21,250 to American Friends of MaTaN, Levittown, PA, 2011.
$2,000 to American Jewish Joint Distribution Committee, New York, NY, 2011.
$1,500 to Leukemia & Lymphoma Society, White Plains, NY, 2011.
$1,000 to Cystic Fibrosis Foundation, Bethesda, MD, 2011.

5563
AIG Disaster Relief Fund-New York ✧
180 Maiden Ln.
New York, NY 10038
Main URL: http://www.aig.com/citizenship_3171_437858.html

Established in 2003 in NY.
Donors: Starr Foundation; American International Group, Inc.

Foundation type: Company-sponsored foundation.
Financial data (yr. ended 12/31/13): Assets, $60,828 (M); gifts received, $1,205,626; expenditures, $1,245,626; qualifying distributions, $1,241,774; giving activities include $1,195,000 for 11 grants (high: $300,000; low: $10,000).
Purpose and activities: The foundation supports programs designed to assist victims of natural and manmade disasters around the world.
Fields of interest: Disasters, preparedness/ services; American Red Cross; Human services.
Type of support: Emergency funds.
Limitations: Applications not accepted. Giving on a national basis, with emphasis on Washington, DC and Tokyo, Japan. No grants to individuals.
Application information: Contributes only to pre-selected organizations.
Officers and Directors:* Jeffrey J. Hurd,* Pres.; Tal S. Kaissar,* V.P.; Christina L. Pretto,* V.P.; Kathleen E. Shannon,* Secy.; Brian T. Schreiber,* Treas.
EIN: 743085338

5564
AIG Foundation, Inc. ✧
c/o Vasyl Tsykulyak
175 Water St., 19th Fl.
New York, NY 10038

Established in 2005 in NY.
Donor: American International Group, Inc.
Foundation type: Company-sponsored foundation.
Financial data (yr. ended 12/31/13): Assets, $3,395 (M); gifts received, $1,135,428; expenditures, $1,135,428; qualifying distributions, $1,135,428; giving activities include $981,920 for 186 grants to individuals (high: $7,000; low: $560).
Purpose and activities: The foundation awards college scholarships to dependents of employees of American International Group, Inc.
Fields of interest: Higher education.
Type of support: Employee-related scholarships.
Limitations: Applications not accepted. Giving on a national and international basis in areas of company operations.
Publications: Corporate giving report.
Application information: Contributes only through employee-related scholarships.
Trustees: Kevin M. Carome; Washington C. Dender; Loren M. Starr.
EIN: 203713472

5565
AJG Foundation ✧
c/o Addie J. Guttag
575 Park Ave., Apt. 1603
New York, NY 10065-7332

Established in 2007 in NY.
Donor: Addie J. Guttag.
Foundation type: Independent foundation.
Financial data (yr. ended 12/31/13): Assets, $12,852,892 (M); expenditures, $701,465; qualifying distributions, $688,136; giving activities include $648,400 for 26 grants (high: $77,250; low: $500).
Fields of interest: Health organizations; Human services; Children, services; Jewish agencies & synagogues.
Limitations: Applications not accepted. Giving primarily in CA and NY.
Application information: Contributes only to pre-selected organizations.
Officer: Addie J. Guttag, Pres.
EIN: 208304634
Selected grants: The following grants are a representative sample of this grantmaker's funding activity:
$70,000 to American Jewish World Service, New York, NY, 2011.
$50,000 to American Jewish World Service, New York, NY, 2011.
$30,000 to International Rescue Committee, New York, NY, 2011.
$30,000 to Partners in Health, Boston, MA, 2011.
$10,000 to Village Health Works, New York, NY, 2011.
$5,000 to African Services Committee, New York, NY, 2011.
$5,000 to Human Rights First, New York, NY, 2011.
$5,000 to South Africa Development Fund, Boston, MA, 2011.
$2,625 to GlobalGiving Foundation, Washington, DC, 2011.
$1,000 to Keep a Child Alive, Brooklyn, NY, 2011.

5566
Alavi Foundation ✧
650 5th Ave., Ste. 2406
New York, NY 10019-6108 (212) 944-8333
Contact: Hanieh Safakamal, Fin. Mgr.
FAX: (212) 921-0325;
E-mail: info@alavifoundation.org; Main URL: http://www.alavifoundation.org

Incorporated in 1973 in NY.
Foundation type: Independent foundation.
Financial data (yr. ended 03/31/13): Assets, $112,290,806 (M); gifts received, $10,833; expenditures, $4,426,052; qualifying distributions, $3,478,426; giving activities include $1,815,800 for 31 grants (high: $403,000; low: $3,000), $648,690 for foundation-administered programs and $18,754 for loans/program-related investments.
Purpose and activities: A primary aim of the foundation is to promote harmony and understanding among people of different religions. Another of its basic aims is to promote the study of the humanities, arts, and pure and applied sciences. It also gives to organizations that are involved in the teaching of Islamic or Persian culture.
Fields of interest: Arts; Education; Human services; Islam.
Type of support: Continuing support; Building/ renovation; Program-related investments/loans; Student loans—to individuals.
Limitations: Applications accepted. Giving on a national basis. No support for political organizations. No grants to individuals, (except for scholarships).
Publications: Grants list; IRS Form 990 or 990-PF printed copy available upon request.
Application information: Student scholarship program has been suspended. Application form not required.
Initial approach: See foundation web site for approach for each individual program
Copies of proposal: 1
Deadline(s): None
Board meeting date(s): Bimonthly
Officers and Directors:* Hoshang Ahmadi, Pres.; Alireza Ebrhamimi,* Secy.; Ali Babiran, Treas.; Hassan Hassani.
Number of staff: 1 full-time professional; 3 full-time support.
EIN: 237345978

5567
Sidney and Beatrice Albert Foundation ✧
20 Corporate Woods, 5th Fl.
Albany, NY 12211 (518) 465-4500
Contact: Marvin Honig Esq., Treas.

Established in 1994 in NY.
Donor: Beatrice Albert Charitable Trust.
Foundation type: Independent foundation.
Financial data (yr. ended 05/31/13): Assets, $671,319 (M); gifts received, $300,000; expenditures, $608,877; qualifying distributions, $604,700; giving activities include $604,700 for 80 grants (high: $60,000; low: $100).
Fields of interest: Media, radio; Arts; Education; Health care; Health organizations, association; Human services; Residential/custodial care, hospices; United Ways and Federated Giving Programs; Jewish agencies & synagogues.
Type of support: General/operating support.
Limitations: Applications accepted. Giving primarily in NY. No grants to individuals.
Application information: Application form required.
Initial approach: Letter
Deadline(s): None
Officers and Directors:* Isadore Cassuto,* Pres.; Charles E. Gregory, Jr.,* V.P.; Marvin Honig,* Treas.
EIN: 223267816

5568
The Alexander Family Foundation ✧
c/o Margo N. Alexander
15 E. 26th St., Apt. 10A
New York, NY 10010-1424

Established in 2000 in NY.
Donor: Margo N. Alexander.
Foundation type: Independent foundation.
Financial data (yr. ended 12/31/12): Assets, $1,044,166 (M); gifts received, $43,598; expenditures, $478,325; qualifying distributions, $452,165; giving activities include $452,165 for grants.
Fields of interest: Higher education; Human services; International affairs, public policy; International relief.
Limitations: Applications not accepted. Giving primarily in CA and New York, NY. No grants to individuals.
Application information: Contributes only to pre-selected organizations.
Officer and Trustees:* Margo N. Alexander,* Pres.; James R. Alexander; Nichol C. Alexander; Robert C. Alexander.
EIN: 134140292

5569
Alexander Foundation, Inc. ✧
c/o Connifer Capital
9 W. 57th St., Ste. 5000
New York, NY 10019

Donor: Gregory Alexander.
Foundation type: Independent foundation.
Financial data (yr. ended 12/31/13): Assets, $29,097,766 (M); gifts received, $1,500,000;

expenditures, $1,587,266; qualifying distributions, $1,305,497; giving activities include $1,300,000 for 8 grants (high: $750,000; low: $10,000).
Fields of interest: Environment; Animals/wildlife, preservation/protection; Animals/wildlife.
Limitations: Applications not accepted. Giving primarily in Washington, DC, the Bronx and New York, NY, and Arlington, VA.
Application information: Contributes only to pre-selected organizations.
Trustees: Gregory Alexander; Jennifer Chiu; Scott M. O'Connell.
EIN: 135221910

5570
Alfiero Family Charitable Foundation ✧
100 Corporate Pkwy., Ste. 130
Amherst, NY 14226-1200
Contact: Salvatore H. Alfiero, Chair.

Established in 1989 in NY.
Donor: Salvatore H. Alfiero.
Foundation type: Independent foundation.
Financial data (yr. ended 12/31/12): Assets, $4,590,993 (M); expenditures, $671,476; qualifying distributions, $664,176; giving activities include $664,176 for 14 grants (high: $250,000; low: $500).
Purpose and activities: Giving primarily for higher education, as well as a heritage organization supporting the Marine Corps, and children, youth, and social services.
Fields of interest: Media/communications; Historical activities; Higher education; Education; Hospitals (specialty); Cancer; Human services; Children/youth, services.
Type of support: General/operating support.
Limitations: Applications not accepted. Giving primarily in NY; some funding also in VA.
Application information: Contributes only to pre-selected organizations.
Managers: Charles C. Alfiero; James J. Alfiero; Salvatore H. Alfiero; Victor S. Alfiero.
EIN: 110036051

5571
Alison Foundation ✧
160 W. 75th St., Apt. 4A
New York, NY 10023

Established in 2004 in NY.
Donors: Ronald H. Fielding; Donna M. Fielding.
Foundation type: Independent foundation.
Financial data (yr. ended 12/31/13): Assets, $11,548,356 (M); gifts received, $110,148; expenditures, $635,022; qualifying distributions, $610,000; giving activities include $610,000 for 3 grants (high: $300,000; low: $10,000).
Fields of interest: Museums (specialized); Performing arts, theater; Higher education; Zoos/zoological societies; Health organizations, association; Youth development; Social sciences, research.
Limitations: Applications not accepted. Giving primarily in San Francisco, CA, Annapolis, MD and NY. No grants to individuals.
Application information: Contributes only to pre-selected organizations.
Officer: Daniel Fielding, Secy.
Trustee: Ronald H. Fielding.
EIN: 200226054

5572
All the Way Foundation ✧
c/o Four M Investments LLC
7 Renaissance Sq., 5th Fl.
White Plains, NY 10601

Foundation type: Independent foundation.
Financial data (yr. ended 06/30/13): Assets, $1,961,595 (M); expenditures, $852,197; qualifying distributions, $849,527; giving activities include $845,575 for 22 grants (high: $295,000; low: $1,000).
Fields of interest: Museums (art); Education; Health organizations; Human services; Foundations (private independent); United Ways and Federated Giving Programs.
Limitations: Applications not accepted. Giving primarily in NY. No grants to individuals.
Application information: Contributes only to pre-selected organizations.
Officers: Michael Mehiel, Chair.; Anna Marie Cotter, Treas.
EIN: 133976406

5573
The Allen Family Foundation, Inc. ✧
(formerly The Bedminster Fund, Inc.)
c/o Keswick Mgmt.
99 Park Ave., 24th Fl.
New York, NY 10016-0313

Incorporated in 1948 in NY.
Donors: A. Christine Allen; Douglas E. Allen; Philip Allen; Dorothy D. Eweson†.
Foundation type: Independent foundation.
Financial data (yr. ended 06/30/13): Assets, $12,391,998 (M); gifts received, $460,410; expenditures, $800,407; qualifying distributions, $719,500; giving activities include $719,500 for grants.
Purpose and activities: Giving primarily for education, health care, the arts, and welfare agencies. Grants only to present beneficiary organizations and to special proposals developed by the directors; additional requests seldom considered.
Fields of interest: Arts; Elementary/secondary education; Education; Environment; Hospitals (general); Human services.
Type of support: General/operating support; Continuing support; Annual campaigns; Capital campaigns; Building/renovation; Conferences/seminars.
Limitations: Applications not accepted. Giving primarily in MA, NJ, and NY. No grants to individuals; no loans.
Application information: Contributes only to pre-selected organizations.
Board meeting date(s): Nov. and as required
Officers and Directors:* Philip D. Allen,* Pres.; Christine Allen,* V.P.; Martin C. Zetterberg,* V.P.; Eileen B. Kane, Secy.; James J. Ruddy, Treas.; Alexandra F. Allen; Andrew D. Allen; Christopher D. Allen; Douglas E. Allen; Elisabeth F. Allen; Nicholas E. Allen; Dorothy D. Caplow; Theodore Caplow.
Number of staff: 1 part-time professional.
EIN: 136083684
Selected grants: The following grants are a representative sample of this grantmaker's funding activity:
$100,000 to Berkshire School, Sheffield, MA, 2013. For financial aid endowment.
$21,000 to Second Stage Theater, New York, NY, 2013. For general support toward 2012 Season.
$5,000 to Cape Eleuthera Foundation, Lawrenceville, NJ, 2013. For Deep Creek Middle School and Resource Center.
$5,000 to Tampa Museum of Art, Tampa, FL, 2013. To Benefit Exhibitions and Educational Programs.
$5,000 to United Methodist Committee on Relief, New York, NY, 2013. To advance No. 901670, Oklahoma Tomato Efforts.
$1,000 to Puppies Behind Bars, New York, NY, 2013. For annual budgetary requirements.
$1,000 to University of Virginia, Charlottesville, VA, 2013. For In honor of Katherine Allen's 20th Reunion.

5574
The Herbert Allen Foundation ✧
711 5th Ave.
New York, NY 10022-3194

Established in 1994 in NY.
Foundation type: Independent foundation.
Financial data (yr. ended 12/31/13): Assets, $11,697,313 (M); expenditures, $517,446; qualifying distributions, $504,942; giving activities include $502,000 for 18 grants (high: $150,000; low: $1,000).
Purpose and activities: Funding primarily for education, human services, and to a hospital.
Fields of interest: Education; Environment, natural resources; Hospitals (general); Human services; Children/youth, services.
Type of support: General/operating support.
Limitations: Applications not accepted. Giving primarily in New York, NY. No grants to individuals.
Application information: Contributes only to pre-selected organizations.
Officers and Directors:* Susan K. Allen,* Pres.; Bradley A. Roberts,* V.P. and Secy.; Herbert A. Allen III,* V.P. and Treas.
EIN: 133791176
Selected grants: The following grants are a representative sample of this grantmaker's funding activity:
$200,000 to Hackley School, Tarrytown, NY, 2011.
$60,000 to Prep for Prep, New York, NY, 2011.
$50,000 to New York-Presbyterian Fund, New York, NY, 2011.
$50,000 to New York-Presbyterian Fund, New York, NY, 2011.
$35,000 to New York-Presbyterian Fund, New York, NY, 2011.
$30,000 to New York University, New York, NY, 2011.
$15,000 to Center for the New Economy, San Juan, PR, 2011.
$15,000 to City Harvest, New York, NY, 2011.
$15,000 to Fresh Air Fund, New York, NY, 2011.
$5,000 to Central Park Conservancy, New York, NY, 2011.

5575
Allyn Foundation, Inc. ✧
P.O. Box 22
Skaneateles, NY 13152-0022 (315) 685-5059
Contact: Meg M. O'Connell, Exec. Dir.
E-mail: info@allynfoundation.org; E-mail for questions regarding application:

anye@allynfoundation.org; Main URL: http://www.allynfoundation.org
Grants List: http://www.allynfoundation.org/index.php?page=recent-grants

Incorporated in 1956 in NY.
Donors: William Noah Allyn†; William G. Allyn†; Welch Allyn, Inc.
Foundation type: Independent foundation.
Financial data (yr. ended 12/31/13): Assets, $29,995,396 (M); gifts received, $200,000; expenditures, $1,632,773; qualifying distributions, $1,387,415; giving activities include $1,231,333 for 198 grants (high: $100,000; low: $250), and $5,000 for 1 employee matching gift.
Purpose and activities: Giving primarily to improve the quality of life in Central New York. Emphasis placed upon health, human services, education, and youth and families.
Fields of interest: Arts; Higher education; Education; Health care; Human services; Children/youth, services; Family services; Community/economic development; Foundations (community).
Type of support: Annual campaigns; Capital campaigns; Building/renovation; Equipment; Seed money; Scholarship funds; Consulting services; Matching/challenge support.
Limitations: Applications accepted. Giving limited to Onondaga and Cayuga counties in NY. No support for religious programs. No grants to individuals, or for endowment funds for fundraising; no loans.
Publications: Application guidelines; Grants list.
Application information: Application form required.
Initial approach: Application form on foundation web site
Copies of proposal: 1
Deadline(s): Apr. 1, July 1, Sept. 1, and Nov. 1
Board meeting date(s): 4 times per year
Final notification: Within 60 days of the deadline
Officers: W. Scott Allyn, M.D., Pres.; Elsa A. Soderberg, V.P.; Lew F. Allyn, Secy.; Eric Allyn, Treas.; Margaret M. O'Connell, Exec. Dir.
Directors: Amy Allyn; David Allyn; Dawn N. Allyn; Janet J. Allyn; Laura A. Allyn; William "Bill" Allyn; Dr. Barbara Connor; Crystal Cosentino; Dr. Cornelius Murphy; Margaret Ogden; Jon Soderberg; Libby Soderberg; Dr. Maureen Soderberg; Peer Allyn Soderberg, M.D.; Peter H. Soderberg.
Number of staff: 1 full-time professional; 1 part-time support.
EIN: 156017723
Selected grants: The following grants are a representative sample of this grantmaker's funding activity:
$129,000 to Central New York Community Foundation, Syracuse, NY, 2012. For Syracuse Say Yes to Educ., IDEAS Fund, Cayuga Comm. Fund, Women's Fund of CNY.
$50,000 to ProLiteracy Worldwide, Syracuse, NY, 2012. For Life Links Program.
$33,500 to Onondaga Community College Foundation, Syracuse, NY, 2012. For Community Scholars Program, Operating support and Director's donation.
$30,000 to Le Moyne College, Syracuse, NY, 2012. For W.G. Allyn Scholarships.
$25,000 to Schweinfurth Memorial Art Center, Auburn, NY, 2012. For Auburn Arts Initiative.
$13,500 to Matthew House, Auburn, NY, 2012. For annual operations fund + director's donations.
$10,000 to Cayuga Museum of History and Art, Auburn, NY, 2012. For capacity building grant.
$8,075 to Child Care Solutions, Syracuse, NY, 2012. For early childhood initiative grant.
$3,000 to Tau Beta Pi Association, Knoxville, TN, 2012. For Director's donation.
$1,000 to ARISE, Inc., Syracuse, NY, 2012. For ARISE at the Farm Program.

5576
Alper Family Foundation ✧
c/o BCRS Assocs., LLC
77 Water St., 9th Fl.
New York, NY 10005-4414

Established in 1991 in NY.
Donor: Andrew M. Alper.
Foundation type: Independent foundation.
Financial data (yr. ended 02/28/13): Assets, $11,921,947 (M); gifts received, $1,762,500; expenditures, $1,317,391; qualifying distributions, $1,275,750; giving activities include $1,275,000 for 3 grants (high: $1,000,000; low: $25,000).
Purpose and activities: Giving primarily for higher education.
Fields of interest: Higher education; Education; Hospitals (general); Big Brothers/Big Sisters; Human services.
Limitations: Applications not accepted. Giving primarily in Chicago, IL and New York, NY. No grants to individuals; no loans.
Application information: Contributes only to pre-selected organizations.
Trustees: Andrew M. Alper; Sharon Sadow Alper.
EIN: 133634384
Selected grants: The following grants are a representative sample of this grantmaker's funding activity:
$1,000,000 to University of Chicago, Chicago, IL, 2011.
$275,000 to Mount Sinai Medical Center, New York, NY, 2011.
$25,000 to University of Chicago, Chicago, IL, 2011.
$1,000 to Columbia Grammar and Preparatory School, New York, NY, 2011.

5577
Alpern Family Foundation, Inc. ✧
c/o Weitzman & Rubin, PC
400 Jericho Tpke., Ste. 205
Jericho, NY 11753-1320

Established in 1952.
Donors: Bernard E. Alpern†; Bernard E. Alpern 1978 Trust; Lloyd J. Alpern 1971 Charitable Remainder Unitrust; Lloyd J. Alpern 1980 Trust.
Foundation type: Independent foundation.
Financial data (yr. ended 12/31/12): Assets, $14,509,266 (M); gifts received, $65,000; expenditures, $864,187; qualifying distributions, $751,287; giving activities include $639,000 for 70 grants (high: $100,000; low: $1,000).
Purpose and activities: Support for medical research, particularly cancer, as well as for children, youth, and social services, the arts, and Jewish organizations.
Fields of interest: Arts; Medical school/education; Education; Cancer research; Human services; Children/youth, services; Jewish federated giving programs; Jewish agencies & synagogues; Women.
Type of support: Research.
Limitations: Applications not accepted. Giving primarily in New York, NY. No grants to individuals.
Application information: Contributes only to pre-selected organizations.
Officers and Directors:* Martin H. Schneider,* Pres.; Rochelle A. Rubin,* V.P. and Exec. Dir.; Barbara Nagel,* Secy.; Steven I. Rubin,* Treas.; Richard L. Alpern.
EIN: 136100302

5578
The Alpert Family Foundation, Inc. ✧
17 Linden Dr.
Purchase, NY 10577-1438

Established in 1995 in NY.
Donor: Norman W. Alpert.
Foundation type: Independent foundation.
Financial data (yr. ended 11/30/13): Assets, $0 (M); gifts received, $697,834; expenditures, $713,336; qualifying distributions, $713,309; giving activities include $713,309 for 76 grants (high: $80,000; low: $36).
Purpose and activities: Giving primarily for education, and to Jewish organizations.
Fields of interest: Higher education; Education; Health organizations, association; Jewish federated giving programs; Jewish agencies & synagogues.
Limitations: Applications not accepted. Giving primarily in MA and RI, some giving also in NY. No grants to individuals.
Application information: Contributes only to pre-selected organizations.
Officers: Norman W. Alpert, Pres.; Jane Alpert, V.P.
Director: William Goldberg.
EIN: 133745910
Selected grants: The following grants are a representative sample of this grantmaker's funding activity:
$315,000 to Brown University, Providence, RI, 2011.
$80,000 to Brown University, Providence, RI, 2011.
$50,000 to Brown University, Providence, RI, 2011.
$40,000 to Brown University, Providence, RI, 2011.
$1,000 to Columbia University, New York, NY, 2011.

5579
Altman Foundation ✧
521 5th Ave., 35th Fl.
New York, NY 10175-3599 (212) 682-0970
Contact: Karen L. Rosa, V.P. and Exec. Dir.; Jeremy Tennenbaum, C.F.O.
E-mail: info@altman.org; Main URL: http://www.altmanfoundation.org
Grants List: http://www.altmanfoundation.org/grants.html

Incorporated in 1913 in NY.
Donors: Benjamin Altman†; Col. Michael Friedsam†.
Foundation type: Independent foundation.
Financial data (yr. ended 12/31/13): Assets, $258,641,797 (M); expenditures, $16,203,255; qualifying distributions, $13,572,079; giving activities include $10,971,550 for 178 grants (high: $180,000; low: $2,500), $138,269 for 42 employee matching gifts, and $500,000 for 1 loan/program-related investment.
Purpose and activities: The foundation's mission is to support programs and institutions that enrich the quality of life in New York City, with a particular focus on initiatives that help individuals, families and communities benefit from the services and

opportunities that will enable them to achieve their full potential.
Fields of interest: Arts; Education, early childhood education; Elementary school/education; Secondary school/education; Education; Palliative care; Health care; Mental health/crisis services; Health organizations; Employment; Housing/shelter, development; Human services; Youth, services; Family services; Aging, centers/services; Infants/toddlers; Children/youth; Children; Youth; Adults; Aging; Young adults; Minorities; African Americans/Blacks; Hispanics/Latinos; Women; Girls; Adults, women; Young adults, female; Men; Infants/toddlers, male; Boys; Adults, men; Young adults, male; Terminal illness, people with; Immigrants/refugees; Economically disadvantaged.
Type of support: Management development/capacity building; Program development; Technical assistance; Program evaluation; Program-related investments/loans; Employee matching gifts.
Limitations: Applications accepted. Giving limited to NY State, and almost exclusively to the boroughs of New York City. No grants to individuals, or for building funds, the purchase of capital equipment, or for galas and other fundraising events.
Publications: Application guidelines; Annual report (including application guidelines).
Application information: The foundation does not accept applications via e-mail or fax. Application form required.
Initial approach: Please review the foundation's mission, values, operating principles, and funding limitations as they appear on the Guidelines page of the foundation's web site before considering which specific program area is applicable to the funding request.
Copies of proposal: 1
Deadline(s): None
Board meeting date(s): 6 times per year
Final notification: Several weeks
Officers and Trustees:* Jane B. O'Connell,* Pres.; Karen L. Rosa, V.P. and Exec. Dir.; John W. Townsend IV,* V.P. and Treas.; Julia V. Shea,* Secy.; James M. Burke; Beverly F. Chase; Wilfred A. Finnegan; William A. Goodloe; Maurice A. Selinger, Jr.; Patricia J. Volland.
Number of staff: 9 full-time professional; 4 full-time support.
EIN: 131623879
Selected grants: The following grants are a representative sample of this grantmaker's funding activity:
$500,000 to Fund for Public Schools, New York, NY, 2012. For years two and three of NYC Summer Quest, a three-year multifaceted approach to improving, expanding, and sustaining summer learning opportunities for NYC public school students.
$325,000 to Queens Museum of Art, Flushing, NY, 2012. For Art and Literacy for New New Yorkers, plan for the nation's first-ever public library in art museum, and implement Collaborative Action Research assessment results to improve teaching practice and enhance student impact.
$325,000 to Sponsors for Educational Opportunity, New York, NY, 2013. To help support SEO's 'OpportunityX2' expansion initiative.
$300,000 to Primary Care Development Corporation, New York, NY, 2012. For the development of a care coordination model for use by primary care providers, to pilot the model with clinics and practices serving low-income Brooklyn residents, and disseminate results.
$250,000 to Mayors Fund to Advance New York City, New York, NY, 2012. For the New York City Housing and Neighborhood Recovery Donors Collaborative.
$220,000 to United Neighborhood Houses of New York, New York, NY, 2013. For general support of UNH's efforts to strengthen the capacity of its members and improve the human services fields in which they operate.
$180,000 to Community Health Care Association of New York State, New York, NY, 2013. To help support NYC-based Federally Qualified Health Centers in their efforts to facilitate enrollment of uninsured patients into public or commercial health insurance through the NYS Health Benefit Exchange.
$150,000 to Catholic Charities Community Services, Archdiocese of New York, New York, NY, 2012. For general operating support and capacity building work with federated agencies.
$150,000 to Cooper-Hewitt Museum, The Smithsonians National Museum of Design, New York, NY, 2013. To help support DesignPrep, the Cooper-Hewitt's design education and career preparation program for underserved New York City high school students.
$150,000 to Mayors Fund to Advance New York City, New York, NY, 2013. For the WorkAdvance program in New York City and to help provide the local match for a Social Innovation Fund grant.
$60,000 to Jewish Home Lifecare, New York, NY, 2012. For the Geriatric Career Development program for at-risk high-school youth.
$60,000 to Jewish Home Lifecare, New York, NY, 2013. To help support the Geriatric Career Development program for at-risk high-school youth.
$55,000 to New York Academy of Medicine, New York, NY, 2012. For a needs assessment aimed at informing efforts to enhance health programs and services at New York City's Innovative Senior Centers.
$50,000 to Brooklyn Academy of Music, Brooklyn, NY, 2013. For capacity building support for BAM's Education programming expansion in the Richard B. Fisher Building.
$50,000 to Center for Childrens Initiatives, New York, NY, 2013. To help support training and consultation to early childhood programs to implement the Devereux Early Childhood Assessment System and promote the social/emotional development of young children.
$50,000 to Childrens Storefront, New York, NY, 2013. To help support the High School Placement and Alumni Relations Initiative.
$50,000 to Local Initiatives Support Corporation, New York, NY, 2012. For the First Responder Initiative to help New York City community development corporations stabilize current activities and assets.
$50,000 to Reach Out and Read of Greater New York, New York, NY, 2012. To help provide New York City children and families with pediatric literacy counseling and support.
$50,000 to Support Center for Nonprofit Management, New York, NY, 2013. For Executive Transition Management and turnaround and restructuring services for the New York City nonprofit sector.
$45,000 to Cool Culture, Brooklyn, NY, 2012. For Literacy Through Culture, which offers professional development to early childhood educators and free access to the arts for families from low-income communities.

5580
The Jeffrey A. Altman Foundation, Inc. ✧
c/o Jeffrey A. Altman, Owl Creek Asset Mgmt.
640 5th Ave., 20th Fl.
New York, NY 10019-6102

Established in 1997 in NY.
Donor: Jeffrey A. Altman.
Foundation type: Independent foundation.
Financial data (yr. ended 11/30/13): Assets, $10,292,000 (M); gifts received, $1,292,041; expenditures, $2,956,506; qualifying distributions, $2,915,386; giving activities include $2,847,892 for 41 grants (high: $1,189,625; low: $100).
Fields of interest: Higher education; Health organizations, association; Human services; Children/youth, services.
Type of support: General/operating support.
Limitations: Applications not accepted. Giving primarily in LA and NY. No grants to individuals.
Application information: Contributes only to pre-selected organizations.
Directors: Georgia Altman; Jeffrey A. Altman; Lawrence Altman.
EIN: 133979282

5581
Altman/Kazickas Foundation ✧
c/o Dorian A. Vergos & Co., LLC
352 7th Ave., Ste. 1501
New York, NY 10001-0064

Established in 1996 in NY.
Donors: Robert C. Altman; Roger C. Altman.
Foundation type: Independent foundation.
Financial data (yr. ended 04/30/13): Assets, $598,977 (M); gifts received, $1,526,535; expenditures, $1,796,326; qualifying distributions, $1,763,297; giving activities include $1,763,067 for 74 grants (high: $160,000; low: $100).
Purpose and activities: Giving primarily for arts and cultural programs, education, social services, and Roman Catholic churches.
Fields of interest: Museums (natural history); Arts; Education; Health organizations; Human services; Children/youth, services; International affairs; Community/economic development; Catholic agencies & churches.
Limitations: Applications not accepted. Giving primarily in NY. No grants to individuals.
Application information: Contributes only to pre-selected organizations.
Trustees: Richard M. Altman; Roger C. Altman; Jurate Kazickas.
EIN: 133944577
Selected grants: The following grants are a representative sample of this grantmaker's funding activity:
$47,500 to Conservation International, Arlington, VA, 2011.
$35,000 to Council on Foreign Relations, New York, NY, 2011.
$25,000 to American Heart Association, Dallas, TX, 2011.
$25,000 to Human Rights First, New York, NY, 2011.
$25,000 to Phoenix House, New York, NY, 2011.
$25,000 to United Negro College Fund, Fairfax, VA, 2011.
$10,000 to City University of New York, New York, NY, 2011.
$1,000 to National Museum of the American Indian, Washington, DC, 2011.

5582
The Altschul Foundation ✧
c/o Daniel L. Kurtz Esq., Skadden Arps
4 Times Sq., 26th Fl.
New York, NY 10036-6522

Incorporated in 1941 in NY.
Donors: Louis Altschul†; Jeanette Cohen Altschul†.
Foundation type: Independent foundation.
Financial data (yr. ended 06/30/13): Assets, $11,821,896 (M); expenditures, $743,350; qualifying distributions, $567,318; giving activities include $563,000 for 55 grants (high: $30,000; low: $1,000).
Purpose and activities: Areas of concern include the arts, education, the environment, health, human services, social action, and youth development.
Fields of interest: Arts; Education; Health care; Human services; Jewish agencies & synagogues.
Type of support: General/operating support; Continuing support; Research.
Limitations: Applications not accepted. Giving primarily in New York, NY. No grants to individuals.
Application information: Contributes only to pre-selected organizations.
Board meeting date(s): 3 times per year
Officers and Trustees:* Susan Rothstein-Schwimmer,* Pres.; William Rothstein,* V.P. and Secy.; Daniel L. Kurtz, Esq.,* Treas.
EIN: 136400009

5583
The Altus One Fund, Inc. ✧
c/o Randall R. Weisenburger
437 Madison Ave., 9th Fl.
New York, NY 10022-7001

Established in 1999 in NY.
Donor: Orchard, Stanwich & Pierce Trusts.
Foundation type: Independent foundation.
Financial data (yr. ended 12/31/13): Assets, $4,569,601 (M); expenditures, $2,260,229; qualifying distributions, $2,239,100; giving activities include $2,239,100 for 25 grants (high: $625,000; low: $700).
Purpose and activities: Giving primarily for the arts, education, health, and human services.
Fields of interest: Performing arts; Higher education; Education; Hospitals (general); Health organizations, association; Medical research, institute; Human services; Foundations (private grantmaking).
Limitations: Applications not accepted. Giving primarily in NY. No grants to individuals.
Application information: Contributes only to pre-selected organizations.
Officers: Randall R. Weisenburger, Pres. and Secy.; John Wren, V.P.
EIN: 510388792

5584
The Alvarez Educational and Charitable Foundation Inc. ✧
c/o Alvarez & Marsal, Inc.
600 Madison Ave., 8th Fl.
New York, NY 10022-4834

Established in 1996 in NJ.
Donors: Abigail C. Alvarez; Antonio C. Alvarez.
Foundation type: Independent foundation.
Financial data (yr. ended 12/31/13): Assets, $3,373,351 (M); gifts received, $2,004,512; expenditures, $888,232.
International interests: Philippines.
Type of support: Scholarship funds.
Limitations: Applications not accepted. Giving primarily in New York, NY; some funding also in the Philippines.
Application information: Unsolicited requests for funds not accepted.
Officers: Antonio C. Alvarez, Pres.; Abigail C. Alvarez, V.P.; Dawn M. Marsal-Wallin, Treas.
EIN: 223479932

5585
American Academy of Arts and Letters ✧
(formerly American Academy & Institute of Arts and Letters)
633 W. 155th St.
New York, NY 10032-7501 (212) 368-5900
Contact: Virginia Dajani, Exec. Dir.
FAX: (212) 491-4615;
E-mail: academy@artsandletters.org; Main URL: http://www.artsandletters.org

Established in 1898 as the National Institute of Arts and Letters. The American Academy of Arts and Letters was founded in 1904. In 1976 the two merged into The American Academy and Institute of Arts and Letters. In 1993, name changed to American Academy of Arts and Letters.
Donors: Mildred B. Strauss†; Channing Pollock†; Archer M. Huntington†; Charles Ives†; Katharine Lane Weems†.
Foundation type: Operating foundation.
Financial data (yr. ended 12/31/13): Assets, $80,370,111 (M); gifts received, $601,737; expenditures, $3,359,157; qualifying distributions, $1,992,110; giving activities include $1,061,083 for grants to individuals, and $2,901,062 for foundation-administered programs.
Purpose and activities: A private operating foundation. Awards by nomination only to individuals for extraordinary achievement in literature, music, and the fine arts. The academy does not give grants. It awards prizes for outstanding artistic achievement.
Fields of interest: Visual arts; Performing arts, music composition; Literature.
Limitations: Applications accepted. Giving on a national basis. No support for the performing arts (except for Richard Rodgers Awards for Musical Theater).
Publications: Informational brochure.
Application information: Applications accepted only for the Richard Rodgers Awards for the Musical Theater. Applications for other prizes not accepted under any circumstances. Award nominations made by membership recommendations only. The Academy will not respond to unsolicited requests for nomination consideration from individuals or organizations. Application form required.
Initial approach: Send SASE for application form for Richard Rodgers Awards for the Musical Theater, or download application from foundation web site
Copies of proposal: 1
Deadline(s): Nov. 1
Final notification: Mar.
Officers and Directors:* Ned Rorem,* Pres.; Will Barnet,* V.P., Art; Varujan Boghosian,* V.P., Art; Jane Wilson,* V.P., Art; Shirley Hazzard, V.P., Literature; Alison Lurie,* V.P., Literature; Ezra Laderman,* V.P., Music; John Hollander,* Secy.; Henry N. Cobb,* Treas.; Virginia Dajani, Exec. Dir.
Number of staff: 8 full-time professional.
EIN: 130429640
Selected grants: The following grants are a representative sample of this grantmaker's funding activity:
$70,000 to Second Stage Theater, New York, NY, 2012. For Richard Rodgers Award for Musical Theater Production Award for Dogfight by Peter Duchan, Benj Pasek, and Justin Paul.
$25,600 to American Academy in Rome, New York, NY, 2012. For Rome Fellowships in Literature Fellowships to two young writers of promise for a one-year residency at the American Academy in Rome.

5586
The American Art Foundation, Inc. ✧
(doing business as The American Contemporary Art Foundation, Inc.)
c/o Lisa Somar
767 5th Ave., 40th Fl.
New York, NY 10153-0003

Established in 1999 in DE and NY.
Donors: Leonard A. Lauder; Mrs. Estee Lauder†; Lauder Foundation, Inc.
Foundation type: Independent foundation.
Financial data (yr. ended 06/30/13): Assets, $35,936,945 (M); gifts received, $9,889,500; expenditures, $3,090,664; qualifying distributions, $2,794,864; giving activities include $2,696,105 for 4 grants (high: $2,150,000; low: $50,000).
Purpose and activities: The foundation acquires, preserves, loans and donates works of art to public museums, libraries, universities, galleries and other institutions for public display and education.
Fields of interest: Museums (art).
Limitations: Applications not accepted. Giving primarily in New York, NY. No grants to individuals.
Application information: Contributes only to pre-selected organizations.
Officers: Leonard A. Lauder, Pres.; Carol Boulanger, V.P.; Meredith Edwards, Secy.; Kevin Dieterich, Treas.
Trustee: William Lauder.
EIN: 134069969

5587
American Express Charitable Fund ✧
200 Vesey St., 48th Fl.
New York, NY 10285-1000
Application address for organizations located outside of Phoenix, AZ, south FL, and Salt Lake City, UT: 3 World Financial Ctr., M.C. 01-48-04, New York, NY 10285-4804; E-mail for Phoenix, AZ: American Express Co., c/o Community Affairs, PhoenixLOIs@aexp.com; E-mail for south Florida: American Express Co., c/o Community Affairs, FtLauderdaleLOIs@aexp.com; E-mail for Salt Lake City, UT: American Express Co., c/o Community Affairs, SaltLakeCityLOIs@aexp.com; Main URL: http://about.americanexpress.com/csr/e-driven.aspx

Established in 2007 in NY.
Donor: American Express.
Foundation type: Company-sponsored foundation.
Financial data (yr. ended 12/31/12): Assets, $8,426,200 (M); expenditures, $9,950,546;

qualifying distributions, $9,950,546; giving activities include $2,836,750 for 254 grants (high: $461,750; low: $500), and $7,042,649 for employee matching gifts.
Purpose and activities: The fund supports programs designed to promote historic preservation; leadership; and community service.
Fields of interest: Arts, cultural/ethnic awareness; Museums; Performing arts; Historic preservation/historical societies; Arts; Higher education; Education; Food services; Disasters, preparedness/services; American Red Cross; YM/YWCAs & YM/YWHAs; Human services; Community/economic development; Foundations (community); United Ways and Federated Giving Programs; Leadership development; Public affairs.
Type of support: General/operating support; Annual campaigns; Building/renovation; Program development; Employee volunteer services; Sponsorships; Employee matching gifts; Employee-related scholarships.
Limitations: Applications accepted. Giving primarily on a national basis in areas of company operations, with emphasis on Phoenix, AZ, Los Angeles and San Francisco, CA, Washington, DC, southern FL, Atlanta, GA, Chicago, IL, Boston, MA, New York, NY, Philadelphia, PA, Dallas and Houston, TX, and Salt Lake City, UT. No support for discriminatory organizations, religious organizations not of direct benefit to the entire community, or political organizations. No grants to individuals (except for employee-related scholarships), or for fundraising, goodwill advertising, souvenir journals, or dinner programs, travel, books, magazines, or articles in professional journals, endowments or capital campaigns, traveling exhibitions, or sports sponsorships.
Publications: Application guidelines; Grants list; Program policy statement.
Application information: A full proposal may be requested at a later date. Historic preservation applications are by invitation only. Leadership applications for youth leadership programs are discouraged. Organizations receiving support of at least $7,500 are asked to provide a final report. Application form required.
Initial approach: Complete online eligibility quiz and application
Deadline(s): None
Final notification: 3 to 4 months
Officers and Trustees:* Timothy J. McClimon,* Pres.; Mary Ellen Craig, Secy.; David L. Yowan, Treas.; Tammy D. Fried, Counsel; Vernon E. Jordan, Jr.; Frank P. Popoff.
EIN: 261607898
Selected grants: The following grants are a representative sample of this grantmaker's funding activity:
$250,000 to American Red Cross National Headquarters, Washington, DC, 2012. For Disaster Relief.
$250,000 to Mayors Fund to Advance New York City, New York, NY, 2012. For Disaster Relief.
$123,500 to JK Group, Global Volunteer Action Fund, Plainsboro, NJ, 2012. For Serve2Gether Grants.
$50,000 to Young at Art Childrens Museum, Davie, FL, 2012.
$45,000 to Community Foundation of Broward, Fort Lauderdale, FL, 2012.
$45,000 to Urban League of Broward County, Fort Lauderdale, FL, 2012.
$30,000 to Arizona State University Foundation for a New American University, Tempe, AZ, 2012.
$25,000 to Volunteer Action Center of Broward County, Lauderhill, FL, 2012.
$10,000 to Child Crisis Center-East Valley, Mesa, AZ, 2012.
$10,000 to Sit-In Movement, Greensboro, NC, 2012.

5588
American Express Foundation ✧
World Financial Ctr.
200 Vesey St., 48th Fl.
New York, NY 10285-4804
Main URL: http://about.americanexpress.com/csr/?inav=about_CorpResponsibility
Grants List: http://about.americanexpress.com/csr/docs/2012grantslist.pdf

Incorporated in 1954 in NY.
Donor: American Express Co.
Foundation type: Company-sponsored foundation.
Financial data (yr. ended 12/31/12): Assets, $2,205,372 (M); gifts received, $2,205,372; expenditures, $8,754,117; qualifying distributions, $8,753,670; giving activities include $8,711,000 for 163 grants (high: $1,000,000; low: $4,000).
Purpose and activities: The foundation supports programs designed to promote historic preservation; leadership; and community service.
Fields of interest: Visual arts; Museums; Performing arts; Historic preservation/historical societies; Arts; Higher education; Education; Hospitals (general); Food services; Food banks; Food distribution, meals on wheels; Disasters, preparedness/services; American Red Cross; Children/youth, services; Human services; Economic development; Nonprofit management; Community/economic development; Foundations (community); Voluntarism promotion; Leadership development; Public affairs.
Type of support: General/operating support; Continuing support; Management development/capacity building; Annual campaigns; Emergency funds; Program development; Conferences/seminars.
Limitations: Applications accepted. Giving on a national and international basis in areas of company operations with emphasis on greater Phoenix, AZ, Los Angeles and San Francisco, CA, Washington, DC, south FL, Atlanta, GA, Chicago, IL, Boston, MA, New York, NY, Philadelphia, PA, Puerto Rico, Houston, TX, Salt Lake City, UT, Argentina, Australia, Canada, China, France, Germany, Hong Kong, India, Italy, Japan, Mexico, Netherlands, Singapore, Spain, Taiwan, and the United Kingdom. No support for discriminatory organizations, religious organizations not of direct benefit to the entire community, or political organizations. No grants to individuals, or for fundraising, goodwill advertising, souvenir journals, or dinner programs, travel, books, magazines, or articles in professional journals, endowments or capital campaigns, traveling exhibitions, or sports sponsorships.
Publications: Application guidelines; Grants list; Program policy statement.
Application information: A full proposal may be requested at a later date. Historic preservation applications are by invitation only. Leadership applications for youth leadership programs are discouraged. Organizations receiving support of at least $7,500 are asked to provide a final report. Application form required.
Initial approach: Complete online eligibility quiz and application
Deadline(s): None
Board meeting date(s): Biannually
Final notification: 3 to 4 months
Officers and Trustees:* Thomas Schick,* Chair.; Timothy J. McClimon, Pres.; Mary Ellen Craig, Compt. and Secy.; Kenneth I. Chenault; Edward P. Gilligan; Daniel T. Henry; Stephen J. Squeri.
EIN: 136123529
Selected grants: The following grants are a representative sample of this grantmaker's funding activity:
$1,000,000 to Smithsonian Institution, Washington, DC, 2012. For special projects.
$375,000 to New York University, New York, NY, 2012. For special projects.
$300,000 to National Academy Foundation, New York, NY, 2012. For leadership.
$158,000 to Common Purpose International, London, England, 2012. For international work.
$150,000 to Feeding America, Chicago, IL, 2012. For community service.
$150,000 to Harlem Childrens Zone, New York, NY, 2012. For community service.
$100,000 to Taproot Foundation, San Francisco, CA, 2012. For community service.
$50,000 to Junior Achievement International China, Raleigh, NC, 2012. For international work.
$40,000 to Asociacion Amigos del Museo Nacional de Bellas Artes, Buenos Aires, Argentina, 2012. For international work.
$25,000 to STRIVE, New York, NY, 2012. For leadership.

5589
American Foundation for Basic Research in Israel ✧
c/o Polakoff
225 W. 34th St., Ste. 1513
New York, NY 10122-1511

Donor: The Cambr Charitable Foundation Trust.
Foundation type: Independent foundation.
Financial data (yr. ended 12/31/12): Assets, $12,563,384 (M); gifts received, $50,000; expenditures, $1,019,161; qualifying distributions, $847,795; giving activities include $804,000 for 2 grants (high: $460,000; low: $344,000).
Fields of interest: Science, research; Science, formal/general education.
Limitations: Applications not accepted. Giving primarily in Jerusalem, Israel. No grants to individuals.
Application information: Contributes only to pre-selected organizations.
Officers and Directors:* Joshua Jortner,* Pres.; Michael A. Varet, Esq.*, V.P.; Alex Keynan,* Secy.; Meir Zadok, M.D.*, Treas.; Michael S. Brown, M.D.; Paul Marks, M.D.; Mark Rattner.
EIN: 133590595

5590
American Friends of Tenuvas Sadie ✧
4918 Ft. Hamilton Pkwy., Ste. 2nd Fl.
Brooklyn, NY 11219-3344 (718) 972-2500
Contact: Norma Dreyfuss, Tr.

Established in 2003 in NY.
Donors: Norma Dreyfuss; Alternate Staffing; Inch Knocker LLC.
Foundation type: Independent foundation.
Financial data (yr. ended 12/31/13): Assets, $201,281 (M); gifts received, $888,135;

expenditures, $687,065; qualifying distributions, $687,000; giving activities include $687,000 for 2 grants (high: $396,000; low: $291,000).
Fields of interest: Jewish agencies & synagogues.
Type of support: General/operating support.
Limitations: Applications not accepted. No grants for individuals.
Application information: Unsolicited requests for funds not accepted.
Trustees: Norma Dreyfuss; Shulamis Gelbwachs.
EIN: 432019169

5591
Ames-Amzalak Memorial Trust ✧ ☆
180 Office Park Way, Ste. 2000
Pittsford, NY 14534-1762
Contact: Myrl S. Gelb, Tr.

Established in 1997 in NY.
Foundation type: Independent foundation.
Financial data (yr. ended 04/30/13): Assets, $5,030,529 (M); expenditures, $586,097; qualifying distributions, $566,226; giving activities include $539,465 for 81 grants (high: $110,000; low: $500).
Fields of interest: Museums; Arts; Education; Hospitals (general); Health organizations; Medical research; Human services; Children/youth, services; Jewish federated giving programs; Christian agencies & churches; Jewish agencies & synagogues.
Limitations: Applications not accepted. Giving primarily in NY. No grants to individuals.
Application information: Contributes only to pre-selected organizations.
Trustees: Jay Gelb; Myrl Gelb; Justin Vigdor, Esq.; Robert Vigdor.
EIN: 161530490
Selected grants: The following grants are a representative sample of this grantmaker's funding activity:
$16,430 to Jewish Home and Infirmary of Rochester New York Foundation, Rochester, NY, 2011.
$14,000 to Mary Cariola Childrens Center, Rochester, NY, 2011.
$8,000 to University of Rochester, Rochester, NY, 2011.
$6,109 to Temple Brith Kodesh, Rochester, NY, 2011.
$3,500 to Sojourner House, Rochester, NY, 2011.
$3,000 to Bivona Child Advocacy Center, Rochester, NY, 2011.
$3,000 to United States Holocaust Memorial Museum, Washington, DC, 2011.
$2,500 to Advertising Council of Rochester, Rochester, NY, 2011.
$2,000 to HCR Cares, Rochester, NY, 2011.
$1,600 to American Cancer Society, Rochester, NY, 2011.

5592
Amicus Foundation Inc. ✧
c/o Philip Mintz
29 W. 38th St., 14th Fl.
New York, NY 10018-2048

Established in 1976.
Foundation type: Independent foundation.
Financial data (yr. ended 10/31/13): Assets, $10,529,548 (M); expenditures, $456,730; qualifying distributions, $424,865; giving activities include $420,000 for 11 grants (high: $175,000; low: $500).
Purpose and activities: Giving primarily to a film festival, as well as for education and hospitals.
Fields of interest: Media, film/video; Education; Hospitals (general); Human services; Foundations (private grantmaking).
Limitations: Applications not accepted. Giving primarily in FL. No grants to individuals.
Application information: Unsolicited requests for funds not accepted.
Officers and Directors:* Leigh Weiner,* Pres.; Sharyn Weiner, V.P.; Theodore Schiffman, Esq.*, Treas.
EIN: 136075489

5593
The Carol A. Ammon Foundation, Inc. ✧
(formerly The Ammon Family Foundation, Inc.)
c/o The Ayco Co., LP
P.O. Box 860
Saratoga Springs, NY 12866-0860

Established in 2004 in NY.
Donor: Carol A. Ammon.
Foundation type: Independent foundation.
Financial data (yr. ended 12/31/13): Assets, $22,499,817 (M); gifts received, $800,002; expenditures, $858,734; qualifying distributions, $686,455; giving activities include $560,000 for grants.
Fields of interest: Higher education; Health organizations, association; Human services.
Type of support: General/operating support.
Limitations: Applications not accepted. Giving primarily in CT and DE. No grants to individuals.
Application information: Contributes only to pre-selected organizations.
Officers and Directors:* Marie E. Pinizzotto, C.E.O. and Exec. Dir.; Carol A. Ammon,* Pres.; Ashley de Simone.
EIN: 202029151

5594
The Ammon Foundation ✧
c/o Sweeney, Gallo, Reich and Bolz LLP
95-25 Queens Blvd., 11th Fl.
Rego Park, NY 11374-4505

Established in 1988 in NY.
Donors: Generosa Ammon†; R. Theodore Ammon†.
Foundation type: Independent foundation.
Financial data (yr. ended 11/30/13): Assets, $12,510,158 (M); expenditures, $628,793; qualifying distributions, $595,898; giving activities include $550,000 for 16 grants (high: $100,000; low: $5,000).
Fields of interest: Education; Hospitals (general); Medical research, institute; Human services; Children/youth, services.
Type of support: General/operating support; Scholarship funds.
Limitations: Applications not accepted. Giving primarily in NY. No grants to individuals.
Application information: Contributes only to pre-selected organizations.
Trustees: Michael G. Dowd; Gerard J. Sweeney.
EIN: 136904321

5595
The Jack and Mimi Leviton Amsterdam Foundation ✧ ☆
71 Broad Brook Rd.
Bedford Hills, NY 10507-2207

Established in 1977 in DE.
Donors: Jack Amsterdam†; Dasha Epstein.
Foundation type: Independent foundation.
Financial data (yr. ended 12/31/13): Assets, $1,810,994 (M); expenditures, $498,424; qualifying distributions, $491,984; giving activities include $484,520 for 56 grants (high: $125,000; low: $100).
Purpose and activities: Giving primarily for the performing arts, education, and medical research.
Fields of interest: Arts; Education; Human services.
Type of support: General/operating support; Research.
Limitations: Applications not accepted. Giving primarily in the New York, NY, area. No grants to individuals.
Application information: Contributes only to pre-selected organizations.
Officers: Dasha Epstein, Pres.; Danielle Epstein, V.P.
EIN: 510220854

5596
Anderson Family Charitable Fund ✧
c/o Bessemer Trust
630 5th Ave.
New York, NY 10111-0100

Established in 2005 in DE.
Donor: Marjorie A. Matheson.
Foundation type: Independent foundation.
Financial data (yr. ended 12/31/13): Assets, $10,952,744 (M); expenditures, $1,859,484.
Fields of interest: Health care, clinics/centers; Health organizations; Human services; Family services.
Type of support: General/operating support.
Limitations: Applications not accepted. Giving primarily in FL and NY. No grants to individuals.
Application information: Contributes only to pre-selected organizations.
Officers and Directors:* Marjorie A. Matheson,* Pres. and Treas.; Holly Hewitt Bard,* Secy.
EIN: 204125250

5597
Keith & Peggy Anderson Family Foundation ✧
c/o R. Mazza, Ayco
P.O. Box 860
Saratoga Springs, NY 12866-0860

Established in 2005 in NY.
Donor: Keith T. Anderson.
Foundation type: Independent foundation.
Financial data (yr. ended 12/31/12): Assets, $20,613,824 (M); gifts received, $5,122,533; expenditures, $2,575,125; qualifying distributions, $2,574,000; giving activities include $2,574,000 for grants.
Fields of interest: Elementary/secondary education; Higher education; Human services.
Limitations: Applications not accepted. Giving primarily in the U.S., with emphasis on NY and TX. No grants to individuals.

Application information: Contributes only to pre-selected organizations.
Officers and Directors:* Keith T. Anderson,* Pres. and Treas.; Peggy A. Anderson,* V.P. and Secy.; Clint D. Carlson.
EIN: 203268603

5598
Andor Capital Management Foundation ✧
c/o Andor Capital Mgmt., LLC
4 International Dr., Ste. 100
Rye Brook, NY 10573-1065

Established in 2001 in CT.
Donors: Daniel C. Benton; Douglas Mueller; Aimee Mueller; Peter Streinger; Kevin O'Brien; Jeanine O'Brien; Charlie Hannigan; Katherine Bailon; Julia Dailey; John Levinson; Ellen Levinson; Cheryl Warren; Moshe Metzger; Jose Fernandez; Nancy Fernandez; Walter G. Schendel III; Mark Bertagnolli; Robert Boroujerdi; Michael Fisher; Seth Ostrie.
Foundation type: Independent foundation.
Financial data (yr. ended 08/31/13): Assets, $13,255,291 (M); expenditures, $3,232,260; qualifying distributions, $3,231,390; giving activities include $3,227,000 for 15 grants (high: $1,000,000; low: $5,000).
Purpose and activities: Giving primarily to human service organizations, including organizations which support the families of fallen and/or injured military personnel; funding also for children and family services, as well as for programs and services to families who have lost loved ones on Sept. 11, 2001.
Fields of interest: Hospitals (specialty); Disasters, 9/11/01; Safety/disasters; Human services; Children/youth, services; Family services; Military/veterans.
Limitations: Applications not accepted. Giving primarily in CT, and New York, NY. No grants to individuals.
Application information: Contributes only to pre-selected organizations.
Officers: Stella Buono, Pres.; Kevin O'Brien, Secy.
Director: Daniel Benton.
EIN: 061631047

5599
The Androcles Foundation, Inc. ✧
c/o Lamb & Barnosky, LLP
534 Broadhollow Rd., Ste. 210
Melville, NY 11747-9034

Established in 2004 in NY.
Donors: LLYR Charitable Annuity Trust; Jane H. Perkins Charitable Lead Annuity Trust.
Foundation type: Independent foundation.
Financial data (yr. ended 12/31/13): Assets, $39,614,045 (M); gifts received, $4,311,012; expenditures, $1,823,976; qualifying distributions, $1,551,211; giving activities include $1,500,000 for 57 grants (high: $65,000; low: $10,000).
Fields of interest: Education; Animal welfare; Health care; Food services; Housing/shelter, development; Human services; Foundations (private grantmaking).
Limitations: Applications not accepted. Giving in the U.S., with emphasis on CA, Washington, DC, and NY. No grants to individuals.
Application information: Contributes only to pre-selected organizations.
Officers: Jennifer Perkins Fitzgerald, Pres.; Roy Perkins, Sr. V.P.; Timothy Perkins, Secy.-Treas.
EIN: 201514742
Selected grants: The following grants are a representative sample of this grantmaker's funding activity:
$80,000 to Challenged Athletes Foundation, San Diego, CA, 2012. To support Physically Disabled During Physical Fitness and Competitive Athletics.
$50,000 to Direct Relief International, Santa Barbara, CA, 2012. For hurricane disaster relief.
$45,000 to New York Public Library, New York, NY, 2012. For educational charity.
$35,000 to Gallery North, Setauket, NY, 2012. For contemporary art museum.
$30,000 to Project Medishare for Haiti, Miami, FL, 2012. For Sharing Human and Technical Resources with its Haitian Partners to Achieve Quality Healthcare and Development Services for All.
$20,000 to Catholic Charities of the Diocese of Santa Rosa, Santa Rosa, CA, 2012. For religious charitable grant.
$20,000 to Ceres Community Project, Sebastopol, CA, 2012. For Community Outreach by Teaching Healthy Consumption for People, Communities and the Planet through Organic Foods.
$20,000 to Food Animal Concerns Trust, Chicago, IL, 2012. For Public Health Concerns.
$20,000 to Redwood Gospel Mission, Santa Rosa, CA, 2012. For Ending Community Hunger.
$10,000 to Polaris Project, Washington, DC, 2012. For Combat Human Trafficking and Modern-Day Slavery.

5600
Angel Foundation ✧
c/o Bessemer Trust Co., N.A.
630 5th Ave.
New York, NY 10111-0100

Established in 2006 in NY.
Donors: Edward T. Anderson; Angel Charitable Remainder Annuity Trust.
Foundation type: Independent foundation.
Financial data (yr. ended 12/31/13): Assets, $10,904,168 (M); gifts received, $3,380,725; expenditures, $2,832,615; qualifying distributions, $2,771,160; giving activities include $2,757,500 for 21 grants (high: $1,250,000; low: $500).
Fields of interest: Elementary/secondary education; Higher education; Education.
Limitations: Applications not accepted. Giving primarily in MA. No grants to individuals.
Application information: Contributes only to pre-selected organizations.
Trustee: Bessemer Trust Co., N.A.
EIN: 204591909
Selected grants: The following grants are a representative sample of this grantmaker's funding activity:
$251,500 to Noble and Greenough School, Dedham, MA, 2011.
$126,000 to Dedham Country Day School, Dedham, MA, 2011.
$47,000 to Neighborhood House Charter School, Dorchester, MA, 2011.
$25,000 to Cape Eleuthera Foundation, Lawrenceville, NJ, 2011.
$20,000 to Conservation Law Foundation, Boston, MA, 2011.
$5,000 to Miss Porters School, Farmington, CT, 2011.
$2,500 to Maine Coast Heritage Trust, Topsham, ME, 2011.
$1,000 to Cotting School, Lexington, MA, 2011.

5601
Animal Farm Foundation, Inc. ✧ ☆
P.O. Box 624
Bangall, NY 12506-0624
E-mail: grantsandawards@animalfarmfoundation.org; Main URL: http://www.animalfarmfoundation.org
Facebook: https://www.facebook.com/animalfarmfoundation
Flickr: https://www.flickr.com/photos/animalfarmfoundation
Pinterest: http://www.pinterest.com/animalfarmfndtn/
Twitter: https://twitter.com/AnimalFarmFndtn
Vimeo: http://vimeo.com/animalfarmfoundation
Wordpress: http://animalfarmfoundation.wordpress.com/

Established in 1985 in NY.
Donors: Jane R. Berkey; Sam Dworkis; Andrew Saul; Denise Saul.
Foundation type: Independent foundation.
Financial data (yr. ended 06/30/13): Assets, $2,537,589 (M); gifts received, $2,893,000; expenditures, $1,856,121; qualifying distributions, $1,792,103; giving activities include $456,324 for 233 grants (high: $16,550; low: $50).
Purpose and activities: Giving primarily to secure equal treatment and opportunity for pit bull dogs.
Fields of interest: Animal welfare.
Type of support: General/operating support.
Limitations: Applications not accepted. Giving primarily in MO. No grants to individuals.
Application information: Unsolicited requests for funds not accepted.
Officers: Jane R. Berkey, Pres.; Peggy Gordijn, V.P.; Donald Cleary, Secy.-Treas.; Stacey Coleman, Exec. Dir.
Board Members: Diana M. Gurieva; Andrew Saul; Ledy Vankavage, Esq.
EIN: 222386955
Selected grants: The following grants are a representative sample of this grantmaker's funding activity:
$1,000 to Animal Legal Defense Fund, Cotati, CA, 2011.

5602
The Aotearoa Foundation ✧
c/o Deborah A. Rutigliano
101 Park Ave.
New York, NY 10178-0002
GiveSmart: http://www.givesmart.org/Stories/Donors/Julian-Robertson,-Jr-
Julian H. Robertson, Jr.'s Giving Pledge Profile: http://glasspockets.org/philanthropy-in-focus/eye-on-the-giving-pledge/profiles/robertson

Established in 2004 in NY.
Donors: Josephine T. Robertson†; Julian H. Robertson, Jr.
Foundation type: Independent foundation.
Financial data (yr. ended 12/31/12): Assets, $37,172,519 (M); expenditures, $1,700,372; qualifying distributions, $1,690,362; giving activities include $1,473,569 for 7 grants (high: $748,717; low: $7,754).

Fields of interest: Higher education; Education; Environment, natural resources.
Limitations: Applications not accepted. Giving primarily in New York, NY, and New Zealand; some giving also in San Francisco, CA. No grants to individuals.
Application information: Contributes only to pre-selected organizations.
Trustees: John Hood; Julian H. Robertson, Jr.
EIN: 201464742

5603
Appel Family Foundation ✧
c/o Robert J. Appel
700 Park Ave.
New York, NY 10021-4930

Established in 1997 in NY.
Donors: Robert Appel; Helen Appel; Susan C. Slavin; Debra L. Weinberg.
Foundation type: Independent foundation.
Financial data (yr. ended 06/30/13): Assets, $51,260 (M); expenditures, $490,000; qualifying distributions, $490,000; giving activities include $490,000 for grants.
Fields of interest: Arts; Education; Human services.
Type of support: General/operating support.
Limitations: Applications not accepted. Giving primarily in NY. No grants to individuals.
Application information: Unsolicited requests for funds not accepted.
Directors: Helen Appel; Robert Appel; Susan C. Slavin; Debra L. Weinreich.
EIN: 113433017

5604
The Appleman Foundation, Inc. ✧
c/o Bessemer Trust Co.
630 5th Ave.
New York, NY 10111-0001

Incorporated in 1952 in FL.
Donors: Nathan Appleman†; Appleman Charitable Trust; and members of the Appleman family.
Foundation type: Independent foundation.
Financial data (yr. ended 12/31/13): Assets, $32,222,105 (M); expenditures, $9,820,354; qualifying distributions, $9,728,621; giving activities include $9,686,128 for 48 grants (high: $6,750,000; low: $200).
Purpose and activities: Giving primarily for Jewish organizations; funding also for hospitals, the arts, and human services.
Fields of interest: Arts; Education; Hospitals (general); Human services; Jewish federated giving programs; Jewish agencies & synagogues.
Type of support: Research.
Limitations: Applications not accepted. Giving primarily in New York, NY. No grants to individuals.
Application information: Contributes only to pre-selected organizations.
Officers: Susan A. Unterberg, Pres.; Ellen Unterberg Celli, V.P.; James Satloff, Secy.-Treas.
EIN: 136154978

5605
Hyman & Ann Arbesfeld Foundation Inc. ✧ ☆
c/o San Carlos
150 E. 50th St.
New York, NY 10022-9500 (212) 697-4800
Contact: Hyman Arbesfeld, Dir.

Established in 1984 in NY.
Donors: Ann Arbesfeld; Hyman Arbesfeld.
Foundation type: Independent foundation.
Financial data (yr. ended 11/30/13): Assets, $6,964,940 (M); gifts received, $1,886,141; expenditures, $837,832; qualifying distributions, $833,460; giving activities include $832,635 for 97 grants (high: $737,000; low: $18).
Purpose and activities: Support for Jewish educational institutions and service organizations.
Fields of interest: Theological school/education; Education; Human services; Jewish agencies & synagogues.
Type of support: General/operating support.
Limitations: Applications accepted. Giving primarily in New York, NY. No grants to individuals.
Publications: Annual report.
Application information: Application form required.
Initial approach: Letter
Deadline(s): None
Board meeting date(s): Dec., June
Directors: Ann Arbesfeld; Benjamin Arbesfeld; Hyman Arbesfeld.
EIN: 133253358

5606
Archangel Michael Foundation ✧
c/o Bessemer Trust Co.
630 5th Ave.
New York, NY 10111-0100

Established in 1998 in CA.
Donor: Michael Huffington.
Foundation type: Independent foundation.
Financial data (yr. ended 09/30/13): Assets, $8,722,636 (M); expenditures, $483,269; qualifying distributions, $435,852; giving activities include $425,003 for 2 grants (high: $425,000; low: $3).
Fields of interest: Medical school/education; Education; Foundations (private grantmaking).
Limitations: Applications not accepted. Giving primarily in CA. No grants to individuals.
Application information: Contributes only to pre-selected organizations.
Trustee: Michael Huffington.
EIN: 957059949
Selected grants: The following grants are a representative sample of this grantmaker's funding activity:
$500,000 to Saint Sophia Foundation, Los Angeles, CA, 2011.

5607
Arctos Foundation ✧ ☆
c/o Crowe Horwath LLP
488 Madison Ave., 3rd Fl.
New York, NY 10022-5734

Donor: George Vojta†.
Foundation type: Independent foundation.
Financial data (yr. ended 12/31/12): Assets, $9,588,860 (M); gifts received, $3,981,176; expenditures, $3,849,813; qualifying distributions, $3,765,057; giving activities include $3,722,000 for 11 grants (high: $3,530,000; low: $2,000).
Fields of interest: Education; Human services.
Limitations: Applications not accepted. Giving in the U.S., with some emphasis on GA and MN.
Application information: Unsolicited requests for funds not accepted.
Officer and Directors:* Christopher Vojta,* Pres.; Timothy Vojta.
EIN: 800561039

5608
Arcus Foundation
(formerly Jon L. Stryker Foundation)
44 W. 28th St., 17th Fl.
New York, NY 10001-4212 (212) 488-3000
Contact: Carol Snapp, Comms. Mgr.
FAX: (212) 488-3010; Main URL: http://www.arcusfoundation.org
Arcus Foundation's Philanthropy Promise: http://www.ncrp.org/philanthropys-promise/who
Arcus Great Apes: https://www.facebook.com/arcusgreatapes
Arcus Great Apes: https://plus.google.com/114673463697672363328/posts
Arcus Great Apes: https://twitter.com/ArcusGreatApes
Arcus LGBT: https://www.facebook.com/arcuslgbt
Arcus LGBT: https://plus.google.com/108620803757236306194/posts
Arcus LGBT: https://twitter.com/ArcusLGBT
E-Newsletter: http://www.arcusfoundation.org/news/
Grants Database: http://www.arcusfoundation.org/grantees/

Established in 1997 in MI.
Donor: Jon L. Stryker.
Foundation type: Independent foundation.
Financial data (yr. ended 12/31/13): Assets, $169,472,585 (M); gifts received, $16,943,465; expenditures, $39,031,711; qualifying distributions, $38,817,986; giving activities include $30,035,825 for 285 grants (high: $4,599,299; low: $24).
Purpose and activities: The mission of the foundation is to achieve social justice that is inclusive of sexual orientation, gender identity and race, and to ensure conservation and respect of the great apes.
Fields of interest: Animals/wildlife, endangered species; Animals/wildlife, sanctuaries; Animals/wildlife, special services; Civil/human rights, LGBTQ; Civil/human rights; LGBTQ.
Type of support: General/operating support; Management development/capacity building; Capital campaigns; Building/renovation; Endowments; Program development; Conferences/seminars; Publication; Curriculum development; Technical assistance; Consulting services; Program evaluation; Employee matching gifts; Matching/challenge support.
Limitations: Applications accepted. Giving on a national basis, with some emphasis on MI, especially southwest MI. Giving on an international basis, with emphasis on Africa, the Middle East and Southeast Asia. No support for lobby groups or political campaigns. No grants to individuals, or for religious or political activities, scholarships, or for medical research or film production projects.
Publications: Annual report (including application guidelines); Newsletter.

Application information: After review of funding request, the foundation may request a Letter of Inquiry and a subsequent full Proposal, which includes the submission of additional organizational and project-specific documentation. Application form not required.

Initial approach: Online submission of initial funding concept

Deadline(s): Varies

Board meeting date(s): Four board meetings annually

Final notification: 3-4 weeks after initial funding request is received

Officers and Directors:* Jon L. Stryker,* Pres.; Annette Lanjouw, V.P., Strategic Initiatives and Great Apes Prog.; Jason McGill, V.P., Social Justice Prog.; Thomas W. Nichols, V.P., Finance and Opers.; Cindy Rizzo, V.P., Impact and Learning; Bryan E. Simmons, V.P., Global Comms.; Linda Ho, Cont.; Kevin Jennings, Exec. Dir.; Stephen Bennett; Evelynn M. Hammonds; Janet Mock; Catherine Pino; Slobodan Randjelovic; Jeff Trandahl; Darren Walker.

Number of staff: 21

EIN: 383332791

Selected grants: The following grants are a representative sample of this grantmaker's funding activity:

$2,700,000 to Save the Chimps, Fort Pierce, FL, 2012. For chimpanzee care and organizational management and development.

$1,000,000 to Jane Goodall Institute for Wildlife Research, Education and Conservation, Vienna, VA, 2012. For Implementation of Great Apes CAP, payable over 3.00 years.

$1,000,000 to United States Department of State, Washington, DC, 2012. For Global Equality Fund, payable over 1.25 years.

$600,000 to Astraea Lesbian Foundation for Justice, New York, NY, 2012. For LGBT Racial Justice Collaborative Fund, payable over 2.00 years.

$600,000 to The Orangutan Project, South Perth, Austria, 2012. For Hutan-Kinabatangan Orangutan Conservation Project in Saba, Malaysia, payable over 3.00 years.

$400,000 to Center for American Progress, Washington, DC, 2012. For State Marriages Initiatives.

$400,000 to Community Initiatives, San Francisco, CA, 2012. For Council for Global Equality, payable over 2.00 years.

$400,000 to Lukuru Wildlife Research Foundation, Circleville, OH, 2012. For Community Integration into Protection of the TL2 Landscape, payable over 2.00 years.

$216,160 to African Wildlife Foundation, Washington, DC, 2012. For International Gorilla Conservation Programme.

$100,000 to Equal Rights Trust, London, England, 2012. For Promoting LGBT Rights in Kenya.

5609
Jerome & Lorraine Aresty Charitable Foundation ✧

c/o Alfred Dunner, Inc.
1411 Broadway
New York, NY 10018-3496

Established in 2003 in NJ and FL.

Donors: Jerome Aresty; Lorraine Aresty.

Foundation type: Independent foundation.

Financial data (yr. ended 12/31/13): Assets, $22,600,464 (M); gifts received, $1,000,000; expenditures, $1,222,615; qualifying distributions, $1,165,310; giving activities include $1,123,000 for 47 grants (high: $200,000; low: $500).

Fields of interest: Education; Agriculture/food; Human services; Jewish federated giving programs; Jewish agencies & synagogues.

Limitations: Applications not accepted. Giving in the U.S., with emphasis on CA, CO, and FL. No grants to individuals.

Application information: Unsolicited requests for funds not accepted.

Officers: Lorraine Aresty, Pres.; James Aresty, Secy.

Trustee: Karen Kustel.

EIN: 061725894

Selected grants: The following grants are a representative sample of this grantmaker's funding activity:

$100,000 to Jewish Federation of South Palm Beach County, Boca Raton, FL, 2011. For general fund.

$50,000 to Morristown Memorial Hospital, Morristown, NJ, 2011. For general fund.

$10,000 to American Civil Liberties Union, New York, NY, 2011. For general fund.

$10,000 to NARAL Pro-Choice America, Washington, DC, 2011. For general fund.

$7,500 to 10,000 Degrees, San Rafael, CA, 2011. For general fund.

$7,500 to Central Asia Institute, Bozeman, MT, 2011. For general fund.

$7,500 to Glide Foundation, San Francisco, CA, 2011. For general fund.

$7,500 to Project Open Hand, San Francisco, CA, 2011. For general fund.

$5,000 to Environmental Defense Fund, New York, NY, 2011. For general fund.

$5,000 to Rocky Mountain Institute, Snowmass, CO, 2011. For general fund.

5610
The Catherine and Joseph Aresty Foundation Inc. ✧

c/o Alfred Dunner, Inc.
1411 Broadway
New York, NY 10018-3496

Established in 1997 in NY; funded in 2002.

Donors: Joseph Aresty; Catherine Aresty; Steven Aresty.

Foundation type: Independent foundation.

Financial data (yr. ended 07/31/13): Assets, $18,265,001 (M); expenditures, $1,014,241; qualifying distributions, $992,509; giving activities include $902,500 for 27 grants (high: $100,000; low: $7,500).

Fields of interest: Historical activities; Education; Health care; Human services; Christian agencies & churches; Hispanics/Latinos.

Limitations: Applications not accepted. Giving primarily in New York, NY. No grants to individuals.

Application information: Contributes only to pre-selected organizations.

Officers: Catherine Aresty, Chair.; Joseph Aresty, Vice-Chair.; Steven Aresty, Secy.-Treas.

EIN: 133962647

Selected grants: The following grants are a representative sample of this grantmaker's funding activity:

$50,000 to City Harvest, New York, NY, 2011. For general fund.

$50,000 to Food Bank for New York City, New York, NY, 2011. For general fund.

$50,000 to Planned Parenthood of New York City, New York, NY, 2011. For general fund.

$25,000 to University of Pennsylvania, Philadelphia, PA, 2011. For general fund.

$25,000 to West Side Campaign Against Hunger, New York, NY, 2011. For general fund.

$7,500 to Jay Heritage Center, Rye, NY, 2011. For general fund.

$6,000 to Symphony Space, New York, NY, 2011. For general fund.

$2,500 to Emelin Theater, Mamaroneck, NY, 2011. For general fund.

$2,500 to Fresh Air Fund, New York, NY, 2011. For general fund.

5611
Arkell Hall Foundation, Inc. ✧

P.O. Box 240
Canajoharie, NY 13317-0240 (518) 673-5417
Contact: Joseph A. Santangelo, Pres.
Additional address: 68 Front St., Canajoharie, NY 13317; Main URL: http://www.arkell.org

Incorporated in 1948 in NY.

Donor: Mrs. F.E. Barbour†.

Foundation type: Independent foundation.

Financial data (yr. ended 11/30/13): Assets, $55,439,955 (M); gifts received, $91,306; expenditures, $2,934,675; qualifying distributions, $2,345,844; giving activities include $929,082 for 33 grants (high: $546,612; low: $45), and $1,433,762 for 1 foundation-administered program.

Purpose and activities: The foundation maintains multi-purpose senior citizen residential and service facilities in Canajoharie, NY; it also does general local giving, with emphasis on higher education, including scholarship funds, hospitals, and health and social services, including youth agencies.

Fields of interest: Arts; Education; Youth development.

Type of support: Building/renovation; Equipment; Scholarship funds.

Limitations: Applications not accepted. Giving limited to Canajoharie, NY. No grants to individuals, or for multi-year commitments, travel, conferences or other personal expenses; no loans.

Application information: The foundation is not accepting proposals at this time. See foundation web site for updates in this area.

Board meeting date(s): Feb., May, Aug., and Oct.

Officers: Joseph A. Santangelo, Pres.; Ron Limoncelli, V.P.; Charles Tallent, Treas.

Trustees: Joyce Dresser; Carol Edwards; William Smith.

Number of staff: 2 full-time professional; 1 part-time professional; 2 full-time support.

EIN: 141343077

5612
Louis Armstrong Educational Foundation, Inc. ✧

c/o Howard Schain
10 E. 40th St., Ste. 2710
New York, NY 10016-0301

Established in 1988 in NY.

Donor: Lucille Armstrong†.

Foundation type: Independent foundation.

Financial data (yr. ended 06/30/13): Assets, $3,684,699 (M); gifts received, $4,000; expenditures, $830,473; qualifying distributions, $560,000; giving activities include $560,000 for 16 grants (high: $180,000; low: $5,000).

Purpose and activities: Giving primarily for education and the musical arts.
Fields of interest: Performing arts centers; Performing arts, music; Arts; Higher education; Education; Hospitals (general).
Limitations: Applications not accepted. Giving primarily in the greater metropolitan New York, NY, area. No grants to individuals.
Application information: Contributes only to pre-selected organizations.
Officers: Stanley Crouch, Pres.; Robin Bell-Stevens, V.P.; Edward Berman, Secy.; Howard Schain, Treas.; Jackie Harris, Exec. Dir.
Directors: David Chevan; Lisa Cohen; Oscar Cohen; Gwen DeLuca; Susan Devens; Wynton Marsalis; Dan Morgenstern; Robert O'Meally; Jeffrey Rosenstock; George Wein.
EIN: 132659286

5613
The Armstrong Foundation, Inc. ✧ ☆
c/o The Ayco Co., LP-NTG
P.O. Box 15014
Albany, NY 12212-5014

Donors: C. Michael Armstrong; Sarah Anne Armstrong; Armstrong Family Foundation.
Foundation type: Independent foundation.
Financial data (yr. ended 10/31/13): Assets, $31,044,378 (M); gifts received, $27,917,492; expenditures, $590,826; qualifying distributions, $517,817; giving activities include $517,817 for 54 grants (high: $50,000; low: $500).
Fields of interest: Arts; Health care; Human services; Christian agencies & churches.
Limitations: Applications not accepted. Giving primarily in Naples, FL.
Application information: Unsolicited requests for funds not accepted.
Officers: C. Michael Armstrong, Pres.; Sarah Anne Armstrong, Secy.; Linda Rittenhouse, Treas.
EIN: 461632281

5614
Arnhold Foundation, Inc. ✧
c/o Joel E. Sammet & Co., LLP
15 Maiden Ln., Ste. 500
New York, NY 10038-5117 (212) 269-8628

Established in 1988 in NY.
Donors: Henry H. Arnhold; John P. Arnhold; Bruder-Stiftung; Clarisse Arnhold; Michele Arnhold†.
Foundation type: Independent foundation.
Financial data (yr. ended 12/31/12): Assets, $336,292,609 (M); gifts received, $2,015,761; expenditures, $16,881,221; qualifying distributions, $14,217,917; giving activities include $14,201,917 for 194 grants (high: $6,298,250; low: $100).
Purpose and activities: Giving primarily to arts and cultural programs, education, natural resource conservation and protection, animal welfare and human services.
Fields of interest: Museums; Performing arts; Arts; Education; Environment, natural resources; Animal welfare; Human services.
Limitations: Applications not accepted. Giving primarily in CT and in New York, NY. No grants to individuals.
Application information: Contributes only to pre-selected organizations.
Officers: Henry H. Arnhold, Pres.; John P. Arnhold, Secy.-Treas.
EIN: 133456684

5615
The Arnow Family Fund, Inc. ✧
675 3rd Ave., 27th Fl.
New York, NY 10017

Established in 1984 in NY.
Donors: Robert H. Arnow; Joan W. Arnow.
Foundation type: Independent foundation.
Financial data (yr. ended 12/31/13): Assets, $24,927,847 (M); expenditures, $1,389,760; qualifying distributions, $1,179,833; giving activities include $1,145,000 for 17 grants (high: $235,000; low: $25,000).
Purpose and activities: Giving for higher education, Jewish temples, art and cultural organizations, and human services.
Fields of interest: Arts; Higher education; Human services; Jewish agencies & synagogues.
Limitations: Applications not accepted. Giving primarily in NY. No grants to individuals.
Application information: Contributes only to pre-selected organizations.
Officers and Directors:* David Arnow,* Pres.; Peter Arnow,* V.P.; Joshua Arnow,* Secy.; Ruth Arnow,* Treas.; Kathi Arnow; Madeleine J. Arnow; Elyse Arnow Brill.
EIN: 133188773

5616
J. Aron Charitable Foundation, Inc. ✧
c/o Aleen Goldberg
100 Jericho Quadrangle
Jericho, NY 11753 (212) 832-3405

Incorporated in 1934 in NY.
Donors: Nicole A. Hardin Trust; Members of the Aron family.
Foundation type: Independent foundation.
Financial data (yr. ended 12/31/13): Assets, $6,033,677 (M); gifts received, $6,659; expenditures, $1,212,227; qualifying distributions, $1,047,120; giving activities include $861,130 for 61 grants (high: $260,000; low: $350).
Purpose and activities: Giving primarily for hospitals and health associations, cultural programs, social service and youth agencies, Jewish welfare funds, education, and to an oceanographic institute.
Fields of interest: Museums; Arts; Higher education; Education; Hospitals (general); Health organizations, association; Medical research, institute; Human services; Youth, services; Jewish federated giving programs; Marine science.
Type of support: General/operating support; Annual campaigns; Capital campaigns; Building/renovation; Program development; Research.
Limitations: Applications not accepted. Giving in the U.S., with emphasis on CT, New Orleans, LA, and New York, NY. No grants to individuals.
Application information: Contributes only to pre-selected organizations.
Board meeting date(s): Apr., July, Sept., and Dec.
Officers and Directors:* Peter A. Aron,* Pres. and Exec. Dir.; Hans G. Jepson,* V.P. and Secy.-Treas.; Robert Aron,* V.P.; Charles R. Schulman; Ronald Stein; Martha Ward.
Number of staff: 2 full-time professional; 1 full-time support; 1 part-time support.
EIN: 136068230

5617
The Jeffrey H. and Shari L. Aronson Family Foundation ✧
c/o BCRS Associates, LLC
77 Water St., 9th Fl.
New York, NY 10005-4401

Established in 2005 in NY.
Donor: Jeffrey H. Aronson.
Foundation type: Independent foundation.
Financial data (yr. ended 12/31/13): Assets, $102,053,966 (M); gifts received, $30,000,000; expenditures, $2,545,365; qualifying distributions, $2,367,461; giving activities include $2,331,426 for 45 grants (high: $1,007,100; low: $500).
Fields of interest: Higher education; Jewish federated giving programs; Jewish agencies & synagogues.
Limitations: Applications not accepted. Giving primarily in Baltimore, MD, and New York, NY. No grants to individuals.
Application information: Contributes only to pre-selected organizations.
Trustees: Jeffrey H. Aronson; Shari L. Aronson.
EIN: 206760231
Selected grants: The following grants are a representative sample of this grantmaker's funding activity:
$552,600 to Johns Hopkins University, Baltimore, MD, 2011.
$100,000 to New York University, New York, NY, 2011.
$10,000 to Jewish Museum, New York, NY, 2011.
$10,000 to Jewish Museum, New York, NY, 2011.
$10,000 to Teach for America, New York, NY, 2011.
$5,000 to American Jewish Committee, New York, NY, 2011.
$5,000 to University of Pittsburgh, Pittsburgh, PA, 2011.
$5,000 to White Plains Hospital Center, White Plains, NY, 2011.

5618
The Arrison Family Charitable Foundation ✧
35 Lincoln Pkwy.
Buffalo, NY 14222-1229 (716) 881-0760
Contact: Clement R. Arrison, Tr.

Established in 1989 in NY.
Foundation type: Independent foundation.
Financial data (yr. ended 12/31/12): Assets, $1,311,658 (M); expenditures, $557,062; qualifying distributions, $551,825; giving activities include $551,825 for 2 grants (high: $500,000; low: $51,825).
Purpose and activities: Giving primarily to a private foundation; support also for the performing arts and human services.
Fields of interest: Performing arts, orchestras; Human services; Foundations (private grantmaking).
Limitations: Applications accepted. Giving primarily in Buffalo, NY.
Application information: Application form not required.
Initial approach: Proposal
Deadline(s): None

Trustees: Clement R. Arrison; Craig Arrison; Karen Arrison; Barbara Regan.
EIN: 223021980

5619
Ashner Family Evergreen Foundation ✧
2 Jericho Plz., Wing A, Ste. 111
Jericho, NY 11753-1681

Established in 2003 in NY.
Donors: Michael Ashner; Susan Ashner.
Foundation type: Independent foundation.
Financial data (yr. ended 12/31/13): Assets, $3,410,044 (M); gifts received, $768,794; expenditures, $1,034,962; qualifying distributions, $978,992; giving activities include $978,992 for 34 grants (high: $603,830; low: $100).
Fields of interest: Hospitals (general); Human services; Jewish federated giving programs; Children/youth; Children; Military/veterans.
Type of support: Scholarship funds; Continuing support; Building/renovation; Annual campaigns.
Limitations: Applications not accepted. Giving on a national basis and in Israel. No support for political organizations.
Application information: Unsolicited requests for funds not accepted.
Officers: Susan Ashner, Pres.; Michael Ashner, Secy.-Treas.
Number of staff: 1 part-time support.
EIN: 010772925
Selected grants: The following grants are a representative sample of this grantmaker's funding activity:
$26,000 to North Shore Hebrew Academy, Great Neck, NY, 2011.
$6,000 to Center for Jewish History, New York, NY, 2011.
$3,600 to Mid-Island Y Jewish Community Center, Plainview, NY, 2011.
$2,500 to America-Israel Cultural Foundation, New York, NY, 2011.
$2,000 to Susan G. Komen for the Cure, Philadelphia, PA, 2011.
$1,000 to Doc to Dock, Brooklyn, NY, 2011.
$1,000 to Dowling College, Oakdale, NY, 2011.

5620
The Assael Foundation ✧
589 5th Ave., Ste. 1154
New York, NY 10017

Established in 1992 in NY.
Donors: Salvador J. Assael; Baruch Assael; Esther Posin; Christina Lang Assael.
Foundation type: Independent foundation.
Financial data (yr. ended 12/31/13): Assets, $4,001,818 (M); expenditures, $893,757; qualifying distributions, $881,842; giving activities include $875,000 for 7 grants (high: $554,000; low: $1,000).
Purpose and activities: Giving primarily for education and the arts.
Fields of interest: Arts, cultural/ethnic awareness; Museums; Performing arts; Arts; Elementary/secondary education; Education, special; Education; Children, services; International development; Jewish agencies & synagogues.
International interests: Israel.
Limitations: Applications not accepted. Giving primarily in NY, with emphasis on the New York metropolitan area. No grants to individuals.
Application information: Contributes only to pre-selected organizations.
Officers: Christina Lang Assael, Chair. and Pres.; Bandana Kumar, Secy.-Treas.
Trustees: Marc D. Angel; John D. Block; Ephraim Propp; Benjamin Zucker.
EIN: 133683069

5621
Assurant Foundation ✧
(formerly Fortis Foundation)
1 Chase Manhattan Plz., 41st Fl.
New York, NY 10005
Main URL: http://www.assurant.com/about/corporateresponsibility/assurant_foundation.html

Established in 1982 in NY.
Donors: Time Insurance Co.; Fortis Insurance Co.; Fortis, Inc.; Fortis Benefits Insurance Co.; Assurant, Inc.
Foundation type: Company-sponsored foundation.
Financial data (yr. ended 12/31/12): Assets, $9,603,401 (M); gifts received, $1,803,071; expenditures, $3,127,494; qualifying distributions, $3,048,367; giving activities include $2,564,540 for 350 grants (high: $351,406; low: $50), and $483,827 for 1 employee matching gift.
Purpose and activities: The foundation supports organizations involved with education, health, nutrition, housing, human services, and community development. Special emphasis is directed toward health and wellness; homes and property; and hometown help.
Fields of interest: Museums (art); Education; Health care; Nutrition; Housing/shelter; Family services; Human services; Community/economic development.
Type of support: General/operating support; Program development; Employee matching gifts.
Limitations: Applications not accepted. Giving primarily in areas of company operations in the New York, NY, metropolitan area. No support for religious or political organizations. No grants to individuals or for lobbying or fundraising.
Trustees: Robert Pollock; Sylvia Wagner; Allen Walker.
EIN: 133156497

5622
The Atlantic Foundation of New York ✧ ☆
c/o The Atlantic Philanthropies
75 Varick St., 17th Fl.
New York, NY 10017-1950 (212) 916-7300
E-mail: USA@atlanticphilanthropies.org
Charles F. Feeney's Giving Pledge Profile: http://glasspockets.org/philanthropy-in-focus/eye-on-the-giving-pledge/profiles/feeney

Established in 1989 in NY.
Donors: Atlan Management Corp.; Interpacific Holdings, Inc.; General Atlantic Corp.
Foundation type: Independent foundation.
Financial data (yr. ended 12/31/13): Assets, $4,912,777 (M); expenditures, $2,330,118; qualifying distributions, $2,316,641; giving activities include $2,316,641 for 11 grants (high: $500,000; low: $100,000).
Purpose and activities: The purpose of the foundation is to bring about lasting changes that will improve the lives of disadvantaged and vulnerable people.
Fields of interest: Human services; Native Americans/American Indians.
Limitations: Applications not accepted. Giving in the U.S., with some emphasis on MT. No grants to individuals.
Publications: Financial statement.
Application information: Contributes only to pre-selected organizations.
Officers and Directors:* Gara LaMarche,* Pres.; Colin McCrea, Sr. V.P., Progs.; Deborah R. Phillips, Sr. V.P., Group Svcs. and Eval.; Cynthia Richards,* V.P.; David Sternlieb, Secy.; Philip Coates, C.I.O.; Harvey Dale; Christine V. Downton; Charles F. Feeney; William Hall; Sara Lawrence-Lightfoot; Elizabeth J. McCormack; Thomas N. Mitchell; Cecilia Munoz; Peter Smitham; Frederick A.O. Schwarz, Jr.; Michael I. Sovern; Cummings V. Zuill.
EIN: 133562971
Selected grants: The following grants are a representative sample of this grantmaker's funding activity:
$600,000 to Georgetown University, Washington, DC, 2012. For technical assistance to the state-based KidsWell collaborative to work with federal and state.
$250,000 to Indian Law Resource Center, Helena, MT, 2012. To help end violence against American Indian and Alaska Native women and girls.
$200,000 to NAACP Legal Defense and Educational Fund, New York, NY, 2012. For the Criminal Justice Project by continuing to fund three community organizers.
$85,650 to Grantmakers in Health, Washington, DC, 2012. To improve health care delivery for low-income older adults with multiple health problems.

5623
Lily Auchincloss Foundation, Inc. ✧
16 E. 79th St., Ste. 31
New York, NY 10075-0150 (212) 737-9533
Contact: Alexandra A. Herzan, Pres.
E-mail: info@lilyauch.org; Main URL: http://www.lilyauch.org
Grants List: http://www.lilyauch.org/allgrants.html

Established in 1985 in NY; incorporated in 1997.
Donors: Lily Auchincloss†; Hedwig A. van Ameringen†; Lily Auchincloss Foundation.
Foundation type: Independent foundation.
Financial data (yr. ended 12/31/13): Assets, $53,786,905 (M); expenditures, $2,943,901; qualifying distributions, $2,863,291; giving activities include $2,175,000 for 174 grants (high: $80,000; low: $15).
Purpose and activities: The foundation supports art, education, human services, and preservation/environment programs located within the five boroughs of New York City.
Fields of interest: Visual arts; Museums; Historic preservation/historical societies; Arts; Elementary/secondary education; Libraries (public); Education, services; Education; Environment, water resources; Environment, land resources; Environment, beautification programs; Environmental education; Recreation, parks/playgrounds; Youth development; Human services; Neighborhood centers; Children/youth, services; Aging, centers/services; Minorities/immigrants, centers/services.

Type of support: General/operating support; Capital campaigns; Program development; Matching/challenge support.
Limitations: Applications accepted. Giving limited to the five boroughs of New York City. No support for hospitals, nursing homes, substance abuse or mental health programs, schools and universities. No grants to individuals, or for organizations with a fiscal sponsor or for research projects.
Publications: Application guidelines; Grants list; Multi-year report; Program policy statement (including application guidelines).
Application information: The foundation only accepts online applications through its website. The application is available one month prior to each deadline. A complete list of grants awarded is available on foundation web site. Application guidelines available on foundation web site. Application form not required.
Initial approach: Submit application online via foundation web site only
Copies of proposal: 1
Deadline(s): Mar. 15, Aug. 15, and Dec. 15
Board meeting date(s): Apr., June, and Dec.
Final notification: Apr., June, and Dec.
Officers and Directors:* Alexandra A. Herzan,* Pres. and Treas.; Paul K. Herzan,* V.P.; Steadman H. Westergaard,* Secy.; James Gara; Lynne Harlow; Janet Levoff; Lee A. Link.
Number of staff: 2 part-time professional.
EIN: 133935995
Selected grants: The following grants are a representative sample of this grantmaker's funding activity:
$40,000 to Fountain House, New York, NY, 2012. For general operating support.
$20,000 to Big Apple Circus, Brooklyn, NY, 2012. For general operating support.
$15,000 to Advocates for Children of New York, New York, NY, 2012. For general operating support.
$15,000 to Bronx River Alliance, Bronx, NY, 2012. For general operating support.
$15,000 to Cathedral Church of Saint John the Divine, New York, NY, 2012. For general operating support.
$15,000 to Coro Eastern Center, New York, NY, 2012. For Immigrant Civic Leadership Program.
$10,000 to BRIC Arts Media Bklyn, Brooklyn, NY, 2012. For contemporary art exhibition program.
$10,000 to Bronx Museum of the Arts, Bronx, NY, 2012. For general operating support.
$10,000 to Chess in the Schools, New York, NY, 2012. For school programs.
$10,000 to East Side House, Bronx, NY, 2012. For youth and adult education services.
$5,000 to A.I.R. Gallery, Brooklyn, NY, 2012.
$5,000 to Food Bank for New York City, New York, NY, 2012. For emergency relief due to Hurricane Sandy.
$5,000 to Indo-American Arts Council, New York, NY, 2012. For emergency relief due to Hurricane Sandy.

5624
August 11 2003 Trust ✧
c/o Access Inc.
730 5th Ave., 20 Fl.
New York, NY 10019-4105

Established in DE.
Foundation type: Independent foundation.
Financial data (yr. ended 12/31/12): Assets, $19,840,958 (M); expenditures, $473,624; qualifying distributions, $449,973; giving activities include $447,798 for 42 grants (high: $32,239; low: $1,000).
Fields of interest: Arts; Education; Jewish federated giving programs; Jewish agencies & synagogues.
Limitations: Applications not accepted. Giving in the U.S., with emphasis on New York, NY.
Application information: Contributes only to pre-selected organizations.
Trustee: Cptc, LLC.
EIN: 206031077
Selected grants: The following grants are a representative sample of this grantmaker's funding activity:
$25,000 to Global Poverty Project, New York, NY, 2012. To support Prevention of Global Poverty.
$19,808 to Hawn Foundation, Santa Monica, CA, 2012. To support Children Education.
$15,000 to Scenarios USA, Brooklyn, NY, 2012. For the media.
$10,000 to American Fund for Charities, Wilmington, DE, 2012. To support Positive Wordly Changes.
$10,000 to Kids in Distress, Wilton Manors, FL, 2012. For Preventing Child Abuse.
$5,715 to New York Academy of Sciences, New York, NY, 2012. For the sciences.
$5,000 to Homes for Our Troops, Taunton, MA, 2012. For injured veterans.
$1,500 to American Jewish Committee, New York, NY, 2012. To support Jewish Community and Democratic Values.

5625
The Augustine Foundation ✧
c/o D. Weishselbaum, CPA
147-40 77th Rd.
Queens, NY 11367-3429
Application address: c/o Stephen Greisgraber, 302 Bedford Ave., Brooklyn, NY 11221

Established in 1980 in NY.
Donor: Rose L. Augustine†.
Foundation type: Independent foundation.
Financial data (yr. ended 06/30/13): Assets, $20,601,441 (M); expenditures, $819,950; qualifying distributions, $576,279; giving activities include $576,279 for 27 grants (high: $60,000; low: $2,400).
Purpose and activities: Giving primarily for the arts and Jewish education.
Fields of interest: Arts; Education; Jewish agencies & synagogues.
Limitations: Applications accepted. Giving in the U.S., with emphasis on NY. No grants to individuals.
Application information: Application form not required.
Initial approach: Proposal
Deadline(s): None
Officers: Stephen Griesgraber, Pres.; Leo Mavrovtis, Secy.
Directors: Sharon Isbin; H. Zeisel.
EIN: 132997450
Selected grants: The following grants are a representative sample of this grantmaker's funding activity:
$49,780 to California State University, Long Beach, CA, 2011.
$5,000 to Long Island University, Brookville, NY, 2011.

5626
Avalon Foundation ✧
c/o BCRS Associates, LLC
77 Water St., 9th Fl.
New York, NY 10005-4414
Contact: Michael D. Mccarthy, Tr.

Established in 1987 in NY.
Donor: Michael D. McCarthy.
Foundation type: Independent foundation.
Financial data (yr. ended 01/31/13): Assets, $9,619,788 (M); expenditures, $1,257,924; qualifying distributions, $1,201,425; giving activities include $1,201,175 for 14 grants (high: $200,000; low: $50).
Fields of interest: Human services; Foundations (private operating).
Limitations: Applications not accepted. Giving in New York, NY. No grants to individuals; no loans.
Application information: Contributes only to pre-selected organizations.
Trustees: Deborah Berg McCarthy; Jonathan L. Cohen; Michael D. McCarthy.
EIN: 133437931
Selected grants: The following grants are a representative sample of this grantmaker's funding activity:
$1,125 to Princeton University, Princeton, NJ, 2013. For All Contributions Were Made to the general purposes Fund of Public Charitable Organizations That Were Classified Under Section 501C (3) of the Internal Revenue Code.

5627
Milton and Sally Avery Arts Foundation ✧
300 Central Park W., Ste. 16J
New York, NY 10024 (212) 595-7338
Contact: March A. Cavanaugh, Tr.

Established in 1983 in NY.
Donor: Sally M. Avery†.
Foundation type: Independent foundation.
Financial data (yr. ended 12/31/12): Assets, $1,622,423 (M); expenditures, $558,542; qualifying distributions, $485,250; giving activities include $485,250 for 52 grants (high: $181,500; low: $3,500).
Purpose and activities: Awards restricted to art education, with emphasis on the visual arts, and to further the development of artists through nonprofit institutions, and to artists' communities and residency programs.
Fields of interest: Arts education; Visual arts, sculpture; Visual arts, painting; Arts; Elementary/secondary education; Higher education.
Type of support: Professorships; Fellowships; Internship funds; Scholarship funds.
Limitations: Applications accepted. Giving primarily in NY. No support for religious or political organizations. No grants to individuals.
Publications: Annual report.
Application information: Application form required.
Initial approach: Letter
Copies of proposal: 1
Deadline(s): None
Trustees: March A. Cavanaugh; Philip G. Cavanaugh; Sean A. Cavanaugh; Harvey Shipley Miller.
EIN: 133093638

5628
The AVI CHAI Foundation ✧
(formerly AVI CHAI - A Philanthropic Foundation)
1015 Park Ave.
New York, NY 10028-0904 (212) 396-8850
Contact: Yossi Prager, Exec. Dir., North America
FAX: (212) 396-8833; E-mail: info@avichaina.org; Additional/mailing address (Israel office): P.O. Box 7617, Jerusalem, 91076 tel.: (02) 621-5300, fax: (02) 621-5331, e-mail: office@avichai.org.il; Main URL: http://www.avichai.org
Blog: http://avichai.org/blog/
Facebook: https://www.facebook.com/AviChaiFoundation
LinkedIn: http://www.linkedin.com/company/the-avi-chai-foundation/
Twitter: https://twitter.com/AVICHAIFDN

Established in 1984 in NY.
Donor: Zalman C. Bernstein‡.
Foundation type: Independent foundation.
Financial data (yr. ended 12/31/12): Assets, $570,152,807 (M); gifts received, $156,289; expenditures, $43,019,901; qualifying distributions, $50,422,671; giving activities include $35,460,993 for 77 grants (high: $12,258,995; low: $2,500), $75,000 for 1 grant to an individual, $909,756 for foundation-administered programs and $7,342,500 for 10 loans/program-related investments (high: $1,000,000; low: $250,000).
Purpose and activities: The foundation is committed to the perpetuation of the Jewish people, Judaism, and the centrality of the state of Israel to the Jewish people. The objectives of the foundation are to encourage those of the Jewish faith towards greater commitment to Jewish observance and lifestyle by increasing their understanding, appreciation, and practice of Jewish traditions, customs, and laws; and to encourage mutual understanding and sensitivity among Jews of different religious backgrounds and commitments to observance.
Fields of interest: Education; Human services; Youth, services; Jewish federated giving programs.
International interests: Israel.
Type of support: Program development; Conferences/seminars; Curriculum development; Research; Program-related investments/loans.
Limitations: Applications not accepted. Giving primarily in North America and Israel. No grants for building projects or deficits.
Publications: Annual report.
Application information: Unsolicited requests for funds not accepted.
Board meeting date(s): 3 times a year
Officers and Trustees:* Mem Dryan Bernstein,* Chair.; Azriel Novick, C.F.O.; Yossi Prager, Exec. Dir., North America; Eli Silver, Exec. Dir., Israel; Samuel "Buddy" Silberman, Tr. Emeritus; Henry Taub, Tr. Emeritus; Meir Buzaglo; Avital Darmon; Alan R. Feld; Arthur W. Fried; Lauren K. Merkin; George Rohr; Lief D. Rosenblatt; Ruth R. Wisse.
Number of staff: 7 full-time professional; 4 full-time support.
EIN: 133252800

5629
AXA Foundation, Inc. ✧
(formerly The Equitable Foundation, Inc.)
1290 Ave. of the Americas, 12th Fl.
New York, NY 10104-0101 (212) 314-3662
Contact: Faith Frank, Chair., C.E.O., and Pres.
FAX: (212) 314-4480; E-mail for AXA Achievement Community Scholarships: axacommunity@scholarshipamerica.org; Main URL: http://www.axa-foundation.com

Established in 1986 in NY.
Donors: The Equitable Cos. Inc.; The Equitable Life Assurance Society of the U.S.; AXA Financial, Inc.; The MONY Group, Inc.
Foundation type: Company-sponsored foundation.
Financial data (yr. ended 12/31/12): Assets, $29,713,201 (M); expenditures, $4,861,682; qualifying distributions, $4,544,183; giving activities include $1,925,390 for 35 grants (high: $328,750; low: $600), and $1,637,473 for 5,254 employee matching gifts.
Purpose and activities: The foundation supports programs designed to improve the quality of life in communities where AXA Financial has a presence. The foundation operates and awards college scholarships through AXA Achievement, a program which provides youth with advice and access to succeed in college.
Fields of interest: Higher education; Youth; Minorities.
Type of support: General/operating support; Scholarship funds; Employee matching gifts; Employee-related scholarships; Scholarships—to individuals.
Limitations: Giving on a national basis with some emphasis in Washington, DC, St. Peter, MN, and New York, NY. No support for private foundations or religious or international organizations. No grants to individuals (except for scholarships), or for capital campaigns, or media-related projects.
Publications: Application guidelines.
Application information: Unsolicited requests for non-AXA Achievement scholarships are not accepted. Application form required.
Initial approach: Complete online application for AXA Achievement Scholarships and AXA Achievement Community Scholarships
Deadline(s): Dec. 1 for AXA Achievement Scholarships; Feb. 1 for AXA Achievement Community Scholarships
Board meeting date(s): As needed
Final notification: Mid-Mar. for AXA Achievement Scholarships
Officers and Directors:* Faith Frank,* Chair., Pres., and C.E.O.; Jan Goldstein, Secy.; John C. Taroni, Treas.; Mark Pearson; Amy Radin.
Number of staff: 3 full-time professional.
EIN: 131340512
Selected grants: The following grants are a representative sample of this grantmaker's funding activity:
$670,000 to Scholarship America, Saint Peter, MN, 2012. For AXA Achievement U.S. News Scholarship awards.
$602,000 to Scholarship America, Saint Peter, MN, 2012. For AXA Achievement Community Scholarship awards.
$200,005 to American Red Cross National Headquarters, Washington, DC, 2013. For Disaster Responder Program.
$200,000 to National Congress of Parents and Teachers, Alexandria, VA, 2012. For general support.
$100,000 to National Association for College Admission Counseling, Arlington, VA, 2012. For National College Fairs.

5630
Marvin Azrak and Sons Foundation ✧
10 W. 33rd St., Rm. 516
New York, NY 10001-3306 (212) 947-9600
Contact: Marvin Azrak, Mgr.

Established in 1994 in NY.
Donors: Adam Azrak; Elliot Azrak; Marvin Azrak; Victor Azrak; members of the Azrak family.
Foundation type: Independent foundation.
Financial data (yr. ended 12/31/12): Assets, $2,629,666 (M); gifts received, $1,029,837; expenditures, $1,027,423; qualifying distributions, $1,000,703; giving activities include $1,000,703 for 160 grants (high: $100,800; low: $18).
Purpose and activities: Giving primarily for Jewish agencies, temples, and schools.
Fields of interest: Education; Jewish federated giving programs; Jewish agencies & synagogues.
Limitations: Giving primarily in NJ, and New York, NY. No grants to individuals.
Application information:
Initial approach: Letter
Deadline(s): None
Officers: Victor Azrak, Pres.; Elliott Azrak, Treas.; Marvin Azrak, Mgr.
Trustees: Adam Azrak.
EIN: 133771410

5631
B & S Charity Foundation Inc ✧ ☆
1269 45th St.
Brooklyn, NY 11219-2000

Established in 2004 in NY.
Foundation type: Independent foundation.
Financial data (yr. ended 12/31/13): Assets, $0 (M); expenditures, $814,998; qualifying distributions, $814,940; giving activities include $814,940 for 2 grants (high: $814,500; low: $440).
Fields of interest: Jewish agencies & synagogues.
Limitations: Applications not accepted.
Application information: Unsolicited requests for funds not accepted.
Officer: Bere Weber, Pres.
EIN: 030546555

5632
Bachmann Strauss Family Fund ✧
(formerly The Bachmann Foundation)
c/o Bender Lane Advisory, Attn.: Joe Vet
P.O. Box 38016
Albany, NY 12203-8016

Incorporated in 1949 in NY.
Donors: Louis Bachmann‡; Thomas W. Strauss; B. Bachmann; GST Charitable Lead Trust.
Foundation type: Independent foundation.
Financial data (yr. ended 12/31/13): Assets, $7,888,978 (M); expenditures, $606,530; qualifying distributions, $519,535; giving activities include $518,900 for 90 grants (high: $210,000; low: $100).
Fields of interest: Museums (art); Performing arts; Arts; Education; Hospitals (general); Health organizations, association; Medical research, institute; Human services; Jewish federated giving programs; Jewish agencies & synagogues.
Limitations: Applications not accepted. No grants to individuals.

Application information: Contributes only to pre-selected organizations.
Officers: Barbara Bachmann Strauss, Pres.; Thomas W. Strauss, V.P. and Treas.
EIN: 136043497

5633
Rose M. Badgeley Residuary Charitable Trust ✧

c/o HSBC Bank USA, N.A.
452 5th Ave, 13th Fl.
New York, NY 10018-2706
FAX: (212) 525-2395; Application address: c/o HSBC Bank USA, attn.: Marianne Caskran, 452 5th Ave., New York, NY 10018, tel.: (212) 525-2418, e-mail: marianne.caskran@hsbcpb.com; additional contact: Gregory Otis; e-mail: gregory.otis@hsbcpb.com

Trust established in 1976 in NY.
Donor: Rose Badgeley†.
Foundation type: Independent foundation.
Financial data (yr. ended 01/31/13): Assets, $23,595,629 (M); expenditures, $1,330,317; qualifying distributions, $1,170,680; giving activities include $1,120,500 for 80 grants (high: $125,000; low: $2,000).
Purpose and activities: The trust provides support to a variety of nonprofit organizations. The scope of its distributions includes support for the benefit of religious, charitable, scientific, literary, or educational purposes, or to such corporations or other organizations having such purposes, which HSBC, the trustee, in its sole discretion, may select. Such selections and appointments shall include purposes that are for the benefit and cure of alcoholism, general education, medical and scientific research and education, or medical and hospital care.
Fields of interest: Education; Health care; Alcoholism; Medical research; Human services.
Type of support: General/operating support; Continuing support; Equipment; Program development; Research.
Limitations: Giving primarily in the greater metropolitan New York, NY, area. No grants to individuals or for capital campaigns.
Publications: Application guidelines.
Application information: Contact trust for application and application guidelines. Application form required.
Initial approach: Telephone, letter or e-mail
Copies of proposal: 1
Deadline(s): Submit proposal postmarked no earlier than Dec. 1 and no later than Mar. 15
Board meeting date(s): June
Final notification: Usually within a month after grant committee meeting in June if approved
Trustee: HSBC Bank USA, N.A.
EIN: 136744781
Selected grants: The following grants are a representative sample of this grantmaker's funding activity:
$125,000 to Samuel Waxman Cancer Research Foundation, New York, NY, 2012.
$25,000 to Childrens Hospital at Montefiore, Bronx, NY, 2012.
$25,000 to New York University, New York, NY, 2012.
$20,000 to Alzheimers Association, New York City Chapter, New York, NY, 2012.
$20,000 to Boys Club of New York, New York, NY, 2012.
$20,000 to Lenox Hill Neighborhood House, New York, NY, 2012.
$20,000 to Metropolitan Opera Guild, New York, NY, 2012.
$17,500 to American Federation for Aging Research, New York, NY, 2012.
$10,000 to Henry Street Settlement, New York, NY, 2012.
$10,000 to New York City Ballet, New York, NY, 2012.

5634
The Bahnik Foundation, Inc. ✧

c/o Roger L. Bahnik
190 Pine Hollow Rd.
Oyster Bay, NY 11771-4704

Established in 1994 in NY.
Donors: Roger L. Bahnik; Lore Bahnik.
Foundation type: Independent foundation.
Financial data (yr. ended 04/30/13): Assets, $22,262,240 (M); gifts received, $432,578; expenditures, $957,378; qualifying distributions, $929,100; giving activities include $929,100 for grants.
Purpose and activities: Giving primarily for education, community development and human services.
Fields of interest: Higher education; Hospitals (general); Boys & girls clubs; Human services; Children/youth, services; Family services; Community/economic development.
Type of support: Continuing support; Annual campaigns; Capital campaigns; Scholarship funds.
Limitations: Applications not accepted. Giving primarily on Long Island, NY. No grants to individuals.
Application information: Contributes only to pre-selected organizations.
Board meeting date(s): Nov.
Officers: Roger L. Bahnik, Pres.; Claude Bahnik, V.P.; Michele Bahnik Mercier, V.P.; Lore Bahnik, Secy.
EIN: 113216930
Selected grants: The following grants are a representative sample of this grantmaker's funding activity:
$110,000 to First Presbyterian Church, Oyster Bay, NY, 2011. For general purposes.
$75,000 to Interfaith Nutrition Network, Hempstead, NY, 2011. For general purposes.
$11,100 to East Woods School, Oyster Bay, NY, 2011. For general purposes.
$10,000 to Cold Spring Harbor Laboratory, Cold Spring Harbor, NY, 2011. For general purposes.
$10,000 to Community Foundation of Oyster Bay, Oyster Bay, NY, 2011. For general purposes.
$10,000 to Doubleday Babcock Senior Center, Oyster Bay, NY, 2011. For general purposes.
$10,000 to Friends of the Bay, Oyster Bay, NY, 2011. For general purposes.
$10,000 to Theodore Roosevelt Sanctuary, Oyster Bay, NY, 2011. For general purposes.
$3,500 to UNICEF, New York, NY, 2011. For general purposes.
$1,000 to Oyster Bay Historical Society, Oyster Bay, NY, 2011. For general purposes.

5635
The Cameron and Jane Baird Foundation ✧

(formerly The Cameron Baird Foundation)
726 Exchange St., Ste. 800
Buffalo, NY 14210-1465

Trust established in 1960 in NY.
Donor: Members of the family of Cameron Baird.
Foundation type: Independent foundation.
Financial data (yr. ended 12/31/13): Assets, $52,928,261 (M); expenditures, $3,283,923; qualifying distributions, $3,000,469; giving activities include $2,979,500 for 123 grants (high: $700,000; low: $2,000).
Purpose and activities: Giving primarily for music and cultural programs, education, social services, family planning, conservation, and civil rights.
Fields of interest: Performing arts, orchestras; Arts; Secondary school/education; Higher education; Environment, natural resources; Reproductive health, family planning; Civil/human rights.
Limitations: Applications not accepted. Giving primarily in NY, with emphasis on the Buffalo area. No support for religious organizations. No grants to individuals.
Application information: Contributes only to pre-selected organizations. Unsolicited requests for funds not considered or acknowledged.
Board meeting date(s): Annually
Trustees: Brent D. Baird; Brian D. Baird; Bridget B. Baird; Bruce C. Baird; Peter C. Clauson; Brenda Baird Senturia.
EIN: 166029481

5636
The Baird Foundation ✧

11 Summer St., 4th Fl.
Buffalo, NY 14209-2256 (716) 883-2429
Contact: Catherine F. Schweitzer, Exec. Dir.

Trust established in 1947 in NY.
Donors: Flora M. Baird†; Frank B. Baird, Jr.†; Cameron Baird†; William C. Baird†.
Foundation type: Independent foundation.
Financial data (yr. ended 12/31/13): Assets, $11,104,056 (M); expenditures, $757,014; qualifying distributions, $678,921; giving activities include $519,458 for 171 grants (high: $50,000; low: $33).
Purpose and activities: Giving primarily for the arts, children, youth and social services, and medical research.
Fields of interest: Museums; Performing arts; Performing arts, orchestras; Historic preservation/historical societies; Arts; Education; Environment; Animal welfare; Hospitals (general); Boys & girls clubs; Human services; Children/youth, services; Disabilities, people with; Economically disadvantaged.
Type of support: General/operating support; Capital campaigns; Equipment; Research; Matching/challenge support.
Limitations: Applications accepted. Giving primarily in the western NY area. No grants to individuals.
Publications: Grants list.
Application information: Application form required.
Initial approach: Letter
Copies of proposal: 5
Deadline(s): None
Officer: Catherine F. Schweitzer, Exec. Dir.

Trustees: Arthur W. Cryer; Robert J.A. Irwin; William B. Irwin.
Number of staff: 1 full-time professional; 1 part-time support.
EIN: 166023080

5637
Bais Ephraim Charitable Foundation Trust ✧

8 Boxwood Ln.
Monsey, NY 10952-2925
Contact: Ari Margulies, Tr.

Established in 2001 in NY.
Donors: Reizel Ledreich; Ari Margulies; Aryeh Margulies; David Margulies; Esther Margulies; Goldy Margulies; Harry Margulies; Solomon Margulies; David's Cookies Inc.
Foundation type: Independent foundation.
Financial data (yr. ended 09/30/13): Assets, $747,069 (M); gifts received, $490,000; expenditures, $490,664; qualifying distributions, $466,996; giving activities include $466,996 for grants.
Purpose and activities: Giving primarily to Jewish agencies, temples, and schools.
Fields of interest: Education; Jewish agencies & synagogues.
Application information: Application form required.
Initial approach: Letter
Deadline(s): None
Trustees: Ari Margulies; Goldy Margulies.
EIN: 116548272

5638
Mr. and Mrs. Robert C. Baker Family Foundation ✧

c/o National Realty and Development Corp.
3 Manhattanville Rd., Ste. 202
Purchase, NY 10577-2122 (914) 694-4444
Contact: Robert C. Baker, Pres.

Established in 1995 in NY.
Donor: Robert C. Baker.
Foundation type: Independent foundation.
Financial data (yr. ended 12/31/13): Assets, $2,041,899 (M); gifts received, $2,867,309; expenditures, $948,417; qualifying distributions, $948,417; giving activities include $948,417 for 74 grants (high: $250,000; low: $25).
Purpose and activities: Giving primarily for the arts, education, health care, and Jewish organizations.
Fields of interest: Museums (art); Performing arts, opera; Arts; Higher education; Medical school/education; Education; Hospitals (general); Health care; Health organizations, association; Cancer research; Human services; Children/youth, services; Jewish federated giving programs; Jewish agencies & synagogues.
Limitations: Applications accepted. Giving primarily in the greater metropolitan New York, NY, area. No grants to individuals.
Application information: Application form not required.
Initial approach: Proposal
Deadline(s): None
Officer: Robert C. Baker, Pres.
EIN: 133798665
Selected grants: The following grants are a representative sample of this grantmaker's funding activity:
$1,000 to Jazz at Lincoln Center, New York, NY, 2012. For In honor of Bob Appel.
$500 to Hofstra University, Hempstead, NY, 2012. For In honor of Robert and Florence Kaufman.
$500 to Williams Syndrome Association, Troy, MI, 2012. For In honor of Michele Felsher Walk for Williams NYC.
$150 to Central Park Conservancy, New York, NY, 2012. For In honor of Bambi Felberbaum.
$150 to Central Park Conservancy, New York, NY, 2012. For In honor of Adrien Arpel.
$150 to Central Park Conservancy, New York, NY, 2012. For In honor of Jay Furman.

5639
The Alec Baldwin Foundation, Inc. ✧

c/o Smith & Co.
509 Madison Ave., 4th Fl.
New York, NY 10022-5501
Facebook: https://www.facebook.com/AlecBaldwinFoundation
Twitter: https://twitter.com/ABFalecbaldwin

Established in 2006 in NY.
Donor: Alexander R. Baldwin, III.
Foundation type: Independent foundation.
Financial data (yr. ended 12/31/13): Assets, $1,213,829 (M); gifts received, $3,254,661; expenditures, $3,097,407; qualifying distributions, $3,097,157; giving activities include $3,097,157 for 159 grants (high: $500,000; low: $234).
Purpose and activities: Giving primarily for higher education and the performing arts.
Fields of interest: Media, radio; Performing arts, dance; Performing arts, theater; Arts; Higher education; Education; Environment, natural resources; Health organizations, association; Cancer; Human services; Foundations (private grantmaking).
Limitations: Applications not accepted. Giving primarily in NY. No grants to individuals.
Application information: Contributes only to pre-selected organizations.
Directors: Alexander R. Baldwin, III; Brendan O'Connell; Dan Wechsler.
EIN: 205062031

5640
The David M. & Barbara Baldwin Foundation, Inc. ✧

c/o McGrath, Doyle & Phair
150 Broadway
New York, NY 10038-4311

Established in 1986 in NJ.
Donor: David M. Baldwin.
Foundation type: Independent foundation.
Financial data (yr. ended 11/30/13): Assets, $7,155,025 (M); gifts received, $200,000; expenditures, $834,254; qualifying distributions, $797,262; giving activities include $783,000 for 41 grants (high: $500,000; low: $100).
Purpose and activities: Giving primarily for hospitals and health associations; funding also for education.
Fields of interest: Performing arts, theater; Higher education; Environment; Hospitals (general); Health organizations, association; Christian agencies & churches.
Limitations: Applications not accepted. Giving primarily in FL, NJ, NY, and PA. No grants to individuals.
Application information: Contributes only to pre-selected organizations.
Officers: David M. Baldwin, Pres.; Barbara Baldwin, V.P.; Charles J. Gengler, V.P.; Nicholas Jacangelo, Secy.-Treas.
EIN: 133391384

5641
The Banfi Vintners Foundation ✧

(formerly The Villa Banfi Foundation)
1111 Cedar Swamp Rd.
Glen Head, NY 11545-2109 (516) 686-2506
Contact: Frank Savino, Treas.
Main URL: http://www.banfiwines.com/about/mission-statement/

Established in 1982 in NY.
Donor: Banfi Products Corp.
Foundation type: Independent foundation.
Financial data (yr. ended 12/31/12): Assets, $12,016,640 (M); expenditures, $605,821; qualifying distributions, $592,150; giving activities include $585,000 for 71 grants (high: $99,000; low: $300).
Purpose and activities: Giving primarily for higher education through scholarships, fellowships and grants-in-aid. In addition, each year the foundation provides scholarships for students at select hospitality and business colleges to travel to Italy for seminars on that nation's wine and food culture.
Fields of interest: Higher education; Hospitals (general); Health organizations, association; Human services; International affairs, goodwill promotion.
Limitations: Giving primarily in, but not limited to CA, MA and NY.
Application information:
Deadline(s): None
Board meeting date(s): Nov.
Officers and Directors:* Joan C. Nolan, Secy.; Frank Savino, Treas.; Philip D. Calderone,* Exec. Dir.; Cristina N. Mariani; Harry F. Mariani; James W. Mariani; John Mariani.
EIN: 112622792

5642
The Brett Barakett Foundation ✧ ☆

(formerly The Brett and Patricia Barakett Foundation)
c/o Tremblant Partners
767 5th Ave.
New York, NY 10153-0023

Established in 2004 in NY.
Donor: Brett Barakett.
Foundation type: Independent foundation.
Financial data (yr. ended 12/31/13): Assets, $9,908,794 (M); gifts received, $1,000,000; expenditures, $578,568; qualifying distributions, $574,374; giving activities include $574,374 for 33 grants (high: $200,925; low: $500).
Fields of interest: Higher education; Education; Hospitals (general); Recreation; United Ways and Federated Giving Programs.
Limitations: Applications not accepted. Giving primarily in NY. No grants to individuals.
Application information: Contributes only to pre-selected organizations.
Officers: Brett Barakett, Pres.; James Eckert, Secy.; Alicia Patrimonio, Treas.
EIN: 200832184

5643

Timothy and Michele Barakett Foundation ✧

c/o TRB Advisors
767 5th Ave., 12th Fl.
New York, NY 10153-0023

Established in 2007 in NY.
Donor: Timothy Barakett.
Foundation type: Independent foundation.
Financial data (yr. ended 12/31/12): Assets, $48,936,401 (M); gifts received, $96,000; expenditures, $3,198,130; qualifying distributions, $2,896,850; giving activities include $2,896,850 for 48 grants (high: $800,000; low: $500).
Fields of interest: Elementary/secondary education; Higher education; Libraries (public); Hospitals (general); Parkinson's disease research.
Limitations: Applications not accepted. Giving primarily in MA and NY. No grants to individuals.
Application information: Contributes only to pre-selected organizations.
Trustees: Michele Barakett; Timothy Barakett.
EIN: 266140904

5644

The Barker Welfare Foundation ✧

P.O. Box 2
Glen Head, NY 11545-0002 (516) 759-5592
Contact: Sarane H. Ross, Pres.
FAX: (516) 759-5497;
E-mail: SusanDeMaio@barkerwelfare.org; Main URL: http://www.barkerwelfare.org

Incorporated in 1934 in IL.
Donor: Mrs. Charles V. Hickox†.
Foundation type: Independent foundation.
Financial data (yr. ended 09/30/13): Assets, $114,149,298 (M); expenditures, $3,788,718; qualifying distributions, $3,361,821; giving activities include $2,951,719 for 320 grants (high: $75,000; low: $500).
Purpose and activities: The mission of the Barker Welfare Foundation is to make grants to qualified charitable organizations whose initiatives improve the quality of life, with an emphasis on strengthening youth and families and to reflect the philosophy of Catherine B. Hickox, the Founder. Grants to established organizations and charitable institutions, with emphasis on youth and families, museums and the fine and performing arts, child welfare and youth agencies, health services and rehabilitation, welfare, aid to the handicapped, family planning, libraries, the environment, recreation, and programs for the elderly.
Fields of interest: Visual arts; Museums; Arts; Libraries/library science; Environment; Health care; Mental health/crisis services; Recreation; Human services; Children/youth, services; Disabilities, people with.
Type of support: General/operating support; Continuing support; Annual campaigns; Capital campaigns; Building/renovation; Equipment.
Limitations: Giving primarily in Chicago, IL, Michigan City, IN, and New York, NY. Requests for funding in Chicago will no longer be accepted unless invited (initiated) by the foundation. No support for political activities, start-up organizations, national health, welfare, or education agencies, institutions or funds, including private or public schools. No grants to individuals, or for endowment funds, seed money, emergency funds, deficit financing, scholarships, fellowships, medical or scientific research, films or videos, or conferences; no loans.
Publications: Application guidelines; Annual report (including application guidelines).
Application information: Proposals must be completed according to the foundation's guidelines and grants process in order to be considered for funding. Grants to Chicago agencies are by invitation only. Proposals sent by fax not considered. Application information available on foundation web site. Application form required.
Initial approach: 2- to 3-page letter of inquiry or online inquiry through web site. A telephone call is also suggested to determine if the applicant falls within the general current policy of the foundation
Copies of proposal: 2
Deadline(s): Feb. 1 and Aug. 1
Board meeting date(s): May and Oct.
Final notification: After board meeting for positive responses; any time for negative responses
Officers and Directors:* Sarane H. Ross,* Pres.; Katrina H. Becker,* V.P.; Danielle H. Moore,* Secy.; Thomas P. McCormick,* Treas.; Diane Curtis; Frances B. Hickox; James A.B. Hickox; Alline Matheson; Sarane R. O'Connor; Alexander B. Ross; Sarane H. Ross; Stephen B. Ross.
Number of staff: 2 full-time professional; 1 part-time support.
EIN: 366018526

5645

Lawrence & Isabel Barnett Charitable Foundation, Inc. ✧

c/o Citrin
709 Westchester Ave.
White Plains, NY 10604-3167

Donor: Lawrence R. Barnett†.
Foundation type: Independent foundation.
Financial data (yr. ended 08/31/13): Assets, $26,057,998 (M); gifts received, $461,650; expenditures, $1,889,284; qualifying distributions, $1,643,333; giving activities include $1,643,333 for 17 grants (high: $1,000,000; low: $5,000).
Fields of interest: Higher education; ALS.
Limitations: Applications not accepted. Giving primarily in CA.
Application information: Contributes only to pre-selected organizations.
Officer and Directors:* Lawrence R. Barnett, Jr.,* Secy.; James Joseph Barnett; Laurey J. Barnett.
EIN: 202761633
Selected grants: The following grants are a representative sample of this grantmaker's funding activity:
$500,000 to Amyotrophic Lateral Sclerosis Association, Calabasas Hills, CA, 2011.
$200,000 to Stanford University, Stanford, CA, 2011.
$40,000 to New York University, New York, NY, 2011.
$25,000 to Ohio State University, Columbus, OH, 2011.
$10,000 to Stanford University, Stanford, CA, 2011.
$10,000 to Stanford University, Stanford, CA, 2011.
$10,000 to Stanford University, Law School, Stanford, CA, 2011.
$10,000 to Stanford University, Stanford, CA, 2011.
$10,000 to Stanford University, Stanford, CA, 2011.
$1,000 to Cystic Fibrosis Foundation, Bethesda, MD, 2011.

5646

Baron Capital Foundation ✧

c/o Ronald Baron, Baron Capital Group Inc.
767 5th Ave., 49th Fl.
New York, NY 10153-0023

Established in 2007 in NY.
Donor: BAMCO, Inc.
Foundation type: Independent foundation.
Financial data (yr. ended 12/31/13): Assets, $12,223,914 (M); gifts received, $1,417,246; expenditures, $1,417,652; qualifying distributions, $1,414,986; giving activities include $1,412,123 for 51 grants (high: $450,000; low: $1,000).
Fields of interest: Medical school/education; Jewish federated giving programs; Jewish agencies & synagogues.
Limitations: Applications not accepted. Giving primarily in New York, NY.
Application information: Contributes only to pre-selected organizations.
Trustees: David R. Baron; Michael R. Baron; Ronald Baron.
EIN: 142004657
Selected grants: The following grants are a representative sample of this grantmaker's funding activity:
$100,000 to University of Pennsylvania, Philadelphia, PA, 2011.
$100,000 to Weill Medical College of Cornell University, New York, NY, 2011.
$75,000 to American Friends of the Israel Museum, New York, NY, 2011.
$75,000 to Prostate Cancer Foundation, Santa Monica, CA, 2011.
$50,000 to Big Apple Circus, Brooklyn, NY, 2011.
$50,000 to Jewish Center of the Hamptons, East Hampton, NY, 2011.
$5,000 to Emory University, Atlanta, GA, 2011.
$2,500 to Breast Cancer Research Foundation, New York, NY, 2011.
$2,500 to Jewish Board of Family and Childrens Services, New York, NY, 2011.
$2,500 to Lincoln Center Theater, New York, NY, 2011.

5647

The Greater Barrington Foundation, Inc. ✧

(doing business as The Barrington Foundation)
7-11 S. Broadway, Ste. 200
White Plains, NY 10601-3520
Mailing address: c/o David H. Strassler, P.O. Box 750, Great Barrington, MA 01230-0750

Established in 1978 in DE.
Donors: Samuel A. Strassler†; David Strassler; Lorna Strassler; Robert Strassler; Abbie Strassler; Gary Strassler; Alan Strassler; Matthew Strassler; Karen Strassler.
Foundation type: Independent foundation.
Financial data (yr. ended 12/31/13): Assets, $1,801,644 (M); gifts received, $1,164,250; expenditures, $873,586; qualifying distributions, $871,450; giving activities include $871,450 for 114 grants (high: $87,500; low: $500).
Purpose and activities: Giving primarily to Jewish federated giving programs and Jewish agencies and temples, as well as for higher education and human services; some giving also for the arts and cultural programs.
Fields of interest: Arts; Education; Jewish agencies & synagogues.

Type of support: Annual campaigns; Capital campaigns; Endowments; Scholarship funds.
Limitations: Applications accepted. Giving primarily in MA, with emphasis on Boston and Great Barrington, and New York, NY. No grants to individuals.
Application information: Application form not required.
Initial approach: Proposal
Deadline(s): None
Officers: David H. Strassler, Pres.; Robert B. Strassler, Secy.-Treas.
EIN: 132930849
Selected grants: The following grants are a representative sample of this grantmaker's funding activity:
$61,000 to Clark University, Worcester, MA, 2011.
$50,000 to Jewish Federation of the Berkshires, Pittsfield, MA, 2011.
$36,650 to Mahaiwe Performing Arts Center, Great Barrington, MA, 2011.
$35,000 to Washington Institute for Near East Policy, Washington, DC, 2011.
$31,500 to Planned Parenthood, National, New York, NY, 2011.
$9,000 to Broadway Cares/Equity Fights AIDS, New York, NY, 2011.
$8,000 to Hospice Care in the Berkshires, Pittsfield, MA, 2011.
$5,000 to Human Rights Watch, New York, NY, 2011.
$5,000 to Nature Conservancy, Arlington, VA, 2011.
$4,500 to Community Legal Services and Counseling Center, Cambridge, MA, 2011.

5648
Theodore H. Barth Foundation, Inc. ✧
45 Rockefeller Plz., 20th Fl., Ste. 2006
New York, NY 10111-0100
Contact: Ellen S. Berelson, Pres.
E-mail: barthfoundation@earthlink.net

Incorporated in 1953 in DE.
Donor: Theodore H. Barth†.
Foundation type: Independent foundation.
Financial data (yr. ended 12/31/13): Assets, $25,302,188 (M); expenditures, $1,369,667; qualifying distributions, $1,118,373; giving activities include $900,000 for 68 grants (high: $125,000; low: $1,000).
Fields of interest: Performing arts; Performing arts, opera; Arts; Higher education; Health care; Human services.
Type of support: General/operating support; Continuing support; Annual campaigns; Endowments; Program development; Seed money.
Limitations: Giving primarily in New York, NY, and Washington, DC; giving also in MA and VA. No grants to individuals directly, or for capital projects.
Publications: Application guidelines.
Application information: Telephone inquiries will not be accepted. Application form not required.
Initial approach: Letter
Copies of proposal: 1
Deadline(s): None
Final notification: Dec.
Officers and Trustees:* Ellen S. Berelson,* Pres. and Treas.; Lois M. Herrmann,* V.P.; Lawrence M. Franks,* Secy.
EIN: 136103401

5649
Jack & Miriam Basch Foundation, Inc. ✧
1755 58th St.
Brooklyn, NY 11204-2236

Established in 1990 in NY.
Donors: Jack Basch; Miriam Basch.
Foundation type: Independent foundation.
Financial data (yr. ended 12/31/12): Assets, $5,356,842 (M); gifts received, $1,850,000; expenditures, $822,924; qualifying distributions, $820,011; giving activities include $819,761 for 45 grants.
Fields of interest: Education; Jewish agencies & synagogues.
Limitations: Applications not accepted. Giving primarily in Brooklyn, NY; some funding also in NJ. No grants to individuals.
Application information: Contributes only to pre-selected organizations.
Officers: Jack Basch, Pres.; Miriam Basch, V.P.; Michael Inzlicht, Secy.
EIN: 113030983

5650
Sandra Atlas Bass & Edythe & Sol G. Atlas Fund, Inc. ✧
c/o Atlas Fund, Inc.
185 Great Neck Rd.
Great Neck, NY 11021-3326

Established in 1962 in NY.
Donors: Sol G. Atlas; Sandra Atlas Bass.
Foundation type: Independent foundation.
Financial data (yr. ended 12/31/12): Assets, $87,643 (M); gifts received, $2,424,480; expenditures, $2,439,460; qualifying distributions, $2,439,460; giving activities include $2,435,900 for 193 grants (high: $110,000; low: $500).
Purpose and activities: Giving primarily for health associations, animal welfare, children, youth and social services, including services for people who are blind; funding also for Jewish organizations.
Fields of interest: Animal welfare; Hospitals (general); Health organizations; Human services; Children/youth, services; Jewish agencies & synagogues; Blind/visually impaired.
Limitations: Applications not accepted. Giving primarily in the metropolitan New York, NY, area, with emphasis on Long Island.
Application information: Unsolicited requests for funds not accepted.
Officers: Sandra Atlas Bass, Pres.; Morton Bass, V.P.; Robert Zabelle, Secy.; Lincoln Page, Treas.
EIN: 116036928

5651
Bat Hanadiv Foundation No. 3 ✧
c/o Carter, Ledyard & Milburn LLP
2 Wall St.
New York, NY 10005-2072
Application address: c/o Yad Hanadiv, 16 Ibn Gvirol St., 92430 Jerusalem, Israel; Application e-mail: website@yadhanadiv.org.il

Established in 1981.
Donors: Bat Hanadiv Foundation; Bat Hanadiv Foundation No. 2.
Foundation type: Independent foundation.
Financial data (yr. ended 12/31/13): Assets, $1,134,111,098 (M); expenditures, $36,502,761; qualifying distributions, $23,119,943; giving activities include $23,119,943 for grants.
Purpose and activities: Grants primarily for higher and other education; support also for conservation, youth and social service agencies, and cultural programs.
Fields of interest: Arts; Environment, natural resources; Human services; Youth, services.
International interests: Israel.
Type of support: General/operating support; Equipment; Program development.
Limitations: Applications accepted. Giving primarily in Israel.
Application information: Grants are administered by Yad Hanadiv. All grantseekers must follow the guidelines on web site http://yadhanadiv.org.il.
Initial approach: See Yad Hanadiv web site for guidelines and eligibility
Trustee: Yad Hanadiv.
EIN: 133091620

5652
The Bay and Paul Foundations, Inc. ✧
(formerly Josephine Bay Paul and C. Michael Paul Foundation, Inc.)
17 W. 94th St., 1st Fl.
New York, NY 10025-7116 (212) 663-1115
Contact: Frederick Bay, C.E.O. and Pres.
FAX: (212) 932-0316;
E-mail: info@bayandpaulfoundations.org; Main URL: http://www.bayandpaulfoundations.org

Established in 2005 in NY.
Donors: Josephine Bay Paul†; Charles Ulrick Bay†.
Foundation type: Independent foundation.
Financial data (yr. ended 12/31/12): Assets, $71,635,854 (M); expenditures, $5,489,268; qualifying distributions, $4,559,383; giving activities include $3,473,026 for 234 grants (high: $200,000; low: $170).
Purpose and activities: Support for organizations demonstrating or developing pre-collegiate educational restructuring; support projects which reinforce the centrality of the arts in pre-collegiate curricula. The foundation also has an interest in projects seeking to sustain the earth's biodiversity. K-12 math and science, arts-in-education: grants are limited to the New York, NY, metropolitan area.
Fields of interest: Arts education; Education, research; Elementary school/education; Secondary school/education; Education; Environment.
Type of support: General/operating support; Continuing support; Program development; Conferences/seminars; Seed money; Research; Technical assistance; Matching/challenge support.
Limitations: Giving limited to the NY metropolitan area for Math/Science and Arts Education; giving on a national basis otherwise. No support for sectarian religious programs, or to other than publicly recognized charities. No grants to individuals, or for building campaigns.
Application information: See foundation web site for the most current application updates and information.
Board meeting date(s): Feb., May, and Nov.
Officers and Directors:* David Bury,* Chair.; Frederick Bay,* C.E.O. and Pres.; Dianne J. Daniels, C.O.O. and Fiscal Off.; Synnova B. Hayes, V.P., Admin. and Progs.; Kenneth D. Hurwitz,* Secy.-Treas.; Rebecca Adamson; Corinne Steel; Khalif Williams.

Number of staff: 2 full-time professional; 3 part-time professional; 2 full-time support.
EIN: 131991717
Selected grants: The following grants are a representative sample of this grantmaker's funding activity:
$20,000 to Scenic Hudson, Poughkeepsie, NY, 2011.
$20,000 to Symphony Space, New York, NY, 2011.
$10,000 to Dynamic Forms, New York, NY, 2011.
$10,000 to Historic Cherry Hill, Albany, NY, 2011.
$10,000 to New York Sun Works, New York, NY, 2011.
$10,000 to Wave Hill, Bronx, NY, 2011.
$9,000 to Houston Zoo, Houston, TX, 2011.
$6,000 to Community-Word Project, New York, NY, 2011.
$5,000 to Brooklyn Childrens Museum, Brooklyn, NY, 2011.
$5,000 to W N Y C Radio, New York, NY, 2011.

5653
The Howard Bayne Fund ✧
c/o Simpson Thacher & Bartlett LLP
425 Lexington Ave.
New York, NY 10017-3909

Incorporated in 1960 in NY.
Donor: Daphne Shih†.
Foundation type: Independent foundation.
Financial data (yr. ended 12/31/13): Assets, $16,887,335 (M); expenditures, $944,103; qualifying distributions, $830,019; giving activities include $804,500 for 116 grants (high: $56,000; low: $500).
Purpose and activities: Giving primarily for education and the arts.
Fields of interest: Museums; Museums (art); Performing arts, theater; Performing arts, music; Performing arts, orchestras; Historic preservation/historical societies; Arts; Higher education; Education; Environment, natural resources; Human services; Family services; Religion.
Type of support: Annual campaigns; Capital campaigns.
Limitations: Applications not accepted. Giving primarily in CT, FL, MA, NJ, NY, and RI, with some emphasis on the New York, NY, area. No grants to individuals.
Application information: Contributes only to pre-selected organizations.
Board meeting date(s): Between Oct. and Dec.
Officers and Directors:* Gurdon B. Wattles,* Pres.; Daisy Paradis,* V.P.; David A. Shevlin, Secy.-Treas.; Diana de Vegh; Pierre J. de Vegh; Alexander B. Wattles; Gurdon S. Wattles; Elizabeth W. Wilkes.
EIN: 136100680

5654
B'Chaya Moshe Charitable Trust ✧
3478 Bedford Ave.
Brooklyn, NY 11210-5235

Established in 2005 in NY.
Donors: Barry Braunstein; Jacqueline Braunstein; Chaya Bleier; Israel Braunstein; Moses & Yetta Charitable Trust.
Foundation type: Independent foundation.
Financial data (yr. ended 12/31/12): Assets, $2,273,734 (M); gifts received, $551,200; expenditures, $493,542; qualifying distributions, $493,192; giving activities include $493,192 for 24 + grants.
Purpose and activities: Giving primarily to Jewish agencies, temples, and schools.
Fields of interest: Elementary/secondary education; Jewish agencies & synagogues.
Limitations: Applications not accepted. Giving primarily in Brooklyn, NY. No grants to individuals.
Application information: Contributes only to pre-selected organizations.
Trustees: Barry Braunstein; Jacqueline Braunstein.
EIN: 206433749

5655
BCHB, Inc. ✧
c/o Hertz, Herson & Co., LLP
477 Madison Ave., 10th Fl.
New York, NY 10022-5802

Established in 1997 in DE and NY.
Donors: Bella Wexner Charitable Remainder Unitrust; Susan Wexner Revocable Trust.
Foundation type: Independent foundation.
Financial data (yr. ended 03/31/13): Assets, $35,818,286 (M); expenditures, $1,735,466; qualifying distributions, $1,586,081; giving activities include $1,582,452 for 7 grants (high: $500,000; low: $2).
Fields of interest: Health care; Jewish federated giving programs; Jewish agencies & synagogues.
Limitations: Applications not accepted. Giving primarily in New York, NY, and Israel. No grants to individuals.
Application information: Contributes only to pre-selected organizations.
Officer and Directors:* Susan R. Wexner,* Pres. and Secy.-Treas.; Dr. Saul G. Agus; Raymond Kanner; Gregg H. Levy, Esq.; Michael S. Oberman, Esq.; Mark W. Saks, Esq.; Walter Stern.
EIN: 133997366
Selected grants: The following grants are a representative sample of this grantmaker's funding activity:
$500,000 to Museum of Jewish Heritage, New York, NY, 2013. For general support for the museum's educational Programs.

5656
Beal Family Foundation ✧ ☆
c/o Related Companies LP
60 Columbus Cir., 18th Fl.
New York, NY 10023-5802

Established in NY.
Donors: Bruce A. Beal, Jr.; Kathryn Beal; Stephen M. Ross.
Foundation type: Independent foundation.
Financial data (yr. ended 12/31/13): Assets, $2,895,571 (M); gifts received, $3,875,000; expenditures, $1,255,625; qualifying distributions, $1,254,125; giving activities include $1,252,500 for 12 grants (high: $1,000,000; low: $500).
Fields of interest: Museums; Hospitals (general).
Limitations: Applications not accepted. Giving primarily in New York, NY. No grants to individuals.
Application information: Unsolicited requests for funds not accepted.
Trustees: Bruce A. Beal, Jr.; Kathryn Beal.
EIN: 455092245

5657
Nancy & Joachim Bechtle Foundation ✧
c/o B. Strauss Assoc., Ltd.
307 5th Ave., 8th Fl.
New York, NY 10016-6517

Established in 2006 in CA.
Donors: Joachim Bechtle; Nancy Bechtle.
Foundation type: Independent foundation.
Financial data (yr. ended 08/31/13): Assets, $1,172,122 (M); gifts received, $755,483; expenditures, $615,278; qualifying distributions, $606,890; giving activities include $605,210 for 54 grants (high: $80,000; low: $50).
Fields of interest: Museums; Performing arts; Education; Recreation, parks/playgrounds.
Limitations: Applications not accepted. No grants to individuals.
Application information: Contributes only to pre-selected organizations.
Officers: Nancy Bechtle, Pres.; Joachim Bechtle, C.F.O. and Secy.
EIN: 208007210
Selected grants: The following grants are a representative sample of this grantmaker's funding activity:
$1,000 to Trust for Public Land, San Francisco, CA, 2011. For general support.

5658
Geoffrey Beene Foundation ✧
13 E. 69th St., Ste. 2R
New York, NY 10021-4968

Established in 2007 in NY.
Donor: Geoffrey Beene†.
Foundation type: Independent foundation.
Financial data (yr. ended 12/31/12): Assets, $47,213,508 (M); expenditures, $3,460,882; qualifying distributions, $3,310,739; giving activities include $3,100,931 for 18 grants (high: $2,000,000; low: $20).
Fields of interest: Scholarships/financial aid; Hospitals (specialty); Cancer research; Alzheimer's disease research.
Limitations: Applications not accepted. Giving primarily in New York, NY.
Application information: Contributes only to pre-selected organizations.
Officer: Mara Hutton, Exec. V.P.
Trustee: G. Thompson Hutton.
EIN: 436936635

5659
The Beker Foundation ✧
c/o The Millburn Corp.
1270 Ave. of the Americas, 11th Fl.
New York, NY 10020-1702

Established in 1984 in NY.
Donor: Harvey Beker.
Foundation type: Independent foundation.
Financial data (yr. ended 12/31/12): Assets, $30,875,181 (M); expenditures, $2,072,451; qualifying distributions, $1,924,200; giving activities include $1,823,737 for 80 grants (high: $250,000; low: $100).
Purpose and activities: Giving primarily for Jewish education and Jewish organizations.
Fields of interest: Higher education; Education; Health organizations, association; Human services;

Jewish federated giving programs; Jewish agencies & synagogues.
Limitations: Applications not accepted. Giving primarily in MA and NY. No grants to individuals.
Application information: Contributes only to pre-selected organizations.
Officers: Harvey Beker, Pres.; Jayne Beker, Secy.
Directors: George E. Crapple; Sheri Gurock; Alison Judd.
EIN: 133249239

5660
Robert A. and Renee E. Belfer Family Foundation ✧
c/o Belfer Mgmt., LLC
767 5th Ave., 46th Fl.
New York, NY 10153-0023 (212) 508-9500
Contact: Robert A. Belfer, Pres.

Established in 1990 in NY.
Donors: Robert A. Belfer; Jack Resnick & Sons, Inc.; Belfer Two Corp.
Foundation type: Independent foundation.
Financial data (yr. ended 12/31/12): Assets, $16,490,248 (M); gifts received, $1,968,665; expenditures, $9,373,313; qualifying distributions, $9,335,005; giving activities include $9,335,005 for 60 grants (high: $4,000,000; low: $150).
Purpose and activities: Giving primarily for the arts, education, health organizations and Jewish causes.
Fields of interest: Museums (art); Museums (ethnic/folk arts); Performing arts centers; Arts; Elementary/secondary education; Higher education; Medical school/education; Education; Cancer; Health organizations; Medical research, institute; Human services; Jewish federated giving programs; Jewish agencies & synagogues.
Limitations: Applications accepted. Giving primarily in New York, NY; some giving also in Houston, TX. No grants to individuals.
Application information:
Initial approach: Letter
Deadline(s): None
Officer: Robert A. Belfer, Pres. and Secy.
Trustees: Laurence D. Belfer; Renee E. Belfer.
EIN: 136935616

5661
Belvedere Charitable Foundation ✧ ☆
1251 Ave. of the Americas, 17th Fl.
New York, NY 10020-1104

Established in 2006 in NY.
Donors: Louis M. Bacon; Michael Daffey.
Foundation type: Independent foundation.
Financial data (yr. ended 12/31/12): Assets, $208,970 (M); gifts received, $418,026; expenditures, $463,873; qualifying distributions, $463,617; giving activities include $461,085 for 10 grants (high: $199,060; low: $1,592).
Fields of interest: Education; Human services.
Limitations: Applications not accepted. Giving primarily in the U.K. No grants to individuals.
Application information: Unsolicited requests for funds not accepted.
Officers: Louis M. Bacon, Pres.; Lawrence M. Noe, V.P.; Chaz Rockey, Treas.
EIN: 980509706

5662
Helen Andrus Benedict Foundation, Inc. ✧
c/o The Philanthropic Group
630 5th Ave., 20th Fl.
New York, NY 10111-0100 (212) 501-7785
Contact: Barbara R. Greenberg, Staff Consultant
FAX: (212) 501-7788; E-mail: info@habf.org; Main URL: http://www.habf.org

Established in 1997 in NY.
Donor: John E. Andrus Memorial, Inc.
Foundation type: Independent foundation.
Financial data (yr. ended 12/31/13): Assets, $18,326,654 (M); expenditures, $794,329; qualifying distributions, $771,435; giving activities include $567,650 for 13 grants (high: $120,000; low: $1,250).
Purpose and activities: The foundation is committed to creating good places for people to grow old while maintaining the maximum possible levels of independence. An important component of such an elder-friendly community is the opportunity for older people to remain actively engaged in the life of their communities.
Fields of interest: Aging, centers/services.
Type of support: Program-related investments/loans; General/operating support.
Limitations: Applications not accepted. Giving primarily in Westchester County, NY with emphasis on the city of Yonkers. No grants to individuals.
Publications: Grants list.
Application information: Grants are made by invitation only.
Officers and Directors:* Bob Hedlund,* Pres.; John J. Lynagh, Secy.; Beth Shogren,* Treas.; Colby L. Andrus, Jr.; Elizabeth H. Andrus; Davis Benedict; Bob Cadoux; Carol M. Cardon; Marc de Venoge; Jocelyn Downie; Irene Gutheil; McCain McMurray; Andrew Sherman.
EIN: 133940833

5663
Frances & Benjamin Benenson Foundation, Inc. ✧
708 3rd Ave., 28th Fl.
New York, NY 10017-4232 (212) 867-0990
Contact: Bruce W. Benenson

Established in 1983 in NY.
Donors: Charles B. Benenson†; Marx Realty & Improvement Co., Inc.
Foundation type: Independent foundation.
Financial data (yr. ended 11/30/13): Assets, $35,809,066 (M); expenditures, $3,055,776; qualifying distributions, $2,461,661; giving activities include $2,409,475 for 25 grants (high: $612,450; low: $20).
Purpose and activities: Support primarily for human services, arts and culture, education, health care, and community development.
Fields of interest: Museums; Arts; Elementary/secondary education; Higher education; Education; Health care; Health organizations, association; Human services; Jewish agencies & synagogues.
Type of support: Continuing support; Endowments.
Limitations: Applications accepted. Giving on a national basis. No grants to individuals.
Application information: Application form not required.
Initial approach: Proposal
Deadline(s): None
Officers: Bruce W. Benenson, Co-Pres.; Frederick C. Benenson, Co-Pres.; Lawrence B. Benenson, Co-Pres.; Richard Kessler, V.P.; Deborah Ciolfi, Secy.; David Thomas, Treas.
EIN: 133267113
Selected grants: The following grants are a representative sample of this grantmaker's funding activity:
$150,000 to Museum of Modern Art, New York, NY, 2011.
$100,000 to UJA-Federation of New York, New York, NY, 2011.
$50,000 to American Civil Liberties Union Foundation, New York, NY, 2011.
$50,000 to Doctors Without Borders USA, New York, NY, 2011.
$50,000 to New York University, New York, NY, 2011.
$50,000 to New York-Presbyterian Hospital, New York, NY, 2011.
$35,000 to Nature Conservancy, New York, NY, 2011.
$25,000 to New York-Presbyterian Fund, New York, NY, 2011.
$20,000 to Center for Constitutional Rights, New York, NY, 2011.
$10,000 to American Folk Art Museum, New York, NY, 2011.

5664
The Robert and Nettie Benenson Foundation ✧ ☆
20 W. 55th St., 6th Fl.
New York, NY 10019-5373

Established about 1957 in NY.
Foundation type: Independent foundation.
Financial data (yr. ended 12/31/13): Assets, $2,266,439 (M); gifts received, $3,000,000; expenditures, $3,146,939; qualifying distributions, $3,146,624; giving activities include $3,136,800 for 8 grants (high: $3,000,000; low: $500).
Purpose and activities: Giving to higher education and the arts.
Fields of interest: Performing arts; Higher education; Health organizations, association; United Ways and Federated Giving Programs; Jewish agencies & synagogues.
Type of support: General/operating support.
Limitations: Applications not accepted. Giving primarily in NC and NY. No grants to individuals.
Application information: Unsolicited requests for funds not accepted.
Officers: Gladys S. Benenson, Pres.; Lisa Quattrocchi, Secy.; Albert Fleischman, Treas.
EIN: 510173119

5665
The Edward H. Benenson Foundation Inc. ✧
(formerly RNB Foundation, Inc.)
20 W. 55th St., Ste. 6
New York, NY 10019-5373

Established in 1955 in NY.
Foundation type: Independent foundation.
Financial data (yr. ended 12/31/13): Assets, $11,609,308 (M); gifts received, $5,007; expenditures, $682,855; qualifying distributions, $682,225; giving activities include $681,000 for 41 grants (high: $252,500; low: $250).

Fields of interest: Arts; Education; Human services; Jewish federated giving programs; Jewish agencies & synagogues.
Limitations: Applications not accepted. Giving primarily in FL, NY, and RI. No grants to individuals.
Application information: Contributes only to pre-selected organizations.
Officers: Gladys S. Benenson, Pres.; Lisa Benenson Quattrocchi, Secy.; Albert Fleischman, Treas.
EIN: 136162730

5666
The Berg Family Foundation ✧
9 Elmhirst Dr.
Old Westbury, NY 11568-1007 (516) 626-1868
Contact: Alfred Berg, Tr.; Gayle Berg, Tr.

Established in 2007 in NY.
Donors: Alfred Berg; Gayle Berg.
Foundation type: Independent foundation.
Financial data (yr. ended 12/31/12): Assets, $7,711,798 (M); gifts received, $1,468,906; expenditures, $630,304; qualifying distributions, $595,390; giving activities include $595,390 for grants.
Fields of interest: Higher education; Jewish federated giving programs.
Limitations: Applications accepted. Giving primarily in NY; some funding also in MA.
Application information: Application form required.
Initial approach: Letter
Deadline(s): None
Trustees: Alfred K. Berg; Gayle R. Berg.
EIN: 260745467

5667
The David Berg Foundation, Inc. ✧
16 E. 73rd St., Ste. 1R
New York, NY 10021-4129 (212) 517-8634
Contact: Michele Tocci, Pres.
FAX: (212) 517-8636;
E-mail: mtocci@bergfoundation.org

Established in 1994 in NY.
Donor: David Berg Settlor Trust.
Foundation type: Independent foundation.
Financial data (yr. ended 12/31/12): Assets, $94,343,132 (M); gifts received, $5,131,606; expenditures, $6,655,068; qualifying distributions, $5,505,457; giving activities include $4,711,643 for 94 grants (high: $1,000,000; low: $5,000).
Fields of interest: Museums; Historic preservation/historical societies; Legal services; Jewish agencies & synagogues.
International interests: England; Israel.
Type of support: General/operating support; Continuing support; Annual campaigns; Equipment; Program development; Conferences/seminars; Professorships; Publication; Curriculum development; Fellowships; Scholarship funds; Research; Exchange programs.
Limitations: Applications accepted. Giving primarily in New York, NY. No grants to individuals.
Publications: Application guidelines; Grants list.
Application information: Application form not required.
Initial approach: Letter
Copies of proposal: 1
Deadline(s): Mar. 15 (for June); June 25 (for Nov.); and Nov. 15 (for Feb.)
Board meeting date(s): June, Oct., and Feb.
Officers: Michele C. Tocci, Pres.; William D. Zabel, V.P.; Jerome Zoffer, Secy.-Treas.
Number of staff: 1 full-time professional; 1 part-time professional; 1 part-time support.
EIN: 133753217

5668
The Berkowitz Family Charitable Trust ✧
(formerly The Berkowitz Family Charitable Trust)
1665 47th St.
Brooklyn, NY 11204-1142

Established in 1992 in NY and NJ.
Donors: Israel Berkowitz; Leopold Berkowitz; Morris Berkowitz; Frady Zyskind; Khal Binyomin Dovid; Joel Gold; Brooklyn Queens Nursing Home; Yeshiva Novominsk; Yeshiva Imrei Yosef.
Foundation type: Independent foundation.
Financial data (yr. ended 12/31/12): Assets, $11,551,378 (M); gifts received, $314,000; expenditures, $804,354; qualifying distributions, $716,484; giving activities include $716,484 for grants.
Purpose and activities: Giving primarily to Jewish agencies, temples, and schools.
Fields of interest: Education; Jewish agencies & synagogues.
Limitations: Applications not accepted. Giving primarily in Brooklyn, NY. No grants to individuals.
Application information: Contributes only to pre-selected organizations.
Trustees: Israel Berkowitz; Leopold Berkowitz; Morris Berkowitz; Frady Zyskind.
EIN: 226585269

5669
The Judy & Howard Berkowitz Foundation ✧
c/o The Ayco Co., LP
P.O. Box 860
Saratoga Springs, NY 12866-0860
Contact: Joseph N. Vet

Established in 1987 in NY.
Donors: Howard P. Berkowitz; Judith R. Berkowitz.
Foundation type: Independent foundation.
Financial data (yr. ended 03/31/13): Assets, $88,600 (M); gifts received, $650,000; expenditures, $636,465; qualifying distributions, $627,175; giving activities include $627,175 for grants.
Purpose and activities: Giving primarily for the arts, particularly the performing arts, as well as for education, health and human services, and Jewish agencies.
Fields of interest: Performing arts; Arts; Higher education, university; Education; Hospitals (general); Health organizations, association; Human services; Children/youth, services; International affairs; Jewish federated giving programs; Jewish agencies & synagogues.
Limitations: Applications not accepted. Giving primarily in New York, NY. No grants to individuals.
Application information: Contributes only to pre-selected organizations.
Trustees: Howard P. Berkowitz; Judith R. Berkowitz; Roger S. Berkowitz; Sandra L. Berkowitz.
EIN: 133371065
Selected grants: The following grants are a representative sample of this grantmaker's funding activity:
$200,000 to New-York Historical Society, New York, NY, 2011.
$150,000 to Rockefeller University, New York, NY, 2011.
$40,000 to Vail Valley Foundation, Avon, CO, 2011.
$25,000 to New-York Historical Society, New York, NY, 2011.
$25,000 to Rockefeller University, New York, NY, 2011.
$25,000 to Rockefeller University, New York, NY, 2011.
$25,000 to Rockefeller University, New York, NY, 2011.
$20,000 to New-York Historical Society, New York, NY, 2011.
$8,000 to New-York Historical Society, New York, NY, 2011.
$5,000 to New York Public Library, New York, NY, 2011.

5670
The Robert Berne Foundation ✧
45 W. 60th St., Ste. 34E
New York, NY 10023-7949

Donors: Vivian Milstein; Robert Berne; Vivian L. Milstein Descendant's Trust.
Foundation type: Independent foundation.
Financial data (yr. ended 12/31/12): Assets, $1,562,802 (M); gifts received, $1,600,000; expenditures, $1,778,115; qualifying distributions, $1,777,785; giving activities include $1,777,785 for 36 grants (high: $600,000; low: $50).
Fields of interest: Higher education; Human services; YM/YWCAs & YM/YWHAs; Philanthropy/voluntarism.
Limitations: Applications not accepted. Giving primarily in New York, NY.
Application information: Contributes only to pre-selected organizations.
Trustees: Robert Berne; Patricia Puma.
EIN: 256912398

5671
The Eddie and Rachelle Betesh Family Foundation, Inc. ✧
c/o Saramax Apparel
1372 Broadway, 7th Fl.
New York, NY 10018-6107

Established in 1998 in DE and NY.
Donors: Eddie Betesh; Rachelle Betesh.
Foundation type: Independent foundation.
Financial data (yr. ended 12/31/12): Assets, $1,329,484 (M); gifts received, $1,673,600; expenditures, $1,697,457; qualifying distributions, $1,697,142; giving activities include $1,696,621 for 360 grants (high: $227,500; low: $18).
Purpose and activities: Giving primarily to Jewish agencies, temples, and schools.
Fields of interest: Education; Jewish federated giving programs; Jewish agencies & synagogues.
Limitations: Applications not accepted. Giving primarily in NY. No grants to individuals.
Application information: Contributes only to pre-selected organizations.
Officers: Eddie Betesh, Pres.; Rachelle Betesh, Treas.
EIN: 133981963

5672
The BFF Foundation, Inc. ✧
1428 36th St., Ste. 200
Brooklyn, NY 11218-3765

Established in 1996 in NY.
Donor: Joseph Bistritzky.
Foundation type: Operating foundation.
Financial data (yr. ended 12/31/12): Assets, $29,780,007 (M); expenditures, $1,422,057; qualifying distributions, $1,370,355; giving activities include $1,370,230 for 65 grants (high: $300,000; low: $36).
Purpose and activities: Giving primarily for Jewish organizations, temples, and schools.
Fields of interest: Elementary/secondary education; Jewish agencies & synagogues.
Type of support: Grants to individuals.
Limitations: Applications not accepted. Giving primarily in NJ and Brooklyn, NY.
Application information: Unsolicited requests for funds not accepted.
Officers: Joseph Bistritzky, Pres.; Yehudis Gold, Secy.; Sheila Bistritzky, Treas.
EIN: 113261912
Selected grants: The following grants are a representative sample of this grantmaker's funding activity:
$180 to Ezrat Israel, Brooklyn, NY, 2012. To Further Jewish Causes Further Jewish Causes.

5673
Bialkin Family Foundation ✧
c/o Skadden, Arps, Slate, Meagher & Flom LLP
4 Times Sq.
New York, NY 10036-6515

Established in 1968 in NY.
Donors: Kenneth J. Bialkin; Ann E. Bialkin.
Foundation type: Independent foundation.
Financial data (yr. ended 12/31/13): Assets, $19,165,660 (M); expenditures, $929,580; qualifying distributions, $767,020; giving activities include $757,103 for 124 grants (high: $100,000; low: $150).
Purpose and activities: Giving primarily to Jewish causes; some funding also for the arts.
Fields of interest: Arts, association; Arts; Elementary/secondary education; Higher education; Education; Human services; Children/youth, services; Jewish federated giving programs; Jewish agencies & synagogues.
Limitations: Applications not accepted. Giving primarily in New York, NY. No grants to individuals.
Application information: Contributes only to pre-selected organizations.
Officers and Directors:* Kenneth J. Bialkin,* Pres.; Ann E. Bialkin,* Sr. V.P.; Johanna Bialkin, V.P.; Lisa Bialkin, V.P.; Jonathan L. Koslow, Secy.
EIN: 237003181

5674
Margaret T. Biddle Foundation ✧
c/o Cullen and Dykman
100 Quentin Roosevelt Blvd., Ste. 402
Garden City, NY 11530-4843

Incorporated in 1952 in NY.
Donor: Margaret T. Biddle†.
Foundation type: Independent foundation.
Financial data (yr. ended 12/31/13): Assets, $373,491 (M); expenditures, $2,617,677; qualifying distributions, $2,611,587; giving activities include $2,580,000 for 17 grants (high: $500,000; low: $5,000).
Fields of interest: Environment, natural resources; Environment; Human services; Children/youth, services.
Type of support: General/operating support.
Limitations: Applications not accepted. Giving in the U.S., with emphasis on Washington, DC, MA and TX. No grants to individuals.
Application information: Contributes only to pre-selected organizations.
Officers and Directors:* Peter B. Schulze,* Pres.; Christian C. Hohenlohe, V.P. and Secy.; Richard A. Smith,* V.P. and Treas.; Catherine H. Jacobus, V.P.; Charles T. Schulze.
EIN: 131936016
Selected grants: The following grants are a representative sample of this grantmaker's funding activity:
$200,000 to Mercy Ships Foundation, Lindale, TX, 2012. For general corporate purposes of donee.

5675
Big Guy Foundation, Inc. ✧
P.O. Box 203
Mill Neck, NY 11765-0203 (516) 671-0746
Contact: Susan Altamore Carusi, Exec. V.P.

Established in 2004 in NY.
Donors: Bruce J. Carusi; Susan Altamore Carusi; James Fantaci; Anna Fantaci; Ted Lachowicz; Cheryl Lachowicz.
Foundation type: Operating foundation.
Financial data (yr. ended 12/31/13): Assets, $249,167 (M); gifts received, $964,000; expenditures, $791,354; qualifying distributions, $791,354; giving activities include $126,170 for 51 grants (high: $39,000; low: $100), and $665,003 for 84 grants to individuals (high: $1,000; low: $5).
Fields of interest: Education.
Limitations: Applications accepted. Giving primarily in NY.
Application information: Application form required.
Initial approach: Request application
Copies of proposal: 1
Deadline(s): None
Officers: Bruce Carusi, Pres.; Susan Altamore Carusi, Exec. V.P. and Secy.-Treas.; Steven Altamore, V.P.; Navila Armon, V.P.; Leonard Shavel, V.P.
EIN: 542118808
Selected grants: The following grants are a representative sample of this grantmaker's funding activity:
$4,000 to Adelphi University, Garden City, NY, 2011.

5676
William Bingham 2nd Betterment Fund ✧
c/o Christine O'Donnell, US Trust
114 W. 47th St., NY8-114-10-02
New York, NY 10036-1510 (646) 855-1011
Contact: Christine O'Donnell, V.P., US Trust
FAX: (646) 855-5463;
E-mail: betterment@ustrust.com

Foundation type: Independent foundation.
Financial data (yr. ended 12/31/13): Assets, $38,017,489 (M); expenditures, $2,254,917; qualifying distributions, $2,037,412; giving activities include $1,667,577 for 119 grants (high: $50,000; low: $715).
Purpose and activities: Giving primarily for education, the environment, health care, philanthropy and voluntarism, and creative economy.
Fields of interest: Education; Environment; Health care; Philanthropy/voluntarism; Economics.
Type of support: General/operating support; Capital campaigns.
Limitations: Applications accepted. Giving limited to ME. No support for religious activities or programs. No grants to individuals.
Publications: Application guidelines; Grants list.
Application information: Online application on foundation web site. Application form required.
Initial approach: Proposal
Deadline(s): Jan. 31., Apr. 30, and Sept. 30
Board meeting date(s): Mar., June, and Dec.
Final notification: 2-3 months
Trustees: William P. Clough III; Carol Berg Geist; Martin J. Grohman; Andrew L. Tansey; William B. Winship; Carolyn S. Wollen; Bank of America, N.A.
EIN: 136072625
Selected grants: The following grants are a representative sample of this grantmaker's funding activity:
$75,000 to University of New England, Biddeford, ME, 2012. For unrestricted general support.
$50,000 to Maine Medical Center, Portland, ME, 2012. For unrestricted general support.
$30,000 to Community Concepts, Lewiston, ME, 2012. For unrestricted general support.
$30,000 to La Arts, Lewiston, ME, 2012. For unrestricted general support.
$25,000 to Androscoggin Land Trust, Auburn, ME, 2012. For unrestricted general support.
$25,000 to Maine Community Foundation, Ellsworth, ME, 2012. For unrestricted general support.
$25,000 to University of Southern Maine, Portland, ME, 2012. For unrestricted general support.
$20,000 to Consumers for Affordable Health Care Foundation, Augusta, ME, 2012. For unrestricted general support.
$15,000 to Audubon Society, Maine, Falmouth, ME, 2012. For unrestricted general support.
$15,000 to Preble Street, Portland, ME, 2012. For unrestricted general support.

5677
The Birkelund Fund ✧
c/o Barry M. Strauss Assoc., Ltd.
307 5th Ave., 8th Fl.
New York, NY 10016-6517

Established in 1989 in DE and NY.
Donor: John P. Birkelund.
Foundation type: Independent foundation.
Financial data (yr. ended 04/30/13): Assets, $7,298,932 (M); gifts received, $834,750; expenditures, $1,573,656; qualifying distributions, $1,519,240; giving activities include $1,518,600 for 37 grants (high: $1,025,000; low: $200).
Purpose and activities: Giving primarily for education, including a public library; some giving also for the arts, and health and human services.
Fields of interest: Museums (art); Arts; Higher education; Libraries (public); Education; Health care; Human services; International affairs.

Limitations: Applications not accepted. Giving primarily in CT, NJ, NY, and RI. No grants to individuals.
Application information: Contributes only to pre-selected organizations.
Officer: John P. Birkelund, Pres. and Treas.
Director: Kenneth W. Orce.
EIN: 133539224
Selected grants: The following grants are a representative sample of this grantmaker's funding activity:
$4,015,000 to Princeton University, Princeton, NJ, 2011. For general support.
$1,500,000 to Saint Lukes School, New York, NY, 2011. For general support.
$580,000 to Frick Collection, New York, NY, 2011. For general support.
$510,000 to Teach for America, New York, NY, 2011. For general support.
$410,000 to National Humanities Center, Research Triangle Park, NC, 2011. For general support.
$25,000 to New York Public Library, New York, NY, 2011. For general support.
$25,000 to Our Lady Queen of Angels School, New York, NY, 2011. For general support.
$20,000 to Brown University, Providence, RI, 2011. For general support.
$20,000 to Carnegie Hall Society, New York, NY, 2011. For general support.
$20,000 to Princeton University, Princeton, NJ, 2011. For general support.
$15,000 to Council on Foreign Relations, New York, NY, 2011. For general support.
$10,000 to American Academy in Berlin, New York Office, New York, NY, 2011. For general support.
$10,000 to Brown University, Providence, RI, 2011. For general support.
$10,000 to Teach for America, New York, NY, 2011. For general support.
$2,000 to American Academy of Arts and Sciences, Cambridge, MA, 2011. For general support.
$2,000 to Columbia University, New York, NY, 2011. For general support.
$1,000 to Mayo Foundation, Rochester, MN, 2011. For general support.

5678
Herbert & Diane Bischoff Foundation ✧ ☆
51 E. 42nd St., 11th Fl.
New York, NY 10017-5404

Donor: Boar's Head Provisions Co., Inc.
Foundation type: Independent foundation.
Financial data (yr. ended 07/31/13): Assets, $10,126,856 (M); expenditures, $638,213; qualifying distributions, $524,108; giving activities include $493,105 for 10 grants (high: $100,000; low: $3,105).
Fields of interest: Health care; Human services; Community/economic development.
Limitations: Applications not accepted. Giving primarily in New York, NY.
Application information: Contributes only to pre-selected organizations.
Trustee: Eric Bischoff.
EIN: 262515244
Selected grants: The following grants are a representative sample of this grantmaker's funding activity:
$250,000 to Convent of the Sacred Heart, New York, NY, 2011.

5679
Donald F. and Edna G. Bishop Scholarship Foundation ✧
(also known as Bishop Scholarship Foundation)
c/o Chemung Canal Trust Company
P.O. Box 1522
Elmira, NY 14902-1522

Established in 1989 in NY.
Donors: Donald Bishop; Edna G. Bishop‡.
Foundation type: Independent foundation.
Financial data (yr. ended 09/30/13): Assets, $14,908,353 (M); expenditures, $779,249; qualifying distributions, $706,705; giving activities include $706,705 for grants.
Fields of interest: Higher education, university; Hospitals (general).
Type of support: Scholarship funds.
Limitations: Applications not accepted. Giving primarily in NY and PA. No grants to individuals (directly).
Application information: Contributes only to pre-selected organizations.
Trustee: Chemung Canal Trust Company.
EIN: 166332120
Selected grants: The following grants are a representative sample of this grantmaker's funding activity:
$26,000 to DYouville College, Buffalo, NY, 2011. For scholarship awards.
$26,000 to University of Rochester, Rochester, NY, 2011. For scholarship awards.
$22,358 to Downstate Medical Center, Brooklyn, NY, 2011. For scholarship awards.
$21,750 to Hartwick College, Oneonta, NY, 2011. For scholarship awards.
$13,000 to Cedarville University, Cedarville, OH, 2011. For scholarship awards.
$13,000 to Clarkson University, Potsdam, NY, 2011. For scholarship awards.
$13,000 to Cornell University, Ithaca, NY, 2011. For scholarship awards.
$13,000 to Houghton College, Houghton, NY, 2011. For scholarship awards.
$13,000 to University of Vermont, Burlington, VT, 2011. For scholarship awards.
$13,000 to Worcester Polytechnic Institute, Worcester, MA, 2011. For scholarship awards.

5680
The BL Squared Foundation ✧ ☆
10 E. 40th St., 22nd Fl.
New York, NY 10016-0201

Established in 1997 in NY.
Donors: Stanley Bernstein; Sandy Liebhard; Mel Lifshitz; Sandy Bernstein; Vivian Bernstein.
Foundation type: Operating foundation.
Financial data (yr. ended 12/31/12): Assets, $5,089,199 (M); expenditures, $476,250; qualifying distributions, $466,000; giving activities include $466,000 for 11 grants (high: $100,000; low: $1,000).
Fields of interest: Jewish agencies & synagogues.
Limitations: Applications not accepted. Giving primarily in NY. No grants to individuals.
Application information: Contributes only to pre-selected organizations.
Trustees: Stanley Bernstein; Sandy Liebhard.
EIN: 137104062

5681
Leon Black Family Foundation Inc. ✧
9 W. 57th St., 43rd Fl.
New York, NY 10019-2700

Established in 1997 in DE and NY.
Donor: Leon D. Black.
Foundation type: Independent foundation.
Financial data (yr. ended 12/31/12): Assets, $8,935 (M); gifts received, $1,000,000; expenditures, $1,000,000; qualifying distributions, $1,000,000; giving activities include $1,000,000 for grants.
Fields of interest: Education; Jewish federated giving programs.
Limitations: Applications not accepted. Giving primarily in New York, NY. No grants to individuals.
Application information: Contributes only to pre-selected organizations.
Officers: Leon D. Black, Pres. and Treas.; Debra R. Black, V.P. and Secy.
Director: Jeffrey Epstein.
EIN: 133947890

5682
Nancy & Robert S. Blank Foundation ✧ ☆
c/o Whitcom Partners
375 Park Ave., Ste. 3800
New York, NY 10152-3899

Established in 1993 in PA.
Donors: Robert S. Blank; Nancy L. Blank; Matthew S. Blank; Samuel A. Blank; Wendy Blank Chaikin.
Foundation type: Independent foundation.
Financial data (yr. ended 08/31/13): Assets, $2,039,351 (M); gifts received, $15,000; expenditures, $581,090; qualifying distributions, $577,274; giving activities include $577,274 for 40 grants (high: $322,335; low: $100).
Purpose and activities: Giving primarily for Jewish federated giving programs and education.
Fields of interest: Higher education; Higher education, university; Human services; Jewish federated giving programs; Jewish agencies & synagogues.
Type of support: General/operating support.
Limitations: Applications not accepted. Giving primarily in NY. No grants to individuals.
Application information: Unsolicited requests for funds not accepted.
Officers: Robert S. Blank, Pres.; Nancy L. Blank, V.P.
EIN: 232738179
Selected grants: The following grants are a representative sample of this grantmaker's funding activity:
$10,000 to Alzheimers Association, Atlanta, GA, 2011.
$2,500 to Teach for America, New York, NY, 2011.

5683
Adele and Leonard Block Foundation, Inc. ✧
499 7th Ave., 21st Fl., South Tower
New York, NY 10018-6803 (917) 339-0344
Contact: Thomas Block, V.P.
E-mail: Tblock@blockbuildingsllc.com

Established in 1945 in NJ.
Donors: Leonard Block‡; Adele G. Block; Adele G. Block Revocable Trust.
Foundation type: Independent foundation.

Financial data (yr. ended 11/30/13): Assets, $5,007,347 (M); expenditures, $1,203,213; qualifying distributions, $1,189,378; giving activities include $1,189,378 for 75 grants (high: $150,000; low: $100).
Purpose and activities: Giving primarily for the arts, as well as for education, health, and human services.
Fields of interest: Museums; Performing arts, theater; Arts; Education; Hospitals (general); Health care; Health organizations; Eye research; Human services; Foundations (private grantmaking).
Type of support: General/operating support.
Limitations: Applications accepted. Giving primarily in New York, NY; some funding also in Washington, D.C.
Application information: Application form required.
Initial approach: Letter
Deadline(s): None
Officers and Directors:* Peggy Block Danziger,* Pres.; Adele G. Block,* V.P.; Thomas Block,* V.P.; Philip Heimlich,* Secy.; Robert Heun, Treas.
EIN: 226026000

5684
Bloomberg Philanthropies ✧
(formerly The Bloomberg Family Foundation, Inc.)
c/o Geller & Co.
909 3rd Ave., 16th Fl.
New York, NY 10022-4797
Main URL: http://www.bloomberg.org
Blog: http://www.bloomberg.org/blog
Bloomberg Philanthropies' Instagram: http://instagram.com/bloombergdotorg
Facebook: https://www.facebook.com/bloombergdotorg
Michael Bloomberg's Giving Pledge Profile: http://glasspockets.org/philanthropy-in-focus/eye-on-the-giving-pledge/profiles/bloomberg
Twitter: https://twitter.com/bloombergdotorg

Established in 2006.
Donor: Michael R. Bloomberg.
Foundation type: Independent foundation.
Financial data (yr. ended 12/31/13): Assets, $5,402,611,056 (M); gifts received, $351,835,466; expenditures, $270,900,330; qualifying distributions, $205,049,182; giving activities include $204,007,709 for 69 grants (high: $46,000,000; low: $23,374).
Purpose and activities: The mission is to ensure better, longer lives for the greatest number of people. The organization focuses on five key areas for creating lasting change: public health, environment, education, government innovation and the arts.
Fields of interest: Arts; Education; Environment; Public health; Philanthropy/voluntarism; African Americans/Blacks.
Type of support: Program-related investments/loans.
Limitations: Applications not accepted. Giving primarily in NY and on an international basis, with an emphasis in India and Switzerland. No grants to individuals.
Publications: Annual report.
Application information: Unsolicited requests for funds not accepted.
Officer and Directors:* Patricia E. Harris,* Chair. and C.E.O.; Tenley Albright; Emma Bloomberg; Georgina Bloomberg; Michael R. Bloomberg; Cory A. Booker; David L. Boren; Jeb Bush; Kenneth I. Chenault; D. Ronald Daniel; Manny Diaz; Fiona Druckenmiller; Patti E. Harris; Walter Isaacson; Maya Lin; John J. Mack; Joseph McShane, S.J.; Mike Mullen, USN (ret.); Sam Nunn; Samuel J. Palmisano; Hank M. Paulson, Jr.; Alfred Sommer; Martin Sorrell; Anne M. Tatlock; Dennis Walcott.
EIN: 205602483
Selected grants: The following grants are a representative sample of this grantmaker's funding activity:
$15,000,000 to Sierra Club Foundation, San Francisco, CA, 2012. To encourage use of clean energy and reduce coal dependency in the US.
$12,200,000 to World Health Organization, Geneva, Switzerland, 2012. To promote road safety in low-middle income countries.
$7,644,000 to Campaign for Tobacco-Free Kids, Washington, DC, 2012. For programs to reduce tobacco use.
$5,400,000 to Living Cities: The National Community Development Initiative, New York, NY, 2012. To replicate financial empowerment centers in cities across the US.
$3,744,000 to World Lung Foundation, New York, NY, 2012. To collaborate with Gates Foundation to reduce tobacco use.
$3,330,000 to MDRC, New York, NY, 2012. To improve outcomes for black and hispanic youth.
$2,300,000 to Johns Hopkins University, Bloomberg School of Public Health, Baltimore, MD, 2012. To promote road safety in low-middle income countries.
$2,081,300 to Louisville, City of, Louisville, KY, 2012. To fund innovation in city government.
$2,000,000 to Environmental Defense Fund, New York, NY, 2012. To minimize impact that the extraction of natural gas has on the environment.
$2,000,000 to Nonprofit Finance Fund, New York, NY, 2012. For arts programs tied to economic development.

5685
Blue Ridge Foundation New York ✧
(formerly Rubicon Foundation)
150 Court St., 2nd Fl.
Brooklyn, NY 11201-6274 (718) 923-1400
FAX: (718) 923-2869; E-mail: info@brfny.org; Main URL: http://www.brfny.org
Facebook: https://www.facebook.com/blueridgefoundationnewyork
Twitter: https://twitter.com/blue_ridge

Established in 1993 in NY.
Donors: John A. Griffin; Blue Ridge Capital LLC.
Foundation type: Independent foundation.
Financial data (yr. ended 11/30/13): Assets, $2,034,902 (M); gifts received, $2,840,000; expenditures, $1,784,985; qualifying distributions, $2,032,054; giving activities include $860,549 for 20 grants (high: $250,000; low: $250), and $550,000 for 4 loans/program-related investments (high: $250,000; low: $100,000).
Purpose and activities: The grantmaker supports social change strategies that operate in high poverty communities and connect people to the opportunities, resources and support they need to fulfill their full potential. The foundation supports start-up organizations in New York City only, helping to develop organizations by providing opportunities for capacity development.
Fields of interest: Education; Youth development; Children/youth, services; Community/economic development; Venture philanthropy.
Type of support: Management development/capacity building.
Limitations: Applications not accepted. Giving primarily in New York, NY. No support for organizations that are more than 2 years old, or for charter or private schools, theater groups, filmmaking, sports or athletic organizations, organizations that exist solely to publish curriculum, books or other media, or organizations that only provide services to constituencies outside of the U.S.
Application information: The foundation is currently not accepting applications. See foundation web site for updates in this matter.
Officers and Trustees:* John Griffin,* Pres.; Homer Smith, Treas.; Richard Bello; Amy M. Griffin; John Kirtley.
EIN: 137029270

5686
Edith C. Blum Foundation, Inc. ✧
c/o EisnerAmper, LLP
750 3rd Ave.
New York, NY 10017-2703
E-mail: info@ecbfoundation.org; Application address: 396 Washington St., Box 309, Wellesley, MA 02481; tel.: (646) 494-4205

Established in 1990 in NY as successor to the Edith C. Blum Foundation.
Donor: Edith C. Blum Foundation.
Foundation type: Independent foundation.
Financial data (yr. ended 09/30/13): Assets, $18,486,749 (M); expenditures, $1,117,997; qualifying distributions, $1,014,354; giving activities include $922,500 for 45 grants (high: $150,000; low: $5,000).
Purpose and activities: Giving primarily for the arts, education, health, Jewish organizations, and human services, including services for people who are blind.
Fields of interest: Performing arts; Performing arts, theater; Arts; Higher education; Education; Medical research, institute; Human services; Jewish federated giving programs; Jewish agencies & synagogues; Blind/visually impaired.
Limitations: Giving primarily in New York, NY. No grants to individuals.
Application information: Application form not required.
Deadline(s): None
Officers and Directors:* Roy R. Friedman,* Pres. and Treas.; Nancy R. Green,* Secy.; Seth A. Friedman.
EIN: 133564317
Selected grants: The following grants are a representative sample of this grantmaker's funding activity:
$175,000 to American Committee for the Weizmann Institute of Science, New York, NY, 2011.
$165,000 to American Friends of the Hebrew University, New York, NY, 2011.
$75,000 to Rockefeller University, New York, NY, 2011.
$55,000 to Weill Medical College of Cornell University, New York, NY, 2011.
$50,000 to Dana-Farber Cancer Institute, Boston, MA, 2011.
$15,000 to Macula Vision Research Foundation, West Conshohocken, PA, 2011.
$10,000 to Metropolitan Museum of Art, New York, NY, 2011.
$10,000 to UJA-Federation of New York, New York, NY, 2011.

$5,000 to Food Bank for New York City, New York, NY, 2011.
$5,000 to Henry Street Settlement, New York, NY, 2011.

5687
The Mitchell J. Blutt and Margo K. Blutt Family Foundation ✧ ☆
c/o Mitchell Blutt
57 E. 90th St.
New York, NY 10128

Established in 1999 in NY.
Donors: Mitchell J. Blutt; Alpha Corp.
Foundation type: Independent foundation.
Financial data (yr. ended 11/30/13): Assets, $2,753 (M); gifts received, $886,000; expenditures, $885,245; qualifying distributions, $883,705; giving activities include $881,800 for 24 grants (high: $679,000; low: $500).
Fields of interest: Arts; Higher education; Education; Jewish agencies & synagogues; Religion.
Limitations: Applications not accepted. Giving primarily in NY and PA. No grants to individuals.
Application information: Unsolicited requests for funds not accepted.
Directors: Margo K. Blutt; Mitchell J. Blutt.
EIN: 134053216
Selected grants: The following grants are a representative sample of this grantmaker's funding activity:
$679,000 to University of Pennsylvania Press, Philadelphia, PA, 2013.
$68,200 to Peconic Land Trust, Southampton, NY, 2013.
$33,000 to Weill Medical College of Cornell University, New York, NY, 2013.
$31,000 to New York City Ballet, New York, NY, 2013.
$12,500 to Collegiate School, New York, NY, 2013.
$7,500 to School of American Ballet, New York, NY, 2013.
$6,000 to Columbia Grammar and Preparatory School, New York, NY, 2013.
$5,400 to Professional Childrens School, New York, NY, 2013.
$2,000 to Creative Arts Workshops for Kids, New York, NY, 2013.
$2,000 to Nypweill Cornell Medical College, New York, NY, 2013.

5688
BMS Family Foundation ✧
131 Jericho Tpke., Ste. 400
Jericho, NY 11753-1017

Donors: B. Silver; M. Silver.
Foundation type: Independent foundation.
Financial data (yr. ended 12/31/13): Assets, $22,881,980 (M); gifts received, $2,000,000; expenditures, $2,001,191; qualifying distributions, $2,000,000; giving activities include $2,000,000 for 1 grant.
Fields of interest: Philanthropy/voluntarism.
Limitations: Applications not accepted. Giving primarily in Covington, KY.
Application information: Contributes only to pre-selected organizations.
Officers: M. Silver, Pres. and Treas.; B. Silver, V.P.; Jay D. Waxenberg, Secy.
EIN: 461082072

5689
The Bnai Jacob Foundation ✧
(formerly Jonathan Strasser Foundation)
61-35 Dry Harbor Rd.
Middle Village, NY 11379-1528

Established in 1989 in NY.
Donor: Jonathan Strasser.
Foundation type: Independent foundation.
Financial data (yr. ended 10/31/13): Assets, $53,556,587 (M); gifts received, $1,000,000; expenditures, $3,041,001; qualifying distributions, $2,727,466; giving activities include $2,433,930 for grants.
Fields of interest: Jewish agencies & synagogues.
Limitations: Applications not accepted. Giving primarily in NY. No grants to individuals.
Application information: Contributes only to pre-selected organizations.
Trustee: Jonathan Strasser.
EIN: 112993178

5690
Elmer and Mamdouha Bobst Foundation, Inc. ✧
70 Washington Sq. S., Ste. 1209
New York, NY 10012-1019

Incorporated in 1968 in NY.
Donors: Elmer H. Bobst†; Mamdouha Bobst.
Foundation type: Independent foundation.
Financial data (yr. ended 12/31/13): Assets, $49,276,967 (M); expenditures, $5,591,060; qualifying distributions, $5,267,400; giving activities include $5,203,500 for 16 grants (high: $2,500,000; low: $500).
Purpose and activities: Giving primarily for higher education; funding also for hospitals, and children and social services.
Fields of interest: Higher education; Higher education, university; Animal welfare; Veterinary medicine, hospital; Hospitals (general); Cancer; Human services; Children/youth, services.
Limitations: Applications not accepted. Giving primarily in New York, NY; funding also in Beirut, Lebanon.
Publications: Annual report; Informational brochure.
Application information: Contributes only to pre-selected organizations.
Officers: Mamdouha S. Bobst, Pres.; Charles Goodfellow, V.P.; Randa Haffar, Secy.; Robert Task, Treas.
Directors: Farouk El-Sayed; Patricia Nixon Cox.
EIN: 132616114

5691
The Alexander Bodini Foundation ✧
(formerly The Alexander Bodini Charitable Foundation)
825 5th Ave.
New York, NY 10065
Contact: Angie Lo, Treas.

Donors: ACP Luxury Corp.; ACP MacDouglas Corp.; The Alexander Charitable Trust; ACP Holdings Inc.
Foundation type: Independent foundation.
Financial data (yr. ended 12/31/12): Assets, $913,285 (M); gifts received, $777,795; expenditures, $836,591; qualifying distributions, $804,059; giving activities include $801,295 for 33 grants (high: $210,000; low: $1,000).
Fields of interest: Arts; Education.
Limitations: Applications accepted. Giving primarily in New York, NY.
Application information: Application form required.
Initial approach: Proposal
Deadline(s): None
Officers: Daniele D. Bodini, Pres.; Angie Lo, Treas.
EIN: 203286810

5692
The Bodman Foundation ✧
767 3rd Ave., 4th Fl.
New York, NY 10017-2023 (212) 644-0322
Contact: John B. Krieger, Secy., Exec. Dir. and Asst. Treas.
FAX: (212) 759-6510;
E-mail: main@achelis-bodman-fnds.org; Main URL: http://www.achelis-bodman-fnds.org

Incorporated in 1945 in NJ.
Donors: George M. Bodman†; Louise C. Bodman†.
Foundation type: Independent foundation.
Financial data (yr. ended 12/31/12): Assets, $57,175,047 (M); expenditures, $3,359,242; qualifying distributions, $3,110,019; giving activities include $2,857,700 for 124 grants (high: $200,000; low: $400).
Purpose and activities: Support largely for poor and disconnected youth; K-12 education, with preference for school reform projects, charter schools, and school choice programs rather than nonprofits that provide direct services in public schools; arts and cultural programs in New York City and northern New Jersey; medical research. Other interests include voluntarism, entrepreneurship, strengthening the two-parent family, fatherhood (and father absence), promoting the institution of marriage, job training and placement, faith-based programs, prevention and early intervention, and measurable participant outcomes and program results, parent involvement, consumer choice, and innovation and cost-saving approaches.
Fields of interest: Arts; Education, reform; Elementary/secondary education; Health care, cost containment; Substance abuse, prevention; Medical research, institute; Employment, services; Children/youth, services; Family services; Family services, adolescent parents; Public policy, research; Children/youth; Youth; Disabilities, people with; Physically disabled; Military/veterans; Offenders/ex-offenders; Substance abusers; Economically disadvantaged.
Type of support: General/operating support; Equipment; Program development; Conferences/seminars; Publication; Seed money; Curriculum development; Scholarship funds; Research; Technical assistance; Program evaluation; Matching/challenge support.
Limitations: Applications accepted. Giving primarily in northern NJ and New York, NY. Generally, no support for political organizations, international projects, government agencies, public schools, (except charter schools), nonprofit programs and services mostly funded or wholly reimbursed by government, small performing arts groups, or national health or mental health organizations. No grants to individuals; generally no grants for travel, endowments, capital campaigns, housing, annual appeals, dinner functions, fundraising events, deficit financing, or films; no loans.
Publications: Application guidelines; Financial statement; Grants list.

Application information: Unless requested, do not send CDs, DVDs, discs, tapes, or proposals through the internet. Application guidelines and procedures are available on foundation web site. Application form not required.
Initial approach: Letter or short proposal
Copies of proposal: 1
Deadline(s): None
Board meeting date(s): Usually May, Sept., and Dec..
Final notification: 5 to 6 weeks
Officers and Trustees:* John N. Irwin III,* Chair. and C.E.O.; Russell P. Pennoyer,* Pres.; Peter Frelinghuysen,* V.P.; Mary S. Phipps,* V.P.; John B. Krieger, Secy. and Exec. Dir.; Horace I. Crary, Jr.,* Treas.; Hon. Walter J.P. Curley; Leslie Lenkowsky; Tatiana Pouschine.
Number of staff: 1 full-time professional; 2 part-time support.
EIN: 136022016
Selected grants: The following grants are a representative sample of this grantmaker's funding activity:
$400,000 to Rockefeller University, New York, NY, 2013. For Bio-Imaging Resource Center, payable over 2.25 years.
$75,000 to Fresh Air Fund, New York, NY, 2013. For Immigrant Outreach Project, payable over 1.25 years.
$75,000 to Gilder Lehrman Institute of American History, New York, NY, 2013. For New York City afterschool education programs for adolescents.
$75,000 to New-York Historical Society, New York, NY, 2013. For an exhibition, Chinese American: Exclusion/Inclusion, payable over 1.50 years.
$75,000 to Texas A & M University, College Station, TX, 2012. For Project on Religion and Politics in the Middle East, payable over 2.00 years.
$75,000 to We Can Do Better New Jersey for Kids, Mount Laurel, NJ, 2013. For general operating support, payable over 1.25 years.
$60,000 to National Council on Teacher Quality, Washington, DC, 2013. To publish Teacher Prep Review 2.0 and District Attendance Study.
$50,000 to American Council of Trustees and Alumni, Washington, DC, 2012. For Future of Academic Freedom project, payable over 1.50 years.
$50,000 to Center for Hearing and Communication, New York, NY, 2013. For Family Resource Center.
$50,000 to Foundation for Cultural Review, New York, NY, 2013. For general operating support, payable over 1.25 years.
$50,000 to Historic Districts Council, New York, NY, 2012. For Missing Historic District Street Signs.
$50,000 to Hudson Institute, Washington, DC, 2012. For America's Secrecy Wars by Gabriel Schoenfeld.
$50,000 to Institute for American Values, New York, NY, 2012. For The Social Costs and Benefits of Legalizing Commercial Casino Gambling in the State of New York, payable over 1.50 years.
$50,000 to Intrepid Sea-Air-Space Museum, New York, NY, 2012. For Project Enterprise, payable over 1.50 years.
$50,000 to Manhattan Institute for Policy Research, New York, NY, 2012. For Empire Center for New York State Policy, payable over 1.50 years.
$50,000 to National Council on Teacher Quality, Washington, DC, 2012. For National Review of Teacher Preparation Programs, payable over 1.50 years.
$50,000 to New York Botanical Garden, Bronx, NY, 2012. For general operating support, payable over 1.50 years.
$50,000 to TEAM Academy, Friends of, Newark, NJ, 2013. For start-up and first-year expenses of Seek Academy, payable over 1.50 years.
$25,000 to New York City Ballet, New York, NY, 2013. For general operating support.
$25,000 to Riverside Films, New York, NY, 2012. For production of a documentary titled Don Quixote in Newark, payable over 1.25 years.

5693
Bodner Family Foundation, Inc. ✧
152 W. 57th St.
New York, NY 10019-3386 (212) 581-0500
Contact: David Bodner, Pres.

Established in 1999 in NY.
Donors: David Bodner; Huberfeld Family Foundation.
Foundation type: Independent foundation.
Financial data (yr. ended 12/31/12): Assets, $24,113,599 (M); gifts received, $1,900,000; expenditures, $3,459,342; qualifying distributions, $3,422,050; giving activities include $3,422,050 for 14 grants (high: $2,685,000; low: $1,000).
Fields of interest: Jewish agencies & synagogues.
Limitations: Giving primarily in Brooklyn, NY.
Application information:
Initial approach: Letter
Deadline(s): None
Officers and Directors:* David Bodner,* Pres.; Naomi Bodner,* Secy.-Treas.; Moishe Bodner.
EIN: 134042545

5694
The Stanley and Roberta Bogen Charitable Foundation ✧
c/o Graf Repetti Co.
1114 6th Ave.
New York, NY 10036-7703

Established in 2008 in NY.
Donors: Roberta Bogen; Stanley Bogen.
Foundation type: Independent foundation.
Financial data (yr. ended 12/31/12): Assets, $1,265,683 (M); gifts received, $703,485; expenditures, $550,046; qualifying distributions, $545,967; giving activities include $545,967 for grants.
Fields of interest: Education; Environment; Human services.
Limitations: Applications not accepted.
Application information: Unsolicited requests for funds not accepted.
Trustee: Roberta Bogen; Stanley Bogen.
EIN: 943457573

5695
The Boisi Family Foundation ✧
c/o BCRS Assocs., LLC
77 Water St., 9th Fl.
New York, NY 10005-4401
GiveSmart: http://www.givesmart.org/Stories/Donors/Geoff-Boisi

Established in 1983 in NY.
Donors: Geoffrey T. Boisi; Norine I. Boisi.
Foundation type: Independent foundation.
Financial data (yr. ended 02/28/13): Assets, $699,969 (M); gifts received, $1,050,000; expenditures, $1,263,491; qualifying distributions, $1,246,597; giving activities include $1,241,237 for 35+ grants (high: $200,000).
Purpose and activities: Giving primarily for education, human services, and youth mentoring programs.
Fields of interest: Education; Youth development, adult & child programs; Human services.
Limitations: Applications not accepted. Giving primarily in New York, NY, and Washington, DC. No grants to individuals, or for scholarships; no loans.
Application information: Contributes only to pre-selected organizations.
Director: Robin Melvin.
Trustees: Geoffrey T. Boisi; Norine I. Boisi.
EIN: 133165815
Selected grants: The following grants are a representative sample of this grantmaker's funding activity:
$100,000 to National Leadership Roundtable on Church Management, Washington, DC, 2011. For general purpose.
$25,000 to Library of Congress, Washington, DC, 2011. For general purpose.
$25,000 to Society of Jesus of New England, Watertown, MA, 2011. For general purpose.
$24,873 to Foundations and Donors Interested in Catholic Activities, Washington, DC, 2011. For general purpose.
$15,000 to Music City Bowl, Nashville, TN, 2011. For general purpose.
$10,000 to Center for Advancing Health, Washington, DC, 2011. For general purpose.
$10,000 to Inner-City Scholarship Fund, New York, NY, 2011. For general purpose.
$7,500 to Foundations and Donors Interested in Catholic Activities, Washington, DC, 2011. For general purpose.
$5,000 to LIFT, Washington, DC, 2011. For general purpose.
$4,000 to Spence-Chapin Services to Families and Children, New York, NY, 2011. For general purpose.

5696
Botwinick-Wolfensohn Foundation, Inc. ✧
1350 Ave. of the Americas, Ste. 2900
New York, NY 10019-4801

Established in 1952 in NY.
Donors: James D. Wolfensohn; Benjamin Botwinick†; Edward Botwinick; Bessie Botwinick†.
Foundation type: Independent foundation.
Financial data (yr. ended 12/31/12): Assets, $13,969,677 (M); expenditures, $760,930; qualifying distributions, $716,140; giving activities include $716,140 for grants.
Purpose and activities: Emphasis on Israeli and Jewish interests, medical research, and social services.
Fields of interest: Performing arts, music; Education; Medical research, institute; Human services; Jewish agencies & synagogues.
International interests: Israel.
Type of support: General/operating support; Continuing support; Annual campaigns; Capital campaigns; Building/renovation; Program development; Seed money; Scholarship funds; Research.
Limitations: Applications not accepted. Giving primarily in New York, NY. No grants to individuals.
Application information: Unsolicited requests for funds not accepted.
Board meeting date(s): Annually in the fall

Officers and Directors:* James D. Wolfensohn,* Chair.; Edward Botwinick,* Pres.; Adam R. Wolfensohn,* V.P.; Elaine R. Wolfensohn,* V.P.; Andrew Botwinick,* Co-Secy.; Sara R. Wolfensohn,* Co-Secy.; Naomi R. Wolfensohn,* Treas.; Victoria Brown.
Number of staff: 1 part-time professional.
EIN: 136111833

5697
The Bouncer Foundation, Inc. ✧
17 East 62nd St.
New York, NY 10021-7204

Established in 2000 in DE.
Donor: Jonathan D. Sackler.
Foundation type: Independent foundation.
Financial data (yr. ended 12/31/13): Assets, $4,189 (M); gifts received, $1,263,446; expenditures, $1,278,471; qualifying distributions, $1,174,071; giving activities include $1,174,071 for 15 grants (high: $240,000; low: $7,500).
Fields of interest: Higher education; Education; Human services; Children.
Limitations: Applications not accepted. Giving primarily in CA, CT, DC, and NY. No grants to individuals.
Application information: Contributes only to pre-selected organizations.
Officers and Directors:* Jonathan D. Sackler,* Pres.; Mary Corson,* V.P. and Secy.-Treas.
EIN: 134119735
Selected grants: The following grants are a representative sample of this grantmaker's funding activity:
$500,000 to Lagniappe Project of New Orleans, New Orleans, LA, 2011.
$300,000 to Yale University, New Haven, CT, 2011.
$10,000 to Philanthropy Roundtable, Washington, DC, 2011.
$5,000 to Alliance for School Choice, Washington, DC, 2011.

5698
The Boxer Foundation ✧ ☆
66 Commack Rd., Ste. 201
Commack, NY 11725-3489

Established in 1985 in NY.
Donor: Leonard Boxer.
Foundation type: Independent foundation.
Financial data (yr. ended 11/30/13): Assets, $9,427,340 (M); expenditures, $512,274; qualifying distributions, $466,276; giving activities include $442,774 for 59 grants (high: $100,000; low: $50).
Purpose and activities: Funding primarily for hospitals and health care, and for Jewish agencies and temples.
Fields of interest: Arts; Higher education; Education; Hospitals (general); Health organizations, association; Human services; Jewish agencies & synagogues.
Type of support: General/operating support.
Limitations: Applications not accepted. Giving primarily in the greater metropolitan New York, NY, area, including Long Island. No grants to individuals.
Application information: Contributes only to pre-selected organizations.
Officer: Steven Boxer, Mgr.
EIN: 133345823

5699
Brach Family Foundation, Inc. ✧
1600 63rd St.
Brooklyn, NY 11204-2713 (718) 236-8000
Contact: Zigmond Brach, Pres.

Established in 1991 in NY.
Donors: Zigmond Brach; Sound Around, Corp.; United Talmudical Academy; Congregation Tifereth Uziel; Congregation Zichron Mayer Zvi; Yeshiva Imrei Yosef Spinka.
Foundation type: Independent foundation.
Financial data (yr. ended 12/31/13): Assets, $14,298,664 (M); gifts received, $2,200,000; expenditures, $1,628,694; qualifying distributions, $1,622,524; giving activities include $1,622,524 for 593 grants (high: $150,000; low: $72).
Purpose and activities: Giving primarily to Jewish agencies, temples, and schools.
Fields of interest: Education; Jewish agencies & synagogues.
Type of support: General/operating support; Research.
Limitations: Applications accepted. Giving primarily in Brooklyn, NY.
Application information: Application form not required.
Initial approach: Proposal
Deadline(s): None
Officer: Zigmond Brach, Pres.
EIN: 113067698

5700
Brach Foundation ✧ ☆
40 Ranick Rd.
Hauppauge, NY 11788

Donor: Samuel Brach.
Foundation type: Independent foundation.
Financial data (yr. ended 12/31/13): Assets, $11,456 (M); gifts received, $433,000; expenditures, $429,636; qualifying distributions, $433,000; giving activities include $433,000 for 24 grants (high: $70,000; low: $3,000).
Fields of interest: Jewish agencies & synagogues.
Limitations: Applications not accepted. Giving primarily in Brooklyn, NY. No grants to individuals.
Application information: Contributes only to pre-selected organizations.
Officer: Samuel Brach, Pres.
Directors: Abraham Brach; Zivia Brach.
EIN: 263850684

5701
The Richard and Susan Braddock Family Foundation, Inc. ✧
10 Gracie Sq., Apt. 9F
New York, NY 10028-8031

Established in 1999 in NY.
Donors: Richard S. Braddock; Susan Braddock; Jennifer Braddock Gerber.
Foundation type: Independent foundation.
Financial data (yr. ended 11/30/13): Assets, $8,435,073 (M); expenditures, $1,403,666; qualifying distributions, $1,331,485; giving activities include $1,296,100 for grants.
Purpose and activities: Giving primarily for the arts, education, and human services.
Fields of interest: Performing arts; Performing arts centers; Arts; Elementary/secondary education; Education; Human services.
Limitations: Applications not accepted. Giving primarily in NY. No grants to individuals.
Application information: Contributes only to pre-selected organizations.
Officer: Jennifer Braddock Gerber, Pres.
Directors: Richard S. Braddock; Susan S. Braddock.
EIN: 061565971

5702
Braka Philanthropic Foundation ✧ ☆
c/o Michele Needle
450 7th Ave., 45th Fl.
New York, NY 10123-0207

Established in 1994 in NJ.
Donors: Ivor Braka; David Braka; Benjamin Braka; Centunan Management, Corp.
Foundation type: Independent foundation.
Financial data (yr. ended 12/31/12): Assets, $10,511,483 (M); gifts received, $304,584; expenditures, $502,209; qualifying distributions, $486,042; giving activities include $486,042 for grants.
Purpose and activities: Giving primarily to Jewish organizations.
Fields of interest: Elementary/secondary education; Education; Human services; Jewish federated giving programs; Jewish agencies & synagogues.
Limitations: Applications not accepted. Giving primarily in FL and NY. No grants to individuals.
Application information: Contributes only to pre-selected organizations.
Officers: Benjamin Braka, Mgr.; David Braka, Mgr.; Ivor Braka, Mgr.
EIN: 226643642

5703
Branta Foundation, Inc. ✧
c/o Perelson Weiner
1 Dag Hammarskjold Plz., 42nd Fl.
New York, NY 10017-2286

Established in 1955 in NY.
Donors: Harvey Picker†; Harvey Picker Trust; Harvey Picker Revocable Trust.
Foundation type: Independent foundation.
Financial data (yr. ended 05/31/13): Assets, $32,590,381 (M); expenditures, $1,895,226; qualifying distributions, $2,476,833; giving activities include $2,476,833 for 5 grants (high: $1,000,000; low: $50,000).
Purpose and activities: Giving primarily for healthcare and the environment.
Fields of interest: Higher education; Environment; Health care; Human services.
Type of support: General/operating support.
Limitations: Applications not accepted. Giving primarily in ME and NY; funding also in MA. No grants to individuals.
Application information: Contributes only to pre-selected organizations.
Officers and Directors:* Frances Hamill,* Pres.; Gale Picker,* V.P.; Christine Beshar,* Secy.; Robert Beshar,* Treas.
EIN: 136130955

Selected grants: The following grants are a representative sample of this grantmaker's funding activity:
$1,000,000 to Natural Resources Defense Council, New York, NY, 2012.
$333,333 to Camden Public Library, Camden, ME, 2012.

5704
Daniel L. Nir & Jill E. Braufman Family Foundation, Inc. ✧
4 E. 66th St., 5th Fl.
New York, NY 10065-6548

Established in NY.
Donors: Daniel L. Nir; Jill E. Braufman; Daniel L. Nir and Jill E. Braufman Family.
Foundation type: Independent foundation.
Financial data (yr. ended 12/31/12): Assets, $1,549,961 (M); gifts received, $415,800; expenditures, $1,319,052; qualifying distributions, $1,289,756; giving activities include $1,282,447 for 101+ grants (high: $149,382).
Fields of interest: Arts; Education; Hospitals (general); Health organizations, association; Human services; Jewish federated giving programs; Jewish agencies & synagogues.
Limitations: Applications not accepted. Giving primarily in NY.
Application information: Contributes only to pre-selected organizations.
Officers: Jill E. Braufman, Pres.; Barry S. Berger, Secy.; Daniel L. Nir, Treas.
EIN: 300218951

5705
The L. Bravmann Foundation, Inc. ✧
3333-B Henry Hudson Pkwy., Apt. 6E
Riverdale, NY 10463-3241

Established in 1964 in NY.
Donors: Ludwig Bravmann; Lotte Bravmann.
Foundation type: Independent foundation.
Financial data (yr. ended 06/30/13): Assets, $21,681,215 (M); gifts received, $850,110; expenditures, $972,961; qualifying distributions, $941,252; giving activities include $941,252 for grants.
Purpose and activities: Giving primarily for Jewish welfare and Jewish agencies.
Fields of interest: Education; Human services; Jewish federated giving programs; Jewish agencies & synagogues.
Type of support: Capital campaigns; Building/renovation; Emergency funds; Scholarship funds.
Limitations: Applications not accepted. Giving primarily in New York, NY. No grants to individuals.
Application information: Contributes only to pre-selected organizations.
Officers and Directors:* Ludwig Bravmann,* Pres.; Lotte Bravmann,* Secy.-Treas.; Carol Bravmann; Judith E. Kaufthal; Matthew Maryles; Shimon Wolf.
EIN: 136168525
Selected grants: The following grants are a representative sample of this grantmaker's funding activity:
$3,000 to North Shore Hebrew Academy, Great Neck, NY, 2011.

5706
The Brennan Charitable Foundation Inc. ✧
c/o T. Kwiatkowski
131 Tulip Ave.
Floral Park, NY 11001

Donor: John V. Brennan.
Foundation type: Independent foundation.
Financial data (yr. ended 12/31/13): Assets, $1,976,339 (M); gifts received, $959,958; expenditures, $1,294,488; qualifying distributions, $1,283,667; giving activities include $1,282,000 for 6 grants (high: $1,000,000; low: $10,000).
Fields of interest: Education; Housing/shelter; Religion.
Limitations: Applications not accepted. Giving primarily in NY.
Application information: Unsolicited requests for funds not accepted.
Officers and Directors:* John V. Brennan,* Pres.; John O. Brennan,* Secy.; Anita M. Brennan,* Treas.; Paul F. Brennan; Marybeth B. Magee.
EIN: 113374432

5707
B. H. Breslauer Foundation, Inc. ✧ ☆
c/o Berge & Assoc., Inc.
25 W. 45th St., Ste. 504
New York, NY 10036-4902 (646) 326-9216
Contact: Ivan S. Rosenblum, Treas.
FAX: (212) 719-3925;
E-mail: bhbreslauerfdn@gmail.com

Established in 2003 in NY.
Donors: Antiquarian Book Foundation; Cambridge in America; University of California-Berkeley; UCLA Foundation; Newberry Library; American Friends for Charities; Art Institute of Chicago; Cotsen Library - Princeton; Ohio State University; University of Virginia; University of Pennsylvania; Grand Valley State University; Georgetown University; Americans for Oxford; McGill University; Morgan Library & Museum; Royal Oak Foundation; Chazen Museum of Art; Grolier Club; National Gallery of Art; Columbia University; Metropolitan Museum of Art; John Carter Brown Library; University of South Carolina; Oberlin College; Friends of The National Libraries; Bidwell Library; National Sporting Library; Johns Hopkins Library; Friends of Milton College; Association du Mecenat de Institut; Staats Bibliotek Berlin; American Antiquarian Society; North American Foundation for University of Manchester; Winterthur.
Foundation type: Independent foundation.
Financial data (yr. ended 12/31/13): Assets, $4,887,744 (M); expenditures, $1,155,172; qualifying distributions, $1,082,030; giving activities include $1,010,085 for 18 grants (high: $241,159; low: $4,050).
Purpose and activities: Funding of acquisitions for rare books and related materials for rare book libraries.
Fields of interest: Arts; Higher education; Philanthropy/voluntarism.
Limitations: Applications accepted. Giving on a national basis. No support for non-501(c)(3) organizations.
Publications: Annual report.
Application information: Application should include a statement of how the material to be acquired is appropriate to the applicant's collection. Application form not required.
Initial approach: Letter or e-mail
Copies of proposal: 3
Deadline(s): None
Final notification: Within 30 days
Officers: Felix Oyens, Pres.; William Voelkle, V.P.; Ivan S. Rosenblum, Secy.-Treas.
Number of staff: None.
EIN: 134076763
Selected grants: The following grants are a representative sample of this grantmaker's funding activity:
$100,000 to Friends of the National Libraries, London, England, 2012. For endowment.
$74,610 to University of South Carolina, Columbia, SC, 2012. For Boyuin Book of Hours.
$60,000 to American Antiquarian Society, Worcester, MA, 2012.
$37,200 to Staatsbibliothek zu Berlin, Berlin, Germany, 2012. For Maren Manuscript.
$22,500 to Staatsbibliothek zu Berlin, Berlin, Germany, 2012. For Catalogue of Books 1796.
$8,000 to Oberlin College, Oberlin, OH, 2012. For Miniature of Crucifixion 15th Century.
$8,000 to University of Pennsylvania, Philadelphia, PA, 2012. For Manuscript Asylum for Female Ophans.

5708
The Deborah Loeb Brice Foundation ✧
c/o Levin Capital Strategies, LP
595 Madison Ave., 17th Fl.
New York, NY 10022-1907

Donor: Deborah L. Brice.
Foundation type: Independent foundation.
Financial data (yr. ended 12/31/13): Assets, $42,558,953 (M); expenditures, $2,687,845; qualifying distributions, $2,442,821; giving activities include $2,441,936 for 28 grants (high: $600,000; low: $1,000).
Purpose and activities: Giving primarily to U.S.-based organizations for the benefit of the arts in London, England; some funding also for education.
Fields of interest: Museums (art); Arts; Education.
International interests: England.
Limitations: Applications not accepted. Giving primarily in the U.S., with emphasis on NY. No grants to individuals.
Application information: Contributes only to pre-selected organizations.
Trustees: Deborah L. Brice; Taran Davies; John A. Levin; Jerome A. Manning; Alexa Model.
EIN: 237065499

5709
William L. Bricker Trust ✧
c/o Access Inc.
730 5th Ave., 20th Fl.
New York, NY 10019-4105

Established in 2008 in DE.
Foundation type: Independent foundation.
Financial data (yr. ended 12/31/10): Assets, $57,492,238 (M); expenditures, $14,551,323; qualifying distributions, $14,502,586; giving activities include $14,237,177 for 60 grants (high: $9,487,200; low: $1,500).
Fields of interest: Education; Youth development; Jewish agencies & synagogues.
Limitations: Applications not accepted. Giving primarily in New York, NY.

Application information: Unsolicited requests for funds not accepted.
Trustee: CPTC, LLC.
EIN: 866324455

5710
Bright Horizon Foundation ✧
c/o Laura B. Carroll, The Ayco Co.
P.O. Box 860
Saratoga Springs, NY 12866-0860

Established in 2000 in DE and NY.
Donors: Louis Salkind; Deborah Rennels.
Foundation type: Independent foundation.
Financial data (yr. ended 12/31/13): Assets, $105,480,161 (M); gifts received, $7,870,381; expenditures, $5,569,584; qualifying distributions, $5,534,676; giving activities include $5,525,000 for 12 grants (high: $2,000,000; low: $10,000).
Fields of interest: Environment, natural resources; Human services; Foundations (public); Foundations (community); Public policy, research.
Type of support: General/operating support.
Limitations: Applications not accepted. Giving primarily in NY; some giving also in CA, GA, MA and VA. No grants to individuals.
Application information: Contributes only to pre-selected organizations.
Directors: Deborah Rennels; Louis Salkind.
EIN: 134121003

5711
The Bristol-Myers Squibb Foundation, Inc.
(formerly The Bristol-Myers Fund, Inc.)
345 Park Ave., 3rd Fl.
New York, NY 10154-0004 (212) 546-4000
Contact: John L. Damonti, Pres.
E-mail: bms.foundation@bms.com; E-mail for Together on Diabetes in the U.S: Patricia Doykos, patricia.doykos@bms.com or togetherondiabetes@bms.com; Contact for Mental Health & Well-Being: Catharine Grimes, e-mail: Catharine.Grimes@bms.com; Contact for Secure the Future - Technical Assistance and Skills Transfer Program: Secure the Future, P.O. Box 1408, Bedfordview, 2008, South Africa, tel.: +21 11 456 6400, fax: +27 11 456 6589, e-mail: archie.smuts@bms.com or beryl.mohr@bms.com; Main URL: http://www.bms.com/foundation/Pages/home.aspx
Mental Health & Well-Being in the U.S. Grant Recipients: http://www.bms.com/Documents/foundation/Mental-Health-Fact-sheet.pdf
Secure the Future Grant Recipients: http://www.securethefuture.com/our_experience/funding/

Incorporated in 1982 in FL as successor to a foundation established in 1953.
Donor: Bristol-Myers Squibb Co.
Foundation type: Company-sponsored foundation.
Financial data (yr. ended 12/31/13): Assets, $81,880,667 (M); gifts received, $2,823,034; expenditures, $34,554,247; qualifying distributions, $31,251,274; giving activities include $31,251,274 for 223 grants (high: $2,296,652).
Purpose and activities: The mission of the Bristol-Myers Squibb Foundation is to promote health equity and improve the health outcomes of populations disproportionately affected by serious diseases and health conditions. The Foundation's Mental Health & Well-Being initiative in the U.S. focuses funding on addressing the mental health and reintegration needs of returning military service members, veterans and their families.
Fields of interest: Higher education; Medical school/education; Education; Health care, public policy; Health care, equal rights; Medical care, community health systems; Hospitals (general); Health care, clinics/centers; Pharmacy/prescriptions; Public health; Public health, STDs; Public health, communicable diseases; Palliative care; Nursing care; Health care; Mental health, treatment; Mental health/crisis services; Cancer; AIDS; Diabetes; Health organizations; Cancer research; AIDS research; American Red Cross; Residential/custodial care, hospices; Human services; Military/veterans' organizations; Children; Aging; African Americans/Blacks; Women; Military/veterans; Economically disadvantaged.
International interests: Africa; China; Europe; India; Japan; Sub-Saharan Africa.
Type of support: General/operating support; Continuing support; Management development/capacity building; Program development; Seed money; Curriculum development; Research; Technical assistance; Employee volunteer services; Program evaluation; Employee matching gifts; Employee-related scholarships; In-kind gifts.
Limitations: Applications accepted. Giving primarily in areas of company operations in Redwood, CA, Wallingford, CT, Washington, DC, Tampa, FL, Mount Vernon, IN, Waltham, MA, Hopewell, New Brunswick, Plainsboro, Princeton, and West Windsor, NJ, New York and Syracuse, NY, TX, Seattle, WA, Africa (especially Sub-Saharan Africa), China, Democratic Republic of Congo, Ethiopia, Europe, India, Japan, Kenya, Lesotho, Swaziland, Tanzania, Taiwan, Thailand, and Zimbabwe. No support for political, fraternal, social, or veterans' organizations, religious or sectarian organizations not of direct benefit to the entire community, or federated campaign-supported organizations. No grants to individuals (except for employee-related scholarships), or for endowments, capital campaigns, debt reduction, conferences, sponsorships, or independent medical research, or specific public broadcasting or films; no loans.
Publications: Application guidelines; Grants list; Informational brochure; Program policy statement.
Application information: Organizations receiving support are asked to submit biannual reports and a final report. Application form required.
Initial approach: Complete online application; complete online application for Secure the Future - Technical Assistance and Skills Transfer Programme
Deadline(s): None
Board meeting date(s): Dec. and as needed
Final notification: 6 to 8 weeks
Officers and Directors:* Lamberto Andreotti, Chair.; John L. Damonti,* Pres.; Mary Vanhatten, Secy.; Jeffrey Galik, Treas.; Charles Bancroft; Giovanni Caforio, M.D.; Sandra Leung.
Number of staff: 6 full-time professional; 4 full-time support.
EIN: 133127947
Selected grants: The following grants are a representative sample of this grantmaker's funding activity:
$1,982,155 to Duke University, Durham, NC, 2012.
$1,946,443 to American Academy of Family Physicians Foundation, Leawood, KS, 2012.
$1,927,960 to National Council on Aging, Washington, DC, 2012.
$588,200 to Give an Hour, Bethesda, MD, 2012.
$250,000 to National Alliance on Mental Illness Georgia, Atlanta, GA, 2012.
$91,653 to Health Oriented Programmes and Education, Lucknow, India, 2012.
$68,153 to Luthando Neuropsychiatric HIV Clinic, Johannesburg, South Africa, 2012.
$65,367 to Hospice Casa Sperantei Foundation, Brasov, Romania, 2012.
$50,000 to Montclair State University Foundation, Montclair, NJ, 2012.

5712
The Bristol-Myers Squibb Patient Assistance Foundation, Inc. ✧
345 Park Ave.
New York, NY 10154-0004 (800) 736-0003
FAX: (866) 736-1611; Application address: P.O. Box 220769, Charlotte, NC 28222-0769; Main URL: http://www.bmspaf.org/index.html

Established in 1999 in NJ as a company-sponsored operating foundation.
Donors: E.R. Squibb & Sons, Inc.; E.R. Squibb & Sons, L.L.C.; Bristol-Myers Squibb Co.; Otsuka American Pharmaceutical, Inc.; BMS/Sanofi Pharmaceuticals Partnership.
Foundation type: Operating foundation.
Financial data (yr. ended 12/31/13): Assets, $17,738,435 (M); gifts received, $822,067,084; expenditures, $823,164,602; qualifying distributions, $811,433,684; giving activities include $811,433,684 for grants to individuals.
Purpose and activities: The foundation provides prescription medicines to patients with financial hardships who have no private prescription drug insurance and are not eligible for prescription drug coverage through Medicaid or other government programs.
Fields of interest: Economically disadvantaged.
Type of support: Grants to individuals; Donated products.
Limitations: Applications accepted. Giving on a national basis.
Publications: Application guidelines; Informational brochure.
Application information: Applications must be completed by the patient and a healthcare provider. Applications for medications Erbitux, Ixempra, Sprycel, and Yervoy must be requested via telephone. Application form required.
Initial approach: Download application form and fax or mail to foundation
Deadline(s): 1 month prior to need
Officers and Trustees:* John L. Damonti,* Chair.; Alicia Coghlan, V.P.; Harvey Kaish, Secy.; David Levi, Treas.; Laura Bessen; John Elicker; Janet Loesberg; Ronald C. Miller; Raymond Sacchetti.
EIN: 223622487

5713
The Daniel and Estrellita Brodsky Family Foundation ✧
400 W. 59th St., 3rd Fl.
New York, NY 10019-1105
Contact: Daniel Brodsky, Tr.

Established in 1999 in NY.
Donor: Daniel Brodsky.
Foundation type: Independent foundation.

Financial data (yr. ended 12/31/12): Assets, $0 (M); gifts received, $1,000,000; expenditures, $1,611,590; qualifying distributions, $1,609,750; giving activities include $1,609,750 for 58 grants (high: $250,000; low: $500).
Purpose and activities: Giving primarily for arts and culture, particularly to museums and Hispanic cultural organizations; funding also for education, health associations, and social services.
Fields of interest: Museums (art); Arts; Higher education.
Limitations: Applications accepted. Giving primarily in New York, NY.
Application information: Application form required.
Initial approach: Letter
Trustees: Daniel Brodsky; Estrellita Brodsky.
EIN: 134065150

5714
The Brodsky Family Foundation ✧
400 W. 59th St.
New York, NY 10019-1105

Established in 1984 in NY.
Donor: Nathan Brodsky†.
Foundation type: Independent foundation.
Financial data (yr. ended 12/31/12): Assets, $14,609,317 (M); expenditures, $792,000; qualifying distributions, $789,500; giving activities include $787,000 for 34 grants (high: $200,000; low: $2,000).
Purpose and activities: Giving primarily for the arts, health care and medical research, and social services.
Fields of interest: Arts; Higher education; Medical school/education; Education; Health care; Health organizations; Human services.
Type of support: General/operating support; Seed money.
Limitations: Applications not accepted. Giving primarily in NY.
Application information: Contributes only to pre-selected organizations.
Trustees: Hady Amr; Thea Amr; Katherine Brodsky; Shirley Brodsky.
EIN: 133236064
Selected grants: The following grants are a representative sample of this grantmaker's funding activity:
$10,000 to New York University, Law School (Public Interest Law Center), New York, NY, 2012. For general.
$10,000 to Princeton University, Woodrow Wilson School, Princeton, NJ, 2012. For general.

5715
The Samuel Bronfman Foundation ✧
(formerly The Edgar M. Bronfman Family Foundation, Inc.)
595 Madison Ave., 16th Fl.
New York, NY 10022-1907 (212) 572-1025
E-mail: info@thesbf.org; Main URL: http://www.thesbf.org
Edgar M. Bronfman's Giving Pledge Profile: http://glasspockets.org/philanthropy-in-focus/eye-on-the-giving-pledge/profiles/bronfman-edgar
Twitter: http://twitter.com/BronfmanFound

Re-established in 2005 in DE; originally established in 1995 in NY.
Donor: Edgar M. Bronfman, Sr.†.
Foundation type: Independent foundation.
Financial data (yr. ended 12/31/13): Assets, $480,977 (M); gifts received, $1,538,952; expenditures, $1,477,697; qualifying distributions, $1,420,576; giving activities include $1,110,000 for 17 grants (high: $335,000; low: $10,000).
Purpose and activities: The foundation seeks to inspire a renaissance of Jewish life. The foundation's work is informed by the following four principles: 1) Jewish Renaissance is Grounded in Jewish Learning: through this principal, the foundation seeks to facilitate exploration of Jewish identity and meaningful engagement with Jewish life; 2) Jewish Youth Shape the Future of Jewish People: the foundation indicates that Jewish youth possess exceptional vision and talent, and that they must be empowered to lead the Jewish people and the world community; 3) Vibrant Jewish Communities are Open and Inclusive: the foundation supports a culture of pluralism and mutual respect that celebrates diverse expressions of Jewish life; and 4) All Jews are a Single Family: the foundation affirms the unity of the Jewish people, throughout the world and in Israel.
Fields of interest: Elementary/secondary education; Higher education; Jewish federated giving programs; Jewish agencies & synagogues.
Type of support: General/operating support.
Limitations: Applications not accepted. Giving primarily in Washington, DC and NY, with some giving in UT. No grants to individuals, or for new gifts to endowments.
Application information: Contributes only to pre-selected organizations.
Officers and Directors:* Adam R. Bronfman,* Managing Dir.; Dana Raucher, Exec. Dir.; Leigh Garofalow, Dir., Fin. and Opers.
EIN: 141918185
Selected grants: The following grants are a representative sample of this grantmaker's funding activity:
$25,000 to American Jewish World Service, New York, NY, 2012. For General Charitable Support - No Designation.

5716
The Clarissa and Edgar Bronfman Jr. Foundation ✧
c/o Baker Tilly
1 Penn Plz., Ste. 3000
New York, NY 10119

Donors: The Ann L. Bronfman Trust; Ann L. Bronfman†.
Foundation type: Independent foundation.
Financial data (yr. ended 12/31/13): Assets, $10,294,606 (M); gifts received, $1,089,257; expenditures, $1,407,179; qualifying distributions, $1,342,121; giving activities include $1,336,307 for 26 grants (high: $363,000; low: $30).
Fields of interest: Education; Human services.
Limitations: Applications not accepted.
Application information: Unsolicited requests for funds not accepted.
Officers: Edgar Bronfman, Jr., Pres.; Clarissa Bronfman, Secy.
EIN: 452529185

5717
The Andrea and Charles Bronfman Philanthropies, Inc. ✧
110 E. 59th St., 26th Fl.
New York, NY 10022-1327 (212) 931-0100
E-mail: info@acbp.net; Main URL: http://www.acbp.net
Charles Bronfman's Giving Pledge Profile: http://glasspockets.org/philanthropy-in-focus/eye-on-the-giving-pledge/profiles/bronfman-charles
GiveSmart: http://www.givesmart.org/Stories/Donors/Charles-Bronfman

Established in 1998 in DE and NY.
Donors: Charles R. Bronfman; Andrea M. Bronfman†; Ellen Hauptman; Philippa Cohen; Jeremy Cohen; Andrew Hauptman; Canary/Manitoba Foundation; Edgar Miles Bronfman Trust; Phyllis Lambert Trust; CRB Prize; The CRB Foundations; The Canary Charitable Foundation; The Manitoba Foundation; Judy and Michael Steinhardt Foundation; Charles and Lynn Schusterman Family Foundation; FJC.
Foundation type: Operating foundation.
Financial data (yr. ended 12/31/12): Assets, $10,011,566 (M); gifts received, $5,633,460; expenditures, $8,882,907; qualifying distributions, $8,641,197; giving activities include $4,271,997 for 78 grants (high: $1,563,667; low: $25), and $6,292,071 for 1 foundation-administered program.
Purpose and activities: The organization operates and supports programs in Canada, Israel and the United States to strengthen the unity of the Jewish people, to improve the quality of life in Israel and to promote Canadian heritage. Ultimately, the philanthropies seek to span the separations created by geography, culture, and the requirements of daily life with a bridge built on the willingness of individuals in search of community, identity, and meaning. It operates in a framework of continuing innovation, have an ability to bear risk, and continually emphasizes quality, value creation and building.
Fields of interest: Education; Human services; Jewish agencies & synagogues.
International interests: Canada; Israel.
Type of support: General/operating support; Program development; Conferences/seminars; Seed money; Curriculum development; Research; Technical assistance; Consulting services; Employee matching gifts.
Limitations: Applications not accepted. Giving primarily in NY, Canada, and Israel. No grants to individuals.
Application information: Contributes only to pre-selected organizations.
Officers and Directors:* Charles R. Bronfman,* Chair.; Jeffrey Solomon,* Pres.; John Hoover, Sr. V.P., and C.F.O.; Janet Aviad, Sr. V.P., Israel; Sharna Goldseker, V.P.; William J. Powers, Secy.; Richard P. Doyle, Treas.; William Zabel.
Number of staff: 9 full-time professional; 3 full-time support.
EIN: 133984936

5718
Brooklyn Community Foundation ✧
(formerly Independence Community Foundation)
45 Main St., Ste. 409
Brooklyn, NY 11201-1093 (347) 750-2310
Contact: Michael Burke, C.O.O.

FAX: (718) 722-5757;
E-mail: info@brooklyncommunityfoundation.org;
Main URL: http://
www.brooklyncommunityfoundation.org/
Facebook: http://www.facebook.com/pages/
Brooklyn-Community-Foundation/128582045333
Flickr: http://www.flickr.com/photos/dogoodbklyn/
Grants Database: http://
www.brooklyncommunityfoundation.org/grants/
at-a-glance
Twitter: http://www.twitter.com/DoGoodBklyn

Established in 1998 in NY; reincorporated as a Community Foundation in December 2008.
Donors: Independence Community Bank Corp.; Rockefeller Brothers Fund; Penguin Putnam Inc.; St. Joseph Hill Academy.
Foundation type: Community foundation.
Financial data (yr. ended 12/31/12): Assets, $59,914,853 (M); gifts received, $2,563,964; expenditures, $5,585,681; giving activities include $3,370,114 for 77+ grants (high: $150,000).
Purpose and activities: The foundation seeks to improve the lives of people in Brooklyn, NY by strengthening communities through local giving, grantmaking and community service.
Fields of interest: Arts; Education; Environment, beautification programs; Health care; Agriculture/food; Housing/shelter, development; Youth development, services; Human services; Community/economic development.
Type of support: General/operating support; Management development/capacity building; Capital campaigns; Equipment; Land acquisition; Endowments; Emergency funds; Program development; Publication; Seed money; Internship funds; Scholarship funds; Research; Technical assistance; Consulting services; Sponsorships; Program-related investments/loans; Employee matching gifts; Matching/challenge support.
Limitations: Applications not accepted. Giving limited to Brooklyn, NY. No support for religious purposes. No grants to individuals, or for tickets for dinners, golf outings, or fundraising events.
Publications: Annual report; Financial statement; Grants list; Informational brochure; Newsletter; Occasional report.
Application information: It has been a very active year for the Brooklyn Community Foundation. Thanks to the generosity of donors, the foundation has made more than $2 million in grants from the Brooklyn Recovery Fund to the neighborhoods that suffered the most damage from Superstorm Sandy: Coney Island, Sheepshead Bay, Canarsie, Red Hook, and Gerritsen Beach. With national funding the foundation has launched a new project to create healthier environments and improve access to healthy, affordable food options in and around three Brooklyn public housing communities in Red Hook, Fort Greene and Brownsville. The foundation has also published the first results on a multi-year initiative to improve educational outcomes for students in Bedford Stuyvesant School District 16, the lowest performing school district in Brooklyn. During the leadership transition, the Board has launched a review of grant making and programming strategies to ensure that the foundation is continuing to address the needs of Brooklyn's communities. Given the importance and breadth of this work, we have decided to suspend this year's open competitive grant process. The foundation does not do this lightly and regret any difficulties this may present to nonprofit partners. The goal is to ensure that the foundation continues to raise and deploy resources to best address the needs of Brooklyn's communities well into the future. The foundation will continue to work together with all who love, live and work in Brooklyn to build an even stronger culture of giving and service to the borough.
Board meeting date(s): Mar., June, Sept., and Dec.
Officers and Directors:* Alan H. Fishman,* Chair.; Hildy Simmons, Vice-Chair.; Marilyn G. Gelber, Pres.; Alexander Villari, V.P., Devel. and External Affairs; Michael Burke,* C.O.O.; Maria Fiorini Ramirez,* Treas.; Martin Baumrind; Robert B. Catell; Rohit M. Desai; Donald H. Elliott; Edward F. Genter, Jr.; Ralph Herzka; Emma Jordan-Simpson; Malcolm MacKay; Richard W. Moore; Constance Rogers Roosevelt; Michael Sherman; Claire Silberman.
Number of staff: 6 full-time professional; 2 full-time support.
EIN: 113422729
Selected grants: The following grants are a representative sample of this grantmaker's funding activity:
$200,000 to Prospect Park Alliance, Brooklyn, NY, 2012.
$150,000 to Pratt Center for Community Development, Brooklyn, NY, 2012.
$150,000 to Weeksville Heritage Center, Brooklyn, NY, 2012.
$50,000 to Good Shepherd Services, New York, NY, 2012.
$40,000 to Green Guerillas, New York, NY, 2012.
$25,000 to Brooklyn Public Library, Brooklyn, NY, 2012.
$25,000 to Girls for Gender Equity, Brooklyn, NY, 2012.
$15,000 to University Settlement Society of New York, New York, NY, 2012.
$10,000 to Brighton Ballet Theater Company, Brooklyn, NY, 2012.
$10,000 to Carroll Gardens Association, Brooklyn, NY, 2012.

5719
Gladys Brooks Foundation ✧
1055 Franklin Ave., Ste. 208
Garden City, NY 11530-2903 (516) 746-6103
Contact: Jessica L. Rutledge
E-mail: kathy@gladysbrooksfoundation.org; Main URL: http://www.gladysbrooksfoundation.org
Grants List: http://
www.gladysbrooksfoundation.org/
annual-report.html

Established in 1981 in NY.
Donor: Gladys Brooks Thayer‡.
Foundation type: Independent foundation.
Financial data (yr. ended 12/31/13): Assets, $37,410,183 (M); expenditures, $1,911,319; qualifying distributions, $1,686,610; giving activities include $1,435,782 for 17 grants (high: $190,000; low: $10,000).
Purpose and activities: The foundation's primary purpose is to provide for the intellectual, moral, and physical welfare of the people of this country by establishing and supporting nonprofit libraries, educational institutions, hospitals, and clinics.
Fields of interest: Higher education; Libraries/library science; Hospitals (general); Health care.
Type of support: Building/renovation; Equipment; Endowments; Scholarship funds.
Limitations: Applications accepted. Giving generally limited to CT, DE, FL, IL, IN, LA, MA, MD, ME, NH, NJ, NY, OH, PA, RI, TN, and VT. No grants to individuals, or for research or salaries.
Publications: Application guidelines; Annual report; Annual report (including application guidelines); Grants list; Program policy statement.
Application information: Electronic submissions are not accepted. The foundation encourages early filing of the application. Application form required.
Initial approach: Use application form on foundation web site, or letter requesting application form
Copies of proposal: 2
Deadline(s): Generally within 45 days from the date of the letter from the foundation furnishing the application to the applicant. See web site for detailed information regarding deadlines
Board meeting date(s): Monthly
Final notification: Dec.
Officers and Governors:* James J. Daly,* Chair.; Thomas Q. Morris, M.D.*, Secy.; Christopher R. Hawkins; Bank of America, N.A.
Number of staff: 1 full-time professional.
EIN: 132955337
Selected grants: The following grants are a representative sample of this grantmaker's funding activity:
$100,000 to Georgetown University, Washington, DC, 2012. For library endowment.
$100,000 to Good Neighbor Health Clinic, White River Junction, VT, 2012. For Dental Equipment and Student Externships.
$100,000 to New York University, New York, NY, 2012. For library technology.
$100,000 to Weeks Medical Center, Lancaster, NH, 2012. For medical simulation equipment.
$50,000 to Mount Washington Observatory, North Conway, NH, 2012. For Library Artifacts Displays.
$10,000 to New York Academy of Medicine, New York, NY, 2012. For technology equipment.

5720
Himan Brown Charitable Trust ✧
c/o Pryor Cashman
7 Times Sq.
New York, NY 10036-6524

Established in NY.
Donor: Himan Brown‡.
Foundation type: Independent foundation.
Financial data (yr. ended 03/31/13): Assets, $100,616,849 (M); expenditures, $4,708,413; qualifying distributions, $4,114,648; giving activities include $3,594,739 for 86 grants (high: $1,000,000; low: $650).
Fields of interest: Arts; Education; Environment; Aging, centers/services.
Limitations: Applications not accepted. Giving in the U.S., with emphasis on New York, NY. No grants to individuals.
Application information: Unsolicited requests for funds not accepted.
Trustee: Richard L. Kay.
EIN: 276669056

5721
Brownington Foundation, Inc. ✧ ☆
c/o Morris & McVeigh LLP
767 3rd Ave.
New York, NY 10017-2023

Established about 1970 in NY.
Donor: Mary J. Tweedy‡.
Foundation type: Independent foundation.
Financial data (yr. ended 12/31/13): Assets, $10,066,149 (M); expenditures, $634,280; qualifying distributions, $584,694; giving activities include $561,500 for 92 grants (high: $50,000; low: $500).
Purpose and activities: Giving primarily for secondary and higher education; support also social services, including services for people who are blind, as well as for health organizations.
Fields of interest: Education; Health organizations; Medical research, institute; Human services.
Limitations: Applications not accepted. No grants to individuals.
Application information: Contributes only to pre-selected organizations.
Officers: Margot T. Eagan, Pres.; Leonard B. Boehner, V.P.; Michael D. Savage, V.P.; Clare T. McMorris, Treas.
EIN: 237043230
Selected grants: The following grants are a representative sample of this grantmaker's funding activity:
$50,000 to Asia Society, New York, NY, 2011. For general funding.
$30,000 to World Learning, Brattleboro, VT, 2011. For general funding.
$5,000 to American Foundation for the Blind, New York, NY, 2011. For general funding.
$5,000 to Sierra Club, Chicago, IL, 2011. For general funding.
$3,000 to Innocence Project, New York, NY, 2011. For general funding.
$2,000 to Teach for America, New York, NY, 2011. For general funding.
$1,000 to Learning Ally, Princeton, NJ, 2011. For general funding.
$1,000 to National Public Radio, Washington, DC, 2011. For general funding.

5722
Brownstone Family Foundation ✧ ☆
(formerly Lucien & Ethel Brownstone Foundation, Inc.)
350 5th Ave., Ste. 6407
New York, NY 10118-6407

Established in 1953.
Donors: Clyde R. Brownstone; Ethel Brownstone Residuary Trust.
Foundation type: Independent foundation.
Financial data (yr. ended 02/28/13): Assets, $9,862,899 (M); gifts received, $2,759; expenditures, $616,463; qualifying distributions, $510,267; giving activities include $510,267 for 70 grants (high: $62,000; low: $150).
Purpose and activities: Giving primarily for education and human services; funding also for hospitals, the arts, and private grantmaking foundations.
Fields of interest: Arts; Higher education; Libraries (public); Education; Hospitals (general); Public health; Crime/law enforcement, police agencies; Human services; Foundations (private grantmaking).
Limitations: Applications not accepted. Giving primarily in the metropolitan New York, NY, area; giving also in MO. No grants to individuals.
Application information: Contributes only to pre-selected organizations.
Officers: Clyde R. Brownstone, Pres.; Diane Brownstone, V.P.; Jennifer Brownstone, V.P.; Spencer Brownstone, V.P.
EIN: 136138834
Selected grants: The following grants are a representative sample of this grantmaker's funding activity:
$135,000 to New York Restoration Project, New York, NY, 2011.
$43,000 to Ackerman Institute for the Family, New York, NY, 2011.
$21,000 to Educational Alliance, New York, NY, 2011.
$20,000 to Visiting Nurse Service of New York, New York, NY, 2011.
$5,000 to New York University Langone Medical Center, New York, NY, 2011.
$2,500 to Mount Sinai Hospital, New York, NY, 2011.
$2,145 to Association to Benefit Children, New York, NY, 2011.
$2,000 to Lenox Hill Hospital, New York, NY, 2011.
$1,000 to Charity: Water, New York, NY, 2011.
$1,000 to Charity: Water, New York, NY, 2011.

5723
The Brunckhorst Foundation ✧
6800 Jericho Tpke.
Syosset, NY 11791-4436

Established in 1968.
Donors: Barbara Brunckhorst; Barbara Brunckhorst 2010 Trust; Lilian Edith Brunckhorst 2002 Trust.
Foundation type: Independent foundation.
Financial data (yr. ended 12/31/13): Assets, $92,337,056 (M); gifts received, $20,209,911; expenditures, $4,139,681; qualifying distributions, $3,916,635; giving activities include $3,900,000 for 19 grants (high: $700,000; low: $75,000).
Purpose and activities: Giving primarily for environmental conservation.
Fields of interest: Education; Environment, natural resources; Animal welfare; Animals/wildlife, preservation/protection; Reproductive health, family planning.
Limitations: Applications not accepted. Giving primarily in CA, FL, NY and VA. No grants to individuals.
Application information: Contributes only to pre-selected organizations.
Trustees: Barbara Brunckhorst; Frank Brunckhorst III; Richard Todd Stravitz.
EIN: 237000850

5724
The BTMU Foundation, Inc. ✧
(formerly The BTM Foundation, Inc.)
1251 Ave. of the Americas, 37th Fl.
New York, NY 10020-1104 (212) 782-4627
Contact: Beth Gilroy, V.P.

Established in 1997 in NY.
Donors: The Bank of Tokyo, Mitsubishi Trust Co.; The Bank of Tokyo, Mitsubishi UFJ Trust Co.; Union Bank, N.A.
Foundation type: Company-sponsored foundation.
Financial data (yr. ended 12/31/13): Assets, $5,216,874 (M); gifts received, $5,000; expenditures, $426,781; qualifying distributions, $420,250; giving activities include $420,000 for 60 grants (high: $50,000; low: $500).
Purpose and activities: The foundation supports nonprofit organizations involved with education, community development, and human services. Special emphasis is directed toward programs serving low and moderate income people and neighborhoods.
Fields of interest: Arts education; Education, reading; Health care; Food services; Housing/shelter, development; Aging, centers/services; Urban/community development; Community/economic development; Physically disabled; Mentally disabled; Economically disadvantaged.
Type of support: General/operating support; Program development.
Limitations: Applications accepted. Giving primarily in New York, NY. No support for political, religious, sectarian, fraternal, veterans, labor, or lobbying organizations. No grants to individuals, or for advertising, fundraising, capital campaigns, tickets or memberships, or debt reduction.
Publications: Application guidelines; Grants list.
Application information: Application form required.
Initial approach: Complete application form
Copies of proposal: 1
Deadline(s): Apr. 30 for Community Dev Financial Institutions, June 30 for non CDFI organizations
Board meeting date(s): 4th quarter
Officers and Directors:* Katsumi Hatao,* Chair.; Johannes Worsoe,* Pres.; Elizabeth Lyman, Sr. V.P.; Beth Gilroy, V.P.; J.J. Ko, V.P.; Andrew Rasanen, V.P.; Thomas Pennington, Secy.; Thomas Greene, Treas.; Noriaki Goto; David Gruppo; Keiichi Hotta; Anthony Marino; Toshihide Motoshita; Isaac Shapiro.
EIN: 133916201
Selected grants: The following grants are a representative sample of this grantmaker's funding activity:
$5,000 to Women in Need, New York, NY, 2012. For New York City Grants for Urban Communities.

5725
The Peter and Carmen Lucia Buck Foundation, Inc.
(also known as The PCLB Foundation)
157 E. 86th St., 5th Fl.
New York, NY 10028-2175 (212) 360-6173
Contact: Carrie Schindele, V.P., Progs. and Admin.
FAX: (212) 360-6175;
E-mail: info@pclbfoundation.org; Main URL: http://www.pclbfoundation.org
Grants List: http://www.pclbfoundation.org/grantees.html

Established in 1999 in CT.
Donor: Peter Buck.
Foundation type: Independent foundation.
Financial data (yr. ended 06/30/14): Assets, $405,083,689 (M); gifts received, $41,313,440; expenditures, $17,799,500; qualifying distributions, $17,029,138; giving activities include $15,203,021 for grants.
Purpose and activities: The purpose of the foundation is to enhance the quality of life through grants to charitable organizations. The foundation supports organizations in the following areas: 1) Community Services; 2) Danbury Area, with emphasis on services for homeless and elderly in the Danbury, CT region; 3) Education, with emphasis on charter schools, advocacy, and teacher/leader development; 4) Land Conservation, with emphasis on land conservation and smart growth in the

Hudson River Valley; and 5) Medical, with emphasis on patient services, pharmacy services, and global capacity building.
Fields of interest: Education; Environment, land resources; Health care; Youth development; Human services.
International interests: Brazil.
Type of support: General/operating support; Program development; Program-related investments/loans.
Limitations: Applications not accepted. Giving emphasis is on CT and NY; some contributions to national organizations. No grants to individuals or ticketed events.
Application information: Applications by invitation only. If invited, applicant must complete a written application. Site visit required prior to receipt of a grant award. Unsolicited requests for funds not accepted but telephone calls (not e-mails) are welcome.
Board meeting date(s): May and Oct.
Officers and Directors:* Christopher Buck,* Pres.; Carrie Schindele, V.P., Progs. and Admin.; Michael Buck,* Secy.; William Buck,* Treas.; D. Ben Benoit, Exec. Dir.; Vera Lourenco.
Number of staff: 6 full-time professional; 1 part-time professional; 1 full-time support; 1 part-time support.
EIN: 061547852
Selected grants: The following grants are a representative sample of this grantmaker's funding activity:
$2,500,000 to Achievement First, New Haven, CT, 2014. For general operating support.
$300,000 to Northeast Charter Schools Network, Albany, NY, 2014. For general operating support.
$250,000 to Jumoke Academy, Hartford, CT, 2014. For Connecticut Operations.
$250,000 to Scenic Hudson, Poughkeepsie, NY, 2014. For general operating support.
$125,000 to Connecticut Pre-Engineering Program, Middletown, CT, 2014. For general operating support.
$100,000 to Direct Relief International, Santa Barbara, CA, 2014. For Direct Relief USA.
$100,000 to Doctors Without Borders USA, New York, NY, 2014. For general operating support.
$100,000 to Land Trust Alliance, Washington, DC, 2014. For general operating support.
$95,000 to Danbury Senior Center, Danbury, CT, 2014. For general operating support.

5726
Buffalo Sabres Alumni Association ✧

c/o Robert Travis
45 Bryant Woods N.
Amherst, NY 14228-3600 (716) 630-2400
Contact: Robert Travis, Treas. and Dir.
Main URL: http://www.sabresalumni.com/
Flickr: https://www.flickr.com/photos/84418649@N04/
Scholarship address: The Buffalo Sabres Alumni Scholarship Program, c/o Buffalo Sabres Alumni Assoc., First Niagara Ctr., 1 Seymour H. Knox III Plz., Buffalo, NY 14203

Established in 1989 in NY.
Foundation type: Independent foundation.
Financial data (yr. ended 12/31/12): Assets, $544,185 (M); expenditures, $1,282,422; qualifying distributions, $623,020; giving activities include $623,020 for 44 grants (high: $218,300; low: $280).
Fields of interest: Scholarships/financial aid; Health organizations, association.
Type of support: Scholarships—to individuals; General/operating support; Scholarship funds.
Limitations: Applications accepted. Giving limited to western NY; scholarships funding includes Southern Ontario, Canada.
Application information: See foundation web site for scholarship application form. Application form required.
Initial approach: Letter on organization's letterhead
Deadline(s): None, for grants; July 1, for scholarships
Officers and Directors:* Rob Ray,* Pres.; Darryl Shannon,* V.P.; Robert Travis,* Treas.; Cliff Benson; Jay McKee; Craig Muni; Michael Peca; Andrew Peters; Larry Playfair; Ric Seiling; Derek Smith.
EIN: 161356116

5727
Henrietta B. & Frederick H. Bugher Foundation ✧

(also known as Bugher Foundation)
c/o The Daniel Adams Co.
P.O. Box 555
Barneveld, NY 13304-0555
E-mail: dan@bugher.org; Main URL: http://www.bugher.org/

Established in 1961 in DC.
Donor: Frederick McLean Bugher†.
Foundation type: Independent foundation.
Financial data (yr. ended 08/31/13): Assets, $42,232,848 (M); expenditures, $2,224,024; qualifying distributions, $2,035,530; giving activities include $1,740,000 for 10 grants (high: $415,000; low: $50,000).
Purpose and activities: Giving is focused on cardiovascular research and treatment. Within these areas, the foundation seeks to fund seminal projects- those judged to be both important and unique which otherwise might have difficulty finding initial funding. The foundation works at the leading edge of this research, funding innovative projects under the highest quality investigators and institutions.
Fields of interest: Heart & circulatory research.
Type of support: Research.
Limitations: Applications not accepted. Giving primarily to national organizations in New York, NY, and Dallas, TX. No grants to individuals, or for general funding, equipment, facilities, or indirect expenses over 10 percent.
Application information: Unsolicited requests for funds not accepted.
Board meeting date(s): Quarterly
Trustees: Bruce H. Adams; Bryan G. Adams; Daniel Nelson Adams, Jr.; Robert A. Robinson; Gayllis Ward.
EIN: 526034266
Selected grants: The following grants are a representative sample of this grantmaker's funding activity:
$415,000 to American Heart Association, Dallas, TX, 2013. To fund Collaborative Awards and Meetings for the ASA-Bugher Centers of Excellence in Stroke.
$300,000 to American Heart Association, Dallas, TX, 2013. For stroke prevention.
$50,000 to American Heart Association, Dallas, TX, 2013. To Fund Saving Lives in Greater Hartford through.
$50,000 to American Heart Association, Dallas, TX, 2013. To Fund Saving Lives in Greater Hartford through Mission: Lifeline.
$50,000 to National Stroke Association, Centennial, CO, 2013. For the Mobile Aps Research Project.

5728
The William C. Bullitt Foundation, Inc. ✧

220 5th Ave., 2nd Fl.
New York, NY 10001-7708 (212) 485-6006
Contact: Christy Pennoyer
E-mail: info@wcbullittfound.org; Main URL: http://www.wcbullittfound.org/
Grants List: http://www.wcbullittfound.org/grants

Established in 2001 in DE.
Donor: Anne M. Bullitt†.
Foundation type: Independent foundation.
Financial data (yr. ended 12/31/12): Assets, $16,475,274 (M); gifts received, $25,039; expenditures, $1,365,935; qualifying distributions, $887,000; giving activities include $887,000 for grants.
Purpose and activities: Giving primarily to organizations that: 1) promote government integrity and protect civil liberties and human rights; 2) help economically and socially disadvantaged children and families achieve the tools necessary to lead independent and productive lives; and 3) protect the natural environment through land conservation and raising public awareness of environmental threats and solutions.
Fields of interest: Environment, land resources; Environment; Human services; Children/youth, services; Civil/human rights; Economically disadvantaged.
Limitations: Applications not accepted. Giving primarily in CT, and the greater New York metropolitan area.
Publications: Grants list.
Application information: Unsolicited requests for funds not accepted.
Officers and Trustees:* Tracy Pennoyer,* Pres.; Sharon Myrie, V.P.; Dana W. Hiscock, Secy.; Robert Pennoyer, Treas.; Christy Pennoyer.
EIN: 134183316

5729
The Burch Foundation ✧

(also known as The Burch Family Foundation)
c/o Robert L. Burch, III
1 Rockefeller Plz., A Jones Co.
New York, NY 10020-2003

Established in 2000 in NY.
Donors: Robert L. Burch III; Jonathan Manufacture Corp.
Foundation type: Independent foundation.
Financial data (yr. ended 12/31/12): Assets, $28,673,775 (M); expenditures, $2,020,711; qualifying distributions, $1,403,393; giving activities include $1,391,000 for 28 grants (high: $520,000; low: $250).
Fields of interest: Higher education; Education; Eye diseases; Eye research; Human services.
Type of support: Research.

Limitations: Applications not accepted. No grants to individuals.
Application information: Contributes only to pre-selected organizations.
Board meeting date(s): Jan. 1
Directors: Catherine C. Burch; Dale J. Burch; Robert L. Burch; Robert L. Burch III.
Number of staff: None.
EIN: 134144134

5730
Burke Family Foundation ✧
41 Central Park W., Apt. 11A
New York, NY 10023

Established in 2001 in PA.
Donors: Stephen B. Burke; Gretchen H. Burke.
Foundation type: Independent foundation.
Financial data (yr. ended 12/31/13): Assets, $351,968 (M); gifts received, $2,362; expenditures, $1,843,059; qualifying distributions, $1,840,657; giving activities include $1,840,657 for 87 grants (high: $300,000; low: $250).
Purpose and activities: Giving primarily for education; some funding also for a children's hospital.
Fields of interest: Education; Hospitals (specialty).
Limitations: Applications not accepted. Giving primarily in the Philadelphia, PA, area. No grants to individuals.
Application information: Contributes only to pre-selected organizations.
Trustees: Gretchen H. Burke; Stephen B. Burke.
EIN: 256699573
Selected grants: The following grants are a representative sample of this grantmaker's funding activity:
$5,000 to Teach for America, Philadelphia, PA, 2012. To Help Fund the Operating Budgets of the Various 501(c)(3) Charitable Organizations.
$250 to Project HOME, Philadelphia, PA, 2012. To Help Fund the Operating Budgets of the Various 501 (c)(3) Charitable Organization Help Fund the Operating Budgets of the Various 501(c)(3) Charitable Organizations.

5731
The Burke Family Foundation ✧
c/o L.H. Frishkoff Co.
529 5th Ave., 9th Fl.
New York, NY 10017-4608

Established in NJ.
Donors: James J. Burke, Jr.; Jeanne J. Burke; James J. Burke, Jr. 2002 Charitable Lead Annuity Trust; James J. Burke 2002 Health and Educational Trust.
Foundation type: Independent foundation.
Financial data (yr. ended 12/31/13): Assets, $6,691,994 (M); gifts received, $3,038; expenditures, $879,250; qualifying distributions, $825,490; giving activities include $820,200 for 12 grants (high: $603,500; low: $600).
Purpose and activities: Giving primarily for higher education; some funding also for the arts.
Fields of interest: Museums (natural history); Performing arts, theater; Arts; Elementary/ secondary education; Higher education; Medical research, institute.
Limitations: Applications not accepted. Giving primarily in NJ, NY, and RI.
Application information: Contributes only to pre-selected organizations.
Trustees: Brian Burke; James J. Burke, Jr.; James J. Burke III; Jeanne J. Burke; Jennifer J. Burke; Philippa C. Burke.
EIN: 223341317

5732
Jacob Burns Foundation, Inc. ✧
c/o Barry Shenkman
335 Manville Rd.
Pleasantville, NY 10570-2118

Incorporated in 1957 in NY.
Donors: Mary Elizabeth Hood†; Jacob Burns†; Rosalie A. Goldberg; Rosalie Burns Charitable Lead Trust.
Foundation type: Independent foundation.
Financial data (yr. ended 12/31/13): Assets, $15,996,967 (M); expenditures, $1,324,774; qualifying distributions, $929,063; giving activities include $703,994 for 83 grants (high: $160,027; low: $100).
Purpose and activities: Giving primarily for the arts, education, social services, and Jewish organizations.
Fields of interest: Media, film/video; Media, television; Museums; Performing arts; Performing arts, theater; Performing arts, opera; Arts; Higher education; Law school/education; Education; Human services; Jewish agencies & synagogues.
Type of support: Annual campaigns; Capital campaigns; Program development; Conferences/ seminars; Curriculum development.
Limitations: Applications not accepted. Giving primarily in NY; some giving also in Washington, DC. No grants to individuals.
Application information: Contributes only to pre-selected organizations.
Board meeting date(s): Quarterly
Officers: Barry A. Shenkman, Pres.; Rosalie A. Goldberg, V.P.; Jamie Shenkman, Secy.
Number of staff: 1 full-time professional; 1 part-time support.
EIN: 136114245

5733
Butler Conservation Fund, Inc. ✧
(formerly Gilbert & Ildiko Butler Foundation, Inc.)
60 Cutter Mill Rd., Ste. 212
Great Neck, NY 11021-3104 (212) 303-0216
FAX: (516) 466-4795; Main URL: http://butlerconservationfund.org/
Grants List: http://butlerconservationfund.org/grantees/

Established in 1988 in MA.
Donors: Gilbert Butler; Butler Capital Corp.
Foundation type: Company-sponsored foundation.
Financial data (yr. ended 12/31/12): Assets, $141,229,394 (M); expenditures, $7,972,059; qualifying distributions, $5,722,164; giving activities include $5,284,938 for 40 grants (high: $1,297,275; low: $250).
Purpose and activities: The foundation supports programs designed to conserve, restore, and protect the environment.
Fields of interest: Historic preservation/historical societies; Environment, natural resources; Environment, water resources; Environment, land resources; Botanical gardens; Environmental education; Environment; Animal welfare; Animals/ wildlife; Recreation, parks/playgrounds.
Type of support: General/operating support; Capital campaigns; Program development; Research.
Limitations: Applications not accepted. Giving primarily in MA, ME, NY, SC, and VA; giving also to national organizations.
Publications: Financial statement; Grants list; IRS Form 990 or 990-PF printed copy available upon request.
Application information: Unsolicited applications are not accepted.
Officers and Directors:* Gilbert Butler,* Chair., Pres., and Treas.; Anthony P. Grassi,* Vice-Chair.; Dhruvika Patel Amin, V.P., Finance & Admin.; Christopher (Kim) Elliman,* V.P.; Tomer Inbar, Secy.; Dana Beach; Peter Lehner; Kristine McDivitt Tompkins.
EIN: 043032409

5734
The Gilbert and Ildiko Butler Family Foundation, Inc. ✧ ☆
60 Cutter Mill Rd.
Great Neck, NY 11021-3104

Established in 2006 in MA.
Donors: Gilbert Butler; Ildiko Butler.
Foundation type: Company-sponsored foundation.
Financial data (yr. ended 12/31/12): Assets, $9,945,908 (M); expenditures, $720,979; qualifying distributions, $565,105; giving activities include $553,183 for 60 grants (high: $200,000; low: $100).
Fields of interest: Performing arts, music; Performing arts, education; Arts; Education; Human services; Children/youth, services.
Type of support: General/operating support.
Limitations: Applications not accepted. Giving primarily in NY. No grants to individuals.
Application information: Contributes only to pre-selected organizations.
Officer: Gilbert Butler, Pres. and Treas.
Directors: Fred Butler; Ildiko Butler; Emily Rafferty; Winthrop Rutherfurd, Jr.
EIN: 270141384

5735
J. E. & Z. B. Butler Foundation, Inc. ✧
780 3rd Ave., 15th Fl.
New York, NY 10017-2024

Established in 1958.
Donors: Zella B. Butler†; Jack E. Butler†.
Foundation type: Independent foundation.
Financial data (yr. ended 12/31/13): Assets, $88,995,556 (M); expenditures, $6,286,910; qualifying distributions, $4,718,472; giving activities include $4,362,699 for 108 grants (high: $317,000; low: $5,000).
Purpose and activities: Giving primarily for education, hospitals and health organizations, including children's hospitals and other children, youth and social services; funding also for Jewish organizations.
Fields of interest: Arts; Education, special; Education; Hospitals (general); Hospitals (specialty); Health organizations, association; Human services; YM/YWCAs & YM/YWHAs; Children/youth, services; Community development,

public/private ventures; Jewish federated giving programs; Jewish agencies & synagogues.
Limitations: Applications not accepted. Giving primarily in MA and New York, NY. No grants to individuals.
Application information: Contributes only to pre-selected organizations.
Board meeting date(s): Apr., Sept., and Dec.
Officers and Directors:* Beatrice B. Doniger,* Co-Chair.; Ruth B. Pearson,* Co-Chair.; Bruce Doniger,* Pres. and C.F.O.; Patricia Goldman,* V.P. and Secy.-Treas.; Carol Parrish,* V.P.
EIN: 136082916

5736
Catherine & Paul Buttenwieser Foundation ✧
c/o Barry M. Strauss Assocs., Ltd.
307 5th Ave., 8th Fl.
New York, NY 10016-6517

Established in 1993 in MA.
Donors: Paul A. Buttenwieser; Catherine F. Buttenwieser.
Foundation type: Independent foundation.
Financial data (yr. ended 09/30/13): Assets, $448,584 (M); gifts received, $813,396; expenditures, $509,637; qualifying distributions, $504,608; giving activities include $502,608 for 125 grants (high: $40,800; low: $100).
Fields of interest: Museums (art); Performing arts, ballet; Performing arts, theater; Performing arts, music; Performing arts, orchestras; Performing arts, opera; Arts; Education; Health organizations; Human services; Jewish federated giving programs.
Limitations: Applications not accepted. Giving primarily in Boston, MA. No grants to individuals.
Application information: Contributes only to pre-selected organizations.
Trustees: Catherine F. Buttenwieser; Paul A. Buttenwieser.
EIN: 043216632
Selected grants: The following grants are a representative sample of this grantmaker's funding activity:
$25,000 to City Year, Boston, MA, 2011. For general support.
$25,000 to Harvard University, Cambridge, MA, 2011. For general support.
$10,000 to Year Up, Boston, MA, 2011. For general support.
$1,000 to Bend the Arc: A Jewish Partnership for Justice, New York, NY, 2011. For general support.
$1,000 to Mercy Corps, Portland, OR, 2011. For general support.

5737
The Butters Foundation ✧ ☆
c/o Vittoria Purdy & Cavallaro LLP
1 Rockefeller Plz., Ste. 321
New York, NY 10020-2134

Donors: Julius Gaudio; The Buffin Foundation; Julius Gaudio.
Foundation type: Independent foundation.
Financial data (yr. ended 12/31/12): Assets, $54,392,933 (M); gifts received, $7,000,000; expenditures, $2,203,337; qualifying distributions, $2,031,185; giving activities include $2,000,000 for 1 grant.
Fields of interest: Foundations (public).
Limitations: Applications not accepted.
Application information: Unsolicited requests for funds not accepted.
Officers: Julius Gaudio, Pres. and Treas.; Alfred Cavallaro, Secy.
EIN: 453597259

5738
Bydale Foundation ✧
c/o U.S. Trust
114 W. 47th St., NY8-114-10-02
New York, NY 10036
Contact: Christine O'Donnell, Agent
E-mail: christine.l.o'donnell@ustrust.com; Main URL: http://fdnweb.org/bydale

Incorporated in 1965 in DE.
Donor: James P. Warburg†.
Foundation type: Independent foundation.
Financial data (yr. ended 12/31/13): Assets, $13,811,191 (M); expenditures, $557,239; qualifying distributions, $536,360; giving activities include $498,500 for 54 grants (high: $30,000; low: $1,000).
Purpose and activities: Giving primarily for the environment, human rights, women's rights, social justice, and poetry.
Fields of interest: Arts; Environment, research; Environment, public policy; Civil/human rights, women; Civil liberties, reproductive rights; Civil/human rights; Women; Economically disadvantaged.
Type of support: General/operating support; Program development; Matching/challenge support.
Limitations: Applications accepted. Giving in Westchester County, NY, NC and Israel. No grants to individuals, or for annual campaigns, emergency funds, deficit financing, endowment funds, demonstration projects, capital funds, scholarships, or fellowships; no loans.
Application information: Unsolicited Inquiry Application Forms are accepted, but the foundation receives many more applications than it funds. Only the foundation's application form is accepted. Application form required.
Initial approach: See foundation web site for details
Copies of proposal: 1
Deadline(s): Aug. 1
Board meeting date(s): Dec.
Final notification: By Dec. 31
Officers and Trustees:* Joan M. Warburg,* Pres.; Frank J. Kick, Treas.; Sarah W. Bliumis-Dunn; James P. Warburg, Jr.; Jennifer Warburg; Philip N. Warburg.
Number of staff: 1 part-time professional; 1 part-time support.
EIN: 136195286
Selected grants: The following grants are a representative sample of this grantmaker's funding activity:
$30,000 to Friends of Israels Environment, Studio City, CA, 2011.
$25,000 to Americans for Peace Now, Washington, DC, 2011.
$25,000 to Grassroots Policy Project, Cambridge, MA, 2011.
$25,000 to National People's Action, Chicago, IL, 2011.
$20,000 to Global Workers Justice Alliance, Brooklyn, NY, 2011.
$20,000 to Planned Parenthood of Southern New England, New Haven, CT, 2011.
$15,000 to Group I Acting Company, New York, NY, 2011.
$10,000 to Equality Now, New York, NY, 2011.
$7,500 to Conservation Law Foundation, Boston, MA, 2011.
$5,000 to Womens eNews, New York, NY, 2011.

5739
C & Y Foundation, Inc. ✧
218 Broadway
Lawrence, NY 11559-1502

Established in 2002 in NY.
Donors: Aliza Friedman; Benny Friedman; Miriam Friedman; Joseph Friedman; Investors Trust.
Foundation type: Independent foundation.
Financial data (yr. ended 12/31/13): Assets, $9,380,096 (M); gifts received, $50,000; expenditures, $496,250; qualifying distributions, $495,000; giving activities include $495,000 for 7 grants (high: $175,000; low: $10,000).
Fields of interest: Jewish agencies & synagogues.
Type of support: General/operating support.
Limitations: Applications not accepted. Giving primarily in Brooklyn, NY; some giving in Lakewood, NJ and Monsey, NY. No grants to individuals.
Application information: Contributes only to pre-selected organizations.
Officers: Chana Friedman, Pres.; Joseph Friedman, V.P.
EIN: 043666136

5740
The Calamus Foundation, Inc. ✧
1325 6th Ave., 27th Fl.
New York, NY 10019-6026
Contact: Brian O'Donnell, Exec. Dir.
E-mail: bodonnell@calamusfoundation.org; Main URL: http://www.calamusfoundation.org

Established in 1995 in FL.
Donor: Saul Kaplan†.
Foundation type: Independent foundation.
Financial data (yr. ended 12/31/12): Assets, $11,412,186 (M); expenditures, $3,060,266; qualifying distributions, $2,825,112; giving activities include $2,781,000 for 31 grants (high: $375,000; low: $1,000).
Purpose and activities: The foundation makes grants to qualifying charitable organizations for programs and activities in the following areas: care and support services to individuals with HIV, and services to the gay and lesbian community that promote and support its formation, growth, identity, general wellbeing and social and legal rights.
Fields of interest: Legal services; LGBTQ.
Limitations: Giving in the U.S., with emphasis on NY.
Publications: Application guidelines.
Application information: Formal grant requests are by invitation only, upon review of organization introduction form.
Initial approach: Use organization introduction form on foundation web site
Deadline(s): None
Officer and Directors:* Louis Bradbury,* Pres.; Brian O'Donnell, Exec. Dir.; James S. Marcus; James M. Rosenberg; Michael Sheafe; Jeffrey B. Soref.
EIN: 650508548

5741
The CAMBR Charitable Foundation Trust ✧
c/o George V. Delson Assocs.
885 2nd Ave., 26th Fl.
New York, NY 10017-2201

Established in 1996 in NY.
Donors: Allen Skolnick; Connie Skolnick; Barry Skolnick; CAMBR Co.; CAMBR Labs.
Foundation type: Independent foundation.
Financial data (yr. ended 01/31/12): Assets, $23,630,683 (M); gifts received, $7,305,000; expenditures, $762,113; qualifying distributions, $712,747; giving activities include $708,423 for 35 grants (high: $200,000; low: $36).
Purpose and activities: Giving primarily for education, human services, Jewish organizations, and to a biology institute.
Fields of interest: Education; Human services; Biology/life sciences; Jewish agencies & synagogues.
Limitations: Applications not accepted. Giving primarily in NY. No grants to individuals.
Application information: Contributes only to pre-selected organizations.
Trustees: Allen Skolnick; Connie Skolnick.
EIN: 116462058
Selected grants: The following grants are a representative sample of this grantmaker's funding activity:
$65,000 to American Jewish Committee, New York, NY, 2011.

5742
Ruth Camp Campbell Charitable Trust ✧
(formerly Ruth Camp McDougall Charitable Trust)
140 Broadway, 4th Fl.
New York, NY 10005-1108
Application address: c/o Brown Brothers Harriman Trust Co., N.A., 227 W. Trade St., Ste. 2100, Charlotte, NC 28202; tel. (212) 493-8000

Established in 1976 in VA.
Donor: Ruth Camp McDougall‡.
Foundation type: Independent foundation.
Financial data (yr. ended 12/31/13): Assets, $15,139,703 (M); expenditures, $837,739; qualifying distributions, $767,452; giving activities include $700,710 for 175 grants (high: $115,360; low: $500).
Fields of interest: Higher education; Education; Hospitals (general); Health organizations, association; Human services; Children/youth, services; Foundations (private grantmaking); Christian agencies & churches; Protestant agencies & churches.
Type of support: Grants to individuals.
Limitations: Applications accepted. Giving in the U.S., with emphasis on FL, NC, SC and VA.
Application information:
Initial approach: Letter
Deadline(s): None
Directors: John M. Camp III; Harry W. Walker.
Trustee: Brown Brothers Harriman Trust Co., N.A.
EIN: 546162697
Selected grants: The following grants are a representative sample of this grantmaker's funding activity:
$5,000 to Camp Pasquaney, Hebron, NH, 2011. For general support.

5743
The Canaday Family Charitable Trust ✧
(formerly Canaday Educational and Charitable Trust)
1 Bryant Park
NY1-100-28-05
New York, NY 10036-6715 (646) 855-1011
Contact: Christine O'Donnell, V.P., Bank of America, N.A.
FAX: (646) 855-5463;
E-mail: canaday@ustrust.com; Main URL: http://www.canadayfamily.org/
Grants List: http://www.canadayfamily.org/list.html

Trust established in 1945 in OH.
Donors: Ward M. Canaday‡; Mariam C. Canaday‡; Doreen Spitzer Trust.
Foundation type: Independent foundation.
Financial data (yr. ended 12/31/13): Assets, $45,871,572 (M); gifts received, $512,365; expenditures, $2,222,643; qualifying distributions, $1,902,438; giving activities include $1,855,320 for 62 grants (high: $100,000; low: $200).
Purpose and activities: Giving primarily to organizations that work in Vermont to improve the lives of children and families, promote environmental education and conservation, and preserve the environment.
Fields of interest: Environment, natural resources; Environmental education; Children/youth, services; Family services; Children; Youth; Young adults.
Type of support: Program development.
Limitations: Applications accepted. Giving primarily in VT. No support for private foundation or organizations lacking 501(c)(3) status. No grants to individuals, or for capital campaigns or endowments.
Publications: Grants list.
Application information: Application guidelines available on foundation web site. Organizations in which the foundation is interested will be contacted and invited to submit a formal grant proposal. Application form not required.
Initial approach: Letter or inquiry submitted through foundation web site
Copies of proposal: 1
Deadline(s): Feb. 1 for letters of inquiry
Board meeting date(s): Annually
Final notification: July
Trustee: Bank of America, N.A.
EIN: 912158408

5744
The Canary Charitable Foundation ✧
c/o First Spring Corp.
499 Park Ave., 26th Fl.
New York, NY 10022-1240

Established in 1998 in DE.
Donors: Charles de Gunzburg; Carob Trust.
Foundation type: Independent foundation.
Financial data (yr. ended 12/31/13): Assets, $11,478,117 (M); gifts received, $1,028,030; expenditures, $2,084,081; qualifying distributions, $2,068,665; giving activities include $2,055,150 for 23 grants (high: $250,000; low: $1,000).
Fields of interest: Museums; Performing arts; Arts; Education; Human services; Jewish federated giving programs; Jewish agencies & synagogues.
Limitations: Applications not accepted. Giving primarily in New York, NY.
Application information: Unsolicited requests for funds not accepted.
Officers: Charles De Gunzburg, Chair. and Pres.; Kenneth N. Munsen, V.P.; Lee Cornell, Secy.-Treas.
Directors: Nathalie De Gunzburg; Guido Goldman; Leonard M. Nelson.
EIN: 134005475

5745
W. P. Carey Foundation
c/o Juliana K. Harris, Exec. Dir.
50 Rockefeller Plz.
New York, NY 10020-1605
Contact: Juliana Harris, Exec. Dir

Established in 1991 in PA.
Donor: William P. Carey‡.
Foundation type: Independent foundation.
Financial data (yr. ended 12/31/13): Assets, $32,741,656 (M); gifts received, $3,529,949; expenditures, $8,885,574; qualifying distributions, $8,760,419; giving activities include $8,272,458 for 17 grants (high: $4,300,000; low: $66), $27,551 for 7 employee matching gifts, and $23,799 for foundation-administered programs.
Purpose and activities: Giving primarily for international relief and education.
Fields of interest: Higher education; Education.
Limitations: Applications not accepted. Giving on a national basis. No grants to individuals.
Application information: Contributes only to pre-selected organizations.
Officers, Directors and Trustees:* Francis J. Carey,* Chair.; Francis J. Carey III,* Pres.; Zachary J. Pack,* C.O.O.; Juliana K. Harris, Secy. and Exec. Dir.; Ricardo A. Vasquez, Treas.; J. Samuel Armstrong IV; William Bast; Gwendolyn G. Bond; Trevor P. Bond; Elizabeth P. Carey; Emily N. Carey; J. Meade Carey; Laura G. Carey; William P. Carey II; Christopher E. Franklin; Benjamin H. Griswold IV; Donald F. MacMaster, Jr.; Frances W. MacMaster; John Miller; John J. Park; Douglas S. Parvis; A. Patterson Pendleton III; Marjorie B. Tompkins.
EIN: 133597510
Selected grants: The following grants are a representative sample of this grantmaker's funding activity:
$3,000,000 to Johns Hopkins University, Carey Business School, Baltimore, MD, 2012.
$2,000,000 to Arizona State University, Tempe, AZ, 2012.
$501,662 to New York-Presbyterian Hospital, New York, NY, 2012.
$501,662 to University of Maryland-College Park, College Park, MD, 2012.
$250,961 to Public School of Germantown, Germantown Academy, Fort Washington, PA, 2012.
$50,000 to Gilman School, Baltimore, MD, 2012.
$25,000 to Pomfret School, Pomfret, CT, 2012.
$25,000 to University of Pennsylvania, Philadelphia, PA, 2012.
$20,000 to Baltimore School for the Arts Foundation, Baltimore, MD, 2012.
$10,000 to Appalachian State University Foundation, Boone, NC, 2012.

5746
The Carmel Hill Fund ✧
(formerly Ruane Family Fund)
767 5th Ave., Ste. 4701
New York, NY 10153-4798
Contact: Arlene Farrand-Borgerson, Exec. Dir.

E-mail for Arlene Farrand-Borgerson: arlene@ruanecunniff.com

Established in 1986 in NY.
Donors: William J. Ruane‡; The Riordan Fund; American Institute of Foreign Studies.
Foundation type: Independent foundation.
Financial data (yr. ended 12/31/12): Assets, $257,571,751 (M); gifts received, $19,705,502; expenditures, $17,950,557; qualifying distributions, $12,107,803; giving activities include $8,025,373 for 48 grants (high: $2,500,000; low: $500).
Purpose and activities: Giving primarily for education, children and social services, and mental health organizations; some funding also for the arts.
Fields of interest: Arts; Higher education; Education; Mental health/crisis services; Human services; Children/youth, services.
Limitations: Applications not accepted. Giving primarily in NY. No grants to individuals.
Application information: Contributes only to pre-selected organizations.
Officer: Arlene Farrand-Borgerson, Exec. Dir.
Trustees: George J. Gillespie, III; Robert D. Goldfarb.
Number of staff: 22 full-time professional; 5 part-time support.
EIN: 136881103
Selected grants: The following grants are a representative sample of this grantmaker's funding activity:
$2,500,000 to Save the Children Federation, Fairfield, CT, 2012.
$1,500,000 to Columbia University, New York, NY, 2012.
$1,166,977 to Denver Public Schools, Denver, CO, 2012.
$581,039 to Childrens Aid Society, New York, NY, 2012.
$567,492 to New York City Department of Education, New York, NY, 2012.
$550,000 to Brain and Behavior Research Foundation, New York, NY, 2012.
$433,091 to Saint Paul School, New York, NY, 2012.
$250,000 to District of Columbia College Access Program, Washington, DC, 2012.
$119,564 to Monroe City School District, Monroe, LA, 2012.
$75,500 to University of Louisiana at Lafayette, Lafayette, LA, 2012.

5747
Carnegie Corporation of New York ✧

437 Madison Ave.
New York, NY 10022-7003 (212) 371-3200
Contact: Nicole Howe Buggs, Assoc. Corp. Secy. and Dir., Grants Management; Bonnie Rivers, Assoc. Dir., Grants Mgmt.
FAX: (212) 754-4073; E-mail: info@carnegie.org; E-mail for Nicole Howe Buggs: nb@carnegie.org; Main URL: http://www.carnegie.org
Andrew Carnegie Medal of Philanthropy: http://carnegiemedals.org/
E-Newsletter: http://carnegie.org/news/grants-in-action/enews-sign-up/
Facebook: https://www.facebook.com/pages/Carnegie-Corporation-of-New-York/145973965440671
Google Plus: https://plus.google.com/106331518092409117369/posts
Grants Database: http://www.carnegie.org/sub/program/grantsearch.html
iTunes: http://itunes.apple.com/us/podcast/carnegie-corporation-new-york/id275515669?ign-mpt=uo%3D4
LinkedIn: http://www.linkedin.com/company/37222/
Pinterest: http://pinterest.com/carnegiecorp/
RSS Feed: http://carnegie.org/news/rss-subscribe/
Teacher Appreciation: http://greatteaching.carnegie.org/
Twitter: http://www.twitter.com/carnegiecorp
Vimeo: http://vimeo.com/carnegiecorp
Vimeo: http://vimeo.com/channels/ccny/videos
YouTube: http://www.youtube.com/user/carnegiecorpofny

Incorporated in 1911 in NY.
Donor: Andrew Carnegie‡.
Foundation type: Independent foundation.
Financial data (yr. ended 09/30/13): Assets, $3,033,694,178 (M); expenditures, $163,242,397; qualifying distributions, $150,462,931; giving activities include $129,848,165 for 445 grants (high: $3,938,945; low: $1,500), $50,000 for 1 grant to an individual, $482,380 for employee matching gifts, and $3,184,598 for foundation-administered programs.
Purpose and activities: As a grantmaking foundation, Carnegie Corporation of New York seeks to carry out Andrew Carnegie's vision of philanthropy, which he said should aim 'to do real and permanent good in this world.' Currently the foundation's work is focused in two integrated programs: the National Program, which includes support for education as a pathway to citizenship; and the International Program, which addresses international peace and security issues.
Fields of interest: Education, reform; Teacher school/education; Libraries, archives; Education, reading; International peace/security; International affairs, arms control; International affairs, national security; Civil/human rights, immigrants; Civil rights, voter education.
International interests: Africa; China; Russia; Sub-Saharan Africa.
Type of support: General/operating support; Continuing support; Program development; Conferences/seminars; Publication; Curriculum development; Research; Technical assistance; Program evaluation; Employee matching gifts.
Limitations: Applications accepted. Giving primarily for U.S. projects, although some grants are made to selected countries in Sub-Saharan Africa. No support for U.S. libraries, cultural institutions, programs or facilities of community-based educational or human services institutions, churches or religious organizations. No grants directly to individuals for scholarships or fellowships, travel, capital campaigns, or endowments, buildings or fundraising drives, deficits.
Publications: Application guidelines; Annual report; Grants list; Occasional report.
Application information: If the project is judged to be within the current program priorities of the corporation, the applicant will be asked to present the narrative and budget in the corporation's format. Before a grant is made, additional materials would be required, including a formal request from the head of the institution involved.Only full proposals that have been invited will be considered. Application form required.
Initial approach: Online application via grantmaker web site. Submit only one
Copies of proposal: 1
Deadline(s): None
Board meeting date(s): Mar., June, and Sept., and Dec.
Final notification: 4-6 weeks to respond to letter of inquiry
Officers and Trustees:* Thomas H. Kean,* Chair.; Kurt L. Schmoke, Vice-Chair.; Vartan Gregorian,* Pres.; Ellen Bloom, V.P., C.A.O. and Corp. Secy.; Robert J. Seman, V.P. and C.F.O.; Deana Arsenian, V.P., Intl. Prog., and Prog. Dir., Russia and Eurasia; Michele Cahill, V.P., Natl. Prog., and Prog. Dir., Urban Education; Meredith Jenkins, V.P. and Co-C.I.O.; Kim Y. Lew, V.P. and Co-C.I.O.; Laverne Evans Srinivasan, V.P., Education Prog.; David Hamburg, Pres. Emeritus; Pedro Aspe; Lionel Barber; Richard Beattie; Geoffrey T. Boisi; Ralph J. Cicerone; Jared L. Cohon; John J. Degioia; Amb. Edward P. Djerejian; John S. Hendricks; Susan Hockfield; Stephen A. Oxman; Don Michael Randel; Louise Richardson; Janet L. Robinson; Jorge Sampaio; Anne Tatlock; Ann Claire Williams; James Wolfensohn; Judy Woodruff.
Number of staff: 38 full-time professional; 33 full-time support; 1 part-time support.
EIN: 131628151

5748
The Carson Family Charitable Trust ✧

c/o US Trust
114 W. 47th St.
New York, NY 10036-1510

Established in 1990 in NY.
Donors: Russell L. Carson; Judith M. Carson.
Foundation type: Independent foundation.
Financial data (yr. ended 12/31/12): Assets, $26,058,298 (M); gifts received, $15,895,725; expenditures, $19,404,094; qualifying distributions, $18,878,008; giving activities include $18,725,000 for 97 grants (high: $1,000,000; low: $5,000).
Purpose and activities: Funding primarily for poverty relief and community development in New York City.
Fields of interest: Museums (art); Higher education; Environment, natural resources; Public health; Human services; Community/economic development.
Type of support: General/operating support.
Limitations: Applications not accepted. Giving primarily in New York, NY. No grants to individuals.
Application information: Contributes only to pre-selected organizations.
Trustees: Cecily M. Carson; Edward S. Carson; Judith M. Carson; Russell L. Carson; Bank of America, N.A.
EIN: 136957038
Selected grants: The following grants are a representative sample of this grantmaker's funding activity:
$1,000,000 to Endowment for Inner-City Education, New York, NY, 2012.
$1,000,000 to Harlem Childrens Zone, New York, NY, 2012.
$1,000,000 to New York Genome Center, New York, NY, 2012.
$1,000,000 to New York-Presbyterian Hospitals Healthcare System, New York, NY, 2012.
$1,000,000 to Robin Hood Foundation, New York, NY, 2012.
$500,000 to Rockefeller University, New York, NY, 2012.

$400,000 to Saint Lukes-Roosevelt Hospital Center, New York, NY, 2012.
$300,000 to New-York Historical Society, New York, NY, 2012.
$250,000 to Robin Hood Foundation, New York, NY, 2012. For Unrestricted General Support.
$100,000 to Kenyon College, Gambier, OH, 2012.

5749
The Thomas & Agnes Carvel Foundation ✧

35 E. Grassy Sprain Rd.
Yonkers, NY 10710-4612 (914) 793-7300
Contact: Peter Smith, Pres.

Established in 1976 in NY.
Donors: Thomas Carvel‡; Agnes Carvel‡; The Agnes Carvel 1991 Trust; Thomas Carvel Unitrust Remainderman.
Foundation type: Independent foundation.
Financial data (yr. ended 11/30/13): Assets, $38,802,170 (M); gifts received, $720,000; expenditures, $2,888,393; qualifying distributions, $2,378,337; giving activities include $2,237,500 for 127 grants (high: $500,000; low: $200).
Purpose and activities: Giving primarily for health care, including hospitals and children's hospitals, funding also for the arts, and children, youth and social services, and for higher education.
Fields of interest: Performing arts, music; Arts; Secondary school/education; Higher education; Hospitals (general); Hospitals (specialty); Health care; Cancer; Human services; Children/youth, services.
Type of support: Scholarship funds; Program development; Building/renovation; Research; Matching/challenge support.
Limitations: Applications accepted. Giving primarily in Westchester County, NY. No support for political and international organizations.
Application information:
Initial approach: Letter
Copies of proposal: 1
Deadline(s): Oct. 1
Board meeting date(s): Jan., Mar., May, July, and Nov.
Officers: Peter Smith, Pres.; Salvador Molella, V.P.; Marie Holcombe, Treas.
Directors: Brendan Byrne; Betty Godley.
Number of staff: 2 part-time professional; 2 full-time support.
EIN: 132879673
Selected grants: The following grants are a representative sample of this grantmaker's funding activity:
$250,000 to Cardinal McCloskey School and Home for Children, Valhalla, NY, 2011.
$250,000 to Elizabeth Seton Pediatric Center, New York, NY, 2011.
$50,000 to Hudson River Museum of Westchester, Yonkers, NY, 2011.
$50,000 to Saint Martin de Porres Academy, New Haven, CT, 2011.
$35,000 to Seton Hall University, South Orange, NJ, 2011.
$19,387 to Temple Sharey Tefilo-Israel, South Orange, NJ, 2011.
$15,000 to Feel Better Kids, Uniondale, NY, 2011.
$10,000 to Childrens Village, Dobbs Ferry, NY, 2011.
$10,000 to Park Performing Arts Center, Union City, NJ, 2011.
$5,000 to Seton Hall Preparatory School, West Orange, NJ, 2011.

5750
Cattaraugus Region Community Foundation ✧

(formerly Greater Olean Community Foundation)
120 N. Union St.
Olean, NY 14760-2735 (716) 372-4433
Contact: Karen Niemic Buchheit, Exec. Dir.; Ryan Michelle Wilcox, Dir., Comms. and Donor Svcs.
FAX: (716) 372-7912;
E-mail: foundation@cattfoundation.org; Additional e-mail: karen@cattfoundation.org; Main
URL: http://www.cattfoundation.org
Facebook: http://www.facebook.com/cattfoundation
LinkedIn: https://www.linkedin.com/company/cattaraugus-region-community-foundation
RSS Feed: http://cattfoundation.org/feed/
Twitter: https://twitter.com/CattFoundation

Established in 1994 in NY.
Foundation type: Community foundation.
Financial data (yr. ended 12/31/13): Assets, $12,664,215 (M); gifts received, $1,484,560; expenditures, $864,517; giving activities include $586,058 for 8+ grants (high: $160,461), and $81,938 for 51 grants to individuals.
Purpose and activities: The foundation receives and administers funds for charitable purposes primarily in the Cattaraugus County (NY) region, but also has funds for support in McKean County (PA) and some other areas. Grantmaking priorities include education, health, youth, scholarships, the arts, community development and human services.
Fields of interest: Arts; Secondary school/education; Education; Health care; Human services; Community/economic development; Youth; Military/veterans; Economically disadvantaged.
Type of support: Building/renovation; Continuing support; Curriculum development; Endowments; Equipment; General/operating support; Matching/challenge support; Program development; Scholarships—to individuals.
Limitations: Applications accepted. Giving generally limited to the southwest NY and northwest PA, primarily serving Cattaraugus County (NY), but also some support in McKean County (PA). No support for promotion of individual religious beliefs or religious activities. No grants for individuals (except for scholarships), or for for-profit organizations or services primarily supported by tax dollars.
Publications: Application guidelines; Annual report; Financial statement; Newsletter.
Application information: Visit foundation web site for application form and guidelines. Application form required.
Initial approach: E-mail or call foundation
Copies of proposal: 1
Deadline(s): May 1 and Nov. 1 for Community Fund; other funds have rolling deadlines.
Board meeting date(s): 3rd Friday in January, March, May, September and November
Final notification: Within 60 days
Officers and Directors:* Carol Stitt,* Pres.; Wendy Brand, V.P.; Doug Price,* Secy.; Mike Kasperski,* Treas.; Karen Niemic Buchheit, Exec. Dir.; Vicki Blessing; Ted Branch; R. Dennis Casey; Barbara Chew; Anthony Evans; Karen Fohl; Steve Foster; Eric Garvin; Dr. Naheed Hilal; Dr. Yogi Kothari; Dennis Pezzimenti; Robert Simon; Larry Sorokes; Audra Stevens; Ward Wilday; Theresa Raftis.
Number of staff: 1 full-time professional; 1 part-time professional.
EIN: 161468127

5751
The Caudill Family Foundation, Inc. ✧

c/o Laura Carroll, The Ayco Company
P.O. Box 860
Saratoga Springs, NY 12866-0860

Donor: W. Lowry Caudill.
Foundation type: Independent foundation.
Financial data (yr. ended 12/31/13): Assets, $427,719 (M); gifts received, $811,582; expenditures, $637,150; qualifying distributions, $625,733; giving activities include $625,733 for 8 grants (high: $247,358; low: $2,500).
Fields of interest: Higher education; Human services; Protestant agencies & churches.
Limitations: Applications not accepted. Giving primarily in NC. No grants to individuals.
Application information: Contributes only to pre-selected organizations.
Directors: Jeffrey Caudill; Sarah Caudill; Susan S. Caudill; Walter Lowry Caudill; Alfred G. Childers.
EIN: 200241846
Selected grants: The following grants are a representative sample of this grantmaker's funding activity:
$166,000 to Aldersgate United Methodist Church, Durham, NC, 2011. For general charitable purposes.

5752
The Joseph & Trina Cayre Foundation, Inc. ✧

(formerly Jack & Grace Cayre Foundation)
141 5th Ave., 2nd Fl.
New York, NY 10010-7105 (212) 726-0773
Contact: Joseph Cayre, Pres.

Established in 1988 in DE.
Donors: Joseph Cayre; Kenneth Cayre; Stanley Cayre; Daniel Cayre; Michael Haddad; Jack Cayre; Michael Cayre; Steven Cayre; Grace Cayre; Murray Hill Properties; Stillwater; Boston National Title LLC.
Foundation type: Independent foundation.
Financial data (yr. ended 12/31/12): Assets, $226,058 (M); gifts received, $792,855; expenditures, $1,754,860; qualifying distributions, $1,754,001; giving activities include $1,754,001 for 165 grants (high: $577,509; low: $18).
Purpose and activities: Giving primarily to Jewish agencies and temples and for Jewish education.
Fields of interest: Education; Human services; Jewish federated giving programs; Jewish agencies & synagogues.
Limitations: Giving primarily in NY, with strong emphasis on Brooklyn. No grants to individuals.
Application information: Application form not required.
Initial approach: Letter
Deadline(s): None
Officers: Joseph Cayre, Pres.; Trina Cayre, V.P.
EIN: 133494146
Selected grants: The following grants are a representative sample of this grantmaker's funding activity:
$75,000 to Prostate Cancer Foundation, Santa Monica, CA, 2011.
$5,000 to Chai Lifeline, New York, NY, 2011.

5753
The Kenneth & Lillian Cayre Foundation, Inc. ✧
1350 Broadway, Ste. 1010
New York, NY 10018 (212) 840-5588
Contact: Kenneth Cayre, Pres.

Established in 1993 in DE.
Donors: Jack K. Cayre; Kenneth Cayre; Nathan Cayre; Grace K. Cayre; Michelle Cayre; Raquel Cayre; Lillian Cayre; Jack K. Cayre Irrevocable Grantor Trust; Nathan Cayre Irrevocable Grantor Trust; Grace Cayre Irrevocable Grantor Trust; Rachel Cayre Irrevocable Grantor Trust; Michelle Cayre Irrevocable Grantor Trust.
Foundation type: Independent foundation.
Financial data (yr. ended 12/31/13): Assets, $4,385,799 (M); expenditures, $794,399; qualifying distributions, $744,260; giving activities include $744,260 for 134 grants (high: $40,000; low: $26).
Fields of interest: Education; Agriculture/food; Human services.
Limitations: Applications accepted. Giving primarily in NJ and NY. No grants to individuals.
Application information: Application form required.
Initial approach: Letter
Deadline(s): None
Officers: Kenneth Cayre, Pres.; Lillian Cayre, V.P.
EIN: 133746793

5754
The Michael & Shirley Cayre Foundation ✧ ☆
141 5th Ave., 2nd Fl.
New York, NY 10010-7105 (212) 726-0773
Contact: Michael Cayre, Pres.

Established in 2000 in DE.
Donors: Michael Cayre; Shirley Cayre.
Foundation type: Independent foundation.
Financial data (yr. ended 12/31/13): Assets, $47,286 (M); gifts received, $535,654; expenditures, $669,805; qualifying distributions, $582,410; giving activities include $86,310 for 7 grants (high: $75,000; low: $1,800), and $496,100 for 10 grants to individuals (high: $412,000; low: $500).
Fields of interest: Jewish agencies & synagogues.
Limitations: Applications accepted. Giving primarily in Brooklyn, NY.
Application information: Application form required.
Initial approach: Proposal
Deadline(s): None
Officers: Michael Cayre, Pres.; Shirley Cayre, V.P.
EIN: 134109353

5755
The Stanley & Frieda Cayre Foundation, Inc. ✧
1407 Broadway, 41st Fl.
New York, NY 10018-2348 (212) 789-7000
Contact: Stanley Cayre, Pres.

Established in 1993 in DE.
Donors: Stanley Cayre; Grace S. Cayre; Aurora Capital Assocs., LLC.
Foundation type: Independent foundation.
Financial data (yr. ended 12/31/13): Assets, $10,027,934 (M); expenditures, $854,133; qualifying distributions, $763,034; giving activities include $763,034 for 91 grants (high: $333,333; low: $101).
Purpose and activities: Giving primarily to Jewish organizations, temples and schools.
Fields of interest: Elementary/secondary education; Education; Human services; Jewish agencies & synagogues.
Limitations: Giving primarily in NY.
Application information: Application form required.
Initial approach: Letter
Deadline(s): None
Officers: Stanley Cayre, Pres.; Frieda Cayre, V.P.
EIN: 133746789

5756
The Central National-Gottesman Foundation ✧
c/o Steven Eigen
3 Manhattanville Rd.
Purchase, NY 10577-2110 (914) 696-9062
Contact: Christine Royer
Application address: 417 Riverside Dr., New York, NY 10025

Established in 1981 in NY.
Donor: Central National-Gottesman, Inc.
Foundation type: Company-sponsored foundation.
Financial data (yr. ended 12/31/13): Assets, $29,838,053 (M); expenditures, $969,799; qualifying distributions, $799,161; giving activities include $200,038 for 55 grants (high: $56,058; low: $500), and $541,488 for 45 grants to individuals (high: $17,058; low: $2,042).
Purpose and activities: The foundation supports hospitals and organizations involved with higher education, pulp and paper industry, and the visually impaired.
Fields of interest: Higher education; Hospitals (general); Business/industry; United Ways and Federated Giving Programs; Jewish federated giving programs; Blind/visually impaired.
Type of support: General/operating support; Employee-related scholarships.
Limitations: Applications accepted. Giving primarily in NY. No grants to individuals (except for employee-related scholarships).
Application information: Application form required.
Initial approach: Completed application form
Deadline(s): None
Officer: Kenneth L. Wallach, Pres.; Steven Eigen, Treas.
Director: Andrew Wallach.
EIN: 133047546
Selected grants: The following grants are a representative sample of this grantmaker's funding activity:
$125,000 to Doctors Without Borders USA, New York, NY, 2011.
$50,000 to National Book Foundation, New York, NY, 2011.
$32,628 to Boston College, Chestnut Hill, MA, 2011.
$27,708 to University of Vermont, Burlington, VT, 2011.
$21,050 to Pennsylvania State University, University Park, PA, 2011.
$8,920 to Poets and Writers, New York, NY, 2011.
$7,500 to Alliance for Young Artists and Writers, New York, NY, 2011.
$3,500 to University of Maine Pulp and Paper Foundation, Orono, ME, 2011.
$2,000 to Connecticut Childrens Medical Center Foundation, Hartford, CT, 2011.
$2,000 to Mercy Hospital, Portland, ME, 2011.

5757
Central New York Community Foundation, Inc. ✧
431 East Fayette St., Ste. 100
Syracuse, NY 13202 (315) 422-9538
Contact: Peter A. Dunn, C.E.O.; For grants: Olive Sephuma, Dir., Community Grantmaking
FAX: (315) 471-6031; E-mail: info@cnycf.org; Grant inquiry e-mail: olive@cnycf.org; Main URL: http://www.cnycf.org
Eventbrite: http://www.eventbrite.com/o/central-new-york-community-foundation-285082707?s=1804557
Facebook: http://www.facebook.com/cnycf
Flickr: http://www.flickr.com/photos/cnycf/
LinkedIn: http://www.linkedin.com/company/central-new-york-community-foundation?goback=.cps_1286159727066_1
RSS Feed: https://cnycf.wordpress.com/feed/
Twitter: https://twitter.com/CNYCF
YouTube: http://www.youtube.com/user/CNYCF

Incorporated in 1927 in NY; reorganized in 1951.
Foundation type: Community foundation.
Financial data (yr. ended 03/31/13): Assets, $143,992,070 (M); gifts received, $12,114,557; expenditures, $10,847,470; giving activities include $8,337,264 for grants.
Purpose and activities: The mission of the foundation is to enhance the quality of life for those who live and work within the community by: 1) encouraging the growth of a permanent charitable endowment to meet the community's changing opportunities and needs; 2) providing donors and their diverse philanthropic interests with vehicles to make giving easy, personally satisfying and effective; 3) serving as a catalyst, neutral convener, and facilitator, stimulating and promoting collaborations among various organizations to accomplish common objectives; and 4) carrying out a strategic grant making program that is flexible, visionary, and inclusive.
Fields of interest: Humanities; Historic preservation/historical societies; Arts; Child development, education; Adult education—literacy, basic skills & GED; Education; Environment; Health care; Recreation; Child development, services; Human services; Community/economic development; Homeless.
Type of support: Employee matching gifts; Curriculum development; Consulting services; Management development/capacity building; Capital campaigns; Building/renovation; Equipment; Program development; Publication; Seed money; Scholarship funds; Research; Technical assistance; Scholarships—to individuals; Matching/challenge support.
Limitations: Applications accepted. Giving limited to Onondaga and Madison counties, NY. No support for religious purposes. No grants to individuals (except for scholarships), or for deficit financing, endowment funds, fellowships, operating budgets, medical or academic research (except where directed by a donor), or travel expenses; no loans.
Publications: Annual report (including application guidelines); Informational brochure (including application guidelines); Newsletter.
Application information: Visit foundation web site for application form and guidelines. Faxed

applications are not accepted. Application form required.

Initial approach: Contact program staff
Copies of proposal: 1
Deadline(s): Apr., July, and Sept.
Board meeting date(s): Mar., June, Sept., and Dec.
Final notification: June, Sept. and Dec.

Officers and Directors:* Linda Dickerson Hartsock,* Chair.; David J. Moynihan,* Vice-Chair.; Peter A. Dunn, C.E.O. and Pres.; John G. Eberle,* V.P., Grants and Community Initiatives; Jennifer Owens, V.P., Devel. and Mktg.; Liz Cavallaro,* C.F.O.; Richard D. Hole,* Treas.; J. Andrew Breuer; William C. Brod; Craig Buckhout; Evelyn Carter; David A. Holstein; Steven Jacobs; Ellen Percy Kraly, Ph.D.; Timothy Penix; J. Daniel Pluff; Brian Pollard, D.D.S.; Rita L. Reicher, Ph.D.; M. Jack Rudnick; Corinne R. Smith, Ph.D.; Michael J. Wamp; Gwen Webber-McLeod; Maryann M. Winters.
Number of staff: 10 full-time professional; 4 full-time support.
EIN: 150626910

5758
Century 21 Associates Foundation, Inc. ✧
(formerly Gindi Associates Foundation, Inc.)
22 Cortlandt St.
New York, NY 10007-3107

Established in 1982 in NJ.
Donors: Century 21, Inc.; ASG Equities LLC.
Foundation type: Company-sponsored foundation.
Financial data (yr. ended 05/31/13): Assets, $4,783,143 (M); gifts received, $6,500,000; expenditures, $8,043,164; qualifying distributions, $8,027,042; giving activities include $7,967,116 for 1,314 grants (high: $500,000; low: $36).
Purpose and activities: The foundation supports organizations involved with education, human services, and Judaism.
Fields of interest: Higher education; Theological school/education; Education; Human services; Jewish federated giving programs; Jewish agencies & synagogues.
Type of support: General/operating support; Continuing support; Sponsorships.
Limitations: Applications not accepted. Giving primarily in NJ and Brooklyn and New York, NY. No grants to individuals.
Application information: Contributes only to pre-selected organizations.
Trustees: Abraham Gindi; Raymond Gindi; Sam Gindi.
EIN: 222412138
Selected grants: The following grants are a representative sample of this grantmaker's funding activity:
$60,000 to South Africa Financing Enterprise, Inc., New York, NY, 2011.
$52,000 to Sephardic Food Fund, New York, NY, 2011.
$50,000 to Museum of Jewish Heritage, New York, NY, 2011.
$26,000 to Foundation Bnei Levy, New York, NY, 2011.
$26,000 to Mattan Basseter, New York, NY, 2011.
$25,000 to UJA-Federation of New York, New York, NY, 2011.
$24,000 to Chai Lifeline, New York, NY, 2011.
$20,000 to Shuvi Nafshi Foundation, New York, NY, 2011.
$10,000 to Jewish National Fund, Rockville Centre, NY, 2011.
$10,000 to Western Wall Heritage Foundation, New York, NY, 2011.

5759
Chada Foundation, Inc. ✧
c/o A. Scherzer
4 Executive Blvd., Ste. 202
Suffern, NY 10901-4190

Established in 1991 in NY.
Donors: Esther Reichman; Asher Scharf; David Scharf Family Trust; So Charitable Trust; Chesed Global Foundation.
Foundation type: Independent foundation.
Financial data (yr. ended 11/30/13): Assets, $1,449,965 (L); gifts received, $166,500; expenditures, $520,828; qualifying distributions, $441,419; giving activities include $441,110 for grants.
Fields of interest: Jewish agencies & synagogues.
Limitations: Applications not accepted. Giving primarily in NY. No grants to individuals.
Application information: Unsolicited requests for funds not accepted.
Officers: Esther Reichman, Pres.; Asher Scharf, V.P. and Secy.
Directors: Moses Scharf; Helene Teitelbaum.
EIN: 133650373

5760
Dorothy Jordan Chadwick Fund ✧
Bank of America Tower
1 Bryant Park
New York, NY 10036

Trust established in 1957 in NY.
Donors: Dorothy J. Chadwick†; Dorothy R. Kidder†.
Foundation type: Independent foundation.
Financial data (yr. ended 05/31/14): Assets, $18,393,548 (M); expenditures, $1,114,469; qualifying distributions, $1,001,488; giving activities include $961,920 for 37 grants (high: $118,990; low: $2,500).
Purpose and activities: Giving primarily to organizations of interest to the family, with emphasis on purposes initiated by the fund. These interests include environmental and wildlife conservation, and non-traditional developmental education.
Fields of interest: Education; Environment; Animals/wildlife, preservation/protection; Health care; Human services.
Type of support: General/operating support; Continuing support; Capital campaigns; Building/renovation; Program development; Seed money; Research.
Limitations: Applications not accepted. Giving in the U.S., with emphasis on MA. No grants to individuals.
Application information: Unsolicited requests for funds not accepted.
Trustees: Katherine K. Hildner; Randolph K. Luskey; Bank of America, N.A.
EIN: 136069950
Selected grants: The following grants are a representative sample of this grantmaker's funding activity:
$65,000 to African Wildlife Foundation, Washington, DC, 2011.
$60,000 to African Wildlife Foundation, Washington, DC, 2011.
$30,000 to Living Classrooms Foundation, Baltimore, MD, 2011.
$25,000 to Food and Friends, Washington, DC, 2011.
$20,000 to Ocean Conservancy, Washington, DC, 2011.
$20,000 to Proctor Academy, Andover, NH, 2011.
$10,000 to Ocean Foundation, Washington, DC, 2011.
$5,000 to Conservation International, Arlington, VA, 2011.
$5,000 to National Aquarium in Baltimore, Baltimore, MD, 2011.
$5,000 to Ocean Awareness Project, Washington, DC, 2011.

5761
Chaim Foundation ✧
c/o HIS
1310 48th St.
Brooklyn, NY 11219-3159

Established in NY.
Donors: Harry Silber; Rabbi Chaim Fortang; Jack Eizikowitz; Micha Kaufman; Jerry Weissman; Huberfeld.
Foundation type: Operating foundation.
Financial data (yr. ended 12/31/12): Assets, $0 (M); gifts received, $1,500; expenditures, $665,497; qualifying distributions, $665,497; giving activities include $665,497 for 39 grants (high: $150,000; low: $4,000).
Purpose and activities: Giving primarily to Jewish agencies, temples, and schools.
Fields of interest: Education; Human services; Jewish agencies & synagogues.
Limitations: Applications not accepted. Giving primarily in NY. No grants to individuals.
Application information: Contributes only to pre-selected organizations.
Trustees: Eva Silber; Harry Silber.
EIN: 113247210

5762
Challenger Foundation ✧
(formerly The Corrigan Foundation)
P.O. Box 73
Bowling Green Sta.
New York, NY 10274-0073

Established in 1996 in NY.
Donors: E. Gerald Corrigan; Goldman Sachs & Co.
Foundation type: Independent foundation.
Financial data (yr. ended 07/31/13): Assets, $22,354,066 (M); expenditures, $912,156; qualifying distributions, $874,000; giving activities include $874,000 for 26 grants (high: $250,000; low: $2,000).
Purpose and activities: Giving primarily for education, health organizations and human services, as well as for research in international economics and finance.
Fields of interest: Higher education; Education; Hospitals (general); Health organizations, association; Human services; Economics.
Type of support: General/operating support.
Limitations: Applications not accepted. Giving primarily in CT and NY; funding also in Washington, DC, and MA. No grants to individuals.

Application information: Contributes only to pre-selected organizations.
Trustees: E. Gerald Corrigan; Elizabeth A. Corrigan; Karen B. Corrigan; Cathy E. Minehan.
EIN: 137109402
Selected grants: The following grants are a representative sample of this grantmaker's funding activity:
$250,000 to Massachusetts General Hospital, Boston, MA, 2011. For general charitable purposes.
$100,000 to Massachusetts General Hospital, Boston, MA, 2011. For general charitable purposes.
$25,000 to Fairfield University, Fairfield, CT, 2011. For general charitable purposes.
$25,000 to University of Rochester, Rochester, NY, 2011. For general charitable purposes.
$20,000 to Aspen Institute, Washington, DC, 2011. For general charitable purposes.
$15,000 to American Museum of Natural History, New York, NY, 2011. For general charitable purposes.
$15,000 to Boston Municipal Research Bureau, Boston, MA, 2011. For general charitable purposes.
$15,000 to Fordham University, Bronx, NY, 2011. For general charitable purposes.
$15,000 to Group of Thirty, Washington, DC, 2011. For general charitable purposes.
$10,000 to Groundwork, Inc., Brooklyn, NY, 2011. For general charitable purposes.

5763
The Charina Endowment Fund, Inc. ✧

(formerly The HWG Fund, Inc.)
c/o Richard L. Menschel
375 Park Ave., Ste. 1602
New York, NY 10152-1600

Established in 1992 in NY.
Donor: Horace W. Goldsmith Foundation.
Foundation type: Independent foundation.
Financial data (yr. ended 12/31/13): Assets, $292,663,159 (M); expenditures, $12,742,087; qualifying distributions, $11,726,534; giving activities include $11,343,000 for 48 grants (high: $1,000,000; low: $25,000).
Purpose and activities: The fund supports cultural programs, including performing arts and museums. Support also for hospitals and education, with emphasis on higher education.
Fields of interest: Visual arts; Museums; Performing arts, theater; Arts; Education, research; Higher education; Business school/education; Libraries (public); Environment, natural resources; Hospitals (general); Medical care, rehabilitation; Aging, centers/services; Homeless, human services; Children/youth; Children; Economically disadvantaged.
Type of support: General/operating support; Continuing support; Income development; Annual campaigns; Capital campaigns; Building/renovation; Land acquisition; Endowments; Debt reduction; Emergency funds; Professorships; Seed money; Curriculum development; Fellowships; Scholarship funds; Research; Matching/challenge support.
Limitations: Applications not accepted. Giving primarily in New York. No grants to individuals.
Application information: Unsolicited requests for funds not accepted.
Officers and Directors:* Richard L. Menschel,* Pres. and Treas.; Ronay A. Menschel,* Secy.; Robert B. Menschel.
Number of staff: 1 part-time professional; 3 part-time support.
EIN: 133675545
Selected grants: The following grants are a representative sample of this grantmaker's funding activity:
$1,000,000 to Cornell University, Ithaca, NY, 2012.
$1,000,000 to Cornell University, Ithaca, NY, 2012. For general support.
$1,000,000 to Harvard University, Cambridge, MA, 2012. For general support.
$750,000 to Hospital for Special Surgery, New York, NY, 2012.
$500,000 to Harvard University, Cambridge, MA, 2012. For grant to School of Public Health in Boston.
$500,000 to International Rescue Committee, New York, NY, 2012.
$300,000 to Seventh Regiment Armory Conservancy, New York, NY, 2012.
$300,000 to Seventh Regiment Armory Conservancy, New York, NY, 2012. For general support.
$250,000 to Central Park Conservancy, New York, NY, 2012.
$200,000 to Rockefeller University, New York, NY, 2012.
$150,000 to Human Rights First, New York, NY, 2012. For general support.
$150,000 to Urban Assembly, New York, NY, 2012. For general support.
$100,000 to Lincoln Center Theater, New York, NY, 2012. For general support.
$100,000 to New York University, School of Medicine, New York, NY, 2012.
$100,000 to Wikimedia Foundation, San Francisco, CA, 2012.
$84,000 to Uncommon Schools, New York, NY, 2012.

5764
Charina Foundation, Inc. ✧

c/o BCRS Assocs.
77 Water St., 9th Fl.
New York, NY 10005-4414
Contact: Richard L. Menschel, Pres.

Incorporated in 1980 in NY.
Donors: Richard L. Menschel; The Menschel Foundation.
Foundation type: Independent foundation.
Financial data (yr. ended 08/31/13): Assets, $28,191,037 (M); expenditures, $1,236,286; qualifying distributions, $1,225,390; giving activities include $1,212,010 for 285 grants (high: $100,000; low: $250).
Purpose and activities: Emphasis on arts and culture, including museums, health services, medical research, and hospitals; higher and other education; Jewish organizations, including welfare funds; recreation; and community development.
Fields of interest: Museums; Arts; Higher education; Business school/education; Medical school/education; Education; Hospitals (general); Medical care, rehabilitation; Health care; Medical research, institute; Legal services; Recreation; Community/economic development; Jewish agencies & synagogues; Children.
Type of support: General/operating support; Continuing support; Income development; Annual campaigns; Capital campaigns; Building/renovation; Equipment; Land acquisition; Endowments; Debt reduction; Emergency funds; Professorships; Seed money; Curriculum development; Fellowships; Scholarship funds; Research; Matching/challenge support.
Limitations: Applications not accepted. Giving primarily in New York, NY. No grants to individuals.
Application information: Contributes only to pre-selected organizations.
Officers and Directors:* Richard L. Menschel,* Pres. and Treas.; Ronay Menschel,* Secy.; Eugene P. Polk.
Number of staff: None.
EIN: 133050294

5765
Chatterjee Charitable Foundation ✧

888 7th Ave., Ste. 3000
New York, NY 10106-0001

Established in 1995 in NY.
Donors: Purnendu Chatterjee; Sidhartha Maitra; Subir K. Sanyal.
Foundation type: Independent foundation.
Financial data (yr. ended 11/30/13): Assets, $8,912,742 (M); expenditures, $918,151; qualifying distributions, $914,861; giving activities include $911,247 for 17 grants (high: $386,047; low: $500).
Purpose and activities: Giving primarily for higher education as well as to Asian and Indian organizations, and to an institute for molecular medicine.
Fields of interest: Higher education; Education; Medical research, institute; Human services.
International interests: India.
Limitations: Applications not accepted. Giving primarily in New York, NY. No grants to individuals.
Application information: Contributes only to pre-selected organizations.
Director: Purnendu Chatterjee.
EIN: 137072667

5766
Chautauqua Region Community Foundation, Inc. ✧

418 Spring St.
Jamestown, NY 14701-5332 (716) 661-3390
Contact: Randall J. Sweeney, Exec. Dir.; For grant and scholarship inquiries: Lisa W. Lynde, Prog. Off.
FAX: (716) 488-0387; E-mail: llynde@crcfonline.org; Grant inquiries tel.: (716) 661-3392; Main URL: http://www.crcfonline.org
Facebook: http://www.facebook.com/CRCFOnline
Google Plus: https://plus.google.com/u/0/108261437264599744516/about
RSS Feed: http://crcfonline.org/feed/
YouTube: http://www.youtube.com/crcfonline
Scholarship inquiries e-mail: llynde@crcfonline.org;
Kids First Mini-Grants
e-mail: jdiethrick@crcfonline.org

Incorporated in 1978 in NY.
Foundation type: Community foundation.
Financial data (yr. ended 12/31/13): Assets, $79,452,997 (M); gifts received, $1,343,280; expenditures, $3,271,269; giving activities include $1,497,489 for 71+ grants (high: $30,061; low: $45), and $895,073 for 693 grants to individuals.
Purpose and activities: The foundation seeks to enrich the quality of life in the Chautauqua region.
Fields of interest: Arts; Libraries/library science; Education; Housing/shelter, development; Children/youth, services; Human services;

Community/economic development; Government/public administration.
Type of support: Program development; General/operating support; Continuing support; Building/renovation; Equipment; Emergency funds; Conferences/seminars; Publication; Seed money; Scholarships—to individuals; Matching/challenge support.
Limitations: Applications accepted. Giving limited to the southern Chautauqua County, NY, area. No support for religious purposes (excluding church related requests supported by the Karl Peterson Fund only). No grants to individuals (except for scholarship grants), or for debt retirement.
Publications: Application guidelines; Annual report (including application guidelines); Informational brochure; Newsletter.
Application information: The foundation is now accepting all grant applications through the www.chautauquagrants.org web site. Please register with the web site and follow the appropriate steps. Application form required.
Initial approach: Create online profile
Deadline(s): Mar. 31, June 30, and Dec. 1 for Community Service grants; last Fri. of each month for Fields-of-Interest grants
Board meeting date(s): Monthly
Final notification: Generally 3-4 months
Officers and Directors:* Jennifer L. Gibson,* Pres.; Pamela D. Noll,* V.P.; Carol S. Hay,* Secy.; Denise R. Jones,* Treas.; Randall J. Sweeney, Exec. Dir.; Michael C. Bird; Christy Brecht; Donald L. Butler; Dr. Ronald W. Kohl; Dana Lundberg; Peter Stark; Stephen J. Wright.
Number of staff: 7 full-time professional.
EIN: 161116837

5767
The Chazen Foundation ✧
c/o Chazen Capital Partners
150 E. 58th St. 27th Fl.
New York, NY 10155-0002 (212) 888-7800

Established in 1985 in NY.
Donors: Jerome Chazen; Simona Chazen; Jerome Chazen & Graf Repetti & Co., LLP.
Foundation type: Independent foundation.
Financial data (yr. ended 12/31/12): Assets, $8,168,678 (M); expenditures, $2,235,019; qualifying distributions, $2,074,225; giving activities include $1,876,780 for 37 grants (high: $861,942; low: $1,034), and $10,500 for grants to individuals.
Purpose and activities: Giving primarily for Jewish agencies and temples, higher education, the arts, particularly art museums, health associations, and human services.
Fields of interest: Museums (art); Performing arts, opera; Arts; Higher education; Health organizations, association; Human services; Jewish federated giving programs; Jewish agencies & synagogues.
International interests: Israel.
Type of support: General/operating support; Capital campaigns; Building/renovation; Professorships; Scholarship funds; Grants to individuals; Scholarships—to individuals.
Limitations: Giving primarily in the northeastern U.S., and in Madison, WI.
Publications: Application guidelines; Informational brochure.
Application information:
Initial approach: Letter
Deadline(s): None
Trustees: Jerome Chazen; Simona Chazen.
Number of staff: 1 part-time professional; 1 part-time support.
EIN: 133229474
Selected grants: The following grants are a representative sample of this grantmaker's funding activity:
$861,942 to University of Wisconsin Foundation, Madison, WI, 2012. For general support-cash contributions.

5768
Chehebar Family Foundation, Inc. ✧
1000 Pennsylvania Ave.
Brooklyn, NY 11207-8417

Incorporated in 1985 in NY.
Donors: Albert Chehebar; Isaac Shehebar; Jack Chehebar; Joseph Chehebar; Hyman Escava; Rainbow Store, Inc.; Rainbow Apparel Companies; Baraka Realty; Skiva International; Joseph Chehebar Family Foundation; Middlegate Securities, Ltd.; Ahaba Ve Ahva Congregation; Charles Kushner; Ike Rudy; Magen Israel Society; Klatskin Associates LLC; Sitt Asset Mgmt. LLC; The Harvey and Shelli Dachs Charitable Foundation; Crown Acquisitions Inc.; Central Mills, Inc.; Ahi Ezer Congregation.
Foundation type: Independent foundation.
Financial data (yr. ended 12/31/12): Assets, $9,433,552 (M); gifts received, $3,306,426; expenditures, $2,735,272; qualifying distributions, $2,674,882; giving activities include $2,674,882 for 1,496 grants (high: $101,000; low: $36).
Purpose and activities: Giving primarily to Jewish temples, agencies, and schools.
Fields of interest: Elementary/secondary education; Jewish federated giving programs; Jewish agencies & synagogues.
Limitations: Applications not accepted. Giving primarily in the greater metropolitan New York, NY, area, with emphasis on Brooklyn. No grants to individuals.
Application information: Unsolicited requests for funds not accepted.
Directors: Albert Chehebar; Jack Chehebar; Joseph Chehebar; Isaac Shehebar.
EIN: 133178015

5769
Joseph Chehebar Family Foundation ✧
1000 Pennsylvania Ave.
Brooklyn, NY 11207-8417

Established in 1998 in NY.
Donors: Joseph Chehebar; Isaac Shehebar; Joseph Benun; Isaac A. Gindi; Middlegate Securities, Ltd.
Foundation type: Independent foundation.
Financial data (yr. ended 12/31/12): Assets, $2,088,944 (M); gifts received, $3,825,000; expenditures, $1,724,859; qualifying distributions, $1,724,834; giving activities include $1,724,834 for 317 grants (high: $250,000; low: $5).
Purpose and activities: Giving primarily to Jewish agencies, temples, and schools.
Fields of interest: Elementary/secondary education; Jewish agencies & synagogues.
Limitations: Applications not accepted. Giving primarily in NY. No grants to individuals.
Application information: Contributes only to pre-selected organizations.
Manager: Joseph Chehebar, Pres.; Gabriel Y. Chehebar, V.P.; Abraham Y. Chehebar, Treas.
EIN: 113388342

5770
The Chernin Family Foundation, Inc. ✧
c/o Executive Monetary Mgmt.
220 E. 42nd St., 32nd Fl.
New York, NY 10017-5814

Established in 2000 in DE.
Donors: Peter Chernin; Megan Chernin.
Foundation type: Independent foundation.
Financial data (yr. ended 12/31/12): Assets, $468,323 (M); gifts received, $920,308; expenditures, $1,084,943; qualifying distributions, $1,072,530; giving activities include $1,072,530 for 28 grants (high: $500,000; low: $200).
Purpose and activities: Giving primarily for higher education, as well as for health care and the environment.
Fields of interest: Higher education; Education; Environment; Health care; Health organizations, association.
Limitations: Applications not accepted. Giving primarily in NY. No grants to individuals.
Application information: Contributes only to pre-selected organizations.
Officers: Peter Chernin, Pres.; Megan Chernin, V.P. and Treas.
Directors: David Chernin; John Chernin; Margaret Chernin.
EIN: 522281012

5771
Michael Chernow Trust ✧
P.O. Box 197
Larchmont, NY 10538-0197 (914) 834-1900
Contact: Gordon S. Oppenheimer Esq.

Established in 1975 in NY.
Foundation type: Independent foundation.
Financial data (yr. ended 06/30/13): Assets, $4,889,627 (M); expenditures, $624,609; qualifying distributions, $483,950; giving activities include $483,950 for grants.
Fields of interest: Performing arts, opera; Higher education; Hospitals (general); Health organizations; Human services; Jewish federated giving programs; Biology/life sciences; Jewish agencies & synagogues; Economically disadvantaged.
Type of support: General/operating support; Continuing support; Research.
Limitations: Applications accepted. Giving primarily in NY. No grants to individuals.
Application information: Application form not required.
Initial approach: Proposal
Deadline(s): None
Trustees: Martin P. Krasner; Edward Streim; Lynn Streim.
EIN: 136758226
Selected grants: The following grants are a representative sample of this grantmaker's funding activity:
$1,000 to Youth America Grand Prix, New York, NY, 2013. For general charitable support.

5772
Chesed Foundation of America ✧
c/o Sabr Group
126 E. 56th St., 15th Fl., No. 1520
New York, NY 10022-3613
Contact: Henry Reinhold

Donors: George Karfunkel; Michael Karfunkel; Karfunkel Family Foundation.
Foundation type: Independent foundation.
Financial data (yr. ended 06/30/13): Assets, $292,833,249 (M); gifts received, $15,205,000; expenditures, $11,222,228; qualifying distributions, $11,154,544; giving activities include $11,154,544 for 228 grants (high: $500,000; low: $72).
Purpose and activities: Giving primarily to cover operating expenses for schools and synagogues, as well as for educational scholarships and assistance for the needy.
Fields of interest: Elementary/secondary education; Jewish federated giving programs; Jewish agencies & synagogues.
Limitations: Applications not accepted.
Application information: Unsolicited requests for funds not accepted.
Officers: George Karfunkel, Pres.; Rene Karfunkel, V.P.
Trustee: Ann Karfunkel.
EIN: 133922068

5773
The Chesed Global Foundation, Inc. ✧
c/o Eli Robins
247 W. 35th St., 14th Fl.
New York, NY 10001-1908

Established in 1991 in NY.
Donors: Esther Scharf; Jane Holtzer; Densco Corp.; Sarpin Developments, LP; Charles Scharf; Sharon Scharf.
Foundation type: Independent foundation.
Financial data (yr. ended 12/31/12): Assets, $3,321,614 (M); expenditures, $672,654; qualifying distributions, $666,380; giving activities include $665,471 for grants.
Purpose and activities: Giving for Jewish causes, with emphasis on the advancement of education and assistance to the needy.
Fields of interest: Jewish agencies & synagogues.
Limitations: Applications not accepted. No grants to individuals.
Application information: Contributes only to pre-selected organizations.
Officers: Ester Scharf, Pres.; Samuel Offen, V.P. and Secy.
Director: Charles Scharf.
EIN: 133648412

5774
The Y.C. Ho/Helen & Michael Chiang Foundation ✧
Park West Finance Sta.
P.O. Box 20845
New York, NY 10025-0013
E-mail: info@hochiangfoundation.org; Main URL: http://hochiangfoundation.org/
Grants List: http://hochiangfoundation.org/grants.html

Established in 2004 in NY.
Donor: Y.C. Ho†.
Foundation type: Independent foundation.
Financial data (yr. ended 04/30/13): Assets, $66,816,163 (M); expenditures, $3,224,312; qualifying distributions, $3,224,187; giving activities include $3,013,496 for 54 grants (high: $250,000; low: $4,275).
Purpose and activities: The mission of The Y.C. Ho/Helen and Michael Chiang Foundation is to improve palliative care and the quality of life for persons of all age groups with serious illnesses.
Fields of interest: Palliative care; Health care.
Type of support: General/operating support.
Limitations: Applications not accepted. Giving primarily in New York, NY. No grants to individuals.
Application information: Contributes only to pre-selected organizations.
Officers and Directors:* Bessie Chiang, M.D.*, Pres. and Treas.; Michael Chiang,* V.P.; Helen Chiang, Secy.; Patricia J. Diaz, Exec. Dir.
EIN: 050613835
Selected grants: The following grants are a representative sample of this grantmaker's funding activity:
$250,000 to Columbia University, New York, NY, 2011.
$200,000 to Beth Israel Medical Center, New York, NY, 2011.
$200,000 to Englewood Hospital and Medical Center, Englewood, NJ, 2011.
$188,000 to Childrens Hospital of Philadelphia, Philadelphia, PA, 2011.
$150,000 to New York-Presbyterian Fund, New York, NY, 2011.
$100,000 to Columbia University, New York, NY, 2011.
$37,000 to Jewish Board of Family and Childrens Services, New York, NY, 2011.
$25,000 to Comfort Zone Camp, Richmond, VA, 2011.
$25,000 to Flying Horse Farms, Columbus, OH, 2011.
$25,000 to Third Street Music School Settlement, New York, NY, 2011.

5775
Judith L. Chiara Charitable Fund Inc. ✧
c/o Levin Capital Strategies
595 Madison Ave., 16th Fl.
New York, NY 10022-1907

Established in 1997 in NY.
Foundation type: Independent foundation.
Financial data (yr. ended 10/31/13): Assets, $11,481,531 (M); expenditures, $693,166; qualifying distributions, $605,000; giving activities include $605,000 for 8 grants (high: $425,000; low: $5,000).
Purpose and activities: Giving primarily for human services, particularly an organization serving individuals affected by substance addiction, incarceration, and HIV/AIDS; support also for the arts and education.
Fields of interest: Arts; Higher education; Education; Health organizations, association; Human services; Foundations (private grantmaking).
Limitations: Applications not accepted. Giving primarily in NY; support also in CA. No grants to individuals.
Application information: Contributes only to pre-selected organizations.
Trustees: John T. Beaty, Jr.; Jerome Manning; Robert Bernhard.
EIN: 311577990
Selected grants: The following grants are a representative sample of this grantmaker's funding activity:
$375,000 to Exponents, New York, NY, 2010.
$375,000 to Exponents, New York, NY, 2011.
$150,000 to Lyford Cay Foundation, Nassau, Bahamas, 2011.
$100,000 to Lyford Cay Foundation, New York, NY, 2010.
$55,000 to Teamwork Foundation, Bronx, NY, 2011.
$25,000 to Union Station Foundation, Pasadena, CA, 2011.
$3,410 to Metropolitan Opera, New York, NY, 2011.

5776
Chiaroscuro Foundation ✧
415 Madison Ave., 15th Fl.
New York, NY 10017-1111

Established in 2006 in NY.
Donors: Sean Fieler; Dr. John Templeton; Dr. Josephine Templeton; Daniel Schreck.
Foundation type: Independent foundation.
Financial data (yr. ended 12/31/13): Assets, $163,074 (M); gifts received, $7,787,267; expenditures, $7,801,982; qualifying distributions, $7,725,134; giving activities include $7,174,392 for 132 grants (high: $1,000,000; low: $100).
Fields of interest: Human services; Foundations (private grantmaking); Christian agencies & churches; Catholic agencies & churches.
Limitations: Applications not accepted. Giving primarily in the U.S., with emphasis on Washington, DC, and New York, NY. No grants to individuals.
Application information: Contributes only to pre-selected organizations.
Officers and Directors:* Sean Fieler,* Pres.; Ana Cecilia Fieler,* Secy.; Erin Lynn Collins.
EIN: 205858767

5777
Chronic Fatigue Initiative, Inc. ✧ ☆
c/o Glenn H. Hutchins
9 W. 57th St., 32nd Fl.
New York, NY 10019-2701

Established in NY.
Donors: Glenn H. Hutchins; Hutchins Family Foundation, Inc.
Foundation type: Independent foundation.
Financial data (yr. ended 12/31/13): Assets, $850,655 (M); gifts received, $2,350,000; expenditures, $1,764,130; qualifying distributions, $1,764,130; giving activities include $1,438,947 for 8 grants (high: $1,001,924; low: $17,924).
Fields of interest: Higher education; Hospitals (general); Health care.
Limitations: Applications not accepted. Giving in the U.S., with emphasis on NY.
Application information: Unsolicited requests for funds not accepted.
Officers: Glenn H. Hutchins, Chair.; Scott A. Carlson, Exec. Dir.
EIN: 272589147

5778
Louis P. Ciminelli Family Foundation ✧
2421 Main St.
Buffalo, NY 14214-2365

Established in 2006 in NY.
Donor: Louis P. Ciminelli.
Foundation type: Independent foundation.
Financial data (yr. ended 12/31/12): Assets, $12,585,378 (M); gifts received, $2,000,000; expenditures, $1,000,010; qualifying distributions, $931,779; giving activities include $931,779 for grants.
Fields of interest: Performing arts, orchestras; Arts.
Limitations: Applications not accepted. Giving primarily in Buffalo, NY.
Application information: Unsolicited requests for funds not accepted.
Officers: Louis C. Ciminelli, Pres.; Annlouise Ciminelli, V.P.; Matthew Ciminelli, V.P.; Nina Ciminelli, V.P.; Frank L. Ciminelli II, Secy.-Treas.
EIN: 204411791

5779
Cinereach Ltd. ✧
126 5th Ave., 5th Fl.
New York, NY 10011-5606 (212) 727-3224
FAX: (212) 727-3282; E-mail: grants@cinereach.org; Reach Film Fellowship e-mail: info@thereachfilmfellowship.org; Additional e-mail: info@cinereach.org; Main URL: http://www.cinereach.org/
Facebook: http://www.facebook.com/pages/Cinereach-Ltd/40157889652?ref=search&sid=1237983244.79003529..1
Organization Blog: http://www.cinereach.org/cinereach-blog
Twitter: http://twitter.com/Cinereach

Established in 2005 in NY.
Donors: Butterfield Trust Bermuda Ltd; San Francisco Film Society.
Foundation type: Operating foundation.
Financial data (yr. ended 06/30/13): Assets, $6,668,883 (M); gifts received, $4,130,750; expenditures, $3,348,620; qualifying distributions, $3,340,581; giving activities include $1,086,573 for 13 grants (high: $500,000; low: $10,638).
Purpose and activities: Cinereach supports feature-length nonfiction and fiction films that are at the intersection of engaging storytelling, visual artistry, and vital subject matter.
Fields of interest: Media, film/video.
Limitations: Applications accepted. Giving primarily in New York, NY. No support for films under 70 minutes in length (short film applicants should refer to Reach Film Fellowship), or for student films; no organizational support. No grants for capital or endowment campaigns, multi-year grants, individual scholarships for study or travel, or for film outreach and distribution activities.
Publications: Application guidelines; Grants list.
Application information: Application form required.
Initial approach: Use online application center on foundation web site for initial registration and to submit a letter of inquiry, or to view application forms with DVD film sample
Deadline(s): See foundation web site for current deadlines
Officers: Joachim Schuetz, Treas.; Philipp Engelhorn, Exec. Dir.
Director: Bruce Rabb.
EIN: 202946241
Selected grants: The following grants are a representative sample of this grantmaker's funding activity:
$105,263 to Women Make Movies, New York, NY, 2011.
$93,684 to International Documentary Association, Los Angeles, CA, 2011.
$90,426 to Independent Feature Project, Brooklyn, NY, 2011.
$86,021 to San Francisco Film Society, San Francisco, CA, 2011.
$69,893 to ArteEast, Brooklyn, NY, 2011.
$57,895 to Film Forum, New York, NY, 2011.
$37,234 to Big Mouth Productions, New York, NY, 2011.
$31,915 to Fractured Atlas, New York, NY, 2011.
$31,579 to Working Films, Wilmington, NC, 2011.
$26,316 to Center for Independent Documentary, Sharon, MA, 2011.

5780
Citi Foundation ✧
(formerly Citigroup Foundation)
1 Court Sq., Fl. 43
Long Island City, NY 11120
Contact: Lia Cartagena, Grants Assoc.
E-mail: citifoundation@citi.com; Main URL: http://www.citifoundation.com
Grants Database: http://www.citifoundation.com/citi/foundation/partnerships/grant.htm

Established in 1994 in NY.
Donors: Citicorp; Citibank, N.A.; Citigroup Inc.; Citigroup Venture Capital Ltd.; Charles Prince.
Foundation type: Company-sponsored foundation.
Financial data (yr. ended 12/31/13): Assets, $50,165,877 (M); gifts received, $78,000,460; expenditures, $78,372,566; qualifying distributions, $78,372,150; giving activities include $78,372,150 for 653 grants (high: $3,650,000; low: $20,000).
Purpose and activities: The foundation supports programs designed to promote economic progress and improve the lives of people in low-income communities around the world. The foundation invests in efforts that increase financial inclusion, catalyze job opportunities for youth, and reimagine approaches to building economically vibrant cities.
Fields of interest: Higher education; Education, services; Employment, services; Employment, training; Housing/shelter, development; Disasters, preparedness/services; Youth development, adult & child programs; Youth development, business; Human services, financial counseling; Community/economic development, management/technical assistance; Community development, neighborhood development; Economic development; Urban/community development; Business/industry; Community development, small businesses; Microfinance/microlending; Community/economic development; Financial services; Leadership development; Youth; Minorities; Women; Economically disadvantaged.
Type of support: Continuing support; Management development/capacity building; Capital campaigns; Program development; Faculty/staff development; Research; Technical assistance.
Limitations: Applications not accepted. Giving on a national and international basis in Algeria, Argentina, Australia, Bahamas, Bahrain, Bangladesh, Belgium, Brazil, Brunei, Bulgaria, Cameroon, Canada, China, Colombia, Commonwealth of Marianas, Costa Rica, Cote d'Ivoire, Czech Republic, Democratic Rep. of Congo, Denmark, Dominican Republic, Ecuador, Egypt, El Salvador, Finland, France, Germany, Ghana, Greece, Guam, Guatemala, Honduras, Hong Kong, Hungary, India, Indonesia, Ireland, Israel, Italy, Jamaica, Japan, Jordan, Kazakhstan, Kenya, Korea (South), Kuwait, Lebanon, Luxembourg, Malaysia, Morocco, Netherlands, New Zealand, Nicaragua, Nigeria, Norway, Pakistan, Panama, Paraguay, Peru, Philippines, Poland, Portugal, Qatar, Romania, Russia, Senegal, Singapore, Slovakia, South Africa, Spain, Sri Lanka, Sweden, Switzerland, Taiwan, Tanzania, Thailand, Trinidad & Tobago, Tunisia, Turkey, Uganda, Ukraine, United Arab Emirates, United Kingdom, Uruguay, Venezuela, Vietnam, and Zambia. No support for political candidates or religious, veterans', or fraternal organizations not of direct benefit to the entire community. No grants to individuals, or for political causes, memorials, gift matching, fundraising events, telethons, marathons, races, or benefits, advertising, sponsorships, dinners or luncheons, or membership fees.
Publications: Corporate giving report; Grants list; Informational brochure.
Application information: The foundation utilizes an invitation only process; unsolicited proposals are not accepted.
Board meeting date(s): 4-5 times yearly
Officers and Directors:* Edward Skyler,* Chair.; Brandee McHale, Pres.; Roberto Annibale; Francisco Aristeguieta; James C. Cowles; Raymond J. McGuire; Paul McKinnon; William J. Mills; Francesco Vanni d'Archirafi; Alberto Verme.
Number of staff: 22 full-time professional; 2 full-time support; 3 part-time support.
EIN: 133781879
Selected grants: The following grants are a representative sample of this grantmaker's funding activity:
$5,000,000 to Financial Innovations Center, Chicago, IL, 2012. For Financial Capability Innovation Fund.
$200,000 to Neighborhood Reinvestment Corporation, Washington, DC, 2012. For Counselor Training and Technology and Capacity Program.
$160,000 to Junior Achievement Worldwide, Colorado Springs, CO, 2012. For youth financial capability and entrepreneur program in LATAM region.
$40,000 to Local Initiatives Support Corporation, New York, NY, 2012. For Technical Assistance Program.

5781
CJM Foundation ✧
c/o Constance Milstein
545 Madison Ave, Ste. 600
New York, NY 10022-4219

Established in 1996 in NY.
Donors: Seymour Milstein†; Vivian Milstein; Constance Milstein; The VLM Charitable Lead Annuity Trust.
Foundation type: Independent foundation.
Financial data (yr. ended 12/31/13): Assets, $5,283,218 (M); gifts received, $2,152,923; expenditures, $6,361,747; qualifying distributions, $6,283,911; giving activities include $6,283,526 for 28 grants (high: $2,500,000; low: $750).
Fields of interest: Arts; Higher education; Hospitals (general); Human services.

Limitations: Applications not accepted. Giving primarily in NY. No grants to individuals.
Application information: Contributes only to pre-selected organizations.
Trustees: Abigail Black Elbaum; Constance Milstein; Joanna Milstein.
EIN: 137105559
Selected grants: The following grants are a representative sample of this grantmaker's funding activity:
$2,500,000 to New York-Presbyterian Hospital, New York, NY, 2011.
$1,250,000 to New York University, New York, NY, 2011.
$1,000,000 to New York University, New York, NY, 2010.
$700,000 to New York University, New York, NY, 2010.
$700,000 to New York University, New York, NY, 2011.
$200,000 to American Heart Association, Dallas, TX, 2010.
$100,000 to American Heart Association, Dallas, TX, 2010.
$25,000 to New York-Presbyterian Hospital, New York, NY, 2011.
$12,600 to American Heart Association, Dallas, TX, 2010.

5782
Ckew Foundation ✧
c/o James Melcher
58 W. 40th St., 12th Fl.
New York, NY 10018-2658

Established in 2007 in DE.
Donor: James Melcher.
Foundation type: Independent foundation.
Financial data (yr. ended 12/31/13): Assets, $9,137,204 (M); expenditures, $690,017; qualifying distributions, $515,000; giving activities include $515,000 for 16 grants (high: $100,000; low: $10,000).
Fields of interest: Higher education; Education; Human services; Children/youth, services.
Limitations: Applications not accepted. Giving primarily in MA and NY. No grants to individuals.
Application information: Unsolicited requests for funds not accepted.
Officers and Directors:* Kristin Benasich,* Pres. and Treas.; April Benasich,* Secy.; James Melcher.
EIN: 261589685

5783
Liz Claiborne & Art Ortenberg Foundation ✧
(formerly The Ortenberg Foundation)
650 5th Ave., 15th Fl.
New York, NY 10019-6108 (212) 333-2536
Contact: James Murtaugh, Prog. Dir.
FAX: (212) 956-3531; E-mail: lcaof@lcaof.org; Main URL: http://www.lcaof.org/

Established in 1984 in NY.
Donors: Elisabeth Claiborne Ortenberg†; Arthur Ortenberg†.
Foundation type: Independent foundation.
Financial data (yr. ended 12/31/12): Assets, $45,634,044 (M); gifts received, $4,100,000; expenditures, $7,276,958; qualifying distributions, $7,191,554; giving activities include $6,420,570 for 85 grants (high: $417,500; low: $1,000).
Purpose and activities: The board of directors has identified two primary program interests for the foundation: 1) Mitigation of conflict between the land and resource needs of rural communities and conservation of biological diversity; and 2) Implementation of field-based scientific, technical and practical training programs in conservation biology for local people. The foundation typically funds modest, carefully designed field activities—primarily in developing countries and in the northern Rocky Mountains region of the United States—in which local communities have substantial proprietary interest.
Fields of interest: Environment, natural resources; Animals/wildlife, preservation/protection.
International interests: Africa; Asia; Central America; Developing Countries; Oceania; South America.
Type of support: Continuing support; Seed money; Matching/challenge support.
Limitations: Applications accepted. Giving primarily in Third World countries in the Tropics and in the Interior West region of the U.S. No grants for general support, or for underwriting of overhead.
Publications: Application guidelines; Grants list; Informational brochure (including application guidelines).
Application information: Application form not required.
Initial approach: Letter
Copies of proposal: 1
Deadline(s): None
Board meeting date(s): Spring and fall
Final notification: As soon as possible
Directors: Douglas Chadwick; William Conway; William deBuys; Robert Dewar; Grant Parker; Alison Richard; George Schaller; Dr. David Western.
Number of staff: 3 full-time professional.
EIN: 133200329

5784
The Edna McConnell Clark Foundation ✧
415 Madison Ave., 10th Fl.
New York, NY 10017-7949 (212) 551-9100
Contact: Albert Chung, Dir., Comm.
FAX: (212) 421-9325; E-mail: info@emcf.org; Additional e-mail (for Albert Chung): achung@emcf.org; Main URL: http://www.emcf.org
GiveSmart: http://www.givesmart.org/Stories/Donors/Nancy-Roob
Grants Database: http://www.emcf.org/our-grantees/our-grantee-portfolio/
Knowledge Center: http://www.emcf.org/sharing-knowledge/

Incorporated in 1950 in NY and 1969 in DE; the NY corporation merged into the DE corporation in 1974.
Donors: Edna McConnell Clark†; W. Van Alan Clark†.
Foundation type: Independent foundation.
Financial data (yr. ended 09/30/13): Assets, $965,338,606 (M); gifts received, $8,462,163; expenditures, $56,857,041; qualifying distributions, $53,896,375; giving activities include $43,155,001 for 52 grants (high: $6,000,000; low: $8,000), and $6,908,793 for 2 foundation-administered programs.
Purpose and activities: The foundation focuses on strengthening nonprofit youth development organizations so they can better serve more young people with high-quality programs. The foundation's approach to grantmaking is primarily focused on individual institutions. Key to the foundation's approach is a comprehensive, multistage process used to identify promising youth development organizations, assess their overall capabilities, and subsequently invest in the growth of those organizations most capable of benefiting from this kind of support.
Fields of interest: Youth development, services; Youth development; Youth, services; Children/youth; Youth; Young adults; Young adults, female; Young adults, male.
Type of support: Management development/capacity building; General/operating support; Continuing support; Program development; Technical assistance; Consulting services; Program evaluation.
Limitations: Applications not accepted. Giving on a national basis. No grants to individuals, or for capital funds, construction and equipment, endowments, scholarships, fellowships, annual appeals, deficit financing, or matching gifts; no loans to individuals.
Publications: Annual report; Grants list; Occasional report.
Application information: The foundation does not accept unsolicited applications. The foundation invites organizations that think they may qualify for support after reviewing the selection criteria to complete the foundation's online youth organizations Preliminary Application Form.
Board meeting date(s): Mar., June, Sept., and Dec.
Officers and Trustees:* H. Lawrence Clark,* Chair.; Nancy Roob, Pres.; Kelly Fitzsimmons, V.P., Chief Prog. and Strategy Off., Youth Devel. Fund; Ralph Stefano, V.P., Chief Finance and Admin. Off.; Woodrow C. McCutchen, V.P., Sr. Portfolio Mgr., Youth Devel. Fund; William Moon, Cont.; James McConnell Clark, Tr. Emeritus; James McConnell Clark, Jr.; Alice F. Emerson; Simon Hemus; Kevin W. Kennedy; Janice C. Kreamer; Theodore E. Martin; Joyce Shields.
Number of staff: 21 full-time professional; 7 full-time support.
EIN: 237047034
Selected grants: The following grants are a representative sample of this grantmaker's funding activity:
$5,000,000 to Youth Villages, Memphis, TN, 2012. To implement business plan.
$3,500,000 to Harlem Childrens Zone, New York, NY, 2012. For HCZ's $15 million growth capital campaign and implementation of sustainability plan.
$2,067,977 to Building Educated Leaders for Life Foundation, Dorchester, MA, 2012. For BELL's growth, quality, and evaluation goals aligned with Social Innovation Fund objectives.
$1,790,412 to Gateway to College National Network, Portland, OR, 2012. For Gateway to College National Network's growth, quality, and evaluation goals aligned with Social Innovation Fund objectives.
$1,538,774 to Center for Employment Opportunities, New York, NY, 2012. For Center for Employment Opportunities growth, quality, and evaluation goals aligned with Social Innovation Fund objectives.
$1,500,000 to Bridgespan Group, Boston, MA, 2012. For business planning for grantees.
$1,000,000 to National Guard Youth ChalleNGe Program, Arlington, VA, 2012. For implementation of the business plan.
$500,000 to Jim Casey Youth Opportunities Initiative, Saint Louis, MO, 2012. To aid in

developing outcomes for young people transitioning from foster care to adulthood by improving the policies and systems that affect them.
$300,000 to Merrill Rose LLC, New York, NY, 2012. For the Communication Advisory Group's research and creation of a comprehensive communication strategy.
$200,000 to New Door Ventures, San Francisco, CA, 2012. For Propel Next - to assist with program design and performance measurement capacity.

5785
Robert Sterling Clark Foundation, Inc.
135 E. 64th St.
New York, NY 10065-7045 (212) 288-8900
Contact: Laura Wolff, Acting Dir.
FAX: (212) 288-1033; E-mail: rscf@rsclark.org; Main URL: http://www.rsclark.org
Grants Database: http://www.rsclark.org/index.php?page=past-grants
Knowledge Center: http://www.rsclark.org/index.php?page=publications
Robert Sterling Clark Foundation's Philanthropy Promise: http://www.ncrp.org/philanthropys-promise/who

Incorporated in 1952 in NY.
Donor: Robert Sterling Clark†.
Foundation type: Independent foundation.
Financial data (yr. ended 10/31/13): Assets, $95,520,989 (M); expenditures, $6,231,674; qualifying distributions, $5,676,397; giving activities include $4,500,750 for 78 grants (high: $140,000; low: $1,000), and $14,080 for employee matching gifts.
Purpose and activities: The foundation supports projects that: 1) promote international cultural engagement; 2) ensure the effectiveness and accountability of public agencies in New York City and State; and 3) protect access to comprehensive reproductive health through litigation and public policy advocacy in New York State and at the federal level.
Fields of interest: Visual arts; Museums; Performing arts; Performing arts, dance; Performing arts, theater; Performing arts, music; Arts; Environment; Reproductive health, family planning; Human services; Family services; Civil liberties, reproductive rights; Urban/community development; Community/economic development; Public policy, research; Government/public administration; Public affairs; Children/youth; Youth; Aging; Young adults; Women; Adults, women; Economically disadvantaged; Homeless.
International interests: Africa; Global Programs; Latin America; Middle East.
Type of support: Continuing support; Program development; Publication; Research; Employee matching gifts; Exchange programs.
Limitations: Applications accepted. Giving primarily in New York State for the Public Institutions Program; nationally for reproductive rights; and nationally for organizations working in Africa, Latin America, and the Middle East to promote international arts and cultural engagement. No support for religious organizations. No grants to individuals, or for annual campaigns, seed money, emergency funds, deficit financing, capital or endowment funds, general support or scholarships.
Publications: Application guidelines; Annual report (including application guidelines); Grants list; Occasional report; Program policy statement.
Application information: Application form not required.
Initial approach: Proposal (not exceeding 15 pages) and a one-page proposal summary
Copies of proposal: 1
Deadline(s): None
Board meeting date(s): Jan., Apr., July, and Oct.
Final notification: 1 to 6 months
Officers and Directors:* James Allen Smith,* Chair.; Clara Miller,* Treas.; Laura Wolff, Acting Exec. Dir.; Paul R. Dolan; Philip Li; Julie Muraco; John Hoyt Stookey.
Number of staff: 2 full-time professional; 1 full-time support.
EIN: 131957792
Selected grants: The following grants are a representative sample of this grantmaker's funding activity:
$215,000 to Joyce Theater, New York, NY, 2012. For Cuban dance exchange-training, commission, presentations.
$200,000 to Brooklyn Academy of Music, Brooklyn, NY, 2013. For Global BAM Dance Motion USA IV, Dance Africa Festivals and music from Muslim Africa.
$200,000 to Mapp International Productions, New York, NY, 2012. For Africa Contemporary Arts Consortium, payable over 2.00 years.
$200,000 to Mid Atlantic Arts Foundation, Baltimore, MD, 2013. For Southern Exposure: Performing Arts of Latin America tour.
$200,000 to National Performance Network, New Orleans, LA, 2012. For Performing Americas Program - touring residencies, center travel and creative exchanges.
$150,000 to Center for Reproductive Rights, New York, NY, 2013. For litigation and developing new legal arguments, challenging abortion restrictions, and to engage medical and legal scholars in supporting these challenges.
$150,000 to Planned Parenthood Federation of America, New York, NY, 2012. For reproductive rights litigation.
$150,000 to Planned Parenthood Federation of America, New York, NY, 2013. For Public Policy Litigation and Law department to fight laws that limit access to reproductive services.
$140,000 to Center for Reproductive Rights, New York, NY, 2012. For litigation, legal analysis, research and public education to counter abortion restitutions and safeguard reproductive rights and healthcare.
$130,000 to CEC ArtsLink, New York, NY, 2012.
$100,000 to American Civil Liberties Union, Reproductive Freedom Project, New York, NY, 2012. For litigation, policy analysis, public education and advocacy to protect access to abortion and contraception.
$100,000 to Art 21, New York, NY, 2012. For engagement with international audiences.
$100,000 to Art 21, New York, NY, 2012. For engagement with international audiences.
$100,000 to National Womens Law Center, Washington, DC, 2013. For work in New York on Reproductive Rights and Health Program.
$100,000 to New York Foundation for the Arts, Brooklyn, NY, 2013. For Emergency Relief Fund for Hurricane Sandy.
$90,000 to National Family Planning and Reproductive Health Association, Washington, DC, 2013. For advocacy and technical assistance to its members.
$80,000 to National Center for Law and Economic Justice, New York, NY, 2012. For litigation, monitoring implementation of court orders, and advising government officials to ensure that low income New Yorkers receive public benefits to which they are entitled.
$75,000 to Fund for the City of New York, Child Care and Early Education Fund, New York, NY, 2013. For re-granting in support of research, advocacy, public education, and assistance to New York City and New York State officials aimed at improving the quality and availability of early childhood education.
$70,000 to Community Catalyst, MergerWatch, Boston, MA, 2012. To help community activists preserve reproductive health services when secular hospitals become part of religious health systems, to produce public educational materials about consequences of religious restrictions and hospital mergers, and to promote administrative and policy strategies to protect access to reproductive health care.
$70,000 to Community Catalyst, Boston, MA, 2012. To help community activists preserve reproductive health services when secular hospitals become part of religious health systems, to produce public education materials about consequences of religious restrictions and hospital mergers, and to promote administrative and policy strategies to protect access to reproductive health care.
$70,000 to Teachers College Columbia University, New York, NY, 2013. For research, public education, and advocacy regarding New York state policy reforms needed to ensure that all children receive constitutionally mandated sound basic education.
$60,000 to Sexuality Information and Education Council of the U.S., New York, NY, 2013. For public policy work for comprehensive sex education.
$55,000 to Advocates for Children of New York, New York, NY, 2012. For research, advocacy, organizing, and assistance to New York State officials aimed at informing revision of High School graduation requirements and establishing multiple pathways to diploma.
$55,000 to New York Public Interest Research Group Fund, New York, NY, 2012. To educate NYC and NYS policymakers and the public about new waste-to-energy technologies and environmentally preferable alternatives, and to advise them about city contract proposals and appropriate state regulation.
$50,000 to Natural Resources Defense Council, New York, NY, 2012. For New York Solid Waste Initiative including advocacy and assistance to New York City officials, and public education regarding implementation of expanded recycling initiative.
$50,000 to Supportive Housing Network of New York, New York, NY, 2012. For research, policy analysis, and assistance to state policymakers in developing and implementing new supportive housing initiatives for high-cost Medicaid clients.

5786
The Clark Foundation
1 Rockefeller Plz., 31st Fl.
New York, NY 10020-2102 (212) 977-6900
Contact: Doug Bauer, Exec. Dir.

Incorporated in 1931 in NY; merged with Scriven Foundation, Inc. in 1973.
Donor: Members of the Clark family.
Foundation type: Independent foundation.
Financial data (yr. ended 12/31/12): Assets, $471,369,685 (M); gifts received, $500; expenditures, $28,693,172; qualifying distributions, $24,688,706; giving activities include

$14,370,421 for 97 grants (high: $500,000; low: $2,250); and $3,140,989 for 1 foundation-administered program.
Purpose and activities: Support for a hospital and museums in Cooperstown, New York; grants also for charitable and educational purposes, including undergraduate scholarships to students residing in the Cooperstown area. The foundation owns and supports the Clark Sports Center, which is located in Cooperstown. Support also for educational, youth, cultural, and community organizations and institutions in New York City.
Fields of interest: Museums; Education; Employment; Human services; Children/youth, services; Young adults; Economically disadvantaged.
Type of support: General/operating support; Continuing support; Management development/capacity building; Capital campaigns; Building/renovation; Program development; Seed money; Technical assistance; Program-related investments/loans.
Limitations: Applications accepted. Giving primarily in New York City and Cooperstown, NY; scholarships restricted to students residing in the Cooperstown, NY, area. No grants to individuals (except as specified in restricted funds), or for deficit financing or matching gifts.
Publications: Application guidelines; Program policy statement.
Application information: The foundation accepts the New York/ New Jersey Area Common Application Form and the New York/ New Jersey Common Report Form. Application form not required.
Initial approach: Letter
Copies of proposal: 1
Deadline(s): Mar. 31, June 30, Sept. 30 and Dec. 31
Board meeting date(s): Mar., June, Oct., and Dec.
Final notification: 2 to 6 months
Officers and Directors:* Jane Forbes Clark,* Pres.; Gates Helms Hawn,* V.P.; Doug Bauer, Secy. and Exec. Dir.; Kevin S. Moore,* Treas.; Kent L. Barwick; Felicia H. Blum; Terry T. Fulmer; Paul Kellogg; Maureen Killackey, M.D.; Thomas Q. Morris, M.D.; Anne L. Peretz; Karl E. Seib; Paul C. Shiverick; Edward W. Stack; John Hoyt Stookey; Clifton R. Wharton, Jr.
Number of staff: 4 full-time professional; 3 part-time professional; 43 full-time support; 20 part-time support.
EIN: 135616528
Selected grants: The following grants are a representative sample of this grantmaker's funding activity:
$1,500,000 to Clara Welch Thanksgiving Home, Cooperstown, NY, 2012. For general support, payable over 3.00 years.
$450,000 to College for Every Student, Essex, NY, 2013. For Leatherstocking Consortium - payable over two years, payable over 2.00 years.
$400,000 to Nonprofit Finance Fund, New York, NY, 2012. For general support and strategic advisory services for New York City Community Resilience Fund.
$375,000 to Opportunities for a Better Tomorrow, Brooklyn, NY, 2013. For general support for Y Roads Initiative, partnership between OBT and Jamaica YMCA that helps youth and young adults between 16-24 to move their lives in a productive direction with job and educational resources.
$350,000 to SCO Family of Services, Glen Cove, NY, 2013. For Family Dynamics Program and Center for Family Life.
$340,000 to New York State Historical Association, Cooperstown, NY, 2013. For general support and special summer programming.
$325,000 to Uncommon Schools, New York, NY, 2012. For general support for New York City Schools.
$300,000 to Center for Employment Opportunities, New York, NY, 2012. For general support.
$300,000 to Center for Employment Opportunities, New York, NY, 2013. For General Support.
$300,000 to Good Shepherd Services, New York, NY, 2012. For general support.
$300,000 to JobsFirst NYC, New York, NY, 2012. For general support.
$300,000 to Memorial Sloan-Kettering Cancer Center, New York, NY, 2012. For Patient Financial Assistance Program. Grant made from Susan V. Clark Fund, payable over 3.00 years.
$275,000 to New York State Historical Association, Cooperstown, NY, 2012. For general support and special summer programming.
$250,000 to Farmers Museum, Cooperstown, NY, 2013. For General Support and Revamping the Harvest of History Website.
$200,000 to Church Avenue Merchants Block Association, Brooklyn, NY, 2013. For General Support.
$200,000 to Safe Space NYC, Jamaica, NY, 2013. For General Support.
$150,000 to De La Salle Academy, New York, NY, 2013. For General Support for Scholarships and Capital Expenses.
$150,000 to Lenox Hill Neighborhood House, New York, NY, 2012. For general support.
$120,000 to Advocates for Children of New York, New York, NY, 2012. For general support.
$120,000 to Cypress Hills Local Development Corporation, Brooklyn, NY, 2013. For General Support for Young Adult Programs.

5787
The Clinton Family Foundation ✧
P.O. Box 937
Chappaqua, NY 10514-0937

Established in 2001 in NY.
Donors: William Jefferson Clinton; Hillary Rodham Clinton.
Foundation type: Independent foundation.
Financial data (yr. ended 12/31/13): Assets, $4,536,824 (M); gifts received, $3,000,000; expenditures, $1,834,767; qualifying distributions, $1,818,600; giving activities include $1,818,600 for 68 grants (high: $100,000; low: $500).
Purpose and activities: Giving primarily for higher education, health, and social services.
Fields of interest: Arts; Higher education; Health care; Health organizations, association; Human services; International democracy & civil society development; Foundations (private grantmaking); Protestant agencies & churches.
Limitations: Applications not accepted. Giving primarily in AR, NY, and Washington, DC. No grants to individuals.
Application information: Contributes only to pre-selected organizations.
Officers: William Jefferson Clinton, Pres.; Hillary Rodham Clinton, Secy.-Treas.
Director: Chelsea V. Clinton.
EIN: 300048438
Selected grants: The following grants are a representative sample of this grantmaker's funding activity:
$352,000 to Bill, Hillary and Chelsea Clinton Foundation, Little Rock, AR, 2011. For general support.
$100,000 to Delta Research and Educational Foundation, Washington, DC, 2011. For general support.
$100,000 to National Park Foundation, Washington, DC, 2011. For general support.
$100,000 to THEA Foundation, North Little Rock, AR, 2011. For general support.
$50,000 to United Methodist City Society, New York, NY, 2011. For general support.
$50,000 to Vital Voices Global Partnership, Washington, DC, 2011. For general support.
$40,000 to Central Arkansas Library System, Little Rock, AR, 2011. For general support.
$30,000 to National Breast Cancer Coalition, Washington, DC, 2011. For general support.
$25,000 to King Hussein Foundation International, McLean, VA, 2011. For general support.
$25,000 to Saban Free Clinic, Los Angeles, CA, 2011. For general support.

5788
Cloud Mountain Foundation ✧
c/o Wagner, Ferber, Fine & Ackerman PLLC
237 W. 35th St., Ste. 1001
New York, NY 10001

Established in 1999 in MA.
Donor: Benjamin Friedman.
Foundation type: Independent foundation.
Financial data (yr. ended 12/31/12): Assets, $23,431,919 (M); gifts received, $3,415,489; expenditures, $1,141,852; qualifying distributions, $1,137,700; giving activities include $1,137,700 for 60 grants (high: $100,000; low: $2,500).
Fields of interest: Media/communications; Environment; Public affairs.
Limitations: Applications not accepted. Giving primarily in MA and NY. No grants to individuals.
Application information: Contributes only to pre-selected organizations.
Officer: Benjamin Friedman, Pres.
EIN: 043493352

5789
CLRC, Inc. ✧
c/o Hertz, Herson & Co., LLP
477 Madison Ave., 10th Fl.
New York, NY 10022-5802

Established in 1998 in DE and NY.
Donors: Bella Wexner Charitable Remainder Unitrust; Susan Wexner Revocable Trust.
Foundation type: Independent foundation.
Financial data (yr. ended 03/31/13): Assets, $36,333,315 (M); expenditures, $1,780,858; qualifying distributions, $1,608,631; giving activities include $1,605,002 for 9 grants (high: $500,000; low: $2).
Fields of interest: Higher education; Health care; Human services; Children/youth, services; Family services; Jewish federated giving programs.
Limitations: Applications not accepted. Giving primarily in New York, NY and Israel. No grants to individuals.
Application information: Contributes only to pre-selected organizations.
Officer and Directors:* Susan R. Wexner,* Pres. and Secy.-Treas.; Saul G. Agus; Raymond Kanner;

Gregg H. Levy, Esq.; Michael S. Oberman, Esq.; Mark W. Saks, Esq.; Walter Stern.
EIN: 133997365
Selected grants: The following grants are a representative sample of this grantmaker's funding activity:
$150,000 to Gratz College, Melrose Park, PA, 2011.
$100,000 to Gratz College, Melrose Park, PA, 2011.

5790
Coach Foundation, Inc. ✧
c/o Coach, Inc.
516 W. 34th St.
New York, NY 10001-1311
E-mail: coachfoundation@coach.com; Main URL: http://www.coach.com/online/handbags/genWCM-10551-10051-en-/Coach_US/CompanyInformation/CoachFoundation/

Established in 2008 in NY.
Donor: Coach, Inc.
Foundation type: Company-sponsored foundation.
Financial data (yr. ended 06/29/13): Assets, $99,362,321 (M); expenditures, $5,958,809; qualifying distributions, $5,790,010; giving activities include $5,402,959 for 69 grants (high: $2,000,000; low: $2,500), and $387,051 for employee matching gifts.
Purpose and activities: The foundation supports programs designed to empower, educate, and support women and children around the world.
Fields of interest: Secondary school/education; Higher education; Education; Environment; Hospitals (general); Breast cancer; Dispute resolution; Employment, services; Disasters, preparedness/services; American Red Cross; Children, services; Family services; Family services, domestic violence; Women, centers/services; Business/industry; Women.
Type of support: General/operating support; Continuing support; Program development; Scholarship funds; Employee volunteer services; Employee matching gifts.
Limitations: Applications not accepted. Giving primarily in areas of company operations, with some emphasis in New York City; giving also to national organizations.
Publications: Grants list.
Application information: The foundation primarily funds projects recommended by its employees and board members.
Officers and Directors:* Lew Frankfort,* Chair., Pres., and C.E.O.; Jerry Stritzke,* C.O.O.; Todd Kahn,* V.P. and Secy.; Nancy H. Walsh, Treas.; Jane Nielson, C.F.O.; Felice Schulaner, Exec. Dir.; Sarah Dunn; Susan J. Kropf; Jason Weisenfeld.
EIN: 262939018
Selected grants: The following grants are a representative sample of this grantmaker's funding activity:
$100,000 to Children's Defense Fund, Washington, DC, 2011.
$25,000 to Teach for America, New York, NY, 2011.
$15,000 to Autism Speaks, New York, NY, 2011.

5791
Coatue Foundation ✧ ☆
c/o Coatue Management
9 W. 57 St., 25th Fl.
New York, NY 10019-2701

Donor: Coatue Charitable LLC.
Foundation type: Independent foundation.
Financial data (yr. ended 12/31/13): Assets, $17,164,938 (M); gifts received, $9,080,924; expenditures, $2,674,377; qualifying distributions, $2,668,869; giving activities include $2,648,867 for 25 grants (high: $333,333; low: $200).
Fields of interest: Youth development; Human services.
Limitations: Applications not accepted.
Application information: Unsolicited requests for funds not accepted.
Officers: Thomas Laffont, Chair.; Colleen Lynch, Secy.; Jason Schwartz, Treas.; McKenna Moreau, Exec. Dir.
Directors: Joanna Albright; Ben Conte; Philippe Laffont; Jaimin Rangwalla; David Scully; Daniel Senft; Vincent Tortorella; Peter Zhou.
EIN: 452156113

5792
Cohen Brothers Foundation ✧
2053 Ocean Pkwy.
Brooklyn, NY 11223-4044

Established in 2007 in NY.
Donor: Textiles From Europe, Inc.
Foundation type: Independent foundation.
Financial data (yr. ended 06/30/13): Assets, $15,634 (M); gifts received, $571,000; expenditures, $560,624; qualifying distributions, $560,624; giving activities include $558,262 for 40 grants (high: $73,101; low: $1,000).
Purpose and activities: Giving primarily to Jewish agencies, temples, and schools.
Fields of interest: Elementary/secondary education; Jewish agencies & synagogues.
Limitations: Applications not accepted.
Application information: Contributes only to pre-selected organizations.
Trustees: Haskell Cohen; Yomtob Cohen.
EIN: 206261649

5793
The Betsy & Alan D. Cohn Foundation Inc. ✧
c/o Tanton & Co., Attn.: Janet Mulligan
37 W. 57th St., 5th Fl.
New York, NY 10019-6708

Established in 1967 in NY.
Donor: Alan D. Cohn.
Foundation type: Independent foundation.
Financial data (yr. ended 09/30/13): Assets, $14,358,913 (M); expenditures, $522,790; qualifying distributions, $521,346; giving activities include $511,940 for 151 grants (high: $60,000; low: $100).
Purpose and activities: Giving primarily for arts and culture, and Jewish agencies, temples, and federated giving programs; support also for human services.
Fields of interest: Museums; Performing arts, theater; Performing arts, theater (playwriting); Arts; Hospitals (general); Human services; Children/youth, services; Jewish federated giving programs; Jewish agencies & synagogues.
Limitations: Applications not accepted. Giving primarily in New York, NY. No grants to individuals.
Application information: Contributes only to pre-selected organizations.
Officers: Betsy Cohn, Pres.; Alan D. Cohn, V.P.; John Klingenstein, Secy.; Janet L. Mulligan, Treas.
EIN: 237046420

5794
Colad Charitable Trust ✧
c/o Fiduciary Trust Co. Intl.
600 5th Ave.
New York, NY 10020-2302

Established in CA.
Foundation type: Independent foundation.
Financial data (yr. ended 12/31/13): Assets, $10,437,705 (M); expenditures, $528,770; qualifying distributions, $483,073; giving activities include $473,600 for 25 grants (high: $125,000; low: $1,000).
Fields of interest: Health care; Agriculture/food; Youth development; Human services.
Limitations: Applications not accepted. Giving primarily in CA.
Application information: Unsolicited requests for funds not accepted.
Trustees: James M. Davis; Fiduciary Trust Intl. of California.
EIN: 276983865

5795
Kenneth Cole Foundation ✧
c/o TAG Assocs.
75 Rockefeller Plz., Ste. 900
New York, NY 10019-6908

Established in 1994 in NY.
Donors: Kenneth D. Cole; The Wagner Family Foundation; The Harry Walker Agency, Inc.
Foundation type: Independent foundation.
Financial data (yr. ended 04/30/13): Assets, $9,845,364 (M); gifts received, $6,589,440; expenditures, $611,102; qualifying distributions, $599,650; giving activities include $599,650 for 36 grants (high: $200,000; low: $1,000).
Purpose and activities: Giving primarily for AIDS research; funding also for higher education, as well as for health associations.
Fields of interest: Arts; Higher education; Education; Health organizations, association; AIDS research; Human services; Children/youth, services; Family services; Philanthropy/voluntarism.
Limitations: Applications not accepted. Giving primarily in NY; some giving also in Providence, RI. No grants to individuals.
Application information: Contributes only to pre-selected organizations.
Trustees: Kenneth D. Cole; Maria Cuomo Cole.
EIN: 133799161
Selected grants: The following grants are a representative sample of this grantmaker's funding activity:
$237,500 to Columbia University, New York, NY, 2011.
$25,000 to AISH New York, New York, NY, 2011.
$25,000 to Bill, Hillary and Chelsea Clinton Foundation, Little Rock, AR, 2011.
$15,000 to Mary J. Blige and Steve Stoute Foundation for the Advancement of Women Now, New York, NY, 2011.
$10,000 to Child Mind Institute, New York, NY, 2011.
$10,000 to Figure Skating in Harlem, New York, NY, 2011.

$10,000 to Mount Sinai Childrens Center Foundation, New York, NY, 2011.
$10,000 to National Alliance to End Homelessness, Washington, DC, 2011.
$10,000 to Robin Hood Foundation, New York, NY, 2011.
$5,000 to American Cancer Society, New York, NY, 2011.

5796
The Chase and Stephanie Coleman Foundation ✧
c/o Tiger Global
101 Park Ave., 48th Fl.
New York, NY 10178-4799

Established in 2006 in NY.
Donors: Charles P. Coleman III; Stephanie A. Coleman.
Foundation type: Independent foundation.
Financial data (yr. ended 12/31/12): Assets, $36,872,714 (M); gifts received, $36,950,000; expenditures, $2,136,160; qualifying distributions, $2,136,160; giving activities include $2,127,650 for 14 grants (high: $1,000,000; low: $5,000).
Fields of interest: Education; Hospitals (general); Foundations (private grantmaking).
Limitations: Applications not accepted. Giving primarily in NY. No grants to individuals.
Application information: Contributes only to pre-selected organizations.
Trustees: Charles P. Coleman III; Stephanie A. Coleman.
EIN: 830451634

5797
Simon and Eve Colin Foundation ✧
1520 Northern Blvd.
Manhasset, NY 11030-3006 (516) 869-6700
Contact: Fred Colin, Dir.

Established in 1984 in NY.
Donors: Fred Colin; Eva Colin Usdan; Rebecca Colin Seman; Stephen Colin†; Samuel F. Colin; Star Enterprises.
Foundation type: Independent foundation.
Financial data (yr. ended 10/31/13): Assets, $28,412,043 (M); gifts received, $565,480; expenditures, $773,496; qualifying distributions, $699,490; giving activities include $679,295 for 82 grants (high: $112,500; low: $50).
Purpose and activities: Giving primarily for education, hospitals and health organizations, and human services,.
Fields of interest: Higher education; Education; Hospitals (general); Hospitals (specialty); Health organizations; Human services.
Limitations: Applications accepted. Giving primarily in the greater metropolitan New York, NY, area, including Long Island.
Application information: Application form not required.
Initial approach: Proposal
Deadline(s): None
Directors: Barbara F. Colin; Fred Colin; Samuel F. Colin; Rebecca Colin Seaman; Eva Usdan.
EIN: 112676434

5798
Joseph Collins Foundation ✧
c/o Willkie Farr & Gallagher
787 7th Ave.
New York, NY 10019-7099

Incorporated in 1951 in NY.
Donor: Joseph Collins, M.D.†.
Foundation type: Independent foundation.
Financial data (yr. ended 06/30/13): Assets, $23,909,544 (M); expenditures, $1,788,992; qualifying distributions, $1,761,505; giving activities include $1,640,000 for 82 grants to individuals (high: $20,000; low: $20,000).
Purpose and activities: The foundation makes annual grants only to students with inadequate resources, in attendance at medical schools in states east of or contiguous to the Mississippi River, in sums not exceeding $10,000. Grants also for tuition to needy second through fourth year undergraduate medical students on the recommendation of medical school authorities. Students must stand in the upper half of their class, intend to specialize in neurology or psychiatry, or to become a general practitioner, and have outside cultural interests.
Fields of interest: Medical school/education.
Type of support: Grants to individuals.
Limitations: Applications not accepted. Giving limited to students attending accredited medical schools located east of the Mississippi River. No grants for pre-medical or postgraduate medical students.
Publications: Annual report; Program policy statement.
Application information: Unsolicited requests for funds not accepted.
Board meeting date(s): Nov. and as required
Officers and Trustees:* Jack H. Nusbaum,* Pres.; Mark F. Hughes, Jr.,* V.P.; Nora Ann Wallace,* V.P.; Dr. Danielle Lann.
EIN: 136404527

5799
P. & C. Collins Fund ✧
c/o Bessemer Trust
630 5th Ave.
New York, NY 10111-0100
Contact: Paul J. Collins, Pres.

Established in 2000 in DE.
Donor: Paul J. Collins.
Foundation type: Independent foundation.
Financial data (yr. ended 12/31/12): Assets, $7,632,312 (M); expenditures, $1,735,021; qualifying distributions, $1,670,700; giving activities include $1,663,700 for 37 grants (high: $500,000; low: $1,000).
Purpose and activities: Giving primarily for education.
Fields of interest: Arts; Higher education; Education; Environment, natural resources; Health care; Human services.
Limitations: Applications accepted. Giving primarily in FL, MA, NY, and WI. No grants to individuals.
Application information: Application form not required.
Initial approach: Proposal
Deadline(s): None
Officers: Paul J. Collins, Pres.; Jayne M. Kurzman, Secy.; Charles J. Seidler, Jr., Treas.
Directors: Julia D. Collins; Ronald Collins.
EIN: 134112988

5800
The Commonwealth Fund
1 E. 75th St.
New York, NY 10021-2692
Contact: Andrea C. Landes, V.P., Grants Mgmt.
FAX: (212) 606-3500; E-mail: info@cmwf.org; E-mail for questions from grant applicants: grants@cmwf.org; Main URL: http://www.commonwealthfund.org
Blog: http://www.commonwealthfund.org/Publications/Blog.aspx
E-Newsletter: http://www.commonwealthfund.org/Profile/My-Profile.aspx
Facebook: http://www.facebook.com/pages/The-Commonwealth-Fund/102047517918
Foundation Management and Performance: http://www.commonwealthfund.org/About-Us/Foundation-Management-and-Performance.aspx
Grants Database: http://www.commonwealthfund.org/Grants-and-Programs/Search-Grants.aspx
Innovations: http://www.commonwealthfund.org/Innovations.aspx
iTunes: http://phobos.apple.com/WebObjects/MZStore.woa/wa/viewPodcast?id=284038727
Mobile: http://mobile.commonwealthfund.org/
Multimedia: http://www.commonwealthfund.org/Multimedia-Center.aspx
Podcasts: http://www.commonwealthfund.org/podcasts/
RSS Feed: http://feeds.feedburner.com/TheCommonwealthFund
Twitter: http://twitter.com/commonwealthfnd
YouTube: http://www.youtube.com/CommonwealthFund

Incorporated in 1918 in NY.
Donors: Mrs. Stephen V. Harkness†; Edward S. Harkness†; Mrs. Edward S. Harkness†.
Foundation type: Independent foundation.
Financial data (yr. ended 06/30/14): Assets, $762,520,635 (M); expenditures, $39,678,057; qualifying distributions, $32,537,578; giving activities include $17,768,386 for 254 grants (high: $956,666; low: $1,928), $2,628,263 for grants to individuals, and $4,973,275 for foundation-administered programs.
Purpose and activities: The mission of the fund is to promote a high performing healthcare system that achieves better access, improved quality, and greater efficiency, particularly for society's most vulnerable, including low-income people, the uninsured, minority Americans, young children, and elderly adults. The fund carries out this mandate by supporting independent research on health care issues and making grants to improve healthcare practice and policy. An international program in health policy is designed to stimulate innovative policies and practices in the United States and other industrialized countries.
Fields of interest: Health care, financing; Health care; Adults; Aging; Disabilities, people with; Minorities.
International interests: Australia; Canada; New Zealand; United Kingdom.
Type of support: Program development; Fellowships; Research; Program evaluation.
Limitations: Applications accepted. Giving on a national basis. No support for religious organizations for religious purposes, or basic biomedical research. No grants to individuals (except through the Commonwealth Fund's fellowship programs), or for scholarships, general planning or ongoing activities, existing deficits,

endowment or capital costs, construction, renovation, equipment, conferences, symposia, major media projects, or documentaries (unless they are an out growth of one of the fund's programs).

Publications: Annual report; Annual report (including application guidelines); Financial statement; Grants list; Informational brochure; Newsletter; Occasional report; Program policy statement.

Application information: The fund strongly prefers grant applicants submit letters of inquiry using the online application form, however, letters submitted via regular mail or fax will be accepted. The fund acknowledges letters on receipt; applicants are typically advised of results of initial staff review within two months. Application form not required.

Initial approach: Letter of inquiry
Copies of proposal: 1
Board meeting date(s): Apr., July, and Nov.
Final notification: 4-6 weeks

Officers and Directors:* Benjamin K. Chu, M.D.*, Chair.; Cristine Russell,* Vice-Chair.; David Blumenthal,* Pres.; Kathleen Regan, Exec. V.P. and C.O.O.; Donald Moulds, Exec. V. P., Progs.; Melinda Abrams, V.P., Delivery System Reform; Anne-Marie J. Audet, M.D., M.Sc., V.P., Delivery System Reform and Breakthrough Opportunities; Sara Collins, Ph.D., V.P., Health Care Coverage and Access; Diana Davenport, V.P., Admin.; Michelle M. Doty, V.P., Survey Research and Eval.; Stuart Guterman, V.P., Medicare and Cost Control; Andrea C. Landes, V.P., Grants Mgmt.; Robin Osborn, V.P., and Dir., International Prog., Health Policy and Innovation; Barry Scholl, V.P., Comms. and Publishing; Eric C. Schneider, M.D., Sr. V.P., Policy and Research; Rachel Nuzum, V.P., Federal and State Health Policy; Jeffry Haber, Cont.; Maureen Bisognano; Mitchell J. Blutt, M.D.; Sheila P. Burke, R.N., M.P.A.; Michael V. Drake, M.D.; Julio Frenk, M.D.; Kathryn Haslanger; Jane E. Henney, M.D.; Robert C. Pozen; Mark D. Smith, M.D.; Simon Stevens; James R. Tallon; William Y. Yun.

Number of staff: 28 full-time professional; 21 full-time support.

EIN: 131635260

Selected grants: The following grants are a representative sample of this grantmaker's funding activity:
$1,620,000 to Qualis Health, Seattle, WA, 2012. For Transforming Safety-Net Clinics into Patient-Centered Medical Homes, 2012-13.
$800,000 to Harvard University, Cambridge, MA, 2012. For The Mongan Commonwealth Fund Fellowship in Minority Health Policy: Support for Program Direction and Fellowships.
$800,000 to Harvard University, Cambridge, MA, 2013. For The Mongan Commonwealth Fund Fellowship in Minority Health Policy: Support for Program Direction and Fellowships.
$750,000 to Institute for Healthcare Improvement, Cambridge, MA, 2012. For State Action on Avoidable Rehospitalizations (STAAR) Initiative, Phase 4.
$750,000 to Institute for Healthcare Improvement, Cambridge, MA, 2013. For The State Action on Avoidable Rehospitalizations (STAAR) Initiative, Phase 5.
$527,560 to LeadingAge, Washington, DC, 2013. For Leveraging Change Through Engagement: Building on the Advancing Excellence Campaign to Improve Nursing Home Care, Year 6.
$521,386 to Center for Health Policy Development, National Academy for State Health Policy, Portland, ME, 2013. For Strengthening Primary Care Through Multipayer Medical Home Initiatives.
$495,000 to Island Peer Review Organization, Lake Success, NY, 2012. For Profiling the Performance of Health Care Organizations and Systems on WhyNotTheBest.org, Phase 4.
$470,609 to Harris Interactive, Rochester, NY, 2012. For International Health Policy Survey.
$438,223 to LeadingAge, Washington, DC, 2012. For Advancing Excellence in America's Nursing Homes: Accelerating Results Through Coalitions, Year 5.
$399,300 to Princeton Survey Research Associates International, Princeton, NJ, 2012. For The Commonwealth Fund Biennial Health Insurance Survey, 2012.
$200,000 to Project HOPE - The People-to-People Health Foundation, Millwood, VA, 2013. For Web Publishing Alliance with Health Affairs.
$50,000 to Columbia University, New York, NY, 2013. For The Second Opinion: Elevating the Coverage of Health Care Policy.
$49,500 to CUNY TV Foundation, New York, NY, 2013. For Talking Health TV Series on CUNY-TV.

5801
Community Foundation for Greater Buffalo ✧

726 Exchange St., Ste. 525
Buffalo, NY 14210 (716) 852-2857
Contact: Clotilde Perez-Bode Dedecker, C.E.O.; For grants: Darren Penoyer, Prog. Off.
FAX: (716) 852-2861; E-mail: mail@cfgb.org; Grant inquiry e-mail: darrenp@cfgb.org; Main URL: http://www.cfgb.org
Facebook: https://www.facebook.com/pages/Community-Foundation-for-Greater-Buffalo/147489612149

Established in 1919 in New York.

Foundation type: Community foundation.

Financial data (yr. ended 12/31/12): Assets, $258,705,854 (M); gifts received, $20,288,442; expenditures, $14,269,609; giving activities include $9,096,515 for 262+ grants (high: $1,000,000), and $1,971,682 for 1,789 grants to individuals.

Purpose and activities: The foundation's mission is connecting people, ideas and resources to improve lives in Western New York. Community Foundation Competitive Grants are open to nonprofit 501(c)3 organizations operating within the eight counties of Western New York that focus efforts in one of the following areas: 1) improve educational achievement for low-income students; 2) increase racial/ethnic equity; 3) enhance and leverage significant natural resources; and 4) strengthen the region as a center for architecture, arts & culture.

Fields of interest: Humanities; Arts; Education; Environment; Animals/wildlife; Human services.

Limitations: Applications accepted. Giving limited to eight counties in Western New York State. No support for religious purposes or any partisan political activity. No grants for annual events or festivals, or attendance at or sponsorship of fundraising events for organizations.

Publications: Application guidelines; Annual report; Biennial report; Financial statement; Grants list; Newsletter; Occasional report.

Application information: Visit foundation web site for focus areas and application information. Application form required.

Initial approach: Submit letter of inquiry electronically
Deadline(s): Feb. 2 for letter of inquiry; May 15 for full proposal. See foundation website for specific dates
Final notification: Apr. 13 for full grant proposal invitations; Mid-Aug. for notification of funding decisions. See foundation website for specific dates

Trustees: Marsha Joy Sullivan,* Chair.; William Joyce,* Vice-Chair.; Francisco Vasquez, Ph.D.,* Vice-Chair.; Clotilde Perez-Bode Dedecker,* C.E.O. and Pres.; Betsy Constantine, V.P., Giving Strategies; Myra S. Lawrence, V.P., Finance; Cara Matteliano, V.P., Community Impact; Gayle L. Eagan,* Secy.; Gerald Reger, C.F.O. and C.A.O.; Ross Eckert,* Treas.; Colleen Becht, Cont.; Melissa Baumgart; James Biltekoff; Gary Brost; Bonnie Durand; Scott Gardner; Danis Gehl, Ph.D.; Alice Jacobs; Gerard Mazurkiewicz; Alphonso O'Neil-White; Jennifer J. Parker, J.D.; Michael Piette; Anna Saldanha, M.D.; Katie Schneider; Richard Stockton, Ph.D.; John Walsh, III.

Trustees: Jean M. McKeown, V.P., Community Impact.

Number of staff: 17 full-time professional; 2 part-time professional; 2 full-time support.

EIN: 222743917

Selected grants: The following grants are a representative sample of this grantmaker's funding activity:
$101,500 to Saint Columba-Brigid Roman Catholic Church, Buffalo, NY, 2012. For Green and Healthy Homes Initiative.
$70,000 to Read to Succeed Buffalo, Buffalo, NY, 2012. For Project Care.
$52,000 to Cradle Beach Camp, Angola, NY, 2012. For Project SOAR.
$50,000 to People United for Sustainable Housing, Buffalo, NY, 2012. For Green and Healthy Homes Initiative.
$47,323 to Geneseo Migrant Center, Mount Morris, NY, 2012. For increasing health care access for Migrant Farm Workers.
$40,000 to Local Initiatives Support Corporation, Buffalo, NY, 2012. For Promise Neighborhood.
$35,000 to Literacy Volunteers of America, Literacy Volunteers of Buffalo and Erie County, Buffalo, NY, 2012. For after school tutoring program.
$30,000 to Buffalo Olmsted Parks Conservancy, Buffalo, NY, 2012. For Rose Garden Pergola Restoration.
$30,000 to Massachusetts Avenue Project, Buffalo, NY, 2012. For Growing Green Program.
$26,500 to Neighborhood Housing Services of South Buffalo, Buffalo, NY, 2012. For lead paint remediation.
$25,000 to African Cultural Center of Buffalo, Buffalo, NY, 2012. For theater arts program.
$25,000 to Be-A-Friend Program, Big Brothers Big Sisters of Erie County, Buffalo, NY, 2012. For Transforming Buffalo Through and Education Mentoring.
$25,000 to Charter School for Applied Technologies, Buffalo, NY, 2012. For remedial educational programing.
$25,000 to Roycroft Campus Corporation, East Aurora, NY, 2012. For Roycroft Campus Grounds Restoration.
$22,725 to University at Buffalo Foundation, Law School, Buffalo, NY, 2012. For Green and Healthy Homes Initiatives.
$20,000 to Catholic Charities of Buffalo, Buffalo, NY, 2012. For Tomorrow's Youth Today.

$20,000 to Locust Street Neighborhood Art Classes, Buffalo, NY, 2012. For year round children's classes.
$19,650 to Lt. Col. Matt Urban Human Services Center of Western New York, Buffalo, NY, 2012. For Green and Healthy Homes Initiative.
$16,000 to Buffalo Hearing and Speech Center, Buffalo, NY, 2012. For language to literacy program transportation scholarships.
$15,000 to BISON Scholarship Fund, Buffalo, NY, 2012. For scholarships.
$15,000 to New Buffalo, Tonawanda, NY, 2012. For Green and Healthy Home Initiative.
$12,266 to Grassroots Gardens of Buffalo, Buffalo, NY, 2012. For building capacity for community gardens.
$12,000 to Nativity Miguel Middle School of Buffalo, Buffalo, NY, 2012. For Graduate support program.
$10,482 to Salvation Army of Buffalo, Buffalo, NY, 2012. For employment search support.
$10,482 to United Way of Buffalo and Erie County, Buffalo, NY, 2012. For CASH program.
$5,250 to Schiller Park Community Services, Buffalo, NY, 2012. For Teen Theater Workshop.
$5,000 to Belmont Housing Resources for Western New York, Buffalo, NY, 2012. For lead paint remediation.

5802
The Community Foundation for South Central New York, Inc. ✧

520 Columbia Dr., Ste. 100
Johnson City, NY 13790-0000 (607) 772-6773
Contact: For grants: Tina Barber, Prog. Off.
FAX: (607) 722-6752;
E-mail: info@donorswhocare.org; Grant inquiry e-mail: tmbarber@stny.rr.com; Main URL: http://www.cfscny.org
Additional URL: http://www.donorswhocare.org/

Established in 1997 in NY.
Foundation type: Community foundation.
Financial data (yr. ended 12/31/13): Assets, $20,271,535 (M); gifts received, $463,757; expenditures, $1,240,827; giving activities include $657,759 for 45+ grants (high: $31,400), and $20,250 for 17 grants to individuals.
Purpose and activities: The foundation seeks to establish and maintain charitable endowments, donor-advised funds and restricted funds for charitable grants and scholarships in Broome, Chenango, Cortland, Delaware and Tioga Counties, NY.
Fields of interest: Humanities; Arts; Higher education; Education; Hospitals (general); Health care; Youth development; Human services; Community/economic development; Infants/toddlers; Children/youth; Children; Youth; Adults; Aging; Young adults; Disabilities, people with; Physically disabled; Mentally disabled; Women; Infants/toddlers, female; Girls; Adults, women; Young adults, female; Men; Infants/toddlers, male; Boys; Adults, men; Young adults, male; Substance abusers; Single parents; Crime/abuse victims; Economically disadvantaged; Homeless.
Type of support: Management development/capacity building; General/operating support; Continuing support; Capital campaigns; Building/renovation; Equipment; Emergency funds; Program development; Conferences/seminars; Seed money; Curriculum development; Scholarship funds; Technical assistance; Consulting services; Program evaluation; Program-related investments/loans; Scholarships—to individuals; Matching/challenge support.
Limitations: Applications accepted. Giving limited to Broome, Chenango, Delaware, Otsego and Tioga counties, NY. No support for religious purposes. No grants to individuals (except for scholarships), or for program deficits, mortgage payments, operating funds, special events, or individual musical theater productions or performances.
Publications: Application guidelines; Annual report; Financial statement; Grants list; Informational brochure; Newsletter.
Application information: Visit foundation web site for application forms and guidelines. Number of copies vary per application attachment. Application form required.
Initial approach: Telephone to confirm project eligibility
Copies of proposal: 16
Deadline(s): Mar. 2 and Sept. 8
Board meeting date(s): Apr. and Oct.
Final notification: Approx. 8 weeks
Officers and Directors:* Heather M. Cornell,* Chair.; Patrick J. Doyel,* Vice-Chair.; Jane L. Zuckerman,* Secy.; John Mirabito,* Treas.; Diane L. Brown,* Exec. Dir.; Whitney Beal; James C. Daniels, C.P.A.; Carolyn Demtrak; Elysia M. Gudas; Hon. David H. Guy; Jean Levenson; Tyron Muse; Peter G. Newman; Jon J. Sarra; Catherine M. Scarlett.
Number of staff: 3 full-time professional; 1 full-time support.
EIN: 161512085

5803
The Community Foundation for the Greater Capital Region, Inc. ✧

6 Tower Pl.
Albany, NY 12203-3725 (518) 446-9638
Contact: For grants: Jackie Mahoney, V.P., Progs.
FAX: (518) 446-9708; E-mail: info@cfcr.org; Pre-application submission e-mail: jmahoney@cfgcr.org; Main URL: http://www.cfgcr.org
Facebook: https://www.facebook.com/CFGCR

Incorporated in 1968 in NY.
Foundation type: Community foundation.
Financial data (yr. ended 12/31/13): Assets, $63,836,026 (M); gifts received, $2,735,131; expenditures, $5,790,837; giving activities include $4,611,524 for grants.
Purpose and activities: The mission of the foundation is to strengthen the community by attracting charitable endowments both large and small, maximizing benefits to donors, making effective grants, and providing leadership to address community needs.
Fields of interest: Performing arts, music; Medical school/education; Nursing school/education; Adult education—literacy, basic skills & GED; Environment; Art & music therapy; Health care, home services; Health care; AIDS; Crime/violence prevention, abuse prevention; Employment; Disasters, preparedness/services; Children/youth, services; Aging, centers/services; Homeless, human services; Aging; Disabilities, people with; Blind/visually impaired; Deaf/hearing impaired.
Type of support: General/operating support; Income development; Management development/capacity building; Program development; Seed money; Technical assistance; Employee-related scholarships.
Limitations: Applications accepted. Giving primarily in the ten-county Capital Area region, including Albany, Renssalear, Saratoga, and Schenectady, NY. No support for sectarian religious purposes. No grants to individuals (except for scholarships), endowments or foundations, programs the community foundation will have to operate, research, endowments, travel, conferences and speakers' expenses, advertisements in programs, journals or other publications, special events and other fundraising events, annual appeals, or membership contributions.
Publications: Application guidelines; Annual report; Financial statement; Informational brochure; Newsletter.
Application information: Visit foundation web site for application guidelines. Based on pre-application questionnaire, the applicant organization will be screened for eligibility and will either be notified of the reason for ineligibility or will be invited to submit an application; the applicant will be supplied with a grant application form and the deadline for submission. Application form required.
Initial approach: E-mail pre-application questionnaire
Copies of proposal: 1
Deadline(s): Feb. 18 for Impact Grants pre-application questionnaire; Apr. for Impact Grants full application; varies for others
Board meeting date(s): Bimonthly
Final notification: Aug. for Impact Grants notification; varies for others
Officers and Directors:* Deborah Onslow,* Chair.; Ellen Sax,* Vice-Chair.; Susan C. Picotte, Esq.,* 2nd Vice-Chair.; Karen Bilowith,* C.E.O. and Pres.; Jackie Mahoney,* V.P., Progs.; Christine Standish,* Secy.; Anthony J. Capobianco,* Treas.; Robin Wood,* Asst. Secy.; Jeffrey N. Rosenbaum,* Asst. Treas.; Matthew Bender IV; Gary C. Dake; Gloria DeSole; Mark Eagan; Virginia C. Gregg; Nancy E. Hoffman, Esq.; Paul M. Hohenberg; William Kahn; Steven E. Lobel; John A. MacAffer; Kevin M. O'Bryan; Amy S. O'Connor, Esq.; Francis Murdock Pitts; Marcus Q. Pryor; Ann M. Sharpe, Esq.; James A. Sidford; Maggie Vinciguerra; C. Wayne Williams.
Number of staff: 5 full-time professional; 2 part-time professional.
EIN: 141505623

5804
The Community Foundation of Elmira-Corning and the Finger Lakes, Inc. ✧

(formerly The Community Foundation of the Chemung County Area and Corning Community Foundation)
301 S. Main St.
Horseheads, NY 14845 (607) 739-3900
Contact: Randi Hewit, Pres.; Sara Palmer, Dir., Grants and Comms.
FAX: (607) 739-3971;
E-mail: rlh@communityfund.org; Additional e-mail: sep@communityfund.org; Main URL: http://www.communityfund.org
Facebook: http://www.facebook.com/pages/Community-Foundation-of-Elmira-Corning-and-the-Finger-Lakes/404520120537

Established in 1977 in NY as Chemung County; Corning established in 1972 in NY; reincorporated

in 1993 under current name after merger of Community Foundation of Chemung County Area and Corning Community Foundation.
Foundation type: Community foundation.
Financial data (yr. ended 06/30/14): Assets, $45,629,920 (M); gifts received, $2,351,640; expenditures, $2,339,631; giving activities include $1,444,385 for 45+ grants (high: $250,000; low: $50), and $233,675 for 102 grants to individuals.
Purpose and activities: The foundation exists in perpetuity to enhance the quality of life in the community. Guided by a board of civic leaders, the foundation provides a continuing source of funding to benefit the community through scholarships and grants to nonprofit organizations.
Fields of interest: Humanities; Arts; Education; Environment; Animal welfare; Health care; Youth development; Human services; Community development, neighborhood development; Women.
Type of support: Grants to individuals; Emergency funds; Management development/capacity building; Capital campaigns; Building/renovation; Equipment; Endowments; Program development; Conferences/seminars; Publication; Seed money; Curriculum development; Scholarship funds; Research; Technical assistance; Consulting services; Program evaluation; Employee-related scholarships; Scholarships—to individuals; Matching/challenge support.
Limitations: Applications accepted. Giving limited to Chemung, Southeast Steuben, Schuyler and Yates counties of New York. No support for religious purposes. No grants to individuals (except through scholarships for education), or for annual campaigns, special event fundraisers, sponsorships, trips, or deficit funding or debt retirement; no loans.
Publications: Application guidelines; Annual report (including application guidelines); Financial statement.
Application information: Visit foundation web site for application forms and guidelines per grant type. Application form required.
Initial approach: Submit letter of intent for Community Grants
Copies of proposal: 5
Deadline(s): Mar. 1 and Aug. 1 for Letter of Intent for Community Grants; Apr. 1 and Sept. 1 for grant application for Community Grants; Feb. 17 for scholarships
Board meeting date(s): Varies
Final notification: Mid-June and mid-Nov. for Community Grants
Officers and Trustees:* Michael Mustico,* Chair.; Thomas Tranter, Jr.,* Vice-Chair.; Randi Hewit,* Pres.; Clover Drinkwater,* Corporate Secy.; Michael Eisner,* Treas.; Gail Baity; Paige Christian; Mary Beth Conwell; Kimberly Cutler; Lou DiFabio; Chris Fortier; Tom Gough; Carl Hayden; Beth Landin; Judith McInerny; Karen Meriwether; Marc Stemmerman; Douglas Tifft; Tony Tripeny; Scott Welliver.
Number of staff: 4 full-time professional.
EIN: 161100837
Selected grants: The following grants are a representative sample of this grantmaker's funding activity:
$110,000 to Capabilities, Elmira, NY, 2012. For STIRS Co-location Project.
$50,000 to Corning Elmira Musical Arts, Corning, NY, 2012.
$50,000 to Saint Josephs Hospital, Elmira, NY, 2012. For Hospital Rehab Renovation Project.
$29,850 to Southeast Steuben County Library, Corning, NY, 2012.
$10,000 to YWCA of Elmira and the Twin Tiers, Elmira, NY, 2012. For Building Capacity Enhancement: Electrical.
$1,250 to Health Ministry of the Southern Tier, Corning, NY, 2012. For Award for Community Nursing.
$1,200 to Pennsylvania College of Technology, Williamsport, PA, 2012. For scholarship.
$1,000 to Community Career Development Council, Elmira, NY, 2012. For Life: Powered by You.
$1,000 to Puppies Behind Bars, New York, NY, 2012. For general operating support.
$1,000 to Wings of Eagles Discovery Center, Horseheads, NY, 2012. For Summer STEM Programming.

5805
The Community Foundation of Herkimer & Oneida Counties, Inc. ✧

(formerly Utica Foundation, Inc.)
2608 Genesee St.
Utica, NY 13502-6003 (315) 735-8212
Contact: Peggy O'Shea, C.E.O. and Pres.; For grants: Jan Squadrito, Sr. Prog. Off.
FAX: (315) 735-9363;
E-mail: info@foundationhoc.org; Telephone (for grants): 315-735-8212; Main URL: http://www.foundationhoc.org
Facebook: https://www.facebook.com/pages/The-Community-Foundation/201676223188193
Flickr: http://www.flickr.com/photos/foundationhoc/
LinkedIn: http://www.linkedin.com/company/the-community-foundation-of-herkimer-&-oneida-counties
Philanthropy's Promise: http://www.ncrp.org/philanthropys-promise/who
RSS Feed: http://foundationhoc.org/feed/
Twitter: http://www.twitter.com/foundationhoc
YouTube: http://www.youtube.com/user/comfoundation315

Incorporated in 1952 in NY.
Foundation type: Community foundation.
Financial data (yr. ended 12/31/13): Assets, $117,511,869 (M); gifts received, $4,231,375; expenditures, $5,018,360; giving activities include $2,881,430 for 85+ grants (high: $1,501,000).
Purpose and activities: The foundation provides support for programs and projects that: 1) offer the greatest opportunity for positive and significant change in the community; 2) identify and enhance local strengths to address and provide creative solutions for important existing or emerging community issues; 3) develop organizational and/or individual self-sufficiency; 4) focus on identifiable outcomes that will make a difference; 5) leverage investment of other community resources; 6) and improve the quality or scope of charitable works in the community.
Fields of interest: Arts; Higher education; Libraries/library science; Education; Environment; Hospitals (general); Health care; Children/youth, services; Family services; Aging, centers/services; Human services; Economic development; Public affairs.
Type of support: Management development/capacity building; Capital campaigns; Building/renovation; Equipment; Land acquisition; Endowments; Emergency funds; Program development; Conferences/seminars; Seed money; Curriculum development; Fellowships; Scholarship funds; Technical assistance; Consulting services; Program evaluation; Program-related investments/loans; Matching/challenge support.
Limitations: Applications accepted. Giving limited to Herkimer and Oneida counties, NY. No support for religious purposes. No grants or loans to individuals, or for ongoing operating support, maintenance and/or reconstruction for municipal infrastructure (unless it is for a dedicated community space), uniforms and equipment for sports teams, camperships, or multi-year grants or requests that exceed $100,000; no loans to individuals.
Publications: Application guidelines; Annual report; Financial statement; Newsletter.
Application information: Visit foundation web site for application cover sheet and guidelines. Application form required.
Initial approach: Telephone
Copies of proposal: 16
Deadline(s): None
Board meeting date(s): Grants committee meets 5 to 6 times per year
Final notification: 4 to 8 weeks
Officers and Directors:* Keith Fenstemacher,* Chair.; Peggy O'Shea,* C.E.O. and Pres.; Judith V. Sweet,* Secy.-Treas.; Mary Lyons Bradley; Lauren Bull; Richard Callahan; Laura Casamento; Linda Cohen; Randy Cuccaro; Burt Danovitz, Ph.D.; L. Michael Fitzgerald; David Jones; Susan G. Matt; Mary Morse; Richard Tantillo; Rev. Robert Umidi; Eve Van de Wal; Randy Van Wagoner; Bonnie Woods.
Number of staff: 6 full-time professional; 1 full-time support; 1 part-time support.
EIN: 156016932

5806
Community Foundation of Orange County, Inc. ✧ ☆

(formerly Community Foundation of Orange and Sullivan, Inc.)
30 Scott's Corner Dr., Ste. 202
Montgomery, NY 12549-2262 (845) 769-9393
Contact: Karen VanHouten Minogue, Pres. and C.E.O.
FAX: (845) 769-9391; E-mail: admin@cfosny.org; Additional e-mail: vanhouten@cfoc-ny.org; Main URL: http://www.cfoc-ny.org
Facebook: http://www.facebook.com/pages/The-Community-Foundation-of-Orange-and-Sullivan/120738087979457
LinkedIn: https://www.linkedin.com/pub/community-foundation-of-orange-sullivan/67/263/797
RSS Feed: http://www.yourcommunityfoundations.org/feed
Twitter: https://www.twitter.com/CFOCny

Established in 1999 in NY.
Donors: Mr. R.J. Smith; Mrs. R.J. Smith; Provident Bank Charitable Foundation; Gerry Foundation; James Ottaway Jr. Trust.
Foundation type: Community foundation.
Financial data (yr. ended 06/30/14): Assets, $12,318,758 (M); gifts received, $1,783,766; expenditures, $992,250; giving activities include $337,774 for 7+ grants (high: $31,750), and $99,550 for 91 grants to individuals.
Purpose and activities: The foundation, through effective use of its endowment, seeks to enhance the quality of life for those who live and work within Orange County by encouraging the growth of a permanent charitable endowment to meet the

community's immediate and emerging needs, and by providing vehicles for donors with diverse philanthropic interests in a way that makes giving easy, personally satisfying, effective, and lasting.
Fields of interest: Health care; Aging, centers/ services.
Type of support: Student loans—to individuals; Scholarships—to individuals; Scholarship funds; Endowments.
Limitations: Applications accepted. Giving primarily in Orange County and Sullivan County, NY.
Publications: Annual report; Financial statement; Grants list; Informational brochure; Newsletter.
Application information: Application form not required.
Initial approach: Contact foundation
Copies of proposal: 1
Deadline(s): None
Board meeting date(s): Every other month
Officers and Directors:* Derrik Wynkoop,* Chair.; Josh Sommers,* Chair. Elect.; Tim McCausland,* 1st Vice-Chair.; Michael Bonura,* 2nd Vice-Chair.; William Bratton,* 3rd Vice-Chair.; Katharine Fitzgerald,* Secy.; Jack Berkowitz,* Treas.; Christopher Corallo,* Asst. Treas.; Karen VanHouten Minogue, Exec. Dir.; Anne Palmer Moss, Founding Exec. Dir.; David Cocks, Emeritus; Ruth Kassel, Emeritus; James H. Ottaway, Jr., Emeritus; John Davies; Eric Fuentes; Philip Guarnieri; Gerald N. Jacobowitz; Dr. Michelle A. Koury; Wayne Martin; Susan Najork; Bonnie Orr; Andrew Pavloff; Raymond J. Quattrini; Richard Shapiro, Esq.; Gerald J. Skoda; Maggie Smith; R.J. Smith; Joe Vanderhoof; Amanda Ward; Todd Whitney; Dr. Michele Winchester-Vega; Wayne Zanetti.
Number of staff: 1 full-time professional; 1 full-time support; 1 part-time support.
EIN: 061551843

5807
Community Foundation of Tompkins County ✧

200 E. Buffalo St., Ste. 202
Ithaca, NY 14850-4230 (607) 272-9333
Contact: George P. Ferrari, Jr., C.E.O.
FAX: (607) 272-3030; E-mail: info@cftompkins.org; Grant application e-mail: jcotraccia@communityfoundationoftc.org; Main URL: http://www.cftompkins.org
Facebook: https://www.facebook.com/CFTompkins
LinkedIn: http://www.linkedin.com/pub/george-ferrari/22/a96/46
Twitter: http://twitter.com/comfountc

Established in 2000 in NY.
Foundation type: Community foundation.
Financial data (yr. ended 12/31/13): Assets, $13,558,077 (M); gifts received, $2,100,774; expenditures, $1,310,543; giving activities include $962,539 for 58+ grants (high: $50,000; low: $200).
Purpose and activities: The foundation seeks to encourage and develop sustainable philanthropy for a broad range of community efforts by: 1) encouraging the growth of a permanent charitable endowment; 2) making strategic grants as community investments; 3) providing donors with vehicles to make giving easy and effective; and 4) serving as a catalyst and convener.
Fields of interest: General charitable giving.
Type of support: General/operating support; Management development/capacity building; Annual campaigns; Capital campaigns; Building/ renovation; Equipment; Emergency funds; Program development; Film/video/radio; Publication; Seed money; Curriculum development; Technical assistance; Consulting services; Program evaluation; Program-related investments/loans; Matching/challenge support.
Limitations: Applications accepted. Giving primarily in Tompkins County, NY. No support for religious organizations.
Publications: Annual report; Financial statement; Grants list; Informational brochure.
Application information: Visit foundation web site for application guidelines. A letter of inquiry must be submitted before applicants are considered for requests that do not match with any grant cycle priority. Application form required.
Initial approach: Submit letter of inquiry
Deadline(s): May 15 and Oct. 15 for letter of inquiry; Varies for applications
Board meeting date(s): 2nd Mon. of each month
Officers and Directors:* Alan Mathios,* Chair.; Richard Banks,* Chair., Devel. and Community Rels.; Paula Davis,* Chair., Community Impact; Diane McDonough,* Chair., Financial Admin. and Treas.; Carol Travis,* Chair., Women's Fund Advisory; Randy Ehrenberg,* Vice-Chair. and Chair., Nominating and Governance; George P. Ferrari, Jr.,* C.E.O.; Sandy Dhimitri,* Secy.; Mary Berens; Susan Brown; Tom Colbert; Fabina Colon; Ross Feldman; Marcie Finlay; Bob Jewell; Sara Knobel; Robin Masson; Philip McPheron; Alice Moore; Bill Murphy; Susan Murphy; Stephen Pope; Ron Poole; Nancy Potter; Kevin Shreve; Carol Travis; Lucia Tyler; Baruch Whitehead; Stephanie Wiles.
Number of staff: 1 full-time professional; 1 part-time professional; 1 full-time support.
EIN: 161587553

5808
Community Foundations of the Hudson Valley ✧

80 Washington St., Ste. 201
Poughkeepsie, NY 12601-2316 (845) 452-3077
Contact: Andrea L. Reynolds, C.E.O.; For grants: Jennifer Killian, Dir., Progs.
FAX: (845) 452-3083; E-mail: cfdc@cfdcny.org; Additional E-mail: areynolds@cfdcny.org; Grant inquiry e-mail: jkillian@cfhvny.org; Main URL: http://www.cfdcny.org

Established in 1969 in NY.
Donors: McCann Foundation; Lester Freer‡.
Foundation type: Community foundation.
Financial data (yr. ended 06/30/13): Assets, $40,821,833 (M); gifts received, $5,689,714; expenditures, $3,122,522; giving activities include $2,078,692 for 184+ grants (high: $250,000; low: $100), and $275,158 for 222 grants to individuals.
Purpose and activities: The foundation strengthens the community by offering donors the means to establish charitable legacies, by making grants, and by providing leadership to address community needs.
Fields of interest: Arts; Education, early childhood education; Elementary school/education; Secondary school/education; Education; Animal welfare; Health care; Food services; Human services; Nonprofit management.
Type of support: Management development/ capacity building; Equipment; Program development; Seed money; Scholarship funds.
Limitations: Applications accepted. Giving primarily in Dutchess, Putnam, and Ulster counties, NY. No grants to individuals (except through The Area Fund Partnership in Education Grants Program), or for endowment funds, capital campaigns, building funds, land acquisition, matching gifts, deficit financing, operating budgets, or where amount of grant will not make a significant impact on a project; no loans.
Publications: Application guidelines; Annual report; Newsletter; IRS Form 990 or 990-PF printed copy available upon request.
Application information: Visit foundation web site for online application, guidelines, and specific deadlines. Application form required.
Initial approach: Submit application via online application portal
Copies of proposal: 1
Deadline(s): Varies
Board meeting date(s): Jan., Mar., May, Sept., and Nov.
Final notification: Late May and Nov.
Officers and Trustees:* Nancy Rossi Brownell,* Chair.; Bill Brenner,* Vice-Chair., Finance and Treas.; Joseph A. Bonura, Jr.,* Vice-Chair., Dutchess County; John K. Gifford,* Vice-Chair., Audit and Secy.; Sue Hartshorn, Vice-Chair., Devel.; Ann Chambers Meagher,* Vice-Chair., Governance; Arthur R. Upright,* Vice-Chair., Ulster; Jeff Wood,* Vice-Chair., Grants; Andrea L. Reynolds, C.E.O. and Pres.; Kevin J. Quilty, V.P., Ulster; Lisette E. Holmes, C.F.O.; Sandy Arteaga; Ellen L. Baker; Eleanor Charwat; James F. Davenport; Charles A. Freni; Ken Kearney; Peter Krulewitch; John E. Mack IV; Thomas J. Murphy; Patrick Page; Nathaniel S. Prentice; Lorraine M. Roberts; Sheila E. Scott; Steven Tinkelman; Kimberley S. Williams.
Number of staff: 5 full-time professional; 1 full-time support.
EIN: 237026859

5809
Conard-Davis Family Foundation ✧

1202 Lexington Ave.
P.O. Box 106
New York, NY 10028-1425

Established in 2006 in NY.
Donor: Edward W. Conard.
Foundation type: Independent foundation.
Financial data (yr. ended 12/31/12): Assets, $11,468,455 (M); gifts received, $8,066,150; expenditures, $471,052; qualifying distributions, $468,332; giving activities include $468,332 for 12 grants (high: $100,000; low: $10,000).
Fields of interest: Higher education, college; Youth development, services; Christian agencies & churches.
Limitations: Applications not accepted. Giving primarily in NY.
Application information: Unsolicited requests for funds not accepted.
Trustees: Edward J. Conard; Jill A. Davis.
EIN: 207204420

5810
The Edward T. Cone Foundation ✧
c/o McLaughlin & Stern, LLP
260 Madison Ave., Ste. 1800
New York, NY 10016-2401 (212) 448-1100
Contact: T. Randolph Harris, Tr.

Established in 1991 in NJ.
Donors: Edward T. Cone Charitable Lead Annuity Trust 2; Edward T. Cone Charitable Lead Trust; Edward T. Cone Charitable Lead Annuity Trust 3; Edward T. Cone Charitable Lead Annuity Trust 4; Edward T. Cone Charitable Lead Annuity Trust 6.
Foundation type: Independent foundation.
Financial data (yr. ended 12/31/12): Assets, $10,188,002 (M); gifts received, $133,008; expenditures, $2,204,629; qualifying distributions, $2,067,071; giving activities include $1,965,000 for 77 grants (high: $400,000; low: $1,000).
Fields of interest: Performing arts, music; Arts; Higher education; International affairs.
Limitations: Applications not accepted. Giving primarily in NJ. No grants to individuals.
Application information: Contributes only to pre-selected organizations.
Trustees: T. Randolph Harris; George W. Pitcher.
EIN: 133646357

5811
The Robert M. Conway Foundation ✧ ☆
(formerly Robert M. & Lois Conway Foundation)
c/o BCRS Associates, LLC
77 Water St., 9th Fl.
New York, NY 10005-4414

Established in 1982 in NY.
Donors: Robert M. Conway; Ricki Gail Conway.
Foundation type: Independent foundation.
Financial data (yr. ended 09/30/13): Assets, $2,858,379 (M); gifts received, $50,000; expenditures, $753,729; qualifying distributions, $752,079; giving activities include $750,044 for 9 grants (high: $635,644; low: $1,975).
Purpose and activities: Giving primarily to U.S.-based organizations for higher education and the arts.
Fields of interest: Education; Health care; Human services.
Limitations: Applications not accepted. Giving primarily in IL and NY. No grants to individuals, or for scholarships; no loans.
Application information: Contributes only to pre-selected organizations.
Trustees: Robert M. Conway; Robert J. Hurst.
EIN: 133153721
Selected grants: The following grants are a representative sample of this grantmaker's funding activity:
$506,936 to University of Notre Dame, Notre Dame, IN, 2011. For general purpose.
$147,841 to University of Notre Dame, Notre Dame, IN, 2011. For general purpose.
$20,000 to Americans for Oxford, New York, NY, 2011. For general purpose.
$10,000 to University of Chicago, Chicago, IL, 2011. For general purpose.
$7,500 to American Ditchley Foundation, New York, NY, 2011. For general purpose.
$4,625 to American Friends of Covent Garden and the Royal Ballet, New York, NY, 2011. For general purpose.
$1,600 to American Associates of the Royal National Theater, New York, NY, 2011. For general purpose.
$1,000 to FINCA International, Washington, DC, 2011. For general purpose.

5812
The Cooper Family Foundation Inc. ✧
(formerly Milton Cooper Foundation)
3333 New Hyde Park Rd., No. 100
New Hyde Park, NY 11042-0020

Established in 1987 in NY.
Donors: Milton Cooper; Martin S. Kimmel; David Cooper.
Foundation type: Independent foundation.
Financial data (yr. ended 12/31/12): Assets, $10,685,200 (M); gifts received, $60,000; expenditures, $1,695,885; qualifying distributions, $1,695,400; giving activities include $1,693,039 for 53 grants (high: $995,575; low: $100).
Fields of interest: Arts; Higher education; Education; Health care; Health organizations, association; Human services; Jewish federated giving programs; Jewish agencies & synagogues.
Limitations: Applications not accepted. Giving primarily in New York, NY; some funding also in Washington, DC. No grants to individuals.
Application information: Contributes only to pre-selected organizations.
Officers: Milton Cooper, Pres.; Shirley Cooper, V.P.; Arthur Friedman, Secy.; Todd Cooper, Treas.
EIN: 112831400

5813
Harriet & Eli Cooper Foundation ✧
c/o Elaine Roth
3 Parliament Dr.
New City, NY 10956-6905

Established in 1997 in NY.
Donors: Eli Cooper; Harriet Cooper; Avrom Vann; Harry Koslow; Fashion Retailers.
Foundation type: Independent foundation.
Financial data (yr. ended 12/31/13): Assets, $14,485,325 (M); gifts received, $221,000; expenditures, $724,202; qualifying distributions, $724,202; giving activities include $720,750 for 19 grants (high: $150,000; low: $750).
Purpose and activities: Giving primarily for Jewish causes, organizations, and schools; funding also for a cancer hospital.
Fields of interest: Education; Hospitals (specialty); Jewish agencies & synagogues.
Limitations: Applications not accepted. Giving primarily in NY. No grants to individuals.
Application information: Contributes only to pre-selected organizations.
Directors: Aurom R. Vann; Elaine Roth.
EIN: 113378441

5814
The Aaron Copland Fund for Music, Inc. ✧
254 W. 31 St., 15th Fl.
New York, NY 10001-2813 (212) 461-6956
Contact: James M. Kendrick, Secy.
FAX: (212) 810-4567; E-mail: info@coplandfund.org; Main URL: http://www.coplandfund.org

Established in 1991 in NY; funded in 1992.
Donors: Aaron Copland†; Sylvia Goldstein†; Robert Eugene Helps†.
Foundation type: Independent foundation.
Financial data (yr. ended 06/30/13): Assets, $18,878,440 (M); expenditures, $2,780,163; qualifying distributions, $2,648,315; giving activities include $1,692,500 for 259 grants (high: $60,000; low: $250).
Purpose and activities: Giving primarily to encourage and improve public knowledge and appreciation for contemporary American music. The fund has established the Performing Ensembles Program, which awards grants to performing ensembles with a commitment to contemporary American music, and the Recording Program to support recordings, as well as a Supplemental Program for service organizations and others.
Fields of interest: Performing arts, music; Higher education.
Type of support: General/operating support; Program development.
Limitations: Giving primarily in CA, CT, MA and NY. No grants to individuals.
Publications: Application guidelines; Grants list; Informational brochure (including application guidelines).
Application information: Applicants must follow the complete application guidelines with specific instructions on foundation web site. Application form required.
Initial approach: Complete application form on foundation web site
Copies of proposal: 1
Deadline(s): See foundation web site for current deadlines
Officers and Directors:* Christopher Rouse, Pres.; James M. Kendrick, Esq.*, Exec. V.P. and Secy.; Vivian Perlis,* Sr. V.P.; Ellen Taaffe Zwilich,* V.P.; Norman Feit, Treas.; Marin Alsop; William Bolcom; John Corigliano; David Del Tredici; Ursula Oppens; Steven Stucky.
EIN: 133620909
Selected grants: The following grants are a representative sample of this grantmaker's funding activity:
$176,667 to Yale University, New Haven, CT, 2011.
$40,000 to American Symphony Orchestra League, New York, NY, 2011.
$32,500 to New York City Opera, New York, NY, 2011.
$22,500 to Columbia University, New York, NY, 2011.
$13,000 to American Composers Forum, Saint Paul, MN, 2011.
$11,000 to American Composers Forum, Saint Paul, MN, 2011.
$6,500 to Columbia College, Chicago, IL, 2011.
$6,500 to Young Peoples Chorus of New York City, New York, NY, 2011.
$4,000 to New York City Ballet, New York, NY, 2011.
$2,000 to University of Pittsburgh, Pittsburgh, PA, 2011.

5815
The Copper Beech Foundation ✧
c/o Bessemer Trust
630 5th Ave.
New York, NY 10111-0100
Main URL: http://www.copperbeechfoundation.org/

Established in 2001 in NJ.
Donors: Charles Snyder; Susan Snyder.

Foundation type: Independent foundation.
Financial data (yr. ended 12/31/13): Assets, $7,734,543 (M); expenditures, $1,626,568; qualifying distributions, $1,620,995; giving activities include $1,617,646 for 26 grants (high: $275,646; low: $2,000).
Purpose and activities: The foundation seeks to support deserving organizations which work to improve quality of life for all people through education, social services and the arts. Special consideration will be given to those projects that encourage recipients to work toward self-sufficiency.
Fields of interest: Arts; Elementary/secondary education; Health care; Human services; Children/youth, services; Community/economic development.
Type of support: Continuing support.
Limitations: Applications not accepted. Giving primarily in NJ. No grants to individuals.
Application information: Contributes only to pre-selected organizations.
Trustees: Ann Marie Snyder; Charles Snyder; Susan Snyder.
EIN: 223793126
Selected grants: The following grants are a representative sample of this grantmaker's funding activity:
$160,000 to Childrens Aid and Family Services, Paramus, NJ, 2011.
$150,000 to Philip's Academy Charter School, Newark, NJ, 2011.
$75,000 to Village School for Children, Waldwick, NJ, 2011.
$50,000 to Phoenix Center, Nutley, NJ, 2011.
$27,000 to In-Sight Photography Project, Brattleboro, VT, 2011.
$5,000 to Brooklyn Arts Exchange, Brooklyn, NY, 2011.
$5,000 to Pro Arte Chorale, Paramus, NJ, 2011.

5816
The Corey Foundation ✧
2 Waterview Ct.
Riverhead, NY 11901-6312

Established in 1998 in NY.
Donors: Emilie Corey; Michael Corey.
Foundation type: Independent foundation.
Financial data (yr. ended 12/31/13): Assets, $28,144,797 (M); gifts received, $658,000; expenditures, $1,088,448; qualifying distributions, $1,029,229; giving activities include $1,028,400 for 34 grants (high: $400,000; low: $300).
Fields of interest: Performing arts, opera; Arts; Higher education; Education; Health care; Human services; Aging.
Limitations: Applications not accepted. Giving primarily in NY. No grants to individuals.
Application information: Contributes only to pre-selected organizations.
Trustees: Emilie Corey; Michael Corey.
EIN: 113453820
Selected grants: The following grants are a representative sample of this grantmaker's funding activity:
$400,000 to New York City Opera, New York, NY, 2011.
$25,000 to Jazz at Lincoln Center, New York, NY, 2011.
$25,000 to New York Youth Symphony, New York, NY, 2011.
$10,000 to East End Hospice, Westhampton Beach, NY, 2011.
$10,000 to Federation of Protestant Welfare Agencies, New York, NY, 2011. For general support.
$10,000 to Westhampton Beach Performing Arts Center, Westhampton Beach, NY, 2011.
$3,000 to Carter Burden Center for the Aging, New York, NY, 2011. For general support.
$1,600 to Westhampton Beach Performing Arts Center, Westhampton Beach, NY, 2011.
$1,000 to American Museum of Natural History, New York, NY, 2011.
$1,000 to Museum of Modern Art, New York, NY, 2011.

5817
Cornerstone Foundation ✧
1358 47th St.
Brooklyn, NY 11219-2642

Established in 1998 in NY.
Donors: Moses Eckstein; Yitzchok Goldberg; Freehold Kollel.
Foundation type: Independent foundation.
Financial data (yr. ended 10/31/13): Assets, $14,022,322 (M); gifts received, $850,000; expenditures, $980,914; qualifying distributions, $946,940; giving activities include $946,274 for 96 grants (high: $254,790; low: $18).
Purpose and activities: Giving primarily to Jewish agencies, temples, and yeshivas.
Fields of interest: Elementary/secondary education; Human services; Jewish federated giving programs; Jewish agencies & synagogues.
Limitations: Applications not accepted. No grants to individuals.
Application information: Unsolicited requests for funds not accepted.
Director: Moses Eckstein.
EIN: 113462646

5818
Corning Incorporated Foundation ✧
(formerly Corning Glass Works Foundation)
MP-BH-07
Corning, NY 14831-0001
Contact: Karen C. Martin, Pres.
FAX: (607) 974-4756;
E-mail: martinkc@corning.com; Additional contact: Joy M. Huth, Admin. Asst., tel. (607) 974-8722, e-mail: huthjm@corning.com; Main URL: http://www.corningincfoundation.org
Grants List: http://www.corningincfoundation.org/our_programs/grants/2013%20AR.pdf

Incorporated in 1952 in NY.
Donor: Corning Inc.
Foundation type: Company-sponsored foundation.
Financial data (yr. ended 12/31/13): Assets, $9,628,092 (M); gifts received, $7,367,582; expenditures, $7,982,090; qualifying distributions, $7,952,479; giving activities include $6,920,728 for 135 grants (high: $2,730,984; low: $1,000), and $623,647 for employee matching gifts.
Purpose and activities: The Corning Incorporated Foundation is dedicated to improving the quality of life in communities where Corning Incorporated is an active corporate citizen. Grants from the foundation to local organizations and to national institutions support programs and projects in the sectors of education, arts and culture, and health and human services.
Fields of interest: Media/communications; Museums; Arts; Elementary/secondary education; Higher education; Libraries/library science; Education; Hospitals (general); Disasters, preparedness/services; YM/YWCAs & YM/YWHAs; Youth, services; Residential/custodial care, hospices; Human services; Foundations (community); United Ways and Federated Giving Programs.
Type of support: General/operating support; Management development/capacity building; Capital campaigns; Building/renovation; Equipment; Program development; Seed money; Curriculum development; Fellowships; Technical assistance; Program evaluation; Employee matching gifts.
Limitations: Applications accepted. Giving primarily in areas of company operations; giving also to national organizations. No support for political parties, labor or veterans' organizations, religious or fraternal organizations, or volunteer emergency squads. No grants to individuals, or for political campaigns or causes, athletic activities, courtesy advertising, or fundraising.
Publications: Application guidelines; Financial statement; Grants list.
Application information: Letters of inquiry should be no longer than 2 to 3 pages. A full proposal may be requested at a later date. Application form not required.
Initial approach: E-mail or mail letter of inquiry
Copies of proposal: 1
Deadline(s): None
Board meeting date(s): Mar., June, Sept., and Nov.
Final notification: 6 weeks
Officers and Trustees:* E. Marie McKee,* Chair.; Karen C. Martin, Pres.; Linda E. Jolly, Secy.; Mark S. Rogus,* Treas.; Jeffrey W. Evenson; James B. Flaws; Kirk P. Gregg; Vincent P. Hatton; James R. Houghton; Lawrence D. McRae; David L. Morse; Christine M. Pambianchi; Wendell P. Weeks.
Number of staff: 2 full-time professional; 1 full-time support.
EIN: 166051394
Selected grants: The following grants are a representative sample of this grantmaker's funding activity:
$2,730,984 to Corning-Painted Post Area School District, Painted Post, NY, 2013. For elementary and secondary programs.
$2,569,016 to Corning-Painted Post Area School District, Painted Post, NY, 2012. For programs.
$2,057,000 to Corning-Painted Post Area School District, Painted Post, NY, 2012. For programs.
$1,827,816 to Corning-Painted Post Area School District, Painted Post, NY, 2013. For elementary and secondary programs.
$442,000 to United Way of the Southern Tier, Corning, NY, 2013. For program support.
$300,000 to Corning Hospital, Corning, NY, 2013. For new facility.
$125,000 to Chemung Valley Arts Council, Arts of the Southern Finger Lakes, Corning, NY, 2013. For program support and lease hold improvements.
$115,000 to Regional Science and Discovery Center, Corning, NY, 2012. For program support.
$100,000 to Chemung Valley Arts Council, Arts of the Southern Finger Lakes, Corning, NY, 2012. For program support.
$100,000 to One Seventy One Cedar, Corning, NY, 2012. For program support.
$70,000 to Regional Science and Discovery Center, Corning, NY, 2013. For program support.

$65,000 to One Seventy One Cedar, Corning, NY, 2013. For program support and facilities repairs/ maintenance.
$62,086 to Corning Elmira Musical Arts, Corning, NY, 2012. For program support and business plan implementation.
$60,000 to Corning Elmira Musical Arts, Orchestra of the Southern Finger Lakes, Corning, NY, 2013. For program support.
$60,000 to Metropolitan Museum of Art, New York, NY, 2012. For program support.
$27,000 to W S K G Public Telecommunications Council, Binghamton, NY, 2013. For broadcasting underwriting.
$25,000 to Catawba Science Center, Hickory, NC, 2012. For program support.
$15,000 to United Way, Heart of Kentucky, Danville, KY, 2013. For program support.
$10,000 to State University of New York College at Geneseo Foundation, Geneseo, NY, 2012. For Service Learning Course Development Awards.

5819
The Joanne D. Corzine Foundation ✧ ☆
c/o BCRS Assoc., LLC
77 Water St., 9th Fl.
New York, NY 10005

Established in 2002 in NJ.
Donors: The Jon and Joanne Corzine Foundation; Joanne D. Corzine; Joanne D. Brown.
Foundation type: Independent foundation.
Financial data (yr. ended 12/31/13): Assets, $1,662,871 (M); expenditures, $467,802; qualifying distributions, $463,400; giving activities include $459,000 for 18 grants (high: $100,000; low: $1,000).
Fields of interest: Education; Health organizations; Human services.
Limitations: Applications not accepted. Giving primarily in CO, NJ and NY. No grants to individuals.
Application information: Contributes only to pre-selected organizations.
Officer: John P. Barry, V.P.
Trustee: Joanne D. Brown.
EIN: 306034293

5820
Frederic R. Coudert Foundation ✧
c/o CohnReznick LLP
100 Jericho Quadrangle, No. 223
Jericho, NY 11753-2702
Application address: Frederic R. Coudert Foundation, 300 E. 59th St., No. 3102, New York, NY 10022, tel.: (212) 860-0758

Established in 1999 in NY.
Donor: Frederic R. Coudert III.
Foundation type: Independent foundation.
Financial data (yr. ended 12/31/13): Assets, $14,351,616 (M); expenditures, $712,114; qualifying distributions, $638,087; giving activities include $633,587 for 31 grants (high: $141,549; low: $1,000).
Fields of interest: Arts; Education; Environment, water resources; Boys & girls clubs; Aging, centers/ services.
Limitations: Applications accepted. Giving primarily in NY. No grants to individuals.
Application information:
Initial approach: Letter
Deadline(s): None
Trustees: Cynthia Coudert; Margaret M. Coudert; Sandra Coudert.
EIN: 137180778

5821
The Countess Moira Charitable Foundation ✧
P.O. Box 8078
Pelham, NY 10803-8878
Contact: Carolyn Gray, Chair. and Pres.
E-mail: inquiries@countessmoirafdn.org; Main URL: http://www.countessmoirafdn.org

Established in 2000 in NY.
Donors: Edward W.T. Gray III†; Moira Forbes; Countess Moira Forbes Rossi†.
Foundation type: Independent foundation.
Financial data (yr. ended 06/30/13): Assets, $32,838,941 (M); expenditures, $2,116,531; qualifying distributions, $1,760,772; giving activities include $1,744,500 for 24 grants (high: $500,000; low: $7,500).
Purpose and activities: Giving to organizations that provide medical, nutritional and educational programs for children.
Fields of interest: Education; Medical care, in-patient care; Children.
Type of support: Continuing support; General/ operating support.
Limitations: Applications not accepted. Giving primarily in NY. No grants to individuals, or for events or fundraisers.
Publications: IRS Form 990 or 990-PF printed copy available upon request.
Application information: Unsolicited requests for funds not accepted.
Officers: Carolyn B. Gray, Chair. and Pres.; Michele J. Le Moal-Gray, Vice-Chair.; Peter G. Gray, V.P. and Secy.; Taylor T. Gray, V.P. and Treas.
Trustees: Donna M. Fitzgerald; Marc E. Garlasco; Kathleen M. Gray.
EIN: 113551993
Selected grants: The following grants are a representative sample of this grantmaker's funding activity:
$60,000 to Doctors Without Borders USA, New York, NY, 2011.
$50,000 to Blythedale Childrens Hospital, Valhalla, NY, 2011.
$50,000 to Student Conservation Association, Charlestown, NH, 2011.
$40,000 to Saint Dominics Home, Blauvelt, NY, 2011.
$30,000 to Community-Word Project, New York, NY, 2011.
$30,000 to Educational Network of Artists in Creative Theater, New York, NY, 2011.
$30,000 to Southern Poverty Law Center, Montgomery, AL, 2011.
$25,000 to Amyotrophic Lateral Sclerosis Association, Milford, CT, 2011.
$25,000 to Astor Services for Children and Families, Rhinebeck, NY, 2011.

5822
Joyce & Daniel Cowin Foundation ✧
640 Park Ave.
New York, NY 10065

Established in 1957 in NY.
Donors: Sylvia J. Berger; Daniel Cowin; Joyce B. Cowin; The Sylvia J. Berger Foundation.
Foundation type: Independent foundation.
Financial data (yr. ended 12/31/13): Assets, $12,588,078 (M); gifts received, $571,850; expenditures, $924,717; qualifying distributions, $855,492; giving activities include $845,000 for 6 grants (high: $375,000; low: $10,000).
Fields of interest: Museums (art); Arts; Higher education; Jewish agencies & synagogues.
Limitations: Applications not accepted.
Application information: Contributes only to pre-selected organizations.
Officers: Joyce B. Cowin, Chair. and Pres.; Anita S. Rosenbloom, V.P. and Secy.; Justine D. Tenney, Treas.
EIN: 136154142

5823
The Coydog Foundation ✧
25 Central Park W., Apt. 5-Q
New York, NY 10023-7210

Established in 1986 in IL.
Donors: Irving B. Harris†; William Harris Trust.
Foundation type: Independent foundation.
Financial data (yr. ended 12/31/13): Assets, $45,013,913 (M); expenditures, $2,683,779; qualifying distributions, $2,331,855; giving activities include $2,331,855 for 109 grants (high: $450,000; low: $500).
Purpose and activities: Giving primarily for the arts, education, children services, including a children's hospital, and social services.
Fields of interest: Arts; Higher education; Hospitals (specialty); Human services; Children/youth, services.
Limitations: Applications not accepted. Giving primarily in Washington DC, MA and NY. No grants to individuals.
Application information: Contributes only to pre-selected organizations. Unsolicited requests for funds not accepted.
Officers and Directors:* William W. Harris, Chair., Pres. and Treas.; Bordman Lloyd,* V.P. and Secy.; David Harris,* V.P.; Roberta Harris,* V.P.
EIN: 363479461

5824
The Gerald and Daphna Cramer Family Foundation, Inc. ✧
(formerly Gerald B. Cramer Family Foundation, Inc.)
c/o WMKG
185 Crossways Park Dr.
Woodbury, NY 11797-2040 (914) 683-9600
Contact: Gerald Cramer; Christine Stelmack

Established in 1993 in NY.
Donors: Gerald B. Cramer; Daphna Cramer; Members of the Cramer family.
Foundation type: Independent foundation.
Financial data (yr. ended 12/31/12): Assets, $6,791,627 (M); gifts received, $1,557,000; expenditures, $1,376,205; qualifying distributions, $1,325,857; giving activities include $1,325,857 for 48 grants (high: $408,000; low: $7).
Purpose and activities: Giving primarily for higher education, the arts, hospitals and medical research, and to Jewish organizations.

Fields of interest: Museums; Arts; Higher education; Education; Hospitals (general); Hospitals (specialty); Medical research, institute; Jewish agencies & synagogues.
Limitations: Applications not accepted. Giving primarily in NY. No grants to individuals.
Application information: Contributes only to pre-selected organizations.
Officers: Gerald B. Cramer, Pres.; Daphna Cramer, V.P.; Lauren B. Cramer, Secy.
Directors: Douglas Cramer; Kimberly Germ-Cramer; Thomas Cramer; Ron Gallatin; Roy Raskin; Shelley Raskin; Arthur Weiss.
EIN: 133749869

5825
Cranaleith Foundation, Inc. ✧
c/o Francis H. Trainer, Jr., Anchin Block Anchin LLP
1375 Broadway
New York, NY 10018-7032

Established in 1993 in PA.
Donors: Francis H. Trainer; Jeanne A. Trainer; Francis H. Tainer, Jr.
Foundation type: Independent foundation.
Financial data (yr. ended 12/31/13): Assets, $16,316,512 (M); gifts received, $750,000; expenditures, $806,589; qualifying distributions, $643,190; giving activities include $640,926 for 38 grants (high: $250,000; low: $1,000).
Purpose and activities: Giving primarily for education, children, youth and social services, and to a bioethics research institute.
Fields of interest: Higher education; Environment, natural resources; Medical care, bioethics; Human services; Children, services; Spirituality; Disabilities, people with.
Limitations: Applications not accepted. Giving in the U.S., with emphasis on NY. No grants to individuals.
Application information: Contributes only to pre-selected organizations.
Officers: Francis H. Trainer, Jr., Pres.; Jeanne A. Trainer, V.P.
EIN: 232726952
Selected grants: The following grants are a representative sample of this grantmaker's funding activity:
$200,000 to Cranaleith Spiritual Center, Philadelphia, PA, 2011.
$200,000 to Hastings Center, Garrison, NY, 2011.
$25,000 to Food Project, Lincoln, MA, 2011.
$25,000 to International Rescue Committee, New York, NY, 2011.
$25,000 to NPR Foundation, Washington, DC, 2011.
$15,000 to Arzu, Inc., Chicago, IL, 2011.
$15,000 to Nature Conservancy, Boulder, CO, 2011.
$15,000 to Painted Turtle, Santa Monica, CA, 2011.
$10,000 to Smile Train, New York, NY, 2011.

5826
Credit Suisse Americas Foundation ✧
(formerly Credit Suisse First Boston Foundation Trust)
11 Madison Ave., 10th Fl.
New York, NY 10010-3629 (212) 325-2389
Contact: Anne Marie Fell, Dir. of Grantmaking & Comms.
FAX: (212) 538-8347;
E-mail: americas.corporatecitizenship@credit-suisse.com; Additional tel.: (212) 325-5260; Main URL: https://www.credit-suisse.com/us/en/about-us/corporate-responsibility/philanthropy/global/americas.html
Core Engagement Grantees: https://www.credit-suisse.com/responsibility/doc/core_grantees_2010.pdf
Credit Suisse Americas Foundation Video: https://multimedia.credit-suisse.com/app/player/index.cfm?fuseaction=OpenMultimedia&aoid=355802&coid=268640&lang=EN&popup=true
Education Grantees: https://www.credit-suisse.com/responsibility/doc/education_grantees_2010.pdf

Established in 1959 in MA.
Donors: Credit Suisse First Boston Corp.; Credit Suisse First Boston LLC; Credit Suisse USA.
Foundation type: Company-sponsored foundation.
Financial data (yr. ended 12/31/12): Assets, $29,521,058 (M); gifts received, $4,252,840; expenditures, $6,027,133; qualifying distributions, $5,841,732; giving activities include $5,833,157 for 333 grants.
Purpose and activities: The foundation supports organizations that engage Credit Suisse and create educational opportunities for disadvantaged young people.
Fields of interest: Elementary school/education; Secondary school/education; Teacher school/education; Education; Health care, clinics/centers; Food services; Food banks; Housing/shelter, development; Disasters, preparedness/services; Recreation, parks/playgrounds; Youth development, centers/clubs; Big Brothers/Big Sisters; Youth development, business; American Red Cross; Family services; Human services; Microfinance/microlending; Voluntarism promotion; United Ways and Federated Giving Programs; Youth; Economically disadvantaged.
Type of support: General/operating support; Management development/capacity building; Program development; Employee volunteer services; Matching/challenge support.
Limitations: Applications not accepted. Giving primarily in areas of company operations, with emphasis on New York, NY; giving also in Los Angeles and San Francisco, CA, Washington, DC, Miami, FL, Atlanta, GA, Boston, MA, Baltimore, MD, Chicago, IL, Raleigh-Durham, NC, Princeton, NJ, Conshohocken, PA, Dallas and Houston, TX, and in Nassau, Bahamas, Sao Paulo, Brazil, and Toronto, Canada. No support for religious organizations not of direct benefit to the entire community, veterans', fraternal, or political organizations, private or grantmaking foundations, colleges or universities, or K-12 schools. No grants to individuals, or for scholarships, capital campaigns, endowments, dinners or events, medical research, political causes, or sponsorships; no matching gifts.
Application information: Unsolicited applications are currently not accepted.
Board meeting date(s): Quarterly
Officers and Trustees:* Dean Wilson Ervin,* Chair.; Douglas L. Paul, Vice-Chair.; Amy Cerciello, Secy.; Eric Eckholdt, Exec. Dir.; Jim Amine; Nicole Arnaboldi; Rob Basso; Stephen Hilton; Grace J. Koo; Tim O'Hare; Mike Paliotta; Antonio Quintella; D. Neil Radey; Robert S. Shafir; Peter Skoglund; Fred Terrell; Lewis H. Wirshba.
Number of staff: 6 full-time professional.
EIN: 900647568

5827
Cricket Island Foundation ✧
(formerly The Cricket Island Foundation)
c/o Elizabeth Sak, Exec. Dir.
25 E. 21st St., 7th Fl.
New York, NY 10010-6207 (212) 782-3730
Contact: Elizabeth Sak, Exec. Dir.; Jenny Peters, Dir., Finance and Opers.; Hana Sun, Prog. Assoc.
FAX: (212) 228-5275;
E-mail: info@cricketisland.org; Additional e-mail: grants@cricketisland.org; Main URL: http://www.cricketisland.org
Blog: http://www.cricketisland.org/news/
Grants List: http://www.cricketisland.org/wp-content/uploads/cricket-island-grant-summary.pdf

Established in 2000 in NY.
Donors: David K. Welles; Georgia E. Welles; Jeffrey F. Welles; David K. Welles, Jr.; Peter C. Welles; Christopher S. Welles; Virginia W. Jordan; Brooke Jordan.
Foundation type: Independent foundation.
Financial data (yr. ended 12/31/13): Assets, $44,101,284 (M); expenditures, $2,308,459; qualifying distributions, $2,032,174; giving activities include $1,417,432 for 66 grants (high: $100,000; low: $3,000).
Purpose and activities: The mission of the foundation is to develop the capacity and commitment of young people to improve their lives, communities and the world around them. The foundation supports organizations that offer meaningful opportunities for young people to contribute to positive societal change.
Fields of interest: Education, public policy; Education, reform; Youth development, alliance/advocacy; Youth development, public policy; Youth development, reform; Civil/human rights, alliance/advocacy; Community/economic development, alliance/advocacy; Community development, citizen coalitions; Youth.
Type of support: General/operating support; Continuing support; Management development/capacity building; Conferences/seminars; Technical assistance; Consulting services.
Limitations: Applications not accepted. Giving primarily in regional cohorts: currently New York, NY and Chicago, IL. No support for general recreational activities or organizations, academic and classroom based training programs, tutoring or job training programs, or for groups that don't involve youth in community change. No grants for scholarships, internships, direct school-based support, individual fellowships, or capital campaigns.
Publications: Grants list.
Application information: Unsolicited requests for funds not accepted. Applications by invitation only; funds currently committed.
Board meeting date(s): Apr. and Nov.
Officers and Directors:* Jeffrey F. Welles,* Chair. and Pres.; Georgia E. Welles,* V.P.; Ginny Jordan, Secy.; Taylor Jordan, Treas.; Elizabeth Sak, Exec. Dir.; Luke Jernagan; Nicole Jordan; Adam Miranda; Cameron Miranda; Berkley Welles; Christopher S. Welles; Hope J. Welles; Maud Welles; Peter Welles; Rene Welles; Ted Welles.
Number of staff: 2 full-time professional; 1 part-time support.
EIN: 341925915
Selected grants: The following grants are a representative sample of this grantmaker's funding activity:

$80,000 to Youth Ministries for Peace and Justice, Bronx, NY, 2012. For Special project Year 1 of 3.
$35,000 to Crossroads Fund, Chicago, IL, 2012. For general purposes (FL).
$33,000 to New Yorkers for Children, New York, NY, 2012. For special project (FL), Year 1 of 3.
$25,000 to Youth United for Change, Philadelphia, PA, 2012. For general purposes (LG).
$20,000 to Flanbwayan Haitian Literacy Project, Brooklyn, NY, 2012. For general purposes year 1 of 3.
$8,000 to Youth United for Change, Philadelphia, PA, 2012. For special project (CB).
$3,000 to Youth United for Change, Philadelphia, PA, 2012. For special project (OF).
$1,950 to Philanthropy New York, New York, NY, 2012. For special project (FL).
$1,500 to Independent Sector, Washington, DC, 2012. For general support (FL).

5828
The Crisp Family Foundation ✧

(formerly The Peter O. Crisp Fund)
c/o WithumSmith+Brown, PC
1411 Broadway, 9th Fl.
New York, NY 10018-3496

Established in 1993 in NY.
Donor: Peter O. Crisp.
Foundation type: Independent foundation.
Financial data (yr. ended 12/31/13): Assets, $7,524,957 (M); gifts received, $1,100,242; expenditures, $1,470,357; qualifying distributions, $1,415,227; giving activities include $1,411,242 for 58 grants (high: $350,500; low: $30).
Purpose and activities: Giving primarily for health and human services.
Fields of interest: Elementary/secondary education; Education; Health care; Cancer; Children/youth, services; Community/economic development.
Limitations: Applications not accepted. Giving primarily in NY. No grants to individuals.
Application information: Contributes only to pre-selected organizations.
Trustee: Peter O. Crisp.
EIN: 137028080

5829
Theodore L. Cross Family Charitable Foundation ✧ ☆

300 Old Country Rd.
Mineola, NY 11501

Established in 1994 in NJ.
Donor: Theodore L. Cross.
Foundation type: Independent foundation.
Financial data (yr. ended 12/31/12): Assets, $17,918,717 (M); expenditures, $963,117; qualifying distributions, $880,000; giving activities include $880,000 for grants.
Fields of interest: Education; Health care; Human services.
Limitations: Applications not accepted. Giving primarily in MA and NY; some funding nationally. No grants to individuals.
Application information: Unsolicited requests for funds not accepted.
Trustees: Adrienne Cannella; Amanda B. Cross; Mary Cross; John W. Halloran; Lisa W. Pownall-Gray.
EIN: 043254361

5830
The Charles and Mary Crossed Foundation ✧

1675 Clover St.
Rochester, NY 14618-2517

Established in 1993 in NY.
Donors: Carol N. Crossed; Richard C. Crossed.
Foundation type: Independent foundation.
Financial data (yr. ended 12/31/13): Assets, $12,159,116 (M); gifts received, $475; expenditures, $1,438,168; qualifying distributions, $1,438,168; giving activities include $1,332,697 for 90 grants (high: $421,992; low: $100).
Fields of interest: Education; Civil/human rights; Public affairs.
Limitations: Applications not accepted. No grants to individuals.
Application information: Unsolicited request for funds not accepted.
Officers: Carol N. Crossed, Pres.; Jessica Shanahan, Secy.; David Crossed, Treas.
Directors: Andrew I. Crossed; Katherine Crossed; Nicholas Crossed; Amy Crossed Rieck.
EIN: 161440339

5831
Lewis B. & Dorothy Cullman Foundation, Inc. ✧

c/o Boyce Hughes & Farrell LLP
30 Jericho Exec. Plz., Ste. 200W
Jericho, NY 11753-1028

Established in 1958 in NY.
Donors: Dorothy F. Cullman‡; Lewis B. Cullman.
Foundation type: Independent foundation.
Financial data (yr. ended 11/30/13): Assets, $1,277,274 (M); expenditures, $1,439,885; qualifying distributions, $1,415,419; giving activities include $1,401,564 for grants.
Fields of interest: Museums; Performing arts; Arts; Higher education.
Limitations: Applications not accepted. Giving primarily in MD and NY. No grants to individuals.
Application information: Contributes only to pre-selected organizations.
Officers and Directors:* Lewis B. Cullman,* Pres.; Edgar M. Cullman, Jr., V.P.; Denise Peppas, Secy.; Nikken C. Sverre-Cullman,* Treas.
Number of staff: 1 part-time professional; 1 full-time support.
EIN: 510243747
Selected grants: The following grants are a representative sample of this grantmaker's funding activity:
$2,000,000 to Museum of Modern Art, New York, NY, 2011. For general support.
$600,000 to Johns Hopkins University, Baltimore, MD, 2011. For general support.
$600,000 to Johns Hopkins University, Baltimore, MD, 2011. For general support.
$500,000 to Chess in the Schools, New York, NY, 2011. For general support.
$250,000 to American Museum of Natural History, New York, NY, 2011. For general support.
$50,000 to American Academy in Rome, New York, NY, 2011. For general support.
$45,244 to Film Odyssey, Washington, DC, 2011. For general support.
$25,000 to Sarah Lawrence College, Bronxville, NY, 2011. For general support.
$25,000 to Watermill Center, Water Mill, NY, 2011. For general support.
$10,000 to Four Freedoms Park Conservancy, Franklin D. Roosevelt Four Freedoms Park, New York, NY, 2011. For general support.

5832
James H. Cummings Foundation, Inc. ✧

120 W. Tupper St., Ste. 201
Buffalo, NY 14201-2170 (716) 874-0040
Contact: Brigid H. Doherty, Secy. and Exec. Dir.
FAX: (716) 854-2659;
E-mail: bdoherty@jameshcummings.com; Main URL: http://www.jameshcummings.com

Incorporated in 1962 in NY.
Donor: James H. Cummings‡.
Foundation type: Independent foundation.
Financial data (yr. ended 05/31/13): Assets, $33,710,899 (M); expenditures, $2,289,524; qualifying distributions, $1,925,691; giving activities include $1,805,821 for 36 grants (high: $500,000; low: $1,000).
Purpose and activities: Giving exclusively for charitable purposes in advancing medical science, research, and education in selected cities in the U.S. and Canada, and for charitable work among underprivileged boys and girls, and aged and infirm persons in designated areas. Priority is given to medical proposals and capital projects, particularly for equipment needs of various kinds.
Fields of interest: Medical school/education; Hospitals (general); Biomedicine; Medical research, institute; Human services; Children/youth, services; Aging, centers/services; Aging; Economically disadvantaged.
International interests: Canada.
Type of support: Capital campaigns; Building/renovation; Equipment; Land acquisition; Seed money; Research; Matching/challenge support.
Limitations: Applications accepted. Giving limited to Toronto, Ontario, Canada, and to Hendersonville, NC, and Buffalo, NY. No support for national health organizations. No grants to individuals, or for annual campaigns, program support, endowment funds, operating budgets, program costs, emergency funds, deficit financing, scholarships, fellowships, publications, conferences, contingency reserves, or continuing support; no loans.
Publications: Annual report (including application guidelines).
Application information: Application form not required.
Initial approach: Preliminary letter (no more than 2 pages) or telephone inquiry is encouraged
Copies of proposal: 6
Deadline(s): 4 weeks prior to board meetings
Board meeting date(s): Quarterly, usually in Feb., May, Sept. and Dec.
Final notification: 1 to 4 weeks
Officers and Directors:* Charles F. Kreiner, Jr., Pres.; Richard C. Bryan, Jr., V.P.; Brigid Doherty, Secy. and Exec. Dir.; William L. Joyce,* Treas.; Christopher T. Greene; Robert J.A. Irwin; Theodore I. Putnam, M.D.
Number of staff: 1 part-time professional; 1 part-time support.
EIN: 160864200
Selected grants: The following grants are a representative sample of this grantmaker's funding activity:

$100,000 to Roswell Park Alliance Foundation, Buffalo, NY, 2013. For Construction of Clinical Science Center.
$50,000 to Medaille College, Buffalo, NY, 2013. For Vernier Technology.
$45,000 to United Way of Buffalo and Erie County, Buffalo, NY, 2013. For Health and Wellness Campaign.
$30,000 to Upstate New York Transplant Services, Buffalo, NY, 2013. For Walk-In Refrigerator and Freezer Construction.
$25,000 to Baker Victory Services, Lackawanna, NY, 2013. For new boiler.
$25,000 to Buffalo State College Foundation, Buffalo, NY, 2013. For Equipment for Science Facility.
$25,000 to Four Seasons Hospice, Flat Rock, NC, 2013. For Exam Tables, Education Kiosk Hardware and Check-In Hardware.
$17,000 to Daemen College, Amherst, NY, 2013. For Physical Therapy Wound Clinic.
$15,000 to Bristol Home, Buffalo, NY, 2013. For porch renovations.
$2,000 to Western New York Grantmakers Association, Buffalo, NY, 2013. For annual fee.

5833
The Nathan Cummings Foundation ✧

475 10th Ave., 14th Fl.
New York, NY 10018-9715 (212) 787-7300
Contact: Ernest Tollerson, Interim C.E.O. and Pres.
FAX: (212) 787-7377;
E-mail: contact@nathancummings.org; Main URL: http://www.nathancummings.org
E-Newsletter: http://www.nathancummings.net/all-news

Established in 1949 in IL.
Donor: Nathan Cummings†.
Foundation type: Independent foundation.
Financial data (yr. ended 12/31/12): Assets, $407,948,470 (M); expenditures, $27,252,765; qualifying distributions, $24,330,693; giving activities include $18,799,000 for 286 grants (high: $600,000; low: $500), and $306,347 for foundation-administered programs.
Purpose and activities: The foundation is rooted in the Jewish tradition and committed to democratic values and social justice, including fairness, diversity, and community. It seeks to build a socially and economically just society that values nature and protects the ecological balance for future generations; promotes humane health care; and fosters arts and culture that enriches communities.
Fields of interest: Media/communications; Media, film/video; Media, television; Media, print publishing; Media, radio; Web-based media; Media, journalism; Performing arts (multimedia); Environment, alliance/advocacy; Environment, public policy; Environment, reform; Environment, climate change/global warming; Health care, alliance/advocacy; Health care, administration/regulation; Health care, public policy; Health care, reform; Health care, equal rights; Public health, environmental health; Health organizations, association; Civil/human rights, equal rights; Civil/human rights, advocacy; Civil rights, voter education; Civil liberties, advocacy; Labor rights; Environmental and resource rights; Religion, interfaith issues; Spirituality; African Americans/Blacks; Economically disadvantaged.
International interests: Israel.
Type of support: General/operating support; Management development/capacity building; Program development; Conferences/seminars; Seed money; Fellowships; Research; Program evaluation.
Limitations: Applications not accepted. Giving primarily in the U.S., with some support to work in Israel. No support for specific diseases, Holocaust-related projects, foreign-based organizations, or community based organizations that do not plan to replicate their program(s) regionally or nationally. No grants for scholarships, sponsorships, projects with no plans for replication, endowments or capital campaigns.
Publications: Annual report; Financial statement; Grants list; Newsletter; Occasional report; Program policy statement.
Application information: Unsolicited requests for funds not accepted. See foundation web site for updates.
Board meeting date(s): Spring and fall
Officers and Trustees:* Adam N. Cummings,* Chair.; James K. Cummings,* Vice-Chair.; Ernest Tollerson,* Interim C.E.O. and Pres.; Bill Dempsey, Sr. V.P., Finance; Maurine D. Knighton, Sr. V.P., Opers.; Jaimie Mayer Phinney,* Secy.; Roberta Friedman Cummings,* Treas.; Rahman Mohamad, Cont.; Beatrice Cummings Mayer, Tr. Emeritus; Hannah Cummings; Jason Cummings; Rick Cummings; Ruth Cummings; Sonia Simon Cummings; Danielle Durchslag; Sophal Ear; Andrew Lee; Jane M. Saks; Tricia Rose.
Number of staff: 8 full-time professional; 12 full-time support; 1 part-time support.
EIN: 237093201
Selected grants: The following grants are a representative sample of this grantmaker's funding activity:
$950,000 to New Israel Fund, New York, NY, 2011. For Women and the Environment: Agents of Change in Israel, initiative to create a more vibrant, just, and peaceful Israel through supporting women as agents of change and developing a pro-active environmental movement. Women and the Environment includes three initiatives: 1) The NCF/NIF Women's Initiative to harness the energies of women to create change by advancing the rights and status of disempowered populations to create a more just and vibrant society. The Initiative seeks to cultivate projects in the Orthodox Jewish and Palestinian-Israeli sectors that mobilize women through leadership development, advocacy, networks, and collaborations. 2) The Dafna Fund (DF) to support the work of the NCF/NIF Women's Initiative developing feminist leadership and supporting projects between feminist and mainstream institutions. 3) The Green Environment Fund (GEF) to develop and advance a positive, proactive vision of Israel's future that integrates environmental sustainability and broadly-shared economic prosperity.
$600,000 to Community Catalyst, Boston, MA, 2011. For the Affordable Care Act Implementation Fund, a project of Community Catalyst, to strengthen state-based systems of advocacy that have the potential to significantly impact implementation of the Affordable Care Act. Over the next two years, Community Catalyst will engage national, state and local funders and provide timely and strategic grants from this pooled fund to state-based advocacy organizations that will promote consumer interests as national health reform is implemented, payable over 2.00 years.
$600,000 to Rockefeller Philanthropy Advisors, New York, NY, 2011. For the Breakthrough Institute, a project of the Rockefeller Philanthropy Advisors, Inc. Breakthrough will publish a series of reports, articles, and policy briefs aimed at changing the way Americans think about and craft environmental, energy and economic competitiveness policy. These reports will tell the story of how America's lack of a significant and permanent commitment to innovation is putting the American economy and the American Dream in peril; how dealing with sustainability, poverty and inequality, and reducing the debt and deficit, will require economic growth; and why key elements of the solution must be greater innovation, productivity, and manufacturing. Breakthrough is poised to make the case for a new and more energetic liberalism that can appeal to American moderates, centrists, and reasonable conservatives on economic, tax and fiscal, environmental and energy policies, payable over 2.00 years.
$300,000 to University of Wisconsin, Madison, WI, 2011. For the Center for State Innovation (CSI), a project of the University of Wisconsin, Madison, as it continues to provide state government executives with evidence-based policy support and technical assistance to develop, refine and implement high-quality, innovative and sustainable policies in important areas of state concern, including health, the environment, economic development, public safety and transportation. CSI will develop and package policy options, provide technical assistance in state-based and regional implementation strategies and promote the importance of state-level policy innovation and experimentation, payable over 1.50 years.
$150,000 to Efforts of Grace, New Orleans, LA, 2011. For general support to use art and culture to foster greater equity and social justice in the rebuilding of New Orleans.
$100,000 to Evidence, Inc., Brooklyn, NY, 2011. For a collaborative project that addresses themes of social justice explored in Ronald K. Brown's original dance work, Gatekeepers. The project will provide opportunities for elders and youth in locations nationwide to interact in ways designed to encourage collective responsibility and strengthen communities.
$86,160 to Information Technology and Innovation Foundation, Washington, DC, 2011. For Energy Innovation Tracker: Mapping and Tracking Investments in Clean Energy Innovation. To support the Energy Innovation Tracker initiative, a project of the Information Technology and Innovation Foundation. The second phase in the Tracker project aims to expand the database to include all public energy investments such as tax expenditures, state investments, and other energy policies in addition to the federal budget as well as private sector energy investments. With these additional datasets, policymakers would have access to the complete U.S. energy innovation investment picture and be able to make the most informed decisions on new clean energy policy.
$85,000 to National Physicians Alliance Foundation, Washington, DC, 2011. For general support to the National Physician's Alliance Foundation (NPAF) to provide doctors with the necessary tools to advocate for effective, patient-centered implementation of the Affordable Care Act. In the coming year, NPAF will work with professional associations and other allies to educate doctors, patients and policy makers regarding the power of health system reforms to

reduce disparities in health and improve health care overall. NPAF will mobilize its network of physicians to act as public spokespeople about the benefits of reform for doctors and patients, with a particular focus on outreach to women and seniors.
$50,000 to Aaron Davis Hall, Harlem Stage, New York, NY, 2011. For project support for WaterWorks, a theater series that commissions leading contemporary performing artists to create provocative commentary on current social issues. The work is contextualized through regular community engagement activities that draw audiences into the creative process and involve them in addressing pressing social challenges. Funding would support the continuing development of three mainstage works: Makandal, about modern-day immigration issues; visible/invisible, on the topic of the Great Migration: and, Holding it Down: The Veterans' Dreams Project, which addresses the impact of war on communities of color.
$50,000 to Backbone Campaign, Vashon, WA, 2011. For Artful Activism. Support for a multi-year training project for progressive activists and organizations nationwide who are working toward human dignity, environmental sustainability, justice and peace.

5834
The Frances L. & Edwin L. Cummings Memorial Fund ✧

501 5th Ave., Ste. 708
New York, NY 10017-7843 (212) 286-1778
Contact: Elizabeth H. Costas, Exec. Dir.
FAX: (212) 682-9458;
E-mail: info@cummingsfund.org; All e-mail should be addressed to: Dottye Chew; Main URL: http://fdnweb.org/cummings
Grants List: http://fdnweb.org/cummings/grants/year/2013/

Established in 1982 in NY.
Donors: Edwin L. Cummings†; Frances L. Cummings†.
Foundation type: Independent foundation.
Financial data (yr. ended 07/31/13): Assets, $34,408,951 (M); expenditures, $1,957,685; qualifying distributions, $1,826,104; giving activities include $1,494,000 for 54 grants (high: $45,000; low: $2,000).
Purpose and activities: The fund's primary interest is in the piloting or expansion of new, innovative programs of organizations operating in New York, NY, and its more urbanized surrounding areas in northeastern NJ (Bergen, Essex, Hudson, Passaic and Union counties). The fund has a particular interest in programs serving young people. Funding interests include 1) Education, especially programs that serve public school children from disadvantaged backgrounds, 2) Social welfare, especially programs addressing issues including child abuse, parent education, juvenile delinquency, teenage pregnancy, housing and homelessness, youth employment and job training, and 3) Health care, particularly for institutions and programs that serve economically and socially disadvantaged people.
Fields of interest: Elementary/secondary education; Elementary/secondary school reform; Vocational education; Adult education—literacy, basic skills & GED; Hospitals (general); Medical care, rehabilitation; Health care; Mental health/crisis services; Crime/violence prevention, youth; Crime/violence prevention, child abuse; Employment, services; Human services; Children/youth, services; Youth, pregnancy prevention; Child development, services; Family services, parent education; Children/youth; Youth; Young adults; Minorities; Economically disadvantaged; Homeless.
Type of support: Program development; Seed money; Technical assistance; Consulting services; Matching/challenge support.
Limitations: Applications accepted. Giving primarily in New York, NY and 5 counties in northeastern NJ (Bergen, Essex, Hudson, Passaic and Union). No support for cultural arts, alcoholism or drug addiction treatment programs, camping programs, day care programs for children and adults, environmental programs, private elementary and secondary schools, programs for senior citizens, soup kitchens and/or food banks, public policy and/or lobbying groups, well-endowed institutions, or legal aid programs. No grants to individuals, or for capital building campaigns, general operating support, moving expenses, conferences, media projects, publications, scholarships, public opinion polls and surveys, annual fundraising campaigns, or research conducted by individuals, soup kitchens and/or food banks, or for equipment.
Publications: IRS Form 990 or 990-PF printed copy available upon request.
Application information: The fund will consider up to 2 different requests at any given time. Proposals should be paginated and then clipped or stapled together, not permanently bound. Faxed or e-mailed proposals are not accepted. Application form not required.
Initial approach: Proposal, (with cover letter and brief executive summary) preferably no more than 7 pages. No more than 10 pages for those organizations submitting two requests. Send either U.S. mail or by messenger
Copies of proposal: 4
Deadline(s): Apr. 1 or Oct. 1
Board meeting date(s): June and Dec.
Final notification: 10 days following board meeting
Officers: Dorothy Riley-Chew, Secy.; Elizabeth Costas, Exec. Dir.
Trustees: J. Andrew Lark, Esq.; The BNY Mellon, N.A.
Board of Advisors: Sean Delany; Julie Floch; Anne Nordeman; Sarah Rosen.
Number of staff: 1 full-time professional; 1 full-time support.
EIN: 136814491

5835
The John P. & Constance A. Curran Charitable Foundation ✧

100 Scarborough Station Rd.
Scarborough, NY 10510-2028

Established in 1997 in NY.
Donors: John P. Curran; Constance A. Curran.
Foundation type: Independent foundation.
Financial data (yr. ended 12/31/13): Assets, $5,767,732 (M); expenditures, $589,520; qualifying distributions, $527,645; giving activities include $525,000 for 20 grants (high: $140,000; low: $5,000).
Purpose and activities: Giving primarily for education.
Fields of interest: Education; Community/economic development; Catholic agencies & churches.
International interests: Ireland.
Type of support: General/operating support; Continuing support; Annual campaigns; Capital campaigns; Building/renovation; Program development; Curriculum development; Scholarship funds; Research.
Limitations: Applications not accepted. Giving primarily in NY. No grants to individuals, or for the arts, debt reduction, or travel.
Application information: Contributes only to pre-selected organizations.
Trustees: Constance A. Curran; John P. Curran; Meredith Curran; Sean Curran.
EIN: 133923928
Selected grants: The following grants are a representative sample of this grantmaker's funding activity:
$140,000 to Ossining Union Free School District, Ossining, NY, 2011.
$50,000 to Ossining Childrens Center, Ossining, NY, 2011.
$35,000 to My Sisters Place, White Plains, NY, 2011.
$30,000 to Aquinas High School, Bronx, NY, 2011.
$30,000 to Read Alliance, New York, NY, 2011.
$15,000 to Harlem Academy, New York, NY, 2011.
$15,000 to Project EXTRA!, Laconia, NH, 2011.
$10,000 to Grace Opportunity Project, New York, NY, 2011.
$10,000 to Saint Aloysius School, New York, NY, 2011.
$10,000 to Under 21, New York, NY, 2011.

5836
Ravenel and Elizabeth Curry Foundation ✧

(formerly Ravenel B. Curry III Foundation)
c/o Elizabeth Curry
435 E. 52nd St., Ste. 4C
New York, NY 10022-6445

Established in 1974 in NY.
Donors: Elizabeth R. Curry; Ravenel B. Curry III.
Foundation type: Independent foundation.
Financial data (yr. ended 11/30/13): Assets, $94,406,188 (M); gifts received, $15,030,000; expenditures, $4,807,758; qualifying distributions, $4,674,226; giving activities include $4,669,375 for 30 grants (high: $1,004,500; low: $1,000).
Purpose and activities: Giving primarily for education, the arts, and human services.
Fields of interest: Performing arts; Performing arts, theater; Arts; Higher education; Education; Human services; Foundations (community).
Limitations: Applications not accepted. Giving primarily in New York, NY; some funding also in Washington, DC, and Charlotte, NC. No grants to individuals.
Application information: Contributes only to pre-selected organizations.
Officers: Ravenel B. Curry, Pres.; Elizabeth R. Curry, Secy.-Treas.
EIN: 237411083

5837
The Cushman Foundation ✧

c/o Anthos USA, Inc.
245 Park Ave., 32nd Fl.
New York, NY 10167 (212) 704-3100

Established in 1999 in NY.
Donors: Anthony Brenninkmeyer; Stiftung Auxilium.
Foundation type: Independent foundation.

Financial data (yr. ended 12/31/13): Assets, $10,045,907 (M); expenditures, $552,382; qualifying distributions, $520,458; giving activities include $515,600 for grants.
Fields of interest: Education; Human services; Religion.
Limitations: Applications not accepted. Giving primarily in NY.
Application information: Unsolicited requests for funds not accepted.
Trustees: Eric Beveridge; Anthony Brenninkmeyer; David J. Vezeris.
EIN: 134086187
Selected grants: The following grants are a representative sample of this grantmaker's funding activity:
$50,000 to Woodstock Theological Center, Washington, DC, 2012. For John Fontana Gift Matching Pledge.
$30,000 to Woodstock Theological Center, Washington, DC, 2012. For Catholic Higher Education Project.
$9,500 to Partners in Health, Boston, MA, 2012. For Per Frank's request for general support.
$3,000 to Intrepid Fallen Heroes Fund, New York, NY, 2012. For Per Frank's request for the Center for the Intrepid in San Antonio, TX.
$2,000 to America Magazine, New York, NY, 2012. For continued support of the Publication.
$1,000 to Mustard Seed Migrant Ministry, Goshen, NY, 2012. For Program servicing migrant workers in Orange County N.Y.
$500 to Memorial Sloan-Kettering Cancer Center, New York, NY, 2012.
$500 to Metropolitan Museum of Art, New York, NY, 2012. For sustaining membership.
$300 to White Plains Hospital Center, White Plains, NY, 2012. To support of community hospital system.

5838
Theresa A. Cwierzyk and Sidney Gordon Trust Fund ✧
110-11 Queens Blvd., Ste. 10C
Forest Hills, NY 11375-5437

Established in NY.
Donor: Theresa A. Cwierzyk†.
Foundation type: Independent foundation.
Financial data (yr. ended 12/31/13): Assets, $3,518,396 (M); expenditures, $1,234,921; qualifying distributions, $1,231,299; giving activities include $1,227,500 for 2 grants (high: $1,200,000; low: $27,500).
Fields of interest: Homeless, human services.
Limitations: Applications not accepted. Giving primarily in New York, NY.
Application information: Contributes only to pre-selected organizations.
Trustee: Anthony Ricchuiti.
EIN: 276098574

5839
Cypress Foundation, Inc. ✧
c/o Sandler O'Neill & Partners, LP
1251 Ave. of the Americas, 6th Fl.
New York, NY 10017-5001

Established in 1992 in NY.
Donors: Herman Sandler; James Dunne III.
Foundation type: Independent foundation.
Financial data (yr. ended 12/31/13): Assets, $5,501,037 (M); gifts received, $500; expenditures, $513,620; qualifying distributions, $506,950; giving activities include $506,950 for 26 grants (high: $240,000; low: $450).
Fields of interest: Higher education; Education; Health organizations; Human services.
Limitations: Applications not accepted. Giving primarily in Notre Dame, IN and the metropolitan New York, NY, area. No grants to individuals.
Application information: Contributes only to pre-selected organizations.
Officers: James Dunne, Chair.; Jonathan Doyle, V.P.; Fred D. Price, V.P.; May Della Pietra, Secy.-Treas.
EIN: 133667026
Selected grants: The following grants are a representative sample of this grantmaker's funding activity:
$2,500 to University of Mississippi, University, MS, 2011.

5840
Renee & Ezra Dabah Charitable Foundation, Inc. ✧ ☆
c/o Krusch & Modell
10 Rockefeller Plz., Ste. 710
New York, NY 10020-1903

Established in 1998 in NY.
Donors: Ezra Dabah; Renee Dabah.
Foundation type: Independent foundation.
Financial data (yr. ended 12/31/13): Assets, $47,191 (M); expenditures, $722,715; qualifying distributions, $720,805; giving activities include $720,805 for 378 grants (high: $26,000; low: $26).
Purpose and activities: Giving primarily to Jewish organizations, temples, and schools; funding also for health associations, and children, youth and social services.
Fields of interest: Education; Health care; Jewish agencies & synagogues.
Limitations: Applications not accepted. Giving primarily in NY; some giving in Israel. No grants to individuals.
Application information: Contributes only to pre-selected organizations.
Officers: Ezra Dabah, Pres.; Eva Dabah Yagoda, V.P.; Renee Dabah, Secy.-Treas.
EIN: 133986707

5841
James D'Addario Family Foundation, Inc. ✧ ☆
45 Clock Tower Ln.
Old Westbury, NY 11568-1003

Established in 1998 in NY.
Donors: James D'Addario; Janet D'Addario.
Foundation type: Independent foundation.
Financial data (yr. ended 05/31/13): Assets, $551,047 (M); gifts received, $798,711; expenditures, $536,855; qualifying distributions, $535,080; giving activities include $535,080 for 37 grants (high: $225,000; low: $25).
Fields of interest: Higher education; Hospitals (general); Pediatrics research; Crime/violence prevention, gun control; Human services; Christian agencies & churches.
Type of support: General/operating support.
Limitations: Applications not accepted. Giving primarily in NY. No grants to individuals.
Application information: Contributes only to pre-selected organizations.
Officers: James D'Addario, Pres.; Janet D'Addario, Secy.-Treas.
Directors: Robert D'Addario; Amy D'Addario Hinchey; Julie Zerbo.
EIN: 113440871
Selected grants: The following grants are a representative sample of this grantmaker's funding activity:
$1,000 to American Cancer Society, Atlanta, GA, 2011.

5842
Daedalus Foundation, Inc. ✧
c/o Altman, Greenfield & Selvaggi
200 Park Avenue S., 8th Fl.
New York, NY 10003-1526

Established in 1988 in NY.
Donors: L. Diane Sawyer; Mike Nichols.
Foundation type: Independent foundation.
Financial data (yr. ended 12/31/13): Assets, $2,116,003 (M); gifts received, $515,712; expenditures, $565,995; qualifying distributions, $544,000; giving activities include $544,000 for 16 grants (high: $250,000; low: $1,000).
Purpose and activities: Giving primarily for children and social services, the arts, and health associations.
Fields of interest: Arts; Education; Hospitals (general); Health organizations, association; Human services; Children/youth, services; Foundations (public).
Type of support: General/operating support.
Limitations: Applications not accepted. Giving primarily in KY, MA, NJ and NY. No grants to individuals.
Application information: Unsolicited requests for funds not accepted.
Officers: Mike Nichols, Chair.; L. Diane Sawyer, Pres.; Max Nichols, V.P.
Board Members: Daisy Nichols; Jenny Nichols.
EIN: 133489057

5843
Filomena M. D'Agostino Foundation ✧
950 3rd Ave., 32nd Fl.
New York, NY 10022-2717 (212) 486-8615
Contact: David Malkin, V.P.

Established in 1990 in NY.
Donor: Filomena M. D'Agostino Greenberg.
Foundation type: Independent foundation.
Financial data (yr. ended 02/28/13): Assets, $27,116,080 (M); expenditures, $1,396,521; qualifying distributions, $1,317,433; giving activities include $1,312,500 for 25 grants (high: $350,000; low: $2,500).
Purpose and activities: Giving primarily for health organizations and medical research, children, youth and social services, museums, and to a law school.
Fields of interest: Media, television; Museums (art); Museums (natural history); Law school/education; Health organizations, association; Multiple sclerosis; Medical research, institute; Alzheimer's disease research; Human services; Children/youth, services; Blind/visually impaired.

Limitations: Giving primarily in New York, NY. No grants to individuals.
Application information: Application form not required.
Initial approach: Letter
Deadline(s): None
Officers and Directors:* Max D'Agostino,* V.P.; David Malkin,* V.P.; Lorene A. Corrado,* Co-Secy.-Treas.; Jessica A. Malkin,* Co-Secy.-Treas.
EIN: 133548660
Selected grants: The following grants are a representative sample of this grantmaker's funding activity:
$10,000 to Center for Hearing and Communication, New York, NY, 2013. To Carry Out Charitable, Educational, and Scientific Functions Within the Purview of Section 501 (c)(3) of the IRC of 1954.

5844
The Damial Foundation, Inc. ✧
c/o Mark J. Krinsky, C.P.A.
655 Madison Ave., 11th Fl.
New York, NY 10065-8043

Established in 1992 in NY and DE.
Donors: Laurence A. Tisch†; Daniel R. Tisch; Wilma S. Tisch.
Foundation type: Independent foundation.
Financial data (yr. ended 12/31/13): Assets, $31,397,172 (M); gifts received, $9,953,500; expenditures, $6,589,063; qualifying distributions, $6,395,000; giving activities include $6,394,390 for 28 grants (high: $2,000,000; low: $1,000).
Fields of interest: Higher education; Theological school/education; Education; Hospitals (general); Health organizations, association; Multiple sclerosis research; Human services; Jewish federated giving programs; Jewish agencies & synagogues.
Limitations: Applications not accepted. Giving primarily in CT, NY, OH, and RI. No grants to individuals.
Application information: Contributes only to pre-selected organizations.
Officers: Daniel R. Tisch, Pres.; Bonnie J. Tisch, Sr. V.P.; Barry L. Bloom, Secy.-Treas.
EIN: 133693581

5845
The Charles A. Dana Foundation, Inc. ✧
(doing business as The Dana Foundation)
505 5th Ave., 6th Fl.
New York, NY 10017-4921
Contact: Burton M. Mirsky, V.P., Finance
FAX: (212) 317-8721; E-mail: danainfo@dana.org; E-mail for grants inquires: grantsinfo@dana.org; Main URL: http://www.dana.org
Blog: http://danablog.org/
E-Newsletter: http://www.dana.org/MemberLogin.aspx?ReturnUrl=%2fmembership%2fSubscriptions.aspx
Facebook: https://www.facebook.com/danafoundation
Knowledge Center: http://www.dana.org/About/
Podcasts: http://www.dana.org/Publications/Multimedia/Webcasts/
Twitter: http://twitter.com/dana_fdn
YouTube: http://www.youtube.com/channel/UC5M4LiJrdoLXeIGIgJ0jydg

Incorporated in 1950 in CT.
Donors: Charles A. Dana†; Eleanor Naylor Dana†.
Foundation type: Independent foundation.
Financial data (yr. ended 12/31/13): Assets, $242,498,391 (M); expenditures, $15,632,384; qualifying distributions, $14,403,590; giving activities include $9,469,162 for 183 grants (high: $2,598,469; low: $2,500), $26,460 for employee matching gifts, and $4,995,201 for 4 foundation-administered programs.
Purpose and activities: Principal interests are in health and science, particularly neuroscience.
Fields of interest: Neuroscience; Health organizations; Brain research; Medical research; Science.
Type of support: Research; Employee matching gifts.
Limitations: Applications accepted. Giving on a national basis. No grants to individuals, or for annual operating costs, deficit reduction, capital campaigns, or individual sabbaticals.
Publications: Application guidelines; Annual report (including application guidelines); Financial statement; Informational brochure (including application guidelines); Newsletter; Occasional report.
Application information: Please see the program pages on the foundation's web site for each programs application process and deadlines. Application form not required.
Deadline(s): Varies
Board meeting date(s): Apr. Sept., and Dec.
Final notification: Varies
Officers and Directors:* Edward F. Rover,* Chair. and Pres.; Barbara E. Gill, Exec. V.P., Public Affairs; Burton M. Mirsky, Exec. V.P., Finance; Barbara Rich, Ed.D., Exec. V.P., Comms.; Brigida C. Gay, Cont.; Edward Bleier; Wallace L. Cook; Charles A. Dana III; Steven E. Hyman, M.D.; Ann McLaughlin Korologos; LaSalle D. Leffall, M.D.; Hildegarde E. Mahoney; Peter A. Nadosy; Herbert J. Siegel.
Number of staff: 46
EIN: 066036761
Selected grants: The following grants are a representative sample of this grantmaker's funding activity:
$4,750,000 to Dana-Farber Cancer Institute, Boston, MA, 2012. For Clinical and Translational Research Neuroscience-related.
$2,701,468 to Dana Alliance for Brain Initiatives, New York, NY, 2012. For public education campaign on neuroscience research.
$2,000,000 to Washington University, School of Medicine, Saint Louis, MO, 2012. For Neuroimaging.
$450,000 to University of Michigan, Medical School, Ann Arbor, MI, 2012. For neuroimmunology research.
$250,000 to Johns Hopkins University, Baltimore, MD, 2012. For Clinical Neuroscience Research.
$150,000 to Emory University, School of Medicine, Atlanta, GA, 2012. For Clinical Neuroscience Research.
$150,000 to Reading Team, New York, NY, 2012. For general support.
$150,000 to Yale University, School of Medicine, New Haven, CT, 2012. For Neuroimaging.
$100,000 to Duke University, School of Medicine, Durham, NC, 2012. For brain and immuno-imaging research.
$15,000 to Saint Georges School, Middletown, RI, 2012. For general support.

5846
Dancing Tides Foundation, Inc. ✧
c/o Seth Starr, FLSV LLP
1475 Franklin Ave.
Garden City, NY 11530-1662

Established in 2001 in NJ.
Donor: Peter Muller.
Foundation type: Independent foundation.
Financial data (yr. ended 12/31/12): Assets, $30,333,561 (M); expenditures, $1,572,935; qualifying distributions, $1,552,874; giving activities include $1,541,554 for 62 grants (high: $750,000; low: $100).
Fields of interest: Community/economic development; Foundations (public); Economically disadvantaged.
Limitations: Applications not accepted. Giving primarily in New York, NY. No grants to individuals.
Application information: Unsolicited requests for funds not accepted.
Trustees: Nathan E. Arnell; Jillian Muller; Peter Muller; Seth Starr.
EIN: 010553351

5847
Elaine Dannheisser Foundation ✧
c/o Schulte Roth & Zabel
919 3rd Ave., 24th Fl.
New York, NY 10022-3902

Established in 2002 in NY.
Donor: Elaine Dannheisser†.
Foundation type: Independent foundation.
Financial data (yr. ended 12/31/13): Assets, $2,921,051 (M); expenditures, $598,339; qualifying distributions, $564,579; giving activities include $552,000 for 7 grants (high: $400,000; low: $2,500).
Purpose and activities: Giving primarily for the arts.
Fields of interest: Arts education; Museums (art); Performing arts, dance; Performing arts, theater; Art & music therapy.
Limitations: Applications not accepted. Giving primarily in New York, NY. No grants to individuals.
Application information: Contributes only to pre-selected organizations.
Trustees: Susan C. Frunzi; William D. Zabel.
EIN: 137317069
Selected grants: The following grants are a representative sample of this grantmaker's funding activity:
$300,000 to Museum of Modern Art, New York, NY, 2012. To support of Art Programs.
$40,000 to National Dance Institute, New York, NY, 2012. For Series Support of In-School Program.
$2,500 to Foundation for Contemporary Arts, New York, NY, 2012. To support of General Art Programs.

5848
The Daphne Foundation
25 E. 21st St.
New York, NY 10010 (212) 782-3711
Contact: Yvonne L. Moore, Exec. Dir.
FAX: (212) 228-5275;
E-mail: info@daphnefoundation.org; Main URL: http://www.daphnefoundation.org
Grants List: http://www.daphnefoundation.org/domestic-grantees.htm

The Daphne Foundation's Philanthropy Promise: http://www.ncrp.org/philanthropys-promise/who

Established in 1990 in CA and NY.
Donors: Abigail E. Disney; Pierre Hauser II.
Foundation type: Independent foundation.
Financial data (yr. ended 06/30/13): Assets, $8,564,075 (M); expenditures, $656,774; qualifying distributions, $592,386; giving activities include $499,710 for 16 grants (high: $35,000; low: $5,000).
Purpose and activities: The foundation funds programs that confront the causes and consequences of poverty in the 5 boroughs of New York City. The foundation has a particular interest in grassroots and emerging organizations which engage their members in the creation and implementation of long-term solutions to intractable social problems. The foundation believes it should fund in a manner that reinforces and facilitates the work of the programs it funds and that the most inventive and humane solutions to social problems often come from the people most affected by those problems.
Fields of interest: Education, reading; AIDS; Legal services; Children/youth, services; Family services; Women; Economically disadvantaged.
Type of support: Continuing support; General/operating support.
Limitations: Giving limited to the five boroughs of New York City. No grants to individuals, or for capital campaigns.
Publications: Grants list.
Application information: Visit foundation web site for current application instructions.
Board meeting date(s): May and Nov.
Officers and Directors:* Abigail E. Disney,* Co-Pres.; Pierre Hauser II,* Co-Pres.; Deborah S. Howes,* Secy.; Leah Doyle Coleman,* Treas.; Yvonne L. Moore, Exec. Dir.
Number of staff: 1 full-time professional.
EIN: 954288541
Selected grants: The following grants are a representative sample of this grantmaker's funding activity:
$70,000 to Picture the Homeless, Bronx, NY, 2011. For general support.
$50,000 to Fund for the City of New York, New York, NY, 2011. For general support.
$35,000 to Abraham House, Bronx, NY, 2011. For general support.
$35,000 to Amethyst Womens Project, Brooklyn, NY, 2011. For general support.
$35,000 to Battered Womens Resource Center, New York, NY, 2011. For general support.
$35,000 to Community Voices Heard, New York, NY, 2011. For general support.
$35,000 to Fresh Youth Initiatives, New York, NY, 2011. For general support.
$35,000 to Hour Children, Long Island City, NY, 2011. For general support.
$35,000 to Research Foundation of the City University of New York, New York, NY, 2011. For general support.
$30,000 to JSI Research and Training Institute, Boston, MA, 2011. For general support.

5849
The Philippe and Deborah Dauman Foundation ✧
c/o Deborah Dauman
121 E. 65th St.
New York, NY 10065-7006 (212) 846-4900
Contact: Philippe P. Dauman, Pres.

Established in 2000 in NY.
Donors: Philippe P. Dauman; Deborah Ross Dauman.
Foundation type: Independent foundation.
Financial data (yr. ended 12/31/12): Assets, $8,309,801 (M); gifts received, $2,807,400; expenditures, $517,596; qualifying distributions, $458,595; giving activities include $458,210 for 18 grants (high: $200,000; low: $60).
Fields of interest: Arts; Higher education, university; Law school/education; Education; Health care; Boys & girls clubs; Human services; American Red Cross; Children/youth, services.
Limitations: Applications accepted. Giving primarily in NY.
Application information: Application form not required.
Initial approach: Proposal
Deadline(s): None
Officers: Philippe P. Dauman, Pres.; Deborah Ross Dauman, Secy.-Treas.
EIN: 134097014
Selected grants: The following grants are a representative sample of this grantmaker's funding activity:
$200,000 to KIPP Foundation, New York, NY, 2011.
$100,000 to Lenox Hill Hospital, New York, NY, 2011.
$10,000 to Gods Love We Deliver, New York, NY, 2011.
$2,000 to Museum of the City of New York, New York, NY, 2011.
$1,000 to Museum of Modern Art, New York, NY, 2011.
$1,000 to Yale University, New Haven, CT, 2011.

5850
The Davenport-Hatch Foundation ✧
P.O. Box 124
Penfield, NY 14526-0124
Contact: Tom Hildebrandt, Dir.

Incorporated in 1952 in NY.
Donor: Augustus Hatch†.
Foundation type: Independent foundation.
Financial data (yr. ended 05/31/13): Assets, $39,652,804 (M); expenditures, $1,997,676; qualifying distributions, $1,855,817; giving activities include $1,658,266 for 89 grants (high: $120,955; low: $2,500).
Purpose and activities: Giving primarily for the arts, health care and medical research, children, youth and social services, and Christian ministries and organizations.
Fields of interest: Museums; Performing arts; Arts; Higher education; Education; Hospitals (general); Health organizations, association; Human services; YM/YWCAs & YM/YWHAs; Children/youth, services.
Type of support: Capital campaigns; Building/renovation; Equipment; Seed money; Scholarship funds.
Limitations: Giving primarily in the greater Rochester, NY, area. No grants to individuals.
Application information: Unsolicited requests for funds are generally not accepted. Application form not required.
Initial approach: Letter
Copies of proposal: 1
Deadline(s): None
Board meeting date(s): Approximately the 15th of Feb., June, and Oct.
Final notification: 3 weeks after board meeting; positive responses only
Directors: William L. Ely; A. Thomas Hildebrandt; Mary Hildebrandt; Molly E. Martin; William T. Knoble; David H. Taylor; David H. Taylor, Jr.; Douglas F. Taylor; Shirley Warren; Taylor F. Warren.
Trustee: Meanning and Napier.
EIN: 166027105
Selected grants: The following grants are a representative sample of this grantmaker's funding activity:
$50,000 to American Cancer Society, Atlanta, GA, 2011.
$5,000 to National Kidney Foundation, New York, NY, 2011.
$3,000 to Crohns and Colitis Foundation of America, New York, NY, 2011.

5851
The Neil Barsky and Juan S. Davidson Foundation ✧
(formerly Barsky Family Foundation)
c/o Barsky Ventures, LLC
250 W. 57th St., Ste. 2514
New York, NY 10107-2500

Established in 2006 in NY.
Donor: Neil S. Barsky.
Foundation type: Independent foundation.
Financial data (yr. ended 12/31/13): Assets, $7,557,896 (M); gifts received, $707,700; expenditures, $1,765,472; qualifying distributions, $1,745,196; giving activities include $1,745,196 for 33 grants (high: $950,000; low: $750).
Fields of interest: Higher education; Health organizations, association; Human services; United Ways and Federated Giving Programs.
Limitations: Applications not accepted. Giving primarily in New York, NY. No grants to individuals.
Application information: Contributes only to pre-selected organizations.
Trustee: Neil S. Barsky.
EIN: 208113017

5852
The Michel David-Weill Foundation ✧
c/o Bruce Oberfest & Assocs.
287 King St.
Chappaqua, NY 10514-3431

Established in 1984 in NY.
Donor: Michel David-Weill.
Foundation type: Independent foundation.
Financial data (yr. ended 06/30/13): Assets, $337,846 (M); gifts received, $1,552,169; expenditures, $2,845,202; qualifying distributions, $2,830,066; giving activities include $2,829,929 for 8 grants (high: $1,000,000; low: $8,086).
Fields of interest: Museums (art); Hospitals (general); Jewish federated giving programs.
Limitations: Applications not accepted. Giving primarily in Paris, France, as well as New York, NY. No grants to individuals.

Application information: Unsolicited requests for funds not accepted.
Officers and Directors:* Michel David-Weill,* Pres.; Helene David-Weill,* V.P.; Bruce Oberfest, Secy.-Treas.
Number of staff: 2
EIN: 133240809
Selected grants: The following grants are a representative sample of this grantmaker's funding activity:
$400,000 to UJA-Federation of New York, New York, NY, 2011. For general purpose.
$200,000 to French-American Foundation, New York, NY, 2011. For general purpose.

5853
Charles A. & Marna Davis Foundation ✧
c/o BCRS Assocs., LLC
77 Water St., 9th Fl.
New York, NY 10005-4401

Established in 1987 in NY.
Donors: Charles A. Davis; Charles A. Davis II; Charles A. David Trust; Charles A. Davis Charitable Lead Annuity Trust.
Foundation type: Independent foundation.
Financial data (yr. ended 04/30/13): Assets, $4,282,707 (M); gifts received, $530,000; expenditures, $552,223; qualifying distributions, $549,569; giving activities include $547,684 for 52 grants (high: $253,559; low: $25).
Fields of interest: Higher education; Health care; Human services; Foundations (public).
Limitations: Applications not accepted. Giving primarily in Greenwich, CT and Burlington, VT. No grants to individuals; no loans or scholarships.
Application information: Contributes only to pre-selected organizations.
Trustees: Charles A. Davis; Marna Davis.
EIN: 133437924
Selected grants: The following grants are a representative sample of this grantmaker's funding activity:
$243,236 to University of Vermont, Burlington, VT, 2011.
$25,000 to Ocean Reef Foundation, Key Largo, FL, 2011.
$20,000 to Brunswick School, Greenwich, CT, 2011.
$20,000 to New York Police and Fire Widows and Childrens Benefit Fund, New York, NY, 2011.
$16,800 to China Care Foundation, Westport, CT, 2011.
$5,000 to Governor Dummer Academy, Byfield, MA, 2011.
$5,000 to Ocean Reef Medical Center Foundation, Key Largo, FL, 2011.
$1,500 to Saint Lawrence University, Canton, NY, 2011.
$1,000 to Friends of Alta, Alta, UT, 2011.
$1,000 to Shelburne Museum, Shelburne, VT, 2011.

5854
The Donald F. and Maxine B. Davison Foundation ✧
P.O. Box 608
Churchville, NY 14428-0608

Established in 2002 in NY.
Donor: Maxine B. Davison.
Foundation type: Independent foundation.
Financial data (yr. ended 12/31/13): Assets, $10,734,428 (M); expenditures, $529,285; qualifying distributions, $464,605; giving activities include $445,000 for 27 grants (high: $50,000; low: $3,000).
Fields of interest: Arts; Higher education; Education.
Limitations: Applications not accepted. Giving primarily in NY. No grants to individuals.
Application information: Contributes only to pre-selected organizations.
Trustees: Michael Baum; Timothy L. Baum; Patrick R. George; Todd D. Green.
EIN: 306010237

5855
DBID, Inc. ✧
477 Madison Ave., 10th Fl.
New York, NY 10022-5802

Established in 1998 in DE and NY.
Donors: Bella Wexner Charitable Remainder Unitrust; Susan Wexner Revocable Trust.
Foundation type: Independent foundation.
Financial data (yr. ended 03/31/13): Assets, $26,598,969 (M); expenditures, $1,330,761; qualifying distributions, $1,163,867; giving activities include $1,159,202 for 16 grants (high: $750,000; low: $2).
Fields of interest: Hospitals (general); Economic development.
Limitations: Applications not accepted. Giving primarily in NY and Israel. No grants to individuals.
Application information: Contributes only to pre-selected organizations.
Officer and Directors:* Susan R. Wexner,* Pres. and Secy.-Treas.; Saul G. Agus; Raymond Kanner; Gregg H. Levy, Esq.; Michael S. Oberman, Esq.; Mark Saks, Esq.; Walter Stern.
EIN: 133997364
Selected grants: The following grants are a representative sample of this grantmaker's funding activity:
$1,000 to Ohel Childrens Home and Family Services, Brooklyn, NY, 2011.

5856
Sarah K. de Coizart Article TENTH Perpetual Charitable Trust ✧
(formerly Sarah K. de Coizart Perpetual Charitable Trust)
c/o JPMorgan Private Bank, N.A., Private Foundation Svcs.
270 Park Ave., 16th Fl.
New York, NY 10017-2014
Contact: Connie Giampapa, Prog. Off.; Jonathan Horowitz, Prog. Officer
FAX: (212) 464-2304; E-mail for Connie Giampapa: connie.a.giampapa@jpmorgan.com; E-mail for Jonathan.g.horowitz@jpmorgan.com; E-mail for Carolyn O'Brien: carolyn.r.obrien@jpmorgan.com; Main URL: http://fdnweb.org/decoizart
Grants List: http://fdnweb.org/decoizart/grants/year/2012/

Established in 1992 in NY.
Foundation type: Independent foundation.
Financial data (yr. ended 01/31/14): Assets, $35,582,522 (M); expenditures, $1,765,565; qualifying distributions, $1,659,568; giving activities include $1,484,000 for 30 grants (high: $124,000; low: $10,000).
Purpose and activities: Giving primarily for the environment and species conservation and for blindness-related services and research. Additional discretionary grants may be made to specific organizations and program areas that were of interest to Mrs. de Coizart.
Fields of interest: Higher education; Environment, natural resources; Environmental education; Eye diseases; Eye research.
Type of support: Program development.
Limitations: Applications accepted. Giving primarily in the northeast region of the U.S. No support for organizations lacking 501(c)(3) status. No grants to individuals, or for matching gifts; no loans.
Publications: Application guidelines; Grants list.
Application information: All application materials must be submitted online. Grants range in size from $20,000 to $100,000 per year. See foundation web site for application guidelines and requirements. Application form required.
Initial approach: Proposal
Copies of proposal: 1
Deadline(s): Aug. 15 for proposals
Board meeting date(s): July and Dec.
Final notification: Jan.
Trustees: Richard Bartholomae; JPMorgan Chase Bank, N.A.
EIN: 137046581
Selected grants: The following grants are a representative sample of this grantmaker's funding activity:
$376,000 to Notre Dame Academy, Worcester, MA, 2012. For first installment of a $500,000 grant to convert the former carriage house into a World Language and International Communication Hub.
$100,000 to Foundation Fighting Blindness, Columbia, MD, 2012. For retinal degenerative disease research.
$75,000 to Appalachian Mountain Club, Boston, MA, 2012. For final installment of a $150,000 grant for the Upper Androscoggin River Watershed Protection Initiative in northern Maine and New Hampshire.
$75,000 to Nature Conservancy, Vermont Chapter, New York, NY, 2012. For final installment of a $150,000 grant for the Vermont Chapter's participation in the Connecticut River Initiative.
$75,000 to Scenic Hudson, Poughkeepsie, NY, 2012. For first installment of a $150,000 grant for the Saving the Land that Matters Most campaign.
$50,000 to Brown University, Providence, RI, 2012. For first installment of a $100,000 grant for the BlindFind project.
$50,000 to Gulf of Maine Research Institute, Portland, ME, 2012. For research project to assess the lives and interactions of key, imperiled fish species in the Gulf of Maine.
$50,000 to National Wildlife Federation, Northeast Resource Center, Montpelier, VT, 2012. For final installment of a $100,000 grant for the development and implementation of a plan to protect the Parker River Wildlife Refuge.
$50,000 to NatureServe, Arlington, VA, 2012. For final installment of a $100,000 grant for the protection of northeastern bumble bees and dragonflies.
$40,000 to Mark Skinner Library, Manchester, VT, 2012. For technology enhancements.

5857

The Edmond de Rothschild Foundation ✧
c/o Proskauer Rose LLP
11 Times Sq.
New York, NY 10036-8299

Incorporated in 1963 in NY.
Donor: Edmond de Rothschild†.
Foundation type: Independent foundation.
Financial data (yr. ended 12/31/13): Assets, $46,038,587 (M); expenditures, $6,954,700; qualifying distributions, $6,214,309; giving activities include $4,693,170 for 19 grants (high: $1,497,326; low: $5,000).
Fields of interest: Arts education; Arts; Higher education; Medical research, institute; Human services.
Limitations: Applications not accepted. Giving primarily in New York, NY, with some funding in CO; giving internationally in France, Spain and Switzerland. No grants to individuals.
Application information: Contributes only to pre-selected organizations.
Board meeting date(s): As required
Officers and Directors:* Benjamin de Rothschild,* Chair.; Ariane de Rothschild,* Pres.; Firoz Ladak,* Exec. V.P. and Treas.; Valerie Monchi,* V.P.; Francois Morin,* V.P.; Philip M. Susswein, Secy.; Nadine de Rothschild.
Number of staff: 1 part-time professional.
EIN: 136119422

5858

Thompson Dean Family Foundation ✧
c/o Regen, Benz & MacKenzie
57 W. 38th St., 3rd Fl.
New York, NY 10018-5500

Established in 1998 in NY.
Donor: Thompson Dean III.
Foundation type: Independent foundation.
Financial data (yr. ended 12/31/12): Assets, $8,568,405 (M); gifts received, $6,378,933; expenditures, $2,122,014; qualifying distributions, $2,120,120; giving activities include $2,090,000 for 19 grants (high: $725,000; low: $5,000).
Fields of interest: Higher education; Education; Human services.
Type of support: General/operating support.
Limitations: Applications not accepted. Giving primarily in MA, NY and VA. No grants to individuals.
Application information: Contributes only to pre-selected organizations.
Officers and Directors:* Thompson Dean III,* Chair.; Caroline W. Dean,* Pres.; Hume R. Steyer, Secy.
EIN: 133942201

5859

The Raymond Debbane Family Foundation ✧
c/o The Invus Group LLC, Raymond Debbane
750 Lexington Ave.
New York, NY 10022-2050

Established in 2001 in NY.
Donor: Raymond Debbane.
Foundation type: Independent foundation.
Financial data (yr. ended 02/28/13): Assets, $23,980,972 (M); gifts received, $18,078,456; expenditures, $1,536,861; qualifying distributions, $1,509,055; giving activities include $1,504,000 for 21 grants (high: $700,000; low: $3,500).
Purpose and activities: Giving primarily for the arts, education, international policy programs, and human services.
Fields of interest: Museums (history); Higher education; Education; Human services; International affairs; Economics.
Limitations: Applications not accepted. Giving primarily in Washington, DC and New York, NY; some giving also in Brussels, Belgium. No grants to individuals.
Application information: Contributes only to pre-selected organizations.
Officers: Raymond Debbane, Pres.; Jessica Packer, Secy.; Sacha Lainovic, Treas.
EIN: 134053653
Selected grants: The following grants are a representative sample of this grantmaker's funding activity:
$225,000 to Connecticut College, New London, CT, 2011.
$25,000 to Action Against Hunger USA, New York, NY, 2011.
$20,000 to Eparchy of Saint Maron of Brooklyn, Brooklyn, NY, 2011.
$20,000 to Lycee Francais de New York, New York, NY, 2011.
$20,000 to Rene Moawad Foundation, Washington, DC, 2011.
$20,000 to Stanford University, Stanford, CA, 2011.
$10,000 to Ronald McDonald House Charities, Oak Brook, IL, 2011.
$5,000 to Alliance Francaise of Greenwich, Greenwich, CT, 2011.
$5,000 to Atlas Economic Research Foundation, Washington, DC, 2011.
$5,000 to Charities Aid Foundation America, Alexandria, VA, 2011.

5860

The Debs Foundation ✧
c/o Richard A. Debs
1 Beekman Pl., Apt. 7A
New York, NY 10022-8057

Established in 1991 in DE and CT.
Donors: Richard A. Debs; Richard A. Debs Revocable Trust.
Foundation type: Independent foundation.
Financial data (yr. ended 12/31/13): Assets, $973,787 (M); gifts received, $100,000; expenditures, $536,802; qualifying distributions, $516,119; giving activities include $507,950 for 89 grants (high: $100,000; low: $100).
Purpose and activities: Giving primarily to cultural, historical, and educational institutions.
Fields of interest: Museums (art); Performing arts; Historic preservation/historical societies; Arts; Higher education; Education; Human services.
Limitations: Applications not accepted. No grants to individuals.
Application information: Contributes only pre-selected organizations.
Officers: Richard A. Debs, Pres.; Barbara K. Debs, V.P.
Directors: Elizabeth A. Debs; Nicholas A. Debs.
EIN: 133639449

5861

The Ira W. DeCamp Foundation ✧
c/o JPMorgan Chase Bank, Fdn. Svcs.
270 Park Ave., 16th Fl.
New York, NY 10017
Contact: Contact for Community Health: Casey Castaneda, Prog. Off.; Contact for Foster Care: Connie Giampapa, Prog. Off.; Contact for Workforce Development: Jonathan Horowitz, Prog. Off
Main URL: http://fdnweb.org/decamp
Grants List: http://fdnweb.org/decamp/grants/year/contributions/

Trust established in 1970 in NY.
Donor: Elizabeth DeCamp McInerny†.
Foundation type: Independent foundation.
Financial data (yr. ended 10/31/13): Assets, $83,413,775 (M); expenditures, $4,128,110; qualifying distributions, $3,793,983; giving activities include $3,430,000 for 20 grants.
Purpose and activities: Grants for community-based health care, foster care, and workforce development.
Fields of interest: Health care; Employment; Children, foster care.
Type of support: Capital campaigns; Management development/capacity building; Program development.
Limitations: Applications accepted. Giving primarily in New York, NY. No support for private foundations. No grants to individuals, or for general support, land acquisition, matching gifts, publications, conferences, endowment funds, operating budgets, continuing support, annual campaigns, emergency funds, scholarships, fellowships, or deficit financing; no loans.
Publications: Application guidelines; Grants list.
Application information: All application materials must be submitted online. See foundation web site for full application requirements. Application form not required.
Initial approach: Proposal (3 pages maximum) to be submitted online via foundation web site
Copies of proposal: 1
Deadline(s): Mar. 15
Board meeting date(s): July and Oct.
Final notification: Summer
Trustee: JPMorgan Chase, N.A.
EIN: 510138577
Selected grants: The following grants are a representative sample of this grantmaker's funding activity:
$175,000 to Community Health Care Association of New York State, New York, NY, 2012. For first installment of a $350,000 grant to support the creation of the Center for Primary Care Informatics, a statewide warehouse of primary health care data.
$150,000 to Community Service Society of New York, New York, NY, 2012. For first installment of a $300,000 grant to support the Advancing Affordable Health Care in New York State initiative.
$150,000 to United Hospital Fund of New York, New York, NY, 2012. For final installment of a $300,000 grant for the Next Step in Care program.
$100,000 to Advocates for Children of New York, New York, NY, 2012. For final installment of a $200,000 grant for Project Achieve.
$100,000 to Brownsville Community Development Corporation, Brooklyn, NY, 2012. For first installment of a $200,000 grant for the Brownsville Multiservice Family Health Center satellite at Ashford Street.
$100,000 to Childrens Aid Society, New York, NY, 2012. For first installment of a $200,000 grant to

expand its health information technology capacity in its primary care network.
$80,000 to Legal Services NYC, New York, NY, 2012. For the Brooklyn Family Defense Project restricted to the social work program.
$75,000 to Fortune Society, Long Island City, NY, 2012. For final installment of a $150,000 grant for the expansion of the organization's sector-based workforce development program.
$75,000 to Per Scholas, Bronx, NY, 2012. For final installment of a $175,000 grant to hire Executive Vice President.
$50,000 to Youth Communication/New York Center, New York, NY, 2012. For first installment of a $100,000 grant for the Represent writers programs.

5862
The David A. Dechman Foundation ✧
c/o Marcum LLP
750 3rd Ave., 11th Fl.
New York, NY 10017-2716

Established in 1999 in NY.
Donor: David A. Dechman.
Foundation type: Independent foundation.
Financial data (yr. ended 03/31/13): Assets, $4,638,092 (M); gifts received, $502,150; expenditures, $633,628; qualifying distributions, $616,128; giving activities include $616,128 for grants.
Fields of interest: Museums (art); Arts; Education; Health organizations, association; Cancer; Human services; Foundations (private operating); LGBTQ.
Limitations: Applications not accepted. Giving primarily in CO, MA, and NY. No grants to individuals.
Application information: Contributes only to pre-selected organizations.
Trustee: David A. Dechman.
EIN: 134087830
Selected grants: The following grants are a representative sample of this grantmaker's funding activity:
$250,000 to Museum of Modern Art, New York, NY, 2011. For general purpose.
$50,000 to GLSEN, New York, NY, 2011. For general purpose.
$30,000 to Dana-Farber Cancer Institute, Boston, MA, 2011. For general purpose.
$25,000 to Dana-Farber Cancer Institute, Boston, MA, 2011. For general purpose.
$15,000 to Museum of Modern Art, New York, NY, 2011. For general purpose.
$8,500 to Museum of Modern Art, New York, NY, 2011. For general purpose.
$5,000 to Museum of Modern Art, New York, NY, 2011. For general purpose.
$2,500 to Freedom to Marry, New York, NY, 2011. For general purpose.
$1,000 to In the Life Media, New York, NY, 2011. For general purpose.
$1,000 to Museum of the City of New York, New York, NY, 2011. For general purpose.

5863
Dr. G. Clifford & Florence B. Decker Foundation ✧
8 Riverside Dr.
Binghamton, NY 13905-4612 (607) 722-0211
Contact: Gerald E. Putman, Exec. Dir.
E-mail: deckerfn@pronetisp.net

Established in 1979 in NY.
Donor: G. Clifford Decker, M.D.†.
Foundation type: Independent foundation.
Financial data (yr. ended 12/31/13): Assets, $36,746,541 (M); expenditures, $1,845,496; qualifying distributions, $1,413,996; giving activities include $1,238,349 for 15 grants (high: $500,000; low: $2,700).
Purpose and activities: The purpose of the foundation is to assist bona fide charitable organizations, focusing primarily on educational, medical and medical research institutions, and cultural and human service organizations providing principal service to residents of Broome County, NY. This assistance is in the form of grants that may be used for capital projects or new and innovative projects and programs. Efforts are directed toward helping organizations provide programs to earn income and thus become more self-sufficient.
Fields of interest: Arts; Education; Health care; Medical research, institute; Human services.
Type of support: Capital campaigns; Building/renovation; Equipment; Program development.
Limitations: Applications not accepted. Giving limited to Broome County, NY. No support for religious organizations for religious purposes. No grants to individuals, or for endowments, operating expenses, continuing support, or for travel and trips.
Application information: Unsolicited requests for funds not accepted.
Board meeting date(s): Apr., June, Oct., and Dec.
Officers and Trustees:* Ferris G. Akel,* Chair.; John T. Fitzsimmons,* Vice-Chair.; Mary Lou Faust,* Secy.; Douglas R. Johnson,* Treas.; Gerald E. Putman, Exec. Dir.; James A. Carrigg; Suzanne F. Hester; James E. Leonard.
Number of staff: 1 full-time professional; 1 part-time support.
EIN: 161131704

5864
Dedalus Foundation, Inc. ✧
3 Columbus Cir.
New York, NY 10019-1903
Contact: Richard Rubin, Chair.
E-mail: grants@dedalusfoundation.org; Main URL: http://www.dedalusfoundation.org

Established in 1981 in CT.
Donors: Robert Motherwell†; Renate Motherwell.
Foundation type: Operating foundation.
Financial data (yr. ended 12/31/12): Assets, $55,739,228 (M); expenditures, $4,632,325; qualifying distributions, $4,094,245; giving activities include $608,250 for 38 grants (high: $50,000; low: $7,500), $171,000 for 29 grants to individuals, and $3,314,995 for foundation-administered programs.
Purpose and activities: The foundation seeks to educate the public about modern art and modernism, and the art of Robert Motherwell. Proposals should be made within the context of one of the foundation's programs: 1) Arts Education (supports symposiums and lectures, K-12 programs, community-based programs, residencies, fellowship programs, educational programs at museums, art schools, colleges, and universities); 2) Research and Publication (supports scholarly research on modern art and modernism; exhibition catalogues; the publication of scholarly books and periodicals); 3) Archives and Conservation (supports projects focused on the science and practice of the conservation and restoration of works of art, and the processing, description, cataloging, and preservation of archival materials, as well as oral history programs); and 4) Curatorial (supports exhibitions of modern and contemporary art; and programs in curatorial studies).
Fields of interest: Arts, research; Arts education.
Type of support: Conferences/seminars; Publication; Seed money; Fellowships; Internship funds; Scholarship funds; Research; Grants to individuals; In-kind gifts.
Limitations: Applications accepted. Giving on a national basis. No support for the commissioning of works of art. No grants to individuals (except for fellowships), or for capital campaigns, or general operating expenses.
Publications: Application guidelines.
Application information: Applicants for Institutional Initiatives should follow the Institutional Initiatives Application Requirements on foundation web site.
Initial approach: Letter of introduction via e-mail.
Copies of proposal: 1
Deadline(s): Mar. 15 (for spring applications), Oct. 15 (for fall applications)
Board meeting date(s): Spring and fall
Officers and Directors:* Richard Rubin,* Chair.; Jack Flam,* C.E.O. and Pres.; Steven R. Howard,* Secy.; Morgan Spangle,* Treas. and Exec. Dir.; John Elderfield; Katy Rogers; David Rosand.
Number of staff: 4 full-time professional; 9 full-time support; 6 part-time support.
EIN: 133091704
Selected grants: The following grants are a representative sample of this grantmaker's funding activity:
$37,500 to Museum of Modern Art, New York, NY, 2012. For New York University.
$25,000 to Detroit Institute of Arts, Detroit, MI, 2012. For Conservation of Tony Smith's sculpture Gracehoper.
$25,000 to Whitney Museum of American Art, New York, NY, 2012. For conservation efforts.
$20,000 to Academy Art Museum, Easton, MD, 2012. For Exhibition.
$20,000 to Independent Curators International, New York, NY, 2012. For Educational initiative The Curatorial Intensive.
$20,000 to Institute of Contemporary Art, Boston, MA, 2012. For Exhibition.
$20,000 to Wichita State University Foundation, Wichita, KS, 2012. For Edwin A Ulrich Museum of Art.
$15,000 to Wadsworth Atheneum Museum of Art, Hartford, CT, 2012. For Exhibition MATRIX.
$10,500 to New York City Department of Education, New York, NY, 2012. For NYC public high school scholarships for studio art and art history.
$10,000 to Stony Brook Foundation, Stony Brook, NY, 2012. For Exhibition Men of Fire Jose Clemente Orozco and Jackson Pollock.

5865
The Deerfield Partnership Foundation ✧
780 3rd Ave., 37th Fl.
New York, NY 10017-2024 (212) 551-1600
Contact: Allison Schultz, Secy.
FAX: (212) 599-3075;
E-mail: aschultz@deerfield.com; Main URL: http://www.deerfield.com/Foundation.aspx

Established in 2005 in NY.
Donor: Deerfield Management Company.
Foundation type: Company-sponsored foundation.

Financial data (yr. ended 12/31/12): Assets, $3,856,598 (M); gifts received, $1,919,432; expenditures, $2,721,242; qualifying distributions, $2,522,073; giving activities include $2,502,535 for 15 grants (high: $725,000; low: $13,080).
Purpose and activities: The foundation supports programs designed to invest in healthcare for those in need on a local and a global scale. Special emphasis is directed toward programs that benefit children.
Fields of interest: Secondary school/education; Education; Hospitals (general); Health care, clinics/centers; Health care; Family services; Homeless, human services; Human services; Children.
Type of support: General/operating support; Continuing support; Program development.
Limitations: Applications not accepted. Giving primarily in New York, NY.
Publications: Newsletter.
Application information: Contributes only to pre-selected organizations.
Officers: Alexander Kristofcak, Chair.; Terence Kamal, Pres.; Karen Arnone, V.P.; Nelson Barriocanal, V.P.; Brian Bizoza, V.P.; Alex Kamal, V.P.; Allison Schultz, Secy.; Cristina Hohlman, Treas.
EIN: 050618950
Selected grants: The following grants are a representative sample of this grantmaker's funding activity:
$448,000 to Partners in Health, Boston, MA, 2012. For Fund the Manufacturing of Nourimanba Bars for Malnutrition.
$298,000 to New York Foundling Hospital, New York, NY, 2012. For Enhanced Medical Home Program.
$144,000 to American Jewish Joint Distribution Committee, New York, NY, 2012. For Fund Surgeries for Sick Kids in Ethiopia.
$111,372 to Little Sisters of the Assumption Family Health Service, New York, NY, 2012. For Infant Mortality and Asthma Program.
$65,000 to Coalition for the Homeless, New York, NY, 2012. For Fund a Child Advocate.
$60,000 to IVUmed, Salt Lake City, UT, 2012. For Fund Pediatric Surgery Workshops in Rwanda and Zambia.

5866
Lydia Collins deForest Charitable Trust ✧

c/o U.S. Trust, Bank of America Private Wealth Mgmt.
1 Bryant Park NY1-100-28-05
New York, NY 10036
Contact: Ken Goody
E-mail: kenneth.l.goody@ustrust.com; E-mail to discuss application process or for questions: ny.grantmaking@ustrust.com (the name of the foundation should be included in the subject line); Main URL: http://www.bankofamerica.com/grantmaking

Established in 2002 in NJ.
Donor: Lydia Collins deForest†.
Foundation type: Independent foundation.
Financial data (yr. ended 02/28/14): Assets, $10,353,516 (M); expenditures, $556,044; qualifying distributions, $487,482; giving activities include $450,000 for 21 grants (high: $50,000; low: $5,000).
Purpose and activities: The trust supports organizations that provide services to those who are visually limited, churches and organizations affiliated with the Protestant Episcopal Church in the United States and other religious organizations in union with or recognized by the Episcopal Church, and organizations that provide services to those who are homeless, unemployed, or substance-dependent.
Fields of interest: Education; Substance abuse, services; Employment, services; Human services; Salvation Army; Family services; Protestant agencies & churches; Blind/visually impaired.
Limitations: Applications accepted. Giving primarily in NJ and in the greater New York, NY metropolitan area. No grants to individuals.
Publications: Application guidelines.
Application information:
Deadline(s): Nov. 30
Final notification: Feb. 28
Trustees: Robert B. Bourne; Jean F. Marano; Bank of America, N.A.
EIN: 030433603
Selected grants: The following grants are a representative sample of this grantmaker's funding activity:
$50,000 to Calvary Episcopal Church, Summit, NJ, 2012. For Stained Glass Restoration Project. Funds will support the conservation and restoration of the five windows with the most critical issues, including the Tiffany rose window.
$45,000 to Lighthouse International, New York, NY, 2012. For general operating support.
$40,000 to Family Promise, Summit, NJ, 2012. For general operating support in support of its New Jersey Affiliates.
$40,000 to Philip's Academy Charter School, Newark, NJ, 2012. For continued general operating support, including its Student Scholarship Program and Faculty Support Program.
$40,000 to Salvation Army New Jersey Divisional Headquarters, Union, NJ, 2012. For Union City Corps Soup Kitchen, Statewide Service Extension Program, and Statewide Emergency Medication Program.
$25,000 to Greater Newark Conservancy, Newark, NJ, 2012. For Greater Newark Conservancy's Newark Prisoner Re-Entry Initiative Job Training Program.
$25,000 to Habcore, Red Bank, NJ, 2012. For general operating support to enhance the case management services offered to disabled residents of affordable housing.
$20,000 to Episcopal Diocese of Newark, Newark, NJ, 2012. For Diocesan Pilgrimage to Israel: The Holy Land, Walking in the Footsteps of Jesus. To provide subsidy for 29 participating Diocese of Newark clergy.
$20,000 to Helen Keller International, New York, NY, 2012. For ChildSight New Jersey program to bring education into focus for economically disadvantaged children in New Jersey public schools.
$20,000 to Oceans Harbor House, Toms River, NJ, 2012. For general operating support to maintain and enhance housing, case management, and supportive services (e.g., counseling, educational pursuits, career development).

5867
Lawrence J. & Florence A. DeGeorge Charitable Trust ✧

c/o Deutsche Bank Trust Co., N.A.
P.O. Box 1297, Church St. Sta.
New York, NY 10008-1297

Established in 1994 in FL.
Donors: Lawrence J. DeGeorge; Florence A. DeGeorge.
Foundation type: Independent foundation.
Financial data (yr. ended 01/31/14): Assets, $61,280,632 (M); expenditures, $5,151,040; qualifying distributions, $3,864,228; giving activities include $3,837,022 for 8 grants (high: $2,100,000; low: $25,000).
Purpose and activities: Giving primarily for health associations, medical research, and children and youth services.
Fields of interest: Animal welfare; Health organizations, association; Medical research, institute; Boys & girls clubs; Children/youth, services; Philanthropy/voluntarism.
Limitations: Applications not accepted. Giving primarily in FL. No grants to individuals.
Application information: Contributes only to pre-selected organizations.
Trustees: Florence A. DeGeorge; Lawrence J. DeGeorge; Deutsche Bank Trust Co., N.A.
EIN: 137053836

5868
The Peter and Jeri Dejana Family Foundation ✧ ☆

30 Sagamore Hill Dr.
Port Washington, NY 11050-2110
Contact: Peter Dejana, Tr.

Donor: Peter Dejana.
Foundation type: Independent foundation.
Financial data (yr. ended 12/31/13): Assets, $19,459,538 (M); gifts received, $1,000,000; expenditures, $857,956; qualifying distributions, $850,028; giving activities include $718,200 for 51 grants (high: $94,000; low: $600).
Fields of interest: Education; Cancer; Human services; Jewish agencies & synagogues; Religion.
Type of support: General/operating support.
Limitations: Applications accepted. Giving primarily in NY.
Application information: Application form required.
Initial approach: Proposal
Deadline(s): None
Trustee: Peter Dejana.
EIN: 276985468

5869
Robert & Pamela Delaney Family Foundation ✧

(formerly Delaney Family Foundation)
c/o BCRS Associates, LLC
77 Water St., 9th Fl.
New York, NY 10005-4414
Contact: Robert V. Delaney, Tr.

Established in 1997 in NJ.
Donors: Robert V. Delaney; Pamela J. Crais.
Foundation type: Independent foundation.
Financial data (yr. ended 06/30/13): Assets, $6,775,962 (M); gifts received, $2,559,000; expenditures, $1,103,159; qualifying distributions, $1,090,000; giving activities include $1,090,000 for grants.
Fields of interest: Higher education; Education; Protestant agencies & churches.
Limitations: Applications not accepted. Giving primarily in Clinton, NY; funding also in Easton, PA. No grants to individuals.

Application information: Contributes only to pre-selected organizations.
Trustees: Pamela J. Craig; Matthew Delaney; Robert V. Delaney.
EIN: 133984315
Selected grants: The following grants are a representative sample of this grantmaker's funding activity:
$28,000 to Saint Pauls Episcopal Church, Westfield, NJ, 2011. For general purpose fund.
$10,000 to Comprehensive Development, New York, NY, 2011. For general purpose fund.
$5,000 to Hamilton College, Clinton, NY, 2011. For general purpose fund.

5870
The Della Rosa Family Foundation ✧
c/o BCRS Associates, LLC
77 Water St., 9th Fl.
New York, NY 10005-4401

Established in 1994 in NJ.
Donor: Joseph Della Rosa.
Foundation type: Independent foundation.
Financial data (yr. ended 08/31/13): Assets, $8,700,808 (M); expenditures, $783,592; qualifying distributions, $777,400; giving activities include $772,200 for 12 grants (high: $500,000; low: $2,000).
Fields of interest: Secondary school/education; Higher education.
Limitations: Applications not accepted. Giving primarily in Washington, DC; giving also in NJ and NY. No grants to individuals.
Application information: Contributes only to pre-selected organizations.
Trustees: Cheryl Della Rosa; Joseph Della Rosa.
EIN: 133797964
Selected grants: The following grants are a representative sample of this grantmaker's funding activity:
$25,000 to Georgetown University, Washington, DC, 2011. For general purpose.
$25,000 to Student/Partner Alliance, Millburn, NJ, 2011. For general purpose.
$2,500 to ArtsConnection, New York, NY, 2011. For general purpose.
$2,500 to Childrens Hearing Institute, New York, NY, 2011. For general purpose.

5871
The Gladys Krieble Delmas Foundation ✧
275 Madison Ave., 33rd Fl.
New York, NY 10016-1101 (212) 687-0011
Contact: Rachel Kimber, Fdn. Admin.
FAX: (212) 687-8877; E-mail: info@delmas.org;
Main URL: http://www.delmas.org

Established in 1976 in NY.
Donors: Gladys V.K. Delmas†; Jean Paul Delmas†.
Foundation type: Independent foundation.
Financial data (yr. ended 12/31/13): Assets, $47,226,337 (M); expenditures, $3,138,527; qualifying distributions, $2,352,036; giving activities include $1,722,146 for 156 grants (high: $100,000; low: $300), and $184,385 for 36 grants to individuals (high: $15,500; low: $1,100).
Purpose and activities: The foundation supports the humanities, research libraries, and New York City performing arts organizations, and has a particular interest in encouraging Venetian scholarship.
Fields of interest: Performing arts; Humanities; Libraries/library science.
International interests: Italy.
Type of support: Scholarship funds; General/operating support; Continuing support; Program development; Conferences/seminars; Curriculum development; Fellowships; Research.
Limitations: Applications accepted. Giving on a national basis to organizations, but only in New York, NY, for performing arts grants; giving for individual research projects conducted in Venice or the Veneto, Italy. Research libraries primarily directed toward European and American letters. No grants to individuals (except for advanced research in Venice and the Veneto), or for building campaigns; no loans.
Publications: Application guidelines; Financial statement; Grants list.
Application information: Application guidelines available on foundation web site. Application form required for grants for Independent Research on Venetian History and Culture. Application form not required.
Initial approach: Letter, not exceeding 2 pages
Copies of proposal: 1
Deadline(s): Dec. 15 for grants for Independent Research on Venetian History and Culture
Board meeting date(s): Varies
Final notification: Apr. 1 for grants for Independent Research on Venetian History and Culture
Trustees: James S. Grubb; Joseph C. Mitchell; Deirdre C. Stam.
Number of staff: 1 full-time professional; 1 part-time professional.
EIN: 510193884
Selected grants: The following grants are a representative sample of this grantmaker's funding activity:
$30,000 to Kenyon College, Gambier, OH, 2012. For Art and Identity: The Holocaust and Cultural Ownership in the 21st Century interdisciplinary series of readings, exhibitions, lectures, films, and discussions presented by the Kenyon Review and the Graham Gund Gallery.
$25,000 to New York Shakespeare Festival, New York, NY, 2012. For summer season of Shakespeare in the Park.
$15,000 to Athenaeum of Philadelphia, Philadelphia, PA, 2012. For technical creation of the catalog and the exhibition of the Albert Morton Turner collections.
$15,000 to Center for Book Arts, New York, NY, 2012. For cataloging the Center's Reference Library.
$15,000 to Museum of Modern Art, New York, NY, 2012. For processing the Victor D'Amico Papers collection and making the collection publicly available.
$15,000 to New York State Archives Partnership Trust, Albany, NY, 2012. For Publication support for the New York Archives magazine.
$15,000 to Oregon Historical Society, Portland, OR, 2012. For conversion of the Library's photograph catalog containing images of individuals dating from circa 1850 to 1980.
$15,000 to University of Wisconsin Foundation, Madison, WI, 2012. For the History of Cartography Project's editorial staff for 24 months.
$10,000 to Grolier Club of the City of New York, New York, NY, 2012. For an exhibition of the careers and accomplishments of women in science.
$10,000 to Wells College, Aurora, NY, 2012. For Victor Hammer Fellowship for the 2012-2013 academic year.

5872
Demartini Family Foundation ✧
8 Elm Rock Rd.
Bronxville, NY 10708-4203

Established in 2001 in NY.
Donor: Richard M. Demartini.
Foundation type: Independent foundation.
Financial data (yr. ended 09/30/13): Assets, $3,797,122 (M); expenditures, $1,126,442; qualifying distributions, $1,058,458; giving activities include $1,054,638 for 48 grants (high: $220,588; low: $500).
Purpose and activities: Giving primarily to an art museum, as well as for education, health care and human services.
Fields of interest: Museums (art); Education; Reproductive health, family planning; Health care; Cancer research; Human services.
Type of support: General/operating support; Income development; Annual campaigns; Program development; Matching/challenge support.
Limitations: Applications not accepted. Giving primarily in NY; giving also in CA, CT, DC, TN, and VT. No grants to individuals.
Application information: Contributes only to pre-selected organizations.
Trustees: Jennifer L. Brorsen; Richard M. Demartini.
EIN: 946781245
Selected grants: The following grants are a representative sample of this grantmaker's funding activity:
$175,000 to NARAL Pro-Choice America Foundation, Washington, DC, 2011.

5873
Frederick and Nancy DeMatteis Family Charitable Trust ✧
(also known as The DeMatteis Family Foundation)
c/o The DeMatteis Family Foundation
P.O. Box 25
Glen Head, NY 11545-0025 (516) 705-4974
Contact: Robert F. Vizza Ph.D., Pres.
Main URL: http://foundationcenter.org/grantmaker/dematteis/

Established in 2001 in NY.
Donors: Frederick DeMatteis†; Nancy DeMatteis; 2001 Frederick DeMatteis Revocable Trust.
Foundation type: Independent foundation.
Financial data (yr. ended 12/31/13): Assets, $29,702,244 (M); expenditures, $2,193,302; qualifying distributions, $2,014,417; giving activities include $1,770,000 for 8 grants (high: $1,000,000; low: $12,500).
Purpose and activities: The mission of the foundation is to make life better by serving human needs through support of institutions involved in education, health, human services, medical research, social services, and the arts.
Fields of interest: Arts; Education; Health care; Medical research, institute; Human services.
Type of support: Building/renovation; Equipment; Program development; Research; Matching/challenge support.
Limitations: Applications accepted. Giving primarily in the metropolitan New York, NY, area. No grants to individuals, or for operating deficits, general operating support, endowments, unrestricted funds, or annual appeals; no loans.
Publications: Application guidelines; Informational brochure.

Application information: See foundation web site for full application requirements. Application form required.

Initial approach: 1-page letter of inquiry
Copies of proposal: 1
Deadline(s): 1 month prior to quarterly board meeting
Board meeting date(s): Quarterly
Final notification: 1 week after board meeting

Officers and Trustees:* Nancy DeMatteis,* Chair.; Robert F. Vizza, Ph.D., Pres.; Richard F. DeMatteis; Scott L. DeMatteis; Linda Langer; Donald M. Schaeffer; Tracey Serko; Stanley Sirote.
Number of staff: 1 part-time professional; 1 full-time support.
EIN: 137294014
Selected grants: The following grants are a representative sample of this grantmaker's funding activity:
$1,000,000 to Cold Spring Harbor Laboratory, Cold Spring Harbor, NY, 2010.
$1,000,000 to Cold Spring Harbor Laboratory, Cold Spring Harbor, NY, 2012.
$250,000 to Hofstra University, Hempstead, NY, 2010. For general grant.
$250,000 to Hofstra University, Hempstead, NY, 2012.
$200,000 to Westhampton Beach Performing Arts Center, Westhampton Beach, NY, 2010. For general grant.
$150,000 to Saint Vincents Services, Brooklyn, NY, 2010. For general grant.
$150,000 to Saint Vincents Services, Brooklyn, NY, 2012.
$125,000 to Friends Academy, Locust Valley, NY, 2012.
$100,000 to Villanova University, Villanova, PA, 2010. For general grant.
$100,000 to Westhampton Beach Performing Arts Center, Westhampton Beach, NY, 2012.
$100,000 to Wheelchair Classics Charities, Jackson Heights, NY, 2012.
$100,000 to Wheelchair Classics Charities, Jackson Heights, NY, 2010. For general grant.
$87,500 to Raymond F. Kravis Center for the Performing Arts, West Palm Beach, FL, 2012.
$55,000 to Raymond F. Kravis Center for the Performing Arts, West Palm Beach, FL, 2010. For general grant.
$50,000 to Palm Beach Pops, West Palm Beach, FL, 2012.
$20,000 to SCO Family of Services, Glen Cove, NY, 2012.

5874
The Derfner Foundation ✧ ☆

(formerly Harold and Helen Derfner Foundation)
245 E. 80th St.
New York, NY 10075-0506

Established in 1992 in NY and FL.
Donors: Michael Braunstein; Barbara Braunstein; Leslie Crosse; Harold Derfner†; Helen Derfner†.
Foundation type: Independent foundation.
Financial data (yr. ended 12/31/12): Assets, $72,086,843 (M); gifts received, $2,335,156; expenditures, $1,888,838; qualifying distributions, $1,837,500; giving activities include $1,837,500 for grants.
Fields of interest: Hospitals (general); Human services; Jewish federated giving programs; Jewish agencies & synagogues.
Limitations: Applications not accepted. Giving primarily in FL and NY. No grants to individuals.
Application information: Contributes only to pre-selected organizations.
Trustee: Jay Lieberman.
EIN: 133661341

5875
The Herman Deutsch Charity Foundation ✧

c/o Cliffside
119-19 Graham Ct.
Flushing, NY 11354-1047

Established in 2007 in NY.
Donors: Anna Deutsch; Jack Deutsch; Esther Friedman; Gloria Lieberman; BDG Foundation; Jacob Davidowitz; Elizabeth Goldbaum; Jerry Solomon.
Foundation type: Independent foundation.
Financial data (yr. ended 12/31/13): Assets, $130,403 (M); gifts received, $900,000; expenditures, $791,169; qualifying distributions, $790,625; giving activities include $790,079 for 106 grants (high: $325,000; low: $10).
Fields of interest: Jewish agencies & synagogues.
Limitations: Applications not accepted. Giving primarily in NY. No grants to individuals.
Application information: Contributes only to pre-selected organizations.
Trustees: Anna Deutsch; Jack Deutsch.
EIN: 260580855
Selected grants: The following grants are a representative sample of this grantmaker's funding activity:
$18,000 to Shaarei Arazim of Monsey, Monsey, NY, 2011.
$10,100 to Mesivta Yeshiva Rabbi Chaim Berlin, Brooklyn, NY, 2011.
$7,000 to Yeshiva of Far Rockaway, Far Rockaway, NY, 2011.
$5,520 to Yeshiva Darchei Torah, Far Rockaway, NY, 2011.
$5,000 to Yeshivas Mir Yerushalayim, Brooklyn, NY, 2011.
$5,000 to Yeshivas Mir Yerushalayim, Brooklyn, NY, 2011.
$4,000 to Bais Yaakov of Spring Valley, Monsey, NY, 2011.
$3,950 to Torah Academy for Girls, Far Rockaway, NY, 2011.

5876
Deutsche Bank Americas Foundation ✧

(formerly BT Foundation)
60 Wall St., NYC60-2312
New York, NY 10005-2858
FAX: (212) 797-2255; Main URL: https://www.db.com/cr/en/society/index.htm
Grants List: https://www.db.com/usa/docs/2012_Americas_Philanthropic_Grants_FINAL.pdf
Twitter: http://twitter.com/DBFoundation

Established in 1986 in NY.
Donors: Bankers Trust Co.; BT Capital Corp.; Deutsche Bank Americas Holding Corp.
Foundation type: Company-sponsored foundation.
Financial data (yr. ended 12/31/12): Assets, $26,436,075 (M); gifts received, $11,843,785; expenditures, $12,054,238; qualifying distributions, $13,798,449; giving activities include $8,030,500 for 277 grants (high: $250,000; low: $500), $3,950,285 for 2,652 employee matching gifts, and $1,810,000 for loans/program-related investments.
Purpose and activities: The foundation supports organizations involved with the environment, health, employment, affordable housing, disaster relief, human services, youth, minorities, immigrants, and economically disadvantaged people. Special emphasis is directed toward programs designed to encourage sustainable community development; promote wider access to quality education; and foster the arts to enrich areas where Deutsche Bank does business.
Fields of interest: Visual arts; Museums; Museums (art); Performing arts, music; Arts; Elementary/secondary education; Higher education; Education, services; Education, e-learning; Education; Environment, climate change/global warming; Environment, energy; Environment; Hospitals (general); Optometry/vision screening; Employment, training; Employment; Housing/shelter, development; Housing/shelter; Disasters, preparedness/services; YM/YWCAs & YM/YWHAs; Children/youth, services; Human services, financial counseling; Homeless, human services; Human services; Community development, neighborhood development; Business/industry; Community development, small businesses; Community/economic development; Mathematics; Engineering/technology; Science; Youth; Minorities; Immigrants/refugees; Economically disadvantaged.
International interests: Canada; Latin America.
Type of support: General/operating support; Continuing support; Management development/capacity building; Building/renovation; Program development; Seed money; Curriculum development; Technical assistance; Employee volunteer services; Sponsorships; Program-related investments/loans; Employee matching gifts; Matching/challenge support; Mission-related investments/loans.
Limitations: Applications accepted. Giving on a national basis in areas of company operations with emphasis on NY, Argentina, Brazil, Canada, Chile, Latin America, Mexico, and Peru. No support for political candidates, veterans', military, or fraternal organizations, United Way agencies not providing a fundraising waiver, professional or trade associations, discriminatory organizations, organizations that employ adversarial and/or confrontational tactics, or organizations that are not in full compliance with anti-terrorism laws. No grants to individuals, or for endowments, capital campaigns, legal advocacy, or religious purposes.
Publications: Application guidelines; Corporate giving report; Newsletter.
Application information: Letters of intent should not exceed 3 pages in length. A full proposal may be requested at a later date. The foundation utilizes a Request for Proposal (RFP) process for most programs. Support is limited to 3 years in length. Application form not required.

Initial approach: Letter of intent
Deadline(s): None

Officers and Directors:* Seth Waugh,* Chair.; Gary S. Hattem,* Pres.; Nicole Rodriguez Leach, V.P.; Sam Marks, V.P.; Alessandra Digiusto, Secy.-Treas. and C.A.O.; Jorge Arce; Gary Beyer; Jacques Brand; Robert Dibble; Christopher Habig; Frank Kelly; Roelfien Kuijpers; Erich Mauff; Jeffrey Mayer; Joseph Polizzotto; Akbar Poonawala.
Number of staff: 3 full-time professional; 3 full-time support.
EIN: 133321736

Selected grants: The following grants are a representative sample of this grantmaker's funding activity:
$250,000 to Local Initiatives Support Corporation, New York, NY, 2012. For first installment of multi-year grant in support of College Ready Communities.
$250,000 to Resource Foundation, New York, NY, 2012. For Latin America Grants.
$200,000 to AmeriCares, Stamford, CT, 2012. For immediate disaster relief, tri-state area.
$166,667 to Living Cities: The National Community Development Initiative, New York, NY, 2012.
$100,000 to Enterprise Community Partners, New York, NY, 2012. For a multi-year grant for general operating support and the Gotham Gala.
$75,000 to Weeksville Heritage Center, Brooklyn, NY, 2012. For Art and Enterprise Art and Emerging Technology.
$30,000 to Homeless Planning Council of Delaware, Wilmington, DE, 2012. For Comprehensive Affordable Housing Plan.
$25,000 to Parodneck Foundation for Self-Help Housing and Community Development, New York, NY, 2012. For Working Capital VIII.
$15,000 to Global Heritage Fund, Palo Alto, CA, 2012. For Patronato Cultural del Peru.
$10,000 to Neighborhood House Charter School, Dorchester, MA, 2012. For the Early Childhood Literacy Program.

5877
The Devlin Foundation ✧
680 5th Ave., Ste. 2201
New York, NY 10019-5429 (212) 339-0100
Contact: Michael Devlin, V.P.

Established in 1998 in TX.
Donors: Robert M. Devlin; Katharine B. Devlin.
Foundation type: Independent foundation.
Financial data (yr. ended 12/31/13): Assets, $17,789,918 (M); expenditures, $1,120,643; qualifying distributions, $1,003,946; giving activities include $922,735 for 47 grants (high: $310,000; low: $150).
Purpose and activities: Giving primarily for education and the arts.
Fields of interest: Museums; Performing arts, theater; Arts; Higher education; Human services; Children/youth, services.
Type of support: General/operating support; Scholarship funds.
Limitations: Applications not accepted. Giving primarily in CT and NY; some funding nationally.
Application information: Unsolicited requests for funds not accepted.
Officers: Katharine B. Devlin, Pres.; Erin C. Devlin, Exec. V.P.; Matthew B. Devlin, V.P.; Michael Devlin, V.P.; Robert M. Devlin, V.P.
EIN: 760574063

5878
The Dewan Foundation ✧ ☆
c/o Tiger Global
101 Park Ave., 48th Fl.
New York, NY 10178-4799

Established in NY.
Donors: Feroz Dewan; Erica Dewan.
Foundation type: Independent foundation.
Financial data (yr. ended 12/31/12): Assets, $17,933,910 (M); gifts received, $19,173,182; expenditures, $1,027,891; qualifying distributions, $1,014,317; giving activities include $1,000,000 for 1 grant.
Fields of interest: Education, services.
Limitations: Applications not accepted. Giving primarily in New York, NY.
Application information: Unsolicited requests for funds not accepted.
Trustees: Erica Dewan; Feroz Dewan.
EIN: 266476207

5879
Dewar Foundation, Inc. ✧
16 Dietz St.
Oneonta, NY 13820-1800 (607) 432-3530

Incorporated in 1947 in NY.
Donors: Jessie Smith Dewar‡; James A. Dewar‡; Frank Getman.
Foundation type: Independent foundation.
Financial data (yr. ended 12/31/13): Assets, $12,514,968 (M); expenditures, $660,570; qualifying distributions, $618,100; giving activities include $618,100 for 81 grants (high: $55,000; low: $1,000).
Purpose and activities: Giving primarily for education, health organizations, youth and social services, and Protestant agencies and churches.
Fields of interest: Arts; Education; Hospitals (general); Health organizations, association; Human services; Children/youth, services; Community/economic development; Protestant agencies & churches.
Type of support: Continuing support; Annual campaigns; Building/renovation; Endowments; Program development; Scholarship funds.
Limitations: Applications accepted. Giving limited to the greater Oneonta, NY, area. No grants to individuals.
Application information: Application form required.
Initial approach: Letter
Deadline(s): None
Officers: Michael F. Getman, Pres.; John M. Pontius, V.P.; William Pirone, Secy.-Treas.
Directors: Vincent Foti; Geoffrey A. Smith.
EIN: 166054329
Selected grants: The following grants are a representative sample of this grantmaker's funding activity:
$50,000 to Hartwick College, Oneonta, NY, 2012. For scholastic.

5880
Miriam and Arthur Diamond Charitable Trust ✧
c/o Withers Bergman LLP
430 Park Ave., 10th Fl.
New York, NY 10022-3505
Contact: Jay H. McDowell, Tr.
FAX: (212) 848-9888;
E-mail: Jay.McDowell@withers.us.com

Established in 1996 in NY.
Foundation type: Independent foundation.
Financial data (yr. ended 12/31/13): Assets, $37,457,654 (M); expenditures, $1,704,119; qualifying distributions, $1,618,022; giving activities include $1,340,000 for 8 grants (high: $750,000; low: $5,000).
Purpose and activities: Giving primarily for aid to frail elderly residents of the New York City area, as well as for the arts, hospitals including medical research, and health and human services.
Fields of interest: Performing arts; Performing arts centers; Arts; Hospitals (general); Genetic diseases and disorders research; Cancer research; Human services; American Red Cross; Jewish federated giving programs; Adults; Aging; Physically disabled; Terminal illness, people with; Economically disadvantaged.
Type of support: General/operating support; Annual campaigns; Emergency funds.
Limitations: Applications accepted. Giving primarily in New York, NY; some funding nationally. No grants to individuals.
Publications: Annual report.
Application information: Application form not required.
Initial approach: Letter
Copies of proposal: 1
Deadline(s): None
Board meeting date(s): As required
Final notification: Varies
Trustees: Jay H. McDowell.
EIN: 137093689
Selected grants: The following grants are a representative sample of this grantmaker's funding activity:
$850,000 to UJA-Federation of New York, New York, NY, 2011.

5881
The Robert & Jennifer Diamond Family Foundation ✧ ☆
c/o Clarfeld Financial Advisors, Inc.
560 White Plains Rd., 5th Fl.
Tarrytown, NY 10591-5113

Established in 2003 in DE.
Donor: Robert E. Diamond, Jr.
Foundation type: Independent foundation.
Financial data (yr. ended 03/31/13): Assets, $6,382,691 (M); expenditures, $1,506,303; qualifying distributions, $1,432,030; giving activities include $1,432,030 for 12 grants (high: $773,058; low: $20,000).
Fields of interest: Higher education; Education.
Type of support: Continuing support; Annual campaigns; Capital campaigns; Building/renovation; Fellowships; Scholarship funds.
Limitations: Applications not accepted. Giving in the U.S., with emphasis on ME; some giving also in the U.K. No grants to individuals.
Application information: Contributes only to pre-selected organizations.
Directors: Jennifer Diamond; Nell Diamond; Robert E. Diamond, Jr.; Robert E. Diamond III; Teresa Jane Taylor; Paul Wrobleski.
EIN: 200618456

5882
Irene Diamond Fund ✧
750 3rd Ave.
New York, NY 10017-2703
Contact: Jane Silver, Pres.

Established in 1994 in NY.
Donor: Irene Diamond‡.
Foundation type: Independent foundation.

Financial data (yr. ended 12/31/12): Assets, $45,565,329 (M); expenditures, $55,705,684; qualifying distributions, $52,910,465; giving activities include $52,171,755 for grants.
Purpose and activities: Giving for pre-determined projects in New York, NY, for medical research on HIV/AIDS and immunology, human rights and for the performing arts.
Fields of interest: Arts; Medical research; Civil/human rights.
Limitations: Applications not accepted. Giving primarily in NY. No grants to individuals.
Application information: Contributes only to pre-selected organizations.
Officers and Board Members:* Jane Silver,* Pres. and Secy,; Peter Kimmelman,* Treas.
Number of staff: 1 full-time professional; 1 part-time professional; 1 full-time support; 1 part-time support.
EIN: 132678431

5883
Valerie & Charles Diker Fund, Inc. ✧
c/o Diker Mgmt., Attn.: Charles Diker
730 5th Ave., 15th Fl.
New York, NY 10019-4105

Established in 1961 in NY.
Donors: Charles Diker; Valerie Diker.
Foundation type: Independent foundation.
Financial data (yr. ended 11/30/13): Assets, $11,074,822 (M); gifts received, $13,062; expenditures, $1,649,591; qualifying distributions, $1,628,800; giving activities include $1,583,664 for 137 grants (high: $560,640; low: $50).
Purpose and activities: Giving primarily to Jewish organizations and temples, and for education, and the arts.
Fields of interest: Museums; Museums (art); Performing arts centers; Performing arts, dance; Arts; Elementary school/education; Higher education; Cancer research; Human services; Children/youth, services; United Ways and Federated Giving Programs; Jewish federated giving programs; Jewish agencies & synagogues.
Limitations: Applications not accepted. Giving primarily in New York, NY. No grants to individuals.
Application information: Contributes only to pre-selected organizations.
Directors: Charles Diker; Valerie Diker.
EIN: 136075504

5884
The Diller-von Furstenberg Family Foundation ✧
(doing business as The Diller Foundation)
c/o Sarah Knutson, Arrow Investments, Inc.
555 W. 18th St., 2nd Fl.
New York, NY 10011-2822
Main URL: http://dvfff.org/
Barry Diller and Diane von Furstenberg's Giving Pledge Profile: http://glasspockets.org/philanthropy-in-focus/eye-on-the-giving-pledge/profiles/diller
RSS Feed: http://dvfff.org/feed/

Established in 1986 in CA.
Donors: Barry Diller; Ranger Investments, L.P.
Foundation type: Independent foundation.
Financial data (yr. ended 12/31/12): Assets, $50,016,678 (M); gifts received, $42,389,954; expenditures, $9,735,597; qualifying distributions, $9,617,122; giving activities include $9,597,284 for 91 grants (high: $2,000,000; low: $1,000).
Purpose and activities: The foundation aims to positively impact the world by improving people's lives and strengthening communities. To achieve this objective, the foundation supports organizations which either provide people opportunities for which they would not otherwise have access, or which sustainably improve a community as a whole.
Fields of interest: Arts, alliance/advocacy; Media/communications; Performing arts, theater; Arts; Elementary/secondary education; Higher education; Education; Hospitals (general); Health care; Health organizations, association; Cancer; AIDS; Cancer, leukemia research; Human services; Children/youth, services; Foundations (private grantmaking).
Type of support: Research.
Limitations: Applications not accepted. Giving primarily in CA and New York, NY. No grants to individuals.
Application information: Contributes only to pre-selected organizations.
Officers and Directors:* Barry Diller,* Pres.; Alexandre Von Furstenberg,* Secy.; Diane Von Furstenberg; Tatiana Von Furstenberg.
EIN: 954081892

5885
The Dillon Fund ✧
99 Park Ave., 24th Fl.
New York, NY 10016-1601

Incorporated in 1922 in NY.
Donors: C. Douglas Dillon; Clarence Dillon‡; Susan S. Dillon.
Foundation type: Independent foundation.
Financial data (yr. ended 12/31/13): Assets, $35,598,467 (M); expenditures, $1,261,678; qualifying distributions, $1,063,250; giving activities include $1,043,500 for 62 grants (high: $350,000; low: $1,000).
Fields of interest: Arts; Education; Environment, natural resources; Hospitals (general); Human services.
Type of support: General/operating support; Continuing support; Annual campaigns; Capital campaigns; Building/renovation; Endowments; Publication.
Limitations: Applications not accepted. Giving in the U.S., with some emphasis on MD, ME, and NY. No grants to individuals; no loans.
Application information: Contributes only to pre-selected organizations. Unsolicited applications not considered.
Officers and Directors:* Joan M. Frost,* Pres.; James J. Ruddy, V.P.; Judy Monge, Secy.; Donald Barclay, Treas.; Douglas D. Bryan; Sophie Bryan; Douglas Collins; Frances Collins; Mark M. Collins, Jr.; Phyllis Dillon Collins; Charlotte Cunningham; Robert De Luxembourg; Katherine S. Groome.
Number of staff: 1 part-time professional.
EIN: 136400226
Selected grants: The following grants are a representative sample of this grantmaker's funding activity:
$2,500 to Harvard University, John F. Kennedy School of Government, Cambridge, MA, 2012.

5886
The DiMenna Foundation, Inc. ✧
(formerly The DiMenna Family Foundation, Inc.)
10 E. 67th St.
New York, NY 10065-5805

Established in 1998 in CT and NY.
Donor: Joseph A. DiMenna.
Foundation type: Independent foundation.
Financial data (yr. ended 12/31/12): Assets, $23,675,509 (M); expenditures, $1,367,664; qualifying distributions, $1,290,455; giving activities include $1,270,000 for 1 grant.
Fields of interest: Museums; Elementary/secondary education; Education; Hospitals (general); Human services; Community/economic development.
Limitations: Applications not accepted. Giving primarily in New York, NY; some funding also in Memphis, TN. No grants to individuals.
Application information: Contributes only to pre-selected organizations.
Officers: Joseph A. DiMenna, Pres.; Kevin P. Cannon, Secy.
Director: Diana DiMenna.
EIN: 061534269
Selected grants: The following grants are a representative sample of this grantmaker's funding activity:
$1,270,000 to Harlem Childrens Zone, New York, NY, 2012. For Educational and Recreational Services for Harlem Families.

5887
The Frank DiMino Family Trust ✧ ☆
(formerly The Raymond DiMino Memorial Foundation)
290 Linden Oaks
Rochester, NY 14625-2815
E-mail: wmasucci@fdfamilyoffice.org

Established in 1988 in NY.
Donor: Frank DiMino.
Foundation type: Independent foundation.
Financial data (yr. ended 06/30/13): Assets, $14,237,317 (M); gifts received, $3,000,012; expenditures, $536,579; qualifying distributions, $516,104; giving activities include $429,000 for 1 grant.
Fields of interest: Arts; Hospitals (general); Human services; Community/economic development.
Limitations: Applications not accepted. Giving primarily in Rochester, NY. No grants to individuals.
Application information: Contributes only to pre-selected organizations.
Trustees: Richard A. Calabrise; Kimberly D'Amico; Anthony DiMino; Frank DiMino; Ronald DiMino; Mary Kay DiMino-Lara; Rebecca Bree Guelli; William Masucci.
EIN: 222985922

5888
The Dinan Family Foundation ✧
(formerly James G. Dinan Foundation, Inc.)
767 5th Ave., 17th Fl.
New York, NY 10153

Established in 1997 in NY.
Donors: James G. Dinan; Elizabeth R. Miller.
Foundation type: Independent foundation.

Financial data (yr. ended 06/30/13): Assets, $31,737,965 (M); gifts received, $7,800,000; expenditures, $1,285,730; qualifying distributions, $952,900; giving activities include $952,900 for 50 grants (high: $125,000; low: $1).
Fields of interest: Museums; Performing arts centers; Arts; Education; Hospitals (general); Foundations (public).
Limitations: Applications not accepted. Giving primarily in New York, NY. No grants to individuals.
Application information: Contributes only to pre-selected organizations.
Officers: James G. Dinan, Pres. and Treas.; Elizabeth Miller, Secy.
Director: William A. Dinan.
EIN: 133976827
Selected grants: The following grants are a representative sample of this grantmaker's funding activity:
$50,000 to Parkinsons Disease Foundation, New York, NY, 2011.
$25,000 to Breakthrough Collaborative, San Francisco, CA, 2011.
$10,000 to Saint Jude Childrens Research Hospital, Memphis, TN, 2011.
$9,000 to American Cancer Society, Atlanta, GA, 2011.
$2,500 to American Cancer Society, Atlanta, GA, 2011.

5889
The Discount Foundation
115 S. Oxford St., No. 569
Brooklyn, NY 11217-1607 (646) 558-6020
Contact: Susan Wefald, Exec. Dir.
E-mail: hallen@discountfoundation.org; Main URL: http://www.discountfoundation.org
Grants Database: http://www.discountfoundation.org/search_grants
The Discount Foundation's Philanthropy Promise: http://www.ncrp.org/philanthropys-promise/who

Established in 1977.
Donors: Jeffrey W. Zinsmeyer; Garfield Trust.
Foundation type: Independent foundation.
Financial data (yr. ended 09/30/13): Assets, $3,104,071 (M); expenditures, $1,403,079; qualifying distributions, $1,361,745; giving activities include $1,165,000 for 35 grants (high: $110,000; low: $2,000).
Purpose and activities: Giving primarily to improve job opportunities, wages, and benefits for poor and working people, including workfare participants; empower poor and working people by strengthening their collective institutions, specifically community-based organizations, churches and congregations, and labor organizations, and encouraging relationships among these institutions; and advance innovative public policies designed to secure jobs with livable wages, benefits, and career opportunities for poor and working people.
Fields of interest: Employment; Community/economic development; Public policy, research; Minorities; African Americans/Blacks; Immigrants/refugees; Economically disadvantaged; Homeless.
Type of support: General/operating support.
Limitations: Applications not accepted. Giving on a national basis. No support for government agencies, schools, or religious programs. No grants to individuals, or for capital campaigns or projects, endowments, publications, research projects, or tours or trips.
Application information: Unsolicited requests for funds are currently not accepted. Refer to foundation web site for updates in this area.
Officers and Directors:* Jeffrey W. Zinsmeyer,* Pres. and Treas.; Thomas R. Asher,* Secy.; Susan Wefald, Exec. Dir.; Deepak Bhargava; Sarita Gupta; Angelica Sala; Margery A. Tabankin; Dorian Warren.
Number of staff: 1 part-time professional.
EIN: 521095120
Selected grants: The following grants are a representative sample of this grantmaker's funding activity:
$110,000 to Center for Popular Democracy, Brooklyn, NY, 2013. For National Warehouse Worker Organizing Initiative.
$50,000 to Jobs with Justice Education Fund, Washington, DC, 2013. For Change WalMart Change the Economy campaign.
$50,000 to National Domestic Workers Alliance, New York, NY, 2013. For domestic worker campaigns in Atlanta and Massachusetts.
$30,000 to Center for Community Change, Washington, DC, 2013. For project support of the Jobs with Economy Project.
$30,000 to Center for Community Change, Washington, DC, 2013. For project support of Promise Arizona.
$30,000 to Voces de la Frontera, Milwaukee, WI, 2013. For general operating support.
$25,000 to New World Foundation, New York, NY, 2013. For the Lift Fund.
$5,000 to Jobs with Justice Education Fund, Washington, DC, 2013. For united Workers Congress.
$5,000 to National Domestic Workers Alliance, New York, NY, 2013. For We Belong Together Campaign.
$3,000 to National Employment Law Project, Washington, DC, 2013. For meeting travel.

5890
The Ditmars Foundation Inc. ✧
c/o Kalmanwitz & Lee, C.A.P.S, PLLC
575 8th Ave., Ste. 1706
New York, NY 10018-7439

Established in 1995 in NY.
Donors: Tibor Klein; York Home Care, LLC; Skatz Realty Corp.; Gershon Klein; Gcsym Realty LLC; Madison York ALP; S&K Woodhaven Associates LLC; Aliah Home Care Inc.; KF Elmhurst Holding LLC.
Foundation type: Independent foundation.
Financial data (yr. ended 12/31/13): Assets, $20,720 (M); gifts received, $1,048,000; expenditures, $1,037,985; qualifying distributions, $1,037,985; giving activities include $1,035,510 for 102 grants (high: $339,020; low: $50).
Fields of interest: Elementary/secondary education; Jewish federated giving programs; Jewish agencies & synagogues.
Limitations: Applications not accepted. Giving primarily in NY. No grants to individuals.
Application information: Contributes only to pre-selected organizations.
Officers: Tibor Klein, Pres.; Chaim Klein, V.P.; Gershon Klein, V.P.; Miriam Klein, Treas.
EIN: 133861379

5891
Dobkin Family Foundation ✧
c/o BCRS Assocs., LLC
77 Water St., 9th Fl.
New York, NY 10005-4401

Established in 1984 in NY.
Donors: Eric S. Dobkin; Barbara Dobkin.
Foundation type: Independent foundation.
Financial data (yr. ended 03/31/13): Assets, $48,752,367 (M); expenditures, $8,272,447; qualifying distributions, $7,046,697; giving activities include $6,740,983 for 196 grants (high: $1,000,000; low: $200).
Purpose and activities: Giving primarily to Jewish organizations and higher education, and for human services.
Fields of interest: Museums; Arts; Higher education; Health organizations, association; Human services; Women, centers/services; Jewish federated giving programs; Jewish agencies & synagogues; Women.
International interests: Israel.
Type of support: General/operating support.
Limitations: Applications not accepted. Giving primarily in New York, NY. No grants to individuals.
Application information: Contributes only to pre-selected organizations.
Trustees: Barbara Dobkin; Eric S. Dobkin; Rachel L. Dobkin.
EIN: 133248042

5892
Cleveland H. Dodge Foundation, Inc. ✧
420 Lexington Ave., Ste. 2331
New York, NY 10170-2332 (212) 972-2800
Contact: Phyllis M. Criscuoli, Exec. Dir.
FAX: (212) 972-1049;
E-mail: info@chdodgefoundation.org; Main URL: http://www.chdodgefoundation.org

Incorporated in 1917 in NY.
Donors: Cleveland H. Dodge†; Cleveland H. Dodge, Jr.
Foundation type: Independent foundation.
Financial data (yr. ended 12/31/13): Assets, $48,003,383 (M); expenditures, $2,115,589; qualifying distributions, $1,756,482; giving activities include $1,307,637 for 272 grants (high: $125,000; low: $33).
Purpose and activities: The purpose of the foundation is to promote the well-being of mankind throughout the world. Grants for a selected list of international organizations in the Near East, including those working toward reversing global overpopulation; grants also to a selected few national agencies in the U.S., the balance directed to organizations located in New York City. Most grants in the U.S. for higher and secondary education, youth agencies and child welfare, and cultural programs.
Fields of interest: Arts; Secondary school/education; Higher education; Children/youth, services; Population studies.
International interests: Middle East.
Type of support: Building/renovation; Equipment; Endowments; Employee matching gifts; Matching/challenge support.
Limitations: Applications accepted. Giving primarily in New York, NY and to national organizations. No support for health care, or schools, colleges, and universities, except those that the foundation has consistently supported. No grants to individuals,

including scholarships and fellowships, or for general purposes, medical and other research; no loans.
Publications: Annual report; Financial statement; Grants list; Program policy statement.
Application information: Application guidelines available on foundation web site. Application form not required.
Initial approach: Letter
Copies of proposal: 1
Deadline(s): Submit letter prior to the 15th of Jan., Apr., and Sept.
Board meeting date(s): Mar., June, and Nov.
Final notification: Within 3 months of submitting the proposal
Officers and Directors:* William Dodge Rueckert,* Pres.; Catherine O. Kerr, V.P.; Louis E. Black,* Secy.; Phyllis M. Criscuoli, Treas. and Exec. Dir.; Bayard Dodge; Robert Garrett; Bolling W. Haxall, Jr.; Alfred H. Howell, Jr.; Sally Dodge Mole; Elizabeth Olmsted-Perry; Bayard D. Rea; Ingrid R. Warren; Peter K. Weidlein.
Number of staff: 1 full-time professional.
EIN: 136015087
Selected grants: The following grants are a representative sample of this grantmaker's funding activity:
$50,000 to American Museum of Natural History, New York, NY, 2012. For Educational Department Programs.
$50,000 to Wildlife Conservation Society, Bronx, NY, 2012. For its Children's Zoo Renovations project, Bronx Zoo.
$25,000 to Covenant House, New York, NY, 2012. For its Regional Training Center.
$25,000 to Wells College, Aurora, NY, 2012. For its Pauline M. Dodge '16 Scholarship Fund.
$19,000 to Antique Boat Museum, Clayton, NY, 2012. For its renovation project.
$15,000 to Near East Foundation, Syracuse, NY, 2012. For major annual grants.
$10,000 to International House, New York, NY, 2012. For its Paul A. Volcker Fund.
$10,000 to White Mountain School, Bethlehem, NH, 2012. For D. Matching Plan B Grants.
$5,000 to Good Shepherd Services, New York, NY, 2012. For its Brooklyn Frontier School.
$5,000 to YMCA of Greater New York, New York, NY, 2012. For B. Regular Annual Grants.

5893
The Henry L. and Grace Doherty Charitable Foundation, Inc. ✧
c/o McGrath, Doyle & Phair
150 Broadway, Ste. 1212
New York, NY 10038-4499 (212) 571-2300
Contact: Walter R. Brown, Pres. and Dir.

Incorporated in 1947 in DE.
Donors: Mrs. Henry L. Doherty†; Helen Lee Lassen†.
Foundation type: Independent foundation.
Financial data (yr. ended 12/31/13): Assets, $21,235,838 (M); expenditures, $1,213,742; qualifying distributions, $1,071,778; giving activities include $953,650 for 89 grants (high: $251,000; low: $100).
Purpose and activities: Primarily to promote the marine sciences and education, and to assist institutions engaged in oceanographic activities. Only limited expansion of activities is anticipated in the foreseeable future.
Fields of interest: Higher education; Human services; Marine science.
Type of support: Seed money; Research; Matching/challenge support.
Limitations: Applications accepted. Giving on a national basis. No grants to individuals, or for building funds or construction equipment.
Application information:
Initial approach: Letter
Copies of proposal: 1
Deadline(s): None
Board meeting date(s): As required
Officers and Directors:* Walter R. Brown,* Pres.; James R. Billingsley,* V.P. and Treas.; James R. Billingsley, Jr.,* Secy.; Helen Lee Billingsley; Kiyoko O. Brown; Jeffrey Masterson; Jacob C. Rardin IV.
EIN: 136401292

5894
DOJ Support Organization ✧
(formerly Daughters of Jacob Geriaatric Ctr.)
1160 Teller Ave.
Bronx, NY 10456-4145

Foundation type: Independent foundation.
Financial data (yr. ended 12/31/11): Assets, $564,673 (M); gifts received, $13,100; expenditures, $1,742,259; qualifying distributions, $968,133; giving activities include $913,582 for 1 grant.
Fields of interest: Nursing home/convalescent facility.
Limitations: Applications not accepted. Giving primarily in The Bronx, NY.
Application information: Contributes only to pre-selected organizations.
Officers: Howard Modlin, Pres.; Christopher Pignone, Cont.; Arthur Webb, Acting Exec. Dir.
Trustees: Henry Burr; David Dworsky; Margot Modlin; Gerald Wechter.
EIN: 131740106

5895
Dolan Children's Foundation ✧
c/o William A. Frewin, Jr.
340 Crossways Park Dr.
Woodbury, NY 11797-2050 (516) 803-9200
Contact: Robert Vizza, Pres.

Established in 1986 in NY.
Donors: Charles F. Dolan; Helen Dolan.
Foundation type: Independent foundation.
Financial data (yr. ended 12/31/13): Assets, $91,722,473 (M); expenditures, $1,535,119; qualifying distributions, $1,410,000; giving activities include $1,410,000 for 12 grants (high: $400,000; low: $14,000).
Fields of interest: Human services; Catholic agencies & churches.
Type of support: Capital campaigns; Building/renovation; Equipment; Land acquisition; Program development; Research; Matching/challenge support.
Limitations: Applications accepted. Giving primarily in Long Island and New York, NY.
Publications: Application guidelines.
Application information: Application form required.
Initial approach: Letter
Copies of proposal: 3
Deadline(s): None
Board meeting date(s): Mar., June, Sept., Nov.
Officers: Robert Vizza,* Pres.; Renzo Mori, V.P.
Director: Thomas Dolan.
EIN: 113379933
Selected grants: The following grants are a representative sample of this grantmaker's funding activity:
$562,500 to East Woods School, Oyster Bay, NY, 2011.
$126,930 to Oyster Bay Historical Society, Oyster Bay, NY, 2011.

5896
Dolan Family Foundation ✧
c/o Tax Dept.
340 Crossways Park Dr.
Woodbury, NY 11797-2050 (516) 803-9200
Contact: Robert Vizza, Pres.

Established in 1987 in NY.
Donors: Charles F. Dolan; Helen A. Dolan; Dolan Children's Foundation.
Foundation type: Independent foundation.
Financial data (yr. ended 11/30/13): Assets, $56,435,394 (M); gifts received, $400,000; expenditures, $1,974,985; qualifying distributions, $1,909,456; giving activities include $1,871,000 for 14 grants (high: $1,000,000; low: $5,000).
Fields of interest: Hospitals (general); Human services.
Type of support: Building/renovation; Equipment; Program development; Research; Matching/challenge support.
Limitations: Giving primarily in the greater metropolitan New York, NY, area, including Long Island. No grants to individuals.
Publications: Application guidelines; Informational brochure.
Application information:
Initial approach: Brief summary
Deadline(s): None
Officers: Robert Vizza, Pres.; Renzo Mori, V.P.
Director: Thomas Dolan.
EIN: 113129948
Selected grants: The following grants are a representative sample of this grantmaker's funding activity:
$81,000 to Upper Valley Haven, White River Junction, VT, 2011.

5897
Angelo Donghia Foundation, Inc. ✧
c/o Levy Sonet & Siegel, LLP
630 3rd Ave., 23rd Fl.
New York, NY 10017-6731

Established in 2001 in NY.
Donor: Angelo Donghia†.
Foundation type: Independent foundation.
Financial data (yr. ended 12/31/13): Assets, $19,776,227 (M); expenditures, $942,430; qualifying distributions, $761,582; giving activities include $698,500 for 13 grants (high: $100,000; low: $28,500).
Purpose and activities: Giving primarily for scholarship funds for interior design students; funding also for AIDS research.
Fields of interest: Visual arts, design; Hospitals (general); AIDS research.
Type of support: Scholarship funds.
Limitations: Applications not accepted. Giving primarily in NY.

Application information: Unsolicited requests for funds not accepted.
Officers and Trustees:* Steven G. Sonet, Esq.*, Pres.; James T. Nerangis, Esq.*, Secy.; Alan M. Siegel,* Treas.
EIN: 133523056
Selected grants: The following grants are a representative sample of this grantmaker's funding activity:
$100,000 to Alpha Workshops, New York, NY, 2012. For grant to Support Advanced Design Training Programs for HIV Positive Individuals.
$35,000 to Florida State University, Tallahassee, FL, 2012. For grant to Support Various Interior Design Initiatives and Programs.
$30,000 to Miami University, School of Fine Arts, Oxford, OH, 2012. For Senior Student Scholarship Award.
$21,584 to University of Cincinnati, Cincinnati, OH, 2012. For Senior Student Scholarship Award.

5898
David Donner Family Charitable Foundation ✧ ☆
1440 54th St., Apt. 1H
Brooklyn, NY 11219-4230

Established in NY.
Donors: David A. Donner; Shulamith Donner.
Foundation type: Independent foundation.
Financial data (yr. ended 06/30/13): Assets, $693,214 (M); gifts received, $242,654; expenditures, $695,028; qualifying distributions, $688,240; giving activities include $688,240 for 42 grants (high: $120,000; low: $180).
Fields of interest: Jewish agencies & synagogues.
Limitations: Applications not accepted. Giving primarily in NY.
Application information: Unsolicited requests for funds not accepted.
Trustees: David A. Donner; Shulamith Dunner.
EIN: 050548804

5899
The William H. Donner Foundation ✧
520 White Plains Rd., Ste. 500
Tarrytown, NY 10591-5118 (914) 524-0404
Contact: Deirdre Feeney, Prog. Mgr.
FAX: (914) 524-0407; E-mail: dfeeney@donner.org; Additional tel.: (212) 949-5213; Main URL: http://www.donner.org

Incorporated in 1961 in DC.
Donor: William H. Donner†.
Foundation type: Independent foundation.
Financial data (yr. ended 10/31/13): Assets, $163,455,874 (M); expenditures, $7,718,970; qualifying distributions, $5,263,550; giving activities include $4,644,152 for 181 grants (high: $150,000; low: $1,585).
Purpose and activities: Giving primarily for international development and relief services, education, arts and culture, and public affairs.
Fields of interest: Arts; Elementary/secondary education; Education; Animals/wildlife; Human services; International development; International relief; International affairs; Philanthropy/voluntarism; Public affairs.
Type of support: General/operating support; Program development.
Limitations: Applications not accepted. Giving primarily in CA, CO, Washington, DC and NY, with some giving in VA.
Application information: Only applications invited by the foundation will be considered.
Board meeting date(s): Sept.
Officers and Trustees:* Rebecca D. Winsor,* Pres.; William M. Spencer III,* V.P.; Alexander B. Donner,* Secy.; Hon. Curtin Winsor, Jr.,* Treas.; David W. Donner; Deborah Donner; Joseph W. Donner III; Joseph W. Donner, Jr.; Timothy E. Donner; Anita Winsor Edwards; Stephanie K. Hanson; Sharon W. Lainhant; Brittany D. Roy; Dillon Roy; M. Hunter Spencer; Robert D. Spencer; Monica Winsor.
Number of staff: 1 full-time professional; 3 part-time professional; 1 full-time support; 1 part-time support.
EIN: 231611346
Selected grants: The following grants are a representative sample of this grantmaker's funding activity:
$616,750 to Fidelity Charitable Gift Fund, Covington, KY, 2012.
$150,000 to Smithsonian Institution, Washington, DC, 2012.
$110,662 to Nature Conservancy, Boulder, CO, 2012.
$100,000 to Donors Trust, Alexandria, VA, 2012.
$61,000 to Oakland Schools Foundation, Oakland, CA, 2012.
$50,000 to Carter Center, Atlanta, GA, 2012.
$50,000 to Synergos Institute, New York, NY, 2012.
$40,000 to Paws 2 Help, West Palm Beach, FL, 2012.
$35,000 to National Outdoor Leadership School, Lander, WY, 2012.
$15,000 to Star Kids Scholarship Program, Middletown, RI, 2012.

5900
Donovan Foundation ✧
c/o Michael Donovan
1040 5th Ave., Ste. 2A
New York, NY 10028-0137

Established in 1999 in NY.
Donor: Michael D.S. Donovan.
Foundation type: Independent foundation.
Financial data (yr. ended 12/31/13): Assets, $4,244,376 (M); gifts received, $320,000; expenditures, $513,985; qualifying distributions, $807,349; giving activities include $465,779 for 20 grants (high: $68,400; low: $4,500).
Purpose and activities: Giving primarily for higher education.
Fields of interest: Higher education; Education; United Ways and Federated Giving Programs.
Limitations: Applications not accepted. Giving primarily in NY and VA; some funding also in Washington, DC. No grants to individuals.
Application information: Contributes only to pre-selected organizations.
Trustees: Stephen A. Briganti; Linda Ramsey Donovan; Michael D.S. Donovan.
Number of staff: 1 part-time professional.
EIN: 137205869

5901
Harry and Misook Doolittle Foundation ✧ ☆
43 Crane Rd.
Scarsdale, NY 10583-4214
Contact: Harry Doolittle, Secy.-Treas.
E-mail: harry.doolittle@gmail.com

Established in 2001 in NY.
Donors: Exclusively Misook, Inc.; Harry Doolittle.
Foundation type: Independent foundation.
Financial data (yr. ended 12/31/13): Assets, $3,271,858 (M); expenditures, $689,458; qualifying distributions, $658,747; giving activities include $658,362 for 5 grants (high: $608,320; low: $1,000).
Purpose and activities: The foundation supports organizations involved with arts and culture, health, food services, human services, and Christianity.
Fields of interest: Arts; Health care; Food services; Human services; United Ways and Federated Giving Programs; Christian agencies & churches.
Type of support: Annual campaigns; Capital campaigns; Program development; Cause-related marketing; Sponsorships.
Limitations: Applications not accepted. Giving primarily in NY. No grants to individuals.
Officers: Misook Doolittle, Pres.; Harry Doolittle, Secy.-Treas.
Number of staff: None.
EIN: 134145966

5902
Doty Family Foundation ✧
c/o BCRS Assocs., LLC
77 Water St., 9th Fl.
New York, NY 10005-4401

Established in 1977 in NY.
Donor: George E. Doty.
Foundation type: Independent foundation.
Financial data (yr. ended 02/28/14): Assets, $8,220,530 (M); expenditures, $2,100,128; qualifying distributions, $2,039,133; giving activities include $2,010,826 for 152 grants (high: $500,000; low: $150).
Purpose and activities: Grants only for churches and charitable organizations with which members of the family are involved.
Fields of interest: Education; Human services; Catholic agencies & churches.
Limitations: Applications not accepted. Giving on a national basis. No support for organizations that directly contradict the teachings of the Catholic Church. No grants to individuals.
Application information: Only charities in which Doty family members are actively involved are considered. Unsolicited requests for funds not considered.
Board meeting date(s): First Wed. in April
Officers: Anne Marie Paine, Chair. and Secy.; Barbara E. Doty, Treas.
Trustees: Christopher S. Doty; Virginia M. Doty; William W. Doty.
EIN: 132921496

5903
Dove Givings Foundation ✧
c/o OTA, LLC
1 Manhattanville Rd.
Purchase, NY 10577
Application address: Kevin Heneghan, 222 Purchase St., P.O. Box 316. Rye, NY 10580, tel: (914) 460-4040

Established in 1995 in NY.
Donors: Kevin J. Heneghan; Eileen Heneghan.
Foundation type: Operating foundation.
Financial data (yr. ended 12/31/13): Assets, $2,036,076 (M); gifts received, $64,969; expenditures, $467,217; qualifying distributions, $733,329; giving activities include $326,684 for 19 grants (high: $63,000; low: $3,000), and $139,835 for 18 grants to individuals (high: $25,000; low: $260).
Purpose and activities: Giving primarily for needy children and families, and to Christian causes.
Fields of interest: Education; Human services; Family services; Christian agencies & churches; Economically disadvantaged.
Type of support: Grants to individuals.
Limitations: Applications accepted. Giving primarily in NY.
Application information: Application form required.
Initial approach: Letter
Deadline(s): None
Officers: Kevin J. Heneghan, Pres.; Eileen Heneghan, V.P.; Richard Cayne, Secy.-Treas.
EIN: 133795957

5904
Dove Givings Foundation II ✧
1 Manhattanville Rd.
Purchase, NY 10577-2101

Established in 2001 in NY.
Donors: Kevin Heneghan; Eileen Heneghan; EH Limited Partnership; EH Family LP; Lookout Dover Partners; Leventhal Family Charitable Foundation; Dove Givings Foundation; Earliene Shipper.
Foundation type: Operating foundation.
Financial data (yr. ended 12/31/13): Assets, $319,994 (M); gifts received, $620,431; expenditures, $705,681; qualifying distributions, $705,250; giving activities include $705,250 for 27 grants (high: $175,000; low: $100).
Purpose and activities: Giving primarily to Christian organizations and churches, as well as for education and human services.
Fields of interest: Education; Human services; Children/youth, services; Family services; Christian agencies & churches.
Limitations: Applications not accepted. Giving in the U.S., with emphasis on NY. No grants to individuals.
Application information: Contributes only to pre-selected organizations.
Officers: Kevin J. Heneghan, Pres.; Eileen Heneghan, V.P.
EIN: 134188889

5905
Zichron Zvi Dovid Inc. ✧
1619 48th St.
Brooklyn, NY 11204

Established in 2003 in NY.
Donors: Chaim Zeiger; Leah Obstfeld; Jerusalem Capital LLC; Reuven D. Dessler; Joseph Meisels.
Foundation type: Independent foundation.
Financial data (yr. ended 06/30/13): Assets, $1,561,153 (M); gifts received, $19,900; expenditures, $617,793; qualifying distributions, $614,590; giving activities include $614,590 for grants.
Fields of interest: Jewish agencies & synagogues.
Limitations: Applications not accepted. Giving primarily in NY.
Application information: Unsolicited requests for funds not accepted.
Officers: Solomon Mayer, Pres.; Chanie Ainhorn, V.P.; Jakob Ainhorn, Treas.
EIN: 743099923
Selected grants: The following grants are a representative sample of this grantmaker's funding activity:
$50,000 to Kedushat Zion, Brooklyn, NY, 2011.
$40,000 to Yeshiva Chasam Sofer, Brooklyn, NY, 2011.
$25,000 to Yeshiva Chasam Sofer, Brooklyn, NY, 2011.
$5,000 to Bonei Olam, Brooklyn, NY, 2011.
$1,000 to Bnos Zion of Bobov, Brooklyn, NY, 2011.

5906
Dow Jones Foundation ✧
1211 Ave. of the Americas
New York, NY 10036-8701

Donor: Dow Jones & Company, Inc.
Foundation type: Independent foundation.
Financial data (yr. ended 06/30/13): Assets, $726,308 (M); gifts received, $1,100,000; expenditures, $1,171,077; qualifying distributions, $1,170,883; giving activities include $1,170,883 for grants.
Fields of interest: Education; Human services.
Limitations: Applications not accepted. Giving in the U.S., with emphasis on CA, NJ, and NY.
Application information: Unsolicited requests for funds not accepted.
Officers and Directors:* Mark Jackson,* Chair. and Pres.; Bradley Rolston,* V.P., and Secy.-Treas.; Paula Keve,* V.P.; Mark Musgrave,* V.P.; Richard Levine; Raju Narisetti.
EIN: 271756118
Selected grants: The following grants are a representative sample of this grantmaker's funding activity:
$170,283 to National Merit Scholarship Corporation, Evanston, IL, 2013. To provide Efficient and Effective Scholarship Program Management.
$40,000 to Neue Galerie New York, New York, NY, 2013. For Museum Devoted to Art.
$36,000 to New York University, New York, NY, 2013. To promote Literacy, Education, and Culture.
$25,000 to Inter American Press Association, Miami, FL, 2013. For Defending Freedom of Expression and Press Throughout the Americas.
$25,000 to Reporters Committee for Freedom of the Press, Arlington, VA, 2013. To promote Journalism Standards and Press Freedoms.
$20,000 to National Association of Black Journalists, College Park, MD, 2013. To provide Quality Programs and Services to and Advocates on Behalf of Black Journalists Worldwide.

5907
William C. Dowling Jr. Foundation ✧
c/o Belair & Evans
61 Broadway
New York, NY 10006-2701 (212) 344-3900
Contact: John T. Evans, Pres.

Established in 2003.
Donor: William C. Dowling Trust, Jr.
Foundation type: Independent foundation.
Financial data (yr. ended 12/31/13): Assets, $22,684,998 (M); expenditures, $1,067,492; qualifying distributions, $804,456; giving activities include $457,750 for 33 grants (high: $200,000; low: $100).
Purpose and activities: Giving primarily for education and human services.
Fields of interest: Museums (art); Higher education; Law school/education; Medical school/education; Hospitals (general); Human services; Catholic agencies & churches.
Limitations: Applications accepted. Giving primarily in NY.
Application information: Application form required.
Initial approach: Letter
Deadline(s): None
Officers: John T. Evans, Pres.; Stephen S. Kurcias, C.F.O.; Marie Evans, V.P.
EIN: 470933520

5908
Doreen Downs Miller Foundation, Inc. ✧
c/o BCRS Associates, LLC
77 Water St., 9th Fl.
New York, NY 10005

Established in NY.
Donors: Doreen D. Miller; John D. and Doreen Miller Foundation.
Foundation type: Independent foundation.
Financial data (yr. ended 06/30/13): Assets, $6,160,326 (M); expenditures, $645,137; qualifying distributions, $613,111; giving activities include $575,365 for 33 grants (high: $225,000; low: $500).
Fields of interest: Higher education; Human services; Children/youth, services; Family services, parent education.
Limitations: Applications not accepted. Giving primarily in New York, NY; some funding also in CA. No grants to individuals.
Application information: Contributes only to pre-selected organizations.
Officer and Director:* Doreen D. Miller,* Pres. and Treas.
EIN: 743116739
Selected grants: The following grants are a representative sample of this grantmaker's funding activity:
$250,000 to California Parenting Institute, Santa Rosa, CA, 2011.
$199,000 to Adelphi University, Garden City, NY, 2011.
$80,000 to Early Years Institute, Plainview, NY, 2011.
$50,000 to Washington University, Saint Louis, MO, 2011.
$12,500 to United Way of Long Island, Deer Park, NY, 2011.
$12,000 to Alliance for Childhood, New York, NY, 2011.
$7,525 to University of Pennsylvania, Philadelphia, PA, 2011.

$5,000 to W N Y C Radio, New York, NY, 2011.
$1,000 to Friends Academy, Locust Valley, NY, 2011.
$1,000 to Long Island University, Brookville, NY, 2011.

5909
Dreams R US Foundation ✧
(formerly The Pace Foundation)
37 Valentine Rd.
Shoreham, NY 11786-1243

Established in 1995 in NY.
Donor: Ben Pace†.
Foundation type: Independent foundation.
Financial data (yr. ended 12/31/13): Assets, $15,965,484 (M); gifts received, $2,820; expenditures, $1,060,259; qualifying distributions, $795,316; giving activities include $795,316 for 17 grants (high: $150,000; low: $10,000).
Fields of interest: Education; Human services; United Ways and Federated Giving Programs; Catholic agencies & churches.
Limitations: Applications not accepted. Giving primarily in NY; some funding also in PA. No grants to individuals.
Application information: Contributes only to pre-selected organizations.
Trustees: Carol Gbur; Alicia M. Pace; Meghan E. Pace; Kerry A. Pace-McVeigh.
EIN: 116458173

5910
Dreitzer Foundation Inc. ✧
c/o Alan Seget, Esq.
60 E. 42nd St.
New York, NY 10165-0009

Established in 1958 in NY.
Donors: Albert J. Dreitzer†; Mildred H. Dreitzer†.
Foundation type: Independent foundation.
Financial data (yr. ended 12/31/12): Assets, $8,129,058 (M); expenditures, $509,016; qualifying distributions, $450,000; giving activities include $450,000 for 18 grants (high: $100,000; low: $10,000).
Purpose and activities: Giving primarily for the arts, education, and human services.
Fields of interest: Arts; Elementary/secondary education; Education; Human services; Children/youth, services; Homeless, human services; Women.
Type of support: General/operating support.
Limitations: Applications not accepted. Giving primarily in New York, NY.
Application information: Contributes only to pre-selected organizations.
Officers: Judith Wallach, Pres.; Steven Halpern, V.P.; Amy Laff, V.P.; Diane Wallach, V.P.; Alan D. Seget, Secy.-Treas.
EIN: 136162509
Selected grants: The following grants are a representative sample of this grantmaker's funding activity:
$60,000 to Project CURE, Centennial, CO, 2012. For Haiti Relief $5,000.
$50,000 to Equality Now, New York, NY, 2012. For ending violence and discrimination against women and girls around the world.
$20,000 to Fistula Foundation, San Jose, CA, 2012. For Medical Education and Research.
$15,000 to Feminist Majority Foundation, Arlington, VA, 2012. For Furthering Equality, Promoting Non-Violence, Justice, Peace and Economic Development, Enhancing Feminist Leadership, Promoting Learning and Research for the Furtherance of Feminist Ideas and Studies, and Providing Education and Training for Feminist Activ.
$15,000 to Innocence Project, New York, NY, 2012. To assist prisoners who could be proven innocent through DNA testing.
$15,000 to One Stop Senior Services, New York, NY, 2012. To improve the quality of life of older New Yorkers.
$10,000 to Calvary Hospital, Bronx, NY, 2012. For providing palliative care for adult advantaged cancer patients in the United States.
$10,000 to Girls Learn International, New York, NY, 2012. For Human Rights Education.
$10,000 to Lawyers Alliance for New York, New York, NY, 2012. For help nonprofit organizations to accomplish their missions and operate effective services for low-income New Yorkers.

5911
Peggy and Millard Drexler Foundation ✧
770 Broadway, 12th Fl.
New York, NY 10003-9512

Established in 1998 in CA.
Donors: Millard S. Drexler; Peggy F. Drexler.
Foundation type: Independent foundation.
Financial data (yr. ended 12/31/13): Assets, $5,485,274 (M); expenditures, $1,163,009; qualifying distributions, $1,122,352; giving activities include $1,063,600 for 21 grants (high: $500,000; low: $500).
Purpose and activities: Giving primarily for education, youth-related causes, human services, and environmental preservation.
Fields of interest: Child development, education; Education; Environment, natural resources; Hospitals (general); Health organizations, association; Human services; Jewish federated giving programs; Jewish agencies & synagogues.
Limitations: Applications not accepted. Giving primarily in CA, NY, and MA. No grants to individuals.
Application information: Contributes only to pre-selected organizations.
Officers: Millard S. Drexler, Chair. and Treas.; Peggy F. Drexler, Pres.
EIN: 522106490

5912
The Camille and Henry Dreyfus Foundation, Inc. ✧
555 Madison Ave., 20th Fl.
New York, NY 10022-3301 (212) 753-1760
Contact: Mark J. Cardillo Ph.D., Exec. Dir.
E-mail: admin@dreyfus.org; Main URL: http://www.dreyfus.org

Incorporated in 1946 in NY.
Donor: Camille Dreyfus†.
Foundation type: Independent foundation.
Financial data (yr. ended 12/31/12): Assets, $93,637,833 (M); expenditures, $4,803,372; qualifying distributions, $4,319,873; giving activities include $71,872 for 4 grants (high: $35,000; low: $10,000), and $2,837,592 for grants to individuals.
Purpose and activities: To advance the sciences of chemistry, biochemistry, chemical engineering, and related sciences as a means of improving human relations and circumstances. The foundation assists organizations which afford facilities for the production, collection, or dissemination of scientific information; support mainly for postsecondary academic institutions through sponsorship of Dreyfus New Faculty in Chemistry Program, the Dreyfus Teacher-Scholar Awards Programs, the Dreyfus Special Grant Program in the Chemical Sciences, the Dreyfus Faculty Start-Up Grant Program for Undergraduate Institutions, and the Dreyfus Postdoctoral Program in Environmental Chemistry.
Fields of interest: Engineering school/education; Chemistry; Science.
Type of support: Equipment; Program development; Seed money; Fellowships; Research.
Limitations: Applications accepted. Giving only on a national basis. No grants to individuals who are not sponsored or nominated by a nonprofit or educational institution, or for specific research projects, emergency funds, deficit financing, land acquisition, endowments, capital construction, or renovation; no loans.
Application information: Candidates for awards must be nominated by applying academic institution; individual applications not accepted; nomination forms required for all programs. Application form required.
Initial approach: Preliminary letter for Special Grant Program in the Chemical Sciences
Copies of proposal: 5
Deadline(s): Current information available on foundation web site
Board meeting date(s): Jan., Apr., July, and Oct.
Final notification: 4 to 5 months
Officers and Directors:* Henry C. Walter, Pres.; Dorothy Dinsmoor,* V.P. and Secy.; H. Scott Walter,* Treas., and Chair., Fin. and Audit Comm.; Mark J. Cardillo, Exec. Dir.; Marye Anne Fox, Ph.D., Chair., Scientific Affairs Comm.; John R.H. Blum; John I. Brauman; Edward A. Reilly; Matthew V. Tirrell; Richard N. Zare.
Number of staff: 2 full-time professional; 1 full-time support.
EIN: 135570117

5913
Jean and Louis Dreyfus Foundation, Inc. ✧
315 Madison Ave., Ste. 900
New York, NY 10017-5405 (212) 599-1931
Contact: Ms. Edmee de M. Firth, V.P. and Exec. Dir.
FAX: (212) 599-2956; E-mail: info@jldreyfus.org; E-mail for general inquiries: Jessica Keuskamp, Prog. Dir.: jk@jldreyfus.org; Main URL: http://www.jldreyfus.org
Grants List: http://www.jldreyfus.org/recentgrants.html

Incorporated about 1979 in NY.
Donor: Louis Dreyfus†.
Foundation type: Independent foundation.
Financial data (yr. ended 12/31/13): Assets, $17,158,283 (M); expenditures, $937,862; qualifying distributions, $830,748; giving activities include $691,500 for 44 grants (high: $50,000; low: $5,000).
Purpose and activities: Giving primarily for aging, the arts, education and social services.
Fields of interest: Arts; Adult education—literacy, basic skills & GED; Education, reading; Education;

Health care; Employment, training; Nutrition; Housing/shelter, homeless; Human services; Children/youth, services; Aging, centers/services; Women, centers/services; Aging; Economically disadvantaged.
Type of support: General/operating support; Capital campaigns; Program development; Matching/challenge support.
Limitations: Giving limited to New York, NY. No grants to individuals.
Publications: Application guidelines; Annual report; Grants list.
Application information: Letters of inquiry are currently only accepted from organizations that have a prior relationship with the foundation. All other inquires will not be accepted at this time. Refer to foundation web site for updates in this area.
Initial approach: Letter of inquiry (2 pages) from organizations familiar to the foundation
Deadline(s): Jan. 15 and July 15
Board meeting date(s): May and Nov.
Officers and Directors:* Nicholas L.D. Firth,* Pres.; Edmee de M. Firth,* V.P. and Exec. Dir.; Katie Firth Bank,* V.P.; Karen L. Rosa; Winthrop Rutherfurd, Jr.
Number of staff: 1 part-time professional; 1 full-time support.
EIN: 132947180

5914
Mmac Drizin Charitable Foundation ✧ ☆

447 Crown St.
Brooklyn, NY 11225-3119
Contact: Mendel Drizin, Dir.

Donor: Mendel Drizin.
Foundation type: Independent foundation.
Financial data (yr. ended 05/31/13): Assets, $146,636 (M); gifts received, $590,000; expenditures, $486,916; qualifying distributions, $486,916; giving activities include $486,916 for 78 grants (high: $50,000; low: $150).
Fields of interest: Jewish agencies & synagogues.
Application information: Application form required.
Initial approach: Letter
Deadline(s): None
Directors: Channy Drizin; Mendel Drizin.
EIN: 452831875

5915
Druckenmiller Foundation ✧

c/o Duquesne Capital Mgmt.
40 W. 57th St., 25th Fl.
New York, NY 10019-4001 (212) 404-1150
GiveSmart: http://www.givesmart.org/Stories/Donors/Stanley-Druckenmiller

Established in 1993 in NY.
Donor: Stanley F. Druckenmiller.
Foundation type: Independent foundation.
Financial data (yr. ended 11/30/13): Assets, $971,517,239 (M); expenditures, $75,433,345; qualifying distributions, $74,483,000; giving activities include $74,292,500 for 46 grants (high: $40,100,000; low: $5,000), and $177,000 for 30 grants to individuals (high: $13,500; low: $500).
Purpose and activities: The foundation provides scholarships to students who, within the past year, have caddied at Oakmont Country Club in PA.
Fields of interest: Higher education, university.
Type of support: Scholarships—to individuals.
Limitations: Applications accepted. Giving primarily to students residing in PA.
Application information: Scholarship applicant must supply transcript and letters of recommendation. Scholarships are paid to the school, and not directly to the student. Application form required.
Deadline(s): July 1
Trustees: Fiona Druckenmiller; Stanley F. Druckenmiller.
EIN: 133735187
Selected grants: The following grants are a representative sample of this grantmaker's funding activity:
$15,000,000 to Harlem Childrens Zone, New York, NY, 2012. For general support.
$12,000,000 to Stanford University, Stanford, CA, 2012. For general support.
$5,000,000 to Brown University, Providence, RI, 2012. For general support.
$3,500,000 to Environmental Defense Fund, New York, NY, 2012. For general support.
$800,000 to College Summit, Washington, DC, 2012. For general support.
$250,000 to Bowdoin College, Brunswick, ME, 2012. For general support.
$150,000 to Cape Eleuthera Foundation, Lawrenceville, NJ, 2012. For general support.
$100,000 to Yale University, New Haven, CT, 2012. For general support.
$10,000 to New York City Mission Society, New York, NY, 2012. For general support.
$10,000 to Ubuntu Education Fund, New York, NY, 2012. For general support.

5916
G. & E. Dubin Family Foundation ✧

c/o D. DePaoli, WTAS LLC
1177 Ave. of Americas, 18th Fl.
New York, NY 10036-2706 (212) 287-4287
Application address: c/o J. Kearsey, Highbridge Capital Mgmt., 40 W. 57th St., 33rd Fl., New York, NY 10019; tel.: (212) 287-4752
Glenn and Eva Dubin's Giving Pledge Profile: http://glasspockets.org/philanthropy-in-focus/eye-on-the-giving-pledge/profiles/dubin

Donors: Glenn R. Dubin; Eva Andersson Dubin.
Foundation type: Independent foundation.
Financial data (yr. ended 12/31/12): Assets, $37,108,782 (M); gifts received, $5,756,715; expenditures, $3,923,986; qualifying distributions, $3,802,250; giving activities include $3,800,000 for 1 grant.
Fields of interest: Hospitals (general).
Limitations: Applications accepted. Giving primarily in New York, NY. No grants to individuals, or for scholarships; no loans.
Application information: Application form not required.
Initial approach: Letter
Deadline(s): None
Trustees: Eva Andersson Dubin; Glenn R. Dubin.
EIN: 137265141

5917
Doris Duke Charitable Foundation ✧

650 5th Ave., 19th Fl.
New York, NY 10019-6108 (212) 974-7000
FAX: (212) 974-7590; Main URL: http://www.ddcf.org
Grantee Spotlight: http://www.ddcf.org/Grants/Grantee-Spotlight/
Grants Database: http://www.ddcf.org/Grants/Grant-Recipients/
Knowledge Center: http://www.ddcf.org/What-Were-Learning/
Twitter: http://twitter.com/DorisDukeFdn

Established in 1996 in NY.
Donor: Doris Duke‡.
Foundation type: Independent foundation.
Financial data (yr. ended 12/31/13): Assets, $1,859,405,732 (M); expenditures, $95,245,619; qualifying distributions, $83,234,494; giving activities include $75,080,723 for 283 grants (high: $3,261,117; low: $2,819), and $170,238 for 9 foundation-administered programs.
Purpose and activities: The mission of the foundation is to improve the quality of people's lives through grants supporting the performing arts, environmental conservation, medical research and the prevention of child abuse. In addition to its grantmaking activities, the foundation will support three affiliated operating foundations: Duke Farms Foundation, the Doris Duke Foundation for Islamic Art, and the Newport Restoration Foundation.
Fields of interest: Performing arts; Performing arts, dance; Performing arts, theater; Performing arts, music; Environment, natural resources; Animals/wildlife, preservation/protection; Medical research; Crime/violence prevention, child abuse.
Type of support: Employee matching gifts.
Limitations: Applications accepted. Giving on a national basis. No support for toxic issues, litigation, the visual arts, museums or galleries, or arts programs for rehabilitative or therapeutic purposes. No grants to individuals (except through special foundation programs), or for conferences or publications.
Application information: The foundation staff responds to all letters of inquiry, however, it should be noted that very few grants result from unsolicited letters of inquiry. Do not send binders, books, CDs, videotapes, or audiotapes.
Initial approach: Online Letter of inquiry (2 pages)
Final notification: 2 months for letter of inquiry
Officers and Trustees:* John E. Zuccotti,* Chair.; Anthony S. Fauci, M.D., Vice-Chair.; Peter Simmons, C.O.O.; Edward P. Henry, Pres.; Eileen Oberlander, Cont. and Dir., Finance; Jeffrey Heil, C.I.O.; Marion Oates Charles, Emeritus; Anne Hawley, Emeritus; John J. Mack, Emeritus; Harry B. Demopoulos, M.D.; James F. Gill; Kathy Halbreich; Nannerl O. Keohane; Angela K. Mwanza; Peter A. Nadosy; William H. Schlesinger; Nicholas Scoppetta; Jide Zeitlin.
EIN: 137043679
Selected grants: The following grants are a representative sample of this grantmaker's funding activity:
$6,203,000 to Open Space Conservancy, New York, NY, 2013. For Southeastern Resilient Landscapes Initiative, payable over 3.50 years.
$6,000,000 to Open Space Conservancy, New York, NY, 2012. To protect sites in the Northeast/Mid-Atlantic region of the United States that can enable wildlife adaptation to climate change, payable over 3.50 years.

$5,775,000 to Doris Duke Charitable Foundation, New York, NY, 2012. For first cohort of Leading Artists Award recipients selected for funding through the Doris Duke Performing Artists Awards Program, payable over 5.25 years.
$5,184,758 to New England Foundation for the Arts, Boston, MA, 2013. For National Dance Project, payable over 3.00 years.
$4,155,000 to Wildlife Conservation Society, Bronx, NY, 2012. Toward Climate Adaptation Fund, a re-granting program to support applied projects that demonstrate effective interventions for wildlife adaptation to climate change, payable over 4.00 years.
$3,330,000 to New England Foundation for the Arts, Boston, MA, 2012. For the National Dance Project, payable over 2.00 years.
$2,636,000 to Fund for Public Health in New York, New York, NY, 2012. For Adolescent Pregnancy Prevention in Schools (APPS) Program, payable over 3.00 years.
$2,500,000 to Children and Family Futures, Irvine, CA, 2013. For integration of parent training and additional family services in family drug courts, payable over 3.00 years.
$1,500,000 to University of North Carolina, Chapel Hill, NC, 2013. For Additional support for the PHIT Partnership in Zambia, payable over 2.50 years.
$905,000 to Foundation for the National Institutes of Health, Bethesda, MD, 2012. To support students in cycles of the National Institutes of Health Medical Research Scholars Program, payable over 3.00 years.
$486,000 to Georgetown University, Washington, DC, 2012. For research project, Can Enhancing Left Lateralization Using Transcranial Direct Current Stimulation Improve Recovery from Post-Stroke Aphasia, payable over 3.00 years.
$486,000 to University of California, San Francisco, CA, 2013. For Electrocorticography based control of anthropomorphic upper limb exoskeleton, payable over 3.00 years.
$486,000 to University of Pennsylvania, Philadelphia, PA, 2013. For role for peripheral blood monocytes in regulating tumor biology in pancreatic cancer, payable over 3.00 years.
$250,000 to Common Ground Communities, Community Solutions, New York, NY, 2012. To support implementation and assessment of a community systems approach to improving outcomes for children.
$250,000 to Community Foundation of New Jersey, Morristown, NJ, 2013. For projects of the New Jersey Recovery Fund that enhance community resilience to climate change in the wake of Superstorm Sandy, payable over 2.00 years.
$100,000 to Energy Foundation, San Francisco, CA, 2012. To support coordinated analysis of potential for philanthropy's impact on Building Retrofits, payable over 1.50 years.
$64,800 to University of California, San Francisco, CA, 2013. For Etiology of non-malarial febrile illnesses in Ugandan children, payable over 1.50 years.
$59,355 to Mid Atlantic Arts Foundation, Baltimore, MD, 2012. For French American Jazz Exchange, payable over 2.25 years.
$50,000 to National Academy of Sciences, Washington, DC, 2013. For the planning meeting: Investing in Young Children Globally (iYCG).
$40,000 to Performance Space 122, Brooklyn, NY, 2013. To host Ryan Holsopple at Performance Space 122 to imagine and explore new approaches to building demand for contemporary dance and theater, payable over 1.25 years.

5918
Doris Duke Foundation ✧ ☆

650 5th Ave., 19th Fl.
New York, NY 10019-6108 (908) 243-3619
Main URL: http://www.ddcf.org
Grantee Spotlight: http://www.ddcf.org/Grants/Grantee-Spotlight/
Grants Database: http://www.ddcf.org/Grants/Grant-Recipients/
Twitter: http://twitter.com/DorisDukeFdn

Incorporated in 1934 in DE.
Donors: Doris Duke†; Doris Duke Charitable Foundation.
Foundation type: Independent foundation.
Financial data (yr. ended 12/31/13): Assets, $18,898,985 (M); gifts received, $12,600,000; expenditures, $3,948,166; qualifying distributions, $3,882,713; giving activities include $3,746,676 for 15 grants (high: $925,000; low: $10,000), and $62,334 for employee matching gifts.
Purpose and activities: Giving primarily to improve the quality of people's lives through grants supporting the performing arts, environmental conservation, medical research and the prevention of child maltreatment, and through preservation of the cultural and environmental legacy Doris Duke's properties.
Fields of interest: Arts; Education; Health care.
Type of support: General/operating support.
Limitations: Applications accepted. Giving primarily in NJ and NY. No support for religious organizations for sectarian purposes. No grants to individuals, or for building or capital funds, publications, or general operating expenses.
Application information: See foundation web site for complete application guidelines. Application form required.
Initial approach: Letter of Inquiry
Copies of proposal: 2
Officers: John Zuccotti, Chair.; Anthony S. Fauci,* Vice-Chair.; Edward P. Henry, Pres.; Peter Simmons, Treas. and C.O.O.; Elizabeth Fader, Secy.
Directors: Harry Demopoulos; James F. Gill; Kathy Halbreich; Anne Hawley; Nannerl O. Keohane; Angela K. Mwanza; Perer A. Nadosy; William H. Schlesinger; Nicholas Scoppetta; Jide Zeitlin.
EIN: 131655241
Selected grants: The following grants are a representative sample of this grantmaker's funding activity:
$575,000 to Doris Duke Monument Foundation, Providence, RI, 2012. For the Maya Lin project renovating Queen Anne Square in Newport RI.
$2,000 to Achieve Minneapolis, Minneapolis, MN, 2012. For matching.

5919
Doris Duke Foundation for Islamic Art ✧

650 5th Ave., 19th Fl.
New York, NY 10019-6108 (212) 974-7000
FAX: (212) 974-7590;
E-mail: buildingbridgesprogram@ddcf.org; Main URL: http://www.ddfia.org/

Established in 1996.
Donor: Doris Duke Charitable Foundation.
Foundation type: Operating foundation.
Financial data (yr. ended 12/31/13): Assets, $34,538,919 (M); gifts received, $6,275,981; expenditures, $6,331,320; qualifying distributions, $1,536,304; giving activities include $1,505,000 for 14 grants (high: $756,250; low: $2,500), $31,304 for 11 employee matching gifts, and $3,854,368 for foundation-administered programs.
Purpose and activities: Giving to increase Americans' understanding of Muslim cultures through the arts and media. The foundation also owns and operates Shangri La, a center for Islamic arts and cultures, offering guided tours, residencies for scholars and artists, performances and symposia. See foundation web site for Shangri La programs.
Fields of interest: Arts; Human services.
Limitations: Applications not accepted. Giving limited to the U.S. No support for individual artists or individual artists' projects (one-of concerts of festivals, films, etc). No grants to individuals, or for films or other artistic ventures.
Application information: Contributes only to pre-selected organizations.
Officers: Edward P. Henry, Pres.; Peter Simmons, C.O.O.; Deborah A. Pope, Exec. Dir.; Marie Clark, Mgr.
Directors: Carol Doran-Khewhok; Anne Hawley; Peter A. Nadosy; William H. Schlesinger; John Zuccotti.
EIN: 050523809
Selected grants: The following grants are a representative sample of this grantmaker's funding activity:
$300,000 to Sundance Institute, Los Angeles, CA, 2012. For continuation of the Islamic Film Festival Initiative.
$297,475 to Arts Midwest, Minneapolis, MN, 2012. For Enhancing America's Understanding of Muslim Societies through Arts, Culture and Media.
$54,173 to Asia Society, New York, NY, 2012. For expansion of Creative Muslim Voices in Asia.
$50,000 to Museum of Arts and Design, New York, NY, 2012. For public Programming to complement the exhibit, Doris Duke's Shangri La Architecture, Landscape, and Islamic Art.
$25,000 to Newark Museum Association, Newark, NJ, 2012. For public Programming to complement the exhibit, Beauty and Belief Crossing Bridges with the Arts of Islamic Culture.
$25,000 to Portland Art Museum, Portland, OR, 2012. For public Programming to complement the exhibit, Beauty and Belief Crossing Bridges with the Arts of Culture.

5920
The Gay T. and Haskell A. Duncan Foundation, Inc. ✧

(formerly The Haskell and Gay Duncan Foundation, Inc.)
c/o Myer, Greene & Degge
P.O. Box 930
Pearl River, NY 10965-0930

Established in 1999 in NC.
Donors: Haskell A. Duncan; U.S. Dept. of Agriculture.
Foundation type: Independent foundation.
Financial data (yr. ended 12/31/13): Assets, $18,900,590 (M); gifts received, $14,274; expenditures, $744,619; qualifying distributions, $637,232; giving activities include $585,504 for 5 grants (high: $350,000; low: $3,451).

Purpose and activities: Giving primarily for higher education, and to Baptist organizations and churches.
Fields of interest: Higher education; Protestant agencies & churches.
Limitations: Applications not accepted. Giving primarily in NC. No grants to individuals.
Application information: Unsolicited requests for funds not accepted.
Officers: Wayne E. Jordan, Pres.; Samuel V. Barefoot, V.P.; Mark D. Vaughn, Secy.-Treas.
EIN: 562163266
Selected grants: The following grants are a representative sample of this grantmaker's funding activity:
$300,000 to Campbell University, Dinity School, Buies Creek, NC, 2012. For Endow a Chair to Teach Church Music.
$26,040 to Catawba College, Salisbury, NC, 2012. For Gay and Haskell Duncan Annual Scholarship Fund.

5921
Clarence and Anne Dillon Dunwalke Trust ✧

c/o Keswick Mgmt.
99 Park Ave., 24th Fl.
New York, NY 10016-1601

Trust established in 1969 in NY.
Donor: Clarence Dillon‡.
Foundation type: Independent foundation.
Financial data (yr. ended 06/30/13): Assets, $32,413,247 (M); expenditures, $2,584,582; qualifying distributions, $2,458,748; giving activities include $2,434,745 for 85 grants (high: $1,017,000; low: $1,000).
Purpose and activities: Emphasis on hospitals, education, public affairs, the arts, and community funds. Grants primarily to present beneficiary organizations and for special proposals developed by the trustees.
Fields of interest: Arts; Higher education; Education; Environment, natural resources; Medical research, institute; Boys & girls clubs; Children/youth, services; United Ways and Federated Giving Programs; Public policy, research; Protestant agencies & churches.
Type of support: General/operating support; Continuing support; Annual campaigns; Capital campaigns; Building/renovation; Endowments; Fellowships; Research.
Limitations: Applications not accepted. Giving primarily in FL, ME, NJ and NY. No grants to individuals; no loans.
Application information: Contributes only to pre-selected organizations.
Board meeting date(s): Nov. and as required
Officer: Eileen Kane, Secy.
Trustees: Alexandra F. Allen; Andrew D. Allen; Christine Allen; Christopher D. Allen; Nicholas E. Allen; Philip D. Allen; Sophie Bryan; Theodore Caplow, Jr.; Douglas Collins; Frances Collins; Mark M. Collins, Jr.; Phyllis D. Collins; Joan M. Frost; Robert Luxembourg; James J. Ruddy; Katherine Stillman; Martin C. Zetterberg.
Number of staff: 1 part-time professional.
EIN: 237043773
Selected grants: The following grants are a representative sample of this grantmaker's funding activity:
$200,000 to University of Washington, Seattle, WA, 2011.
$100,000 to Saint Pauls School, Concord, NH, 2011.
$90,000 to Islesboro Affordable Property, Islesboro, ME, 2011.
$80,000 to Islesboro Community Center, Islesboro, ME, 2011.
$50,000 to World Wildlife Fund, Washington, DC, 2011. For general support.
$35,000 to Metropolitan Opera, New York, NY, 2011. For annual budgetary needs.
$32,000 to New York Sun Works, New York, NY, 2011.
$10,000 to Big Tree Boating Association, Islesboro, ME, 2011. For annual budgetary needs.
$10,000 to Christ Church, Dark Harbor, Islesboro, ME, 2011.
$10,000 to Living Classrooms Foundation, Baltimore, MD, 2011. For annual budgetary needs.

5922
The Durst Family Foundation ✧

1 Bryant Park
New York, NY 10036-6715

Established in 2000 in NY.
Foundation type: Independent foundation.
Financial data (yr. ended 12/31/12): Assets, $9,970,835 (M); expenditures, $935,329; qualifying distributions, $700,000; giving activities include $700,000 for grants.
Fields of interest: Education; Agriculture/food; Human services; Children/youth, services.
Limitations: Applications not accepted. Giving primarily in New York, NY. No grants to individuals.
Application information: Contributes only to pre-selected organizations.
Officers and Directors: Wendy Durst Kreeger, Pres.; Leslie B. Durst, V.P.; Nan Rothschild Cooper,* Secy.; Laurel Durst Strong, Treas.; Helena Durst; Keith Kreeger; Emily Rothchild.
EIN: 522262647

5923
Dyson Foundation ✧

25 Halcyon Rd.
Millbrook, NY 12545-6137 (845) 677-0644
Contact: Diana M. Gurieva, Exec. V.P.
FAX: (845) 677-0650; E-mail: info@dyson.org; Main URL: http://www.dysonfoundation.org

Trust established in 1956 in NY; incorporated in 1957 in DE.
Donors: Charles H. Dyson‡; Margaret M. Dyson‡.
Foundation type: Independent foundation.
Financial data (yr. ended 12/31/12): Assets, $244,956,597 (M); expenditures, $25,126,786; qualifying distributions, $21,787,519; giving activities include $18,667,714 for 209 grants (high: $2,500,000; low: $500), and $25,000 for 1 loan/program-related investment.
Purpose and activities: The foundation supports nonprofit organizations in the Mid-Hudson Valley of NY in a variety of fields and makes grants that are linked to the interests of the family of the president, Robert R. Dyson. To best support the most vulnerable people and communities in the foundation's region, the foundation will focus on organizations and activities that address basic needs such as food, housing, health care, and other human services. In addition, there will also be funds available through the capacity-building Mini-Grant Program and the Nonprofit Strategic Restructuring Initiative.
Fields of interest: Education; Health care; Agriculture/food; Housing/shelter; Youth development; Human services; Children/youth, services; Community/economic development; Philanthropy/voluntarism, management/technical assistance; Economically disadvantaged.
Type of support: Annual campaigns; Building/renovation; Capital campaigns; Consulting services; Continuing support; Equipment; General/operating support; Management development/capacity building; Matching/challenge support; Program development; Program evaluation; Program-related investments/loans; Scholarship funds; Technical assistance.
Limitations: Applications accepted. Giving primarily in Dutchess County, NY, and organizations providing services in Dutchess County; limited grants to other Mid-Hudson Valley counties (Columbia, Greene, Orange, Putnam and Ulster counties). National and other grants on a solicited basis. No support for international organizations. No grants to individuals, or for debt reduction, direct mail campaign or fundraising events.
Publications: Annual report (including application guidelines); Grants list; Informational brochure; Occasional report.
Application information: No new applications will be accepted for environmental, historic preservation, or capital projects. The foundation will consider limited funding to arts organizations or projects that provide management support or training to other arts organizations, and to arts organizations or projects that can demonstrate the potential to increase local tourism and employment and/or other local economic development as a result of their efforts. The foundation has its own application forms available on its grants portal. The foundation also accepts the Dutchess County Common Grant Application and Philanthropy New York's New York/New Jersey area Common Application Form. Application form required.
Initial approach: Submit letter of inquiry online via new grants portal
Copies of proposal: 1
Deadline(s): None
Board meeting date(s): Quarterly
Final notification: Three to six months
Officers and Directors:* Robert R. Dyson,* Pres.; Diana M. Gurieva, Exec. V.P.; John S. FitzSimmons, Secy.; Christopher Dyson,* Treas.; Molly Dyson; Raymond A. Lamontagne; Timmian C. Massie; Jode Millman.
Number of staff: 5 full-time professional; 4 full-time support.
EIN: 136084888
Selected grants: The following grants are a representative sample of this grantmaker's funding activity:
$5,000,000 to Cornell University, Ithaca, NY, 2013. Toward Robert R. Dyson Professorship of Management in Samuel Curtis Johnson Graduate School of Management, to be housed at the new Cornell Tech campus in New York City, payable over 7.00 years.
$2,500,000 to Washington and Lee University, Lexington, VA, 2012. For multi-year grant toward the Center for Global Learning, which will enhance international education at the university, payable over 5.00 years.
$1,000,000 to Media Matters for America, Washington, DC, 2013. For general operating support, payable over 4.00 years.

$750,000 to Family Services, Poughkeepsie, NY, 2013. For general operating support, payable over 3.00 years.
$500,000 to Poughkeepsie-Highland Railroad Bridge Company, Poughkeepsie, NY, 2012. Toward the purchase of a parcel of land that will connect the eastern end of the Walkway Over the Hudson to the Dutchess County Rail Trail.
$500,000 to Saint Francis Hospital, Poughkeepsie, NY, 2012. Toward expansion of the hospital's emergency psychiatric facility.
$500,000 to YMCA of the Capital District, Albany, NY, 2012. Toward a new YMCA facility in Greene County, payable over 1.75 years.
$475,000 to Community Foundation of Dutchess County, Poughkeepsie, NY, 2013. For general operating support and toward a strengthened presence in Putnam County, payable over 3.50 years.
$450,000 to Planned Parenthood of the Mid-Hudson Valley, Poughkeepsie, NY, 2013. For general operating support, payable over 3.00 years.
$250,000 to Purple Heart Hall of Honor, Newburgh, NY, 2013. For capital support to enhance and expand National Purple Heart Hall of Honor.
$125,000 to Hudson River Housing, Poughkeepsie, NY, 2012. For general operating support.
$100,000 to Center for Governmental Research, Rochester, NY, 2013. Toward feasibility study on possibility of consolidating Department of Health and Department of Mental Hygiene in Dutchess County.
$75,000 to People Projects to Empower and Organize the Psychiatrically Labeled, Poughkeepsie, NY, 2012. For general operating support.
$30,000 to Dutchess Day School, Millbrook, NY, 2012. For general operating support.
$24,000 to Young Rhinebeck, Rhinebeck, NY, 2013. Toward Life, Learning and Language program, summer and after-school program for Rhinebeck elementary school students whose families do not speak English as their first language, payable over 2.00 years.
$20,000 to YMCA of Newburgh, Newburgh, NY, 2012. Toward the implementation of a merger with a childcare center in Dutchess County, as part of the Foundation's Strategic Restructuring Initiative.
$16,000 to Dutchess County Arts Council, Poughkeepsie, NY, 2012. Toward a feasibility study for the development of a Poughkeepsie Community Art Museum.
$15,000 to Friends of Seniors of Dutchess County, Poughkeepsie, NY, 2013. Toward mileage reimbursement for volunteer drivers who transport seniors citizens to medical appointments.
$10,000 to GuideStar USA, Williamsburg, VA, 2013. For general operating support.

5924
The E & SS Foundation, Inc. ✧ ☆
c/o Tiger Global
9 W. 57th St., 35th Fl.
New York, NY 10019

Established in DE.
Donor: Scott L. Shleifer.
Foundation type: Independent foundation.
Financial data (yr. ended 12/31/13): Assets, $617,478 (M); expenditures, $4,601,436; qualifying distributions, $4,476,436; giving activities include $4,475,350 for 36 grants (high: $736,850; low: $1,000).
Fields of interest: Education; Health care; Human services; Jewish federated giving programs.
Limitations: Applications not accepted. Giving primarily in New York, NY.
Application information: Unsolicited requests for funds not accepted.
Directors: Elena Shleifer; Scott L. Shleifer.
EIN: 460666419

5925
Sarita Kenedy East Foundation, Inc. ✧
19 Mountain Ave.
Mount Kisco, NY 10549-1321

Established in 1962 in NY.
Donor: Sarita Kenedy East†.
Foundation type: Independent foundation.
Financial data (yr. ended 12/31/13): Assets, $19,670,308 (M); expenditures, $1,061,697; qualifying distributions, $888,259; giving activities include $872,515 for 50 grants (high: $75,000; low: $5,000).
Purpose and activities: Giving primarily to Roman Catholic organizations and social services.
Fields of interest: Human services; Catholic agencies & churches; Economically disadvantaged.
Type of support: General/operating support; Continuing support; Seed money.
Limitations: Applications not accepted. Giving primarily in NY and MA. No grants to individuals.
Application information: Contributes only to pre-selected organizations.
Board meeting date(s): As necessary
Officers and Directors:* Patrick P. Grace,* Pres.; Theresa Grace Sears, V.P. and Secy.-Treas.; Justine M. Carr, V.P.; Noreen Doyle,* Treas.; Margaret F. Grace.
Number of staff: 1 part-time support.
EIN: 136116447

5926
East Hill Foundation ✧
17 Island St.
P.O. Box 547
North Tonawanda, NY 14120-5705 (716) 204-0204, ext. 201
Contact: Michele R. Schmidt
FAX: (716) 694-6353;
E-mail: mschmidt@easthillfdn.org; Additional e-mail: info@easthillfdn.org; Main URL: http://www.easthillfdn.org

Established in 1986 in NY.
Donors: Eleanor Greatbatch; Warren Greatbatch.
Foundation type: Independent foundation.
Financial data (yr. ended 12/31/13): Assets, $22,398,789 (M); gifts received, $3,425; expenditures, $1,551,956; qualifying distributions, $1,255,781; giving activities include $824,199 for 64 grants (high: $100,000; low: $150), and $189,967 for 1 foundation-administered program.
Purpose and activities: The foundation is currently concentrating on projects that serve basic human needs for the Western New York community.
Fields of interest: Arts; Education; Animal welfare; Health care; Youth development.
Type of support: Building/renovation; Equipment; Program development.
Limitations: Applications accepted. Giving primarily in the eight counties of Allegany, Cattaraugus, Chautauqua, Erie, Genesee, Niagara, Orleans and Wyoming of western NY. No support for religious organizations for direct religious purposes. No grants to individuals, or for endowments, technology, private education, scholarships, salaries or travel expenses.
Publications: Application guidelines; Grants list; Informational brochure (including application guidelines).
Application information: Refer to foundation web site for specific application guidelines which must be followed. Applications sent by fax are not considered. Application form required.
Board meeting date(s): Semiannually
Officers: Warren D. Greatbatch, Pres. and Treas.; Ami Greatbatch, V.P.; John E. Siegel, Secy.
Directors: Tommie Greatbatch; Jenny Pierce; Julia Spitz.
Number of staff: 1 full-time professional.
EIN: 161441497

5927
Eastern Star Hall and Home Foundation, Inc. ✧
c/o Pounder Hall
1400 Utica St., P.O. Box 106
Oriskany, NY 13424-0106

Established in 1986 in NY.
Donors: Hilda Brooks†; Mildred Niley†; Althea Julson†; Geraldine Bear†; Lucile Sotherden; Dors S. Bliss†; Natalie Hermann†; Kathryn Martin†; Marilyn Castleman†; Martha Burdick†; Tucker Anthony; Essig Family Trust; Mildred Schneider†; Iris Casey Trust; Helen Bronk; A. Somers Gardner Trust; Anna Mae Stewart†; Order of the Eastern Star; Clifford Scarlett†; Trustees of the Eastern Star Hall; Elia Juchter†; Gladys Hart†; Thelma Seavey Trust; Ann Alsheimen†; John Cole†; J. Bleich Kolhmeir; W.H. Albery Society.
Foundation type: Independent foundation.
Financial data (yr. ended 06/30/13): Assets, $9,303,137 (M); gifts received, $23,380; expenditures, $1,554,907; qualifying distributions, $1,438,535; giving activities include $1,438,535 for grants.
Fields of interest: Human services; Residential/custodial care, senior continuing care; Aging.
Type of support: Endowments.
Limitations: Applications not accepted. Giving primarily in Oriskany, NY. No grants to individuals.
Publications: Annual report.
Application information: Contributes only to pre-selected organizations.
Board meeting date(s): Apr., July, Oct., and Dec.
Officers: Karen Marshall-King, Pres.; Burniece Herendeen, Recording Secy.
Directors: John Butcher; Sally Clarke; Ruth Howe; Isabelle Keuther; Ronald Myers.
EIN: 133458370

5928
Fred Ebb Foundation ✧
40 W. 20th St., 11th Fl.
New York, NY 10011-4211
E-mail: info@fredebbfoundation.org; Main URL: http://www.fredebbfoundation.org
Application address: c/o Roundabout Theatre, 231 W. 39th St., Ste. 1200, New York, NY 10018

Established in 2005 in NY.
Donor: Fred Ebb†.

Foundation type: Operating foundation.
Financial data (yr. ended 12/31/12): Assets, $27,821,621 (M); expenditures, $1,542,112; qualifying distributions, $1,542,112; giving activities include $1,300,000 for 1 grant, and $50,000 for 1 grant to an individual.
Purpose and activities: The foundation provides an annual award to one or more persons working in the field of musical theater as composers and/or lyricists. Funding also for Broadway Cares/Equity Fights AIDS.
Fields of interest: Performing arts, theater (musical); AIDS.
Type of support: Grants to individuals.
Limitations: Applications accepted. Giving primarily in New York, NY.
Application information: Applications only accepted for musical theater award and are accepted by mail or delivery. See foundation web site for guidelines and application form in this area. Contributes only to pre-selected organizations for grants. Application form required.
Deadline(s): Applications accepted June 2-30
Final notification: Nov.
Officer: Mitchell Bernard, Pres.
EIN: 202184998

5929
The Eberstadt-Kuffner Fund, Inc. ✧
(formerly The Vera and Walter Eberstadt Foundation)
c/o Anchin
1375 Broadway
New York, NY 10018-7001

Established in 1967 in NY.
Donors: Vera Eberstadt; Walter Eberstadt; Helene Kuffner†.
Foundation type: Independent foundation.
Financial data (yr. ended 12/31/13): Assets, $15,868,085 (M); gifts received, $261,000; expenditures, $631,735; qualifying distributions, $514,840; giving activities include $510,460 for 66 grants (high: $121,750; low: $100).
Fields of interest: Media, television; Museums; Arts; Higher education; Environment, natural resources; Human services.
Limitations: Applications not accepted. Giving primarily in NY. No grants to individuals.
Application information: Contributes only to pre-selected organizations.
Officer: E. Richard Baum, Treas.
Directors: Vera Eberstadt; Walter Eberstadt; Daniel L. Mosley.
EIN: 136225395
Selected grants: The following grants are a representative sample of this grantmaker's funding activity:
$138,229 to Frick Collection, New York, NY, 2011.
$50,000 to THIRTEEN, New York, NY, 2011.
$20,000 to Memorial Sloan-Kettering Cancer Center, New York, NY, 2011.
$10,000 to World Policy Institute, New York, NY, 2011.
$7,500 to Leo Baeck Institute, New York, NY, 2011.
$6,000 to New School, New York, NY, 2011.
$5,000 to Marthas Vineyard Hospital, Oak Bluffs, MA, 2011.
$3,500 to Trinity Episcopal School, New York, NY, 2011.
$2,337 to Museum of Modern Art, New York, NY, 2011.
$1,500 to Human Rights First, New York, NY, 2011.

5930
William & Dewey Edelman Charitable Trust ✧
c/o Kenneth L. Stein
5 Woods Witch Ln.
Chappaqua, NY 10514-1223

Established in 2007 in NY.
Donors: William Edelman Trust; Dewey Edelman†.
Foundation type: Independent foundation.
Financial data (yr. ended 12/31/13): Assets, $18,976,194 (M); expenditures, $874,181; qualifying distributions, $803,912; giving activities include $784,500 for 9 grants (high: $350,000; low: $3,500).
Fields of interest: Higher education; Human services; Jewish federated giving programs; Jewish agencies & synagogues.
Limitations: Applications not accepted. Giving primarily in New York, NY. No grants to individuals.
Application information: Unsolicited requests for funds not accepted.
Trustees: Kenneth L. Stein; Nancy C. Stein.
EIN: 137109390

5931
The Thomas J. Edelman Family Foundation ✧
49 Lawrence Ave.
Lawrence, NY 11559-1446

Established in 1998.
Donors: Alex Edelman; Susan Edelman.
Foundation type: Independent foundation.
Financial data (yr. ended 12/31/13): Assets, $236,592 (M); gifts received, $835,000; expenditures, $609,180; qualifying distributions, $609,180; giving activities include $607,360 for 81 grants (high: $286,000; low: $75).
Purpose and activities: Giving primarily for Jewish education.
Fields of interest: Education; Jewish agencies & synagogues.
Limitations: Applications not accepted. Giving primarily in NY. No grants to individuals.
Application information: Contributes only to pre-selected organizations.
Officers: Alex Edelman, Pres.; Jeffrey Edelman, V.P.; Fay Greenberg, V.P.; Susan Edelman, Treas.
EIN: 113455820

5932
The Thomas J. Edelman Foundation ✧
c/o Thomas J. Edelman
667 Madison Ave.
New York, NY 10065

Established in 1993 in NY.
Donor: Thomas J. Edelman.
Foundation type: Independent foundation.
Financial data (yr. ended 12/31/13): Assets, $26,649,725 (M); expenditures, $740,646; qualifying distributions, $673,469; giving activities include $671,140 for 25 grants (high: $250,000; low: $175).
Fields of interest: Higher education; Education; Human services.
Type of support: General/operating support.
Limitations: Applications not accepted. Giving primarily in NY; funding also in CT and Washington, DC. No grants to individuals.
Application information: Contributes only to pre-selected organizations.
Officer: Thomas J. Edelman, Pres.
Director: Cornelia S. Edelman.
EIN: 133762804
Selected grants: The following grants are a representative sample of this grantmaker's funding activity:
$288,000 to Hotchkiss School, Lakeville, CT, 2011.
$261,000 to Georgetown University, Washington, DC, 2011.
$127,800 to Lenox Hill Neighborhood House, New York, NY, 2011.
$7,500 to Wildlife Rescue Center of the Hamptons, Hampton Bays, NY, 2011.
$5,000 to Guild Hall of East Hampton, East Hampton, NY, 2011.
$2,000 to American Society for the Prevention of Cruelty to Animals, New York, NY, 2011.
$1,000 to Pestalozzi US Childrens Charity, New York, NY, 2011.
$1,000 to Princeton University, Princeton, NJ, 2011.

5933
Michael & Florence Edelstein Foundation, Inc. ✧
880 5th Ave., Ste. 14F
New York, NY 10021-5260
Application address: Florence Edelstein, Dir., 2207 Coney Island Ave., Brooklyn, NY, 11223, tel.: (718) 627-7177

Established in 2005 in NY.
Donors: Michael Edelstein; Florence Edelstein.
Foundation type: Independent foundation.
Financial data (yr. ended 12/31/13): Assets, $12,985 (M); gifts received, $800,000; expenditures, $810,983; qualifying distributions, $810,983; giving activities include $810,983 for 62 grants (high: $300,000; low: $25).
Fields of interest: Education; Human services; Jewish agencies & synagogues.
Limitations: Applications accepted. Giving primarily in New York, NY.
Application information: Application form required.
Initial approach: Proposal
Deadline(s): 60 to 90 days before approved
Directors: Florence Edelstein; Michael Edelstein.
EIN: 202417292
Selected grants: The following grants are a representative sample of this grantmaker's funding activity:
$50,000 to Israel Cancer Research Fund, New York, NY, 2011.
$1,000 to Simon Wiesenthal Center, Los Angeles, CA, 2011.

5934
Bilquis Edhi Relief Foundation, Inc. ✧
45-11 National St.
Corona, NY 11368-2741

Established in 1998.
Donors: Ali Haider; Tariq Mahmood, M.D.; Hisham Salimi; Pakistan League of USA.
Foundation type: Independent foundation.
Financial data (yr. ended 12/31/12): Assets, $7,285,351 (M); gifts received, $5,293,814; expenditures, $8,261,546; qualifying distributions, $7,742,502; giving activities include $7,742,502

for 1 grant, and $33,721 for foundation-administered programs.
Purpose and activities: Giving to foundations that help the poor and needy people of the world, specifically those who are victims of natural disasters.
Fields of interest: International relief.
Type of support: General/operating support.
Limitations: Applications not accepted. Giving primarily in Karachi, Pakistan. No grants to individuals.
Application information: Unsolicited requests for funds not accepted.
Officers: Bilquis Edhi, Pres.; Abdul S. Edhi, V.P.; Qutub Edhi, Secy.
EIN: 113454067

5935
The Edlow Family Fund, Inc. ✧
35 E. 85th St., Apt. 5-E
New York, NY 10028-0966

Established in 1983 in NY.
Donors: Kenneth Lewis Edlow; Donald Edlow; Mary Edlow.
Foundation type: Independent foundation.
Financial data (yr. ended 11/30/13): Assets, $12,031,344 (M); expenditures, $614,256; qualifying distributions, $602,725; giving activities include $602,725 for 87 grants (high: $183,700; low: $100).
Purpose and activities: Support for Jewish welfare and other Jewish concerns; support also for education, and the arts.
Fields of interest: Museums; Performing arts, theater; Arts; Higher education; Education; Human services; Jewish federated giving programs; Jewish agencies & synagogues.
Type of support: Continuing support.
Limitations: Applications not accepted. Giving primarily in New York, NY. No grants to individuals.
Publications: Annual report.
Application information: Contributes only to pre-selected organizations.
Officers: Mary Edlow, Pres. and Treas.; Kenneth Lewis Edlow, V.P. and Secy.
Directors: Brian Lewis Edlow; Donald William Edlow; Elizabeth Fielding Edlow.
EIN: 133190911
Selected grants: The following grants are a representative sample of this grantmaker's funding activity:
$10,000 to Compassion and Choices, Denver, CO, 2011.
$10,000 to Planned Parenthood of New York City, New York, NY, 2011.
$7,500 to Population Council, New York, NY, 2011.

5936
The Edouard Foundation Inc. ✧
c/o Fourpoints Asset Management Inc.
1 Penn Plz., Ste. 1628
New York, NY 10119-1628

Established in 1987 in NY.
Donor: Christopher E. Finch.
Foundation type: Independent foundation.
Financial data (yr. ended 12/31/13): Assets, $12,980,230 (M); expenditures, $632,956; qualifying distributions, $496,554; giving activities include $493,500 for 60 grants (high: $25,500; low: $500).
Purpose and activities: The foundation is committed to funding programs which improve the quality of life primarily in the communities in which the directors reside. The funding is focused in the areas of human services, education, health care, art, animal welfare, environmental protection, and disaster relief.
Fields of interest: Health care; Health organizations, association; Human services; Children/youth, services; International relief; International human rights; United Ways and Federated Giving Programs; Jewish agencies & synagogues; Disabilities, people with; Economically disadvantaged.
Type of support: General/operating support; Emergency funds; Program development; Research.
Limitations: Applications not accepted. Giving primarily in CT, NY, TX, and the U.S. Virgin Islands; some funding nationally. No grants to individuals.
Application information: Contributes only to pre-selected organizations.
Board meeting date(s): Oct.
Officers: Christopher Finch, Pres.; Sandra Finch-Nguyen, V.P.; Ronald Finch, V.P.; Edwin A. Margolius, Secy.; Aaron Finch, Treas.
EIN: 133446831

5937
Educational Support Foundation, Inc. ✧
(formerly Leon & Irene Scharf Foundation, Inc.)
1659 58th St.
Brooklyn, NY 11204-2144

Established in 1963 in NY.
Donors: Leon Scharf; Irene Scharf; S. Schoferig; Chada Foundation; Franconia Foundation; Scharf, Scharf, & Beer; Weinreb Management; Nazel Family Trust; Cong Ahavas Tzedokah Vchese; MS Associates, LLC; RB Associates, LLC; Zichran Yitchok.
Foundation type: Independent foundation.
Financial data (yr. ended 05/31/13): Assets, $22,968,217 (M); gifts received, $884,000; expenditures, $3,267,874; qualifying distributions, $3,129,641; giving activities include $3,121,732 for 1 grant.
Purpose and activities: Giving primarily to Jewish agencies and temples and to yeshivas.
Fields of interest: Elementary/secondary education; Jewish agencies & synagogues.
Limitations: Applications not accepted. Giving primarily in NY. No grants to individuals.
Application information: Contributes only to pre-selected organizations.
Officers: Irene Scharf, Mgr.; Leon Scharf, Mgr.
EIN: 136159760

5938
Cheryl C. & Blair Effron Family Foundation ✧
c/o Alan Frankel FLSV LLP
1475 Franklin Ave.
Garden City, NY 11530

Established in 2002 in NY.
Donor: Blair Effron.
Foundation type: Independent foundation.
Financial data (yr. ended 12/31/13): Assets, $7,348,159 (M); gifts received, $112,665; expenditures, $687,689; qualifying distributions, $640,250; giving activities include $640,000 for 4 grants (high: $290,000; low: $50,000).
Fields of interest: Museums (art); Performing arts centers; Education; Human services.
Type of support: General/operating support.
Limitations: Applications not accepted. Giving primarily in New York, NY. No grants to individuals.
Application information: Contributes only to pre-selected organizations.
Officers: Blair Effron, Pres. and Treas.; Cheryl Cohen Effron, V.P. and Secy.
Directors: Drew Effron; Cathy Lasry.
EIN: 010720431

5939
EGL Charitable Foundation ✧
c/o Gruss and Co., Inc.
40 W. 57th St., No. 1440
New York, NY 10019-4001 (212) 446-4268
Contact: Evelyn Lipper, Pres.

Established in NY.
Donor: Evelyn Lipper.
Foundation type: Independent foundation.
Financial data (yr. ended 08/31/13): Assets, $164,575,075 (M); gifts received, $6,752; expenditures, $7,210,618; qualifying distributions, $5,603,359; giving activities include $5,568,576 for 26+ grants (high: $1,000,000).
Fields of interest: Education; Jewish federated giving programs; Jewish agencies & synagogues.
Limitations: Giving primarily in NJ and NY.
Application information:
Initial approach: Letter
Deadline(s): None
Officers: Evelyn Lipper, Pres.; Tina Guberman, Secy.-Treas.
EIN: 273667312
Selected grants: The following grants are a representative sample of this grantmaker's funding activity:
$1,056,175 to Albert Einstein College of Medicine of Yeshiva University, Bronx, NY, 2011. For general support.
$1,000,000 to Congregation Bnai Jeshurun, New York, NY, 2011. For general support.
$804,000 to Jewish National Fund, Rockville Centre, NY, 2011. For general support.
$304,600 to Columbia University, New York, NY, 2011. For general support.
$262,238 to Museum of Jewish Heritage, New York, NY, 2011. For general support.
$165,617 to Jewish Community Center in Manhattan, New York, NY, 2011. For general support.
$150,000 to Ohr HaLimud/The Multi-Sensory Learning Center, Brooklyn, NY, 2011. For general support.
$133,000 to Dorot, New York, NY, 2011. For general support.
$100,000 to Friends of Ir David, Brooklyn, NY, 2011. For general support.
$44,100 to Temple Rodef Shalom, Falls Church, VA, 2011. For general support.

5940
EHA Foundation, Inc. ✧
c/o Kelley Drye & Warren, LLP
101 Park Ave., 30th Fl.
New York, NY 10178-3099
Contact: Christina M. Mason, Secy.

Established in 1996 in NY.
Donors: Ruth Uris†; Linda M. Sanger.
Foundation type: Independent foundation.
Financial data (yr. ended 01/31/13): Assets, $25,436,304 (M); expenditures, $2,063,198; qualifying distributions, $1,680,915; giving activities include $1,680,915 for grants.
Purpose and activities: Giving primarily for education and the arts.
Fields of interest: Arts; Elementary/secondary education; Higher education; Libraries (public); Education; Human services.
Type of support: General/operating support; Continuing support; Building/renovation; Program development; Seed money; Fellowships; Scholarship funds; Matching/challenge support.
Limitations: Applications not accepted. Giving primarily in MA, and NY. No grants to individuals.
Application information: Contributes only to pre-selected organizations. Unsolicited requests for funds not accepted.
Officers: Linda M. Sanger, Pres.; Abbie W. Sanger, V.P.; Terence D. Sanger, V.P.; Victoria Sanger, V.P.; Christina M. Mason, Secy.; Michael S. Insel, Treas.
EIN: 133898642
Selected grants: The following grants are a representative sample of this grantmaker's funding activity:
$250,000 to Oakwood School, North Hollywood, CA, 2011. For general support.
$200,000 to New York Public Library, New York, NY, 2011. For general support.
$100,000 to United Neighborhood Houses of New York, New York, NY, 2011. For general support.
$60,000 to Childrens Aid Society, New York, NY, 2011. For general support.
$50,000 to Kinhaven Music School, Bethlehem, PA, 2011. For general support.
$50,000 to Metropolitan Opera, New York, NY, 2011. For general support.
$40,000 to Teachers and Writers Collaborative, New York, NY, 2011. For general support.
$35,000 to American Repertory Theater, Cambridge, MA, 2011. For general support.
$25,000 to Green Guerillas, New York, NY, 2011. For general support.
$10,000 to Temple Israel of Hollywood, Los Angeles, CA, 2011. For general support.

5941
Ehrenkranz Family Foundation ✧
c/o Joel S. Ehrenkranz
375 Park Ave., Ste. 2800
New York, NY 10152-2899

Established in 1997 in NY.
Donor: Joel S. Ehrenkranz.
Foundation type: Independent foundation.
Financial data (yr. ended 12/31/13): Assets, $11,744,779 (M); gifts received, $4,071,630; expenditures, $3,333,056; qualifying distributions, $3,311,220; giving activities include $3,308,460 for 62 grants (high: $1,054,400; low: $100).
Purpose and activities: Giving primarily for higher education, health care, and the arts; funding also for Jewish organizations and social services.
Fields of interest: Museums; Performing arts centers; Arts; Higher education; Education; Hospitals (general); Human services; Jewish agencies & synagogues.
Limitations: Applications not accepted. Giving primarily in New York, NY. No grants to individuals.
Application information: Contributes only to pre-selected organizations.
Trustees: Anne B. Ehrenkranz; Joel S. Ehrenkranz.
EIN: 133977888
Selected grants: The following grants are a representative sample of this grantmaker's funding activity:
$1,054,400 to Museum of Modern Art, New York, NY, 2013. For general support.
$910,000 to Museum of Modern Art, New York, NY, 2012.
$850,000 to Lincoln Center for the Performing Arts, New York, NY, 2012.
$750,000 to Mount Sinai Medical Center, New York, NY, 2012.
$550,100 to Hospital for Special Surgery, New York, NY, 2013. For general support.
$550,000 to Lincoln Center for the Performing Arts, New York, NY, 2013. For general support.
$548,000 to Hospital for Special Surgery, New York, NY, 2012.
$344,000 to Institute of Fine Arts Foundation, New York, NY, 2013. For general support.
$290,000 to New York University, New York, NY, 2012.
$255,550 to Icahn School of Medicine at Mount Sinai, New York, NY, 2012.
$200,000 to Whitney Museum of American Art, New York, NY, 2012.
$200,000 to Whitney Museum of American Art, New York, NY, 2013. For general support.
$100,000 to Foundation for Contemporary Arts, New York, NY, 2012.
$60,000 to Dalton Schools, New York, NY, 2013. For general support.
$55,000 to Visiting Nurse Service of New York, New York, NY, 2012.
$52,500 to Blythedale Childrens Hospital, Valhalla, NY, 2013. For general support.
$35,000 to Rye Country Day School, Rye, NY, 2012.
$30,000 to University of Pennsylvania, Philadelphia, PA, 2013. For general support.
$25,000 to Graduate Center Foundation, School of Journalism, New York, NY, 2013. For general support.
$25,000 to Rye Country Day School, Rye, NY, 2013. For general support.

5942
Einhorn Family Charitable Trust ✧
c/o Greenlight Capital, Inc.
140 E. 45th St., 24th Fl.
New York, NY 10017-7142
Contact: David Einhorn, Tr.

Established in 2002 in NY.
Donors: David Einhorn; Cheryl Einhorn.
Foundation type: Independent foundation.
Financial data (yr. ended 12/31/12): Assets, $6,508,888 (M); gifts received, $31,352,000; expenditures, $26,161,878; qualifying distributions, $26,495,144; giving activities include $24,936,333 for 53 grants (high: $4,869,491; low: $100), $2,082 for 17 employee matching gifts, and $333,333 for 1 loan/program-related investment.
Fields of interest: Higher education; International affairs; Foundations (private grantmaking); Jewish agencies & synagogues.
Type of support: Program-related investments/loans.
Limitations: Applications not accepted. Giving primarily in NY. No grants to individuals.
Application information: Contributes only to pre-selected organizations.
Officers: Harry Bradler, C.F.O.; Jennifer Hoos Rothberg, Exec. Dir.
Trustees: Cheryl Einhorn; David Einhorn.
EIN: 226921358
Selected grants: The following grants are a representative sample of this grantmaker's funding activity:
$4,869,491 to City Year, Boston, MA, 2012. For general support and culture behavior initiative.
$4,646,600 to Robin Hood Foundation, New York, NY, 2012. For general support and Robin Hood Relief Fund.
$2,044,439 to Interfaith Youth Core, Chicago, IL, 2012. For general support and leadership initiatives.
$1,750,000 to Ashoka: Innovators for the Public, Arlington, VA, 2012. For Ashoka Empathy Initiative.
$1,700,000 to Columbia University, New York, NY, 2012. For Brain-Gut Initiative.
$1,500,000 to Playworks, Oakland, CA, 2012. For general support.
$1,001,000 to Repair the World, New York, NY, 2012. For general support.
$500,000 to Roots of Empathy, Toronto, Canada, 2012. For general support.
$500,000 to Tony Blair Faith Foundation-US, Washington, DC, 2012. For general support.
$150,000 to Education Reform Now, New York, NY, 2012. For general support.

5943
The Einhorn Family Foundation ✧
c/o BCRS Assocs., Inc.
77 Water St., 9th Fl.
New York, NY 10005-4414

Established in 1989 in NJ.
Donor: Steven G. Einhorn.
Foundation type: Independent foundation.
Financial data (yr. ended 01/31/13): Assets, $1,014,015 (M); gifts received, $2,920,000; expenditures, $1,946,127; qualifying distributions, $1,942,527; giving activities include $1,942,527 for grants.
Purpose and activities: Giving primarily for health organizations, including a hearing center, and Jewish federated programs and agencies.
Fields of interest: Arts; Education; Speech/hearing centers; Health care; Human services; Jewish federated giving programs; Jewish agencies & synagogues.
Limitations: Applications not accepted. Giving primarily in New York, NY. No grants to individuals.
Application information: Contributes only to pre-selected organizations.
Trustees: Shelley Einhorn; Steven G. Einhorn.
EIN: 133531970

5944
Eisenberg Family Foundation, Inc. ✧
2917 Ave. I
Brooklyn, NY 11210-2934

Established in 2000 in NY.
Donors: Solomon Eisenberg; Joseph H. & Miriam F. Wells Foundation, Inc.
Foundation type: Independent foundation.
Financial data (yr. ended 12/31/12): Assets, $4,677,840 (M); expenditures, $534,693; qualifying distributions, $503,489; giving activities include $503,489 for 21+ grants (high: $87,038).
Purpose and activities: Giving primarily to Jewish temples, yeshivas, and to a rabbinical college.
Fields of interest: Elementary/secondary education; Theological school/education; Jewish agencies & synagogues.
Limitations: Applications not accepted. No grants to individuals.
Application information: Contributes only to pre-selected organizations.
Directors: Edward H. Birnbaum; Miriam Eisenberg; Solomon Eisenberg.
EIN: 113543069

5945
Elbogen Family Charitable Trust ✧
1650 49th St.
Brooklyn, NY 11204-1133

Established in 2000 in NY.
Donor: Aaron Elbogen.
Foundation type: Independent foundation.
Financial data (yr. ended 12/31/12): Assets, $9,594,538 (M); gifts received, $150,000; expenditures, $445,435; qualifying distributions, $438,620; giving activities include $438,620 for grants.
Fields of interest: Elementary/secondary education; Jewish agencies & synagogues.
Limitations: Applications not accepted. No grants to individuals.
Application information: Contributes only to pre-selected organizations.
Trustees: Aaron Elbogen; Chaya Elbogen.
EIN: 116552018

5946
The Elishis Family Foundation ✧
c/o Oracle Advisory Svcs., LLC
100 Grand St., Apt. 4
New York, NY 10013-2674

Established in 1999 in NY.
Donors: Isser Elishis; Brenda Elishis; David Elishis†; Tony Inder Reiden.
Foundation type: Independent foundation.
Financial data (yr. ended 12/31/12): Assets, $42,511 (M); gifts received, $794,200; expenditures, $877,397; qualifying distributions, $877,094; giving activities include $877,094 for 193 grants (high: $100,000; low: $18).
Fields of interest: Jewish agencies & synagogues.
Limitations: Applications not accepted. Giving primarily in Brooklyn and New York, NY; funding also in Toronto, Ontario, Canada. No grants to individuals.
Application information: Contributes only to pre-selected organizations.
Officers and Director:* Brenda Elishis,* Pres.; Isser Elishis, V.P. and Mgr.
EIN: 113502742

5947
The Elkes Foundation ✧
c/o Davidson, Dawson & Clark LLP
60 E. 42nd St., 38th Fl.
New York, NY 10165-3802 (917) 388-9505

Established in 1989 in NY.
Donors: Terrence A. Elkes†; Elkes Trust.
Foundation type: Operating foundation.
Financial data (yr. ended 11/30/13): Assets, $63,737,189 (M); gifts received, $2,901,968; expenditures, $2,397,822; qualifying distributions, $1,649,790; giving activities include $1,649,790 for 49 grants (high: $250,000; low: $200).
Purpose and activities: Giving primarily for education and health organizations.
Fields of interest: Arts; Higher education; Health organizations; Diabetes; Jewish agencies & synagogues.
Limitations: Applications not accepted. Giving in the U.S., with emphasis on San Francisco, CA, and NY. No grants to individuals.
Application information: Contributes only to pre-selected organizations.
Trustees: Daniel A. Elkes; David A. Elkes; Steven A. Elkes.
EIN: 133497016

5948
Thomas and Jeanne Elmezzi Private Foundation ✧
(also known as The Jet Foundation)
31-10 23rd St.
Astoria, NY 11106-4585 (718) 204-5029
Contact: Jose Rivero, Chair.; Christopher Cutter, Prog. Officer
FAX: (347) 710-1370; E-mail: admin@elmezzi.org;
Main URL: http://www.elmezzi.org
Foundation RSS Feed: http://elmezzi.org/?feed=rss

Established in 1996 in NY.
Donors: Thomas Elmezzi†; Jeanne Elmezzi†; The Thomas Elmezzi Revocable Trust; The Thomas and Jeanne Elmezzi Charitable Remainder Annuity Trust; Jeanne Elmezzi Chariable Unitrust.
Foundation type: Independent foundation.
Financial data (yr. ended 12/31/12): Assets, $38,086,491 (M); gifts received, $373,039; expenditures, $4,369,135; qualifying distributions, $4,100,422; giving activities include $3,298,064 for 95 grants (high: $1,200,000; low: $1,000).
Purpose and activities: The foundation's mission is to encourage and support programs that directly provide assistance to individuals who due to either environment or circumstance have not had the opportunity or ability to live independent and productive lives. Such challenges may be physical, medical, economic, environmental or geographical. The foundation strives to have a direct and measurable impact on the quality of individual lives, through direct sponsorship and/or innovative program design and development.
Fields of interest: Education; Geriatrics; Medical research; Children/youth, services; Community/economic development.
Type of support: Management development/capacity building; Endowments; Program development; Technical assistance.
Limitations: Giving primarily in New York City, with emphasis on the Long Island City and Astoria neighborhoods in Queens. No support for housing, international organizations (except for some disasters) and foreign travel or study. No grants for individuals, annual appeals, dinners, fundraising events, capital campaigns, loans and deficit financing.
Publications: Grants list; Occasional report; IRS Form 990 or 990-PF printed copy available upon request.
Application information: Unsolicited proposals not accepted. Proposals are by invitation only, upon review of initial e-mail.
Initial approach: E-mail to ascertain interest
Board meeting date(s): Ongoing
Officers and Trustees:* Jose Rivero,* Chair. and Pres.; Stephen J. Saft,* Secy.; Alfred LaRosa, Treas.; Dominick Fortino; Allen Freed; Lynn Grossman; Nivia Pedroza; Jack Sollazzo.
Number of staff: 2 full-time professional.
EIN: 113343740

5949
Emerald Foundation, Inc. ✧
c/o Marianne Gerschel
780 3rd Ave., 24th Fl.
New York, NY 10017-2024 (212) 888-2069

Established in 1998 in NY.
Foundation type: Independent foundation.
Financial data (yr. ended 12/31/13): Assets, $36,380,195 (M); expenditures, $2,274,154; qualifying distributions, $2,120,494; giving activities include $1,500,000 for 11 grants (high: $150,000; low: $75,000).
Purpose and activities: Giving primarily to medical research.
Fields of interest: Higher education; Hospitals (general); Medical research, institute.
Limitations: Applications not accepted.
Application information: Proposals only accepted upon request.
Officer and Director:* Marianne Gerschel,* Pres.
EIN: 133912580
Selected grants: The following grants are a representative sample of this grantmaker's funding activity:
$150,000 to Rockefeller University, New York, NY, 2012. For explore the role of a novel population of dendritic cells called IKDCs and their precursors as important modulators of the immune response to viral infection of the brain.
$150,000 to Rockefeller University, New York, NY, 2012. To use autologous apoptotic tumor and dendritic cells obtained from brain tumor patients as autologous tumor vaccine that uses naturally occurring tumor immunity to fight the disease.
$150,000 to Samuel Waxman Cancer Research Foundation, New York, NY, 2012. To support a collaboration between 4 scientists at 3 institutions with the goal of targeting the HER family of proteins and their signaling pathways in brain cancer.
$150,000 to Whitehead Institute for Biomedical Research, Cambridge, MA, 2012. To determine the roles for individual microRNA-target interactions in both mammalian development and cancer.
$125,000 to Samuel Waxman Cancer Research Foundation, New York, NY, 2012. To expand the collaboration between scientists of the Samuel Waxman Cancer Research Foundation and of the Shanghai Institute of Hematology with the goal of identifying new and more powerful drugs that can restore normal differentiation and cell growth to leu.
$75,000 to Rockefeller University, New York, NY, 2012. To investigate how TGF-beta signaling

controls skin stem cell behavior and how this becomes deregulated in the formation of squamous cell carcinoma.

5950
Fred L. Emerson Foundation, Inc. ✧
5654 South Street Rd.
Auburn, NY 13021-9602 (315) 253-9621
Contact: Daniel J. Fessenden, Exec. Dir.
E-mail: dan@emersonfoundation.com; E-mail for proposal information:
info@emersonfoundation.com

Incorporated in 1943 in DE.
Donor: Fred L. Emerson†.
Foundation type: Independent foundation.
Financial data (yr. ended 12/31/13): Assets, $84,399,975 (M); expenditures, $4,385,419; qualifying distributions, $3,719,787; giving activities include $3,208,204 for 73 grants (high: $750,000; low: $1,000).
Purpose and activities: Giving to private colleges and universities, community funds, and a library; grants also for youth and social service agencies and cultural programs.
Fields of interest: Arts; Higher education; Libraries/library science; Human services; Children/youth, services; United Ways and Federated Giving Programs.
Type of support: Annual campaigns; Capital campaigns; Building/renovation; Equipment; Endowments; Emergency funds; Program development; Internship funds; Scholarship funds; Research; Matching/challenge support.
Limitations: Applications accepted. Giving primarily in Auburn, Cayuga County, and upstate NY. No grants to individuals, or for deficit financing; no loans. Support for operating budgets is discouraged.
Publications: Application guidelines.
Application information: Application form not required but preferred.
Initial approach: Letter, telephone, or proposal
Copies of proposal: 1
Deadline(s): Proposals accepted on an ongoing basis
Board meeting date(s): Quarterly
Final notification: 2 to 3 weeks after board meetings
Officers and Directors:* Anthony D. Franceschelli,* Pres.; Kristen E. Rubacka,* V.P.; W. Gary Emerson,* Treas.; Daniel J. Fessenden,* Secy. and Exec. Dir.; Ann M. Dugan; Christopher S. Emerson; Heather A. Emerson; Peter J. Emerson; Daniel M. Myers; Lori E. Robinson; Sally E. Wagner.
Number of staff: 1 full-time professional; 1 full-time support.
EIN: 156017650

5951
Emes Foundation, Inc. ✧
1575 50th St., Ste. 201
Brooklyn, NY 11219-3752

Established in 2001 in NY.
Donors: The Emunah Trust; Manuel Scharf; Educational Support Foundation; MSS Trust Assocs.; Leon Scharf Trust f/b/o Manuel.
Foundation type: Independent foundation.
Financial data (yr. ended 09/30/13): Assets, $6,830,842 (M); gifts received, $292,000; expenditures, $1,332,896; qualifying distributions, $1,295,970; giving activities include $1,287,020 for 1+ grant.
Fields of interest: Education; Human services.
Limitations: Applications not accepted. No grants to individuals.
Application information: Contributes only to pre-selected organizations.
Officers and Directors:* Manuel Scharf,* Pres.; Chava Scharf,* V.P.; Yisroel Scharf,* Secy.-Treas.
EIN: 113640577

5952
EMLE, Inc. ✧
477 Madison Ave., 10th Fl.
New York, NY 10022-5841

Established in 1998 in DE and NY.
Donors: Bella Wexner Charitable Remainder Unitrust; Susan Wexner Revocable Trust.
Foundation type: Independent foundation.
Financial data (yr. ended 03/31/13): Assets, $31,886,290 (M); expenditures, $1,590,764; qualifying distributions, $1,452,021; giving activities include $1,447,356 for 9 grants (high: $500,000; low: $2).
Purpose and activities: Giving primarily for Jewish education and other Jewish organizations, including a Jewish museum.
Fields of interest: Higher education; Jewish agencies & synagogues.
Limitations: Applications not accepted. Giving primarily in NY and Israel. No grants to individuals.
Application information: Contributes only to pre-selected organizations.
Officer and Directors:* Susan R. Wexner,* Pres. and Secy.-Treas.; Saul G. Agus; Raymond Kanner; Gregg H. Levy, Esq.; Michael S. Oberman, Esq.; Mark Saks, Esq.; Walter Stern.
EIN: 133997362
Selected grants: The following grants are a representative sample of this grantmaker's funding activity:
$400,000 to International March of the Living, New York, NY, 2013. For general operating support for the organization's educational Programming.
$179,505 to Yeshiva University, New York, NY, 2013. For teacher training fellowship Program which provides a master's degree and supported induction of Program participants.
$100,000 to Gift of Life Bone Marrow Foundation, Boca Raton, FL, 2013. For general operating support for the organization's medical and research Programming.

5953
Empire State Foundation ✧
100A Broadway, Ste. 227
Brooklyn, NY 11249-6031
Contact: Samuel Schwartz, Tr.

Established in 2007 in NY.
Donors: Samuel Schwartz; Chaya Landau; Erika Schwartz; Berish Brauner; NY Commerical Financial; Michael Schwartz.
Foundation type: Independent foundation.
Financial data (yr. ended 12/31/12): Assets, $1,523,825 (M); gifts received, $677,905; expenditures, $621,432; qualifying distributions, $619,187; giving activities include $619,187 for grants.
Purpose and activities: Giving primarily Jewish agencies, temples, and schools.
Fields of interest: Education; Jewish agencies & synagogues.
Application information: Application form required.
Initial approach: Letter
Deadline(s): None
Trustees: Barnard Schwartz; Samuel Schwartz.
EIN: 300456687

5954
The Charles Engelhard Foundation ✧
Olympic Twrs.
645 5th Ave., 7th Fl.
New York, NY 10022-5910
Contact: Mary Ogorzaly, Secy.
FAX: (212) 935-2434;
E-mail: mary@engelhardhanovia.com

Incorporated in 1949 in NJ.
Donors: Charles Engelhard†; Jane Engelhard†; Engelhard Hanovia, Inc.; and others.
Foundation type: Independent foundation.
Financial data (yr. ended 12/31/13): Assets, $98,985,891 (M); expenditures, $10,619,797; qualifying distributions, $10,227,540; giving activities include $9,900,375 for 197 grants (high: $650,001; low: $500).
Purpose and activities: Emphasis on higher and secondary education, and cultural, medical, religious, wildlife, and conservation organizations.
Fields of interest: Arts; Secondary school/education; Higher education; Environment, natural resources; Animals/wildlife, preservation/protection; Biomedicine; Medical research, institute; Religion; Youth.
Type of support: General/operating support; Continuing support; Annual campaigns; Capital campaigns; Building/renovation; Endowments; Program development; Conferences/seminars; Professorships; Film/video/radio; Publication; Scholarship funds; Research; Matching/challenge support.
Limitations: Applications not accepted. Giving on a national basis. No support for political organizations. No grants to individuals.
Publications: Financial statement.
Application information: Giving only to organizations known to the trustees. Unsolicited requests for funds not considered.
Board meeting date(s): Quarterly
Officers: Mary Ogorzaly, Secy.; Edward G. Beimfohr, Treas.
Trustees: Sophie Engelhard Craighead; Anne E. de la Renta; Charlene B. Engelhard; Susan O'Connor; Sally E. Pingree.
Number of staff: 1 full-time professional; 2 part-time professional.
EIN: 226063032
Selected grants: The following grants are a representative sample of this grantmaker's funding activity:
$550,000 to Georgetown University, Washington, DC, 2012.
$408,000 to Refugees International, Washington, DC, 2012.
$215,000 to Hana Spiritual Retreat, Hana, HI, 2012.
$160,000 to National Gallery of Art, Washington, DC, 2012.
$150,000 to Orion Society, Great Barrington, MA, 2012.

$140,000 to Doctors Without Borders USA, New York, NY, 2012.
$100,000 to Craighead Beringia South, Kelly, WY, 2012.
$35,000 to Ma Ka Hana Ka Ike Building Program, Hana, HI, 2012.
$30,000 to Catholic Relief Services, Baltimore, MD, 2012.
$10,000 to Chinati Foundation, Marfa, TX, 2012.

5955
Englander Foundation, Inc. ✧
740 Park Ave.
New York, NY 10021-4251

Established in 1991 in NY.
Donors: Israel A. Englander; Englander Capital Corp.
Foundation type: Independent foundation.
Financial data (yr. ended 11/30/13): Assets, $1,167,843 (M); gifts received, $1,575,000; expenditures, $3,038,897; qualifying distributions, $3,038,897; giving activities include $3,023,837 for 33 grants (high: $2,600,000; low: $500).
Purpose and activities: Giving primarily for Jewish agencies and temples; some funding for education and human services.
Fields of interest: Elementary/secondary education; Theological school/education; Human services; Jewish federated giving programs; Jewish agencies & synagogues.
International interests: Israel.
Type of support: General/operating support; Continuing support; Annual campaigns; Capital campaigns; Building/renovation.
Limitations: Applications not accepted. Giving primarily in the metropolitan New York, NY, area and PA. No grants to individuals.
Publications: Financial statement; Grants list.
Application information: Contributes only to pre-selected organizations.
Officers: Israel A. Englander, Pres.; Lenard Brafman, V.P.; Allan S. Sexter, Secy.; Steven C. Weidman, Treas.
EIN: 133640833
Selected grants: The following grants are a representative sample of this grantmaker's funding activity:
$5,000 to Mechon Hadar, New York, NY, 2012. For Aid the Donee Organization in Carrying Out Its Exempt Functions.

5956
Enterprise Foundation Trust ✧
c/o Daniel R. Eule
888 7th Ave., 33rd Fl.
New York, NY 10106-0001

Established in 1995 in NY.
Donor: Robert Soros.
Foundation type: Independent foundation.
Financial data (yr. ended 11/30/13): Assets, $5,776,478 (M); expenditures, $791,320; qualifying distributions, $785,500; giving activities include $785,000 for 35 grants (high: $550,000; low: $500).
Fields of interest: Performing arts; Arts; Higher education; Hospitals (general); Health care; Human services; Foundations (private grantmaking).
Limitations: Applications not accepted. Giving primarily in NY. No grants to individuals.
Application information: Contributes only to pre-selected organizations.
Trustees: Melissa Schiff Soros; Robert Soros.
EIN: 137029291

5957
The Eppley Foundation for Research, Inc. ☆
Box 359
244 Madison Ave.
New York, NY 10016
Contact: Ingrid Eisenstadter, Dir. of Grants
Main URL: http://foundationcenter.org/grantmaker/eppley/

Established in 1947 in RI.
Donor: Marion Eppley†.
Foundation type: Independent foundation.
Financial data (yr. ended 12/31/13): Assets, $2,604,351 (M); gifts received, $192,832; expenditures, $496,446; qualifying distributions, $478,402; giving activities include $460,723 for 19 grants (high: $35,000; low: $10,000).
Purpose and activities: Giving focuses on the following areas of interest: innovative medical investigations, endangered animals and ecosystems, and climate change.
Fields of interest: Environment; Animals/wildlife, research; Biomedicine; Medical research, institute; Medical research; Agriculture; Physical/earth sciences; Chemistry; Biology/life sciences.
Type of support: Research.
Limitations: Applications accepted. No support for social sciences, computer sciences, educational programs, or for research involving AIDS, cancer or heart disease.
Publications: Application guidelines; Informational brochure; Program policy statement.
Application information: Please go to the foundation web site and read the information there before applying. All submissions must start with an e-mailed Letter of Inquiry, not to exceed 4 pages, describing the project and qualifications, goals, novelty, and the broader ramifications of the work once completed. It is preferred that the LOI is in the body of the e-mail, but it may also be a Word doc attachment (not docx, or .pdf). Full proposals must be accompanied by the foundation's application form and at least 2 letters of reference from qualified individuals who are familiar with the work proposed. Mail a print copy of the proposal and all attachments to Ingrid Eisenstadter at the foundation address above. Simultaneously, e-mail the proposal, application form and all attachments to Ingrid Eisenstadter at the e-mail address on the foundation web page, at the URL above. Send the proposal and application form as Word docs, not docx or .pdf (attachments may be any format). Grants are made only to nonprofit education and research organizations with a U.S. base to receive the funds. Application form required.
Initial approach: Letter of inquiry
Copies of proposal: 2
Deadline(s): Letters of Inquiry must be received by Mar. 15 or Sept. 15. If a full proposal is invited, deadlines for receipt are Apr. 15 and Oct. 15
Board meeting date(s): June and Dec.
Final notification: Within two weeks of board meetings
Officers: Joan Winant, Pres.; Amy S. Saar, Secy.
Director: John Winant, M.D.
Number of staff: 1 part-time professional; 1 part-time support.
EIN: 050258857
Selected grants: The following grants are a representative sample of this grantmaker's funding activity:
$15,000 to Audubon Society of New York City, New York, NY, 2013. Toxins-uptake analysis of herring gulls in NY Harbor after Superstorm Sandy, to compare with pre-Sandy database of waterbirds as bioindicators in the polluted waters of this denssely populated harbor.
$13,900 to Natural History Museum of Los Angeles County, Los Angeles, CA, 2013. Evolution and Paleobiology of Primitive Birds to study in China fossils of the Mesozoic bird, Confuciousornis sanctus, at the crossroads of dinosaur-to-bird evolution.
$10,000 to Utah Valley University, Orem, UT, 2013. Innovations in breast cancer research; Real-time tissue analysis, to reduce multiple surgeries due to cancer in the margins of tissues removed.

5958
Epstein Teicher Philanthropies ✧
(formerly Epstein Philanthropies)
c/o Milton S. Teicher
10 Rockefeller Plz., Ste. 1015
New York, NY 10019

Established in 1977 in NY.
Donors: Thomas Epstein†; William A. Epstein†; Florence E. Teicher†.
Foundation type: Independent foundation.
Financial data (yr. ended 12/31/13): Assets, $32,180,186 (M); expenditures, $2,169,440; qualifying distributions, $1,759,250; giving activities include $1,759,250 for 58 grants (high: $150,000; low: $750).
Purpose and activities: Giving primarily for the arts, education, and human rights.
Fields of interest: Museums; Arts; Education; Health care; Human services; International human rights; Jewish agencies & synagogues.
Limitations: Applications not accepted. Giving primarily in New York, NY. No support for religious or political organizations. No grants to individuals.
Application information: Contributes only to pre-selected organizations.
Officers: Seth Teicher, Pres.; Jane E. Heffner, V.P. and Secy.; Adrienne Simpson, Treas.
EIN: 132902852
Selected grants: The following grants are a representative sample of this grantmaker's funding activity:
$90,000 to Human Rights Watch, New York, NY, 2011.
$25,000 to American Civil Liberties Union, New York, NY, 2011.
$20,000 to American Jewish World Service, New York, NY, 2011.
$15,000 to Food Bank for New York City, New York, NY, 2011.
$15,000 to Jewish Guild for the Blind, New York, NY, 2011.
$10,000 to BronxWorks, Bronx, NY, 2011.

5959
The Equipart Foundation ✧
2323 Eastchester Rd.
Bronx, NY 10469-5910

Established in 1986 in NY.
Donors: Arnold Berkowitz; Joseph Brachfeld; Isaac Goldbrenner; Israel Hartman; Equipart Assocs.; BHC Co.; Shamai & Richu Hartman Family Foundation.
Foundation type: Independent foundation.
Financial data (yr. ended 06/30/13): Assets, $334,889 (M); gifts received, $992,000; expenditures, $970,368; qualifying distributions, $969,545; giving activities include $969,545 for 191+ grants (high: $116,197).
Purpose and activities: Giving primarily to Jewish agencies, temples, and schools.
Fields of interest: Education; Jewish agencies & synagogues.
Type of support: General/operating support.
Limitations: Applications not accepted. Giving primarily in NY. No grants to individuals.
Application information: Contributes only to pre-selected organizations.
Directors: Joseph Brachfeld; Isaac Goldbrenner; Israel Hartman.
EIN: 133355056

5960
ESL Charitable Foundation ✧
225 Chestnut St.
Rochester, NY 14604-2424 (585) 336-1000
Contact: Francine Patella-Ryan

Established in 2004 in NY.
Donor: ESL Federal Credit Union.
Foundation type: Independent foundation.
Financial data (yr. ended 12/31/13): Assets, $0 (M); gifts received, $438,275; expenditures, $438,275; qualifying distributions, $438,250; giving activities include $438,250 for 46 grants (high: $105,000; low: $150).
Fields of interest: Arts; Health organizations, association; Human services; Community/ economic development; United Ways and Federated Giving Programs.
Type of support: General/operating support.
Limitations: Applications accepted. Giving primarily in Rochester, NY. No grants to individuals.
Application information: Application form required.
Initial approach: Letter
Deadline(s): None
Officers: David Fiedler, Pres.; William Freeman, V.P.; Faheem A. Masood, 1st V.P.; Arline Santiago, V.P. and Secy.; Marueen Wolfe, V.P. and Treas.
EIN: 820548352
Selected grants: The following grants are a representative sample of this grantmaker's funding activity:
$552,000 to United Way of Greater Rochester, Rochester, NY, 2012. For Public Affairs/Society Benefit.
$6,042 to Rochester Roots, Rochester, NY, 2012. For Education; Health and Human Services.
$560 to Greece Central School District, Rochester, NY, 2012. For arts and culture, education.

5961
Essel Foundation, Inc. ✧
c/o Constance Lieber
2500 Westchester Ave.
Purchase, NY 10577-2540

Established in 1966.
Donors: Stephen Lieber; Constance Lieber; Stephen A. Lieber Trust.
Foundation type: Independent foundation.
Financial data (yr. ended 11/30/13): Assets, $79,982,632 (M); gifts received, $1,888,386; expenditures, $9,176,508; qualifying distributions, $9,127,396; giving activities include $9,127,396 for 7 grants (high: $7,142,425; low: $5,000).
Purpose and activities: Support for research in neuroscience, biological psychiatry, and higher education.
Fields of interest: Higher education; Neuroscience research.
Type of support: General/operating support; Research.
Limitations: Applications not accepted. Giving in the greater metropolitan New York, NY, area, including Nassau and Westchester counties; funding also in MD. No grants to individuals.
Application information: Contributes only to pre-selected organizations.
Officers: Constance Lieber, Pres.; Samuel Lieber, Secy.-Treas.
Trustee: Janice Lieber.
EIN: 136191234
Selected grants: The following grants are a representative sample of this grantmaker's funding activity:
$2,025,000 to Brain and Behavior Research Foundation, New York, NY, 2012. For unrestricted support.
$1,000,000 to Lieber Institute, Baltimore, MD, 2012. For unrestricted support.
$500,000 to New York-Presbyterian Fund, New York, NY, 2012. For unrestricted support.
$300,000 to Brain and Behavior Research Foundation, New York, NY, 2012. For unrestricted support.
$50,000 to UJA-Federation of New York, New York, NY, 2012. For unrestricted support.
$25,000 to Israel Leadership Institute, Sderot, Israel, 2012. For unrestricted support.

5962
The ETZ Chaim Charitable Trust ✧ ☆
1520 50th St.
Brooklyn, NY 11219-3745

Established in 1997 in NY.
Donors: Saul Wolf; Chaim Wolf; Chayem Meisels; Shaindy Meisels; Carter Enterprises, LLC; Deborah Wolf.
Foundation type: Independent foundation.
Financial data (yr. ended 12/31/13): Assets, $20,042,705 (M); gifts received, $5,887,144; expenditures, $1,037,162; qualifying distributions, $1,015,850; giving activities include $1,015,850 for 30 grants (high: $150,000; low: $1,000).
Fields of interest: Jewish agencies & synagogues; General charitable giving.
Limitations: Applications not accepted. Giving primarily in MA and NY. No grants to individuals.
Application information: Contributes only to pre-selected organizations.
Trustees: Deborah Wolf; Saul Wolf.
EIN: 137138977

5963
Eveillard Family Charitable Trust ✧
c/o Elizabeth M. Eveillard
3 E. 84th St., No. 7
New York, NY 10028-0407

Established in 2004 in NY.
Donors: Elizabeth M. Eveillard; Gamco Investors, Inc.
Foundation type: Independent foundation.
Financial data (yr. ended 12/31/13): Assets, $25,800,041 (M); expenditures, $1,988,613; qualifying distributions, $1,930,958; giving activities include $1,920,998 for 59 grants (high: $187,260; low: $100).
Purpose and activities: Giving primarily to the opera and higher education.
Fields of interest: Performing arts, opera; Arts; Higher education; Human services; Christian agencies & churches.
Limitations: Applications not accepted. Giving primarily in MA and NY. No grants to individuals.
Application information: Contributes only to pre-selected organizations.
Trustees: Elizabeth M. Eveillard; Jean-Marie R. Eveillard; Pauline M. Eveillard; Suzanne M. Eveillard.
EIN: 566648252

5964
Everett Foundation, Inc. ✧
150 E. 69th St.
New York, NY 10021-5704

Incorporated in 1957 in NY.
Donors: Henry Everett†; Edith B. Everett; David F. Everett; Carolyn Everett.
Foundation type: Independent foundation.
Financial data (yr. ended 12/31/13): Assets, $8,049,189 (M); expenditures, $1,102,674; qualifying distributions, $1,071,963; giving activities include $1,050,429 for 48 grants (high: $128,650; low: $100).
Purpose and activities: Giving primarily to Jewish organizations, as well as for education and human services.
Fields of interest: Arts; Higher education; Education; Botanical gardens; Human services; Jewish federated giving programs; Jewish agencies & synagogues.
Limitations: Applications not accepted. Giving primarily in the metropolitan New York, NY, area; some funding also in Washington, DC. No support for hospitals, motion pictures, videos, or theatrical plays. No grants to individuals, or for capital campaigns, conferences, annual campaigns, endowments, and operating support.
Application information: Contributes only to pre-selected organizations.
Officers and Directors:* Edith B. Everett, Chair. and Pres.; David F. Everett,* V.P.; Mark Levenfus,* Treas.; Daniel Reingold.
EIN: 116038040

5965
The Fairfield Foundation ✧
c/o Hughes Hubbard & Reed, LLP
1 Battery Park Plz.
New York, NY 10004-1482
Contact: Kenneth R. Page

Foundation type: Independent foundation.
Financial data (yr. ended 12/31/13): Assets, $8,847,939 (M); expenditures, $546,488; qualifying distributions, $482,000; giving activities include $482,000 for 28 grants (high: $90,000; low: $2,500).

Fields of interest: Education; Health care; Public affairs.
Limitations: Applications accepted. Giving primarily in Salisbury, CT.
Application information: Application form required.
Initial approach: Letter
Deadline(s): None
Trustees: David F. Harris; G. Anne Harris; John M. Harris.
EIN: 806135476
Selected grants: The following grants are a representative sample of this grantmaker's funding activity:
$2,500 to Yankee Golden Retriever Rescue, Hudson, MA, 2012. For community service.

5966
The Falcon Fund Foundation ✧ ☆
(formerly The Icarus Foundation)
c/o BSK
111 Washington Ave.
Albany, NY 12210-2214

Established in 1999 in MA.
Donors: Jean J. Beard; The 2004 Falcon Fund C.L.T.
Foundation type: Independent foundation.
Financial data (yr. ended 12/31/13): Assets, $2,656,416 (M); gifts received, $425,201; expenditures, $780,667; qualifying distributions, $778,500; giving activities include $778,500 for 16 grants (high: $350,000; low: $1,000).
Fields of interest: Education; Human services; Public affairs.
Limitations: Applications not accepted. Giving primarily in MA, NY, and Washington, DC. No grants to individuals.
Application information: Contributes only to pre-selected organizations.
Officer and Trustees:* Jean J. Beard,* Secy.; John R. Aldrich; Anson H. Beard; James McCook Beard; Leila J. Linen.
EIN: 141818663
Selected grants: The following grants are a representative sample of this grantmaker's funding activity:
$25,000 to Corlears School, New York, NY, 2011.
$20,000 to Brandywine Conservancy, Chadds Ford, PA, 2011.
$15,000 to Fractured Atlas, New York, NY, 2011.
$15,000 to Prep for Prep, New York, NY, 2011.
$10,000 to Spelman College, Atlanta, GA, 2011.
$2,000 to Treehouse Foundation, Easthampton, MA, 2011.
$1,000 to Trevor Day School, New York, NY, 2011.

5967
Falconwood Foundation, Inc. ✧
257 Park Ave. S., 7th Fl.
New York, NY 10010-7304
Contact: Stanley A. Lefkowitz, V.P., Secy., and Dir.

Established in 1987 in NY.
Donors: Henry G. Jarecki; John Jarecki; Thomas A. Jarecki; Divonne Holmes A'Court; Philip Chapman; Susan Chapman; Andrew R. Jarecki; Stanley A. Lefkowitz; Nicholas M. Jarecki; Classical Theatre of Harlem; The Brightwater Fund; Eugene D. Jarecki; Lianna Jarecki; Maxson D. Jarecki; Paul Brody; Samantha Brody; The Brightwater Fund; Antony Detre; The Claudio Reyna Foundation.
Foundation type: Independent foundation.
Financial data (yr. ended 12/31/13): Assets, $6,167 (M); gifts received, $3,995,300; expenditures, $4,031,465; qualifying distributions, $4,031,465; giving activities include $3,983,200 for 93 grants (high: $1,037,500; low: $200).
Fields of interest: Arts; Higher education; Education; Hospitals (general); Human services.
Limitations: Applications accepted. Giving primarily in NY.
Application information: Application form not required.
Initial approach: Proposal
Deadline(s): None
Officers and Directors:* Henry G. Jarecki,* Pres. and Treas.; Stanley A. Lefkowitz,* V.P. and Secy.; Thomas A. Russo.
EIN: 133456475

5968
The Fanwood Foundation ✧
c/o Bessemer Trust
630 5th Ave.
New York, NY 10111-0100
Application address: c/o Victor E.D. King, 435 W. 7th St., Plainfield, NJ 07060, tel.: (908) 756-7804

Trust established in 1940 in NJ.
Donor: Dorothy W. Stevens.
Foundation type: Independent foundation.
Financial data (yr. ended 12/31/13): Assets, $13,698,972 (M); expenditures, $669,751; qualifying distributions, $609,845; giving activities include $501,700 for 192 grants (high: $35,000; low: $250).
Fields of interest: Arts; Education; Environment, natural resources; Environment; Animals/wildlife; Hospitals (general); Hospitals (specialty); Christian agencies & churches.
Type of support: General/operating support; Annual campaigns; Land acquisition; Endowments.
Limitations: Applications accepted. No support for religious or political organizations. No grants to individuals.
Publications: Annual report.
Application information: Application form required.
Initial approach: Proposal
Copies of proposal: 1
Deadline(s): None
Board meeting date(s): Various
Trustees: Victor E.D. King; J. Whitney Stevens; Robert T. Stevens; Whitney Stevens.
EIN: 136051922

5969
Max & Marian Farash Charitable Foundation ✧
255 East Ave.
Rochester, NY 14604-2625 (585) 218-9855
FAX: (585) 546-1714;
E-mail: info@farashfoundation.org; Main URL: http://www.farashfoundation.org
Farash Prize for Social Entrepreneurship: http://www.farashfoundation.org/Default.aspx?RD=2275

Established in 1988 in NY.
Foundation type: Independent foundation.
Financial data (yr. ended 12/31/12): Assets, $257,912,246 (M); gifts received, $971,774; expenditures, $43,905,614; qualifying distributions, $10,259,672; giving activities include $6,965,011 for 166 grants (high: $790,000; low: $42).
Purpose and activities: Giving primarily for arts and culture, education, entrepreneurship, and Jewish life.
Fields of interest: Arts; Higher education; Human services; Jewish federated giving programs; Jewish agencies & synagogues.
Type of support: Emergency funds; General/operating support; Annual campaigns; Capital campaigns; Scholarship funds.
Limitations: Applications accepted. Giving primarily in Monroe and Ontario counties in NY. No grants to individuals directly, or for general operating support.
Publications: Application guidelines.
Application information: Application form not required.
Initial approach: Use application process on foundation web site
Deadline(s): See foundation web site for current deadlines
Officers and Trustees:* Nathan J. Robfogel, Esq.*, Chair.; Hollis S. Budd, Exec. Dir.; Matthew Aroesty; Kenneth D. Bell; Lynn Farash; Edward Hourihan, Jr.; Thomas H. Jackson; Howard Konar; Hoffman Moka Lantum, M.D., Ph.D; Theresa Mazzullo; Alvin L. Ureles, M.D.; Gregory Wolcott.
EIN: 222948675

5970
The Gloria and Hilliard Farber Foundation ✧
980 5th Ave., Apt. 17B
New York, NY 10021

Established in 2000 in NY.
Donors: Gloria Farber; Hilliard Farber; Hilliard Farber & Co., Inc.
Foundation type: Independent foundation.
Financial data (yr. ended 05/31/13): Assets, $1,069,188 (M); gifts received, $100,000; expenditures, $501,630; qualifying distributions, $489,616; giving activities include $485,504 for 21 grants (high: $123,574; low: $1,000).
Fields of interest: Child development, education; Education; Human services; Youth, services.
Limitations: Applications not accepted. Giving primarily in New York, NY. No grants to individuals.
Application information: Unsolicited requests for funds not accepted.
Directors: Gloria Farber; Hilliard Farber; Jennifer Farber; Melissa Farber.
EIN: 134132864
Selected grants: The following grants are a representative sample of this grantmaker's funding activity:
$53,500 to Columbia University, New York, NY, 2011.
$1,000 to New York Live Arts, New York, NY, 2011.
$1,000 to Young Israel of Great Neck, Great Neck, NY, 2011.

5971
The Fascitelli Family Foundation ✧
170 East End Ave., Apt. 17 A/B
New York, NY 10128-7681

Established in 1993 in NY.
Donors: Michael D. Fascitelli; Elizabeth Cogan Fascitelli.
Foundation type: Independent foundation.

Financial data (yr. ended 01/31/13): Assets, $19,684,107 (M); gifts received, $3,380,549; expenditures, $1,555,198; qualifying distributions, $1,332,128; giving activities include $1,332,128 for 83 grants (high: $250,000; low: $250).
Purpose and activities: Giving primarily for education, and health associations, including a mental health center for children.
Fields of interest: Arts; Elementary/secondary education; Higher education; Education; Health care; Health organizations, association; Human services.
Limitations: Applications not accepted. Giving primarily in New York, NY; some funding also in NH and RI. No grants to individuals.
Application information: Contributes only to pre-selected organizations.
Officers: Elizabeth Cogan Fascitelli, Treas.; Michael D. Fascitelli, Mgr.
EIN: 133748071
Selected grants: The following grants are a representative sample of this grantmaker's funding activity:
$300,000 to Dartmouth College, Hanover, NH, 2011.
$10,000 to Columbia University, New York, NY, 2011.
$5,000 to Aspen Institute, Washington, DC, 2011.
$5,000 to Childrens Tumor Foundation, New York, NY, 2011.
$5,000 to Nature Conservancy, Arlington, VA, 2011.
$5,000 to New York City Opera, New York, NY, 2011.
$5,000 to Teach for America, New York, NY, 2011.
$2,500 to Cystic Fibrosis Foundation, Bethesda, MD, 2011.
$1,000 to City of Hope, Duarte, CA, 2011.
$1,000 to Right to Play International, Toronto, Canada, 2011.

5972
George H. Fearons, III Charitable Trust ✧ ☆
Church St. Station
P.O. Box 1297
New York, NY 10009-8957

Donor: George Fearons†.
Foundation type: Independent foundation.
Financial data (yr. ended 07/31/13): Assets, $9,865,837 (M); gifts received, $306,124; expenditures, $590,046; qualifying distributions, $541,847; giving activities include $500,001 for 2 grants (high: $426,300; low: $73,701).
Fields of interest: Education; Catholic agencies & churches.
Limitations: Applications not accepted. Giving primarily in VT.
Application information: Unsolicited requests for funds not accepted.
Trustee: Deutsche Bank Trust Co., N.A.
EIN: 452899447

5973
The Feil Family Foundation ✧
(formerly Louis & Gertrude Feil Foundation, Inc.)
370 7th Ave., Ste. 618
New York, NY 10001-3912

Established in 1977 in NY.
Donors: Louis Feil†; Gertrude Feil†; Gertrude Feil Marital Trust; Charitable Lead Annuity Trust A; Charitable Lead Annuity Trust B; Charitable Lead Annuity Trust C; Charitable Lead Annuity Trust D; Charitable Lead Annuity Trust E.
Foundation type: Independent foundation.
Financial data (yr. ended 06/30/14): Assets, $1,489,230 (M); gifts received, $1,000,000; expenditures, $4,411,050; qualifying distributions, $4,410,800; giving activities include $4,410,800 for 32 grants (high: $4,000,000; low: $1,000).
Purpose and activities: Giving primarily for health and human services, higher education, and to Jewish agencies, temples, and schools.
Fields of interest: Elementary/secondary education; Higher education; Law school/education; Hospitals (general); Health organizations, association; Medical research, institute; Human services; Children/youth, services; Jewish federated giving programs; Jewish agencies & synagogues.
Limitations: Applications not accepted. Giving primarily in NY. No grants to individuals.
Application information: Contributes only to pre-selected organizations.
Officers: Jeffrey Feil, Pres.; Carole Feil, V.P. and Secy.; Jay Anderson, Treas.
EIN: 132958414
Selected grants: The following grants are a representative sample of this grantmaker's funding activity:
$25,000 to Madison Square Park Conservancy, New York, NY, 2013. For park conservancy.
$10,000 to Lenox Hill Hospital, New York, NY, 2013. For special events funding.
$10,000 to Safe Horizon, New York, NY, 2013. For family assistance programs.
$5,000 to Union Square Partnership, New York, NY, 2013. For Beautification Programs.

5974
Susan & Leonard Feinstein Foundation ✧
(formerly Feinstein Family Foundation)
c/o Bed Bath & Beyond
2 Jericho Plz.
Jericho, NY 11753-1681 (516) 822-3254

Established in 1992.
Donors: Leonard Feinstein; Amy Feinstein.
Foundation type: Independent foundation.
Financial data (yr. ended 06/30/13): Assets, $80,554,422 (M); expenditures, $5,888,440; qualifying distributions, $5,861,304; giving activities include $5,852,731 for 130 grants (high: $2,500,000; low: $100).
Purpose and activities: Giving primarily for the arts, particularly museums, health care, and to Jewish agencies and temples.
Fields of interest: Museums; Arts; Hospitals (general); Health care; Health organizations, association; Jewish federated giving programs; Jewish agencies & synagogues.
Limitations: Applications not accepted. Giving primarily in NY. No grants to individuals.
Application information: Contributes only to pre-selected organizations.
Officers and Trustee:* Susan Feinstein,* Vice-Chair.; Leonard Feinstein, Pres.; Amy Feinstein, Secy.
EIN: 113131761
Selected grants: The following grants are a representative sample of this grantmaker's funding activity:
$2,500,000 to Feinstein Institute for Medical Research, Manhasset, NY, 2013. For general support.
$416,667 to New Museum of Contemporary Art, New York, NY, 2013. For general support.
$375,000 to UJA-Federation of New York, New York, NY, 2013. For general support.
$350,000 to Friends of the Israel Defense Forces, National/New York Tri-State Region, New York, NY, 2013. For general support.
$225,000 to American Friends of Shalva, New York, NY, 2013. For general support.
$196,164 to PEF Israel Endowment Funds, New York, NY, 2013. For general support.
$100,000 to Jewish Communal Fund of New York, New York, NY, 2013. For general support.
$50,000 to American Ballet Theater, New York, NY, 2013. For general support.
$30,000 to Friends of ELNET, Northbrook, IL, 2013. For general support.
$20,000 to Project Renewal, New York, NY, 2013. For general support.

5975
Fernleigh Foundation ✧
1 Rockefeller Plz., 31st Fl.
New York, NY 10020-2003

Established in 1993 in NY.
Donor: Jane F. Clark.
Foundation type: Independent foundation.
Financial data (yr. ended 12/31/12): Assets, $12,320,053 (M); expenditures, $1,150,648; qualifying distributions, $1,020,450; giving activities include $1,020,450 for 8 grants (high: $600,000; low: $500).
Fields of interest: Museums; Nursing home/convalescent facility; Athletics/sports, equestrianism; Human services.
Limitations: Applications not accepted. Giving primarily in Cooperstown, NY; funding also in Williamstown, MA, Gladstone, NJ, and Cold Spring, NY.
Application information: Contributes only to pre-selected organizations.
Officers and Directors:* Jane F. Clark,* Pres.; Edward W. Stack,* V.P.; Kathleen F. Keslter, Secy.; Kevin S. Moore,* Treas.
EIN: 137027378

5976
Fifth & Pacific Foundation ✧
(formerly Liz Claiborne Foundation)
1441 Broadway
New York, NY 10018-1805 (212) 626-5704
Contact: Sheila M. Renovitch, Dir.; Alison Mathias, Prog. Off.
FAX: (212) 626-1841;
E-mail: Foundation@fnpc.com; Main URL: http://www.fifthandpacific.com/web/guest/foundation
Featured Grants: http://www.fifthandpacific.com/web/guest/featuredgrants

Established in 1981 in NY.
Donors: Liz Claiborne Inc.; Fifth & Pacific Companies, Inc.
Foundation type: Company-sponsored foundation.
Financial data (yr. ended 12/31/12): Assets, $26,812,256 (M); expenditures, $1,571,398; qualifying distributions, $1,466,906; giving

activities include $1,402,082 for 252 grants (high: $250,000; low: $20).
Purpose and activities: The foundation supports programs designed to promote women's economic self-sufficiency. Special emphasis is directed toward women affected by domestic violence who are transitioning from poverty into successful independent living.
Fields of interest: Employment, services; Employment, training; Family services, domestic violence; Human services; Economic development; Women.
Type of support: General/operating support; Annual campaigns; Program development; Technical assistance; Employee matching gifts; Matching/challenge support.
Limitations: Applications accepted. Giving primarily in areas of company operations with emphasis on Los Angeles County, CA, Hudson County, NJ, and New York, NY; limited giving also to national organizations. No support for political organizations, or religious, fraternal, or veterans' organizations. No grants to individuals, or for capital campaigns, equipment, professional meetings, conferences, or symposia, endowments, research, technical assistance, media projects, fundraising events, sponsorships, or journal advertisements.
Publications: Application guidelines.
Application information: Application form not required.
Initial approach: Download proposal cover sheet and mail proposal and cover sheet to foundation
Copies of proposal: 1
Deadline(s): None
Board meeting date(s): Quarterly
Final notification: 5 days following board meetings
Officers and Directors :* John Moroz,* Chair.; Alison Mathias, Secy. and Prog. Off.; John Engeman, Treas.; Sheila Renovitch, Fdn. Dir.; Diana Buchman; Jerome Chazen; Elaine Goodell; Roberta Karp; Craig Leavitt; William McComb; Jane Randel; Nick Rubino.
Number of staff: 2 full-time professional.
EIN: 133060673
Selected grants: The following grants are a representative sample of this grantmaker's funding activity:
$75,000 to Joyful Heart Foundation, New York, NY, 2012. For No More Project.
$65,000 to Sanctuary for Families, New York, NY, 2011.
$50,000 to Rising Tide Capital, Jersey City, NJ, 2011.
$50,000 to Womens Initiative for Self Employment, San Francisco, CA, 2011. For Women's Initiative in the New York City metropolitan area.
$45,000 to Hot Bread Kitchen, Brooklyn, NY, 2012.
$30,000 to Women in Non Traditional Employment Roles, Los Angeles, CA, 2011.

5977
FIMF, Inc. ✧
477 Madison Ave., 10th Fl.
New York, NY 10022-2027

Established in 1995 in DE and NY.
Foundation type: Independent foundation.
Financial data (yr. ended 12/31/13): Assets, $32,898,836 (M); expenditures, $1,495,036; qualifying distributions, $1,394,191; giving activities include $1,384,726 for 25 grants (high: $392,208; low: $26).
Purpose and activities: Giving primarily to Jewish organizations.
Fields of interest: Higher education; Education; Human services; Children/youth, services; Jewish agencies & synagogues.
International interests: Israel.
Limitations: Applications not accepted. Giving primarily in New York, NY, and in Tel Aviv, Israel. No grants to individuals.
Application information: Contributes only to pre-selected organizations.
Officer and Directors:* Susan Wexner,* Pres. and Secy.-Treas.; Saul G. Agus; Raymond Kanner; Gregg H. Levy, Esq.; Michael S. Oberman, Esq.; Mark Saks, Esq.; Walter Stern.
EIN: 134072661

5978
Finneran Family Foundation ✧
c/o Anchin, Block & Anchin
1375 Broadway
New York, NY 10018-7001

Established in 1986 in NY.
Donors: William B. Finneran; Exop Investors LLC; William B. Finneran Thru Exop Investors LP.
Foundation type: Independent foundation.
Financial data (yr. ended 11/30/13): Assets, $4,123,502 (M); gifts received, $1,381,419; expenditures, $588,947; qualifying distributions, $554,213; giving activities include $507,410 for 27 grants (high: $200,000; low: $500).
Purpose and activities: Giving primarily for education, health, and human services.
Fields of interest: Museums; Performing arts; Performing arts centers; Higher education; Hospitals (general); Health organizations, association; Boys & girls clubs; Human services; Children/youth, services; Youth, services; Catholic agencies & churches.
Limitations: Applications not accepted. Giving primarily in NY and PA. No grants to individuals.
Application information: Unsolicited requests for funds not accepted.
Officer: William B. Finneran, Pres.
EIN: 133447863

5979
First Niagara Foundation
(formerly First Niagara Bank Foundation)
726 Exchange St., Ste. 900
Buffalo, NY 14210-1452 (716) 270-8675
Contact: Elizabeth S. Gurney, Exec. Dir.; Florine Luhr, Fdn. Admin.
FAX: (716) 819-5160; E-mail: florine.luhr@fnfg.com; Main URL: https://www.firstniagara.com/About_Us/Community_Commitment/Community_Commitment.aspx

Established in 1998 in NY.
Donors: Niagara Bancorp, Inc.; First Niagara Financial Group, Inc.; Lockport Savings Bank; First Niagara Bank.
Foundation type: Company-sponsored foundation.
Financial data (yr. ended 12/31/13): Assets, $32,696,352 (M); expenditures, $9,326,337; qualifying distributions, $9,326,337; giving activities include $9,326,337 for grants.
Purpose and activities: The foundation supports organizations involved with mentoring and children and youth. Giving is limited to areas of company operations.
Fields of interest: Arts, single organization support; Arts education; Education, single organization support; Higher education; Adult education—literacy, basic skills & GED; Education; Health care; Food banks; Food distribution, meals on wheels; Housing/shelter, management/technical assistance; Housing/shelter, single organization support; Housing/shelter, information services; Housing/shelter, public education; Housing/shelter, formal/general education; Housing/shelter, development; Housing/shelter, rehabilitation; Housing/shelter, home owners; Recreation, community; Youth development, alliance/advocacy; Youth development, single organization support; Boys & girls clubs; Youth development, adult & child programs; Big Brothers/Big Sisters; Youth development; Children/youth, services; Residential/custodial care; Community development, neighborhood development; Economic development; Community development, small businesses; Children/youth; Children; Youth; Young adults; Economically disadvantaged.
Type of support: Program development; Employee volunteer services; Sponsorships.
Limitations: Applications accepted. Giving limited to areas of company operations in CT, Western MA, Upstate and Hudson Valley NY, and PA. No support for organizations with limited availability to the general public; political organizations, candidates or lobbying efforts; national or international organizations, unless their programs have significant local impact; organizations that discriminate based on: age, race, color, sex, religion, national origin, disability, marital status, receipt of public assistance, sexual orientation, or military status. No grants to individuals or programs that benefit specific individuals.
Publications: Application guidelines; Corporate giving report.
Application information: Contributions are limited to one donation per organization in any given year. Organizations receiving Mentoring Matters support are asked to submit a final report. Application form required.
Initial approach: Complete online application at www.firstniagara.com
Copies of proposal: 1
Deadline(s): 90 days prior to need
Board meeting date(s): Quarterly
Final notification: 90 days from receipt
Officers and Directors:* Mark Rendulic, Pres.; Rose Melisz, Secy.; Ann Segarra, Treas.; Daniel E. Cantara; Peter Cosgrove; Robert Kane; Paul McCraven; Todd Moules; David Ring; Cathie Schaffer; Buford Sears.
Number of staff: 2 full-time professional.
EIN: 161549641
Selected grants: The following grants are a representative sample of this grantmaker's funding activity:
$125,000 to Big Brothers Big Sisters Southeastern Pennsylvania, Philadelphia, PA, 2013. For mentoring program.
$125,000 to United Way of Allegheny County, Pittsburgh, PA, 2013. For Be a 6th Grade Mentor Program.
$50,000 to Be-A-Friend Program, Big Brothers Big Sisters of Erie County, Buffalo, NY, 2013. For Tranforming Buffalo Through Mentoring and Education Program.

$50,000 to Central New York Community Foundation, Syracuse, NY, 2013. For Say Yes Syracuse Mentoring Program.
$50,000 to Mass Mentoring Partnership, Boston, MA, 2013. For youth mentoring.

5980
Harry and Jane Fischel Foundation ✧
875 Ave. of the Americas, Ste. 1701
New York, NY 10001-3507 (212) 599-2828
FAX: (212) 867-8512;
E-mail: info@fischelfoundation.org; Application e-mail: grants@fischelfoundation.org; Main URL: http://fischelfoundation.org/

Incorporated in 1932 in NY.
Donor: Harry Fischel†.
Foundation type: Independent foundation.
Financial data (yr. ended 12/31/13): Assets, $13,774,680 (M); expenditures, $1,133,993; qualifying distributions, $659,765; giving activities include $425,470 for 15 grants (high: $377,000; low: $50).
Purpose and activities: Organized to develop Talmudic research to aid Jewish knowledge and to present the Orthodox Jewish contributions to civilization. Funding also to an institute which includes a school for training judges for religious courts, publishes tracts in the field of religious law, and researches and republishes Talmudic commentary in new editions utilizing heretofore unknown manuscripts; some giving also for Jewish education and temples.
Fields of interest: Education; Jewish agencies & synagogues.
International interests: Israel.
Type of support: General/operating support.
Limitations: Giving primarily in NY; some giving also in Israel. No grants to individuals.
Publications: Application guidelines.
Application information: Complete application guidelines available on foundation website. Application form required.
Initial approach: E-mail grant application form on foundation web site to specific application e-mail address
Officers and Directors:* Chief Rabbi Shear-Yashuv Cohen,* Chair.; Seth M. Goldstein,* Pres.; Rabbi Hillel Reichel,* 1st V.P.; Chaim Stepelman,* 2nd V.P.; Rabbi Aaron I. Reichel, Esq.*, Secy.; Avishai Kraus, Esq.; David S. Locker; Donald Moses; Deborah Stepelman.
Number of staff: 1 part-time professional; 2 part-time support.
EIN: 135677832
Selected grants: The following grants are a representative sample of this grantmaker's funding activity:
$25,500 to Yeshiva University, New York, NY, 2011.
$14,756 to Mesorah Heritage Foundation, Brooklyn, NY, 2011.

5981
The Fischer Family Foundation ✧
c/o Timeworks International, Inc.
449 20th St.
Brooklyn, NY 11215-6247

Donors: Chaim Fischer; CRF Charitable Lead Trust; Timesworks Worldwide, LLC; Stuhrling Palace LLC; Stuhrling Original, LLC.
Foundation type: Independent foundation.
Financial data (yr. ended 12/31/12): Assets, $36,172 (M); gifts received, $523,000; expenditures, $499,053; qualifying distributions, $498,699; giving activities include $498,699 for grants.
Purpose and activities: Giving primarily to Jewish agencies, temples, and schools.
Fields of interest: Elementary/secondary education; Human services; Jewish federated giving programs; Jewish agencies & synagogues.
Limitations: Applications not accepted. No grants to individuals.
Application information: Contributes only to pre-selected organizations.
Trustee: Chaim Fischer.
EIN: 510474134

5982
The Fisher Brothers Foundation, Inc. ✧
c/o Fisher Brothers
299 Park Ave.
New York, NY 10171-0001
Main URL: http://www.fisherbrothers.com/about/philanthropies/3

Established in 1981 in NY.
Donors: Fisher Brothers; Fisher Park Lane Co.; Fisher Capital Assets; 1345 Cleaning Service Co. II LP; 299 Cleaning Service Co. II LP; Plaza Cleaning Service Co. II LP; 605 Cleaning Service Co. II LP; Columbia Cleaning; Fisher 120 Wall; Fisher 92nd St.; FSAR Fee Associates; Rancho Road Development; Park Clipper Leasing Associates; Sandhurst Associates; Zachary & Elizabeth Fisher Charitable Trust.
Foundation type: Company-sponsored foundation.
Financial data (yr. ended 12/31/12): Assets, $44,315 (M); gifts received, $2,900,000; expenditures, $3,123,910; qualifying distributions, $3,096,892; giving activities include $3,086,782 for 54 grants (high: $1,197,600; low: $500).
Purpose and activities: The foundation supports police agencies and fire departments and organizations involved with arts and culture, health, golf, military and veterans, and Judaism.
Fields of interest: Museums; Performing arts centers; Arts; Hospitals (general); Health care; Crime/law enforcement, police agencies; Disasters, fire prevention/control; Athletics/sports, golf; Jewish federated giving programs; Military/veterans' organizations; Jewish agencies & synagogues.
Type of support: Program development; General/operating support; Annual campaigns; Scholarship funds.
Limitations: Applications not accepted. Giving limited to New York, NY. No grants to individuals.
Application information: Contributes only to pre-selected organizations.
Directors: Arnold Fisher; Kenneth Fisher; Winston C. Fisher.
EIN: 133118286
Selected grants: The following grants are a representative sample of this grantmaker's funding activity:
$749,200 to Intrepid Museum Foundation, New York, NY, 2011.
$136,000 to Charity: Water, New York, NY, 2011.
$115,150 to Lincoln Center for the Performing Arts, New York, NY, 2011.
$75,000 to Fisher House Foundation, Rockville, MD, 2011.
$25,000 to Beth Israel Medical Center, New York, NY, 2011.
$11,000 to Metropolitan Museum of Art, New York, NY, 2011.
$5,000 to Skyscraper Museum, New York, NY, 2011.
$2,500 to Museum of the City of New York, New York, NY, 2011.
$2,000 to Columbus Citizens Foundation, New York, NY, 2011.

5983
Eileen Fisher Foundation ✧ ☆
c/o Marilyn Calister, WTAS LLC
1177 Avenue of the Americas, 18th Fl.
New York, NY 10036-2714

Established in 2004 in NY.
Donor: Eileen Fisher.
Foundation type: Independent foundation.
Financial data (yr. ended 11/30/13): Assets, $4,869,669 (M); gifts received, $1,500,000; expenditures, $1,081,014; qualifying distributions, $1,006,500; giving activities include $1,006,500 for 12 grants (high: $745,000; low: $500).
Fields of interest: Performing arts centers; Education; Health organizations; Community/economic development.
Type of support: General/operating support.
Limitations: Applications not accepted. Giving primarily in NY. No grants to individuals.
Application information: Unsolicited requests for funds not accepted.
Trustee: Eileen Fisher.
EIN: 331113151

5984
The Fishoff Family Foundation ✧
c/o Mimi
240 Viola Rd.
Monsey, NY 10952-1731

Established in 1982 in NY.
Donors: Benjamin Fishoff; Marilyn Fishoff†; Donald Fishoff; Henry M. Shapiro; Avi Fishoff; Meryl Gross; Saul D. Levy; Interocean Industries, Inc.; Regina Weinstock; Zev Maybruck; Louis Gellis.
Foundation type: Independent foundation.
Financial data (yr. ended 07/31/13): Assets, $6,280,921 (M); gifts received, $13,000; expenditures, $523,148; qualifying distributions, $493,265; giving activities include $493,265 for grants.
Purpose and activities: Support primarily for Jewish organizations, temples, and schools.
Fields of interest: Elementary/secondary education; Human services; Jewish agencies & synagogues.
Limitations: Applications not accepted. Giving primarily in Brooklyn and Queens, NY. No grants to individuals.
Application information: Contributes only to pre-selected organizations.
Officer: Benjamin Fishoff, Pres.
Directors: Abraham Fishoff; Donald Fishoff; Barbara Gold; Meryl Gross; Regina Weinstock.
EIN: 133076576

5985
Lawton W. Fitt and James I. McLaren Foundation ✧ ☆
Bowling Green Sta.
P.O. Box 73
New York, NY 10274-0073

Established in 1996 in NY.
Donors: Lawton W. Fitt; James McLaren.
Foundation type: Independent foundation.
Financial data (yr. ended 09/30/13): Assets, $7,180,517 (M); expenditures, $467,548; qualifying distributions, $447,750; giving activities include $447,750 for 24 grants (high: $100,000; low: $100).
Purpose and activities: Giving primarily for international relations and education; some giving also for the arts and social services.
Fields of interest: Performing arts; Arts; Higher education; Education; Health care; Health organizations, association; Youth development; Human services; International development; United Ways and Federated Giving Programs.
Limitations: Applications not accepted. Giving primarily in NY and VA. No grants to individuals, or for scholarships; no loans.
Application information: Contributes only to pre-selected organizations.
Trustees: Lawton W. Fitt; James I. McLaren.
EIN: 133919763

5986
The Flaherty Family Foundation ✧ ☆
130 E. 95th St.
New York, NY 10128-1705

Established in 1996 in DE and NY.
Donors: Peter A. Flaherty; Pamela Flaherty.
Foundation type: Independent foundation.
Financial data (yr. ended 10/31/13): Assets, $528,297 (M); gifts received, $856,456; expenditures, $433,482; qualifying distributions, $431,209; giving activities include $428,650 for 34 grants (high: $200,000; low: $100).
Fields of interest: Higher education; Human services.
Type of support: General/operating support.
Limitations: Applications not accepted. Giving primarily in NY and OH. No grants to individuals.
Application information: Contributes only to pre-selected organizations.
Officers: Peter A. Flaherty, Pres.; Jonathan P. Flaherty, Treas.
Trustee: Pamela P. Flaherty.
EIN: 133919502
Selected grants: The following grants are a representative sample of this grantmaker's funding activity:
$200,000 to Johns Hopkins University, Baltimore, MD, 2011.
$200,000 to Rockefeller University, New York, NY, 2011.
$70,000 to TechnoServe, Washington, DC, 2011.
$50,000 to Kenyon College, Gambier, OH, 2011.
$10,000 to Educators for Excellence, New York, NY, 2011.
$10,000 to Johns Hopkins University, Baltimore, MD, 2011.
$8,000 to TechnoServe, Washington, DC, 2011.
$5,000 to Rockefeller University, New York, NY, 2011.
$2,120 to TechnoServe, Washington, DC, 2011.
$2,000 to New York Stem Cell Foundation, New York, NY, 2011.

5987
The Fledgling Fund ✧
162 5th Ave., Ste. 901
New York, NY 10010-5967
E-mail: info@thefledglingfund.org; Main URL: http://www.thefledglingfund.org
Blog: http://www.thefledglingfund.org/blog/
Facebook: http://www.facebook.com/pages/The-Fledgling-Fund/101890706557481
Pinterest: http://pinterest.com/fledglingfund/
Twitter: http://twitter.com/fledglingfund
YouTube: http://www.youtube.com/user/TheFledglingFund

Donor: Diana Barrett.
Foundation type: Independent foundation.
Financial data (yr. ended 12/31/12): Assets, $16,026,983 (M); gifts received, $225,500; expenditures, $2,251,997; qualifying distributions, $2,233,829; giving activities include $1,577,300 for 114 grants (high: $60,000; low: $250).
Purpose and activities: The fund seeks to improve the lives of vulnerable individuals, families and communities by supporting innovative media projects that target entrenched social problems.
Fields of interest: Media, film/video; Environment, beautification programs; Environment; Health care; Substance abuse, prevention; Housing/shelter; Children/youth, services; International affairs; Civil/human rights, advocacy.
Type of support: Film/video/radio.
Limitations: Giving on a national and international basis. No support for youth media programs.
Publications: Application guidelines.
Application information: Full applications are by invitation only, upon review of letter of inquiry. If the applicant is involved with more than one project that fits the foundation's guidelines, they are welcome to submit separate letters of inquiry for each. All applicants must have a fiscal sponsor based in the U.S. This does not need to be in place for applicants to submit the letter of inquiry or the application, but it must be in place for the funds to be disbursed. Application form required.
Initial approach: Complete foundation online letter of inquiry
Deadline(s): See foundation web site
Officers and Directors:* Diana Barrett,* Pres. and Secy.; Bob Vila,* V.P.; Robert Connor, V.P.; Christopher Vila,* V.P.; Jessica Wolfe, V.P.
Number of staff: 1 full-time professional; 2 part-time professional.
EIN: 202450707
Selected grants: The following grants are a representative sample of this grantmaker's funding activity:
$40,000 to International Documentary Association, Los Angeles, CA, 2012. For Cafeteria Man.
$25,000 to International Documentary Association, Los Angeles, CA, 2012. For Brooklyn Castle (formerly Chess Movie).
$25,000 to International Documentary Association, Los Angeles, CA, 2012. For Escape Fire The Fight To Rescue American Healthcare.
$25,000 to International Documentary Association, Los Angeles, CA, 2012. For Girls on the Wall.
$20,000 to Documentary Educational Resources, Watertown, MA, 2012. For The Awra Amba Experience.
$20,000 to International Documentary Association, Los Angeles, CA, 2012. For 25 to Life.
$20,000 to International Documentary Association, Los Angeles, CA, 2012. For CITIZEN CORP (Working Title).
$20,000 to Pulitzer Center on Crisis Reporting, Washington, DC, 2012. For Easy Like Water.
$20,000 to San Francisco Film Society, San Francisco, CA, 2012. For MissRepresentation org-Town Hall Forums.
$15,000 to Coruway Film Institute, Portsmouth, NH, 2012. For The Schooting Beauty Patch.

5988
Stephanie & Lawrence Flinn, Jr. Charitable Trust ✧
555 Theodore Fremd Ave., Apt. C-207
Rye, NY 10580-1451

Donor: Lawrence Flinn, Jr.
Foundation type: Independent foundation.
Financial data (yr. ended 12/31/13): Assets, $21,564,255 (M); expenditures, $1,771,268; qualifying distributions, $1,098,845; giving activities include $1,098,845 for 89 grants (high: $347,063; low: $5).
Fields of interest: Arts; Education; Environment.
Limitations: Applications not accepted. Giving primarily in NY.
Application information: Contributes only to pre-selected organizations.
Trustees: Lawrence Flinn, Jr.; Stephanie Flinn.
EIN: 266135172

5989
The Flom Family Foundation ✧
4 Times Sq.
New York, NY 10036-6518

Established in 1988 in NY.
Donors: Claire Flom; Joseph H. Flom‡.
Foundation type: Independent foundation.
Financial data (yr. ended 12/31/12): Assets, $29,948,872 (M); gifts received, $30,000,000; expenditures, $897,718; qualifying distributions, $855,750; giving activities include $854,750 for 16 grants (high: $119,000; low: $19,000).
Fields of interest: Elementary/secondary education; Higher education; Human services; Children/youth, services.
Type of support: Program development; Seed money; Curriculum development.
Limitations: Applications not accepted. Giving primarily in New York, NY. No grants to individuals, or for endowment or building funds, fellowships, travel, or operating expenses; no program-related investments.
Application information: Contributes only to pre-selected organizations.
Officers and Directors:* Robert C. Sheehan,* Pres.; Jason Flom,* V.P.; Peter Flom,* Secy.; Earle Yaffa,* Treas.; Eric J. Friedman; Nancy Laing.
Number of staff: 1 part-time professional.
EIN: 133499384

5990
J. C. Flowers Foundation ✧ ☆
c/o J. C . Flowers & Co.
717 5th Ave.
New York, NY 10022
Main URL: http://www.jcflowersfoundation.org/

Donors: J. Christopher Flowers; E. Neville Isdell.
Foundation type: Independent foundation.
Financial data (yr. ended 12/31/12): Assets, $363,875 (M); gifts received, $1,468,250; expenditures, $1,164,802; qualifying distributions, $1,144,302; giving activities include $929,936 for 25 grants (high: $200,000; low: $1,000).
Fields of interest: Health care; Human services; Christian agencies & churches.
Limitations: Applications not accepted. Giving primarily in New York, NY; funding also in Angola, England, Namibia, Zambia, and Zimbabwe.
Application information: Unsolicited requests for funds not accepted.
Officers: J. Christopher Flowers, Pres.; Susan Lassen, Exec. Dir.
Trustee: Anne Flowers.
EIN: 272142340
Selected grants: The following grants are a representative sample of this grantmaker's funding activity:
$125,000 to Episcopal Relief and Development, New York, NY, 2012. To Strengthen Malaria Control.
$55,508 to Interfaith Center of New York, New York, NY, 2012. For Reintegrate Parolees Into Productive Society.
$10,000 to Naval Institute Foundation, Annapolis, MD, 2012. For education in national defense.
$2,300 to Autism Speaks, New York, NY, 2012. For Research and Awareness in Autism.
$1,930 to University of the South, Sewanee, TN, 2012. For Theological Scholarship for African Priests Fund.

5991
The Foop Foundation ✧
c/o Poof Apparel Corp.
1407 Broadway, Ste. 900
New York, NY 10018-5109

Foundation type: Independent foundation.
Financial data (yr. ended 12/31/13): Assets, $162,830 (M); gifts received, $623,800; expenditures, $698,170; qualifying distributions, $698,899; giving activities include $698,899 for 524 grants (high: $55,703; low: $26).
Purpose and activities: Giving primarily to Jewish agencies, temples, and schools.
Fields of interest: Education; Jewish agencies & synagogues.
Limitations: Applications not accepted.
Application information: Unsolicited requests for funds not accepted.
Trustees: Albert Habert; David Shalom; Elliot Terzi.
EIN: 266721306
Selected grants: The following grants are a representative sample of this grantmaker's funding activity:
$10,000 to Chai Lifeline, New York, NY, 2011.

5992
Leo and Julia Forchheimer Foundation ✧ ☆
(formerly The Forchheimer Foundation)
c/o Golenbock, Eiseman, Assor, Bell & Peskoe, LLP
437 Madison Ave., 35th Fl.
New York, NY 10022-7001

Established about 1957 in NY.
Donor: Leo Forchheimer†.
Foundation type: Independent foundation.
Financial data (yr. ended 12/31/13): Assets, $1,054,496 (M); expenditures, $618,917; qualifying distributions, $618,917; giving activities include $575,000 for 1 grant.
Purpose and activities: Giving primarily to a Modern Orthodox Jewish day school in Riverdale, NY.
Fields of interest: Elementary/secondary education.
Limitations: Applications not accepted. Giving primarily in Riverdale, NY.
Application information: Contributes only to pre-selected charitable organizations.
Officer and Director:* Michael Jesselson,* Secy.
Number of staff: None.
EIN: 136075112

5993
The Ford Family Foundation ✧
(formerly The David B. & Virginia M. Ford Foundation)
c/o BCRS Assocs., LLC
77 Water St., 9th Fl.
New York, NY 10005-4414

Established in 1986 in PA.
Donor: David B. Ford.
Foundation type: Independent foundation.
Financial data (yr. ended 06/30/13): Assets, $15,682,266 (M); gifts received, $15; expenditures, $1,147,822; qualifying distributions, $987,478; giving activities include $973,963 for 128 grants (high: $70,000; low: $250).
Purpose and activities: Giving primarily for the arts, education, health associations, and human services.
Fields of interest: Arts; Higher education; Education; Animals/wildlife, preservation/protection; Animals/wildlife, bird preserves; Health organizations, association; Human services.
Limitations: Applications not accepted. Giving primarily in New York, NY, and PA; funding also in Newport, RI. No grants to individuals; no loans.
Application information: Contributes only to pre-selected organizations.
Trustees: David B. Ford; David B. Ford, Jr.; James M. Ford; Virginia M. Ford.
EIN: 133385063
Selected grants: The following grants are a representative sample of this grantmaker's funding activity:
$1,979,000 to Vanguard Charitable Endowment Program, Boston, MA, 2011. For general purpose fund.
$100,000 to University of Pennsylvania, Philadelphia, PA, 2011. For general purpose fund.
$100,000 to University of Pennsylvania, Philadelphia, PA, 2011. For general purpose fund.
$30,000 to Bryn Mawr Film Institute, Bryn Mawr, PA, 2011. For general purpose fund.
$25,000 to National Urban Squash and Education Association, Roxbury Crossing, MA, 2011. For general purpose fund.
$20,000 to Bryn Mawr Hospital Foundation, Bryn Mawr, PA, 2011. For general purpose fund.
$15,000 to Norman Bird Sanctuary, Middletown, RI, 2011. For general purpose fund.
$10,000 to Salve Regina University, Newport, RI, 2011. For general purpose fund.
$6,000 to Philadelphia Orchestra Association, Philadelphia, PA, 2011. For general purpose fund.
$5,000 to New York Downtown Hospital, New York, NY, 2011. For general purpose fund.

5994
Ford Foundation
320 E. 43rd St.
New York, NY 10017-4801 (212) 573-5000
Contact: Secy.
FAX: (212) 351-3677;
E-mail: secretary@fordfoundation.org; Main URL: http://www.fordfoundation.org
Blog: http://www.fordfoundation.org/equals-change
Employment Feed: http://www.fordfoundation.org/feeds/employment
E-Newsletter: http://www.fordfoundation.org/About-Us#sign-up
Facebook: https://www.facebook.com/FordFound
Flickr: http://www.flickr.com/photos/ford-foundation/
Ford Foundation's Philanthropy Promise: http://www.ncrp.org/philanthropys-promise/who
Foundation News: http://www.fordfoundation.org/newsroom
GiveSmart: http://www.givesmart.org/Stories/Donors/Darren-Walker
Grantee Perception Report: http://www.fordfoundation.org/pdfs/grants/Ford%20Foundation_Grantee%20Perception%20Report_04-02-13.pdf
Grants Database: http://www.fordfoundation.org/grants/search
Issues Center: http://www.fordfoundation.org/issues
Knowledge Center: http://www.fordfoundation.org/impact
Multimedia: http://www.fordfoundation.org/library/search?contenttype=6
News Feed: http://www.fordfoundation.org/feeds/newsroom
Regional Priorities Center: http://www.fordfoundation.org/regions
Twitter: https://twitter.com/FordFoundation
Vimeo: http://vimeo.com/fordfoundation
YouTube: http://www.youtube.com/fordfoundationTV

Established in 1936 in MI.
Donors: Henry Ford†; Edsel Ford†.
Foundation type: Independent foundation.
Financial data (yr. ended 12/31/13): Assets, $12,259,961,589 (M); expenditures, $706,760,799; qualifying distributions, $682,832,765; giving activities include $558,468,518 for 2,745 grants (high: $8,320,000; low: $5,000), $1,867,365 for employee matching gifts, $3,647,699 for foundation-administered programs and $21,167,832 for 9 loans/program-related investments (high: $5,000,000; low: $504,595).
Purpose and activities: The foundation supports visionary leaders and organizations working on the frontlines of social change worldwide. Its goals for more than half a century have been to strengthen democratic values, reduce poverty and injustice, promote international cooperation, and advance human achievement. The foundation focuses on

eight issues: 1) Human Rights; 2) Democratic and Accountable Government; 3) Educational Opportunity and Scholarship; 4) Economic Fairness; 5) Metropolitan Opportunity; 6) Sustainable Development; 7) Freedom of Expression; and 8) Gender, Sexuality and Reproductive Justice.
Fields of interest: Media/communications; Media, film/video; Museums; Performing arts; Performing arts, dance; Performing arts, theater; Performing arts, music; Arts; Education, research; Secondary school/education; Higher education; Education; Environment, natural resources; Environment; Reproductive health; Reproductive health, sexuality education; AIDS; Crime/violence prevention, abuse prevention; Legal services; Employment; Agriculture; Housing/shelter, development; Youth development, research; Human services; Women, centers/services; Minorities/immigrants, centers/services; International economic development; International human rights; International affairs; Civil rights, race/intergroup relations; Civil/human rights; Economic development; Urban/community development; Rural development; Community/economic development; Philanthropy/voluntarism; Social sciences; Economics; Law/international law; Government/public administration; Public affairs, citizen participation; Leadership development; Religion, interfaith issues; Youth; Minorities; Asians/Pacific Islanders; African Americans/Blacks; Hispanics/Latinos; Indigenous peoples; Women; AIDS, people with; Immigrants/refugees; Economically disadvantaged; LGBTQ.
International interests: Africa; Asia; Latin America; Middle East.
Type of support: General/operating support; Continuing support; Management development/capacity building; Endowments; Program development; Program evaluation; Program-related investments/loans; Employee matching gifts.
Limitations: Applications accepted. Giving in the United States, Africa, the Middle East, Asia, Latin America and the Caribbean, and also on a global basis, with a focus on eight core issues. No support for programs for which substantial support from government or other sources is readily available, or for religious sectarian activities. No grants for construction or maintenance of buildings, undergraduate scholarships, or for purely personal or local needs. The vast majority of foundation grants go to organizations. Historically, the foundation has provided a very limited number of fellowship opportunities for individuals, focusing on advanced degrees in areas of interest to the foundation. When available, recipients are selected by universities and other organizations that receive grants from the foundation to support fellowships.
Publications: Annual report; Informational brochure; Occasional report.
Application information: Prospective applicants are advised to carefully review the foundation's initiatives online, and to download and review the Grant Application Guide for additional details about the grant-review process at http://www.fordfoundation.org/pdfs/grants/grant-application-guide.pdf. Application form not required.

Initial approach: After reviewing the Grant Application Guide, submit an inquiry online using the Grant Inquiry Form (http://www.fordfoundation.org/grants/select-country-or-region)
Copies of proposal: 1
Deadline(s): None, grants are made throughout the year
Final notification: Three months from the time a formal proposal is submitted for a potential grant to be fully reviewed

Officers and Trustees:* Kofi Appenteng,* Chair.; Darren Walker, Pres.; Martin Abregu, Vice President for Democracy, Rights and Justice; Eric Doppstadt, Vice President and Chief Investment Officer; John W. Bernstein, Vice President, Treasurer and Chief Financial Officer; Samantha Gilbert, Vice President, Talent and HR; Kenneth T. Monteiro, Vice President, Secy. and Genl. Counsel; Hilary Pennington, Vice President for Education, Creativity and Free Expression; Alfred Ironside, V.P., Global Communications; Francisco Cigarroa; Tim Berners-Lee; Martin Eakes; Amy Falls; Juliet V. Garcia; Irene Hirano Inouye; J. Clifford Hudson; Robert S. Kaplan; Lourdes Lopez; Thurgood Marshall, Jr.; Paula Moreno; N.R. Narayana Murthy; Peter A. Nadosy; Cecile Richards.
Number of staff: 254 full-time professional; 116 full-time support.
EIN: 131684331
Selected grants: The following grants are a representative sample of this grantmaker's funding activity:
$2,200,000 to National Employment Law Project, New York, NY, 2014. For general support to promote policies and programs that create good jobs, strengthen upward mobility, enforce worker rights and improve programs for the unemployed.
$1,350,000 to PICO National Network, Oakland, CA, 2014. For general support for faith-based racial and economic justice organizing and program support for civic engagement efforts.
$1,300,000 to NAACP Legal Defense and Educational Fund, New York, NY, 2014. To transform promise of equality into reality for black Americans and core support for Political Participation Program and activities to support leadership transition.
$1,225,000 to Center for Responsible Lending, Durham, NC, 2014. For general support to promote fair and affordable access to consumer and mortgage credit for low income households.
$1,000,000 to Minnesota Public Radio, Saint Paul, MN, 2014. For Marketplace public radio program's Wealth and Poverty Desk to produce and distribute original reporting and analysis on economic disparity and inequity in the United States.
$1,000,000 to Rights and Resources Institute, Washington, DC, 2014. For general support to promote global commitment and action toward policy, market and legal reforms that secure local communities' and indigenous people's rights to own, control and benefit from natural resources.
$900,000 to Communities Foundation of Texas, Dallas, TX, 2014. For grantmaking and activities of Educate Texas Rio Grande Valley Collective Impact Action Plan to transform poorest region in Texas by focusing on college readiness and success.
$500,000 to Natural Resources Defense Council, New York, NY, 2014. To explore pre-development needs, investment opportunities, requirements and federal policy reforms for community scale infrastructure deployment that supports environmental, economic and social benefits.
$350,000 to Advocates for Youth, Washington, DC, 2014. For national communications and social media strategy and advance positive public narrative surrounding youth sexuality, reproductive health and rights.
$200,000 to Jordan Davis Movie, LLC, San Francisco, CA, 2014. To produce 3 1/2 Minutes, documentary film about public safety and criminal justice system as revealed through story of creation and spread of stand your ground laws.
$100,000 to Data and Society Research Institute, New York, NY, 2014. To develop collaborations among civil rights leaders, technologists and researchers to consider how emergent data practices affect criminal justice, education, employment, finance, housing and health.

5995
The Edward E. Ford Foundation ✧

26 Court St., Ste. 2200
Brooklyn, NY 11242-1122 (718) 596-1950
Contact: John C. Gulla, Exec. Dir.
FAX: (718) 596-1988; E-mail: office@eeford.org; Main URL: http://www.eeford.org

Trust established in 1957 in NY.
Donor: Edward E. Ford†.
Foundation type: Independent foundation.
Financial data (yr. ended 09/30/13): Assets, $64,064,564 (M); expenditures, $3,317,701; qualifying distributions, $3,048,020; giving activities include $2,498,977 for 35 grants (high: $250,000; low: $7,500).
Purpose and activities: Grants for independent secondary education only. Independent secondary schools must hold full and active membership in National Association of Independent Schools to be eligible for consideration.
Fields of interest: Secondary school/education.
Type of support: Annual campaigns; Capital campaigns; Building/renovation; Equipment; Endowments; Program development; Conferences/seminars; Seed money; Curriculum development; Scholarship funds; Research; Matching/challenge support.
Limitations: Giving limited to the U.S. and its protectorates. No support for public elementary or college-level schools, schools that have been applicants within the last three years, or schools that do not have individual membership in NAIS (National Association of Independent Schools). No grants to individuals, or for emergency funds or deficit financing.
Publications: Application guidelines.
Application information: Application guidelines available on foundation web site. Grant requests of $100,000 from schools and associations will not be accepted. Applicants must request space on agenda prior to submitting a proposal. Application form required.

Initial approach: Telephone
Copies of proposal: 18
Deadline(s): See foundation web site for current deadlines
Board meeting date(s): Apr., June, and Nov.
Final notification: 6 weeks for formal reply; informal reply sooner

Officers and Advisory Board:* Walter Burgin,* Chair.; William L. Menard,* Vice-Chair.; John C. Gulla,* Exec. Dir.; George J. Gillespie III, Honorary Board Member; Phillips Smith, Honorary Board Member; Gillian Attfield; Christopher Brooks; Nancy R. Cavanaugh; Gillian R. Christensen; Philip V. Havens; David J. Hubbard; Edward F. Menard; Dr. John K. Prentiss; Tyler Tingley.
Trustee: JPMorgan Chase Bank, N.A.

Number of staff: 1 full-time professional; 1 full-time support.
EIN: 136047243

5996
Fordham Street Foundation ✧
c/o K & L Gates
599 Lexington Ave.
New York, NY 10022-6030
Contact: Judy Bigelow
E-mail: info@fordhamstreet.org; WA tel.: (425) 451-2516; Main URL: http://www.fordhamstreet.org

Established in 2003 in WA.
Donor: Judith A. Bigelow.
Foundation type: Independent foundation.
Financial data (yr. ended 06/30/13): Assets, $9,960,125 (M); gifts received, $313,780; expenditures, $580,708; qualifying distributions, $507,500; giving activities include $507,500 for 24 grants (high: $40,000; low: $10,000).
Purpose and activities: The foundation is currently limiting its funding to minority academic achievement.
Fields of interest: Child development, education; Education.
Limitations: Applications accepted. Giving in the U.S., with emphasis on the Pacific Northwest, particularly WA. No grants to individuals or private foundations.
Publications: Application guidelines; Grants list.
Application information: Application information available on foundation web site. Application form not required.
Initial approach: Proposal
Deadline(s): Jan. 15
Board meeting date(s): Apr. or early May
Officers: Judith A. Bigelow, Pres.; Lisa L. Johnsen, Secy.
EIN: 200532818
Selected grants: The following grants are a representative sample of this grantmaker's funding activity:
$50,000 to Partners in School Innovation, San Francisco, CA, 2011.
$30,000 to First Place, Seattle, WA, 2011.
$30,000 to Lets Get Ready, New York, NY, 2011.
$25,000 to Breakthrough Collaborative, San Francisco, CA, 2011.
$20,000 to Humanities Washington, Seattle, WA, 2011.
$20,000 to New Futures, Burien, WA, 2011.
$20,000 to Powerful Schools, Seattle, WA, 2011.
$20,000 to Technology Access Foundation, Seattle, WA, 2011.
$20,000 to Washington Tennis and Education Foundation, Washington, DC, 2011.
$10,000 to Solid Ground, Seattle, WA, 2011.

5997
Forst Family Foundation ✧
Bowling Green Sta.
P.O. Box 73
New York, NY 10274-0073

Established in 1999 in NY.
Donors: Edward C. Forst; Susan R. Forst.
Foundation type: Independent foundation.
Financial data (yr. ended 05/31/13): Assets, $24,966 (M); expenditures, $944,700; qualifying distributions, $939,781; giving activities include $939,781 for 12 grants (high: $919,981; low: $100).
Purpose and activities: Giving primarily for higher education; funding also for health care and human services.
Fields of interest: Higher education; Health care; Human services.
Limitations: Applications not accepted. Giving primarily in CT and NY. No grants to individuals.
Application information: Contributes only to pre-selected organizations.
Trustees: Edward C. Forst; Susan R. Forst.
EIN: 134046414

5998
The Kat Foundation ✧
(formerly The George W. & Patricia A. Wellde Foundation)
Bowling Green Sta.
P.O. Box 73
New York, NY 10274-0073

Established in 1993 in NY.
Donors: George W. Wellde, Jr.; Patricia A. Wellde.
Foundation type: Independent foundation.
Financial data (yr. ended 07/31/13): Assets, $17,823,991 (M); gifts received, $1,049,459; expenditures, $934,731; qualifying distributions, $774,205; giving activities include $774,205 for 31 grants (high: $60,000; low: $100).
Purpose and activities: Giving primarily for higher and other education.
Fields of interest: Elementary/secondary education; Higher education; Public affairs.
Limitations: Applications not accepted. Giving primarily in AZ, NY, and VA; funding also in Washington, DC. No grants to individuals, or for scholarships; no loans.
Application information: Contributes only to pre-selected organizations.
Trustees: George W. Wellde, Jr.; Patricia A. Wellde.
EIN: 133749673
Selected grants: The following grants are a representative sample of this grantmaker's funding activity:
$50,000 to George Washington University, Washington, DC, 2011.
$35,000 to Council on Foreign Relations, New York, NY, 2011.
$25,000 to Arzu, Inc., Chicago, IL, 2011.
$3,305 to Council on Foreign Relations, New York, NY, 2011.
$2,000 to Waterside School, Stamford, CT, 2011.
$1,000 to ACT, Inc., Iowa City, IA, 2011.
$1,000 to Spence School, New York, NY, 2011.

5999
The Kellner Foundation ✧ ☆
c/o Kellner Capital, LLC
900 3rd Ave., 14th Fl.
New York, NY 10022-4728

Established in 1996 in NY.
Donors: George A. Kellner; Martha Kellner.
Foundation type: Independent foundation.
Financial data (yr. ended 12/31/13): Assets, $3,309,494 (M); expenditures, $656,281; qualifying distributions, $587,967; giving activities include $587,967 for 3 grants (high: $388,879; low: $3,000).
Fields of interest: Performing arts, opera; Higher education; Business school/education; Education.
Limitations: Applications not accepted. Giving primarily in NY. No grants to individuals.
Application information: Contributes only to pre-selected organizations.
Trustees: Catherine Kellner; George Kellner; Martha Kellner; Peter Kellner.
EIN: 137084979

6000
Foundation 14 ✧
(formerly Jill & Darius Bikoff Foundation)
c/o The Observatory US, Inc.
17-20 Whitestone Expwy., Ste. 403
Whitestone, NY 11357-3000

Established in 2007 in NY.
Donor: J. Darius Bikoff.
Foundation type: Independent foundation.
Financial data (yr. ended 12/31/13): Assets, $53,992,073 (M); expenditures, $2,735,309; qualifying distributions, $2,624,000; giving activities include $2,622,500 for 17 grants (high: $1,090,000; low: $2,500).
Fields of interest: Museums (art); Arts; Prostate cancer; Jewish agencies & synagogues.
Limitations: Applications not accepted. Giving primarily in CA and NY.
Application information: Contributes only to pre-selected organizations.
Officers: J. Darius Bikoff, Pres. and Treas.; Jill Bikoff, V.P.; Hanan Goldenthal, Secy.
EIN: 261082338

6001
Foundation for a Just Society ✧
160 5th Ave., 7th Fl.
New York, NY 10010-7003

Established in 2010 in NY.
Donors: Audrey Simons; Audrey Simons Delaware Trust; Audrey Simons Delaware Trust II.
Foundation type: Independent foundation.
Financial data (yr. ended 12/31/13): Assets, $172,663,785 (M); gifts received, $55,306,584; expenditures, $4,925,445; qualifying distributions, $4,669,475; giving activities include $4,013,449 for 48 grants (high: $216,949; low: $500).
Purpose and activities: Giving to advance social justice, especially for discriminated populations.
Fields of interest: Human services; Civil/human rights; Community/economic development.
Limitations: Applications not accepted. Giving primarily in the U.S., Africa, Asia and Latin America.
Application information: Unsolicited requests for funds not accepted.
Officers: Audrey Simons, Pres.; Jessica Hawrys, V.P.; Kyla Barkin, Secy.-Treas.
Directors: Kady Safar; Elizabeth Simons.
EIN: 273345774
Selected grants: The following grants are a representative sample of this grantmaker's funding activity:
$400,000 to Stichting Mama Cash, Amsterdam, Netherlands, 2012. For Mama Cash's Strategic Grantmaking and Work to Influence Philanthropy : In 2013 and 2014, Mama Cash will provide grants and accompaniment support to human rights organizations led by marginalized women, girls and trans people in the thematic areas of Body (bodily

integrity), Money (economic justice) and Voice (agency and participation). Mama Cash will fund national and regional women's funds that support grassroots women's groups and that work to influence local philanthropy from a feminist perspective. All of our grantee-partners work to challenge the status quo that pushes women, girls and trans people to the margins, payable over 2.00 years.
$300,000 to Global Fund for Women, San Francisco, CA, 2012. The Global Fund for Women envisions equitable, just world in which women and girls have voice, choice, and resources to realize their full potential. The Global Fund seeks to achieve universal human rights for women and girls by investing in, connecting, and advocating for women-led solutions to local, regional, and transnational challenges. The Global Fund is the world's largest public foundation investing exclusively in women's rights worldwide throughout 174 countries, consistently ranking among the top sources of funding for more than 4,500 women-led, grassroots, and civil society organizations in developing countries. The Global Fund brings women's organizations and donors across the globe together in international network committed to a world of equality and social justice, payable over 2.00 years.
$300,000 to Partners Asia, Seattle, WA, 2012. payable over 2.00 years.
$300,000 to Womens Refugee Commission, New York, NY, 2012. payable over 2.00 years.
$200,000 to Asylum Access, Oakland, CA, 2012. Asylum Access is international nonprofit working to empower refugees to assert their fundamental rights in Africa, Asia and Latin America. Founded in 2005, Asylum Access helps refugee women assert their rights to seek safety, access employment, education, healthcare and seek protection from further injustice. Using innovative model that includes a combination of grassroots legal assistance and broader advocacy efforts, Asylum Access has transformed the human rights landscape for almost 1,000,000 refugees in just five years, payable over 2.00 years.
$160,000 to Planned Parenthood Southeast, Atlanta, GA, 2012. A clear correlation exists between poverty and access to quality reproductive health services in the United States. Nowhere is this felt more strongly than in the southern states of Alabama and Mississippi. Compared to other groups within the U.S., low-income women and youth in the south experience significantly worse health outcomes, greater difficulty accessing health services and lower quality care. Low-income women in the South experience significantly higher rates of unintended pregnancy, STDs-including HIV/AIDS-and breast and cervical cancer than their counterparts living in other areas of the country. In these tough economic times, more women than ever need access to essential health care services. Our program focuses not only on delivering quality medical care but on providing health education to reduce health disparities in our community. Our health centers provide basic gynecological care including: physical exams, birth control methods, sexually transmitted disease testing and treatment, HIV testing and counseling, medical referral, and health education and promotion, payable over 2.00 years.
$150,000 to Global Alliance Against Traffic in Women Thailand, Bangkok, Thailand, 2012. payable over 2.00 years.
$80,000 to Adhikaar for Human Rights and Social Justice, Woodside, NY, 2012. With a general operating support from the Foundation for a Just Society Adhikaar will expand and deepen our Workers' Rights program, a multi-pronged approach seeking long-term, systematic changes while addressing immediate needs of low-wage Nepali-speaking workers. Recognizing their interconnected needs, Adhikaar's Workers' Rights Program includes English classes, skill training, and job training. It assists workers to claim unpaid wages and seek workplace justice. It facilitates opportunities to share stories of struggles and victories, meet with elected officials, speak at rallies from New York to Washington, DC, collaborate with other workers' rights groups, and take on leadership positions within Adhikaar. Next year, Adhikaar will continue to focus on raising awareness and implementing the Domestic Workers Bill of Rights, as well as developing new standards for the domestic work industry. The Foundation support will allow Adhikaar to lead a multi-sector, multi-ethnic coalition to create a healthy nail salon industry in New York, payable over 2.00 years.
$75,000 to Freedom Network USA, Dallas, TX, 2012. The Freedom Network, as a national human rights movement seeks support to strengthen our infrastructure, continue to expand our media and communication efforts and provide continued support to our training arm, The Freedom Network Training Institute. Support for these efforts will enable us to build on our successful advocacy strategy, broaden the national and international audience through electronic media platforms and continue the essential work of educating communities across the United States and beyond to identify and assist trafficked and enslaved people. The competing voices in this country demand that the FN maintain its' national presence, its production of position papers, advocacy materials, training curricula, and widespread use of social media. With the support of FJS we can continue our work, engage survivors as partners in our leadership structure, advocate for better services, educate a wide audience about root causes and promote a deliberate, coordinated approach grounded in reality, not scare tactics or alarmist rhetoric.
$75,000 to National Latina Institute for Reproductive Health, New York, NY, 2012.

6002
Foundation for Arts Initiatives ✧ ☆
(formerly American Center Foundation)
375 Greenwich St.
New York, NY 10013
Main URL: http://www.ffaiarts.net/

Established in DE.
Foundation type: Independent foundation.
Financial data (yr. ended 08/31/13): Assets, $20,868,437 (M); expenditures, $1,279,828; qualifying distributions, $1,152,805; giving activities include $725,840 for 27 grants (high: $56,000; low: $5,000), and $112,500 for 15 grants to individuals (high: $7,500; low: $7,500).
Purpose and activities: Giving primarily to: encourage original and experimental thinking in the visual arts; support new ventures in the contemporary arts that may be at an especially critical point in their development; help organizations involved with emerging or under-recognized artists, particularly those run by artists themselves or in areas where there is a lack of institutional resources for contemporary artists.
Fields of interest: Arts; Education; Human services.
Limitations: Applications not accepted. Giving primarily on a national and international basis.
Application information: Unsolicited requests for funds not accepted.
Officers and Board Members:* Frederick B. Henry,* Chair. and Treas.; Marie-Claude Beaud,* Vice-Chair.; Kynaston McShine,* Vice-Chair.; Joan Weakley, Secy.; Manuel J. Borja-Villel; Christophe Girard; Claire Hsu; Vasif Kortun; Ann Philbin; William Wells.
EIN: 986000319
Selected grants: The following grants are a representative sample of this grantmaker's funding activity:
$60,000 to Centre for the Study of Developing Societies, Delhi, India, 2011.

6003
Foundation for Child Development ✧
295 Madison Ave., 40th Fl.
New York, NY 10017-6304 (212) 867-5777
Contact: Mark Bogosian, Comms. and Grants Off.
FAX: (212) 867-5844; E-mail: info@fcd-us.org; Main URL: http://www.fcd-us.org
E-Newsletter: http://www.fcd-us.org/whats-new/subscribe
Grants Database: http://www.fcd-us.org/grants/search
RSS Feed: http://www.fcd-us.org/whats-new
Twitter: http://twitter.com/fcdusorg
Program e-mail: ysp@fcd-us.org

Incorporated as a voluntary agency in 1900 in NY and established as the Association for the Aid of Crippled Children in 1908; current name adopted in 1972, affirming a broader focus on children at risk.
Donors: Milo M. Belding†; Annie K. Belding†; and others.
Foundation type: Independent foundation.
Financial data (yr. ended 03/31/13): Assets, $99,997,180 (M); gifts received, $21,000; expenditures, $5,158,021; qualifying distributions, $4,399,367; giving activities include $2,515,945 for 17 grants (high: $726,295; low: $7,500).
Purpose and activities: The Foundation for Child Development (FCD) is a national, private philanthropy dedicated to the principle that all families should have the social and material resources to raise their children to be healthy, educated and productive members of their communities. The foundation seeks to understand children, particularly the disadvantaged, and to promote their well-being. The foundation believes that families, schools, nonprofit organizations, businesses and government at all levels share complementary responsibilities in the critical task of raising new generations.
Fields of interest: Education, reform; Education, early childhood education; Public policy, research; Children; Immigrants/refugees.
Type of support: Fellowships; Endowments; General/operating support; Continuing support; Program development; Conferences/seminars; Publication; Seed money; Research; Technical assistance.
Limitations: Applications not accepted. Giving on a national basis. No support for the direct provision of pre-kindergarten education, child care, or health care. No grants for capital campaigns, endowments,

or for the purchase, construction, or renovation of buildings.
Publications: Annual report; Grants list; Informational brochure; Newsletter; Occasional report; Program policy statement.
Application information: Unsolicited requests for funds not accepted.
Board meeting date(s): Mar., June, and Oct.
Officers and Directors:* David Lawrence, Jr.,* Chair.; Margaret Beale Spencer, Ph.D.*, Vice-Chair.; Jessica Chao, Interim C.E.O. and C.O.O.; Ruby Takanishi, Ph.D.*, Pres.; Hirokazu Yoshikawa,* Secy.; Ellen Berland Gibbs, Treas.; Eugene E. Garcia; Walter Giles; Robert P. Morgenthau; Andrew D. Racine, M.D., Ph.D.; Margarita Rosa; Joseph Youngblood II.
Number of staff: 5 full-time professional; 1 part-time professional; 1 part-time support.
EIN: 131623901
Selected grants: The following grants are a representative sample of this grantmaker's funding activity:
$723,481 to Foundation for Child Development, New York, NY, 2012. For FCD Changing Faces of Americas Children - Young Scholars Program. Goals of Program are to stimulate both basic and policy-relevant research about early education, health and well-being of children living in immigrant families from birth to age ten, particularly those who are living in low-income families; and to support young investigators from the behavioral and social sciences or in an allied professional field who are untenured but in tenure-track positions or who have received tenure in the last four years from a college or university in the United States.
$714,500 to New America Foundation, Washington, DC, 2012. For Pre-K-3rd Education Reform Initiative and to support the inclusion of PreK data in the New America Foundations Federal Education Budget Project, payable over 2.00 years.
$220,000 to Migration Policy Institute, Washington, DC, 2012. For public symposium to highlight policy-relevant research generated from the first decade of the FCD Young Scholars Program, and invitational workshop on future research and field-building;, payable over 1.50 years.
$200,000 to University of Minnesota, Minneapolis, MN, 2012. For research and evaluation of Midwest expansion of Child-Parent (PreK-3rd) Center Education Program, payable over 2.00 years.
$197,580 to Foundation for Child Development, New York, NY, 2012. For the PreK-3rd Research and Evaluation Convening which will produce four papers and a technical manual on the design of PreK-3rd evaluations, payable over 1.50 years.
$106,370 to Duke University, Durham, NC, 2012. For continuing development, maintenance and promotion of FCD Child Well-Being Index (CWI), payable over 1.50 years.
$102,000 to University of Chicago, Chicago, IL, 2012. To support two case studies of birth-to-college approach to public education as developed by the University's Urban Education Institute and Ounce of Prevention Fund, payable over 2.00 years.
$61,168 to North Carolina Central University, Durham, NC, 2012. For continuing development, maintenance and promotion of FCD Child Well-Being Index (CWI).
$57,786 to Rockefeller Archive Center, Sleepy Hollow, NY, 2012. For the FCD Digitization Project, payable over 2.00 years.
$30,000 to Migration Policy Institute, Washington, DC, 2012. Toward support of Transatlantic Learning Community on Early Childhood Issues.

6004
Foundation to Promote Open Society
224 W. 57th St.
New York, NY 10019-3212 (212) 548-0600
Main URL: http://www.opensocietyfoundations.org/

Established in 2008 in DE and NY.
Donors: George Soros; Open Society Institute.
Foundation type: Independent foundation.
Financial data (yr. ended 12/31/13): Assets, $3,330,839,478 (M); gifts received, $784,245; expenditures, $423,874,068; qualifying distributions, $382,640,801; giving activities include $380,512,799 for 1,074 grants (high: $10,000,000; low: $1,500).
Fields of interest: Education; Human services; Philanthropy/voluntarism.
Limitations: Applications not accepted. Giving primarily in Washington, DC and Albany and New York, NY.
Application information: Unsolicited requests for funds not accepted.
Officers and Directors:* George Soros,* Chair.; Jonathan Soros,* Co-Vice-Chair.; Aryeh Neier,* Co-Vice-Chair.; Ricardo A. Castro, Secy.; Daniel R. Eule, Treas.; Susan C. Frunzi; William D. Zabel.
EIN: 263753801
Selected grants: The following grants are a representative sample of this grantmaker's funding activity:
$41,915,199 to Open Society Institute, Budapest, Hungary, 2013. For activities and programs promoting open, democratic societies around the world.
$10,000,000 to Higher Achievement Program, Washington, DC, 2012. For general support.
$9,000,000 to Ms. Foundation for Women, Brooklyn, NY, 2012. For general support.
$6,000,000 to Boston Community Capital, Boston, MA, 2012. For general support.
$4,014,588 to Chancellor Masters and Scholars of the University of Cambridge, West Nyack, NY, 2013. For the Paul Collier Professor of Economic Policy.
$2,500,000 to Demos: A Network for Ideas and Action, New York, NY, 2012. For general support.
$125,000 to Bill of Rights Defense Committee, Northampton, MA, 2013. For general support.
$125,000 to Lambda Legal Defense and Education Fund, New York, NY, 2012. For renewal support for Lambda Legal's Fair Courts Project.
$115,000 to Pacific Environment, San Francisco, CA, 2013. For civil society growth in China by providing capacity building and technical support to a growing network of grassroots non-governmental organizations.
$100,000 to Black Star Project, Chicago, IL, 2013. For general support.
$85,941 to Georgetown University, Washington, DC, 2012. To facilitate the completion of the International Migrants' Bill of Rights and develop a tool for its widespread application.

6005
Fourdoves Foundation ✧
132 Perry St., Ste. 2B
New York, NY 10014-7811

Donor: Trace Foundation.
Foundation type: Independent foundation.
Financial data (yr. ended 12/31/12): Assets, $13,953,622 (M); gifts received, $16,876,545; expenditures, $3,527,788; qualifying distributions, $3,451,938; giving activities include $3,435,000 for 1 grant.
Purpose and activities: Giving primarily to a foundation that is dedicated to preserving the Tibetan culture.
Fields of interest: Foundations (private grantmaking).
Limitations: Applications not accepted. Giving primarily in New York, NY.
Application information: Contributes only to pre-selected organizations.
Officers: Andrea Soros Colombel, Pres. and Treas.; Eric Colombel, V.P.
EIN: 455403404

6006
The Four-Four Foundation, Inc. ✧
c/o Bessemer Trust
630 5th Ave.
New York, NY 10111-0100

Established in 1994 in WI.
Foundation type: Independent foundation.
Financial data (yr. ended 12/31/13): Assets, $34,813,271 (M); expenditures, $1,758,987; qualifying distributions, $1,644,322; giving activities include $1,550,000 for 112 grants (high: $150,000; low: $1,000).
Fields of interest: Arts; Education; Environment, natural resources; Medical care, rehabilitation; Public health; Health organizations.
Type of support: Continuing support; Annual campaigns; Capital campaigns; Building/renovation; Endowments; Professorships.
Limitations: Applications not accepted. Giving primarily in Milwaukee, WI. No grants to individuals.
Application information: Contributes only to pre-selected organizations. Unsolicited requests for funds not accepted.
Board meeting date(s): Between June and Sept.
Officers and Directors:* Sally S. Manegold,* Pres.; Robert H. Manegold,* V.P. and Treas.; Lynn M. Rix,* Secy.; Katherine M. Biersach; Joan M. Dukes.
EIN: 391867243
Selected grants: The following grants are a representative sample of this grantmaker's funding activity:
$150,000 to University Lake School, Hartland, WI, 2011.
$105,000 to Skylight Music Theatre Corp, Milwaukee, WI, 2011.
$15,000 to Dartmouth College, Hanover, NH, 2011.
$15,000 to Milwaukee Art Museum, Milwaukee, WI, 2011.

6007
Francqui Foundation ✧
(formerly Foundation Francqui Belgium)
c/o Lutz and Carr
300 E. 42nd St.
New York, NY 10017-5947 (212) 697-2299

Foundation type: Independent foundation.
Financial data (yr. ended 12/31/13): Assets, $50,246,778 (M); expenditures, $2,024,405; qualifying distributions, $1,951,263; giving

activities include $809,012 for 4 grants (high: $332,000; low: $109,029).
Purpose and activities: Giving primarily for Belgian scholars and education.
Fields of interest: Higher education.
International interests: Belgium.
Limitations: Applications not accepted. Giving limited to Belgium. No grants to individuals.
Application information: Unsolicited requests for funds not accepted.
Officers and Directors:* Mark Eyskens,* Chair.; Herman Balthazar,* Vice-Chair.; Etienne Viscount Davignon,* Exec. Dir.; Thierry Baron Boon; Emile Knight Boulpaep; Jacques Baron Brotchi; Paul Baron De Meester; Frederic Count Francqui; Daniel Baron Janssen; Francoise Masai; Pierre Van Moebeke; Niceas Baron Schamp; Alexander Sevrin; Anton Van Rossum; Piet Baron Van Waeyenberge.
EIN: 986001286

6008
The Herbert & Noemi Frank Family Foundation ✧ ☆

214 Ditmas Ave.
Brooklyn, NY 11218-4904 (718) 941-4200
Contact: Barry Frank, Tr.

Established in 1999 in NY.
Donors: Herbert Frank; Noemi Frank; Barry Frank; Joseph Frank; Art Flock and Screen Inc.; 125 North Industrial Boulevard LLC.
Foundation type: Independent foundation.
Financial data (yr. ended 12/31/13): Assets, $8,624,661 (M); gifts received, $1,100,000; expenditures, $568,037; qualifying distributions, $567,251; giving activities include $567,251 for grants.
Type of support: General/operating support.
Limitations: Applications accepted. Giving primarily in NY. No grants to individuals.
Application information: Application form required.
Initial approach: Letter
Deadline(s): None
Trustees: Barry Frank; Herbert Frank; Noemi Frank.
EIN: 113522063

6009
The Regina Bauer Frankenberg Foundation ✧

c/o JPMorgan Chase Bank, N.A., Private Foundation Svcs.
270 Park Ave., 16th Fl.
New York, NY 10017
Contact: Carolyn O'Brien, Prog. Off.
FAX: (212) 464-2304;
E-mail: carolyn.r.obrien@jpmoran.com; Main URL: http://fdnweb.org/frankenberg
Grants List: http://fdnweb.org/frankenberg/grants/year/contributions/

Established in 1994 in NY.
Donor: Regina Bauer Frankenberg†.
Foundation type: Independent foundation.
Financial data (yr. ended 12/31/13): Assets, $22,586,519 (M); expenditures, $1,077,163; qualifying distributions, $910,084; giving activities include $859,742 for 16 grants (high: $150,000; low: $4,742).
Purpose and activities: Giving exclusively for animal welfare, particularly for the protection of endangered wild animals or threatened species by supporting conservation and research, and for strengthening the capacity of organizations working to reduce the homelessness, mistreatment and euthanasia of companion animals through adoption, training, spaying/neutering, and other programs.
Fields of interest: Animal welfare; Animals/wildlife, preservation/protection.
Type of support: Capital campaigns; Management development/capacity building; Program development.
Limitations: Applications accepted. Giving for companion animals limited to New York, NY; giving for wildlife on a national and international scope. No support for private foundations, or for organizations that will engage in or supply animals for vivisection. No grants to individuals, or for matching gifts; no loans.
Publications: Application guidelines; Grants list.
Application information: Application materials must be submitted online via foundation web site. Application form not required.
Initial approach: Proposal (3 pages maximum)
Copies of proposal: 1
Deadline(s): July 1
Board meeting date(s): Nov.
Final notification: Dec. 31
Trustee: JPMorgan Chase Bank, N.A.
Number of staff: None.
EIN: 133741659
Selected grants: The following grants are a representative sample of this grantmaker's funding activity:
$150,000 to Mayors Alliance for NYCs Animals, New York, NY, 2011. For final installment of a $275,000 grant for general operating support.
$100,000 to Friends of Animals, Darien, CT, 2011. For final installment of a $200,000 grant for the Spay and Neuter Project.
$100,000 to Humane Society of the United States, Washington, DC, 2011. For final installment of a $200,000 grant for the Stop Puppy Mills Campaign and for the Animal Fighting and Cruelty Rescue Fund.
$50,000 to Bideawee, New York, NY, 2011. For a customized transport van.
$50,000 to Fauna and Flora International, Washington, DC, 2011. For first installment of a $100,000 grant to help mitigate human-carnivore conflict in Georgia.
$50,000 to Humane Society of New York, New York, NY, 2011. For endoscopy unit for its clinic.
$50,000 to University of Montana Foundation, Montana Cooperative Wildlife Research Unit, Missoula, MT, 2011. For first installment of a $150,000 grant for efforts to monitor and protect gray wolves.
$45,000 to African Wildlife Foundation, Washington, DC, 2011. For second installment of a $135,000 grant for the creation of the Iyondje Community Bonobo Reserve.
$40,000 to North Shore Animal League, Port Washington, NY, 2011. For endoscopy unit for its clinic.
$40,000 to Northern Rockies Conservation Cooperative, Jackson, WY, 2011. For first installment of $80,000 grant for the Peoples and Carnivores program.

6010
The Frankfort Family Foundation ✧

c/o Anchin, Block & Anchin LLP
1375 Broadway
New York, NY 10018-7001

Established in 2003 in NJ.
Donors: Lewis Frankfort; Roberta Frankfort.
Foundation type: Independent foundation.
Financial data (yr. ended 12/31/13): Assets, $3,254,661 (M); gifts received, $2,000,255; expenditures, $1,983,501; qualifying distributions, $1,978,556; giving activities include $1,973,381 for 36 grants (high: $600,020; low: $125).
Fields of interest: Higher education; Education; Health care; Human services; Jewish agencies & synagogues.
Limitations: Applications not accepted. Giving primarily in NJ and NY. No grants to individuals.
Application information: Contributes only to pre-selected organizations.
Trustees: Lewis Frankfort; Roberta Frankfort.
EIN: 200383031
Selected grants: The following grants are a representative sample of this grantmaker's funding activity:
$250,051 to Teach for America, Newark, NJ, 2011.
$250,000 to Teach for America, Newark, NJ, 2011.
$200,086 to New York City Center, New York, NY, 2011.
$150,018 to New Jersey SEEDS, Newark, NJ, 2011.
$100,000 to New York City Center, New York, NY, 2011.
$57,300 to New York City Center, New York, NY, 2011.
$30,000 to Teach for America, Newark, NJ, 2011.
$25,050 to Columbia University, New York, NY, 2011.
$25,050 to Hunter College Foundation, New York, NY, 2011.
$15,000 to New York City Center, New York, NY, 2011.

6011
The Freed Foundation

825 3rd Ave., Ste. 224
New York, NY 10022-7519 (212) 520-8399
Contact: Grants Committee; Grants Inquiries
E-mail: freedfoundationnyc@verizon.net

Incorporated in 1954 in Washington, DC.
Donors: Frances W. Freed†; Gerald A. Freed†; Allie S. Freed†.
Foundation type: Independent foundation.
Financial data (yr. ended 12/31/13): Assets, $20,529,524 (M); expenditures, $947,670; qualifying distributions, $902,119; giving activities include $702,260 for 21 grants (high: $150,000; low: $1,760).
Purpose and activities: Support for all aspects of animal welfare, and mental health.
Fields of interest: Animal welfare; Animals/wildlife, preservation/protection; Mental health, counseling/support groups; Mental health, disorders; Nutrition; Safety/disasters.
Type of support: General/operating support; Annual campaigns; Capital campaigns; Building/renovation; Equipment.
Limitations: Applications accepted. Giving primarily in the New York City metropolitan area. No grants to individuals, or for research, conferences and meetings, and international programs.
Application information: Letters of Inquiry, proposals, and inquiries accepted by e-mail only. Applicants should only submit the 28 application requirements and any additional information upon request from the foundation, after initial Letter of Inquiry has been considered. Grants are one time

only, applicants must re-apply each time for further funding. Application form not required.
Initial approach: E-mail Letter of Inquiry
Copies of proposal: 1
Board meeting date(s): Nov. 27, 2015
Final notification: Oct. 31
Officers and Directors:* Elizabeth Freed,* Pres. and Treas.; Steven Douenias, Secy.; William Mitchell.
Number of staff: 1 full-time professional.
EIN: 526047591
Selected grants: The following grants are a representative sample of this grantmaker's funding activity:
$350,000 to North Shore Animal League, Port Washington, NY, 2012. For Recovery Center.
$75,000 to Boys Club of New York, New York, NY, 2012. For Staff Psychologist.
$50,000 to Community Hope, Parsippany, NJ, 2012. For Veteran's Housing.
$50,000 to Deborah Hospital Foundation, Browns Mills, NJ, 2012. For Women's Health.
$25,000 to Cancer Support Community, New York, NY, 2012. For support group.
$20,000 to Americas Vetdogs, Smithtown, NY, 2012. For Golf Tounament.
$20,000 to Riverdale Mental Health Association, Bronx, NY, 2012. For Mental Health.
$20,000 to Search and Care, New York, NY, 2012. For Social Worker.
$15,000 to Stray from the Heart, New York, NY, 2012. For Website Upgrade.
$10,000 to Pesach Tikvah Hope Development, Brooklyn, NY, 2012. For Social Worker.
$10,000 to Training Institute for Mental Health, New York, NY, 2012. For Counseling.
$5,000 to Children of the Night, Van Nuys, CA, 2012. For Children's Housing.
$2,000 to National Hypertension Association, New York, NY, 2012. For Vital Program.

6012
Freeman Foundation ✧
c/o Rockefeller Trust Company, N.A.
10 Rockefeller Plz., 3rd Fl.
New York, NY 10020-1903 (212) 549-5270
Contact: George S. Tsandikos
Application address: 499 Taber Hill Rd., Stowe, VT 05672

Established in 1978 in VT.
Donors: Houghton Freeman; Mansfield Freeman†; members of the Freeman family.
Foundation type: Independent foundation.
Financial data (yr. ended 12/31/12): Assets, $301,224,960 (M); expenditures, $16,639,783; qualifying distributions, $14,911,925; giving activities include $13,817,869 for 98 grants (high: $1,560,000; low: $3,500).
Purpose and activities: Support primarily for the promotion of international understanding, farmland preservation projects in the state of VT and special projects in HI.
Fields of interest: Education, public education; Environment, natural resources; International affairs, goodwill promotion; International studies.
International interests: Asia.
Type of support: General/operating support; Land acquisition; Program development; Professorships; Curriculum development; Fellowships; Scholarship funds; Research; Exchange programs; Matching/challenge support.
Limitations: Applications accepted. Giving primarily in VT for conservation and environment grants; Asian studies grants are awarded nationally. No grants to individuals, or for endowments or capital campaigns.
Publications: Annual report.
Application information: Application form not required.
Initial approach: Letter
Copies of proposal: 7
Deadline(s): One month before meetings
Board meeting date(s): Quarterly
Officer and Trustees:* Graeme Freeman, Pres.; Doreen Freeman; George B. Snell.
Number of staff: 4
EIN: 132965090
Selected grants: The following grants are a representative sample of this grantmaker's funding activity:
$1,560,000 to Wesleyan University, Middletown, CT, 2012.
$1,300,000 to Association of Children's Museums, Arlington, VA, 2012.
$750,000 to National Association of Japan-America Societies, Washington, DC, 2012.
$500,000 to Blakemore Foundation, Seattle, WA, 2012.
$494,073 to Columbia University, Weatherhead East Asian Institute, New York, NY, 2012.
$480,000 to University of Hawaii Foundation, Honolulu, HI, 2012.
$217,400 to University of Pittsburgh, Asian Studies Center, Pittsburgh, PA, 2012.
$100,000 to George Washington University, Washington, DC, 2012.
$90,000 to East-West Center Foundation, Honolulu, HI, 2012.
$60,000 to Historic Hawaii Foundation, Honolulu, HI, 2012.

6013
Marina Kellen French Foundation ✧
c/o JES, LLP
15 Maiden Ln.
New York, NY 10038

Established in 2001 in NY.
Donors: Michael Kellen French; A.M. & S.M. Kellen Foundation.
Foundation type: Independent foundation.
Financial data (yr. ended 12/31/12): Assets, $10,034,927 (M); expenditures, $1,015,685; qualifying distributions, $593,506; giving activities include $593,506 for grants.
Fields of interest: Arts; Human services.
Limitations: Applications not accepted. No grants to individuals.
Application information: Contributes only to pre-selected organizations.
Officer: Andrew Gundlach, Treas.
Trustee: Marina Kellen French.
EIN: 137270721

6014
Frey Family Foundation, Inc. ✧
c/o Harbor Financial Management, LLC
40 N. Country Rd.
Port Jefferson, NY 11777

Established in NY.
Donor: Robert Frey.
Foundation type: Independent foundation.
Financial data (yr. ended 12/31/12): Assets, $7,379,659 (M); expenditures, $598,579; qualifying distributions, $596,978; giving activities include $596,978 for 20 grants (high: $309,209; low: $100).
Fields of interest: Higher education; Hospitals (general); Health organizations, association; Human services; Religion.
Limitations: Applications not accepted. Giving primarily in NY, with some emphasis on Port Jefferson.
Application information: Contributes only to pre-selected organizations.
Officers: Robert Frey, Pres.; Stephen Rizzo, Secy.; Kathryn Frey, Treas.
EIN: 113640474

6015
Fribourg Family Foundation ✧
277 Park Ave., 50th Fl.
New York, NY 10172-0003

Established in 2000 in NY.
Donors: Michel Fribourg†; Mary Ann Fribourg; Paul Fribourg; Charles Fribourg.
Foundation type: Independent foundation.
Financial data (yr. ended 12/31/13): Assets, $305,058 (M); gifts received, $14,000; expenditures, $664,469; qualifying distributions, $664,343; giving activities include $664,108 for 30 grants (high: $154,385; low: $500).
Purpose and activities: Giving primarily for the arts, higher and other education, health organizations, particularly a hospital, human services, and to Jewish organizations.
Fields of interest: Arts; Higher education; Education; Hospitals (general); Health organizations, association; Human services; Jewish agencies & synagogues.
Limitations: Applications not accepted. Giving primarily in New York, NY. No grants to individuals.
Application information: Contributes only to pre-selected organizations.
Directors: Charles Fribourg; Mary Ann Fribourg; Paul Jules Fribourg; Teresa E. McCaslin; Susan McIntyre.
EIN: 134148779

6016
The Fridolin Charitable Trust ✧
483 10th Ave., 2nd Fl.
New York, NY 10018-1118

Established in 2006 in NY.
Donor: Fred Howard†.
Foundation type: Independent foundation.
Financial data (yr. ended 12/31/13): Assets, $47,235,880 (M); gifts received, $66,671; expenditures, $2,707,357; qualifying distributions, $2,421,661; giving activities include $2,083,226 for 74 grants (high: $104,922; low: $1,000).
Fields of interest: Higher education; Education; Hospitals (general); Human services; Children/youth, services.
Limitations: Applications not accepted. Giving primarily in New York and in Israel; some giving nationally.
Application information: Contributes only to pre-selected organizations.
Trustees: Ursula Kalish; Bonnie Kaye; Herbert Kozlov; Ada Samuelsson; Michael Wahl.
EIN: 546717390

Selected grants: The following grants are a representative sample of this grantmaker's funding activity:
$116,000 to New York University, School of Medicine, New York, NY, 2011.
$100,000 to Givat Haviva Educational Foundation, New York, NY, 2011.
$99,397 to Washington University, Saint Louis, MO, 2011.
$80,000 to Mount Sinai Medical Center, New York, NY, 2011.
$50,000 to AISH New York, New York, NY, 2011.
$50,000 to Boomer Esiason Foundation, New York, NY, 2011.
$50,000 to Global Kids, New York, NY, 2011.
$35,000 to Learning Through an Expanded Arts Program, New York, NY, 2011.
$35,000 to Pepperdine University, Malibu, CA, 2011.
$25,000 to Under 21, New York, NY, 2011.

6017
The Barry Friedberg and Charlotte Moss Family Foundation ✧ ☆

134 E. 71st St., 38th Fl.
New York, NY 10021-5011

Established in 1998 in NY.
Donors: Barry S. Friedberg; Charlotte Moss.
Foundation type: Independent foundation.
Financial data (yr. ended 05/31/13): Assets, $2,469,328 (M); gifts received, $198,880; expenditures, $515,138; qualifying distributions, $507,824; giving activities include $507,574 for 81 grants (high: $100,000; low: $1).
Purpose and activities: Giving primarily for the performing arts, education, children, youth and social services, and health associations.
Fields of interest: Museums (art); Performing arts; Performing arts, ballet; Arts; Higher education; Education; Health organizations, association; Medical research, institute; Human services; Children/youth, services; United Ways and Federated Giving Programs.
Limitations: Applications not accepted. Giving primarily in San Francisco, CA and New York, NY. No grants to individuals.
Application information: Contributes only to pre-selected organizations.
Trustees: Barry S. Friedberg; Charlotte A. Moss.
EIN: 137154197
Selected grants: The following grants are a representative sample of this grantmaker's funding activity:
$100,000 to California College of the Arts, San Francisco, CA, 2011.
$25,000 to Thomas Jefferson Foundation, Charlottesville, VA, 2011.
$15,000 to Council on Foreign Relations, New York, NY, 2011.
$13,500 to Glaucoma Foundation, New York, NY, 2011.
$6,000 to Teach for America, New York, NY, 2011.
$5,000 to Bone Marrow Foundation, New York, NY, 2011.
$4,000 to School of American Ballet, New York, NY, 2011.
$3,500 to American Hospital of Paris Foundation, New York, NY, 2011.
$2,500 to Aspen Valley Medical Foundation, Aspen, CO, 2011.
$2,000 to New York City Ballet, New York, NY, 2011.

6018
The Claire Friedlander Family Foundation ✧ ☆

c/o Peter J. Klein
223 Wall St., Ste. 411
Huntington, NY 11743-2060
E-mail: information@cffamilyfoundation.org; Main URL: http://www.cffamilyfoundation.org
Facebook: https://www.facebook.com/pages/Claire-Friedlander-Family-Foundation/199109633584012?ref_type=bookmark
Twitter: https://twitter.com/clairefriedlan1
YouTube: https://www.youtube.com/user/cffamilyfoundation/videos

Established in NY.
Donor: Claire Friedlander†.
Foundation type: Independent foundation.
Financial data (yr. ended 06/30/13): Assets, $17,279,303 (M); expenditures, $2,513,902; qualifying distributions, $2,437,539; giving activities include $2,075,500 for 83 grants (high: $1,000,000; low: $25).
Purpose and activities: The foundation is devoted to promoting tolerance throughout the world, proliferation of the arts, and advocacy for people who need help.
Fields of interest: Arts.
Limitations: Applications not accepted. Giving primarily in NY.
Application information: Unsolicited requests for funds not accepted.
Officers: Peter J. Klein, Pres. and Treas.; Irene M. Klein, V.P.; Adam J. Gottlieb, Secy.
EIN: 263850557

6019
Friedman Family Foundation ✧

(formerly Stephen & Barbara Friedman Foundation)
c/o BCRS Assocs., LLC
77 Water St., 9th Fl.
New York, NY 10005-4414 (212) 440-0800

Established in 1979 in NY.
Donors: Stephen B. Friedman; Barbara Friedman.
Foundation type: Independent foundation.
Financial data (yr. ended 07/31/13): Assets, $18,512,141 (M); gifts received, $9,104,713; expenditures, $3,132,718; qualifying distributions, $3,049,738; giving activities include $3,048,433 for 109 grants (high: $1,000,000; low: $180).
Purpose and activities: Giving primarily for education, health, a cancer hospital, human services, and Jewish organizations.
Fields of interest: Higher education; Medical school/education; Hospitals (specialty); Cancer; Human services; Jewish federated giving programs; Jewish agencies & synagogues.
Limitations: Applications not accepted. Giving primarily in NY. No grants to individuals.
Application information: Contributes only to pre-selected organizations.
Trustees: Barbara Friedman; Stephen Friedman.
EIN: 133025979

6020
Brian P. Friedman Family Foundation ✧

c/o Brain P. Frideman
520 Madison Ave., 10th Fl.
New York, NY 10022-4213

Established in 1992 in NY.
Donor: Brian P. Friedman.
Foundation type: Independent foundation.
Financial data (yr. ended 12/31/13): Assets, $11,563,761 (M); expenditures, $1,267,445; qualifying distributions, $1,224,914; giving activities include $1,224,029 for 54 grants (high: $500,000; low: $50).
Fields of interest: Education; Jewish federated giving programs; Jewish agencies & synagogues.
Limitations: Applications not accepted. Giving primarily in NY. No grants to individuals.
Application information: Contributes only to pre-selected organizations.
Officers and Directors:* Brian P. Friedman,* Pres.; Barbara J. Shulman,* Secy.-Treas.; Etta Brandman; Daniel Friedman; Julia Friedman.
EIN: 133705915

6021
Richard A. and Susan P. Friedman Family Foundation ✧

Bowling Green Sta.
P.O. Box 73
New York, NY 10274-0073

Established in 1991 in NY.
Donors: Richard A. Friedman; Goldman Sachs & Co.
Foundation type: Independent foundation.
Financial data (yr. ended 06/30/13): Assets, $13,615,688 (M); gifts received, $9,963,409; expenditures, $4,108,311; qualifying distributions, $4,052,622; giving activities include $4,052,622 for 57 grants (high: $3,000,000; low: $100).
Fields of interest: Higher education; Hospitals (general); Human services; Jewish federated giving programs; Jewish agencies & synagogues.
Limitations: Applications not accepted. Giving primarily in the metropolitan New York, NY, area, as well as in Providence, RI. No grants to individuals.
Application information: Contributes only to pre-selected organizations.
Trustee: Richard A. Friedman.
EIN: 133634385
Selected grants: The following grants are a representative sample of this grantmaker's funding activity:
$1,000,000 to Brown University, Providence, RI, 2011.
$125,000 to National Museum of American Jewish History, Philadelphia, PA, 2011. For general charitable purposes.
$100,000 to American Israel Education Foundation, Washington, DC, 2011. For general charitable purposes.
$50,000 to Central Synagogue, New York, NY, 2011. For general charitable purposes.
$48,000 to Mount Sinai Hospital, New York, NY, 2011. For general charitable purposes.
$25,000 to American Friends of Shalva, New York, NY, 2011. For general charitable purposes.
$25,000 to American Jewish Committee, New York, NY, 2011. For general charitable purposes.
$25,000 to New York Needs You, New York, NY, 2011. For general charitable purposes.
$10,000 to New York Public Library, New York, NY, 2011. For general charitable purposes.
$10,000 to UJA-Federation of New York, New York, NY, 2011. For general charitable purposes.

6022
Dr. Gerald J. and Dorothy R. Friedman Medical Foundation, Inc. ✧
c/o CohnReznick LLP
1212 6th Ave.
New York, NY 10036

Established in 1992 in FL.
Donors: Gerald J. Friedman; Dorothy Friedman; Jane Friedman.
Foundation type: Independent foundation.
Financial data (yr. ended 06/30/13): Assets, $11,883,380 (M); expenditures, $1,738,815; qualifying distributions, $1,686,099; giving activities include $1,678,716 for 33 grants (high: $1,102,302; low: $500).
Fields of interest: Arts; Education; Human services; Children/youth, services; Jewish agencies & synagogues.
Limitations: Applications not accepted. Giving primarily in the metropolitan New York, NY, area. No grants to individuals.
Application information: Contributes only to pre-selected organizations.
Officers: Jane Friedman, Pres.; Susan Thomases, Exec. V.P.; Jennifer Gerson, V.P.; Judith Kennedy, V.P.; Mark Satlof, V.P.; Lewis Bernstein, Secy.-Treas.
EIN: 650416767
Selected grants: The following grants are a representative sample of this grantmaker's funding activity:
$40,000 to Columbia University, School of Social Work, New York, NY, 2013. For general activities.

6023
The Gerald J. and Dorothy R. Friedman New York Foundation for Medical Research ✧
c/o CohnReznick LLP
1212 6th Ave.
New York, NY 10036-1602

Established in 1999 in NY.
Donors: Dorothy Friedman; Gerald J. Friedman†.
Foundation type: Independent foundation.
Financial data (yr. ended 02/28/13): Assets, $23,122,148 (M); expenditures, $3,234,417; qualifying distributions, $2,981,791; giving activities include $2,838,916 for 8 grants (high: $2,354,916; low: $2,000).
Purpose and activities: Giving primarily to organizations involved in medical research.
Fields of interest: Health care; Health organizations; Medical research.
Limitations: Applications not accepted. Giving primarily in NY; giving also in MA. No grants to individuals.
Application information: Contributes only to pre-selected organizations.
Officers: Jane Friedman, Pres.; Susan Thomases, Exec. V.P.; Judith Kennedy, V.P.; Mark Satlof, V.P.; Lewis Bernstein, Secy.-Treas.
Director: Dorothy Friedman.
EIN: 134034562

6024
Friends of the Congressional Glaucoma Caucus Foundation, Inc. ✧
69-44 76th St.
Middle Village, NY 11379-2829
Contact: S.J. "Bud" Grant, C.E.O
E-mail: RichardGrant716@aol.com; Toll free tel.: (877) 611-4232; Nassau County, NY tel.: (516) 327-2236, fax: (516) 327-0260; Main URL: http://glaucomacongress.org

Established in 2000 in NY.
Donors: Pharmacia & Upjohn, Inc.; Pfizer Inc.; Allergan, Inc.; CDC of Health and Human Services Dept.
Foundation type: Operating foundation.
Financial data (yr. ended 12/31/12): Assets, $136,894 (M); gifts received, $2,044,805; expenditures, $2,201,638; qualifying distributions, $2,372,945; giving activities include $484,456 for 12 grants (high: $225,000; low: $4,500), and $1,871,131 for 1 foundation-administered program.
Purpose and activities: The foundation is dedicated to supporting the activities of the Congressional Glaucoma Caucus, a group of United States Congress members who are dedicated to helping all Americans fight the scourge of glaucoma and other eye diseases. The foundation awards grants to organizations to provide diagnostic screening opportunities and follow up for high risk glaucoma population groups in their home districts across the nation.
Fields of interest: Health care, rural areas; Public health; Eye diseases.
Type of support: Consulting services; Fellowships; Curriculum development; General/operating support.
Limitations: Applications accepted. Giving on a national basis. No grants to individuals.
Application information: See foundation web site for downloading of the Medical School Student Sight Saver Program application form. Application form not required.
Initial approach: Letter or telephone
Copies of proposal: 1
Deadline(s): None
Board meeting date(s): Quarterly
Final notification: 3 months
Officers: Robert J. Bishop, J.D., Chair.; Stanley J. "Bud" Grant, C.E.O. and Pres.; Randall D. Bloomfield, M.D., V.P. and Secy.; Philip Ragusa, Treas.
Directors: John J. Abbott, Ph.D.; Judy Collins; Rev. Dr. Floyd Flake; S. Dorothy Anne Fitzgibbons, OP; Edward Greissing; Roger C. Herdman, M.D.; Joseph M. Mattone, J.D.; Hon. Raymond J. McGrath; Carrie Ann Stevens; Robert C. Wertz, J.D.
EIN: 134098767
Selected grants: The following grants are a representative sample of this grantmaker's funding activity:
$4,500 to New York Medical College, Valhalla, NY, 2012. For Glaucoma Medical Research.

6025
William Froelich Foundation ✧ ☆
c/o Rifkin and Lubcher, LLP
424 Madison Ave., 3rd Fl.
New York, NY 10017 (212) 888-8350
Contact: Beverly Hall, Tr.

Established in 1999 in NY.
Donor: William G. Froelich†.
Foundation type: Independent foundation.
Financial data (yr. ended 05/31/13): Assets, $2,131,410 (M); gifts received, $2,094,703; expenditures, $565,958; qualifying distributions, $551,115; giving activities include $527,000 for 26 + grants (high: $102,000).
Purpose and activities: Giving for alternative medicine and education.
Fields of interest: Education; Health care; Youth development.
Type of support: General/operating support.
Limitations: Applications accepted. Giving primarily in CT, IL and MA. No grants to individuals.
Application information: Application form required.
Initial approach: Proposal
Deadline(s): None
Trustees: Gene Franklin; Beverly Hall; David Rimmer.
EIN: 311624502
Selected grants: The following grants are a representative sample of this grantmaker's funding activity:
$17,500 to Nantucket Arts Council, Nantucket, MA, 2011.
$10,000 to Worldwide Fistula Fund, Saint Louis, MO, 2011.
$5,000 to Giraffe Project, Langley, WA, 2011.
$5,000 to Metta Institute, Sausalito, CA, 2011.
$1,000 to Nantucket Historical Association, Nantucket, MA, 2011.

6026
The Frog Rock Foundation ✧
P.O. Box 865
Chappaqua, NY 10514-0865 (914) 273-1375
Contact: Margie Orell, Exec. Dir.
E-mail: frogrockfoundation@gmail.com; Main URL: http://www.frogrockfoundation.org

Established in 2000 in NY.
Donor: Janet Inskeep Benton.
Foundation type: Independent foundation.
Financial data (yr. ended 12/31/13): Assets, $18,127,797 (M); expenditures, $917,950; qualifying distributions, $825,912; giving activities include $800,414 for 12 grants (high: $195,421; low: $8,280).
Purpose and activities: The foundation will fund organizations working with economically disadvantaged children in Westchester County, NY, to promote early childhood learning and development, and to provide opportunities for intellectual and personal enrichment to children of all ages.
Fields of interest: Children/youth, services.
Type of support: Program development; Seed money; Curriculum development; Program evaluation.
Limitations: Applications accepted. Giving limited to Westchester County, NY. No support for religious organizations (though churches and religious organizations may be eligible to receive funding for activities that are non-sectarian and benefit the larger community), or programs or research to address specific physical conditions, or medical or psychological diagnoses. No grants to individuals, or for endowments or scholarships. Very limited consideration for capital campaigns.
Publications: Application guidelines.
Application information: Full proposals are by invitation only. Application form required.

Initial approach: Use Initial Request form on foundation web site
Deadline(s): None
Board meeting date(s): Mar. 15, June 15, Oct. 15, and Dec. 15
Officer: Janet Inskeep Benton, Pres.; Margery Orell, Exec. Dir.
Trustee: Elisabeth C. Naman.
Number of staff: 1 part-time professional.
EIN: 134127228

6027
Alex & Ruth Fruchthandler Foundation Inc. ✧
111 Broadway, 20th Fl.
New York, NY 10006-1901

Established in 1945 in NY.
Donors: Olympia & York Financial Co.; Fruchthandler Bros. Enterprises; Abraham H. Fruchthandler; Ruth Fruchthandler; Rabbi Chaim Berlin; FBE Limited LLC.
Foundation type: Independent foundation.
Financial data (yr. ended 12/31/12): Assets, $20,567,278 (M); gifts received, $17,000; expenditures, $609,819; qualifying distributions, $609,819; giving activities include $606,869 for 265 grants (high: $150,000; low: $5).
Purpose and activities: Support primarily for Jewish organizations, including yeshivas.
Fields of interest: Elementary/secondary education; Jewish agencies & synagogues.
Limitations: Applications not accepted. No grants to individuals.
Application information: Contributes only to pre-selected organizations.
Officers: Abraham Fruchthandler, Pres.; Baruch Dov Fruchthandler, C.F.O.; Zachary Fruchthandler, Secy.-Treas.
Directors: Joseph Fruchthandler; Solomon Fruchthandler.
EIN: 136156031

6028
Shmuel Fuchs Foundation Inc. ✧
1109 E. 22nd St.
Brooklyn, NY 11210-3619

Established in 1997 in NY.
Donors: Bernard Fuchs; Morris Fuchs.
Foundation type: Independent foundation.
Financial data (yr. ended 12/31/13): Assets, $3,354,212 (M); gifts received, $600,000; expenditures, $512,906; qualifying distributions, $512,906; giving activities include $507,850 for 216 grants (high: $196,100; low: $50).
Purpose and activities: Giving primarily to Jewish organizations, temples, and schools.
Fields of interest: Education; Jewish federated giving programs; Jewish agencies & synagogues.
Limitations: Applications not accepted. Giving primarily in NY, with emphasis on Brooklyn. No grants to individuals.
Application information: Contributes only to pre-selected organizations.
Officers: Morris Fuchs, Pres.; Rachel Fuchs, Secy.
EIN: 113372438
Selected grants: The following grants are a representative sample of this grantmaker's funding activity:
$35,000 to Yeshiva Torah Vodaath, Brooklyn, NY, 2011.
$2,160 to Beth Medrash Elyon, Monsey, NY, 2011.
$1,800 to Congregation Chazon Avrohom, Brooklyn, NY, 2011.
$1,800 to Haazinu Charitable Foundation, Brooklyn, NY, 2011.
$1,500 to Bais Yaakov High School of Lakewood, Lakewood, NJ, 2011.

6029
Helene Fuld Health Trust ✧
c/o HSBC Bank USA
452 5th Ave., 13th Fl.
New York, NY 10018-2706 (212) 525-2418
Contact: Marianne Caskran; Gregory Otis
FAX: (212) 525-2395;
E-mail: marianne.caskran@hsbcpb.com; Gregory Otis, email: gregory.otis@hsbcpb.com

Trust established in 1951 in NJ; activated in 1969 as successor to Helene Fuld Health Foundation; incorporated in 1935.
Donors: Leonhard Felix Fuld†; Florentine M. Fuld†.
Foundation type: Independent foundation.
Financial data (yr. ended 09/30/13): Assets, $136,286,252 (M); expenditures, $7,078,900; qualifying distributions, $6,411,021; giving activities include $6,186,073 for 14 grants (high: $1,300,000; low: $165,000).
Purpose and activities: The primary mission of the trust is to support and promote the health, welfare, and education of student nurses. The first priority of the trust is financial aid to nursing students. Acknowledging the increased complexity of and sophisticated knowledge required for health care delivery, the trust will give preference to programs that offer BSN degrees and higher. The trust will seek opportunities to establish endowed scholarships for students in baccalaureate programs at selected nursing schools through an invitational process. The trust will continue to award grants to leading nursing schools and other organizations which undertake innovative programs designed to develop and expand the professional and leadership skills of nursing students, faculty, and administration.
Fields of interest: Nursing school/education; Education; Nursing care.
Type of support: Endowments; Curriculum development; Scholarship funds.
Limitations: Applications not accepted. Giving on a national basis. No grants to individuals; no loans.
Application information: Grants made by invitation only.
Trustee: HSBC Bank USA, N.A.
EIN: 136309307
Selected grants: The following grants are a representative sample of this grantmaker's funding activity:
$1,300,000 to Emory University, Atlanta, GA, 2013. To promote program and study in nursing field.
$1,197,000 to University of Pennsylvania, School of Nursing, Claire M. Fagin, Philadelphia, PA, 2013. To promote program and study in nursing field.
$944,073 to Johns Hopkins University, Baltimore, MD, 2013. To promote program and study in nursing field.
$320,000 to Boston College, Chestnut Hill, MA, 2013. To promote program and study in nursing field.
$320,000 to Duke University, Durham, NC, 2013. To promote program and study in nursing field.
$320,000 to New York University, New York, NY, 2013. To promote program and study in nursing field.
$320,000 to Ohio State University Foundation, School of Nursing, Columbus, OH, 2013. To promote program and study in nursing field.
$320,000 to University of Arizona, Tucson, AZ, 2013. To promote program and study in nursing field.
$320,000 to University of Portland, School of Nursing, Portland, OR, 2013. To promote program and study in nursing field.
$165,000 to Columbia University, New York, NY, 2013. To promote program and study in nursing field.

6030
Fund for Life Foundation Inc. ✧
1428 36th St., Ste. 200
Brooklyn, NY 11218-3765

Established in 1996 in NY.
Donors: Harry Reichman; Greater Windows & Doors.
Foundation type: Independent foundation.
Financial data (yr. ended 12/31/12): Assets, $31,267,824 (M); gifts received, $8,499; expenditures, $2,366,376; qualifying distributions, $2,130,410; giving activities include $2,077,231 for 135 grants (high: $674,000; low: $18).
Purpose and activities: Giving primarily to Jewish organizations, temples, and yeshivas.
Fields of interest: Education; Jewish agencies & synagogues.
Limitations: Applications not accepted. Giving primarily in Brooklyn, NY. No grants to individuals.
Application information: Contributes only to pre-selected organizations.
Officers: Harry Reichman, Pres.; Chaya Reichman, Treas.
Director: Simon Reichman.
EIN: 113239215

6031
The Gaisman Foundation Inc. ✧
1112 Park Ave.
New York, NY 10128-1235

Incorporated in 1934 in DE.
Donor: Henry J. Gaisman†.
Foundation type: Independent foundation.
Financial data (yr. ended 12/31/13): Assets, $146,654,132 (M); gifts received, $980,784; expenditures, $4,847,846; qualifying distributions, $2,609,940; giving activities include $2,609,940 for 18 grants (high: $1,156,540; low: $600).
Fields of interest: Higher education; Hospitals (general); Medical research, institute; Catholic agencies & churches.
Limitations: Applications not accepted. Giving primarily in NY. No grants to individuals.
Application information: Contributes only to pre-selected organizations.
Officer: Eric W. Waldman, Chair.
Director: Kimberly Waldman.
EIN: 136129464

6032
The Galasso Foundation ✧
P.O. Box 685
Clarence, NY 14031-0685
E-mail: galasso@rdinet.net

Established in 1963 in NY.
Donors: August J. Galasso; Susquehanna Motel Corp.
Foundation type: Independent foundation.
Financial data (yr. ended 12/31/13): Assets, $9,352,516 (M); expenditures, $624,590; qualifying distributions, $472,992; giving activities include $447,355 for 67 grants (high: $60,000; low: $50).
Purpose and activities: Giving primarily for education and to Roman Catholic organizations and churches.
Fields of interest: Secondary school/education; Higher education; Education; Catholic agencies & churches.
Type of support: General/operating support; Continuing support; Annual campaigns; Capital campaigns; Building/renovation; Scholarship funds; Employee matching gifts; Matching/challenge support.
Limitations: Applications not accepted. Giving primarily in upstate NY, with emphasis on Buffalo and Lancaster. No grants to individuals.
Application information: Contributes only to pre-selected organizations.
Board meeting date(s): May and Sept.
Trustees: Emil J. Galasso; Martin A. Galasso; August J. Gillon; Paul M. Gonzalez; J. Michael Kelleher.
Number of staff: 1 part-time professional.
EIN: 166031447

6033
The Ganger Foundation, Inc. ✧
c/o Ira Ganger
34 Herrick Dr.
Lawrence, NY 11559-1528

Established in 1993 in NY.
Donors: Ira Ganger; Joe Ganger; AMEREX (USA), Inc.
Foundation type: Independent foundation.
Financial data (yr. ended 04/30/13): Assets, $2,227,606 (M); gifts received, $1,050,332; expenditures, $815,873; qualifying distributions, $795,251; giving activities include $794,514 for 205 grants (high: $100,000; low: $25).
Purpose and activities: Giving primarily for Jewish agencies and temples.
Fields of interest: Jewish federated giving programs; Jewish agencies & synagogues.
Limitations: Applications not accepted. Giving primarily in New York, NY. No grants to individuals.
Application information: Contributes only to pre-selected organizations.
Officer: Ira Ganger, Mgr.
Trustees: Aviva Ganger; Shoshana Ganger.
EIN: 113162524

6034
Ganzi Family Foundation ✧
c/o Victor F. Ganzi
126 E. 56th St., 14th Fl.
New York, NY 10022-3613

Established in FL.
Donor: Victor Ganzi.
Foundation type: Independent foundation.
Financial data (yr. ended 12/31/12): Assets, $10,900,273 (M); gifts received, $1,580,830; expenditures, $587,105; qualifying distributions, $505,000; giving activities include $497,500 for 15 grants (high: $100,000; low: $1,000).
Fields of interest: Education; Human services.
Limitations: Applications not accepted.
Application information: Unsolicited requests for funds not accepted.
Trustees: Edward S. Binnie; Victoria G. Binnie; Patricia M. Ganzi; Victor F. Ganzi; Danielle G. Hauck; Jonathan M. Hauck; Ronald S. Kochman.
EIN: 271538063
Selected grants: The following grants are a representative sample of this grantmaker's funding activity:
$100,000 to Chaminade High School, Mineola, NY, 2011.
$52,500 to Saint Albans School, Washington, DC, 2011.
$50,000 to Boys and Girls Club, Madison Square, New York, NY, 2011.
$25,000 to Central Park Conservancy, New York, NY, 2011.
$2,500 to American Society for the Prevention of Cruelty to Animals, New York, NY, 2010. For general support.
$2,500 to So Others Might Eat, Washington, DC, 2011.
$2,500 to So Others Might Eat, Washington, DC, 2010. For general support.
$2,500 to University of Pennsylvania, Philadelphia, PA, 2011.

6035
The Story Garschina Foundation ✧ ☆
c/o Kenneth Garschina
1 Gramercy Park W.
New York, NY 10003-1714

Donor: Kenneth Garschina.
Foundation type: Independent foundation.
Financial data (yr. ended 12/31/13): Assets, $20,218,940 (M); gifts received, $9,988,050; expenditures, $1,191,430; qualifying distributions, $1,191,000; giving activities include $1,191,000 for 11 grants (high: $500,000; low: $1,000).
Fields of interest: Education; Health care; Public policy, research.
Limitations: Applications not accepted. Giving primarily in NJ and NY.
Application information: Unsolicited requests for funds not accepted.
Director: Kenneth Garschina.
EIN: 454039101

6036
GBRG, Inc. ✧
477 Madison Ave., 10th Fl.
New York, NY 10022-5841

Established in 1995 in DE and NY.
Foundation type: Independent foundation.
Financial data (yr. ended 12/31/13): Assets, $33,558,190 (M); expenditures, $1,575,221; qualifying distributions, $1,455,060; giving activities include $1,445,595 for 25 grants (high: $485,000; low: $26).
Fields of interest: Elementary/secondary education; Human services; Children/youth, services; Jewish federated giving programs; Jewish agencies & synagogues.
International interests: Israel.
Type of support: General/operating support.
Limitations: Applications not accepted. Giving primarily in Jerusalem, Israel. No grants to individuals.
Application information: Contributes only to pre-selected organizations.
Officer and Directors:* Susan Wexner,* Pres. and Secy.-Treas.; Saul G. Agus; Raymond Kanner; Gregg H. Levy, Esq.; Michael S. Oberman, Esq.; Mark Saks, Esq.; Walter Stern.
EIN: 134072646

6037
Bruce G. Geary Foundation ✧
698 Forest Ave.
Staten Island, NY 10310-2507

Established in 2007 in NY.
Donor: Bruce G. Geary.
Foundation type: Independent foundation.
Financial data (yr. ended 12/31/13): Assets, $23,538,067 (M); expenditures, $1,412,883; qualifying distributions, $1,015,358; giving activities include $917,684 for 36 grants (high: $127,684; low: $10,000).
Fields of interest: Animal welfare; Zoos/zoological societies.
Limitations: Applications not accepted. Giving primarily in NY. No grants to individuals.
Application information: Contributes only to pre-selected organizations.
Officers: Raymond J. Pezzoli, Pres.; Cathy Carlson, V.P.; Mathew Smith, Secy.-Treas.
Director: John Kosinski.
EIN: 208075415
Selected grants: The following grants are a representative sample of this grantmaker's funding activity:
$100,000 to Staten Island Zoological Society, Staten Island, NY, 2011. For general charitable purpose.

6038
Gebbie Foundation, Inc. ✧
215 Cherry St.
Jamestown, NY 14701-5203 (716) 487-1062
Contact: Gregory J. Edwards, C.E.O.
FAX: (716) 484-6401; E-mail: info@gebbie.org; Email: gedwards@gebbie.org; Main URL: http://www.gebbie.org
Facebook: https://www.facebook.com/pages/Gebbie-Foundation/318313207852

Incorporated in 1964 in NY.
Donors: Marion B. Gebbie†; Geraldine G. Bellinger†.
Foundation type: Independent foundation.
Financial data (yr. ended 12/31/12): Assets, $72,651,029 (M); expenditures, $3,919,839; qualifying distributions, $3,698,376; giving activities include $3,143,190 for 18+ grants (high: $1,877,019), and $25,000 for 1 employee matching gift.
Purpose and activities: Grants primarily for the arts, children and youth services, community development, education, and human services. The foundation's strategic focus is to rejuvenate

downtown Jamestown, New York, through economic development.
Fields of interest: Arts; Education; Human services; Children/youth, services; Community/economic development.
Type of support: General/operating support; Continuing support; Annual campaigns; Capital campaigns; Building/renovation; Equipment; Endowments; Seed money; Scholarship funds; Program-related investments/loans; Matching/challenge support.
Limitations: Applications accepted. Giving primarily in Chautauqua County in western NY, especially the Jamestown, NY, area. No support for sectarian or religious organizations, or for United Way-funded agencies, unless there is a strong link to the foundation's strategic focus. No grants to individuals.
Publications: Application guidelines; Grants list.
Application information: The foundation will accept full proposals from 501(c)(3) organizations that have submitted a Letter of Inquiry and received a written approval in response, or have received an invitation from the foundation. Complete application guidelines available on foundation web site.
Initial approach: Letter of inquiry (1-2 pages)
Copies of proposal: 1
Deadline(s): None
Board meeting date(s): Quarterly
Final notification: 1 to 4 months
Officers and Directors:* Gregory J. Edwards, C.E.O.; Daniel Kathman,* Pres.; Jonathan Taber,* V.P.; Nancy Gleason,* Secy.; Rodney Drake,* Treas.; Dr. Lynn Dunham; Rhoe B. Henderson, III; Tory Irgang; Kristy B. Zabrodsky.
Number of staff: 1 full-time professional; 3 full-time support.
EIN: 166050287

6039
Lawrence M. Gelb Foundation, Inc. ✧
c/o Proskauer Rose LLP
11 Times Sq.
New York, NY 10036-8299
Contact: Robert M. Kaufman, Secy.-Treas.

Established in 1957 in NY.
Donors: Lawrence M. Gelb†; Richard L. Gelb†; Bruce S. Gelb; Lawrence N. Gelb; BSG Revocable Trust.
Foundation type: Independent foundation.
Financial data (yr. ended 12/31/13): Assets, $2,996,676 (M); gifts received, $449,360; expenditures, $571,629; qualifying distributions, $538,770; giving activities include $534,000 for 74 grants (high: $82,000; low: $1,000).
Purpose and activities: Support primarily for private secondary and higher education; some support also for cultural programs and hospitals.
Fields of interest: Arts; Secondary school/education; Higher education; Hospitals (general).
Limitations: Applications accepted. Giving on a national basis. No grants to individuals.
Application information:
Initial approach: Letter
Deadline(s): None
Board meeting date(s): Various
Officers and Directors:* Bruce S. Gelb,* Chair.; Phyllis N. Gelb,* Pres.; Robert M. Kaufman,* Secy. -Treas.; Wilbur H. Friedman; John T. Gelb; Lawrence N. Gelb.
EIN: 136113586

Selected grants: The following grants are a representative sample of this grantmaker's funding activity:
$1,000 to Scenic Hudson, Poughkeepsie, NY, 2012. For environmental.

6040
Michael E. Gellert Trust ✧
750 3rd Ave., Ste. 3300
New York, NY 10017-2703

Established in 1962 in NY.
Donors: Michael E. Gellert; Mary C. Gellert.
Foundation type: Independent foundation.
Financial data (yr. ended 06/30/13): Assets, $19,402,464 (M); expenditures, $3,811,637; qualifying distributions, $3,672,289; giving activities include $3,575,254 for 71 grants (high: $1,229,400; low: $500).
Purpose and activities: Giving primarily for education and the arts.
Fields of interest: Performing arts; Performing arts, opera; Arts; Higher education; Education; Human services; International human rights.
Limitations: Applications not accepted. Giving primarily in CT, MA, and NY. No grants to individuals.
Application information: Contributes only to pre-selected organizations.
Trustees: Catherine A. Gellert; David B. Spohn Gellert; Michael E. Gellert; Hugh McLoughlin.
EIN: 136093842
Selected grants: The following grants are a representative sample of this grantmaker's funding activity:
$233,500 to Harvard University, Cambridge, MA, 2011. For general support.
$224,333 to New York City Opera, New York, NY, 2011. For general support.
$103,000 to American Academy of Arts and Sciences, Cambridge, MA, 2011. For general support.
$100,000 to Carnegie Institution of Washington, Washington, DC, 2011. For general support.
$77,710 to Lincoln Center for the Performing Arts, New York, NY, 2011. For general support.
$35,000 to Council on Foreign Relations, New York, NY, 2011. For general support.
$12,525 to International Womens Health Coalition, New York, NY, 2011. For general support.
$10,000 to Black Rock Forest Consortium, Cornwall, NY, 2011. For general support.
$1,570 to Elaine Kaufman Cultural Center, New York, NY, 2011. For general support.
$1,540 to Bank Street College of Education, New York, NY, 2011. For general support.

6041
Jacques & Natasha Gelman Foundation Inc. ✧ ☆
c/o McLaughlin & Stern, LLP
260 Madison Ave., 18th Fl.
New York, NY 10016-2401
Contact: Janet C. Neschis, Tr.

Donor: Jacques & Natasha GelmanTrust.
Foundation type: Independent foundation.
Financial data (yr. ended 11/30/13): Assets, $34,418,184 (M); gifts received, $32,130,193; expenditures, $1,242,945; qualifying distributions, $1,121,019; giving activities include $923,750 for 14 grants (high: $400,000; low: $2,500).
Fields of interest: Arts education; Museums (art); Arts.
Limitations: Applications accepted. Giving primarily in New York, NY.
Application information:
Initial approach: Proposal
Trustees: Marylin G. Diamond; Janet C. Neschis.
EIN: 462953602

6042
Genesis Foundation Inc.
505 Park Ave., 4th Fl.
New York, NY 10022-1106 (212) 421-1185
Contact: Carolina Esquenazi, Pres.; Cristina Gutierrez de Pineres, Exec. Dir.
E-mail: genesis@genesis-foundation.org; Additional tel.: (212) 421-1149; Main URL: http://www.genesis-foundation.org
Facebook: http://www.facebook.com/pages/Genesis-Foundation/227677570578716
Twitter: http://twitter.com/GenesisColombia
Vimeo: http://vimeo.com/genesisfoundation

Established in 2001 in FL.
Donors: Genesis Endowment; ReMax of Georgia; Belive; Daniel Roitman; Edmundo Esquenazi; Greenlight Capital; Jim Marilyn Simons; JPMorgan Chase; Prince Capital; Sources of Hope Foundation; Quadrant Capital; Becky Mayer; Jimmy Mayer; Challenge Me Now.
Foundation type: Independent foundation.
Financial data (yr. ended 12/31/12): Assets, $1,504,623 (M); gifts received, $978,896; expenditures, $1,185,376; qualifying distributions, $745,336; giving activities include $745,336 for grants, and $902,368 for foundation-administered programs.
Purpose and activities: The foundation supports successful programs aimed at enhancing quality education with the purpose of providing underserved Colombian children better opportunities to develop and succeed, contributing to a more equal society.
Fields of interest: Education, management/technical assistance; Education, reform; Education, equal rights; Education, formal/general education; Elementary/secondary education; Education, early childhood education; Secondary school/education; Education, drop-out prevention; Education, reading; Education, community/cooperative; Education, computer literacy/technology training; Education, e-learning; Education; Children/youth.
International interests: Colombia.
Type of support: Management development/capacity building; Equipment; Program development; Curriculum development.
Limitations: Applications not accepted. Giving primarily in Colombia. However, the foundation is willing to consider transferring education methodologies to organizations in other countries.
Publications: Annual report; Grants list; Informational brochure; Newsletter; Occasional report.
Application information: Unsolicited requests for funds not accepted.
Board meeting date(s): May and Nov.
Officers: Carolina Esquenazi-Shaio, Pres.; Herbert Selzer, Secy.; Cristina Gutierrez de Pineres, Exec. Dir.
Directors: Jaime Bermudez; Juan Carlos Garcia; Andrea Lawson; Susie Mayer.
Number of staff: 6 full-time professional; 1 part-time professional.
EIN: 912120744

6043
Gerry Charitable Trust ✧
(also known as Peggy N. & Roger G. Gerry Charitable Trust)
c/o McLaughlin & Stern, LLP
260 Madison Ave.
New York, NY 10016-2401
FAX: (212) 448-6260;
E-mail: hheld@mclaughlinstern.com

Established in NY in 1978.
Donors: Roger G. Gerry‡; Peggy N. Gerry‡.
Foundation type: Independent foundation.
Financial data (yr. ended 12/31/13): Assets, $23,242,620 (M); expenditures, $1,010,983; qualifying distributions, $834,099; giving activities include $756,246 for 17 grants (high: $186,246; low: $5,000).
Fields of interest: Historic preservation/historical societies; Arts; Environment.
Type of support: General/operating support; Annual campaigns; Capital campaigns; Building/renovation; Land acquisition; Endowments; Matching/challenge support.
Limitations: Applications not accepted. Giving primarily in NY, with emphasis on Long Island. No grants to individuals.
Application information: Unsolicited requests for funds strongly discouraged.
Trustee: BNY Mellon, N.A.
Advisory Committee: Robert B. Mackay; Theodore S. Wickersham.
EIN: 136753033

6044
Gerry Foundation, Inc. ✧
P.O. Box 311
Liberty, NY 12754-0311 (845) 295-2400
Contact: Darrell Supak

Established in 1997 in NY.
Donors: Alan Gerry; Ron Greenberg; Stuart Salenger; Sandra Gerry; Empire State Development Corp.; EDI-Special Projects Program; Granite Assocs., LP; New York State Dept. of Economic Development; Dormitory Dept. of New York State; New York State Urban Development Corp.; Stillwater Farms, Inc.; Goldman Sachs Philanthropy Fund; Citigroup Global Impact Funding Trust, Inc.; Morgan Stanley Smith Barney Global; National Philanthropy Trust; Ullman Family Partnership; ASG Realty, LLC; U.S. Dept. of Housing and Urban Development.
Foundation type: Operating foundation.
Financial data (yr. ended 12/31/13): Assets, $124,594,203 (M); gifts received, $15,341,943; expenditures, $6,480,573; qualifying distributions, $4,901,098; giving activities include $2,168,485 for 11 grants (high: $2,000,000; low: $250), and $280,238 for foundation-administered programs.
Purpose and activities: Giving primarily to the arts, including a museum, community development and human services.
Fields of interest: Higher education; Health care, clinics/centers; Human services; Community/economic development; Foundations (community).
Type of support: Program-related investments/loans.
Limitations: Applications accepted. Giving primarily in Sullivan County, NY.
Application information:
Initial approach: Letter
Deadline(s): None
Officers and Directors:* Darlene Fedun, C.E.O.; Alan Gerry,* Pres.; Eric Frances, C.F.O.; Christopher Grillo, V.P.; Louis J. Boyd, Secy.-Treas.; Adam Gerry; Annelise Gerry; Robyn Gerry; Sandra Gerry.
EIN: 141798234

6045
The Patrick A. Gerschel Foundation ✧
600 Madison Ave., 16th Fl.
New York, NY 10022-1615

Established in 1986 in NY.
Donor: Patrick A. Gerschel.
Foundation type: Independent foundation.
Financial data (yr. ended 12/31/12): Assets, $5,859,706 (M); expenditures, $861,145; qualifying distributions, $835,250; giving activities include $832,900 for 8 grants (high: $500,000; low: $1,000).
Fields of interest: Museums; Higher education; International affairs, goodwill promotion.
Type of support: Research.
Limitations: Applications not accepted. Giving primarily in NY. No grants to individuals.
Application information: Contributes only to pre-selected organizations.
Officers and Director:* Patrick A. Gerschel,* Pres.; Jonathan Botwinick, V.P.
EIN: 133317180

6046
The Gershwind Family Foundation ✧
152 W. 57th St., 56th Fl.
New York, NY 10019-3310

Established in 1998 in NY.
Donor: Marjorie Gershwind Fiverson.
Foundation type: Independent foundation.
Financial data (yr. ended 12/31/13): Assets, $14,369,663 (M); expenditures, $1,963,447; qualifying distributions, $1,930,953; giving activities include $1,930,953 for 28 grants (high: $1,501,174; low: $500).
Purpose and activities: Giving primarily for education and to Jewish agencies and temples; funding also for a hospital.
Fields of interest: Higher education; Education; Hospitals (general); Health care; Jewish federated giving programs; Jewish agencies & synagogues.
Limitations: Applications not accepted. Giving primarily in NY. No grants to individuals.
Application information: Contributes only to pre-selected organizations.
Officers and Directors:* Marjorie Gershwind Fiverson,* Pres.; Stacey Bennett,* V.P.; Erik Gershwind,* V.P.; J. Robert Small, Secy.-Treas.
EIN: 113359917

6047
Gerson Family Foundation, Inc. ✧
19 W. 95th St.
New York, NY 10025-6755

Established in 1993 in NY.
Donors: James Gerson; Ruth Joffe‡; Barbara N. Gerson.
Foundation type: Independent foundation.
Financial data (yr. ended 09/30/13): Assets, $11,762,498 (M); expenditures, $549,882; qualifying distributions, $519,119; giving activities include $513,300 for 71 grants (high: $136,500; low: $500).
Purpose and activities: Giving primarily for education and to Jewish organizations.
Fields of interest: Higher education; Education; Human services; United Ways and Federated Giving Programs; Jewish federated giving programs; Jewish agencies & synagogues.
Limitations: Applications not accepted. Giving primarily in New York, NY. No grants to individuals.
Application information: Contributes only to pre-selected organizations.
Officers: James Gerson, Pres.; Barbara N. Gerson, Secy.
Directors: Frederick E. Gerson; Kara O. Gerson; Simon F. Gerson; Richard A. Krantz.
EIN: 133750336
Selected grants: The following grants are a representative sample of this grantmaker's funding activity:
$117,000 to Jewish Communal Fund of New York, New York, NY, 2011.
$50,000 to Arbor Brothers, New York, NY, 2011.
$10,000 to Bowdoin College, Brunswick, ME, 2011.
$10,000 to Congregation Bnai Israel, Bridgeport, CT, 2011.
$10,000 to Dartmouth College, Hanover, NH, 2011.
$10,000 to National Council of Jewish Women, New York, NY, 2011.
$5,000 to Congregation Rodeph Sholom, New York, NY, 2011.
$1,000 to Bend the Arc: A Jewish Partnership for Justice, New York, NY, 2011.
$1,000 to Breakthrough Collaborative, San Francisco, CA, 2011.
$1,000 to Young Womens Leadership Foundation, New York, NY, 2011.

6048
Malcolm Gibbs Foundation, Inc. ✧
14 E. 60th St., No. 702
New York, NY 10022-7125

Established in 1999 in NY.
Donors: The Green Fund, Inc.; Cynthia G. Colin Charitable Lead Trust.
Foundation type: Independent foundation.
Financial data (yr. ended 01/31/14): Assets, $17,184,854 (M); gifts received, $43,371; expenditures, $820,856; qualifying distributions, $560,962; giving activities include $451,825 for 72 grants (high: $85,000; low: $250).
Purpose and activities: Giving primarily for the performing arts, education, and human services; funding also for a hospital.
Fields of interest: Performing arts; Arts; Higher education; Hospitals (general); Human services.
Limitations: Applications not accepted. Giving primarily in MA and NY. No grants to individuals.
Application information: Contributes only to pre-selected organizations.
Officers: Ann Colin Herbst, Chair.; Laura Colin Klein, Pres.
EIN: 134041340

6049
The Rosamond Gifford Charitable Corporation ✧
(also known as The Gifford Foundation)
100 Clinton Sq.
126 N. Salina St., 3rd Fl.
Syracuse, NY 13202-1059 (315) 474-2489
Contact: Kathy Goldfarb-Findling, Exec. Dir.
FAX: (315) 475-4983;
E-mail: contact@giffordfoundation.org; Main URL: http://www.giffordfoundation.org
Facebook: http://www.facebook.com/GiffordFoundation?ref=ts
Twitter: https://twitter.com/GiffordCNY

Incorporated in 1954 in NY.
Donor: Rosamond Gifford†.
Foundation type: Independent foundation.
Financial data (yr. ended 12/31/12): Assets, $20,168,619 (M); gifts received, $99,454; expenditures, $1,652,882; qualifying distributions, $1,458,081; giving activities include $796,730 for 71+ grants (high: $316,506).
Purpose and activities: Giving support for educational, scientific, social, and religious needs in Onondaga, Oswego, and Madison Counties, NY. Particular interest in issues around youth violence, employment for youth, and neighborhood revitalization.
Fields of interest: Arts; Higher education; Hospitals (general); Crime/violence prevention; Youth development; Human services; Children/youth, services; Aging, centers/services.
Type of support: General/operating support; Capital campaigns; Building/renovation; Equipment; Land acquisition; Emergency funds; Program development; Conferences/seminars; Seed money; Curriculum development; Research; Technical assistance; Program evaluation; Matching/challenge support.
Limitations: Giving limited to organizations in or serving Madison, Onondaga and Oswego Counties in NY; the "What If..." Mini Grants program is limited to Syracuse, NY. No grants to individuals, or for endowment funds, continuing support.
Publications: Application guidelines; Annual report; Program policy statement.
Application information: Proposals are by invitation only. Application guidelines available on foundation web site. E-mailed or faxed applications not accepted. Application form not required.
Initial approach: Use Grant Inquiry Form on foundation web site, or telephone foundation
Copies of proposal: 1
Deadline(s): Deadlines are rolling and will be announced at an intake meeting
Board meeting date(s): Monthly
Final notification: 2-3 months
Officers and Trustees:* Laurence G. Bousquet,* Pres.; Ben Walsh,* V.P.; Jaime Alicea,* Secy.; Eric Allyn,* Treas.; Dirk Sonneborn, Exec. Dir.; Joseph Charles; Michael Feng; Monique Fletcher; Vincent B. Love; Gwyn Mannion; Cynthia B. Morrow, M.D.; Kathy O'Connell; M. Catherine Richardson; Merike Treier.
Number of staff: 5 full-time professional; 1 full-time support.
EIN: 150572831

6050
Gilder Foundation, Inc. ✧
c/o Anchin
1375 Broadway
New York, NY 10018-7001 (212) 840-3456
Contact: Daniella Muhling, Grants Admin.

Established in 1965 in NY.
Donors: Richard Gilder; Great Circle Trust.
Foundation type: Independent foundation.
Financial data (yr. ended 12/31/13): Assets, $61,351,238 (M); expenditures, $26,122,473; qualifying distributions, $25,666,427; giving activities include $25,279,850 for 185 grants (high: $10,000,000; low: $200).
Purpose and activities: Support for libraries, scholarship funds, and secondary education; support also for recreational programs, public affairs organizations, and cultural groups.
Fields of interest: Arts; Education; Recreation; Economic development; Public affairs, association.
Type of support: General/operating support; Continuing support; Annual campaigns; Capital campaigns; Endowments; Fellowships; Scholarship funds.
Limitations: Applications not accepted. Giving primarily in NY. No grants to individuals.
Application information: Contributes only to pre-selected organizations.
Officers: Richard Gilder, Pres.; Patrick Duff, V.P.; Howard Rothman, Secy.; Richard Schneidman, Treas.
Number of staff: 2 part-time professional; 1 part-time support.
EIN: 136176041
Selected grants: The following grants are a representative sample of this grantmaker's funding activity:
$750,000 to Gilder Lehrman Institute of American History, New York, NY, 2012.
$750,000 to Gilder Lehrman Institute of American History, New York, NY, 2012.
$750,000 to New-York Historical Society, New York, NY, 2012.
$500,000 to Central Park Conservancy, New York, NY, 2012.
$250,000 to Thomas Jefferson Foundation, Charlottesville, VA, 2012.
$250,000 to Yale University, New Haven, CT, 2012.
$50,000 to Acumen Fund, New York, NY, 2012.
$7,500 to Farm School, Athol, MA, 2012.
$5,000 to New Yorkers for Parks, New York, NY, 2012.
$5,000 to Vermont Humanities Council, Montpelier, VT, 2012.

6051
The Gillespie Family Fund, Inc. ✧
c/o Cravath, Swaine & Moore
825 8th Ave.
New York, NY 10019-7475

Established in 2007 in NY; successor to the Charitable Trust dated 4/28/83.
Donors: George J. Gillespie III; Charitable Trust dated 4/28/83.
Foundation type: Independent foundation.
Financial data (yr. ended 12/31/13): Assets, $1,135,041 (M); expenditures, $475,481; qualifying distributions, $468,320; giving activities include $468,320 for 44 grants (high: $50,000; low: $500).
Fields of interest: Education; Hospitals (general); Catholic agencies & churches.
Limitations: Applications not accepted. Giving primarily in CT and NY. No grants to individuals.
Application information: Contributes only to pre-selected organizations.
Officers and Directors:* George J. Gillespie III,* Chair. and Secy.; Myles D. Gillespie,* Pres. and Treas.; Eileen D. Gillespie.
EIN: 260709512
Selected grants: The following grants are a representative sample of this grantmaker's funding activity:
$5,000 to Visiting Nurse Service of New York, New York, NY, 2012. For general support.

6052
Howard Gilman Foundation, Inc. ✧
810 7th Ave., 24th Fl.
New York, NY 10019-5873
Contact: Stephen W. Cropper, V.P.
Main URL: http://www.gilmanfoundation.org/gilman/
Scholarship address (for children of employees of the foundation: c/o Howard Gilman Scholarship Prog., P.O. Box 6730, Princeton, NJ 08541, tel.: (609) 243-6549

Incorporated in 1981 in DE.
Donors: Gilman Investment Co.; Gilman Paper Co.; Gilman Securities Corp.; Howard Gilman†; Sylvia P. Gilman†.
Foundation type: Independent foundation.
Financial data (yr. ended 12/31/12): Assets, $156,577,326 (M); gifts received, $72,970; expenditures, $6,814,141; qualifying distributions, $6,512,494; giving activities include $1,797,500 for 20 grants (high: $500,000; low: $1,000), $30,400 for 7 grants to individuals (high: $5,000; low: $2,500), and $4,529,728 for 1 foundation-administered program.
Purpose and activities: The mission of the foundation is to preserve and protect those areas Howard Gilman considered vulnerable and in need of help. These include the conservation of endangered animals, the support and nourishment of the arts, as well as the funding of medical research in the fields of HIV/AIDS and cardiology.
Fields of interest: Performing arts; Performing arts, dance; Performing arts, theater; Education; Animals/wildlife, preservation/protection; Medical research, institute; Heart & circulatory research; AIDS research; Family services.
Type of support: General/operating support; Continuing support; Building/renovation; Program development; Seed money; Curriculum development; Fellowships; Internship funds; Research; Scholarships—to individuals; Matching/challenge support.
Limitations: Applications accepted. Giving primarily in the metropolitan New York, NY, area. No support for political or religious organizations. No grants to individuals (except for scholarships), capital investments, or deficit operations.
Publications: Informational brochure; Program policy statement.
Application information: Scholarship applicants must complete a preprinted application and questionnaire. Application form not required.
Initial approach: Letter
Deadline(s): None for grants, Dec. 15 for scholarship applications

Officers and Directors:* Mary C. Farrell,* Pres.; Stephen W. Cropper,* V.P. and Secy.-Treas.; Daniel L. Kurtz; Marvin S. Rosen; Joseph M. Samulski.
Number of staff: 1 part-time support.
EIN: 133097486

6053
Bernard F. and Alva B. Gimbel Foundation, Inc. ✧

271 Madison Ave., Ste. 605
New York, NY 10016-1001 (212) 684-9110
Contact: Leslie Gimbel, C.E.O. and Pres.
FAX: (212) 684-9114; Main URL: http://www.gimbelfoundation.org
Grants List: http://www.gimbelfoundation.org/grants.html

Incorporated in 1943 in NY.
Donors: Bernard F. Gimbel†; Alva B. Gimbel†.
Foundation type: Independent foundation.
Financial data (yr. ended 12/31/13): Assets, $55,741,896 (M); expenditures, $4,683,376; qualifying distributions, $3,906,198; giving activities include $3,544,250 for 99 grants (high: $125,000; low: $900).
Purpose and activities: Support for education, workforce/economic development, criminal justice, civil legal services, reproductive rights, the environment, and for advocacy in these areas.
Fields of interest: Environment; Legal services; Employment, training; Civil liberties, reproductive rights; Economic development.
Type of support: General/operating support; Continuing support; Program development.
Limitations: Applications accepted. Giving for direct services is limited to New York City programs. No support for individual schools, short-term educational programs or workshops, mentoring, after-school or summer programs, film projects, or direct service programs outside New York City. No grants to individuals.
Publications: Application guidelines; Grants list.
Application information: Applications by fax not accepted. Full proposals accepted by invitation only following review of a Letter of Inquiry. The foundation makes very few new grants each year. For this reason, interested applicants are encouraged to contact the offices before submitting a letter of inquiry. The foundation is no longer accepting requests for funds in the area of education. Application form not required.

Initial approach: Prospective applicants should submit a two- to three-page letter of inquiry through the online system on foundation web site
Copies of proposal: 1
Deadline(s): None, for letters of inquiry; Early Feb. and early Sept. for proposals
Board meeting date(s): June and Dec.
Final notification: Varies

Officers and Directors:* Leslie Gimbel,* C.E.O. and Pres.; Lynn S. Stern,* V.P.; Stephen D. Greenberg,* Treas.; Hope G. Solinger,* Honorary Chairperson; Thomas S.T. Gimbel; Alva G. Greenberg; Spencer Greenberg; Judy Mendelsund; Nicholas S.G. Stern.
Number of staff: 2 full-time professional; 1 full-time support.
EIN: 136090843
Selected grants: The following grants are a representative sample of this grantmaker's funding activity:
$125,000 to Earthjustice, San Francisco, CA, 2012. For general support.
$100,000 to Center for Reproductive Rights, New York, NY, 2012. For U.S. Program.
$100,000 to Lawyers for Children, New York, NY, 2012. For general support.
$100,000 to Union of Concerned Scientists, Cambridge, MA, 2012. For general support.
$75,000 to Advocates for Children of New York, New York, NY, 2012. For general support.
$75,000 to Fifth Avenue Committee, Brooklyn, NY, 2012. For general support.
$75,000 to Per Scholas, Bronx, NY, 2012. For IT Training Program.
$75,000 to Planned Parenthood of New York City, New York, NY, 2012. For general support.
$65,000 to League of Conservation Voters Education Fund, Washington, DC, 2012. For general support.
$60,000 to South Brooklyn Legal Services, Brooklyn, NY, 2012. For Employment Projects.
$60,000 to U.S. Green Building Council, New York Chapter, New York, NY, 2012. For general support.
$50,000 to Center for Court Innovation, New York, NY, 2012. For QUEST Futures and Juvenile Mental Health Programs.
$50,000 to Center for Family Representation, New York, NY, 2012. For general support.
$50,000 to CERES, Boston, MA, 2012. For general support.
$50,000 to DreamYard Drama Project, Bronx, NY, 2012. For In-school Programs/Bronx Arts Learning Community.
$50,000 to Nontraditional Employment for Women, New York, NY, 2012. For general support.
$50,000 to Reproductive Health Access Project, New York, NY, 2012. For general support.
$40,000 to Pratt Center for Community Development, Brooklyn, NY, 2012. For Urban Manufacturing Programs.
$40,000 to Sentencing Project, Washington, DC, 2012. For general support.

6054
The Ralph S. Gindi Private Foundation ✧

c/o Jeff Gindi
15 W. 34th St.
New York, NY 10001-3015

Established in 1998 in NY.
Donors: Jeffrey Gindi; Eli Gindi; Irwin Gindi; Jason Gindi; Randy Gindi; Crown Kings Highway LLC; Ahi Ezer Congregation.
Foundation type: Independent foundation.
Financial data (yr. ended 12/31/12): Assets, $310,374 (M); gifts received, $1,070,000; expenditures, $1,058,462; qualifying distributions, $1,058,462; giving activities include $1,057,736 for 299 grants (high: $135,130; low: $18).
Purpose and activities: Giving primarily to Jewish agencies, temples, and schools.
Fields of interest: Education; Jewish federated giving programs; Jewish agencies & synagogues.
Limitations: Applications not accepted. Giving primarily in New York, NY. No grants to individuals.
Application information: Contributes only to pre-selected organizations.
Officers: Jeffrey Gindi, Pres.; Irwin Gindi, V.P.; Eli Gindi, Secy.; Elliot H. Levine, Treas.
EIN: 113431763

6055
Kermit Gitenstein Foundation Inc. ✧

c/o Steven Schlesinger
300 Garden City Plz.
Garden City, NY 11530-3302

Established in 1969.
Donors: Steven R. Schlesinger; Shirley Gitenstein†; Aaron Gitenstein†.
Foundation type: Independent foundation.
Financial data (yr. ended 12/31/11): Assets, $266,097 (M); gifts received, $4,565,938; expenditures, $4,431,979; qualifying distributions, $4,300,000; giving activities include $4,300,000 for 2 grants (high: $4,250,000; low: $50,000).
Fields of interest: Hospitals (general); Health care; Human services.
Type of support: General/operating support; Research.
Limitations: Applications not accepted. Giving primarily in NY and in Israel. No grants to individuals.
Application information: Contributes only to pre-selected organizations.
Trustee: Steven R. Schlesinger.
EIN: 237032219

6056
The Glades Foundation ✧

c/o Sullivan & Cromwell LLP
125 Broad St., Ste. 2534
New York, NY 10004-2498

Established in 1991 in NY.
Donors: Mark F. Dalton; Paul Tudor Jones II.
Foundation type: Independent foundation.
Financial data (yr. ended 12/31/13): Assets, $492,369 (M); gifts received, $1,100,000; expenditures, $660,630; qualifying distributions, $652,830; giving activities include $645,145 for 20 grants (high: $150,000; low: $1,000).
Purpose and activities: Giving primarily for higher education, youth and social services, and the arts.
Fields of interest: Arts; Higher education, university; Human services; Children/youth, services; Foundations (private grantmaking).
Limitations: Applications not accepted. Giving in the U.S., with emphasis on CO and NY; some funding also in Geneva, Switzerland. No grants to individuals.
Application information: Contributes only to pre-selected organizations.
Trustees: James I. Black III; Mark F. Dalton.
EIN: 136986506
Selected grants: The following grants are a representative sample of this grantmaker's funding activity:
$300,000 to Vanderbilt University, Law School, Nashville, TN, 2011.
$65,000 to Sheridan Arts Foundation, Telluride, CO, 2011.
$55,500 to Robin Hood Foundation, New York, NY, 2011.
$50,000 to Buoniconti Fund to Cure Paralysis, Miami, FL, 2011.
$50,000 to Everglades Foundation, Palmetto Bay, FL, 2011.
$35,000 to Memorial Sloan-Kettering Cancer Center, New York, NY, 2011.
$25,000 to American Enterprise Institute for Public Policy Research, Washington, DC, 2011.
$25,000 to Americas Foundation for Chess, Bellevue, WA, 2011.

$10,000 to Harlem Childrens Zone, New York, NY, 2011.
$10,000 to Way to Work, New York, NY, 2011.

6057
The Glens Falls Foundation ✧
237 Glen St.
Glens Falls, NY 12801 (518) 761-7350
Contact: D. Michael Niles, Business Admin.
FAX: (518) 798-8620;
E-mail: administrator@glensfallsfoundation.org;
Main URL: http://www.glensfallsfoundation.org

Established in 1939 in NY by declaration of trust.
Foundation type: Community foundation.
Financial data (yr. ended 12/31/13): Assets, $15,140,899 (M); gifts received, $29,832; expenditures, $523,330; giving activities include $283,448 for 13+ grants (high: $65,000), and $147,225 for 85 grants to individuals.
Purpose and activities: Giving solely to promote the mental, moral, and physical improvement of the people of Glens Falls and environs. Direct financial aid to individuals limited to scholarships to medical students and to students at Dartmouth and Harvard colleges. All other scholarships are awarded through area institutions.
Fields of interest: Human services; Community/economic development.
Type of support: Capital campaigns; Building/renovation; Equipment; Land acquisition; Emergency funds; Program development; Conferences/seminars; Seed money; Research; Scholarships—to individuals; Matching/challenge support.
Limitations: Applications accepted. Giving limited to Warren, Washington, and northern Saratoga counties, NY. No grants for annual campaigns, continuing support, or endowment funds; no loans; no direct scholarship grants (except for medical students and students at Dartmouth and Harvard colleges).
Publications: Application guidelines; Annual report; Informational brochure.
Application information: Visit foundation web site for application form and guidelines. Application form required.
Initial approach: Submit application
Copies of proposal: 2
Deadline(s): Mar. 20, June 20, Sept. 20, and Dec. 20
Board meeting date(s): 2nd Wed. in Jan., Apr., July, and Oct.
Final notification: Applicants will receive a written notice of the Committee's Decision within ten (10) business days of the meeting.
Officers and Distribution Committee:* Donna Metivier Perkett,* Chair.; Mark L. Behan,* Vice-Chair.; Elizabeth Barton-Navitsky; Cheryl Hogan; Stacey Mandelbaum, M.D.; Paul R. McPhillips; Kathryn O'Keeffe, M.D.
Trustee: TD Bank, N.A.
EIN: 146036390

6058
The Glickenhaus Foundation ✧
8 Kendall Ave.
Sleepy Hollow, NY 10591-2211

Incorporated in 1960 in NY.
Donors: Seth M. Glickenhaus; Sarah Glickenhaus.
Foundation type: Independent foundation.
Financial data (yr. ended 11/30/13): Assets, $11,041,348 (M); gifts received, $1,800,000; expenditures, $2,701,105; qualifying distributions, $2,419,993; giving activities include $2,411,575 for 48 grants (high: $2,000,000; low: $50).
Purpose and activities: Giving primarily for human services.
Fields of interest: Museums; Medical school/education; Education; Health organizations, association; Cancer; Human services; Children/youth, services; Jewish agencies & synagogues; Aging.
Type of support: Endowments; Emergency funds; Research.
Limitations: Applications accepted. Giving primarily in the greater metropolitan New York, NY, area, including Westchester County.
Application information: Application form not required.
Initial approach: Letter
Deadline(s): None
Officers: Nancy G. Pier, Pres.; James Glickenhaus, Secy.-Treas.
Number of staff: 1 full-time support.
EIN: 136160941

6059
Rick and Susan Goings Foundation ✧ ☆
c/o Bessemer Trust
630 5th Ave., Ste. 3425
New York, NY 10111-0100

Established in 2007 in FL.
Donor: Everett V. Goings.
Foundation type: Independent foundation.
Financial data (yr. ended 12/31/13): Assets, $13,603,130 (M); expenditures, $524,114; qualifying distributions, $512,841; giving activities include $510,341 for 25 grants (high: $200,000; low: $1,000).
Fields of interest: Boys & girls clubs; United Ways and Federated Giving Programs.
Limitations: Applications not accepted. No grants to individuals.
Application information: Contributes only to pre-selected organizations.
Trustees: Everett V. Goings; Susan Porcaro Goings.
EIN: 260769554

6060
Gold Family Foundation ✧
1 Carter Ln.
Monsey, NY 10952-1108

Established in 1998 in NY.
Donors: Mendel Gold; Israel Gold.
Foundation type: Operating foundation.
Financial data (yr. ended 12/31/11): Assets, $10,449,080 (M); gifts received, $1,535,430; expenditures, $530,431; qualifying distributions, $528,980; giving activities include $528,980 for 39 grants (high: $164,250; low: $180).
Purpose and activities: Giving primarily to Jewish agencies, temples, and schools.
Fields of interest: Education; Jewish agencies & synagogues.
Limitations: Applications not accepted. Giving primarily in NY, with emphasis on Brooklyn and Monsey; some funding also in Lakewood, NJ. No grants to individuals.
Application information: Contributes only to pre-selected organizations.
Officer: Mendel Gold, Pres.
EIN: 134001734

6061
Bradley L. Goldberg Family Foundation ✧
(formerly The Bradley L. Goldberg Charitable Trust)
P.O. Box 737
Mamaroneck, NY 10543-0737

Established in 1984 in NY.
Donors: Bradley L. Goldberg; Dexter Jennison Assocs.
Foundation type: Independent foundation.
Financial data (yr. ended 12/31/13): Assets, $6,893,191 (M); gifts received, $287,200; expenditures, $670,548; qualifying distributions, $669,425; giving activities include $668,250 for 40 grants (high: $255,250; low: $1,000).
Purpose and activities: Giving primarily for animal welfare, conservation, human welfare, and the arts.
Fields of interest: Museums (art); Arts; Environment; Animal welfare; Animals/wildlife, preservation/protection; Human services.
Limitations: Applications not accepted. Giving primarily in NY. No grants to individuals.
Application information: Contributes only to pre-selected organizations.
Officer: Bradley L. Goldberg, Chair.; Sunny Goldberg, Secy.
Board Members: Lilli Goldberg Lawner.
EIN: 136847767

6062
Goldberg/Nash Family Foundation ✧
(formerly Beth Nash & Joshua Nash Charitable Trust)
c/o Ulysses Mgmt., LLC
1 Rockefeller Plz., 20th Fl.
New York, NY 10020-2003

Established in 1989 in NY.
Donor: Joshua Nash.
Foundation type: Independent foundation.
Financial data (yr. ended 06/30/13): Assets, $2,633,707 (M); gifts received, $3,659,473; expenditures, $1,153,179; qualifying distributions, $1,151,329; giving activities include $1,044,439 for 98 grants (high: $170,000; low: $100).
Fields of interest: Arts, association; Museums; Museums (ethnic/folk arts); Arts; Higher education; Education; Hospitals (general); Health organizations, association; Human services; Jewish federated giving programs; Jewish agencies & synagogues.
Limitations: Applications not accepted. Giving primarily in New York, NY. No grants to individuals.
Application information: Contributes only to pre-selected organizations.
Trustees: Beth Nash; Joshua Nash.
EIN: 133560261
Selected grants: The following grants are a representative sample of this grantmaker's funding activity:
$50,000 to American Israel Education Foundation, Washington, DC, 2011.
$50,000 to American Jewish Committee, New York, NY, 2011.
$20,000 to Jewish Theological Seminary of America, New York, NY, 2011.

$15,000 to American Friends of the Israel Museum, New York, NY, 2011.
$15,000 to American Jewish Committee, New York, NY, 2011.
$10,000 to American Friends of the Israel Museum, New York, NY, 2011.
$10,000 to American Friends of the Israel Museum, New York, NY, 2011.
$4,940 to American Jewish Committee, New York, NY, 2011.
$2,600 to Childrens Aid Society, New York, NY, 2011.
$2,500 to Human Rights First, New York, NY, 2011.

6063
The Goldie Anna Charitable Trust ✧
c/o Kenneth L. Stein
5 Woods Witch Ln.
Chappaqua, NY 10514-1223

Established about 1977 in NY.
Foundation type: Independent foundation.
Financial data (yr. ended 12/31/13): Assets, $27,406,794 (M); expenditures, $1,301,961; qualifying distributions, $1,184,241; giving activities include $1,162,012 for 166 grants (high: $105,000; low: $250).
Purpose and activities: Giving primarily for higher education, including some support in Israel, medical research, hospitals, Jewish giving, cultural organizations, and the elderly and disadvantaged.
Fields of interest: Arts; Higher education; Education; Health organizations; Human services; Jewish agencies & synagogues; Economically disadvantaged.
International interests: Israel.
Limitations: Applications not accepted. Giving primarily in the metropolitan New York, NY, area.
Application information: Contributes only to pre-selected organizations. Unsolicited requests for funds not accepted.
Trustees: Emily C. Sharko; Eric C. Stein; Kenneth L. Stein; Nancy C. Stein; Peter C. Stein.
EIN: 132897474
Selected grants: The following grants are a representative sample of this grantmaker's funding activity:
$10,000 to Columbia University, Law School, New York, NY, 2012. For General Operating Support and Specified Charitable Purposes.
$2,500 to Stanford University, Bing School, Stanford, CA, 2012. For General Operating Support and Specified Charitable Purposes.

6064
The Lillian Goldman Charitable Trust ✧
c/o Holland & Knight
31 W. 52 St.
New York, NY 10019-6118
Contact: Donald Goldsmith

Established in 1995 in NY.
Donors: Sol Goldman†; The Sol Goldman Charitable Trust.
Foundation type: Independent foundation.
Financial data (yr. ended 12/31/12): Assets, $26,512,397 (M); expenditures, $7,688,227; qualifying distributions, $7,012,339; giving activities include $6,915,584 for 86 grants (high: $1,000,000; low: $3,662).
Fields of interest: Arts; Higher education; Botanical gardens; Health organizations, association; Human services.
Limitations: Applications not accepted. Giving primarily in New York, NY; funding also in England and Italy. No grants to individuals.
Application information: Contributes only to pre-selected organizations.
Trustees: Sara Goldman Arno; Amy Goldman Fowler; Cary Fowler; Donald A. Goldsmith; Neil Hamilton; Robin Kemper; Carroll Stevens.
EIN: 137048279

6065
The Sol Goldman Charitable Trust ✧
1185 6th Ave., 10th Fl.
New York, NY 10036-2604 (212) 265-2280
Contact: Jane H. Goldman, Tr.

Established in 1988 in NY; funded in 1990.
Donor: Sol Goldman†.
Foundation type: Independent foundation.
Financial data (yr. ended 12/31/13): Assets, $104,457,624 (M); expenditures, $7,021,688; qualifying distributions, $6,743,265; giving activities include $6,732,950 for 53 grants (high: $2,000,000; low: $1,000).
Purpose and activities: Giving primarily to Jewish organizations, health organizations, and education.
Fields of interest: Education; Health organizations, association; Human services; YM/YWCAs & YM/YWHAs; Jewish agencies & synagogues.
Limitations: Giving primarily in New York, NY. No grants to individuals.
Application information: Application form not required.
Initial approach: Proposal
Deadline(s): None
Trustees: Allan H. Goldman; Jane H. Goldman; Louisa Little.
EIN: 133577310
Selected grants: The following grants are a representative sample of this grantmaker's funding activity:
$2,000,000 to Yale University, New Haven, CT, 2011.
$1,000,000 to Brown University, Providence, RI, 2011.
$932,666 to Johns Hopkins University, Baltimore, MD, 2011.
$300,000 to Central Florida Hillel, Orlando, FL, 2011.
$150,000 to New York City Center, New York, NY, 2011.
$100,000 to Israel Museum, Jerusalem, Israel, 2011.
$25,000 to Mannes College of Music, New York, NY, 2011.
$25,000 to New York Shakespeare Festival, New York, NY, 2011.
$25,000 to Ramaz School, New York, NY, 2011.
$25,000 to Roundabout Theater Company, New York, NY, 2011.

6066
Joyce and Irving Goldman Family Foundation, Inc. ✧
(formerly Irving Goldman Foundation, Inc.)
417 5th Ave., Ste. 400
New York, NY 10016-2239 (212) 624-4300
Contact: Benjamin Binswanger, Exec. Dir.
E-mail: jigff@jigff.org

Established in 1984 in NY.
Donors: Goldman Children Trust; Goldman Grandchildren Trust.
Foundation type: Independent foundation.
Financial data (yr. ended 12/31/13): Assets, $160,372,311 (M); gifts received, $4,456,648; expenditures, $7,442,933; qualifying distributions, $6,551,741; giving activities include $6,366,454 for 136 grants (high: $500,000; low: $500).
Purpose and activities: Grants are made in the following three issue areas: Jewish life, medical education and community health in Israel's Negev region, and breast cancer cure/eradication.
Fields of interest: Medical school/education; Cancer; Jewish agencies & synagogues.
Type of support: General/operating support; Continuing support; Program development; Conferences/seminars; Seed money; Research; Program evaluation.
Limitations: Applications accepted. Giving primarily in Israel and the U.S., with special emphasis on NY. No grants to individuals, or for capital requests.
Application information: Consideration for support is primarily through invitation to organizations working in the foundation's areas of interest. Unsolicited letters of inquiry are reviewed; unsolicited proposals are discouraged and should not be submitted unless by invitation from foundation staff. Application form not required.
Initial approach: Letter of inquiry
Copies of proposal: 1
Deadline(s): None
Board meeting date(s): Ongoing
Final notification: Acknowledgment of application immediately; decision within 3-9 months
Officers and Director:* Dorian Goldman,* Pres.; Lloyd Goldman, Secy.; Katja Goldman, Treas.; Benjamin Binswanger, Exec. Dir.
Number of staff: 1 full-time professional.
EIN: 133216152
Selected grants: The following grants are a representative sample of this grantmaker's funding activity:
$510,000 to North Shore-Long Island Jewish Health System Foundation, Great Neck, NY, 2012. For General Operating Support.
$500,000 to American Associates, Ben-Gurion University of the Negev, New York, NY, 2012. For Project Support.
$300,000 to National Breast Cancer Coalition Fund, Washington, DC, 2012. For General Operating Support.
$200,000 to American Jewish Committee, New York, NY, 2012. For Project Support.
$200,000 to UJA-Federation of New York, New York, NY, 2012. For General Operating Support.
$170,000 to Kivunim, New York, NY, 2012. For General Operating Support.
$125,000 to Reboot, Inc., New York, NY, 2012. For Project Support.
$110,000 to Congregation Bnai Jeshurun, New York, NY, 2012. For General Operating Support.
$45,000 to Fund for Public Schools, New York, NY, 2012. For General Operating Support.
$30,000 to Andrea and Charles Bronfman Philanthropies, New York, NY, 2012. For Project Support.

6067
Amy P. Goldman Foundation ✧
c/o Donald Goldsmith, Tr., Holland and Knight LLP
31 W. 52nd St.
New York, NY 10019-6118

Established in 2007 in NY.
Donor: Amy P. Goldman.
Foundation type: Independent foundation.
Financial data (yr. ended 04/30/12): Assets, $89,444,032 (M); gifts received, $2,000,000; expenditures, $568,153; qualifying distributions, $509,888; giving activities include $501,000 for 9 grants (high: $200,000; low: $6,000).
Fields of interest: Education; Botanical gardens.
Limitations: Applications not accepted. Giving primarily in IA, NC, and NY. No grants to individuals.
Application information: Contributes only to pre-selected organizations.
Officers and Trustees:* Amy Goldman,* Pres.; Diana M. Gurieva,* Secy.; Donald A. Goldsmith, Esq.*, Treas.
EIN: 204853144

6068
Herman Goldman Foundation ✧
44 Wall St., Ste. 1212
New York, NY 10005-2401 (212) 461-2132
Contact: Richard K. Baron, Exec. Dir.
E-mail: goldfound@aol.com

Incorporated in 1943 in NY.
Donor: Herman Goldman†.
Foundation type: Independent foundation.
Financial data (yr. ended 02/28/13): Assets, $19,274,290 (M); expenditures, $1,582,066; qualifying distributions, $1,196,778; giving activities include $879,000 for 82+ grants.
Purpose and activities: Emphasis on enhancing the quality of life through innovative grants in four main areas: 1) Health - to achieve effective delivery of physical and mental health care services; 2) Social Justice - to develop organizational, social, and legal approaches to aid deprived or handicapped people; 3) Education - for new or improved counseling for effective preschool, vocational and paraprofessional training; and 4) the Arts - to increase opportunities for talented youth to receive training and for less affluent individuals to attend quality presentations; some aid for programs relating to nationwide problems.
Fields of interest: Performing arts; Education, early childhood education; Vocational education; Education; Health care; Mental health/crisis services; Health organizations, association; Crime/law enforcement; Human services; Disabilities, people with; Economically disadvantaged.
Type of support: General/operating support; Continuing support; Annual campaigns; Capital campaigns; Building/renovation; Endowments; Program development; Seed money; Fellowships; Internship funds; Scholarship funds; Research.
Limitations: Applications accepted. Giving primarily in the metropolitan New York, NY, area. No support for religious organizations. No grants to individuals, or for emergency funds.
Publications: Annual report (including application guidelines).
Application information: NY/NJ Area Common Application Form accepted. Application form not required.
Initial approach: Proposal
Copies of proposal: 1
Deadline(s): None
Board meeting date(s): Monthly; grants considered in Apr., July, and Nov.
Final notification: 2 to 3 months
Officers and Directors:* Alan Michigan,* Pres.; David A. Brauner,* V.P.; Charles A. Damato,* V.P.; Michael J. Clain,* Secy.; Michael L. Goldstein,* Treas.; Richard K. Baron, Exec. Dir.; Mel P. Barkan; Jules M. Baron; John H.F. Enteman; Donald Gibson; David R. Kay; Alan Nisselson; Christopher C. Schwabacher; Howard L. Simon; Roy M. Sparber.
Number of staff: 2 full-time professional.
EIN: 136066039

6069
Robert I. Goldman Foundation ✧ ☆
c/o R. Rothberg; Cooley, LLP
1114 Ave. of the Americas, 46th Fl.
New York, NY 10036

Established in 2005 in NY.
Donors: Robert I. Goldman†; Brown Charitable Rem Unitrust.
Foundation type: Independent foundation.
Financial data (yr. ended 12/31/13): Assets, $9,982,290 (M); expenditures, $594,126; qualifying distributions, $533,053; giving activities include $505,000 for 20 grants (high: $175,000; low: $2,000).
Fields of interest: Museums (ethnic/folk arts); Higher education; Education; Cancer; Alzheimer's disease; Medical research, institute; Human services.
Limitations: Applications not accepted. Giving primarily in CA, Washington, DC, IL and NY.
Application information: Contributes only to pre-selected organizations.
Officers: Olexa Celine Mandelbaum, Chair.; Melva Bucksbaum, Vice-Chair. and Treas.; Richard S. Rothberg, Secy.
EIN: 202371917
Selected grants: The following grants are a representative sample of this grantmaker's funding activity:
$130,000 to Baum Foundation, San Francisco, CA, 2011.
$25,000 to Alzheimers Association, Chicago, IL, 2011.
$25,000 to Breast Cancer Research Foundation, New York, NY, 2011.
$25,000 to Saint Jude Childrens Research Hospital, Memphis, TN, 2011.
$15,000 to Aspen Community Foundation, Aspen, CO, 2011.
$15,000 to Buoniconti Fund to Cure Paralysis, Miami, FL, 2011.
$15,000 to Business Executives for National Security, Washington, DC, 2011.

6070
The Goldman Sachs Foundation ✧
(formerly Goldman Sachs Charitable Fund)
200 West St., 29th Fl.
New York, NY 10282-2198 (212) 902-3246
Contact: Brenda Lee, Grants Admin.
E-mail: gsfoundation@gs.com; E-mail for 10,000 Small Businesses: 10000SmallBusinesses@gs.com; Main URL: http://www.goldmansachs.com/citizenship/index.html

Established in 1999 in NY.
Donors: Goldman, Sachs & Co.; MTGLQ Investors, L.P.; Goldman Sachs Group, Inc.
Foundation type: Company-sponsored foundation.
Financial data (yr. ended 12/31/12): Assets, $588,543,934 (M); gifts received, $10,243,500; expenditures, $42,776,915; qualifying distributions, $39,768,844; giving activities include $36,658,124 for grants.
Purpose and activities: The foundation supports strategic programs that include 10,000 Women and 10,000 Small Businesses.
Fields of interest: Education; Community development, small businesses; Community/economic development.
International interests: Africa; Asia; Europe; Middle East; United Kingdom.
Type of support: Continuing support; Program development.
Limitations: Applications not accepted. Giving on a national and international basis primarily in areas of company operations in Asia, Africa, the Middle East, and the United Kingdom. No support for political causes, campaigns, or candidates. No grants for political fundraising events.
Publications: Informational brochure.
Application information: Contributes only to pre-selected organizations and individuals.
Officers and Directors:* John F.W. Rogers,* Chair.; Dina H. Powell, Pres.; Peter M. Fahey,* V.P.; Robert J. Katz,* V.P.; Eileen M. Dillion; Lisa D. Hancock; Katherine Jollon; Matthew LoCurto; Noa Meyer; Beverly L. O'Toole; Benjamin J. Radar; Emmett St. John.
EIN: 311678646
Selected grants: The following grants are a representative sample of this grantmaker's funding activity:
$2,445,810 to Houston Community College System Foundation, Houston, TX, 2012. To implement the 10,000 Small Businesses initiative in the greater Houston area.
$2,091,833 to Long Beach City College Foundation, Long Beach, CA, 2012. To implement the 10,000 Small Businesses initiative in the Los Angeles metropolitan region.
$2,081,787 to Babson College, Babson Park, MA, 2012. To develop, implement and deliver the 10,000 Small Businesses curriculum nationally and to train faculty across the initiative.
$1,690,212 to LaGuardia Community College of the City University of New York, Long Island City, NY, 2012. To implement the 10,000 Small Businesses initiative in the greater New York area.
$1,413,107 to Manchester Metropolitan University, Centre for Enterprise, Manchester, England, 2012. To implement the 10,000 Small Businesses initiative in Manchester, England.
$1,402,434 to Delgado Community College Foundation, New Orleans, LA, 2012. To implement the 10,000 Small Businesses initiative in the greater New Orleans area.
$1,302,047 to Cuyahoga Community College, Cleveland, OH, 2012. To implement the 10,000 Small Businesses initiative in the greater Cleveland Area.
$1,283,984 to Aston University, Aston Business School, Birmingham, England, 2012. To implement the 10,000 Small Businesses initiative in Birmingham, England.
$1,211,695 to Initiative for a Competitive Inner-City, Roxbury, MA, 2012. To coordinate the participant outreach and recruitment and selection process

nationally for the 10,000 Small Businesses initiative.
$455,909 to Thunderbird, The Garvin School of International Management, Glendale, AZ, 2012. To implement the 10,000 Women Training Program in Afghanistan in collaboration with The America University in Afghanistan (AUAF).

6071
Barbara Lubin Goldsmith Foundation ✧
(formerly Goldsmith-Perry Philanthropies, Inc.)
550 Park Ave., Ste. 17E
New York, NY 10065-7345

Established in 1969 in NY.
Donors: Joseph I. Lubin†; Barbara Lubin Goldsmith Charitable Trust.
Foundation type: Independent foundation.
Financial data (yr. ended 12/31/13): Assets, $2,188,759 (M); expenditures, $768,765; qualifying distributions, $717,432; giving activities include $621,707 for 99 grants (high: $100,000; low: $45).
Purpose and activities: Giving primarily for the arts, higher and other education, health organizations and human services.
Fields of interest: Arts; Higher education; Education; Health organizations; Human services; Jewish agencies & synagogues.
Limitations: Applications not accepted. Giving primarily in Middletown, CT, and New York, NY. No grants to individuals.
Application information: Unsolicited requests for funds not accepted.
Officers and Directors:* Barbara Lubin Goldsmith,* Pres.; Alice Elgart,* Secy.
Number of staff: 1
EIN: 237031986
Selected grants: The following grants are a representative sample of this grantmaker's funding activity:
$50,000 to New York University, New York, NY, 2011.
$35,000 to Council on Foreign Relations, New York, NY, 2011.
$6,950 to Aspen Institute, Washington, DC, 2011.
$4,640 to New York City Center, New York, NY, 2011.
$2,500 to Phoenix House, New York, NY, 2011.
$1,000 to Boys and Girls Clubs of America, Atlanta, GA, 2011.
$1,000 to Planned Parenthood Federation of America, New York, NY, 2011.
$1,000 to Teach for America, New York, NY, 2011.
$1,000 to University of Pennsylvania, Philadelphia, PA, 2011.

6072
Horace W. Goldsmith Foundation ✧
375 Park Ave., Ste. 1602
New York, NY 10152-1600
Contact: William A. Slaughter, C.E.O.
E-mail: hwgf1@verizon.net

Incorporated in 1955 in NY.
Donor: Horace W. Goldsmith†.
Foundation type: Independent foundation.
Financial data (yr. ended 12/31/13): Assets, $563,410,104 (M); expenditures, $26,357,738; qualifying distributions, $18,874,107; giving activities include $18,115,168 for 239 grants (high: $500,000; low: $5,000).
Purpose and activities: Support for cultural programs, including the performing arts and museums; Jewish and Israeli charitable organizations; hospitals and other health care organizations; and education, especially higher education.
International interests: Israel.
Limitations: Applications not accepted. Giving on a worldwide basis. No grants to individuals.
Application information: Unsolicited applications are not accepted; foundation grants are internally initiated.
Board meeting date(s): 4 times a year
Officers and Managing Directors:* William A. Slaughter,* C.E.O.; Charles L. Slaughter,* C.F.O.; Thomas R. Slaughter; R. James Slaughter.
Number of staff: 1 full-time support.
EIN: 136107758
Selected grants: The following grants are a representative sample of this grantmaker's funding activity:
$750,000 to University of Virginia, Law School, Charlottesville, VA, 2013.
$500,000 to Jerusalem Foundation, New York, NY, 2013.
$500,000 to National Constitution Center, Philadelphia, PA, 2013.
$500,000 to Yale University, Law School, New Haven, CT, 2013.
$400,000 to Metropolitan Opera, New York, NY, 2013.
$250,000 to University of California San Francisco Foundation, Madison Clinic for Pediatric Diseases, San Francisco, CA, 2013.
$100,000 to University of California San Francisco Foundation, Global Health Sciences, San Francisco, CA, 2013.
$83,334 to PATH, Seattle, WA, 2013.
$75,000 to World Affairs Council of Northern California, San Francisco, CA, 2013.
$33,000 to Smithsonian American Art Museum, Washington, DC, 2013.

6073
Abraham and Mildred Goldstein Charitable Trust ✧
c/o Withumsmith+Brown PC
1411 Broadway, 9th Fl.
New York, NY 10018

Established in 1997 in NY.
Donors: Abraham Goldstein†; Mildred Goldstein†.
Foundation type: Independent foundation.
Financial data (yr. ended 12/31/12): Assets, $15,734,421 (M); expenditures, $1,594,124; qualifying distributions, $1,435,000; giving activities include $1,435,000 for grants.
Fields of interest: Higher education; Medical school/education; Health care; Jewish agencies & synagogues.
Limitations: Applications not accepted. Giving primarily in NY. No grants to individuals.
Application information: Contributes only to pre-selected organizations.
Trustees: K. Baptiste; Hirschell E. Levine.
EIN: 137061296

6074
Arlene & Arnold Goldstein Family Foundation ✧ ☆
c/o Samson Mgmt.
97-77 Queens Blvd.
Rego Park, NY 11374-3395

Established in 1996 in NY.
Donor: Arnold Goldstein.
Foundation type: Independent foundation.
Financial data (yr. ended 12/31/13): Assets, $1,552,205 (M); gifts received, $443,865; expenditures, $581,344; qualifying distributions, $445,544; giving activities include $445,544 for 57 grants (high: $100,000; low: $100).
Purpose and activities: Giving primarily to Jewish federated giving programs and other Jewish organizations, as well as for health associations and hospitals, and for human services.
Fields of interest: Arts; Higher education; Hospitals (general); Health organizations; Human services; United Ways and Federated Giving Programs; Jewish federated giving programs; Jewish agencies & synagogues.
Limitations: Applications not accepted. Giving primarily in New York, NY. No grants to individuals.
Application information: Contributes only to pre-selected organizations.
Trustees: Arlene Goldstein; Arnold Goldstein.
EIN: 137091014

6075
The Goldstein Family Foundation ✧
c/o Arthur Fox, CPA
420 Lexington Ave., Ste. 1733
New York, NY 10170-1734

Established in 1984 in NY.
Donor: Jerome Goldstein.
Foundation type: Independent foundation.
Financial data (yr. ended 11/30/13): Assets, $14,490,319 (M); expenditures, $902,147; qualifying distributions, $700,899; giving activities include $683,515 for 75 grants (high: $300,000; low: $115).
Fields of interest: Arts; Higher education; Education; Environment; Hospitals (general); Jewish federated giving programs; Jewish agencies & synagogues.
Limitations: Applications not accepted. Giving primarily in New York, NY; some funding also in NJ. No grants to individuals.
Application information: Contributes only to pre-selected organizations.
Officers: Jerome R. Goldstein, Pres.; Dorothy L. Goldstein, V.P.; Bettina L. Decker, Secy.-Treas.
EIN: 133192220

6076
The Leslie & Roslyn Goldstein Foundation ✧
c/o MGI Repetti LLP
500 5th Ave., 5th Fl.
New York, NY 10110-0501

Established in 1980 in CT.
Donors: Leslie Goldstein; Roslyn Goldstein.
Foundation type: Independent foundation.
Financial data (yr. ended 11/30/13): Assets, $33,844,659 (M); expenditures, $1,699,350; qualifying distributions, $1,696,850; giving

activities include $1,691,850 for 36 grants (high: $258,000; low: $100).
Purpose and activities: Giving primarily for the arts, health, human services, and to Jewish organizations.
Fields of interest: Arts; Hospitals (general); Health care; Breast cancer research; Human services; Jewish federated giving programs; Jewish agencies & synagogues.
Type of support: Annual campaigns; Capital campaigns; Building/renovation.
Limitations: Applications not accepted. Giving primarily in New York, NY. No grants to individuals.
Application information: Contributes only to pre-selected organizations.
Board meeting date(s): Varies
Trustee: Roslyn Goldstein.
EIN: 061035614

6077
The B. Thomas Golisano Foundation ✧
c/o Fishers Asset Mgmt.
1 Fishers Rd.
Pittsford, NY 14534-9511 (585) 340-1203
Contact: Ann M. Costello, Dir.
FAX: (585) 340-1204;
E-mail: info@GolisanoFoundation.org; Main URL: http://www.golisanofoundation.org
Facebook: https://www.facebook.com/pages/The-Golisano-Foundation/118294264855416
Grants List: http://www.golisanofoundation.org/grants.html

Established in 1985 in NY.
Donor: B. Thomas Golisano.
Foundation type: Independent foundation.
Financial data (yr. ended 10/31/13): Assets, $28,934,513 (M); expenditures, $1,162,771; qualifying distributions, $1,122,254; giving activities include $927,000 for 26 grants (high: $361,000; low: $5,000).
Purpose and activities: Support for programs that create opportunities for people with developmental disabilities to achieve maximum potential and be active in their communities.
Fields of interest: Disabilities, people with.
Type of support: General/operating support; Capital campaigns; Building/renovation; Equipment; Seed money; Program evaluation; Matching/challenge support.
Limitations: Applications accepted. Giving limited to the greater Rochester, NY area. No support for municipal programs. No grants to individuals, or for fund-raising events, medical research, or for endowments.
Publications: Application guidelines; Annual report; Grants list; Program policy statement.
Application information: Grantmakers Forum of New York's Common Grant Application Form accepted. Application form required.
Initial approach: Telephone or letter of inquiry with application
Copies of proposal: 2
Deadline(s): 4 weeks prior to board meeting
Board meeting date(s): Quarterly; usually 4th Wed. of Jan., Apr., July and Oct.
Final notification: Within 2 weeks after board meeting
Director: Ann M. Costello.
Trustees: G. Thomas Clark; Dr. William Destler; B. Thomas Golisano; Charles Graham; Patricia Malgieri; James D. Murray.
Number of staff: 1 part-time professional; 1 part-time support.
EIN: 222692938

6078
Perry & Donna Golkin Family Foundation ✧
c/o KKR Financial Svcs. Co. LLC
730 5th Ave., 8th Fl.
New York, NY 10019-4105

Established in 1997 in NY.
Donor: Perry Golkin.
Foundation type: Independent foundation.
Financial data (yr. ended 11/30/13): Assets, $13,523,910 (M); gifts received, $3,965,039; expenditures, $697,666; qualifying distributions, $659,075; giving activities include $636,420 for 5 grants (high: $125,000; low: $100).
Purpose and activities: Giving primarily for higher and other education and human services.
Fields of interest: Elementary/secondary education; Higher education; Human services.
Limitations: Applications not accepted. Giving primarily in New York, NY and Philadelphia, PA. No grants to individuals.
Application information: Contributes only to pre-selected organizations.
Trustees: David L. Golkin; Donna Golkin; Dorie C. Golkin; Gregory W. Golkin; Perry Golkin.
EIN: 133928587

6079
The William and Estelle Golub Foundation, Inc. ✧
461 Nott St.
Schenectady, NY 12308-1812

Established in 1986 in NY.
Donors: William Golub†; Estelle Golub†; Neil M. Golub Trust.
Foundation type: Independent foundation.
Financial data (yr. ended 12/31/13): Assets, $20,330,842 (M); expenditures, $1,280,696; qualifying distributions, $1,267,422; giving activities include $1,125,992 for 161 grants (high: $340,000; low: $50).
Purpose and activities: Giving primarily for health organizations, including a camp for children with critical illnesses; funding also for social services, federated giving programs, and Jewish organizations.
Fields of interest: Hospitals (general); Health organizations, association; Human services; Children/youth, services; United Ways and Federated Giving Programs; Jewish federated giving programs.
Type of support: General/operating support.
Limitations: Applications not accepted. Giving primarily in Albany and Schenectady, NY. No grants to individuals.
Application information: Contributes only to pre-selected organizations.
Officers and Trustees:* Neil M. Golub,* Pres.; Mona Golub, Secy.; Jane Golub.
EIN: 222809785
Selected grants: The following grants are a representative sample of this grantmaker's funding activity:
$100,000 to Wildwood Foundation, Schenectady, NY, 2011.
$79,600 to Double H Hole in the Woods Ranch, Lake Luzerne, NY, 2011.
$70,000 to Ellis Hospital Foundation, Schenectady, NY, 2011.
$38,000 to United Way of the Capital Region, Enola, PA, 2011.
$35,000 to Rensselaer Polytechnic Institute, Troy, NY, 2011.
$30,600 to Proctors Theater, Schenectady, NY, 2011.
$25,000 to Union College, Schenectady, NY, 2011.
$22,500 to Clowns on Rounds, Albany, NY, 2011.
$19,750 to Muscular Dystrophy Association, Albany, NY, 2011.
$17,850 to American Heart Association, Dallas, TX, 2011.

6080
The Michael Gordon Foundation, Inc. ✧
c/o Baker Tilly Virchow Krause,LLP
1 Penn Plz., Ste. 3000
New York, NY 10119-0032

Established in 1991 in NY.
Donor: Michael Gordon†.
Foundation type: Independent foundation.
Financial data (yr. ended 12/31/13): Assets, $13,960,465 (M); expenditures, $667,245; qualifying distributions, $534,335; giving activities include $421,995 for 40 grants (high: $25,000; low: $1,825).
Fields of interest: Secondary school/education; Education.
Limitations: Applications not accepted. Giving primarily in the metropolitan New York, NY, area.
Application information: Contributes only to pre-selected organizations.
Officers: Thomas Tillander, Pres.; William McSherry, Secy.; John Tillander, Treas.
EIN: 133585393
Selected grants: The following grants are a representative sample of this grantmaker's funding activity:
$29,400 to Hawthorne Foundation, Hawthorne, NY, 2011.
$26,050 to Bishop Kearney High School, Brooklyn, NY, 2011.
$24,849 to Parkside School, New York, NY, 2011.
$23,350 to Notre Dame Academy, Staten Island, NY, 2011.
$22,374 to McCarton School, New York, NY, 2011.
$20,000 to Fontbonne Hall Academy, Brooklyn, NY, 2011.
$20,000 to Gillen Brewer School, New York, NY, 2011.
$20,000 to Saint John Villa Academy, Staten Island, NY, 2011.
$20,000 to Staten Island Academy, Staten Island, NY, 2011.
$15,000 to Saint Saviour High School, Brooklyn, NY, 2011.

6081
The John R. and Kiendl Dauphinot Gordon Fund ✧
(formerly The John R. Gordon Fund)
c/o Sullivan & Cromwell LLP
125 Broad St.
New York, NY 10004-2498

Established in 1988 in NY.

Donors: Albert H. Gordon; John R. Gordon; Kiendl Dauphinot Gordon.
Foundation type: Independent foundation.
Financial data (yr. ended 12/31/12): Assets, $79,848 (M); gifts received, $1,584,504; expenditures, $1,668,083; qualifying distributions, $1,668,083; giving activities include $1,665,566 for 35 grants (high: $511,500; low: $200).
Fields of interest: Arts; Education; Health organizations; Protestant agencies & churches.
Limitations: Applications not accepted. Giving primarily in New York, NY and in Philadelphia, PA. No grants to individuals.
Application information: Contributes only to pre-selected organizations.
Trustees: John R. Gordon; Kiendl Dauphinot Gordon.
EIN: 136920431

6082
The Kathy and Al Gordon Fund ✧
570 Park Ave., No. 7B
New York, NY 10021

Established in 2004 in NY.
Foundation type: Independent foundation.
Financial data (yr. ended 12/31/13): Assets, $186,185 (M); gifts received, $511,500; expenditures, $490,103; qualifying distributions, $480,485; giving activities include $480,485 for 6 grants (high: $113,335; low: $1,400).
Fields of interest: Higher education; Education; Athletics/sports, racquet sports; Catholic agencies & churches.
Limitations: Applications not accepted. Giving primarily in NY; funding also in NH. No grants to individuals.
Application information: Contributes only to pre-selected organizations.
Trustees: Kathleen Gordon; Nancy Mulligan; William A. Oates.
EIN: 306073441

6083
Owen T. Gorman & Alice M. Gorman Testamentary Charitable Trust ✧
(doing business as The Gorman Foundation)
447 Kinsley St.
Sherrill, NY 13461-1349 (315) 363-0170
Contact: Amanda Larson, Pres.
FAX: (315) 366-0170;
E-mail: amanda@gormanfoundation.org; Main URL: http://www.gormanfoundation.org

Established in 2003 in NY.
Donors: Alice M. Gorman†; Owen Gorman†; Catherine Cummings Gorman†.
Foundation type: Independent foundation.
Financial data (yr. ended 12/31/12): Assets, $13,633,673 (M); expenditures, $921,976; qualifying distributions, $880,735; giving activities include $547,888 for 58 grants (high: $250,000; low: $75).
Purpose and activities: Giving primarily to organizations that support: 1) faith in action programs, particularly programs and services designed to help people in need gain access to healthcare, education, food, and shelter; 2) the environment, particularly efforts to support sustainable farming programs, and to preserve biodiversity, rehabilitate wildlife, and care for homeless, domestic animals; and 3) community education and enhancement projects, particularly outreach programs that enhance community well being, or preserve historical areas of interest.
Fields of interest: Education; Health care; Human services; Children; Immigrants/refugees; Economically disadvantaged; Homeless.
International interests: Lithuania; Sri Lanka.
Type of support: General/operating support; Continuing support; Building/renovation; Emergency funds; Program development; Scholarship funds; Program-related investments/loans.
Limitations: Applications accepted. Giving limited to Madison County, NY. No grants to individuals, or for debt reduction drives, or lobbying activities as defined by the IRS; no grants to organizations that do not agree with the foundation's policy on non-discrimination.
Publications: Application guidelines; Grants list; Informational brochure; Informational brochure (including application guidelines).
Application information: Hard copy applications are not accepted. Online applications only. Application form required.
Initial approach: Use online application form via foundation web site
Deadline(s): None
Final notification: Approx. 3 months
Officers and Trustees:* Joanne G. Larson,* Chair. and C.I.O.; Amanda Larson,* Pres. and C.O.O.; James F. Sullivan, Sr.,* V.P.
Number of staff: 2 full-time professional; 1 part-time professional; 1 part-time support.
EIN: 226927092
Selected grants: The following grants are a representative sample of this grantmaker's funding activity:
$10,000 to Great Swamp Conservancy, Canastota, NY, 2012. To transform a barn into a community outreach center and natural history museum.
$5,000 to Oneida Community Mansion House, Oneida, NY, 2012. For furniture renovations and lounge carpeting.
$2,250 to Samaritan Center, Syracuse, NY, 2012. For a soup kitchen for those in need.
$2,010 to American Cancer Society, Utica, NY, 2012. For Oneida Relay For Life which supports cancer research, education and advocacy efforts.
$500 to Madison County Historical Society, Oneida, NY, 2012. For Hop Fest, annual event that promotes the art of craft brewing and central New York's influence on the hop industry.

6084
The Gorter Family Foundation ✧
(formerly Green Bay Foundation)
c/o BCRS Assocs., LLC
77 Water St., 9th Fl.
New York, NY 10005-3701

Established in 1977 in IL.
Donors: James P. Gorter; Audrey F. Gorter.
Foundation type: Independent foundation.
Financial data (yr. ended 12/31/12): Assets, $22,140,381 (M); gifts received, $1,070,727; expenditures, $1,760,784; qualifying distributions, $1,239,230; giving activities include $1,220,823 for 101 grants (high: $200,000; low: $2).
Purpose and activities: Giving primarily for education, health organizations, and human services.
Fields of interest: Higher education; Hospitals (general); Health organizations, association; Human services; Children/youth, services; United Ways and Federated Giving Programs; Christian agencies & churches.
Type of support: General/operating support.
Limitations: Applications not accepted. Giving primarily in FL, IL and NC. No grants to individuals, or for scholarships; no loans.
Application information: Contributes only to pre-selected organizations.
Officer and Directors:* James P. Gorter,* Pres.; Audrey F. Gorter; David F. Gorter; Lauren A. Gorter; Mary Gorter Krey; Bradley R. Krey.
EIN: 362950350
Selected grants: The following grants are a representative sample of this grantmaker's funding activity:
$1,000 to Duke University, School of Environment, Durham, NC, 2012. For All Contributions Were Made to the general purposes Fund of Public Charitable Organizations That Were Classified Under Section 501(c)(3) of the Internal Revenue Code.
$1,000 to Duke University, School of Environment, Durham, NC, 2012. For All Contributions Were Made to the general purposes Fund of Public Charitable Organizations That Were Classified Under Section 501(c)(3) of the Internal Revenue Code.
$500 to Duke University, School of Nursing, Durham, NC, 2012. For All Contributions Were Made to the general purposes Fund of Public Charitable Organizations That Were Classified Under Section 501(c)(3) of the Internal Revenue Code.
$500 to Duke University, School of Nursing, Durham, NC, 2012. For All Contributions Were Made to the general purposes Fund of Public Charitable Organizations That Were Classified Under Section 501(c)(3) of the Internal Revenue Code.
$100 to Family Network, Highland Park, IL, 2012. For All Contributions Were Made to the general purposes Fund of Public Charitable Organizations That Were Classified Under Section 501(c)(3) of the Internal Revenue Code.

6085
Adolph and Esther Gottlieb Foundation, Inc. ✧
380 West Broadway
New York, NY 10012-5115 (212) 226-0581
Contact: Sanford Hirsch, Exec. Dir.
FAX: (212) 274-1476;
E-mail: shirsch@gottliebfoundation.org; Main URL: http://www.gottliebfoundation.org

Established in 1976 in NY.
Donors: Adolph Gottlieb†; Esther Gottlieb†; Alice Yamin†; Ann Cooper†.
Foundation type: Independent foundation.
Financial data (yr. ended 06/30/13): Assets, $32,911,466 (M); expenditures, $1,244,487; qualifying distributions, $1,106,168; giving activities include $548,500 for 33 grants to individuals.
Purpose and activities: The foundation maintains two separate grant programs: 1) Individual support program for painters, sculptors, and printmakers who have worked at least 20 years in a mature phase of their art, and are in current financial need; and 2) Emergency assistance program for painters, sculptors, and printmakers who have worked at least 10 years in a mature phase of their art and are in current financial need in excess of and unrelated to their normal economic situation, and which is the result of a recent emergency occurrence such as a fire, flood or medical emergency.

Fields of interest: Visual arts; Visual arts, sculpture; Visual arts, painting; Economically disadvantaged.
Type of support: Emergency funds; Grants to individuals.
Limitations: Giving on a national and international basis. No support for charitable organizations, educational institutions or projects, artists working in crafts, or for dental work, or chronic situations. No grants for capital improvements, or for debt.
Publications: Application guidelines; Informational brochure.
Application information: Application information available on foundation web site. Application form required.
Initial approach: Letter only, requesting application form for Individual Support program; letter or telephone for Emergency Assistance program
Copies of proposal: 1
Deadline(s): Dec. 15 for Individual Support Program grants; none for Emergency Assistance Program
Board meeting date(s): Annually
Final notification: Mar.
Officers and Directors:* Robert Mangold, Pres.; Charlotta Kotik,* V.P.; Gordon Marsh,* V.P.; Sanford Hirsch,* Secy.-Treas. and Exec. Dir.; Lynda Benglis.
Number of staff: 3 full-time professional; 1 part-time professional; 1 part-time support.
EIN: 132853957

6086
Gould Family Foundation ✧
c/o Baker & McKenzie LLP
229 Christie St., Ste. 816
New York, NY 10002
Contact: Edwin S. Matthews, Jr., Tr.; Anthony Gould

Established in 2003 in NY.
Donor: Lois Gould.
Foundation type: Independent foundation.
Financial data (yr. ended 12/31/13): Assets, $27,075,338 (M); expenditures, $1,403,533; qualifying distributions, $1,283,525; giving activities include $1,020,000 for 21 grants (high: $150,000; low: $5,000).
Purpose and activities: The foundation funds creative projects for fundamental social change.
Fields of interest: Museums; Performing arts; Arts; Higher education; Environment; Animals/wildlife; International human rights.
International interests: Developing Countries.
Limitations: Giving primarily in CT, Washington, DC, New York, NY, and in Kenya, South Africa, and Guatemala.
Application information: Application form not required.
Initial approach: Letter
Copies of proposal: 1
Deadline(s): None
Trustees: Anthony Gould; Edwin S. Matthews, Jr.
EIN: 020595263
Selected grants: The following grants are a representative sample of this grantmaker's funding activity:
$75,000 to Rocky Mountain Institute, Boulder, CO, 2012. For Technical support for the preparation of a comprehensive energy strategy for the state of Connecticut.
$40,000 to Steep Rock Association, Washington Depot, CT, 2012. For Preservation of land and design of footbridge in preserve.
$20,000 to After School Arts Program, Washington Depot, CT, 2012. To enable children to engage in artistic and cultural activities.

6087
Edwin Gould Foundation ✧
55 Exchange Pl., 6th Fl.
New York, NY 10005-3301 (212) 982-5200
Contact: Cynthia Rivera Weissblum, C.E.O. and Pres.
FAX: (212) 982-6886; Main URL: http://www.edwingouldfoundation.org/

Incorporated in 1923 in New York, NY.
Foundation type: Independent foundation.
Financial data (yr. ended 12/31/13): Assets, $42,442,166 (M); gifts received, $75,655; expenditures, $2,629,355; qualifying distributions, $2,114,675; giving activities include $914,004 for 27 grants (high: $508,464; low: $500).
Purpose and activities: The foundation champions innovative organizations that create bold, best-in-class solutions to increase the number of college graduates from under-resourced communities. They seek to accomplish this by seeding and growing educational models that empower motivated, yet underserved students to enter college, graduate and advance society. The foundation seeks to provide educational support where the system leaves off, with a focus on supplemental education initiatives that help students succeed. The foundation has a deep, long-term approach to grantmaking through investment in Gould Partners over the long-term, to provide them with the additional resources and office space needed to work, grow and collaborate.
Fields of interest: Elementary/secondary education; Higher education; Higher education, college; Youth; Young adults; Young adults, female; Young adults, male; Economically disadvantaged.
Type of support: Management development/capacity building; Program development; Seed money; Curriculum development; Program evaluation.
Limitations: Applications not accepted. Giving primarily in New York, NY, and throughout the U.S. for advocacy. No support for organizations that do not focus on preparation for and persistence to college graduation for motivated yet underserved youth. No grants to individuals, or for building or endowment funds, or matching gifts; no loans.
Application information: Unsolicited requests for funds not accepted.
Officers and Trustees:* Mark Bieler,* Chair.; Cynthia Rivera Weissblum,* C.E.O. and Pres.; Nana Tam, Treas.; Michael W. Osheowitz,* Chair. Emeritus; Steven Brown; Anthony Carnevale; Nicole M. Chestang; Steven Gross; Lofton Holder; Truda Jewitt; Edward A. Lesser; Roszell Mack III; Josh Parker; Alan Weinstein.
Advisors: Marc Porter Magee; Thomas L. Webber.
Number of staff: 5 full-time professional; 1 full-time support.
EIN: 135675642

6088
The Florence Gould Foundation ✧
c/o Cahill Gordon & Reindel LLP
80 Pine St., Ste. 2133
New York, NY 10005-1702 (212) 701-3400
Contact: John R. Young, Pres.

Incorporated in 1957 in NY.
Donor: Florence J. Gould†.
Foundation type: Independent foundation.
Financial data (yr. ended 12/31/12): Assets, $65,904,584 (M); expenditures, $7,523,346; qualifying distributions, $7,141,506; giving activities include $6,682,739 for 82 grants (high: $1,400,000; low: $165).
Purpose and activities: Essential aim is to promote French-American amity and understanding.
Fields of interest: Arts.
International interests: France.
Limitations: Applications accepted. Giving primarily in the U.S. and France. No grants to individuals.
Application information: Application form not required.
Initial approach: Letter or telephone inquiry
Copies of proposal: 1
Deadline(s): None
Board meeting date(s): As necessary
Final notification: Varies
Officers and Directors:* John R. Young,* Pres.; Walter C. Cliff,* V.P. and Secy.; Ursula Cliff; Katusha Davison.
Number of staff: 1 full-time professional.
EIN: 136176855
Selected grants: The following grants are a representative sample of this grantmaker's funding activity:
$1,400,000 to Metropolitan Museum of Art, New York, NY, 2012. For FG Gallery Bonnard and Vuillard.
$1,000,000 to Grolier Club of the City of New York, New York, NY, 2012. For Mary Young Fund.
$500,000 to Harvard University, Cambridge, MA, 2012. For FG Gallery in Art Museums.
$400,000 to French American Cultural Exchange, New York, NY, 2012. For program support.
$250,000 to American Friends of the Paris Opera and Ballet, New York, NY, 2012. For US tour.
$250,000 to French Regional American Museum Exchange, Los Angeles, CA, 2012. For endowment for FRAME programs.
$100,000 to French-American Foundation, New York, NY, 2012. For Courants program.
$43,000 to Mackinac Associates, Mackinaw City, MI, 2012. For translation of French documents of Colonial Michilimackinac.
$25,000 to French-American Cultural Foundation, Washington, DC, 2012. For France Magazine.
$15,000 to French-American Aid for Children, New York, NY, 2012. For general support.

6089
The Gould-Shenfeld Family Foundation ✧
(formerly The Gould Family Charitable Foundation of New York)
60 Cuttermill Rd.
Great Neck, NY 11021-3152

Established in 1995 in NY.
Donors: Fredric H. Gould; Jeffrey Gould; Matthew Gould; Steven Shenfeld; REIT Management Corp. 401K; REIT Management Corp. Pension.
Foundation type: Independent foundation.
Financial data (yr. ended 12/31/12): Assets, $2,829,448 (M); gifts received, $433,682; expenditures, $1,217,481; qualifying distributions, $1,214,423; giving activities include $1,189,023 for 197 grants (high: $345,000; low: $50).
Purpose and activities: Giving primarily for Jewish organizations, as well as for the arts, health, and children, youth and social services.

Fields of interest: Arts; Education; Health organizations, association; Human services; Children/youth, services; Jewish federated giving programs; Jewish agencies & synagogues.
Limitations: Applications not accepted. Giving primarily in New York, NY. No grants to individuals.
Application information: Contributes only to pre-selected organizations.
Trustees: Fredric H. Gould; Helaine Gould; Jeffrey A. Gould; Matthew J. Gould; Wendy Shenfeld.
EIN: 113262391

6090
The Grace and Mercy Foundation, Inc. ✧
c/o Tiger Asia
101 Park Ave., 48th Fl.
New York, NY 10178-4799

Established in 2006 in NY.
Donors: Sung Kook Hwang; Chung Ko; Jensen Ko; Tiger Asia Management; Hwang Donor Advised Fund at Fuller.
Foundation type: Independent foundation.
Financial data (yr. ended 12/31/12): Assets, $68,839,374 (M); gifts received, $23,603; expenditures, $6,981,773; qualifying distributions, $6,938,479; giving activities include $5,648,178 for 61 grants (high: $670,000; low: $250).
Fields of interest: Theological school/education; Education; Health care; Human services; Protestant agencies & churches.
Limitations: Applications not accepted. Giving primarily in New York, NY; funding also in CA. No grants to individuals.
Application information: Contributes only to pre-selected organizations.
Officers and Directors:* Mark W. Shaw, Pres.; Becky Hwang,* V.P.; Jeanne Cox, Secy.; Patrick Halligan, Treas.; Sung Kook Hwang.
EIN: 208050779

6091
The Perry and Martin Granoff Family Foundation, Inc. ✧
c/o Hogan Lovells US LLP, Attn.: SF
875 3rd Ave.
New York, NY 10022-6225

Established in 1993 in NJ.
Donor: Martin J. Granoff.
Foundation type: Independent foundation.
Financial data (yr. ended 12/31/13): Assets, $46,737 (M); gifts received, $81,314; expenditures, $655,371; qualifying distributions, $650,833; giving activities include $650,833 for 28 grants (high: $128,333; low: $500).
Purpose and activities: Giving primarily for the arts and education; funding also for Jewish federated giving programs.
Fields of interest: Performing arts; Performing arts, ballet; Performing arts, theater; Higher education; Education; Jewish federated giving programs.
Limitations: Applications not accepted. Giving primarily in MA, NY, and RI. No grants to individuals.
Application information: Contributes only to pre-selected organizations.
Officers and Trustees:* Martin J. Granoff,* Pres.; Perry Granoff,* V.P.; Michael Granoff, Secy.-Treas.
EIN: 521647009

Selected grants: The following grants are a representative sample of this grantmaker's funding activity:
$300,000 to Salk Institute for Biological Studies, La Jolla, CA, 2011. For general purpose.
$200,000 to City College 21st Century Foundation, New York, NY, 2011. For general purpose.
$100,000 to American Israel Education Fund, Troy, MI, 2011. For general purpose.
$100,000 to National World War II Memorial, Washington, DC, 2011. For general purpose.

6092
Eugene and Emily Grant Family Foundation ✧
277 Park Ave., 47th Fl.
New York, NY 10172-0003 (212) 688-4700
Contact: Eugene M. Grant, Tr.

Established in 1998 in NY.
Donors: Eugene M. Grant; Terry E. Grant; Sol Heligman†.
Foundation type: Independent foundation.
Financial data (yr. ended 12/31/13): Assets, $6,524,030 (M); gifts received, $10,000,000; expenditures, $21,603,952; qualifying distributions, $21,508,406; giving activities include $21,508,406 for grants.
Purpose and activities: Giving primarily to Jewish agencies, the arts and health care; support also to American and Israeli universities, environmental conservation, intermarriage, and Holocaust studies.
Fields of interest: Performing arts, music; Performing arts, orchestras; Performing arts, opera; History/archaeology; Arts; Higher education, university; Environment, natural resources; Health care; Health organizations, association; Jewish federated giving programs; Jewish agencies & synagogues.
International interests: Israel.
Limitations: Applications accepted. Giving in the U.S. and Israel.
Application information: Application form not required.
Initial approach: Letter
Deadline(s): None
Trustees: Emily Grant; Eugene M. Grant.
EIN: 133997005

6093
William T. Grant Foundation ✧
570 Lexington Ave., 18th Fl.
New York, NY 10022-6837 (212) 752-0071
Contact: Grants Coord.
FAX: (212) 752-1398; E-mail: info@wtgrantfdn.org; Main URL: http://www.wtgrantfdn.org/
Blog: http://blog.wtgrantfoundation.org/
Twitter: https://twitter.com/wtgrantfdn
YouTube: http://www.youtube.com/channel/UCGmhupKeS_x6HOjrofY1p9A

Incorporated in 1936 in DE.
Donor: William T. Grant†.
Foundation type: Independent foundation.
Financial data (yr. ended 12/31/12): Assets, $291,967,654 (M); expenditures, $16,027,377; qualifying distributions, $14,945,698; giving activities include $9,990,715 for 111 grants (high: $567,745; low: $8,315).
Purpose and activities: The mission of the foundation is to help create a society that values young people and enables them to reach their full potential. In pursuit of this goal, the foundation invests in research and in people and projects that use evidence-based approaches. Current grantmaking for research, policy analyses, and evaluations of interventions is restricted to the three interrelated topics that follow: 1) Youth Development: Understanding how youth develop strengths and assets such as the skills and relationships that contribute to their development and well-being; 2) Improving Systems, Organizations, and Programs: Understanding how to improve the quality of youth-serving systems, organizations, and programs; and 3) Adults' Use of Evidence and Their Views of Youth: Understanding how adults who are key constituents (influential policymakers, practitioners, scholars, advocates, and members of the media) view youth, and the policies and services that affect youth. The foundation also supports promising post-doctoral scholars from diverse disciplines through the William T. Grant Scholars Program, and through Youth Service Grants. Support also for local programs in the Tri-State area that actively engage young people and enable them to reach their full potential.
Fields of interest: Education, research; Youth development; Social sciences, research; Psychology/behavioral science; Social sciences, interdisciplinary studies; Social sciences; Public policy, research.
Type of support: Program development; Conferences/seminars; Publication; Fellowships; Research; Program evaluation.
Limitations: Applications accepted. Giving on a national basis; giving limited to NY, NJ, and CT for youth service grants. No grants to individuals or for annual fundraising campaigns, equipment and materials, land acquisition, building or renovation projects, operating budgets, endowments, or scholarships; no loans.
Publications: Application guidelines; Annual report; Financial statement; Grants list; Informational brochure; Informational brochure (including application guidelines).
Application information: Letter of inquiry may be submitted online via foundation web site. The foundation will invite applicants to submit proposals through its web site following review of the letter of inquiry. Application to William T. Grant Scholars Program by nomination only. The foundation accepts the New York/ New Jersey Area Common Application Form. Application form not required.
Initial approach: Letter of inquiry for major grants
Copies of proposal: 6
Deadline(s): See foundation web site for current deadlines
Board meeting date(s): Quarterly
Final notification: Following each quarterly board meeting
Officers and Trustees:* Henry E. Gooss,* Chair.; Christine James-Brown,* Vice-Chair.; Adam Gamoran,* Pres.; Deborah E. McGinn, V.P., Finance and Admin.; Vivian Tseng, V.P., Progs.; Russell Pennoyer,* Secy.-Treas.; Margaret R. Burchinal; Prudence L. Carter; Scott Evans; Olivia Golden; Nancy Gonzales; Andrew C. Porter; Kenneth Prewitt; Judson Reis.
Number of staff: 5 full-time professional; 13 full-time support.
EIN: 131624021
Selected grants: The following grants are a representative sample of this grantmaker's funding activity:

$567,745 to Forum for Youth Investment, Washington, DC, 2012. For Bridging Research, Policy, and Practice in Youth Development.
$492,070 to Ohio State University, Columbus, OH, 2012. For study, Activity Space, Social Network, and Community Influences on Adolescent Risk.
$316,382 to Northwestern University, Evanston, IL, 2012. For research project, The Causes of Truancy and Dropout: A Mixed-Methods Experimental Study in Chicago Public Schools.
$300,000 to University of Chicago, Chicago, IL, 2012. For research project, Improving Studies of the Impact of Group Level Interventions on Program Quality and Youth Outcomes.
$293,703 to Johns Hopkins University, Bloomberg School of Public Health, Baltimore, MD, 2012. For research project, Observing the Setting-level Impact of a High School Behavioral Change Intervention: A 60 School Randomized Trial.
$255,898 to Stanford University, Stanford, CA, 2012. For research by Federal policymakers on Student and School Success.
$234,578 to University of California, Berkeley, CA, 2012. For research project, From Users to Coproducers of Research Evidence: A Study of Place-Based Research Partnerships.
$74,548 to University of Michigan, Ann Arbor, MI, 2012. For project, The Role of Research in Enhancing Family Planning and Pregnancy Prevention for Teens.
$64,942 to University of Chicago, Chicago, IL, 2012. For research project Consequences of the Within-Race Gender Imbalance in the College Campus Setting.
$25,000 to Teachers College Columbia University, New York, NY, 2012. For research project, Are We Learning From K-12 Philanthropic Investments?.

6094
Grateful Foundation Inc. ✧
411 Theodore Fremd Ave.
New York, NY 10177-0073

Established in 1987 in DE.
Donor: Jordan Seaman.
Foundation type: Independent foundation.
Financial data (yr. ended 10/31/13): Assets, $9,658,089 (M); expenditures, $513,674; qualifying distributions, $440,250; giving activities include $440,250 for grants.
Purpose and activities: Giving primarily for the arts, health, and children, youth and social services.
Fields of interest: Arts; Hospitals (general); Health organizations, association; Human services; Children/youth, services.
Type of support: Research.
Limitations: Applications not accepted. Giving primarily in NY. No grants to individuals.
Application information: Contributes only to pre-selected organizations.
Officers: Jordan Seaman, Pres.; Alan Ast, Treas.
EIN: 112897411

6095
Peter T. & Laura M. Grauer Foundation ✧
c/o Geller Fos
P.O. Box 1510
New York, NY 10150

Established in 1989 in NY and DE.
Donors: Peter T. Grauer; Laura Grauer.
Foundation type: Independent foundation.
Financial data (yr. ended 12/31/13): Assets, $1,347,019 (M); gifts received, $2,424,076; expenditures, $1,202,000; qualifying distributions, $1,199,250; giving activities include $1,196,500 for 41 grants (high: $158,000; low: $2,000).
Purpose and activities: Giving primarily for education and human services.
Fields of interest: Elementary/secondary education; Higher education; Education; Health organizations, association; Human services; Family services.
Limitations: Applications not accepted. Giving primarily in CT and NC.
Application information: Contributes only to pre-selected organizations.
Officers: Peter T. Grauer, Pres. and Treas.; Laura M. Grauer, V.P.
EIN: 521702126

6096
Jonathan Grayer Charitable Trust ✧
c/o Barry Horowitz, Withumsmith+Brown
1411 Broadway, 9th Fl.
New York, NY 10018-3496

Established in NY.
Donor: Jonathan Grayer.
Foundation type: Independent foundation.
Financial data (yr. ended 11/30/13): Assets, $1,171,292 (M); gifts received, $135; expenditures, $1,791,562; qualifying distributions, $1,781,885; giving activities include $1,781,500 for 11 grants (high: $1,500,000; low: $1,000).
Fields of interest: Education; Cancer; Medical research; Human services; Jewish agencies & synagogues.
Limitations: Applications not accepted. Giving primarily in NY. No grants to individuals.
Application information: Contributes only to pre-selected organizations.
Trustees: Fern Grayer; Jonathan Grayer; Lewis Grossman.
EIN: 137394495
Selected grants: The following grants are a representative sample of this grantmaker's funding activity:
$100,000 to Harvard University, Cambridge, MA, 2011.
$40,000 to Rye Country Day School, Rye, NY, 2011.
$10,000 to Legal Momentum: Advancing Womens Rights, New York, NY, 2011.
$5,000 to JumpStart, Cleveland, OH, 2011.
$5,000 to Rye Free Reading Room, Rye, NY, 2011.
$1,500 to Humane Education Advocates Reaching Teachers, Mamaroneck, NY, 2011.
$1,000 to UJA-Federation of New York, New York, NY, 2011.

6097
Great Island Foundation ✧
c/o Withumsmith+Brown P.C.
1411 Broadway, 9th Fl.
New York, NY 10018

Established in 1994 in DE.
Donors: Eliot Chace Nolen; Wilson Nolen; National Indemnity Co.
Foundation type: Independent foundation.
Financial data (yr. ended 12/31/12): Assets, $28,195,718 (M); expenditures, $760,984; qualifying distributions, $661,702; giving activities include $638,464 for grants.
Purpose and activities: Giving primarily for art museums and the performing arts; some funding for education and human services.
Fields of interest: Museums (art); Performing arts; Arts; Elementary/secondary education; Higher education; Education; Human services; Children/youth, services; United Ways and Federated Giving Programs; Christian agencies & churches.
Limitations: Applications not accepted. Giving primarily in New York, NY; some funding also in CT and MA. No grants to individuals.
Application information: Contributes only to pre-selected organizations. Unsolicited requests for funds not accepted.
Directors: Eliot Chace Nolen; Wilson Nolen.
EIN: 134049061

6098
Greater Impact Foundation ✧
(formerly Trani Family Foundation)
c/o Marvin Adler, C.P.A.
24 Louis Dr.
Melville, NY 11747-1911

Established in 2007 in CT.
Donors: John M. Trani; Carol A. Trani.
Foundation type: Independent foundation.
Financial data (yr. ended 06/30/13): Assets, $17,024,637 (M); gifts received, $5,070,000; expenditures, $985,106; qualifying distributions, $917,264; giving activities include $917,264 for 16 grants (high: $728,264; low: $1,000).
Fields of interest: Higher education; Hospitals (general); Human services; International relief; Foundations (public); Christian agencies & churches.
Limitations: Applications not accepted. Giving primarily in CA, FL, LA, NJ and NY. No grants to individuals.
Application information: Contributes only to pre-selected organizations.
Trustees: Carol A. Trani; John M. Trani.
EIN: 261431577
Selected grants: The following grants are a representative sample of this grantmaker's funding activity:
$135,000 to Food for the Poor, Coconut Creek, FL, 2011.
$36,820 to Food for the Poor, Coconut Creek, FL, 2011.
$30,000 to American Cancer Society, Oklahoma City, OK, 2011.
$3,000 to National Foundation for Cancer Research, Bethesda, MD, 2011.
$1,000 to Easter Seals, Chicago, IL, 2011.

6099
Greater Rochester Health Foundation ✧
150 State St., Ste. 100
Rochester, NY 14614-1353 (585) 258-1799
Contact: John Urban, C.E.O.
FAX: (585) 258-1711; E-mail: jurban@thegrhf.org; Telephone for John Urban: (585) 258-1704; Main URL: http://www.thegrhf.org
E-Newsletter: http://www.thegrhf.org/news-and-reports/newsletters/

Established in 2005 in NY.
Donor: MVP Health Plan, Inc.

Foundation type: Independent foundation.
Financial data (yr. ended 12/31/12): Assets, $229,582,553 (M); gifts received, $26,638,706; expenditures, $10,984,269; qualifying distributions, $9,369,920; giving activities include $5,127,195 for grants.
Purpose and activities: Giving to improve the health status of residents of the Rochester, New York, community, including people whose unique healthcare needs have not been met because of race, ethnicity or income.
Fields of interest: Health care; Children; Youth; Adults; Minorities; African Americans/Blacks; Women; Adults, women; Men; Adults, men; Economically disadvantaged.
Type of support: Equipment; Program development; Program evaluation; Program-related investments/loans.
Limitations: Giving in the greater Rochester, NY area, including Monroe, Genesee, Livingston, Ontario, Orleans, Seneca, Wayne, Wyoming, and Yates counties. No support for political or lobbying organizations or for purely educational or research programs. No grants for formal research, capital expenses that are not integral to a program initiative that the foundation supports, capital campaigns, scholarships or sponsorships for events or purchase of healthcare services.
Publications: Application guidelines; Financial statement; Grants list; Informational brochure; Multi-year report; Occasional report; Occasional report (including application guidelines); Program policy statement.
Application information: Prospective grantees should talk about their projects with foundation staff if they have questions about eligibility for funding. Application form required.
Initial approach: Online
Deadline(s): Varies
Board meeting date(s): Quarterly
Final notification: Varies
Officers and Directors:* John Urban,* C.E.O. and Pres.; Bonnie DeVinney, V.P. and Chief Prog. Off.; Thomas G. Wesley, V.P. and C.F.O; Erika F. Augustine, M.D.; Essie L. Calhoun; William G. Clark; James G. Gould; G. Jean Howard; Carlos R. Ortiz, M.D.; Geoffrey Rosenberg; Bogen Vargas, Ed.D.; James H. Waters; Bridgette Wiefling, M.D.
Number of staff: 12 full-time support.
EIN: 134301222

6100
Green Charitable Foundation, Inc. ✧
14 E. 60th St., Ste. 702
New York, NY 10022-7125

Established in 1999 in NY.
Donor: The Green Fund, Inc.
Foundation type: Independent foundation.
Financial data (yr. ended 01/31/14): Assets, $15,956,908 (M); expenditures, $882,968; qualifying distributions, $787,376; giving activities include $682,795 for 35 grants (high: $225,000; low: $250).
Purpose and activities: Giving primarily for higher education, particularly law schools.
Fields of interest: Arts; Higher education; Law school/education; Education; Hospitals (general); Jewish agencies & synagogues.
Limitations: Applications not accepted. No grants to individuals.
Application information: Contributes only to pre-selected organizations.
Officers: Patricia Green, Pres.; Louis Green, Secy.; Catherine Green, Treas.
EIN: 134041346
Selected grants: The following grants are a representative sample of this grantmaker's funding activity:
$8,000 to American Jewish Committee, New York, NY, 2011.
$1,500 to Asia Society, New York, NY, 2011.

6101
The Green Fund, Inc. ✧
14 E. 60th St., Ste. 702
New York, NY 10022-7125

Incorporated in 1947 in NY.
Donors: Evelyn Green Davis†; Louis A. Green†.
Foundation type: Independent foundation.
Financial data (yr. ended 01/31/14): Assets, $25,785,237 (M); expenditures, $1,964,162; qualifying distributions, $1,618,572; giving activities include $1,450,050 for 37 grants (high: $735,750; low: $750).
Purpose and activities: Giving primarily for higher education, community development, and human services.
Fields of interest: Arts; Higher education; Education; Human services; Community/economic development; Jewish federated giving programs; Jewish agencies & synagogues.
Limitations: Applications not accepted. Giving primarily in the metropolitan New York, NY, area. No grants to individuals.
Application information: Unsolicited requests for funds not accepted.
Board meeting date(s): Varies
Officers: Cynthia Green Colin, Pres.; Patricia Green, Treas.
Number of staff: 1 full-time professional.
EIN: 136160950

6102
Glenn Greenberg and Linda Vester Foundation ✧
c/o Brave Warrior Capital Inc.
12 E. 49th St.
New York, NY 10017-1028

Established in 2003 in NY.
Donors: Glenn H. Greenberg; Linda J. Vester; Glenn Greenberg Charitable Lead Annuity Trust.
Foundation type: Independent foundation.
Financial data (yr. ended 12/31/13): Assets, $10,470,023 (M); gifts received, $3,824,471; expenditures, $2,829,250; qualifying distributions, $2,784,250; giving activities include $2,784,000 for 35 grants (high: $600,000; low: $5,000).
Purpose and activities: Giving primarily for education and the arts.
Fields of interest: Media, film/video; Arts; Higher education; Education; Human services; Children/youth, services; Foundations (public).
Limitations: Applications not accepted. Giving primarily in CT and NY. No grants to individuals.
Application information: Contributes only to pre-selected organizations.
Officers and Directors:* Linda J. Vester,* Pres.; Glenn H. Greenberg,* Secy.-Treas.; Gregory Greenberg; Spencer Greenberg.
EIN: 200405627
Selected grants: The following grants are a representative sample of this grantmaker's funding activity:
$400,000 to Trinity Episcopal School, New York, NY, 2011.
$200,000 to Facing History and Ourselves National Foundation, Brookline, MA, 2011.
$200,000 to Robin Hood Foundation, New York, NY, 2011.
$100,000 to Columbia University, New York, NY, 2011.

6103
The David and Alan Greene Family Foundation, Inc. ✧
(formerly The David J. Greene Foundation, Inc.)
c/o The Greene Group
605 3rd Ave.
New York, NY 10158-0180

Incorporated in 1966 in NY.
Donors: David J. Greene†; Allan I. Greene; and members of the Greene family.
Foundation type: Independent foundation.
Financial data (yr. ended 12/31/13): Assets, $22,727,605 (M); gifts received, $394,923; expenditures, $1,227,156; qualifying distributions, $1,156,355; giving activities include $1,151,680 for 119 grants (high: $310,000; low: $5).
Purpose and activities: Giving primarily for education, health organizations, children, youth and social services, and Jewish agencies and temples.
Fields of interest: Arts; Higher education; Education; Hospitals (specialty); Health care; Health organizations, association; Human services; Children/youth, services; Jewish federated giving programs; Jewish agencies & synagogues.
Type of support: General/operating support.
Limitations: Applications not accepted. Giving primarily in the metropolitan New York, NY, area, including Long Island and Westchester County; some funding in CA. No grants to individuals.
Application information: Contributes only to pre-selected organizations.
Board meeting date(s): Mar., June, Sept., and Dec.
Officers: Alan I. Greene, Pres.; Michael C. Greene, V.P.; Robert Ravitz, V.P.; James Greene, Treas.
EIN: 136209280
Selected grants: The following grants are a representative sample of this grantmaker's funding activity:
$226,500 to UJA-Federation of New York, New York, NY, 2011.
$160,900 to Feinstein Institute for Medical Research, Manhasset, NY, 2011.

6104
Jerome L. Greene Foundation, Inc. ✧
c/o Christina McInerney
146 Central Park West, Ste. 1E
New York, NY 10023-6297

Established in 1978.
Donors: Jerome L. Greene†; Dawn M. Greene†.
Foundation type: Independent foundation.
Financial data (yr. ended 12/31/13): Assets, $315,308,325 (M); gifts received, $6,080,000; expenditures, $102,776,753; qualifying distributions, $101,409,933; giving activities

include $100,947,352 for 33 grants (high: $92,260,000; low: $75).
Purpose and activities: Giving primarily for higher education, as well as for the arts, a medical center and other health organizations.
Fields of interest: Media, radio; Museums (ethnic/folk arts); Performing arts; Arts; Higher education; Higher education, university; Hospitals (specialty); Health organizations.
Limitations: Applications not accepted. Giving primarily in New York, NY. No grants to individuals.
Application information: Contributes only to pre-selected organizations.
Officer and Director:* Christina McInerney, Pres.
EIN: 132960852

6105
The Greenwall Foundation ✧
420 Lexington Ave., Ste. 2500
New York, NY 10170-0020
Contact: Bernard Lo M.D., C.E.O. and Pres.
E-mail: admin@greenwall.org; Main URL: http://www.greenwall.org
Grants Database: http://www.greenwall.org/grants.php

Incorporated in 1949 in NY.
Donors: Anna A. Greenwall†; Frank K. Greenwall†.
Foundation type: Independent foundation.
Financial data (yr. ended 12/31/13): Assets, $96,052,112 (M); expenditures, $3,690,773; qualifying distributions, $2,849,539; giving activities include $1,979,295 for 25 grants (high: $265,611; low: $3,000), and $172,146 for 1 foundation-administered program.
Purpose and activities: Grantmaking will focus solely on building and enriching the Greenwall Faculty Scholars Program in Bioethics.
Fields of interest: Medical care, bioethics.
Type of support: Research.
Limitations: Applications accepted. Giving nationally for bioethics. No grants for building or endowment funds, operating budgets, annual campaigns, deficit financing, or conferences; no loans.
Publications: Financial statement; IRS Form 990 or 990-PF printed copy available upon request.
Application information: See foundation web site for specific application instructions which must be followed. Application form not required.
Initial approach: Letter of intent to be submitted through link on foundation web site
Copies of proposal: 1
Deadline(s): Nov. (See foundation web site for current date)
Board meeting date(s): May and Nov.
Final notification: After next board meeting
Officers and Directors:* Christine K. Cassel, M.D.*, Chair.; Joseph G. Perpich, M.D., J.D.*, Vice-Chair.; Bernard Lo, M.D.*, C.E.O. and Pres.; T. Dennis Sullivan,* Secy.-Treas.; Ann Alpers; Mark Barnes; George L. Bunting, Jr.; Jason H. Karlawish, M.D.; Joel W. Motley; Gayle Pemberton, Ph.D.; Richard L. Salzer, Jr., M.D.; James A. Tulsky, M.D.
Number of staff: 1 full-time professional; 2 full-time support.
EIN: 136082277

6106
The William and Mary Greve Foundation, Inc. ✧
665 Broadway, Ste. 1001
New York, NY 10012-2330

Incorporated in 1964 in NY.
Donor: Mary P. Greve†.
Foundation type: Independent foundation.
Financial data (yr. ended 12/31/13): Assets, $26,776,684 (M); expenditures, $2,666,524; qualifying distributions, $2,151,509; giving activities include $1,748,876 for 65+ grants (high: $100,000).
Purpose and activities: Grants largely for education and related fields, U.S.-Eastern Europe relations, the performing arts, and the environment.
Fields of interest: Media, film/video; Performing arts; Arts; Education; Environment; International affairs, goodwill promotion.
Type of support: General/operating support; Continuing support; Endowments; Matching/challenge support.
Limitations: Applications not accepted. Giving on a national basis, with emphasis on NY and VA. No grants to individuals, or for scholarships or fellowships; no loans.
Application information: Contributes only to pre-selected organizations.
Board meeting date(s): Varies
Officers and Directors:* John W. Kiser III,* Chair.; Anthony C.M. Kiser,* Pres.; Jennifer Franklin, Secy.; Fritz Link; James W. Sykes, Jr.
Number of staff: 1 full-time professional; 1 part-time professional; 1 part-time support.
EIN: 136020724
Selected grants: The following grants are a representative sample of this grantmaker's funding activity:
$98,350 to Merrimack College, North Andover, MA, 2012. For In continuing support of the Center for the Study of Jewish-Christian Muslim Relations and Programs to expand the mission of promoting tolerance and interfaith understanding.
$50,000 to Land Trust Alliance, Washington, DC, 2012. For a matching grant Program to develop accreditation Programs for land trusts.
$35,750 to Belle Meade School, Sperryville, VA, 2012. For a matching grant to create community service projects and internships for the high school students.
$30,000 to Kid Pan Alley, Charlottesville, VA, 2012. For a challenge grant to raise funds for Programs for underserved children to develop song-writing skills and to create music.
$28,000 to Publicolor, New York, NY, 2012. For Programs to assist students in need with their education and to help them prepare for college and/or career.
$25,000 to Peconic Land Trust, Southampton, NY, 2012. For conserving Long Island's working farms and natural lands.
$25,000 to Scenic Hudson, Poughkeepsie, NY, 2012. For general operations aimed at protecting the Hudson River Valley and increasing public access to the Hudson river.
$20,000 to High Country News, Paonia, CO, 2012. For in Department journalism on the subject of the American west's natural resources.
$20,000 to Merrimack College, North Andover, MA, 2012. To support of the development of Interfaith courses for graduate and undergraduate students and to supplement executive functions.
$15,000 to New Yorkers for Parks, New York, NY, 2012. For general operations relating to the building, protection, and promotion of City Parks and open spaces.

6107
John & Amy Griffin Foundation ✧
(formerly John A. Griffen Foundation, Inc.)
c/o Blue Ridge Capital LLC, Attn.: John Griffin, Tr.
660 Madison Ave.
New York, NY 10065-8405

Established in 2001 in NY.
Donor: John A. Griffin.
Foundation type: Independent foundation.
Financial data (yr. ended 11/30/13): Assets, $26,843,288 (M); gifts received, $21,115,776; expenditures, $8,766,813; qualifying distributions, $8,703,813; giving activities include $8,684,188 for 39 grants (high: $1,777,523; low: $5,000).
Fields of interest: Education; Foundations (private grantmaking).
Limitations: Applications not accepted. Giving primarily in NY and VA.
Application information: Contributes only to pre-selected organizations.
Officers and Directors:* John A. Griffin,* Pres.; Richard Bello, Secy.-Treas.; Amy M. Griffin.
EIN: 020562020
Selected grants: The following grants are a representative sample of this grantmaker's funding activity:
$750,000 to KIPP New York, New York, NY, 2011. For general support.
$500,000 to Saint Annes Belfield School, Charlottesville, VA, 2010.
$500,000 to Saint Annes Belfield School, Charlottesville, VA, 2011.
$500,000 to Tiger Foundation, New York, NY, 2011. For general support.
$495,115 to iMentor, New York, NY, 2011.
$453,243 to University of Virginia McIntire School of Commerce Foundation, Charlottesville, VA, 2011. For annual support.
$380,000 to Robin Hood Foundation, New York, NY, 2011. For program support.
$350,000 to iMentor, New York, NY, 2010.
$250,000 to Lance Armstrong Foundation, Austin, TX, 2011. For general support.
$200,000 to Virginia Athletics Foundation, Charlottesville, VA, 2011. For general support.
$100,000 to Stanford University, Graduate School of Business, Stanford, CA, 2011.
$100,000 to Thomas Jefferson Foundation, Charlottesville, VA, 2010.
$100,000 to University of Virginia, Charlottesville, VA, 2010.
$98,000 to Robin Hood Foundation, New York, NY, 2010.
$67,500 to Boys Club of New York, New York, NY, 2011. For general support.
$57,200 to American Museum of Natural History, New York, NY, 2010. For general support.
$25,000 to Buckley School, New York, NY, 2010.
$25,000 to Teach for America, New York, NY, 2010.

6108
The Griffin-Cole Fund ✧
Bowling Green Sta.
P.O. Box 73
New York, NY 10274-0073

Established in 1996 in NJ.
Donors: Christopher A. Cole; Goldman Sachs & Co.
Foundation type: Independent foundation.
Financial data (yr. ended 07/31/13): Assets, $27,531,970 (M); gifts received, $3,538,500; expenditures, $1,790,518; qualifying distributions, $1,534,080; giving activities include $1,534,080 for 38 grants (high: $550,000; low: $100).
Fields of interest: Elementary/secondary education; Higher education; Environment, natural resources; Human services.
Type of support: General/operating support.
Limitations: Applications not accepted. Giving primarily in Princeton, NJ. No grants to individuals.
Application information: Contributes only to pre-selected organizations.
Trustees: Christopher A. Cole; Barbara Griffin-Cole.
EIN: 137109406
Selected grants: The following grants are a representative sample of this grantmaker's funding activity:
$900,000 to Princeton University, Princeton, NJ, 2011. For general purposes.
$250,000 to Stony Brook-Millstone Watershed Association, Pennington, NJ, 2011. For general purposes.
$200,000 to Princeton Healthcare System Foundation, Princeton, NJ, 2011. For general purposes.
$100,000 to Phillips Academy, Andover, MA, 2011. For general purposes.
$20,000 to Childrens Hospital of Philadelphia, Philadelphia, PA, 2011. For general purposes.
$5,000 to D and R Greenway Land Trust, Princeton, NJ, 2011. For general purposes.
$5,000 to Nature Conservancy, Arlington, VA, 2011. For general purposes.
$5,000 to Princeton University, Princeton, NJ, 2011. For general purposes.
$2,500 to New Jersey Conservation Foundation, Far Hills, NJ, 2011. For general purposes.
$1,000 to HiTOPS, Princeton, NJ, 2011. For general purposes.

6109
Grigg-Lewis Foundation, Inc. ✧
76 West Ave.
Lockport, NY 14094-3641 (716) 478-0002
Contact: William B. May, Exec. Dir.
FAX: (716) 478-0281;
E-mail: grigglewis@grigglewis.org; Main URL: http://www.grigglewis.org

Established in 1968 in NY.
Donor: Henrietta G. Lewis†.
Foundation type: Independent foundation.
Financial data (yr. ended 12/31/13): Assets, $45,211,559 (M); expenditures, $2,671,474; qualifying distributions, $2,485,316; giving activities include $2,092,751 for 109 grants (high: $250,000; low: $500), and $195,000 for 1 loan/program-related investment.
Purpose and activities: Giving primarily for youth, cultural and educational programs, senior programs, local tourism, preservation and restoration of local history, community health, and human services.
Fields of interest: Historic preservation/historical societies; Arts; Education; Human services; Youth, services; Aging, centers/services; Community/economic development.
Type of support: General/operating support; Continuing support; Capital campaigns; Building/renovation; Equipment; Emergency funds; Program development; Conferences/seminars; Research; Matching/challenge support.
Limitations: Applications accepted. Giving primarily in Lockport and Eastern Niagara County, NY. No support for religious or political organizations. No grants to individuals, or for scholarships.
Publications: Application guidelines; Annual report; Program policy statement.
Application information: The submission of an online application via foundation web site is by invitation only, after review of letter of inquiry. Application form required.
Initial approach: Letter of inquiry via U.S. mail or e-mail
Copies of proposal: 1
Deadline(s): Letters of inquiry should be submitted 1-month before application deadline; see foundation web site for current application deadlines
Board meeting date(s): Quarterly
Officers and Directors:* Christa Caldwell,* Pres.; R. Thomas Weeks,* V.P.; William B. May,* Secy. and Exec. Dir.; Dan L. Wilson,* Treas.; Brian F. Costello; Mary F. Murphy.
Number of staff: 1 full-time professional; 1 full-time support.
EIN: 161550858
Selected grants: The following grants are a representative sample of this grantmaker's funding activity:
$18,400 to YMCA of Lockport, Lockport, NY, 2012. For human service.

6110
The William and Sue Gross Family Foundation ✧
c/o The Ayco Co., L.P.
P.O. Box 15014
Albany, NY 12212-5014

Established in 2005 in CA.
Donors: William Gross; Sue Gross.
Foundation type: Independent foundation.
Financial data (yr. ended 12/31/12): Assets, $387,741,509 (M); expenditures, $16,695,650; qualifying distributions, $16,033,000; giving activities include $16,033,000 for 25 grants (high: $5,000,000; low: $3,000).
Fields of interest: Museums; Higher education; Higher education, university; Hospitals (general); Human services; Foundations (private grantmaking); Protestant agencies & churches; Catholic agencies & churches.
Limitations: Applications not accepted. Giving primarily in CA, NY and Washington, DC.
Application information: Contributes only to pre-selected organizations.
Officers: William Gross, Pres.; Sue Gross, Secy.
Trustees: Jeffrey Gross; Jennifer Gross; Nicholas Gross.
EIN: 050563132
Selected grants: The following grants are a representative sample of this grantmaker's funding activity:
$150,000 to James Hines Teacher of the Year Foundation, Costa Mesa, CA, 2011. For awards for outstanding teachers.
$10,000 to Life Rolls On Foundation, Culver City, CA, 2011. For general support.

6111
Gross Foundation, Inc. ✧
P.O. Box 040308
Parkville Sta.
Brooklyn, NY 11204-0308 (718) 851-7724
Contact: Dov Gross, Dir.

Established in 1991 in NY.
Donors: Chaim Gross; Arie Herzog; Pinchus Gross; Esther Gross; Naftali Weiser; Esther Weiser; Shea Rosenfeld; Rachel Rosenfeld; David Spira; Daniel Gross; Robert Kaszovitz.
Foundation type: Independent foundation.
Financial data (yr. ended 02/28/13): Assets, $49,849,931 (M); expenditures, $2,366,263; qualifying distributions, $2,326,767; giving activities include $2,326,767 for grants.
Purpose and activities: Giving primarily for Orthodox Jewish educational and charitable organizations and temples.
Fields of interest: Education; Jewish agencies & synagogues.
Limitations: Applications accepted. Giving primarily in NY. No grants to individuals.
Application information: Application form not required.
Initial approach: Letter
Deadline(s): None
Directors: Dov Gross; Faigie Gross; Pincus Gross.
EIN: 113006419
Selected grants: The following grants are a representative sample of this grantmaker's funding activity:
$100,000 to American Friends of MESHI, Staten Island, NY, 2012.

6112
Vicki & Michael Gross Foundation Inc. ✧
930 Park Ave.
New York, NY 10028-0209

Donors: Michael Gross; Vicki Gross.
Foundation type: Independent foundation.
Financial data (yr. ended 12/31/13): Assets, $2,377,845 (M); expenditures, $1,298,570; qualifying distributions, $1,290,795; giving activities include $1,290,795 for 48 grants (high: $250,000; low: $100).
Purpose and activities: Giving primarily for medical research, educational purposes, and underprivileged children.
Fields of interest: Museums; Arts; Higher education; Health organizations, association; Jewish agencies & synagogues.
Limitations: Applications not accepted. Giving primarily in NY. No grants to individuals.
Application information: Unsolicited requests for funds not accepted.
Directors: Michael Gross; Vicki Gross; Mark Klein.
EIN: 134098501

6113
The Grubman Compton Foundation ✧
(formerly Eric P. Grubman Foundation)
c/o BCRS Associates, LLC
77 Water St., 9th Fl.
New York, NY 10005-4414

Established in 1996 in NJ.
Donor: Eric P. Grubman.
Foundation type: Independent foundation.

Financial data (yr. ended 07/31/13): Assets, $1,746,189 (M); gifts received, $149,520; expenditures, $657,154; qualifying distributions, $637,150; giving activities include $635,500 for 19 grants (high: $250,000; low: $500).
Fields of interest: Elementary/secondary education; Education; Human services; Foundations (private grantmaking); Protestant agencies & churches.
Limitations: Applications not accepted. Giving primarily in MD, NJ and NY. No grants to individuals.
Application information: Contributes only to pre-selected organizations.
Trustees: Elizabeth K. Compton; Eric P. Grubman.
EIN: 133936474
Selected grants: The following grants are a representative sample of this grantmaker's funding activity:
$100,000 to Overlook Hospital Foundation, Summit, NJ, 2011.
$50,000 to Connection for Women and Families, Summit, NJ, 2011.
$50,000 to Overlook Hospital Foundation, Summit, NJ, 2011.
$50,000 to Overlook Hospital Foundation, Summit, NJ, 2011.
$49,000 to Overlook Hospital Foundation, Summit, NJ, 2011.
$10,000 to Readworks Inc., Brooklyn, NY, 2011.
$10,000 to Student Sponsor Partners, New York, NY, 2011.
$10,000 to Teach for America, New York, NY, 2011.
$5,000 to New York Cares, New York, NY, 2011.
$5,000 to Our House Foundation, Murray Hill, NJ, 2011.

6114
Emanuel & Riane Gruss Charitable Foundation, Inc. ✧
180 E. 79th St., Apt. 15G
New York, NY 10075-0569

Established in 1978 in NY.
Donors: Emanuel Gruss; Riane Gruss; O. and R. Gruss Charitable and Educational Foundation.
Foundation type: Independent foundation.
Financial data (yr. ended 03/31/13): Assets, $28,833,273 (M); expenditures, $1,380,867; qualifying distributions, $1,311,156; giving activities include $1,298,406 for 30 grants (high: $1,000,000; low: $20).
Purpose and activities: Giving primarily for Jewish secular and religious organizations, the arts, and social services.
Fields of interest: Arts; Human services; Jewish agencies & synagogues.
Limitations: Applications not accepted. Giving primarily in New York, NY. No grants to individuals.
Application information: Contributes only to pre-selected organizations.
Officers: Riane Gruss, Pres.; Emanuel Gruss, V.P.
Directors: Brenda Gruss; Leslie Gruss.
EIN: 132969811

6115
The Harry Frank Guggenheim Foundation ✧
25 W. 53rd St., 16th Fl.
New York, NY 10019-5401 (646) 428-0971
Contact: Staff
FAX: (646) 428-0981; E-mail: info@hfg.org; Main URL: http://www.hfg.org

Incorporated in 1929 in NY.
Donor: Harry Frank Guggenheim†.
Foundation type: Operating foundation.
Financial data (yr. ended 12/31/13): Assets, $61,897,813 (M); expenditures, $4,472,219; qualifying distributions, $3,487,019; giving activities include $700,866 for 46 grants (high: $102,516; low: $500), $797,000 for 44 grants to individuals (high: $40,000; low: $1,000), and $3,411,179 for foundation-administered programs.
Purpose and activities: Grants for research projects at the postdoctoral level (though not necessarily requiring a Ph.D.) directed toward providing a better understanding of violence, aggression, and dominance in relation to social change; Dissertation Fellowship program to support individuals only during the writing of their Ph.D. dissertation; research grants can be applied for directly. Primary areas of support include anthropology, biological sciences, sociology, history, political science, and psychology.
Fields of interest: History/archaeology; Crime/law enforcement; Child development, services; International peace/security; International affairs, arms control; International affairs, foreign policy; International human rights; International affairs; Civil rights, race/intergroup relations; Biology/life sciences; Science; Social sciences; Anthropology/sociology; Psychology/behavioral science; Political science; Law/international law; International studies; Public policy, research; Government/public administration; Public affairs; Minorities.
Type of support: Fellowships; Research; Employee matching gifts; Grants to individuals.
Limitations: Applications accepted. Giving on a national and international basis. No grants for capital or endowment funds, or for matching funds; no loans. No funds for overhead costs of institutions, travel to professional meetings, publications, conferences (except for those organized by the foundation), subsidiaries, self-education, elaborate fixed equipment, or pre-doctoral support (apart from that indirectly involved in research assistantships and except for a special program of support for dissertation writing).
Publications: Application guidelines; Multi-year report; Occasional report.
Application information: Application guidelines and application forms may be downloaded on foundation Web site. Application form required.
Initial approach: Letter or telephone
Copies of proposal: 4
Deadline(s): Feb. 1 for Ph.D. support; Aug. 1 for research grants
Board meeting date(s): June and Dec.
Final notification: Within 3 days of meeting
Officers and Directors:* Peter O. Lawson-Johnston,* Chair.; Josiah Bunting III,* Pres.; Deirdre Hamill, Treas.; William Bardel; Tina Bennett; Dana Draper; Victor Davis Hanson; Donald C. Hood; Patrick Lang; Carol Langstaff; Lewis H. Lapham; Peter Lawson-Johnston II; Reeve Lindbergh; Gillian Lindt; Tania L.J. McCleery; J.M. Millbank III; Thomas Piper III; Lois Dickson Rice; Andrew Roberts; Patricia Rosenfield; Brogann Sanderson; Kirk Unruh.
Lifetime Directors: James B. Edwards; James Hester; Theodore Lockwood.
Number of staff: 4 full-time professional; 1 part-time professional.
EIN: 136043471

6116
John Simon Guggenheim Memorial Foundation ✧
90 Park Ave.
New York, NY 10016-1302 (212) 687-4470
Contact: Edward Hirsch, Pres.
FAX: (212) 697-3248; E-mail: fellowships@gf.org; Main URL: http://www.gf.org
E-Newsletter: http://list-manage.com/subscribe?u=59d983d0914a509b37f82546c&id=5039a73dec

Incorporated in 1925 in NY.
Donors: Simon Guggenheim†; Mrs. Simon Guggenheim†.
Foundation type: Independent foundation.
Financial data (yr. ended 12/31/12): Assets, $238,109,536 (M); gifts received, $1,030,793; expenditures, $16,867,864; qualifying distributions, $11,924,881; giving activities include $8,069,150 for 325 grants to individuals (high: $55,000; low: $5,000).
Purpose and activities: Fellowships offered to further the development of scholars and artists by assisting them to engage in research in any field of knowledge and creation in any of the arts, under the freest possible conditions and irrespective of race, color, or creed. Fellowships are awarded by the trustees upon nomination by a Committee of Selection. Awards are made to citizens and permanent residents of the U.S., Canada, Latin America, and the Caribbean.
Fields of interest: Visual arts; Humanities; Science; Social sciences.
International interests: Canada; Caribbean; Latin America.
Type of support: Fellowships.
Limitations: Applications accepted. Giving to citizens and permanent residents of the U.S., Canada, Latin America, and the Caribbean. No grants for endowments, operating budgets, special projects, or any other expenses of institutions.
Publications: Application guidelines; Annual report; Financial statement; Informational brochure (including application guidelines).
Application information: Grants are awarded to individuals rather than institutions. Application guidelines available on Web site. Application form required.
Initial approach: Online
Copies of proposal: 1
Deadline(s): Sept. 19 for U.S. and Canada; Dec. 1 for Latin America and the Caribbean
Board meeting date(s): Apr., June, and as required
Final notification: Approximately 6 months
Officers and Trustees:* William P. Kelly,* Chair.; Edward Hirsch,* Pres.; Robert A. Caro; Joel Conarroe; Dorothy Tapper Goldman; Michael Hegarty; Dwight E. Lee; Joyce Carol Oates; A. Alex Porter; Joseph A. Rice; Richard A. Rifkind; Stacy Schiff; Charles P. Stevenson, Jr.; Waddell W. Stillman; Patrick J. Waide, Jr.; Ellen Taaffe Zwilich.
Number of staff: 8 full-time professional; 12 full-time support.
EIN: 135673173

6117
Aaron & Marion Gural Foundation ✧
c/o Newmark and Company
125 Park Ave., 11th Fl.
New York, NY 10017-2049

Established in 1986 in NY.
Donors: Aaron Gural†; Jane Gural Senders; The Aaron N. Gural Charitable Lead Annuity Trust.
Foundation type: Independent foundation.
Financial data (yr. ended 12/31/13): Assets, $2,280,745 (M); gifts received, $350,000; expenditures, $704,354; qualifying distributions, $693,008; giving activities include $681,662 for grants.
Purpose and activities: Giving primarily to Jewish organizations, temples, and schools; funding also for the arts, higher education, and children, youth, and social services.
Fields of interest: Museums (art); Performing arts centers; Higher education; Medical school/education; Education; Hospitals (general); Health organizations, association; Human services; Jewish federated giving programs; Jewish agencies & synagogues.
Limitations: Applications not accepted. Giving primarily in the metropolitan New York, NY, area, including Long Island; some funding nationally. No grants to individuals.
Application information: Contributes only to pre-selected organizations.
Officer: Jeffrey Gural, Pres.
Directors: Barbara Gural; Jane Gural Senders.
EIN: 133377362

6118
J. Gurwin Foundation Inc. ✧ ☆
40 E. 83rd St., No. 8E
New York, NY 10028-0843

Incorporated in 1959 in NY.
Donors: Joseph Gurwin; Eric Gurwin; Laura Flug; Kings Point Industries, Inc.; Danielle Flug; Laura Flug.
Foundation type: Independent foundation.
Financial data (yr. ended 07/31/13): Assets, $17,373,028 (M); expenditures, $571,122; qualifying distributions, $511,680; giving activities include $511,680 for 24 grants (high: $112,500; low: $100).
Purpose and activities: Giving primarily for Jewish organizations, schools, and federated giving programs.
Fields of interest: Arts; Education; Human services; Jewish agencies & synagogues.
Limitations: Applications not accepted. Giving primarily in NY. No grants to individuals.
Application information: Contributes only to pre-selected organizations.
Officers: Joseph Gurwin, Pres.; Eric Gurwin, V.P.; Laura Flug, Secy.-Treas.
EIN: 136059258

6119
The Robert G. & Ellen S. Gutenstein Foundation, Inc. ✧
c/o Coopersmith, Simon & Vogel, PC
50 Charles Lindbergh Blvd., Ste. 605
Uniondale, NY 11553-3626

Established in 1967 in DE and NY.
Donors: Robert G. Gutenstein; Ellen S. Gutenstein.
Foundation type: Independent foundation.
Financial data (yr. ended 10/31/13): Assets, $9,030,749 (M); gifts received, $100,000; expenditures, $476,902; qualifying distributions, $450,101; giving activities include $445,445 for 168 grants (high: $31,200; low: $35).
Purpose and activities: Giving for higher education, Jewish organizations, and arts and cultural institutes.
Fields of interest: Higher education, university; Education; Hospitals (general); Jewish agencies & synagogues.
Limitations: Applications not accepted. Giving primarily in NJ, NY, and PA. No grants to individuals.
Application information: Contributes only to pre-selected organizations.
Officers: Robert G. Gutenstein, Pres.; Ellen S. Gutenstein, V.P.; Charles Salomon, Secy.
EIN: 136227087
Selected grants: The following grants are a representative sample of this grantmaker's funding activity:
$10,000 to University of Pennsylvania, Philadelphia, PA, 2011. For general support.
$2,500 to Cancer Care, New York, NY, 2011. For general support.
$2,000 to American Cancer Society, Atlanta, GA, 2011. For general support.
$2,000 to Fresh Air Fund, New York, NY, 2011. For general support.
$2,000 to World Learning, Brattleboro, VT, 2011. For general support.
$1,500 to Union for Reform Judaism, New York, NY, 2011. For general support.
$1,000 to Feeding America, Chicago, IL, 2011. For general support.

6120
Ron and Stacey Gutfleish Foundation ✧
298 Scarborough Rd.
Briarcliff Manor, NY 10510-2065

Donors: Ron Gutfleish; Stacey Gutfleish.
Foundation type: Independent foundation.
Financial data (yr. ended 06/30/13): Assets, $22,540,399 (M); gifts received, $3,000,000; expenditures, $1,512,006; qualifying distributions, $1,178,950; giving activities include $1,171,500 for 15 grants (high: $400,000; low: $500).
Fields of interest: Higher education; Human services.
Limitations: Applications not accepted. Giving in the U.S., with emphasis on NY and RI. No grants to individuals.
Application information: Contributes only to pre-selected organizations.
Directors: Ron Gutfleish; Stacey Gutfleish.
EIN: 753205276
Selected grants: The following grants are a representative sample of this grantmaker's funding activity:
$375,000 to Brown University, Providence, RI, 2011.
$50,000 to Boys and Girls Club, Madison Square, New York, NY, 2011.
$25,000 to Center for Food Action in New Jersey, Englewood, NJ, 2011.
$25,000 to University of California, Berkeley, CA, 2011.
$20,000 to Multiple Sclerosis Society, National, New York, NY, 2011.
$2,500 to Adventure Cycling Association, Missoula, MT, 2011.
$2,000 to International Mountain Bicycling Association, Boulder, CO, 2011.
$2,000 to Pan-Massachusetts Challenge, Needham, MA, 2011.
$1,000 to Childrens Hospital Los Angeles, Los Angeles, CA, 2011.
$1,000 to Johns Hopkins University, Baltimore, MD, 2011.

6121
Stella and Charles Guttman Foundation, Inc.
122 E. 42nd St. Ste. 2010
New York, NY 10168-2101
Contact: Elizabeth Olofson, Exec. Dir.
FAX: (212) 371-8936;
E-mail: eolofson@guttmanfoundation.org; Main URL: http://www.guttmanfoundation.org/

Incorporated in 1959 in NY.
Donors: Charles Guttman†; Stella Guttman†.
Foundation type: Independent foundation.
Financial data (yr. ended 12/31/13): Assets, $27,865,017 (M); expenditures, $26,730,663; qualifying distributions, $26,313,490; giving activities include $25,485,000 for 50 grants (high: $24,500,000; low: $1,000).
Purpose and activities: At present, the foundation intends to direct a substantial portion of its grantmaking to programs that serve low income infants, toddlers and preschoolers as they transition to kindergarten. Special emphasis will be placed on programs that improve quality, expand services and create a strong continuum of care for children ages 0-3 in high-need neighborhoods.
Fields of interest: Education, early childhood education.
Type of support: General/operating support; Continuing support; Program development.
Limitations: Applications accepted. Giving primarily in the five boroughs of New York, NY. No support for religious organizations for religious purposes, or for public interest litigation or antivivisectionist causes. No grants to individuals, or for foreign travel or foreign study.
Application information: An application form will be provided at the discretion of the foundation.
Initial approach: 2 or 3-page letter of inquiry
Deadline(s): Rolling
Board meeting date(s): Quarterly
Final notification: 4 to 6 weeks
Officers and Directors:* Ernest Rubenstein,* Pres.; Peter A. Herbert,* V.P.; Susan Butler Plum,* Secy.; Robert S. Gassman,* Treas.; Elizabeth Olofson, Exec. Dir.; Patricia L. Francy; Benjamin Herbert; Sr. Paulette Lo Monaco.
Number of staff: 4 full-time professional.
EIN: 136103039

6122
H & M Charitable Fund, Inc. ✧
1448 E. 8th St.
Brooklyn, NY 11230-6403
Contact: Harry Muller, Tr.

Established in 1984 in NY.
Donors: Harry Muller; Hyman Muller.
Foundation type: Independent foundation.
Financial data (yr. ended 10/31/11): Assets, $9,258,561 (M); expenditures, $2,234,014; qualifying distributions, $2,145,817; giving activities include $2,127,770 for 71 grants (high: $290,000; low: $360).
Purpose and activities: Giving primarily for Jewish agencies, temples, and schools.

Fields of interest: Education; Jewish agencies & synagogues.
Type of support: General/operating support.
Limitations: Giving primarily in Brooklyn, NY. No grants to individuals.
Application information: Application form not required.
Initial approach: Letter
Deadline(s): None
Trustees: Harry Muller; Hyman Muller.
EIN: 112720493

6123
H. & Y. Charitable Foundation, Inc. ✧ ☆
1651 46th St.
Brooklyn, NY 11204-1123

Established in 2007 in NY.
Donor: Economy Freight, Inc.
Foundation type: Independent foundation.
Financial data (yr. ended 05/31/13): Assets, $462,507 (M); gifts received, $155,000; expenditures, $672,011; qualifying distributions, $628,643; giving activities include $628,643 for 59 grants (high: $190,000; low: $54).
Fields of interest: Jewish agencies & synagogues.
Type of support: General/operating support.
Limitations: Applications not accepted. No grants to individuals.
Application information: Unsolicited requests for funds not accepted.
Directors: Hershel Kaufman; Isabelle Kaufman; Miriam Kaufman; Yidle Kaufman.
EIN: 260413034

6124
The Marc Haas Foundation, Inc. ✧
c/o Weisermazars LLP
135 W. 50th St.
New York, NY 10020-1201 (212) 812-7000
Contact: Robert H. Haines, Pres.

Established in 1985 in NY.
Foundation type: Independent foundation.
Financial data (yr. ended 12/31/12): Assets, $105,480,065 (M); expenditures, $7,215,587; qualifying distributions, $5,934,766; giving activities include $5,606,000 for 173 grants (high: $200,000; low: $5,000).
Purpose and activities: Giving primarily for the arts and education.
Fields of interest: Museums (specialized); Performing arts; Arts; Higher education; Education; Hospitals (general); Health organizations, association.
Type of support: General/operating support; Fellowships.
Limitations: Giving primarily on a national basis, with emphasis on New York, NY. No loans or program-related investments.
Application information: Application form not required.
Initial approach: Letter
Deadline(s): None
Officers and Directors:* Stanley S. Shuman,* Chair. and Secy.; Robert H. Haines,* Pres. and Treas.; Sydney R. Shuman; Judy E. Tenney.
EIN: 133073137

6125
The Habe Foundation ✧ ☆
c/o Janet L. Mulligan, Tanton Co. LLP
37 W. 57th St., 5th Fl.
New York, NY 10019-3411

Established in 2004 in NY.
Donors: John Klingenstein; Nancy Simpkins.
Foundation type: Independent foundation.
Financial data (yr. ended 12/31/13): Assets, $10,773,572 (M); expenditures, $508,436; qualifying distributions, $455,399; giving activities include $453,000 for 16 grants (high: $100,000; low: $2,500).
Fields of interest: Museums (natural history); Education.
Limitations: Applications not accepted. Giving in the U.S., with emphasis on CT and NY.
Application information: Unsolicited requests for funds not accepted.
Officers: Nancy K. Simpkins, Pres.; Thomas D. Klingenstein, V.P. and Secy.; Andrew D. Klingenstein, Treas.
EIN: 201366114

6126
The Mark D. Hostetter and Alexander N. Habib Foundation ✧
c/o Mark D. Hostetter, Esq.
306 W. 98th St.
New York, NY 10025

Established in 1997 in MA.
Donor: Mark D. Hostetter.
Foundation type: Independent foundation.
Financial data (yr. ended 12/31/13): Assets, $25,328,019 (M); expenditures, $1,268,495; qualifying distributions, $1,212,688; giving activities include $1,209,500 for 18 grants (high: $678,000; low: $1,000).
Purpose and activities: Giving primarily for Presbyterian churches and agencies, funding also for education, including a seminary, and for gay and lesbian concerns.
Fields of interest: Theological school/education; Education; Civil/human rights, LGBTQ; Protestant agencies & churches.
Limitations: Applications not accepted. Giving primarily in New York, NY. No grants to individuals.
Application information: Contributes only to pre-selected organizations.
Trustees: Alexander N. Habib; Mark D. Hostetter.
EIN: 043386858
Selected grants: The following grants are a representative sample of this grantmaker's funding activity:
$105,000 to Family Equality Council, Boston, MA, 2011.
$95,000 to New York Theological Seminary, New York, NY, 2011.
$40,000 to Presbyterian Conference Association, Holmes, NY, 2011.
$13,000 to Presbyterian Church USA, Louisville, KY, 2011.
$10,000 to Breast Cancer Research Foundation, New York, NY, 2011.
$10,000 to Presbyterian Welcome, New York, NY, 2011.
$2,500 to Westminster Presbyterian Church, Tiburon, CA, 2011.
$1,500 to Gay and Lesbian Alliance Against Defamation, Los Angeles, CA, 2011.

6127
Hagedorn Foundation
225 Bryant Ave.
Roslyn Harbor, NY 11576-1153 (516) 767-5754
E-mail: Info@hagedornfoundation.org; Application address: P.O. Box 888, Port Washington, NY 11050-0888; Main URL: http://www.hagedornfoundation.org
Hagedorn Foundation's Philanthropy Promise: http://www.ncrp.org/philanthropys-promise/who

Established in 2007 in NY.
Donors: Horace Hagedorn Foundation; Seedworks.
Foundation type: Independent foundation.
Financial data (yr. ended 12/31/12): Assets, $31,994,459 (M); expenditures, $5,469,061; qualifying distributions, $5,257,037; giving activities include $4,460,823 for 58 grants (high: $665,000; low: $75).
Purpose and activities: Giving primarily to support and promote social equity on Long Island, New York.
Fields of interest: Children, services; Civil/human rights, equal rights.
Limitations: Giving primarily in Long Island, NY. No grants to individuals, or for scholarships, fellowships, deficit reduction, emergency funding, capital campaigns, political programs or endowments.
Publications: Application guidelines.
Application information: If using e-mail, please attach the Concept Paper (as a Word document) to an e-mail with the following subject line: "Concept Paper for HF Funding." Without this subject line, the foundation's online server will reject the e-mail. Full proposals are by invitation only, after review of concept paper. Reports, videos or other attachments are not accepted with the concept paper.
Initial approach: Concept paper (no more than 2 pages) via e-mail or U.S. mail
Deadline(s): None
Officers and Director:* Amy Hagedorn,* Pres.; Lisa O'Beirne, V.P.; Annamarie Quinlan, Secy.; Rob McMahon, Treas.; Darren Sandow, Exec. Dir.
Number of staff: 3 full-time professional; 3 full-time support.
EIN: 260370010

6128
Hagedorn Fund ✧
c/o JPMorgan Chase Bank, N.A., Private Foundation Svcs.
270 Park Ave., 16th Fl.
New York, NY 10017-2014
Contact: Jonathan G. Horowitz, Prog. Off.
FAX: (212) 464-2304;
E-mail: jonathan.g.horowitz@jpmchase.com; Main URL: http://fdnweb.org/hagedorn
Grants List: http://fdnweb.org/hagedorn/grants/category/contributions/

Trust established in 1953 in NY.
Donor: William Hagedorn‡.
Foundation type: Independent foundation.
Financial data (yr. ended 12/31/13): Assets, $53,244,519 (M); expenditures, $2,709,479; qualifying distributions, $2,427,626; giving activities include $2,200,000 for 65 grants (high: $100,000; low: $1,000).
Purpose and activities: Giving primarily for health (including cancer, HIV/AIDS, blindness), gardens,

social services, youth, education, senior services, and housing and community development.
Fields of interest: Education; Botanical gardens; Health care; Cancer; AIDS; Housing/shelter; Youth development; Human services; Community/economic development; Aging; Blind/visually impaired.
Type of support: General/operating support; Capital campaigns; Program development.
Limitations: Applications not accepted. Giving primarily in New York, NY. No support for private foundations. No grants to individuals, or for continuing support, seed money, emergency funds, deficit financing, endowment funds, matching gifts, special projects, publications, or conferences; no loans.
Publications: Grants list.
Application information: Unsolicited proposals are not accepted.
Board meeting date(s): Nov.
Trustees: John J. Kindred III; Malcolm E. Martin; JPMorgan Chase Bank, N.A.
EIN: 136048718
Selected grants: The following grants are a representative sample of this grantmaker's funding activity:
$100,000 to Citymeals-on-Wheels, New York, NY, 2012. For general operating support, with additional $50,000 one time grant for Hurricane Sandy relief work.
$95,000 to Food Bank for New York City, New York, NY, 2012. For general operating support, with additional $50,000 one time grant for Hurricane Sandy relief work.
$80,000 to Salvation Army of Greater New York, New York, NY, 2012. For general operating support, with additional $50,000 one time grant for Hurricane Sandy relief work.
$50,000 to New York University, School of Medicine, Aging and Dementia Research Center, New York, NY, 2012. For Alzheimer's research.
$50,000 to Wells College, Aurora, NY, 2012. For the annual fund and faculty professional development program.
$40,000 to HealthCare Chaplaincy, New York, NY, 2012. For general operating support and the development of a certification program for palliative care chaplains.
$35,000 to Cancer Research Institute, New York, NY, 2012. For general operating support.
$30,000 to DonorsChoose.org, New York, NY, 2012. For 40 literacy projects in the Bronx.
$30,000 to New York Botanical Garden, Bronx, NY, 2012. For the Plant Records Office and general operating support.
$25,000 to Cathedral Church of Saint John the Divine, New York, NY, 2012. For the Cathedral Community Cares Program.

6129
Peter and Helen Haje Foundation ✧
44 W. 77th St., Ste. 14W
New York, NY 10024-5150

Established in 2000 in NY.
Donor: Peter R. Haje.
Foundation type: Independent foundation.
Financial data (yr. ended 12/31/12): Assets, $6,258,636 (M); expenditures, $825,751; qualifying distributions, $767,692; giving activities include $767,692 for 46 grants (high: $125,000; low: $4).
Purpose and activities: Support primarily for higher education and the performing arts.
Fields of interest: Performing arts; Higher education; Law school/education; Education; Human services; Children/youth, services.
Limitations: Applications not accepted. Giving primarily in New York, NY. No grants to individuals.
Application information: Contributes only to pre-selected organizations.
Officers: Peter R. Haje, Chair.; Helen Haje, Pres. and Treas.; Katie Haje, V.P. and Secy.; Michael Haje, V.P.
EIN: 134112185

6130
Hansen Family Foundation Inc. ✧
c/o Bessemer Trust
630 5th Ave.
New York, NY 10111-0001

Established in 2000 in WI.
Donors: Donna L. Hansen; John J. Hansen.
Foundation type: Independent foundation.
Financial data (yr. ended 12/31/13): Assets, $15,224,643 (M); expenditures, $874,743; qualifying distributions, $779,174; giving activities include $765,946 for 26 grants (high: $200,000; low: $46).
Purpose and activities: Giving primarily for education, and human services.
Fields of interest: Higher education; Education; Human services; Foundations (private grantmaking); Catholic agencies & churches.
Limitations: Applications not accepted. Giving primarily in La Crosse, WI. No grants to individuals.
Application information: Contributes only to pre-selected organizations.
Officers: Donna L. Hansen, Chair.; John J. Hansen, Pres.; Mary B. Brennan, 1st V.P.; Paul E. Hansen, 2nd V.P.; Amy L. Hansen-Strom, Secy.; Mark W. Hansen, Treas.
EIN: 392011330

6131
Ralph J. Harary Foundation, Inc. ✧
c/o Moret Group
1411 Broadway, 7th Fl.
New York, NY 10018

Established in 1984 in NJ.
Donors: Ralph J. Harary; Joseph Harary; Jacques Moret, Inc.; SBH Intimates Inc.; HBS Associates; H. Best Ltd.; High Point Design LLC.
Foundation type: Independent foundation.
Financial data (yr. ended 12/31/13): Assets, $205,094 (M); gifts received, $2,150,000; expenditures, $2,225,112; qualifying distributions, $2,224,858; giving activities include $2,224,858 for 490 grants (high: $168,763; low: $18).
Purpose and activities: Funding primarily to Jewish organizations, temples, schools, and federated giving programs.
Fields of interest: Elementary/secondary education; Human services; Jewish federated giving programs; Jewish agencies & synagogues.
Limitations: Applications not accepted. Giving primarily in New York, NY. No grants to individuals.
Application information: Contributes only to pre-selected organizations.
Officers: Joseph Harary, C.F.O.; Gloria Harary, V.P.; Ralph J. Harary, Mgr.
EIN: 222457455

6132
Harbor Lights Foundation ✧
c/o BCRS Assocs., LLC
77 Water St., 9th Fl.
New York, NY 10005

Established in 1980 in CT.
Donor: J. Fred Weintz, Jr.
Foundation type: Independent foundation.
Financial data (yr. ended 04/30/13): Assets, $16,279,460 (M); gifts received, $496,431; expenditures, $811,684; qualifying distributions, $679,928; giving activities include $659,400 for 92 grants (high: $200,000; low: $250).
Purpose and activities: Giving primarily for education and human services.
Fields of interest: Arts; Education; Health organizations; Human services.
Limitations: Applications not accepted. Giving in the U.S., with some emphasis on CA, CT, and NY. No grants to individuals, or for scholarships; no loans.
Application information: Contributes only to pre-selected organizations.
Trustees: Elizabeth Weintz Cerf; H. Frederick Krimendahl II; Polly Weintz Sanna; Eric Cortelyou Weintz; J. Fred Weintz, Jr.; Karl Frederick Weintz.
EIN: 133052490
Selected grants: The following grants are a representative sample of this grantmaker's funding activity:
$120,000 to AmeriCares, Stamford, CT, 2011.
$100,000 to Stanford University, Stanford, CA, 2011.
$25,000 to Christ Church, Greenwich, CT, 2011.
$25,000 to University of Denver, Denver, CO, 2011.
$15,000 to Federation of Protestant Welfare Agencies, New York, NY, 2011.
$10,000 to Greenwich Hospital, Greenwich, CT, 2011.
$8,000 to HALO Trust USA, Washington, DC, 2011.
$5,000 to Sierra Club Foundation, San Francisco, CA, 2011.
$3,000 to Stanford University, Stanford, CA, 2011.
$2,000 to Preservation Society of Newport County, Newport, RI, 2011.

6133
The Keith Haring Foundation, Inc. ✧
676 Broadway, 5th Fl.
New York, NY 10012-2319
Contact: Julia Gruen, Exec. Dir.
E-mail: jgruen@haring.com; Additional e-mail: fkrieger@haring.com; Main URL: http://www.haring.com/kh_foundation/
Blog: http://www.keithharingfoundationarchives.wordpress.com
Grants List: http://www.haring.com/kh_foundation/grants
Tumblr: http://keithharing.tumblr.com/
Twitter: http://twitter.com/KeithHaring

Established in 1989 in NY.
Donors: Keith Haring‡; ACT-UP.
Foundation type: Independent foundation.
Financial data (yr. ended 09/30/13): Assets, $41,775,667 (M); gifts received, $1,300; expenditures, $3,397,095; qualifying distributions,

$2,512,360; giving activities include $1,153,450 for 47 grants (high: $250,000; low: $500).
Purpose and activities: Giving primarily to organizations which provide educational opportunities to underprivileged children, and to organizations which engage in research and care with respect to AIDS and HIV infection. The foundation also maintains a collection of art along with archives which facilitate historical research about Keith Haring and the times and places in which he lived and worked. The foundation supports arts and educational institutions by funding exhibitions, educational programs, acquisitions and publications that serve to contextualize and illuminate the artist's work and philosophy.
Fields of interest: Arts education; Health care; AIDS; AIDS research; Children, services; Children/youth; Children; Youth; Minorities; African Americans/Blacks; Hispanics/Latinos; AIDS, people with; Economically disadvantaged; LGBTQ.
Type of support: Continuing support; Curriculum development.
Limitations: Applications accepted. Giving primarily in New York, NY. No support for religious or political organizations. No grants to individuals directly. No grants to organizations lacking 501(c)(3) status.
Publications: Application guidelines; Grants list.
Application information: Application form and guidelines available on foundation web site. Application form required.
Officers: Gilbert Vazquez, Vice-Pres.; David Stark, Secy.; Allen Haring, Treas.; Julia Gruen, Exec. Dir.
Trustees: Judith Cox; Tom Eccles; Kristen Haring.
Number of staff: 4 full-time professional; 3 part-time professional.
EIN: 110249024

6134
The Harkness Foundation for Dance, Inc. ✧

145 E. 48th St., Ste. 26C
New York, NY 10017-1259
Contact: Theodore S. Bartwink, Treas., Exec. Dir., and Dir.

Established in 1936 as William Hale Harkness Foundation in NY; Harkness Ballet Foundation established in 1959 in NY; adopted current name in 1973.
Donors: William Hale Harkness†; Rebekah Harkness†.
Foundation type: Independent foundation.
Financial data (yr. ended 12/31/13): Assets, $12,588,138 (M); expenditures, $1,253,967; qualifying distributions, $1,024,921; giving activities include $766,950 for 122 grants (high: $72,500; low: $1,000).
Purpose and activities: Support primarily for arts and cultural programs.
Fields of interest: Performing arts; Performing arts, dance; Arts.
Type of support: General/operating support; Program development; Curriculum development; Scholarship funds.
Limitations: Applications accepted. Giving primarily in NY. No support for private schools, or for religious organizations. No grants to individuals, or for endowments, capital projects, or for film and video projects.
Publications: Application guidelines.
Application information: Application form required.
Initial approach: Letter
Copies of proposal: 1
Deadline(s): None
Board meeting date(s): Quarterly
Officers and Directors:* William A. Perlmuth,* Pres.; Etta Brandman,* V.P. and Secy.; Theodore S. Bartwink,* Treas. and Exec. Dir.
Number of staff: 1 full-time professional; 1 full-time support.
EIN: 131926551

6135
William F. Harnisch Foundation Inc ✧

c/o William F. Harnisch
P.O. Box 366
East Quogue, NY 11942-0366

Established in 1997 in NY.
Donor: William F. Harnisch.
Foundation type: Independent foundation.
Financial data (yr. ended 12/31/13): Assets, $8,184,534 (M); expenditures, $1,110,689; qualifying distributions, $1,103,837; giving activities include $1,084,930 for 47 grants (high: $250,000; low: $40).
Fields of interest: Arts; Education; Health organizations, association; Foundations (community).
Limitations: Applications not accepted. Giving primarily in GA and NY. No grants to individuals.
Application information: Contributes only to pre-selected organizations.
Officers: William F. Harnisch, Pres.; Michelle Teramo, Secy.
Directors: Ruth Ann Harnisch; Laura Scott.
EIN: 113353576
Selected grants: The following grants are a representative sample of this grantmaker's funding activity:
$50,000 to Baruch College Fund, New York, NY, 2012. For Harnisch Scholars.
$10,000 to Baruch College Fund, New York, NY, 2012. For Baruch Tribute Dinner.
$10,000 to Citymeals-on-Wheels, New York, NY, 2012. For Citymeals Dineout Program.
$10,000 to Lubavitch Youth Organization, Brooklyn, NY, 2012. For Grand National Testimony.
$1,500 to Wildlife Conservation Society, Bronx, NY, 2012. For general operations support.

6136
Gladys and Roland Harriman Foundation ✧

c/o Brown Brothers Harriman Trust Co., LLC
140 Broadway, 11th Fl.
New York, NY 10005-1108
Contact: Barbara O'Connell, Secy.

Established in 1966 in NY.
Donors: Roland Harriman†; Gladys Harriman†.
Foundation type: Independent foundation.
Financial data (yr. ended 12/31/13): Assets, $129,038,797 (M); expenditures, $7,894,368; qualifying distributions, $7,364,099; giving activities include $7,115,728 for 146 grants (high: $400,000; low: $500).
Purpose and activities: Giving primarily for education; support also for youth and social service agencies, arts and cultural organizations, and health agencies and hospitals.
Fields of interest: Education; Hospitals (general); Health care; Health organizations, association; Human services; Children/youth, services.
Type of support: Endowments; Capital campaigns; Annual campaigns; General/operating support; Employee matching gifts; Matching/challenge support.
Limitations: Applications accepted. Giving on a national basis. No grants to individuals.
Application information: Application form not required.
Initial approach: Letter
Copies of proposal: 1
Deadline(s): Oct. 1
Board meeting date(s): May and Nov.
Final notification: 1 month
Officers and Directors:* Elbridge T. Gerry, Jr.,* Pres.; Thomas F. Dixon,* V.P.; Barbara O'Connell,* Secy.; Anna T. Korniczky, Treas.; Hillary A. Dixon; Anthony T. Enders; Kitty Northrop Friedman; Elbridge T. Gerry III; Wilhelm E. Northrop.
Number of staff: 2 full-time professional; 2 full-time support.
EIN: 510193915
Selected grants: The following grants are a representative sample of this grantmaker's funding activity:
$1,000,000 to Boys Club of New York, New York, NY, 2012. For general support.
$400,000 to American Red Cross National Headquarters, Washington, DC, 2012. For general support.
$250,000 to Weill Medical College of Cornell University, New York, NY, 2012. For general support.
$200,000 to Rensselaerville Institute, Delmar, NY, 2012. For general support.
$150,000 to American Museum of Natural History, New York, NY, 2012. For general support.
$100,000 to Memorial Sloan-Kettering Cancer Center, New York, NY, 2012. For general support.
$64,000 to New England Villages, Pembroke, MA, 2012. For general support.
$25,000 to California Science Center, Los Angeles, CA, 2012. For general support.
$20,000 to Girl Scouts of the U.S.A., Council of Greater New York, New York, NY, 2012. For general support.
$10,000 to Grace Opportunity Project, New York, NY, 2012. For general support.

6137
Mary W. Harriman Foundation ✧

c/o Brown Brothers Harriman Trust Co.
140 Broadway, 11th Fl.
New York, NY 10005-1108
Contact: Barbara O'Connell, Secy.

Established in 1925 in NY; incorporated in 1973.
Donor: Mary W. Harriman†.
Foundation type: Independent foundation.
Financial data (yr. ended 12/31/12): Assets, $28,437,406 (M); expenditures, $1,314,207; qualifying distributions, $1,247,133; giving activities include $1,182,500 for 106 grants (high: $50,000; low: $1,000).
Fields of interest: Media, television; Media, radio; Performing arts; Arts; Elementary/secondary education; Higher education; Education; Animals/wildlife; Hospitals (general); Health organizations, association; Human services; Children/youth, services; Children/youth; Children; Disabilities, people with; Deaf/hearing impaired.
Type of support: General/operating support; Continuing support; Annual campaigns; Capital campaigns.

Limitations: Applications accepted. Giving primarily in the metropolitan New York, NY, area, and in New York State; some funding nationally, particularly in CO, CT, MA and VT. No grants to individuals.
Application information: Application form not required.
Initial approach: Typewritten proposal
Copies of proposal: 1
Deadline(s): None
Board meeting date(s): May
Final notification: 1 month
Officers and Directors:* David H. Mortimer,* Pres.; Kathleen L.F. Ames,* V.P.; Barbara O'Connell, Secy.; Anna T. Korniczky, Treas.; Marjorie Northrop Friedman.
Number of staff: 2 full-time professional; 2 full-time support.
EIN: 237356000
Selected grants: The following grants are a representative sample of this grantmaker's funding activity:
$50,000 to American Assembly, New York, NY, 2011. For general purpose.
$35,000 to New York City Ballet, New York, NY, 2011. For general purpose.
$31,000 to Good Samaritan Hospital, Suffern, NY, 2011. For general purpose.
$30,000 to Bates College, Lewiston, ME, 2011. For general purpose.
$25,000 to Land Trust Alliance, Washington, DC, 2011. For general purpose.
$25,000 to Palisades Interstate Park Commission, Bear Mountain, NY, 2011. For general purpose.
$12,500 to Visiting Nurse Service of New York, New York, NY, 2011. For general purpose.
$10,000 to Brearley School, New York, NY, 2010. For general purpose.
$10,000 to Dartmouth College, Tuck School of Business, Hanover, NH, 2011. For general purpose.
$10,000 to Seventh Regiment Armory Conservancy, New York, NY, 2011. For general purpose.
$8,000 to Everglades Foundation, Palmetto Bay, FL, 2011. For general purpose.

6138
J. Ira & Nicki Harris Family Foundation, Inc. ✧
c/o BCRS Assocs., LLC
77 Water St., 9th Fl.
New York, NY 10005-4401

Established in 2008 in NY.
Foundation type: Independent foundation.
Financial data (yr. ended 03/31/13): Assets, $29,006,246 (M); expenditures, $826,940; qualifying distributions, $746,587; giving activities include $633,066 for 70 grants (high: $100,000; low: $200).
Fields of interest: Museums; Performing arts centers; Arts; Higher education; Health organizations, association; Medical research, institute; Human services; Jewish federated giving programs; Jewish agencies & synagogues.
Limitations: Applications not accepted. Giving primarily in FL, IL, MI, and NY. No grants to individuals.
Application information: Contributes only to pre-selected organizations.
Officers and Directors:* J. Ira Harris,* Pres.; Nicki Harris,* V.P.; Jacqueline Harris Hochberg,* Secy.; Jonathan M. Harris,* Treas.; David Moore; Bruce Moskowitz; Craig Shadur.
EIN: 260818520
Selected grants: The following grants are a representative sample of this grantmaker's funding activity:
$400,000 to New York University Langone Medical Center, New York, NY, 2011. For general purpose.
$100,000 to Raymond F. Kravis Center for the Performing Arts, West Palm Beach, FL, 2011. For general purpose.
$10,000 to Hospital for Special Surgery, New York, NY, 2011. For general purpose.

6139
J. Ira and Nicki Harris Family Foundation, Inc. ✧
(formerly J. Ira and Nicki Harris Foundation, Inc.)
c/o BCRS Assocs., LLC
77 Water St., 9th Fl.
New York, NY 10005-4401

Established in FL.
Donors: J. Ira Harris; Maize and Blue Charitable Trust.
Foundation type: Independent foundation.
Financial data (yr. ended 03/31/13): Assets, $2,633,140 (M); gifts received, $815,001; expenditures, $860,732; qualifying distributions, $850,600; giving activities include $850,600 for 55 grants (high: $200,000; low: $300).
Fields of interest: Museums; Performing arts centers; Arts; Health organizations; Human services.
Type of support: General/operating support.
Limitations: Applications not accepted. Giving primarily in Washington, DC, Palm Beach and West Palm Beach, FL, Chicago, IL, and New York, NY. No grants to individuals.
Application information: Contributes only to pre-selected organizations.
Officers and Directors:* Jacqueline Harris Hochberg,* Pres. and Secy.; Nicki Harris,* V.P.; Jonathan M. Harris,* Treas.; David Moore; Bruce Moskowitz; Craig Shadur.
EIN: 650805468
Selected grants: The following grants are a representative sample of this grantmaker's funding activity:
$200,000 to Museum of Science and Industry, Chicago, IL, 2011. For general purpose.
$125,000 to National Museum of American Jewish History, Philadelphia, PA, 2011. For general purpose.
$50,000 to John F. Kennedy Center for the Performing Arts, Washington, DC, 2011. For general purpose.
$37,500 to City Parks Foundation, New York, NY, 2010. For general purpose.
$25,000 to Child Mind Institute, New York, NY, 2011. For general purpose.
$25,000 to YM-YWHA, 92nd Street, New York, NY, 2011. For general purpose.
$13,000 to Museum of Science and Industry, Chicago, IL, 2010. For general purpose.
$10,000 to Lincoln Center for the Performing Arts, New York, NY, 2011. For general purpose.
$10,000 to Museum of Science and Industry, Chicago, IL, 2011. For general purpose.
$5,000 to Des Moines Art Center, Des Moines, IA, 2010. For general purpose.
$5,000 to MorseLife Foundation, West Palm Beach, FL, 2010. For general purpose.
$2,500 to American Friends of the Israel Museum, New York, NY, 2011. For general purpose.
$2,500 to Childrens Museum of Manhattan, New York, NY, 2011. For general purpose.
$2,500 to Federation Employment and Guidance Service, New York, NY, 2010. For general purpose.
$2,500 to Roundabout Theater Company, New York, NY, 2010. For general purpose.
$2,000 to Jewish Museum, New York, NY, 2010. For general purpose.
$1,000 to Palm Beach Police Foundation, Palm Beach, FL, 2010. For general purpose.

6140
Matthew and Jennifer Harris Family Foundation ✧ ☆
12 E. 49th St., 38th Fl.
New York, NY 10017-8220

Established in NY.
Donors: Matthew Harris; Jennifer Harris.
Foundation type: Independent foundation.
Financial data (yr. ended 12/31/12): Assets, $0 (M); gifts received, $504,005; expenditures, $504,005; qualifying distributions, $500,000; giving activities include $500,000 for 1 grant.
Fields of interest: Animals/wildlife.
Limitations: Applications not accepted. Giving primarily in Washington, DC.
Application information: Unsolicited requests for funds not accepted.
Trustees: Jennifer Harris; Matthew C. Harris.
EIN: 456661063

6141
The Jeffrey and Jamie Harris Family Foundation Trust ✧
400 W. 12th St., No. 9C
New York, NY 10014-1861

Established in 2001 in NY.
Donor: Jeffrey A. Harris.
Foundation type: Independent foundation.
Financial data (yr. ended 11/30/13): Assets, $18,714,304 (M); gifts received, $448,327; expenditures, $907,373; qualifying distributions, $900,831.
Fields of interest: Arts; Education; Medical research; Human services; Children/youth, services; Jewish federated giving programs; Jewish agencies & synagogues.
Limitations: Applications not accepted. Giving primarily in New York, NY. No grants to individuals.
Application information: Unsolicited requests for funds not accepted.
Trustees: Daniel Harris; Jamie Harris; Jeffrey A. Harris; Rachel H. Harris.
EIN: 137273247

6142
Francena T. Harrison Foundation Trust ✧ ☆
Church St. Station
P.O. Box 1297
New York, NY 10008-1297

Established in 1986 in VA.
Donor: Francena T. Harrison†.
Foundation type: Independent foundation.
Financial data (yr. ended 04/30/13): Assets, $5,884,399 (M); expenditures, $700,324; qualifying distributions, $662,804; giving activities

include $632,500 for 17 grants (high: $100,000; low: $5,000).
Purpose and activities: Giving primarily to cultural institutions.
Fields of interest: Museums; Performing arts centers; Performing arts, theater; Performing arts, opera; Performing arts, music ensembles/groups; Elementary school/education; Higher education, university; Human services.
Type of support: General/operating support.
Limitations: Applications not accepted. Giving primarily in NY. No grants to individuals.
Application information: Contributes only to pre-selected organizations.
Trustee: Deutsche Bank Trust Co., N.A.
EIN: 136911262
Selected grants: The following grants are a representative sample of this grantmaker's funding activity:
$70,000 to Metropolitan Opera, New York, NY, 2011.
$50,000 to University of Richmond, Richmond, VA, 2011.
$25,000 to Historic Morven, Princeton, NJ, 2011.
$25,000 to Juilliard School, New York, NY, 2011.
$25,000 to Music Academy of the West, Santa Barbara, CA, 2011.
$25,000 to Trinity Counseling Service, Princeton, NJ, 2011.
$20,000 to Virginia Museum of Fine Arts, Richmond, VA, 2011.
$10,000 to Lincoln Center Theater, New York, NY, 2011.
$10,000 to Metropolitan Opera Guild, New York, NY, 2011.
$10,000 to Solomon R. Guggenheim Museum, New York, NY, 2011.

6143
Griffith R. Harsh, IV and Margaret C. Whitman Charitable Foundation ✧
c/o The Ayco Co.
P.O. Box 860
321 Broadway
Saratoga Springs, NY 12866-0860

Established in 2006 in CA.
Donors: Griffith R. Harsh IV; Margaret C. Whitman.
Foundation type: Independent foundation.
Financial data (yr. ended 12/31/12): Assets, $108,220,048 (M); gifts received, $140,121; expenditures, $5,135,446; qualifying distributions, $4,495,700; giving activities include $4,487,700 for 10 grants (high: $2,000,000; low: $200).
Purpose and activities: Giving primarily for education, as well as for health organizations, particularly neurosurgery research.
Fields of interest: Education; Environment; Health organizations; Medical research, institute; Neuroscience research.
Limitations: Applications not accepted. Giving primarily in CA, and New York, NY.
Application information: Contributes only to pre-selected organizations.
Trustees: Griffith R. Harsh IV; Margaret C. Whitman.
EIN: 208033091

6144
The John A. Hartford Foundation, Inc. ✧
55 E. 59th St., 16th Fl.
New York, NY 10022-1713
Contact: Corinne H. Rieder, Exec. Dir. and Treas.
FAX: (212) 593-4913; E-mail: mail@jhartfound.org;
Main URL: http://www.jhartfound.org
CEP Study: http://www.jhartfound.org/images/uploads/resources/Final_2010_Grantee_Perception_Report_John_A._Hartford_Foundation_Public_Version.pdf
E-Newsletter: http://www.jhartfound.org/news-events/enewsletter/
Facebook: http://www.facebook.com/jhartfound?ref=ts
health AGEnda Blog: http://www.jhartfound.org/blog/
Publications: http://www.jhartfound.org/news-events/publications/
Twitter: https://twitter.com/jhartfound
YouTube: https://www.youtube.com/user/jhartfound

Established in 1929; incorporated in 1942 in NY.
Donors: John A. Hartford†; George L. Hartford†.
Foundation type: Independent foundation.
Financial data (yr. ended 12/31/13): Assets, $555,995,058 (M); expenditures, $28,283,489; qualifying distributions, $23,268,232; giving activities include $17,130,348 for 59 grants (high: $3,570,613; low: $306), $1,123,475 for employee matching gifts, and $743,683 for 4 foundation-administered programs.
Purpose and activities: The mission of the foundation is to improve the health older Americans. The foundation addresses the unique health needs of the elderly, including long-term care, the use of medication in chronic health problems, increasing the nation's geriatric research and training capability, and improving the integration of financing and care delivery for comprehensive geriatric services.
Fields of interest: Health care; Geriatrics; Aging, centers/services; Aging.
Type of support: Technical assistance; Matching/challenge support; General/operating support; Conferences/seminars; Continuing support; Curriculum development; Employee matching gifts; Fellowships; Management development/capacity building; Program development; Program evaluation; Publication; Research; Scholarship funds.
Limitations: Giving on a national basis. No grants to individuals (including student loans or scholarships), or for annual or capital campaigns, building renovations, equipment, seed money, emergency or endowment funds, or deficit financing.
Publications: Application guidelines; Annual report; Financial statement; Grants list; Newsletter; Program policy statement.
Application information: Unsolicited full proposals or applications not accepted. See foundation's web site for exact guidelines. Do not send correspondence by fax or e-mail. Application form not required.
Initial approach: Review program areas (see website). May submit a brief letter of inquiry if project falls within this focus
Copies of proposal: 1
Board meeting date(s): Mar., June, Sept., and Dec.
Final notification: 6 weeks
Officers and Trustees:* Norman H. Volk,* Chair.; Kathryn D. Wriston,* Pres.; Corinne H. Rieder, Exec. Dir. and Treas.; Eva Cheng, Cont. and Dir., Finance; Barbara Paul Robinson, Secy.; John H. Allen; John J. Curley; Charles A. Dana; Lile R. Gibbons; John R. Mach, Jr.; Audrey A. McNiff; Christopher T.H. Pell; Margaret L. Wolff.
Number of staff: 10 full-time professional; 5 full-time support; 1 part-time support.
EIN: 131667057
Selected grants: The following grants are a representative sample of this grantmaker's funding activity:
$3,350,428 to American Federation for Aging Research, New York, NY, 2012. For Centers of Excellence in Geriatric Medicine and Training National Program Office.
$1,992,999 to Gerontological Society of America, Washington, DC, 2012. For Hartford Geriatric Social Work Faculty Scholars Program and National Network.
$1,464,106 to American Federation for Aging Research, New York, NY, 2012. For Paul B. Beeson Career Development Awards in Aging Research Partnership.
$991,519 to Gerontological Society of America, Washington, DC, 2012. For Hartford Doctoral Fellows in Geriatric Social Work Program renewal.
$607,196 to American Geriatrics Society, New York, NY, 2012. For Geriatrics for Specialists Initiative.
$257,791 to Association of Directors of Geriatric Academic Programs, New York, NY, 2012. For geriatric leadership development program.
$208,569 to Oregon Health and Science University, Portland, OR, 2012. For Hartford Center of Gerontological Nursing Excellence renewal.
$145,979 to AARP Foundation, Washington, DC, 2012. For professional partners supporting family caregiving - Phase II.

6145
Shamai & Richu Hartman Family Foundation ✧
1639 52nd St.
Brooklyn, NY 11204-1419

Established in 1993 in NY.
Donors: Alexander Hartman; Sima Hartman.
Foundation type: Independent foundation.
Financial data (yr. ended 11/30/13): Assets, $11,671,416 (M); expenditures, $790,762; qualifying distributions, $780,987; giving activities include $780,987 for 13+ grants (high: $705,500).
Purpose and activities: Giving primarily to Jewish agencies, temples, and schools.
Fields of interest: Elementary/secondary education; Jewish federated giving programs; Jewish agencies & synagogues.
Limitations: Applications not accepted. Giving primarily in New York. No grants to individuals.
Application information: Contributes only to pre-selected organizations.
Trustees: Joseph Brachfeld; Isaac Goldbrenner; Alexander Hartman; Israel Hartman.
EIN: 113189198

6146
William A. Haseltine Charitable Foundation ✧
c/o Citrin Cooperman & Co.
529 5th Ave.
New York, NY 10017-4608

Established in 2001 in DC.

Donor: William A. Haseltine.
Foundation type: Independent foundation.
Financial data (yr. ended 12/31/12): Assets, $7,968,326 (M); expenditures, $693,839; qualifying distributions, $647,682; giving activities include $647,682 for grants.
Fields of interest: Arts; Health organizations; Human services.
Limitations: Applications not accepted. Giving primarily in Washington, DC, and New York, NY. No grants to individuals.
Application information: Contributes only to pre-selected organizations.
Trustee: William A. Haseltine.
EIN: 134158761

6147
The Hauser Foundation, Inc. ✧
c/o Rita E. Hauser
700 Park Ave., Ste. 8
New York, NY 10021-7098
FAX: (212) 956-3618;
E-mail: rita@hauserfoundation.org

Established in 1989 in NY.
Donors: Gustave M. Hauser; Rita E. Hauser.
Foundation type: Independent foundation.
Financial data (yr. ended 11/30/13): Assets, $34,949,915 (M); expenditures, $3,890,290; qualifying distributions, $3,683,851; giving activities include $3,549,000 for 29 grants (high: $2,000,000; low: $100).
Purpose and activities: Giving primarily for legal and graduate education, and international affairs; some support for cultural organizations and the arts.
Fields of interest: Media/communications; Visual arts; Performing arts; Performing arts, music; Arts; International peace/security; International affairs, foreign policy; International human rights; Law/international law; Public policy, research; Government/public administration; Women.
International interests: Israel; Middle East.
Type of support: Annual campaigns; Capital campaigns; Endowments; Program development; Conferences/seminars.
Limitations: Applications not accepted. Giving on a national basis. No support for religious organizations. No grants to individuals.
Application information: Unsolicited requests for funds not accepted.
Board meeting date(s): Fall
Officers and Directors:* Rita E. Hauser,* Pres.; Gustave M. Hauser, V.P. and Secy.-Treas.; Ronald J. Stein.
Number of staff: 1 full-time support.
EIN: 110016142
Selected grants: The following grants are a representative sample of this grantmaker's funding activity:
$1,000,000 to Lincoln Center for the Performing Arts, New York, NY, 2011.
$150,000 to New America Foundation, Washington, DC, 2011.
$125,000 to Hunter College Foundation, New York, NY, 2011.
$100,000 to International Peace Institute, New York, NY, 2011.
$100,000 to Paley Center for Media, New York, NY, 2011.
$50,000 to RAND Corporation, Santa Monica, CA, 2011.
$20,000 to Cleveland Clinic, Cleveland, OH, 2011.
$15,000 to Council on Foreign Relations, New York, NY, 2011.
$10,000 to Columbia University, Middle East Institute, New York, NY, 2011.

6148
The Havens Relief Fund Society ✧
475 Riverside Dr., Rm. 1940
New York, NY 10115-0023
Contact: Allison S. McDermott, Exec. Dir.
E-mail: info@havensfund.org; Main URL: http://www.havensfund.org

Incorporated in 1870 in NY.
Donors: Charles Gerard Havens†; The Philanthropic Collaborative; The Clarkson Family Foundation.
Foundation type: Operating foundation.
Financial data (yr. ended 12/31/12): Assets, $26,114,200 (M); gifts received, $57,941; expenditures, $1,339,081; qualifying distributions, $1,198,991; giving activities include $753,518 for grants to individuals.
Purpose and activities: Since its founding, the Society's purpose has remained the same: to relieve the suffering caused by a setback in the life of a New York City resident by providing a modest financial boost at a critical time in that person's life. In doing so, the Society's goal is to help the beneficiary overcome an obstacle that stands between him/her and self-sufficiency. The Society works with a network of dedicated individuals called "Almoners" - derived from "the giving of alms" - many of whom work in the New York City's health and social services agencies or serve as religious and community representatives.
Fields of interest: Economically disadvantaged.
Type of support: Grants to individuals.
Limitations: Applications not accepted. Giving limited to New York, NY. No support for institutions, organizations, or agencies.
Application information: Unsolicited requests for funds not accepted.
Board meeting date(s): Feb. and Dec. and May
Officers and Board Members:* Regina S. Peruggi,* Pres.; Paul J. Brignola,* V.P.; Christy Pennoyer,* Secy.; Jose A. Tavares,* Treas.; Allison S. McDermott, Exec. Dir.; Jane Aoyama-Martin, Esq.; Hon. Deborah A. Batts; Hon. P. Kevin Castel; Bayard D. Clarkson, M.D.; David C. Condliffe, Esq.; Daniel P. Davidson; Abigail Jones Feder; Anna M. Irwin; Dianne Mack; Samuel L. Morgan, Ed.D.; Suzanne M. Murphy; Stephanie Nickerson, Ph.D.; David L. Plimpton, Ph.D.; David F. Sternleib; Hon. Laura Taylor Swain; Hon. Robert W. Sweet; Jose Tavares; Thomas D. Thatcher II; George A. von Hassel.
Number of staff: 2 full-time professional.
EIN: 135562382

6149
Hayden Family Foundation ✧
c/o Marilyn Carter, WTAS, Inc.
1177 Ave. of the Americas, 18th Fl.
New York, NY 10036-2714

Established in 1984 in NY.
Donors: Richard M. Hayden; Susan Hayden.
Foundation type: Independent foundation.
Financial data (yr. ended 02/28/13): Assets, $11,387,546 (M); gifts received, $3,000,000; expenditures, $1,658,294; qualifying distributions, $1,033,195; giving activities include $1,015,950 for 34 grants (high: $237,585; low: $390).
Purpose and activities: Giving primarily for education, arts and culture, health and human services.
Fields of interest: Arts; Higher education; Education; Health care; Health organizations, association; Human services.
International interests: England.
Limitations: Applications not accepted. Giving primarily in the U.S. and London, England. No grants to individuals, or for scholarships, gifts; no loans.
Publications: Financial statement; Grants list.
Application information: Contributes only to pre-selected organizations.
Trustees: Lindsay Hayden; Richard M. Hayden; Susan F. Hayden.
EIN: 133248046
Selected grants: The following grants are a representative sample of this grantmaker's funding activity:
$200,000 to Yale University, New Haven, CT, 2011.
$100,000 to Yale University, New Haven, CT, 2011.
$25,000 to University of Pennsylvania, Philadelphia, PA, 2011.
$5,000 to Georgetown University, Washington, DC, 2011.
$5,000 to Yale University, New Haven, CT, 2011.

6150
Charles Hayden Foundation ✧
140 Broadway, 51st Fl.
New York, NY 10005-1108 (212) 785-3677
Contact: Kenneth D. Merin, C.E.O. and Pres.
FAX: (212) 785-3689;
E-mail: info@charleshaydenfoundation.org; Boston Office: c/o GMA, 77 Summer St., 8th Fl., Boston, MA 02110, tel.: (617) 426-7080, ext. 306; Main URL: http://www.charleshaydenfoundation.org
Grants Database: http://www.charleshaydenfoundation.org/grants.php

Incorporated in 1937 in NY.
Donor: Charles Hayden†.
Foundation type: Independent foundation.
Financial data (yr. ended 06/30/13): Assets, $316,296,920 (M); expenditures, $17,613,117; qualifying distributions, $15,551,064; giving activities include $13,861,307 for 174 grants (high: $520,000; low: $500).
Purpose and activities: To promote the mental, moral and physical development of children and youth ages five to eighteen, especially low-income youth, in the Boston, MA and New York, NY metropolitan areas. Program support grants are available for the expansion of programs with well-defined goals that are expected to be met in a specified time frame. "Bricks and mortar" capital support grants are available for renovation, expansion, construction, and acquisition of physical facilities and purchase of non-expendable equipment.
Fields of interest: Museums (children's); Elementary school/education; Secondary school/education; Education; Youth development; Children/youth, services.
Type of support: Continuing support; Building/renovation; Equipment; Land acquisition; Program development; Matching/challenge support.
Limitations: Applications accepted. Giving limited to the metropolitan Boston, MA, and New York, NY areas (including the city of Newark, NJ). No support for fraternal groups, religious organizations other

than community youth-related projects, arts exposure programs, institutions of higher education except to support work on precollegiate programs (other than recruitment programs for a particular college), hospitals, hospices, or projects essentially medical in nature. No grants to individuals, or for endowment funds, operating budgets, fellowships, annual campaigns, emergency funds, deficit financing, publications, or conferences; no loans.
Publications: Application guidelines; Grants list.
Application information: Foundation requires using Philanthropy New York and Associated Grant Makers Common Grant Application forms; Boston area, 2 copies of proposal (one copy sent to New York City and one copy sent to Boston, MA); 1 copy for the NY/NJ area. Application form required.

Initial approach: Proposal
Deadline(s): None
Board meeting date(s): 10 times per year
Final notification: Approximately 2 months

Officers and Trustees:* Dean H. Steeger,* Chair.; Kenneth D. Merin,* C.E.O. and Pres.; Carol Van Atten, V.P., Progs.; Robert Andrews,* Secy.; Robert Howitt,* Treas.; Kristen J. McCormack.
Number of staff: 4 full-time professional.
EIN: 135562237
Selected grants: The following grants are a representative sample of this grantmaker's funding activity:
$520,000 to Hunts Point Alliance for Children, Bronx, NY, 2013. Toward the continuing services provided for children in the Hunts Point area of the Bronx.
$500,000 to American Museum of Natural History, New York, NY, 2013. Toward the Dome Screen replacement and the new Space Show V.
$450,000 to TEAM Academy, Newark, NJ, 2013. For their Newark expansion.
$375,000 to Sports and Arts in Schools Foundation, Woodside, NY, 2013. For their Summer School Sports and Arts Day Camps, their Middle School Academics and Sports Summer Camps, and toward the Hayden Scholars Program and the extended day program at PS 180.
$200,000 to Boys and Girls Club, Madison Square, New York, NY, 2013. Toward support of their Teen Campus Program.
$200,000 to Summer Search New York City, New York, NY, 2013. For their New York and Boston programs.
$150,000 to New Visions for Public Schools, New York, NY, 2013. For their co-curricular and extracurricular activities.
$60,000 to YMCA of Greater Boston, Boston, MA, 2013. Toward teen programming at the Roxbury Y, in support of the Grove Hall Initiative.
$51,500 to Link Community School, Newark, NJ, 2013. For the school year.
$50,000 to Shakespeare Society, New York, NY, 2013. For the Hunts Point Children's Shakespeare Ensemble.

6151
The Edward W. Hazen Foundation, Inc.

333 7th Ave., 14th Fl.
New York, NY 10001-5004 (212) 889-3034
Contact: Lori Bezahler, Pres. and Secy.
FAX: (212) 889-3039;
E-mail: hazen@hazenfoundation.org; Main URL: http://www.hazenfoundation.org/
The Edward W. Hazen Foundation's Philanthropy Promise: http://www.ncrp.org/philanthropys-promise/who

Incorporated in 1925 in CT.
Donors: Edward Warriner Hazen†; Helen Russell Hazen†; Lucy Abigail Hazen†; Mary Hazen Arnold†.
Foundation type: Independent foundation.
Financial data (yr. ended 12/31/13): Assets, $24,941,691 (M); expenditures, $1,514,049; qualifying distributions, $1,320,389; giving activities include $849,363 for 77 grants (high: $100,000; low: $50).
Purpose and activities: The foundation's work is currently focused on public education and youth development. In the area of public education, interest is primarily in parent and community organizing and training around school reform issues. Similarly, in the area of youth development, proposals which focus on training young people to become community or peer organizers around concrete social issues are favored. Funding is targeted at community-based and grassroots organizations.
Fields of interest: Education, public education; Youth development.
Type of support: Mission-related investments/loans; General/operating support; Program development; Employee matching gifts.
Limitations: Applications not accepted. Giving on a national basis, with emphasis on Los Angeles, CA, Miami Dade County, FL, New York, NY, and the Delta Region of MS. No support for service-oriented programs or projects in medicine or health sciences, engineering, law, public and business administration, juvenile justice, or schools or school districts. No grants to individuals, or for annual campaigns, deficit financing, building deficits, capital or endowment funds, scholarships, research, or fellowships.
Publications: Annual report; Grants list.
Application information: Unsolicited requests for funds not accepted. Periodically, the foundation will issue requests for proposals and calls for letters of inquiry. Organizations that wish to receive a RFP should call the foundation and leave a message on voicemail extension No. 7, or submit a request with organizational contact information at the contact us page of the foundation's website, or send an e-mail with the subject: RFP Request.

Board meeting date(s): Spring and fall

Officers and Trustees:* Sonia Jarvis, Chair.; Beverly Cross,* Vice-Chair.; Lori Bezahler,* Pres. and Secy.; Michael Lent,* Treas.; Jennifer Arwade; Charles Fields; Angela Sanbrano; Rachel Tompkins; Lorelei Villarosa.
Number of staff: 2 full-time professional; 2 full-time support; 1 part-time support.
EIN: 060646671

6152
Healey Family Foundation ✧

c/o BCRS Assocs., LLC
77 Water St., 9th Fl.
New York, NY 10005-4401

Established in 1989 in NJ.
Donor: Thomas J. Healey.
Foundation type: Independent foundation.
Financial data (yr. ended 04/30/13): Assets, $16,123,095 (M); expenditures, $954,679; qualifying distributions, $796,197; giving activities include $776,035 for 136 grants (high: $62,500; low: $3).
Fields of interest: Education; Health care; Human services; Catholic agencies & churches.
Limitations: Applications not accepted. Giving primarily in Washington, DC, NJ, and NY. No grants to individuals.
Application information: Contributes only to pre-selected organizations.
Trustees: Margaret S. Healey; Megan H. Hagerty; Thomas J. Healey; Thomas Jeremiah Healey.
EIN: 133531967
Selected grants: The following grants are a representative sample of this grantmaker's funding activity:
$100,000 to National Leadership Roundtable on Church Management, Washington, DC, 2011.
$25,000 to Foundations and Donors Interested in Catholic Activities, Washington, DC, 2011.
$25,000 to Seton Hall University, South Orange, NJ, 2011.
$20,000 to Marthas Vineyard Hospital, Oak Bluffs, MA, 2011.
$10,000 to Woodstock Theological Center, Washington, DC, 2011.
$8,000 to Birth Haven, Newton, NJ, 2011.
$6,000 to American Enterprise Institute for Public Policy Research, Washington, DC, 2011.
$5,000 to Casa Cornelia Law Center, San Diego, CA, 2011.
$5,000 to Trustees of Reservations, Beverly, MA, 2011.
$4,000 to RENEW International, Plainfield, NJ, 2011.

6153
Health Foundation For Western and Central New York ✧

(formerly Community Health Foundation of Western & Central New York, Inc.)
Larkin at Exchange
726 Exchange St., Ste. 518
Buffalo, NY 14210-1485 (716) 852-3030
Contact: Ann F. Monroe, Pres.
FAX: (716) 852-3131; Syracuse, NY office: 431 E. Fayette St., Ste. 250, Syracuse, NY 13202, tel.: (315) 671-0057, fax: (315) 218-7314; Main URL: http://www.hfwcny.org
E-Newsletter: http://www.chfwcny.org/Tools/ContactManager/frontend/register.asp?reset=1&strPath=/tools/contactManager/frontend/viewprofile.asp
Grants List: http://www.chfwcny.org/Tools/ContactManager/frontend/itemlist.asp?reset=1&type=16
LinkedIn: http://www.linkedin.com/company/health-foundation-for-western-and-central-new-york

Established in 2001 in NY.
Donors: Univera Heathcare- CNY, Inc.; Genesee Valley Group Health Assoc.
Foundation type: Independent foundation.
Financial data (yr. ended 12/31/12): Assets, $112,576,513 (M); gifts received, $170,246; expenditures, $5,453,210; qualifying distributions, $4,910,690; giving activities include $2,572,511 for 87 grants (high: $745,351; low: $250), and $1,950,977 for foundation-administered programs.
Purpose and activities: The foundation is dedicated to improving the health and health care of the people and communities of western and central New York. Frail elders and children in communities of poverty are the current priority focus areas.
Fields of interest: Medical care, community health systems; Health care; Foundations (community); Children; Aging; Economically disadvantaged.

Type of support: Management development/capacity building; Building/renovation; Program development; Conferences/seminars; Fellowships; Scholarship funds; Technical assistance; Consulting services; Program evaluation; Matching/challenge support.
Limitations: Applications accepted. Giving limited to select counties in western and central NY (Allegany, Cattaraugus, Chautauqua, Erie, Genesee, Niagara, Orleans and Wyoming in western NY, and Cayuga, Cortland, Herkimer, Madison, Oneida, Onondaga, Oswego and Tompkins in central NY).
Publications: Application guidelines; Annual report; Grants list; Newsletter.
Application information: Check foundation web site for current Requests for Proposals. Application form not required.
Initial approach: Telephone call, letter of intent or e-mail
Board meeting date(s): Bimonthly
Officers and Trustees:* Angel "Lito" Guttierez,* Chair.; Stephen J. Suhowatsky, Vice-Chair.; Ann F. Monroe, Pres.; Amber L. Slichta, V.P.; Sally Berry,* Secy.; Vincent J. Mancuso,* Treas.; Lisa Alford; Marilyn J. Baader; Joseph J. Cozzo; Denise Dunford, DNS, FNP, RN; Catherine A. Gale, Esq.; Arthur R. Goshin, M.D., M.P.H.; Robert A. Ludwig; James L. Magavern; Eugene Meeks; David A. Milling, M.D.; Patricia J. Numann, M.D.; Peter J. O'Neill; Leola Rodgers; C. Anthony Rider, CPA; Theodore J. Scallon; Melva D. Visher; L. Thomas Wolff, M.D.
Number of staff: 2 full-time professional; 1 part-time professional; 1 full-time support; 2 part-time support.
EIN: 223804398

6154
The Austin & Gabriela Hearst Foundation ✧

(formerly The Austin Hearst Foundation)
c/o Grassi & Co.
488 Madison Ave.
New York, NY 10022-5702

Established in 1998 in NJ.
Donor: Austin Hearst.
Foundation type: Independent foundation.
Financial data (yr. ended 12/31/13): Assets, $185,571 (M); gifts received, $454,500; expenditures, $507,462; qualifying distributions, $508,399; giving activities include $499,135 for 4 grants (high: $351,635; low: $20,000).
Fields of interest: Museums; Education; Human services; Children, services.
Limitations: Applications not accepted. Giving primarily in CT and NY. No grants to individuals.
Application information: Contributes only pre-selected organizations.
Trustees: Austin Hearst; Steven M. Loeb; Jaime Taicher.
EIN: 226748476

6155
The Hearst Foundation, Inc. ✧

Hearst Twrs.
300 W. 57th St., 26th Fl.
New York, NY 10019-3741 (212) 649-3750
Contact: Paul I. Dinovitz, Exec. Dir.
E-mail: hearst.ny@hearstfdn.org; Address for applicants from west of the Mississippi River: 90 New Montgomery St., Ste. 1212, San Francisco, CA 94105, tel.: (415) 908-4500, fax: (415) 348-0887; E-mail: hearst.sf@hearstfdn.org; Main URL: http://www.hearstfdn.org/
Grants Database: http://www.hearstfdn.org/grants_home.php

Incorporated in 1945 in NY.
Donor: William Randolph Hearst†.
Foundation type: Independent foundation.
Financial data (yr. ended 12/31/13): Assets, $314,425,053 (M); expenditures, $15,902,992; qualifying distributions, $12,690,918; giving activities include $11,310,000 for 135 grants (high: $350,000; low: $25,000).
Purpose and activities: The Hearst Foundations are national philanthropic resources for organizations working in the fields of culture, education, health and social services. The Hearst Foundations identify and fund outstanding nonprofits to ensure that people of all backgrounds in the United States have the opportunity to build healthy, productive and inspiring lives.
Fields of interest: Arts, cultural/ethnic awareness; Arts education; Museums; Performing arts; Performing arts, education; Arts; Higher education; Graduate/professional education; Theological school/education; Adult education—literacy, basic skills & GED; Hospitals (general); Medical care, rehabilitation; Public health; Medical research, institute; Medical research; Employment, services; Housing/shelter; Youth development, services; Children/youth, services; Family services; Human services; Homeless, human services; Rural development; Children/youth; Adults; Aging; Minorities; African Americans/Blacks; Hispanics/Latinos; Native Americans/American Indians; Women; Men; Economically disadvantaged; Homeless.
Type of support: General/operating support; Capital campaigns; Endowments; Program development; Fellowships; Scholarship funds; Research; Technical assistance; Matching/challenge support.
Limitations: Applications accepted. Giving limited to the U.S. and its territories. No support for public policy, or public policy research, advocacy, or foreign countries. No grants to individuals, or for media or publishing projects, conferences, workshops, seminars, seed funding, multi-year grants, special events, tables, or advertising for fundraising events; no loans or program-related investments.
Publications: Application guidelines.
Application information: All applications must be submitted via the Hearst Foundations' Online Application portal. The Hearst Foundations no longer accept applications or materials through the mail. Please see the Hearst Foundations' website for more information. Application form not required.
Initial approach: Please visit the Hearst Foundations' website to learn about the steps for seeking funding
Deadline(s): None
Board meeting date(s): Mar., June, Sept., and Dec.
Directors: James M. Asher; Anissa Boudjakdji Balson; David J. Barrett; Frank A. Bennack, Jr.; John G. Conomikes; Lisa H. Hagerman; George R. Hearst III; William R. Hearst III; Gilbert C. Maurer; Mark F. Miller; Virginia Randt; Mitchell Scherzer; Steven R. Swartz.
EIN: 136161746

6156
William Randolph Hearst Foundation ✧

Hearst Twrs.
300 W. 57th St., 26th Fl.
New York, NY 10019-3741 (212) 649-3750
Contact: Paul I. Dinovitz, Exec. Dir.
E-mail: hearst.ny@hearstfdn.org; Address for applicants from West of the Mississippi: 90 New Montgomery St., Ste. 1212, San Francisco, CA 94105, tel.: (415) 908-4500, E-mail: hearst.sf@hearstfdn.org; Main URL: http://www.hearstfdn.org
Grants Database: http://www.hearstfdn.org/grants_home.php

Incorporated in 1948 in CA.
Donor: William Randolph Hearst†.
Foundation type: Independent foundation.
Financial data (yr. ended 12/31/13): Assets, $690,210,340 (M); expenditures, $34,212,057; qualifying distributions, $27,224,741; giving activities include $19,803,587 for 161 grants (high: $1,250,000; low: $25,000), and $2,712,171 for 2 foundation-administered programs.
Purpose and activities: The Hearst Foundations are national philanthropic resources for organizations working in the fields of culture, education, health and social services. The Hearst Foundations identify and fund outstanding nonprofits to ensure that people of all backgrounds in the United States have the opportunity to build healthy, productive and inspiring lives.
Fields of interest: Arts, cultural/ethnic awareness; Arts education; Museums; Performing arts; Performing arts, education; Arts; Higher education; Graduate/professional education; Theological school/education; Adult education—literacy, basic skills & GED; Hospitals (general); Medical care, rehabilitation; Public health; Medical research, institute; Medical research; Employment, services; Housing/shelter; Youth development, services; Human services; Children/youth, services; Family services; Homeless, human services; Rural development; Children/youth; Adults; Aging; Minorities; African Americans/Blacks; Hispanics/Latinos; Native Americans/American Indians; Women; Men; Economically disadvantaged; Homeless.
Type of support: General/operating support; Capital campaigns; Endowments; Program development; Fellowships; Scholarship funds; Research; Technical assistance; Matching/challenge support.
Limitations: Applications accepted. Giving limited to the U.S. and its territories. No support for public policy, public schools, advocacy, or foreign countries. No grants to individuals, or for media projects, conferences, workshops, seminars, multi-year grants, publishing projects, special events, seed funding, public policy research, tables, or advertising for fundraising events; no loans or program-related investments.
Publications: Application guidelines.
Application information: All applications must be submitted via the Hearst Foundations' Online Application portal. The Hearst Foundations no longer accept applications or materials through the mail. Please see the Hearst Foundations' web site for more information. Application form not required.
Initial approach: Please visit the Hearst Foundations' web site to learn about the steps for seeking funding
Deadline(s): None
Board meeting date(s): Mar., June, Sept., and Dec.

Directors: James M. Asher; Anissa Boudjakdji Balson; David J. Barrett; Frank A. Bennack, Jr.; John G. Conomikes; Lisa H. Hagerman; George R. Hearst III; William R. Hearst III; Gilbert C. Maurer; Mark F. Miller; Virginia Randt; Mitchell Scherzer; Steven R. Swartz.
Number of staff: 3 full-time professional; 1 full-time support.
EIN: 136019226

6157
Heckscher Foundation for Children

123 E. 70th St.
New York, NY 10021-5006 (212) 744-0190
Contact: Heather Sutton, Sr. Prog. Off.
FAX: (212) 744-2761;
E-mail: grants@heckscherfoundation.org; Main URL: http://www.heckscherfoundation.org
Facebook: https://www.facebook.com/HeckscherFoundation
Instagram: http://www.instagram.com/heckscherfoundation#
Twitter: https://www.twitter.com/HeckscherFnd

Incorporated in 1921 in NY.
Donor: August Heckscher†.
Foundation type: Independent foundation.
Financial data (yr. ended 12/31/13): Assets, $297,685,633 (M); expenditures, $14,601,444; qualifying distributions, $12,311,347; giving activities include $10,474,429 for 113 grants (high: $500,000).
Purpose and activities: The foundation defines its mission as "leveling the playing field for underserved youth." Its goal is to foster venture philanthropy using three principal funding strategies: 1) Catalytic Giving identifies approaches that have the potential for wide application but which have not reached a scale broad enough to attract investment by larger private foundations or government; 2) Strategic Partnerships promotes collaborations between not for profits, for profits and the public sector toward a common goal; 3) Targeted Problem Solving defines a specific challenge that has a practical solution attainable within a reasonable time and budget, and that encourages creative problem solvers to test that solution. The challenge often addresses barriers to equal opportunity either overlooked or under appreciated.
Fields of interest: Arts education; Health care; Employment; Recreation; Youth, services; Infants/toddlers; Children/youth; Children; Girls; Boys.
Type of support: Curriculum development; Matching/challenge support; Program development; Program evaluation.
Limitations: Applications not accepted. Giving primarily in the greater New York, NY, area. No grants to individuals, annual campaigns, fundraising events, political efforts, or endowment funds.
Application information: Funding by invitation only. Unsolicited requests for funds not accepted.
Officers and Trustees:* Howard G. Sloane,* Chair. and C.E.O.; Arthur J. Smadbeck,* Vice-Chair. and Treas.; Gail Meyers,* Vice-Chair.; Ourania Vokolos-Zias, V.P., Finance and Admin.; Mark Magowan,* Secy.; Virginia Sloane,* Pres. Emeritus; Hilary Azrael; Mark Beck; Philippe Laub; Kathryn Meyers; Alexander Sloane; Jake Sloan; Nessia Sloane; Jeffrey Smadbeck; Lou Smadbeck; Louis Smadbeck, Jr.; Mark Smadbeck; Paul Smadbeck; David Tillson.
Senior Staff: Indya Hartley, Grants Mgr.; Shelby Marzouk, Prog. Off.; Heather Sutton, Sr. Prog. Off.
Number of staff: 2 full-time professional; 7 full-time support.
EIN: 131820170
Selected grants: The following grants are a representative sample of this grantmaker's funding activity:
$1,200,000 to Central Park Conservancy, New York, NY, 2011. For East 79th Street Playground Renovation.
$500,000 to Success Charter Network, New York, NY, 2011. For T School.
$319,875 to Single Stop USA, New York, NY, 2011. For Single Stop Community College Initiative.
$272,719 to Harvard University, Center for Public Interest Careers (CPIC) at Harvard College, Cambridge, MA, 2011. For CPIC-Heckscher Fund for Service Internship (FSI) Program Fiscal Year.
$250,000 to Miami Art Museum of Dade County, Miami, FL, 2011. For MAM Education and Community Outreach Programs.
$125,000 to Summer Camp Opportunities Provide An Edge, New York, NY, 2011. For SCOPE Campership Program.
$50,000 to Crenulated Company, Bronx, NY, 2011. For New Settlement's College Access Center at DreamYard Preparatory Academy.
$30,000 to Ramapo for Children, Rhinebeck Campus, Rhinebeck, NY, 2011. For Camp Ramapo - A Summer Learning Experience for Children with Special Needs.
$25,000 to New York Shakespeare Festival, New York, NY, 2011. For The Shakespeare Initiative.
$5,000 to Inwood House, New York, NY, 2011. For Holiday Giving 2011.

6158
Heineman Foundation for Research, Educational, Charitable and Scientific Purposes, Inc. ✧

c/o Brown Brothers Harriman Trust Co.
140 Broadway
New York, NY 10005-1108
E-mail: info@heinemanfoundation.org

Incorporated in 1947 in DE.
Donor: Dannie N. Heineman†.
Foundation type: Independent foundation.
Financial data (yr. ended 12/31/12): Assets, $16,390,900 (M); expenditures, $967,910; qualifying distributions, $848,847; giving activities include $798,500 for 18 grants (high: $125,000; low: $17,000).
Purpose and activities: Giving primarily for programs that enable economically challenged women to enter and remain in the workplace, environmental research that will help prevent, reduce and/or eliminate water degradation, live music performance for education and outreach, research into prevention and treatment of childhood illnesses, programs that enable youth to think, create, and communicate effectively, and programs that support and promote high achievement in music, science, and literature.
Fields of interest: Performing arts, music; Environment, water resources; Health care; Youth; Women.
Type of support: General/operating support; Endowments; Program development; Publication; Seed money; Fellowships; Research; Technical assistance.
Limitations: Giving limited to CT, FL, IL, MA, ME, MT, NC, NH, and NY. No support for political or religious activities. No grants to individuals.
Application information: Electronic proposals are preferred. Telephone calls are not accepted. Application form not required.
Copies of proposal: 1
Deadline(s): Sept. 1, no later than 5:00pm eastern time
Board meeting date(s): Nov.
Final notification: Dec.
Officers and Directors:* C. David Bergendahl,* Pres.; Alexandra Rose, V.P.; Agnes Gautier,* Secy.; Alexander Bergendahl, Treas.; Anders Bergendahl; Molly Cummings; Joan Heineman-Schur; June C. Heineman Morris; Madeleine Paternot; Stephan Paternot; Ann R. Podlipny; Lucia Rose Podlipny; Magda Podlipny; Aaron Rose; David H. Rose; Gina Rose; James A. Rose, Ph.D.; Marian Rose, Ph.D.; Simon Rose; Sonia Rose; Michael Schur, M.D.; and 5 additional directors.
EIN: 136082899

6159
Heisman Trophy Trust ✧

111 Broadway, Ste. 103A
New York, NY 10006-1958
E-mail: info@Heisman.com; Main URL: http://www.heisman.com/

Established in NY.
Donors: Orange Bowl Committee; Valero Alamo Bowl; Electronic Arts Inc.
Foundation type: Operating foundation.
Financial data (yr. ended 10/30/13): Assets, $14,588,597 (M); gifts received, $32,000; expenditures, $2,641,839; qualifying distributions, $1,246,725; giving activities include $1,246,725 for 95 grants (high: $51,158; low: $1,000).
Fields of interest: Education; Health organizations, association; Human services; Catholic agencies & churches.
Limitations: Applications not accepted.
Application information: Unsolicited requests for funds not accepted.
Officer and Directors:* William J. Dockery,* Pres.; Robert Whalen, Jr., Exec. Dir.; Michael Comeford, Esq.; James Corcoran; Anne Fitzpatrick-Donahue; N. Richard Kalikow; Vasili Krishnamurti; Brian Obergfell; Carol Pisano; Sanford Wurmfeld.
EIN: 137052079
Selected grants: The following grants are a representative sample of this grantmaker's funding activity:
$32,600 to New York City Mission Society, New York, NY, 2011.
$32,600 to New York City Mission Society, New York, NY, 2011.
$25,000 to Achilles International, New York, NY, 2011.
$15,000 to United Cerebral Palsy of New York City, New York, NY, 2011.
$7,000 to First Tee, Saint Augustine, FL, 2011.
$5,000 to Guiding Eyes for the Blind, Yorktown Heights, NY, 2011.
$3,000 to Marine Corps Scholarship Foundation, Alexandria, VA, 2011.
$1,500 to Special Olympics South Carolina, Columbia, SC, 2011.

6160
The Leona M. and Harry B. Helmsley Charitable Trust ✧
230 Park Ave., Ste. 659
New York, NY 10169-0698 (212) 679-3600
E-mail: grants@helmsleytrust.org; Additional address: 3130 W. 57th St., Ste. 112, Sioux Falls, SD 57108, tel.: (605) 361-9848; Main URL: http://www.helmsleytrust.org/
Grants Database: http://helmsleytrust.org/grants/

Established in 1999 in NY.
Donors: Leona M. Helmsley†; Sierra Towers & Fresh Meadows, LLP; Eastdil Realty, Inc., LLC; Helmsley Enterprises, Inc.
Foundation type: Independent foundation.
Financial data (yr. ended 03/31/13): Assets, $4,241,501,002 (M); gifts received, $97,478,331; expenditures, $242,309,685; qualifying distributions, $222,718,960; giving activities include $210,352,475 for 378 grants (high: $15,018,000; low: $913).
Purpose and activities: The trust aspires to improve lives by supporting effective nonprofits. Grantmaking focuses on four main areas: health and medical research, human services, education, and conservation. The trust, which is administered by four trustees selected by Leona Helmsley, also awards grants in other areas.
Fields of interest: Education; Environment; Hospitals (general); Health care; Digestive diseases; Diabetes; Diabetes research; Medical research; Human services; Philanthropy/voluntarism.
Limitations: Applications not accepted. Giving primarily in NY. No grants to individuals.
Application information: Contributes only to pre-selected organizations.
Officers: John R. Ettinger, C.E.O.; Leigh Bonney, C.F.O.; Nicholas Milowski, Cont.; Rosalind M. Hewsenian, C.I.O.
Trustees: John Codey; Sandor Frankel; David Panzirer; Walter Panzirer.
Investment Committee: Linda B. Strumpf, Chair.; Deborah L. Allinson, Vice Chair.; Sandor Frankel; Howard Marks; Robert H. Niehaus; David Panzirer; Remy W. Trafelet.
EIN: 137184401
Selected grants: The following grants are a representative sample of this grantmaker's funding activity:
$15,018,000 to Salk Institute for Biological Studies, La Jolla, CA, 2013. For study at Helmsley Center for Genomic Medicine, The Role of Inflammation in Chronic Disease.
$9,333,334 to New York-Presbyterian Fund, New York, NY, 2013. To expand Center for Advanced Digestive Care.
$3,659,757 to Weizmann Institute of Science, Rehovot, Israel, 2013. For New Options for Solar Energy Conversion to Electricity and Biofuel.
$3,500,000 to Hadassah College Jerusalem, Jerusalem, Israel, 2013. For Building of an Interdisciplinary Science Center.
$2,643,033 to Clalit Health Services, Tel Aviv, Israel, 2013. For Electronic Medical Records and E-Pharmacy for Israel's Rural Southern Periphery.
$1,480,960 to Student Achievement Partners, New York, NY, 2013. For Empowering All Students to Achieve the Core.
$500,000 to Juvenile Diabetes Research Foundation International, New York, NY, 2013. For Research in Type 1 Diabetes.
$251,500 to Diabetic Youth Foundation, Concord, CA, 2013. For Diabetes Camperships for Low-Income Youth.
$250,000 to Young Womens Leadership Foundation, New York, NY, 2013. For the Collegebound Initiative in 2 Bronx Schools.
$212,000 to Center for Excellence in Health Care Journalism, Columbia, MO, 2013. For Training Resources for Health Journalists.

6161
Stephen and Ruth Hendel Foundation ✧
10 Dundee Rd.
Larchmont, NY 10538-1446

Established in 1989 in NY.
Donor: Stephen Hendel.
Foundation type: Independent foundation.
Financial data (yr. ended 02/28/13): Assets, $224,212 (M); gifts received, $1,050,000; expenditures, $919,255; qualifying distributions, $915,679; giving activities include $915,679 for 35 grants (high: $223,500; low: $100).
Purpose and activities: Giving primarily for performing arts, education, including a Jewish seminary, human services, and Jewish organizations.
Fields of interest: Performing arts, theater; Higher education; Theological school/education; Health organizations, association; Human services; Jewish federated giving programs; Jewish agencies & synagogues.
Limitations: Applications not accepted. Giving primarily in CT and NY. No grants to individuals.
Application information: Contributes only to pre-selected organizations.
Trustees: Myron Hendel; Ruth Hendel; Stephen Hendel.
EIN: 133532037
Selected grants: The following grants are a representative sample of this grantmaker's funding activity:
$33,800 to SeaChange Capital Partners, New York, NY, 2011.
$25,000 to Culture Project, New York, NY, 2011.
$25,000 to Saint Anns Warehouse, Brooklyn, NY, 2011.
$15,000 to World Music Productions, Brooklyn, NY, 2011.
$12,500 to Bill T. Jones/Arnie Zane Dance Company, New York, NY, 2011.
$12,500 to Bill T. Jones/Arnie Zane Dance Company, New York, NY, 2011.
$10,800 to New York Shakespeare Festival, New York, NY, 2011.
$10,000 to LAByrinth, Inc., New York, NY, 2011.
$10,000 to Play Company, New York, NY, 2011.
$5,000 to New Group, New York, NY, 2011.

6162
The Joan C. & David L. Henle Foundation ✧ ☆
c/o BCRS Assocs., LLC
77 Water St., 9th Fl.
New York, NY 10005-4401

Established in 1996 in NY.
Donor: David L. Henle.
Foundation type: Independent foundation.
Financial data (yr. ended 08/31/13): Assets, $2,363,065 (M); gifts received, $1,106,459; expenditures, $2,198,851; qualifying distributions, $2,185,528; giving activities include $2,183,093 for 49 grants (high: $881,297; low: $50).
Fields of interest: Higher education; Education; Environment, natural resources; Health organizations, association; Human services; Children/youth, services.
Limitations: Applications not accepted. Giving in the U.S., with emphasis on NY. No grants to individuals; no loans or scholarships.
Application information: Contributes only to pre-selected organizations.
Trustees: David L. Henle; Joan C. Henle.
EIN: 137103244
Selected grants: The following grants are a representative sample of this grantmaker's funding activity:
$100,000 to Union College, Schenectady, NY, 2011.
$5,000 to Harlem Childrens Zone, New York, NY, 2011.
$5,000 to Teach for America, New York, NY, 2011.
$1,900 to Graham-Windham, New York, NY, 2011.
$1,000 to Bronxville School Foundation, Bronxville, NY, 2011.
$1,000 to Janada L. Batchelor Foundation for Children, Tulsa, OK, 2011.

6163
Hermione Foundation ✧
c/o Laura J. Sloate
35 E. 75th St., Apt. 16C
New York, NY 10021-2762
Contact: Donna Leone, Tr.

Established in 1992 in NY.
Donor: Laura J. Sloate.
Foundation type: Independent foundation.
Financial data (yr. ended 12/31/12): Assets, $84,526 (M); gifts received, $393,640; expenditures, $1,140,558; qualifying distributions, $1,126,946; giving activities include $1,126,946 for 30 grants (high: $547,870; low: $100).
Fields of interest: Performing arts, music; Performing arts, opera; Arts; Higher education; Libraries (public); Hospitals (general); Health organizations; Human services; Jewish agencies & synagogues.
Type of support: General/operating support; Continuing support; Endowments; Emergency funds; Program development; Conferences/seminars; Scholarship funds; Research; Program-related investments/loans.
Limitations: Applications not accepted. Giving primarily in NY. No grants to individuals.
Application information: Unsolicited requests for funds not accepted.
Board meeting date(s): May 15
Officer: Laura J. Sloate, Pres.
Trustees: Nesli Basgoz; Donna Leone; Michael J. Schwartz.
EIN: 133673826

6164
The F. B. Heron Foundation
100 Broadway, 17th Fl.
New York, NY 10005-4506 (212) 404-1800
Contact: John Seidl, Exec. Asst.
FAX: (212) 404-1805; E-mail: info@heronfdn.org; Main URL: http://www.fbheron.org/
Facebook: https://www.facebook.com/heronfdn

Idea Factory: http://fbheron.org/idea-factory/
Knowledge Center: http://fbheron.issuelab.org/home
LinkedIn: https://www.linkedin.com/company/the-f-b-heron-foundation
Twitter: https://twitter.com/FBHeron

Established in 1992 in DE.
Foundation type: Independent foundation.
Financial data (yr. ended 12/31/13): Assets, $291,570,556 (M); expenditures, $9,704,177; qualifying distributions, $15,256,246; giving activities include $6,809,063 for grants.
Purpose and activities: The foundation exists solely to serve a public purpose—making investments that further the ability of people and communities to move out of poverty and thrive. This purpose guides not only the foundation's grantmaking, but the use of all of its resources, including investment capital, so that it can use them fully to contribute to the reduction of poverty, the widening of opportunity, and the improvement in material and social well-being for disadvantaged people and communities. The Heron investment policy reflects its intent to balance the social and financial return on all assets, and to select opportunities for deploying capital, whether as grants or as investments, so as to maximize the combination of both kinds of return within each.
Fields of interest: Employment; Economic development.
Type of support: General/operating support; Continuing support; Capital campaigns; Technical assistance; Program-related investments/loans; Employee matching gifts; Matching/challenge support; Mission-related investments/loans.
Limitations: Applications accepted. Giving primarily on a national basis. No grants to individuals.
Publications: Annual report (including application guidelines); Grants list; Occasional report.
Application information: Potential grantees should have one of their primary grant-makers contact Heron on their behalf. Information available on the foundation's web site. Application form not required.
Initial approach: Letter, e-mail or telephone
Deadline(s): None
Board meeting date(s): Quarterly
Officers and Directors:* Buzz Schmidt,* Chair.; Clara Miller,* Pres.; Ian Magee, V.P., Finance and Opers. and Secy.-Treas.; James A. Joseph; William F. McCalpin; John Otterlei; Anne Wade.
Number of staff: 15 full-time professional; 1 part-time professional; 1 full-time support; 1 part-time support.
EIN: 133647019
Selected grants: The following grants are a representative sample of this grantmaker's funding activity:
$1,500,000 to Housing Partnership Network, Boston, MA, 2013. For Enterprise Capital.
$1,250,000 to Buffalo Niagara Medical Campus, Buffalo, NY, 2013. For Enterprise Capital.
$1,000,000 to Paraprofessional Healthcare Institute, Bronx, NY, 2013. For Enterprise Capital.
$1,000,000 to Sustainability Accounting Standards Board, San Francisco, CA, 2013. For Enterprise Capital.
$250,000 to Neighborhood Reinvestment Corporation, Washington, DC, 2012.
$250,000 to Reinvestment Fund, Philadelphia, PA, 2012.
$154,000 to Nonprofit Finance Fund, New York, NY, 2013. For Heron Fellowship.
$150,000 to CoopMetrics, Andover, MA, 2012. For Data Visualization development.
$150,000 to CoopMetrics, Andover, MA, 2013. For Join Practice Fellowship.
$150,000 to Housing Assistance Council, Washington, DC, 2012.
$150,000 to Kuyasa Fund, Cape Town, South Africa, 2012. For microloans to low-income households for home improvement.
$150,000 to Sustainability Accounting Standards Board, San Francisco, CA, 2012.
$150,000 to Tides Foundation, San Francisco, CA, 2013. For General Support.
$125,000 to United Way of New York City, New York, NY, 2013. For General Support.
$75,000 to Financial Innovations Center, Chicago, IL, 2012.
$75,000 to Reinvestment Partners, Durham, NC, 2012.
$65,000 to Proyecto Azteca, San Juan, TX, 2012.
$50,000 to National Federation of Community Development Credit Unions, New York, NY, 2012.
$4,000 to Community Foundation of Southeastern Massachusetts, New Bedford, MA, 2013. For General Support.
$2,500 to Urban Ventures Leadership Foundation, Minneapolis, MN, 2013. For General Support.

6165
The Jim and Robin Herrnstein Foundation Inc. ✧ ☆
c/o Cohnreznick LLP
1212 6th Ave., 14th Fl.
New York, NY 10036-1600 (212) 826-6000
Contact: Robeson M. Herrnstein, Pres. and Secy.

Donors: Robeson M. Herrnstein; James R. Herrnstein.
Foundation type: Independent foundation.
Financial data (yr. ended 11/30/13): Assets, $4,329,966 (M); gifts received, $5,000,000; expenditures, $670,034; qualifying distributions, $670,034; giving activities include $652,090 for 5 grants (high: $400,000; low: $5,890).
Fields of interest: Health care; Human services; Community/economic development.
Limitations: Applications accepted. Giving primarily in MA.
Application information: Application form not required.
Initial approach: Proposal
Deadline(s): None
Officers and Board Members:* Robeson M. Herrnstein,* Pres. and Secy.; James R. Herrinstein,* V.P. and Treas.
EIN: 461591770

6166
Abraham & Esther Hersh Foundation, Inc. ✧
587 5th Ave., 10th Fl.
New York, NY 10017-8744

Established in 1994 in NY.
Donors: Chi Yueh Chen; Ahron Hersh; Toby Hersh; Rosetti Handbags, Ltd.; Castle Equity Group, LLC; Horizon Equity Group, LLC.
Foundation type: Independent foundation.
Financial data (yr. ended 10/31/13): Assets, $1,715,268 (M); gifts received, $700,000; expenditures, $1,034,793; qualifying distributions, $1,034,338; giving activities include $1,034,338 for 76 grants (high: $169,500; low: $100).
Purpose and activities: Giving primarily to Jewish federated giving programs and Jewish agencies, temples, and schools.
Fields of interest: Education; Jewish federated giving programs; Jewish agencies & synagogues.
Limitations: Applications not accepted. Giving primarily in West Deal, NJ, and Brooklyn, NY. No grants to individuals.
Application information: Contributes only to pre-selected organizations.
Directors: Ahron Hersh; Toby Hersh.
EIN: 113188332

6167
Arthur N. Hershaft Foundation ✧ ☆
c/o Levene, Gouldin & Thompson, LLP
450 Plaza Dr.
Vestal, NY 13850-3657

Established in 1988 in NY.
Donors: Arthur N. Hershaft; Carol H. Hershaft‡.
Foundation type: Independent foundation.
Financial data (yr. ended 12/31/13): Assets, $2,737,061 (M); expenditures, $472,989; qualifying distributions, $470,216; giving activities include $447,459 for 66 grants (high: $100,000; low: $80).
Purpose and activities: Giving primarily for human services and Jewish organizations.
Fields of interest: Health organizations, association; Human services; Jewish federated giving programs; Jewish agencies & synagogues.
Limitations: Applications not accepted. Giving primarily in CT and NY. No grants to individuals.
Application information: Contributes only to pre-selected organizations.
Trustees: Arthur N. Hershaft; Janet Hershaft; Michael H. Zuckerman, Esq.
EIN: 226462965
Selected grants: The following grants are a representative sample of this grantmaker's funding activity:
$100,000 to Albert Einstein College of Medicine of Yeshiva University, Bronx, NY, 2011.
$100,000 to Albert Einstein College of Medicine of Yeshiva University, Bronx, NY, 2011.
$25,000 to Albert Einstein College of Medicine of Yeshiva University, Bronx, NY, 2011.

6168
Hershman Family Foundation Inc. ✧ ☆
43 Willow Rd.
Woodsburgh, NY 11598-2228 (516) 869-5400
Contact: Ronnie A. Hershman, Pres.; Hannah Hershman, V.P.

Established in 1993 in NY.
Donors: Ronnie A. Hershman; Hannah Hershman.
Foundation type: Independent foundation.
Financial data (yr. ended 08/31/13): Assets, $277,924 (M); gifts received, $393,000; expenditures, $425,550; qualifying distributions, $420,828; giving activities include $420,828 for 38 grants (high: $160,000; low: $200).
Purpose and activities: Giving primarily for Jewish organizations.
Fields of interest: Jewish federated giving programs; Jewish agencies & synagogues.

Limitations: Applications accepted. Giving primarily in NY. No grants to individuals.
Application information: Application form required.
Initial approach: Letter
Deadline(s): None
Officers: Ronnie A. Hershman, Pres.; Hannah Hershman, V.P.
EIN: 113178650

6169
The Hertz Foundation Inc. ✧ ☆
18 Christmas Hill Rd.
Monsey, NY 10952-3803 (845) 490-6060
Contact: Shloime Silbiger, Treas.

Established in NJ.
Donor: Nathan Stern.
Foundation type: Independent foundation.
Financial data (yr. ended 12/31/13): Assets, $492,021 (M); gifts received, $1,184,000; expenditures, $849,510; qualifying distributions, $849,510; giving activities include $848,180 for 8 grants (high: $770,000; low: $180).
Fields of interest: Jewish agencies & synagogues.
Limitations: Applications accepted. Giving primarily in Brooklyn, NY.
Application information: Application form not required.
Initial approach: Proposal
Deadline(s): None
Officer and Directors: Shloime Silbiger,* Treas.; Nathan Stern; Nechama Stern.
EIN: 452747826

6170
Hettinger Foundation ✧
c/o Oberfest
P.O. Box 318
Chappaqua, NY 10514-0318

Trust established in 1961 in NY.
Donors: Albert J. Hettinger, Jr.†; John Hettinger†.
Foundation type: Independent foundation.
Financial data (yr. ended 12/31/13): Assets, $23,929,452 (M); expenditures, $963,742; qualifying distributions, $900,572; giving activities include $900,000 for 20 grants (high: $375,000; low: $5,000).
Fields of interest: Higher education; Education; Health organizations; Human services.
Type of support: General/operating support; Scholarship funds.
Limitations: Applications not accepted. Giving in the U.S., with emphasis on NY. No grants to individuals.
Application information: Contributes only to pre-selected organizations.
Trustees: Betty Hettinger; Corinna Hettinger; William R. Hettinger.
Number of staff: None.
EIN: 136097726

6171
The Andrew R. Heyer and Mindy B. Heyer Foundation ✧
c/o Andrew Heyer
55 Cushman Rd.
Scarsdale, NY 10583-3403

Established in 2000 in NY.
Donors: Andrew R. Heyer; Mindy B. Heyer.
Foundation type: Independent foundation.
Financial data (yr. ended 09/30/13): Assets, $1,529,591 (M); gifts received, $1,135,249; expenditures, $798,302; qualifying distributions, $783,394; giving activities include $783,394 for 12 grants (high: $432,715; low: $200).
Fields of interest: Higher education; Education; Human services; Jewish agencies & synagogues.
Limitations: Applications not accepted. Giving primarily in PA and NY.
Application information: Unsolicited requests for funds not accepted.
Trustees: Andrew R. Heyer; Mindy B. Heyer.
EIN: 134146979

6172
The Heyman-Merrin Foundation ✧
c/o Anchin
1375 Broadway
New York, NY 10018-7001

Established in 2006 in NY.
Donor: Seth Merrin.
Foundation type: Independent foundation.
Financial data (yr. ended 12/31/11): Assets, $20,972 (M); gifts received, $400,000; expenditures, $462,159; qualifying distributions, $459,849; giving activities include $457,499 for 13 grants (high: $165,000; low: $999).
Purpose and activities: Giving primarily to Jewish organizations; funding also for education, and children and youth services.
Fields of interest: Higher education; Children/youth, services; Jewish federated giving programs; Jewish agencies & synagogues.
Limitations: Applications not accepted. Giving primarily in New York, NY.
Application information: Contributes only to pre-selected organizations.
Trustees: Anne Heyman; Seth Merrin.
EIN: 206796212
Selected grants: The following grants are a representative sample of this grantmaker's funding activity:
$165,000 to Tufts University, Medford, MA, 2011.
$55,000 to Abraham Joshua Heschel School, New York, NY, 2011.
$25,000 to UJA-Federation of New York, New York, NY, 2011.

6173
Hickrill Foundation, Inc. ✧
c/o Norman Foundation Inc.
147 E. 48th St.
New York, NY 10017-1223
Contact: Denie S. Weil, V.P. and Secy.

Incorporated in 1946 in NY.
Donors: Debbie Weil Harrington; John Timothy W. Harrington; Samuel P. Harrington; The Norman Foundation; Eliza H. Myers; Amanda E. Weil; Denie S. Weil; Frank A. Weil; Sandison E. Weil; William S. Weil; Deborah W. Harrington; Samuel P. Harrington.
Foundation type: Independent foundation.
Financial data (yr. ended 12/31/13): Assets, $7,087,948 (M); gifts received, $202,149; expenditures, $516,183; qualifying distributions, $445,771; giving activities include $438,747 for 128 grants (high: $300,000; low: $100).
Purpose and activities: The foundation primarily supports a selected few community organizations in the communities of the members of the foundation, and a very few special projects of particular interest to members of the foundation.
Fields of interest: Community/economic development.
Limitations: Applications accepted. Giving on a national basis. No grants to individuals.
Application information: Application form required.
Initial approach: Letter
Deadline(s): None
Officers: Frank A. Weil, Pres.; Denie S. Weil, V.P. and Secy.
EIN: 136002949

6174
The Rita and Alex Hillman Foundation ✧
(formerly The Alex Hillman Family Foundation)
200 Park Ave. S., Ste. 1705
New York, NY 10003-1503
Main URL: http://www.rahf.org/

Incorporated in 1966 in NY.
Donors: Alex L. Hillman†; Rita K. Hillman†.
Foundation type: Independent foundation.
Financial data (yr. ended 12/31/12): Assets, $98,225,189 (M); expenditures, $4,179,156; qualifying distributions, $3,196,281; giving activities include $2,692,206 for 25 grants (high: $750,000; low: $500).
Purpose and activities: Giving primarily for higher education, with emphasis on schools of nursing; support also for the arts.
Fields of interest: Museums; Performing arts; Performing arts, music; Arts; Higher education; Nursing school/education; Hospitals (general); Jewish agencies & synagogues.
Type of support: General/operating support.
Limitations: Applications not accepted. Giving primarily in the metropolitan New York, NY, area, and in Philadelphia, PA. No grants to individuals, or for continuing support.
Application information: Contributes only to pre-selected organizations.
Board meeting date(s): Semiannually
Officers: James Marcus, Pres.; Henry Christensen III, Secy.-Treas.
Directors: Polly Beere; Paul Garfinkle; William M. Griffin; Raymond J. McGuire; Ahrin Mishan.
EIN: 132560546
Selected grants: The following grants are a representative sample of this grantmaker's funding activity:
$750,000 to University of Pennsylvania, School of Nursing, Philadelphia, PA, 2012. For nursing education.
$121,770 to Lenox Hill Hospital, New York, NY, 2012. For nursing education.

6175
Rochelle and David A. Hirsch Foundation ✧
c/o David Hirsch
910 5th Ave.
New York, NY 10021-4155

Established in 2002 in NY.
Donors: David A. Hirsch; Stephen Colman; Rochelle C. Hirsch.
Foundation type: Independent foundation.
Financial data (yr. ended 12/31/13): Assets, $16,484,048 (M); gifts received, $1,000,000;

expenditures, $706,003; qualifying distributions, $692,412; giving activities include $692,412 for 130 grants (high: $30,000; low: $36).
Fields of interest: Museums; Arts; Higher education; Human services; Jewish agencies & synagogues.
Limitations: Applications not accepted. No grants to individuals.
Application information: Contributes only to pre-selected organizations.
Officers: David A. Hirsch, Pres.; Rochelle C. Hirsch, V.P.; Jeffrey M. Hirsch, Secy.; Jason T. Hirsch, Treas.
EIN: 550809138
Selected grants: The following grants are a representative sample of this grantmaker's funding activity:
$5,000 to Alan T. Brown Foundation to Cure Paralysis, New York, NY, 2011.
$1,500 to Aleph Society, New York, NY, 2011.

6176
His Will Foundation ✧
(formerly The Azariah Foundation)
c/o BCRS Group Assocs., LLC
77 Water St., 9th Fl.
New York, NY 10005-4401

Established in 2000 in NJ.
Donor: John E. Urban.
Foundation type: Independent foundation.
Financial data (yr. ended 08/31/13): Assets, $10,433,411 (M); expenditures, $3,182,031; qualifying distributions, $3,070,000; giving activities include $3,070,000 for 5 grants (high: $2,000,000; low: $20,000).
Fields of interest: Higher education; Christian agencies & churches.
Limitations: Applications not accepted. Giving primarily in NJ, TX, and Purcellville, VA. No grants to individuals, or for scholarships; no loans.
Application information: Contributes only to pre-selected organizations.
Trustees: Carolyn L. Urban; John E. Urban.
EIN: 134043877
Selected grants: The following grants are a representative sample of this grantmaker's funding activity:
$250,000 to Family Educators Alliance of South Texas, San Antonio, TX, 2011.
$200,000 to Patrick Henry College, Purcellville, VA, 2011.
$50,000 to Pillar of Fire, Zarephath, NJ, 2011.
$20,000 to Patrick Henry College, Purcellville, VA, 2011.

6177
Peter & Stacy Hochfelder Charitable Foundation, Inc. ✧ ☆
2 Lincoln Ln.
Purchase, NY 10577-2304

Established in 1994 in NY.
Donors: Peter Hochfelder; Stacy Hochfelder.
Foundation type: Independent foundation.
Financial data (yr. ended 12/31/13): Assets, $28,405 (M); gifts received, $809,849; expenditures, $781,779; qualifying distributions, $781,754; giving activities include $781,754 for 48 grants (high: $246,950; low: $180).
Purpose and activities: Giving primarily for higher education, health care, including health associations and hospitals, human services, and Jewish organizations and education.
Fields of interest: Higher education; Hospitals (general); Health organizations, association; Human services; Jewish federated giving programs; Jewish agencies & synagogues.
Limitations: Applications not accepted. Giving primarily in NY. No grants to individuals.
Application information: Contributes only to pre-selected organizations.
Officers: Peter Hochfelder, Pres.; Mitchell Kuflik, V.P.; Stacy Hochfelder, Secy.
EIN: 133799164
Selected grants: The following grants are a representative sample of this grantmaker's funding activity:
$5,000 to National Tay-Sachs and Allied Diseases Association, Boston, MA, 2011.
$2,500 to Columbia University, New York, NY, 2011.
$1,000 to American Cancer Society, Atlanta, GA, 2011.

6178
Hochstein Foundation, Inc. ✧
c/o Withumsmith and Brown, P.C.
1411 Broadway, 9th Fl.
New York, NY 10018-3496

Established in 1960 in NY.
Donor: Bernard Hochstein†.
Foundation type: Independent foundation.
Financial data (yr. ended 12/31/12): Assets, $76,131,722 (M); gifts received, $1,324,515; expenditures, $3,280,079; qualifying distributions, $3,020,600; giving activities include $3,020,500 for 8 grants (high: $2,095,000; low: $3,500).
Purpose and activities: Giving primarily to Jewish agencies, temples, and schools.
Fields of interest: Education; Human services; Jewish federated giving programs; Jewish agencies & synagogues.
Type of support: General/operating support.
Limitations: Applications not accepted. Giving primarily in the metropolitan New York, NY, area. No grants to individuals.
Application information: Contributes only to pre-selected organizations.
Board Members: Michael Hochstein; Miriam Hochstein; Richard Hochstein; Stephen Hochstein.
EIN: 136161765

6179
Hod Foundation ✧
c/o Amtrust Financial
59 Maiden Ln., 6th Fl.
New York, NY 10038-4502 (212) 639-5100
Contact: Henry Reinhold, Tr.

Established in 2000 in NY.
Donors: Michael Karfunkel; Karfunkel Family Foundation.
Foundation type: Independent foundation.
Financial data (yr. ended 06/30/13): Assets, $286,689,211 (M); expenditures, $5,350,896; qualifying distributions, $5,332,300; giving activities include $5,332,300 for 125 grants (high: $3,000,000; low: $500).
Purpose and activities: Giving primarily to Jewish agencies, temples, and schools.
Fields of interest: Elementary/secondary education; Jewish agencies & synagogues.
Limitations: Giving primarily in NY. No grants to individuals.
Application information: Application form not required.
Initial approach: Letter
Deadline(s): None
Directors: Barry Karfunkel; Leah Karfunkel; Michael Karfunkel; Robert Karfunkel; Henry Reinhold; Jeffrey Weissmann.
EIN: 133922069

6180
Hoerle Foundation ✧
c/o Stone Run Capital, LLC
551 5th Ave., 33 Fl.
New York, NY 10176-3399
Contact: Robert F. Hoerle, Pres.

Established in 1987 in NY.
Donors: Robert F. Hoerle; Sheila A. Hoerle.
Foundation type: Independent foundation.
Financial data (yr. ended 12/31/13): Assets, $18,271,196 (M); gifts received, $289,843; expenditures, $1,005,137; qualifying distributions, $829,359; giving activities include $829,359 for 37 grants (high: $500,000; low: $135).
Purpose and activities: Giving primarily for education.
Fields of interest: Arts; Higher education; Education; Human services; Aging; Girls; Boys; Military/veterans.
Type of support: General/operating support; Annual campaigns; Emergency funds; Scholarship funds; Matching/challenge support.
Limitations: Applications accepted. Giving primarily in NY. No grants to individuals.
Application information: Application form not required.
Initial approach: Letter
Copies of proposal: 1
Deadline(s): None
Board meeting date(s): Dec.
Officers : Robert F. Hoerle, Pres.; Sheila A. Hoerle, V.P.; Pierre J. De Vegh, Treas.
Number of staff: None.
EIN: 133419592

6181
The Jane and Michael Hoffman Foundation ✧ ☆
c/o Riverstone Holdings
712 5th Ave., 36 Fl.
New York, NY 10019-4137

Established in NY.
Donors: Michael Hoffman; Jane Hoffman.
Foundation type: Independent foundation.
Financial data (yr. ended 12/31/13): Assets, $2,083,426 (M); gifts received, $250; expenditures, $564,550; qualifying distributions, $564,550; giving activities include $556,100 for 19 grants (high: $300,000; low: $250).
Fields of interest: Arts; Education; Health organizations.
Limitations: Applications not accepted. Giving primarily in NY; funding also in IL.
Application information: Unsolicited requests for funds not accepted.

Trustees: Jane Hoffman; Michael Hoffman.
EIN: 277098234

6182
Marion & Maximilian Hoffman Foundation ✧

6000 Northern Blvd.
P.O. Box 130
East Norwich, NY 11732-1601
Contact: Ursula C. Niarakis, Pres.

Established in 1984 in NY.
Donors: Marion O. Hoffman; Maximilian Hoffman†.
Foundation type: Independent foundation.
Financial data (yr. ended 06/30/13): Assets, $25,213,624 (M); expenditures, $1,484,483; qualifying distributions, $1,181,217; giving activities include $1,053,965 for 7 grants (high: $1,000,000; low: $300).
Purpose and activities: Giving primarily for natural resource conservation; funding also for human services.
Fields of interest: Environment, natural resources; Environment; Human services; Foundations (private grantmaking).
Limitations: Applications not accepted. Giving primarily in East Norwich and New York, NY. No grants to individuals.
Application information: Contributes only to pre-selected organizations.
Officers: Ursula C. Niarakis, Pres.; William Niarakis, V.P.
Director: Margareta Jackel.
EIN: 112697957

6183
The Hollyhock Foundation, Inc. ✧

c/o Robert A. Karr
55 E. 59th St., 15th Fl.
New York, NY 10022-1112

Established in 2002 in NY.
Donor: Robert A. Karr.
Foundation type: Operating foundation.
Financial data (yr. ended 12/31/12): Assets, $309,974,921 (M); gifts received, $5,000,000; expenditures, $12,785,281; qualifying distributions, $14,022,201; giving activities include $12,134,500 for 35 grants (high: $5,900,000; low: $500), and $1,875,000 for 1 loan/program-related investment.
Purpose and activities: Giving primarily for human services, particularly for the fight against poverty; funding also for education.
Fields of interest: Higher education; Education; Human services; Foundations (private grantmaking); Foundations (public); Catholic agencies & churches; Economically disadvantaged.
Limitations: Applications not accepted. Giving primarily in CA and New York, NY; some funding also in NM. No grants to individuals.
Application information: Contributes only to pre-selected organizations.
Officers: Robert A. Karr, Pres.; Susanne Karr, V.P.; Timothy K. McManus, Secy.-Treas.
EIN: 542091336
Selected grants: The following grants are a representative sample of this grantmaker's funding activity:
$1,500,000 to Robin Hood Foundation, New York, NY, 2012. For Aid for Those Living in Poverty.
$1,000,000 to Harvard University, Cambridge, MA, 2012. For Graduate School of Education for the Doctorate in Education Leadership Fund.
$1,000,000 to Relay Graduate School of Education, New York, NY, 2012. For Development of Online Curriculum and Expenses for GSE Lab School Project.
$350,000 to Good Shepherd Services, New York, NY, 2012. To provide Family Support, Education and Job Programs for High Need Communities.
$50,000 to Harvard University, Cambridge, MA, 2012. For the Graduate School of Education and for the Hollyhock Foundation Fellowship.
$25,000 to Williams College, Williamstown, MA, 2012. For Graduate Program in Art History Annual Fund.
$10,000 to Riverdale Country School, Bronx, NY, 2012. To support Operating Costs of the School.
$5,000 to Amos House, Providence, RI, 2012. To support Operating Costs in Honor of Mike Costa.
$5,000 to Impact OASIS, Middletown, NJ, 2012. To Promote Support for Autistic Adults.
$5,000 to PAVE Academy Charter School, Brooklyn, NY, 2012. For general support for Education at Charter School.

6184
Jacob L. and Lillian Holtzmann Foundation ✧

c/o Marks Paneth LLP
685 3rd Ave.
New York, NY 10017

Established in 1958 in NY.
Donors: Jacob L. Holtzmann†; Lillian Holtzmann†; Howard M. Holtzmann, Esq.
Foundation type: Independent foundation.
Financial data (yr. ended 12/31/13): Assets, $17,490,409 (M); gifts received, $100,000; expenditures, $1,176,230; qualifying distributions, $1,106,381; giving activities include $1,091,950 for 63 grants (high: $250,000; low: $100).
Purpose and activities: Giving primarily for education, Jewish organizations and temples, human services, and the arts.
Fields of interest: Arts; Elementary/secondary education; Higher education; Health organizations, association; Human services; Jewish federated giving programs; Jewish agencies & synagogues.
Limitations: Applications not accepted. Giving primarily in New York, NY; some funding also in CT. No grants to individuals.
Application information: Contributes only to pre-selected organizations.
Trustees: Howard M. Holtzmann, Esq.; Susan H. Richardson.
Number of staff: 1 part-time professional; 1 part-time support.
EIN: 136174349
Selected grants: The following grants are a representative sample of this grantmaker's funding activity:
$35,000 to Yale University, Law School, New Haven, CT, 2012. For general contribution.

6185
Horncrest Foundation, Inc. ✧

6 Sleator Dr.
Ossining, NY 10562-3918 (914) 941-5533
Contact: Lawrence Blau, Pres.

Established in 1960 in NY.
Foundation type: Independent foundation.
Financial data (yr. ended 09/30/13): Assets, $2,844,790 (M); expenditures, $3,436,546; qualifying distributions, $3,405,819; giving activities include $3,386,938 for 162 grants (high: $593,839).
Fields of interest: Higher education; Medical school/education.
Type of support: General/operating support; Seed money; Scholarship funds; Matching/challenge support.
Limitations: Applications accepted. Giving primarily St. Louis, MO and NY. No grants to individuals.
Application information: Application form not required.
Deadline(s): None
Officers: Lawrence Blau, Pres.-Treas.; Olivia Blau, V.P. and Secy.
EIN: 136021261
Selected grants: The following grants are a representative sample of this grantmaker's funding activity:
$230,000 to Grace United Methodist Church, Saint Louis, MO, 2013. For Capital Building Project and Food Pantry.
$198,000 to Washington University, Saint Louis, MO, 2013. For William L. Becker Endowed Fund.
$50,000 to Hailey's Hope Foundation, Goshen, NY, 2013. For General Budget.
$50,000 to International Sculpture Center, Hamilton, NJ, 2013. To support Conference.
$48,000 to Operation Food Search, Saint Louis, MO, 2013. For General Budget.
$35,000 to Moun Pou Moun Haiti, Saint Louis, MO, 2013. For General Budget.
$34,000 to AmeriCares, Stamford, CT, 2013. To support services.
$18,000 to Meds and Food for Kids, Saint Louis, MO, 2013. For General Budget.
$15,000 to Americans for the Arts, Washington, DC, 2013. For General Budget.
$15,000 to Yale University, Dwight Hall, New Haven, CT, 2013. For General Budget.

6186
The G. & B. Horowitz Family Foundation, Inc. ✧

(formerly Gedale B. and Barbara S. Horowitz Foundation)
c/o Cleary Gottlieb
1 Liberty Plz.
New York, NY 10006-1404

Established in 1970 in NY.
Donors: Gedale B. Horowitz; Barbara S. Horowitz; Gedale B. Horowitz Charitable Lead Trust; Gedale B. & Barbara S. Horowitz March 31, 1994 Charitable Lead Annuity Trust.
Foundation type: Independent foundation.
Financial data (yr. ended 06/30/13): Assets, $3,047,654 (M); gifts received, $400,100; expenditures, $515,439; qualifying distributions, $509,869; giving activities include $509,869 for grants.
Purpose and activities: Grants primarily for higher education, including a Conservative Jewish rabbinical seminary, as well as for the arts, particularly museums; funding also for Jewish organizations and temples.
Fields of interest: Museums (art); Higher education; Theological school/education; Health

organizations; Human services; Jewish federated giving programs; Jewish agencies & synagogues.
Type of support: General/operating support.
Limitations: Applications not accepted. Giving primarily in New York, NY. No grants to individuals.
Application information: Contributes only to pre-selected organizations.
Officers: Gedale B. Horowitz, Pres.; Ruth Horowitz, V.P.; Seth Horowitz, V.P.; Steven M. Loeb, Secy.
EIN: 237101730
Selected grants: The following grants are a representative sample of this grantmaker's funding activity:
$52,500 to Columbia University, Law School, New York, NY, 2013. For general unrestricted.

6187
The Mr. and Mrs. Raymond J. Horowitz Foundation for the Arts, Inc. ✧

c/o Warren Adelson
823 Park Ave.
New York, NY 10021-2849

Donor: Margaret Horowitz†.
Foundation type: Independent foundation.
Financial data (yr. ended 12/31/12): Assets, $12,725,436 (M); expenditures, $2,332,406; qualifying distributions, $2,286,202; giving activities include $2,202,500 for 22 grants (high: $250,000; low: $35,000).
Fields of interest: Museums; Museums (art).
Limitations: Applications not accepted. Giving primarily in CT, NY, and PA. No grants to individuals.
Application information: Contributes only to pre-selected organizations.
Officers and Directors:* Warren Adelson,* Pres.; Elaine M. Reich,* V.P.; Michael Simches, Secy.; Steven L. Ingerman,* Treas.; Judith Babcok; Max Berry.
EIN: 133699100

6188
Redlich Horwitz Foundation ✧

P.O. Box 449
Suffern, NY 10901-0449

Established in 1986 in NJ.
Donors: Robert Horwitz; Catherine Redlich.
Foundation type: Independent foundation.
Financial data (yr. ended 12/31/12): Assets, $29,052,967 (M); gifts received, $5,907,590; expenditures, $725,753; qualifying distributions, $641,150; giving activities include $641,150 for 10 grants (high: $300,000; low: $2,000).
Purpose and activities: Giving primarily for education and social services.
Fields of interest: Higher education; Education; Human services; Children/youth, services.
Limitations: Applications not accepted. Giving primarily in NJ and NY; some funding also in IL and MI.
Application information: Contributes only to pre-selected organizations.
Officer: Robert Horwitz,* Pres.
Trustee: Catherine Redlich.
EIN: 222798198

6189
Max and Sunny Howard Memorial Foundation ✧

355 Lexington Ave., 6th Fl.
New York, NY 10017-6603 (212) 557-5666
Contact: Maurice Rosen, Treas.

Donor: Sunny Rice Howard†.
Foundation type: Independent foundation.
Financial data (yr. ended 12/31/13): Assets, $12,882,496 (M); expenditures, $874,579; qualifying distributions, $659,000; giving activities include $659,000 for 31 grants (high: $52,000; low: $5,000).
Fields of interest: Higher education; Human services; Jewish agencies & synagogues.
Limitations: Applications accepted. Giving primarily in New York, NY. No grants to individuals.
Application information: Application form required.
Initial approach: Letter
Deadline(s): None
Officers: Naomi B. Sinnreich, Pres.; Aaron Scherer, Secy.; Maurice Rosen, Treas.
EIN: 273130549

6190
Huberfeld Family Foundation, Inc. ✧

152 W. 57th St.
New York, NY 10019-3386 (212) 581-0500
Contact: Murray Huberfeld, Pres.

Established in 1999 in NY.
Donors: Huberfeld-Bodner Family Foundation; Murray Huberfeld; Jessica Beren; Rachel Huberfield; Alexander Huberfield; Ariela Huberfield; Jacob Huberfield.
Foundation type: Independent foundation.
Financial data (yr. ended 12/31/13): Assets, $43,288,785 (M); gifts received, $2,400,000; expenditures, $3,177,897; qualifying distributions, $3,109,731; giving activities include $3,109,731 for 88 grants (high: $900,000; low: $360).
Purpose and activities: Giving primarily to Jewish organizations, temples, and schools.
Fields of interest: Education; Human services; Jewish agencies & synagogues.
Limitations: Applications accepted. Giving primarily in the greater metropolitan New York, NY, area, including Long Island.
Application information: Application form required.
Initial approach: Letter
Deadline(s): None
Officers and Directors:* Murray Huberfeld,* Pres.; Rachel Huberfeld,* Secy.-Treas.; Jessica Beren; Alexander Huberfeld.
EIN: 134042543

6191
Hudson River Bancorp, Inc. Foundation ✧

P.O. Box 1189
Hudson, NY 12534-0076 (518) 671-6226
Contact: Holly Rappleyea, Secy.
Main URL: http://www.hrbtfoundation.com

Established in 1998 in NY.
Donors: Hudson River Bank & Trust Co.; Carl Florio.
Foundation type: Company-sponsored foundation.
Financial data (yr. ended 03/31/14): Assets, $14,918,661 (M); gifts received, $1,100; expenditures, $1,207,426; qualifying distributions, $681,667; giving activities include $652,821 for 128 grants (high: $100,000; low: $25).
Purpose and activities: The foundation supports programs designed to address healthcare; community development; education and youth; arts and culture; historic preservation; and environmental protection.
Fields of interest: Historic preservation/historical societies; Arts; Education; Environment, natural resources; Hospitals (general); Health care; Youth, services; Community/economic development.
Type of support: General/operating support; Capital campaigns; Building/renovation; Equipment; Program development; Scholarship funds.
Limitations: Applications accepted. Giving primarily in upstate NY. No support for political groups or religious groups for sectarian purposes. No grants to individuals or for debt liquidation.
Application information: Application form required.
Initial approach: Telephone call
Deadline(s): Telephone call
Officers: Marilyn A. Herrington, Pres.; Tony Jones, V.P.; Holly Rappleyea, Secy.; Carl A. Florio, Treas.
Directors: Joseph Phelan; Sid Richter.
EIN: 223595668
Selected grants: The following grants are a representative sample of this grantmaker's funding activity:
$100,000 to Columbia-Greene Hospital Foundation, Hudson, NY, 2011.
$20,000 to Columbia Opportunities, Hudson, NY, 2011.
$10,000 to Columbia Land Conservancy, Chatham, NY, 2011.
$10,000 to Equine Advocates, Chatham, NY, 2011.
$10,000 to Hawthorne Valley School, Ghent, NY, 2011.
$7,500 to Northeast Parent and Child Society, Schenectady, NY, 2011.
$7,500 to Northern Dutchess Hospital Foundation, Rhinebeck, NY, 2011.
$5,000 to Germantown Library, Germantown, NY, 2011.
$5,000 to Proctors Theater, Schenectady, NY, 2011.
$4,500 to STRIDE, Inc., Rensselaer, NY, 2011.

6192
Geoffrey C. Hughes Foundation, Inc. ✧

c/o Cahill Gordon & Reindel LLP
80 Pine St., Ste. 2133
New York, NY 10005-1702 (212) 701-3400
Contact: John R. Young, Pres.

Established in 1991 in NY.
Donor: Geoffrey C. Hughes†.
Foundation type: Independent foundation.
Financial data (yr. ended 03/31/13): Assets, $30,087,357 (M); expenditures, $1,552,511; qualifying distributions, $1,435,028; giving activities include $1,390,567 for 23 grants (high: $250,000; low: $10,000).
Purpose and activities: Support primarily for environmental protection, opera, and ballet, with preference given to organizations supported by Mr. Hughes during his lifetime.
Fields of interest: Performing arts, ballet; Performing arts, opera; Higher education; Environment, natural resources.
Limitations: Applications accepted. Giving on a national basis. No grants to individuals.
Application information: Application form not required.

Initial approach: Letter of inquiry or telephone
Copies of proposal: 1
Deadline(s): None
Board meeting date(s): As necessary
Final notification: Varies

Officers and Directors:* John R. Young,* Pres.; Ursula Cliff,* V.P. and Secy.; Walter C. Cliff,* V.P. and Treas.
EIN: 133622255
Selected grants: The following grants are a representative sample of this grantmaker's funding activity:
$200,000 to Nature Conservancy, Arlington, VA, 2011.
$186,664 to University of Kentucky, Lexington, KY, 2011.
$100,000 to New York City Ballet, New York, NY, 2011.
$100,000 to New York City Opera, New York, NY, 2011.
$20,000 to Housatonic Valley Association, Cornwall Bridge, CT, 2011.

6193
The Charles Evans Hughes Memorial Foundation, Inc. ✧

c/o Philantropy Advisors
P.O. Box 20486
New York, NY 10021-0068
Contact: Lauren Katowitz Shenfield, Secy.
E-mail: cehfdn@philanthropyadvisorsny.org; Main URL: http://cehughesfoundation.org

Incorporated in 1962 in NY.
Donors: Catherine Hughes Waddell†; Chauncey L. Waddell†.
Foundation type: Independent foundation.
Financial data (yr. ended 12/31/13): Assets, $15,588,108 (M); expenditures, $1,037,987; qualifying distributions, $945,181; giving activities include $778,250 for 47 grants (high: $60,000; low: $1,000).
Purpose and activities: Giving primarily to organizations engaged in: 1) education, including legal education 2) legal and human rights 3) protecting the environment 4) American arts and culture.
Fields of interest: Arts; Law school/education; Education; Environment; Legal services; Civil/human rights.
Type of support: Continuing support; Annual campaigns.
Limitations: Applications not accepted. Giving primarily in New York, NY. No grants to individuals.
Application information: Unsolicited requests for funds not accepted.
Board meeting date(s): May and Oct.

Officers and Directors:* Wendy Williamson,* Pres.; Sandra H. Waddell,* V.P.; Lauren Katzowitz Shenfield,* Secy.-Treas.; Mary B. Conrad,* Treas.; Christopher Angell; William G. Kirkland; Karen A.G. Loud; Susan Johnson McLean; Sandra Waddell; Theodore H. Waddell.
Number of staff: None.
EIN: 136159445
Selected grants: The following grants are a representative sample of this grantmaker's funding activity:
$60,000 to Legal Aid Society, New York, NY, 2011.
$50,000 to Environmental Defense Fund, New York, NY, 2011.
$50,000 to National Trust for Historic Preservation, Washington, DC, 2011.
$50,000 to Natural Resources Defense Council, New York, NY, 2011.
$50,000 to New York Community Trust, Donors Education Collaborative, New York, NY, 2011.
$25,000 to Alvin Ailey Dance Foundation, New York, NY, 2011.
$25,000 to Brennan Center for Justice, New York, NY, 2011.
$25,000 to Jazz at Lincoln Center, New York, NY, 2011.
$25,000 to National Womens Law Center, Washington, DC, 2011.
$25,000 to New York Legal Assistance Group, New York, NY, 2011.

6194
Hugoton Foundation ✧

900 Park Ave., Ste. 17E
New York, NY 10075-0280 (212) 734-5447
Contact: Joan K. Stout, Pres.

Established in 1981 in DE.
Donor: Wallace Gilroy†.
Foundation type: Independent foundation.
Financial data (yr. ended 12/31/13): Assets, $45,001,788 (M); expenditures, $2,126,443; qualifying distributions, $2,089,757; giving activities include $1,846,500 for 85 grants (high: $150,000; low: $2,000).
Purpose and activities: Giving primarily to augment health care.
Fields of interest: Higher education; Medical school/education; Nursing school/education; Hospitals (general); Health care; Human services; Catholic agencies & churches.
Type of support: Equipment; Program development; Research.
Limitations: Giving primarily in Miami, FL and New York, NY. No grants to individuals.
Application information:
Initial approach: Proposal
Copies of proposal: 1
Deadline(s): None
Board meeting date(s): As necessary

Officers and Directors:* Joan K. Stout, Pres.; Ray E. Stout,* V.P.; Joan M. Stout,* Secy.; Jean C. Stout,* Treas.; Frank S. Fejes; John K. Stout.
Number of staff: 1 full-time professional.
EIN: 341351062
Selected grants: The following grants are a representative sample of this grantmaker's funding activity:
$250,000 to Archdiocese of New York, New York, NY, 2012. To restore St Patrick's Cathedral.
$85,000 to Miami Dade College, Miami, FL, 2012. For School of Nursing Muse Patient Simulator.
$65,000 to Lenox Hill Hospital, New York, NY, 2012. For Plastic Surgery Fellowship.
$50,000 to Archdiocese of Miami, Miami Shores, FL, 2012. To support Ecumenical Healthcare.
$50,000 to Barry University, Miami Shores, FL, 2012. For Fund the Purchase of Medical Equipment.
$25,000 to Lenox Hill Hospital, New York, NY, 2012. For Upgrade of Nurses Resource Center.
$25,000 to Xavier Society for the Blind, New York, NY, 2012. To support Mission for Blind.
$12,000 to Marian Center School and Services, Miami Gardens, FL, 2012. For replacement of infrastructure.
$10,000 to Eternal Word Television Network, Irondale, AL, 2012. For religious television programming.
$10,000 to USO World Headquarters, Arlington, VA, 2012. For Christmas Convoy.

6195
Hultquist Foundation, Inc. ✧

202 N. Main St., 4th Fl.
Jamestown, NY 14701-5208 (716) 664-5210
Contact: Tom Flowers, Pres.

Established in 1965 in NY.
Foundation type: Independent foundation.
Financial data (yr. ended 06/30/13): Assets, $14,993,092 (M); expenditures, $987,821; qualifying distributions, $891,938; giving activities include $882,808 for 17 grants (high: $250,000; low: $4,200).
Purpose and activities: Giving primarily for higher education and human services.
Fields of interest: Higher education; Human services; YM/YWCAs & YM/YWHAs; Human services, mind/body enrichment; United Ways and Federated Giving Programs.
Type of support: General/operating support; Continuing support; Annual campaigns; Capital campaigns; Building/renovation; Equipment; Land acquisition.
Limitations: Applications accepted. Giving limited to Chautauqua County, NY, with emphasis on Jamestown, NY. No grants to individuals.
Application information: Application form required.
Initial approach: Letter
Copies of proposal: 4
Deadline(s): Generally in June and Dec.
Board meeting date(s): Quarterly

Officers: Thomas I. Flowers, Pres.; John K. Plumb, V.P.; Stephen J. Wright, V.P.; William L. Wright, V.P.; Robert F. Rohm, Jr., Secy.-Treas.
EIN: 160907729
Selected grants: The following grants are a representative sample of this grantmaker's funding activity:
$250,000 to Jamestown Community College, Jamestown, NY, 2013. For Jamestown Campus Science Building.
$35,000 to Boys and Girls Club of Jamestown, Jamestown, NY, 2013. For roof replacement.
$35,000 to Chautauqua Institution, Chautauqua, NY, 2013. For Music School Festival Orchestra.

6196
Hunter Douglas Foundation Inc. ✧

1 Blue Hill Plz.
Pearl River, NY 10965-3104 (845) 664-7000
Contact: Kathy O'Keefe

Established as a company-sponsored operating foundation in 1999 in NJ.
Donor: Hunter Douglas, Inc.
Foundation type: Operating foundation.
Financial data (yr. ended 12/31/12): Assets, $92,844 (M); gifts received, $644,086; expenditures, $625,996; qualifying distributions, $625,996; giving activities include $425,000 for 2 grants (high: $275,000; low: $150,000), and $197,250 for 87 grants to individuals (high: $5,000; low: $500).
Purpose and activities: The foundation supports organizations involved with the 9/11 disaster and

awards college scholarships to children of employees of Hunter Douglas, Inc.
Fields of interest: Education; Disasters, 9/11/01; Human services.
Type of support: Employee-related scholarships.
Limitations: Applications accepted. Giving limited to Upper Saddle River, NJ and NY.
Application information: Application form required.
Initial approach: Letter
Deadline(s): Annually by mid-Sept.
Officers and Directors:* Gordon Khan,* V.P.; Arthur Lorenz,* V.P.; Marvin Hopkins.
EIN: 223694713

6197
The Hunter Foundation ✧
477 Madison Ave., 10th Fl.
New York, NY 10022

Established in NY.
Donor: Allan B. Hunter.
Foundation type: Independent foundation.
Financial data (yr. ended 12/31/12): Assets, $3,337,888 (M); expenditures, $585,231; qualifying distributions, $552,758; giving activities include $548,614 for 39 grants (high: $489,000; low: $50).
Purpose and activities: Giving primarily for higher education.
Fields of interest: Arts; Higher education, college; Education; Hospitals (general); Health care; Human services.
Limitations: Applications not accepted. Giving primarily in NH. No grants to individuals.
Application information: Contributes only to pre-selected organizations.
Trustees: Andre Hunter; Kelly Hunter.
EIN: 136094021

6198
Syde Hurdus Foundation, Inc. ✧
(formerly Syde Hurdus 1992 Charitable Trust)
c/o Reedsmith-Gilberti
599 Lexington Ave., 22nd Fl.
New York, NY 10022-6030

Established in 1992 in NY.
Donor: Syde Hurdus‡.
Foundation type: Independent foundation.
Financial data (yr. ended 08/31/13): Assets, $17,162,544 (M); expenditures, $1,122,151; qualifying distributions, $791,500; giving activities include $791,500 for 40 grants (high: $100,000; low: $2,000).
Purpose and activities: Giving primarily for health care and medical research, and children, youth and social services.
Fields of interest: Hospitals (general); Health care; Health organizations, association; Medical research, institute; Human services; Children/youth, services; Foundations (private grantmaking).
Limitations: Applications not accepted. Giving primarily in NY; some funding also in CA. No grants to individuals.
Application information: Contributes only to pre-selected organizations.
Officers and Directors:* Herbert S. Fitzgibbon,* V.P.; Lawrence F. Gilberti,* Secy.; Herbert Botwinick,* Treas.
EIN: 113163290

Selected grants: The following grants are a representative sample of this grantmaker's funding activity:
$100,000 to ReSurge International, Mountain View, CA, 2011.
$40,000 to American Academy in Rome, New York, NY, 2011.
$35,000 to Lighthouse International, New York, NY, 2011.
$25,000 to Friends of Nick, New York, NY, 2011.
$20,000 to Goods for Good, New York, NY, 2011.
$20,000 to Manhattan Institute for Policy Research, New York, NY, 2011.
$15,000 to Cystic Fibrosis Foundation, New York, NY, 2011.
$15,000 to New York Junior Tennis League, Woodside, NY, 2011.
$12,500 to Saint Francis Hospital Foundation, Roslyn, NY, 2011.
$5,000 to Gildas Club Worldwide, New York, NY, 2011.

6199
The Hurford Foundation ✧
c/o Davidson, Dawson & Clark, LLP
60 E. 42nd St.
New York, NY 10165-0001

Established in 1986.
Donors: John B. Hurford‡; BEA Assocs., Inc.
Foundation type: Independent foundation.
Financial data (yr. ended 12/31/13): Assets, $12,203,403 (M); expenditures, $1,239,025; qualifying distributions, $1,052,080; giving activities include $924,809 for 15 grants (high: $281,476; low: $5,000).
Fields of interest: Arts; Higher education; Human services; Children/youth, services; International affairs, foreign policy; International affairs.
Type of support: General/operating support.
Limitations: Applications not accepted. Giving primarily in NY. Generally no grants to individuals.
Application information: Unsolicited requests for funds not accepted.
Board meeting date(s): Quarterly
Officers and Directors:* Robert C. Miller, Pres. and Treas.; Jayne M. Kurzman,* V.P.; William W. Priest, Jr.,* Secy.
EIN: 133394688
Selected grants: The following grants are a representative sample of this grantmaker's funding activity:
$215,500 to Foreign Policy Association, New York, NY, 2011.
$150,000 to Council on Foreign Relations, New York, NY, 2011.
$125,000 to National Endowment for Democracy, Washington, DC, 2011.
$100,000 to Save the Children Federation, Fairfield, CT, 2011.
$50,000 to Freedom House, New York, NY, 2011.
$50,000 to Humanity in Action, New York, NY, 2011.
$15,000 to Global Network Foundation, Atlanta, GA, 2011.
$15,000 to One To World, New York, NY, 2011.
$5,000 to Henry L. Stimson Center, Washington, DC, 2011.

6200
Hurst Family Foundation ✧
(formerly The Robert J. Hurst Foundation)
c/o Crestview Partners
667 Madison Ave., 10th Fl.
New York, NY 10065

Established in 1997 in NY.
Donors: Robert J. Hurst; RJH Investment Partners, L.P.
Foundation type: Independent foundation.
Financial data (yr. ended 12/31/12): Assets, $41,903,373 (M); gifts received, $3,001,945; expenditures, $3,966,836; qualifying distributions, $3,785,546; giving activities include $3,779,296 for 74 grants (high: $1,000,000; low: $25).
Fields of interest: Arts; Education; Health care; Human services; Jewish federated giving programs; Jewish agencies & synagogues.
Limitations: Applications not accepted. Giving primarily in NY. No grants to individuals.
Application information: Contributes only to pre-selected organizations.
Trustees: Alexander B. Hurst; Amanda K. Hurst; Robert J. Hurst; Soledad D. Hurst.
EIN: 311568195

6201
Hutchins Family Foundation, Inc. ✧
c/o Glenn H. Hutchins, Silver Lake Partners
9 W. 57th St., 32nd Fl.
New York, NY 10019-2603

Established in 2004 in NY.
Donor: Glenn H. Hutchins.
Foundation type: Independent foundation.
Financial data (yr. ended 12/31/13): Assets, $9,778,660 (M); gifts received, $8,637,057; expenditures, $9,704,491; qualifying distributions, $9,704,491; giving activities include $9,295,138 for 24 grants (high: $3,145,234; low: $300).
Fields of interest: Higher education; Education; Medical research, institute; Social sciences, public policy.
Limitations: Applications not accepted. Giving primarily in MA, NJ, and NY; funding also in Washington, DC. No grants to individuals.
Application information: Contributes only to pre-selected organizations.
Officers and Trustee:* Glenn H. Hutchins,* Chair. and Treas.; Deborah D. Hutchins, Pres. and Secy.; Scott A. Carlson, Exec. Dir.
EIN: 371501785

6202
Mary J. Hutchins Foundation, Inc. ✧
c/o TCC Group
31 W. 27th St., 4th Fl.
New York, NY 10001-6914

Incorporated in 1935 in NY.
Donors: Mary J. Hutchins‡; Caspar J. Voorhis‡; Waldo H. Hutchins, Jr.‡; Waldo Hutchins Jr. Non Exempt Trust; Waldo Hutchins Generation Skipping Transfer Exempt Trust.
Foundation type: Independent foundation.
Financial data (yr. ended 12/31/13): Assets, $37,020,785 (M); expenditures, $1,680,637; qualifying distributions, $1,542,761; giving activities include $1,360,000 for 43 grants (high: $60,000; low: $10,000).

Purpose and activities: The foundation supports social services organizations serving low-income populations in New York City. There is some support for health services to the same populations.
Fields of interest: Health care; Human services; Economically disadvantaged.
Type of support: General/operating support; Program development; Grants to individuals.
Limitations: Applications not accepted. Giving primarily in the New York, NY, area. No support for educational purposes or national health funds. No grants for seed money, scholarships, or annual campaigns.
Application information: Unsolicited requests for proposals not accepted.
Board meeting date(s): Mar., June, Sept., and Dec.
Officers and Directors:* Elizabeth E. Hutchins,* Pres.; Carol Gallo, V.P.; Edwin Sheffield,* V.P.; Hildy J. Simmons,* V.P.; Sidney S. Whelan, Jr.,* V.P.
EIN: 136083578

6203
IBM International Foundation ✧
(formerly IBM South Africa Projects Fund)
New Orchard Rd.
Armonk, NY 10504-1709
Contact: Judy Chin, Fdn. Mgr.
Main URL: http://www.ibm.com/ibm/responsibility/
IBM Fellowship Grants Website: http://www.ibm.com/developerworks/university/phdfellowship/
KidSmart Early Learning Program Website: http://www.kidsmartearlylearning.org/
E-mail for IBM Fellowship Grants: phdfellow@us.ibm.com

Established in 1985 in NY.
Donor: International Business Machines Corp.
Foundation type: Company-sponsored foundation.
Financial data (yr. ended 12/31/12): Assets, $193,326,732 (M); gifts received, $24,567,673; expenditures, $23,839,105; qualifying distributions, $23,813,698; giving activities include $12,291,100 for grants, and $9,326,905 for employee matching gifts.
Purpose and activities: The foundation supports organizations involved with arts and culture, K-12 education, the environment, health, employment, human services, diversity, science, public policy research, and minorities.
Fields of interest: Arts; Elementary/secondary education; Education, early childhood education; Education, continuing education; Education, reading; Health care; Human services; Civil/human rights, equal rights; Science, formal/general education; Mathematics; Physics; Engineering/technology; Computer science; Engineering; Science; Public policy, research; Disabilities, people with; Minorities.
International interests: Africa; Asia; Canada; Europe; Latin America.
Type of support: Employee matching gifts; Fellowships; General/operating support; Program development.
Limitations: Applications accepted. Giving on a national and international basis, with some emphasis in CA and NY, and in Africa, Asia, Canada, Europe, and Latin America. No support for fraternal, labor, political, or religious organizations or private or parochial schools. No grants to individuals (except for fellowships), or for scholarships, capital campaigns, fundraising, construction or renovation projects, chairs, endowments, conferences, symposia, or sports competitions.
Application information: Proposals should be no longer than 2 pages. Additional information may be requested at a later date. Applicants must be nominated by a faculty member for IBM Fellowship Grants. Application form not required.
Initial approach: Proposal; complete online nomination form for IBM Fellowship Grants
Copies of proposal: 1
Deadline(s): None; Sept. 22 to Nov. 2 for IBM Fellowship Grants
Final notification: 1 month
Officers and Directors:* Samuel J. Palmisano,* Chair.; John C. Iwata,* Vice-Chair.; Stanley S. Litow,* Pres.; Michelle Browdy, Secy.; Robert Del Bene, Treas.; Nick D'Anniballe, Cont.; Jennifer Crozier; Mark Loughridge.
Number of staff: 1 full-time professional.
EIN: 133267906

6204
The Carl C. Icahn Foundation ✧ ☆
c/o Icahn Assoc. Holding LLC
767 5th Ave., Ste. 4700
New York, NY 10153-0023 (212) 702-4300
Contact: Gail Golden-Icahn, V.P.
Carl Icahn's Giving Pledge Profile: http://glasspockets.org/philanthropy-in-focus/eye-on-the-giving-pledge/profiles/icahn

Established in 1980 in NY and DE.
Donor: Carl C. Icahn.
Foundation type: Independent foundation.
Financial data (yr. ended 11/30/13): Assets, $29,032,527 (L); gifts received, $35,050; expenditures, $1,192,437; qualifying distributions, $740,894; giving activities include $730,500 for 29 grants (high: $500,000; low: $1,000).
Fields of interest: Arts; Higher education; Hospitals (general); Health organizations, association; Recreation; Children/youth, services; Jewish agencies & synagogues.
Type of support: General/operating support; Annual campaigns; Building/renovation; Matching/challenge support.
Limitations: Applications accepted. Giving primarily in NJ and New York, NY. No grants to individuals.
Application information: Application form required.
Initial approach: Letter
Deadline(s): None
Board meeting date(s): As necessary
Officers and Director:* Carl C. Icahn,* Pres. and Treas.; Gail Golden-Icahn, V.P. and Secy.
Number of staff: 1
EIN: 133091588

6205
The IF Foundation ✧
(formerly The Iovino Family Foundation)
26-15 Ulmer St.
College Point, NY 11356-1144 (718) 554-2961
FAX: (718) 554-2799; Main URL: http://www.if-foundation.org
Facebook: https://www.facebook.com/if.foundation
Twitter: https://twitter.com/Theiffoundation

Established in 2001 in NY.
Donors: Michael Capasso; Robert Hood; David Horowitch; Mary Iovino; Thomas Iovino; Mitch Levine; Bernard London; Charles Magrath; Peter Pace; Paul Posillico; Judlau Contracting, Inc.; The Iovino Charitable Lead Annuity Trust; Spearin, Preston and Burrows, Inc.; J-Track LLC; Midland Tech LLC; TC Electric LLC; Grassi and Co.; Posillico Foundation; T and Company Moriarty; Redwood Contracting; Arthur Corwin/Moretrench; St. James Church; The Better U Foundation.
Foundation type: Independent foundation.
Financial data (yr. ended 12/31/13): Assets, $2,647,946 (M); gifts received, $758,933; expenditures, $1,057,261; qualifying distributions, $527,916; giving activities include $527,916 for grants.
Purpose and activities: Giving primarily for Episcopal churches, and for higher and other education; funding also for human services.
Fields of interest: Higher education; Education; Human services; Family services; Protestant agencies & churches.
Limitations: Applications not accepted. Giving primarily in NY. No grants to individuals.
Publications: Annual report.
Application information: Contributes only to pre-selected organizations.
Officers and Trustees:* Thomas Iovino,* Pres.; Frank Cara; Dale Okonow.
EIN: 113619538

6206
IFF Foundation Inc. ✧
521 W. 57th St.
New York, NY 10019-2929
Contact: Carol Brys, Corp. Comms.

Incorporated in 1963 in NY.
Donor: International Flavors & Fragrances, Inc.
Foundation type: Company-sponsored foundation.
Financial data (yr. ended 12/31/13): Assets, $190,771 (M); gifts received, $668,052; expenditures, $517,438; qualifying distributions, $515,943; giving activities include $157,117 for 20 grants (high: $35,000; low: $1,568), and $358,826 for 1 employee matching gift.
Purpose and activities: The foundation supports police agencies and organizations involved with arts and culture, education, health, genetic diseases, cancer, cancer research, and human services.
Fields of interest: Museums (art); Performing arts centers; Arts; Higher education; Education; Hospitals (general); Health care; Genetic diseases and disorders; Cancer; Cancer, leukemia; Breast cancer; Cancer research; Crime/law enforcement, police agencies; American Red Cross; Children, services; Human services; United Ways and Federated Giving Programs; Women.
Type of support: General/operating support; Annual campaigns; Program development; Publication; Employee volunteer services; Sponsorships; Employee matching gifts.
Limitations: Applications not accepted. Giving limited to areas of company operations in NJ and New York, NY. No support for sectarian or religious organizations not of direct benefit to the entire community, political, fraternal, social, or other membership organizations, or organizations whose combined administrative, management, and fundraising expenses exceed 30% of the organization's total budget. No grants to individuals, or for capital campaigns or endowments.

Application information: Contributes only to pre-selected organizations.
Officers and Directors: Angelica T. Cantlon,* Pres.; Anne Chwat,* V.P. and Secy.; Kevin C. Berryman,* V.P.; Richard A. O'Leary, V.P.; Robert G. Anderson, Treas.
EIN: 136159094
Selected grants: The following grants are a representative sample of this grantmaker's funding activity:
$25,000 to American Jewish Committee, New York, NY, 2011.

6207
IIMI, Inc. ✧
477 Madison Ave., 10th Fl.
New York, NY 10022-5841

Established in 1997 in DE and NY.
Donor: Susan Wexner Revocable Trust.
Foundation type: Independent foundation.
Financial data (yr. ended 06/30/13): Assets, $26,064,435 (M); expenditures, $1,248,942; qualifying distributions, $1,140,657; giving activities include $1,133,959 for 14 grants (high: $500,000; low: $1).
Fields of interest: Education; Human services; Children/youth, services; International development; Jewish federated giving programs; Jewish agencies & synagogues.
International interests: Israel.
Limitations: Applications not accepted. Giving in Israel and to national organizations for the benefit of Israel, primarily in New York, NY. No grants to individuals.
Application information: Contributes only to pre-selected organizations.
Officer and Directors:* Susan Wexner,* Pres. and Secy.-Treas.; Saul G. Agus; Raymond Kanner; Gregg H. Levy, Esq.; Michael S. Oberman, Esq.; Mark Saks, Esq.; Walter Stern.
EIN: 134077817
Selected grants: The following grants are a representative sample of this grantmaker's funding activity:
$282,000 to Israel Museum, Jerusalem, Israel, 2011.
$50,000 to National Ramah Commission, New York, NY, 2011.
$2,500 to PEF Israel Endowment Funds, New York, NY, 2011.
$1,500 to Jewish Foundation for Group Homes, Rockville, MD, 2011.
$1,500 to PEF Israel Endowment Funds, New York, NY, 2011.

6208
Elizabeth & Frank Ingrassia Foundation ✧
c/o The Ayco Co., L.P.
P.O. Box 15014
Albany, NY 12212-5014

Established in 1994 in NY.
Donor: Francis J. Ingrassia.
Foundation type: Independent foundation.
Financial data (yr. ended 09/30/13): Assets, $3,603,505 (M); expenditures, $469,424; qualifying distributions, $425,000; giving activities include $425,000 for 4 grants (high: $200,000; low: $50,000).
Purpose and activities: Giving primarily for education, juvenile diabetes research, and to Catholic churches.
Fields of interest: Higher education; Education; Diabetes research; Catholic agencies & churches.
Limitations: Applications not accepted. Giving primarily in NY; some giving also in PA. No grants to individuals, or for scholarships; no loans.
Application information: Contributes only to pre-selected organizations.
Trustees: Francis J. Ingrassia; Elizabeth McCaul.
EIN: 133801229
Selected grants: The following grants are a representative sample of this grantmaker's funding activity:
$250,000 to Friends Academy, Locust Valley, NY, 2011. For general charitable purposes.
$230,000 to Lehigh University, Bethlehem, PA, 2011. For general charitable purposes.
$10,000 to Church of the Resurrection, New York, NY, 2011. For general charitable purposes.

6209
Inmaat Foundation ✧ ☆
c/o Victoria Purdy & Cavallaro LLP
1 Rockefeller Plz., Ste. 321
New York, NY 10020-2134 (212) 977-3535

Donor: The Buffin Foundation.
Foundation type: Independent foundation.
Financial data (yr. ended 12/31/13): Assets, $38,463,939 (M); expenditures, $2,419,983; qualifying distributions, $2,116,696; giving activities include $2,011,500 for 59 grants (high: $300,000; low: $5,000).
Fields of interest: Human services.
Limitations: Applications not accepted. Giving primarily in NY.
Application information: Unsolicited request for funds not accepted.
Officers: Chandra Jessee, Pres. and Treas.; Alfred Cavallaro, Secy.
EIN: 453814655

6210
Interlaken Foundation, Inc. ✧
c/o Robert G. Wilmers
350 Park Ave., 6th Fl.
New York, NY 10022-6081

Established in 2001 in NY.
Donors: Robert G. Wilmers; Gertrude Wilmers.
Foundation type: Independent foundation.
Financial data (yr. ended 06/30/13): Assets, $26,354,787 (M); gifts received, $2,819,039; expenditures, $494,792; qualifying distributions, $490,045; giving activities include $486,845 for 7 grants (high: $250,000; low: $1,000).
Fields of interest: Museums; Performing arts, theater; Higher education; Environment; Safety/disasters; International affairs, public policy.
Limitations: Applications not accepted. Giving primarily in MA. No grants to individuals.
Application information: Contributes only to pre-selected organizations.
Officer: Robert G. Wilmers, Pres.
EIN: 522339479
Selected grants: The following grants are a representative sample of this grantmaker's funding activity:
$204,845 to Canisius College, Buffalo, NY, 2013. For organization's charitable use.

6211
International Federation of Red Cross and Red Crescent Societies at the United Nations, Inc. ✧
420 Lexington Ave., Ste. 2811
New York, NY 10170-2811

Established in 1992 in NY.
Foundation type: Independent foundation.
Financial data (yr. ended 12/31/12): Assets, $939,490 (M); gifts received, $1,713,131; expenditures, $2,442,340; qualifying distributions, $1,287,487; giving activities include $1,287,487 for 17 grants (high: $212,206; low: $14,250).
Fields of interest: American Red Cross; International relief.
International interests: Global Programs; Switzerland.
Limitations: Applications accepted. Giving on an international basis, with emphasis on Geneva, Switzerland.
Application information:
Initial approach: Letter
Deadline(s): Dec. 31
Officers: Elise Baudot-Queguiner; Siddarth Chatterjee; Andrew Rizk.
EIN: 133682664

6212
The Inzlicht Heritage Foundation ✧ ☆
3A Vincent Rd.
Spring Valley, NY 10977-3830

Donors: Michael Inzlicht; Pearl Inzlicht; Arthur Meisels.
Foundation type: Independent foundation.
Financial data (yr. ended 12/31/13): Assets, $7,665,199 (M); gifts received, $6,600,000; expenditures, $659,492; qualifying distributions, $599,629; giving activities include $599,629 for grants.
Fields of interest: Education; Human services; Jewish agencies & synagogues.
Limitations: Applications not accepted.
Application information: Unsolicited requests for funds not accepted.
Directors: David Inzlicht; Michael Inzlicht; Pearl Inzlicht.
EIN: 200431670

6213
The Iris Foundation ✧
224 W. 57th St.
New York, NY 10019-3212

Established in 1991 in NY.
Donors: George Soros; Murray Weber; Andrea Colombel; Eric Colombel; Susan Soros; Tivadar Charitable Lead Trust; George Soros 1982 Charitable Lead Trust; Soros Foundation; Open Society Institute.
Foundation type: Independent foundation.
Financial data (yr. ended 08/31/13): Assets, $197,030,802 (M); expenditures, $11,178,467; qualifying distributions, $8,271,241; giving activities include $8,195,144 for 6 grants (high: $8,115,517; low: $1,000).

Purpose and activities: Giving primarily for higher education.
Fields of interest: Museums (art); Higher education.
Type of support: General/operating support.
Limitations: Applications not accepted. Giving primarily in NY; some giving also in London, UK. No grants to individuals.
Application information: Contributes only to pre-selected organizations.
Officers and Trustees:* George Soros,* Co-Chair.; Susan Weber Soros,* Co-Chair.; William D. Zabel.
EIN: 136977690
Selected grants: The following grants are a representative sample of this grantmaker's funding activity:
$8,115,517 to Bard College, Annandale on Hudson, NY, 2013. For ongoing activities.
$62,500 to Metropolitan Museum of Art, New York, NY, 2013. For unrestricted support.

6214
Isdell Foundation ✧
c/o Aristela Capital LLC
136 Madison Ave., 3rd Fl.
New York, NY 10016-6711 (212) 842-8900
Contact: Kevin Toner, Pres.
Main URL: http://www.isdell.org/

Established in 1994 in NY.
Donor: Kevin Toner.
Foundation type: Independent foundation.
Financial data (yr. ended 12/31/13): Assets, $12,555,069 (M); expenditures, $853,228; qualifying distributions, $830,400; giving activities include $830,400 for 12 grants (high: $300,000; low: $5,000).
Purpose and activities: Giving for international affairs and public affairs.
Fields of interest: International affairs; Public affairs.
Type of support: Seed money; Research; Publication; Program evaluation; Program development; Management development/capacity building; General/operating support; Conferences/seminars.
Limitations: Applications accepted. Giving on a national basis.
Publications: Application guidelines.
Application information: Application form required.
Initial approach: Letter
Deadline(s): Dec. 31
Officer: Kevin Toner, Pres.
Director: Yodon Thonden.
EIN: 223341359

6215
Island Outreach Foundation, Inc. ✧
150 Senix Ave.
Center Moriches, NY 11934-0122

Established in NY.
Donor: Priscilla Knapp.
Foundation type: Independent foundation.
Financial data (yr. ended 05/31/13): Assets, $32,835,636 (M); expenditures, $2,166,275; qualifying distributions, $1,869,714; giving activities include $1,869,714 for 39 grants (high: $400,000; low: $1,000).
Fields of interest: Health care; Cancer research; Housing/shelter; Human services; United Ways and Federated Giving Programs; Catholic federated giving programs.
Limitations: Applications not accepted. Giving primarily in Long Island and New York, NY.
Application information: Contributes only to pre-selected organizations.
Directors: Danielle Knapp; David Knapp; Michele Knapp; Margaret King; Janice Taraskas.
EIN: 260734110

6216
A. C. Israel Foundation, Inc. ✧
12 E. 49th St., 41st Fl.
New York, NY 10017-8298

Incorporated in 1967 in DE as successor to the foundation of the same name incorporated in 1946 in NY.
Donors: Adrian C. Israel‡; Adrian & James, Inc.; Stanley Aberman; A.C. Israel Enterprises, Inc.
Foundation type: Independent foundation.
Financial data (yr. ended 12/31/13): Assets, $32,428,982 (M); expenditures, $1,293,904; qualifying distributions, $1,144,404; giving activities include $1,144,404 for 72 grants (high: $310,000; low: $100).
Purpose and activities: Giving primarily for education, hospitals and health associations, and human services.
Fields of interest: Arts; Secondary school/education; Higher education; Hospitals (general); Hospitals (specialty); Health organizations, association; Human services.
Type of support: General/operating support.
Limitations: Applications not accepted. Giving primarily in CA, CT, MA, and NY. No grants to individuals.
Application information: Contributes only to pre-selected organizations.
Officers and Directors:* Thomas C. Israel,* Pres.; Gregory H. Warner, V.P. and Secy.-Treas.; Barry W. Gray,* V.P.; Lawrence E. Kraus, V.P.; Virginia J. Goldstein.
EIN: 516021414
Selected grants: The following grants are a representative sample of this grantmaker's funding activity:
$624,000 to Phillips Academy, Andover, MA, 2011. For general support.
$200,000 to Scripps Foundation for Medicine and Science, San Diego, CA, 2011. For general support.
$25,000 to Anti-Defamation League of Bnai Brith, New York, NY, 2011. For general support.
$10,000 to Riverdale Country School, Bronx, NY, 2011. For general support.

6217
Ittleson Foundation, Inc. ✧
15 E. 67th St., 5th Fl.
New York, NY 10021-5804 (212) 794-2008
Contact: Anthony C. Wood, Exec. Dir.
FAX: (212) 794-0351; Main URL: http://www.ittlesonfoundation.org

Trust established in 1932 in NY.
Donors: Henry Ittleson‡; Blanche F. Ittleson‡; Henry Ittleson, Jr.‡; Lee F. Ittleson‡; Nancy S. Ittleson‡.
Foundation type: Independent foundation.
Financial data (yr. ended 12/31/13): Assets, $14,288,717 (M); expenditures, $1,152,706; qualifying distributions, $1,107,560; giving activities include $613,600 for 29 grants (high: $300,000; low: $500).
Purpose and activities: The foundation provides seed money for start-up programs and pilot and demonstration projects with a plan for national dissemination in the areas of AIDS and mental health.
Fields of interest: Mental health/crisis services; AIDS.
Type of support: Program development; Publication; Seed money; Research; Technical assistance; Matching/challenge support.
Limitations: Applications accepted. Giving on a national basis. No support for the humanities or cultural projects, general education, social service agencies offering direct service to people in local communities, or projects or organizations that are international in scope or purpose. No grants to individuals, or for continuing support, scholarships, fellowships, internships, annual or capital campaigns, travel, emergency or endowment funds, biomedical research, or deficit financing; no loans.
Publications: Annual report (including application guidelines).
Application information: Application guidelines available on foundation web site. Application form not required.
Initial approach: Letter of inquiry
Copies of proposal: 1
Deadline(s): Sept. 1
Board meeting date(s): Annually
Final notification: 3 weeks to 3 months
Officers and Directors:* H. Anthony Ittleson,* Chair. and Pres.; Pamela Lee Syrmis,* V.P.; Anthony C. Wood,* Secy. and Exec. Dir.; Henry P. Davison II, Treas.; Andrew Auchincloss; H. Philip Ittleson; Stephanie Ittleson; Christina Ittleson Smith; Victor Syrmis, M.D.
Number of staff: 1 full-time professional; 1 part-time support.
EIN: 510172757
Selected grants: The following grants are a representative sample of this grantmaker's funding activity:
$600,000 to Brown University, Providence, RI, 2012. For green and sustainable initiatives campus-wide, including the new athletics quadrangle, in association with the naming of the new green quadrangle located in front of the new Fitness Center and Aquatics Center.
$40,000 to City Health Works, New York, NY, 2012. For City Health Works! is organization dedicated to advancing the use of the role of community health workers in the United States by creating a low-cost and high-performing operational model for the delivery of evidence-based interventions by peer coaches.
$20,000 to Darkness to Light, Charleston, SC, 2012. For One-time grant to launch, in partnership with Stop It Now! a national movement against child sexual abuse. Leadership will be provided to advance child abuse prevention through national policy mandates and funding. A model for the cooperative development.

6218
J. & AR Foundation ✧
c/o Anchin Block & Anchin LLP
1375 Broadway
New York, NY 10018-7001

Established in 1990 in NY.

Donors: Janet C. Ross; Arthur Ross†; Arthur Ross Foundation.
Foundation type: Independent foundation.
Financial data (yr. ended 12/31/13): Assets, $35,632,280 (M); gifts received, $39,229; expenditures, $1,124,347; qualifying distributions, $911,616; giving activities include $779,250 for 67 grants (high: $341,500; low: $500).
Fields of interest: Museums (natural history); Historic preservation/historical societies; Arts; Higher education; Botanical gardens; Medical research.
Limitations: Applications not accepted. Giving primarily in NY. No grants to individuals.
Application information: Contributes only to pre-selected organizations.
Trustees: George J. Gillespie III; Janet C. Ross.
EIN: 136962028
Selected grants: The following grants are a representative sample of this grantmaker's funding activity:
$50,000 to Asia Society, New York, NY, 2011.
$25,000 to Japan Society, New York, NY, 2011.
$4,000 to Nature Conservancy, Arlington, VA, 2011.
$1,500 to Citizens for NYC, New York, NY, 2011.
$1,000 to American Jewish Committee, New York, NY, 2011.

6219
The Jacobson Family Foundation ✧
152 W. 57th St., 56th Fl.
New York, NY 10019-3386

Established in 1997 in NY.
Donor: Mitchell Jacobson.
Foundation type: Independent foundation.
Financial data (yr. ended 12/31/12): Assets, $33,614,306 (M); gifts received, $13,268,850; expenditures, $3,583,356; qualifying distributions, $3,500,134; giving activities include $3,500,134 for 68 grants (high: $1,743,089; low: $100).
Purpose and activities: Giving primarily for higher education, health care, Jewish organizations, and social services.
Fields of interest: Higher education; Hospitals (general); Health care; Medical research, institute; Human services; Foundations (private grantmaking); Jewish federated giving programs; Jewish agencies & synagogues.
Limitations: Applications not accepted. Giving primarily in New York, NY. No grants to individuals.
Application information: Contributes only to pre-selected organizations.
Officers and Directors:* Kathy Howard Jacobson,* Pres.; Erik Gershwind,* V.P.; Mitchell Jacobson,* V.P.; J. Robert Small, Secy.-Treas.
EIN: 133922461

6220
Richard & Natalie Jacoff Foundation, Inc. ✧
c/o Brown Rudnick, LLP
7 Times Sq., 46th Fl.
New York, NY 10036-6536

Established in 1985 in NY.
Donors: Richard Jacoff†; Natalie Jacoff.
Foundation type: Independent foundation.
Financial data (yr. ended 12/31/13): Assets, $12,869,255 (M); expenditures, $1,024,289; qualifying distributions, $979,500; giving activities include $979,500 for 55 grants (high: $100,000; low: $1,000).
Fields of interest: Museums; Arts; Higher education; Higher education, college; Hospitals (general); Health care; Medical research, institute; Cancer research; Food services; Food banks; Human services; Military/veterans' organizations.
Type of support: General/operating support.
Limitations: Applications not accepted. Giving primarily in MA and NY. No grants to individuals.
Application information: Contributes only to pre-selected organizations.
Officers and Directors:* Rachel Mildred Jacoff,* Pres.; Kenneth R. Asher,* V.P. and Secy.; Steven F. Wasserman.
EIN: 133316233
Selected grants: The following grants are a representative sample of this grantmaker's funding activity:
$20,000 to American Academy in Rome, New York, NY, 2011.
$20,000 to Dana-Farber Cancer Institute, Boston, MA, 2011.
$20,000 to Doctors Without Borders USA, New York, NY, 2011.
$20,000 to Greater Boston Food Bank, Boston, MA, 2011.
$20,000 to Massachusetts Soldiers Legacy Fund, Amherst, MA, 2011.
$20,000 to National Military Family Association, Alexandria, VA, 2011.
$20,000 to Pine Street Inn, Boston, MA, 2011.
$20,000 to Rosies Place, Boston, MA, 2011.
$5,000 to Woodrow Wilson National Fellowship Foundation, Princeton, NJ, 2011.
$3,000 to Longy School of Music, Cambridge, MA, 2011.

6221
JAF Foundation ✧ ☆
P.O. Box 1307
Southampton, NY 11969-1307

Established in NY.
Donor: Juergen A. Friedrich.
Foundation type: Independent foundation.
Financial data (yr. ended 12/31/13): Assets, $12,064,838 (M); expenditures, $583,133; qualifying distributions, $551,245; giving activities include $536,737 for 6 grants (high: $500,000; low: $5,000).
Purpose and activities: Giving primarily for education, as well as for environmental conservation, and children, youth and social services.
Fields of interest: Education; Environment; Hospitals (general); Human services; Children/youth, services.
Limitations: Applications not accepted. Giving primarily in NY. No grants to individuals.
Application information: Contributes only to pre-selected organizations.
Officers: Juergen A. Friedrich, Pres.; Anke Beck-Friedrich, V.P. and Co-Treas.; Thomas Oplinger, Co-Treas.
Director: Jeffrey Tarrant.
EIN: 200510367

6222
The Rona Jaffe Foundation ✧
21 Wildwood Dr.
Dix Hills, NY 11746-6039

Established in NY.
Donor: Rona F. Jaffe†.
Foundation type: Independent foundation.
Financial data (yr. ended 09/30/13): Assets, $40,549,979 (M); expenditures, $2,916,901; qualifying distributions, $2,372,401; giving activities include $2,051,780 for 81 grants (high: $150,000; low: $1,000), and $180,000 for 6 grants to individuals (high: $30,000; low: $30,000).
Purpose and activities: Giving primarily for health organizations and human services; grant awards also to selected individuals to support their writing.
Fields of interest: Literature; Cancer; Health organizations; Parkinson's disease research; Food distribution, groceries on wheels; Human services; Jewish agencies & synagogues.
Type of support: General/operating support; Grants to individuals.
Limitations: Applications not accepted. Giving on a national basis.
Application information: Unsolicited requests for funds not accepted.
Officers and Trustees:* Robert Wishnew,* Pres. and Treas.; Alan C. Rothfeld, Exec. V.P. and Secy.; Beth McCabe; Marc N. Simon.
EIN: 133383860

6223
The Jaharis Family Foundation, Inc. ✧
499 Park Ave., 23rd Fl.
New York, NY 10022-1240
Contact: Kathryn Jaharis, Pres.

Established in 1986 in FL.
Donors: Michael Jaharis, Jr.; Mary Jaharis; The 1998 Katina Charitable Trust; The 1998 MJ Trust; The 1998 Katina Charitable Trust No. 2.
Foundation type: Independent foundation.
Financial data (yr. ended 09/30/13): Assets, $229,621,808 (M); expenditures, $17,569,398; qualifying distributions, $14,346,665; giving activities include $14,346,665 for 52 grants (high: $2,250,000; low: $2,000).
Fields of interest: Museums; Arts; Higher education; Medical school/education; Education; Hospitals (general); Human services; Orthodox agencies & churches.
Type of support: Building/renovation; Endowments; Scholarship funds; Research; Matching/challenge support.
Limitations: Giving primarily in FL, IL, NY, MA and PA. No grants to individuals.
Application information: Application form not required.
Deadline(s): None
Officers and Directors:* Kathryn Jaharis,* Pres. and Treas.; Pelagia Sotirhos Nicholson, Secy.; Steven K. Aronoff; Kevin Ferro; Mary Jaharis; Michael Jaharis; Steven Jaharis.
EIN: 592751110
Selected grants: The following grants are a representative sample of this grantmaker's funding activity:
$2,100,000 to Haverford College, Haverford, PA, 2012.
$1,250,000 to DePaul University, Chicago, IL, 2012.

$1,000,000 to Art Institute of Chicago, Chicago, IL, 2012.
$1,000,000 to Columbia University, New York, NY, 2012.
$1,000,000 to North Park University, Chicago, IL, 2012.
$510,000 to Orpheon, The Little Orchestra Society, New York, NY, 2012.
$500,000 to Carroll University, Waukesha, WI, 2012.
$429,571 to Metropolitan Opera, New York, NY, 2012.
$200,000 to Archive of Contemporary Music, New York, NY, 2012.
$100,000 to Tufts University, School of Medicine, Medford, MA, 2012. For grant to Medical School in Boston.

6224
JAM Anonymous Foundation, Inc. ✧
(formerly The Dakota Foundation, Inc.)
c/o CAB
950 3rd Ave., 20th Fl.
New York, NY 10022-2705
Application address: c/o Nancy B. Mulheren, Rumson Mgmt., 95 Ave. of Two Rivers, Rumson, NJ 07760-1703, tel.: (732) 450-0488

Established in 1984 in NJ.
Donors: John Mulheren†; Nancy B. Mulheren; John Mulheren, Jr.
Foundation type: Independent foundation.
Financial data (yr. ended 10/31/13): Assets, $54,800 (M); gifts received, $147,240; expenditures, $1,342,641; qualifying distributions, $1,342,221; giving activities include $1,296,841 for 37 grants (high: $525,000; low: $300), and $45,380 for 2 grants to individuals (high: $33,435; low: $11,945).
Purpose and activities: Giving primarily for the arts, education and human services. The foundation also sponsors a college scholarship program which includes tuition, fees, room, and board for 4 years, as long as the student maintains a 2.0 average. In order to be nominated, the student must be a resident of Rumson or Fair Haven, NJ, (at least through the high school years), with average grades from B- to C. The student's financial needs are evidenced by a FAFSA report. The program is searching for "late bloomers" who lack encouragement to attend college, who may have fallen through the cracks or who may have had a life-altering experience, and who are willing to attend college outside of New Jersey.
Fields of interest: Performing arts centers; Higher education; Education; Human services.
Type of support: General/operating support; Scholarships—to individuals.
Limitations: Applications accepted. Giving primarily in NJ; funding also in Salem, VA.
Application information: Application form not required.
Initial approach: Proposal
Deadline(s): None
Officer: Nancy B. Mulheren, Pres.
Trustees: Stephen Cutler; Alexander Mulheren; Michael Walker.
EIN: 222621688

6225
Jana Foundation Inc. ✧
(formerly Aaron H. & Dorothy S. Rubin Foundation)
c/o Alan Seget, Davidson, Dawson, and Clark, LLP
60 E. 42nd St., 38th Fl.
New York, NY 10165-3897

Established in 1970 in NY.
Donors: Andrew Auerbach; Arnold Auerbach; Justine Auerbach†; Nina Auerbach.
Foundation type: Independent foundation.
Financial data (yr. ended 12/31/13): Assets, $25,307,823 (M); expenditures, $1,401,889; qualifying distributions, $1,254,882; giving activities include $1,199,000 for 66+ grants (high: $290,000).
Fields of interest: Arts; Higher education; Health care; Health organizations; Human services; Jewish agencies & synagogues; Women.
Limitations: Applications not accepted. Giving primarily in CT and NY. No grants to individuals.
Application information: Contributes only to pre-selected organizations.
Directors: Nina Auerbach; D. Rosen; A. Seget.
EIN: 133574540

6226
Jandon Foundation ✧
c/o Donald Cecil
3 Stratford Rd.
Harrison, NY 10528-1115 (914) 995-8620
Main URL: http://jandonfoundation.org/
Twitter: https://twitter.com/jandonscholars
Scholarship address: c/o Westchester County Board of Legislators, 148 Maritine Ave., 8th Fl., White Plains, NY 10601; Additional scholarship contact: Anand Singh, Westchester County Board of Legislators, tel.: (914) 995-2016, fax: (914) 995-3884,
e-mail: AnandS@westchesterlegislators.com

Established in 1966 in NY.
Donors: Donald Cecil; Jane Cecil.
Foundation type: Independent foundation.
Financial data (yr. ended 12/31/13): Assets, $14,045,646 (M); gifts received, $670,000; expenditures, $572,344; qualifying distributions, $726,376; giving activities include $377,550 for grants, and $172,941 for grants to individuals.
Purpose and activities: Giving primarily for the arts, education, and youth and social services. Fifteen scholarships are also made to low-income academic achievers who are graduating seniors from a Westchester County, NY, public high school, and will attend a 4-year accredited university and obtain a bachelor's degree.
Fields of interest: Arts; Higher education; Education; Human services; Children/youth, services.
Type of support: Scholarships—to individuals.
Limitations: Giving primarily in Westchester County, NY. No grants for program-related investments; no loans.
Publications: Application guidelines.
Application information: Unsolicited requests for funds not accepted for grants. Refer to foundation web site for scholarship application form and guidelines. Application form required.
Deadline(s): See foundation web site for current scholarship deadline
Officers and Directors:* Donald Cecil,* Pres.; Alec Cecil,* V.P.; Leslie Cecil,* V.P.; Jane Cecil,* Secy.-Treas.; James C. Michael; Diane Zultowsky.
EIN: 136199442
Selected grants: The following grants are a representative sample of this grantmaker's funding activity:
$5,000 to Brown University, Providence, RI, 2012. For charitable and educational.

6227
The JCT Foundation ✧
c/o Jeff C. Tarr
145 Central Park W., Ste. 25C
New York, NY 10023-2004

Established in 1984 in NY.
Donor: Jeff C. Tarr.
Foundation type: Independent foundation.
Financial data (yr. ended 12/31/13): Assets, $16,696,068 (M); gifts received, $203,393; expenditures, $8,610,923; qualifying distributions, $8,574,034; giving activities include $8,570,334 for 79 grants (high: $2,000,000; low: $175).
Fields of interest: Arts; Higher education; Education; Environment, natural resources; Human services.
Limitations: Applications not accepted. Giving primarily in New York, NY. No grants to individuals.
Application information: Contributes only to pre-selected organizations.
Directors: Jeff C. Tarr; Patricia G. Tarr.
Trustees: Jeff Tarr, Jr.; Jennifer Tarr.
EIN: 133237111

6228
Jewish Foundation for Education of Women ✧
135 E. 64 St.
New York, NY 10065-7045 (212) 288-3931
Contact: Elizabeth Leiman Kraiem, Exec. Dir.
FAX: (212) 288-5798; E-mail: info@jfew.org; Main URL: http://www.jfew.org

Incorporated in 1884 in NY as Hebrew Technical School for Girls.
Donors: Erika Rindler Urbach Living Trust; The Betsy and Alan Cohn Foundation; Sonya Cohen Revocable Trust; Lisbeth Jacobs.
Foundation type: Independent foundation.
Financial data (yr. ended 06/30/13): Assets, $75,814,810 (M); gifts received, $54,066; expenditures, $3,325,416; qualifying distributions, $3,208,474; giving activities include $2,495,453 for 28 grants (high: $206,750; low: $4,032), and $205,500 for 33 grants to individuals (high: $10,000; low: $1,500).
Purpose and activities: The foundation is a New York City-based, non-sectarian organization helping women with financial need to meet their educational and career goals through scholarships and opportunities for professional development. In partnership with schools and non-profits, it fosters a community of women dedicated to education, professional achievement and contributing to society.
Fields of interest: Scholarships/financial aid; Women.
Type of support: Fellowships.
Limitations: Applications accepted. Giving limited to scholarships and related programming for female

citizens and permanent residents with demonstrated financial need. The foundation has a strong preference for those living within the lower 8 counties of NY State. No grants for general support, operating budgets, capital or endowment funds, matching gifts, research, special projects, publications, or conferences.
Publications: Newsletter.
Application information: The foundation will consider letters of inquiry for scholarship programs at the Associates, Bachelors and Graduate levels in the following areas: Health Professions; Math, Science and Technology; Aging Society; Public and Communal Service. Letters of inquiry may be up to three pages, plus a budget. They should take into account the characteristics of our programs and include the following information: Selection criteria and process for intended scholarship recipients, which should be consistent with JFEW's eligibility requirements and include a minimum GPA of at least 3.0; Graduation rates of students with these criteria; Job placement rates of students who graduate with these criteria; Profiles of typical students in the program and examples of what they do when they graduate; How the program will create a cohort of scholarship recipients; Proposed programming, summer internships or supportive services for the cohort and how this will contribute to student growth and development; Method of program evaluation. Application information available on foundation web site. Application form not required.
Initial approach: Letter
Copies of proposal: 1
Deadline(s): See foundation web site for current deadline
Board meeting date(s): Quarterly
Final notification: By Jan. 31
Officers and Directors:* Sharon L. Weinberg,* Chair.; Jill W. Smith,* Pres.; Phyllis Korff,* V.P.; Lisa C. Liman,* Secy.; Harold J. Levy, Treas.; Elizabeth Leiman Kraiem, Exec. Dir.; Neil R. Grabois, Dir. Emeritus; Alan R. Kahn, Dir. Emeritus; Irving Kahn, Dir. Emeritus; Ruth Messinger, Dir. Emeritus; James Wood, Dir. Emeritus; Jean G. Bronstein; Alan D. Cohn; Marcia Goldsmith; Suzanne H. Keusch; Reeva S. Mager; Louise Mirrer; Marcy Russo; Susan Schatz; Marion Spanbock; Ann Tanenbaum; Andrew Vogelstein; David Weiner.
Number of staff: 1 full-time professional; 1 full-time support.
EIN: 131860415

6229
Jewish Spirit, Inc. ✧
1531 58th St.
Brooklyn, NY 11219-4748

Donors: Yehuda Akerman; Ahron Eber; Meir Levin; American Friends Of Heritage, Inc.; Arevim Philanthropic Group; National Society Of Hebrew Day Schools; Kolisaus Associated; AFIKIM; World Zionist Organization; Zvi Ryzman; Avshalom Baskin; David Hager Foundation; Maharal Institute; Meir Eronfroind; Bronxwood Home for the Aged Inc.; Robert de Rothchild; Robert Deutch Petery Sanders; Paul Singer; Robby Moyal Zohara Joelle; Thermofoil Doors Inc.
Foundation type: Independent foundation.
Financial data (yr. ended 12/31/13): Assets, $66,893 (M); gifts received, $1,225,007; expenditures, $1,177,056; qualifying distributions, $1,134,388; giving activities include $1,134,388 for 11 grants (high: $475,127; low: $30,000).
Fields of interest: Jewish agencies & synagogues.
Limitations: Applications not accepted. Giving primarily in Jerusalem, Israel; some giving also in Hallandale, FL.
Application information: Contributes only to pre-selected organizations.
Officers: Zev Oratz, Pres.; Isaac Mordecai Bukowsky, Secy.; Shlomo Kushelevsky, Treas.
EIN: 264037735

6230
Yibing and Ping Jiang Foundation ✧ ☆
c/o Schiff Hardin LLP
666 5th Ave., Ste. 1700
New York, NY 10103-0001

Established in 2006 in NY.
Donors: Ping Jiang; Yibing Guan.
Foundation type: Independent foundation.
Financial data (yr. ended 12/31/13): Assets, $12,725,620 (M); gifts received, $600,000; expenditures, $1,245,153; qualifying distributions, $1,245,153; giving activities include $1,182,800 for 5 grants (high: $1,060,000; low: $300).
Fields of interest: Arts; Education.
International interests: China.
Limitations: Applications not accepted. Giving primarily in MN and NY; with some giving in Jiangsu, China. No grants to individuals.
Application information: Contributes only to pre-selected organizations.
Officers: Ping Jiang, Pres.; Yibing Guan, V.P. and Secy.
EIN: 205945642

6231
JJR Foundation ✧
c/o Eisneramper LLP
750 3rd Ave., 16th Fl.
New York, NY 10017

Established in 1993 in NY.
Donors: Joshua Ruch; Habib Kairouz; Human Genome Sciences NY Inc.; Millenium Pharmaceuticals; Shire Pharmaceuticals.
Foundation type: Independent foundation.
Financial data (yr. ended 09/30/13): Assets, $13,067,452 (L); gifts received, $397,435; expenditures, $562,014; qualifying distributions, $544,337; giving activities include $538,785 for 2 grants (high: $518,785; low: $20,000).
Fields of interest: Jewish federated giving programs.
Limitations: Applications not accepted. Giving primarily in New York, NY. No grants to individuals.
Application information: Contributes only to pre-selected organizations.
Trustees: Joshua Ruch; Julia M. Ruch.
EIN: 133740793

6232
The Joelson Foundation ✧
1841 Broadway, Ste. 1008
New York, NY 10023-7646
Contact: Barbara J. Fife, Pres.; Lynn M. Argenziano, Admin.

Established in 1966 in NY.
Donors: Julius Joelson†; Grt. Grand Charitable Remainder Unitrust; K. Campbell Charitable Remainder Trust.
Foundation type: Independent foundation.
Financial data (yr. ended 03/31/13): Assets, $19,468,800 (M); gifts received, $86,275; expenditures, $1,329,219; qualifying distributions, $1,208,426; giving activities include $923,881 for 200 grants (high: $50,000; low: $72).
Purpose and activities: Giving primarily for the arts, with emphasis on the performing arts, health, education, and social services; giving also to Jewish organizations.
Fields of interest: Museums; Performing arts; Performing arts, theater; Arts; Higher education; Education; Environment, natural resources; Health care; Human services; Children/youth, services; Jewish federated giving programs; Jewish agencies & synagogues.
Type of support: Matching/challenge support; General/operating support; Continuing support; Capital campaigns; Annual campaigns.
Limitations: Applications not accepted. Giving primarily in New York, NY; some funding also in CA and MA. No grants to individuals.
Application information: Contributes only to pre-selected organizations.
Officers: Barbara J. Fife, Pres.; Joseph C. Mitchell, Secy.-Treas.
Directors: Andrew Fife; Howard Fife; Richard Fife; Stephen Fife; Evelyn Segal Lipton; Margaret Segal; Rosalind Segal.
EIN: 136220799

6233
The 1994 Elizabeth R. Johnson Charitable Trust ✧
c/o Cohnreznick
1212 Avenue of the Americas
New York, NY 10036-1602

Established in 1994 in NY.
Donor: Elizabeth Ross Johnson.
Foundation type: Independent foundation.
Financial data (yr. ended 12/31/12): Assets, $7,252,989 (M); expenditures, $610,530; qualifying distributions, $600,000; giving activities include $600,000 for 5 grants (high: $250,000; low: $50,000).
Purpose and activities: Giving primarily for children and social services, including U.S.-based organizations which support programs in Cambodia.
Fields of interest: Museums (art); Higher education, college; Education; Environment; Animal welfare; Alzheimer's disease; Human services; Children/youth, services; Children.
International interests: Cambodia.
Limitations: Applications not accepted. Giving primarily in Chicago, IL and New York, NY. No grants to individuals.
Application information: Contributes only to pre-selected organizations.
Trustees: Betty Wold Johnson; Elizabeth Ross Johnson.
EIN: 137046313
Selected grants: The following grants are a representative sample of this grantmaker's funding activity:
$50,000 to Intrepid Fallen Heroes Fund, New York, NY, 2012. For public affairs.

6234
The 1994 Christopher W. Johnson Charitable Trust No. 33 ✧
(formerly The Christopher W. Johnson Charitable Trust)
c/o The Johnson Co., Inc.
610 5th Ave., 2nd Fl.
New York, NY 10020-0100

Established in 1994 in NY.
Donors: Betty W. Johnson; Christopher W. Johnson.
Foundation type: Independent foundation.
Financial data (yr. ended 12/31/13): Assets, $11,912,684 (M); expenditures, $461,670; qualifying distributions, $441,450; giving activities include $440,000 for 2 grants (high: $250,000; low: $190,000).
Fields of interest: Children/youth, services.
Limitations: Applications not accepted. Giving primarily in Austin, TX; some funding also in New York, NY. No grants to individuals.
Application information: Unsolicited requests for funds not accepted.
Trustees: Betty W. Johnson; Christopher W. Johnson.
EIN: 137046311

6235
Christian A. Johnson Endeavor Foundation ✧
1060 Park Ave.
New York, NY 10128-1033
Contact: Julie J. Kidd, Pres.

Incorporated in 1952 in NY.
Donors: Christian A. Johnson‡; Charlotte Johnson Charitable Lead Trust.
Foundation type: Independent foundation.
Financial data (yr. ended 12/31/13): Assets, $214,030,415 (M); expenditures, $9,818,071; qualifying distributions, $9,294,970; giving activities include $7,558,321 for 64 grants (high: $3,000,000; low: $500).
Purpose and activities: Giving concentrated on private institutions of higher learning at the baccalaureate level in the United States and Europe and performing arts organizations in New York City; occasional support for perceived needs in other areas of education and the arts.
Fields of interest: Arts; Higher education; Education.
International interests: Europe.
Type of support: General/operating support; Program development; Seed money; Curriculum development; Matching/challenge support.
Limitations: Applications accepted. Giving primarily in the U.S. and Central and Eastern Europe. Generally, no support for government agencies, or for community or neighborhood projects, religious institutions, or for health care. Generally, no grants to individuals, or for annual campaigns, emergency funds, deficit financing, land acquisitions, building projects, medical research; no loans (except for program-related investments).
Publications: Application guidelines; Financial statement; Program policy statement.
Application information: Application form not required.
Initial approach: Letter of inquiry
Copies of proposal: 1
Board meeting date(s): Spring

Officers and Trustees:* Julie J. Kidd,* Pres. and Treas.; Christen L. Kidd, Secy.; Donald W. Harward; Ann B. Spence.
Number of staff: 3 full-time professional; 1 full-time support.
EIN: 136147952
Selected grants: The following grants are a representative sample of this grantmaker's funding activity:
$3,000,000 to Bard College, Annandale on Hudson, NY, 2013. For general operating support.
$1,042,000 to Bard College, Annandale on Hudson, NY, 2013. For general operating support.
$479,722 to Bratislava International School of Liberal Arts, Bratislava, Slovenia, 2013. To repurchase garden property.
$460,851 to Bratislava International School of Liberal Arts, Bratislava, Slovenia, 2013. For general operating support.
$85,175 to Great Lakes Colleges Association, Ann Arbor, MI, 2013. For Global Liberal Arts Alliance courses.
$58,000 to Franklin and Marshall College, Lancaster, PA, 2013. For Writing Across the Curriculum.
$51,113 to National Humanities Center, Research Triangle Park, NC, 2013. For education programs expansion.
$50,000 to San Francisco Film Society, San Francisco, CA, 2013. For Nuclear Documentary Outreach Campaign.
$25,000 to W N Y C Radio, New York, NY, 2013. For Superstorm Sandy Coverage.
$25,000 to Wells College, Aurora, NY, 2013. For Lisa Marsh Ryerson '81 Presidential Fund for Student Success.

6236
The Jane Botsford Johnson Foundation ✧
c/o The Johnson Company, Inc.
610 5th Ave., 2nd Fl.
New York, NY 10020-2403

Foundation type: Independent foundation.
Financial data (yr. ended 12/31/13): Assets, $3,946,113 (M); expenditures, $2,888,909; qualifying distributions, $2,858,914; giving activities include $2,856,858 for 9 grants (high: $822,140; low: $20,000).
Fields of interest: Education; Health care.
Limitations: Applications not accepted. Giving primarily in AR, CA, DE, MA, NC, and TX.
Application information: Contributes only to pre-selected organizations.
Officers: Jane Botsford Johnson, Pres.; Ira Akselrad, V.P. and Secy.; Kenneth J. Drummond, V.P.; Christopher W. Johnson, V.P.; Joel Latman, Treas.
EIN: 264227067

6237
Suzanne M. Nora Johnson and David G. Johnson Foundation ✧
Bowling Green Sta.
P.O. Box 73
New York, NY 10274-0073

Established in 1993 in NY and CA.
Donor: Suzanne M. Nora Johnson.
Foundation type: Independent foundation.
Financial data (yr. ended 01/31/13): Assets, $10,215,216 (M); gifts received, $1,402,723; expenditures, $2,283,135; qualifying distributions, $2,245,339; giving activities include $2,245,339 for 117 grants (high: $800,000; low: $14).
Fields of interest: Museums (art); Higher education; Education; Health organizations, association; Human services; American Red Cross; Public affairs, association; Government/public administration; Catholic agencies & churches.
Limitations: Applications not accepted. Giving primarily in CA, NY, and Washington, DC. No grants to individuals; no loans.
Application information: Contributes only to pre-selected organizations.
Trustees: David G. Johnson; Suzanne M. Nora Johnson.
EIN: 133748062
Selected grants: The following grants are a representative sample of this grantmaker's funding activity:
$800,000 to Brookings Institution, Washington, DC, 2011. For general charitable purposes.
$400,000 to Museum of Contemporary Art, Los Angeles, CA, 2011. For general charitable purposes.
$125,000 to Yale University, New Haven, CT, 2011. For general charitable purposes.
$100,000 to Carnegie Institution of Washington, Washington, DC, 2011. For general charitable purposes.
$75,000 to Public Counsel, Los Angeles, CA, 2011. For general charitable purposes.
$75,000 to TechnoServe, Washington, DC, 2011. For general charitable purposes.
$35,000 to Council on Foreign Relations, New York, NY, 2011. For general charitable purposes.
$25,000 to Aspen Institute, Washington, DC, 2011. For general charitable purposes.
$25,000 to Dream Foundation, Santa Barbara, CA, 2011. For general charitable purposes.
$25,000 to RAND Corporation, Santa Monica, CA, 2011. For general charitable purposes.

6238
The Johnson Foundation ✧
17 Christopher St.
New York, NY 10014-3518

Established in 1992 in NY and DE.
Donors: Peter James Johnson, Sr.; Peter James Johnson, Jr.; Aaron Seligson.
Foundation type: Independent foundation.
Financial data (yr. ended 06/30/13): Assets, $6,772,368 (M); gifts received, $37,710; expenditures, $437,365; qualifying distributions, $427,244; giving activities include $424,000 for 18 grants (high: $100,000; low: $500).
Fields of interest: Education; Human services; Catholic agencies & churches.
Type of support: General/operating support; Continuing support; Research.
Limitations: Applications not accepted. Giving primarily in NY. No grants to individuals.
Application information: Unsolicited requests for funds not accepted.
Officers and Directors:* Christopher Johnson,* Chair. and Pres.; Peter James Johnson, Jr.,* V.P. and Secy.; Veronica Johnson,* Treas.; Blanche A. Johnson; Veronica F. Johnson.
EIN: 133696561
Selected grants: The following grants are a representative sample of this grantmaker's funding activity:
$100,000 to Archdiocese of New York, New York, NY, 2011.

$28,000 to Marymount School, New York, NY, 2011.
$26,000 to Pepperdine University, Malibu, CA, 2011.
$25,000 to Alfred E. Smith Memorial Foundation, New York, NY, 2011.
$10,000 to Brigham and Women's Hospital, Boston, MA, 2011.
$10,000 to New York Downtown Hospital, New York, NY, 2011.
$10,000 to Young Womens Leadership Foundation, New York, NY, 2011.
$5,000 to Horatio Alger Association of Distinguished Americans, Alexandria, VA, 2011.
$5,000 to New-York Historical Society, New York, NY, 2011.
$5,000 to Saint Josephs Church, New York, NY, 2011.

6239
The Thomas Phillips and Jane Moore Johnson Foundation
(also known as Johnson Family Foundation)
55 Exchange Pl., Ste. 404
New York, NY 10005-2035 (212) 343-1102
Contact: Andrew Lane, Exec. Dir.; Samantha Franklin, Prog. Off.
Main URL: http://www.jffnd.org
Facebook: https://www.facebook.com/pages/Johnson-Family-Foundation/222004264480124
Twitter: https://twitter.com/JohnsonFamFound

Established in 1990 in PA.
Donors: Thomas Phillips Johnson, Sr.†; Thomas Phillips Johnson, Jr.; James Moore Johnson.
Foundation type: Independent foundation.
Financial data (yr. ended 12/31/13): Assets, $83,744,205 (M); expenditures, $4,088,223; qualifying distributions, $3,742,814; giving activities include $3,000,000 for 53 grants (high: $380,000; low: $10,000).
Purpose and activities: Giving for the development of healthy, vibrant and just communities where individuals, families and the next generation of leaders will thrive. The foundation funds programs to improve the health of our environment; promote equality and social progress; and support education and youth. Its grantmaking is place-based and, in environmental health and LGBT issues, national in scope.
Fields of interest: Arts; Education; Environmental education; Environment; Human services; Civil/human rights, LGBTQ; Public affairs; Children/youth; Youth; Adults; Adults, women; Economically disadvantaged; LGBTQ.
Type of support: Annual campaigns; Continuing support; General/operating support; Management development/capacity building; Matching/challenge support; Program development; Program evaluation; Publication; Research.
Limitations: Applications not accepted. Giving on a national basis; with emphasis on New York City, NY and VT. No grants to individuals.
Publications: Grants list.
Application information: Unsolicited requests for funds not accepted.
Board meeting date(s): Jan. and Aug.
Officers and Trustees:* Thomas P. Johnson, Jr.,* Pres.; James M. Johnson,* Chair.; Asa J. Johnson,* Secy.; Jesse D. Johnson,* Treas.; Andrew Lane, Exec. Dir.
Number of staff: 2 full-time professional.
EIN: 256357015

6240
Willard T. C. Johnson Foundation, Inc. ✧
c/o The Johnson Company, Inc.
610 5th Ave., 2nd Fl.
New York, NY 10020-2403 (212) 891-4087
Contact: Robert W. Johnson IV, Pres.

Incorporated in 1979 in NY.
Donors: Willard T.C. Johnson†; Keith W. Johnson†.
Foundation type: Independent foundation.
Financial data (yr. ended 12/31/13): Assets, $57,827,262 (M); expenditures, $2,222,616; qualifying distributions, $2,051,441; giving activities include $2,041,250 for 12 grants (high: $450,000; low: $25,000).
Fields of interest: Museums; Higher education; Hospitals (general); Hospitals (specialty); Cancer; Medical research, institute; Lupus research; Human services.
Limitations: Applications accepted. Giving primarily in NJ and NY. No grants to individuals.
Application information: Application form not required.
Deadline(s): None
Officers and Directors:* Betty W. Johnson,* Chair.; Robert W. Johnson IV,* Pres.; Christopher W. Johnson,* V.P. and Secy.-Treas.
EIN: 132993310

6241
The Johnson Street Foundation ✧ ☆
c/o Leonard Orr
850 7th Ave., Ste. 701
New York, NY 10019-4642

Established in 2007 in NY.
Donors: Elizabeth B. Orr; Leonard Orr; Elizabeth Buckner.
Foundation type: Independent foundation.
Financial data (yr. ended 12/31/13): Assets, $10,699,548 (M); expenditures, $2,019,681; qualifying distributions, $1,979,909; giving activities include $1,766,983 for 20 grants (high: $177,867; low: $25,000).
Fields of interest: Health care; Human services.
Limitations: Applications not accepted. Giving primarily in NY.
Application information: Unsolicited requests for funds not accepted.
Officer: Frank Wolf, Exec. Dir.
Directors: Elizabeth Buckner; Leonard Orr.
EIN: 137579596

6242
Daisy Marquis Jones Foundation ✧
1600 South Ave., Ste. 250
Rochester, NY 14620-3921 (585) 461-4950
Contact: Donald W. Whitney, Pres.
FAX: (585) 461-9752; E-mail: mail@dmjf.org; Main URL: http://www.dmjf.org

Established in 1968 in NY.
Donors: Daisy Marquis Jones†; Leo M. Lyons†.
Foundation type: Independent foundation.
Financial data (yr. ended 12/31/13): Assets, $53,426,095 (M); gifts received, $40,000; expenditures, $2,292,510; qualifying distributions, $2,201,628; giving activities include $1,825,120 for grants.
Purpose and activities: The foundation's mission is to improve the well-being of residents of Yates and Monroe Counties, NY, and of the City of Rochester, in particular. A central concern is disadvantaged children and families, and the neighborhoods in which they live. The foundation believes that it can best serve those in need by granting time-limited support to nonprofit organizations with programs or projects that provide access to health care, attend to the needs of young children and senior citizens or help families develop economic security. The foundation also looks for programs that: give people the tools they need to help themselves; encourage collaboration among agencies and between individuals and agencies; have measurable outcomes; make long-term commitments to specific neighborhoods.
Fields of interest: Education, early childhood education; Children, services; Community/economic development; Public affairs; Children/youth; Aging; Women; Economically disadvantaged.
Type of support: General/operating support; Building/renovation; Program development; Technical assistance; Matching/challenge support.
Limitations: Applications accepted. Giving limited to Monroe and Yates counties, NY, with emphasis on Rochester. No support for the arts, religious purposes, private schools, local chapters of national health-related organizations, or private foundations. No grants to individuals, or for endowment funds, research, scholarships, fellowships, or annual campaigns.
Publications: Application guidelines; Annual report; Annual report (including application guidelines); Grants list.
Application information: The foundation accepts the Grantmakers Forum of New York Common Application Form which is available on the foundation's web site, as are the application guidelines and procedures. Application form required.
Initial approach: Letter of inquiry, or visit foundation web site for inquiry form
Copies of proposal: 1
Deadline(s): None
Board meeting date(s): Monthly (except July and Aug.)
Final notification: 2 to 3 months
Officer and Trustees:* Donald W. Whitney,* Pres.; Roger L. Gardner; C. John Matteson.
Number of staff: 1 full-time professional; 1 full-time support.
EIN: 237000227

6243
The JPB Foundation ✧
9 W. 57th St., 38th Fl.
New York, NY 10019-2701
Contact: Sonia Mohan, Dir. Admin. and Opers.
Main URL: http://jpbfoundation.org/

Donor: Jeffrey M. Picower†.
Foundation type: Independent foundation.
Financial data (yr. ended 12/31/13): Assets, $2,318,642,200 (M); gifts received, $1,185,300,750; expenditures, $93,866,862; qualifying distributions, $84,760,654; giving activities include $78,051,333 for 120 grants (high: $6,100,000; low: $1,000).
Purpose and activities: The mission of the foundation is to enhance the quality of life in the United States through transformational initiatives that promote the health of our communities by creating opportunities for those living in poverty,

enabling pioneering medical research, and enriching and sustaining our environment.
Fields of interest: Environment; Medical research; Economically disadvantaged.
Limitations: Applications not accepted. Giving on a national basis.
Application information: Contributes only to pre-selected organizations.
Officers and Trustees:* Barbara Picower,* Chair. and Pres.; April C. Freilich,* C.O.O.; Gerald McNamara,* C.I.O.; Susan C. Frunzi; Joshua Henri Hochschuler; Martin R. Post; William D. Zabel.
EIN: 900747216
Selected grants: The following grants are a representative sample of this grantmaker's funding activity:
$4,300,000 to Harlem Childrens Zone, New York, NY, 2012. For Harlem Children's Zone Healthy Living Initiative.
$3,000,000 to Planned Parenthood Federation of America, New York, NY, 2012. For Breast Southern Access Project.
$2,500,000 to Public Interest Projects, New York, NY, 2012. For General Operating Support for the Four Freedoms Fund.
$1,000,000 to Immigrant Legal Resource Center, San Francisco, CA, 2012. For the New Americans Collaboration.
$975,000 to Northwestern University, Feinberg School of Medicine, Department of Physiology, Evanston, IL, 2012. For Molecular and Cellular Mechanisms of Parkinson's Disease.
$700,000 to Johns Hopkins University, School of Medicine, Baltimore, MD, 2012. For Characterization of the Parkin/PINK/PARIS Pathway of Neurodegeneration in Parkinson's Disease.
$646,387 to University of Michigan, Ann Arbor, MI, 2012. For the University's Center for Managing Chronic Disease's Accelerating Team Impact.
$579,724 to Guttmacher Institute, New York, NY, 2012. For Identifying Pathways to Improve Contraceptive Use. A Longitudinal Study.
$504,835 to Center for American Progress, Washington, DC, 2012. For the Our Future, Together Initiative.
$75,000 to Community Funds, New York, NY, 2012. For Donor Advised Fund.

6244
The JPMorgan Chase Foundation ✧
(formerly The Chase Manhattan Foundation)
270 Park Ave., 4th Fl.
New York, NY 10017-2014 (212) 270-0471
E-mail address for regional contacts: Africa, Europe, and the Middle East: bi.x.amosu@jpmorgan.com; Argentina: Maria.S.Urribarri@jpmchase.com; Asia and
Pacific: apac.corporate.responsibility@jpmorgan.com; Brazil: rentata.biselli@jpmorgan.com;
Canada: renee.l.tremblay@jpmorgan.com;
Chile: alejandra.x.gallo@jpmorgan.com;
Colombia: ximena.cardenas@jpmorgan.com and andrea.valero@jpmchase.com;
Mexico: olivia.zubieta@jpmorgan.com; Multi-Region and Latin
America: David.A.Goldberg@jpmchase.com; and Peru: karla.a.stammer@jpmorgan.com; Main URL: http://www.jpmorganchase.com/corporate/Corporate-Responsibility/corporate-philanthropy.htm

Incorporated in 1969 in NY; name changed in 2001 as a result of the merger of Chase Manhattan Corp. with J.P. Morgan & Co. Inc.
Donors: The Chase Manhattan Bank; JPMorgan Chase Bank, N.A.; Chatham Ventures, Inc.; CMRCC, Inc.; Chemical Investments, Inc.; Bank One Investment Corp.
Foundation type: Company-sponsored foundation.
Financial data (yr. ended 12/31/12): Assets, $328,377,669 (M); gifts received, $169,958,084; expenditures, $116,731,589; qualifying distributions, $115,541,284; giving activities include $115,516,001 for 9,096 grants (high: $2,370,000; low: $1).
Purpose and activities: The foundation supports programs designed to promote affordable housing; economic growth and workforce readiness; and financial capability. Special emphasis is directed toward neighborhoods located in areas of JPMorgan Chase's major operations.
Fields of interest: Arts education; Museums; Museums (art); Arts; Education, reform; Elementary/secondary education; Higher education; Teacher school/education; Adult/continuing education; Education, services; Education, reading; Education; Employment, services; Employment, training; Employment; Food services; Housing/shelter, development; Housing/shelter, home owners; Housing/shelter; Youth development; YM/YWCAs & YM/YWHAs; Children/youth, services; Family services; Human services, financial counseling; Community development, neighborhood development; Economic development; Urban/community development; Community development, small businesses; Microfinance/microlending; Community/economic development; Financial services; Leadership development; Public affairs; Economically disadvantaged.
Type of support: General/operating support; Continuing support; Management development/capacity building; Building/renovation; Program development; Conferences/seminars; Curriculum development; Technical assistance; Employee volunteer services; Sponsorships; Program-related investments/loans; Employee matching gifts.
Limitations: Applications accepted. Giving in areas of company operations in AZ, CA, CO, Fairfield and New Haven, CT, Washington, DC, DE, FL, Atlanta, GA, ID, IL, IN, KY, LA, Boston, MA, MI, MN, St. Louis and Springfield, MO, NJ, NV, OH, OK, OR, Philadelphia, PA, TX, UT, WA, WI, and WV, with emphasis on NY; giving also to U.S.-based international organizations active in areas of company operations abroad in Africa, Argentina, Asia, Brazil, Canada, Chile, Columbia, Europe, Latin America, Mexico, the Middle East, and Peru. No support for religious, fraternal, social, or other membership organizations not of direct benefit to the entire community, athletic teams, health or medical-related organizations, discriminatory organizations, parent teacher associations, private schools, public agencies, or volunteer operated organizations. No grants to individuals, or for capital campaigns or endowments, scholarships or tuition assistance, advertising, fundraising, or debt reduction.
Publications: Application guidelines; Corporate giving report; Newsletter.
Application information: A full proposal may be requested at a later date. Grants are administered by Community Relations Officers in each market region. Please visit website for regional contact information. Unsolicited applications from organizations in Europe, the Middle East, and Africa are currently not accepted. Application form required.
Initial approach: Complete online letter of inquiry form; non-U.S.-based organizations should e-mail a short preliminary proposal to regional grants coordinator
Deadline(s): None
Officers: Bruce McNamer, C.E.O.; Dalila Wilson-Scott, Pres.
EIN: 237049738
Selected grants: The following grants are a representative sample of this grantmaker's funding activity:
$2,370,000 to American Red Cross of Greater Columbus, Columbus, OH, 2012. For program support.
$1,925,000 to Seattle Art Museum, Seattle, WA, 2012. For program support.
$1,840,000 to Local Initiatives Support Corporation, New York, NY, 2012. For program support.
$1,330,000 to Enterprise Community Partners, Columbia, MD, 2012. For program support.
$870,000 to City Year, Wilmington, DE, 2012. For program support.
$550,000 to United Way of New York City, New York, NY, 2012. For program support.
$50,000 to Associacao Ubadora Social Gastromotiva, Sao Paulo, Brazil, 2012. For program support.
$40,000 to Kingsborough Community College Foundation, Brooklyn, NY, 2012. For program support.
$30,000 to YWCA of Fort Worth and Tarrant County, Fort Worth, TX, 2012. For program support.

6245
The JVZ Foundation ✧
c/o James C. Zelter
45 E. 82nd St., Ste. 8E
New York, NY 10028

Established in 2007 in NY.
Donors: James C. Zelter; Vivian Zelter.
Foundation type: Independent foundation.
Financial data (yr. ended 12/31/13): Assets, $1,018,789 (M); gifts received, $1,002,343; expenditures, $508,533; qualifying distributions, $505,160; giving activities include $154,461 for 23 grants (high: $50,000; low: $360).
Fields of interest: Elementary/secondary education; Higher education.
Limitations: Applications not accepted. No grants to individuals.
Application information: Unsolicited requests for funds not accepted.
Trustees: James C. Zelter; Vivian Zelter.
EIN: 208042292

6246
K.W. Charitable Foundation ✧
4706 18th Ave.
Brooklyn, NY 11204-1260

Established in 1998 in NY.
Donors: Robert Wolf; Wolf Family Trust.
Foundation type: Independent foundation.
Financial data (yr. ended 12/31/12): Assets, $11,908,123 (M); gifts received, $1,850,000; expenditures, $847,196; qualifying distributions,

$821,727; giving activities include $821,727 for grants.
Fields of interest: Jewish agencies & synagogues.
Limitations: Applications not accepted. No grants to individuals.
Application information: Contributes only to pre-selected organizations.
Trustee: Robert Wolf.
EIN: 113366771

6247
Max Kade Foundation, Inc. ✧
6 E. 87th St., 5th Fl.
New York, NY 10128-0505 (646) 672-4354
Contact: Lya Friedrich Pfeifer J.D., Pres. and Treas.
Main URL: http://www.maxkadefoundation.org

Incorporated in 1944 in NY.
Donor: Max Kade†.
Foundation type: Independent foundation.
Financial data (yr. ended 12/31/12): Assets, $87,533,520 (M); expenditures, $5,795,414; qualifying distributions, $5,769,756; giving activities include $5,146,332 for 201 grants (high: $300,000; low: $1,000).
Purpose and activities: The foundation promotes Germanic studies and transatlantic exchange through the support of existing programs and new indicatives related to German studies which encourage a positive relationship between German-speaking countries and the U.S. The foundation supports initiatives which promote international understanding by sponsoring exchange programs between Germany, Austria and the U.S. such as post-doctoral research exchange programs, visiting faculty exchange programs, and exchange programs of undergraduate and graduate students both in the U.S. and abroad.
Fields of interest: Language/linguistics; Literature; Higher education; Biomedicine; Medical research, institute; Physical/earth sciences; Chemistry; Engineering; Biology/life sciences.
International interests: Austria; Europe; Germany.
Type of support: Program development; Professorships; Exchange programs.
Limitations: Applications accepted. Giving primarily in the U.S. and Europe. No grants to individuals, or for operating budgets, capital funds, development campaigns, or endowment funds; no loans.
Publications: Application guidelines; Occasional report.
Application information: Larger grant proposals will be submitted for approval to the board of directors. E-mail submissions not accepted.
Initial approach: Letter or proposal
Deadline(s): None
Board meeting date(s): Bi-annually
Officers and Directors:* Lya Friedrich Pfeifer,* Pres. and Treas.; Berteline Baier Dale,* Secy.; Reinhard Augustin; Guenter Blobel; Fritz Kade, Jr., M.D.
Number of staff: 4 full-time professional.
EIN: 135658082

6248
Kadrovach/Duckworth Family Foundation ✧
c/o BCRS Assocs., LLC
77 Water St., 9th Fl.
New York, NY 10005-4401
Contact: Connie K. Duckworth
GiveSmart: http://www.givesmart.org/Stories/Donors/Connie-K—Duckworth

Established in 1991 in IL.
Donor: Connie K. Duckworth.
Foundation type: Independent foundation.
Financial data (yr. ended 02/28/13): Assets, $10,782,257 (M); expenditures, $571,488; qualifying distributions, $478,207; giving activities include $474,000 for 22 grants (high: $100,000; low: $500).
Fields of interest: Education; Health care; Human services.
Limitations: Applications not accepted. Giving primarily in IL; some funding also in CA, NY and PA. No grants to individuals; no loans or scholarships.
Application information: Contributes only to pre-selected organizations.
Trustees: Connie K. Duckworth; Thomas J. Duckworth; David B. Ford.
EIN: 133634387
Selected grants: The following grants are a representative sample of this grantmaker's funding activity:
$75,000 to Global Heritage Fund, Palo Alto, CA, 2011.
$72,500 to University of Pennsylvania, Philadelphia, PA, 2011.
$55,000 to Church of the Holy Spirit, Lake Forest, IL, 2011.
$50,000 to Arzu, Inc., Chicago, IL, 2011.
$50,000 to Global Heritage Fund, Palo Alto, CA, 2011.
$50,000 to Lake Forest Academy, Lake Forest, IL, 2011.
$40,000 to Lake Forest Open Lands Association, Lake Forest, IL, 2011.
$25,000 to Claremont McKenna College, Claremont, CA, 2011.
$25,000 to Global Heritage Fund, Palo Alto, CA, 2011.
$25,000 to Lake Forest Academy, Lake Forest, IL, 2011.

6249
John and Elaine Kanas Family Foundation ✧
c/o Kathleen Hallinan
445 Broadhollow Rd.
Melville, NY 11747-3669
Application address: c/o Capital One Bank, N.A., Attn.: John A. Kanas, Pres., 265 Broadhollow Rd., Melville, NY 11747

Established in 1998 in NY.
Donors: John A. Kanas; Elaine Kanas.
Foundation type: Independent foundation.
Financial data (yr. ended 12/31/12): Assets, $0 (M); gifts received, $1,289,000; expenditures, $5,164,379; qualifying distributions, $5,126,300; giving activities include $5,126,300 for 47 grants (high: $2,000,000; low: $100).
Fields of interest: Secondary school/education; Higher education; Medical school/education; Education; Health organizations; Human services; Christian agencies & churches; Protestant agencies & churches.
Limitations: Giving primarily in NY.
Application information: Application form not required.
Initial approach: Letter
Deadline(s): None
Officers: John A. Kanas, Pres.; Elaine Kanas, V.P.
Directors: Patricia Blake; Kathy Hallinan.
EIN: 113440709

6250
Rita J. and Stanley H. Kaplan Family Foundation, Inc. ✧
866 United Nations Plz., Ste. 306
New York, NY 10017-1822 (212) 688-1047

Incorporated in 1984 in NY.
Donors: Stanley H. Kaplan†; Rita J. Kaplan; The Rita J. and Stanley H. Kaplan Trust; The Rita J. and Stanley H. Kaplan Charitable Lead Unitrust.
Foundation type: Independent foundation.
Financial data (yr. ended 12/31/13): Assets, $26,103,691 (M); gifts received, $44,834; expenditures, $2,018,508; qualifying distributions, $1,791,996; giving activities include $1,532,704 for 129 grants (high: $243,389; low: $100).
Purpose and activities: Support for cultural programs, including music, arts, theater, performing arts, and museums; libraries; medical research and education, including mental illness, AIDS and cancer research; social and family services, including programs for the homeless, children, and women; Jewish giving, including Jewish education; and organizations promoting human rights and pluralism in Israel and the U.S.
Fields of interest: Arts; Theological school/education; Education; Health care; Civil/human rights, advocacy; Jewish federated giving programs; Jewish agencies & synagogues.
Type of support: Annual campaigns; Continuing support; Endowments; Fellowships; General/operating support; Program development; Research; Scholarship funds; Seed money.
Limitations: Applications not accepted. Giving primarily in Boston, MA, and New York, NY; giving also in Israel. No grants to individuals.
Application information: Contributes only to pre-selected organizations.
Board meeting date(s): May, Aug. and Nov.
Officers: Susan Beth Kaplan, Pres.; Nancy Kaplan Belsky, V.P.; Rita J. Kaplan, V.P.; Scott Kaplan Belsky, Secy.-Treas.; Gali Cooks, Exec. Dir.
Number of staff: 2 full-time professional; 1 full-time support.
EIN: 133221298

6251
Robert S. Kaplan Foundation ✧
c/o Goldman Sachs & Co., Family Office
P.O. Box 73
Bowling Green Sta.
New York, NY 10274-0073

Established in 1991 in NY.
Donor: Robert S. Kaplan.
Foundation type: Independent foundation.
Financial data (yr. ended 03/31/13): Assets, $16,859,731 (M); expenditures, $2,043,987; qualifying distributions, $1,983,237; giving activities include $1,983,237 for grants.
Purpose and activities: Giving primarily to Jewish organizations, and for higher and other education, including a Jewish theological seminary; funding also for health and human services.
Fields of interest: Theological school/education; Jewish federated giving programs; Philanthropy/voluntarism; Jewish agencies & synagogues.

Limitations: Applications not accepted. Giving in the U.S., with emphasis on NY; some emphasis also on Lawrence, KS. No grants to individuals; no loans.
Application information: Contributes only to pre-selected organizations.
Trustee: Robert S. Kaplan.
EIN: 133637444

6252
The J. M. Kaplan Fund, Inc. ✧
261 Madison Ave., 19th Fl.
New York, NY 10016-2303 (212) 767-0630
Contact: Angela Carabine, Grants Mgr.
FAX: (212) 767-0639; E-mail: info@jmkfund.org; Application address for Furthermore Grants in Publishing program:, c/o Ann Birckmayer, Prog. Assoc., P.O. Box 667, Hudson, NY 12534; tel.: (518) 828-8900; Main URL: http://www.jmkfund.org

Incorporated in 1948 in NY as Faigel Leah Foundation, Inc.; The J.M. Kaplan Fund, Inc., a DE corporation, merged with it in 1975 and was renamed The J.M. Kaplan Fund, Inc.
Donor: Members of the J.M. Kaplan family.
Foundation type: Independent foundation.
Financial data (yr. ended 12/31/12): Assets, $134,314,281 (M); expenditures, $10,938,592; qualifying distributions, $7,873,165; giving activities include $6,638,149 for 383 grants (high: $280,000; low: $75).
Purpose and activities: Giving primarily in three areas: environment, historic preservation, and human migrations. The fund offers program-related investments to encourage ventures of particular interest. The fund also has a trustee-initiated grants program that considers grant requests invited by the trustees.
Fields of interest: Historic preservation/historical societies; Environment, natural resources; Environment; Human services; International migration/refugee issues; Community/economic development.
Type of support: General/operating support; Continuing support; Program development; Publication; Seed money; Research; Technical assistance; Program-related investments/loans.
Limitations: Applications accepted. Giving primarily in New York City; cross-borders of North America; and worldwide. No grants to individuals, including scholarships and fellowships, or for construction or building programs, endowment funds, operating budgets of educational or medical institutions, film or video, or sponsorship of books, dances, plays, or other works of art.
Publications: Annual report (including application guidelines).
Application information: Proposals received by fax will not be considered.
Initial approach: 2- to 3-page letter of inquiry
Copies of proposal: 1
Deadline(s): None; requests received after Oct. 1 will be carried over to next year
Board meeting date(s): Quarterly
Final notification: Applicants will be notified within approximately 6 weeks of receipt of letter of inquiry if they are to submit a full proposal
Officers and Trustees:* Peter W. Davidson,* Chair.; William P. Falahee, Cont.; Joan K. Davidson,* Pres. Emeritus; Betsy Davidson; Bradford Davidson; J. Matthew Davidson; Caio Fonseca; Elizabeth K. Fonseca; Isabel Fonseca; Quina Fonseca; Mary E. Kaplan; Richard D. Kaplan.
Number of staff: 4 full-time professional; 1 full-time support.
EIN: 136090286
Selected grants: The following grants are a representative sample of this grantmaker's funding activity:
$280,000 to Occidental College, Los Angeles, CA, 2012. To establish endowed fund for The Richard C. Cornuelle Fellowship Program.
$200,000 to National Parks Conservation Association, Washington, DC, 2012. For New York/ New Jersey Harbor Coalition.
$200,000 to World Monuments Fund, New York, NY, 2012. For 1) Restoration of the Ani Cathedral 2) Restoration of Ani Chruch of the Redeemer.
$150,000 to Manhattan Institute for Policy Research, New York, NY, 2012. For Social Entrepreneuship Initiative.
$100,000 to Migration Policy Institute, Washington, DC, 2012. For E Pluribus Unum National Awards Program.
$45,000 to University of Miami, Coral Gables, FL, 2012. For Havana: Its Architecture and Urbanism.
$12,000 to Rocky Mountain Institute, Boulder, CO, 2012. For General Support.
$10,000 to American Civil Liberties Union Foundation, New York, NY, 2012. For Stop Solitary Campaign.
$5,000 to Old Dartmouth Historical Society, New Bedford Whaling Museum, New Bedford, MA, 2012. For the book, The Arctic Region.
$5,000 to Urban Assembly, New York, NY, 2012. For General Support.

6253
The Kapnick Foundation Trust ✧
P.O. Box 73
Bowling Green Sta.
New York, NY 10274-0073

Established in IL.
Donor: Scott B. Kapnick.
Foundation type: Independent foundation.
Financial data (yr. ended 12/31/13): Assets, $53,749,369 (M); expenditures, $8,138,295; qualifying distributions, $7,833,964; giving activities include $5,816,474 for 30 grants (high: $1,800,000; low: $440).
Fields of interest: Performing arts, opera; Higher education; Libraries (special); Education; Human services.
Limitations: Applications not accepted. Giving primarily in CA, MA, and NY.
Application information: Contributes only to pre-selected organizations.
Officer: Scott B. Kapnick, Treas.
Trustees: Kathleen G. Kapnick; Richard B. Kapnick.
EIN: 367434011

6254
Mel Karmazin Foundation ✧
1 Central Park W., Ste. 48B
New York, NY 10023-7703

Established in DE and NY in 1998.
Donors: Melvin Karmazin; Karmazin Trust; Karmazin Trust II.
Foundation type: Independent foundation.
Financial data (yr. ended 12/31/12): Assets, $11,507,391 (M); gifts received, $10,000,000; expenditures, $3,195,328; qualifying distributions, $3,243,350; giving activities include $3,045,880 for 30 grants (high: $793,450; low: $1,000).
Purpose and activities: Giving primarily for medical research, particularly for autism, as well as for children and social services.
Fields of interest: Autism; Medical research, institute; Human services; Children/youth, services.
Limitations: Applications not accepted. Giving primarily in NY. No grants to individuals.
Application information: Contributes only to pre-selected organizations.
Trustees: Dina K. Elkins; Melvin Karmazin.
EIN: 311620186

6255
Iris & Saul Katz Family Foundation, Inc. ✧
(formerly The Iris & Saul Katz Foundation, Inc.)
111 Great Neck Rd., Ste. 408
Great Neck, NY 11021-5404 (516) 773-3800
Contact: Saul B. Katz, Pres.

Established in 1982 in DE and NY.
Donor: Saul B. Katz.
Foundation type: Independent foundation.
Financial data (yr. ended 12/31/12): Assets, $863,256 (M); gifts received, $1,338,056; expenditures, $3,051,755; qualifying distributions, $461,860; giving activities include $461,860 for 39 grants (high: $210,000; low: $100).
Fields of interest: Higher education; Education; Health organizations, association; Human services; Jewish agencies & synagogues.
Limitations: Applications accepted. Giving primarily in NY, with some emphasis on Long Island.
Application information: Application form required.
Initial approach: Letter
Deadline(s): None
Officer and Directors:* Saul B. Katz,* Pres.; David M. Katz; Iris J. Katz.
EIN: 112626656

6256
Alex Katz Foundation, Inc. ✧
c/o A. Kozak & Company, LLP
192 Lexington Ave., Ste. 1100
New York, NY 10016-6823

Established in 2005 in NY.
Donor: Alex Katz.
Foundation type: Operating foundation.
Financial data (yr. ended 12/31/13): Assets, $26,951,486 (M); gifts received, $2,500,000; expenditures, $2,078,956; qualifying distributions, $1,909,909; giving activities include $1,860,145 for 50 grants (high: $302,500; low: $450).
Fields of interest: Museums (art).
Limitations: Applications not accepted. Giving primarily in ME; funding also in Boston, MA. No grants to individuals.
Application information: Contributes only to pre-selected organizations.
Officers and Directors:* Alex Katz,* Pres.; Ada Katz,* V.P.; Vivien Bittencourt Katz,* Secy.; Vincent Katz,* Treas.
EIN: 510529249

6257
The Jane and Robert Katz Foundation ✧
Bowling Green Station
P.O. Box 73
New York, NY 10274-0073

Established in 1989 in NY.
Donors: Robert J. Katz; Goldman Sachs & Co.
Foundation type: Independent foundation.
Financial data (yr. ended 02/28/13): Assets, $2,287,992 (M); expenditures, $1,505,384; qualifying distributions, $1,476,585; giving activities include $1,476,585 for 76 grants (high: $360,000; low: $100).
Purpose and activities: Giving primarily for education, human services, Jewish organizations, and to a donor advised fund.
Fields of interest: Elementary/secondary education; Higher education; Law school/education; Human services; Foundations (public); Jewish federated giving programs; Jewish agencies & synagogues.
Limitations: Applications not accepted. Giving primarily in New York, NY, and Boston, MA. No grants to individuals, or for scholarships; no loans.
Application information: Contributes only to pre-selected organizations.
Trustees: Jane L. Katz; Robert J. Katz.
EIN: 133534735
Selected grants: The following grants are a representative sample of this grantmaker's funding activity:
$5,000 to Harvard University, Law School, Cambridge, MA, 2013. For general charitable purposes.

6258
The Katzenberger Foundation, Inc. ✧
200 Park Ave. S., Ste. 1700
New York, NY 10003-1531 (212) 315-5575
Contact: Abner J. Golieb, Pres.

Incorporated in 1952 in NY.
Donors: Walter B. Katzenberger†; Helen Katherine Katzenberger†.
Foundation type: Independent foundation.
Financial data (yr. ended 12/31/13): Assets, $15,019,993 (M); expenditures, $915,328; qualifying distributions, $745,501; giving activities include $675,500 for 27 grants (high: $75,000; low: $5,000).
Fields of interest: Performing arts centers; Arts; Elementary/secondary education; Higher education; Human services; Children/youth, services.
Type of support: General/operating support; Continuing support; Annual campaigns; Emergency funds.
Limitations: Applications accepted. Giving primarily in AZ, Chicago, IL, and NY. No support for religious organizations (except for Christian Science organizations), or for medical or medical research organizations. No grants to individuals, or for scholarships; no loans.
Publications: Annual report; Financial statement.
Application information: Application form not required.
Initial approach: Proposal
Copies of proposal: 1
Deadline(s): Sept. 1
Officers and Directors:* Abner J. Golieb,* Pres.; Edward Davis,* Secy.; Margaret G. Axelrod,* Treas.; John A. Golieb.
EIN: 136094434
Selected grants: The following grants are a representative sample of this grantmaker's funding activity:
$40,000 to United Negro College Fund, Fairfax, VA, 2011.
$15,000 to Ronald McDonald House Charities, Oak Brook, IL, 2011.
$10,000 to Avenues to Independence, Park Ridge, IL, 2011.
$10,000 to Teach for America, New York, NY, 2011.
$5,500 to Child Crisis Center-East Valley, Mesa, AZ, 2010.
$5,000 to Avenues to Independence, Park Ridge, IL, 2011.
$5,000 to Child Crisis Center-East Valley, Mesa, AZ, 2011.
$5,000 to Guiding Eyes for the Blind, Yorktown Heights, NY, 2011.

6259
Henry and Elaine Kaufman Foundation Inc. ✧
590 Madison Ave., 5th Fl.
New York, NY 10022-2524 (212) 758-7100
Contact: Henry Kaufman, Pres. and Treas.; Elaine Kaufman, V.P.

Established in 1969.
Donors: Elaine Kaufman; Henry Kaufman; Henry Kaufman Charitable Lead Trust.
Foundation type: Independent foundation.
Financial data (yr. ended 12/31/12): Assets, $19,024,517 (M); gifts received, $2,230,632; expenditures, $1,850,665; qualifying distributions, $1,702,834; giving activities include $1,701,834 for 126 grants (high: $200,000; low: $100).
Purpose and activities: Support primarily for Jewish organizations, museums and other cultural institutions, and education; funding also for human services and hospitals.
Fields of interest: Museums; Arts; Higher education; Business school/education; Education; Animal welfare; Hospitals (general); Human services; Jewish federated giving programs; Jewish agencies & synagogues.
Type of support: General/operating support; Annual campaigns.
Limitations: Applications accepted. Giving primarily in the metropolitan New York, NY, area, including portions of NJ; some funding also in Atlanta, GA.
Application information: Application form required.
Initial approach: Letter
Deadline(s): None
Officers and Directors:* Henry Kaufman,* Pres. and Treas.; Elaine Kaufman,* V.P.; Daniel S. Kaufman,* Secy.; Craig S. Kaufman; Glenn D. Kaufman.
EIN: 237045903

6260
The Kautz Family Foundation ✧
c/o BCRS Assocs., LLC
77 Water St., 9th Fl.
New York, NY 10005-4414

Established in 1981 in NY.
Donors: James C. Kautz; Peter Levy; Ron Tauber; Bob Friedman; Ann Brown Farrell; Martha Barnes Miller.
Foundation type: Independent foundation.
Financial data (yr. ended 02/28/13): Assets, $30,420,253 (M); gifts received, $578,051; expenditures, $1,492,069; qualifying distributions, $1,432,467; giving activities include $1,431,717 for 31 grants (high: $1,000,000; low: $7).
Purpose and activities: Giving primarily for the arts and higher and other education; funding also for children, youth, and social services, and for the arts.
Fields of interest: Arts; Education, association; Higher education; Education; Hospitals (specialty); Health organizations, association; Human services; Children/youth, services.
Type of support: Continuing support; Annual campaigns; Capital campaigns; Endowments; Fellowships.
Limitations: Applications not accepted. Giving primarily in AZ, NY and OH. No grants to individuals; no loans.
Application information: Contributes only to pre-selected organizations.
Trustees: Daniel P. Cunningham; Daniel B. Kautz; James C. Kautz; Leslie B. Kautz.
EIN: 133103149
Selected grants: The following grants are a representative sample of this grantmaker's funding activity:
$1,000,000 to University of Cincinnati Foundation, Cincinnati, OH, 2013. For Organizations That Were Classified Under Section 501 C (3) of the Internal Revenue Code.

6261
Laurie Kayden Foundation ✧
c/o Phillips Nizer
666 5th Ave.
New York, NY 10103-0001
Contact: R. Horan

Established in 1990 in NY.
Donor: Suzanne Kayden†.
Foundation type: Independent foundation.
Financial data (yr. ended 12/31/13): Assets, $17,713,780 (M); expenditures, $1,188,139; qualifying distributions, $1,115,085; giving activities include $886,000 for 53 grants (high: $64,000; low: $1,000).
Fields of interest: Health organizations, association; Jewish federated giving programs; Jewish agencies & synagogues.
Limitations: Applications not accepted. Giving primarily in New York, NY. No grants to individuals.
Application information: Contributes only to pre-selected organizations.
Trustees: Robert Horan; Andrew J. Tunick.
EIN: 133557216

6262
The Kaye Family Foundation ✧
c/o C. Judge, The Ayco Co., L.P.
321 Broadway
P.O. Box 860
Saratoga Springs, NY 12866-4110

Established in 1999 in NY.
Donors: Charles R. Kaye; Sheryl J. Kaye.
Foundation type: Independent foundation.
Financial data (yr. ended 11/30/13): Assets, $3,052,714 (M); gifts received, $3,653,036; expenditures, $794,371; qualifying distributions, $769,320; giving activities include $769,320 for 57 grants (high: $400,000; low: $15).
Fields of interest: Higher education; Education; Hospitals (general); Health organizations,

association; International economic development; Jewish agencies & synagogues.
Limitations: Applications not accepted. Giving primarily in New York and Westchester counties, NY. No grants to individuals.
Application information: Contributes only to pre-selected organizations.
Trustees: Charles R. Kaye; Sheryl Kaye.
EIN: 134092284

6263
The Harvey & Gloria Kaylie Foundation, Inc. ✧
5 Fir Dr.
Kings Point, NY 11024-1528

Established in 1999 in NY.
Donors: Scientific Components Corp.; Harvey Kaylie.
Foundation type: Company-sponsored foundation.
Financial data (yr. ended 12/31/12): Assets, $13,081,848 (M); gifts received, $1,698,800; expenditures, $3,780,767; qualifying distributions, $3,773,134; giving activities include $3,773,134 for 71 grants (high: $865,000; low: $90).
Purpose and activities: The foundation supports organizations involved with education, health, cancer research, human services, and Judaism.
Fields of interest: Secondary school/education; Higher education; Education; Health care; Cancer research; Children, services; Family services; Human services; Jewish federated giving programs; Jewish agencies & synagogues.
Type of support: General/operating support; Matching/challenge support.
Limitations: Applications not accepted. Giving primarily in Brooklyn and New York, NY. No grants to individuals.
Application information: Contributes only to pre-selected organizations.
Officers and Directors:* Harvey Kaylie,* Pres.; Gloria W. Kaylie,* V.P.; Roberta Kaylie,* Secy.; Alicia Kaylie Yacoby,* Treas.
EIN: 113502781

6264
Kazickas Family Foundation Inc. ✧
120 E. 38th St.
New York, NY 10016-2602

Established in 1998 in NY.
Donors: Victor Gruodis; John A. Kazickas; Joseph M. Kazickas; Joseph P. Kazickas; Michael Kazickas.
Foundation type: Independent foundation.
Financial data (yr. ended 12/31/13): Assets, $15,032,671 (M); expenditures, $890,968; qualifying distributions, $542,326; giving activities include $537,326 for 67 grants (high: $42,000; low: $15).
Purpose and activities: Giving primarily for education and human services, particularly Lithuanian causes.
Fields of interest: Museums (children's); Arts; Higher education; Human services; Children/youth, services.
Limitations: Applications not accepted. Giving primarily in New York, NY. No grants to individuals.
Application information: Contributes only to pre-selected organizations.
Officers and Directors:* Jurate Kazickas,* Pres.; John A. Kazickas, Secy.-Treas.; Joseph M. Kazickas; Joseph P. Kazickas; Michael V. Kazickas.
EIN: 134011883

6265
William H. Kearns Foundation ✧ ☆
c/o Robert J. Hughes, Marks Paneth & Shron LLP
685 3rd Ave.
New York, NY 10017-6723

Established in 1965.
Foundation type: Independent foundation.
Financial data (yr. ended 12/31/13): Assets, $9,838,259 (M); expenditures, $903,544; qualifying distributions, $673,200; giving activities include $506,000 for 16 grants (high: $150,000; low: $1,000).
Purpose and activities: Giving primarily for the arts, education, human services, and to a hospital.
Fields of interest: Performing arts, orchestras; Arts; Education; Hospitals (general); Human services.
Limitations: Applications not accepted. Giving primarily in CA and NY. No grants to individuals.
Application information: Unsolicited requests for funds not accepted.
Officers: Milton Warshaw, Pres. and Treas.; Maxine D. Prisyon, V.P. and Secy.
EIN: 136199107
Selected grants: The following grants are a representative sample of this grantmaker's funding activity:
$150,000 to Santa Barbara Cottage Hospital, Santa Barbara, CA, 2013.
$125,000 to University of California, Santa Barbara, CA, 2013.
$100,000 to Santa Barbara Symphony Orchestra Association, Santa Barbara, CA, 2013.
$50,000 to Metropolitan Museum of Art, New York, NY, 2013.
$25,000 to Museum of Modern Art, New York, NY, 2013.
$7,000 to Social Venture Network, San Francisco, CA, 2013.
$5,000 to Food for Needy, New York, NY, 2013.
$2,500 to Music Academy of the West, Santa Barbara, CA, 2013.
$2,500 to Santa Barbara Foundation, Santa Barbara, CA, 2013.
$1,000 to Youth and Family Services, Rapid City, SD, 2013.

6266
The Ernest and Nancy Keet Foundation ✧
62 Moir Rd.
P.O. Box 1199
Saranac Lake, NY 12983-7199
E-mail: Trustee@Keet-Foundation.org; Fax: (208) 275-7423 (Idaho number); Main URL: http://www.keet-foundation.org
Grants List: http://www.keet-foundation.org/Past_Support.htm

Established in 1986 in CT.
Donor: Ernest E. Keet.
Foundation type: Independent foundation.
Financial data (yr. ended 12/31/13): Assets, $24,239,788 (M); expenditures, $1,139,195; qualifying distributions, $1,098,272; giving activities include $1,098,272 for grants.
Purpose and activities: Giving primarily for medical research and education, as well as for hunger relief, wilderness preservation, protecting civil liberties, and cultural development.
Fields of interest: Museums (natural history); Arts; Libraries/library science; Education; Environment; Medical research; Disasters, Hurricane Katrina; Human services.
Type of support: General/operating support.
Limitations: Giving primarily in NY, particularly the Adirondack Mountain region. No grants to individuals.
Publications: Application guidelines; IRS Form 990 or 990-PF printed copy available upon request.
Application information: See foundation web site for specific application instructions and Grant Request Form. Application form required.
Trustees: Bonnie Falkenstine Keet; Ernest E. Keet; Nancy R. Keet.
EIN: 222784895

6267
Keidan Family Foundation, Inc. ✧ ☆
c/o David B. Keidan
750 3rd Ave., 6th Fl.
New York, NY 10017-2715

Established in 2006 in NY.
Donor: David B. Keidan.
Foundation type: Independent foundation.
Financial data (yr. ended 12/31/13): Assets, $4,863,627 (M); expenditures, $1,344,376; qualifying distributions, $1,342,126; giving activities include $1,342,000 for 25 grants (high: $850,000; low: $1,000).
Fields of interest: Hospitals (general); Jewish federated giving programs; Jewish agencies & synagogues.
Limitations: Applications not accepted. Giving primarily in NY. No grants to individuals.
Application information: Contributes only to pre-selected organizations.
Officers: David B. Keidan, Pres.; Georgia Keidan, V.P.; Jonathan Keidan, Secy.; Amanda Keidan, Treas.
EIN: 562618835

6268
Anna-Maria & Stephen Kellen Foundation, Inc. ✧
c/o Joel E. Sammet & Co., LLP
15 Maiden Ln., Ste. 500
New York, NY 10038-5117 (212) 269-8628

Established in 1984.
Donors: Stephen M. Kellen‡; Anna-Maria Kellen.
Foundation type: Independent foundation.
Financial data (yr. ended 04/30/13): Assets, $558,011,142 (M); gifts received, $85,000,000; expenditures, $29,509,417; qualifying distributions, $19,238,505; giving activities include $18,304,468 for 130 grants (high: $3,578,400; low: $250).
Purpose and activities: Giving primarily for cultural programs, including a music school, a school of design, museums, and performing arts groups; support also for higher and secondary education, Protestant churches, and media and communications.
Fields of interest: Media/communications; Museums; Performing arts, music; Arts; Secondary

school/education; Higher education; Medical care, outpatient care; Protestant agencies & churches.
Limitations: Applications not accepted. Giving primarily in New York, NY. No grants to individuals.
Application information: Contributes only to pre-selected organizations.
Officers and Directors:* Michael Kellen,* Pres.; Marina K. French,* V.P.; Andrew Gundlach, Secy.-Treas.; Nina M. Gorrissen.
EIN: 133173593
Selected grants: The following grants are a representative sample of this grantmaker's funding activity:
$3,828,550 to Cancer Research Institute, New York, NY, 2012. For general support.
$3,578,400 to Cancer Research Institute, New York, NY, 2013. For general support.
$3,057,935 to American Academy in Berlin, New York, NY, 2012. For general support.
$2,250,438 to American Academy in Berlin, New York Office, New York, NY, 2013. For general support.
$2,250,000 to Weill Medical College of Cornell University, New York, NY, 2013. For general support.
$1,560,000 to Metropolitan Museum of Art, New York, NY, 2012. For general support.
$1,500,000 to Curtis Institute of Music, Philadelphia, PA, 2013. For general support.
$1,050,000 to Metropolitan Opera Guild, New York, NY, 2012. For general support.
$750,000 to Hospital for Special Surgery, New York, NY, 2012. For general support.
$750,000 to Hospital for Special Surgery, New York, NY, 2013. For general support.
$723,500 to Carnegie Hall Corporation, New York, NY, 2012. For general support.
$560,000 to Metropolitan Museum of Art, New York, NY, 2013. For general support.
$535,000 to National Gallery of Art, Washington, DC, 2013. For general support.
$500,000 to Mayo Clinic, Rochester, MN, 2012. For general support.
$365,000 to Icahn School of Medicine at Mount Sinai, New York, NY, 2012. For general support.
$75,000 to American Ballet Theater, New York, NY, 2013. For general support.
$75,000 to Mayo Clinic, Rochester, MN, 2013. For general support.
$53,210 to Saint Bernards School, New York, NY, 2013. For general support.
$50,000 to Skidmore College, Saratoga Springs, NY, 2012. For general support.
$50,000 to Women Make Movies, New York, NY, 2012. For general support.

6269
J. C. Kellogg Foundation, Inc. ✧

c/o IAT Reinsurance Co., Ltd.
48 Wall St., 30th Fl.
New York, NY 10005-2915
Contact: Mike Pickett

Established in 1954 in NY.
Donors: Morris W. Kellogg; James C. Kellogg IV; Elizabeth I. Kellogg; Richard I. Kellogg; Peter R. Kellogg; 120 Broadway Partners.
Foundation type: Independent foundation.
Financial data (yr. ended 08/31/13): Assets, $91,682,277 (M); gifts received, $2,773,500; expenditures, $5,847,149; qualifying distributions, $5,163,902; giving activities include $5,157,317 for 167 grants (high: $500,000; low: $125).
Purpose and activities: The foundation seeks to provide creative financial support and other assistance to organizations serving a variety of community and educational needs.
Fields of interest: Elementary/secondary education; Higher education; Education; Hospitals (general); Health organizations, association; Boys & girls clubs; Human services; Children/youth, services; Foundations (community); United Ways and Federated Giving Programs.
Limitations: Applications not accepted. Giving primarily in MA, NJ, and NY. No grants to individuals.
Application information: Contributes only to pre-selected organizations.
Officers: James C. Kellogg IV, Pres. and Treas.; Peter R. Kellogg, V.P.
Trustees: Nancy K. Gifford; Morris W. Kellogg; Richard I. Kellogg.
EIN: 136092448
Selected grants: The following grants are a representative sample of this grantmaker's funding activity:
$1,000,000 to YMCA of Eastern Union County, Elizabeth, NJ, 2011.
$500,000 to Berkshire School, Sheffield, MA, 2011.
$500,000 to Berkshire School, Sheffield, MA, 2011.
$200,000 to Berkshire School, Sheffield, MA, 2011.
$100,000 to CEC Stuyvesant Cove, New York, NY, 2011.
$95,000 to Heartworks, Bernardsville, NJ, 2011.
$75,000 to Christodora, New York, NY, 2011.
$45,000 to Bridges Outreach, Summit, NJ, 2011.
$10,000 to Kent Place School, Summit, NJ, 2011.
$10,000 to Thompson Island Outward Bound Education Center, Boston, MA, 2011.

6270
Peter R. & Cynthia K. Kellogg Foundation ✧

c/o IAT RE, Ltd.
48 Wall St., 30th Fl.
New York, NY 10005-2915 (212) 389-5830

Established in 1983 in NJ.
Donors: Charles K. Kellogg; Lee I. Kellogg; Peter R. Kellogg; IAT Syndicate, Inc.; Peter R. Kellogg Corp.
Foundation type: Independent foundation.
Financial data (yr. ended 06/30/13): Assets, $103,158,746 (M); gifts received, $4,823,275; expenditures, $6,195,254; qualifying distributions, $5,446,478; giving activities include $5,446,478 for 506 grants (high: $1,000,000; low: $50).
Purpose and activities: Giving primarily for education.
Fields of interest: Museums; Historic preservation/historical societies; Arts; Education; Recreation; Children/youth, services.
Limitations: Applications not accepted. Giving primarily in MA and NJ. No grants to individuals.
Application information: Contributes only to pre-selected organizations.
Officers: Peter R. Kellogg, Pres.; Cynthia K. Kellogg, Secy.; Marguerite R. Gorman, Treas.
EIN: 222472914
Selected grants: The following grants are a representative sample of this grantmaker's funding activity:
$1,000,000 to Berkshire School, Sheffield, MA, 2013.
$250,000 to Catskill Mountain Foundation, Hunter, NY, 2013.
$130,000 to Audubon South Carolina, Harleyville, SC, 2013.
$100,000 to Project Self Sufficiency, New York, NY, 2013.
$30,000 to National Sailing Hall of Fame and Museum, Annapolis, MD, 2013.
$10,000 to Belleayre Conservatory, Highmount, NY, 2013.
$10,000 to East Harlem School at Exodus House, New York, NY, 2013.
$5,000 to Birth Haven, Newton, NJ, 2013.
$2,500 to Bayshore Discovery Project, Port Norris, NJ, 2013.
$1,000 to United States Equestrian Team Foundation, Gladstone, NJ, 2013.

6271
Ellsworth Kelly Foundation, Inc. ✧

P.O. Box 220
Spencertown, NY 12165-0220

Established in 1991 in NY.
Donors: Ellsworth Kelly; Christopher Burge.
Foundation type: Independent foundation.
Financial data (yr. ended 12/31/13): Assets, $30,639,426 (M); gifts received, $2,032,500; expenditures, $1,211,854; qualifying distributions, $1,003,541; giving activities include $1,000,000 for 10 grants (high: $300,000; low: $50,000).
Purpose and activities: Giving primarily for the arts, particularly art museums, as well as for environmental conservation, and community development.
Fields of interest: Museums (art); Arts; Environment, natural resources; Animals/wildlife, bird preserves; Community/economic development; Foundations (community).
Limitations: Applications not accepted. Giving primarily in MA and NY. No grants to individuals.
Application information: Contributes only to pre-selected organizations.
Officers and Directors:* Ellsworth Kelly,* Pres.; Jack Shear,* Secy.-Treas.; Roberta Bernstein; Emily Pulitzer.
EIN: 223132379

6272
The Barbara and Gil Kemp Foundation Inc ✧ ☆

c/o Ken Greenhut McGladrey LLP
1185 Ave. of the Americas, 19th Fl.
New York, NY 10036-2602

Established in NY.
Donors: Giles K. Kemp; Barbara G. Kemp.
Foundation type: Independent foundation.
Financial data (yr. ended 12/31/12): Assets, $13,400,318 (M); expenditures, $1,655,235; qualifying distributions, $944,045; giving activities include $944,045 for grants.
Fields of interest: Education; Human services.
Limitations: Applications not accepted. Giving in the U.S., with some emphasis on CA and NY.
Application information: Unsolicited requests for funds not accepted.
Officers: Giles K. Kemp, Pres.; Barbara G. Kemp, V.P.
Directors: David G. Kemp; Rebecca L. Kemp.
EIN: 203834827

6273
Thomas L. Kempner, Jr. Foundation ✧
65 E. 55th St., 19th Fl.
New York, NY 10022-3355

Established in 1987 in NY.
Donor: Thomas L. Kempner, Jr.
Foundation type: Independent foundation.
Financial data (yr. ended 12/31/12): Assets, $49,004,002 (M); gifts received, $1,683,334; expenditures, $2,075,546; qualifying distributions, $2,008,110; giving activities include $1,996,272 for 8 grants (high: $600,000; low: $10,000).
Purpose and activities: Giving primarily for higher and other education; funding also for a medical center and a park conservancy.
Fields of interest: Higher education; Medical school/education; Education; Environment; Hospitals (general).
Limitations: Applications not accepted. Giving primarily in New Haven, CT and New York, NY. No grants to individuals.
Application information: Contributes only to pre-selected organizations.
Officers: Thomas L. Kempner, Jr., Pres.; Katheryn C. Patterson, Secy.
Directors: Thomas N. Kempner; Trevor Kempner.
EIN: 133407819

6274
The Karen A. & Kevin W. Kennedy Foundation ✧
P. O. Box 73
Bowling Green Sta.
New York, NY 10274-0073

Established 1985.
Donor: Kevin W. Kennedy.
Foundation type: Independent foundation.
Financial data (yr. ended 04/30/13): Assets, $1,168,360 (M); gifts received, $738,100; expenditures, $673,277; qualifying distributions, $669,277; giving activities include $669,277 for 89 grants (high: $100,000; low: $250).
Purpose and activities: Giving primarily for the arts, conservation, education, health care and human services.
Fields of interest: Performing arts, opera; Arts; Higher education; Medical school/education; Nursing school/education; Environment, natural resources; Health care; Human services.
Type of support: General/operating support; Continuing support; Annual campaigns; Capital campaigns; Building/renovation; Endowments; Emergency funds; Professorships; Fellowships; Scholarship funds.
Limitations: Applications not accepted. Giving primarily in MA, NJ, and NY. No grants to individuals, or for scholarships; no loans.
Application information: Contributes only to pre-selected organizations.
Trustees: Coleman W. Kennedy; Karen A. Kennedy; Kevin W. Kennedy; William F. Kennedy.
EIN: 133318161
Selected grants: The following grants are a representative sample of this grantmaker's funding activity:
$1,000 to Columbia University, School of Nursing, New York, NY, 2013. For All contributions were made to the general purposes fund of public charitable organizations that were classified under section 501(c)(3) of the Internal Revenue Code.

6275
Ada Howe Kent Foundation ✧
c/o Curtis, Mallet-Prevost, et al.
101 Park Ave., Ste. 3500
New York, NY 10178-0061

Incorporated in 1962 in DE.
Donor: Marjorie K. Kilpatrick†.
Foundation type: Independent foundation.
Financial data (yr. ended 09/30/13): Assets, $13,754,277 (M); expenditures, $614,589; qualifying distributions, $564,162; giving activities include $470,000 for 25 grants (high: $75,000; low: $1,000).
Fields of interest: Higher education; Education; Human services.
Limitations: Applications not accepted. Giving primarily in CT, MA and NY. No grants to individuals.
Application information: Contributes only to pre-selected organizations.
Officers: Henry P. Renard, V.P. and Treas.; Samuel R. Campbell, V.P.; Edward Ortiz, V.P.; Sabine Renard, V.P.
EIN: 136066978
Selected grants: The following grants are a representative sample of this grantmaker's funding activity:
$75,000 to Cornell University, Ithaca, NY, 2011.
$75,000 to Smith College, Northampton, MA, 2011.
$55,000 to Middlesex School, Concord, MA, 2011.
$50,000 to Cornell University, Ithaca, NY, 2011.
$50,000 to Harvard University, Cambridge, MA, 2011.
$30,000 to International Service Fellowship, Upper Darby, PA, 2011.
$10,000 to New School, New York, NY, 2011.
$5,000 to Isabella Stewart Gardner Museum, Boston, MA, 2011.
$5,000 to Juilliard School, New York, NY, 2011.
$1,000 to Sherman Chamber Ensemble, Sherman, CT, 2011.

6276
Keren Keshet - The Rainbow Foundation ✧
1015 Park Ave.
New York, NY 10028-0904
Contact: Linda Sakacs, Secy.

Established in 1999 in NY.
Donor: Zalman C. Bernstein†.
Foundation type: Independent foundation.
Financial data (yr. ended 12/31/13): Assets, $240,246,269 (M); gifts received, $2,120,000; expenditures, $19,496,218; qualifying distributions, $12,562,165; giving activities include $10,098,957 for 14 grants (high: $4,000,000; low: $2,500), and $43,267 for 3 grants to individuals (high: $30,000; low: $1,935).
Purpose and activities: Giving primarily for Jewish educational and cultural programs.
Fields of interest: Education.
Limitations: Applications not accepted. Giving primarily on a national basis and in Israel.
Application information: Unsolicited requests for funds not accepted.
Board meeting date(s): Monthly
Officers: Arthur W. Fried, Pres.; Mem Dryan Bernstein, V.P. and Treas.; Linda Sakacs, Secy.
Number of staff: 1 full-time professional; 3 part-time professional; 5 full-time support; 2 part-time support.
EIN: 134069592
Selected grants: The following grants are a representative sample of this grantmaker's funding activity:
$10,515,000 to Jewish Communal Fund of New York, New York, NY, 2012. For program support.
$5,000,000 to Jewish Communal Fund of New York, New York, NY, 2012. For program support.
$2,722,174 to Keren Keshet, Jerusalem, Israel, 2012. For program support.
$2,616,367 to Jewish Community High School of the Bay, San Francisco, CA, 2012. For operating support.
$726,532 to 1210 Scott Street, New York, NY, 2012. For operating support.
$100,000 to Bureau of Jewish Education, San Francisco, CA, 2012. For program support.
$50,000 to Rabbi Jacob Joseph School, Staten Island, NY, 2012. For operating support.
$30,000 to Jewish Funders Network, New York, NY, 2012. For operating support and program support.
$5,000 to Jewish Community Federation of San Francisco, the Peninsula, Marin and Sonoma Counties, San Francisco, CA, 2012. For operating support.

6277
Keshet Foundation ✧
c/o Dekel II, LLC
1700 Broadway, Ste. 2000
New York, NY 10019-2300

Established in 1997 in NY.
Donors: Rebecca Gridish; Eli Gridish; RLTS II; National Society of Hebrew Day Schools; Tzohar Foundation.
Foundation type: Independent foundation.
Financial data (yr. ended 11/30/13): Assets, $311,567 (M); gifts received, $2,487,969; expenditures, $2,369,264; qualifying distributions, $2,366,995; giving activities include $2,366,995 for 75 grants (high: $180,000; low: $1,800).
Fields of interest: Jewish agencies & synagogues.
Limitations: Applications not accepted. Giving primarily in NY.
Application information: Unsolicited requests for funds not accepted.
Trustees: Estanne Abraham; Eli Gridish; Rebecca Gridish.
EIN: 137132997

6278
The Khatib Foundation Inc. ✧ ☆
111 Cherry Valley Ave.
Garden City, NY 11530-1570

Established in 1999 in NY.
Donors: Reza Khatib, M.D.; Georgianna Khatib.
Foundation type: Independent foundation.
Financial data (yr. ended 12/31/13): Assets, $73,888 (M); gifts received, $635,000; expenditures, $612,761; qualifying distributions, $612,833; giving activities include $612,833 for 16 grants (high: $468,763; low: $100).
Fields of interest: Higher education, university; Health care.
Type of support: General/operating support.
Limitations: Applications not accepted. Giving primarily in FL. No grants to individuals.
Application information: Unsolicited requests for funds not accepted.

Directors: Georgianna Khatib; Reza Khatib, M.D.
EIN: 113522346

6279
The Peter and Eaddo Kiernan Foundation ✧ ☆
c/o BCRS Assoc., LLC
77 Water St., 9th Fl.
New York, NY 10005-4414

Established in 1991 in NY.
Donor: Peter D. Kiernan.
Foundation type: Independent foundation.
Financial data (yr. ended 05/31/13): Assets, $188,008 (M); gifts received, $540,356; expenditures, $446,785; qualifying distributions, $446,785; giving activities include $445,133 for 13 grants (high: $100,000; low: $550).
Fields of interest: Higher education; Education; Foundations (public).
Limitations: Applications not accepted. No grants to individuals or for scholarships; no loans.
Application information: Contributes only to pre-selected organizations.
Trustees: Eaddo H. Kiernan; Peter D. Kiernan.
EIN: 133637705
Selected grants: The following grants are a representative sample of this grantmaker's funding activity:
$220,000 to Christopher and Dana Reeve Foundation, Short Hills, NJ, 2011. For general purpose fund.
$200,000 to Christopher and Dana Reeve Foundation, Short Hills, NJ, 2011. For general purpose fund.
$100,000 to Robin Hood Foundation, New York, NY, 2011. For general purpose fund.
$50,000 to Trout Unlimited, New York, NY, 2011. For general purpose fund.
$25,000 to Alfred E. Smith Memorial Foundation, New York, NY, 2011. For general purpose fund.
$25,000 to University of Virginia Darden School Foundation, Charlottesville, VA, 2011. For general purpose fund.
$10,000 to New York-Presbyterian Hospital, New York, NY, 2011. For general purpose fund.
$8,200 to Ubuntu Education Fund, New York, NY, 2011. For general purpose fund.
$3,711 to University of Virginia Fund, Charlottesville, VA, 2011. For general purpose fund.
$1,000 to Newport Art Museum and Art Association, Newport, RI, 2011. For general purpose fund.

6280
The Kilts Family Foundation ✧
(formerly The Atlas Heritage Foundation)
c/o The Ayco Co., LP
P.O. Box 860
Saratoga Springs, NY 12866-0860

Established in 2000 in DE.
Donor: James M. Kilts.
Foundation type: Independent foundation.
Financial data (yr. ended 12/31/12): Assets, $11,096,803 (M); expenditures, $1,308,659; qualifying distributions, $1,190,100; giving activities include $1,190,100 for 19 grants (high: $600,000; low: $100).
Fields of interest: Higher education.
Limitations: Applications not accepted. Giving primarily in Chicago, IL; some giving also in NY. No grants to individuals.
Application information: Contributes only to pre-selected organizations.
Officers: James M. Kilts, Pres.; Sandra M. Kilts, V.P. and Secy.
Directors: James M. Kilts, Jr.; Sarah Kilts.
EIN: 134147482

6281
The Kimmel Family Foundation ✧
(formerly Martin S. Kimmel Foundation)
280 Madison Ave., Ste. 1007
New York, NY 10016-0881

Established in 1994 in NY.
Donor: Martin S. Kimmel†.
Foundation type: Independent foundation.
Financial data (yr. ended 12/31/12): Assets, $39,885,674 (M); expenditures, $4,048,240; qualifying distributions, $4,031,000; giving activities include $4,031,000 for grants.
Fields of interest: Education; Jewish agencies & synagogues.
Limitations: Applications not accepted. Giving primarily in New York, NY; funding also in Washington, DC. No grants to individuals.
Application information: Contributes only to pre-selected organizations.
Trustees: David Cooper; Adam P. Kimmel.
EIN: 137024058

6282
The Kimmelman Family Foundation ✧
c/o BCRS Group/Marcum & Kliegman, LLP
750 3rd Ave., 11th Fl.
New York, NY 10017-2703

Established in 1997 in NJ.
Donor: Douglas W. Kimmelman.
Foundation type: Independent foundation.
Financial data (yr. ended 08/31/13): Assets, $179,747 (M); gifts received, $1,786,292; expenditures, $1,951,855; qualifying distributions, $1,945,815; giving activities include $1,939,800 for 46 grants (high: $500,000; low: $250).
Purpose and activities: Giving primarily for education and human services.
Fields of interest: Elementary/secondary education; Higher education; Education; Human services; Foundations (private grantmaking).
Limitations: Applications not accepted. Giving primarily in NJ; some funding also in CA. No grants to individuals; no loans.
Application information: Contributes only to pre-selected organizations.
Trustees: Carol Kimmelman; Douglas W. Kimmelman.
EIN: 133933319
Selected grants: The following grants are a representative sample of this grantmaker's funding activity:
$350,000 to Stanford University, Stanford, CA, 2011.
$250,000 to Blair Academy, Blairstown, NJ, 2011.
$100,000 to Blair Academy, Blairstown, NJ, 2011.
$100,000 to Far Hills Country Day School, Far Hills, NJ, 2011.
$50,000 to Foundation for Morristown Medical Center, Morristown, NJ, 2011.
$40,000 to Harlem RBI, New York, NY, 2011.
$25,200 to Far Hills Country Day School, Far Hills, NJ, 2011.
$25,000 to Princeton University, Princeton, NJ, 2011.
$25,000 to USTA Serves, White Plains, NY, 2011.
$25,000 to USTA Serves, White Plains, NY, 2011.

6283
The King Street Charitable Trust ✧
c/o King Street Capital Mgmt. LLC
65 E. 55th St., 30th Fl.
New York, NY 10022-3358

Established in 2004 in NY.
Donors: Brian J. Higgins; O. Francis Biondi, Jr.; Franklin Edmonds; King Street Capital Advisors; King Street Capital Mgmt. LP.
Foundation type: Independent foundation.
Financial data (yr. ended 12/31/13): Assets, $95,012,286 (M); gifts received, $152,000; expenditures, $9,872,037; qualifying distributions, $9,727,492; giving activities include $9,720,992 for 122 grants (high: $2,260,000; low: $20).
Fields of interest: Arts; Elementary/secondary education; Higher education; Education; Hospitals (specialty); Health organizations, association; Medical research, institute; Human services; Children/youth, services.
Limitations: Applications not accepted. Giving primarily in NY.
Application information: Unsolicited requests for funds not accepted.
Trustees: O. Francis Biondi, Jr.; Brian J. Higgins.
EIN: 137425331
Selected grants: The following grants are a representative sample of this grantmaker's funding activity:
$2,000,000 to Harlem Childrens Zone Promise Academy Charter School, New York, NY, 2011.
$500,000 to New York-Presbyterian Hospital, New York, NY, 2011.
$500,000 to Pierpont Morgan Library, New York, NY, 2011.
$500,000 to Villanova University, Villanova, PA, 2011.
$200,000 to Endowment for Inner-City Education, New York, NY, 2011.
$100,000 to Memorial Sloan-Kettering Cancer Center, Society of, New York, NY, 2011.
$75,000 to Christiana Care Health System, Wilmington, DE, 2011.
$50,000 to Brearley School, New York, NY, 2011.
$50,000 to Memorial Sloan-Kettering Cancer Center, Society of, New York, NY, 2011.
$25,000 to Brain Trauma Foundation, New York, NY, 2011.

6284
Mark and Anla Cheng Kingdon Fund ✧
c/o Anla Cheng Kingdon
152 W. 57th St., 50th Fl.
New York, NY 10019-3310 (212) 333-0100

Established in 1997 in NY.
Donors: Mark Kingdon; Anla Cheng Kingdon; M. Kingdon Charitable Lead Annuity Trust; M. Kingdon Charitable Lead Annuity Trust II; M. Kingdon Charitable Lead Annuity Trust III.
Foundation type: Independent foundation.

Financial data (yr. ended 12/31/13): Assets, $124,895,535 (M); gifts received, $11,267,959; expenditures, $10,874,995; qualifying distributions, $10,744,417; giving activities include $10,610,885 for 69 grants (high: $4,020,000; low: $100).
Purpose and activities: Giving primarily for the arts, education, and human services.
Fields of interest: Arts; Higher education; Health organizations, association; Human services; Children, services; Jewish federated giving programs; Jewish agencies & synagogues.
Limitations: Applications not accepted. Giving primarily in NY. No grants to individuals.
Application information: Contributes only to pre-selected organizations.
Officers and Director:* Mark Kingdon,* Chair.; Anla Cheng Kingdon, Secy.
EIN: 133948023
Selected grants: The following grants are a representative sample of this grantmaker's funding activity:
$4,250,000 to Columbia University, New York, NY, 2012. For general support.
$4,020,000 to Columbia University, New York, NY, 2013. For general support.
$2,483,875 to China Institute in America, New York, NY, 2012. For general support.
$2,100,000 to Harlem Childrens Zone, New York, NY, 2012. For general support.
$2,050,000 to Harlem Childrens Zone, New York, NY, 2013. For general support.
$1,375,750 to China Institute in America, New York, NY, 2013. For general support.
$550,000 to Jewish National Fund, Rockville Centre, NY, 2013. For general support.
$500,000 to Jewish Agency for Israel, New York, NY, 2013. For general support.
$401,000 to Carnegie Hall Corporation, New York, NY, 2012. For general support.
$400,000 to Carnegie Hall Corporation, New York, NY, 2013. For general support.
$205,000 to Columbia University, New York, NY, 2012. For general support.
$122,613 to Riverdale Country School, Bronx, NY, 2012. For general support.
$105,000 to Human Rights Watch, New York, NY, 2013. For general support.
$100,000 to Human Rights Watch, New York, NY, 2012. For general support.
$75,000 to Columbia University, Columbia College, New York, NY, 2013. For general support and for Columbia College Fund.
$63,200 to Community Impact, New York, NY, 2012. For general support.
$47,500 to Committee of 100, New York, NY, 2012. For general support.
$40,425 to Community Impact, New York, NY, 2013. For general support.
$25,000 to New York City Center, New York, NY, 2013. For general support.
$10,000 to THIRTEEN, WNET Channel 13, New York, NY, 2012. For general support.

6285
Kinney Drugs Foundation, Inc. ✧

29 E. Main St.
Gouverneur, NY 13642-1401
Main URL: http://www.kinneydrugsfoundation.com

Established as a company-sponsored operating foundation in 2002 in NY.
Donors: Kinney Drugs, Inc.; Mary Kinney Trust.
Foundation type: Operating foundation.
Financial data (yr. ended 12/31/12): Assets, $3,089,003 (M); gifts received, $629,620; expenditures, $838,291; qualifying distributions, $798,728; giving activities include $604,920 for 118 grants (high: $136,167; low: $50).
Purpose and activities: The foundation supports programs designed to help people live healthier lives within communities served by Kinney Drugs.
Fields of interest: Public health school/education; Hospitals (general); Health care, clinics/centers; Health care, EMS; Health care, home services; Health care; Cancer; Heart & circulatory diseases; Disasters, fire prevention/control; American Red Cross; Children/youth, services; Aging, centers/services; Developmentally disabled, centers & services; Human services.
Type of support: General/operating support; Annual campaigns; Capital campaigns; Building/renovation; Equipment; Sponsorships.
Limitations: Applications accepted. Giving limited to areas of company operations, primarily in central and northern NY and VT. No grants to individuals.
Publications: Application guidelines; Annual report; Financial statement; Grants list; Informational brochure.
Application information: Application form required.
Initial approach: Complete online application form
Deadline(s): 1 month before board meeting
Board meeting date(s): 3rd Wed. of Feb., Mar., Apr., May, July, Aug., Oct., and Dec
Officers and Directors:* Mark Brackett, R.Ph.*, Pres.; Rich McNulty,* V.P; Stephen McCoy,* Secy.-Treas.; Bernie Alden; Richard Cognetti; Fred Haggerty, R.Ph.; Owen Halloran, R.Ph.; Rebecca Horn; Timothy O'Connor, R.Ph.; Charles Owen, R.Ph.; James Spencer; Norton Taylor, R.Ph.; Daniel Villa, R.Ph.; Warren Wolfson.
EIN: 030406308
Selected grants: The following grants are a representative sample of this grantmaker's funding activity:
$10,000 to Disabled Persons Action Organization, Watertown, NY, 2012. To support Concert Series.
$7,500 to Claxton-Hepburn Medical Center Foundation, Ogdensburg, NY, 2012. For Donation for Infant Warmer.
$5,500 to Crouse Health Foundation, Syracuse, NY, 2012. For Golf - Gala.
$5,000 to Hospice of Jefferson County, Watertown, NY, 2012. For Sailing Event.
$5,000 to Watertown Urban Mission, Watertown, NY, 2012. For Critical Needs Program.
$4,500 to Alice Hyde Medical Center, Malone, NY, 2012. For Golf Event/Silver and Black Gala.
$2,500 to River Hospital Foundation, Alexandria Bay, NY, 2012. For donation for equipment purchases.
$500 to Carthage Area Hospital, Carthage, NY, 2012. For Comedy Night Event.
$200 to Auburn Memorial Hospital, Auburn, NY, 2012. For 16th Annual Golf Tournament.

6286
The Conrad and Virginia Klee Foundation, Inc. ✧

84 Court St., Ste. 500
Binghamton, NY 13901-3310 (607) 722-2266
Contact: Judith C. Peckham, Exec. Dir.
FAX: (607) 722-2264;
E-mail: kleefoundation@stny.rr.com; Main URL: http://www.kleefoundation.org
Grants List: http://www.kleefoundation.org/grants/index.html

Incorporated in 1957 in NY.
Donors: Conrad C. Klee†; Virginia Klee†.
Foundation type: Independent foundation.
Financial data (yr. ended 12/31/13): Assets, $19,288,118 (M); expenditures, $970,769; qualifying distributions, $892,428; giving activities include $780,998 for 18 grants (high: $227,000; low: $5,000).
Purpose and activities: Giving primarily for the arts, health care, and human services.
Fields of interest: Arts; Health care; Human services; Children/youth, services.
Type of support: Equipment; Program development; Fellowships.
Limitations: Giving limited to Broome County, NY. No support for religious or political organizations. No grants to individuals.
Publications: Application guidelines; Annual report; Grants list.
Application information: Complete application guidelines available on foundation web site. Application form required.
Initial approach: E-mail or telephone call
Copies of proposal: 1
Deadline(s): See foundation web site for current deadlines
Board meeting date(s): Apr., May, Oct. and Nov.
Final notification: 4-6 weeks
Officers and Directors:* Lawrence Anderson,* Chair.; Patricia Ingraham, Ph.D.*, Vice-Chair.; Arthur Orr,* Secy.-Treas.; Judith C. Peckham, Exec. Dir.; Ron Akel; Linda Biemer; Armond R. George; Gary Holcomb; William J. Orband, Jr.; Prakash Ramanathan.
Number of staff: 1 part-time professional; 1 part-time support.
EIN: 156019821
Selected grants: The following grants are a representative sample of this grantmaker's funding activity:
$150,000 to Catholic Charities of Broome County, Binghamton, NY, 2012. For Capital Purpose Or Operating.

6287
The Reb Ephraim Chaim & Miriam Rochel Klein Charitable Foundation ✧

614 Ave. J
Brooklyn, NY 11230-3504

Established in 1989 in NY.
Donors: Abraham Klein; Sarah Dinah Klein; L. Rubin; Abraham Leizirowitz; Stuart Schlesinger; Barbara Hurwitz; Beach Terrace Care Center; Fairview Nursing Care Center, Inc.; Grandell Rehabilitation; Hyde Park Nursing Home, Inc.; Oceanside Care Center; Park Terrace Care Center; Queens Nassau Nursing Home; Talmide Chidishei Harim.
Foundation type: Independent foundation.
Financial data (yr. ended 12/31/12): Assets, $54,594,452 (M); expenditures, $4,136,444; qualifying distributions, $4,028,631; giving activities include $4,006,981 for 181 grants (high: $1,000,000; low: $100).
Purpose and activities: Giving primarily to Jewish agencies, temples, and schools.

Fields of interest: Elementary/secondary education; Human services; Jewish federated giving programs; Jewish agencies & synagogues; Religion.
International interests: Israel.
Limitations: Applications not accepted. Giving primarily in Brooklyn, NY; some giving nationally, as well as in Israel. No grants to individuals.
Application information: Contributes only to pre-selected organizations.
Directors: Mordechai Klein; Sarah Dinah Klein.
EIN: 223000780

6288
Klein Family Foundation ✧
c/o Park Terrace Care Ctr.
109-40 Saultell Ave.
Corona, NY 11368-4012
Contact: Abraham N. Klein, Tr.

Established in 1999 in NY.
Donors: Chana Brauner; Abraham Klein; Sarah Dinah Klein; Rifka Green; Bracha Weits; Sara Dina Klein Irrevocable Trust; Lincoln Avenue Realty Co.; Northern Manhattan Nursing; Fairview Nursing Center Inc.; Medford Multicare Center; Beach Terrace Care Center; Grandell Rehabilitation; Queens Nassau Nursing Home; Park Terrace Care Center; Oceanside Care Center; Manhattan Nursing Home Realty Inc.
Foundation type: Independent foundation.
Financial data (yr. ended 12/31/12): Assets, $48,829,688 (M); gifts received, $250,000; expenditures, $2,306,306; qualifying distributions, $2,141,388; giving activities include $2,133,856 for 249 grants (high: $600,000; low: $96).
Purpose and activities: Giving primarily to Jewish agencies, temples, and schools.
Fields of interest: Education; Jewish agencies & synagogues.
Limitations: Applications not accepted. Giving primarily in Brooklyn, NY, and Israel. No grants to individuals.
Application information: Contributes only to pre-selected organizations.
Trustees: Abraham Klein; Sarah Dinah Klein.
EIN: 134092608

6289
Calvin Klein Family Foundation ✧
(formerly Calvin & Kelly Klein Foundation, Inc.)
c/o PAF Calvin Klein Studio
545 W. 25th St., 18th Fl.
New York, NY 10001-5501

Established in 1987 in DE.
Donor: Calvin Klein.
Foundation type: Independent foundation.
Financial data (yr. ended 10/31/13): Assets, $1,252,191 (M); gifts received, $1,366,537; expenditures, $1,023,700; qualifying distributions, $1,021,960; giving activities include $1,021,960 for 19 grants (high: $250,000; low: $500).
Fields of interest: Museums (art); Higher education; Education; Medical care, outpatient care; AIDS; Food distribution, groceries on wheels; Gay men.
Type of support: General/operating support; Annual campaigns; Research.
Limitations: Applications not accepted. Giving primarily in New York, NY. No grants to individuals.
Application information: Contributes only to pre-selected organizations.
Officers: Calvin Klein, Pres.; Richard Norton, C.F.O.
Director: Kelly Klein.
EIN: 133472787

6290
The Kleinman Family Foundation ✧
171 Kings Hwy.
Brooklyn, NY 11223-1023

Established in 2003 in NY.
Donor: Martin Kleinman.
Foundation type: Independent foundation.
Financial data (yr. ended 12/31/12): Assets, $12,129,762 (M); expenditures, $4,186,597; qualifying distributions, $4,107,315; giving activities include $4,107,315 for grants.
Purpose and activities: Giving primarily to Jewish agencies, temples, and schools.
Fields of interest: Elementary/secondary education; Jewish agencies & synagogues.
Limitations: Applications not accepted. Giving primarily in Brooklyn, NY. No grants for individuals.
Application information: Contributes only to pre-selected organizations.
Officers: Martin Kleinman, Pres. and Treas.; Beth Kleinman, Secy.
Directors: Aliza Freedman; Joseph S. Kleinman; Deena Schuss.
EIN: 200136129
Selected grants: The following grants are a representative sample of this grantmaker's funding activity:
$750,000 to Congregation Beth Medrash Govoha, Brooklyn, NY, 2011. For general support.
$500,000 to Yeshiva Darchei Torah, Far Rockaway, NY, 2011. For general support.
$400,000 to Mesorah Heritage Foundation, Brooklyn, NY, 2011. For general support.
$300,000 to Shekel Hakodesh, Brooklyn, NY, 2011. For general support.
$300,000 to Yeshivas Novominsk-Kol Yehuda, Brooklyn, NY, 2011. For general support.
$250,000 to Congregation Darchei Noam, Oceanside, NY, 2011. For general support.
$100,000 to Mesorah Heritage Foundation, Brooklyn, NY, 2011. For general support.
$50,000 to Center for Initiatives in Jewish Education, New York, NY, 2011. For general support.
$18,000 to Ichud Mosdos Hachinuch in Brooklyn, Brooklyn, NY, 2011. For general support.
$18,000 to Yeshivat Imrei Daat, American Friends of, Brooklyn, NY, 2011. For general support.

6291
Andrew & Julie Klingenstein Family Fund Inc. ✧
c/o Janet L. Mulligan, Tanton and Co. LLP
37 W. 57th St., 5th Fl.
New York, NY 10019-3411

Established in 2000 in MD.
Donors: Andrew Klingenstein; Andrew Klingenstein Charitable Lead Trust; John Klingenstein; Patricia Klingenstein.
Foundation type: Independent foundation.
Financial data (yr. ended 12/31/13): Assets, $17,221,502 (M); gifts received, $66,212; expenditures, $696,067; qualifying distributions, $621,303; giving activities include $607,266 for 52 grants (high: $60,000; low: $250).
Purpose and activities: Giving primarily for education and health organizations.
Fields of interest: Elementary/secondary education; Higher education; Education; Medical care, bioethics; Health organizations; Jewish agencies & synagogues.
Limitations: Applications not accepted. Giving primarily in Washington, DC. No grants to individuals.
Application information: Contributes only to pre-selected organizations.
Officers: Julie Klingenstein, Pres.; Thomas D. Klingenstein, V.P.; Andrew Klingenstein, Secy.-Treas.
EIN: 522126870

6292
The Esther A. & Joseph Klingenstein Fund, Inc.
125 Park Ave., Ste. 1700
New York, NY 10017-5529 (212) 492-6195
Contact: Andrew D. Klingenstein, Pres.; Kathleen Pomerantz, V.P.
FAX: (212) 492-7007;
E-mail: kathleen.pomerantz@klingenstein.com;
Main URL: http://www.klingfund.org

Incorporated in 1945 in NY.
Donors: Esther A. Klingenstein†; Joseph Klingenstein†; John Klingenstein.
Foundation type: Independent foundation.
Financial data (yr. ended 09/30/13): Assets, $91,013,473 (M); expenditures, $1,726,374; qualifying distributions, $1,079,674; giving activities include $721,681 for 21+ grants (high: $137,106).
Purpose and activities: Primary interests in basic neuroscience research and independent school education.
Fields of interest: Elementary/secondary education; Higher education; Hospitals (general); Medical research, institute; Epilepsy research; Neuroscience research; Civil liberties, first amendment; Public policy, research.
Type of support: General/operating support; Continuing support; Program development; Conferences/seminars; Publication; Seed money; Fellowships; Research; Grants to individuals.
Limitations: Applications accepted. Giving primarily in NY. No grants to individuals (except for Neuroscience Fellowship Program), or for building or endowment funds.
Publications: Informational brochure.
Application information: Online application is required for the Klingenstein Neuroscience Fellowship Awards. Application form not required.
Initial approach: Letter or proposal
Copies of proposal: 1
Deadline(s): See fund web site for current deadline information for the Klingenstein Fellowship Awards
Board meeting date(s): Generally 4 or 5 times a year
Officers and Directors:* Andrew D. Klingenstein,* Pres.; Julie Klingenstein; Patricia D. Klingenstein; Thomas D. Klingenstein; Sally Klingenstein Martell; Nancy Perlman; Nancy K. Simpkins.
Number of staff: 2 full-time professional; 2 part-time professional; 1 full-time support.
EIN: 136028788

6293
Frederick & Sharon Klingenstein Fund ✧
c/o Tanton & Co., LLP
37 W. 57th St., 5th Fl.
New York, NY 10019-3411

Established in 1997 in NY.
Donor: Frederick A. Klingenstein.
Foundation type: Independent foundation.
Financial data (yr. ended 12/31/12): Assets, $18,418,056 (M); expenditures, $980,312; qualifying distributions, $506,977; giving activities include $500,789 for 53 grants (high: $297,661; low: $85).
Purpose and activities: Giving primarily for the arts, particularly museums, as well as for education, with emphasis on a medical school; some funding also for health, children, youth, and social services.
Fields of interest: Museums; Museums (natural history); Arts; Higher education; Medical school/education; Education; Hospitals (general); Human services; Children/youth, services; Community/economic development; Jewish agencies & synagogues.
Limitations: Applications not accepted. Giving primarily in New York, NY.
Application information: Contributes only to pre-selected organizations.
Trustee: Frederick A. Klingenstein.
EIN: 061471980

6294
John & Patricia Klingenstein Fund ✧
c/o Tanton & Co., LLP
37 W. 57th St., 5th Fl.
New York, NY 10019-3411

Established in 1999 in NY.
Donors: John Klingenstein; John Klingenstein 1999 Trust.
Foundation type: Independent foundation.
Financial data (yr. ended 12/31/12): Assets, $43,709,086 (M); gifts received, $1,648,933; expenditures, $2,485,308; qualifying distributions, $2,225,468; giving activities include $2,225,468 for grants.
Purpose and activities: Giving primarily for education and to an historical society.
Fields of interest: Museums (natural history); Historic preservation/historical societies; Education.
Limitations: Applications not accepted. Giving primarily in CT and NY. No grants to individuals.
Application information: Contributes only to pre-selected organizations.
Trustees: Kenneth H. Fields; John Klingenstein; Patricia Klingenstein.
EIN: 134062589

6295
The Knapp Foundation Inc. ✧ ☆
(formerly Silver Marshall Foundation, Inc.)
1740 Broadway, 3rd Fl.
New York, NY 10019-4315
Application address: c/o Charles Knapp, 2 Rectory Ln. S., Scarsdale, NY 10583

Established in 1979 in DE.
Donor: Russell S. Knapp†.
Foundation type: Independent foundation.
Financial data (yr. ended 12/31/13): Assets, $15,708,852 (M); gifts received, $9,925,163; expenditures, $1,049,877; qualifying distributions, $890,000; giving activities include $890,000 for 10 grants (high: $250,000; low: $25,000).
Fields of interest: Higher education; Medical school/education; Education; Health care; Health organizations.
Type of support: General/operating support; Scholarship funds.
Limitations: Applications accepted. Giving primarily in New York, NY. No grants to individuals.
Application information: Application form required.
Initial approach: Proposal
Deadline(s): June 30
Officers: Albert Knapp, V.P.; Leonard S. Schwartz, V.P.; Emily Knapp, Secy.; Charles Knapp, Treas.
EIN: 132979552

6296
Knapp-Swezey Foundation, Inc. ✧
P.O. Box 2549
Patchogue, NY 11772-0886
Contact: Priscilla S. Knapp, Pres.

Established in 1989 in NY.
Donors: Priscilla S. Knapp; Carroll Swezey; Carolyn Maust.
Foundation type: Independent foundation.
Financial data (yr. ended 06/30/13): Assets, $35,783,089 (M); gifts received, $40,070; expenditures, $4,185,300; qualifying distributions, $3,953,235; giving activities include $3,953,235 for 80 grants (high: $1,195,000; low: $250).
Fields of interest: Arts; Education; Hospitals (general); Health organizations, association; Boys & girls clubs; Human services; Youth, services; Military/veterans; Economically disadvantaged.
Type of support: Continuing support; Annual campaigns; Building/renovation; Scholarship funds.
Limitations: Applications accepted. Giving primarily in the Suffolk County, NY, area, with emphasis on the town of Brookhaven. No support for religious organizations. No loans to individuals.
Application information: Application form not required.
Initial approach: Letter
Copies of proposal: 1
Deadline(s): None
Board meeting date(s): Quarterly
Final notification: Next board meeting
Officers: Priscilla Knapp, Pres.; Nancy Swezey, Secy.; William L. Knapp, Treas.
Trustees: Danielle Knapp; David E. Knapp; Jane Knapp; Carolyn Maust; John J. Roe III; Dorothy Swezey; John Swezey; Jerome Teich.
EIN: 113038738
Selected grants: The following grants are a representative sample of this grantmaker's funding activity:
$60,000 to Boy Scouts of America, Medford, NY, 2011.
$20,000 to Three Village Historical Society, Setauket, NY, 2011.
$5,000 to Federation of Organizations, West Babylon, NY, 2011.
$2,000 to Maryhaven Center of Hope, Port Jefferson, NY, 2011.

6297
Alice F. & Cortland J. Knipe Charitable Trust ✧
P.O. Box 1297
Church St. Station
New York, NY 10009-8957

Donor: Cortland J. Knipe†.
Foundation type: Independent foundation.
Financial data (yr. ended 11/30/13): Assets, $18,400,677 (M); expenditures, $874,921; qualifying distributions, $829,742; giving activities include $795,000 for 11 grants (high: $250,000; low: $25,000).
Fields of interest: Education; Health care; Human services.
Limitations: Applications not accepted.
Application information: Unsolicited requests for funds not accepted.
Trustees: Richard A. Nelson; Deutsche Bank Trust Co.
EIN: 262077849

6298
Knott Family Foundation ✧
485 Underhill Rd., Ste. 205
Syosset, NY 11791-3434

Established in 2003 in NY.
Donor: David M. Knott.
Foundation type: Independent foundation.
Financial data (yr. ended 12/31/12): Assets, $2,335,636 (M); gifts received, $151,300; expenditures, $648,825; qualifying distributions, $643,700; giving activities include $643,200 for 19 grants (high: $106,500; low: $500).
Fields of interest: Education; Health care; Boys & girls clubs.
Limitations: Applications not accepted. Giving primarily in NY. No grants to individuals.
Application information: Unsolicited requests for funds not accepted.
Officer and Director:* David M. Knott,* Pres.
EIN: 200495479

6299
The Seymour H. Knox Foundation ✧
1 Seneca Tower
Buffalo, NY 14203-2843 (716) 854-6811

Incorporated in 1945 in NY.
Donors: Seymour H. Knox†; Marjorie K.C. Klopp†; Dorothy K.G. Rogers†.
Foundation type: Independent foundation.
Financial data (yr. ended 12/31/13): Assets, $20,967,758 (M); expenditures, $1,379,385; qualifying distributions, $1,095,581; giving activities include $940,100 for 105 grants (high: $152,800; low: $200).
Fields of interest: Arts education; Arts; Education; Environment, natural resources; Animals/wildlife, preservation/protection; Health care; Human services; United Ways and Federated Giving Programs.
Type of support: General/operating support.
Limitations: Giving primarily in the Buffalo, NY, area. No grants to individuals.
Application information:
Initial approach: Letter
Deadline(s): None

Officers and Directors:* Hazard K. Campbell,* Chair.; Northrup R. Knox, Jr.,* Pres.; Seymour H. Knox IV,* V.P. and Secy.; Benjamin K. Campbell,* V.P. and Treas.; Charles W. Banta.
EIN: 160839066
Selected grants: The following grants are a representative sample of this grantmaker's funding activity:
$12,500 to Gow School, South Wales, NY, 2012. For science and technology.
$10,000 to Buffalo and Erie County Historical Society, Buffalo, NY, 2012. For The 150th Anniversary Event.
$2,500 to Westminster Presbyterian Church, Buffalo, NY, 2012. For general operating need.
$2,000 to BISON Scholarship Fund, Buffalo, NY, 2012. For Scholarship to Buffalo's Low Income Children.
$1,600 to Preservation League of New York State, Albany, NY, 2012. For Honoring - the Margaret L. Wendt Foundation.

6300
The Kohlberg Foundation, Inc. ✧
111 Radio Cir.
Mount Kisco, NY 10549-2609 (914) 242-2385
Contact: Nancy White McCabe, Exec. V.P. and Exec. Dir.
FAX: (914) 242-7284; E-mail: dehaan@kfound.org; Main URL: http://www.kohlbergfoundation.org/

Established in 1989 in NY.
Donor: The Kohlberg Foundation.
Foundation type: Independent foundation.
Financial data (yr. ended 12/31/13): Assets, $306,932,183 (M); gifts received, $4,500,000; expenditures, $26,390,111; qualifying distributions, $24,392,685; giving activities include $23,450,701 for 100 grants (high: $4,000,000; low: $300).
Purpose and activities: Support for environmental and conservation programs, integrative medicine, community, educational and cultural organizations.
Fields of interest: Environment; Health organizations, association; Medical research, institute; Children/youth, services.
International interests: Mexico.
Type of support: Program-related investments/loans; Annual campaigns; Land acquisition; Program development; Seed money; Program evaluation.
Limitations: Applications not accepted. Giving primarily in the U.S., with emphasis on CA and MA; giving also in Baja CA, Mexico. No grants to individuals.
Publications: Annual report.
Application information: Contributes only to pre-selected organizations.
Board meeting date(s): Spring and Fall
Officers and Trustees:* Jerome Kohlberg,* Chair. and Pres.; Nancy White McCabe,* Exec. V.P. and Exec. Dir.; Jennifer Magnone,* Secy.; Leslie G. Fagen.
Number of staff: 4 full-time professional; 1 full-time support.
EIN: 133496263

6301
Zichron Moshe Vesther Kohn Foundation ✧ ☆
768 Bedford Ave.
Brooklyn, NY 11205-1508

Established in NY.
Donors: Nachum Sherman; Kohn Family Trust; New Century Mgmt. Svcs. LLC; Blum Foundation.
Foundation type: Independent foundation.
Financial data (yr. ended 12/31/12): Assets, $0 (M); gifts received, $435,644; expenditures, $455,330; qualifying distributions, $453,761; giving activities include $453,761 for grants.
Fields of interest: Jewish agencies & synagogues.
Limitations: Applications not accepted. Giving primarily in NY. No grants to individuals.
Application information: Contributes only to pre-selected organizations.
Trustees: Herb Kohn; Sara Kohn.
EIN: 113435079

6302
Kopf Family Foundation ✧ ☆
(formerly Kopf Foundation, Inc.)
c/o Kelley, Drye & Warren LLP
101 Park Ave., 30th Fl.
New York, NY 10178-0001

Incorporated in 1967 in NY.
Donor: R.C. Kopf†.
Foundation type: Independent foundation.
Financial data (yr. ended 12/31/13): Assets, $14,897,174 (M); expenditures, $854,871; qualifying distributions, $672,126; giving activities include $518,268 for grants.
Purpose and activities: Giving primarily for higher and other education; funding also for a hospital foundation.
Fields of interest: Higher education; Business school/education; Hospitals (general).
Type of support: General/operating support; Continuing support; Seed money; Fellowships; Scholarship funds; Matching/challenge support.
Limitations: Applications not accepted. Giving primarily in FL, MA, and NY. No grants to individuals.
Application information: Contributes only to pre-selected organizations.
Officers: Patricia Colagiuri, Pres.; Nancy Sue Mueller, V.P.; Michael S. Insel, Esq., Secy.; Brenda Helies, Treas.
EIN: 136228036

6303
Hyman Korman Family Foundation ✧
c/o Brown Brothers Harriman Tr. Co., N.A.
140 Broadway
New York, NY 10005-1108

Trust established in 1947 in PA.
Donors: Hyman Korman, Inc.; I. Barney Moss†; Berton E. Korman; Leonard I. Korman; Steven H. Korman; Members of the Korman family.
Foundation type: Independent foundation.
Financial data (yr. ended 12/31/13): Assets, $11,396,732 (M); expenditures, $582,987; qualifying distributions, $490,695; giving activities include $487,750 for 10 grants (high: $120,000; low: $5,000).
Purpose and activities: Giving primarily for Jewish agencies and temples, and for higher education.
Fields of interest: Museums (ethnic/folk arts); Elementary/secondary education; Higher education; Medical care, outpatient care; Jewish federated giving programs; Jewish agencies & synagogues.
Limitations: Applications not accepted. Giving primarily in PA. No grants to individuals.
Application information: Contributes only to pre-selected organizations.
Trustees: Berton E. Korman; Leonard I. Korman; Steven H. Korman.
EIN: 236297326
Selected grants: The following grants are a representative sample of this grantmaker's funding activity:
$170,000 to Public School of Germantown, Fort Washington, PA, 2011.
$102,500 to Albert Einstein Healthcare Network, Philadelphia, PA, 2011.
$100,000 to Jewish Federation of Greater Philadelphia, Philadelphia, PA, 2011.
$15,000 to Jefferson Foundation, Philadelphia, PA, 2011.
$10,000 to Cystic Fibrosis Foundation, Broomall, PA, 2011.
$10,000 to Philadelphia Jewish Archives Center, Philadelphia, PA, 2011.
$10,000 to Talmudical Yeshiva of Philadelphia, Philadelphia, PA, 2011.
$5,000 to United Way of Bucks County, Fairless Hills, PA, 2011.

6304
Emily Davie and Joseph S. Kornfeld Foundation
41 Schermerhorn St., Ste. 208
Brooklyn, NY 11201-4802 (718) 624-7969
Contact: Bobye G. List, Exec. Dir.
FAX: (718) 834-1204;
E-mail: office@kornfeldfdn.org; Main URL: http://kornfeldfdn.org
Additional URL: http://www.kornfeldfdn.org
Grants List: http://fdnweb.org/kornfeld/recent-grants/

Established in 1979.
Donor: Emily Davie Kornfeld†.
Foundation type: Independent foundation.
Financial data (yr. ended 12/31/13): Assets, $31,588,802 (M); expenditures, $2,030,715; qualifying distributions, $1,872,430; giving activities include $1,600,000 for 22 grants (high: $600,000; low: $5,000; average: $10,000–$50,000).
Purpose and activities: The Foundation supports: 1) Literacy enrichment programs for New York City public school children that focus on arts education and professional development, in collaboration with Columbia University Teachers College Reading and Writing Project; 2) Robert Packard Center for ALS Research at Johns Hopkins Medical School; 3) Grants in palliative care and bioethics, currently focused on the National Palliative Care Research Center at Mount Sinai School of Medicine and the Kornfeld Program in Bioethics and Patient Care, administered by The Greenwall Foundation.
Fields of interest: Education, management/technical assistance; Elementary/secondary education; Medical school/education; Education, reading; Health care, ethics; Palliative care; Health care; Medical research, institute.
Type of support: Program development; Seed money; Curriculum development; Research; Program evaluation.

Limitations: Applications accepted. Giving limited to the continental U.S., with emphasis on New York, NY, for educational grants.
Publications: Annual report (including application guidelines); Grants list.
Application information: The foundation will no longer be accepting grants for after school programs. Bioethics grantmaking now restricted to Kornfeld Program in Bioethics and Patient Care program. Application information available on foundation Web site. The grants listed in current program areas include major ongoing commitments undertaken pursuant to this strategy. Accordingly, only minimal grants to other organizations will be available in the near future. Application form not required.
Initial approach: Letter
Copies of proposal: 1
Deadline(s): Mar. 15, July 15, and Nov. 15
Board meeting date(s): Feb., May, and Oct.
Final notification: Winter, spring, and fall
Officers and Directors:* Christopher C. Angell,* Pres.; Emme L. Deland,* V.P. and Treas.; Barry H. Smith, M.D.*, Secy.; Bobye G. List, Exec. Dir.
Number of staff: 1 full-time professional; 1 part-time support.
EIN: 133042360
Selected grants: The following grants are a representative sample of this grantmaker's funding activity:
$185,000 to Johns Hopkins University, Baltimore, MD, 2013. For Annual Scientific Symposium and Clinician Forum.
$150,000 to Henry Street Settlement, New York, NY, 2013. For expansion of Studiolab Integrate programming, payable over 3.00 years.
$100,000 to Brooklyn Academy of Music, Brooklyn, NY, 2013. For Brooklyn Reads, payable over 2.00 years.
$100,000 to Brooklyn Museum, Brooklyn Institute of Arts and Sciences, Brooklyn, NY, 2013. For Expanded Focus Unit Program, payable over 2.00 years.
$80,000 to Orchestra of Saint Lukes, New York, NY, 2013. For YOSL: Youth Orchestra of St. Lukes, payable over 2.00 years.
$60,000 to New-York Historical Society, New York, NY, 2013. For Art of History Professional Development Program, payable over 2.00 years.
$54,000 to Ethical Culture Fieldston School, New York, NY, 2013. For Young Dancemakers Company, payable over 2.00 years.
$35,000 to Public School 15 the Patrick F. Daly School, Brooklyn, NY, 2013. For Library Power Launch.
$30,000 to Metropolitan Opera Guild, New York, NY, 2013. For COBALT (Comprehensive Opera-Based Arts Learning and Teaching).
$10,000 to Orchestra of Saint Lukes, New York, NY, 2013. For general operating support.

6305
The Kraus Family Foundation ✧
Bowling Green Sta.
P.O. Box 73
New York, NY 10274-0073

Established in 1996 in NY.
Donor: Peter S. Kraus.
Foundation type: Independent foundation.
Financial data (yr. ended 08/31/13): Assets, $11,098,997 (M); gifts received, $750; expenditures, $3,281,912; qualifying distributions, $3,250,431; giving activities include $3,250,431 for 95 grants (high: $1,000,000; low: $100).
Purpose and activities: Giving primarily for the arts, particularly to art museums; funding also for education.
Fields of interest: Museums (art); Arts; Higher education; Education; Environment, land resources; Hospitals (general); Human services; Foundations (private grantmaking); Jewish agencies & synagogues.
Type of support: General/operating support.
Limitations: Applications not accepted. Giving primarily in CT and NY; some giving also in CA. No grants to individuals.
Application information: Contributes only to pre-selected organizations.
Trustees: Jill G. Kraus; Peter S. Kraus.
EIN: 133921376

6306
The Marie-Josee and Henry R. Kravis Foundation, Inc. ✧
c/o KKR Financial Svcs. Co., LLC
730 Fifth Ave., 8th Fl.
New York, NY 10019-4105 (212) 271-9933

Established in 1985 in NY.
Donor: Henry R. Kravis.
Foundation type: Independent foundation.
Financial data (yr. ended 11/30/13): Assets, $1,065,003 (M); expenditures, $21,805,950; qualifying distributions, $21,645,891; giving activities include $21,627,496 for 108 grants (high: $5,000,000; low: $200).
Purpose and activities: Support primarily for education, arts and culture, including a museum, and for social services.
Fields of interest: Museums; Arts; Higher education; Education; Human services.
Type of support: General/operating support.
Limitations: Applications not accepted. Giving primarily in NY. No grants to individuals.
Application information: Contributes only to pre-selected organizations.
Officers and Directors:* Henry R. Kravis,* Chair.; Lesley Harrison, Secy.; James M. Goldrick, Treas.; Richard I. Beattie.
EIN: 133341521
Selected grants: The following grants are a representative sample of this grantmaker's funding activity:
$5,000,000 to Claremont McKenna College, Claremont, CA, 2013.
$5,000,000 to Columbia University, New York, NY, 2013.
$2,000,000 to Museum of Modern Art, New York, NY, 2013.
$1,500,000 to Philharmonic-Symphony Society of New York, New York, NY, 2013.
$625,000 to Museum of Modern Art, New York, NY, 2013.
$500,000 to Claremont McKenna College, Claremont, CA, 2013.
$500,000 to Loomis Chaffee School, Windsor, CT, 2013.
$312,000 to Museum of Modern Art, New York, NY, 2013.
$200,000 to Loomis Chaffee School, Windsor, CT, 2013.
$25,000 to Studio Museum in Harlem, New York, NY, 2013.

6307
The Raymond and Bessie Kravis Foundation ✧
c/o KKR Financial Svcs. Co., LLC
730 5th Ave., 8th Fl.
New York, NY 10019-2601

Established in 1992 in OK.
Donors: Bessie R. Kravis†; Raymond Field Kravis†.
Foundation type: Independent foundation.
Financial data (yr. ended 12/31/13): Assets, $34,116,358 (M); expenditures, $1,308,849; qualifying distributions, $1,147,130; giving activities include $947,500 for 11 grants (high: $250,000; low: $10,000).
Purpose and activities: Giving primarily for the arts and higher education.
Fields of interest: Museums (art); Performing arts centers; Arts; Higher education.
Limitations: Applications not accepted. Giving primarily in Tulsa, OK. No grants to individuals.
Application information: Contributes only to pre-selected organizations.
Trustees: George R. Kravis II; Henry R. Kravis; Kimberly R. Kravis; Robert S. Kravis.
EIN: 731393621

6308
Samuel H. Kress Foundation ✧
174 E. 80th St.
New York, NY 10075-0439 (212) 861-4993
Contact: Wyman Meers, Prog. Admin.
FAX: (212) 628-3146;
E-mail: wyman.meers@kressfoundation.org; E-mail for grant and fellowship inquiries: info@kressfoundation.org; Main URL: http://www.kressfoundation.org

Incorporated in 1929 in NY.
Donors: Samuel H. Kress†; Claude W. Kress†; Rush H. Kress†.
Foundation type: Independent foundation.
Financial data (yr. ended 06/30/13): Assets, $88,824,967 (M); expenditures, $6,751,482; qualifying distributions, $5,206,354; giving activities include $4,111,761 for 237 grants (high: $300,000; low: $49), and $19,442 for 1 foundation-administered program.
Purpose and activities: Giving through five main programs: 1) fellowships for pre-doctoral research in art history; 2) advanced training and research in conservation of works of art; 3) development of scholarly resources in the fields of art history and conservation; 4) conservation and restoration of monuments in Europe; and 5) occasional related projects.
Fields of interest: Visual arts; Museums; History/archaeology; Arts.
International interests: Europe.
Type of support: Conferences/seminars; Professorships; Publication; Fellowships; Internship funds; Research; Employee matching gifts.
Limitations: Applications accepted. Giving primarily in the U.S. and Europe. No support for the purchase of works of art. No grants for living artists, or for operating budgets, continuing support, annual campaigns, endowments, deficit financing, capital funds exhibitions, or films; no loans.
Publications: Application guidelines; Annual report (including application guidelines).
Application information: Application forms required for fellowships in art history and interpretive

fellowships. Applications sent by fax not considered. Application form not required.
Initial approach: Proposal
Copies of proposal: 1
Deadline(s): Nov. 30 for research fellowships in art history; Received by Mar. 10 for conservation fellowships, Apr. 1 for interpretive fellowships; Quarterly submission deadlines: Jan. 15, Apr. 1, and Oct. 1
Board meeting date(s): Annually in winter, spring and fall
Final notification: 3 months
Officers and Trustees:* Frederick W. Beinecke,* Chair.; Max Marmor,* Pres.; David Rumsey, Secy.-Treas.; Elizabeth Eveillard; Carmela Vircillo Franklin; William Higgins; Cheryl Hurley; Barbara A. Shailor; Daniel H. Weiss.
Number of staff: 4 full-time professional; 1 part-time professional.
EIN: 131624176
Selected grants: The following grants are a representative sample of this grantmaker's funding activity:
$89,000 to National Gallery of Art, Washington, DC, 2012. To develop Kress Collection History and Conservation Database.
$83,000 to Yale University, New Haven, CT, 2012. For Summer Teachers Institute in Technical Art History.
$80,000 to American Academy in Rome, New York, NY, 2012. For Rome Prize Pre-doctoral Fellowships in Art History.
$75,000 to Allentown Art Museum, Allentown, PA, 2012. For exhibition, Shared Treasure: The Legacy of Samuel H. Kress.
$50,000 to Smithsonian Institution, Washington, DC, 2012. For World War II-era Provenance Webpage Project.
$48,500 to Middlebury College, Middlebury, VT, 2012. For Summer Language School Scholarships.
$35,000 to Indianapolis Museum of Art, Indianapolis, IN, 2012. For 21st Century Voices Oral History Project.
$26,000 to Art Institute of Chicago, Chicago, IL, 2012. For Teaching Institute in Museum Education program.
$25,000 to Frick Collection, New York, NY, 2012. For meeting on digitization of key photo archives in the US and Europe.
$10,000 to French Regional American Museum Exchange, Los Angeles, CA, 2012. For exhibition, Caravaggio and His Followers.

6309
Jeannette & H. Peter Kriendler Charitable Trust ✧
c/o Fiduciary Trust International
600 5th Ave.
New York, NY 10020-2302

Established in 1986 in NY.
Donors: H. Peter Kriendler†; Maxwell C.C. Kriendler Unitrust.
Foundation type: Independent foundation.
Financial data (yr. ended 12/31/13): Assets, $13,107,583 (M); expenditures, $809,428; qualifying distributions, $736,494; giving activities include $695,000 for 66 grants (high: $30,000; low: $2,000).
Fields of interest: Arts; Health organizations, association; Human services; International affairs; Jewish agencies & synagogues.
Limitations: Applications not accepted. Giving primarily in NY. No grants to individuals.
Application information: Contributes only to pre-selected organizations.
Trustees: Blair Axel; John Kriendler.
EIN: 136880589
Selected grants: The following grants are a representative sample of this grantmaker's funding activity:
$20,000 to Cornell University, Ithaca, NY, 2011. For general charitable purposes.

6310
Guru Krupa Foundation Inc. ✧
P.O. Box 81
Jericho, NY 11753-0081 (631) 704-2776
Contact: Mukund Padmanabhan, Pres.
E-mail: mp@guru-krupa.org; Main URL: http://www.guru-krupa.org

Established in 2008 in NY.
Donor: Mukund Padmanabhan.
Foundation type: Independent foundation.
Financial data (yr. ended 06/30/13): Assets, $21,768,211 (M); gifts received, $11,500,000; expenditures, $919,201; qualifying distributions, $900,967; giving activities include $900,967 for 14 grants (high: $250,000; low: $20,000).
Purpose and activities: Giving primarily for: 1) Social projects that aim to improve the lives of impoverished people who do not have access to basic material needs; 2) Educational projects to fund fellowships at well recognized universities; and 3) Religious and Cultural projects that support activities related to preserving and nurturing the Hindu Dharmic way of life.
Fields of interest: Education; Hinduism; Economically disadvantaged.
Limitations: Applications accepted. Giving primarily in MD, MO and NY; funding also in Tamil Nadu, India.
Publications: Application guidelines.
Application information: Application form required.
Initial approach: Proposal
Deadline(s): None
Officers and Director:* Mukund Padmanabhan,* Pres.; Lalit Bahl, Secy.-Treas.
Trustee: Deepak Nayak.
EIN: 261900576
Selected grants: The following grants are a representative sample of this grantmaker's funding activity:
$100,000 to UCLA Foundation, Los Angeles, CA, 2011.
$11,803 to Children International, Kansas City, MO, 2011.

6311
Mitchell and Karen Kuflik Charitable Foundation ✧
15 Franklin Ln.
Harrison, NY 10528-1105

Established in 1999 in NY.
Donors: Mitchell Kuflik; Karen Kuflik.
Foundation type: Independent foundation.
Financial data (yr. ended 12/31/12): Assets, $109,895 (M); gifts received, $1,242,874; expenditures, $1,250,333; qualifying distributions, $1,246,470; giving activities include $1,246,470 for 81 grants (high: $516,600; low: $100).
Purpose and activities: Giving primarily to Jewish agencies, temples, and schools.
Fields of interest: Education; Human services; Jewish agencies & synagogues.
Limitations: Applications not accepted. Giving primarily in NY. No grants to individuals.
Application information: Contributes only to pre-selected organizations.
Officers: Mitchell Kuflik, Pres.; Karen Kuflik, V.P.
EIN: 137197004

6312
Jesse and Joan Kupferberg Family Foundation ✧
c/o Martin R. Kupferberg
131-38 Sanford Ave.
Flushing, NY 11355-4231

Established in 2001 in NY.
Donor: Jesse M. Kupferberg.
Foundation type: Independent foundation.
Financial data (yr. ended 11/30/13): Assets, $10,979,843 (M); expenditures, $515,755; qualifying distributions, $476,566; giving activities include $470,000 for 21 grants (high: $105,000; low: $1,000).
Fields of interest: Education; Autism; Medical research; Jewish agencies & synagogues.
Limitations: Applications not accepted. Giving primarily in NY. No grants to individuals.
Application information: Unsolicited requests for funds not accepted.
Trustees: Liane S. Carter; Martin R. Kupferberg.
EIN: 061636088
Selected grants: The following grants are a representative sample of this grantmaker's funding activity:
$175,000 to Brandeis University, Waltham, MA, 2011.
$75,000 to Autism Speaks, New York, NY, 2011.
$15,000 to Citizens United for Research in Epilepsy, Chicago, IL, 2011.
$15,000 to MATAN: The Gift of Jewish Learning for Every Child, White Plains, NY, 2011.
$10,000 to Anti-Defamation League of Bnai Brith, New York, NY, 2011.
$10,000 to Ramapo for Children, Rhinebeck, NY, 2011.
$5,000 to Dorot, New York, NY, 2011.
$3,000 to Queens Library Foundation, Jamaica, NY, 2011.
$1,000 to New York Gilbert and Sullivan Players, New York, NY, 2011.

6313
The Kupferberg Foundation ✧
c/o Max Kupferberg
131-38 Sanford Ave.
Flushing, NY 11355-4231

Established in 1961 in NY.
Donors: Jesse Kupferberg; Max Kupferberg; Kepco, Inc.
Foundation type: Company-sponsored foundation.
Financial data (yr. ended 11/30/13): Assets, $13,238,205 (M); expenditures, $702,004; qualifying distributions, $625,324; giving activities include $605,500 for 30 grants (high: $173,000; low: $2,000).
Purpose and activities: The foundation supports organizations involved with arts and culture,

education, health, autism, eye disease research, human services, and Judaism.
Fields of interest: Education; Health care; Science.
Type of support: General/operating support.
Limitations: Applications not accepted. Giving primarily in New York and Queens, NY. No grants to individuals.
Application information: Contributes only to pre-selected organizations.
Officer: Max Kupferberg, Pres.
Trustees: Martin Kupferberg; Saul Kupferberg.
EIN: 116008915
Selected grants: The following grants are a representative sample of this grantmaker's funding activity:
$20,000 to Autism Speaks, Port Chester, NY, 2011.
$12,000 to Queens Botanical Garden Society, Flushing, NY, 2011.
$12,000 to Ramapo for Children, Rhinebeck, NY, 2011.
$9,000 to MATAN: The Gift of Jewish Learning for Every Child, White Plains, NY, 2011.
$5,000 to Anti-Defamation League of Bnai Brith, New York, NY, 2011. For general support.
$5,000 to Saint Francis Hospital, Roslyn, NY, 2011.
$3,000 to Ackerman Institute for the Family, New York, NY, 2011. For general support.
$3,000 to Crohns and Colitis Foundation of America, Garden City, NY, 2011. For general support.
$3,000 to Queens Museum of Art, Flushing, NY, 2011. For general support.
$2,000 to International Rescue Committee, New York, NY, 2011. For general support.

6314
The Kurz Family Foundation Ltd. ✧
c/o Baker Tilly Virchow Krause, LLP
1 Penn Plz., Ste. 3000
New York, NY 10119

Established in 1992 in NY.
Donor: Herbert Kurz.
Foundation type: Independent foundation.
Financial data (yr. ended 12/31/13): Assets, $80,204,551 (M); expenditures, $3,485,531; qualifying distributions, $1,804,868; giving activities include $1,780,000 for 75 grants (high: $300,000; low: $500).
Fields of interest: Higher education; Environment, natural resources; Hospitals (general); Human services; Children/youth, services; International peace/security; Community/economic development; Jewish agencies & synagogues.
Limitations: Applications not accepted. Giving primarily in NY. No grants to individuals.
Application information: Contributes only to pre-selected organizations.
Officers and Directors:* Herbert Kurz,* Chair.; Ellen Kurz,* Secy.; Leonard Kurz,* Treas.; Brenda D. Neal.
EIN: 133680855

6315
Gloria and Richard Kushel Foundation ✧ ☆
1135 Greacen Point Rd.
Mamaroneck, NY 10543-4612

Established in 2007 in NY.
Donors: John Richard Kushel; Gloria Joan Kushel.
Foundation type: Independent foundation.
Financial data (yr. ended 12/31/13): Assets, $2,336,677 (M); gifts received, $302,835; expenditures, $485,115; qualifying distributions, $484,730; giving activities include $484,730 for 24 grants (high: $246,330; low: $100).
Fields of interest: Education; Health care; Human services.
Limitations: Applications not accepted. No grants to individuals.
Application information: Unsolicited requests for funds not accepted.
Directors: Gloria Joan Kushel; John Richard Kushel; Stephen Kushel.
EIN: 261397530

6316
L. & L. Foundation ✧
48 Lawrence Ave.
Lawrence, NY 11559-1436
Contact: Joshua Guttman, Mgr.

Foundation type: Independent foundation.
Financial data (yr. ended 12/31/12): Assets, $4,780,827 (M); expenditures, $494,065; qualifying distributions, $449,796; giving activities include $449,796 for grants.
Fields of interest: Jewish agencies & synagogues.
Limitations: Giving primarily in NY.
Trustee: Joshua Guttman.
EIN: 113416458

6317
The L.E. Charitable Trust ✧
1453 50th St.
Brooklyn, NY 11219-3632

Established in 1992 in NY.
Donors: Ludvik Hilman; Eva Hilman.
Foundation type: Independent foundation.
Financial data (yr. ended 11/30/13): Assets, $13,688,447 (M); gifts received, $309,954; expenditures, $708,742; qualifying distributions, $681,069; giving activities include $680,260 for grants.
Purpose and activities: Giving primarily to Jewish organizations.
Fields of interest: Education; Jewish agencies & synagogues.
Limitations: Applications not accepted. Giving limited to Brooklyn, NY. No grants to individuals.
Application information: Contributes only to pre-selected organizations.
Trustees: Eva Hilman; Abraham Loeffler; Miriam Shimon.
EIN: 113133027

6318
The Lachman Family Foundation Inc. ✧
c/o David B. Petshaft PC
138 Rolling Hill Rd.
Manhasset, NY 11030-2517

Established in 2002 in NY.
Donor: Leon Lachman.
Foundation type: Independent foundation.
Financial data (yr. ended 12/31/12): Assets, $11,119,593 (M); gifts received, $1,000,505; expenditures, $446,164; qualifying distributions, $442,000; giving activities include $442,000 for grants.
Fields of interest: Performing arts, orchestras; Higher education; Health sciences school/education; Scholarships/financial aid; International relief, 2004 tsunami.
Limitations: Applications not accepted. Giving primarily in MD, NY and WI. No grants to individuals.
Application information: Contributes only to pre-selected organizations.
Officers and Directors:* Leon Lachman,* Pres. and Treas.; Joan Lachman,* V.P. and Secy.; Julie Lachman,* V.P.; Lawrence Lachman,* V.P.; David B. Petshaft,* V.P.
EIN: 320033014

6319
Laffont Family Foundation ✧ ☆
c/o Coatue Management
9 W. 57th St., 25th Fl.
New York, NY 10019-2701

Donors: Philippe Laffont; Laffont 2009 Charitable Lead Unity Trust; Coatue Management, LLC.
Foundation type: Independent foundation.
Financial data (yr. ended 12/31/13): Assets, $85,772 (M); gifts received, $890,651; expenditures, $5,851,778; qualifying distributions, $5,850,058; giving activities include $5,845,615 for 4 grants (high: $4,000,000; low: $345,615).
Fields of interest: Health care; Agriculture/food; Human services.
Limitations: Applications not accepted.
Application information: Unsolicited requests for funds not accepted.
Officers: Philippe Laffont, Pres.; Ana Luisa Diez De Rivera, Treas.
EIN: 271517424

6320
Lake Road Foundation ✧
(formerly Lowenstein Family Foundation)
c/o Leonard Schwartz
1740 Broadway, 3rd Fl.
New York, NY 10019-4315

Established in 1993 in DE.
Donor: Richard Lowenstein.
Foundation type: Independent foundation.
Financial data (yr. ended 04/30/13): Assets, $21,497,348 (M); expenditures, $1,032,653; qualifying distributions, $1,029,703; giving activities include $1,028,845 for 41 grants (high: $150,000; low: $250).
Fields of interest: Museums; Performing arts, theater; Performing arts, opera; Higher education, university; Homeless, human services; Jewish federated giving programs; Jewish agencies & synagogues.
Limitations: Applications not accepted. Giving primarily in NY. No grants to individuals.
Application information: Unsolicited requests for funds not accepted.
Officers: Wendy Sandler, Pres.; Neil Sandler, Secy.; Michael Lowenstein, Treas.
EIN: 133745065

6321
Lambert Family Foundation ✧
c/o Bessemer Trust Co., N.A.
630 5th Ave.
New York, NY 10111-0001 (212) 708-9216
Contact: Bill Lambert, Tr.; Sheila Lambert, Tr.; Phineas Lambert, Tr.

Established in 2001 in NY.
Donors: Bill Lambert; Sheila Lambert; Phineas Lambert; Lambert Family Foundation.
Foundation type: Independent foundation.
Financial data (yr. ended 12/31/13): Assets, $18,999,341 (M); expenditures, $1,006,140; qualifying distributions, $973,151; giving activities include $968,266 for 58 grants (high: $123,000; low: $850).
Purpose and activities: Giving primarily for education, women's issues (including health education and civil rights and liberties), and for organizations that provide health care, shelter, food and other services to poor and disadvantaged persons.
Fields of interest: Secondary school/education; Higher education; Education; Health care; Human services; Jewish agencies & synagogues; Women; Economically disadvantaged.
Limitations: Applications accepted. Giving primarily in NY. No grants to individuals.
Application information: Application form required.
Initial approach: Letter
Deadline(s): None
Trustees: Bill Lambert; Phineas Lambert; Sheila Lambert.
EIN: 316665497

6322
Ralph Landau Foundation ✧
c/o Listowel Inc.
2 Park Ave., Ste. 1525
New York, NY 10016-5701

Established in DE.
Donors: The Ralph Landau 1995 Trust; Claire Landau†.
Foundation type: Independent foundation.
Financial data (yr. ended 12/31/12): Assets, $55,742,835 (M); gifts received, $1,693,791; expenditures, $3,072,555; qualifying distributions, $2,913,109; giving activities include $2,667,329 for 32 grants (high: $750,000; low: $250).
Fields of interest: Higher education; Biology/life sciences.
Type of support: General/operating support.
Limitations: Applications not accepted. Giving primarily in NY and PA. No grants to individuals.
Application information: Contributes only to pre-selected organizations.
Officers: Laurie J. Landau, Pres.; Edward F. Rover, Secy.-Treas.
EIN: 132895717

6323
The Landegger Charitable Foundation, Inc. ✧
4 International Dr., Ste. 300
Rye Brook, NY 10573-1065

Established in 1975 DE and FL.
Foundation type: Independent foundation.
Financial data (yr. ended 10/31/13): Assets, $7,892,206 (M); expenditures, $658,249; qualifying distributions, $597,630; giving activities include $589,500 for 54 grants (high: $401,000; low: $250).
Purpose and activities: Giving primarily for higher education, health associations, and social services.
Fields of interest: Higher education; Education; Health organizations, association; Human services; Protestant agencies & churches.
Limitations: Applications not accepted. Giving primarily in CT and NY. No grants to individuals.
Application information: Unsolicited requests for funds not accepted.
Officers: George F. Landegger, Pres.; Carl Landegger, Treas.
EIN: 510180544
Selected grants: The following grants are a representative sample of this grantmaker's funding activity:
$8,000 to Abraham House, Bronx, NY, 2011.
$5,000 to Aish HaTorah, Airmont, NY, 2011.
$2,000 to Achilles International, New York, NY, 2011.

6324
Landy Family Foundation ✧ ☆
c/o Warburg Pincus, LLC, Attn.: Joseph P. Landy
450 Lexington Ave., 32nd Fl.
New York, NY 10017-3904

Established in 2001 in NY.
Donor: Joseph P. Landy.
Foundation type: Independent foundation.
Financial data (yr. ended 07/31/13): Assets, $5,077,137 (M); expenditures, $1,112,185; qualifying distributions, $1,051,417; giving activities include $1,051,417 for 18 grants (high: $768,916; low: $2,500).
Fields of interest: Arts; Higher education; Education; Health organizations; Boy scouts; Human services; Children/youth, services.
Limitations: Applications not accepted. Giving primarily in NY. No grants to individuals.
Application information: Contributes only to pre-selected organizations.
Trustees: Joseph P. Landy; Mary P. Landy.
EIN: 912172209
Selected grants: The following grants are a representative sample of this grantmaker's funding activity:
$200,000 to University of Pennsylvania, Philadelphia, PA, 2011.
$10,000 to Community Service Associates, Mount Vernon, NY, 2011.
$10,000 to Concordia College, Bronxville, NY, 2011.
$10,000 to Susan G. Komen for the Cure, Dallas, TX, 2011.
$7,500 to Bronxville School Foundation, Bronxville, NY, 2011.
$3,500 to Cathedral Education Cluster, Bridgeport, CT, 2011.
$2,500 to AIDS Walk Boston, Boston, MA, 2011.
$2,500 to Bereavement Center of Westchester, Scarsdale, NY, 2011.
$2,500 to Phoenix House Foundation, New York, NY, 2011.
$1,000 to Little Baby Face Foundation, New York, NY, 2011.

6325
The Randi and Clifford Lane Foundation, Inc. ✧
105 Wilbur Pl.
Bohemia, NY 11716-2426

Established in 2001 in NY.
Donors: Clifford Lane; Randi Lane; ILC Holdings, Inc.; Mildred Lane†.
Foundation type: Independent foundation.
Financial data (yr. ended 12/31/12): Assets, $17,911,525 (M); expenditures, $1,074,132; qualifying distributions, $978,675; giving activities include $978,675 for 39 grants (high: $250,000; low: $225).
Fields of interest: Hospitals (general); Cancer; Medical research, institute; Children/youth, services; Jewish federated giving programs.
Limitations: Applications not accepted. Giving primarily in NY. No grants to individuals.
Application information: Contributes only to pre-selected organizations.
Officers: Clifford Lane, Pres.; Randi Lane, V.P.
Director: Terrence M. Bennett.
EIN: 113635985

6326
Eugene M. Lang Foundation ✧
535 5th Ave., Ste. 906
New York, NY 10017-8007 (212) 949-4100
Contact: Eugene M. Lang, Tr.

Established in 1968 in NY.
Donor: Eugene M. Lang.
Foundation type: Independent foundation.
Financial data (yr. ended 12/31/13): Assets, $19,841,016 (M); expenditures, $22,111,369; qualifying distributions, $21,914,958; giving activities include $21,758,928 for grants.
Purpose and activities: Giving primarily for an arts center, higher and other education, cultural programs, and health and hospitals, including medical research.
Fields of interest: Performing arts; Arts; Education, early childhood education; Higher education; Education; Hospitals (general); Health care; Health organizations, association; Medical research, institute; Children/youth; Children.
Type of support: General/operating support; Continuing support; Annual campaigns; Program development; Conferences/seminars; Professorships; Seed money; Fellowships; Internship funds; Scholarship funds.
Limitations: Applications accepted. Giving primarily in Washington, DC, NY and neighboring areas, including PA. No grants to individuals, or for building funds, equipment and materials, capital or endowment funds, deficit financing, publications, or matching gifts; no loans.
Publications: Annual report (including application guidelines); Grants list; Program policy statement.
Application information: Application form required.
Initial approach: Letter
Deadline(s): None
Trustees: Eugene M. Lang; Jane Lang; Kristina Lang; Lucy Lang; Stephen Lang; Lauren McGrail; Paul Sprenger.
Number of staff: 2 full-time professional.
EIN: 136153412

6327
The Jacob and Valeria Langeloth Foundation ✧
275 Madison Ave., 33rd Fl.
New York, NY 10016-1101 (212) 687-1133
Contact: Andrea Fionda, Prog. Off.
FAX: (212) 687-8877;
E-mail: afionda@langeloth.org; Main URL: http://www.langeloth.org
Facebook: https://www.facebook.com/TheLangelothFoundation
Twitter: https://twitter.com/LangelothFndn

Incorporated in 1915 in NY as the Valeria Home; renamed in 1975.
Donor: Jacob Langeloth†.
Foundation type: Independent foundation.
Financial data (yr. ended 11/30/13): Assets, $97,333,332 (M); expenditures, $5,806,700; qualifying distributions, $4,971,789; giving activities include $4,458,279 for 52 grants (high: $400,000; low: $2,500).
Purpose and activities: The foundation's grantmaking program is centered on the concepts of health and well-being. The foundation's purpose is to promote and support effective and creative programs, practices and policies related to healing from illness, accident, physical, social or emotional trauma and to extend the availability of programs that promote healing to underserved populations, with a focus on justice-involved people. The foundation believes that justice-involved people experience disproportionately higher rates of infectious and chronic diseases, substance abuse, mental illness, and trauma than the general population. As such, jails and prisons represent one of the largest target populations for public health services in America, and are important sites for improving the overall health and well-being of communities. The foundation is interested in projects that seek to improve the physical and mental health of individuals involved in the criminal justice system. Programs focusing on alternatives to incarceration, detention, and reentry will be considered. While the foundation does not support prevention projects, it is interested in programs that seek to reduce recidivism.
Fields of interest: Health care; Adults; Mentally disabled; Minorities; African Americans/Blacks; Hispanics/Latinos; Native Americans/American Indians; Offenders/ex-offenders; Substance abusers; Immigrants/refugees; Economically disadvantaged; Homeless; LGBTQ.
Type of support: Program development; Program evaluation; Matching/challenge support.
Limitations: Applications accepted. Giving primarily in NY and for projects that hold promise of national impact or extensive replication. No support for preventive medicine, or for children or end-of-life issues. No grants to individuals, or for annual campaigns, capital campaigns, building or renovation projects, or budgetary relief.
Publications: Grants list.
Application information: Potential applicants must register project ideas on foundation's web site. Letters of intent and proposals are accepted by invitation only following online project registration. Unsolicited letters of intent or proposals not accepted. Registrations only accepted via foundation's online registration system. Application form required.
Initial approach: Online registration for letter of intent
Copies of proposal: 5
Deadline(s): See foundation web site for current deadline
Board meeting date(s): Apr. and Oct.
Final notification: Varies
Officer: Scott Moyer, Pres.
Number of staff: 3 full-time professional.
EIN: 131773646

6328
Irving Langer Charitable Trust ✧
1465A Flatbush Ave.
Brooklyn, NY 11210-2498

Established in 1999 in NY.
Donor: Irving Langer.
Foundation type: Independent foundation.
Financial data (yr. ended 12/31/12): Assets, $14,957 (M); gifts received, $93,509; expenditures, $801,143; qualifying distributions, $798,168; giving activities include $798,168 for grants.
Purpose and activities: Giving primarily to Jewish organizations, temples and schools.
Fields of interest: Elementary/secondary education; Jewish agencies & synagogues.
Limitations: Applications not accepted. Giving primarily in NY. No grants to individuals.
Application information: Unsolicited requests for funds not accepted.
Director: Irving Langer.
EIN: 116449730

6329
Lanza Family Foundation ✧
c/o O'Connor Davies Munns & Dobbins, LLP
500 Mamaroneck Ave.
Harrison, NY 10528-1633

Established in 1996 in NY.
Donors: Frank Lanza†; Patricia Lanza; The Lanza Family Foundation; Lanza Family Charitable Lead Annuity Trust; Lanza Family Charitable Lead Trust.
Foundation type: Independent foundation.
Financial data (yr. ended 06/30/13): Assets, $1,389,367 (M); gifts received, $2,635,000; expenditures, $2,693,100; qualifying distributions, $2,674,200; giving activities include $2,667,000 for 31 grants (high: $455,000; low: $5,000).
Purpose and activities: Giving primarily to help minorities overcome financial impediments in order to have equal opportunities.
Fields of interest: Education; Human services; Children/youth, services; Women, centers/services; Community/economic development; Foundations (private grantmaking).
Type of support: Scholarship funds.
Limitations: Applications not accepted. Giving primarily in Westchester County and New York, NY. No grants to individuals directly.
Application information: Unsolicited requests for funds not accepted.
Board meeting date(s): Apr. 1
Officer: Patricia Lanza, Pres. and Secy.
Trustee: Anthony Lanza.
EIN: 133922706
Selected grants: The following grants are a representative sample of this grantmaker's funding activity:
$100,000 to UNICEF, New York, NY, 2013. For Snowflake Ball.

6330
A.B. Lapine Charitable Trust ✧
1 HSBC Ctr., 23rd Fl.
Buffalo, NY 14203-2885

Established in NY.
Foundation type: Independent foundation.
Financial data (yr. ended 01/31/12): Assets, $5,647,013 (M); expenditures, $766,075; qualifying distributions, $690,000; giving activities include $585,497 for 3 grants (high: $195,166; low: $195,165).
Fields of interest: Residential/custodial care, senior continuing care.
Limitations: Applications not accepted. Giving primarily in Rochester, NY.
Application information: Unsolicited requests for funds not accepted.
Trustee: HSBC Bank, USA.
EIN: 456633621
Selected grants: The following grants are a representative sample of this grantmaker's funding activity:
$195,166 to Jewish Home and Infirmary of Rochester New York Foundation, Rochester, NY, 2012. For general charitable purposes.
$195,166 to Saint Anns Home Foundation, Rochester, NY, 2012. For general charitable purposes.

6331
LaSalle Adams Fund ✧
c/o Fiduciary Trust Co. International
600 5th Ave.
New York, NY 10020-2326

Established in 1953 in IL; incorporated in 1999 in NY.
Donor: Sydney Stein, Jr.†.
Foundation type: Independent foundation.
Financial data (yr. ended 12/31/12): Assets, $24,688,430 (M); expenditures, $1,505,138; qualifying distributions, $1,108,706; giving activities include $990,000 for 14 grants (high: $450,000; low: $20,000).
Purpose and activities: Giving primarily for environmental and wildlife conservation and protection.
Fields of interest: Environment, natural resources; Animals/wildlife, preservation/protection; Philanthropy/voluntarism.
International interests: Canada; Mexico.
Type of support: Land acquisition; Program development; Seed money; Program evaluation; Matching/challenge support.
Limitations: Applications not accepted. Giving primarily in the Rocky Mountain states. No grants to individuals.
Application information: Contributes only to pre-selected organizations.
Board meeting date(s): 3 times a year
Officers: Edith Carol Stein, Pres. and Treas.; Nancy C. Stein, V.P. and Secy.; Susan S. Stein, Vice-Secy.
EIN: 161562907

6332
William & Mildred Lasdon Foundation ✧
650 Park Ave., Apt. 6-F
New York, NY 10065-5986 (212) 935-3916
Contact: Nanette L. Laitman, Tr.

Established in 1947 in DE.
Donors: Jacob S. Lasdon; William S. Lasdon; Mildred D. Lasdon‡; Nanette L. Leitman; Bonnie Eletz; Cathy Seligman.
Foundation type: Independent foundation.
Financial data (yr. ended 12/31/12): Assets, $21,916,335 (M); gifts received, $40,000; expenditures, $2,792,033; qualifying distributions, $2,587,366; giving activities include $2,416,300 for 69 grants (high: $1,000,000; low: $50).
Purpose and activities: Giving primarily for arts and culture, particularly museums, as well as for Jewish agencies and temples.
Fields of interest: Museums; Arts; Hospitals (general); Jewish federated giving programs; Jewish agencies & synagogues.
Limitations: Applications accepted. Giving primarily in New York, NY. No grants to individuals.
Application information: Application form not required.
Initial approach: Proposal
Deadline(s): None
Trustees: Bonnie Eletz; Nanette L. Laitman; Cathy Seligman.
EIN: 237380362

6333
Albert and Mary Lasker Foundation, Inc. ✧
110 E. 42nd St., Ste. 1300
New York, NY 10017-8532 (212) 286-0222
Contact: Maria Freire Ph.D., Pres.
FAX: (212) 286-0924;
E-mail: info@laskerfoundation.org; Additional e-mail for applications: dkeegan@laskerfoundation.org;
Main URL: http://www.laskerfoundation.org
Multimedia: http://www.laskerfoundation.org/media/video.htm
Scholars inquiry: Charles R. Dearolf, Ph.D., Asst. Dir. for Intramural Research, National Institutes of Health, Bldg. 1, Rm. 152, Bethesda, MD 20892, e-mail: laskerScholar@nih.gov

Incorporated in 1942 in NY.
Donors: Albert Davis Lasker‡; Mary Woodard Lasker‡; Christopher Brody; John R. Considine; Cathy Sulzberger; Frances L. Brody Living Trust.
Foundation type: Operating foundation.
Financial data (yr. ended 12/31/12): Assets, $66,678,481 (M); gifts received, $495,771; expenditures, $3,383,575; qualifying distributions, $2,983,002; giving activities include $750,215 for 8 grants (high: $125,000; low: $215), and $2,277,184 for foundation-administered programs.
Purpose and activities: To foster the prevention and treatment of disease and disability by honoring excellence in basic and clinical science, and through public education and research advocacy.
Fields of interest: Health care; Biomedicine; Health organizations; Medical research; Biology/life sciences.
Type of support: Grants to individuals.
Limitations: Giving on a international basis.
Publications: Application guidelines.
Application information: Application form required.
Initial approach: Telephone or e-mail
Copies of proposal: 1
Deadline(s): None
Officers and Directors:* Alfred Sommer, M.D.*, Chair.; Claire Pomeroy, M.D., MBA*, Pres.; John R. Considine,* Secy.-Treas.; James W. Fordyce,* Chair. Emeritus; Purnell W. Choppin, M.D., Dir., Emeritus; Barbara Barrett; Christopher W. Brody; Anthony B. Evnin, Ph.D.; Marshall Fordyce; Joseph Goldstein, M.D.; Jordan U. Gutterman, M.D.; Sherry Lansing; George P. Noon, M.D.; William J. "Mike" Overlock; George Roche; Solomon H. Snyder; Russell W. Steenberg; Robert Tjian, Ph.D.; Elias A. Zerhouni, M.D.
Number of staff: 2 full-time professional; 2 part-time professional.
EIN: 131680062

6334
The Leonard and Evelyn Lauder Foundation ✧
c/o Lisa Somar
767 5th Ave., 40th Fl.
New York, NY 10153-0003 (212) 284-2764
Contact: Joan Krupskas, Secy.-Treas.

Established in 2001 in DE.
Donors: Mrs. Estee Lauder‡; Leonard A. Lauder; Evelyn H. Lauder‡; The Lauder Foundation; EL 2002 Trust.
Foundation type: Independent foundation.
Financial data (yr. ended 12/31/12): Assets, $3,986,037 (M); expenditures, $6,353,485; qualifying distributions, $6,330,035; giving activities include $6,315,267 for 81 grants (high: $2,500,000; low: $500).
Purpose and activities: Giving primarily for education, health care, and human services.
Fields of interest: Arts education; Museums; Performing arts; Performing arts centers; Arts; Higher education; Environment; Health care; Health organizations, association; Breast cancer research; Recreation, parks/playgrounds; Human services; Foundations (community); Jewish agencies & synagogues.
Limitations: Applications not accepted. Giving primarily in New York, NY, with some funding in CA. No grants to individuals.
Application information: Contributes only to pre-selected organizations.
Officers and Directors:* Leonard A. Lauder,* Pres.; Joel Ehrenkranz,* V.P.; Deborah Krulewitch,* V.P.; George Schiele,* V.P.; Joan Krupskas, Secy.; Kevin Dieterich,* Treas.
EIN: 134139448
Selected grants: The following grants are a representative sample of this grantmaker's funding activity:
$2,500,000 to Mount Sinai Hospital, New York, NY, 2012.
$1,705,000 to Aspen Institute, Queenstown, MD, 2012.
$258,000 to Society of the Four Arts, Palm Beach, FL, 2012.
$252,000 to Alzheimers Drug Discovery Foundation, New York, NY, 2012.
$184,700 to Breast Cancer Research Foundation, New York, NY, 2012.
$125,000 to U.S. Foundation for Queen's University at Kingston, Washington, DC, 2012.
$116,667 to Aspen Art Museum, Aspen, CO, 2012.
$112,500 to Lincoln Center for the Performing Arts, New York, NY, 2012.
$50,000 to Hand in Hand for Haiti, San Francisco, CA, 2012.
$24,000 to Whitney Museum of American Art, New York, NY, 2012.

6335
The Ronald & Jo Carole Lauder Foundation ✧
767 5th Ave., Ste. 4200
New York, NY 10153-0023

Established in DE.
Donor: Ronalds S. Lauder.
Foundation type: Independent foundation.
Financial data (yr. ended 12/31/12): Assets, $248,272 (M); gifts received, $1,175,000; expenditures, $1,091,850; qualifying distributions, $1,079,250; giving activities include $1,079,225 for 88 grants (high: $200,000; low: $40).
Fields of interest: Museums (art); Arts; Higher education; Education; Health care.
Limitations: Giving primarily in New York, NY.
EIN: 273866350

6336
The Ronald S. Lauder Foundation ✧
767 5th Ave., Ste. 4200
New York, NY 10153-0185 (212) 319-6300
Contact: George Ban, C.E.O. and Exec. V.P.
RSS Feed: http://feeds.feedburner.com/ronaldlauder
Twitter: http://twitter.com/ronaldlauderfou

Established in 1987 in NY.
Donors: Estee Lauder‡; Ronald S. Lauder; Estee Lauder, Inc.; Chaim Z. Roswaski; Aba M. Dunner; Olaf Ossmann; The Estee Lauder 2002 Trust; Jewish Renaissance Foundation; The Taube Foundation for Jewish Life; Jewish Agency for Israel; Chesed Congregation of America; Conference of European Rabbis; Shuvo Yisroel Charity; Javne Fund; Zentgralrat Der Juden; Juedicshe Gemeinde Hamburg; Union of Orthodox Jewish Congregation; Rothschild Foundation; Canadian Foundation; Stenham Trustees Limited.
Foundation type: Operating foundation.
Financial data (yr. ended 12/31/12): Assets, $99,216,644 (M); gifts received, $80,872,566; expenditures, $12,140,979; qualifying distributions, $11,467,508; giving activities include $3,591,399 for 29 grants (high: $445,000; low: $7,350), and $5,339,848 for 4 foundation-administered programs.
Purpose and activities: Giving primarily for Central and Eastern European organizations dedicated to revitalization of Jewish life through educational and cultural programs, and the preservation of Jewish monuments and buildings; support also for a nonsectarian international student exchange program at the secondary level.
Fields of interest: Historic preservation/historical societies; Arts; Elementary/secondary education; Education; Jewish agencies & synagogues; Religion.
International interests: Austria; Belarus; Bulgaria; Czech Republic; Eastern Europe; Estonia; Europe; Germany; Hungary; Latvia; Lithuania; Moldova; Poland; Romania; Slovakia; Ukraine.
Type of support: General/operating support; Continuing support; Building/renovation; Program development; Grants to individuals; Exchange programs.
Limitations: Applications not accepted. Giving primarily in Central and Eastern Europe.
Publications: Financial statement; Informational brochure; Newsletter.
Application information: Unsolicited requests for funds are not considered.
Board meeting date(s): Varies

Officers and Directors:* Ronald S. Lauder,* Chair. and Pres.; Rabbi Joshua Spinner, C.E.O. and Exec. V.P.; Rabbi Jacob I. Biderman,* V.P. for Education; David Gerson, Treas.; Dr. George Ban; Malcolm Hoenlein.
EIN: 133445910

6337
Lauder Foundation Inc. ✧
c/o Lisa Somer
767 5th Ave., 40th Fl.
New York, NY 10153-0003

Incorporated in 1962 in NY.
Donors: Estee Lauder‡; Joseph H. Lauder‡; Leonard A. Lauder; Ronald S. Lauder; Evelyn Lauder‡; William Lauder; Estee Lauder, Inc.; LWG Family Partners; EL 2002 Trust.
Foundation type: Independent foundation.
Financial data (yr. ended 11/30/12): Assets, $46,055,073 (M); expenditures, $3,707,407; qualifying distributions, $3,674,491; giving activities include $3,606,764 for 99 grants (high: $1,000,000; low: $250).
Fields of interest: Performing arts centers; Higher education, university; Medical research, institute.
Type of support: General/operating support; Continuing support; Annual campaigns; Capital campaigns.
Limitations: Applications not accepted. Giving in the U.S., with emphasis on New York, NY. No grants to individuals.
Application information: Contributes only to pre-selected organizations.
Officers and Directors:* Leonard A. Lauder,* Pres.; Joel Ehrenkranz,* V.P.; George Schiele,* V.P.; Joan Krupskas, Secy.-Treas.
EIN: 136153743

6338
Laurents/Hatcher Foundation Inc ✧ ☆
(formerly Laurents Foundation)
608 Northville Tpke.
Riverhead, NY 11901-4717
Application address: c/o Scott Goldman, P.O. Box 1187, New Brunswick, NJ 08901, tel.: (732) 846-2895

Established in 1965 in NY.
Donor: Arthur Laurents‡.
Foundation type: Independent foundation.
Financial data (yr. ended 12/31/13): Assets, $19,756,603 (M); gifts received, $1,060,668; expenditures, $1,842,561; qualifying distributions, $929,755; giving activities include $700,000 for 13 grants (high: $175,000; low: $10,000).
Fields of interest: Performing arts; Education; Human services.
Limitations: Applications not accepted. Giving primarily in NJ and NY. No grants to individuals.
Application information: Unsolicited requests for funds not accepted.
Officer and Directors:* David Saint,* Pres.; Patricia McCorkle,* Secy.; Judith Rubin,* Treas.
EIN: 136114331

6339
Lavelle Fund for the Blind, Inc. ✧
307 W. 38th St., Ste. 2010
New York, NY 10018-9507 (212) 668-9801
Contact: Andrew S. Fisher, Exec. Dir.
FAX: (212) 668-9803;
E-mail: afisher@lavellefund.org; Main URL: http://www.lavellefund.org/
Grants List: http://www.lavellefund.org/grants.html

Established in 1999; Converted to an independent foundation in 2003.
Foundation type: Independent foundation.
Financial data (yr. ended 12/31/13): Assets, $122,125,872 (M); expenditures, $5,811,709; qualifying distributions, $6,161,011; giving activities include $4,448,941 for grants, and $1,200,000 for 1 loan/program-related investment.
Purpose and activities: The fund is dedicated to supporting programs that promote the spiritual, moral, intellectual, and physical development of blind and low-vision people of all ages, together with programs that help people avoid vision loss. Priority is given to agencies that concentrate on serving the New York City metropolitan area.
Fields of interest: Eye diseases; Disabilities, people with.
Type of support: General/operating support; Program development; Scholarship funds.
Limitations: Applications accepted. Giving primarily in the New York City metropolitan area. No grants to individuals, or for deficit reduction, emergency funds, medical research programs, conferences or media events (unless an integral part of a broader program of direct service), or advocacy programs; no loans.
Publications: Informational brochure (including application guidelines).
Application information: Application guidelines available on foundation web site. New York/New Jersey Area Common Grant Application Form accepted. Application form not required.
Initial approach: Letter of inquiry on organization's letterhead
Copies of proposal: 1
Deadline(s): None
Board meeting date(s): Quarterly
Final notification: 1 week
Officers and Trustees:* Daniel M. Callahan,* Pres.; John J. Caffrey,* V.P. and Treas.; Andrew S. Fisher, Secy. and Exec. Dir.; Nancy L. Brown; Sr. Mary Flood, M.D., Ph.D.; Michael A. Lemp, M.D.; J. Robert Lunney; Hon. Kevin B. McGrath, Jr.; Jane B. O'Connell; Paul A. Sidoti, M.D.
Number of staff: 2 full-time professional.
EIN: 131740463
Selected grants: The following grants are a representative sample of this grantmaker's funding activity:
$337,650 to Helen Keller International, New York, NY, 2013. For ChildSight Program free vision, screenings, examinations, and prescription eyesglasses to needy students in public and parochial middle schools located in New York City.
$200,000 to Visions Services for the Blind and Visually Impaired, New York, NY, 2013. To launch employer-centered and guided job training and placement program for adults who are legally blind and reside in NYC or Long Island.
$175,000 to Central Association for the Blind and Visually Handicapped, Utica, NY, 2013. For HVAC and insulation systems of headquarters building.
$172,814 to Beneficent Technology, Palo Alto, CA, 2013. For educational materials for people in India who are blind and visually impaired.
$160,000 to Goodwill Industries of Greater New York and Northern New Jersey, Astoria, NY, 2013. To train blind working age adults for call-center work and place these trainees in paid call-center and customer service jobs.
$140,000 to Seva Foundation, Berkeley, CA, 2013. To improve access and utilization of Primary Eye Care Centers (PECC) and new eye hospital in Nepal and Vision Centers (VCs) in North India and increase efficiency and productivity of facilities.
$135,000 to Seva Foundation, Berkeley, CA, 2013. For consortium of global eye care organizations.
$100,000 to Olmsted Center for Sight, Buffalo, NY, 2013. To establish satellite low vision clinic in Buffalo's inner suburban ring, increasing the combined total of Olmsted low vision patients served.
$88,600 to Helen Keller Services for the Blind, Brooklyn, NY, 2013. For national program to train people as adaptive technology trainers for people who are deaf-blind.
$39,671 to Seton Hall University, South Orange, NJ, 2013. For scholarship for students who are legally blind.

6340
LCU Fund for Women's Education ✧
(formerly LCU Foundation)
244 5th Ave., Ste. 200
New York, NY 10001-7604 (212) 627-4555
FAX: (212) 631-7449; E-mail: lcufund@gmail.com;
Main URL: http://www.lcufund.org
Facebook: https://www.facebook.com/LCUFund
Twitter: https://twitter.com/lcufund

Established in 1858 in NY.
Foundation type: Independent foundation.
Financial data (yr. ended 12/31/13): Assets, $18,160,324 (M); gifts received, $19,215; expenditures, $767,182; qualifying distributions, $666,310; giving activities include $556,000 for 15 grants (high: $80,000; low: $15,000).
Purpose and activities: Giving primarily to colleges and universities for housing stipends for female students.
Fields of interest: Higher education; Graduate/professional education; Housing/shelter; Women.
Limitations: Applications not accepted. Giving limited to New York, NY. No grants to individuals.
Publications: Annual report; Financial statement; Newsletter.
Application information: Contributes only to pre-selected organizations.
Officers: Holly Hughes, Pres.; Tina Donovan, V.P.; Mary Jo Mullan, Secy.; Carol Starmack, Treas.; Sara Espinosa, Exec. Dir.
Number of staff: 1 full-time professional.
EIN: 135562262
Selected grants: The following grants are a representative sample of this grantmaker's funding activity:
$85,000 to City College of the City University of New York, New York, NY, 2012.
$65,000 to Lehman College of the City University of New York, Bronx, NY, 2012.
$50,000 to Phillips Beth Israel School of Nursing, New York, NY, 2013.
$35,000 to John Jay College of Criminal Justice of the City University of New York, New York, NY, 2012.

6341
The Frances Lear Foundation ✧
c/o O'Connor Davies, LLP
665 5th Ave.
New York, NY 10022

Established in 2000 in DE.
Donor: The North Star Fund, Inc.
Foundation type: Independent foundation.
Financial data (yr. ended 12/31/13): Assets, $10,663,375 (M); expenditures, $984,914; qualifying distributions, $865,622; giving activities include $838,500 for 29 grants (high: $250,000; low: $2,500).
Fields of interest: Performing arts, ballet; Arts; Health organizations; Human services.
Limitations: Applications not accepted. Giving primarily in NY. No grants to individuals.
Application information: Contributes only to pre-selected organizations.
Officer: Thomas R. Asher, Secy.
Directors: Daniel R. Katz; Dr. Jonathan LaPook; Kate Breckir Lear; Maggie Lear.
EIN: 043489966

6342
The Lebensfeld Foundation ✧
c/o Sullivan & Cromwell LLP
125 Broad St.
New York, NY 10004-2498 (212) 558-4000
Contact: Robert J. Giuffra, Jr. Esq., V.P. and Secy.-Treas.

Incorporated in 1959 in NY.
Donor: Harry Lebensfeld Revocable Trust.
Foundation type: Independent foundation.
Financial data (yr. ended 08/31/13): Assets, $23,789,080 (M); expenditures, $1,220,075; qualifying distributions, $1,218,460; giving activities include $1,214,200 for 45 grants (high: $200,000; low: $5,000).
Purpose and activities: Giving primarily for the arts, education and health organizations.
Fields of interest: Arts; Elementary/secondary education; Higher education; Education; Health organizations; Medical research, institute; United Ways and Federated Giving Programs.
Limitations: Applications accepted. Giving primarily in NJ and NY. No grants to individuals.
Application information: Application form not required.
Initial approach: Proposal
Deadline(s): None
Officers and Trustees:* Andrew G. Pietrini,* Pres.; Robert J. Giuffra, Jr., V.P. and Secy.-Treas.; Lauri Pietrini.
EIN: 136086169
Selected grants: The following grants are a representative sample of this grantmaker's funding activity:
$100,000 to Bancroft Neurohealth, Haddonfield, NJ, 2011. For general support.

6343
Patrick P. Lee Foundation ✧
45 Bryant Woods N.
Amherst, NY 14228-3600 (716) 844-3100
FAX: (716) 844-3117;
E-mail: info@patrickleefoundation.org; Main URL: http://www.patrickpleefoundation.org
All Grants: http://www.patrickpleefoundation.org/work/
Behavioral Health Grants: http://www.patrickpleefoundation.org/work/behavioral-health/
Education Grants: http://www.patrickpleefoundation.org/work/education/
Human and Community Services Grants: http://www.patrickpleefoundation.org/work/human-community-services/
Medical Care and Research Grants: http://www.patrickpleefoundation.org/work/medical-care-research/

Donor: Patrick P. Lee.
Foundation type: Independent foundation.
Financial data (yr. ended 12/31/12): Assets, $26,902,969 (M); gifts received, $308,188; expenditures, $1,627,909; qualifying distributions, $1,520,406; giving activities include $1,388,557 for 63 grants (high: $200,000; low: $500).
Purpose and activities: Giving primarily for behavioral health, education, medical care and research, and human services.
Fields of interest: Higher education; Health care; Human services; Children/youth, services; Family services; Catholic agencies & churches.
Limitations: Applications accepted. Giving primarily in Buffalo, NY. No support for political activities. No grants to individuals or for deficit financing, capacity building funds, seed funds or program-related investments.
Application information: Application guidelines available on foundation web site. Application form required.
Initial approach: Letter of intent
Deadline(s): Jan. 15 for behavioral health; Apr. 15 for education; July 15 for medical care and research; Oct. 15 for human services
Board meeting date(s): Mar. June, Sept., and Dec.
Final notification: Apr. and Oct.
Officers and Directors:* Patrick P. Lee,* Chair.; Mark O'Donnell,* Exec. Dir.; Glenda M. Cadawallader; David C. Hohn, M.D.; David C. Horan; Robert J. Lane, Jr.; Christopher J. Lee; Cynthia R. Lee; Michele R. Lee; Jennifer McNamara; Barbara R. Rhee; John Rhee, M.D.; Lee Wortham.
EIN: 453845576
Selected grants: The following grants are a representative sample of this grantmaker's funding activity:
$194,500 to Ocean Reef Cultural Center, Key Largo, FL, 2012. For capital campaign.
$30,000 to Niagara Hospice, Lockport, NY, 2012. For general purposes.
$25,000 to Hope of Buffalo, Buffalo, NY, 2012. For Program - Family Reuniting.
$10,000 to Friends of Night People, Buffalo, NY, 2012. For Program - Satellite Feeding Program.
$5,000 to Hilbert College, Hamburg, NY, 2012. For 2 Year Grant - Scholarship Endowment.

6344
Leeds Family Foundation ✧
c/o Lipsky, Goodkin & Co.
120 W. 45th St., 7th Fl.
New York, NY 10036-4041 (212) 840-6444
Contact: Laurence C. Leeds, Jr., Tr.

Established in 1999 in NY.
Donors: Laurence C. Leeds, Jr.; Dalia Leeds.
Foundation type: Independent foundation.
Financial data (yr. ended 12/31/12): Assets, $20,949,994 (M); expenditures, $1,314,504; qualifying distributions, $1,083,733; giving activities include $1,080,548 for 60 grants (high: $350,175; low: $75).
Fields of interest: Arts; Higher education; Education; Health care, clinics/centers; Health organizations; Human services.
Limitations: Giving primarily in CT and NY. No grants to individuals.
Application information: Application form not required.
Initial approach: Letter of request
Deadline(s): None
Trustees: Dalia Leeds; Laurence C. Leeds, Jr.
EIN: 137219856

6345
Lisa and Michael Leffell Family Foundation ✧
600 Madison Ave., 20th Fl.
New York, NY 10022-1615 (646) 532-2445
Contact: Stacey Popovsky, Exec. Dir.

Established in 1999 in NY.
Donor: Michael Leffell.
Foundation type: Independent foundation.
Financial data (yr. ended 12/31/13): Assets, $28,755,935 (M); gifts received, $273,662; expenditures, $1,522,846; qualifying distributions, $1,209,664; giving activities include $480,705 for grants.
Purpose and activities: The foundation is dedicated to inspiring passion for Jewish education and strengthening the security and vibrancy of the State of Israel. To build strong support for Israel, The foundation advances initiatives that educate and engage opinion leaders to become effective advocates of Israel and research issues impacting the Jewish community. To pursue these goals, the foundation fosters strategic partnerships, collaboration, and ongoing communication with other foundations, organizations, and individuals to leverage opportunities for cooperation and change.
Fields of interest: Higher education; Education; Human services; Jewish federated giving programs; Public policy, research; Jewish agencies & synagogues.
Limitations: Applications not accepted. Giving primarily in Worcester, MA and in Westchester County and New York, NY. No grants to individuals.
Application information: Contributes only to pre-selected organizations.
Officer: Stacey Popovsky, Exec. Dir.
Trustees: Lisa Leffell; Michael Leffell.
EIN: 316633021

6346
Edith and Herbert Lehman Foundation, Inc. ✧
c/o Wendy Lehman Lash
151 E. 79th St.
New York, NY 10075-0564

Incorporated in 1952 in NY.
Donors: Edith A. Lehman†; Herbert H. Lehman†.
Foundation type: Independent foundation.
Financial data (yr. ended 09/30/13): Assets, $8,003,198 (M); expenditures, $611,792; qualifying distributions, $482,161; giving activities include $473,000 for 46 grants (high: $69,000; low: $1,000).
Purpose and activities: Giving primarily for the arts and education.
Fields of interest: Arts; Higher education; Education; Animals/wildlife; Health care; Human services; Children, services.
International interests: United Kingdom.
Type of support: Equipment; General/operating support; Continuing support; Annual campaigns; Capital campaigns; Building/renovation; Endowments; Emergency funds; Professorships; Seed money; Curriculum development.
Limitations: Applications not accepted. Giving primarily in NY. No support for political organizations. No grants to individuals.
Publications: Annual report.
Application information: Proposals are accepted by invitation only. Preference is given to organizations which historically have been of interest to the Lehman family and to those in which the family is personally involved.
Board meeting date(s): Quarterly
Officer and Directors:* Wendy Lehman Lash,* Pres.; Robert C. Graham, Jr.; Abigail S. Lash; Emily Altschul Miller; Catherine J. Wise; Deborah Wise.
EIN: 136094015

6347
Robert Lehman Foundation, Inc. ✧
488 Madison Ave., 9th Fl.
New York, NY 10022-5723
Contact: Francesca C. Valerio, Exec. Dir.
FAX: (212) 593-9175;
E-mail: info@robertlehmanfoundation.org; Main URL: http://www.robertlehmanfoundation.org

Incorporated in 1943 in NY.
Donor: Robert Lehman†.
Foundation type: Independent foundation.
Financial data (yr. ended 09/30/13): Assets, $53,201,981 (M); expenditures, $4,450,482; qualifying distributions, $3,978,121; giving activities include $3,465,966 for 52 grants (high: $1,500,000; low: $250).
Purpose and activities: Support for the maintenance, conservation, and preservation of the Robert Lehman collection at the Metropolitan Museum of Art; giving to museums, arts organizations, educational institutions and other cultural organizations with the goal of enhancing the role of the visual arts within American and world culture.
Fields of interest: Visual arts.
Limitations: Applications accepted. Giving primarily in the northeastern U.S., with emphasis on New York, NY.
Publications: Application guidelines.
Application information: Beginning in 2012, organizations that have received Robert Lehman Foundation grants for four consecutive years will not be eligible for consideration of further grants for a period of two years. The foundation has adopted this policy due to the significant increase in the number of proposals received by the foundation, and in order to release funds for new and deserving institutions. Please note that this policy does not apply to the Edwin L. Weisl Jr. Lectureship program. Application guidelines available on foundation web site.
Initial approach: Upload proposal and documents via foundation web site
Deadline(s): Apr. 1 and Sept. 1
Board meeting date(s): Generally in May and Oct.
Officers and Directors:* Philip H. Isles,* Pres.; Michael M. Thomas,* Treas.; Francesca C. Valerio, Exec. Dir.; Robert A. Bernhard; Robert Owen Lehman; Marie Rolf; Angela Weisl.
Number of staff: 2 full-time professional.
EIN: 136094018

6348
Leibowitz and Greenway Family Charitable Foundation ✧
234 Clinton St.
Brooklyn, NY 11201-6208

Established in 2000 in FL and NY.
Donors: Lawrence Leibowitz; Dorothy Liebowitz†; Dorothy E. Leibowitz Family Trust; Dorothy E. Leibowitz Charitable Lead Trust.
Foundation type: Independent foundation.
Financial data (yr. ended 12/31/12): Assets, $10,177,221 (M); gifts received, $350,000; expenditures, $588,169; qualifying distributions, $542,000; giving activities include $542,000 for grants.
Fields of interest: Health organizations, association; Human services; Children/youth, services.
Limitations: Applications not accepted. Giving in the U.S., with emphasis on New York, NY. No grants to individuals.
Application information: Contributes only to pre-selected organizations.
Trustees: Tara Greenway-Leibowitz; Lawrence Leibowitz.
EIN: 656358233

6349
The Leir Foundation, Inc. ✧
570 Lexington Ave., 33rd Fl.
New York, NY 10022-6837

Established in 1996 in CT.
Donors: Henry J. Leir†; Louis Lipton; The Ridgefield Foundation.
Foundation type: Independent foundation.
Financial data (yr. ended 12/31/12): Assets, $53,195,071 (M); expenditures, $5,131,650; qualifying distributions, $3,776,550; giving activities include $3,776,550 for 80 grants (high: $1,450,000; low: $400).
Fields of interest: Museums (art); Higher education; Human services; Children, services; Jewish federated giving programs; Jewish agencies & synagogues.
International interests: Germany; Luxembourg.
Limitations: Applications not accepted. Giving primarily in CT, with emphasis on Ridgefield, MA, and New York, NY; funding also in Mauth, Germany and Luxembourg. No grants to individuals.
Application information: Contributes only to pre-selected organizations.
Officers and Directors:* Arthur S. Hoffman,* Pres. and Treas.; Margot Gibis,* V.P.; Anthony J. Cernera,* Secy.; Stuart Silver; Jean Wagener.
EIN: 061466481
Selected grants: The following grants are a representative sample of this grantmaker's funding activity:
$90,000 to Young Adult Institute, New York, NY, 2012. For relief of disadvantage.
$10,000 to Tanenbaum Center for Interreligious Understanding, New York, NY, 2012. For interreligious understanding.
$10,000 to World Wildlife Fund, Washington, DC, 2012. For Museum and cultural.

6350
Lemberg Foundation, Inc. ✧
430 Park Ave., Ste. 505
New York, NY 10022-3540 (212) 682-9595
Contact: John Usdan, Pres.

Incorporated in 1945 in NY.
Donors: Samuel Lemberg†; Suzanne L. Usdan Charitable Lead Annuity Trust.
Foundation type: Independent foundation.
Financial data (yr. ended 12/31/13): Assets, $40,938,676 (M); gifts received, $403,825; expenditures, $2,667,352; qualifying distributions, $2,245,394; giving activities include $2,245,394 for 50 grants (high: $1,000,000; low: $1,000).
Purpose and activities: Giving primarily for arts and culture, education, children and youth services, and Jewish federated giving programs and temples.
Fields of interest: Museums; Performing arts; Arts; Higher education; Human services; Children/youth, services; Jewish federated giving programs; Jewish agencies & synagogues.
Type of support: Building/renovation; Endowments; Program development; Fellowships; Scholarship funds; Research.
Limitations: Applications accepted. Giving primarily in NY. No grants for matching gifts.
Application information:
Initial approach: Letter, proposal, or telephone
Copies of proposal: 1
Deadline(s): None
Board meeting date(s): As required
Officers: John Usdan, Pres.; Adam Usdan, V.P. and Treas.; Esme Usdan, Secy.
Director: Dale Lewis.
Number of staff: 2 part-time support.
EIN: 136082064

6351
Robert and Roni Lemle Family Foundation ✧
c/o Robert S. Lemle
1201 Rxr Plz.
Uniondale, NY 11556

Established in 2003 in NY.
Donors: Robert S. Lemle; Gertrude Lemle.
Foundation type: Independent foundation.
Financial data (yr. ended 12/31/12): Assets, $9,999,668 (M); expenditures, $585,305; qualifying distributions, $523,900; giving activities include $523,900 for grants.

Fields of interest: Museums (specialized); Higher education; Education.
Limitations: Applications not accepted. No grants to individuals.
Application information: Contributes only to pre-selected organizations.
Trustees: Robert S. Lemle; Roni S. Lemle.
EIN: 200389244

6352
Reginald A. & Elizabeth S. Lenna Foundation, Inc. ✧
(doing business as The Lenna Foundation)
P.O. Box 13
Lakewood, NY 14750-0013 (716) 763-0823
Contact: Joseph C. Johnson, Pres.
E-mail: lennafoundation@windstream.net

Established in 1985 in NY.
Donors: Reginald A. Lenna†; Elizabeth S. Lenna†.
Foundation type: Independent foundation.
Financial data (yr. ended 12/31/13): Assets, $33,965,953 (M); gifts received, $18,131,634; expenditures, $1,072,314; qualifying distributions, $1,073,453; giving activities include $982,460 for 42 grants (high: $150,000; low: $500).
Fields of interest: Historic preservation/historical societies; Arts; Education; Environment; Hospitals (general); Human services; YM/YWCAs & YM/YWHAs; Children, day care; Community/economic development; Infants/toddlers; Children/youth; Youth; Hispanics/Latinos; Girls; Boys; Economically disadvantaged.
Type of support: General/operating support; Management development/capacity building; Annual campaigns; Capital campaigns; Building/renovation; Equipment; Scholarship funds; Technical assistance; Matching/challenge support.
Limitations: Applications accepted. Giving primarily in southwestern NY. No support for municipal or religious organizations. No grants to individuals.
Application information: Chautauqua Regional Community Foundation http://www.chautauquagrants.org application form accepted. Application form required.
Initial approach: Letter of interest (2 page maximum)
Copies of proposal: 2
Deadline(s): Mar. 10 and July 31
Board meeting date(s): Apr., May, Aug., and Nov.
Final notification: 90 days
Officers: Joseph Johnson, Pres.; Florence Cass, Secy.; Randy Ordines, Treas.
Directors: Anne Kohl; Thomas Price.
Number of staff: 1 part-time professional; 1 part-time support.
EIN: 112800733
Selected grants: The following grants are a representative sample of this grantmaker's funding activity:
$50,000 to WCA Hospital, Jamestown, NY, 2012. For emergency department.
$35,000 to Jamestown Community College, Jamestown, NY, 2012. For Arts and Sciences Building 3rd Floor Renovation.
$31,500 to Arts Council for Chautauqua County, Jamestown, NY, 2012. For Wrfa-Lp Capital Needs $5000, Daily Operations $26,500.
$28,000 to YWCA of Jamestown, Jamestown, NY, 2012. For Team - Provide Teaching Nursery and Critical Social Work Services.
$10,000 to Chautauqua Lake Association, Lakewood, NY, 2012. For Lake Maintenance.
$6,700 to Reg Lenna Civic Center, Jamestown, NY, 2012. For Arts Council Merger.
$6,000 to Jamestown Community Learning Council, Jamestown, NY, 2012. For Parents As Teachers Program.
$5,000 to Patterson Library, Westfield, NY, 2012. For capital repairs.
$2,050 to Chautauqua Regional Youth Ballet, Jamestown, NY, 2012. For Spring Gala.

6353
Lerner Family Foundation ✧
c/o Marcum LLP
10 Melville Park Rd.
Melville, NY 11747-3146

Established in 1997 in MD.
Donors: Mark Lerner; Traci Lerner.
Foundation type: Independent foundation.
Financial data (yr. ended 11/30/13): Assets, $8,992,276 (M); gifts received, $2,140,000; expenditures, $2,354,681; qualifying distributions, $2,325,317; giving activities include $2,320,274 for 37 grants (high: $550,000; low: $25).
Purpose and activities: Giving primarily for health organizations, as well as for education, human services, and Jewish organizations.
Fields of interest: Education; Health organizations, association; Human services; Jewish federated giving programs; Jewish agencies & synagogues.
Type of support: General/operating support; Capital campaigns.
Limitations: Applications not accepted. Giving primarily in Baltimore, MD, New York, NY, and Philadelphia, PA. No grants to individuals.
Application information: Contributes only to pre-selected organizations.
Trustees: Mark Lerner; Traci Lerner.
EIN: 522073256

6354
Naftali Tzvi Leshkowitz Memorial Foundation ✧ ☆
270 Madison Ave., 17th Fl.
New York, NY 10016-0601
Contact: C.H. Leshkowitz, Tr.

Established in 1986 in NY.
Donors: C.H. Leshkowitz; Joseph Leshkowitz.
Foundation type: Independent foundation.
Financial data (yr. ended 12/31/12): Assets, $4,358,044 (M); gifts received, $507,000; expenditures, $604,733; qualifying distributions, $578,620; giving activities include $578,620 for grants.
Purpose and activities: Giving primarily for education, human services, Jewish organizations and educational institutions.
Fields of interest: Education; Human services; Jewish federated giving programs; Jewish agencies & synagogues.
Limitations: Applications not accepted. Giving primarily in NY. No grants to individuals.
Application information: Contributes only to pre-selected organizations.
Trustees: C.H. Leshkowitz; Joseph Leshkowitz.
EIN: 133394520

6355
The Lessing Family Foundation ✧
c/o Stephen & Sandra Lessing
9 Snake Hill Rd.
Cold Spring Harbor, NY 11724-1105

Established in 2003 in NY.
Donors: Stephen M. Lessing; Sandra M. Lessing; Morton S. Bouchard III.
Foundation type: Independent foundation.
Financial data (yr. ended 12/31/13): Assets, $835,445 (M); gifts received, $501,445; expenditures, $660,235; qualifying distributions, $655,000; giving activities include $650,000 for 1 grant.
Purpose and activities: Giving primarily for scientific research.
Fields of interest: Education; Science.
Limitations: Applications not accepted. Giving primarily in NY. No grants to individuals.
Application information: Unsolicited requests for funds not accepted.
Trustees: Sandra Lessing; Stephen M. Lessing.
EIN: 030518473
Selected grants: The following grants are a representative sample of this grantmaker's funding activity:
$200,000 to Cold Spring Harbor Laboratory, Cold Spring Harbor, NY, 2011.
$25,000 to Fairfield University, Fairfield, CT, 2011.

6356
The Letterman Foundation for Courtesy and Grooming ✧
(formerly American Foundation for Courtesy and Grooming)
c/o Geller Family Office Svcs.
P.O. Box 1510
New York, NY 10150

Established in 1993 in NY.
Donors: David Letterman; Creative Artists Agency.
Foundation type: Independent foundation.
Financial data (yr. ended 12/31/13): Assets, $79,049 (M); gifts received, $15,000; expenditures, $554,790; qualifying distributions, $540,253; giving activities include $540,253 for 39 grants (high: $207,968; low: $500).
Fields of interest: Education; Health organizations, association; Housing/shelter, development; Human services; Children/youth, services.
Limitations: Applications not accepted. Giving primarily in IN and NY; some funding also in MT. No grants to individuals.
Application information: Contributes only to pre-selected organizations.
Officers: David Letterman, Pres.; R. Letterman, V.P. and Secy.
EIN: 223250026

6357
Leventhal Family Charitable Foundation ✧
(formerly Ira and Beth Leventhal Foundation)
c/o OTA LLC
1 Manhattanville Rd.
Purchase, NY 10577-2100

Established in NY.
Donors: Ira Leventhal; Beth Leventhal; Institute for Student Achievement.
Foundation type: Operating foundation.

Financial data (yr. ended 12/31/13): Assets, $4,893,284 (M); gifts received, $268,453; expenditures, $1,471,565; qualifying distributions, $1,470,750; giving activities include $1,470,750 for 34 grants (high: $250,000; low: $200).
Purpose and activities: Giving primarily for Jewish organizations; some funding for social services, as well as for health organizations, and higher education.
Fields of interest: Arts; Higher education; Law school/education; Human services; Children/youth, services; Jewish federated giving programs; Jewish agencies & synagogues.
Limitations: Applications not accepted. Giving primarily in NY. No grants to individuals.
Application information: Contributes only to pre-selected organizations.
Officers: Beth Leventhal, Pres.; Ira Leventhal, V.P.; Richard Cayne, Secy.
Directors: Daniel Leventhal; Jonathan Leventhal; Michael Leventhal.
EIN: 134092955

6358
The Pary & Abdulrahim Levian Charitable Foundation ✧

235 Great Neck Rd.
Great Neck, NY 11021-2802

Established in 2003 in NY.
Donors: Edmond Levian; Lawrence Levian; Moossa Levian; Pary Levian; Levian Corp.; Shlomo Basslian.
Foundation type: Independent foundation.
Financial data (yr. ended 12/31/13): Assets, $2,400,136 (M); gifts received, $1,500,000; expenditures, $706,990; qualifying distributions, $706,715; giving activities include $706,715 for 4 grants (high: $486,000; low: $26,000).
Fields of interest: Education; Jewish agencies & synagogues.
Limitations: Applications not accepted. Giving primarily in NY. No grants to individuals.
Application information: Contributes only to pre-selected organizations.
Directors: Edmond Levian; Lawrence Levian; Moossa Levian; Pary Levian.
EIN: 061684665

6359
William and Mildred Levine Foundation ✧ ☆

2921 Brighton-Henrietta Town Line Rd.
Rochester, NY 14623-2748

Established in 1987 in NY.
Donors: William Levine; Mildred Levine; M&T Bank.
Foundation type: Independent foundation.
Financial data (yr. ended 12/31/13): Assets, $10,246,652 (M); expenditures, $538,930; qualifying distributions, $525,100; giving activities include $525,100 for 3 grants (high: $500,000; low: $100).
Fields of interest: Hospitals (specialty); Jewish federated giving programs; Jewish agencies & synagogues; Children.
Type of support: General/operating support.
Limitations: Applications not accepted. Giving primarily in Rochester and Fishers, NY. No grants to individuals.
Application information: Unsolicited requests for funds not accepted.
Officers and Directors:* Todd Levine,* Pres.; Elena Oliveri,* Secy.-Treas.; Richard Levine; Barbara Slater.
EIN: 161310753
Selected grants: The following grants are a representative sample of this grantmaker's funding activity:
$350,000 to EquiCenter, Honeoye Falls, NY, 2011.
$20,000 to University of Rochester, Rochester, NY, 2011.
$4,000 to Quad A for Kids, Rochester, NY, 2011.
$2,161 to Temple Brith Kodesh, Rochester, NY, 2011.
$1,500 to Jewish Home and Infirmary of Rochester New York Foundation, Rochester, NY, 2011.

6360
Laurence W. Levine Foundation Inc. ✧

c/o Fiduciary Trust Co. Intl.
600 5th Ave.
New York, NY 10020-2302

Established in 1994 in FL.
Donor: Laurence W. Levine‡.
Foundation type: Independent foundation.
Financial data (yr. ended 12/31/13): Assets, $17,323,899 (M); expenditures, $849,641; qualifying distributions, $775,523; giving activities include $699,814 for 47 grants (high: $50,000; low: $814).
Fields of interest: Arts; Health care; Human services; Jewish agencies & synagogues.
Limitations: Applications not accepted. Giving primarily in NY. No grants to individuals.
Application information: Unsolicited requests for funds not accepted.
Officers and Directors:* Susan Kane,* Pres. and Treas.; Jay Levine,* V.P.; Eric Kane, Secy.; Beth Feldman; Russell Kane; James Levine; Michael Levine; Lesley Logue.
EIN: 650535001
Selected grants: The following grants are a representative sample of this grantmaker's funding activity:
$20,000 to Young Survival Coalition, New York, NY, 2012. To honor.

6361
Levitt Foundation, Inc. ✧

c/o Philanthropic Group
630 5th Ave., 20th Fl.
New York, NY 10111-0100 (212) 501-7785
Contact: Barbara R. Greenberg
FAX: (212) 501-7788;
E-mail: BGreenberg@philanthropicgroup.com; Main URL: http://fdnweb.org/levitt
Grants List: http://fdnweb.org/levitt/grants-approved/

Incorporated in 1949 in NY.
Donors: Levitt and Sons, Inc.; Abraham Levitt‡; Alfred Levitt‡; William Levitt.
Foundation type: Independent foundation.
Financial data (yr. ended 04/30/14): Assets, $17,544,978 (M); expenditures, $846,739; qualifying distributions, $789,829; giving activities include $700,900 for 56 grants (high: $64,000; low: $1,000).
Purpose and activities: The foundation is interested in youth-powered food justice as it relates to children and youth living in the five boroughs of New York City and Long Island, New York. The foundation funds programs that: enable young people ages 6 to 18 to learn about healthy eating and food systems, and to take action to increase access to affordable fresh foods in their own neighborhoods; provide children and youth with ongoing opportunities to build their confidence and self-esteem, citizenship skills and leadership abilities; and are sponsored by neighborhood and community-based organizations (rather than schools).
Fields of interest: Nutrition; Agriculture/food; Children/youth, services; Community development, neighborhood development.
Type of support: Program development; Internship funds.
Limitations: Applications not accepted. Giving limited to Long Island and New York, NY. No grants to individuals.
Publications: Grants list.
Application information: Unsolicited requests for funds not accepted.
Board meeting date(s): 3 times per year
Officers and Directors:* Elaine S. Hutchinson,* Pres.; Gregg Walker,* Secy.; Carlos Garcia-Tunon,* Treas.; John M. Brickman; Loren S. Harris; Tracy Green Landauer; Blondel A. Pinnock.
EIN: 136128226
Selected grants: The following grants are a representative sample of this grantmaker's funding activity:
$55,000 to City Parks Foundation, New York, NY, 2013. For Learning Gardens Leadership Program in four community gardens in the Bronx, Brooklyn, and Queens. Working after-school and during summer, youth learn about food systems, practice gardening skills, master community outreach techniques, and lead garden activities for neighborhood children and adults.
$51,000 to Project MOST, East Hampton, NY, 2013. For food justice learning and action projects for children enrolled in Seedling after-school and summer programs in the Village of Springs, Long Island.
$50,000 to Center for Family Life in Sunset Park, Brooklyn, NY, 2013. For Sunset Park Food Justice Program.
$50,000 to Childrens Aid Society, New York, NY, 2013. For Youth Food Justice Program in three neighborhoods in East Harlem and the South Bronx.
$50,000 to Cypress Hills Local Development Corporation, Brooklyn, NY, 2013. For Youth Food Justice Initiative. Young people in after-school and summer programs learn about food production and access to fresh healthy food.
$45,000 to BronxWorks, Bronx, NY, 2013. To fund HYPHEN project. South Bronx teens will test soil quality, plant and grow vegetables, prepare healthy meals, create composting bins, develop and distribute flyers, posters and a Facebook page that promote healthy eating, and conduct public presentations in their neighborhoods.
$45,000 to Queens Community House, Forest Hills, NY, 2013. For Pomonok Food Justice Leadership Program.
$40,000 to Added Value and Herban Solutions, Brooklyn, NY, 2013. For Summer Youth Food Justice Program. Red Hook teens grow and harvest produce to be sold at the farmers market, distributed to CSA members, and donated to people in need.
$40,000 to Brotherhood/Sister Sol, New York, NY, 2013. For Gaia Food Empowerment Project, to launch new Hamilton Height Urban Farmer Market and publish Gaia, Corner youth-powered neighborhood magazine.

$40,000 to Childrens Museum of the Arts, New York, NY, 2013. To fund FOOD, project operated by Open Road of New York in five low-income neighborhoods in lower Manhattan, the north shore of Staten Island, Fort Greene and Crown Heights in Brooklyn, and Jamaica, Queens. Teens design and build productive gardens and collaborate with USDA School Food and NYC Garden to School initiatives to increase the amount of healthy food offered on menus in school cafeterias and summer feeding programs for children and youth.
$30,000 to Just Food, New York, NY, 2013. To support teens across the City who train as Community Chefs, lead cooking demonstrations at farmer markets and spread the word about healthy eating.
$30,000 to Open Space Institute, New York, NY, 2013. For BK Farmyards Summer Youth Farm Leaders Program in East Flatbush, Brooklyn.
$25,000 to Concrete Safaris, New York, NY, 2013. To fund food justice project in East Harlem on public housing grounds at Jefferson Houses and Washington Houses. Young people create and maintain edible gardens, teach volunteers to garden, conduct public health research, and present educational workshops about food insecurity and obesity.
$20,000 to United Community Centers, Brooklyn, NY, 2013. To enhance East New York Farms program by creating opportunities for young people to function as peer leaders in urban farming and farmers market activities.
$12,500 to North Shore Child and Family Guidance Center, Roslyn Heights, NY, 2013. To support farming experiences for teens enrolled in the Wilderness Program. Young people plant, mulch, weed, and harvest vegetables at the Fox Hollow Farm in South Huntington and donate their produce to families in need.

6362
The Paul and Karen Levy Family Foundation ✧

c/o Schwartz & Co.
2580 Sunrise Hwy.
Bellmore, NY 11710-3608
Contact: Paul Levy, Tr.

Established in 1997 in NY.
Donors: Paul Levy; Karen Levy.
Foundation type: Independent foundation.
Financial data (yr. ended 12/31/12): Assets, $367,965 (M); gifts received, $1,575,000; expenditures, $1,614,029; qualifying distributions, $1,609,099; giving activities include $1,609,099 for 21 grants (high: $500,000; low: $500).
Purpose and activities: Giving primarily for higher education, as well as for the arts, Jewish organizations, and social services.
Fields of interest: Museums; Arts; Higher education; Law school/education; Human services; Jewish federated giving programs.
Limitations: Giving primarily in NY and PA; some giving nationally.
Application information: Application form not required.
Initial approach: Letter
Deadline(s): None
Trustee: Paul Levy.
EIN: 133982379

6363
Jerome Levy Foundation ✧

1 Rockefeller Plz., 20th Fl.
New York, NY 10020-2017
Main URL: http://leonlevyfoundation.org/
Shelby White's Giving Pledge Profile: http://glasspockets.org/philanthropy-in-focus/eye-on-the-giving-pledge/profiles/levy

Trust established in 1955 in NY.
Donors: Leon Levy†; S. Jay Levy†.
Foundation type: Independent foundation.
Financial data (yr. ended 10/31/13): Assets, $48,043,161 (M); gifts received, $23,394,881; expenditures, $1,847,152; qualifying distributions, $1,827,317; giving activities include $1,826,567 for 13 grants (high: $666,667; low: $2,500).
Fields of interest: Museums; Higher education; Environment, land resources; Hospitals (general); Human services; Civil/human rights; Jewish federated giving programs.
Limitations: Applications not accepted. Giving primarily in the metropolitan New York, NY, area. No grants to individuals.
Application information: Contributes only to pre-selected organizations.
Trustee: Shelby White.
EIN: 136159573

6364
Leon Levy Foundation ✧

One Rockefeller Plaza, 20th Fl.
New York, NY 10020-2003
Contact: John W. Bernstein, Pres. and C.F.O.; Nina Berg, Dir., Admin.
FAX: (212) 455-6231; E-mail for Nina Berg: nina.berg@leonlevy.org; Main URL: http://www.leonlevy.org

Established in 2004 in NY.
Donor: Leon Levy†.
Foundation type: Independent foundation.
Financial data (yr. ended 12/31/12): Assets, $442,526,524 (M); expenditures, $35,765,202; qualifying distributions, $30,679,681; giving activities include $29,317,508 for 184 grants (high: $7,240,208; low: $200), and $561,357 for foundation-administered programs.
Purpose and activities: Giving primarily for higher education and the arts.
Fields of interest: Arts, multipurpose centers/programs; Museums; History/archaeology; Higher education; Botanical/horticulture/landscape services; Civil liberties, advocacy; Biology/life sciences; Science.
Limitations: Applications not accepted. Giving primarily in New York, NY. No grants to individuals.
Application information: Contributes only to pre-selected organizations.
Board meeting date(s): Quarterly
Trustees: John Bernstein; Elizabeth B. Moynihan; Shelby White.
Number of staff: 4 full-time professional.
EIN: 306085406
Selected grants: The following grants are a representative sample of this grantmaker's funding activity:
$7,240,208 to New York University, New York, NY, 2012. For project support.
$4,007,287 to Institute for Advanced Study, Princeton, NJ, 2012. For project support.
$1,669,375 to Brooklyn Public Library, Brooklyn, NY, 2012. For project support.
$1,375,000 to Friends of the Israel Antiquities Authoritity, New York, NY, 2012. For project support.
$1,019,805 to Harvard University, Semitic Museum, Cambridge, MA, 2012. For White Levy Program for Archaeological Publications project.
$901,000 to Brooklyn Botanic Garden, Brooklyn, NY, 2012. For general operating support.
$143,446 to Woodrow Wilson International Center for Scholars, Washington, DC, 2012. For project support.
$19,925 to University of Massachusetts, Amherst, MA, 2012. For project support/general operating support.
$15,000 to Garden Conservancy, Cold Spring, NY, 2012. For general operating support.
$10,000 to PEN American Center, New York, NY, 2012. For general operating support.

6365
Reginald F. Lewis Foundation, Inc. ✧

115 E. 57th St., Ste. 1430
New York, NY 10022-2110
Contact: Beverly A. Cooper, Dir.

Established in 1987 in NY.
Donors: Reginald F. Lewis†; Loida N. Lewis; Leslie Lewis Sword; Christina S.N. Lewis.
Foundation type: Independent foundation.
Financial data (yr. ended 06/30/13): Assets, $21,854,125 (M); expenditures, $1,343,649; qualifying distributions, $1,343,649; giving activities include $1,123,056 for 77 grants (high: $500,000; low: $228).
Fields of interest: Arts; Libraries (public); Education; Children.
Application information: Application form required.
Initial approach: Letter
Deadline(s): None
Directors: Beverly A. Cooper; Anthony S. Fugett; Christina Lewis Halpern; Loida N. Lewis.
EIN: 133429965
Selected grants: The following grants are a representative sample of this grantmaker's funding activity:
$15,000 to University of Michigan, Ann Arbor, MI, 2011.

6366
The Lichtenstein Family Foundation ✧

1531 54th St.
Brooklyn, NY 11219-4346

Established in 1997 in NY.
Donor: George Lichtenstein.
Foundation type: Independent foundation.
Financial data (yr. ended 12/31/13): Assets, $940,930 (M); expenditures, $441,290; qualifying distributions, $431,521; giving activities include $427,000 for 19 grants (high: $67,600; low: $3,600).
Purpose and activities: Giving primarily to Jewish agencies, temples, and schools.
Fields of interest: Education; Jewish agencies & synagogues.
Limitations: Applications not accepted. Giving primarily in Brooklyn, NY. No grants to individuals.
Application information: Unsolicited requests for funds not accepted.
Directors: Alan Lichtenstein; George Lichtenstein; David Singer.
EIN: 113377455

6367
Lightfighter Trust ✧
(formerly Rosh Foundation)
c/o BCRS Assocs., LLC
77 Water St., 9th Fl.
New York, NY 10005-4401
Contact: Robin Chemers Neustein, Tr.

Established in 1991 in NY.
Donor: Robin Chemers Neustein.
Foundation type: Independent foundation.
Financial data (yr. ended 03/31/13): Assets, $25,621,319 (M); gifts received, $1,405,471; expenditures, $2,855,869; qualifying distributions, $2,756,613; giving activities include $2,655,129 for 9 grants (high: $2,255,325; low: $804).
Purpose and activities: Giving primarily for higher education, and to a donor advised fund.
Fields of interest: Higher education; Foundations (public).
Type of support: Scholarship funds.
Limitations: Applications not accepted. Giving primarily in the metropolitan New York, NY, area; funding also in Cincinnati, OH, and Providence, RI. No grants to individuals or for scholarships; no loans.
Application information: Contributes only to pre-selected organizations.
Trustee: Robin Chemers Neustein.
EIN: 133637441
Selected grants: The following grants are a representative sample of this grantmaker's funding activity:
$200,000 to Rockefeller University, New York, NY, 2013. For Collaborative Science Campaign.
$100,000 to Hope for Heroism, Seattle, WA, 2013. For peer-to-peer healing of wounded combat soldiers.
$75,000 to Bronx Veterans Medical Research Foundation, Bronx, NY, 2013. For Direct research grant to support research project, Psychobiology of Suicidal Behavior Among Military Veterans.
$20,000 to Rockefeller University, New York, NY, 2013. For Whitehead Presidential Scholarships.
$1,000 to Iraq and Afghanistan Veterans of America, New York, NY, 2013. For general support for veterans organization.
$1,000 to Puppies Behind Bars, New York, NY, 2013. For Dog Tags Initiative for wounded veterans.

6368
The Lincoln Fund ✧ ☆
c/o Weber Moses Co.
225 Broadway, No. 2420
New York, NY 10007-3001
Application address: c/o Martha McLanahan, Pres., 295 Madison Ave., New York, NY 10017

Incorporated in 1898 in NY.
Foundation type: Independent foundation.
Financial data (yr. ended 06/30/13): Assets, $7,024,919 (M); expenditures, $527,743; qualifying distributions, $468,000; giving activities include $468,000 for 19 grants (high: $75,000; low: $14,000).
Purpose and activities: Giving primarily for educational programs, youth organizations, and human services.
Fields of interest: Secondary school/education; Higher education; Nursing school/education; Education; Human services; Children/youth, services.
Type of support: Continuing support; Program development; Seed money; Scholarship funds; Matching/challenge support.
Limitations: Applications accepted. Giving limited to the greater metropolitan New York, NY, area. No grants to individuals, or for building or endowment funds, operating budgets, or general corporate purposes.
Application information: Application form not required.
Initial approach: Letter
Copies of proposal: 1
Deadline(s): None
Board meeting date(s): Mar., June, Sept., and Dec.
Officers: Martha McLanahan, Pres.; Christopher O'Malley, Secy.; Christopher S. Moore,* Treas.
Directors: Richard Brown; Iris Chen; Rosemary Ordonez Jenkins; Keith Thomas.
Number of staff: 1 part-time support.
EIN: 131740466
Selected grants: The following grants are a representative sample of this grantmaker's funding activity:
$35,000 to East Harlem Tutorial Program, New York, NY, 2011.
$25,000 to Harlem Educational Activities Fund, New York, NY, 2011.
$25,000 to National Medical Fellowships, New York, NY, 2011.
$25,000 to Saint Joseph School, Bronx, NY, 2011.
$20,000 to Inwood House, New York, NY, 2011.
$16,500 to Riverdale Mental Health Association, Bronx, NY, 2011.
$15,000 to Kingsbridge Heights Community Center, Bronx, NY, 2011.

6369
Linden Trust For Conservation ✧
(formerly Lawrence and Dana Linden Family Foundation)
156 W. 56th St., Ste. 1100
New York, NY 10019-3927 (212) 991-3730
FAX: (646) 225-7116; Main URL: http://www.lindentrust.org

Established in 1993 in NY.
Donors: Lawrence H. Linden; Dana Linden; Goldman Sachs & Co.
Foundation type: Independent foundation.
Financial data (yr. ended 12/31/12): Assets, $26,675,790 (M); gifts received, $1,801,565; expenditures, $4,032,960; qualifying distributions, $3,832,407; giving activities include $2,042,473 for 34 grants (high: $412,963; low: $4,876), and $1,170,000 for 1 foundation-administered program.
Fields of interest: Higher education; Environment; Animals/wildlife, preservation/protection.
Limitations: Applications not accepted. Giving primarily in Washington, DC, MA, and New York, NY. No grants, or scholarships, gifts, or loans to individuals.
Application information: Contributes only to pre-selected organizations.
Officers: Roger Ullman, Exec. Dir.; Marsha Hahn, Dir., Fin. and Admin.
Trustee: Lawrence H. Linden.
EIN: 133748063

6370
Lindenbaum Family Charitable Trust ✧
c/o Linda Lindenbaum
998 5th Ave., Ste. 7/8E
New York, NY 10028-0102

Established in 1989 in NY.
Donors: Samuel H. Lindenbaum; Belle Lindenbaum; Lindenbaum GST Charitable Trust; Linda Lindenbaum.
Foundation type: Independent foundation.
Financial data (yr. ended 09/30/13): Assets, $809,233 (M); gifts received, $23,079; expenditures, $469,789; qualifying distributions, $466,953; giving activities include $465,103 for 44 grants (high: $100,000; low: $100).
Fields of interest: Museums (art); Performing arts, dance; Arts; Human services; Jewish agencies & synagogues.
Limitations: Applications not accepted. Giving primarily in New York, NY. No grants to individuals.
Application information: Unsolicited requests for funds not accepted.
Trustee: Linda Lindenbaum.
EIN: 136929327

6371
Lindmor Foundation, Inc. ✧
c/o BCRS Associates, LLC
77 Water St., 9th Fl.
New York, NY 10005

Donor: Arthur J. Reimers III.
Foundation type: Independent foundation.
Financial data (yr. ended 12/31/13): Assets, $38,635,819 (M); expenditures, $2,405,138; qualifying distributions, $1,863,756; giving activities include $1,848,256 for 18 grants (high: $1,100,000; low: $6).
Fields of interest: Foundations (community).
Limitations: Applications not accepted. Giving primarily in CT.
Application information: Unsolicited requests for funds not accepted.
Officers and Directors:* Lindsay J.H. Reimers,* Pres.; Arthur J. Reimers III,* V.P. and Secy.-Treas.; Caitlin L. Reimers; Megan C. Reimers; Sarah E.M. Reimers.
EIN: 263631010

6372
The Fay J. Lindner Foundation ✧
1161 Meadowbrook Rd.
North Merrick, NY 11566-1332

Established in 1966.
Donor: Fay J. Lindner‡.
Foundation type: Independent foundation.
Financial data (yr. ended 08/31/13): Assets, $40,075,859 (M); expenditures, $2,322,251; qualifying distributions, $2,178,804; giving activities include $2,058,027 for 110 grants (high: $183,769; low: $200).
Purpose and activities: Giving primarily for the performing arts, education, health organizations, children, youth, and social services, and Jewish organizations.
Fields of interest: Performing arts; Higher education; Hospitals (general); Health care; Health organizations, association; Human services; Children/youth, services; Family services;

Residential/custodial care, hospices; Foundations (private grantmaking); Jewish federated giving programs.
Type of support: Building/renovation; Program development; Seed money; Fellowships; Program-related investments/loans.
Limitations: Applications not accepted. Giving primarily on Long Island, NY. No grants to individuals.
Application information: Contributes only to pre-selected organizations.
Officers and Directors:* Robert M. Goldberg,* Pres.; Norman A. Schefer, V.P. and Secy.-Treas.; Robin Goldberg,* Secy.; David S. Goldberg.
Board Member: Norman Gross.
EIN: 116043320
Selected grants: The following grants are a representative sample of this grantmaker's funding activity:
$51,564 to Cornell University, Ithaca, NY, 2011.
$25,782 to American Cancer Society, Atlanta, GA, 2011.
$25,782 to American Heart Association, Dallas, TX, 2011.
$25,782 to Muscular Dystrophy Association, Tucson, AZ, 2011.
$10,000 to Juvenile Diabetes Research Foundation International, New York, NY, 2011.
$5,000 to Amyotrophic Lateral Sclerosis Association, Calabasas Hills, CA, 2011.
$5,000 to Columbia University, New York, NY, 2011.
$5,000 to Cystic Fibrosis Foundation, Bethesda, MD, 2011.
$3,000 to Covenant House, New York, NY, 2011.
$2,000 to Crohns and Colitis Foundation of America, New York, NY, 2011.

6373
Robert and Teresa Lindsay Family Foundation ✧
630 5th Ave., 30th Fl.
New York, NY 10111-0100 (212) 651-1100

Established in 1997 in NY.
Donor: Robert D. Lindsay.
Foundation type: Independent foundation.
Financial data (yr. ended 09/30/13): Assets, $212,679 (M); gifts received, $2,578,000; expenditures, $2,577,490; qualifying distributions, $2,566,410; giving activities include $2,566,250 for 16 grants (high: $1,000,000; low: $1,250).
Purpose and activities: Giving primarily for education; funding also for social services.
Fields of interest: Higher education; Education; Health care; Human services; United Ways and Federated Giving Programs.
Limitations: Applications accepted. Giving primarily in NH and NY. No grants to individuals.
Application information:
Initial approach: Letter
Deadline(s): None
Trustees: Robert D. Lindsay; Teresa Lindsay.
EIN: 137142605
Selected grants: The following grants are a representative sample of this grantmaker's funding activity:
$1,000,000 to Saint Pauls School, Concord, NH, 2013. For general support.
$800,000 to Cold Spring Harbor Laboratory, Cold Spring Harbor, NY, 2012. For general support.
$600,000 to Cold Spring Harbor Laboratory, Cold Spring Harbor, NY, 2013. For general support.
$250,500 to Wildlife Conservation Society, Bronx, NY, 2012. For general support.
$250,000 to Stanford University, Stanford Fund, Stanford, CA, 2012. For general support.
$200,000 to Harvard College Fund, Cambridge, MA, 2013. For general support.
$200,000 to Stanford University, Stanford, CA, 2013. For general support for Bing Overseas Study Program.
$200,000 to Stanford University, Stanford Fund, Stanford, CA, 2013. For general support.
$100,000 to Juilliard School, New York, NY, 2013. For general support.
$75,000 to Juilliard School, New York, NY, 2012. For general support.
$65,000 to Second Stage Theater, New York, NY, 2012. For general support.
$63,240 to Saint Johns Episcopal Church of Cold Spring Harbor, Cold Spring Harbor, NY, 2012. For general support.
$60,000 to Cambodian Childrens Fund, Santa Monica, CA, 2013. For general support.
$50,000 to Pan-Massachusetts Challenge, Needham, MA, 2012. For general support.
$25,000 to Boys Club of New York, New York, NY, 2012. For general support.
$25,000 to Jazz at Lincoln Center, New York, NY, 2012. For general support.
$10,000 to Americans Aiding Refugees, Houston, TX, 2013. For general support.
$10,000 to Hunter College Foundation, New York, NY, 2012. For general support for Lindsay Book Project.

6374
The Link Foundation ✧
c/o Binghamton University Foundation
P.O. Box 6005
Binghamton, NY 13902-6005
Contact: Martha J. Gahring
Application address: P.O. Box 6005 Bringhamton, NY 13902-6005; Main URL: http://www.linkfoundation.org

Established in 1953 in NY.
Donors: Edwin A. Link†; Mrs. Edwin A. Link†; Lawrence Clayton; L-3 Link Communications; Link Div. of CAE.
Foundation type: Independent foundation.
Financial data (yr. ended 06/30/13): Assets, $11,044,705 (M); gifts received, $17,390; expenditures, $518,726; qualifying distributions, $452,000; giving activities include $452,000 for grants.
Purpose and activities: The foundation supports programs to foster the theoretical basis, practical knowledge, and application of energy, simulation, and ocean engineering and instrumentation research, and to disseminate the results of that research through lectures, seminars and publications.
Fields of interest: Environment, energy; Marine science; Space/aviation; Engineering/technology.
Type of support: Continuing support; Fellowships; Research.
Limitations: Applications accepted. Giving primarily in FL and NY. No grants to individuals (except through programs).
Publications: Informational brochure (including application guidelines).
Application information: Application form required.
Initial approach: Letter
Copies of proposal: 1
Deadline(s): Jan. 15
Board meeting date(s): Feb. and June
Final notification: Mar.
Officers and Trustees:* Dr. Thomas F. Kelly,* Chair; Dr. Jimmie Anne Haisley,* Secy.; Douglas R. Johnson,* Treas.; Dr. Andrew M. Clark; David Gdovin.
Number of staff: 1 part-time professional.
EIN: 536011109

6375
George Link, Jr. Foundation, Inc. ✧
200 Park Ave., 54th Fl.
New York, NY 10166-0005
Contact: Joseph Samulski, Treas.

Incorporated in 1980 in NY.
Donor: George Link, Jr.†.
Foundation type: Independent foundation.
Financial data (yr. ended 12/31/12): Assets, $33,272,763 (M); expenditures, $1,956,217; qualifying distributions, $1,638,586; giving activities include $1,610,000 for 65 grants (high: $85,000; low: $5,000).
Purpose and activities: Giving primarily for hospitals and medical research, higher and secondary education, culture and fine arts, Roman Catholic organizations, schools, churches and missions, and children, youth, and social services.
Fields of interest: Museums (art); Arts; Secondary school/education; Higher education; Hospitals (general); Medical research, institute; Human services; Children/youth, services; Christian agencies & churches; Catholic agencies & churches.
Type of support: General/operating support; Continuing support; Management development/capacity building; Program development; Scholarship funds; Matching/challenge support.
Limitations: Giving primarily in NJ and NY. No grants to individuals, or for general support, operating budgets, continuing support, annual campaigns, seed money, emergency funds, deficit financing, equipment, land acquisition, renovation projects, or matching gifts; no loans.
Application information: Application form not required.
Initial approach: Letter of Inquiry
Copies of proposal: 1
Deadline(s): None
Board meeting date(s): Monthly except July and Aug.
Final notification: 6 weeks
Officers: Raymond Dorado, Chair.; Kerry M. Link, M.D., Vice-Chair.; William Norden, V.P.; Josephine Woodward, Secy.; Joseph M. Samulski, Treas.
EIN: 133041396

6376
Linville Family Foundation ✧ ☆
c/o BBH & Co.
140 Broadway, 5th Fl.
New York, NY 10005

Established in 2001 in NY.
Donors: Clarence Linville; Susanne Gay Linville; Linville Trust; Linville NTC Charitable Lead Unity Trust.
Foundation type: Independent foundation.
Financial data (yr. ended 12/31/13): Assets, $15,096,901 (M); gifts received, $3,917,200; expenditures, $677,729; qualifying distributions,

$621,620; giving activities include $609,000 for 64 grants (high: $120,000; low: $500).
Fields of interest: Arts; Higher education; Environment; Medical research, institute; Christian agencies & churches.
Limitations: Applications not accepted. No grants to individuals.
Application information: Unsolicited requests for funds not accepted.
Trustees: James Coker Linville; John Evans Linville.
EIN: 137177348
Selected grants: The following grants are a representative sample of this grantmaker's funding activity:
$6,000 to Columbia University, School of Law, New York, NY, 2012. For general support.

6377
The Bari Lipp Foundation, Inc. ✧
c/o Ayco Co. L.P., David Quinn
P.O. Box 15014
Albany, NY 12212-5014 (518) 640-5000

Established in 1996 in NY.
Donor: Robert I. Lipp.
Foundation type: Independent foundation.
Financial data (yr. ended 12/31/12): Assets, $30,013,625 (M); expenditures, $3,427,911; qualifying distributions, $3,328,231; giving activities include $3,328,231 for 75 grants (high: $1,500,000; low: $4).
Purpose and activities: Giving primarily for the arts, particularly the ballet, as well as for education, health, and human services.
Fields of interest: Performing arts, ballet; Arts; Higher education; Human services; Children/youth, services.
Limitations: Applications not accepted. Giving primarily in MA and NY. No grants to individuals.
Application information: Contributes only to pre-selected organizations.
Directors: Jeffrey D. Lipp; Robert I. Lipp; Wendy A. Lipp.
EIN: 133921302

6378
The Lisabeth Foundation ✧
(formerly The Seldon Foundation)
c/o Patty Carcano
4 International Dr., Ste. 100
Rye Brook, NY 10573-1065

Established in 1999 in NY.
Donor: Daniel C. Benton.
Foundation type: Independent foundation.
Financial data (yr. ended 11/30/13): Assets, $12,559,887 (M); expenditures, $2,408,930; qualifying distributions, $2,404,982; giving activities include $2,401,000 for 21 grants (high: $1,000,000; low: $1,000).
Purpose and activities: Giving primarily to health organizations, and for children and youth services.
Fields of interest: Health organizations, association; Human services; Children/youth, services.
Limitations: Applications not accepted. Giving primarily in NY. No grants to individuals.
Application information: Contributes only to pre-selected organizations.
Trustees: Daniel C. Benton; Kevin E. O'Brien.
EIN: 066486254

6379
The Lucius N. Littauer Foundation, Inc. ✧
220 5th Ave., 19th Fl.
New York, NY 10001 (212) 697-2677
Contact: Alan Divack, Prog. Off.
E-mail: info@littauerfoundation.org; Main URL: http://littauerfoundation.org/

Incorporated in 1929 in NY.
Donor: Lucius N. Littauer‡.
Foundation type: Independent foundation.
Financial data (yr. ended 12/31/13): Assets, $44,253,675 (M); expenditures, $2,979,350; qualifying distributions, $2,814,399; giving activities include $2,625,749 for 140 grants (high: $435,000; low: $1,000), and $41,762 for 26 employee matching gifts.
Purpose and activities: Grants for scholarly research on Jewish studies, for the endowment of Judaica book funds at university libraries, for medical ethics and palliative medical care, and NY public projects.
Fields of interest: Humanities; History/archaeology; Language/linguistics; Literature; Higher education; Environment; Medical care, bioethics; Palliative care; Social sciences; Political science; Jewish agencies & synagogues; Religion.
International interests: Israel.
Type of support: Endowments; Program development; Publication; Seed money; Research; Employee matching gifts; Matching/challenge support.
Limitations: Applications accepted. Giving primarily in NY for medical ethics, and environmental related projects. No support for religious programs. No grants to individuals.
Application information: See foundation web site for application guidelines and online application. Application form required.
Board meeting date(s): Annually and as required
Officers and Directors:* Robert D. Frost,* Pres.; Noah Perlman, Secy.; Geula R. Solomon, Treas.; Charles Berlin; Berthold Bilski; Mark A. Bilski; George Harris; Sarah K. Levy; Henry A. Lowet; Peter J. Solomon.
Number of staff: 1 part-time professional; 1 part-time support.
EIN: 131688027

6380
The Litwin Foundation, Inc. ✧
1200 Union Tpke.
New Hyde Park, NY 11040-1708
Contact: Leonard Litwin, Pres.

Established in 1989 in NY.
Donors: Leonard Litwin; Woodbourne Foundation.
Foundation type: Independent foundation.
Financial data (yr. ended 12/31/12): Assets, $15,795,814 (M); gifts received, $4,500,000; expenditures, $6,374,849; qualifying distributions, $6,321,663; giving activities include $6,321,663 for grants.
Purpose and activities: Giving primarily for disease research organizations, children's services, human services, education, and the environment.
Fields of interest: Museums; Education; Environment, natural resources; Hospitals (general); Health organizations, association; Medical research, institute; Human services; Children/youth, services; Jewish agencies & synagogues; Aging; Disabilities, people with; Homeless.
Type of support: General/operating support; Research.
Limitations: Applications not accepted. Giving primarily in New York, NY. No grants to individuals.
Application information: Unsolicited requests for funds not accepted.
Officers and Directors:* Leonard Litwin,* Pres.; Diane Miller,* V.P.; Carole Pittelman,* Treas.; Richard Cohen; Seymour D. Reich; Howard Swarzman.
EIN: 133501980

6381
The Ernest and Joan Liu Foundation ✧ ☆
c/o BCRS Assocs., LLC
77 Water St., 9th Fl.
New York, NY 10005-4401

Established in 1989 in NJ.
Donors: Ernest S. Liu; Joan S. Liu.
Foundation type: Independent foundation.
Financial data (yr. ended 03/31/13): Assets, $9,305,024 (M); gifts received, $6,100; expenditures, $492,343; qualifying distributions, $450,095; giving activities include $447,045 for 8 grants (high: $435,000; low: $45).
Fields of interest: Higher education; Protestant agencies & churches.
Type of support: General/operating support.
Limitations: Applications not accepted. Giving primarily in Ithaca and New York, NY. No grants to individuals.
Application information: Contributes only to pre-selected organizations.
Trustees: Erica Sze-Hua Liu; Ernest S. Liu; Joan S. Liu.
EIN: 133531987
Selected grants: The following grants are a representative sample of this grantmaker's funding activity:
$380,800 to Cornell University, Ithaca, NY, 2011.
$5,000 to Chinatown Health Clinic Foundation, New York, NY, 2011.

6382
The Liu Foundation ✧
27 William St., 11th Fl.
New York, NY 10005-2701 (212) 966-1059
Contact: Yvonne Liu, Pres. and Dir.

Established in 1997 in NY.
Donors: Arthur Liu; Yvonne Liu.
Foundation type: Independent foundation.
Financial data (yr. ended 12/31/13): Assets, $3,533,955 (M); expenditures, $693,430; qualifying distributions, $649,356; giving activities include $636,500 for 10 grants (high: $200,000; low: $10,000).
Purpose and activities: Giving primarily for community programs and education.
Fields of interest: Higher education; Scholarships/financial aid; Cancer; Big Brothers/Big Sisters; Human services.
Type of support: General/operating support.
Limitations: Applications accepted. Giving primarily in New York, NY. No grants to individuals.
Application information: Application form not required.
Initial approach: Proposal
Deadline(s): None

Officers and Directors:* Yvonne Liu,* Pres.; Laura Parsons,* V.P.; Wyna Liu,* Secy.; Whiting Wu,* Treas.; Fred Teng.
EIN: 133945839
Selected grants: The following grants are a representative sample of this grantmaker's funding activity:
$50,000 to Chinese-American Planning Council, New York, NY, 2012. For Project Gateway Program.

6383
The Loeb Family - Third Point Foundation ✧

(formerly Daniel S. Loeb - Third Point Foundation)
15 Central Park W., Ph. 39
New York, NY 10023-7719

Established in 2000 in NY.
Donors: Daniel S. Loeb; Third Point LLC.
Foundation type: Independent foundation.
Financial data (yr. ended 12/31/12): Assets, $21,837,802 (M); gifts received, $21,923,237; expenditures, $4,606,340; qualifying distributions, $4,568,878; giving activities include $4,566,212 for 136 grants (high: $798,500; low: $100).
Fields of interest: Museums (art); Arts; Higher education; Education; Human services; Children/youth, services; Philanthropy/voluntarism.
Limitations: Applications not accepted. Giving primarily in the metropolitan New York, NY, area. No grants to individuals.
Application information: Contributes only to pre-selected organizations.
Officers and Directors:* Daniel S. Loeb,* Pres.; John Josephson, Secy.; Nicole Nadal, Treas.; Margaret M. Loeb; Carter Pottash.
EIN: 522251371

6384
Arthur L. Loeb Foundation, Inc. ✧

c/o Laurence I. Foster, CPA
270 Madison Ave., 16th Fl.
New York, NY 10016-0601

Established around 1977 in NY.
Donor: Arthur L. Loeb.
Foundation type: Independent foundation.
Financial data (yr. ended 11/30/13): Assets, $2,381,686 (M); expenditures, $1,475,898; qualifying distributions, $1,441,480; giving activities include $1,430,238 for 111 grants (high: $100,000; low: $500).
Purpose and activities: Giving for higher education, cultural institutes, Jewish organizations, social services, health services, and boys and girls clubs.
Fields of interest: Museums; Museums (art); Performing arts; Performing arts, theater; Performing arts, opera; Arts; Higher education; Hospitals (specialty); Health organizations, association; Food distribution, meals on wheels; Boys & girls clubs; Human services; Community development, citizen coalitions; Community development, neighborhood associations.
Limitations: Applications not accepted. Giving primarily in New York, NY; funding also in Cambridge, MA. No grants to individuals.
Application information: Contributes only to pre-selected organizations.
Officers and Directors:* Arthur L. Loeb,* Pres.; William L. Bernard,* V.P.; Jerome A. Manning,* Secy.-Treas.
EIN: 132933768

6385
John L. Loeb, Jr. Foundation ✧ ☆

c/o Barry M. Strauss Assocs., Ltd.
307 5th Ave., 8th Fl.
New York, NY 10016-6517

Established in 1964.
Donor: John L. Loeb, Jr.
Foundation type: Independent foundation.
Financial data (yr. ended 12/31/13): Assets, $5,563,786 (M); expenditures, $1,857,269; qualifying distributions, $1,830,159; giving activities include $1,687,463 for 115 grants (high: $581,680; low: $40).
Purpose and activities: Giving primarily for education, Jewish organizations, health organizations and human services.
Fields of interest: Arts; Higher education; Education; Environment; Health organizations, association; Human services; International affairs; Foundations (private grantmaking); Religion, public policy; Jewish agencies & synagogues.
Limitations: Applications not accepted. Giving primarily in NY. No grants to individuals.
Application information: Contributes only to pre-selected organizations.
Officer: John L. Loeb, Jr., Pres. and Treas.
EIN: 136142345
Selected grants: The following grants are a representative sample of this grantmaker's funding activity:
$600,000 to George Washington Institute for Religious Freedom, New York, NY, 2011. For general support.
$5,000 to ACCION International, Washington, DC, 2011. For general support.

6386
Frederick Loewe Foundation, Inc. ✧ ☆

c/o Baker Tilly, LLP
1 Penn Plz., Ste. 3000
New York, NY 10119-0032
Main URL: http://www.frederickloewe.org

Established in 1959 in NY.
Donor: Frederick Loewe†.
Foundation type: Independent foundation.
Financial data (yr. ended 12/31/13): Assets, $9,239,057 (M); expenditures, $601,495; qualifying distributions, $463,924; giving activities include $443,000 for grants.
Purpose and activities: Giving primarily for the arts, particularly theater, and education.
Fields of interest: Arts, association; Arts education; Performing arts; Performing arts, theater; Arts; Higher education; Jewish agencies & synagogues.
Limitations: Applications not accepted. Giving primarily in NY. No grants to individuals.
Application information: Contributes only to pre-selected organizations.
Officers: Emily Altman, Pres. and Treas.; Dara Altman, V.P.
Board Members: Paul Epstein; Michael Lennon.
EIN: 136111444

6387
Loewenberg Foundation, Inc. ✧

900 3rd Ave., Ste. 1002
New York, NY 10022-3310 (212) 753-4100
Contact: Diana Loewenberg, Pres., Treas. and Dir.

Established in 1959 in NY.
Donors: Ralph E. Loewenberg; Kurt Loewenberg†.
Foundation type: Independent foundation.
Financial data (yr. ended 10/31/13): Assets, $19,982,702 (M); expenditures, $1,278,112; qualifying distributions, $960,750; giving activities include $960,000 for 4 grants (high: $825,000; low: $10,000).
Fields of interest: Foundations (community); Jewish federated giving programs; Jewish agencies & synagogues.
Type of support: Research.
Limitations: Applications accepted. Giving primarily in New York, NY. No grants to individuals.
Application information:
Initial approach: Letter
Deadline(s): None
Officers and Directors:* Diana Loewenberg,* Pres. and Treas.; Jeffrey N. Grabel,* Secy.; Frederick Lubcher.
EIN: 136075586
Selected grants: The following grants are a representative sample of this grantmaker's funding activity:
$750,000 to New York Community Trust, New York, NY, 2011.
$25,000 to Israel Project, Washington, DC, 2011.
$25,000 to Leo Baeck Institute, New York, NY, 2011.
$25,000 to Storm King Art Center, Mountainville, NY, 2011.

6388
Loews Foundation ✧

c/o Tax Dept.
655 Madison Ave., 9th Fl.
New York, NY 10065 (212) 521-2500
Contact: Alan Momeyer, V.P., Corp. Human Resources

Trust established in 1957 in NY.
Donors: Loews Corp.; Loews Hotel Holding Corp.; Marcus Loew Booking Agency.
Foundation type: Company-sponsored foundation.
Financial data (yr. ended 12/31/13): Assets, $268,034 (M); gifts received, $500,000; expenditures, $497,716; qualifying distributions, $496,336; giving activities include $496,336 for 27 grants (high: $100,381; low: $225).
Purpose and activities: The foundation supports police agencies and parks and organizations involved with arts and culture, education, children and youth, business, and voluntarism promotion.
Fields of interest: Arts; Education; Human services.
Type of support: Annual campaigns; Program development; Scholarship funds; Employee matching gifts; Employee-related scholarships.
Limitations: Applications accepted. Giving primarily in NY. No grants to individuals (except for employee-related scholarships).
Application information: Application form not required.
Initial approach: Completed application form
Board meeting date(s): As required
Trustees: Peter W. Keegan; Andrew H. Tisch; Ed Unneland.
EIN: 136082817

Selected grants: The following grants are a representative sample of this grantmaker's funding activity:
$22,165 to United Way of New York City, New York, NY, 2011.
$15,000 to New York Cares, New York, NY, 2011.
$12,000 to Dress for Success New Orleans, New Orleans, LA, 2011.
$10,000 to American Friends of the Hebrew University, New York, NY, 2011.
$10,000 to Yeshiva University, New York, NY, 2011.
$5,000 to New York City Police Foundation, New York, NY, 2011.
$1,000 to United Negro College Fund, Fairfax, VA, 2011.

6389
Loewy Family Foundation Inc. ✧
80 Wall St., No. 1018
New York, NY 10005-3601 (212) 269-2466
Contact: John P. Reiner, Secy.-Treas.

Established in 1966 in NY.
Donors: Alfred Loewy†; Edna Loewy Butler†.
Foundation type: Independent foundation.
Financial data (yr. ended 06/30/13): Assets, $9,510,888 (M); expenditures, $538,991; qualifying distributions, $451,332; giving activities include $451,332 for grants.
Purpose and activities: Giving primarily for higher education.
Fields of interest: Elementary/secondary education; Higher education.
Type of support: Equipment; Program development; Fellowships; Scholarship funds; Research.
Limitations: Applications accepted. Giving primarily in Washington, DC, NM, NY, PA, and VA. No grants to individuals.
Application information: Application form required.
Initial approach: Proposal in letter form
Copies of proposal: 1
Deadline(s): None
Officers and Directors:* Brigitte Loewy Linz, Chair. and Pres.; Erik A. Hanson, C.P.A.*, V.P.; Peter Erwin Linz,* V.P.; Edward B. Pennfield,* V.P.; Mischa A. Zabotin,* V.P.; John P. Reiner,* Secy.-Treas.
EIN: 136225288
Selected grants: The following grants are a representative sample of this grantmaker's funding activity:
$256,666 to Lehigh University, Bethlehem, PA, 2013. For Permanent Support for a Substantial Portion of Laboratory Equipment.
$30,000 to Mohonk Preserve, New Paltz, NY, 2013. To Enhance and Maximize the Capacity to Extract and Apply Data and Recruit Scientists.
$20,000 to Catching the Dream, Albuquerque, NM, 2013. For Scholarships for Needy Native Americans to Obtain Engineering/Science.
$20,000 to Lehigh University, Bethlehem, PA, 2013. To Develop Two Field-Based Student Internships at Wyuman Gordon.
$16,666 to Whitehead Institute for Biomedical Research, Cambridge, MA, 2013. To Fund the Loewy Family Foundation Core Facilities Innovation Fund.

6390
The Lone Rock Foundation, Inc. ✧ ☆
(formerly Herring Creek Foundation, Inc.)
c/o BCRS Assocs., LLC
77 Water St., 9th Fl.
New York, NY 10005-3701

Established in 1994 in NY.
Donors: Susan Scheuer; Jonathan Lipnick.
Foundation type: Independent foundation.
Financial data (yr. ended 12/31/11): Assets, $10,318 (M); gifts received, $10,000; expenditures, $601,930; qualifying distributions, $593,236; giving activities include $593,236 for 3 grants (high: $567,236; low: $1,000).
Fields of interest: Foundations (public); Jewish agencies & synagogues.
Limitations: Applications not accepted. Giving primarily in MA and NY. No grants to individuals.
Application information: Unsolicited requests for funds not accepted.
Officers: Susan Scheuer, Pres.; Jonathan Lipnick, Secy.
Director: Judith Scheuer.
EIN: 133783380

6391
Longwell Family Foundation ✧
c/o The Ayco Company
P.O. Box 860
Saratoga Springs, NY 12866-0860

Established in TX.
Donors: Harry Longwell; Norma Longwell.
Foundation type: Independent foundation.
Financial data (yr. ended 12/31/13): Assets, $8,420,735 (M); gifts received, $2,399,850; expenditures, $765,788; qualifying distributions, $753,500; giving activities include $753,500 for 28 grants (high: $120,000; low: $3,500).
Fields of interest: Education; Health care; Human services; Catholic agencies & churches.
Limitations: Applications not accepted. Giving primarily in LA, MT, and TX.
Application information: Unsolicited requests for funds not accepted.
Trustees: Brent John Longwell; Garett John Longwell; Harry John Longwell III; Harry L. Longwell; Norma Longwell; Paxton John Longwell.
EIN: 205970193

6392
The Lopatin Family Foundation ✧ ☆
c/o BCRS Assocs., LLC
77 Water St., 9th Fl.
New York, NY 10005-3701

Established in 1994 in NY.
Donors: Jonathan M. Lopatin; Brenda Lopatin.
Foundation type: Independent foundation.
Financial data (yr. ended 08/31/13): Assets, $13,221,044 (M); expenditures, $603,432; qualifying distributions, $514,547; giving activities include $424,850 for 29 grants (high: $200,000; low: $200).
Purpose and activities: Giving primarily for Jewish organizations.
Fields of interest: Theological school/education; Education; Mental health, association; Human services; Jewish federated giving programs; Jewish agencies & synagogues.
Limitations: Applications not accepted. Giving primarily in the greater metropolitan New York, NY, area. No grants to individuals, or for scholarships; no loans.
Application information: Contributes only to pre-selected organizations.
Trustee: Jonathan M. Lopatin.
EIN: 133797381

6393
The Lucille Lortel Foundation, Inc. ✧
322 8th Ave., 21st. Fl.
New York, NY 10001-6763 (212) 924-2817
FAX: (212) 989-0036; E-mail: jshubart@lortel.org; Main URL: http://www.lortel.org/llf.cfm

Established in 1980 in NY.
Donor: Lucille Lortel Schweitzer†.
Foundation type: Independent foundation.
Financial data (yr. ended 06/30/13): Assets, $31,937,633 (M); expenditures, $1,346,256; qualifying distributions, $1,051,588; giving activities include $705,000 for 13+ grants (high: $408,000), and $1,923 for foundation-administered programs.
Purpose and activities: Giving primarily to small and mid-size nonprofit theater companies and organizations in New York, NY.
Fields of interest: Performing arts, theater; Arts.
Type of support: General/operating support.
Limitations: Applications not accepted. Giving primarily in New York, NY. No support for religious or political organizations. No grants to individuals.
Application information: Unsolicited requests for funds not accepted.
Officers and Directors:* James J. Ross,* Pres.; Richard M. Ticktin,* Secy.; Michael Hecht,* Treas.; George Forbes,* Exec. Dir.
Number of staff: None.
EIN: 133036521

6394
Lostand Foundation, Inc. ✧
c/o Jonathan F.P. Rose
33 Katonah Ave.
Katonah, NY 10536-2103

Established in 1997 in NY.
Donors: Jonathan F.P. Rose; Sandra Rose; NYS Energy Research and Development; Riverview Property LLC.
Foundation type: Independent foundation.
Financial data (yr. ended 10/31/13): Assets, $15,344,010 (M); gifts received, $1,499,986; expenditures, $2,292,516; qualifying distributions, $1,663,995; giving activities include $1,652,640 for 58 grants (high: $1,107,344; low: $750).
Purpose and activities: Giving primarily for the arts, the environment, education, and Jewish organizations.
Fields of interest: Museums (natural history); Performing arts; Arts; Higher education; Education; Environment, natural resources; Human services; Jewish federated giving programs; Jewish agencies & synagogues.
Limitations: Applications not accepted. Giving primarily in NY. No grants to individuals.
Application information: Contributes only to pre-selected organizations.

Officers: Jonathan F.P. Rose, Pres.; Diana C. Rose, V.P. and Secy.; Ariel Flores, Treas.
EIN: 133945705
Selected grants: The following grants are a representative sample of this grantmaker's funding activity:
$1,525,813 to Garrison Institute, Garrison, NY, 2011.
$250,000 to American Museum of Natural History, New York, NY, 2011.
$225,000 to Natural Resources Defense Council, New York, NY, 2011.
$35,000 to Enterprise Community Partners, Columbia, MD, 2011.
$25,000 to Mind and Life Institute, Hadley, MA, 2011.
$10,000 to American Associates of the Royal National Theater, New York, NY, 2011.
$10,000 to Dia Center for the Arts, New York, NY, 2011.
$10,000 to Trust for Public Land, San Francisco, CA, 2011.
$2,500 to Lincoln Center Theater, New York, NY, 2011.
$1,000 to Rocky Mountain Institute, Snowmass, CO, 2011.

6395
Leon Lowenstein Foundation, Inc.
150 E. 58th St., 16th Fl.
New York, NY 10155-1601 (212) 319-0670
Contact: Alice Eaton, Exec. Dir.

Incorporated in 1941 in NY.
Donor: Leon Lowenstein‡.
Foundation type: Independent foundation.
Financial data (yr. ended 12/31/13): Assets, $122,556,449 (M); expenditures, $7,282,518; qualifying distributions, $6,872,358; giving activities include $6,130,325 for 120 grants (high: $500,000; low: $725).
Purpose and activities: The foundation supports a wide range of projects nationwide. Program areas include education, health and the environment with a particular interest in innovative, scale-able, and transformative projects and organizations.
Fields of interest: Education; Environment; Health care.
Type of support: General/operating support; Program development; Seed money; Matching/challenge support.
Limitations: Applications accepted. Giving primarily in the metropolitan New York, NY, area. No support for international organizations. No grants to individuals.
Application information: NY/NJ Common Application Form is accepted, but not required. Application form not required.
Initial approach: Letter
Copies of proposal: 1
Deadline(s): None
Board meeting date(s): Twice per year
Final notification: 3 months
Officers and Directors:* Kim Bendheim,* Co-Chair.; Joanna Schulman,* Co-Pres.; Lynn B. Thoman,* Co-Pres.; Bernard O. Rapoport, Secy.-Treas.; Alice Eaton, Exec. Dir.; John M. Bendheim, Sr.; John M. Bendheim, Jr.; Joanne Bendheim; Thomas Wright.
Number of staff: 2 full-time professional; 1 part-time support.
EIN: 136015951

Selected grants: The following grants are a representative sample of this grantmaker's funding activity:
$1,275,000 to North Shore-Long Island Jewish Health System Foundation, Great Neck, NY, 2012.
$1,000,000 to Princeton University, Princeton, NJ, 2012.
$550,000 to Jewish Community Center in Manhattan, New York, NY, 2012.
$500,000 to Memorial Sloan-Kettering Cancer Center, New York, NY, 2012.
$350,000 to University of Pennsylvania, Wharton School of Business, Philadelphia, PA, 2012.
$295,000 to Planned Parenthood of New York City, New York, NY, 2012.
$75,000 to Westchester Jewish Community Services, White Plains, NY, 2012.
$50,000 to Early Care and Learning Council, Albany, NY, 2012.
$50,000 to Public Health Solutions, New York, NY, 2012.
$25,000 to University of Pennsylvania, Center for Healthcare Improvement and Patient Safety (CHIPS), Philadelphia, PA, 2012.

6396
Lubo Fund, Inc. ✧
c/o Norman Foundation Inc.
147 E. 48th St.
New York, NY 10017-1223

Incorporated in 1958 in GA.
Donors: Belinda Reusch; Lucinda W. Bunnen; Robert L. Bunnen; Robert L. Bunnen, Jr.; Melissa Bunnen Jernigan; members of the Bunnen family.
Foundation type: Independent foundation.
Financial data (yr. ended 12/31/12): Assets, $9,058,581 (M); gifts received, $58,377; expenditures, $559,760; qualifying distributions, $456,120; giving activities include $446,326 for 120 grants (high: $111,000; low: $3).
Purpose and activities: Giving primarily for the arts, education and human services.
Fields of interest: Visual arts, photography; Performing arts; Arts; Education; Environment; Health organizations, association; Human services; Jewish agencies & synagogues.
Type of support: General/operating support; Continuing support; Annual campaigns; Emergency funds; Program development; Publication; Seed money; Matching/challenge support.
Limitations: Applications not accepted. Giving primarily in GA, with emphasis on Atlanta. No grants to individuals, or for land acquisition, renovation projects, endowment funds, scholarships, fellowships, research, or conferences; no loans.
Application information: Unsolicited requests for funds not accepted.
Board meeting date(s): July
Officers: Lucinda W. Bunnen, Pres.; Dr. Robert L. Bunnen, Sr., V.P. and Secy.
EIN: 586043631

6397
Theodore Luce Charitable Trust ✧
c/o JPMorgan Chase Bank, N.A., Private Foundation Svcs.
270 Park Ave., 16th Fl.
New York, NY 10017-2014
Contact: Connie Giampapa, Prog. Off.
FAX: (212) 464-2304;
E-mail: connie.a.giampapa@jpmorgan.com; Main URL: http://fdnweb.org/luce
Grants List: http://fdnweb.org/luce/grants/category/contributions/

Established in the 1940s in NY.
Foundation type: Independent foundation.
Financial data (yr. ended 07/31/13): Assets, $13,227,116 (M); expenditures, $808,519; qualifying distributions, $688,584; giving activities include $655,000 for 17 grants (high: $80,000; low: $5,000).
Purpose and activities: Giving primarily to programs that assist young people, ages 8-18, in developing competencies that will enable them to grow, develop their skills and become healthy, responsible and caring youth and adults. The foundation is particularly interested in programs for low-income youth that operate year-round, and address academics, personal and social competence, health and physical well-being, preparation for work, special interests and talents, leadership and citizenship and/or parent involvement. The trust also seeks to support youth development organizations in one of two areas: program enhancement or capacity building.
Fields of interest: Youth development; Children/youth; Youth; LGBTQ.
Type of support: General/operating support; Program development.
Limitations: Applications not accepted. Giving limited to New York, NY. No support for organizations lacking 501(c)(3) status. No grants to individuals, or for matching gifts; no loans.
Publications: Grants list.
Application information: Proposals accepted by invitation only. Invitations will be mailed in Feb. and grant awards will be announced in July.
Board meeting date(s): July
Trustee: JPMorgan Chase Bank, N.A.
EIN: 136029703
Selected grants: The following grants are a representative sample of this grantmaker's funding activity:
$45,000 to Abraham House, Bronx, NY, 2011. For the after-school program.
$45,000 to Harlem Educational Activities Fund, New York, NY, 2011. For first installment of a $90,000 grant for the Continuum program.
$45,000 to StreetSquash, New York, NY, 2011. For first installment of a $90,000 grant for general operating support.
$45,000 to Womens Housing and Economic Development Corporation, Bronx, NY, 2011. For first installment of a $90,000 grant for Project STEP.
$40,000 to Coalition for Hispanic Family Services, Brooklyn, NY, 2011. For final installment of a $75,000 grant for the Arts and Literacy program.
$40,000 to Goddard-Riverside Community Center, New York, NY, 2011. For the Youth Connections program.
$40,000 to Good Shepherd Services, New York, NY, 2011. For final installment of $80,000 grant for the Beacon programs.
$40,000 to Groundwork, Inc., Brooklyn, NY, 2011. For final installment of $80,000 grant for Middle Ground.
$40,000 to Ifetayo Cultural Arts Facility, Brooklyn, NY, 2011. For final installment of a $75,000 grant for general operating support.
$35,000 to Rocking the Boat, Bronx, NY, 2011. For final installment of a $70,000 grant for general operating support.

6398
The Henry Luce Foundation, Inc.

51 Madison Ave., 30th Fl.
New York, NY 10010-1603 (212) 489-7700
Contact: Michael Gilligan, Pres.
FAX: (212) 581-9541; E-mail: hlf1@hluce.org; Main URL: http://www.hluce.org

Incorporated in 1936 in NY.
Donors: Henry R. Luce†; Clare Boothe Luce†.
Foundation type: Independent foundation.
Financial data (yr. ended 12/31/13): Assets, $867,417,767 (M); expenditures, $47,056,152; qualifying distributions, $40,430,346; giving activities include $33,549,708 for grants, $559,126 for grants to individuals, and $445,309 for employee matching gifts.
Purpose and activities: Grants for specific projects in the broad areas of Asian affairs, American art, public policy and the environment, theology, advancement of women in science and engineering, and higher education. The Luce Scholars Program gives a select group of young Americans, not Asian specialists, a year's work experience in East and Southeast Asia. Asia grants support the creation of new scholarly and public resources on East and Southeast Asia as well as innovative cultural and intellectual exchange between the Asia-Pacific and the United States. The Henry R. Luce Professorship Program, which supports innovative programs at private colleges and universities, no longer accepts proposals for new grants. The Clare Boothe Luce Program is designed to enhance the careers of women in science and engineering through scholarships, fellowships, and professorships at invited institutions. Funding in the arts focuses on research, scholarship and exhibitions in American art; direct support for specific projects at major museums and service organizations; dissertation support for topics in American art history through the American Council of Learned Societies. Theology grants are made primarily to seminaries and divinity schools for educational purposes. The Henry Luce III Theology Fellows Program is administered through the Association of Theological Schools. Public Policy grants are to support the development of public leadership and to promote best practices in philanthropy, and the Environment grants are made to support the study of critical issues and environmental training and research.
Fields of interest: Visual arts; Museums; Humanities; Theology; Higher education; Theological school/education; Environment; Engineering/technology; Social sciences; International studies; Public policy, research.
International interests: Eastern Asia; Southeastern Asia.
Type of support: General/operating support; Program development; Professorships; Fellowships; Internship funds; Scholarship funds; Research; Employee matching gifts; Grants to individuals; Matching/challenge support.
Limitations: Applications accepted. Giving on a national and international basis; international activities limited to East and Southeast Asia. No support for medical or healthcare projects. No grants to individuals (except for specially designated programs), or for endowments, domestic building campaigns, annual fund drives; no loans.
Publications: Biennial report (including application guidelines); Grants list; Program policy statement.
Application information: Nominees for Luce Scholars Program accepted from invited institutions only; Clare Boothe Luce Program by invitation to institutions only, individual applications cannot be considered; Luce Fun in American Art requires prior inquiry by Apr.1. Application form not required.
Initial approach: Letter
Copies of proposal: 1
Deadline(s): June 15, for American Art; Nov. 1 for Luce Scholars nominations; all others, no specific deadlines
Board meeting date(s): Mar., June and Nov.
Officers and Directors:* Margaret Boles Fitzgerald,* Chair.; Michael Gilligan,* Pres.; Toby Volkman, Secy. and Dir., Policy Initiatives; Staci Salomon, C.F.O. and Treas.; Robert E. Armstrong, Dir., Emeritus; John C. Evans, Dir., Emeritus; James T. Laney, Dir., Emeritus; Terrence B. Adamson; Elizabeth Broun; Mary Brown Bullock; Claire L. Gaudiani; Kenneth T. Jackson; Debra S. Knopman; H. Christopher Luce; Thomas L. Pulling; David V. Ragone; George E. Rupp.
Number of staff: 11 full-time professional; 1 part-time professional; 8 full-time support; 2 part-time support.
EIN: 136001282
Selected grants: The following grants are a representative sample of this grantmaker's funding activity:
$2,500,000 to Yale University, Jackson Institute for Global Affairs, New Haven, CT, 2011. For Henry R. Luce Directors Fund, payable over 4.25 years.
$540,000 to Tufts University, Fletcher School of Law and Diplomacy, Medford, MA, 2011. For a collaborative research project on religious claims, nationalism and human suffering, payable over 3.00 years.
$500,000 to Metropolitan Museum of Art, New York, NY, 2011. To support the reinstallation of the American Paintings Collection.
$500,000 to Villanova University, Villanova, PA, 2011. For Clare Boothe Luce Professorships, payable over 5.00 years.
$300,000 to Aspen Institute, Washington, DC, 2011. To inform Members of Congress about international issues, payable over 2.00 years.
$300,000 to Council of Independent Colleges, Washington, DC, 2011. To strengthen and expand leadership development programs for college and university administrators, payable over 3.00 years.
$300,000 to Link Media, San Francisco, CA, 2011. To support news, cultural and current affairs programming on East and Southeast Asia, payable over 2.00 years.
$300,000 to Seattle University, School of Theology and Ministry, Seattle, WA, 2011. To develop an educational model to prepare students for ministry in a religiously diverse world, payable over 3.00 years.
$285,000 to Washington University, Saint Louis, MO, 2011. To identify the relationships among learning styles of first-year students, attrition from the Sciences, Technology, Engineering and Mathematics (STEM), and faculty teaching strategies, payable over 4.00 years.
$100,000 to ASIANetwork, Bloomington, IL, 2011. To formulate plans for Program on Asian Studies and Environment as part of Luce Initiative on Asian Studies and the Environment (LIASE). LIASE aspires to encourage innovative approaches to Asian studies teaching and research at the undergraduate level through the lens of the environment and sustainable development, payable over 2.00 years.

6399
The Luckow Family Foundation, Inc. ✧

c/o Jeff Reynolds, IAT RE
48 Wall St., 30th Fl.
New York, NY 10005-2915

Established in 1996 in NJ.
Donors: Robert Luckow; The Robert W. Luckow Corp.; Education for Youth Society; Stefani Luckow Trust.
Foundation type: Independent foundation.
Financial data (yr. ended 09/30/13): Assets, $8,630,468 (M); gifts received, $1,935,786; expenditures, $941,895; qualifying distributions, $922,294; giving activities include $921,845 for 90 grants (high: $400,000; low: $100).
Purpose and activities: Giving primarily for education, health associations, human services, and Roman Catholic churches and schools.
Fields of interest: Education; Health organizations, association; Autism research; Human services; Catholic agencies & churches.
Limitations: Applications not accepted. No grants to individuals.
Application information: Contributes only to pre-selected organizations.
Officers: Robert W. Luckow, Pres.; Audrey J. Luckow, V.P. and Secy.-Treas.; Michael P. Luckow, V.P.; Stephanie A. Luckow, V.P.; Donald Leigh Meyers, V.P.
EIN: 223479153
Selected grants: The following grants are a representative sample of this grantmaker's funding activity:
$100,000 to Academy of Holy Angels, New Orleans, LA, 2010.
$10,000 to American Cancer Society, Atlanta, GA, 2011.
$7,500 to Adaptive Sports Foundation, Windham, NY, 2010.
$5,000 to Adaptive Sports Foundation, Windham, NY, 2010.
$2,500 to Academy of Holy Angels, New Orleans, LA, 2010.
$2,500 to Healing the Children, Spokane, WA, 2011.
$1,500 to American Cancer Society, Atlanta, GA, 2011.
$1,000 to Academy of Holy Angels, New Orleans, LA, 2010.
$1,000 to American Heart Association, Dallas, TX, 2011.
$1,000 to American Heart Association, Dallas, TX, 2011.
$1,000 to Fairleigh Dickinson University, Teaneck, NJ, 2011.
$1,000 to Fairleigh Dickinson University, Teaneck, NJ, 2011.

6400
Lui and Wan Foundation ✧

P.O. Box 150, Murray Hill Sta.
New York, NY 10156-0150 (212) 689-4939
Contact: Livia S. Wan Lui, Treas.

Established in 2001 in NY.
Donors: Francis C. Lui; Livia S. Wan Lui; Francis C. Lui Trust.
Foundation type: Independent foundation.
Financial data (yr. ended 02/28/13): Assets, $11,207,392 (M); expenditures, $519,837; qualifying distributions, $506,000; giving activities include $506,000 for grants.

Purpose and activities: Giving primarily to a women's health center.
Fields of interest: Higher education; Hospitals (general); Women.
Type of support: General/operating support.
Limitations: Applications accepted. Giving primarily in New York, NY; some giving also in McLean, VA.
Application information: Application form required.
Initial approach: Letter
Deadline(s): None
Officers: Lawrence Lui, Pres.; Yvonne Lui, Secy.; Livia Wan Lui, Treas.
Directors: Deborah Chan; Flora R. Si.
EIN: 134161117
Selected grants: The following grants are a representative sample of this grantmaker's funding activity:
$25,000 to Vassar College, Poughkeepsie, NY, 2011.

6401
Lupus Clinical Trials Consortium, Inc. ✧
221 E. 48th St., 2nd Fl.
New York, NY 10017-1559 (212) 593-7227
E-mail: info@lupus-consortium.org; Main URL: http://lupusclinicaltrials.org

Established in 2002.
Foundation type: Independent foundation.
Financial data (yr. ended 12/31/12): Assets, $756,476 (M); gifts received, $4,700,000; expenditures, $4,380,030; qualifying distributions, $4,337,779; giving activities include $959,600 for 17 grants (high: $137,250; low: $1,800), and $4,337,781 for foundation-administered programs.
Purpose and activities: The consortium provides infrastructure support grants to academic institutions to support readiness for testing new lupus therapies.
Fields of interest: Lupus; Lupus research.
Limitations: Applications not accepted. Giving limited to the U.S. and Canada.
Application information: Contributes only to pre-selected organizations.
Officers and Trustees:* Katherine M. Snider,* Pres.; Arnold M. Snider,* V.P. and Treas.; Stephen A. Paget, M.D.*, Secy.; Joseph E. Craft, M.D.; Bevra H. Hahn, M.D.; Matthew H. Liang, M.D., M.P.H.; Michael D. Lockshin, M.D.
EIN: 412068934
Selected grants: The following grants are a representative sample of this grantmaker's funding activity:
$33,600 to University of Rochester, Rochester, NY, 2012. For Contribution for Testing Lupus.

6402
Georges Lurcy Charitable and Educational Trust ✧
1633 Broadway, 32nd Fl.
New York, NY 10019-6708
Contact: Seth E. Frank, Tr.

Established in 1985 in NY.
Donor: Georges Lurcy†.
Foundation type: Independent foundation.
Financial data (yr. ended 06/30/13): Assets, $30,163,418 (M); expenditures, $1,348,317; qualifying distributions, $993,300; giving activities include $993,300 for grants.
Purpose and activities: Support primarily for education including fellowships for students of American colleges or universities to study in France, and students of French colleges or universities to study in the U.S.; some support for cultural organizations.
Fields of interest: Arts; Higher education.
International interests: France.
Type of support: Fellowships.
Application information: Fellowship applicants from America must be recommended by their universities; applicants from France must apply to the Franco-American Commission for Educational Exchange. Applicants cannot apply directly to the foundation.
Trustees: Alan S. Bernstein; Daniel L. Bernstein; Georges Lurcy Bernstein; Seth E. Frank.
EIN: 136372044
Selected grants: The following grants are a representative sample of this grantmaker's funding activity:
$22,500 to Brown University, Providence, RI, 2013. For charitable deduction.

6403
Helen & Rita Lurie Foundation ✧
c/o A. Lesk-Fried Frank
1 New York Plz.
New York, NY 10004-1902

Established in NY.
Donors: Helen Lurie†; Philip Morris Cos. Inc.
Foundation type: Independent foundation.
Financial data (yr. ended 10/31/13): Assets, $10,878,413 (M); expenditures, $645,980; qualifying distributions, $530,000; giving activities include $530,000 for 9 grants (high: $200,000; low: $15,000).
Fields of interest: Medical school/education; Jewish federated giving programs.
Type of support: General/operating support; Scholarship funds.
Limitations: Applications not accepted. Giving primarily in New York, NY. No grants to individuals.
Application information: Contributes only to pre-selected organizations.
Directors: Helen Armel; Ann B. Lesk; Frederick Lubcher; Joseph A. Stern.
EIN: 133316656

6404
The Ronald P. and Susan E. Lynch Foundation ✧
c/o Katten Muchin Rosenman LLP
575 Madison Ave.
New York, NY 10022-2588

Established in 1985 in NY.
Donors: Ronald P. Lynch†; Susan E. Lynch.
Foundation type: Independent foundation.
Financial data (yr. ended 12/31/13): Assets, $19,517,590 (M); gifts received, $1,500,000; expenditures, $749,170; qualifying distributions, $746,137; giving activities include $732,518 for 24 grants (high: $162,000; low: $1,000).
Fields of interest: Museums; Higher education; Medical school/education; Education; Cancer research; Catholic agencies & churches.
Limitations: Applications not accepted. Giving primarily in NY. No grants to individuals.
Application information: Contributes only to pre-selected organizations.
Trustees: Charles R. Lynch; Susan E. Lynch.
EIN: 136863977

6405
The Lynton Foundation ✧ ☆
c/o Carol Lynton
33 W. 81st St.
New York, NY 10024-6009

Established in 1993 in NY.
Donors: Marion Lynton; Carol Lynton; Michael Lynton; Lili Lynton; Lynton Asset LP.
Foundation type: Independent foundation.
Financial data (yr. ended 12/31/13): Assets, $8,123,890 (M); gifts received, $45,831; expenditures, $660,385; qualifying distributions, $619,304; giving activities include $619,304 for 26 grants (high: $250,000; low: $250).
Purpose and activities: Giving primarily for education and health organizations.
Fields of interest: Arts; Higher education; Education; Health organizations, association.
Limitations: Applications not accepted. Giving primarily in NY. No grants to individuals.
Application information: Contributes only to pre-selected organizations.
Trustees: Carol Lynton; Michael Lynton.
EIN: 133743511

6406
The M & T Charitable Foundation ✧
1 M&T Plaza, 3rd Fl.
Buffalo, NY 14203-2309 (716) 848-3804
Contact: Joe Cassidy; Shelly C. Drake, Pres.
FAX: (716) 848-7318; E-mail: sdrake@mtb.com; Main URL: https://www.mtb.com/aboutus/community/Pages/TheMTCharitableFoundation.aspx

Established in 1993 in NY.
Donors: Manufacturers and Traders Trust Co.; M&T Bank; New York State Extended Day Grant.
Foundation type: Company-sponsored foundation.
Financial data (yr. ended 12/31/13): Assets, $5,176,431 (M); gifts received, $11,000,000; expenditures, $19,423,925; qualifying distributions, $19,423,925; giving activities include $19,423,925 for 3,532 grants (high: $1,000,000; low: $25).
Purpose and activities: The foundation supports organizations involved with arts and culture, education, health, human services, and civic affairs.
Fields of interest: Museums (art); Performing arts; Arts; Secondary school/education; Higher education; Education; Health care; American Red Cross; Youth, services; Human services; United Ways and Federated Giving Programs; Public policy, research; Public affairs.
Type of support: General/operating support; Income development; Management development/capacity building; Annual campaigns; Capital campaigns; Building/renovation; Equipment; Program development; Film/video/radio; Publication; Curriculum development; Scholarship funds; Research; Employee volunteer services; Sponsorships; Matching/challenge support.
Limitations: Applications accepted. Giving primarily in areas of company operations in Washington, DC, DE, MD, Albany, Buffalo, Fishkill, New York,

Rochester, Southern Tier, Syracuse, and Tarrytown, NY, Altoona, Harrisburg, Hanover, Lancaster, Philadelphia, Pottsville, Reading, Wilkes-Barre, Williamsport, and York , PA, VA, and Toronto, Ontario Canada. No support for political organizations, candidates, or lobbying organizations, fraternal or veterans' organizations, sports teams, national or international organizations (unless their programs have significant local impact), or religious organizations not of direct benefit to the entire community. No grants to individuals.
Publications: Application guidelines.
Application information: Visit website for application addresses. Requests are reviewed by local Charitable Contributions Committees. Proposals from organizations located in Buffalo, NY must be submitted through a M&T Bank sponsor. Proposals from Rochester, NY must include a Logic Model form. Proposals should be no longer than 1 to 2 pages. A Supplemental Questionnaire is required for requests of $10,000 or more. Arts and cultural organizations applying for contributions of $10,000 or more in MD, NY, and PA should submit a data profile through the Cultural Data Project. Application form required.
Initial approach: Download application form and mail proposal and application form to nearest application address
Copies of proposal: 1
Deadline(s): Contact nearest application address for deadlines
Board meeting date(s): Monthly
Final notification: Varies depending on amount requested
Officers and Directors:* Shelley C. Drake,* Chair. and Pres.; Robert W. Bauchman, V.P.; Keith M. Belanger, V.P.; Beth Beshaw, V.P.; Peter M. Black, V.P.; Nancy E. Brock, V.P. and Prog. Dir.; Ira A. Brown, V.P.; Daniel J. Burns, V.P.; Sara A. Cardillo, V.P.; David K. Chamberlain, V.P.; Atwood Collins III, V.P.; R. Joe Crosswhite, V.P.; Mark J. Czarnecki,* V.P.; Scott E. Dagenais, V.P.; James J. Donavan, V.P.; Ralph W. Emerson, Jr., V.P.; Steven I. Flax, V.P.; Stephen A. Foreman, V.P.; Brian E. Hickey, V.P.; Philip H. Johnson, V.P.; Michael T. Keegan, V.P.; Frederick M. Krajacic, V.P.; Nicholas P. Lambrow, V.P.; William C. Long, V.P.; Paula Mandell, V.P.; Gino A. Martocci, V.P.; Michael S. Murchie, V.P.; Thomas J. Murphy, V.P.; Allen J. Naples, V.P.; Peter G. Newman, V.P.; Robert H. Newman, Jr., V.P.; Kevin J. Pearson, V.P.; J. Michael Riley, V.P.; Gerald R. Siuda, V.P.; Glenn R. Small, V.P.; Darlene A. Spychala, V.P.; Alissa M. Viti, V.P.; Jeffrey A. Wellington, V.P.; Marie King, Secy.; Michael P. Pinto,* Treas.; Drew J. Pfirrman; Robert G. Wilmers.
EIN: 161448017
Selected grants: The following grants are a representative sample of this grantmaker's funding activity:
$334,750 to Banking Partnership for Community Development, New York, NY, 2012.
$224,518 to Buffalo Promise Neighborhood, Buffalo, NY, 2012.
$150,000 to Albright-Knox Art Gallery, Buffalo, NY, 2012.
$100,000 to Christiana Care Health System, Wilmington, DE, 2012.
$50,000 to Buffalo State College Foundation, Buffalo, NY, 2012.
$12,500 to Greater Baltimore Committee Foundation, Baltimore, MD, 2012.
$10,000 to American Red Cross, Buffalo, NY, 2012.
$10,000 to Bayhealth Foundation, Dover, DE, 2012.
$10,000 to Graycliff Conservancy, Derby, NY, 2012.
$10,000 to Janus School, Mount Joy, PA, 2012.

6407
The M&E Foundation ✧ ☆
(formerly Moric & Elsa Bistricer Foundation)
c/o Moric Bistricer
4611 12th Ave.
Brooklyn, NY 11219-2539

Established in 1988 in NY.
Donors: Moric Bistricer; Elsa Bistricer; Eliza Bistricer; 1999 Bistricer Family Trust; MB 2006 Lead Trust.
Foundation type: Independent foundation.
Financial data (yr. ended 04/30/13): Assets, $13,388,400 (M); gifts received, $271,250; expenditures, $682,834; qualifying distributions, $680,725; giving activities include $680,486 for 47 grants (high: $510,820; low: $100).
Purpose and activities: Giving primarily to Jewish organizations for the purpose of advancing education and assisting the needy.
Fields of interest: Human services; Jewish agencies & synagogues.
Limitations: Applications not accepted. Giving primarily in Brooklyn, NY. No grants to individuals.
Application information: Unsolicited requests for funds not accepted.
Officer: Moric Bistricer, Fdn. Mgr.
Director: Eliza Bisticer.
EIN: 112914881

6408
The M.A.C. AIDS Fund
(formerly The M.A.C. Global Foundation)
130 Prince St., 2th Fl.
New York, NY 10012-3101 (212) 965-6300
Contact: Nancy Mahon, Exec. Dir.
FAX: (212) 372-6171;
E-mail: macaidsf@maccosmetics.com; Main
URL: http://www.macaidsfund.org
Twitter: https://twitter.com/macaidsfund

Established in 2000 in NY.
Donors: Make-Up Art Cosmetics Inc.; Estee Lauder Companies, Inc.
Foundation type: Independent foundation.
Financial data (yr. ended 06/30/13): Assets, $23,384,196 (M); gifts received, $23,858,792; expenditures, $23,290,100; qualifying distributions, $22,923,470; giving activities include $21,588,838 for 322 grants (high: $2,683,438; low: $130).
Purpose and activities: Giving primarily to AIDS research, outreach and resource organizations.
Fields of interest: AIDS; Food services; Human services; International affairs.
Limitations: Applications accepted. Giving on a national basis, with some emphasis on CA and NY; giving on an international basis, with some emphasis on Ontario, Canada. No grants to individuals; general operating expenses. deficit reduction; endowments, capital casts, conferences, summits, briefings, research, or multi-year granting.
Publications: Application guidelines.
Application information: See the fund's web site for each program's deadlines and eligibility criteria.
Initial approach: Online application and eligibility quiz
Deadline(s): Varies
Board meeting date(s): Quarterly, usually Mar., June, Sept. and Dec.
Final notification: Varies
Officers and Directors:* John D. Demsey,* Chair.; Jennifer Balbier,* Secy.; Carey Maloney,* Treas.; Nancy Mahon,* Exec. Dir.; Bruce Hunter,* Exec. Prog. Dir., Canadian Office; Frank Doyle; James Gager; Peter Jueptner; Quarraisha Abdool Karim, Ph.D.; Nancy M. Louden; Sara Moss; Ian Ness; Jean W. Pape, M.D.; Charles Richards; Karen Buglisi Weiler; Clyde Williams; Tracey Travis; Reggie Van Lee.
EIN: 134144722
Selected grants: The following grants are a representative sample of this grantmaker's funding activity:
$2,683,438 to Tides Foundation, San Francisco, CA, 2013. For AIDS prevention/care.
$2,225,000 to AIDS United, Washington, DC, 2013. For AIDS prevention/care.
$1,000,000 to Agency for International Development, Washington, DC, 2013. For AIDS prevention/care.
$1,000,000 to Doctors Without Borders USA, New York, NY, 2013. For AIDS prevention/care.
$575,000 to UNICEF, New York, NY, 2013. For AIDS prevention/care.
$330,000 to mothers2mothers, Cape Town, South Africa, 2013. For AIDS prevention/care.
$279,000 to Ashoka: Innovators for the Public, Arlington, VA, 2013. For AIDS prevention/care.
$250,000 to Broadway Cares/Equity Fights AIDS, Equity Fights AIDS, New York, NY, 2013. For AIDS prevention/care.
$250,000 to PMTCT Business Leadership Council Foundation, New York, NY, 2013. For AIDS prevention/care.
$25,000 to Law Foundation of Silicon Valley, San Jose, CA, 2013. For AIDS prevention/care.

6409
Ma'asim Tovim Foundation ✧
1342 E. 5th St.
Brooklyn, NY 11230-4626 (718) 758-9424
Contact: Shoshana Grossman

Established in 1998 in NY.
Donors: Focus Camera LLC; APB Real Estate Trust; A&E Realty; 4510-4526 Realty Corp.; Bridgegate Sales; BF Kent Property Holdings Trust; HRM SLM Realty Trust; FCR Guardian Trust; Malbur Realty Trust.
Foundation type: Independent foundation.
Financial data (yr. ended 12/31/13): Assets, $3,694,762 (M); gifts received, $441,500; expenditures, $560,952; qualifying distributions, $560,952; giving activities include $559,604 for 32 grants (high: $132,249; low: $1,000).
Fields of interest: Human services; Jewish agencies & synagogues.
Limitations: Applications accepted. Giving primarily in NY.
Application information: Application form required.
Initial approach: Letter
Deadline(s): None
Trustees: A. Berkowitz; E. Berkowitz; H. Berkowitz; M. Berkowitz; S. Silberstein.
EIN: 133978279
Selected grants: The following grants are a representative sample of this grantmaker's funding activity:
$2,500 to Congregation Ateres Shalom, Brooklyn, NY, 2012. For Synagogue Maintenance.

6410
Mab Foundation ✧
c/o Meridian
1 Battery Park Plz.
New York, NY 10004-1405

Established in 1997 in NY.
Donors: Aron Birnbaum; AMB Charitable Lead Trust.
Foundation type: Independent foundation.
Financial data (yr. ended 12/31/12): Assets, $1,246,031 (M); gifts received, $915,200; expenditures, $601,072; qualifying distributions, $588,600; giving activities include $588,600 for grants.
Fields of interest: Jewish agencies & synagogues.
Limitations: Applications not accepted. Giving primarily in NY. No grants to individuals.
Application information: Unsolicited requests for funds not accepted.
Trustees: Aaron Birnbaum; Alisa Birnbaum.
EIN: 113409995

6411
Christy and John Mack Foundation ✧
(formerly The C. J. Mack Foundation)
6 Club Rd.
Rye, NY 10580-1613

Established in 1993 in NY and DE.
Donors: Christy K. Mack; John J. Mack.
Foundation type: Independent foundation.
Financial data (yr. ended 12/31/12): Assets, $21,765,236 (M); gifts received, $797,234; expenditures, $3,638,992; qualifying distributions, $3,484,718; giving activities include $3,484,718 for 27 grants (high: $580,000; low: $1,500).
Purpose and activities: Giving primarily for hospitals, education, and the arts, including a public television station.
Fields of interest: Media, film/video; Arts; Higher education; Education; Hospitals (general); Health organizations, association; Human services.
Limitations: Applications not accepted. Giving primarily in NC and NY. No grants to individuals.
Application information: Contributes only to pre-selected organizations.
Officer: Christy K. Mack, Pres.
Director: John J. Mack.
EIN: 133746731

6412
The Earle I. Mack Foundation, Inc. ✧
c/o Spector, Foo, Weissman
1979 Marcus Ave., Ste. E-146
Lake Success, NY 11042-1068

Established in 2002 in NJ.
Donors: Earle I. Mack; Drexel University; Ruth Mack.
Foundation type: Independent foundation.
Financial data (yr. ended 12/31/13): Assets, $10,257,373 (M); gifts received, $7,227,525; expenditures, $1,443,603; qualifying distributions, $1,161,736; giving activities include $1,161,736 for 171 grants (high: $100,000; low: $170).
Purpose and activities: Giving primarily for education, the arts, social services, and for medical research for various cancers.
Fields of interest: Museums (art); Arts; Education; Cancer research; Prostate cancer research; Human services; Foundations (private grantmaking); Jewish agencies & synagogues.
Limitations: Applications not accepted. Giving primarily in NY.
Application information: Contributes only to pre-selected organizations.
Officer: Earle I. Mack, Pres.
Trustees: David Mack; Richard Mack.
EIN: 911981393

6413
The MacMillan Family Foundation, Inc. ✧
c/o Geller & Co., LLC
909 3rd Ave., 16th Fl.
New York, NY 10022-4757
Duncan and Nancy MacMillan's Giving Pledge Profile: http://glasspockets.org/philanthropy-in-focus/eye-on-the-giving-pledge/profiles/macmillan

Established in 2002 in NJ.
Donors: Duncan MacMillan; Nancy MacMillan.
Foundation type: Independent foundation.
Financial data (yr. ended 12/31/12): Assets, $80,780,278 (M); gifts received, $35,316,792; expenditures, $3,728,716; qualifying distributions, $3,322,942; giving activities include $3,279,500 for 27 grants (high: $2,000,000; low: $2,000).
Fields of interest: Arts; Higher education; Health care; Medical research, institute; Human services.
Limitations: Applications not accepted. Giving primarily in MD, NJ, and NY. No grants to individuals.
Application information: Contributes only to pre-selected organizations.
Officers and Directors:* Duncan MacMillan,* Pres.; Nancy MacMillan,* Secy.-Treas.; Alissa C. MacMillan; Kevin MacMillan.
EIN: 481286405

6414
Josiah Macy Jr. Foundation
44 E. 64th St.
New York, NY 10065-7306 (212) 486-2424
Contact: George E. Thibault M.D., Pres.; Peter Goodwin M.B.A., C.O.O. and Treas.
FAX: (212) 644-0765;
E-mail: info@macyfoundation.org; Main URL: http://www.macyfoundation.org
LinkedIn: http://www.linkedin.com/groups?home=&gid=4215159
Twitter: http://twitter.com/macyfoundation

Incorporated in 1930 in NY.
Donor: Kate Macy Ladd‡.
Foundation type: Independent foundation.
Financial data (yr. ended 06/30/13): Assets, $144,037,503 (M); expenditures, $9,786,597; qualifying distributions, $8,563,244; giving activities include $6,093,628 for 58 grants (high: $325,575; low: $20), $161,710 for employee matching gifts, and $464,352 for foundation-administered programs.
Purpose and activities: Major interest in medicine and health. Support for enhancing and improving health professional and medical education in ways that will better the health of the public. The foundation's grantmaking is focused on projects that: a) Demonstrate or encourage interprofessional education and teamwork among health care professionals;b) Teach principles of patient safety, quality improvement, and system performance;c) Develop new models for clinical education, including community-based models;d)Increase the diversity of the health care professional workforce through career development for underrepresented minorities; and c) Improve education for the care of underserved populations.
Fields of interest: Medical school/education; Nursing school/education; Public health school/education; Health sciences school/education; Health care; Minorities; African Americans/Blacks; Hispanics/Latinos; Native Americans/American Indians; Women; Economically disadvantaged.
Type of support: Program development; Conferences/seminars; Publication; Curriculum development; Fellowships; Program evaluation; Employee matching gifts; Matching/challenge support.
Limitations: Applications accepted. Giving on a national basis. No grants to individuals, or for travel, capital funds, operating budgets, general undesignated support annual fund appeals, financing, construction or renovation projects, research, scholarships, or fellowships; no loans.
Publications: Application guidelines; Annual report; Financial statement; Grants list; Informational brochure; Newsletter; Occasional report; Program policy statement.
Application information: Additional program information is available on the foundation's web site. The foundation no longer accepts submission of applications via mail or e-mail. Application form required.
Initial approach: Letter of inquiry via foundation's web site
Copies of proposal: 1
Deadline(s): None
Board meeting date(s): Jan., May, and Oct.
Final notification: Within 3 months
Officers and Directors:* William H. Wright II,* Chair.; George E. Thibault, M.D.*, Pres.; Peter Goodwin, C.O.O. and Treas.; David Blumenthal, M.D., MPP; George Campbell, Jr., Ph.D.; Linda Cronenwett, Ph.D., R.N.; Harvey V. Fineberg, M.D., Ph.D.; Linda Fried, M.D., MPH; Terry Fulmer, Ph.D., R.N.; Henry P. Johnson; Paul G. Ramsey, M.D.; George Rupp, Ph.D; Steven M. Sayfer, M.D.; Gregory H. Warner, M.B.A.
Number of staff: 2 full-time professional; 1 part-time professional; 3 full-time support.
EIN: 135596895
Selected grants: The following grants are a representative sample of this grantmaker's funding activity:
$400,000 to Institute on Medicine as a Profession, New York, NY, 2012. For Educating and Training to Professionalism Initiative.
$375,000 to Institute of Medicine, Washington, DC, 2012. For Governance and Financing of Graduate Medical Education.
$325,575 to University of Virginia, Charlottesville, VA, 2013. For Bridging the Gap: Developing, Implementing, and Assessing the Impact of Innovative Undergraduate Interprofessional Education (IPE) Experiences Based on Collaborative Care Best Practice Models.
$317,650 to Columbia University, New York, NY, 2013. For Reframing the Academic Medical Center through Interprofessional Effectiveness: Toward Justice, Safety, and Kindness.
$304,937 to National Health Policy Forum, Washington, DC, 2012. For Innovations in Education and Training for 21st Century Health Care Workforce.
$300,000 to Association of American Medical Colleges, Washington, DC, 2013. For Education in

Pediatrics Across the Continuum - A Competency-based Medical Education Pilot.
$300,000 to University of Minnesota, Minneapolis, MN, 2013. For National Center for Interprofessional Practice and Education.
$280,669 to Research Foundation of the City University of New York, New York, NY, 2012. For Hunter College and Weill Cornell Medical College to develop ITEACH (Integrating Transdisciplinary Education at Cornell/Hunter).
$257,751 to Arizona State University Foundation for a New American University, Tempe, AZ, 2013. For Interprofessional Primary Care Curriculum: Implementation and Evaluation.
$229,370 to University of Colorado, Denver, CO, 2012. To develop longitudinal, interprofessional and team building curriculum that integrated into preclinical and clinical training for all health professions students at UCD Anschutz Medical Campus.
$211,958 to New York University Langone Medical Center, New York, NY, 2012. For NYU 3T: Teaching, Technology, Teamwork.
$204,209 to American Academy of Family Physicians, Leawood, KS, 2012. For Tracking the output of Graduate Medical Education: How are Teaching Hospitals and Teaching Health Centers Meeting Society's Needs?.
$154,937 to National Health Policy Forum, Washington, DC, 2013. For Innovations in Education and Training for a 21st Century Health Care Workforce: Education and Dialogue for Federal Policy Makers.
$150,000 to National Health Policy Forum, Washington, DC, 2012. For Innovations in Education and Training for 21st Century Health Care Workforce: Education and Dialogue for Federal Policy Makers.
$150,000 to Project HOPE - The People-to-People Health Foundation, Millwood, VA, 2013. For Thematic Issue and Briefing on Creating the Optimal Health Care Work Force.
$145,885 to Massachusetts General Hospital, Boston, MA, 2013. For Improving Quality and Safety for Diverse Populations: An Innovative Multidisciplinary Curriculum.
$139,000 to University of Colorado, Boulder, CO, 2013. For Macy Faculty Scholar.
$135,090 to Oregon Health and Science University, Portland, OR, 2012. For Macy Faculty Scholar.
$75,000 to Institute of Medicine, Washington, DC, 2013. For Global Forum on Innovation in Health Professionals Education.
$57,893 to Geisinger Center for Health Research, Danville, PA, 2012. For Hands on Quality Improvements The Physician-Nurse Relationship.

6415
The Jamie Maguire Family Foundation ✧

c/o The Ayco Co., NTG
P.O. Box 15014
Albany, NY 12212-5014

Established in PA.
Donors: James MaGuire, Jr.; Lisa MaGuire.
Foundation type: Independent foundation.
Financial data (yr. ended 12/31/13): Assets, $4,862,427 (M); gifts received, $1,358,205; expenditures, $1,164,129; qualifying distributions, $1,127,124; giving activities include $1,127,124 for 93 grants (high: $180,000; low: $50).
Fields of interest: Higher education; Education; Human services; Foundations (private grantmaking).
Limitations: Applications not accepted. Giving primarily in PA, with emphasis on Philadelphia. No grants to individuals.
Application information: Contributes only to pre-selected organizations.
Trustees: Jamie MaGuire, Jr.; Lisa MaGuire.
EIN: 263338477

6416
The Maguire Foundation ✧

c/o The Ayco Co.-NTG
P.O. Box 15014
Albany, NY 12212-5014

Established in 2000 in PA.
Donors: James J. Maguire; Frances Maguire.
Foundation type: Independent foundation.
Financial data (yr. ended 12/31/12): Assets, $85,615,104 (M); gifts received, $20,000,006; expenditures, $5,840,591; qualifying distributions, $5,716,898; giving activities include $5,567,662 for 86 grants (high: $1,000,000; low: $50).
Purpose and activities: Giving primarily for education; funding also for social services, and Roman Catholic organizations and churches.
Fields of interest: Arts; Higher education; Education; Health organizations, association; Human services; Children/youth, services; Catholic federated giving programs; Catholic agencies & churches.
Limitations: Applications not accepted. Giving primarily in Philadelphia, PA. No grants to individuals.
Application information: Contributes only to pre-selected organizations.
Officers: James J. Maguire, Pres.; Frances M. Maguire, Secy.-Treas.
EIN: 233057805
Selected grants: The following grants are a representative sample of this grantmaker's funding activity:
$1,080,000 to Saint Josephs University, Philadelphia, PA, 2011. For general support.
$1,000,000 to Gwynedd-Mercy University, Gwynedd Valley, PA, 2011. For general support.
$500,000 to Pennsylvania Academy of the Fine Arts, Philadelphia, PA, 2011. For general support.
$500,000 to University of Pennsylvania, Philadelphia, PA, 2011. For general support.
$325,514 to Pennsylvania School for the Deaf, Philadelphia, PA, 2011. For general support.
$260,000 to Cristo Rey Philadelphia High School, Philadelphia, PA, 2011. For general support.
$100,000 to Philadelphia Museum of Art, Philadelphia, PA, 2011. For general support.
$50,000 to Gwynedd-Mercy University, Gwynedd Valley, PA, 2011. For general support.
$50,000 to Woodmere Art Museum, Philadelphia, PA, 2011. For general support.
$25,000 to Pennsylvania Academy of the Fine Arts, Philadelphia, PA, 2011. For general support.

6417
The Mai Family Foundation ✧

c/o Cranemere
135 E. 57th St., 31 Fl.
New York, NY 10022

Established in 1996 in NY.
Donor: Vincent A. Mai.
Foundation type: Independent foundation.
Financial data (yr. ended 12/31/12): Assets, $25,148,997 (M); expenditures, $3,003,440; qualifying distributions, $3,913,821; giving activities include $2,867,300 for 59 grants (high: $350,000; low: $5,000), and $1,000,000 for 1 loan/program-related investment.
Fields of interest: Arts; Education; Health organizations; Human services; Children/youth, services.
Limitations: Applications not accepted. Giving primarily in Washington, DC and New York, NY; some funding also in CA and CO. No grants to individuals.
Application information: Contributes only to pre-selected organizations.
Officers and Directors:* Anne Mai,* Pres.; Vincent A. Mai,* V.P.; Chiara Mai,* Secy.; Rebecca Mai,* Treas.; James Mai; Timothy Mai; David Mitnick.
EIN: 133915987

6418
A. L. Mailman Family Foundation, Inc. ✧

707 Westchester Ave.
White Plains, NY 10604-3102
FAX: (914) 686-5519; E-mail: info@mailman.org

Established in 1976 in FL as the Dr. Marilyn M. Segal Foundation, Inc.
Donors: Abraham L. Mailman‡; The Mailman Foundation, Inc.
Foundation type: Independent foundation.
Financial data (yr. ended 12/31/13): Assets, $17,326,751 (M); expenditures, $770,914; qualifying distributions, $648,120; giving activities include $598,150 for 19 grants (high: $100,000; low: $1,000).
Purpose and activities: Giving to enhance the ability of families and communities to nurture their children by focusing on early childhood care and education, particularly for infants and toddlers.
Fields of interest: Education, early childhood education; Infants/toddlers.
Type of support: Technical assistance; Research; Publication; Program development; Curriculum development.
Limitations: Applications not accepted. Giving on a national basis; some emphasis on MA, NY, and Washington, DC. No support for locally based service organizations or programs, or for religious organizations. No grants to individuals, operating budgets, or for capital expenditures endowment campaigns.
Publications: Grants list; Program policy statement.
Application information: Contributes only to pre-selected organizations.
Board meeting date(s): Apr. and Oct.
Officers and Trustees:* Wendy S. Masi,* Chair.; Richard D. Segal,* Pres.; Michael Walden, Secy.-Treas.; Arran Bardige; Betty S. Bardige; Kori Bardige; Patricia S. Lieberman; Rachel Masi; Greg Segal.
Number of staff: 1 full-time professional; 1 full-time support.
EIN: 510203866
Selected grants: The following grants are a representative sample of this grantmaker's funding activity:
$50,000 to Fund for the City of New York, New York, NY, 2012. For Child Care and Early Education Fund.

6419
The Mailman Foundation, Inc. ✧
c/o Hecht & Co.
622 3rd Ave., 8th Fl.
New York, NY 10017-6707
GiveSmart: http://www.givesmart.org/Josh-Mailman

Incorporated in 1943 in DE.
Donors: Joseph L. Mailman†; Joseph S. Mailman†; Joshua L. Mailman; Phyllis Mailman.
Foundation type: Independent foundation.
Financial data (yr. ended 12/31/12): Assets, $28,443,312 (M); expenditures, $2,115,991; qualifying distributions, $1,905,480; giving activities include $1,877,500 for 38 grants (high: $1,512,590; low: $620).
Purpose and activities: Giving primarily for the arts, education, and human services.
Fields of interest: Museums (art); Performing arts, theater; Performing arts, music; Arts; Higher education; Education; Human services.
Limitations: Applications not accepted. Giving primarily in NY. No grants to individuals.
Application information: Contributes only to pre-selected organizations.
Officers and Trustees:* Joan M. Wolfe, Pres.; Phyllis Mailman, V.P.; Johanna L. Wolfe,* V.P.; Judson A. Wolfe, V.P.; Olivia L. Wolfe, V.P.; Joseph V. Hastings, Secy.-Treas.
EIN: 136161556

6420
The Joshua Mailman Foundation ✧
c/o Hecht & Co.
350 5th Ave., 68th Fl.
New York, NY 10018-6710
GiveSmart: http://www.givesmart.org/Stories/Donors/Josh-Mailman

Established in 2006 in NY.
Foundation type: Independent foundation.
Financial data (yr. ended 12/31/12): Assets, $13,632,749 (M); expenditures, $846,151; qualifying distributions, $753,884; giving activities include $717,884 for 57 grants (high: $100,000; low: $800).
Fields of interest: Performing arts, theater; Arts; Human services.
Limitations: Applications not accepted. Giving primarily in NY. No grants to individuals.
Application information: Contributes only to pre-selected organizations.
Officers: Joshua Mailman, Pres.; Phyllis Mailman, V.P.; Joseph V. Hastings, Secy.-Treas.
EIN: 205520413

6421
Makioka Foundation ✧ ☆
c/o BCRS Associates, LLC
77 Water St., 9th Fl.
New York, NY 10005-3701

Established in 1993 in NY.
Donors: Jun Makihara; Megumi Oka.
Foundation type: Independent foundation.
Financial data (yr. ended 02/28/13): Assets, $4,324,505 (M); expenditures, $667,597; qualifying distributions, $641,850; giving activities include $639,050 for 39 grants (high: $500,000; low: $200).
Fields of interest: Arts; Education; Community/economic development.
Limitations: Applications not accepted. Giving primarily in Boston, MA. No grants to individuals; no loans or scholarships.
Application information: Unsolicited requests for funds not accepted.
Trustees: Jun Makihara; Megumi Oka.
EIN: 133748081

6422
Malkin Fund, Inc. ✧
c/o Malkin Holdings, LLC
1 Grand Central Pl.
New York, NY 10165-0006

Established in 1994 in NY.
Donors: Peter L. Malkin; Isabel W. Malkin; Cynthia M. Blumenthal; Scott D. Malkin; Legacy Venture III.
Foundation type: Independent foundation.
Financial data (yr. ended 12/31/12): Assets, $8,980,773 (M); gifts received, $2,893,323; expenditures, $2,673,326; qualifying distributions, $2,667,391; giving activities include $2,662,122 for 340 grants (high: $380,570; low: $2).
Purpose and activities: Giving primarily for higher education, the arts, health, and human services.
Fields of interest: Museums; Performing arts; Historic preservation/historical societies; Arts; Elementary/secondary education; Higher education; Higher education, university; Education; Animal welfare; Health organizations, association; Human services; Children/youth, services; Jewish federated giving programs.
Limitations: Applications not accepted. Giving primarily in the Northeast, with emphasis on CT, MA, and NY. No grants to individuals.
Application information: Contributes only to pre-selected organizations.
Officers: Peter L. Malkin, Chair.; Isabel W. Malkin, Pres. and Treas.
Director: Scott D. Malkin.
EIN: 133749046
Selected grants: The following grants are a representative sample of this grantmaker's funding activity:
$10,000 to Harvard College Parents Fund, Cambridge, MA, 2012. For charitable grant.

6423
The Diane and Darryl Mallah Family Foundation ✧
479 Greenbriar Ct.
Roslyn, NY 11576-3071

Donors: Diane Mallah; Darryl Mallah; Joel Mallah; Yvette Mallah.
Foundation type: Independent foundation.
Financial data (yr. ended 12/31/13): Assets, $1,111,448 (M); gifts received, $1,750,000; expenditures, $1,215,888; qualifying distributions, $1,215,888; giving activities include $1,215,888 for 32 grants (high: $350,000; low: $488).
Fields of interest: Hospitals (general); Health care; Health organizations, association; Jewish agencies & synagogues.
Limitations: Applications not accepted. Giving primarily in NY.
Application information: Contributes only to pre-selected organizations.
Directors: Martin Major; Darryl Mallah; Diane Mallah.
EIN: 208075586

6424
The Yvette and Joel Mallah Family Foundation ✧
P.O. Box 1297
Bridgehampton, NY 11932-1297

Established in 1999 in NY.
Donors: Joel Mallah; Darryl Mallah; Sheldon Mallah; Barry Mallah; Yvette Mallah.
Foundation type: Independent foundation.
Financial data (yr. ended 12/31/13): Assets, $2,578,046 (M); expenditures, $1,021,900; qualifying distributions, $1,021,900; giving activities include $1,000,300 for 13 grants (high: $650,000; low: $300).
Fields of interest: Higher education; Hospitals (general); Human services.
Limitations: Applications not accepted. Giving primarily in NY. No grants to individuals.
Application information: Contributes only to pre-selected organizations.
Trustees: Joel Mallah; Yvette Mallah.
EIN: 137172805

6425
The Manton Foundation ✧
c/o JPMorgan Chase Bank, NY1-K348
270 Park Ave., 16th Fl.
New York, NY 10017-2014 (212) 464-2487
Contact: Casey Castaneda, V.P. and Prog. Off., JPMorgan Chase Bank
E-mail: casey.b.castaneda@jpmchase.com

Established in 1991 in NY.
Donors: Sir Edwin Manton†; Lady Manton†.
Foundation type: Independent foundation.
Financial data (yr. ended 12/31/12): Assets, $505,453,334 (M); expenditures, $31,605,042; qualifying distributions, $30,201,722; giving activities include $30,047,816 for 26 grants (high: $5,000,000; low: $5,000).
Fields of interest: Historical activities; Arts; Education; Health care; Medical research.
Type of support: Capital campaigns; Building/renovation; Endowments; Research; Matching/challenge support.
Limitations: Applications not accepted. Giving primarily in New England. No grants to individuals or for loans.
Application information: Contributes only to pre-selected organizations.
Board meeting date(s): Mar., July and Nov.
Trustees: Julia G. Morton Krapf; Diana H. Morton; Sandra T. Morton Niles.
EIN: 133636372
Selected grants: The following grants are a representative sample of this grantmaker's funding activity:
$10,000,000 to Sterling and Francine Clark Art Institute, Williamstown, MA, 2012. For British Collection and Research Center.
$5,000,000 to Tate, London, England, 2012. For gallery improvements to Millbank Street location.
$3,350,000 to Children's Hospital Corporation, Boston, MA, 2012. For Manton Center for Orphan Diseases.

$2,500,000 to Southcoast Health Systems, New Bedford, MA, 2012. To construct Center for Cancer Care.
$2,000,000 to Fenn School, Concord, MA, 2012. To construct library and science center.
$1,811,500 to Yale University, New Haven, CT, 2012. For genetics research to develop a dyslexia screen.
$1,500,000 to Hotchkiss School, Lakeville, CT, 2012. For infrastructure at farm property.
$1,000,000 to North Bennet Street School, Boston, MA, 2012. To purchase school building.
$500,000 to Sherborn Library, Sherborn, MA, 2012. To construct Children's Room and treehouse.
$250,000 to Bostonian Society, Boston Historical Society and Museum, Boston, MA, 2012. For capital support to restore Old State House.

6426
Many Voices Foundation ✧ ☆
c/o Laura Carroll, The Ayco Co., A Goldman Sachs Co.
321 Broadway
P.O. Box 860
Saratoga Springs, NY 12866-4110

Established in 2000 in DE and MA.
Donor: Maximilian Dana Stone.
Foundation type: Independent foundation.
Financial data (yr. ended 12/31/13): Assets, $36,505,427 (M); gifts received, $5,430,250; expenditures, $9,522,832; qualifying distributions, $9,446,014; giving activities include $9,441,660 for 3 grants (high: $6,506,257; low: $600,000).
Fields of interest: Hospitals (specialty); Health care; Economically disadvantaged.
Limitations: Applications not accepted. Giving primarily in Boston, MA and New York, NY. No grants to individuals.
Application information: Contributes only to pre-selected organizations.
Officer: Maximilian Dana Stone, Pres. and Treas.
EIN: 134144617
Selected grants: The following grants are a representative sample of this grantmaker's funding activity:
$6,506,257 to Partners in Health, Boston, MA, 2013. For improving the health of poor and marginalized people.
$2,335,403 to Robin Hood Foundation, New York, NY, 2013. For help poverty in New York City.
$600,000 to Children's Hospital Corporation, Boston, MA, 2013. To provide patients with highest quality care.
$75,000 to Neighborhood Trust Financial Partners, New York, NY, 2012. To Promote Economic Empowerment By Increasing Access to Financial Services.
$35,000 to Turnaround for Children, New York, NY, 2012. For Helping Public Schools Create Positive Learning Environments.
$13,000 to Massachusetts General Hospital, Boston, MA, 2012. To provide Patients with Highest Quality Care and Expand in Healthcare Research.

6427
Robert Mapplethorpe Foundation, Inc. ✧
c/o Michael Stout, Esq.
477 Madison Ave., 15 Fl.
New York, NY 10022-5835 (212) 755-3025
Contact: Ms. Joree Adilman
FAX: (212) 941-4764;
E-mail: info@mapplethorpe.org; Main URL: http://www.mapplethorpe.org/foundation.html

Established in 1988 in NY.
Donor: Robert Mapplethorpe†.
Foundation type: Independent foundation.
Financial data (yr. ended 05/31/13): Assets, $230,542,028 (M); expenditures, $3,134,860; qualifying distributions, $1,855,946; giving activities include $1,251,686 for 42 grants.
Purpose and activities: Support for medical research to advance the cure and treatment of AIDS and HIV infection; support also for photography as an art form through assisting museums, universities, and other institutions, and by publishing quality books and materials.
Fields of interest: Visual arts, photography; Museums; Arts; AIDS; Medical research, institute; AIDS research.
Type of support: Program development; Publication; Research.
Limitations: Applications accepted. Giving on a national basis. No support for social services or for international organizations that are based outside of the U.S. No grants to individuals.
Publications: Application guidelines.
Application information: Application form not required.
Initial approach: E-mail or letter
Copies of proposal: 1
Deadline(s): None
Board meeting date(s): Approximately every 3 months
Final notification: Approximately 1 week after board meeting
Officer and Directors:* Michael Ward Stout,* Pres.; Dimitri Levas; Burton G. Lipsky; Eric Johnson; Stewart Shining.
Number of staff: 2 full-time professional; 1 full-time support; 2 part-time support.
EIN: 133480472

6428
The James S. Marcus Foundation ✧
c/o BCRS Assocs., LLC
77 Water St., 9th Fl.
New York, NY 10005-4401

Established in 1969 in NY.
Donor: James S. Marcus.
Foundation type: Independent foundation.
Financial data (yr. ended 05/31/13): Assets, $4,771,204 (M); expenditures, $538,754; qualifying distributions, $533,054; giving activities include $529,848 for 92 grants (high: $25,000; low: $100).
Purpose and activities: Giving primarily to the arts with emphasis on the performing arts, particularly music and the opera; some giving also for education, a hospital, and human services.
Fields of interest: Performing arts; Performing arts, music; Performing arts, orchestras; Performing arts, opera; Arts; Higher education; Animal welfare; Hospitals (general); Human services.
Limitations: Applications not accepted. Giving primarily in the New York, NY, area, including Long Island, particularly East Hampton. No grants to individuals (including scholarships); no loans.
Application information: Contributes only to pre-selected organizations.
Trustees: H. Frederick Krimendahl II; Ellen F. Marcus; James S. Marcus.
EIN: 237044611
Selected grants: The following grants are a representative sample of this grantmaker's funding activity:
$13,800 to Animal Medical Center, New York, NY, 2011. For general purpose.

6429
Mariposa Foundation, Inc. ✧
31 W. 27th St., 4th Fl.
New York, NY 10001-6953
E-mail: info@mariposafoundation.org; Main URL: http://www.mariposafoundation.org

Established around 1976.
Donor: Lewis W. Bernard.
Foundation type: Independent foundation.
Financial data (yr. ended 12/31/12): Assets, $79,463,947 (M); gifts received, $1,495,111; expenditures, $5,045,821; qualifying distributions, $4,506,870; giving activities include $4,259,000 for 46 grants (high: $800,000; low: $5,000).
Purpose and activities: Giving primarily for social services, the arts, and for education.
Fields of interest: Arts; Education; Environment; Hospitals (general); Human services; Children/youth, services.
Limitations: Applications not accepted. Giving primarily in New York, NY. No grants to individuals.
Application information: Contributes only to pre-selected organizations. Proposals are by invitation only.
Officers: Lewis W. Bernard, Pres. and Treas.; Jill V. Bernard, V.P. and Secy.; Claire E. Bernard, V.P.
Director: Adam T. Bernard.
Number of staff: 1 full-time support.
EIN: 510170409

6430
Mark Family Foundation ✧
c/o BCRS Associates, LLC
77 Water St., 9th Fl.
New York, NY 10005

Established in 1994 in NY.
Donors: Morris Mark; Susan Mark.
Foundation type: Independent foundation.
Financial data (yr. ended 11/30/13): Assets, $3,103,053 (M); gifts received, $485,953; expenditures, $762,909; qualifying distributions, $758,033; giving activities include $747,914 for 91 grants (high: $125,000; low: $95).
Purpose and activities: Giving primarily for Jewish federated giving programs, the arts, education, health care, and medical research.
Fields of interest: Arts; Education; Health organizations, association; Human services; Jewish federated giving programs; Jewish agencies & synagogues.
Limitations: Applications not accepted. Giving primarily in NY. No grants to individuals.
Application information: Contributes only to pre-selected organizations.
Trustees: Morris Mark; Susan Mark.
EIN: 137052586

6431
The Markle Foundation ✧
(also known as The John and Mary R. Markle Foundation)
10 Rockefeller Plz., 16th Fl.
New York, NY 10020-1903 (212) 713-7600
Contact: Zoe Baird, Pres.
FAX: (212) 765-9690; E-mail: info@markle.org; Main URL: http://www.markle.org/
RSS Feed Directory: http://www.markle.org/stay-connected/rss-feeds
Twitter: http://twitter.com/marklefdn

Incorporated in 1927 in NY.
Donors: John Markle†; Mary Markle†.
Foundation type: Independent foundation.
Financial data (yr. ended 06/30/13): Assets, $143,158,120 (M); expenditures, $11,888,917; qualifying distributions, $10,011,750; giving activities include $1,906,793 for 17 grants (high: $456,859; low: $2,695), and $6,264,603 for 2 foundation-administered programs.
Purpose and activities: The mission of the foundation is to use emerging communication and information technologies to address critical public needs, with emphasis on health, and national and economic security.
Fields of interest: Public policy, research.
Type of support: Endowments.
Limitations: Applications not accepted. Giving primarily in Washington, DC, and New York, NY.
Publications: IRS Form 990 or 990-PF printed copy available upon request.
Application information: The foundation directly supports its work in health and national security.
Officers and Directors:* Lewis B. Kaden,* Chair.; Zoe Baird,* Pres.; Karen Byers, C.F.O. and Secy.-Treas.; Sen. Slade Gorton; Suzanne Nora Johnson; Gilman Louie; Herbert Pardes, M.D.; Edward Rover; Stanley Shulman; Debora Spar.
Number of staff: 15 full-time professional; 4 part-time professional; 2 full-time support; 1 part-time support.
EIN: 131770307
Selected grants: The following grants are a representative sample of this grantmaker's funding activity:
$664,989 to Center for Democracy and Technology, Washington, DC, 2012.
$301,600 to Aspen Institute, Washington, DC, 2012.
$200,018 to National Partnership for Women and Families, Washington, DC, 2012.
$98,680 to Center for Public Integrity, Washington, DC, 2012.
$80,000 to Center for a New American Security, Washington, DC, 2012.
$25,000 to Brookings Institution, Washington, DC, 2012.

6432
Nancy and Edwin Marks Family Foundation ✧
(formerly Marks Family Foundation)
c/o Carl Marks & Co.
900 3rd Ave., 33rd Fl.
New York, NY 10022-4775
Contact: Katherine Liebman, Exec. Dir.

Established in 1986 in NY.
Donors: Edwin S. Marks†; Nancy A. Marks.
Foundation type: Independent foundation.
Financial data (yr. ended 06/30/13): Assets, $16,494,687 (M); expenditures, $610,395; qualifying distributions, $568,286; giving activities include $483,000 for 31 grants (high: $60,000; low: $500).
Purpose and activities: Giving primarily for early childhood education.
Fields of interest: Arts; Human services; Children/youth, services.
Type of support: General/operating support.
Limitations: Giving primarily in New York, NY. No grants to individuals.
Application information:
Initial approach: Proposal
Deadline(s): None
Officers and Directors:* Nancy A. Marks,* Pres. and Secy.; Katherine Liebman, Exec. Dir.; Carolyn Marks; Constance Marks Miller.
EIN: 133385770
Selected grants: The following grants are a representative sample of this grantmaker's funding activity:
$175,000 to Harlem Childrens Zone, New York, NY, 2011.
$100,000 to Children of Bellevue, New York, NY, 2011.
$60,000 to Visiting Nurse Service of New York, New York, NY, 2011.
$50,000 to DreamYard Drama Project, Bronx, NY, 2011.
$45,100 to Parent-Child Home Program, Garden City, NY, 2011.
$25,000 to AnimalKind, Hudson, NY, 2011.
$25,000 to Charter Oak Challenge Foundation, Westport, CT, 2011.
$25,000 to Samaritan Foundation, Briarwood, NY, 2011.
$15,000 to Fishermans Mark, Lambertville, NJ, 2011.
$15,000 to United States Fund for UNICEF, New York, NY, 2011.

6433
Tony and Renee Marlon Charitable Foundation ✧
c/o Christine O'Donnell, US Trust
114 W. 47th St., NY8-114-10-02
New York, NY 10036-1510

Established in 2006 in NV.
Donors: Anthony Marlon; Renee Marlon.
Foundation type: Independent foundation.
Financial data (yr. ended 12/31/12): Assets, $32,838,680 (M); expenditures, $2,728,618; qualifying distributions, $1,879,374; giving activities include $1,784,806 for 41 grants (high: $175,000; low: $1,000).
Fields of interest: Hospitals (general); Human services.
Limitations: Applications not accepted. Giving primarily in NH and NV.
Application information: Unsolicited requests for funds not accepted.
Officers: Anthony Marlon, Pres.; Renee Marlon, V.P.; Anthony Marlon, Secy.-Treas.
Directors: Brad Marlon; Robert Marlon; Jeannine Ann Zeller.
EIN: 205104500
Selected grants: The following grants are a representative sample of this grantmaker's funding activity:
$100,000 to College of the Holy Cross, Worcester, MA, 2012. To provide Educational Support.
$100,000 to Park City Performing Arts Foundation, Park City, UT, 2012. To provide Support to Performing Arts.
$34,450 to YMCA of Southern Nevada, Las Vegas, NV, 2012. To provide Support for Children's Summer Camp.
$25,000 to Families First of the Greater Seacoast, Portsmouth, NH, 2012. For Health and Family Services.
$25,000 to Foundation for an Independent Tomorrow, Las Vegas, NV, 2012. To Provide Support for Education, Training, and Employment Preparation.
$25,000 to Nevada Policy Research Institute, Las Vegas, NV, 2012. For Seeks Private Solutions to Public Challenges Facing Nevada.
$20,000 to Three Square, Las Vegas, NV, 2012. To support Hunger Relief Programs.
$10,000 to Cornerstone School, Stratham, NH, 2012. To provide Education Support.
$10,000 to Rebuilding All Goals Efficiently, Las Vegas, NV, 2012. To provide Assistance for the Elderly and Disabled.
$10,000 to Rockingham Community Action, Portsmouth, NH, 2012. For senior citizen support.

6434
The Yacov and Rita Marmurstein Charitable Foundation Trust ✧
c/o Rita Marmurstein
5307 17th Ave.
Brooklyn, NY 11204-1424

Established in 1999.
Donors: Yacov Marmurstein; Rita Marmurstein; Jacob Marmurstein; Private One of NY, LLC; Zev Marmurstein; Renee Marmurstein; Citysights LLC.
Foundation type: Independent foundation.
Financial data (yr. ended 12/31/12): Assets, $5,586,792 (M); gifts received, $2,225,000; expenditures, $2,513,706; qualifying distributions, $2,446,990; giving activities include $2,446,990 for grants.
Fields of interest: Jewish agencies & synagogues.
Limitations: Applications not accepted. Giving primarily in Brooklyn, NY. No grants to individuals.
Application information: Contributes only to pre-selected organizations.
Trustees: Rita Marmurstein; Yacov Marmurstein.
EIN: 116532361

6435
Donald B. Marron Charitable Trust ✧
c/o Marron Family Office
9 W. 57th St., 31st. Fl.
New York, NY 10019-2701 (212) 884-0198
Contact: Donald B. Marron, Tr.

Established in 2000 in NY.
Donor: Donald B. Marron.
Foundation type: Independent foundation.
Financial data (yr. ended 12/31/12): Assets, $14,556,873 (M); gifts received, $3,600,000; expenditures, $4,984,116; qualifying distributions, $4,966,304; giving activities include $4,947,524 for 57 grants (high: $1,067,850; low: $100).
Purpose and activities: Giving primarily for the arts, particularly an art museum, as well as for education and human services; funding also for a cancer center.

Fields of interest: Museums (art); Arts; Libraries (public); Education; Cancer research; Human services.
Limitations: Giving primarily in New York, NY.
Application information:
Initial approach: Letter
Deadline(s): None
Trustee: Donald B. Marron.
EIN: 137260354

6436
Marrus Family Foundation, Inc. ✧
(formerly David & Judith Marrus Foundation, Inc.)
c/o Levine & Seltzer
500 5th Ave., 37th Fl.
New York, NY 10110

Established in 1994 in NY.
Donors: David Marrus; Judith Marrus; Michael Marrus; Lauren Marrus.
Foundation type: Independent foundation.
Financial data (yr. ended 12/31/13): Assets, $14,164,179 (M); expenditures, $812,727; qualifying distributions, $801,657; giving activities include $661,745 for 97 grants (high: $60,000; low: $50).
Fields of interest: Arts; Education; Hospitals (general); Hospitals (specialty); Children/youth, services; Women, centers/services; Jewish agencies & synagogues.
Limitations: Applications not accepted. Giving primarily in MA, NY, and RI. No grants to individuals.
Application information: Contributes only to pre-selected organizations.
Officers: Michael Marrus, Pres.; David Marrus, V.P.; Judith Marrus, Secy.; Andrew Marrus, Treas.
EIN: 136279584

6437
Virginia Cretella Mars Foundation ✧
c/o Brown Brothers Harriman Trust Co., N.A.
140 Broadway, 4th Fl.
New York, NY 10005-1108
Contact: Kenneth Moy

Established in 1994 in DE.
Donor: Virginia C. Mars Charitable Lead Trust.
Foundation type: Independent foundation.
Financial data (yr. ended 12/31/13): Assets, $14,763,993 (M); gifts received, $444,859; expenditures, $678,571; qualifying distributions, $581,011; giving activities include $570,315 for 36 grants (high: $200,000; low: $9,315).
Purpose and activities: Giving primarily for education.
Fields of interest: Visual arts; Performing arts; Elementary school/education; Secondary school/education; Higher education; Environment.
Type of support: General/operating support; Land acquisition; Seed money; Curriculum development.
Limitations: Applications accepted. Giving primarily in Washington, DC, Baltimore, MD, NH, and Philadelphia, PA. No grants to individuals.
Application information: Application form required.
Initial approach: Letter
Deadline(s): Oct. 31
Officers: Stephanie J. Schuetz,* Pres.; Pamela D. Mars-Wright,* V.P.; Bernadette Russell,* Secy.; Victoria B. Mars,* Treas.
Directors: Marijke E. Mars; Valerie A. Mars; Kimberly V. Spina; Christopher M. White; Justin F. White.
EIN: 133798973

6438
The Marsal Family Foundation ✧ ☆
c/o Alvarez & Marsal Inc.
600 Madison Ave., 8th Fl.
New York, NY 10022-7616

Established in 1996 in CO.
Donors: Bryan Marsal; Kathleen Marsal; The Bryan P. Marsal 2010 Clat Co.; Alska Trust Co.
Foundation type: Independent foundation.
Financial data (yr. ended 12/31/13): Assets, $358,971 (L); gifts received, $500,264; expenditures, $572,074; qualifying distributions, $568,548; giving activities include $568,548 for 29 grants (high: $264,800; low: $100).
Fields of interest: Elementary/secondary education; Higher education; United Ways and Federated Giving Programs.
Limitations: Applications not accepted. Giving primarily in MI, NH, and NY. No grants to individuals.
Application information: Contributes only to pre-selected organizations.
Officers: Bryan Marsal, Pres.; Kathleen Marsal, V.P.
EIN: 841367157

6439
The Margot Marsh Biodiversity Foundation ✧
c/o First Republic Investment Mgmt.
1230 Ave. of the Americas
New York, NY 10020-1513

Established in 1996 in CA.
Foundation type: Independent foundation.
Financial data (yr. ended 12/31/13): Assets, $6,288,750 (M); expenditures, $765,723; qualifying distributions, $708,741; giving activities include $621,700 for 31 grants (high: $135,000; low: $10,000).
Purpose and activities: Support for organizations which operate wildlife and conservation protection programs on a worldwide basis.
Fields of interest: Environment, natural resources; Animals/wildlife, preservation/protection.
Type of support: Program development; Research.
Limitations: Applications not accepted. Giving primarily in Arlington, VA; some funding also in CA, NE, NY, PA, TX and Washington D.C. No grants to individuals.
Application information: Contributes only to pre-selected organizations.
Officers: Russell Mittermeier, Pres.; H. Williamson Ghriskey, Jr., V.P.; Mildred Basden, Secy.
EIN: 330683174

6440
Martin Family Foundation ✧
c/o Marcum LLP
750 3rd Ave., 11th Fl.
New York, NY 10017-2703

Established in 1989 in CA.
Donors: Eff W. Martin; Goldman Sachs & Co.
Foundation type: Independent foundation.
Financial data (yr. ended 12/31/13): Assets, $5,646,609 (M); expenditures, $850,792; qualifying distributions, $798,569; giving activities include $619,799 for 29 grants (high: $100,000; low: $500).
Fields of interest: Performing arts, orchestras; Higher education; Human services; Foundations (private grantmaking).
Limitations: Applications not accepted. Giving primarily in CA and VA. No grants to individuals.
Application information: Contributes only to pre-selected organizations.
Officer: Betty Ann Boeving, Exec. Dir.
Trustees: Andrew D. Martin; Eff W. Martin; Patricia M. Martin.
EIN: 133532032

6441
The V. & L. Marx Foundation ✧
14 Brookline Rd.
Scarsdale, NY 10583-6004 (201) 767-6270
Contact: Jennifer Gruenberg, Pres.

Established in 2004 in NY.
Donors: Jan Borgia‡; The Virginia and Leonard Marx Foundation.
Foundation type: Independent foundation.
Financial data (yr. ended 12/31/13): Assets, $99,064,172 (M); expenditures, $4,338,951; qualifying distributions, $4,159,355; giving activities include $4,152,000 for 110 grants (high: $914,000; low: $1,000).
Purpose and activities: Giving primarily for higher education, as well as for the arts, hospitals, medical research, and social services.
Fields of interest: Arts; Higher education; Hospitals (general); Medical research, institute; Human services; Children/youth, services; Foundations (private grantmaking).
Limitations: Applications accepted. Giving primarily in NY.
Application information: Application form required.
Initial approach: Letter (via U.S. mail)
Deadline(s): None
Officers: Jennifer Gruenberg, Pres.; Leonard Gruenberg, V.P. and C.F.O.; Wendy Gruenberg, Secy.; Jon Gruenberg, Treas.
EIN: 030536676
Selected grants: The following grants are a representative sample of this grantmaker's funding activity:
$15,000 to Dartmouth College, Hanover, NH, 2011.
$10,000 to Planned Parenthood of New York City, New York, NY, 2011.
$10,000 to Teach for America, New York, NY, 2011.
$5,000 to A Better Chance, New York, NY, 2011.
$5,000 to Israel Cancer Research Fund, New York, NY, 2011.
$5,000 to Parkinsons Disease Foundation, New York, NY, 2011.
$5,000 to Trout Unlimited, Arlington, VA, 2011.
$5,000 to Yale University, New Haven, CT, 2011.
$3,500 to American Jewish Committee, New York, NY, 2011.

6442
The William Marx Foundation ✧ ☆
c/o Wiss and Co. LLP
14 Penn Plz., Ste. 300
New York, NY 10122-0401

Donors: Helen Schulman Marx; William Marx; Cynthia Marks.
Foundation type: Independent foundation.
Financial data (yr. ended 10/31/13): Assets, $393,019 (M); expenditures, $469,930; qualifying distributions, $461,745; giving activities include $455,495 for 28 grants (high: $100,000; low: $100).
Purpose and activities: Giving primarily for health organizations and hospice care, as well as for social services, and Jewish organizations.
Fields of interest: Health care; Health organizations, association; Human services; Residential/custodial care, hospices; Civil/human rights; Foundations (private grantmaking); Jewish federated giving programs; Jewish agencies & synagogues.
Limitations: Applications not accepted. Giving primarily in Washington, DC, FL and NY. No grants to individuals.
Application information: Unsolicited requests for funds not accepted.
Officers: Cynthia Marks, Pres.; Laurie Lederman, V.P.
EIN: 116020448
Selected grants: The following grants are a representative sample of this grantmaker's funding activity:
$100,000 to Anti-Defamation League of Bnai Brith, New York, NY, 2011.
$50,000 to Hospice Care Network, Fresh Meadows, NY, 2011.
$25,000 to Boca Raton Regional Hospital Foundation, Boca Raton, FL, 2011.
$25,000 to Jewish Federation of South Palm Beach County, Boca Raton, FL, 2011.
$25,000 to New England Villages, Pembroke, MA, 2011.
$25,000 to UJA-Federation of New York, New York, NY, 2011.
$10,000 to Hands On Tzedakah, Boca Raton, FL, 2011.
$10,000 to Retreat, The, East Hampton, NY, 2011.
$5,000 to Adults and Children with Learning and Developmental Disabilities, Bethpage, NY, 2011.
$1,000 to Doctors Without Borders USA, New York, NY, 2011.

6443
The Page and Otto Marx, Jr. Foundation ✧
1983 Marcus Ave., Ste. 137
New Hyde Park, NY 11042-1009

Established in 1984 in NY.
Donors: Otto Marx, Jr.; Page M. Marx‡.
Foundation type: Independent foundation.
Financial data (yr. ended 12/31/13): Assets, $19,241,053 (M); expenditures, $1,026,826; qualifying distributions, $868,021; giving activities include $819,000 for 56 grants (high: $120,000; low: $250).
Purpose and activities: Giving primarily for education, health care and health associations.
Fields of interest: Arts; Education; Health care; Health organizations, association; Human services.
Limitations: Applications not accepted. Giving in the U.S., primarily in NJ, NY, and PA. No grants to individuals.
Application information: Contributes only to pre-selected organizations.
Officers and Directors:* Bruce J. Westcott,* Pres.; Joseph W. Levy,* V.P. and Treas.; Jeffrey S. Levin, Secy.; Jill S. Levy; Helen D. Westcott.
EIN: 133200783
Selected grants: The following grants are a representative sample of this grantmaker's funding activity:
$120,000 to Pennington School, Pennington, NJ, 2011. For scholarship.
$21,000 to Johns Hopkins Medicine, Baltimore, MD, 2011.
$20,000 to Alzheimers Association, Chicago, IL, 2011.
$14,500 to Memphis Zoo, Memphis, TN, 2011.
$10,000 to Harlem Arts Alliance, New York, NY, 2011.
$9,000 to New York Academy of Medicine, New York, NY, 2011.
$5,000 to Art Resources Transfer, New York, NY, 2011.
$4,500 to Family and Childrens Aid, Danbury, CT, 2011.
$4,250 to American Lung Association, New York, NY, 2011.
$4,000 to Chewonki Foundation, Development Office, Wiscasset, ME, 2011.

6444
Massry Charitable Foundation, Inc. ✧
c/o Norman Massry
255 Washington Ave. Ext.
Albany, NY 12205-5533

Established in 1994 in NY.
Donor: Morris Massry.
Foundation type: Independent foundation.
Financial data (yr. ended 12/31/13): Assets, $29,849,463 (M); gifts received, $1,979,212; expenditures, $1,338,021; qualifying distributions, $1,179,286; giving activities include $1,179,286 for 64 grants (high: $205,000; low: $100).
Purpose and activities: Giving primarily for education, health and human services, federated giving programs, and Jewish organizations.
Fields of interest: Higher education; Education; Health care; Human services; Family services; United Ways and Federated Giving Programs; Jewish federated giving programs; Jewish agencies & synagogues.
Limitations: Applications not accepted. Giving primarily in MA and NY. No grants to individuals.
Application information: Unsolicited requests for funds not accepted.
Officers: Morris Massry, Pres.; Esther Massry, V.P.; Norman Massry, Secy.-Treas.
EIN: 141777179

6445
Mater Dei Foundation, Inc. ✧
c/o Edwards Wildman Palmer, LLP
750 Lexington Ave., 9th Fl.
New York, NY 10022
Application address: c/o, Stephen D. Pryor, 1415 S. Voss, Ste. 110-256, Houston, TX 77057

Donors: Stephen D. Pryor; Katherine A. Pryor.
Foundation type: Independent foundation.
Financial data (yr. ended 11/30/13): Assets, $1,114,592 (M); gifts received, $2,350,000; expenditures, $2,015,873; qualifying distributions, $2,015,873; giving activities include $1,668,500 for 1 grant.
Fields of interest: Religion.
Limitations: Applications accepted. Giving primarily in Kericho, Kenya.
Application information: Application form required.
Initial approach: Letter
Deadline(s): None
Officers and Directors:* Stephen D. Pryor,* Pres.; Katherine A. Pryor,* Secy.
EIN: 261577359

6446
The G. Harold & Leila Y. Mathers Charitable Foundation ✧
118 N. Bedford Rd., Ste. 203
Mount Kisco, NY 10549-2555 (914) 242-0465
Contact: James H. Handelman, Exec. Dir.
FAX: (914) 242-0665;
E-mail: admin@mathersfoundation.org; Additional e-mail (for James H. Handelman): jh@mathersfoundation.org; Main URL: http://www.mathersfoundation.org

Established in 1975 in NY.
Donors: G. Harold Mathers‡; Leila Y. Mathers‡.
Foundation type: Independent foundation.
Financial data (yr. ended 12/31/12): Assets, $203,465,494 (M); expenditures, $15,433,353; qualifying distributions, $11,856,322; giving activities include $11,672,561 for 56 grants (high: $1,000,001; low: $5,000).
Purpose and activities: The foundation is primarily interested in supporting fundamental basic research in the life sciences. Support is provided for specific projects from established researchers at top universities and independent research institutions within the United States.
Fields of interest: Science, research; Biology/life sciences.
Type of support: General/operating support; Research.
Limitations: Applications accepted. Giving on a national basis. No grants to individuals.
Publications: Application guidelines.
Application information: General inquiries can be made via e-mail. Specific detailed queries must be received by mail. Application form not required.
Initial approach: Letter
Copies of proposal: 1
Deadline(s): None
Board meeting date(s): 2 or 3 times per year
Final notification: Within 90 days of submission of request
Officers and Directors:* Donald E. Handelman,* Pres.; William R. Handelman,* V.P.; John Young,* Secy.; Richard Handelman, Treas.; James H. Handelman, Exec. Dir.; David Boyle; William S. Miller.
Number of staff: 1 full-time professional; 1 full-time support.
EIN: 237441901
Selected grants: The following grants are a representative sample of this grantmaker's funding activity:
$1,000,001 to University of California at San Diego, Center for Academic Research and Training in Anthropogeny, La Jolla, CA, 2012. For general support.
$586,666 to Yale University, School of Medicine, New Haven, CT, 2012. For research project, Epigenetic Programming piRNAs Mammal.

$500,000 to Stanford University, Stanford, CA, 2012. For research project, Neural Function: Molecules to Network.
$497,284 to University of California at San Diego, La Jolla, CA, 2012. For research project, Renew Molecular Glycobiology Research.
$402,394 to Rockefeller University, New York, NY, 2012. For research project, Tracing the Evolution of Conserved Behavior.
$348,592 to University of California at San Diego, La Jolla, CA, 2012. For research, Interactions Drosophila Brain.
$342,698 to Harvard University, Cambridge, MA, 2012. For grant to School of Medicine in Boston for research project, Circadian Clocks-Molecular Regulators.
$333,334 to California Institute of Technology, Pasadena, CA, 2012. For research project, Consciousness Medial Temporal Lobe.
$188,438 to Washington University, Saint Louis, MO, 2012. For research project, Neuronal Circuit Function in the Olfactory System.
$142,418 to Brandeis University, Waltham, MA, 2012. For research, Imaging Molecular Mech Transcription.

6447
Pierre and Tana Matisse Charitable Foundation ✧

1 E. 53rd St.
New York, NY 10022-4200 (212) 355-6269
Contact: Sandra Carnielli, Exec. Dir.

Established in 1995 in DE and NY.
Donors: Maria-Gaetana Matisse; The Maria-Gaetana Matisse Revocable Trust.
Foundation type: Independent foundation.
Financial data (yr. ended 12/31/12): Assets, $216,682,629 (M); expenditures, $3,534,615; qualifying distributions, $3,090,567; giving activities include $1,830,300 for 48 grants (high: $403,000; low: $350), and $260,670 for foundation-administered programs.
Fields of interest: Museums (art); Arts; Education; Foundations (private grantmaking).
Limitations: Giving primarily in New York, NY, some funding also in Phnom Penh, Cambodia. No grants to individuals.
Application information:
Initial approach: Letter
Deadline(s): None
Officers and Directors:* Robert H. Horowitz,* Pres. and Treas.; Oliver G. Bernier,* V.P. and Secy.; Janos Farkas,* V.P.; Sandra Carnielli, Exec. Dir.
EIN: 133838457

6448
The Mayday Fund ✧

c/o SPG
127 W. 26th St., Ste. 800
New York, NY 10001-6869 (212) 366-6970
Contact: Christina Spellman, Exec. Dir.
FAX: (212) 366-6979;
E-mail: inquiry@maydayfund.org; Main URL: http://www.maydayfund.org/
Grants List: http://www.maydayfund.org/maydaygrants.html
Application fax: (301) 654-1589,
e-mail: ghertz@burnesscommunications.com

Established in 1992 in NY.
Donors: Shirley S. Katzenbach‡; John C. Beck; Pamela M. Thye; Caroline N. Sidnam; Harold L. Messenger.
Foundation type: Independent foundation.
Financial data (yr. ended 12/31/13): Assets, $27,149,332 (M); expenditures, $1,339,784; qualifying distributions, $1,310,179; giving activities include $819,434 for 16 grants (high: $200,000; low: $1,950), and $243,927 for 1 foundation-administered program.
Purpose and activities: The foundation is dedicated to the reduction of the profound human problems associated with physical pain and its consequences. The fund is particularly interested in projects that result in clinical interventions to reduce the toll of physical pain, pediatric pain, pain in non-verbal populations, and pain in the context of emergency medicine. The fund also promotes networking between veterinary and human medicine.
Fields of interest: Medical research.
International interests: Canada.
Type of support: Research.
Limitations: Giving on a national basis. No grants to individuals, or generally for endowments, capital projects, equipment, general operating expenses, ongoing activities, or annual fundraising drives.
Publications: Annual report; Financial statement; Grants list.
Application information: Mail and phone contacts only after initial e-mail communications. Application form not required.
Initial approach: E-mail to Exec. Dir.
Copies of proposal: 1
Deadline(s): None
Board meeting date(s): Quarterly
Final notification: 1-6 weeks
Officer: Christina Spellman, Exec. Dir.
Trustees: John C. Beck; Robert D.C. Meeker, Jr.; Caroline N. Sidnam; Pamela M. Thye.
EIN: 133645438
Selected grants: The following grants are a representative sample of this grantmaker's funding activity:
$100,000 to Yale University, School of Medicine, New Haven, CT, 2012. For Implementation of a VA Stepped Care Model of Pain Management partnership with the Donaghue Foundation.
$91,092 to University of Chicago, School of Medicine, Chicago, IL, 2012. For Emergency Department Management of Pain in Older Adults.
$12,000 to Gerontological Society of America, Washington, DC, 2012. For Mayday Fund Add-on for Graduate Nursing or Post-Doctoral Research on Pain reissue of the balance of a grant in support of the Hartford Building Academic Geriatric Nursing Initiative made originally to the American Academy of Nursing in 2006.
$2,130 to Council on Foundations, Arlington, VA, 2012. For Contribution for General Operations.

6449
The Louis B. Mayer Foundation ✧

c/o Emily Grand
275 Madison Ave., Ste. 401
New York, NY 10016-1101 (212) 812-4362
Contact: Emily Grand, Admin.

Established in 1947 in CA.
Donor: Louis B. Mayer‡.
Foundation type: Independent foundation.
Financial data (yr. ended 12/31/13): Assets, $12,265,149 (M); expenditures, $594,151; qualifying distributions, $502,976; giving activities include $475,000 for 13 grants (high: $100,000; low: $5,000).
Purpose and activities: Support for cutting edge medical research for the treatment of cancer and for film preservation.
Fields of interest: Media, film/video; Performing arts, dance; Cancer; Medical research.
Type of support: Continuing support; Program development; Research.
Limitations: Applications not accepted. Giving on a national basis. No support for filmmaking. No grants to individuals; no loans.
Application information: Contributes only to pre-selected organizations.
Board meeting date(s): Semi-annually
Officers and Trustees:* Robert A. Gottlieb,* Pres.; Carol Farkas,* Secy.-Treas.; Elliot R. Cattarulla.
EIN: 952232340
Selected grants: The following grants are a representative sample of this grantmaker's funding activity:
$100,000 to Miami City Ballet, Miami Beach, FL, 2012. For general support.
$75,000 to Film Foundation, New York, NY, 2012. For preservation of Michael Powell-Emeric Pressburger film, The Tales of Hoffman and Michael Powell's Bluebeard's Castle.
$75,000 to Mount Sinai Medical Center, New York, NY, 2012. For Dr. Valentin Fuster's Grenada Heart Project.
$50,000 to Dana-Farber Cancer Institute, Boston, MA, 2012. For prostate cancer molecular research database project.
$30,000 to University of California, Los Angeles, CA, 2012. For UCLA Film and Television Archive to restore Now I'll Tell with Spencer Tracy.
$29,500 to George Eastman House/International Museum of Photography and Film, Rochester, NY, 2012. For preservation of Thirty Years of Motion Pictures.
$25,000 to New York Public Library, New York, NY, 2012. For the performing arts, preservation of the Mikhail Baryshnikov Archive.
$20,000 to Berkeley Art Museum and Pacific Film Archive, Berkeley, CA, 2012. For CineFiles Film Document Imaging Project.
$10,000 to George Eastman House/International Museum of Photography and Film, Rochester, NY, 2012. For L. Jeffrey Selznick School of Film Preservation.

6450
Mazel Charitable Trust ✧ ☆

4721 17th Ave.
Brooklyn, NY 11204-1119

Established in 1999.
Donors: Judah Blau; Marilyn Blau; TPE Inc.; Avrohom Blau.
Foundation type: Independent foundation.
Financial data (yr. ended 12/31/13): Assets, $396,171 (M); gifts received, $700,000; expenditures, $592,800; qualifying distributions, $592,800; giving activities include $591,800 for grants.
Type of support: General/operating support.
Limitations: Applications not accepted. No grants to individuals.
Application information: Unsolicited requests for funds not accepted.
Trustees: Judah Blau; Marilyn Blau.
EIN: 116466161

6451
MBIA Foundation, Inc. ✧
113 King St.
Armonk, NY 10504-1611 (914) 765-3834
Contact: Jean McGovern, Secy.
E-mail: Jean.McGovern@mbia.com; Additional tel.: (914) 273-4545; Main URL: http://www.mbia.com/about/about_foundation.html

Established in 2001 in NY.
Donors: Optinuity Alliance Resources Corporation; MBIA Insurance Corp.; John Caouette; Francie Heller; Kathleen Okenica; Kevin D. Silva; Kutak Rock LLP; Richard L. Weil; Moody's Corp.
Foundation type: Company-sponsored foundation.
Financial data (yr. ended 12/31/13): Assets, $11,041,333 (M); gifts received, $3,000,000; expenditures, $1,956,128; qualifying distributions, $1,818,967; giving activities include $1,818,967 for 558 grants (high: $40,000; low: $30).
Purpose and activities: The foundation supports programs designed to serve children and families through education; health services; and human services.
Fields of interest: Museums; Arts; Elementary school/education; Higher education; Law school/education; Education; Health care; Diabetes; Medical research; Food banks; Family services; Family services, parent education; Human services; Community/economic development; Christian agencies & churches; Religion; Children.
Type of support: Continuing support; Building/renovation; Program development; Employee volunteer services; Sponsorships; Employee matching gifts.
Limitations: Applications accepted. Giving primarily in areas of company operations, with emphasis on CT, NJ, NY, and PA. No support for discriminatory organizations, political or lobbying organizations, religious, fraternal, athletic, social, or veterans' organizations not of direct benefit to the entire community, or umbrella agencies such as the United Way. No grants to individuals, or for general operating support, fundraising activities related to individual sponsorship, capital campaigns, endowments, or fundraising events.
Publications: Application guidelines.
Application information: A site visit may be requested. Organizations receiving support are asked to submit a post grant evaluation report. Application form required.
Initial approach: Contact foundation for application form
Deadline(s): Nov. 26
Officers and Directors:* Kimberly Osgood,* Pres.; Chuck Chaplin,* V.P.; Bill Fallon, V.P; Jean McGovern,* Secy.; Joseph Buonadonna,* Treas.; Robert Alan; Jennifer C. Cronin; Charlie Hannigan; Rich McKay; Susan A. Voltz.
EIN: 134163899
Selected grants: The following grants are a representative sample of this grantmaker's funding activity:
$200 to University of Virginia, Darden School, Charlottesville, VA, 2012. For education.
$100 to University of Virginia, Darden School, Charlottesville, VA, 2012. For education.

6452
MBK Educational Foundation, Inc. ✧
252 7th Ave., Ste. 8J
New York, NY 10001-7337

Donor: Michael B. Kim.
Foundation type: Independent foundation.
Financial data (yr. ended 12/31/13): Assets, $3,502,280 (M); gifts received, $260,000; expenditures, $1,755,966; qualifying distributions, $1,760,550; giving activities include $1,750,000 for 2 grants (high: $1,500,000; low: $250,000).
Fields of interest: Higher education.
Limitations: Applications not accepted. Giving primarily in Haverford, PA; some funding also in Seoul, South Korea.
Application information: Contributes only to pre-selected organizations.
Officer and Director:* Mimi Okkyung Kim,* Pres.
EIN: 262987483
Selected grants: The following grants are a representative sample of this grantmaker's funding activity:
$1,000,000 to Haverford College, Haverford, PA, 2012. For the Construction of a New Dormitory at Haverford College.

6453
James J. McCann Charitable Trust ✧
(also known as McCann Foundation)
35 Market St.
Poughkeepsie, NY 12601-3214 (845) 452-3085
Contact: Michael G. Gartland, Tr.

The foundation was established in 1967, the trust in 1969. They function as a single combined entity.
Donor: James J. McCann†.
Foundation type: Independent foundation.
Financial data (yr. ended 12/31/12): Assets, $27,953,518 (M); expenditures, $2,127,700; qualifying distributions, $1,818,060; giving activities include $1,661,348 for 141 grants (high: $230,900; low: $600).
Purpose and activities: Giving primarily for the arts, education, health, children and social services, sports associations, and Christian agencies and churches.
Fields of interest: Performing arts, opera; Arts; Higher education; Education; Hospitals (general); Health care; Recreation, association; Human services; Children/youth, services; Christian agencies & churches.
Type of support: Continuing support; Annual campaigns; Building/renovation; Equipment; Land acquisition; Conferences/seminars; Publication; Seed money; Fellowships; Scholarship funds.
Limitations: Applications accepted. Giving primarily in Poughkeepsie and Dutchess County, NY. No grants to individuals, or for operating budgets, emergency or endowment funds, deficit financing, or matching gifts; generally no loans.
Publications: Annual report.
Application information: Application form required.
Initial approach: Proposal
Copies of proposal: 1
Deadline(s): None
Final notification: None
Officer: Maureen Breslin, Mgr.
Trustees: Richard V. Corbally; Michael G. Gartland.
Number of staff: 1 part-time professional; 1 part-time support.

6454
The McCarthy Charities Inc. ✧
P.O. Box 1090
Troy, NY 12181-1090
Grants List: http://www.mccarthyfamilyfdn.org/history.html

Incorporated in 1917 in NY.
Donors: Robert H. McCarthy†; Lucy A. McCarthy†; Peter F. McCarthy†; Peter H. McCarthy†.
Foundation type: Independent foundation.
Financial data (yr. ended 12/31/13): Assets, $12,146,794 (M); expenditures, $671,850; qualifying distributions, $667,200; giving activities include $511,805 for 73 grants (high: $100,000; low: $150).
Purpose and activities: Giving for local Roman Catholic church support and church-related education and welfare agencies; support also for community funds, social service agencies, and local hospitals.
Fields of interest: Arts; Education; Hospitals (general); Human services; Catholic federated giving programs; Catholic agencies & churches.
Type of support: General/operating support; Continuing support; Annual campaigns; Capital campaigns; Program development; Seed money; Scholarship funds; Program evaluation; Matching/challenge support.
Limitations: Applications not accepted. Giving primarily in the Rensselaer County, NY, area. No grants to individuals.
Application information: Contributes only to pre-selected organizations.
Officers: Christopher Connally, Co-Pres.; Lucy McCarthy, Co-Pres.; Denis McCarthy, V.P.; Roseanne McCathy Lobitz, Secy.; Robert P. McCarthy, Treas.
Directors: Bridget McCarthy; Pamela McCarthy; Winifred McCarthy; Mary Katherine Sheridan.
Trustee: Laura McCarthy.
Number of staff: 1 part-time professional.
EIN: 146019064

6455
Brian A. McCarthy Foundation, Inc. ✧
c/o O'Connor Davies, LLP
665 5th Ave.
New York, NY 10022-5305
E-mail: brianamccarthyfoundation@gmail.com; Main URL: http://www.brianamccarthy.com
Grants List: http://www.brianamccarthy.com/grants.html

Foundation type: Independent foundation.
Financial data (yr. ended 12/31/13): Assets, $9,637,889 (M); expenditures, $504,155; qualifying distributions, $431,475; giving activities include $430,000 for 8 grants (high: $80,000; low: $50,000).
Purpose and activities: Giving primarily for gay, lesbian, bisexual, and transgender health, education, culture, and well-being with an emphasis on HIV research and prevention, and housing and anti-violence programs for LGBT youth.
Fields of interest: Health care, clinics/centers; AIDS; AIDS research; Neighborhood centers; LGBTQ.
Limitations: Applications not accepted. Giving primarily in the metropolitan New York, NY, area. No grants to individuals.
Publications: Financial statement.

Application information: Contributes only to pre-selected organizations.
Officer and Director:* Brian A. McCarthy,* Pres.
EIN: 262804661
Selected grants: The following grants are a representative sample of this grantmaker's funding activity:
$100,000 to Ali Forney Center, New York, NY, 2012. For funding for the opening and operation of the nation's first 24-Hour Drop-In Center for homeless LGBT youth. Programs will include 24 Hour Access to Meals, Showers, Clothing and Laundry, 24 hour HIV support services, 24 hour Mental Health Services and Overn.

6456
Michael W. McCarthy Foundation, Inc. ✧ ☆

1065 Old Country Rd., Ste. 207
Westbury, NY 11590-5628

Foundation type: Independent foundation.
Financial data (yr. ended 12/31/13): Assets, $8,997,336 (M); expenditures, $851,392; qualifying distributions, $696,914; giving activities include $471,985 for 21 grants (high: $110,000; low: $600).
Fields of interest: Education; Autism; Human services.
Limitations: Applications not accepted. Giving primarily in NY.
Application information: Contributes only to pre-selected organizations.
Officers: Giovanna McCarthy, Mgr.; Patrick C. McCarthy, Mgr.
EIN: 260675307
Selected grants: The following grants are a representative sample of this grantmaker's funding activity:
$100,000 to Christmas Magic, Hauppauge, NY, 2012. For General Operating to Help Provide Holiday Gifts to Underprivileged Children Throughout Suffolk County, Long Island.
$30,000 to Autism Speaks, New York, NY, 2012. For Financial Support for Those Who Struggle with Autism.
$25,000 to Concern for Independent Living, Medford, NY, 2012. To Help Finance Housing and Services for Persons Challenged with Psychiatric Or Other Disabilities and Those with Very Low Incomes.

6457
The Stephanie and Carter McClelland Foundation ✧

c/o Cohnreznick LLP
1212 6th Ave.
New York, NY 10036-1600

Established in 1997 in NY.
Donors: W. Carter McClelland; Stephanie McClelland.
Foundation type: Independent foundation.
Financial data (yr. ended 11/30/13): Assets, $104,614 (M); gifts received, $1,861,382; expenditures, $1,800,322; qualifying distributions, $1,795,250; giving activities include $1,795,250 for 17 grants (high: $1,500,000; low: $500).
Purpose and activities: Giving primarily for higher education and the arts.
Fields of interest: Performing arts, theater; Performing arts, education; Arts; Higher education; Education; Human services.
Limitations: Applications not accepted. Giving primarily in NY; some funding also in Stanford, CA. No grants to individuals.
Application information: Contributes only to pre-selected organizations.
Trustees: Stephanie P. McClelland; W. Carter McClelland.
EIN: 137154217

6458
McCormick Family Foundation ✧

1100 Wehrle Dr., 2nd Fl.
Buffalo, NY 14221

Established in 2003 in PA.
Donors: Margaret O. McCormick; Vance C. McCormick Trust; Anne McCormick Trust; Margaret McCormick Trust.
Foundation type: Independent foundation.
Financial data (yr. ended 12/31/13): Assets, $17 (M); gifts received, $548,220; expenditures, $548,216; qualifying distributions, $523,100; giving activities include $523,100 for 43 grants (high: $40,000; low: $1,000).
Fields of interest: Performing arts; Higher education; Human services.
Limitations: Applications not accepted. Giving primarily in PA. No grants to individuals.
Application information: Contributes only to pre-selected organizations.
Officer: Larry A. Hartman, Exec. Dir.
EIN: 300166827
Selected grants: The following grants are a representative sample of this grantmaker's funding activity:
$35,000 to Boys and Girls Club of Central Pennsylvania, Harrisburg, PA, 2011.
$10,000 to Central Pennsylvania Food Bank, Harrisburg, PA, 2011. For general funding.

6459
The John J. McDonnell and Margaret T. O'Brien Foundation ✧

c/o Rich May PC, Eric Freedgood, Pinnacle Association
335 Madison Ave.
New York, NY 10017-4627

Established in 2007 in NY.
Donor: Margaret T. O'Brien‡.
Foundation type: Independent foundation.
Financial data (yr. ended 12/31/13): Assets, $12,156,298 (M); expenditures, $806,750; qualifying distributions, $545,683; giving activities include $543,600 for 25 grants (high: $102,500; low: $5,000).
Fields of interest: Education; Liver disorders; Medical research, institute; Boys & girls clubs; Human services.
Limitations: Applications not accepted. Giving primarily in MA and NY.
Application information: Unsolicited requests for funds not accepted.
Trustees: Eric Freedgood; Walter L. Landergan, Jr.
EIN: 510644921

6460
Dextra Baldwin McGonagle Foundation, Inc. ✧

c/o O'Connor Davies, LLP
665 5th Ave.
New York, NY 10022-5305
Contact: Jonathan G. Spanier, Pres.

Incorporated in 1967 in NY.
Donor: Dextra Baldwin McGonagle‡.
Foundation type: Independent foundation.
Financial data (yr. ended 12/31/13): Assets, $19,881,362 (M); expenditures, $1,085,102; qualifying distributions, $909,695; giving activities include $763,938 for 30 grants (high: $130,000; low: $1,000).
Purpose and activities: Primary areas of interest include hospitals, the medical sciences, and medical research, including cancer research; grants also for higher and medical education, social service agencies, and cultural programs.
Fields of interest: Arts; Higher education; Medical school/education; Hospitals (general); Health care; Cancer; Biomedicine; Medical research, institute; Cancer research; Human services; Biology/life sciences; Aging.
Type of support: Annual campaigns; Equipment; Endowments; Seed money; Scholarship funds; Research.
Limitations: Applications accepted. Giving primarily in CA and NY. No grants to individuals, or for matching gifts.
Application information: Application form not required.
Initial approach: 1-page summary of proposal
Copies of proposal: 1
Deadline(s): None
Board meeting date(s): As required
Officers and Directors:* Maury L. Spanier,* Chair.; Jonathan G. Spanier, Pres. and Treas.; David B. Spanier,* V.P. and Secy.
Number of staff: 1 full-time professional; 1 part-time professional; 3 part-time support.
EIN: 136219236
Selected grants: The following grants are a representative sample of this grantmaker's funding activity:
$40,000 to Westchester Land Trust, Bedford Hills, NY, 2012. For land preservation.
$10,000 to Columbia University, Law School, New York, NY, 2012. For scholarships.

6461
The Donald C. McGraw Foundation, Inc. ✧

c/o Deutsche Trust Co. of NY
P.O. Box 1297
Church St. Sta.
New York, NY 10008-1297

Incorporated in 1963 in NY.
Donors: Donald C. McGraw‡; D. McGraw Charitable Trust; Donald C. McGraw Charitable Lead Annuity Trust.
Foundation type: Independent foundation.
Financial data (yr. ended 01/31/13): Assets, $42,192,854 (M); gifts received, $91,600; expenditures, $1,703,731; qualifying distributions, $1,630,353; giving activities include $1,580,000 for 49 grants (high: $250,000; low: $5,000).
Purpose and activities: Giving primarily for health care and medical research, as well as for museums, education, and human services.

Fields of interest: Museums; Elementary/secondary education; Health care; Health organizations, association; Medical research; Human services; Residential/custodial care, hospices.
Limitations: Applications not accepted. Giving primarily to FL and MA. No grants to individuals.
Application information: Contributes only to pre-selected organizations.
Officer: Donald C. McGraw III, Pres.
Directors: J. Patterson Cooper; David W. McGraw; Robert L.W. McGraw.
EIN: 136165603
Selected grants: The following grants are a representative sample of this grantmaker's funding activity:
$350,000 to Community Hospice of Northeast Florida, Jacksonville, FL, 2011.
$200,000 to Mayo Clinic Jacksonville, Jacksonville, FL, 2011.
$50,000 to Berkshire Taconic Community Foundation, Sheffield, MA, 2011.
$50,000 to Heritage Museums and Gardens, Sandwich, MA, 2011.
$50,000 to Multiple Sclerosis Society, National, New York, NY, 2011.
$50,000 to YMCA of Cape Cod, West Barnstable, MA, 2011.
$30,000 to Cape Cod Academy, Osterville, MA, 2011.
$25,000 to Berkshire Country Day School, Lenox, MA, 2011.
$25,000 to Berkshire Museum, Pittsfield, MA, 2011.
$25,000 to Cape Cod Hospital, Hyannis, MA, 2011.

6462
Elizabeth McGraw Foundation, Inc. ✧
c/o Deutsche Bank Trust Co. of NY
P.O. Box 1297
Church St. Sta.
New York, NY 10008-1297

Established in 1990 in NY.
Donor: Donald C. McGraw Foundation, Inc.
Foundation type: Independent foundation.
Financial data (yr. ended 09/30/13): Assets, $27,473,533 (M); expenditures, $1,572,581; qualifying distributions, $1,510,445; giving activities include $1,490,000 for 13 grants (high: $600,000; low: $20,000).
Fields of interest: Museums (art); Performing arts, ballet; Performing arts, opera; Higher education; Health care; Human services.
Limitations: Applications not accepted. Giving primarily in FL and MA; funding also in DE. No grants to individuals.
Application information: Contributes only to pre-selected organizations.
Officers: John L. McGraw, Pres.; John Cady, Secy.
Directors: Edie Murphy; John L. McGraw, Jr.; Ms. Lee McGraw.
EIN: 133591829

6463
The D.J. McManus Foundation Inc. ✧
c/o Jason D. McManus
420 W. Broadway, PH A
New York, NY 10012-3741 (212) 874-7426
Contact: Deborah H.M. McManus, Pres.

Established in 1999 in NY.
Donors: Deborah H.M. McManus; Jason D. McManus.
Foundation type: Independent foundation.
Financial data (yr. ended 12/31/13): Assets, $13,418,804 (M); gifts received, $619,778; expenditures, $577,632; qualifying distributions, $470,247; giving activities include $470,247 for 83 grants (high: $57,500; low: $10).
Purpose and activities: Giving primarily for the arts, education, human services, and for community programs.
Fields of interest: Arts; Higher education; Environment, natural resources; Human services; Children/youth, services; Community/economic development.
Limitations: Applications accepted. Giving primarily in NY; some funding nationally. No grants to individuals.
Application information: Application form required.
Initial approach: Letter on corporate letterhead
Deadline(s): None
Officers: Deborah H.M. McManus, Pres.; Sophie McManus, V.P.; Jason D. McManus, Secy.
EIN: 134080144

6464
Joanna McNeil Trust ✧
(formerly The Phelps Trust)
c/o Brown Brothers Harriman Trust Co.
140 Broadway, 5th Fl.
New York, NY 10005-1108

Established in 1997 in PA.
Donor: Robert L. McNeil, Jr. 2000 Trust.
Foundation type: Independent foundation.
Financial data (yr. ended 12/31/13): Assets, $12,654,839 (M); expenditures, $736,201; qualifying distributions, $616,015; giving activities include $616,000 for 4 grants (high: $220,000; low: $45,000).
Fields of interest: Performing arts, music; Arts; Education.
Type of support: General/operating support.
Limitations: Applications not accepted. Giving limited to Philadelphia, PA. No grants to individuals.
Application information: Contributes only to pre-selected organizations.
Trustee: Joanne McNeil Lewis.
EIN: 526854625
Selected grants: The following grants are a representative sample of this grantmaker's funding activity:
$50,000 to Princeton University, Princeton, NJ, 2012. For Restricted to the Aspire Campaign.
$45,000 to Springside School, Philadelphia, PA, 2012. For Restricted to the Next Step Scholar Program.

6465
John P. & Anne Welsh McNulty Foundation ✧
c/o BCRS Assocs., LLC
77 Water St., 9th Fl.
New York, NY 10005-4401

Established in 1985 in FL.
Donors: John P. McNulty‡; Anne Welsh McNulty.
Foundation type: Independent foundation.
Financial data (yr. ended 12/31/13): Assets, $48,628,122 (M); gifts received, $915,315; expenditures, $2,304,029; qualifying distributions, $2,101,246; giving activities include $1,510,135 for 61 grants (high: $200,000; low: $100).
Purpose and activities: Giving primarily for higher education, the arts, and human services.
Fields of interest: Performing arts, opera; Arts; Higher education; Education; Human services; Children/youth, services; Public affairs.
Limitations: Applications not accepted. Giving primarily in FL, NY and PA; some funding also in CO. No grants to individuals or for scholarships; no loans.
Application information: Contributes only to pre-selected organizations.
Trustee: Anne Welsh McNulty.
EIN: 521445003

6466
The Scott & Suling Mead Foundation ✧
Bowling Green Sta.
P.O. Box 73
New York, NY 10274-0073

Established in 1996 in DC.
Donor: E. Scott Mead.
Foundation type: Independent foundation.
Financial data (yr. ended 04/30/13): Assets, $7,958,353 (M); expenditures, $1,391,845; qualifying distributions, $1,100,890; giving activities include $1,100,890 for 32 grants (high: $500,000; low: $201).
Purpose and activities: Giving primarily for education and health associations.
Fields of interest: Arts; Higher education, university; Education; Health organizations, association; Children/youth, services.
Limitations: Applications not accepted. Giving primarily in London, England; funding also in CA, MA, and PA. No grants to individuals.
Application information: Contributes only to pre-selected organizations.
Trustees: E. Scott Mead; Suling C. Mead; Hope Mead Wynn.
EIN: 133921104
Selected grants: The following grants are a representative sample of this grantmaker's funding activity:
$400,000 to Phillips Academy, Andover, MA, 2011. For general charitable purposes.
$251,000 to Harvard University, Cambridge, MA, 2011. For general charitable purposes.
$50,000 to Ushers New Look, Duluth, GA, 2011. For general charitable purposes.
$50,000 to Ushers New Look, Duluth, GA, 2011. For general charitable purposes.
$3,750 to Royal Opera House, London, England, 2011. For general charitable purposes.
$2,500 to Albuquerque Academy, Albuquerque, NM, 2011. For general charitable purposes.

6467
George and Margaret Mee Charitable Foundation ✧
The Waldron Bldg.
80 Exchange St., Ste. 3
Binghamton, NY 13901-3400 (607) 722-0181
Contact: Deborah S. Manley, Admin.
FAX: (607) 722-0215; Main URL: http://www.meefoundation.org/

Established in 2003 in PA.

Donor: Margaret Mee.
Foundation type: Independent foundation.
Financial data (yr. ended 12/31/13): Assets, $22,735,796 (M); expenditures, $1,126,645; qualifying distributions, $966,753; giving activities include $867,856 for 32 grants (high: $100,000; low: $1,000).
Purpose and activities: Giving primarily for health care, including a hospital, the humanities, community services, education, recreation, and arts and culture.
Fields of interest: Arts; Education; Hospitals (general); Health organizations; Human services.
Limitations: Applications accepted. Giving primarily in Broome and Delaware counties, NY, and Cameron County, PA. No support for religious organizations. No grants to individuals.
Publications: Application guidelines; Grants list.
Application information: Formal applications are by invitation only, after review of Initial Inquiry Form. Inquiry forms may be downloaded from foundation web site. Application form required.
Initial approach: Contact foundation office to discuss nature of request and eligibility
Deadline(s): Mar. 31, June 30, Sept. 30, and Dec. 31
Board meeting date(s): Feb., May, Aug. and Nov.
Final notification: Within two weeks of Feb. meeting
Officers: John T. Rogers, Pres.; John L. Mallery, V.P.; Dwight R. Ball, Secy.-Treas.
Directors: Bruce M. Edwards; David E. Guloien.
EIN: 562313198
Selected grants: The following grants are a representative sample of this grantmaker's funding activity:
$25,000 to Catholic Charities of Broome County, Binghamton, NY, 2012. Toward the Costs of the Construction and Renovation at the Main Street Location.
$16,434 to Family Enrichment Network, Johnson City, NY, 2012. For 22 New Laptop Computers, Secure Storage Cart and Software to Computerize the GED Program.

6468
Meehan Foundation ✧ ☆
c/o T. Meehan, Meehan & Assoc., LLC
39 Broadway, 36th Fl.
New York, NY 10006-3003

Established in 1996 in NY.
Donors: Emily Souvaine Meehan; Terence S. Meehan.
Foundation type: Independent foundation.
Financial data (yr. ended 12/31/13): Assets, $10,972,928 (M); expenditures, $688,651; qualifying distributions, $569,029; giving activities include $533,500 for 14 grants (high: $270,000; low: $1,000).
Purpose and activities: Giving primarily for research in mental health, particularly bipolar research; funding also for education and human services.
Fields of interest: Education; Mental health/crisis services; Medical research, institute; Human services.
Limitations: Applications not accepted. Giving primarily in CT, Washington, DC, MA, NJ, and New York, NY. No grants to individuals.
Application information: Contributes only to pre-selected organizations.
Trustees: Emily Souvaine Meehan; Terence S. Meehan.
EIN: 137099577

6469
The Mehra Family Foundation ✧ ☆
Bowling Green Sta.
P.O. Box 73
New York, NY 10274-0073

Established in 1999 in CT.
Donor: Sanjeev Mehra.
Foundation type: Independent foundation.
Financial data (yr. ended 10/31/13): Assets, $8,548,081 (M); gifts received, $2,742,540; expenditures, $480,614; qualifying distributions, $471,585; giving activities include $471,585 for 25 grants (high: $250,000; low: $25).
Fields of interest: Higher education; Education; Human services; Religion.
Limitations: Applications not accepted. Giving in the U.S., with emphasis on CT and MA; funding also in Rutland, England. No grants to individuals.
Application information: Contributes only to pre-selected organizations.
Trustees: Karen Petersen Mehra; Sanjeev Mehra.
EIN: 134091997
Selected grants: The following grants are a representative sample of this grantmaker's funding activity:
$250,000 to Harvard College, Cambridge, MA, 2013. For general charitable purpose.
$160,000 to Harvard College, Cambridge, MA, 2013. For general charitable purpose.
$5,000 to Elon University, Elon, NC, 2013. For general charitable purpose.

6470
The Andrew W. Mellon Foundation
140 E. 62nd St.
New York, NY 10065-8124 (212) 838-8400
Contact: Michele S. Warman, V.P., General Counsel and Secy.
FAX: (212) 888-4172; E-mail: inquiries@mellon.org; Main URL: http://www.mellon.org
Knowledge Center: http://www.mellon.org/news-publications/

Trust established in 1940 in DE as Avalon Foundation; incorporated in 1954 in NY; merged with Old Dominion Foundation and renamed The Andrew W. Mellon Foundation in 1969.
Donors: Ailsa Mellon Bruce†; Paul Mellon†.
Foundation type: Independent foundation.
Financial data (yr. ended 12/31/13): Assets, $6,188,229,000 (M); expenditures, $282,423,144; qualifying distributions, $234,372,144; giving activities include $232,931,088 for 486 grants (high: $3,750,000; low: $2,900), $1,441,056 for employee matching gifts, and $100,000 for 1 loan/program-related investment.
Purpose and activities: The foundation's grantmaking philosophy is to build, strengthen and sustain institutions and their core capacities, rather than be a source for narrowly defined projects. As such, it develops thoughtful, long-term collaborations with grant recipients and invests sufficient funds for an extended period to accomplish the purpose at hand and achieve meaningful results. Institutions and programs receiving support are often leaders in fields of foundation activity, but they may also be promising newcomers, or in a position to demonstrate new ways of overcoming obstacles to achieve program goals. The foundation concentrates most of its grantmaking in a few areas: higher education, art history, conservation, museums, performing arts, scholarly communications and information technology.
Fields of interest: Museums; Performing arts; Humanities; Arts; Higher education; Environment; Public affairs.
Type of support: Program-related investments/loans; Continuing support; Endowments; Program development; Fellowships; Research; Matching/challenge support.
Limitations: Applications accepted. Giving on a national basis with some international giving, primarily focused on South Africa. No support for primarily local organizations. No grants to individuals (including scholarships).
Publications: Annual report; Grants list.
Application information: Please direct inquiries to appropriate program officers. Contact should be by writing or e-mail. Unsolicited applications are accepted but most proposals are by invitation. The program officer will provide instructions after reviewing the initial letter. Application form not required.
Initial approach: Letter
Copies of proposal: 1
Deadline(s): None
Board meeting date(s): Mar., June, Sept., and Dec.
Officers and Trustees:* W. Taylor Reveley III,* Chair.; Earl Lewis, Pres.; John E. Hull, V.P., Finance and C.I.O.; Michele S. Warman, V.P., Genl. Counsel and Secy.; Philip E. Lewis, V.P.; Mariet Westermann, V.P.; Danielle S. Allen; Lewis W. Bernard; Richard Brodhead; Katherine G. Farley; Kathryn A. Hall; Paul LeClerc; Glenn D. Lowry; Eric M. Mindich; Sarah E. Thomas.
Number of staff: 55 full-time professional; 17 full-time support; 1 part-time support.
EIN: 131879954
Selected grants: The following grants are a representative sample of this grantmaker's funding activity:
$4,407,000 to American Council of Learned Societies, New York, NY, 2013. To continue support for a program enabling non-academic organizations to appoint PhDs in the humanities to postdoctoral positions, payable over 4.50 years.
$4,000,000 to Council on Library and Information Resources, Washington, DC, 2013. For a regranting program that would provide awards for cataloging unprocessed library and archival collections, payable over 4.50 years.
$3,750,000 to New York Foundation for the Arts, Brooklyn, NY, 2013. For the New York Theater Program, payable over 2.50 years.
$3,406,350 to United Negro College Fund, Washington, DC, 2013. For the renewal of the United Negro College Fund consortium's Mellon Mays Undergraduate Fellowship program, payable over 4.00 years.
$3,000,000 to University of Illinois at Urbana-Champaign, Illinois Program for Research in the Humanities, Urbana, IL, 2013. For a collaboration of interdisciplinary humanities centers at 15 research-extensive institutions, payable over 3.00 years.
$2,000,000 to American Academy of Arts and Sciences, Cambridge, MA, 2013. To increase

endowment for ongoing maintenance and development of the Humanities Indicators, payable over 5.00 years.
$2,000,000 to New York University, New York, NY, 2013. For initiatives at the intellectual and institutional intersection of urban studies and the humanities, payable over 5.00 years.
$577,000 to Washington and Lee University, Lexington, VA, 2013. For international education initiatives, payable over 4.00 years.
$450,000 to University of California, Los Angeles, CA, 2013. For the digitization and transcription of ancient cuneiform texts from museums around the world to build a comprehensive digital library for cuneiform studies, payable over 2.00 years.
$279,100 to Duke University, Durham, NC, 2013. For a New Directions Fellowship for Professor, payable over 3.00 years.

6471
The Alice Pack and L. Thomas Melly Foundation ✧

(formerly L. Thomas Melly Foundation)
c/o BCRS Assocs., LLC
77 Water St., 9th Fl.
New York, NY 10005-3720

Established in 1969 in NY.
Donors: L. Thomas Melly; Alice Pack Melly.
Foundation type: Independent foundation.
Financial data (yr. ended 05/31/13): Assets, $5,779,236 (M); expenditures, $472,319; qualifying distributions, $462,275; giving activities include $458,190 for 51 grants (high: $200,000; low: $20).
Fields of interest: Museums (art); Arts; Elementary/secondary education; Higher education; Education; Health care; Human services; Family services; Christian agencies & churches.
Limitations: Applications not accepted. No grants to individuals.
Application information: Contributes only to pre-selected organizations.
Trustees: Alice P. Melly; David Randolph Melly; Laura A. Melly; Lee Scott Melly; L. Thomas Melly; Thomas L. Melly.
EIN: 237059703
Selected grants: The following grants are a representative sample of this grantmaker's funding activity:
$19,500 to Trinity College, Hartford, CT, 2011. For general purpose fund.
$12,000 to Rocky Mountain Institute, Snowmass, CO, 2011. For general purpose fund.
$10,000 to Hill School, Pottstown, PA, 2011. For general purpose fund.
$7,500 to Kent School, Kent, CT, 2011. For general purpose fund.
$5,000 to Metropolitan Museum of Art, New York, NY, 2011. For general purpose fund.
$5,000 to Sarasota Memorial Healthcare Foundation, Sarasota, FL, 2011. For general purpose fund.
$5,000 to Shelter for the Homeless, Stamford, CT, 2011. For general purpose fund.
$5,000 to Smith College, Northampton, MA, 2011. For general purpose fund.
$5,000 to Solar Energy International, Carbondale, CO, 2011. For general purpose fund.
$3,000 to National Outdoor Leadership School, Lander, WY, 2011. For general purpose fund.

6472
The Melohn Foundation, Inc. ✧

c/o Melohn Properties
1995 Broadway
New York, NY 10023-5882 (212) 787-2500

Established in 1965 in NY.
Donors: Alfons Melohn; Leon Melohn; and members of the Melohn family.
Foundation type: Independent foundation.
Financial data (yr. ended 07/31/13): Assets, $15,412,744 (M); expenditures, $2,606,367; qualifying distributions, $1,482,796; giving activities include $1,472,255 for 46 grants (high: $1,302,460; low: $100).
Purpose and activities: Giving primarily for Jewish agencies, temples, and schools.
Fields of interest: Elementary/secondary education; Jewish federated giving programs; Jewish agencies & synagogues.
Limitations: Applications accepted. Giving primarily in Brooklyn and New York, NY. No grants to individuals.
Application information: Application form required.
Initial approach: Letter
Deadline(s): None
Officers: Martha Melohn, Pres.; Leon Melohn, V.P.; Alfons Melohn, Secy.
EIN: 136197827
Selected grants: The following grants are a representative sample of this grantmaker's funding activity:
$752,100 to Agudath Israel of America, New York, NY, 2011.
$21,250 to Manhattan Day School, New York, NY, 2011.
$10,625 to Bikur Cholim of Manhattan, New York, NY, 2011.
$10,000 to Chabad, New York, NY, 2011.
$8,500 to Congregation Yetev Lev, Brooklyn, NY, 2011.
$5,000 to Bonei Olam, Brooklyn, NY, 2011.
$5,000 to Chai Lifeline, New York, NY, 2011.
$2,500 to Ahavas Chesed, Brooklyn, NY, 2011.
$1,800 to American Friends of Yad Eliezer, Brooklyn, NY, 2011.
$1,700 to Yeshiva Torah Vodaath, Brooklyn, NY, 2011.

6473
The Robert and Joyce Menschel Family Foundation ✧

(formerly The Robert and Joyce Menschel Foundation)
c/o BRCS Assocs., LLC
77 Water St., 9th Fl.
New York, NY 10005-4401

Established in 1958 in NY.
Donor: Robert B. Menschel.
Foundation type: Independent foundation.
Financial data (yr. ended 10/31/13): Assets, $22,544,321 (M); expenditures, $1,049,412; qualifying distributions, $1,044,787; giving activities include $1,039,277 for 169 grants (high: $159,000; low: $100).
Fields of interest: Arts; Higher education; Hospitals (general); Human services.
Limitations: Applications not accepted. Giving on a national basis. No grants to individuals.
Application information: All grants initiated by the foundation.
Officers: Robert B. Menschel, Pres.; Joyce F. Menschel, V.P. and Secy.
Directors: Henry Christensen III; David F. Menschel; Lauren E. Menschel.
Number of staff: None.
EIN: 136098443

6474
Mercer Family Foundation ✧

240 Riverside Blvd., Apt. 24A
New York, NY 10069-1024

Established in 2004 in NY.
Donor: Robert Mercer.
Foundation type: Independent foundation.
Financial data (yr. ended 12/31/12): Assets, $37,625,310 (M); gifts received, $4,003,629; expenditures, $11,702,665; qualifying distributions, $11,677,197; giving activities include $11,677,197 for 22 grants (high: $3,000,000; low: $2,905).
Purpose and activities: Giving primarily for human services, public policy organizations, health organizations, and to a media research center.
Fields of interest: Media/communications; Health organizations; Human services; Foundations (private grantmaking); Social sciences, public policy.
Limitations: Applications not accepted. Giving primarily in IL, NY, TX, and VA. No grants to individuals.
Application information: Contributes only to pre-selected organizations.
Director: Rebekah Mercer.
EIN: 201982204
Selected grants: The following grants are a representative sample of this grantmaker's funding activity:
$2,186,215 to State University of New York at Stony Brook, Stony Brook, NY, 2011.
$1,800,000 to Media Research Center, Reston, VA, 2011.
$1,000,000 to George W. Bush Foundation, Dallas, TX, 2011.
$965,000 to Oregon Institute of Science and Medicine, Cave Junction, OR, 2011.
$444,000 to Heartland Institute, Chicago, IL, 2011.
$250,000 to Illinois Policy Institute, Chicago, IL, 2011.
$100,000 to Barry Goldwater Institute for Public Policy Research, Phoenix, AZ, 2011.
$100,000 to Manhattan Institute for Policy Research, New York, NY, 2011.
$85,000 to Special Operations Warrior Foundation, Tampa, FL, 2011.
$50,000 to Council for National Policy, Washington, DC, 2011.

6475
The Sue and Eugene Mercy, Jr. Foundation, Inc. ✧

c/o BCRS Associates, LLC
77 Water St., 9th Fl.
New York, NY 10005-4401

Established in 1967 in NY.
Donor: Eugene Mercy, Jr.
Foundation type: Independent foundation.
Financial data (yr. ended 12/31/13): Assets, $5,141,931 (M); expenditures, $628,957; qualifying distributions, $593,369; giving activities

include $592,075 for 116 grants (high: $58,910; low: $100).
Purpose and activities: Giving primarily for the arts, education, environmental conservation, hospitals and health organizations, and human services.
Fields of interest: Museums; Performing arts; Education; Environment, natural resources; Hospitals (general); Health organizations, association; Human services; Jewish agencies & synagogues.
Limitations: Applications not accepted. Giving primarily in New York, NY. No grants to individuals.
Application information: Contributes only to pre-selected organizations.
Officers: Eugene Mercy, Jr., Pres.; Robert E. Mnuchin, Secy.
Directors: Aaron Daniels; Andrew Seth Mercy; Eugene Mercy III.
EIN: 136217050
Selected grants: The following grants are a representative sample of this grantmaker's funding activity:
$50,000 to Beth Israel Medical Center, New York, NY, 2011.
$25,000 to Humanity in Action, New York, NY, 2011.
$25,000 to Publicolor, New York, NY, 2011.
$15,000 to Central Park Conservancy, New York, NY, 2011.
$15,000 to Loomis Chaffee School, Windsor, CT, 2011.
$15,000 to Museum of Modern Art, New York, NY, 2011.
$10,000 to New York Service for the Handicapped, New York, NY, 2011.
$2,630 to Central Synagogue, New York, NY, 2011.
$2,500 to American Jewish Committee, New York, NY, 2011.
$2,500 to Bachmann-Strauss Dystonia and Parkinson Foundation, New York, NY, 2011.

6476
The Meringoff Family Foundation, Inc. ✧

c/o Meringoff Equities
30 W. 26th St.
New York, NY 10010-2011

Established in 2007 in NY.
Donor: Stephen J. Meringoff.
Foundation type: Independent foundation.
Financial data (yr. ended 12/31/13): Assets, $1,738,496 (M); gifts received, $119,517; expenditures, $1,298,444; qualifying distributions, $1,285,647; giving activities include $1,273,300 for 30 grants (high: $202,500; low: $500).
Fields of interest: Performing arts; Education; Health organizations.
Limitations: Applications not accepted. Giving primarily in NY. No grants to individuals.
Application information: Contributes only to pre-selected organizations.
Officer: Stephen J. Meringoff, Pres.
EIN: 208968264

6477
Mertz Gilmore Foundation ✧

(formerly Joyce Mertz-Gilmore Foundation)
218 E. 18th St.
New York, NY 10003-3694 (212) 475-1137
Contact: Jay Beckner, Pres.
FAX: (212) 777-5226;
E-mail: info@mertzgilmore.org; Main URL: http://www.mertzgilmore.org
Grants List: http://www.mertzgilmore.org/index.php/programs/grants-lists
LinkedIn: http://www.linkedin.com/company/mertz-gilmore-foundation?goback=.cps_1286206604270_1

Incorporated in 1959 in NY.
Donors: Robert Gilmore‡; Joyce Mertz‡.
Foundation type: Independent foundation.
Financial data (yr. ended 12/31/13): Assets, $125,045,056 (M); gifts received, $3,200,000; expenditures, $8,548,950; qualifying distributions, $7,961,786; giving activities include $6,175,250 for 248 grants (high: $250,000; low: $1,000), and $300,000 for 1 loan/program-related investment.
Purpose and activities: Current concerns include human rights, the environment, and New York City cultural, social, and civic concerns.
Fields of interest: Performing arts, dance; Environment, energy; Community/economic development, equal rights; Community development, citizen coalitions; Community/economic development.
Type of support: Program-related investments/loans; General/operating support; Continuing support; Program development; Seed money; Technical assistance; Matching/challenge support.
Limitations: Applications accepted. Giving on a national basis for Human Rights; also giving in the Northeast and New York City for Climate Change Solutions, and in New York City for Dance and Communities programs. No support for sectarian religious concerns. No grants to individuals, or for endowments, annual fund appeals, fundraising events, conferences, workshops, publications, film or media projects, scholarships, research, fellowships, or travel.
Publications: Annual report.
Application information: Please submit an online inquiry letter (not a full proposal) of no more than three pages describing the mission of the organization and the purpose of the request. The online inquiry form can be found on foundation web site. Staff will respond to all communications, and, if appropriate, invite a full proposal. Do not submit videos, CDs, audiocassettes, press clippings, books, or other materials unless they are requested. The foundation accepts the New York/ New Jersey Area Common Application Form and the New York/ New Jersey Common Report Form. Application form required.
Initial approach: Online letter of inquiry submission
Copies of proposal: 1
Deadline(s): See web site for current deadlines
Board meeting date(s): Apr. and Nov. for grant decisions
Final notification: Within 2 weeks
Officers and Directors:* Mikki Shepard,* Chair.; Jay Beckner,* Pres.; Lukas Haynes, V.P.; Laura Butzel,* Secy.; Rini Banerjee,* Treas.; Larry E. Condon,* Chair. Emeritus; Elizabeth Burke Gilmore, Dir. Emerita; Jared Bernstein; Phil Radford; Andrea Sholler; Clara Torres-Spelliscy.
Number of staff: 7 full-time professional; 3 full-time support; 3 part-time support.
EIN: 132872722
Selected grants: The following grants are a representative sample of this grantmaker's funding activity:
$200,000 to Public Justice Foundation, Washington, DC, 2011. For Rotating Fund.
$160,000 to Make the Road New York, Brooklyn, NY, 2011. For general support.
$150,000 to Progressive America Fund, New York, NY, 2011. For Center for Working Families: Green Jobs / Green New York Project.
$140,000 to Fifth Avenue Committee, Brooklyn, NY, 2011. For South Brooklyn Accountable Development Initiative.
$100,000 to Brooklyn Academy of Music, Brooklyn, NY, 2011. For Dance Commissions and Presentations at BAM Richard B. Fisher Building.
$100,000 to Danspace Project, New York, NY, 2011. For general support.
$100,000 to Supportive Housing Network of New York, New York, NY, 2011. For Green Supportive Housing Initiative.
$70,000 to Pratt Center for Community Development, Brooklyn, NY, 2011. For general support.
$40,000 to Sustainable Markets Foundation, New York, NY, 2011. For general support for Eco-Accountability Project in Alexandria, VA.
$20,000 to Thelma Hill Performing Arts Center, Brooklyn, NY, 2011. For Souls of Our Feet: People of Color Dance Festival.

6478
The Mesdag Family Foundation ✧ ☆

c/o BCRS Assocs., LLC
77 Water St., 9th Fl.
New York, NY 10005-4414

Established in 1991 in NY.
Donors: T. Willem Mesdag; Goldman Sachs & Co.
Foundation type: Independent foundation.
Financial data (yr. ended 03/31/13): Assets, $16,656,308 (M); expenditures, $824,486; qualifying distributions, $608,090; giving activities include $602,340 for 35 grants (high: $250,000; low: $1).
Purpose and activities: Giving primarily for higher education and the arts.
Fields of interest: Museums (art); Performing arts, music; Performing arts, opera; Higher education; Medical school/education; Athletics/sports, water sports; International affairs.
Type of support: General/operating support; Scholarship funds.
Limitations: Applications not accepted. Giving primarily in CA; funding also in CO, Cambridge, MA, and Princeton, NJ. No grants to individuals.
Application information: Contributes only to pre-selected organizations.
Trustees: Lisa Ann Mesdag; T. Willem Mesdag.
EIN: 133651269
Selected grants: The following grants are a representative sample of this grantmaker's funding activity:
$25,000 to Northwestern University, Evanston, IL, 2011. For general purpose.
$25,000 to Northwestern University, Evanston, IL, 2011. For general purpose.
$14,650 to Los Angeles Philharmonic Association, Los Angeles, CA, 2011. For general purpose.
$10,000 to Aspen Institute, Washington, DC, 2011. For general purpose.
$10,000 to Human Rights Watch, New York, NY, 2011. For general purpose.
$10,000 to International Medical Corps, Los Angeles, CA, 2011. For general purpose.

$9,810 to Human Rights Watch, New York, NY, 2011. For general purpose.
$9,770 to Museum of Contemporary Art, Tucson, AZ, 2011. For general purpose.
$4,838 to Independence Pass Foundation, Aspen, CO, 2011. For general purpose.
$2,500 to Rape Foundation, Santa Monica, CA, 2011. For general purpose.

6479
MetLife Foundation ✧
1095 Ave. of the Americas
New York, NY 10036-6797 (212) 578-6272
Contact: A. Dennis White, C.E.O. and Pres.
FAX: (212) 578-0617;
E-mail: metlifefoundation@metlife.com; Main URL: https://www.metlife.com/metlife-foundation/
MetLife Foundation Video Gallery: https://www.metlife.com/metlife-foundation/video/index.html

Incorporated in 1976 in NY.
Donor: Metropolitan Life Insurance Co.
Foundation type: Company-sponsored foundation.
Financial data (yr. ended 12/31/13): Assets, $180,391,744 (M); gifts received, $45,000,000; expenditures, $43,455,281; qualifying distributions, $43,377,574; giving activities include $41,591,899 for 550 grants (high: $3,600,000; low: $250), $896,951 for 762 employee matching gifts, and $250,000 for 1 loan/program-related investment.
Purpose and activities: The foundation supports programs designed to empower communities and bring financial inclusion to low-income individuals and families. Special emphasis is directed toward programs designed to promote access to knowledge; access to services; and access to insights.
Fields of interest: Media, television; Museums (art); Arts; Higher education; Education, services; Education; Public health; Health care; Alzheimer's disease; Alzheimer's disease research; Food banks; Housing/shelter; Youth development, adult & child programs; Girl scouts; Youth development, business; Youth development; Children/youth, services; Family services; Human services, financial counseling; Human services; Urban/community development; Social entrepreneurship; Microfinance/microlending; Community/economic development; Financial services; Leadership development; Public affairs; Adults; Aging; Disabilities, people with; Physically disabled; Minorities; Asians/Pacific Islanders; African Americans/Blacks; Hispanics/Latinos; Native Americans/American Indians; Women; Girls; Young adults, female; Men; Boys; Young adults, male; Military/veterans; Economically disadvantaged; Homeless; LGBTQ.
Type of support: General/operating support; Continuing support; Management development/capacity building; Program development; Publication; Scholarship funds; Research; Employee volunteer services; Program evaluation; Program-related investments/loans; Employee matching gifts; Employee-related scholarships; In-kind gifts.
Limitations: Applications accepted. Giving on a national and international basis, with emphasis in CA, CT, DC, FL, IL, MA, NJ, NY, PA, TX, Brazil, India, Latin America, Mexico, Peru, and South Korea. No support for private foundations, religious, fraternal, athletic, political, or social organizations, hospitals, local chapters of national organizations, disease-specific organizations, labor groups, organizations primarily engaged in patient care or direct treatment, drug treatment centers, community health clinics, or elementary or secondary schools. No grants to individuals (except for employee-related scholarships), or for endowments, courtesy advertising, or festival participation.
Publications: Annual report (including application guidelines); Corporate giving report (including application guidelines); Financial statement.
Application information: Grant requests outside of the financial inclusion priority area are by invitation only. Application form required.
Initial approach: Complete online eligibility quiz and application for financial inclusion requests
Copies of proposal: 1
Deadline(s): None for financial inclusion grants
Officers and Directors:* Michael Zarcone,* Chair.; A. Dennis White,* C.E.O. and Pres.; Phyllis Zanghi, Counsel and Secy.; Jonathan Rosenthal,* Treas.; Robert C. Tarnok, Cont.; Frans Hijkoop; Michel Khalaf; Maria R. Morris; Oscar Schmidt; Eric Steigerwalt; Christopher Townsend.
Number of staff: None.
EIN: 132878224
Selected grants: The following grants are a representative sample of this grantmaker's funding activity:
$600,000 to Trust for Public Land, San Francisco, CA, 2012. For More Parks for More People.
$410,000 to National Association of Secondary School Principals, Reston, VA, 2012. For NASSP Breakthrough Schools Program.
$250,000 to Childrens Health Fund, New York, NY, 2012. For Healthy Kids, Healthy Smiles Initiative.
$250,000 to Generations United, Washington, DC, 2012. For Stronger Together: Developing Youth Intergenerational Entrepreneurs and Recognizing Excellence in Intergenerational Communities.
$200,000 to Partners for Livable Communities, Washington, DC, 2012. For MetLife Foundation City Leaders Institute for Aging in Place.
$200,000 to Reach Out and Read, Boston, MA, 2012. For Supporting Military Families.
$125,000 to Smithsonian Institution, Washington, DC, 2012. For Smithsonian Community Grant Program.
$100,000 to Smithsonian Institution, Washington, DC, 2012. For Black Wings: American Dreams of Flight.
$50,000 to Fifth Avenue Committee, Brooklyn, NY, 2012. For Affordable Housing, Workforce and Economic Development in South Brooklyn.
$50,000 to Partners for Livable Communities, Washington, DC, 2012. For Institutions as Fulcrums of Change: Creative Re-imagining of Community Assets to Meet the Challenges of the Next Decade.
$50,000 to Studio in a School Association, Studio in a School, New York, NY, 2012. For Art and Healthy Living.
$2,000 to Ronald McDonald House of Delaware, Wilmington, DE, 2012. For Volunteer Project Fund - Ronald McDonald House of Delaware Meal Program.

6480
Edward & Sandra Meyer Foundation, Inc. ✧
c/o Ocean Road Advisors
767 5th Ave., 18th Fl.
New York, NY 10153-0023 (212) 599-3500

Established in 1966.
Donor: Edward H. Meyer.
Foundation type: Independent foundation.
Financial data (yr. ended 12/31/12): Assets, $66,549,277 (M); expenditures, $3,720,680; qualifying distributions, $3,461,158; giving activities include $3,203,785 for 75 grants (high: $2,000,000; low: $100).
Purpose and activities: Giving primarily for Jewish agencies and federated giving programs, as well as for the arts, and education; funding also for a medical center.
Fields of interest: Museums; Performing arts, theater; Performing arts, orchestras; Arts; Education; Hospitals (general); Health care; United Ways and Federated Giving Programs; Jewish federated giving programs; Jewish agencies & synagogues.
Limitations: Applications not accepted. Giving primarily in the New York, NY, area, and PA. No grants to individuals.
Application information: Contributes only to pre-selected organizations.
Officers: Edward H. Meyer, Pres. and Treas.; Sandra Meyer, Secy.
Directors: Anthony Meyer; Margaret Meyer.
EIN: 136204325

6481
The Meyer Foundation ✧
c/o Oberfest
P.O. Box 318
Chappaqua, NY 10514-0318

Established in 1985 in NY.
Donors: George J. Ames†; Vincent Meyer.
Foundation type: Independent foundation.
Financial data (yr. ended 12/31/13): Assets, $13,754,361 (M); gifts received, $600,000; expenditures, $848,033; qualifying distributions, $800,392; giving activities include $800,000 for 3 grants (high: $400,000; low: $200,000).
Fields of interest: Higher education; Human services; Jewish federated giving programs.
Type of support: General/operating support; Research.
Limitations: Applications not accepted. Giving primarily in New York, NY. No grants to individuals.
Application information: Contributes only to pre-selected organizations.
Officers: Vincent Meyer, Pres.; Francois Voss, Secy.; Bruce Oberfest, Treas.
EIN: 133317912

6482
The Michaels Family Foundation Inc. ✧
(formerly The Lorne Michaels Foundation, Inc.)
c/o Hecht & Co. PC, Broadway Video
1619 Broadway, 9th Fl.
New York, NY 10019-7444

Established in 1990 in DE and NY.
Donors: Lorne Michaels; Broadway Video, Inc.
Foundation type: Independent foundation.
Financial data (yr. ended 12/31/13): Assets, $1,378 (M); gifts received, $452,799; expenditures, $499,731; qualifying distributions, $488,680; giving activities include $485,000 for 15 grants (high: $250,000; low: $500).
Fields of interest: Arts, alliance/advocacy; Education, fund raising/fund distribution; Higher

education, university; Education; Human services; International relief; Protestant agencies & churches.
Limitations: Applications not accepted. Giving primarily in NY. No grants to individuals.
Application information: Contributes only to pre-selected organizations.
Officers: Lorne Michaels, Pres. and Treas.; Alice Michaels, V.P. and Secy.
EIN: 133584269

6483
Middle Road Foundation ✧
(formerly The Anchorage Charitable Fund)
P.O. Box 287440
New York, NY 10128-7440

Established in 1982 in NY.
Donors: Elizabeth R. Varet; William Rosenwald Family Fund Inc.; Hudson Charitable Fund.
Foundation type: Independent foundation.
Financial data (yr. ended 04/30/13): Assets, $18,995,767 (M); gifts received, $657,412; expenditures, $1,194,394; qualifying distributions, $1,052,555; giving activities include $982,567 for 117 grants (high: $250,000; low: $150).
Fields of interest: Health organizations, association; Medical research, institute; Jewish agencies & synagogues.
Limitations: Applications not accepted. Giving primarily in New York, NY. No grants to individuals.
Application information: Contributes only to pre-selected organizations.
Board meeting date(s): As necessary
Officers and Directors:* Elizabeth R. Varet,* Chair.; Michael A. Varet,* Pres. and Treas.; Sarah R. Varet, V.P. and Secy.; David R. Varet, V.P.; Joseph R. Varet, V.P.
EIN: 133202345
Selected grants: The following grants are a representative sample of this grantmaker's funding activity:
$5,000 to Yale University, Law School, New Haven, CT, 2013. For general support.

6484
Robert & Bethany Millard Charitable Foundation ✧
(formerly Robert B. Millard Charitable Foundation)
c/o CBIZ Mahoney Cohen
111 W. 40th St.
New York, NY 10018-2506

Established in 1989 in NY.
Donor: Robert B. Millard.
Foundation type: Independent foundation.
Financial data (yr. ended 12/31/13): Assets, $20,752,046 (M); gifts received, $4,266,990; expenditures, $1,551,949; qualifying distributions, $1,542,037; giving activities include $1,522,594 for 41 grants (high: $1,002,896; low: $50).
Purpose and activities: Giving primarily for the arts and higher education.
Fields of interest: Museums; Arts; Higher education; Education; Jewish federated giving programs.
Limitations: Applications not accepted. Giving primarily in New York, NY; funding also in MA. No grants to individuals.
Application information: Contributes only to pre-selected organizations.
Trustees: Bethany Millard; Robert B. Millard.
EIN: 133566723

6485
Millbrook Tribute Garden, Inc. ✧
P.O. Box D
Millbrook, NY 12545-0128

Incorporated in 1943 in NY.
Foundation type: Independent foundation.
Financial data (yr. ended 09/30/13): Assets, $47,311,799 (M); expenditures, $1,925,189; qualifying distributions, $1,510,423; giving activities include $1,204,900 for 58 grants (high: $210,000; low: $500).
Purpose and activities: Emphasis on secondary education, church support, child welfare, hospitals, and civic projects; operates and maintains a playground and memorial park in honor of war veterans.
Fields of interest: Elementary/secondary education; Hospitals (general); Children/youth, services; Government/public administration; Christian agencies & churches; Protestant agencies & churches; Catholic agencies & churches.
Type of support: General/operating support; Capital campaigns; Scholarship funds.
Limitations: Applications accepted. Giving primarily in Millbrook and Poughkeepsie, NY. No grants to individuals.
Application information: Application form required.
Initial approach: Letter
Deadline(s): None
Officers: Oakleigh B. Thorne, Pres.; Felicitas S. Thorne, V.P.; George Whalen III, Secy.; George T. Whalen, Jr., Treas.
Trustees: Oakleigh Thorne; Robert W. Whalen.
EIN: 141340079

6486
Pierson K. Miller Trust ✧ ☆
1100 Wehrle Dr., 2nd Fl.
Buffalo, NY 14221

Established in PA.
Foundation type: Independent foundation.
Financial data (yr. ended 12/31/13): Assets, $10,585,322 (M); expenditures, $550,202; qualifying distributions, $481,040; giving activities include $481,040 for 5 grants (high: $192,416; low: $48,104).
Fields of interest: Historic preservation/historical societies; YM/YWCAs & YM/YWHAs; Protestant agencies & churches.
Limitations: Applications not accepted. Giving primarily in PA.
Application information: Unsolicited request for funds not accepted.
Trustee: M&T Trust Co.
EIN: 166552192

6487
Milliken Foundation ✧
c/o Citibank, N.A.
1 Court Sq., 17th Fl.
Long Island City, NY 11120

Trust established in 1945 in NY.
Donor: Milliken and Co.
Foundation type: Company-sponsored foundation.
Financial data (yr. ended 12/31/13): Assets, $4,626,706 (M); gifts received, $489,087; expenditures, $535,750; qualifying distributions, $492,931; giving activities include $491,000 for 19 grants (high: $150,000; low: $1,000).
Purpose and activities: The foundation supports organizations involved with arts and culture, education, muscular dystrophy, human services, and community development.
Fields of interest: Arts education; Media/communications; Arts; Elementary/secondary education; Higher education; Education; Muscular dystrophy; Boys & girls clubs; YM/YWCAs & YM/YWHAs; Children/youth, services; Human services; Community/economic development; United Ways and Federated Giving Programs.
Type of support: General/operating support.
Limitations: Applications not accepted. Giving in areas of company operations, with emphasis on SC. No grants to individuals.
Application information: Contributes only to pre-selected organizations.
Trustee: Citibank, N.A.
Advisory Committee: G. Ashley Allen; Gerrish H. Milliken; Justine V.R. Russell; Joseph M. Sailey.
EIN: 136055062
Selected grants: The following grants are a representative sample of this grantmaker's funding activity:
$150,000 to Northside Development Corporation, Spartanburg, SC, 2013. For general support.
$87,000 to Arts Partnership of Greater Spartanburg, Spartanburg, SC, 2013. For general support.
$50,000 to Charles Lea Center Foundation, Spartanburg, SC, 2013. For general support.
$50,000 to LaGrange Academy, LaGrange, GA, 2013. For general support.
$47,000 to United Way, 2013. For general support.
$20,000 to Mobile Meals of Spartanburg County, Spartanburg, SC, 2013. For general support.
$18,000 to March of Dimes Foundation, White Plains, NY, 2013. For general support.
$10,000 to Junior Achievement of Upstate South Carolina, Greenville, SC, 2013. For general support.
$10,000 to South Carolina Institute of Medicine and Public Health, Columbia, SC, 2013. For general support.

6488
Paul and Irma Milstein Foundation ✧
335 Madison Ave., Ste. 1500
New York, NY 10017-4611
Secondary contact: Irma Milstein, Dir.

Established in 1995.
Donors: Paul Milstein†; Irma Milstein; PIM Holding Co.
Foundation type: Independent foundation.
Financial data (yr. ended 12/31/13): Assets, $1,256,532 (M); gifts received, $6,100,250; expenditures, $6,170,945; qualifying distributions, $6,170,930; giving activities include $6,159,350 for 11 grants (high: $2,000,000; low: $5,000).
Purpose and activities: Giving to a public library and for education, the arts and Jewish causes.
Fields of interest: Museums; Secondary school/education; Higher education; Libraries (public); Jewish federated giving programs; Jewish agencies & synagogues.
Limitations: Applications not accepted. Giving primarily in New York, NY. No grants to individuals.
Application information: Contributes only to pre-selected organizations.

Directors: Roslyn M. Meyer; Edward Milstein; Howard Milstein; Irma Milstein; Barbara M. Zalaznick.
EIN: 133771891

6489
The Joan Mitchell Foundation, Inc. ✧
545 W. 25th St., 15th Fl.
New York, NY 10001-5501 (212) 524-0100
FAX: (212) 524-0101;
E-mail: info@joanmitchellfoundation.org; Main URL: http://joanmitchellfoundation.org/
Facebook: http://www.facebook.com/pages/Joan-Mitchell-Foundation/133626328055?ref=search

Established in 1993 in NY.
Donor: Joan Mitchell†.
Foundation type: Independent foundation.
Financial data (yr. ended 12/31/13): Assets, $274,412,544 (M); expenditures, $8,007,268; qualifying distributions, $9,242,894; giving activities include $401,925 for 16 grants (high: $25,000; low: $1,000), $1,230,850 for 76 grants to individuals (high: $75,000; low: $1,500), and $6,219,834 for foundation-administered programs.
Purpose and activities: The Joan Mitchell Foundation seeks to demonstrate that painting and sculpture are significant cultural necessities. To further this mandate, the foundation provides grants, stipends and scholarships for painters and sculptors. The foundation also seeks out avenues to meet the needs of artists such as colloquiums and workshops, classes and other resource facilities. These educational activities are to further the development of painters and sculptors. Applications are accepted only in the field of art.
Fields of interest: Arts; Scholarships/financial aid.
Type of support: Grants to individuals; Scholarships—to individuals.
Limitations: Giving in the U.S., with some emphasis on New Orleans, LA, and NY.
Application information: Grants for individual artists are awarded through nomination only. There is no open application process in this area. Application form required.
Initial approach: Letter
Deadline(s): See application form for deadlines
Officers and Directors:* Alejandro Anreus, Ph.D.*, Pres.; Tomie Arai, V.P.; Michele Tortelli, Secy.; Theodore Berger, Treas.; John Koos, Emeritus; Carolyn Somers, Emeritus; Ronald Bechet; Dan Bergman; Tyrone Mitchell; Yolanda Shashaty.
EIN: 113161054

6490
Mitsubishi Corporation Foundation for the Americas ✧
(also known as MC Foundation for the Americas)
(formerly Mitsubishi International Corporation Foundation)
655 3rd Ave.
New York, NY 10017-5617 (212) 605-2314
Contact: Joseph P. Reganato, Secy.
E-mail: mic.foundation@org.mitsubishicorp.com; Main URL: http://www.mitsubishicorp.com/us/en/csr/foundation.html

Established in 1992 in NY.
Donors: Mitsubishi Corp.; Mitsubishi International Corp.
Foundation type: Company-sponsored foundation.
Financial data (yr. ended 12/31/13): Assets, $2,389,375 (M); expenditures, $538,324; qualifying distributions, $536,175; giving activities include $520,747 for 17 grants (high: $50,000; low: $10,000).
Purpose and activities: The foundation supports programs designed to promote the physical and social environments in which we live. Special emphasis is directed toward biodiversity conservation; sustainable development; environmental justice; and environmental education.
Fields of interest: Environment, natural resources; Environment, water resources; Environment, land resources; Environment, forests; Botanical gardens; Environmental education; Environment; Human services; Civil/human rights.
International interests: Latin America.
Type of support: General/operating support; Continuing support; Land acquisition; Program development; Conferences/seminars; Research; Employee volunteer services; Sponsorships; Program-related investments/loans; Mission-related investments/loans.
Limitations: Applications accepted. Giving primarily in the Americas, with emphasis on areas of company operations; giving also in Latin America. No support for religious, political, or lobbying organizations, or discriminatory organizations. No grants to individuals.
Publications: Application guidelines; Grants list.
Application information: Application form required.
Initial approach: Letter
Copies of proposal: 1
Deadline(s): None
Board meeting date(s): Fall
Final notification: Summer
Officers and Directors:* Yasuyuki Sugura,* Pres.; Joseph P. Reganato, Secy.; Naoki Tsuruta, Treas.; Tracy L. Austin,* Exec. Dir.; Jaruki Hayashi; Katsuhiro Ito; Ryugo Izumda; Hidemoto Mizuhara; Yoshyuki Nojima; Seiji Shiraki.
Number of staff: 3 part-time professional; 1 part-time support.
EIN: 133676166

6491
The Mitsui U.S.A. Foundation ✧
200 Park Ave.
New York, NY 10166-0001
Main URL: http://www.mitsui.com/us/en/index.html

Established in 1987 in NY.
Donors: Mitsui & Co. (U.S.A.), Inc.; Intercontinental Terminals Co. LCC; Sunwise Technologies Inc.; Mitsui Foods Intl.; Mitsui Plastics, Inc.
Foundation type: Company-sponsored foundation.
Financial data (yr. ended 03/31/14): Assets, $15,564,224 (M); gifts received, $22,500; expenditures, $858,717; qualifying distributions, $769,775; giving activities include $743,305 for 161 grants (high: $48,000; low: $25).
Purpose and activities: The foundation supports programs designed to promote education; community welfare and disabled individuals welfare; and arts and culture. Special emphasis is directed toward programs designed to promote international understanding and deepen U.S.-Japan relations.
Fields of interest: Arts education; Arts; Education; Human services; International exchange, students; International affairs; Community/economic development; Disabilities, people with.
Type of support: Employee volunteer services; Conferences/seminars; Fellowships; Scholarship funds; Sponsorships; Employee matching gifts; Employee-related scholarships; Scholarships—to individuals; Exchange programs.
Limitations: Applications not accepted. Giving primarily in areas of company operations in Los Angeles, CA, Chicago, IL, and New York, NY. No support for discriminatory organizations, religious, fraternal, veterans', or athletic organizations, or political and lobbying groups. No grants to individuals (except for scholarships), or for endowments, building campaigns, advertisements, film or television productions, social events, galas, or dinner tables or tickets; no in-kind or non-monetary support.
Publications: Informational brochure.
Application information: Contributes only to pre-selected organizations.
Officers and Directors:* Mitsuhiko Kwai,* Pres.; Eric B. Campbell, V.P.; Janet E. Garland, Secy.; Anthony Pensabene,* Treas.; Glenn Clarke; Keiichi Furihata; Yoshiyuki Kawashima; Osamu Nagao.
EIN: 133415220
Selected grants: The following grants are a representative sample of this grantmaker's funding activity:
$50,000 to Council on Foreign Relations, New York, NY, 2012.
$50,000 to Scholarship America, Saint Peter, MN, 2012.
$31,250 to Scholarship America, Saint Peter, MN, 2012.
$30,000 to Council on Foreign Relations, New York, NY, 2012.
$30,000 to Partnership for New York City, New York, NY, 2012.
$18,750 to Scholarship America, Saint Peter, MN, 2012.

6492
Mizuho USA Foundation, Inc. ✧
(formerly The IBJ Foundation, Inc.)
1251 Ave. of the Americas, 31st Fl.
New York, NY 10020-1104 (212) 282-4192
Contact: Lesley Palmer, Exec. Dir.
FAX: (212) 282-4250;
E-mail: mizuho.usa.foundation@mizuhocbus.com; Main URL: http://www.mizuhocbk.com/americas/community/foundation/index.html
Grants List: http://www.mizuhocbk.com/americas/community/foundation/pdf/mizuhousafdn_2012release.pdf

Established in 1989 in NY.
Donors: The Industrial Bank of Japan Trust Co.; Mizuho Corporate Bank (USA); The Industrial Bank of Japan, Ltd.; Mizuho Securities USA Inc.; DKB Foundation.
Foundation type: Company-sponsored foundation.
Financial data (yr. ended 12/31/13): Assets, $14,513,773 (M); gifts received, $68,815; expenditures, $855,491; qualifying distributions, $782,512; giving activities include $722,902 for 35 grants (high: $123,392; low: $860).
Purpose and activities: The foundation supports organizations involved with workforce development, affordable housing, and economic development. Special emphasis is directed toward programs designed to promote the development of urban neighborhoods.

Fields of interest: Employment, training; Employment; Housing/shelter, home owners; Housing/shelter; Human services, financial counseling; Homeless, human services; Community/economic development, management/technical assistance; Community development, neighborhood development; Economic development; Community development, small businesses; Community/economic development; Economically disadvantaged.
Type of support: Continuing support; Management development/capacity building; Program development; Seed money; Technical assistance; Employee volunteer services; Employee matching gifts.
Limitations: Applications accepted. Giving limited to New York, NY. No support for discriminatory, religious or sectarian, fraternal, veterans', labor, athletic, or political organizations. No grants to individuals, or for building or construction, capital campaigns, general operating support, endowments, capital campaigns, fundraising, dinners, benefits, sporting events, journal advertising, or tickets.
Publications: Application guidelines; Grants list; Informational brochure (including application guidelines).
Application information: Concept paper should be no longer than 3 pages and may be submitted using the NY/NJ Common Area Application Form. A full proposal may be requested at a later date. Multi-year funding is not automatic. Application form not required.
Initial approach: Mail concept paper
Copies of proposal: 1
Deadline(s): 1st weekday in July
Board meeting date(s): Nov.
Final notification: Within 8 weeks following deadlines
Officers and Directors:* Merlin E. Nelson,* Chair.; Hideki Shirato,* Pres.; Koji Nishiwaki,* Secy.; Paul Dankers, Treas.; Lesley Palmer, Exec. Dir.; Leah Markham, Prog. Off.; John H. Higgs; Shinya Wako.
Number of staff: None.
EIN: 133550008
Selected grants: The following grants are a representative sample of this grantmaker's funding activity:
$100,000 to Nonprofit Finance Fund, New York, NY, 2012. For New York City Community Resilience Fund.
$76,000 to Financial Clinic, New York, NY, 2012. For New Ground: A Foundation to Build Wealth Pilot Program.
$75,000 to Center for New York City Neighborhoods, New York, NY, 2012. For Housing Mobility Pilot Program.
$75,000 to Womens Housing and Economic Development Corporation, Bronx, NY, 2012. For Childcare Improvement Project.
$50,000 to New York City Workforce Development Fund, New York, NY, 2012. For New York Alliance for Careers in Healthcare.
$50,000 to Trust for Public Land, New York, NY, 2012. For New York City Playgrounds Program.
$40,000 to Pratt Center for Community Development, Brooklyn, NY, 2012. For Retrofit Block by Block: Standardizing Retrofits in NYC's Small Homes.
$35,000 to ACCION East, New York, NY, 2012. For Certified Credit Counselor Pilot Program.

6493
Mnuchin Foundation ✧
c/o BCRS Associates, LLC
77 Water St., 9th Fl.
New York, NY 10005

Established in 1980 in NY.
Donors: Robert E. Mnuchin; C&M Arts LP.
Foundation type: Independent foundation.
Financial data (yr. ended 04/30/13): Assets, $9,215,959 (M); expenditures, $667,382; qualifying distributions, $552,641; giving activities include $552,641 for grants.
Purpose and activities: Giving primarily for the arts, education, hospitals, human services, and Jewish organizations.
Fields of interest: Arts; Education; Hospitals (general); Human services; Jewish federated giving programs.
Limitations: Applications not accepted. Giving primarily in New York, NY. No grants to individuals.
Application information: Contributes only to pre-selected organizations.
Officer and Trustees:* Robert E. Mnuchin,* Secy.; Eugene Mercy, Jr.; Adriana Mnuchin.
EIN: 133050751
Selected grants: The following grants are a representative sample of this grantmaker's funding activity:
$1,000 to Student Advocacy, Elmsford, NY, 2013. For All Contributions Were Made to the general purposes Fund of Public Charitable Organizations That Were Classified Under Section 501(c)(3) of the Internal Revenue Code.

6494
The Steven and Heather Mnuchin Foundation ✧
(formerly The Steven T. Mnuchin Foundation)
c/o BCRS Assocs., LLC
77 Water St., 9th Fl.
New York, NY 10005-4401

Established in 1996 in NY.
Donors: Steven T. Mnuchin; Heather Mnuchin.
Foundation type: Independent foundation.
Financial data (yr. ended 11/30/13): Assets, $5,901,714 (M); gifts received, $550,000; expenditures, $597,485; qualifying distributions, $589,235; giving activities include $587,100 for 35 grants (high: $100,000; low: $75).
Purpose and activities: Giving primarily for the arts, education, hospitals, social services, and Jewish organizations and temples.
Fields of interest: Museums; Museums (art); Arts; Education; Hospitals (general); Cancer research; Food services; Jewish agencies & synagogues.
Limitations: Applications not accepted. Giving primarily in CA and NY. No grants to individuals; no loans or scholarships.
Application information: Contributes only to pre-selected organizations.
Trustees: Heather Crosby Mnuchin; Robert E. Mnuchin; Steven T. Mnuchin.
EIN: 133990500

6495
Leo Model Foundation, Inc. ✧
c/o Peter Model
500 E. 63rd St., No. 24K
New York, NY 10065-7946
Additional address: c/o Model Entities, 1500 Walnut St., Ste. 1300, Philadelphia, PA 19103

Established in 1970 in NY.
Donors: Model Charitable Lead Trust; Jane and Leo Model Foundation; Leo Model‡.
Foundation type: Independent foundation.
Financial data (yr. ended 12/31/13): Assets, $46,557,215 (M); expenditures, $2,449,505; qualifying distributions, $2,245,867; giving activities include $2,215,229 for 154 grants (high: $200,000; low: $250).
Purpose and activities: Support for museums and the arts, secondary and higher education (including colleges and universities), and public interest organizations.
Fields of interest: Museums; Arts; Higher education; Education; Environment; Human services; International peace/security; International migration/refugee issues; Public affairs.
International interests: Israel.
Limitations: Applications not accepted. Giving primarily in New York, NY, and Philadelphia, PA. No grants to individuals.
Application information: Contributes only to pre-selected organizations.
Board meeting date(s): Mar.
Officers and Directors:* Allen Model,* Chair.; Peter H. Model,* Pres.; Pamela Model,* V.P.; Marjorie Russel,* Secy.-Treas.; Roberta Gausas; Paul Model.
Number of staff: 1 part-time support.
EIN: 237084119

6496
The Mollylou Foundation ✧
c/o O'Connor, Davies, LLP
665 5th Ave.
New York, NY 10022-5305

Established in 1998 in NY and DE.
Donors: Sidney Lerner; Harriet Heilburnn‡.
Foundation type: Independent foundation.
Financial data (yr. ended 12/31/13): Assets, $14,130,681 (M); expenditures, $611,094; qualifying distributions, $611,094; giving activities include $604,108 for 7 grants (high: $344,762; low: $1,000).
Fields of interest: Higher education; Medical school/education; Health care, public policy.
Limitations: Applications not accepted. No grants to individuals.
Application information: Unsolicited requests for funds not accepted.
Officers and Directors:* Sidney Lerner,* Pres. and Treas.; Helaine Lerner,* Secy.
EIN: 134011378

6497
The Ambrose Monell Foundation ✧
c/o Fulton, Rowe, & Hart
1 Rockefeller Plz., Ste. 301
New York, NY 10020-2002 (212) 586-0700
Contact: Ambrose K. Monell, Pres.

FAX: (212) 245-1863;
E-mail: info@monellvetlesen.org; Main URL: http://www.monellvetlesen.org/
Grants List: http://www.monellvetlesen.org/monell/grants.htm

Incorporated in 1952 in NY.
Donor: Maude Monell Vetlesen†.
Foundation type: Independent foundation.
Financial data (yr. ended 12/31/13): Assets, $283,652,930 (M); expenditures, $12,342,966; qualifying distributions, $10,969,739; giving activities include $10,615,833 for 161 grants (high: $1,000,000; low: $2,500).
Purpose and activities: Giving for the improvement of the physical, mental, and moral condition of humanity throughout the world. Giving largely for hospitals and health services, scientific research, museums, performing arts, and other cultural activities, and higher and secondary education; support also for social services, research in political science, mental health, and aid to the handicapped.
Fields of interest: Education; Animal welfare; Hospitals (general); Health care; Mental health/crisis services; Health organizations, association; Alcoholism; Medical research, institute; AIDS research; Human services; Physical/earth sciences; Political science; Public policy, research; Aging; Disabilities, people with.
Type of support: General/operating support; Continuing support; Annual campaigns; Capital campaigns; Building/renovation; Equipment; Curriculum development; Scholarship funds; Research; Matching/challenge support.
Limitations: Applications accepted. Giving primarily in NY. No grants to individuals.
Publications: Application guidelines; Annual report; Financial statement; Grants list.
Application information: The foundation accepts full proposals by invitation only. Full proposals are reviewed twice yearly: June and Dec. Application guidelines for full proposals available on foundation web site. Application form not required.
Initial approach: Letter of inquiry (not to exceed 3 pages)
Copies of proposal: 1
Deadline(s): Apr. 30 and Oct. 31
Board meeting date(s): June and Dec.
Final notification: Decision within 4-6 weeks (positive responses only)
Officers and Directors:* Ambrose K. Monell,* Pres. and Treas.; Maurizio J. Morello, Exec. V.P.; Eugene P. Grisanti,* V.P.; George Rowe, Jr.,* V.P.; Kristen G. Pemberton, Secy.
EIN: 131982683
Selected grants: The following grants are a representative sample of this grantmaker's funding activity:
$625,000 to Monell Chemical Senses Center, Philadelphia, PA, 2012. For general purposes.
$350,000 to THIRTEEN, New York, NY, 2012. For General purposes.
$250,000 to Massachusetts General Hospital, MGH Cancer Center, Boston, MA, 2012. For general purposes.
$225,000 to Dana-Farber Cancer Institute, Boston, MA, 2012. For General purposes.
$100,000 to Cancer Research Institute, New York, NY, 2012. For cancer vaccine research program.
$100,000 to New York Botanical Garden, Bronx, NY, 2012. For Plant Genomics Program.
$50,000 to Kennedy Krieger Institute, Baltimore, MD, 2012. For General purposes.
$25,000 to Cooper-Hewitt Museum, The Smithsonians National Museum of Design, New York, NY, 2012. For general purposes.
$25,000 to Saint Georges School, Middletown, RI, 2012. For general purposes.

6498
The Monteforte Foundation, Inc. ✧
c/o Felix Partners
712 5th Ave., 20th Fl.
New York, NY 10019-4108

Established in 1992 in NJ.
Donors: Willem Kooyker; Judith-Ann Corrente.
Foundation type: Independent foundation.
Financial data (yr. ended 08/31/13): Assets, $23,914,646 (M); gifts received, $7,531,801; expenditures, $13,815,158; qualifying distributions, $13,797,057; giving activities include $13,764,209 for 33 grants (high: $5,000,000; low: $250).
Fields of interest: Arts; Education; Human services.
Type of support: Annual campaigns.
Limitations: Applications not accepted. Giving primarily in NJ and NY. No grants to individuals.
Application information: Contributes only to pre-selected organizations.
Officers and Trustees:* Judith-Ann Corrente,* Pres.; Willem Kooyker,* V.P.; Carmela June Bruno,* Secy.; Noah Schankler, Treas.
EIN: 223198329
Selected grants: The following grants are a representative sample of this grantmaker's funding activity:
$6,560,735 to Metropolitan Opera, New York, NY, 2012.
$5,000,000 to Baruch College of the City University of New York, New York, NY, 2013.
$3,615,620 to Metropolitan Opera, New York, NY, 2013.
$2,641,500 to Lawrenceville School, Lawrenceville, NJ, 2013.
$1,700,000 to National Mentoring Partnership, Alexandria, VA, 2012.
$1,105,000 to Princeton University, Princeton, NJ, 2012.
$1,000,000 to National Mentoring Partnership, Alexandria, VA, 2013.
$581,621 to Oliver Scholars Program, New York, NY, 2012.
$501,000 to Far Hills Country Day School, Far Hills, NJ, 2012.
$364,000 to W N Y C Radio, New York, NY, 2013.
$296,300 to Oliver Scholars Program, New York, NY, 2013.
$198,050 to Metropolitan Museum of Art, New York, NY, 2012.
$144,710 to Lang Lang International Music Foundation, New York, NY, 2013.
$140,000 to Orpheus Chamber Orchestra, New York, NY, 2012.
$57,000 to Mass Mentoring Partnership, Boston, MA, 2012.
$52,500 to Lawrenceville School, Lawrenceville, NJ, 2012.
$50,000 to Lang Lang International Music Foundation, New York, NY, 2012.
$37,200 to Delbarton School, Morristown, NJ, 2013.
$25,000 to Brown University, Providence, RI, 2013.
$15,000 to Gotham Chamber Opera, New York, NY, 2013.

6499
The Moody's Foundation ✧
c/o Mgr., Philanthropy Progs.
7 World Trade Ctr.
250 Greenwhich St., 14th Fl.
New York, NY 10007-2140 (212) 553-3667
E-mail: philanthropy@moodys.com; Main URL: http://www.moodys.com/Pages/itc003.aspx
Euro Challenge on Facebook: https://www.facebook.com/eurochallengecompetition
Euro Challenge on Twitter: https://twitter.com/eurochallenge
Moody's In The Community Video: http://v3.moodys.com/sites/products/ProductAttachments/moodys%20foundation.wmv
Moody's Mega Math Challenge on Facebook: https://www.facebook.com/m3challenge
Moody's Mega Math Challenge on Twitter: https://twitter.com/m3challenge
Moody's Mega Math Challenge on YouTube: http://www.youtube.com/watch?v=Pgcbw1sP0Lc&list=PL0C3D55F2E8B6A33B

Established in 2002 in NY.
Donor: Moody's Investors Service, Inc.
Foundation type: Company-sponsored foundation.
Financial data (yr. ended 12/31/12): Assets, $16,274,669 (M); gifts received, $10,000,000; expenditures, $4,709,188; qualifying distributions, $4,709,133; giving activities include $4,239,280 for 84+ grants (high: $801,500).
Purpose and activities: The foundation supports organizations involved with arts and culture, education, health, workforce development, hunger, housing, human services, economic development, microfinance, mathematics, economics, civic affairs, minorities, and women.
Fields of interest: Arts; Elementary/secondary education; Secondary school/education; Higher education; Business school/education; Education; Hospitals (general); Health care; Employment, services; Food services; Housing/shelter; Disasters, preparedness/services; American Red Cross; Human services; Economic development; Microfinance/microlending; Mathematics; Economics; Public affairs; Minorities; Women.
Type of support: General/operating support; Continuing support; Management development/capacity building; Annual campaigns; Equipment; Program development; Fellowships; Scholarship funds; Research; Employee volunteer services; Employee matching gifts; Employee-related scholarships.
Limitations: Applications accepted. Giving primarily in areas of company operations in San Francisco, CA, New York, NY, West Chester, PA, and London, England. No support for political candidates or lobbying organizations, fraternal, labor, religious, or similar organizations not of direct benefit to the entire community, or anti-business groups. No grants to individuals, or for travel, national conferences, sponsorships or advertising, team sponsorships, or athletic scholarships; generally, no support for general operating costs or capital campaigns.
Publications: Application guidelines; Corporate giving report; Grants list; Newsletter; Program policy statement.
Application information: Letters of inquiry should be no longer than 1 page. Telephone calls during the application process are not encouraged. A full proposal may be requested at a later date.

Multi-year funding is not automatic. Application form not required.
Initial approach: Mail or e-mail letter of inquiry
Deadline(s): None
Board meeting date(s): Quarterly
Final notification: Up to 8 weeks
Officers and Directors:* Frances G. Laserson,* Pres.; Elizabeth M. McCarroll, V.P.; Jane B. Clark, Secy.; Jeffrey R. Hare, Treas.; Mark E. Almeda; Robert Fauber; John J. Goggins; Linda S. Huber; Michel F. Madelain; Lisa Simone Westlake.
EIN: 134200757

6500
The Moore Charitable Foundation, Inc. ✧
c/o Moore Capital Mgmt., LLC
1251 Ave. of the Americas, 17th Fl.
New York, NY 10020-1104
Contact: Ann Stevenson-Colley, Exec. VP.

Established in 1992 in NY; funded in 1993.
Donors: Carl Palash; David Waddill; Moore Capital Mgmt., LLC; One to One Charitable Foundation.
Foundation type: Independent foundation.
Financial data (yr. ended 12/31/12): Assets, $54,927,450 (M); gifts received, $45,000,000; expenditures, $7,729,549; qualifying distributions, $7,726,775; giving activities include $6,740,418 for 217 grants (high: $500,000; low: $500).
Purpose and activities: Giving primarily for the arts, higher education, environmental conservation, health and human services.
Fields of interest: Arts; Education; Environment, natural resources; Hospitals (general); Health organizations; Human services.
Limitations: Applications not accepted. Giving primarily in the U.S., with emphasis on CO, Washington, DC and NY. No grants to individuals.
Application information: Contributes only to pre-selected organizations. Unsolicited requests for funds not considered.
Officers: Louis M. Bacon, Pres.; Ann Stevenson-Colley, Exec. V.P.; Lawrence M. Noe, V.P.; Paul Stimson, V.P.; Chaz Rockey, Treas.
EIN: 133741954

6501
David and Katherine Moore Family Foundation ✧
c/o D'Arcangelo Co.
800 Westchester Ave., N-400
Rye Brook, NY 10573-1301 (914) 694-4600
Contact: Katherine C. Moore, Tr.
E-mail: pwarner@darcangelo.com

Established in 1997 in NY.
Donors: David E. Moore, Sr.; Katherine C. Moore.
Foundation type: Independent foundation.
Financial data (yr. ended 12/31/12): Assets, $19,523,608 (M); gifts received, $44,598; expenditures, $1,119,477; qualifying distributions, $1,056,462; giving activities include $1,048,250 for 36 grants (high: $350,000; low: $250).
Fields of interest: Reproductive health, family planning; Human services; Foundations (community).
Type of support: General/operating support; Continuing support; Annual campaigns; Capital campaigns; Endowments; Scholarship funds.
Limitations: Applications accepted. Giving primarily in the northeastern U.S., with emphasis on NY.
Application information: The foundation generally does not accept unsolicited requests for funds. Application form not required.
Deadline(s): None
Board meeting date(s): Dec.
Trustees: Katherine C. Moore; Richard W. Moore.
EIN: 137103979
Selected grants: The following grants are a representative sample of this grantmaker's funding activity:
$350,000 to Westchester Community Foundation, Hartsdale, NY, 2012. For Moore Donor Advised Fund.
$115,500 to Westchester Community Foundation, Hartsdale, NY, 2012. For Katherine and David Moore Fund for Community Development.
$50,000 to Westchester Community Foundation, Hartsdale, NY, 2012. For Hurricane Sandy Relief Fund.
$35,000 to Planned Parenthood Federation of America, New York, NY, 2012. For America's Global Partners Program and General Support.
$20,000 to Family Care International, New York, NY, 2012. For Women's Reproductive Health.
$3,500 to Planned Parenthood League of Massachusetts, Boston, MA, 2012. For general support and Global Partners.

6502
Edward S. Moore Family Foundation, Inc. ✧
202 11th St.
Brooklyn, NY 11215-3916

Established in 2005 in NY.
Foundation type: Independent foundation.
Financial data (yr. ended 03/31/13): Assets, $20,872,226 (M); expenditures, $1,099,348; qualifying distributions, $911,200; giving activities include $911,200 for grants.
Purpose and activities: Giving primarily for social services and education.
Fields of interest: Arts; Higher education; Education; Human services; Children/youth, services; Family services.
Limitations: Applications not accepted. Giving primarily in CT and NY.
Application information: Contributes only to pre-selected organizations.
Officers and Directors:* Marion M. Gilbert,* Pres.; Roger Gilbert,* V.P.; Katrina Gilbert Millard,* Secy.; Jeffrey Z. Gilbert,* Treas.; Jane Gilbert; Louisa Gilbert.
EIN: 200249777
Selected grants: The following grants are a representative sample of this grantmaker's funding activity:
$80,000 to Inspirica, Stamford, CT, 2011. For general support.
$40,000 to Sanctuary for Families, New York, NY, 2011. For general support.
$30,000 to Womens Prison Association and Home, New York, NY, 2011. For general support.
$25,000 to Family and Childrens Agency, Norwalk, CT, 2011. For general support.
$23,500 to Childrens Aid Society, New York, NY, 2011. For general support.
$20,000 to Barnard College, New York, NY, 2011. For general support.
$20,000 to Carver Foundation of Norwalk, Norwalk, CT, 2011. For general support.
$20,000 to Clearpool, Carmel, NY, 2011. For general support.
$15,000 to Brooklyn Academy of Music, Brooklyn, NY, 2011. For general support.
$10,000 to Connecticut Center for School Change, Hartford, CT, 2011. For general support.

6503
Moore for Kids ✧ ☆
(formerly America's Children's Fund)
3792 Ridge Rd.
Cambria, NY 14094 (214) 668-8854
Contact: Robert Moore, Mgr.

Established in UT.
Donors: Kristi Moore; Robert Moore.
Foundation type: Independent foundation.
Financial data (yr. ended 12/31/13): Assets, $394,938 (M); gifts received, $750,000; expenditures, $771,371; qualifying distributions, $729,500; giving activities include $729,500 for 7 grants (high: $500,000; low: $3,500).
Fields of interest: Health care; Cancer research.
Limitations: Applications accepted. Giving primarily in CA and NY.
Application information:
Initial approach: Letter
Deadline(s): None
Officers: Kristi Moore, Mgr.; Robert Moore, Mgr.
EIN: 261557732

6504
Marion Moore Foundation, Inc. ✧
c/o Alston & Bird LLP
90 Park Ave., 12th Fl.
New York, NY 10016-1387

Established in 2004 in CT.
Foundation type: Independent foundation.
Financial data (yr. ended 12/31/12): Assets, $10,961,725 (M); gifts received, $175; expenditures, $1,611,188; qualifying distributions, $1,189,538; giving activities include $845,000 for 53 grants (high: $40,000; low: $2,500).
Fields of interest: Museums; Performing arts, music; Education; Health care; Human services; Children/youth, services.
Limitations: Applications not accepted. Giving primarily in CT and NY. No grants to individuals.
Application information: Contributes only to pre-selected organizations.
Officers and Directors:* John W. Cross III,* Pres.; John F. Baron, Secy.; Cynthia Page Cross; John W. Cross IV; Gracia T. Willis; Lois Cross Willis.
EIN: 200249695
Selected grants: The following grants are a representative sample of this grantmaker's funding activity:
$25,000 to Greenwich Hospital, Greenwich, CT, 2012. For general support of Charitable and Scientific Organization.
$25,000 to New York Botanical Garden, Bronx, NY, 2012. For general support of Charitable and Educational Organization.
$15,000 to Moore Memorial Library, Greene, NY, 2012. For Charitable and Educational Organization.
$15,000 to Multiple Myeloma Research Foundation, Norwalk, CT, 2012. For Charitable, Scientific and Educational.
$15,000 to Yale University, New Haven, CT, 2012. For charitable and educational.

$5,000 to Adaptive Sports Foundation, Windham, NY, 2012. For general support of Charitable Organization.

6505
The Tom and Judy Moore Foundation ✧

1133 5th Ave.
New York, NY 10128-0123

Established in NY.
Donors: Thomas A. Moore; Judith Livingston Moore.
Foundation type: Independent foundation.
Financial data (yr. ended 12/31/13): Assets, $1,497,309 (M); gifts received, $674,637; expenditures, $2,028,444; qualifying distributions, $2,027,500; giving activities include $2,027,500 for 14 grants (high: $520,000; low: $2,500).
Fields of interest: Elementary/secondary education; Higher education; Law school/education; Human services; Foundations (private grantmaking); Catholic agencies & churches.
Limitations: Applications not accepted. Giving primarily in IN and NY. No grants to individuals.
Application information: Contributes only to pre-selected organizations.
Officers: Thomas A. Moore, Pres.; Judith Livingston Moore, V.P. and Secy.-Treas.
Director: Mary Rose Smith.
EIN: 201258563
Selected grants: The following grants are a representative sample of this grantmaker's funding activity:
$200,000 to Hofstra University, Hempstead, NY, 2011.

6506
John E. Morgan Foundation, Inc. ✧

c/o Bessemer Trust
630 5th Ave.
New York, NY 10111-0100
Application address: c/o James R. Zigmant, Treas., P.O. Box 349, Tamaqua, PA 18252-0349

Established in PA.
Foundation type: Independent foundation.
Financial data (yr. ended 12/31/13): Assets, $76,906,051 (M); gifts received, $7,106,684; expenditures, $3,544,024; qualifying distributions, $3,495,135; giving activities include $3,325,918 for 50 grants (high: $500,000; low: $2), and $2,500 for 1 grant to an individual.
Purpose and activities: Giving primarily for higher education.
Fields of interest: Higher education; Hospitals (general); Human services.
Type of support: Scholarship funds.
Limitations: Applications accepted. Giving primarily in PA, with emphasis on Hershey and Lehigh.
Application information:
Initial approach: Letter
Deadline(s): None
Officers and Directors:* James R. Zigmant,* Vice-Chair. and Treas.; John Eddy,* V.P.; Jay R. Wagner,* Secy.; Joe Zizelmann.
EIN: 562290010

6507
Morgan Stanley Foundation, Inc. ✧

(formerly Morgan Stanley Foundation)
c/o Community Affairs
1585 Broadway, 23rd Fl.
New York, NY 10036-8200 (212) 296-3600
FAX: (646) 519-5460;
E-mail: whatadifference@morganstanley.com;
E-mail for Richard B. Fisher Scholarship Program: richardbfisherprogram@morganstanley.com; Main URL: http://www.morganstanley.com/globalcitizen/ms_foundation.html

Trust established in 1961 in NY.
Donors: Morgan Stanley Group Inc.; Morgan Stanley & Co. Inc.; Morgan Stanley, Dean Witter, Discover & Co.; Morgan Stanley Dean Witter & Co.; Morgan Stanley.
Foundation type: Company-sponsored foundation.
Financial data (yr. ended 12/31/12): Assets, $55,817,750 (M); gifts received, $4,905,673; expenditures, $9,937,056; qualifying distributions, $9,937,056; giving activities include $9,937,056 for 857 grants (high: $2,500,000; low: $500).
Purpose and activities: The foundation supports programs designed to promote children's health, diversity education, and employee community involvement.
Fields of interest: Elementary/secondary education; Secondary school/education; Higher education; Education; Hospitals (general); Health care, clinics/centers; Health care; Pediatrics; Food services; Food banks; Nutrition; Disasters, preparedness/services; American Red Cross; Human services; Civil/human rights, equal rights; Children; Youth; Disabilities, people with; Minorities; Economically disadvantaged.
Type of support: General/operating support; Continuing support; Program development; Fellowships; Internship funds; Scholarship funds; Employee volunteer services; Scholarships—to individuals.
Limitations: Applications accepted. Giving primarily in areas of company operations, with emphasis on the Phoenix, AZ, Los Angeles and San Francisco, CA, Wilmington, DE, Chicago, IL, MA, New York, NY, Columbus, OH, Philadelphia, PA, Dallas and Houston, TX, and Salt Lake City, UT, metropolitan areas; giving also to national organizations. No support for local organizations with which Morgan Stanley employees are not involved, political candidates or lobbying organizations, religious, fraternal, or professional sports organizations, or individual performing arts organizations. No grants to individuals (except for Morgan Stanley Scholarship Initiatives), or for capital campaigns or endowments, dinners, walks or runs, golf events, political causes or campaigns, or documentaries or productions.
Publications: Application guidelines; Corporate giving report.
Application information: Letters of inquiry should be no longer than 1 to 2 pages. Morgan Stanley initiates the majority of grants. Priority is given to national initiatives and those serving multiple cities across the U.S. Support for local organizations serving only one metropolitan area or state is limited to organizations with which Morgan Stanley employees volunteer and is coordinated through the Volunteer Incentive Program. Application form not required.
Initial approach: Letter of inquiry for Global Alliance for Children's Health or Richard B. Scholars Program
Deadline(s): Varies for Richard B. Scholars Program
Board meeting date(s): Mar., June, Sept., and Dec.
Officers and Trustees:* Carla Harris,* Chair.; Joan E. Steinberg,* Pres.; Matt Berke; Marilyn Booker; Charlie Chasin; Jeff Brodsky; Audrey Choi; Jeanmarie McFadden; Kathleen McCabe; Bill McMahon; Shelley O'Connor; Mary Lou Peters; James A. Rosenthal.
EIN: 261226280

6508
The William C. and Susan F. Morris Foundation ✧ ☆

c/o Cove Point Holdings, LLC
60 E. 42nd St., No. 3210
New York, NY 10165-0056 (212) 599-3388

Established in 2000 in DE.
Donor: William Morris.
Foundation type: Independent foundation.
Financial data (yr. ended 12/31/13): Assets, $9,379,240 (M); expenditures, $2,269,703; qualifying distributions, $2,265,295; giving activities include $2,265,000 for 3 grants (high: $1,250,000; low: $15,000).
Fields of interest: Performing arts, opera.
Limitations: Applications not accepted. Giving primarily in New York, NY. No grants to individuals.
Application information: Contributes only to pre-selected organizations.
Officers: William Morris, Chair., Pres. and Treas.; Susan Morris, V.P. and Secy.
EIN: 134128044

6509
Morse Family Foundation, Inc. ✧

(formerly Enid & Lester S. Morse, Jr. Foundation, Inc.)
c/o Lester Morse Co.
60 E. 42nd St., Ste. 1807
New York, NY 10165-6210
Contact: Lester S. Morse, Jr., Secondary, Contact: Enid W. Morse V.P.

Established in 1967 in NY.
Donor: Lester S. Morse, Jr.
Foundation type: Independent foundation.
Financial data (yr. ended 03/31/13): Assets, $5,734,108 (M); gifts received, $870; expenditures, $1,479,624; qualifying distributions, $1,435,425; giving activities include $1,431,025 for 208 grants (high: $250,000; low: $100).
Purpose and activities: Giving primarily for the arts, particularly museums and music schools; funding also for education, environmental conservation, and health and human services.
Fields of interest: Museums; Performing arts; Performing arts centers; Performing arts, dance; Performing arts, music; Performing arts, education; Arts; Higher education; Education; Environment; Hospitals (general); Health care; Health organizations, association; Human services; Jewish federated giving programs.
Type of support: Annual campaigns; Capital campaigns; Building/renovation.
Limitations: Applications not accepted. Giving primarily in New York, NY; some funding nationally, particularly in CT. No grants to individuals.

Application information: Contributes only to pre-selected organizations.
Board meeting date(s): Apr.
Officers: Lester S. Morse, Jr., Pres.; Enid W. Morse, V.P.; Douglas A. Morse, Treas.
EIN: 136220174
Selected grants: The following grants are a representative sample of this grantmaker's funding activity:
$7,500 to New York City Ballet, New York, NY, 2011. For general support.
$5,000 to Planned Parenthood of New York City, New York, NY, 2011. For general support.
$2,750 to New York City Ballet, New York, NY, 2011. For general support.
$2,500 to New York City Ballet, New York, NY, 2011. For general support.
$2,500 to New York City Opera, New York, NY, 2011. For general support.
$1,000 to Big Brothers Big Sisters of New York City, New York, NY, 2011. For general support.

6510
Morse Hill Foundation, Inc. ✧
20 Corporate Woods Blvd., Ste. 600
Albany, NY 12211-2396

Established in 1990 in NY.
Donors: Kathleen M. Picotte†; Michael B. Picotte; KMP Charitable Trust II; KMP Charitable Trust VI; KMP Trust II.
Foundation type: Independent foundation.
Financial data (yr. ended 12/31/13): Assets, $12,093,535 (M); gifts received, $9,430; expenditures, $558,559; qualifying distributions, $504,888; giving activities include $461,981 for 15 grants (high: $200,000; low: $5,000).
Purpose and activities: Giving primarily for education and social services.
Fields of interest: Higher education; Education; Human services; Children/youth, services; Family services.
Limitations: Applications not accepted. Giving in the U.S., with emphasis on NY, as well as some emphasis on Sheffield, MA. No grants to individuals.
Application information: Contributes only to pre-selected organizations.
Officers: Michael B. Picotte, Pres.; Margaret L. Picotte, V.P. and Treas.
Directors: Joseph M. Picotte; Michelle H. Picotte; Nicole L. Picotte; Dan Sleasman.
EIN: 223083890
Selected grants: The following grants are a representative sample of this grantmaker's funding activity:
$25,000 to Villanova University, Villanova, PA, 2012. To the Office of Learning Support Services.
$10,000 to Capital Region Youth Tennis Foundation, Albany, NY, 2012. For gift to 15-LOVE's College Prep and Leadership Training Program.

6511
Henry and Lucy Moses Fund, Inc. ✧
c/o Moses and Singer
405 Lexington Ave.
New York, NY 10174-0001 (212) 554-7800
Contact: Irving Sitnick, Pres.

Incorporated in 1942 in NY.
Donors: Henry L. Moses†; Lucy G. Moses†; Lucy G. Moses Trust; Henry L. Moses Trust.
Foundation type: Independent foundation.
Financial data (yr. ended 12/31/13): Assets, $475,013 (M); gifts received, $5,166,000; expenditures, $5,199,994; qualifying distributions, $5,178,090; giving activities include $5,166,000 for 96+ grants (high: $250,000; low: $5,000).
Purpose and activities: Support for hospitals; Jewish and other welfare funds; higher and legal education and educational programs for minorities; social service agencies, including those for youth, child welfare, minorities, the aged, and the handicapped; arts and cultural programs, including dance; and environmental concerns, including Central Park in New York, NY.
Fields of interest: Performing arts; Performing arts, dance; Performing arts, music; Arts; Higher education; Environment; Hospitals (general); Human services; Children/youth, services; Aging, centers/services; Jewish federated giving programs; Disabilities, people with.
Type of support: General/operating support; Continuing support; Annual campaigns; Endowments; Professorships; Scholarship funds; Research; Matching/challenge support.
Limitations: Applications not accepted. Giving primarily in the New York, NY, area. No grants to individuals; no loans.
Application information: Contributes only to pre-selected organizations.
Board meeting date(s): Usually in Feb., May, Aug., and Oct.
Officers and Directors:* Irving Sitnick,* Pres.; Joseph Fishman,* V.P. and Secy-Treas.; Alvin H. Schulman, V.P. and Secy.
EIN: 136092967

6512
The Mozilo Family Foundation ✧
c/o The Ayco Company, LP - NTG
P.O. Box 15014
Albany, NY 12212-5014

Established in 1997 in CA.
Donors: Angelo R. Mozilo; Phyllis G. Mozilo.
Foundation type: Independent foundation.
Financial data (yr. ended 12/31/13): Assets, $14,644,459 (M); gifts received, $690,334; expenditures, $1,259,392; qualifying distributions, $1,249,048; giving activities include $1,249,048 for 14 grants (high: $333,333; low: $10,000).
Fields of interest: Performing arts; Higher education; Hospitals (general); Catholic agencies & churches.
Limitations: Applications not accepted. Giving primarily in CA and WA. No grants to individuals.
Application information: Contributes only to pre-selected organizations.
Officers: Angelo R. Mozilo, Pres.; Christy Mozilo Larsen, Secy.; Phyllis G. Mozilo, Treas.
EIN: 954617492
Selected grants: The following grants are a representative sample of this grantmaker's funding activity:
$333,333 to Providence Tarzana Medical Center, Tarzana, CA, 2010. For general charitable purpose.
$333,333 to Providence Tarzana Medical Center, Tarzana, CA, 2011. For general charitable purposes.
$285,715 to Flintridge Sacred Heart Academy, La Canada Flintridge, CA, 2011. For general charitable purposes.
$80,000 to Mayfield Senior School of the Holy Child Jesus, Pasadena, CA, 2011. For general charitable purposes.
$52,500 to Holy Family Services Adoption and Foster Care, Los Angeles, CA, 2011. For general charitable purposes.
$50,000 to Eisenhower Medical Center, Rancho Mirage, CA, 2011. For general charitable purposes.
$25,000 to Gonzaga University, Spokane, WA, 2011. For general charitable purposes.
$10,000 to Villa Scalabrini Retirement Center, Sun Valley, CA, 2011. For general charitable purposes.

6513
Mule Family Foundation ✧ ☆
c/o BCRS Associates, LLC
77 Water St., 9th Fl.
New York, NY 10005-3801

Established in 1994 in NY.
Donor: Edward A. Mule.
Foundation type: Independent foundation.
Financial data (yr. ended 08/31/13): Assets, $17,616,210 (M); gifts received, $9,919,699; expenditures, $440,735; qualifying distributions, $431,735; giving activities include $429,050 for 37 grants (high: $200,000; low: $200).
Fields of interest: Elementary/secondary education; Higher education; Hospitals (general); Mental health, association; Cancer research; Boys & girls clubs; Human services; Protestant agencies & churches.
Type of support: General/operating support.
Limitations: Applications not accepted. Giving primarily in Greenwich, CT and New York, NY. No grants to individuals.
Application information: Unsolicited requests for funds not accepted.
Trustee: Edward A. Mule.
EIN: 133801234
Selected grants: The following grants are a representative sample of this grantmaker's funding activity:
$200,000 to Greenwich Country Day School, Greenwich, CT, 2011.
$50,000 to InMotion, New York, NY, 2011.
$25,000 to Greenwich Academy, Greenwich, CT, 2011.
$25,000 to New York University, New York, NY, 2011.
$5,000 to Greenwich Country Day School, Greenwich, CT, 2011.
$2,500 to Greenwich Academy, Greenwich, CT, 2011.
$2,500 to Teach for America, New York, NY, 2011.
$2,300 to Greenwich Academy, Greenwich, CT, 2011.
$1,000 to MFY Legal Services, New York, NY, 2011.
$1,000 to MFY Legal Services, New York, NY, 2011.

6514
The Vincent Mulford Foundation ✧
P.O. Box 635
Tuxedo Park, NY 10987-0635
Contact: Christian R. Sonne, Tr.
E-mail: info@mulfordfdn.org; Main URL: http://www.mulfordfdn.org

Trust established in 1951 in NJ.
Donors: Walter Moor†; Vincent S. Mulford†; Edith Mulford†; Donald Mulford†; Vincent S. Mulford, Jr.†.
Foundation type: Independent foundation.
Financial data (yr. ended 12/31/13): Assets, $13,400,845 (M); expenditures, $1,169,243;

qualifying distributions, $1,148,565; giving activities include $1,137,480 for 82 grants (high: $77,000; low: $500).
Purpose and activities: Giving to improve the lives of others, particularly the least fortunate. Giving for the provision of permanent and transitional housing for the homeless, and to support efforts of those at risk of losing their housing to retain it.
Fields of interest: Housing/shelter, public education; Housing/shelter, homeless; Housing/shelter; Homeless, human services; Homeless.
Type of support: General/operating support; Continuing support; Annual campaigns; Capital campaigns; Building/renovation; Emergency funds; Seed money; Matching/challenge support.
Limitations: Applications accepted. Giving limited to Boston, MA, and its western suburbs (metrowest), and New York, NY. No support for governmental organizations or advocacy groups. No grants to individuals.
Publications: Application guidelines; Informational brochure (including application guidelines).
Application information: A substantial portion of available funding is already committed to program areas long supported by family members. These include emergency services, support of micro-enterprise, and provision of educational and social tools to disadvantaged individuals. The foundation is not currently accepting proposals in these program areas from organizations that are new to the foundation. Please send proposals in duplicate. Proposals sent by fax or e-mail will not be accepted. AGM Common Proposal Form accepted. Application form required.
Initial approach: Letter or proposal
Copies of proposal: 2
Deadline(s): Mar. 1 and Sept. 1
Final notification: Early June and early Dec.
Trustees: Madeleine B. Grant; Christian R. Sonne.
Number of staff: 1 part-time support.
EIN: 226043594
Selected grants: The following grants are a representative sample of this grantmaker's funding activity:
$50,000 to American Red Cross in Greater New York, New York, NY, 2012. For Disaster Relief Fund and International Response Fund.
$50,000 to Center for Urban Community Services, New York, NY, 2012. To finance new 102 unit permanent supportive housing building in Bronx.
$35,000 to Lenox Hill Neighborhood House, New York, NY, 2012. For equipment and furniture for newly renovated Women's Mental Health Shelter in New York's Park Avenue Armory.
$35,000 to Project Renewal, New York, NY, 2012. For new residence in Bronx studio apartments for homless adults diagnosed with substance abuse disorder or mental illness.
$30,000 to Neighborhood Development Corporation of Jamaica Plain, Jamaica Plain, MA, 2012. For former nursing home to offer respite care beds for homeless people and small units for previously homeless people.
$25,000 to Find Aid for the Aged, New York, NY, 2012. For renovation of penthouse of former Woodstock Hotel to create housing units for indigent elderly.
$20,000 to New Alternatives for Children, New York, NY, 2012. To offer direct financial assistance to families with one or more medically fragile children to help secure or maintain housing.
$15,000 to Crittenton, Inc., Boston, MA, 2012. For comprehensive surveillance system at shelter for young homeless mothers.
$9,000 to Boston Rescue Mission, Boston, MA, 2012. To restore housing in danger of being condemned, thereby preventing homelessness.
$5,000 to Little Sisters of the Assumption Family Health Services, Project Hope, Roxbury, MA, 2012. For housing services program provide eviction prevention and emergency services to low-income families.

6515
Donald R. Mullen Family Foundation, Inc. ✧
546 5th Ave., 20th Fl.
New York, NY 10036-5000

Established in 2004 in NY.
Donors: Donald R. Mullen; Donald R. Mullen, Jr.
Foundation type: Independent foundation.
Financial data (yr. ended 12/31/13): Assets, $58,122 (M); gifts received, $755,997; expenditures, $1,050,593; qualifying distributions, $1,042,000; giving activities include $1,042,000 for 81 grants (high: $200,000; low: $200).
Fields of interest: Arts; Higher education; Education; Health care; Health organizations, association; Human services.
Limitations: Applications not accepted. Giving primarily in NY. No grants to individuals.
Application information: Contributes only to pre-selected organizations.
Officer: Donald R. Mullen, Jr., Mgr.
EIN: 200786906

6516
The Hilda Mullen Foundation ✧
c/o Milbank Tweed Hadley & McCloy
1 Chase Manhattan Plz.
New York, NY 10005-1413

Established in 1997 in NY.
Donors: Lois Q. Whitman; Martin J. Whitman.
Foundation type: Independent foundation.
Financial data (yr. ended 12/31/13): Assets, $8,624,383 (M); expenditures, $1,852,231; qualifying distributions, $1,827,148; giving activities include $1,822,973 for 46 grants (high: $500,000; low: $1,000).
Purpose and activities: Giving primarily for human rights, education, health services, and Jewish agencies.
Fields of interest: Higher education; Education; Environment; Health care; Human services; International human rights; Civil/human rights; Jewish agencies & synagogues.
Limitations: Applications not accepted. Giving primarily in NY, with emphasis on the metropolitan New York, NY, area; some funding nationally. No grants to individuals.
Application information: Contributes only to pre-selected organizations.
Trustees: Lois Q. Whitman; Martin J. Whitman.
EIN: 137120449

6517
The Murphy Family Foundation ✧
(formerly The Philip D. & Tammy S. Murphy Foundation)
Bowling Green Sta.
P.O. Box 73
New York, NY 10274-0073

Established in 1993 in NY.
Donors: Philip D. Murphy; Tammy S. Murphy; Goldman Sachs.
Foundation type: Independent foundation.
Financial data (yr. ended 07/31/13): Assets, $11,522,263 (M); expenditures, $501,850; qualifying distributions, $445,750; giving activities include $445,750 for 14 grants (high: $100,000; low: $250).
Fields of interest: Elementary/secondary education; Education; Hospitals (general); Health organizations, association; Crime/violence prevention, domestic violence; Human services; Salvation Army.
Limitations: Applications not accepted. Giving primarily in NJ, VA and Washington D.C. No grants to individuals.
Application information: Contributes only to pre-selected organizations.
Trustees: Philip D. Murphy; Tammy S. Murphy.
EIN: 133742910
Selected grants: The following grants are a representative sample of this grantmaker's funding activity:
$200,000 to Rumson Country Day School, Rumson, NJ, 2011. For general purpose.
$100,000 to 180 Turning Lives Around, Hazlet, NJ, 2011. For general purpose.
$100,000 to 180 Turning Lives Around, Hazlet, NJ, 2011. For general purpose.
$100,000 to Monmouth Medical Center, Long Branch, NJ, 2011. For general purpose.
$25,000 to Monmouth Conservation Foundation, Middletown, NJ, 2011. For general purpose.
$25,000 to Playwrights Horizons, New York, NY, 2011. For general purpose.
$5,000 to Boston Medical Center, Boston, MA, 2011. For general purpose.
$5,000 to College Foundation of the University of Virginia, Charlottesville, VA, 2011. For general purpose.
$1,000 to Columbia University, New York, NY, 2011. For general purpose.
$1,000 to Monmouth Medical Center Foundation, Long Branch, NJ, 2011. For general purpose.

6518
Mutual of America Foundation ✧
320 Park Ave.
New York, NY 10022-6839 (212) 224-1147
Contact: Thomas Gilliam, Chair. and C.E.O.; Theodore Herman, Vice-Chair.
FAX: (212) 207-3001;
E-mail: thomas.gilliam@mutualofamerica.com; Main URL: http://www.mutualofamerica.com/cpa/CommunityPartnershipAward
Community Partnership Award Winners: http://www.mutualofamerica.com/about/cpa2010winners.asp?pst=yes

Established in 1989.
Donor: Mutual of America Life Insurance Co.
Foundation type: Company-sponsored foundation.
Financial data (yr. ended 12/31/13): Assets, $511,270 (M); gifts received, $3,339,544; expenditures, $3,341,544; qualifying distributions, $3,341,544; giving activities include $2,839,732 for 1,196 grants (high: $432,160; low: $25).
Purpose and activities: The foundation supports organizations involved with education, and health and human services.
Fields of interest: Secondary school/education; Higher education; Education; Health care, patient

services; Health care; Disasters, preparedness/services; Girl scouts; Children/youth, services; Homeless, human services; Human services; United Ways and Federated Giving Programs.
Type of support: Employee matching gifts; General/operating support.
Limitations: Applications accepted. Giving primarily in CA, Washington, DC, GA, IL, NV, TN, TX, and WI.
Publications: Application guidelines; Annual report; Informational brochure (including application guidelines).
Application information: Proposals should be no longer than 3 pages. Application form required.
Initial approach: Download application form and mail proposal and application form to foundation for Community Partnership Award
Copies of proposal: 1
Deadline(s): Apr. 1 for Community Partnership Award
Board meeting date(s): Mar., May, June, Sept., and Nov.
Officers and Directors:* Thomas Gilliam,* Chair., Pres. and C.E.O.; Theodore L. Herman,* Vice-Chair.; William S. Conway,* C.O.O.; John R. Greed,* Sr. Exec. V.P. and C.F.O.; James J. Roth,* Exec. V.P., Secy., and Genl. Counsel; George L. Medlin, Exec. V.P. and Treas.; Diane Aramony,* Exec. V.P.; John Corrigan, Exec. V.P.; Scott Rothstein, Exec. V.P.
EIN: 133443360

6519
Mys Family US Charitable Foundation Inc. ✧ ☆

c/o M. Safra Co.
499 Park Ave., 11th Fl.
New York, NY 10022-1378

Donors: Bullion Ltd.; Jacob M. Safra; Edmond M. Safra.
Foundation type: Independent foundation.
Financial data (yr. ended 06/30/13): Assets, $19,885,382 (M); gifts received, $4,000,000; expenditures, $1,852,711; qualifying distributions, $2,519,807; giving activities include $1,345,000 for 9 grants (high: $500,000; low: $95,000).
Fields of interest: Higher education, university; Hospitals (general); Cancer; Community/economic development; Jewish agencies & synagogues.
Limitations: Applications not accepted. Giving primarily in New York, NY.
Application information: Unsolicited requests for funds not accepted.
Officers: Jacob M. Safra, Pres.; Edmond M. Safra, V.P. and Secy.-Treas.
EIN: 270521354

6520
Naddisy Foundation, Inc. ✧

c/o Invus Financial Advisors, LLC
126 E. 56th St., 20th Fl.
New York, NY 10022-3613

Established in 2002 in NY.
Donor: Sacha Lainovic.
Foundation type: Independent foundation.
Financial data (yr. ended 12/31/13): Assets, $21,626,991 (M); expenditures, $2,807,449; qualifying distributions, $2,782,316; giving activities include $2,782,316 for 8 grants (high: $1,342,316; low: $10,000).
Purpose and activities: Giving primarily for higher education, health, and human services.
Fields of interest: Secondary school/education; Higher education; Education; Cancer; Medical research, institute; Human services; Catholic agencies & churches.
Limitations: Applications not accepted. Giving in the U.S., with emphasis on NY. No grants to individuals.
Application information: Contributes only to pre-selected organizations.
Officers and Director:* Sacha Lainovic,* Pres.; Rebecca Lainovic, Secy.-Treas.
EIN: 050544092

6521
Paul S. Nadler Family Charitable Trust ✧

247 W. 87th St., Ste. 4J
New York, NY 10024-2848

Established in 2001 in NJ.
Donor: Paul S. Nadler†.
Foundation type: Independent foundation.
Financial data (yr. ended 12/31/13): Assets, $16,982,352 (M); expenditures, $1,050,402; qualifying distributions, $817,500; giving activities include $817,500 for 65 grants (high: $72,500; low: $500).
Fields of interest: Human services; Jewish agencies & synagogues.
Limitations: Applications not accepted. Giving primarily in NY. No grants to individuals.
Application information: Contributes only to pre-selected organizations.
Trustees: Beverly Nadler; David Nadler; Julie Nadler; Saul Nadler; Saul Nadler.
EIN: 226886319

6522
Nakash Family Foundation ✧

c/o Jordache Enterprises Inc.
1400 Broadway, 14th Fl.
New York, NY 10018-5300

Established in 1984 in NY.
Donors: Jordache Ltd.; Jordache Enterprises, Inc.; Nakash Holding LLC.
Foundation type: Company-sponsored foundation.
Financial data (yr. ended 12/31/12): Assets, $1,380,994 (M); gifts received, $950,000; expenditures, $1,159,186; qualifying distributions, $1,086,193; giving activities include $1,086,193 for grants.
Purpose and activities: The foundation supports organizations involved with theological education and Judaism.
Fields of interest: Jewish agencies & synagogues; Religion.
Type of support: General/operating support.
Limitations: Applications not accepted. No grants to individuals.
Application information: Unsolicited requests for funds not accepted.
Officers: Joseph Nakash, Pres.; Avi Nakash, V.P.; Ralph Nakash, Secy.-Treas.
EIN: 133030267

6523
The Naomi Prawer Kadar Foundation, Inc ✧ ☆

5 Woodland Ct.
Bedford, NY 10506-2034 (212) 574-6170
E-mail: grants@naomi.org; Additional email: info@naomi.org; Main URL: http://www.naomi.org

Established in NY.
Donor: Avraham Kadar.
Foundation type: Independent foundation.
Financial data (yr. ended 06/30/13): Assets, $41,436 (M); gifts received, $1,690,460; expenditures, $1,665,715; qualifying distributions, $1,517,827; giving activities include $1,517,827 for 10 grants (high: $400,000; low: $3,600).
Purpose and activities: The foundation supports Jewish culture, Jewish educational growth and Yiddish-language learning. The foundation also supports the training of the next generation of teachers in all fields and to inspire youth and learners of all ages, as well as it supports medical advances specifically in the field of oncology.
Fields of interest: Teacher school/education; Education; Medical research; Jewish agencies & synagogues.
Application information: Refer to foundation web site for specific application opportunities and deadlines.
Officers: Avraham Kadar, M.D., Pres.; Einat Kadar, V.P.; Maya Kadar, V.P.; Nadav Kadar, V.P.
EIN: 273144255

6524
NAON, Inc. ✧

477 Madison Ave., 10th Fl.
New York, NY 10022-5841

Established in 2000 in NY and DE.
Donor: Susan R. Wexner.
Foundation type: Independent foundation.
Financial data (yr. ended 12/31/13): Assets, $28,057,603 (M); expenditures, $1,315,647; qualifying distributions, $1,219,799; giving activities include $1,211,203 for 28 grants (high: $303,000; low: $22).
Purpose and activities: Giving primarily for Jewish education, temples, and organizations.
Fields of interest: Higher education; Education; Jewish agencies & synagogues.
International interests: Israel.
Limitations: Applications not accepted. Giving primarily in New York, NY, and Israel. No grants to individuals.
Application information: Contributes only to pre-selected organizations.
Officer and Directors:* Susan R. Wexner,* Pres. and Secy.-Treas.; Saul G. Agus; Raymond Kanner; Gregg H. Levy, Esq.; Michael S. Oberman, Esq.; Mark Saks, Esq.; Walter Stern.
EIN: 134099539

6525
Nash Family Foundation

25 W. 45th St., Ste. 1400
New York, NY 10036-4902
Contact: Judith Ginsberg, Exec. Dir.
E-mail: info@nashff.org; Additional e-mail: judith@nashff.org

Established in 1964 in NY.

Donors: Jack Nash‡; Leon Levy‡; Helen Nash.
Foundation type: Independent foundation.
Financial data (yr. ended 06/30/13): Assets, $47,164,915 (M); expenditures, $10,733,144; qualifying distributions, $10,295,809; giving activities include $9,591,810 for 253 grants (high: $1,000,000; low: $18).
Purpose and activities: Support primarily for underserved Jewish populations, arts and culture, health care organizations.
Fields of interest: Arts; Elementary/secondary education; Theological school/education; Human services; Jewish agencies & synagogues; Adults; Aging; Young adults; Disabilities, people with; Physically disabled; Mentally disabled; Economically disadvantaged.
International interests: Israel.
Type of support: Program development; General/operating support; Management development/capacity building; Building/renovation; Seed money.
Limitations: Applications accepted. Giving primarily in New York, NY and Israel. No support for political organizations. No grants to individuals or for conferences.
Application information: All doctors, fellows, medical professionals, fiscal sponsors, and other interested parties should please note the discontinuation of the Nash Family Foundation Medical Training Fellowship Program and the Fellowship program. No further applications will be accepted for this program. Application form not required.
Initial approach: Telephone, letter or e-mail
Copies of proposal: 2
Deadline(s): None
Board meeting date(s): Throughout the year
Final notification: 6 months
Officers and Directors:* Helen Nash,* Chair.; Joshua Nash, Pres.; Pamela Rohr, Exec. V.P.; Morris H. Rosenthal, Secy.-Treas.; Judith Ginsberg, Exec. Dir.; Todd Lang, Tr.
Number of staff: 1 full-time professional; 1 part-time professional; 1 full-time support.
EIN: 136168559
Selected grants: The following grants are a representative sample of this grantmaker's funding activity:
$1,000,000 to North Shore-Long Island Jewish Health System, Westbury, NY, 2013. For CLL (chronic lymphocytic leukemia) Clinical and Basic Research Programs.
$1,000,000 to Ramaz School, New York, NY, 2013. For Ramaz/KJ 2010 Fund.
$500,000 to UJA-Federation of New York, New York, NY, 2013. For Capital Campaign for Jewish Homes.
$250,000 to M.Y. Keren Hashluchim, Brooklyn, NY, 2013. For Passover.
$100,000 to Dorot, New York, NY, 2013. For Homeless Prevention Program, Wellness program, and other work.
$63,000 to Foundation for Jewish Culture, New York, NY, 2013. For Scholarships.
$51,200 to Metropolitan Council on Jewish Poverty, New York, NY, 2013. For Feinberg Senior Residence.
$19,850 to Friends of ELIYA-USA, Westlake Village, CA, 2013. For Purchase of Tech Equipment for Israel Association for the Advancement of Blind and Visually Impaired Children.
$11,667 to American Friends of Hala, Cleveland Heights, OH, 2013. For Maintenance Fund.
$10,000 to Friends of the Israel Antiquities Authoritity, New York, NY, 2013. For Lod Mosaic Exhibition Berlin.

6526
National Fuel Gas Company Foundation ✧
6363 Main St.
Williamsville, NY 14221-5855 (716) 857-7861
Contact: Emily L. Ciraolo
E-mail: ciraoloe@natfuel.com

Established in NY.
Donor: National Fuel Gas Company.
Foundation type: Company-sponsored foundation.
Financial data (yr. ended 09/30/13): Assets, $1,692,896 (M); gifts received, $1,000,025; expenditures, $839,038; qualifying distributions, $839,038; giving activities include $838,782 for 1,627 grants (high: $70,000; low: $25).
Purpose and activities: The foundation matches contributions made by its employees to nonprofit organizations; also a small number of grants on a case by case basis. Special emphasis is directed toward programs that promote community development. Support is limited to areas of company operations in western New York and northwestern Pennsylvania.
Fields of interest: Health organizations; Human services; Community/economic development.
Type of support: Annual campaigns; Capital campaigns; Scholarship funds.
Limitations: Applications accepted. Giving limited to areas of company operations in western NY and northwestern PA. No support for political organizations or candidates, sports teams, or religious or sectarian organizations. No grants to individuals or for lobbying efforts.
Application information: Application form required.
Initial approach: Completed application form
Copies of proposal: 1
Deadline(s): None
Board meeting date(s): Quarterly
Officers and Directors:* David F. Smith,* Pres.; Paula M. Ciprich,* V.P. and Secy.; D.L. DeCarolis,* V.P. and Treas.; A.M. Cellino,* V.P.; Ronald J. Tanski,* V.P.; C.M. Carlotti.
EIN: 201860605
Selected grants: The following grants are a representative sample of this grantmaker's funding activity:
$25,000 to Kaleida Health Foundation, Buffalo, NY, 2011.
$25,000 to Urban League of Buffalo, Buffalo, NY, 2011.
$6,000 to Boys and Girls Club of Erie, Erie, PA, 2011.
$5,000 to American Cancer Society, Atlanta, GA, 2011.
$5,000 to Elk Regional Health System, Saint Marys, PA, 2011.
$5,000 to Erie Art Museum, Erie, PA, 2011.
$5,000 to Gannon University, Erie, PA, 2011.
$4,904 to United Way of Erie County, Erie, PA, 2011.
$4,627 to Catholic Charities of Buffalo, Buffalo, NY, 2011.
$2,081 to PXE International, Washington, DC, 2011.

6527
The National Grid Foundation ✧
(formerly The KeySpan Foundation)
175 E. Old Country Rd.
Hicksville, NY 11801-4257 (516) 545-5147
Contact: Robert G. Keller, Exec. Dir.
FAX: (516) 545-6094; Main URL: http://www2.nationalgridus.com/corpinfo/community/foundation_all.jsp

Established in 1998 in NY.
Donors: MarketSpan Corp.; KeySpan Corp.
Foundation type: Company-sponsored foundation.
Financial data (yr. ended 12/31/12): Assets, $31,230,911 (M); expenditures, $1,781,209; qualifying distributions, $1,293,300; giving activities include $1,293,300 for grants.
Purpose and activities: The foundation supports organizations involved with education and the environment.
Fields of interest: Elementary/secondary education; Higher education; Scholarships/financial aid; Education; Environment, natural resources; Environment, beautification programs; Environment; United Ways and Federated Giving Programs.
Type of support: Program development; Scholarship funds.
Limitations: Applications accepted. Giving primarily in areas of company operations in MA and Brooklyn, Long Island, Nassau, Queens, and Staten Island, NY. No support for religious, political, or fraternal organizations. No grants to individuals, or for capital campaigns or endowments, advertisements, or tables or tickets at dinners or other functions.
Publications: Application guidelines; Annual report.
Application information: Support is limited to 1 contribution per organization during any given year. Application form required.
Initial approach: Complete online eligibility quiz and application
Copies of proposal: 1
Deadline(s): Oct. 31
Board meeting date(s): Quarterly
Final notification: 60 to 90 days
Officers and Directors:* Basil A. Paterson,* Chair.; Donald H. Elliot,* Vice-Chair.; Albert Wiltshire, Vice-Chair.; Robert G. Keller, Pres.; Jean T. Tesoriero, Secy.; Michael J. Taunton,* Treas.; Stephen W. McCaffrey, Chief Counsel; Robert B. Catell; Eileen R. Cohen; Susan M. Crossett; Carmen Fields; George Mayhew; Rev. Gary V. Simpson.
Number of staff: 1 full-time professional; 1 full-time support.
EIN: 113466416

6528
National Hockey League Foundation ✧
1185 Ave. of the Americas, 15th Fl.
New York, NY 10036-2601

Established in 1991 in NY.
Donors: National Hockey League; Athletic Sport Fund of America; Norwalk Police Union Show Fund; Richmond Hockey Fights Cancer; United Charitable Programs.
Foundation type: Company-sponsored foundation.
Financial data (yr. ended 06/30/13): Assets, $2,338,911 (M); gifts received, $414,357; expenditures, $670,783; qualifying distributions, $659,200; giving activities include $503,437 for 103 grants (high: $50,000; low: $300).
Purpose and activities: The foundation supports museums and organizations involved with education, health, cancer, sports, and children and youth.
Fields of interest: Museums; Education; Hospitals (general); Health care, clinics/centers; Health care, patient services; Health care; Cancer; Athletics/sports, amateur leagues; Athletics/sports, winter

sports; Boy scouts; Children/youth, services; Jewish federated giving programs.
Type of support: General/operating support; Equipment; Sponsorships; Program development; Scholarship funds.
Limitations: Applications not accepted. Giving primarily in CA, CO, MA, MI, NC, and NY. No grants to individuals.
Application information: Contributes only to pre-selected organizations.
Officers: William Daly, Pres.; Bernadette Mansur, V.P. and Secy.; Craig C. Harnett, Treas.
Directors: Joseph De Sousa; David Zimmerman.
EIN: 133498589
Selected grants: The following grants are a representative sample of this grantmaker's funding activity:
$205,000 to Companions in Courage Foundation, Huntington, NY, 2011.
$100,000 to Leukemia & Lymphoma Society, White Plains, NY, 2011.
$40,000 to Autism Speaks, New York, NY, 2011. For fundraiser.
$15,000 to Childrens Hospital of Pittsburgh Foundation, Pittsburgh, PA, 2011.
$10,000 to Friends of Independent Schools and Better Education, Tacoma, WA, 2011.
$10,000 to Kevin Guest House, Buffalo, NY, 2011.
$10,000 to UJA-Federation of New York, New York, NY, 2011.
$10,000 to USA Hockey Foundation, Colorado Springs, CO, 2011. For sponsorship.
$7,500 to Boys Club of New York, New York, NY, 2011. For fundraiser.
$5,000 to Friends of Kids With Cancer, Saint Louis, MO, 2011.

6529
National Mah Jongg League Foundation, Inc. ✧
c/o Samuel Greenberg & Co.
1430 Broadway, No. 1615
New York, NY 10018-3356

Established in 1995 in NY.
Donor: National Mah Jongg League, Inc.
Foundation type: Independent foundation.
Financial data (yr. ended 02/28/13): Assets, $0 (M); gifts received, $700,000; expenditures, $629,054; qualifying distributions, $624,250; giving activities include $624,250 for 12 grants (high: $495,250; low: $1,000).
Purpose and activities: Giving primarily for health organizations, particularly a children's hospital.
Fields of interest: Hospitals (specialty); Health organizations; Children/youth, services.
Limitations: Applications not accepted. Giving in the U.S. with emphasis on NY. No grants to individuals.
Application information: Unsolicited requests for funds not accepted.
Officers: David Unger, Pres.; Larry Unger, V.P.; Ruth Unger, V.P.; Marilyn Starr, Secy.; Norman Greenberg, Treas.
EIN: 133791092

6530
Nazarian Family Foundation ✧ ☆
c/o Marks Paneth LLP
88 Froehlich Farm Blvd.
Woodbury, NY 11797

Established in 1987 in NJ.
Donors: Nazar Nazarian; Artemis Nazarian; Seta Albrecht; Levon Nazarian.
Foundation type: Independent foundation.
Financial data (yr. ended 11/30/13): Assets, $8,247,915 (M); gifts received, $377,000; expenditures, $1,585,661; qualifying distributions, $1,566,750; giving activities include $1,565,000 for 30 grants (high: $1,391,100; low: $100).
Purpose and activities: Giving primarily for higher education and to Armenian organizations.
Fields of interest: Higher education; Education; Ethnic studies.
International interests: Armenia.
Limitations: Applications not accepted. Giving primarily in NY. No grants to individuals.
Application information: Unsolicited requests for funds not accepted.
Directors: Seta Albrecht; Artemis Nazarian; Levon Nazarian; Nazar Nazarian.
EIN: 112889824
Selected grants: The following grants are a representative sample of this grantmaker's funding activity:
$127,850 to Armenian General Benevolent Union, New York, NY, 2011.
$11,000 to Fund for Armenian Relief, New York, NY, 2011.
$10,000 to Boston University, Boston, MA, 2011.
$6,750 to Bergen Community College Foundation, Paramus, NJ, 2011.
$5,000 to Napa Valley Education Foundation, Napa, CA, 2011.
$5,000 to Saint Nersess Armenian Seminary, New Rochelle, NY, 2011.
$2,000 to Clark University, Worcester, MA, 2011.

6531
NBC Universal Foundation ✧
(formerly Universal Studios Foundation, Ltd.)
c/o NBC Universal
30 Rockefeller Plz.
New York, NY 10012-0015
Contact: Jennifer Fitzgerald
Main URL: http://corporate.comcast.com/our-values/community-investment/philanthropy-partnerships
Grants List: http://corporate.comcast.com/csr2013/2013-foundation-giving

Incorporated in 1956 in CA.
Donors: Universal Studios, Inc.; NBC Universal, Inc.
Foundation type: Company-sponsored foundation.
Financial data (yr. ended 12/31/13): Assets, $19,111,486 (M); gifts received, $3,000,000; expenditures, $2,449,831; qualifying distributions, $2,442,265; giving activities include $2,310,000 for 57 grants (high: $100,000; low: $25,000).
Purpose and activities: The foundation supports organizations involved with arts and culture, education, the environment, employment, community and economic development, and civic affairs.
Fields of interest: Arts; Secondary school/education; Education; Environment; Employment; Economic development; Community/economic development; Engineering/technology; Public affairs.
Type of support: General/operating support; Program development.
Limitations: Applications accepted. Giving primarily in CA, CT, Washington, DC, Miami, FL, Chicago, IL, New York, NY, Philadelphia, PA, and Dallas and Fort-Worth, TX. No support for private foundations or organizations with overhead expenses exceeding 15 percent of the total project budget. No grants for endowments or major equipment purchases, capital campaigns, annual fundraising events or fund drives, partisan lobbying or political campaigns or activities, individual film or television projects, sponsorship of special events, debt reduction, or religious or sectarian purposes.
Publications: Application guidelines.
Application information: Applications are only accepted for the 21st Century Solutions Initiative in August. Applying organizations must have been in existence for more than two years and have an annual operating budget of more than $300,000. Application form required.
Initial approach: Visit local NBC station websites for 21st Century Solutions Initiative
Deadline(s): June 2 to Aug. 8 for 21st Century Solutions Initiative
Final notification: Dec. for 21st Century Solutions Initiative
Officers and Directors:* Adam Miller,* Pres.; Maren Christensen,* Exec. V.P. and Secy.; Christy Rupert Shibata,* Exec. V.P. and Treas.; Elizabeth Colleton,* V.P.; Patricia Fili-Krushel; Cindy Gardner; Charisse Lillie; Craig P. Robinson; Valari Staab.
Number of staff: 2 full-time professional.
EIN: 136096061
Selected grants: The following grants are a representative sample of this grantmaker's funding activity:
$100,000 to Motion Picture and Television Fund, Woodland Hills, CA, 2011.
$50,000 to Sponsors for Educational Opportunity, New York, NY, 2011.
$45,000 to Committee for Hispanic Children and Families, New York, NY, 2011.
$37,500 to City Year, Boston, MA, 2011.
$35,000 to Lawrence Hall Youth Services, Chicago, IL, 2011.
$35,000 to Urban Arts Partnership, New York, NY, 2011.
$25,000 to Aspire of Illinois, Westchester, IL, 2011.
$20,000 to Camp Fire USA, Fort Worth, TX, 2011.
$20,000 to Hispanic Unity of Florida, Hollywood, FL, 2011.
$20,000 to STRIVE DC, Washington, DC, 2011.

6532
The NBI Foundation, Inc. ✧
(also known as The Urban Foundation USA, Inc.)
c/o Bencivenga Ward & Co., C.P.A.s PC
420 Columbus Ave., Ste. 304
Valhalla, NY 10595-1382

Established in 1985 in NY.
Donors: Johnson & Johnson Corp.; American Express Foundation; Global Initiative Partners; Tupperware Brands Corp.; Cisco; Smith Richardson Foundation Inc.; N. Colin Lind.
Foundation type: Independent foundation.
Financial data (yr. ended 06/30/13): Assets, $83,815 (M); gifts received, $1,248,602; expenditures, $1,418,054; qualifying distributions, $1,403,934; giving activities include $1,387,611 for 11 grants (high: $657,061; low: $1,050).
Purpose and activities: The foundation seeks to improve the quality of life of South African communities, particularly in an urban context, and to promote peaceful structural change in relation to fundamental aspects of community needs.
Fields of interest: Urban/community development.

International interests: Southern Africa.
Limitations: Applications not accepted. Giving primarily in South Africa.
Application information: Unsolicited requests for funds not accepted.
Officers: Lauretta J. Bruno, Chair.; Henry R. Slack, V.P.; Robert Pilkington, Secy.
Directors: Theuns Eloff; Gillian Hutchings; A.M. Rosholt.
EIN: 521402447

6533
The Nduna Foundation ✧
(formerly Amy L. Robbins Foundation)
c/o Perelson Weiner LLP
One Dag Hammarskjold Plz., 42 Fl.
New York, NY 10017-2201 (212) 605-3100

Established in 2007 in NY.
Donors: Amy L. Robbins; Larry Robbins.
Foundation type: Independent foundation.
Financial data (yr. ended 12/31/12): Assets, $5,991,629 (M); gifts received, $7,676,548; expenditures, $8,181,514; qualifying distributions, $8,172,244; giving activities include $7,934,961 for 23 grants (high: $1,175,000; low: $1,000).
Purpose and activities: The foundation focuses efforts and investments on improving the lives of children everywhere. In particular, with improved nutrition and food security; supporting those who work diligently to treat and eliminate pediatric HIV/AIDS in developing countries; supporting innovative education programs; on conservation and wildlife restoration efforts in the U.S. and in Africa.
Fields of interest: Elementary/secondary education; Education; Environment, natural resources; Health care; International development; International affairs.
International interests: Africa.
Limitations: Applications not accepted. Giving primarily in NY. No grants to individuals.
Application information: Unsolicited requests for funds not accepted.
Officer and Trustee:* Amy L. Robbins,* Exec. Dir.
EIN: 261641882
Selected grants: The following grants are a representative sample of this grantmaker's funding activity:
$1,175,000 to Human Rights Watch, New York, NY, 2012. For general support.
$1,000,000 to United States Fund for UNICEF, New York, NY, 2012. For general support.
$600,000 to Millennium Promise Alliance, New York, NY, 2012. For general support.
$593,961 to Witness, Inc., Brooklyn, NY, 2012. For general support.
$575,000 to Allen-Stevenson School, New York, NY, 2012. For general support.
$500,000 to Better World Fund, Santa Cruz, CA, 2012. For general support.
$500,000 to CDC Foundation, Atlanta, GA, 2012. For general support.
$500,000 to Mary Robinson Foundation, Dublin, Ireland, 2012. For general support.
$500,000 to Teach for All, New York, NY, 2012. For general support.
$100,000 to EngenderHealth, New York, NY, 2012. For general support.

6534
Daniel M. Neidich & Brooke Garber Foundation ✧
c/o The Ayco Co., LP, Attn.: C. Denisulk
P.O. Box 860
Saratoga Springs, NY 12866-0860

Established in 1985 in NY.
Donor: Daniel M. Neidich.
Foundation type: Independent foundation.
Financial data (yr. ended 01/31/13): Assets, $2,526,714 (M); expenditures, $2,230,681; qualifying distributions, $1,940,982; giving activities include $1,940,982 for grants.
Purpose and activities: Giving primarily for the arts, education, children, youth, and social services, medical research, and to Jewish organizations.
Fields of interest: Museums; Museums (art); Performing arts, theater; Arts; Elementary/secondary education; Higher education; Education; Medical research, institute; Human services; Children/youth, services; Foundations (private grantmaking); Jewish federated giving programs; Jewish agencies & synagogues.
Limitations: Applications not accepted. Giving primarily in New York, NY, as well as in East Hampton and Southampton, NY; some funding nationally. No grants to individuals.
Application information: Contributes only to pre-selected organizations.
Trustees: Brooke Garber Neidich; Daniel M. Neidich.
EIN: 133318126
Selected grants: The following grants are a representative sample of this grantmaker's funding activity:
$437,500 to Whitney Museum of American Art, New York, NY, 2011. For general purpose.
$300,000 to Chapin School, New York, NY, 2011. For general purpose.
$239,680 to Child Mind Institute, New York, NY, 2011. For general purpose.
$200,000 to Brown University, Providence, RI, 2011. For general purpose.
$64,767 to Whitney Museum of American Art, New York, NY, 2011. For general purpose.
$20,000 to Central Synagogue, New York, NY, 2011. For general purpose.
$15,840 to Central Synagogue, New York, NY, 2011. For general purpose.
$10,000 to Chapin School, New York, NY, 2011. For general purpose.
$4,800 to Child Mind Institute, New York, NY, 2011. For general purpose.
$2,600 to Lincoln Center Theater, New York, NY, 2011. For general purpose.

6535
LeRoy Neiman Foundation, Inc. ✧
1 W. 67th St., Ste. 303
New York, NY 10023-6200

Established in 1987 in NY.
Donors: LeRoy Neiman†; Janet Neiman.
Foundation type: Independent foundation.
Financial data (yr. ended 12/31/13): Assets, $244,227,919 (M); gifts received, $236,488,294; expenditures, $2,894,006; qualifying distributions, $2,206,970; giving activities include $1,517,755 for 10 grants (high: $600,000; low: $2,500).
Fields of interest: Arts; Higher education; Human services; United Ways and Federated Giving Programs.
Limitations: Applications not accepted. Giving primarily in IL, NJ, and NY. No grants to individuals.
Application information: Contributes only to pre-selected organizations.
Officers: Steven Bond, Pres.; Janet Neiman, V.P.; William Joseph, Secy.; James A. Purdy, Treas.
Director: Heather Byrne Long.
EIN: 133385053
Selected grants: The following grants are a representative sample of this grantmaker's funding activity:
$500,000 to School of the Art Institute of Chicago, Chicago, IL, 2012. For Leroy Neiman Student Center.
$300,000 to Arts Horizons, Englewood, NJ, 2012. For Leroy Neiman Art Center.

6536
Kanfei Nesharim Foundation ✧
156 W. 56th St., Ste. 1701
New York, NY 10019-3877

Established in 2005 in CT.
Donors: Four Ark Charitable Lead Trust; Harry Skydell.
Foundation type: Independent foundation.
Financial data (yr. ended 12/31/13): Assets, $3,047,481 (M); gifts received, $1,988,534; expenditures, $937,196; qualifying distributions, $937,196; giving activities include $879,820 for 154 grants (high: $101,100; low: $18), and $7,000 for 8 grants to individuals (high: $1,500; low: $500).
Purpose and activities: Giving primarily to Jewish agencies, temples, and schools.
Fields of interest: Education; Jewish agencies & synagogues.
Limitations: Applications not accepted. Giving primarily in NJ and NY.
Application information: Unsolicited requests for funds not accepted.
Officers: Lyudmila Koyenova, Secy.; David Camhi, Treas.
Trustee: Carey Wolchock.
EIN: 206609618
Selected grants: The following grants are a representative sample of this grantmaker's funding activity:
$52,000 to Congregation Ahavas Tzdokah V Chesed, Brooklyn, NY, 2011.
$50,850 to Yeshiva Ketana of Manhattan, New York, NY, 2011.
$40,000 to West Side Kollel Torah Center, New York, NY, 2011.
$27,900 to Jewish Communal Fund of New York, New York, NY, 2011.
$26,000 to Bonei Olam, Brooklyn, NY, 2011.
$20,000 to Mesivta Yeshiva Rabbi Chaim Berlin, Brooklyn, NY, 2011.
$19,410 to American Friends of Migdal Ohr, New York, NY, 2011.
$8,000 to Ramaz School, New York, NY, 2011.
$4,600 to Ohr Somayach International, Brooklyn, NY, 2011.
$3,600 to Keren Yehoshua V Yisroel, Lakewood, NJ, 2011.

6537
The John and Wendy Neu Family Foundation, Inc. ✧
120 5th Ave., No. 600
New York, NY 10011-5614 (646) 467-6700

Established in 1990 in NY.
Donors: Hugo Neu Corp.; Flynn-Learner.
Foundation type: Independent foundation.
Financial data (yr. ended 12/31/12): Assets, $6,800,594 (M); expenditures, $5,523,248; qualifying distributions, $5,522,250; giving activities include $5,522,250 for 46 grants (high: $1,000,000; low: $250).
Purpose and activities: Giving primarily for animal welfare; support also for hospitals and rehabilitation centers. Some giving for environmental conservation.
Fields of interest: Museums; Education; Environment; Animal welfare; Hospitals (general); Youth development.
Limitations: Applications not accepted. Giving primarily in NJ and NY. No grants to individuals.
Application information: Contributes only to pre-selected organizations.
Officer and Directors:* John L. Neu,* Pres.; Robert T. Neu; Wendy K. Neu.
EIN: 133731089

6538
The Neuberger Berman Foundation ✧
(formerly The Lehman Brothers Foundation)
605 3rd Ave.
New York, NY 10158-0180
Contact: Melissa Papini, Grants Mgr.
Main URL: https://www.nb.com/corporate_social_responsibility/

Established in 2000 in NY.
Donors: Judy Vale; Lehman Brothers Holdings Inc.; Joseph M. Gregory; LB Foundation; The Action Fund of Lehman Brothers Holdings; The Donna and Marvin Schwartz Foundation.
Foundation type: Company-sponsored foundation.
Financial data (yr. ended 11/30/13): Assets, $10,907,706 (M); gifts received, $831,510; expenditures, $1,337,904; qualifying distributions, $1,386,551; giving activities include $1,132,000 for 53 grants (high: $200,000; low: $10,000), and $96,500 for 6 grants to individuals (high: $27,500; low: $1,500).
Purpose and activities: The foundation supports programs designed to help at-risk children and youth achieve their potential through educational enrichment; and promote academic success, independence, and economic sustainability. Special emphasis is directed toward programs designed to ensure that young people receive school readiness and educational enrichment opportunities; and help older youth on that path to economic independence through job readiness, college preparedness, and financial literacy training.
Fields of interest: Museums; Higher education; Education, services; Education; Employment, services; Youth development; YM/YWCAs & YM/YWHAs; Children/youth, services; Human services, financial counseling; Children; Youth.
International interests: Africa; Asia; India; Latin America.
Type of support: General/operating support; Continuing support; Capital campaigns; Building/renovation; Emergency funds; Program development; Employee volunteer services; Program evaluation.
Limitations: Applications not accepted. Giving in the U.S., with emphasis on NY; funding also in England and India. No support for religious, political, or fraternal organizations or discriminatory organizations.
Application information: Contributes only to pre-selected organizations and individuals.
Officers and Directors: Elizabeth R. Cribbs, Pres.; Melissa J. Papini, V.P. and Secy.; David Pedowitz, Treas.; Ingrid S. Dyott; Francine S. Kittredge; Kyle Y. Ridaught; Judith M. Vale; Heather P. Zuckerman.
EIN: 311736689

6539
The Neuwirth Foundation, Inc. ✧
c/o Cummings and Carroll
175 Great Neck Rd., No. 405
Great Neck, NY 11021-3343

Established in 1991 in NY.
Donor: Marvin R. Neuwirth.
Foundation type: Independent foundation.
Financial data (yr. ended 08/31/13): Assets, $7,144,944 (M); expenditures, $619,311; qualifying distributions, $571,590; giving activities include $571,590 for grants.
Purpose and activities: Giving primarily for health associations and hospitals; funding also for Jewish and other federated giving programs, and the arts.
Fields of interest: Arts; Environment, natural resources; Hospitals (general); Health organizations, association; Cancer; Alzheimer's disease research; Foundations (private grantmaking); Jewish federated giving programs.
Limitations: Applications not accepted. Giving primarily in Hartford, CT, and NY. No grants to individuals.
Application information: Contributes only to pre-selected organizations.
Officers and Directors:* Marvin R. Neuwirth, Chair.; Barbara Braun,* Pres.; Felice Neuwirth,* V.P; Robert Halper, Secy.; Richard J. Birnbach,* Treas.
EIN: 113048776
Selected grants: The following grants are a representative sample of this grantmaker's funding activity:
$187,000 to Alzheimers Association, Chicago, IL, 2011.
$86,000 to Nature Conservancy, Arlington, VA, 2011.
$5,000 to Multiple Sclerosis Society, National, New York, NY, 2011.

6540
The New Brook Charitable Foundation, Inc. ✧ ☆
(formerly Gerald David Neuman Foundation, Inc.)
5 Briarwood
Suffern, NY 10901-3601

Established in 1981 in NY.
Donors: Sandy Kornfeld; Gerald Neuman; Baruch Singer; Neal Neuman.
Foundation type: Independent foundation.
Financial data (yr. ended 12/31/12): Assets, $7,242,719 (M); gifts received, $299,711; expenditures, $643,425; qualifying distributions, $638,967; giving activities include $638,967 for grants.
Purpose and activities: Giving primarily to Jewish temples and yeshivas.
Fields of interest: Elementary/secondary education; Theological school/education; Human services; Jewish federated giving programs; Jewish agencies & synagogues.
Limitations: Applications not accepted. Giving primarily in Brooklyn, NY. No grants to individuals.
Application information: Contributes only to pre-selected organizations.
Trustees: Rabbi Martin Laufer; Martin Leventhal; Vera Neuman.
EIN: 222979993

6541
New Tamarind Foundation, Inc. ✧ ☆
c/o O'Connor Davies Munns and Dobbins
665 5th Ave.
New York, NY 10022-5305

Donors: Helaine Lerner; Harriet Heilbrunn Trust; Robert Heilbrunn Trust; Marital Trust; Harriet Heilbrunn‡.
Foundation type: Independent foundation.
Financial data (yr. ended 06/30/13): Assets, $77,342,834 (M); gifts received, $63,739,901; expenditures, $2,180,255; qualifying distributions, $2,180,255; giving activities include $2,161,948 for 13 grants (high: $911,309; low: $100).
Fields of interest: Performing arts, theater; Higher education; Jewish federated giving programs.
Limitations: Applications not accepted. Giving primarily in NY.
Application information: Unsolicited requests for funds not accepted.
Officers and Directors:* Helaine Lerner,* Pres.; Joan Rechnitz, Secy.-Treas.
EIN: 263324875

6542
The New Yankee Stadium Community Benefits Fund, Inc. ✧
199 Lincoln Ave., Ste. 313
Bronx, NY 10454-3707 (347) 591-4767
Contact: Veronica Torres
E-mail: bronxyankeefund@gmail.com; Main URL: http://bronxyankeefund.org/

Established in NY.
Foundation type: Independent foundation.
Financial data (yr. ended 12/31/12): Assets, $145,525 (M); gifts received, $925,998; expenditures, $888,721; qualifying distributions, $754,821; giving activities include $754,821 for 109 grants (high: $15,000; low: $500).
Purpose and activities: Giving primarily to improve the quality of life in the Bronx by addressing civic, socioeconomic and/or educational needs and providing social arts, health, cultural, and recreational opportunities.
Fields of interest: Arts; Education; Health care; Athletics/sports, amateur leagues; Human services; Youth.
Limitations: Applications accepted. Giving primarily in the Bronx section of NY.
Publications: Application guidelines.
Application information: The fund's three different application forms: Large Grants, Small Grants, and Little League, may be downloaded from fund web site. Little League applications are for Bronx little leagues only. Application form required.
Initial approach: Submit appropriate application form via regular U.S. Mail
Deadline(s): See fund web site for current deadlines
Officers: Serafin U. Mariel, Chair.; Ted Jefferson, Secy.; Susan Goldy, Treas.

Board Members: Bishop Ronald Bailey; Robert Crespo; Leo Martinez; Harold Silverman.
EIN: 141979116
Selected grants: The following grants are a representative sample of this grantmaker's funding activity:
$5,900 to Wave Hill, Bronx, NY, 2012. For funding for the Organization's Purpose.

6543
The New York Community Bank Foundation ✧

(formerly The Roslyn Savings Foundation)
c/o New York Community Bank
1400 Old Northern Blvd.
Roslyn, NY 11576-2127 (516) 484-1344
Contact: Marian Conway, Exec. Dir.
FAX: (516) 484-1599;
E-mail: mconway@roslynsavingsfoundation.org; Additional contact: Cindy Krezel, Prog. Off, ckkrezel@roslynsavinigsfoundation.org; Main URL: http://www.roslynsavingsfoundation.org
Grants List: http://www.roslynsavingsfoundation.org/new-pastgrants.htm

Established in 1997 in NY.
Donor: Roslyn Bancorp, Inc.
Foundation type: Company-sponsored foundation.
Financial data (yr. ended 12/31/13): Assets, $24,902,709 (M); expenditures, $2,030,779; qualifying distributions, $1,820,736; giving activities include $1,541,303 for 188 grants (high: $50,000; low: $100).
Purpose and activities: The foundation supports organizations involved with arts and culture, education, health, hunger, and human services. Special emphasis is directed toward programs designed to promote community development; expand home ownership opportunities; and provide access to affordable housing.
Fields of interest: Museums; Arts; Higher education; Libraries (public); Education; Hospitals (general); Health care, clinics/centers; Health care; Food services; Housing/shelter, home owners; Housing/shelter; Family services; Human services; Community/economic development.
Type of support: General/operating support; Continuing support; Capital campaigns; Equipment; Endowments; Program development; Scholarship funds; Sponsorships.
Limitations: Applications accepted. Giving primarily in Long Island and Queens, NY. No support for religious, political, or fraternal organizations. No grants to individuals.
Publications: Application guidelines; Grants list.
Application information: Letters of inquiry should be no longer than 1 to 2 pages. Letters of inquiry should list any grants or contributions received from the banks in the New York Community Bank family. Multi-year funding is not automatic. Organizations receiving support are asked to submit periodic progress reports. A site visit may be requested. Application form not required.
Initial approach: Letter of inquiry
Copies of proposal: 1
Deadline(s): None
Board meeting date(s): Quarterly
Final notification: Within 3 months
Officers and Directors:* John R. Bransfield, Jr.,* Chair.; Maureen E. Clancy,* Pres.; R. Patrick Quinn, Secy.; Thomas Calabrese,* Treas.; Marian Conway, Exec. Dir.; Thomas Calabrese; Dominick Ciampa; Joseph R. Ficalora; Michael J. Levine; James O'Donavan; John M. Tsimbinos; Gerry Voutsinas.
Number of staff: 2 full-time professional.
EIN: 113354472

6544
The New York Community Trust ✧

909 3rd Ave., 22nd Fl.
New York, NY 10022-4752 (212) 686-0010
Contact: For grant inquiries: Mary Gentile, Exec. Asst., Grants and Special Projects
FAX: (212) 532-8528; E-mail: aw@nyct-cfi.org; Tel. for grant inquiries: (212) 686-0010, ext. 554; Main URL: http://www.nycommunitytrust.org
E-Newsletter: http://www.nycommunitytrust.org/tabid/251/default.aspx
Facebook: https://www.facebook.com/pages/The-New-York-Community-Trust/206444912741562?v=wall
GiveSmart: http://www.givesmart.org/Stories/Donors/Lorie-Slutsky
Grants List: http://www.nycommunitytrust.org/GrantSeekers/RecentGrants/tabid/208/Default.aspx
Twitter: http://twitter.com/nycommtrust

Established in 1924 in NY by resolution and declaration of trust.
Foundation type: Community foundation.
Financial data (yr. ended 12/31/13): Assets, $2,443,372,250 (M); gifts received, $145,051,661; expenditures, $156,377,606; giving activities include $144,241,100 for grants.
Purpose and activities: Priority given to applications for projects having particular significance for the New York City area.
Fields of interest: Historic preservation/historical societies; Arts; Education, public education; Child development, education; Education; Environment; Health care; Substance abuse, services; Mental health/crisis services; Health organizations, association; Cancer; AIDS; Biomedicine research; Crime/violence prevention, domestic violence; Legal services; Employment; Food services; Housing/shelter, development; Youth development; Children/youth, services; Family services; Aging, centers/services; Women, centers/services; Homeless, human services; Human services; Civil/human rights, immigrants; Civil/human rights, minorities; Civil/human rights, disabled; Civil/human rights, women; Civil/human rights, aging; Civil/human rights, LGBTQ; Civil liberties, reproductive rights; Community/economic development; Government/public administration; Disabilities, people with; Girls; Young adults, female.
Type of support: Income development; Management development/capacity building; Program development; Publication; Seed money; Fellowships; Scholarship funds; Research; Technical assistance; Consulting services; Program evaluation; Employee matching gifts.
Limitations: Applications accepted. Giving limited to the metropolitan New York, NY, area. No support for religious purposes. No grants to individuals (except for scholarships), or for deficit financing, emergency funds, building campaigns, films, endowment funds, capital projects or general operating support.
Publications: Application guidelines; Annual report; Financial statement; Grants list; Informational brochure (including application guidelines); Newsletter; Occasional report; Program policy statement (including application guidelines).
Application information: Visit foundation web site for application cover sheet and guidelines. Please submit all written materials before calling the foundation to discuss ideas. Faxed or e-mailed proposals are not accepted. The foundation accepts the New York/ New Jersey Area Common Application Form. Application form required.
Initial approach: Submit proposal with cover letter
Copies of proposal: 1
Deadline(s): Oct. 15, Feb. 14, and June 13
Board meeting date(s): Feb., Apr., June, July, Oct., and Dec.
Final notification: Apr. 30, Oct. 30, and Dec. 31
Officers and Directors:* Charlynn Goins,* Chair.; Lorie A. Slutsky,* Pres.; Robert V. Edgar, V.P., Donor Rels.; Mercedes M. Leon, V.P., Admin.; Jenny Patricia, V.P., Grants; Gay Young, V.P., Donor Svcs.; Alan Holzer, C.F.O.; Mary Z. Greenebaum, C.I.O.; Heidi Hotzler, Cont.; Jane L. Wilton, Genl. Counsel; Jamie Drake; Roger Juan Maldonado; Anne Moore, M.D.; Raffiq Nathoo; Valerie S. Peltier; Judith O. Rubin; Barron "Buzz" Tenny; Ann Unterberg; Mary Kay Vyskocil; Jason H. Wright.
Trustee Banks: Bank of America, N.A.; Bessemer Trust Co., N.A.; BNY Mellon, N.A.; Brown Brothers Harriman Trust Co.; Citigroup; Deutsche Bank Americas; Fiduciary Trust Co. International; HSBC Bank USA, N.A.; JPMorgan Chase Bank, N.A.; Lehman Brothers Trust Co., N.A.; Merrill Lynch Trust Co.; Rockefeller Trust Co.; Bank of America, N.A.
Number of staff: 23 full-time professional; 1 part-time professional; 18 full-time support; 1 part-time support.
EIN: 133062214
Selected grants: The following grants are a representative sample of this grantmaker's funding activity:
$5,000,000 to Hunter College Foundation, Lois V. and Samuel J. Silberman School of Social Work, New York, NY, 2012. For Silberman Endowment.
$3,000,000 to Henry Schein Cares Foundation, Melville, NY, 2012. For general support.
$1,000,000 to Sesame Workshop, New York, NY, 2012. For general support of the Sesame Learning Project.
$950,000 to Bridge Fund of New York, New York, NY, 2012. For cash assistance and employment services for families that are at risk of losing their homes in high-need neighborhoods.
$600,000 to New York Botanical Garden, Bronx, NY, 2012. For general support.
$5,000 to Catholic Social Services of Morris County, Dover, NJ, 2012. For general support.
$5,000 to Environmental Defense Fund, New York, NY, 2012. For general support.
$5,000 to Metropolitan Opera Association, New York, NY, 2012. For general support.
$3,332 to Lawrence Hospital, Bronxville, NY, 2012. For general support.
$3,000 to Saint Bonaventure University, Saint Bonaventure, NY, 2012. For a scholarship award.

6545
New York Crohns Foundation ✧

1200 Union Tpke.
New Hyde Park, NY 11040-1708 (718) 343-6400
Contact: Howard Swarzman, Secy.-Treas.

Established in 1998 in NY.

Donors: Leonard Litwin; Michael Kerr; Litwin Foundation; M&R Management.
Foundation type: Independent foundation.
Financial data (yr. ended 12/31/13): Assets, $293,299 (M); gifts received, $1,055,000; expenditures, $1,000,275; qualifying distributions, $1,000,000; giving activities include $990,000 for 3 grants (high: $480,000; low: $110,000).
Purpose and activities: Giving primarily for health care and medical research for the cure of Crohn's disease.
Fields of interest: Hospitals (general); Health care; Digestive diseases; Medical research.
Limitations: Applications accepted. Giving primarily in New York, NY.
Application information: Application form required.
Initial approach: Letter
Copies of proposal: 1
Deadline(s): None
Officers and Directors:* Leonard Litwin,* Pres.; Michael Kerr,* V.P.; Carole Pittelman,* V.P.; Howard Swarzman,* Secy.-Treas.
EIN: 113437172

6546
New York Foundation

10 E. 34th St., 10th Fl.
New York, NY 10016-4327 (212) 594-8009
Contact: Maria Mottola, Exec. Dir.
E-mail: info@nyf.org; Main URL: http://www.nyf.org/
Big Ideas. Locally Grown.: http://nyf.org/category/blog/
Grants Database: http://www.nyf.org/grants-database
Knowledge Center: http://nyf.issuelab.org/
New York Foundation's Philanthropy Promise: http://www.ncrp.org/philanthropys-promise/who
Newsmakers: http://nyf.org/category/newsmakers/
Twitter: https://twitter.com/TheNYFoundation

Incorporated in 1909 in NY.
Donors: Louis A. Heinsheimer†; Alfred M. Heinsheimer†; Lionel J. Salomon†.
Foundation type: Independent foundation.
Financial data (yr. ended 12/31/13): Assets, $65,741,696 (M); gifts received, $312,875; expenditures, $4,694,379; qualifying distributions, $4,146,660; giving activities include $3,035,344 for grants.
Purpose and activities: The New York Foundation is a steadfast supporter of community organizing and advocacy in New York City. It believes that the resilience and vitality of its neighborhoods is the city's greatest resource. Its grants support community-initiated solutions to solve local problems, constituents mobilizing for adequate and equitable resources, and groups organizing a collective voice among those whose voices have not been heard.
Fields of interest: Housing/shelter, development; Youth development, services; Human services; Children/youth, services; Aging, centers/services; Minorities/immigrants, centers/services; Homeless, human services; Civil/human rights, alliance/advocacy; Civil/human rights, immigrants; Civil/human rights, minorities; Civil/human rights, disabled; Civil/human rights, women; Civil/human rights, aging; Civil/human rights, LGBTQ; Civil rights, race/intergroup relations; Civil liberties, reproductive rights; Community/economic development; Youth; Aging; Disabilities, people with; Minorities; African Americans/Blacks; Hispanics/Latinos; AIDS, people with; Immigrants/refugees; Economically disadvantaged; Homeless; Migrant workers; LGBTQ.
Type of support: General/operating support; Continuing support; Management development/capacity building; Program development; Seed money; Technical assistance.
Limitations: Applications accepted. Giving limited to local programs in the five boroughs of New York City. The foundation does not consider requests outside New York City except from organizations working on statewide issues of concern to youth, the elderly, or the poor. The foundation's charter prohibits it from making grants outside the United States. No grants to individuals, or for capital campaigns, research studies, films, conferences, or publications (except for those initiated by the foundation).
Publications: Application guidelines; Annual report (including application guidelines); Grants list.
Application information: Fax submissions are not accepted.
Initial approach: A simple first step is to complete the Initial Funding Request (a form which can be found on foundation web site), and send via U.S. mail or e-mail to: requests@nyf.org. When request is e-mailed, applicant must save the completed Initial Funding Request as a Word document or PDF and send as an attachment.
Copies of proposal: 1
Deadline(s): Mar. 1, July 1, and Nov. 1
Board meeting date(s): Feb., June, and Oct.
Final notification: 3 to 6 months
Officers and Trustees:* Marlene Provizer,* Chair.; Glenn E. Martin,* Vice-Chair.; Roger Schwed,* Secy.; Gail Gordon,* Treas.; Maria Mottola, Exec. Dir.; Rose Dobrof, DSW, Tr. Emeritus; Rosa Alfonso-McGoldrick; Seth Borgos; Kerry-Anne Edwards; Carla Franklin; Stephen Heyman; Wayne Ho; Susan A. Kaplan; Lillian Llambelis; Fitzgerald Miller; Mike Pratt; David Rivel; Aida Rodriguez; Fatima Shama; Dawn Walker; John Weiler; Kyung Yoon.
Number of staff: 3 full-time professional; 2 full-time support.
EIN: 135626345
Selected grants: The following grants are a representative sample of this grantmaker's funding activity:
$86,000 to Community Resource Exchange, New York, NY, 2012. For individual technical assistance to New York Foundation grantees.
$50,000 to National Employment Law Project, New York, NY, 2012. To launch a new campaign to raise New York States minimum wage.
$45,000 to CDC Kids N Teens Program, Staten Island, NY, 2012. For a safe space on the North Shore of Staten Island for refugee children and other underprivileged children to learn and explore.
$45,000 to Jacob A. Riis Neighborhood Settlement, Long Island City, NY, 2012. For a civic engagement and legal services program for immigrants.
$45,000 to New York Students Rising, Voorheesville, NY, 2012. For a network of students from across New York State organizing to increase access to affordable quality public higher education.
$45,000 to Project Hospitality, EyeOpeners: Youth Against Violence, Staten Island, NY, 2012. For a campaign to address the escalating violence between African American and Latin youth in Port Richmond.
$45,000 to Rights for Imprisoned People with Psychiatric Disabilities, New York, NY, 2012. For a grassroots, direct-action organization that demands justice for imprisoned people with psychiatric disabilities.
$42,500 to Asian American Federation of New York, New York, NY, 2012. For a community organizing center that serves the Southeast Asian community in New York City through programs that provide community organizing, healing, education, arts, culture, language, and improving access to social services.
$7,500 to Immigrant Defense Project, New York, NY, 2012. To hire information technology consultant to upgrade the capability of its Web site.
$5,000 to New York Communities Organizing Fund, Brooklyn, NY, 2012. To meet the urgent needs of residents following Hurricane Sandy.

6547
New York Jets Foundation, Inc. ✧ ☆

c/o The Johnson Co.
610 5th Ave., 2nd Fl.
New York, NY 10020 (973) 549-4800
Contact: Brian Friedman, Treas. and Tr.
Application address: c/o New York Jets LLC, 1 Jets Dr., Florham Park, NJ 07932; Main URL: http://www.newyorkjets.com

Established in 1969.
Donors: Bett Wold Johnson, Inc.; NFL Charities; New York Mercantile Exchange, Inc.; NFL Youth Football Fund; Kraft Total; Paul Tudor Jones.
Foundation type: Company-sponsored foundation.
Financial data (yr. ended 12/31/13): Assets, $5,255,860 (M); gifts received, $2,070,202; expenditures, $1,029,180; qualifying distributions, $550,414; giving activities include $521,522 for 77 grants (high: $145,145; low: $426).
Purpose and activities: The foundation supports programs designed to promote youth education, fitness, and health with an emphasis on disadvantaged communities.
Fields of interest: Education; Health care; Human services.
Type of support: General/operating support; Program development; Scholarship funds.
Limitations: Applications accepted. Giving primarily in Chicago, IL, NJ, and NY.
Application information: Application form required.
Initial approach: Letter
Deadline(s): None
Officers and Trustees:* Robert Wood Johnson IV,* Chair.; Neil J. Burmeister,* V.P.; Brian Friedman,* Treas.
EIN: 237108291

6548
New York Life Foundation

51 Madison Ave.
New York, NY 10010-1655 (212) 576-7341
Contact: Christine Park, Pres.
E-mail: NYLFoundation@newyorklife.com; Additional tel.: (212) 576-3466; Main URL: http://www.newyorklife.com/foundation
A Child In Grief Website: http://www.newyorklife.com/achildingrief
Grants List: http://www.newyorklife.com/nyl/v/index.jsp?contentId=18000&vgnextoid=10126f21189d2210a2b3019d221024301cacRCRD
New York Life Foundation Grief Guide: http://www.newyorklife.com/nyl/v/index.jsp?

contentId=17798&vgnextoid=1ec16f21189d2210a2b3019d221024301cacRCRD

Established in 1979 in NY.
Donor: New York Life Insurance Co.
Foundation type: Company-sponsored foundation.
Financial data (yr. ended 12/31/13): Assets, $115,811,533 (M); gifts received, $31,191,376; expenditures, $14,779,444; qualifying distributions, $14,730,927; giving activities include $13,839,189 for 543 grants (high: $801,800; low: $100), and $882,701 for employee matching gifts.
Purpose and activities: The foundation supports organizations and programs that benefit young people, particularly in the areas of mentoring, safe places to learn and grow, educational enhancement opportunities, and childhood bereavement.
Fields of interest: Elementary/secondary education; Child development, education; Education, reading; Education; Mental health, grief/bereavement counseling; Disasters, preparedness/services; Recreation, camps; Boys & girls clubs; Youth development, adult & child programs; Youth development, citizenship; Youth development; Children/youth; Children; Economically disadvantaged.
International interests: Mexico.
Type of support: General/operating support; Continuing support; Program development; Curriculum development; Employee volunteer services; Employee matching gifts; Employee-related scholarships.
Limitations: Applications not accepted. Giving primarily in New York and Westchester County, NY; giving also to national organizations that serve multiple cities. No support for religious or sectarian organizations not of direct benefit to the entire community, or fraternal, social, professional, veterans', athletic, or discriminatory organizations. No grants to individuals (except for employee-related scholarships), or for seminars, conferences, or trips, endowments, memorials, or capital campaigns, fundraising events, telethons, races, or other benefits, goodwill advertising, or basic or applied research.
Publications: Annual report; Grants list.
Application information: Unsolicited applications are not accepted. The foundation practices an invitation only practice for giving.
Board meeting date(s): Apr. and Nov.
Officers and Directors:* Theodore A. Mathas,* Chair.; Frank M. Boccio, Vice-Chair.; Heather Nesle Nesle, Pres.; John Y. Kim, Exec. V.P.; Arthur H. Seter, Sr. V.P., Investments; Byran Boudreau, V.P., Investments; Karen Bain, V.P., Tax; Anna L. Bidwell, Assoc. Genl. Counsel & Secy.; Kathleen T. Davenport; Sheila K. Davidson.
Number of staff: 5 full-time professional; 1 full-time support.
EIN: 132989476

6549
The New York State Health Foundation ✧
(also known as NYSHealth)
1385 Broadway, 23rd Fl.
New York, NY 10018-6001 (212) 664-7656
FAX: (646) 421-6029; E-mail: Info@NYSHealth.org; Main URL: http://www.nyshealthfoundation.org
E-Newsletter: http://visitor.r20.constantcontact.com/manage/optin/ea?v=001Wa58ZNPFtyVYtil_DggXSw%3D%3D
Facebook: http://www.facebook.com/NewYorkStateHealthFoundation
Grants Database: http://www.nyshealthfoundation.org/content/grant
Health Care Impact: http://nyshealthfoundation.org/about-us/measuring-our-impact
Knowledge Center: http://www.nyshealthfoundation.org/section/resources
LinkedIn: http://www.linkedin.com/company/nys-health-foundation?trk=hb_tab_compy_id_598148
RSS Feed: http://www.nyshealthfoundation.org/index.xml
Twitter: http://twitter.com/nys_health

Established in 2002 in NY. Changed status to a private foundation in 2005. Operations began in 2006.
Donor: Empire Blue Cross/Blue Shield.
Foundation type: Independent foundation.
Financial data (yr. ended 12/31/13): Assets, $287,629,473 (M); gifts received, $305,000; expenditures, $15,597,879; qualifying distributions, $14,133,834; giving activities include $9,839,176 for 185 grants (high: $574,090; low: $500), and $1,633,699 for 3 foundation-administered programs.
Purpose and activities: The New York State Health Foundation (NYSHealth) is a private, statewide foundation dedicated to improving the health of all New Yorkers. To achieve meaningful impact, the foundation makes grants, informs health care policy and practice, and spreads effective programs that work to improve New York's health system. Today, NYSHealth focuses most of its activities and grantmaking in three strategic priority areas: (1) expanding health care coverage; (2) improving diabetes prevention; and (3) advancing primary care. The foundation also focuses on the health and wellbeing of returning veterans and their families and manages a Special Projects Fund to support projects consistent with NYSHealth's mission but outside of its priority areas.
Fields of interest: Health care, public policy; Medical care, community health systems; Medical care, outpatient care; Health care, clinics/centers; Dental care; Health care, rural areas; Public health; Health care, insurance; Health care, cost containment; Health care, financing; Health care; Diabetes.
Limitations: Applications accepted. Giving limited to NY.
Publications: Financial statement; Grants list; Informational brochure (including application guidelines); Multi-year report.
Application information:
Initial approach: See web site for current RFPs: http://nyshealthfoundation.org/grant-seekers
Officers and Directors:* Robert G. Smith,* Chair.; James R. Knickman, C.E.O. and Pres.; David Sandman, Sr. V. P.; Jacqueline Martinez Garcel, V.P.; Nick Smirensky, C.I.O.; Paul Bader; LaRay Brown; Jo-Ann Costantino; Margaret I. Cuomo, M.D.; Paul Francis; Marc Gourevitch, M.D., M.P.H.; Jane Steiner Hoffman; John T. Lane.
EIN: 300127892

6550
Samuel I. Newhouse Foundation, Inc. ✧
c/o Advance Finance Group LLC
1440 Broadway, 12th Fl.
New York, NY 10018-2301 (212) 588-2200
Contact: Steven Markovits

Incorporated in 1945 in NY.
Donors: Samuel I. Newhouse, Sr.‡; Mitzi E. Newhouse‡; The Conde Nast Publications, Inc.; Advance Publications, Inc.
Foundation type: Independent foundation.
Financial data (yr. ended 10/31/13): Assets, $139,274,587 (M); gifts received, $44,756,500; expenditures, $16,240,468; qualifying distributions, $15,255,946; giving activities include $15,195,946 for 189 grants (high: $1,500,000; low: $500), and $60,000 for 8 grants to individuals (high: $12,000; low: $6,000).
Purpose and activities: The foundation established the Newhouse Communications Center at Syracuse University for education and research in mass communications. The foundation makes some awards to artists with disabilities.
Fields of interest: Media/communications; Media, print publishing; Performing arts, music; Arts; Secondary school/education; Higher education; Hospitals (general); Human services; Children/youth, services; United Ways and Federated Giving Programs; Jewish federated giving programs; Disabilities, people with.
Type of support: Grants to individuals.
Limitations: Applications accepted. Giving primarily in New York City.
Application information: Application form not required.
Initial approach: Letter
Deadline(s): None
Officers and Directors:* Samuel I. Newhouse, Jr.,* Pres. and Treas.; Donald E. Newhouse,* V.P. and Secy.
EIN: 116006296
Selected grants: The following grants are a representative sample of this grantmaker's funding activity:
$1,500,000 to Syracuse University, Syracuse, NY, 2013.
$1,500,000 to Yale University, New Haven, CT, 2013.
$1,000,000 to American Red Cross, Alabama Region Office, Hoover, AL, 2013.
$600,000 to New York City Opera, New York, NY, 2013.
$524,500 to UJA-Federation of New York, New York, NY, 2013.
$350,000 to National Dance Institute, New York, NY, 2013.
$50,000 to New Orleans Public Library Foundation, New Orleans, LA, 2013.
$46,200 to United Way of Central Alabama, Birmingham, AL, 2013.
$20,000 to Citizens Committee for Children of New York, New York, NY, 2013.
$15,000 to New Orleans Museum of Art, New Orleans, LA, 2013.

6551
The New-Land Foundation, Inc. ✧
1114 Ave. of the Americas
New York, NY 10036-7798 (212) 479-6162

Incorporated in 1941 in NY.
Donor: Muriel M. Buttinger‡.
Foundation type: Independent foundation.
Financial data (yr. ended 12/31/12): Assets, $25,253,886 (M); expenditures, $1,925,541; qualifying distributions, $1,687,780; giving activities include $1,611,819 for 111 grants (high: $50,000; low: $5,000).

Purpose and activities: Giving primarily for civil rights, the environment, population control, and peace and arms control.
Fields of interest: Museums (specialized); Environment; Human services; International affairs, arms control; Civil/human rights; Population studies.
International interests: England.
Type of support: General/operating support; Continuing support; Annual campaigns; Program development; Seed money; Research; Matching/challenge support.
Limitations: Giving primarily in CA, CO, Washington, DC, and New York, NY; some funding also in London, England. No support for educational institutions, medicine, religion and general social programs. No grants to individuals or for capital campaigns, publications, films, endowment campaigns, building campaigns, or conferences; no loans.
Publications: Application guidelines.
Application information: Application form required.
Initial approach: Proposal (no more than 5 pages), or contact foundation for specific application requirements
Copies of proposal: 1
Deadline(s): Feb. 1 and Aug. 1
Board meeting date(s): Spring and fall
Final notification: Positive responses only; June 1 (spring cycle) and Dec. 31 (fall cycle)
Officers and Directors:* Hal Harvey,* Pres.; Constance Harvey,* V.P.; Renee G. Schwartz,* Secy.-Treas.; Anne Ehrlich; Ann Harvey; Joan Harvey; George Perkovich, Ph.D.
EIN: 136086562

6552
The Lizbeth & Frank Newman Charitable Foundation ✧
40 E. 61st St., No. 15B
New York, NY 10065-8033
Contact: Mary Reen, Treas.

Established in 1999 in NY.
Donors: Frank N. Newman; Lizabeth Newman.
Foundation type: Independent foundation.
Financial data (yr. ended 12/31/13): Assets, $17,978 (M); gifts received, $460,000; expenditures, $490,231; qualifying distributions, $470,956; giving activities include $434,250 for 6 grants (high: $108,000; low: $1,250).
Purpose and activities: Giving primarily to performing arts and cultural institutions.
Fields of interest: Museums; Performing arts centers; Arts; Higher education; Education.
Limitations: Applications not accepted. Giving primarily in NY. No grants to individuals.
Application information: Contributes only to pre-selected organizations.
Officers: Frank Newman, Pres.; Lizabeth Newman, V.P. and Secy.; Mary Reen, Treas.
EIN: 134067790

6553
The Howard and Maryam Newman Family Foundation, Inc. ✧
c/o Maryam Newman
346 Pine Brook Rd.
Bedford, NY 10506-1618

Established in 2005 in NY.
Donor: Howard Newman.
Foundation type: Independent foundation.
Financial data (yr. ended 11/30/13): Assets, $8,664,281 (M); gifts received, $328,165; expenditures, $1,104,015; qualifying distributions, $1,083,390; giving activities include $1,083,390 for 34 grants (high: $250,000; low: $100).
Fields of interest: Arts; Higher education, university; Health organizations; Human services; Biology/life sciences.
Limitations: Applications not accepted. Giving primarily in CA, CT and NY. No grants to individuals.
Application information: Unsolicited requests for funds not accepted.
Officers: Howard H. Newman, Pres.; Zeena M. Meurer, V.P.; Elizabeth V. Newman, Secy.; Maryam R. Newman, Treas.
EIN: 201999992

6554
The Barnett and Annalee Newman Foundation ✧ ☆
c/o John Silberman Assocs., PC
145 E. 57th St.
New York, NY 10022-2141

Established in 1996 in NY.
Donor: Annalee Newman†.
Foundation type: Independent foundation.
Financial data (yr. ended 12/31/13): Assets, $36,358,150 (M); expenditures, $1,118,914; qualifying distributions, $1,235,000; giving activities include $335,000 for 2 grants (high: $300,000; low: $35,000), and $900,000 for 6 grants to individuals (high: $150,000; low: $150,000).
Purpose and activities: Giving primarily to artists whose prior artistic achievements best embody the spirit of individualism and independence of Barnett Newman.
Fields of interest: Arts.
Limitations: Applications not accepted. Giving primarily in New York, NY; funding also in Minneapolis, MN.
Application information: Unsolicited requests for funds not accepted.
Trustees: Paula Pelosi; Frank Stella.
EIN: 137105549

6555
Newman-Tanner Foundation ✧
c/o Harold Tanner
950 3rd Ave.
New York, NY 10022-2705
Established in 1990 in NY.
Donors: Estelle Newman Tanner; Harold Tanner.
Foundation type: Independent foundation.
Financial data (yr. ended 12/31/13): Assets, $2,080,524 (M); gifts received, $448,170; expenditures, $887,222; qualifying distributions, $864,962; giving activities include $864,700 for 80 grants (high: $100,000; low: $100).
Purpose and activities: Giving primarily for education and social services; funding also for Jewish organizations.
Fields of interest: Higher education; Human services; Jewish federated giving programs.
Limitations: Applications not accepted. Giving primarily in NY. No grants to individuals.
Application information: Contributes only to pre-selected organizations.
Trustees: Karen Tanner Allen; David A. Tanner; Estelle Newman Tanner; Harold Tanner; James M. Tanner.
EIN: 136942897
Selected grants: The following grants are a representative sample of this grantmaker's funding activity:
$100,000 to Lincoln Center for the Performing Arts, New York, NY, 2011. For general fund.
$1,500 to Philharmonic-Symphony Society of New York, New York, NY, 2011. For general fund.

6556
Henry Nias Foundation, Inc. ✧
180 E. Prospect Ave.
Mamaroneck, NY 10543-3709
Application address: c/o Richard Edelman, Treas., 277 Glendale Dr., Carthage, NC 28327, tel.: (910) 947-5460

Incorporated in 1955 in NY.
Donor: Henry Nias†.
Foundation type: Independent foundation.
Financial data (yr. ended 11/30/13): Assets, $28,879,017 (M); expenditures, $1,338,549; qualifying distributions, $1,101,834; giving activities include $889,500 for 52 grants (high: $55,000; low: $1,000).
Purpose and activities: Giving primarily for the arts, higher education, health care, youth and social services, and to Jewish organizations.
Fields of interest: Museums; Performing arts; Performing arts, theater; Performing arts, orchestras; Arts; Higher education; Education; Hospitals (general); Health care; Human services; Children/youth, services; Jewish federated giving programs; Jewish agencies & synagogues.
Type of support: Continuing support.
Limitations: Applications accepted. Giving primarily in the metropolitan New York, NY, area.
Application information: Application form not required.
Initial approach: Proposal
Deadline(s): Aug.
Final notification: Grants paid in Nov.
Officers: Stanley Edelman, M.D., Chair.; Charles D. Fleischman, Pres.; Richard J. Edelman, Treas.; William F. Rosenberg, Emeritus Dir.
Directors: Catherine Edelman; Ellen Fleischman-Litsky; Victoria E. Tate; Beth Zweibel.
EIN: 136075785

6557
Nicholas Family Charitable Trust ✧ ☆
c/o Nicholas J Nicholas, Jr.
190 Riverside Dr., Ste. 11 C
New York, NY 10024-1008

Established in 1992 in NY.
Donors: Nicholas J. Nicholas, Jr.; Llewellyn J. Nicholas; Alexandra Nicholas.
Foundation type: Independent foundation.
Financial data (yr. ended 12/31/13): Assets, $1,087,950 (M); gifts received, $308,606; expenditures, $522,091; qualifying distributions, $521,975; giving activities include $517,200 for 44 grants (high: $175,275; low: $100).
Purpose and activities: Giving for higher and other education, cultural programs, and human services.

Fields of interest: Arts; Higher education; Education; Environment, natural resources; Human services.
Type of support: General/operating support; Capital campaigns.
Limitations: Applications not accepted. Giving primarily in MA and NY. No grants to individuals.
Application information: Contributes only to pre-selected organizations.
Trustees: Alexandra Nicholas; Llewellyn J. Nicholas; Nicholas J. Nicholas, Jr.
EIN: 136990536
Selected grants: The following grants are a representative sample of this grantmaker's funding activity:
$2,000 to Teach for America, New York, NY, 2012. For general appeal.

6558
The Nicholson Foundation ✧
419 E. 50th St.
New York, NY 10022-8074 (212) 953-9200
Contact: Jan Nicholson, Pres.
Main URL: http://www.thenicholsonfoundation-newjersey.org/

Established in 1980 in NJ.
Donor: Marion G. Nicholson.
Foundation type: Independent foundation.
Financial data (yr. ended 12/31/12): Assets, $63,349,238 (M); gifts received, $5,000,874; expenditures, $10,532,584; qualifying distributions, $9,909,079; giving activities include $7,629,439 for 95 grants (high: $734,645; low: $1,000), and $1,710,325 for foundation-administered programs.
Purpose and activities: Giving primarily to address the complex needs of vulnerable populations in New Jersey's urban areas by encouraging the reform of health and human services delivery systems.
Fields of interest: Higher education; Education; Human services; Community/economic development.
Limitations: Applications not accepted. Giving primarily in NJ and NY. No grants to individuals.
Application information: Contributes only to pre-selected organizations.
Officers and Trustees:* Barbara Nicholson McFadyen,* Chair.; Jan Nicholson,* Pres. and Treas.; Marion G. Nicholson,* Secy.
EIN: 222344110
Selected grants: The following grants are a representative sample of this grantmaker's funding activity:
$734,645 to Newark Now, Newark, NJ, 2012. For the operation of four Family Success Centers in Newark and the overall coordination of the Newark Family Success Center Network.
$348,126 to Rutgers, The State University of New Jersey, Newark, NJ, 2012. To Fund T E E M Gateway program to support at-risk youth.
$284,375 to Family Connections, East Orange, NJ, 2012. For the Orange Family Success Center.
$282,961 to Cooper Foundation, Camden, NJ, 2012. For the Coalition to become a successful Medicaid Accountable Organization.
$247,848 to Family Intervention Services, East Orange, NJ, 2012. For technical assistance that FIS's National Institute for Family Success is providing the NJ DCF.
$191,400 to Blessed Ministries, Inc., South Orange, NJ, 2012. To provide job placements and retention services for at least 80 work ready individuals who are involved with the criminal justice system.
$109,193 to Essex County Family Justice Center, Newark, NJ, 2012. For the Center's administrative staff and infrastructure to operate as a single-stop resource center for victims of domestic violence in Essex County.
$91,943 to Third Sector New England, Boston, MA, 2012. For Implementation of Diploma Plus model in 3 Newark Schools for a period of 3 years.
$90,000 to New Jersey Institute of Technology, Newark, NJ, 2012. For the hospital in recruiting women to enroll in the program that offers prenatal, post natal and pediatric care in group settings.
$31,250 to Family Intervention Services, East Orange, NJ, 2012. For the continuation of The National Institute for Family Success to provide technical assistance and training to the Family Success Centers throughout the state and to develop performance outcomes.

6559
The Robert and Kate Niehaus Foundation ✧
c/o Robert H. Niehaus
770 Park Ave.
New York, NY 10021-4153

Established in 1998 in NY.
Donor: Robert H. Niehaus.
Foundation type: Independent foundation.
Financial data (yr. ended 12/31/12): Assets, $27,929,903 (M); gifts received, $86,400; expenditures, $3,173,673; qualifying distributions, $2,924,676; giving activities include $2,910,024 for 9 grants (high: $1,000,000; low: $24).
Purpose and activities: Giving primarily for a cancer hospital, as well as for education and social entrepreneurship.
Fields of interest: Education; Hospitals (specialty); Social entrepreneurship.
Limitations: Applications not accepted. Giving primarily in New York, NY.
Application information: Contributes only to pre-selected organizations.
Officers: Kate Niehaus, Pres.; Robert H. Niehaus, V.P. and Treas.
Director: Jerome L. Levine.
EIN: 134007527

6560
John H. & Ethel G. Noble Charitable Trust ✧
c/o Deutsche Bank Trust Co., N.A.
P.O. Box 1297
Church St. Sta.
New York, NY 10008-1297

Established in 1969 in CT.
Donors: Ethel G. Noble‡; John H. Noble‡.
Foundation type: Independent foundation.
Financial data (yr. ended 05/31/14): Assets, $20,410,297 (M); expenditures, $1,160,702; qualifying distributions, $1,051,396; giving activities include $983,362 for 22 grants (high: $100,000; low: $20,000).
Purpose and activities: Grants for organizations that provide shelter or support to the low-income aged and places for the care and treatment of crippled or handicapped children.
Fields of interest: Hospitals (general); Medical care, rehabilitation; Health care; Aging, centers/services; Aging; Disabilities, people with.
Limitations: Applications not accepted. Giving limited to CT, FL, and NY. No grants to individuals.
Application information: Contributes only to pre-selected organizations.
Trustee: Deutsche Bank Trust Co., N.A.
EIN: 136307313

6561
Edward John Noble Foundation, Inc. ✧
32 E. 57th St., 19th Fl.
New York, NY 10022-2513 (212) 759-4212
Contact: E.J. Noble Smith, Chair. and Pres.

Trust established in 1940 in CT; incorporated in 1982.
Donors: Edward John Noble‡; St. Catherine's Island Foundation, Inc.
Foundation type: Independent foundation.
Financial data (yr. ended 12/31/13): Assets, $109,266,517 (M); expenditures, $7,737,264; qualifying distributions, $6,795,275; giving activities include $5,289,692 for 32 grants (high: $2,500,000; low: $1,900).
Purpose and activities: Grants to major cultural organizations in New York City, especially for educational programs and management training internships. Selected projects concerned with conservation and ecology primarily related to activities on an island off the coast of GA. Supports programs to improve educational opportunities for gifted and talented disadvantaged children in NY. Programs in health education efforts related to family planning and population education.
Fields of interest: Performing arts, music; Arts; Education; Environment, natural resources; Environment; Reproductive health, family planning.
Type of support: General/operating support; Continuing support; Endowments; Program development; Internship funds; Matching/challenge support.
Limitations: Applications accepted. Giving primarily in the metropolitan New York, NY, area for arts organizations; St. Catherine's Island, GA, and the eastern states for conservation projects and family planning; and the Northeast for private colleges and universities. No grants to individuals, or for publications, building funds, equipment, television, films, or performances; no loans.
Publications: Biennial report (including application guidelines).
Application information: Application form not required.
Initial approach: Brief letter
Copies of proposal: 1
Deadline(s): None
Board meeting date(s): Dec.
Final notification: 3 months
Officers and Directors:* E.J. Noble Smith,* Chair. and Pres.; Jeremy T. Smith,* Vice-Chair. and V.P.; Deborah Menton-Nightlinger, Secy. and Exec. Dir.; E. Mary Heffernan, Treas.; June Noble Larkin,* Chair. Emeritus; Harold B. Johnson; Daniel L. Mosley, Esq.; David S. Smith; Edward N. Smith; Jordan V. Smith; Maribeth Smith; Sarah N. Smith; William Z. Smith.
Number of staff: 3 full-time professional; 1 full-time support; 1 part-time support.
EIN: 061055586
Selected grants: The following grants are a representative sample of this grantmaker's funding activity:

$2,500,000 to Saint Catherines Island Foundation, Midway, GA, 2012. For general support.
$500,000 to Juilliard School, New York, NY, 2012. For capital campaign.
$500,000 to Lincoln Center for the Performing Arts, New York, NY, 2012. For capital campaign.
$375,000 to Community Funds, New York, NY, 2012. For JTS Fund.
$200,000 to Calm Air Visibility Unlimited, Universal City, TX, 2012. For general support.
$200,000 to Calm Air Visibility Unlimited, Universal City, TX, 2012. For general support.
$100,000 to Charleston School of Law Foundation, Charleston, SC, 2012. For scholarships.
$82,355 to State University of New York Potsdam College, Community Performance Series, Potsdam, NY, 2012. For Residency in the Arts and outreach.
$70,000 to Community Funds, New York, NY, 2012. For WainWright Fund.
$50,000 to Lincoln Center for the Performing Arts, New York, NY, 2012. For internship program.

6562
The Nola Foundation ✧
c/o John A. Gacinski
200 Madison Ave., 5th Fl.
New York, NY 10016-3912

Established in 1998 in DE.
Donors: Susan and Elihu Rose Foundation, Inc.; Amy Rose Silverman.
Foundation type: Independent foundation.
Financial data (yr. ended 12/31/12): Assets, $8,586,585 (M); gifts received, $1,789,245; expenditures, $532,465; qualifying distributions, $492,364; giving activities include $492,364 for grants.
Fields of interest: Education; Health organizations, association; Human services; YM/YWCAs & YM/YWHAs; Jewish agencies & synagogues.
Limitations: Applications not accepted. Giving primarily in New York, NY. No grants to individuals.
Application information: Contributes only to pre-selected organizations.
Officers and Directors:* Amy Rose Silverman,* Pres.; Jeffrey Silverman,* V.P.
EIN: 134014432

6563
Nonna's Garden ✧
17-20 Whitestone Expwy., Ste. 501
Whitestone, NY 11357-3000

Established in 2007 in NY.
Donors: Michael Repole; Peaceworks Holdings, LLC.
Foundation type: Independent foundation.
Financial data (yr. ended 12/31/13): Assets, $9,313,051 (M); gifts received, $10,750; expenditures, $528,966; qualifying distributions, $435,000; giving activities include $435,000 for 13 grants (high: $140,000; low: $2,500).
Fields of interest: Higher education, university; Hospitals (specialty); Health organizations, association; Cancer; Skin disorders.
Limitations: Applications not accepted. Giving primarily in New York, NY. No grants to individuals.
Application information: Contributes only to pre-selected organizations.
Trustees: Maria A. Repole; Michael Repole.
EIN: 137548350

Selected grants: The following grants are a representative sample of this grantmaker's funding activity:
$50,000 to Columbia University, New York, NY, 2011. For general contribution.
$10,000 to Thrivewell Cancer Foundation, San Antonio, TX, 2011. For general contribution.

6564
Norcross Wildlife Foundation, Inc. ✧
250 W. 88th St., Ste. 806
Caller Box No. 611
New York, NY 10024-1767 (212) 362-4831
Contact for questions, application process, or if applicant is unable to submit an application via e-mail: John McMurray, Prog. Off., tel.: (718) 791-2094; e-mail: john@norcrossws.org; Main URL: http://www.norcrossws.org

Established in 1964 in NY.
Donors: Arthur D. Norcross‡; June Norcross Webster‡.
Foundation type: Independent foundation.
Financial data (yr. ended 12/31/13): Assets, $53,738,941 (M); expenditures, $3,304,681; qualifying distributions, $3,646,110; giving activities include $988,839 for grants, and $681,000 for 3 loans/program-related investments (high: $250,000; low: $201,000).
Purpose and activities: The foundation makes only restricted grants for land protection, program-related office and field equipment/technology, and public education materials. Limited support for community service work confined to the NYC metropolitan area, and the towns near the Norcross Wildlife Sanctuary.
Fields of interest: Environment, natural resources; Environment; Animals/wildlife, preservation/protection.
Type of support: Building/renovation; Equipment; Land acquisition; Publication; Program-related investments/loans.
Limitations: Applications accepted. Giving primarily in North America, with some giving in Canada. No support for animal welfare or wildlife rehabilitation. No grants to individuals, or for operating support, fundraising, overhead expenses, salaries, research endowments, conferences, matching gifts, or multi-year grants.
Publications: Application guidelines; Annual report (including application guidelines); Grants list.
Application information: The foundation will accept grant requests only for amounts under $10,000. Grants average less than $5,000. Fax, express mail applications or proposals without an attached application form not accepted; no 990-PF forms or annual reports required; only 1 copy of IRS letter is required. See foundation web site for complete application guidelines. Application form required.
Initial approach: Use online application form via foundation web site
Copies of proposal: 1
Deadline(s): None
Board meeting date(s): Quarterly
Officers: Angelica Braestrup, Chair.; Jennifer Grossman, Vice-Chair.; Richard S. Reagan, Secy.; Charles Baeder, Treas.; Karen Outlaw, Exec. Dir.
Directors: Liz Austin; Chad Blocker; Whit Fosburgh; Arthur D. Norcross, Jr.; Richard Stebbins; Sol Watson.
Number of staff: 3 full-time professional; 1 full-time support.
EIN: 132041622

6565
Norman Foundation, Inc.
147 E. 48th St.
New York, NY 10017-1223
Contact: June Makela
Norman Foundation's Philanthropy Promise: http://www.ncrp.org/philanthropys-promise/who

Incorporated in 1935 in NY.
Donors: Aaron E. Norman‡; Normandie Foundation, Inc.
Foundation type: Independent foundation.
Financial data (yr. ended 12/31/12): Assets, $23,245,921 (M); expenditures, $1,446,518; qualifying distributions, $1,201,123; giving activities include $941,211 for 86 grants (high: $25,000; low: $1,000).
Purpose and activities: The foundation funds in two broad areas: economic justice and environmental justice. The foundation is interested in community-based organizing projects that could have a potentially national impact as well as provide potential models for social change. Collaborative projects welcome.
Fields of interest: Environment, legal rights; Employment; Civil/human rights; Economic development; Community/economic development; Public affairs; Minorities; Economically disadvantaged.
Type of support: General/operating support; Continuing support; Program development; Seed money; Matching/challenge support.
Limitations: Applications accepted. Giving limited to the U.S. No support for universities or direct social service agencies. No grants to individuals, or for building or endowment funds, publications, conferences, capital funding projects, fundraising, research, scholarships, films, and arts projects or fellowships.
Publications: Application guidelines; Financial statement; Grants list.
Application information: Application form required.
Initial approach: Letter
Copies of proposal: 1
Deadline(s): None
Board meeting date(s): 3 times per year
Officers: Honor Lassalle, Pres.; Alice Franklin, V.P.; Amanda Weil, V.P.; Margaret Norman, Secy.; Melissa Bunnen, Treas.
Number of staff: 1 part-time professional; 1 part-time support.
EIN: 131862694

6566
Normandie Foundation, Inc. ✧
c/o Norman Foundation
147 E. 48th St.
New York, NY 10017
Contact: Abigail Norman, Pres.

Incorporated in 1966 in NY.
Donors: Andrew E. Norman‡; The Aaron E. Norman Fund, Inc.; Sarah Norman.
Foundation type: Independent foundation.
Financial data (yr. ended 12/31/13): Assets, $12,324,742 (M); gifts received, $14,976; expenditures, $640,732; qualifying distributions, $526,838; giving activities include $514,503 for 47 grants (high: $34,000; low: $3).
Purpose and activities: Grants primarily for civil liberties and the environment; support also for civic, charitable, educational, and cultural institutions.

Fields of interest: Environment; Civil/human rights; Community/economic development.
Type of support: General/operating support; Continuing support; Annual campaigns; Seed money.
Limitations: Applications accepted. No support for religious organizations. No grants to individuals, or for conferences, building or endowment funds, scholarships, fellowships, or matching gifts; generally no loans.
Application information: Application form required.
Initial approach: Letter
Deadline(s): None
Officers: Abigail Norman, Pres.; Margaret Norman, Secy.-Treas.
Number of staff: None.
EIN: 136213564

6567
Northern New York Community Foundation, Inc. ✧
(formerly Watertown Foundation, Inc.)
120 Washington St., Ste. 400
Watertown, NY 13601-3330 (315) 782-7110
Contact: Rande S. Richardson, Exec. Dir.; Max DelSignore, Coord., Donor Svcs.
FAX: (315) 782-0047; E-mail: info@nnycf.org; Additional e-mail: rande@nnycf.org; Grant inquiry e-mail: rande@nnycf.org; Main URL: http://www.nnycf.org
Facebook: http://www.facebook.com/nnycf
Grants List: http://www.nnycf.org/grantrecipients.asp?mm=5

Incorporated in 1929 in NY.
Foundation type: Community foundation.
Financial data (yr. ended 12/31/12): Assets, $43,840,804 (M); gifts received, $3,021,398; expenditures, $2,812,964; giving activities include $1,307,385 for 21+ grants (high: $100,000), and $748,118 for grants to individuals.
Purpose and activities: The foundation raises, manages and administers an endowment and collection of funds for the benefit of the community, built and added to by gifts from individuals and organizations committed to meeting the changing needs of Northern New York.
Fields of interest: Arts; Education; Health care; Human services.
Type of support: Annual campaigns; Capital campaigns; Building/renovation; Equipment; Land acquisition; Program development; Conferences/seminars; Publication; Seed money; Scholarship funds; Technical assistance; Scholarships—to individuals; Matching/challenge support.
Limitations: Applications accepted. Giving limited to organizations and individuals in Jefferson and Lewis counties, NY. No support for churches or religious organizations (except where projects clearly benefit the entire community). No grants to individuals (except for scholarships), or for endowment funds or deficit financing.
Publications: Annual report; Grants list; Newsletter.
Application information: Visit foundation web site for more information, and to request grant application guidelines.
Initial approach: Letter, telephone, or e-mail
Copies of proposal: 1
Deadline(s): Jan. 24, Apr. 18, Aug. 15, and Oct. 17 for grants; Apr. 1 for scholarships
Board meeting date(s): Mar., June, Oct., and Dec.
Final notification: 1 to 2 months for grants; June 1 for scholarships
Officers and Directors:* Cathy M. Pircsuk,* Pres.; Joseph W. Russell,* V.P.; Linda S. Merrell,* Secy.-Treas.; Rande S. Richardson, Exec. Dir.; Shari Scott, Cont.; William J. Bonisteel; Bernard H. Brown, Jr.; Michael J. Burgess; Katherine F. Fenlon; Gregory A. Gardner; Susan B. Horr; Harold B. Johnson II; Laurel W. Pike; Jude Renzi; Jacquelyn A. Schell; Jay Stone; Stephen J. Todd; Peter J. Whitmore.
Number of staff: 1 full-time professional; 1 full-time support; 1 part-time support.
EIN: 156020989

6568
Northfield Bank Foundation ✧
1731 Victory Blvd.
Staten Island, NY 10314-3511 (718) 303-4265
Contact: Diane Senerchia, Exec. Dir.
FAX: (718) 448-5035;
E-mail: info@northfieldbankfoundation.org;
Additional tel.: (732) 587-2225; Main URL: http://www.northfieldbankfoundation.org

Established in 2007 in NY.
Foundation type: Company-sponsored foundation.
Financial data (yr. ended 12/31/13): Assets, $17,054,048 (M); expenditures, $774,999; qualifying distributions, $767,256; giving activities include $674,484 for 125 grants (high: $40,000; low: $100).
Purpose and activities: The foundation supports organizations involved with education, health, human services, community development, civic affairs, and projects designed to improve quality of life.
Fields of interest: Performing arts; Performing arts centers; Higher education; Education; Hospitals (general); Health care, clinics/centers; Health care; Children/youth, services; Human services; Community/economic development; Public affairs.
Type of support: General/operating support; Building/renovation; Equipment; Program development; Scholarship funds; Sponsorships.
Limitations: Applications accepted. Giving in areas of company operations, specifically in Brooklyn and Staten Island, NY, and in Central NJ. No support for political organizations.
Publications: Application guidelines; Annual report.
Application information: A formal grant application package may be requested a later date. Organizations receiving support are asked to submit a final report. Application form required.
Initial approach: Download application form and mail application form and preliminary proposal summary to foundation
Deadline(s): None
Board meeting date(s): Quarterly
Officers and Directors:* Susan Lamberti,* Chair.; John W. Alexander,* Pres. and C.E.O.; Steven M. Klein, Treas.; Diane Senerchia, Exec. Dir.; Stanley A. Applebaum; John R. Bowen; Lucille Chazanoff; John P. Connors, Jr.; John DePierro; Albert J. Regen.
EIN: 261317178

6569
Novartis US Foundation ✧
(formerly Sandoz Foundation of America)
230 Park Ave., 21st FL
New York, NY 10169-2403
Main URL: http://www.us.novartis.com/novartis-us-foundation/index.shtml

Incorporated in 1965 in DE; adopted current name in 1997 following a merger with the Ciba Educational Foundation, Inc.
Donors: Sandoz Corp.; Novartis Inc.
Foundation type: Company-sponsored foundation.
Financial data (yr. ended 12/31/13): Assets, $26,699,643 (M); gifts received, $1,042,901; expenditures, $1,488,011; qualifying distributions, $1,121,587; giving activities include $85,000 for 2 grants (high: $50,000; low: $35,000), and $1,036,587 for 1 employee matching gift.
Purpose and activities: The foundation matches contributions made by its employees to nonprofit organizations.
Fields of interest: Education; Public affairs.
Type of support: Employee matching gifts.
Limitations: Applications not accepted. Giving on a national basis, with emphasis on areas of company operations. No support for religious organizations or social, labor, veterans', fraternal, athletic, or alumni organizations.
Application information: Contributes only to pre-selected organizations and through employee matching gifts.
Board meeting date(s): As required
Trustees: Brenda Blanchard; James Elkin; Meryl Zausner.
Officers: Robert E. Pelzer, Chair.; Barry Rosenfield, Secy.; Kenneth Schuster, Treas.; Edgar Butz, Exec. Dir.
EIN: 136193034

6570
NoVo Foundation ✧
(formerly The Spirit Foundation)
535 Fifth Ave., 33rd. Fl.
New York, NY 10017-0051
Contact: Kelly Merryman, Opers. Mgr.
E-mail for Kelly Merryman:
Kmerryman@novofoundation.org; Main URL: http://www.novofoundation.org
GiveSmart: http://www.givesmart.org/Stories/Donors/Jennifer-and-Peter-Buffett
NoVo Foundation's Philanthropy Promise: http://www.ncrp.org/philanthropys-promise/who
Warren Buffett's Giving Pledge Profile: http://glasspockets.org/philanthropy-in-focus/eye-on-the-giving-pledge/profiles/buffett

Established in 1999 in NE; classified as a private operating foundation in 2000; reclassified as an independent foundation in 2001.
Donor: Warren E. Buffett.
Foundation type: Independent foundation.
Financial data (yr. ended 12/31/12): Assets, $264,168,686 (M); gifts received, $53,089,976; expenditures, $63,715,651; qualifying distributions, $62,552,448; giving activities include $56,715,829 for 111 grants (high: $10,943,660; low: $2,500), and $1,996,916 for foundation-administered programs.
Purpose and activities: NoVo Foundation seeks to foster a paradigm shift from domination to partnership. Funds are primarily directed toward the empowerment of women and girls, social emotional

learning for all, and support for men and boys as their roles transform toward a more balanced society. Strategies include: Education and economic empowerment for young women and girls in the developing world. Ending violence against women and girls. Leadership development for women and men who share our commitment to shifting the paradigm from domination to partnership. Research and advocacy. Advancement of social emotional learning (SEL).
Fields of interest: Youth development, equal rights; Human services, equal rights; Child development, services; Women, centers/services; Civil/human rights, equal rights; Civil/human rights, women; Community/economic development; Women; Girls.
Limitations: Applications not accepted. No grants to individuals.
Publications: Annual report.
Application information: Unsolicited requests for funds not accepted.
Board meeting date(s): May 5 and Nov. 24
Officer and Directors:* Jennifer Buffett,* Co.-Chair., Pres. and Treas.; Peter Buffett,* Co.-Chair.; Aaron Stern, Secy.; Pamela Shifman, Exec. Dir.
Number of staff: 7 full-time professional; 2 full-time support.
EIN: 470824753
Selected grants: The following grants are a representative sample of this grantmaker's funding activity:
$13,000,000 to NIKE Foundation, Beaverton, OR, 2012. For Girl Effect, project to help adolescent girls to end poverty for themselves and the world.
$4,633,660 to New World Foundation, New York, NY, 2012. For Local Economies Projecta (LEP), which explores and promotes strategies for cultivating local living economies within initial geographic focus on Hudson Valley of New York State. Local living economies are rooted in local ownership of businesses, local government and public institutions (eg. schools and hospitals) procurement practices and policies that are based on principals of fair trade, living wages, democratic practice and environmental stewardship. LEP has designated local food systems as key entry point to building a sustainable economy.
$3,735,735 to International Rescue Committee, New York, NY, 2012. For project support, Women and Girls Rebuilding Nations.
$1,400,000 to Turnaround for Children, New York, NY, 2012. For General Support.
$1,200,000 to V-Day, New York, NY, 2012. For General Support.
$450,000 to Business Alliance for Local Living Economies, Oakland, CA, 2012. For General Support.
$250,000 to Austin Independent School District, Austin, TX, 2012. For Project Support, Collaborating Districts Initiative.
$125,000 to Fractured Atlas, New York, NY, 2012. For Project Support, The Bully Project.
$100,000 to International Rescue Committee, New York, NY, 2012. For project support, Women and Girls Rebuilding Nations.
$50,000 to New Organizing Institute Education Fund, Washington, DC, 2012. For Project Support, Ultra Violet.

6571
Jessie Smith Noyes Foundation, Inc.

6 E. 39th St., 12th Fl.
New York, NY 10016-0112 (212) 684-6577
Contact: Victor De Luca, Pres.
FAX: (212) 689-6549; E-mail: noyes@noyes.org; Main URL: http://www.noyes.org
E-Newsletter: http://www.noyes.org/maillist/
Jessie Smith Noyes Foundation's Philanthropy Promise: http://www.ncrp.org/philanthropys-promise/who
Twitter: http://twitter.com/NoyesFoundation

Incorporated in 1947 in NY.
Donor: Charles F. Noyes‡.
Foundation type: Independent foundation.
Financial data (yr. ended 12/31/12): Assets, $44,391,249 (M); gifts received, $430,000; expenditures, $3,512,519; qualifying distributions, $3,062,721; giving activities include $1,942,560 for 141 grants (high: $75,000; low: $250), and $12,150 for foundation-administered programs.
Purpose and activities: The foundation envisions a socially just and environmentally sustainable society in which all people are able to gain the knowledge and build the power they need to exercise their rights and participate fully in the economic, social and political decisions that affect their lives and communities. The foundation supports grassroots organizations and movements in the United States, that are working to change environmental, social, economic, and political conditions to bring about a more just, equitable, and sustainable world.
Fields of interest: Environment, toxics; Environment; Agriculture; Civil liberties, reproductive rights; Adults; Minorities; Asians/Pacific Islanders; African Americans/Blacks; Hispanics/Latinos; Native Americans/American Indians; Indigenous peoples; Women; Adults, women; Immigrants/refugees; Economically disadvantaged; Migrant workers.
Type of support: General/operating support; Continuing support; Program development; Seed money; Mission-related investments/loans.
Limitations: Applications accepted. Giving limited to the U.S. No grants to individuals, or for scholarships, fellowships, endowment funds, deficit financing, capital construction funds, or general fundraising drives; generally no support for conferences, research, college and university based programs, or media; no loans.
Publications: Application guidelines; Financial statement; Grants list; Newsletter; Occasional report; Program policy statement.
Application information: Full proposal will be requested after review of letter of intent, background of organization, summary of activities for funding and expected outcome. The foundation encourages requests that address multiple priorities, as well as those that bring together organizations and activists from diverse movements. The foundation prefers to make general support grants and does not limit the number of renewal grants. It believes this helps organizations increase and sustain their effectiveness. The foundation seeks out organizations led by people of color and/or working in low income communities. It supports efforts to develop the leadership skills of, and foster the participation by, low income people and people of color. It encourages requests that address multiple priorities, as well as those that bring together organizations and activists from diverse movements. With first time grants, it tries to bring diverse voices and approaches, and young people into the movements for social change. It makes grants throughout the U.S. in both rural and urban communities. Application form required.
Initial approach: 1- or 2-page web-based letter of inquiry (through foundation web site), including budget estimate
Copies of proposal: 1
Deadline(s): None
Board meeting date(s): Spring, summer, and fall
Final notification: Within 6 weeks of receipt of letters; within 2 weeks of board meetings for final proposals
Officers and Directors:* Jenifer Getz, Chair.; Martha Matsuoka,* Vice-Chair.; Victor De Luca, Pres.; Wendy Holding,* Secy.; Nicholas Jacangelo,* Treas.; Dorothy Anderson; Rachel Anderson; Nikhil Aziz; George Beardsley; Jim Enote; Steven Godeke; Keecha Harris; Jaribu Hill; Nick Jacangelo; Joan Lisi; Arlene Rodriguez; Lenora Suki; Ann Wiener.
Number of staff: 2 full-time professional; 2 part-time professional; 2 part-time support.
EIN: 135600408
Selected grants: The following grants are a representative sample of this grantmaker's funding activity:
$100,000 to Comite de Apoyo a los Trabajadores Agricolas, Glassboro, NJ, 2012. For CATAs project will build the advocacy capacity of the Latino farmworker community to address food policy issues as they relate to labor rights issues.
$100,000 to East Michigan Environmental Action Council, Detroit, MI, 2012. For East Michigan Environmental Action Council (EMEAC) which will bring our youth work and food justice work together to lay the foundation for a youth-led food justice network in Detroit.
$90,000 to Alaska Community Action on Toxics, Anchorage, AK, 2012. For general support for statewide work for environmental and reproductive justice issues by supporting and assisting communities and Native tribes in Alaska, payable over 2.00 years.
$90,000 to Southwest Workers Union, San Antonio, TX, 2012. For Southwest Workers Union proposal to elevate our culturally-competent approach to food justice to the federal level through support of urban agriculture, farm to school programs and access to affordable, healthy food.
$60,000 to National Latina Institute for Reproductive Health, New York, NY, 2012. For general support to ensure the reproductive health and rights of Latinas nationwide through education, policy and advocacy initiatives, and community mobilization, payable over 2.00 years.
$50,000 to Farmworker Association of Florida, Apopka, FL, 2012. For general support for a statewide farmworker organization of Latino and immigrant farmworkers organizing on workplace, health, environmental and political issues, payable over 2.00 years.
$50,000 to Right to the City Alliance, New York, NY, 2012. For general support for a national coalition of urban base-building organizations, payable over 2.00 years.
$20,000 to Community Environmental Legal Defense Fund, Mercersburg, PA, 2012. For general support to help communities promote sustainable development by reining in corporate power and asserting local democratic control.
$20,000 to Missouri Rural Crisis Center, Columbia, MO, 2012. For general support to challenge corporate control of the food supply, and to create a sustainable, locally-based agriculture and food system.
$15,000 to National Womens Health Network, Washington, DC, 2012. For project support to protect and advance reproductive rights within the

context of health care reform by educating and mobilizing women through the Raising Women's Voices for the Health Care We Need campaign.

6572
Jane W. Nuhn Charitable Trust ✧
c/o Van DeWater & Van DeWater
P.O. Box 112
Poughkeepsie, NY 12602-0112
Contact: Michael De Cordova, Tr.

Established in 1988 in NY.
Foundation type: Independent foundation.
Financial data (yr. ended 12/31/13): Assets, $11,136,732 (M); expenditures, $583,584; qualifying distributions, $477,131; giving activities include $431,225 for 17 grants (high: $60,000; low: $1,500).
Purpose and activities: Giving primarily for the arts, higher education, and human services.
Fields of interest: Arts, multipurpose centers/programs; Arts; Higher education; Human services; Protestant agencies & churches.
Type of support: General/operating support; Building/renovation; Equipment; Endowments; Matching/challenge support.
Limitations: Applications accepted. Giving primarily in Dutchess County, NY, with some emphasis on Poughkeepsie. No grants to individuals.
Publications: Annual report.
Application information:
Initial approach: Letter
Deadline(s): None
Board meeting date(s): Quarterly
Trustees: Edward V.K. Cunningham, Jr.; Michael De Cordova; Noel De Cordova, Jr.
EIN: 146134057
Selected grants: The following grants are a representative sample of this grantmaker's funding activity:
$25,000 to Mill Street Loft, Poughkeepsie, NY, 2012. For youth outreach program.
$25,000 to Scenic Hudson, Poughkeepsie, NY, 2012. For City of Beacon Waterfront Project.
$20,000 to Bannerman Castle Trust, Glenham, NY, 2012. For rehabilitation project.
$15,000 to Bard College, Annandale on Hudson, NY, 2012. For music festival.
$2,000 to New Day Repertory Company, Poughkeepsie, NY, 2012. For Black Nativity Program.

6573
NYSE Euronext Foundation, Inc. ✧
(formerly New York Stock Exchange Foundation, Inc.)
20 Broad St., 19th Fl.
New York, NY 10005
Contact: Michelle Greene, Exec. Dir.
FAX: (212) 656-5629; E-mail: foundation@nyx.com; Main URL: http://www.nyx.com/nyse-euronext-foundation

Incorporated in 1983 in NY.
Donors: Charity Folks, Inc., Inc.; New York Stock Exchange LLC; Merrill Lynch, Pierce, Fenner & Smith Inc.
Foundation type: Company-sponsored foundation.
Financial data (yr. ended 12/31/12): Assets, $9,481,200 (M); gifts received, $63,949; expenditures, $2,856,944; qualifying distributions, $2,787,757; giving activities include $2,312,188 for 51 grants (high: $427,516; low: $5,000), and $427,516 for 433 employee matching gifts.
Purpose and activities: The foundation supports programs designed to promote financial literacy; entrepreneurship; economic empowerment; and community.
Fields of interest: Medical care, rehabilitation; Nutrition; Housing/shelter; Youth development; Human services, financial counseling; Human services; Business/industry; Microfinance/microlending; Community/economic development; Economics; Children; Minorities; Economically disadvantaged; Homeless.
Type of support: General/operating support; Annual campaigns; Capital campaigns; Program development; Scholarship funds; Research; Employee volunteer services; Sponsorships; Employee matching gifts.
Limitations: Applications accepted. Giving primarily in areas of company operations in New York, NY. No support for businesses, political, fraternal, or religious organizations, discriminatory organizations, donor advised funds, or private foundations. No grants to individuals, or for tickets to dinners, receptions, or other fundraising events.
Publications: Application guidelines; Annual report (including application guidelines).
Application information: Proposals should be no longer than 3 to 6 pages in length. Organizations receiving support are asked to submit a final report. Application form not required.
Initial approach: Mail grant application cover sheet and proposal to foundation
Copies of proposal: 1
Deadline(s): None
Board meeting date(s): Rolling
Final notification: Varies
Officers and Directors:* Duncan L. Niederauer,* Chair.; Janet M. McGinness,* Secy.; Michael S. Geltzeiler,* Treas.; Stephane P. Biehler, Cont.; Michelle D. Greene,* Exec. Dir.; Patrick D. Armstrong; Mary L. Brienza; Arthur D. Cashin, Jr.; Dominique Cerruti; Scott Cutler; Thomas J. Facchine; Thomas Farley; Scott Hill; Kelly Loeffler; Joseph Mecane; Patrick T. Murphy; David C. O'Day; Richard A. Rosenblatt; Edward G. Schreier; Daniel W. Tandy.
EIN: 133203195

6574
The Oceanic Heritage Foundation ✧
c/o Carter Ledyard & Milburn LLP
2 Wall St.
New York, NY 10005-2072

Established in 1998 in DE and MO.
Donors: John K. Menoudakos; Chryssanthy L. Menoudakos.
Foundation type: Independent foundation.
Financial data (yr. ended 12/31/13): Assets, $10,419,200 (M); gifts received, $2,067,341; expenditures, $2,003,165; qualifying distributions, $1,779,204; giving activities include $1,674,000 for 88 grants (high: $200,000; low: $5,000).
Purpose and activities: Giving only to organizations deemed worthy by the foundation.
Fields of interest: Arts; Higher education; Health care.
Limitations: Applications not accepted. Giving limited to areas of geographic interest, as determined by the foundation. No grants to individuals.
Application information: Contributes only to pre-selected organizations. Unsolicited requests for funds will neither be accepted or acknowledged.
Officers and Directors:* Chryssanthy L. Menoudakos,* Pres.; John K. Menoudakos,* V.P.
EIN: 431836518
Selected grants: The following grants are a representative sample of this grantmaker's funding activity:
$200,000 to Metropolitan Museum of Art, New York, NY, 2012. For American Wing Conservation and Training.
$172,000 to Metropolitan Museum of Art, New York, NY, 2012. For American Wing Conservation.
$133,000 to American Farm School, New York, NY, 2012. For preschool project.
$25,000 to American Farm School, New York, NY, 2012. For scholarship benefit.
$25,000 to Metropolitan Museum of Art, New York, NY, 2012. For Civil War and American Art Exhibition.
$20,000 to George W. Bush Foundation, Dallas, TX, 2012. For MSM and AREL Education Programs.
$20,000 to New York Public Library, New York, NY, 2012. For Summer Reading and Writing Program.
$15,000 to Alvin Ailey American Dance Theater, New York, NY, 2012. For Ailey II.
$15,000 to American Museum of Natural History, New York, NY, 2012. For Science Mentoring and STEM Programs.
$15,000 to Museum of Modern Art, New York, NY, 2012. For Family Lab Interactive Spaces.

6575
The Jane and Daniel Och Family Foundation ✧
c/o BCRS Assocs., LLC
77 Water St., 9th Fl.
New York, NY 10005-3701

Established in 2008 in NY.
Donor: Daniel S. Och.
Foundation type: Independent foundation.
Financial data (yr. ended 12/31/12): Assets, $159,065,060 (M); gifts received, $28,000,000; expenditures, $19,457,150; qualifying distributions, $18,574,222; giving activities include $18,560,286 for 27 grants (high: $2,500,000; low: $13,936).
Fields of interest: Hospitals (general); Human services; Foundations (private independent); Jewish federated giving programs.
Limitations: Applications not accepted. Giving primarily in New York, NY; some giving also in Boston, MA.
Application information: Contributes only to pre-selected organizations.
Trustees: Daniel S. Och; Jane C. Och.
EIN: 263791338
Selected grants: The following grants are a representative sample of this grantmaker's funding activity:
$3,000,000 to University of Pennsylvania, Philadelphia, PA, 2012. For general support.
$2,500,000 to New York-Presbyterian Fund, New York, NY, 2012. For general support.
$2,500,000 to Solomon Schechter Day School of Essex and Union, West Orange, NJ, 2012. For general support.
$2,176,350 to UJA-Federation of New York, New York, NY, 2012. For general support.
$2,002,750 to Robin Hood Foundation, New York, NY, 2012. For general support.

$1,000,000 to Birthright Israel Foundation, New York, NY, 2012. For general support.
$1,000,000 to Birthright Israel Foundation, New York, NY, 2012. For general support.
$1,000,000 to Solomon Schechter Day School of Essex and Union, West Orange, NJ, 2012. For general support.
$500,000 to Birthright Israel Foundation, New York, NY, 2012. For general operating support.
$50,000 to White Plains Hospital Center, White Plains, NY, 2012. For general support.

6576
OCLO, Inc. ✧

c/o Hertz, Herson & Co., LLP
477 Madison Ave., 10th Fl.
New York, NY 10022

Established in 1999 in DE and NY.
Donors: Susan R. Wexner; Naon, Inc.
Foundation type: Independent foundation.
Financial data (yr. ended 12/31/13): Assets, $40,300,613 (M); expenditures, $1,836,384; qualifying distributions, $1,731,611; giving activities include $1,729,589 for 12 grants (high: $1,000,000; low: $39).
Purpose and activities: Giving primarily to Jewish organizations.
Fields of interest: Education; Health organizations; United Ways and Federated Giving Programs; Jewish agencies & synagogues.
Limitations: Applications not accepted. Giving primarily in Washington, DC, New York, NY, and in Jerusalem, Israel. No grants to individuals.
Application information: Contributes only to pre-selected organizations.
Officer and Directors:* Susan R. Wexner,* Pres. and Secy.-Treas.; Saul G. Agus; Raymond Kanner; Gregg H. Levy, Esq.; Michael S. Oberman, Esq.; Mark W. Saks, Esq.; Walter Stern.
EIN: 522171831

6577
O'Connor Family Foundation ✧ ☆

c/o O'Connor Capital Partners
535 Madison Ave., 23rd Fl.
New York, NY 10022

Established in 2006 in NY.
Donors: Joan B. O'Connor; Jeremiah W. O'Connor†.
Foundation type: Independent foundation.
Financial data (yr. ended 12/31/13): Assets, $10,952,301 (M); expenditures, $561,252; qualifying distributions, $515,867; giving activities include $514,250 for 42 grants (high: $110,000; low: $250).
Fields of interest: Elementary/secondary education; Catholic agencies & churches.
Limitations: Applications not accepted. Giving primarily in NY. No grants to individuals.
Application information: Unsolicited requests for funds not accepted.
Trustees: John O'Connor; Joan B. O'Connor; Roger D. Turner.
EIN: 137557714
Selected grants: The following grants are a representative sample of this grantmaker's funding activity:
$50,000 to Partners in Health, Boston, MA, 2011.
$21,000 to Our Lady of Florida Spiritual Center, North Palm Beach, FL, 2011.
$12,000 to Gregorian University Foundation, New York, NY, 2011.
$10,000 to Bronxville School Foundation, Bronxville, NY, 2011.
$10,000 to Heritage Museums and Gardens, Sandwich, MA, 2011.
$10,000 to Memorial Sloan-Kettering Cancer Center, New York, NY, 2011.
$5,000 to Cape Cod Healthcare Foundation, Hyannis, MA, 2011.
$5,000 to Stamford Hospital, Stamford, CT, 2011.
$3,500 to Saint Josephs Seminary, Yonkers, NY, 2011.
$2,000 to Brunswick School, Greenwich, CT, 2011.

6578
A. Lindsay and Olive B. O'Connor Foundation ✧

731 Main St.
P.O. Box D
Hobart, NY 13788-0404 (607) 538-9248
FAX: (607) 538-1650;
E-mail: office@theoconnorfoundation.org; Main URL: http://theoconnorfoundation.org/
Grants List: http://theoconnorfoundation.org/recent_grants.html

Trust established in 1965 in NY.
Donor: Olive B. O'Connor†.
Foundation type: Independent foundation.
Financial data (yr. ended 12/31/13): Assets, $68,849,995 (M); expenditures, $3,559,777; qualifying distributions, $2,982,721; giving activities include $2,688,014 for 302 grants (high: $159,302; low: $250).
Purpose and activities: Emphasis on quality of life, including hospitals, libraries, community centers, higher education, nursing and other vocational education, child development and youth agencies, religious organizations, museums, and historic restoration; support also for civic affairs and town, village, and environmental conservation and improvement.
Fields of interest: Arts, alliance/advocacy; Visual arts, architecture; Museums; Performing arts; History/archaeology; Historic preservation/historical societies; Arts; Education, early childhood education; Child development, education; Vocational education; Higher education; Business school/education; Libraries/library science; Environment, natural resources; Environment; Animal welfare; Animals/wildlife, preservation/protection; Hospitals (general); Nursing care; Substance abuse, services; Alcoholism; Crime/violence prevention, youth; Employment; Agriculture; Housing/shelter, development; Human services; Children/youth, services; Child development, services; Women, centers/services; Rural development; Community/economic development; United Ways and Federated Giving Programs; Religious federated giving programs; Biology/life sciences; Economics; Government/public administration; Christian agencies & churches; Protestant agencies & churches; Religion; Children/youth; Children; Youth; Aging; Young adults; Physically disabled; Women; Girls; Adults, women; Young adults, female; Boys; Adults, men; Young adults, male; Economically disadvantaged.
Type of support: Continuing support; Income development; Management development/capacity building; Annual campaigns; Capital campaigns; Building/renovation; Equipment; Land acquisition; Endowments; Emergency funds; Program development; Conferences/seminars; Publication; Seed money; Scholarship funds; Research; Technical assistance; Program-related investments/loans; Matching/challenge support.
Limitations: Applications accepted. Giving primarily in Delaware County, NY, and 7 contiguous rural counties in upstate NY (Broome, Chenango, Greene, Otsego, Schoharie, Sullivan, and Ulster). No grants to individuals, or for salaries, debt repayment, operating budgets, or deficit financing.
Publications: Application guidelines; Grants list; Multi-year report; Program policy statement.
Application information: Complete application guidelines and form are available by contacting the foundation. Application form required.
Initial approach: Letter or telephone
Copies of proposal: 1
Deadline(s): Apr. 1 and Sept. 1 for grants over $5,000; 1st of each month for grants under $5,000
Board meeting date(s): May or June and Sept. or Oct.; committee meets monthly to consider grants under $5,000
Final notification: 7 to 10 days after semiannual meeting
Officers and Directors:* Donald F. Bishop II,* Chair. and Exec. Dir.; Charlotte Bishop Hill,* Vice-Chair.; Pamela Hill, Exec. Secy. and Treas.; Amy Bishop; Lindsay Bishop; Robert L. Bishop II; Suzanne Hill; William J. Murphy; Eugene Peckham.
Trustee: Chemung Canal Trust Co.
Number of staff: 2 full-time professional; 1 part-time professional.
EIN: 166063485

6579
Ralph E. Ogden Foundation, Inc. ✧

Pleasant Hill Rd.
P.O. Box 290
Mountainville, NY 10953-0290

Incorporated in 1947 in DE.
Donors: Ralph E. Ogden†; H. Peter Stern; Margaret H. Ogden†.
Foundation type: Independent foundation.
Financial data (yr. ended 12/31/12): Assets, $38,140,275 (M); expenditures, $2,774,606; qualifying distributions, $2,369,590; giving activities include $1,661,190 for 56 grants (high: $1,055,000; low: $1,000).
Purpose and activities: Giving primarily for the arts and education.
Fields of interest: Arts; Education; International affairs.
Limitations: Applications not accepted. Giving primarily in Mountainville and New York, NY. No grants to individuals.
Application information: Contributes only to pre-selected organizations.
Officers: Beatrice Stern, Pres. and Treas.; Elisabeth Ellen Stern, V.P.
Directors: Lucy Cohan; Peter Erwin; Peter Lamb; Joan O. Stern; John Peter Stern.
EIN: 141455902
Selected grants: The following grants are a representative sample of this grantmaker's funding activity:
$1,055,000 to Storm King Art Center, Mountainville, NY, 2012. For Furtherance of the Arts.
$15,000 to Center for Constitutional Rights, New York, NY, 2012. To support Educational Institution.

$10,000 to Grassroots International, Boston, MA, 2012. For International Welfare.
$7,500 to Georgetown Day School, Washington, DC, 2012. To support Education Institution.

6580
Ohel Harav Yehoshua Boruch Foundation, Inc. ✧
1180 Ocean Pkwy., Ste. 3A
Brooklyn, NY 11230-4033

Established in 1994 in NY.
Donors: Ben Landa; Josh Farkovits; Esther Farkovits; Meir Fischil; Teddy Pollack.
Foundation type: Independent foundation.
Financial data (yr. ended 12/31/12): Assets, $15,861,791 (M); gifts received, $550,000; expenditures, $737,200; qualifying distributions, $737,200; giving activities include $737,200 for 11 grants (high: $250,000; low: $1,000).
Purpose and activities: Giving primarily to Jewish temples and schools.
Fields of interest: Education; Jewish agencies & synagogues.
Limitations: Applications not accepted. Giving primarily in NY. No grants to individuals.
Application information: Contributes only to pre-selected organizations.
Officers: Ben Landa, Pres.; Esther Farkovitz, V.P. and Treas.; Dena Hersh, Secy.
EIN: 113201774

6581
Norio Ohga Foundation ✧
550 Madison Ave., 35th Fl.
New York, NY 10022-3211
Application address: c/o Kenneth Nees, V.P. and Secy., 1470 Royal Harbour Ct., No. 522, Fort Myers, FL 33908

Established in 1991 in NY.
Donor: Sony Corp. of America.
Foundation type: Independent foundation.
Financial data (yr. ended 12/31/13): Assets, $499,426 (M); expenditures, $560,626; qualifying distributions, $560,000; giving activities include $560,000 for 2 grants (high: $550,000; low: $10,000).
Purpose and activities: Support for the arts, primarily for the benefit of the Tokyo Philharmonic Orchestra.
Fields of interest: Arts, association; Performing arts, orchestras.
Type of support: General/operating support; Capital campaigns; Scholarship funds.
Limitations: Applications accepted. Giving primarily in FL, NY, in Tokyo, Japan. No grants to individuals.
Application information: Application form required.
Initial approach: Letter
Deadline(s): None
Officers and Directors:* Midori Ohga,* Pres.; Kenneth L. Nees, V.P. and Secy.; H. Paul Burak,* V.P.; Mark E. Kahil,* V.P.
EIN: 133617866

6582
The Ohrstrom Foundation, Inc. ✧
c/o O'Connor, Davies, Munns & Dobbins, LLP
665 Fifth Ave.
New York, NY 10022-5305
E-mail: cgallo@tccgrp.com

Incorporated in 1953 in DE.
Donor: Members of the Ohrstrom family.
Foundation type: Independent foundation.
Financial data (yr. ended 05/31/13): Assets, $88,058,660 (M); expenditures, $4,523,514; qualifying distributions, $4,375,634; giving activities include $4,192,609 for 27 grants (high: $1,032,607; low: $10,000).
Fields of interest: Education; Environment, natural resources; Human services; Philanthropy/voluntarism, management/technical assistance.
Type of support: General/operating support; Continuing support; Annual campaigns; Building/renovation; Equipment; Land acquisition; Endowments; Emergency funds; Program development; Seed money; Matching/challenge support.
Limitations: Applications not accepted. Giving in the U.S., with emphasis on MA and VA. No grants to individuals, or for deficit financing, scholarships, fellowships, research, special projects, publications, or conferences; no loans.
Application information: Contributes only to pre-selected organizations.
Officers and Directors:* W. Carey Crane III,* V.P.; Kristiane C. Graham,* V.P.; Clarke Ohrstrom,* V.P.; George F. Ohrstrom, V.P.; Jennifer L. Franklin, Secy.; Mark J. Ohrstrom,* Treas.; Magalen O. Bryant, Dir. Emeritus; Winifred O. Nichols; Christopher Ohrstrom.
EIN: 546039966

6583
George L. Ohrstrom, Jr. Foundation ✧
c/o OD, LLP
665 5th Ave.
New York, NY 10022-5305

Established in NY.
Donor: George L. Ohrstrom, Jr.†.
Foundation type: Independent foundation.
Financial data (yr. ended 12/31/13): Assets, $65,608,639 (M); expenditures, $3,092,470; qualifying distributions, $2,443,469; giving activities include $2,370,000 for 79 grants (high: $500,000; low: $2,500).
Fields of interest: Libraries (public); Environment; Human services; Foundations (private grantmaking); Foundations (public).
Type of support: General/operating support.
Limitations: Applications not accepted. Giving in the U.S., with emphasis on NY and VA. No grants to individuals.
Application information: Contributes only to pre-selected organizations.
Officers: Alan Berlin, Co-Chair.; Donald Grant Calder, Co-Chair.; Wright R.S. Ohrstrom, Co-Chair.; David W. Laughlin, Treas.
EIN: 133415874

6584
The John R. Oishei Foundation ✧
726 Exchange Street, Ste. 510
Buffalo, NY 14210 (716) 856-9490
Contact: Robert D. Gioia, Pres.
FAX: (716) 856-9493; E-mail: info@oishei.org; Main URL: http://www.oishei.org
CEP Study: http://www.oishei.org/index.php/about-us/km/grantee-perception-report-2010
E-Newsletter: http://www.oishei.org/index.php/about-us/media-room/news
Facebook: https://www.facebook.com/pages/The-John-R-Oishei-Foundation/172658236100389
Grants List: http://www.oishei.org/index.php/about-us/km/grantmaking
LinkedIn: http://www.linkedin.com/company/the-john-r.-oishei-foundation?trk=fc_badge
Twitter: https://twitter.com/OisheiFndtn

Incorporated in 1941 in NY.
Donors: Peter C. Cornell Trust; John R. Oishei†; R. John Oshei†; Jean R. Oshei; Oishei Consolidated Trust No. 1; Oishei Consolidated Trust No. 2.
Foundation type: Independent foundation.
Financial data (yr. ended 12/31/12): Assets, $255,827,396 (M); gifts received, $945,977; expenditures, $23,392,259; qualifying distributions, $18,893,957; giving activities include $17,421,218 for 216 grants (high: $1,007,827; low: $250).
Purpose and activities: The foundation strives to be a catalyst for change to enhance economic vitality and the quality of life for the Buffalo Niagara region.
Fields of interest: Arts; Secondary school/education; Higher education; Health care; Medical research, institute; Human services; Community/economic development; Science, research.
Type of support: Mission-related investments/loans; General/operating support; Management development/capacity building; Program development; Professorships; Seed money; Curriculum development; Scholarship funds; Research; Program evaluation; Program-related investments/loans; Matching/challenge support.
Limitations: Applications accepted. Giving limited to the Buffalo, NY, area. No support for religious organizations for sectarian or propagation of faith purposes. No grants to individuals, organizations which make grants to others, or lobbying or advocacy for specific political candidates or legislation.
Publications: Annual report; Grants list; Informational brochure (including application guidelines).
Application information: Full application guidelines are available on the foundation web site. Application form not required.
Initial approach: Letter of inquiry via online process
Copies of proposal: 1
Deadline(s): None
Board meeting date(s): Bimonthly
Final notification: Within 3 to 6 months
Officers and Directors:* James M. Wadsworth,* Chair.; Mary S. Martino,* Vice-Chair.; Robert D. Gioia, Pres.; Paul T. Hogan, Exec. V.P.; Blythe T. Merrill, Sr. V.P., Progs.; Karen Lee Spaulding, V.P., Philanthropic Support; Gayle L. Houck, Secy., Cont., and Grants Mgr.; Edward F. Walsh, Jr.,* Treas.; Robert M. Bennett; Ruth D. Bryant; Florence M. Conti; William G. Giesel, Jr.; Luke T. Jacobs; Ann M. McCarthy.
Number of staff: 4 full-time professional; 1 full-time support.
EIN: 160874319

Selected grants: The following grants are a representative sample of this grantmaker's funding activity:
$1,007,827 to Buffalo Independent Secondary School Network, Buffalo, NY, 2012. For JROF scholarship program.
$500,000 to Canisius College, Buffalo, NY, 2012. For Phase I to develop the Science Hall.
$350,000 to Buffalo Society of Natural Sciences, Buffalo Museum of Science, Buffalo, NY, 2012. For Development and installation of the Health Sciences and Earth Systems Science Studios.
$310,000 to Western New York Association of Homes and Services for the Aging, Getzville, NY, 2012. For Implement the regional Framework for Change initiative (now the WNY Alliance for Person-Centered Care).
$100,000 to Buffalo Center for Arts and Technology, Buffalo, NY, 2012. For BATC Center.
$87,500 to Wellness Institute of Greater Buffalo and Western New York, Buffalo, NY, 2012. For Buffalo CarShare - shared staff position and a match for commercial support.
$50,000 to National Center for Arts and Technology, Pittsburgh, PA, 2012. For planning and implementation work needed to launch the Buffalo Arts and Technology Center.
$20,000 to Niagara Community Action Program, Niagara Falls, NY, 2012. For basic human needs.

6585
Olayan Charitable Trust ✧
c/o Olayan America Corp.
505 Park Ave., 11th Fl.
New York, NY 10022

Established in 1993 in NY.
Donors: Hutham S. Olayan; Olayan America Corp.
Foundation type: Independent foundation.
Financial data (yr. ended 12/31/13): Assets, $1,983,814 (M); gifts received, $8,060,000; expenditures, $729,169; qualifying distributions, $728,800; giving activities include $728,800 for 11 grants (high: $192,500; low: $2,500).
Purpose and activities: Giving primarily for education, particularly to a university in Beirut; funding also for a cancer hospital.
Fields of interest: Higher education; Hospitals (specialty); Cancer; Human services.
International interests: Middle East.
Limitations: Applications not accepted. Giving primarily in NY and in Beirut, Lebanon. No grants to individuals.
Application information: Contributes only to pre-selected organizations.
Trustees: Nazeeh S. Habachy; Hutham S. Olayan.
EIN: 137031747

6586
The Old Boys Foundation ✧ ☆
c/o Lipsky Goodkin & Co.
120 W. 45th St., 7th Fl.
New York, NY 10036-4041

Established in DE.
Donor: Maurice E. Pinto.
Foundation type: Independent foundation.
Financial data (yr. ended 12/31/12): Assets, $1,441,980 (M); expenditures, $1,371,095; qualifying distributions, $1,236,700; giving activities include $1,236,700 for grants.
Fields of interest: Education.
Type of support: General/operating support.
Limitations: Applications not accepted. Giving primarily in NY. No grants to individuals.
Application information: Contributes only to pre-selected organizations.
Officers and Directors:* Maurice E. Pinto,* Pres.; Elizabeth A. Pinto,* Secy.-Treas.
EIN: 522060504

6587
Olive Bridge Fund ✧
c/o DZ Capital, LLC
767 5th Ave., 12th Fl.
New York, NY 10153

Incorporated in 1952 in NY.
Donors: Harold F. Linder†; Joshua Steiner; Susan E. Linder; Elizabeth Steiner; Daniel L. Steiner; Prudence L. Steiner.
Foundation type: Independent foundation.
Financial data (yr. ended 12/31/12): Assets, $26,900,705 (M); expenditures, $1,185,101; qualifying distributions, $1,099,345; giving activities include $1,085,954 for 68 grants (high: $100,000; low: $3).
Fields of interest: Arts; Higher education; Education; Health care; Health organizations, association; Human services; Jewish agencies & synagogues.
Type of support: General/operating support.
Limitations: Applications not accepted. Giving primarily in MA, NY and OR. No grants to individuals.
Application information: Contributes only to pre-selected organizations.
Officers: Prudence L. Steiner, Pres. and Secy.; Elizabeth Steiner Hayward, V.P.; Joshua L. Steiner, V.P.
Trustee: Susan E. Linder.
EIN: 136161669

6588
Morton & Carole Olshan Foundation ✧
600 Madison Ave., 14th Fl.
New York, NY 10022

Established in 1991 in NY.
Donors: Morton Olshan; Carole Olshan.
Foundation type: Independent foundation.
Financial data (yr. ended 12/31/13): Assets, $4,990 (M); gifts received, $485,000; expenditures, $511,798; qualifying distributions, $507,765; giving activities include $507,765 for 14 grants (high: $150,000; low: $500).
Purpose and activities: The foundation provides aid to those in need of assistance.
Fields of interest: Education; Human services; Jewish federated giving programs; Jewish agencies & synagogues.
Limitations: Applications not accepted. Giving primarily in NY. No grants to individuals.
Application information: Unsolicited requests for funds not accepted.
Officers and Directors:* Morton Olshan,* Pres.; Carole Olshan,* V.P.; Robert Steinberg.
EIN: 133601794

6589
The T. D. & M. A. O'Malley Foundation, Inc. ✧
c/o Berdon, LLP
360 Madison Ave.
New York, NY 10017-1111

Established in 1985 in CT.
Donor: Thomas D. O'Malley.
Foundation type: Independent foundation.
Financial data (yr. ended 09/30/13): Assets, $1,352,989 (M); expenditures, $1,492,676; qualifying distributions, $1,477,950; giving activities include $1,474,000 for 15 grants (high: $437,500; low: $250).
Purpose and activities: Giving primarily for education, health care and medical research, including childhood illness.
Fields of interest: Higher education; Education; Hospitals (general); Hospitals (specialty); Medical research, institute; Children.
Limitations: Applications not accepted. Giving primarily in Riverdale, NY; giving also in CT, with emphasis on Greenwich, and in Washington, DC; some funding also in Pasadena, CA. No grants to individuals.
Application information: Contributes only to pre-selected organizations.
Officers: Thomas D. O'Malley, Pres. and Treas.; Mary Alice O'Malley, V.P. and Secy.
EIN: 061157580

6590
Omer Foundation ✧ ☆
c/o Moses & Singer
405 Lexington Ave.
New York, NY 10174-0002

Donor: Claire Friedlander†.
Foundation type: Independent foundation.
Financial data (yr. ended 12/31/13): Assets, $11,884,333 (M); expenditures, $691,684; qualifying distributions, $595,898; giving activities include $581,000 for 24 grants (high: $80,000; low: $7,000).
Fields of interest: Health organizations; Human services.
Limitations: Applications not accepted. Giving primarily in New York, NY.
Application information: Unsolicited requests for funds not accepted.
Trustee: Jay Fialkoff.
EIN: 800094281
Selected grants: The following grants are a representative sample of this grantmaker's funding activity:
$10,000 to Herbert G. Birch Services, New York, NY, 2011.

6591
The Timothy J. and Linda D. O'Neill Foundation ✧ ☆
c/o Goldman Sachs & Co., Family Office
Bowling Green Sta.
P.O. Box 73
New York, NY 10274-0073

Established in 1991 in NY.
Donor: Timothy J. O'Neill.
Foundation type: Independent foundation.

Financial data (yr. ended 04/30/13): Assets, $5,235,883 (M); expenditures, $1,014,296; qualifying distributions, $1,013,350; giving activities include $1,013,350 for 22 grants (high: $500,000; low: $350).
Purpose and activities: Giving primarily for education, health organizations, and children and youth services, including a children's hospital, and social services.
Fields of interest: Higher education; Education; Hospitals (specialty); Health organizations; Human services; Children/youth, services.
Limitations: Applications not accepted. Giving primarily in CT, Washington DC, and NY. No grants to individuals.
Application information: Contributes only to pre-selected organizations.
Trustees: Linda D. O'Neill; Timothy J. O'Neill.
EIN: 133642501
Selected grants: The following grants are a representative sample of this grantmaker's funding activity:
$500,000 to Georgetown University, Washington, DC, 2013. For general support.
$400,000 to Greenwich Academy, Greenwich, CT, 2013. For general support.
$46,000 to Mount Sinai Hospital, New York, NY, 2013. For general support.
$10,000 to Greenwich Academy, Greenwich, CT, 2012. For general support.
$10,000 to Kennebunkport Conservation Trust, Cape Porpoise, ME, 2012. For general support.
$10,000 to Kennebunkport Conservation Trust, Cape Porpoise, ME, 2013. For general support.
$10,000 to New York Foundling Hospital, New York, NY, 2012. For general support.
$10,000 to New York Foundling Hospital, New York, NY, 2013. For general support.
$10,000 to New York-Presbyterian Hospital, New York, NY, 2012. For general support.
$10,000 to Weill Medical College of Cornell University, New York, NY, 2013. For general support.

6592
The Opatrny Family Foundation ✧

(formerly Donald C. and Judith T. Opatrny, Jr. Charitable Foundation)
c/o BCRS Assocs., LLC
77 Water St., 9th Fl.
New York, NY 10005-4414

Established in 1988 in NY.
Donor: Donald C. Opatrny, Jr.
Foundation type: Independent foundation.
Financial data (yr. ended 05/31/13): Assets, $1,159,378 (M); gifts received, $775,000; expenditures, $1,200,510; qualifying distributions, $1,196,110; giving activities include $1,192,825 for 17 grants (high: $600,000; low: $250).
Fields of interest: Higher education.
Limitations: Applications not accepted. Giving primarily in New London, CT, and Ithaca, NY. No grants to individuals.
Application information: Contributes only to pre-selected organizations.
Trustees: Donald C. Opatrny, Jr.; Judith T. Opatrny.
EIN: 133502411
Selected grants: The following grants are a representative sample of this grantmaker's funding activity:
$1,000,000 to Cornell University, Ithaca, NY, 2011. For general purpose.
$600,000 to Connecticut College, New London, CT, 2011. For general purpose.

6593
Open Society Institute ✧

224 W. 57th St.
New York, NY 10019-3212 (212) 548-0600
Contact: Inquiry Mgr.
FAX: (212) 548-4600; Baltimore, MD office: 201 N. Charles St., Ste. 1300, Baltimore, MD 21201, tel.: (410) 234-1091; Washington, DC office: 1730 Pennsylvania Ave. N.W., 7th fl., Washington, DC 20006, tel.: 202-721-5600; Main URL: http://www.opensocietyfoundations.org/
Blog: http://blog.soros.org/
E-Newsletter: http://www.soros.org/resources/newsletters
Facebook: http://www.facebook.com/OpenSocietyFoundations
Open Society Foundations Instagram: http://instagram.com/opensocietyfoundations
Open Society Institute: United States RSS: http://feeds.feedburner.com/OpenSocietyInstituteUnitedStates
Open Society Institute's Philanthropy Promise: http://www.ncrp.org/philanthropys-promise/who
OSI - Baltimore: http://twitter.com/OSIBaltimore
Podcasts: http://www.soros.org/resources/multimedia/podcasts
RSS Directory: http://www.soros.org/feeds
Twitter: http://www.twitter.com/opensociety

Established in 1993 in NY.
Donor: George Soros.
Foundation type: Operating foundation.
Financial data (yr. ended 12/31/12): Assets, $685,871,435 (M); gifts received, $202,281,105; expenditures, $586,306,761; qualifying distributions, $642,804,792; giving activities include $444,471,445 for 526 grants (high: $245,000,000; low: $600), $9,998,480 for 862 grants to individuals (high: $120,020; low: $79), and $1,393,873 for 419 employee matching gifts.
Purpose and activities: The Open Society Institute (OSI), a private operating and grantmaking foundation, aims to shape public policy to promote democratic governance, human rights, and economic, legal, and social reform. On a local level, OSI implements a range of initiatives to support the rule of law, education, public health, and independent media. At the same time, OSI works to build alliances across borders and continents on issues such as combating corruption and rights abuses. OSI was created in 1993 by investor and philanthropist George Soros to support his foundations in Central and Eastern Europe and the former Soviet Union. Those foundations were established, starting in 1984, to help countries make the transition from communism. OSI has expanded the activities of the Soros foundations network to other areas of the world where the transition to democracy is of particular concern. The Soros foundations network encompasses foundations, offices, initiatives, and grantees in more than 60 countries and regions including: Asia, Southeast Asia, Central Asia, and Caucasus, Latin America and the Caribbean Central and South Eastern Europe, Africa, the Baltics, and North America.
Fields of interest: Media/communications; Arts; Education; Reproductive health; Public health; Palliative care; Crime/law enforcement; International economic development; International human rights; Civil/human rights; Law/international law; Children/youth; Children; Youth; Disabilities, people with; Blind/visually impaired; Mentally disabled; Minorities; African Americans/Blacks; Hispanics/Latinos; Indigenous peoples; Girls; Offenders/ex-offenders; Substance abusers; AIDS, people with; Terminal illness, people with; Immigrants/refugees; Economically disadvantaged; Migrant workers; LGBTQ.
International interests: Africa; Asia; Caribbean; Central Asia; Eastern Europe; Global Programs; Latin America; Southeastern Asia.
Type of support: General/operating support; Continuing support; Program development; Professorships; Publication; Fellowships; Internship funds; Scholarship funds; Research; Technical assistance; Program-related investments/loans; Employee matching gifts; Grants to individuals; Scholarships—to individuals.
Limitations: Applications accepted. Giving on a national and international basis. No support for political parties or organizations connected to political parties.
Publications: Annual report; Informational brochure; Newsletter; Program policy statement.
Application information: For program application guidelines and deadlines see foundation web site. The site includes a wizard to help determine eligibility and submit an inquiry electronically. Application form not required.
Initial approach: Letter of inquiry, only if grantseeker does not have internet access
Officers and Trustees:* George Soros,* Chair.; Christopher Stone, Pres.; Stewart J. Paperin, Exec. V.P. and Treas.; Annette Laborey, V.P.; Ricardo A. Castro, Secy. and Genl. Counsel; Maija Arbolino, C.F.O.; Leon Botstein; Jonathan Soros.
EIN: 137029285
Selected grants: The following grants are a representative sample of this grantmaker's funding activity:
$245,000,000 to Foundation to Promote Open Society, New York, NY, 2012. For charitable activities and programs promoting open, democratic societies both in the United States and abroad.
$40,000,000 to Foundation to Promote Open Society, New York, NY, 2012. For charitable activities and programs promoting open, democratic societies both in the United States and abroad.
$12,766,016 to Open Society Foundation - London, London, England, 2012. For charitable activities promoting open societies worldwide.
$10,100,000 to Open Society Institute, Budapest, Hungary, 2012. For general support.
$5,313,556 to Soros Foundation-Romania, Bucharest, Romania, 2012. For general support to the Foundation in its transition into a fully independent entity.
$4,466,948 to Stefan Batory Foundation, Warsaw, Poland, 2012. For general support to the EU7 Foundations as they transition into independent entities.
$3,578,878 to Nadace Open Society Fund Praha, Prague, Czech Republic, 2012. For funds to the EU7 countries to support their transition into fully independent entities.
$3,535,722 to Open Society Institute-Sofia, Sofia, Bulgaria, 2012. For general support to the Foundation as it transitions to become a fully independent entity.
$2,660,305 to Open Estonia Foundation, Tallinn, Estonia, 2012. For general support to the EU7

Foundations as they transition into independent entities.
$2,308,099 to Open Society Institute-Macedonia, Skopje, Macedonia, 2012. For general support for the foundation's charitable activities, including but not limited to: accelerating the EU accession of Macedonia, promoting the integration of Roma and socially marginalized groups, encouraging civic participation, reviving civil society, developing local democracy, and promoting multiethnic and open society values.

6594
Oppenheim Family Fund, Inc. ✧
c/o James Ferrara, Anchin, Block & Anchin LLP
1375 Broadway
New York, NY 10018-7086

Established in 1961.
Donors: William J. Oppenheim; Paula K. Oppenheim.
Foundation type: Independent foundation.
Financial data (yr. ended 08/31/13): Assets, $13,375,897 (M); expenditures, $685,441; qualifying distributions, $551,518; giving activities include $547,018 for 98 grants (high: $50,000; low: $75).
Purpose and activities: Giving primarily for education, health, social services and Jewish organizations.
Fields of interest: Higher education; Education; Hospitals (general); Health organizations, association; Human services; Jewish federated giving programs; Jewish agencies & synagogues.
Limitations: Applications not accepted. Giving primarily in Greenwich, CT, and New York, NY. No grants to individuals.
Application information: Contributes only to pre-selected organizations.
Officers: Paula K. Oppenheim, Pres.; Lisa Oppenheim Schultz, Secy.; William J. Oppenheim, Jr., Treas.
EIN: 136158857
Selected grants: The following grants are a representative sample of this grantmaker's funding activity:
$5,000 to Abraham Fund Initiatives, New York, NY, 2011.
$1,000 to Ackerman Institute for the Family, New York, NY, 2011.

6595
The Winifred and William O'Reilly Foundation ✧
c/o Bell & Co.
122 E. 42nd St., 31th Fl.
New York, NY 10168-0002

Established in 2005 in NY.
Donors: William O'Reilly; Maureen O'Reilly; Bill Me Inc.; Richard W. Hotes.
Foundation type: Independent foundation.
Financial data (yr. ended 09/30/13): Assets, $357,154 (M); gifts received, $2,050,269; expenditures, $1,859,757; qualifying distributions, $1,847,655; giving activities include $1,847,655 for 84 grants (high: $1,015,000; low: $500).
Fields of interest: Arts; Education; Human services; Children/youth.
Limitations: Applications not accepted. Giving primarily in CA and NY. No grants to individuals.
Application information: Contributes only to pre-selected organizations.
Officers and Directors:* William O'Reilly,* Pres.; Edgar Royce,* V.P.; Evan R. Bell,* Secy.-Treas.
EIN: 202226224

6596
Orentreich Family Foundation ✧
909 5th Ave.
New York, NY 10021-4187

Established in 1986 in NY.
Donors: David Orentreich; Norman Orentreich; Orentreich Medical Group.
Foundation type: Independent foundation.
Financial data (yr. ended 09/30/13): Assets, $20,113,780 (M); expenditures, $1,343,759; qualifying distributions, $1,177,026; giving activities include $1,156,746 for 79 grants (high: $294,100; low: $1,000).
Fields of interest: Museums (art); Arts; Human services; Jewish agencies & synagogues.
Limitations: Applications not accepted. Giving primarily in New York, NY. No grants to individuals.
Application information: Contributes only to pre-selected organizations.
Trustees: David Orentreich; Norman Orentreich.
EIN: 136879797

6597
The William R. Orthwein, Jr. & Laura Rand Orthwein Foundation ✧
c/o Morgan Stanley Trust, N.A.
1 New York Plz., 7th Fl.
New York, NY 10004-1913

Established in MO.
Donors: William R. Orthwein; Laura R. Orthwein; The LRO 10-Year Charitable Lead Annuity Trust; The LRO 15-Year Charitable Lead Annuity Trust.
Foundation type: Independent foundation.
Financial data (yr. ended 11/30/13): Assets, $63,758,624 (M); gifts received, $1,630,891; expenditures, $4,005,363; qualifying distributions, $3,295,720; giving activities include $3,176,573 for 55 grants (high: $237,086; low: $5,000).
Purpose and activities: Giving primarily for the arts, education, hospitals, including a children's hospital, and to other children, youth, and social services.
Fields of interest: Museums (specialized); Arts; Elementary/secondary education; Higher education; Hospitals (general); Hospitals (specialty); Human services; Children/youth, services.
Limitations: Applications not accepted. Giving primarily in St. Louis, MO. No grants to individuals.
Application information: Contributes only to pre-selected organizations.
Trustees: Stephen C. Jones; Morgan Stanley Trust, N.A.
EIN: 200257512

6598
The Arthur and Mae Orvis Foundation, Inc. ✧
(formerly The Arthur Emerton Orvis Foundation)
1540 Broadway, 24th Fl.
New York, NY 10036-4039 (646) 218-7594
Contact: Paul M. Frank, Pres.

Established in 1967 in NY.
Donor: Mae Zenke Orvis‡.
Foundation type: Independent foundation.
Financial data (yr. ended 12/31/13): Assets, $11,954,381 (M); expenditures, $943,450; qualifying distributions, $799,625; giving activities include $715,000 for 17 grants (high: $150,000; low: $2,500).
Purpose and activities: Giving primarily for cultural institutions, and for nursing.
Fields of interest: Performing arts, music; Performing arts, orchestras; Performing arts, opera; Arts; Higher education; Nursing school/education.
Limitations: Applications accepted. Giving limited to Honolulu, HI, Reno, NV, and New York, NY. No grants to individuals.
Application information: Application form required.
Initial approach: Proposal
Deadline(s): None
Officers: Paul M. Frank, Pres.; John A. Gibbons, V.P.; Roger M. Gerber, Treas.; Darcy Katris, Secy.
Board Members: Ruth O. Bingham; Ernest J. Maupin; Grover O'Neill.
EIN: 136217675
Selected grants: The following grants are a representative sample of this grantmaker's funding activity:
$50,000 to Hawaii Opera Theater, Honolulu, HI, 2011.
$45,000 to Sierra Arts Foundation, Reno, NV, 2011.
$35,000 to University of Nevada Reno Foundation, Reno, NV, 2011.
$30,000 to Manhattan School of Music, New York, NY, 2011.
$25,000 to Hawaii Opera Theater, Honolulu, HI, 2011.
$25,000 to Hawaii Opera Theater, Honolulu, HI, 2011.
$25,000 to Nevada Museum of Art, Reno, NV, 2011.
$15,000 to Manhattan School of Music, New York, NY, 2011.
$15,000 to Nevada Museum of Art, Reno, NV, 2011.
$15,000 to University of Nevada Reno Foundation, Reno, NV, 2011.

6599
The O'Shea Family Foundation ✧
(formerly The Robert J. and Michele K. O'Shea Foundation)
c/o BCRS Assocs., LLC
77 Water St., 9th Fl.
New York, NY 10005-3701

Established in 1996 in NJ.
Donor: Robert J. O'Shea.
Foundation type: Independent foundation.
Financial data (yr. ended 10/31/13): Assets, $36,308,054 (M); gifts received, $5,030,000; expenditures, $1,324,150; qualifying distributions, $1,313,023; giving activities include $1,313,015 for 38 grants (high: $1,100,000; low: $115).
Fields of interest: Higher education; Education; Health care; Human services.
Limitations: Applications not accepted. Giving primarily in NJ, with some emphasis on Wyckoff; some funding nationally, particularly in NY. No grants to individuals or for scholarships; no loans.
Application information: Contributes only to pre-selected organizations.
Trustees: Michele K. O'Shea; Robert J. O'Shea.
EIN: 133926380

Selected grants: The following grants are a representative sample of this grantmaker's funding activity:
$950,000 to Fordham University, New York, NY, 2011. For general purpose.
$75,000 to Fordham University, New York, NY, 2011. For general purpose.
$20,000 to Emily Krzyzewski Family Life Center, Durham, NC, 2011. For general purpose.
$4,000 to Duke University, Durham, NC, 2011. For general purpose.
$3,000 to YMCA, Wyckoff Family, Wyckoff, NJ, 2011. For general purpose.
$2,500 to Shelter Our Sisters, Hackensack, NJ, 2011. For general purpose.
$2,000 to Fordham University, New York, NY, 2011. For general purpose.
$1,675 to Emily Krzyzewski Family Life Center, Durham, NC, 2011. For general purpose.

6600
Ostrovsky Family Fund, Inc. ✧
c/o Cornick Garber & Sandler LLP
825 3rd Ave., 4th Fl.
New York, NY 10022-9524

Established in 1987 in NY.
Donors: Vivian S. Ostrovsky; LKC Foundation; EST Assocs. LP; Jet Lag Productions LLC.
Foundation type: Independent foundation.
Financial data (yr. ended 11/30/13): Assets, $1,342,687 (M); gifts received, $512,000; expenditures, $733,885; qualifying distributions, $697,410; giving activities include $671,048 for 13 grants (high: $150,000; low: $5,000).
Fields of interest: Arts; Jewish federated giving programs.
International interests: Israel.
Type of support: Continuing support.
Limitations: Applications not accepted. Giving primarily in New York, NY. No grants to individuals.
Application information: Contributes only to pre-selected organizations.
Officer: Vivian S. Ostrovsky, Pres.
Director: Rose Ostrovsky.
EIN: 133389580

6601
O'Sullivan Foundation ✧
c/o The Ayco Company, L.P.-NTG
P.O. Box 15014
Albany, NY 12212-5014

Established in 1999 in TX.
Donor: Sean M. O'Sullivan.
Foundation type: Independent foundation.
Financial data (yr. ended 12/31/13): Assets, $16,503,694 (M); expenditures, $2,367,507; qualifying distributions, $2,311,756; giving activities include $2,311,756 for 6 grants (high: $1,800,000; low: $3,500).
Fields of interest: Education; Human services; Community/economic development.
Limitations: Applications not accepted. Giving primarily in VA and GA. No grants to individuals.
Application information: Contributes only to pre-selected organizations.
Trustees: Anne S. O'Sullivan; Marie T. O'Sullivan; Sean M. O'Sullivan.
EIN: 066487034

6602
The O'Toole Family Foundation ✧
c/o Ayco Company - NTG
P.O. Box 15014
Albany, NY 12212-5014

Established in 1993 in NJ.
Donor: Terence M. O'Toole.
Foundation type: Independent foundation.
Financial data (yr. ended 03/31/13): Assets, $21,777,367 (M); gifts received, $8,732,909; expenditures, $1,084,380; qualifying distributions, $1,049,371; giving activities include $1,049,371 for 33 grants (high: $500,000; low: $50).
Fields of interest: Arts; Higher education; Education; Health organizations, association; Medical research, institute; Athletics/sports, racquet sports; Human services; Children/youth, services.
Limitations: Applications not accepted. Giving primarily in CA, NJ and PA. No grants to individuals; no loans.
Application information: Contributes only to pre-selected organizations.
Trustees: Paula M. O' Toole; Terence M. O' Toole.
EIN: 133748068
Selected grants: The following grants are a representative sample of this grantmaker's funding activity:
$25,000 to City Squash, Bronx, NY, 2011. For general charitable purposes.
$20,000 to Pingry School, Martinsville, NJ, 2011. For general charitable purposes.
$10,000 to Child Mind Institute, New York, NY, 2011. For general charitable purposes.
$5,000 to Aspen Institute, New York, NY, 2011. For general charitable purposes.
$5,000 to Duke University, Durham, NC, 2011. For general charitable purposes.
$1,500 to Student/Partner Alliance, Millburn, NJ, 2011. For general charitable purposes.
$1,500 to Student/Partner Alliance, Millburn, NJ, 2011. For general charitable purposes.
$1,000 to Family Connections, East Orange, NJ, 2011. For general charitable purposes.

6603
Nicholas B. Ottaway Foundation, Inc. ✧
P.O. Box 401
Campbell Hall, NY 10916-0401 (845) 636-4260
Contact: Bonnie Burgoyne, Secy.
E-mail: bonnie.burgoyne@gmail.com

Established in 1968 in NY.
Donor: Members of the Ottaway family.
Foundation type: Independent foundation.
Financial data (yr. ended 05/31/13): Assets, $11,029,776 (M); gifts received, $28,994; expenditures, $788,451; qualifying distributions, $680,455; giving activities include $669,486 for 27 grants (high: $83,000; low: $7,000).
Purpose and activities: Giving primarily to 1) education programs or institutions at all levels that support educational opportunity for the economically disadvantaged, 2) journalism programs or projects which improve the quality of journalism in all its forms or defend freedom of the press anywhere in the world, and 3) programs and projects in new areas chosen by the foundation's trustees from time to time.
Fields of interest: Media, print publishing; Education; Human services; Community/economic development.
Type of support: General/operating support; Continuing support; Capital campaigns; Seed money; Curriculum development.
Limitations: Applications accepted. Giving on a national basis with emphasis on Washington, DC, MA and NY.
Application information: Application form required.
Initial approach: Letter
Copies of proposal: 1
Deadline(s): Mar. 31
Board meeting date(s): June
Final notification: 1-week
Officers and Trustees:* Dr. Frank Alexei Sherer,* Pres.; Alexandra H. Ottaway,* V.P.; Bonnie Burgoyne, Exec. Dir and Secy.; Eric B. Ottaway, Treas.; Henry Nault; Lisa Orloff; Audra Ottaway; Christopher H. Ottaway; David Ottaway; James H. Ottaway, Jr.; James W. Ottaway; Marina S. Ottaway; Mary Ottaway; Robin Ottaway; Ruth B. Ottaway; Katrin Ottaway-Velder; Christine Sherer; Ruth O. Sherer.
Number of staff: 1 part-time professional.
EIN: 141505939
Selected grants: The following grants are a representative sample of this grantmaker's funding activity:
$25,000 to Maine Center for Public Interest Reporting, Hallowell, ME, 2013. For journalism.
$7,500 to Metropolitan Opera Guild, New York, NY, 2013. For arts in the community.

6604
The Overbrook Foundation
122 E. 42nd St., Ste. 2500
New York, NY 10168-2500 (212) 661-8710
Contact: Nikole LaVelle, Asst. Grants Mgr.
FAX: (212) 661-8664;
E-mail: website@overbrook.org; Main URL: http://www.overbrook.org
The Overbrook Foundation Blog: http://www.overbrook.org/blog/
The Overbrook Foundation's Philanthropy Promise: http://www.ncrp.org/philanthropys-promise/who
Twitter: https://twitter.com/OverbrookFnd

Incorporated in 1948 in NY.
Donors: Frank Altschul†; Helen G. Altschul†; Arthur G. Altschul†; Margaret A. Lang†.
Foundation type: Independent foundation.
Financial data (yr. ended 12/31/13): Assets, $177,403,440 (M); expenditures, $9,477,665; qualifying distributions, $6,812,900; giving activities include $5,348,036 for 142 grants (high: $163,999; low: $250).
Purpose and activities: The foundation is a progressive family foundation that supports organizations advancing human rights and conserving the natural environment.
Fields of interest: Environment, natural resources; International human rights; Civil/human rights, advocacy; Civil liberties, advocacy; Civil liberties, reproductive rights; Civil/human rights; Children/youth; Children; Adults; Indigenous peoples; Women; Girls; Young adults, female; LGBTQ.
International interests: Latin America.
Type of support: General/operating support; Program development; Fellowships.
Limitations: Giving primarily in the U.S. and Latin America, with emphasis on Brazil, Mexico, Ecuador and Central America. No grants to individuals or for debt reduction.

Publications: Application guidelines; Financial statement; Grants list; Program policy statement.
Application information: The foundation no longer accepts unsolicited requests for new projects or operating support from organizations not currently funded by the foundation. Grant requests are now by invitation only for organizations advancing human rights and the environment.
Board meeting date(s): 3 times per year, dates vary
Officers and Directors:* Aaron Labaree, Chair.; Emily Altschul-Miller,* Vice-Chair. and Secy.; Carolyn J. Cole,* Vice-Chair. and Treas.; Stephen A. Foster, C.E.O. and Pres.; Mary Greco, C.F.O. and Grants Mgr.; Robert C. Graham, Jr., Dir. Emeritus; Charles Altschul; Stephen F. Altschul; Cooper Cox; Julie Graham; Kathryn G. Graham; Frances Labaree; Elizabeth Lindemann; Dinorah Matias-Melendez; Isaiah Orozco.
Number of staff: 5 full-time professional; 2 part-time professional.
EIN: 136088860
Selected grants: The following grants are a representative sample of this grantmaker's funding activity:
$150,000 to Public Interest Projects, New York, NY, 2012. For the U.S. Human Rights Fund.
$100,000 to Center for Reproductive Rights, New York, NY, 2012. For U.S. Legal Program and Latin America Regional Office.
$100,000 to Proteus Fund, Amherst, MA, 2013. For Civil Marriage Collaborative.
$80,000 to Root Capital, Cambridge, MA, 2012. For Fostering Innovation and Biodiversity Conservation in Ecuador, Mexico and Nicaragua.
$75,000 to Rainforest Alliance, New York, NY, 2012. For Achieve Conservation and Community Development through Healthy Sustainable Tourism Destinations.
$75,000 to Rainforest Alliance, New York, NY, 2013. For Achieve Conservation and Community Development through Healthy Sustainable Tourism Destinations.
$75,000 to United Republic Education Fund, Florence, MA, 2013. For General Operating Support.
$55,000 to Grist Magazine, Seattle, WA, 2013. For General Operating Support.
$55,000 to W N Y C Radio, New York, NY, 2012. For general operating support and for reporting from Mexico.
$50,000 to Movement Strategy Center, Oakland, CA, 2013. For General Operating Support.
$50,000 to University of Chile, Human Rights Center, Law School, Santiago, Chile, 2012. For International Human Rights Fellowship Program.
$50,000 to University of Chile, Human Rights Center, Law School, Santiago, Chile, 2013. For 2013 International Human Rights Fellowship Program.
$40,000 to American Jewish World Service, New York, NY, 2013. For Promoting Human Rights for Marginalized People in Latin America.
$40,000 to Breakthrough, New York, NY, 2012. For General Operating Support.
$40,000 to Story of Stuff Project, Berkeley, CA, 2013. For General Operating Support.
$40,000 to W N Y C Radio, New York, NY, 2013. For On the Media.
$35,000 to Indian Law Resource Center, Helena, MT, 2012. For Protecting Maya Q'eqchi' Land and Resource Rights in Guatemala.
$35,000 to Indian Law Resource Center, Helena, MT, 2013. For Protecting Maya Q'eqchi' Land and Resource Rights in Guatemala.
$30,000 to Hampshire College, Civil Liberties and Public Policy Program, Amherst, MA, 2012. For Training New Generations of Reproductive Rights Advocates, Activists, Practitioners and Leaders.
$25,000 to National Public Radio, Washington, DC, 2012. For Coverage of the Environment and Human Rights.

6605
Overdeck Family Foundation, Inc. ✧ ☆
c/o Tanya M. Sheehan
100 Ave. of the Americas, 16th Fl.
New York, NY 10013-1689
E-mail: info@overdeck.org; Main URL: http://overdeck.org

Foundation type: Independent foundation.
Financial data (yr. ended 12/31/13): Assets, $164,295,728 (M); expenditures, $4,826,198; qualifying distributions, $3,853,989; giving activities include $3,838,560 for 14 grants (high: $1,500,000; low: $22,950).
Purpose and activities: Giving primarily to improve K-12 math and science education.
Fields of interest: Education.
Limitations: Giving primarily in New Jersey.
Application information: Application information available on foundation web site.
Officers and Directors:* John A. Overdeck,* Pres.; Laura B. Overdeck,* Secy.; Tanya M. Sheehan, Treas.
EIN: 264377643

6606
Overhills Foundation ✧
c/o DAB Management Co., LLC
377 Oak St., No. 405-7
Garden City, NY 11530-6559

Established in 2000 in DE.
Donors: Omnibus Charitable Trust; Underhill Foundation; Wild Wings Foundation; A.M. Rockefeller Trust; A.R. Rockefeller Charitable Trust; Underhill Charitable Trust.
Foundation type: Independent foundation.
Financial data (yr. ended 11/30/12): Assets, $12,897,170 (M); expenditures, $746,539; qualifying distributions, $673,500; giving activities include $673,500 for grants.
Fields of interest: Arts; Higher education; Education; Environment, formal/general education; Environment, natural resources.
Limitations: Applications not accepted. Giving primarily in CT and NY. No grants to individuals.
Application information: Contributes only to pre-selected organizations.
Officers and Directors:* Ann R. Elliman,* Pres.; Edward H. Elliman,* V.P.; Lucia Brown Evans,* V.P.; Christopher J. Elliman,* Secy.-Treas.
EIN: 133922745
Selected grants: The following grants are a representative sample of this grantmaker's funding activity:
$39,000 to White Birch Community Center, Henniker, NH, 2011.
$35,000 to Yale University, School of Forestry and Environmental Studies, New Haven, CT, 2011.
$32,500 to Open Space Institute, New York, NY, 2011.
$25,000 to Nature Conservancy, Keene Valley, NY, 2011.
$25,000 to Wilderness Society, Washington, DC, 2011.
$20,000 to Adirondack Council, Elizabethtown, NY, 2011.
$10,000 to National Trust for Historic Preservation, Washington, DC, 2011.
$8,750 to National Trust for Historic Preservation, Washington, DC, 2011.
$4,000 to American Ballet Theater, New York, NY, 2011.
$3,000 to Merry-Go-Round, Greenwich, CT, 2011.

6607
Overlook International Foundation Inc. ✧
c/o Inverness Counsel Inc.
845 3rd Ave., 8th Fl.
New York, NY 10022-6601

Established in 2004 in MI.
Donors: Richard H. Lawrence; Dee M. Lawrence; Grantham Foundation; Fondazione del Ceresio; 2032 Trust.
Foundation type: Independent foundation.
Financial data (yr. ended 12/31/12): Assets, $18,994,286 (M); gifts received, $11,000,000; expenditures, $882,503; qualifying distributions, $746,950; giving activities include $746,950 for grants.
Fields of interest: Education; Health organizations, public education; Health organizations; Human services.
Limitations: Applications not accepted. Giving primarily in CA and CT.
Application information: Contributes only to pre-selected organizations.
Officers: Richard H. Lawrence, Pres.; Dee M. Lawrence, V.P.; Philip S. Lawrence, Secy.-Treas.
EIN: 201164239

6608
The Paestum Foundation, Inc. ✧
c/o Hecht & Co., PC
350 5th Ave., 68th Fl.
New York, NY 10118

Established in 2000 in DE and NY.
Donors: Arthur Ross†; Arthur Ross Foundation.
Foundation type: Independent foundation.
Financial data (yr. ended 09/30/13): Assets, $31,657,161 (M); expenditures, $1,626,337; qualifying distributions, $1,388,594; giving activities include $1,210,000 for 11 grants (high: $540,000; low: $5,000).
Purpose and activities: Giving primarily to a charitable gift fund, and to a university's school of art.
Fields of interest: Arts education; Philanthropy/voluntarism.
Limitations: Applications not accepted. Giving primarily in New York, NY. No grants to individuals.
Application information: Contributes only to pre-selected organizations.
Officers and Directors:* Michael Rudell,* Pres.; Michael Hecht,* Treas.
EIN: 134082016

6609
The Palette Fund, Inc. ✧
1201 Broadway, Ste. 504
New York, NY 10001-5405 (646) 861-3292
FAX: (212) 214-0816;
E-mail: info@thepalettefund.org; Main URL: http://www.thepalettefund.org/
Facebook: https://www.facebook.com/thepalettefund
Pinterest: https://www.pinterest.com/palettefund/
RSS Feed: http://www.thepalettefund.org/feed/
Tumblr: http://thepalettefund.tumblr.com/
Twitter: https://twitter.com/PaletteFund
YouTube: http://www.youtube.com/user/ThePaletteFund

Established in NY.
Foundation type: Independent foundation.
Financial data (yr. ended 12/31/12): Assets, $20,912,442 (M); gifts received, $4,201,246; expenditures, $1,670,687; qualifying distributions, $1,493,673; giving activities include $944,205 for 37 grants (high: $172,667; low: $350).
Purpose and activities: Giving primarily for nutrition and wellness, and to LGBT causes.
Fields of interest: Cancer; Health organizations; Nutrition; Human services; LGBTQ.
Limitations: Giving primarily in CA and NY.
Publications: Application guidelines.
Application information: Letters of intent and grant proposals are accepted by invitation only. Complete application guidelines are available online.
Initial approach: Email inquiry
Deadline(s): Check foundation web site for current deadlines
Officers and Directors:* Peter Benassi,* Chair.; Terrence Meck,* Pres. and Exec. Dir.; Kristin Resnansky,* Secy.-Treas.; Todd Sears.
EIN: 262736653

6610
William S. Paley Foundation, Inc. ✧
c/o Bencivenga Ward & Co. CPAs PC
420 Columbus Ave., Ste. 304
Valhalla, NY 10595-1382 (914) 769-5005
Contact: Patrick S. Gallagher, Exec. Dir.

Incorporated in 1936 in NY.
Donor: William S. Paley†.
Foundation type: Independent foundation.
Financial data (yr. ended 12/31/12): Assets, $120,094,806 (M); expenditures, $6,840,541; qualifying distributions, $5,454,039; giving activities include $4,850,190 for 33 grants (high: $2,100,000; low: $2,500).
Purpose and activities: Endowment funds held for and emphasis on the Museum of Television and Radio and the Greenpark Foundation (Paley Park). Support for other museums, health services, education, and cultural programs.
Fields of interest: Museums; Arts; Education; Health care.
Type of support: General/operating support; Continuing support; Annual campaigns.
Limitations: Applications accepted. Giving primarily in NY. No grants to individuals.
Application information: Application form not required.
Initial approach: Proposal
Copies of proposal: 1
Deadline(s): None
Board meeting date(s): Nov.
Officers and Directors:* Henry A. Kissinger,* Chair.; William C. Paley,* V.P.; Daniel L. Mosley,* Secy.-Treas.; Patrick S. Gallagher,* Exec. Dir.; George J. Gillespie III.
Number of staff: 1 full-time professional; 1 part-time professional.
EIN: 136085929
Selected grants: The following grants are a representative sample of this grantmaker's funding activity:
$2,100,000 to Paley Center for Media, New York, NY, 2011. For program support.
$1,000,000 to Paley Center for Media, New York, NY, 2011. For deficit.
$500,000 to Paley Center for Media, New York, NY, 2011. For Paley Television Festival.
$498,901 to Paley Center for Media, New York, NY, 2011. For deficit.
$425,000 to GreenPark Foundation, Valhalla, NY, 2011. For Paley Park program support.
$238,262 to Paley Center for Media, New York, NY, 2011.
$100,000 to Museum of Modern Art, New York, NY, 2011. For program support.
$52,135 to Paley Center for Media, New York, NY, 2011. For PCM Awards.
$25,000 to Paley Center for Media, New York, NY, 2011. For Bennack Theater.
$25,000 to Portland Museum of Art, Portland, ME, 2011. For annual fund.

6611
The Palm Foundation ✧
Bowling Green Sta.
P.O. Box 73
New York, NY 10274-0073

Established in 1993 in NY.
Donor: Gregory K. Palm.
Foundation type: Independent foundation.
Financial data (yr. ended 04/30/13): Assets, $11,230,365 (M); gifts received, $20,000; expenditures, $528,110; qualifying distributions, $515,700; giving activities include $515,700 for 19 grants (high: $332,000; low: $700).
Purpose and activities: Giving primarily for the arts and to a charitable gift fund.
Fields of interest: Arts; Libraries (public); Education; Foundations (public).
Limitations: Applications not accepted. Giving primarily in New York, NY and Cincinnati, OH. No grants to individuals; no loans or scholarships.
Application information: Contributes only to pre-selected organizations.
Trustees: Gregory K. Palm; Jennifer Palm; Katherine Palm; Susan Rose Palm.
EIN: 133748059
Selected grants: The following grants are a representative sample of this grantmaker's funding activity:
$10,000 to Memorial Sloan-Kettering Cancer Center, New York, NY, 2013. For All contributions were made to the general purposes fund or public charitable organizations that were classified under section 501(c)(3) the Internal Revenue Code.

6612
The Panaphil Foundation ✧
c/o TCC Group
31 W. 47th St., 4th Fl.
New York, NY 10001

Established in 1990 in PA and NY.
Donor: Frances A. Velay†.
Foundation type: Independent foundation.
Financial data (yr. ended 12/31/12): Assets, $78,668,056 (M); expenditures, $3,464,619; qualifying distributions, $2,589,898; giving activities include $2,315,000 for 27 grants (high: $1,000,000; low: $25,000).
Purpose and activities: Giving primarily for environmental concerns, particularly an ocean conservancy, preservation of animal and plant species threatened with extinction, and prevention of cruelty to animals.
Fields of interest: Environment, natural resources; Animal welfare; Human services.
Limitations: Applications not accepted. Giving primarily on the East Coast. No grants to individuals.
Application information: Contributes only to pre-selected organizations.
Trustees: Dan McCarthy; Barbara Paul Robinson, Esq.; Christopher J. Velay.
EIN: 136959472
Selected grants: The following grants are a representative sample of this grantmaker's funding activity:
$150,000 to Natural Resources Defense Council, New York, NY, 2012. For Oceans Initiative.
$50,000 to Conservation International, Arlington, VA, 2012. For Freshwater Turtle and Tortoise Work.
$50,000 to Greenpeace Fund, Washington, DC, 2012. For Oceans Program.
$25,000 to Wildlife Conservation Society, Bronx, NY, 2012. For Regional Turtle Conservation Initiative in Myanmar.

6613
Pannonia Foundation ✧
c/o Marks Paneth, et al.
685 3rd Ave., 4th Fl.
New York, NY 10017-6707

Established in 2003 in NY.
Donor: The Celeste & Adam Bartos Charitable Trust.
Foundation type: Independent foundation.
Financial data (yr. ended 12/31/13): Assets, $7,662,424 (M); gifts received, $1,914,475; expenditures, $891,887; qualifying distributions, $834,726; giving activities include $818,480 for 65 grants (high: $205,850; low: $500).
Fields of interest: Museums; Arts; Libraries/library science; Education; Hospitals (general); Human services.
Limitations: Applications not accepted. Giving primarily in the five boroughs of New York City. No grants to individuals.
Application information: Contributes only to pre-selected organizations.
Directors: Adam Bartos; Robert J. Hughes; Mahnaz Ispahani.
EIN: 134112882
Selected grants: The following grants are a representative sample of this grantmaker's funding activity:
$285,000 to American Museum of the Moving Image, Astoria, NY, 2011.
$97,490 to New York Public Library, New York, NY, 2011.
$70,000 to Wellesley College, Wellesley, MA, 2011.
$61,000 to Dalton Schools, New York, NY, 2011.
$25,000 to New York-Presbyterian Hospital, New York, NY, 2011.
$20,000 to Rhode Island School of Design, Providence, RI, 2011.

$15,000 to Council on Foreign Relations, New York, NY, 2011.
$7,500 to American Civil Liberties Union Foundation, New York, NY, 2011.
$3,500 to Drawing Center, New York, NY, 2011.
$2,500 to Seeds of Peace, New York, NY, 2011.

6614
Chang K. Park Foundation ✧
7 Terrace Cir.
Armonk, NY 10504-1112

Established in 2008 in NY.
Donor: Chang K. Park.
Foundation type: Independent foundation.
Financial data (yr. ended 06/30/13): Assets, $11,427,940 (M); gifts received, $5,150,000; expenditures, $1,842,137; qualifying distributions, $1,805,427; giving activities include $1,805,427 for 7 grants (high: $1,000,000; low: $30,000).
Fields of interest: Theological school/education; Education; Protestant agencies & churches.
Limitations: Applications not accepted. Giving primarily in DC and NY. No grants to individuals.
Application information: Contributes only to pre-selected organizations.
Officer: Chang K. Park, C.E.O.
EIN: 261535704
Selected grants: The following grants are a representative sample of this grantmaker's funding activity:
$150,000 to Demos: A Network for Ideas and Action, New York, NY, 2011. For general support.
$100,000 to Tulane University Medical Center, New Orleans, LA, 2011. For general support.

6615
Park Foundation, Inc. ✧
P.O. Box 550
Ithaca, NY 14851-0550 (607) 272-9124
Contact: Jon Jensen, Exec. Dir.
FAX: (607) 272-6057;
E-mail: info@parkfoundation.org; Street Address: 301 E. State St., Ithaca, N.Y., 14850; Main URL: http://www.parkfoundation.org

Established in 1966.
Donors: RHP, Inc.; Roy H. Park†.
Foundation type: Independent foundation.
Financial data (yr. ended 12/31/12): Assets, $366,405,008 (M); expenditures, $22,168,578; qualifying distributions, $19,736,469; giving activities include $17,814,586 for 380 grants (high: $645,046; low: $20), and $500,000 for 1 loan/program-related investment.
Purpose and activities: Giving primarily for scholarships in higher education, quality public affairs media that heightens public awareness of critical issues, and protection of the environment. In addition to these core program areas, interests include a broad range of charitable giving in communities where the trustees reside.
Fields of interest: Media/communications; Media, television; Media, print publishing; Higher education; Environment, water resources; Animal welfare.
Type of support: Mission-related investments/loans; General/operating support; Continuing support; Management development/capacity building; Program development; Film/video/radio; Scholarship funds; Program-related investments/loans; Employee matching gifts; Matching/challenge support.
Limitations: Applications accepted. Giving limited to the eastern U.S., primarily in central NY, Washington, DC, and NC. No grants to individuals.
Publications: Application guidelines; Grants list; Program policy statement.
Application information: See web site for application requirements. Application form required.
Initial approach: Letter of inquiry, telephone or application (see website)
Copies of proposal: 1
Deadline(s): Quarterly: Jan. 3, Apr. 4, July 7 and Sept. 26
Board meeting date(s): Mar., June, Sept., and Dec.
Final notification: Within 3 months
Officers and Directors:* Adelaide P. Gomer,* Pres.; Alicia P. Wittink,* V.P.; William L. Bondurant,* Secy.-Treas.; Jon Jensen, Exec. Dir.; Jay R. Halfon; Richard G. Robb; Jerome B. Libin.
Number of staff: 7 full-time professional.
EIN: 166071043
Selected grants: The following grants are a representative sample of this grantmaker's funding activity:
$645,046 to North Carolina State University, Park Scholarships Program, Raleigh, NC, 2012. For Park Scholarships and recruitment selection activities.
$600,000 to W G B H Educational Foundation, Boston, MA, 2012. For FRONTLINE Series Support.
$500,200 to Ithaca College, Ithaca, NY, 2012. For a cohort of Park Scholars.
$500,000 to Independent Production Fund, New York, NY, 2012. For the multimedia project, Moyers and Company.
$487,782 to North Carolina State University, Park Scholarships Program, Raleigh, NC, 2012. For Park Scholarships and recruitment selection activities.
$125,000 to Food and Water Watch, Washington, DC, 2012. For National Water Campaign to stop the private control of water and protect and conserve the nation's water resources.
$125,000 to Southern Environmental Law Center, Charlottesville, VA, 2012. To protect water quality and improve water management efforts in North Carolina and the Southeast U.S.
$25,000 to American University, Washington, DC, 2012. For final production and outreach activities related to the documentary, Shooting in the Wild, which will raise awareness of the environmental, wildlife and ethical issues surrounding the documentary filmmaking industry.
$25,000 to Golden Opportunity Go, Ithaca, NY, 2012. For providing tutoring to low-income students.
$15,000 to Common Dreams, Portland, ME, 2012. For general operating support.

6616
Jim and Shirley Parke Foundation ✧ ☆
c/o The Ayco Co., LP - NTG
P.O. Box 15014
Albany, NY 12212-5014

Established in 2001 in CT.
Donors: Jim A. Parke; Shirley Parke.
Foundation type: Independent foundation.
Financial data (yr. ended 12/31/13): Assets, $2,153,712 (M); gifts received, $1,017,013; expenditures, $476,597; qualifying distributions, $471,000; giving activities include $471,000 for 9 grants (high: $150,000; low: $1,000).
Fields of interest: Foundations (public).
Limitations: Applications not accepted. Giving primarily in CT. No grants to individuals.
Application information: Unsolicited requests for funds not accepted.
Directors: Jim A. Parke; Shirley Parke.
EIN: 061603828

6617
Parkview Foundation ✧
2600 Nostrand Ave.
Brooklyn, NY 11210-4601

Established in 2000 in NY.
Donors: Issack Bernstein; Parkview Realty Co.
Foundation type: Independent foundation.
Financial data (yr. ended 06/30/13): Assets, $4,377,007 (M); gifts received, $5,457; expenditures, $753,996; qualifying distributions, $536,050; giving activities include $536,050 for 13 grants (high: $195,450; low: $300).
Purpose and activities: Giving primarily to Jewish agencies, temples, and schools.
Fields of interest: Education; Jewish federated giving programs; Jewish agencies & synagogues.
Limitations: Applications not accepted. Giving primarily in Brooklyn, NY. No grants to individuals.
Application information: Unsolicited requests for funds not accepted.
Trustees: Issack Bernstein; Jerome Lieberman.
EIN: 113544307
Selected grants: The following grants are a representative sample of this grantmaker's funding activity:
$6,000 to Bais Rivka Rochel, Lakewood, NJ, 2011.

6618
The Parsons Family Foundation ✧
c/o Tag Assocs., LLC
75 Rockefeller Plz., Ste. 900
New York, NY 10019-6999

Established in 1995 in NY and DE.
Donor: Richard D. Parsons.
Foundation type: Independent foundation.
Financial data (yr. ended 12/31/13): Assets, $693,719 (M); gifts received, $229,568; expenditures, $716,843; qualifying distributions, $708,390; giving activities include $708,390 for 36 grants (high: $250,000; low: $500).
Fields of interest: Museums (art); Museums (ethnic/folk arts); Museums (natural history); Education; Human services.
Limitations: Applications not accepted. Giving primarily in NY. No grants to individuals.
Application information: Contributes only to pre-selected organizations.
Officers and Directors:* Laura A. Parsons,* Pres.; Richard D. Parsons,* Secy.-Treas.; Gregory A. Parsons; Leslie J. Parsons; Rebecca L. Parsons.
EIN: 133864478

6619
Ann Parsons Memorial Foundation ✧
c/o Troutman Sanders LLP, Carol F. Burger, Esq.
405 Lexington Ave., 8th Fl
New York, NY 10174-0002

Established in 1994 in TX.
Foundation type: Independent foundation.

Financial data (yr. ended 12/31/13): Assets, $23,037,413 (M); expenditures, $549,284; qualifying distributions, $546,724; giving activities include $546,724 for 6 grants (high: $220,400; low: $22,040).
Purpose and activities: Giving primarily for medical research and health organizations.
Fields of interest: Arts, single organization support; Health organizations; AIDS; Alzheimer's disease; Cancer research; Orthodox agencies & churches.
Limitations: Applications not accepted. Giving primarily in CA, TX and VA. No grants to individuals.
Application information: Contributes only to pre-selected organizations.
Officers and Directors:* Roger Parsons,* Pres.; Sofia Kartsotis,* Secy.; Kathy K. Elliot,* Treas.; Mary Beth Cook; Bill Kartsotis.
EIN: 752550555

6620
Paulson Family Foundation ✧
1251 Ave. of the Americas, 50th Fl.
New York, NY 10020-1104 (212) 350-5151
Contact: John Paulson, Pres. and Treas.

Donor: John Paulson.
Foundation type: Independent foundation.
Financial data (yr. ended 12/31/12): Assets, $490,890,813 (M); gifts received, $24,000,000; expenditures, $27,422,106; qualifying distributions, $27,393,106; giving activities include $27,374,743 for 40 grants (high: $10,050,000; low: $1,000).
Fields of interest: Education; Environment; Human services.
Limitations: Applications accepted. Giving primarily in New York, NY.
Officer and Director:* John Paulson,* Pres. and Treas.
EIN: 263922995
Selected grants: The following grants are a representative sample of this grantmaker's funding activity:
$10,050,000 to Central Park Conservancy, New York, NY, 2012. For unrestricted support.
$5,569,458 to Benefactors of Ecuador, New York, NY, 2012. For unrestricted support.
$3,110,000 to Spence School, New York, NY, 2012. For unrestricted support.
$2,150,000 to New York University, New York, NY, 2012. For unrestricted support.
$1,500,000 to UJA-Federation of New York, New York, NY, 2012. For unrestricted support.
$1,010,000 to Harvard University, Cambridge, MA, 2012. For unrestricted support.
$666,000 to New Visions for Public Schools, New York, NY, 2012. For unrestricted support.
$623,635 to Friends of Fondation de France, New York, NY, 2012. For unrestricted support.
$285,000 to Friends of the Israel Defense Forces, New York, NY, 2012. For unrestricted support.
$125,000 to New York Public Library, New York, NY, 2012. For unrestricted support.

6621
PB Foundation, Inc. ✧
1 Penn Plz.
New York, NY 10119-0001

Donors: John J. Ryan; Michael I. Schneider; William S. Roman; Christopher E. Reseign; Keith J. Hawksworth; Richard Jakelski; PB Americas Inc.; Parsons Brinckerhoff, Inc.; Parsons Brinckerhoff Construction Svcs.; Parsons Brinckerhoff Quade & Douglas, Inc.; Parsons Brinckehroff Group, Inc.; PB Services Inc.
Foundation type: Operating foundation.
Financial data (yr. ended 12/31/13): Assets, $13,003 (M); gifts received, $540,354; expenditures, $542,690; qualifying distributions, $542,640; giving activities include $542,640 for 19 + grants (high: $100,790).
Purpose and activities: Giving primarily for organizations and foundations concerning engineering and construction; funding also for health organizations.
Fields of interest: Education; Breast cancer; Health organizations; Engineering/technology.
Limitations: Applications not accepted.
Application information: Unsolicited requests for funds not accepted.
Officer and Trustees:* Judith Cooper,* Chair.; David McAlister; Patrick Schaffner.
EIN: 134187790

6622
PBHP, Inc. ✧
c/o Hertz, Herson & Co., LLP
477 Madison Ave., 10th Fl.
New York, NY 10022-5841

Established in 1999 in DE and NY.
Donors: Susan R. Wexner; Naon, Inc.
Foundation type: Independent foundation.
Financial data (yr. ended 12/31/13): Assets, $36,791,785 (M); expenditures, $1,655,030; qualifying distributions, $1,613,569; giving activities include $1,611,547 for 12 grants (high: $600,000; low: $26).
Fields of interest: Theological school/education; Education; Health care; Human services; Foundations (private independent); Jewish agencies & synagogues.
Limitations: Applications not accepted. Giving primarily in New York, NY and in Israel. No grants to individuals.
Application information: Contributes only to pre-selected organizations.
Officer and Directors:* Susan R. Wexner,* Pres. and Secy.-Treas.; Saul G. Agus; Raymond Kanner; Gregg H. Levy, Esq.; Michael S. Oberman, Esq.; Mark W. Saks, Esq.; Walter Stern.
EIN: 522171835

6623
Pearson-Rappaport Foundation ✧
c/o Ayco Co.-NTG
P.O. Box 15014
Albany, NY 12212-5014

Established in 1997 in CT.
Donors: Andrall E. Pearson; Jill P. Rappaport; Joanne P. Pearson; Alan H. Rappaport.
Foundation type: Independent foundation.
Financial data (yr. ended 12/31/13): Assets, $2,500,149 (M); expenditures, $781,232; qualifying distributions, $760,065; giving activities include $760,065 for 49 grants (high: $100,000; low: $500).
Fields of interest: Museums; Higher education; Business school/education; Education; Hospitals (general); Health organizations, association; Human services; Children/youth, services; Christian agencies & churches.
Limitations: Applications not accepted. Giving primarily in FL and NY. No grants to individuals.
Application information: Contributes only to pre-selected organizations.
Trustees: Joanne P. Pearson; Alan H. Rappaport; Jill P. Rappaport.
EIN: 061484929

6624
Peco Foundation ✧
1 Penn Plz., 4th Fl., Ste. 440
New York, NY 10119-0002

Established in 1969 in NY.
Donors: Catherine G. Curran; Catherine G. Curran Trust; Constance Curran McPhee; Peter Curran.
Foundation type: Independent foundation.
Financial data (yr. ended 12/31/12): Assets, $21,040,079 (M); expenditures, $1,079,214; qualifying distributions, $1,008,374; giving activities include $961,887 for 188 grants (high: $50,000; low: $450).
Purpose and activities: Giving for arts and culture, and human services.
Fields of interest: Museums (art); Performing arts; Historic preservation/historical societies; Arts; Education; Environment, natural resources; Human services.
Type of support: General/operating support.
Limitations: Applications not accepted. Giving primarily in New York, NY. No grants to individuals.
Application information: Contributes only to pre-selected organizations.
Board meeting date(s): Dec.
Officers: Peter Curran, Pres.; Constance Curran McPhee, V.P.
EIN: 237031675

6625
Donald A. Pels Charitable Trust ✧
63 E. 79th St., Apt. 4B
New York, NY 10021-0228

Established in 1992 in NY.
Donor: Donald A. Pels.
Foundation type: Independent foundation.
Financial data (yr. ended 12/31/13): Assets, $41,382,416 (M); gifts received, $13,788; expenditures, $1,001,532; qualifying distributions, $977,310; giving activities include $963,625 for 61 grants (high: $125,000; low: $500).
Purpose and activities: Giving primarily to cultural institutions and for education.
Fields of interest: Museums (art); Performing arts centers; Arts; Higher education; Environment, natural resources; Health organizations; Human services; Civil/human rights, single organization support.
Type of support: General/operating support.
Limitations: Applications not accepted. Giving primarily in NY. No grants to individuals.
Application information: Contributes only to pre-selected organizations.
Trustee: Donald A. Pels.
EIN: 136998091

6626
Shannon and Andrew S. Penson Foundation ✧
551 5th Ave., 34th Fl.
New York, NY 10176-3499

Established in 2002 in NY.
Donors: Andrew S. Penson; Shannon S. Penson.
Foundation type: Independent foundation.
Financial data (yr. ended 12/31/13): Assets, $2,859,515 (M); gifts received, $3,250,000; expenditures, $3,984,026; qualifying distributions, $3,972,889; giving activities include $3,961,366 for 313 grants (high: $1,000,000; low: $108).
Purpose and activities: Giving primary to Jewish agencies, temples, and schools.
Fields of interest: Elementary/secondary education; Jewish agencies & synagogues.
Limitations: Applications not accepted. No grants to individuals.
Application information: Contributes only to pre-selected organizations.
Trustees: Andrew S. Penson; Shannon S. Penson; Citibank, N.A.
EIN: 134226290

6627
The PepsiCo Foundation, Inc. ✧
700 Anderson Hill Rd.
Purchase, NY 10577-1401
Main URL: http://www.pepsico.com/Purpose/Global-Citizenship

Incorporated in 1962 in NY.
Donor: PepsiCo, Inc.
Foundation type: Company-sponsored foundation.
Financial data (yr. ended 12/31/13): Assets, $56,552,966 (M); gifts received, $15,000,000; expenditures, $32,323,539; qualifying distributions, $32,229,824; giving activities include $31,730,571 for grants.
Purpose and activities: The foundation supports programs designed to encourage healthy lifestyles; improve availability of affordable nutrition; provide access to water; enhance sustainable agriculture capability; promote job readiness; and empower women and girls.
Fields of interest: Higher education; Education, reading; Education; Environment, water pollution; Environment, water resources; Public health; Public health, physical fitness; Public health, clean water supply; Health care; Employment, training; Employment; Food services; Food banks; Nutrition; Agriculture/food; Disasters, preparedness/services; Safety/disasters; Children, services; Civil/human rights, equal rights; Economic development; United Ways and Federated Giving Programs; Minorities; Women; Girls; Economically disadvantaged.
International interests: Africa; Asia; Bangladesh; Ghana; India.
Type of support: General/operating support; Continuing support; Management development/capacity building; Program development; Employee volunteer services; Employee matching gifts; Employee-related scholarships; Scholarships—to individuals; In-kind gifts.
Limitations: Applications not accepted. Giving on a national and international basis, with emphasis on Washington, DC, FL, IL, MA, NY, TX, and VA, and in Africa, Asia, Bangladesh, Canada, China, Ghana, India, Mexico, and the United Kingdom. No support for private charities or foundations, religious organizations, political candidates or organizations, discriminatory organizations, or legislative organizations, or for playgrounds, or sports fields. No grants to individuals (except for employee-related and Diamond scholarships), or for political causes or campaigns, endowments or capital campaigns, equipment, film, music, TV, video, or media productions, sports sponsorships, performing arts tours, or association memberships.
Publications: Program policy statement.
Application information: Unsolicited letters of inquiry or proposals are currently not accepted.
Officers and Directors:* Indra K. Nooyi,* Chair.; Larry Thompson, Pres.; Sue Tsokris, V.P.; Christine Griff, Secy.; Tessa Hilado, Treas.; Zein Abdalla; Saad Abdul-Latif; Al Carey; Brian Cornell; Rich Delaney; Enderson Guimaraes; Hugh F. Johnston; Mehmood Khan; Cynthia M. Trudell; James Wilkinson.
Number of staff: 2 full-time professional; 2 full-time support.
EIN: 136163174
Selected grants: The following grants are a representative sample of this grantmaker's funding activity:
$3,423,930 to Scholarship America, Saint Peter, MN, 2012. For employee scholarships.
$2,520,643 to Johns Hopkins University, Baltimore, MD, 2012. For program to increase graduation rates.
$2,016,000 to Give2Asia, San Francisco, CA, 2012. For Water China Project.
$2,000,000 to Water.org, Kansas City, MO, 2012. For Water India Project.
$1,500,000 to Inter-American Development Bank, Washington, DC, 2012. To support AquaFund, which provides grants that contribute to the achievement of the water-related Millennium Development Goals and the targets established under the IDB's Water and Sanitation Initiative.
$625,000 to Diplomacy Center Foundation, Washington, DC, 2012. For Elements of Diplomacy exhibit.
$333,000 to Plaza de Cultura y Artes Foundation, LA Plaza de Cultura y Artes, Los Angeles, CA, 2012. For Edible Teaching Garden, which demonstrates from compost to harvest in a year round organic growing environment.
$140,240 to National Merit Scholarship Corporation, Evanston, IL, 2012. For merit and achievement scholarships.
$50,000 to National Association of Hispanic Journalists, Washington, DC, 2012. For scholarships.

6628
Perelman Family Foundation ✧
35 E. 62nd St.
New York, NY 10065-8014
Ronald Perelman's Giving Pledge Profile: http://glasspockets.org/philanthropy-in-focus/eye-on-the-giving-pledge/profiles/perelman

Established in 1999 in NY.
Donors: R G I Group Incorporated; Ronald O. Perelman.
Foundation type: Independent foundation.
Financial data (yr. ended 12/31/12): Assets, $51,796 (M); gifts received, $10,451,967; expenditures, $10,461,067; qualifying distributions, $10,460,967; giving activities include $10,460,967 for 32 grants (high: $3,125,000; low: $1,000).
Fields of interest: Arts; Hospitals (general); Health organizations, association; Human services; United Ways and Federated Giving Programs; Jewish agencies & synagogues.
Limitations: Applications not accepted. Giving primarily in NY. No grants to individuals.
Application information: Contributes only to pre-selected organizations.
Officers and Directors:* Ronald O. Perelman,* Chair. and C.E.O.; Barry F. Schwartz,* Exec. Vice-Chair. and C.A.O.; Paul G. Savas, Exec. V.P., Fin.; Michael C. Borofsky, Sr. V.P. and Secy.; Adam F. Ingber, Sr. V.P., Taxation; Debra G. Perelman,* Sr. V.P.; Christine Taylor, Sr. V.P.; Alison Horowitz, V.P., Treas., and Cont.; Gary Rozenshteyn, V.P., Taxation; JoAnne deFreitas, V.P.; Hope G. Perelman, V.P.; Joshua G. Perelman, V.P.; Steven G. Perelman, V.P.
EIN: 134008528
Selected grants: The following grants are a representative sample of this grantmaker's funding activity:
$3,125,000 to New York-Presbyterian Hospital, New York, NY, 2012.
$2,500,000 to Weill Medical College of Cornell University, New York, NY, 2012.
$1,702,967 to Carnegie Hall Corporation, New York, NY, 2012.
$350,000 to Ohr Torah Institutions of Israel, New York, NY, 2012.
$250,000 to Machne Israel, Brooklyn, NY, 2012.
$200,000 to Arizona State University Foundation for a New American University, Tempe, AZ, 2012.
$193,500 to Nison Pinson Foundation, New York, NY, 2012.
$150,000 to Machne Israel, Brooklyn, NY, 2012.
$140,000 to Machne Israel, Brooklyn, NY, 2012.
$100,000 to Columbia University Medical Center, New York, NY, 2012.

6629
The Pershing Square Foundation ✧
c/o Marcum LLP
10 Melville Park Rd.
Melville, NY 11747-3146
Main URL: http://www.pershingsquarefoundation.org
Bill and Karen Ackman's Giving Pledge Profile: http://glasspockets.org/philanthropy-in-focus/eye-on-the-giving-pledge/profiles/ackman

Established in 2007 in NY.
Donors: William Ackman; Karen Ackman; Nicholas Botta; Roy Katzovicz; Lawrence D. Ackman; Pershing Square Capital Mgmt.
Foundation type: Independent foundation.
Financial data (yr. ended 09/30/13): Assets, $79,862,242 (M); gifts received, $10,000,000; expenditures, $32,498,127; qualifying distributions, $32,341,208; giving activities include $31,135,657 for 80 grants (high: $5,139,426; low: $1,000).
Purpose and activities: Giving primarily for community development, education, the arts, human services, health organizations, and Jewish organizations.
Fields of interest: Historic preservation/historical societies; Arts; Education; Health organizations; Human services; Social entrepreneurship; Community/economic development; Foundations (public); Jewish federated giving programs;

Leadership development; Jewish agencies & synagogues.
Limitations: Applications accepted. Giving on a world wide basis with an emphasis on New York, NY and NJ.
Application information: Eligibility includes that applicants should have at least 3 years of experience running their own laboratories and may have up to 10 years of experience. Principal Investigators (PIs) must hold a faculty appointment at an academic research institution in the New York area at the level of Assistant or Associate Professor (or equivalent). The New York area includes New York City and Long Island.
Initial approach: One-page, LOI online application period is open Dec. 2 through Jan. 20.
Deadline(s): By Feb. 17 selected applicants are invited to submit full length proposals. March 31 is the deadline for selected applicants to submit full length proposals.
Final notification: Prize winners notified in May; Projects start in the Summer.
Officers: Paul Bernstein, C.E.O.; Amy Herskovitz, Exec. V.P.; Olivia Tournay Flatto, Exec. Dir., Pershing Square Sohn Cancer Research Alliance.
Trustee: Karen Ackman; William Ackman.
EIN: 208068401
Selected grants: The following grants are a representative sample of this grantmaker's funding activity:
$5,139,426 to Foundation for Newarks Future, Newark, NJ, 2013. For general support.
$2,000,000 to Friends of the High Line, New York, NY, 2013. For Pershing Square Beams.
$2,000,000 to Harvard University, Cambridge, MA, 2013. For grant to School of Medicine in Boston for Quadrangle Professorship of Global Health.
$2,000,000 to Human Rights Watch, New York, NY, 2013. For unrestricted support.
$1,966,667 to Root Capital, Cambridge, MA, 2013. For Scaling Impact Plan.
$1,000,000 to Signature Theatre Company, New York, NY, 2013. For capital support.
$350,000 to New York Junior Tennis League, Woodside, NY, 2013. For Cary Leeds Center.
$175,000 to Big Mouth Productions, New York, NY, 2013. For E-Team documentary film.
$125,000 to Minds Matter of NYC, New York, NY, 2013. For organizational growth and development.
$100,000 to Silk Road Project, Boston, MA, 2013. For Sound of Silk documentary film, Silk Road Fellowship Program.

6630
Peter G. Peterson Foundation ✧

888-C Eighth Ave.
P.O. Box 144
New York, NY 10019-8511 (212) 542-9200
Contact: Rikard Treiber, Dir., Grants Mgmt.
FAX: (212) 542-9250; E-mail: inquiries@pgpf.org;
Main URL: http://pgpf.org/
Blog: http://www.pgpf.org/blog
E-Newsletter: http://www.pgpf.org/Registration.aspx?ref=/Media/Video/2009/09/Fiscal-Wake-Up-Tour-Online-Dave-Walker.aspx
Facebook: http://www.facebook.com/pages/Peter-G-Peterson-Foundation/15503839732
GiveSmart: http://www.givesmart.org/Stories/Donors/Pete-Peterson
Multimedia: http://www.pgpf.org/Media/Video/2009/09/Fiscal-Wake-Up-Tour-Online-Dave-Walker.aspx
Peter G. Peterson's Giving Pledge Profile: http://glasspockets.org/philanthropy-in-focus/eye-on-the-giving-pledge/profiles/peterson
RSS Feed: http://www.pgpf.org/blog/publicfeed
Twitter: https://twitter.com/pgpfoundation
YouTube: https://www.youtube.com/user/pgpfoundation

Established in 2008.
Donors: Peter G. Peterson; David M. Walker; Warren E. Buffett; Georges Marciano.
Foundation type: Independent foundation.
Financial data (yr. ended 03/31/13): Assets, $484,815,258 (M); expenditures, $18,384,080; qualifying distributions, $16,328,050; giving activities include $8,871,984 for 36 grants (high: $1,546,984; low: $10,000), and $19,234,256 for 3 foundation-administered programs.
Purpose and activities: The mission is to increase public awareness of the nature and urgency of key fiscal challenges threatening America's future and to accelerate action on them. To address these challenges successfully, the foundation works to bring Americans together to find and implement sensible, long-term solutions that transcend age, party lines and ideological divides in order to achieve real results.
Fields of interest: Health care, cost containment; Health care, financing; International affairs, national security; Public affairs, finance; Public affairs, citizen participation.
Type of support: Research; Internship funds; Curriculum development; Conferences/seminars.
Limitations: Applications accepted. Giving limited to the U.S. to nonprofits that are regional or national in scope and have the ability to implement programming nationwide. No support for other private grantmaking foundations, foreign organizations, or for political, social or fraternal organizations. No grants to individuals, or for general operating support, unrestricted purposes, indirect expenses, ongoing funding, capital campaigns, annual appeals, ongoing sponsorships, fundraising events, or to underwrite chairs, endowments or scholarships sponsored by academic or nonprofit institutions.
Publications: Financial statement; Informational brochure; Newsletter; Occasional report.
Application information: The foundation gives only in pre-selected program areas. Application form required.
Initial approach: Submit initial inquiry via inquiries@pgpf.org. If invited, a proposal will be requested
Copies of proposal: 1
Deadline(s): Initial inquiries are accepted throughout the year
Final notification: Varies
Officers and Directors:* Peter G. Peterson,* Chair.; Michael Peterson,* Pres. and C.O.O.; Susan Tanaka, V.P., Policy and Research; Loretta Ucelli, V.P., Comms. and Public Affairs; Moshe Mandelbaum, C.F.O.; Joan Ganz Cooney.
Number of staff: 17 full-time professional; 5 full-time support; 2 part-time support.
EIN: 260316905
Selected grants: The following grants are a representative sample of this grantmaker's funding activity:
$1,250,000 to Concord Coalition, Arlington, VA, 2012. For efforts to educate the public about the causes and consequences of federal budget deficits, the long-term challenges facing America's unsustainable entitlement programs, and how to build a sound foundation for economic growth.
$585,000 to Teachers College Columbia University, New York, NY, 2012. For promotion, implementation and evaluation of a new curriculum to help high school students understand the facts, significance and consequences of the nation's fiscal challenges.
$500,000 to Clinton Global Initiative, New York, NY, 2012. For the development and execution of Up to Us, a nationwide campus competition empowering university students to create campaigns that educate and engage their peers on the United States fiscal challenges and their impact on economic opportunity, investment in the future, and other concerns of future generations, payable over 2.00 years.
$500,000 to Research Foundation of the City University of New York, New York, NY, 2012. For a comprehensive analysis of the fiscal challenges faced by six heavily populated states and the development of recommendations to improve long-term fiscal sustainability.
$450,000 to Net Impact: New Leaders for Better Business, San Francisco, CA, 2012. For the development and execution of Up to Us, a nationwide campus competition empowering university students to create campaigns that educate and engage their peers on the United States fiscal challenges and their impact on economic opportunity, investment in the future, and other concerns of future generations, payable over 1.25 years.
$300,000 to Henry L. Stimson Center, Washington, DC, 2012. For analysis of alternative defense strategy and mission choices as part of the Budgeting for Foreign Affairs and Defense program.
$250,000 to Clinton Global Initiative, New York, NY, 2012. For CGI Americas meeting and discussions on how to improve the nation's long-term economic competitiveness.
$250,000 to Coalition to Transform Advanced Care, Washington, DC, 2012. For the replication of health care models that ensure compassionate, coordinated care for individuals with advanced illness.
$250,000 to Committee for Economic Development, Washington, DC, 2012. For the Fiscal Health Initiative, a program providing nonpartisan analysis on long-term fiscal challenges and conducting outreach to the business community in support of more sustainable policies.
$57,500 to Concord Coalition, Arlington, VA, 2012. For the Peter G. Peterson Foundation Fiscal Internship Program.

6631
Carroll Petrie Foundation ✧

c/o RSSM
757 3rd Ave., 6th Fl.
New York, NY 10017-2059

Established in 1996 in DE & NY.
Donor: Carroll M. Petrie.
Foundation type: Independent foundation.
Financial data (yr. ended 12/31/13): Assets, $3,588,452 (M); gifts received, $1,000,787; expenditures, $1,454,761; qualifying distributions, $1,421,056; giving activities include $1,411,600 for 5 grants (high: $1,000,000; low: $1,600).
Fields of interest: Museums (art); Animal welfare.
Limitations: Applications not accepted. Giving primarily in Southampton and New York, NY. No grants to individuals.

Application information: Contributes only to pre-selected organizations.
Board meeting date(s): May
Officers and Directors:* Jay B. Goldberg,* Pres.; William D. Zabel,* Secy.; Camille Manning; Carolina Portago; Theodora Portago; David J. Stoll.
EIN: 133912203

6632
The Carroll and Milton Petrie Foundation, Inc. ✧

767 Third Ave., Fl. 37
New York, NY 10017-2077 (212) 806-6115
Contact: Beth J. Lief, Exec. Dir.
FAX: (212) 826-8627;
E-mail: petriefoundation@gmail.com

Established in 2005 in NY as a successor to The Carrol and Milton Petrie Foundation.
Donor: Milton Petrie†.
Foundation type: Independent foundation.
Financial data (yr. ended 12/31/12): Assets, $20,504,227 (M); gifts received, $3,483,321; expenditures, $5,591,168; qualifying distributions, $5,430,514; giving activities include $5,236,320 for 28 grants (high: $1,025,000; low: $25,000).
Purpose and activities: The foundation's mission is to promote quality education for the more than 1.5 million students who attend public schools in New York City. There are two channels through which the foundation supports doing this: 1) To advance the likelihood that students at the City University of New York and at other notable colleges can survive emergencies and stay in school to finish their degrees; and 2) To build the expertise of teachers and principals to help them become effective in middle and high schools in the New York City Department of Education, so that vulnerable and disadvantaged students can succeed at graduating ready for college.
Fields of interest: Elementary/secondary education; Higher education.
Type of support: Continuing support; Emergency funds; Curriculum development; Consulting services.
Limitations: Applications not accepted. Giving primarily in New York, NY. No grants to individuals.
Application information: Unsolicited requests for funds not accepted.
Officers and Directors:* Carroll Petrie,* Chair.; Jerome A. Manning,* Pres.; Jean L. Troubh, V.P.; Charles A. Klein,* Secy.; Etta Brandman, Treas.; Beth Lief, Exec. Dir.; Michael Goldberg; Paul O. LeClerc.
EIN: 201451752
Selected grants: The following grants are a representative sample of this grantmaker's funding activity:
$1,762,070 to New Visions for Public Schools, New York, NY, 2012. To launch Literacy Initiative for development, adoption and scaling of Common core literacy curricula in and beyond New Visions schools.
$1,200,000 to Internationals Network for Public Schools, New York, NY, 2012. To develop and support quality evaluations of teachers of immigrants students and to implement Common Core Standards in curriculum that meets the needs of students who are English language learners.
$1,185,000 to Urban Assembly, New York, NY, 2012. To transform literacy instruction and to align teachers' instructional practice with Common Core Standards in Urban Assembly schools.
$1,000,000 to New York University, New York, NY, 2011.
$727,000 to Turnaround for Children, New York, NY, 2011.
$727,000 to Turnaround for Children, New York, NY, 2011.
$557,236 to Bard College, Annandale on Hudson, NY, 2011.
$500,000 to Police Athletic League, New York, NY, 2011.
$500,000 to Police Athletic League, New York, NY, 2011.
$500,000 to Teach for America, New York, NY, 2011. For general support.
$500,000 to Teach for America, New York, NY, 2011.
$407,236 to Bard College, Annandale on Hudson, NY, 2011.
$372,875 to New Teacher Center, Santa Cruz, CA, 2011. For accelerating teacher and leader effectiveness through mentoring for new teachers.
$350,000 to New York Public Library, New York, NY, 2011.
$300,000 to Expeditionary Learning Outward Bound, New York, NY, 2012. To strengthen professional development for schools by aligning curriculum and support Common Core Standards and improve student achievement.
$175,000 to Brandeis University, Waltham, MA, 2011.

6633
The Pfizer Foundation, Inc. ✧

235 E. 42nd St.
New York, NY 10017-5703
Main URL: http://www.pfizer.com/responsibility

Incorporated in 1953 in Brooklyn, NY.
Donor: Pfizer Inc.
Foundation type: Company-sponsored foundation.
Financial data (yr. ended 12/31/12): Assets, $191,472,395 (M); expenditures, $22,200,652; qualifying distributions, $21,513,192; giving activities include $9,957,810 for grants, and $11,099,462 for employee matching gifts.
Purpose and activities: The foundation supports programs designed to promote access to quality healthcare; nurture innovation; and support the community involvement of Pfizer colleagues.
Fields of interest: Higher education; Education, services; Education; Animals/wildlife; Health care, public policy; Medicine/medical care, public education; Medical care, community health systems; Health care, patient services; Health care; Cancer; Lung diseases; AIDS; Children, services; International development; Philanthropy/voluntarism; United Ways and Federated Giving Programs; Science, formal/general education; Mathematics; Science; Women.
Type of support: General/operating support; Continuing support; Management development/capacity building; Building/renovation; Program development; Curriculum development; Technical assistance; Employee volunteer services; Sponsorships; Program evaluation; Employee matching gifts.
Limitations: Applications not accepted. Giving on a national and international basis. No support for political organizations. No grants to individuals, or for capital campaigns or scholarships; no loans to individuals.
Publications: Corporate giving report; Grants list; Program policy statement.
Application information: Contributes only to pre-selected organizations.
Board meeting date(s): As required
Officers and Directors:* William C. Steere, Jr.,* Chair.; Sally Susman, Vice-Chair.; Caroline Roan, Pres.; Dezarie Mayers, Secy.; Richard Passov, Treas.; Anneka Norgren, Exec. Dir.; C. L. Clemente; Frank D'Amelio; Kirsten Lund-Jurgensen; Gary Nicholson; David Simmons.
EIN: 136083839
Selected grants: The following grants are a representative sample of this grantmaker's funding activity:
$3,009,000 to Give2Asia, San Francisco, CA, 2012. For Global Health.
$1,300,000 to Grantmakers in Aging, Arlington, VA, 2012. For Global Health.
$491,608 to United Way, Greater Kalamazoo, Kalamazoo, MI, 2012.
$337,849 to United Way of Southeastern Connecticut, Gales Ferry, CT, 2012.
$250,000 to Hurricane Sandy New Jersey Relief Fund, Mendham, NJ, 2012. For Disaster Relief Grants.
$250,000 to United Way of Southeastern Connecticut, Gales Ferry, CT, 2012. For Disaster Relief Grants.
$200,000 to Direct Relief International, Santa Barbara, CA, 2012. For focusing relief efforts on immediate and near-term support for the health facilities that serve people who rely on the nonprofit healthcare safety net for essential services.
$25,000 to American Humane Association, Englewood, CO, 2012. For Disaster Relief Grants.
$2,568 to United Fund, Westfield, Westfield, NJ, 2012. For United Way.
$1,073 to Deborah Hospital Foundation, Browns Mills, NJ, 2012. For United Way.

6634
Pfizer Patient Assistance Foundation, Inc. ✧

235 E. 42nd St.
New York, NY 10017-5703 (866) 706-2400
Application address: Pfizer Connection to Care Prog., P.O. Box 66585, St. Louis, MO 63166; Pfizer MAINTAIN, P.O. Box 66549, St. Louis, MO 63166; Tel. for Sharing the Care Prog.: (800) 984-1500; Tel. for Pfizer Bridge Prog.: (800) 645-1280; Main URL: http://www.pfizerhelpfulanswers.com/pages/misc/Default.aspx

Donor: Pfizer Inc.
Foundation type: Operating foundation.
Financial data (yr. ended 12/31/12): Assets, $17,817,709 (M); gifts received, $526,763,045; expenditures, $528,618,809; qualifying distributions, $518,220,470; giving activities include $105,425,527 for grants, and $410,301,026 for grants to individuals.
Purpose and activities: The foundation provides Pfizer medicines to uninsured, underinsured, and economically disadvantaged patients in need through health centers, hospitals, and healthcare providers. Patient assistance is administered through Pfizer Helpful Answers, a joint program of Pfizer, Inc. and the Pfizer Patient Assistance Foundation.
Fields of interest: Hospitals (general); Health care, clinics/centers; Pharmacy/prescriptions; Economically disadvantaged.
Type of support: Donated products; In-kind gifts.

Limitations: Applications accepted. Giving on a national basis and in Puerto Rico, and the US Virgin Islands.
Publications: Application guidelines; Informational brochure.
Application information: Application form required.
Initial approach: Download application and mail to application address
Deadline(s): None
Officers and Directors:* Caroline Roane,* Chair.; Daniel Murphy, Secy.; Diane Krisko, Treas.; Gary Pelletier, Exec. Dir.; Elizabeth Barrett; William Kennally; Jim Sage; Amy Schmeltz.
EIN: 261437283

6635
The Carl and Lily Pforzheimer Foundation, Inc. ✧
950 3rd Ave., 30th Fl.
New York, NY 10022-2705
Contact: Carl H. Pforzheimer III, Pres.

Incorporated in 1942 in NY.
Donor: Members of the Pforzheimer family.
Foundation type: Independent foundation.
Financial data (yr. ended 12/31/13): Assets, $527,718 (M); gifts received, $156,246; expenditures, $2,142,933; qualifying distributions, $2,102,137; giving activities include $1,754,167 for 22 grants (high: $1,026,667; low: $2,000), and $258,534 for foundation-administered programs.
Purpose and activities: The foundation maintains publishing and research activities in connection with the Carl H. Pforzheimer Library collection at the New York Public Library in the general field of American and English literature; giving primarily for higher and secondary education; support also for libraries, and cultural programs, public administration, a national municipal organization, and health care.
Fields of interest: Performing arts; Performing arts, theater; Language/linguistics; Literature; Arts; Secondary school/education; Higher education; Adult education—literacy, basic skills & GED; Libraries/library science; Education, reading; Education; Nursing care; Youth development, citizenship; Government/public administration; Public affairs, citizen participation.
Type of support: Endowments; Program development; Professorships; Publication; Seed money; Fellowships; Internship funds; Scholarship funds; Matching/challenge support.
Limitations: Applications accepted. Giving on a national basis. No support for religious or political organizations. No grants to individuals, or for building funds; no loans.
Application information: Application form not required.
Initial approach: Letter or proposal
Copies of proposal: 1
Deadline(s): None
Board meeting date(s): Apr., Oct., and Dec.
Final notification: Generally, following board meeting
Officers and Directors:* Carl H. Pforzheimer III,* Pres. and Treas.; Nancy P. Aronson,* V.P.; Martin F. Richman, Secy.; Anthony L. Ferranti, Compt.; Edgar D. Aronson; Edith S. Aronson; George L.K. Frelinghuysen; Carol K. Pforzheimer; Elizabeth S. Pforzheimer; Gary M. Pforzheimer; Richard M. Sallick.
Number of staff: 3 full-time professional; 1 part-time professional; 2 full-time support.
EIN: 135624374
Selected grants: The following grants are a representative sample of this grantmaker's funding activity:
$1,026,667 to New York Public Library, New York, NY, 2012. To be used for the Manuscripts and Archives Department and the General Research Division.
$200,000 to Marine Corps Heritage Foundation, Dumfries, VA, 2012. To finance immersion exhibit at the Marine Corps Museum.
$200,000 to Marine Military Academy, Harlingen, TX, 2012. To endow a fund to provide two student scholarships annually.
$25,000 to Art Education for the Blind, New York, NY, 2012. For its Art Beyond Sight online project.
$20,000 to McLean Hospital, Belmont, MA, 2012. For its Program in Education, Afterschool, and Resiliency (PEAR).
$10,000 to American Council of Learned Societies, New York, NY, 2012. For the endowment being collected for the Oscar Handlin fellowship.
$5,000 to Hudson Valley Shakespeare Festival, Cold Spring, NY, 2012. For its Arts-in-education Program.

6636
Philippe Foundation, Inc. ✧
c/o Four Points Asset Management, Inc.
1 Penn Plz., Ste. 1628
New York, NY 10119-1628
Contact: Beatrice Philippe, Pres. and Dir.; Alain Philippe, V.P.

Incorporated in 1953 in NY.
Donors: Alain Philippe; Anne-Marie Philippe; Beatrice Philippe; Pierre Philippe; Anne B. Vaysee; Jacques Vaysse; Zoltan Hankovszky; Daniel Philippe; Isabelle Philippe; European-American Economic Corp.
Foundation type: Independent foundation.
Financial data (yr. ended 12/31/13): Assets, $7,536,774 (M); gifts received, $52,601; expenditures, $614,109; qualifying distributions, $579,669; giving activities include $548,942 for 105 grants (high: $12,000; low: $1,351).
Purpose and activities: Support primarily for the exchange of physicians and scientists between the U.S. and France for advanced study and scientific research, emphasizing cancer research.
Fields of interest: Cancer research; Science.
International interests: France.
Type of support: Conferences/seminars; Fellowships; Internship funds; Research; Grants to individuals; Exchange programs.
Limitations: Applications accepted. Giving on a national basis; funding also in France.
Publications: Application guidelines.
Application information: Application form not required.
Initial approach: Proposal
Copies of proposal: 3
Deadline(s): None
Officers and Directors:* Beatrice Philippe,* Pres.; Louiza Ferrara, V.P.; Alain Philippe,* V.P.; Jacques B. Vaysse, V.P.; Zoltan Hankovszky, Secy.; Patricia Reischour, Treas.; Benjamin Grenier; Irving London; Dominique Meyer; Helene Philippe-Grenier; Anne Philippe-Vaysse.
EIN: 136087157

6637
Phillips-Van Heusen Foundation, Inc. ✧
200 Madison Ave., 10th Fl.
New York, NY 10016-3903 (212) 381-3500
Contact: Emanuel Chirico, Chair.
FAX: (212) 381-3960; Main URL: http://www.pvhcsr.com/csr2013/community/article/impact-through-global-partnership

Incorporated in 1969 in NY.
Donor: Phillips-Van Heusen Corp.
Foundation type: Company-sponsored foundation.
Financial data (yr. ended 12/31/13): Assets, $6,768,453 (M); gifts received, $10,992,214; expenditures, $9,523,243; qualifying distributions, $10,992,214; giving activities include $9,523,243 for 389 grants (high: $425,100; low: $50).
Purpose and activities: The foundation supports programs designed to improve the lives of women and children in need through safe spaces, education, and amenities to enhance quality of life.
Fields of interest: Museums; Arts; Higher education; Education; Health care, clinics/centers; Health care, patient services; Health care; Cancer; Crime/violence prevention, domestic violence; Disasters, preparedness/services; Safety/disasters; Recreation, camps; Boys & girls clubs; American Red Cross; Children/youth, services; Family services; Human services; International development; Business/industry; United Ways and Federated Giving Programs; Children; Women; Economically disadvantaged.
Type of support: General/operating support; Continuing support; Annual campaigns; Emergency funds; Program development; Scholarship funds; Research.
Limitations: Applications accepted. Giving on national basis in areas of company operations, with emphasis on New York, NY; giving also to national organizations. No grants to individuals.
Application information: The foundation primarily provides funding through established partnerships. Application form not required.
Initial approach: Proposal
Copies of proposal: 1
Deadline(s): None
Officers: Emanuel Chirico, Chair.; Guy Vickers, Pres.; Mark D. Fischer, V.P.; Bruce Goldstein, V.P.; Dana Perlman, V.P.; Michael A. Shaffer, V.P.
EIN: 237104639
Selected grants: The following grants are a representative sample of this grantmaker's funding activity:
$350,127 to Leukemia & Lymphoma Society, White Plains, NY, 2011.
$319,221 to Save the Children Federation, Fairfield, CT, 2011.
$144,279 to Save the Children Federation, Fairfield, CT, 2011.
$50,000 to Autism Speaks, New York, NY, 2011.
$47,070 to Leukemia & Lymphoma Society, White Plains, NY, 2011.
$35,000 to Save the Children Federation, Fairfield, CT, 2011.
$25,000 to Lupus Foundation of America, Washington, DC, 2011.
$20,548 to Save the Children Federation, Fairfield, CT, 2011.
$10,938 to Autism Speaks, New York, NY, 2011.
$3,000 to Foundation Fighting Blindness, Columbia, MD, 2011.

6638
Picket Family Foundation Inc. ✧
c/o Gotham Organization Inc.
1010 Ave. of the Americas
New York, NY 10018-5490

Established in 2008 in NY.
Donor: Gotham Organization Inc.
Foundation type: Independent foundation.
Financial data (yr. ended 12/31/13): Assets, $2,392,861 (M); gifts received, $300,000; expenditures, $506,700; qualifying distributions, $490,397; giving activities include $490,250 for 14 grants (high: $133,000; low: $1,000).
Fields of interest: Performing arts centers; Higher education, university; Hospitals (general); Jewish federated giving programs.
Limitations: Applications not accepted. Giving primarily in Bronx and New York, NY.
Application information: Unsolicited requests for funds not accepted.
Officers and Directors:* Joel I. Picket,* Pres.; Joan R. Picket,* V.P.; Allison D. Fehrenbaker,* Secy.; David L. Picket,* Treas.; Lawrence G. Fehrenbaker; Rona J. Picket.
EIN: 263870611

6639
John D. Picotte Family Foundation ✧
(formerly Equinox Foundation, Inc.)
20 Corporate Woods Blvd., Ste. 600
Albany, NY 12211-2396

Established in 1990 in NY.
Donors: John D. Picotte; KMP Trust I; KMP Trust V; KMP Charitable Lead Trust I; KMP Charitable Lead Trust V.
Foundation type: Independent foundation.
Financial data (yr. ended 12/31/13): Assets, $14,495,386 (M); gifts received, $44,685; expenditures, $672,092; qualifying distributions, $626,684; giving activities include $581,650 for 82 grants (high: $150,000; low: $200).
Purpose and activities: Giving primarily for education and human services; funding also for health organizations, and to museums.
Fields of interest: Museums; Higher education; Education; Hospitals (general); Medical research, institute; Human services.
Type of support: Annual campaigns.
Limitations: Applications not accepted. Giving primarily in Albany and New York, NY. No grants to individuals.
Application information: Contributes only to pre-selected organizations.
Officers: John D. Picotte, Pres.; Michelle R. Leclair, Secy.; Margaret P. MacClarence, Treas.
Directors: Brooke A. Picotte; John D. Picotte, Jr.; Margaret Hines Picotte.
EIN: 223109260
Selected grants: The following grants are a representative sample of this grantmaker's funding activity:
$100,000 to Albany Medical Center Foundation, Albany, NY, 2012. For 2nd payment of a 10-year ($1,000,000) pledge to support the Lifeline Campaign.
$47,500 to Alfred E. Smith Memorial Foundation, New York, NY, 2012. To the Alfred E. Smith Memorial Foundation; supports and aids the children living in poverty.
$10,000 to Capital Region Youth Tennis Foundation, Albany, NY, 2012. For CF-2012 grant for the Book Clubs, College Prep, Leadership Training Program, and the Summer Book Giveaway Program.
$8,500 to Albany Symphony Orchestra, Albany, NY, 2012. For CF-2012 grant for the Adopt-A-School Program.
$8,000 to Schenectady Inner City Ministry, Schenectady, NY, 2012. For CF-2012 grant for the Schenectady Damien Center.
$8,000 to Trinity Institution, Albany, NY, 2012. For CF-2012 support for capacity building.
$7,500 to Parsons Child and Family Center, Albany, NY, 2012. For CF-2012 grant for the Capital Region Child and Adolescent Mobile Crisis Team.
$4,000 to Village Community School, New York, NY, 2012. For BAP-2012 gift to the Annual Fund.
$1,500 to Berkshire School, Sheffield, MA, 2012. For MPM-2012 gift to the Parents Fund.
$1,500 to Dana-Farber Cancer Institute, Boston, MA, 2012. For JDP/MHP-2012 gift for matching grant from Harbor Consulting IP Services, Inc.

6640
Piece by Piece Productions Inc ✧ ☆
c/o Anchin Block & Anchin LLP
1375 Broadway
New York, NY 10018-7001

Established in NY.
Donor: Wendy Vanden Heuvel.
Foundation type: Operating foundation.
Financial data (yr. ended 08/31/13): Assets, $178,809 (M); gifts received, $1,068,411; expenditures, $1,108,836; qualifying distributions, $1,033,116; giving activities include $502,500 for 4 grants (high: $290,000; low: $10,000).
Fields of interest: Media, film/video; Arts.
Limitations: Applications not accepted. Giving primarily in New York, NY.
Application information: Unsolicited requests for funds not accepted.
Officers and Directors:* Wendy Vanden Heuvel,* Pres.; Luly Santangelo,* Secy.; Philipe Goldin,* Treas.; Etta Brandman.
EIN: 311693404
Selected grants: The following grants are a representative sample of this grantmaker's funding activity:
$80,000 to Rattlestick Productions, New York, NY, 2011. For general fund.
$9,850 to Williamstown Theater Foundation, Williamstown, MA, 2011. For general fund.

6641
The Pindaros Foundation, Inc. ✧ ☆
c/o Marks, Paneth & Shron LLP
685 3rd Ave.
New York, NY 10017-6707

Established in 2002 in NJ.
Donors: P. Roy Vagelos; Vagelos Family Trust; Vagelos Family Charitable Lead Annuity Trust.
Foundation type: Independent foundation.
Financial data (yr. ended 12/31/13): Assets, $94,229,200 (M); gifts received, $844,663; expenditures, $718,689; qualifying distributions, $553,490; giving activities include $548,240 for 19 grants (high: $200,000; low: $500).
Fields of interest: Education.
Limitations: Applications not accepted. Giving primarily in NY. No grants to individuals.
Application information: Contributes only to pre-selected organizations.
Officers: P. Roy Vagelos, Pres.; Randall Vagelos, V.P.; Andrew Vagelos, Secy.; Cynthia Vagelos Roberts, Treas.
EIN: 010623055
Selected grants: The following grants are a representative sample of this grantmaker's funding activity:
$3,565,100 to University of Pennsylvania, Philadelphia, PA, 2011. For general support.
$186,576 to Rahway Public Schools, Rahway, NJ, 2011. For general support.
$100,000 to Barnard College, New York, NY, 2011. For general support.
$13,280 to University of Pennsylvania, Philadelphia, PA, 2011. For general support.
$10,000 to Brown University, Providence, RI, 2011. For general support.
$10,000 to Palo Alto Partners in Education, Palo Alto, CA, 2011. For general support.
$7,000 to Hackley School, Tarrytown, NY, 2011. For general support.
$5,000 to Harvard University, Cambridge, MA, 2011. For general support.

6642
Pine Tree Foundation of New York ✧
c/o Janet L. Mulligan, Tanton Co.
37 W. 57th St., 5th Fl.
New York, NY 10019-3411

Established in 2002 in NY.
Donor: Charles J. Tanenbaum.
Foundation type: Independent foundation.
Financial data (yr. ended 12/31/12): Assets, $11,204,249 (M); expenditures, $567,233; qualifying distributions, $473,602; giving activities include $473,602 for grants.
Fields of interest: Arts; Higher education, university; Libraries (special).
Type of support: General/operating support.
Limitations: Applications not accepted. Giving primarily in CA and NY. No grants to individuals.
Application information: Contributes only to pre-selected organizations.
Trustees: Kenneth Gliedman; Szlvia Szmuk Tanenbaum.
EIN: 137308483

6643
The Pinkerton Foundation ✧
610 5th Ave., Ste. 316
New York, NY 10020-2403 (212) 332-3385
Contact: Richard Smith, Pres.
FAX: (212) 332-3399;
E-mail: pinkfdn@pinkertonfdn.org; Main URL: http://www.thepinkertonfoundation.org

Incorporated in 1966 in DE.
Donor: Robert A. Pinkerton‡.
Foundation type: Independent foundation.
Financial data (yr. ended 12/31/13): Assets, $668,363,451 (M); expenditures, $30,414,261; qualifying distributions, $26,440,172; giving activities include $24,021,758 for 197+ grants.
Purpose and activities: Giving to economically disadvantaged children, youth, and families; support also for severely learning-disabled children and adults of borderline intelligence. The foundation is also interested in endeavors that strengthen

youth programming in poor communities; and programs that develop an individual's competencies, instill values, and increase opportunities to participate in society.
Fields of interest: Employment, services; Children/youth, services; Children; Youth; Economically disadvantaged.
Type of support: General/operating support; Management development/capacity building; Program development; Seed money; Research; Technical assistance; Matching/challenge support.
Limitations: Applications accepted. Giving primarily in New York, NY. No support for medical research, the media, the direct provision of health care, or religious education. Generally no grants to individuals, or for emergency assistance, conferences, publications, media, building renovations, or other capital projects, unless they are integrally related to foundation's program objectives or an outgrowth of grantee's programs; no loans.
Publications: Application guidelines; Grants list.
Application information: The foundation accepts the New York/ New Jersey Area Common Application Form and the New York/ New Jersey Common Report Form. Application form required.
Initial approach: Letter (no more than 2 pages)
Copies of proposal: 1
Deadline(s): Submit proposal by Feb. 1 for May meeting and Sept. 1 for Dec. meeting
Board meeting date(s): May and Dec.
Officers and Trustees:* George J. Gillespie III,* Chair.; Richard M. Smith,* Pres.; Jill Bregenzer, V.P., Fin. and Admin.; Joan Colello,* Secy. and Exec. Dir. Emeritus; Daniel L. Mosley,* Treas.; Robert R. Gould; James Piereson; Marnie S. Pillsbury.
Number of staff: 2 full-time professional; 1 part-time professional; 1 part-time support.
EIN: 136206624
Selected grants: The following grants are a representative sample of this grantmaker's funding activity:
$618,372 to After-School Corporation, New York, NY, 2012. For operating support.
$482,143 to Center on Media, Crime and Justice, New York, NY, 2012. For operating support.
$405,000 to City Year, Boston, MA, 2012. For operating support.
$300,000 to Fostering Change for Children, Rocky Point, NY, 2012. For operating support.
$203,673 to Youth Communication/New York Center, New York, NY, 2012. For operating support.
$100,000 to Getting Out and Staying Out, New York, NY, 2012. For operating support.
$100,000 to Groundwork, Inc., Brooklyn, NY, 2012. For operating support.
$100,000 to Henry Street Settlement, New York, NY, 2012. For operating support.
$80,000 to Queens Library Foundation, Jamaica, NY, 2012. For operating support.
$50,000 to Reel Works Teen Filmmaking, Brooklyn, NY, 2012. For operating support.

6644
Planning and Art Resources for Communities Inc. ✧
P.O. Box 6437
New York, NY 10150-6421
FAX: (646) 383-6999;
E-mail: info@theparcfoundation.org; Main URL: http://www.theparcfoundation.org

Established in 2006 in NY.
Donor: David Deutsch.
Foundation type: Independent foundation.
Financial data (yr. ended 10/31/13): Assets, $42,519,502 (M); expenditures, $2,084,546; qualifying distributions, $1,631,393; giving activities include $1,381,239 for 25 grants (high: $150,000; low: $1,000).
Purpose and activities: Giving to strengthen communities in need by serving as a catalyst for the development and promotion of contemporary architecture and art.
Fields of interest: Arts; Environment; Animals/wildlife; Health care, association.
Type of support: Program-related investments/loans.
Limitations: Applications not accepted. Giving in the U.S. with emphasis on NY. No grants to individuals.
Application information: Contributes only to pre-selected organizations.
Officers and Directors:* David Deutsch,* Chair. and Pres.; Victoria Sambunaris,* Secy.; Megan Wurth,* Fdn. Mgr; Shawn Ganon.
EIN: 134350414

6645
Henry B. Plant Memorial Fund, Inc. ✧
c/o Withumsmith + Brown PC
1411 Broadway, 9th Fl.
New York, NY 10018-3496

Incorporated in 1947 in NY.
Donor: Amy P. Statter.
Foundation type: Independent foundation.
Financial data (yr. ended 12/31/12): Assets, $12,209,300 (M); expenditures, $674,042; qualifying distributions, $620,000; giving activities include $620,000 for grants.
Purpose and activities: Giving primarily for arts and culture, education, health, and human services.
Fields of interest: Arts, multipurpose centers/programs; Arts; Education; Health organizations, association; Human services.
Limitations: Applications not accepted. Giving primarily in CT and NY; some funding also in MA. No grants to individuals.
Application information: Contributes only to pre-selected organizations.
Officers: Phyllis Oxman, Pres.; Amy Roberts Lee, V.P.; Christine O'Donnell, Secy.-Treas.
Number of staff: 1 part-time professional.
EIN: 136077327

6646
The Kronhill Pletka Foundation ✧ ☆
123A W. 69th St.
New York, NY 10023-5127
E-mail: info@kronhillpletkafoundation.org; Application email: LOI@kronhillpletkafoundation.org; Main URL: http://www.kronhillpletkafoundation.org/index.html

Established in 2007 in NY.
Foundation type: Independent foundation.
Financial data (yr. ended 12/31/13): Assets, $6,150,936 (M); expenditures, $552,104; qualifying distributions, $506,278; giving activities include $474,889 for 18 grants (high: $154,947; low: $250).
Fields of interest: Higher education; Jewish agencies & synagogues.
Limitations: Applications accepted. Giving primarily in New York, NY. No grants to individuals.
Publications: Application guidelines.
Application information: The specific project proposal should not exceed 1,000 words. See foundation web site for specific application guidelines.
Initial approach: Letter of intent via e-mail
Deadline(s): 1st Fri. of Feb., May, Aug. and Nov.
Officer and Trustee:* Irene Pletka,* Chair. and Pres.
EIN: 261466252

6647
PLM Foundation ✧
545 Madison Ave., Ste. 600
New York, NY 10022-4219 (212) 339-2100

Established in 1996 in NY.
Donors: Philip L. Milstein; Vivian Milstein; The VLM Charitable Lead Annuity Trust.
Foundation type: Independent foundation.
Financial data (yr. ended 12/31/12): Assets, $8,380,999 (M); gifts received, $2,153,768; expenditures, $6,406,016; qualifying distributions, $6,306,822; giving activities include $6,304,034 for 113 grants (high: $2,500,000; low: $41).
Purpose and activities: Giving primarily for higher education, including a university library; funding also for the arts, particularly for a performing arts center, and for social services.
Fields of interest: Museums (art); Arts; Higher education; Business school/education; Libraries (school); Education; Health care; Human services; YM/YWCAs & YM/YWHAs; Jewish agencies & synagogues.
Limitations: Applications not accepted. Giving primarily in NY. No grants to individuals.
Application information: Contributes only to pre-selected organizations.
Trustees: Cheryl Milstein; Philip L. Milstein.
EIN: 137105558
Selected grants: The following grants are a representative sample of this grantmaker's funding activity:
$2,500,000 to New York-Presbyterian Fund, New York, NY, 2012.
$500,000 to Columbia University, New York, NY, 2012.
$500,000 to Lincoln Center for the Performing Arts, New York, NY, 2012.
$400,000 to W N E T.Org, New York, NY, 2012.
$300,000 to YM-YWHA, 92nd Street, New York, NY, 2012.
$250,000 to Lincoln Center for the Performing Arts, New York, NY, 2012.
$100,000 to THIRTEEN, New York, NY, 2012.
$50,000 to New York University, Stern School of Business, New York, NY, 2012.
$50,000 to New York-Presbyterian Fund, New York, NY, 2012.
$24,905 to Community Impact, New York, NY, 2012.

6648
Plum Beach Foundation ✧
14 Plum Beach Point Rd.
Sands Point, NY 11050-1314 (212) 697-1000
Contact: Michael Nierenberg, Tr.
Application address: c/o Citrin Cooperman, 529 5th Ave., New York, NY 10017

Established in 2006 in NY.
Donor: Michael B. Nierenberg.
Foundation type: Independent foundation.
Financial data (yr. ended 12/31/12): Assets, $246,171 (M); gifts received, $138,625; expenditures, $503,541; qualifying distributions, $501,360; giving activities include $501,135 for 22 grants (high: $258,100; low: $100).
Purpose and activities: Giving primarily for health organizations, social services, and Jewish agencies and temples.
Fields of interest: Health organizations, association; Cancer; Medical research, institute; Human services; Jewish agencies & synagogues.
Limitations: Applications accepted. Giving primarily in NY.
Application information: Application form required.
Initial approach: Letter
Deadline(s): None
Trustees: Elin Nierenberg; Michael B. Nierenberg.
EIN: 203849330

6649
Joe Plumeri Foundation, Inc. ✧ ☆
c/o Ayco Co., LP
P.O. Box 860
Saratoga Springs, NY 12866-0860

Established in 2005 in NY.
Donor: Joseph J. Plumeri.
Foundation type: Operating foundation.
Financial data (yr. ended 12/31/13): Assets, $18,980,404 (M); gifts received, $18,678,000; expenditures, $1,420,522; qualifying distributions, $1,379,832; giving activities include $1,379,832 for 19 grants (high: $202,324; low: $1,000).
Fields of interest: Higher education; Medical school/education; Education; Mental health/crisis services; Human services.
Type of support: General/operating support.
Limitations: Applications not accepted. Giving primarily in NY and VA. No grants to individuals.
Application information: Unsolicited requests for funds not accepted.
Officers: Joseph J. Plumeri, Pres.; Jay Plumeri, V.P.
EIN: 331126619

6650
The Pollock-Krasner Foundation, Inc. ✧
863 Park Ave.
New York, NY 10075-0380 (212) 517-5400
Contact: Caroline Black, Prog. Off.
FAX: (212) 288-2836; E-mail: grants@pkf.org; E-mail for application-related questions: grantapplication@pkf.org; Main URL: http://www.pkf.org
Grants List: http://www.pkf.org/recent_grantees.html

Established in 1984 in DE.
Donor: Lee Krasner†.
Foundation type: Independent foundation.
Financial data (yr. ended 06/30/13): Assets, $65,271,620 (M); gifts received, $6,880; expenditures, $5,015,860; qualifying distributions, $3,913,078; giving activities include $381,000 for 18 grants (high: $200,000; low: $4,000), and $2,098,500 for grants to individuals.
Purpose and activities: Giving primarily to aid, internationally, those individuals who have worked as artists over a significant period of time. The foundation's dual criteria for grants are recognizable artistic merit and financial need, whether professional, personal or both.
Fields of interest: Visual arts.
Type of support: Grants to individuals.
Limitations: Giving on a national and international basis. No grants for past debt, legal fees, purchase of real estate, tuition reimbursement, moving expenses, costs of installations, commissions or projects ordered by others, or individual grants to students, photographers, commercial, performance, or video artists, filmmakers or craftsmen.
Publications: Application guidelines; Annual report; Informational brochure (including application guidelines).
Application information: Complete application guidelines and procedures available on foundation web site. Application form required.
Initial approach: Online application link on foundation web site
Deadline(s): None
Board meeting date(s): Regularly throughout the year
Final notification: Up to 9 months
Officers and Directors:* Charles C. Bergman,* C.E.O. and Chair.; Samuel Sachs II,* Pres.; Kerrie Buitrago, Exec. V.P.
Number of staff: 5 full-time professional; 2 full-time support.
EIN: 133255693

6651
The Polo Ralph Lauren Foundation ✧
c/o Mahoney Cohen
1065 Ave. of the Americas
New York, NY 10018-1847
Main URL: http://global.ralphlauren.com/en-us/about/philanthropy/pages/default.aspx

Established in 2001 in NY.
Donors: Polo Ralph Lauren Corp.; Jones Apparel Group, Inc.; L'Oreal USA; New Times Group Holdings Ltd.; Ralph Lauren Media Polo.com; Winnitex Ltd.; Kuohwa Garment & Enamel Industry Co., Inc.; Yee Tung Garment Co., Ltd.; Timemax International, Ltd.; Mo Villa Productions, Inc.; Bathco (The Navy Yard); Beijing Industrial Development Co. Ltd.; Peter S. Goldstein.
Foundation type: Company-sponsored foundation.
Financial data (yr. ended 03/31/12): Assets, $16,637,976 (M); gifts received, $4,959,380; expenditures, $3,940,659; qualifying distributions, $3,857,426; giving activities include $3,857,426 for 26 grants (high: $3,209,350; low: $1,000).
Purpose and activities: The foundation supports programs designed to promote care; education; and service in underserved communities.
Fields of interest: Secondary school/education; Education; Hospitals (general); Cancer; Breast cancer; Housing/shelter, development; Recreation, parks/playgrounds; Children/youth, services; Community/economic development; Economically disadvantaged.
Type of support: Scholarship funds; General/operating support; Program development; Employee volunteer services.
Limitations: Applications not accepted. Giving primarily in CA, Washington, DC, MD, MN, NC, NJ, and NY, and in Switzerland. No support for political campaigns. No grants to individuals.
Application information: Contributes only to pre-selected organizations.
Officers and Directors:* Ralph Lauren,* Chair.; David Lauren, Pres.; Paul Campbell, V.P.; Bette-Ann Gwathmey, V.P.; Avery Fischer, Secy.; Tracy Travis,* Treas.; Arthur Crispo, Exec. Dir.; Roger Farah; Mitchell Kosh.
EIN: 522316766

6652
The William G. Pomeroy Foundation ✧
P.O. Box 3327
Syracuse, NY 13220-3327 (315) 476-3000
Contact: Paula Miller, Tr.
Main URL: http://www.wgpfoundation.org/

Established in 2005 in NY.
Donor: William G. Pomeroy.
Foundation type: Independent foundation.
Financial data (yr. ended 12/31/13): Assets, $26,122,222 (M); gifts received, $3,975,038; expenditures, $885,626; qualifying distributions, $875,998; giving activities include $868,597 for 83 grants (high: $585,000; low: $100).
Fields of interest: Historic preservation/historical societies; Cancer, leukemia; Salvation Army; Foundations (community).
Limitations: Applications accepted. Giving generally limited to the central NY area.
Application information:
Initial approach: Letter
Deadline(s): None
Trustees: Paula Miller; Sandra Pomeroy; William G. Pomeroy.
EIN: 206572301

6653
The Generoso Pope Foundation ✧
(formerly The Pope Foundation)
1 Generoso Pope Pl.
Tuckahoe, NY 10707 (914) 793-7777
Contact: David Pope, C.E.O.
FAX: (914) 793-7748; Main URL: http://www.gpfny.org

Incorporated in 1947 in NY.
Donor: Generoso Pope†.
Foundation type: Independent foundation.
Financial data (yr. ended 12/31/12): Assets, $13,142,767 (M); expenditures, $2,386,061; qualifying distributions, $1,874,932; giving activities include $1,007,967 for 65 grants (high: $291,750; low: $390).
Purpose and activities: Giving primarily for education, human services, Roman Catholic organizations, and to Italian heritage causes. Scholarships for higher education also available for students who are residents of Westchester, NY, possess a minimum GPA of 3.0, who have competitive SAT scores, who are active in community services, and who are of at least 50 percent Italian heritage.
Fields of interest: Arts, cultural/ethnic awareness; Higher education; Education; Medical research, institute; Human services; Catholic agencies & churches.
Type of support: General/operating support; Scholarships—to individuals.
Limitations: Giving primarily in the metropolitan New York, NY, area, including Westchester County.
Application information:
Initial approach: Letter
Deadline(s): None

Officers: Edith A. Pope, Chair.; David Anthony Pope, C.E.O. and Pres.; Catherine E. Pope, V.P. and Secy.
EIN: 136096193
Selected grants: The following grants are a representative sample of this grantmaker's funding activity:
$291,750 to Westchester Italian Cultural Center, Tuckahoe, NY, 2012. For Cultural Awareness of Italian Heritage.
$5,000 to Adelphi University, Garden City, NY, 2012. For educational.

6654
Porticus North America Foundation ✧
(formerly The Humanitas Foundation)
PO Box 1690
New York, NY 10163-1690 (212) 704-2300
FAX: (212) 704-2301;
E-mail: porticusnorthamerica@porticus.com; Canada Address: 1267 Cornwall Rd., Ste. 200, Oakville, Ontario, L6J 7T5; tel.: 905-338-2992; fax: 905-338-1651; Main URL: http://www.porticusna.com

Established in 1979.
Donors: American Retail Group, Inc.; American Retail Properties, Inc.; Argidius Foundation.
Foundation type: Independent foundation.
Financial data (yr. ended 12/31/12): Assets, $574,035 (M); gifts received, $5,340,240; expenditures, $5,717,832; qualifying distributions, $5,717,372; giving activities include $5,717,372 for grants.
Purpose and activities: The foundation is a small, private foundation that supports projects sponsored by Catholic organizations in the United States. Through its grantmaking it seeks to foster church renewal, improve Catholic education, and serve the disadvantaged. It has a sister foundation in Canada known as the Ansgar Charitable Foundation. Grants are only for Roman Catholic organizations within the U.S.
Fields of interest: Catholic agencies & churches.
Type of support: General/operating support; Management development/capacity building; Equipment; Program development; Conferences/seminars; Seed money; Curriculum development; Research; Technical assistance; Consulting services; Matching/challenge support.
Limitations: Applications accepted. Giving on a national basis. No support for individual parishes, schools or colleges not solicited by the foundation. No grants to individuals, or for scholarships, endowments, large construction projects, or capital campaigns.
Publications: Application guidelines.
Application information: See foundation proposal guidelines. Application form required.
Initial approach: Submit a proposal letter no more than two pages
Copies of proposal: 1
Deadline(s): Mar. 30, June 30, Sept. 30 and Dec. 31
Board meeting date(s): Apr. and Oct.
Final notification: Following board meeting
Officer: Anthony P. Mullen, Pres.
Number of staff: 2 full-time professional; 1 full-time support.
EIN: 133005012
Selected grants: The following grants are a representative sample of this grantmaker's funding activity:
$250,000 to Catholic Charities USA, Alexandria, VA, 2012. To plan and implement ten regional gatherings promoting poverty reduction programming to local charity agencies.
$250,000 to Roman Catholic Archdiocese of Boston, Braintree, MA, 2012. To retain two fundraising consulting firms for services to parishes for increased offertory programs benefitting both the parishes and the Archdiocese.
$177,950 to National Religious Vocation Conference, Chicago, IL, 2012. To strengthen, enhance, and promote vocations to religious life in the United States.
$164,000 to Roundtable Association of Catholic Diocesan Social Action Directors, Washington, DC, 2012. To support Welcoming the Stranger and Restorative Justice ministries through conferences and virtual training.
$146,000 to Jesuit Secondary Education Association, Washington, DC, 2012. For Blended Learning project in Jesuit High School and Mission Formation.
$110,000 to Vernon Avenue Project, Brooklyn, NY, 2012. Toward funds for start-up cost of setting up a food-related retail/wholesale business that will train/employ 20 young males.
$75,000 to Seton Hall University, South Orange, NJ, 2012. To establish the Micah Institute for Business Ethics as a collaborative cross-disciplinary institute at the Stillman School of Business.
$64,375 to National Federation for Catholic Youth Ministry, Washington, DC, 2012. To support and implement the Transforming Adolescent Catechesis.
$53,890 to University of Notre Dame, Notre Dame, IN, 2012. Toward PROCLAIM!: An ongoing Faith Formation program for Lay Volunteer ministers.
$44,000 to Sisters of the Order of Saint Dominic, Hicksville, NY, 2012. To support of North Fork Spanish Apostolate.

6655
The Poses Family Foundation ✧
145 Hudson St., Apt. 5B
New York, NY 10013-2150

Established in 2004 in NJ.
Donor: Frederic Poses.
Foundation type: Independent foundation.
Financial data (yr. ended 12/31/12): Assets, $460,931,335 (M); gifts received, $6,425,258; expenditures, $17,453,444; qualifying distributions, $13,831,029; giving activities include $12,918,372 for 186 grants (high: $4,752,551; low: $100), and $1,340,000 for 4 foundation-administered programs.
Purpose and activities: Giving primarily for education, as well as for the arts, human services, health organizations, and Jewish organizations.
Fields of interest: Arts; Elementary/secondary education; Education, special; Higher education; Education; Health organizations, association; Children/youth, services; Family services; Jewish agencies & synagogues.
Limitations: Applications not accepted. Giving primarily in New York, NY; funding also in San Francisco, CA. No grants to individuals.
Application information: Contributes only to pre-selected organizations.
Trustee: Frederic Poses.
EIN: 206375470

6656
The Powers Family Foundation ✧
c/o Raiche Ende Malter and Co. LLP
475 Park Ave. S., 31st. Fl.
New York, NY 10016-6901

Established in 1991 in NY.
Donor: John J. Powers.
Foundation type: Independent foundation.
Financial data (yr. ended 06/30/13): Assets, $12,180,148 (M); expenditures, $619,698; qualifying distributions, $600,078; giving activities include $586,000 for 18 grants (high: $385,000; low: $500).
Purpose and activities: Giving primarily for education.
Fields of interest: Higher education; Education; Health organizations.
Limitations: Applications not accepted. Giving primarily in MA and NY. No grants to individuals.
Application information: Contributes only to pre-selected organizations.
Trustees: Charles A. Davis; John J. Powers; Linda E. Powers.
EIN: 133637704
Selected grants: The following grants are a representative sample of this grantmaker's funding activity:
$50,000 to Fibrolamellar Cancer Foundation, Greenwich, CT, 2011. For general charitable purposes.
$25,000 to Tuesdays Children, Manhasset, NY, 2011. For general charitable purposes.
$16,500 to University of Durham, Durham, England, 2011. For general charitable purposes.
$10,000 to Laurel Mountain Christian Camp, Rector, PA, 2011. For general charitable purposes.
$10,000 to Mentoring Partnership of Long Island, Hauppauge, NY, 2011. For general charitable purposes.
$10,000 to Saint Aloysius School, New York, NY, 2011. For general charitable purposes.
$10,000 to Stone Point Capital Foundation, Greenwich, CT, 2011. For general charitable purposes.
$5,000 to Freedom Alliance, Dulles, VA, 2011. For general charitable purposes.
$5,000 to Trinity-Pawling School, Pawling, NY, 2011. For general charitable purposes.
$2,000 to Brick Presbyterian Church, New York, NY, 2011. For general charitable purposes.

6657
Tina & Steven Price Charitable Foundation ✧
c/o Tag Assoc., LLC
810 7th Ave., 7th Fl.
New York, NY 10019-5890

Established in 2003 in NY.
Donors: Steven Price; Tina Price; Robert Price; Price 2006 Family Trust.
Foundation type: Independent foundation.
Financial data (yr. ended 12/31/13): Assets, $9,106,897 (M); gifts received, $1,058,370; expenditures, $1,708,710; qualifying distributions, $1,672,202; giving activities include $1,672,202 for 47 grants (high: $600,000; low: $50).
Purpose and activities: Giving primarily to Jewish organizations and for social services.
Fields of interest: Higher education; Human services; Children/youth, services; Jewish

federated giving programs; Jewish agencies & synagogues.
Limitations: Applications not accepted. Giving primarily in New York, NY. No grants to individuals.
Application information: Contributes only to pre-selected organizations.
Trustees: Steven Price; Tina Price.
EIN: 206019600
Selected grants: The following grants are a representative sample of this grantmaker's funding activity:
$270,700 to UJA-Federation of New York, New York, NY, 2011.

6658
Price Chopper's Golub Foundation ✧
(formerly Golub Foundation)
461 Nott St.
Schenectady, NY 12308-1812 (518) 356-9450
FAX: (518) 374-4259; Application address: P.O. Box 1074, Schenectady, NY 12301; Additional tel.: (877) 877-0870; Main URL: http://www.pricechopper.com/community/golub-foundation

Established in 1981 in NY.
Donors: Jane Golub; Neil M. Golub; Golub Corp.
Foundation type: Company-sponsored foundation.
Financial data (yr. ended 03/31/14): Assets, $35,515 (M); gifts received, $1,175,000; expenditures, $1,293,662; qualifying distributions, $1,203,901; giving activities include $1,203,901 for 1,093 grants (high: $125,000; low: $35).
Purpose and activities: The foundation supports organizations involved with arts and culture, education, health, youth development, and human services and awards college scholarships to students located in areas of company operations.
Fields of interest: Museums; Arts; Higher education; Education; Hospitals (general); Health care; Youth development; YM/YWCAs & YM/YWHAs; Human services; United Ways and Federated Giving Programs; Minorities.
Type of support: General/operating support; Continuing support; Annual campaigns; Capital campaigns; Building/renovation; Program development; Scholarship funds; Sponsorships; Employee matching gifts; Scholarships—to individuals; Donated products.
Limitations: Applications accepted. Giving limited to areas of company operations in CT, MA, NH, NY, PA, and VT. No grants to individuals (except for scholarships), or for annual meetings, endowments, film or video projects, advertising, travel, conferences, conventions, or symposiums, publishing, or capital campaigns of national, religious, or political organizations.
Publications: Application guidelines; Informational brochure (including application guidelines).
Application information: Proposals and letters of request should be submitted using organization letterhead. An application form is required for scholarships. A personal interview may be required for scholarships. Support is limited to 1 contribution per organization during any given year.
Initial approach: Proposal; complete online application for scholarships; letter of request to nearest store facility for product donations
Deadline(s): 6 to 8 weeks prior to need; Mar. 15 for scholarships; 4 to 5 weeks prior to need for product donations
Final notification: 3 to 4 months; Apr. 15 for scholarships
Trustees: Pamela Cerrone; Warren Cressman; Jane Golub; Wes Holloway; Heidi Reali.
EIN: 222341421
Selected grants: The following grants are a representative sample of this grantmaker's funding activity:
$58,750 to United Jewish Federation of Northeastern New York, Albany, NY, 2011.
$36,000 to Muscular Dystrophy Association, Albany, NY, 2011.
$25,000 to Whitney M. Young Jr. Foundation, Albany, NY, 2011.

6659
The Price Family Foundation, Inc. ✧
(formerly Michael F. Price Foundation, Inc.)
c/o Michael F. Price
667 Madison Ave., 25th Fl.
New York, NY 10065-8025
Contact: Joanne Duhl, Exec. Dir.

Established in 1997 in NJ.
Donor: Michael F. Price.
Foundation type: Independent foundation.
Financial data (yr. ended 11/30/13): Assets, $20,741,090 (M); gifts received, $11,608,875; expenditures, $13,372,507; qualifying distributions, $13,129,905; giving activities include $12,944,208 for 62 grants (high: $7,943,746; low: $500).
Purpose and activities: Giving primarily for higher education, children's services, and hospitals.
Fields of interest: Higher education; Hospitals (general); Children/youth, services; Children/youth; Children; Young adults; Economically disadvantaged.
Limitations: Applications accepted. Giving primarily in NJ and New York City, NY. No grants to individuals.
Publications: Annual report.
Application information: Application form not required.
Initial approach: Letter
Deadline(s): None
Officers: Michael F. Price, Mgr.; Joanne Duhl, Exec. Dir.
Trustees: Martin Bernstein; Claudia Forbs; Jennifer C. Price; Jordan M. Price.
Number of staff: 1 full-time professional.
EIN: 223483367
Selected grants: The following grants are a representative sample of this grantmaker's funding activity:
$400,000 to SCO Family of Services, Glen Cove, NY, 2013.
$216,258 to Albert Einstein Medical Center, Philadelphia, PA, 2013. For early childhood programs.
$177,472 to Good Shepherd Services, New York, NY, 2013.
$150,000 to East Harlem Tutorial Program, New York, NY, 2013.
$150,000 to Friends of the Children New York, New York, NY, 2013.
$135,000 to Childrens Aid Society, New York, NY, 2013.
$100,000 to New Heights Youth, New York, NY, 2013.
$95,653 to Global Health Institute, New York, NY, 2013.
$75,000 to Bottom Line, Brooklyn, NY, 2013.
$25,000 to New York Cares, New York, NY, 2013.

6660
Vivian G. Prins Foundation ✧ ☆
c/o Anchin
1375 Broadway
New York, NY 10018-7001

Established in 2005 in NY.
Foundation type: Independent foundation.
Financial data (yr. ended 12/31/13): Assets, $3,365,510 (M); expenditures, $1,058,556; qualifying distributions, $1,023,243; giving activities include $1,009,000 for 5 grants (high: $334,000; low: $25,000).
Fields of interest: Jewish agencies & synagogues.
Limitations: Applications not accepted. No grants to individuals.
Application information: Contributes only to pre-selected organizations.
Trustee: Jerome A. Manning, Esq.
EIN: 203156955

6661
Project Home Again Foundation ✧
c/o Bryan Cave LLP
1290 Ave. of the Americas
New York, NY 10104-3399
Application address: P.O. Box 851008, New Orleans, LA 70185-1008; tel.: (504) 529-3522; Main URL: http://www.projecthomeagain.net
Application inquiry URL: http://www.nola.gov/softseconds

Donors: The Riggio Foundation; Greater New Orleans Foundation; New Orleans Redevelopment Authority.
Foundation type: Operating foundation.
Financial data (yr. ended 03/31/13): Assets, $16,642,684 (M); gifts received, $1,697,693; expenditures, $3,398,321; qualifying distributions, $3,247,787; giving activities include $98,739 for 4 grants (high: $50,000; low: $1,345), and $1,694,042 for 67 grants to individuals (high: $33,360; low: $16,400).
Purpose and activities: Giving to low and moderate income families in New Orleans, LA, who, due to Hurricane Katrina, own homes that are uninhabitable in Gentilly (Planning District 6) in Orleans Parish.
Fields of interest: Housing/shelter; Disasters, Hurricane Katrina; Economically disadvantaged.
Limitations: Applications accepted. Giving primarily in New Orleans, LA.
Publications: Application guidelines.
Application information: See http://www.nola.gov/softseconds/ for guidelines and details regarding eligibility. Application form required.
Deadline(s): Telephone foundation for deadline
Officers and Directors:* Leonard Riggio,* Pres.; Louise Riggio,* Secy.; Maria Florez, Treas.; William Lynch; Carey C. Shea.
EIN: 208733214

6662
Morris and Anna Propp Sons Fund, Inc. ✧
405 Park Ave., Ste. 1103
New York, NY 10022-9410

Incorporated in 1944 in NY.
Donor: Members of the Propp family.
Foundation type: Independent foundation.

Financial data (yr. ended 12/31/13): Assets, $17,118,362 (M); expenditures, $1,523,586; qualifying distributions, $1,457,950; giving activities include $1,457,950 for 106 grants (high: $200,000; low: $250).
Purpose and activities: Giving primarily for Jewish welfare funds, temple support, and religious education; some support for higher education.
Fields of interest: Museums; Higher education; Theological school/education; Health care; Human services; Jewish federated giving programs; Jewish agencies & synagogues.
Limitations: Applications not accepted. Giving primarily in NY. No grants to individuals.
Application information: Contributes only to pre-selected organizations.
Directors: Helen Heller; Gail Propp; Morris S. Propp.
Number of staff: 2 part-time support.
EIN: 136099110

6663
The Prospect Hill Foundation, Inc. ✧
99 Park Ave., Ste. 2220
New York, NY 10016-1601 (212) 370-1165
FAX: (212) 599-6282;
E-mail: grants@prospect-hill.org; Main URL: http://www.prospect-hill.org/

Incorporated in 1960 in NY; absorbed The Frederick W. Beinecke Fund in 1983.
Donor: William S. Beinecke.
Foundation type: Independent foundation.
Financial data (yr. ended 06/30/13): Assets, $61,506,165 (M); expenditures, $3,288,537; qualifying distributions, $3,000,010; giving activities include $2,533,412 for grants.
Purpose and activities: The foundation's mission is to advance the human experience while ensuring the well being of the earth. The foundation pursues this mission by making grants in four main program areas: 1) environmental conservation - to support conservation strategies that protect natural systems and to improve air quality for the benefit of human and ecological health; 2) nuclear nonproliferation - to limit the spread of nuclear weapons by providing reliable information to U.S. policy makers, the media, and the public; 3) reproductive health and rights - to support the right of women and men to be informed of and have access to safe, effective, affordable and acceptable methods of fertility regulation of their choice; and 4) criminal justice - to promote a fair and humane criminal justice system. In addition, the foundation makes a number of core grants that support the general philanthropic interests and goals of the foundation's directors and their family.
Fields of interest: Arts; Education; Environment, natural resources; Reproductive health, family planning; Courts/judicial administration; International affairs, arms control.
Type of support: Mission-related investments/loans; General/operating support; Capital campaigns; Land acquisition; Employee matching gifts; Matching/challenge support.
Limitations: Applications not accepted. Giving primarily on a national basis with emphasis on MA, NJ, NY, and RI. No support for sectarian religious activities, political organizations or non-tax exempted organizations. No grants to individuals, or for basic scientific research.
Publications: Financial statement; Grants list; Informational brochure.
Application information: Unsolicited requests for funds not accepted. Applications are by invitation only. Invited applicants should see the foundation web site for specific guidelines.
Board meeting date(s): 3 times annually
Officers and Directors:* William S. Beinecke,* Chair.; John B. Beinecke,* Pres.; Frederick W. Beinecke,* V.P. and Secy.; Robert J. Barletta, Treas.; Penny Fujiko Willgerodt, Exec. Dir.; Benjamin B. Beinecke; Frances G. Beinecke; Jacob S. Beinecke; Elizabeth B. Elston; Mary B. Elston; Sarah Beinecke Richardson; Jesse W. Smith; Carrie Elston Tunick.
Number of staff: 1 full-time professional; 1 part-time support.
EIN: 136075567

6664
Providence Foundation Inc. ✧
1637 50th St.
Brooklyn, NY 11204-1154

Established in 1997 in NY.
Donors: Michael Melnicke; Samuel Chmelnicki; Jack Rosen; Mr. Weingarten; Abraham Rubenfeld; Matityahu Tenenbaum; Aron Cytryn.
Foundation type: Independent foundation.
Financial data (yr. ended 06/30/13): Assets, $11,226,505 (M); gifts received, $1,862,483; expenditures, $659,339; qualifying distributions, $623,194; giving activities include $587,050 for 39 grants (high: $261,000; low: $250).
Purpose and activities: Giving primarily to Jewish organizations, temples, and schools.
Fields of interest: Education; Human services; Jewish agencies & synagogues.
Limitations: Applications not accepted. Giving primarily in Brooklyn, NY; some funding also in Los Angeles, CA. No grants to individuals.
Application information: Contributes only to pre-selected organizations.
Officer and Directors:* Michael Melnicke,* Pres.; Cila Chmelnicki; Samuel Chmelnicki; Breindy Melnicke.
EIN: 113350828
Selected grants: The following grants are a representative sample of this grantmaker's funding activity:
$1,000 to Congregation Ateres Shalom, Brooklyn, NY, 2011.

6665
Benjamin & Seema Pulier Charitable Foundation Inc. ✧ ☆
7 Cobblestone Ct.
Centerport, NY 11721-1162

Established in 1993 in NY.
Foundation type: Independent foundation.
Financial data (yr. ended 12/31/12): Assets, $9,041,189 (M); expenditures, $583,193; qualifying distributions, $492,500; giving activities include $492,500 for 9 grants (high: $200,000; low: $300).
Purpose and activities: Giving primarily for education and health care, particularly to an institute for research and treatment of kidney disease, as well as to Jewish organizations.
Fields of interest: Museums (specialized); Higher education; Health organizations, association; Medical research, institute; Human services; Jewish federated giving programs; Jewish agencies & synagogues.
Limitations: Applications not accepted. Giving primarily in FL, MA, and NY. No grants to individuals.
Publications: Financial statement.
Application information: Contributes only to pre-selected organizations.
Officers and Directors:* Solomon J. Freedman,* Pres.; Sol Karsch,* V.P.; Bruce A. Rosen,* Secy.-Treas.
EIN: 133683886

6666
The Pumpkin Foundation ✧
575 Lexington Ave., 33rd Fl.
New York, NY 10022-6156

Established in 1969.
Donors: Joseph H. Reich; Carol F. Reich; Janet Reich Elsbach; Deborah Reich.
Foundation type: Independent foundation.
Financial data (yr. ended 06/30/13): Assets, $8,604,283 (M); expenditures, $1,259,616; qualifying distributions, $1,155,939; giving activities include $1,153,804 for 30 grants (high: $500,000; low: $200).
Purpose and activities: Giving primarily for education, as well as for the arts, health organizations, and children and social services.
Fields of interest: Performing arts; Arts; Education; Health organizations, association; Human services; Children/youth, services.
Limitations: Applications not accepted. Giving primarily in New York, NY. No grants to individuals.
Application information: Contributes only to pre-selected organizations.
Trustees: Janet Reich Elsbach; Tracy S. Nagler; Carol F. Reich; Joseph H. Reich.
Number of staff: 1 full-time professional.
EIN: 136279814

6667
The Purchase Fund ✧
c/o Barry M. Strauss Assocs., Ltd.
307 5th Ave., 8th Fl.
New York, NY 10016-6517

Established in 1992 in NY.
Donor: Peter M. Flanigan.
Foundation type: Independent foundation.
Financial data (yr. ended 09/30/13): Assets, $615,762 (M); gifts received, $841,566; expenditures, $662,282; qualifying distributions, $655,338; giving activities include $653,513 for 51 grants (high: $100,543; low: $150).
Fields of interest: Arts; Education; Health organizations, association; Human services; Catholic agencies & churches.
Limitations: Applications not accepted. Giving on a national basis, with emphasis on NY and RI. No grants to individuals.
Application information: Contributes only to pre-selected organizations.
Trustees: Megan F. Flanigan; Robert W. Flanigan; Timothy P. Flanigan; Brigid S. Flanigan Lezak.
EIN: 137005756
Selected grants: The following grants are a representative sample of this grantmaker's funding activity:
$40,000 to Missionaries of Charity, Bronx, NY, 2011. For general support.

$25,500 to Princeton University, Princeton, NJ, 2011. For general support.
$1,000 to Childrens Scholarship Fund, New York, NY, 2011. For general support.
$1,000 to Harvard University, Cambridge, MA, 2011. For general support.

6668
The Puth Family Foundation ✧ ☆
(formerly John and Betsey Puth Foundation)
c/o Ayco Company LP - National Tax Group
P.O. Box 15014
Albany, NY 12112-5014

Established in 1987 in IL.
Donors: John W. Puth; David W. Puth; Castle Foundation; Leslie A. Puth.
Foundation type: Independent foundation.
Financial data (yr. ended 12/31/13): Assets, $5,059,561 (M); gifts received, $1,856,225; expenditures, $661,114; qualifying distributions, $654,944; giving activities include $654,944 for 75 grants (high: $125,000; low: $100).
Fields of interest: Museums; Performing arts, theater; Performing arts, music; Arts; Education, special; Higher education; Christian agencies & churches; Blind/visually impaired.
Limitations: Applications not accepted. Giving primarily in IL, MA and NY. No grants to individuals.
Application information: Contributes only to pre-selected organizations.
Officers: John W. Puth, Pres.; David W. Puth, V.P.; Leslie A. Puth, V.P.; Betsey L. Puth, Treas.
EIN: 363478673
Selected grants: The following grants are a representative sample of this grantmaker's funding activity:
$75,000 to Robin Hood Foundation, New York, NY, 2010.
$50,000 to Moravian College, Bethlehem, PA, 2011.
$40,000 to Brooklyn Museum, Brooklyn, NY, 2011.
$20,000 to Kenilworth Union Church, Kenilworth, IL, 2010.
$15,000 to Kenilworth Union Church, Kenilworth, IL, 2011.
$10,000 to Lehigh University, Bethlehem, PA, 2010.
$10,000 to Moravian College, Bethlehem, PA, 2011.
$10,000 to Moravian College, Bethlehem, PA, 2010.
$10,000 to Music Institute of Chicago, Wilmette, IL, 2011.
$10,000 to Music Institute of Chicago, Wilmette, IL, 2011.
$7,500 to Music Institute of Chicago, Wilmette, IL, 2011.
$7,500 to North Shore Senior Center, Northfield, IL, 2011.
$6,000 to Music Institute of Chicago, Wilmette, IL, 2010.
$5,000 to Field Museum of Natural History, Chicago, IL, 2011.
$5,000 to Loblollypop Foundation, Hobe Sound, FL, 2010.
$5,000 to Lyric Opera of Chicago, Chicago, IL, 2010.
$5,000 to North Shore Senior Center, Northfield, IL, 2010.
$2,500 to Geneva Foundation of Presbyterian Homes, Evanston, IL, 2011.
$2,000 to Geneva Foundation of Presbyterian Homes, Evanston, IL, 2010.
$1,000 to Old Elm Scholarship Foundation, Highland Park, IL, 2010.

6669
Pzena Charitable Foundation Inc. ✧
c/o Richard Pzena
791 Park Ave., Apt. 5B
New York, NY 10021

Established in 2005 in NJ.
Donor: Richard Pzena.
Foundation type: Independent foundation.
Financial data (yr. ended 12/31/13): Assets, $1,109,513 (M); expenditures, $582,285; qualifying distributions, $577,388; giving activities include $575,328 for 27 grants (high: $190,000; low: $100).
Fields of interest: Education; Jewish federated giving programs; Jewish agencies & synagogues.
Limitations: Applications accepted. Giving primarily in MA and NY. No grants to individuals.
Application information: Application form not required.
Initial approach: Proposal
Deadline(s): None
Trustees: Jeffrey Pzena; Richard Pzena; Robin Pzena.
EIN: 203706307

6670
Leslie C. Quick, Jr. & Regina A. Quick Charitable Trust Foundation ✧
c/o BCRS Assocs., LLC
77 Water St., 9th Fl.
New York, NY 10005-4414

Established in 1988 in FL.
Donors: Leslie C. Quick, Jr.†; Regina A. Quick†; Leslie and Regina Quick Charitable Lead Trust.
Foundation type: Independent foundation.
Financial data (yr. ended 10/31/13): Assets, $6,221,000 (M); gifts received, $4,882,348; expenditures, $3,750,324; qualifying distributions, $3,746,074; giving activities include $3,681,199 for 104 grants (high: $450,000; low: $100).
Purpose and activities: Support primarily for education, Roman Catholic churches, a mission, and a diocese; grants also for hospitals and medical research.
Fields of interest: Elementary/secondary education; Higher education; Health organizations, association; Medical research, institute; Catholic agencies & churches.
Limitations: Applications not accepted. Giving primarily in CA, FL and NY. No grants to individuals.
Application information: Contributes only to pre-selected organizations.
Trustees: Nancy Q. Gibson; Mary Q. Pedersen; Christopher C. Quick; Leslie C. Quick III; Peter Quick; Thomas C. Quick.
EIN: 650083436
Selected grants: The following grants are a representative sample of this grantmaker's funding activity:
$250,000 to Dana-Farber Cancer Institute, Boston, MA, 2012. For general support.
$225,000 to Schwab Charitable Fund, San Francisco, CA, 2012. For general support.
$225,000 to Schwab Charitable Fund, San Francisco, CA, 2012. For general support.
$225,000 to Schwab Charitable Fund, San Francisco, CA, 2012. For general support.
$217,857 to Schwab Charitable Fund, San Francisco, CA, 2012. For general support.
$80,000 to Partnership for Inner-City Education, New York, NY, 2012. For general support.
$75,000 to Jefferson Scholars Foundation, Charlottesville, VA, 2012. For general support.
$25,000 to Fairfield University, Fairfield, CT, 2012. For general support.
$25,000 to Palm Healthcare Foundation, West Palm Beach, FL, 2012. For general support.
$15,000 to Easter Seal Society of Volusia and Flagler Counties, Daytona Beach, FL, 2012. For general support.

6671
Radif Chesed Foundation ✧ ☆
1434 58th St.
Brooklyn, NY 11219-4646

Established in 2006 in NY.
Donor: Dovid Isaac Rabinowitz.
Foundation type: Independent foundation.
Financial data (yr. ended 12/31/12): Assets, $530,452 (M); gifts received, $50,000; expenditures, $608,773; qualifying distributions, $601,200; giving activities include $601,200 for grants.
Fields of interest: Jewish agencies & synagogues.
Limitations: Applications not accepted. Giving primarily in Brooklyn, NY. No grants to individuals.
Application information: Contributes only to pre-selected organizations.
Trustees: Dovid Isaac Rabinowitz; Rivka Rabinowitz.
EIN: 208068241

6672
Radio Drama Network, Inc. ✧
c/o Pryor Cashman LLP
7 Times Sq.
New York, NY 10036-6569
Contact: Richard Kay, Pres.

Established in 1990 in NY.
Donor: Himan Brown†.
Foundation type: Independent foundation.
Financial data (yr. ended 06/30/13): Assets, $16,628,827 (M); expenditures, $1,295,150; qualifying distributions, $1,198,000; giving activities include $1,198,000 for grants.
Fields of interest: Media, television; Higher education.
Limitations: Applications not accepted. Giving primarily in New York, NY. No grants to individuals.
Application information: Unsolicited requests for funds not accepted.
Board meeting date(s): June and Dec.
Officers and Directors:* Melina Brown,* Pres.; Richard Kay, Secy.; Mrs. Barrie Brown, V.P.; Eli Kopelman, Treas.
Number of staff: 2 part-time support.
EIN: 133253712

6673
Raether 1985 Charitable Trust ✧
c/o Kohlberg, Kravis, Roberts & Co.
9 W. 57th St., Ste. 4200
New York, NY 10019-2601

Established in 1985 in NY.
Donors: Paul E. Raether; Wendy S. Raether.
Foundation type: Independent foundation.
Financial data (yr. ended 11/30/13): Assets, $37,082,548 (M); expenditures, $6,829,501; qualifying distributions, $6,670,083; giving activities include $6,635,093 for 94 grants (high: $1,050,000; low: $100).
Purpose and activities: Funding primarily for education and for a boys and girls club. Funding also for human services and health care.
Fields of interest: Arts; Elementary/secondary education; Higher education, college; Health organizations; Medical research, institute; Boys & girls clubs; Human services.
Type of support: General/operating support.
Limitations: Applications not accepted. Giving primarily in CT and NY. No grants to individuals.
Application information: Contributes only to pre-selected organizations.
Trustees: Paul E. Raether; Wendy S. Raether; Holly Werner.
EIN: 136855420

6674
The Stewart J. Rahr Foundation ✧
725 Fifth Ave., 24th Fl.
New York, NY 10022-2519
E-mail: info@rahrfoundation.org; Main URL: http://www.rahrfoundation.org

Established in 2010 in NY.
Donor: Stewart J. Rahr.
Foundation type: Independent foundation.
Financial data (yr. ended 12/31/12): Assets, $110,561,355 (M); expenditures, $5,764,734; qualifying distributions, $5,192,500; giving activities include $5,192,500 for 46 grants (high: $1,000,000; low: $2,500).
Purpose and activities: Giving primarily to support youth, education, and medical research.
Fields of interest: Education; Medical research; Youth.
Application information: Application form available on foundation web site.
Officers: Stewart J. Rahr, Pres. and Treas.; Steven Burns, V.P. and Secy.
EIN: 274275648

6675
The Raiff Foundation ✧
c/o Robert M. Raiff
152 W. 57th St., 29th Fl.
New York, NY 10019-3310

Established in 1995 in NY.
Donor: Robert M. Raiff.
Foundation type: Independent foundation.
Financial data (yr. ended 12/31/13): Assets, $11,256,322 (M); expenditures, $587,052; qualifying distributions, $565,600; giving activities include $565,600 for 11 grants (high: $355,000; low: $5,000).
Fields of interest: Higher education; Hospitals (general); Medical research, institute; Philanthropy/voluntarism; Jewish agencies & synagogues.
Type of support: Annual campaigns; Emergency funds.
Limitations: Applications not accepted. Giving primarily in New York, NY, Cincinnati, OH, and Providence, RI.
Application information: Unsolicited requests for funds not accepted.
Officer: Sheldon Brody, Treas.
Trustee: Robert M. Raiff.
EIN: 137070078
Selected grants: The following grants are a representative sample of this grantmaker's funding activity:
$310,000 to Fidelity Charitable Gift Fund, Boston, MA, 2010.
$10,000 to Stanford University, Stanford, CA, 2011.
$5,000 to Rhode Island Foundation, Providence, RI, 2011.

6676
Randa Foundation ✧ ☆
120 W. 45th St.
New York, NY 10036

Donors: Randa Corp.; Randa Accessories Leather Goods, LLC; Randa Luggage, LLC; Market Connect Group, Inc.; Audrey Spiegel; Jeffrey Spiegel.
Foundation type: Independent foundation.
Financial data (yr. ended 12/31/12): Assets, $43,124 (M); gifts received, $448,750; expenditures, $604,471; qualifying distributions, $603,850; giving activities include $603,850 for grants.
Fields of interest: Education; International affairs; Philanthropy/voluntarism.
Limitations: Applications not accepted. Giving primarily in RI.
Application information: Unsolicited requests for funds not accepted.
Officers and Directors:* Audrey Spiegel,* Pres.; Jeffrey Spiegel,* Secy.; Grace Spiegel; Justin Spiegel.
EIN: 274240245

6677
The Randolph Foundation ✧
255 E. 49th St. , Ste. 23D
New York, NY 10017-1534 (212) 752-7148
Contact: Heather R. Higgins, Tr.

Established in 2003 in NY.
Foundation type: Independent foundation.
Financial data (yr. ended 12/31/13): Assets, $57,255,248 (M); expenditures, $4,505,324; qualifying distributions, $3,396,727; giving activities include $2,043,250 for 118 grants (high: $200,000; low: $100).
Fields of interest: Higher education; Education; Cystic fibrosis research; Human services; Civil/human rights; Foundations (private grantmaking); Social sciences, public policy; Public affairs.
Application information: Application form required.
Initial approach: Letter
Deadline(s): None
Officers and Trustees:* Heather R. Higgins,* Pres.; James E. Higgins,* Treas.; Joann Beyer; Polly Jackson Friess; R. Randolph Richardson.
EIN: 470892971

6678
The Michael and Paula Rantz Foundation ✧
c/o BCRS Assocs., LLC
77 Water St., 9th Fl.
New York, NY 10005-4401

Established in 1994 in CT.
Donor: Michael G. Rantz.
Foundation type: Independent foundation.
Financial data (yr. ended 05/31/13): Assets, $10,488,401 (M); gifts received, $995,662; expenditures, $519,440; qualifying distributions, $462,624; giving activities include $460,624 for 56 grants (high: $50,000; low: $500).
Fields of interest: Higher education, university; Medical school/education; Education; Arthritis; YM/YWCAs & YM/YWHAs; Civil/human rights, disabled; Protestant agencies & churches.
Limitations: Applications not accepted. Giving primarily in New York, NY and CA. No grants to individuals; no loans or scholarships.
Application information: Contributes only to pre-selected organizations.
Trustees: Michael G. Rantz; Paula Anne Rantz.
EIN: 133792291
Selected grants: The following grants are a representative sample of this grantmaker's funding activity:
$5,000 to University of Chicago, Booth School of Business, Chicago, IL, 2013. For All Contributions Were Made to the general purposes Fund of Public Charitable Organizations That Were Classified Under Section 501(c)(3) of the Internal Revenue Code.

6679
V. Kann Rasmussen Foundation ✧
475 Riverside Dr., Ste. 900
New York, NY 10115-0066 (212) 812-4271
Contact: Irene Krarup, Assoc. Dir.
FAX: (212) 812-4299; E-mail: ikrarup@vkrf.org; E-mail for Letters of Inquiry: grants@vkrf.org; Main URL: http://www.vkrf.org/

Established in 1991 in MA.
Donor: The Velux Trust.
Foundation type: Independent foundation.
Financial data (yr. ended 06/30/13): Assets, $85,409,661 (M); gifts received, $2,607,952; expenditures, $4,575,328; qualifying distributions, $4,197,655; giving activities include $3,437,005 for 47 grants (high: $250,000; low: $3,407), and $150,000 for foundation-administered programs.
Purpose and activities: Giving primarily for the environment. The foundation favors projects that: 1) take stock of the scale of the environmental problems, 2) use a systems approach to achieve change, 3) link policy, advocacy, and practical solution, 4) have international significance and perspective, even if U.S. based, and 5) are based on original thinking and creative ideas. The foundation currently only evaluates projects within the categories of: Ecosystems Resilience, Protection and Restoration, (research and tools of relevance to large scale geographic areas including many countries and continents; natural greenhouse gas sequestration and storage with large scale impact potential, and agro-biodiversity); Framework of Ecological Stability (economic models of living within global limits and practical implementation of change to a stable global ecosystem, and sustainable production and land use); and Communication and Leadership (communicating

value-based living with sustainable use of water, energy, and food resources, new innovative initiatives to enhance international cooperation and knowledge-sharing, and next generation leadership).
Fields of interest: Higher education; Environment, natural resources; Environment; Medical research, institute.
Type of support: General/operating support; Program development; Mission-related investments/loans.
Limitations: Applications accepted. Giving in the U.S., with emphasis on CA, CT, MA, NY, and Washington, DC. No support for general operations of well-established NGO programs, large membership organizations or networks, government organizations, established university research programs, or for organizations whose job it is to re-grant funding received. No grants to individuals, or for scholarships, candidates for political office, conservative projects focused on one single species, book, magazine, or web-based publishing, film, TV, radio, or video projects, medical research, health care, construction or endowment campaigns, U.S. projects with a specific local, state, or regional focus, non-US projects focused on single countries, regions, or specific continents, or for benefits or annual fundraising campaigns.
Publications: Application guidelines; Informational brochure; Occasional report.
Application information: Full proposals are by invitation only. See foundation web site for specific information regarding page restrictions for supplemental information. Application form not required.

Initial approach: Letter of inquiry (2 pages maximum), e-mail only
Copies of proposal: 1
Deadline(s): See foundation web site for current deadlines
Board meeting date(s): Mar./Apr. and Oct./Nov.
Final notification: 30 days or see foundation web site

Officer and Trustees:* Hans Kann Rasmussen,* Chair.; Lois E. H. Smith, Ph.D., M.D.*, Managing Dir.; Irene Krarup, Assoc. Dir.; Anne-Margrete Ogstrup-Pedersen; Astrid Kann Rasmussen; Kristian Kann Rasmussen.
EIN: 223101266

6680
Rattner Family Foundation Inc. ✧

(formerly Steven L. Rattner and P. Maureen White Foundation, Inc.)
998 5th Ave., 9th Fl.
New York, NY 10028-0102

Established in 1989 in NY.
Donors: Steven L. Rattner; The Steven Rattner 2000 LT Trust; 2000 LTT Asset Corp.
Foundation type: Independent foundation.
Financial data (yr. ended 12/31/12): Assets, $9,779,442 (M); gifts received, $9,142,154; expenditures, $1,252,036; qualifying distributions, $1,138,655; giving activities include $1,132,810 for grants.
Purpose and activities: Giving primarily for higher education; support also for cultural institutions, and human services.
Fields of interest: Museums; Arts; Higher education; Education; Human services; International relief.
Limitations: Applications not accepted. Giving primarily in New York, NY. No grants to individuals.
Application information: Contributes only to pre-selected organizations.
Officers and Director:* Steven L. Rattner, Pres.; P. Maureen White,* V.P. and C.F.O.; Michael Minars, Secy.-Treas.
EIN: 133519099

6681
Rauch Foundation ✧

229 7th St., Ste. 306
Garden City, NY 11530-5766 (516) 873-9808
Contact: Emilia Pitrelli
FAX: (516) 873-0708; E-mail for concept papers: info@rauchfoundation.org; Main URL: http://www.rauchfoundation.org
Facebook: https://www.facebook.com/rauchfoundation
Grants Database: http://www.rauchfoundation.org/for-grantees/grants-database/
LinkedIn: http://www.linkedin.com/company/rauch-foundation
Twitter: https://twitter.com/rauchfoundation

Incorporated in 1960 in NY.
Donors: Philip Rauch‡; Louis J. Rauch‡; Ruth T. Rauch; Philip J. Rauch, Jr.; Nancy R. Douzinas.
Foundation type: Independent foundation.
Financial data (yr. ended 11/30/13): Assets, $85,245,772 (M); expenditures, $6,042,042; qualifying distributions, $5,435,355; giving activities include $3,956,340 for 96 grants (high: $450,000; low: $50).
Purpose and activities: The foundation's mission is to: 1) promote positive outcomes for young children, ages newborn to 6, with particular focus on those with a disadvantaged socio-economic start. The foundation's first priority is to support programs that facilitate systemic change for those children and their families; 2) to protect the environment and improve the quality of life on Long Island, NY, and in MD; and 3) to strengthen the organizational effectiveness of nonprofit institutions that work on these issues through capacity building and leadership development. The foundation focuses its work in the places where Rauch family members have lived and worked— Long Island, NY, and MD.
Fields of interest: Education, early childhood education; Environment; Family services; Community/economic development.
Type of support: General/operating support; Program development; Conferences/seminars; Seed money; Technical assistance; Consulting services; Program evaluation; Matching/challenge support.
Limitations: Applications accepted. Giving primarily in Nassau and Suffolk counties, NY; some giving also in MD. Generally, no grants to individuals, capital expenditures, or emergency funding.
Publications: Application guidelines; Occasional report; Program policy statement.
Application information: The foundation requests that organizations not send videotapes. Application guidelines available on foundation web site. Application form not required.

Initial approach: Concept paper (no more than 3 pages)
Copies of proposal: 1
Deadline(s): None
Board meeting date(s): Feb., June, and Oct.
Final notification: Approx. 60 days

Officer and Trustees:* Nancy Rauch Douzinas,* Pres.; Jennifer Marino Rojas, V.P., Grants and Opers.; Philip J. Rauch; Ruth F. Douzinas; George W. Frank; Drew Halevy; Lance E. Lindblom; Lisa Mars; John Treiber; Reginald Tuggle; Eva D. Veson; John Wenzel.
Number of staff: 4 full-time professional; 1 part-time professional; 2 full-time support.
EIN: 112001717

6682
The Morton and Beverley Rechler Family Foundation, Inc. ✧

c/o Katzman, Weinstein & Co., LLP
131 Jericho Tpke., Ste. 400
Jericho, NY 11753-1017

Established in 1986 in FL.
Donors: Morton Rechler; Beverley Rechler; Yvetta Rechler-Newman; Bennett Rechler; Hannah Rabinowitz.
Foundation type: Independent foundation.
Financial data (yr. ended 12/31/13): Assets, $10,890,773 (M); expenditures, $717,739; qualifying distributions, $708,000; giving activities include $708,000 for 3 grants (high: $700,000; low: $3,000).
Purpose and activities: Giving to Jewish agencies, education, and community services.
Fields of interest: Higher education; Education; Human services; Jewish federated giving programs; Jewish agencies & synagogues.
Limitations: Applications not accepted. Giving primarily in New York, NY. No grants to individuals.
Application information: Contributes only to pre-selected organizations.
Officers: Morton Rechler, Pres.; Beverley Rechler, Secy.; Bennett Rechler, Treas.
Directors: Hannah Rabinowitz; Yvetta Rechler-Newman.
EIN: 592828631

6683
Red Crane Foundation ✧

(formerly Joseph & Carson Gleberman Foundation)
c/o Goldman Sachs & Co.
P.O. Box 73
Bowling Green Sta.
New York, NY 10274-0073

Established in 1991 in NY.
Donor: Joseph H. Gleberman.
Foundation type: Independent foundation.
Financial data (yr. ended 03/31/13): Assets, $44,979,994 (M); gifts received, $6,216,250; expenditures, $6,131,745; qualifying distributions, $5,917,521; giving activities include $5,917,521 for 41 grants (high: $2,000,000; low: $500).
Purpose and activities: Giving primarily for arts and cultural programs, education, natural resource conservation and protection, health associations, and human services.
Fields of interest: Arts; Education; Environment, natural resources; Health organizations, association; Human services; Jewish agencies & synagogues.
Limitations: Applications not accepted. Giving in the U.S., with strong emphasis on NY. No grants to individuals.
Application information: Contributes only to pre-selected organizations.
Trustees: Carson Gleberman; Joseph H. Gleberman.
EIN: 133632753

Selected grants: The following grants are a representative sample of this grantmaker's funding activity:
$1,000,000 to Nature Conservancy, New York City Office, New York, NY, 2011. For general support.
$1,000,000 to Stanford University, Stanford, CA, 2011. For general support.
$25,000 to Ethical Culture Fieldston School, New York, NY, 2011. For general support.
$20,000 to American Museum of Natural History, New York, NY, 2011. For general support.
$20,000 to Page Seventy-Three Productions, Brooklyn, NY, 2011. For general support.
$15,000 to Central Park Conservancy, New York, NY, 2011. For general support.
$10,000 to Cancer Research Institute, New York, NY, 2011. For general support.
$10,000 to Hospital for Special Surgery, New York, NY, 2011. For general support.
$10,000 to Manhattan Theater Club, New York, NY, 2011. For general support.

6684
The Reed Foundation, Inc. ✧

500 5th Ave., Ste. 2222
New York, NY 10110-0004
E-mail: lathamdc@thereedfoundation.org; Main URL: http://www.thereedfoundation.org

Incorporated in 1949 in NY.
Donor: Samuel Rubin†.
Foundation type: Independent foundation.
Financial data (yr. ended 12/31/13): Assets, $20,927,530 (M); expenditures, $2,580,566; qualifying distributions, $2,576,600; giving activities include $867,524 for 59 grants (high: $150,000; low: $140), and $485,351 for 27 grants to individuals (high: $40,000; low: $4,700).
Purpose and activities: The foundation's focus is on the support of programs in the arts, related libraries, social services, and both domestic and international civil rights. The arts and literature of the Caribbean Basin, through programs at a university and a research institute, are of major interest at present.
Fields of interest: Visual arts; Museums (art); Performing arts; Performing arts, opera; Arts; Higher education; Libraries/library science; Education; Human services; Civil/human rights.
International interests: Caribbean.
Type of support: General/operating support; Continuing support; Endowments; Program development; Fellowships; Scholarship funds; Research; Exchange programs; Matching/challenge support.
Limitations: Applications not accepted. Giving primarily in the metropolitan New York, NY, area; some limited funding also in the Caribbean Basin.
Publications: Program policy statement.
Application information: Unsolicited requests for funds not accepted.
Board meeting date(s): Varies
Officers and Directors:* Reed Rubin,* Pres.; Lara R. Rubin,* V.P.; Jane Gregory Rubin,* Secy.; Maia A. Rubin, Treas.; Peter L. Rubin.
Number of staff: 3 full-time professional.
EIN: 131990017

6685
Regals Foundation ✧

(formerly The Atticus Foundation)
c/o Regals Mgmt., LP
152 W. 57th St.
New York, NY 10019-3386 (212) 256-8489
Contact: David Slager, Tr.

Established in 1997 in NY.
Donors: Timothy R. Barakett; Nathaniel Rothschild; Atticus Capital LLC; Matthew J. Edmunds; David Slager; Dilan Siritunga.
Foundation type: Independent foundation.
Financial data (yr. ended 12/31/13): Assets, $49,104 (M); gifts received, $1,802,500; expenditures, $2,814,129; qualifying distributions, $2,810,289; giving activities include $2,806,952 for 31 grants (high: $1,015,000; low: $100).
Purpose and activities: Giving primarily for social services, education, health, and Jewish organizations and temples.
Fields of interest: Education; Hospitals (general); Health organizations, association; Medical research, institute; Human services; Children/youth, services; Foundations (private grantmaking); Jewish federated giving programs; Jewish agencies & synagogues.
Type of support: General/operating support.
Limitations: Giving primarily in NY. No grants to individuals.
Application information: Application form not required.
Initial approach: Letter
Deadline(s): None
Trustees: Yuri Musayev; David Slager.
EIN: 133981257
Selected grants: The following grants are a representative sample of this grantmaker's funding activity:
$2,280,000 to Jewish Communal Fund of New York, New York, NY, 2012.
$2,000,000 to Chabad-Lubavitch of Midtown Center, New York, NY, 2012.
$1,120,000 to Machne Israel, Brooklyn, NY, 2012.
$180,000 to Congregation Birchos Yosef, Spring Valley, NY, 2012.
$124,000 to M.Y. Keren Hashluchim, Brooklyn, NY, 2012.
$30,000 to Jewish Childrens Museum, Brooklyn, NY, 2012.
$25,000 to American Friends of Otzar Hessed, New York, NY, 2012.
$15,000 to Congregation Oholey Yakov of Boyom, Brooklyn, NY, 2012.
$10,000 to Congregation Hari, Spring Valley, NY, 2012.

6686
The Dorothy and Marshall M. Reisman Foundation ✧

(doing business as The Reisman Foundation)
P.O. Box 130
Dewitt, NY 13214-0130
Contact: Robert R. Falter, Tr.
E-mail: robertrfalter@reismanfoundation.org; Main URL: http://www.reismanfoundation.org

Established in 1991 in NY.
Donors: Dorothy Reisman†; Marshall M. Reisman†.
Foundation type: Independent foundation.
Financial data (yr. ended 01/31/14): Assets, $33,083,877 (M); expenditures, $1,542,845; qualifying distributions, $885,249; giving activities include $642,475 for 53 grants (high: $100,000; low: $450).
Fields of interest: Arts; Higher education; Health care.
Type of support: Scholarship funds; Program development; Management development/capacity building; General/operating support; Equipment; Curriculum development; Conferences/seminars; Capital campaigns; Building/renovation.
Limitations: Applications accepted. Giving primarily in NY, with emphasis on Syracuse; funding also in Montego Bay, Jamaica.
Publications: Application guidelines.
Application information: Application form not required.
Initial approach: Letter
Deadline(s): None
Trustee: Robert R. Falter.
Number of staff: 1 full-time professional; 1 part-time support.
EIN: 166353565
Selected grants: The following grants are a representative sample of this grantmaker's funding activity:
$900,000 to Central New York Community Foundation, Syracuse, NY, 2012.
$500,000 to Cazenovia College, Cazenovia, NY, 2012.
$250,000 to Ronald McDonald House Charities of Central New York, Syracuse, NY, 2012. For capital campaign.
$75,000 to Central New York Community Foundation, Syracuse, NY, 2013.
$50,000 to Central New York Community Foundation, Syracuse, NY, 2013.
$50,000 to Saint Josephs Hospital Foundation, Syracuse, NY, 2013.
$30,000 to Boys and Girls Club of Syracuse, Syracuse, NY, 2013.
$28,300 to Onondaga Historical Association, Syracuse, NY, 2012.
$25,000 to ProLiteracy Worldwide, Syracuse, NY, 2013.
$20,000 to Crouse Health Foundation, Syracuse, NY, 2012.
$16,733 to Cazenovia College, Cazenovia, NY, 2012.
$14,000 to United Way of Central New York, Syracuse, NY, 2013.
$10,000 to Crouse Health Foundation, Syracuse, NY, 2013.
$10,000 to Redhouse Arts Center, Syracuse, NY, 2013.
$2,000 to Grantmakers Forum of New York, Rochester, NY, 2012.

6687
Mahir A. & Helene Reiss Foundation, Inc. ✧

444 Madison Ave., Ste. 1800
New York, NY 10022-6949
Contact: Mahir Reiss, Dir.

Established in 1981 in NY.
Donors: Mahir A. Reiss; Helene Reiss; Rumelt Family Trust; Bedford Family LLC.
Foundation type: Independent foundation.
Financial data (yr. ended 12/31/13): Assets, $31,367 (M); gifts received, $1,445,000; expenditures, $1,465,600; qualifying distributions, $1,465,600; giving activities include $1,463,716 for grants.

Purpose and activities: Giving primarily to Jewish agencies, temples, and schools.
Fields of interest: Elementary/secondary education; Jewish federated giving programs; Jewish agencies & synagogues.
Limitations: Applications accepted. Giving primarily in NY.
Application information: Application form required.
Initial approach: Letter
Deadline(s): None
Director: Mahir A. Reiss.
EIN: 133050322

6688
Beatrice Renfield Foundation ✧

(formerly Harold and Beatrice Renfield Foundation, Inc.)
888 Park Ave.
New York, NY 10021-0235
Contact: Jean Renfield-Miller, Pres.

Established in 1974 in NY.
Donor: Beatrice Renfield†.
Foundation type: Independent foundation.
Financial data (yr. ended 12/31/12): Assets, $13,191,090 (M); gifts received, $30,308; expenditures, $835,675; qualifying distributions, $673,204; giving activities include $645,800 for 25 grants (high: $200,000; low: $300).
Purpose and activities: Giving primarily for education, including a nursing school, and for human services.
Fields of interest: Arts; Higher education; Nursing school/education; Education; Human services.
Limitations: Giving primarily in New York, NY; some funding also in New Haven, CT. No support for private foundations. No grants to individuals.
Application information:
Initial approach: Letter
Deadline(s): None
Officers: Jean Renfield-Miller, Pres.; Joseph Renfield, V.P. and Treas.
Directors: Dr. Attallah Kappas; Kate Maitland; Martin J. Milston; Robert Renfield; D. Carrington Renfield-Miller.
EIN: 510156925
Selected grants: The following grants are a representative sample of this grantmaker's funding activity:
$25,000 to Yale University, School of Nursing, New Haven, CT, 2012. For Unrestricted use by donee.

6689
The Burton P. and Judith B. Resnick Foundation ✧ ☆

c/o Jack Resnick & Sons, Inc.
110 E. 59th St.
New York, NY 10022-1308

Established in 1989 in NY.
Donors: Burton P. Resnick; Judith P. Resnick; Jack and Pearl Resnick Charitable Trust No. 2.
Foundation type: Independent foundation.
Financial data (yr. ended 03/31/13): Assets, $7,597,453 (M); expenditures, $1,029,678; qualifying distributions, $1,021,865; giving activities include $1,019,102 for 12 grants (high: $325,000; low: $8,200).
Fields of interest: Museums (ethnic/folk arts); Arts; Medical school/education; Jewish agencies & synagogues.
Limitations: Applications not accepted. Giving primarily in New York, NY. No grants to individuals.
Application information: Contributes only to pre-selected organizations.
Officers and Directors:* Burton P. Resnick,* Pres. and Treas.; Judith B. Resnick,* V.P. and Secy.; Steven J. Rotter.
EIN: 133524116
Selected grants: The following grants are a representative sample of this grantmaker's funding activity:
$22,568 to Carnegie Hall Society, New York, NY, 2012.
$15,000 to Westport Country Playhouse, Westport, CT, 2012.
$14,515 to Whitney Museum of American Art, New York, NY, 2012.
$8,500 to American Friends of the Israel Museum, New York, NY, 2012.

6690
The Ira M. Resnick Foundation, Inc. ✧

133 E. 58th St., Ste. 705
New York, NY 10022-1236
Contact: Ira M. Resnick, Pres.

Established in 1994 in NY.
Donor: Ira M. Resnick.
Foundation type: Independent foundation.
Financial data (yr. ended 05/31/13): Assets, $1,070,396 (M); gifts received, $1,000,000; expenditures, $1,025,415; qualifying distributions, $890,820; giving activities include $890,820 for grants.
Purpose and activities: Giving primarily for the arts, health associations, children, youth and social services, and to Jewish organizations.
Fields of interest: Museums; Performing arts; Arts; Education; Health organizations, association; Human services; Children/youth, services; Jewish agencies & synagogues.
Limitations: Applications not accepted. Giving primarily in NY.
Application information: Contributes only to pre-selected organizations.
Officers: Ira M. Resnick, Pres.; Gilbert A. Wang, Secy.-Treas.
Director: Paula S. Resnick.
EIN: 133775995
Selected grants: The following grants are a representative sample of this grantmaker's funding activity:
$25,000 to Los Angeles Opera Company, Los Angeles, CA, 2011.
$5,000 to Alzheimers Association, Chicago, IL, 2011.
$5,000 to Simon Wiesenthal Center, Los Angeles, CA, 2011.
$3,750 to American Cancer Society, Atlanta, GA, 2011.
$1,500 to American Jewish World Service, New York, NY, 2011.
$1,000 to Cystic Fibrosis Foundation, Bethesda, MD, 2011.
$1,000 to Film Foundation, Los Angeles, CA, 2011.
$1,000 to New York City Rescue Mission, New York, NY, 2011.
$1,000 to Special Olympics, Washington, DC, 2011.

6691
The Resource Foundation, Inc. ✧

(formerly Simpson Family Foundation, Inc.)
c/o A. J. Signorile
10 Park Ave.
New York, NY 10016-4338

Established in 1987 in CT.
Donors: Roy B. Simpson; Edith J. Simpson; Roy B. Simpson, Jr.
Foundation type: Independent foundation.
Financial data (yr. ended 12/31/12): Assets, $10,379,873 (M); gifts received, $450,000; expenditures, $837,441; qualifying distributions, $755,120; giving activities include $708,510 for 70 grants (high: $97,710; low: $95).
Purpose and activities: Giving primarily for the arts, particularly museums, education, social services, and religious purposes.
Fields of interest: Museums; Performing arts; Performing arts, orchestras; Historic preservation/historical societies; Arts; Education; Human services; Family services; United Ways and Federated Giving Programs; Protestant agencies & churches; Religion.
Limitations: Applications not accepted. Giving primarily in Greenwich, CT and NY, with some giving in PA. No grants to individuals.
Application information: Contributes only to pre-selected organizations.
Officers and Directors:* Roy B. Simpson,* Chair.; Edith J. Simpson,* Pres.; Roy B. Simpson, Jr.,* Treas.
EIN: 222870501

6692
Review Foundation ✧

20 Corporate Woods Blvd.
Albany, NY 12211-2396

Established in 1993 in NY.
Donors: Rhea P. Clark; KMP Charitable Trust VII; Kathleen Picotte; MJP International Fund; KMP Charitable Lead Trust III; RPC Charitable Lead Annuity Trust.
Foundation type: Independent foundation.
Financial data (yr. ended 12/31/13): Assets, $12,460,485 (M); gifts received, $387,833; expenditures, $565,698; qualifying distributions, $506,218; giving activities include $455,436 for 74 grants (high: $30,000; low: $500).
Fields of interest: Education; Hospitals (general); Human services; United Ways and Federated Giving Programs; Christian agencies & churches.
Limitations: Applications not accepted. Giving primarily in NY. No grants to individuals.
Application information: Contributes only to pre-selected organizations.
Officers: Rhea P. Clark, Pres.; James Clark, Jr., V.P.; Kathleen Clark, Secy.; Elizabeth Clark, Treas.
EIN: 223252633
Selected grants: The following grants are a representative sample of this grantmaker's funding activity:
$30,000 to Academy of the Holy Names, Albany, NY, 2012. For the recipients of the Academy of the Holy Names Partners in Education Program-St. Casmir Scholars.
$25,000 to Albany Symphony Orchestra, Albany, NY, 2012. For 2nd installment of 4-year ($100,000) pledge.
$6,000 to Amherst College, Amherst, MA, 2012. For donation to the alumni fund.

$5,000 to Academy of the Holy Names, Albany, NY, 2012. For sponsorship of the NYC Ballet at Saratoga for Girls Night Out.
$5,000 to La Salle School Foundation, Albany, NY, 2012. For general donation to the Annual Appeal.
$5,000 to Maria College, Albany, NY, 2012. For donation to the Sister Laureen Fitzgerald-Presidential Scholarship.
$5,000 to Trinity College, Hartford, CT, 2012. For donation for the college.
$1,500 to Siena College, Loudonville, NY, 2012. For gift to the Annual Fund.

6693
Charles H. Revson Foundation, Inc.
55 E. 59th St., 23rd Fl.
New York, NY 10022-1701 (212) 935-3340
Contact: Julie A. Sandorf, Pres.
FAX: (212) 688-0633;
E-mail: info@revsonfoundation.org; Main URL: http://www.revsonfoundation.org
Twitter: https://twitter.com/Revson_Fdn

Incorporated in 1956 in NY.
Donor: Charles H. Revson†.
Foundation type: Independent foundation.
Financial data (yr. ended 12/31/13): Assets, $162,376,020 (M); expenditures, $11,326,562; qualifying distributions, $8,265,119; giving activities include $6,828,749 for 75 grants (high: $800,000; low: $3,000).
Purpose and activities: Grants for urban affairs and public policy, with a special emphasis on New York, NY, problems, as well as national policy issues; education, including higher education; biomedical research; and Jewish Life.
Fields of interest: Media/communications; Higher education; Education; Community/economic development, public education; Biology/life sciences; Public policy, research; Government/public administration; Public affairs.
International interests: Israel.
Type of support: Continuing support; Program development; Fellowships; Internship funds; Research; Program-related investments/loans.
Limitations: Applications accepted. Giving primarily in New York, NY and Israel. No support for local or national health appeals. No grants to individuals generally, or for film projects, endowments, capital or building campaigns or fundraising dinner events.
Application information: The foundation will contact within two weeks only selected applicants. Application form not required.
Initial approach: Online Letter of Inquiry. Do not send LOI by mail
Copies of proposal: 1
Deadline(s): None
Board meeting date(s): 3 times per year
Final notification: 6 months
Officers and Directors:* Reynold Levy,* Chair.; Julie A. Sandorf, Pres.; Azade Ardali, C.F.O. and C.A.O.; Cheryl Cohen Effron,* Secy.; Azade Ardali, C.F.O. and C.A.O.; Gerald Rosenfeld,* Treas.; Karen Yu, Cont.; Stacy S. Dick; Suzanne Gluck; Jeffrey Goldberg; Sharon Greenberger; Dr. Steven Hyman; Charles H. Revson, Jr.; Dr. Clifford Tabin.
Number of staff: 3 full-time professional; 5 full-time support; 1 part-time support.
EIN: 136126105
Selected grants: The following grants are a representative sample of this grantmaker's funding activity:
$864,400 to New York University, School of Law, New York, NY, 2012. For continued support of Charles H. Revson Law Students Public Interest Fellowship Program (LSPIN), enabling New York area law students to work at public interest law organizations in the summers; and for Public Interest/Public Service Legal Career Fair held by NYU.
$500,000 to Lincoln Center for the Performing Arts, New York, NY, 2012. To rebuild and rename Charles H. Revson fountain.
$500,000 to W N Y C Radio, New York, NY, 2012. To develop new model for building and sustaining high-quality local public affairs journalism and establish new models of community engagement.
$400,000 to PEF Israel Endowment Funds, New York, NY, 2012. For Sheatufim-The Israel Center for Civil Society to establish, with Israeli philanthropic partners, the Opportunity Fund for Civic Service, independent collaborative of Israeli and North American philanthropies that will allocate enrichment program funding competitively to "best practice" NGOs that oversee Government-funded civic service slots for disadvantaged Israeli youth; and a rigorous evaluation of the economic and social impact of civic service on volunteers' lives.
$169,000 to ReServe Elder Service, New York, NY, 2012. For Queens Library Project.
$95,930 to Rockefeller University, New York, NY, 2012. For fellow in Charles H. Revson Senior Fellowship in Biomedical Science Program.
$95,407 to New York Press Association Scholarship Foundation, Albany, NY, 2012. To expand NYPA's work to strengthen the financial and organizational stability of New York City's ethnic and community press by training publications in best practices and increasing ad revenues.
$89,714 to New York University, New York, NY, 2012. For fellow in Charles H. Revson Senior Fellowship in Biomedical Science Program.
$50,000 to Harvard University, Cambridge, MA, 2012. For Public Service Venture Fund at Harvard Law School.
$30,000 to Friends of the Library of the Supreme Court of Israel, New Haven, CT, 2012. For English translation and online posting of significant opinions of 2008, 2009, and 2010 terms of Israeli Supreme Court.

6694
Reynolds Family Foundation ✧ ☆
c/o The Ayco Company, L.P. - NTG
P.O. Box 15014
Albany, NY 12212-5014

Established in 2007 in MA.
Donor: Robert L. Reynolds.
Foundation type: Independent foundation.
Financial data (yr. ended 12/31/13): Assets, $7,554,423 (M); gifts received, $1,960,952; expenditures, $457,018; qualifying distributions, $449,700; giving activities include $449,700 for 12 grants (high: $100,000; low: $10,000).
Fields of interest: Higher education, college; Athletics/sports, winter sports; Athletics/sports, golf.
Limitations: Applications not accepted. Giving primarily in MA and UT. No grants to individuals.
Application information: Contributes only to pre-selected organizations.
Trustees: Laura Caro Reynolds; Robert L. Reynolds.
EIN: 261458354
Selected grants: The following grants are a representative sample of this grantmaker's funding activity:
$50,000 to Points of Light Institute, Atlanta, GA, 2011. For general charitable purposes.

6695
Rheuminations, Inc. ✧
142 W. 57th St., Ste. 15A
New York, NY 10019

Established in 2000 in NJ.
Donors: Arnold H. Snider; Katherine M. Snider; Snider Holdings, LLC.
Foundation type: Operating foundation.
Financial data (yr. ended 12/31/12): Assets, $8,792,332 (M); gifts received, $7,000,000; expenditures, $7,013,279; qualifying distributions, $6,766,923; giving activities include $4,760,000 for 2 grants (high: $4,700,000; low: $60,000), and $1,365,256 for foundation-administered programs.
Fields of interest: Hospitals (general); Hospitals (specialty); Lupus; Lupus research.
Limitations: Applications not accepted. Giving primarily in NY; some giving also in San Francisco, CA and in Vancouver, Canada. No grants to individuals.
Application information: Contributes only to pre-selected organizations.
Officers and Trustees:* Katherine M. Snider,* Pres.; Arnold H. Snider,* V.P. and Treas.; Gina Del Giudice, M.D.*, Secy.; Nancy S. Hearne.
EIN: 223723547

6696
The Rice Family Foundation ✧
256 Bedford Banksville Rd.
Bedford, NY 10506-1923

Established in 1989 in NY.
Donors: Henry Hart Rice†; Edward Hart Rice; Eve Hart Rice.
Foundation type: Independent foundation.
Financial data (yr. ended 12/31/13): Assets, $54,986,711 (M); expenditures, $4,695,145; qualifying distributions, $3,647,614; giving activities include $3,646,000 for 42 grants (high: $1,000,000; low: $1,000).
Purpose and activities: Giving primarily for higher educational institutions, cultural programs, and health and human service agencies.
Fields of interest: Arts; Higher education; Health care; Human services.
Limitations: Applications not accepted. Giving primarily in NY; support also in CT and Washington, DC. No grants to individuals.
Application information: Contributes only to pre-selected organizations.
Board meeting date(s): Annually
Officers: Margaret S. Rice, Pres.; Edward Hart Rice, V.P. and Secy.; Eve Hart Rice, V.P. and Treas.
EIN: 133542090

6697
Rich Family Foundation ✧
(formerly Rich Foundation)
P.O. Box 245
Buffalo, NY 14240-0245
Contact: Robert E. Rich, Jr., Chair.

Established in 1961.
Donors: Rich Products Corp.; Robert E. Rich, Sr.‡.
Foundation type: Company-sponsored foundation.
Financial data (yr. ended 12/31/13): Assets, $8,579,334 (M); gifts received, $2,400,000; expenditures, $1,234,859; qualifying distributions, $1,216,620; giving activities include $1,198,381 for 74 grants (high: $300,000; low: $50).
Purpose and activities: The foundation supports organizations involved with performing arts, education, health, cancer research, fishing, and business and industry.
Fields of interest: Education; Health care; Human services.
Type of support: General/operating support; Continuing support; Annual campaigns; Sponsorships.
Limitations: Applications accepted. Giving primarily in FL and Buffalo and Cheektowaga, NY.
Application information: Application form required.
Initial approach: Letter
Deadline(s): None
Officers: Robert E. Rich, Jr., Chair.; Melinda Rich, Pres.; Mary Pat O'Connor, Secy. and Exec. Dir.; Joseph W. Segarra, Treas.
EIN: 166026199

6698
Mary Lea Johnson Richards 1997 Charitable Trust ✧

c/o O'Connor Davies
665 5th Ave.
New York, NY 10022

Established in 1996 in FL.
Donor: Elaine J. Wold.
Foundation type: Independent foundation.
Financial data (yr. ended 11/30/13): Assets, $1,303,668 (M); expenditures, $1,020,665; qualifying distributions, $1,009,674; giving activities include $1,000,000 for 1 grant.
Fields of interest: Arts; Children/youth, services; Foundations (private operating).
Limitations: Applications not accepted. Giving primarily in FL and NY. No grants to individuals.
Application information: Contributes only to pre-selected organizations.
Officers and Trustees:* Alexander D. Forger,* Mgr.; Diana E. Marszalek,* Mgr.; Kenneth Mersel,* Mgr.
EIN: 656236791
Selected grants: The following grants are a representative sample of this grantmaker's funding activity:
$55,000 to New York Center for Children, New York, NY, 2011. For general purposes.
$20,000 to Broadway Cares/Equity Fights AIDS, New York, NY, 2011. For general purposes.
$5,000 to American Cancer Society, New York, NY, 2011. For general purposes.
$3,000 to Lighthouse International, New York, NY, 2011. For general purposes.
$2,000 to New York Eye and Ear Infirmary, New York, NY, 2011. For general purposes.

6699
Bruce and Avis Richards Family Foundation ✧

15 Central Park W., Apt. 12A
New York, NY 10023-7714

Established in 2006 in NY.
Donors: Avis Richards; Bruce Richards.
Foundation type: Independent foundation.
Financial data (yr. ended 12/31/13): Assets, $3,068,561 (M); gifts received, $681,000; expenditures, $706,939; qualifying distributions, $703,217; giving activities include $703,217 for 18 grants (high: $201,935; low: $5,000).
Fields of interest: Education; Human services.
Limitations: Applications not accepted. Giving primarily in MA and New York, NY.
Application information: Unsolicited requests for funds not accepted.
Officers: Bruce Richards, Pres.; Avis Richards, V.P.
EIN: 208034361

6700
The Richardson Foundation ✧

(formerly Frank E. and Nancy M. Richardson Foundation)
c/o F.E. Richardson & Co.
245 Park Ave., 41st Fl.
New York, NY 10167-0002

Established in 1987 in NY.
Donors: Frank E. Richardson III; Deutsche Bank AG; Frank E. Richardson.
Foundation type: Independent foundation.
Financial data (yr. ended 12/31/13): Assets, $2,820,438 (M); gifts received, $660,257; expenditures, $761,213; qualifying distributions, $722,102; giving activities include $722,102 for 40 grants (high: $614,632; low: $100).
Purpose and activities: Giving primarily for the arts and education.
Fields of interest: Museums (art); Performing arts; Performing arts, ballet; Performing arts, opera; Arts; Higher education; Libraries (public); Education; Hospitals (general); Health organizations, association; Human services.
Type of support: General/operating support.
Limitations: Applications not accepted. Giving primarily in NY; some giving also in VT. No grants to individuals.
Application information: Contributes only to pre-selected organizations.
Trustee: Frank E. Richardson.
EIN: 133440317
Selected grants: The following grants are a representative sample of this grantmaker's funding activity:
$109,070 to Metropolitan Museum of Art, New York, NY, 2011. For general operating support.
$100,000 to New York University Langone Medical Center, New York, NY, 2011. For general operating support.
$98,200 to New York City Ballet, New York, NY, 2011. For general operating support.
$50,000 to Council on Foreign Relations, New York, NY, 2011. For general operating support.
$20,000 to William J. Gould Associates, Monterey, MA, 2011. For general operating support.
$10,000 to New Visions for Public Schools, New York, NY, 2011. For general operating support.
$5,000 to Manhattan Institute for Policy Research, New York, NY, 2011. For general operating support.
$2,500 to Metropolitan Opera, New York, NY, 2011. For general operating support.
$2,000 to Frick Collection, New York, NY, 2011. For general operating support.
$2,000 to New-York Historical Society, New York, NY, 2011. For general operating support.

6701
Richenthal Foundation ✧

28 Greene St., No. 5E
New York, NY 10013-2559 (212) 472-0831
Contact: David Richenthal, Tr.

Established in 1964 in NY.
Donor: Richenthal Trust.
Foundation type: Independent foundation.
Financial data (yr. ended 12/31/13): Assets, $14,604,736 (M); expenditures, $1,468,520; qualifying distributions, $521,610; giving activities include $521,610 for 52 grants (high: $85,000; low: $110).
Fields of interest: Performing arts, theater; Arts; Education; Human services.
Limitations: Applications accepted. Giving primarily in New York, NY. No grants to individuals.
Application information: Application form required.
Initial approach: Letter
Deadline(s): None
Trustees: Peter M. Graham; David Richenthal.
EIN: 136113616

6702
Richman Family Foundation ✧

(formerly The Fred & Rita Richman Foundation)
261 5th Ave.
New York, NY 10016-7701

Established in 1985 in NY.
Donors: Fred Richman; Richloom Sales Corp.; Richloom Fabrics Group, Inc.
Foundation type: Independent foundation.
Financial data (yr. ended 11/30/13): Assets, $41,782,802 (M); gifts received, $337,335; expenditures, $2,479,001; qualifying distributions, $1,769,429; giving activities include $1,431,324 for 1 grant.
Fields of interest: Jewish federated giving programs.
Limitations: Applications not accepted. Giving primarily in NY. No grants to individuals.
Application information: Contributes only to pre-selected organizations.
Directors: Fred Richman; James Richman; Rita Richman.
EIN: 133332711
Selected grants: The following grants are a representative sample of this grantmaker's funding activity:
$1,342,000 to Jewish Communal Fund of New York, New York, NY, 2011.

6703
Richmond County Savings Foundation ✧

900 South Ave., Exec. Ste. 17
Staten Island, NY 10314-7869 (718) 568-3516
Contact: Cesar J. Claro, Exec. Dir.
FAX: (718) 568-3551; E-mail: staff@rcsf.org; Additional tels.: (718) 568-3517 and (718) 568-3631; Main URL: http://www.rcsf.org

Established in 1998 in DE.
Donors: Richmond County Financial Corp.; New York Community Bancorp., Inc.
Foundation type: Company-sponsored foundation.
Financial data (yr. ended 12/31/12): Assets, $62,967,349 (M); expenditures, $3,744,806; qualifying distributions, $3,605,646; giving activities include $3,052,020 for 193 grants (high: $750,000; low: $95).

Purpose and activities: The foundation supports programs designed to advance educational opportunity; enrich cultural development; and strengthen health and human services.
Fields of interest: Museums; Arts; Higher education; Education; Environment, natural resources; Landscaping; Environment, beautification programs; Environment; Hospitals (general); Food services; Food banks; Housing/shelter; Human services; Community development, neighborhood development; Community/economic development.
Type of support: General/operating support; Management development/capacity building; Annual campaigns; Capital campaigns; Building/renovation; Equipment; Endowments; Program development; Conferences/seminars; Publication; Research; Technical assistance; Sponsorships; Matching/challenge support.
Limitations: Applications accepted. Giving primarily in areas of company operations in Staten Island, NY. No support for political organizations or private non-operating foundations. No grants to individuals.
Publications: Application guidelines; Annual report; Informational brochure; Newsletter.
Application information: The foundation awards general grants of up to $5,000 and board grants for requests over $5,000. Organizations requesting a grant over $10,000 are required to submit a summary of their proposed request on organization letterhead. Additional information, a grantee interview, or a site visit may be requested. Organizations receiving grants of more than $10,000 will be required to file a final report. Application form required.
Initial approach: Complete online application form or download application form and mail to foundation; download application form and mail to foundation for RCSF Green Challenge
Copies of proposal: 1
Deadline(s): None; Dec. 1 for RCSF Green Challenge
Board meeting date(s): Quarterly
Final notification: Jan. for RCF Green Challenge
Officers and Directors:* Michael F. Manzulli,* Chair. and Pres.; Kim Seggio, Secy. and Sr. Prog. Off.; Thomas R. Cangemi,* Treas.; Cesar J. Claro, Exec. Dir.; Godfrey H. Carstens, Jr.; Edward Cruz; Alfred B. Curtis, Jr.; Robert S. Farrell; Joseph R. Ficalora; William C. Frederick; Caroline Diamond Harrison; James L. Kelley; Patrick F.X. Nilan.
Number of staff: 4 full-time support.
EIN: 061503051

6704
The Anita B. and Howard S. Richmond Foundation Inc. ✧ ☆

(formerly Kings Point Richmond Foundation, Inc.)
266 W. 37th St., 17th Fl., Ste. 17th Fl.
New York, NY 10018-6609 (212) 594-9518
Contact: Lawrence S. Richmond, V.P., Treas. and Dir.

Established in 1965 in NY.
Donors: Howard S. Richmond; Lawrence Richmond; Phillip Richmond; Robert Richmond; Elizabeth Richmond-Schulman; Connaught Music Inc.; Cromwell Music Inc.; Essex Music Inc.; Folyways Music Publishers Inc.; Elizabeth R. Schulman; The Richmond Organization Inc.; The Richmond Foundation.
Foundation type: Independent foundation.
Financial data (yr. ended 12/31/13): Assets, $7,751,356 (M); gifts received, $2,573,650; expenditures, $5,388,266; qualifying distributions, $5,340,450; giving activities include $5,340,450 for 71 grants (high: $5,110,000; low: $100).
Purpose and activities: Giving primarily to health associations, including a children's hospital, education, and social services, including a free cancer support community group.
Fields of interest: Museums (children's); Arts; Higher education; Education; Hospitals (general); Health organizations, association; Human services; Children, services; United Ways and Federated Giving Programs; Jewish agencies & synagogues.
Limitations: Applications accepted. Giving primarily in CA and CT. No grants to individuals.
Application information: Application form not required.
Initial approach: Letter
Deadline(s): None
Officers and Directors:* Elizabeth Schulman,* Pres.; Frank Richmond,* V.P. and Treas.; Lawrence S. Richmond,* V.P.; Phillip Richmond,* V.P.; Robert M. Richmond,* V.P.; Bernard D. Gartlir, Secy.
EIN: 136180873

6705
The Ridgefield Foundation ✧

c/o Arthur S. Hoffman
570 Lexington Ave., 33rd Fl.
New York, NY 10022-6837

Incorporated in 1956 in NY.
Donors: Henry J. Leir†; Erna D. Leir†; Continental Ore Corp.; International Ore and Fertilizer Corp.; Joan Corley.
Foundation type: Independent foundation.
Financial data (yr. ended 12/31/12): Assets, $78,428,025 (M); expenditures, $5,459,329; qualifying distributions, $3,514,750; giving activities include $3,514,750 for grants.
Purpose and activities: Giving primarily for education, the arts, human services, and Jewish organizations.
Fields of interest: Arts; Higher education; Education; Human services; Jewish federated giving programs; Jewish agencies & synagogues.
Limitations: Applications not accepted. Giving primarily in CT, MA, and NY; funding also in Germany and Luxembourg. No grants to individuals, or for scholarships, fellowships, or matching gifts; no loans.
Application information: Contributes only to pre-selected organizations.
Board meeting date(s): Oct.
Officers and Directors:* Arthur S. Hoffman,* Pres. and Treas.; Margot Gibis,* V.P.; Anthony J. Cernera,* Secy.; Stuart Silver; Jean Wagener.
Number of staff: 1 part-time professional.
EIN: 136093563

6706
The Riedman Foundation ✧

45 East Ave., 8th Fl.
Rochester, NY 14604-2219 (585) 232-4424
Contact: John R. Riedman, Mgr.

Established in 1980 in NY.
Donors: John R. Riedman; Susan Holliday; Katherine Griswold; Riedman Corp.
Foundation type: Independent foundation.
Financial data (yr. ended 12/31/12): Assets, $13,965,814 (M); gifts received, $63,495; expenditures, $858,956; qualifying distributions, $828,928; giving activities include $807,712 for 21 grants (high: $430,000; low: $500).
Fields of interest: Museums; Museums (science/technology); Arts; Education; Animals/wildlife, fisheries; Zoos/zoological societies; Hospitals (general); Children/youth, services; Community/economic development.
Type of support: General/operating support.
Limitations: Applications accepted. Giving primarily in Rochester, NY.
Application information: Application form not required.
Initial approach: Proposal
Deadline(s): None
Manager: John R. Riedman.
EIN: 222279168
Selected grants: The following grants are a representative sample of this grantmaker's funding activity:
$427,500 to Rochester General Hospital, Rochester, NY, 2011. For unrestricted gift.
$10,000 to Saint John Fisher College, Rochester, NY, 2011. For unrestricted gift.
$7,000 to Rochester Philharmonic Orchestra, Rochester, NY, 2011. For unrestricted gift.
$5,000 to Rochester Institute of Technology, Rochester, NY, 2011. For unrestricted gift.
$5,000 to Rochester Museum and Science Center, Rochester, NY, 2011. For unrestricted gift.
$5,000 to Rochester Public Library, Rochester, NY, 2011. For unrestricted gift.
$1,250 to School of the Holy Childhood, Rochester, NY, 2011. For unrestricted gift.

6707
The Rieger Charitable Foundation Trust ✧

c/o Abraham Rieger, Meron Mgmt.
1846 50th St.
Brooklyn, NY 11204-1252 (718) 436-2326

Established in 1998 in NY.
Donors: Abraham Jacob Rieger; Rachel Rieger; A & E Trust; Triangle Trust.
Foundation type: Independent foundation.
Financial data (yr. ended 12/31/12): Assets, $2,118,695 (M); gifts received, $600,000; expenditures, $663,747; qualifying distributions, $663,050; giving activities include $663,050 for 26 grants (high: $297,000; low: $250).
Purpose and activities: Giving primarily to Jewish agencies, temples, and schools.
Fields of interest: Elementary/secondary education; Jewish agencies & synagogues.
Limitations: Giving primarily in Brooklyn, NY.
Application information: Application form not required.
Initial approach: Letter
Deadline(s): None
Directors: Abraham Rieger; David Rieger; Rachel Rieger.
EIN: 116508164

6708
The Dennis L. Riese Foundation ✧

c/o Ann Martinez
604 5th Ave.
New York, NY 10020-2304

Established in 2006 in NY.
Donor: Dennis L. Riese.
Foundation type: Independent foundation.
Financial data (yr. ended 11/30/13): Assets, $3,076,045 (M); gifts received, $1,675,000; expenditures, $541,130; qualifying distributions, $540,130; giving activities include $538,333 for 6 grants (high: $160,000; low: $10,000).
Fields of interest: Education; Medical research; Children/youth, services; Jewish agencies & synagogues.
Limitations: Applications not accepted. Giving primarily in NY. No grants to individuals.
Application information: Contributes only to pre-selected organizations.
Directors: Dennis L. Riese; Lauren Riese; Randi Riese; Victoria Riese; James Rosenzweig.
EIN: 203955152

6709
The Riggio Foundation ✧
c/o Maria Florez, LR Enterprises Mgmt., BDO USA LLP
122 5th Ave., Ste. 10
New York, NY 10011-5605

Established in 1994 in NY.
Donor: Leonard Riggio.
Foundation type: Independent foundation.
Financial data (yr. ended 08/31/13): Assets, $70,752,499 (M); expenditures, $2,157,986; qualifying distributions, $1,783,891; giving activities include $1,783,891 for 69 grants (high: $141,642; low: $150).
Purpose and activities: Giving primarily for the arts; funding also for human services, higher education, hospitals and health associations, and children's services.
Fields of interest: Arts, multipurpose centers/programs; Museums; Museums (art); Performing arts; Arts; Higher education; Hospitals (general); Health organizations, association; Disasters, 9/11/01; Human services; Children, services.
Type of support: General/operating support; Capital campaigns.
Limitations: Applications not accepted. Giving primarily in NY, with emphasis on the greater metropolitan New York City area; some funding on a national basis. No grants to individuals.
Application information: Contributes only to pre-selected organizations.
Trustees: Leonard Riggio; Louise Riggio.
EIN: 137039631
Selected grants: The following grants are a representative sample of this grantmaker's funding activity:
$300,000 to Secretarial Center, Chicago, IL, 2013.
$200,000 to United Federation of Teachers, New York, NY, 2013.
$141,642 to Equine Advocates, Chatham, NY, 2013.
$100,000 to Adelphi University, Garden City, NY, 2013.
$100,000 to Buoniconti Fund to Cure Paralysis, Miami, FL, 2013.
$65,000 to Omega Horse Rescue and Rehabilitation Center, Airville, PA, 2013.
$50,000 to Detroit Rescue Mission Ministries, Detroit, MI, 2013.
$50,000 to Grabhorn Institute, San Francisco, CA, 2013.
$25,000 to Grayson-Jockey Club Research Foundation, Lexington, KY, 2013.
$25,000 to UrbanGlass, Brooklyn, NY, 2013.

6710
Riley Family Foundation ✧
c/o Raich Ende Malter & Co., LLP
475 Park Ave. S., 31st Fl.
New York, NY 10016-6902

Established in 1991 in NY.
Donor: James P. Riley, Jr.
Foundation type: Independent foundation.
Financial data (yr. ended 02/28/13): Assets, $13,875,430 (M); gifts received, $400; expenditures, $820,046; qualifying distributions, $695,145; giving activities include $695,145 for grants.
Fields of interest: Higher education; Hospitals (general); Health organizations, association; Human services; Foundations (private grantmaking); Catholic agencies & churches.
Type of support: General/operating support.
Limitations: Applications not accepted. Giving primarily in New York, NY. No grants to individuals; no loans.
Application information: Contributes only to pre-selected organizations.
Officers: James P. Riley, Jr., Pres.; Brigid A. Riley, V.P.; Courtney Riley, V.P.; Shannon C. Riley, V.P.; Kerrylynn Riley, Exec. Dir.; Ellen C. Riley, Secy.-Treas.
EIN: 133638509
Selected grants: The following grants are a representative sample of this grantmaker's funding activity:
$3,050 to Villanova University, Villanova, PA, 2013. For The Organization's Primary Activity Is to Support By Contributions, Other Organizations Qualifying for Exemption Under Section 501(c)(3) of the Internal Revenue Code. the Trustees Choose These Organizations Based Upon Their Knowledge of the Organizations'.

6711
The Ripple Foundation ✧
c/o Malkin Holdings LLC
1 Grand Central Pl.
New York, NY 10165-0001

Established in 1999 in DE.
Donors: Anthony E. Malkin; Rachelle B. Malkin; Legacy Venture III LLC.
Foundation type: Independent foundation.
Financial data (yr. ended 12/31/13): Assets, $10,949,934 (M); gifts received, $3,624,488; expenditures, $1,359,811; qualifying distributions, $1,353,158; giving activities include $1,350,693 for 37 grants (high: $600,000; low: $255).
Purpose and activities: Giving primarily for education, the arts and the environment.
Fields of interest: Arts; Elementary/secondary education; Higher education; Environment, natural resources; Children/youth, services.
Limitations: Applications not accepted. Giving primarily in Cambridge, MA, and New York, NY.
Application information: Contributes only to pre-selected organizations.
Officer: Anthony E. Malkin, Pres.
Director: Rachelle B. Malkin.
EIN: 134081347

6712
May Ellen and Gerald Ritter Foundation ✧
61 Oliver St., Apt. 3Y
Brooklyn, NY 11209-8615
Contact: Vincent Rohan, Pres.
FAX: (718) 745-2095; E-mail: megritterfdn@aol.com

Established in 1980 in NY.
Donors: Gerald Ritter†; May Ellen Ritter†.
Foundation type: Independent foundation.
Financial data (yr. ended 12/31/13): Assets, $12,957,740 (M); expenditures, $1,430,073; qualifying distributions, $1,257,378; giving activities include $1,084,295 for 50 grants (high: $200,000; low: $1,000).
Purpose and activities: Giving primarily for the arts, education, hospitals and health care, human services, and to Catholic federated giving programs, agencies and churches; the foundation will, however consider all religions.
Fields of interest: Arts; Education; Hospitals (general); Health care; Human services; Catholic federated giving programs; Catholic agencies & churches; Religion; Infants/toddlers; Children/youth; Children; Youth; Adults; Aging; Young adults; Disabilities, people with; Physically disabled; Blind/visually impaired; Mentally disabled; Minorities; African Americans/Blacks; Hispanics/Latinos; Indigenous peoples; Women; Girls; Adults, women; Men; Boys; Adults, men; Military/veterans; Offenders/ex-offenders; Substance abusers; AIDS, people with; Single parents; Crime/abuse victims; Terminal illness, people with; Immigrants/refugees; Economically disadvantaged; Homeless.
Type of support: General/operating support; Continuing support; Annual campaigns; Capital campaigns; Building/renovation; Equipment; Endowments; Program development; Professorships; Seed money; Fellowships; Scholarship funds; Research.
Limitations: Applications accepted. Giving primarily in, but not limited to, the metropolitan New York, NY, area. No grants to individuals.
Application information: Application form not required.
Initial approach: Letter. Telephone inquires not accepted.
Deadline(s): None
Board meeting date(s): Annually
Officers: Vincent Rohan, Pres. and Treas.; Terri Rohan, V.P.; Alexander V. Rohan, Esq., Secy.
EIN: 136114269

6713
The Riversville Foundation ✧
c/o Ann Thivierge
1100 Park Ave., Apt. 12A
New York, NY 10128
Application address: c/o Arthur Thivierge, 440 Alexian Way, Apt. 58, Signal Mountain, TN 37377, tel.: (423) 886-0758

Established in 2000 in NY.
Donors: Barton M. Biggs†; Richard Fisher.
Foundation type: Independent foundation.
Financial data (yr. ended 12/31/13): Assets, $42,072,531 (M); gifts received, $18,922,609; expenditures, $1,635,156; qualifying distributions, $1,493,399; giving activities include $1,425,900 for 15 grants (high: $455,400; low: $10,000).
Purpose and activities: Giving primarily for higher education.

Fields of interest: Higher education; Education; Human services; Children/youth, services.
Limitations: Applications accepted. Giving in the U.S., with emphasis on NY.
Application information: Application form required.
Initial approach: Letter
Deadline(s): None
Trustees: Ann D. Thivierge; Arthur Thivierge.
EIN: 066504128
Selected grants: The following grants are a representative sample of this grantmaker's funding activity:
$180,000 to Spelman College, Atlanta, GA, 2011.
$150,000 to DePaul University, Chicago, IL, 2011.
$96,000 to Howard University, Washington, DC, 2011.
$72,000 to Claflin University, Orangeburg, SC, 2011.
$21,848 to Guilford College, Greensboro, NC, 2011.
$20,000 to Waterlines, Santa Fe, NM, 2011.
$7,000 to Elihu Club, New Haven, CT, 2011.

6714
The Leandro P. Rizzuto Foundation ✧
c/o Paul Weiss, Rifkind, Wharton & Garr
1285 Ave. of the Americas
New York, NY 10019-6031

Established in 2003 in DE.
Donors: Leandro P. Rizzuto; Patrick Yanotta.
Foundation type: Independent foundation.
Financial data (yr. ended 12/31/12): Assets, $280,743 (M); gifts received, $560,000; expenditures, $651,500; qualifying distributions, $650,000; giving activities include $650,000 for grants.
Fields of interest: Hospitals (general); Cancer; Medical research.
Limitations: Applications not accepted. Giving primarily in Boston, MA and New York, NY. No grants to individuals.
Application information: Contributes only to pre-selected organizations.
Officer: Leandro P. Rizzuto, Mgr.
Trustee: James M. Dubin.
EIN: 306068334

6715
Robbins Foundation ✧
(formerly Larry Robbins Foundation)
c/o Glenview Capital Mgmt.
767 5th Ave., 44th Fl.
New York, NY 10153-0023

Established in 2008 in NY.
Donors: Lawrence Robbins; Mercury Foundation of New York.
Foundation type: Independent foundation.
Financial data (yr. ended 12/31/12): Assets, $47,421,857 (M); gifts received, $130,000; expenditures, $8,167,110; qualifying distributions, $8,104,735; giving activities include $8,053,122 for 38 grants (high: $3,787,500; low: $100).
Fields of interest: Museums (ethnic/folk arts); Education; Hospitals (specialty); Cancer research; Youth development; Jewish federated giving programs.
Limitations: Applications not accepted. Giving primarily in Chicago, IL and New York, NY.
Application information: Contributes only to pre-selected organizations.
Trustee: Lawrence Robbins.
EIN: 261578481
Selected grants: The following grants are a representative sample of this grantmaker's funding activity:
$3,787,500 to Robin Hood Foundation, New York, NY, 2012. To fight poverty in New York City.
$1,795,656 to UJA-Federation of New York, New York, NY, 2012. For general support.
$1,502,000 to KIPP New York, New York, NY, 2012. For general support.
$433,333 to Teach for America, New York, NY, 2012. For general support.
$228,500 to Allen-Stevenson School, New York, NY, 2012. For general support.
$33,333 to Relay Graduate School of Education, New York, NY, 2012. For general support.
$25,000 to LIFT, Washington, DC, 2012. For general support.
$15,000 to University of Pennsylvania, Philadelphia, PA, 2012. For general support.
$10,000 to Icahn School of Medicine at Mount Sinai, New York, NY, 2012. For general support.
$10,000 to Village Academies Network, Harlem Village Academies, New York, NY, 2012. For general support.

6716
Jerome Robbins Foundation ✧
156 W. 56th St., Ste. 900
New York, NY 10019 (212) 367-8956
Contact: Christopher Pennington, Exec. Dir.
FAX: (212) 367-8966;
E-mail: pennington@jeromerobbins.org; Main URL: http://www.jeromerobbins.org

Established about 1970 in NY.
Donor: Jerome Robbins†.
Foundation type: Independent foundation.
Financial data (yr. ended 12/31/12): Assets, $17,413,619 (M); gifts received, $35,000; expenditures, $2,844,791; qualifying distributions, $2,384,241; giving activities include $1,969,054 for 143 grants (high: $550,000; low: $750), and $24,000 for 1 in-kind gift.
Purpose and activities: Financial support for dance, theater and organizations dedicated to serving those with HIV and AIDS with an emphasis on the artistic community.
Fields of interest: Performing arts, dance; Performing arts, ballet; Performing arts, theater.
Limitations: Applications accepted. Giving primarily in New York, NY.
Publications: Application guidelines; Grants list.
Application information: The foundation strongly urges that all applications for theater and dance be preceded by videotape or DVD. Thereafter, the foundation will inform the applicant whether a proposal should be submitted for further consideration. AIDS-related applications will be considered only for those programs that address HIV and AIDS as the disease impacts artists and the arts, most specifically those in the performing arts. Applications are not accepted for the New Essential Works (NEW) Program. Application form not required.
Initial approach: Proposal not exceeding 2 pages (excluding financials) by U.S. mail, or by e-mail in WordPerfect, Microsoft Word or PDF formats
Copies of proposal: 4
Deadline(s): Feb.1, July 1 and Nov. 1
Board meeting date(s): Quarterly
Final notification: 3 to 4 months
Officer: Christopher Pennington, Exec. Dir.
Trustees: Allen Greenberg; Daniel Stern.
Number of staff: 1 full-time professional.
EIN: 136021425

6717
A.M. Roberts Charitable Foundation ✧
c/o Morgan Stanley Private Bank, N.A.
1 New York Plz., 7th Fl.
New York, NY 10004

Established in 2003 in FL.
Donors: Alfred M. Roberts, Jr.; A. M. Roberts Marital Trust f/b/o Dorothy.
Foundation type: Independent foundation.
Financial data (yr. ended 12/31/13): Assets, $19,669,077 (M); expenditures, $3,067,258; qualifying distributions, $2,901,394; giving activities include $2,755,376 for 7 grants (high: $2,553,500; low: $5,000).
Purpose and activities: The foundation's primary mission is to benefit charitable organizations in the two communities in which Cmdr. Roberts made his home— Jacksonville and northern Florida and Watch Hill, Westerly, Rhode Island. A particular focus is to identify unmet community needs and to develop innovative strategies to address them.
Fields of interest: Historic preservation/historical societies; Education; Environment, plant conservation; Animal welfare.
Type of support: Continuing support; Capital campaigns; Seed money.
Limitations: Applications not accepted. Giving primarily in Jacksonville and northern FL and Westerly, RI.
Application information: Unsolicited requests for funds not accepted.
Board meeting date(s): Semi-annually as needed
Trustees: Chaplin Bradford Barnes; Morgan Stanley Private Bank, N.A.
EIN: 226948512

6718
Robertson Foundation ✧
c/o Deborah Rutigliano
101 Park Ave.
New York, NY 10178-0002 (212) 984-5714
Main URL: http://www.robertsonfoundation.org
GiveSmart: http://www.bridgespan.org/Philanthropy-Advice/Philanthropist-Spotlights/Stories/Donors/Julian-Robertson,-Jr.aspx#.VAYRPNJdWE4
Julian H. Robertson, Jr.'s Giving Pledge Profile: http://glasspockets.org/philanthropy-in-focus/eye-on-the-giving-pledge/profiles/robertson

Established in 1996 in NY.
Donor: Julian H. Robertson, Jr.
Foundation type: Independent foundation.
Financial data (yr. ended 11/30/13): Assets, $732,721,762 (M); expenditures, $105,785,297; qualifying distributions, $102,444,745; giving activities include $99,597,042 for 148 grants (high: $14,000,000; low: $600).
Purpose and activities: Support for education, general and rehabilitative medicine, medical research and philanthropy and voluntarism.

Fields of interest: Arts; Education; Hospitals (general); Youth development, centers/clubs; Protestant agencies & churches.
Limitations: Applications not accepted. Giving on a national basis. No grants to individuals.
Application information: Contributes only to pre-selected organizations.
Officer and Trustees:* John Hood, C.E.O. and Pres.; Phoebe Boyer, Exec. Dir.; John Griffen; Alexandra Robertson; Alexander Tucker Robertson; Julian H. Robertson, Jr.; Julian Hart Robertson III; Julian Spencer Robertson; Sarah Robertson; Aaron Stern.
Number of staff: 8 full-time professional.
EIN: 137068398
Selected grants: The following grants are a representative sample of this grantmaker's funding activity:
$8,146,935 to Robertson Scholars Program, Chapel Hill, NC, 2012. For general support.
$7,600,000 to Memorial Sloan-Kettering Cancer Center, New York, NY, 2012. For general support.
$7,285,800 to New York Stem Cell Foundation, New York, NY, 2012. For general support.
$7,000,000 to Environmental Defense Fund, New York, NY, 2012. For general support.
$5,000,000 to East Lake Foundation, Atlanta, GA, 2012. For general support.
$2,837,000 to CF Foundation, Atlanta, GA, 2012. For general support.
$1,200,000 to World Resources Institute, Washington, DC, 2012. For general support.
$332,800 to Focused Ultrasound Surgery Foundation, Charlottesville, VA, 2012. For general support.
$125,000 to Hollins University, Roanoke, VA, 2012. For general support.
$75,000 to New York-Presbyterian Hospital, New York, NY, 2012. For general support.

6719
The Robertson Scholars Program ✧

125 Park Ave., 16th Fl.
New York, NY 10001-0064 (212) 984-5711
Mailing address for Duke University office: Smith Warehouse, Bay 7 N., Fl. 2, Box 90753, Durham, NC 27708-0753; mailing address for UNC-Chapel Hill office: Rm. 023 Graham Memorial Bldg., Campus Box 1301, The University of North Carolina at Chapel Hill, Chapel Hill, NC 27599-1301
Facebook: https://www.facebook.com/RobertsonProgram
Twitter: https://twitter.com/RobertsonPrgm

Established in 2008 in NC.
Donor: Robertson Foundation.
Foundation type: Independent foundation.
Financial data (yr. ended 06/30/13): Assets, $323 (M); gifts received, $8,059,656; expenditures, $8,060,502; qualifying distributions, $8,060,502; giving activities include $7,329,072 for 2 grants (high: $5,505,574; low: $1,823,498).
Purpose and activities: The Robertson Scholars Program is a highly selective scholarship program that supplements the curricula of Duke University or University of North Carolina - Chapel Hill with unique experiences contributing to the development of a student's leadership potential. Students are accepted into the program each year after extensive application and interview process designed to identify leaders.
Fields of interest: Higher education.
Limitations: Applications not accepted. Giving primarily in NC.
Application information: Contributes only to pre-selected organizations.
Officers: Anthony S. Brown, Pres.; Allen Chan, Exec. Dir.
Directors: Richard Brodhead; Dr. John Hood; Julian H. Robertson, Jr.; Dr. Aaron Stern; Holden Thorp.
EIN: 202479103
Selected grants: The following grants are a representative sample of this grantmaker's funding activity:
$5,505,574 to Duke University, Durham, NC, 2013. For general support.
$1,823,498 to University of North Carolina, Chapel Hill, NC, 2013. For general support.

6720
The Jim and Linda Robinson Foundation, Inc. ✧ ☆

c/o The Ayco Co., LLP, Ral Mazza
P.O. Box 860
Saratoga Springs, NY 12866-0860

Established in NY.
Donors: Ral Mazza; Linda Gosden Robinson; James D. Robinson III.
Foundation type: Independent foundation.
Financial data (yr. ended 12/31/13): Assets, $364,170 (M); expenditures, $531,462; qualifying distributions, $517,074; giving activities include $517,074 for 43 grants (high: $100,000; low: $100).
Fields of interest: Arts; Education; Health care.
Limitations: Applications not accepted. Giving primarily in NY. No grants to individuals.
Application information: Contributes only to pre-selected organizations.
Officers: James D. Robinson III, Pres.; Linda G. Robinson, V.P. and Treas.; Karen Marshon, Secy.
EIN: 133981478

6721
Robinson-Broadhurst Foundation, Inc. ✧

c/o Diane E. Frazee
101 Main St.
P.O. Box 160
Stamford, NY 12167-1140 (607) 652-2508
Contact: Charles K. McKenzie, Pres. and Exec. Dir.
FAX: (607) 652-2453; E-mail: rbfi@stny.rr.com; Main URL: http://www.robinsonbroadhurstfoundationinc.com/

Established in 1984 in NY.
Donors: Anna Broadhurst†; R. Avery Robinson†; Winnie M. Robinson†.
Foundation type: Independent foundation.
Financial data (yr. ended 04/30/13): Assets, $50,643,559 (M); expenditures, $2,717,376; qualifying distributions, $2,328,752; giving activities include $2,128,396 for 94 grants (high: $227,800; low: $600).
Purpose and activities: Giving primarily for local community services.
Fields of interest: Arts; Health care; Community/economic development; Government/public administration.
Type of support: Building/renovation; Equipment; Scholarship funds; Matching/challenge support.
Limitations: Applications accepted. Giving limited to Winchendon, MA; and Stamford and Worcester, NY. No grants to individuals, or for annual operating expenditures or debt reduction.
Publications: Application guidelines; Informational brochure.
Application information: Application form available on foundation web site. Application form required.
Deadline(s): Dec. 31
Board meeting date(s): May
Officers and Trustees:* Charles "Lad" McKenzie,* Pres. and Exec. Dir.; Ralph Beisler,* V.P. and Secy.; Ernest "Bud" Fletcher, Jr.,* Treas.; Martin "Skip" Parks; Donald VanEtten.
Number of staff: 1 full-time professional; 1 full-time support.
EIN: 222558699
Selected grants: The following grants are a representative sample of this grantmaker's funding activity:
$227,800 to Wendell P. Clark Memorial YMCA, Winchendon, MA, 2012.
$200,000 to Winchendon, Town of, Winchendon, MA, 2012. For public schools.
$72,584 to Stamford Health Care Society, Stamford, NY, 2012. For Robinson Terrace.
$52,851 to Stamford Central School, Stamford, NY, 2012. For Camp HERE.
$39,871 to Stamford Central School, Stamford, NY, 2012.
$38,000 to Winchendon, Town of, Winchendon, MA, 2012.
$25,000 to Catskill Area Hospice and Palliative Care, Oneonta, NY, 2012.
$21,920 to Winchendon Historical Society, Winchendon, MA, 2012.

6722
Rochester Area Community Foundation ✧

500 East Ave.
Rochester, NY 14607-1912 (585) 271-4100
Contact: For grants: Mary Harstein, Prog. Admin.
FAX: (585) 271-4292; E-mail: mcole@racf.org; Grant application E-mail: mhartstein@RACF.org; Main URL: http://www.racf.org
Facebook: http://facebook.com/pages/Rochester-Area-Community-Foundation/106070818124?ref=ts
Scholarship inquiry tel.: (585) 341-4357

Incorporated in 1972 in NY.
Foundation type: Community foundation.
Financial data (yr. ended 03/31/14): Assets, $302,577,291 (M); gifts received, $25,998,475; expenditures, $25,835,277; giving activities include $21,600,650 for grants.
Purpose and activities: Giving for broad purposes related to community betterment, including education, the environment, arts and cultural programs, historic preservation, health services, especially for youth, community development and responsibility, and social services, including family and legal services, minorities, women, and youth. Scholarship recipients are chosen by institutions. Primary interests include early childhood education, community development, including leadership programs for young people, after-school program quality, civic engagement, and strengthening families and children.
Fields of interest: Historic preservation/historical societies; Arts; Education, early childhood education; Child development, education; Education, services; Education; Environment, natural resources; Environment; Health care; Recreation; Youth development, services; Children/youth, services; Child development, services; Family services; Women, centers/services; Minorities/

immigrants, centers/services; Human services; Community/economic development; Children/youth; Children; Youth; Aging; Minorities; Women; Girls.
Type of support: General/operating support; Management development/capacity building; Building/renovation; Equipment; Program development; Conferences/seminars; Publication; Seed money; Scholarship funds; Technical assistance; Consulting services; Program evaluation.
Limitations: Applications accepted. Giving limited to Genesee, Livingston, Monroe, Ontario, Orleans, and Wayne counties, NY, except for donor-designated funds. No support for religious projects. No grants to individuals (except from restricted funds), or for capital or annual campaigns, debt reduction, special events, land acquisition, or endowment or emergency funds.
Publications: Annual report (including application guidelines); Biennial report (including application guidelines); Financial statement; Grants list; Informational brochure; Newsletter; Program policy statement.
Application information: Visit foundation web site for application forms and specific guidelines per grant type. Application form required.
Initial approach: Submit application form and attachments
Copies of proposal: 1
Deadline(s): Varies
Board meeting date(s): Jan., Feb., Mar., May, June, July, Oct. and Nov.
Final notification: Ongoing
Officers and Board Members:* Kathy Nixon,* Chair.; Jennifer Leonard, C.E.O. and Pres.; Mary F. Holleran, V.P., Comms.; Dana K. Miller, V.P., Advancement; Hank Rubin, V.P., Community Progs.; Amy S. Vars, V.P., Finance and Admin.; Susan Acker; Carol Adams; Robert D. Baden; Edward D. Bloom; Philip L. Burke; Jeremy A. Cooney; Jose Coronas; Malik Evans; David R. Ferris; Michael G. Kane; Hoffman Moka Lantum, M.D., Ph.D.; Laura Loomis; Laura J. "Jinny" Loomis; Rev. Marvin A. McMickle; Carolyn G. Nussbaum; Kevin J. Parker, Ph.D.; Edward Radin; Thomas S. Richards; Richard J. Riedman; David Still; Elizabeth A. Thorley; Kim VanGelder; David P. Veniskey; Judy von Bucher; Thomas F. Warfield; Mary Worboys-Turner; Heidi N. Zimmer-Meyer.
Number of staff: 11 full-time professional; 2 part-time professional; 7 full-time support; 1 part-time support.
EIN: 237250641
Selected grants: The following grants are a representative sample of this grantmaker's funding activity:
$500,000 to University of Rochester, Memorial Art Gallery, Rochester, NY, 2012.
$302,000 to Arizona Community Foundation, Phoenix, AZ, 2012. For Season For Sharing Campaign.
$200,000 to Rochester General Hospital Foundation, Rochester, NY, 2012. For Bullis Spring: Newark-Wayne Community Hospital Emergency Room Expansion and Renovation.
$110,240 to Catholic Charities of Wayne County, Newark, NY, 2012. For Bullis Summer: Early Intervention Program.
$100,000 to Association for the Blind and Visually Impaired-Goodwill Industries, Rochester, NY, 2012. For the construction of New Centennial Campus.
$18,074 to United Way of Greater Rochester, Rochester, NY, 2012. For annual giving.
$15,000 to Childrens Institute, Rochester, NY, 2012. For Partners in Family Child Care.
$15,000 to Rochester Arts Festival, Rochester, NY, 2012. For Other Fall: Rochester International Fringe Festival.
$13,304 to Rochester City School District, Rochester, NY, 2012. For 3rd grade Dictionary Program.
$10,000 to Hearing and Speech Center of Rochester, Rochester, NY, 2012. For Summer Services Outreach Program.
$3,000 to Jewish Community Federation of Greater Rochester, Rochester, NY, 2012. For UJA campaign.
$3,000 to Saint Lukes Community House, Nashville, TN, 2012. For Child Development/Early Literacy Program.
$2,500 to Wings of Eagles Discovery Center, Horseheads, NY, 2012. For Expansion of E-Mission Educational Program.
$2,000 to Al Sigl Center for Rehabilitation Agencies, Rochester, NY, 2012. For general support.
$2,000 to Our Lady of Mercy High School, Rochester, NY, 2012. For general support.

6723
Rockefeller Brothers Fund, Inc.
475 Riverside Dr., Ste. 900
New York, NY 10115-0066 (212) 812-4200
Contact: Lisa A. Gilson, Grants Managment Analyst
FAX: (212) 812-4299; E-mail: grantsmgmt@rbf.org; Main URL: http://www.rbf.org
CEP Study: http://www.rbf.org/resource/2010-grantee-and-applicant-perception-reports
David Rockefeller's Giving Pledge Profile: http://glasspockets.org/philanthropy-in-focus/eye-on-the-giving-pledge/profiles/rockefeller
E-Newsletter: http://rbf.us1.list-manage.com/subscribe/post?u=8ced17726d46f75e118db9da7&id=2a6d5fa7b5
Facebook: http://www.facebook.com/pages/Rockefeller-Brothers-Fund/181125435234193
Grants Database: http://www.rbf.org/content/grants-search
Knowledge Center: http://www.rbf.org/news-and-resources
Twitter: http://twitter.com/rockbrosfund/
YouTube: http://www.youtube.com/user/RBFCommunications

Incorporated in 1940 in NY.
Donors: John D. Rockefeller, Jr.†; Martha Baird Rockefeller†; Abby Rockefeller Mauze†; David Rockefeller; John D. Rockefeller III†; Laurance S. Rockefeller†; Nelson A. Rockefeller†; Winthrop Rockefeller†.
Foundation type: Independent foundation.
Financial data (yr. ended 12/31/13): Assets, $870,572,218 (M); gifts received, $2,237,209; expenditures, $49,650,766; qualifying distributions, $40,859,797; giving activities include $27,351,089 for 334 grants (high: $500,000; low: $1,500), $48,015 for 120 employee matching gifts, and $4,500,429 for 3 foundation-administered programs.
Purpose and activities: The Rockefeller Brothers Fund promotes social change that contributes to a more just, sustainable, and peaceful world. Through its grantmaking, the Fund supports efforts to expand knowledge, clarify values and critical choices, nurture creative expression, and shape public policy. The Fund's programs are intended to develop leaders, strengthen institutions, engage citizens, build community, and foster partnerships that include government, business, and civil society. Respect for cultural diversity and ecological integrity pervades the Fund's activities.
Fields of interest: Arts, alliance/advocacy; Arts, cultural/ethnic awareness; Environment, alliance/advocacy; Environment, public policy; Environment, government agencies; Environment, pollution control; Environment, climate change/global warming; Environment, natural resources; Environment, energy; Environment, forests; Environmental education; Environment; International peace/security; Civil/human rights, public policy; Civil/human rights, government agencies; Civil rights, voter education; Public affairs, election regulation.
International interests: China; Hungary; Israel; Kosovo; Montenegro; Serbia.
Type of support: Program-related investments/loans; Program evaluation; Employee matching gifts; General/operating support; Matching/challenge support; Program development; Technical assistance.
Limitations: Applications accepted. Giving primarily in the United States and internationally, with an emphasis on pivotal places: Southern China and the Western Balkans. No grants to individuals, or for land acquisitions or building funds.
Publications: Annual report; Grants list; Occasional report; IRS Form 990 or 990-PF printed copy available upon request.
Application information: Application guidelines available on foundation web site.
Initial approach: Online letter of inquiry and preliminary grant compatibility quiz
Deadline(s): See foundation web site
Board meeting date(s): Mar., June, and Nov.
Final notification: 3 months
Officers and Trustees:* Valerie Rockefeller Wayne,* Chair.; Joseph A. Pierson,* Vice-Chair.; Stephen B. Heintz,* Pres.; Elizabeth C. Campbell, V.P., Progs.; Geraldine F. Watson, V.P., Opers. and Finance; Nancy L. Muirhead, Corp. Secy.; David Rockefeller, Advisory Tr.; Anne Bartley; Nicholas Burns; Wendy Gordon; Miranda M. Kaiser; Hugh Lawson; Daniel Levy; Vali Nasr; Peter M. O'Neill; Marnie Pillsbury; Kavita Ramdas; Justin Rockefeller; Steven C. Rockefeller; Arlene Shuler; Marsha Simms.
Number of staff: 19 full-time professional; 28 full-time support.
EIN: 131760106

6724
The Rockefeller Foundation ✧
420 5th Ave.
New York, NY 10018-2702 (212) 869-8500
Main URL: http://www.rockefellerfoundation.org/
Blog: http://www.rockefellerfoundation.org/blog
Centennial Innovation Challenge: http://challenge.rockefellerfoundation.org/
E-Newsletter: http://www.rockefellerfoundation.org/sign-up
Facebook: http://www.facebook.com/rockefellerfoundation
Grants Database: http://www.rockefellerfoundation.org/grants/search
RSS Feed: http://www.rockefellerfoundation.org/rockfound.xml
Twitter: https://twitter.com/RockefellerFdn
YouTube: http://www.youtube.com/RockefellerFound

Incorporated in 1913 in NY.
Donor: John D. Rockefeller, Sr.‡.
Foundation type: Independent foundation.
Financial data (yr. ended 12/31/13): Assets, $4,121,465,814 (M); expenditures, $201,185,881; qualifying distributions, $190,491,092; giving activities include $135,931,282 for 673 grants (high: $7,200,000; low: $1,000), $366,371 for 8 grants to individuals (high: $230,000; low: $1,140), $1,520,137 for 287 employee matching gifts, $4,284,482 for 1 foundation-administered program and $4,400,839 for 8 loans/program-related investments (high: $1,750,000; low: $45,593).
Purpose and activities: Operating both within the United States and around the world, the Rockefeller Foundation supports work that expands opportunity and strengthens resilience to social, economic, health and environmental challenges, affirming its pioneering philanthropic mission since 1913 to "promote the well-being" of humanity.
Fields of interest: Environment, climate change/global warming; Health care; International economic development; Community/economic development.
International interests: Global Programs.
Type of support: General/operating support; Continuing support; Program development; Conferences/seminars; Publication; Seed money; Curriculum development; Fellowships; Research; Technical assistance; Program-related investments/loans; Employee matching gifts; Scholarships—to individuals.
Limitations: Applications accepted. Giving primarily in New York City, Africa, North America, and Southeast Asia. No grants to individuals for personal aid, or, except in rare cases, for endowment funds or building or operating funds.
Publications: Annual report (including application guidelines); Financial statement; Grants list.
Application information: Organizations submitting inquiries that foundation staff thinks might contribute to a defined area of work will be asked to submit a full proposal. Please do not send a proposal by mail or e-mail unless invited to do so. See foundation web site for the Ballagio Center application information. Application form not required.
Initial approach: Online funding inquiry form
Copies of proposal: 1
Deadline(s): April 1 for Centennial Innovation Challenge
Board meeting date(s): Apr., Aug., and Dec.
Final notification: 6 to 8 weeks
Officers and Trustees:* David Rockefeller, Jr.,* Chair.; Dr. Judith Rodin,* Pres.; Peter Madonia, C.O.O.; Neill Coleman, V.P., Global Communications; Zia Khan, V.P., Initiatives and Strategy; Shari L. Patrick, Genl. Counsel and Corp. Secy.; Ellen Taus, C.F.O. and Treas.; Donna Dean, C.I.O.; Dominick Impemba, Cont.; Ann M. Fudge; Helene D. Gayle; Alice S. Huang; Martin L. Leibowitz; Yifei Li; Monica Lozano; Strive Masiyiwa; Diana Natalicio; Dr. Ngozi Okonjo-Iweala; Richard D. Parsons; John W. Rowe; Ravi Venkatesan.
Number of staff: 171 full-time professional; 2 part-time professional.
EIN: 131659629
Selected grants: The following grants are a representative sample of this grantmaker's funding activity:
$31,350,000 to Rockefeller Philanthropy Advisors, Philanthropic Collaborative, New York, NY, 2013. For use by 100 Resilient Cities in support of 100 Resilient Cities Centennial Challenge, which aims to build cities' capacity globally to maintain and recover critical functions in the face of shocks and stresses, payable over 1.50 years.
$5,000,000 to Alliance for a Green Revolution in Africa, Nairobi, Kenya, 2012. Toward initiating work relevant to new strategy and Rockefeller Foundation's new Issue Areas.
$5,000,000 to Asian Development Bank, Manila, Philippines, 2013. Toward establishing Urban Climate Change Resilience Trust Fund, multi-donor trust fund that will scale-up investment in urban climate change resilience building in 25 cities in Asia by supporting integration of climate change resilience into city-wide and sectoral planning, regulations and investment, payable over 8.25 years.
$4,750,000 to Smart Growth America, Washington, DC, 2013. Toward advocacy campaign, Transportation for America (T4 America), that seeks to advance more sustainable and equitable national transportation policies to improve the lives of low-income and vulnerable people and its development of mission-related, member-focused strategy, payable over 2.50 years.
$3,840,000 to Ghana Ministry of Communications, Accra, Ghana, 2013. Toward creating a center in Accra to provide direct and indirect jobs to high potential, disadvantaged youth to transform Ghana's Business Process Outsourcing landscape, payable over 3.25 years.
$2,250,000 to Living Cities: The National Community Development Initiative, Washington, DC, 2013. For general support of mission to advance opportunity and prosperity in U.S. cities and their low-income populations, payable over 3.00 years.
$2,150,000 to Smart Growth America, Washington, DC, 2012. Toward advocacy campaign, Transportation for America (T4 America), that seeks to advance more sustainable and equitable national transportation policies to improve the lives of low-income and vulnerable people.
$2,000,000 to Oceana, Washington, DC, 2013. For two complementary studies focused on identifying policy reform options in five countries and international subsidy reform solutions to reverse the global decline in fish stocks and ensure livelihoods for poor and vulnerable small-scale fishers, payable over 1.50 years.
$1,999,965 to Wildlife Conservation Society, Bronx, NY, 2012. For collaboration with Harvard University and other partners to conduct pilot projects in Indonesia and Madagascar examining the relationship between conserved ecosystems and improved human health, ultimately resulting in the identification of policy and management changes that would improve both the state of the environment and the health of poor or vulnerable people.
$1,641,250 to World Health Organization, Geneva, Switzerland, 2012. To develop a strategy toward a United Nations General Assembly resolution on Universal Health Coverage and embedding it within the post-2015 agenda, developing a framework for its definition, goals, indicators, targets, timelines and monitoring mechanisms, and conducting consultations to implement country-level strategies for achieving it.
$1,250,000 to Social Finance, Boston, MA, 2012. Toward a guarantee facility to leverage commercially-oriented capital to capitalize a social impact bond addressing workforce development for formerly incarcerated individuals in New York and to ensure the catalytic use of philanthropic funds to engage the broader capital markets in creating a sustainable social impact bond market to scale solutions to poor or vulnerable populations in the U.S.
$1,000,000 to PATH, Seattle, WA, 2013. To develop information technology systems as a means of enhancing design and rollout of Universal Health Coverage within countries of the Joint Learning Network, payable over 2.00 years.
$325,000 to Indian Council for Research on International Economic Relations, New Delhi, India, 2012. For research in four Asian Cities Climate Change Resilience Network cities in India (Surat, Gorakhpur, Pune and Cochin) to enable a robust policy dialogue with government and the private sector on strengthening the economic competitiveness of cities by investing in urban climate change resilience.
$310,504 to Georgetown University, O'Neill Institute for National and Global Health Law, Washington, DC, 2012. To establish secretariat for the Joint Action and Learning Initiative on National and Global Responsibilities for Health international multi-organization effort to foster universal health coverage research, policy and framework development.
$300,000 to Piedmont Environmental Council, Warrenton, VA, 2012. For project, Coalition for Smarter Growth, to conduct a public education and communications campaign to help build support for Bus Rapid Transit investments in Montgomery County, Maryland and to extract lessons about effective communications strategies around Bus Rapid Transit projects.
$280,380 to Institute for Social and Environmental Transition, Boulder, CO, 2013. For project to generate new knowledge and evidence on impact of land conversion and development on peri-urban areas of cities, drawing on case studies from Can Tho, Da Nang, Quy Nhon and Hue, Vietnam and provide recommendations to urban development authorities on how to reduce climate and social vulnerabilities in order to strengthen resilience, as part of the Asian Cities Climate Change Resilience Network (ACCCRN), payable over 2.50 years.
$250,000 to University of Pennsylvania, Institute for Urban Research, Philadelphia, PA, 2013. To design and convene multi-stakeholder event on The Future of Transforming Cities, to be held at the Rockefeller Foundation Bellagio Center, resulting in a dynamic, interactive, wide-ranging exploration of future trends and a corresponding publication, payable over 1.25 years.
$200,000 to Impact Investment Shujog Limited, Singapore, Singapore, 2013. Toward Assistance for Capacity Building and Technical Service program, which provides technical assistance to high-impact social enterprises in Asia in order to help address urgent social and environmental problems, payable over 1.25 years.
$200,000 to Villgro, Chennai, India, 2012. Toward Social Entrepreneur and Enterprise Development (SEED), program which trains early-stage social entrepreneurs to refine their business model and scale their social impact to create positive benefits for poor or vulnerable people in India.

6725
The David Rockefeller Fund, Inc. ✧
30 Rockefeller Plz., Rm. 5600
New York, NY 10112-0002 (212) 649-5631
Contact: Marianna S. Schaffer, Dir. of Progs.

FAX: (212) 765-6817; E-mail: info@drfund.org; Main URL: http://www.drfund.org
David Rockefeller's Giving Pledge Profile: http://glasspockets.org/philanthropy-in-focus/eye-on-the-giving-pledge/profiles/rockefeller

Established in 1989 in NY.
Donor: David Rockefeller.
Foundation type: Independent foundation.
Financial data (yr. ended 12/31/12): Assets, $4,891,417 (M); gifts received, $1,250,000; expenditures, $1,628,763; qualifying distributions, $1,382,118; giving activities include $1,332,200 for 128 grants (high: $230,000; low: $500).
Purpose and activities: The fund currently has four primary program areas: Community, Arts, Criminal Justice, and Environment. The Community grants program (referred to as the Citizenship Program from 1990 to 2009) continues to support more than 80 local non-profit organizations annually with grants ranging from $500 to $10,000. Since its inception, the Community Program has awarded grants totaling over $3.35 million. The Arts Program focuses on access and engagement; Criminal Justice promotes a more humane and fair criminal justice system; and Environment addresses climate change and local sustainability efforts. Between 2001 and 2009, the Fund awarded grants totaling over $3.8 million to more than 70 organizations in the Arts, Criminal Justice, and Environment program areas. Please see Programs for more detailed information. In addition to the program areas outlined above, the fund underwrites a number of initiatives designed to encourage family members' individual philanthropic involvement and interests, as well as collaborative grantmaking by the family.
Fields of interest: Historic preservation/historical societies; Arts; Education; Environment; Health care; Agriculture/food, alliance/advocacy; Agriculture/food, association; Agriculture, sustainable programs; Recreation; Civil/human rights, advocacy; Community/economic development; Youth; Offenders/ex-offenders; Economically disadvantaged.
Type of support: Program-related investments/loans; Program development; General/operating support; Emergency funds; Continuing support.
Limitations: Applications not accepted. Giving primarily in Community Program: Giving limited to Mount Desert Island, ME, the Tarrytown area in Westchester County, NY, and the Livingston Communities of Columbia County, NY; Arts Program: Giving limited to New York City, NY; giving in NY and on a national basis for the Criminal Justice and Environment Programs. No grants to individuals, or for film/video projects.
Publications: Annual report.
Application information: Unsolicited proposals are not accepted for any of the fund's programs.
Board meeting date(s): Spring and fall
Officers and Directors:* David Kaiser,* Chair.; Stephen Heintz,* Pres.; Marianna Schaffer, Secy.; James Sligar,* Treas.; Marnie S. Pillsbury, Exec. Dir.; Peggy Dulany; Neva Goodwin; Adam Growald; Danny Growald; Paul Growald; Miranda Kaiser; Michael Lambert; Rebecca Rockefeller Lambert; Michael Quattrone; Camilla Rockefeller; Susan Cohn Rockefeller.
Number of staff: 1 full-time professional; 1 part-time professional; 1 part-time support.
EIN: 133533359
Selected grants: The following grants are a representative sample of this grantmaker's funding activity:
$230,000 to Rockefeller Philanthropy Advisors, New York, NY, 2012. For DRF Trustee (Discretionary).
$1,500 to Westchester Land Trust, Bedford Hills, NY, 2012. For DRF Westchester County.
$1,000 to Olana Partnership, Hudson, NY, 2012. For DRF Columbia County.
$1,000 to Westside Food Pantry, Southwest Harbor, ME, 2012. For DRF Maine.

6726
Alexander J. Roepers Foundation ✧
c/o Atlantic Investment Mgmt.
666 5th Ave., 34th Fl.
New York, NY 10103-3401

Established in NY.
Donor: Alexander J. Roepers.
Foundation type: Independent foundation.
Financial data (yr. ended 12/31/13): Assets, $3,654,084 (M); gifts received, $2,250,000; expenditures, $1,949,314; qualifying distributions, $1,948,052; giving activities include $1,946,540 for grants.
Fields of interest: Business school/education; Libraries/library science; Education; Hospitals (specialty); Cancer; Protestant agencies & churches.
Limitations: Applications not accepted. Giving primarily in Stonington, CT and New York, NY.
Application information: Contributes only to pre-selected organizations.
Trustee: Alexander J. Roepers.
EIN: 206373575

6727
Amy Falls and Hartley Rogers Foundation ✧
c/o Hartley R. Rogers
159 Factory Pond Rd.
Locust Valley, NY 11560

Established in 2005 in NY.
Donors: Hartley R. Rogers; Amy Falls.
Foundation type: Independent foundation.
Financial data (yr. ended 12/31/12): Assets, $2,307,958 (M); expenditures, $1,309,788; qualifying distributions, $1,270,587; giving activities include $1,266,787 for 38 grants (high: $365,000; low: $92).
Purpose and activities: Giving primarily for higher and other education, and the arts.
Fields of interest: Performing arts, opera; Historical activities, genealogy; Arts; Higher education; Education; Environment.
Limitations: Applications not accepted. Giving primarily in MA and New York, NY. No grants to individuals.
Application information: Unsolicited requests for funds not accepted.
Trustees: Amy Falls; Hartley R. Rogers.
EIN: 203997010

6728
The David & Tricia Rogers Foundation ✧
c/o BCRS Associates LLC
77 Water St., 9th Fl.
New York, NY 10005-4414

Established in 1994 in CT.
Donors: J. David Rogers; Tricia Rogers.
Foundation type: Independent foundation.
Financial data (yr. ended 02/28/13): Assets, $6,508,865 (M); expenditures, $700,792; qualifying distributions, $694,284; giving activities include $692,134 for 22 grants (high: $600,000; low: $200).
Fields of interest: Education; Health organizations; Protestant agencies & churches.
Limitations: Applications not accepted. Giving primarily in CT, NY and PA. No grants to individuals, or for scholarships; no loans.
Application information: Unsolicited requests for funds not accepted.
Trustees: J. David Rogers; Tricia Rogers.
EIN: 133789004

6729
The Felix and Elizabeth Rohatyn Foundation, Inc. ✧
(formerly Felix G. Rohatyn Foundation)
c/o Marcum LLP
750 3rd Ave., 11th Fl.
New York, NY 10017-2703
Contact: Felix G. Rohatyn, Pres.

Established in 1968.
Donors: Felix G. Rohatyn; Elizabeth F. Rohatyn.
Foundation type: Independent foundation.
Financial data (yr. ended 12/31/13): Assets, $1,359,256 (M); gifts received, $1,410,000; expenditures, $1,176,443; qualifying distributions, $1,168,589; giving activities include $1,160,428 for 60 grants (high: $250,000; low: $400).
Fields of interest: Arts; Libraries (public); Education; Human services.
Type of support: General/operating support; Program development.
Limitations: Applications accepted. Giving primarily in the New York, NY, area. No grants to individuals.
Application information: Application form not required.
Initial approach: Letter
Deadline(s): None
Board meeting date(s): Quarterly
Officers and Directors:* Felix G. Rohatyn,* Chair. and Pres.; Nicolas Rohatyn,* V.P.; Elizabeth F. Rohatyn,* Secy.
Number of staff: 1 part-time professional.
EIN: 237015644

6730
The George Rohr Foundation, Inc. ✧ ☆
c/o Ulysses Management, LLC
1 Rockefeller Plz., 20th Fl.
New York, NY 10020-2017

Established in 1986 in NY.
Donor: George Rohr.
Foundation type: Independent foundation.
Financial data (yr. ended 12/31/12): Assets, $2,240,764 (M); gifts received, $501,938; expenditures, $3,757,895; qualifying distributions, $3,746,832; giving activities include $3,000,001 for 2 grants (high: $3,000,000; low: $1), and $713,259 for foundation-administered programs.
Fields of interest: Foundations (public).
Limitations: Applications not accepted. Giving primarily in MA. No grants to individuals.
Application information: Unsolicited requests for funds not accepted.

Officers: George Rohr, Pres.; Pamela Rohr, V.P.; Debra K. Niderberg, Exec. Dir.
EIN: 133267203

6731
Rose Family Foundation ✧ ☆
P.O. Box 228
York, NY 14592

Established in 1998 in DE and NY.
Donor: Marian H. Rose.
Foundation type: Independent foundation.
Financial data (yr. ended 12/31/13): Assets, $5,319,971 (M); expenditures, $512,527; qualifying distributions, $458,820; giving activities include $453,280 for 4 grants (high: $150,000; low: $55,280).
Fields of interest: Arts; Environment; Recreation.
Limitations: Applications not accepted. Giving primarily in NY and Sante Fe, NM. No grants to individuals.
Application information: Contributes only to pre-selected organizations.
Officers: Simon M. Rose, Pres.; Ann R. Podlipny, V.P.; David H. Rose, Secy.; James A. Rose, Treas.
Director: Marian H. Rose.
EIN: 134016964
Selected grants: The following grants are a representative sample of this grantmaker's funding activity:
$60,000 to Randalls Island Sports Foundation, New York, NY, 2011.

6732
Marshall Rose Family Foundation, Inc. ✧
(formerly Jill & Marshall Rose Foundation, Inc.)
c/o Georgetown GP
667 Madison Ave.
New York, NY 10065-8029

Established around 1980.
Donors: Marshall Rose; Alan R. Grossman.
Foundation type: Independent foundation.
Financial data (yr. ended 11/30/13): Assets, $4,727,358 (M); gifts received, $40,000; expenditures, $553,180; qualifying distributions, $553,060; giving activities include $553,060 for 36 grants (high: $50,000; low: $250).
Fields of interest: Arts; Higher education; Theological school/education; Education; Human services; Jewish federated giving programs; Jewish agencies & synagogues.
Type of support: General/operating support; Annual campaigns; Endowments; Curriculum development.
Limitations: Applications not accepted. No grants to individuals.
Application information: Contributes only to pre-selected organizations.
Directors: Simeon Brinberg; Marshall Rose.
EIN: 133036439
Selected grants: The following grants are a representative sample of this grantmaker's funding activity:
$25,000 to Ohio State University, Columbus, OH, 2011.
$1,000 to Horace Mann School, Riverdale, NY, 2011.
$1,000 to Horace Mann School, Riverdale, NY, 2011.

6733
Adam R. Rose Foundation ✧
200 Madison Ave., 5th Fl.
New York, NY 10016-3912

Established in 1996 in DE.
Donors: Adam Rose; Sandra P. Rose.
Foundation type: Independent foundation.
Financial data (yr. ended 12/31/13): Assets, $39,160 (M); gifts received, $1,645,000; expenditures, $1,645,626; qualifying distributions, $1,643,868; giving activities include $1,641,800 for 53 grants (high: $512,000; low: $100).
Purpose and activities: Giving for the arts, education, and the environment.
Fields of interest: Arts; Education; Environment, natural resources; Botanical gardens.
Limitations: Applications not accepted. Giving primarily in FL and NY. No grants to individuals.
Application information: Contributes only to pre-selected organizations.
Officer: Adam R. Rose, Pres. and Treas.
EIN: 137095495

6734
Billy Rose Foundation, Inc. ✧
100 N. Village Ave., Ste. 35
Rockville Centre, NY 11570-3712
Contact: Terri C. Mangino

Incorporated in 1958 in NY.
Donor: Billy Rose†.
Foundation type: Independent foundation.
Financial data (yr. ended 12/31/13): Assets, $11,636,360 (M); expenditures, $981,430; qualifying distributions, $835,977; giving activities include $786,000 for 39 grants (high: $135,000; low: $1,000).
Purpose and activities: Support for the fine and performing arts, and for education.
Fields of interest: Arts, research; Visual arts; Museums; Performing arts; Performing arts, orchestras; Arts; Higher education; Libraries (public); Education.
Type of support: Program development; Research.
Limitations: Applications accepted. Giving primarily in New York, NY. No grants to individuals.
Application information: Application form required.
Initial approach: Letter
Deadline(s): None
Board meeting date(s): Usually in June
Officers: John Wohlstetter, Chair. and Treas.; James R. Cherry, Jr., Pres.; Edward J. Walsh, Jr., V.P. and Secy.; James M.C. Nasby, V.P.
Number of staff: 1 full-time professional.
EIN: 136165466
Selected grants: The following grants are a representative sample of this grantmaker's funding activity:
$135,000 to American Friends of the Israel Museum, New York, NY, 2011.
$30,000 to Fordham University, Bronx, NY, 2011.
$25,000 to New York City Ballet, New York, NY, 2011.

6735
The Deborah Rose Foundation ✧
200 Madison Ave., 5th Fl.
New York, NY 10016-3912

Established in 1999 in DE.
Donors: Deborah Rose; Sandra P. Rose.
Foundation type: Independent foundation.
Financial data (yr. ended 12/31/12): Assets, $5,849,314 (M); gifts received, $4,648,200; expenditures, $3,972,439; qualifying distributions, $3,933,439; giving activities include $3,933,439 for 41 grants (high: $1,000,000; low: $5,000).
Purpose and activities: Giving primarily for higher education; funding also for human services, and to a scientific research organization.
Fields of interest: Higher education; Education; Human services; Science, research.
Limitations: Applications not accepted. Giving primarily in CT and Washington, DC, and MA. No grants to individuals.
Application information: Contributes only to pre-selected organizations.
Officers and Director:* Deborah Rose,* Pres. and Treas.; John A. Gacinski, Secy.
EIN: 134088811

6736
Frederick P. & Sandra P. Rose Foundation ✧
c/o Adam R. Rose
200 Madison Ave., 5th Fl.
New York, NY 10016-3912

Established in 1982 in DE.
Donors: Frederick P. Rose†; Sandra Priest Rose; Samuel and David Rose Charitable Foundation.
Foundation type: Independent foundation.
Financial data (yr. ended 11/30/13): Assets, $438,747 (M); gifts received, $1,730,000; expenditures, $2,406,067; qualifying distributions, $2,400,273; giving activities include $2,394,180 for 117 grants (high: $400,000; low: $250).
Purpose and activities: Giving primarily for performing arts and other cultural organizations; support also for higher education.
Fields of interest: Museums; Performing arts; Arts; Higher education; Human services.
Limitations: Applications not accepted. Giving primarily in New York, NY. No grants to individuals.
Application information: Contributes only to pre-selected organizations.
Officers and Directors:* Sandra Priest Rose,* Pres.; Jonathan F.P. Rose,* V.P.; Adam R. Rose,* Secy.-Treas.; Deborah Rose.
EIN: 133136740

6737
Susan and Elihu Rose Foundation, Inc. ✧
c/o John A. Gacinski
200 Madison Ave., 5th Fl.
New York, NY 10016-3912

Established in 1988 in DE.
Donors: Elihu Rose; Susan W. Rose; Samuel and David Rose Charitable Foundation.
Foundation type: Independent foundation.
Financial data (yr. ended 12/31/12): Assets, $15,415,763 (M); gifts received, $5,250,000; expenditures, $6,051,729; qualifying distributions, $5,953,479; giving activities include $5,953,479 for 181 grants (high: $2,625,000; low: $300).
Purpose and activities: Support primarily for the arts, education, and Jewish giving.
Fields of interest: Performing arts; Historic preservation/historical societies; Arts; Higher education; Health organizations, association;

Human services; Jewish federated giving programs; Jewish agencies & synagogues.
Type of support: Annual campaigns; Capital campaigns; Building/renovation; Endowments.
Limitations: Applications not accepted. Giving primarily in New York, NY. No grants to individuals.
Application information: Contributes only to pre-selected organizations.
Officer and Directors:* Elihu Rose,* Pres. and Secy.; Susan Rose.
EIN: 133484181
Selected grants: The following grants are a representative sample of this grantmaker's funding activity:
$3,000,000 to Seventh Regiment Armory Conservancy, Park Avenue Armory, New York, NY, 2011.
$200,000 to National Museum of American History, Washington, DC, 2011.
$100,185 to Hospital for Special Surgery, New York, NY, 2011.
$100,000 to Carnegie Hall Society, New York, NY, 2011.
$100,000 to Hospital for Special Surgery, New York, NY, 2011.
$100,000 to Juilliard School, New York, NY, 2011.
$100,000 to Juilliard School, New York, NY, 2011.
$58,333 to Hospital for Special Surgery, New York, NY, 2011.
$25,000 to International Center of Photography, New York, NY, 2011.
$15,000 to Juilliard School, New York, NY, 2011.

6738
Daniel and Joanna S. Rose Fund, Inc. ✧
200 Madison Ave., 5th Fl.
New York, NY 10016-3903
GiveSmart: http://www.givesmart.org/Stories/Donors/Daniel-Rose

Established in 1988 in DE.
Donors: Daniel Rose; Samuel and David Rose Charitable Foundation.
Foundation type: Independent foundation.
Financial data (yr. ended 12/31/12): Assets, $2,584,296 (M); gifts received, $6,807,000; expenditures, $5,950,792; qualifying distributions, $5,910,220; giving activities include $5,910,220 for 219 grants (high: $1,250,000; low: $15).
Fields of interest: Arts; Higher education; Education; Environment, land resources; Human services; Jewish federated giving programs.
Limitations: Applications not accepted. Giving primarily in DC and NY. No grants to individuals.
Application information: Contributes only to pre-selected organizations.
Officer and Director:* Daniel Rose,* Pres.
EIN: 133484179

6739
The Benjamin M. Rosen Family Foundation ✧
c/o Benjamin M. Rosen
1 Central Park W.
New York, NY 10023-7703

Established in 1998 in NY.
Donor: Benjamin M. Rosen.
Foundation type: Independent foundation.
Financial data (yr. ended 12/31/13): Assets, $1,824,993 (M); expenditures, $538,452; qualifying distributions, $526,036; giving activities include $505,202 for 64 grants (high: $135,000; low: $100).
Fields of interest: Museums; Museums (art); Arts; Education; Hospitals (specialty); Health organizations.
Limitations: Applications not accepted. Giving primarily in NY. No grants to individuals.
Application information: Unsolicited requests for funds not accepted.
Trustees: Benjamin M. Rosen; Donna Rosen; Frederic A. Rubenstein.
EIN: 134034465

6740
The Abner Rosen Foundation, Inc. ✧
40 E. 69th St.
New York, NY 10021-5016

Established in DE.
Donor: Miriam N. Rosen†.
Foundation type: Independent foundation.
Financial data (yr. ended 06/30/13): Assets, $10,935,371 (M); gifts received, $2,949,612; expenditures, $2,521,228; qualifying distributions, $2,434,230; giving activities include $2,434,230 for 6 grants (high: $1,000,000; low: $250).
Fields of interest: Museums; Higher education.
Limitations: Applications not accepted. Giving primarily in New York, NY. No grants to individuals.
Application information: Contributes only to pre-selected organizations.
Officers and Directors:* Jonathan P. Rosen,* Pres.; Jeanette D. Rosen,* Treas.; Sarah Rosen.
EIN: 133841307
Selected grants: The following grants are a representative sample of this grantmaker's funding activity:
$1,000,000 to New York University, New York, NY, 2011. For general support.
$200,000 to Central Park Conservancy, New York, NY, 2011. For general support.
$194,374 to Cornell University, Ithaca, NY, 2011. For general support.
$166,667 to Pierpont Morgan Library, New York, NY, 2011. For general support.
$30,000 to Icahn School of Medicine at Mount Sinai, New York, NY, 2011. For general support.

6741
Joseph Rosen Foundation, Inc. ✧
P.O. Box 334
Lenox Hill Sta.
New York, NY 10021-0036

Incorporated in 1948 in NY.
Donors: Jonathan P. Rosen; Tranel, Inc.; The Abner Rosen Foundation, Inc.
Foundation type: Independent foundation.
Financial data (yr. ended 06/30/13): Assets, $31,683,162 (M); gifts received, $500,000; expenditures, $3,538,611; qualifying distributions, $2,018,888; giving activities include $2,018,888 for 230 grants (high: $500,000; low: $2).
Purpose and activities: Giving primarily for education, the arts, medical research, human services and Jewish organizations.
Fields of interest: Museums; Arts; Higher education; Education; Health care; Health organizations, association; Medical research, institute; Cancer research; Human services; Jewish federated giving programs; Jewish agencies & synagogues.
Limitations: Applications not accepted. Giving primarily in NY. No grants to individuals.
Application information: Contributes only to pre-selected organizations.
Officers: Jonathan P. Rosen, Pres. and Secy.; Jeannette Rosen, V.P. and Treas.
EIN: 136158412
Selected grants: The following grants are a representative sample of this grantmaker's funding activity:
$300,000 to Yale University, New Haven, CT, 2011.
$10,000 to Amherst College, Amherst, MA, 2011.

6742
Reb Moishe Rosen Fund Inc. ✧
271 Madison Ave., Ste. 22
New York, NY 10016-1001

Established in NY.
Donors: Charles Alpert; Joseph Alpert.
Foundation type: Independent foundation.
Financial data (yr. ended 06/30/13): Assets, $233,628 (M); gifts received, $720,000; expenditures, $757,625; qualifying distributions, $757,500; giving activities include $757,500 for grants.
Purpose and activities: Giving primarily to Jewish agencies, temples, and schools.
Fields of interest: Elementary/secondary education; Jewish agencies & synagogues.
Limitations: Applications not accepted. Giving primarily in NY. No support for private foundations. No grants to individuals, or for scholarships.
Application information: Contributes only to pre-selected organizations.
Officers: Ori Alpert, Secy.; Charles Alpert, Treas.
EIN: 116036649
Selected grants: The following grants are a representative sample of this grantmaker's funding activity:
$10,000 to Chai Lifeline, New York, NY, 2011.

6743
Sunny and Abe Rosenberg Foundation, Inc. ✧
P.O. Box 237198
Ansonia Sta.
New York, NY 10023-0033
Contact: Maryanne Passafiume
E-mail: mpassafiume@rosenbergfoundation.org

Incorporated in 1966 in NY.
Donors: Abraham Rosenberg†; Sonia Rosenberg†.
Foundation type: Independent foundation.
Financial data (yr. ended 12/31/12): Assets, $19,780,072 (M); gifts received, $115,000; expenditures, $1,281,775; qualifying distributions, $577,955; giving activities include $577,955 for grants.
Purpose and activities: The foundation centers its giving around foster care.
Fields of interest: Education; Children/youth, services.
Type of support: General/operating support; Continuing support; Program development; Seed money; Curriculum development; Research; Program evaluation.
Limitations: Applications not accepted. Giving primarily in New York, NY. No support for private

foundations. No grants to individuals, or for capital campaigns.
Application information: Unsolicited requests for funds not accepted.
Board meeting date(s): Spring and fall
Officers: Susan B. Goldstein, Pres.; Danielle Goldstein, Secy.; Darin Goldstein, Treas.
Number of staff: 2 full-time professional; 1 part-time professional; 1 part-time support.
EIN: 136210591

6744
The Rosenblatt Charitable Trust ✧ ☆
160 E. 72nd St., Apt. 7
New York, NY 10021-4357

Established in NY.
Donor: Lief D. Rosenblatt.
Foundation type: Independent foundation.
Financial data (yr. ended 12/31/13): Assets, $16,306,004 (M); expenditures, $3,073,930; qualifying distributions, $3,055,735; giving activities include $3,053,000 for 24 grants (high: $1,172,000; low: $7,000).
Fields of interest: Higher education; Jewish agencies & synagogues.
Limitations: Applications not accepted. Giving primarily in Washington, DC, and New York, NY.
Application information: Unsolicited requests for funds not accepted.
Trustee: Lief D. Rosenblatt.
EIN: 356876040

6745
Rosenblatt Family Foundation ✧
155 Riverside Dr.
New York, NY 10024-2207

Incorporated in 1956 in NY.
Donors: Marcus Retter; Betty Retter‡; C. Rosenblatt.
Foundation type: Independent foundation.
Financial data (yr. ended 12/31/12): Assets, $4,612,717 (M); expenditures, $1,243,444; qualifying distributions, $590,788; giving activities include $590,788 for grants.
Purpose and activities: Giving primarily to Jewish temples and yeshivas.
Fields of interest: Education; Human services; Jewish agencies & synagogues.
International interests: Israel.
Limitations: Applications not accepted. Giving primarily in NY.
Application information: Contributes only to pre-selected organizations.
Officers: Mary Schreiber, Pres.; Daniel Retter, V.P.; Leah Eisenberg, Treas.; Margot Pollak, Secy.
EIN: 136145385

6746
Daniel Rosenblum Family Foundation Inc. ✧
c/o ED&F Man Inc.
140 E. 45th St., 42nd Fl.
New York, NY 10017

Established in 1989 in NY.
Donor: Daniel Rosenblum.
Foundation type: Independent foundation.
Financial data (yr. ended 12/31/13): Assets, $1,693,811 (M); gifts received, $250; expenditures, $654,148; qualifying distributions, $627,016; giving activities include $623,456 for 22 grants (high: $308,000; low: $500).
Purpose and activities: Giving primarily for education, health, human services, and Jewish agencies and temples.
Fields of interest: Education; Health organizations; Medical research, institute; Human services; Jewish agencies & synagogues.
Limitations: Applications not accepted. Giving primarily in New York, NY. No grants to individuals.
Application information: Unsolicited requests for funds not accepted.
Officer and Directors:* Daniel Rosenblum,* Pres. and Treas.; Leonard Rosenblum; N. Barry Ross.
EIN: 133520602
Selected grants: The following grants are a representative sample of this grantmaker's funding activity:
$75,000 to Columbia Grammar and Preparatory School, New York, NY, 2011.
$50,000 to Cambridge in America, New York, NY, 2011.
$25,000 to Allen-Stevenson School, New York, NY, 2011.
$15,000 to McLean Hospital, Belmont, MA, 2011.
$10,000 to Bnai Brith International, Washington, DC, 2011.
$7,500 to Hampton Synagogue, Westhampton Beach, NY, 2011.
$7,440 to Park Avenue Synagogue, New York, NY, 2011.
$5,000 to New Yorks Finest Foundation, New York, NY, 2011.
$5,000 to Per Scholas, Bronx, NY, 2011.

6747
The Max & Morton M. Rosenfeld Foundation, Inc. ✧ ☆
c/o Berdon LLP
360 Madison Ave.
New York, NY 10017-7111

Established in 1945 in DE.
Foundation type: Independent foundation.
Financial data (yr. ended 11/30/13): Assets, $1,070,292 (M); gifts received, $2,840; expenditures, $2,162,127; qualifying distributions, $2,139,176; giving activities include $2,139,176 for 2 grants (high: $1,069,588; low: $1,069,588).
Fields of interest: Arts; Education; ALS research; Legal services; Human services; Jewish federated giving programs; Jewish agencies & synagogues.
Type of support: General/operating support.
Limitations: Applications not accepted. Giving primarily in New York, NY; some giving also in MA and Portland, ME. No grants to individuals.
Application information: Unsolicited requests for funds not accepted.
Directors: Suzanne Lehmann; Michael Rosenfeld; Maxine Sclar.
EIN: 136137869

6748
The Rosenkranz Foundation, Inc. ✧
590 Madison Ave., 30th Fl.
New York, NY 10022-8547 212 303-4322
FAX: 212 303-4475;
E-mail: info@rosenkranzfdn.org; Main URL: http://www.rosenkranzfdn.org/
GiveSmart: http://www.givesmart.org/Stories/Donors/Robert-Rosenkranz

Established in 1997 in DE and NY.
Donors: Robert Rosenkranz; Dick Weismann; Thomas Lee; Shelby White; Van David Greenfield; Stanley Shuman; Sydney Shuman; Willem Kookyer; Paul E. Singer; Ken Brody; Donald A. Sherman; Christopher Howard Browne; Judith-Ann Corrente; Richard Gilder, Jr.; Anita Wien; Byron Wien; Newsweek.
Foundation type: Independent foundation.
Financial data (yr. ended 10/31/13): Assets, $30,489,147 (M); expenditures, $2,364,874; qualifying distributions, $1,937,000; giving activities include $1,918,904 for 52 grants (high: $800,849; low: $250), and $1,050,849 for 2 foundation-administered programs.
Purpose and activities: Giving primarily for arts and culture, as well as for higher education.
Fields of interest: Performing arts; Arts; Higher education; Education; Foundations (private grantmaking).
Limitations: Applications not accepted. Giving primarily in New York, NY. No grants to individuals.
Application information: Contributes only to pre-selected organizations.
Officers and Directors:* Robert Rosenkranz,* Pres.; Stephanie Hessler,* V.P.; Salvatore Arena, Treas.; Dana Wolfe, Exec. Dir.; Alexandra Munro; Nicholas Quinn Rosenkranz.
Number of staff: 1 full-time professional; 1 part-time professional.
EIN: 133940017

6749
Juliet Rosenthal Foundation, Inc. ✧
1370 Broadway
New York, NY 10018-7302

Established in 1958 in NY.
Donor: Rosenthal & Rosenthal, Inc.
Foundation type: Independent foundation.
Financial data (yr. ended 12/31/13): Assets, $9,484,957 (M); gifts received, $300,000; expenditures, $500,365; qualifying distributions, $461,162; giving activities include $456,198 for 27 grants (high: $140,000; low: $447).
Purpose and activities: Giving primarily for health care and human services.
Fields of interest: Higher education; Education; Hospitals (specialty); Cancer; Health organizations; Medical research, institute; Human services; Jewish federated giving programs.
Limitations: Applications not accepted. Giving primarily in New York, NY. No grants to individuals or for program-related investments.
Application information: Contributes only to pre-selected organizations.
Officers: Stephen Rosenthal, Pres.; Robert Prizer, V.P.; Eric Rosenthal, Treas.
EIN: 136161085

6750

The Edward John & Patricia Rosenwald Foundation ✧

c/o Anchin, Block & Anchin LLP
1375 Broadway
New York, NY 10018-7001

Established in 2004 in NY.
Donor: Edward John Rosenwald, Jr.
Foundation type: Independent foundation.
Financial data (yr. ended 12/31/13): Assets, $144,221 (M); gifts received, $1,412,125; expenditures, $2,299,000; qualifying distributions, $2,290,875; giving activities include $2,278,250 for 76 grants (high: $301,000; low: $250).
Fields of interest: Museums (art); Higher education; Health organizations; Jewish federated giving programs; Jewish agencies & synagogues.
Limitations: Applications not accepted. Giving primarily in New York, NY; some giving also in Hanover, NH. No grants to individuals.
Application information: Contributes only to pre-selected organizations.
Officers: Edward John Rosenwald, Jr., Pres.; Patricia Rosenwald, V.P.
Director: Lawrence B. Buttenwieser.
EIN: 743107995

6751

Alice Rosenwald Fund ✧ ☆

(formerly The Rose Shield Fund)
c/o Eisneramper LLP, J. Zbar
750 3rd Ave., 22nd Fl.
New York, NY 10017-4011

Established in 1982 in NY.
Donors: Alice R. Sigelman; William Rosenwald Family Fund Inc.; Alice Rosenwald; JJG Foundation.
Foundation type: Independent foundation.
Financial data (yr. ended 04/30/13): Assets, $24,999,943 (M); gifts received, $6,541,107; expenditures, $783,968; qualifying distributions, $648,104; giving activities include $525,417 for 14 grants (high: $250,000; low: $250), and $60,000 for 3 grants to individuals (high: $25,000; low: $10,000).
Fields of interest: Historic preservation/historical societies; Higher education; Medical school/education; Education; Hospitals (specialty); Health care.
Limitations: Applications not accepted. Giving primarily in New York, NY; funding also in MA.
Application information: Unsolicited requests for funds not accepted.
Officers and Directors:* Alice Rosenwald,* Pres.; David Buss,* V.P.; James Ledley,* Secy.; Joel Zbar, Treas.
EIN: 133174406

6752

Leo Rosner Foundation, Inc. ✧

6 Westway
White Plains, NY 10605-3523 (914) 682-2800
Contact: William D. Robbins, Pres.

Established in 1960 in NY.
Foundation type: Independent foundation.
Financial data (yr. ended 10/31/13): Assets, $11,377,250 (M); expenditures, $621,992; qualifying distributions, $530,268; giving activities include $422,100 for 31 grants (high: $50,000; low: $5,000).
Fields of interest: Museums (specialized); Arts; Higher education; Education; Hospitals (general); Human services; Community/economic development; Jewish federated giving programs; Jewish agencies & synagogues.
Type of support: Program development; Conferences/seminars; Scholarship funds.
Limitations: Applications accepted. Giving primarily in CT and NY.
Application information: Application form not required.
Initial approach: Proposal
Deadline(s): None
Board meeting date(s): Mid-Oct.
Officers and Directors:* William D. Robbins,* Pres.; Mildred R. Caplow,* V.P.; June Rosner,* V.P.; Marcy Wachtel,* V.P.; Amy H. Caplow Chan,* Secy.-Treas.
Number of staff: 1 part-time professional.
EIN: 136161637
Selected grants: The following grants are a representative sample of this grantmaker's funding activity:
$25,000 to Cornell University, Ithaca, NY, 2011.
$25,000 to New York University, New York, NY, 2011.
$20,000 to Coalition for the Homeless, New York, NY, 2011.
$15,000 to Mount Sinai Hospital, New York, NY, 2011.
$15,000 to National Museum of Women in the Arts, Washington, DC, 2011.
$12,500 to Neighborhood Coalition for Shelter, New York, NY, 2011.
$10,000 to Philharmonic-Symphony Society of New York, New York, NY, 2011.
$7,500 to Ackerman Institute for the Family, New York, NY, 2011.
$5,000 to Central Synagogue, New York, NY, 2011.
$5,000 to Southern Institute for Education and Research, New Orleans, LA, 2011.

6753

Alfred & Jane Ross Foundation, Inc. ✧

c/o Hecht & Co.
350 5th Ave., 68th Fl.
New York, NY 10118

Established in 1992 in DE.
Donors: Arthur Ross†; Jane Ross.
Foundation type: Independent foundation.
Financial data (yr. ended 12/31/13): Assets, $18,815,740 (M); expenditures, $908,698; qualifying distributions, $840,987; giving activities include $827,750 for 66 grants (high: $187,000; low: $250).
Purpose and activities: Giving primarily for art, with some emphasis on music, and cultural institutes, education, and youth services.
Fields of interest: Performing arts, opera; Arts; Higher education; Education; Youth, services; International exchange, arts; International affairs, foreign policy.
Limitations: Applications not accepted. Giving primarily in New York, NY. No grants to individuals.
Application information: Contributes only to pre-selected organizations.
Officers: Alfred F. Ross, Pres.; Jane Ross, V.P. and Secy.; Michael Hecht, Treas.
EIN: 133680380
Selected grants: The following grants are a representative sample of this grantmaker's funding activity:
$4,000 to New York University, New York, NY, 2012. For Steinhardt travel grant.
$1,500 to World Security Institute, Washington, DC, 2012. For JRL.
$1,000 to Columbia University, Law School, New York, NY, 2012. For unrestricted general support.

6754

The Dorothea Haus Ross Foundation ✧

1036 Monroe Ave.
Rochester, NY 14620-1725 (585) 473-6006
Contact: Wayne S. Cook, Fdn. Exec.
FAX: (585) 473-6007;
E-mail: rossfoundation@frontiernet.net; Main URL: http://www.dhrossfoundation.org

Established in 1979 in NY.
Donor: Dorothea Haus Ross†.
Foundation type: Independent foundation.
Financial data (yr. ended 12/31/13): Assets, $17,738,758 (M); expenditures, $951,271; qualifying distributions, $840,778; giving activities include $559,624 for 53 grants (high: $33,300; low: $2,500).
Purpose and activities: Giving to advance the moral, mental, and physical well-being of children of all races and creeds in all parts of the world; and to aid and assist in providing for the basic needs of food, shelter, and education of such children by whatever means and methods necessary or advisable. The foundation provides direct aid and assistance to vulnerable children between the ages of 0-18, including those who are ill, orphaned, disabled, injured, disfigured, abused and malnourished or have limited access to education.
Fields of interest: Child development, education; Medical care, rehabilitation; Health care; Health organizations, association; Pediatrics; Children/youth, services; Child development, services; Infants/toddlers; Children/youth; Children; Youth; Physically disabled; Blind/visually impaired; Deaf/hearing impaired; Mentally disabled; Native Americans/American Indians; Girls; Boys; Economically disadvantaged.
Type of support: Building/renovation; Equipment; Emergency funds; Program development; Publication; Seed money; Matching/challenge support.
Limitations: Applications accepted. Giving on a national and international basis (with the following exceptions: Burma, Cuba, Liberia, Libya, North Korea, Sierra Leone, Somalia, Sudan, Nigeria and Zimbabwe). Non-U.S. charities must find a U.S. charity or a Religious Order located near them that has a U.S. affiliate office. No support for day care or public education in America, or to non-U.S. countries where there is war, widespread violence, or where a breakdown of law and order exists or is probable, or to non-U.S. countries where grants are prohibited by the U.S. Department of the Treasury as listed in the Office of Foreign Assets Control Program Summary (OFAC). No grants to individuals, or for operating budgets, continuing support, annual campaigns, deficit financing, conferences, or fellowships; no loans.
Publications: Application guidelines; Annual report; Grants list.
Application information: Grant proposals are by invitation only, upon review of letter of inquiry. See foundation web site for guidelines. The foundation

is less interested in larger projects or capital campaigns that are better left to larger foundations and organizations. Water projects are limited to schools, orphanages and medical centers where children predominate. Organizations applying to the foundation from outside the U.S. should call or e-mail the office for further instructions, or to clarify if whether or not grants are permissible in their country under U.S. law. Application form not required.

Initial approach: 1-2 page letter of inquiry via e-mail or telephone
Deadline(s): None
Board meeting date(s): Feb., May, Aug., and Nov.
Final notification: Within 3 weeks for letters of inquiry

Officer and Trustees:* Wayne S. Cook, Ph.D.*, Fdn. Exec.; Charles C. Chamberlain; Kathryn C. Chamberlain; Edward C. Radin III, Esq.; Bank of America, N.A.
Number of staff: 1 full-time professional; 1 part-time support.
EIN: 161080458

6755
Billie and George Ross Foundation Inc. ✧ ☆

10 Thixton Dr.
Hewlett Harbor, NY 11557-2632

Established in 2002 in NY.
Donors: Billie D. Ross; George H. Ross; Shawn Maher.
Foundation type: Operating foundation.
Financial data (yr. ended 12/31/13): Assets, $1,616,165 (M); gifts received, $425,000; expenditures, $1,003,601; qualifying distributions, $1,003,251; giving activities include $1,002,316 for grants.
Fields of interest: Hospitals (specialty); Medical care, rehabilitation.
Limitations: Applications not accepted. Giving primarily in PA. No grants to individuals.
Application information: Unsolicited requests for funds not accepted.
Directors: Billie D. Ross; George H. Ross; Nanci Ross; Stephanie Suskin.
EIN: 412065250

6756
Rostrust Foundation ✧ ☆

1759 49th St.
Brooklyn, NY 11204-1217

Established in 1998 in NY.
Donors: Chany Rosenberg; Joseph Landau; New York Life Insurance Co.; Abraham Shaulson; Premier Store Fixtures; Emes Foundation; The Funds for Life Foundation.
Foundation type: Independent foundation.
Financial data (yr. ended 04/30/13): Assets, $6,727,413 (M); gifts received, $109,265; expenditures, $581,292; qualifying distributions, $570,763; giving activities include $570,763 for 60 grants (high: $150,000; low: $100).
Fields of interest: Jewish agencies & synagogues.
Limitations: Applications accepted. Giving primarily in Brooklyn and New York, NY. No grants to individuals.
Application information: Application form required.

Initial approach: Letter
Deadline(s): None

Trustee: Michael Rosenberg.
EIN: 137111711
Selected grants: The following grants are a representative sample of this grantmaker's funding activity:
$15,000 to Bobover Yeshiva Bnei Zion, Brooklyn, NY, 2011.
$2,500 to Bobover Yeshiva Bnei Zion, Brooklyn, NY, 2011.

6757
Steven J. and Robin Rotter Family Foundation ✧ ☆

110 E. 59th St., 34th Fl.
New York, NY 10022-1308

Donor: Steven J. Rotter.
Foundation type: Independent foundation.
Financial data (yr. ended 11/30/13): Assets, $3,434,365 (M); expenditures, $530,220; qualifying distributions, $526,970; giving activities include $524,396 for 41 grants (high: $235,000; low: $150).
Fields of interest: Arts; Education; Jewish federated giving programs; Religion.
Limitations: Applications not accepted. Giving primarily in New York, NY.
Application information: Unsolicited requests for funds not accepted.
Officer: Steven J. Rotter, Pres.
Directors: Adam Rotter; Robin Rotter.
EIN: 261444241

6758
Rowan Family Foundation, Inc. ✧

927 5th Ave.
New York, NY 10021-2650
Contact: Marc Rowan, Dir.; Carolyn Rowan, Dir.

Established in 2005 in NY.
Donors: Marc Rowan; Carolyn Rowan.
Foundation type: Independent foundation.
Financial data (yr. ended 12/31/12): Assets, $15,653,831 (M); gifts received, $20,500,000; expenditures, $6,695,363; qualifying distributions, $6,695,363; giving activities include $6,695,113 for 119 grants (high: $3,500,000; low: $100).
Fields of interest: Arts; Higher education; Education; Medical research, institute; Human services; Jewish agencies & synagogues.
Limitations: Applications not accepted. Giving primarily in NY.
Application information: Contributes only to pre-selected organizations.
Directors: Michael Gross; Carolyn Rowan; Marc Rowan.
EIN: 202213142
Selected grants: The following grants are a representative sample of this grantmaker's funding activity:
$200,000 to Columbia Grammar and Preparatory School, New York, NY, 2011.
$125,000 to Youth Renewal Fund, New York, NY, 2011.
$100,000 to Imagination Productions, Jerusalem U, New York, NY, 2011.

6759
Rowe Family Charitable Trust ✧

c/o The Ayco Co.
P.O. Box 15014
Albany, NY 12212-5014

Established in IL.
Donor: John W. Rowe.
Foundation type: Independent foundation.
Financial data (yr. ended 12/31/13): Assets, $17,291,457 (M); expenditures, $1,981,364; qualifying distributions, $1,900,000; giving activities include $1,900,000 for 7 grants (high: $500,000; low: $25,000).
Fields of interest: Arts; Higher education; Education.
Limitations: Applications not accepted. Giving primarily in Chicago, IL.
Application information: Contributes only to pre-selected organizations.
Trustees: Jeanne M. Rowe; John W. Rowe; William J. Rowe.
EIN: 208255907
Selected grants: The following grants are a representative sample of this grantmaker's funding activity:
$500,000 to Noble Network of Charter Schools, Chicago, IL, 2011.
$450,000 to Illinois Institute of Technology, Chicago, IL, 2011.
$375,000 to University of Wisconsin Foundation, Madison, WI, 2011.
$250,000 to Field Museum of Natural History, Chicago, IL, 2011.
$210,000 to Noble Network of Charter Schools, Chicago, IL, 2011.
$125,000 to Big Shoulders Fund, Chicago, IL, 2011.
$25,000 to Ann and Robert H. Lurie Children's Hospital of Chicago, Chicago, IL, 2011.
$25,000 to Dominican University, River Forest, IL, 2011.
$25,000 to Joffrey Ballet, Chicago, IL, 2011.

6760
RTS Family Foundation ✧

c/o C. Vanburen, The AYCO Co., LP
321 Broadway
P.O. Box 860
Saratoga Springs, NY 12866-0860

Established in 1998 in NJ.
Donor: Richard T. Santulli.
Foundation type: Independent foundation.
Financial data (yr. ended 12/31/13): Assets, $18,825,523 (M); expenditures, $3,196,180; qualifying distributions, $3,006,200; giving activities include $3,004,700 for 52 grants (high: $800,000; low: $2,600).
Purpose and activities: Giving primarily for social services.
Fields of interest: Education, ESL programs; Employment, training; Human services; Children/youth, services; Family services; Catholic agencies & churches.
Limitations: Applications not accepted. Giving primarily in NY and PA. No grants to individuals.
Application information: Contributes only to pre-selected organizations.
Trustees: Pat Hartigan; Mary McGrory; Margaret Santulli; Richard T. Santulli.
EIN: 237997212

6761
Lawrence Ruben Foundation ✧
(formerly The Selma and Lawrence Ruben Foundation)
c/o Ruben Companies, Dante Maliwat
600 Madison Ave., 21st Fl.
New York, NY 10022-1615

Established in 1982 in NY.
Donors: Lawrence Ruben; Selma Ruben.
Foundation type: Independent foundation.
Financial data (yr. ended 12/31/13): Assets, $4,886,674 (M); expenditures, $639,264; qualifying distributions, $629,471; giving activities include $625,000 for 1 grant.
Fields of interest: Higher education; Medical school/education.
Limitations: Applications not accepted. Giving primarily in New York, NY. No grants to individuals.
Application information: Contributes only to pre-selected organizations.
Directors: Rochelle Kivell; Lawrence Ruben; Lenore Ruben; Richard Ruben.
EIN: 133124700

6762
The Marilyn and Barry Rubenstein Family Foundation ✧
68 Wheatley Rd.
Brookville, NY 11545-2922

Established in 1992 in NY.
Donors: Barry Rubenstein; Marilyn Rubenstein; Seneca Ventures; Woodland Venture Fund.
Foundation type: Independent foundation.
Financial data (yr. ended 06/30/13): Assets, $1,457,642 (M); gifts received, $450,000; expenditures, $706,215; qualifying distributions, $701,284; giving activities include $701,284 for grants.
Purpose and activities: Giving primarily to Jewish affiliated institutions and for health care.
Fields of interest: Museums (ethnic/folk arts); Elementary/secondary education; Hospitals (general); Health organizations, association; Medical research, institute; Children/youth, services; Jewish federated giving programs; Jewish agencies & synagogues.
Type of support: Continuing support; Annual campaigns; Capital campaigns; Building/renovation.
Limitations: Applications not accepted. Giving primarily in NY. No grants to individuals.
Application information: Contributes only to pre-selected organizations.
Trustees: Barry Rubenstein; Brian Rubenstein; Marilyn Rubenstein; Rebecca Rubenstein.
EIN: 116417671

6763
The Rubin Family Foundation, Inc. ✧
1441 59th St.
Brooklyn, NY 11219-5017

Established in 1991 in NY.
Donors: Liebel Rubin; Abraham Klein; Solomon Rubin; Long Beach Grandell Co., Inc.; Oceanside Care Center Inc., Inc.; Park Terrace Care Center; Beach Terrace Care Center; Queens Nassau Nursing Home; Yeshiva B'nai Zion.
Foundation type: Independent foundation.
Financial data (yr. ended 12/31/12): Assets, $23,321,985 (M); gifts received, $550,000; expenditures, $1,533,619; qualifying distributions, $1,352,205; giving activities include $1,341,700 for 64 grants (high: $126,000; low: $500).
Purpose and activities: Giving primarily to Jewish agencies, temples, and schools.
Fields of interest: Education; Jewish agencies & synagogues.
Limitations: Applications not accepted. Giving primarily in Brooklyn, NY.
Application information: Contributes only to pre-selected organizations.
Officers: Liebel Rubin, Pres.; Dorothy Rubin, V.P.
Directors: Sara Heller; Marvin Rubin; Solomon Rubin.
EIN: 113047773

6764
Samuel Rubin Foundation, Inc. ✧
777 United Nations Plz.
New York, NY 10017-3521 (212) 697-8945
Contact: Lauranne Jones, Grants Admin.
FAX: (212) 682-0886;
E-mail: joneslauranne@gmail.com; Main URL: http://www.samuelrubinfoundation.org

Established in 1958 in NY.
Donors: Samuel Rubin†; Samuel Rubin Foundation, Inc.
Foundation type: Independent foundation.
Financial data (yr. ended 06/30/13): Assets, $11,609,544 (M); expenditures, $847,966; qualifying distributions, $738,987; giving activities include $603,500 for 46 grants (high: $100,000; low: $500).
Purpose and activities: Grants for the pursuit of peace and justice; for an equitable reallocation of the world's resources; and to promote social, economic, political, civil, and cultural rights.
Fields of interest: Higher education; International peace/security; International affairs, arms control; International affairs, foreign policy; International human rights; Civil/human rights; Women.
Type of support: Film/video/radio; General/operating support; Seed money.
Limitations: Applications accepted. Giving on a national and international basis. No grants to individuals, or for endowments, scholarships, or building funds.
Publications: Grants list; Program policy statement.
Application information: Applications sent by e-mail or fax will not be accepted, nor will telephone solicitations. Application form not required.
Initial approach: Proposal (no more than 5 pages)
Deadline(s): First Fri. in Jan., May, and Sept.
Board meeting date(s): 3 times per year; generally at the end of Feb., June, and Oct.
Final notification: 2 weeks following board meetings
Officers: Cora Weiss, Pres.; Judy Weiss, V.P.; Peter Weiss, Treas.
Directors: Alison R. Bernstein; Daniel Weiss; Tamara Weiss.
Number of staff: 2 full-time professional.
EIN: 136164671

6765
The Shelley & Donald Rubin Foundation, Inc. ✧
17 W. 17th St., 9th Fl.
New York, NY 10011-5510 (646) 839-5911
FAX: (212) 645-3206; E-mail: info@sdrubin.org; Main URL: http://www.sdrubin.org
Grants Database: http://www.sdrubin.org/grants

Established in 1991 in NY.
Donors: Suman Jain; Donald Rubin; Shelley Rubin; Global Leadership Foundation.
Foundation type: Independent foundation.
Financial data (yr. ended 06/30/13): Assets, $8,124,425 (M); gifts received, $91,000; expenditures, $5,307,913; qualifying distributions, $5,264,114; giving activities include $3,243,117 for 161 grants (high: $200,000; low: $600).
Purpose and activities: Giving primarily to arts and culture, with a strong commitment to Himalayan art; health and human services; and civil liberty and social justice.
Fields of interest: Arts, cultural/ethnic awareness; Museums (ethnic/folk arts); Arts; Higher education; Adult education—literacy, basic skills & GED; Education; Environment; Children.
Limitations: Giving primarily in the New York City metropolitan area; funding also in the Himalayan region. No grants to individuals, or for fundraising activities, capital funds, direct services, operating support, scholarships, fellowships, building funds, endowment funds, or for the delivery of direct services.
Publications: Application guidelines.
Application information: The foundation's grants to educational institutions are for direct program expenses only. No part of such a grant can be used for overhead or indirect costs. Application form not required.
Initial approach: Letter of intent via e-mail
Copies of proposal: 1
Deadline(s): None
Board meeting date(s): Quarterly
Final notification: Within 90 days
Officer and Directors:* Donald Rubin,* Pres. and Exec. Dir.; Shelley Rubin; Harvey Sigelbaum.
Number of staff: 3 part-time professional.
EIN: 133639542

6766
The Rubin-Henry Family Foundation ✧
c/o Howard Rubin
120 East End Ave., Apt. 2A
New York, NY 10028-7552

Established in 2000 in NY.
Donors: Mary Henry; Howard Rubin.
Foundation type: Independent foundation.
Financial data (yr. ended 08/31/13): Assets, $793,965 (M); gifts received, $1,238,500; expenditures, $855,930; qualifying distributions, $847,280; giving activities include $847,280 for grants.
Fields of interest: Education; Human services; Children/youth, services.
Limitations: Applications not accepted. Giving primarily in NY. No grants to individuals.
Application information: Contributes only to pre-selected organizations.
Trustees: Mary Henry; Howard Rubin.
EIN: 137255537

Selected grants: The following grants are a representative sample of this grantmaker's funding activity:
$10,000 to Cystic Fibrosis Foundation, Bethesda, MD, 2011.
$10,000 to Swim Across America, Boston, MA, 2011.
$1,000 to Alzheimers Association, Chicago, IL, 2011.

6767
May and Samuel Rudin Family Foundation, Inc. ✧

c/o Rudin
345 Park Ave.
New York, NY 10154-0004 (212) 407-2512
Contact: Mark L. Bodden, Admin. and Prog. Dir.

Established in 1996 in NY.
Donors: 345 Park Avenue L.P.; 215 E. 68th St. L.P.; 211 E. 70th St. L.P.; 845 3rd L.P.; 40 E. 52nd L.P.; 41 Madison L.P.
Foundation type: Independent foundation.
Financial data (yr. ended 12/31/13): Assets, $6,672 (M); gifts received, $5,025,000; expenditures, $5,041,219; qualifying distributions, $5,041,219; giving activities include $4,392,744 for 198 grants (high: $470,000; low: $300).
Purpose and activities: Grants are mainly to charitable organizations, museums, and educational institutions in New York City.
Fields of interest: Museums; Arts; Higher education; Education; Human services; Jewish federated giving programs.
Type of support: General/operating support.
Limitations: Applications accepted. Giving primarily in New York, NY.
Application information: Application form not required.
Initial approach: Letter
Copies of proposal: 1
Deadline(s): Oct. 15th
Final notification: Varies
Officers and Directors:* Jack Rudin,* Chair.; Beth Rudin DeWoody,* Pres.; Eric C. Rudin,* V.P. and Secy.-Treas.; James Carlton DeWoody III,* V.P.; Kyle Hardin DeWoody,* V.P.; Grant Johnson, V.P.; Madeleine Rudin Johnson,* V.P.; David B. Levy,* V.P.; Katherine L. Rudin,* V.P.; Samantha Mia Rudin,* V.P.; William C. Rudin,* V.P.; Michael P.H. Rudin.
EIN: 133875171
Selected grants: The following grants are a representative sample of this grantmaker's funding activity:
$650,000 to UJA-Federation of New York, New York, NY, 2011.
$132,571 to Whitney Museum of American Art, New York, NY, 2011.
$90,000 to New York University, New York, NY, 2011.
$50,000 to City University of New York, Honors College, New York, NY, 2011.
$30,000 to Memorial Sloan-Kettering Cancer Center, New York, NY, 2011.
$25,000 to American Museum of Natural History, New York, NY, 2011.
$25,000 to HealthCare Chaplaincy, New York, NY, 2011.
$15,000 to Rockefeller University, New York, NY, 2011.
$5,000 to Visiting Nurse Service of New York, New York, NY, 2011.

6768
The Rudin Foundation, Inc. ✧

c/o Rudin Mgmt.
345 Park Ave.
New York, NY 10154-0004 (212) 407-2512
Contact: Mark L. Bodden, Admin. & Prog. Dir.

Incorporated in 1960 in NY.
Donors: Clarkton Estates, Inc.; Corliss Estates, Inc.; Graceton Estates, Inc.; Marshall Estates, Inc.; Rudin Estates Co., LP; Taylor Estates, Inc.; 136 East 55th Street, Inc.; 144 West Corp.; 415 Madison, Inc.; 295 Central Park W., Inc.; Lexington 55th St.; Croston Estates, Inc.; Norwin Estates, Inc.; Clarkdale Estates, Inc.
Foundation type: Independent foundation.
Financial data (yr. ended 12/31/13): Assets, $123,637 (M); gifts received, $1,337,500; expenditures, $1,346,390; qualifying distributions, $1,346,390; giving activities include $1,203,636 for 107 grants (high: $280,000; low: $500).
Purpose and activities: Giving to the arts, education, health and human services, and to Jewish and Roman Catholic organizations.
Fields of interest: Arts, alliance/advocacy; Arts; Higher education; Hospitals (general); Human services; Community/economic development; Jewish federated giving programs; Catholic agencies & churches.
Limitations: Applications accepted. Giving primarily in New York, NY. No grants to individuals.
Application information:
Initial approach: Letter
Copies of proposal: 1
Deadline(s): Oct. 15
Final notification: Varies
Officers and Directors:* Jack Rudin,* Chair.; Beth Rudin DeWoody,* Pres.; Jeffrey Steinman,* Exec. V.P.; Samantha Rudin Earls, V.P.; Madeleine Rudin Johnson,* V.P.; John Lewin,* V.P.; Stephen Lewin,* V.P.; Eric C. Rudin,* V.P.; William C. Rudin,* V.P.; Gregory Sills,* V.P.; John L. Sills,* V.P.; Robert Steinman,* V.P.; Andrew Migdon,* Secy.; David B. Levy,* Treas.
EIN: 136113064
Selected grants: The following grants are a representative sample of this grantmaker's funding activity:
$30,000 to Jewish Theological Seminary of America, New York, NY, 2011. For general support.
$20,000 to Roundabout Theater Company, New York, NY, 2011.
$10,000 to Skyscraper Museum, New York, NY, 2011.
$5,000 to Big Brothers Big Sisters of New York City, New York, NY, 2011. For general support.
$5,000 to Childrens Aid Society, New York, NY, 2011. For general support.
$5,000 to Girls Incorporated, New York, NY, 2011. For general support.
$2,500 to Prospect Park Alliance, Brooklyn, NY, 2011.

6769
The Louis and Rachel Rudin Foundation, Inc. ✧

c/o Rudin Mgmt.
345 Park Ave.
New York, NY 10154-0004 (212) 407-2512
Contact: Mark L. Bodden, V.P.

Incorporated in 1968 in NY.
Foundation type: Independent foundation.
Financial data (yr. ended 12/31/13): Assets, $121,730,541 (M); expenditures, $6,073,198; qualifying distributions, $4,142,880; giving activities include $3,821,000 for 26 grants (high: $690,000; low: $10,000).
Purpose and activities: Grants to medical and nursing schools only for educational training programs.
Fields of interest: Medical school/education; Nursing school/education.
Type of support: Scholarship funds.
Limitations: Applications accepted. Giving primarily in New York, NY. No grants to individuals, or for building funds.
Application information: Application form not required.
Initial approach: Letter
Copies of proposal: 1
Deadline(s): Oct. 15
Final notification: Varies
Officers and Directors:* Jack Rudin,* Chair.; Beth Rudin DeWoody,* Pres.; Stephen Lewin,* Exec. V.P.; Eric C. Rudin,* V.P. and Secy.; Jeffrey Steinman,* V.P. and Treas.; Mark L. Bodden, V.P.; Madeleine Rudin Johnson,* V.P.; John Lewin,* V.P.; Katherine L. Rudin,* V.P.; Samantha Mia Rudin,* V.P.; William C. Rudin,* V.P.; Peter D. Steinman,* V.P.
EIN: 237039549
Selected grants: The following grants are a representative sample of this grantmaker's funding activity:
$255,000 to New York University, New York, NY, 2011.
$230,000 to City University of New York, New York, NY, 2011.
$190,000 to New York University, School of Medicine, New York, NY, 2011.
$140,000 to Helene Fuld College of Nursing, New York, NY, 2011.
$50,000 to New York Medical College, Valhalla, NY, 2011.
$25,000 to College of New Rochelle, New Rochelle, NY, 2011.
$25,000 to Pace University, Pleasantville, NY, 2011.
$25,000 to Rockefeller University, New York, NY, 2011.
$20,000 to College of Mount Saint Vincent, Riverdale, NY, 2011.

6770
Peter B. & Adeline W. Ruffin Foundation, Inc. ✧

1192 Park Ave., Ste. 14A
New York, NY 10128-1314
Contact: Edward G. McAnaney, Pres.

Established in 1964 in NY.
Foundation type: Independent foundation.
Financial data (yr. ended 11/30/13): Assets, $27,656,717 (M); expenditures, $2,512,346; qualifying distributions, $2,260,885; giving activities include $2,251,000 for 66 grants (high: $600,000; low: $500).
Purpose and activities: Support for minority scholarship funds.
Fields of interest: Secondary school/education; Higher education; Education; Human services; Youth; Minorities; Native Americans/American Indians; Economically disadvantaged.

Type of support: Annual campaigns; General/operating support; Capital campaigns; Endowments; Professorships; Scholarship funds.
Limitations: Applications not accepted. Giving primarily in CT, Washington, DC, NJ, NY, PA, and VA. No grants to individuals.
Publications: Annual report.
Application information: Contributes only to pre-selected organizations.
Officer and Trustees:* Edward G. McAnaney,* Pres., Treas., and Mgr.; Sheila K. Kostanecki; Brian T. McAnaney; Kevin G. McAnaney.
Number of staff: 1 part-time professional.
EIN: 136170484
Selected grants: The following grants are a representative sample of this grantmaker's funding activity:
$200,000 to Woodberry Forest School, Woodberry Forest, VA, 2012. For endowed professorship.
$5,000 to Golden Gate University, Law School, San Francisco, CA, 2012. For unrestricted.

6771
The Richard W. Rupp Foundation ✧ ☆
1806 Liberty Bldg.
Buffalo, NY 14202-3618

Established in 1998 in NY.
Donor: Richard W. Rupp.
Foundation type: Independent foundation.
Financial data (yr. ended 12/31/13): Assets, $10,318,059 (M); expenditures, $567,265; qualifying distributions, $468,508; giving activities include $420,000 for 47 grants (high: $40,000; low: $1,000).
Fields of interest: Human services.
Type of support: General/operating support.
Limitations: Applications not accepted. Giving primarily in Buffalo, NY. No grants to individuals.
Application information: Contributes only to pre-selected organizations.
Directors: Chester E. Borczynski; Peter J. Brevorka; Christina D. Rupp; Susan S. Rupp; William R. Rupp.
EIN: 161551594

6772
The ILR Ruth Foundation, Inc. ✧
1 Rockefeller Plz., 29th Fl.
New York, NY 10020-2021
Application address: c/o William Schwartz, Secy., 1 World Financial Ctr., New York, NY 10281; tel.: (212) 504-6399

Donor: Ira Leon Rennert.
Foundation type: Independent foundation.
Financial data (yr. ended 12/31/13): Assets, $0 (M); gifts received, $3,133,908; expenditures, $3,133,908; qualifying distributions, $3,133,908; giving activities include $3,095,190 for 2 grants (high: $2,895,190; low: $200,000).
Fields of interest: Human services; Public affairs.
Limitations: Applications accepted. Giving primarily in Jerusalem, Israel.
Application information: Application form required.
Initial approach: Letter
Deadline(s): None
Officers: Ira Leon Rennert, Chair.; Ari E.Y.M. Rennert, Pres.; Ingeborg Rennert, V.P.; William Schwartz, Secy.
EIN: 273349255
Selected grants: The following grants are a representative sample of this grantmaker's funding activity:
$965,690 to Keren Ruth Bat Sarah, Jerusalem, Israel, 2012.

6773
RZH Foundation ✧
c/o Meridian Capital Group LLC
P.O. Box 422
Bowling Green Sta.
New York, NY 10274-0422

Established in 1994 in NY.
Donors: Ralph Herzka; Interlink I Charitable Trust; Interlink III Charitable Trust; Interlink VI Charitable Trust.
Foundation type: Independent foundation.
Financial data (yr. ended 12/31/12): Assets, $41,131,592 (M); gifts received, $8,422,000; expenditures, $2,567,878; qualifying distributions, $2,507,750; giving activities include $2,507,750 for 221+ grants (high: $346,250).
Purpose and activities: Giving primarily to Jewish agencies, temples, and schools.
Fields of interest: Elementary/secondary education; Jewish agencies & synagogues.
Limitations: Applications not accepted. Giving primarily in NY. No grants to individuals.
Application information: Contributes only to pre-selected organizations.
Trustees: Judy Herzka; Ralph Herzka.
EIN: 113242489

6774
S & G Foundation, Inc. ✧
c/o The Ayco Co.
P.O. Box 860
Saratoga Springs, NY 12866-0860 518) 886-4220

Established around 1995 in WY.
Donors: Gale L. Davis; Shelby M.C. Davis.
Foundation type: Independent foundation.
Financial data (yr. ended 06/30/13): Assets, $743,848,993 (M); gifts received, $261,408,871; expenditures, $17,695,689; qualifying distributions, $17,039,583; giving activities include $16,939,509 for 62 grants (high: $12,582,580; low: $45).
Purpose and activities: Giving primarily for arts, educational institutions and organizations, and Christian agencies and churches.
Fields of interest: Arts; Higher education; Education; Environment; Christian agencies & churches.
Type of support: General/operating support.
Limitations: Applications not accepted. Giving primarily on the East Coast, with emphasis on FL, MA, ME, NJ, and NY; some giving also in NM, RI and VT. No grants to individuals.
Application information: Contributes only to pre-selected organizations.
Officers: Shelby M.C. Davis, Pres.; Gale L. Davis, Secy.-Treas.
Directors: Lancing Davis; Mary Ann McGrath.
EIN: 364193183
Selected grants: The following grants are a representative sample of this grantmaker's funding activity:
$16,000,000 to Vanguard Charitable Endowment Program, Boston, MA, 2012. For general support.
$12,582,580 to Vanguard Charitable Endowment Program, Boston, MA, 2013. For general support.
$1,710,854 to Westminster College, Fulton, MO, 2013. For general support.
$1,244,549 to United World College of the American West, Montezuma, NM, 2013. For general support.
$992,121 to Luther College, Decorah, IA, 2012. For general support.
$518,105 to Macalester College, Saint Paul, MN, 2013. For general support.
$443,392 to Methodist University, Fayetteville, NC, 2013. For general support.
$410,000 to Brown University, Providence, RI, 2012. For general support.
$150,000 to Institute for Shipboard Education, Semester at Sea, Charlottesville, VA, 2012. For general support.
$127,802 to Vanguard Charitable Endowment Program, Boston, MA, 2012. For general support.
$54,000 to United World College Costa Rica, San Jose, Costa Rica, 2012. For general support.
$52,544 to United World College of the American West, Montezuma, NM, 2012. For general support.
$40,000 to University of Florida, Gainesville, FL, 2013. For general support.
$20,800 to United World College of the American West, Montezuma, NM, 2012. For Experiment in International Living (EIL) summer program.
$20,000 to College of Idaho, Caldwell, ID, 2013. For general support.
$20,000 to Lake Forest College, Lake Forest, IL, 2012. For general support.
$20,000 to University of Florida, Gainesville, FL, 2012. For general support.
$20,000 to Vassar College, Poughkeepsie, NY, 2013. For general support.
$16,667 to Carleton College, Northfield, MN, 2013. For general support.
$10,000 to Bucknell University, Lewisburg, PA, 2013. For general support.

6775
Andrew Sabin Family Foundation ✧
P.O. Box 5026
East Hampton, NY 11937-6091

Established in 2007 in NY.
Donors: Andrew Sabin; Annette Sabin; Sabin Commodities, Inc.; Fraydun Foundation Inc.
Foundation type: Independent foundation.
Financial data (yr. ended 12/31/13): Assets, $14,378,012 (M); gifts received, $3,357,830; expenditures, $3,044,725; qualifying distributions, $3,021,058; giving activities include $2,887,279 for 245 grants (high: $285,000; low: $10).
Fields of interest: Higher education; Environment; Health organizations, association; Cancer; Human services; Children/youth, services; Jewish agencies & synagogues.
Limitations: Applications not accepted. Giving in the U.S., with emphasis on NY. No grants to individuals.
Application information: Contributes only to pre-selected organizations.
Director: Andrew E. Sabin.
EIN: 208729425
Selected grants: The following grants are a representative sample of this grantmaker's funding activity:
$246,250 to Conservation International, Arlington, VA, 2011.

$125,000 to Yale University, New Haven, CT, 2011.
$38,000 to Earthjustice, San Francisco, CA, 2011.
$15,000 to Buoniconti Fund to Cure Paralysis, Miami, FL, 2011.
$15,000 to Childrens Scholarship Fund, New York, NY, 2011.
$13,000 to Asia Society, New York, NY, 2011.
$11,000 to Swim Across America, Boston, MA, 2011.
$10,000 to Phoenix House, New York, NY, 2011.
$10,000 to Smile Train, New York, NY, 2011.
$7,000 to American Jewish World Service, New York, NY, 2011.

6776
The Else Sackler Charitable Foundation ✧

c/o Pillsbury Winthrop
1540 Broadway
New York, NY 10036-4039

Established in 2000 in NY.
Donor: The Else Sackler Charitable Remainder Trust.
Foundation type: Independent foundation.
Financial data (yr. ended 12/31/13): Assets, $1,994,304 (M); expenditures, $1,131,573; qualifying distributions, $1,052,257; giving activities include $1,025,000 for 7 grants (high: $500,000; low: $5,000).
Purpose and activities: Giving primarily to Jewish federated giving programs.
Fields of interest: Foundations (private independent); Jewish federated giving programs.
Limitations: Applications not accepted. Giving primarily in New York, NY; some funding also in Boston, MA. No grants to individuals.
Application information: Contributes only to pre-selected organizations.
Officers: Dr. Elizabeth A. Sackler, Pres.; Dr. Carol Master, V.P. and Treas.; Susan P. Serota, Esq., Secy.
EIN: 133933972

6777
The Arthur M. Sackler Foundation ✧ ☆

461 E. 57th St.
New York, NY 10022 (212) 980-5400
Contact: Elizabeth A. Sackler, C.E.O.

Established in 1965 in NY; classified as a private operating foundation in 1977.
Donors: Arthur M. Sackler; Elizabeth A. Sackler; Carol Master; The Else Sackler Charitable Foundation.
Foundation type: Operating foundation.
Financial data (yr. ended 12/31/13): Assets, $25,188,314 (M); expenditures, $1,837,929; qualifying distributions, $1,750,048; giving activities include $1,123,150 for 9 grants (high: $400,000; low: $3,550).
Purpose and activities: Support primarily for the arts.
Fields of interest: Museums (art); Arts; Religion.
Type of support: Program development; Publication.
Application information: Application form required.
Initial approach: Letter
Deadline(s): None
Officers: Elizabeth A. Sackler, C.E.O. and Pres.; Carol Master, Chair. and V.P.; Laurie Sackler, Secy.-Treas.
Number of staff: 8 full-time professional; 1 full-time support; 1 part-time support.
EIN: 521074954
Selected grants: The following grants are a representative sample of this grantmaker's funding activity:
$40,000 to Santa Barbara Museum of Art, Santa Barbara, CA, 2012. For donation of art that was previously on loan.

6778
The Elizabeth A. Sackler Foundation, Inc. ✧

461 E. 57th St.
New York, NY 10022-3003

Established in 2001 in NY.
Donors: Dr. Elizabeth A. Sackler; Arthur Sackler; Laurie Sackler; Laura Sackler Tancredi; Beverly Sackler; Else Sackler Charitable Foundation.
Foundation type: Independent foundation.
Financial data (yr. ended 12/31/13): Assets, $290,741 (M); gifts received, $786,991; expenditures, $641,580; qualifying distributions, $641,580; giving activities include $527,753 for 1 grant, and $641,580 for foundation-administered programs.
Fields of interest: Museums (art).
Type of support: General/operating support.
Limitations: Applications not accepted. Giving primarily in Brooklyn, NY. No grants to individuals.
Application information: Contributes only to pre-selected organizations.
Directors: Janet Bajan; Janet McKay; Dr. Elizabeth A. Sackler.
EIN: 134180717

6779
The Mortimer D. Sackler Foundation, Inc. ✧

17 E. 62nd St.
New York, NY 10065-7204

Established in 1967 in NY.
Donors: M.D. Sackler‡; T.E. Sackler; T. Lefcourt; K.A. Sackler; S.S. Sackler Hunt; M.D.A. Sackler; M.T. Sackler; S.D. Sackler; Mi D. Sackler; Varns Investments, Ltd.; PLP Associates Holdings Inc.; Purdue Pharma, Inc.; The Varus Trust; The Medichem Trust.
Foundation type: Independent foundation.
Financial data (yr. ended 12/31/12): Assets, $8,442,410 (M); expenditures, $1,999,050; qualifying distributions, $1,998,300; giving activities include $1,998,300 for 50 grants (high: $525,000; low: $1,000).
Fields of interest: Arts; Education; Health organizations; Economics; Political science.
Type of support: General/operating support.
Limitations: Applications not accepted. Giving primarily in New York, NY. No grants to individuals.
Application information: Contributes only to pre-selected organizations.
Officers and Directors:* I. Sackler Lefcourt,* Pres.; K.A. Sackler,* V.P. and Secy.; M.D.A. Sackler,* V.P. and Treas.; S.D. Sackler Dalrymple,* V.P.; S.S. Sackler Hunt,* V.P.; Mi D. Sackler,* V.P.; M.T. Sackler,* V.P.; T.E. Sackler,* V.P.; L.J. Schreyer; C.B. Mitchell; H. Shaw.
EIN: 237022461
Selected grants: The following grants are a representative sample of this grantmaker's funding activity:
$10,000 to Metropolitan Museum of Art, New York, NY, 2012. For acquisitions committee.

6780
Raymond and Beverly Sackler Foundation, Inc. ✧

17 E. 62nd St.
New York, NY 10065-7204

Established in 1967 in NY.
Donors: Raymond R. Sackler, M.D.; Richard S. Sackler, M.D.; Jonathan D. Sackler; Beverly Sackler.
Foundation type: Operating foundation.
Financial data (yr. ended 12/31/13): Assets, $9,294,108 (M); gifts received, $95,000; expenditures, $6,910,590; qualifying distributions, $6,820,115; giving activities include $5,550,000 for 7 grants (high: $3,000,000; low: $50,000).
Fields of interest: Medical school/education; Medical research.
Type of support: General/operating support.
Limitations: Applications not accepted. Giving primarily in Washington, DC and New York, NY. No grants to individuals.
Application information: Contributes only to pre-selected organizations.
Officers and Directors:* Jonathan D. Sackler,* C.E.O. and Pres.; Raymond R. Sackler, M.D., V.P.; Richard S. Sackler, M.D.*, V.P.; Beverly Sackler,* Secy.-Treas.
Number of staff: 7 full-time professional; 5 part-time professional.
EIN: 237022467

6781
Joseph Safra Foundation, Inc. ✧

(also known as Safra Foundation, Inc.)
546 5th Ave.
New York, NY 10036-5000

Established in 2002 in NY.
Donor: Safra National Bank of New York.
Foundation type: Independent foundation.
Financial data (yr. ended 12/31/13): Assets, $20,863,236 (M); gifts received, $5,000,000; expenditures, $4,113,523; qualifying distributions, $4,083,129; giving activities include $4,083,129 for 59 grants (high: $1,249,999; low: $1,000).
Purpose and activities: Giving primarily to Jewish organizations, federated giving programs and schools; some funding for health organizations.
Fields of interest: Education; Health organizations; Jewish federated giving programs; Jewish agencies & synagogues.
Limitations: Applications not accepted. Giving primarily in Brooklyn and New York, NY. No grants to individuals.
Application information: Contributes only to pre-selected organizations.
Directors: Carlos Bertaco Bomfim; Steven Montague; Jacob Safra; Joseph Yacoub Safra.
EIN: 131640434

6782
Russell Sage Foundation ✧
112 E. 64th St.
New York, NY 10065-7307
Contact: Christopher Brogna, C.F.O.
FAX: (212) 371-4761; E-mail: info@rsage.org; Main URL: http://www.russellsage.org
Blog: http://www.russellsage.org/blog
Facebook: https://www.facebook.com/russellsagefoundation
Twitter: http://www.twitter.com/russellsagefdn
YouTube: http://www.youtube.com/user/RussellSageFdn?feature=mhee

Incorporated in 1907 in NY.
Donor: Mrs. Russell Sage‡.
Foundation type: Operating foundation.
Financial data (yr. ended 08/31/13): Assets, $279,298,445 (M); expenditures, $12,911,260; qualifying distributions, $11,342,604; giving activities include $3,614,910 for 70 grants (high: $338,223; low: $429), and $10,483,123 for foundation-administered programs.
Purpose and activities: The foundation is a private operating foundation devoted exclusively to the conduct and dissemination of research in the social sciences. Its current programs include research on the causes and consequences of the decline in demand for low-skilled workers in advanced economies; the adaptation of U.S. immigrants and their children to American society; the social effects of rising economic inequality, efforts by American institutions to accommodate greater racial and ethnic diversity; and a variety of smaller special projects and research initiatives. The foundation sponsors a Visiting Scholar Program in which individual scholars and collaborative groups pursue research and writing projects related to the foundation's interests at its headquarters in New York City for periods of up to one year. The foundation also provides support for scholars at other institutions to pursue research projects that advance the foundation's research interests. The foundation disseminates the resulting research findings through its own book publishing program.
Fields of interest: Social sciences.
Type of support: Program development; Conferences/seminars; Publication; Research; Employee matching gifts.
Limitations: Applications accepted. Giving on a national basis. No grants for capital or endowment funds, independent ongoing activities of other institutions, scholarships, annual campaigns, emergency funds, deficit financing, operating budgets, or continuing support; no loans.
Publications: Application guidelines; Biennial report; Financial statement; Informational brochure (including application guidelines); Newsletter.
Application information: Application information available on foundation's web site. Awards are given to post-Ph.D.'s only. Application form not required.
Initial approach: Letter of inquiry
Copies of proposal: 2
Deadline(s): All major proposals must be submitted 8 weeks prior to board meetings
Board meeting date(s): Feb., June, and Nov.
Final notification: 3 months
Officers and Trustees:* Robert E. Denham,* Chair.; Sheldon Danziger,* Pres.; Shelley E. Taylor,* Treas.; Christopher Brogna, C.F.O.; Larry M. Bartels; Kenneth D. Brody; Karen S. Cook; W. Bowman Cutter III; Kathryn Edin; Lawrence F. Katz; Nicholas Lemann; Sara S. McLanahan; Claude M. Steele; Richard H. Thaler.
Number of staff: 10 full-time professional; 19 full-time support; 9 part-time support.
EIN: 131635303
Selected grants: The following grants are a representative sample of this grantmaker's funding activity:
$200,000 to University of Massachusetts, Amherst, MA, 2011. For Working Group: Care Work in United States.
$150,000 to Massachusetts Institute of Technology, Cambridge, MA, 2011. For Employment Policy Research Network.
$88,368 to Stanford University, Stanford, CA, 2011. For Measuring Intergenerational Economic Mobility with Tax-Return Data: Toward IRS Platform.
$76,231 to University of Colorado, Boulder, CO, 2011. For immigration, internal migration, and local labor market adjustment following the US housing bust.
$33,000 to Graduate Center Foundation, New York, NY, 2011. For interviews with Occupy Wall Street Movement.

6783
The Sagner Family Foundation ✧
c/o Deborah Sagner
210 Central Park S., Apt. 20C
New York, NY 10019 (908) 305-1020
Contact: Deborah Sagner, Pres.

Established in 1961 in NJ.
Donors: Ruth Levin Sagner; Alan Sagner; The Deborah S. Buurma Charitable Foundation.
Foundation type: Independent foundation.
Financial data (yr. ended 12/31/12): Assets, $11,992,006 (M); gifts received, $20,000; expenditures, $689,394; qualifying distributions, $461,568; giving activities include $461,568 for 68 grants (high: $66,500; low: $40).
Purpose and activities: Giving primarily for the arts, Jewish organizations, and social services.
Fields of interest: Performing arts; Arts; Education; Housing/shelter, services; Human services; Children/youth, services; Family services; Jewish federated giving programs; Public affairs; Jewish agencies & synagogues; Economically disadvantaged.
Limitations: Applications accepted. Giving primarily in CA, FL, MA, NJ and NY. No grants to individuals.
Application information: Application form not required.
Initial approach: Proposal
Deadline(s): None
Officers: Alan Sagner, Chair.; Deborah Sagner, Pres.; Mary Baltycki, Secy.-Treas.
Trustee: Rachel Buurma; Jacob Burma.
EIN: 221711646

6784
The Salmon Foundation, Inc. ✧
275 Madison Ave., Ste. 401
New York, NY 10016-1101
Contact: Emily Grand, Admin.

Established in 1991 in NY.
Donor: Lois S. Duffey.
Foundation type: Independent foundation.
Financial data (yr. ended 12/31/13): Assets, $18,804,407 (M); gifts received, $510,275; expenditures, $845,247; qualifying distributions, $814,874; giving activities include $721,000 for 43 grants (high: $50,000; low: $1,000).
Purpose and activities: Giving primarily for children and family services, and education.
Fields of interest: Education; Children/youth, services.
Limitations: Applications not accepted. Giving limited to areas in CO, CT, MD and VT. No grants to individuals.
Application information: Unsolicited applications are not generally considered, because the board is focused on director-initiated projects.
Board meeting date(s): June and Nov.
Officers and Directors:* Amanda D. Rutledge,* Pres; Sarah J. Rutledge, Secy.; Catherine D. MacGlashan,* Treas.; Diana C. Duffey; Harry J. Duffey III; Patricia D. Parkhurst; Peter L. Rutledge.
EIN: 133637630
Selected grants: The following grants are a representative sample of this grantmaker's funding activity:
$50,000 to Kristin Brooks Hope Center, Washington, DC, 2012. For Veteran Housing and Peer to Peer Hotline.
$35,000 to Family Place, Norwich, VT, 2012. For Shelter and Children's Services Programs.
$35,000 to Wesley College, Dover, DE, 2012. For Salmon Scholarships to support students with need.
$30,000 to Child and Family Agency of Southeastern Connecticut, New London, CT, 2012. For staff positions for enrichment activities.
$30,000 to Dartmouth College, Hanover, NH, 2012. For Inpatient Child Life Specialist Position at Children's Hospital.
$25,000 to Delaware Valley College, Doylestown, PA, 2012. For Salmon Scholarship Fund for deserving students with need.
$25,000 to In the Arena, Cambridge, MA, 2012. For mentor athlete program for children in Colorado and Vermont.
$25,000 to Saint Timothys School, Stevenson, MD, 2012. For financial aid to returning student in need who would otherwise not be able to return.

6785
The Richard Salomon Family Foundation, Inc. ✧
(formerly Richard & Edna Salomon Foundation, Inc.)
610 5th Ave., Ste. 506
New York, NY 10020-2403

Established in 1964 in NY.
Donors: Richard B. Salomon‡; Richard E. Salomon; Edna Salomon‡.
Foundation type: Independent foundation.
Financial data (yr. ended 12/31/13): Assets, $17,290,924 (M); expenditures, $1,081,563; qualifying distributions, $812,500; giving activities include $775,025 for 35 grants (high: $100,000; low: $2).
Purpose and activities: Giving for education, cancer research, and human services.
Fields of interest: Museums (art); Elementary/secondary education; Higher education; Education; Cancer research; Human services; International affairs, foreign policy.
Type of support: General/operating support.
Limitations: Applications not accepted. Giving primarily in New York, NY and Providence, RI. No grants to individuals.
Application information: Contributes only to pre-selected organizations.

Officers: David Salomon, Chair.; Robyn S. Transport, Treas.; Jennifer Salomon, Exec. Dir.
Directors: Evanne S. Gargiulo; Marlene Hess; Laura A. Landro; Frederick Lubcher; Christina Salomon; Richard E. Salomon.
EIN: 136163521

6786
The Gary Saltz Foundation, Inc. ✧
c/o SF Capital Group, LLC
150 E. 52nd St., 10th Fl.
New York, NY 10022-6094

Incorporated in 1985 in NY.
Donors: Jack Saltz; Anita Saltz†; Leonard Saltz Charitable Lead Annuity Trust; Ronald Saltz Charitable Lead Annuity Trust; Susan Saltz Charitable Lead Annuity Trust.
Foundation type: Independent foundation.
Financial data (yr. ended 04/30/13): Assets, $46,859,902 (M); gifts received, $3,068,025; expenditures, $3,164,176; qualifying distributions, $2,897,667; giving activities include $2,896,917 for 36 grants (high: $650,000; low: $293).
Purpose and activities: Giving primarily for higher education and the arts.
Fields of interest: Museums (natural history); Arts; Higher education; Education; Human services; Children/youth, services; Jewish agencies & synagogues.
Type of support: Research.
Limitations: Applications not accepted. Giving primarily in New York, NY; some giving in Los Angeles, CA. No grants to individuals.
Application information: Contributes only to pre-selected organizations.
Officers: Jack Saltz, Pres.; Ronald Saltz, V.P.; Susan Saltz, Secy.; Leonard Saltz, Treas.
EIN: 133267114
Selected grants: The following grants are a representative sample of this grantmaker's funding activity:
$500,000 to Brown University, Providence, RI, 2011. For general contribution.
$255,000 to Stanford University, Stanford, CA, 2011. For general contribution.
$220,000 to Alliance for Childrens Rights, Los Angeles, CA, 2011. For general contribution.
$200,000 to New Visions Foundation, Santa Monica, CA, 2011. For general contribution.
$100,000 to World Union for Progressive Judaism, New York, NY, 2011. For general contribution.
$65,000 to A Window Between Worlds, Venice, CA, 2011. For general contribution.
$50,000 to Child Mind Institute, New York, NY, 2011. For general contribution.
$35,000 to Nightingale-Bamford School, New York, NY, 2011. For general contribution.
$25,000 to North Carolina Outward Bound School, Asheville, NC, 2011. For general contribution.
$20,000 to Venice Family Clinic, Venice, CA, 2011. For general contribution.

6787
The Jack & Anita Saltz Foundation ✧
c/o SF Capital Group, LLC
150 E. 52nd St., 28th Fl.
New York, NY 10022-6017

Established in 1997 in NY.
Donors: Jack Saltz; Anita Saltz†.
Foundation type: Independent foundation.
Financial data (yr. ended 12/31/13): Assets, $1,885,418 (M); expenditures, $667,592; qualifying distributions, $646,106; giving activities include $645,856 for 53 grants (high: $250,000; low: $250).
Purpose and activities: Giving primarily for medical research, Jewish organizations, and social services.
Fields of interest: Arts; Medical school/education; Hospitals (general); Health organizations, association; Medical research, institute; Diabetes research; Human services; Children/youth, services; Jewish federated giving programs; Jewish agencies & synagogues.
Limitations: Applications not accepted. Giving primarily in the metropolitan New York, NY, area. No grants to individuals.
Application information: Contributes only to pre-selected organizations.
Officers: Jack Saltz, Pres.; Ronald I. Saltz, Secy.; Leonard B. Saltz, Treas.
Director: Susan Saltz.
EIN: 133914629
Selected grants: The following grants are a representative sample of this grantmaker's funding activity:
$271,500 to UJA-Federation of New York, New York, NY, 2011.
$250,000 to Weill Medical College of Cornell University, New York, NY, 2011.
$25,000 to Memorial Sloan-Kettering Cancer Center, New York, NY, 2011.
$10,000 to American Jewish Committee, New York, NY, 2011.
$10,000 to Kildonan School, Amenia, NY, 2011.
$7,000 to National Jewish Health, Denver, CO, 2011.
$5,000 to Blythedale Childrens Hospital, Valhalla, NY, 2011.
$5,000 to Lincoln Center for the Performing Arts, New York, NY, 2011.
$5,000 to Teach for America, New York, NY, 2011.
$3,000 to American Museum of Natural History, New York, NY, 2011.

6788
The Fan Fox and Leslie R. Samuels Foundation, Inc. ✧
350 5th Ave., Ste. 4301
New York, NY 10118-4301 (212) 239-3030
Contact: Joseph C. Mitchell, Chair.
FAX: (212) 239-3039; E-mail: info@samuels.org;
Main URL: http://www.samuels.org

Incorporated in 1959 in UT; reincorporated in 1981 in NY.
Donors: Leslie R. Samuels†; Fan Fox Samuels†.
Foundation type: Independent foundation.
Financial data (yr. ended 07/31/13): Assets, $172,740,509 (M); expenditures, $8,497,705; qualifying distributions, $7,303,114; giving activities include $5,829,258 for 224 grants (high: $265,100; low: $25), and $718 for 2 employee matching gifts.
Purpose and activities: Grants for the performing arts, and health care and social services for the elderly, including palliative and end-of-life care, health systems, and quality measurement.
Fields of interest: Performing arts; Performing arts, dance; Performing arts, theater; Performing arts, music; Performing arts, opera; Medical care, outpatient care; Health care, support services; Palliative care; Housing/shelter, aging; Human services; Aging.
Type of support: Program development; Seed money; Program evaluation.
Limitations: Applications accepted. Giving limited to New York City. No support for education. No grants to individuals, or for scholarships, fellowships, or film or video projects.
Publications: Application guidelines; Grants list.
Application information: Do not submit musical scores. Application form not required.
Initial approach: Letter of inquiry not exceeding 3 typed pages
Copies of proposal: 1
Deadline(s): Mar. 1, June 1, Sept. 1, and Dec.1
Board meeting date(s): Jan., Apr., July, Oct., and as necessary
Final notification: 3 months
Officers and Directors:* Joseph C. Mitchell,* Chair.; Robert Marx,* Pres.; Julio Urbina, V.P. and Dir., Healthy Aging Prog.; Michael L. Ziegler, Secy.; Alexandra Francis, Cont.; Marvin A. Kaufman, Chair. Emeritus; Joseph W. Polisi; Jacqueline M. Taylor; Michael L. Ziegler.
Number of staff: 4 full-time professional; 2 full-time support.
EIN: 133124818

6789
The Mara & Ricky Sandler Foundation ✧
c/o Eminence Partners
65 E. 55th St., 25th Fl.
New York, NY 10022-3364

Established in NY.
Donors: Mara Sandler; Ricky Sandler.
Foundation type: Independent foundation.
Financial data (yr. ended 12/31/12): Assets, $10,567,759 (M); gifts received, $2,806,355; expenditures, $1,030,043; qualifying distributions, $1,015,190; giving activities include $1,002,500 for 88 grants (high: $125,000; low: $100).
Purpose and activities: Giving primarily for the arts, education, health, Jewish organizations, and children and social services.
Fields of interest: Arts; Higher education; Health organizations, association; Human services; Children/youth, services; Jewish federated giving programs.
Limitations: Applications not accepted. Giving primarily in the metropolitan New York, NY, area; some funding elsewhere in the U.S., particularly in Madison, WI. No grants to individuals.
Application information: Contributes only to pre-selected organizations.
Trustees: Mara Sandler; Ricky Sandler.
EIN: 412091688

6790
The Sands Family Foundation, Inc. ✧
(formerly The Mac and Sally Sands Foundation, Inc.)
c/o Constellation Brands, Inc.
207 High Point Dr., Bldg. 100
Victor, NY 14564-1061

Established in 1959 in NY.
Donors: Robert Sands; Richard Sands; Marilyn Sands.
Foundation type: Independent foundation.
Financial data (yr. ended 12/31/13): Assets, $17,851,286 (M); gifts received, $7,002,500;

expenditures, $1,631,634; qualifying distributions, $1,626,000; giving activities include $1,626,000 for 18 grants (high: $250,000; low: $1,000).
Fields of interest: Performing arts, ballet; Higher education; Education; Human services.
Limitations: Applications not accepted. Giving primarily in Rochester, NY. No grants to individuals.
Application information: Contributes only to pre-selected organizations.
Officers: Robert Sands, Pres. and Treas.; Richard Sands, V.P. and Secy.
EIN: 546052978

6791
The Sandy Hill Foundation ✧
15 Boulevard
Hudson Falls, NY 12839-1001 (518) 791-3490
Contact: Nancy Juckett Brown, Tr.
Scholarship application address: P.O. Box 607, Williston, VT 05495,
e-mail: njbrown@sandyhillfoundation.org

Established in 1953.
Donor: J. Walter Juckett.
Foundation type: Independent foundation.
Financial data (yr. ended 08/31/13): Assets, $8,355,434 (M); expenditures, $520,184; qualifying distributions, $483,452; giving activities include $359,779 for 86 grants (high: $100,000; low: $250), and $88,000 for 44 grants to individuals (high: $2,000; low: $2,000).
Purpose and activities: Giving primarily for the arts and culture, higher education, hospitals, health associations, children's and social services, and federated giving programs. Also offers scholarship grants for college education to assist young men and women graduating from designated local area schools.
Fields of interest: Arts; Higher education; Hospitals (general); Health organizations, association; Human services; Children/youth, services; Community/economic development; United Ways and Federated Giving Programs.
Type of support: General/operating support.
Limitations: Applications accepted. Giving primarily in the greater Hudson Falls, NY, area. No grants to individuals directly.
Application information: Application form required.
Initial approach: Proposal
Deadline(s): Apr. 1 for scholarships
Trustees: Nancy Juckett Brown; Stephen J. Brown; Timothy S. Brown.
EIN: 146018954
Selected grants: The following grants are a representative sample of this grantmaker's funding activity:
$1,000 to Warm the Children, Higganum, CT, 2011.

6792
Santa Maria Foundation, Inc. ✧
19 Mountain Ave.
Mount Kisco, NY 10549-1321

Established in 1978 in NY.
Donors: J. Peter Grace†; Margaret F. Grace.
Foundation type: Independent foundation.
Financial data (yr. ended 12/31/12): Assets, $7,332,899 (M); expenditures, $734,498; qualifying distributions, $667,320; giving activities include $647,625 for 35 grants (high: $85,000; low: $5,000).
Purpose and activities: Giving primarily for Roman Catholic churches and organizations, including Catholic schools; funding also for other education.
Fields of interest: Higher education; Education; Human services; Catholic agencies & churches.
Type of support: General/operating support; Continuing support; Seed money.
Limitations: Applications not accepted. Giving primarily in NY. No grants to individuals.
Application information: Contributes only to pre-selected organizations.
Officers and Directors:* Margaret F. Grace, Co-Pres.; Patrick P. Grace,* Co-Pres.; Theresa Grace Sears,* V.P. and Secy.; Nora Grace O'Donnell,* V.P. and Treas.
EIN: 132938749

6793
Theresa Patnode Santmann Foundation, Inc. ✧
(formerly Santmann Foundation, Inc.)
66 Cedar Ln.
Babylon, NY 11702-3809

Established in 2004 in NY.
Donor: Theresa M. Santmann.
Foundation type: Independent foundation.
Financial data (yr. ended 12/31/12): Assets, $2,034,374 (M); gifts received, $2,001,050; expenditures, $543,975; qualifying distributions, $542,550; giving activities include $542,550 for 18 grants (high: $155,000; low: $1,000).
Fields of interest: Elementary/secondary education; Hospitals (general); Human services; Economically disadvantaged.
Type of support: General/operating support.
Limitations: Applications not accepted. Giving primarily in NY, with emphasis on Long Island. No grants to individuals.
Application information: Contributes only to pre-selected organizations.
Director: Theresa M. Santmann.
EIN: 201513997

6794
The Lawrence and Carol Saper Foundation ✧
c/o BCRS Associates, LLC
77 Water St., 9th Fl.
New York, NY 10005

Established in 1996 in NY.
Donor: Lawrence Saper.
Foundation type: Independent foundation.
Financial data (yr. ended 12/31/12): Assets, $12,974,637 (M); gifts received, $1,000,000; expenditures, $551,867; qualifying distributions, $501,925; giving activities include $500,675 for 33 grants (high: $80,800; low: $500).
Fields of interest: Arts; Cancer research; Human services; International affairs; Jewish agencies & synagogues.
Type of support: General/operating support.
Limitations: Applications not accepted. Giving primarily in NY; some funding also in London, England. No grants to individuals.
Application information: Contributes only to pre-selected organizations.
Officers: Lawrence Saper, Pres.; Carol Saper, V.P.; Martin Nussbaum, Secy.
EIN: 133946616

6795
The Sapling Foundation ✧
c/o Ted Conferences
250 Hudson St., No. 1002
New York, NY 10013-1413

Established in 1995 in CA.
Donors: Aditya Agarwal; Nili Agassi; Ravin Agarwal; Steve Anderson; Adrian Aoun; Vincent Argiro; Gregory Arnold; John Arnold; Brain Ascher; Kristine Ashe.
Foundation type: Independent foundation.
Financial data (yr. ended 12/31/13): Assets, $45,332,516 (M); gifts received, $13,781,765; expenditures, $51,370,916; qualifying distributions, $14,220,835; giving activities include $1,050,000 for 5 grants (high: $500,000; low: $50,000).
Purpose and activities: Giving primarily to the environment, and to U.S.-based organizations that support global health and poverty issues.
Fields of interest: International affairs.
Limitations: Applications not accepted. Giving primarily in CA, NY, VA, and WA; some giving also in London, UK. No grants to individuals.
Application information: Contributes only to pre-selected organizations.
Officers: Christopher Anderson, Pres.; Yesenia Martinez, Co-Secy.; Thomas Valentino, Co-Secy. and C.F.O.
EIN: 943235545

6796
The Sapp Family Foundation ✧ ☆
P.O. Box 73, Bowling Green Sta.
New York, NY 10274-0073

Established in 1991 in NY.
Donor: Richard A. Sapp.
Foundation type: Independent foundation.
Financial data (yr. ended 04/30/13): Assets, $9,948,676 (M); expenditures, $590,707; qualifying distributions, $500,000; giving activities include $500,000 for 2 grants (high: $250,000; low: $250,000).
Fields of interest: Education.
Limitations: Applications not accepted. Giving primarily in Carlsbad, CA; some giving also in Duluth, GA. No grants to individuals.
Application information: Contributes only to pre-selected organizations.
Trustees: Richard A. Sapp; Shari M. Sapp.
EIN: 133632757

6797
Louisa Stude Sarofim Foundation ✧
c/o WTAS LLC
1177 Ave. of the Americas, 18th Fl.
New York, NY 10036-2714

Established in 1991.
Donor: Louisa Stude Sarofim.
Foundation type: Independent foundation.
Financial data (yr. ended 12/31/12): Assets, $14,212,928 (M); expenditures, $6,551,964; qualifying distributions, $6,350,000; giving activities include $5,350,000 for 3 grants (high: $5,000,000; low: $100,000).
Purpose and activities: Giving primarily for the arts and education; funding also for an animal shelter medical program.

Fields of interest: Performing arts, music; Arts; Elementary/secondary education; Animal welfare.
Limitations: Applications not accepted. Giving primarily in Sante Fe, NM, and Houston, TX. No grants to individuals.
Application information: Contributes only to pre-selected organizations.
Trustees: Mary L. Porter; Allison Sarofim; Christopher Sarofim; Louisa S. Sarofim.
EIN: 760347329

6798
The Sato Family Foundation, Inc ✧
c/o Colibri
237 W. 37th St., 10th Fl.
New York, NY 10018-5704

Established in 2001 in NY.
Donors: Joseph Wechsler; Samuel Wechsler; MTS Assocs. LLC.
Foundation type: Independent foundation.
Financial data (yr. ended 12/31/13): Assets, $6,041,896 (M); expenditures, $460,452; qualifying distributions, $444,479; giving activities include $441,200 for 15 grants (high: $145,000; low: $200).
Purpose and activities: Giving primarily to Jewish agencies and federated giving programs.
Fields of interest: Minorities/immigrants, centers/services; Jewish federated giving programs; Jewish agencies & synagogues.
Limitations: Applications not accepted. Giving on a national and international basis, with emphasis on Brooklyn, NY, and Antwerp, Belgium.
Application information: Unsolicited requests for funds not accepted.
Directors: Joseph Wechsler; Samuel Wechsler.
EIN: 134140924

6799
Save the Starfish Foundation ✧
(formerly Geds Help Fund Foundation)
625 Rexcorp Plz.
Uniondale, NY 11556-3815
Contact: Scott Rechler, Dir.

Established in 2001 in NY.
Donors: Scott Rechler; Deborah Rechler.
Foundation type: Independent foundation.
Financial data (yr. ended 12/31/13): Assets, $199,561 (M); gifts received, $674,281; expenditures, $910,861; qualifying distributions, $910,861; giving activities include $910,676 for 43 grants (high: $331,741; low: $250).
Fields of interest: Museums (children's); Higher education; Health care; Human services; Family services; Family services, counseling.
Limitations: Applications accepted. Giving primarily in Long Island, NY.
Application information: Application form required.
Initial approach: Proposal
Deadline(s): None
Directors: Jordan Heller; Deborah Rechler; Scott Rechler.
EIN: 113613923

6800
The Schaffner Family Foundation ✧
252 7th Ave., Ste. 17M
New York, NY 10001-7351
E-mail: val@nabigallery.com

Established in 2002 in NY.
Donor: Schaffner Family Foundation.
Foundation type: Independent foundation.
Financial data (yr. ended 12/31/12): Assets, $5,264,005 (M); expenditures, $891,196; qualifying distributions, $751,965; giving activities include $751,965 for grants.
Fields of interest: Arts; Environment; Human services; International affairs.
International interests: Africa; Asia.
Type of support: General/operating support; Continuing support; Annual campaigns; Capital campaigns; Building/renovation; Land acquisition; Emergency funds; Program development; Conferences/seminars; Film/video/radio; Publication; Seed money; Scholarship funds; Research; Matching/challenge support.
Limitations: Applications not accepted. Giving primarily in NY. No grants to individuals.
Application information: Contributes only to pre-selected organizations.
Trustees: Elizabeth B. Schaffner; Timothy Schaffner; Valentine Schaffner.
EIN: 383652881
Selected grants: The following grants are a representative sample of this grantmaker's funding activity:
$50,000 to Greenpeace, Washington, DC, 2012. For Habitat Restoration.
$50,000 to Oxfam America, Washington, DC, 2012. For global education.

6801
Morris and Alma Schapiro Fund ✧
(formerly M. A. Schapiro Fund)
c/o Anchin, Block & Anchin LLP
1375 Broadway
New York, NY 10018-7001
Contact: Richard Baum

Established in 1955 in NY.
Donors: Morris A. Schapiro†; Morris A. Schapiro Charitable Unitrust.
Foundation type: Independent foundation.
Financial data (yr. ended 12/31/13): Assets, $105,990,178 (M); gifts received, $3,424,617; expenditures, $6,471,212; qualifying distributions, $5,631,249; giving activities include $5,566,257 for 107 grants (high: $600,000; low: $5,000).
Purpose and activities: Giving primarily for the arts, education, and to health organizations.
Fields of interest: Arts, formal/general education; Museums (art); Arts; Higher education; Education; Hospitals (general); Health organizations.
Limitations: Applications not accepted. Giving primarily in New York, NY. No grants to individuals.
Application information: Contributes only to pre-selected organizations.
Officers: Daniel E. Schapiro, V.P.; Stephen J. Paluszek, Treas.
EIN: 136089254
Selected grants: The following grants are a representative sample of this grantmaker's funding activity:
$83,333 to New York University, School of Medicine, New York, NY, 2012. For general purposes.
$25,000 to Columbia University, School of the Arts, New York, NY, 2012. For general purposes.
$20,000 to New York University, School of Medicine, New York, NY, 2012. For general purposes.

6802
The Schenectady Foundation ✧
376 Broadway, Fl. 2
Schenectady, NY 12305 (518) 393-9500
Contact: Robert A. Carreau, Exec. Dir.
E-mail: racarreau@schenectadyfoundation.org; Main URL: http://www.schenectadyfoundation.org

Established in 1963 in NY.
Donors: Eleanor F. Green†; Mabel Birdsall†; Agnes Macdonald†; Laura Ayer†; S. Wells Corbin†; John N. Erbacher†; Kathryn Rice†; Martin Rice†; Willis R. Whitney†; Herman Blumer†; Patrick Garey†; Irving Handelman†; Sara Handelman†; Adelaide Parker†; Alice Stackpole†; Charles W. Carl, Jr.†; Edna Wood†; General Electric Foundation.
Foundation type: Community foundation.
Financial data (yr. ended 12/31/13): Assets, $18,310,987 (M); gifts received, $368,689; expenditures, $1,014,679; giving activities include $970,107 for 26+ grants (high: $165,616).
Purpose and activities: The foundation seeks to assist and promote the welfare of Schenectady County, New York and the people who live and/or work there. Support for general charitable purposes; awards scholarships to graduating seniors of Schenectady County, NY, high schools planning to enter the teaching profession.
Fields of interest: Education; Animals/wildlife, preservation/protection; Health care; Youth development; Child development, services; Community/economic development; Engineering/technology; Children.
Type of support: General/operating support; Capital campaigns; Building/renovation; Equipment; Land acquisition; Seed money; Scholarship funds; Research; Matching/challenge support.
Limitations: Applications accepted. Giving limited to Schenectady County, NY. No support for religious organizations for religious purposes. No grants for operating budgets, continuing support, annual campaigns, emergency or deficit financing, general or special endowments, demonstration projects, publications, or conferences or seminars; no loans.
Publications: Application guidelines; Annual report; Grants list; Informational brochure.
Application information: Visit foundation Web site for application guidelines. Application form required.
Initial approach: Letter of Inquiry (no longer than 2 pages)
Copies of proposal: 1
Deadline(s): None
Board meeting date(s): Mar., June, Sept., and Dec.
Officers and Directors:* Jennifer Kenneally,* Chair.; Robert Bylancik,* Vice-Chair.; Deborah Mullaney,* Secy.; Robert T. Cushing,* Co-Treas.; Herbert L. Shultz, Jr.,* Co-Treas.; Michael Ozimek,* Asst. Treas.; Robert A. Carreau, Exec. Dir.; Teresa Little; Joseph Tardi.
Trustee Banks: KeyBank; Trustco Bank.
EIN: 146019650

6803
The Schenker Family Foundation ✧
c/o Curtis Schenker
1175 Park Ave., Apt. 8A
New York, NY 10128-1211

Established in 1998 in NY.
Donors: Curtis Schenker; Leo Schenker; CJS Partnership.
Foundation type: Independent foundation.
Financial data (yr. ended 12/31/12): Assets, $368,284 (M); gifts received, $848,800; expenditures, $593,722; qualifying distributions, $591,992; giving activities include $591,992 for grants.
Purpose and activities: Giving primarily for education, health, children and youth services, social services, and Jewish organizations.
Fields of interest: Education; Health organizations, association; Medical research, institute; Human services; Children/youth, services; Jewish federated giving programs; Jewish agencies & synagogues.
Type of support: General/operating support.
Limitations: Applications not accepted. Giving primarily in the greater metropolitan New York, NY, area. No grants to individuals.
Application information: Contributes only to pre-selected organizations.
Officer: Livia Schenker, Secy.
Directors: Curtis Schenker; Leo Schenker; Jeffrey Schwarz.
EIN: 133992998

6804
The Scherman Foundation, Inc.
16 E. 52nd St., Ste. 601
New York, NY 10022-5306 (212) 832-3086
Contact: Environment, Arts, Strengthening NYC Communities: Mike Pratt, Pres. and Exec. Dir.; Reproductive Rights and Justice, Strenghtening NYC Communities: Alexis Aviles, Prog. Off.; Help with Electronic Applications: Zabrina Collaza, Prog. Asst.; Admin. and Bookkeeping: Catherine Porter
FAX: (212) 838-0154; E-mail: info@scherman.org; Additional e-mail address for applications: submissions@scherman.org. Please type SUPPORT REQUEST in the subject line.; Main URL: http://www.scherman.org
The Scherman Foundation's Philanthropy Promise: http://www.ncrp.org/philanthropys-promise/who

Incorporated in 1941 in NY.
Donors: Katharine S. Rosin†; Karen R. Sollins; Members of the Scherman family.
Foundation type: Independent foundation.
Financial data (yr. ended 12/31/12): Assets, $108,620,554 (M); gifts received, $6,103,625; expenditures, $3,702,806; qualifying distributions, $3,196,835; giving activities include $2,415,100 for 70 grants (high: $90,000; low: $2,000), and $3,250 for employee matching gifts.
Purpose and activities: Grants largely for the environment, reproductive rights and services, human rights and liberties, the arts, and social welfare. In the social welfare field, grants are made to New York City organizations concerned with social justice, community organizing, and community development. Arts grants are limited to New York City.
Fields of interest: Performing arts; Performing arts, dance; Performing arts, theater; Performing arts, music; Environment, alliance/advocacy; Environment, natural resources; Environment, water resources; Environment, energy; Environment; Reproductive health, family planning; Legal services; Human services; Civil/human rights, advocacy; Civil/human rights, minorities; Civil liberties, reproductive rights; Civil/human rights; Community/economic development, alliance/advocacy; Urban/community development; Community/economic development; Minorities; Economically disadvantaged.
Type of support: Annual campaigns; Continuing support; General/operating support; Matching/challenge support; Technical assistance.
Limitations: Applications accepted. Giving in NY and nationally in all areas, except for the arts and social welfare, which is limited to New York City. No support for colleges, universities, or other higher educational institutions. No grants to individuals, or for building or endowment funds, capital campaigns scholarships, fellowships, conferences or symposia, specific media or arts production, medical, science or engineering research.
Publications: Annual report (including application guidelines); Grants list.
Application information: Application guidelines and form available on foundation web site. The foundation does not accept proposals via fax or the Internet. Do not submit video or audio cassettes or CDs, unless requested to do so.
Initial approach: Letter of Intent via foundation web site
Copies of proposal: 1
Deadline(s): Rolling basis for Core Fund and Annual for Rosin Fund (see Grantmaking Programs and Guidelines on foundation web site).
Board meeting date(s): Quarterly
Final notification: Within 8 weeks
Officers and Directors:* Karen R. Sollins,* Chair.; Mike Pratt, Pres.; Susanna Bergtold,* Secy.; Hillary Brown; Miriam Buhl; David R. Jones; Gordon N. Litwin; John J. O'Neil; Marcia Thompson; John Wroclawski.
Number of staff: 2 full-time professional; 2 full-time support.
EIN: 136098464
Selected grants: The following grants are a representative sample of this grantmaker's funding activity:
$90,000 to Center for Reproductive Rights, New York, NY, 2012. For general support 2-year grant.
$80,000 to 350.org, Washington, DC, 2012. For general support. 2-year grant.
$75,000 to Make the Road New York, Brooklyn, NY, 2012. For general support 2-year grant.
$50,000 to CERES, Boston, MA, 2012. For Climate Activities 2-year grant.
$50,000 to MinKwon Center for Community Action, Flushing, NY, 2012. For general support 2-year grant.
$50,000 to National Latina Institute for Reproductive Health, New York, NY, 2012. For general support 2-year grant.
$50,000 to Project on Government Oversight, Washington, DC, 2012. For general support. 2-year grant.
$50,000 to Youth Ministries for Peace and Justice, Bronx, NY, 2012. For general support 2-year grant.
$45,000 to Brooklyn Academy of Music, Brooklyn, NY, 2012. For general support. 2-year grant.
$25,000 to Vineyard Theater and Workshop Center, New York, NY, 2012. For general support. 2-year grant.

6805
The Schiff Foundation
1177 Ave. of the Americas, 42nd Fl.
New York, NY 10036-2714 (212) 655-7044
Contact: David T. Schiff, Pres.
FAX: (212) 259-3896;
E-mail: gorilla@kuhnloebco.com; Additional tel: (212) 259-3800; tel for Peter G. Schiff: (516) 364-5544; e-mail for Peter G. Schiff: pschiff@northwoodventures.com

Incorporated in 1946 in NY.
Donors: John M. Schiff†; Edith B. Schiff†; David T. Schiff; Peter G. Schiff.
Foundation type: Independent foundation.
Financial data (yr. ended 12/31/13): Assets, $12,792,127 (M); expenditures, $731,599; qualifying distributions, $608,845; giving activities include $608,845 for 102 grants (high: $90,000; low: $250).
Purpose and activities: Giving for special medical programs, certain youth and social service agencies, museums, animal welfare, and education; funds substantially committed to organizations of interest to the donors.
Fields of interest: Museums; Arts; Education; Animal welfare; Health care; Human services; Children/youth, services.
Type of support: General/operating support; Annual campaigns; Capital campaigns; Program development.
Limitations: Applications not accepted. Giving primarily in NY. No grants to individuals.
Application information: Contributes only to pre-selected organizations.
Officers and Directors:* David T. Schiff,* Pres.; Peter G. Schiff,* V.P.; Laura A. Gallagher, Secy.; Andrew N. Schiff,* Treas.
EIN: 136088221
Selected grants: The following grants are a representative sample of this grantmaker's funding activity:
$50,000 to Weill Medical College of Cornell University, New York, NY, 2012. For capital campaign.
$30,000 to Hofstra University, Hempstead, NY, 2012. For capital campaign.
$28,250 to Wildlife Conservation Society, Bronx, NY, 2012. For general support.
$25,000 to Deerfield Academy, Deerfield, MA, 2012. For capital campaign.
$25,000 to Lincoln Center for the Performing Arts, New York, NY, 2012. For general support.
$24,700 to Animal Medical Center, New York, NY, 2012. For general support.
$19,500 to Metropolitan Museum of Art, New York, NY, 2012. For general support and acquisitions.
$17,000 to Jazz at Lincoln Center, New York, NY, 2012. For general support.
$12,000 to Saint James Church, New York, NY, 2012. For general support and capital campaign.
$10,000 to Brown University, Providence, RI, 2012. For general support.
$10,000 to Jewish Board of Family and Childrens Services, New York, NY, 2012. For general support.
$7,000 to Metropolitan Opera, New York, NY, 2012. For general support.
$5,000 to Citizens Budget Commission, New York, NY, 2012. For general support.
$5,000 to Henry Street Settlement, New York, NY, 2012. For general support.
$5,000 to Lake Forest College, Lake Forest, IL, 2012. For general support.

$5,000 to Natural Resources Defense Council, New York, NY, 2012. For general support.

6806
Jeannette F. Schlobach Article 4 Trust ✧
c/o Mark Dennis, C.P.A.
504 Haight Ave.
Poughkeepsie, NY 12603-2479

Established in 2001 in NY.
Foundation type: Independent foundation.
Financial data (yr. ended 12/31/13): Assets, $10,889,333 (M); expenditures, $1,701,032; qualifying distributions, $1,579,905; giving activities include $1,579,905 for 8 grants (high: $1,010,000; low: $2,000).
Purpose and activities: Giving primarily for the arts, education, health care, and social services.
Fields of interest: Arts; Higher education; Health care; Human services.
Limitations: Applications not accepted. Giving primarily in NY, with emphasis on Poughkeepsie. No grants to individuals.
Application information: Contributes only to pre-selected organizations.
Trustee: Mark V. Dennis.
EIN: 226863221
Selected grants: The following grants are a representative sample of this grantmaker's funding activity:
$29,799 to Grace Smith House, Poughkeepsie, NY, 2012. For domestic.

6807
Schlosstein Hartley Foundation ✧
c/o Barry M. Strauss Assocs., Ltd.
307 5th Ave., 8th Fl.
New York, NY 10016-6517

Established in 2000 in NY.
Donor: Ralph L. Schlosstein.
Foundation type: Independent foundation.
Financial data (yr. ended 09/30/13): Assets, $6,921,577 (M); gifts received, $1,449; expenditures, $686,138; qualifying distributions, $676,210; giving activities include $674,500 for 64 grants (high: $140,000; low: $100).
Purpose and activities: Giving primarily for higher and other education, as well as for the arts, health organizations, and social services.
Fields of interest: Arts; Higher education; Education; Health organizations, association; Human services; Social sciences, public policy.
Limitations: Applications not accepted. Giving primarily in NY. No grants to individuals.
Application information: Unsolicited requests for funds not accepted.
Trustees: Jane Hartley; Ralph L. Schlosstein.
EIN: 137268307
Selected grants: The following grants are a representative sample of this grantmaker's funding activity:
$200,000 to Dartmouth College, Hanover, NH, 2011. For general support.
$30,000 to Mayors Fund to Advance New York City, New York, NY, 2011. For general support.
$20,000 to Council on Foreign Relations, New York, NY, 2011. For general support.
$16,000 to Conservation International, Arlington, VA, 2011. For general support.
$5,000 to City University of New York, New York, NY, 2011. For general support.
$5,000 to Malaria No More, New York, NY, 2011. For general support.

6808
The Kilian J. and Caroline F. Schmitt Foundation, Inc. ✧ ☆
1570 East Ave.
Rochester, NY 14610 (585) 244-4821
Contact: Alfred M. Hallenbeck, Secy.
E-mail: ahallenbeck83@gmail.com

Established in 1991 in NY as successor to Kilian J. and Caroline F. Schmitt Foundation.
Donors: Kilian J. Schmitt†; Caroline F. Schmitt†.
Foundation type: Independent foundation.
Financial data (yr. ended 02/28/13): Assets, $11,423,577 (M); expenditures, $621,860; qualifying distributions, $567,924; giving activities include $515,086 for 33 grants (high: $215,000; low: $500).
Purpose and activities: Giving primarily for higher education, health care, and human services.
Fields of interest: Performing arts, orchestras; Higher education; Health care; Medical research; Human services; American Red Cross.
Type of support: General/operating support; Annual campaigns; Capital campaigns; Equipment; Endowments.
Limitations: Applications accepted. Giving primarily in the metropolitan Rochester, NY, area. No grants to individuals.
Application information: Application form required.
Initial approach: Completed application form
Deadline(s): None
Officers: Robert H. Fella, Pres.; Alfred M. Hallenbeck, Secy.; Gary J. Lindsay, Treas.
Directors: James R. Dray; Leon Fella; Megan Henry; James D. Ryan, Jr.
EIN: 223087449
Selected grants: The following grants are a representative sample of this grantmaker's funding activity:
$215,000 to University of Rochester, Rochester, NY, 2011.
$5,000 to Veterans Outreach Center, Rochester, NY, 2011. For operating funds.
$4,000 to Rochester Institute of Technology, Rochester, NY, 2011.
$2,000 to Susan B. Anthony House, Rochester, NY, 2011. For operating funds.
$1,500 to Rochester Museum and Science Center, Rochester, NY, 2011.
$1,000 to Cameron Community Ministries, Rochester, NY, 2011. For operating funds.
$1,000 to Lifetime Assistance Foundation, Rochester, NY, 2011.
$1,000 to Lifetime Care, Rochester, NY, 2011.
$1,000 to Memorial Sloan-Kettering Cancer Center, New York, NY, 2011.
$1,000 to University of Rochester Medical Center, Rochester, NY, 2011. For operating funds.

6809
Adolph & Ruth Schnurmacher Foundation, Inc. ✧
551 5th Ave., Ste. 1210
New York, NY 10176-1299
Contact: Janet Plotkin, Pres.
FAX: (212) 972-2303;
E-mail: arsfoundation@gmail.com; Additional e-mail: info@arsfoundation.com; Main URL: http://www.arsfoundation.com

Established in 1977 in NY.
Donors: Adolph Schnurmacher†; Ruth Schnurmacher†.
Foundation type: Independent foundation.
Financial data (yr. ended 12/31/13): Assets, $21,206,441 (M); expenditures, $1,957,753; qualifying distributions, $1,764,190; giving activities include $1,422,900 for 127 grants (high: $63,500; low: $250).
Purpose and activities: The foundation's mission is to make a positive difference in the lives of others. It has a variety of focuses including (but not limited to) human and social services, the arts, children and the elderly, and health care.
Fields of interest: Arts; Education; Health organizations, association; Human services; Public affairs.
Type of support: General/operating support; Continuing support; Annual campaigns; Equipment; Emergency funds; Curriculum development; Scholarship funds; Research; Matching/challenge support.
Limitations: Applications accepted. Giving in the metropolitan New York, NY, area, including Fairfield County, CT. No support for political organizations. No grants to individuals.
Publications: IRS Form 990 or 990-PF printed copy available upon request.
Application information: Applicants should not submit tapes, compact disks or DVDs unless requested to do so. Application form not required.
Initial approach: Letter
Copies of proposal: 1
Deadline(s): None
Board meeting date(s): 6 to 8 times a year
Final notification: None
Officers and Trustees:* Janet Plotkin,* Pres.; Amanda Plotkin,* V.P.; Carolyn Plotkin,* V.P.; Jonathan Plotkin,* V.P.; Fred Plotkin,* Secy.-Treas.
Number of staff: 1 full-time support; 4 part-time support.
EIN: 132938935
Selected grants: The following grants are a representative sample of this grantmaker's funding activity:
$57,500 to Levitt Pavilion, Friends of the, Westport, CT, 2011.
$50,000 to Fairfield University, Fairfield, CT, 2011. For program support.
$43,500 to Salvation Army of Greater New York, New York, NY, 2011. For program support and relief.
$35,000 to Optometric Center of New York, New York, NY, 2011. For merit scholarships.
$25,000 to Anti-Defamation League of Bnai Brith, New York, NY, 2011. For general support.
$15,000 to AmeriCares Free Clinics, Stamford, CT, 2011. For general support.
$15,000 to Mid-Fairfield Child Guidance Center, Norwalk, CT, 2011. For program support.

6810
Charles and Mildred Schnurmacher Foundation, Inc. ✧
155 E. 55th St., Ste. 6J
New York, NY 10022-4020 (212) 838-7766
Contact: Ira J. Weinstein, Pres.

FAX: (212) 888-7360;
E-mail: grants@charlesandmildred.org; Main URL: http://www.charlesandmildred.org

Established in 1977 in NY.
Donor: Charles M. Schnurmacher‡.
Foundation type: Independent foundation.
Financial data (yr. ended 12/31/13): Assets, $15,973,578 (M); expenditures, $1,614,558; qualifying distributions, $1,397,897; giving activities include $1,055,500 for 96 grants (high: $125,000; low: $250).
Purpose and activities: Support primarily for music organizations, art therapy, social services, health care, Jewish agencies and temples, food banks, animal spay-neuter programs, botanical gardens and garden restoration. Limited funding for mental health treatment.
Fields of interest: Arts; Education; Botanical gardens; Animal population control; Hospitals (general); Mental health, treatment; Medical research, institute; Food banks; Human services, victim aid; Jewish federated giving programs; Jewish agencies & synagogues; Children; Physically disabled; Deaf/hearing impaired; Native Americans/American Indians; Crime/abuse victims; Homeless; Gay men.
Type of support: General/operating support; Continuing support; Management development/capacity building; Equipment; Emergency funds; Program development; Publication; Seed money; Curriculum development; Internship funds; Scholarship funds; Research; Technical assistance; Matching/challenge support.
Limitations: Applications accepted. Giving limited to the metropolitan New York, NY area, and southern CA but all requests will be considered. No grants to individuals or charities without an IRS determination letter.
Publications: Annual report; Grants list.
Application information: Application information available on foundation web site. Application form not required.
Initial approach: Letter (preferred)
Copies of proposal: 3
Deadline(s): None
Board meeting date(s): 6 times per year, and special meetings as needed
Final notification: Up to 2 months
Officers and Directors:* Ira J. Weinstein,* Pres.; Barbara Packer, Esq.*, V.P. and Secy.; Peter Weinstein, DVM*, V.P.
Number of staff: 1 part-time support.
EIN: 132937218

6811
Schon Family Foundation ✧
1534 53rd St.
Brooklyn, NY 11204

Established in 1992 in NY.
Donors: Henry A. Schon; Baron Schon; Heidi Gelley; Abraham Shaulson; Mesivta Torah Institute; Anna Schon; Eli Weinstein; Henna Two LLC.
Foundation type: Independent foundation.
Financial data (yr. ended 12/31/13): Assets, $21,836,479 (M); gifts received, $650,000; expenditures, $1,131,800; qualifying distributions, $1,078,918; giving activities include $1,074,760 for 43 grants (high: $202,700; low: $250).
Purpose and activities: Giving primarily to Jewish temples and schools.
Fields of interest: Education; Jewish agencies & synagogues.
Limitations: Applications not accepted. Giving primarily in Brooklyn, NY. No grants to individuals.
Application information: Contributes only to pre-selected organizations.
Officers: Henry A. Schon, Pres.; Anna Schon, V.P.; Heidi Gelley, Secy.
Director: Baron Schon.
EIN: 113133066

6812
A. and R. Schonberger Family Foundation, Inc. ✧ ☆
5117 14th Ave.
Brooklyn, NY 11219-3628

Donor: Alfred Schonberger.
Foundation type: Independent foundation.
Financial data (yr. ended 12/31/12): Assets, $1,377,175 (M); gifts received, $458,333; expenditures, $529,751; qualifying distributions, $527,800; giving activities include $527,800 for grants.
Limitations: Applications not accepted.
Application information: Unsolicited requests for funds not accepted.
Officers: A. Schonberger, Pres.; N. Tessler, Secy.; J. Schonberger, Treas.
EIN: 861144704

6813
The Schumann Media Center, Inc. ✧
(formerly The Schumann Center for Media and Democracy, Inc.)
250 W. 57th St., Ste. 715
New York, NY 10107-0003
Contact: Lynn C. Welhorsky, V.P., Admin.

Incorporated in 1961 in NJ.
Donors: Florence F. Schumann‡; John J. Schumann, Jr.‡.
Foundation type: Independent foundation.
Financial data (yr. ended 12/31/12): Assets, $29,034,683 (M); expenditures, $4,542,620; qualifying distributions, $4,397,115; giving activities include $2,878,770 for 20 grants (high: $750,000; low: $3,770).
Purpose and activities: Grants for programs in effective governance and the environment.
Fields of interest: Media/communications; Higher education; Public affairs, citizen participation.
Type of support: General/operating support; Continuing support; Program development; Matching/challenge support.
Limitations: Applications not accepted. Giving primarily in New York, NY; some funding nationally. No grants to individuals, or for annual campaigns, capital campaigns, deficit financing, equipment and materials, land acquisition, or endowment funds; no loans.
Application information: Currently, the foundation is not accepting any proposals for consideration.
Board meeting date(s): Feb., June, and Oct.
Officers and Trustees:* Joan Konner,* Chair.; Bill D. Moyers,* Pres.; Lynn C. Welhorsky, V.P., Admin.; Michael J. Johnston,* V.P.; Beth Yingling, Secy.-Treas.; W. Ford Schumann,* Chair. Emeritus; David S. Bate, Trustee Emeritus; Robert M. Herbert; R. Ford Schumann.
Number of staff: 2 full-time professional.
EIN: 226044214

6814
Schwartz Family Foundation ✧
c/o BCRS Assocs., LLC
77 Water St., 9th Fl.
New York, NY 10005-4414

Established in 1991 in NY.
Donors: Mark Schwartz; Lisa Schwartz.
Foundation type: Independent foundation.
Financial data (yr. ended 04/30/13): Assets, $2,664,213 (M); expenditures, $1,511,690; qualifying distributions, $1,511,690; giving activities include $1,510,910 for 9 grants (high: $500,000; low: $800).
Purpose and activities: Giving primarily for higher education, hospitals and human services.
Fields of interest: Higher education; Hospitals (general); Human services; Foundations (private grantmaking).
Limitations: Applications not accepted. Giving primarily in Bedford, Katonah, Mount Kisco, and New York, NY; funding also in Cambridge and Boston, MA. No grants to individuals, or for scholarships; no loans.
Application information: Contributes only to pre-selected organizations.
Trustees: Lisa H. Schwartz; Mark Schwartz.
EIN: 133632755
Selected grants: The following grants are a representative sample of this grantmaker's funding activity:
$500,000 to Massachusetts General Hospital, Boston, MA, 2012.
$500,000 to Massachusetts General Hospital, Boston, MA, 2012.
$500,000 to Massachusetts General Hospital, Boston, MA, 2012.
$500,000 to Massachusetts General Hospital, Boston, MA, 2012.
$50,000 to Harvard University, Cambridge, MA, 2012.
$30,000 to Westchester Land Trust, Bedford Hills, NY, 2012.
$25,000 to Westchester Land Trust, Bedford Hills, NY, 2012.
$10,000 to Community Center, Katonah, NY, 2012.
$3,250 to Culinary Institute of America, Hyde Park, NY, 2012.
$1,000 to Katonah Village Library, Katonah, NY, 2012.

6815
Schwartz Family Foundation ✧
c/o Alan Schwartz Guggenheim Partners
330 Madison Ave., 15th Fl.
New York, NY 10017-5032
Contact: Alan Schwartz, Tr.

Established in 1997 in NY.
Donors: Alan D. Schwartz; Nancy M. Seaman.
Foundation type: Independent foundation.
Financial data (yr. ended 12/31/12): Assets, $20,086,830 (M); gifts received, $2,394,150; expenditures, $1,807,974; qualifying distributions, $1,748,700; giving activities include $1,748,700 for grants.
Purpose and activities: Giving primarily for education, health organizations, social services.

Fields of interest: Higher education; Education; Health organizations, association; Human services; Children/youth, services; Foundations (private grantmaking).
Limitations: Applications not accepted. Giving in the U.S., with strong emphasis on NC and NY. No grants to individuals.
Application information: Contributes only to pre-selected organizations.
Trustees: Alan D. Schwartz; Nancy M. Seaman.
EIN: 137138217

6816
The Eric & Erica Schwartz Family Foundation ✧
(formerly Schwartz Foundation)
Bowling Green Sta.
P.O. Box 73
New York, NY 10274-0073

Established in 1996 in NY.
Donor: Eric S. Schwartz.
Foundation type: Independent foundation.
Financial data (yr. ended 08/31/13): Assets, $8,224,050 (M); gifts received, $1,521,509; expenditures, $1,787,316; qualifying distributions, $1,780,300; giving activities include $1,780,300 for 18 grants (high: $525,000; low: $500).
Fields of interest: Libraries (public); Education; Human services; Jewish federated giving programs; Jewish agencies & synagogues.
Limitations: Applications not accepted. Giving primarily in NY and Washington, DC. No grants to individuals, or for scholarships; no loans.
Application information: Contributes only to pre-selected organizations.
Trustees: Eric S. Schwartz; Erica Schwartz.
EIN: 133957291

6817
Peter A. and Marion W. Schwartz Family Foundation Trust ✧
5337 Black Point Rd.
Canandaigua, NY 14424-8217

Established in 1997 in CT.
Donors: Peter A. Schwartz; Marion W. Schwartz.
Foundation type: Independent foundation.
Financial data (yr. ended 12/31/13): Assets, $26,720,030 (M); gifts received, $257,500; expenditures, $1,287,554; qualifying distributions, $1,219,059; giving activities include $1,219,059 for 59 grants (high: $225,000; low: $1,000).
Purpose and activities: Giving primarily for the arts, education, and human services.
Fields of interest: Museums (natural history); Higher education; Cancer; Medical research; Human services.
Limitations: Applications not accepted. Giving primarily in CT and NY. No grants to individuals.
Application information: Contributes only to pre-selected organizations.
Trustees: Marion W. Schwartz; Peter A. Schwartz.
EIN: 066447457
Selected grants: The following grants are a representative sample of this grantmaker's funding activity:
$35,000 to Multiple Sclerosis Society, National, New York, NY, 2011. For general support.
$10,000 to Autism Speaks, New York, NY, 2011. For general support.
$10,000 to Volunteers of America, Alexandria, VA, 2011. For general support.

6818
Deborah and Daniel Schwartz Foundation ✧
c/o Daniel Schwartz
767 5th Ave., 17th Fl.
New York, NY 10153-0028

Established in 1999 in NY.
Donors: Daniel Schwartz; Deborah Schwartz.
Foundation type: Independent foundation.
Financial data (yr. ended 06/30/13): Assets, $16,553,094 (M); gifts received, $2,000,000; expenditures, $2,434,291; qualifying distributions, $2,244,026; giving activities include $2,244,026 for 42 grants (high: $360,000; low: $26).
Fields of interest: Higher education; Education; Jewish federated giving programs; Jewish agencies & synagogues.
Limitations: Applications not accepted. Giving primarily in New York, NY. No grants to individuals.
Application information: Contributes only to pre-selected organizations.
Officers: Daniel Schwartz, Pres.; Deborah Schwartz, Secy.
Director: Gabriella Major.
EIN: 134089802
Selected grants: The following grants are a representative sample of this grantmaker's funding activity:
$200,000 to American Friends of Shalva, New York, NY, 2011.
$100,000 to Salanter Akiba Riverdale Academy, Riverdale, NY, 2011.

6819
The Donna and Marvin Schwartz Foundation ✧
c/o Neuberger & Berman
605 3rd Ave.
New York, NY 10158-3698

Established in 1997 in NY.
Donors: Donna Schwartz; Marvin C. Schwartz.
Foundation type: Independent foundation.
Financial data (yr. ended 04/30/13): Assets, $94,730,892 (M); expenditures, $4,627,315; qualifying distributions, $4,434,461; giving activities include $4,434,461 for 92+ grants (high: $1,500,000).
Purpose and activities: Giving primarily for the arts, Jewish federated giving programs, education, health and human services.
Fields of interest: Museums; Performing arts, opera; Arts; Higher education; Environment, natural resources; Health organizations, association; Medical research, institute; Cancer research; Human services; Community/economic development; United Ways and Federated Giving Programs; Jewish federated giving programs; Jewish agencies & synagogues.
Limitations: Applications not accepted. Giving primarily in NY, with emphasis on the greater metropolitan New York, NY, area, including Long Island and Westchester. No grants to individuals.
Application information: Contributes only to pre-selected organizations.
Trustees: Donna Schwartz; Marvin C. Schwartz.
EIN: 137114848

6820
Scotts Miracle-Gro Foundation ✧
c/o Rob McMahon
800 Port Washington Blvd.
Port Washington, NY 11050-3720

Established in 2001 in OH.
Donors: The Hagedorn Family Foundation, Inc.; The Scotts Company, Inc.; Hagedorn Partnership LP; The Scotts Miracle-Gro Co.
Foundation type: Company-sponsored foundation.
Financial data (yr. ended 12/31/13): Assets, $137,360 (M); gifts received, $633,333; expenditures, $532,146; qualifying distributions, $488,908; giving activities include $488,908 for 2 grants (high: $418,908; low: $70,000).
Fields of interest: Children, services.
Limitations: Applications not accepted. Giving primarily in NY. No grants to individuals.
Application information: Contributes only to pre-selected organizations.
Officers and Directors:* Sue Hagedorn,* Pres.; Rob McMahon,* Secy.-Treas.; Jim Hagedorn; Larry Hilsheimer; Su Lok; Hope Reeves.
EIN: 311799491
Selected grants: The following grants are a representative sample of this grantmaker's funding activity:
$360,000 to Ohio College Access Network, Columbus, OH, 2012. To assist with college applications.

6821
The Thomas P. & Cynthia D. Sculco Foundation ✧
c/o Cynthia D. Sculco
132 E. 95th St.
New York, NY 10128-1705 (212) 606-1777
Contact: Thomas P. Sculco M.D., Pres.

Established in 1997 in NY.
Donors: Thomas P. Sculco, M.D.; Cynthia D. Sculco.
Foundation type: Independent foundation.
Financial data (yr. ended 02/28/13): Assets, $13,635,794 (M); gifts received, $859,552; expenditures, $606,390; qualifying distributions, $518,914; giving activities include $518,914 for grants.
Purpose and activities: Giving primarily for education.
Fields of interest: Performing arts, theater; Performing arts, opera; Higher education; Hospitals (general); Arthritis.
Limitations: Applications accepted. Giving primarily in NY. No grants to individuals.
Application information: Application form required.
Initial approach: Letter
Deadline(s): None
Officers: Thomas P. Sculco, M.D., Pres.; Cynthia D. Sculco, Secy.
EIN: 133952927

6822
The Scully-Peretsman Foundation ✧
9 E. 79th St.
New York, NY 10075-0123

Established in 1997 in NY.
Donors: Robert W. Scully; Nancy B. Peretsman.
Foundation type: Independent foundation.

Financial data (yr. ended 12/31/13): Assets, $46,417,142 (M); expenditures, $5,814,040; qualifying distributions, $5,445,369; giving activities include $5,445,369 for 44 grants (high: $2,041,052; low: $639).
Fields of interest: Education; Human services.
Limitations: Applications not accepted. Giving primarily in New York, NY. No grants to individuals.
Application information: Contributes only to pre-selected organizations.
Trustees: Nancy B. Peretsman; Emma C. Scully; Robert W. Scully.
EIN: 133982344
Selected grants: The following grants are a representative sample of this grantmaker's funding activity:
$3,140,178 to Princeton University, Princeton, NJ, 2011. For grant made in form of stock.
$2,041,052 to Princeton University, Princeton, NJ, 2013. For grant made in form of stock.
$1,293,470 to Princeton University, Princeton, NJ, 2012. For grant made in form of stock.
$1,020,526 to Institute for Advanced Study, Princeton, NJ, 2013. For grant made in form of stock.
$1,020,526 to Teach for America, New York, NY, 2013. For grant made in form of stock.
$744,165 to Teach for America, New York, NY, 2012. For grant made in form of stock.
$523,365 to Metropolitan Museum of Art, New York, NY, 2011. For grant made in form of stock.
$471,012 to Metropolitan Museum of Art, New York, NY, 2013. For grant made in form of stock.
$418,692 to Teach for America, New York, NY, 2011. For grant made in form of stock.
$250,000 to Harvard University, Cambridge, MA, 2013. For grant to School of Business in Boston.
$132,174 to American Museum of Natural History, New York, NY, 2012. For grant made in form of stock.
$99,637 to New Schools Fund, Oakland, CA, 2012. For grant made in form of stock.
$94,000 to Educators for Excellence, New York, NY, 2013. For grant made in form of stock.
$94,000 to Teach for All, New York, NY, 2013. For grant made in form of stock.
$93,664 to Education Reform Now, New York, NY, 2011. For grant made in form of stock.
$86,000 to Educators for Excellence, New York, NY, 2012.
$80,418 to New Leaders for New Schools, New York, NY, 2011. For grant made in form of stock.
$78,419 to New School, New York, NY, 2011. For grant made in form of stock.
$75,000 to American Museum of Natural History, New York, NY, 2013.
$75,000 to Lincoln Center for the Performing Arts, New York, NY, 2011.
$51,569 to Teach for America, New York, NY, 2011. For grant made in form of stock.
$50,000 to Harvard University, Cambridge, MA, 2012.
$25,000 to Advocates for Children of New York, New York, NY, 2013.
$25,000 to Association of Art Museum Curators Foundation, New York, NY, 2012.
$23,500 to Young Womens Leadership Foundation, New York, NY, 2013. For grant made in form of stock.
$15,000 to Young Womens Leadership Foundation, New York, NY, 2012.
$13,096 to New School, New York, NY, 2012.
$12,892 to Metropolitan Opera, New York, NY, 2011. For grant made in form of stock.
$10,000 to Museum of American Finance, New York, NY, 2011.
$10,000 to Saint Johns University, Jamaica, NY, 2012.

6823
The SDA Foundation ✧
c/o Goldberg Lindsay & Co. LLC
630 5th Ave., 30th Fl.
New York, NY 10111-0001 (212) 651-1100

Established in 2000 in NY.
Donor: Alan E. Goldberg.
Foundation type: Independent foundation.
Financial data (yr. ended 12/31/13): Assets, $7,153 (M); gifts received, $5,520,000; expenditures, $5,513,695; qualifying distributions, $5,499,094; giving activities include $5,498,934 for 32 grants (high: $760,000; low: $1,000).
Purpose and activities: Giving primarily for health care, particularly hospitals and medical research, as well as for Jewish education and to Jewish organizations.
Fields of interest: Higher education; Education; Hospitals (general); Medical research, institute; Cancer research; Human services; Jewish federated giving programs; Jewish agencies & synagogues.
Limitations: Applications accepted. Giving primarily in New York, NY. No grants to individuals.
Application information:
Initial approach: Letter
Deadline(s): None
Trustees: Alan E. Goldberg; Miriam P. Goldberg.
EIN: 137235530
Selected grants: The following grants are a representative sample of this grantmaker's funding activity:
$3,699,000 to Yeshiva University, New York, NY, 2012. For general support.
$920,000 to Mount Sinai Hospital, New York, NY, 2012. For general support.
$500,000 to New York-Presbyterian Hospital, New York, NY, 2012. For general support.
$300,000 to Riverdale Jewish Center, Bronx, NY, 2012. For general support.
$250,000 to Congregation Agudath Israel of Boro Park, Brooklyn, NY, 2012. For general support.
$250,000 to Ohr Torah Institutions of Israel, New York, NY, 2012. For general support.
$105,000 to Young Israel of Riverdale, Bronx, NY, 2012. For general support.
$100,000 to Israel Healthcare Foundation, New York, NY, 2012. For general support.
$100,000 to Jewish Center of Atlantic Beach, Atlantic Beach, NY, 2012. For general support.
$100,000 to Rabbi Isaac Elchanan Theological Seminary, New York, NY, 2012. For general support.

6824
The Sealark Foundation, Inc. ✧
c/o Bessemer Trust Co., N.A.
630 5th Ave.
New York, NY 10111-0001

Established in 1997 in DE.
Donor: James M. Clark.
Foundation type: Independent foundation.
Financial data (yr. ended 12/31/13): Assets, $22,786,934 (M); expenditures, $1,104,236; qualifying distributions, $1,015,181; giving activities include $1,015,000 for 7 grants (high: $200,000; low: $15,000).
Purpose and activities: Giving primarily for education and for oceanographic research.
Fields of interest: Education; Health care; Marine science.
Limitations: Applications not accepted. Giving primarily in CT, MA, and TX. No grants to individuals.
Application information: Contributes only to pre-selected organizations.
Board meeting date(s): Varies
Officers: James M. Clark, Pres.; James M. Clark, Jr., V.P. and Secy.; Mrs. James M. Clark, Treas.
Number of staff: None.
EIN: 133747240
Selected grants: The following grants are a representative sample of this grantmaker's funding activity:
$100,000 to Saint Alcuin Montessori School, Dallas, TX, 2011.
$15,000 to Waveny Care Center, New Canaan, CT, 2011.

6825
Beatrice & Samuel A. Seaver Foundation ✧
c/o WithumSmith+Brown, PC
1411 Broadway, 9th Fl.
New York, NY 10018-3496

Established in 1986 in NY.
Donors: Beatrice Seaver‡; John Cohen.
Foundation type: Independent foundation.
Financial data (yr. ended 11/30/13): Assets, $91,270,989 (M); expenditures, $4,554,410; qualifying distributions, $4,370,671; giving activities include $3,422,867 for 56 grants (high: $1,000,000; low: $500).
Purpose and activities: Giving primarily for medical education and research, hospitals, cancer care, human services, and Jewish organizations.
Fields of interest: Hospitals (general); Genetic diseases and disorders research; Autism research; Jewish agencies & synagogues.
Type of support: Research.
Limitations: Applications not accepted. Giving primarily in New York, NY. No grants to individuals.
Application information: Contributes only to pre-selected organizations.
Trustees: John Cohen; Hirschell E. Levine.
EIN: 133251432

6826
Sebonack Foundation ✧ ☆
270 S. Service Rd., Ste. 45
Melville, NY 11747-2339 (631) 622-9401
Contact: Christine Tourtoulis

Established in NY.
Donor: Michael C. Pascucci.
Foundation type: Independent foundation.
Financial data (yr. ended 09/30/13): Assets, $3,816,689 (M); expenditures, $1,161,352; qualifying distributions, $1,161,063; giving activities include $1,153,248 for 25 grants (high: $245,000; low: $250).
Fields of interest: Higher education; Human services; Economically disadvantaged.
Limitations: Applications accepted. Giving primarily in NY; funding also in PA. No grants to individuals.
Application information: Application form required.

Initial approach: Completed application form
Deadline(s): None
Officers and Directors:* Michael C. Pascucci,* Pres.; Christopher S. Pascucci,* V.P.; Ralph P. Pascucci,* V.P.; Peter I. Cavallaro, Secy.; Charles E. Becker, Jr., Treas.
EIN: 205411954

6827
Secunda Family Foundation, Inc. ✧
c/o Geller & Co.
P.O. Box 1510
New York, NY 10150-1510
Thomas and Cynthia Secunda's Giving Pledge Profile: http://glasspockets.org/philanthropy-in-focus/eye-on-the-giving-pledge/profiles/secunda

Established in 2006 in DE.
Donor: Thomas F. Secunda.
Foundation type: Independent foundation.
Financial data (yr. ended 12/31/12): Assets, $88,722,915 (M); gifts received, $44,995,013; expenditures, $3,775,187; qualifying distributions, $3,574,405; giving activities include $3,551,000 for 31 grants (high: $1,500,000; low: $2,000).
Fields of interest: Performing arts; Higher education; Education; Environment; Health organizations; Jewish federated giving programs.
Limitations: Applications not accepted. Giving primarily in NY and Washington, DC; some funding also in MD. No grants to individuals.
Application information: Contributes only to pre-selected organizations.
Officers: Thomas F. Secunda, Pres. and Treas.; Cynthia Secunda, V.P. and Secy.
EIN: 205968142
Selected grants: The following grants are a representative sample of this grantmaker's funding activity:
$1,500,000 to National Parks Conservation Association, Washington, DC, 2012. For Advocacy, Endowment for N/E Regional Office, Unrestricted.
$5,000 to National Parks Conservation Association, Washington, DC, 2012. For general purposes contribution - Ted Smith Memorial Fund.

6828
The Nathan & Lena Seiler Family Foundation Inc. ✧
c/o Lenat Co.
315 Westchester Ave.
Port Chester, NY 10573-3868

Established in 1981 in NY.
Donors: Lena Seiler†; Nathan Seiler.
Foundation type: Independent foundation.
Financial data (yr. ended 12/31/13): Assets, $4,397,976 (M); expenditures, $594,992; qualifying distributions, $553,960; giving activities include $553,960 for 39 grants (high: $100,000; low: $500).
Purpose and activities: Giving primarily to Jewish organizations, temples, and schools.
Fields of interest: Education; Human services; Jewish federated giving programs; Jewish agencies & synagogues.
Limitations: Applications not accepted. Giving primarily in the greater New York, NY, area. No grants to individuals.
Application information: Unsolicited requests for funds not accepted.
Officers: Gloria S. Deitsch, Pres.; Irving Kaplan, V.P. and Secy.; Betty S. Cohen, Treas.
EIN: 133106906
Selected grants: The following grants are a representative sample of this grantmaker's funding activity:
$10,000 to Innocence Project, New York, NY, 2011.

6829
Select Equity Group Foundation ✧
380 Lafayette St., 6th Fl.
New York, NY 10003-6933
Contact: Robert Wilson, Exec. Dir.
E-mail: rwilson@selectequity.com; Main URL: https://www.selectequity.com/foundation.aspx

Established in 2000 in NY.
Donor: Select Equity Group, Inc.
Foundation type: Company-sponsored foundation.
Financial data (yr. ended 12/31/12): Assets, $1,582,431 (M); expenditures, $1,801,655; qualifying distributions, $1,798,276; giving activities include $1,503,295 for 312 grants (high: $75,000; low: $45).
Purpose and activities: The foundation supports organizations involved with arts and culture, education, the environment, health, cancer, kidney disease, human services, youth development, international economic development, and civil and human rights.
Fields of interest: Arts; Secondary school/education; Education; Environment, water resources; Environment; Health care; Cancer; Kidney diseases; Youth development; Children, services; Human services; International economic development; Civil/human rights.
Type of support: General/operating support; Program development; Scholarship funds; Employee matching gifts.
Limitations: Applications not accepted. Giving primarily in AL, CA, MA, IL, NJ, TX, and VA, with emphasis on NY. No grants to individuals.
Application information: Contributes only to pre-selected organizations. Preference is given to organizations endorsed by Select Equity employees.
Board meeting date(s): Four times a year
Trustees: John Britton; George S. Loening; Darren Seirer; Amor Towles.
EIN: 134148796
Selected grants: The following grants are a representative sample of this grantmaker's funding activity:
$75,000 to Childrens Aid Society, New York, NY, 2011.
$75,000 to Row New York, Long Island City, NY, 2011.
$50,000 to Equal Justice Initiative of Alabama, Montgomery, AL, 2011.
$50,000 to TEAK Fellowship, New York, NY, 2011.
$41,875 to Damon Runyon Cancer Research Foundation, New York, NY, 2011.
$30,000 to Publicolor, New York, NY, 2011.
$26,850 to Charity: Water, New York, NY, 2011.
$18,450 to Posse Foundation, New York, NY, 2011.
$18,000 to Harlem RBI, New York, NY, 2011.
$15,600 to New York Theater Workshop, New York, NY, 2011.

6830
Selz Foundation, Inc. ✧
c/o Selz Capital
1370 Ave. of the Americas, 24th Fl.
New York, NY 10019-4602 (212) 554-5044
Contact: Bernard T. Selz, Pres.

Established in 1983 in NY.
Donors: Bernard T. Selz; Ermitage Selz Fund.
Foundation type: Independent foundation.
Financial data (yr. ended 12/31/13): Assets, $151,690,630 (M); gifts received, $7,387,949; expenditures, $8,094,904; qualifying distributions, $8,094,904; giving activities include $8,000,978 for 133+ grants (high: $1,300,000).
Fields of interest: Museums; Arts; Education; Environment, natural resources; Animals/wildlife; Children/youth, services.
Type of support: General/operating support; Program development; Professorships.
Limitations: Applications not accepted. Giving primarily in NY. No grants to individuals.
Application information: Unsolicited requests for funds not accepted.
Officers and Directors:* Bernard T. Selz,* Pres.; Arnold Syrop,* V.P.; Lisa Selz, Secy.-Treas.
Number of staff: 3 part-time support.
EIN: 133180806

6831
Semlitz/Glaser Foundation ✧ ☆
1 Gracie Sq., Apt. 11
New York, NY 10028-8001

Established in 1991 in NY.
Donors: Stephen M. Semlitz; Cathy Glaser.
Foundation type: Independent foundation.
Financial data (yr. ended 04/30/13): Assets, $2,564 (M); gifts received, $521,000; expenditures, $503,476; qualifying distributions, $499,951; giving activities include $499,951 for 25 grants (high: $443,077; low: $36).
Purpose and activities: Giving primarily for medical research, particularly to a foundation for migraine research; funding also for education and human services.
Fields of interest: Arts; Education; Health care; Health organizations; Medical research, institute; Food distribution, meals on wheels; Human services; Children/youth, services; United Ways and Federated Giving Programs; Jewish agencies & synagogues.
Type of support: Continuing support; Annual campaigns; Capital campaigns; Building/renovation; Equipment; Emergency funds; Curriculum development; Scholarship funds; Research.
Limitations: Applications not accepted. Giving primarily in New York, NY. No grants to individuals.
Application information: Contributes only to pre-selected organizations.
Trustees: Cathy Glaser; Stephen M. Semlitz.
EIN: 133632754
Selected grants: The following grants are a representative sample of this grantmaker's funding activity:
$300,000 to Migraine Research Foundation, New York, NY, 2011.

6832
Seneca Foods Foundation ✧
3736 S. Main St.
Marion, NY 14505-9751 (315) 926-8100
Contact: Kraig H. Kayser, C.E.O. and Pres.
E-mail: foundation@senecafoods.com; Main URL: http://www.senecafoods.com/seneca-foods-foundation

Established in 1988 in NY.
Donor: Seneca Foods Corp.
Foundation type: Company-sponsored foundation.
Financial data (yr. ended 03/31/14): Assets, $5,031,835 (M); gifts received, $2,000,000; expenditures, $2,289,423; qualifying distributions, $2,274,219; giving activities include $2,263,648 for grants.
Purpose and activities: The foundation supports programs designed to promote education and employment; and youth development.
Fields of interest: Elementary/secondary education; Education, early childhood education; Higher education; Education, services; Education, drop-out prevention; Education; Crime/violence prevention, abuse prevention; Crime/violence prevention, child abuse; Employment, services; Employment, job counseling; Employment; Youth development, adult & child programs; Youth development; Children/youth, services; United Ways and Federated Giving Programs; Leadership development; Youth.
Type of support: General/operating support; Building/renovation; Program development; Scholarship funds.
Limitations: Applications accepted. Giving primarily in areas of company operations in Modesto, CA, Sarasota, FL, Buhl and Payette, ID, Princeville, IL, Arlington, Blue Earth, Glencoe, Rochester, and Montgomery, MN, Geneva, Leicester, Marion, and Penn Yan, NY, Lebanon, PA, Dayton, Sunnyside, and Yakima, WA, and Baraboo, Cambria, Clyman, Cumberland, Gillett, Janesville, Maryville, Oakfield, Plainfield, and Ripon, WI. No support for religious organizations not of direct benefit to the entire community, or legislative organizations. No grants to individuals, or for endowments, capital campaigns, fundraising events, sponsorships, propaganda, or academic, medical, or scientific research; no product donations.
Publications: Application guidelines; Program policy statement.
Application information: Grants are limited to organizations with documented performance results. Organizations applying for support must include performance outcomes and performance data to be eligible for funding. Support is limited to 1 contribution per organization during any given year. Priority is given to organizations with Seneca employee or retiree volunteer involvement. Application form required.
Initial approach: Download application form and mail to foundation
Deadline(s): None
Officers and Directors:* Arthur S. Wolcott,* Chair.; Kraig H. Kayser,* C.E.O. and Pres.; Jeffrey L. Van Riper, Secy.; Roland E. Breunig, Treas.; Susan W. Stuart.
EIN: 222996324
Selected grants: The following grants are a representative sample of this grantmaker's funding activity:
$2,900 to American Cancer Society, Atlanta, GA, 2012.

6833
The Setton Foundation ✧
85 Austin Blvd.
Commack, NY 11725-5701

Established in 2000 in NY.
Donors: Setton International Foods of Brooklyn; Imani Bros.; Setton's International Foods, Inc.; Bank of America, N.A.
Foundation type: Independent foundation.
Financial data (yr. ended 12/31/13): Assets, $6,135,749 (M); gifts received, $3,005,640; expenditures, $1,773,849; qualifying distributions, $1,785,410; giving activities include $1,785,410 for 685 grants (high: $175,000; low: $15).
Purpose and activities: Giving primarily to Jewish agencies, temples, and schools.
Fields of interest: Education; Jewish agencies & synagogues.
Limitations: Applications not accepted. No grants to individuals.
Application information: Contributes only to pre-selected organizations.
Officers and Directors:* Joshua Setton,* Pres. and Secy.; Morris Setton,* V.P.; Rachel Souede.
EIN: 113577481
Selected grants: The following grants are a representative sample of this grantmaker's funding activity:
$10,000 to American Friends of the Hebrew University, New York, NY, 2011.
$1,800 to American Friends of the Hebrew University, New York, NY, 2011.
$1,800 to Amyotrophic Lateral Sclerosis Association, Calabasas Hills, CA, 2011.
$1,800 to Autism Speaks, New York, NY, 2011.
$1,800 to Saint Jude Childrens Research Hospital, Memphis, TN, 2011.
$1,800 to Yeshiva University, New York, NY, 2011.
$1,500 to American Heart Association, Dallas, TX, 2011.

6834
Seven Turns Fund, Inc. ✧ ☆
(formerly Rizavi Friedland Foundation, Inc.)
c/o BNLY Group LLC
2150 Broadway, PH. 2A
New York, NY 10023-3801

Established in 2006 in NY.
Donors: Shaiza Rizavi; Jonathan Friedland.
Foundation type: Independent foundation.
Financial data (yr. ended 11/30/13): Assets, $3,067,911 (M); gifts received, $348,598; expenditures, $525,038; qualifying distributions, $521,551; giving activities include $517,828 for 40 grants (high: $50,000; low: $1,000).
Fields of interest: Museums (natural history); Performing arts, music; Higher education; Business school/education; Education; Environment, natural resources; Christian agencies & churches.
Limitations: Applications not accepted. No grants to individuals.
Application information: Contributes only to pre-selected organizations.
Directors: Jonathan Friedland; Dara Metz; Shaiza Rizavi.
EIN: 203992304

6835
Shaarei Halacha, Inc. ✧
1840 58th St.
Brooklyn, NY 11204-2027

Foundation type: Independent foundation.
Financial data (yr. ended 12/31/13): Assets, $756,900 (M); expenditures, $529,500; qualifying distributions, $526,500; giving activities include $526,500 for 1 grant.
Fields of interest: Theological school/education; Jewish agencies & synagogues.
Type of support: General/operating support.
Limitations: Applications not accepted. Giving primarily in Brooklyn, NY. No grants to individuals.
Application information: Unsolicited requests for funds not accepted.
Officers: Mark I. Ettinger, Pres.; Binyomin Webster, Co-Secy.; Moshe Weiss, Co-Secy.
EIN: 113519604

6836
Zichron Shaindel Foundation ✧
1303 53rd St., Ste. 106
Brooklyn, NY 11219-3823

Foundation type: Independent foundation.
Financial data (yr. ended 12/31/11): Assets, $19,000 (M); gifts received, $150,000; expenditures, $596,650; qualifying distributions, $603,650; giving activities include $600,150 for grants.
Trustees: Naftali Horowitz; Chana Neustein; Jacob Zimmerman.
EIN: 272770833

6837
Shanken Family Foundation ✧ ☆
387 Park Ave. S.
New York, NY 10016-8810 (212) 684-4884
Contact: Marvin R. Shanken, Dir.

Established in 1999 in NY.
Donor: M. Shanken Communications, Inc.
Foundation type: Company-sponsored foundation.
Financial data (yr. ended 12/31/13): Assets, $3,373,546 (M); gifts received, $300,000; expenditures, $428,340; qualifying distributions, $420,500; giving activities include $420,500 for grants.
Purpose and activities: The foundation supports medical centers and organizations involved with education, Autism, diabetes research, disability services, civil and human rights, and Judaism.
Fields of interest: Education; Medical research; Human services.
Type of support: General/operating support; Program development; Research.
Limitations: Applications accepted. Giving primarily in CT, FL, and New York, NY. No grants to individuals.
Application information: Application form required.
Initial approach: Proposal
Deadline(s): None
Final notification: Within 2 months
Officer: Mel Manion, Treas.
Director: Marvin R. Shanken.
EIN: 134027049

6838
Shapiro-Silverberg Foundation ✧
c/o Anchin Block & Anchin, LLP
1375 Broadway
New York, NY 10018-7001

Established in 2000 in NY.
Donors: John M. Shapiro; Shonni J. Silverberg.
Foundation type: Independent foundation.
Financial data (yr. ended 12/31/13): Assets, $49,880,968 (M); gifts received, $4,223,517; expenditures, $2,943,874; qualifying distributions, $2,825,450; giving activities include $2,824,700 for 48 grants (high: $1,000,000; low: $1,000).
Fields of interest: Arts; Higher education; Education; Children/youth, services; Jewish federated giving programs; Jewish agencies & synagogues.
Limitations: Applications not accepted. Giving in the U.S., with emphasis on CT and NY. No grants to individuals.
Application information: Contributes only to pre-selected organizations.
Trustees: John M. Shapiro; Shonni J. Silverberg.
EIN: 134151366

6839
The Evelyn Sharp Foundation ✧
708 3rd Ave., Ste. 1005
New York, NY 10017-4113 (212) 758-0024
Contact: Mary Cronson, Pres.

Established in 1952 in NY.
Donor: Evelyn Sharp†.
Foundation type: Independent foundation.
Financial data (yr. ended 12/31/13): Assets, $12,566,986 (M); expenditures, $552,455; qualifying distributions, $540,752; giving activities include $510,400 for 49 grants (high: $50,000; low: $1,000).
Fields of interest: Arts education; Museums; Performing arts; Performing arts, theater; Arts; Higher education; Hospitals (general).
Limitations: Applications accepted. Giving primarily in New York, NY. No grants to individuals.
Application information: Generally contributes to pre-selected organizations. Application form not required.
Initial approach: Proposal
Deadline(s): None
Officers and Trustees:* Mary Cronson,* Pres.; Paul Cronson,* V.P.; David Finkelstein,* Secy.-Treas.
EIN: 136119532
Selected grants: The following grants are a representative sample of this grantmaker's funding activity:
$25,000 to Peddie School, Hightstown, NJ, 2012. To fund endowment.
$10,000 to Vassar College, Poughkeepsie, NY, 2012. To fund educational programs.
$5,000 to Brooklyn Academy of Music, Brooklyn, NY, 2012. For fund theater and dance operations.
$1,100 to CentraState Healthcare Foundation, Freehold, NJ, 2012. To fund operations.

6840
The Shaw Family Endowment Fund ✧
c/o Scott Barley
120 W. 45th St., 39th Fl.
New York, NY 10036-4041

Established in 2007 in NY.
Donors: David E. Shaw; Beth K. Shaw.
Foundation type: Independent foundation.
Financial data (yr. ended 12/31/13): Assets, $21,599,982 (M); gifts received, $19,589; expenditures, $7,246,442; qualifying distributions, $7,232,205; giving activities include $7,223,000 for 38 grants (high: $1,000,000; low: $500).
Fields of interest: Arts; Elementary/secondary education; Higher education; Law school/education; Medical school/education; Education; Hospitals (general); Hospitals (specialty); Prostate cancer; Jewish agencies & synagogues.
Limitations: Applications not accepted. Giving primarily in New York, NY; some giving also in CA, CT, DC, MA, NJ, and RI. No grants to individuals.
Application information: Contributes only to pre-selected organizations.
Officers: Beth K. Shaw, Pres.; David E. Shaw, Secy.-Treas.
EIN: 260476590
Selected grants: The following grants are a representative sample of this grantmaker's funding activity:
$1,000,000 to City College Fund, New York, NY, 2011. For Kobliner Chair in Education.
$1,000,000 to Harvard University, Cambridge, MA, 2011. For general support.
$1,000,000 to Princeton University, Princeton, NJ, 2011. For general support.
$1,000,000 to Stanford University, Stanford, CA, 2011. For general support.
$1,000,000 to Yale University, New Haven, CT, 2011. For general support.
$500,000 to Brown University, Providence, RI, 2011. For general support.
$500,000 to Columbia University, New York, NY, 2011. For general support.
$500,000 to Horace Mann School, Riverdale, NY, 2011. For capital campaign.
$200,000 to Brown University, Providence, RI, 2011. For general support.
$50,000 to Horace Mann School, Riverdale, NY, 2011. For annual fund.

6841
Ralph C. Sheldon Foundation, Inc. ✧
P.O. Box 417
Jamestown, NY 14702-0417 (716) 664-9890
Contact: Linda V. Swanson, Exec. Dir.
FAX: (716) 483-6116;
E-mail: info@rcsheldonfoundation.org; Main URL: http://www.rcsheldonfoundation.org/
New Site for Area Common Application: http://www.chautauquagrants.org

Incorporated in 1948 in NY.
Donors: Julia S. Livengood†; Isabell M. Sheldon†; Isabella M. Sheldon Trust.
Foundation type: Independent foundation.
Financial data (yr. ended 12/31/13): Assets, $13,618,138 (M); gifts received, $1,742,006; expenditures, $2,319,914; qualifying distributions, $2,157,073; giving activities include $2,045,441 for 107 grants (high: $156,000; low: $200).
Purpose and activities: Support for youth development organizations, community improvement, cultural organizations, hospitals, social service organizations, and education in Southern Chautauqua County, NY.
Fields of interest: Visual arts; Performing arts; Performing arts, theater; Arts; Libraries/library science; Education; Environment; Hospitals (general); Human services; Youth, services; Community/economic development.
Type of support: General/operating support; Annual campaigns; Capital campaigns; Building/renovation; Equipment; Emergency funds; Matching/challenge support.
Limitations: Applications accepted. Giving limited to southern Chautauqua County, NY. No support for religious organizations. No grants to individuals.
Publications: Application guidelines; Financial statement.
Application information: Application form required.
Initial approach: Application is submitted electronically at http://www.chautauquagrants.org
Deadline(s): Mar. 1, July 1, Sept. 1 and Dec. 1
Board meeting date(s): Quarterly
Final notification: Immediately after determination
Officers and Directors:* Barclay O. Wellman,* Pres.; Betsy Shults, V.P.; Mark Hampton,* Secy.; Kelly Dawson,* Treas.; Linda V. Swanson, Exec. Dir.; Raymond Fashano; Peter B. Sullivan; Alexis Theofilactidis.
Number of staff: 1 full-time professional; 1 full-time support.
EIN: 166030502
Selected grants: The following grants are a representative sample of this grantmaker's funding activity:
$216,902 to WCA Hospital, Jamestown, NY, 2012. For capital projects.
$157,500 to YMCA of Jamestown, Jamestown, NY, 2012. For program support and capital support.
$147,200 to United Way of Southern Chautauqua County, Jamestown, NY, 2012. For human services program support.
$100,000 to Jamestown Community College, Jamestown, NY, 2012. For building renovations.
$81,300 to Arts Council for Chautauqua County, Jamestown, NY, 2012. For program support and operating support.
$80,000 to Chautauqua Striders Youth Development Coalition, Jamestown, NY, 2012. For youth mentoring and tutoring programs.
$67,700 to James Prendergast Library Association, Jamestown, NY, 2012. For books and library materials.
$55,000 to Jamestown Community Learning Council, Jamestown, NY, 2012. For program support.
$50,000 to Cornell Cooperative Extension, Jamestown, NY, 2012. For Four-H Club Programs.
$42,250 to Chautauqua Lake Association, Lakewood, NY, 2012. For lake maintenance projects.

6842
The Shelter Hill Foundation ✧
c/o BCRS Associates, LLC
77 Water St., 9th Fl.
New York, NY 10005-4401

Established in 2004 in NY.
Donors: Paul Shiverick; Elizabeth Shiverick; Seminole Management Co., Inc.
Foundation type: Independent foundation.
Financial data (yr. ended 12/31/13): Assets, $58,059,408 (M); gifts received, $7,565,000; expenditures, $1,988,804; qualifying distributions, $1,983,804; giving activities include $1,975,209 for 48 grants (high: $715,000; low: $50).
Fields of interest: Education; Cancer research; Catholic agencies & churches.

Limitations: Applications not accepted.
Application information: Unsolicited requests for funds not accepted.
Officers: Paul Shiverick, Pres.; Elizabeth Shiverick, V.P.
EIN: 416539096
Selected grants: The following grants are a representative sample of this grantmaker's funding activity:
$20,000 to Society for the Protection of New Hampshire Forests, Concord, NH, 2012. For All Contributions Were Made to the general purposes Fund of Public Charitable Organizations That Were Classified Under Section 501(c)(3) of the Internal Revenue Code. All Contributions Were Made to the general purposes Fund of Public Charitable Organizations.

6843
The Walter V. and Judith L. Shipley Family Foundation ✧
(formerly WJS Foundation, Inc.)
c/o TAG Associates, LLC
810 7th Ave., 7th Fl.
New York, NY 10019-5890

Established in 1997 in NJ.
Donors: Walter V. Shipley; Judith L. Shipley.
Foundation type: Independent foundation.
Financial data (yr. ended 12/31/13): Assets, $5,325,962 (M); expenditures, $828,944; qualifying distributions, $804,115; giving activities include $804,115 for 38 grants (high: $190,115; low: $1,000).
Purpose and activities: Giving primarily for the arts, particularly a museum of natural, history, as well as for education, human services, and to a YMCA.
Fields of interest: Museums (natural history); Arts; Higher education; Education; Human services; YM/YWCAs & YM/YWHAs.
Limitations: Applications not accepted. Giving primarily in NJ and NY. No grants to individuals.
Application information: Contributes only to pre-selected organizations.
Officers and Directors:* Walter V. Shipley,* Pres.; Judith L. Shipley,* V.P. and Secy.; Allison P. Shipley, Treas.; Barbara S. Shipley; Dorothy S. Shipley; John P. Shipley; Pamela J. Shipley.
EIN: 223514762

6844
Shippy Foundation ✧
c/o The Clark Estates Inc.
1 Rockefeller Plz., 31st Fl.
New York, NY 10020-2011

Established in DE.
Donors: Eve C. Labouisse†; Sotheby's, Inc.
Foundation type: Independent foundation.
Financial data (yr. ended 12/31/12): Assets, $28,470,924 (M); expenditures, $1,776,072; qualifying distributions, $1,614,558; giving activities include $1,440,000 for 45 grants (high: $65,000; low: $1,000).
Fields of interest: Education.
Limitations: Applications not accepted. Giving primarily in DC, MA, and NY.
Application information: Contributes only to pre-selected organizations.
Officers and Directors:* Anne L. Peretz,* Pres.; Evgenia S. Peretz,* V.P. and Secy.; David L. Farnsworth,* V.P. and Treas.; Anne E. Farnsworth,* V.P.; Jesse W. Peretz,* V.P.
EIN: 204083744

6845
Susan Stein Shiva Foundation ✧
c/o Baker Tilly Virchow Krause LLP
1 Penn Plz., Ste. 3000
New York, NY 10119-0032 (212) 697-6900

Established in 1997 in CA.
Donors: Doris Stein Charitable Lead Trust No. 2; Doris Stein Charitable Lead Trust No. 4.
Foundation type: Independent foundation.
Financial data (yr. ended 12/31/12): Assets, $21,974,869 (M); gifts received, $529,817; expenditures, $1,608,174; qualifying distributions, $1,434,941; giving activities include $1,412,895 for 134 grants (high: $377,000; low: $500).
Purpose and activities: Giving primarily for health care, education and the arts.
Fields of interest: Museums; Performing arts; Performing arts, theater; Arts; Higher education; Health care.
Limitations: Applications accepted. Giving primarily in New York, NY. No grants to individuals.
Application information: Application form not required.
Initial approach: Letter
Deadline(s): None
Officer: Alexandra Shiva, Pres.
Director: Andrew Shiva.
EIN: 954620752

6846
The Edith Glick Shoolman Children's Foundation ✧
Cherokee Sta.
P.O. Box 20763
New York, NY 10021-0075
E-mail: info@shoolman.org; Main URL: http://www.shoolman.org
Grants List: http://www.shoolman.org/EGSCF/index.php/grantees2/2013-grantees

Established in NY.
Donor: Edith Glick Shoolman†.
Foundation type: Independent foundation.
Financial data (yr. ended 12/31/13): Assets, $24,341,304 (M); expenditures, $1,888,938; qualifying distributions, $1,800,352; giving activities include $1,730,422 for 45 grants (high: $201,190; low: $2,000).
Purpose and activities: Giving to foster the health, education, and well-being of children.
Fields of interest: Child development, education; Child development, services; Children.
Type of support: General/operating support.
Limitations: Giving primarily in the metropolitan New York, NY and Boston, MA, areas. No support for organizations lacking 501(c)(3) status. No grants to individuals, or for pure medical research; also, no funding to endowments, or for annual appeals, or capital improvements other than in connection with the implementation of a specific program being supported; no support for events or outings.
Publications: Application guidelines; Grants list.
Application information: New unsolicited applications for funding will only be accepted from organizations which provide services in the New York City Metropolitan Area. Only online applications are accepted. Please contact the foundation directly for any hardships with online submissions. Application form required.
Initial approach: Letter of inquiry via foundation web site
Deadline(s): None, for letters of inquiry
Officers and Trustees:* Henry L. Berman,* Pres.; Deborah B. Breznay,* Exec. Dir.
EIN: 043414101
Selected grants: The following grants are a representative sample of this grantmaker's funding activity:
$100,000 to Fund for Public Health in New York, New York, NY, 2011.
$100,000 to Queens Library Foundation, Jamaica, NY, 2011.
$100,000 to Raising A Reader Massachusetts, Boston, MA, 2011.
$85,326 to Ackerman Institute for the Family, New York, NY, 2011.
$72,391 to Parent-Child Home Program, Garden City, NY, 2011.
$60,000 to University Settlement Society of New York, New York, NY, 2011.
$50,000 to Boston Chinatown Neighborhood Center, Boston, MA, 2011.
$34,696 to Family Life Academy, Bronx, NY, 2011.
$25,000 to Boston Childrens Chorus, Boston, MA, 2011.
$25,000 to Harlem Academy, New York, NY, 2011.

6847
The Shoreland Foundation ✧
38 Camel Hollow Rd.
Lloyd Harbor, NY 11743-1604

Established in 1994 in NY.
Donors: Anthony W. Wang; Lulu Wang.
Foundation type: Independent foundation.
Financial data (yr. ended 12/31/12): Assets, $29,979,106 (M); expenditures, $6,024,807; qualifying distributions, $5,698,233; giving activities include $5,642,128 for 41 grants (high: $3,000,000; low: $100).
Purpose and activities: Giving primarily to higher education and the arts, including art and cultural museums.
Fields of interest: Arts, cultural/ethnic awareness; Museums; Museums (art); Higher education.
Type of support: General/operating support; Endowments.
Limitations: Applications not accepted. Giving primarily in NY and MA. No grants to individuals.
Application information: Contributes only to pre-selected organizations.
Officers: Lulu C. Wang, Pres.; Anthony W. Wang, V.P.; Carol-Ann Mealey, Secy.
EIN: 113241828

6848
The SHS Foundation ✧
c/o Richard Feldman
7 Penn Plz., No. 900
New York, NY 10001-3993 (212) 245-6754

Established in 2002 in NY.
Donors: Samuel H. Scripps†; Richard E. Feldman; SHS Trust.
Foundation type: Independent foundation.
Financial data (yr. ended 12/31/13): Assets, $58,151,967 (M); expenditures, $5,429,409;

qualifying distributions, $4,807,504; giving activities include $4,807,504 for 28 grants (high: $1,180,000; low: $5,000).
Purpose and activities: Giving primarily for the performing arts; funding also for education.
Fields of interest: Performing arts, dance; Performing arts, theater; Arts; Education.
Limitations: Applications not accepted. Giving primarily in NY.
Application information: Contributes only to pre-selected organizations.
Officers and Directors:* Sara Throne,* Secy.; Richard E. Feldman,* Mgr.; Susan Manzo.
EIN: 256819008
Selected grants: The following grants are a representative sample of this grantmaker's funding activity:
$2,050,000 to American Dance Festival, New York, NY, 2012.
$1,100,000 to Theater for a New Audience, New York, NY, 2012.
$1,076,000 to Brooklyn Academy of Music, Brooklyn, NY, 2012.
$1,000,000 to Paul Taylor Dance Company, New York, NY, 2012.
$228,187 to Bala Music and Dance Association, Old Lyme, CT, 2012.
$200,000 to Shen Wei Dance Arts, New York, NY, 2012.
$130,000 to Cocoon Theater, Rhinebeck, NY, 2012.
$100,000 to Aaron Davis Hall, Harlem Stage, New York, NY, 2012.
$100,000 to Ballet Hispanico of New York, New York, NY, 2012.
$50,000 to Alvin Ailey American Dance Theater, New York, NY, 2012.

6849
The Shtesl Family Foundation ✧ ☆
150 Heyward St., 3rd Fl.
Brooklyn, NY 11206-5059

Donors: Unique Sales of USA, Inc.; Joel Shtesl.
Foundation type: Independent foundation.
Financial data (yr. ended 12/31/13): Assets, $15,384 (M); gifts received, $450,050; expenditures, $467,549; qualifying distributions, $467,022; giving activities include $465,757 for 288 grants (high: $40,000; low: $18).
Fields of interest: Jewish agencies & synagogues.
Limitations: Applications not accepted.
Application information: Unsolicited requests for funds not accepted.
Trustee: Ascher Shtesl.
EIN: 273815914

6850
The Shubert Foundation, Inc. ✧
234 W. 44th St.
New York, NY 10036-3909 (212) 944-3777
Contact: Vicki Reiss, Exec. Dir.
FAX: (212) 944-3767; Main URL: http://www.shubertfoundation.org

Incorporated in 1945 in DE as the Sam S. Shubert Foundation; current name adopted in 1971.
Donors: Lee Shubert†; J.J. Shubert†.
Foundation type: Independent foundation.
Financial data (yr. ended 05/31/13): Assets, $409,983,016 (M); gifts received, $143,221; expenditures, $27,708,663; qualifying distributions, $22,800,422; giving activities include $21,502,000 for 504 grants (high: $300,000; low: $10,000), and $518,972 for foundation-administered programs.
Purpose and activities: To build and perpetuate the live performing arts, particularly the professional theater, in the United States. Emphasis is on theater and a secondary focus on dance. Support for theatrical organizations with demonstrated artistic and administrative track records, and arts-related institutions necessary to maintain and support the theater. The foundation also operates a theatrical archive. Grants almost always made exclusively for general operating funds.
Fields of interest: Performing arts; Performing arts, dance; Performing arts, theater; Performing arts, education.
Type of support: General/operating support.
Limitations: Applications accepted. Giving limited to the U.S. No grants to individuals, or for capital or endowment funds, conduit organizations, renovation projects, media (TV, radio or film), audience development, direct subsidy of reduced-price admissions, no loans.
Publications: Annual report (including application guidelines).
Application information: The foundation does not acknowledge receipt of proposals. Interviews with applicants are granted by appointment. Unaudited financial statements are not accepted. Grant requests must be submitted on the foundation's current application form. Application form is available on foundation web site. Aug.-Dec. E-mailed applications will not be accepted. Review web site for additional application requirements for each program area. Application form required.
Initial approach: Letter or telephone
Copies of proposal: 2
Deadline(s): Dance, Arts-related, and Education: Oct. 15; Theater: Dec. 1
Final notification: Late May
Officers and Directors:* Philip J. Smith,* Chair.; Michael I. Sovern,* Pres.; Vicki Reiss, Exec. Dir.; Wyche Fowler, Jr.; Diana Phillips; Lee J. Seidler; Stuart Subotnick; Robert E. Wankel.
Number of staff: 2 full-time professional; 1 full-time support.
EIN: 136106961
Selected grants: The following grants are a representative sample of this grantmaker's funding activity:
$300,000 to Chicago Theater Group, Chicago, IL, 2012. For General Operating Support.
$300,000 to South Coast Repertory Theater, Costa Mesa, CA, 2012. For General Operating Support.
$300,000 to Vivian Beaumont Theater, New York, NY, 2012. For General Operating Support.
$240,000 to Playwrights Horizons, New York, NY, 2012. For General Operating Support.
$235,000 to Roundabout Theater Company, New York, NY, 2012. For General Operating Support.
$230,000 to Manhattan Theater Club, New York, NY, 2012. For General Operating Support.
$230,000 to New York Shakespeare Festival, New York, NY, 2012. For General Operating Support.
$225,000 to Ballet Theater Foundation, New York, NY, 2012. For General Operating Support.
$220,000 to Washington Drama Society, Washington, DC, 2012. For General Operating Support.
$25,000 to DOVA, Inc., New York, NY, 2012. For General Operating Support.

6851
The Shulsky Foundation ✧
200 W. 57th St., Ste. 801
New York, NY 10019

Established in 1996 in NY.
Donors: Rena Shulsky; Rubin Shulsky†; 1220 Broadway, LLC.
Foundation type: Independent foundation.
Financial data (yr. ended 11/30/13): Assets, $150,807 (M); gifts received, $1,144,157; expenditures, $994,282; qualifying distributions, $991,657; giving activities include $856,657 for 11 grants (high: $250,000; low: $15,373).
Fields of interest: Higher education; Hospitals (general); Health organizations; Medical research, institute; Deaf/hearing impaired.
Limitations: Applications not accepted. Giving primarily in MA, MN and New York, NY. No grants to individuals.
Application information: Unsolicited requests for funds not accepted.
Trustee: Rena Shulsky.
EIN: 137079079

6852
Sidewalk Angels Foundation ✧ ☆
P.O. Box 356
Bedford Hills, NY 10507-0356
E-mail: info@sidewalkangelsfoundation.org; Main URL: http://www.sidewalkangelsfoundation.org/
Facebook: https://www.facebook.com/sidewalkangels
Twitter: http://twitter.com/sidewalkangels

Established in 2004 in NY.
Donors: Marisol Thomas; Rob Thomas; New Bidnis Inc.; Music Mastermind Inc.
Foundation type: Operating foundation.
Financial data (yr. ended 12/31/13): Assets, $40,062 (M); gifts received, $393,782; expenditures, $464,398; qualifying distributions, $435,000; giving activities include $435,000 for 18 grants (high: $230,000; low: $5,000).
Purpose and activities: The foundation seeks through its efforts to encourage people to locally address problems such as animals that have been abandoned and abused as well as people who are destitute, homeless, or cannot afford proper medical care.
Fields of interest: Animal welfare; Homeless, human services; Economically disadvantaged; Homeless.
Limitations: Applications not accepted. Giving in the U.S., with emphasis on NY.
Application information: Unsolicited requests for funds not accepted.
Officers: Marisol Thomas, Pres.; Robert Thomas, V.P.; Maria Maldonado, Secy.; Greg Prato, Treas.
Directors: Michael Lippman; Jeff Maldonado; Melissa Lopez Maldonado.
EIN: 200285336

6853
Harold W. Siebens Charitable Foundation, Inc. ✧
c/o McDermott Will & Emery LLP
340 Madison Ave., 17th Fl.
New York, NY 10173-1922

Established in 2001 in NY, IA, and MO.

Donors: Famsea Corp.; Seafam Corp.; Seacay Corp.
Foundation type: Independent foundation.
Financial data (yr. ended 12/31/13): Assets, $3,546,641 (M); gifts received, $5,398,508; expenditures, $5,692,533; qualifying distributions, $5,680,595; giving activities include $5,101,304 for 80+ grants (high: $750,000).
Fields of interest: Education; Health care; Food banks; Housing/shelter; Human services; Children/youth, services; Family services.
Type of support: General/operating support; Building/renovation; Endowments; Emergency funds; Program development; Scholarship funds.
Limitations: Applications not accepted. Giving primarily in IA, MO and TX. No grants to individuals.
Application information: Contributes only to pre-selected organizations.
Directors: Henry Christensen III; Heather Rae Johnson; James G. McKee; Jay E. Rivlin; Stewart D. Siebens; W. Carter Siebens.
EIN: 133666768

6854
The William & Sylvia Silberstein Foundation, Inc. ✧

1600 Harrison Ave.
Mamaroneck, NY 10543-3126

Established in 1969 in NY.
Donors: William Silberstein†; Sylvia Silberstein.
Foundation type: Independent foundation.
Financial data (yr. ended 11/30/13): Assets, $12,949,933 (M); expenditures, $694,372; qualifying distributions, $563,650; giving activities include $549,500 for 16 grants (high: $168,000; low: $2,500).
Purpose and activities: Support primarily for education and health care.
Fields of interest: Higher education; Hospitals (general); Health organizations, association; Human services.
Limitations: Applications not accepted. Giving primarily in CT and New York, NY. No grants to individuals.
Application information: Contributes only to pre-selected organizations.
Officers: Bruce Silberstein, Pres.; Debra Dietz, V.P.; Mary Farren, Secy.; William Conron, Treas.
EIN: 237108375

6855
Marty and Dorothy Silverman Foundation ✧

c/o L. Silverman
830 3rd Ave., 6th Fl.
New York, NY 10022-6566

Established in 1986.
Donor: Marty Silverman†.
Foundation type: Independent foundation.
Financial data (yr. ended 07/31/13): Assets, $491,883,075 (M); gifts received, $15,000; expenditures, $19,446,248; qualifying distributions, $40,240,320; giving activities include $12,254,454 for 182+ grants (high: $1,000,000), and $27,985,866 for 10 loans/program-related investments.
Purpose and activities: Support for programs that address the special needs of indigent senior citizens, including nursing homes and hospitals. Grants may also be made to educational and cultural organizations, and health and welfare agencies.
Fields of interest: Arts; Education, association; Hospitals (general); Health organizations, association; Human services; Aging, centers/services; Aging.
Type of support: Program-related investments/loans.
Limitations: Applications not accepted. Giving primarily in NY. No grants to individuals.
Application information: Contributes only to pre-selected organizations.
Officers and Directors:* Lorin Silverman,* Pres. and Treas.; Patty Lipshutz,* V.P. and Secy.; Allison Silverman; Seth Silverman.
EIN: 222777449
Selected grants: The following grants are a representative sample of this grantmaker's funding activity:
$1,000,000 to Hebrew Home for the Aged at Riverdale, Riverdale, NY, 2013.
$1,000,000 to New York City Energy Efficiency Corporation, New York, NY, 2013.
$550,000 to New Economy Project, New York, NY, 2012.
$500,000 to Albany Medical Center Foundation, Albany, NY, 2012.
$500,000 to American Jewish Joint Distribution Committee, New York, NY, 2013.
$250,000 to Citymeals-on-Wheels, New York, NY, 2012.
$242,900 to New York Legal Assistance Group, New York, NY, 2013.
$228,500 to New York Civil Liberties Union Foundation, New York, NY, 2012.
$220,000 to THIRTEEN, New York, NY, 2012.
$212,500 to Jewish Association for Services for the Aged, New York, NY, 2013.
$210,000 to Earthjustice, San Francisco, CA, 2012.
$210,000 to Vermont Law School, South Royalton, VT, 2012.
$180,000 to Dorot, New York, NY, 2012.
$175,000 to Human Rights First, New York, NY, 2012.
$166,667 to Project Vote/Voting for America, Washington, DC, 2013.
$165,000 to W N Y C Radio, New York, NY, 2013.
$151,105 to New York Legal Assistance Group, New York, NY, 2012.
$60,000 to Mount Sinai Medical Center, New York, NY, 2013.
$35,000 to Family Service Society of Yonkers, Yonkers, NY, 2013.
$30,000 to Rockaway Waterfront Alliance, Far Rockaway, NY, 2013.

6856
The Raine & Stanley Silverstein Family Foundation, Inc. ✧ ☆

c/o Krusch & Modell
10 Rockefeller Plz., Ste. 710
New York, NY 10020-1966

Established in 1996 in NY.
Donors: Raine Silverstein; Stanley Silverstein.
Foundation type: Independent foundation.
Financial data (yr. ended 11/30/13): Assets, $111,540 (M); gifts received, $497,634; expenditures, $632,010; qualifying distributions, $608,611; giving activities include $608,611 for 93 grants (high: $96,780; low: $36).
Purpose and activities: Giving primarily for Jewish higher education, human services, and to Jewish agencies and temples.
Fields of interest: Higher education; Human services; Jewish agencies & synagogues.
Limitations: Applications not accepted. Giving primarily in NY. No grants to individuals.
Application information: Unsolicited requests for funds not accepted.
Officers: Stanley Silverstein, Pres.; Raine Silverstein, V.P. and Treas.; Nina Miner, V.P.; Flori Silverstein, V.P.
EIN: 113353084

6857
Silverweed Foundation, Inc. ✧

c/o Anchin Block & Anchin, LLP
1375 Broadway
New York, NY 10018-7001

Established in 1989 in DE and NY.
Donor: Doris Freedman.
Foundation type: Independent foundation.
Financial data (yr. ended 12/31/13): Assets, $8,056,873 (M); expenditures, $1,272,679; qualifying distributions, $1,146,103; giving activities include $953,125 for 42 grants (high: $131,000; low: $1,000).
Purpose and activities: Giving primarily for education, the arts and to Jewish agencies and temples.
Fields of interest: Arts; Higher education; Law school/education; Education; Human services; Jewish federated giving programs; Jewish agencies & synagogues.
Limitations: Applications not accepted. Giving primarily in New York, NY; some funding also in CT and RI. No grants to individuals.
Application information: Contributes only to pre-selected organizations.
Officers: Karen Freedman, Pres.; Susan K. Freedman, V.P. and Secy.; Nina P. Freedman, V.P. and Treas.
Number of staff: 1 full-time professional.
EIN: 133496446
Selected grants: The following grants are a representative sample of this grantmaker's funding activity:
$235,000 to Brown University, Providence, RI, 2011.
$125,000 to Ethical Culture Fieldston School, New York, NY, 2011.
$11,500 to Mayors Fund to Advance New York City, New York, NY, 2011.
$10,000 to American Jewish World Service, New York, NY, 2011.
$7,500 to Natural Resources Defense Council, New York, NY, 2011.

6858
The Slomo and Cindy Silvian Foundation, Inc. ✧

150 Broadhollow Rd., Ste. 304
Melville, NY 11747-4907
Main URL: http://www.silvianfoundation.org/

Established in 2005 in NY.
Donor: Cindy Silvian†.
Foundation type: Independent foundation.
Financial data (yr. ended 12/31/13): Assets, $44,408,333 (M); gifts received, $380,000;

expenditures, $1,790,067; qualifying distributions, $1,571,542; giving activities include $1,007,500 for 79 grants (high: $50,000; low: $750).
Purpose and activities: Giving primarily for Jewish education, and to other Jewish agencies.
Fields of interest: Education; Jewish agencies & synagogues.
Limitations: Applications not accepted. Giving primarily in NY.
Application information: Contributes only to pre-selected organizations.
Officers and Directors:* Daniel S. Komansky, Pres.; Hon. Jack Mackston,* Secy.; David Grossman,* Treas.
EIN: 342037021
Selected grants: The following grants are a representative sample of this grantmaker's funding activity:
$23,000 to Albany Law School, Albany, NY, 2012. For education and medical care.
$18,000 to Jewish Foundation for the Righteous, New York, NY, 2012. For Jewish Philanthropy.
$15,000 to New York University, School of Law, New York, NY, 2012. For education.
$12,500 to Columbia University Medical Center, Department of Ophthalmology, New York, NY, 2012. For medical research.
$12,500 to Zion Orphanage, Fresh Meadows, NY, 2012. For children's welfare.

6859
William E. Simon Foundation, Inc. ✧
(formerly William E. & Carol G. Simon Foundation, Inc.)
140 E. 45th St., Ste. 14D
New York, NY 10017-7136 (212) 661-8366
FAX: (212) 661-9450;
E-mail: info@wesimonfoundation.org; Main URL: http://www.wesimonfoundation.org
Grants Database: http://www.wesimonfoundation.org/index.php?option=com_content&view=article&id=3&Itemid=7

Established in 1967 in NJ.
Donor: William E. Simon†.
Foundation type: Independent foundation.
Financial data (yr. ended 12/31/12): Assets, $92,523,052 (M); gifts received, $9,917,714; expenditures, $13,791,598; qualifying distributions, $13,036,832; giving activities include $11,315,938 for 344 grants (high: $460,728; low: $25).
Purpose and activities: The main purpose of the foundation is to assist those in need by providing the means through which they may help themselves. The foundation seeks to fund programs that are effective in promoting independence and responsibility.
Fields of interest: Education; Human services; Children/youth, services; Religion; General charitable giving; Economically disadvantaged.
Type of support: General/operating support; Scholarship funds; Employee matching gifts; Matching/challenge support.
Limitations: Applications not accepted. Giving on a national basis, with emphasis on New York, NY, and Los Angeles and the San Francisco Bay Area, CA. No support for foreign charities. No grants to individuals.
Publications: Grants list; Informational brochure.
Application information: The foundation staff reviews proposals on an invitational basis only. Unsolicited proposals are not accepted.
Board meeting date(s): Varies
Officers and Directors:* J. Peter Simon,* Co-Chair.; William E. Simon, Jr.,* Co-Chair.; James Piereson,* Pres.; Aimee Simon Bloom; Katie Morris; Daniel L. Mosley; Julie Simon Munro; Leigh Simon Porges; Mary B. Simon Streep; William T. Wachenfeld.
Number of staff: 1 full-time professional; 1 full-time support; 1 part-time support.
EIN: 136217788
Selected grants: The following grants are a representative sample of this grantmaker's funding activity:
$460,728 to Foundation for Morristown Medical Center, Morristown, NJ, 2012.
$370,000 to Philanthropy Roundtable, Washington, DC, 2012.
$350,000 to Charter Fund, Broomfield, CO, 2012.
$300,000 to Manhattan Institute for Policy Research, New York, NY, 2012.
$300,000 to Witherspoon Institute, Princeton, NJ, 2012.
$135,000 to Princeton University, Department of Politics, Princeton, NJ, 2012.
$100,000 to Covenant House New Jersey, Newark, NJ, 2012.
$25,000 to Manhattan Institute for Policy Research, New York, NY, 2012.
$20,000 to Foundation for Morristown Medical Center, Morristown, NJ, 2012.
$20,000 to Morristown-Beard School, Morristown, NJ, 2012.

6860
The Nick Simons Foundation ✧
160 5th Ave., 7th Fl.
New York, NY 10010-7003
Main URL: http://nicksimonsfoundation.org
Gradian Health Systems: http://www.gradianhealth.org/company/
James and Marilyn Simons's Giving Pledge Profile: http://glasspockets.org/philanthropy-in-focus/eye-on-the-giving-pledge/profiles/simons
Nick Simons Institute: http://www.nsi.edu.np/?site=yes

Established in 2006 in NY.
Donors: James Simons; Nick Simons†.
Foundation type: Independent foundation.
Financial data (yr. ended 06/30/13): Assets, $56,863,913 (M); gifts received, $5,400,000; expenditures, $5,424,650; qualifying distributions, $5,170,694; giving activities include $2,325,529 for 27 grants (high: $1,785,000; low: $100).
Purpose and activities: The Nick Simons Foundation is a private family foundation formed to honor the memory of Nick Simons and his love for Nepal. The Foundation aims to perpetuate his interest in developing countries through its mission to improve health and medical care, especially for rural and remote communities in Nepal. Special emphasis is directed toward the development and technology of the Universal Anesthesia Machine (UAM), a low cost trolley-based workstation providing inhalation anesthesia brought to market by Gradian Health Systems, a wholly-owned subsidiary of the Nick Simons Foundation; training for rural health care workers; curricula development; training site start-ups; and programs that help retain health care workers in the field.
Fields of interest: Hospitals (general); Health care; Anesthesiology; Rural development.
International interests: Nepal.
Type of support: General/operating support; Program development.
Limitations: Applications not accepted. Giving primarily in the U.S. and in Nepal.
Application information: Contributes only to pre-selected organizations. The Foundation's main grantees are the Nick Simons Institute (NSI) and Gradian Health Systems.
Officers: James Simons, Pres.; Marilyn Simons, Secy.-Treas.
Trustees: Caitlin Heising; Mark Heising; Audrey Simons; Laura Baxter Simons; Liz Simons; Nat Simons.
EIN: 203101239

6861
The Simons Foundation ✧
160 5th Ave., 7th Fl.
New York, NY 10010-7037 (646) 654-0066
Contact: Marilyn Simons, Pres.
E-mail: admin@simonsfoundation.org; Main URL: http://www.simonsfoundation.org
James and Marilyn Simons's Giving Pledge Profile: http://glasspockets.org/philanthropy-in-focus/eye-on-the-giving-pledge/profiles/simons
Knowledge Center: https://sfari.org/news-and-opinion
On SFARI Blog: https://sfari.org/news-and-opinion/blog/going-on-sfari
Vimeo: http://vimeo.com/simonsfoundation

Established in 1994 in NY.
Donor: James Simons.
Foundation type: Independent foundation.
Financial data (yr. ended 12/31/13): Assets, $2,170,686,615 (M); gifts received, $84,000,000; expenditures, $212,915,163; qualifying distributions, $179,640,382; giving activities include $178,889,844 for grants, $750,538 for in-kind gifts, and $25,129,417 for foundation-administered programs.
Purpose and activities: The primary mission of the foundation is to advance the frontiers of research in the basic sciences and mathematics.
Fields of interest: Autism research; Science, research; Mathematics.
Type of support: General/operating support; Capital campaigns; Endowments; Professorships; Research.
Publications: Annual report; Financial statement.
Application information: The foundation does not accept proposals outside its established programs. In almost all cases grants are made in response to announced requests for proposals and funding decisions are made through a peer-reviewed proposal process. See foundation web site for requests for applications.
Board meeting date(s): Throughout the year
Officers and Trustees:* James H. Simons, Ph.D.*, Chair.; Marilyn Simons,* Pres.; Maria Adler, C.F.O. and Treas.; Marion Greenup, V.P., Admin.; Patricia Weisenfeld, V.P., Special Initiatives; Fang Han, Cont.; David Eisenbud; Gerald D. Fischbach; Mark Silber.
Number of staff: 2 part-time professional; 1 full-time support.
EIN: 133794889

Selected grants: The following grants are a representative sample of this grantmaker's funding activity:
$16,000,000 to Institute for Advanced Study, Princeton, NJ, 2012. For Simons Foundation Simonyi Endowment Fund.
$13,700,000 to Math for America, New York, NY, 2012. For operating support.
$11,250,008 to New York Genome Center, New York, NY, 2012. For New York Genome Center.
$9,000,000 to Stony Brook Foundation, Stony Brook, NY, 2012. For unrestricted support.
$6,557,422 to Cold Spring Harbor Laboratory, Cold Spring Harbor, NY, 2012. For research to understand the genetic basis of autism.
$124,320 to Stanford University, Stanford, CA, 2012. For CLARITY circuit-dynamics and connectivity of autism-related behavior.
$100,000 to Institute for Advanced Study, Princeton, NJ, 2012. For annual support.
$66,000 to California Institute of Technology, Pasadena, CA, 2012. For Simons Investigator in Physics.
$7,000 to Dartmouth College, Hanover, NH, 2012. For Noncommutative Dynamical Systems.

6862
The Paul E. Singer Foundation ✧
40 W. 57th St., 4th Fl.
New York, NY 10019-4001

Donor: Paul E. Singer.
Foundation type: Independent foundation.
Financial data (yr. ended 11/30/13): Assets, $281,193,219 (M); gifts received, $61,000,000; expenditures, $14,824,821; qualifying distributions, $14,794,488; giving activities include $13,836,960 for 42 grants (high: $8,788,500; low: $1,000).
Fields of interest: Education; Health care; Cancer; Cancer, leukemia; Human services; Jewish agencies & synagogues.
Limitations: Applications not accepted. Giving primarily in Washington, DC and New York, NY.
Application information: Contributes only to pre-selected organizations.
Officers and Directors:* Paul E. Singer,* Pres. and Treas.; Myron Kaplan,* Secy.; Annie Dickerson; Terry Kassel; Dan Senor.
EIN: 272009342

6863
The Sirus Fund ✧
c/o Susan Helpern, EisnerAmper LLP
750 3rd Ave., 21st Fl.
New York, NY 10017-2703
Contact: Susan U. Halpern, Pres.

Established in 1996 in NY.
Donor: Susan U. Halpern.
Foundation type: Independent foundation.
Financial data (yr. ended 06/30/13): Assets, $13,162,387 (M); gifts received, $20,000; expenditures, $1,216,003; qualifying distributions, $1,116,752; giving activities include $1,067,290 for 55 grants (high: $100,000; low: $300).
Purpose and activities: Giving primarily for services to young children in the metropolitan New York, NY, area.
Fields of interest: Education, early childhood education; Higher education; Child development, services; Family services.
Type of support: General/operating support; Continuing support; Program development.
Limitations: Applications not accepted. Giving primarily in the metropolitan New York, NY, area. No support for religious organizations. No grants to individuals.
Application information: Unsolicited requests for funds not accepted.
Board meeting date(s): June and Sept.
Officer and Trustee:* Susan U. Halpern,* Pres.
Number of staff: None.
EIN: 137100236

6864
The Sister Fund ✧
79 5th Ave., 4th Fl.
New York, NY 10003-3034 (212) 260-4446
FAX: (212) 260-4633; E-mail: info@sisterfund.org; Main URL: http://www.sisterfund.org

Donors: Lauren Embrey; Carol Andreae; Robert Morrison; Susan Morrison; Cynda Collins Arsenault; Helen Lakelly Hunt; Trea C. Yip; Abigail Disney; Gayle Embrey; Jacquelyn and Gregory Zehner Foundation; Tides Foundation; Dobkin Family Foundation; Harnisch Foundation; Silverleaf Foundation; Starry Night Foundation; Winds of Change Foundation; Rockefeller Philanthropy Advisors; Ruth & Charles Sharp Foundation; Jacquelyn Zehner; Ms. Foundation for Women; Michael Campbell; Katherine Grover; Alida Messinger; Lindsay Shea; Stephens Foundation; The Novo Foundation; The Harold & Kayrita Anderson Fam. Foundation; Swanee Hunt Family Foundation.
Foundation type: Independent foundation.
Financial data (yr. ended 12/31/13): Assets, $9,370,346 (M); gifts received, $27,780; expenditures, $1,641,655; qualifying distributions, $1,587,271; giving activities include $949,823 for 79 grants (high: $100,000; low: $400), $87,323 for 3 in-kind gifts, and $160,852 for foundation-administered programs.
Purpose and activities: The fund believes that women can transform faith, and faith can transform feminism. It funds this kind of transformation in a variety of contexts. It is committed to woman-centered philanthropy and the empowerment of faith-based women, because it believes the energy of love heals. The fund provides grants, technical support, communication tools, and networking opportunities in a variety of forms. A portion of the fund's resources is dedicated to broader ideas and initiatives that help create a just and sustainable world. These efforts are led by the fund's donor family.
Fields of interest: Higher education; Theological school/education; Women, centers/services; Christian agencies & churches; Religion.
Limitations: Applications not accepted. Giving in the U.S., with emphasis on New York, NY.
Application information: Unsolicited requests for funds not accepted.
Officers and Trustees:* Helen Lakelly Hunt,* Pres.; Harville Hendrix,* V.P.; Vincent McGee,* Secy.; Lorelei Williams, Interim Exec. Dir.; Kanyere Eaton.
EIN: 133501674

6865
Sitchin Foundation Inc. ✧
c/o Salo Aizenberg
31 Bloomingdale Dr.
Scarsdale, NY 10583 (917) 363-4919
Contact: Salo Aizenberg, Secy. and Dir.

Donor: Zecharia Sitchin†.
Foundation type: Independent foundation.
Financial data (yr. ended 12/31/13): Assets, $5,807,420 (M); gifts received, $162,482; expenditures, $534,279; qualifying distributions, $499,094; giving activities include $457,926 for 38 grants (high: $150,000; low: $50).
Fields of interest: Education; Recreation; Human services.
Application information: Application form required.
Initial approach: Letter
Deadline(s): None
Officers and Directors:* Amnon Sitchin,* V.P.; Salo Aizenberg,* Secy.; Arthur Feldman,* Treas.; Janet Sitchin.
EIN: 260814762

6866
Joseph Jack Sitt 1986 Charitable Trust ✧ ☆
c/o Joseph J. Satt
25 W. 39th St., 11th Fl.
New York, NY 10018-3805

Established in 1986 in NY.
Donor: Joseph J. Sitt.
Foundation type: Independent foundation.
Financial data (yr. ended 12/31/12): Assets, $9,158,478 (M); expenditures, $560,640; qualifying distributions, $560,388; giving activities include $560,388 for grants.
Purpose and activities: Giving primarily for Jewish organizations.
Fields of interest: Museums (ethnic/folk arts); Education; Jewish federated giving programs; Jewish agencies & synagogues.
Limitations: Applications not accepted. Giving primarily in Brooklyn and New York, NY. No grants to individuals.
Application information: Unsolicited requests for funds not accepted.
Trustee: Joseph J. Sitt.
EIN: 133406764

6867
SJS Charitable Trust ✧
c/o WTAS
1177 Ave. of the Americas
New York, NY 10036

Donor: Sandra Leitner.
Foundation type: Independent foundation.
Financial data (yr. ended 12/31/12): Assets, $23,258,788 (M); expenditures, $1,144,720; qualifying distributions, $1,085,880; giving activities include $1,085,880 for 25 grants (high: $371,000; low: $500).
Fields of interest: Christian agencies & churches.
Limitations: Applications not accepted. Giving primarily in New York, NY.
Application information: Unsolicited requests for funds not accepted.

Trustees: Arthur Alexander; Sandra Shahinian Leitner.
EIN: 270653520

6868
Skadden Foundation ✧
(formerly Skadden, Arps, Slate, Meagher & Flom Fellowship Foundation)
360 Hamilton Ave.
White Plains, NY 10601-1811 (212) 735-2956
Contact: Susan Butler Plum, Secy.
FAX: (917) 777-2956;
E-mail: susan.plum@skadden.com; Application address: Skadden Fellowship Program, 4 Times Sq., Rm. 29-218, New York, NY 10036; Main URL: http://www.skaddenfellowships.org/
Fellows: http://www.skaddenfellowships.org/fellows-list

Established in 1988 in NY.
Donor: Skadden, Arps, Slate, Meagher & Flom.
Foundation type: Company-sponsored foundation.
Financial data (yr. ended 12/31/12): Assets, $9,878,610 (M); gifts received, $4,077,400; expenditures, $4,008,674; qualifying distributions, $3,992,696; giving activities include $3,347,701 for 87 grants (high: $129,682; low: $1,713), and $62,373 for 13 grants to individuals (high: $9,148; low: $150).
Purpose and activities: The foundation awards fellowships to graduating law students and outgoing judicial clerks who create projects at public interest organizations designed to provide legal services to the poor, the elderly, the disabled, and those deprived of their civil rights or human rights; and grants to former Skadden Fellows who want to undertake new initiatives on behalf of their clients.
Fields of interest: Law school/education; Civil/human rights, advocacy; Civil/human rights; Leadership development; Aging; Disabilities, people with; Economically disadvantaged.
Type of support: Fellowships; Grants to individuals.
Limitations: Applications accepted. Giving on a national basis, with emphasis on Berkeley, Los Angeles, Oakland, San Diego, and San Francisco, CA, Washington, DC, Chicago, IL, MA, and Bronx, Brooklyn, and New York, NY. No grants to individuals who do not secure a potential position with a sponsoring public interest organization.
Publications: Application guidelines.
Application information: Letters for Flom Memorial Incubator Grants should describe the applicant's career trajectory, the inspiration for the project, and the proposed plan for grant funds. Fellows who have been awarded a FIG must wait two years before reapplying.
Initial approach: Download application form and mail application form and supporting materials for fellowships; letter to foundation for Flom Memorial Incubator Grants
Copies of proposal: 1
Deadline(s): Oct. 6 for fellowships; Jan. 15 and July 15 for Flom Memorial Incubator Grants
Board meeting date(s): Dec. 4
Final notification: Dec. 5
Officers and Trustees: Lauren Aguiar, Pres.; Thomas J. Allingham II, V.P.; C. Benjamin Crisman, Jr., V.P.; Susan Butler Plum, Secy.; Chris Fulton, Treas.; Eric J. Friedman; Barry H. Garfinkel; Hon. Judith S. Kaye; Jose Lozano; Suzanne Mckechnie Klahr; Martha Minow; Michael H. Schill; Kurt Schmoke; Robert C. Sheehan; Solomon Watson IV; Joy Ziegeweid.
Number of staff: 1 full-time professional; 1 part-time support.
EIN: 133455231

6869
Skirball Foundation ✧
31 W. 52nd St., 21st Fl.
New York, NY 10019-6396 (212) 832-8500
Contact: Martin Blackman, Pres.

Established in 1950 in OH.
Donors: Members of the Skirball family; Skirball Investment Co.
Foundation type: Independent foundation.
Financial data (yr. ended 12/31/13): Assets, $15,210,851 (M); expenditures, $17,718,217; qualifying distributions, $16,987,515; giving activities include $15,186,499 for 95 grants (high: $7,875,000; low: $1,000).
Purpose and activities: Giving primarily for Jewish welfare and temple support; support also for education, the arts, and medicine.
Fields of interest: Media/communications; Arts; Education; Human services; Jewish federated giving programs; Jewish agencies & synagogues.
Limitations: Applications accepted. Giving primarily in CA. No grants to individuals.
Application information: Contributes primarily to pre-selected organizations and accepts limited applications for funds.
Officers and Trustees:* Martin Blackman,* C.E.O. and Pres.; Marvin Goldstein, V.P., Secy. and C.F.O.; Robert D. Goldfarb,* Treas.; Nympha H. Cody, Cont.; Uri D. Herscher.
EIN: 346517957
Selected grants: The following grants are a representative sample of this grantmaker's funding activity:
$5,336,009 to Skirball Cultural Center, Los Angeles, CA, 2012. For Operating Funds.
$2,412,900 to Hebrew Union College-Jewish Institute of Religion, New York, NY, 2012. For Operating Funds.
$1,187,500 to University of California, Los Angeles, CA, 2012. For Operating Funds.
$842,597 to Geffen Playhouse, Los Angeles, CA, 2012. For Operating Funds.
$539,138 to Skirball Cultural Center, Los Angeles, CA, 2012. For Operating Funds.
$250,000 to Venice Family Clinic, Venice, CA, 2012. For Operating Funds.
$249,830 to Childrens Hospital Los Angeles, Los Angeles, CA, 2012. For Operating Funds.
$100,000 to SRN Corporation, Mamaroneck, NY, 2012. For Operating Funds.
$50,000 to Inner-City Scholarship Fund, New York, NY, 2012. For Operating Funds.
$50,000 to Lower East Side Tenement Museum, New York, NY, 2012. For Operating Funds.

6870
Alan B. Slifka Foundation, Inc. ✧
477 Madison Ave., 8th Fl.
New York, NY 10022-5802 (212) 303-9470
Contact: Sarah Silver, Exec. Dir.
E-mail: programofficer@halcyonllc.com

Established in 1963 in NY.
Donors: Alan B. Slifka†; Sylvia Slifka†.
Foundation type: Independent foundation.
Financial data (yr. ended 11/30/13): Assets, $59,197,283 (M); gifts received, $33,136,287; expenditures, $8,088,837; qualifying distributions, $8,012,668; giving activities include $7,202,903 for 123 grants (high: $1,485,500; low: $50).
Purpose and activities: Support primarily for Jewish interest projects and cultural activities and for endeavors that promote coexistence and a world safe for difference.
Fields of interest: International peace/security; International affairs; Jewish agencies & synagogues; Religion, interfaith issues; Religion.
International interests: Israel; Middle East.
Type of support: Research; General/operating support; Continuing support; Program development; Seed money; Curriculum development; Program evaluation; Matching/challenge support.
Limitations: Applications accepted. No support for political organizations, environmental, medical, or health-related fields. No grants to individuals, or for endowments, for-profit organizations or acquisitions of land. Generally no grants for major equipment purchases, individual research or media projects.
Application information: Telephone or e-mail the foundation for a copy of the current guidelines which has all the necessary information for applying.
Initial approach: Letter
Copies of proposal: 1
Board meeting date(s): Varies
Officers and Board Members:* Riva Ritro Slitka, Pres.; Shira Levin,* Secy.; Rachelle Markowitz, Treas.; Sarah Silver, Exec. Dir.; Gary Gladstein; Judith Eigen Sarna.
Number of staff: 3 full-time professional; 1 full-time support.
EIN: 136192257
Selected grants: The following grants are a representative sample of this grantmaker's funding activity:
$1,062,500 to Brandeis University, Waltham, MA, 2012.
$1,000,000 to Abraham Joshua Heschel School, New York, NY, 2012.
$600,000 to Abraham Fund Initiatives, New York, NY, 2012.
$600,000 to Abraham Fund Initiatives, New York, NY, 2012.
$200,000 to American Friends of the Israel Museum, New York, NY, 2012.
$100,000 to Harvard-Westlake School, North Hollywood, CA, 2012.
$50,000 to Big Apple Circus, Brooklyn, NY, 2012.
$25,000 to Shalom Hartman Institute of North America, New York, NY, 2012.
$17,500 to Santa Barbara Bowl Foundation, Santa Barbara, CA, 2012.
$10,000 to PEF Israel Endowment Funds, New York, NY, 2012.

6871
Joseph & Sylvia Slifka Foundation, Inc. ✧
c/o Hecht & Co. PC
350 5th Ave., 68th Fl.
New York, NY 10118-6710

Established in 1944 in NY.
Donors: Joseph Slifka†; Sylvia Slifka†; Barbara Slifka.
Foundation type: Independent foundation.
Financial data (yr. ended 10/31/13): Assets, $39,580,496 (M); expenditures, $8,721,036; qualifying distributions, $8,466,724; giving

activities include $8,443,334 for 34 grants (high: $2,000,000; low: $10,000).
Purpose and activities: Giving primarily for higher education and Jewish activities and philanthropy.
Fields of interest: Museums; Performing arts, ballet; Education; Jewish federated giving programs.
Limitations: Applications not accepted. Giving primarily in the metropolitan New York, NY, area. No grants to individuals.
Application information: Contributes only to pre-selected organizations.
Officers and Trustees:* Barbara S. Slifka,* Pres.; Michael Hecht,* V.P. and Treas.; John J. O'Neil,* Secy.
EIN: 136106433
Selected grants: The following grants are a representative sample of this grantmaker's funding activity:
$2,000,000 to New York City Ballet, New York, NY, 2012.
$1,000,000 to Big Apple Circus, Brooklyn, NY, 2012.
$1,000,000 to Graduate Center Foundation, New York, NY, 2012.
$500,000 to Jewish Communal Fund of New York, New York, NY, 2012.
$500,000 to Nature Conservancy, South Fork/Shelter Island Chapter, East Hampton, NY, 2012.
$500,000 to Robin Hood Foundation, New York, NY, 2012.
$500,000 to Solomon R. Guggenheim Foundation, New York, NY, 2012.
$350,000 to Peconic Land Trust, Southampton, NY, 2012.
$250,000 to Thomas Moran Trust, East Hampton, NY, 2012.
$150,000 to Childrens Storefront, New York, NY, 2012.

6872
Alfred P. Sloan Foundation ✧
630 5th Ave., Ste. 2550
New York, NY 10111-0242 (212) 649-1649
Contact: Paul L. Joskow, Pres.
FAX: (212) 757-5117; Main URL: http://www.sloan.org
Twitter: https://twitter.com/SloanFoundation

Incorporated in 1934 in DE.
Donors: Alfred P. Sloan, Jr.†; Irene Jackson Sloan†; New Castle Corp.
Foundation type: Independent foundation.
Financial data (yr. ended 12/31/13): Assets, $1,888,720,791 (M); expenditures, $103,206,694; qualifying distributions, $92,111,806; giving activities include $75,360,005 for 318 grants (high: $3,806,541; low: $6,500), $6,731,580 for 138 grants to individuals (high: $50,000; low: $27,269), and $664,463 for 4 foundation-administered programs.
Purpose and activities: Grants are made primarily to support original research and broad-based education related to science, technology, economic performance and the quality of American life. The foundation has a deep-rooted belief that carefully reasoned systematic understanding of the forces of nature and society, when applied inventively and wisely, can lead to a better world for all. In each of its grants programs, the foundation seeks proposals for original projects with a high expected return to society which are led by outstanding individuals or teams and for which funding from the private sector, government or other foundations is not yet widely available.
Fields of interest: Higher education; Safety/disasters, research; Family services; Science, administration/regulation; Science, research; Science, information services; Science, public education; Science, formal/general education; Science; Engineering/technology; Science; Economics.
Type of support: Research; Program evaluation.
Limitations: Applications accepted. Giving primarily focused on U.S. institutions with occasional grants to foreign institutions. No support for creative or performing arts (except for those that educate the public about science), or for humanities, religion, or primary or secondary education, or for projects aimed at pre-college students or for-profit institutions. No grants to individuals (except for research and publication), or for endowment or building funds, medical research, or equipment not related directly to foundation-supported projects; no loans.
Publications: Application guidelines; Annual report; Grants list; Informational brochure (including application guidelines); IRS Form 990 or 990-PF printed copy available upon request.
Application information: Nomination forms available on foundation web site for fellowship candidates; direct applications not accepted. Application procedures are available at http://www.sloan.org/apply. Application form not required.
Initial approach: Letter of inquiry
Copies of proposal: 1
Deadline(s): Rolling deadlines
Board meeting date(s): Quarterly
Final notification: Early in year for research fellowships; within 3 months for others
Officers and Trustees:* Sandra O. Moose,* Chair.; Paul L. Joskow,* Pres.; Leslie Lin,* Sr. V.P., Finance and Opers.; William B. Petersen,* Sr. V.P. and C.I.O.; Gail M. Pesyna,* V.P., Human Resources and Prog. Management; Daniel L. Goroff,* V.P., Progs.; Doron Weber,* V.P., Progs.; Christopher T. Sia,* Treas. and Chief Tech. Off.; Cynthia Barnhart; Francine Berman; Bonnie L. Bassler; Richard Bernstein; Kevin Burke; Mary Schmidt Campbell; Frederick Henderson; Freeman A. Hrabowski III; Peter S. Kim; Robert Litterman; James Poterba; Michael Purugganan; Marta Tienda.
Number of staff: 30
EIN: 131623877
Selected grants: The following grants are a representative sample of this grantmaker's funding activity:
$10,000,000 to Astrophysical Research Consortium, Seattle, WA, 2012. For the Sloan Digital Sky Survey IV, which will study the history of the Milky Way, the evolution of galaxies, and the expansion of the Universe and dark energy over the last 12 billion years, payable over 6.00 years.
$3,458,800 to National Action Council for Minorities in Engineering, White Plains, NY, 2012. To fund obligations in the Minority Ph.D. program and the Sloan Indigenous Graduate Partnership, payable over 5.00 years.
$3,200,145 to University of Texas, Austin, TX, 2012. To follow up the original nationally representative High School and Beyond (HSB) study to produce a valuable new data infrastructure and research findings about the foundation for working longer, payable over 3.00 years.
$3,000,000 to New York Genome Center, New York, NY, 2012. Toward New York Genome Center, payable over 3.00 years.
$1,200,000 to Digital Public Library of America, Boston, MA, 2012. To launch Digital Public Library of America (DPLA) as independent, national organization and hire executive director and two key staff to begin operations and scale up for the first two years, payable over 2.00 years.
$1,199,471 to Dartmouth College, Hanover, NH, 2012. To increase understanding of how recessions, including the Great Recession, affect the labor market activities and retirement of older Americans, payable over 4.00 years.
$685,950 to Mozilla Foundation, Mountain View, CA, 2012. To improve the quality of software produced by scientists, and to drive the development of tools, practices, and diverse community around digitally networked science, payable over 2.00 years.
$385,328 to Massachusetts Institute of Technology, Cambridge, MA, 2012. To examine the impacts of online working paper repositories on the diffusion of scholarly ideas, payable over 2.00 years.
$249,739 to Harvard University, Cambridge, MA, 2012. To examine the transmission of human associated microbes by public transportation surfaces, payable over 2.00 years.
$140,000 to International Association for Research in Income and Wealth, Ottawa, Canada, 2012. To study and share improvements for estimating gross domestic product.
$125,000 to W E T A-Greater Washington Educational Telecommunications Association, Arlington, VA, 2012. To enhance public understanding of the issues raised by aging U.S. workforce.
$100,000 to San Jose State University, San Jose, CA, 2012. For Winner of the 2012 Alfred P. Sloan Award for Best Practices for Faculty Retirement Transitions.
$50,000 to University of Victoria, Victoria, Canada, 2012. For Alfred P. Sloan Research Fellowship in Ocean Science, payable over 2.00 years.

6873
SMBC Global Foundation Inc. ✧ ☆
(formerly Sumitomo Bank Global Foundation)
277 Park Ave., 5th FL
New York, NY 10172-0002 (212) 224-4440
Contact: Makoto Takashima, Pres. and Dir.
Main URL: https://www.smbcgroup.com/

Established in 1994 in DE and NY.
Donors: Sumitomo Bank Capital Markets, Inc.; SMBC Capital Markets, Inc.
Foundation type: Company-sponsored foundation.
Financial data (yr. ended 12/31/13): Assets, $15,013,089 (M); expenditures, $801,426; qualifying distributions, $725,311; giving activities include $455,001 for 133 grants (high: $79,210; low: $20).
Purpose and activities: The foundation supports organizations involved with arts and culture, education, and human services.
Fields of interest: Arts; Education; Human services.
Type of support: Annual campaigns; Employee matching gifts; General/operating support; Scholarship funds.
Limitations: Applications accepted. Giving primarily in the NY Metro area and Asia. No support for political, religious, or discriminatory organizations. No grants to individuals directly.
Application information: Application form not required.

Initial approach: Request application form
Deadline(s): None
Officers and Directors:* Makoto Takashima,* Pres.; Jane Hutta, Secy.; Kei Ueda, Treas.; William Haney; Naoya Miyagaki; D. Scarborough Smith III.
EIN: 133766226
Selected grants: The following grants are a representative sample of this grantmaker's funding activity:
$50,000 to Manhattan Theater Club, New York, NY, 2012. For MTC's 2012 Benefit fundraiser.
$25,000 to Manhattan Theater Club, New York, NY, 2012. For MTCs 2012 Benefit fundraiser.
$25,000 to New York Cares, New York, NY, 2012. For grant to support volunteer projects to help homelessness hunger aids education seniors and the elderly HIV/AIDS the environment urban renewal.
$10,000 to Columbia University, New York, NY, 2012. To raise funds in order to find and train the next generation of acholans on Jape.
$10,000 to Japan Day, New York, NY, 2012. For Japan Day st Central Park, a festival to educate New Yorker's about the Japanese culture.
$10,000 to Japan Day, New York, NY, 2012. For Japan Day at Central Park, a festival to educate New Yorker's about the Japanese culture.
$1,000 to Houston Public Media Foundation, Houston, TX, 2012. For the organization's service for cultivating and engaging community resources to support its mission of opening minds changing lives and.
$1,000 to San Marino Schools Foundation, San Marino, CA, 2012. For In support for the organization's activity to raise money on behalf of the San Marino Unified School District.
$75 to Society for the Preservation of New England Antiquities, Boston, MA, 2012. For grant in support of preserving and presenting New England heritage.
$25 to Washington University, Saint Louis, MO, 2012. For In support for the organization's educational activities.

6874
Donald and Paula Smith Family Foundation, Inc. ✧
152 W. 57th St., 22nd Fl.
New York, NY 10019-3310

Established in 2000 in NJ.
Donors: Donald Smith; Paula Smith.
Foundation type: Operating foundation.
Financial data (yr. ended 08/31/13): Assets, $100,388,102 (M); gifts received, $10,595,837; expenditures, $8,680,263; qualifying distributions, $3,884,805; giving activities include $3,882,855 for 34 grants (high: $2,500,000; low: $50).
Fields of interest: Recreation, parks/playgrounds; Civil liberties, first amendment; Public affairs.
Limitations: Applications not accepted. Giving primarily in Washington, DC and NY. No grants to individuals.
Application information: Contributes only to pre-selected organizations.
Officers: Donald Smith, Pres. and Treas.; Paula Smith, V.P. and Secy.
Directors: Gary Gerstein; Julie Smith; Laura Smith.
EIN: 223732524
Selected grants: The following grants are a representative sample of this grantmaker's funding activity:
$1,200,000 to Vanguard Charitable Endowment Program, Boston, MA, 2011.

6875
The Matthew & Tracy Smith Foundation ✧ ☆
c/o Anchin Block & Anchin LLP
1375 Broadway
New York, NY 10018

Donors: Matthew Smith; Tracy Smith.
Foundation type: Independent foundation.
Financial data (yr. ended 09/30/13): Assets, $2,263,175 (M); gifts received, $7,530; expenditures, $512,631; qualifying distributions, $501,853; giving activities include $501,853 for 26 grants (high: $395,000; low: $500).
Fields of interest: Arts; Education; Human services.
Type of support: General/operating support.
Limitations: Applications not accepted. Giving primarily in FL.
Application information: Unsolicited requests for funds not accepted.
Trustees: Matthew Smith; Tracy Smith.
EIN: 276974020

6876
R. C. Smith Foundation, Inc. ✧
35 W. Main St.
P.O. Box 552
Norwich, NY 13815-0552 (607) 336-5850
Contact: Richard M. Runyon, Exec. Dir.
FAX: (607) 334-8121;
E-mail: rcsmithfoundation@frontiernet.net; Main URL: http://www.rcsmithfoundation.org

Established in 2005 in NY.
Donor: Robert C. Smith†.
Foundation type: Operating foundation.
Financial data (yr. ended 12/31/13): Assets, $18,320,082 (M); expenditures, $951,673; qualifying distributions, $849,982; giving activities include $822,883 for 43 grants (high: $180,000; low: $1,000).
Purpose and activities: Giving primarily for community activities and betterment, as well as for religious agencies.
Fields of interest: Catholic agencies & churches; Religion; Children/youth; Economically disadvantaged.
Type of support: Emergency funds.
Limitations: Applications accepted. Giving primarily in Chenango County, NY.
Publications: Application guidelines; Annual report; Grants list.
Application information: Application guidelines and form available on foundation web site. Application form required.
Initial approach: Use application format on foundation web site
Copies of proposal: 10
Deadline(s): Quarterly: Jan. 1, Apr. 1, July 1, and Oct. 1
Board meeting date(s): Quarterly, in Jan., Apr., July, and Oct.
Officers and Directors:* William Troxell,* Pres.; Betsy Baio,* V.P.; Thomas C. Emerson, Secy.; William Acee,* Treas.; Richard M. Runyon,* Exec. Dir.; Gary Brookins; Mary W. Davis; Pegi LoPresti; Nancy Ritzel.
EIN: 201893940
Selected grants: The following grants are a representative sample of this grantmaker's funding activity:
$50,000 to Chenango Memorial Hospital, Norwich, NY, 2012. For Equipment and Interior Renovations.
$15,000 to Hospice of Chenango County, Norwich, NY, 2012. For patient medication support.
$13,849 to Chenango County Historical Society, Norwich, NY, 2012. For Building Expansion, Renovation and Furnishings.

6877
George D. Smith Fund, Inc. ✧
c/o L.W. Milas & W.B. Norden, Seyfarth Shaw, LLP
620 8th Ave., Ste. 3200
New York, NY 10018-1415 (212) 218-3316
Contact: Lawrence W. Milas, V.P.

Incorporated in 1956 in DE.
Donor: George D. Smith, Sr.†.
Foundation type: Independent foundation.
Financial data (yr. ended 12/31/13): Assets, $112,061,228 (M); expenditures, $16,968,905; qualifying distributions, $16,903,839; giving activities include $16,900,100 for 11 grants (high: $5,000,000; low: $100).
Fields of interest: Media, television; Higher education; Biomedicine; Medical research, institute.
Type of support: Research.
Limitations: Applications not accepted. Giving primarily in CA.
Application information: Unsolicited requests for funds not considered.
Officers: George D. Smith, Jr., Pres. and Secy.-Treas.; Lawrence W. Milas, V.P.; Camilla M. Smith, V.P.
Director: Sarah A. Smith.
EIN: 136138728
Selected grants: The following grants are a representative sample of this grantmaker's funding activity:
$5,000,000 to Stanford Hospital and Clinics, Stanford, CA, 2013. For general support.
$5,000,000 to Stanford University Medical Center Auxiliary, Stanford, CA, 2012. For general support.
$5,000,000 to University of California San Francisco Foundation, San Francisco, CA, 2012. For general support.
$5,000,000 to University of California San Francisco Foundation, San Francisco, CA, 2013. For general support.
$2,000,000 to Teachers College Columbia University, New York, NY, 2013. For general support.
$1,200,000 to Carter Center, Atlanta, GA, 2013. For general support.
$1,200,000 to National Public Radio, Washington, DC, 2012. For general support.
$1,200,000 to NPR Foundation, Washington, DC, 2013. For general support.
$1,100,000 to Carter Center, Atlanta, GA, 2012. For general support.
$800,000 to Planned Parenthood Federation of America, New York, NY, 2012. For general support.
$800,000 to Planned Parenthood Federation of America, New York, NY, 2013. For general support.
$500,000 to University of Utah, Salt Lake City, UT, 2012. For general support.
$500,000 to University of Utah, Salt Lake City, UT, 2013. For general support.
$500,000 to W G B H Educational Foundation, Boston, MA, 2012. For general support.
$500,000 to W G B H Educational Foundation, Boston, MA, 2013. For general support.
$300,000 to University of Utah, Marriott Library, Salt Lake City, UT, 2012. For general support.

$300,000 to University of Utah, Marriott Library, Salt Lake City, UT, 2013. For general support.

6878
John Ben Snow Memorial Trust ✧
50 Presidential Plz., Ste. 106
Syracuse, NY 13202-2279
Contact: (For NY): Jonathan L. Snow, Tr.
E-mail: johnbensnow@verizon.net; Regional offices: c/o Valerie Macfie, Tr., 3587 Rte. 9 N., No. 304, Freehold, NJ 07728, e-mail: vmacfiejbs.nj@gmail.com; c/o Emelie M. Williams, Tr., P.O. Box 5605, Reno, NV 89513, e-mail: jbs.nevada@gmail.com; Main URL: http://www.johnbensnow.com/jbsmt

Established in 1975 in NY.
Donor: John Ben Snow†.
Foundation type: Independent foundation.
Financial data (yr. ended 12/31/13): Assets, $28,969,858 (M); expenditures, $1,454,280; qualifying distributions, $1,288,580; giving activities include $1,167,450 for 84 grants (high: $80,000; low: $1,000).
Purpose and activities: Support primarily for higher education, scholarship funds, the humanities and cultural institutions, especially libraries, the performing arts, theater, and historical preservation; environmental groups; media and communications; and community development. Support also for organizations for people who are handicapped.
Fields of interest: Media, print publishing; Performing arts; Performing arts, theater; Historic preservation/historical societies; Arts; Higher education; Libraries/library science; Education; Environment; Health organizations, association; Children/youth, services; Youth, services; Community/economic development; Children/youth; Disabilities, people with.
Type of support: Building/renovation; Equipment; Program development; Publication; Seed money; Curriculum development; Fellowships; Scholarship funds; Matching/challenge support.
Limitations: Applications accepted. Giving primarily in NJ, NV, and central NY. No support for unspecified projects, religious organizations, or for-profit groups. No grants to individuals, or for operating budgets, endowment funds, or contingency financing; no loans.
Publications: Annual report (including application guidelines); Grants list.
Application information: Contact closest regional office. Refer to foundation web site for grant application procedures. Application form required.
Initial approach: Letter of inquiry by Jan. 1 of the year for which funding is requested
Copies of proposal: 1
Deadline(s): Apr. 1 of the year for which funding is requested
Board meeting date(s): June
Final notification: July 1
Trustees: Valerie MacFie; Jonathan L. Snow; Emelie Melton Williams; BNY Mellon, N.A.
Number of staff: None.
EIN: 134941102

6879
The Ted Snowdon Foundation ✧
(formerly The Snowdon Foundation)
50 Riverside Dr., No. 15-C
New York, NY 10024-6508
Contact: Edward W. Snowdon, Jr., Pres.
E-mail: snowdonfound@aol.com; Tel./Fax: (212) 787-2413

Established in 1997 in DE and NY.
Donor: Edward W. Snowdon, Jr.
Foundation type: Independent foundation.
Financial data (yr. ended 04/30/13): Assets, $4,052,419 (M); expenditures, $854,026; qualifying distributions, $772,000; giving activities include $772,000 for grants.
Purpose and activities: Giving to promote research and study, production and dissemination of the performing arts, and to encourage interest in many forms of artistic endeavor; provide financial aid and assistance to organizations attending principally to the concerns and needs of the lesbian and gay community.
Fields of interest: Performing arts, theater; Performing arts, theater (musical); Performing arts, opera; Arts; Health care; AIDS; Human services; Civil/human rights, LGBTQ; LGBTQ.
Limitations: Applications accepted. Giving primarily in New York, NY. No grants to individuals.
Publications: Application guidelines.
Application information: Unsolicited proposals are not considered.
Initial approach: 1-page letter of introduction requesting the grant application procedure
Deadline(s): Feb. 1 and Aug. 1
Board meeting date(s): Apr. and Oct.
Final notification: Apr. 30 and Oct. 31
Officers and Directors:* Edward W. Snowdon, Jr., Pres.; Richard W. Snowdon,* V.P.; Robert S. Blaustein, Secy.; Deborah Ensign.
Number of staff: 1 part-time support.
EIN: 133948662
Selected grants: The following grants are a representative sample of this grantmaker's funding activity:
$11,000 to New Dramatists, New York, NY, 2013. For General Grants to Donee.

6880
Beatrice Snyder Foundation ✧
c/o Arthur V. Fox, CPA, P.C.
126 E. 56th St., 12th Fl.
New York, NY 10022-3613

Established in 1998.
Donors: Harold Snyder†; Beryl L. Snyder; Jay Snyder; Brian Snyder.
Foundation type: Independent foundation.
Financial data (yr. ended 05/31/13): Assets, $28,821,846 (M); gifts received, $413,000; expenditures, $1,545,066; qualifying distributions, $1,470,300; giving activities include $1,470,300 for 44 grants (high: $175,000; low: $1,000).
Purpose and activities: Giving primarily for education, human services, and hospitals.
Fields of interest: Education; Hospitals (general); Human services; Foundations (private grantmaking).
Limitations: Applications not accepted. Giving primarily in NY. No grants to individuals.
Application information: Contributes only to pre-selected organizations.
Trustees: Beryl L. Snyder; Brian S. Snyder; Jay T. Snyder.
EIN: 223595071

6881
The SO Charitable Trust ✧
c/o Alpine Resources LLC, Oded Aboodi
P.O. Box 5028
New York, NY 10150-5028

Established in 1980 in NJ.
Donors: Oded Aboodi; Moses Marx; Kenneth Wang; Vera Wang-Becker; Victor Yen; Vincent Yen; Summer Assocs.; The Courtside Charitable Foundation.
Foundation type: Independent foundation.
Financial data (yr. ended 11/30/13): Assets, $2,305,025 (M); gifts received, $720,940; expenditures, $447,177; qualifying distributions, $447,177; giving activities include $447,177 for 165 grants (high: $99,289; low: $100).
Purpose and activities: Giving primarily for Jewish education, agencies and temples; funding also for the arts, children and social services, education and health care.
Fields of interest: Museums; Arts; Elementary/secondary education; Higher education; Theological school/education; Education; Health care; Health organizations, association; Human services; Children, services; Jewish federated giving programs; Jewish agencies & synagogues.
Limitations: Applications not accepted. Giving primarily in the metropolitan New York, NY, area, including Long Island and Westchester; some funding nationally, particularly in FL and NJ. No grants to individuals.
Application information: Contributes only to pre-selected organizations.
Trustees: Oded Aboodi; Solomon M. Weiss.
EIN: 133050892

6882
The Jonathan Sobel and Marcia Dunn Foundation ✧
P.O. Box 73, Bowling Green Sta.
New York, NY 10274-0073

Established in 1999 in NY.
Donor: Jonathan Sobel.
Foundation type: Independent foundation.
Financial data (yr. ended 11/30/13): Assets, $49,406 (M); expenditures, $886,410; qualifying distributions, $876,271; giving activities include $876,271 for 51 grants (high: $200,000; low: $100).
Purpose and activities: Giving primarily for the arts, education, health, and Jewish agencies and temples.
Fields of interest: Museums; Arts; Education; Hospitals (specialty); Health organizations, association; Jewish agencies & synagogues.
Limitations: Applications not accepted. Giving primarily in New York, NY. No grants to individuals.
Application information: Contributes only to pre-selected organizations.
Trustees: Marcia Dunn; Jonathan Sobel.
EIN: 134050663

6883
The Robert and Karen Sobel Charitable Foundation ✧
20 Westerleigh Rd.
Purchase, NY 10577-2505

Established in 1999 in NY.
Donors: Robert J. Sobel; Karen Sobel.
Foundation type: Independent foundation.
Financial data (yr. ended 12/31/13): Assets, $459,626 (M); gifts received, $1,062,500; expenditures, $728,853; qualifying distributions, $727,390; giving activities include $727,390 for 24 grants (high: $550,000; low: $100).
Fields of interest: Arts; Education, early childhood education; Higher education; Health organizations; Jewish federated giving programs; Jewish agencies & synagogues.
Limitations: Applications not accepted. Giving primarily in NY. No grants to individuals.
Application information: Contributes only to pre-selected organizations.
Officers: Robert J. Sobel, Pres.; Karen Sobel, V.P.
EIN: 137196988
Selected grants: The following grants are a representative sample of this grantmaker's funding activity:
$1,000 to Leukemia & Lymphoma Society, White Plains, NY, 2011.

6884
Dr. Robert C. and Tina Sohn Foundation ✧
(formerly Sohn Foundation)
825 3rd Ave., 20th Fl.
New York, NY 10022-7519 (212) 408-0590
Main URL: http://www.sohnfoundation.org

Established in 1993.
Donors: Robert C. Sohn; Tina Sohn.
Foundation type: Independent foundation.
Financial data (yr. ended 12/31/13): Assets, $7,166,002 (M); expenditures, $818,581; qualifying distributions, $718,060; giving activities include $531,000 for 64 grants (high: $50,000; low: $500).
Purpose and activities: Giving primarily for the environment, alternative health care, human services, education, and the arts.
Fields of interest: Arts; Education; Environment; Health care; Human services.
Type of support: General/operating support.
Limitations: Giving primarily in MA and NY. No grants for deficits, endowments, annual appeals, dinners, special fundraising, or financing; no loans.
Publications: Application guidelines.
Application information: Application guidelines available on foundation web site.
Initial approach: Letter
Officers and Trustees:* Barry R. Shapiro,* C.E.O. and Pres.; Norman Leben,* Exec. V.P. and C.F.O.; Ray Kasevich; Stella Lellos; William Leone.
EIN: 990306576
Selected grants: The following grants are a representative sample of this grantmaker's funding activity:
$50,000 to Jewish Board of Family and Childrens Services, New York, NY, 2010.
$50,000 to Jewish Board of Family and Childrens Services, New York, NY, 2011.
$25,000 to Shakespeare and Company, Lenox, MA, 2010.
$15,000 to Figure Skating in Harlem, New York, NY, 2011.
$15,000 to Healthy Schools Network, Albany, NY, 2010.
$10,000 to Careers Through Culinary Arts Program, New York, NY, 2011.
$10,000 to Council on the Environment, New York, NY, 2011.
$10,000 to Education Through Music, New York, NY, 2011.
$10,000 to Family Life Academy, Bronx, NY, 2011.
$10,000 to Figure Skating in Harlem, New York, NY, 2010.
$10,000 to Harlem Academy, New York, NY, 2011.
$10,000 to Humane Farming Association, San Rafael, CA, 2010.
$10,000 to New York Botanical Garden, Bronx, NY, 2011.
$10,000 to Queens Botanical Garden Society, Flushing, NY, 2010.
$5,635 to National Center for Disability Services, Albertson, NY, 2011.
$5,000 to Community Access to the Arts, Great Barrington, MA, 2011.
$5,000 to UPROSE, Brooklyn, NY, 2010.

6885
Peter J. Solomon Foundation ✧
(formerly Peter J. & Linda N. Solomon Foundation)
c/o Barry M. Strauss Assocs., Ltd.
307 5th Ave., 8th Fl.
New York, NY 10016-6517

Established in 1986 in NY.
Donors: Peter J. Solomon; Peter J. Solomon Charitable Remainder Unitrust; Jeanette R. Solomon Trust.
Foundation type: Independent foundation.
Financial data (yr. ended 03/31/13): Assets, $11,259,376 (M); gifts received, $906,967; expenditures, $876,187; qualifying distributions, $681,629; giving activities include $674,604 for 74 grants (high: $169,433; low: $1).
Purpose and activities: Giving primarily for the arts and to cultural organizations; support also for human services, and to a cancer hospital.
Fields of interest: Media, radio; Performing arts, theater; Arts; Higher education; Education; Hospitals (specialty); Health organizations; Human services; Jewish federated giving programs; Jewish agencies & synagogues.
Type of support: Annual campaigns; Capital campaigns; Building/renovation; Endowments; Scholarship funds.
Limitations: Applications not accepted. Giving primarily in New York, NY. No grants to individuals.
Application information: Contributes only to pre-selected organizations.
Trustee: Peter J. Solomon.
EIN: 133384028
Selected grants: The following grants are a representative sample of this grantmaker's funding activity:
$85,000 to Council on Foreign Relations, New York, NY, 2011.
$75,000 to Harvard University, Cambridge, MA, 2011.
$10,000 to American Rivers, Washington, DC, 2011.
$2,000 to Planned Parenthood of New York City, New York, NY, 2011.
$1,000 to Tufts University, Medford, MA, 2011.

6886
Alfred Z. Solomon Testamentary Trust ✧
P.O. Box 108
Saratoga Springs, NY 12866 (518) 584-1500

Established in 2005 in NY.
Donor: Alfred L. Solomon†.
Foundation type: Independent foundation.
Financial data (yr. ended 12/31/13): Assets, $7,286,669 (M); expenditures, $581,843; qualifying distributions, $537,079; giving activities include $518,316 for 21 grants (high: $300,000; low: $1,000).
Fields of interest: Museums (specialized); Performing arts, theater; Historical activities; Arts; Education; Health care; Food services; American Red Cross; Salvation Army; Jewish agencies & synagogues.
Limitations: Applications accepted. Giving primarily in Saratoga Springs, NY.
Application information: Application form required.
Initial approach: Proposal
Deadline(s): Nov. 1
Trustees: Victoria Garlanda; Harry D. Snyder.
EIN: 137430894

6887
The Solomon Wilson Family Foundation, Inc. ✧ ☆
915 Broadway, Ste. 1408
New York, NY 10010-7143 (516) 874-8800
Contact: Frederick R. Wilson

Established in 2000 in NY.
Donor: Frederick R. Wilson.
Foundation type: Independent foundation.
Financial data (yr. ended 12/31/12): Assets, $48,240 (M); gifts received, $400,155; expenditures, $789,271; qualifying distributions, $788,900; giving activities include $788,900 for grants.
Fields of interest: Education; Community/economic development.
Limitations: Applications accepted. Giving primarily in CT and NY. No grants to individuals.
Application information:
Initial approach: Letter
Deadline(s): None
Officers and Directors:* Frederick R. Wilson, Pres. and Treas.; Joanne S. Wilson,* V.P. and Secy.; Susan G. Soloman.
EIN: 134092426

6888
Paul & Daisy Soros Fellowships for New Americans ✧
(formerly Paul & Daisy Soros Foundation)
400 W. 59th St., 4th Fl.
New York, NY 10019-1105 (212) 547-6926
FAX: (212) 548-4623;
E-mail: pdsoros_fellows@sorosny.org; Main URL: http://www.pdsoros.org

Established in 1994 in NY.
Donor: Paul Soros.
Foundation type: Independent foundation.
Financial data (yr. ended 12/31/12): Assets, $48,405,686 (M); gifts received, $331,782; expenditures, $4,382,955; qualifying distributions, $4,168,190; giving activities include $963,239 for 8 grants (high: $300,000; low: $20,000), and

$2,401,386 for 86 grants to individuals (high: $57,500; low: $5,000).
Purpose and activities: Grants to new Americans for graduate study. Giving limited to permanent U.S. residents, naturalized U.S. citizens, and U.S.-born applicants who are the children of two naturalized U.S. citizens.
Fields of interest: Education; Adults; Immigrants/refugees.
Type of support: Fellowships; Grants to individuals.
Limitations: Applications accepted. Giving on a national basis. No grants for academic fees other than tuition.
Publications: Application guidelines; Informational brochure; Newsletter.
Application information: Application forms, guidelines, and guidance for recommenders for the Fellowship for New Americans are available on foundation web site. Application form required.
Initial approach: See Web site for details
Deadline(s): Nov. 1 (it is encouraged that materials be submitted prior to this date)
Board meeting date(s): Feb. and Oct. of each year.
Final notification: 2 months from Nov. 1
Director: Yulian Ramos, Deputy Dir.; Stanley J. Heginbotham.
Trustee: Daisy Soros.
Number of staff: 2 full-time professional; 1 full-time support.
EIN: 137057096

6889
Alexander Soros Foundation ✧
c/o SFM LLC
888 7th Ave., 33rd Fl.
New York, NY 10106

Donor: Alexander Soros.
Foundation type: Independent foundation.
Financial data (yr. ended 12/31/13): Assets, $1,520,681 (M); gifts received, $1,000,000; expenditures, $482,209; qualifying distributions, $482,209; giving activities include $481,667 for 5 grants (high: $150,000; low: $65,000).
Fields of interest: Education; Human services; Jewish agencies & synagogues; Religion.
Type of support: General/operating support.
Limitations: Applications not accepted. Giving primarily in San Francisco, CA and New York, NY.
Application information: Unsolicited requests for funds not accepted.
Trustee: Alexander Soros.
EIN: 453133937

6890
Jennifer and Jonathan Allan Soros Foundation ✧
c/o SFM
888 7th Ave., 33rd. Fl.
New York, NY 10106-0001

Established in 2009 in NY.
Donors: Jonathan Soros; Allasor Corporation; Geosor Corp.
Foundation type: Independent foundation.
Financial data (yr. ended 12/31/12): Assets, $84,355,662 (M); expenditures, $4,090,174; qualifying distributions, $4,010,174; giving activities include $3,984,000 for 31 grants (high: $925,000; low: $5,000).
Fields of interest: Education; Human services; Civil liberties, death penalty issues.
Limitations: Applications not accepted. Giving in the U.S., with emphasis on NY; some emphasis also on NC. No grants to individuals.
Application information: Contributes only to pre-selected organizations.
Officers: Jonathan Soros, Chair.; Jennifer Allan, Pres.; Daniel R. Eule, Secy.-Treas.
EIN: 800464952

6891
Soros Fund Charitable Foundation ✧
(formerly SGM Scholarship Foundation)
888 7th Ave., 33rd Fl.
New York, NY 10106-0011

Established in 1986 in NY.
Donors: George Soros; Soros Charitable Foundation; Soros Foundation-Hungary; Centennial Foundation.
Foundation type: Independent foundation.
Financial data (yr. ended 12/31/13): Assets, $280,421,230 (M); expenditures, $9,095,745; qualifying distributions, $8,932,052; giving activities include $8,932,052 for 485 grants (high: $1,150,000; low: $75).
Purpose and activities: Awards scholarships to students who have demonstrated an ability for contributing to the scientific, cultural, or economic development of China, and fellowships to individuals involved in the fields of culture, economics, and science. The scholarships and fellowships may be used for trips to the U.S. and other countries by Chinese nationals and trips to China by non-Chinese nationals. Support also for international organizations and U.S. philanthropic organizations supporting international issues.
Fields of interest: Education; Health care; Health organizations, association; Human services; Children/youth, services; International affairs, goodwill promotion; Civil rights, race/intergroup relations; Christian agencies & churches; Jewish agencies & synagogues.
International interests: Eastern Asia.
Type of support: General/operating support; Fellowships; Scholarship funds.
Limitations: Applications not accepted. Giving primarily in CT, NJ, and NY. No grants to individuals.
Application information: Contributes only to pre-selected organizations.
Officers and Directors:* Gary Gladstein,* Pres.; Daniel R. Eule,* V.P. and Secy.; Maryann Canfield, Treas.; Armando Belly; Alexander Soros; George Soros; Jonathan Allan Soros; Robert Soros; William D. Zabel.
EIN: 133388177

6892
Martin and Toni Sosnoff Foundation ✧
(formerly Martin T. Sosnoff Foundation)
P.O. Box 135
Rhinebeck, NY 12572-0135

Established in 1978 in NY.
Donors: Martin T. Sosnoff; Toni Sosnoff.
Foundation type: Independent foundation.
Financial data (yr. ended 11/30/13): Assets, $15,179,517 (M); gifts received, $2,874,400; expenditures, $2,412,129; qualifying distributions, $2,322,643; giving activities include $2,322,643 for 39 grants (high: $750,000; low: $17).
Purpose and activities: Giving primarily for the performing arts, as well as for medical school education and to a hospital.
Fields of interest: Performing arts; Performing arts centers; Performing arts, ballet; Medical school/education; Hospitals (general).
Type of support: General/operating support; Building/renovation.
Limitations: Applications not accepted. Giving primarily in NY. No support for private foundations. No grants to individuals.
Application information: Contributes only to pre-selected organizations.
Trustees: Martin T. Sosnoff; Toni Sosnoff.
EIN: 222231640

6893
Source of Hope Foundation ✧
c/o Stephen Robert, Tr.
667 Madison Ave., Ste. 17B
New York, NY 10065-8029 (212) 583-7002
E-mail: gina@sourceofhope.com; Main URL: http://www.sourceofhope.com/

Established in NY.
Donors: Stephen Robert; Pilar Crespi Robert.
Foundation type: Independent foundation.
Financial data (yr. ended 06/30/13): Assets, $23,929,195 (M); gifts received, $1,100,000; expenditures, $3,694,346; qualifying distributions, $3,681,214; giving activities include $3,426,200 for 26 grants (high: $1,000,000; low: $500).
Purpose and activities: The mission of the foundation is to help people in desperate need through a holistic approach that supplies sustainable aid in the form of food, water, health care, education and micro-finance.
Fields of interest: Housing/shelter, temporary shelter; Human services.
Limitations: Applications not accepted. Giving primarily in NY and OR.
Application information: Unsolicited requests for funds not accepted.
Officers: Stephen Robert, Chair. and Co-C.E.O.; Pilar Crespi Robert, Co-C.E.O. and Pres.
EIN: 264380918

6894
The Sparkplug Foundation ✧ ☆
Park West Finance Station
P.O. Box 20956
New York, NY 10025-0016 (877) 866-8285
E-mail: info@sparkplugfoundation.org; Tel./Fax: (877) 866-8285; Main URL: http://www.sparkplugfoundation.org/
Grants Database: http://sparkplugfoundation.org/past-grants

Established in 2003 in NY.
Donors: Felice Gelman; Yoram Gelman; Emmaia Gelman.
Foundation type: Independent foundation.
Financial data (yr. ended 12/31/13): Assets, $5,846,258 (M); expenditures, $582,222; qualifying distributions, $440,665; giving activities include $439,480 for 55 grants (high: $10,100; low: $4,000).
Purpose and activities: Giving is focused on providing seed money for new organizations,

projects or ideas. The foundation makes one-time grants for activities which create sustainable organizing and communities, while recognizing the importance of developing individual cultures by favoring projects that promote diversity. The main areas of focus are music, education, and grassroots organizations, as well as exploring funding projects in the area of alternative and sustainable energies.
Fields of interest: Performing arts, music ensembles/groups; Education; Environment; International human rights; International migration/refugee issues; International affairs; Community/economic development; Science; Young adults; Minorities; Asians/Pacific Islanders; African Americans/Blacks; Hispanics/Latinos; Native Americans/American Indians; Indigenous peoples; Adults, women; AIDS, people with; Immigrants/refugees; LGBTQ.
International interests: East Jerusalem; Israel; West Bank/Gaza (Palestinian Territories).
Type of support: Management development/capacity building; Program development; Conferences/seminars; Publication; Seed money; Curriculum development; Research; Technical assistance; Program evaluation; Grants to individuals.
Limitations: Applications accepted. Giving to every state in the USA. Some giving in Israel for projects that involve Palestinian communities. No support for university-based projects, or for non-secular activities. No grants to non-501(c)(3) organizations unless they have a fiscal sponsor. No grants for performances, tickets or tuitions, equipment, computers or for operating support.
Application information: Complete application guidelines and deadlines available on foundation web site. Application form required.
Initial approach: Submit preliminary questionnaire on foundation web site
Copies of proposal: 1
Board meeting date(s): Within 4 weeks of deadline dates
Final notification: Usually within 1 month
Trustees: Felice Gelman; Yoram Gelman; Emmaia Gelman.
Number of staff: 1 part-time professional.
EIN: 331033952

6895
The Sperry Fund ✧
99 Park Ave., Ste. 2220
New York, NY 10016-1601
Contact: Thomas L. Parkinson Ph.D., Prog. Dir.
Scholarship program URL: http://foundationcenter.org/grantmaker/beinecke/index.html, tel.: (610) 395-5560, e-mail: BeineckeScholarship@earthlink.net

Established in 1962 in NY.
Foundation type: Independent foundation.
Financial data (yr. ended 06/30/13): Assets, $16,710,206 (M); gifts received, $10,000; expenditures, $1,041,824; qualifying distributions, $963,069; giving activities include $255,000 for 12 grants (high: $25,000; low: $10,000), and $578,274 for grants to individuals.
Purpose and activities: The foundation provides scholarships for the graduate education of young men and women of exceptional promise through the Beinecke Scholarship Program.
Fields of interest: Education.
Type of support: Program development; Scholarships—to individuals.
Limitations: Applications not accepted. Giving primarily in NY.
Publications: Informational brochure.
Application information: College or university must be invited to nominate juniors for scholarship program; completion of application form required for nominees. Applications outside the nomination process not considered. See scholarship web site for guidelines.
Officers and Directors:* Frederick W. Beinecke, Pres.; John B. Beinecke,* V.P.; R. Scott Greathead,* Secy.; Robert J. Barletta, Treas.; William S. Beinecke; Frances Beinecke Elston; Sarah Beinecke Richardson; Melvyn L. Shaffir.
Number of staff: 1 part-time support.
EIN: 136114308

6896
The Speyer Family Foundation, Inc. ✧
(formerly Tishman Speyer Properties Foundation, Inc.)
45 Rockefeller Plz., 7th Fl.
New York, NY 10111-0100 (212) 715-0300

Established in NY.
Donors: Katherine G. Farley; Jerry I. Speyer; Robert Speyer; Tishman Speyer Properties, LP.
Foundation type: Independent foundation.
Financial data (yr. ended 09/30/13): Assets, $706,478 (M); gifts received, $5,277,585; expenditures, $5,112,618; qualifying distributions, $5,109,267; giving activities include $5,109,267 for 40 grants (high: $2,000,000; low: $1,000).
Purpose and activities: Giving primarily for museums, education, health care, and the arts.
Fields of interest: Museums (art); Museums (natural history); Performing arts; Arts; Higher education; Education; Hospitals (general); Health organizations; Human services; International human rights; Civil/human rights, immigrants; Jewish agencies & synagogues.
Limitations: Applications not accepted. Giving primarily in New York, NY. No grants to individuals.
Application information: Contributes only to pre-selected organizations.
Officers: Jerry I. Speyer, Pres.; Katherine G. Farley, V.P.; Linda Szoldatits, Secy.; Richard Welch, Treas.
Directors: Holly Lipton; Valerie Peltier; Robert Speyer.
EIN: 136158848
Selected grants: The following grants are a representative sample of this grantmaker's funding activity:
$2,000,000 to Museum of Modern Art, New York, NY, 2012.
$2,000,000 to New York-Presbyterian Fund, New York, NY, 2013. For general support.
$1,000,000 to Lincoln Center for the Performing Arts, New York, NY, 2012.
$350,000 to Columbia University, New York, NY, 2012.
$333,334 to Dalton Schools, New York, NY, 2013. For general support.
$333,333 to Dalton Schools, New York, NY, 2012.
$250,000 to Lincoln Center for the Performing Arts, New York, NY, 2012.
$250,000 to Yale University, New Haven, CT, 2012.
$250,000 to Yale University, New Haven, CT, 2013. For general support.
$240,000 to New York Community Trust, New York, NY, 2012.
$200,000 to International Rescue Committee, New York, NY, 2013. For program support.
$200,000 to New York Genome Center, New York, NY, 2013. For research.
$150,000 to Community Funds, New York, NY, 2013. For general support.
$100,000 to Dalton Schools, New York, NY, 2012.
$100,000 to Fidelity Charitable Gift Fund, Boston, MA, 2012.
$100,000 to Foundation for Contemporary Arts, New York, NY, 2013. For performances.
$100,000 to International Rescue Committee, New York, NY, 2013. For program support.
$80,000 to Museum of Modern Art, New York, NY, 2012. For exhibition.
$50,000 to Lincoln Center Theater, New York, NY, 2013. For performances.
$50,000 to Yale University, New Haven, CT, 2013. For general support.

6897
Marc & Diane Spilker Foundation ✧
Bowling Green Sta.
P.O. Box 73
New York, NY 10274-0073

Established in 1996 in NY.
Donor: Marc Spilker.
Foundation type: Independent foundation.
Financial data (yr. ended 04/30/13): Assets, $11,572,217 (M); gifts received, $1,186,380; expenditures, $577,097; qualifying distributions, $546,282; giving activities include $546,282 for 32 grants (high: $200,000; low: $100).
Fields of interest: Arts; Education; Human services; Jewish federated giving programs; Jewish agencies & synagogues.
International interests: Israel.
Type of support: General/operating support.
Limitations: Applications not accepted. Giving primarily in FL and NY. No grants to individuals; no loans or scholarships.
Application information: Contributes only to pre-selected organizations.
Trustees: Diane Spilker; Marc Spilker.
EIN: 133933345

6898
Spinal Muscular Atrophy Foundation ✧
(also known as SMA Foundation)
888 7th Ave., Ste. 400
New York, NY 10106-0401 (646) 253-7100
FAX: (212) 247-3079;
E-mail: info@smafoundation.org; Toll-free tel. (outside of NY only): (877) 386-3762; Main URL: http://www.smafoundation.org/
Twitter: https://twitter.com/smafoundation

Established in 2003 in NY.
Donors: Loren Eng; Dinakar Singh; Muneer Satter; Jason Amiss; John Zacamy; Richard Perry; Phillip D. Murphy; Timothy Dattels; Eric Mandelblatt; Deborah Heine; Bryan White; Christine White; Cynthia Joyce; James & Chantel Sheridan Foundation; The Shea Megale Fund Corp.; The Jonathan Leff Family Fund; Jonathan L. Cohen; Association Francaise Contre Les Myopath; Goldman Sachs & Co.; Jackie Nydick; Jay Nydick; Helen Meates; Coulter 2006 Management Trust; Kristine Johnson; Doyle Busskohl; Jane Bisskohl; Satter Foundation; Holly Beach Public Library; Vishwa Singh; TPG Holding LP; Beth Kojima; Chris Kojima; Genzyme Corporation; Santhera Pharmaceuticals; Credit Agricole Asset

Management; Matthew Browe; Julie Oh; TPG Axon Capital.
Foundation type: Independent foundation.
Financial data (yr. ended 12/31/13): Assets, $1,058,832 (M); gifts received, $3,264,191; expenditures, $3,580,888; qualifying distributions, $3,349,031; giving activities include $1,018,560 for 8 grants (high: $634,320; low: $15,000), and $903,309 for foundation-administered programs.
Purpose and activities: The mission of the foundation is to accelerate the development of a treatment or a cure for spinal muscular atrophy (SMA), the number one genetic killer of infants and toddlers.
Fields of interest: Spine disorders.
Type of support: Research.
Limitations: Applications not accepted. Giving primarily in CA, MA, MD, NY and PA. No grants for salaries, construction, computer equipment, memberships (in scientific societies), office supplies, tuitions, or for publication costs.
Application information: Unsolicited requests for funds not accepted.
Officers and Directors:* Dinakar Singh,* Chair.; Karen S. Chen, Ph.D., C.O.O.; Loren A. Eng,* Pres.; David M. Weil, Esq.*, Treas.; Wendy Belzberg, Dir. Emeritus; Darryl C. De Vivo, M.D., Dir. Emeritus; Susan S. Lin, Dir. Emeritus; Douglas G. Cole, M.D.; Gerald Fischbach, M.D.; Andrew Knight; Jonathan Leff; Srin Madipalli; Helen Meates, Esq.; Stephen Mikita, Esq.; Juli Oh, Esq.; Simon H. Prisk, Esq.
EIN: 010759380
Selected grants: The following grants are a representative sample of this grantmaker's funding activity:
$165,045 to University of Southern California, Los Angeles, CA, 2012. For Examination of Neuromuscular Junctions in Sma Mice.
$70,361 to Johns Hopkins University, School of Medicine, Baltimore, MD, 2012. For Pathology of Sma.
$30,000 to Emory University, Atlanta, GA, 2012. For The Role of SMN in Axonal Localization of MRNP Complexes.
$25,000 to University of Pennsylvania, Philadelphia, PA, 2012. For Investigation of Muscle Phenotype in Sma Mice.
$17,000 to Beth Israel Deaconess Medical Center, Boston, MA, 2012. For Measuring Disease Programression in Spinal Muscular Atrophy Through the Use of Electrical Impedance Myography.

6899
The Spingold Foundation, Inc. ✧ ☆
(formerly Nate B. and Frances Spingold Foundation, Inc.)
c/o Skadden, Arps, Slate, Meagher & Flom LLP
4 Times Sq., Ste. 26-326
New York, NY 10036-6522

Incorporated in 1955 in NY.
Donors: Frances Spingold†; Nathan Breither Spingold†.
Foundation type: Independent foundation.
Financial data (yr. ended 11/30/13): Assets, $10,794,767 (M); expenditures, $638,254; qualifying distributions, $494,000; giving activities include $454,750 for grants.
Fields of interest: Arts; Education; Environment; Health care; Mental health/crisis services; Youth development; Human services; Aging, centers/services; Civil/human rights; Community/economic development.
Type of support: General/operating support; Continuing support; Annual campaigns; Program development; Seed money.
Limitations: Applications not accepted. Giving primarily in the metropolitan New York, NY, area. No grants to individuals.
Application information: Contributes only to pre-selected organizations. Unsolicited requests for funds not considered or acknowledged.
Board meeting date(s): 2-3 times annually
Officers and Directors:* Daniel L. Kurtz,* Pres.; Lorance Hockert,* Secy.-Treas.; Elizabeth Olofson; Ruth Rosenblatt.
EIN: 136107659

6900
Bernard and Anne Spitzer Charitable Trust ✧
(formerly The Bernard & Anne Spitzer Foundation, Inc.)
730 5th Ave., Ste. 2202
New York, NY 10019-4105 (212) 765-5170

Established around 1982 in NY as a successor to The Bernard and Anne Spitzer Foundation, Inc.
Donors: Bernard Spitzer; Anne Spitzer.
Foundation type: Independent foundation.
Financial data (yr. ended 12/31/12): Assets, $67,497,659 (M); gifts received, $3,800,000; expenditures, $7,041,404; qualifying distributions, $4,545,093; giving activities include $4,544,722 for 43 grants (high: $1,010,000; low: $22).
Purpose and activities: Support primarily for the arts, health associations, education, and Jewish organizations.
Fields of interest: Arts; Higher education; Education; Health organizations, association; Jewish federated giving programs.
Type of support: General/operating support.
Limitations: Applications accepted. Giving primarily in NY. No grants to individuals.
Application information: Application form required.
Initial approach: Proposal
Deadline(s): None
Trustees: Anne Spitzer; Bernard Spitzer; Daniel Evan Spitzer; Eliot Laurence Spitzer.
EIN: 137298842

6901
The Seth Sprague Educational and Charitable Foundation
c/o U.S. Trust
114 W. 47th St.
New York, NY 10036-1592 (646) 855-1011
Contact: Christine O'Donnell, U.S. Trust

Trust established in 1939 in NY.
Donor: Seth Sprague†.
Foundation type: Independent foundation.
Financial data (yr. ended 12/31/13): Assets, $74,952,995 (M); expenditures, $3,533,638; qualifying distributions, $3,320,900; giving activities include $3,060,000 for 243 grants (high: $50,000; low: $1,000).
Purpose and activities: Program priorities in New York, NY, consist of: 1) Arts- priorities include audience engagement for ages 20s to 30s and underserved communities; 2) Education- priorities include professional development and school-day enrichment programs operating in public schools; and 3) Housing and basic needs - priorities include services to support homeless individuals or those at-risk of losing their homes, food distribution and nutrition programs, and comprehensive services for at-risk populations. Program priorities in Boston and Cape Cod, MA, San Diego, CA, and ME include: health care, education, human and social services, environment and the arts.
Fields of interest: Arts; Education; Environment, natural resources; Health care; Food banks; Human services.
Type of support: General/operating support; Program development; Matching/challenge support.
Limitations: Applications accepted. Giving primarily in NY, Boston and Cape Cod, MA, ME, and San Diego, CA. No grants to individuals, or for building funds; no loans.
Application information: Arts in education is no longer a priority of the foundation. Application form not required.
Initial approach: 3-5 page narrative proposal
Copies of proposal: 1
Deadline(s): Apr. 1 and Sept. 1
Board meeting date(s): June and Nov.
Final notification: June and Dec.
Trustees: Rebecca Greenleaf Clapp; Irene de Watteville; Patricia Dunnington.
EIN: 136071886

6902
Spunk Fund, Inc. ✧
780 3rd Ave., 24th Fl.
New York, NY 10017-2024 (212) 980-8880
E-mail: mg@spunkfund.com

Incorporated in 1981 in NY.
Donor: Marianne Gerschel.
Foundation type: Independent foundation.
Financial data (yr. ended 12/31/13): Assets, $22,649,928 (M); gifts received, $424,311; expenditures, $1,521,669; qualifying distributions, $1,236,160; giving activities include $733,480 for 21 grants (high: $150,000; low: $1,000).
Purpose and activities: Supports initiatives that contribute to the enrichment and well-being of children and adolescents, including medical and psychological research, education, cultural programs, and programs for the prevention and treatment of child abuse and neglect. Giving also for international programs that enhance the quality of life and create opportunities for less-advantaged children.
Fields of interest: Arts; Child development, education; Elementary school/education; Education; Crime/violence prevention, child abuse; Children/youth, services; Child development, services; Family services; Economically disadvantaged.
Type of support: General/operating support; Seed money; Research.
Limitations: Applications accepted. Giving on a national basis. No grants to individuals, or for capital programs.
Publications: Informational brochure (including application guidelines).
Application information: The fund will request proposals from organizations in which it is interested; unsolicited proposals not considered. Application form required.
Initial approach: Letter of inquiry
Copies of proposal: 1
Deadline(s): Letters of inquiry accepted year round; requested proposals due Apr. 1

Board meeting date(s): June
Final notification: July 1
Officers and Directors:* Marianne Gerschel,* Pres. and Treas.; Andrew W. Heymann,* Secy.; Gerard E. Heymann.
Number of staff: 2 full-time professional; 1 part-time professional; 4 full-time support.
EIN: 133116094
Selected grants: The following grants are a representative sample of this grantmaker's funding activity:
$90,000 to University of Minnesota Foundation, Minneapolis, MN, 2012. To support the following components of the Resilience Development Study. 1)Gene Expression: RNA Sample Collection and Investigation of Epigenetic Processes, and 2) Statistical Analysis of Multi-level Processes in Predicting Diverse Outcomes.
$65,000 to University of Minnesota Foundation, Minneapolis, MN, 2012. To support the following components of the Resilience Development Study. 1) Gene Expression: RNA Sample Collection and Investigation of Epigenetic Processes, 2) Inflammation/Immune Functioning in maltreated children, 3)Continuation of Neurophysiological Assessment.
$50,000 to Liberty Science Center, Jersey City, NJ, 2012. To support Partners in Science, a Program that matches high-achieving high school students with professionals in STEM fields.
$40,000 to Good Shepherd Services, New York, NY, 2012. To support social, interpersonal, educational, and vocational services that Good Shepherd clients require for a successful transition into autonomous adulthood.
$30,000 to Harlem Academy, New York, NY, 2012. To support continued development, evaluation, and revision of Harlem Academy's middle school Program.
$18,000 to Nation Institute, New York, NY, 2012. To support U S based interviews and background research concerning the life and death of Vietnam reporter, Alex Shimkin.
$7,500 to De La Salle Academy, New York, NY, 2012. To support a Program to ensure that all De La Salle students are able to visit the boarding schools to which they are applying.

6903
St. Faith's House Foundation ✧ ☆
c/o Brenda P. Foley, C.P.A.
257 Main St.
North Creek, NY 12853-0570
Contact: Ann D. Phillips
E-mail: drew@bestweb.net; Additional address: 16 Crest Dr., Tarrytown, NY 10591

Incorporated in 1901 in NY as St. Faith's House; reorganized in 1973 as a private foundation.
Foundation type: Independent foundation.
Financial data (yr. ended 06/30/13): Assets, $9,851,003 (M); expenditures, $600,308; qualifying distributions, $435,000; giving activities include $435,000 for grants.
Purpose and activities: Giving for homeless children, pregnancy prevention programs for at-risk teens, and tuition assistance for day care. Grants limited to organizations that provide services to children and young people of Westchester County, New York.
Fields of interest: Children/youth, services; Children, day care; Family services; Homeless, human services; Infants/toddlers; Children/youth; Children.
Type of support: Continuing support; Program development; Matching/challenge support.
Limitations: Applications accepted. Giving restricted to Westchester County, NY. No support for public or private institutions. No grants to individuals, or for building, capital campaigns or endowment funds.
Publications: Application guidelines.
Application information: Application form required.
Initial approach: Proposal
Copies of proposal: 12
Deadline(s): Sept. 1 and Mar. 1
Board meeting date(s): May and Nov.
Directors: Shari K. Bloom; Barbara Bush Bunges; Bruce E. Clark; Marilyn Dimling; Sarah Gardner; Jody Hansen; Mary Jean Keenan; Heather Kenny; Mary Alice Lyman; Drusilla R. Van Hengel.
Officers: Patricia Ellis, Pres.; Robert C. Myers, Secy.; Michael Lowry, Treas.
Number of staff: None.
EIN: 131740123

6904
St. George's Society of New York
216 E. 45th St., Ste. 901
New York, NY 10017-3304 (212) 682-6110
Contact: John Shannon, Exec. Dir.; Samantha Hamilton, Dir., Devel. and Membership
FAX: (212) 682-3465;
E-mail: info@stgeorgessociety.org; Main
URL: http://www.stgeorgessociety.org
Facebook: https://www.facebook.com/pages/St-Georges-Society-of-New-York/162723030430738

Established in 1770 in NY.
Donors: Charlotte M. F. Bentley†; British Embassy; DeCoizart Charitable Trust; Andrew MacKenzie Hay†; Florence Davis; Francis Finlay; Richard Grasso; Sir Deryck C. Maughan; Sir Edwin Manton†; William R. Miller; Martin Sullivan; Aetna; Citigroup UK; D'Amato & Lynch; HSBC Bank USA, N.A.; McGraw Hill Companies; Sherman & Sterling; Skaden Arps; JPMorgan Chase Bank, N.A.; Starr Foundation; Revolution Studios; CSFB; Bloomberg; Sony Corp.; AIG; WWP/Young & Rubicam; Hearst Corp.; Sir Howard Stringer; R. Brandon Fradd; Mark C. Pigott; PACCAR, Inc.; Ford Motor Co.
Foundation type: Operating foundation.
Financial data (yr. ended 12/31/13): Assets, $12,890,253 (M); gifts received, $959,690; expenditures, $1,558,123; qualifying distributions, $1,447,643; giving activities include $227,899 for 6 grants (high: $99,332; low: $200), $552,070 for 108 grants to individuals, and $885,782 for foundation-administered programs.
Purpose and activities: A private operating foundation dedicated to helping men and women from the United Kingdom and the British Commonwealth and their children who find themselves in need, trouble, sickness or other adversity in the New York, NY, area. The Society has two main areas of endeavor, its Beneficiary Program to support the elderly and disabled, and its Scholarship Program to assist outstanding students with university tuition.
Fields of interest: Higher education, university; Health care.
International interests: United Kingdom.
Type of support: Emergency funds; Grants to individuals.
Limitations: Giving limited to the metropolitan New York, NY, area.
Publications: Annual report; Newsletter.
Application information: Applicant must be a native of the United Kingdom or the British Commonwealth, residing in the New York, NY, metropolitan region, with a legal status. Personal interviews and visits from the Society's social worker. Application form not required.
Initial approach: Letter or telephone
Copies of proposal: 1
Deadline(s): None
Board meeting date(s): Quarterly
Final notification: 4-6 weeks
Officers and Directors:* Robert J.K. Titley,* Pres.; Richard Sexton, MBE*, 1st V.P.; Philip Warner, OBE*, 2nd V.P.; Paul Beresford-Hill, MBE, Secy.; Stephen J. Storen, Treas.; Lewis Stetson Allen; Ceasae Anquillare, JP; Andrew Booth; Philippa Cheetham; Duncan Edwards; June Felix; Susan Lopez; Geneive Brown Metzger; Jigs Patel; Peter Selman; Nicholas C. Walsh; Stuart Welburn.
Number of staff: 3 full-time professional; 2 part-time professional; 1 full-time support.
EIN: 237426425

6905
St. Giles Foundation ✧
(formerly The House of St. Giles the Cripple)
880 3rd Ave., Ste. 1211
New York, NY 10022-4730

Established around 1979.
Foundation type: Independent foundation.
Financial data (yr. ended 03/31/13): Assets, $25,316,463 (M); gifts received, $47,204; expenditures, $1,309,867; qualifying distributions, $930,000; giving activities include $930,000 for grants.
Purpose and activities: Giving primarily for hospitals, particularly children's hospitals, and to organizations that help people who are handicapped, particularly youth; special interest in medical sciences, and children's orthopedics.
Fields of interest: Hospitals (general); Hospitals (specialty); Medical research; Children/youth, services; Disabilities, people with.
Type of support: General/operating support; Equipment; Research.
Limitations: Applications not accepted. Giving primarily in New York, NY.
Application information: Contributes only to pre-selected organizations.
Officers: Richard T. Arkwright, Pres.; Edward Ridley Finch, Jr., V.P.; Henry A. Braun, Secy.; Robert B. MacKay, Treas.
Trustees: Jill Ann Arkwright; James Hamerschlag.
EIN: 111630806
Selected grants: The following grants are a representative sample of this grantmaker's funding activity:
$375,000 to Hospital for Special Surgery, New York, NY, 2013. For St Giles Education Conference Center to Help Facilitate the Educational Opportunities and Provide a New Children's Pavilion to the Hospital.
$30,000 to Pediatric Orthopaedic Society of North America, Rosemont, IL, 2013. For Arthur H Memorial Award for Medical Research.
$10,000 to Pediatric Orthopaedic Society of North America, Rosemont, IL, 2013. For St Giles Young Investigator Award for Medical Research.

6906
The Stainman Family Foundation, Inc. ✧
c/o Arthur J. Stainman
320 E. 72nd St.
New York, NY 10021-4769

Established in NY.
Donors: Arthur J. Stainman; Lois Stainman.
Foundation type: Independent foundation.
Financial data (yr. ended 12/31/12): Assets, $17,820,975 (M); gifts received, $1,664,952; expenditures, $972,618; qualifying distributions, $874,719; giving activities include $874,719 for grants.
Fields of interest: Arts; Food banks; Human services.
Limitations: Applications not accepted. Giving primarily in NY. No grants to individuals.
Application information: Contributes only to pre-selected organizations.
Officers: Arthur J. Stainman, Pres.; Lois Stainman, V.P.; Evan Stainman, Secy.
EIN: 133980213

6907
The Elizabeth and Oliver Stanton Foundation ✧
(formerly The Oliver & Elizabeth Stanton Foundation)
c/o Transammonia Inc.
320 Park Ave.
New York, NY 10022-6815

Established in 2000 in NY.
Donors: Herta Schloss‡; Oliver K. Stanton; Ronald P. Stanton; Transammonia, Inc.
Foundation type: Independent foundation.
Financial data (yr. ended 12/31/13): Assets, $10,858,648 (M); expenditures, $1,692,150; qualifying distributions, $1,644,642; giving activities include $1,644,642 for 32 grants (high: $428,000; low: $5,000).
Purpose and activities: Giving primarily for Jewish organizations and temples; funding also for education, human services, and the arts.
Fields of interest: Arts; Higher education; Education; Health organizations; Human services; Jewish federated giving programs; Jewish agencies & synagogues.
Limitations: Applications not accepted. Giving primarily in New York, NY. No grants to individuals.
Application information: Contributes only to pre-selected organizations.
Officers: Elizabeth Stanton, Pres.; Oliver K. Stanton, V.P.; Fred M. Lowenfels, Secy.; Edward G. Weiner, Treas.
EIN: 134138465

6908
The Stanton Foundation ✧
(formerly Ruth and Frank Stanton Fund)
c/o Baker Tilly
One Penn Plz., Ste. 3000
New York, NY 10119-0002 (212) 697-6900

Established in 1991 in NY.
Donors: Frank Stanton‡; The Frank Stanton 2002 Trust.
Foundation type: Independent foundation.
Financial data (yr. ended 12/31/12): Assets, $221,311,214 (M); gifts received, $50,000; expenditures, $14,524,018; qualifying distributions, $13,094,275; giving activities include $12,558,266 for 44 grants (high: $6,111,645; low: $5,000).
Fields of interest: Higher education; Animal welfare; Human services; Community/economic development; Social sciences, public policy.
Limitations: Applications not accepted. Giving primarily in Boston and Cambridge, MA. No grants to individuals.
Application information: Contributes only to pre-selected organizations.
Trustees: Elisabeth K. Allison; Andrew H. Weiss.
EIN: 133598005
Selected grants: The following grants are a representative sample of this grantmaker's funding activity:
$6,111,645 to Massachusetts Institute of Technology, Cambridge, MA, 2012.
$2,512,500 to Harvard University, Cambridge, MA, 2012.
$1,848,000 to Wikimedia Foundation, San Francisco, CA, 2012.
$375,000 to Stanford University, Stanford, CA, 2012.

6909
The Starfish Group ✧
c/o Anchin Block & Anchin
1375 Broadway
New York, NY 10018-7001

Established in 2000 in NY.
Donors: Virginia Gilder; Great Circle Trust.
Foundation type: Independent foundation.
Financial data (yr. ended 12/31/12): Assets, $210,984 (M); gifts received, $321,760; expenditures, $482,988; qualifying distributions, $473,988; giving activities include $469,920 for 27 grants (high: $75,000; low: $500).
Purpose and activities: Giving primarily for education and human services; funding also to foundations which support the sport of rowing.
Fields of interest: Arts; Libraries (public); Education; Legal services; Human services; Foundations (private grantmaking).
Limitations: Applications not accepted. Giving on a national basis, with emphasis on New York, NY, and Seattle, WA. No grants to individuals.
Application information: Contributes only to pre-selected organizations.
Officers: Britt-Louise Gilder, Co-Pres.; Virginia Anne Gilder, Co-Pres.; Margaret Mathews, Secy.; Lynn Slaughter, Treas.
Director: Adrienne Morris.
EIN: 134128526

6910
The Starker Family Foundation Inc. ✧
c/o JAD Consulting LLC
61 Broadway, Ste. 512
New York, NY 10006-2744

Established in NY.
Donor: Steven Starker.
Foundation type: Independent foundation.
Financial data (yr. ended 09/30/13): Assets, $962,055 (M); expenditures, $607,145; qualifying distributions, $561,370; giving activities include $495,425 for 130 grants (high: $100,000; low: $50).
Fields of interest: Education; Health care; Health organizations, association; Medical research, institute; Human services; Children/youth, services; Jewish federated giving programs; Jewish agencies & synagogues.
Limitations: Applications not accepted. No grants to individuals.
Application information: Contributes only to pre-selected organizations.
Officers: Steven Starker, Pres. and Treas.; Farrel Starker, V.P. and Secy.; Stuart Dix, V.P.; Ray Starker, V.P.
EIN: 133986718
Selected grants: The following grants are a representative sample of this grantmaker's funding activity:
$25,000 to Autism Speaks, New York, NY, 2011.
$10,000 to Cystic Fibrosis Foundation, Bethesda, MD, 2011.
$5,000 to Chai Lifeline, New York, NY, 2011.
$5,000 to Myasthenia Gravis Foundation of America, Saint Paul, MN, 2011.
$5,000 to Teach for America, New York, NY, 2011.
$3,500 to Cystic Fibrosis Foundation, Bethesda, MD, 2011.
$2,500 to Columbia University, New York, NY, 2011.
$2,500 to Leukemia & Lymphoma Society, White Plains, NY, 2011.
$2,500 to Saint Jude Childrens Research Hospital, Memphis, TN, 2011.
$1,000 to Hole in the Wall Gang Fund, New Haven, CT, 2011.

6911
The Starr Foundation ✧
399 Park Ave., 17th Fl.
New York, NY 10022-4614 (212) 909-3600
FAX: (212) 750-3536; Main URL: http://www.starrfoundation.org/

Incorporated in 1955 in NY.
Donor: Cornelius V. Starr‡.
Foundation type: Independent foundation.
Financial data (yr. ended 12/31/13): Assets, $1,371,638,088 (M); gifts received, $50,000; expenditures, $100,462,579; qualifying distributions, $85,739,685; giving activities include $83,168,245 for grants.
Purpose and activities: The foundation makes grants in a number of areas, including education, medicine and health care, human needs, public policy, culture and the environment.
Fields of interest: Arts; Higher education; Education; Environment; Health care; Health organizations, association; Medical research; Human services; Social sciences; Children; Youth; Adults; Aging; Disabilities, people with; Blind/visually impaired; Deaf/hearing impaired; Military/veterans; Immigrants/refugees; Economically disadvantaged.
International interests: Asia.
Type of support: General/operating support; Continuing support; Management development/capacity building; Capital campaigns; Building/renovation; Endowments; Emergency funds; Program development; Professorships; Fellowships; Scholarship funds; Research; Employee matching gifts; Employee-related scholarships; Exchange programs; Matching/challenge support.
Limitations: Applications not accepted. Giving on a national and international basis, with emphasis on New York, NY and Asia. No support for religious

institutions (except for non-denominational human services). No grants to individuals (except for children of C.V. Starr & Co. and Starr International Co. employees, pursuant to a qualified scholarship program).
Publications: IRS Form 990 or 990-PF printed copy available upon request.
Application information: The foundation does not accept unsolicited applications. Unsolicited applications will be declined summarily and will not be saved by the foundation.
Board meeting date(s): Six times per year
Officers and Directors:* Maurice R. "Hank" Greenberg,* Chair.; Florence A. Davis,* Pres.; Paula S. Lawrence, V.P.; Martha Livingston, V.P.; Joan Katz, Corp. Secy. of the Board; Howard I. Smith,* Treas.; Corinne Greenberg; T.C. Hsu; Bertil Lundqvist; Edward E. Matthews.
Number of staff: 8 full-time professional; 1 part-time professional; 4 full-time support.
EIN: 136151545
Selected grants: The following grants are a representative sample of this grantmaker's funding activity:
$50,000,000 to Weill Medical College of Cornell University, New York, NY, 2012. For tri-institutional stem cell initiative, involving collaboration of Weill Cornell, Rockefeller University and Memorial-Sloan Kettering, payable over 4.00 years.
$20,000,000 to Harlem Childrens Zone, New York, NY, 2010. For Sustainability Plan, payable over 5.00 years.
$10,000,000 to New York University, New York, NY, 2012. For Maurice R. Greenberg Scholarship Fund, payable over 4.00 years.
$10,000,000 to Starr Cancer Consortium, Cambridge, MA, 2013. For renewed support.
$10,000,000 to Weill Medical College of Cornell University, New York, NY, 2012. For capital support for new research facility, payable over 5.00 years.
$900,000 to Weill Medical College of Cornell University, New York, NY, 2012. For basic science research, payable over 5.00 years.
$500,000 to Baruch College of the City University of New York, New York, NY, 2012. For general support of the Starr Career Services Center, payable over 5.00 years.
$500,000 to Baruch College of the City University of New York, New York, NY, 2012. To establish Maurice R. Greenberg Scholarship Fund.
$500,000 to Building Educated Leaders for Life Foundation, New York, NY, 2012. For general operating support, payable over 3.00 years.
$100,000 to Innocence Project, New York, NY, 2013. For general operating support.
$50,000 to New York Public Library, New York, NY, 2012. For general operating support.
$50,000 to New York Public Library, New York, NY, 2013. For general operating support.
$50,000 to Philharmonic-Symphony Society of New York, New York, NY, 2013. For general operating support.

6912
The Staten Island Foundation ✧

(formerly SI Bank & Trust Foundation)
260 Christopher Ln., Ste. 3B
Staten Island, NY 10314-1658 (718) 697-2831
Contact: C.E.O.: Betsy Dubovsky, Exec. Dir.; Program: Laura Jean Watters, Prog. Off.
FAX: (718) 697-3180;
E-mail: dubovsky@thestatenislandfoundation.org; Additional e-mail: watters@thestatenislandfoundation.org; Main URL: http://www.thestatenislandfoundation.org/

Established as a company-sponsored foundation in 1998 in DE and NY; status changed to independent foundation in 2004.
Donors: Staten Island Savings Bank; SI Bank & Trust.
Foundation type: Independent foundation.
Financial data (yr. ended 06/30/14): Assets, $78,882,083 (M); gifts received, $1,070,000; expenditures, $4,632,093; qualifying distributions, $4,107,744; giving activities include $3,524,190 for 114 grants (high: $250,000; low: $100).
Purpose and activities: The mission of the foundation is to improve the quality of life on Staten Island, particularly for the least advantaged, with a focus on strengthening the community, and improving education, health, and the arts. Strategies to accomplish the mission include financial support through grants; providing leadership for the community; convening and collaborating with grantee partners, funders, and other entities in order to share best practices; and building the capacity of local organizations to better fulfill their missions. All organizations and the individuals working with them learn continually from the results of their activities and services. Applying that learning in order to improve is of particular interest of the foundation. In its grantmaking, the foundation looks to fund opportunities that educate Staten Island organizations and individuals in a way that leads to their learning. The foundation defines learning as a positive change in behavior. Foundation grants are an investment in these changes. The foundation's definition of a successful investment includes strong results for program participants, and strong learnings for the organizations in which the foundation invests.
Fields of interest: Arts; Education; Health care; Housing/shelter; Human services; Community/economic development; Infants/toddlers; Children/youth; Youth; Adults; Young adults; Disabilities, people with; Physically disabled; Mentally disabled; Minorities; African Americans/Blacks; Hispanics/Latinos; Substance abusers; Immigrants/refugees; Economically disadvantaged; Homeless.
Type of support: General/operating support; Management development/capacity building; Program development; Technical assistance; Sponsorships; Employee matching gifts; Matching/challenge support.
Limitations: Giving limited to Staten Island, NY. No support for political causes, candidates, or lobbying efforts, fraternal or veterans organizations, business, professional, or civic associations or clubs, animal welfare groups, cemetery associations, or private foundations. No grants to individuals, or for renovations/repairs to places of worship, yearbook advertisements, research including medical research, memorial fundraising events, or tickets to fundraising events.
Publications: Application guidelines; Biennial report.
Application information: An application form is available online upon invitation. Application form required.
Initial approach: Telephone or e-mail to discuss proposal. If proposal is approved, URL link will be provided for online application
Deadline(s): 2 months prior to board meeting
Board meeting date(s): Jan., Apr. July and Oct.
Final notification: 2 months
Officers and Directors:* Allan Weissglass,* Chair.; Kathryn Krause Rooney, Vice-Chair.; Jill O'Donnell Tormey, Secy.; Lenore Puleo,* Treas.; Betsy Dubovsky, Exec. Dir.; Alice B. Diamond; Denis Kelleher; Daniel Master; Dolores Morris.
Number of staff: 3 full-time professional.
EIN: 133993115
Selected grants: The following grants are a representative sample of this grantmaker's funding activity:
$150,000 to FSG Social Impact Advisors, Boston, MA, 2012. To plan and implement Steering Committee and Community Wellness for Tackling Youth Substance Abuse.
$150,000 to Richmond University Medical Center, Staten Island, NY, 2013. For Executive Director and staff of the Richmond University Medical Center Foundation, Inc. Project.
$150,000 to Staten Island Partnership for Community Wellness, Staten Island, NY, 2013. For continued support for year one implementation of the Tackling Youth Substance Abuse Initiative, aimed at systemic change in youth substance abuse in Staten Island.
$100,000 to Staten Island Partnership for Community Wellness, Staten Island, NY, 2012. To implement Tackling Youth Substance Abuse Initiative.
$65,000 to Elias Bernstein Intermediate School No. 7, Staten Island, NY, 2013. For the 2012 Literacy Grant: The Leader in Me at I.S. 7.
$50,000 to City Harvest, New York, NY, 2012. For Stapleton Mobile Market.
$50,000 to Community Health Action of Staten Island, Staten Island, NY, 2013. For nurse navigators on a mobile unit to connect people to primary health care, chronic disease management, mental health services, and secure supports to maintain health such as health insurance, food and nutrition and prescription drug assistance.
$50,000 to Council on the Arts and Humanities for Staten Island, Staten Island, NY, 2012. For arts in education regrant project.
$50,000 to Council on the Arts and Humanities for Staten Island, Staten Island, NY, 2013. For Arts Investment Regrants for Schools program.
$50,000 to Eden II School for Autistic Children, Staten Island, NY, 2013. For unforeseen expenses related to Hurricane Sandy's damage to buildings and effect on the operating budget.
$50,000 to Food Bank for New York City, New York, NY, 2012. For Staten Island Tax and Benefits Assistance Program.
$50,000 to Lifestyles for the Disabled, Staten Island, NY, 2012. For Access for Everyone project, renovations to Lifestyles Educational Center in order to be ADA complaint.
$50,000 to Neighborhood Housing Services of Staten Island, Staten Island, NY, 2012. For Foreclosure Intervention and Financial Stabilization Initiative.
$50,000 to Partnership with Children, New York, NY, 2013. For Open Heart-Open Mind Program (OHOM).
$50,000 to Police Athletic League, New York, NY, 2012. For Summer Day Camp at PS 14/PS 13.
$50,000 to Read Alliance, New York, NY, 2012. For Success Starts Early and Summer Reading Program.
$50,000 to Staten Island Childrens Museum, Staten Island, NY, 2012. For SERVE (Service Enhancements to Reshape Visitor Experience) Project.
$42,000 to Staten Island Ballet Theater, Staten Island, NY, 2013. For ArtsCAN Project.

$30,000 to Staten Island NFP Association, Staten Island, NY, 2013. To convene a multi-stakeholder collaboration of organizations and civic groups involved in post-Sandy storm recovery work in order to increase their organizational capacity to serve those who most need assistance.
$20,000 to Public School 39, Staten Island, NY, 2013. For the 2012 Literacy Grant: Covey: 7 Habits for Happy Healthy Kids - The Leader in Me.

6913
The Statler Foundation ✧
1207 Delaware Ave.
Plaza Suites., No. 222
Buffalo, NY 14209-1458 (716) 852-1104
Contact: Bernard A. Tolbert, Chair.

Trust established in 1934 in NY.
Donor: Ellsworth Milton Statler†.
Foundation type: Independent foundation.
Financial data (yr. ended 12/31/13): Assets, $33,247,020 (M); expenditures, $1,854,176; qualifying distributions, $1,361,010; giving activities include $1,044,033 for grants.
Purpose and activities: Education and research for the benefit of the hotel industry in the U.S. Income used for awards to colleges and schools teaching hotel techniques and for grants to schools and others for research projects and for programs to train and increase the proficiency of hotel workers. The foundation also supports culinary arts and hotel management programs.
Fields of interest: Vocational education; Business school/education.
Type of support: Building/renovation; Equipment; Professorships; Research.
Limitations: Giving primarily in western NY. No grants for scholarships.
Application information: The scholarship program is offered only to students in Western New York. Application form is required for scholarship applicants. Application form not required.
Initial approach: Letter
Copies of proposal: 13
Board meeting date(s): Monthly
Trustees: Robert Bennett; Marguerite Collesano; William J. Cunningham, Jr.; Peter J. Fiorella, Jr.; Edward M. Flynn; Ernestine R. Green; Carlo M. Perfetto; Arthur V. Sabia; Herb M. Siegel; Bernard A. Tolbert; Peter A. Vinolus.
Number of staff: 1 full-time professional.
EIN: 131889077

6914
The Robert K. Steel Family Foundation ✧
c/o BCRS Assocs., LLC
77 Water St., 9th Fl.
New York, NY 10005-4401

Established in 1989 in NY.
Donors: Robert K. Steel; Gillian Steel; Robert K. Steel Family; Goldman, Sachs & Co.
Foundation type: Independent foundation.
Financial data (yr. ended 04/30/13): Assets, $10,198,804 (M); gifts received, $350,000; expenditures, $1,487,633; qualifying distributions, $1,301,245; giving activities include $1,299,550 for 153 grants (high: $200,000; low: $100).
Purpose and activities: Giving primarily for higher education, and to health associations and hospitals.
Fields of interest: Arts; Higher education; Health care; Health organizations, association; Protestant agencies & churches.
Type of support: General/operating support; Annual campaigns; Capital campaigns; Endowments.
Limitations: Applications not accepted. Giving in the U.S., with emphasis on Washington, DC, and NY. No grants to individuals.
Application information: Contributes only to pre-selected organizations.
Trustee: Gillian V. Steel.
EIN: 133531990
Selected grants: The following grants are a representative sample of this grantmaker's funding activity:
$666,667 to Aspen Institute, Washington, DC, 2012. For general support.
$325,000 to SeaChange Capital Partners, New York, NY, 2012. For general support.
$200,000 to Duke University, Durham, NC, 2012. For general support.
$200,000 to Hospital for Special Surgery, New York, NY, 2013. For general support.
$200,000 to SeaChange Capital Partners, New York, NY, 2012. For general support.
$125,000 to REACH Prep, Stamford, CT, 2012. For general support.
$100,000 to Akanksha Fund, New York, NY, 2012. For general support.
$100,000 to Akanksha Fund, New York, NY, 2012. For general support.
$100,000 to Boy Scouts of America, Greater New York Councils, New York, NY, 2013. For general support.
$100,000 to Duke University, Durham, NC, 2012. For general support.
$100,000 to New York Botanical Garden, Bronx, NY, 2013. For general support.
$100,000 to Right to Play USA, New York, NY, 2013. For general support.
$100,000 to SeaChange Capital Partners, New York, NY, 2013. For general support.
$60,000 to Aspen Institute, Washington, DC, 2013. For general support.
$50,000 to Aspen Institute, Washington, DC, 2012. For general support.
$50,000 to Partnership for Public Service, Washington, DC, 2013. For general support.
$50,000 to W E T A-Greater Washington Educational Telecommunications Association, http://www.thebetterangelssociety.org/, Arlington, VA, 2013. For general support for The Better Angels Society, membership organization making philanthropic donation to the making of historical documentaries.
$25,000 to Harvard University, Cambridge, MA, 2013. For general support.
$25,000 to Posse Foundation, New York, NY, 2012. For general support.
$15,000 to Hospital for Special Surgery, New York, NY, 2013. For general support.

6915
The Steele-Reese Foundation ✧
32 Washington Sq. W.
New York, NY 10011-9156 (212) 505-2696
Contact: William T. Buice
Additional address: c/o Charles U. Buice, 242 Bergen St., No. 2, Brooklyn, NY 11217; e-mail: charles@steele-reese.org; proposal information address for Kentucky Programs: Judy K. Owens, 2613 Clubside Ct., Lexington. KY 40513, tel. and fax: (859) 313-5225; e-mail: jkowensjd@aol.com; for projects in Idaho and Montana: c/o Linda Tracy, P.O. Box 8311, Missoula, MT 59807-8311; tel.: (406) 207-7984; fax: (207) 470-3872; e-mail: linda@steele-reese.org; Main URL: http://www.Steele-Reese.org

Trust established in 1955 in NY.
Donors: Eleanor Steele Reese†; Emmet P. Reese†.
Foundation type: Independent foundation.
Financial data (yr. ended 08/31/13): Assets, $31,388,265 (M); expenditures, $2,421,879; qualifying distributions, $2,191,996; giving activities include $1,984,475 for 78 grants (high: $62,500; low: $3,500).
Purpose and activities: Giving principally to aid organized charities in southern Appalachia, Idaho and Montana. Support for rural education (primarily elementary and secondary), rural social services, rural conservation and preservation, rural health, and rural arts and humanities. For students who have graduated from one of the four high schools in Lemhi or Custer Counties, ID, the foundation has set up scholarship endowments at the following twelve western colleges and universities: Albertson College of Idaho, Brigham Young University, Brigham Young University— Idaho, The College of Southern Idaho, Gonzaga University, Idaho State University, Lewis & Clark College, Pacific Lutheran University, Reed College, The University of Idaho, The University of Montana, and Western Montana College.
Fields of interest: Humanities; Elementary/secondary education; Education; Environment, natural resources; Environment; Health care; Health organizations, association; Human services; Children/youth, services; Family services; Rural development.
Type of support: General/operating support; Management development/capacity building; Equipment; Land acquisition; Endowments; Professorships; Scholarship funds; Matching/challenge support.
Limitations: Applications accepted. Giving primarily to rural communities in ID, MT, and the Appalachian Mountain region of KY. No support for community chests, efforts to influence school board and other elections, recreational facilities, athletic or academic competitions, or efforts to promulgate religious or political beliefs. No grants for continuing support, annual campaigns, conferences or workshops, seed money, emergency or building funds, deficit financing, research, travel, endowments for small organizations, computers or other technology used for instruction in schools; no loans; grants to individuals confined to scholarships and paid through institutions.
Publications: Annual report (including application guidelines); Grants list.
Application information: The foundation now requests that applicants submit application materials electronically via its secure web application portal. High school seniors in Lemhi and Custer counties, ID, should apply for scholarships through their schools. The colleges and universities administer every detail of the scholarship programs autonomously, without participation by the foundation. Application form not required.
Initial approach: Online via foundation web site. Applicants are also encouraged to contact the foundation's Appalachian Dir., Judy Owens, or Western Dir., Linda Tracy to discuss project prior to submitting an application
Copies of proposal: 2
Deadline(s): Mar. 1

Board meeting date(s): Monthly
Final notification: Late June/early July
Trustees: Charles U. Buice; William T. Buice III; JPMorgan Chase Bank, N.A.
Number of staff: 2 part-time professional.
EIN: 136034763
Selected grants: The following grants are a representative sample of this grantmaker's funding activity:
$75,000 to Steele Memorial Benefit Association, Salmon, ID, 2011. For general support.
$50,000 to Idaho Community Foundation, Boise, ID, 2011. For general support.
$50,000 to Intermountain Children's Home, Helena, MT, 2011. For general support.
$50,000 to Lotts Creek Community School, Hazard, KY, 2011. For general support.
$40,000 to Hazard-Perry County Community Ministries, Hazard, KY, 2011. For general support.
$40,000 to Kentucky Historical Society Foundation, Frankfort, KY, 2011. For general support.
$40,000 to Western Sustainability Exchange, Livingston, MT, 2011. For general support.
$30,000 to homeWORD, Missoula, MT, 2011. For general support.
$25,000 to Hopa Mountain, Bozeman, MT, 2011. For general support.
$20,000 to Defenders of Wildlife, Washington, DC, 2011. For general support.

6916
The Meir and Ruth Stefansky Charitable Trust ✧
3 Roman Blvd.
Monsey, NY 10952-3105

Established in 2005 in NY.
Donor: Meir Stefansky.
Foundation type: Operating foundation.
Financial data (yr. ended 01/31/13): Assets, $108,168 (M); gifts received, $410,000; expenditures, $439,136; qualifying distributions, $430,961; giving activities include $32,900 for grants, and $47,100 for 2 grants to individuals (high: $40,000; low: $7,100).
Purpose and activities: Giving to Jewish scholars who shed insight into complex areas of Jewish law.
Fields of interest: Jewish agencies & synagogues.
Type of support: Grants to individuals.
Limitations: Applications not accepted. Giving primarily in Israel.
Application information: Unsolicited requests for funds not accepted.
Officer: N.B. Spitzer, Admin.
Trustees: Meir Stefansky; Ruth Stefansky.
EIN: 200699712

6917
Steffens 21st Century Foundation II ✧
65 E. 55th St., 32nd Fl.
New York, NY 10022-3356

Established in 2001 in NY.
Donors: John L. Steffens; Louise C. Steffens.
Foundation type: Independent foundation.
Financial data (yr. ended 12/31/13): Assets, $4,653,182 (M); expenditures, $885,683; qualifying distributions, $865,500; giving activities include $865,500 for 19 grants (high: $250,000; low: $2,000).
Purpose and activities: Giving primarily for education and human services; funding also for a hospital.
Fields of interest: Higher education; Education; Hospitals (general); Human services.
Limitations: Applications not accepted. Giving primarily in NH, NJ and NY. No grants to individuals.
Application information: Contributes only to pre-selected organizations.
Officer: John L. Steffens, Pres.
EIN: 137284293
Selected grants: The following grants are a representative sample of this grantmaker's funding activity:
$25,000 to Princeton Day School, Princeton, NJ, 2012. For education school support.
$2,000 to North Shore Land Alliance, Old Westbury, NY, 2012. For Nature Preservation Program Support.

6918
Joseph F. Stein Family Foundation Inc. ✧
(formerly The Steiro Foundation, Inc.)
30 Glenn St.
White Plains, NY 10603-3254

Established in 2002 in NY.
Donors: Stuart M. Stein; Anne S. Squadron; Brian T. Kloza; David Plotkin; Edward H. Cohen; Elaine S. Stein; Jerold Goldberg; Martin S. Barbar; Nancy Rozen Feibus; Roger Stein; Susan Melchner; Toby Stein Rozen; Norton Spiel; Robert Spielman; Charles Selig, Jr.; Mrs. Charles Selig, Jr.; Robert Grossman; Wiss & Co; Elaine S. Stein Revocable Trust; Tiberiu Weisz; Martin Feinstein; Lawrence Chodor.
Foundation type: Independent foundation.
Financial data (yr. ended 12/31/13): Assets, $14,081,816 (M); gifts received, $79,000; expenditures, $886,121; qualifying distributions, $681,821; giving activities include $581,020 for 103 grants (high: $63,000; low: $100).
Purpose and activities: Giving primarily for education, health organizations and hospitals, and to Jewish organizations.
Fields of interest: Arts; Higher education; Education; Hospitals (general); Health organizations, association; Human services; Children/youth, services; Jewish federated giving programs; Jewish agencies & synagogues.
Type of support: General/operating support.
Limitations: Applications not accepted. No grants to individuals.
Application information: Unsolicited requests for funds not accepted.
Officers: Stuart M. Stein, Pres.; Michael R. Rozen, V.P.; Toby S. Rozen, V.P.; Roni L. Stein, Secy.; Arthur J. Feibus, Treas.
Director: Neil Rozen.
EIN: 134144648
Selected grants: The following grants are a representative sample of this grantmaker's funding activity:
$24,500 to Tucson Hebrew Academy, Tucson, AZ, 2011.
$13,500 to Jewish National Fund, Rockville Centre, NY, 2011.
$10,250 to New York-Presbyterian Hospital, New York, NY, 2011.
$10,000 to Boston University, Boston, MA, 2011.
$10,000 to Columbia University, New York, NY, 2011.
$5,000 to Crohns and Colitis Foundation of America, New York, NY, 2011.
$5,000 to University of Pennsylvania, Philadelphia, PA, 2011.
$5,000 to University of Rochester, Rochester, NY, 2011.
$4,630 to New York City Center, New York, NY, 2011.
$2,700 to American Cancer Society, Atlanta, GA, 2011.

6919
The Lazar and Sofia Stein Memorial Foundation ✧
c/o WeiserMazars
135 W. 50th St., Ste. 14
New York, NY 10020

Established in 1999 in NY.
Donor: Martin Stein.
Foundation type: Independent foundation.
Financial data (yr. ended 08/31/13): Assets, $255,424 (M); gifts received, $800,000; expenditures, $1,021,116; qualifying distributions, $1,011,001; giving activities include $1,011,001 for 7 grants (high: $600,000; low: $501).
Purpose and activities: Giving primarily to Jewish agencies, temples, and schools.
Fields of interest: Education; Jewish agencies & synagogues.
Limitations: Applications not accepted. Giving primarily in Brooklyn, NY. No grants to individuals.
Application information: Contributes only to pre-selected organizations.
Officers: Martin Stein, Pres.; Arlyne Stein, Secy.; Steven N. Stein, Treas.
EIN: 134119091

6920
Joseph S. & Diane H. Steinberg 1992 Charitable Trust ✧
c/o Leucadia National Corp.
315 Park Ave. S., 20th Fl.
New York, NY 10010-3607
Contact: Joseph S. Steinberg, Tr.

Established in 1992 in NY.
Donors: Joseph S. Steinberg; Diane H. Steinberg.
Foundation type: Independent foundation.
Financial data (yr. ended 06/30/13): Assets, $48,657,291 (M); gifts received, $3,126,500; expenditures, $4,418,311; qualifying distributions, $4,066,338; giving activities include $4,066,338 for 62 grants (high: $1,030,000; low: $300).
Purpose and activities: Giving primarily for the arts and education.
Fields of interest: Arts, cultural/ethnic awareness; Performing arts centers; Arts; Higher education; Botanical gardens; Health care; Jewish federated giving programs; Jewish agencies & synagogues.
Limitations: Applications not accepted. Giving primarily in NY; some funding also in MA. No grants to individuals.
Application information: Contributes only to pre-selected organizations.
Trustees: Diane H. Steinberg; Joseph S. Steinberg.
EIN: 137002791

6921
The Harold & Mimi Steinberg Charitable Trust ✧
c/o Schulte Roth & Zabel, LLP
919 3rd Ave.
New York, NY 10022-3903 (212) 758-0404

Established in 1986 in NY.
Donor: Harold Steinberg†.
Foundation type: Independent foundation.
Financial data (yr. ended 12/31/12): Assets, $100,757,497 (M); expenditures, $7,256,630; qualifying distributions, $6,486,718; giving activities include $6,135,666 for 210 grants (high: $375,000; low: $500), and $251,070 for foundation-administered programs.
Purpose and activities: Giving primarily for arts and cultural organizations, higher education, and the environment.
Fields of interest: Visual arts; Performing arts; Performing arts, theater; Performing arts, theater (playwriting); Higher education; Libraries/library science; Hospitals (general); Human services; Jewish federated giving programs.
Limitations: Applications not accepted. Giving primarily in New York, NY. No grants to.
Application information: Contributes only to pre-selected organizations.
Trustees: Carole A. Krumland; James D. Steinberg; Michael A. Steinberg; Seth Weingarten; William D. Zabel.
EIN: 133383348

6922
The Steinberg Family Fund, Inc. ✧
c/o Arthur Fox, C.P.A.
420 Lexington Ave., Ste. 1733
New York, NY 10170-1734

Established in 1984 in NY.
Donor: Robert Steinberg.
Foundation type: Independent foundation.
Financial data (yr. ended 11/30/13): Assets, $10,638,744 (M); expenditures, $584,331; qualifying distributions, $575,925; giving activities include $573,425 for 37 grants (high: $105,000; low: $250).
Purpose and activities: Giving primarily for Jewish schools and organizations; funding also for health associations.
Fields of interest: Elementary/secondary education; Pediatrics research; Jewish federated giving programs; Jewish agencies & synagogues.
Limitations: Applications not accepted. Giving primarily in CT and NY. No grants to individuals.
Application information: Contributes only to pre-selected organizations.
Officers: Robert Steinberg, Pres.; Suzanne Steinberg, V.P. and Treas.
EIN: 133254493
Selected grants: The following grants are a representative sample of this grantmaker's funding activity:
$5,000 to Greenwich Hospital, Greenwich, CT, 2011.
$5,000 to Greenwich Hospital, Greenwich, CT, 2011.
$1,000 to Greenwich Library, Greenwich, CT, 2011.

6923
The Judy and Michael Steinhardt Foundation ✧
712 5th Ave., 34th Fl.
New York, NY 10019-4108
GiveSmart: http://www.givesmart.org/Stories/Donors/Michael-Steinhardt

Established in 1986 in NY.
Donor: Michael H. Steinhardt.
Foundation type: Independent foundation.
Financial data (yr. ended 09/30/13): Assets, $8,843,945 (M); gifts received, $25,400,130; expenditures, $15,349,939; qualifying distributions, $14,814,658; giving activities include $14,814,428 for 138 grants (high: $2,000,000; low: $500).
Purpose and activities: Giving primarily to educational programs for children, as well as for recent immigrants to Israel.
Fields of interest: Higher education; Education; Human services; Jewish federated giving programs; Jewish agencies & synagogues.
International interests: Israel.
Limitations: Applications not accepted. Giving primarily in NY. No grants to individuals.
Application information: Contributes only to pre-selected organizations.
Trustees: Judith Steinhardt; Michael H. Steinhardt.
EIN: 133357500

6924
Edward & Joan B. Steiniger Charitable Foundation ✧
1 Court Sq., 19th Fl.
Long Island City, NY 11120

Established in 1990 in NY.
Donor: Pamela S. Saelzler Trust.
Foundation type: Independent foundation.
Financial data (yr. ended 12/31/13): Assets, $28,372,570 (M); expenditures, $1,467,629; qualifying distributions, $1,211,909; giving activities include $1,142,345 for 4 grants (high: $448,326; low: $100,000).
Purpose and activities: Giving primarily for Roman Catholic education, including a seminary, a Roman Catholic archdiocese, and a Roman Catholic federated giving program.
Fields of interest: Theological school/education; Education; Catholic federated giving programs; Catholic agencies & churches.
Limitations: Applications not accepted. Giving primarily in the metropolitan New York, NY, area. No grants to individuals.
Application information: Contributes only to pre-selected organizations.
Trustees: Howard G. Seitz; Citibank, N.A.; Archdiocese of New York.
EIN: 133585674

6925
Ernest E. Stempel Foundation ✧
c/o JPMorgan Chase Bank, N.A.
270 Park Ave.
New York, NY 10017-2014 (212) 464-1937
Contact: James P. Largey

Established in 1994 in DE.
Donors: Ernest E. Stempel†; Saltus Grammar School.
Foundation type: Independent foundation.
Financial data (yr. ended 12/31/13): Assets, $29,546,107 (M); gifts received, $120,660; expenditures, $1,614,860; qualifying distributions, $1,460,932; giving activities include $1,393,336 for 32 grants (high: $338,384; low: $10,000).
Fields of interest: Museums (marine/maritime); Higher education; Law school/education; Education; Zoos/zoological societies; Hospitals (general); Human services.
International interests: Bermuda.
Limitations: Applications not accepted. Giving primarily in DE and NY, as well as in Bermuda. No grants to individuals.
Application information: Contributes only to pre-selected organizations.
Trustees: Diana S. Bergquist; Calvin B. Stempel; Neil F. Stempel.
EIN: 510363381

6926
The Daniel and Nanna Stern Family Foundation ✧
650 Madison Ave., 26th Fl.
New York, NY 10022-1029 (212) 610-9006
Contact: Ann Colucci

Established in 2006 in DE.
Donor: Daniel Stern.
Foundation type: Independent foundation.
Financial data (yr. ended 12/31/13): Assets, $33,646 (M); gifts received, $601,750; expenditures, $591,962; qualifying distributions, $588,750; giving activities include $588,750 for 7 grants (high: $150,500; low: $23,750).
Fields of interest: Media, film/video; Media, television; Performing arts centers; Arts; Education; Hospitals (general).
Limitations: Applications accepted. Giving primarily in New York, NY. No grants to individuals.
Application information: Application form required.
Initial approach: Letter
Deadline(s): None
Officer and Directors:* Daniel Stern,* Chair.; Diane Lichtenstein; Nanna Stern.
EIN: 205993432

6927
Thomas D. & Denise R. Stern Family Foundation ✧
c/o Anchin, Block & Anchin, LLP
1375 Broadway
New York, NY 10018-7001

Established in 2001 in NY.
Donors: Thomas D. Stern; Denise Stern.
Foundation type: Independent foundation.
Financial data (yr. ended 12/31/13): Assets, $11,235,826 (M); gifts received, $1,684,656; expenditures, $981,812; qualifying distributions, $929,750; giving activities include $929,500 for 17 grants (high: $200,000; low: $2,500).
Purpose and activities: Giving primarily for diabetes and medical research, Jewish organizations and education.
Fields of interest: Higher education; Education; Diabetes research; Medical research; Jewish federated giving programs.
Limitations: Applications not accepted. Giving primarily in FL, MA, and NY, some giving also in NH. No grants to individuals.

Application information: Contributes only to pre-selected organizations.
Trustees: Denise R. Stern; Thomas D. Stern.
EIN: 134195656
Selected grants: The following grants are a representative sample of this grantmaker's funding activity:
$367,150 to Diabetes Research Foundation, Chicago, IL, 2011.
$200,000 to Birthright Israel Foundation, New York, NY, 2011.

6928
Bernice and Milton Stern Foundation ✧
c/o Phillips Gold & Co., C.P.A.s
1430 Broadway, 6th Fl.
New York, NY 10018-3308 (212) 730-1112
Contact: Bernice Stern, Pres.

Established in 1982 in DE.
Donor: Bernice Stern.
Foundation type: Independent foundation.
Financial data (yr. ended 04/30/13): Assets, $7,614,897 (M); expenditures, $1,398,997; qualifying distributions, $1,296,388; giving activities include $1,138,400 for 10+ grants (high: $250,000).
Purpose and activities: Giving primarily for education, and children, youth and social services. The foundation funds study and program development on issues affecting the lives of needy children and families through the Stern Institute for Family Life Education of the Children's Aid Society.
Fields of interest: Performing arts, theater; Arts; Education; Human services; Neighborhood centers; Children/youth, services; Foundations (private grantmaking).
Type of support: Continuing support.
Limitations: Applications not accepted. Giving primarily in the metropolitan New York, NY, area; some funding also Boise, ID, and Boston, MA. No grants to individuals.
Application information: Contributes only to pre-selected organizations.
Officers: Bernice Stern, Pres.; Wendy S. Pesky, V.P.
Directors: Michael Stern; Peter Stern; Robert Stern.
EIN: 510264122
Selected grants: The following grants are a representative sample of this grantmaker's funding activity:
$250,000 to Lee Pesky Learning Center, Boise, ID, 2011.
$250,000 to Stern Center for Language and Learning, Williston, VT, 2011.
$200,000 to Kingsbridge Heights Community Center, Bronx, NY, 2011.
$136,875 to Morris and Bessie Altman Foundation, Shelburne, VT, 2011.
$100,000 to Childrens Aid Society, New York, NY, 2011.
$75,000 to Find Your Voice, New York, NY, 2011.
$15,000 to United Neighbors of East Midtown, New York, NY, 2011.
$2,000 to Beth Israel Foundation, New York, NY, 2011.

6929
The Joyce C. Stern Foundation ✧ ☆
424 W. End Ave., No. 1FN
New York, NY 10024
Contact: Tiffany Herlands

Established in 2006 in NY.
Donor: Gustav and Irene Stern Foundation.
Foundation type: Independent foundation.
Financial data (yr. ended 09/30/13): Assets, $6,150,817 (M); expenditures, $687,552; qualifying distributions, $641,151; giving activities include $588,500 for 12 grants (high: $240,000; low: $1,000).
Fields of interest: Higher education, university; Education; Health care; Religion.
Limitations: Applications not accepted. Giving primarily in NJ and New York, NY. No grants to individuals.
Application information: Unsolicited requests for funds not accepted.
Officers: Joyce C. Herlands, Pres.; Ronny Barnea, Secy.; Tiffany Herlands, Treas.
EIN: 204435816
Selected grants: The following grants are a representative sample of this grantmaker's funding activity:
$240,000 to Columbia University, New York, NY, 2013. For educational.
$105,000 to Chabad of the West Side, New York, NY, 2013. For religious.
$100,000 to Christopher and Dana Reeve Foundation, Short Hills, NJ, 2013.
$70,000 to Metropolitan Opera, New York, NY, 2013.
$25,000 to Yeshiva University, New York, NY, 2013. For educational.
$10,000 to American Lung Association, Washington, DC, 2013. For scientific purposes.
$10,000 to Buoniconti Fund to Cure Paralysis, Miami, FL, 2013. For scientific purposes.
$10,000 to Lymphoma Foundation, New York, NY, 2013. For scientific purposes.
$5,000 to American Museum of Natural History, New York, NY, 2013. For educational.
$2,500 to Congregation Shearith Israel, New York, NY, 2013. For religious.

6930
Sternberg Charitable Trust ✧ ☆
85 Bellevue Ave.
Rye, NY 10580-1840

Established in 1994 in NY.
Donor: Stuart L. Sternberg.
Foundation type: Independent foundation.
Financial data (yr. ended 12/31/13): Assets, $10,630,167 (M); gifts received, $3,610,979; expenditures, $441,526; qualifying distributions, $431,495; giving activities include $428,610 for 37 grants (high: $250,000; low: $100).
Purpose and activities: Giving primarily for the arts, education, health organizations, social services, the environment, religion, and the arts.
Fields of interest: Arts; Elementary/secondary education; Environment, natural resources; Health care; Health organizations, association; Human services; Foundations (public).
Limitations: Applications not accepted. Giving primarily in NY. No grants to individuals.
Application information: Contributes only to pre-selected organizations.
Trustees: Lisa Sternberg; Stuart L. Sternberg.
EIN: 137046097

6931
The Ernst C. Stiefel Foundation ✧
c/o Hughes Hubbard & Reed
1 Battery Park Plz.
New York, NY 10004-1482
Contact: Kenneth R. Page, Tr.

Established in 1997 in NY.
Donor: Ernst C. Stiefel†.
Foundation type: Independent foundation.
Financial data (yr. ended 12/31/13): Assets, $3,371,425 (M); expenditures, $545,075; qualifying distributions, $525,000; giving activities include $525,000 for 16 grants (high: $75,000; low: $10,000).
Fields of interest: Performing arts, music; Arts; Higher education; Education; Human services.
Type of support: General/operating support; Continuing support; Research; Matching/challenge support.
Limitations: Applications accepted. Giving primarily in New York, NY. No grants to individuals.
Application information: Application form required.
Initial approach: Letter
Copies of proposal: 1
Deadline(s): None
Final notification: Upon review and decision by Trustees
Trustees: Robert J. Gellert; Kenneth R. Page.
EIN: 137117155
Selected grants: The following grants are a representative sample of this grantmaker's funding activity:
$200,000 to Caramoor Center for Music and the Arts, Katonah, NY, 2011.
$75,000 to Manhattan Theater Club, New York, NY, 2011.
$75,000 to Music Conservatory of Westchester, White Plains, NY, 2011.
$60,000 to New York City Rescue Mission, New York, NY, 2011.
$50,000 to Selfhelp Community Services, New York, NY, 2011.
$50,000 to United Neighbors of East Midtown, New York, NY, 2011.
$35,000 to Dorot, New York, NY, 2011.
$35,000 to Gotham Chamber Opera, New York, NY, 2011.
$35,000 to One Stop Senior Services, New York, NY, 2011.
$25,000 to W N Y C Foundation, New York, NY, 2011.

6932
Stockman Family Foundation Trust ✧
P.O. Box 1297
Church St. Sta.
New York, NY 10008-1297
Application address: c/o Hervey S. Stockman, Jr., Pres., 4475 N. Ocean Blvd., No. 5-B, Delray Beach, FL 33483, tel.: (561) 265-0244

Established in 1990 in NM.
Donors: Hervey S. Stockman; Sarah A. Stockman†.
Foundation type: Independent foundation.
Financial data (yr. ended 11/30/13): Assets, $19,507,406 (M); expenditures, $1,072,244; qualifying distributions, $1,024,680; giving activities include $983,457 for 29 grants (high: $100,000; low: $5,350).
Purpose and activities: Grants are made to organizations to advance the knowledge and

practice of conservation of historic and artistic property in the museum and university domain.
Fields of interest: Museums; Historic preservation/historical societies; Education.
Limitations: Applications accepted. Giving in the U.S. No support for political organizations. No grants to individuals.
Publications: Application guidelines.
Application information: Application form not required.
Initial approach: Proposal
Deadline(s): None
Final notification: 2-3 months
Officers: Hervey S. Stockman, Jr., Pres.; Karl W. Gustafson, Treas.
Directors: Pamela Proctor; Allison A. Stockman; Charles C. Stockman; Robert P. Stockman.
Trustee: Deutsche Bank Trust Co., N.A.
EIN: 856104630

6933
The Stony Point Foundation ✧
c/o BCRS Assocs., LLC, Attn.: John O. Downing
77 Water St., 9th Fl.
New York, NY 10005-4401

Established in 1993 in NY.
Donor: John O. Downing.
Foundation type: Independent foundation.
Financial data (yr. ended 01/31/13): Assets, $13,744,603 (M); expenditures, $720,117; qualifying distributions, $541,050; giving activities include $541,050 for grants.
Purpose and activities: Giving primarily for education, the environment, and human services.
Fields of interest: Museums; Elementary/secondary education; Higher education; Environment, natural resources; Human services.
Limitations: Applications not accepted. Giving in the U.S., with emphasis on CT, NJ, TN, and VT. No grants to individuals or for scholarships; no loans.
Application information: Contributes only to pre-selected organizations.
Trustees: Frances V.S. Downing; John O. Downing.
EIN: 133766973
Selected grants: The following grants are a representative sample of this grantmaker's funding activity:
$250,000 to Vanderbilt University, Nashville, TN, 2011. For general purpose.
$150,000 to Hotchkiss School, Lakeville, CT, 2011. For general purpose.
$75,000 to Madeira School, McLean, VA, 2011. For general purpose.
$75,000 to Shelburne Museum, Shelburne, VT, 2011. For general purpose.
$7,500 to Shelburne Museum, Shelburne, VT, 2011. For general purpose.
$5,000 to Vanderbilt University, Nashville, TN, 2011. For general purpose.
$3,000 to Hotchkiss School, Lakeville, CT, 2011. For general purpose.
$3,000 to Montana Land Reliance, Helena, MT, 2011. For general purpose.
$2,000 to New Jersey Highlands Coalition, Boonton, NJ, 2011. For general purpose.
$2,000 to South Carolina Coastal Conservation League, Charleston, SC, 2011. For general purpose.

6934
The Philip A. and Lynn Straus Foundation, Inc. ✧
1037 Constable Dr. S.
Mamaroneck, NY 10543-4702
Contact: Lynn G. Straus, Pres.
E-mail: lynngstraus@me.com

Incorporated about 1957 in NY.
Donors: Lynn G. Straus; Philip A. Straus†.
Foundation type: Independent foundation.
Financial data (yr. ended 03/31/13): Assets, $14,252,892 (M); gifts received, $15,461; expenditures, $1,065,842; qualifying distributions, $938,960; giving activities include $931,600 for 100 grants (high: $250,000; low: $100).
Purpose and activities: Giving primarily for education from birth to age 21, the arts, libraries, civil rights and human services.
Fields of interest: Museums; Arts; Libraries/library science; Education; Human services; Civil/human rights; Infants/toddlers; Children; Mentally disabled; Minorities; Women; Infants/toddlers, female; Infants/toddlers, male; Immigrants/refugees; Economically disadvantaged.
Type of support: Continuing support; Annual campaigns; Capital campaigns; Building/renovation; Endowments; Emergency funds; Program development; Curriculum development; Scholarship funds.
Limitations: Applications not accepted. Giving on a national basis. No support for religious organizations. No grants to individuals.
Application information: Contributes only to pre-selected organizations.
Officer: Lynn G. Straus, Pres.
Trustees: Donald Roy Straus; Katherine Bea Straus; Philip A. Straus, Jr.
Number of staff: None.
EIN: 136161223

6935
The Stringer Foundation ✧
10 Park Ave., Ste. 2A
New York, NY 10016-4338
Contact: Donald R. Wall, Exec. Dir.
E-mail: drwell@optonline.net

Established in 1995 in NY.
Donor: Tipton S. Conrad.
Foundation type: Independent foundation.
Financial data (yr. ended 06/30/13): Assets, $23,054,299 (M); expenditures, $1,152,329; qualifying distributions, $895,000; giving activities include $895,000 for grants.
Fields of interest: Adult education—literacy, basic skills & GED; Education, reading; Animal welfare; Reproductive health, family planning; Human services; Children/youth, services.
Limitations: Applications not accepted. Giving primarily in CA and NY. No support for organizations lacking 501(c)(3) status, or religious or political organizations; generally no support for organizations that limit their work to a group of people determined by race, sex or origin.
Application information: Unsolicited requests for funds not accepted.
Board meeting date(s): June
Officers and Directors:* Tipton S. Conrad,* Pres.; Donald R. Wall, Secy.-Treas. and Exec. Dir.; Barbara Schacter.
Number of staff: 1
EIN: 113288229
Selected grants: The following grants are a representative sample of this grantmaker's funding activity:
$100,000 to New York University Langone Medical Center, New York, NY, 2011. For operations.
$30,000 to Urban Assembly, New York, NY, 2011. For operations.
$20,000 to Reach Out and Read, Boston, MA, 2011. For operations.
$10,000 to American Society for the Prevention of Cruelty to Animals, New York, NY, 2011. For operations.
$5,000 to Haven Hills, Canoga Park, CA, 2011. For operations.
$5,000 to University of Maryland-College Park, College Park, MD, 2011. For operations.

6936
Strypemonde Foundation ✧
1384 Park Ln.
Pelham Manor, NY 10803-3514

Established in 1999 in NY.
Donor: Paul Francis.
Foundation type: Independent foundation.
Financial data (yr. ended 06/30/13): Assets, $14,259,164 (M); expenditures, $1,094,113; qualifying distributions, $807,793; giving activities include $807,793 for grants.
Fields of interest: Arts; Secondary school/education; Higher education, university; Human services; Children/youth, services.
Type of support: General/operating support; Continuing support; Annual campaigns; Equipment; Program development; Research.
Limitations: Applications not accepted. Giving primarily in Westchester County and New York, NY. No grants to individuals.
Application information: Contributes only to pre-selected organizations.
Officers: Titia Hulst, Pres.; Paul Francis, V.P. and Secy.
Number of staff: None.
EIN: 137204588
Selected grants: The following grants are a representative sample of this grantmaker's funding activity:
$40,000 to New York University, Law School, New York, NY, 2013. For educational.

6937
The Stuart Family Foundation, Inc. ✧ ☆
c/o Karen Larkin, The Ayco Co., LP
P.O. Box 860
Saratoga Springs, NY 12866-0860

Established in 1995 in NY.
Donor: Scott M. Stuart.
Foundation type: Independent foundation.
Financial data (yr. ended 11/30/13): Assets, $7,712,588 (M); expenditures, $917,767; qualifying distributions, $910,535; giving activities include $910,535 for 27 grants (high: $250,027; low: $500).
Purpose and activities: Giving primarily for higher education, medical research, and social services.
Fields of interest: Higher education; Education; Medical research, institute; Human services; Children/youth, services.

Limitations: Applications not accepted. Giving primarily in CA, CT, NH, and NY. No grants to individuals.
Application information: Contributes only to pre-selected organizations.
Trustees: Lisa G. Stuart; Scott M. Stuart.
EIN: 133861861
Selected grants: The following grants are a representative sample of this grantmaker's funding activity:
$502,046 to Dartmouth College, Hanover, NH, 2011. For general charitable purposes.
$493,384 to Dartmouth College, Hanover, NH, 2011. For general charitable purposes.
$50,000 to Greenwich Country Day School, Greenwich, CT, 2011. For general charitable purposes.
$50,000 to Greenwich Country Day School, Greenwich, CT, 2011. For general charitable purposes.
$40,000 to Waterside School, Stamford, CT, 2011. For general charitable purposes.
$25,000 to Memorial Sloan-Kettering Cancer Center, New York, NY, 2011. For general charitable purposes.
$17,500 to Memorial Sloan-Kettering Cancer Center, New York, NY, 2011. For general charitable purposes.
$2,500 to Dartmouth College Fund, Hanover, NH, 2011. For general charitable purposes.
$2,500 to Good Shepherd Nativity Mission School, New Orleans, LA, 2011. For general charitable purposes.
$1,000 to Prep for Prep, New York, NY, 2011. For general charitable purposes.

6938
The Julius Stulman Foundation, Inc. ✧
c/o S. Stulman
151 Central Park W.
New York, NY 10023-1514

Established in 1998 in FL.
Foundation type: Independent foundation.
Financial data (yr. ended 12/31/13): Assets, $4,030,772 (M); expenditures, $674,166; qualifying distributions, $638,098; giving activities include $621,460 for 27 grants (high: $211,800; low: $200).
Fields of interest: Education; Human services; Jewish federated giving programs; Jewish agencies & synagogues.
Limitations: Applications not accepted. Giving primarily in CT, NY, and WI. No grants to individuals.
Application information: Contributes only to pre-selected organizations.
Officers and Directors:* Stephen L. Stulman,* Pres.; Jessica R. Sheinman,* V.P.; James K. Stulman,* Secy.; Andrea S. Dennett,* Treas.; Laura Cooper.
EIN: 311550822
Selected grants: The following grants are a representative sample of this grantmaker's funding activity:
$3,500 to Ohavi Zedek Synagogue, Burlington, VT, 2012. For religious activities.
$1,000 to Bi-Cultural Day School, Stamford, CT, 2012. For educational, cultural.

6939
Stuntz Family Foundation ✧
c/o Eisneramper LLP
750 3rd Ave., 16th Fl.
New York, NY 10017-2716

Established in 1997 in NY.
Donors: Mayo Stuntz; Elizabeth Stuntz; Mayo S. Stuntz, Jr.
Foundation type: Independent foundation.
Financial data (yr. ended 11/30/13): Assets, $9,235,889 (M); gifts received, $38,585; expenditures, $524,827; qualifying distributions, $444,580; giving activities include $433,860 for 33 grants (high: $75,000; low: $500).
Purpose and activities: Giving primarily for education and human services, as well as for Jewish organizations.
Fields of interest: Education; Human services; Jewish agencies & synagogues.
Limitations: Applications not accepted. Giving primarily in NY. No grants to individuals.
Application information: Contributes only to pre-selected organizations.
Officer: Mayo S. Stuntz, Jr., Pres.
Director: Elizabeth Stuntz.
EIN: 133979253

6940
Jay and Kelly Sugarman Foundation ✧
c/o Jay Sugarman
1114 Ave. of the Americas
New York, NY 10036

Established in 2004 in NY.
Donors: Jay Sugarman; Kelly Sugarman.
Foundation type: Independent foundation.
Financial data (yr. ended 12/31/12): Assets, $2,280,119 (M); expenditures, $667,990; qualifying distributions, $638,372; giving activities include $598,222 for 26 grants (high: $219,600; low: $1,000).
Purpose and activities: Giving primarily for the arts, education, and human services.
Fields of interest: Performing arts, theater; Arts; Education; Health organizations, association; Human services; Children/youth, services.
Limitations: Applications not accepted. Giving primarily in New York, NY. No grants to individuals.
Application information: Contributes only to pre-selected organizations.
Officers: Jay Sugarman, Pres. and Treas.; Kelly Sugarman, V.P.; Wendy Forshay, Secy.
EIN: 200911399
Selected grants: The following grants are a representative sample of this grantmaker's funding activity:
$73,430 to Robin Hood Foundation, New York, NY, 2012. For poverty programs.
$10,000 to Turnaround for Children, New York, NY, 2012. For youth development Programs.
$2,500 to Covenant Preparatory School, Hartford, CT, 2012. For the Tyler Copp Memorial Fund.
$2,500 to Southampton Fresh Air Home, Southampton, NY, 2012. For physically challenged children.
$1,200 to Lighthouse International, New York, NY, 2012. For general purposes of organization.
$1,000 to New Venture Fund, Washington, DC, 2012. For the Every Mother Counts Program.

6941
The Sullivan Family Foundation ✧ ☆
c/o BCRS Associates, LLC
77 Water St., 9th Fl.
New York, NY 10005-4414

Established in 1989 in MA.
Donors: Daniel J. Sullivan, Jr.; Marjorie O. Sullivan.
Foundation type: Independent foundation.
Financial data (yr. ended 05/31/13): Assets, $1,505,186 (M); gifts received, $595,593; expenditures, $925,387; qualifying distributions, $917,170; giving activities include $915,000 for 4 grants (high: $500,000; low: $20,000).
Fields of interest: Hospitals (general).
Limitations: Applications not accepted. Giving primarily in Boston, MA. No grants to individuals.
Application information: Contributes only to pre-selected organizations.
Trustees: Daniel J. Sullivan, Jr.; Marjorie O. Sullivan.
EIN: 133531989
Selected grants: The following grants are a representative sample of this grantmaker's funding activity:
$280,000 to Massachusetts General Hospital, Boston, MA, 2011.
$250,000 to Massachusetts General Hospital, Boston, MA, 2011.
$10,000 to JFYNetWorks, Boston, MA, 2011.

6942
The Sulzberger Foundation, Inc. ✧
620 8th Ave., 16th Fl.
New York, NY 10018-1618

Incorporated in 1956 in NY.
Donors: Arthur Hays Sulzberger‡; Iphigene Ochs Sulzberger‡; Marian S. Heiskell; Ruth S. Holmberg; Judith P. Sulzberger; Arthur Ochs Sulzberger‡.
Foundation type: Independent foundation.
Financial data (yr. ended 12/31/12): Assets, $30,758,999 (M); expenditures, $3,041,126; qualifying distributions, $2,759,426; giving activities include $2,689,000 for 2 grants (high: $2,189,000; low: $500,000).
Fields of interest: Museums (specialized); Foundations (public).
Type of support: General/operating support; Continuing support; Annual campaigns; Building/renovation; Endowments; Emergency funds; Program development; Internship funds; Scholarship funds.
Limitations: Applications not accepted. Giving primarily in Cincinnati, OH; some funding also in Washington, DC. No grants to individuals, or for matching gifts; no loans.
Application information: The foundation is not currently accepting applications.
Board meeting date(s): Jan. and as required
Officers: Marian S. Heiskell, Pres.; Ruth S. Holmberg, V.P.
Trustee: Arthur Ochs Sulzberger.
Number of staff: 1 part-time professional; 2 part-time support.
EIN: 136083166

6943
Sumitomo Corporation of America Foundation ✧
600 3rd Ave.
New York, NY 10016-2001
Main URL: http://www.sumitomocorp.com/about/community.html

Established in 2004 in NY.
Donor: Sumitomo Corporation of America "SCOA".
Foundation type: Company-sponsored foundation.
Financial data (yr. ended 03/31/13): Assets, $9,108,003 (M); expenditures, $594,283; qualifying distributions, $551,061; giving activities include $530,165 for 24 grants (high: $150,000; low: $165).
Purpose and activities: The foundation supports organizations involved with arts and culture, education, relief assistance, and social services. Special emphasis is directed toward programs designed to enhance understanding in the United States of Japan, its people, culture, and society through research, education, and cultural initiatives.
Fields of interest: Arts, cultural/ethnic awareness; Performing arts; Arts; Higher education; Education; Disasters, preparedness/services; Children/youth, services; Human services; Community/economic development.
Type of support: Sponsorships; General/operating support; Research.
Limitations: Applications not accepted. Giving primarily in areas of company operations, with emphasis on NY. No grants to individuals.
Application information: Contributes only to pre-selected organizations.
Officers and Directors:* Hideki Iwasawa,* Pres.; Elizabeth Peters,* Secy.; Masao Hirota,* Treas.; William Kane; Shinichi Watabe.
EIN: 202103634

6944
Solon E. Summerfield Foundation, Inc. ✧
1270 Ave. of the Americas, Ste. 2114
New York, NY 10020-1806
E-mail: info@summerfieldfoundation.org; Main URL: http://summerfieldfoundation.org

Incorporated in 1939 in NY.
Donor: Solon E. Summerfield†.
Foundation type: Independent foundation.
Financial data (yr. ended 12/31/13): Assets, $74,019,482 (M); expenditures, $3,221,523; qualifying distributions, $2,747,358; giving activities include $2,193,468 for 94 grants (high: $272,537; low: $1,000).
Purpose and activities: Giving primarily for the arts, educational and scholarship opportunities, medical research, and social services.
Fields of interest: Arts education; Higher education; Hospitals (general); Health care; Health organizations; Medical research, institute; Human services; Children/youth, services.
Type of support: General/operating support; Capital campaigns; Endowments; Scholarship funds; Matching/challenge support.
Limitations: Applications accepted. Giving on a national basis, with emphasis on the East Coast. No grants to individuals, or for fund raising events or benefits.
Application information: Application information and letter of inquiry form available on foundation web site. Eligible foundations will be invited to submit a full proposal. Attachments to the LOI are not accepted. Application form not required.
Initial approach: On-line letter of inquiry only (no more than 1 page)
Deadline(s): Feb. 1 and Aug. 1, for letter of inquiry; Feb. 28 and July 30 for invited applications
Board meeting date(s): Biannually
Final notification: June and Nov.
Officers and Directors:* Thomas C. Treeger,* Pres.; Karen Prager Balliet, V.P. and Secy.; Mark A. Cogen, V.P. and Treas.; Ruth P. Cogen,* V.P.; Jennifer Treeger Peters,* V.P.
Number of staff: 1 full-time support; 3 part-time support.
EIN: 131797260

6945
The John and Jayne Summers Foundation, Inc. ✧
P.O. Box 60620
Rochester, NY 14606-0620

Established in 2000 in NY.
Donors: John M. Summers; Jayne C. Summers†; Richard Sand; Danny Wegman; John C. Pyles; Steriliz LLC.
Foundation type: Independent foundation.
Financial data (yr. ended 12/31/13): Assets, $12,047,687 (M); gifts received, $914,269; expenditures, $2,018,578; qualifying distributions, $1,749,243; giving activities include $1,749,243 for 24 grants (high: $1,300,000; low: $1,000).
Fields of interest: Higher education; Education; Health organizations, association; Human services.
Limitations: Applications not accepted. Giving primarily in Rochester, NY. No grants to individuals.
Application information: Contributes only to pre-selected organizations.
Officers: John M. Summers, Pres.; Eugene W. Baldino, V.P. and Treas.; Kenneth A. Marvald, V.P.; Susan L. Conrado, Secy.
Directors: Douglas J. Summers; Todd D. Summers.
EIN: 161596923

6946
Sun Hill Foundation ✧
c/o DRM Group LLC
26 Railroad Ave., No. 229
Babylon, NY 11702-2216

Established in 1992 in CT as partial successor to the Tudor Foundation.
Donors: Edwin A. Malloy†; Susan R. Malloy.
Foundation type: Independent foundation.
Financial data (yr. ended 12/31/13): Assets, $9,952,341 (M); expenditures, $617,138; qualifying distributions, $527,445; giving activities include $527,445 for 45 grants (high: $50,000; low: $1,000).
Purpose and activities: Giving primarily for education and social services.
Fields of interest: Arts; Higher education; Law school/education; Education; Environment, natural resources; Medical research, institute; Human services; Jewish federated giving programs; Jewish agencies & synagogues.
Limitations: Applications not accepted. Giving primarily in CT, Washington, DC, the greater Boston, MA, area, New York, NY and South Royalton, VT. No grants to individuals.
Publications: Annual report.
Application information: Unsolicited requests for funds not accepted.
Officers: Susan R. Malloy, Pres.; Timon J. Malloy, Secy.; Jennifer Malloy Combs, Treas.
EIN: 061326091

6947
Surdna Foundation, Inc. ✧
330 Madison Ave., 30th Fl.
New York, NY 10017-5001 (212) 557-0010
Contact: Phillip Henderson, Pres.
FAX: (212) 557-0003; E-mail: grants@surdna.org; Main URL: http://www.surdna.org
E-Newsletter: http://visitor.constantcontact.com/manage/optin/ea?v=001qgl9GeY_mqQM45bpB_NAiA%3D%3D
Grantee Perception Report: http://www.surdna.org/publications-resources/102.html
Grants Database: http://www.surdna.org/what-we-fund/search-our-grants.html
Knowledge Center: http://www.surdna.org/what-were-learning.html
Twitter: http://twitter.com/surdna_fndn

Incorporated in 1917 in NY.
Donor: John E. Andrus†.
Foundation type: Independent foundation.
Financial data (yr. ended 06/30/13): Assets, $929,596,379 (M); expenditures, $44,766,655; qualifying distributions, $34,643,450; giving activities include $34,643,450 for 501 grants (high: $800,000; low: $100).
Purpose and activities: The foundation seeks to foster just and sustainable communities in the United States guided by principles of social justice and distinguished by healthy environments, strong local economies, and thriving cultures. The foundation focuses on three core areas: 1) Sustainable Environments; 2) Strong Local Economies; and 3) Thriving Cultures.
Fields of interest: Arts, alliance/advocacy; Arts, association; Arts, cultural/ethnic awareness; Arts education; Environment, energy; Environment; Employment; Economic development; Urban/community development; Community/economic development; Public affairs, citizen participation.
Type of support: General/operating support; Continuing support; Management development/capacity building; Program development; Program-related investments/loans; Employee matching gifts.
Limitations: Applications accepted. Giving on a national basis. No support for international projects, or programs addressing direct job training, toxics, hazardous waste, environmental education, sustainable agriculture, or food production. No grants for individuals, endowments/land acquisition, capital campaigns or construction.
Publications: Annual report (including application guidelines); Grants list.
Application information: Online applications encouraged. Applicants should check guidelines and eligibility requirements prior to initiating the application process. The foundation funds the Andrus Family Fund that defines and manages its own grantmaking program and process. For more information see http://www.affund.org. Application form required.
Initial approach: Online at foundation web site
Copies of proposal: 1
Deadline(s): None

Board meeting date(s): Feb., May, and Sept.
Final notification: 90 days for letters of inquiry; approximately 12 weeks for full proposals
Officers and Directors:* Jocelyn Downie,* Chair.; Peter B. Benedict II, Vice-Chair.; Phillip Henderson, Pres.; Marc de Venoge, C.F.O. and C.A.O.; Lawrence S.C. Griffith, M.D., Secy. and Interim-Treas.; Bruce Abernethy; Elizabeth H. Andrus; Judy Belk; Carra Cote-Ackah; John F. Hawkins; Kelly D. Nowlin; Tracy Palandjian; Michael S. Spensley; Gwen Walden.
Number of staff: 19 full-time professional; 4 full-time support; 1 part-time support.
EIN: 136108163
Selected grants: The following grants are a representative sample of this grantmaker's funding activity:
$750,000 to Boston Arts Academy Foundation, Boston, MA, 2012. To further strengthen the Surdna Arts Teachers Fellowship program by supporting its transition to a new home at the Center for Arts in Education at Boston Arts Academy. The program will be renamed: National Arts Teachers Fellowship, payable over 3.00 years.
$700,000 to Reconnecting America, Oakland, CA, 2013. For Transportation for America's (T4A) efforts to help cities and states implement the 2012 Transportation Reauthorization Act, as well as efforts to leverage innovative financing of sustainable infrastructure investments, payable over 2.00 years.
$500,000 to Center for Neighborhood Technology, Chicago, IL, 2013. For the establishment of wet weather retrofit ('Wetrofit) services in Chicago area communities that support stormwater management and provide data and advocacy tools to spur similar market-based solutions in other cities, payable over 2.00 years.
$500,000 to Green for All, Oakland, CA, 2012. For general operating funds, including support for policy advocacy, efforts to strengthen local leadership, and initiatives to scale economic development models that result in inclusive green economy strong enough to lift people out of poverty, payable over 2.00 years.
$500,000 to Nonprofit Finance Fund, New York, NY, 2013. For ArtPlace to initiate a third round of grantmaking; stage a national tour to promote Vibrancy Indicators; make its first loans; stage a convening of creative placemakers; and craft a strategy for extended federal alignment.
$425,000 to Reconnecting America, Washington, DC, 2012. For general support to strengthen transit-oriented development implementation, federal policy development and communications, payable over 2.00 years.
$419,000 to Family Alternatives, Minneapolis, MN, 2012. For youth to learn skills and strategies for life transitions; update social workers and foster parents on transition theory and facilitate its use; collaborate with the University of St. Thomas study, payable over 3.00 years.
$400,000 to National Domestic Workers Alliance, New York, NY, 2012. For research, communications and strategic campaigns that strengthen local and regional economies by creating jobs, workforce training and improved working conditions in the domestic work and home care industries, payable over 2.00 years.
$300,000 to Los Angeles Alliance for a New Economy, Los Angeles, CA, 2013. To launch a five-year national transportation procurement initiative to integrate job creation and quality standards into the purchasing strategy for clean energy vehicles and vehicle parts manufactured for public transit, payable over 3.00 years.
$300,000 to National Employment Law Project, New York, NY, 2013. For general support for NELP's work to improve the quality of low wage jobs, strengthen the economic security safety net, and enhance workers' access to education and training that will improve their workforce mobility, payable over 2.00 years.
$270,000 to Maryland Institute College of Art, Baltimore, MD, 2012. For mentoring, support, and financial aid to high school students and visual art teachers engaged in intensive, summer residency, studio art experiences that will increase skills for both college preparedness/teacher quality and impact, payable over 3.00 years.
$115,000 to Political Economy Research Institute, Amherst, MA, 2012. For continued support for PERI's Green Economy program to provide qualitative analysis of green economic policy issues for decision makers, and broaden the reach of its findings among the media, the economics profession, and the public.
$110,000 to Job Opportunities Task Force, Baltimore, MD, 2013. To strengthen connections between workers and training opportunities; to better link workforce and infrastructure development; and to advance policies that create stronger pathways into careers and promote healthy workplaces.
$100,000 to College for Creative Studies, Detroit Creative Corridor Center, Detroit, MI, 2012. For the development and implementation of a Delivery Co-Operative for creative sector entrepreneurs; and to craft a state-wide advocacy campaign to increase support to Michigan's creative economy initiatives, payable over 2.00 years.
$100,000 to Ella Baker Center for Human Rights, Oakland, CA, 2013. To support Communities United for Clean Energy and Jobs for Clean Energy and Jobs to build a strong and equitable environmental movement among people of color and low-income communities in California that can be a model for national efforts.
$90,000 to Casa Valentina, Miami, FL, 2012. To expand 'Successful Transitions' program. To replicate 'Successful Transitions' across all services, including newly added programs for young men and young mothers aging out of foster care.
$75,000 to Community Labor United, Boston, MA, 2013. To promote a comprehensive proposal for a State Infrastructure Bank that adheres to equitable economic and environmental indicators.
$75,000 to Next American City, Philadelphia, PA, 2013. To build a sustained dialogue about equitable economic development strategies through a daily online column and three long-form investigative articles.
$75,000 to Urban Bush Women, Brooklyn, NY, 2012. For continued support for Urban Bush Women's Summer Leadership Institute in New Orleans, a ten-day training for dance professionals, community-based artists and organizers.
$70,000 to Foundry Theater, New York, NY, 2013. For the premiere production of a new theatrical work exploring the contemporary US policing and prison practices and transformative justice, and accompanying Foundry Dialogues series.

6948
The Jeff Sutton Charitable Foundation ✧
500 5th Ave., 54th Fl.
New York, NY 10110-0001

Established in NY.
Donor: Jeff Sutton.
Foundation type: Independent foundation.
Financial data (yr. ended 12/31/13): Assets, $150,835 (M); expenditures, $1,833,925; qualifying distributions, $1,833,925; giving activities include $1,810,000 for 2 grants (high: $1,800,000; low: $10,000).
Fields of interest: Jewish federated giving programs.
Limitations: Applications not accepted. Giving in New York, NY.
Application information: Contributes only to pre-selected organizations.
Officers: Jeff Sutton, Pres.; Elliot H. Levine, Treas.
EIN: 137557698

6949
Ruth & David Sutton Family Foundation ✧
1 E. 33rd St., 7th Fl.
New York, NY 10016-2831

Established in 1993 in NY.
Donors: David Sutton; Paul Sutton; Ruth Sutton; Steven Sutton; Cudlie Accessories, LLC; DS Associates; David Sutton Ira First Clearing Corp.; Ruth Sutton National Financial Services; Sutton Holdings GP.
Foundation type: Independent foundation.
Financial data (yr. ended 05/31/13): Assets, $522,482 (M); gifts received, $350,000; expenditures, $506,999; qualifying distributions, $499,894; giving activities include $499,894 for grants.
Fields of interest: Education; Jewish agencies & synagogues.
Type of support: General/operating support.
Limitations: Applications not accepted. No grants to individuals.
Application information: Contributes only to pre-selected organizations.
Trustees: Paul Sutton; Steven Sutton.
EIN: 137014537

6950
Albert & Melissa Sutton Foundation, Inc. ✧ ☆
c/o E.S. Sutton, Inc.
1400 Broadway, 26th Fl.
New York, NY 10018-5396 (212) 944-9494

Established in 2002 in NY.
Donors: Albert J. Sutton; E.S. Sutton, Inc.; Extra Sportswear, Inc.
Foundation type: Independent foundation.
Financial data (yr. ended 12/31/13): Assets, $8,754,319 (M); expenditures, $1,981,094; qualifying distributions, $1,897,815; giving activities include $1,897,815 for 168 grants (high: $1,000,000; low: $36).
Fields of interest: Education; Human services; Jewish agencies & synagogues.
Limitations: Applications not accepted. No grants to individuals.
Application information: Contributes only to pre-selected organizations.
Directors: Albert J. Sutton; Eileen Sutton; Melissa Sutton.
EIN: 113639224

6951
The Sutton Trust Foundation ✧
c/o Wiggin and Dana
450 Lexington Ave., Ste. 3800
New York, NY 10017-3913

Established in 2005 in NY.
Donors: Richard Perry; Rebecca C. Byrne; James R. Byrne; Michael Carpenter; Mrs. Michael Carpenter; Sir Peter Lampl; D.F.K. Finlay; Martin J. Sullivan; Christopher Wright; Auda Advisor Associates; Scott Lampl Trust; Perry Capital; Perry Partners; EMG Madonna Educational Foundation; Geoffrey Scott Walker; Chatterjee Charitable Foundation.
Foundation type: Independent foundation.
Financial data (yr. ended 12/31/13): Assets, $446,246 (M); gifts received, $385,882; expenditures, $458,186; qualifying distributions, $439,773; giving activities include $437,732 for 9 grants (high: $139,065; low: $3,750).
Fields of interest: Higher education.
Limitations: Applications not accepted. Giving primarily in England. No grants to individuals.
Application information: Unsolicited requests for funds not accepted.
Trustees: Bruce Hood; Sir Peter Lampl; Erica Walker.
EIN: 201886191

6952
SVM Foundation ✧
c/o Philip L. Milstein
545 Madison Ave., 6th Fl., Ste. 600
New York, NY 10022-4608

Established in 1996 in NY.
Donors: Seymour Milstein†; Vivian Milstein.
Foundation type: Independent foundation.
Financial data (yr. ended 12/31/13): Assets, $2,757,750 (M); expenditures, $526,087; qualifying distributions, $518,885; giving activities include $518,500 for 8 grants (high: $350,000; low: $1,000).
Fields of interest: Arts; Higher education; Foundations (private grantmaking); Jewish federated giving programs; Jewish agencies & synagogues.
Type of support: Grants to individuals.
Limitations: Applications not accepted. Giving primarily in NY.
Application information: Unsolicited requests for funds not accepted.
Trustees: Constance J. Milstein; Philip L. Milstein; Vivian Milstein.
EIN: 137105557
Selected grants: The following grants are a representative sample of this grantmaker's funding activity:
$600,000 to North Carolina Blumenthal Performing Arts Center, Charlotte, NC, 2011.
$515,000 to Metropolitan Opera, New York, NY, 2011.

6953
The Swartz Foundation ✧
6 Light House Point Rd.
Lloyd Harbor, NY 11743-1010
Main URL: http://www.theswartzfoundation.org
Twitter: http://twitter.com/SwartzCompNeuro

Established in 1995 in NY.
Donors: Dr. Jerome Swartz; JSwartz Charitable Lead Trust.
Foundation type: Independent foundation.
Financial data (yr. ended 10/31/11): Assets, $9,026,185 (M); gifts received, $138,500; expenditures, $2,075,049; qualifying distributions, $1,915,973; giving activities include $1,692,500 for 12 grants (high: $380,000; low: $10,000).
Purpose and activities: The mission of the Swartz foundation is to explore the application of physics, mathematics, and computer engineering principles to neuroscience, as a path to better understanding the brain-mind relationship. Giving primarily to establish research centers devoted to advancing computational neuroscience.
Fields of interest: Higher education; Science, research.
Limitations: Applications not accepted. Giving primarily in CA, CT, MA, NJ, and NY. No grants to individuals.
Application information: Contributes only to pre-selected organizations.
Officer: Paul Kelly, C.F.O.
Trustees: James P. King; Dr. Jerome Swartz.
EIN: 116447242

6954
Swartz Foundation Trust ✧
c/o Brandywine (PTS)
880 3rd Ave., 3rd Fl.
New York, NY 10022-4730

Established in NJ.
Donor: James R. Swartz.
Foundation type: Independent foundation.
Financial data (yr. ended 12/31/12): Assets, $44,881,595 (M); expenditures, $7,149,835; qualifying distributions, $6,727,157; giving activities include $6,686,446 for 81 grants (high: $5,000,000; low: $200).
Purpose and activities: Giving primarily for the arts, human services, YMCAs, and to evangelical Christian organizations and churches.
Fields of interest: Performing arts; Arts; Higher education; Human services; YM/YWCAs & YM/YWHAs; Christian agencies & churches.
Limitations: Applications not accepted. Giving primarily in CA, MA, and UT; some funding also in PA.
Application information: Contributes only to pre-selected organizations.
Officer: James R. Swartz, Pres.
EIN: 226554026

6955
Swieca Family Foundation ✧
950 3rd Ave., 23rd Fl.
New York, NY 10022

Established in NY.
Donors: Henry Swieca; Esther Swieca; Dubin and Swieca Capital Management Inc.; Henry Swieca 2001 Charitable Trust; Henry Swieca 2002 Charitable Trust; Henry Swieca 2003 Charitable Trust; Henry Swieca 2007 Charitable Trust.
Foundation type: Independent foundation.
Financial data (yr. ended 12/31/13): Assets, $33,382,736 (M); expenditures, $949,105; qualifying distributions, $877,370; giving activities include $817,434 for 93 grants (high: $146,960; low: $36).
Fields of interest: Education; Human services; Jewish agencies & synagogues.
Limitations: Applications not accepted. Giving primarily in NY. No grants to individuals.
Application information: Contributes only to pre-selected organizations.
Trustees: Esther Swieca; Henry Swieca.
EIN: 137437179

6956
The Edward P. Swyer Foundation, Inc. ✧
10 Executive Park Dr.
Albany, NY 12203-3716
Contact: Sandra Tatem, Treas.

Established in 2005 in NY.
Donor: Edward P. Swyer.
Foundation type: Independent foundation.
Financial data (yr. ended 12/31/13): Assets, $3,736,651 (M); expenditures, $617,040; qualifying distributions, $591,835; giving activities include $591,835 for 22 grants (high: $250,000; low: $2,500).
Fields of interest: Museums (specialized); Higher education; YM/YWCAs & YM/YWHAs; Law/international law.
Type of support: Program development; Professorships; Capital campaigns; Annual campaigns.
Limitations: Applications not accepted. Giving primarily in Albany, NY. No grants to individuals.
Application information: Contributes only to pre-selected organizations.
Officers: Edward P. Swyer, Pres.; Sandra Tatem, Treas.
Director: Julius Oestreicher.
Number of staff: None.
EIN: 342056927
Selected grants: The following grants are a representative sample of this grantmaker's funding activity:
$25,000 to National Museum of Dance, Saratoga Springs, NY, 2012. For Unrestricted Charitable Grants to 501 (c)(3) Organizations.

6957
Sykes Family Foundation ✧
c/o MJSM
P.O. Box 331
Plainview, NY 11803

Established in 1993 in CA.
Donors: Gene T. Sykes; Tracy M. Sykes.
Foundation type: Independent foundation.
Financial data (yr. ended 06/30/13): Assets, $13,534,949 (M); expenditures, $1,009,302; qualifying distributions, $905,280; giving activities include $905,280 for 17 grants (high: $500,000; low: $250).
Purpose and activities: Giving primarily for the environment, including a conservation association, as well as for education and human services.
Fields of interest: Elementary/secondary education; Environment; Health organizations; Human services.
Type of support: General/operating support.
Limitations: Applications not accepted. Giving primarily in CA and Washington, D.C. No grants to individuals; no loans.
Application information: Contributes only to pre-selected organizations.

Trustees: Gene T. Sykes; Tracy M. Sykes.
EIN: 133748075
Selected grants: The following grants are a representative sample of this grantmaker's funding activity:
$500,000 to National Parks Conservation Association, Washington, DC, 2011. For general purpose.
$70,000 to Saint Matthews Parish School, Pacific Palisades, CA, 2011. For general purpose.
$27,620 to Museum Associates, Los Angeles County Museum of Art (LACMA), Los Angeles, CA, 2011. For general purpose.
$10,000 to Saint Matthews Parish School, Pacific Palisades, CA, 2011. For general purpose.
$10,000 to Telluride Foundation, Telluride, CO, 2011. For general purpose.
$10,000 to Telluride Foundation, Telluride, CO, 2011. For general purpose.
$5,000 to Columbia University, New York, NY, 2011. For general purpose.
$2,000 to Telluride Academy, Telluride, CO, 2011. For general purpose.
$1,000 to Telluride Academy, Telluride, CO, 2011. For general purpose.

6958
The Tahari Family Foundation ✧ ☆
c/o Marcum LLP
10 Melville Park Rd.
Melville, NY 11747-3146 (631) 414-4000
Contact: Elie Tahari, Pres.

Established in 2005 in NY.
Donors: Elie Tahari; Husein Jafferjee; Elie Tahari Ltd.
Foundation type: Independent foundation.
Financial data (yr. ended 12/31/13): Assets, $1,870 (M); gifts received, $467,920; expenditures, $473,133; qualifying distributions, $472,134; giving activities include $471,000 for 10 grants (high: $215,000; low: $1,000).
Fields of interest: Arts; Human services; Foundations (private grantmaking); Jewish agencies & synagogues.
Limitations: Applications accepted. Giving primarily in New York, NY.
Application information: Application form required.
Initial approach: Letter
Deadline(s): None
Officer: Elie Tahari, Pres.
EIN: 206739119
Selected grants: The following grants are a representative sample of this grantmaker's funding activity:
$150,000 to Friends of the Israel Defense Forces, New York, NY, 2012. For educational, cultural, recreational.
$5,000 to Women in Need, New York, NY, 2012. For homeless women.
$1,500 to Southampton Hospital Foundation, Southampton, NY, 2012. For health care services.

6959
J. T. Tai & Company Foundation, Inc. ✧
18 E. 67th St.
New York, NY 10065-5827
Contact: F. Richard Hsu, Pres.

Incorporated in 1983 in DE.
Donors: J.T. Tai & Co., Inc.; Jun Tsei Tai†.
Foundation type: Independent foundation.
Financial data (yr. ended 12/31/13): Assets, $125,726,815 (M); expenditures, $6,208,687; qualifying distributions, $4,341,076; giving activities include $4,157,000 for 68 grants (high: $305,000; low: $3,500).
Purpose and activities: Giving primarily for higher education and health care.
Fields of interest: Higher education; Medical school/education; Health care; Christian agencies & churches.
Type of support: Scholarship funds; Research; Fellowships; Exchange programs; General/operating support.
Limitations: Applications not accepted. Giving on a national basis. No grants to individuals.
Application information: Contributes only to pre-selected organizations.
Officers and Directors:* F. Richard Hsu,* Pres.; Y.C. Chen,* Secy.; K.W. Hsu; Ming Chen Hsu.
EIN: 133157279

6960
The Ping Y. Tai Foundation, Inc. ✧
c/o Shapiro & Duffalo, C.P.A., P.C.
110 E. 59th St., 22nd Fl.
New York, NY 10022-1304

Established in 1997 in NY.
Donors: Ping Y. Tai†; J.T. Tai & Co., Inc.
Foundation type: Independent foundation.
Financial data (yr. ended 11/30/12): Assets, $22,154,156 (M); expenditures, $1,213,842; qualifying distributions, $1,106,968; giving activities include $1,100,000 for 20 grants (high: $100,000; low: $20,000).
Fields of interest: Health care, association; Hospitals (general); Medical research, institute; Human services; United Ways and Federated Giving Programs.
Type of support: General/operating support.
Limitations: Applications not accepted. Giving primarily in NY. No grants to individuals.
Application information: Contributes only to pre-selected organizations.
Officers: Michael Duffalo, Pres.; Yueh Chuen Chen, Secy.-Treas.
EIN: 133980789

6961
Tanaka Memorial Foundation, Inc. ✧
711 5th Ave., 16th Fl.
New York, NY 10022-3111 (212) 601-9244
Contact: Kenji Tanaka, Chair.

Established in 1991 in NY.
Donor: Tanaka Ikubikai Educational Corp.
Foundation type: Independent foundation.
Financial data (yr. ended 06/30/13): Assets, $16,668,309 (M); expenditures, $894,640; qualifying distributions, $586,625; giving activities include $586,625 for grants.
Purpose and activities: Giving primarily for higher education, including support for Asian studies through programs and scholarship funds, arts, and human services.
Fields of interest: Performing arts centers; Higher education; Education.
International interests: United Kingdom.
Type of support: General/operating support; Capital campaigns; Endowments; Scholarship funds.
Limitations: Applications accepted. Giving on a national and international basis, with emphasis on New York, NY, Washington, DC, and England. No grants to individuals.
Application information: Application form not required.
Initial approach: Proposal
Deadline(s): None
Officers and Directors:* Kenji Tanaka,* Chair.; Taeko Tanaka,* Vice-Chair.; Makiko Tanaka,* Pres.; Kimiko Tanaka,* V.P.; Takeshi Hashimoto, Secy.; Tokiwa Morimoto, Treas.; Kiyoshi Okada; Yoshihiro Tajima; Takeshi Ueshima.
EIN: 110235010
Selected grants: The following grants are a representative sample of this grantmaker's funding activity:
$30,000 to Hope College, Holland, MI, 2013. For Financial Assistance to International Students.
$10,000 to Bates College, Lewiston, ME, 2013. For Programs in Asian Studies.
$10,000 to Carleton College, Northfield, MN, 2013. To Expand International Understanding.
$10,000 to Illinois Wesleyan University, Bloomington, IL, 2013. For Endowment of International Scholarship.
$10,000 to McKendree University, Lebanon, IL, 2013. To Help Fund Scholarships.
$10,000 to Trinity College, Hartford, CT, 2013. To Help Outstanding Lead Among Liberal Arts College.

6962
Lisa and Steven Tananbaum Family Foundation ✧
10 Loden Ln.
Purchase, NY 10577-2310

Donors: Lisa Tananbaum; Steve A. Tananbaum.
Foundation type: Independent foundation.
Financial data (yr. ended 12/31/12): Assets, $13,881,747 (M); gifts received, $1,469,367; expenditures, $886,310; qualifying distributions, $829,411; giving activities include $829,411 for 30 grants (high: $501,000; low: $466).
Purpose and activities: Giving primarily for museums, education, social services, and Jewish organizations.
Fields of interest: Museums (art); Museums (ethnic/folk arts); Elementary/secondary education; Higher education; Human services; Jewish federated giving programs; Jewish agencies & synagogues.
Limitations: Applications not accepted. Giving primarily in New York, NY.
Application information: Contributes only to pre-selected organizations.
Trustees: Lisa Tananbaum; Steve A. Tananbaum.
EIN: 137378428

6963
Tandon Family Foundation, Inc. ✧
c/o M. Baharestani, CPA
148 Madison Ave., 11th Fl.
New York, NY 10016-6700

Established in NY.
Donors: Chandrika Tandon; Ranjan Tandon.
Foundation type: Independent foundation.
Financial data (yr. ended 12/31/13): Assets, $22,032,208 (M); expenditures, $4,027,263; qualifying distributions, $3,899,093; giving

activities include $3,540,607 for 23 grants (high: $1,500,000; low: $101).
Purpose and activities: Giving primarily for U.S.-based organizations and programs concerning India.
Fields of interest: Arts; Education; Hinduism.
International interests: India.
Limitations: Applications not accepted. Giving primarily in New Haven, CT, and New York, NY. No grants to individuals.
Application information: Contributes only to pre-selected organizations.
Directors: Martin Baharestani; Deven Sharma; Chandrika Tandon; Lita Tandon; Ranjan Tandon.
EIN: 043744965

6964
Tansy Charitable Foundation ✧
c/o Eric Wepsic
1166 Ave. of the Americas, 9th Fl.
New York, NY 10036-2708

Donor: Eric Wepsic.
Foundation type: Independent foundation.
Financial data (yr. ended 12/31/13): Assets, $89,507,521 (M); gifts received, $18,000,000; expenditures, $2,007,685; qualifying distributions, $2,004,660; giving activities include $2,000,000 for 1 grant.
Fields of interest: Environment, natural resources.
Limitations: Applications not accepted. Giving primarily in New York, NY.
Application information: Contributes only to pre-selected organizations.
Trustee: Eric Wepsic.
EIN: 276377439

6965
The Pamela and Laurence Tarica Foundation ✧ ☆
6 Sloanes Ct.
Sands Point, NY 11050-1231

Established in NY.
Donors: Lawrence Tarica; Pamela Tarica.
Foundation type: Independent foundation.
Financial data (yr. ended 12/31/12): Assets, $2,334,570 (M); expenditures, $436,546; qualifying distributions, $426,187; giving activities include $424,437 for 123 grants (high: $68,550; low: $18).
Fields of interest: ALS; Human services; Jewish agencies & synagogues.
Limitations: Applications not accepted.
Application information: Unsolicited requests for funds not accepted.
Officers and Directors:* Lawrence Tarica,* Pres.; Pamela Tarica,* V.P.; James Tarica.
EIN: 274057867

6966
TE Connectivity Foundation ✧
(formerly Tyco Electronics Foundation)
c/o Tyco Electronics Corp.
1100 Wehrle Dr., 2nd Fl.
Buffalo, NY 14221 (717) 564-0100
Contact: Mary J. Rakoczy
E-mail: TEFoundation@te.com; Application Address: P.O. Box 3608, Harrisburg, PA 17105.; Main URL: http://www.te.com/en/about-te/responsibility/community.html

Established in 1977 in PA.
Donors: AMP Inc.; Tyco Electronics.
Foundation type: Company-sponsored foundation.
Financial data (yr. ended 12/31/13): Assets, $22,412,015 (M); gifts received, $56,500; expenditures, $1,133,458; qualifying distributions, $1,066,075; giving activities include $1,020,147 for 151 grants (high: $82,800; low: $200).
Purpose and activities: The foundation supports programs designed to address disaster relief and human services; the environment; health and wellness; and education and technology.
Fields of interest: Elementary/secondary education; Education; Environment, energy; Environment; Health care; Disasters, preparedness/services; Human services; Business/industry; Community/economic development; United Ways and Federated Giving Programs; Mathematics; Engineering/technology; Engineering; Science.
Type of support: General/operating support; Program development; Research; Employee volunteer services.
Limitations: Applications accepted. Giving primarily in areas of company operations, with emphasis on Menlo Park and northern CA, Boston, MA, NC, Harrisburg and central PA, and SC. No support for private foundations, national organizations, service clubs, or fraternal, social, labor, or trade organizations, discriminatory organizations, or religious organizations not of direct benefit to the entire community. No grants to individuals, or for administrative or overhead expenses for research, political campaigns, or programs posing a potential conflict of interest; no loans or investments.
Publications: Application guidelines.
Application information: Application form required.
Initial approach: E-mail foundation for grant application
Copies of proposal: 1
Deadline(s): None
Trustee: M&T Trust Co.
Officer: Mary J, Rakoczy, Exec. Dir.
Number of staff: 1 full-time professional.
EIN: 232022928
Selected grants: The following grants are a representative sample of this grantmaker's funding activity:
$45,000 to Lehigh University, Bethlehem, PA, 2011.
$35,000 to North Carolina A & T State University, Greensboro, NC, 2011.
$20,000 to MATHCOUNTS Foundation, Alexandria, VA, 2011.
$20,000 to National Engineers Week Foundation, Alexandria, VA, 2011.
$20,000 to Thaddeus Stevens Foundation, Lancaster, PA, 2011.
$10,000 to College Possible, Saint Paul, MN, 2011.
$10,000 to Tech Museum of Innovation, San Jose, CA, 2011.
$5,000 to Minnesota Childrens Museum, Saint Paul, MN, 2011.
$5,000 to Society of Automotive Engineers Foundation, Warrendale, PA, 2011.
$5,000 to Works, The, Bloomington, MN, 2011.

6967
The Teagle Foundation Incorporated ✧
c/o Jennifer Dale
570 Lexington Ave., 38th Fl.
New York, NY 10022-6837
E-mail: info@teaglefoundation.org; Main URL: http://www.teaglefoundation.org/

Foundation type: Independent foundation.
Financial data (yr. ended 06/30/13): Assets, $146,322,906 (M); gifts received, $1,000; expenditures, $9,499,994; qualifying distributions, $6,909,510; giving activities include $5,814,727 for 194 grants (high: $139,000; low: $50), and $50,489 for foundation-administered programs.
Purpose and activities: The foundation intends to be an influential national voice and a catalyst for change in higher education to improve undergraduate student learning in the arts and sciences.
Fields of interest: Higher education; Human services.
Limitations: Applications not accepted. Giving primarily in New York, NY.
Application information: Unsolicited requests for funds not accepted.
Officers and Directors:* Walter C. Teagle III,* Chair.; Judith R. Shapiro,* Pres.; Desiree Vazquez, Secy.; Eli Weinberg, Treas.; Kenneth P. Cohen; Andrew Delbanco; Blanche Goldenburg; William Chester Jordan; Jayne Keith; Richard J. Light; Richard L. Morrill; Philip B. Pool, Jr.; Grant Porter; Barbara Paul Robinson; Cornelia Small; Pauline Yu.
EIN: 201370387

6968
Teferes Foundation ✧
59 Maiden Ln., 6th Fl.
New York, NY 10038-4502 (212) 220-7120
Contact: Barry Zyskind, Pres.

Established in 2007 in NY.
Donors: Barry Zyskind; Harry Schlachter.
Foundation type: Independent foundation.
Financial data (yr. ended 12/31/12): Assets, $4,403,682 (M); gifts received, $2,909,640; expenditures, $856,184; qualifying distributions, $681,030; giving activities include $681,030 for grants.
Fields of interest: Jewish federated giving programs; Jewish agencies & synagogues.
Application information: Application form required.
Initial approach: Letter
Deadline(s): None
Officers and Directors:* Barry Zyskind,* Pres.; Stuart Hollander,* V.P.; Stephen Ungar, Secy.; Esther Zyskind.
EIN: 205428853

6969
Richard and Mary Templeton Foundation ✧
c/o Ayco Company L.P., NTG
P.O. Box 15014
Albany, NY 12212-5014

Established in 2003 in TX.
Donors: Mary Templeton; Richard Templeton.
Foundation type: Independent foundation.
Financial data (yr. ended 12/31/13): Assets, $21,675,760 (M); gifts received, $4,542,000;

expenditures, $626,620; qualifying distributions, $620,000; giving activities include $620,000 for 35 grants (high: $100,000; low: $2,500).
Purpose and activities: Giving primarily for education, particularly a Roman Catholic high school, as well as to other Catholic schools and organizations.
Fields of interest: Secondary school/education; Higher education; Education; United Ways and Federated Giving Programs; Catholic agencies & churches.
Limitations: Applications not accepted. Giving primarily in TX. No grants to individuals.
Application information: Contributes only to pre-selected organizations.
Trustees: Mary Templeton; Richard Templeton.
EIN: 200321164

6970
Tensor Foundation ✧
P.O. Box 149
Dobbs Ferry, NY 10522-0149

Established in 1993 in NY.
Donors: Archie C. McKellar; Marie T. McKellar.
Foundation type: Independent foundation.
Financial data (yr. ended 12/31/13): Assets, $4,084,724 (M); gifts received, $7,090; expenditures, $554,989; qualifying distributions, $528,192; giving activities include $520,000 for 3 grants (high: $300,000; low: $20,000).
Fields of interest: Environment, water resources; Mathematics.
Limitations: Applications not accepted. Giving primarily in Dobbs Ferry, NY; support also in Washington, DC. No grants to individuals.
Application information: Contributes only to pre-selected organizations.
Trustees: Archie C. McKellar; Marie T. McKellar.
EIN: 137017367
Selected grants: The following grants are a representative sample of this grantmaker's funding activity:
$200,000 to Mathematical Association of America, Washington, DC, 2011.

6971
Terra Nova Foundation ✧
c/o Technical Services of N.A.
60 E. 42nd St.
P.O. Box 4566
New York, NY 10163-4566

Established in 1997 in NY.
Donor: Charles P. Stevenson, Jr.
Foundation type: Independent foundation.
Financial data (yr. ended 12/31/13): Assets, $22,054 (M); gifts received, $660,000; expenditures, $1,171,480; qualifying distributions, $1,171,060; giving activities include $1,171,060 for 18 grants (high: $1,016,110; low: $100).
Fields of interest: Higher education; Human services.
Type of support: General/operating support.
Limitations: Applications not accepted. Giving in the U.S., with emphasis on NY. No grants to individuals.
Application information: Contributes only to pre-selected organizations.
Trustees: Inez E. D'Arcangelo; Charles P. Stevenson, Jr.
EIN: 133948138

6972
Terumah Foundation, Inc. ✧
c/o Phillipe Katz, Secy.
160 Broadway, 1st Fl.
New York, NY 10038-4297

Established in 1993 in NY.
Donors: Moses Marx; Max Czapski‡; Daniel Stein; United Equities Commodities Co.; K'Hal Adath Jeshrun; Afikim; Momar Corp.
Foundation type: Independent foundation.
Financial data (yr. ended 12/31/13): Assets, $52,047,512 (M); gifts received, $11,744,000; expenditures, $3,030,261; qualifying distributions, $3,017,516; giving activities include $3,013,800 for 175 grants (high: $350,000; low: $100).
Purpose and activities: Giving primarily to Jewish organization, temples, and schools.
Fields of interest: Elementary/secondary education; Jewish agencies & synagogues.
Limitations: Applications not accepted. Giving primarily in NY. No grants to individuals.
Application information: Contributes only to pre-selected organizations.
Officers and Directors:* Moses Marx,* Pres.; Joseph Fink,* V.P.; Phillipe Katz,* Secy.; Marga Marx,* Treas.; Eva Fink; Esther Katz.
EIN: 133694180

6973
The Textor Family Foundation ✧
c/o BCRS Assocs., LLC
77 Water St., 9th Fl.
New York, NY 10005-4401

Established in 1991 in NY.
Donors: Donald F. Textor; Elaine R. Textor; EOG Resources, Inc.
Foundation type: Independent foundation.
Financial data (yr. ended 05/31/13): Assets, $15,398,200 (M); gifts received, $1,171,000; expenditures, $2,957,342; qualifying distributions, $2,929,785; giving activities include $2,926,250 for 34 grants (high: $1,000,000; low: $50).
Purpose and activities: Giving primarily for higher and other education.
Fields of interest: Elementary/secondary education; Higher education; Education; Health organizations, association; Human services.
Limitations: Applications not accepted. Giving primarily in NY; some funding also in Washington, DC, and Bethlehem, PA. No contributions, grants, gifts, loans or scholarships to individuals.
Application information: Contributes only to pre-selected organizations.
Trustees: Donald F. Textor; Elaine R. Textor.
EIN: 133637703
Selected grants: The following grants are a representative sample of this grantmaker's funding activity:
$750,000 to Lehigh University, Bethlehem, PA, 2011.
$500,000 to Georgetown University, Washington, DC, 2011.
$250,000 to Chaminade High School, Mineola, NY, 2011.
$250,000 to Lehigh University, Bethlehem, PA, 2011.
$50,000 to Futures in Education Foundation, Brooklyn, NY, 2011.
$25,000 to Trinity-Pawling School, Pawling, NY, 2011.
$18,650 to Saint Dominic High School, Oyster Bay, NY, 2011.
$15,000 to Portledge School, Locust Valley, NY, 2011.
$10,000 to Lehigh University, Bethlehem, PA, 2011.

6974
Theobald Foundation ✧ ☆
c/o Bessemer Trust Co., N.A.
630 5th Ave., 34th Fl.
New York, NY 10111-0100

Established in 1993 in IL.
Donors: Regina Mahon; Thomas C. Theobald.
Foundation type: Independent foundation.
Financial data (yr. ended 10/31/13): Assets, $4,561,984 (M); gifts received, $815,126; expenditures, $1,101,335; qualifying distributions, $1,090,649; giving activities include $1,083,450 for 75 grants (high: $904,000; low: $350).
Purpose and activities: Giving primarily for education.
Fields of interest: Museums; Higher education; Higher education, college (community/junior); Education; Human services.
Limitations: Applications not accepted. Giving primarily in IL, MA and OH. No grants to individuals.
Application information: Unsolicited requests for funds not accepted.
Trustees: Stephen B. Theobald; Thomas C. Theobald.
EIN: 367085378
Selected grants: The following grants are a representative sample of this grantmaker's funding activity:
$40,000 to Cincinnati Zoo and Botanical Garden, Cincinnati, OH, 2011.
$15,000 to United Way of Greenwich, Greenwich, CT, 2011.
$13,500 to Central Park Conservancy, New York, NY, 2011.
$11,100 to Bruce Museum, Greenwich, CT, 2011.
$10,000 to Harlem Childrens Zone, New York, NY, 2011.
$7,000 to Citymeals-on-Wheels, New York, NY, 2011.
$7,000 to Mount Notre Dame High School, Cincinnati, OH, 2011.
$3,000 to Nature Conservancy, East Hampton, NY, 2011.
$2,000 to Boys and Girls Club, Kips Bay, Bronx, NY, 2011.
$2,000 to Doctors Without Borders USA, New York, NY, 2011.

6975
The Thompson Family Foundation, Inc. ✧
(formerly The Wade F. B. Thompson Charitable Foundation, Inc.)
230 Park Ave., Ste. 1541
New York, NY 10169-1541

Established in 1986 in CT.
Donors: Wade F.B. Thompson‡; Wade F.B. Thompson Trust.
Foundation type: Independent foundation.
Financial data (yr. ended 05/31/14): Assets, $545,757,504 (M); expenditures, $26,393,130; qualifying distributions, $24,671,053; giving

activities include $24,184,083 for 86 grants (high: $8,043,930; low: $5,000).
Purpose and activities: Giving primarily for historical preservation, health organizations, and human services.
Fields of interest: Museums; Historic preservation/historical societies; Arts; Health organizations, association; Cancer research; Prostate cancer research; Recreation, parks/playgrounds; Human services; Community/economic development.
Type of support: General/operating support; Annual campaigns; Building/renovation; Land acquisition; Seed money.
Limitations: Applications not accepted. Giving primarily in CT and the greater New York, NY, area. No grants to individuals.
Application information: Contributes only to pre-selected organizations.
Officers: Angela E. Thompson, Pres.; Charles A.Y. Thompson, V.P.; Alan Siegel, Secy.; Amanda J.T. Riegel, Treas.
EIN: 061194385
Selected grants: The following grants are a representative sample of this grantmaker's funding activity:
$50,000 to City Harvest, New York, NY, 2013. To Aid the Donee Organization Out Its Exempt Purpose.
$10,000 to New York Restoration Project, New York, NY, 2013. To Aid the Donee Organization Out Its Exempt Functions.

6976
Three Little Pigs Foundation ✧
c/o William E. Ford
1212 5th Ave., Apt. 8A
New York, NY 10029-5217

Established in 2003 in NY.
Donor: William E. Ford.
Foundation type: Independent foundation.
Financial data (yr. ended 12/31/13): Assets, $7,636,949 (M); gifts received, $1,090,600; expenditures, $3,444,541; qualifying distributions, $3,416,875; giving activities include $3,416,875 for 17 grants (high: $1,500,000; low: $5,000).
Purpose and activities: Giving primarily for education; funding also for museums, as well as for a cancer hospital.
Fields of interest: Museums; Higher education; Hospitals (specialty).
Limitations: Applications not accepted. Giving primarily in MA and NY. No grants to individuals.
Application information: Contributes only to pre-selected organizations.
Officers: William E. Ford, Pres.; Richard Gold, Secy.
EIN: 200512645

6977
The Tianaderrah Foundation ✧
130 Butternut Rd.
P.O. Box 639
Unadilla, NY 13849-0139

Established in 1996 in NY.
Donor: Robert L. Gipson.
Foundation type: Independent foundation.
Financial data (yr. ended 12/31/13): Assets, $46,205,712 (M); expenditures, $2,102,639; qualifying distributions, $2,100,000; giving activities include $2,100,000 for 91 grants (high: $300,000; low: $1,000).
Purpose and activities: Giving primarily to organizations which are devoted to education, medicine, social welfare, the arts, historical preservation, religion and the environment.
Fields of interest: Historic preservation/historical societies; Arts; Higher education; Education; Health organizations, association; Community/economic development; Religion.
Limitations: Applications accepted. Giving primarily in NY and NJ. No grants to individuals.
Application information: Application form required.
Initial approach: Letter
Deadline(s): None
Trustees: Robert L. Gipson; Thomas L. Gipson; Sally Gipson Tully.
EIN: 166445118
Selected grants: The following grants are a representative sample of this grantmaker's funding activity:
$200,000 to Sofia American Schools, Princeton, NJ, 2011.
$100,000 to Bulgarian American Society, Bulgaria, 2011. For general funds.
$25,000 to Hunter College Foundation, New York, NY, 2011. For scholarship.
$10,000 to Delaware County Historical Association, Delhi, NY, 2011. For general funds.

6978
The Tiffany & Co. Foundation ✧
200 Fifth Ave.
New York, NY 10010-3302
Contact: Anisa Kamadoli Costa, Chair. and Pres.
E-mail: foundation@tiffany.com; Main URL: http://www.tiffanyandcofoundation.org
Grants Database: http://www.tiffanyandcofoundation.org/grants/
Grants Map: http://www.tiffanyandcofoundation.org/grants/map/

Established in 2000 in NY.
Donor: Tiffany & Co.
Foundation type: Company-sponsored foundation.
Financial data (yr. ended 12/31/12): Assets, $23,440,999 (M); expenditures, $6,001,344; qualifying distributions, $5,820,000; giving activities include $5,820,000 for 32 grants (high: $1,000,000; low: $25,000).
Purpose and activities: The foundation supports programs designed to protect the beauty of nature and the creativity of human nature. Special emphasis is directed toward programs designed to preserve the arts and promote environmental conservation.
Fields of interest: Arts education; Visual arts; Visual arts, design; Museums; Arts; Environment, research; Environment, natural resources; Environment, water resources; Environment, land resources; Botanical/horticulture/landscape services; Environment, beautification programs; Environment; Recreation, parks/playgrounds; Urban/community development; Geology.
Type of support: Continuing support; General/operating support; Program development; Research.
Limitations: Applications accepted. No support for religious, political, social, or fraternal organizations, or organizations that do not have tax-exempt status under Section 501(c)(3) of the Internal Revenue Code, or the equivalent. No grants to individuals, or for capital campaigns, fundraising benefits or events, or athletic events; no product donations.
Publications: Application guidelines; Program policy statement.
Application information: Additional information may be requested at a later date. Application form required.
Initial approach: Complete online letter of inquiry
Deadline(s): Rolling
Board meeting date(s): Twice annually
Final notification: 3 months
Officers and Directors:* Anisa Kamadoli Costa,* Chair. and Pres.; Leigh M. Harlan, Secy.; Michael W. Connolly, Treas.; Patrick B. Dorsey; James N. Fernandez; Michael J. Kowalski.
EIN: 134096178
Selected grants: The following grants are a representative sample of this grantmaker's funding activity:
$500,000 to Trust for Public Land, San Francisco, CA, 2011. For Campaign to Save Cathuenga Park, Home of Hollywood Sign and for permanent protection of Cathuenga Park to become part of Griffin Park.
$200,000 to Environmental Defense Fund, New York, NY, 2011. For Coral Wildlife Campaign.
$200,000 to Trout Unlimited, Arlington, VA, 2011. For Abandoned Hard Rock Mine Restoration Program in the American West.
$150,000 to Wildlife Conservation Society, Bronx, NY, 2011. For continued support of Global Coral Reef Conservation Program in Coral Triangle community-based management strategic for global protection of coral and climate change adaptation strategies.
$150,000 to World Wildlife Fund, Washington, DC, 2011. For Mining and Sustainable Land use Management in and around Protected and Sensitive Ecosystems Project.
$100,000 to Alaska Conservation Foundation, Anchorage, AK, 2011. For Bristol Bay Regional Vision Project.
$75,000 to World Monuments Fund, New York, NY, 2011. For general operating support.
$50,000 to Bard College, Annandale on Hudson, NY, 2011. For publication, A History of the Decorative and Applied Arts and Design, 1400-2000 comprehensive history of decorative arts.
$40,000 to African Wildlife Foundation, Washington, DC, 2011. To design and plan phase of education center at Chobe National Park, which seek to serve meeting place for land and wildlife conservation in Africa's Kazungula Heartland.
$26,000 to Metropolitan Museum of Art, New York, NY, 2011. For Tiffany & Co Foundation Curatorial Internship in American Decorative Arts.

6979
Tiger Baron Foundation, Inc. ✧
233 Broadway, Ste. 2200
New York, NY 10279 (212) 273-3719
Contact: Grace Lyu-Volckhausen, Pres.

Established in 2002 in DE and NJ.
Donor: Grace Lyu-Volckhausen.
Foundation type: Operating foundation.
Financial data (yr. ended 12/31/13): Assets, $42,856,153 (M); expenditures, $2,269,351; qualifying distributions, $1,950,634; giving activities include $1,670,386 for 141 grants (high: $106,085; low: $500).
Fields of interest: Performing arts, theater; Arts; Education; Environment; Human services.
Limitations: Applications accepted. Giving primarily in NY. No grants to individuals.
Application information:

Initial approach: Proposal
Deadline(s): None
Officers: Grace Lyu-Volckhausen, Pres. and Treas.; Alexander Louis Volckhausen, V.P.; Sharon Lyu-Volckhausen, Secy.
EIN: 752979875

6980
Tiger Foundation ✧
101 Park Ave., 21st Fl.
New York, NY 10178-4799 (212) 984-2565
Contact: Amy Barger, Mgr. Dir.
FAX: (212) 949-9778;
E-mail: info@tigerfoundation.org; Physical address: 125 Park Ave., 16th Fl., New York, NY 10017; Main URL: http://www.tigerfoundation.org
GiveSmart: http://www.bridgespan.org/Philanthropy-Advice/Philanthropist-Spotlights/Stories/Donors/Julian-Robertson,-Jr.aspx#.VAcss9JdWE5
Grants List: http://www.tigerfoundation.org/index.php?/our_grantees/
Julian H. Robertson, Jr.'s Giving Pledge Profile: http://glasspockets.org/philanthropy-in-focus/eye-on-the-giving-pledge/profiles/robertson

Established in 1989 in NY.
Donors: Julian H. Robertson, Jr.; Tiger Management LLC employees.
Foundation type: Independent foundation.
Financial data (yr. ended 06/30/13): Assets, $141,389,067 (M); gifts received, $12,920,361; expenditures, $22,226,620; qualifying distributions, $21,921,421; giving activities include $19,280,000 for 95 grants (high: $500,000; low: $10,000), and $1,420,785 for 2 foundation-administered programs.
Purpose and activities: Giving provided to organizations working to break the cycle of poverty in New York City, rather than those which merely alleviate its symptoms. Seeking to provide families with the tools necessary to attain self-sufficiency and build productive lives. To this end, support is to a variety of educational, vocational, and social service and youth development programs designed to catch children and families before they slip into a cycle of poverty and despair, as well as those programs designed to enable individuals to end their dependence on public assistance.
Fields of interest: Education; Employment, services; Youth development, services; Children/youth, services; Family services; Human services; Economically disadvantaged.
Type of support: General/operating support; Continuing support; Management development/capacity building; Program development; Technical assistance; Program evaluation.
Limitations: Applications accepted. Giving primarily in New York, NY. No support for political organizations or public policy. No grants to individuals, or for endowments, annual or capital campaigns, benefits, legal aid, obligations or debt.
Publications: Application guidelines; Grants list.
Application information: Application form required.
Initial approach: Online application process
Copies of proposal: 1
Deadline(s): None
Board meeting date(s): Quarterly
Officers: Charles Buice, Pres.; Michelle Butynes, Cont.
Number of staff: 8 full-time professional; 1 part-time professional.
EIN: 133555671
Selected grants: The following grants are a representative sample of this grantmaker's funding activity:
$500,000 to Uncommon Schools, New York, NY, 2013. For General Support for New York City.
$450,000 to New Alternatives for Children, New York, NY, 2013. For General Support.
$450,000 to Success Charter Network, New York, NY, 2013. For General Support.
$400,000 to Center for Employment Opportunities, New York, NY, 2013. For General Operating Support for New York City Operations.
$400,000 to Lending Education Assistance Program, Brooklyn, NY, 2013. For General Support.
$400,000 to SCO Family of Services, Glen Cove, NY, 2013. For Early Childhood Program.
$225,000 to Project Renewal, New York, NY, 2013. For Next Step Employment Program.
$200,000 to East Side House, Bronx, NY, 2013. For Disconnected Youth Prevention Initiative.
$200,000 to Highbridge Community Life Center, Bronx, NY, 2013. For General Support.
$175,000 to Village Academies Network, New York, NY, 2013. For General Support.

6981
The Tikvah Fund ✧
165 E. 56th St., 4th Fl.
New York, NY 10022-6607 (212) 796-1672
Contact: Roger Hertog, Chair.
FAX: (646) 514-5915; E-mail: info@tikvahfund.org; Main URL: http://tikvahfund.org/
GiveSmart: http://www.givesmart.org/Stories/Donors/Roger-Hertog

Established in 1992 in NY.
Donor: Zalman C. Bernstein†.
Foundation type: Independent foundation.
Financial data (yr. ended 12/31/12): Assets, $152,877,561 (M); expenditures, $15,759,065; qualifying distributions, $15,174,055; giving activities include $6,337,805 for 41 grants, $212,930 for 13 grants to individuals, and $1,625,514 for foundation-administered programs.
Purpose and activities: Giving primarily for Jewish affairs. Makes grants and program-related investments to companies located in areas of high unemployment or development in Israel, and to companies that are owned by or employ new immigrants or veteran soldiers.
Fields of interest: Religion, public policy; Jewish agencies & synagogues.
International interests: Israel.
Limitations: Applications not accepted. Giving primarily in NY and NJ; some giving in Israel.
Application information: Unsolicited requests for funds not accepted.
Officers and Directors:* Roger Hertog,* Chair.; Maryana Geller, Cont.; Eric Cohen, Exec. Dir.; Elliott Abrams; Mem Dryan Bernstein; Arthur Fried; William Kristol; Jay Lefkowitz; Sallai Meridor; Jehuda Reinharz.
EIN: 133676152
Selected grants: The following grants are a representative sample of this grantmaker's funding activity:
$2,500,000 to Shalem Foundation, New York, NY, 2012. For general support.
$676,400 to Princeton University, Princeton, NJ, 2012. For program support.
$652,692 to New York University, Tikvah Center for Law and Jewish Civilization, New York, NY, 2012. For program support.
$642,941 to New York University, School of Law, New York, NY, 2012. For program support.
$387,217 to Ein Prat Academy for Leadership, Alon, West Bank/Gaza (Palestinian Territories), 2012. For general support and program support.
$223,467 to El Haprat, KFar Adumin, Israel, 2012. For program support.
$125,000 to American Friends of JSC, Teaneck, NJ, 2012. For program support.
$100,598 to Hebrew University of Jerusalem, Jerusalem, Israel, 2012. For program support.
$75,000 to Forum for Jewish Leadership, London, England, 2012. For general support.
$30,000 to Maayanot Yeshiva High School for Girls, Teaneck, NJ, 2012. For program support.

6982
Time Warner Foundation, Inc. ✧
(formerly AOL Time Warner Foundation)
1 Time Warner Ctr.
New York, NY 10019-6038
Contact: Lisa Quiroz, Pres.
E-mail: foundation@timewarner.com; Main URL: http://www.timewarnerfoundation.org/
Time Warner Blog: http://www.timewarner.com/blog/category/time-warner-foundation
Time Warner Foundation Videos: http://www.timewarnerfoundation.org/videos

Established in 1997 in VA.
Donors: America Online, Inc.; AOL Time Warner Inc.; Time Warner Inc.
Foundation type: Company-sponsored foundation.
Financial data (yr. ended 12/31/12): Assets, $7,049,490 (M); expenditures, $3,640,000; qualifying distributions, $3,640,000; giving activities include $3,640,000 for 30 grants (high: $500,000; low: $25,000).
Purpose and activities: The foundation supports programs designed to create, develop, and produce work that reflects the voices and experiences of the world, which is critical to sustaining a culturally rich, vibrant and informed community; and promote college access and college advocacy.
Fields of interest: Media/communications; Media, film/video; Media, television; Media, journalism; Museums; Performing arts, theater; Higher education; Education; Disasters, 9/11/01.
Type of support: Capital campaigns; General/operating support; Building/renovation; Program development.
Limitations: Applications not accepted. Giving primarily in Washington, DC and New York, NY. No support for political, labor, religious, or fraternal organizations or amateur or professional sports groups. No grants to individuals, or for book publication, or film or music production.
Application information: Contributes only to pre-selected organizations.
Officers and Directors:* Lisa Garcia Quiroz,* Pres.; Brenda C. Karickhoff, V.P. and Secy.; Daniel J. Osheyack, V.P.; Rosa Olivares, Treas.; Pascal Desroches, C.F.O.; Philip Sanchez, Assoc. Dir.; Molly Battin; Sofia Chang; Michael Ellenberg; Sue Fleishman; Gary L. Ginsberg; Lisa Gregorian; Karen Magee; Vinnie Malhotra; Olaf Olafsson; Quentin Shaffer; Greg Silverman; Misty Skedgell.
EIN: 541886827

6983
The Tinker Foundation Inc. ✧
55 E. 59th St., 21st Fl.
New York, NY 10022-1112 (212) 421-6858
Contact: Renate Rennie, Chair. and Pres.
FAX: (212) 223-3326; E-mail: tinker@tinker.org;
Main URL: http://www.tinker.org
Grants Database: http://www.tinker.org/grants

Trust established in 1959 in NY; incorporated in 1975 in NY.
Donor: Edward Larocque Tinker‡.
Foundation type: Independent foundation.
Financial data (yr. ended 12/31/13): Assets, $87,372,209 (M); expenditures, $5,447,316; qualifying distributions, $4,703,185; giving activities include $3,375,250 for 58+ grants (high: $400,000).
Purpose and activities: The mission of the foundation is to promote the development of an equitable, sustainable, and productive society in Latin America and to enhance the understanding in the U.S. of Latin America and of how U.S. policies may impact the region. Grants are awarded primarily in the areas of democratic governance, education, and sustainable resource management. More limited support is given for projects addressing U.S. policy toward Latin America and Antarctica.
Fields of interest: Education; Environment, natural resources; Environment; International affairs, goodwill promotion; International affairs, foreign policy; International affairs; Marine science; Economics; Political science; Public policy, research; Government/public administration.
International interests: Antarctica; Latin America; Mexico.
Type of support: Program development; Conferences/seminars; Seed money; Research.
Limitations: Applications accepted. Giving limited to projects related to Latin America and Antarctica. No support for projects concerned with health or medical issues or the arts and humanities. No grants to individuals, or for building or endowment funds, equipment, annual campaigns, operating budgets, annual appeals or production costs for film, television, and radio projects.
Publications: Application guidelines; Annual report.
Application information: Application form for Institutional Grants available on foundation web site. Use application guidelines and proposal cover sheet found on the web site or in paper copy, available upon request. Travel to Iberia is no longer supported through Field Research Grants. Application form required.
Initial approach: Letter of Inquiry or full proposal via foundation web site for Institutional Grants; download complete application package and forms from foundation web site for Field Research Grants
Copies of proposal: 2
Deadline(s): For Institutional Grants: Mar. 1 and Sept. 15; for Field Research Grants: Oct. 1
Board meeting date(s): June and Dec.
Final notification: 2 weeks after board meetings
Officers and Directors:* Renate Rennie,* Chair. and Pres.; Alan Stoga,* Secy.; Kathleen Waldron,* Treas.; John H. Coatsworth; Sally Grooms Cowal; Arturo C. Porzecanski; Luis Rubio; Susan L. Segal; Bradford K. Smith.
Number of staff: 5 full-time professional; 1 part-time professional; 1 full-time support; 1 part-time support.
EIN: 510175449
Selected grants: The following grants are a representative sample of this grantmaker's funding activity:
$1,000,000 to Pro Mujer, New York, NY, 2012. For Scaling Up Pro Mujer's Programs, payable over 5.00 years.
$550,000 to Scientific Committee on Antarctic Research, Cambridge, England, 2013. To award Martha T. Muse Prize for Science and Policy in Antarctica, payable over 5.00 years.
$514,000 to Scientific Committee on Antarctic Research, Cambridge, England, 2013. To administer Martha T. Muse Prize for Science and Policy in Antarctica, payable over 5.00 years.
$475,000 to Association of the Bar of the City of New York Fund, New York, NY, 2012. For Promoting and Facilitating Cross-border Pro Bono Initiatives to Increase Access to Justice and Advance the Public Interest in Latin America, payable over 3.00 years.
$438,000 to Duke University, Durham, NC, 2012. For Linking Users and Providers of Environmental Services in Mexico: Lessons from a Policy Experiment in Facilitating Local Water Institutions, payable over 3.00 years.
$399,000 to Fundacion Futuro Latinoamericano, Quito, Ecuador, 2013. To scale up lessons learned in water governance in vulnerable cities in the Andean Region, payable over 3.00 years.
$298,000 to Environmental Law Institute, Washington, DC, 2012. For Implementing Mexico's Constitutional Right to Water, payable over 2.00 years.
$240,000 to Columbia University, New York, NY, 2012. For Innovative Imaging of Changing Ice Sheets in Antarctica, payable over 3.00 years.
$210,000 to Comunidad y Biodiversidad, Guaymas, Mexico, 2012. For Building Fisheries Resilience: An Incentive-based Approach, payable over 2.00 years.
$200,000 to Fabretto Childrens Foundation, Arlington, VA, 2012. For Adapting Curriculum to Nicaraguan Contexts: Developing and Contextualizing the Sistema de Apredizaje Tutorial (SAT) Curriculum to Enhance Student Learning, Professional Development, and Human Capital, payable over 2.00 years.
$200,000 to Scientific Committee on Antarctic Research, Cambridge, England, 2013. For Antarctic and Southern Ocean Science Horizon Scan: A Tribute to Martha T. Muse, payable over 2.00 years.
$170,000 to Pro Bono Foundation, Santiago, Chile, 2013. For project, Expanding Access to Justice by Creating New Models for Pro Bono Services, payable over 2.00 years.
$160,000 to ConTextos, Chicago, IL, 2012. For Improving Teacher Practice and Education Quality at Public Schools in El Salvador, payable over 2.25 years.
$151,000 to Due Process of Law Foundation, Washington, DC, 2013. To promote judicial independence and transparency in Latin America, payable over 2.00 years.
$150,000 to Americas Society, New York, NY, 2013. For Americas Quarterly: The Policy Journal for Our Hemisphere, payable over 2.00 years.
$45,000 to University of California at San Diego, Center for Iberian and Latin American Studies, La Jolla, CA, 2013. For Tinker Field Research Grants Program, payable over 3.00 years.
$45,000 to University of Illinois at Urbana-Champaign, Center for Latin American and Caribbean Studies, Urbana, IL, 2012. For Tinker Field Research Grants, payable over 3.00 years.
$30,000 to State University of New York at Stony Brook, Latin American and Caribbean Studies Center, Stony Brook, NY, 2013. For Tinker Field Research Grants Program, payable over 3.00 years.
$10,000 to Americas Society, New York, NY, 2012. For Culture Department: Literature and Visual Arts Programs.
$10,000 to Reaching U, A Foundation for Uruguay, New York, NY, 2013. For general support.

6984
The Lizzie and Jonathan Tisch Family Foundation ✧ ☆
655 Madison Ave., 11th Fl.
New York, NY 10065-8043

Donor: Joan H. Tisch.
Foundation type: Independent foundation.
Financial data (yr. ended 12/31/13): Assets, $10,905,153 (L); gifts received, $13,630,125; expenditures, $2,840,893; qualifying distributions, $2,765,800; giving activities include $2,760,214 for 21 grants (high: $1,250,000; low: $1,500).
Fields of interest: Arts; Health care; Agriculture/food.
Limitations: Applications not accepted.
Application information: Unsolicited requests for funds not accepted.
Officer: Barry L. Bloom, Mgr.
Trustees: Elizabeth S. Tisch; Jonathan M. Tisch.
EIN: 462435208

6985
The Steve Tisch Family Foundation ✧
655 Madison Ave, 11th Fl.
New York, NY 10065-8043

Established in 1998 in NY.
Donors: Preston R. Tisch; Joan H. Tisch.
Foundation type: Independent foundation.
Financial data (yr. ended 12/31/13): Assets, $15,226,469 (M); gifts received, $3,082,100; expenditures, $3,099,609; qualifying distributions, $3,051,071; giving activities include $3,024,341 for 50 grants (high: $895,725; low: $2,500).
Fields of interest: Museums (art); Breast cancer; AIDS research; Food distribution, meals on wheels.
Limitations: Applications not accepted. Giving primarily in CA, CT and NY. No grants to individuals.
Application information: Contributes only to pre-selected organizations.
Trustee: Steven E. Tisch.
EIN: 134037377
Selected grants: The following grants are a representative sample of this grantmaker's funding activity:
$50,000 to Whitney Museum of American Art, New York, NY, 2012. For All contributions were made to further educational, religious, medical, cultural, societal and environmental causes.
$5,000 to New York University, Tisch School of the Arts, New York, NY, 2012. For All contributions were made to further educational, religious, medical, cultural, societal and environmental causes.

6986
The Alice M. & Thomas J. Tisch Foundation, Inc. ✧
c/o Mark J. Krinsky
655 Madison Ave., 11th Fl.
New York, NY 10065-8043

Established in 1992 in NY and DE.
Donors: Laurence A. Tisch‡; Thomas J. Tisch; Wilma S. Tisch.
Foundation type: Independent foundation.
Financial data (yr. ended 12/31/13): Assets, $55,833,229 (M); gifts received, $4,378,500; expenditures, $17,108,229; qualifying distributions, $17,030,909; giving activities include $17,009,117 for 145 grants (high: $9,527,109; low: $250).
Purpose and activities: Giving primarily for education, arts, health services, youth services, and Jewish agencies and temples.
Fields of interest: Museums (art); Performing arts; Arts; Higher education; Education; Hospitals (general); Health organizations, association; Human services; Children, services; Jewish federated giving programs; Public policy, research; Jewish agencies & synagogues.
Limitations: Applications not accepted. Giving primarily in New York, NY. No grants to individuals.
Application information: Contributes only to pre-selected organizations.
Officers: Thomas J. Tisch, Pres.; Alice M. Tisch, Sr. V.P.; Barry L. Bloom, Secy.-Treas.
EIN: 133693582
Selected grants: The following grants are a representative sample of this grantmaker's funding activity:
$18,792,818 to Brown University, Providence, RI, 2012. For annual fund.
$2,000,000 to Collegiate School, New York, NY, 2012.
$748,000 to Museum of Modern Art, New York, NY, 2012.
$615,000 to New York City Opera, New York, NY, 2012.
$446,490 to New York University, New York, NY, 2012.
$269,925 to Brearley School, New York, NY, 2012.
$250,000 to Museum Associates, Los Angeles County Museum of Art, Los Angeles, CA, 2012.
$225,000 to American Friends of the Israel Museum, New York, NY, 2012.
$65,000 to Young Womens Leadership Foundation, New York, NY, 2012.
$25,000 to Classical American Homes Preservation Trust, New York, NY, 2012.

6987
The Andrew & Ann Tisch Foundation, Inc. ✧
655 Madison Ave., 11th Fl.
New York, NY 10065-8043

Established in 1992 in NY.
Donors: Laurence A. Tisch‡; Wilma S. Tisch.
Foundation type: Independent foundation.
Financial data (yr. ended 12/31/13): Assets, $30,742,726 (M); gifts received, $4,378,500; expenditures, $1,139,990; qualifying distributions, $977,500; giving activities include $964,788 for 43 grants (high: $150,000; low: $250).
Purpose and activities: Giving primarily for education and Jewish agencies; some funding also for human services, and medical research.
Fields of interest: Higher education; Medical research, institute; Human services; Children/youth, services; Jewish federated giving programs; Philanthropy/voluntarism; Jewish agencies & synagogues; Women.
Limitations: Applications not accepted. Giving primarily in New York, NY. No grants to individuals.
Application information: Contributes only to pre-selected organizations.
Officers and Directors:* Andrew H. Tisch,* Pres.; Ann R. Tisch,* Sr. V.P.; Barry L. Bloom, Secy.-Treas.
EIN: 133693583

6988
Tisch Foundation, Inc. ✧
655 Madison Ave., 11th Fl.
New York, NY 10065-8043 (212) 521-2930

Incorporated in 1957 in FL.
Donors: Hotel Americana; Tisch Hotels, Inc.; members of the Tisch family; and closely held corporations.
Foundation type: Independent foundation.
Financial data (yr. ended 12/31/13): Assets, $18,538,605 (M); expenditures, $8,393,479; qualifying distributions, $8,303,397; giving activities include $8,296,927 for 71 grants (high: $6,000,000; low: $25).
Purpose and activities: Emphasis on higher education, including institutions in Israel, and research-related programs; support also for Jewish organizations and welfare funds, museums, and secondary education.
Fields of interest: Museums; Secondary school/education; Higher education; AIDS; Medical research, institute; Human services; Jewish federated giving programs; Jewish agencies & synagogues.
International interests: Israel.
Type of support: Continuing support; Building/renovation; Equipment; Research.
Limitations: Applications not accepted. Giving primarily in NY. No grants to individuals, or for endowment funds, scholarships, fellowships, or matching gifts; no loans.
Application information: Contributes only to pre-selected organizations.
Board meeting date(s): Mar., June, Sept., Dec., and as required
Officers and Directors:* Joan H. Tisch,* Co-Pres.; Wilma S. Tisch,* Co-Pres.; Andrew H. Tisch, V.P.; Daniel R. Tisch, V.P.; James S. Tisch, V.P.; Jonathan M. Tisch, V.P.; Laurie M. Tisch, V.P.; Steven E. Tisch, V.P.; Thomas J. Tisch,* V.P.; Barry L. Bloom,* Secy.-Treas.
EIN: 591002844
Selected grants: The following grants are a representative sample of this grantmaker's funding activity:
$6,000,150 to New York University, New York, NY, 2012. For general support.
$1,500,000 to Skidmore College, Saratoga Springs, NY, 2012. For general support.
$505,000 to Museum of Modern Art, New York, NY, 2012. For general support.
$500,000 to Gay Mens Health Crisis, New York, NY, 2012. For general support.
$500,000 to Gunnery, Washington, CT, 2012. For general support.
$250,000 to Ethical Culture Fieldston School, New York, NY, 2012. For general support.
$50,000 to Carnegie Hall Society, New York, NY, 2012. For general support.
$25,000 to World Trade Center Memorial Foundation, New York, NY, 2012. For general support.
$10,000 to Childrens Museum of Manhattan, New York, NY, 2012. For general support.
$10,000 to Lincoln Center for the Performing Arts, New York, NY, 2012. For general support.

6989
The James S. & Merryl H. Tisch Foundation, Inc. ✧
c/o Mark J. Krinsky, CPA
655 Madison Ave., 11th Fl.
New York, NY 10065-8043

Established in 1992 in DE and NY.
Donors: Laurence A. Tisch‡; James S. Tisch; Wilma S. Tisch.
Foundation type: Independent foundation.
Financial data (yr. ended 12/31/13): Assets, $24,108,314 (M); gifts received, $4,378,500; expenditures, $5,909,171; qualifying distributions, $5,881,012; giving activities include $5,871,942 for 37 grants (high: $5,006,012; low: $500).
Purpose and activities: Giving primarily for education, and children and youth services; funding also for the arts, health associations, social services, and Jewish organizations.
Fields of interest: Arts; Education, association; Higher education; Education; Health organizations, association; Human services; Children/youth, services; Jewish federated giving programs; Social sciences, public policy; Jewish agencies & synagogues.
Limitations: Applications not accepted. Giving primarily in New York, NY. No grants to individuals.
Application information: Contributes only to pre-selected organizations.
Officers and Directors:* James S. Tisch,* Pres.; Merryl H. Tisch,* Sr. V.P.; Barry L. Bloom, Secy.-Treas.
EIN: 133693587

6990
The Laurie M. Tisch Foundation, Inc. ✧
655 Madison Ave., 11th Fl.
New York, NY 10065-8043

Established in 1992 in NY and DE.
Donors: S. Donald Sussman; Preston Robert Tisch‡; Joan H. Tisch; The Sussman Family Foundation.
Foundation type: Independent foundation.
Financial data (yr. ended 12/31/13): Assets, $105,304,228 (M); gifts received, $7,975,600; expenditures, $15,470,410; qualifying distributions, $15,156,149; giving activities include $13,843,261 for 116 grants (high: $3,880,415; low: $300).
Purpose and activities: Giving primarily for the arts; funding also for education and social services.
Fields of interest: Museums (art); Performing arts; Performing arts centers; Arts; Education; Human services.
Limitations: Applications not accepted. Giving primarily in New York, NY. No grants to individuals.
Application information: Contributes only to pre-selected organizations.
Officers: Laurie M. Tisch, C.E.O. and Pres.; Richard E. Luftglass, V.P., Secy. and Exec. Dir.; Barry L. Bloom, Treas.
EIN: 133693585
Selected grants: The following grants are a representative sample of this grantmaker's funding activity:
$1,985,000 to Teachers College Columbia University, New York, NY, 2012.
$1,154,765 to Whitney Museum of American Art, New York, NY, 2012.
$1,010,500 to Yeshiva University, Cardozo School of Law, New York, NY, 2012.

$585,200 to Lincoln Center for the Performing Arts, New York, NY, 2012.
$474,578 to Mayors Fund to Advance New York City, New York, NY, 2012.
$400,500 to Skidmore College, Saratoga Springs, NY, 2012.
$252,334 to Childrens Museum of Manhattan, New York, NY, 2012.
$166,666 to Hunter College Foundation, New York, NY, 2012.
$150,000 to Echoing Green, New York, NY, 2012.
$25,000 to Four Freedoms Park Conservancy, Franklin D. Roosevelt Four Freedoms Park, New York, NY, 2012.

6991
The Steve Tisch Foundation ✧
655 Madison Ave., 11th Fl.
New York, NY 10065-8043

Foundation type: Independent foundation.
Financial data (yr. ended 12/31/13): Assets, $5,818,254 (M); expenditures, $459,667; qualifying distributions, $445,492; giving activities include $443,282 for 5 grants (high: $100,000; low: $47,790).
Fields of interest: Media, film/video; Performing arts, theater; Elementary school/education; Higher education.
Limitations: Applications not accepted. Giving primarily in Medford, MA; some giving also in Los Angeles, CA and Salt Lake City, UT.
Application information: Contributes only to pre-selected organizations.
Trustee: Steven E. Tisch.
EIN: 264740521

6992
The Wilma S. and Laurence A. Tisch Foundation ✧ ☆
655 Madison Ave., 11th Fl.
New York, NY 10065-8043

Established in 2011 in NY.
Donor: Wilma S. Tisch.
Foundation type: Independent foundation.
Financial data (yr. ended 12/31/13): Assets, $24,070,197 (M); gifts received, $15,241,559; expenditures, $17,944,462; qualifying distributions, $17,555,245; giving activities include $17,552,726 for 46 grants (high: $10,000,000; low: $500).
Fields of interest: Arts; Education; Hospitals (general); Health organizations; Human services.
Limitations: Applications not accepted. Giving primarily in New York, NY.
Application information: Contributes only to pre-selected organizations.
Trustees: Andrew H. Tisch; Daniel R. Tisch; James S. Tisch; Thomas J. Tisch; Wilma S. Tisch.
EIN: 456431332

6993
Dan and Sheryl Tishman Family Foundation ✧
100 Park Ave.
New York, NY 10017-5516 (212) 399-3600
Contact: Daniel R. Tishman, Dir.; Sheryl C. Tishman, Dir.

Donors: Daniel R. Tishman; Sheryl C. Tishman.
Foundation type: Independent foundation.
Financial data (yr. ended 12/31/12): Assets, $247,944 (M); gifts received, $2,137,785; expenditures, $2,113,254; qualifying distributions, $2,109,000; giving activities include $2,109,000 for grants.
Fields of interest: Education; Health care; Religion.
Limitations: Applications accepted. Giving primarily in New York, NY.
Application information: Application form required.
Initial approach: Letter
Deadline(s): None
Directors: Bob Kerrey; Daniel R. Tishman; Sheryl C. Tishman; John A. Vissicchio; Ed Zukerman.
EIN: 450612382

6994
Barbara and Donald Tober Foundation ✧
c/o Sugar Foods Corp.
950 3rd Ave.
New York, NY 10022-2705

Established in 1999 in NY.
Donors: Barbara Tober; Donald G. Tober.
Foundation type: Independent foundation.
Financial data (yr. ended 12/31/12): Assets, $948,866 (M); gifts received, $1,024,381; expenditures, $612,802; qualifying distributions, $605,638; giving activities include $601,710 for 113 grants (high: $160,000; low: $100).
Fields of interest: Arts; Education; Environment.
Limitations: Applications not accepted. Giving primarily in New York, NY. No grants to individuals.
Application information: Contributes only to pre-selected organizations.
Trustees: Myron Stein; Barbara Tober; Donald G. Tober; Jack Vivinetto.
EIN: 137192894

6995
Tomorrow Foundation ✧
430 Park Ave., 6th Fl.
New York, NY 10022-1029

Established in 1997 in NY.
Donors: Robert F.X. Sillerman; Laura Baudo Sillerman.
Foundation type: Independent foundation.
Financial data (yr. ended 12/31/13): Assets, $139,178 (M); gifts received, $510,000; expenditures, $879,577; qualifying distributions, $892,948; giving activities include $892,948 for 12 grants (high: $365,000; low: $1,500).
Purpose and activities: Giving primarily for higher education.
Fields of interest: Arts; Higher education; Human services; Children/youth, services.
Limitations: Applications not accepted. Giving primarily in NY. No grants to individuals.
Application information: Unsolicited requests for funds not accepted.
Officers: Laura Baudo Sillerman, Pres.; John Coughlan, V.P.; Mitchell Nelson, V.P.
EIN: 133930172

6996
Tortora Sillcox Family Foundation ✧
(formerly Tortora Family Foundation)
c/o BCRS Assocs., LLC
77 Water St., 9th Fl.
New York, NY 10005-4414

Established in 1999 in NY.
Donors: Leslie C. Tortora; Leslie C. Sillcox; Mark Sillcox.
Foundation type: Independent foundation.
Financial data (yr. ended 03/31/13): Assets, $37,672,474 (M); gifts received, $806,747; expenditures, $3,503,103; qualifying distributions, $3,207,837; giving activities include $3,134,124 for 20 grants (high: $475,000; low: $9).
Fields of interest: Higher education; Education; Health organizations; Foundations (private grantmaking).
Limitations: Applications not accepted. Giving primarily in Hartford, CT and New York, NY. No grants to individuals.
Application information: Contributes only to pre-selected organizations.
Trustees: Leslie C. Sillcox; Mark E. Sillcox.
EIN: 134088705
Selected grants: The following grants are a representative sample of this grantmaker's funding activity:
$288,000 to Fund for Public Schools, New York, NY, 2011.
$250,000 to State University of New York Regents Research Fund, Albany, NY, 2011.
$250,000 to Urban Assembly, New York, NY, 2011.
$175,000 to Trinity College, Hartford, CT, 2011.
$150,000 to Uncommon Schools, New York, NY, 2011.
$50,000 to Computers for Youth Foundation, New York, NY, 2011.

6997
Toshiba America Foundation ✧ ☆
c/o Prog. Office
1251 Ave. of the Americas, 41st Fl.
New York, NY 10020-4110 (212) 596-0620
Contact: Laura Cronin, Dir.
FAX: (212) 221-1108;
E-mail: foundation@tai.toshiba.com; Main URL: http://www.taf.toshiba.com
6-12 Grants: http://www.toshiba.com/taf/pop_612_grants_10.html
K-5 Grants: http://www.toshiba.com/taf/pop_k5_grants_10.html

Established in 1990 in NY.
Donors: Toshiba America, Inc.; Toshiba Corporation.
Foundation type: Company-sponsored foundation.
Financial data (yr. ended 03/31/13): Assets, $9,988,028 (M); expenditures, $678,327; qualifying distributions, $652,500; giving activities include $544,105 for 125 grants (high: $50,000; low: $265).
Purpose and activities: The foundation supports schools and organizations involved with K-12 science and mathematics education.
Fields of interest: Elementary/secondary education; Science, formal/general education; Mathematics.
Type of support: Equipment; Program development.
Limitations: Applications accepted. Giving on a national basis, with some emphasis on areas of company operations in CA, IL, NJ, NY, TN, and TX. No support for religious or political organizations,

teacher training institutes, or discriminatory organizations. No grants to individuals, or for professional development, capital campaigns, endowments, start-up needs, general operating support, conferences, building, computer hardware or materials, audio-visual equipment, videos, textbooks, independent study, fundraising, dinners, special events, educational research, after-school programs, or educational summer programs.
Publications: Application guidelines; Corporate giving report; Grants list; Informational brochure (including application guidelines); Newsletter; Occasional report.
Application information: Applicants are encouraged to contact the foundation to discuss project ideas prior to applying. Organizations receiving support are asked to submit a final report. Application form required.
Initial approach: Download application form and mail to foundation
Copies of proposal: 2
Deadline(s): Oct. 1 for K-5 Grant Program; None for 6-12 Grant Program requests of up to $5,000; Feb. 1 and Aug. 2 for 6-12 Grant Program requests over $5,000
Board meeting date(s): Mar. and Sept.
Final notification: 3 months; Mar. and Sept. for 6-12 Grant Program requests over $5,000
Officers and Directors:* John A. Anderson, Jr.,* Pres.; Thomas Gallatin, Secy.; Wayne Chau, Treas.; Shinichiro Akiba; Yoshihide Fuji; Tetsuo Kadoya; Mark Mathews; Toshiya Miyaguchi; Hideya Sakaida; Mark Simons; Atsushi Tanaka.
Number of staff: 2 full-time professional.
EIN: 133596612

6998
Tova Foundation ✧
13 Schunnemunk Rd.
Monroe, NY 10950-6225

Established in 1998 in NY.
Donors: B & H Foto and Electronics; Rueben Rosenburg Fdn.; Olam Chesed Yiboneh.
Foundation type: Independent foundation.
Financial data (yr. ended 12/31/13): Assets, $1,595,040 (M); expenditures, $476,003; qualifying distributions, $472,500; giving activities include $472,500 for 2 grants (high: $302,500; low: $170,000).
Fields of interest: Human services; Jewish federated giving programs; Jewish agencies & synagogues.
Limitations: Applications not accepted. Giving primarily in NY. No grants to individuals.
Application information: Contributes only to pre-selected organizations.
Trustees: David Mendolowitz; Abe Schwartz.
EIN: 134016145
Selected grants: The following grants are a representative sample of this grantmaker's funding activity:
$515,000 to Congregation Ahavas Tzdokah V Chesed, Brooklyn, NY, 2012.
$320,000 to Khal Chesed Lashem, Brooklyn, NY, 2012.

6999
Tower Family Fund, Inc. ✧
369 Franklin St.
Buffalo, NY 14202-1702

Established in 2006 in NY.
Donors: Peter Tower; Peter Tower Assocs., LP.
Foundation type: Independent foundation.
Financial data (yr. ended 12/31/13): Assets, $39,534,386 (M); gifts received, $500,000; expenditures, $3,207,919; qualifying distributions, $2,990,051; giving activities include $2,901,007 for 44 grants (high: $1,291,669; low: $500).
Fields of interest: Performing arts, orchestras; Arts; Human services; Children/youth, services.
Limitations: Applications not accepted. Giving primarily in MA, and Buffalo, NY. No grants to individuals.
Application information: Contributes only to pre-selected organizations.
Officers and Directors:* Peter Tower,* Pres.; John N. Blair,* V.P.; Mollie T. Byrnes,* Secy.; Cynthia T. Doyle,* Treas.
EIN: 205848514
Selected grants: The following grants are a representative sample of this grantmaker's funding activity:
$200,000 to New Profit, Boston, MA, 2011.
$60,000 to Pathways for Children, Gloucester, MA, 2011.
$50,000 to Peer Health Exchange, San Francisco, CA, 2011.
$50,000 to Stand for Children Leadership Center, Portland, OR, 2011.
$30,000 to Trustees of Reservations, Beverly, MA, 2011.
$25,000 to Albright-Knox Art Gallery, Buffalo, NY, 2011.
$25,000 to Buffalo Philharmonic Orchestra, Buffalo, NY, 2011.
$25,000 to Massachusetts General Hospital, Boston, MA, 2011.
$25,000 to YMCA of Marthas Vineyard, Vineyard Haven, MA, 2011.
$5,000 to Heifer Project International, Little Rock, AR, 2011.

7000
The Peter and Elizabeth C. Tower Foundation ✧
2351 N. Forest Rd., Ste. 106
Getzville, NY 14068-1225 (716) 689-0370
Contact: Tracy A. Sawicki, Exec. Dir.
FAX: (716) 689-3716;
E-mail: info@thetowerfoundation.org; Tel. for Donald W. Matteson: (716) 689-0370, ext. 207; Main URL: http://www.thetowerfoundation.org
E-Newsletter: http://www.thetowerfoundation.org/Home/Email
Facebook: https://www.facebook.com/thetowerfoundation
LinkedIn: http://www.linkedin.com/company/the-peter-and-elizabeth-c-tower-foundation?trk=company_logo
RSS Feed: http://www.thetowerfoundation.org/blog
Twitter: https://twitter.com/towerfdn

Established in 1990 in NY.
Donors: Elizabeth C. Tower; Peter Tower; Peter Tower, Inc.; Peter Tower Living Trust.
Foundation type: Independent foundation.
Financial data (yr. ended 12/31/13): Assets, $81,423,410 (M); gifts received, $147; expenditures, $6,913,207; qualifying distributions, $6,516,750; giving activities include $5,417,659 for 168 grants (high: $619,721; low: $200).
Purpose and activities: The foundation has four primary funding categories: mental health, substance abuse, learning disabilities, and intellectual disabilities. It also has another category: organizational capacity building, which provides support to eligible organizations that offer programs and services in its primary funding categories.
Fields of interest: Elementary/secondary education; Education, early childhood education; Education; Substance abuse, services; Mental health, treatment; Mental health/crisis services; Children/youth; Youth; Disabilities, people with; Mentally disabled; Substance abusers.
Type of support: Management development/capacity building; Program development; Seed money; Technical assistance; Program evaluation; Matching/challenge support.
Limitations: Giving primarily in Barnstable, Dukes, Essex, and Nantucket counties in MA, and Erie and Niagara counties in NY, and for organizations serving residents of these areas. No support for political campaigns or attempts to influence legislation. No grants to individuals or for general operating support, capital campaigns or capital improvement, or scholarships.
Publications: Application guidelines; Grants list; Program policy statement.
Application information: Application guidelines updated annually; please see foundation web site for current guidelines.
Initial approach: Request for proposal
Board meeting date(s): Quarterly
Officer: Tracy A. Sawicki, Exec. Dir.
Trustees: John N. Blair; Deborah Brayton; John H. Byrnes; Mollie Tower Byrnes; Cynthia Tower Doyle; Robert M. Doyle; Sherif A. Nada; Donna Owens; Joseph J. Rosa; Elizabeth C. Tower; Peter Tower.
Number of staff: 5 full-time professional; 1 full-time support.
EIN: 166350753

7001
Towerbrook Foundation ✧
Park Ave. Tower
65 E. 55th St., 27 Fl.
New York, NY 10022-3362 (212) 699-2200
Contact: Jennifer Glassman, Treas.; Filippo Cardini, Secy.
FAX: (917) 591-9851;
E-mail: contact@towerbrook.com; Additional tel.: (212) 699-2278; Main URL: http://www.towerbrook.com/towerbrook-foundation/

Established in 2006 in NY.
Donor: Towerbrook Capital Partners LP.
Foundation type: Company-sponsored foundation.
Financial data (yr. ended 12/31/12): Assets, $8,399,762 (M); expenditures, $1,704,432; qualifying distributions, $1,697,682; giving activities include $1,668,006 for 104 grants (high: $220,000; low: $150).
Purpose and activities: The foundation supports organizations involved with education, health, bone diseases, allergies research, employment, youth development, human services, international development, philanthropy, and military and veterans.
Type of support: General/operating support; Annual campaigns; Equipment; Program development; Scholarship funds.
Limitations: Giving primarily in areas of company operations in CT, MA , and NY, and in Finland, Italy, and the United Kingdom.

Application information:
Initial approach: Contact foundation for application information
Officers and Directors:* Neal Moszkowski,* Co-Chair.; Ramez Sousou, Co-Chair.; Filippo Cardini, Secy.; Jennifer Glassman,* Treas.; Jonathan Bilzin; Robin Esterson; Niclas Gabran; Winston Ginsberg; Hugh Harper; Gordon Holmes; Brian Jacobsen; Michael Karangelen; Adam McLain; Axel Meyersiek; Travis Nelson; Andrew Rolfe; Ian Sacks; Karim Saddi; Patrick Smulders; John Sinik.
EIN: 743182897

7002
Toyota USA Foundation
c/o Fdn. Admin.
601 Lexington Ave., 49th Fl.
New York, NY 10022-4611 (212) 715-7486
E-mail: ToyotaPhilanthropy@Toyota.com; Tel. for questions about online applications: (212) 715-7490; Main URL: http://www.toyota.com/usa/community/articles/community_grants_foundation.html

Established in 1987 in CA.
Donors: Toyota Motor Sales, U.S.A., Inc.; Toyota Motor Manufacturing North America, Inc.
Foundation type: Company-sponsored foundation.
Financial data (yr. ended 06/30/12): Assets, $103,052,108 (M); expenditures, $5,911,294; qualifying distributions, $5,175,610; giving activities include $5,156,919 for 25 grants (high: $1,800,000; low: $20,000).
Purpose and activities: The foundation supports organizations involved with K-12 education. Special emphasis is directed toward math, science, and environmental science.
Fields of interest: Elementary/secondary education; Higher education; Environment, natural resources; Environment; Youth, services; Science, formal/general education; Mathematics; Science.
Type of support: Equipment; Program development; Curriculum development; Program evaluation.
Limitations: Giving primarily in areas of major company operations in AZ, CA, Washington, DC, IL, MD, NM, NY, and TX; giving also to national organizations. No support for discriminatory organizations, government agencies, private or public K-12 schools, religious, fraternal, or lobbying organizations, or political parties or candidates. No grants to individuals, or for general operating support, annual campaigns, or debt reduction, endowments, capital campaigns, fundraising events, or construction or equipment, conferences, meals, or travel, or publication subsidies, advertising, or mass mailings.
Publications: Application guidelines; Grants list.
Application information: Grants range from $50,000 to $200,000. A site visit may be requested. Additional information may be requested at a later date.
Initial approach: Complete online application
Deadline(s): None
Board meeting date(s): Twice per year
Final notification: Up to 6 months
Officers and Directors:* Michael Rouse, Pres.; Dian Ogilvie,* Secy.; Hiroshi Nishida,* Treas.; Tetsuo Agata; Chuck Brown; Barbra Cooper; Robert C. Daly; Katsuyuki Kusakawa; Jim Lentz; Patricia Salas Pineda; Steve St. Angelo; Shigeki Terashi; James Weisman.
Number of staff: 2 full-time professional; 1 full-time support.
EIN: 953255038

7003
Trace Foundation ✧
132 Perry St., Ste. 2B
New York, NY 10014-2703 (212) 367-7380
FAX: (212) 367-7383; E-mail: info@trace.org; Main URL: http://www.trace.org
E-Newsletter: http://www.trace.org/contact-us
Facebook: http://www.facebook.com/TraceFoundation
Flickr: http://www.flickr.com/photos/tracefoundation
Twitter: http://twitter.com/tracefoundation
YouTube: http://www.youtube.com/user/tracefoundation

Established in 1993 in NY.
Donors: Andrea Soros; George Soros.
Foundation type: Independent foundation.
Financial data (yr. ended 12/31/12): Assets, $1,392,516 (M); gifts received, $3,397,414; expenditures, $6,072,400; qualifying distributions, $5,133,815; giving activities include $3,391,067 for grants.
Purpose and activities: The foundation supports the continuity, development, and vitality of Tibetan communities. It works to better people's lives and reinforce the uniqueness of Tibetan culture, language, and places.
Fields of interest: Arts, cultural/ethnic awareness; Media, film/video; Visual arts; Libraries/library science; Education; International development; Community/economic development, management/technical assistance; Philanthropy/voluntarism.
International interests: China.
Type of support: Research; Publication; Grants to individuals; Fellowships; Scholarship funds.
Limitations: Giving primarily in China.
Publications: Application guidelines; Annual report; Informational brochure; Newsletter; Occasional report.
Application information: See foundation web site for scholarship and fellowship information and application forms. Application form required.
Initial approach: Submit appropriate application form on foundation web site. Letter of inquiry required
Copies of proposal: 1
Trustees: Eric Colombel; Andrea Soros.
Number of staff: 1 full-time professional; 2 full-time support.
EIN: 137008868

7004
Travis Foundation ✧ ☆
1 Court Sq., 19th Fl.
Long Island City, NY 11120-0001

Established in IL.
Donors: Dempsey J. Travis†; Moselynne E. Travis†.
Foundation type: Independent foundation.
Financial data (yr. ended 12/31/13): Assets, $15,095,911 (M); gifts received, $343,029; expenditures, $675,394; qualifying distributions, $604,458; giving activities include $515,000 for 3 grants (high: $255,000; low: $5,000).
Fields of interest: Higher education, university; Education.
Limitations: Applications accepted. Giving primarily in IL.
Application information: Application form required.
Initial approach: Request application form
Deadline(s): None
Trustee: Citibank, N.A.
EIN: 356890246

7005
Triad Foundation, Inc.
P.O. Box 4440
Ithaca, NY 14852-4440 (607) 257-1133
Contact: Joanne V. Florino, Exec. Dir.
FAX: (607) 257-5203;
E-mail: JVF@triadfoundation.org

Established in 2002; funded by transfer of assets from Park Foundation, Inc. in Feb., 2003.
Donors: Roy Hampton Park, Jr.; Park Foundation, Inc.
Foundation type: Independent foundation.
Financial data (yr. ended 12/31/12): Assets, $258,595,165 (M); expenditures, $13,529,058; qualifying distributions, $11,735,121; giving activities include $10,426,118 for 306 grants (high: $500,000; low: $300), and $9,263 for 27 employee matching gifts.
Purpose and activities: Giving primarily for graduate fellowships, educational programs serving children and youth, marine and tropical ecology, scientific research, and human services.
Fields of interest: Education; Environment, water resources; Human services; Children/youth, services.
Type of support: General/operating support; Management development/capacity building; Program development; Conferences/seminars; Seed money; Fellowships; Internship funds; Research; Technical assistance; Employee matching gifts; Matching/challenge support.
Limitations: Applications accepted. Giving primarily in Tampa, FL, Charlotte, NC, and Tompkins County, NY. No grants to individuals, or for endowments or capital campaigns.
Publications: Application guidelines.
Application information: Application form required.
Initial approach: Letter or telephone
Copies of proposal: 1
Deadline(s): Rolling basis
Board meeting date(s): Quarterly
Final notification: 2 months
Officers and Directors:* Roy Hampton Park, Jr.,* Chair. and Pres.; Roy H. Park III,* V.P. and Secy.; Elizabeth P. Fowler,* V.P. and Treas.; Joanne V. Florino, Exec. Dir.; Caitlyn Schryver, Dir., Finance.
Number of staff: 2 full-time professional; 3 part-time professional; 2 full-time support.
EIN: 300108102
Selected grants: The following grants are a representative sample of this grantmaker's funding activity:
$500,000 to American Enterprise Institute for Public Policy Research, Washington, DC, 2012. For The Road to Freedom project.
$455,456 to University of North Carolina, School of Journalism and Mass Communication, Chapel Hill, NC, 2012. For Roy H. Park Fellowships over a period of five years, payable over 5.00 years.
$300,000 to Frameworks of Tampa Bay, Tampa, FL, 2012. For key staff ($250,000), general operating support ($30,000), and a match for funds raised during the appeal at the Heads and Hearts Awards Luncheon ($20,000).

$150,000 to Harvest Center, Charlotte, NC, 2012. For the development of a real estate fund ($50,000), purchase of a pre-owned 15' box truck ($15,000), new position of Transformation Program Director ($50,000), and general operating support ($35,000).
$100,000 to Moving Picture Institute, New York, NY, 2012. For general operating support.
$20,000 to Tompkins Cortland Community College Foundation, Dryden, NY, 2012. For TC3's nursing program with the purchase of the Pyxis Medstation medication administration system.
$20,000 to Young Life in Tampa, Tampa, FL, 2012. For mentoring programs, specifically for staff expenses for the Tampa Urban Area Program ($11,000) and the South Tampa Program ($9,000).
$15,000 to Media Research Center, Reston, VA, 2012. For MRC's media watchdog efforts.
$15,000 to Powerstories Theater of Tampa Bay, Tampa, FL, 2012. For Girlstories Leadership Theatre and workshop programs.
$10,000 to Charlotte Center for Urban Ministry, Charlotte, NC, 2012. To support the Urban Ministry Center's efforts to end chronic homelessness in Charlotte.
$10,000 to Safe Alliance, Charlotte, NC, 2012. For UFS domestic violence programs.
$5,000 to Clare Boothe Luce Policy Institute, Herndon, VA, 2012. For the Institute's training and mentoring program.

7006
The Troy Savings Bank Charitable Foundation, Inc. ✧

32 2nd St.
P.O. Box 598
Troy, NY 12181-0598 (518) 720-0004
Contact: Leslie A. Cheu, Exec. Dir.
FAX: (518) 720-0008;
E-mail: info@tsbfoundation.org; E-mail for Leslie A. Cheu, Exec. Dir.: lcheu@tsbfoundation.org; Main URL: http://www.tsbfoundation.org

Established in 1998 in NY as a company-sponsored foundation; status changed to independent foundation in 2004.
Donors: The Troy Savings Bank; Troy Financial Corp.
Foundation type: Independent foundation.
Financial data (yr. ended 12/31/13): Assets, $15,710,090 (M); expenditures, $861,869; qualifying distributions, $743,199; giving activities include $570,488 for 65 grants (high: $213,150; low: $200).
Purpose and activities: The foundation supports organizations involved with arts and culture, community development, and youth development.
Fields of interest: Arts; Housing/shelter; Human services; Children/youth; Youth; Economically disadvantaged; Homeless.
Type of support: Continuing support; Capital campaigns; Equipment; Program development; Curriculum development; Matching/challenge support.
Limitations: Applications accepted. Giving primarily in NY, with emphasis on Albany, Greene, Rensselaer, Saratoga, Schenectady, Schoharie, Warren, and Washington counties. No support for political, labor or fraternal organizations. No grants to individuals.
Publications: Application guidelines; Informational brochure.
Application information: See foundation web site for specific application information. Application form required.
Initial approach: Letter (for requests under $1,000), telephone to Exec. Dir. (for requests greater than $1,000)
Deadline(s): Varies. Please contact the Exec. Dir.
Board meeting date(s): Quarterly, with distribution meetings generally held in Jan., Apr., July and Oct.
Final notification: 8 to 10 weeks
Officers and Directors:* Daniel J. Hogarty, Jr.,* Pres.; George H. Arakelian, Secy.; Leslie A. Cheu, Exec. Dir.; Dr. Michael E. Fleming; Willie A. Hammett; Thomas B. Healy; Morris Massry; Edward G. O'Haire.
Number of staff: 2 full-time professional.
EIN: 141813865
Selected grants: The following grants are a representative sample of this grantmaker's funding activity:
$10,000 to Albany Medical Center Foundation, Albany, NY, 2012. For Hospital Capital Campaign.
$10,000 to Parsons Child and Family Center, Albany, NY, 2012. For Post Adoption Resource Center.
$7,500 to Food Pantries for the Capital District, Albany, NY, 2012. For Food Express Delivery Program.
$5,000 to Arts Center of the Capital Region, Troy, NY, 2012. For Arts Access Program for Youth.
$4,250 to Albany Symphony Orchestra, Albany, NY, 2012. For Rehearsals 2010/2011 Performance Season.
$1,000 to Schenectady County Community College, Schenectady, NY, 2012. For annual fund 2012.
$250 to Troy Area United Ministries, Troy, NY, 2012. For Spring Appeal 2012.

7007
Mildred Faulkner Truman Foundation ✧ ☆

c/o M&T Bank
1100 Wehrle Dr., 2nd Fl.
Buffalo, NY 14221-7748 (716) 842-5506
E-mail: info@mftf.net; Main URL: http://www.mftf.net/

Established in 1985 in NY.
Donor: Mildred Faulkner Truman†.
Foundation type: Independent foundation.
Financial data (yr. ended 08/31/13): Assets, $6,852,299 (M); expenditures, $715,730; qualifying distributions, $605,858; giving activities include $605,858 for 38 grants (high: $67,500; low: $1,000).
Purpose and activities: Giving primarily to organizations which enhance the benefit and residents of Tioga County, NY. The foundation wishes to accomplish this mission by encouraging grant requests for critical needs, capital projects, and seed money for new and special projects or programs.
Fields of interest: Historic preservation/historical societies; Higher education; Higher education, college (community/junior); Libraries (public); Education; Athletics/sports, amateur leagues; Human services; Community development, neighborhood development.
Type of support: Capital campaigns; Building/renovation; Equipment; Emergency funds; Program development; Seed money; Scholarship funds; Matching/challenge support.
Limitations: Applications accepted. Giving primarily in Owego and Tioga counties, NY. No grants to individuals.
Publications: Annual report (including application guidelines).
Application information: Completed applications can be mailed or deposited in the drop box located in the basement lobby of M&T Bank at the corner of Front and Church Sts., Owego, NY, during normal banking hours. Application form and guidelines are available on foundation web site. Application form required.
Initial approach: Proposal
Copies of proposal: 11
Deadline(s): 5 weeks prior to board meeting
Board meeting date(s): Jan., Apr., June, Sept.
Final notification: 1 week after board meeting
Officer: Irene C. Graven, Exec. Dir.
Trustee: M&T Bank.
Number of staff: 1 part-time professional.
EIN: 166271201
Selected grants: The following grants are a representative sample of this grantmaker's funding activity:
$15,000 to Broome Community College, Binghamton, NY, 2011.
$15,000 to State University of New York at Binghamton Foundation, Binghamton, NY, 2011.
$15,000 to Tompkins Cortland Community College Foundation, Dryden, NY, 2011.
$11,400 to Coburn Free Library, Owego, NY, 2011.
$6,636 to Boys and Girls Clubs of Tioga County, Owego, NY, 2011.
$2,000 to Community Care Network of Nichols, Nichols, NY, 2011.
$1,000 to Owego Marketplace, Owego, NY, 2011.

7008
The Donald J. Trump Foundation ✧

c/o WeiserMazars LLP
60 Crossways Park Dr., No. 301
Woodbury, NY 11797-2018
Application address: c/o Donald J. Trump, Pres., The Trump Organization, 725 5th Ave., New York, NY 10022

Established in 1987 in NY.
Donors: Donald J. Trump; Alfons J. Schmitt; Maurice R. Povich; Beth Schwartz; Jayson Schwartz; Corinna Jones; Charles Evans; Joel Pashcow; Kinray, Inc.; Trump Park Ave., LLC; Mr. White LLC; NCL America, Inc.; Stark Carpet Corp.; People Magazine; The Charles Evans Foundation; World Wrestling Entertainment.
Foundation type: Independent foundation.
Financial data (yr. ended 12/31/12): Assets, $1,718,511 (M); gifts received, $1,249,746; expenditures, $1,717,394; qualifying distributions, $1,717,394; giving activities include $1,712,089 for 76 grants (high: $200,000; low: $1,000).
Purpose and activities: Giving primarily for health organizations, youth development, and social services.
Fields of interest: Museums; Education; Hospitals (general); Health care; Health organizations; Medical research, institute; Youth development; Human services; Foundations (public).
Limitations: Giving primarily in New York, NY; some funding also in MA.
Application information: Application form not required.
Initial approach: Letter
Deadline(s): None

Officers: Donald J. Trump, Pres.; Allen Weisselberg, Treas.
Directors: Donald J. Trump, Jr.; Eric F. Trump; Ivanka M. Trump.
EIN: 133404773

7009
Trust for Mutual Understanding ✧
6 W. 48th St., 12th Fl.
New York, NY 10036-1802 (212) 843-0404
Contact: Jennifer P. Goodale, Exec. Dir.; Barbara Lanciers, Dir.
FAX: (212) 843-0344; E-mail: tmu@tmuny.org; Main URL: http://www.tmuny.org
Blog: http://www.tmuny.org/connect/blog
E-Newsletter: http://www.tmuny.org/connect/tmuniverse
Facebook: http://www.facebook.com/pages/Trust-for-Mutual-Understanding/112446932323
Grants Database: http://www.tmuny.org/grantees

Established in 1984 in NY.
Foundation type: Independent foundation.
Financial data (yr. ended 12/31/13): Assets, $41,944,320 (M); expenditures, $3,152,399; qualifying distributions, $2,932,678; giving activities include $1,912,408 for 113 grants (high: $140,000; low: $400).
Purpose and activities: Support to American nonprofit organizations for professional exchanges in the arts and environmental fields between the United States, Russia, and Eastern and Central Europe. Support is provided for travel and related expenses for exchange projects that involve direct, in-depth professional interaction, with the potential for sustained collaboration; that show evidence of professional accomplishment and innovation; and/or that respond to social contexts and engage local communities.
Fields of interest: Visual arts; Museums; Performing arts; Performing arts, dance; Performing arts, theater; Performing arts, music; Historic preservation/historical societies; Arts; Environment, natural resources; Environment; Animals/wildlife, preservation/protection; International exchange.
International interests: Albania; Armenia; Azerbaijan; Belarus; Bosnia and Herzegovina; Bulgaria; Croatia; Czech Republic; Estonia; Georgia; Hungary; Kazakhstan; Kosovo; Kyrgyz Republic; Latvia; Lithuania; Macedonia; Moldova; Mongolia; Montenegro; Poland; Romania; Russia; Serbia; Slovakia; Slovenia; Tajikistan; Turkmenistan; Ukraine; Uzbekistan.
Type of support: Exchange programs.
Limitations: Applications accepted. Giving for exchanges between the U.S. and Russia, and Central and Eastern Europe. No support for one-person exhibitions of work by living artists, solo performance tours or youth programs. No grants to individuals, or for fellowships for individual research or academic study, operating expenses, capital campaigns, construction costs, salaries, honoraria or fees, student exchanges, performing or visual arts competitions, literature or publication projects, library acquisitions or equipment purchases, film production, media training, mass communication programs, activities pertaining to arms control or security issues, economic development, medicine, public health, agriculture, activities in which only a single participant is involved, multi-year commitments, retroactive funding, or, except in special circumstances, interregional travel or travel by project participants in their home countries.
Publications: Application guidelines; Annual report; Grants list; Newsletter.
Application information: The trust has recently transitioned to an online application. Grants are made only to tax-exempt organizations in the United States for exchange projects involving Russia, Central Asia, Mongolia and the Caucasus, and Eastern and Central Europe. Grant funds may only be used for international travel costs. Application form required.
Initial approach: Letter of Inquiry (refer to form on foundation web site); initial contact should be established at least 3 months prior to the application deadline
Copies of proposal: 1
Deadline(s): May 1 and Nov. 1 (for initial inquiry); Feb. 1 and Aug. 1 (for full application)
Board meeting date(s): Spring and fall
Final notification: Within 2 weeks (for initial inquiry)
Director and Trustees:* Jennifer P. Goodale,* Exec. Dir.; Richard S. Lanier; Elizabeth J. McCormack; Marcia McLean; Blaire Ruble.
Board of Advisors: Laura Chasin; Wade Greene; William H. Luers; Isaac Shapiro; Arlene Shuler; Irina Yurna.
Number of staff: 3 full-time professional; 1 part-time professional; 1 part-time support.
EIN: 133212724

7010
Tsadra Foundation ✧
P.O. Box 20192
New York, NY 10014-0710
E-mail: info@tsadra.org; Main URL: http://www.tsadra.org
Advanced Studies Scholarship e-mail: studyscholarship@tsadra.org, Advanced Contemplative Scholarship e-mail: contemplativescholarship@tsadra.org

Established in 2000 in NY.
Donors: Eric Colombel; Andrea Soros; Leon Sauke; Trace Foundation.
Foundation type: Independent foundation.
Financial data (yr. ended 12/31/12): Assets, $558,487 (M); gifts received, $2,350,540; expenditures, $2,296,085; qualifying distributions, $1,790,610; giving activities include $604,917 for 31 grants (high: $208,511; low: $4,377), and $875,050 for grants to individuals.
Purpose and activities: Giving primarily for the combined study and practice of Tibetan Buddhism in the west. The foundation also awards scholarships for both advanced Buddhist studies and advanced contemplative training.
Fields of interest: Education; International development; Buddhism.
Type of support: General/operating support; Program development; Fellowships.
Limitations: Applications not accepted. Giving in the U.S., with emphasis on CA, as well as in Canada, France, India and Nepal.
Application information: Unsolicited requests for funds not accepted.
Officers: Eric Colombel, Pres.; Drupgyu Anthony Chapman, V.P., and Dir., Contemplative Scholarships.
EIN: 137224970
Selected grants: The following grants are a representative sample of this grantmaker's funding activity:
$22,000 to Naropa University, Boulder, CO, 2012. For Lama Tenpa Gyaltsen leading retreat and assisting trans.

7011
Tuft Family Foundation ✧
c/o Bowling Green Station
P.O. Box 73
New York, NY 10274-0073

Established in 1987 in NY.
Donor: Thomas E. Tuft.
Foundation type: Independent foundation.
Financial data (yr. ended 08/31/13): Assets, $12,338,956 (M); gifts received, $625,000; expenditures, $1,015,411; qualifying distributions, $965,442; giving activities include $953,127 for 49 grants (high: $400,000; low: $1).
Purpose and activities: Giving primarily for the arts, health, children, youth and social services, and Jewish federated giving programs.
Fields of interest: Museums (art); Performing arts, theater; Arts; Hospitals (general); Health organizations, association; Human services; Children/youth, services; Jewish federated giving programs.
Limitations: Applications not accepted. Giving primarily in New York, NY. No grants to individuals.
Application information: Contributes only to pre-selected organizations.
Trustees: Lewis M. Eisenberg; Diane H. Tuft; Thomas E. Tuft.
EIN: 133437888
Selected grants: The following grants are a representative sample of this grantmaker's funding activity:
$132,500 to International Center of Photography, New York, NY, 2011.
$26,600 to Mount Sinai Hospital, New York, NY, 2011.
$25,000 to Cancer Research Institute, New York, NY, 2011.
$25,000 to Robin Hood Foundation, New York, NY, 2011.
$25,000 to Village Academies Network, New York, NY, 2011.
$18,000 to UJA-Federation of New York, New York, NY, 2011.
$10,000 to Bachmann-Strauss Dystonia and Parkinson Foundation, New York, NY, 2011.
$10,000 to Student Sponsor Partners, New York, NY, 2011.
$9,250 to Perlman Music Program, New York, NY, 2011.
$5,000 to Childrens Hospital of Philadelphia, Philadelphia, PA, 2011.

7012
Turn 2 Foundation, Inc. ✧
215 Park Ave. S., Ste. 1905
New York, NY 10003-1617 (212) 475-2339
FAX: (212) 475-3378;
E-mail: mail@turn2foundation.org; Main URL: http://derekjeter.mlb.com/NASApp/mlb/players/jeter_derek/turn2/overview.jsp
Alternate URL: http://www.turn2foundation.org

Established in 1996 in MI.

Donors: 78/79 York Assocs., LLC; Acclaim Entertainment; All American Collectibles; AXA Foundation Charitable Gift Fund; Bank of America, N.A.; BBDO; Bestfoods; Bloomberg; Cantor Fitzgerald Securities; Collins Building Services; ConAgra Foods, Inc.; Raniero Cortina, Jr.; Credit Suisse First Boston LLC; Jack Critchfield; Danker-Basham Foundation; Del Frisco's New York; Disney Worldwide Services, Inc.; Dittman Incentive Marketing; Drew Doscher; Richard C. Dresdale; Ernst & Young, LLP; Fenway Partners; Fleer Trading Cards; FleetBoston Financial Corp.; Forbes Foundation; Thomas Geller; Jason Giambi; Goldman Sachs; IMG; Interviewing Services of America; Derek Jeter; JPMorgan Chase Bank, N.A.; Daniel Keith; Kellogg Co.; James Krivacs; Victoria Krivacs; Matt Lalin; Dan LaVecchia; Howard Lutnick; Marquis Jet; Millsport; Nature's Therapy, Inc.; NetJets Aviation, Inc.; New York Mercantile Exchange; NFL Ventures LP; Nike, Inc.; Omdusa, Inc.; The Packer Family Foundation; Partnership for a Drug-Free America; Pepsi Cola Company; Pfizer Inc.; Pharmacia & Upjohn, Inc.; PricewaterhouseCoopers; Pro Performance Sports, LLC; The Promotions Network; Prudential Financial; Quaker Oates Co.; Rockmont Mgmt. Partners; Philip Rogers; Schenker Family Foundation; Seminole Hard Rock Hotel & Casino; Christopher D. Smithers Foundation; Adele Smithers-Fornaci; Sport Fun, Inc.; Steiner Sports Memorabilia; Straub Lincoln Mercury; Chris Sullivan; Take 2 Interactive; Thomas Terrill; Time, Inc.; Tri State Quality Ford Dealers; Turn 2 Enterprises, Inc.; Turn 2, Inc.; Twenty Ones, Inc.; The Upper Deck Co.; Visual Architectural Designs.
Foundation type: Independent foundation.
Financial data (yr. ended 12/31/11): Assets, $4,458,410 (M); gifts received, $3,188,467; expenditures, $2,280,416; qualifying distributions, $2,262,306; giving activities include $610,355 for 25 grants (high: $202,044; low: $2,500), and $1,538,718 for foundation-administered programs.
Purpose and activities: Giving to create and support signature programs and activities that motivate young people to turn away from drugs and alcohol and "TURN 2" healthy lifestyles. Through these ventures, the foundation strives to create outlets that promote and reward academic excellence, leadership development and positive behavior. Turn 2's goal is to see the children of these programs grow safely and successfully into adulthood and become the leaders of tomorrow.
Fields of interest: Secondary school/education; Substance abuse, prevention; Substance abuse, treatment; Recreation, parks/playgrounds; Boys & girls clubs; Human services; Children/youth, services; Foundations (community).
Limitations: Applications not accepted. Giving primarily in and around the Tampa, FL, Kalamazoo, MI, and New York, NY, areas. No support for organizations lacking 501(c)(3) status. No grants to individuals, or for endowment funds, building or renovation projects, or conferences or travel expenses.
Application information: Going forward, Turn 2 will focus its funding on maintaining and enhancing its signature programs and will no longer accept new grant requests or proposals.
Board meeting date(s): Jan. and July
Officers and Directors:* Derek S. Jeter, Chair.; Dr. S. Charles Jeter, Vice-Chair.; Sharlee Jeter, Pres. and Secy.; Todd Smith,* V.P.; Dorothy Jeter, Treas.
EIN: 341847687

7013
Robert L. Turner Charitable Trust ✧
31 E. 72nd St., Ste. 8A-8B
New York, NY 10021-4131

Established in 2005 in NY.
Donor: Robert L. Turner.
Foundation type: Independent foundation.
Financial data (yr. ended 12/31/12): Assets, $74,621 (M); gifts received, $592,869; expenditures, $805,165; qualifying distributions, $805,165; giving activities include $805,165 for 10 grants (high: $743,765; low: $1,000).
Purpose and activities: Giving primarily for the arts, particularly the opera; funding also for human services and medical research.
Fields of interest: Performing arts, opera; Arts; Medical research, institute; Human services.
Limitations: Applications not accepted. Giving primarily in New York, NY. No grants to individuals.
Application information: Contributes only to pre-selected organizations.
Director: Robert L. Turner.
EIN: 206386088

7014
Isaac H. Tuttle Fund ✧
1155 Park Ave.
New York, NY 10128-1209 (212) 831-0429
Contact: Stephanie A. Raneri, Exec. Dir.
FAX: (212) 426-5684; E-mail: info@tuttlefund.org;
Main URL: http://www.tuttlefund.org
Grants List: http://www.tuttlefund.org/grants/recent-grants

Incorporated in 1872 as a public charity; status changed to a private foundation in 2001.
Donors: Martin S. Paine Foundation; Mary Caroline Phelps Trust.
Foundation type: Independent foundation.
Financial data (yr. ended 12/31/13): Assets, $46,467,234 (M); gifts received, $1,180,149; expenditures, $2,253,854; qualifying distributions, $2,133,002; giving activities include $680,000 for 23 grants (high: $40,000; low: $10,000), $521,534 for grants to individuals, and $1,037,209 for foundation-administered programs.
Purpose and activities: The fund gives direct financial support to elderly individuals (65 years of age or older, unless there are compelling circumstances that merit consideration), and nonprofit community-based organizations that provide services to seniors in the borough of Manhattan in New York City, with the goal of enabling older persons to continue living in their own homes so long as they are physically and mentally able to do so. Applicants must have been productive, contributing members of their communities during their working years.
Fields of interest: Aging, centers/services; Aging.
Type of support: General/operating support; Continuing support; Building/renovation; Equipment; Program development; Technical assistance; Grants to individuals.
Limitations: Applications accepted. Giving limited to applicants residing in the borough of Manhattan in NY.
Publications: Application guidelines; Financial statement.
Application information: Contact Exec. Dir. for grants, or Stipend Prog. Dir. for stipends. Application form required for stipends. Formal proposals are by invitation, only after telephone, e-mail or letter of inquiry contact. Application form required.
Initial approach: Telephone, e-mail or letter of inquiry to Exec. Dir.
Copies of proposal: 1
Deadline(s): 3 months prior to board meetings for grants and stipends
Board meeting date(s): 5 times per year
Final notification: Following board meetings
Officers and Trustees:* Molly O. Parkinson,* Pres.; Kenneth R. Page,* V.P.; Christine Valentine,* Secy.; Anne H. Lindgren,* Treas.; Stephanie A. Raneri, Exec. Dir.; Paul J. Benziger, Jr.; Shirley B. Bresler; Susan L. Burden; Susan P. Cole; William H. Forsyth, Jr.; Charles B. Grace III; John C. Harpole; Martha V. Johns; Ann R. Loeb; K.C. Maurer; The Rev. Edward D. Pardoe III; Oscar S. Straus III; M. Antoinette Thomas.
Number of staff: 6 full-time professional; 1 full-time support.
EIN: 135628325

7015
The C. & J. Unanue Foundation, Inc. ✧
c/o Bessemer Trust Co., N.A.
630 5th Ave.
New York, NY 10111-0001

Established in 1995 in NJ.
Donors: Joseph A. Unanue; Carmen Unanue; Joseph A. Unanue Charitable Lead Trust; Ferolie Family Foundation; Marabel Unanue.
Foundation type: Independent foundation.
Financial data (yr. ended 06/30/13): Assets, $16,444,300 (M); gifts received, $9,732; expenditures, $777,842; qualifying distributions, $710,000; giving activities include $710,000 for grants.
Purpose and activities: Giving primarily for higher education, and to Hispanic arts and cultural organizations.
Fields of interest: Museums (ethnic/folk arts); Performing arts, dance; Arts; Higher education; Education; Hispanics/Latinos.
Limitations: Applications not accepted. Giving primarily in NJ and New York, NY. No grants to individuals.
Application information: Contributes only to pre-selected organizations.
Officers and Trustees:* Carmen Unanue,* Pres.; Andrew Unanue,* V.P.; Joseph A. Unanue,* Secy.-Treas.
EIN: 223382542
Selected grants: The following grants are a representative sample of this grantmaker's funding activity:
$300,000 to Seton Hall University, South Orange, NJ, 2011.
$40,000 to Resource Foundation, Baton Rouge, LA, 2011.
$10,000 to Bergen Catholic High School, Oradell, NJ, 2011.
$5,000 to Robin Hood Foundation, New York, NY, 2011.

7016
Unbound Philanthropy
101 Avenue of the Americas, Ste. 1400
New York, NY 10013-1941 (212) 219-1009
FAX: (212) 219-1129;
E-mail: mail@unboundphilanthropy.org; Additional

address: 70 Crowcross St., Farrington, London, UK, EC1 M 6EJ; tel.: (020) 7251-9304; Main URL: http://www.unboundphilanthropy.org
Grants List: http://www.unboundphilanthropy.org/grantees.php

Established in 2004 in HI.
Donors: William Huntington Reeves; Deborah K. Berger.
Foundation type: Independent foundation.
Financial data (yr. ended 12/31/13): Assets, $166,080,781 (M); gifts received, $14,000,000; expenditures, $11,215,029; qualifying distributions, $11,177,732; giving activities include $7,946,975 for 95 grants (high: $417,647; low: $6,250).
Purpose and activities: The grantmaker is dedicated to securing justice and opportunity for migrants and refugees.
Fields of interest: Education; Human services; Philanthropy/voluntarism; Children/youth; Women; Immigrants/refugees.
International interests: Africa; United Kingdom.
Limitations: Applications not accepted. Giving on a national basis and in the U.S. and the U.K. No grants to individuals.
Publications: Grants list.
Application information: Contributes only to pre-selected organizations.
Officers and Directors:* - Deborah K. Berger,* Pres. and Secy.; Taryn Higashi, Exec. Dir.; Kiki Fordham; Bill Reeves; Hilary Weinstein; Kiki Fordham.
Number of staff: 3 full-time professional.
EIN: 830411606
Selected grants: The following grants are a representative sample of this grantmaker's funding activity:
$500,000 to International Rescue Committee, New York, NY, 2012. For Strengthening Capacities for the Field of Education in Emergencies through NGO-University Partnership, payable over 2.00 years.
$304,755 to Public Interest Projects, New York, NY, 2012. For Four Freedoms Fund.
$300,000 to National Immigration Law Center, Los Angeles, CA, 2012. For support of United We DREAM, including provision of rapid response resources to help implement the new Deferred Action Policy for DREAMers.
$300,000 to United We Dream Network, Washington, DC, 2012. To provide rapid response support to United We DREAM Network to publicize and offer support to affiliates on assisting youth eligible for the new Deferred Action for Childhood Arrivals policy.
$265,000 to New York Community Trust, New York, NY, 2012. For BDEK Fund in Community Funds, Inc.
$250,000 to American Civil Liberties Union Foundation, New York, NY, 2012. For Immigrant Rights Project, payable over 2.00 years.
$100,000 to Brookings Institution, Washington, DC, 2012. For continuation of work advancing quality education in conflict contexts.
$100,000 to International Rescue Committee, New York, NY, 2012. For Inter-Agency Network for Education in Emergencies, payable over 1.25 years.
$100,000 to Public Interest Projects, New York, NY, 2012. For Define American.
$80,500 to International Rescue Committee, New York, NY, 2012. For University of Nairobi (UoN) Interim Grant.

7017
Union Square Fund ✧
c/o Marks Paneth & Shron LLP
685 3rd Ave.
New York, NY 10017-8408

Established in 1997 in NY.
Foundation type: Independent foundation.
Financial data (yr. ended 12/31/13): Assets, $60,539,693 (M); expenditures, $1,752,747; qualifying distributions, $1,068,174; giving activities include $968,972 for 8 grants (high: $563,972; low: $25,000).
Fields of interest: Education; Health organizations; Nonprofit management.
Limitations: Applications not accepted. Giving primarily in San Francisco, CA; funding also in the Boston, MA, area, and New York, NY. No grants to individuals.
Publications: Informational brochure.
Application information: Contributes only to pre-selected organizations.
Officers: Jeane Ungerleider, Pres.; Steven C. Baum, Secy.-Treas.
Directors: Nan Arons; Anne Peretz.
Number of staff: None.
EIN: 311574700

7018
United Armenian Charities, Inc. ✧
41 Elizabeth St., Ste. 502
New York, NY 10013-4503 (212) 334-0990

Established in 1951 in NY.
Donor: Dadour Dadourian.
Foundation type: Independent foundation.
Financial data (yr. ended 12/31/12): Assets, $13,329,665 (M); expenditures, $1,037,978; qualifying distributions, $621,000; giving activities include $621,000 for 23 grants (high: $117,000; low: $3,000).
Purpose and activities: Grants primarily for Armenian religious support; grants also for Armenian education and social services.
Fields of interest: Orthodox agencies & churches; Religion.
Type of support: General/operating support.
Limitations: Applications accepted. Giving primarily in NY.
Application information: Application form not required.
Initial approach: Proposal
Deadline(s): None
Trustees: Melanie Dadourian; Stephen Dadourian; Heather Weber.
EIN: 136125023

7019
United States-Japan Foundation ✧
145 E. 32nd St., 12th Fl.
New York, NY 10016-6055 (212) 481-8753
FAX: (212) 481-8762; E-mail: info@us-jf.org; Tokyo office address: Reinanzaka Bldg. 1F, 1-14-2 Akasaka, Minato-ku, Tokyo 107-0052, Japan, tel.: (03) 3586-0541; fax: (03) 3586-1128; e-mail: infotokyo-usjf@nifty.com; Main URL: http://www.us-jf.org
Sign up for current newsletter: http://www.us-jf.org/

Foundation incorporated in 1980 in NY.
Donor: The Nippon Foundation.
Foundation type: Independent foundation.
Financial data (yr. ended 12/31/12): Assets, $82,370,054 (M); gifts received, $86,675; expenditures, $3,557,026; qualifying distributions, $1,045,523; giving activities include $1,045,523 for 36 grants (high: $78,426; low: $3,000).
Purpose and activities: The United States-Japan Foundation is committed to promoting stronger ties between Americans and Japanese by supporting projects that foster mutual knowledge and education, deepen understanding, create effective channels of communication, and address common concerns in an increasingly interdependent world. The current focus of grantmaking activities is in the areas of communication/public opinion, precollege education and policy studies.
Fields of interest: Elementary school/education; Secondary school/education; Education; Environment, energy; Environment; International economic development; International affairs, foreign policy; International affairs; Economics; Public policy, research; Government/public administration; Youth; Adults.
International interests: Asia; Japan.
Type of support: Program development; Publication; Curriculum development; Research; Matching/challenge support.
Limitations: Applications accepted. Giving primarily in the U.S. and Japan. No support for projects in the arts involving performances, exhibitions, or productions, or for sports exchanges or student exchanges. No grants to individuals, or for building or endowment funds, capital campaigns, deficit operations.
Publications: Application guidelines; Financial statement; Grants list.
Application information: The foundation only accepts unsolicited letters of inquiry, not proposals. Application guidelines available on foundation web site. Application form not required.
Initial approach: Letter (no longer than 4 pages)
Copies of proposal: 2
Deadline(s): July 15 and Dec. 15
Board meeting date(s): Apr. and Oct.
Final notification: 1 to 3 months
Officers and Trustees:* James W. Lintott,* Chair.; George R. Packard,* Pres.; Jane Mack Gould; Akinori Horii; Hon. Yoriko Kawaguchi; Dr. Shin'ichi Kitaoka; Akira Kojima; Hon. Taro Kono; Dr. Alexandra Munroe; Satoru Murase; Thomas W. Strauss; Daniel Tani; Takeshi Ueshima.
Honorary Advisors: Hon. Jimmy Carter; Hon. Thomas S. Foley.
Number of staff: 8 full-time professional; 1 full-time support.
EIN: 133054425
Selected grants: The following grants are a representative sample of this grantmaker's funding activity:
$2,370,000 to Foundation for International School of Asia Karuizawa, Tokyo, Japan, 2013. For scholarships for American junior and high school students to attend International School of Asiafs 2013 summer school and to support international negotiation and leadership classes.
$74,701 to Mercy College, Dobbs Ferry, NY, 2013. For Japan-focused professional development program for in-service and pre-service middle school teachers in four school districts in Westchester County, New York.
$56,709 to Middlebury College, Middlebury, VT, 2013. For education program designed to promote awareness of nonproliferation and international peace and security issues and develop critical

thinking skills among high school students in the US and Japan.
$50,000 to International Center for Journalists, Washington, DC, 2013. For media fellowships to prepare and send three selected US journalists on 12-day reporting tour to Japan.
$50,000 to Japanese Medical Society of America, New York, NY, 2013. To support travel to Tohoku for group of 9/11 survivors, Rotarians, and trauma experts to share post disaster recovery experiences with victims in Japan.
$50,000 to Midori Foundation, Midori and Friends, New York, NY, 2013. For music education programs in underprivileged elementary schools in New York City area, including Journey to Japan program.
$50,000 to National Committee on American Foreign Policy, New York, NY, 2013. For conference and meetings to identify common interests of US, Japan, China, and ROK.
$50,000 to New York Foundation for the Arts, Artspire, Brooklyn, NY, 2013. For Hand in Hand program to bring high school students from Tohoku, Japan to perform in Rose Theater at Jazz at Lincoln Center.
$39,941 to University of Virginia, Charlottesville, VA, 2013. For scriptwriting and research for documentary film titled, The Slow Way Home.
$30,000 to Ohio Northern University, Ada, OH, 2013. For sixth annual US-Japan Camp, offers innovative academically oriented immerson program to American high school students interested in Japanese language and cultural.

7020
The United Ten Foundation, Inc. ✧ ☆
3611 14th Ave., Rm. 400
Brooklyn, NY 11218-3750

Established in 2006 in NY.
Donor: Abraham Hoffman.
Foundation type: Independent foundation.
Financial data (yr. ended 12/31/12): Assets, $1,460,430 (M); gifts received, $800,650; expenditures, $788,319; qualifying distributions, $787,910; giving activities include $787,910 for 12 + grants (high: $702,000).
Fields of interest: Jewish agencies & synagogues.
Limitations: Applications not accepted. Giving primarily in NY.
Application information: Unsolicited requests for funds not accepted.
Officers: Abraham Hoffman, Pres.; Peggy Hoffman, Secy.
EIN: 204263188

7021
Marjorie & Clarence E. Unterberg Foundation, Inc. ✧
c/o Unterberg Capital LLC
126 E. 56th St., 26th Fl.
New York, NY 10022-3613

Established in 1994 in NY.
Donors: Mary A. Debare; Thomas I. Unterberg; Andrew Arno.
Foundation type: Independent foundation.
Financial data (yr. ended 12/31/12): Assets, $7,524,941 (M); gifts received, $2,158,946; expenditures, $1,815,687; qualifying distributions, $1,724,620; giving activities include $1,724,620 for grants.
Fields of interest: Performing arts, theater; Arts; Higher education; Education; Animals/wildlife, preservation/protection; Hospitals (general); Human services; Jewish federated giving programs.
Limitations: Applications not accepted. Giving primarily in NJ and NY. No grants to individuals.
Application information: Contributes only to pre-selected organizations.
Officers: Thomas I. Unterberg, Pres.; Mary A. Debare, V.P. and Secy.; Andrew Arno, Treas.
EIN: 133792809

7022
Uphill Foundation ✧
31 W. 27th St., 4th Fl.
New York, NY 10001-6914

Established in 2000 in PA.
Donor: Frances A. Velay†.
Foundation type: Independent foundation.
Financial data (yr. ended 12/31/12): Assets, $23,281,115 (M); expenditures, $1,580,225; qualifying distributions, $1,322,288; giving activities include $1,235,000 for 18 grants (high: $500,000; low: $15,000).
Purpose and activities: Giving primarily for human services.
Fields of interest: Arts; Education; Environment; Human services; Children/youth, services; International relief; Economically disadvantaged.
Limitations: Applications not accepted. Giving primarily in AR, NY, and VA. No grants to individuals.
Application information: Contributes only to pre-selected organizations.
Trustees: Dan McCarthy; Barbara Paul Robinson; Christophe Velay.
EIN: 137196672

7023
H. van Ameringen Foundation ✧
509 Madison Ave.
New York, NY 10022-5501 (212) 758-6221
Contact: Kenneth A. Kind, Pres.
FAX: (212) 688-2105; E-mail: info@vanamfound.org; E-mail for LOI: Letterofinquiry@vanamfound.org; Main URL: http://www.vanamfound.org/
H. van Ameringen Foundation's Philanthropy Promise: http://www.ncrp.org/philanthropys-promise/who

Established in 1967 in NY.
Donor: Henry P. van Ameringen.
Foundation type: Independent foundation.
Financial data (yr. ended 12/31/13): Assets, $39,681,377 (M); gifts received, $12,426,733; expenditures, $14,149,324; qualifying distributions, $14,144,708; giving activities include $14,134,000 for 122 grants (high: $4,250,000; low: $1,000).
Purpose and activities: Funding for programs in mental-health agencies.
Fields of interest: Media/communications; Vocational education; Education; Health care; Mental health/crisis services; Crime/law enforcement, correctional facilities; Housing/shelter; Family services, domestic violence; Aging, centers/services.
Type of support: General/operating support; Program development; Seed money; Matching/challenge support.
Limitations: Applications accepted. Giving primarily in New York, NY and Philadelphia, PA. No grants to individuals, or for endowments, capital projects, annual fund-raising drives, or in support of international activities and institutions.
Publications: Application guidelines.
Application information: Proposals are by invitation only.
Initial approach: Letter of inquiry
Copies of proposal: 1
Deadline(s): Letter of inquiry: Nov. 10 for Mar. meeting; Mar. 10 for June meeting; and June 10 for Nov. meeting
Board meeting date(s): Mar., June and Nov.
Officers and Directors:* Kenneth A. Kind,* Pres. and Treas.; Steadman Westergaard,* V.P. and Secy.; Eleanor Sypher, Exec. Dir.; Judith Beck; Alexandra Herzan; Christina Kind; Patricia Kind; Andrew Kindfuller; Valerie Kind-Rubin; Laura K McKenna; Clarence J. Sundram; Henry P. van Ameringen.
Number of staff: 1 part-time professional.
EIN: 136215329

7024
van Ameringen Foundation, Inc.
509 Madison Ave.
New York, NY 10022-5501 (212) 758-6221
Contact: Kenneth A. Kind, Pres. and Treas.
FAX: (212) 688-2105; E-mail: info@vanamfound.org; Letter of Inquiry e-mail: Letterofinquiry@vanamfound.org; Main URL: http://www.vanamfound.org/
van Ameringen Foundation's Philanthropy Promise: http://www.ncrp.org/philanthropys-promise/who

Incorporated in 1950 in NY.
Donor: Arnold Louis van Ameringen†.
Foundation type: Independent foundation.
Financial data (yr. ended 12/31/13): Assets, $95,086,433 (M); expenditures, $4,996,823; qualifying distributions, $4,368,793; giving activities include $3,848,500 for 84 grants (high: $250,000; low: $5,000).
Purpose and activities: Grants primarily to promote mental health and social welfare through preventive measures, treatment, and rehabilitation. Support also for the field of psychiatry. Within its broad focus on mental health, the foundation is interested in encouraging and attracting innovative and practical programs in areas which: 1) increase the accessibility of the poor and needy to mental health services; and 2) offer preventative and early intervention strategies.
Fields of interest: Mental health, treatment; Mental health/crisis services; Infants/toddlers; Children/youth; Youth; Aging; Mentally disabled; Hispanics/Latinos; Military/veterans; Offenders/ex-offenders; Crime/abuse victims; Immigrants/refugees; Economically disadvantaged; Homeless.
Type of support: Technical assistance; General/operating support; Management development/capacity building; Program development; Program-related investments/loans; Seed money.
Limitations: Applications accepted. Giving primarily in metropolitan New York, NY, and Philadelphia, PA. No support for international activities and institutions, or for programs for the mentally retarded, the physically handicapped, drug abuse, or alcoholism. No grants or loans to individuals, or for endowments, annual campaigns, deficit financing,

emergency funds, capital campaigns, scholarships, or fellowships.
Publications: Application guidelines; Annual report; Financial statement; Grants list.
Application information: Proposals received after a deadline will not be considered for the upcoming meeting. New York/New Jersey Area Common Application accepted but not required. Application form not required.
Initial approach: Letter of inquiry
Copies of proposal: 1
Deadline(s): For Letters of Inquiry: Mar. 10 (for June meeting), June 10 (for Nov. meeting), and Nov. 10 (for Mar. meeting)
Board meeting date(s): Mar., June, and Nov.
Final notification: Within 60 days
Officers and Directors:* Kenneth A. Kind,* Pres. and Treas.; Steadman Westergaard,* V.P. and Secy.; Eleanor K. Sypher, Exec. Dir.; Judith Beck; Alexandra Herzan; Christina Kind; Patricia Kind; Valerie Kind-Rubin; Andrew Kindfuller; Laura K. McKenna; Clarence J. Sundram; Henry P. van Ameringen.
Number of staff: 1 full-time professional; 1 full-time support.
EIN: 136125699
Selected grants: The following grants are a representative sample of this grantmaker's funding activity:
$150,000 to International Center for Clubhouse Development, New York, NY, 2012. For training and accreditation progams to develop and support strong clubhouses for mentally ill worldwide.
$125,000 to Hamilton-Madison House, New York, NY, 2012. For expansion of psychological internship program to recruit and train five PhD-level interns, who are bilingual, to treat Asian Americans.
$125,000 to Hudson Guild, New York, NY, 2012. For start-up of satellite mental-health clinic at Public School 363 on the Lower East Side.
$70,000 to Housing and Services, New York, NY, 2012. To increase psychiatric hours at two residences for formerly homeless.
$62,000 to Human Development Services of Westchester, Mamaroneck, NY, 2012. For representative payee coordintor who helps housed mentally ill clients with financial management.
$50,000 to Girls Educational and Mentoring Services, New York, NY, 2012. For mental health services for girls and young women who have experienced sexual exploitation and domestic trafficking.
$50,000 to Greenwich House, New York, NY, 2012. For delivery of Child-Parent Psychotherapy for abused and traumatized children, infants to age seven, and their non-offending family members.
$50,000 to Iraq and Afghanistan Veterans of America, New York, NY, 2012. For mental-health awareness, outreach, and advocacy campaign nationwide.
$50,000 to Jewish Family Service Agency of Central New Jersey, Elizabeth, NJ, 2012. For social workers providing play therapy to underserved, emotionally disturbed children, ages 2 to 11, and their families.
$50,000 to Legal Aid Society, New York, NY, 2012. Toward salary of full-time social worker in Immigration Law Unit to address needs of immigrant clients with mental illness, who are often in detention.

7025
The George M. Van Cleave Family Foundation ✧
c/o BCRS Assocs., LLC
100 Water St., 9th Fl.
New York, NY 10005-3701

Established in 2005 in NY.
Donor: George M. Van Cleave.
Foundation type: Independent foundation.
Financial data (yr. ended 12/31/12): Assets, $9,778,356 (M); gifts received, $4,953,005; expenditures, $942,727; qualifying distributions, $789,991; giving activities include $632,280 for 13 grants (high: $450,000; low: $1,000).
Fields of interest: Hospitals (general); Health organizations; Human services; Protestant agencies & churches.
Limitations: Applications not accepted. Giving in the U.S., with emphasis on NY. No grants to individuals.
Application information: Contributes only to pre-selected organizations.
Officers: George M. Van Cleave, Chair.; Karen L. Van Cleave, Pres. and Treas.; Jo Ann Van Cleave, V.P.; Paul R. Van Cleave, V.P.; Diane Beresford, Secy.
EIN: 202789576

7026
The Miles Hodsdon Vernon Foundation, Inc. ✧ ☆
P.O. Box 701
Sleepy Hollow, NY 10591-0701 (914) 923-8499
Contact: Dennis M. Fitzgerald, Pres., Secy., and Dir.

Incorporated in 1953 in NY.
Donors: Miles Hodsdon Vernon†; Martha Hodsdon Kinney†; Louise Hodsdon†.
Foundation type: Independent foundation.
Financial data (yr. ended 12/31/13): Assets, $9,170,330 (M); expenditures, $894,771; qualifying distributions, $529,220; giving activities include $489,500 for 35 grants (high: $80,500; low: $500).
Purpose and activities: Giving primarily for education and human services.
Fields of interest: Secondary school/education; Education; Human services; YM/YWCAs & YM/YWHAs; Children/youth, services; Christian agencies & churches; Economically disadvantaged.
Type of support: Scholarship funds; Research.
Limitations: Applications accepted. Giving primarily in NH, NJ, NY, and PA. No grants to individuals directly.
Application information: Application form required.
Initial approach: Contact foundation for application form
Deadline(s): None
Final notification: Positive responses only
Officers and Directors:* Dennis M. Fitzgerald,* Pres. and Co-Secy.; Linda T. Murray,* V.P. and Co-Secy.; Michele C. Fitzgerald; Eloise T. Schundler.
EIN: 136076836

7027
The G. Unger Vetlesen Foundation ✧
c/o Fulton, Rowe, & Hart
1 Rockefeller Plz., Ste. 301
New York, NY 10020-2002 (212) 586-0700
Contact: Ambrose K. Monell, Pres.
FAX: (212) 245-1863;
E-mail: info@monellvetlesen.org; Main URL: http://www.monellvetlesen.org/

Incorporated in 1955 in NY.
Donor: George Unger Vetlesen†.
Foundation type: Independent foundation.
Financial data (yr. ended 12/31/13): Assets, $151,620,365 (M); expenditures, $6,231,617; qualifying distributions, $5,700,911; giving activities include $5,532,500 for 29 grants (high: $600,000; low: $2,500).
Purpose and activities: Established a biennial international science award for discoveries in the earth sciences; grants for biological, geophysical, and environmental research, including scholarships, and cultural organizations, including those emphasizing Norwegian-American relations and maritime interests. Support also for public policy research and libraries.
Fields of interest: Arts; Libraries/library science; Environment; Marine science; Physical/earth sciences; Engineering/technology; Biology/life sciences; Science; Public policy, research.
Type of support: General/operating support; Continuing support; Annual campaigns; Capital campaigns; Building/renovation; Equipment; Endowments; Program development; Professorships; Scholarship funds; Research.
Limitations: Applications accepted. Giving primarily in NY; some giving in other areas. No grants to individuals.
Publications: Application guidelines; Annual report; Financial statement; Grants list.
Application information: Full proposals are accepted by invitation only following positive response to letter of inquiry. Unsolicited full proposals will not be reviewed. Application form not required.
Initial approach: Letter of inquiry (not exceeding 3 pages)
Copies of proposal: 1
Deadline(s): None for letters of inquiry; Apr. 30 and Oct. 31 for full proposals
Board meeting date(s): June and Dec.
Final notification: Positive responses are sent within 4-6 weeks
Officers and Directors:* Ambrose K. Monell,* Pres. and Treas.; Maurizio J. Morello, Exec. V.P.; Eugene P. Grisanti,* V.P.; Kristen G. Pemberton, Secy.; Dr. Gary K. Beauchamp.
EIN: 131982695

7028
VHIV, Inc. ✧
(formerly The Bella Wexner Charitable Foundation)
477 Madison Ave., 10th Fl.
New York, NY 10022-5841

Established in 1990 in OH.
Donors: Bella Wexner; Susan R. Wexner Revocable Trust.
Foundation type: Independent foundation.
Financial data (yr. ended 12/31/13): Assets, $43,227,495 (M); expenditures, $2,081,059; qualifying distributions, $1,923,071; giving activities include $1,911,782 for 15 grants (high: $500,000; low: $33).
Fields of interest: Youth development; Jewish federated giving programs; Jewish agencies & synagogues.
International interests: Israel.

Limitations: Applications not accepted. Giving in Israel. No grants to individuals.
Application information: Contributes only to pre-selected organizations.
Officer and Directors:* Susan R. Wexner,* Pres. and Secy.-Treas.; Saul G. Agus; Raymond Kanner; Gregg H. Levy, Esq.; Michael S. Oberman, Esq.; Mark Saks, Esq.; Walter Stern.
EIN: 311324522

7029
The Harriet and Esteban Vicente Foundation, Inc. ✧
110 W. 40th St., Ste. 402
New York, NY 10018-8572 (914) 834-2272
Contact: Robert S. Warshaw; Susan Newman
FAX: (914) 834-2207;
E-mail: rwarshaw@fifthavenuelaw.com

Established in 2001 in NY.
Donors: Harriet G. Vicente‡; Harriet Vincente Revocable Trust.
Foundation type: Independent foundation.
Financial data (yr. ended 12/31/12): Assets, $18,782,453 (M); gifts received, $733,209; expenditures, $1,643,430; qualifying distributions, $1,557,326; giving activities include $747,823 for 7 grants (high: $342,295; low: $100).
Fields of interest: Museums (art); Human services; Jewish federated giving programs.
Limitations: Applications not accepted. Giving primarily in NY and in Madrid, Spain.
Application information: Contributes only to pre-selected organizations.
Officers and Trustees:* Robert S. Warshaw,* Chair. and Secy.; Michael R. Stein,* Pres. and Treas.; Kevin Consey, Exec. Dir.
Number of staff: 2 full-time professional; 2 part-time professional.
EIN: 134182614

7030
The Vidda Foundation ✧
250 W. 57th St., Ste. 1928
New York, NY 10107-1914
Contact: John B. Roberts, Admin.
E-mail: info@vidda.org; Main URL: http://www.vidda.org

Established in 1979 in NY.
Donor: Ursula Corning‡.
Foundation type: Independent foundation.
Financial data (yr. ended 05/31/13): Assets, $9,696,188 (M); gifts received, $251; expenditures, $891,192; qualifying distributions, $824,779; giving activities include $751,500 for 40 grants (high: $175,000; low: $2,500).
Purpose and activities: Giving primarily for supporting programs that will have a lasting impact in the areas of conservation, education, health care, human services and the arts.
Fields of interest: Humanities; Arts; Education; Environment, beautification programs; Environment; Animal welfare; Animals/wildlife, preservation/protection; Medical care, in-patient care; Human services; Children/youth, services; Aging, centers/services; Economic development; Community/economic development; Protestant agencies & churches.
Type of support: General/operating support; Continuing support; Annual campaigns; Building/renovation; Endowments; Program development; Seed money; Research.
Limitations: Applications accepted. Giving primarily in NY. No grants to individuals.
Publications: Application guidelines; Financial statement.
Application information: New York/New Jersey Area Common Grant Application Form is required from proposed grantees that receive a positive response to their letter of intent. Please refer to application guidelines on foundation web site; telephone calls, or faxed or e-mailed letters of interest are not accepted. Application form not required.
Initial approach: Letter of interest (2 pages maximum)
Copies of proposal: 1
Deadline(s): None (for letters of interest)
Board meeting date(s): Nov. and May
Final notification: Approximately 3 months
Officer and Trustees:* Gerald E. Rupp,* Chair.; John A. Downey, M.D.; Stephen Evans; Helen C. Evarts; Ian H. Fraser; John B. Roberts.
EIN: 132981105
Selected grants: The following grants are a representative sample of this grantmaker's funding activity:
$175,000 to Columbia University, New York, NY, 2011. For unrestricted operating grant.
$80,000 to American Museum of Natural History, New York, NY, 2011.
$25,000 to Central Park Conservancy, New York, NY, 2011. For unrestricted operating grant.
$25,000 to Madison Avenue Presbyterian Church, New York, NY, 2011. For unrestricted operating grant.
$25,000 to Student Conservation Association, Charlestown, NH, 2011.
$15,000 to Wildlife Conservation Society, Bronx, NY, 2011. For unrestricted operating grant.
$10,000 to Bhutan Foundation, Washington, DC, 2011.
$10,000 to Childrens Tumor Foundation, New York, NY, 2011. For unrestricted operating grant.
$10,000 to Fountain House, New York, NY, 2011. For unrestricted operating grant.
$10,000 to New York City Marble Cemetery, New York, NY, 2011. For unrestricted operating grant.

7031
The Vilcek Foundation, Inc. ✧
(formerly The Friderika Fischer Foundation)
167 E. 73rd St.
New York, NY 10021-4160 (212) 472-2500
Contact: Rick A. Kinsel, Exec. Dir.
FAX: (212) 472-4720; E-mail: info@vilcek.org; Main URL: http://www.vilcek.org
Facebook: http://www.facebook.com/vilcekfoundation
Grants List: http://www.vilcek.org/about/grants.html
Twitter: https://twitter.com/Vilcek
YouTube: http://www.youtube.com/user/VilcekFoundation

Established in 2000 in NY. Classified as a private operating foundation in 2001.
Donor: Jan Vilcek.
Foundation type: Operating foundation.
Financial data (yr. ended 11/30/13): Assets, $114,955,867 (M); gifts received, $1,135,005; expenditures, $4,214,841; qualifying distributions, $5,036,647; giving activities include $255,332 for 14 grants (high: $55,299; low: $3,000), $410,000 for 9 grants to individuals (high: $100,000; low: $35,000), and $1,998,682 for foundation-administered programs.
Purpose and activities: The foundation honors foreign-born scientists and artists living in the U.S. who have made outstanding contributions to U.S. society that benefit mankind. Each year the foundation bestows upon certain individuals the Vilcek Prize to honor such achievement in biomedical research and in arts or humanities. Giving primarily for higher education and to fund a research project to develop treatments for chronic inflammatory auto-immune diseases.
Fields of interest: Media, film/video; Arts; Higher education; Medical school/education; Medical research, institute.
Type of support: Conferences/seminars; Research.
Limitations: Applications not accepted. Giving in the U.S., with some emphasis on CA, HI, NM, NY, OK and TX.
Publications: Grants list.
Application information: Unsolicited requests for funds not accepted.
Officers and Directors:* Jan Vilcek, M.D, Ph.D.*, Pres. and Treas.; Marica Vilcek,* V.P. and Secy.; Rick A. Kinsel,* Exec. Dir.; Richard Gaddes; S. Peter Ludwig; Joan Massague; Christina Mossaides Strassfield.
Number of staff: 4 full-time professional.
EIN: 510404790

7032
The Viola Fund ✧
(formerly The Mandrake Fund)
c/o Alan S. Honig, C.P.A.
1501 Broadway, Ste. 1313
New York, NY 10036-5505

Established in 1987 in NY.
Donors: Milton A. Kimmelman; Abby K. Leigh; Mitch Leigh.
Foundation type: Independent foundation.
Financial data (yr. ended 12/31/13): Assets, $12,601,280 (M); gifts received, $1,715,464; expenditures, $781,531; qualifying distributions, $712,000; giving activities include $712,000 for 20 + grants (high: $350,000).
Fields of interest: Arts; Education; Environment; Health care; Human services.
Limitations: Applications not accepted. No grants to individuals.
Application information: Unsolicited requests for funds not accepted.
Trustees: Abby K. Leigh; David Leigh; Mitch Leigh; Rebecca Leigh.
EIN: 133398045

7033
Vital Projects Fund, Inc. ✧
c/o Robert B. Menschel
375 Park Ave., Ste. 1602
New York, NY 10152-1600

Established in 1992 in NY, funded in 2006.
Donor: Horace W. Goldsmith‡.
Foundation type: Independent foundation.
Financial data (yr. ended 12/31/13): Assets, $291,788,646 (M); expenditures, $12,825,425; qualifying distributions, $11,780,177; giving activities include $11,257,000 for 121 grants (high: $900,000; low: $10,000).

Purpose and activities: The fund primarily supports cultural programs, including performing arts and museums, support also for hospitals, and higher education.
Fields of interest: Visual arts; Museums; Performing arts, dance; Performing arts, theater; Performing arts, music; Arts; Education, research; Higher education; Libraries/library science; Education; Environment, natural resources; Hospitals (general); Medical care, rehabilitation; Health care; Medical research, institute; Cancer research; AIDS research; Medical research; Crime/law enforcement; Human services; Homeless, human services; International relief; Disabilities, people with.
Type of support: General/operating support; Continuing support; Income development; Annual campaigns; Capital campaigns; Building/renovation; Land acquisition; Endowments; Debt reduction; Emergency funds; Professorships; Curriculum development; Fellowships; Scholarship funds; Research; Matching/challenge support.
Limitations: Applications not accepted. Giving on a national basis. No grants to individuals, or for scholarships or loans to individuals.
Application information: Unsolicited requests for funds not accepted.
Officers and Directors:* Robert B. Menschel,* Chair. and Treas.; David F. Menschel,* Pres.; Lauren E. Menschel, Secy.; Richard B. Menschel; Ronay Menschel.
Number of staff: 1 part-time professional; 3 part-time support.
EIN: 133711340
Selected grants: The following grants are a representative sample of this grantmaker's funding activity:
$900,000 to Metropolitan Museum of Art, New York, NY, 2013.
$750,000 to New York-Presbyterian Hospital, Weill Cornell Medical School, New York, NY, 2013.
$275,000 to Texas Defender Service, Austin, TX, 2013.
$200,000 to New York-Presbyterian Hospital, North Campus, New York, NY, 2013.
$150,000 to American Civil Liberties Union Foundation, New York, NY, 2013.
$100,000 to Equal Justice Initiative of Alabama, Montgomery, AL, 2013.
$50,000 to Mayo Clinic, Rochester, MN, 2013.
$50,000 to Public Art Fund, New York, NY, 2013.
$50,000 to Southern Center for Human Rights, Atlanta, GA, 2013.
$50,000 to Yale University, Yale Law School, New Haven, CT, 2013.

7034
The John and Barbara Vogelstein Foundation ✧
(formerly John L. Vogelstein Charitable Trust)
c/o Warburg Pincus
450 Lexington Ave., 32nd Fl.
New York, NY 10017-3904

Established in 1999 in NY.
Donors: John L. Vogelstein Revocable Trust; John L. Vogelstein.
Foundation type: Independent foundation.
Financial data (yr. ended 11/30/13): Assets, $3,019,050 (M); gifts received, $6,344,914; expenditures, $4,483,301; qualifying distributions, $4,432,000; giving activities include $4,432,000 for 72 grants (high: $1,000,000; low: $1,000).
Purpose and activities: Giving primarily for education, and the arts, particularly the performing arts as well as for health and human services.
Fields of interest: Museums (art); Performing arts, ballet; Arts; Elementary/secondary education; Higher education; Education; Hospitals (general); Reproductive health, family planning; Health organizations, association; Medical research, association; Human services; Children/youth, services; Jewish agencies & synagogues.
Limitations: Applications not accepted. Giving primarily in the metropolitan New York, NY, area. No grants to individuals.
Application information: Contributes only to pre-selected organizations. Unsolicited requests for funds are not accepted.
Trustees: Andrew A. Vogelstein; Barbara Manfrey Vogelstein; Hans A. Vogelstein; John L. Vogelstein.
EIN: 137177278

7035
The Volcker Family Foundation, Inc. ✧ ☆
c/o Hill Rivkins & Hayden, LLP
45 Broadway, Ste. 1500
New York, NY 10006-3007
Application address: c/o Paul A. Volcker, 610 5th Ave., Ste. 410, New York, NY 10020, tel.: (212) 218-7878

Established in 1996 in DE.
Donor: Paul A. Volcker.
Foundation type: Independent foundation.
Financial data (yr. ended 12/31/13): Assets, $4,561,639 (M); expenditures, $5,319,168; qualifying distributions, $5,305,000; giving activities include $5,305,000 for 2 grants (high: $5,300,000; low: $5,000).
Purpose and activities: Giving primarily for educational and medical organizations.
Fields of interest: Higher education; Education; Health care; International affairs.
Limitations: Applications accepted. Giving primarily in Washington, DC, NJ and New York, NY.
Officers and Directors:* Paul A. Volcker,* Pres.; Ernesto V. Luzzatto, Secy.-Treas.; Anthony J. Dowd; James P. Volcker; Janis Volcker Zima.
EIN: 133917327

7036
Barry and Teri Volpert Foundation ✧ ☆
c/o BCRS Associates, LLC
77 Water St., 9th Fl.
New York, NY 10005-4414

Established in 1995 in NY.
Donor: Barry S. Volpert.
Foundation type: Independent foundation.
Financial data (yr. ended 08/31/13): Assets, $2,920,636 (M); expenditures, $671,890; qualifying distributions, $652,982; giving activities include $645,191 for 78 grants (high: $100,000; low: $25).
Purpose and activities: Giving primarily for higher education, the arts, and Jewish organizations.
Fields of interest: Museums; Museums (art); Museums (ethnic/folk arts); Arts; Higher education; Education; Human services; Jewish federated giving programs; Jewish agencies & synagogues.
Limitations: Applications not accepted. Giving primarily in NY. No grants to individuals.
Application information: Contributes only to pre-selected organizations.
Trustees: Joel Beckman; Barry S. Volpert; Teri C. Volpert.
EIN: 133802670
Selected grants: The following grants are a representative sample of this grantmaker's funding activity:
$460,000 to Amherst College, Amherst, MA, 2011. For general purpose.
$35,000 to Jewish Museum, New York, NY, 2011. For general purpose.
$25,000 to FINCA International, Washington, DC, 2011. For general purpose.
$20,000 to Jewish Museum, New York, NY, 2011. For general purpose.
$12,500 to Jewish Museum, New York, NY, 2011. For general purpose.
$7,450 to Congregation Rodeph Sholom, New York, NY, 2011. For general purpose.
$2,500 to American Museum of Natural History, New York, NY, 2011. For general purpose.
$2,500 to Congregation Rodeph Sholom, New York, NY, 2011. For general purpose.
$1,780 to Jewish Museum, New York, NY, 2011. For general purpose.
$1,000 to College Summit, Washington, DC, 2011. For general purpose.

7037
The von der Heyden Family Foundation ✧ ☆
25 Central Park West, Ste. 24K
New York, NY 10023-7200

Established in 1994 in CT.
Donors: Ingolf M. von der Heyden; Karl M. von der Heyden.
Foundation type: Independent foundation.
Financial data (yr. ended 12/31/13): Assets, $4,132,381 (M); gifts received, $355,454; expenditures, $676,622; qualifying distributions, $669,501; giving activities include $661,824 for 32 grants (high: $326,546; low: $50).
Purpose and activities: Giving primarily for education.
Fields of interest: Arts; Education; Human services.
Limitations: Applications not accepted. Giving primarily in NC and NY. No grants to individuals.
Application information: Contributes only to pre-selected organizations.
Trustees: D. James Gillespie; Ellen M. Gillespie; Eric M. von der Heyden; Heike von der Heyden; Karl M. von der Heyden; Mary Ellen von der Heyden.
EIN: 061410915

7038
Voya Foundation ✧
(formerly ING Foundation)
230 Park Ave., 15th Fl.
New York, NY 10169
Contact: Rhoda Mims, Pres.; Chip Wheeler, Dir. Community Rels.
E-mail: voyafoundation@voya.com; Main URL: http://ing.us/about-ing/responsibility

Established in 1990 in MN.
Donors: ReliaStar Financial Corp.; Northern Life Insurance Co.; ReliaStar Bankers Security Life Insurance Co.; ReliaStar United Services Life Insurance Co.; ReliaStar Life Insurance Co.

Foundation type: Company-sponsored foundation.
Financial data (yr. ended 12/31/12): Assets, $2,049,840 (M); gifts received, $5,020,478; expenditures, $2,632,651; qualifying distributions, $2,633,058; giving activities include $2,592,641 for 2,196 grants (high: $569,100; low: $3).
Purpose and activities: The foundation supports programs designed to promote financial literacy and children's education.
Fields of interest: Elementary/secondary education; Education; Disasters, preparedness/services; Girls clubs; Youth development, business; Children/youth, services; Human services, financial counseling; Economic development; Children/youth; Minorities; Economically disadvantaged.
Type of support: Continuing support; Program development; Conferences/seminars; Scholarship funds; Research; Cause-related marketing; Employee volunteer services; Sponsorships; Program evaluation; Employee matching gifts.
Limitations: Applications accepted. Giving on a national basis in areas of company operations, with emphasis on CA, CO, CT, DE, FL, GA, MA, MN, NY, PA, and TX; giving also to national organizations. No support for religious organizations not of direct benefit to the entire community, private foundations, fraternal organizations, social clubs, labor organizations, lobbying or political organizations, sports teams, or discriminatory organizations. No grants to individuals, or for capital campaigns, endowments, general or administrative costs, institutional, civic, or commemorative advertising, fashion shows, pageants, golf tournaments, athletic events, conferences, workshops, or other meetings, travel, benefits, performances, testimonial dinners, or other fundraising activities.
Publications: Annual report (including application guidelines); Informational brochure.
Application information: Mailed, e-mailed, or hard copy applications are not accepted. Requests under $2,500 are not considered. Additional information may be requested at a later date. Support is limited to 1 contribution per organization during any given year. Multi-year funding is not automatic. Organizations receiving support are asked to submit twice-yearly impact data. Application form required.
Initial approach: Complete online application form
Deadline(s): May 15, Aug. 29, and Nov. 7
Board meeting date(s): Feb., May, Aug., and Nov.
Final notification: June 15 and Sept. 14
Officers and Directors:* Rodney O. Martin,* Chair.; Rhoda Mims,* Pres.; Jennifer Ogren, Secy.; David S. Pendergrass,* Treas.; Mary E. Beams; Jeffery T. Becker; Donald W. Britton; Bridget M. Healy; Alain Karaoglan; Kevin D. Silva; Michael Smith; Ewout Steenbergen.
Number of staff: None.
EIN: 411682766

7039
Sue and Edgar Wachenheim Foundation ✧
3 Manhattanville Rd.
Purchase, NY 10577-2116
Contact: Edgar Wachenheim III, C.E.O. and Pres.

Established in 1969 in NY.
Donors: Sue W. Wachenheim; Edgar Wachenheim III; Greenhaven Assocs.
Foundation type: Independent foundation.
Financial data (yr. ended 10/31/13): Assets, $207,299,587 (M); expenditures, $7,208,400; qualifying distributions, $7,206,400; giving activities include $7,204,400 for 44 grants (high: $4,000,000; low: $100).
Purpose and activities: Giving primarily for higher education and for health and human services.
Fields of interest: Arts; Higher education; Libraries/library science; Education; Health care; Human services.
Type of support: Annual campaigns; Capital campaigns; Building/renovation; Scholarship funds.
Limitations: Applications not accepted. Giving primarily in NY. No grants to individuals.
Application information: Contributes only to pre-selected organizations.
Officers and Directors:* Edgar Wachenheim III,* C.E.O. and Pres.; Sue W. Wachenheim,* V.P.; Kim Wachenheim Wagman,* Secy.; Lance R. Wachenheim,* Treas.; Chris A. Wachenheim.
Number of staff: None.
EIN: 237011002
Selected grants: The following grants are a representative sample of this grantmaker's funding activity:
$4,000,000 to Metropolitan Museum of Art, New York, NY, 2013. For general support.
$1,250,000 to Metropolitan Museum of Art, New York, NY, 2013. For general support.
$1,000,000 to Metropolitan Museum of Art, New York, NY, 2012. For general support.
$1,000,000 to Metropolitan Museum of Art, New York, NY, 2012. For general support.
$1,000,000 to Metropolitan Museum of Art, New York, NY, 2012. For general support.
$420,000 to Metropolitan Museum of Art, New York, NY, 2012. For general support.
$400,000 to New York Public Library, New York, NY, 2013. For general support.
$350,000 to Williams College, Williamstown, MA, 2012. For general support.
$350,000 to Williams College, Williamstown, MA, 2012. For general support.
$302,500 to Skidmore College, Saratoga Springs, NY, 2012. For general support.
$300,000 to Skidmore College, Saratoga Springs, NY, 2013. For general support.
$200,000 to Metropolitan Museum of Art, New York, NY, 2013. For general support.
$125,000 to Metropolitan Museum of Art, New York, NY, 2013. For general support.
$125,000 to Metropolitan Museum of Art, New York, NY, 2013. For general support.
$125,000 to New York Public Library, New York, NY, 2012. For general support.
$125,000 to New York Public Library, New York, NY, 2013. For general support.
$102,500 to Rye Country Day School, Rye, NY, 2013. For general support.
$100,000 to Metropolitan Museum of Art, New York, NY, 2013. For general support.
$77,500 to Rye Country Day School, Rye, NY, 2012. For general support.
$50,000 to Metropolitan Museum of Art, New York, NY, 2012. For general support.

7040
Wachtell, Lipton, Rosen & Katz Foundation ✧
51 W. 52nd St.
New York, NY 10019-6119

Established in 1981 in NY.
Donor: Wachtell, Lipton, Rosen & Katz.
Foundation type: Company-sponsored foundation.
Financial data (yr. ended 09/30/13): Assets, $18,411,365 (M); gifts received, $10,000,209; expenditures, $1,850,659; qualifying distributions, $1,850,250; giving activities include $1,850,000 for grants (high: $1,050,000; low: $25,000).
Purpose and activities: The foundation supports medical centers and organizations involved with education, 9/11 memorials, justice, law, Judaism, and people of color.
Fields of interest: Health care; Medical research; Human services.
Type of support: General/operating support; Annual campaigns; Scholarship funds.
Limitations: Applications not accepted. Giving limited to New York, NY. No grants to individuals.
Application information: Contributes only to pre-selected organizations.
Board meeting date(s): As necessary
Officers and Directors:* Martin Lipton,* Pres.; Herbert M. Wachtell,* V.P. and Secy.; Constance Monte,* V.P. and Treas.; Edward D. Herlihy,* V.P.; Daniel A. Neff,* V.P.; Jodi D. Schwartz,* V.P.
EIN: 133099901
Selected grants: The following grants are a representative sample of this grantmaker's funding activity:
$303,600 to Legal Aid Society, New York, NY, 2011.
$300,000 to New York University Langone Medical Center, New York, NY, 2011.
$300,000 to Prep for Prep, New York, NY, 2011.
$150,000 to New York University, New York, NY, 2011.
$104,000 to Childrens Aid Society, New York, NY, 2011.
$35,000 to University of Chicago, School of Law, Chicago, IL, 2011.
$30,000 to University of Pennsylvania, School of Law, Philadelphia, PA, 2011.
$25,000 to Prodigal Sons and Daughters Redirection Services, East Orange, NJ, 2011.
$25,000 to Stanford University, Law School, Stanford, CA, 2011.
$10,000 to George Washington University, School of Law, Washington, DC, 2011.

7041
The Walbridge Fund ✧
c/o Arthur Yorke Allen
1095 Park Ave.
New York, NY 10128-1154

Established in 1997 in NY.
Donor: George W. Perkins, Jr.‡.
Foundation type: Independent foundation.
Financial data (yr. ended 12/31/13): Assets, $84,251,231 (M); expenditures, $6,239,334; qualifying distributions, $5,872,000; giving activities include $5,872,000 for 83 grants (high: $1,000,000; low: $5,000).
Purpose and activities: Giving primarily for education, human services, and the environment.
Fields of interest: Arts; Education; Environment, natural resources; Health organizations, association; Human services.
Limitations: Applications not accepted. Giving primarily in NY and UT. No grants to individuals.
Application information: Contributes only to pre-selected organizations.
Officers: Jennifer P. Speers, Pres.; Nancy F. Perkins, V.P.; Harriet Savage, Secy.; Arthur Yorke Allen, Treas.
EIN: 133936131

Selected grants: The following grants are a representative sample of this grantmaker's funding activity:
$725,000 to Dutchess Day School, Millbrook, NY, 2011. For general support.
$200,000 to Glynwood Center, Cold Spring, NY, 2011. For general support.
$150,000 to Scenic Hudson, Poughkeepsie, NY, 2011. For general support.
$50,000 to Foundation for Community Health, Sharon, CT, 2011. For general support.
$50,000 to Millbrook Fire Department, Millbrook, NY, 2011. For general support.
$35,000 to Tracy Aviary, Salt Lake City, UT, 2011. For general support.
$25,000 to American Agora Foundation, New York, NY, 2011. For general support.
$25,000 to American Council on Germany, New York, NY, 2011. For general support.
$21,000 to New York Theological Seminary, New York, NY, 2011. For general support.
$15,000 to Utah Rivers Council, Salt Lake City, UT, 2011. For general support.

7042
Walentas Foundation, Ltd. ✧ ☆
45 Main St., Ste.602
Brooklyn, NY 11201-1099 (718) 222-2500
Contact: David C. Walentas, Pres. and Treas.

Donors: David C. Walentas; Jane L. Walentas.
Foundation type: Independent foundation.
Financial data (yr. ended 12/31/13): Assets, $0 (M); gifts received, $960,000; expenditures, $968,753; qualifying distributions, $968,753; giving activities include $944,705 for 65 grants (high: $155,000; low: $1,000).
Fields of interest: Arts; Education; Environment.
Limitations: Applications accepted. Giving primarily in New York, NY.
Application information: Application form required.
Initial approach: Proposal
Deadline(s): Feb 28.
Officers: David C. Walentas, Pres.and Treas.; Jed Walentas, V.P.; Jane L. Walentas, Secy.
EIN: 455331864

7043
The Wallace Foundation ✧
(formerly Wallace-Reader's Digest Funds)
5 Penn Plz., 7th Fl.
New York, NY 10001-1837 (212) 251-9700
Contact: Grants Admin.
FAX: (212) 679-6990;
E-mail: grantrequest@wallacefoundation.org; Main URL: http://www.wallacefoundation.org
Facebook: https://www.facebook.com/pages/The-Wallace-Foundation/376102262278
Google Plus: https://plus.google.com/118367860292395448396/posts
Grants Database: http://www.wallacefoundation.org/learn-about-wallace/GrantsPrograms/our-grantees/Pages/default.aspx
Knowledge Center: http://www.wallacefoundation.org/KnowledgeCenter/Pages/default.aspx
Pinterest: http://pinterest.com/wallacefdn/
RSS Feed: http://www.wallacefoundation.org/Pages/rss-feed.aspx
The Wallace Foundation's Philanthropy Promise: http://www.ncrp.org/philanthropys-promise/who
Twitter: http://twitter.com/WallaceFdn
YouTube: http://www.youtube.com/WallaceFdn

The Wallace Foundation is the current manifestation of the philanthropic legacy of DeWitt and Lila Acheson Wallace, who created a series of family foundations in the mid 1950s and 1960s. By 2003, the various foundations had merged and adopted the current name. Immediately prior to this merger, there were two foundations known as the Lila Wallace-Reader's Digest Fund and the DeWitt Wallace-Reader's Digest Fund.
Donors: DeWitt Wallace†; Lila Acheson Wallace†.
Foundation type: Independent foundation.
Financial data (yr. ended 12/31/13): Assets, $1,514,962,198 (M); gifts received, $1,594,938; expenditures, $73,367,260; qualifying distributions, $61,462,148; giving activities include $61,436,628 for 169 grants (high: $4,000,000; low: $250), and $25,520 for employee matching gifts.
Purpose and activities: The Wallace Foundation seeks to improve education and enrichment for disadvantaged children. The foundation has an unusual approach: funding projects to test innovative ideas for solving important social problems, conducting research to find out what works and what doesn't and to fill key knowledge gaps; and then communicating the results to help others.
Fields of interest: Arts; Education, services; Education, community/cooperative; Education; Leadership development; Children/youth.
Type of support: General/operating support; Program development; Conferences/seminars; Publication; Research; Technical assistance; Program evaluation; Employee matching gifts.
Limitations: Applications accepted. Giving on a national basis. No support for religious or fraternal organizations; environmental or conservation programs, health, medical or social service programs, international programs, or for private foundations. No grants to individuals, or for annual funds, emergency funds, capital campaigns, historical restorations, or deficit financing.
Publications: Annual report (including application guidelines); Financial statement; Grants list; Occasional report; Program policy statement (including application guidelines).
Application information: Unsolicited proposals are rarely funded. Application guidelines can be found on foundation web site.
Initial approach: E-mail
Deadline(s): None
Officers and Directors:* Kevin W. Kennedy,* Chair.; William I. Miller,* Pres.; Kenneth Austin, Corp. Secy. and Sr. Counsel; Stacy. J. Martin, C.F.O. and Treas.; Rob D. Nagel, C.I.O.; Lawrence T. Babbio, Jr.; Candace K. Beinecke; Linda Darling-Hammond; Augusta Souza Kappner; Ann S. Moore; Joseph W. Polisi; Debora L. Spar; Amor H. Towles; Mary Beth West.
Number of staff: 36 full-time professional; 7 full-time support.
EIN: 136183757
Selected grants: The following grants are a representative sample of this grantmaker's funding activity:
$3,740,000 to EdVestors, Boston, MA, 2012. For arts learning for children in Boston Public Schools.
$2,443,000 to RAND Corporation, Santa Monica, CA, 2012. To conduct evaluation of six school districts summer learning programs and produce public report.
$1,800,000 to Charlotte-Mecklenburg Board of Education, Charlotte, NC, 2012. To participate in Wallace's Principal Pipeline initiative.
$1,000,000 to Pittsburgh Public Schools, Pittsburgh, PA, 2012. For Summer Learning Program, as part of Wallace Summer Learning District Demonstration Project.
$765,000 to Grand Rapids, City of, Grand Rapids, MI, 2012. To participate in Wallace's System Building Initiative.
$250,000 to Council of the Great City Schools, Washington, DC, 2012. To conduct analysis of instructional superintendent position in six Principal Pipeline districts.
$200,000 to Education Development Center, New York, NY, 2012.
$150,000 to Education Trust, Washington, DC, 2012. For conferences.
$125,000 to After School Matters, Chicago, IL, 2012. To create cash reserve fund for organizations receiving intensive financial management training in Strengthening Financial Management Initiative.

7044
Mary and James G. Wallach Foundation ✧
3 Manhattanville Rd.
Purchase, NY 10577-2116

Established in 1968 in NY.
Donors: James G. Wallach; Asgot Securities, Inc.
Foundation type: Independent foundation.
Financial data (yr. ended 10/31/13): Assets, $44,602,179 (M); expenditures, $1,901,735; qualifying distributions, $1,820,841; giving activities include $1,788,106 for 32 grants (high: $853,072; low: $460).
Fields of interest: Museums (art); Performing arts, orchestras; Arts; Education; Health care; Human services; Jewish agencies & synagogues.
Limitations: Applications not accepted. Giving primarily in NY. No grants to individuals.
Application information: Contributes only to pre-selected organizations.
Officers: Mary Wallach, Pres.; Andrew Wallach, V.P.; Kenneth Wallach, V.P.; Scott Wallach, V.P.; Howard Herman, Secy.-Treas.
EIN: 136278694
Selected grants: The following grants are a representative sample of this grantmaker's funding activity:
$246,900 to Philharmonic-Symphony Society of New York, New York, NY, 2011. For general purpose.
$83,000 to Central Park Conservancy, New York, NY, 2011. For general purpose.
$32,500 to Westchester Community College Foundation, Valhalla, NY, 2011. For general purpose.
$25,000 to New York Public Library, New York, NY, 2011. For general purpose.
$24,755 to Metropolitan Opera, New York, NY, 2011. For general purpose.
$20,500 to Columbia University, New York, NY, 2011. For general purpose.
$10,875 to Rockefeller University, New York, NY, 2011. For general purpose.
$8,813 to Metropolitan Museum of Art, New York, NY, 2011. For general purpose.
$8,000 to Japan Society, New York, NY, 2011. For general purpose.

$6,500 to Urban Assembly, New York, NY, 2011. For general purpose.

7045
The Mark A. & Lisa J. Walsh Foundation ✧
c/o DDK & Co., LLP
1 Penn Plz., 54th Fl.
New York, NY 10119-0002

Established in 2005 in NY.
Donors: Mark A. Walsh; Lisa J. Walsh.
Foundation type: Independent foundation.
Financial data (yr. ended 12/31/12): Assets, $9,009,715 (M); gifts received, $3,008,264; expenditures, $720,636; qualifying distributions, $695,500; giving activities include $695,500 for grants.
Fields of interest: Higher education; Education; Health organizations, association; Cancer; Medical research, institute.
Type of support: General/operating support.
Limitations: Applications not accepted. Giving primarily in CA, CT and NY. No grants to individuals.
Application information: Contributes only to pre-selected organizations.
Trustees: Lisa J. Walsh; Mark A. Walsh.
EIN: 203911283

7046
The Rosalind P. Walter Foundation ✧
435 E. 52nd St.
New York, NY 10022-6445

Established in 1951 as the Walter Foundation.
Donors: Henry G. Walter, Jr.†; Rosalind P. Walter.
Foundation type: Independent foundation.
Financial data (yr. ended 12/31/13): Assets, $1,984,511 (M); gifts received, $1,707,970; expenditures, $2,082,627; qualifying distributions, $2,067,660; giving activities include $2,065,650 for 38 grants (high: $400,000; low: $150).
Fields of interest: Media/communications; Media, television; Museums (natural history); Higher education; Animals/wildlife; Athletics/sports, racquet sports; Boys & girls clubs; Human services; United Ways and Federated Giving Programs.
Limitations: Applications not accepted. Giving primarily in NY. No grants to individuals.
Application information: Contributes only to pre-selected organizations.
Trustee: Rosalind P. Walter.
EIN: 136177284
Selected grants: The following grants are a representative sample of this grantmaker's funding activity:
$100,000 to Long Island University, Brookville, NY, 2011.
$4,500 to Long Island University, Brookville, NY, 2011.

7047
The Wang Family Charitable Foundation ✧ ☆
P.O. Box 5028
New York, NY 10150-5028

Established in NY.
Foundation type: Independent foundation.
Financial data (yr. ended 10/31/13): Assets, $825,319 (M); expenditures, $705,042; qualifying distributions, $704,732; giving activities include $704,732 for 3 grants (high: $500,000; low: $4,732).
Fields of interest: Arts; Education; Health care.
Type of support: General/operating support.
Limitations: Applications not accepted. Giving primarily in MA, New York, NY and PA. No grants to individuals.
Application information: Contributes only to pre-selected organizations.
Trustee: Oded Aboodi.
EIN: 133192845
Selected grants: The following grants are a representative sample of this grantmaker's funding activity:
$500,000 to New York-Presbyterian Hospital, New York, NY, 2013. For general purposes.
$200,000 to University of Pennsylvania, Philadelphia, PA, 2013. For scholarships.
$4,732 to Solomon R. Guggenheim Foundation, New York, NY, 2013. For general purposes.

7048
The Warburg Pincus Foundation ✧
450 Lexington Ave., 32nd Fl.
New York, NY 10017-3200

Established in 2000 in NY.
Donors: Warburg Pincus Partners LLC; Warburg Pincus & Co.
Foundation type: Company-sponsored foundation.
Financial data (yr. ended 11/30/12): Assets, $1,330,595 (M); gifts received, $710,525; expenditures, $3,095,014; qualifying distributions, $3,053,637; giving activities include $3,053,637 for 141 grants (high: $500,000; low: $250).
Purpose and activities: The foundation supports parks and organizations involved with arts and culture, education, health, human services, and international affairs.
Fields of interest: Arts, cultural/ethnic awareness; Performing arts, theater; Arts; Higher education; Education, reading; Education; Health care, volunteer services; Hospitals (general); Health care, clinics/centers; Health care; Recreation, parks/playgrounds; Youth, services; Human services; International development; International relief; International affairs.
Type of support: Annual campaigns; Program development; General/operating support.
Limitations: Applications not accepted. Giving primarily in CA, CT, GA, MA, New York, NY, and PA. No grants to individuals.
Application information: Contributes only to pre-selected organizations.
Officers and Directors:* Charles R. Kaye,* Co-Pres.; Joseph P. Landy,* Co-Pres.; Scott A. Arenare,* Secy.; Timothy J. Curt,* Treas.; Steve G. Glenn.
EIN: 134148834

7049
The Michael and Kim Ward Foundation ✧
(formerly The Michael Ward Foundation)
c/o The Ayco Co., NTG
P.O. Box 15014
Albany, NY 12212-5014

Established in 2010 in FL.
Donor: Michael J. Ward.
Foundation type: Independent foundation.
Financial data (yr. ended 12/31/13): Assets, $6,386,836 (M); gifts received, $1,155,434; expenditures, $2,988,680; qualifying distributions, $2,954,700; giving activities include $2,954,700 for 31 grants (high: $500,000; low: $2,500).
Purpose and activities: Giving primarily for the assistance of young people with learning, emotional or physical disabilities, and at-risk youth who live in underserved communities, belong to low-income families, and/or face educational or social barriers due to family or other circumstances.
Fields of interest: Middle schools/education; Charter schools; Higher education; Children; Youth; Disabilities, people with; Physically disabled; Economically disadvantaged.
Limitations: Applications not accepted. Giving primarily in the Jacksonville, FL, area.
Application information: Unsolicited requests for funds not accepted.
Trustees: Kim Anspach Ward; Michael Ward.
EIN: 276692318

7050
The Andy Warhol Foundation for the Visual Arts ✧
65 Bleecker St., 7th Fl.
New York, NY 10012-2420 (212) 387-7555
Contact: Rachel Bers, Prog. Dir.
FAX: (212) 387-7560;
E-mail: info@warholfoundation.org; E-mail for proposals: deadline@warholfoundation.org; Main URL: http://www.warholfoundation.org
Grants Database: http://www.warholfoundation.org/grant/index.html#/2009

Established in 1987 in NY.
Donor: Andy Warhol†.
Foundation type: Independent foundation.
Financial data (yr. ended 04/30/13): Assets, $327,697,626 (M); expenditures, $21,353,867; qualifying distributions, $15,974,019; giving activities include $12,298,779 for 139 grants (high: $1,500,000; low: $10,000).
Purpose and activities: The foundation's purpose is the advancement of the visual arts. The foundation's principal activities are twofold: it awards grants to nonprofit cultural organizations working in the visual arts; and it has responsibility for all aspects of its collection of Andy Warhol's art.
Fields of interest: Visual arts; Museums; Arts, artist's services; Arts.
Type of support: Fellowships; Program development; Conferences/seminars; Publication; Research.
Limitations: Applications accepted. Giving on a national basis. No grants to individuals.
Publications: Application guidelines; Biennial report; Financial statement; Grants list; Multi-year report.
Application information: Application form not required.
Initial approach: Letter
Copies of proposal: 1
Deadline(s): Mar. 1 and Sept. 1
Board meeting date(s): Apr., June, Oct., and Dec.
Final notification: Jan.1 and July 1
Officers and Directors:* Michael Straus, Chair.; Joel Wachs,* Pres.; Donald Warhola,* V.P.; K.C. Maurer, C.F.O. and Treas.; Mark Allen; James Keith Brown; Igor DaCosta; Courtney Fink; Jonathan Lee; Sarah Elizabeth Lewis; Shirin Neshat; Lawrence Rinder;

Trevor Schoonmaker; Cindy Sherman; Olga Viso; Carrie Mae Weems; Adam D. Weinberg; Julian Zugazagoitia.
Number of staff: 22 full-time professional; 2 part-time professional.
EIN: 133410749
Selected grants: The following grants are a representative sample of this grantmaker's funding activity:
$1,500,000 to Creative Capital Foundation, New York, NY, 2013. For General operating support.
$1,000,000 to New York Foundation for the Arts, Brooklyn, NY, 2013. For Emergency Fund for regranting to individual artists affected by Hurricane Sandy.
$900,000 to Creative Capital Foundation, New York, NY, 2013. For Arts Writers Initiative.
$325,000 to Andy Warhol Museum, Pittsburgh, PA, 2013. For General support.
$177,600 to Diverse Works, Houston, TX, 2013. For Warhol Initiative.
$40,000 to Isabella Stewart Gardner Museum, Boston, MA, 2013. For Residency and exhibition program support.
$25,000 to Coney Island, USA, Brooklyn, NY, 2013. For Emergency Fund for Visual Arts Organizations affected by Hurricane Sandy.
$25,000 to Dia Center for the Arts, New York, NY, 2013. For Emergency Fund for Visual Arts Organizations affected by Hurricane Sandy.
$25,000 to Eyebeam Atelier, New York, NY, 2013. For Emergency Fund for Visual Arts Organizations affected by Hurricane Sandy.
$15,000 to Long Beach Island Foundation of the Arts and Sciences, Long Beach Township, NJ, 2013. For Emergency Fund for Visual Arts Organizations affected by Hurricane Sandy.

7051
The Warnaco Foundation ✧
200 Madison Ave.
New York, NY 10016

Established in 2007 in DE.
Donor: Warnaco, Inc.
Foundation type: Company-sponsored foundation.
Financial data (yr. ended 12/31/12): Assets, $116,686 (M); gifts received, $440,541; expenditures, $519,228; qualifying distributions, $519,228; giving activities include $483,363 for grants.
Fields of interest: Breast cancer; Athletics/sports, water sports; Youth development, centers/clubs.
Limitations: Applications not accepted. Giving primarily in CA and CO.
Application information: Contributes only to pre-selected organizations.
Officers and Directors:* Elizabeth Wood,* Pres.; Ericka Alford, Secy.; Jay A. Galluzzo; Joseph R. Gromek; Lawrence R. Rutkowski.
EIN: 562675524

7052
The Warner Foundation ✧
c/o Paul Gartner
12 Garey Dr.
Chappaqua, NY 10514-1302

Established in 2001 in NY.
Donors: Douglas & Ann Warner Charitable Trust; Douglas Warner Trust.
Foundation type: Independent foundation.
Financial data (yr. ended 12/31/13): Assets, $2,088,972 (M); expenditures, $7,074,869; qualifying distributions, $6,971,125; giving activities include $6,960,000 for 12 grants (high: $580,000; low: $580,000).
Fields of interest: Health care; Health organizations; Agriculture/food.
Limitations: Applications not accepted. Giving primarily in New York, NY. No grants to individuals.
Application information: Contributes only to pre-selected organizations.
Officers: Susan Reed, Pres.; Joan Warner, V.P. and Treas.; Paul Gartner, Secy.
Directors: Theresa Comer; Theodore Warner.
EIN: 010620097

7053
The Joseph Leroy and Ann C. Warner Fund, Inc. ✧
2 Rector St., 20th Fl.
New York, NY 10006-1819 (212) 619-2501
Contact: Michael Stalonas, Exec. Dir.
FAX: (212) 587-0075; E-mail: warnerfund@aol.com; Main URL: http://www.warnerfund.org

Established in 1998 in NY.
Foundation type: Independent foundation.
Financial data (yr. ended 12/31/12): Assets, $17,991,846 (M); expenditures, $1,494,710; qualifying distributions, $1,236,884; giving activities include $1,027,501 for 31 grants (high: $75,000; low: $1).
Purpose and activities: Grants are made for the benefit of children in foster care, and children with disabilities.
Fields of interest: Elementary school/education; Education, special; Children, foster care; Children, services; Infants/toddlers; Children/youth; Children; Youth; Disabilities, people with; Physically disabled; Blind/visually impaired; Deaf/hearing impaired; Mentally disabled; Girls; Young adults, female; Boys; Young adults, male; Terminal illness, people with.
Type of support: General/operating support; Continuing support; Management development/ capacity building; Building/renovation; Equipment; Emergency funds; Program development; Publication; Seed money; Curriculum development; Scholarship funds; Research; Program evaluation.
Limitations: Applications accepted. Giving primarily in the metropolitan New York, NY, area.
Publications: Application guidelines.
Application information: Full proposals are by invitation only, after review of letter of inquiry. The foundation accepts the New York/ New Jersey Area Common Application Form. Application form required.
Initial approach: Letter of inquiry
Copies of proposal: 1
Deadline(s): None
Officers and Directors:* Jo Ann Ferdinand,* Pres.; Barbara Fei,* Secy.; Rachel Ferdinand,* Treas.; Michael Stalonas, Exec. Dir.
Number of staff: 1 full-time professional.
EIN: 113426508

7054
The Riley J. & Lillian N. Warren and Beatrice W. Blanding Foundation ✧
6 Ford Ave.
Oneonta, NY 13820-1818 (607) 432-6724
Contact: William H. Hulbert, Tr.

Trust established in 1972 in NY.
Donor: Beatrice W. Blanding‡.
Foundation type: Independent foundation.
Financial data (yr. ended 12/31/13): Assets, $24,411,180 (M); expenditures, $1,246,037; qualifying distributions, $1,235,347; giving activities include $1,051,000 for 53 grants (high: $150,000; low: $1,500).
Fields of interest: Arts; Elementary/secondary education; Higher education; Education; Hospitals (general); Human services; Children/youth, services; Protestant agencies & churches; Disabilities, people with.
Limitations: Applications accepted. Giving primarily in the Oneonta, NY, area.
Application information: Application form required.
Initial approach: Letter
Deadline(s): Nov. 1
Trustees: Richard A. Harlem; Maureen P. Hulbert; William H. Hulbert.
EIN: 237203341
Selected grants: The following grants are a representative sample of this grantmaker's funding activity:
$200,000 to Hartwick College, Oneonta, NY, 2011. For general fund.
$150,000 to Aurelia Osborn Fox Memorial Hospital Foundation, Oneonta, NY, 2011.
$25,000 to Catskill Symphony Orchestra, Oneonta, NY, 2011. For general fund.
$10,000 to Habitat for Humanity of Otsego County, Oneonta, NY, 2011.
$10,000 to Pathfinder Village, Edmeston, NY, 2011.
$10,000 to Saint Lawrence University, Canton, NY, 2011.
$10,000 to United Way of Delaware and Otsego Counties, Oneonta, NY, 2011.
$5,000 to Oneonta Concert Association, Oneonta, NY, 2011. For general support.
$5,000 to Upper Catskill Community Council of the Arts, Oneonta, NY, 2011.
$5,000 to Villanova University, Villanova, PA, 2011.

7055
The Bert & Sandra Wasserman Foundation ✧
126 E. 56th St., Ste. 12N
New York, NY 10022-3613

Established in 1997 in NY.
Donors: Bert W. Wasserman; Sandra K. Wasserman.
Foundation type: Independent foundation.
Financial data (yr. ended 12/31/13): Assets, $16,633,880 (M); gifts received, $1,000,000; expenditures, $701,616; qualifying distributions, $681,950; giving activities include $681,950 for 7 grants (high: $303,600; low: $1,750).
Purpose and activities: Giving primarily for education, Jewish organizations, medical research, and the arts.
Fields of interest: Arts; Higher education; Medical research, institute; Jewish federated giving programs; Jewish agencies & synagogues.

Limitations: Applications not accepted. Giving primarily in New York, NY. No grants to individuals.
Application information: Contributes only to pre-selected organizations.
Officers and Directors:* Sandra K. Wasserman,* Pres. and Treas.; Debra Wasserman,* V.P. and Secy.
EIN: 133961422
Selected grants: The following grants are a representative sample of this grantmaker's funding activity:
$50,000 to Memorial Sloan-Kettering Cancer Center, New York, NY, 2011.
$18,015 to Metropolitan Opera, New York, NY, 2011.
$18,000 to Project Kesher, Evanston, IL, 2011.
$18,000 to UJA-Federation of New York, New York, NY, 2011.
$8,600 to Gurwin Jewish Geriatric Foundation, Commack, NY, 2011.
$5,000 to Boca Raton Regional Hospital, Boca Raton, FL, 2011.
$3,600 to Prep for Prep, New York, NY, 2011.

7056
Water Cove Charitable Foundation ✧
c/o Ayco Co., Tax Dept.
P.O. Box 15014
Albany, NY 12212-5014

Established in 1999 in MA.
Donors: Bruce I. Sachs; Kimberlie T. Sachs.
Foundation type: Independent foundation.
Financial data (yr. ended 12/31/13): Assets, $3,827,999 (M); gifts received, $363,378; expenditures, $580,201; qualifying distributions, $567,000; giving activities include $567,000 for 36 grants (high: $350,000; low: $250).
Fields of interest: Health organizations, association; Human services; Children/youth, services.
Limitations: Applications not accepted. Giving primarily in MA. No grants to individuals.
Application information: Contributes only to pre-selected organizations.
Trustees: Bruce I. Sachs; Kimberlie T. Sachs.
EIN: 046905190
Selected grants: The following grants are a representative sample of this grantmaker's funding activity:
$1,000,000 to Accelerated Cure Project, Waltham, MA, 2011. For general purpose.
$10,000 to Accelerated Cure Project, Waltham, MA, 2011. For general purpose.
$10,000 to Boston Home, Boston, MA, 2011. For general purpose.
$10,000 to Myelin Repair Foundation, Saratoga, CA, 2011. For general purpose.
$1,000 to Guiding Eyes for the Blind, Yorktown Heights, NY, 2011. For general purpose.
$1,000 to H. Lee Moffitt Cancer Center and Research Institute, Tampa, FL, 2011. For general purpose.
$1,000 to Salvation Army, Canton, MA, 2011. For general purpose.

7057
Waterston Family Foundation ✧
c/o Zeiderman
170 Avery Rd.
Garrison, NY 10524-4103

Established in 2007 in NY.
Donors: Samuel Waterston; Lynn Waterston.
Foundation type: Independent foundation.
Financial data (yr. ended 12/31/13): Assets, $1,778,176 (M); expenditures, $720,504; qualifying distributions, $720,275; giving activities include $720,275 for grants.
Fields of interest: Performing arts, theater; Arts; Environment; Human services.
Limitations: Applications not accepted. Giving primarily in NY.
Application information: Contributes only to pre-selected organizations.
Officers: Samuel Waterston, Pres.; Lynn Waterston, Secy.
EIN: 260697604

7058
The Thomas J. Watson Foundation ✧
11 Park Pl., Ste. 1503
New York, NY 10007-2816
FAX: (212) 245-8860; E-mail: tjw@tjwf.org; Main URL: http://www.watsonfellowship.org
Going Solo: The Watson Journey: http://www.watsonfellowship.org/site/what/SoloVideo.html

Trust established in 1961 in NY.
Donors: Jeannette K. Watson†; Arthur K. Watson†; Thomas J. Watson, Jr.†; Mrs. John N. Irwin II†; Helen W. Buckner†.
Foundation type: Independent foundation.
Financial data (yr. ended 05/31/13): Assets, $88,202,077 (M); expenditures, $3,550,784; qualifying distributions, $2,913,550; giving activities include $1,259,661 for grants to individuals.
Purpose and activities: The grantmaker sponsors a fellowship program for independent study and travel abroad for graduating seniors of the private colleges and universities which are listed on the foundation's web site.
Fields of interest: Higher education; Education.
Type of support: General/operating support; Continuing support; Fellowships.
Limitations: Giving on a national basis. No grants to individuals (except for seniors attending the 50 member colleges of The Watson Fellowship Program).
Publications: Informational brochure.
Application information: Applicants for fellowships must be nominated by a participating private college or university and must be a graduating senior; independent applications not accepted. For information about the Watson Fellowship Program and a list of the participating colleges, see foundation web site. Application form required.
Copies of proposal: 1
Deadline(s): See foundation web site for current deadline
Board meeting date(s): As required
Final notification: Approximately Mar. 15
Advisory Committee: Liz Buckner; Walker Buckner; John Irwin, III; David McKinney; Daniel L. Mosley; Jeanne Olivier; Stuart Watson; Thomas J. Watson III.
Directors: Chris Kasabach; Frank Wolf.
Trustee: JPMorgan Chase Bank, N.A.
Number of staff: 4 full-time professional.
EIN: 136038151

7059
The Charles R. & Winifred R. Weber Foundation ✧
c/o Carter Ledyard & Milburn LLP
2 Wall St.
New York, NY 10005-2072

Established in 1999 in NY.
Donor: Mrs. Charles R. Weber.
Foundation type: Independent foundation.
Financial data (yr. ended 12/31/13): Assets, $11,523,348 (M); gifts received, $425; expenditures, $865,627; qualifying distributions, $735,156; giving activities include $700,000 for 12 grants (high: $150,000; low: $5,000).
Fields of interest: Health organizations, association; Big Brothers/Big Sisters; Children/youth, services; Jewish agencies & synagogues.
Limitations: Applications not accepted. Giving primarily in FL, NY, OH, PA, and RI. No grants to individuals.
Application information: Contributes only to pre-selected organizations.
Officers: Daniel J. McSwiggan, V.P. and Secy.; Robert Frankel, V.P. and Treas.
EIN: 136167132
Selected grants: The following grants are a representative sample of this grantmaker's funding activity:
$130,000 to Big Brothers Big Sisters of New York City, New York, NY, 2011.
$125,000 to Agudath Israel of America, New York, NY, 2011.
$100,000 to Providence College, Providence, RI, 2011.
$25,000 to Bonei Olam, Brooklyn, NY, 2011.
$10,000 to Calvary Hospital, Bronx, NY, 2011.
$10,000 to Saint Josephs University, Philadelphia, PA, 2011.

7060
Weeden Foundation ✧
35 Adams St., Ground Fl.
Bedford Hills, NY 10507-1819
Contact: Donald A. Weeden, Exec. Dir.; Gillian Beach, Research Asst.
FAX: (914) 864-1377; E-mail: info@weedenfdn.org; Main URL: http://www.weedenfdn.org
Grants Database: http://www.weedenfoundation.org/Weeden-Foundation-Grantees.php

Established 1963 in CA.
Donors: Frank Weeden†; Alan N. Weeden; Donald E. Weeden; John D. Weeden; William F. Weeden, M.D.; Frank Weeden Fund; Holloman-Price Fdn.
Foundation type: Independent foundation.
Financial data (yr. ended 12/31/12): Assets, $32,894,789 (M); gifts received, $8,586,167; expenditures, $6,109,178; qualifying distributions, $5,136,244; giving activities include $4,497,975 for grants.
Purpose and activities: Giving primarily to environmental organizations working to preserve biological diversity. Program interests also include organizations working to stabilize human population and organizations working to address the over consumption of the earth's resources.
Fields of interest: Environment, natural resources; Environment; Population studies.
International interests: Chile; Russia.

Type of support: General/operating support; Continuing support; Land acquisition; Emergency funds; Program development; Seed money; Program-related investments/loans.
Limitations: Applications accepted. Giving on a national and international basis, primarily in northern CA, the Pacific Northwest, Latin America (Chile), Central Siberia and the Altai Republic in Russia. No grants to individuals, or for multi-year requests; generally no funding for films, conferences, or scientific research.
Publications: Application guidelines; Annual report; Financial statement; Program policy statement.
Application information: The foundation strongly encourages potential applicants to submit a letter of inquiry before presenting a complete proposal. Proposal guidelines available on foundation web site. Application form not required.
Initial approach: Letter of inquiry via e-mail or U.S. mail only
Copies of proposal: 2
Deadline(s): 6 weeks prior to each board meeting; check web site for dates
Board meeting date(s): 3 times a year
Final notification: 8-10 weeks
Officers and Directors:* Norman Weeden, Ph.D.*, Pres.; Tina Roux, V.P.; H. Leslie Weeden,* Secy.; Bob Weeden, Treas.; Donald A. Weeden, Exec. Dir.; Barbara Daugherty; Alan N. Weeden; Donald E. Weeden; Jack D. Weeden; John D. Weeden; William Weeden, M.D.
Number of staff: 2 full-time professional.
EIN: 946109313
Selected grants: The following grants are a representative sample of this grantmaker's funding activity:
$50,000 to National Tropical Botanical Garden, Kalaheo, HI, 2010.
$50,000 to National Tropical Botanical Garden, Kalaheo, HI, 2011.
$25,000 to Californians for Population Stabilization, Santa Barbara, CA, 2011.
$25,000 to Campana Patagonia Rios Vivos de Ecosistemas, Santiago, Chile, 2010.
$25,000 to Natural Resources Defense Council, New York, NY, 2011.
$25,000 to Nature Conservancy, San Francisco, CA, 2010.
$25,000 to NumbersUSA, Arlington, VA, 2010.
$25,000 to NumbersUSA, Arlington, VA, 2011.
$20,000 to American Rivers, Washington, DC, 2011.
$20,000 to Californians for Population Stabilization, Santa Barbara, CA, 2010.
$20,000 to Center for Immigration Studies, Washington, DC, 2011.
$20,000 to Craighead Institute, Bozeman, MT, 2010.
$20,000 to Endangered Species Coalition, Washington, DC, 2011.
$20,000 to International Projects Assistance Services, Chapel Hill, NC, 2010.
$20,000 to International Projects Assistance Services, Chapel Hill, NC, 2011.
$15,000 to Center for a New American Dream, Charlottesville, VA, 2010.
$15,000 to Population Institute, Washington, DC, 2010.
$10,000 to Institute for Fisheries Resources, Eugene, OR, 2010.
$10,000 to Tuleyome, Woodland, CA, 2011.
$3,000 to American Bird Conservancy, The Plains, VA, 2011.

7061
The Wegman Family Charitable Foundation ✧

(formerly Robert B. Wegman Charitable Foundation)
1500 Brooks Ave.
P.O. Box 30844
Rochester, NY 14603-0844 (585) 328-2550

Established in 1993 in NY.
Donors: Daniel R. Wegman; Robert B. Wegman†.
Foundation type: Independent foundation.
Financial data (yr. ended 12/31/13): Assets, $56,258,939 (M); expenditures, $24,829,656; qualifying distributions, $24,664,500; giving activities include $24,663,000 for 28 grants (high: $10,000,000; low: $6,000).
Purpose and activities: Giving primarily for human services and education.
Fields of interest: Performing arts centers; Secondary school/education; Education; Hospitals (general); Heart & circulatory diseases; Food banks; Human services; Children, services; Youth, services; Community/economic development; United Ways and Federated Giving Programs; Catholic federated giving programs; Disabilities, people with.
Limitations: Applications not accepted. Giving primarily in Rochester, NY. No grants to individuals.
Application information: Contributes only to pre-selected organizations.
Officers and Directors:* Daniel R. Wegman,* Chair., Pres. and Treas.; Margaret F. Wegman,* V.P.; Paul S. Speranza, Jr.,* Secy.
EIN: 223247037
Selected grants: The following grants are a representative sample of this grantmaker's funding activity:
$10,000,000 to University of Rochester, Institute for Data Science, Rochester, NY, 2013. For program support.
$7,000,000 to Golisano Childrens Hospital, Rochester, NY, 2013. For building and program support.
$4,000,000 to Hillside Childrens Center Foundation, Rochester, NY, 2012. For general support.
$4,000,000 to Hillside Childrens Center Foundation, Rochester, NY, 2013. For operating support.
$1,000,000 to Nazareth College of Rochester, Rochester, NY, 2013. For building project to consolidate various health care programs in the community.
$1,000,000 to Rochester Institute of Technology, Rochester, NY, 2012. For general support.
$800,000 to McQuaid Jesuit High School, Rochester, NY, 2012. For general support.
$433,500 to University of Rochester, Rochester, NY, 2012. For general support.
$400,000 to United Way of Greater Rochester, Rochester, NY, 2012. For programs for people in need in the Rochester area.
$249,500 to Our Lady of Mercy High School, Rochester, NY, 2012. For scholarships.
$210,000 to University of Rochester Medical Center, Rochester, NY, 2012. For operating support.
$200,000 to Saint Anns Home Foundation, Rochester, NY, 2012. For general support.
$200,000 to Saint Anns Home Foundation, Rochester, NY, 2013. For general support.
$100,000 to Education Enterprise of New York Foundation, Rochester, NY, 2012. For academic programs.
$63,000 to United Way of Buffalo and Erie County, Buffalo, NY, 2012. For programs for people in need in the greater Buffalo area.

7062
Weil, Gotshal & Manges Foundation Inc. ✧

c/o Tax Dept.
767 5th Ave., Ste. 2330
New York, NY 10153-0001 (212) 310-6813
Contact: Dennis Foley, Dir.

Established in 1983 in NY.
Donors: Weil, Gotshal & Manges LLP; Robert Todd Lang; Ira M. Millstein; Harvey R. Miller.
Foundation type: Company-sponsored foundation.
Financial data (yr. ended 12/31/13): Assets, $4,565,438 (M); expenditures, $1,480,191; qualifying distributions, $1,479,791; giving activities include $1,479,406 for 83 grants (high: $336,600; low: $25).
Purpose and activities: The foundation supports museums and organizations involved with education, legal services, disaster relief, children and youth, international relief, civil and human rights, business, and Judaism.
Fields of interest: Education; Human services; Religion.
Type of support: General/operating support; Scholarship funds.
Limitations: Applications accepted. Giving primarily in NJ and NY. No grants to individuals.
Application information: Application form required.
Initial approach: Proposal
Copies of proposal: 1
Deadline(s): Nov. 1
Directors: Joseph Allerhand; Howard Chatzinoff; Dennis Foley; Thomas Roberts.
EIN: 133158325
Selected grants: The following grants are a representative sample of this grantmaker's funding activity:
$150,000 to Japan Society, New York, NY, 2011.
$30,000 to Pro Bono Partnership, White Plains, NY, 2011.
$20,000 to American Heart Association, Dallas, TX, 2011.
$15,000 to Disabled Sports USA, Rockville, MD, 2011.
$15,000 to Human Rights Watch, New York, NY, 2011.
$12,561 to National Minority Supplier Development Council, New York, NY, 2011.
$10,000 to Mayors Fund to Advance New York City, New York, NY, 2011.
$5,000 to New York City Police Foundation, New York, NY, 2011.
$3,000 to American Heart Association, Dallas, TX, 2011.
$2,000 to Achilles International, New York, NY, 2011.

7063
Theodore & Renee Weiler Foundation Inc. ✧

6800 Jericho Tpke.
Syosset, NY 11791

Established in 1965 in NY.
Donors: Theodore R. Weiler†; Theodore R. Weiler Trust.

Foundation type: Independent foundation.
Financial data (yr. ended 12/31/13): Assets, $8,660,757 (M); expenditures, $1,047,606; qualifying distributions, $1,006,285; giving activities include $974,900 for 100 grants (high: $101,000; low: $500).
Purpose and activities: Giving primarily for arts and culture, hospitals and health associations, children's and human services, and Jewish agencies and temples.
Fields of interest: Museums; Museums (art); Museums (ethnic/folk arts); Performing arts; Performing arts, theater; Arts; Hospitals (general); Health organizations, association; Human services; Children, services; Jewish federated giving programs; Jewish agencies & synagogues.
Limitations: Applications not accepted. Giving primarily in New York, NY; some funding also in FL. No grants to individuals.
Application information: Contributes only to pre-selected organizations.
Officers and Directors:* Alan Safir,* Pres.; Richard Kandel,* Treas. and Mgr.
EIN: 136181441

7064
Joyce & George Wein Foundation Inc. ✧
150 E. 69th St., Ste. 27K
New York, NY 10021-5722

Donor: George Wein.
Foundation type: Independent foundation.
Financial data (yr. ended 09/30/13): Assets, $2,106,932 (M); gifts received, $200,374; expenditures, $438,995; qualifying distributions, $437,261; giving activities include $435,250 for 16 grants (high: $250,000; low: $500).
Fields of interest: Museums; Arts; Education; Religion.
Type of support: General/operating support.
Limitations: Applications not accepted. Giving primarily in New York, NY.
Application information: Unsolicited requests for funds not accepted.
Officers: George Wein, Pres.; Deborah Ross, Secy.
EIN: 261445446

7065
Peter A. and Deborah L. Weinberg Family Foundation ✧
c/o BCRS Assocs., LLC
77 Water St., 9th Fl.
New York, NY 10005-4414

Established in 1996 in CT.
Donor: Peter A. Weinberg.
Foundation type: Independent foundation.
Financial data (yr. ended 07/31/13): Assets, $12,595,465 (M); gifts received, $2,400,000; expenditures, $645,805; qualifying distributions, $612,985; giving activities include $612,925 for 38 grants (high: $250,000; low: $100).
Fields of interest: Higher education; Education; Human services; Children/youth, services.
Limitations: Applications not accepted. Giving in the U.S., with emphasis on Claremont, CA, Greenwich, CT, and New York, NY. No grants to individuals.
Application information: Contributes only to pre-selected organizations.
Trustees: Deborah L. Weinberg; Peter A. Weinberg.
EIN: 133920469

Selected grants: The following grants are a representative sample of this grantmaker's funding activity:
$100,000 to Multiple Myeloma Research Foundation, Norwalk, CT, 2011.
$25,000 to Memorial Sloan-Kettering Cancer Center, New York, NY, 2011.
$18,000 to Family Centers, Greenwich, CT, 2011.
$14,900 to Boys and Girls Club of Greenwich, Greenwich, CT, 2011.
$14,700 to Jackie Robinson Foundation, New York, NY, 2011.
$14,000 to NARAL Pro-Choice America Foundation, Washington, DC, 2011.
$10,000 to Boys and Girls Club of Greenwich, Greenwich, CT, 2011.
$10,000 to Inner-City Scholarship Fund, New York, NY, 2011.
$10,000 to Multiple Myeloma Research Foundation, Norwalk, CT, 2011.
$2,500 to Posse Foundation, New York, NY, 2011.

7066
The John L. and Sue Ann Weinberg Foundation ✧
(formerly The Sue Ann and John L. Weinberg Foundation)
c/o BCRS Assocs., LLC
77 Water St., 9th Fl.
New York, NY 10005-4414

Established in 1959 in NY.
Donors: John L. Weinberg†; Sue Ann Weinberg.
Foundation type: Independent foundation.
Financial data (yr. ended 12/31/13): Assets, $59,288,150 (M); gifts received, $2,000,768; expenditures, $2,953,275; qualifying distributions, $2,676,072; giving activities include $2,555,336 for 276 grants (high: $1,199,996; low: $50).
Purpose and activities: Giving primarily for the arts, particularly museums and the performing arts, as well as for higher education, health, youth development, and social services.
Fields of interest: Museums (art); Performing arts; Historic preservation/historical societies; Arts; Higher education; Hospitals (general); Medical research, institute; Youth development; Human services.
Type of support: General/operating support; Annual campaigns; Capital campaigns; Building/renovation; Endowments; Professorships; Research; Program-related investments/loans.
Limitations: Applications not accepted. Giving primarily in the metropolitan New York, NY area; giving also in Greenwich, CT and DE. No grants to individuals, or for scholarships; no loans.
Application information: Contributes only to pre-selected organizations.
Trustees: Jean Weinberg Rose; Elizabeth Weinberg Smith; John S. Weinberg; Sue Ann Weinberg.
Number of staff: 2 part-time support.
EIN: 136028813

7067
Sidney J. Weinberg, Jr. Foundation ✧
c/o BCRS Assocs., LLC
77 Water St., 9th Fl.
New York, NY 10005-4414

Established in 1979 in NY.
Donors: Sidney J. Weinberg, Jr.; Elizabeth H. Weinberg; Elizabeth W. Smith.
Foundation type: Independent foundation.
Financial data (yr. ended 12/31/13): Assets, $50,528,007 (M); expenditures, $5,077,627; qualifying distributions, $4,697,701; giving activities include $4,670,000 for 47 grants (high: $1,000,000; low: $5).
Purpose and activities: Giving primarily for the arts, education, health and human services.
Fields of interest: Museums (marine/maritime); Performing arts; Performing arts, opera; Historic preservation/historical societies; Arts; Higher education; Education; Environment; Hospitals (general); Health organizations, association; Human services; Community/economic development; United Ways and Federated Giving Programs.
Type of support: General/operating support.
Limitations: Applications not accepted. Giving primarily in MA and New York, NY; some funding also in CA. No grants to individuals or for scholarships; no loans.
Application information: Contributes only to pre-selected organizations.
Trustees: Elizabeth W. Smith; Peter A. Weinberg; Sydney H. Weinberg.
EIN: 132998603

7068
Tin and Boaz Weinstein Foundation ✧
870 5th Ave., Ste. 16A
New York, NY 10065-4907 (917) 653-3269

Established in 2010 in NY.
Donors: Boaz Weinstein; Tali Farhadian Weinstein.
Foundation type: Independent foundation.
Financial data (yr. ended 11/30/11): Assets, $89,568 (M); gifts received, $9,398,062; expenditures, $9,781,730; qualifying distributions, $9,732,630; giving activities include $9,703,224 for 6 grants (high: $9,617,224; low: $5,000).
Fields of interest: Education; Jewish federated giving programs.
Limitations: Applications not accepted. Giving primarily in New York, NY. No grants to individuals.
Application information: Contributes only to pre-selected organizations.
Trustees: Boaz Weinstein; Tali Farhadian Weinstein.
EIN: 274271464

7069
David and Candace Weir Foundation ✧
(formerly Candace King Weir Foundation)
c/o C. L. King & Assocs., Inc.
9 Elk St.
Albany, NY 12207-1002
Contact: Candace K. Weir, Tr.

Established in 1994 in NY.
Donor: Candace K. Weir.
Foundation type: Independent foundation.
Financial data (yr. ended 12/31/12): Assets, $25,539,671 (M); gifts received, $5,000,000; expenditures, $1,011,682; qualifying distributions, $1,001,080; giving activities include $996,400 for 102 grants (high: $504,000; low: $100).
Fields of interest: Museums (art); Historical activities; Arts; Higher education; Environment; Hospitals (general); Human services; Catholic agencies & churches.

Limitations: Applications accepted. Giving primarily in NY. No grants to individuals.
Application information: Application form required.
Initial approach: Letter
Deadline(s): None
Trustees: Meredith Prime; Amelia F. Weir; Candace K. Weir.
EIN: 133797919

7070
Michael & Leah Weisberg Family Foundation ✧
720 Park Ave., Ste. 16A
New York, NY 10021-4954

Established in NY.
Donor: Michael Weisberg.
Foundation type: Independent foundation.
Financial data (yr. ended 12/31/13): Assets, $4,109,674 (M); gifts received, $25,000; expenditures, $470,220; qualifying distributions, $463,724; giving activities include $463,724 for 34 grants (high: $150,000; low: $100).
Fields of interest: Historic preservation/historical societies; Health care; Human services.
Limitations: Applications not accepted. Giving primarily in New York, NY.
Application information: Unsolicited requests for funds not accepted.
Trustees: Leah Weisberg; Michael Weisberg.
EIN: 451539904

7071
Weissman Family Foundation, Inc. ✧
81 Manursing Way
Rye, NY 10580-4311

Established in 1992 in NY.
Donor: George Weissman.
Foundation type: Independent foundation.
Financial data (yr. ended 12/31/13): Assets, $29,766,603 (M); expenditures, $1,574,119; qualifying distributions, $1,511,584; giving activities include $1,505,250 for 109 grants (high: $155,000; low: $500).
Purpose and activities: Giving primarily for education and for human services.
Fields of interest: Arts; Education; Environment; Human services.
Type of support: General/operating support; Continuing support; Annual campaigns; Capital campaigns; Endowments; Emergency funds; Publication; Seed money.
Limitations: Applications not accepted. Giving primarily in New York, NY. No grants to individuals.
Application information: Contributes only to pre-selected organizations.
Officers and Directors: Mildred Weissman,* Pres.; Daniel Weissman,* V.P.; Ellen Weissman,* Secy.; Paul Weissman,* Treas.
Number of staff: 1 part-time support.
EIN: 133688122

7072
The Paul and Harriet Weissman Family Foundation Inc. ✧
(formerly The Paul M. Weissman Family Foundation)
2 Oxford Rd.
White Plains, NY 10605-3603

Established in 1969 in NY.
Donor: Paul M. Weissman.
Foundation type: Independent foundation.
Financial data (yr. ended 02/28/13): Assets, $9,083,908 (M); gifts received, $600,000; expenditures, $1,023,100; qualifying distributions, $1,017,515; giving activities include $1,015,250 for 77 grants (high: $300,000; low: $10).
Purpose and activities: Support primarily for education, the arts, health and social services, and child welfare associations.
Fields of interest: Arts; Elementary/secondary education; Higher education; Education; Hospitals (general); Health care; Human services; Children/youth, services.
Limitations: Applications not accepted. Giving primarily in New York, NY; funding also in White Plains, NY. No grants to individuals.
Application information: Unsolicited requests for funds not accepted.
Officers: Paul M. Weissman, Pres. and Treas.; Harriet L. Weissman, V.P. and Secy.; Michael A. Weissman, V.P.; Peter A. Weissman, V.P.; Stephanie T. Weissman, V.P.
EIN: 237049744
Selected grants: The following grants are a representative sample of this grantmaker's funding activity:
$2,500 to Rye Country Day School, Rye, NY, 2013. For The Purpose of These Contributions Is to Provide the Donee Organizations to Carry Out Their Exempt Functions.

7073
Franklin H. & Ruth L. Wells Foundation ✧ ☆
1100 Wehrle Dr., 2nd Fl.
Buffalo, NY 14221-7748
Contact: Miles J. Gibbons, Jr., Exec. Dir.
E-mail for Miles J. Gibbons, Jr.: mgibbons989@earthlink.net

Established in 1983 in PA.
Donors: Ruth L. Wells Annuity Trust; Frank Wells Marital Trust.
Foundation type: Independent foundation.
Financial data (yr. ended 05/31/13): Assets, $5,069,708 (M); expenditures, $706,450; qualifying distributions, $691,650; giving activities include $625,250 for 36 grants (high: $70,000; low: $750).
Purpose and activities: Startup funding for new programs in education, human services, community development, health care, and cultural arts.
Fields of interest: Arts; Higher education; Education; Health care; Boys & girls clubs; Girl scouts; Human services; YM/YWCAs & YM/YWHAs; Community/economic development.
Type of support: Equipment; Emergency funds; Program development; Seed money.
Limitations: Applications accepted. Giving primarily in Dauphin, Cumberland, and Perry counties, PA. No support for religious activities. No grants to individuals, or for endowments, debts, or capital campaigns.
Application information: Application form not required.
Initial approach: Letter
Copies of proposal: 1
Board meeting date(s): Apr. and Oct.
Officer: Miles J. Gibbons, Jr.,* Exec. Dir.
Trustee: M & T Trust Co.
Number of staff: 1 full-time professional.
EIN: 222541749
Selected grants: The following grants are a representative sample of this grantmaker's funding activity:
$1,000 to United Negro College Fund, Fairfax, VA, 2011.

7074
The Margaret L. Wendt Foundation ✧
40 Fountain Plz., Ste. 277
Buffalo, NY 14202-2220 (716) 855-2146
Contact: Robert J. Kresse, Tr.

Trust established in 1956 in NY.
Donor: Margaret L. Wendt†.
Foundation type: Independent foundation.
Financial data (yr. ended 01/31/14): Assets, $104,394,194 (M); expenditures, $7,550,559; qualifying distributions, $6,560,571; giving activities include $5,581,372 for 164 grants (high: $500,000; low: $315), and $716,089 for 1 loan/program-related investment.
Purpose and activities: Emphasis on education, the arts, and social services; support also for churches and religious organizations, public interest organizations, and youth agencies.
Fields of interest: Historic preservation/historical societies; Arts; Higher education; Theological school/education; Education; Environment, natural resources; Human services; Children/youth, services; Family services; Community/economic development; Religion.
Limitations: Applications accepted. Giving primarily in Buffalo and western NY. No grants to individuals, or for scholarships.
Publications: Application guidelines.
Application information: Application form not required.
Initial approach: Letter or application form
Copies of proposal: 4
Deadline(s): 1 month prior to board meeting
Board meeting date(s): Quarterly; no fixed dates
Final notification: Usually 4 to 6 months
Trustees: Janet L. Day; Robert J. Kresse; Thomas D. Lunt.
Number of staff: 1 part-time support.
EIN: 166030037

7075
Wenner-Gren Foundation for Anthropological Research, Inc. ✧
470 Park Ave. S., 8th Fl.
New York, NY 10016-6818 (212) 683-5000
FAX: (212) 532-1492;
E-mail: inquiries@wennergren.org; Main
URL: http://www.wennergren.org
Blog: http://blog.wennergren.org/
Facebook: http://www.facebook.com/wennergrenfoundation
Grants Database: http://www.wennergren.org/grantees
Twitter: http://twitter.com/wennergrenorg

Incorporated in 1941 at The Viking Fund in DE. Later, it was re-named Wenner-Gren Foundation for Anthropological Research, Inc.
Donor: Axel L. Wenner-Gren†.
Foundation type: Operating foundation.
Financial data (yr. ended 12/31/13): Assets, $177,506,184 (M); expenditures, $8,334,789;

qualifying distributions, $7,255,406; giving activities include $176,280 for 9 grants (high: $25,000; low: $5,000), $4,364,460 for grants to individuals, and $6,957,348 for foundation-administered programs.
Purpose and activities: A private operating foundation; international support of research in all branches of anthropology including cultural/social anthropology, ethnology, biological/physical anthropology, archaeology, and anthropological linguistics, and in closely related disciplines so far as they pertain to human origins, development, and variation; grants-in-aid for programs of research; subsidies for conferences for anthropologists to promote reporting on results of research; publishes a journal and provides clearinghouse services for anthropological information.
Fields of interest: History/archaeology; Language/linguistics; Anthropology/sociology.
Type of support: Conferences/seminars; Publication; Seed money; Fellowships; Research; Grants to individuals.
Limitations: Applications accepted. Giving on a national and international basis. Individuals from all countries are invited to apply for individual research grants. No support for intermediary funding agencies, nonproject personnel, or institutional overhead or support. No grants for salaries or fringe benefits, tuition or travel to meetings, dissertation write-up or revision, publication subvention, or filmmaking. No publication assistance (outside of the Hunt Post-Doctoral Fellowship).
Publications: Application guidelines; Annual report; Annual report (including application guidelines); Financial statement; Grants list; Informational brochure.
Application information: Application form required.
Initial approach: See Programs Page on foundation web site
Deadline(s): Contact foundation for program deadlines
Board meeting date(s): Apr. and Oct.
Final notification: Approximately 6 months after deadline
Officers and Trustees:* Seth Masters,* Chair.; Lorraine Sciarra,* Vice-Chair.; Leslie C. Aiello,* Pres.; Maugha Kenny, V.P., Fin. and Secy.; Lauren Meserve,* Treas.; Dr. Ira Berlin; Dr. John Immerwahr; and 7 additional trustees.
Number of staff: 13
EIN: 131813827

7076
Nina W. Werblow Charitable Trust ✧
c/o Ehrenkranz and Ehrenkranz, LLP
375 Park Ave., Ste. 28
New York, NY 10152-0067 (212) 751-5959
Contact: Roger A. Goldman, Tr.

Established in 1977 in NY.
Donor: Nina W. Werblow†.
Foundation type: Independent foundation.
Financial data (yr. ended 02/28/13): Assets, $10,978,169 (M); expenditures, $993,365; qualifying distributions, $911,512; giving activities include $911,512 for grants.
Purpose and activities: Giving primarily for the arts, education, health organizations and human services.
Fields of interest: Visual arts, photography; Arts; Higher education; Medical school/education; Education; Health care; Health organizations, association; Human services.
Limitations: Applications accepted. Giving limited to New York, NY.
Application information:
Initial approach: Letter
Deadline(s): Sept. 30
Trustees: Joel S. Ehrenkranz; Roger A. Goldman.
EIN: 136742999
Selected grants: The following grants are a representative sample of this grantmaker's funding activity:
$10,000 to Columbia University, Law School, New York, NY, 2013. For unrestricted charitable purposes.
$10,000 to New York University, School of Law Scholarship Program, New York, NY, 2013. For unrestricted charitable purposes.

7077
West Ferry Foundation ✧
c/o Robert G. Wilmers
350 Park Ave., 6th Fl.
New York, NY 10022-6081

Established in 1992 in NY.
Donor: Robert G. Wilmers.
Foundation type: Independent foundation.
Financial data (yr. ended 11/30/13): Assets, $16,625,561 (M); expenditures, $629,324; qualifying distributions, $617,104; giving activities include $613,904 for 9 grants (high: $375,000; low: $904).
Fields of interest: Museums (art); Performing arts; Higher education; Foundations (community); United Ways and Federated Giving Programs.
Limitations: Applications not accepted. Giving primarily in Buffalo and New York, NY and MA. No grants to individuals.
Application information: Contributes only to pre-selected organizations.
Trustee: Robert G. Wilmers.
EIN: 133715532
Selected grants: The following grants are a representative sample of this grantmaker's funding activity:
$50,000 to Lincoln Center Theater, New York, NY, 2011.
$35,000 to Council on Foreign Relations, New York, NY, 2011.
$25,000 to United Way of Buffalo and Erie County, Buffalo, NY, 2011.
$10,000 to Buffalo Prep, Buffalo, NY, 2011.
$10,000 to Harvard College Fund, Cambridge, MA, 2011.
$1,000 to Irish Classical Theater, Buffalo, NY, 2011.

7078
The Western New York Foundation ✧
11 Summer St., 3rd Fl.
Buffalo, NY 14209-2256 (716) 839-4225
Contact: Beth K. Gosch, Exec. Dir.
FAX: (716) 883-1107; E-mail for Beth Kinsman Gosch, Exec. Dir.: bgosch@wnyfoundation.org; Main URL: http://www.wnyfoundation.org
Grants List: http://www.wnyfoundation.org/Tools/Library/frontend/itemlist.asp?reset=1&phase=1&type=1

Incorporated in 1951 in NY as the Wildroot Foundation; present name adopted in 1958.
Donor: Welles V. Moot†.
Foundation type: Independent foundation.
Financial data (yr. ended 03/31/14): Assets, $15,194,481 (M); gifts received, $22,028; expenditures, $735,994; qualifying distributions, $688,071; giving activities include $552,528 for 45 grants (high: $34,000; low: $500).
Purpose and activities: Grants to nonprofit institutions, with emphasis on capital needs, seed funds for new projects, or expanding services. Support primarily for the fine and performing arts, youth agencies, the natural sciences, and social service agencies; some support also for health services and libraries and other educational institutions.
Fields of interest: Visual arts; Museums; Performing arts; Performing arts, dance; Performing arts, theater; Performing arts, music; Arts; Child development, education; Secondary school/education; Libraries (public); Medical care, rehabilitation; Substance abuse, services; Mental health/crisis services; Alcoholism; Legal services; Crime/law enforcement; Housing/shelter, development; Human services; Children/youth, services; Family services; Residential/custodial care, hospices; Aging, centers/services; Women, centers/services; Community/economic development; Infants/toddlers; Children/youth; Adults; Aging; Disabilities, people with; Mentally disabled; Minorities; Homeless.
Type of support: Income development; Capital campaigns; Building/renovation; Equipment; Land acquisition; Emergency funds; Program development; Conferences/seminars; Publication; Seed money; Technical assistance; Program-related investments/loans; Matching/challenge support.
Limitations: Applications accepted. Giving limited to the 8th Judicial District of NY (Erie, Niagara, Genesee, Wyoming, Allegany, Cattaraugus, and Chautauqua counties). No support for hospitals or religious organizations. No grants to individuals, or for scholarships, fellowships, or generally for operating budgets or deficit financing.
Publications: Application guidelines; Annual report (including application guidelines); Informational brochure.
Application information: See foundation web site for complete application guidelines and procedures. Application form required.
Initial approach: Create account on foundation web site
Copies of proposal: 2
Deadline(s): June 30th and Nov. 30th for Alignment Determination Application
Board meeting date(s): 3 or 4 times a year
Final notification: Usually within 3 months
Officers and Trustees:* Jennifer S. Johnson,* Chair.; James A. W. McLeod,* Pres.; John N. Walsh III,* V.P.; Anthony S. Johnson,* Secy.; Theodore V. Burger,* Treas.; Beth Kinsman Gosch, Exec. Dir.; Richard E. Moot, Tr. Emeritus; Paulette M. Crooke; Andrew W. Dorn; Amey D. Moot.
Number of staff: 1 full-time professional; 2 part-time support.
EIN: 160845962
Selected grants: The following grants are a representative sample of this grantmaker's funding activity:
$45,000 to Jericho Road Ministries, Buffalo, NY, 2013. For Jericho Road Health Center Merger.
$30,000 to Buffalo Niagara Riverkeeper, Buffalo, NY, 2013. For Advancement Director.
$30,000 to Buffalo Society of Natural Sciences, Buffalo, NY, 2013. For Science Studios.

$28,000 to Opportunities Unlimited of Niagara, Niagara Falls, NY, 2013. For Sub-Contracting Delivery Truck.
$24,000 to Cradle Beach Camp, Angola, NY, 2013. For research and evaluation.
$20,000 to Community Foundation for Greater Buffalo, Buffalo, NY, 2013. For Say Yes-Buffalo Scholarship.
$10,000 to Community Foundation for Greater Buffalo, Buffalo, NY, 2013. For Fund for the Arts.
$10,000 to Locust Street Neighborhood Art Classes, Buffalo, NY, 2013. For Succession and Sustainability Implementation.
$5,000 to Compass House, Buffalo, NY, 2013. For Capital Improvements - Kitchen.
$5,000 to Richardson Center Corporation, Buffalo, NY, 2013. For website upgrades.

7079
Mrs. Giles Whiting Foundation
(also known as Whiting Foundation)
16 Court St., Ste. 2308
Brooklyn, NY 11241 (718) 701-5962
Contact: Daniel Reid, Exec. Dir.
E-mail: info@whitingfoundation.org; Main URL: http://www.whitingfoundation.org

Incorporated in 1963 in NY.
Donor: Mrs. Giles Whiting‡.
Foundation type: Independent foundation.
Financial data (yr. ended 11/30/12): Assets, $54,247,523 (M); expenditures, $3,018,089; qualifying distributions, $2,682,236; giving activities include $1,717,500 for 32 grants (high: $150,000; low: $1,000), and $400,000 for 16 grants to individuals (high: $25,000; low: $25,000).
Purpose and activities: The foundation is dedicated to the support of the humanities and of literature.
Fields of interest: Humanities; Literature; Higher education.
Limitations: Applications not accepted.
Application information: Unsolicited requests for funds not accepted.
Officers and Trustees:* Antonia M. Grumbach,* Pres.; John N. Irwin III,* V.P. and Treas.; Peter Pennoyer,* V.P.; Kate Torrey,* V.P.; Robin Krause,* Secy.; Daniel Reid, Exec. Dir.
Number of staff: 2 full-time professional; 1 part-time professional.
EIN: 136154484

7080
The Helen Hay Whitney Foundation ✧
20 Squadron Blvd., Ste. 630
New City, NY 10956-5247 (845) 639-6799
Contact: Robert Weinberger, Admin. Dir.
FAX: (845) 639-6798; E-mail: hhwf@earthlink.net; Additional fax: (646) 304-7133; Main URL: http://www.hhwf.org/
Directory of Fellows Search: http://www.hhwf.org/HTMLSrc/Search.html

Charitable trust established in 1943; established as a private foundation in 1947; incorporated in 1951 in NY.
Donor: Mrs. Charles S. Payson‡.
Foundation type: Independent foundation.
Financial data (yr. ended 12/31/12): Assets, $51,969,904 (M); gifts received, $1,724,690; expenditures, $3,660,183; qualifying distributions, $3,296,888; giving activities include $2,880,533 for 59 grants to individuals (high: $54,500; low: $1,000).
Purpose and activities: Giving to support beginning postdoctoral training in basic biomedical research through research fellowships for residents of the United States who are planning to work in laboratories either in the U.S., Canada, or abroad, and also to foreign citizens for research in laboratories in the U.S. only. Fellowships are awarded to individuals but funds are administered largely by research institutions. American citizenship is not required, but foreign nationals are expected to pursue their research in the U.S.
Fields of interest: Medical research.
Type of support: Fellowships.
Limitations: Giving limited to North America, including Canada and Mexico.
Publications: Application guidelines; Annual report; Financial statement; Informational brochure (including application guidelines).
Application information: Application forms available in May on foundation web site. For application guidelines and procedures, and any inquiries, please e-mail or see foundation web site. Application form required.
Initial approach: Complete application form on-line
Deadline(s): Submit proposal anytime from Apr. 15-July 15; deadline July 1
Final notification: 3 months
Officers and Trustees:* Averil Payson Meyer,* Pres.; Stephen C. Harrison, Ph.D.*, V.P. and Chair., Scientific Advisory Comm.; Lisa A. Steiner, M.D.*, V.P.; W. Perry Welch, Treas.; Jerome Gross, M.D., Tr. Emeritus; Thomas M. Jessell, Ph.D.; Payne Middleton; Thomas Sakmar, M.D.; Stephen C. Sherrill; Christopher T. Walsh, Ph.D.
Scientific Advisory Committee: David J. Anderson; Daniel Kahne, Ph.D.; Barbara J. Meyer, Ph.D.; Erin K. O'Shea, Ph.D.; Matthew D. Scharff, M.D.; Julie Theriot, Ph.D.; S. Lawrence Zipursky, Ph.D.
Number of staff: 1 full-time professional.
EIN: 131677403

7081
The Widgeon Point Charitable Foundation ✧
(formerly The Beinecke Foundation, Inc.)
c/o Coopersmith, Simon and Vogel., C.P.A.s, P.C.
50 Charles Lindbergh Blvd., Ste. 605
Uniondale, NY 11553-3650 (516) 483-5800
Contact: Jeffery Coopersmith, C.F.O.

Incorporated in 1966 in NY as The Kerry Foundation, Inc. and absorbed the Edwin J. Beinecke Trust, NY, in April 1985. The new name for the combined foundations was adopted in Dec. 1985.
Donor: Sylvia B. Robinson‡.
Foundation type: Independent foundation.
Financial data (yr. ended 12/31/12): Assets, $58,828,908 (M); gifts received, $53,024; expenditures, $4,053,105; qualifying distributions, $2,945,792; giving activities include $2,292,000 for 145 grants (high: $250,000; low: $100).
Purpose and activities: Giving primarily for education and the arts, particularly museums; funding also for human services.
Fields of interest: Museums (art); Arts; Elementary/secondary education; Higher education; Education; Environment, natural resources; Botanical gardens; Boys clubs; Human services.
Type of support: General/operating support; Capital campaigns; Building/renovation; Equipment; Endowments; Conferences/seminars; Publication.
Limitations: Applications accepted. Giving primarily in CT and NY; some funding also in MA and ME. No grants to individuals; no loans.
Publications: Annual report.
Application information: Application form not required.
Initial approach: Letter
Deadline(s): None
Board meeting date(s): Spring and fall
Officers: John R. Robinson, Pres.; Abigail Phipps Bowers, V.P.; Jeffrey Coopersmith, C.F.O.; Rowland P. Robinson, Treas.
Number of staff: 2 full-time professional; 1 full-time support.
EIN: 136201175

7082
The Wiegers Family Foundation ✧ ☆
c/o Barry M. Strauss Assocs., Ltd.
307 5th Ave., 8th Fl.
New York, NY 10016-6517

Established in 1992 in CO.
Donor: George A. Wiegers.
Foundation type: Independent foundation.
Financial data (yr. ended 02/28/13): Assets, $6,095,397 (M); expenditures, $602,322; qualifying distributions, $531,891; giving activities include $520,296 for 21 grants (high: $300,000; low: $400).
Purpose and activities: Giving primarily for the arts and education.
Fields of interest: Museums (art); Arts; Higher education; Business school/education; Education.
Limitations: Applications not accepted. Giving primarily in CO and NY. No grants to individuals.
Application information: Contributes only to pre-selected organizations.
Trustees: Hans P. Utsch; E. Alexander Wiegers; Elizabeth C. Wiegers; George A. Wiegers.
EIN: 841214070
Selected grants: The following grants are a representative sample of this grantmaker's funding activity:
$15,000 to Denver Art Museum, Denver, CO, 2012. For general support.
$10,000 to Trout Unlimited, Arlington, VA, 2012. For general support.
$5,000 to Denver Public Library, Denver, CO, 2012. For general support.

7083
Malcolm Hewitt Wiener Foundation, Inc. ✧
c/o The Millburn Corp.
1270 Ave. of the Americas
New York, NY 10020-1700
Contact: Christina Padgett

Incorporated in 1984 in NY.
Donor: Malcolm H. Wiener.
Foundation type: Independent foundation.
Financial data (yr. ended 12/31/12): Assets, $46,612,019 (M); expenditures, $3,524,646; qualifying distributions, $3,059,115; giving activities include $2,776,802 for 86 grants (high: $515,000; low: $2).

Purpose and activities: Giving primarily for international affairs, arts and cultural programs, and higher education. Support also for public affairs.
Fields of interest: Museums (art); Humanities; Higher education; International affairs, goodwill promotion; International peace/security; International affairs, foreign policy.
Limitations: Applications not accepted. Giving primarily in CT, NJ, NY and PA. No grants to individuals.
Application information: Contributes only to pre-selected organizations.
Officers and Directors:* Malcolm H. Wiener,* Pres.; Harvey Beker,* V.P.; Gregg Buckbinder, Treas.; George E. Crapple,* V.P.; Martin J. Whitman; Carolyn S. Wiener.
EIN: 133250321

7084
The Wildwood Foundation ✧
(formerly The Morgens East Foundation)
c/o Morgens, Waterfall, Vintiadis
600 5th Ave., 27th Fl.
New York, NY 10020-2307

Established in 1968 in CT.
Donors: Edwin H. Morgens; Howard J. Morgens; Wildwood Trust; Wildwood Charitable Lead Annuity Trust.
Foundation type: Independent foundation.
Financial data (yr. ended 12/31/13): Assets, $25,789,011 (M); expenditures, $1,047,710; qualifying distributions, $1,032,000; giving activities include $1,016,500 for 19 grants (high: $355,000; low: $1,000).
Fields of interest: Museums (natural history); Higher education; Environment, natural resources; United Ways and Federated Giving Programs.
Limitations: Applications not accepted. Giving primarily in NY and CT; some funding also in SC. No grants to individuals.
Application information: Contributes only to pre-selected organizations.
Trustees: Edwin H. Morgens; Lauren Morgens; Linda M. Morgens.
EIN: 316090956
Selected grants: The following grants are a representative sample of this grantmaker's funding activity:
$60,000 to American Museum of Natural History, New York, NY, 2011.
$60,000 to Cornell University, Ithaca, NY, 2011.
$56,000 to Sea Education Association, Woods Hole, MA, 2011.
$54,000 to Connecticut Audubon Society, Fairfield, CT, 2011.
$50,000 to Kalmar Nyckel Foundation, Wilmington, DE, 2011.
$20,000 to Low Country Institute, Okatie, SC, 2011.
$20,000 to Montana Land Reliance, Helena, MT, 2011.
$5,000 to Greens Farms Academy, Greens Farms, CT, 2011.
$2,500 to Montana State University, Bozeman, MT, 2011.

7085
Willumstad Family Charitable Trust ✧
c/o Ayco Co.-National Tax Group
P.O. Box 15014
Albany, NY 12212-5014

Established in 2006 in NY.
Donors: Robert B. Willumstad; Carol A. Willumstad.
Foundation type: Independent foundation.
Financial data (yr. ended 12/31/12): Assets, $212,845 (M); expenditures, $3,408,278; qualifying distributions, $3,400,000; giving activities include $3,400,000 for 1 grant.
Fields of interest: Higher education.
Limitations: Applications not accepted. Giving primarily in Garden City, NY. No grants to individuals.
Application information: Contributes only to pre-selected organizations.
Trustees: Carol A. Willumstad; Robert B. Willumstad.
EIN: 206785538

7086
The Robert W. Wilson Charitable Trust ✧
c/o Robert W. Wilson
520 83rd St., Ste. 1R
Brooklyn, NY 11209-4520 (718) 748-6113

Established in 2003 in NY.
Donors: Robert W. Wilson†; Bowman Family Foundation.
Foundation type: Independent foundation.
Financial data (yr. ended 12/31/13): Assets, $58,996,503 (M); gifts received, $38,764,090; expenditures, $47,307,587; qualifying distributions, $46,463,950; giving activities include $46,086,253 for 51 grants (high: $6,816,340; low: $50).
Purpose and activities: Giving primarily for art museums, civil rights associations, historic preservation/historical societies, and environmental conservation and protection.
Fields of interest: Museums (art); Historic preservation/historical societies; Environment, natural resources; Environment; Civil/human rights, association.
Type of support: Program-related investments/ loans.
Limitations: Applications not accepted. Giving primarily in NY. No grants to individuals.
Application information: Contributes only to pre-selected organizations.
Trustee: Richard Schneidman.
EIN: 516536168
Selected grants: The following grants are a representative sample of this grantmaker's funding activity:
$8,518,762 to World Monuments Fund, New York, NY, 2012. For general support.
$5,000,000 to Wildlife Conservation Society, Bronx, NY, 2012. For general support.
$4,500,000 to New York Public Library, New York, NY, 2012. For general support.
$4,042,703 to Nature Conservancy, Arlington, VA, 2012. For general support.
$3,809,025 to Inner-City Scholarship Fund, New York, NY, 2012. For general support.
$3,089,957 to Institute for Justice, Arlington, VA, 2012. For general support.
$1,025,000 to Vera Institute of Justice, New York, NY, 2012. For general support.
$810,000 to Humane Society of the United States, Washington, DC, 2012. For general support.
$771,341 to Rainforest Alliance, New York, NY, 2012. For general support.
$230,000 to Municipal Art Society of New York, New York, NY, 2012. For general support.

7087
The H. W. Wilson Foundation, Inc. ✧
c/o William Hayden
420 Lexington Ave., Ste. 2450
New York, NY 10017-2403 (212) 972-6490
Contact: William E. Stanton, Pres.

Incorporated in 1952 in NY.
Donors: H.W. Wilson†; Mrs. H.W. Wilson†; The H.W. Wilson Co., Inc.
Foundation type: Independent foundation.
Financial data (yr. ended 11/30/13): Assets, $28,439,761 (M); expenditures, $1,270,187; qualifying distributions, $1,191,888; giving activities include $1,017,500 for 98 grants (high: $100,000; low: $500).
Purpose and activities: Grants largely to accredited library schools for scholarships; support also for cultural programs, including historical societies, and library associations.
Fields of interest: Higher education; Libraries/ library science.
Type of support: Scholarship funds; Research.
Application information: Application form required.
Initial approach: Proposal
Copies of proposal: 1
Deadline(s): None
Officers: William E. Stanton, Pres.; James M. Matarazzo, V.P.; William T. Hayden, Treas.
Director: Harold Regan.
EIN: 237418062

7088
Marie C. and Joseph C. Wilson Foundation
160 Allens Creek Rd.
Rochester, NY 14618-3309 (585) 461-4696
Contact: Carolyn Bick, Opers. Mgr.
FAX: (585) 473-5206;
E-mail: info@mcjcwilsonfoundation.org; Main URL: http://www.mcjcwilsonfoundation.org
Facebook: http://www.facebook.com/pages/ Marie-C-Joseph-C-Wilson-Foundation/ 191324530900131
Marie C. and Joseph C. Wilson Foundation's Philanthropy Promise: http://www.ncrp.org/ philanthropys-promise/who
Twitter: http://www.twitter.com/#!/ MCJCWilsonFdn

Trust established in 1963 in NY.
Donors: Katherine M. Wilson†; Joseph C. Wilson†; Marie C. Wilson†.
Foundation type: Independent foundation.
Financial data (yr. ended 12/31/13): Assets, $20,044,690 (M); expenditures, $1,128,751; qualifying distributions, $961,765; giving activities include $729,547 for 149 grants (high: $25,000; low: $500).
Purpose and activities: The mission of the foundation is to improve the quality of life through initiating and supporting projects that measurably demonstrate a means of creating a sense of belonging within the family and the community. Currently focusing on a strategic initiative to promote transformational housing (see foundation web site).
Fields of interest: Housing/shelter; Community/ economic development.
Type of support: Research; Consulting services; General/operating support; Continuing support; Equipment; Emergency funds; Program development; Conferences/seminars; Seed money;

Fellowships; Scholarship funds; Technical assistance; Program evaluation.
Limitations: Applications accepted. Giving primarily in Rochester, NY. No grants to individuals or for capital campaigns.
Publications: Application guidelines; Annual report; Financial statement; Grants list; Program policy statement.
Application information: See foundation web site for complete application information. Application form required.
Initial approach: Use online application system on foundation web site
Copies of proposal: 1
Deadline(s): Ongoing
Board meeting date(s): Fall or Spring
Final notification: Up to 4 months
Officers and Board of Managers:* Chris Kling,* Co-Chair.; Joseph Wilson,* Co-Chair.; Elenore Garton,* Vice-Chair.; Josh Kling,* Secy.; Scott Wilson,* Treas.; Megan Bell,* Exec. Dir.; Joan Dalbey; T. Dalbey; Joanie Donahue; Katherine Dalbey Ensign; Caitlin Garton; Deirdre Wilson Garton; Josie Garton; Barclay Kling; Breck Kling; Judith W. Martin; Oliver Martin; Jessa McIntosh; Katherine W. Roby; Mimi Tabah; Chris Wilson.
Trustee: JPMorgan Chase Bank, N.A.
Number of staff: 1 part-time professional; 1 part-time support.
EIN: 166042022
Selected grants: The following grants are a representative sample of this grantmaker's funding activity:
$25,000 to Wilson Commencement Park, Rochester, NY, 2012. For grant: Family Support Services.
$19,700 to University of Rochester, Rochester, NY, 2012. For grant: Court Based Mental Health Services.
$15,000 to Center for Youth Services, Rochester, NY, 2012. For grant: New Beginning School Incarcerated Teen.
$10,000 to Stepping Stones Learning Center, Rochester, NY, 2012. For grant; Expansion Program.
$8,000 to University of Rochester, Rochester, NY, 2012. For grant: Mt Hope Family Center Planning Program.
$7,500 to Rochester Area Interfaith Hospitality Network, Rochester, NY, 2012. For grant: Homeless Family Emergency Housing.
$5,000 to American Diabetes Association, Alexandria, VA, 2012. For grant; Safe at School Health Education.
$5,000 to American Lung Association, New York, NY, 2012. For grant: Home Environment Program Asthma.
$5,000 to Nazareth College of Rochester, Rochester, NY, 2012. For grant: Summer Dance Festival.
$3,000 to Wilson Commencement Park, Rochester, NY, 2012. For grant; Snowball Sponsorship.

7089
The Windmill Lane Foundation ✧
c/o Alfred J. Shuman
1 Central Park S.
New York, NY 10019-1629

Established in 2004 in DE.
Donors: Alfred J. Shuman; Stephanie J. Shuman.
Foundation type: Independent foundation.
Financial data (yr. ended 12/31/13): Assets, $6,220,065 (M); gifts received, $319,050; expenditures, $1,570,146; qualifying distributions, $1,540,443; giving activities include $1,534,579 for 35 grants (high: $233,333; low: $2).
Purpose and activities: Giving primarily for the arts and education; funding also for a cancer center.
Fields of interest: Arts, multipurpose centers/programs; Visual arts, photography; Arts; Elementary/secondary education; Education; Hospitals (specialty); Human services.
Limitations: Applications not accepted. Giving primarily in NY.
Application information: Unsolicited requests for funds not accepted.
Officers: Alfred J. Shuman, Pres.; Stephanie Shuman, V.P.
EIN: 202026907
Selected grants: The following grants are a representative sample of this grantmaker's funding activity:
$400,000 to New York City Center, New York, NY, 2011.
$333,333 to Lincoln Center Theater, New York, NY, 2011.
$300,000 to International Center of Photography, New York, NY, 2011.
$250,000 to Memorial Sloan-Kettering Cancer Center, New York, NY, 2010. For general support.
$100,000 to Rockefeller University, New York, NY, 2011.
$50,000 to New York City Center, New York, NY, 2011.
$25,000 to New York City Center, New York, NY, 2011.
$10,000 to New York City Center, New York, NY, 2011.

7090
The Jon & Abby Winkelried Foundation ✧
(formerly The Winkelried Family Foundation)
Bowling Green Sta.
P.O. Box 73
New York, NY 10274-0073

Established in 1991 in NJ.
Donor: Jon Winkelried.
Foundation type: Independent foundation.
Financial data (yr. ended 05/31/13): Assets, $11,832,011 (M); expenditures, $1,496,847; qualifying distributions, $1,490,847; giving activities include $1,490,847 for grants.
Purpose and activities: Giving primarily for education and to Jewish organizations.
Fields of interest: Higher education; Environment, land resources; Health organizations, association; Jewish federated giving programs; Jewish agencies & synagogues.
Limitations: Applications not accepted. Giving primarily in DC, IL, NJ and NY. No grants to individuals; no loans or scholarships.
Application information: Contributes only to pre-selected organizations.
Trustees: Abby Winkelried; Jon Winkelried.
EIN: 133634388
Selected grants: The following grants are a representative sample of this grantmaker's funding activity:
$25,000 to Teach for America, New York, NY, 2011. For general charitable purposes.
$5,000 to Childrens Cause for Cancer Advocacy, Washington, DC, 2011. For general charitable purposes.
$5,000 to Duke University, Durham, NC, 2011. For general charitable purposes.
$5,000 to National Cowgirl Museum and Hall of Fame, Fort Worth, TX, 2011. For general charitable purposes.
$5,000 to Teach for America, New York, NY, 2011. For general charitable purposes.
$4,500 to Tribeca Film Institute, New York, NY, 2011. For general charitable purposes.
$1,000 to MPN Foundation, Chicago, IL, 2011. For general charitable purposes.

7091
Winley Foundation ✧
100 N. Village Ave., Ste. 35
Rockville Centre, NY 11570-3712
E-mail: winleyfoundation@aol.com; Application Address: c/o, Anna M. Barone, Winley Foundation, 2517 Rte. 44, Ste. 11-199, Salt Point, NY 12578, tel.: (845) 489-3373

Established in NY.
Donor: Amory Winthrop Trust.
Foundation type: Independent foundation.
Financial data (yr. ended 12/31/13): Assets, $19,951,653 (M); expenditures, $1,487,898; qualifying distributions, $1,371,000; giving activities include $1,371,000 for 6 grants (high: $435,000; low: $60,000).
Purpose and activities: Giving is limited to the benefit of animals.
Fields of interest: Animal welfare; Animals/wildlife, preservation/protection; Animals/wildlife, sanctuaries.
Limitations: Applications accepted. Giving primarily in the greater metropolitan Washington, DC, area, including MD and VA; giving also in NY and SC. No grants to individuals.
Application information: Application form required.
Initial approach: Typewritten letter
Deadline(s): None
Officers: Heidi Prescott, Pres.; Cathy Liss, V.P.; Edward J. Walsh, Jr., Secy.; Anna M. Barone, Treas.
EIN: 521230146

7092
The Winston Foundation, Inc. ✧
(formerly The Norman and Rosita Winston Foundation, Inc.)
c/o John O'Neil, Paul, Weiss, Rifkind, Wharton & Garrison LLP
1285 Ave. of the Americas
New York, NY 10019-6064
Contact: John J. O'Neil

Incorporated in 1954 in NY.
Donors: Norman K. Winston‡; The N.K. Winston Foundation, Inc.
Foundation type: Independent foundation.
Financial data (yr. ended 06/30/13): Assets, $82,029,139 (M); expenditures, $4,654,976; qualifying distributions, $4,180,418; giving activities include $3,999,500 for 110 grants (high: $435,000; low: $1,000).
Purpose and activities: Giving primarily for higher education, including medical education, as well as for hospitals, and cultural programs.
Fields of interest: Arts; Secondary school/education; Higher education; Medical school/education; Hospitals (general).
Type of support: General/operating support.

Limitations: Applications not accepted. Giving in the U.S., with emphasis on national and local organizations in NY. No grants to individuals.
Application information: Contributes only to pre-selected organizations.
Board meeting date(s): 2 to 4 times per year
Officers and Directors:* Richard A. Rifkind,* Pres.; Lauri Levitt Friedland,* Secy.; Jan Krukowski,* Treas.
EIN: 136161672

7093
Harry Winston Hope Foundation, Inc. ✧ ☆
c/o Harry Winston, Inc.
718 5th Ave.
New York, NY 10019-4102

Established in NY.
Donors: Frederic De Narp; Daniel Rosenblum; Harry Winston, Inc.
Foundation type: Independent foundation.
Financial data (yr. ended 01/31/13): Assets, $2,919 (M); gifts received, $725,000; expenditures, $726,803; qualifying distributions, $726,500; giving activities include $726,500 for 4 grants (high: $600,000; low: $1,500).
Fields of interest: Museums (specialized); Education; Safety/disasters.
Limitations: Applications not accepted. Giving primarily in Washington, DC, MD and NY; funding also in Tokyo, Japan.
Application information: Unsolicited requests for funds not accepted.
Officers and Directors:* Robert Gannicott,* Chair.; Frederic De Narp,* Pres.; Catherine Lacaze, V.P.; Robert Scott,* Secy.-Treas.
EIN: 273042057

7094
The Winters Family Fund ✧ ☆
c/o Berdon, LLP
360 Madison Ave.
New York, NY 10017-7111

Established in 2003 in NY.
Donors: Harold D. Winters; Judith Winters.
Foundation type: Independent foundation.
Financial data (yr. ended 12/31/13): Assets, $14,317,328 (M); expenditures, $638,075; qualifying distributions, $527,950; giving activities include $523,700 for 34 grants (high: $125,000; low: $1,000).
Fields of interest: Hospitals (specialty); Human services.
Limitations: Applications not accepted. Giving primarily in NY. No grants to individuals.
Application information: Unsolicited requests for funds not accepted.
Trustees: Steven J. Meyer; Harold D. Winters; Judith Winters; Laura Winters.
EIN: 137388516

7095
Richard & Elizabeth Witten Family Foundation ✧
c/o BCRS Associates., LLC
77 Water St., 9th Fl.
New York, NY 10005-3701

Established in 1991 in NY.
Donors: Richard E. Witten; Elizabeth Witten.
Foundation type: Independent foundation.
Financial data (yr. ended 05/31/13): Assets, $6,929,083 (M); gifts received, $237,885; expenditures, $994,070; qualifying distributions, $970,970; giving activities include $966,135 for 37 grants (high: $250,000; low: $150).
Purpose and activities: Giving primarily for education; funding also for the arts, social services and to a Jewish temple.
Fields of interest: Arts; Higher education; Education; Hospitals (general); Health care, support services; Human services; Jewish agencies & synagogues.
Limitations: Applications not accepted. Giving primarily in Boston, MA, and Larchmont and New York, NY. No grants to individuals, or for scholarships; no loans.
Application information: Contributes only to pre-selected organizations.
Trustees: Elizabeth H. Witten; Richard E. Witten.
EIN: 133632751
Selected grants: The following grants are a representative sample of this grantmaker's funding activity:
$250,000 to Massachusetts General Hospital, Boston, MA, 2011. For general purpose.
$100,000 to Fidelity Charitable Gift Fund, Boston, MA, 2011. For general purpose.
$100,000 to Massachusetts General Hospital, Boston, MA, 2011. For general purpose.
$36,160 to National Museum of American Jewish History, Philadelphia, PA, 2011. For general purpose.
$25,000 to Columbia University, New York, NY, 2011. For general purpose.
$25,000 to NYU Hospital for Joint Diseases, New York, NY, 2011. For general purpose.
$20,000 to Fresh Air Fund, New York, NY, 2011. For general purpose.
$17,500 to Hunter College Foundation, New York, NY, 2011. For general purpose.
$13,841 to National Museum of American Jewish History, Philadelphia, PA, 2011. For general purpose.
$2,500 to New York Shakespeare Festival, New York, NY, 2011. For general purpose.

7096
WLC and SBC Family Foundation ✧ ☆
c/o Brown Rudnick
7 Times Sq., 47th Fl.
New York, NY 10036-6536

Established in 2007 in CT.
Donor: Peter R. Chapman.
Foundation type: Independent foundation.
Financial data (yr. ended 12/31/13): Assets, $1,583,182 (M); gifts received, $282,193; expenditures, $580,335; qualifying distributions, $538,500; giving activities include $538,500 for 14 grants (high: $356,000; low: $500).
Fields of interest: Education; Youth development; Human services.
Limitations: Applications not accepted. No grants to individuals.
Application information: Unsolicited requests for funds not accepted.
Officer: Kenneth R. Asher, Secy.
Trustees: Peter R. Chapman; Susan Chapman.
EIN: 261291625

7097
Diane & Howard Wohl Family Foundation, Inc. ✧
141 Heather Ln.
Mill Neck, NY 11765-1010

Established in 1999 in NY.
Donor: Howard Wohl.
Foundation type: Independent foundation.
Financial data (yr. ended 12/31/12): Assets, $5,860,092 (M); expenditures, $674,337; qualifying distributions, $657,722; giving activities include $655,534 for 77 grants (high: $90,000; low: $500).
Fields of interest: Arts; Education; Human services; United Ways and Federated Giving Programs; Jewish federated giving programs; Jewish agencies & synagogues.
Type of support: General/operating support.
Limitations: Applications not accepted. Giving primarily in NY. No grants to individuals.
Application information: Contributes only to pre-selected organizations.
Officers: Howard Wohl, Pres.; Diane Wohl, Secy.-Treas.
Directors: Alexander D. Wohl; Allison K. Wohl; Pamela B. Wohl; Hillary J. Wohl Zalon; Zachary Zalon.
EIN: 113493603

7098
Wolfensohn Family Foundation ✧
1350 Ave. of the Americas, Ste. 2900
New York, NY 10019-4801 (646) 731-2700
Contact: Paige Stephens, Asst. Dir.
FAX: (212) 974-1437; E-mail: info@wolfensohn.org; Additional e-mail address: pstephens@wolfensohn.com; Main URL: http://www.wolfensohn.org

Established in 1995 in NY.
Donors: James D. Wolfensohn; EJ Safra Philanthropic Foundation; Brookfield Partners Foundation.
Foundation type: Independent foundation.
Financial data (yr. ended 12/31/12): Assets, $4,136,984 (M); gifts received, $1,339,840; expenditures, $1,630,599; qualifying distributions, $1,470,799; giving activities include $1,176,170 for 170 grants (high: $200,000; low: $35).
Purpose and activities: Giving primarily to arts and cultural programs, environment and community.
Fields of interest: Arts; Education; Environment; Cancer research; Community development, neighborhood development; Jewish agencies & synagogues.
Type of support: General/operating support; Continuing support; Annual campaigns; Capital campaigns; Program development; Seed money; Research; Technical assistance.
Limitations: Applications not accepted. Giving primarily on the East Coast, with emphasis on NY and Washington, DC. Giving for environmental programs in AK and WY. Giving for religious pluralism and Jewish-Arab coexistence in Israel; giving also in Australia and England. No grants to individuals.
Application information: Contributes only to pre-selected organizations.
Board meeting date(s): Once a year, in the fall
Director: Sara R. Wolfensohn.

Trustees: Adam R. Wolfensohn; Elaine R. Wolfensohn; James D. Wolfensohn; Naomi R. Wolfensohn.
Number of staff: 2 full-time professional.
EIN: 133781581
Selected grants: The following grants are a representative sample of this grantmaker's funding activity:
$200,000 to Memorial Sloan-Kettering Cancer Center, New York, NY, 2012. Toward Larry Norton Research Suite in Breast and Imaging Center.
$50,000 to Carnegie Hall Society, New York, NY, 2012. For endowment.
$25,000 to Jewish Theological Seminary of America, New York, NY, 2012. For Louis Marshall Award Dinner honoring Mr. and Mrs Wolfensohn.
$20,000 to Harvard University, Cambridge, MA, 2012. Toward James D. Wolfensohn MBA Fellowship Fund.
$12,500 to Columbia University Medical Center, New York, NY, 2012. For Vision Center and Low Vision Rehabilitation Clinic.
$10,000 to Bretton Woods Committee, Washington, DC, 2012. For work of the committee.
$10,000 to Conservation International, Arlington, VA, 2012. To attend New York Dinner.
$10,000 to Metropolitan Opera Association, New York, NY, 2012. For membership.
$7,500 to International Rescue Committee, New York, NY, 2012. For general support.
$2,500 to Center for Global Development, Washington, DC, 2012. For Partners Council membership.

7099
Louis S. & Molly B. Wolk Foundation ✧
1600 East Ave., Ste. 701
Rochester, NY 14610-1629 (585) 442-6900

Established in 1982 in NY.
Donor: Louis S. Wolk‡.
Foundation type: Independent foundation.
Financial data (yr. ended 12/31/13): Assets, $31,803,854 (M); expenditures, $1,608,818; qualifying distributions, $1,456,402; giving activities include $1,283,750 for 23 grants (high: $200,000; low: $500).
Purpose and activities: Giving primarily to organizations in the greater Rochester, New York area whose goals are focused on health related, educational, geriatric and social issues.
Fields of interest: Health care; Health organizations; Youth development, scouting agencies (general); Human services; Family services, domestic violence; Jewish agencies & synagogues.
Limitations: Applications accepted. Giving primarily in Rochester, NY. No grants to individuals.
Application information: Application form required.
Initial approach: Proposal
Deadline(s): None
Final notification: Monthly
Officers and Trustees:* Alvin L. Ureles, M.D., Chair.; Marvin L. Wolk,* Mgr.; Michael B. Berger; Harold Samloff; David M. Wolk; Jeremy J. Wolk.
EIN: 222405596
Selected grants: The following grants are a representative sample of this grantmaker's funding activity:
$1,000,000 to University of Rochester, Rochester, NY, 2011.
$100,000 to University of Rochester, Rochester, NY, 2011.
$47,500 to Jewish Community Federation of Greater Rochester, Rochester, NY, 2011. For annual campaign.
$46,160 to University of Rochester, Rochester, NY, 2011.
$25,000 to NYSARC, Monroe County Chapter, Rochester, NY, 2011. For general operating fund.
$15,000 to Rochester Regional Community Design Center, Rochester, NY, 2011. For general operating fund.
$3,350 to Temple Brith Kodesh, Rochester, NY, 2011. For general operating fund.

7100
The Wolstencroft Family Foundation ✧
Bowling Green Sta.
P.O. Box 73
New York, NY 10274-0073

Established in 1997 in IL.
Donor: Tracy Wolstencroft.
Foundation type: Independent foundation.
Financial data (yr. ended 12/31/13): Assets, $21,961,185 (M); expenditures, $802,057; qualifying distributions, $710,000; giving activities include $710,000 for 14 grants (high: $150,000; low: $5,000).
Fields of interest: Higher education, college; Animals/wildlife, preservation/protection.
Type of support: General/operating support.
Limitations: Applications not accepted. Giving primarily in CT, NY and ME. No grants to individuals.
Application information: Contributes only to pre-selected organizations.
Trustees: Catherine Wolstencroft; Tracy Wolstencroft.
EIN: 133976344
Selected grants: The following grants are a representative sample of this grantmaker's funding activity:
$100,000 to Brookings Institution, Washington, DC, 2011. For general charitable purposes.
$100,000 to International Rescue Committee, New York, NY, 2011. For general charitable purposes.
$5,000 to Bridges of Understanding Foundation, Washington, DC, 2011. For general charitable purposes.
$5,000 to Sun Valley Writers Conference, Ketchum, ID, 2011. For general charitable purposes.
$2,000 to Audubon Connecticut, Greenwich, CT, 2011. For general charitable purposes.

7101
Woodcock Foundation ✧
c/o Rock Co.
30 Rockefeller Plz.
New York, NY 10112-0015
Contact: Wendy Goldner
Main URL: http://woodcockfdn.org/

Established in NY.
Foundation type: Independent foundation.
Financial data (yr. ended 11/30/13): Assets, $37,919,936 (M); expenditures, $3,471,357; qualifying distributions, $2,639,424; giving activities include $2,200,155 for 19 grants (high: $314,990; low: $2,665), and $357,541 for foundation-administered programs.
Purpose and activities: Giving primarily in the areas of social enterprise, reproductive health and rights, land conservation, media reform and civil society.
Fields of interest: Environment, land resources; Reproductive health, family planning; Human services.
Limitations: Applications not accepted.
Application information: Unsolicited requests for funds not accepted. Applicants who have been invited to submit a proposal should refer to submission process on foundation web site.
Trustees: Olga M. Davidson; Stuart Davidson; Jeremy Guth; Winthrop Rutherfurd, Esq.; Lindsay D. Shea.
EIN: 341606085

7102
Woodshouse Foundation ✧
(formerly The Biggs Foundation)
522 5th Ave., Ste. 1000
New York, NY 10036-7601

Established in 1992 in CT.
Donors: Judith L. Biggs; Wende B. Ractliffe; Barton M. Biggs Charitable Remainder Unitrust.
Foundation type: Independent foundation.
Financial data (yr. ended 12/31/13): Assets, $11,618,463 (M); gifts received, $4,095,032; expenditures, $809,140; qualifying distributions, $759,500; giving activities include $759,500 for 35 grants (high: $150,000; low: $3,000).
Fields of interest: Education; Environment; Animal welfare; Human services.
Limitations: Applications not accepted. Giving primarily in MD and NY; giving also in France.
Application information: Contributes only to pre-selected organizations.
Trustees: Barton W. Biggs; Gretchen Biggs; Wende Biggs Ractliffe.
Board Members: Kanisa Collings; Penelope Hovington; Vincent Black.
EIN: 136983078
Selected grants: The following grants are a representative sample of this grantmaker's funding activity:
$20,000 to Alliance for Childhood, New York, NY, 2011.
$20,000 to National Family Farm Coalition, Washington, DC, 2011.
$10,000 to Nature Institute, Ghent, NY, 2011.
$4,000 to Convoy of Hope, Springfield, MO, 2011.
$3,000 to Alliance for Global Justice, Washington, DC, 2011.

7103
Work Force Investment Board Of Rockland County Inc. ✧ ☆
2 New Hempstead Rd., 1st Fl.
New City, NY 10956

Foundation type: Independent foundation.
Financial data (yr. ended 06/30/13): Assets, $433,900 (M); gifts received, $634,398; expenditures, $634,440; qualifying distributions, $634,440; giving activities include $481,495 for 3 grants (high: $245,868; low: $17,482).
Fields of interest: Youth.
Limitations: Applications not accepted. Giving primarily in New City, NY.
Application information: Unsolicited requests for funds not acceped.
Officer: Richard Struck, Chair.
Directors: Lynne Allen; Bill Boydston; Elaine Cunningham; Martin Devaney; Mike Ditullo; Robert

Dutra; Craig Jacobs; Mary Shinick; Debra Thomas; and 12 additional directors.
EIN: 134147474

7104
The Wright Family Foundation, Inc. ✧
P.O. Box 1046
Schenectady, NY 12301-1046 (518) 347-4530
FAX: (518) 347-6201;
E-mail: info@wrightfamilyfoundation.org; Main URL: http://www.wrightfamilyfoundation.org

Established in 1997 in Schenectady, NY.
Donor: SIGroup, Inc.
Foundation type: Independent foundation.
Financial data (yr. ended 09/30/13): Assets, $20,971,810 (M); expenditures, $912,994; qualifying distributions, $1,258,967; giving activities include $768,706 for 31 grants (high: $104,490; low: $1,200).
Purpose and activities: Funding for community, education, health, social needs, and the arts.
Fields of interest: Arts; Higher education; Libraries (public); Education; Health care; Human services; YM/YWCAs & YM/YWHAs; Community/economic development.
Type of support: Capital campaigns; Building/renovation; Equipment; Matching/challenge support.
Limitations: Applications accepted. Giving limited to Schenectady County, NY, and surrounding counties, Cocke County, TN, and Brazoria County, TX. No support for religious or political organizations. No grants to individuals, or for annual campaigns, athletic events, social functions, advertising, underwriting or administrative support.
Publications: Application guidelines; Annual report.
Application information: Funding requests under $1,000 will not be considered. See foundation website for complete application guidelines and procedures. Application form required.
Initial approach: Online application system on foundation website
Copies of proposal: 1
Deadline(s): Jan. 15, May 15, Aug. 15, and Nov. 15
Board meeting date(s): Quarterly
Officers: Ashley G. Gardner, Chair.; A. Malcolm MacCormick, Vice-Chair.; Linda Nizolek, Secy.; Robert D. McQueen, Treas.; Heather M. Ward, Exec. Dir.
Number of staff: 1 part-time professional.
EIN: 141798255

7105
WSB Family Foundation ✧ ☆
595 New Loudon Rd., Ste. 123
Latham, NY 12110

Donor: Walter S. Borisenok.
Foundation type: Independent foundation.
Financial data (yr. ended 12/31/13): Assets, $6,599,520 (M); gifts received, $129,131; expenditures, $727,569; qualifying distributions, $583,639; giving activities include $583,639 for 27 grants (high: $500,000; low: $75).
Fields of interest: Education; Animals/wildlife; Human services.
Limitations: Applications not accepted. Giving primarily in NY.
Application information: Unsolicited requests for funds not accepted.
Officers: Walter S. Borisenok, Pres.; Michelle C. Borisenok, V.P.; Michael A. Borisenok, Secy.; Nicole W. Borisenok, Treas.
EIN: 461204082

7106
Wunsch Foundation, Inc. ✧ ☆
902 Broadway, Ste. 1603
New York, NY 10010-6029

Incorporated in 1943 in NY.
Donors: Joseph W. Wunsch; Eric M. Wunsch; Samuel Wunsch; WEA Enterprises Co., Inc.; 9th Avenue Equities; 63rd Street Equities.
Foundation type: Independent foundation.
Financial data (yr. ended 12/31/12): Assets, $9,541,875 (M); gifts received, $212,940; expenditures, $459,256; qualifying distributions, $433,345; giving activities include $433,345 for 53 grants (high: $160,000; low: $200).
Purpose and activities: Funding primarily for higher education and for museums.
Fields of interest: Visual arts; Museums; Museums (art); Arts; Education; Health care; Jewish federated giving programs.
Limitations: Applications not accepted. Giving primarily in NY. No grants to individuals.
Application information: Contributes only to pre-selected organizations.
Officers: Eric M. Wunsch, Pres.; Ethel Wunsch, Secy.; Peter Wunsch, Treas.
EIN: 116006013
Selected grants: The following grants are a representative sample of this grantmaker's funding activity:
$13,000 to City Harvest, New York, NY, 2012. For social assistance/poverty.

7107
The YAD Charity Foundation ✧ ☆
(formerly The JHD Charity Foundation)
c/o Cliffside
119-19 Graham Ct.
Flushing, NY 11354-1047

Established in 2007 in NY.
Donors: Jack Deutsch; Moishe Deutsch; Stuart Neuhauser; Yeshiva Tov V'Chesed.
Foundation type: Independent foundation.
Financial data (yr. ended 12/31/13): Assets, $1,558,704 (M); gifts received, $630,073; expenditures, $830,876; qualifying distributions, $822,974; giving activities include $816,070 for 192 grants (high: $125,000; low: $18).
Purpose and activities: Giving primarily to Jewish agencies, temples, and schools.
Fields of interest: Education; Jewish agencies & synagogues.
Limitations: Applications not accepted. Giving primarily in Monsey, NY. No grants to individuals.
Application information: Unsolicited requests for funds not accepted.
Trustees: Jack Deutsch; Moishe Deutsch.
EIN: 260512851
Selected grants: The following grants are a representative sample of this grantmaker's funding activity:
$3,000 to Ahavas Chaverim Gemilas Chesed, Monsey, NY, 2011.

7108
Yad Miriam Foundation Inc. ✧ ☆
c/o Roth & Co., LLP
1428 36th St., Ste. 200
Brooklyn, NY 11218

Established in 2006 in NY.
Donor: Israel M. Tyberg.
Foundation type: Independent foundation.
Financial data (yr. ended 06/30/13): Assets, $954,867 (M); gifts received, $204,920; expenditures, $515,231; qualifying distributions, $509,660; giving activities include $509,660 for 35 grants (high: $55,000; low: $360).
Fields of interest: Jewish agencies & synagogues; Indigenous peoples.
Limitations: Applications not accepted. Giving primarily in NY.
Application information: Contributes only to pre-selected organizations.
Directors: Israel M. Tyberg; Miriam L. Tyberg; Yehudit Zoberman.
EIN: 203992820
Selected grants: The following grants are a representative sample of this grantmaker's funding activity:
$5,500 to Bonei Olam, Brooklyn, NY, 2013. For Helping Infertile Couples.

7109
Yashar Foundation, Inc. ✧ ☆
3266 Bedford Ave.
Brooklyn, NY 11210-4509
Contact: Michael Kaplan, Exec. Dir.

Established in 2007 in NY.
Donors: Joe and Eileen Sutton Foundation; Yumark Enterprises; Ouyalady Corporation.
Foundation type: Independent foundation.
Financial data (yr. ended 12/31/12): Assets, $3,425,676 (M); gifts received, $3,000,000; expenditures, $1,207,255; qualifying distributions, $1,207,255; giving activities include $1,200,441 for 73 grants (high: $106,000; low: $20).
Fields of interest: Education; Jewish agencies & synagogues.
Limitations: Applications accepted. Giving primarily in NY. No grants to individuals.
Application information: Application form not required.
Deadline(s): None
Officer: Michael Kaplan, Exec. Dir.
Directors: Gizelle Kaplan; Yitzcak Kaplan.
EIN: 260770603

7110
YLRY, Inc. ✧
477 Madison Ave., 10th Fl.
New York, NY 10022-5802

Established in 1992 in NY.
Donor: Legacy Heritage Fund, Ltd.
Foundation type: Independent foundation.
Financial data (yr. ended 12/31/13): Assets, $40,725,191 (M); expenditures, $1,924,834; qualifying distributions, $1,752,161; giving activities include $1,743,349 for 14 grants (high: $510,000; low: $35).
Fields of interest: Jewish federated giving programs.
Limitations: Applications not accepted. Giving in Israel and PA. No grants to individuals.

Application information: Contributes only to pre-selected organizations.
Officer and Directors:* Susan R. Wexner,* Pres. and Secy.-Treas.; Saul G. Agus; Raymond Kanner; Gregg H. Levy, Esq.; Michael S. Oberman, Esq.; Mark Saks, Esq.; Walter Stern.
EIN: 133722745

7111
The Young Family Charitable Foundation ✧
c/o EOS Partners, L.P.
320 Park Ave., 22nd Fl.
New York, NY 10022-6815

Established in 1991 in NY.
Donors: Brian D. Young; Anne Young.
Foundation type: Independent foundation.
Financial data (yr. ended 06/30/13): Assets, $346,516 (M); gifts received, $502,670; expenditures, $792,805; qualifying distributions, $791,402; giving activities include $790,000 for 5 grants (high: $500,000; low: $25,000).
Fields of interest: Higher education; Catholic agencies & churches.
Limitations: Applications not accepted. Giving primarily in Cambridge, MA and in Bridgeport, CT. No grants to individuals.
Application information: Contributes only to pre-selected organizations.
Trustee: Brian D. Young.
EIN: 136976453
Selected grants: The following grants are a representative sample of this grantmaker's funding activity:
$1,215,534 to Harvard College Fund, Cambridge, MA, 2011.
$40,000 to Squam Lakes Conservation Society, Holderness, NH, 2011.
$30,000 to Mayors Fund to Advance New York City, New York, NY, 2011.
$5,000 to Holy Family Passionist Retreat Center, West Hartford, CT, 2011.
$3,000 to Bottomless Closet, New York, NY, 2011.

7112
Youths' Friends Association, Inc. ✧
c/o BDO Usa, LLP
100 Park Ave.
New York, NY 10017-5387
Application address: c/o Walter J. Graver, 69 Bayard Cove Rd., Hilton Head, SC 29928

Incorporated in 1950 in NY.
Donors: Johan J. Smit‡; Mrs. Johan J. Smit‡.
Foundation type: Independent foundation.
Financial data (yr. ended 12/31/13): Assets, $10,338,891 (M); expenditures, $577,937; qualifying distributions, $546,957; giving activities include $466,900 for 117 grants (high: $12,000; low: $1,000).
Purpose and activities: Grants largely for international relief, and higher and secondary education, through scholarship support earmarked for high school students; support also for social services, youth, health, and cultural programs.
Fields of interest: Arts; Secondary school/education; Higher education; Health care; Health organizations, association; Human services; Children/youth, services; Children, adoption; International relief; Children; Youth.
Type of support: General/operating support; Seed money; Scholarship funds.
Limitations: Applications accepted. Giving on a national basis. No grants to individuals.
Publications: Financial statement.
Application information: Application form required.
Initial approach: Letter
Copies of proposal: 1
Deadline(s): None
Board meeting date(s): Semiannually
Officers and Directors:* Sheila M. Smit,* Pres.; Stephen C. Smit,* V.P.; Walter J. Graver,* Secy.-Treas.; Evan Kirchen; Helen S. Kirchen; Robert V. Kirchen; Judith L. Rist; Peta Smit Santos; Lisa Smit; Barbara Weiler.
Number of staff: 1 part-time support.
EIN: 136097828

7113
Barbara M. and David Zalaznick Foundation ✧
c/o Eric Kaplan and Barbara Zalaznick
335 Madison Ave., Ste. 1500
New York, NY 10017-4611

Established in 1996 in NY.
Donors: Irma Milstein; Paul Milstein‡; Barbara Zalaznick; David Zalaznick; Milstein Family Foundation.
Foundation type: Independent foundation.
Financial data (yr. ended 12/31/13): Assets, $14,620,990 (M); gifts received, $300,750; expenditures, $2,166,733; qualifying distributions, $2,049,579; giving activities include $2,047,800 for 52 grants (high: $1,560,500; low: $90).
Fields of interest: Performing arts; Arts; Higher education.
Limitations: Applications not accepted. Giving primarily in New York, NY. No grants to individuals.
Application information: Contributes only to pre-selected organizations.
Trustees: Irma Milstein; Barbara Zalaznick; David Zalaznick.
EIN: 133921831

7114
The Zankel Fund ✧
c/o Hecht and Co., P.C.
622 3rd Ave., 68th Fl.
New York, NY 10118

Foundation type: Independent foundation.
Financial data (yr. ended 12/31/12): Assets, $46,696,735 (M); expenditures, $2,644,841; qualifying distributions, $2,474,077; giving activities include $2,464,434 for 141 grants (high: $250,000; low: $400).
Purpose and activities: Giving primarily for the arts and education.
Fields of interest: Performing arts, circus arts; Arts; Higher education; Education; Hospitals (general); Health organizations, association; Human services.
Limitations: Applications not accepted. Giving primarily in New York, NY.
Application information: Contributes only to pre-selected organizations.
Officers and Directors:* James Zankel,* Co-Pres.; Judy Francis Zankel,* Co-Pres.; Mark Zankel,* Co-Pres.
EIN: 352319507

Selected grants: The following grants are a representative sample of this grantmaker's funding activity:
$10,000 to Columbia University, Law School, New York, NY, 2012. For unrestricted charitable purposes.

7115
The Lois and Andrew Zaro Family Charitable Trust ✧
521 5th Ave., Rm. 1804
New York, NY 10175-1804

Established in 2002 in NY.
Donors: Lois Zaro; Andrew Zaro.
Foundation type: Independent foundation.
Financial data (yr. ended 12/31/13): Assets, $824,475 (M); gifts received, $666,290; expenditures, $721,754; qualifying distributions, $719,904; giving activities include $719,804 for 46 grants (high: $192,005; low: $100).
Fields of interest: Arts; Education; Medical research, institute; Jewish agencies & synagogues.
Limitations: Applications not accepted. Giving primarily in New York, NY. No grants to individuals.
Application information: Contributes only to pre-selected organizations.
Trustee: Lois Zaro.
EIN: 306035876

7116
The Zegar Family Foundation ✧
c/o Geller & Co.
P.O. Box 1510
New York, NY 10150-1501
Charles and Merryl Snow Zegar's Giving Pledge Profile: http://glasspockets.org/philanthropy-in-focus/eye-on-the-giving-pledge/profiles/zegar

Established in 2006 in NY.
Donor: Charles M. Zegar.
Foundation type: Independent foundation.
Financial data (yr. ended 12/31/13): Assets, $119,045,173 (M); gifts received, $26,324,931; expenditures, $4,528,944; qualifying distributions, $3,489,994; giving activities include $3,479,994 for 43 grants (high: $1,500,660; low: $1,000).
Fields of interest: Higher education; Hospitals (general); Human services; Foundations (public).
Limitations: Applications not accepted. Giving primarily in New York, NY. No grants to individuals.
Application information: Contributes only to pre-selected organizations.
Trustees: Charles M. Zegar; Merryl Snow Zegar.
EIN: 137548507

7117
The Zegarac-Pollock Family Foundation ✧
2211 Broadway, Ste. 9AB
New York, NY 10024-6263

Donors: Jonathan D. Pollock; Tea Nadezda Zegarac-Pollock.
Foundation type: Independent foundation.
Financial data (yr. ended 12/31/13): Assets, $4,886,047 (M); expenditures, $605,207; qualifying distributions, $605,000; giving activities include $605,000 for 4 grants (high: $500,000; low: $10,000).

Purpose and activities: Giving primarily to an Episcopal school.
Fields of interest: Elementary/secondary education; Health care, single organization support.
Limitations: Applications not accepted. Giving primarily in New York, NY and Cleveland, OH.
Application information: Unsolicited requests for funds not accepted.
Trustees: Jonathan D. Pollock; Tea Nadezda Zegarac-Pollock.
EIN: 271497602
Selected grants: The following grants are a representative sample of this grantmaker's funding activity:
$250,000 to Cleveland Clinic Foundation, Cleveland, OH, 2011.
$25,000 to All Stars Project, New York, NY, 2010.

7118
The Jacquelyn & Gregory Zehner Foundation ✧
c/o BCRS Assocs., LLC
77 Water St., 9th Fl.
New York, NY 10005-4414

Established in 1996 in NY.
Donors: Gregory H. Zehner; Jacquelyn M. Hoffman-Zehner.
Foundation type: Independent foundation.
Financial data (yr. ended 07/31/13): Assets, $13,802,947 (M); expenditures, $820,359; qualifying distributions, $727,290; giving activities include $541,792 for 58 grants (high: $160,000; low: $500).
Fields of interest: Arts; Education; Philanthropy/voluntarism; Christian agencies & churches; Women.
Type of support: General/operating support.
Limitations: Applications not accepted. Giving primarily in New York, NY, San Francisco, CA, CT, and UT. No grants to individuals.
Application information: Contributes only to pre-selected organizations.
Trustees: Jacquelyn M. Hoffman-Zehner; Gregory H. Zehner.
EIN: 133971019
Selected grants: The following grants are a representative sample of this grantmaker's funding activity:
$200,000 to Womens Funding Network, San Francisco, CA, 2011.
$75,000 to Give Me an Answer, New Canaan, CT, 2011.
$25,000 to Global Partners for Development, Rohnert Park, CA, 2011.
$25,000 to Impact Partners, New York, NY, 2011.
$15,000 to Sundance Institute, Park City, UT, 2011.
$10,000 to Acumen Fund, New York, NY, 2011.
$10,000 to K2 the Church, Salt Lake City, UT, 2011.
$10,000 to San Francisco Film Society, San Francisco, CA, 2011.
$5,000 to Hope for Haiti, Naples, FL, 2011.
$5,000 to Love146, New Haven, CT, 2011.

7119
Lillian Zeides Foundation ✧
36 W. 25th St., Apt. 7G
New York, NY 10001-2706

Donor: Lillian Zeides.
Foundation type: Operating foundation.
Financial data (yr. ended 06/30/13): Assets, $2,071,680 (M); expenditures, $2,006,361; qualifying distributions, $1,996,322; giving activities include $1,996,322 for 68 grants (high: $1,000,000; low: $18).
Fields of interest: Education; Human services; Community/economic development; Jewish agencies & synagogues.
Limitations: Applications not accepted.
Application information: Unsolicited requests for funds not accepted.
Officer: Joshua Fisheman, Secy.
Director: Lillian Zeides.
EIN: 270504301
Selected grants: The following grants are a representative sample of this grantmaker's funding activity:
$62,000 to Yeshiva University, New York, NY, 2011.
$1,100 to National Jewish Health, Denver, CO, 2011.

7120
Zichron Avraham Abba Foundation ✧
1360 E. 14th St., Ste. 101
Brooklyn, NY 11230-5961

Established in 1998 in NY.
Donors: Leon Goldenberg; Chaim Goldenberg.
Foundation type: Independent foundation.
Financial data (yr. ended 12/31/13): Assets, $3,305,753 (M); gifts received, $1,470,000; expenditures, $695,279; qualifying distributions, $695,029; giving activities include $695,029 for grants.
Purpose and activities: Giving primarily for Jewish education, temples, and organizations.
Fields of interest: Education; Jewish agencies & synagogues.
Type of support: General/operating support.
Limitations: Applications not accepted. Giving primarily in NY. No grants to individuals.
Application information: Contributes only to pre-selected organizations.
Officers: Leon Goldenberg, Pres.; Agnes Goldenberg, V.P.
Trustee: Chaim Goldenberg.
EIN: 113412101

7121
The Bill and Ann Ziff Foundation ✧
c/o Ziff Brothers Investments, LLC
350 Park Ave., 4th Fl.
New York, NY 10022-6067

Established in 2007 in NY and DE.
Donors: Daniel M. Ziff; Dirk E. Ziff; Robert M. Ziff.
Foundation type: Independent foundation.
Financial data (yr. ended 12/31/13): Assets, $34,487,875 (M); expenditures, $5,551,994; qualifying distributions, $5,536,342; giving activities include $5,521,469 for 35 grants (high: $3,000,000; low: $1,969).
Fields of interest: Performing arts centers; Performing arts, music; Performing arts, opera; Botanical gardens; Environment.
Limitations: Applications not accepted. Giving primarily in New York, NY. No grants to individuals.
Application information: Contributes only to pre-selected organizations.
Officers and Director:* Ann Ziff,* Pres.; Spencer Lehv, V.P. and Treas.; Steven C. Feinman, V.P.; David Gray, Secy.
EIN: 261437399

7122
The Leslie and Daniel Ziff Foundation ✧
(formerly The Daniel M. Ziff Foundation)
c/o ZBI, LLC
350 Park Ave., 4th Fl.
New York, NY 10022-6067

Established in DE.
Donor: Ziff Investment Partnership LP II.
Foundation type: Independent foundation.
Financial data (yr. ended 12/31/13): Assets, $3,555,309 (M); expenditures, $1,233,191; qualifying distributions, $1,230,801; giving activities include $1,229,200 for 12 grants (high: $325,000; low: $2,500).
Fields of interest: Performing arts, dance; Performing arts, ballet; Environment, natural resources; Hospitals (general); Human services.
Limitations: Applications not accepted. Giving primarily in NY. No grants to individuals.
Application information: Contributes only to pre-selected organizations.
Officers: Daniel M. Ziff, Co-Pres.; Leslie Ziff, Co-Pres.; David Gray, V.P. and Secy.; Spencer Lehv, V.P. and Treas.
EIN: 134083253
Selected grants: The following grants are a representative sample of this grantmaker's funding activity:
$750,000 to Natural Resources Defense Council, New York, NY, 2011. For general support.
$700,000 to Community Foundation of Northwest Mississippi, Hernando, MS, 2011.
$300,000 to Chamber of Commerce Foundation, District of Columbia, Washington, DC, 2011.
$200,000 to CEC Stuyvesant Cove, New York, NY, 2011.
$150,000 to Polaris Dance Theater, Portland, OR, 2011.
$50,000 to Girls Club of New York, Lower East Side, New York, NY, 2011.
$30,000 to Northside Center for Child Development, New York, NY, 2011.
$25,000 to American Museum of Natural History, New York, NY, 2011. For general support.
$25,000 to Conservation International, Arlington, VA, 2011. For general support.
$25,000 to Ovarian Cancer Research Fund, New York, NY, 2011. For general support.

7123
The Natasha & Dirk Ziff Foundation ✧
(formerly The Dirk E. Ziff Foundation)
c/o ZBI, LLC
350 Park Ave., 4th Fl.
New York, NY 10022-6022

Established in 2000 in DE.
Donors: Dirk Ziff; Ziff Investment Partnership LP II.
Foundation type: Independent foundation.
Financial data (yr. ended 12/31/13): Assets, $4,973,507 (M); expenditures, $525,078; qualifying distributions, $482,959; giving activities include $441,600 for 4 grants (high: $400,000; low: $8,300).

Fields of interest: Education; Human services; Foundations (private grantmaking).
Limitations: Applications not accepted. Giving primarily in MA and New York, NY. No grants to individuals.
Application information: Contributes only to pre-selected organizations.
Officers: Dirk E. Ziff, Pres.; David Gray, V.P. and Secy.; Spencer Lehv, V.P. and Treas.
Director: Natasha B. Ziff.
EIN: 134083748
Selected grants: The following grants are a representative sample of this grantmaker's funding activity:
$250,000 to Film Society of Lincoln Center, New York, NY, 2011. For general support.
$95,000 to Sea the World Productions, Chilmark, MA, 2011.
$25,000 to FARM Institute, Edgartown, MA, 2011. For general support.
$16,650 to Breast Cancer Research Foundation, New York, NY, 2011. For general support.
$15,000 to Sea the World Productions, Chilmark, MA, 2011.
$8,300 to Gay Mens Health Crisis, New York, NY, 2011. For general support.
$2,500 to Aspen Center for Environmental Studies, Aspen, CO, 2011. For general support.
$2,500 to Aspen Center for Environmental Studies, Aspen, CO, 2011. For general support.

7124
ZIIZ, Inc. ✧
477 Madison Ave., 10th Fl.
New York, NY 10022-5802

Established in 2000 in DE and NY.
Donor: Susan Wexner Revocable Trust.
Foundation type: Independent foundation.
Financial data (yr. ended 03/31/13): Assets, $36,526,645 (M); expenditures, $1,797,872; qualifying distributions, $1,610,018; giving activities include $1,605,255 for 17 grants (high: $500,000; low: $2).
Purpose and activities: Giving primarily for community development, particularly the construction of a pediatric hospital.
Fields of interest: Hospitals (specialty); Economic development; Jewish agencies & synagogues.
Limitations: Applications not accepted. Giving primarily in New York, NY and in Israel. No grants to individuals.
Application information: Contributes only to pre-selected organizations.
Officer and Directors:* Susan Wexner,* Pres. and Secy.-Treas.; Saul Agus; Raymond Kanner; Gregg H. Levy, Esq.; Michael S. Oberman, Esq.; Mark Saks, Esq.; Walter Stern.
EIN: 134031038
Selected grants: The following grants are a representative sample of this grantmaker's funding activity:
$110,000 to Partnership for Excellence in Jewish Education, Boston, MA, 2013. For organization's Programming to improve efficiency of revenue generation in support of Jewish education.

7125
The Zilkha Foundation, Inc. ✧
450 Park Ave., Ste. 2102
New York, NY 10022-2675
Contact: Ezra K. Zilkha, Pres. and Treas.

Incorporated in 1948 in NY.
Donors: Zilkha & Sons, Inc.; Ezra K. Zilkha; Cecile E. Zilkha.
Foundation type: Company-sponsored foundation.
Financial data (yr. ended 08/31/13): Assets, $728,963 (M); gifts received, $450,000; expenditures, $544,221; qualifying distributions, $540,620; giving activities include $536,990 for 47 grants (high: $100,000; low: $50).
Purpose and activities: The foundation supports organizations involved with opera, K-12 and higher education, human services, international affairs, public policy research, and Judaism.
Fields of interest: Performing arts, opera; Elementary/secondary education; Higher education; Human services; International affairs, foreign policy; Jewish federated giving programs; Public policy, research; Jewish agencies & synagogues.
Type of support: General/operating support.
Limitations: Applications not accepted. Giving primarily in New York, NY. No grants to individuals.
Application information: Contributions only to pre-selected organizations.
Board meeting date(s): Dec.
Officers and Directors:* Ezra K. Zilkha,* Pres. and Treas.; Cecile E. Zilkha,* V.P. and Secy.; Donald Zilkha.
EIN: 136090739
Selected grants: The following grants are a representative sample of this grantmaker's funding activity:
$379,500 to Brookings Institution, Washington, DC, 2011.
$123,660 to Metropolitan Opera, New York, NY, 2011.
$95,000 to Wesleyan University, Middletown, CT, 2011.
$93,000 to Lycee Francais de New York, New York, NY, 2011.
$55,000 to Council on Foreign Relations, New York, NY, 2011.
$20,500 to UJA-Federation of New York, New York, NY, 2011.
$20,000 to American Hospital of Paris Foundation, New York, NY, 2011.
$3,000 to French Institute Alliance Francaise, New York, NY, 2011.
$1,000 to French-American Foundation, New York, NY, 2011.
$1,000 to Weill Medical College of Cornell University, New York, NY, 2011.

7126
Barry L. and Jan R. Zubrow Foundation ✧ ☆
c/o BCRS Assocs., LLC
77 Water St., 9th Fl.
New York, NY 10005-4414

Established in 1989 in NY.
Donors: Barry L. Zubrow; Jan Rock Zubrow.
Foundation type: Independent foundation.
Financial data (yr. ended 06/30/13): Assets, $2,685,274 (M); gifts received, $1,668,200; expenditures, $883,557; qualifying distributions, $869,910; giving activities include $868,515 for 38 grants (high: $400,000; low: $200).
Purpose and activities: Giving primarily for higher education, as well as for the arts, and to Jewish organizations and temples.
Fields of interest: Arts; Higher education; Jewish federated giving programs; Jewish agencies & synagogues.
Limitations: Applications not accepted. Giving primarily in NJ, and Ithaca and New York, NY; some funding also in PA. No grants to individuals.
Application information: Contributes only to pre-selected organizations.
Trustees: Richard M. Hayden; Barry L. Zubrow; Jan Rock Zubrow.
EIN: 133532026
Selected grants: The following grants are a representative sample of this grantmaker's funding activity:
$1,300,000 to Cornell University, Ithaca, NY, 2011. For general purpose.
$200,000 to Haverford College, Haverford, PA, 2011. For general purpose.
$100,000 to Far Hills Country Day School, Far Hills, NJ, 2011. For general purpose.
$75,000 to Morristown-Beard School, Morristown, NJ, 2011. For general purpose.
$25,000 to Foundation for Morristown Medical Center, Morristown, NJ, 2011. For general purpose.
$10,000 to Winston School, Short Hills, NJ, 2011. For general purpose.
$7,500 to Sir John Soanes Museum, London, England, 2011. For general purpose.
$7,000 to Metropolitan Opera, New York, NY, 2011. For general purpose.
$5,000 to Corporate Angel Network, White Plains, NY, 2011. For general purpose.
$5,000 to Nantucket Cottage Hospital, Nantucket, MA, 2011. For general purpose.

7127
The Donald & Barbara Zucker Family Foundation ✧
103 W. 55th St.
New York, NY 10019-5306

Established in 2006 in NY.
Donor: Donald Zucker.
Foundation type: Independent foundation.
Financial data (yr. ended 11/30/12): Assets, $23,870,344 (M); gifts received, $10,000,000; expenditures, $3,886,423; qualifying distributions, $3,884,236; giving activities include $3,884,236 for 146 grants (high: $1,600,000; low: $25).
Fields of interest: Museums; Animals/wildlife; Hospitals (general); Jewish agencies & synagogues.
Limitations: Applications not accepted. Giving primarily in NY.
Application information: Contributes only to pre-selected organizations.
Officers: Donald Zucker, Pres.; Barbara Zucker Albinder, V.P.; Laurie Zucker Lederman, V.P.; Barbara Hrbek Zucker, Secy.-Treas.
EIN: 203932106

7128
Roy J. Zuckerberg Family Foundation ✧
(also known as Roy J. Zuckerberg Foundation)
c/o BCRS Assocs., LLC
77 Water St., 9th Fl.
New York, NY 10005-4414

Established in 1980 in NY.

Donor: Roy J. Zuckerberg.
Foundation type: Independent foundation.
Financial data (yr. ended 09/30/13): Assets, $9,004,455 (M); gifts received, $1,733,153; expenditures, $2,537,375; qualifying distributions, $2,416,056; giving activities include $2,415,661 for 149 grants (high: $256,110; low: $36).
Purpose and activities: Giving primarily to museums, hospitals, health associations, human services and Jewish federated giving programs.
Fields of interest: Museums; Hospitals (general); Health organizations, association; Human services; Jewish federated giving programs.
Limitations: Applications not accepted. Giving primarily in the greater metropolitan New York, NY, area. No grants to individuals, or for scholarships; no loans.
Application information: Contributes only to pre-selected organizations.
Trustees: James C. Kautz; Barbara Zuckerberg; Dina R. Zuckerberg; Lloyd P. Zuckerberg; Roy J. Zuckerberg.
EIN: 133052489

7129
Keren Yehuda Zvi Foundation ✧
1541 E. 7th St.
Brooklyn, NY 11230-6407 (718) 435-8555
Contact: Barry Weiss, Tr.; Susana Weiss, Tr.

Established in 1992 in NY.
Donors: Barry Weiss; Susana Weiss.
Foundation type: Independent foundation.
Financial data (yr. ended 12/31/12): Assets, $462,373 (M); gifts received, $550,000; expenditures, $630,078; qualifying distributions, $630,078; giving activities include $630,078 for grants.
Purpose and activities: Giving primarily to yeshivas.
Fields of interest: Education; Philanthropy/voluntarism; Religion.
Type of support: General/operating support.
Limitations: Applications accepted. Giving primarily in Brooklyn, NY. No grants to individuals.
Application information: Application form not required.
Initial approach: Proposal
Deadline(s): None
Trustees: Malka Culang; Barry Weiss; Susana Weiss.
EIN: 113039559

7130
The Martin & Barbara Zweig Foundation Inc. ✧
900 3rd Ave.
New York, NY 10022-4728

Established in 1998 in NY.
Donor: Martin Zweig.
Foundation type: Independent foundation.
Financial data (yr. ended 12/31/13): Assets, $8,467,719 (M); expenditures, $502,610; qualifying distributions, $501,300; giving activities include $500,000 for 1 grant.
Fields of interest: Hospitals (general).
Limitations: Applications not accepted. Giving primarily in NY. No grants to individuals.
Application information: Unsolicited requests for funds not accepted.
Officers: Barbara Zweig, Chair.; Michael Link, Treas.
EIN: 061534181
Selected grants: The following grants are a representative sample of this grantmaker's funding activity:
$333,333 to Mount Sinai Medical Center, Miami Beach, FL, 2011. For general use.
$50,000 to Mount Sinai Medical Center, New York, NY, 2011. For general use.
$15,000 to Harlem Childrens Zone, New York, NY, 2011. For general use.

NORTH CAROLINA

7131
The 25th Century Foundation ✧
1525 W. W.T. Harris Blvd., D1114-044
Charlotte, NC 28288-5709

Established in 2000 in PA.
Donor: J. Marlon Buck, Jr.
Foundation type: Independent foundation.
Financial data (yr. ended 03/31/13): Assets, $15,850,580 (M); expenditures, $722,906; qualifying distributions, $632,000; giving activities include $632,000 for grants.
Fields of interest: Education; Health care; Breast cancer; Human services; Salvation Army; YM/YWCAs & YM/YWHAs.
Limitations: Applications not accepted. Giving primarily in PA. No grants to individuals.
Application information: Unsolicited requests for funds not accepted.
Officers and Directors:* J. Marlon Buck, Jr.,* Chair.; Caroline Buck Rogers,* Pres.; James Buck III,* V.P.; Elia Buck; Elinor Buck; Joseph W. Rogers, Jr.
Trustee: Wells Fargo Bank, N.A.
EIN: 311738216
Selected grants: The following grants are a representative sample of this grantmaker's funding activity:
$50,000 to Canine Partners for Life, Cochranville, PA, 2013. For Start-Up Campaign.
$50,000 to Mann Center for the Performing Arts, Philadelphia, PA, 2013. For Acquisition of Video Screens.
$50,000 to Need in Deed, Philadelphia, PA, 2013. To establish Endowment Fund.
$50,000 to Philadelphia Film Society, Philadelphia, PA, 2013. For Film Projection and Audio/Visual Equipment.
$50,000 to Please Touch Museum, Philadelphia, PA, 2013. For Railway Play Exhibit.
$50,000 to YMCA of Philadelphia and Vicinity, Philadelphia, PA, 2013. For Haverford Twp. Area Y - Family Locker Room.
$25,000 to Educating Communities for Parenting, Philadelphia, PA, 2013. To educate Parents and Children.

7132
Arthur F. & Alice E. Adams Charitable Foundation ✧
c/o Wells Fargo Bank, N.A.
1525 W. W.T. Harris Blvd., D1114-044
Charlotte, NC 28288-5709
Application address: c/o Wells Fargo Bank, N.A., Attn.: Peter Thompson, V.P., tel.: (908) 598-3582; Email: grantadministration@wellsfargo.com; Main URL: https://www.wellsfargo.com/privatefoundationgrants/adams

Established in 1987 in FL.
Donor: Alice E. Adams†.
Foundation type: Independent foundation.
Financial data (yr. ended 09/30/13): Assets, $15,800,159 (M); expenditures, $1,139,106; qualifying distributions, $936,005; giving activities include $817,500 for 26 grants (high: $250,000; low: $5,000).
Purpose and activities: Giving primarily to organizations benefitting arts, culture, humanities, and education.
Fields of interest: Arts; Education; Human services.
Limitations: Applications accepted. Giving primarily in Miami, FL, New York, NY, and Memphis, TN. No grants to individuals.
Application information: See foundation website for complete application guidelines. Application form required.
Deadline(s): Feb. 15
Board meeting date(s): Spring
Officers: Paul L. Guiabo, Pres.; Renee C. Guiabo, Governor.
Trustees: Arete Warren; Wells Fargo Bank, N.A.
EIN: 656003785
Selected grants: The following grants are a representative sample of this grantmaker's funding activity:
$122,000 to Circuit Playhouse, Memphis, TN, 2011.
$50,000 to Preservation League of New York State, Albany, NY, 2011.

7133
Adams-Mastrovich Family Foundation ✧
c/o Wells Fargo Bank N.A., Trust Tax Dept.
1 W. 4th St., 4th Fl., MAC D4000-041
Winston-Salem, NC 27101-3818
E-mail: grantadministration@wellsfargo.com; Main URL: https://www.wellsfargo.com/privatefoundationgrants/adams-mastrovich

Established in 1957 in MN.
Donor: Mary Adams Balmat†.
Foundation type: Independent foundation.
Financial data (yr. ended 12/31/13): Assets, $26,110,523 (M); expenditures, $1,336,384; qualifying distributions, $1,144,786; giving activities include $1,076,000 for 49 grants (high: $250,000; low: $4,000).
Purpose and activities: Giving primarily for the arts, human services, and Roman Catholic agencies and churches.
Fields of interest: Performing arts; Performing arts, music; Arts; Human services; Catholic agencies & churches; Religion.
Type of support: General/operating support; Continuing support; Building/renovation; Equipment; Program development; Scholarship funds.
Limitations: Applications accepted. Giving limited to Los Angeles County, CA, and SD. No support for political organizations. No grants to individuals, or for conferences or seminars, fundraisers, campaigns, endowments, or for travel.
Application information: See foundation website for complete application guidelines. Application form required.
Deadline(s): Aug. 1
Trustee: Wells Fargo Bank, N.A.
EIN: 416014092

7134
Bill and Sharon Allen Family Foundation ✧ ☆
810 Colville Rd.
Charlotte, NC 28207-2312

Established in 2006 in NC.
Donors: Bill Allen; Sharon Allen.
Foundation type: Independent foundation.
Financial data (yr. ended 12/31/13): Assets, $11,610,111 (M); gifts received, $500,000; expenditures, $558,322; qualifying distributions, $437,500; giving activities include $437,500 for 15 grants (high: $200,000; low: $5,000).
Fields of interest: Education; Health organizations; Children.
Limitations: Applications not accepted. Giving primarily in NC. No grants to individuals.
Application information: Contributes only to pre-selected organizations.
Officer and Director:* Bill Allen,* Pres.
Trustee: Jeffrey Scribner.
EIN: 205854617
Selected grants: The following grants are a representative sample of this grantmaker's funding activity:
$20,000 to Community School of the Arts, Charlotte, NC, 2012. For arts education organization.
$20,000 to Girls on the Run International, Charlotte, NC, 2012. For Programs for Preteen Girls.
$15,000 to Texas Rangers Baseball Foundation, Arlington, TX, 2012. For youth health, fitness, and education Programs.
$10,000 to Classroom Central, Charlotte, NC, 2012. To Collect and Distribute Free School Supplies.
$7,500 to YMCA of Greater Charlotte, Charlotte, NC, 2012. For Health, Fitness, and Education Programs.

7135
The Anonymous Fund ✧
P.O. Box 9908
Greensboro, NC 27429-0908

Established in 1995 in NC.
Foundation type: Independent foundation.
Financial data (yr. ended 12/31/13): Assets, $11,086,963 (M); expenditures, $1,512,594; qualifying distributions, $1,378,282; giving activities include $1,270,000 for 23 grants (high: $500,000; low: $10,000).
Purpose and activities: Giving primarily for the arts, education, health care and human services.
Fields of interest: Arts; Higher education; Health care; Human services; United Ways and Federated Giving Programs; Catholic agencies & churches.
Limitations: Applications not accepted. Giving primarily in NC. No grants to individuals.
Application information: Contributes only to pre-selected organizations.
Officers: Joseph M. Bryan, Jr., Pres.; Ronald P. Johnson, Secy.
Trustee: William P. Massey.
EIN: 562152734
Selected grants: The following grants are a representative sample of this grantmaker's funding activity:
$500,000 to Guilford College, Greensboro, NC, 2012. For 1st installment of $1,5 pledge to Bryan Series.
$125,000 to Triad Stage, Greensboro, NC, 2012. For 2nd installment of $375,000 pledge to purchase new facility at 1724 Holbrook Street.
$50,000 to Santa Fe Opera, Santa Fe, NM, 2012. To assist underwriting Maometto II.
$25,000 to Choate Rosemary Hall, Wallingford, CT, 2012. For 3rd installment of $100,000 pledge for Joseph M. Bryan, Jr. Community Service Endowment.

$25,000 to Eastern Music Festival, Greensboro, NC, 2012. For festival.

7136
Anonymous Trust ✧

P.O. Box 31143
Raleigh, NC 27622-1143
Application address: c/o Margaret Turlington, Scholarship Coord., P.O. Box 2087, Clinton, NC 28329; tel.: (910) 385-6716

Established in 2008 in NC.
Donors: Nancy B. Faircloth; Nancy B. Faircloth Trust.
Foundation type: Independent foundation.
Financial data (yr. ended 12/31/13): Assets, $181,220,681 (M); expenditures, $8,866,275; qualifying distributions, $8,416,449; giving activities include $8,175,277 for 37 grants (high: $6,725,464; low: $500), and $176,685 for 33 grants to individuals (high: $26,323; low: $100).
Fields of interest: Higher education.
Limitations: Giving primarily in VA; some giving also in NC and NY. No grants to.
Application information: Applicants for the Simple Gifts Scholarships, the Simple Gifts Fund Sampson County Love of Learning Grant Program, and the Simple Gifts Fund Sampson County Teachers Fellowship Program should visit the Simple Gifts Fund web site at http://www.simplegiftsfund.org/.
Initial approach: Letter
Deadline(s): Dec. 1
Trustees: Anne B. Faircloth; Maria M. Lynch.
EIN: 266220561
Selected grants: The following grants are a representative sample of this grantmaker's funding activity:
$10,000 to United Methodist Church, North Carolina Conference, Garner, NC, 2011.
$5,000 to Historic Preservation Foundation of North Carolina, Raleigh, NC, 2011.

7137
The Edward M. Armfield, Sr. Foundation, Inc. ✧

324 W. Wendover Ave., No. 130
Greensboro, NC 27408-8438
Contact: Melinda W. Oakley

Established in 2000 in NC.
Donor: Edward M. Armfield, Sr.‡.
Foundation type: Independent foundation.
Financial data (yr. ended 12/31/12): Assets, $60,448,098 (M); expenditures, $3,334,797; qualifying distributions, $2,545,954; giving activities include $1,353,632 for grants, and $866,500 for grants to individuals.
Purpose and activities: Giving primarily for education and human services.
Fields of interest: Elementary/secondary education; Higher education; Education; Hospitals (general); YM/YWCAs & YM/YWHAs.
Type of support: Scholarships—to individuals.
Limitations: Applications accepted. Giving primarily in NC.
Application information: Application form required.
Deadline(s): June 15 and Oct. 1
Officer: Steve Joyce, Exec. Dir.
Directors: Adair P. Armfield; W.J. Armfield; Bedford Cannon; Phifer Crute.
EIN: 562156876

7138
Mary Reynolds Babcock Foundation, Inc. ✧

2920 Reynolda Rd.
Winston-Salem, NC 27106-3016 (336) 748-9222
Contact: Justin Maxson, Exec. Dir.
FAX: (336) 777-0095; E-mail: info@mrbf.org; Main URL: http://www.mrbf.org
Blog: http://www.mrbf.org/blog
Grants Database: http://mrbf.org/what-and-where-we-fund
Knowledge Center: http://mrbf.org/resources
Mary Reynolds Babcock Foundation's Philanthropy Promise: http://www.ncrp.org/philanthropys-promise/who
Twitter: https://twitter.com/intent/user?screen_name=mrbf_org&original_referer=http://mrbf.org/

Incorporated in 1953 in NC.
Donors: Betsy Babcock‡; Charles H. Babcock‡; Charles H. Babcock, Jr.‡; Mary Reynolds Babcock‡.
Foundation type: Independent foundation.
Financial data (yr. ended 12/31/13): Assets, $182,397,210 (M); expenditures, $10,557,828; qualifying distributions, $9,033,040; giving activities include $7,440,114 for 143 grants (high: $250,000; low: $250), and $66,503 for foundation-administered programs.
Purpose and activities: The foundation supports people in the southeast to build just and caring communities that nurture people, spur enterprise, bridge differences, and foster fairness. Its mission is to help people and places to move out of poverty and achieve greater social and economic justice. The foundation supports organizations and networks that work across race, ethnic, economic and political differences to make possible a brighter future for all.
Fields of interest: Education; Employment; Housing/shelter; Community/economic development; Children/youth; Adults; Minorities; Economically disadvantaged.
Type of support: Mission-related investments/loans; General/operating support; Program-related investments/loans.
Limitations: Applications accepted. Giving in the southeastern U.S., with emphasis on AL, GA, MS, NC, SC, TN, the Gulf Coast regions of AR and LA, and the Appalachian Regions of KY, VA, and WV. No grants to individuals, or for capital improvements, direct services (such as food or medical assistance), or for satellite operations of organizations outside the southeast.
Publications: Application guidelines; Financial statement; Grants list; Newsletter; Occasional report.
Application information: An Organizational Summary may be completed and submitted online at the Foundation's website. Applications should wait for a response to the summary before submitting a proposal. Application form required.
Initial approach: Organizational summary
Deadline(s): Rolling deadlines
Board meeting date(s): June and Oct.
Officers and Directors:* Wendy S. Johnson,* Pres.; Katherine R. Mountcastle,* V.P.; Dee Davis,* Secy.; Kenneth F. Mountcastle III,* Treas.; Justin Maxson, Exec. Dir.-Elect; Bruce M. Babcock; LaVeeda Battle; Chad Berry; David Dodson; Jerry Gonzalez; Derrick Johnson; Barbara B. Millhouse; Dr. James Mitchell; Katharine B. Mountcastle; Laura L. Mountcastle; Mary Mountcastle; Ivan Kohar Parra; Kevin Trapani.
Number of staff: 5 full-time professional; 1 part-time professional; 4 full-time support.
EIN: 560690140
Selected grants: The following grants are a representative sample of this grantmaker's funding activity:
$450,000 to South Carolina Association of Community Development Corporations, Charleston, SC, 2012. For general operating support and regranting.
$400,000 to Hope Enterprise Corporation, Jackson, MS, 2012. For expansion.
$300,000 to Arkansas Public Policy Panel, Little Rock, AR, 2012. For general operating support and coalition building.
$250,000 to Community Foundation of South Alabama, Mobile, AL, 2012. For project grant to build local capacity for asset development.
$150,000 to CommunityWorks Carolina, Greenville, SC, 2012. For general operating support.
$150,000 to Hispanic Interest Coalition of Alabama, Birmingham, AL, 2012. For general operating support.
$150,000 to Homes of Hope, Greenville, SC, 2012. For general operating support.
$140,000 to Step Up Savannah, Savannah, GA, 2012. For general operating support.
$100,000 to Kentucky Domestic Violence Association, Frankfort, KY, 2012. For the Economic Justice Project in Eastern Kentucky.
$36,000 to Georgia Conference of Black Mayors, Washington, GA, 2012. For general operating support.

7139
The Bank of America Charitable Foundation, Inc. ✧

401 N. Tryon St., NC1-021-02-20
Charlotte, NC 28255-0001 (800) 218-9946
Main URL: http://www.bankofamerica.com/foundation/index.cfm

Established in 1958; reincorporated in 2004.
Donors: Bank of America Corp.; Bank of America, N.A.; FleetBoston Financial Foundation; The Holden Trust; Merrill Lynch & Co., Inc.
Foundation type: Company-sponsored foundation.
Financial data (yr. ended 12/31/12): Assets, $32,075,548 (M); gifts received, $120,576,140; expenditures, $175,303,789; qualifying distributions, $175,299,789; giving activities include $175,299,789 for 45,820 grants (high: $2,560,503; low: $10).
Purpose and activities: The Bank of America Charitable Foundation provides philanthropic support to address specific needs vital to the health of local communities by focusing on community and economic development initiatives, addressing critical human needs such as hunger, and educating the workforce for 21st century jobs. Special emphasis is directed toward programs supporting low and moderate income communities. Support is given primarily in areas of company operations.
Fields of interest: Arts; Secondary school/education; Higher education; Education; Environment; Hospitals (general); Employment, services; Employment, training; Employment; Food services; Food banks; Nutrition; Housing/shelter, owner/renter issues; Housing/shelter, home owners; Housing/shelter; Youth development, adult & child programs; Youth development; Family services; Human services, financial counseling; Homeless, human services; Human services;

Community development, neighborhood development; Community development, small businesses; Community/economic development; United Ways and Federated Giving Programs; Leadership development; Disabilities, people with; Military/veterans; Economically disadvantaged.
Type of support: General/operating support; Continuing support; Management development/ capacity building; Program development; Conferences/seminars; Internship funds; Employee volunteer services; Employee matching gifts; Employee-related scholarships.
Limitations: Applications accepted. Giving on a national and international basis in areas of company operations. No support for discriminatory organizations, political, labor, or fraternal organizations, civic clubs, religious organizations not of direct benefit to the entire community, or public or private pre-K-12 schools. No grants to individuals or for fellowships, sports, athletic events or programs, travel-related events, student trips or tours, development or production of books, films, videos, or televisions programs, or memorial campaigns.
Publications: Application guidelines; Program policy statement.
Application information: Support is limited to 1 contribution per organization during any given year. Application form required.
Initial approach: Complete online eligibility quiz and application
Deadline(s): Jan. 22 to Feb. 14 for Workforce Development and Education; Apr. 21 to May 9 for Community Development; and July 21 to Aug 8 for Basic Human Services
Officers and Directors:* Anne M. Finucane,* Chair.; Kerry H. Sullivan, Pres.; Thomas M. Brantley, Sr. V.P., Tax; Dannielle C. Campos, Sr. V.P.; Anna Cowenhoven, Sr. V.P.; Ximena A. Delgato, Sr. V.P.; Rena M. DeSisto, Sr. V.P.; Stephen B. Fitzgerald, Sr. V.P.; Robert E. Gallery, Sr. V.P.; Angie Garcia-Lathrop, Sr. V.P.; Charles R. Henderson, Jr., Sr. V.P.; Teresa M. Ingwall, Sr. V.P.; Daniel Letendre, Sr. V.P.; Alexandra C. Liftman, Sr. V.P.; Jennifer Locane, Sr. V.P.; Susan Portugal, Sr. V.P.; Tish Secrest, Sr. V.P.; Michael F. Shriver, Sr. V.P.; Brenda L. Suits, Sr. V.P.; Kristen L. Teskey, Sr. V.P.; Melissa Alpert Anguilla, V.P.; Caitlin M. Bell, V.P.; Abigail Goward, V.P.; Erin M. Hinton, V.P.; Colleen O. Johnson, Secy.; Suzette Finger, Treas.; Keith T. Banks; Amy Woods Brinkley; Walter B. Elcock; Janet W. Lamkin; Andrew D. Plepler; Martin Richards; Purna R. Saggurti.
EIN: 200721133
Selected grants: The following grants are a representative sample of this grantmaker's funding activity:
$2,560,503 to Scholarship America, Saint Peter, MN, 2012. For program and operating support.
$2,000,000 to Foundation for the Carolinas, Charlotte, NC, 2012. For program and operating support.
$2,000,000 to Habitat for Humanity International, Americus, GA, 2012. For program and operating support.
$1,250,000 to Local Initiatives Support Corporation, New York, NY, 2012. For program and operating support.
$1,000,000 to Museum of Fine Arts, Boston, MA, 2012. For program and operating support.
$650,000 to Urban League, National, New York, NY, 2012. For program and operating support.
$500,000 to City Year, Boston, MA, 2012. For program and operating support.
$5,000 to Jewish Federation, Greater Miami, Miami, FL, 2012. For program and operating support.
$4,250 to Humanity First USA, Silver Spring, MD, 2012. For program and operating support.
$2,375 to Metrolina Regional Scholars Academy, Charlotte, NC, 2012. For program and operating support.

7140
The Baruch Fund ✧
c/o Richard U. Puryear, CPA
82 Old Pasture Way
Hendersonville, NC 28739-3133
Application address: c/o Rhoda W. Baruch, 5630 Wisconsin Ave., Ste. 905, Chevy Chase, MD 20815

Established about 1964 in MA as the Jordan J. Baruch Foundation.
Donors: Jordan J. Baruch; Rhoda W. Baruch.
Foundation type: Independent foundation.
Financial data (yr. ended 12/31/13): Assets, $5,339,161 (M); expenditures, $887,927; qualifying distributions, $889,069; giving activities include $889,069 for 174 grants (high: $388,415; low: $18).
Purpose and activities: Giving primarily to Jewish organizations and temples; funding also for education, health and human services.
Fields of interest: Education; Health organizations, association; Human services; Jewish federated giving programs; Jewish agencies & synagogues.
Limitations: Applications accepted. Giving primarily in Washington, DC, MA, MD, NJ, and NY. No grants to individuals.
Application information: Application form not required.
Initial approach: Proposal
Deadline(s): None
Trustees: Lawrence K. Baruch; Rhoda W. Baruch.
EIN: 046112483

7141
The Harold H. Bate Foundation, Inc. ✧
3515 Trent Rd.
P.O. Box 14298
New Bern, NC 28561 (252) 638-1998
E-mail: info@batefoundation.org; Main URL: http://www.batefoundation.org

Established in NC.
Foundation type: Independent foundation.
Financial data (yr. ended 12/31/12): Assets, $32,044,995 (M); expenditures, $1,643,938; qualifying distributions, $1,350,028; giving activities include $1,225,400 for 73 grants (high: $200,000; low: $500).
Purpose and activities: Giving primarily for education, youth and recreation organizations, and the quality of life in Craven, Pamlico and Jones counties, and East Carolina University.
Fields of interest: Higher education; Education; Health organizations; Human services; Children/ youth, services; Community/economic development.
Limitations: Giving limited to Craven, Pamlico and Jones counties in NC; funding also for projects connected with East Carolina University in serving eastern North Carolina. No support for religious organizations for theological purposes. No grants to individuals.
Publications: Application guidelines.
Application information: Application form and guidelines are available on foundation web site. Faxed, e-mailed, or handwritten applications, or applications with responses taped onto the form are not accepted. Application form required.
Initial approach: Use application form on foundation web site, or request form from foundation
Deadline(s): May 15 and Oct. 1
Directors: Gary H. Baldree, Sr.; Donald K. Brinkley; Berleen B. Burnette; Robert L. Mattocks II; Marvin B. Mullinix; Silas B. Seymour.
EIN: 562121302
Selected grants: The following grants are a representative sample of this grantmaker's funding activity:
$66,600 to East Carolina University Foundation, Greenville, NC, 2012. For Distinguished Professorship.
$35,000 to East Carolina University Foundation, Greenville, NC, 2012. For Chancellor's Fund - College of Business.
$20,000 to North Carolina Coastal Land Trust, Wilmington, NC, 2012. For land acquisitions.
$15,000 to Eight Days of Hope, Tupelo, MS, 2012. For Pamlico County building materials.
$15,000 to Religious Community Services, New Bern, NC, 2012. For Rent and Utility assistance.
$12,500 to Public Radio East, New Bern, NC, 2012. For emergency funding.
$10,000 to East Carolina University Foundation, Greenville, NC, 2012. For access scholarships.
$10,000 to Easter Seals UCP North Carolina, Raleigh, NC, 2012. For Child Development Center.
$10,000 to Hope Clinic, Bayboro, NC, 2012. For Clinic for uninsured.
$10,000 to Merci Clinic, New Bern, NC, 2012. For Pharmacy assistance Program.

7142
George W. and Ruth R. Baxter Foundation, Inc. ✧
(formerly George W. Baxter Foundation, Inc.)
2115 Rexford Rd., Ste. 211
Charlotte, NC 28211

Established about 1970 in NC.
Donors: George W. Baxter, Sr.†; George W. Baxter Sr. Trust of 2000.
Foundation type: Independent foundation.
Financial data (yr. ended 12/31/13): Assets, $20,042,650 (M); expenditures, $1,089,264; qualifying distributions, $924,888; giving activities include $800,500 for 50 grants (high: $50,000; low: $2,500).
Purpose and activities: Giving primarily to hospitals, health associations, and Christian agencies and churches.
Fields of interest: Elementary/secondary education; Education, special; Education; Hospitals (general); Cancer; Diabetes; Human services; United Ways and Federated Giving Programs; Protestant agencies & churches; Catholic agencies & churches.
Limitations: Applications not accepted. Giving primarily in NC. No grants to individuals.
Application information: Unsolicited requests for funds not accepted.
Officers and Director:* Nolan D. Pace, Jr., Chair.; G. Steven Baxter, Sr., Vice-Chair.; Mark B. Edwards,* Secy.
EIN: 560949547

Selected grants: The following grants are a representative sample of this grantmaker's funding activity:
$25,000 to Aldersgate United Methodist Retirement Community, Charlotte, NC, 2011.

7143
BB&T Charitable Foundation ✧
c/o Branch Banking & Trust, Trust Tax Dept.
P.O. Box 2907
Wilson, NC 27894-2907

Established in 1998 in NC.
Donors: BB&T Corp.; First Virginia Bank.
Foundation type: Company-sponsored foundation.
Financial data (yr. ended 12/31/13): Assets, $227,001 (M); expenditures, $1,202,794; qualifying distributions, $1,197,637; giving activities include $1,196,133 for 31 grants (high: $480,000; low: $450).
Purpose and activities: The foundation supports organizations involved with arts and culture, education, the environment, health, human services, and community development.
Fields of interest: Museums; Arts; Higher education; Education; Environment; Health care; Housing/shelter; Human services; Economic development; Community/economic development; United Ways and Federated Giving Programs.
Type of support: General/operating support; Annual campaigns; Capital campaigns; Building/renovation; Endowments; Emergency funds; Program development; Professorships; Publication; Curriculum development; Scholarship funds; Matching/challenge support.
Limitations: Applications not accepted. Giving primarily in areas of company operations in the mid-Atlantic and southeastern U.S. No grants to individuals.
Application information: Contributes only to pre-selected organizations.
Board meeting date(s): Bi-monthly
Trustee: Branch Banking and Trust Co.
Number of staff: None.
EIN: 562093089

7144
BB&T West Virginia Foundation Inc. ✧
(formerly One Valley Bank Foundation, Inc.)
c/o Trust Tax Dept.
P.O. Box 2907
Wilson, NC 27894-2907 (304) 348-7271
Contact: John M. Barry, Exec. Dir.
Application address: P.O. Box 1793, Charleston, WV 25326.

Established in 1954 in WV.
Donors: One Valley Bank, N.A.; BB&T Corp.; OVB Charitable Trust.
Foundation type: Company-sponsored foundation.
Financial data (yr. ended 12/31/13): Assets, $11,350,271 (M); gifts received, $100,000; expenditures, $608,374; qualifying distributions, $594,188; giving activities include $593,188 for 79 grants (high: $53,000; low: $500).
Purpose and activities: The foundation supports community foundations and organizations involved with arts and culture, education, health, human services, and community economic development.
Fields of interest: Performing arts, orchestras; Arts; Higher education; Libraries (public); Education; Hospitals (general); Health care, clinics/centers; Health care; YM/YWCAs & YM/YWHAs; Human services; Foundations (community); United Ways and Federated Giving Programs.
Type of support: General/operating support.
Limitations: Applications accepted. Giving limited to WV. No grants to individuals.
Application information: Application form required.
Initial approach: Proposal
Copies of proposal: 1
Deadline(s): Nov. 1
Board meeting date(s): As needed
Officer: John M. Barry, Exec. Dir.
Board Members and Trustees:* Phyllis H. Arnold; Calvin E. Barker; Nelle Ratrie Chilton; C. Edward Gaunch; Holmes Morrison; Steven M. Rubin; K. Richard C. Sinclair; Edwin H. Welch.
EIN: 556017269
Selected grants: The following grants are a representative sample of this grantmaker's funding activity:
$5,000 to Natural Capital Investment Fund, Shepherdstown, WV, 2011.
$3,000 to Fellowship of Christian Athletes, Kansas City, MO, 2011.

7145
Elizabeth Hurlock Beckman Award Trust ✧ ☆
1525 W. WT Harris Blvd., D1114-044
Charlotte, NC 28288-0001
E-mail: grantadministration@wellsfargo.com; Main URL: https://www.wellsfargo.com/privatefoundationgrants/beckman

Foundation type: Independent foundation.
Financial data (yr. ended 12/31/12): Assets, $5,967,444 (M); expenditures, $746,821; qualifying distributions, $673,224; giving activities include $550,000 for 22 grants to individuals (high: $25,000; low: $25,000).
Purpose and activities: Grant awards to current and former academic teachers who have inspired students to make significant contributions for the benefit of the community.
Fields of interest: Education; Community/economic development; Public affairs.
Type of support: Grants to individuals.
Limitations: Applications accepted. Giving primarily in CA, FL, GA, MA, NY, WA and WI.
Application information: Recipients must be current or former teachers, professors, or instructors at a college, university, junior college, community college, or technical school located in the United States. Preference will be given to educators who teach or who taught in the fields of psychology, medicine, or law. See foundation website for complete application policies and guidelines. Application form required.
Deadline(s): July 15
Trustee: Wells Fargo Bank, N.A.
Advisory Committee: Geraldine A. Downey; Karen MacCausland Tidmarsh; Carol Goodheart.
EIN: 371564854

7146
John M. Belk Educational Endowment ✧
(also known as John M. Belk Endowment)
5960 Fairview Rd., Ste. 400
Charlotte, NC 28210-3119
Contact: Katherine B. Morris, Vice-Chair.

Established in 1996 in NC.
Donor: John M. Belk.
Foundation type: Independent foundation.
Financial data (yr. ended 12/31/13): Assets, $298,263,000 (M); gifts received, $6,144; expenditures, $4,810,757; qualifying distributions, $3,562,828; giving activities include $3,140,155 for 19 grants (high: $1,000,000; low: $2,500).
Fields of interest: Higher education, university.
Limitations: Applications not accepted. Giving primarily in NC.
Application information: Unsolicited requests for funds not accepted.
Officers: Mary Claudia Belk Pilon, Chair. and Treas.; Katherine Belk Morris, Vice-Chair. and Secy.; Claudia W. Belk, Vice-Chair.; Kristen Teskey, Exec. Dir.
EIN: 561954114
Selected grants: The following grants are a representative sample of this grantmaker's funding activity:
$1,000,000 to Foundation for the Carolinas, Charlotte, NC, 2011.
$50,000 to Fletcher School, Charlotte, NC, 2011.
$18,000 to North Carolina Outward Bound School, Asheville, NC, 2011.

7147
The Katherine and Thomas Belk Foundation, Inc. ✧
2801 W. Tyvola Rd.
Charlotte, NC 28217-4500 (704) 357-1000

Established in 2001 in NC.
Donor: Katherine M. Belk.
Foundation type: Independent foundation.
Financial data (yr. ended 12/31/13): Assets, $6,110,009 (M); expenditures, $1,295,794; qualifying distributions, $1,286,206; giving activities include $1,286,206 for 33 grants (high: $726,706; low: $500).
Purpose and activities: Giving primarily to Presbyterian organizations and churches; funding also for the arts, education, and social services.
Fields of interest: Museums (art); Arts; Higher education; Human services; Protestant agencies & churches.
Limitations: Applications not accepted. Giving primarily in NC.
Application information: Contributes only to pre-selected organizations.
Officers and Directors:* Katherine Belk Morris,* Pres.; H.W. McKay Belk,* V.P.; Thomas M. Belk, Jr.,* V.P.; Katherine M. Belk,* Secy.; John R. Belk,* Treas.
EIN: 562220828
Selected grants: The following grants are a representative sample of this grantmaker's funding activity:
$5,000 to Boy Scouts of America, Charlotte, NC, 2012. For Friends of Scouting Campaign.
$1,000 to Junior League of Charlotte, Charlotte, NC, 2012. For 2012/2013 annual campaign.
$1,000 to Salvation Army, Atlanta, GA, 2012. For annual report.
$1,000 to Sharon Towers, Charlotte, NC, 2012. For Residents Assistance Fund.

7148
The Belk Foundation ✧
2801 W. Tyvola Rd.
Charlotte, NC 28217-4500 (704) 426-8396
Contact: Susan Blount, Admin.
E-mail: info@belkfoundation.org; E-mail for Susan Blount: susan_blount@belk.com; Main URL: http://belkfoundation.org
Grants List: http://www.belkfoundation.org/grants/main-recent-grants

Trust established in 1928 in NC.
Donors: The Belk Department Stores; Matthews Belk; Belk Enterprises; Belk, Inc.
Foundation type: Company-sponsored foundation.
Financial data (yr. ended 05/31/13): Assets, $49,208,620 (M); gifts received, $755,000; expenditures, $2,606,412; qualifying distributions, $2,395,638; giving activities include $2,242,476 for 55 grants (high: $160,000; low: $25,000).
Purpose and activities: The foundation supports programs designed to ensure all students graduate from high school and continue on an intentional path toward college, a career, and quality of life.
Fields of interest: Arts; Secondary school/education; Higher education; Education, services; Education; Hospitals (general); Health care; Breast cancer; Boys & girls clubs; Boy scouts; YM/YWCAs & YM/YWHAs; Children/youth, services; Human services; United Ways and Federated Giving Programs.
Type of support: General/operating support; Continuing support; Annual campaigns; Capital campaigns; Building/renovation; Endowments; Emergency funds; Program development; Scholarship funds; Sponsorships; Matching/challenge support.
Limitations: Applications accepted. Giving primarily in areas of company operations, with emphasis on Birmingham, AL, Atlanta, GA, and Charlotte, NC. No support for private elementary or secondary schools or international organizations. No grants to individuals or for fundraising.
Publications: Application guidelines; Grants list; IRS Form 990 or 990-PF printed copy available upon request.
Application information: Final applications are by invitation only and are issued mid-Feb. and mid-Aug. The foundation awards the majority of its grants to organizations identified by Belk Foundation staff and board. Application form not required.
Initial approach: Complete online eligibility quiz and letter of inquiry form
Deadline(s): None; Apr. 1 and Oct. 1 for applications
Final notification: May and Nov. for applications
Officers and Directors:* Katherine B. Morris,* Chair.; John R. Belk, Vice-Chair. and Treas.; Mary Claudia Belk Pilon,* Secy.; Johanna Edens Anderson, Exec. Dir.; Thomas M. Belk, Jr.; Ophelia Garmon-Brown; Peter Gorman; Louise Martin.
EIN: 270237197
Selected grants: The following grants are a representative sample of this grantmaker's funding activity:
$200,000 to Foundation for the Carolinas, Charlotte, NC, 2013. For Project LIFT, a 5-year Program seeking to narrow the achievement gap by increasing proficiency and graduation rates in West Charlotte.
$110,000 to Fulton County Public Schools, Atlanta, GA, 2013. For Program support for redesigning the district's teacher selection model with The New Teacher Project (TNTP), a national leader in urban teacher recruitment and training.
$60,000 to Charlotte Center for Urban Ministry, Charlotte, NC, 2013. For funding for the library at Moore Place, a Housing First model and proven solution for chronically disabled homeless.
$50,000 to Mecklenburg Citizens for Public Education, Charlotte, NC, 2013. For General operating support for MeckEd, to inform and engage the community around critical issues facing public education.
$50,000 to New Leaders, Charlotte, NC, 2013. For General operating support for New Leaders, which develops transformational school leaders to ensure high academic achievement for all children.
$50,000 to Wingate University, Wingate, NC, 2013. For Capital funding for the Levine College of Health Sciences.
$40,000 to Wings for Kids, Charleston, SC, 2013. For Program support for WINGS, evidence-based social and emotional learning Program, in high-poverty public elementary school sin Fulton County.
$30,000 to YWCA of Birmingham, Birmingham, AL, 2013. For General operating support for the Afterschool Enrichment Program, serving high-poverty and homeless children.
$25,000 to Queens University of Charlotte, Charlotte, NC, 2013. For Program support for the School of Executive Leadership Academy, innovative partnership with the McColl School of Business to develop school leaders.
$20,000 to Foundation for the Carolinas, Charlotte, NC, 2013. For Capital support for the new Regional Center for Philanthropy.

7149
Frank and Lydia Bergen Foundation ✧
1525 W. WT Harris Blvd., D1114-044
Charlotte, NC 28288-5709
Wells Fargo Philanthropic Services, 1 W. 4th St., 6th Fl., Winston-Salem, NC 27101, tel.: (855) 739-2920, e-mail: grantadministration@wellsfargo.com; Main URL: http://www.wellsfargo.com/privatefoundationgrants/bergen

Incorporated in 1983 in NJ.
Donor: Charlotte V. Bergen‡.
Foundation type: Independent foundation.
Financial data (yr. ended 12/31/13): Assets, $9,792,033 (M); expenditures, $547,405; qualifying distributions, $466,013; giving activities include $440,000 for 26 grants (high: $50,000; low: $5,000).
Purpose and activities: Giving primarily to 1) arrange for musical entertainments, concerts and recitals of a character appropriate for the education and instruction of the public in the musical arts, with paramount consideration given to traditional classical music programs, 2) aid worthy students of music in securing a complete and adequate musical education, and 3) aid organizations in their efforts to present fine music to the public, provided that such organizations are operated exclusively for educational purposes.
Fields of interest: Arts education; Performing arts, music; Arts.
Type of support: Program development; Scholarship funds.
Limitations: Applications accepted. Giving primarily in NJ; some funding also in NY. No grants to individuals, or for endowments or general operating support; fundraising events including dinners, benefits and athletic events; no loans.
Application information: Application form required.
Initial approach: See foundation web site
Deadline(s): Apr. 10 or Aug. 15
Trustee: Wells Fargo Bank, N.A.
EIN: 226359304
Selected grants: The following grants are a representative sample of this grantmaker's funding activity:
$60,000 to Montclair State University, Montclair, NJ, 2012. For Cali Connect.
$30,000 to Newark Boys Chorus School, Newark, NJ, 2012. For Music Component of Program.
$15,000 to Harlem School of the Arts, New York, NY, 2012. For music Program overall.
$10,000 to Drew University, Madison, NJ, 2012. For Chamber Music Society Of.
$10,000 to Mid-Atlantic Center for the Arts, Cape May, NJ, 2012. For Cape May Music Festival.
$10,000 to Perkins Center for the Arts, Moorestown, NJ, 2012. For scholarships, concerts, and.

7150
The Mary Duke Biddle Foundation ✧
318 Blackwell St., Ste. 130
PMB 101
Durham, NC 27701-2888 (919) 493-5591
Contact: Douglas C. Zinn, Exec. Dir.
FAX: (919) 489-0118; E-mail: info@mdbf.org; Main URL: http://www.mdbf.org
Grants List: http://www.mdbf.org/RecentGrants.html

Trust established in 1956 in NY.
Donors: Mary Duke Biddle‡; Nicholas Duke Biddle 1960 Trust; Nicholas D. Biddle Trust #2.
Foundation type: Independent foundation.
Financial data (yr. ended 12/31/13): Assets, $30,559,650 (M); gifts received, $275,000; expenditures, $1,703,287; qualifying distributions, $1,327,134; giving activities include $652,750 for 58 grants (high: $402,000; low: $2,000).
Purpose and activities: Support for private higher and secondary education, specified churches, cultural programs, particularly music, dance and theater, projects in the arts, and aid to the community and to the handicapped; half of the income is committed to Duke University.
Fields of interest: Performing arts, dance; Performing arts, theater; Performing arts, music; Arts; Secondary school/education; Higher education; Education; Community/economic development; Children/youth; Disabilities, people with.
Type of support: Program development; Conferences/seminars; Seed money; Fellowships; Scholarship funds; Matching/challenge support.
Limitations: Applications accepted. Giving limited to NC and New York, NY. No support for public education. No grants to individuals, or for building or endowment funds; generally no operating budgets; no loans.
Publications: Annual report.
Application information: Application guidelines available on foundation web site. Application form not required.
Initial approach: E-mail brief letter of inquiry
Copies of proposal: 1

Deadline(s): See foundation web site for current deadlines
Board meeting date(s): Mar., June, Sept., and Dec.
Officers and Trustees:* Mary T. Jones,* Chair.; Thomas S. Kenan III,* Vice-Chair. and Secy.; John G. Mebane, Jr.,* Treas.; Mimi O'Brien, Exec. Dir.; C. Russell Bryan; James D.B.T. Semans; Jon E. Zeljo.
Number of staff: 1 full-time professional; 2 part-time support.
EIN: 136068883

7151
BIN Charitable Foundation ✧

c/o Sarah Fish
3103 Buckingham Rd.
Durham, NC 27707-4505

Established in 1999 in NC.
Donors: Barbara Newborg; Joan Mertens; Brooks Norman Crat.
Foundation type: Independent foundation.
Financial data (yr. ended 12/31/13): Assets, $12,912,393 (M); expenditures, $778,767; qualifying distributions, $1,254,000; giving activities include $627,000 for 29 grants (high: $125,000; low: $2,000).
Purpose and activities: Giving to enhance the Durham, NC and surrounding community by making grants to support environmental concerns, affordable housing, unity of diverse citizens, the arts, and children.
Fields of interest: Housing/shelter, development; Human services; Children/youth, services.
Type of support: Matching/challenge support; Curriculum development; Equipment; Building/renovation; Annual campaigns.
Limitations: Applications not accepted. Giving primarily in NC. No grants to individuals.
Application information: Unsolicited requests for funds not accepted.
Officers: Barbara Newborg, Pres.; Sarah Fish, Secy.; Elissa B. Olszewski, Treas.
EIN: 562111550

7152
Bissell Foundation ✧

13860 Ballantyne Corp. Pl., Ste. 300
Charlotte, NC 28277-3167 (704) 248-2000
Contact: Howard C. Bissell, Pres. and Dir.

Established in 2007 in NC.
Donors: Sara H. Bissell; Howard C. Bissell; Joseph Hallow; Barbara Hallow; Cary Pickard; James J. Bissell; BFLP LLC.
Foundation type: Independent foundation.
Financial data (yr. ended 12/31/13): Assets, $1,252,712 (M); gifts received, $110,373; expenditures, $518,854; qualifying distributions, $500,787; giving activities include $500,134 for 42 + grants (high: $101,000).
Purpose and activities: Giving primarily for education, YMCAs, social services, and to a children's hospital.
Fields of interest: Elementary/secondary education; Higher education; Hospitals (specialty); Human services; YM/YWCAs & YM/YWHAs.
Limitations: Applications accepted. Giving primarily in Charlotte, NC.
Application information: Application form not required.
Initial approach: Proposal
Deadline(s): None
Officers and Directors:* Howard C. Bissell,* Pres.; Edward L. Curran, V.P.; Lars G. Wilson, Secy.-Treas.; Howard Bissell III; James J. Bissell; Margaret G. Bissell; Barbara B. Hallow; Cary B. Sherck.
EIN: 208520020

7153
Blue Cross and Blue Shield of North Carolina Foundation ✧

c/o Grant Review Comm.
P.O. Box 2291
5901 Old Chapel Hill Rd.
Durham, NC 27702-2291 (919) 765-7347
Contact: Jill Mallatratt, Assoc. Project Mgr.
FAX: (919) 765-4243;
E-mail: info@bcbsncfoundation.org; E-mail for Jill Mallatratt: jill.mallatratt@bcbsncfoundation.org; Contact for Health of Vulnerable Populations: Katie Eyes, Sr, Prog. Mgr., tel.: (919) 765-4024, e-mail: katie.eyes@bcbsncfoundation.org; Contact for Healthy Active Communities: Jennifer MacDougall, Prog. Mgr., tel.: (919) 765-2128, e-mail: jennifer.macDougall@bcbsncfoundation.org; Contact for Nonprofit Excellence: Valerie Stewart, Prog. Mgr., tel.: (919) 765-4514, e-mail: valerie.stewart@bcbsncfoundation.org; Additional contact: Michael Gay, Opers. Mgr., tel. (919) 765-2826, e-mail: michael.gay@bcbsncfoundation.org; Main URL: http://www.bcbsnc.com/foundation
Be Active Kids on Facebook: http://www.facebook.com/beactivekids
Grantee Map: http://www.bcbsncfoundation.org/grants/grantee-map/
Grantee Profiles: http://www.bcbsncfoundation.org/grants/grantee-profiles/
Grants Database: http://www.bcbsncfoundation.org/grants/grantee-database/
Multimedia: http://www.bcbsncfoundation.org/about/multimedia
RSS Feed: http://www.bcbsncfoundation.org/feeds/news/
Twitter: http://twitter.com/bcbsncfound

Established in 2000 in NC.
Donors: Blue Cross and Blue Shield of North Carolina, Inc.; Golden Leaf Foundation.
Foundation type: Company-sponsored foundation.
Financial data (yr. ended 06/30/13): Assets, $108,599,272 (M); expenditures, $14,166,230; qualifying distributions, $13,105,245; giving activities include $12,570,885 for 100 grants (high: $4,000,000; low: $1,500), and $518,352 for 4 foundation-administered programs.
Purpose and activities: The foundation supports programs designed to improve the health and well-being of North Carolinians. Special emphasis is directed toward programs designed to attain measurable results and sustained community impact.
Fields of interest: Medical care, community health systems; Health care, clinics/centers; Dental care; Public health; Public health, obesity; Public health, physical fitness; Health care, patient services; Health care; Cancer; Breast cancer; Heart & circulatory diseases; Diabetes; Food services; Nutrition; Athletics/sports, school programs; Children/youth, services; Family services, parent education; Rural development; Leadership development; Aging; Disabilities, people with; Economically disadvantaged.
Type of support: General/operating support; Continuing support; Management development/capacity building; Capital campaigns; Equipment; Program development; Conferences/seminars; Curriculum development; Technical assistance; Consulting services; Program evaluation; Matching/challenge support.
Limitations: Applications accepted. Giving primarily in areas of company operations in NC. No support for religious organizations, individual sports teams, or organizations with the sole purpose of receiving goods and entitlements from other charitable organizations. No grants to individuals, or for bricks and mortar, annual campaigns, political campaigns, religious purposes, endowments, advertising, or direct service or program-related costs including salaries, benefits, materials, or supplies.
Publications: Application guidelines; Annual report; Financial statement; Grants list; IRS Form 990 or 990-PF printed copy available upon request; Program policy statement.
Application information: A full proposal may be requested at a later date for Health of Vulnerable Populations and Healthy Active Communities. Support is limited to 1 contribution per organization during any given year. Application form required.
Initial approach: Complete online application
Deadline(s): Varies - visit website for deadline announcements
Final notification: Varies
Officers and Directors:* J. Bradley Wilson,* Chair.; Kathy Higgins, Pres.; Danielle Breslin, V.P., Opers.; Stran Summers, V.P., Finance; N. King Prather, Secy.; Steve Cherrier, Treas.; Lisa Carey; Daniel E. Glaser; L. Steven Nelson; Maureen O'Connor; Gerald Petkau; John T. Roos.
EIN: 562226009
Selected grants: The following grants are a representative sample of this grantmaker's funding activity:
$2,000,000 to North Carolina Association of Free Clinics, Winston-Salem, NC, 2012. To support existing NCAFC member free clinics and pharmacies and the creation of new free clinics in underserved counties. The focus is on stability and sustainability of all member clinics.
$1,131,000 to North Carolina Department of Agriculture and Consumer Services, Food Distribution Division, Raleigh, NC, 2012. To increase the number of school districts participating in the North Carolina Farm to School Program by expanding the capacity of the Department through the purchase of five tractor-trailers.
$1,000,000 to North Carolina Partnership for Children, Raleigh, NC, 2012. To improve the health of young children, ages 0-5, and child care workers through a statewide strategy of comprehensive coordinated early childhood obesity prevention, outreach and technical assistance that will address change at the individual, programmatic, built environment and policy levels.
$1,000,000 to North Carolina State University, Raleigh, NC, 2012. To increase access to healthy food through establishment of a statewide local food system that serves as a sustainable, replicable model to drive improved health and rural economic development.
$1,000,000 to University of North Carolina at Asheville Foundation, Asheville, NC, 2012. To continue partnership that seeks to discover best practices about health and wellness and broadly

communicating those to the public through undergraduate research, internships, and equipment support for North Carolina Center for Health and Wellness.
$855,000 to Youth Empowered Solutions, Raleigh, NC, 2012. To increase effectiveness of youth advocates in obesity prevention and expand organizational capacity of YES to sustain youth advocacy strategies through organizational restructuring and implementation of a fee-for-service business model.
$150,000 to Farmer Foodshare, Chapel Hill, NC, 2012. For core mission investment to build capacity and move organizational infrastructure from start-up to sustainable for future programmatic growth in areas of supporting farmers, feeding communities healthy food and creating food-access jobs.
$140,400 to MGR Foundation, Chicago, IL, 2012. To increase access to healthy food by implementing GREEN Community Schools and promoting environmental awareness and fully integrate sustainable practices in struggling local communities in the Charlotte-Mecklenburg School District.
$138,543 to East Carolina University, Greenville, NC, 2012. To refine and package MATCH (Motivating Adolescents with Technology to Choose Health) program in an effort to decrease the prevalence of obesity in ten rural eastern North Carolina middle schools. Refinement and packaging will allow the easy replication of the program statewide.
$99,809 to Appalachian Sustainable Agriculture Project, Asheville, NC, 2012. To increase access to healthy, local food in Ashe, Henderson, and Macon counties by improving or developing systems for food procurement, distribution, and marketing systems as well as assisting educational, institutional and retail sites to access and serve this food on a long-term sustainable basis.

7154
The Blumenthal Foundation ✧
P.O. Box 34689
Charlotte, NC 28234-4689 (704) 688-2305
Contact: Philip Blumenthal
FAX: (704) 688-2301;
E-mail: foundation@rscbrands.com; Main URL: http://www.blumenthalfoundation.org

Trust established in 1953 in NC.
Donors: I.D. Blumenthal‡; Herman Blumenthal‡; Radiator Specialty Co.
Foundation type: Independent foundation.
Financial data (yr. ended 12/31/13): Assets, $21,036,297 (M); expenditures, $1,107,087; qualifying distributions, $1,046,116; giving activities include $824,225 for 94 grants (high: $50,000; low: $425).
Purpose and activities: Giving primarily for arts and science, civic and community programs, education, environment, foundation affiliates, health, Jewish institutions and philanthropies, religious and interfaith programs, and social sciences.
Fields of interest: Humanities; Arts; Higher education; Education; Environment; Health care; Human services; Jewish federated giving programs; Jewish agencies & synagogues.
Type of support: General/operating support; Annual campaigns; Capital campaigns; Building/renovation; Endowments; Emergency funds; Program development; Conferences/seminars; Professorships; Publication; Seed money; Research; Matching/challenge support.
Limitations: Giving primarily in NC, with emphasis on Charlotte and Mecklenburg County. No grants to individuals, or for scholarships or fellowships; no loans.
Publications: Application guidelines; Annual report; Grants list; Multi-year report.
Application information: Application form not required.
Initial approach: Letter
Copies of proposal: 1
Deadline(s): None
Board meeting date(s): Mar., June, Sept., and Dec.
Officer and Trustees:* Philip Blumenthal,* Dir.; Alan Blumenthal; Samuel Blumenthal, Ph.D.
Number of staff: 2 full-time professional; 1 part-time professional.
EIN: 560793667
Selected grants: The following grants are a representative sample of this grantmaker's funding activity:
$230,000 to Temple Beth El, Charlotte, NC, 2012. For 4th payment on 5-year $1,150,000.00 grant for Capital and Endowment Campaign.
$25,000 to Foundation for the Carolinas, Charlotte, NC, 2012. For 1st payment on a 5 year commitment for the Carolina Thread Trail Fund.
$20,000 to Penland School of Crafts, Penland, NC, 2012. For 1st payment on 5-year grant for the Campaign for Penland's Future (CPT).
$10,000 to Catawba Lands Conservancy, Charlotte, NC, 2012. For First payment on 5 year grant of $50,000.00 to enable CLC to hire additional staff person to.
$10,000 to Crisis Assistance Ministry, Charlotte, NC, 2012. For General Operating Support - 1st payment on $20,000.00 grant.
$10,000 to Crisis Assistance Ministry, Charlotte, NC, 2012. For 2nd payment on $20,000.00 grant.
$10,000 to Foundation for the Carolinas, Charlotte, NC, 2012. For 2nd and final payment on two-year grant for bronze relief in Legacy Hall of Herman and I D.
$5,000 to Levine Museum of the New South, Charlotte, NC, 2012. For 2nd payment on $10,000 grant for 20th Anniversary celebration.
$3,750 to United Way of Central Carolinas, Charlotte, NC, 2012. For 3rd payment on one-year $15,000 grant.
$3,000 to Dogwood Alliance, Asheville, NC, 2012. For a grant for the Youth Organizing Program.

7155
The Bolick Foundation ✧
P.O. Box 307
Conover, NC 28613-0307

Established in 1967 in NC.
Donor: Southern Furniture Co. of Conover, Inc.
Foundation type: Company-sponsored foundation.
Financial data (yr. ended 06/30/14): Assets, $11,438,594 (M); expenditures, $549,457; qualifying distributions, $429,750; giving activities include $429,750 for 67 grants (high: $100,000; low: $250).
Purpose and activities: The foundation supports organizations involved with historical activities, education, health, human services, international relief, and Christianity.
Fields of interest: Historical activities; Elementary/secondary education; Higher education; Theological school/education; Education; Health care; Boy scouts; YM/YWCAs & YM/YWHAs; Residential/custodial care, hospices; Human services; International relief; Christian agencies & churches.
Type of support: General/operating support; Annual campaigns; Capital campaigns; Building/renovation.
Limitations: Applications not accepted. Giving primarily in NC. No grants to individuals.
Application information: Contributes only to pre-selected organizations.
Trustees: Jerome W. Bolick; Judith L. Bolick; Linda B. Bolick.
EIN: 566086348
Selected grants: The following grants are a representative sample of this grantmaker's funding activity:
$20,000 to Newton Depot Authority, Newton, NC, 2011.
$10,000 to Lutheran Services for the Aging, Salisbury, NC, 2011. For general operating fund.
$5,000 to Palliative CareCenter and Hospice of Catawba Valley, Newton, NC, 2011. For building fund.
$3,000 to Newton-Conover Auditorium Authority, Newton, NC, 2011.
$2,500 to American Heart Association, Charlotte, NC, 2011. For general operating fund.
$2,500 to Independent College Fund of North Carolina, Raleigh, NC, 2011. For general operating fund.
$2,000 to Billy Graham Evangelistic Association, Charlotte, NC, 2011. For general operating fund.
$1,000 to Campus Crusade for Christ International, Orlando, FL, 2011. For general operating fund.
$1,000 to Eastern Catawba Cooperative Christian Ministry, Newton, NC, 2011. For general operating fund.
$1,000 to Family Care Center of Catawba Valley, Hickory, NC, 2011. For general operating fund.

7156
Brady Education Foundation, Inc. ✧
(formerly W.H. Brady Foundation, Inc.)
100 Europa Dr., Ste. 351
Chapel Hill, NC 27517-2389
Contact: Elizabeth P. Pungello, Pres.
E-mail: info@bradyeducationfoundation.org; Stage 1 application e-mail: applications@bradyeducationfoundation.org; Main URL: http://bradyeducationfoundation.org/

Incorporated in 1956 in WI.
Foundation type: Independent foundation.
Financial data (yr. ended 06/30/13): Assets, $13,697,228 (M); expenditures, $774,751; qualifying distributions, $627,131; giving activities include $544,575 for 6 grants (high: $142,816; low: $50,000).
Purpose and activities: Giving to close the achievement gap for children at risk for poor school outcomes due to environmental factors associated with living in poverty. The foundation pursues its mission by promoting collaboration between researchers and educators via the funding of research and program evaluations in education.
Fields of interest: Education; Children; Economically disadvantaged.
Type of support: General/operating support; Continuing support; Management development/capacity building; Capital campaigns; Equipment; Program development; Conferences/seminars; Publication; Curriculum development; Scholarship

funds; Research; Technical assistance; Program evaluation; Matching/challenge support.
Limitations: Giving in the U.S., with emphasis on NC. No support for sectarian programs or umbrella organizations, or for capital projects, research for children at risk of poor school outcomes due to medical conditions, scaling up programs already found to be effective, or for individual providers who wish to increase their center's Early Childhood Environment Rating Scale score or obtain accreditation. Funding to tax-supported institutions extremely limited. No grants to individuals, or for scholarships or operating costs.
Publications: Application guidelines.
Application information: Stage 2 applications are by invitation only, upon review of Stage 1 applications.
Initial approach: Proposal via e-mail in .pdf format using the foundation's Stage 1 application process which is explained on the foundation's web site
Deadline(s): See foundation web site for current deadlines
Officers and Directors:* Elizabeth P. Pungello,* Pres.; Peter J. Lettenberger,* V.P.; James M. Rauh,* Treas.; Frances Campbell, Ph.D.; Barbara Crockett; Mark Kuhn.
Number of staff: 1 part-time support.
EIN: 396064733
Selected grants: The following grants are a representative sample of this grantmaker's funding activity:
$100,000 to University of North Carolina, Chapel Hill, NC, 2011.

7157
Charles I. Branan Trust ✧
1525 W. WT Harris Blvd., D1114-044
Charlotte, NC 28262

Established in 2003 in GA.
Foundation type: Independent foundation.
Financial data (yr. ended 12/31/13): Assets, $27,866,534 (M); expenditures, $1,568,340; qualifying distributions, $1,298,919; giving activities include $1,235,430 for 109 grants (high: $45,000; low: $500).
Fields of interest: Education; Health care; Human services; Children/youth, services; Community/economic development; United Ways and Federated Giving Programs; Protestant agencies & churches.
Limitations: Applications not accepted. Giving primarily in Atlanta, GA.
Application information: Contributes only to pre-selected organizations.
Trustee: Wells Fargo Bank, N.A.
EIN: 586026401
Selected grants: The following grants are a representative sample of this grantmaker's funding activity:
$20,000 to Big Brothers Big Sisters of Metro Atlanta, Atlanta, GA, 2011.
$10,000 to Action Ministries, Atlanta, GA, 2011.

7158
James R. and Bronnie L. Braswell Trust ✧
c/o George C. Bower, Jr.
300 E. Wade St.
Wadesboro, NC 28170-2231

Established in 2001 in NC.
Donors: James R. Braswell‡; The James R. Braswell Marital Trust.
Foundation type: Independent foundation.
Financial data (yr. ended 12/31/13): Assets, $28,779,872 (M); gifts received, $365,061; expenditures, $979,950; qualifying distributions, $800,500; giving activities include $800,500 for 23 grants (high: $95,000; low: $5,000).
Purpose and activities: Giving primarily for education, health organizations, social services, and to United Methodist and other Protestant and Christian churches and organizations.
Fields of interest: Higher education; Education; Health organizations; Human services; Christian agencies & churches; Protestant agencies & churches.
Limitations: Applications not accepted. Giving primarily in NC. No grants to individuals.
Application information: Contributes only to pre-selected organizations.
Trustee: George L. Bower, Jr.
EIN: 736339730
Selected grants: The following grants are a representative sample of this grantmaker's funding activity:
$50,000 to Union County Community Shelter, Monroe, NC, 2012. For shelter for homeless.
$20,000 to Community Health Services of Union County, Monroe, NC, 2012. For Medical Assistance for Disadvantaged.
$10,000 to American Bible Society, New York, NY, 2012. For religious missions.
$10,000 to Boy Scouts of America, Albemarle, NC, 2012. For children's services.
$10,000 to Hospice of Union County, Monroe, NC, 2012. For Medical Services for the Terminally Ill Care of Terminally Ill.
$500 to 24 Hours of Booty, Charlotte, NC, 2012. For Cancer Research and Education.

7159
George Brauninger Trust ✧
c/o Wells Fargo Bank N.A., Trust Tax Dept.
1 W. 4th St., 4th Fl., MAC D4000-041
Winston-Salem, NC 27101-3818

Foundation type: Independent foundation.
Financial data (yr. ended 12/31/13): Assets, $12,942,711 (M); expenditures, $622,793; qualifying distributions, $527,288; giving activities include $495,060 for 2 grants (high: $247,530; low: $247,530).
Purpose and activities: Giving primarily to a YMCA, and to a Lutheran organization.
Fields of interest: Human services; YM/YWCAs & YM/YWHAs; Protestant agencies & churches.
Limitations: Applications not accepted. Giving primarily in NJ.
Application information: Unsolicited requests for funds not accepted.
Trustees: Richard M. Kohn, Esq.; Wells Fargo Bank, N.A.
EIN: 900041483

7160
Broyhill Family Foundation, Inc. ✧
P.O. Box 500
Lenoir, NC 28645-0500

Incorporated in 1945 in NC.
Donors: Broyhill Furniture Industries, Inc.; James E. Broyhill‡; Paul H. Broyhill.
Foundation type: Independent foundation.
Financial data (yr. ended 12/31/13): Assets, $40,773,628 (M); expenditures, $2,207,758; qualifying distributions, $1,970,154; giving activities include $1,481,793 for 188 grants (high: $150,000; low: $150).
Purpose and activities: Support for higher education, health, youth development and welfare, civic and community services, and the free enterprise system.
Fields of interest: Humanities; Arts; Child development, education; Higher education; Health care, research; Recreation, parks/playgrounds; Human services; Social sciences, public policy.
Type of support: Annual campaigns; Capital campaigns; Building/renovation; Endowments; Program development; Curriculum development; Scholarship funds; Research.
Limitations: Applications not accepted. Giving primarily in Caldwell County, NC. No support for religious organizations. No grants to individuals.
Application information: Unsolicited applications from organizations outside of Caldwell County, NC not encouraged.
Board meeting date(s): Quarterly
Officers and Directors:* Paul H. Broyhill,* Chair.; M. Hunt Broyhill,* Pres.; Carol Frye,* Secy.-Treas.; D. Eugene Hendricks,* C.F.O.; Sheila Triplett-Brady,* Exec. Dir.; B. Claire Broyhill; Caron J. Broyhill; Boyd Wilson, Jr.
Number of staff: None.
EIN: 566054119

7161
R. A. Bryan Foundation Inc. ✧
P.O. Box 919
Goldsboro, NC 27533-0919

Established in 1956 in NC.
Donors: R.A. Bryan, Jr.; Ruby M. Bryan‡; Aviation Fuel Terminals, Inc.; Ridgewood, Inc.; T.A. Loving Co.
Foundation type: Independent foundation.
Financial data (yr. ended 12/31/13): Assets, $18,614,672 (M); expenditures, $894,690; qualifying distributions, $811,290; giving activities include $807,590 for 69 grants (high: $102,000; low: $50).
Purpose and activities: Giving to public day schools, higher education, youth services, and health and medical organizations.
Fields of interest: Arts; Higher education; Animals/wildlife, preservation/protection; Health care; Health organizations, association; Cancer; Medical research, institute; Cancer research; Human services; Christian agencies & churches.
Type of support: General/operating support; Continuing support; Annual campaigns; Capital campaigns; Building/renovation; Endowments; Program development; Scholarship funds; Research.
Limitations: Applications not accepted. Giving primarily in NC. No grants to individuals.
Publications: Annual report.
Application information: Unsolicited requests for funds not accepted.
Officer: R.A. Bryan, Jr., Pres.
Directors: R.A. Bryan III; Stephen C. Bryan; Ann Bryan Huffman.
Number of staff: None.
EIN: 566044320

7162
The Joseph M. Bryan Foundation of Greater Greensboro, Inc. ✧
P.O. Box 14829
Greensboro, NC 27415-4829

Established in 1986 in NC.
Donors: Joseph M. Bryan; The Ellison Family Foundation; William A. Stern Foundation; Brooks Pierce McLendon Humphrey & Leonard; Jefferson-Pilot Financial; Lansyr Adams Farm, LLC; New Breed Corporate Services, Inc.; The Rotary Club of Greensboro; Lincoln Financial.
Foundation type: Independent foundation.
Financial data (yr. ended 12/31/12): Assets, $79,788,292 (M); expenditures, $9,003,220; qualifying distributions, $8,092,229; giving activities include $7,260,289 for 75 grants (high: $2,400,000; low: $659).
Purpose and activities: Support for the economic, cultural, educational, and recreational enrichment of the lives of the citizens of the greater Greensboro, NC, area; a primary purpose of the foundation is the making of improvements to and enhancements of the Joseph M. and Kathleen Bryan Park.
Fields of interest: Arts; Higher education; Law school/education; Education; Foundations (private grantmaking).
Type of support: Program-related investments/ loans.
Limitations: Applications not accepted. Giving limited to NC. No grants to individuals.
Application information: Contributes only to pre-selected organizations.
Officers and Directors:* Shirley Frye,* Chair.; E.S. Melvin,* Pres.; J. Edward Kitchen,* V.P.; Carole W. Bruce,* Secy.-Treas.; David G. Altman; Louise F. Brady; Robert E. Long.
EIN: 561548051

7163
Bryson Foundation Limited ✧
408 Parkview Crescent
Chapel Hill, NC 27516

Established in 1991 in IN.
Donor: Vaughn D. Bryson.
Foundation type: Independent foundation.
Financial data (yr. ended 12/31/13): Assets, $13,783,401 (M); expenditures, $1,002,515; qualifying distributions, $874,811; giving activities include $851,560 for 38 grants (high: $603,060; low: $250).
Fields of interest: Arts; Higher education.
Type of support: General/operating support.
Limitations: Applications not accepted. Giving emphasis is on FL and NC. No support for religious or political organizations. No grants to individuals.
Application information: Unsolicited requests for funds not accepted.
Officers: N. Catherine Bryson, Pres.; Nancy F. Bryson, Secy.; Vaughn D. Bryson, Treas.
Directors: William D. Bryson; Jeffrey H. Thomasson.
EIN: 351854017
Selected grants: The following grants are a representative sample of this grantmaker's funding activity:
$250 to Stanford University, Business School, Stanford, CA, 2012. For unrestricted.

7164
Burroughs Wellcome Fund ✧
21 T. W. Alexander Dr.
P.O. Box 13901
Research Triangle Park, NC 27709-3901 (919) 991-5100
Contact: Russell Campbell III, Comms. Off.
FAX: (919) 991-5160; E-mail: info@bwfund.org; Contact info. for Russ Campbell III tel.: (919) 991-5119; fax: (919) 991-5179, e-mail: rcampbell@bwfund.org; Main URL: http://www.bwfund.org
Twitter: https://twitter.com/BWFUND

Incorporated in 1955 in NY.
Donors: Burroughs Wellcome Co.; The Wellcome Trust.
Foundation type: Independent foundation.
Financial data (yr. ended 08/31/13): Assets, $719,935,278 (M); expenditures, $39,319,875; qualifying distributions, $33,322,096; giving activities include $28,407,990 for 699 grants (high: $359,000; low: $500).
Purpose and activities: The fund is an independent private foundation dedicated to advancing the medical sciences by supporting research and other scientific and educational activities. Within this broad mission the Fund has two primary goals: 1) To help scientists early in their careers develop as independent investigators and 2) To advance fields in the basic biomedical sciences that are undervalued or in need of particular encouragement. The fund makes grants primarily to degree-granting institutions on behalf of individual researchers, who must be nominated by their institutions.
Fields of interest: Medical research, institute; Biology/life sciences.
International interests: Canada.
Type of support: Program development; Research.
Limitations: Applications accepted. Giving limited to the U.S. and Canada. No grants to individuals, or for building or endowment funds, equipment, operating budgets, continuing support, annual campaigns, deficit financing, publications, conferences, or matching gifts; no loans.
Publications: Annual report (including application guidelines); Informational brochure (including application guidelines); Newsletter; Occasional report.
Application information: See fund web site for application information. Application form required.
Initial approach: All applications must be submitted electronically. Paper applications are not accepted
Deadline(s): Varies depending on the program. See fund web site for information
Board meeting date(s): Feb., May, July, and Oct.
Final notification: Varies
Officers and Directors:* Carlos J. Bustamante, Ph.D., Chair.; John E. Burris,* Pres.; Steven D. Corman, Hon. Dir.; Philip R. Tracy, J.D., Hon. Dir.; Bruce Alberts; Nancy Andrews; J. Michael Bishop, M.D.; Emery N. Brown, M.D., Ph.D.; Geoff Gerber, Ph.D.; George Langford, Ph.D.; Roderick R. McInnes, M.D., Ph.D.; Carla Shatz; Michael J. Welsh, M.D.; Dyann Wirth, Ph.D.
Number of staff: 17 full-time professional; 4 full-time support; 2 part-time support.
EIN: 237225395
Selected grants: The following grants are a representative sample of this grantmaker's funding activity:
$700,000 to Harvard University, Cambridge, MA, 2012. For grant to School of Medicine in Boston for characterization of non-coding RNAs in pancreatic adenocarcinoma, payable over 5.00 years.
$700,000 to Stanford University, School of Medicine, Stanford, CA, 2012. For Function of the plastid organelle in P. falciparum: beyond isoprenoid precursor biosynthesis and blood stage, payable over 5.00 years.
$700,000 to University of Chicago, Chicago, IL, 2012. For Identification of chromosomal aberrations that cooperate with the human papillomavirus to cause cancer, payable over 5.00 years.
$700,000 to University of Texas Southwestern Medical Center, Dallas, TX, 2012. For akt-mediated regulation of autophagy and tumorigenesis through formation of a beclin 1/keratin intermediate filament complex, payable over 5.00 years.
$180,000 to Hyde County Schools, Swanquarter, NC, 2012. For STEM 4 ME! Academy, payable over 3.25 years.
$180,000 to North Carolina School of Science and Mathematics Foundation, Durham, NC, 2012. For Step Up to STEM, payable over 3.25 years.
$179,931 to Eno River Association, Durham, NC, 2012. For iWalk the Eno II and Outdoor Science Labs: Year-round Science, Engineering, and Nature Inquiries, payable over 3.00 years.
$178,500 to North Carolina State University, Raleigh, NC, 2012. For The Engineering Place, payable over 3.00 years.
$28,950 to Webb A. Murray Elementary School, Hickory, NC, 2012. For Aventuras de Ciencia (Adventures in Science), payable over 3.00 years.
$10,000 to University of California, Los Angeles, CA, 2012. For Nanopatterning Proteins for Enhancement of Bone Cell Adhesion.

7165
Alice Butler Foundation ✧ ☆
(formerly J. D. and Alice Butler Memorial Scholarship Foundation)
c/o Wells Fargo Bank, N.A.
100 N. Main St., 13th Fl.
Winston-Salem, NC 27150-0001 (754) 322-6691
Contact: Maureen Steinlein
FAX: (754) 322-6676;
E-mail: maureen.steinlein@browardschools.com
Application address: c/o Scholarship Coord., Deerfield Beach Senior High School, 910 S.W. 15th St., Deerfield Beach, FL 33461

Established in 1987 in FL.
Foundation type: Independent foundation.
Financial data (yr. ended 08/31/13): Assets, $9,149,915 (M); expenditures, $589,327; qualifying distributions, $519,726; giving activities include $465,673 for grants to individuals.
Purpose and activities: Scholarship awards to graduates of Deerfield Beach Senior High School in Florida.
Fields of interest: Higher education.
Type of support: Scholarships—to individuals.
Limitations: Applications accepted. Giving limited to graduates of Deerfield Beach High School in FL.
Publications: Application guidelines; Informational brochure.
Application information: Individual grantees must receive a diploma from Deerfield Beach High School. Application form required.
Initial approach: Letter requesting application form
Deadline(s): Apr. 21

Board meeting date(s): As necessary
Final notification: 4 months
Trustee: Wells Fargo Bank, N.A.
Number of staff: 1 full-time support.
EIN: 596878169

7166
Porter B. Byrum Charitable Trust ✧ ☆
P.O. Box 11795
Charlotte, NC 28220-1795

Donors: Porter B. Byrum; Park Roads Shopping Centerporter By; Byrum Land and Timber Inc. Porter Byrum.
Foundation type: Independent foundation.
Financial data (yr. ended 12/31/13): Assets, $47,845,571 (M); gifts received, $5,353,127; expenditures, $4,492,388; qualifying distributions, $4,258,140; giving activities include $4,121,100 for 11 grants (high: $1,050,000; low: $100).
Fields of interest: Higher education; Theological school/education; Protestant agencies & churches.
Limitations: Applications not accepted. Giving primarily in NC.
Application information: Contributes only to pre-selected organizations.
Trustee: Porter B. Byrum.
EIN: 266366327

7167
Marie Eccles Caine Charitable Foundation ✧
c/o Wells Fargo Bank, N.A.
1 W. 4th St., 4th Fl., MAC D4000-041
Winston-Salem, NC 27101-3818

Established in 1981 in UT.
Donor: Marie Eccles Caine‡.
Foundation type: Independent foundation.
Financial data (yr. ended 05/31/13): Assets, $11,865,546 (M); expenditures, $584,515; qualifying distributions, $521,341; giving activities include $507,648 for 13 grants (high: $316,568; low: $3,000).
Fields of interest: Arts; Higher education; Education.
Type of support: General/operating support; Continuing support; Program development; Curriculum development; Scholarship funds.
Limitations: Applications not accepted. Giving primarily in Logan and Salt Lake City, UT. No grants to individuals.
Application information: Contributes only to pre-selected organizations.
Board meeting date(s): Varies
Trustee: Wells Fargo Bank, N.A.
EIN: 942764258

7168
Ruth and Henry Campbell Foundation ✧
1525 W. W.T. Harris Blvd., D1114-044
Charlotte, NC 28262-8522
Application address: c/o P.C. Marks, Dir., 150 Fayetteville St., Raleigh, NC 27601, tel.: (919) 881-6497

Established in 1957.
Foundation type: Independent foundation.
Financial data (yr. ended 12/31/13): Assets, $15,122,876 (M); expenditures, $832,152; qualifying distributions, $692,524; giving activities include $642,300 for 75 grants (high: $75,000; low: $1,000).
Fields of interest: Education; Human services; Children/youth, services.
Type of support: Annual campaigns; Capital campaigns; Building/renovation; Scholarship funds.
Limitations: Applications accepted. Giving primarily in VA.
Application information: Application form required.
Initial approach: Letter
Deadline(s): None
Directors: Elizabeth D. Camp; Paul Camp Marks.
Trustee: Wells Fargo Bank, N.A.
EIN: 546031023
Selected grants: The following grants are a representative sample of this grantmaker's funding activity:
$106,700 to Elms Foundation, Franklin, VA, 2011.

7169
The Cannon Foundation, Inc. ✧
P.O. Box 548
Concord, NC 28026-0548 (704) 786-8216
Contact: Frank Davis, Exec. Dir.
FAX: (704) 782-2812;
E-mail: info@cannonfoundation.org; Application address: P.O. Box 548, Concord NC 28026-0548; Main URL: http://www.cannonfoundation.org/

Incorporated in 1943 in NC.
Donors: Charles A. Cannon‡; Cannon Mills Co.
Foundation type: Independent foundation.
Financial data (yr. ended 09/30/13): Assets, $199,116,650 (M); expenditures, $8,936,015; qualifying distributions, $7,533,841; giving activities include $6,793,206 for 115 grants (high: $788,000; low: $198).
Purpose and activities: Support for hospitals, secondary and higher education, and cultural programs; grants also for Protestant church support, and social service and youth agencies.
Fields of interest: Arts; Secondary school/education; Higher education; Hospitals (general); Human services; Children/youth, services; Protestant agencies & churches.
Type of support: Capital campaigns; Building/renovation; Equipment; Debt reduction; Matching/challenge support.
Limitations: Applications accepted. Giving generally limited to NC, with emphasis on Cabarrus County. No grants to individuals, or for operating budgets, salaries, seed money, deficit financing, endowment funds, demonstration projects, research, publications, conferences, seminars, scholarships, or fellowships; no loans; no multi-year grants or frequent grants to the same organization (except for select, historic relationships).
Publications: Application guidelines; Informational brochure (including application guidelines).
Application information: Application guidelines available on foundation web site. Application form required.
Initial approach: Letter, telephone or web site
Copies of proposal: 1
Deadline(s): Jan 5, Apr. 5, July 5, and Oct. 5,
Board meeting date(s): Mar., June, Sept., and Dec.
Final notification: Within 10-12 weeks following each deadline date
Officers and Directors:* William C. Cannon, Jr.,* Pres.; William S. Fisher,* V.P.; Dan L. Gray,* Secy.-Treas.; Frank Davis, Exec. Dir.; William M. Connolly; Winslow H. Galloway; Thomas M. Grady; Robert C. Hayes; George W. Liles, Jr.; Edward K. Prewitt, Jr.; Elizabeth L. Quick.
Number of staff: 2 full-time professional; 3 full-time support.
EIN: 566042532

7170
Cape Fear Memorial Foundation ✧
2508 Independence Blvd., Ste. 200
Wilmington, NC 28412-2493
Contact: Anna Erwin C.P.A., Pres. and Treas.
FAX: (910) 452-5879; E-mail: info@cfmfdn.org; Main URL: http://www.cfmfdn.org

Established in 1996 in NC; converted from the sale of Cape Fear Memorial Hospital to Columbia/HCA.
Donor: Cape Fear Memorial Health Care Corp.
Foundation type: Independent foundation.
Financial data (yr. ended 06/30/13): Assets, $56,000,551 (M); expenditures, $2,691,530; qualifying distributions, $2,545,122; giving activities include $2,308,732 for 59 grants (high: $150,000; low: $250).
Purpose and activities: Giving for health and medical needs.
Fields of interest: Education; Health care; Human services.
Type of support: General/operating support; Continuing support; Income development; Management development/capacity building; Capital campaigns; Building/renovation; Equipment; Land acquisition; Debt reduction; Program development; Publication; Seed money; Curriculum development; Technical assistance; Matching/challenge support.
Limitations: Applications accepted. Giving limited to southeastern NC, generally within a 50-mile radius of Wilmington, NC. No grants to individuals.
Publications: Application guidelines; Grants list; Informational brochure (including application guidelines).
Application information: Letters of inquiry and grant applications should be submitted to the foundation office via regular mail or hand delivery only. Application form required.
Initial approach: Letter of inquiry
Copies of proposal: 2
Deadline(s): Jan. 15 and July 15
Board meeting date(s): Mar. and Sept.
Final notification: Approx. 90 days
Officers and Board Members:* W. Carter Mebane III,* Chair.; James D. Hundley, M.D., F.A.C.O.S*, Vice-Chair.; Anna Erwin, C.P.A.*, Pres. and Treas.; Agnes R. Beane,* Secy.; William H. Cameron; J. Richard Corbett, M.D., F.A.C.R.; R.T. Sinclair, Jr., M.D.; Ronald Sinclair; Robert F. Warwick, C.P.A.; Richard L. Woodbury.
Number of staff: 1 full-time professional; 2 part-time support.
EIN: 561974747
Selected grants: The following grants are a representative sample of this grantmaker's funding activity:
$300,000 to Lower Cape Fear Hospice, Wilmington, NC, 2011.
$90,000 to Cape Fear HealthNet, Wilmington, NC, 2011.
$75,000 to Child Development Center, Wilmington, NC, 2011. For general operating support.
$75,000 to Coastal Horizons Center, Wilmington, NC, 2011.

$55,000 to Boys and Girls Club, Brigade, Wilmington, NC, 2011.
$50,000 to American Heart Association, Greensboro, NC, 2011.
$40,000 to Leading Into New Communities, Wilmington, NC, 2011. For general operating support.
$30,000 to Hope Harbor Home, Supply, NC, 2011.
$20,000 to Special Olympics of North Carolina, Morrisville, NC, 2011. For general operating support.
$15,000 to Phoenix Employment Services of Wilmington, Wilmington, NC, 2011. For general operating support.

7171
Capital Community Foundation, Inc. ✧
615 Oberlin Rd., Ste. 40
Raleigh, NC 27605 (919) 782-0602
Contact: Jennifer Sullivan Munford, C.E.O.
E-mail: info@capitalcf.org; Mailing address: P.O. Box 18902, Raleigh, NC 27619-8902; Main URL: http://www.capitalcf.org

Established in 1995 in NC.
Foundation type: Community foundation.
Financial data (yr. ended 12/31/13): Assets, $16,367,142 (M); gifts received, $1,681,156; expenditures, $1,191,139; giving activities include $964,013 for 126 grants (high: $118,500).
Purpose and activities: The foundation provides donors of all means with a way to maximize their charitable objectives while taking advantage of immediate income tax benefits.
Fields of interest: Education; Environment; Animal welfare; Health care; Human services; Religion.
Type of support: Endowments.
Limitations: Applications not accepted. Giving primarily in the Raleigh, NC area. No support for organizations lacking 501(c)(3) designation. No grants to individuals.
Publications: Financial statement; Informational brochure; Newsletter.
Application information: Contributes only to pre-selected organizations.
Board meeting date(s): Quarterly
Officers and Directors: R. Donavon Munford, Jr.,* Chair.; Jennifer Sullican Munford, C.E.O. and Pres.; Bailey Williams, C.F.O.; J. Stephenson Bryant; Paul Y. Coble; Thomas H. Fetzer, Jr.; Barbara P. King; Gloria C. Sprunt; Richard A. Thompson; Adrian N. Wilson.
Number of staff: 1 full-time professional; 1 part-time professional.
EIN: 561942969

7172
Carlson Family Foundation Inc. ✧
c/o John A. Norton
206 Brookgreen Dr.
Chapel Hill, NC 27516-4462 (919) 604-0842
Contact: Mary N. Owen, Dir.

Established in 2000 in NJ.
Foundation type: Independent foundation.
Financial data (yr. ended 12/31/13): Assets, $21,620,982 (M); expenditures, $1,004,984; qualifying distributions, $910,431; giving activities include $736,125 for 110 grants (high: $30,000; low: $25).
Fields of interest: Education; Environment, natural resources; Health organizations; Cancer research; Human services; Children/youth, services; Foundations (private grantmaking); Foundations (community).
International interests: Spain.
Type of support: General/operating support; Capital campaigns; Matching/challenge support.
Limitations: Applications accepted. Giving primarily in the U.S., with emphasis on KY and NC; some funding also in CT, MD, NY, and Spain.
Application information: Application form required.
Initial approach: Letter
Deadline(s): None
Officers: Paul S. Norton, Pres.; Lenore Trilby Norton, V.P.; Michael A. Norton, Secy.; John A. Norton, Treas.
Directors: Elaine Boylen; James M. Norton; Mary N. Owen.
EIN: 311678303

7173
Mary E. Carnrick Foundation ✧
219 Greenwich Rd.
Charlotte, NC 28211-2315 (704) 365-0390
Contact: A. Stuart McKaig III, Dir.

Established in 1998 in NC.
Donor: Mary E. Carnrick†.
Foundation type: Operating foundation.
Financial data (yr. ended 12/31/13): Assets, $4,923,834 (M); expenditures, $1,142,957; qualifying distributions, $1,120,000; giving activities include $1,120,000 for 58 grants (high: $100,000; low: $5,000).
Fields of interest: Education; Health organizations, association; Children/youth, services; Human services; Christian agencies & churches.
Limitations: Applications accepted. Giving primarily in Charlotte, NC. No grants to individuals.
Application information:
Initial approach: Requst application form
Deadline(s): None
Directors: John Crawford; William L. Maxwell; A. Stuart McKaig III; Barrie L. Wiggins.
EIN: 562114068
Selected grants: The following grants are a representative sample of this grantmaker's funding activity:
$100,000 to Crisis Assistance Ministry, Charlotte, NC, 2011.
$60,000 to Loaves and Fishes, Charlotte, NC, 2011.
$50,000 to Friendship Trays, Charlotte, NC, 2011.
$50,000 to Regent Schools of the Carolinas, Charlotte, NC, 2011.
$40,000 to Charlotte Rescue Mission, Charlotte, NC, 2011.
$30,000 to Mens Shelter of Charlotte, Charlotte, NC, 2011.
$15,000 to Alexander Youth Network, Charlotte, NC, 2011.
$15,000 to Susan G. Komen for the Cure, Charlotte, NC, 2011.
$15,000 to Thompson Child and Family Focus, Matthews, NC, 2011.
$10,000 to American Diabetes Association, Charlotte, NC, 2011.

7174
The Cemala Foundation, Inc. ✧
330 S. Greene St., Ste. 101
Greensboro, NC 27401-2659
Contact: Susan Schwartz, Exec. Dir.; Melissa Burroughs, Asst. Secy.-Treas.
FAX: (336) 272-8153; E-mail: cemala@cemala.org; Additional e-mail address: sschwartz@cemala.org; Main URL: http://www.cemala.org

Established in 1986 in NC.
Donors: Martha A. Cone†; Ceasar Cone II†.
Foundation type: Independent foundation.
Financial data (yr. ended 12/31/13): Assets, $37,220,393 (M); expenditures, $2,085,114; qualifying distributions, $1,895,738; giving activities include $1,523,200 for 50 grants (high: $125,000; low: $500).
Purpose and activities: The foundation's primary purpose is to continue a family tradition of commitment to enhancing the quality of life of the community through grants to qualified charitable organizations. The focus is on projects that foster the foundation's vision statement as indicated on the foundation's web site.
Fields of interest: Performing arts; Arts; Education, association; Child development, education; Higher education; Education, reading; Housing/shelter, development; Human services; Children/youth, services; Infants/toddlers; Children/youth; Children; Youth; Young adults; Minorities; Economically disadvantaged; Homeless.
Type of support: Scholarship funds; Building/renovation; Capital campaigns; Conferences/seminars; Emergency funds; Equipment; Fellowships; General/operating support; Management development/capacity building; Matching/challenge support; Program development; Program evaluation.
Limitations: Applications not accepted. Giving limited to Greensboro, NC, and projects with countywide benefit. No support for sectarian religious activities. No grants to individuals or for annual campaigns, endowments or requests under $1,000.
Publications: Grants list.
Application information: Unsolicited requests for funds not accepted.
Board meeting date(s): May and Nov.
Officers and Directors:* Katherine K. Richmond,* Chair.; Merritt C. Richmond,* Vice-Chair.; Ashley E. Cone,* Secy.; John A. Richmond, Treas.; Susan S. Schwartz, Exec. Dir.; Chester "Trip" Brown; Ceasar Cone III; Kristen G. Cone; Lawrence M. Cone; Walter "Butch" Cone; Daniel Craft; Matthew D. Richmond; Martha C. Wright.
Number of staff: 1 full-time professional; 1 full-time support.
EIN: 561528982

7175
The Chatham Valley Foundation, Inc. ✧ ☆
c/o Wells Fargo Bank, N.A.
1525 W. WT Harris Blvd.
Charlotte, NC 28288-5709

Incorporated in 1962 in GA.
Donors: A.J. Weinberg†; Eliot Goldstein.
Foundation type: Independent foundation.
Financial data (yr. ended 07/31/13): Assets, $7,613,908 (M); expenditures, $669,448; qualifying distributions, $609,833; giving activities

include $608,333 for 12 grants (high: $268,333; low: $5,000).
Purpose and activities: Giving primarily for a local Jewish welfare federation and other Jewish organizations; broad support for local charitable, educational, cultural, and civic activities.
Fields of interest: Arts; Human services; Religion.
Type of support: General/operating support; Annual campaigns; Capital campaigns; Building/renovation; Endowments; Program development.
Limitations: Applications not accepted. Giving primarily in the metropolitan Atlanta, GA, area. No grants to individuals.
Application information: Contributes only to pre-selected organizations.
Board meeting date(s): Aug.
Trustee: Wells Fargo Bank, N.A.
EIN: 586039344

7176
Louis J. Christopher Memorial Charity Fund ✧
1525 W. WT Harris Blvd., D1114-044
Charlotte, NC 28262

Established in 2002 in CA.
Foundation type: Independent foundation.
Financial data (yr. ended 12/31/13): Assets, $15,106,448 (M); expenditures, $989,447; qualifying distributions, $910,833; giving activities include $887,408 for 6 grants (high: $269,606; low: $78,414).
Purpose and activities: Giving primarily for higher education and hospitals, particularly to a children's hospital and for orthopedic research.
Fields of interest: Higher education; Hospitals (specialty); Orthopedics; Residential/custodial care, hospices; Foundations (private grantmaking).
Limitations: Applications not accepted. Giving primarily in Los Angeles, CA. No grants to individuals.
Application information: Contributes only to pre-selected organizations.
Trustee: Wells Fargo Bank, N.A.
EIN: 956019838

7177
The Guilliam H. Clamer Foundation ✧
c/o Wells Fargo Bank, N.A. - Trust Tax Dept.
1 W. 4th St., 4th Fl., MAC D4000-041
Winston-Salem, NC 27101-3818

Supporting organization of Ursinus College, University of Pennsylvania, and The Franklin Institute.
Donor: Guilliam Clamer Trust.
Foundation type: Independent foundation.
Financial data (yr. ended 10/31/13): Assets, $15,999,731 (M); gifts received, $56,341; expenditures, $604,064; qualifying distributions, $508,241; giving activities include $481,000 for 3 grants (high: $240,000; low: $1,000).
Fields of interest: Higher education.
Limitations: Applications not accepted. Giving primarily in Washington, DC, and PA. No grants to individuals.
Application information: Contributes only to pre-selected organizations. Unsolicited requests for funds not considered or acknowledged.
Trustee: Wells Fargo Bank, N.A.
EIN: 236678246

7178
Community Foundation of Burke County ✧
205 N. King St.
Morganton, NC 28655 (828) 437-7105
Contact: Nancy W. Taylor, Exec. Dir.
FAX: (828) 437-0433;
E-mail: info@cfburkecounty.org; Mailing address: P.O. Box 1156, Morganton, NC 28680; Main URL: http://www.cfburkecounty.org

Established in 1999 in NC.
Foundation type: Community foundation.
Financial data (yr. ended 12/31/13): Assets, $15,737,676 (M); gifts received, $1,922,235; expenditures, $938,507; giving activities include $640,982 for 36+ grants (high: $95,546), and $35,336 for 27 grants to individuals.
Purpose and activities: The foundation seeks to encourage, develop and participate in philanthropy by providing flexible giving opportunities, professional support and responsible stewardship for the benefit of donors and qualified recipients.
Fields of interest: Humanities; Arts; Education, early childhood education; Libraries (public); Education; Environment, association; Environment; Health care; Human services; Economic development; Community/economic development; Protestant agencies & churches; Religion.
Limitations: Applications accepted. Giving primarily in Burke County, NC. No support for religious organizations or purposes. No grants to individuals (except for scholarships), or for annual fund campaigns or capital campaigns, augmenting endowments, or underwriting for fundraising events or performances.
Publications: Annual report; Informational brochure; Newsletter.
Application information: Visit foundation web site for application forms and guidelines. Application form required.
Initial approach: Mail, fax, or e-mail Notification of Intent form
Copies of proposal: 1
Deadline(s): June 30 for Letter of Intent, Varies for application
Board meeting date(s): 4th Wed. of each month
Officers and Directors:* J. Rountree Collett, Jr.,* Pres.; John F. Black, Jr.,* V.P.; Martha McMurray-Russ,* Secy.; Phillip E. Church,* Treas.; Nancy W. Taylor, Exec. Dir.; William M. Brinkley; Le N. Ervin; Doris Fullwood; Kelle B. HUffman; Donald J. McCall; Marcus W.H. Mitchell, Jr.; Susan C. Pollpeter; Diana Spangler-Crawford; Benjamin S. Succop; David R. Wiese; V. Otis Wilson, Jr.
Emeritus: John T. Branstrom; Cynthia H. Callaway; Sterling R. Collett III; P. Paul Deaton; Elisabeth C. Ervin; John W. Ervin, Jr.; J. Hugh Fletcher; C. Michael Fulenwider; Susan L. Haire; Charles E. Horton; Jack B. Kirksey; James E. Lowdermilk; Nettie M. McIntosh; W. Harold Mitchell; Barbara C. Norvell; James H. Rostan; Robert T. Turner II; Edward D. Wall; Emily Williamson Gangi; Otto H. Woerner.
Number of staff: 1 part-time professional; 1 full-time support.
EIN: 562170220

7179
Community Foundation of Gaston County, Inc. ✧
1201 E. Garrison Blvd.
Gastonia, NC 28054 (704) 864-0927
Contact: Ernest W. Sumner, Exec. Dir.; For grants: Elizabeth Patton, Grants and Scholarship Coord.
FAX: (704) 869-0222; E-mail: info@cfgaston.org; Additional e-mail: esumner@cfgaston.org; Grant inquiry e-mail: epatton@cfgaston.org; Main URL: http://www.cfgaston.org
LinkedIn: https://www.linkedin.com/company/community-foundation-of-gaston-county
Twitter: https://twitter.com/CommunityFndGC

Incorporated in 1978 in NC.
Foundation type: Community foundation.
Financial data (yr. ended 12/31/13): Assets, $154,704,214 (M); gifts received, $5,476,063; expenditures, $6,147,009; giving activities include $5,286,232 for 94+ grants (high: $249,331).
Purpose and activities: The foundation is the primary steward of philanthropic giving by connecting donors with community needs to enhance the lives of present and future generations.
Fields of interest: Environment; Community/economic development.
Type of support: Scholarships—to individuals; Emergency funds; Capital campaigns; Building/renovation; Equipment; Program development; Seed money; Curriculum development.
Limitations: Applications accepted. Giving primarily in Gaston County, NC. No support for private schools or religious organizations for religious purposes. No grants to individuals (except for scholarship funds), or for operating costs of established programs, exchange programs, fellowships, annual campaigns, deficit financing, continuing support, technical assistance, professorships, or internships.
Publications: Annual report; Informational brochure; Newsletter.
Application information: The foundation will invite applicants to submit a formal proposal based on letter of inquiry; visit foundation web site for more information.
Initial approach: Letter of inquiry
Deadline(s): June 17 for letter of inquiry; July 31 for formal proposal
Board meeting date(s): Quarterly
Officers and Directors:* Dr. Richard E. Rankin, Jr., Pres.; Julia Shovelin, V.P.; Artie Newcombe IV,* Secy.-Treas.; Ernest W. Sumner, Exec. Dir.; Susan Briggs; Robert S. Browne; Merryman Cassels; William P. Carstarphen; Richard K. Craig; Tim Efird; Dr. Herman Gore; Janet A. Jackson; Steven Long; Gene Matthews; Robert S. Pearson; Kim S. Price; David Ratchford; Sally Robinson; Dr. Ed Sadler; Anthony Sigmon; T.J. Solomon; Ronald M. Sytz; Pamela K. Warlick.
Number of staff: 3 full-time professional; 1 full-time support.
EIN: 581340834

7180

Community Foundation of Greater Greensboro, Inc. ✧

(formerly The Foundation of Greater Greensboro, Inc.)
Foundation Place
330 S. Greene St., Ste. 100
Greensboro, NC 27401-2659 (336) 379-9100
Contact: H. Walker Sanders, Pres.; For grants: Kevin Lundy, Prog. Off.
FAX: (336) 378-0725; E-mail: info@cfgg.org; Grant application e-mail: grants@cfgg.org; Grant inquiry e-mail: Klundy@cfgg.org; Main URL: http://www.cfgg.org
E-Newsletter: http://cfgg.org/downloads/newsletters
Facebook: http://www.facebook.com/pages/Community-Foundation-of-Greater-Greensboro/105978283949
Google Plus: https://plus.google.com/115989431304613174269/posts
LinkedIn: http://www.linkedin.com/groups/Community-Foundation-Greater-Greensboro-4512586
Pinterest: http://www.pinterest.com/cfggnews/
RSS Feed: http://cfgg.org/feed
Twitter: https://twitter.com/cfggnews
YouTube: http://www.youtube.com/user/CFGGstories

Established in 1983 in NC.
Foundation type: Community foundation.
Financial data (yr. ended 12/31/13): Assets, $193,467,590 (M); gifts received, $14,006,201; expenditures, $15,727,923; giving activities include $14,098,757 for grants.
Purpose and activities: The foundation is dedicated to strengthening the community for both present and future generations by promoting philanthropy, building a collection of endowment funds, and serving as a leader in shaping effective responses to community issues and opportunities in the greater Greensboro, NC, area.
Fields of interest: Humanities; Arts; Education; Environment; Health care; Health organizations, association; AIDS; Housing/shelter, development; Children/youth, services; Human services; Community development, neighborhood development; Community/economic development; Government/public administration; Infants/toddlers; Children/youth; Children; Youth; Adults; Aging; Young adults; Disabilities, people with; Physically disabled; Blind/visually impaired; Deaf/hearing impaired; Mentally disabled; Minorities; Asians/Pacific Islanders; African Americans/Blacks; Hispanics/Latinos; Native Americans/American Indians; Indigenous peoples; Women; Infants/toddlers, female; Girls; Adults, women; Young adults, female; Men; Infants/toddlers, male; Boys; Adults, men; Young adults, male; Military/veterans; Offenders/ex-offenders; Substance abusers; AIDS, people with; Single parents; Crime/abuse victims; Terminal illness, people with; Immigrants/refugees; Economically disadvantaged; Homeless; Migrant workers; LGBTQ.
Type of support: General/operating support; Continuing support; Income development; Management development/capacity building; Capital campaigns; Building/renovation; Equipment; Land acquisition; Endowments; Emergency funds; Program development; Conferences/seminars; Film/video/radio; Publication; Seed money; Curriculum development; Fellowships; Internship funds; Scholarship funds; Research; Technical assistance; Consulting services; Program evaluation; Program-related investments/loans; Employee-related scholarships; Scholarships—to individuals; Exchange programs; Matching/challenge support.
Limitations: Applications accepted. Giving primarily in the greater Greensboro, NC, area. No support for partisan purposes, or for programs that promote religious instruction or doctrine. No grants to individuals (except for scholarships), or for capital campaigns, debt retirement, endowments, multi-year commitments, debt retirement, or endowments.
Publications: Application guidelines; Annual report; Financial statement; Grants list; Informational brochure; Newsletter; Occasional report; Program policy statement.
Application information: Visit foundation web site for application Cover Sheet and guidelines. Faxed or e-mailed applications are not accepted. The foundation strongly encourages attending a Grantseeker Orientation Workshop held approximately one month prior to each proposal deadline; registration is required. Application form required.
Initial approach: Mail Cover Sheet with proposal, and attachments
Copies of proposal: 1
Deadline(s): Mar. 14 and Aug. 15 for Community Grants Program; varies for others
Board meeting date(s): Monthly
Final notification: Within 10 weeks
Officers and Directors:* Kathy Manning,* Chair.; Mona G. Edwards, C.O.O.; H. Walker Sanders, Pres.; Jacqueline O'Connell, V.P., Finance and Admin. and C.F.O.; Tara McKenzie Sandercock, Sr. V.P., Fdn. and Community Rels.; Lynn Wooten, V.P., Mktg. and Comms.; Michelle Thrift, Cont.; Nancy Brenner; Frances Bullock; Suresh Chandra; Rev. Odell Cleveland; Lowell Easter; John Englar; Rosalind Fuse-Hall; Michelle Gethers-Clark; Jon Glazman; Arlene Gutterman; David Hagan; Ramsey Hamadi; Wallace "Buster" Johnson; Jennifer Koenig; Barbara Lusk; Harold Martin; Susan McDonald; Lawrence McSwain; Bobby Mendez; Ronald Milstein; Karla Munden; Elaine Ostrowski; Martha Peddrick; Reid L. Phillips; Erica Procton; Fairfax Reynolds; Calvin Riley; Terry Simon; Adrian Smith; Tim Tsujii.
Number of staff: 13 full-time professional; 2 part-time professional.
EIN: 561380249
Selected grants: The following grants are a representative sample of this grantmaker's funding activity:
$855,394 to United Methodist Foundation of Western North Carolina, Huntersville, NC, 2012. For general support.
$783,852 to Fellowship Hall, Greensboro, NC, 2012. For general support.
$500,087 to Action Greensboro, Greensboro, NC, 2012. For general support.
$404,767 to Duke University, Duke Cancer Institute, Durham, NC, 2012. For general support.
$314,176 to United Way of Greater Greensboro, Greensboro, NC, 2012. For general support.
$269,417 to Greensboro College, Greensboro, NC, 2012. For general support.
$130,467 to Triad Stage, Greensboro, NC, 2012. For general support.
$123,911 to Greensboro Urban Ministry, Greensboro, NC, 2012. For general support.
$20,000 to North Naples United Methodist Church, Naples, FL, 2012. For general support.
$15,000 to High Point University, High Point, NC, 2012. For general support.

7181

Community Foundation of Henderson County, Inc. ✧

401 N. Main St., 3rd Fl.
P.O. Box 1108
Hendersonville, NC 28792-4915 (828) 697-6224
Contact: McCray V. Benson, C.E.O.; For grants: Kathryn McConnell, V.P., Philanthropy
FAX: (828) 696-4026; E-mail: info@cfhcforever.org; Grant application e-mail: kmcconnell@cfhcforever.org; Main URL: http://www.cfhcforever.org
Facebook: https://www.facebook.com/pages/Community-Foundation-of-Henderson-County/228920600597
LinkedIn: http://www.linkedin.com/company/community-foundation-of-henderson-county?trk=top_nav_home

Incorporated in 1982 in NC.
Foundation type: Community foundation.
Financial data (yr. ended 06/30/13): Assets, $77,635,127 (M); gifts received, $3,662,048; expenditures, $3,782,391; giving activities include $2,308,502 for 62+ grants (high: $293,694), and $187,298 for 128 grants to individuals.
Purpose and activities: The foundation exists to enrich the quality of life in the greater Henderson County, NC, area, through building and increasing endowments in perpetuity.
Fields of interest: Arts; Child development, education; Higher education; Education; Environment; Health care; Disasters, Hurricane Katrina; Child development, services; Aging, centers/services; Homeless, human services; Human services; Community/economic development; Public affairs; Aging; Homeless.
Type of support: Program evaluation; Management development/capacity building; Emergency funds; Equipment; Matching/challenge support; Program development; Scholarships—to individuals; Seed money; Technical assistance.
Limitations: Applications accepted. Giving limited to the Henderson County, NC, area. No support for religious purposes. No grants to individuals (except for scholarships), or for capital campaigns, annual campaigns, fundraising events, or augmenting endowments; no loans.
Publications: Application guidelines; Annual report; Informational brochure; Newsletter.
Application information: Visit foundation Web site for application guidelines. Scholarship availability is announced in November. Application form required.
Initial approach: Letter or telephone
Copies of proposal: 2
Deadline(s): Mar. 1, June 1, Sept. 1, and Dec. 1 for General Grants; Mar. 1 for scholarships
Board meeting date(s): Monthly
Final notification: 2 months
Officers and Directors:* Randolph Romeo,* Chair.; John Bell, Jr.,* Vice-Chair.; McCray V. Benson,* C.E.O. and Pres.; Kathryn McConnell,* V.P., Community Philanthropy; Lauretta Cook,* Secy.; George Bond,* Secy.; Steve Greene,* Treas.; David Marshall,* Asst. Treas.; Les Boyd III; Cindy Causby; Keith Dalbec; Tom Darnall; Gary Eblen; Chuck Edwards; Shirley McGee; Kimbela McMinn; Ron Partin; Pam Prather; Charley Rogers; Kaye Youngblood.

Number of staff: 4 full-time professional; 2 full-time support.
EIN: 561330792

7182
The Community Foundation of Western North Carolina, Inc. ✧
4 Vanderbilt Park Dr., Ste. 300
Asheville, NC 28803 (828) 254-4960
Contact: Diane Crisp, Grants Mgr.
FAX: (828) 251-2258; E-mail: crisp@cfwnc.org; Mailing Address: P.O. Box 1888, Asheville, NC 28802-1888; Main URL: http://www.cfwnc.org
Facebook: http://www.facebook.com/pages/The-Community-Foundation-of-Western-North-Carolina/148250892249
Grants Database: https://www.grantinterface.com/Common/LogOn.aspx?eqs=FzDcrVbouBENQuVFfQC_Gg2
YouTube: http://www.youtube.com/user/cfwnc09

Incorporated in 1978 in NC.
Foundation type: Community foundation.
Financial data (yr. ended 06/30/13): Assets, $211,579,611 (M); gifts received, $16,389,983; expenditures, $11,854,483; giving activities include $8,876,025 for 328+ grants (high: $277,000), and $320,350 for 146 grants to individuals.
Purpose and activities: The Community Foundation of Western North Carolina inspires philanthropy and mobilizes resources to enrich lives and communities in Western North Carolina.
Fields of interest: Arts; Education; Agriculture/food, reform; Children/youth, services; Human services; Nonprofit management; Community/economic development; Infants/toddlers; Children/youth; Women; Girls; Economically disadvantaged.
Type of support: Income development; Management development/capacity building; Equipment; Endowments; Program development; Curriculum development; Scholarship funds; Technical assistance; Program evaluation; Scholarships—to individuals; Matching/challenge support.
Limitations: Applications accepted. Giving limited to Avery, Buncombe, Burke, Cherokee, Clay, Graham, Haywood, Henderson, Jackson, Macon, Madison, McDowell, Mitchell, Polk, Rutherford, Swain, Transylvania, and Yancey counties, NC. No support for religious organizations or sectarian purposes (except from designated funds). No grants to individuals (except for undergraduate student scholarships), or for capital campaigns, endowment funds, start-up funds, or debt retirement.
Publications: Application guidelines; Annual report; Financial statement; Newsletter.
Application information: Visit foundation web site for online application link, guidelines, and specific deadlines. Application form required.
Initial approach: Telephone or e-mail, online letter of intent or application
Copies of proposal: 1
Deadline(s): Varies
Board meeting date(s): Quarterly, 2nd Wed. in Feb., May, Aug., and Nov.
Final notification: Varies
Officers and Directors:* James W. Stickney IV,* Chair.; A.C. Honeycutt, Jr.,* Vice-Chair.; Elizabeth Brazas,* Pres.; Sheryl Aikman, V.P., Devel.; Philip Belcher, V.P., Progs.; Graham Keever, C.F.O.; Laurence Weiss,* Secy.; G. Edward Towson II,* Treas.; Maurean B. Adams; William Clarke; Jennie Eblen; Ernest E. Ferguson; Charles Frederick; Howell A. Hammond; Darryl Hart; Susan Jenkins; Stephanie Norris Kiser; Tina McGuire; Lowell R. Pearlman; Ramona C. Rowe; George W. Saenger; Anna S. "Candy" Shivers; Jerry Stone; Sarah Sparboe Thornburg; Stephen Watson; Sharon Kelly West.
Number of staff: 14 full-time professional; 2 part-time professional; 2 full-time support.
EIN: 561223384
Selected grants: The following grants are a representative sample of this grantmaker's funding activity:
$830,000 to Foundation for Excellence in Mental Health Care, Wilsonville, OR, 2012.
$500,000 to Carleton College, Northfield, MN, 2012.
$101,750 to YMCA Blue Ridge Assembly, Black Mountain, NC, 2012.
$80,000 to Haywood Waterways Association, Waynesville, NC, 2012.
$25,000 to Mountain View Baptist Church, Black Mountain, NC, 2012.
$2,500 to Saint Timothys School, Stevenson, MD, 2012.
$2,500 to United Way of Greater Portland, Portland, ME, 2012.
$2,100 to YWCA of Asheville and Western North Carolina, Asheville, NC, 2012.
$2,000 to Nature Conservancy, Columbia, SC, 2012.
$2,000 to Pisgah Forest Baptist Church, Pisgah Forest, NC, 2012.

7183
Maxwell M. Corpening, Jr. Memorial Foundation ✧
P.O. Box 2400
Marion, NC 28752-2400
Contact: Terri Laws

Established in 1972 in NC.
Donors: Maxwell M. Corpening Memorial Trust; Duke Power Co.; Mrs. M.M. Corpening‡; Duke Energy Foundation.
Foundation type: Operating foundation.
Financial data (yr. ended 12/31/13): Assets, $255,208 (M); gifts received, $635,483; expenditures, $605,313; qualifying distributions, $600,267; giving activities include $430,118 for 10 grants (high: $415,693; low: $300), and $157,478 for grants to individuals.
Purpose and activities: Grants to needy individuals only in McDowell County, NC.
Fields of interest: Economically disadvantaged.
Type of support: Grants to individuals.
Limitations: Giving limited to long-time residents of McDowell County, NC. No grants for the payment of loans and credit cards or for cell phones, cable, and the internet.
Application information: Mailed applications not accepted. Unsolicited requests for funds accepted rom McDowell County, NC residents only. All other unsolicited requests not accepted. Application form required.
Initial approach: Personal interview with completed application
Copies of proposal: 1
Deadline(s): None
Board meeting date(s): Weekly, on Wed.
Final notification: Within 24 hours
Officers and Trustees:* Dudley Greene,* Chair.; Jeff Coffey,* Vice-Chair.; David Wooten,* Treas.
Number of staff: 1 part-time support.
EIN: 237201488
Selected grants: The following grants are a representative sample of this grantmaker's funding activity:
$2,500 to McDowell Mission Ministries, Marion, NC, 2011.
$1,000 to Family Services of McDowell County, Marion, NC, 2011.

7184
Cumberland Community Foundation, Inc. ✧
308 Green St.
P.O. Box 2345
Fayetteville, NC 28301-1703 (910) 483-4449
Contact: Mary M. Holmes, Exec. Dir.
FAX: (910) 483-2905;
E-mail: info@cumberlandcf.org; Additional e-mail: mary@cumberlandcf.org; Main URL: http://www.cumberlandcf.org
Knowledge Center: http://www.cumberlandcf.org/ccf_news.php

Established in 1980 in NC by Dr. Lucile Hutaff.
Donor: Lucile Hutaff‡.
Foundation type: Community foundation.
Financial data (yr. ended 06/30/13): Assets, $65,791,812 (M); gifts received, $4,888,330; expenditures, $4,147,096; giving activities include $3,090,452 for 44+ grants, and $204,750 for grants to individuals.
Purpose and activities: The foundation exists to foster creative change, to encourage and test new ideas, and to work for the common good of all citizens of Cumberland County and the surrounding area by: 1) promoting local philanthropy and its rewards; 2) building and maintaining a permanent endowment for the benefit of the community; 3) providing a flexible vehicle for prospective donors with varied charitable interests and abilities to give; and 4) developing solutions to changing community needs through effective grantmaking.
Fields of interest: Museums; Performing arts; Humanities; History/archaeology; Language/linguistics; Literature; Arts; Child development, education; Vocational education; Higher education; Adult/continuing education; Libraries/library science; Education; Environment, natural resources; Environment; Animals/wildlife, preservation/protection; Reproductive health, family planning; Medical care, rehabilitation; Health care; Substance abuse, services; Mental health/crisis services; AIDS; Crime/violence prevention, youth; Employment; Nutrition; Housing/shelter, development; Recreation; Youth development, services; Children/youth, services; Child development, services; Family services; Residential/custodial care, hospices; Aging, centers/services; Women, centers/services; Minorities/immigrants, centers/services; Homeless, human services; Human services; Civil rights, race/intergroup relations; Civil/human rights; Economic development; Rural development; Community/economic development; Voluntarism promotion; Population studies; Military/veterans' organizations; Leadership development; Children/youth; Youth; Disabilities, people with; Blind/visually impaired; Minorities; Native Americans/American Indians; Women; Economically disadvantaged; Homeless.
Type of support: General/operating support; Income development; Management development/capacity

building; Program development; Conferences/seminars; Publication; Seed money; Scholarship funds; Technical assistance; Program evaluation; Scholarships—to individuals; In-kind gifts; Matching/challenge support.
Limitations: Applications accepted. Giving limited to Cumberland County, NC. No support for religious purposes. No grants to individuals (except for scholarships), or for annual campaigns, special event fundraisers or sponsorships, capital campaigns, endowments, trips for schools or clubs, membership dues, or deficit funding or debt retirement.
Publications: Application guidelines; Annual report; Financial statement; Grants list; Informational brochure; Newsletter; Occasional report; Program policy statement.
Application information: Visit foundation web site for application guidelines. Based on the letter of intent and data form, the foundation's Grants Committee will consider all eligible requests and determine what organizations/projects will be invited to submit a full grant application. Application form required.
Initial approach: Attend Grant Overview Session
Copies of proposal: 1
Deadline(s): Aug. 15 for Community Grants
Board meeting date(s): 2nd Thurs. of every other month
Final notification: Complete review process takes approx. 15 weeks
Officers and Directors:* S. Lynn Legatski,* Pres.; James R. Konneker,* V.P.; Mary M. Holmes, Exec. Dir.; Mary Anne Brooks, C.F.O.; John S. Ayers; Cathy J. Blackwell; Jesse H. Byrd, Jr.; Libby Stanfield Daniel; Dr. Loleta Wood Foster; Ashton L. Fox; Rakesh Gupta, M.D.; Elaine Bryant Hayes; John Healy; Lucy H. Jones; Elizabeth Marler Keeney; O. Raymond Manning, Jr.; Lonnie J. McAllister; Dan K. McNeill; Sandra W. Monroe; Barbara B. Richardson; Emily K. Schaefer; Ole M. Sorensen; Eva C. Williams.
Number of staff: 5 full-time professional; 1 full-time support; 1 part-time support.
EIN: 581406831

7185
The Michael G. Curran Family Foundation ✧
130 Arabella Ct.
Cary, NC 27518-7155
E-mail: mike.curran@curranfoundation.org; Main URL: http://www.curranfoundation.org

Established in 2003 in NC.
Donor: Michael Curran.
Foundation type: Independent foundation.
Financial data (yr. ended 12/31/13): Assets, $10,029,571 (M); gifts received, $8,000; expenditures, $485,388; qualifying distributions, $474,875; giving activities include $469,284 for 9 grants (high: $460,984; low: $100).
Purpose and activities: Giving primarily to create and support programs, projects and services that positively impact the lives of children and young adults.
Fields of interest: Health organizations; Recreation; Human services; Children/youth, services; Christian agencies & churches.
Limitations: Giving primarily in Wake County, NC. No grants to individuals.
Application information: The foundation is not accepting grant inquiries from any new nonprofit organizations at this time.
Director: Michael Curran.
EIN: 061691227
Selected grants: The following grants are a representative sample of this grantmaker's funding activity:
$402,389 to Triangle Aquatic Center, Cary, NC, 2012. For Pmt. for Operations. of Community Facility.

7186
The Curtis Foundation Inc. ✧ ☆
P.O. Box 20443
Raleigh, NC 27619-0443
Contact: Barbara H. Curtis, Secy.-Treas.
Application address: 622 Lakestone Dr., Raleigh, NC 27609, tel.: (919) 781-6119

Donor: Donald W. Curtis.
Foundation type: Independent foundation.
Financial data (yr. ended 11/30/13): Assets, $12,141,160 (M); expenditures, $624,204; qualifying distributions, $502,055; giving activities include $502,055 for 46 grants (high: $152,500; low: $100).
Fields of interest: Higher education; Journalism school/education; Residential/custodial care; Protestant federated giving programs; Christian agencies & churches.
Type of support: General/operating support.
Limitations: Applications accepted. Giving primarily in NC. No support for state supported schools. No grants to individuals.
Application information: Application form required.
Initial approach: Letter
Deadline(s): At least 6 months prior to requested disbursement date
Officers and Trustees:* Donald W. Curtis,* Pres.; Barbara H. Curtis,* Secy.-Treas.; Donna C. McClatchey.
EIN: 561257146

7187
Dalton-Brand Foundation, Inc. ✧ ☆
(formerly Harry L. Dalton Foundation, Inc.)
112 S. Tryon St., Ste. 805
Charlotte, NC 28284-1106 (704) 332-5380
FAX: (704) 332-1972;
E-mail: brand0598@gmail.com

Established about 1954 in NC.
Foundation type: Independent foundation.
Financial data (yr. ended 07/31/13): Assets, $5,294,966 (M); expenditures, $583,108; qualifying distributions, $532,500; giving activities include $532,500 for 33 grants (high: $181,800; low: $200).
Purpose and activities: Giving primarily for education, including higher education; support also for the arts, including a museum, performing arts center and cultural programs; giving also for a Presbyterian church.
Fields of interest: Museums; Arts; Higher education; Education; Human services; Children/youth, services; Community/economic development; Protestant agencies & churches.
Type of support: Capital campaigns; Building/renovation; Endowments.
Limitations: Applications accepted. Giving primarily in Mecklenburg County, NC.
Publications: Annual report.
Application information:
Deadline(s): None
Board meeting date(s): Quarterly
Officers and Director:* Elizabeth D. Brand, Pres. and Treas.; R. Alfred Brand III, V.P.; Deeda M. Coffey,* Secy.
Number of staff: 1 part-time support.
EIN: 566061267
Selected grants: The following grants are a representative sample of this grantmaker's funding activity:
$34,500 to Agnes Scott College, Decatur, GA, 2011.
$5,000 to North Carolina Blumenthal Performing Arts Center, Charlotte, NC, 2011.

7188
Davie Community Foundation, Inc. ✧ ☆
107 N. Salisbury St.
P.O. Box 546
Mocksville, NC 27028-2322 (336) 753-6903
Contact: Jane Simpson, Pres. and C.E.O.
FAX: (336) 753-6904;
E-mail: info@daviefoundation.org; Main URL: http://www.daviefoundation.org
Facebook: http://www.facebook.com/daviefoundation
Flickr: http://www.flickr.com/photos/daviefoundation
Twitter: http://twitter.com/daviefoundation
YouTube: http://www.youtube.com/user/daviefoundation

Established in 1988 in NC; reorganized in 2003.
Foundation type: Community foundation.
Financial data (yr. ended 12/31/13): Assets, $8,127,391 (M); gifts received, $883,913; expenditures, $728,625; giving activities include $484,195 for 128+ grants (high: $31,390).
Purpose and activities: The foundation promotes the well being of the people of Davie County and is operated exclusively for civic, educational, cultural, religious and charitable purposes.
Fields of interest: Education, reading; Children/youth; Youth.
Type of support: General/operating support; Management development/capacity building; Program development; Scholarship funds; Scholarships—to individuals; Matching/challenge support.
Limitations: Applications accepted. Giving limited to Davie County, NC.
Publications: Application guidelines; Annual report; Financial statement; Grants list; Informational brochure; Newsletter.
Application information: Visit foundation web site for application forms and guidelines. If applicants notification of intent form falls within the requirements and interest of the foundation, a grant application will be sent for completion. Application form required.
Initial approach: Mail, fax, or e-mail notification of intent form
Copies of proposal: 1
Deadline(s): Feb. 1. for full grant application; Mar. 5 for scholarships
Board meeting date(s): 2nd Mon. of each month
Final notification: 1 week for full application invitation; June for grant determination

Officers and Directors:* Phillip Fuller,* Chair.; George Webb,* Vice-Chair.; Jane Simpson,* Pres. and C.E.O.; Marlene Shamel,* Secy.; Joan Woodard,* Treas.; J. Chad Bomar; Joel Edwards, M.D.; Christopher Owens, O.D.; Mike Owen; Henry P. VanHoy; Dr. Richard Williams; Zach Wright.
Number of staff: 1 full-time professional; 1 part-time professional; 1 part-time support.
EIN: 581850531

7189
Champion McDowell Davis Charitable Foundation Inc. ✧

(formerly Champion McDowell Davis Charitable Foundation)
P.O. Drawer 2178
Wilmington, NC 28402-2178 (910) 617-5327
Contact: Patricia C. Jenkins, Chair.

Established in 1963 in NC.
Donor: Champion McDowell Davis†.
Foundation type: Independent foundation.
Financial data (yr. ended 12/31/13): Assets, $17,411,855 (M); expenditures, $892,639; qualifying distributions, $857,654; giving activities include $825,500 for 9 grants (high: $730,000; low: $2,500).
Purpose and activities: Giving primarily for health care.
Fields of interest: Health care; Human services; Residential/custodial care, hospices.
Type of support: Capital campaigns; Building/renovation.
Limitations: Applications accepted. Giving primarily in Wilmington, NC. No grants to individuals.
Application information: Application form required.
Initial approach: Proposal
Copies of proposal: 1
Deadline(s): 2 weeks before quarterly meetings
Board meeting date(s): Mar./June
Officers: Patricia C. Jenkins, Chair.; William O.J. Lynch, Secy.; Thomas L. Dodson, Treas.
Directors: Michael C. Brown, Jr.; William H. Cameron; Katherine T. Cammack; Frances H. Goodman; Dan Gottovi; Cyrus D. Hogue, Jr.; John R. Murchison II.
Number of staff: 1 part-time support.
EIN: 566055716

7190
Elmer R. Deaver Foundation, IDT ✧

1525 W. WT Harris Blvd., D1114-044
Charlotte, NC 28288-5709
Application address: c/o Wells Fargo Bank, 1 W. 4th St., D4000-062, Winston-Salem NC 27101-3818, tel.: (855) 739-2920

Established in 1996 in PA.
Donor: Delema Deaver Foundation.
Foundation type: Independent foundation.
Financial data (yr. ended 12/31/13): Assets, $12,643,034 (M); gifts received, $281,011; expenditures, $866,521; qualifying distributions, $787,540; giving activities include $683,080 for 22 + grants (high: $147,443).
Purpose and activities: Giving scholarships for descendants of employees of Quaker City Life Insurance Company, including spouses and dependent children.
Fields of interest: Higher education.
Type of support: Scholarships—to individuals; Endowments.
Limitations: Applications accepted. Giving primarily in PA.
Application information: Refer to https://www.csascholars.org/deaver/index.php for scholarship application information. Application form required.
Deadline(s): Scholarship applicants: see foundation web page for current deadlines
Trustee: Wells Fargo Bank, N.A.
EIN: 237830263
Selected grants: The following grants are a representative sample of this grantmaker's funding activity:
$118,051 to Lincoln University, Lincoln University, PA, 2011. For general support.
$39,350 to Rutgers University Foundation, New Brunswick, NJ, 2011. For general support.
$39,350 to Temple University, Philadelphia, PA, 2011. For general support.
$39,350 to University of Delaware, Newark, DE, 2011. For general support.
$39,350 to Villanova University, Villanova, PA, 2011. For general support.
$8,937 to Bucknell University, Lewisburg, PA, 2011. For general support.
$6,818 to University of Pennsylvania, Philadelphia, PA, 2011. For general support.
$4,650 to Immaculata University, Immaculata, PA, 2011. For general support.
$4,468 to La Salle University, Philadelphia, PA, 2011. For general support.
$2,118 to Drexel University, Philadelphia, PA, 2011. For general support.

7191
The Delta Air Lines Foundation ✧

1525 W. W.T. Harris Blvd., D1114-044
Charlotte, NC 28288-1161 (404) 715-5487
Contact: Scarlett Pressley-Brown, Sr. V.P.
FAX: (404) 715-3267;
E-mail: foundation.delta@delta.com; Application address: Community Affairs, Dept. 979, P.O. Box 20706, Atlanta, GA 30320-6001; Main URL: http://www.delta.com/about_delta/global_good/

Established in 1968 in DE.
Donor: Delta Air Lines, Inc.
Foundation type: Company-sponsored foundation.
Financial data (yr. ended 12/31/12): Assets, $30,465,583 (M); gifts received, $9,950,000; expenditures, $1,976,562; qualifying distributions, $1,815,089; giving activities include $1,795,664 for 12 grants (high: $333,333; low: $50,000).
Purpose and activities: The foundation and Delta Air Lines supports the Delta's Force for Global Good initiative designed to advance global diversity; improve global wellness; improve the environment; and promote arts and culture.
Fields of interest: Historical activities; Historical activities, centennials; Arts; Education, fund raising/fund distribution; Higher education; Environment; Health care; American Red Cross; Civil/human rights, equal rights; Foundations (community).
Type of support: General/operating support; Continuing support; Program development; Sponsorships; Employee matching gifts.
Limitations: Applications accepted. Giving primarily in areas of company operations, with emphasis on Washington, DC, Atlanta, GA, and Fairfax, VA. No support for political organizations, sectarian, religious, denominational organizations, tax-supported city, county or state organizations, fraternal organizations, professional associations, membership groups, or sports organizations. No grants to individuals, or for academic or medical research, or fundraising.
Publications: Application guidelines.
Application information: Funding for new proposals for cash or in-kind support are currently limited. Application form required.
Initial approach: Complete online application for sponsorships
Deadline(s): 90 days prior to need for sponsorships
Board meeting date(s): Mar., June, Sept., and Nov.
Final notification: 4 weeks for sponsorships
Officers and Trustees:* Timothy W. Mapes, Pres.; Scarlet Pressley-Brown, Sr. V.P.; Andrew Nelson, V.P. and Treas.; Frank Wrenn, V.P., Opers.; Julie Young, Secy.; Richard H. Anderson; Edward H. Bastian; Michael H. Campbell; Stephen E. Gorman; Glen W. Hauenstein.
EIN: 586073119

7192
The Dickson Foundation, Inc.

301 S. Tryon St., Ste. 1800
Charlotte, NC 28282-1947 (704) 372-5404
Contact: Alan T. Dickson, Pres.; Susan W. Patterson, Secy.-Treas.

Incorporated in 1944 in NC.
Donor: American and Efird Mills, Inc.
Foundation type: Independent foundation.
Financial data (yr. ended 12/31/12): Assets, $61,428,476 (M); expenditures, $3,263,344; qualifying distributions, $3,147,293; giving activities include $3,002,198 for 267 grants (high: $199,732; low: $100).
Purpose and activities: Giving primarily to local charities including health, human services and education.
Fields of interest: Education, association; Secondary school/education; Higher education; Hospitals (general); Health organizations, association; Human services; YM/YWCAs & YM/YWHAs; Youth, services; Residential/custodial care, hospices; United Ways and Federated Giving Programs.
Type of support: General/operating support; Scholarship funds.
Limitations: Giving primarily in NC. No grants to individuals, or for building or endowment funds.
Application information:
Initial approach: Letter
Deadline(s): None
Board meeting date(s): Annually and as required
Officers and Directors:* R. Stuart Dickson,* Chair.; Rush S. Dickson III,* V.P.; Thomas W. Dickson,* V.P.; Susan W. Patterson, Secy.-Treas.; Christian O. Avery; Jane W. Marley; Alison M. Scott.
EIN: 566022339

7193
Samuel C. Dobbs Trust ✧

c/o Wells Fargo Bank, N.A.
1 W. 4th St., 4th Fl., MAC D4000-041
Winston-Salem, NC 27101-3818

Foundation type: Independent foundation.

Financial data (yr. ended 09/30/13): Assets, $15,592,024 (M); expenditures, $880,832; qualifying distributions, $741,991; giving activities include $710,636 for 2 grants (high: $700,636; low: $10,000).
Fields of interest: Higher education.
Limitations: Applications not accepted. Giving primarily in GA.
Application information: Contributes only to pre-selected organizations.
Trustee: Wells Fargo Bank, N.A.
EIN: 586026550

7194
Dover Foundation, Inc. ✧
P.O. Box 208
Shelby, NC 28151-0208 (704) 487-8888
Contact: Hoyt Q. Bailey, Pres.
FAX: (704) 482-6818; E-mail: doverfnd@shelby.net

Incorporated in 1944 in NC.
Foundation type: Independent foundation.
Financial data (yr. ended 08/31/13): Assets, $17,711,316 (M); expenditures, $1,199,946; qualifying distributions, $1,064,083; giving activities include $949,880 for 131 grants (high: $50,000; low: $50).
Purpose and activities: Giving primarily for the arts, education, health, religion, particularly Baptist and United Methodist churches, and human services.
Fields of interest: Arts; Elementary/secondary education; Higher education; Education; Health organizations, association; Human services; Protestant agencies & churches.
Type of support: General/operating support; Continuing support; Annual campaigns; Capital campaigns; Building/renovation; Endowments; Emergency funds; Professorships; Fellowships; Scholarship funds; Research; Matching/challenge support.
Limitations: Applications accepted. Giving primarily in Cleveland County, NC.
Publications: Informational brochure (including application guidelines).
Application information: Application form required.
Initial approach: Letter
Copies of proposal: 9
Deadline(s): None
Officers: Hoyt Q. Bailey, Pres.; Kathleen H. Wilson, V.P.; Harvey B. Hamrick, Jr., Secy.; J. Linton Suttle, Treas.
Directors: Cynthia B. Buckingham; Melanie Ann Knight.
Number of staff: 1 full-time professional.
EIN: 560769897
Selected grants: The following grants are a representative sample of this grantmaker's funding activity:
$100,000 to Gardner-Webb University, Boiling Springs, NC, 2011.
$51,000 to Greater Cleveland County Baptist Association, Shelby, NC, 2011.
$50,000 to Hospice of Cleveland County, Shelby, NC, 2011.
$40,000 to Humane Society, Cleveland County, Shelby, NC, 2011.
$25,000 to Cleveland-Rutherford Kidney Association, Shelby, NC, 2011.
$25,000 to Destination Cleveland County, Shelby, NC, 2011.
$10,600 to Boys and Girls Club of Cleveland County, Shelby, NC, 2011.
$7,500 to Cleveland County Arts Council, Shelby, NC, 2011.
$7,000 to Princeton University, Princeton, NJ, 2011.
$3,000 to Holy Angels, Belmont, NC, 2011.

7195
The Duke Endowment
800 E. Morehead St.
Charlotte, NC 28202-4012 (704) 376-0291
Contact: Eugene W. Cochrane, Jr., Pres.
FAX: (704) 376-9336; E-mail: infotde@tde.org; E-mail for Charity L. Perkins, Dir., Comms.: cperkins@tde.org; Main URL: http://www.dukeendowment.org
Endowment's largest single philanthropic gift in its 87 years: http://www.youtube.com/watch?v=sZI-TrHam8o
Grants Database: http://www.dukeendowment.org/grants/search-our-grants
RSS Feed: http://www.dukeendowment.org/news/rss
RSS Grants Feed: http://www.dukeendowment.org/for-grantees
YouTube: http://www.youtube.com/dukeendowment

Trust established in 1924 in NJ.
Donor: James Buchanan Duke†.
Foundation type: Independent foundation.
Financial data (yr. ended 12/31/13): Assets, $3,367,128,863 (M); expenditures, $151,257,611; qualifying distributions, $127,729,045; giving activities include $127,729,045 for 388 grants.
Purpose and activities: Grants to nonprofit health care and child care institutions in NC and SC; rural United Methodist churches and its pastors in NC; and Duke, Furman, and Johnson C. Smith Universities, and Davidson College.
Fields of interest: Higher education; Hospitals (general); Palliative care; Health care; Children/youth, services; Protestant agencies & churches.
Type of support: General/operating support; Continuing support; Capital campaigns; Building/renovation; Equipment; Endowments; Emergency funds; Program development; Conferences/seminars; Professorships; Publication; Seed money; Curriculum development; Fellowships; Internship funds; Scholarship funds; Research; Technical assistance; Consulting services; Matching/challenge support.
Limitations: Applications accepted. Giving limited to NC and SC. No grants to individuals or for deficit financing; no loans.
Publications: Application guidelines; Annual report; Annual report (including application guidelines); Grants list; Informational brochure (including application guidelines); Newsletter; Occasional report.
Application information: Application form required.
Initial approach: Letter
Copies of proposal: 1
Deadline(s): June 15 and Dec. 15
Board meeting date(s): First Monday and Tuesday, 10 months of the year
Final notification: 2 to 6 months
Officers and Trustees:* Minor Mickel Shaw,* Chair.; William G. Anlyan, M.D.*, Vice-Chair.; Eugene W. Cochrane, Jr., Pres.; Rhett N. Mabry, V.P.; Arthur E. Morehead IV, V.P.; Mary L. Piepenbring, V.P.; Terri W. Honeycutt, Secy.; Karen H. Rogers, C.F.O.; Hong "Lily" Zhang, Cont.; K. Todd Walker, Managing Dir., Investments; William Barnet III; Dennis M. Campbell, Ph.D.; John F.A.V. Cecil; Harris E. DeLoach, Jr.; Ravenel B. Curry III; Constance F. Gray; Mary D.T. Jones; Thomas S. Kenan III; Charles C. Lucas III; Wilhelmina M. Reuben-Cooke; Russell M. Robinson II; Jean G. Spaulding, M.D.; Kenneth Durham Weeks, Jr., M.D.; Judy Woodruff.
Number of staff: 21 full-time professional; 14 full-time support.
EIN: 560529965
Selected grants: The following grants are a representative sample of this grantmaker's funding activity:
$45,000,000 to Davidson College, Davidson, NC, 2012. To create academic neighborhood that supports the integration of the arts and sciences at Davidson College.
$12,500,000 to Duke University, Durham, NC, 2012. For unrestricted operating support.
$12,500,000 to Duke University, Durham, NC, 2013. For unrestricted operating support.
$4,600,000 to Duke University, Divinity School, Durham, NC, 2013. To continue the Clergy Health Initiative, a program that works to improve and study the health of United Methodist clergy in North Carolina.
$3,850,000 to Duke University, Divinity School, Durham, NC, 2013. For the Thriving Rural Communities Initiative.
$3,404,420 to Davidson College, Davidson, NC, 2013. For the student resilience project at Davidson College, Duke University, Furman University and Johnson C. Smith University.
$3,350,000 to North Carolina Hospital Foundation, Cary, NC, 2012. To implement a rural hospital improvement program in North Carolina.
$3,000,000 to North Carolina Hospital Foundation, Cary, NC, 2012. For the North Carolina Hospital Association Center for Hospital Quality and Patient Safety.
$3,000,000 to South Carolina Hospital Research and Education Foundation, Columbia, SC, 2012. For the South Carolina Program for Quality and Patient Safety.
$2,750,000 to Self Regional Healthcare, Greenwood, SC, 2013. To expand a treatment program for genetic disabilities in South Carolina.
$1,650,000 to South Carolina Hospital Research and Education Foundation, Columbia, SC, 2012. To implement a rural hospital improvement program in South Carolina.
$1,500,000 to Childrens Home Society of North Carolina, Greensboro, NC, 2013. For matching support for the Social Innovation Fund to scale Family Finding throughout North Carolina.
$1,400,000 to Furman University, Greenville, SC, 2012. For unrestricted operating support.
$1,247,000 to Duke University, Divinity School, Durham, NC, 2012. For scholarships for the 2012 Summer Field Education Assistant Pastors program.
$500,000 to Blue Ridge HealthCare Systems, Morganton, NC, 2013. To expand a community network of care for the low-income, uninsured in Burke County.
$350,000 to North Carolina Hospital Foundation, Cary, NC, 2012. For the North Carolina Rural Center.
$225,000 to Partners in Ministry, Laurinburg, NC, 2013. For a community development program.
$175,000 to Duke University, Durham, NC, 2013. To assess the effectiveness of 'flipped classrooms'.
$90,000 to Oriental United Methodist Church, Oriental, NC, 2013. For a community outreach program.

7196
Duke Energy Foundation ✧
(formerly Duke Power Company Foundation)
400 South Tryon St.
P.O. Box 1007
Charlotte, NC 28201-1007 (704) 382-7200
Contact: Alisa McDonald, V.P.
FAX: (704) 382-7600; Address for Share the Warmth Fund: Duke Energy Foundation, P.O. Box 35469, Charlotte, NC 28254; Main URL: http://www.duke-energy.com/community/foundation.asp

Established in 1984 in NC.
Donors: Duke Power Co.; Duke Energy Corp.; Duke Energy Field Services, LP; Duke Energy Business Services; DPC Midstream; Cinergy Foundation.
Foundation type: Company-sponsored foundation.
Financial data (yr. ended 12/31/13): Assets, $20,770,172 (M); gifts received, $29,943,541; expenditures, $26,055,574; qualifying distributions, $26,054,388; giving activities include $24,512,290 for 1,541 grants (high: $1,000,000; low: $50), and $1,539,598 for employee matching gifts.
Purpose and activities: The foundation supports programs designed to promote STEM and early childhood literacy; economic and workforce development; the environment; and community impact and cultural enrichment.
Fields of interest: Arts; Elementary/secondary education; Education, early childhood education; Vocational education; Higher education; Higher education, college (community/junior); Education, reading; Education; Environment, research; Environment, air pollution; Environment, natural resources; Environment, energy; Environmental education; Environment; Animals/wildlife, preservation/protection; Animals/wildlife, endangered species; Employment, training; Employment, retraining; Employment; Safety/disasters; American Red Cross; Human services; Economic development; Business/industry; United Ways and Federated Giving Programs; Mathematics; Engineering/technology; Science; Leadership development; Minorities; Economically disadvantaged.
Type of support: Management development/capacity building; Annual campaigns; Building/renovation; Program development; Scholarship funds; Research; Employee volunteer services; Employee matching gifts; Employee-related scholarships; In-kind gifts; Matching/challenge support.
Limitations: Applications accepted. Giving primarily in areas of company operations in FL, IN, KY, OH, NC, and SC. No support for discriminatory organizations, political organizations or candidates, sports or all-star teams, elementary, secondary, or private schools, parent-teacher associations, religious organizations, or fraternal, veterans', or labor groups. No grants to individuals (except for employee-related scholarships), or for political activities or campaigns, fundraisers, uniforms, religious activities, general operating support, debt reduction, films, video, or television productions, membership or association fees, capital campaigns, investments, or improvements, endowments, conferences, trips, or tours, advertising, dinners, tables, walks, or runs; no utility service reduction.
Publications: Application guidelines; Informational brochure; IRS Form 990 or 990-PF printed copy available upon request; Program policy statement.
Application information: Support is limited to 1 contribution per organization during any given year. Organizations receiving support are asked to submit periodic reports on the measurable results of funded project. Application form required.
Initial approach: Complete online application form
Deadline(s): None for Local Community Development Grants; Apr. to May for Community Impact and Cultural Enrichment; July to Aug. for Environment; and Aug. to Sept. for Economic and Workforce Development
Board meeting date(s): Quarterly
Final notification: 1 to 3 months for Local Community Development Grants; 3 to 5 months
Officers and Trustees: Richard Tyrone Williams, Pres.; Alisa McDonald, V.P.; Kalyn Matthews, Treas.; Dhiaa M. Jamil; Marc E. Manly; B. Keith Trent; Jennifer L. Weber; Lloyd Yates.
Number of staff: 2 full-time professional.
EIN: 581586283
Selected grants: The following grants are a representative sample of this grantmaker's funding activity:
$1,000,000 to Foundation for the Carolinas, Charlotte, NC, 2012.
$790,000 to University of North Carolina at Charlotte Foundation, Charlotte, NC, 2012.
$690,000 to Foundation for the Carolinas, Charlotte, NC, 2012.
$625,000 to Queens University of Charlotte, Charlotte, NC, 2012.
$273,821 to North Carolina Museum of Natural Sciences, Friends of the, Raleigh, NC, 2012.
$250,000 to Chamber of Commerce Foundation of Greater Cincinnati, Cincinnati, OH, 2012.
$20,000 to Lee Institute, Charlotte, NC, 2012.
$20,000 to United Arts Council of Greater Greensboro, Greensboro, NC, 2012.
$15,600 to United Way of Greater High Point, High Point, NC, 2012.
$10,000 to Johnson C. Smith University, Charlotte, NC, 2012.

7197
Duke University Medical School and Hospital Trust ✧ ☆
c/o Wells Fargo Bank, N.A.
1 W. 4th St., 4th Fl., MAC D4000-041
Winston-Salem, NC 27101-3818

Foundation type: Independent foundation.
Financial data (yr. ended 08/31/13): Assets, $14,842,338 (M); expenditures, $769,173; qualifying distributions, $659,825; giving activities include $628,100 for 1 grant.
Fields of interest: Higher education.
Limitations: Applications not accepted. Giving primarily in Durham, NC.
Application information: Contributes only to pre-selected organizations.
Trustee: Wells Fargo Bank, N.A.
EIN: 566036456

7198
E. Claiborne Robins Jr. Charitable Trust ✧
1525 W. WT Harris Blvd., D1114-044
Charlotte, NC 28262-8522

Established in VA.
Donor: E.C. Robins Marital Trust.
Foundation type: Independent foundation.
Financial data (yr. ended 12/31/13): Assets, $40,299,160 (M); expenditures, $1,271,705; qualifying distributions, $1,119,471; giving activities include $1,117,471 for 5 grants (high: $673,500; low: $10,000).
Fields of interest: Historic preservation/historical societies; Education.
Limitations: Applications not accepted. Giving primarily in VA.
Application information: Contributes only to pre-selected organizations.
Trustee: E. Claiborne Robins, Jr.
EIN: 326140103

7199
A. E. Finley Foundation, Inc. ✧
1151 Newton Rd.
Raleigh, NC 27615-5223 (919) 782-0565
Contact: Robert C. Brown, Pres.
E-mail: lesa@aeffinc.org; Additional tel.: (919) 782-0529; fax: (919) 235-3348; Main URL: http://www.aefinleyfoundationinc.org

Incorporated in 1957 in NC.
Donor: A.E. Finley‡.
Foundation type: Independent foundation.
Financial data (yr. ended 12/31/12): Assets, $26,145,209 (M); expenditures, $1,457,333; qualifying distributions, $810,643; giving activities include $559,050 for 89 grants (high: $220,000; low: $100).
Purpose and activities: Support primarily for religion, health care, human services, arts and culture, youth development, and education.
Fields of interest: Arts; Higher education; Education; Human services; Youth, services; Community/economic development; Christian agencies & churches.
Type of support: General/operating support; Continuing support; Annual campaigns; Building/renovation; Equipment; Endowments; Program development; Seed money; Curriculum development; Fellowships; Scholarship funds; Research; Matching/challenge support.
Limitations: Giving primarily in the Triangle area of NC. No support for international or political organizations. No grants to individuals.
Publications: Informational brochure.
Application information:
Initial approach: Letter (via U.S. Mail)
Board meeting date(s): Monthly
Officer and Directors:* Robert C. Brown,* Pres.; Earle Finley; Alton Howard; Ben G. Nottingham; Charles Nottingham III.
Number of staff: 1 full-time professional; 2 part-time professional; 1 full-time support.
EIN: 566057379

7200
Flow Foundation, Inc. ✧
1425 Plaza Dr.
Winston-Salem, NC 27103-1480

Established in 2004 in NC.
Donor: Donald E. Flow.
Foundation type: Independent foundation.
Financial data (yr. ended 12/31/12): Assets, $588,790 (M); gifts received, $1,079,795; expenditures, $805,337; qualifying distributions,

$804,780; giving activities include $804,780 for 38 grants (high: $235,000; low: $200).
Fields of interest: Higher education; Human services; United Ways and Federated Giving Programs.
Limitations: Applications not accepted. Giving primarily in NC and VA. No grants to individuals.
Application information: Contributes only to pre-selected organizations.
Officers: Donald E. Flow, Pres.; Robbin B. Flow, Secy.-Treas.
EIN: 201983806

7201
Food Lion Charitable Foundation, Inc. ✧
2110 Executive Dr.
Salisbury, NC 28147-9007 (704) 633-8250
Contact: Denise Hill, Chair.
FAX: (704) 638-1988; E-mail: flcf@foodlion.com; Application address: Community Rels. Dept., P.O. Box 1330, Salisbury, NC 28145-1330; Main URL: http://charitablefoundation.foodlion.org

Established as a company-sponsored operating foundation in 2001 in NC.
Donor: Food Lion LLC.
Foundation type: Operating foundation.
Financial data (yr. ended 12/31/12): Assets, $419,930 (M); gifts received, $1,013,549; expenditures, $1,051,846; qualifying distributions, $925,850; giving activities include $925,850 for 258+ grants (high: $10,000).
Purpose and activities: The foundation supports programs and agencies designed to feed the hungry with a focus on eliminating hunger.
Fields of interest: Food services; Food banks; Food distribution, meals on wheels; United Ways and Federated Giving Programs.
Type of support: Continuing support; Program development.
Limitations: Applications accepted. Giving primarily in areas of company operations in DE, FL, GA, KY, MD, NC, PA, SC, TN, VA. and WV. No grants to individuals, or for administrative costs.
Publications: Application guidelines.
Application information: Grants range from $2,500 to $5,000. Preference is given to organizations that involve Food Lion associates. Support is limited to 1 contribution per organization during any given year. Organizations receiving support are asked to submit information regarding grant success and outcomes. Application form required.
Initial approach: Download application form and mail to foundation
Deadline(s): Mar. 15 and Sept. 15
Board meeting date(s): Jan., Apr., July, and Oct.
Final notification: May and Nov.
Officers: Denise Hill, Chair.; Lou Delorenzo, V.P.; Chris Dove, Secy.-Treas.
EIN: 562279572
Selected grants: The following grants are a representative sample of this grantmaker's funding activity:
$4,000 to Women Who Care Ministries, Montgomery Village, MD, 2012. For feeding the hungry.

7202
Foundation For The Carolinas ✧
220 N. Tryon St.
Charlotte, NC 28202-3201 (704) 973-4500
Contact: Brian Collier, Sr. V.P.
E-mail: infor@fftc.org; Additional tel.: (800) 973-7244; Additional e-mail: bcollier@fftc.org; Main URL: http://www.fftc.org
Facebook: http://www.facebook.com/pages/Foundation-For-The-Carolinas/150051255018005
Tel. for Q. Austin: (704) 973-4535, e-mail: qaustin@fftc.org

Incorporated in 1958 in NC.
Foundation type: Community foundation.
Financial data (yr. ended 12/31/13): Assets, $1,276,583,309 (M); gifts received, $288,182,455; expenditures, $194,377,441; giving activities include $180,272,727 for grants.
Purpose and activities: The foundation exists to advance philanthropy by serving donors, increasing charitable giving, and improving communities.
Fields of interest: Arts, cultural/ethnic awareness; Historic preservation/historical societies; Arts; Education; Environment; Health care; Health organizations, association; Medical research, institute; Disasters, Hurricane Katrina; Children/youth, services; Aging, centers/services; Human services; Civil/human rights, equal rights; Civil/human rights, minorities; Economic development; Leadership development; Public affairs; Religion; African Americans/Blacks; Economically disadvantaged.
Type of support: Seed money; Scholarship funds; Grants to individuals; Matching/challenge support.
Limitations: Applications accepted. Giving primarily to organizations serving the citizens of NC and SC, with emphasis on the greater Charlotte, NC, region. No grants to individuals (except for scholarships), or for deficit financing, capital campaigns, ongoing operating budgets, publications, conferences, videos, travel, equipment, small businesses, business start-up, or advertising.
Publications: Application guidelines; Annual report (including application guidelines); Newsletter.
Application information: Visit foundation web site for application guidelines per Regional Affiliate Community Foundation grant program and client grantmaking programs. Faxed or e-mail applications are not accepted. Application form required.
Initial approach: Varies
Deadline(s): Varies
Board meeting date(s): Distribution Committee meets 3 times per year
Final notification: 2 months
Officers and Directors:* Chris Kearney,* Chair.; Michael Marsicano, Ph.D., C.E.O. and Pres.; D. Brian Collier, Exec. V.P.; Laura Smith, Exec. V.P.; Holly K. Welch Stubbing, Exec. V.P., In-house Counsel; Laura L. Meyer Wellman, C.E.O. and Pres., E4E Relief; Qiana L. Austin, V.P., Scholarships; Douglas W. Benson, V.P., and Deputy Counsel; Alli Celebron-Brown, V.P., Community Progs.-Affiliates; Meg Kluttz Dees, V.P., Philanthropic Advancement-Affiliates; Alyssa R. Federico, V.P., Finance; Paul Fisher, V.P., Inf. Tech. Opers. and Architecture; Vicki L. Jones, V.P., Product Mgmt.; David W. Julian, V.P., Regional Affiliates; Tara Keener, V.P., Mktg. and Comms.; Carol Morris, V.P., Community Initiatives; Andrea C. Phelps, V.P., Donor Rels.; David Snider, V.P., Community Progs.; Ronald Townsend, V.P., Client Svcs.; Curt Walton, V.P., Real Estate and Facilities Mgmt.; Catherine D. Warfield, V.P., Center for Personal Philanthropy; Debra S. Watt, Sr. V.P., Inf. Tech. and Human Resources; Catherine P. Bessant; Ron Carter, Ph.D.; Eugene "Gene" Flood; W. Barnes Hauptfuhrer; Jewell D. Hoover; James "Jim" Johnston; Howard Levine; Todd Mansfield; Fritz Nauck; Pat Rodgers; Art Rogers; Geri Rucker; Laura Schulte; Ruth Shaw, Ph.D.; Tom E. Smith.
Number of staff: 17 full-time professional; 10 full-time support; 1 part-time support.
EIN: 566047886
Selected grants: The following grants are a representative sample of this grantmaker's funding activity:
$408,000 to Communities in Schools of Charlotte-Mecklenburg, Charlotte, NC, 2012. For general operating support for the Dropout Prevention Programs at CIS-Mecklenburg and Allenbrook Elementary School.
$250,000 to Four-H of North Carolina, NC, 2012. To assist with the building of The Cole Foundation Theater.
$75,000 to Richmond Community College Foundation, Hamlet, NC, 2012. For the Forte Building Renovation and Expansion Project.
$50,000 to Crisis Assistance Ministry, Charlotte, NC, 2012. For the Benefit Bank.
$30,000 to International House of Metrolina, Charlotte, NC, 2012. For the Ginter Immigration Law Clinic in assisting low-income immigrants and refugees with family immigration and naturalization services, while moving later to a new facility on Central Avenue.
$25,000 to Levine Museum of the New South, Charlotte, NC, 2012. For Latino New South.
$8,000 to Iredell-Statesville Schools, Statesville, NC, 2012. For the Presidential Art Show being held at the Department of Education/Washington, DC.
$5,000 to Carolinas Concert Association, Charlotte, NC, 2012. For the Sphinx Virtuosi program.
$5,000 to Family Promise of York County, Rock Hill, SC, 2012. For direct guest assistance, including transportation, medication and other basic necessities.

7203
Samuel & Katharine French Fund ✧
(formerly Samuel H. French III and Katharine Weaver French Fund)
c/o Wells Fargo Bank, N.A., Trust Tax Dept.
1 W. 4th St., 4th Fl., MAC D4000-041
Winston-Salem, NC 27101-3818
E-mail: grantadministration@wellsfargo.com; Main URL: https://www.wellsfargo.com/privatefoundationgrants/french

Established in 1986 in CA.
Donor: French Charitable Remainder Unitrust.
Foundation type: Independent foundation.
Financial data (yr. ended 12/31/13): Assets, $11,433,735 (M); expenditures, $659,943; qualifying distributions, $555,818; giving activities include $528,111 for 56 grants (high: $100,000; low: $150).
Purpose and activities: Support for underprivileged children and the elderly.
Fields of interest: Hospitals (general); Health organizations, association; YM/YWCAs & YM/YWHAs; Children/youth, services; Aging, centers/services; Children; Aging.
Type of support: Building/renovation; Equipment; Program development; Conferences/seminars; Scholarship funds; Research; Matching/challenge support.

Limitations: Applications accepted. Giving limited to San Diego County, CA. No support for start-up organizations. No grants to individuals, or for salaries.
Application information: See foundation website for complete application guidelines. Application form required.
Deadline(s): Apr. 30, Aug. 31, and Dec. 31
Trustee: Wells Fargo Bank, N.A.
EIN: 954111082

7204
The Fund for Democratic Communities ✧ ☆
620 S. Elm St., Ste. 355
Greensboro, NC 27406-1398
E-mail: info@f4dc.org; Main URL: http://www.f4dc.org
Blog: http://f4dc.org/blog/
Facebook: https://www.facebook.com/Fund4DemocraticCommunities
Flickr: https://www.flickr.com/photos/f4dc/
Google Plus: https://plus.google.com/+F4dcOrg/posts
Grants List: http://f4dc.org/programs/grassroots-matching-grants/
Twitter: http://twitter.com/f4dc

Donors: Stephen Johnson; Marnie Thompson; W. Hayden Thompson†; William H. Thompson.
Foundation type: Independent foundation.
Financial data (yr. ended 12/31/13): Assets, $9,319,648 (M); gifts received, $713,248; expenditures, $1,225,607; qualifying distributions, $1,164,465; giving activities include $728,924 for 55 grants (high: $343,292; low: $50), and $1,164,465 for foundation-administered programs.
Purpose and activities: Supports groups that engage in participatory democracy to further their social change objectives; convenes groups and individuals committed to social and economic justice through deepening democratic practice; conducts research; and produces materials to nurture the growth of authentic democracy.
Type of support: General/operating support; Matching/challenge support.
Limitations: Applications accepted. Giving primarily in GA and NC.
Publications: Application guidelines.
Application information: Application form and complete application guidelines available on fund web site. Application form required.
Deadline(s): None
Final notification: 4 weeks
Managing Directors: Marnie Thompson, Co-Managing Director; Ed Whitfield, Co-Managing Director.
EIN: 260344869
Selected grants: The following grants are a representative sample of this grantmaker's funding activity:
$6,826 to Southerners on New Ground, Atlanta, GA, 2012. For Capacity building and general operating support.
$5,000 to Abundance Foundation, Pittsboro, NC, 2012. For Slow Money NC general operating support.
$5,000 to Carolina Common Enterprise, Hendersonville, NC, 2012. For RCDG Match general operating support.
$2,716 to Interactive Resource Center, Greensboro, NC, 2012. For IRC Staff development in grassroots fundraising.
$605 to Alliance for a Just Society, Seattle, WA, 2012. For IPP Conference in Seattle.
$500 to Participatory Budgeting Project, Brooklyn, NY, 2012. For Sponsorship of International PB Conference 3/30/12.

7205
George Foundation, Inc. ✧
P.O. Box 800
Hickory, NC 28603-0800
Contact: Boyd George, Pres.

Established in 1980 in NC.
Donors: Boyd George; G. Lee George†; Merchants Distributors, Inc.; Lowe's Food Stores, Inc.; Institution Food House, Inc.
Foundation type: Independent foundation.
Financial data (yr. ended 11/30/13): Assets, $9,504,836 (M); gifts received, $1,024,500; expenditures, $1,212,985; qualifying distributions, $1,160,900; giving activities include $1,160,900 for 93 grants (high: $600,000; low: $200).
Purpose and activities: Giving primarily for a college; support also for community development and a program fighting hunger.
Fields of interest: Higher education; Food services; Community/economic development.
Limitations: Giving primarily in Hickory, NC. No grants to individuals.
Officers and Trustees:* Boyd George,* Pres.; Kimberly D. George,* V.P.; John B. Orgain,* Secy.; Ron Knedlik,* Treas.; Joyce George Corbett; William R. Waddell.
EIN: 561282417
Selected grants: The following grants are a representative sample of this grantmaker's funding activity:
$500,000 to Lenoir-Rhyne University, Hickory, NC, 2011. For general support.
$1,000 to A Brighter Path Foundation, Winston-Salem, NC, 2011. For general support.
$1,000 to AIDS Leadership Foothills Area Alliance, Hickory, NC, 2011. For general support.

7206
William & Marian Ghidotti Foundation ✧
c/o Wells Fargo Bank, N.A., Trust Tax Dept.
1 W. 4th St., 4th Fl., MAC D4000-041
Winston-Salem, NC 27101-3818
Application address: c/o Wells Fargo Bank, N.A., P.O. Box 63954, MAC A 0330-011, San Francisco, CA 94163, tel.: (800) 352-3705

Established in 1969 in CA.
Donors: William Ghidotti; Marian Ghidotti†.
Foundation type: Independent foundation.
Financial data (yr. ended 12/31/13): Assets, $11,209,076 (M); expenditures, $687,988; qualifying distributions, $634,803.
Purpose and activities: Awards student scholarships to graduating seniors residing in and attending Nevada County, CA, high schools; some support also for the arts, education, health care, human services, and community programs.
Fields of interest: Arts; Education; Health care; Human services; Children/youth, services.
Type of support: Equipment; Scholarships—to individuals.
Limitations: Applications accepted. Giving limited to residents of Nevada County, CA.
Application information: Scholarship applicants should submit Std. Scholarship APF/Transcript of grades, student and family income, and resume. Application form required.
Initial approach: Proposal
Deadline(s): Feb. for new scholarships; Aug. for renewals
Trustee: Wells Fargo Bank, N.A.
EIN: 946181833
Selected grants: The following grants are a representative sample of this grantmaker's funding activity:
$4,000 to Abilene Christian University, Abilene, TX, 2012. For general support grant scholarship.

7207
Gibbs Trust ✧
1525 W. WT Harris Blvd., D1114-044
Charlotte, NC 28288-5709

Foundation type: Independent foundation.
Financial data (yr. ended 11/30/13): Assets, $13,786,925 (M); expenditures, $724,715; qualifying distributions, $586,506; giving activities include $575,000 for 3 grants (high: $287,500; low: $143,750).
Purpose and activities: Giving primarily to Lutheran organizations and churches; some support also for a music foundation.
Fields of interest: Performing arts, music; Protestant agencies & churches.
Limitations: Applications not accepted. Giving primarily in Reading and Mechanicsburg, PA.
Application information: Contributes only to pre-selected organizations.
Trustee: Wells Fargo Bank, N.A.
EIN: 236754370

7208
The Lucille P. and Edward C. Giles Foundation ✧ ☆
(formerly The Edward C. Giles Foundation)
2115 Rexford Rd.
Charlotte, NC 28211-5453

Established in 1981 in NC.
Donor: Lucille P. Giles†.
Foundation type: Independent foundation.
Financial data (yr. ended 12/31/12): Assets, $17,294,241 (M); expenditures, $1,076,971; qualifying distributions, $936,843; giving activities include $845,417 for 13 grants (high: $478,611; low: $6,806).
Purpose and activities: Giving primarily for higher education, particularly scholarships to children of employees of Carauster Industries, Inc. and its subsidiaries, as well as for human services.
Fields of interest: Higher education; Human services; Protestant agencies & churches.
Type of support: Employee-related scholarships.
Limitations: Applications not accepted. Giving primarily in the Charlotte, NC, area.
Application information: Unsolicited requests for funds not accepted.
Board meeting date(s): Spring and late fall
Officers: Bernard Fitzgerald, C.E.O. and Pres.; William Jeffries, V.P.; John V. McIntosh, V.P.; Jan J. Nomina, V.P.; Mark B. Edwards, Secy.-Treas.

Number of staff: 1 part-time professional.
EIN: 581450874

7209
Gipson Family Foundation ✧
609 Brookfield Rd.
Raleigh, NC 27615-1406 (919) 847-8500
Contact: Thomas Gipson, Tr.

Established in 1996 in NC.
Donor: Thomas L. Gipson.
Foundation type: Independent foundation.
Financial data (yr. ended 12/31/13): Assets, $29,260,517 (M); gifts received, $1,770,400; expenditures, $1,194,877; qualifying distributions, $1,193,250; giving activities include $1,193,250 for 35 grants (high: $500,000; low: $250).
Purpose and activities: Giving primarily for social services and to Protestant churches and ministries.
Fields of interest: Human services; Protestant agencies & churches.
Limitations: Applications accepted. Giving primarily in Raleigh, NC, PA and TX.
Application information: Application form not required.
Initial approach: Proposal
Deadline(s): None
Trustees: Elizabeth Cheatham; Cary Gipson; Clay Gipson; Donald Gipson; Patricia C. Gipson; Thomas L. Gipson.
EIN: 562001414

7210
Glass Foundation, Inc. ✧
(formerly Glass Family Foundation, Inc.)
2 Town Square Blvd., Ste. 310
Asheville, NC 28803-8814
E-mail: lnolletti@glassfoundation.org; Main URL: http://www.glassfoundation.org

Established in 2000 in NC.
Donors: Kenneth E. Glass; TECT.
Foundation type: Independent foundation.
Financial data (yr. ended 12/31/12): Assets, $13,535,602 (M); gifts received, $1,420,249; expenditures, $830,606; qualifying distributions, $675,337; giving activities include $675,337 for grants.
Purpose and activities: The foundation believes in helping the Western North Carolina region thrive as a whole community educationally, environmentally, and culturally and offer a distinctive quality of life. The overall vision of the foundation is to enable Western North Carolina to realize a vision of itself as a premier place to both live and work by making the region a center of high quality educational opportunity; helping to preserve a diverse array of natural resources; and by maintaining a rich cultural and historical heritage.
Fields of interest: Education; Environment, natural resources; Health organizations, association; Human services; United Ways and Federated Giving Programs; Children/youth; Youth.
Type of support: Capital campaigns; Building/renovation; Equipment; Land acquisition; Conferences/seminars; Matching/challenge support.
Limitations: Applications accepted. Giving primarily in NC. No grants to individuals.
Publications: Application guidelines.
Application information: Complete application policies and guidelines available on foundation web site. Application form not required.
Initial approach: Submit proposal or e-mail a summary of the project to ensure compatibility prior to submitting proposal
Deadline(s): None
Officers and Directors:* Kenneth E. Glass,* Chair.; Lara Nolletti,* Pres.; Nancy J. Glass,* Secy.; David Nolletti; Bernard Stanek.
Number of staff: 1 part-time professional.
EIN: 562196225

7211
Glenn Family Foundation ✧ ☆
P.O. Box 2736
Winston-Salem, NC 27102-2736

Established in 1987 in NC.
Donors: James K. Glenn; James K. Glenn, Jr.; Frances G. Porter.
Foundation type: Independent foundation.
Financial data (yr. ended 12/31/13): Assets, $4,362,555 (M); expenditures, $3,286,895; qualifying distributions, $3,253,000; giving activities include $3,253,000 for 30 grants (high: $3,006,000; low: $1,000).
Purpose and activities: Giving primarily to Presbyterian churches, as well as for children, youth and social services.
Fields of interest: Arts; Human services; Children/youth, services; Family services; Residential/custodial care, hospices; United Ways and Federated Giving Programs; Protestant agencies & churches.
Type of support: General/operating support; Building/renovation; Professorships.
Limitations: Applications not accepted. Giving primarily in Winston-Salem, NC. No grants to individuals.
Application information: Contributes only to pre-selected organizations.
Directors: Sally G. Blanco; Frances G. Porter.
Officer: J. Kirk Glenn, Jr., Pres. and Treas.
EIN: 581748268
Selected grants: The following grants are a representative sample of this grantmaker's funding activity:
$1,000 to Boy Scouts of America, Old Hickory Council, Winston-Salem, NC, 2012. For general use.

7212
The Goodnight Educational Foundation ✧
100 SAS Campus Dr.
Cary, NC 27513-2414

Established in 1998 in NC.
Donors: James H. Goodnight; Ann B. Goodnight.
Foundation type: Independent foundation.
Financial data (yr. ended 12/31/13): Assets, $120,899,601 (M); expenditures, $2,473,149; qualifying distributions, $2,396,000; giving activities include $2,396,000 for 35 grants (high: $1,818,000; low: $5,000).
Purpose and activities: Giving primarily for higher education and the arts.
Fields of interest: Arts; Elementary/secondary education; Higher education; Education; Human services.
Limitations: Applications not accepted. Giving primarily in NC, with emphasis on Raleigh. No support for political campaigns. No grants to individuals.
Application information: Unsolicited requests for funds not accepted.
Directors: Susan G. Ellis; Ann Baggett Goodnight; James H. Goodnight; Leah A. Goodnight; Donald R. Parker.
EIN: 566533546

7213
Goodrich Foundation ✧
(formerly The Goodrich Foundation, Inc.)
4 Coliseum Centre
2730 W. Tyvola Rd.
Charlotte, NC 28217-4578 (704) 423-7489
Contact: Cynthia Forbes, Mgr., Community Rels.
FAX: (704) 423-7011;
E-mail: cynthia.forbes@utas.utc.com; Main URL: http://utcaerospacesystems.com/Company/Pages/goodrich-foundation.aspx

Established in 1989 in OH.
Donors: The B.F.Goodrich Co.; Goodrich Corp.
Foundation type: Company-sponsored foundation.
Financial data (yr. ended 12/31/13): Assets, $3,991,561 (M); expenditures, $1,812,093; qualifying distributions, $1,778,264; giving activities include $1,762,905 for 61 grants (high: $664,122; low: $997).
Purpose and activities: The foundation supports programs designed to advance K-12 and higher education science, technology, engineering, and math initiatives focused on the next generation of engineering scientists; promote vibrant communities through community revitalization, health and social services, and arts and culture; and build sustainable cities through environmental sustainable practices, projects, and urban green space.
Fields of interest: Museums (science/technology); Arts; Education, reform; Elementary/secondary education; Higher education; Adult/continuing education; Education, services; Education; Environment; Health care; Disasters, preparedness/services; Human services; Community/economic development; United Ways and Federated Giving Programs; Space/aviation; Mathematics; Engineering/technology; Science.
Type of support: General/operating support; Continuing support; Management development/capacity building; Annual campaigns; Program development; Scholarship funds; Research; Employee volunteer services; Use of facilities; Sponsorships; Employee matching gifts; Employee-related scholarships; In-kind gifts; Matching/challenge support.
Limitations: Applications accepted. Giving on a national basis in areas of company operations, with emphasis on Charlotte, NC. No support for private foundations, churches, fraternal, social, labor groups with high fundraising or administrative expenses, political parties or candidates, discriminatory organizations, organizations primarily funded through municipal, country, state, or federal dollars, individual United Way agencies already supported by Goodrich, and international organizations. No grants to individuals, or for endowments, religious programs, lobbying activities, travel, tours, exhibitions, trips, local athletics, sports programs, equipment, courtesy advertising benefits, tables, or tickets.
Publications: Application guidelines.

Application information: Multi-year funding is not automatic. Multi-year funding requests should not exceed 5 years. Telephone calls are not encouraged. Application form required.
Initial approach: Complete online application form
Deadline(s): Mar. 1 and Aug. 1
Board meeting date(s): Quarterly
Final notification: 90 days
Officers: Terrence G. Linnert, Pres.; Jack Carmola, V.P.; Scott Kuechle, Treas.
Number of staff: 1 full-time professional; 1 full-time support.
EIN: 261195329
Selected grants: The following grants are a representative sample of this grantmaker's funding activity:
$100,000 to Association of Graduates of the United States Military Academy, West Point, NY, 2012. For W Point National Confer Ethics in America.
$50,000 to Presbyterian Hospital Foundation, Charlotte, NC, 2012. For mobile health outreach.
$50,000 to University of Akron Foundation, Akron, OH, 2012. For Engineering Program Support College of Engineering.
$30,000 to Habitat for Humanity of Charlotte, Charlotte, NC, 2012. For Goodrich Habit Charlotte Build.
$25,000 to YMCA of Greater Charlotte, Charlotte, NC, 2012. For Y Achievers.
$20,000 to Hope for the Warriors, Jacksonville, NC, 2012. To restore program.
$20,000 to Pats Place Child Advocacy Center, Charlotte, NC, 2012. For family advocate and crisis support.
$15,000 to Habitat for Humanity International, Americus, GA, 2012. For Last Home a Special Project W Orange.
$11,500 to LifeQuest Transitions, Colorado Springs, CO, 2012. For Lifequest Military Transition Functional, Wellness Program.
$5,000 to Special Operations Warrior Foundation, Tampa, FL, 2012. For Wounded Warrior Support.

7214
The Jeff Gordon Children's Foundation ✧
(formerly The Jeff Gordon Foundation)
7575 West Winds Blvd. N.W., Ste., C
Concord, NC 28027-3328 (980) 255-8508
Contact: Grant Program
E-mail: foundation@jgiracing.com; Main URL: http://www.jeffgordonchildrensfoundation.org
ebay: http://cgi3.ebay.com/ws/eBayISAPI.dll?ViewUserPage&userid=jeffgordon4cure
E-Newsletter: http://www.jeffgordonchildrensfoundation.org/site/c.5oIDJRPyGfISF/b.5968399/k.991E/eNewsletter.htm
Facebook: http://www.facebook.com/JGChildrensFoundation?ref=ts
Pinterest: https://www.pinterest.com/jeffgordon4cure/
RSS Feed: http://www.jeffgordonchildrensfoundation.org/site/apps/nl/rss2.asp?c=5oIDJRPyGfISF&b=5968491
Twitter: https://twitter.com/#!/JeffGordon4Cure
YouTube: http://www.youtube.com/user/JeffGordon4Cure

Established in 1999 in NC.
Donors: American Book Wholesale; Greg Biffle; Bristol Motor Speedway; Clarian Health; El DuPont DE Nemours Co.; Eldora Speedway, Inc.; Elkhorn Auto Services LLC; Fox Channel Services LLC; Jeffrey M. Gordon; Jeff Gordon, Inc.; HGJ Licensing LLC; Hendrick Gordon Leasing; Hendrick Motorsports; Rebecca Hoover; ICAP Securities USA LLC; IJO; Int'l Merchandising Corp.; Jimmie Johnson Foundation; Just Marketing, Inc.; Just Rite Acoustics, Inc.; Rebecca Kasten; Kraft Foods Global, Inc.; Lowes; Marcus Pointe Baptist Church; Midwest Maintenance and Construction; Motorsports Authentics; Motorsports Charities; Motorsports Marketing; Music Today LLC; The Nexxus Group; Nicorette; One America; Pacific Technical Resources; Pepsico; Penguin Group; Perfection Products, Inc.; Julian Rawl; RCI North American; Schwan's Home Services; Kiros Sistevans; Speedway Children's Charities; Sprint Nextel; Brad Swaback; Mitchell Swaback Charities, Inc.; Tracie Thompson; Village Pantry; Paul Wellnitz; Rhonda Zamora.
Foundation type: Independent foundation.
Financial data (yr. ended 12/31/12): Assets, $404,026 (M); gifts received, $1,297,726; expenditures, $1,924,804; qualifying distributions, $1,811,789; giving activities include $1,335,544 for 11+ grants (high: $300,000).
Purpose and activities: The foundation supports children battling cancer by funding programs that improve patients' quality of life, treatment programs that increase survivorship and pediatric medical research dedicated to finding a cure. Additionally, the foundation provides support to the Jeff Gordon Children's Hospital in Concord, NC, which serves children in the community by providing a high level of primary and specialty pediatric care.
Fields of interest: Hospitals (specialty); Health care; Cancer; Pediatrics; Medical research, institute; Cancer research; Human services; Children/youth, services; Family services.
Limitations: Giving in the U.S., with emphasis on NC; funding also in IN, MA, and MN. No grants to individuals, or for endowment funds.
Publications: Application guidelines; Annual report; Grants list; Informational brochure.
Application information: Must submit proposal with the Jeff Gordon Foundation grant application form which can be downloaded from foundation web site. Application form required.
Initial approach: Submit application form
Copies of proposal: 1
Deadline(s): Usually in Aug. See foundation web site for current deadline date
Final notification: Dec. 31
Officers and Director:* Jeffrey M. Gordon, Pres.; John S. Bickford, Sr., V.P. and Secy.; Ryan Hutcheson, C.F.O.; Dianne Chipps Bailey; Jeffrey W. Chell, M.D.; Wade Clapp, M.D.; Rick Hendrick; James Reichard; Glenn Schineller.
Number of staff: 1 full-time professional.
EIN: 562174163

7215
William and Patricia Gorelick Family Foundation ✧ ☆
4064 Colony Rd., Ste. 340
Charlotte, NC 28211-5117

Established in 1990 in NC.
Donors: William Gorelick; Todd Gorelick.
Foundation type: Independent foundation.
Financial data (yr. ended 12/31/13): Assets, $5,205,113 (M); expenditures, $502,455; qualifying distributions, $490,372; giving activities include $490,372 for 34 grants (high: $185,950; low: $144).
Purpose and activities: Giving primarily to Jewish organizations and art organizations.
Fields of interest: Museums; Arts; Education; Jewish agencies & synagogues.
Type of support: Annual campaigns; Capital campaigns; Building/renovation; Endowments.
Limitations: Applications not accepted. Giving primarily in NC. No grants to individuals.
Application information: Unsolicited requests for funds not accepted.
Officers: William Gorelick, Pres.; Patricia Gorelick, V.P.; Todd A. Gorelick, Secy.
EIN: 561743190

7216
Gratis Foundation ✧ ☆
(formerly Zaccaria Family Foundation)
1525 W. WT Harris Blvd., D1114-044
Charlotte, NC 28262
Tel. for applications: Wells Fargo Philanthropic Services, Winston-Salem, NC 27101, tel.: (888) 235-4351

Established in MD.
Donors: Adrian Zaccaria; Mary Sandra Zaccaria.
Foundation type: Independent foundation.
Financial data (yr. ended 12/31/13): Assets, $14,024,466 (M); expenditures, $778,432; qualifying distributions, $669,186; giving activities include $643,000 for 59 grants (high: $30,000; low: $1,000).
Fields of interest: Education; Health care; Human services.
Limitations: Applications accepted. Giving primarily in IN, KY, ME, NY and VA. No grants to individuals.
Application information: Application form available at http://www.wellsfargo.com/privatefoundationgrants/gratis. Application form required.
Initial approach: Complete online form application
Deadline(s): Jan. 31, May 31, and Sept. 30
Officer: Justin Zaccaria, Pres. and Secy.-Treas.
Directors: Adrian Zaccaria; Mary Sandra Zaccaria.
EIN: 263639918

7217
The Greater Greenville Foundation, Inc. ✧
625-Suite A, Lynndale Court
P.O. Box 20154
Greenville, NC 27858 (252) 756-8549
Contact: For grants: Charlene Silver, Donor Svcs. Mgr.
FAX: (252) 756-8549;
E-mail: charlene.ggcf@gmail.com; Main URL: http://www.ggcfnc.org

Organized in 1978 as the City of Greenville Foundation Trust; reorganized in 1999 as The Greater Greenville Foundation.
Foundation type: Community foundation.
Financial data (yr. ended 12/31/12): Assets, $8,107,077 (M); gifts received, $1,976,638; expenditures, $1,258,143; giving activities include $738,259 for 22+ grants (high: $120,662).
Purpose and activities: The foundation serves educational, religious and charitable causes, as well as helping nonprofit organizations establish their own gift funds or endowments. The foundation also encourages citizens of Pitt County to support these charitable causes by establishing their own gift

funds and endowments, or by supporting current gift funds and endowments held by the foundation.
Fields of interest: Community/economic development.
Type of support: General/operating support; Annual campaigns; Endowments; Program development; Conferences/seminars; Curriculum development; Scholarship funds; Matching/challenge support.
Limitations: Applications accepted. Giving primarily in Pitt County, NC. No support for sectarian religious purposes. No grants to individuals (except for scholarships), or for long term operating support.
Publications: Application guidelines; Financial statement; Grants list; Informational brochure.
Application information: Visit foundation web site for application information.
Initial approach: Telephone or e-mail
Deadline(s): None
Board meeting date(s): Jan., Apr., July, and Oct.
Final notification: Within 30 days
Officers and Directors:* Dr. Marcus Albernaz,* Pres.; Joel Butler,* V.P.; Melissa Spain,* C.E.O. and Exec. Dir.; Mary Everett,* Secy.; Rebecca Blount,* Treas.; Walter Bolden; Kirk Dominick; Leigh Fanning; James L. Lanier; Marty Measamer; Christian Porter; Dr. Mary Raab; George Saad, Jr.; Bill Taft; Lamont Wooten.
Number of staff: 1 full-time professional; 1 full-time support.
EIN: 562152669

7218
The Gunzenhauser-Chapin Fund Inc. ✧
c/o Piedmont Trust Co.
P.O. Box 20124
Greensboro, NC 27420-0124

Established in 1998 in NC.
Donor: Lynne R. and Karl E. Prickett Fund.
Foundation type: Independent foundation.
Financial data (yr. ended 12/31/13): Assets, $21,533,288 (M); gifts received, $750,000; expenditures, $983,726; qualifying distributions, $883,282; giving activities include $856,500 for 32 grants (high: $299,991; low: $500).
Fields of interest: Environment; Human services; Foundations (community).
Limitations: Applications not accepted. Giving in the U.S., with some emphasis on MA and NY.
Application information: Unsolicited requests for funds not accepted.
Officers: Lynn C. Gunzenhauser, Pres.; Samuel C. Chapin, V.P.; Lisa V. Prochnow, Secy.
Directors: Janine Lynne; Meta L. McDaniel.
EIN: 562089195

7219
Michael W. Haley Foundation Inc. ✧
100 N. Greene St., Ste. 600
Greensboro, NC 27401-2546

Established in 1990 in NC.
Donor: Michael W. Haley.
Foundation type: Independent foundation.
Financial data (yr. ended 10/31/13): Assets, $7,863,778 (M); expenditures, $721,404; qualifying distributions, $713,643; giving activities include $713,643 for 23 grants (high: $500,000; low: $1,000).
Purpose and activities: Giving primarily for education; funding also for health organizations and human services.
Fields of interest: Elementary/secondary education; Higher education; Health organizations, association; Human services.
Limitations: Applications not accepted. Giving primarily in Greensboro, NC. No grants to individuals.
Application information: Contributes only to pre-selected organizations.
Officers and Directors:* Michael W. Haley,* Pres. and Treas.; Lynn C. Haley; Elizabeth L. Stanley; Leigh H. Jones.
EIN: 561720197

7220
The Hallowell Foundation ✧
1525 W. WT Harris Blvd.
Charlotte, NC 28288-5709

Established in 1956 in PA.
Donor: Members of the Hallowell family.
Foundation type: Independent foundation.
Financial data (yr. ended 12/31/12): Assets, $4,589,015 (M); expenditures, $3,912,829; qualifying distributions, $3,871,910; giving activities include $3,870,395 for 18 grants (high: $3,668,395; low: $1,000).
Fields of interest: Higher education; Human services; Foundations (private grantmaking); Foundations (community).
Type of support: General/operating support; Building/renovation.
Limitations: Applications not accepted. Giving primarily in Washington, DC, NY and PA. No grants to individuals.
Application information: Contributes only to pre-selected organizations.
Trustees: Anne H. Miller; Elaine Reed.
EIN: 236234545

7221
The John W. and Anna H. Hanes Foundation ✧
1525 W. WT Harris Blvd., D1114-044
Charlotte, NC 28288-5709 (888) 234-1999
E-mail: grantadministration@wellsfargo.com; Main URL: https://www.wellsfargo.com/privatefoundationgrants/hanes

Trust established in 1947 in NC.
Foundation type: Independent foundation.
Financial data (yr. ended 12/31/13): Assets, $31,290,471 (M); expenditures, $1,769,642; qualifying distributions, $1,564,997; giving activities include $1,495,300 for 44 grants (high: $110,000; low: $3,500).
Purpose and activities: Giving primarily for the arts, education, and human services.
Fields of interest: Historic preservation/historical societies; Arts; Higher education; Environment, natural resources; Environment; Health care; Human services; Children/youth, services.
Type of support: Annual campaigns; Capital campaigns; Building/renovation; Equipment; Land acquisition; Endowments; Emergency funds; Program development; Seed money; Matching/challenge support.
Limitations: Applications accepted. Giving limited to NC, with emphasis on Winston-Salem and Forsyth County. No grants to individuals, or for operating expenses.
Publications: Application guidelines; Program policy statement.
Application information: Application guidelines available on foundation web site. Application form required.
Initial approach: Use online application system on foundation web site
Copies of proposal: 1
Deadline(s): Mar. 15, June 15, Sept. 15 and Dec. 15
Board meeting date(s): Jan., Apr., July, and Oct.
Trustees: F. Borden Hanes, Jr.; Mrs. Drewry H. Nostitz; Robert M. Willis; Ralph H. Womble; Wells Fargo Bank.
EIN: 566037589

7222
James G. Hanes Memorial Fund ✧
(formerly James G. Hanes Memorial Fund/Foundation)
4605 Country Club Rd.
Winston-Salem, NC 27104-3519 (336) 768-8500

Established in 1957 in NC. The James G. Hanes Memorial Fund reincorporated under its current name following the formal merger and transfer of all foundation assets to the fund in Dec. 1991. The foundation terminated in 1992.
Foundation type: Independent foundation.
Financial data (yr. ended 10/31/13): Assets, $20,949,152 (M); expenditures, $117,014; qualifying distributions, $938,740; giving activities include $938,740 for 22 grants (high: $385,908; low: $5,000).
Purpose and activities: Giving primarily for arts and culture, with emphasis on a contemporary art center.
Fields of interest: Museums (art); Arts; Environment, natural resources; Health care; Health organizations; Community/economic development.
Type of support: General/operating support; Annual campaigns; Capital campaigns; Building/renovation; Equipment; Land acquisition; Endowments; Emergency funds; Program development; Conferences/seminars; Publication; Seed money; Research; Matching/challenge support.
Limitations: Applications accepted. Giving primarily in NC, with emphasis on Winston-Salem. No grants to individuals, or for maintenance purposes, or salary requests or funding on a recurring basis.
Publications: Application guidelines; Informational brochure.
Application information: Application form required.
Initial approach: Contact foundation for application form
Copies of proposal: 1
Deadline(s): Jan. 1, Apr. 1, July 1, and Oct. 1
Board meeting date(s): Jan., Apr., Aug., and Oct.
Trustee: Capital Bank.
EIN: 566036987
Selected grants: The following grants are a representative sample of this grantmaker's funding activity:
$33,333 to Winston-Salem State University, Winston-Salem, NC, 2013. For special program support.
$20,000 to Community Education Collaborative, Winston-Salem, NC, 2013. For Community Education Plan.

$7,000 to Forsyth Jail and Prison Ministries, Winston-Salem, NC, 2013. For special project support.

7223
The John W. Harris Family Foundation ✧
4725 Piedmont Row Dr., Ste. 800
Charlotte, NC 28210-4284

Established in NC.
Donor: James J. and Angelia M. Harris Foundation.
Foundation type: Independent foundation.
Financial data (yr. ended 12/31/12): Assets, $1,196,891 (M); expenditures, $577,568; qualifying distributions, $557,534; giving activities include $551,534 for 24 grants (high: $100,000; low: $1,000).
Fields of interest: Education; Human services; Children/youth, services.
Limitations: Applications not accepted.
Application information: Unsolicited requests for funds not accepted.
Trustees: Greg Currie; John W. Harris; John W. Harris III; Sarah H. Hutchinson.
EIN: 263556445

7224
Harvest Charities
(formerly Belk-Simpson Foundation)
1525 W. W.T. Harris Blvd., D1114-044
Charlotte, NC 28262 (864) 255-8231

Trust established in 1944 in SC.
Donors: Belk-Simpson Co.; J. A. Kuhn.
Foundation type: Company-sponsored foundation.
Financial data (yr. ended 12/31/13): Assets, $11,476,023 (M); expenditures, $602,564; qualifying distributions, $539,133; giving activities include $523,500 for 38 grants (high: $60,000; low: $1,000).
Purpose and activities: The foundation supports museums and organizations involved with education, health, human services, and religion.
Fields of interest: Arts; Higher education; Education; YM/YWCAs & YM/YWHAs; United Ways and Federated Giving Programs; Christian agencies & churches; Religion.
Type of support: General/operating support; Capital campaigns; Program development; Scholarship funds.
Limitations: Applications accepted. Giving primarily in Greenville, SC. No grants to individuals.
Application information: Application form required.
Initial approach: Letter or Proposal
Deadline(s): Apr. 1 and Oct. 1
Board meeting date(s): May 1 and Nov. 1
Trustee: Wells Fargo Bank, N.A.
Advisory Board: Claire Efird; John A. Kuhne; Lucy S. Kuhne; William D.S. Kuhne; Nell M. Rice; Caroline Schmitt; Katherine Sullivan.
EIN: 576020261
Selected grants: The following grants are a representative sample of this grantmaker's funding activity:
$150,000 to Converse College, Spartanburg, SC, 2011. For general purpose.
$100,000 to Montreat Presbyterian Church, Montreat, NC, 2011. For general purpose.
$100,000 to Samaritans Purse, Boone, NC, 2011. For general purpose.
$50,000 to Bob Jones University Museum and Gallery, Greenville, SC, 2010. For general support.
$50,000 to Bob Jones University Museum and Gallery, Greenville, SC, 2011. For general purpose.
$25,000 to Converse College, Spartanburg, SC, 2010. For general support.
$25,000 to Converse College, Spartanburg, SC, 2010. For general support.
$10,000 to Crossover Communications International, Columbia, SC, 2010. For general support.
$10,000 to United Way of Collier County, Naples, FL, 2010. For general support.
$5,000 to Camperdown Academy, Greenville, SC, 2011. For general purpose.
$5,000 to First Presbyterian Church, Greenville, SC, 2011. For general purpose.
$2,000 to Clemson University Foundation, Clemson, SC, 2011. For general purpose.

7225
The C. Felix Harvey Foundation, Inc. ✧
P.O. Box 189
Kinston, NC 28502-0189 (252) 523-3862
Contact: Ruth Heath, Secy.-Treas.

Established around 1970 in NC.
Donors: C. Felix Harvey; Margaret B. Harvey; Sunny H. Burrows; John McNairy; Leigh McNairy; Robert Lee; Dixie Denning Supply Co.; Mallard Oil Co.; Harvey's; Harvey Enterprises; Tidewater Transit; Carolina Finance.
Foundation type: Independent foundation.
Financial data (yr. ended 08/31/13): Assets, $12,634,590 (M); gifts received, $350,000; expenditures, $589,935; qualifying distributions, $550,577; giving activities include $539,950 for 47 grants (high: $125,000; low: $250).
Fields of interest: Higher education; Education; Human services; Protestant agencies & churches.
Limitations: Applications accepted. Giving primarily in NC. No grants to individuals.
Application information: Application form required.
Initial approach: Letter
Deadline(s): June 30
Officers: Margaret B. Harvey, Pres.; C. Felix Harvey, V.P.; Leigh H. McNairy, V.P.; Ruth Heath, Secy.-Treas.
EIN: 237038942
Selected grants: The following grants are a representative sample of this grantmaker's funding activity:
$50,000 to Vidant Medical Center Foundation, Greenville, NC, 2011. For operating expenses.
$36,250 to Mount Olive College, Mount Olive, NC, 2011. For operating expenses.
$18,000 to Ron Clark Academy, Atlanta, GA, 2011. For operating expenses.
$12,000 to Duke University, Durham, NC, 2011. For operating expenses.
$10,000 to Blessed Sacrament School, Burlington, NC, 2011. For operating expenses.
$10,000 to Triangle Community Foundation, Durham, NC, 2011. For operating expenses.
$5,000 to United Way, Lenoir/Greene, Kinston, NC, 2011. For operating expenses.
$5,000 to Woodberry Forest School, Woodberry Forest, VA, 2011. For operating expenses.

7226
Weston Havens Foundation ✧
c/o Wells Fargo Bank, N.A.
1 W. 4th St., 4th Fl., MAC D4000-041
Winston-Salem, NC 27101-3818

Established in 2005 in CA.
Donor: Westen Havens Living Trust.
Foundation type: Independent foundation.
Financial data (yr. ended 06/30/13): Assets, $28,238,837 (M); expenditures, $1,599,178; qualifying distributions, $1,419,349; giving activities include $1,350,000 for 3 grants (high: $450,000; low: $450,000).
Fields of interest: Higher education.
Limitations: Applications not accepted. Giving primarily in CA. No grants to individuals.
Application information: Contributes only to pre-selected organizations.
Trustee: Wells Fargo Bank, N.A.
EIN: 306051962
Selected grants: The following grants are a representative sample of this grantmaker's funding activity:
$550,000 to California Institute of Technology, Pasadena, CA, 2011.
$477,412 to Stanford University, Stanford, CA, 2011.
$385,000 to University of California San Francisco Foundation, San Francisco, CA, 2011.

7227
Mariam and Robert Hayes Charitabe Trust ✧
1525 W. WT Harris Blvd.
Charlotte, NC 28262-8522

Established in 2007 in NC.
Donor: Mariam C. Hayes Trust.
Foundation type: Independent foundation.
Financial data (yr. ended 12/31/13): Assets, $42,488,719 (M); expenditures, $2,067,440; qualifying distributions, $1,709,222; giving activities include $1,651,122 for 44 grants (high: $120,000; low: $1,000).
Fields of interest: Arts; Education; Health care; Housing/shelter, rehabilitation; Human services; Christian agencies & churches; Protestant agencies & churches.
Limitations: Applications not accepted. Giving primarily in NC; some giving in CO.
Application information: Unsolicited requests for funds not accepted.
Trustees: William C. Cannon, Jr.; Joseph C. Hunter; Elizabeth L. Quick.
EIN: 266147884
Selected grants: The following grants are a representative sample of this grantmaker's funding activity:
$120,000 to Boy Scouts of America, Central Nc Council, Albemarle, NC, 2012. For general support.
$10,000 to North Carolina Center for International Understanding Council, Research Triangle Park, NC, 2012. For International Education Support.
$2,000 to Barium Springs Home for Children, Barium Springs, NC, 2012. For Drainage Project Secure.

7228
Charles E. Hayworth, Jr. Foundation ✧
(formerly The Charles E. & Pauline Hayworth Foundation)
1525 W. WT Harris Blvd.
Charlotte, NC 28262

Established in 1986 in NC.
Donors: David R. Hayworth; Charles E. Hayworth, Jr.‡; The Hayworth Foundation.
Foundation type: Independent foundation.
Financial data (yr. ended 12/31/13): Assets, $12,055,743 (M); expenditures, $630,246; qualifying distributions, $526,146; giving activities include $500,000 for 9 grants (high: $250,000; low: $5,000).
Fields of interest: Performing arts, theater; Higher education; Religion.
Limitations: Applications not accepted. Giving primarily in NC. No grants to individuals.
Application information: Unsolicited requests for funds not accepted.
Officers: David R. Hayworth, Pres.; Elizabeth L. Quick, V.P. and Secy.; Linwood Davis, V.P. and Treas.
EIN: 570834648
Selected grants: The following grants are a representative sample of this grantmaker's funding activity:
$184,000 to High Point University, High Point, NC, 2011.
$50,000 to West End Ministries, High Point, NC, 2011.
$25,000 to North Carolina Shakespeare Festival, High Point, NC, 2011.
$20,000 to Arts Council, Winston-Salem, NC, 2011.
$15,000 to Boys and Girls Clubs of Greater High Point, High Point, NC, 2011.
$15,000 to United Way of Greater High Point, High Point, NC, 2011.

7229
The Leonard G. Herring Family Foundation ✧
P.O. Box 427
North Wilkesboro, NC 28659-0427 (336) 838-7181
Contact: A . Lee Herring II

Established in 1994 in NC.
Donor: Leonard G. Herring.
Foundation type: Independent foundation.
Financial data (yr. ended 12/31/12): Assets, $19,469,790 (M); expenditures, $744,659; qualifying distributions, $576,098; giving activities include $559,904 for 71 grants (high: $100,000; low: $100).
Fields of interest: Higher education; Environment, natural resources; Health organizations, association; YM/YWCAs & YM/YWHAs; Children/youth, services; Protestant agencies & churches.
Limitations: Applications accepted. Giving primarily in NC. No grants to individuals.
Application information: Application form required.
Initial approach: Letter
Deadline(s): None
Officers: Leonard G. Herring, Pres.; Rozelia S. Herring, V.P.; Sandra Herring Gaddy, Secy.; Albert Lee Herring, Treas.
EIN: 561881015

7230
The Hesburgh-Yusko Scholars Foundation ✧ ☆
2121 N. Lakeshore Dr.
Chapel Hill, NC 27514-2026

Established in NC.
Donors: Mark W. Yusko; Stacey M. Yusko.
Foundation type: Independent foundation.
Financial data (yr. ended 12/31/12): Assets, $6,240,825 (M); gifts received, $2,095,000; expenditures, $2,148,879; qualifying distributions, $2,122,516; giving activities include $2,020,000 for 1 grant, and $2,122,516 for 1 foundation-administered program.
Fields of interest: Education.
Limitations: Applications not accepted. Giving primarily in IN.
Application information: Unsolicited requests for funds not accepted.
Officers: Mark W. Yusko, Pres. and Treas.; Stacey M. Yusko, V.P. and Secy.
Members: Allen Chan; John Yusko; Sara Yusko.
EIN: 271153971

7231
High Point Community Foundation ✧
501 N. Main St., Ste. 2A
High Point, NC 27260 (336) 882-3298
Contact: Paul Lessard, Pres.; For grants: Karol Murks, Dir., Acctg. and Grants
FAX: (336) 882-3293;
E-mail: paul@hpcommunityfoundation.org;
Additional mailing address: P.O. Box 5166, High Point, NC 27262; Grant application tel.: (336) 882-3297; Main URL: http://www.hpcommunityfoundation.org
Facebook: http://www.facebook.com/pages/High-Point-Community-Foundation/370597412973836

Established in 1990 in NC.
Foundation type: Community foundation.
Financial data (yr. ended 06/30/13): Assets, $55,539,078 (M); gifts received, $1,324,853; expenditures, $10,461,512; giving activities include $9,498,178 for 16+ grants (high: $34,624; low: $500).
Purpose and activities: The foundation is dedicated to strengthening a diverse, healthy, and productive community for both present and future generations. The foundation promotes philanthropy, builds and maintains a permanent collection of endowment funds, and serves as a trustworthy partner and leader in responding to community needs.
Fields of interest: Arts; Elementary/secondary education; Education; Health care; Mental health/crisis services; Housing/shelter; Boys & girls clubs; Youth development; Children/youth, services; Human services; Jewish agencies & synagogues.
Type of support: Continuing support; Management development/capacity building; Capital campaigns; Building/renovation; Equipment; Program development; Seed money; Scholarship funds; Matching/challenge support.
Limitations: Applications accepted. Giving limited to Guilford County, NC and surrounding counties. No grants to individuals, or for general operating support, or endowments.
Publications: Application guidelines; Annual report; Grants list; Informational brochure; Newsletter.
Application information: Visit foundation web site for application form and information. "Guidelines for Grantseekers" and "Grants Policies and Procedures" must be reviewed before submitting complete application; materials may be requested from foundation office. Faxed applications are not accepted. Application form required.
Initial approach: Submit application form and attachments
Copies of proposal: 16
Deadline(s): June 1 through Aug. 15
Board meeting date(s): May, Sept., and Dec.
Final notification: Nov.
Officers and Trustees:* Martha Yarborough,* Chair.; Jim Fealy,* Vice-Chair.; Paul Lessard,* Pres.; Kay Maynard,* Secy.; Dan Odom,* Treas.; Elizabeth Aldridge; L'Tanya Bailey; Earl Congdon; Ned Covington; Frosty Culp; Susan Culp; Skip Gilliland; Bill Goodman; Eric Hill; Ken Hughes; Gene Kester; Jennifer Lynch; Judy Mendenhall; David Miller; Molly Millis-Hedgecock; Dan Odom; Melissa Painter; Nido Qubein Samuel; Joe Rawley; Deena Qubein Samuel; Barry Safrit; Gary Simon; Royster Tucker; Jim White; Coy O. Williard; Doug Witcher.
Number of staff: 3 full-time professional; 1 part-time professional.
EIN: 561695787

7232
Hillsdale Fund, Inc. ✧
c/o Piedmont Financial Trust Co.
P.O. Box 20124
Greensboro, NC 27420-0124 (336) 574-8696
Contact: Mary L. Scott, Exec. Dir.

Incorporated in 1963 in NC.
Donors: Margaret R. White; L. Richardson Jr. Charitable Lead Trust; The L. Richardson family.
Foundation type: Independent foundation.
Financial data (yr. ended 12/31/12): Assets, $29,370,705 (M); gifts received, $18,356; expenditures, $1,609,853; qualifying distributions, $1,439,259; giving activities include $1,315,354 for 85 grants (high: $75,000; low: $1,000).
Purpose and activities: Giving primarily for education, natural resource conservation and protection, and arts and culture.
Fields of interest: Arts; Elementary/secondary education; Higher education; Environment; Health organizations; Human services; Children/youth, services; Residential/custodial care, hospices; Protestant agencies & churches.
Limitations: Giving in the U.S., with emphasis on NC. No grants to individuals, or for operating budgets.
Application information: Application form required.
Initial approach: Completed application form
Copies of proposal: 1
Deadline(s): Spring and fall (contact foundation for exact dates)
Board meeting date(s): Usually in Apr. or June and Nov.
Officer and Trustees:* Lunsford Richardson, Jr.,* Pres.; Martin M. Boney; Sion A. Boney III; Laurinda Lowenstein Douglas; Barbara R. Evans; John Peter Gallagher; Margaret W. Gallagher; Louise Boney McCoy; Eudora L. Richardson; James Lunsford Richardson; Lunsford R. Smith; Richard G. Smith III; William L.R. Smith; Margaret R. White.
Number of staff: 1 part-time professional; 1 part-time support.
EIN: 566057433

Selected grants: The following grants are a representative sample of this grantmaker's funding activity:
$25,000 to Action Greensboro, Greensboro, NC, 2012. For The Purpose of Each Grant Is to Assist the Tax Exempt Organization to Carry Out Its Exempt Purpose.

7233
Ella Ann L. and Frank B. Holding Foundation ✧
P.O. Box 1415
Smithfield, NC 27577-1415

Established in 1997 in NC.
Donors: Ella Holding; Frank B. Holding; Ella and Frank Holding Charitable Lead Annuity Trust.
Foundation type: Independent foundation.
Financial data (yr. ended 12/31/13): Assets, $12,638,484 (M); gifts received, $331,919; expenditures, $623,623; qualifying distributions, $565,537; giving activities include $564,000 for 104 grants (high: $87,000; low: $250).
Fields of interest: Higher education, university; Education; Environment; Health care; Protestant agencies & churches.
Limitations: Applications not accepted. Giving primarily in NC.
Application information: Unsolicited requests for funds not accepted.
Officers: Olivia B. Holding, Pres.; Frank B. Holding, Jr., V.P.; Hope Holding Connell, Secy.-Treas.
EIN: 562002528

7234
The Robert P. Holding Foundation, Inc. ✧
(also known as The R.P. Holding Foundation, Inc.)
P.O. Box 1415
Smithfield, NC 27577-1415

Incorporated in 1955 in NC.
Donors: Robert Holding†; Maggie B. Holding.
Foundation type: Independent foundation.
Financial data (yr. ended 12/31/13): Assets, $23,491,295 (M); expenditures, $1,054,088; qualifying distributions, $1,040,816; giving activities include $1,039,494 for 30 grants (high: $210,513; low: $500).
Purpose and activities: Giving primarily for higher education, youth services, and a community foundation, as well as to hospital foundations.
Fields of interest: Higher education; Hospitals (general); Youth, services; Foundations (community).
Type of support: General/operating support; Scholarship funds.
Limitations: Applications not accepted. Giving primarily in NC.
Application information: Unsolicited requests for funds not accepted.
Officers: Frank B. Holding, Pres.; Carmen H. Ames, V.P.; Olivia B. Holding, Secy.; Virginia Hopkins, Treas.
EIN: 566044205

7235
Hommer Foundation Trust ✧
c/o Wells Faro Bank, N.A.-Trust Tax Dept.
1 W. 4th St., 4th Fl., MAC D4000-041
Winston-Salem, NC 27101-3818

Established in 1996 in PA.
Donor: Katheryn M. Hommer.
Foundation type: Independent foundation.
Financial data (yr. ended 12/31/13): Assets, $15,873,009 (M); expenditures, $885,027; qualifying distributions, $825,195; giving activities include $810,000 for 36 grants (high: $100,000; low: $2,500).
Fields of interest: Libraries (public); Education; Protestant agencies & churches.
Limitations: Applications not accepted. Giving primarily in PA.
Application information: Contributes only to pre-selected organizations.
Trustee: Wells Fargo Bank, N.A.
EIN: 232847257
Selected grants: The following grants are a representative sample of this grantmaker's funding activity:
$25,000 to Allentown Art Museum, Allentown, PA, 2012. For grant for 2011 Programs.
$25,000 to Barrett Friendly Library, Cresco, PA, 2012. For library debt amortization.
$20,000 to Lehigh County Conference of Churches, Allentown, PA, 2012. To support Ecumenical Activities.
$15,000 to Community Music School, Allentown, PA, 2012. For Scholarships for Students in Need.

7236
James Daniel Humphrey Foundation ✧
c/o Wells Fargo Bank, N.A.
1525 W. WT Harris Blvd., D1114-044
Charlotte, NC 28288-0001

Established in MN; supporting organization of AFS-USA Inc., St. Paul Area American Red Cross, Bennington College, Camp Fire Boys & Girls, MN Council, National Camp Fire Boys & Girls, Carleton College, Children's Home Society of MIN, Christ Episcopal Church, Social Service League of La Jolla, First Church of Christ Scientist, First Congressional United Church of Christ, First Congregational Church - Rockport, Hamline University, House of Hope Presbyterian Church, Mary Institute, United Way of St. Paul, Mother Church, Presbyterian Homes, Princeton University, St. Paul Academy & Summit School, Presbyterian Church Foundation, Vassar College, Wayzata Community Church Foundation, La Jolla YMCA, YMCA of Greater St. Paul.
Foundation type: Independent foundation.
Financial data (yr. ended 03/31/13): Assets, $31,746,062 (M); expenditures, $1,631,784; qualifying distributions, $1,387,440; giving activities include $1,387,440 for grants.
Fields of interest: Higher education; Human services; YM/YWCAs & YM/YWHAs; Protestant agencies & churches.
Limitations: Applications not accepted. Giving in the U.S., with emphasis on MN.
Application information: Unsolicited requests for funds not considered or acknowledged.
Trustees: Joann "Joan" E. Aalfs; Marvin J. Pertzik; Wells Fargo Bank Minnesota, N.A.
EIN: 416263553
Selected grants: The following grants are a representative sample of this grantmaker's funding activity:
$67,374 to American Red Cross, Minneapolis, MN, 2012. For general support.

7237
Vicky and Sam Hunt Foundation ✧
P.O. Drawer 2440
Burlington, NC 27216

Established in 1998 in NC.
Donors: R. Samuel Hunt III; Victoria S. Hunt; Hunt Electric Supply; Atlas Lighting Products Inc.
Foundation type: Operating foundation.
Financial data (yr. ended 12/31/13): Assets, $494,656 (M); gifts received, $255,000; expenditures, $428,739; qualifying distributions, $425,600; giving activities include $425,600 for 18 grants (high: $300,000; low: $500).
Fields of interest: Higher education; Education; Animals/wildlife.
Limitations: Applications not accepted. Giving primarily in FL and NC. No grants to individuals.
Application information: Unsolicited requests for funds not accepted.
Trustees: R. Samuel Hunt III; R. Samuel Hunt IV; Victoria S. Hunt.
EIN: 562115931
Selected grants: The following grants are a representative sample of this grantmaker's funding activity:
$500,000 to Elon University, Elon, NC, 2012. For Softball Park and Scholarship.
$5,000 to Baton Rouge Area Foundation, Baton Rouge, LA, 2012. For Every Kid a King.

7238
Estelle Hunter Charitable Trust ✧
c/o Wells Fargo Bank, N.A., Trust Tax Dept.
1 W. 4th St., 4th Fl., MAC D4000-041
Winston-Salem, NC 27101-3818

Foundation type: Independent foundation.
Financial data (yr. ended 12/31/13): Assets, $11,678,189 (M); expenditures, $567,287; qualifying distributions, $457,732; giving activities include $428,304 for 4 grants (high: $160,614; low: $53,538).
Purpose and activities: Giving primarily for higher education, and for human services, including a children's home.
Fields of interest: Higher education; Human services; Residential/custodial care; Children.
Limitations: Applications not accepted. Giving primarily in Denver, CO.
Application information: Unsolicited requests for funds not accepted.
Trustee: Wells Fargo Bank, N.A.
EIN: 846016605

7239
The Ireland Family Foundation ✧
113 Kenan St.
Chapel Hill, NC 27516-2527 (919) 537-8735
Contact: Lori Ireland, Pres.
Main URL: http://www.irelandfamilyfoundation.org/

Established in 2000 in NC.
Donors: Lori Ireland; Gregg Alden Ireland.
Foundation type: Independent foundation.
Financial data (yr. ended 12/31/13): Assets, $8,316,633 (M); gifts received, $700,000; expenditures, $888,223; qualifying distributions, $888,223; giving activities include $803,490 for 21 grants (high: $100,000; low: $165).

Purpose and activities: Giving primarily for higher education, autism research, and human services.
Fields of interest: Higher education; Autism research; Human services; Developmentally disabled, centers & services.
Limitations: Applications accepted. Giving primarily in NC; funding also in CA. No grants to individuals.
Application information: Application form required.
Initial approach: Letter
Deadline(s): None
Officers: Lori Ireland, Pres.; Gregg Alden Ireland, V.P.
EIN: 562227048
Selected grants: The following grants are a representative sample of this grantmaker's funding activity:
$3,000 to Mental Health America of the Triangle, Durham, NC, 2012. For Triangle golf outing.

7240
The Jolley Foundation ✧
1525 W. WT Harris Blvd., D1114-044
Charlotte, NC 28262-8522
Application address: c/o Marsha Samellas, Wells Fargo Bank, N.A., P.O. Box 969, Greenville, SC 29602, tel.: (877) 287-0641

Established in 1947 in SC.
Donors: R.A. Jolley, Jr.; James E. Jolley; Mamie J. Bruce.
Foundation type: Independent foundation.
Financial data (yr. ended 12/31/13): Assets, $30,661,013 (M); expenditures, $1,436,880; qualifying distributions, $1,219,974; giving activities include $1,203,000 for grants (high: $150,000; low: $5,000).
Purpose and activities: The foundation awards grants to local charities in the Greenville County, SC, area for health, education, and youth and social services.
Fields of interest: Education; Health organizations; Human services; Children/youth, services.
Type of support: Capital campaigns.
Limitations: Applications accepted. Giving primarily in the Greenville, SC, area. No grants to individuals, or for annual campaigns, operating budgets or endowment funds.
Application information: E-mailed or faxed applications will not be accepted. Application form required.
Initial approach: Request application guidelines
Copies of proposal: 4
Deadline(s): Apr. 1 and Sept. 1
Board meeting date(s): May and Oct.
Trustees: James McDuffie Bruce III; Jolley Bruce Christman; James E. Jolley; Wells Fargo Bank, N.A.
EIN: 576024996
Selected grants: The following grants are a representative sample of this grantmaker's funding activity:
$50,000 to Greenville Tech Foundation, Greenville, SC, 2012. For Ambulance and Mannequin Simulators.
$25,000 to Cancer Society of Greenville County, Greenville, SC, 2012. For Life Saving Medications.
$25,000 to Metropolitan Arts Council, Greenville, SC, 2012. For Smartarts.
$20,000 to Greenville Forward, Greenville, SC, 2012. For Gardening for Food.
$15,000 to Naturaland Trust, Greenville, SC, 2012. For Saving Mtn and Protecting.

7241
The Jonas Foundation ✧
P.O. Box 1650
Lenoir, NC 28645 (828) 728-3271
Contact: A.G. Jonas, Pres. and Treas.
Application address: 1006 Hibriten Dr., Lenior, NC 28645.

Established in 1984 in NC.
Donors: Lenoir Mirror Co.; A.G. Jonas, Sr.; Bly Jonas‡.
Foundation type: Independent foundation.
Financial data (yr. ended 06/30/13): Assets, $9,921,892 (M); expenditures, $481,741; qualifying distributions, $472,000; giving activities include $472,000 for grants.
Fields of interest: Higher education; United Ways and Federated Giving Programs; Protestant agencies & churches.
Limitations: Applications accepted. Giving primarily in Caldwell County, NC. No grants to individuals.
Application information: Application form required.
Initial approach: Letter
Deadline(s): None
Officers: A.G. Jonas, Pres. and Treas.; Linda Jones, V.P.; Joyce Bumgarner, Secy.
EIN: 561459346
Selected grants: The following grants are a representative sample of this grantmaker's funding activity:
$72,540 to Caldwell Memorial Hospital Foundation, Lenoir, NC, 2010.
$44,500 to Caldwell Memorial Hospital Foundation, Lenoir, NC, 2011.
$20,000 to United Way of Caldwell County, Lenoir, NC, 2011.
$15,000 to Childrens Advocacy Center of Caldwell County, Lenoir, NC, 2011.
$15,000 to Lutheran Services for the Aging, Salisbury, NC, 2011.
$10,000 to Habitat for Humanity, Caldwell County, Lenoir, NC, 2011.
$2,000 to Catawba Science Center, Hickory, NC, 2011.
$1,000 to Caldwell Opportunities, Lenoir, NC, 2011.
$1,000 to Education Foundation of Caldwell County, Lenoir, NC, 2011. For scholarship fund.

7242
Seby B. Jones Family Foundation ✧
P.O. Box 19067
Raleigh, NC 27619-9067 (919) 829-2499
Contact: Seby Russell Jones, Secy.

Established in 1983 in NC.
Donors: Seby B. Jones; Christina B. Jones‡; Seby B. Jones Charitable Lead Trust.
Foundation type: Independent foundation.
Financial data (yr. ended 06/30/13): Assets, $11,353,677 (M); gifts received, $400,000; expenditures, $846,946; qualifying distributions, $658,850; giving activities include $658,850 for 75 grants (high: $205,000; low: $100).
Fields of interest: Higher education; Education; Substance abuse, services; Health organizations, association; Human services; Children/youth, services; Foundations (private grantmaking).
Type of support: General/operating support; Building/renovation; Research.
Limitations: Applications accepted. Giving primarily in NC; no giving outside the U.S.
Application information: Application form not required.
Initial approach: Proposal
Copies of proposal: 1
Deadline(s): None
Officers: Robert L. Jones, Chair.; James R. Jones, Pres.; Seby B. Jones, Jr., V.P.; Seby Russell Jones, Secy.; Alice J. Harrod, Treas.
EIN: 311578859
Selected grants: The following grants are a representative sample of this grantmaker's funding activity:
$15,000 to Boy Scouts of America, Occoneechee Council, Raleigh, NC, 2013. For community support.
$1,000 to Adventure Cycling Association, Missoula, MT, 2013. For community awareness.

7243
Jerry and Evon Jordan Foundation ✧
P.O. Box 546
Oakboro, NC 28129-0546
Contact: Jerry A. Jordon, Pres.

Foundation type: Independent foundation.
Financial data (yr. ended 12/31/13): Assets, $43,165 (M); gifts received, $500,000; expenditures, $769,033; qualifying distributions, $769,000; giving activities include $769,000 for 10 grants (high: $610,000; low: $500).
Fields of interest: Recreation; Human services; Christian agencies & churches; Religion.
Limitations: Applications not accepted. Giving primarily in NC. No grants to individuals.
Application information: Contributes only to pre-selected organizations.
Officers: Jerry A. Jordan, Pres.; Trudie Evon Smith Jordan, Secy.
EIN: 263135531
Selected grants: The following grants are a representative sample of this grantmaker's funding activity:
$10,000 to Petty Family Foundation, Randleman, NC, 2011.
$10,000 to Petty Family Foundation, Randleman, NC, 2010.
$1,000 to Mission Baptist Church, Locust, NC, 2010.

7244
William Josef Foundation Inc. ✧
(formerly Satterwhite Family Foundation, Inc.)
1525 W. WT Harris Blvd.
Charlotte, NC 28262

Established in 2006.
Donor: Scott Satterwhite.
Foundation type: Independent foundation.
Financial data (yr. ended 12/31/13): Assets, $20,451,787 (M); gifts received, $5,000,000; expenditures, $1,105,450; qualifying distributions, $983,529; giving activities include $980,925 for 14 grants (high: $350,000; low: $5,000).
Fields of interest: Higher education, university; Education; Food banks.
Limitations: Applications not accepted. Giving primarily in GA. No grants to individuals.
Application information: Unsolicited requests for funds not accepted.
Officers: Scott Satterwhite, Pres.; Patricia Stern, Treas.
EIN: 208075941

Selected grants: The following grants are a representative sample of this grantmaker's funding activity:
$100,000 to Atlanta Community Food Bank, Atlanta, GA, 2011.
$75,000 to Nature Conservancy, Georgia Chapter, Atlanta, GA, 2011.
$50,000 to Tulane University, New Orleans, LA, 2011.
$10,000 to United Way of Haywood County, Waynesville, NC, 2011.

7245
Michael A. Kahn Foundation ✧
c/o Michael A. Kahn
13833 Carowinds Blvd.
Charlotte, NC 28273-4736

Donor: Michael A. Kahn.
Foundation type: Independent foundation.
Financial data (yr. ended 12/31/13): Assets, $7,522,622 (M); gifts received, $4,200; expenditures, $842,237; qualifying distributions, $768,594; giving activities include $768,594 for 23 grants (high: $350,000; low: $500).
Fields of interest: Education; Recreation; Christian agencies & churches.
Limitations: Applications not accepted. Giving primarily in GA.
Application information: Contributes only to pre-selected organizations.
Director: Michael A. Kahn.
EIN: 272449310
Selected grants: The following grants are a representative sample of this grantmaker's funding activity:
$500,000 to Arch Foundation for the University of Georgia, Athens, GA, 2011.
$250,000 to Darlington School, Rome, GA, 2011.
$30,000 to Fellowship of Christian Athletes, Kansas City, MO, 2011.
$20,000 to Fletcher School, Charlotte, NC, 2011.
$10,000 to Shepherd Center Foundation, Atlanta, GA, 2011.
$5,000 to University of Georgia Foundation, Athens, GA, 2011.
$5,000 to William Breman Jewish Home, Atlanta, GA, 2011.

7246
The Kean/Hartquist Foundation ✧
(formerly The Hartquist Foundation)
17404B Randall's Ferry Rd.
Norwood, NC 28128-7460

Established in 1998 in NC.
Donor: Mildred Hartquist Trust.
Foundation type: Independent foundation.
Financial data (yr. ended 12/31/13): Assets, $8,014,418 (M); gifts received, $4,900; expenditures, $796,910; qualifying distributions, $754,900; giving activities include $750,000 for 9 grants (high: $200,000; low: $50,000).
Purpose and activities: Giving primarily for higher education.
Fields of interest: Higher education; Hospitals (general).
Limitations: Applications not accepted. Giving primarily in NC. No grants to individuals.
Application information: Unsolicited requests for funds not accepted.
Officer: Thomas J. Kean, Jr., Treas.
Directors: Janet H. Kean; Teresa Anne Kean; Anne Marie Kean-Teed.
EIN: 911912805

7247
The Greg and India Keith Foundation ✧
c/o Graeme M. Keith Jr.
5201 Gorham Dr.
Charlotte, NC 28226-6407 (704) 364-6105
Contact: India E. Keith, Secy.

Established in 2004 in NC.
Donors: Graeme M. Keith, Jr.; India E. Keith.
Foundation type: Independent foundation.
Financial data (yr. ended 12/31/13): Assets, $4,220,936 (M); gifts received, $1,087,430; expenditures, $899,977; qualifying distributions, $873,535; giving activities include $873,535 for 31 grants (high: $25,000; low: $500).
Fields of interest: Elementary/secondary education; Human services; YM/YWCAs & YM/YWHAs; Christian agencies & churches; Protestant agencies & churches.
Limitations: Applications accepted. Giving primarily in NC; some funding also in CA and TN.
Application information: Application form not required.
Initial approach: Proposal
Deadline(s): None
Officers: Graeme M. Keith, Jr., Pres.; India E. Keith, Secy.
EIN: 202016795

7248
William R. Kenan, Jr. Charitable Trust ✧
Kenan Center
P.O. Box 3858
Chapel Hill, NC 27515-3858
Contact: Richard M. Krasno, Exec. Dir.; Douglas Zinn, Asst. Exec. Dir.

Established in 1965 in NY.
Donor: William R. Kenan, Jr.‡.
Foundation type: Independent foundation.
Financial data (yr. ended 06/30/13): Assets, $570,678,087 (M); expenditures, $27,549,785; qualifying distributions, $24,765,664; giving activities include $22,754,797 for 76 grants (high: $1,996,667; low: $10,000).
Purpose and activities: To support the advancement of education in a broad sense, giving first priority to programs that have the potential to fundamentally improve educational opportunities throughout the United States. In particular, to seek out institutions, programs and activities that hold exceptional promise to become models or guides for more general and lasting value to American society.
Fields of interest: Secondary school/education; Higher education; Education.
Type of support: Endowments; Seed money; Matching/challenge support.
Limitations: Applications not accepted. Giving in the U.S., primarily in states where William R. Kenan, Jr. and his family have had significant interests: FL, KY, NC, and NY. No grants to individuals, or for capital projects (except under special circumstances).
Publications: Annual report.
Application information: Unsolicited requests for funds not accepted.
Board meeting date(s): As required
Officer: Richard M. Krasno, Exec. Dir.; Douglas Zinn, Asst. Exec. Dir.
Trustees: James G. Kenan III; Thomas S. Kenan III; JPMorgan Chase Bank, N.A.
EIN: 136192029
Selected grants: The following grants are a representative sample of this grantmaker's funding activity:
$2,000,000 to University of North Carolina, Chapel Hill, NC, 2011.
$1,666,667 to University of North Carolina, Chapel Hill, NC, 2011.
$1,000,000 to University of North Carolina, Chapel Hill, NC, 2011.
$500,000 to Global Scholars Academy, Durham, NC, 2011.
$453,008 to Global Scholars Academy, Durham, NC, 2011.
$400,000 to Kenan Center, Lockport, NY, 2011.
$250,000 to Mount Vernon Ladies Association, Mount Vernon, VA, 2011.
$100,000 to University of North Carolina Law Foundation, Chapel Hill, NC, 2011.
$55,000 to Lincoln Center for the Performing Arts, New York, NY, 2011.
$50,000 to Kenan Center, Lockport, NY, 2011.

7249
The W. Duke Kimbrell Family Foundation ✧
1525 W. WT Harris Blvd., D1114-044
Charlotte, NC 28262

Established in 2005 in NC.
Donor: W. Duke Kimbrell Agency Investment.
Foundation type: Independent foundation.
Financial data (yr. ended 12/31/13): Assets, $13,363,350 (M); expenditures, $3,434,752; qualifying distributions, $3,348,928; giving activities include $3,348,928 for 24 grants (high: $1,311,000; low: $100).
Fields of interest: Higher education; Education; Botanical gardens; Residential/custodial care, hospices; Foundations (community); Protestant agencies & churches.
Limitations: Applications not accepted. Giving primarily in NC. No grants to individuals.
Application information: Contributes only to pre-selected organizations.
Director: Dan Wilson.
EIN: 203390787

7250
Victor W. Kramer Charitable Trust ✧
1525 W. WT Harris Blvd., D1114-044
Charlotte, NC 28262-8522

Established in AZ.
Donor: Victor Kramer Trust.
Foundation type: Independent foundation.
Financial data (yr. ended 10/31/13): Assets, $12,374,787 (M); gifts received, $800,000; expenditures, $604,980; qualifying distributions, $547,211; giving activities include $499,495 for 13 grants (high: $173,736; low: $10,859).
Fields of interest: Human services; Catholic agencies & churches.
Limitations: Applications not accepted. Giving primarily in AZ.
Application information: Unsolicited request for funds not accepted.

Trustee: Wells Fargo Bank, N.A.
EIN: 276739649

7251
Kulynych Family Foundation II, Inc. ✧
1727 Spring Valley Rd.
Wilkesboro, NC 28697-9516 (336) 667-0346
Contact: Martha W. Eller, Secy.

Established in 1996 in NC.
Donor: Petro Kulynych.
Foundation type: Independent foundation.
Financial data (yr. ended 06/30/13): Assets, $17,487,451 (M); gifts received, $786,025; expenditures, $855,162; qualifying distributions, $749,500; giving activities include $749,500 for grants.
Fields of interest: Elementary/secondary education; Higher education; Education; Health care; Health organizations, association; Human services; Protestant agencies & churches.
Limitations: Applications accepted. Giving primarily in NC. No grants to individuals.
Application information: Application form required.
Initial approach: Letter
Deadline(s): October 3st and April 30th Annually.
Officers: Janice K. Story, Chair. and Treas.; Christina E. Story, Pres.; Thomas E. Story IV, V.P.; Martha W. Eller, Secy.
Director: Ranlet S. Bell.
EIN: 561982360
Selected grants: The following grants are a representative sample of this grantmaker's funding activity:
$1,000 to Emory University, Goizueta Business School, Atlanta, GA, 2013. For general support.
$1,000 to Emory University, School of Law, Atlanta, GA, 2013. For general support.

7252
Petro Kulynych Foundation Inc. ✧
(doing business as Kulynych Family Foundation I)
(also known as Petro Kulynych Foundation, Inc.)
1727 Spring Valley Rd.
Wilkesboro, NC 28697-9516 (336) 667-0346
Contact: Martha W. Eller, Secy.

Established in 1992 in NC.
Donor: Petro Kulynych.
Foundation type: Independent foundation.
Financial data (yr. ended 06/30/13): Assets, $17,504,291 (M); gifts received, $786,025; expenditures, $857,722; qualifying distributions, $751,226; giving activities include $751,226 for grants.
Purpose and activities: Giving primarily for education, health, human services, children's services, and Baptist, Episcopal, and Lutheran churches and organizations.
Fields of interest: Elementary/secondary education; Education; Health care; Health organizations, association; Human services; Children/youth, services; Protestant agencies & churches.
Limitations: Applications accepted. Giving primarily in NC. No grants to individuals.
Application information: Application form required.
Initial approach: Letter
Deadline(s): Oct. 31 and Apr. 30

Officers: Brenda K. Cline, Chair. and Treas.; Laura C. Berry, Pres.; Adam K. Cline, V.P.; Martha W. Eller, Secy.
Director: Ranlet S. Bell.
EIN: 237335353
Selected grants: The following grants are a representative sample of this grantmaker's funding activity:
$20,000 to Samaritan Christian Ministry of Wilkes, Wilkesboro, NC, 2011. For general support.
$15,000 to Avon Old Farms School, Avon, CT, 2011. For general support.
$10,000 to Brenner Childrens Hospital, Winston-Salem, NC, 2011. For general support.
$10,000 to Fletcher School, Charlotte, NC, 2011. For general support.
$10,000 to New Life Mobility Assistance Dogs, Moravian Falls, NC, 2011. For general support.
$10,000 to United Way of Wilkes County, North Wilkesboro, NC, 2011. For general support.
$5,000 to Catawba County Historical Association, Newton, NC, 2011. For general support.
$5,000 to Church at Charlotte, Charlotte, NC, 2011. For general support.
$5,000 to Davidson Day School, Davidson, NC, 2011. For general support.
$2,000 to Senior Services, Winston-Salem, NC, 2011.

7253
The Leever Foundation ✧
900 S. Park Pl.
Hendersonville, NC 28791-1906 (203) 927-5997
Application address: c/o The Duncannon Group, Att.: Carol O"Donnell, 45 Newbridge Cir., Cheshire, CT 06410, tel.: (203) 927-5997

Established in 1991 in CT.
Donors: Harold Leever†; Ruth Ann Leever; Thomas Leever; Harold Leever CLUT.
Foundation type: Independent foundation.
Financial data (yr. ended 12/31/12): Assets, $10,027,287 (M); gifts received, $210,963; expenditures, $1,177,132; qualifying distributions, $1,116,468; giving activities include $1,067,083 for 42 grants (high: $700,000; low: $100).
Fields of interest: Scholarships/financial aid; Health care; Human services; United Ways and Federated Giving Programs; Children/youth; Youth; Economically disadvantaged.
Type of support: Annual campaigns; Capital campaigns; Equipment; Program development; Seed money; Scholarship funds; Matching/challenge support.
Limitations: Applications accepted. Giving primarily in greater Waterbury, CT. No support for religious or political activities. No grants for endowments.
Publications: Application guidelines; Program policy statement.
Application information: Application form required.
Initial approach: Letter of inquiry
Copies of proposal: 8
Board meeting date(s): Feb., May, and Oct.
Officers: Thomas Leever, Pres. and Treas.; Daniel Leever, V.P.; Andrew Leever, Secy.
Directors: Lori Hart; M. Catherine Smith.
EIN: 223115036

7254
Legatus Foundation ✧
1 W. 4th St.
Winston-Salem, NC 27101-3806

Established in 2000 in NC.
Donors: Virginia Durand Shelden†; William Warren Shelden†.
Foundation type: Independent foundation.
Financial data (yr. ended 12/31/13): Assets, $13,445,197 (M); expenditures, $622,246; qualifying distributions, $601,518; giving activities include $586,000 for 53 grants (high: $230,000; low: $500).
Fields of interest: Higher education; Environment, natural resources; Human services; Community/economic development; Foundations (community).
Limitations: Applications not accepted. Giving in the U.S., with emphasis on Winston-Salem, NC. No grants to individuals.
Application information: Contributes only to pre-selected organizations.
Officers and Director:* Ranlet S. Bell,* Pres.; Frank M. Bell, Jr., Secy.-Treas.
EIN: 311737683
Selected grants: The following grants are a representative sample of this grantmaker's funding activity:
$175,000 to Winston-Salem Foundation, Winston-Salem, NC, 2011.
$120,000 to Wake Forest University, Winston-Salem, NC, 2011.
$55,000 to Nature Conservancy, Lander, WY, 2011.
$30,000 to Nature Conservancy, Durham, NC, 2011.
$25,000 to Robert E. Lee Memorial Association, Stratford, VA, 2011.
$10,000 to Brookgreen Gardens, Murrells Inlet, SC, 2010. For general support.
$10,000 to Wake Forest University, Winston-Salem, NC, 2011.
$7,500 to Brookgreen Gardens, Murrells Inlet, SC, 2011.
$5,000 to Grand Teton National Park Foundation, Jackson, WY, 2010. For general support.
$3,000 to Miss Porters School, Farmington, CT, 2011.
$2,000 to South Carolina Environmental Law Project, Georgetown, SC, 2011.
$1,000 to Blue Ridge Parkway Foundation, Winston-Salem, NC, 2011.
$1,000 to South Carolina Environmental Law Project, Georgetown, SC, 2010. For general support.

7255
The Leon Levine Foundation ✧
6000 Fairview Rd., Ste. 1525
Charlotte, NC 28210-2212 (704) 817-6502
Contact: Thomas W. Lawrence III, Treas.
FAX: (704) 817-6515; E-mail for Thomas W. Lawrence: tlawrence@leonlevinefoundation.org; Main URL: http://www.leonlevinefoundation.org/

Established in 1981 in NC.
Donors: Leon Levine; Howard Levine.
Foundation type: Independent foundation.
Financial data (yr. ended 06/30/13): Assets, $338,429,517 (M); expenditures, $17,886,018; qualifying distributions, $15,491,964; giving activities include $14,946,318 for 244 grants (high: $2,000,000; low: $125).
Purpose and activities: Giving primarily to improve and advance the human condition in four major

areas: Education, Healthcare, Jewish Religion and Human Services. The foundation exists to support individuals and institutions seeking to accomplish the following: 1) Supporting the physically, mentally or emotionally ill through medical assistance and scientific research; 2) Pursuing academic excellence and providing access for disadvantaged and deserving individuals; 3) Building Jewish identity and strengthening Jewish Communities locally and worldwide; 4) Eliminating homelessness, alleviating personal crisis, improving the lives of families, children and the elderly and supporting cultural activities; 5) Responding to other emerging issues which could have a significant impact on society.
Fields of interest: Arts; Education; Health care; Human services; Foundations (community); Jewish agencies & synagogues.
Type of support: Capital campaigns; Endowments; Matching/challenge support.
Limitations: Applications accepted. Giving primarily in Charlotte, NC. No support for foreign organizations or 509(a)(3) supporting organizations. No grants to individuals.
Application information: Upon review of the letter of intent, an applicant may be invited to submit a formal proposal. See the foundation's web site for additional information.
Initial approach: Online letter of intent
Deadline(s): For proposals: Apr. 1 for grants made in June; Oct. 1 for grants made in Dec. However, applicants are not guaranteed consideration for that cycle depending on the number of requests already under consideration.
Board meeting date(s): June, Sept., and Dec.
Final notification: 30 days for confirmation of receipt of proposal and in which cycle the foundation expects to consider the application. Successful applicants normally are notified of the board's funding decision within 30-60 days after the decision.
Officers and Directors:* Leon Levine,* Chair. and Pres.; Sandra P. Levine,* V.P. and Secy.; Lindsey O'Neil, Cont.; Thomas W. Lawrence III,* Treas. and Exec. Dir.; Larry Polsky; Michael Richardson.
EIN: 581427515

7256
J. Arnet and Mildred M. Lewis Trust ✧
1525 W. WT Harris Blvd., D1114-044
Charlotte, NC 28262-8522

Established in 2007 in SC.
Donors: Arnet Lewis; William E. McDonald; Mildred Lewis†.
Foundation type: Independent foundation.
Financial data (yr. ended 12/31/13): Assets, $14,477,039 (M); gifts received, $122,318; expenditures, $766,844; qualifying distributions, $661,817; giving activities include $650,001 for 4 grants (high: $213,167; low: $10,500).
Purpose and activities: Giving primarily for hospitals, including a children's hospital, and to Baptist churches.
Fields of interest: Hospitals (general); Hospitals (specialty); Protestant agencies & churches.
Type of support: General/operating support.
Limitations: Applications not accepted. Giving primarily in Tampa, FL, North Myrtle Beach, SC, Memphis, TN, and Richmond, VA. No grants to individuals.
Application information: Contributes only to pre-selected organizations.
Trustee: Wells Fargo Bank, N.A.
EIN: 260454822

7257
George T. Lewis, Jr. 2001 Foundation ✧
3208 Twelve Oaks Pl.
Charlotte, NC 28270-4439

Established in 2004 in NC.
Donors: George T. Lewis†; George T. Lewis Revocable Trust.
Foundation type: Independent foundation.
Financial data (yr. ended 12/31/12): Assets, $35,917,909 (M); gifts received, $193,318; expenditures, $1,879,369; qualifying distributions, $1,638,000; giving activities include $1,620,000 for 29 grants (high: $130,000; low: $15,000).
Fields of interest: Education; Health organizations, association; Children, services; Foundations (community).
Limitations: Applications not accepted. Giving primarily in NC and SC.
Application information: Contributes only to pre-selected organizations.
Officer: James E. Lewis, Pres.
EIN: 043763019

7258
Audrey Love Charitable Foundation ✧
P.O. Box 175
Lake Toxaway, NC 28747-0175
Contact: Paul W. Doll, Jr.

Established in 1994 in DE.
Donor: Audrey B. Love Trust.
Foundation type: Independent foundation.
Financial data (yr. ended 12/31/13): Assets, $43,740,241 (M); expenditures, $1,702,006; qualifying distributions, $1,701,240; giving activities include $1,177,406 for 87 grants (high: $127,000; low: $2,000).
Fields of interest: Performing arts; Arts; Medical school/education; Animals/wildlife; Human services.
Limitations: Applications not accepted. No grants to individuals.
Application information: Contributes only to pre-selected organizations.
Officers and Directors:* Paul W. Doll, Jr.,* Pres.; Gerard B. Bajek,* V.P.; R. Keith McCall; Jeffrey Tanen.
EIN: 222766994
Selected grants: The following grants are a representative sample of this grantmaker's funding activity:
$100,000 to University of Miami, Miami, FL, 2011.
$30,000 to Caramoor Center for Music and the Arts, Katonah, NY, 2011.

7259
Luddy Charitable Foundation ✧
c/o Wells Fargo Bank, N.A.
1525 W. WT Harris Blvd.
Charlotte, NC 28288-5709

Established in 2002 in NC.
Donor: Robert L. Luddy.
Foundation type: Independent foundation.
Financial data (yr. ended 12/31/13): Assets, $1,087,266 (M); gifts received, $2,002,325; expenditures, $2,624,616; qualifying distributions, $2,565,000; giving activities include $2,564,000 for 30 grants (high: $750,000; low: $5,000).
Fields of interest: Education; Human services; Catholic agencies & churches.
Limitations: Applications not accepted. Giving in the U.S., with emphasis on NC. No grants to individuals.
Application information: Contributes only to pre-selected organizations.
Officer: William H. Frances, Jr., Secy.
Director: Robert L. Luddy.
EIN: 113660572
Selected grants: The following grants are a representative sample of this grantmaker's funding activity:
$300,000 to Donors Trust, Alexandria, VA, 2011.
$100,000 to Bishop McDevitt High School, Harrisburg, PA, 2011.
$100,000 to Legion of Christ, Cheshire, CT, 2011.

7260
Donald D. Lynch Family Foundation ✧
108 Artillery Ln.
Raleigh, NC 27615-1507 (919) 846-0830
Contact: Donald D. Lynch, Exec. Dir.
E-mail: dlynch888@bellsouth.net

Established in 1997 in NC.
Donor: Donald D. Lynch.
Foundation type: Independent foundation.
Financial data (yr. ended 06/30/13): Assets, $18,315,866 (M); gifts received, $700,018; expenditures, $807,808; qualifying distributions, $740,787; giving activities include $740,787 for grants.
Purpose and activities: Giving primarily to Roman Catholic organizations that endeavor to relieve human suffering, provide hand-ups, and attempt to become part of the solution. Priority is given to job training, right-to-life projects, evangelization and missionary work (domestic and international).
Fields of interest: Catholic federated giving programs; Catholic agencies & churches.
Limitations: Applications accepted. Giving on a national basis. No support for parishes, dioceses, or organizations receiving government funding. No grants to individuals, or for building projects, campaigns, or tuition.
Publications: Application guidelines.
Application information: Application form required.
Initial approach: E-mail or letter
Copies of proposal: 2
Deadline(s): None
Board meeting date(s): July or Aug.
Officers and Directors:* Dennis Lynch,* Secy.; Donald D. Lynch,* Exec. Dir.; Dow L. Campbell; Susan Lynch Campbell.
Number of staff: 1 part-time professional.
EIN: 562053851
Selected grants: The following grants are a representative sample of this grantmaker's funding activity:
$12,228 to Apostolate for Family Consecration, Bloomingdale, OH, 2013. To complete funding for expenses to the first annual International Missionary Training Seminar for this Pontifically-recognized organization.
$10,000 to Daughters of Mary and Joseph, Rancho Palos Verdes, CA, 2013. To partially fund the budget for the AIDS palliative care outreach Program in Bisheshe, Uganda.

$10,000 to Lamp Ministries, Bronx, NY, 2013. For their ministries in poor parishes in the New York and Newark archdioceses.
$10,000 to Missionaries of the Sacred Hearts of Jesus and Mary, Linwood, NJ, 2013. To complete the funding for a project to purchase solar panels for community drinking water near Sacred Hearts' Catholic Formation House in Ullakwu Village, Imo State, Nigeria.
$5,960 to Archdiocese of Chicago, Chicago, IL, 2013. For 23 bikes and 46 albs to Fr. Max and his Our Lady of Assumption Parish, Buyambi, Uganda for the catechists who service the 23 Mission Stations in the community.
$5,000 to Notre Dame Academy, Toledo, OH, 2013. For our annual payment for the Donna O. Lynch Memorial Scholarship which was established in October, 2000.
$5,000 to Vernon Avenue Project, Brooklyn, NY, 2013. For seed money to open a catering business to attempt to break the cycle of poverty for at-risk youths by developing their potential to be positive citizens through a combination of academic success and work.
$3,300 to Community of Charity and Social Services, Biloxi, MS, 2013. For furniture and chapel furnishings for a structure being used to house priests and seminarians.
$2,800 to Colorado Vincentian Volunteers, Denver, CO, 2013. To cover expenses for the Spring contemplative retreat at St. Benedict's Monastery which is integral to the volunteers' year-of-service experiences.
$2,235 to Franciscan Sisters of Little Falls, Little Falls, MN, 2013. To fund modest updates to the Casa Misionera Franciscana in Managua Nicaragua.

7261
George Henry Mayr Trust ✧
c/o Wells Fargo Bank, N.A., Trust Tax Dept.
1 W. 4th St., 4th Fl., MAC D4000-041
Winston-Salem, NC 27101-3818

Trust established in 1949 in CA.
Donor: George Henry Mayr†.
Foundation type: Independent foundation.
Financial data (yr. ended 12/31/13): Assets, $24,457,429 (M); expenditures, $1,239,215; qualifying distributions, $1,095,534; giving activities include $804,455 for 92 grants (high: $17,270; low: $2,000).
Purpose and activities: Grants to California private schools for scholarships to students who have completed the 8th grade and reside in the state.
Fields of interest: Secondary school/education; Higher education; Education; Minorities.
Type of support: Scholarship funds.
Limitations: Applications not accepted. Giving limited to CA. No support for medical education other than dentistry. No grants to individuals.
Application information: Contributes only to pre-selected organizations.
Board meeting date(s): Quarterly
Officer and Directors:* Natalie Haden O'Connor,* Secy.; Michele McGarry Crahan; Patrick Haden; Catherine Grier Olson.
Trustee: Wells Fargo Bank, N.A.
Number of staff: 1 part-time support.
EIN: 956062009

7262
Alexander McCausland Charitable Trust ✧
1525 W. WT Harris Blvd., D1114-044
Charlotte, NC 28288-0001
Application address: c/o Wells Fargo Philanthropic Services, One W. 4th St., Winston-Salem, NC 27101, tel.: (888) 234-1999; Main URL: https://www.wellsfargo.com/privatefoundationgrants/mccausland

Donor: Alexander Mccausland†.
Foundation type: Independent foundation.
Financial data (yr. ended 12/31/12): Assets, $15,885,440 (M); expenditures, $935,529; qualifying distributions, $777,917; giving activities include $733,751 for 21 grants (high: $100,000; low: $5,000).
Fields of interest: Animals/wildlife; Human services.
Limitations: Applications accepted. Giving in the U.S., with emphasis on VA. No grants to individuals.
Application information: Application form required.
Initial approach: Complete online application form
Deadline(s): Sept. 30
Trustee: Wells Fargo Bank, N.A.
EIN: 376437195
Selected grants: The following grants are a representative sample of this grantmaker's funding activity:
$25,000 to American Humane Association, Washington, DC, 2012. For Red Star Emergency Program.

7263
L. D. McEachern Trust Fund ✧
c/o Wachovia Bank, N.A.
1525 W. WT Harris Blvd., D1114-044
Charlotte, NC 28288-1161

Established in 1992; supporting organization of McEachern Memorial Methodist Church, McEachern Endowment Fund, and Young Harris College; Status changed to private foundation in 2008.
Foundation type: Independent foundation.
Financial data (yr. ended 12/31/13): Assets, $130,879,142 (M); expenditures, $6,222,225; qualifying distributions, $5,528,869; giving activities include $5,400,000 for 3 grants (high: $4,320,000; low: $540,000).
Fields of interest: Higher education, college; Education; Protestant agencies & churches.
Limitations: Applications not accepted. Giving limited to GA. No grants to individuals.
Application information: Contributes only to pre-selected organizations.
Trustee: Wells Fargo Bank, N.A.
EIN: 586255314
Selected grants: The following grants are a representative sample of this grantmaker's funding activity:
$4,160,000 to McEachern Endowment Fund, Powder Springs, GA, 2012.
$520,000 to McEachern Memorial United Methodist Church, Powder Springs, GA, 2012.
$520,000 to Young Harris College, Young Harris, GA, 2012.

7264
Thomas R. & Elizabeth E. McLean Foundation, Inc. ✧
P.O. Box 58329
Fayetteville, NC 28305-8329

Established in 1998 in NC.
Donor: Thomas R. McLean†.
Foundation type: Independent foundation.
Financial data (yr. ended 12/31/13): Assets, $20,922,097 (M); gifts received, $352,246; expenditures, $1,122,975; qualifying distributions, $964,446; giving activities include $860,000 for 14 grants (high: $250,000; low: $5,000).
Purpose and activities: Giving to improve the quality of life in Cumberland County, NC.
Fields of interest: Museums (science/technology); Performing arts, theater; Higher education; YM/YWCAs & YM/YWHAs; Foundations (community).
Limitations: Applications accepted. Giving limited to Cumberland County, NC. No support for religious or political organizations.
Application information: Application form required.
Initial approach: Letter
Deadline(s): None
Board meeting date(s): Monthly
Officers: Alfred Cleveland, Pres.; Harry Shaw, V.P.
Directors: Faison Covington; Jennifer Elam.
EIN: 311470721
Selected grants: The following grants are a representative sample of this grantmaker's funding activity:
$100,000 to Cape Fear Botanical Garden, Fayetteville, NC, 2011.
$100,000 to Cape Fear Botanical Garden, Fayetteville, NC, 2011.
$100,000 to Cross Creek Linear Park, Fayetteville, NC, 2011.
$100,000 to Methodist University, Fayetteville, NC, 2011.
$50,000 to Airborne and Special Operations Museum Foundation, Fayetteville, NC, 2011.

7265
The McMichael Family Foundation ✧
P.O. Box 507
Madison, NC 27025-0507

Established in 1992 in NC.
Donor: Dalton L. McMichael, Sr.†.
Foundation type: Independent foundation.
Financial data (yr. ended 09/30/13): Assets, $54,524,977 (M); expenditures, $3,629,548; qualifying distributions, $2,622,034; giving activities include $2,622,034 for 137 grants (high: $200,000; low: $34).
Purpose and activities: Giving primarily for education, health, human services, and to Protestant churches.
Fields of interest: Higher education; Education; Health care; Human services; Protestant agencies & churches.
Limitations: Applications not accepted. Giving primarily in NC, with some emphasis on Elon, Greensboro, and High Point. No grants to individuals.
Application information: Contributes only to pre-selected organizations.
Officers and Directors:* Dalton L. McMichael, Jr.,* Pres.; Flavel McMichael Godfrey,* V.P.; Whitney

Brigman Heard,* Secy.; Gail McMichael Drew,* Treas.; Anna Drew Kirk; Andrew Martin Miracle.
EIN: 561774976
Selected grants: The following grants are a representative sample of this grantmaker's funding activity:
$400,000 to Elon University, Elon, NC, 2011.
$195,000 to Saint Vincents Foundation, Jacksonville, FL, 2011.
$125,000 to Rescue Missions Ministries, Durham, NC, 2011. For capital campaign.
$100,000 to High Point Regional Health System, High Point, NC, 2011. For capital campaign.
$40,000 to MANNA FoodBank, Asheville, NC, 2011.
$35,000 to Cystic Fibrosis Foundation, Raleigh, NC, 2011. For research.
$35,000 to United Way of Rockingham County, Reidsville, NC, 2011. For general support.
$33,900 to Mountain Housing Opportunities, Asheville, NC, 2011.
$19,000 to Durham Nativity School, Durham, NC, 2011. For scholarship fund.
$10,000 to Cummer Museum of Art and Gardens, Jacksonville, FL, 2011. For general support.

7266
Mebane Charitable Foundation, Inc. ✧

232 S. Main St.
P.O. Box 339
Mocksville, NC 27028-2427 (336) 936-0041
Contact: Larry C. Colbourne, Pres.
FAX: (336) 936-0038;
E-mail: info@mebanefoundation.com; Main URL: http://www.mebanefoundation.com

Established in 1992 in NC.
Donor: G. Allen Mebane IV.
Foundation type: Independent foundation.
Financial data (yr. ended 12/31/13): Assets, $38,251,074 (M); expenditures, $3,331,151; qualifying distributions, $3,226,987; giving activities include $2,674,399 for 52 grants (high: $1,250,000; low: $100).
Purpose and activities: The foundation promotes and supports the highest quality early childhood education initiatives for children in North Carolina. The foundation also supports nonprofit initiatives in Davie and Yadkin counties, NC, that can improve the lifestyle of its citizens.
Fields of interest: Education, early childhood education; Children/youth, services.
Type of support: General/operating support; Continuing support; Annual campaigns; Capital campaigns; Building/renovation; Endowments; Debt reduction; Program development; Seed money; Curriculum development; Scholarship funds; Research; Program evaluation; In-kind gifts; Matching/challenge support.
Limitations: Giving limited to NC. No grants to individuals; no loans.
Publications: Application guidelines; Annual report; Financial statement; Grants list; Multi-year report; Program policy statement.
Application information: Letter of intent form available on foundation web site. Questions regarding letter of intent maybe made by telephone, Mon.-Fri., between 9:00am and 4:00pm. Application form required.
Initial approach: Complete a phone interview with the foundation president
Copies of proposal: 1
Deadline(s): July 1 for consideration at fall board meeting and Jan. 1 for consideration at spring board meeting
Board meeting date(s): 3rd Tues. in Mar. and Sept.
Final notification: 90 days
Officers and Directors:* Marianne Cheek Mebane,* Chair.; Larry C. Colbourne, Pres.; Judy T. Averitte, Secy.; Paul R. Barkus,* Treas.; Roger Berrier; Carl N. Boon; John A. Hilton, Jr.; Rev. John C. Lathrop; Paul H. Livingston, Jr.; Donald C. McMillion; William Mebane; Mary E. Rittling, Ed.D.
Number of staff: 1 full-time professional; 2 full-time support.
EIN: 561853390
Selected grants: The following grants are a representative sample of this grantmaker's funding activity:
$100,000 to Wilkes County Schools, North Wilkesboro, NC, 2012. For board approved.
$5,000 to Harlem Academy, New York, NY, 2012. For Director Advised.

7267
Merancas Foundation, Inc. ✧

(formerly Mermans Foundation, Inc.)
14051 Island Dr.
Huntersville, NC 28078-8954 (704) 992-0705
Contact: Cornelis A.M. Mermans, Pres.
FAX: (704) 992-0706;
E-mail: cmermans@merancas.org; Georgia contact: Attn.: Nicole Mermans, 361 17th St. N.W., Unit 2223, Atlanta, GA 30363, e-mail: nicole@merancas.org; New Jersey contact: Attn.: Jennifer Mermans, 210 Elm Rd., Princeton, NJ 08540, e-mail: jennifer@merancas.org; Main URL: http://merancas.org

Established in 1989 in NC.
Donors: Cornelis A.M. Mermans; Johanna K. Mermans; Andy Mermans; Jennifer E. Mermans; Bryan K. Mermans; Robin B. Mermans; Nicole A. Mermans.
Foundation type: Independent foundation.
Financial data (yr. ended 12/31/12): Assets, $32,399,036 (M); gifts received, $4,000,000; expenditures, $5,369,437; qualifying distributions, $5,365,000; giving activities include $5,365,000 for 97 grants (high: $535,000; low: $1,000).
Purpose and activities: Financially supporting non-profit organizations close to home that prepare children to become productive adults and help adults in need become self-sufficient.
Fields of interest: Education, early childhood education; Vocational education; Education, ESL programs; Health care; Employment, training; Food services; Housing/shelter; Disasters, preparedness/services; Human services; Youth, services.
Type of support: Annual campaigns; Capital campaigns.
Limitations: Applications accepted. Giving primarily in the Charlotte, NC, area, and more recently in GA and NJ. No support for arts organizations, or for political or religious organizations. No grants to individuals.
Application information: Application form not required.
Initial approach: Proposal to closest office location
Copies of proposal: 1
Deadline(s): Feb. and Aug.
Board meeting date(s): Mar. and Sept.
Final notification: 1-3 months
Officers: Cornelis A.M. Mermans, Pres.; Johanna K. Mermans, V.P.; Jennifer E. Mermans, Secy.
Directors: Andy Mermans; Bryan K. Mermans; Nicole A. Mermans; Robin B. Mermans.
Number of staff: None.
EIN: 561677733

7268
The Morehead-Cain Foundation ✧

(formerly The John Motley Morehead Foundation)
P.O. Box 690
Chapel Hill, NC 27514-0690 (919) 962-1201
Contact: Charles E. Lovelace, Jr., Exec. Dir.
FAX: (919) 962-1615;
E-mail: moreheadcain@unc.edu; Toll free tel.: (800) 741-9023; Main URL: http://www.moreheadcain.org/
Facebook: http://www.facebook.com/pages/The-Morehead-Cain-Scholars-Program/37888997921
Morehead-Cain Network: http://www.m-c-network.org
Scholar Videos: http://www.moreheadcain.org/page/scholar-videos
YouTube: http://www.youtube.com/user/MoreheadCain

Trust established in 1945 in NY; Name changed in 207 as a result of a significant gift from the Gordon and Mary Cain Foundation.
Donors: John Motley Morehead III†; The Gordon and Mary Cain Foundation.
Foundation type: Independent foundation.
Financial data (yr. ended 06/30/13): Assets, $192,653,483 (M); gifts received, $1,041,554; expenditures, $11,214,270; qualifying distributions, $8,737,495; giving activities include $1,102,602 for 5 grants (high: $921,039; low: $600), and $5,751,895 for 270 grants to individuals (high: $49,042; low: $500).
Purpose and activities: To attract outstanding, well-rounded students to study at the University of North Carolina at Chapel Hill. Through the Morehead-Cain Scholars Program, the foundation currently makes awards for undergraduate study only at the University of North Carolina at Chapel Hill to graduates of NC high schools. schools outside the state and in Canada, and public schools in the United Kingdom.
Fields of interest: Higher education.
Type of support: Internship funds; Scholarships—to individuals.
Limitations: Applications accepted. Giving primarily to nominated residents of NC; some giving also to out of state residents attending selected secondary schools. International Scholar giving limited to nominees from England and Canada. No support for secondary schools outside NC except by invitation from the foundation.
Publications: Annual report; Informational brochure.
Application information: Nomination form required. Nominations for undergraduate scholarships must be made by secondary schools eligible to participate in the selection process. A form is issued for nominations, which are made in Sept. after a preliminary screening process.
Initial approach: For NC students: nominated by their high school or nominate themselves by applying directly; students in Canada: endorsed by their school or CGEPS, or may apply directly without sponsorship; UK

students not attending an official British Morehead-Lain nominating school may nominate themselves by applying directly, all other students most be nominated
Deadline(s): Oct. 1 for nominations
Board meeting date(s): Mar., Apr., Aug., and Nov.
Final notification: Mar. 1
Officers and Trustees:* Lucy Hanes Chatham,* Chair.; Timothy Brooks Burnett,* Vice-Chair.; Steven R. Michalak, Treas.; Charles E. Lovelace, Jr., Exec. Dir.; David C. Wright,* Genl. Counsel; Holly Cluett Gwynne-Timothy; John A. Larkin, III; George Kennedy Thompson; James D. Weaver; Margaret W. Weaver.
Number of staff: 5 full-time professional; 3 full-time support.
EIN: 560599225
Selected grants: The following grants are a representative sample of this grantmaker's funding activity:
$1,323,307 to University of North Carolina, Chapel Hill, NC, 2012. To support and promote Morehead-Cain Scholars Program and Summer Enrichment Program.
$74,065 to University of North Carolina, Chapel Hill, NC, 2012. To maintain Morehead House facility for distinguished guests.
$15,000 to Morehead Planetarium and Science Center, Chapel Hill, NC, 2012. For general support.
$2,500 to University of North Carolina Educational Foundation, Chapel Hill, NC, 2012. For general support.
$1,800 to North Carolina Network of Grantmakers, Chapel Hill, NC, 2012. For general support.

7269
The Morgan Foundation, Inc. ✧
P.O. Box 1167
Laurel Hill, NC 28351-1167 (910) 462-2016
Contact: James L. Morgan, Jr., Chair. and Pres.
FAX: (910) 462-2019; E-mail: morganco@alltel.net

Established in 1992 in NC as successor to Morgan Trust for Charity, Religion, and Education which was established in 1949.
Donors: Edwin Morgan†; Elise Morgan†; Morgan Mills, Inc.; The Morgan Co. of Laurel Hill, Inc.; Morgan Farms, Inc.; Walden Court, Inc.
Foundation type: Independent foundation.
Financial data (yr. ended 12/31/13): Assets, $3,221,411 (M); expenditures, $755,898; qualifying distributions, $734,394; giving activities include $728,903 for 26 grants (high: $120,000; low: $1,000).
Purpose and activities: Support for higher education, Protestant churches, and community charities.
Fields of interest: Higher education; Education; Community/economic development; Protestant agencies & churches.
Type of support: Continuing support; Annual campaigns; Capital campaigns; Building/renovation; Endowments; Debt reduction; Seed money; Matching/challenge support.
Limitations: Applications accepted. Giving primarily in the Laurel Hill, NC, area. No grants to individuals, or for scholarships or fellowships; no loans. Generally no grants for operating budgets.
Publications: Financial statement.
Application information: Application form not required.
Initial approach: Proposal
Copies of proposal: 1
Deadline(s): None
Board meeting date(s): As required
Officers and Directors:* James L. Morgan, Jr.,* Chair. and Pres.; Elizabeth E. Morgan,* V.P.; Tammy C. Ivey, Secy.-Treas.; Susan M. Farrell.
EIN: 561790979
Selected grants: The following grants are a representative sample of this grantmaker's funding activity:
$160,000 to Montreat College, Montreat, NC, 2012. For Keystone Scholarship Fund/Centennial Campaign.
$160,000 to Montreat Conference Center, Montreat, NC, 2012. For Morgan Youth Endowment Fund.
$5,300 to American Cancer Society, Raleigh, NC, 2012. For Relay for Life/Operating Funds.
$5,000 to Hospice of Scotland County, Laurinburg, NC, 2012. For Richard L. Byrne Memorial Golf Tournament.

7270
Fred M. Klaus and Harold L. Murphy Foundation ✧
c/o Wells Fargo Bank, N.A.
1525 W. WT Harris Blvd., D1114-044
Charlotte, NC 28288-5709

Established in 1990 in FL.
Donors: Fred M. Klaus; Harold L. Murphy.
Foundation type: Independent foundation.
Financial data (yr. ended 04/30/13): Assets, $11,561,655 (M); expenditures, $729,497; qualifying distributions, $439,222; giving activities include $439,222 for grants.
Fields of interest: Human services; American Red Cross; Catholic agencies & churches.
Limitations: Applications not accepted. Giving primarily in FL. No grants to individuals.
Application information: Contributes only to pre-selected organizations.
Trustees: Randy W. Moore; Wells Fargo Bank, N.A.
EIN: 656049287
Selected grants: The following grants are a representative sample of this grantmaker's funding activity:
$15,000 to Monroe Association for Retarded Citizens, Key West, FL, 2013. For Adult Day Training Programs.

7271
Neviaser Charitable Foundation, Inc. ✧
P.O. Box 2907, Trust Tax Dept.
Wilson, NC 27894-2907

Established in 2007 in FL.
Donors: C.M. Neviaser†; Charles Neviaser Trust; Charles Neviaser Marital Trust B.
Foundation type: Independent foundation.
Financial data (yr. ended 12/31/13): Assets, $22,294,381 (M); expenditures, $1,426,777; qualifying distributions, $1,226,666; giving activities include $1,025,000 for 11 grants (high: $300,000; low: $20,000).
Fields of interest: Human services; Residential/custodial care, hospices.
Limitations: Applications not accepted. Giving primarily in Jacksonville, FL.
Application information: Unsolicited requests for funds not accepted.
Directors: Nancy Baker; Tiffany Holbrook; Michael Neviaser.
EIN: 208774946
Selected grants: The following grants are a representative sample of this grantmaker's funding activity:
$100,000 to I. M. Sulzbacher Center for the Homeless, Jacksonville, FL, 2011.
$20,000 to Brooks Health Foundation, Jacksonville, FL, 2011.
$20,000 to Clara White Mission, Jacksonville, FL, 2011.

7272
Nickel Producers Environmental Research Association, Inc. ✧
(also known as NiPERA)
2525 Meridian Pkwy., Ste. 240
Durham, NC 27713-5244 (919) 595-1950
Contact: Hudson K. Bates, Exec. Dir.
FAX: (919) 595-1955; E-mail: nipera@nipera.org; Main URL: http://www.nipera.org

Established in 1980 in NY.
Donors: Anglo Platinum; Billiton; Empress Nickel Refinery, Ltd.; Eramet; Inco, Ltd.; International Cobalt; Nippon Yakin; Noranda; Sumitomo; Pharma; Unicore; Nickel Institute.
Foundation type: Independent foundation.
Financial data (yr. ended 12/31/13): Assets, $799,382 (M); gifts received, $3,516,232; expenditures, $3,550,979; qualifying distributions, $1,447,122; giving activities include $1,447,122 for 62 grants (high: $120,000; low: $755).
Purpose and activities: Giving primarily for research investigations, studies, and surveys relating to occupational health and safety aspects of the nickel producing industries and related environmental matters.
Fields of interest: Higher education; Environment; Health care; Health organizations, association; Safety/disasters; Engineering/technology; Science.
International interests: Canada; Europe; Japan.
Type of support: Fellowships; Research.
Limitations: Giving primarily in the U.S., Europe, Canada, and Japan.
Publications: Annual report.
Application information:
Initial approach: Proposal
Deadline(s): Varies
Board meeting date(s): Sept.
Officers: Tim Aiken, Chair.; David Butler, Secy.; Joe Catalano, Treas.; Hudson K. Bates, Exec. Dir.; Gerald Schuetz, CPA, CGMA, C.F.O.
Board Members: Michael Chalkley; Gordon Hall; Tetsuya Kubota; L.J.G. Nacken; Jacques-Antoine Rondeau; Catherine Tissot-Colle.
EIN: 133070077

7273
North Carolina Community Foundation ✧
4601 Six Forks Rd., Ste. 524
Raleigh, NC 27609-5286 (919) 828-4387
Contact: Jennifer Tolle Whiteside, Pres.; For grants: Sally Migliore, Dir., Community Leadership
FAX: (919) 828-5495;
E-mail: info@nccommunityfoundation.org; Additional tel.: (800) 201-9533; Main URL: http://www.nccommunityfoundation.org
Blog: http://www.nccommunityfoundation.org/blog

Facebook: http://www.facebook.com/pages/North-Carolina-Community-Foundation/55963655306
Flickr: http://www.flickr.com/photos/nccommunityfoundation/
LinkedIn: http://www.linkedin.com/company/2079728?trk=tyah
Twitter: https://twitter.com/NCCF
YouTube: http://www.youtube.com/user/nccommunityfoundatio

Established in 1988 in NC.
Foundation type: Community foundation.
Financial data (yr. ended 03/31/14): Assets, $191,437,016 (M); gifts received, $17,539,706; expenditures, $18,964,993; giving activities include $15,068,652 for 1,112+ grants (high: $1,647,719; low: $90).
Purpose and activities: The foundation's mission is to inspire North Carolinians to make lasting and meaningful contributions to their communities.
Fields of interest: Humanities; Arts; Education; Environment; Animals/wildlife; Health care; Youth development; Human services; Public affairs; Religion; Children/youth; Youth; Adults; Aging; Young adults; Disabilities, people with; Physically disabled; Blind/visually impaired; Deaf/hearing impaired; Mentally disabled; Minorities; Asians/Pacific Islanders; African Americans/Blacks; Hispanics/Latinos; Native Americans/American Indians; Indigenous peoples; Women; Military/veterans; Offenders/ex-offenders; Substance abusers; AIDS, people with; Single parents; Crime/abuse victims; Terminal illness, people with; Immigrants/refugees; Economically disadvantaged; Homeless.
Type of support: Capital campaigns; Building/renovation; Conferences/seminars; Consulting services; Continuing support; Curriculum development; Emergency funds; Employee-related scholarships; Endowments; Equipment; Fellowships; General/operating support; Management development/capacity building; Program development; Program evaluation; Publication; Research; Scholarship funds; Scholarships—to individuals; Technical assistance.
Limitations: Applications accepted. Giving primarily in NC. No grants for annual funds or capital campaigns, or for re-granting by the applicant organization. No loans.
Publications: Application guidelines; Annual report; Financial statement; Grants list; Informational brochure; Newsletter.
Application information: Visit foundation web site for application information per affiliate foundation. Application form required.
Initial approach: Submit online application
Copies of proposal: 1
Deadline(s): Varies
Board meeting date(s): Quarterly
Final notification: Varies
Officers and Directors:* Stuart B. Dorsett,* Chair.; Linda J. Staunch,* Vice-Chair.; Jennifer Tolle Whiteside,* C.E.O. and Pres.; Beth Boney Jenkins, V.P., Devel.; James Bell Black,* Chair., Governance; Rodney E. Martin,* Chair., Grants; Ken G. Reece, Chair., Resource Devel.; Dean E. Painter, Jr.,* Secy.; John Berngartt, C.F.O.; W. Trent Ragland III,* Treas.; James W. Narron,* Immediate Past-Chair.; Annabelle L. Fetterman, Dir. Emeritus; Henry E. Frye, Dir. Emeritus; Martha Guy, Dir. Emeritus; John R. Jordan, Jr., Dir. Emeritus; W. Trent Ragland, Jr., Dir. Emeritus; Sherwood H. Smith, Jr., Dir. Emeritus; Robert L. Jones, Asst. Secy.; Juan Austin; Robert E. Barnhill, Jr.; Laura Beasley; Dr. John Cameron; Brian C. Crutchfield; Sarah Belk Gambrell; Frank B. Gibson, Jr.; Katharine Harrison Hardin; Clyde P. Harris, Jr.; H. Kel Landis; James M. Parrott, Jr.; C. Ron Scheeler; Karen Stiwinter; Elizabeth Hobgood Wellons; Billy T. Woodard.
Number of staff: 23 full-time professional.
EIN: 581661700

7274
The North Carolina GlaxoSmithKline Foundation, Inc. ✧

(formerly The Glaxo Wellcome Foundation)
5 Moore Dr.
P.O. Box 13398
Research Triangle Park, NC 27709-3398 (919) 483-2140
Contact: Marilyn E. Foote-Hudson, Exec. Dir.
FAX: (919) 315-3015;
E-mail: info@ncgskfoundation.org; Contact for Ribbon of Hope: Jesse Rainey, tel.: (303) 632-5590, e-mail: jrainey@mcrel.org or RibbonOfHope@mcrel.org; Main URL: http://www.ncgskfoundation.org/index.html
Additional URL: http://www.mcrel.org/GSKRibbonOfHope
Ribbon of Hope Recipients: http://www2.mcrel.org/NCGSKFRibbonOfHope/recipients13.asp
Traditional Grants Recipients: http://www.ncgskfoundation.org/cp.html
Twitter: https://twitter.com/NCGSKFound

Established in 1986 in NC.
Donors: Glaxo Wellcome Americas Inc.; GlaxoSmithKline Holdings (Americas) Inc.
Foundation type: Company-sponsored foundation.
Financial data (yr. ended 12/31/12): Assets, $59,837,197 (M); gifts received, $163,913; expenditures, $3,915,088; qualifying distributions, $3,755,357; giving activities include $2,950,845 for 25 grants (high: $537,920; low: $2,714).
Purpose and activities: The foundation supports programs designed to promote education, health, and science.
Fields of interest: Museums; Museums (art); Elementary/secondary education; Higher education; Higher education, college (community/junior); Education, reading; Education; Health care, association; Public health; Health care; Children/youth, services; Science; Children/youth; Adults; Minorities.
Type of support: Professorships; Matching/challenge support; Curriculum development; Capital campaigns; Internship funds; Program development; Scholarship funds; Seed money.
Limitations: Applications accepted. Giving primarily in NC. No support for religious, political, or international organizations. No grants to individuals, or for construction, restoration projects, or for general operating costs.
Publications: Annual report (including application guidelines); Grants list.
Application information: Proposals for Ribbon of Hope should be no longer than 10 pages. Support is limited to 1 contribution per organization during any given year. Organizations receiving support are asked to provide interim reports and a final report. Application form not required.
Initial approach: Proposal for Traditional Grants; download application form and e-mail or mail proposal and application form for Ribbon of Hope
Copies of proposal: 1
Deadline(s): Jan. 1, Apr. 1, July 1, and Oct. 1 for Traditional Grants; Apr. 1 and Oct. 1 for Ribbon of Hope
Board meeting date(s): Mar., June, Sept., and Dec.
Final notification: Within 15 days following board meetings for Traditional Grants; Apr. and Nov. for Ribbon of Hope
Officers and Directors:* Robert A. Ingram,* Chair.; Margaret B. Dardess,* Pres.; Paul A. Holcombe, Jr.,* Secy.; Marilyn E. Foote-Hudson, Exec. Dir.; Adrianna Carter, Legal Counsel; Diedre P. Connelly; W. Robert Connor; Shirley T. Frye; Thomas R. Haber; Charles A. Sanders, M.D.; Mark Werner; Janice M. Whitaker.
Number of staff: 2 full-time professional; 1 part-time professional; 1 full-time support.
EIN: 581698610

7275
Nucor Foundation ✧

1915 Rexford Rd.
Charlotte, NC 28211-3465 (704) 367-8662
FAX: (704) 943-7199;
E-mail: scholarshipsupport@nucor.com; Main URL: https://scholarshipapply.nucor.com/

Established in 1973 in NC.
Donor: Nucor Corp.
Foundation type: Company-sponsored foundation.
Financial data (yr. ended 12/31/13): Assets, $109,614 (M); gifts received, $1,800,000; expenditures, $1,848,254; qualifying distributions, $1,848,254; giving activities include $1,847,100 for 725 grants to individuals (high: $6,000; low: $36).
Purpose and activities: The foundation awards undergraduate and vocational education scholarships to children and stepchildren of employees of Nucor Corporation and scholarships to students pursuing degrees in engineering and metallurgy form communities where Nucor operates.
Fields of interest: Vocational education; Higher education; Education.
Type of support: Employee-related scholarships; Scholarships—to individuals.
Limitations: Applications accepted. Giving primarily in areas of company operations.
Application information: Application form required.
Initial approach: Complete online application
Deadline(s): Mar. 1
Directors: Daniel R. Dimicco; James D. Frias; Daniel W. Krug.
EIN: 237318064

7276
The Oak Foundation U.S.A. ✧

55 Vilcom Center Dr., Ste. 340
Chapel Hill, NC 27514-1690
E-mail: oak@oakfnd.org; Additional e-mail (Geneva office): info@oakfnd.ch.; Main URL: http://www.oakfnd.org
Grantee Perception Report: http://www.oakfnd.org/sites/default/files/Oak%20Foundation%20Grantee%20Perception%20Report%202011.pdf
Grants Database: http://www.oakfnd.org/node/3

Established in 1986 in DE.
Donors: The Oak Trust; The Forest Trust.
Foundation type: Independent foundation.

Financial data (yr. ended 12/31/13): Assets, $73,539,978 (M); gifts received, $1,302,000; expenditures, $38,672,242; qualifying distributions, $37,551,455; giving activities include $36,428,746 for 148 grants (high: $2,000,000; low: $15,000).
Purpose and activities: The foundation's giving priorities include child abuse, the environment, especially climate change and marine conservation, human rights, issues affecting women, housing and homelessness, learning differences and special interest grants.
Fields of interest: Environment, climate change/global warming; Environment, natural resources; Environment, water resources; Environment; Learning disorders; Crime/violence prevention, abuse prevention; Crime/violence prevention, domestic violence; Crime/violence prevention, child abuse; Crime/violence prevention, sexual abuse; Housing/shelter, homeless; International human rights; Women.
International interests: Africa; Asia; Bulgaria; Eastern Africa; Ethiopia; Europe; India; Latin America; Latvia; Moldova; Myanmar; Russia; South America; Switzerland; Tanzania; Uganda.
Type of support: General/operating support; Continuing support; Management development/capacity building; Building/renovation; Equipment; Program development; Research; Technical assistance; Program evaluation; Matching/challenge support.
Limitations: Applications accepted. Giving on a national basis. No support for religious organizations for religious purposes or for political candidates. No grants to fundraising drives, events or amounts under $25,000 (except in special circumstances).
Publications: Application guidelines; Annual report (including application guidelines); Grants list; Program policy statement.
Application information: The foundation will respond within two months to inquiries, informing the applicant whether there is sufficient interest to pursue a proposal. If interested, the foundation will request additional information from the organization. Generally grants will not be given for under $25,000. Please see foundation web site for additional information. Application form not required.
Initial approach: Inquiry via e-mail to the appropriate program or letter addressed to the appropriate office; for initial contact, please do not telephone or visit the offices. See foundation web page for contact information for international offices
Copies of proposal: 1
Deadline(s): None
Final notification: Within two months
Officers and Trustees:* Kristian Parker,* Chair.; Natalie Shipton,* Vice-Chair.; Caroline Turner,* Vice-Chair.; Kathleen Cravero-Kristoffersson, Pres.; Gary Goodman, Secy.; Alan M. Parker; Jette Parker.
Advisory Board Members: William Norris; Julie Sandorf.
Number of staff: 3 full-time professional.
EIN: 133321196

7277
Robert S. & Helen P. Odell Fund ✧

(formerly Robert Stewart and Helen Pfeiffer Odell Fund)
c/o Wells Fargo Bank, N.A., Trust Tax. Dept.
1 W. 4th St., 4th Fl., MAC D4000-041
Winston-Salem, NC 27101-3818
Application address: c/o Wells Fargo Bank, Attn.: Eugene Ranchiasci, 420 Montgomery St., 5th Fl., San Francisco, CA 94104-1207, tel.: (412) 396-3215; Main URL: https://www.wellsfargo.com/privatefoundationgrants/odell

Established in 1967 in CA.
Donors: Robert Stewart Odell†; Helen Pfeiffer Odell†.
Foundation type: Independent foundation.
Financial data (yr. ended 12/31/13): Assets, $39,973,745 (M); expenditures, $1,954,096; qualifying distributions, $1,590,789; giving activities include $1,495,000 for 43 grants (high: $100,000; low: $10,000).
Purpose and activities: Giving primarily to education, the performing arts, human services and Catholic agencies.
Fields of interest: Performing arts; Arts; Elementary/secondary education; Higher education; Health organizations, association; Human services; Children/youth, services; Catholic agencies & churches.
Limitations: Giving primarily in the San Francisco Bay Area, CA. No grants to individuals.
Application information: Application form not required.
Initial approach: Letter
Copies of proposal: 1
Deadline(s): None
Board meeting date(s): Quarterly
Trustees: James P. Conn; Paul Fay III; Wells Fargo Bank, N.A.
EIN: 946132116
Selected grants: The following grants are a representative sample of this grantmaker's funding activity:
$100,000 to BASIC Fund, San Francisco, CA, 2011.
$100,000 to Thomas Aquinas College, Santa Paula, CA, 2011.

7278
Oechsle Family Foundation ✧

1525 W. WT Harris Blvd.
Charlotte, NC 28262-8522

Established in 2006 in NC.
Donors: Christa Oechsle; Walter Oechsle.
Foundation type: Independent foundation.
Financial data (yr. ended 12/31/13): Assets, $5,455,687 (M); gifts received, $1,600,000; expenditures, $713,557; qualifying distributions, $711,000; giving activities include $710,000 for 3 grants (high: $500,000; low: $60,000).
Fields of interest: Higher education; Health care; Cancer.
Limitations: Applications not accepted. Giving primarily in PA; some giving also in FL and MA. No grants to individuals.
Application information: Contributes only to pre-selected organizations.
Officers: Walter Oechsle, Pres. and Treas.; Christa Oechsle, V.P. and Secy.
EIN: 204852371

7279
Olin Corporation Charitable Trust

1525 W. W.T. Harris Blvd., D1114-044
Charlotte, NC 28262 (618) 258-2961
Contact: Susan Dona
Application address: 427 N. Shamrock St., East Alton, IL 62024, Tel.: (618) 258-2961

Established in 1945 in MO.
Donor: Olin Corp.
Foundation type: Company-sponsored foundation.
Financial data (yr. ended 06/30/14): Assets, $921,292 (M); gifts received, $500,000; expenditures, $671,197; qualifying distributions, $659,312; giving activities include $651,150 for 141 grants (high: $250,000; low: $50).
Purpose and activities: The foundation supports fire departments and organizations involved with arts and culture, education, health, youth development, human services, business promotion, and mining.
Fields of interest: Arts; Elementary school/education; Higher education; Education; Health care, patient services; Health care; Disasters, fire prevention/control; Youth development, business; Salvation Army; Children/youth, services; Human services; Community development, business promotion; United Ways and Federated Giving Programs; Geology.
Type of support: General/operating support; Continuing support; Annual campaigns; Capital campaigns; Building/renovation; Equipment; Program development; Curriculum development; Scholarship funds; Research; Employee matching gifts.
Limitations: Applications accepted. Giving primarily in areas of company operations in AL, IL, MO, SC, TN, and WA. No grants to individuals or for endowments; no loans.
Application information: Application form not required.
Initial approach: Proposal
Copies of proposal: 1
Deadline(s): None
Officers: Brenda M. Pantalone, Secy.; Thomas J. Fitgerald, Admin.
Trustees: Dennis R. MGough; George H. Pain; Wells Fargo Bank, N.A.
Number of staff: 1 full-time professional; 1 part-time support.
EIN: 436022750
Selected grants: The following grants are a representative sample of this grantmaker's funding activity:
$45,000 to United Way of Greater Saint Louis, Saint Louis, MO, 2011.
$5,450 to United Way of Bradley County, Cleveland, TN, 2011.
$5,000 to American Cancer Society, Atlanta, GA, 2011.
$5,000 to Saint Louis University, Saint Louis, MO, 2011.
$5,000 to Southern Illinois University, Edwardsville, IL, 2011.
$5,000 to United Way, Capital Area, Baton Rouge, LA, 2011.
$4,650 to Clark County School District, Las Vegas, NV, 2011.
$2,500 to University of Illinois Foundation, Urbana, IL, 2011.
$2,500 to University of Rochester, Rochester, NY, 2011.
$1,000 to Mary Bird Perkins Cancer Center, Baton Rouge, LA, 2011.

7280
P & B Foundation ✧
1025 Holleybank Dr.
Matthews, NC 28105-6531 (704) 821-3200
Contact: Larry C. Pratt, Pres. and Secy.

Established in 1970.
Donors: Kurt Cunningham; Pam Cunningham; C. Wilbur Peters; Eli Scholarship Fund; Grace Baptist Church; International Bible College; Providence Development Partners, LLC.
Foundation type: Independent foundation.
Financial data (yr. ended 08/31/13): Assets, $20,928,863 (M); expenditures, $663,456; qualifying distributions, $567,811; giving activities include $456,918 for 28 grants (high: $67,410; low: $100).
Purpose and activities: Giving primarily for Baptist church-related educational and religious institutions.
Fields of interest: Christian agencies & churches; Protestant agencies & churches.
Type of support: General/operating support; Program-related investments/loans.
Limitations: Applications accepted. Giving primarily in AL, NC, MO, OH and VA. No grants to individuals.
Application information: Application form required.
Initial approach: Letter
Deadline(s): None
Officers: Larry C. Pratt, Pres. and Secy.; C. Wilbur Peters, V.P. and Treas.
Directors: Roger Peterson; Barry Shearer.
EIN: 237083912

7281
Palm Beach Community Trust Fund ✧
1525 W. WT Harris Blvd., D1114-044
Charlotte, NC 28262

Established in 1955 in FL.
Donors: Cecil Hackett†; William Regan; Fisher Charitable Trust; Hackett Trust.
Foundation type: Independent foundation.
Financial data (yr. ended 12/31/13): Assets, $20,825,590 (M); expenditures, $941,553; qualifying distributions, $775,905; giving activities include $693,000 for 28 grants (high: $61,470; low: $1,000).
Fields of interest: Higher education; Human services.
Limitations: Applications not accepted. Giving primarily in FL, with some emphasis on West Palm Beach. No grants to individuals.
Application information: Contributes only to pre-selected organizations.
Trustee: Wells Fargo Bank, N.A.
EIN: 510144921
Selected grants: The following grants are a representative sample of this grantmaker's funding activity:
$68,000 to Bethune-Cookman University, Daytona Beach, FL, 2011.
$54,000 to Flagler College, Saint Augustine, FL, 2011.
$50,000 to Kenyon College, Gambier, OH, 2011.
$50,000 to Oberlin College, Oberlin, OH, 2011.
$45,000 to Rollins College, Winter Park, FL, 2011.
$34,000 to Palm Beach Atlantic University, West Palm Beach, FL, 2011.
$31,000 to Southwestern University, Georgetown, TX, 2011.
$30,600 to Bascom Palmer Eye Institute, Miami, FL, 2010.
$28,000 to Austin College, Sherman, TX, 2011.
$28,000 to Wittenberg University, Springfield, OH, 2011.
$14,000 to Cafe Joshua, West Palm Beach, FL, 2010.
$14,000 to South Florida Science Museum, West Palm Beach, FL, 2010.
$8,000 to Spectrum Healthcare Foundation, West Palm Beach, FL, 2010.
$4,000 to Boy Scouts of America, Palm Beach Gardens, FL, 2010.
$4,000 to Girl Scouts of the U.S.A., Jupiter, FL, 2010.

7282
James J. and Mamie R. Perkins Memorial Fund ✧
c/o Bank of America, N.A., P.C. Group
421 Fayetteville St. Mall, NC7-002-17-01
Raleigh, NC 27601-1792
Greenville, NC tel.: (252) 756-8888

Established in 1989 in NC.
Foundation type: Independent foundation.
Financial data (yr. ended 09/30/13): Assets, $12,573,807 (M); expenditures, $654,298; qualifying distributions, $580,310; giving activities include $512,280 for 19 grants (high: $71,129; low: $1,500).
Purpose and activities: Giving primarily for education and human services; funding also for an Episcopal church.
Fields of interest: Arts; Elementary/secondary education; Education; Human services; Community/economic development; Foundations (private grantmaking); Protestant agencies & churches.
Limitations: Applications accepted. Giving limited to Pitt County, NC, with strong emphasis on Greenville. No grants to individuals.
Application information: Application form required.
Initial approach: Letter or telephone requesting application form
Copies of proposal: 4
Deadline(s): None
Board meeting date(s): 1st Tues. of Feb., May, Aug., and Nov.
Officer and Director:* James G. Sullivan,* Chair.
Members: Robert Hudak; Danny McNally.
Trustee: Bank of America, N.A.
EIN: 566325764
Selected grants: The following grants are a representative sample of this grantmaker's funding activity:
$14,302 to Pitt County Educational Foundation, Greenville, NC, 2011.
$10,000 to Greenville Museum of Art, Greenville, NC, 2011.
$3,222 to Greenville Learning Center, Greenville, NC, 2011.

7283
The Pharmacy Network Foundation, Inc. ✧
P.O. Box 31603
Raleigh, NC 27622-1603 (919) 661-8461
Contact: Jimmy S. Jackson, Secy.-Treas.
Application address: 2015 Navan Ln., Garner, NC 27529

Donors: Pharmacy Network National Corp.; United Pharmacy Cooperative Inc.; Pharmacy Network National Corporation Trust.
Foundation type: Company-sponsored foundation.
Financial data (yr. ended 12/31/13): Assets, $17,744,719 (M); expenditures, $1,153,002; qualifying distributions, $835,204; giving activities include $785,000 for 10 grants (high: $625,000; low: $10,000).
Purpose and activities: The foundation supports organizations involved with education and health and awards college scholarships to pharmacy students enrolled at the University of North Carolina at Chapel Hill and Campbell University.
Fields of interest: Education.
Limitations: Applications accepted. Giving limited to NC and SC.
Application information: Application form required.
Initial approach: Letter
Copies of proposal: 1
Deadline(s): None
Board meeting date(s): 4th Tue. of each month
Officers: Mitchell W. Watts, Pres.; J. Andrew Barrett, V.P.; Jimmy S. Jackson, Secy.-Treas.
Directors: Jonathan A. Hill, Sr.; Julian E. Upchurch.
EIN: 561690027
Selected grants: The following grants are a representative sample of this grantmaker's funding activity:
$135,000 to Campbell University, School of Pharmacy, Buies Creek, NC, 2012. For building fund.
$125,000 to Wingate University, School of Pharmacy, Wingate, NC, 2012. For building fund.
$60,000 to Campbell University, School of Pharmacy, Buies Creek, NC, 2012. For Pharmacy Student Scholarships.
$60,000 to Wingate University, School of Pharmacy, Wingate, NC, 2012. For Pharmacy Student Scholarships.

7284
Samuel L. Phillips Family Foundation ✧
1525 W. WT Harris Blvd.
Charlotte, NC 28262-8522

Established in 2000 in NC.
Donors: Samuel L. Phillips; Jewel M. Phillips Irrevocable Trust; Samuel L. Phillips Revocable Trust.
Foundation type: Independent foundation.
Financial data (yr. ended 12/31/13): Assets, $13,409,069 (M); expenditures, $730,757; qualifying distributions, $625,173; giving activities include $588,034 for 18 grants (high: $300,000; low: $500).
Purpose and activities: Giving primarily for higher education and health care, particularly hospitals, and human services.
Fields of interest: Higher education; Hospitals (general); Health care; Human services.
Limitations: Applications not accepted. Giving primarily in NC, with some emphasis on Asheville and Spruce Pine. No grants to individuals, or for annual appeals, membership drives, unrestricted endowment funds, operating expenses, debt retirement of established organizations supported by the United Way, or recurring type grants.
Application information: Contributes only to pre-selected organizations.
Board meeting date(s): Summer (annually)
Officers: Gina A. Phillips, Pres.; Fred L. Stout, V.P.; Van Phillips, Secy.; G. Byron Phillips, Treas.
EIN: 562225556

Selected grants: The following grants are a representative sample of this grantmaker's funding activity:
$171,900 to Mayland Community College, Spruce Pine, NC, 2011. For general purpose.
$9,500 to North Carolina Stage Company, Asheville, NC, 2011. For general purpose.

7285
Piedmont Natural Gas Foundation ✧
4720 Piedmont Row Dr.
Charlotte, NC 28210-4269 (704) 731-4262
Contact: Timothy Greenhouse, Managing Dir., Community Rels.
FAX: (704) 731-4086;
E-mail: timothy.greenhouse@piedmontng.com;
Main URL: http://www.piedmontng.com/ourcommunity/ourfoundation.aspx

Established in 2004 in NC.
Donor: Piedmont Natural Gas Co., Inc.
Foundation type: Company-sponsored foundation.
Financial data (yr. ended 12/31/13): Assets, $7,767,974 (M); gifts received, $500,000; expenditures, $836,110; qualifying distributions, $828,862; giving activities include $761,382 for 99 grants (high: $93,000; low: $150).
Purpose and activities: The foundation supports programs designed to promote environmental stewardship and sustainability; K-12 science, technology, engineering, and math education; workforce development; health and human services; and energy assistance.
Fields of interest: Elementary/secondary education; Vocational education; Higher education, college (community/junior); Education, services; Education, reading; Environment, research; Environment, public policy; Environment, pollution control; Environment, natural resources; Environment, energy; Environmental education; Environment; Dental care; Pharmacy/prescriptions; Health care, patient services; Health care; Substance abuse, services; Mental health/crisis services; Crime/violence prevention; Employment, training; Employment, retraining; Employment; Housing/shelter, temporary shelter; Youth development, adult & child programs; Youth development; Children/youth, services; Developmentally disabled, centers & services; Homeless, human services; Human services; Economic development; United Ways and Federated Giving Programs; Mathematics; Engineering/technology; Science; Leadership development; Economically disadvantaged.
Type of support: Emergency funds; General/operating support; Continuing support; Management development/capacity building; Annual campaigns; Equipment; Program development; Curriculum development; Employee volunteer services.
Limitations: Applications accepted. Giving primarily in areas of company operations in NC, SC, and TN. No support for religious organizations not of direct benefit to the entire community, fraternal or political organizations, athletic organizations, private foundations, social or veterans' organizations, pre-college level private schools, third-party professional fundraising organizations, or private clubs. No grants to individuals, or for scholarships, travel or conferences, controversial social causes, athletic events or programs, or causes from which Piedmont Natural Gas will receive any benefit.
Publications: Application guidelines; Program policy statement.
Application information: Grants are assigned to Community Relations Managers based on the region the organization serves. Grants greater than $10,000 must be reviewed and approved by the board of directors during Foundation board meeting. Only competitive grants have a defined deadline that is specified during the Request for Proposal (RFP) process. Additional information may be requested at a later date. An interview or site visit may be requested. Application form required.
Initial approach: Complete online application form
Copies of proposal: 1
Deadline(s): 6 weeks prior to board meetings; June 28 for Environmental Stewardship & Energy Sustainability
Board meeting date(s): Apr., Aug., and Nov.
Officers and Directors:* Timothy Greenhouse, Chair. and Pres.; George Baldwin, V.P.; Jane R. Lewis-Raymond, Secy.; Robert O. Pritchard, Treas.; Kevin M. O'Hara; Minh Tran; David Trusty; Theresa VonCannon; Ranelle Warfield.
Trustee: Wells Fargo Bank, N.A.
EIN: 201786431

7286
Louis M. Plansoen Charitable Trust ✧ ☆
1525 W. W.T. Harris Blvd., D1114-044
Charlotte, NC 28262

Established in 1991 in PA.
Donor: Louis Plansoen‡.
Foundation type: Independent foundation.
Financial data (yr. ended 12/31/13): Assets, $13,626,945 (M); expenditures, $807,226; qualifying distributions, $737,641; giving activities include $689,769 for 22 grants (high: $300,000; low: $500).
Purpose and activities: Giving primarily to non-denominational or Protestant organizations for religious, charitable, scientific, literary, or educational purposes; giving also for the prevention of cruelty to children or animals and to hospitals whose principal function is providing medical care.
Fields of interest: Higher education; Animal welfare; Hospitals (general); Medical research, institute; Cancer research; Human services; Protestant agencies & churches.
Type of support: General/operating support.
Limitations: Applications not accepted. Giving primarily in NJ. No grants to individuals.
Application information: Unsolicited requests for funds not accepted.
Trustees: Hector L. Plansoen; Helen Post; Johanna Young; Wells Fargo Bank.
EIN: 226322826

7287
The Polk County Community Foundation, Inc. ✧
255 S. Trade St.
Tryon, NC 28782-3707 (828) 859-5314
Contact: Elizabeth Nager, Exec. Dir.; Cathie Campbell, Grants Mgr.
FAX: (828) 859-6122;
E-mail: foundation@polkccf.org; Additional E-mail: ccampbell@polkccf.org; Main URL: http://www.polkccf.org

Incorporated in 1975 in NC.
Foundation type: Community foundation.
Financial data (yr. ended 12/31/13): Assets, $49,417,348 (M); gifts received, $1,162,616; expenditures, $3,102,732; giving activities include $1,930,439 for 32+ grants (high: $120,322), and $314,228 for grants to individuals.
Purpose and activities: The foundation seeks to improve the quality of life in Polk County, NC, and Landrum, SC.
Fields of interest: Humanities; Arts; Education; Environment, natural resources; Health care; Human services; Community/economic development.
Type of support: General/operating support; Continuing support; Capital campaigns; Building/renovation; Equipment; Program development; Conferences/seminars; Publication; Seed money; Curriculum development; Internship funds; Scholarship funds; Scholarships—to individuals; Matching/challenge support.
Limitations: Applications accepted. Giving limited to Polk County, NC, and Landrum, SC. No grants to individuals (except for scholarships), or for debt reduction, medical research, courtesy advertising, benefit tickets, or telephone solicitations.
Publications: Application guidelines; Annual report; Financial statement; Informational brochure (including application guidelines); Occasional report.
Application information: Visit foundation web site for application form, guidelines, and specific deadlines. Faxed or incomplete applications are not accepted. Application form required.
Initial approach: Submit application form and attachments
Copies of proposal: 1
Deadline(s): Varies
Board meeting date(s): Mar., May, June, Sept., Oct., and Nov.
Final notification: Approx. 3 months
Officers and Directors:* Marcy Wright,* Chair.; Donald A. Eifert,* Vice-Chair.; Elizabeth Nager,* Pres. and C.E.O.; Frank Cannon,* Secy.; Sally McPherson,* Treas.; Melanie Campbell-Cobb; Norma Powers; Marilyn Ochs; Kathy Taft; Lois Tirre; Sherril L. Wingo.
Number of staff: 1 full-time professional; 2 part-time professional; 1 full-time support.
EIN: 510168751

7288
John William Pope Foundation ✧
4601 Six Forks Rd., Ste. 300
Raleigh, NC 27609-5271 (919) 861-6445
Contact: James Arthur Pope, Pres.
FAX: (919) 790-9526; E-mail: info@jwpf.org; Main URL: http://www.jwpf.org/
Facebook: https://www.facebook.com/PopeFoundation
Twitter: https://twitter.com/PopeFoundation
YouTube: http://www.youtube.com/user/PopeFoundation

Established in 1986 in NC.
Donor: Members of the Pope family.
Foundation type: Independent foundation.
Financial data (yr. ended 06/30/13): Assets, $145,867,004 (M); expenditures, $10,544,990; qualifying distributions, $9,841,966; giving activities include $9,704,808 for 146 grants (high: $1,000,000; low: $2,500).
Fields of interest: Education; Public policy, research.

Limitations: Applications accepted. Giving primarily in Washington, DC, NC, and VA. No grants to individuals.
Application information: Application guidelines available on foundation web site. Application form not required.
Initial approach: Online application
Deadline(s): Jan. 1
Officers and Directors:* James Arthur Pope,* Chair.; Amanda Joyce Pope,* Vice-Chair.; David W. Riggs, Exec. V.P.; Joyce W. Pope; David Stover.
EIN: 581691765
Selected grants: The following grants are a representative sample of this grantmaker's funding activity:
$1,000,000 to Americans for Prosperity Foundation, Arlington, VA, 2013. For general operating support.
$1,000,000 to University of North Carolina Educational Foundation, Chapel Hill, NC, 2013. For JWP Student Athlete Academic Support Center.
$300,000 to Campbell University, Norman Adrian Wiggins School of Law, Buies Creek, NC, 2013. For Law School building.
$250,000 to Institute for Humane Studies, Arlington, VA, 2013. For capital campaign.
$212,459 to John Locke Foundation, Raleigh, NC, 2013. For general operating support.
$212,459 to John Locke Foundation, Raleigh, NC, 2013. For general operating support.
$140,000 to North Carolina State University, Raleigh, NC, 2013. For Public Choice, Law and Economics.
$115,000 to John William Pope Civitas Institute, Raleigh, NC, 2013. For general operating support.
$50,000 to Institute for Humane Studies, Arlington, VA, 2013. For NC scholarships.
$45,234 to John William Pope Center for Higher Education Policy, Raleigh, NC, 2013. For general operating support.

7289
John A. and Margaret Post Foundation ✧
1525 W. WT Harris Blvd., D1114-044
Charlotte, NC 28262-8522

Established in 1997 in NJ.
Donors: John A. Post; Margaret Post.
Foundation type: Independent foundation.
Financial data (yr. ended 12/31/13): Assets, $23,577,869 (M); gifts received, $2,085,353; expenditures, $1,200,879; qualifying distributions, $1,030,124; giving activities include $1,028,124 for 42 grants (high: $406,287; low: $2,000).
Purpose and activities: Giving primarily to Roman Catholic schools and churches, as well as to human services, and federated giving programs.
Fields of interest: Arts; Education; Human services; United Ways and Federated Giving Programs; Catholic agencies & churches.
Limitations: Applications not accepted. Giving primarily in NJ, with emphasis on Newton and Sparta. No grants to individuals.
Application information: Contributes only to pre-selected organizations.
Officers and Trustees:* John A. Post, Pres.; Margaret Post, V.P.; Heather Villone,* Secy.-Treas.; John Post; Rich Villone.
EIN: 223401833
Selected grants: The following grants are a representative sample of this grantmaker's funding activity:
$25,000 to Christian Health Care Center Foundation, Wyckoff, NJ, 2012. For Longview Living Res/Courtyard for Memory I.
$25,000 to Zoological Society of New Jersey, West Orange, NJ, 2012. For New Sea Lion Exhibit.
$9,000 to Learning Center for Exceptional Children, Clifton, NJ, 2012. For Ada Compliant Wheelchair Accessible Elevator.

7290
Lynn R. and Karl E. Prickett Fund ✧
c/o Piedmont Financial Trust Co.
P.O. Box 20124
Greensboro, NC 27420-0124

Established in 1964 in NC.
Donor: Lynn R. Prickett†.
Foundation type: Independent foundation.
Financial data (yr. ended 06/30/13): Assets, $11,078,838 (M); expenditures, $661,286; qualifying distributions, $600,000; giving activities include $600,000 for grants.
Fields of interest: Education; Human services; Children/youth, services; Foundations (community).
Type of support: General/operating support.
Limitations: Applications not accepted. Giving in the U.S., with emphasis CA, HI, NC and NY.
Application information: Contributes only to pre-selected organizations.
Trustees: Samuel C. Chapin; Lynn C. Gunzenhauser; Katherine Kessner; Meta McDaniel; Lisa V. Prochnow.
EIN: 566064788
Selected grants: The following grants are a representative sample of this grantmaker's funding activity:
$10,000 to Inland Northwest Land Trust, Spokane, WA, 2013. To Assist Each Organization in Carrying Out Its Exempt Purpose.

7291
Provident Benevolent Foundation ✧
(formerly Providence Charitable Foundation)
c/o Wachovia Bank, N.A.
1525 W. WT Harris Blvd.
Charlotte, NC 28288-5709
E-mail: rachel.reilly@wachovia.com

Established in 1989 in NC.
Donors: Jesse J. Thompson†; Sylvia Thompson.
Foundation type: Independent foundation.
Financial data (yr. ended 06/30/14): Assets, $25,020,815 (M); gifts received, $634,950; expenditures, $1,218,135; qualifying distributions, $924,661; giving activities include $856,025 for 69 grants (high: $40,384; low: $2,500).
Purpose and activities: Giving primarily for education, health, and human services.
Fields of interest: Arts; Education; Environment, natural resources; Hospitals (general); Human services; Children/youth, services.
Type of support: General/operating support.
Limitations: Applications not accepted. Giving limited to NC and TN. No grants for endowments or deficit financing.
Application information: Contributes only to pre-selected organizations.
Board meeting date(s): Oct. (annually)
EIN: 581881092
Selected grants: The following grants are a representative sample of this grantmaker's funding activity:
$15,000 to Winston-Salem Industries for the Blind, Winston-Salem, NC, 2011.
$10,000 to Safe Alliance, Charlotte, NC, 2011.

7292
Randleigh Foundation Trust ✧
c/o Thomas S. Kenan III
P.O. Box 4150
Chapel Hill, NC 27515-4150

Established in 1965 in NY.
Donor: William R. Kenan, Jr.†.
Foundation type: Independent foundation.
Financial data (yr. ended 03/31/13): Assets, $23,936,890 (M); expenditures, $1,008,900; qualifying distributions, $954,000; giving activities include $954,000 for grants.
Purpose and activities: Giving primarily for education and the arts.
Fields of interest: Performing arts, theater; Arts; Higher education; Education; Christian agencies & churches.
Type of support: General/operating support; Continuing support.
Limitations: Applications not accepted. Giving primarily in KY and NC; some giving also in RI. No grants to individuals.
Application information: Contributes only to pre-selected organizations.
Board meeting date(s): Annually
Trustees: Annice H. Kenan; James G. Kenan III; Thomas S. Kenan III; Garrett Kirk, Jr.
Number of staff: None.
EIN: 136207897
Selected grants: The following grants are a representative sample of this grantmaker's funding activity:
$50,000 to North Carolina State University, Raleigh, NC, 2013. To provide funding for the university's capital campaign related to improvements to the school's dairy research and teaching farm.
$35,000 to Duplin County Board of Education, Kenansville, NC, 2013. For assistance with general operating expenses and the restoration of Liberty Hall.
$35,000 to Kentucky Educational Television, Lexington, KY, 2013. To provide funds to support the Programs and services of the state of Kentucky's public media organization.
$25,000 to Colorado College, Colorado Springs, CO, 2013. For $5,000 grant was to supplement the college's public interest fellowship Program $20,000 grant was for the President's discretionary fund which provides support to student projects.
$25,000 to Gordon School, East Providence, RI, 2013. For $20,000 grant was provided to the school's capital campaign to assist with needed facility improvements $5,000 grant was provided to the discretionary fund controlled by the school librarian for use in improving library resources.
$25,000 to Woodberry Forest School, Woodberry Forest, VA, 2013. To provide funding for the school's Hill Brown Concert Fund The fund enables the school to sponsor annual organ concert in the chapel utilizing the Kenan Fisk Organ.
$20,000 to Williams College, Williamstown, MA, 2013. To provide funding to support the school's drama and art departments as well as to supplement the annual operating budget.

$10,000 to Crossroads Rhode Island, Providence, RI, 2013. To provide operating funds to support Programs providing basic emergency needs to homeless or at-risk Rhode Islanders.
$10,000 to Henry Morrison Flagler Museum, Palm Beach, FL, 2013. To provide funds to support the museum's music series.
$10,000 to Ounce of Prevention Fund, Chicago, IL, 2013. To provide funding for the organization's home Program which provides child-development and parenting advice to help teen parents create safe and stimulating home environments, and ensure families are connected to medical, dental, mental-health, and other su.

7293
Rasmuson Endowment Trust for the Boy Scouts of America in Alaska ✧

c/o Wells Fargo Bank, N.A., Tax Trust Dept
1 W. 4th St., 4th Fl., MAC D4000-041
Winston-Salem, NC 27101-3818

Established in 2001 in AK; supporting organization of Great Alaska Council, Midnight Sun Council, and Southeast Alaska Area Council.
Donor: Elmer Rasmuson‡.
Foundation type: Independent foundation.
Financial data (yr. ended 12/31/13): Assets, $10,388,589 (M); expenditures, $558,312; qualifying distributions, $474,610; giving activities include $453,523 for 2 grants (high: $284,607; low: $168,916).
Fields of interest: Boy scouts.
Type of support: General/operating support.
Limitations: Applications not accepted. Giving limited to AK. No grants to individuals.
Application information: Contributes only to pre-selected organizations.
Trustee: Wells Fargo Bank, N.A.
EIN: 926031574
Selected grants: The following grants are a representative sample of this grantmaker's funding activity:
$288,628 to Boy Scouts of America, Great Alaska Counsil, Anchorage, AK, 2012. For general support grant.
$157,244 to Boy Scouts of America, Midnight Sun Counsil, Fairbanks, AK, 2012. For general support grant.

7294
Reidsville Area Foundation ✧

124 S. Scales St.
Reidsville, NC 27320-3834
Contact: R. Craig Cardwell, Exec. Dir.
E-mail: rafoundation@bellsouth.net; Main URL: http://www.rafoundation.org
Flickr: https://www.flickr.com/photos/40088270@N08/

Established in 2001 in NC.
Foundation type: Independent foundation.
Financial data (yr. ended 09/30/13): Assets, $32,850,850 (M); gifts received, $6,150; expenditures, $1,875,111; qualifying distributions, $1,773,809; giving activities include $1,518,149 for 73 grants (high: $635,000; low: $250).
Purpose and activities: The foundation provides financial support to programs and initiatives which improve the health, wellness, education, and quality of life of Rockingham County, North Carolina citizens.
Fields of interest: Education; Health care; Infants/toddlers; Children/youth; Youth; Adults; Aging; Young adults; Disabilities, people with; Physically disabled; Mentally disabled; African Americans/Blacks; Hispanics/Latinos; Women; Men; Adults, men; Offenders/ex-offenders; Substance abusers; Single parents; Crime/abuse victims; Terminal illness, people with; Economically disadvantaged; Homeless.
Type of support: Technical assistance; Program evaluation; Continuing support; Consulting services; Capital campaigns; General/operating support; Management development/capacity building; Building/renovation; Equipment; Emergency funds; Program development; Matching/challenge support.
Limitations: Applications accepted. Giving limited to Rockingham County, NC. No support for individual religious or political organizations. No grants to individuals, or for medical research.
Publications: Application guidelines; Grants list.
Application information: Full grant applications are by invitation, only after review of initial Letter of Interest. Application guidelines and forms available on foundation web site. Application form required.
Initial approach: Use Letter of Interest form on foundation web site, or e-mail or telephone for form
Copies of proposal: 1
Deadline(s): Feb. 15 for Letter of Interest; Apr. 1 for Grant Application
Board meeting date(s): June
Final notification: June
Officers: Donna Rothrock, Chair.; Jacob Balsley III, Vice-Chair.; Lafayette Judkins, DDS, Secy.; J. Wayne Keeling, M.D., Treas.; R. Craig Cardwell, Exec. Dir.
Directors: Victor Armstrong; James L. Burston, Ph.D.; Malcolm N. Clark, CPA; Jonathan W. Craig, Jr.; Leon Niegelsky, Jr.; Kenneth G. Norman; J. Scottie Penn; Joe M. Walker, Jr.; Ann D. Willis; Edwin G. Wilson, Jr.
Number of staff: 2 full-time professional.
EIN: 562255809
Selected grants: The following grants are a representative sample of this grantmaker's funding activity:
$7,500 to CenterPoint Human Services, Winston-Salem, NC, 2011.
$7,500 to CenterPoint Human Services, Winston-Salem, NC, 2011.
$6,250 to North Carolina Dental Health Fund, Cary, NC, 2011.
$4,000 to Special Olympics of North Carolina, Morrisville, NC, 2011.

7295
John Rex Endowment ✧

712 W. North St.
Raleigh, NC 27603-1419 (919) 838-1110
Contact: Kevin Cain, C.E.O. and Pres.
E-mail: info@rexendowment.org; Main URL: http://www.rexendowment.org

Established in 2000 in NC; converted from the result of an acquisition of Rex Healthcare.
Foundation type: Independent foundation.
Financial data (yr. ended 12/31/12): Assets, $71,066,233 (M); expenditures, $4,021,206; qualifying distributions, $3,334,715; giving activities include $2,346,986 for 27 grants (high: $371,563; low: $9,570).
Purpose and activities: Giving primarily for healthy weight, injury prevention, mental health, social and emotional well-being, and nonprofit capacity building for children and families in the Wake County, NC, area.
Fields of interest: Health care; Children/youth.
Type of support: Management development/capacity building; Program development; Seed money; Technical assistance; Program evaluation.
Limitations: Applications accepted. Giving limited to Wake, NC and surrounding counties.
Publications: Application guidelines; Annual report; Grants list; Occasional report.
Application information: Application form required.
Initial approach: Use online Grant Management System on foundation web site
Board meeting date(s): Jan., July, and Oct.
Officers and Directors:* Sherry Worth,* Chair.; Jill Wright, M.D.*, Vice-Chair.; Kevin M. Cain,* C.E.O. and Pres.; Virginia Parker,* Secy.; Larry D. Barbour,* Treas.; Linda Butler, M.D.; Janet Cowell; Dick Daugherty; Jill Wells Heath; Tom McGuire; Cathy Moore; Deborah Nelson; George Reed; Ramon Rojano; Jimmy Talton.
Number of staff: 3 full-time professional; 1 part-time professional.
EIN: 311678223

7296
Reynolds American Foundation ✧

(formerly R. J. Reynolds Foundation)
Plaza Bldg., 15th Fl.
P.O. Box 891
Winston-Salem, NC 27102-2959 (336) 741-0106
Contact: Alan Caldwell, Exec. Dir.
E-mail: caldwea1@rjrt.com; Main URL: http://www.rjrt.com/fndnguide.aspx

Established in 1986 in NC.
Donors: RJR Nabisco Holdings Corp.; R.J. Reynolds Tobacco Co.; Nabisco Brands, Inc.; Planters LifeSavers Co.; RJR Tobacco Intl.; RJR Acquisition Corp.; Reynolds American.
Foundation type: Company-sponsored foundation.
Financial data (yr. ended 12/31/12): Assets, $65,885,114 (M); expenditures, $4,461,067; qualifying distributions, $4,125,057; giving activities include $3,633,835 for 42 grants (high: $1,252,142; low: $358), and $465,667 for 397 employee matching gifts.
Purpose and activities: The foundation supports organizations involved with arts and culture, education, community development, and economically disadvantaged people.
Fields of interest: Arts councils; Arts; Child development, education; Elementary school/education; Higher education; Education; American Red Cross; YM/YWCAs & YM/YWHAs; Community/economic development; United Ways and Federated Giving Programs; Economically disadvantaged.
Type of support: Continuing support; Annual campaigns; Capital campaigns; Program development; Scholarship funds; Employee matching gifts; Employee-related scholarships.
Limitations: Applications accepted. Giving primarily in areas of company operations in KY and NC. No support for churches or religious organizations not of direct benefit to the entire community, political candidates or organizations, individual day-care centers, or discriminatory organizations. No grants to individuals (except for employee-related

scholarships), or for endowments, general operating support, travel expenses, or sponsorships.
Publications: Application guidelines.
Application information: Proposals should be no longer than 5 pages. Support is limited to 1 contribution per organization during any given year. Application form not required.
Initial approach: Proposal
Deadline(s): Feb. 1, May 1, Aug. 1, and Nov. 1
Board meeting date(s): Quarterly
Final notification: Mar. 31, June 30, Sept. 30, and Dec. 31
Officers and Directors: John S. (Tripp) Wilson, Pres.; William Nance, V.P.; Fred W. Franklin, Secy.; Dan A. Fawley, Treas.; Alan L. Caldwell, Exec. Dir.; Robert H. Dunham; Nancy H. Hawley; Nancy G. Sturgeon.
Number of staff: 1 full-time professional; 1 full-time support.
EIN: 581681920

7297
Kate B. Reynolds Charitable Trust ✧

(also known as KBR Charitable Trust)
128 Reynolda Village
Winston-Salem, NC 27106-5123 (336) 397-5500
Contact: Karen McNeil-Miller, Pres.; Allen Smart, Dir., Health Care Div.; Joe Crocker, Dir., Poor and Needy Div.
FAX: (336) 723-7765; Toll free tel.: 1-800-485-9080; E-mail for Joe Crocker: joe@kbr.org, e-mail for Allen Smart: Allen@kbr.org; Main URL: http://www.kbr.org
Facebook: https://www.facebook.com/KateBReynoldsTrust
Google Plus: https://plus.google.com/107849778428160345243/about
Kate B. Reynolds Charitable Trust's Philanthropy Promise: http://www.ncrp.org/philanthropys-promise/who
Twitter: http://twitter.com/KateBReynolds

Established in 1947 in NC.
Donor: Kate B. Reynolds†.
Foundation type: Independent foundation.
Financial data (yr. ended 08/31/13): Assets, $532,506,481 (M); expenditures, $28,180,298; qualifying distributions, $25,613,545; giving activities include $22,753,821 for 222 grants (high: $773,728; low: $5,000), and $549,926 for foundation-administered programs.
Purpose and activities: To improve the quality of life and quality of health for the financially needy of North Carolina. The trust accomplishes its work through its two divisions. The Health Care Division and The Poor and Needy Division.
Fields of interest: Education, early childhood education; Middle schools/education; Education; Health care, clinics/centers; Health care, rural areas; Public health, obesity; Health care; Health care, insurance; Substance abuse, services; Mental health, treatment; Mental health/crisis services; Housing/shelter; Human services; Community/economic development.
Type of support: Capital campaigns; Building/renovation; Equipment; Program development; Seed money; Technical assistance; Program evaluation; Matching/challenge support.
Limitations: Applications accepted. Giving limited to NC; Poor and Needy Division limited to Forsyth County; Health Care Division, statewide. No grants to individuals, or for endowment funds or medical research; grants on a highly selective basis for construction of facilities or purchase of equipment.
Publications: Application guidelines; Financial statement; Grants list; Newsletter; Occasional report; Program policy statement.
Application information: Applicants should contact the trust staff to discuss the proposal prior to submitting a written application. Advance consultation is required before an application can be accepted for consideration. Applications will only be accepted online. Application form required.
Initial approach: Telephone inquiry, then in-person advance consult. For the Poor and Needy Division, call to schedule a meeting with a program officer. For the Health Care Division, contact the program associate to discuss your idea and determine if an advance consultation makes sense
Copies of proposal: 1
Deadline(s): 2nd Tues. in Feb. and in Aug.
Final notification: May and Nov.
Trustee: Wells Fargo Bank, N.A.
Officers: Karen McNeil-Miller, Pres.; Allen J. Smart, V.P., Progs.
Number of staff: 11 full-time professional; 1 part-time professional; 3 full-time support.
EIN: 566036515
Selected grants: The following grants are a representative sample of this grantmaker's funding activity:
$3,025,763 to North Carolina Hospital Foundation, Cary, NC, 2014. For Mobile Medication Program, payable over 3.00 years.
$1,484,430 to North Carolina Public Health Foundation, Raleigh, NC, 2014. For Community Transformation Catalyst, payable over 3.00 years.
$1,383,628 to North Carolina Foundation for Advanced Health Programs, Cary, NC, 2013. For community care of North Carolina chronic pain initiative, payable over 2.00 years.
$964,560 to Forsyth County Health Department, Winston-Salem, NC, 2014. For Cleveland Avenue Dental Center Growth and Sustainability Project, payable over 2.00 years.
$773,728 to North Carolina Department of Health and Human Services, Raleigh, NC, 2013. For medication assistance program.
$745,929 to University of North Carolina, Chapel Hill, NC, 2013. For Healthy IDEAS (Identifying Depression, Empowering Activities for Seniors) North Carolina, payable over 3.00 years.
$697,429 to KaBOOM, Washington, DC, 2013. For eliminating play deserts in Beaufort, McDowell, and Halifax Counties.
$519,458 to North Carolina Foundation for Advanced Health Programs, Cary, NC, 2014. For Center of Excellence for Integrated Care (COE), payable over 2.00 years.
$500,000 to Winston-Salem State University Foundation, Winston-Salem, NC, 2013. For Student Success Center at Winston-Salem State University, payable over 2.00 years.
$412,094 to University of North Carolina, Chapel Hill, NC, 2014. For a partnership between emergency medical services and community medicine for improving health and reducing costs for patients with behavioral health emergencies, payable over 2.00 years.
$398,198 to Winston-Salem/Forsyth County Board of Education, Winston-Salem/Forsyth County Schools, Winston-Salem, NC, 2014. For Ready Schools Coordinator, payable over 3.00 years.
$325,478 to East Carolina University, Greenville, NC, 2013. For Tele-TEAM Care: Bringing the Healthcare Team to Needy Diabetic Patients in Underserved Rural Communities, payable over 2.00 years.
$296,175 to Guilford Adult Health, Greensboro, NC, 2013. For integrative behavioral health and primary care within a patient-centered medical home, payable over 2.00 years.
$236,500 to Winston-Salem/Forsyth County Board of Education, Winston-Salem/Forsyth County Schools, Winston-Salem, NC, 2014. For Great Expectations Initiative.
$232,100 to Mental Health Fund, Hickory, NC, 2014. For Project Enhance, payable over 3.00 years.
$192,500 to Building Educated Leaders for Life Foundation, Dorchester, MA, 2013. For Winston-Salem/Forsyth County Schools and BELL Summer Scholars Program.
$137,500 to North Carolina Justice Center, Raleigh, NC, 2013. For building support for Medicaid expansion and ensuring full enrollment in targeted tier one counties.
$130,310 to Enfield, Town of, Parks and Recreation, Enfield, NC, 2014. For enhancing physical activity opportunities in Enfield.
$110,000 to Crosby Scholars Community Partnership, Winston-Salem, NC, 2014. For last dollar grant funding for needy Crosby Scholars.
$83,685 to Roanoke Rapids, City of, Department of Parks and Recreation, Roanoke Rapids, NC, 2013. For Rosemary Mill Village revitalization — Ledgerwood Park.

7298
Z. Smith Reynolds Foundation, Inc. ✧

102 W. 3rd St., Ste. 1110
Winston-Salem, NC 27101-3962 (336) 725-7541
FAX: (336) 725-6069; E-mail: info@zsr.org; Additional tel.: (800) 443-8319; Main URL: http://www.zsr.org
Twitter: https://twitter.com/ZSRFoundation
Vimeo: http://vimeo.com/user18238620
Z. Smith Reynolds Foundation's Philanthropy Promise: http://www.ncrp.org/philanthropys-promise/who

Incorporated in 1936 in NC.
Donors: Nancy S. Reynolds†; Mary Reynolds Babcock†; Richard J. Reynolds, Jr.†; William N. Reynolds†.
Foundation type: Independent foundation.
Financial data (yr. ended 12/31/13): Assets, $16,687,410 (M); gifts received, $18,033,512; expenditures, $17,965,118; qualifying distributions, $17,949,903; giving activities include $14,887,673 for 244 grants (high: $645,000; low: $1,600), $16,285 for employee matching gifts, and $464,775 for foundation-administered programs.
Purpose and activities: The goals of the foundation are: 1) to promote social, economic and environmental justice; 2) to strengthen democracy, through an educated and informed populace; 3) to encourage innovation and excellence in a dynamic nonprofit sector; 4) to support progressive public policy and social change; 5) to foster cooperation and respect among all racial, ethnic, and socio-economic groups; and 6) to build strong, vibrant, economically sound, and peaceful communities. To accomplish its purpose, the foundation currently gives special attention to certain focus areas: community and economic development; environment; democracy and civic engagement; pre-collegiate education; and social

justice and equity (with an emphasis on women and families).
Fields of interest: Education, early childhood education; Child development, education; Elementary school/education; Secondary school/education; Education; Environment, natural resources; Environment; Crime/violence prevention, youth; Crime/violence prevention, domestic violence; Legal services; Housing/shelter, public housing; Women, centers/services; Minorities/immigrants, centers/services; Civil/human rights, formal/general education; Civil/human rights, minorities; Civil/human rights, women; Civil rights, race/intergroup relations; Civil liberties, reproductive rights; Civil/human rights; Rural development; Community/economic development; Voluntarism promotion; Public policy, research; Public affairs, citizen participation; Leadership development; Public affairs; Minorities; African Americans/Blacks; Hispanics/Latinos; Native Americans/American Indians; Women.
Type of support: General/operating support; Continuing support; Program development; Publication; Seed money; Technical assistance; Employee matching gifts; Matching/challenge support.
Limitations: Applications accepted. Giving limited to NC. No support for athletic teams, civic clubs, day care centers, fraternal groups, parent/teachers associations, private K-12 schools, single site public schools, volunteer fire departments, or emergency medical service organizations, art organizations, historic preservation organizations, homeless shelters, or health care (physical and mental health). No grants to individuals (except for Nancy Susan Reynolds Awards and Sabbatical Program), or for endowment funds, equipment purchases, research, athletic events, building projects or renovations (including construction materials and labor costs), capital campaigns, computer hardware or software purchases (where it is the principal purpose of the grant), conferences, seminars, symposiums, fundraising events, initiatives promoting religious education or doctrine, land purchases, payment of debts, salaries for personnel or other general operating expenses in public schools, or after-school programs. Additionally, no grants for adoption and foster care, annual species preservation or rehabilitation, crisis intervention, greenways, senior citizen services, social/human direct services, substance abuse treatment, transitional housing, or treatment or rehabilitation.
Publications: Annual report (including application guidelines); Informational brochure; Informational brochure (including application guidelines); Occasional report.
Application information: Application form available online. Fax, email or letter applications will not be accepted. Application form required.
Initial approach: Letter or telephone for specifics. Review the foundation's web site and then telephone for questions not answered by online resources. All applications must be submitted using the foundation's online application system
Copies of proposal: 1
Deadline(s): For grants, Feb. 1 and Aug. 1; for Sabbatical Program, Nov.
Board meeting date(s): 3rd Fri. in May and Nov.
Final notification: 4 months after deadline
Officers and Trustees:* David L. Neal,* Pres.; Nancy R. Bagley,* V.P.; Lloyd P. Tate, Jr.,* Pres.; Leslie J. Winner, Secy. and Exec. Dir.; John O. McNairy,* Treas.; Katharine B. Mountcastle, Life Tr.; Anita Brown-Graham; Daniel G. Clodfelter; Ilana Dubester; Mary Mountcastle; Stephen L. Neal; Jane S. Patterson; W. Noah Reynolds; Virgil L. Smith; Lloyd P. Tate, Jr.
Number of staff: 7 full-time professional; 1 part-time professional; 6 full-time support.
EIN: 586038145
Selected grants: The following grants are a representative sample of this grantmaker's funding activity:
$3,870,000 to North Carolina Justice Center, Raleigh, NC, 2013. For general operating support.
$1,200,000 to Wake Forest University, Winston-Salem, NC, 2012. For Annual grant, under 1990 contract, for general support, faculty development, and scholarships.
$1,200,000 to Wake Forest University, Winston-Salem, NC, 2013. For Annual grant, under 1990 contract, for general support, faculty development, and scholarships.
$720,000 to Southern Environmental Law Center, Chapel Hill, NC, 2012. For general operating support.
$600,000 to Democracy North Carolina, Durham, NC, 2013. For general operating support.
$600,000 to North Carolina Center for Nonprofits, Raleigh, NC, 2013. For general operating support.
$525,000 to North Carolina Conservation Network, Raleigh, NC, 2013. For general operating support.
$400,000 to Blueprint North Carolina, Raleigh, NC, 2012. For general operating support.
$400,000 to Democracy North Carolina, Durham, NC, 2012. For general operating support.
$375,000 to Legal Aid of North Carolina, Raleigh, NC, 2013. For Home Defense Project.
$375,000 to Planned Parenthood Health Systems, Raleigh, NC, 2012. For general operating support.
$250,000 to Latino Community Development Center, Durham, NC, 2013. For Immigrant Integration Project.
$200,000 to Southern Coalition for Social Justice, Durham, NC, 2012. For general operating support.
$150,000 to Adolescent Pregnancy Prevention Coalition of North Carolina, Durham, NC, 2012. For general operating support.
$110,000 to University of North Carolina, Pembroke, NC, 2013. For School of Education - PREP (Partnership for the Retention of Education Professionals) Project.
$60,000 to University of North Carolina, Pembroke, NC, 2012. For PREP — (Partnership for the Retention of Education Professionals).
$50,000 to Franklin-Vance-Warren Opportunity, Henderson, NC, 2012. For Women's Economic Equity (WEE) Project.
$50,000 to Western North Carolina Alliance, Asheville, NC, 2012. For general operating support.
$40,000 to North Carolina Rural Economic Development Center, Raleigh, NC, 2013. For Pipeline to Success Project.
$30,000 to Neuse River Foundation, New Bern, NC, 2013. For general operating support.

7299
Richard J. and Marie Mallouk Reynolds III Foundation ✧
P.O. Box 29522
Raleigh, NC 27626-0522

Established in 1995 in NC.
Donor: Richard J. Reynolds III†.
Foundation type: Independent foundation.
Financial data (yr. ended 06/30/13): Assets, $16,255,561 (M); expenditures, $850,830; qualifying distributions, $675,000; giving activities include $675,000 for grants.
Purpose and activities: Giving primarily for health organizations and human services, as well as to a YMCA.
Fields of interest: Hospitals (general); Health organizations; Human services; YM/YWCAs & YM/YWHAs; Residential/custodial care, hospices.
Type of support: Building/renovation.
Limitations: Applications not accepted. Giving primarily in NC, with emphasis on Winston-Salem. No grants to individuals.
Application information: Contributes only to pre-selected organizations.
Committee Members: Judge Robert A. Collier, Jr.; M. Robinson; N. Robinson.
Trustee: First Citizens Bank.
EIN: 561925457
Selected grants: The following grants are a representative sample of this grantmaker's funding activity:
$25,000 to Iredell Christian Ministries, Statesville, NC, 2013. For Providing Care for Sick, Aged Or Helpless.

7300
H. Smith Richardson Charitable Trust ✧
(formerly Randolph Foundation)
701 Green Valley Rd., Ste. 300
Greensboro, NC 27408-7096

Trust established in 1976 in NC.
Donors: H. Smith Richardson†; Smith Richardson Foundation, Inc.
Foundation type: Independent foundation.
Financial data (yr. ended 12/31/13): Assets, $62,966,711 (M); expenditures, $2,992,249; qualifying distributions, $2,824,703; giving activities include $2,292,000 for grants.
Purpose and activities: Primary areas of interest include the study and research of cultural values and civic virtues.
Fields of interest: Higher education; Social sciences; Public affairs.
Type of support: Publication; Research.
Limitations: Applications not accepted. Giving primarily in NC. No grants to individuals.
Application information: Contributes only to pre-selected organizations.
Trustees: Nicolas Richardson; Peter L. Richardson; Tyler B. Richardson; E. William Stetson III.
Number of staff: 1 full-time professional; 2 full-time support.
EIN: 237245123

7301
Grace Jones Richardson Testamentary Trust ✧
(formerly Grace Jones Richardson Trust)
c/o Piedmont Financial Trust Co.
P.O. Box 20124
Greensboro, NC 27420-0124

Trust established in 1962 in CT.
Donors: Grace Jones Richardson†; Smith Richardson Foundation.
Foundation type: Independent foundation.
Financial data (yr. ended 12/31/13): Assets, $98,953,122 (M); gifts received, $584,000;

expenditures, $2,123,565; qualifying distributions, $1,871,590; giving activities include $1,689,500 for 426 grants (high: $55,000; low: $1,000).
Purpose and activities: Giving primarily for the arts, education, environmental conservation, health care, and human services.
Fields of interest: Museums (art); Arts; Elementary/secondary education; Higher education; Education; Environment, natural resources; Animals/wildlife, preservation/protection; Health care; Human services; United Ways and Federated Giving Programs; Christian agencies & churches.
Type of support: General/operating support.
Limitations: Applications not accepted. Giving primarily in CO, CT, Washington DC, NC and NY. No grants to individuals.
Application information: Unsolicited requests for funds not accepted. Contributes only to pre-selected organizations.
Board meeting date(s): As required
Trustees: P.L. Richardson; S.S. Richardson; Tyler B. Richardson.
EIN: 066023003

7302
Richmond Community Foundation, Inc. ✧
220 N. Tryon St.
Charlotte, NC 28202-2137 (704) 973-4500

Established in 2001 in NC.
Donors: Richmond Memorial Hospital Foundation; First Union National Bank.
Foundation type: Independent foundation.
Financial data (yr. ended 12/31/12): Assets, $26,929,111 (M); expenditures, $2,047,887; qualifying distributions, $1,933,219; giving activities include $1,800,000 for 7 grants (high: $1,400,000; low: $10,000).
Fields of interest: Education; Health care; Children/youth, services.
Limitations: Applications accepted. Giving primarily in the Richmond County, NC, area. No grants to individuals.
Application information: Application form required.
Deadline(s): Varies
Officers and Directors:* Russell E. Bennett, Jr.,* Chair.; John J. Jackson,* Secy.; Betty Dorsett; Robert E. Hutchinson; Franklin Clay Jenkins; Paul R. Smart; Roger Staley; Bruce Stanback.
EIN: 562168849
Selected grants: The following grants are a representative sample of this grantmaker's funding activity:
$250,000 to Richmond County Health Department, Rockingham, NC, 2012. For Richmond County Care Clinic.
$45,000 to Richmond County Board of Commissioners, Rockingham, NC, 2012. For general program expenses.
$15,000 to Richmond Community College Foundation, Hamlet, NC, 2012. For education and scholarship Programs.

7303
Roanoke-Chowan Foundation, Inc. ✧
P.O. Box 1385
Ahoskie, NC 27910-1385
Contact: Sandra Woodard, Pres.

Established in 1997 in NC.
Donor: Roanoke-Chowan Hospital.
Foundation type: Independent foundation.
Financial data (yr. ended 09/30/13): Assets, $15,165,275 (M); gifts received, $12,996; expenditures, $689,975; qualifying distributions, $634,042; giving activities include $595,741 for 10 grants (high: $232,265; low: $267).
Purpose and activities: Grants are made only to promote the health, wellness, and general well-being of persons living in Bertie, Gates, Hertford, or Northampton, counties in NC.
Fields of interest: Hospitals (general); Health care.
Type of support: General/operating support; Program development.
Limitations: Applications accepted. Giving limited to Bertie, Gates, Hertford, and Northampton counties, NC.
Publications: Application guidelines; Grants list; Informational brochure; Informational brochure (including application guidelines); Occasional report; Program policy statement.
Application information: Application form required.
Initial approach: Proposal
Copies of proposal: 2
Deadline(s): None
Board meeting date(s): Quarterly
Final notification: 3-6 months
Officers: Charles Hughes, Chair.; Cy Grant, Vice-Chair.; Sandra Woodard, Pres.; Reba Green-Holley, Secy.-Treas.
Directors: Michael Alston; Gina Basnight; Ernie Carter; Ernest L. Evans; James W. Mason; Charles L. Revelle III; Carl D. Taylor.
Number of staff: 1 part-time professional; 1 part-time support.
EIN: 561535057
Selected grants: The following grants are a representative sample of this grantmaker's funding activity:
$232,265 to Roanoke-Chowan Hospital, Ahoskie, NC, 2013. For Viquest operations.

7304
Percival Roberts, Jr. Trust ✧
1 W. 4th St., D4000-041
Winston-Salem, NC 27101-5709
E-mail: grantadministration@wellsfargo.com; Main URL: https://www.wellsfargo.com/privatefoundationgrants/roberts

Established in PA.
Foundation type: Independent foundation.
Financial data (yr. ended 12/31/13): Assets, $15,672,644 (M); expenditures, $891,329; qualifying distributions, $793,853; giving activities include $750,233 for 4 grants (high: $240,000; low: $50,000).
Purpose and activities: Giving primarily to children's causes, including children's hospitals; funding also for higher education.
Fields of interest: Higher education; Hospitals (specialty); Children.
Limitations: Applications accepted. Giving primarily in Tampa, FL, and Philadelphia, PA. No grants to individuals.
Application information: See foundation website for complete application guidelines. Application form required.
Deadline(s): Apr. 1
Trustee: Wells Fargo Bank, N.A.
EIN: 236219291
Selected grants: The following grants are a representative sample of this grantmaker's funding activity:
$175,000 to Shriners Hospitals for Children, Tampa, FL, 2011. For general support.

7305
The Blanche and Julian Robertson Family Foundation, Inc. ✧
P.O. Box 4242
Salisbury, NC 28145-4242
Contact: David E. Setzer, Exec. Dir.
FAX: (704) 637-0177;
E-mail: bjrfoundation@bellsouth.net; Additional address: 141 E. Council St., Salisbury, NC 28144; Main URL: http://www.bjrff.org/
Julian H. Robertson, Jr.'s Giving Pledge Profile: http://glasspockets.org/philanthropy-in-focus/eye-on-the-giving-pledge/profiles/robertson

Established in 1997 in NC.
Donor: Julian H. Robertson, Jr.
Foundation type: Independent foundation.
Financial data (yr. ended 12/31/13): Assets, $15,636,933 (M); expenditures, $2,989,162; qualifying distributions, $2,973,077; giving activities include $2,900,606 for 78 grants (high: $383,868; low: $500).
Purpose and activities: The foundation, committed to improving the quality of life in Salisbury, NC, and its surrounding area, is interested in funding programs that address social, family, educational, health, and neighborhood issues, and those which enrich lives through cultural, artistic and recreational opportunities. Preference is given to projects that encourage constructive change, strive toward achieving excellence, and have a significant component of public service.
Fields of interest: Historic preservation/historical societies; Arts; Education; Environment; Health care; Recreation; Youth, services; Family services; Community/economic development; Infants/toddlers; Children/youth; Children; Youth; Adults; Aging; Disabilities, people with; Physically disabled; Mentally disabled; Minorities; African Americans/Blacks; AIDS, people with; Single parents; Crime/abuse victims; Economically disadvantaged; Homeless.
Type of support: General/operating support; Continuing support; Management development/capacity building; Capital campaigns; Building/renovation; Equipment; Land acquisition; Emergency funds; Program development; Conferences/seminars; Film/video/radio; Curriculum development; Scholarship funds; Technical assistance; Program evaluation; Matching/challenge support.
Limitations: Applications accepted. Giving limited to Salisbury, NC, and its surrounding Rowan County area. No support for religious organizations in their sectarian programming. No grants for individual scholarships.
Publications: Application guidelines; Grants list; Informational brochure (including application guidelines); Newsletter; Occasional report.
Application information: Application form required.
Initial approach: Telephone, personal visit, or letter
Copies of proposal: 1
Deadline(s): Mar. 15
Board meeting date(s): Twice a year, as determined by board
Final notification: Upon board's decision and action, usually in mid-May

Officers and Directors:* Margaret H. Kluttz,* Chair.; B. Clay Lindsay, Jr., Vice-Chair.; Lillian L. Morgan, Secy.; David E. Setzer, Exec. Dir.; Timothy L. Bates; Bret R. Busby; Catrelia Hunter; R. Scott Maddox; Alex T. Robertson; Spencer R. Robertson; Wyndham Robertson; Fred J. Stanback, Jr.; Jason A. Walser.
Number of staff: 1 part-time professional.
EIN: 562027907
Selected grants: The following grants are a representative sample of this grantmaker's funding activity:
$140,000 to Housing Authority of the City of Salisbury, Salisbury, NC, 2012. For West End Transformation Plan.
$131,979 to Rowan-Salisbury Schools, Salisbury, NC, 2012. For Elementary Schools iPad project.
$125,000 to Hood Theological Seminary, Salisbury, NC, 2012. For construction of new refectory.
$50,000 to Nazareth Childrens Home, Rockwell, NC, 2012. For construction of cottages.
$50,000 to Waterworks Visual Arts Center, Salisbury, NC, 2012. For operating support.
$40,000 to Rape, Child and Family Abuse Crisis Council of Salisbury-Rowan, Salisbury, NC, 2012. For battered women's shelter.
$20,000 to Rowan Museum, Salisbury, NC, 2012. For summer camps, education projects, and operating support.
$15,000 to Rowan Care Alliance, Salisbury, NC, 2012. To assist AIDS/HIV patients with dental care.
$5,000 to Footprints in the Community, Salisbury, NC, 2012. For summer camp for children with disabilities.
$3,750 to Center for Faith and the Arts, Salisbury, NC, 2012. For Summer Arts Academy for young people.

7306
The Phil & Gerry Rominger Foundation ✧ ☆
(formerly Tomar Foundation, Inc.)
c/o Marsha R. Aksel
100 Chesapeake Way
Chapel Hill, NC 27516-7785

Established in 2001 in NC.
Donor: Phillip E. Rominger‡.
Foundation type: Independent foundation.
Financial data (yr. ended 12/31/12): Assets, $15,217,067 (M); expenditures, $953,786; qualifying distributions, $785,120; giving activities include $785,120 for 7 grants (high: $112,160; low: $112,160).
Fields of interest: Education; Children/youth, services.
Type of support: Research.
Limitations: Applications not accepted. Giving primarily in NC. No grants to individuals.
Application information: Unsolicited requests for funds not accepted.
Officers: Marsha R. Aksel, Pres.; Thomas L. Rominger, V.P.; Richard deButts, C.P.A., Treas.
Trustee: Comerica Bank and Trust, N.A.
Board Members: Pearl Daugherty; Willie Glenn; John Northen; Todd Purich.
EIN: 562253755

7307
S.R.C. Education Alliance ✧
P.O. Box 12053
Research Triangle Park, NC 27709-2053 (919) 941-9400
E-mail: EducationAlliance@src.org; Application e-mail for fellowships and scholarships: apply@src.org; Main URL: http://www.src.org/program/srcea/

Donors: Microelectonics Advanced Research Corp.; Semiconductor Research Corp.; Intel Foundation; IBM; Semiconductor Industry Association.
Foundation type: Company-sponsored foundation.
Financial data (yr. ended 12/31/12): Assets, $899,471 (M); gifts received, $1,383,030; expenditures, $1,615,656; qualifying distributions, $1,616,156; giving activities include $558,986 for 12 grants (high: $75,893; low: $23,000), and $742,522 for 104 grants to individuals (high: $21,000; low: $122).
Purpose and activities: The foundation supports programs designed to promote science and engineering education and the semiconductor industry through university research grants, scholarships, and fellowships.
Fields of interest: Higher education; Engineering school/education; Engineering; Science; Minorities; African Americans/Blacks; Hispanics/Latinos; Native Americans/American Indians; Women.
Type of support: Fellowships; Research; Scholarships—to individuals.
Limitations: Applications accepted. Giving on a national basis, with emphasis on AZ, CA, NC, NY, and OH.
Publications: Application guidelines.
Application information: Application form required.
Initial approach: Download application form or e-mail foundation for application form for fellowships and scholarships
Deadline(s): Mid-Feb for fellowships and scholarships
Final notification: Apr. for fellowships and scholarships
Officers and Directors:* Larry W. Sumney,* C.E.O. and Pres.; Celia I. Merzbacher, V.P., Innovative Partnerships; MaryLisabeth Rich, Exec. Dir.; Steven J. Hillenius; Elizabeth J. Weitzman.
EIN: 581807204

7308
Schumacker Trust ✧
c/o Wells Fargo Bank, N.A., Trust Tax Dept.
1 W. 4th St., 4th Fl., MAC D4000-041
Winston-Salem, NC 27101-3818

Foundation type: Independent foundation.
Financial data (yr. ended 11/30/13): Assets, $18,624,390 (M); expenditures, $838,052; qualifying distributions, $771,627; giving activities include $752,000 for 1 grant.
Fields of interest: Education.
Limitations: Applications not accepted. Giving primarily in Charlottesville, VA.
Application information: Contributes only to pre-selected organizations.
Trustee: Wells Fargo Bank, N.A.
EIN: 237991418

7309
Seven Oaks Farm Foundation ✧
(formerly Daniel J. Stowe Museum Foundation)
P.O. Box 1046
Belmont, NC 28012-1046

Established in 1997 in NC.
Foundation type: Independent foundation.
Financial data (yr. ended 12/31/12): Assets, $17,172,118 (M); expenditures, $967,567; qualifying distributions, $781,887; giving activities include $781,887 for grants.
Fields of interest: Botanical gardens.
Limitations: Applications not accepted. Giving primarily in Belmont, NC. No grants to individuals.
Application information: Contributes only to pre-selected organizations.
Directors:* Catharine Pharr Carstarphen; Daniel Harding Stowe; Richmond Harding Stowe; Robert L. Stowe III.
EIN: 562023128

7310
The Shelton Foundation ✧ ☆
286 Cabernet Ln.
Dobson, NC 27017-6322

Established in 1985 in NC.
Donors: The Shelton Cos.; Charles M. Shelton; R. Edwin Shelton; Ballard G. Norwood.
Foundation type: Company-sponsored foundation.
Financial data (yr. ended 12/31/13): Assets, $1,259,400 (M); gifts received, $47,500; expenditures, $467,121; qualifying distributions, $461,800; giving activities include $411,800 for 14 grants (high: $200,000; low: $250).
Purpose and activities: The foundation supports hospices and hospitals and organizations involved with historic preservation, higher education, and children and youth.
Fields of interest: Education; Community/economic development; Religion.
Type of support: General/operating support.
Limitations: Applications not accepted. Giving limited to NC. No grants to individuals.
Application information: Unsolicited requests for funds not accepted.
Officers: Charles M. Shelton, Pres.; R. Edwin Shelton, V.P.; Cindy McBride, Secy.-Treas.
EIN: 581596729

7311
Shelton H. Short, Jr. Trust ✧
c/o Wells Fargo Bank, N.A.
1525 W. WT Harris Blvd., D1114-044
Charlotte, NC 28288-1114
Application address: c/o Kevin Grogan, Wells Fargo Bank, 1 W. 4th St., D400-062, Winston-Salem, NC 27101-3818, tel.: (336) 747-8173; Main URL: https://www.wellsfargo.com/privatefoundationgrants/short

Established in VA.
Donor: Jean R. Short‡.
Foundation type: Independent foundation.
Financial data (yr. ended 12/31/12): Assets, $28,740,300 (M); expenditures, $1,521,365; qualifying distributions, $1,253,816; giving activities include $1,200,000 for 31 grants (high: $250,000; low: $5,000).

Purpose and activities: Giving primarily for higher education, human services, and to a golf association.
Fields of interest: Higher education; Recreation, association; Human services.
Limitations: Applications accepted. Giving primarily in southeast VA. No grants to individuals.
Application information: See foundation website for complete application guidelines. Application form required.
Deadline(s): May 15 and Oct. 15
Trustee: Wells Fargo Bank, N.A.
EIN: 546140127

7312
The Simpson Foundation ✧
1525 W. WT Harris Blvd., D1114-044
Charlotte, NC 28288-5709 (864) 255-8231
E-mail: grantadministration@wellsfargo.com; Main URL: https://www.wellsfargo.com/privatefoundationgrants/simpson

Trust established in 1956 in SC.
Donors: W.H.B. Simpson‡; Mrs. W.H.B. Simpson; Jack Kuhne; Lucy Kuhne.
Foundation type: Independent foundation.
Financial data (yr. ended 12/31/12): Assets, $28,296,993 (M); expenditures, $1,573,942; qualifying distributions, $1,403,313; giving activities include $1,372,500 for 33 grants (high: $382,000; low: $1,000).
Purpose and activities: Giving primarily for education, human services, health organizations, and to Presbyterian churches.
Fields of interest: Higher education; Education; Animal welfare; Health organizations; Human services; Protestant agencies & churches.
Type of support: Capital campaigns; Matching/challenge support.
Limitations: Applications accepted. Giving primarily in Greenville County, SC. No support for educational purposes. No grants to individuals, or for scholarships; no loans.
Application information: See foundation website for complete application guidelines. Application form required.
Initial approach: Letter or Proposal
Copies of proposal: 2
Deadline(s): Apr. 1 and Oct. 1
Board meeting date(s): Middle of May and Nov.
Trustee: Wells Fargo Bank, N.A.
EIN: 576017451

7313
Slick Family Foundation ✧
4400 Silas Creek Pkwy., No. 302
Winston-Salem, NC 27104-3823

Established in 1997 in NC.
Donors: Earl F. Slick‡; Earl F. Slick Revocable Trust.
Foundation type: Independent foundation.
Financial data (yr. ended 12/31/13): Assets, $16,357,380 (M); expenditures, $972,511; qualifying distributions, $655,450; giving activities include $484,666 for 10 grants (high: $100,000; low: $500).
Fields of interest: Historic preservation/historical societies; Arts; Education; Environment; Zoos/zoological societies; Hospitals (general); Medical research, institute; Human services.
Limitations: Applications not accepted. Giving primarily in NC. No grants to individuals.
Application information: Contributes only to pre-selected organizations.
Officers and Directors:* Phyllis S. Cowell,* Pres.; John F. Cowell,* V.P.; Michelle P. Cowell,* V.P.; Lynn C. Ives,* V.P.; Dana W. Howard, Secy.-Treas.; R. Elaine Addison; Steven L. Wallen.
EIN: 311500854

7314
Carole C. and O. Temple Sloan, Jr. Foundation ✧
4900 Falls of Neuse Rd., Ste. 150
Raleigh, NC 27609-5490 (919) 573-3211
Contact: Cheryl Ligon, Tr.

Established in 1994 in NC.
Donors: O. Temple Sloan, Jr.; O. Temple Sloan, Jr. Charitable Lead Trust; St. Andrews Presbyterian College; Sheser Creek LLC.
Foundation type: Independent foundation.
Financial data (yr. ended 12/31/13): Assets, $26,449,052 (M); gifts received, $5,417,682; expenditures, $1,361,931; qualifying distributions, $1,263,726; giving activities include $1,263,726 for 121 grants (high: $131,500; low: $100).
Purpose and activities: Giving primarily for education, hospitals, and religious organizations.
Fields of interest: Higher education; Hospitals (general); United Ways and Federated Giving Programs; Christian agencies & churches; Protestant agencies & churches.
Type of support: Capital campaigns; Scholarships—to individuals.
Limitations: Applications accepted. Giving primarily in NC; some funding also in MT.
Application information: Application form required.
Initial approach: Proposal
Deadline(s): None
Trustees: Cheryl P. Ligon; Carson S. Henline; Mark Sloan; O. Temple Sloan III; W. Gerald Thornton.
EIN: 561870844

7315
Eddie and Jo Allison Smith Family Foundation, Inc. ✧
(formerly Edward C. Smith, Jr. & Christopher B. Smith Foundation, Inc.)
P.O. Box 1527
Greenville, NC 27835-1527
Contact: Geri Lassiter
FAX: (252) 830-8460;
E-mail: glassiter@gradywhite.com

Established in 1993 in NC.
Donors: Edward C. Smith, Jr.; Christopher B. Smith; C & E Enterprises; Grady-White Boats, Inc.
Foundation type: Independent foundation.
Financial data (yr. ended 06/30/13): Assets, $50,720,406 (M); expenditures, $3,038,860; qualifying distributions, $2,624,263; giving activities include $2,576,639 for 160 grants (high: $674,680; low: $250).
Purpose and activities: Giving primarily for the arts, education, the environment, health, and human services.
Fields of interest: Museums; Arts; Education; Environment, natural resources; Health organizations, association; Human services; Children/youth, services; Protestant agencies & churches.
Limitations: Applications not accepted. Giving primarily in NC; some funding nationally. No grants to individuals.
Application information: Contributes only to pre-selected organizations.
Board meeting date(s): Quarterly
Officers and Directors:* Edward C. Smith, Jr.,* Pres.; Christopher B. Smith,* V.P.; Jo A. Smith,* Secy.; Kristin Carroll; Herman Simon.
Number of staff: 1 part-time support.
EIN: 561844198
Selected grants: The following grants are a representative sample of this grantmaker's funding activity:
$418,000 to Virginia Episcopal School, Lynchburg, VA, 2011. For fund drive.
$210,000 to Virginia Episcopal School, Lynchburg, VA, 2011. For fund drive.
$140,000 to University of North Carolina Educational Foundation, Chapel Hill, NC, 2011.
$100,000 to Pitt County Schools, Greenville, NC, 2011.
$52,500 to Nature Conservancy, Durham, NC, 2011.
$32,200 to Pamlico-Tar River Foundation, Washington, NC, 2011.
$25,000 to Tar River Land Conservancy, Louisburg, NC, 2011. For fund drive.
$15,000 to American Red Cross, Greenville, NC, 2011. For fund drive.
$6,834 to Charlotte Country Day School, Charlotte, NC, 2011.
$2,500 to Compassion International, Colorado Springs, CO, 2011. For fund drive.

7316
Winthrop H. Smith Memorial Foundation, Inc. ✧
100 N. Tryon St., NC1-007-08-29
Charlotte, NC 28202-4000
Application address: c/o LifeCare, Inc., 2 Armstrong Rd., Shelton, CT 06484, tel.: (877) 444-1012

Established in 1962.
Donors: Kenneth C. Iwelumo; Merrill Lynch & Co., Inc.
Foundation type: Independent foundation.
Financial data (yr. ended 12/31/13): Assets, $2,473,232 (M); expenditures, $702,722; qualifying distributions, $611,080; giving activities include $611,080 for 258 grants to individuals (high: $9,424; low: $58).
Purpose and activities: Grants in aid and loans to needy current and retired employees of Merrill Lynch & Co. for emergency relief of personal or family misfortune.
Fields of interest: Safety/disasters.
Type of support: Grants to individuals; Loans—to individuals.
Application information: Application form required.
Initial approach: Proposal
Deadline(s): None
Officers and Trustees:* Christopher L. Hollinger,* Co-Pres.; Erika M. Ross,* Co-Pres.; Akilah L. Weaver,* Secy.; William A. Bridy,* Treas.; Rhonda M. Bethea; Mauro A. Cieri.
EIN: 136160365

7317
Ethel Sergeant Clark Smith Memorial Fund ✧
c/o Wells Fargo Bank
1525 W. WT Harris Blvd., D1114-044
Charlotte, NC 28288-1161 (888) 234-1999
Contact: Kyle J. Quinlivan, Trust Admin.
FAX: (877) 746-5889;
E-mail: grantsadministration@wellsfargo.com; Main URL: https://www.wellsfargo.com/privatefoundationgrants/smith

Established in 1977 in PA.
Donor: Ethel Sergeant Clark Smith†.
Foundation type: Independent foundation.
Financial data (yr. ended 05/31/13): Assets, $13,548,313 (M); expenditures, $683,222; qualifying distributions, $519,067; giving activities include $463,000 for 38 grants (high: $120,000; low: $1,000).
Purpose and activities: Giving for health associations and hospitals, education, including early childhood and secondary schools, child welfare and development, social service organizations, libraries, fine and performing arts groups and culture, museums and historical buildings, recreation, music and drama facilities, and programs for women, the handicapped and exceptional persons, and community reinvestment.
Fields of interest: Visual arts; Museums; Performing arts; Performing arts, theater; Performing arts, orchestras; Historic preservation/historical societies; Arts; Education, early childhood education; Child development, education; Secondary school/education; Higher education; Libraries/library science; Education; Speech/hearing centers; Mental health/crisis services; Health organizations, association; Recreation; Human services; Children/youth, services; Child development, services; Women, centers/services; Community/economic development; Disabilities, people with; Women.
Type of support: General/operating support; Capital campaigns; Building/renovation; Equipment; Emergency funds; Program development; Seed money; Research; Technical assistance; Exchange programs; Matching/challenge support.
Limitations: Applications accepted. Giving limited to southeastern PA, with emphasis on Delaware County. No support for single-disease organizations. No grants to individuals, or for deficit financing, construction or renovations to real estate not owned by the charitable entity, salaries, professional fundraiser fees, scholarships, or fellowships; no gifts longer than 3 years consecutively; no loans.
Publications: Application guidelines; Informational brochure (including application guidelines).
Application information: Application form required.
Initial approach: Apply online via foundation web site
Copies of proposal: 1
Deadline(s): Mar. 1 and Sept. 1
Board meeting date(s): May and Nov. (Advisory Committee)
Final notification: 2 months after trustee meets with advisory committee
Trustee: Wells Fargo Bank, N.A.
EIN: 236648857
Selected grants: The following grants are a representative sample of this grantmaker's funding activity:
$5,000 to Melmark, Berwyn, PA, 2011. For general support.

7318
Snyder's-Lance Foundation ✧
P.O. Box 32368
Charlotte, NC 28232-2368 (704) 554-1421
Contact: Sid Levy, Exec. Dir.

Trust established in 1956 in NC.
Donor: Lance, Inc.
Foundation type: Company-sponsored foundation.
Financial data (yr. ended 12/31/13): Assets, $412,822 (M); expenditures, $654,818; qualifying distributions, $650,830; giving activities include $646,827 for 8 grants (high: $401,750; low: $2,500).
Purpose and activities: The foundation supports hospices and organizations involved with arts and culture, education, hunger, youth development, and business.
Fields of interest: Arts; Education; Human services.
Type of support: General/operating support; Scholarship funds.
Limitations: Applications accepted. Giving primarily in Charlotte, NC. No grants to individuals, or for scholarships or fellowships; no loans.
Application information: Application form not required.
Initial approach: Proposal
Copies of proposal: 1
Deadline(s): None
Board meeting date(s): As required
Officer: Sid Levy, Exec. Dir.
Director: Rick D. Puckett.
Trustee: Bank of America, N.A.
Number of staff: 1
EIN: 566039487
Selected grants: The following grants are a representative sample of this grantmaker's funding activity:
$115,000 to United Way of Central Carolinas, Charlotte, NC, 2011. For general funds.
$25,000 to Armed Forces Foundation, Washington, DC, 2011. For general funds.
$25,000 to Enactus, Springfield, MO, 2011. For general funds.
$10,811 to American Cancer Society, York, PA, 2011. For general funds.
$10,000 to American Heart Association, Dallas, TX, 2011. For general funds.
$10,000 to First Book, Washington, DC, 2011. For general funds.
$10,000 to United Way of Ashland County, Ashland, OH, 2011. For general funds.
$10,000 to YMCA of Greater Charlotte, Charlotte, NC, 2011. For general funds.
$8,500 to Johnson C. Smith University, Charlotte, NC, 2011. For general funds.
$2,500 to Thompson Child and Family Focus, Matthews, NC, 2011. For general funds.

7319
Southern Bank Foundation ✧
P.O. Box 729
Mount Olive, NC 28365-0729 (919) 658-7007
Contact: David L. Sauls, Treas.

Established in 1996 in NC.
Donors: Southern Bank & Trust Co.; Southern Bancshares, Inc.
Foundation type: Company-sponsored foundation.
Financial data (yr. ended 12/31/13): Assets, $13,120,224 (M); expenditures, $613,964; qualifying distributions, $582,675; giving activities include $582,675 for 82 grants (high: $101,000; low: $200).
Purpose and activities: The foundation supports hospitals and organizations involved with education, human services, community development, and Christianity.
Fields of interest: Higher education; Libraries (public); Education; Hospitals (general); Health care; Health organizations; Salvation Army.
Type of support: General/operating support; Annual campaigns; Capital campaigns; Building/renovation; Equipment; Debt reduction; Program development; Scholarship funds.
Limitations: Applications accepted. Giving primarily in eastern NC. No grants to individuals.
Application information: Application form required.
Initial approach: Request application form
Deadline(s): None
Officers: Frank B. Holding, Pres.; William H. Bryan, V.P.; J. Grey Morgan, V.P.; John L. Heeden, Secy.; David L. Sauls, Treas.
Directors: Bynum R. Brown; Hope Holding Connell.
EIN: 562002871
Selected grants: The following grants are a representative sample of this grantmaker's funding activity:
$12,000 to Eastern Carolina Vocational Center, Greenville, NC, 2011.

7320
C. D. Spangler Foundation, Inc. ✧
P.O. Box 36007
Charlotte, NC 28236-6007
Contact: W.D. Cornwell, Jr., V.P. and Secy.-Treas.

Established in 1956 in NC.
Donors: C.D. Spangler†; PTI Investments Inc.; Delcap, Inc.; C.D. Spangler Construction Co.; Delcor, Inc.
Foundation type: Independent foundation.
Financial data (yr. ended 12/31/13): Assets, $110,670,288 (M); expenditures, $3,708,488; qualifying distributions, $3,703,037; giving activities include $3,690,196 for 39 grants (high: $1,000,000; low: $1,000), and $9,718 for employee matching gifts.
Purpose and activities: Giving primarily for higher education.
Fields of interest: Museums; Arts; Higher education; Human services.
Type of support: Employee matching gifts.
Limitations: Applications not accepted. Giving primarily in NC. No grants to individuals.
Application information: Unsolicited requests for funds not considered.
Officers and Directors:* Meredith R. Spangler, Chair.; Abigail R. Spangler,* Pres.; W.D. Cornwell, Jr.,* V.P. and Secy.-Treas.; Denise E. Gardner, V.P.; Anna Spangler Nelson,* V.P.; C.D. Spangler, Jr.
EIN: 566061548
Selected grants: The following grants are a representative sample of this grantmaker's funding activity:
$1,000,000 to Foundation for the Carolinas, Charlotte, NC, 2013. For Project LIFT.
$1,000,000 to Harvard University, Cambridge, MA, 2013. For grant to School of Business in Boston.
$300,000 to Wellesley College, Wellesley, MA, 2013.
$218,000 to Myers Park Baptist Church, Charlotte, NC, 2013.
$200,000 to Teach for America, Charlotte, NC, 2013.

$175,000 to United Way of Central Carolinas, Charlotte, NC, 2013. For program support.
$165,000 to Arts and Science Council of Charlotte-Mecklenburg, Charlotte, NC, 2013. For program support.
$149,000 to Charlotte Symphony Orchestra, Charlotte, NC, 2013. For program support.
$25,000 to North Carolina Dance Theater, Charlotte, NC, 2013. For program support.
$20,000 to Potomac School, McLean, VA, 2013. For capital campaign.

7321
State Employees' Credit Union Foundation ✧
(doing business as SECU Foundation)
P.O. Box 27665
Raleigh, NC 27611-7665 (919) 839-5000
Contact: G. Mark Twisdale, Exec. Dir.
E-mail: secufoundation@ncsecu.org; Toll free tel.: (800) 438-1104; Main URL: http://www.ncsecufoundation.org

Established in 2001 in NC; funding initiated in 2004.
Foundation type: Operating foundation.
Financial data (yr. ended 06/30/13): Assets, $33,023,474 (M); gifts received, $11,229,681; expenditures, $7,088,139; qualifying distributions, $12,181,062; giving activities include $3,095,342 for 8 grants (high: $1,000,000; low: $15,000), $3,955,000 for 1,685 grants to individuals (high: $2,500; low: $750), and $5,094,105 for 5 loans/program-related investments (high: $2,431,770; low: $49,379).
Purpose and activities: The purpose of the foundation is to help identify and address community issues that are beyond the normal scope of State Employees' Credit Union. The foundation will promote local community development primarily through high impact projects in the areas of education, health, and human services.
Fields of interest: Higher education; Education; Health care; Human services.
Type of support: Capital campaigns; Building/renovation; Scholarships—to individuals.
Limitations: Applications accepted. Giving limited to NC. No grants for operational budgets, debt reduction, sponsorship or events.
Publications: Application guidelines; Annual report; Multi-year report.
Application information: There is no formal application process for scholarships; individual recipients are chosen by local area scholarship selection committees. Scholarship eligibility guidelines available on foundation web site. Application form required.
Initial approach: Letter of Interest for grant requests available on foundation's web site
Copies of proposal: 1
Deadline(s): Varies
Board meeting date(s): Quarterly
Officers and Directors:* McKinley Wooten,* Chair.; Jim Johnson,* Vice-Chair.; Cynthia Jolly, Secy.-Treas.; Mark Twisdale, Exec. Dir.; Jim Barber*; Shirley Bell; Bob Brinson; Karan Bunn; Michael Clements; Olson Huff; David King; Tom King; Robert S. Parker; Jo Anne Sanford; Marilyn Sheerer.
EIN: 562255292
Selected grants: The following grants are a representative sample of this grantmaker's funding activity:
$1,250,000 to Winston-Salem Family House, SECU Family House, Winston-Salem, NC, 2012. To provide housing for families while their loved ones are being treated at Forsyth Medical Center or North Carolina Baptist Hospital in Winston-Salem.
$1,000,000 to North Carolina Museum of Natural Sciences, Raleigh, NC, 2012. For construction of Nature Research Center.
$1,000,000 to SECU Cancer Center, Asheville, NC, 2012. For construction.
$1,000,000 to SECU Hospice House of Brunswick, Bolivia, NC, 2012. For construction of Hospice House of Brunswick County, 7-bed facility.
$250,000 to BizKid$, Boston, MA, 2012. Toward production assistance for BizKid$, financial education show for children & youth on public television.
$120,000 to North Carolina State Employees Combined Campaign, Cary, NC, 2012. For general support.
$37,500 to North Carolina Greenpower Corporation, Raleigh, NC, 2012. For general support.
$15,000 to Office of State Personnel, Raleigh, NC, 2012. For State Employees Award of Excellence.

7322
The Stewards Fund ✧
P.O. Box 6575
Raleigh, NC 27628-6575

Established in 1986 in NC.
Donors: Nancy B. Faircloth; Anne B. Faircloth.
Foundation type: Independent foundation.
Financial data (yr. ended 12/31/13): Assets, $18,944,618 (M); expenditures, $4,621,799; qualifying distributions, $4,590,159; giving activities include $4,513,000 for 58 grants (high: $250,000; low: $5,000).
Purpose and activities: Support for organizations meeting basic needs including food, clothing, and shelter in the triangle area of NC only.
Fields of interest: Health care; Food services; Food banks; Food distribution, meals on wheels; Housing/shelter, development; Boys & girls clubs; Human services; Children/youth, services; Family services; Homeless, human services; Religious federated giving programs; Christian agencies & churches; Protestant agencies & churches; Homeless.
Limitations: Applications not accepted. Giving limited to Wake, Durham, and Orange counties, NC. No grants to individuals.
Application information: Contributes only to pre-selected organizations. Unsolicited requests for funds not accepted.
Officers: Anne B. Faircloth, Pres.; Anna Neal Blanchard, Genl. Mgr.
Trustees: Marian Bergdolt; Gordon Grubb; Haywood Holderness; Micheline Malson; Wyndham Robertson; Kathryn West.
Number of staff: 1 part-time support.
EIN: 561482138

7323
Strauss Foundation ✧
1525 W. WT Harris Blvd., D1114-044
Charlotte, NC 28262-8522
Contact: Reginald Middleton, V.P., Wells Fargo

Trust established in 1951 in PA.
Donor: Maurice L. Strauss.
Foundation type: Independent foundation.
Financial data (yr. ended 12/31/13): Assets, $39,901,948 (M); expenditures, $2,354,933; qualifying distributions, $2,150,331; giving activities include $2,039,725 for 320 grants (high: $100,000; low: $100).
Purpose and activities: Emphasis on Jewish welfare funds in the U.S. and Israel, child welfare and youth agencies, education, hospitals, and cultural programs.
Fields of interest: Arts; Higher education; Education; Hospitals (general); Human services; Children/youth, services; Jewish federated giving programs.
International interests: Israel.
Limitations: Applications not accepted. Giving primarily in CA and PA. No grants to individuals.
Application information: Contributes only to pre-selected organizations. Unsolicited applications are not encouraged.
Trustees: Henry A. Gladstone; Scott Rosen Isdaner; Victoria S. Kennedy; Sandra S. Krause; Robert Perry Strauss; Wells Fargo Bank, N.A.
EIN: 236219939
Selected grants: The following grants are a representative sample of this grantmaker's funding activity:
$10,000 to University of Southern California, Los Angeles, CA, 2012. For USC Norris Comprehensive Cancer Center.

7324
The Sunshine Lady Foundation, Inc. ✧
P.O. Box 1074
Morehead City, NC 28557-1074
Contact: Doris B. Buffett, Pres.
E-mail: SLFwebform@gmail.com; Main URL: http://www.sunshinelady.org/
YouTube: http://www.youtube.com/user/sunshineladychannel

Established in 1996 in NC.
Donor: Doris B. Bryant.
Foundation type: Operating foundation.
Financial data (yr. ended 12/31/13): Assets, $22,720,911 (M); gifts received, $1,131,997; expenditures, $7,031,396; qualifying distributions, $6,904,840; giving activities include $6,462,138 for 477 grants (high: $443,455; low: $77).
Purpose and activities: The foundation's mission is to invest in organizations and programs dedicated to providing opportunities for the advancement of education, well being and new life choices for disadvantaged people with special empathy for the working poor and families in crisis.
Fields of interest: Higher education; Education; Health care; Youth development; Human services; Family services, domestic violence; Women.
Type of support: Matching/challenge support.
Limitations: Applications not accepted. Giving on a national basis. No support for religious organizations or for the arts. No grants for payment of medical debt, academic or scientific research, graduate study, or school loans, no conferences, seminars or trips, environmental or animal protection, fundraising events, or for business investments of any type or grants to businesses; no loans of any type.
Application information: Unsolicited requests for grants are not accepted. The Sunshine Lady Foundation directors, staff and volunteers, known as Sunbeams, seek out ways to effectively share financial support, goodwill, energy and vision with

those who need it most, and to encourage collaborative efforts within the community to help achieve this mission. Sunbeams nominate or otherwise introduce eligible candidates to the foundation for funding.
Officers and Directors:* Doris B. Buffett,* Pres.; Diane Grimsley,* V.P. and Treas.; Mitty Beal,* Secy.; Anne Ewing, Exec. Dir.; Alexander Buffett Rozek,* Prog. Dir., Learning by Giving; Rebecca Currie.
Number of staff: 3 full-time professional; 2 part-time professional; 2 part-time support.
EIN: 561977987
Selected grants: The following grants are a representative sample of this grantmaker's funding activity:
$4,000,000 to Learning By Giving Foundation, Boston, MA, 2012.
$381,399 to Rappahannock Council on Domestic Violence, Fredericksburg, VA, 2012. For Capital Campaign.
$140,000 to Hudson Link for Higher Education in Prison, Ossining, NY, 2012.
$124,935 to Chester Upland School of the Arts, Chester, PA, 2012.
$100,000 to Walla Walla Community College, Walla Walla, WA, 2012.
$50,000 to 15th District Court Service Unit, Stafford, VA, 2012. For Discretionary Funds.
$45,000 to Fund for the City of New York, New York, NY, 2012.
$40,000 to Fund for the City of New York, New York, NY, 2012.
$30,000 to Rappahannock Legal Services, Fredericksburg, VA, 2012.
$18,683 to Southside Virginia Community College, Alberta, VA, 2012.

7325
F. W. Symmes Foundation ✧
1525 W. WT Harris Blvd., D1114-044
Charlotte, NC 28288-5709 (888) 234-1999
E-mail: grantadministration@wellsfargo.com; Main URL: https://www.wellsfargo.com/privatefoundationgrants/symmes

Established in 1954 in SC.
Donor: F.W. Symmes†.
Foundation type: Independent foundation.
Financial data (yr. ended 12/31/12): Assets, $13,999,531 (M); expenditures, $707,631; qualifying distributions, $619,701; giving activities include $578,000 for 26 grants (high: $50,000; low: $5,000).
Purpose and activities: Giving primarily for the arts and social services, including a Catholic agency.
Fields of interest: Arts; Education; Human services; YM/YWCAs & YM/YWHAs; Children/youth, services; Catholic agencies & churches.
Limitations: Applications accepted. Giving primarily in the Greenville, SC, area. No grants to individuals.
Application information: Application form required.
Initial approach: Online application form
Deadline(s): Mar. 15 and Sept. 1
Board meeting date(s): May and Oct.
Trustees: O. Perry Earle III; Eleanor Welling; F. McKinnon Wilkinson; Wells Fargo Bank, N.A.
EIN: 576017472

7326
Tannenbaum-Sternberger Foundation, Inc. ✧
(formerly Sigmund Sternberger Foundation, Inc.)
324 W. Wendover Ave., Ste. 118
Greensboro, NC 27404-8438 (336) 274-5761
Contact: Robert O. Klepfer, Jr., Exec. Dir.
FAX: (336) 274-5763;
E-mail: bobklepfer@tsfoundation.com; Mailing address: P.O. Box 41199, Greensboro, NC 27404-1199; Main URL: http://www.TSFoundation.com

Incorporated in 1955 in NC.
Donors: Sigmund Sternberger†; Leah Louise B. Tannenbaum†; Rosa Sternberger Williams†.
Foundation type: Independent foundation.
Financial data (yr. ended 03/31/13): Assets, $16,378,440 (M); expenditures, $984,473; qualifying distributions, $804,001; giving activities include $697,534 for 55 grants (high: $112,500; low: $2,500).
Purpose and activities: Support for higher education, including scholarship funds, and individual scholarships for children and grandchildren of members of the Revolution Masonic Lodge in Greensboro, NC; grants also to 501(c)(3) organizations for purposes benefiting residents of Guilford County, NC.
Fields of interest: Historic preservation/historical societies; Arts; Higher education; Health care; Human services; Community/economic development.
Type of support: Program evaluation; Land acquisition; General/operating support; Management development/capacity building; Capital campaigns; Building/renovation; Equipment; Emergency funds; Program development; Conferences/seminars; Seed money; Internship funds; Scholarship funds; Scholarships—to individuals; Matching/challenge support.
Limitations: Applications accepted. Giving primarily in Guilford County, NC. Generally, no grants to endowment funds.
Publications: Application guidelines; Grants list.
Application information: Application must be submitted online. Application form required.
Initial approach: Letter, e-mail or telephone
Copies of proposal: 1
Deadline(s): Approx. 6 weeks prior to board meeting
Board meeting date(s): Usually in Mar., July, Nov. and as required
Final notification: Within 3 weeks of Board meeting at which grant proposals are considered
Officers and Directors:* Susan M. Tannenbaum,* Chair.; Sigmund I. Tannenbaum, M.D.*, Vice-Chair. and Secy.; Nancy B. Tannenbaum,* Vice-Chair.; John T. Warmath, Jr., Treas.; Robert O. Klepfer, Jr., Exec. Dir.; Edward F. Cone; Michael L. Diamond; Jeanne L. Tannenbaum, M.D.
Number of staff: 1 part-time professional; 1 part-time support.
EIN: 566045483
Selected grants: The following grants are a representative sample of this grantmaker's funding activity:
$50,000 to Duke University, Durham, NC, 2011.
$12,000 to National Conference for Community and Justice, Willowbrook, IL, 2011.
$10,000 to National Black Child Development Institute, Washington, DC, 2011.
$8,000 to Duke University, Durham, NC, 2011.
$8,000 to Wake Forest University, Winston-Salem, NC, 2011.

7327
R. B. Terry Charitable Foundation, Inc. ✧
c/o Charles L. Odom
P.O. Box 2003
High Point, NC 27261-2003

Established in 1998 in NC.
Donors: Randall B. Terry, Jr.†; Dorothy P. Lockwood†.
Foundation type: Independent foundation.
Financial data (yr. ended 12/31/12): Assets, $157,229,840 (M); expenditures, $7,081,438; qualifying distributions, $6,489,500; giving activities include $6,489,500 for 6 grants (high: $3,000,000; low: $1,000).
Purpose and activities: Giving primarily to a boarding school for boys, as well as to a veterinary medical foundation.
Fields of interest: Elementary/secondary education; Education; Animals/wildlife, association; Veterinary medicine; Children/youth, services; Foundations (private grantmaking).
Type of support: General/operating support.
Limitations: Applications not accepted. Giving primarily in Raleigh, NC and Woodberry Forest, VA. No grants to individuals.
Publications: Annual report.
Application information: Contributes only to pre-selected organizations.
Officers and Directors:* Arch K. Schoch IV,* Pres.; Sion boney,* V.P. and Secy.; Oscar Fletcher,* V.P.; Charles L. Odom,* Treas.
EIN: 562066238
Selected grants: The following grants are a representative sample of this grantmaker's funding activity:
$3,000,000 to North Carolina Veterinary Medical Foundation, Raleigh, NC, 2012. For unrestricted support.
$3,000,000 to Woodberry Forest School, Woodberry Forest, VA, 2012. For unrestricted support.
$468,500 to Susies Hope, Winston-Salem, NC, 2012. For unrestricted support.
$10,000 to Montpelier Foundation, Montpelier Station, VA, 2012. For unrestricted support.
$10,000 to United Animal Coalition, Guilford County Animal Shelter, Greensboro, NC, 2012. For unrestricted support.
$1,000 to Exponent Philanthropy, Washington, DC, 2012. For unrestricted support.

7328
Triangle Community Foundation ✧
324 Blackwell St., Ste. 1220
Durham, NC 27701-3690 (919) 474-8370
FAX: (919) 941-9208; E-mail: info@trianglecf.org; Main URL: http://www.trianglecf.org
Blog: http://www.philanthrospeak.com/
E-Newsletter: http://www.trianglecf.org/contact_us/email_newsletters
Facebook: http://www.facebook.com/pages/Triangle-Community-Foundation/113419701016
Flickr: http://www.flickr.com/photos/tricomfdn
Twitter: http://twitter.com/TriComFdn
YouTube: http://www.youtube.com/user/TriangleCF
Scholarship e-mail: gina@trianglecf.org

Incorporated in 1983 in NC.
Foundation type: Community foundation.
Financial data (yr. ended 06/30/13): Assets, $160,631,411 (M); gifts received, $17,192,722; expenditures, $16,013,655; giving activities include $13,365,449 for 383+ grants (high: $1,174,110).
Purpose and activities: The foundation seeks to connect philanthropic resources with community needs, create opportunity for enlightened change, and encourage philanthropy as a way of life.
Fields of interest: Visual arts; Museums; Performing arts; Performing arts, dance; Performing arts, theater; Performing arts, music; Humanities; Historic preservation/historical societies; Arts; Education, early childhood education; Child development, education; Elementary school/education; Vocational education; Higher education; Adult/continuing education; Adult education—literacy, basic skills & GED; Libraries/library science; Education, reading; Education; Environment, natural resources; Environment, energy; Environment; Animal welfare; Animals/wildlife, preservation/protection; Reproductive health, family planning; Medical care, rehabilitation; Health care; Substance abuse, services; Mental health/crisis services; Health organizations, association; AIDS; Alcoholism; Crime/violence prevention, youth; Legal services; Crime/law enforcement; Food services; Housing/shelter, development; Recreation; Youth development, services; Children/youth, services; Child development, services; Family services; Residential/custodial care, hospices; Aging, centers/services; Women, centers/services; Minorities/immigrants, centers/services; Homeless, human services; Human services; International peace/security; Civil rights, race/intergroup relations; Urban/community development; Rural development; Community/economic development; Voluntarism promotion; Government/public administration; Leadership development; Public affairs; Aging; Disabilities, people with; Minorities; Native Americans/American Indians; Women; Economically disadvantaged; Homeless; LGBTQ.
Type of support: Continuing support; Management development/capacity building; Annual campaigns; Capital campaigns; Emergency funds; Program development; Seed money; Scholarship funds; Research; Technical assistance; Program-related investments/loans; Employee matching gifts; Employee-related scholarships; Scholarships—to individuals; In-kind gifts; Matching/challenge support.
Limitations: Applications accepted. Giving limited to Chatham, Durham, Orange, and Wake counties, NC. No grants for budget deficits.
Publications: Annual report; Newsletter.
Application information: Visit foundation web site for guidelines for specific grantmaking programs. Application form required.

Board meeting date(s): Feb., May, Aug., and Nov.

Officers and Directors:* Lacy M. Presnell III,* Chair.; Lori O'Keefe, Pres.; Robert Naylor, C.F.O. and Dir., Admin.; Pat Nathan,* Secy. and Chair., Devel./Donor Engagement Comm.; James A. Stewart,* Treas. and Chair., Finance Comm.; Lindsay Harrell, Cont.; Paul B. Harrison, Chair., Governance Comm.; Tim Gupton, Chair., Audit Comm.; Mark Kuhn, Chair., Investment Comm.; Easter Maynard, Chair., Community Engagement Comm.; Peter J. Meehan,* Chair., Leadership Council; Cecile Noel,* Chair., Philanthropic Svcs. Comm.; C. Perry Colwell,* Asst. Secy.; Farad Ali; Diane Birch; Diane Bonner; Ruth Dzau; Richard B. Guirlinger; Larry Rocamora; Pam Senegal; Michael Schoenfeld; James H. Speed, Jr.; Carl Thompson; Kathryn Williams.
Number of staff: 13 full-time professional; 2 part-time professional.
EIN: 561380796
Selected grants: The following grants are a representative sample of this grantmaker's funding activity:
$790,402 to Community Foundation of Western North Carolina, Asheville, NC, 2013.
$474,860 to Carolina Friends School, Durham, NC, 2013.
$200,000 to YMCA of the Triangle Area, Raleigh, NC, 2013. For the We Build People Campaign.
$145,500 to American Social Health Association, Research Triangle Park, NC, 2013.
$100,000 to Aldersgate United Methodist Church, Chapel Hill, NC, 2013. For the Sanctuary Fund.
$100,000 to North Carolina Museum of History Foundation, Raleigh, NC, 2013. For Chronology Exhibit support.
$4,200 to North Carolina Center for Nonprofits, Raleigh, NC, 2013. To sponsor the NC Center for Nonprofit's Conference.
$3,000 to University of North Carolina, Center for Public Service, Chapel Hill, NC, 2013. For the Ronald Hyatt Rotary Public Service Award.
$2,500 to Tryon Palace Foundation, New Bern, NC, 2013. For the Kay P. Williams Endowment.
$2,250 to SECU Family House at UNC Hospitals, Chapel Hill, NC, 2013.

7329
Philip L. Van Every Foundation ✧

P.O. Box 32368
Charlotte, NC 28232-2368
Contact: Roddey Brown, Exec. Dir.

Established in 1961 in NC.
Donor: Philip Van Every.
Foundation type: Independent foundation.
Financial data (yr. ended 12/31/13): Assets, $36,868,060 (M); expenditures, $1,773,411; qualifying distributions, $1,580,777; giving activities include $1,503,500 for 37 grants (high: $175,000; low: $2,500).
Purpose and activities: Giving for arts and culture, social services, health care and medical research, higher education, and federated giving programs.
Fields of interest: Arts; Higher education; Education; Health care; Health organizations, association; Medical research, institute; Human services; United Ways and Federated Giving Programs.
Limitations: Applications not accepted. Giving primarily in NC and SC. No grants to individuals.
Application information: Contributes only to pre-selected organizations.
Officer: Roddey Brown, Exec. Dir.
Directors: Quincy Foil; Anne Glenn; James S. Howell; Ron Melvin; Dave Singer.
Trustee: Bank of America, N.A.
Number of staff: 1
EIN: 566039337
Selected grants: The following grants are a representative sample of this grantmaker's funding activity:
$50,000 to United Way of Central Carolinas, Charlotte, NC, 2011.
$40,000 to American Red Cross, Greater Carolinas Chapter, Charlotte, NC, 2011.
$25,000 to Charlotte Center for Urban Ministry, Charlotte, NC, 2011.
$25,000 to Crisis Assistance Ministry, Charlotte, NC, 2011.
$25,000 to Heineman Medical Research Center of Charlotte, Charlotte, NC, 2011.
$25,000 to Hospice and Palliative Care Charlotte Region, Charlotte, NC, 2011.
$25,000 to Ronald McDonald House of Charlotte, Charlotte, NC, 2011.
$25,000 to Salvation Army of Charlotte, Charlotte, NC, 2011.
$25,000 to YWCA of the Central Carolinas, Charlotte, NC, 2011.
$5,000 to Make-A-Wish Foundation of Central and Western North Carolina, Charlotte, NC, 2011.

7330
The Edward W. and Stella C. Van Houten Memorial Fund ✧ ☆

c/o Wells Fargo Bank, N.A.
1525 W. WT Harris Blvd.
Charlotte, NC 28288-5709 1-888-234-1999
FAX: 1-877-746-5889;
E-mail: grantsadministration@wellsfargo.com; Main URL: https://www.wellsfargo.com/privatefoundationgrants/vanhouten

Established in 1979 in NJ.
Donor: Stella C. Van Houten†.
Foundation type: Independent foundation.
Financial data (yr. ended 11/30/13): Assets, $19,971,879 (M); expenditures, $758,437; qualifying distributions, $640,291; giving activities include $600,000 for 30 grants (high: $50,000; low: $5,000).
Purpose and activities: Interests include: 1) human service activities in Bergen and Passaic counties in NJ; specific areas of interest include orphaned children, the disabled, and the elderly; 2) hospitals and health organizations in Bergen and Passaic counties, NJ, to improve or expand healthcare services; 3) higher education, primarily medical and nursing training; and 4) education and care of children.
Fields of interest: Arts; Education, early childhood education; Child development, education; Medical school/education; Nursing school/education; Education; Hospitals (general); Nursing care; Health care; Health organizations, association; Biomedicine; Medical research, institute; Human services; Children/youth, services; Child development, services; Aging.
Type of support: Capital campaigns; Building/renovation; Equipment; Program development; Seed money; Scholarship funds.
Limitations: Applications accepted. Giving primarily in NJ. No grants to individuals, or for general operating support or endowments; no loans.
Application information: Complete application guidelines and online application information available on Fund web site.

Deadline(s): Jan 31 and Aug. 1
Board meeting date(s): Mar., June, Sept., and Dec.

Trustee: Wells Fargo Bank, N.A.
EIN: 226311438

7331
R. T. Vanderbilt Trust ✧
1525 W. WT Harris Blvd.
Charlotte, NC 28288-1114

Established in 1951 in CT.
Foundation type: Independent foundation.
Financial data (yr. ended 12/31/13): Assets, $9,207,617 (M); expenditures, $527,962; qualifying distributions, $440,933; giving activities include $424,933 for 76 grants (high: $113,000; low: $500).
Purpose and activities: Giving primarily for education and conservation; support also for health care, and cultural programs.
Fields of interest: Historic preservation/historical societies; Arts; Higher education; Education; Environment, natural resources; Hospitals (general); Health care; Human services.
Type of support: General/operating support; Building/renovation; Endowments; Program development.
Limitations: Applications not accepted. Giving primarily in CT; some giving in ME and NY. No grants to individuals.
Application information: Contributes only to pre-selected organizations.
Board meeting date(s): Apr., June, Sept., and Dec.
Trustees: Hugh B. Vanderbilt, Jr.; Paul Vanderbilt.
Number of staff: 2 part-time support.
EIN: 066040981
Selected grants: The following grants are a representative sample of this grantmaker's funding activity:
$21,000 to American Red Cross, Farmington, CT, 2012. For Ct Victims of Hurricane Sandy.
$1,000 to University of Denver, Denver, CO, 2012. For Greater University Fund.

7332
The VF Foundation ✧
105 Corporate Center Blvd.
Greensboro, NC 27408-3194
Main URL: http://www.vfc.com/corporate-responsibility/social/vf-in-the-community

Established in 2002 in NC.
Donor: V.F. Corp.
Foundation type: Company-sponsored foundation.
Financial data (yr. ended 12/31/13): Assets, $6,582,577 (M); expenditures, $1,749,574; qualifying distributions, $1,806,271; giving activities include $1,743,341 for 174 grants (high: $400,000).
Purpose and activities: The foundation supports organizations involved with arts and culture, education, conservation, diabetes, human services, and economic development.
Fields of interest: Museums; Museums (science/technology); Performing arts, theater; Arts; Education; Environment, natural resources; Diabetes; American Red Cross; Children, services; Family services; Residential/custodial care, hospices; Human services; Economic development; Community/economic development.
Type of support: General/operating support; Capital campaigns; Employee volunteer services; Employee matching gifts.
Limitations: Applications not accepted. Giving primarily in areas of company operations in Greensboro, NC. No support for religious or political organizations. No grants to individuals.
Application information: Contributes only to pre-selected organizations.
Officers and Directors:* Eric C. Wiseman,* Chair.; Patrick Guido, V.P.; Laura Meagher,* Secy.; Susan McDonald,* Treas.
EIN: 562322084
Selected grants: The following grants are a representative sample of this grantmaker's funding activity:
$250,800 to Conservation Alliance, Bend, OR, 2011.
$146,000 to Ronald McDonald House Charities of Atlanta, Atlanta, GA, 2011.
$100,000 to CHAPS Academy, Shiocton, WI, 2011.

7333
Kerry & Simone Vickar Family Foundation ✧
(formerly L. Kerry Vickar Charitable Foundation)
201 S. College St., Ste. 1540
Charlotte, NC 28244-0002

Established in 2003 in NC.
Donor: L. Kerry Vickar.
Foundation type: Independent foundation.
Financial data (yr. ended 12/31/13): Assets, $7,966,840 (M); expenditures, $882,379; qualifying distributions, $803,565; giving activities include $715,153 for 34 grants (high: $100,000; low: $1,000).
Fields of interest: Human services; Children/youth, services; Jewish federated giving programs.
Limitations: Applications not accepted. Giving primarily in FL. No grants to individuals.
Application information: Contributes only to pre-selected organizations.
Officers: Simone D. Vickar, Pres.; Jeffrey R. Gifford, Treas.
Director: L. Kerry Vickar.
EIN: 341974937

7334
The Warner Foundation
(formerly The D. Michael Warner Foundation, Inc.)
4112 Powder Mill Rd.
Chapel Hill, NC 27514-9658 (919) 383-8213
Contact: Michael D. Warner, V.P.
E-mail: info@thewarnerfoundation.org
Warner Foundation's Philanthropy Promise: http://www.ncrp.org/philanthropys-promise/who

Established in 1996 in NC.
Donor: D. Michael Warner.
Foundation type: Independent foundation.
Financial data (yr. ended 12/31/12): Assets, $7,517,981 (M); expenditures, $581,211; qualifying distributions, $529,065; giving activities include $450,000 for 9 grants (high: $120,000; low: $20,000).
Purpose and activities: Giving to North Carolina organizations working to foster long-term improvements in economic opportunities for low-wealth African-Americans.
Fields of interest: Education; Minorities; Economically disadvantaged.
Type of support: Program-related investments/loans; General/operating support; Continuing support; Income development; Management development/capacity building; Program development; Seed money; Technical assistance; Matching/challenge support.
Limitations: Applications accepted. Giving limited to NC. No grants to individuals.
Application information: Application form required.
Initial approach: Contact foundation for application form
Deadline(s): Contact foundation for application deadline
Officers and Board Member:* D. Michael Warner, Chair. and V.P.; Elizabeth B. Craven,* Pres.
Number of staff: 5 full-time professional.
EIN: 561969171

7335
Weaver Foundation, Inc. ✧
324 W. Wendover Ave., Ste. 300
Greensboro, NC 27408-8440 (336) 378-7910
Contact: Kevin Gray, Interim Pres.
FAX: (336) 275-9602;
E-mail: kgray@weaverfoundation.com; Address for inquiries: P.O. Box 26040, Greensboro, NC 27420-6040; Main URL: http://www.weaverfoundation.com
Grants List: http://www.weaverfoundation.com/grants/index.php

Incorporated in 1967 in NC.
Donors: W.H. Weaver†; E.H. Weaver; H. Michael Weaver.
Foundation type: Independent foundation.
Financial data (yr. ended 12/31/12): Assets, $22,188,906 (M); gifts received, $250; expenditures, $1,624,823; qualifying distributions, $1,395,980; giving activities include $1,395,980 for grants.
Purpose and activities: The purpose of the foundation is to help the greater Greensboro, NC, community, enhance and improve the quality of life and the economic environment for its citizens while developing a sense of philanthropy, civic education, and commitment in current and future generations of the founders' families. Focus areas include education, children and youth, environment, reducing poverty, advancement of civil rights, and economic development.
Fields of interest: Arts; Education, early childhood education; Higher education; Education; Environment, natural resources; Environment; Housing/shelter, development; Human services; Children/youth, services; Homeless, human services; Community/economic development; Leadership development; Children/youth; Immigrants/refugees; Economically disadvantaged.
Type of support: General/operating support; Continuing support; Management development/capacity building; Annual campaigns; Capital campaigns; Building/renovation; Equipment; Land acquisition; Endowments; Debt reduction; Emergency funds; Program development; Professorships; Seed money; Scholarship funds; Technical assistance; Consulting services; Program evaluation; Employee matching gifts; Matching/challenge support.
Limitations: Giving limited to the greater Greensboro, NC, area. No support for fraternal or religious organizations. No grants to individuals, or for conferences, travel or group trips, or video productions.
Publications: Annual report; Grants list.
Application information: Unsolicited applications not accepted. Inquiries and information meetings are welcomed. On-line application form required if the organization invited to apply. Application form required.

Initial approach: Telephone, visit, e-mail or a letter of interest submitted through foundation website
Deadline(s): Invited applicants will be given a deadline to complete the application.
Board meeting date(s): Quarterly
Final notification: Generally 3 to 4 weeks
Officers and Trustees:* Katherine Weaver,* Chair.; Ralph Shelton,* Vice-Chair.; Kevin Gray, Pres.; Lee McAllister, V.P.; Elizabeth Green,* Secy.; Mark Wilson, Treas.; Bob Biggerstaff; Ashley Hodges; Sandra Hughes; H. Mike Weaver.
Number of staff: 1 full-time professional.
EIN: 566093527

7336
Wheeler Foundation ✧
(formerly Wheeler Machinery Foundation)
1525 W. WT Harris Blvd.
Charlotte, NC 28262
Application address: c/o Wells Fargo Philanthropic Services, 1 W. 4th St., Winston Salem, NC 27101, tel.: (888) 234-1999

Established in 1992 in UT.
Donors: Don M. Wheeler†; Don M. Wheeler Revocable Trust.
Foundation type: Independent foundation.
Financial data (yr. ended 12/31/13): Assets, $89,196,535 (M); gifts received, $5,000,000; expenditures, $1,460,548; qualifying distributions, $812,173; giving activities include $722,225 for 119 grants (high: $25,000; low: $150).
Fields of interest: Performing arts; Performing arts, theater; Performing arts, orchestras; Higher education, university; Education; Human services.
Type of support: General/operating support.
Limitations: Applications accepted. Giving primarily in Salt Lake City, UT. No grants to individuals.
Application information: Application form required.
Initial approach: Online application form
Deadline(s): Feb. 15 and Aug. 15
Officers and Directors:* Connie Wheeler,* Pres.; Rebecca Davis,* V.P.; Kathy Younker,* V.P.; Alison W. Jensen,* Secy.; Susan Holt,* Treas.
EIN: 870503163

7337
L.E. Wilson Charitable Trust "A" ✧ ☆
c/o Wells Fargo Bank, N.A., Trust Tax Dept.
1 W. 4th St., 4th Fl., MAC D4000-041
Winston-Salem, NC 27101-3818

Established in AL.
Foundation type: Independent foundation.
Financial data (yr. ended 12/31/13): Assets, $13,682,412 (M); expenditures, $647,258; qualifying distributions, $593,685; giving activities include $586,125 for 1 grant.
Fields of interest: Education, single organization support.
Limitations: Applications not accepted. Giving primarily in Sheffield, AL.
Application information: Unsolicited requests for funds not accepted.
Trustee: Wells Fargo Bank, N.A.
EIN: 371565122

7338
The Wilson Family Foundation ✧
(formerly Janet H. and T. Henry Wilson, Jr. Foundation)
P.O. Box 2278
High Point, NC 27261-2278

Established in 1997 in NC.
Donors: Janet Wilson; Henry Wilson; Thomas Henry Wilson Family Foundation.
Foundation type: Independent foundation.
Financial data (yr. ended 12/31/13): Assets, $38,607,231 (M); expenditures, $1,499,279; qualifying distributions, $1,367,500; giving activities include $1,367,500 for 90 grants (high: $205,500; low: $1,000).
Purpose and activities: Giving primarily for education, health, and human services.
Fields of interest: Higher education; Education; Health organizations; Human services; Christian agencies & churches.
Limitations: Applications not accepted. Giving primarily in NC. No grants to individuals.
Application information: Contributes only to pre-selected organizations.
Officers: Janet Wilson, Pres; Amy Wilson Scott, V.P.
Directors: David Wilson; Henry Wilson III.
EIN: 562042058

7339
W. R. Winslow Residuary Trust ✧
c/o Wells Fargo Bank, N.A., IFS Fiduciary Tax Service
1 W. 4th St., 4th Fl.
Winston-Salem, NC 27101-3818

Established in DC; supporting organization of Georgetown University Medical Center; Johns Hopkins University School of Medicine; University of Maryland; North Carolina State University; Virginia Polytechnic Institute and State University; University of Maryland Foundation, Inc.; Children's National Medical Center; Little Sisters of the Poor - Baltimore, MD; Little Sisters of the Poor - D.C.; Salvation Army Trust; Methodist Home of the District of Columbia; Florence Crittenton Home, Inc. of Washington D.C.; and W.R. Winslow Memorial Home.
Foundation type: Independent foundation.
Financial data (yr. ended 12/31/13): Assets, $19,826,159 (M); expenditures, $758,561; qualifying distributions, $708,972; giving activities include $699,999 for 14 grants (high: $126,000; low: $31,889).
Purpose and activities: The trust supports medical schools and other institutions of higher learning to fund scholarships; funding also for human services.
Fields of interest: Medical school/education; Human services.
Type of support: Scholarship funds.
Limitations: Applications not accepted. Giving primarily in Washington, DC; giving also in MD, NC and VA. No grants to individuals.
Application information: Contributes only to pre-selected organizations.
Trustee: Wells Fargo Bank, N.A.
EIN: 526144289

7340
The Winston-Salem Foundation ✧
751 W. 4th St., Ste. 200
Winston-Salem, NC 27101
Contact: Scott F. Wierman, Pres.
FAX: (336) 727-0581;
E-mail: info@wsfoundation.org; Toll free tel.: (866) 227-1209; Grant application e-mail: grants@wsfoundation.org; Additional e-mail: swierman@wsfoundation.org; Main URL: http://www.wsfoundation.org
Facebook: http://www.facebook.com/winstonsalemfoundation

Established in 1919 in NC by declaration of trust.
Foundation type: Community foundation.
Financial data (yr. ended 12/31/13): Assets, $325,704,566 (M); gifts received, $36,716,946; expenditures, $24,896,271; giving activities include $20,965,432 for grants.
Purpose and activities: The foundation invests in the community by making philanthropy and its benefits available to all. The foundation accomplishes this by assisting individuals and organizations with their charitable giving, making grants to nonprofit organizations, providing financial aid to college students and offering community leadership on many issues.
Fields of interest: Arts; Education; Environment; Animals/wildlife; Health organizations; Recreation; Human services; Community/economic development; Youth; African Americans/Blacks; Women.
Type of support: Program evaluation; Building/renovation; Capital campaigns; Consulting services; Emergency funds; Endowments; General/operating support; Income development; Management development/capacity building; Program development; Scholarship funds; Scholarships—to individuals; Seed money; Student loans—to individuals; Technical assistance.
Limitations: Applications accepted. Giving primarily in the greater Forsyth County, NC, area. No support for religious organizations for religious purposes. No grants to individuals (except for scholarships), or for general operating support.
Publications: Application guidelines; Annual report (including application guidelines); Financial statement; Grants list; Informational brochure; Newsletter; Occasional report.
Application information: Visit foundation web site for application forms and guidelines per grant type. Based on the preliminary grant application for Community Grants, the foundation will contact applying organizations as to whether they qualify to submit a full application. Application form required.
Initial approach: Submit preliminary grant application form for Community Grants; varies for others
Copies of proposal: 1
Deadline(s): Bimonthly for preliminary grant application for Community Grants; varies for others
Board meeting date(s): Mar., June, and Oct.
Final notification: Within 30 days for preliminary application determination for Community Grants
Officers and Foundation Committee:* Scott F. Wierman, Pres.; Lisa Purcell, Exec. V.P.; Annette Lynch, V.P., Philanthropic Svcs.; Todd Slate, V.P., Finance and Admin.; Dee Matthews, Compt.; Sen. Linda Garrou; Dr. Gary Green; Tommy L. Hickman; Stan Kelly; M. Carlyle Kinlaw, Jr.; Davida W. Martin; Dr. John D. McConnell; Corena Norris-McCluney; Randall S. Tuttle; Mike Wells; Janet P. Wheeler; Cynthia Williams; Vernon Winters.
Trustees: Bank of America, N.A.; BB&T; First Citizens Bank; SunTrust Bank; Wells Fargo, N.A.

Number of staff: 16 full-time professional; 8 full-time support.
EIN: 566037615
Selected grants: The following grants are a representative sample of this grantmaker's funding activity:
$138,500 to ECHO Council, Winston-Salem, NC, 2012. To foster enriching, trusting, and long-lasting relationships among diverse people.
$125,000 to Winston-Salem Community Development Funders Collaborative, Winston-Salem, NC, 2012. For operating support and technical assistance for mature and emerging community development corporations.
$100,000 to Crosby Scholars Community Partnership, Winston-Salem, NC, 2012. For the capital campaign.
$75,000 to Forsyth Futures, Winston-Salem, NC, 2012. To improve positive outcomes for children, adults, and families.
$75,000 to Senior Services, Winston-Salem, NC, 2012. For part-time senior center program assistant.
$40,000 to Winston-Salem Symphony, Winston-Salem, NC, 2012. For audience development and marketing efforts.
$35,000 to CHANGE, Winston-Salem, NC, 2012. For new fellow position and to expand office manager position.
$25,750 to Carter G. Woodson School of Challenge, Winston-Salem, NC, 2012. To fund a library media specialist for a third year.
$20,000 to SECCA Foundation, Winston-Salem, NC, 2012. For exterior lighting project.
$20,000 to United Way of Forsyth County, Winston-Salem, NC, 2012. To fund the Ten-Year Plan to End Chronic Homelessness.

7341
Women's Independence Scholarship Program, Inc. ✧
4900 Randall Pkwy., Ste. H
Wilmington, NC 28403-2831 (910) 397-7742
Contact: Nancy Soward, Exec. Dir.
FAX: (910) 397-0023; E-mail: nancy@wispinc.org; Main URL: http://www.wispinc.org

Donor: Doris E. Buffett.
Foundation type: Independent foundation.
Financial data (yr. ended 12/31/13): Assets, $21,004,494 (M); gifts received, $740; expenditures, $2,294,341; qualifying distributions, $2,294,341; giving activities include $1,977,682 for 357 grants (high: $102,550; low: $317).
Purpose and activities: The foundation's mission is to enhance efforts to end domestic violence by offering scholarships to survivors of intimate partner abuse and to people who work in the field of domestic violence, as counselors, advocates, and support staff. Scholarship Awards for tuition, books and fees are paid directly to the educational institution.
Fields of interest: Women.
Publications: Newsletter.
Application information: Application guidelines and forms available on foundation web site. Application form required.
Initial approach: Submit on-line application form
Deadline(s): None
Final notification: 2-3 months
Officers: Linda Lytvinenko, Pres.; Nanci McGregor, V.P. and Treas.; Nancy Soward, Secy. and Exec. Dir.
Directors: Diane Grimsley; Ellen Kiernan.
Number of staff: 3 full-time professional; 1 full-time support; 1 part-time support.
EIN: 261956643

7342
Margaret C. Woodson Foundation, Inc. ✧
225 N. Main St.
Salisbury, NC 28144-0829
Application address: Foundation of the Carolinas, 220 N. Tryon St., Charlotte, NC 28202; tel.: (704) 973-4500

Incorporated in 1954 in NC.
Donors: Margaret C. Woodson†; Margaret C. Woodson Trust Co.; US Trust Company of NY.
Foundation type: Independent foundation.
Financial data (yr. ended 12/31/13): Assets, $636,657 (L); gifts received, $915,866; expenditures, $704,314; qualifying distributions, $700,348; giving activities include $625,000 for 22 grants (high: $70,000; low: $1,200).
Purpose and activities: Giving primarily for education and human services, with designated funds for Davidson College, Mary Baldwin College and Barium Springs Childrens Home.
Fields of interest: Museums; Arts; Higher education; Theological school/education; Human services; YM/YWCAs & YM/YWHAs; Children/youth, services.
Type of support: General/operating support.
Limitations: Applications accepted. Giving primarily in Davie and Rowan counties, NC. No grants for research.
Application information: Application form not required.
Initial approach: Letter
Deadline(s): Mar. 1
Officers and Directors:* William G. Johnson,* Pres.; Mary Holt Woodson Murphy,* V.P.; John B.E. Cunningham,* Secy.; Donald D. Sayers,* Treas.; Paul Leake Bernhardt; Charlotte Davis; Robert P. Shay, Jr.; Paul B. Woodson, Jr.
EIN: 566064938

7343
Marian Woodward Ottley-Watertown Trust ✧
(also known as Marian W. Ottley Trust-Watertown)
1525 W. WT Harris Blvd., D1114-044
Charlotte, NC 28288-5709

Established in 1975 in GA.
Donor: Marian W. Ottley†.
Foundation type: Independent foundation.
Financial data (yr. ended 05/31/13): Assets, $16,365,954 (M); expenditures, $874,075; qualifying distributions, $687,125; giving activities include $687,125 for grants.
Purpose and activities: Giving primarily for secondary, elementary, and higher education, social services, and to hospitals.
Fields of interest: Performing arts; Arts; Elementary/secondary education; Higher education; Education; Hospitals (general); Human services; YM/YWCAs & YM/YWHAs; Youth, services.
Type of support: Capital campaigns; Building/renovation; Equipment; Endowments; Scholarship funds.
Limitations: Applications accepted. Giving limited to local organizations in New England and NY, with emphasis on CT. No support for institutions of higher education, or organizations lacking 501(c)(3) tax-exempt status. No grants to individuals, or for general operating funds; generally no multi-year grants.
Publications: Application guidelines.
Application information: Application form required.
Initial approach: Letter (2 pages maximum)
Copies of proposal: 3
Deadline(s): None
Board meeting date(s): May
Officer: Linda Merriman, Secy.
Commitee Members: Craig W. Czarsty, M.D.; Anne Fitzgerald; M. Heminway Merriman II.
Trustee: Wells Fargo Bank, N.A.
EIN: 586222005
Selected grants: The following grants are a representative sample of this grantmaker's funding activity:
$25,000 to Westover School, Middlebury, CT, 2013. For Inspiring Women Campaign.

7344
George & Harriet Woodward Trust ✧
c/o Wells Fargo Bank, N.A., Trust Tax Dept.
1 W. 4th St., 4th Fl., D4000-041
Winston-Salem, NC 27101-3818

Foundation type: Independent foundation.
Financial data (yr. ended 11/30/13): Assets, $28,244,581 (M); expenditures, $1,504,170; qualifying distributions, $1,251,372; giving activities include $1,170,000 for 6 grants (high: $195,000; low: $195,000).
Purpose and activities: Giving primarily for arts and education.
Fields of interest: Arts education; Museums (art); Performing arts, orchestras; Higher education; Physical/earth sciences; Religion.
Type of support: General/operating support.
Limitations: Applications not accepted. Giving primarily in Philadelphia, PA. No grants to individuals.
Application information: Contributes only to pre-selected organizations.
Trustee: Wells Fargo Bank, N.A.
EIN: 237750367
Selected grants: The following grants are a representative sample of this grantmaker's funding activity:
$173,287 to Pennsylvania Academy of the Fine Arts, Philadelphia, PA, 2011. For general support.
$173,287 to Philadelphia Orchestra Association, Philadelphia, PA, 2011. For general support.

7345
Louis Dejoy and Aldona Z. Wos Family Foundation, Inc. ✧
4043 Piedmont Pkwy.
High Point, NC 27265 (336) 232-4874
Contact: Heather Clarke, Secy.-Treas.

Established in 2005 in NC.
Donors: Louis Dejoy; Aldona Z. Wos.
Foundation type: Independent foundation.
Financial data (yr. ended 12/31/13): Assets, $7,135,973 (M); gifts received, $1,000,000; expenditures, $747,718; qualifying distributions, $668,606; giving activities include $668,606 for 29 grants (high: $203,000; low: $100).
Fields of interest: Higher education, university; Education; Human services; United Ways and

Federated Giving Programs; Christian agencies & churches.
Type of support: General/operating support; Capital campaigns.
Limitations: Applications accepted. Giving primarily in NC.
Application information: Application form not required.
Initial approach: Proposal
Deadline(s): None
Officers: Louis Dejoy, Pres.; Aldona Z. Wos, V.P.; Heather Clarke, Secy.-Treas.
EIN: 203466009
Selected grants: The following grants are a representative sample of this grantmaker's funding activity:
$75,000 to Elon University, Elon, NC, 2011.
$25,000 to Episcopal High School, Alexandria, VA, 2011.
$25,000 to Fund for American Studies, Washington, DC, 2011.
$25,000 to George W. Bush Foundation, Dallas, TX, 2011.
$20,000 to Greensboro Ballet, Greensboro, NC, 2011.
$15,000 to Duke University, Durham, NC, 2011.
$10,000 to Columbia University, New York, NY, 2011.
$6,000 to Victims of Communism Memorial Foundation, Washington, DC, 2011.
$5,250 to Institute of World Politics, Washington, DC, 2011. For general operations.
$4,500 to Kosciuszko Foundation, New York, NY, 2011. For general operations.

7346
The Yeargan Foundation Charitable Trust ✧
7777 White Oak Rd.
Garner, NC 27529-8808

Established in 1998.
Donors: Rowann Yeargan; Flora Yeargan†.
Foundation type: Independent foundation.
Financial data (yr. ended 12/31/13): Assets, $19,775,288 (M); expenditures, $637,576; qualifying distributions, $540,744; giving activities include $520,733 for 13 grants (high: $200,000; low: $100).
Purpose and activities: Giving primarily for higher education and to hospices.
Fields of interest: Higher education; Residential/custodial care, hospices; Public affairs, government agencies.
Limitations: Applications not accepted. Giving primarily in NC. No grants to individuals.
Application information: Contributes only to pre-selected organizations.
Trustees: Rowann Yeargan; Sherman Yeargan.
EIN: 581846281
Selected grants: The following grants are a representative sample of this grantmaker's funding activity:
$200,000 to Duke University, Durham, NC, 2011. For endowment.
$193,200 to University of North Carolina, Chapel Hill, NC, 2010. For endowment.
$133,200 to University of North Carolina, Chapel Hill, NC, 2011. For endowment.
$25,000 to Durham Nativity School, Durham, NC, 2011.
$2,000 to Medical Foundation of North Carolina, Chapel Hill, NC, 2011.

7347
John B. & Brownie Young Memorial Fund ✧
c/o BB&T
P.O. Box 2907
Wilson, NC 27894-2907
Scholarship application address: Karen Taber, 230 Frederica St., Owensboro, KY 42301, tel.: (270) 685-4466

Established in 1961 in KY.
Donor: Gates Young Trust.
Foundation type: Independent foundation.
Financial data (yr. ended 12/31/12): Assets, $16,240,918 (M); gifts received, $78,850; expenditures, $1,169,944; qualifying distributions, $1,092,825; giving activities include $1,000,481 for 57 grants (high: $318,487; low: $50).
Purpose and activities: Scholarships to unmarried and full-time students in the school districts of Daviess, McClean, and Owensboro counties in KY.
Fields of interest: Education.
Type of support: Scholarships—to individuals.
Limitations: Giving limited to Davies, McLean, and Owensboro school districts in KY.
Application information: Applications available at area high schools. Application form required.
Deadline(s): Beginning of college year
Trustee: BB&T.
EIN: 616025137
Selected grants: The following grants are a representative sample of this grantmaker's funding activity:
$6,022 to Florida College, Temple Terrace, FL, 2012. For scholarships.

7348
The Yount Foundation, Inc. ✧ ☆
1234 S. Center St.
Hickory, NC 28601-5042

Established in 2006 in NC.
Donors: Benny Yount; Paraount Kia of Asheville; Paramount Motor Sales, LLC; BCL, LLC; Paramount Ford, LLC.
Foundation type: Independent foundation.
Financial data (yr. ended 12/31/12): Assets, $99,716 (M); expenditures, $617,524; qualifying distributions, $593,499; giving activities include $593,499 for 30 grants (high: $235,879; low: $100).
Fields of interest: Higher education; Christian agencies & churches; Protestant agencies & churches.
Limitations: Applications not accepted. Giving primarily in MO and NC.
Application information: Contributes only to pre-selected organizations.
Officers: Benny Yount, Pres.; Cherrie Yount, V.P.; Nick Kincaid, Secy.; Lisa Yount, Treas.
EIN: 205240159

7349
Zinc Saves Kids Inc ✧ ☆
1822 E. NC Hwy 54
Durham, NC 27713

Donors: Goldcorp; International Zinc Association; Weigel Verwaltung BMBH GO; Nyrstar Sanv E; Teck Resources Ltd; Xstrata Zinc; Boliden Commercial Lab; Votorantim Metals Ltd; Kazzinc AP; Penoles Met-Mex La; Mitsui Mining Smelting; Korea Zinc Co Ltd; Hudbay Minerals; Ind Minera Mexico; Portovesme SRL E; Exxaro Resources Ltd SA; Sumitomo Metal Mining AP; Breakwater RES Ltd NA; Hecla Mining; Umicore Zinc Chemicals; Bhp Billiton; Befesa Zinc SLU; Umicore Building Products; JCS Chelyabinsk ZP E; KCM-SA; Votorantim Metals Cajamarquilla; HC Miasteczko E; US Zinc A Votorantim Metals Company; Doe Run Res USA.
Foundation type: Independent foundation.
Financial data (yr. ended 12/31/12): Assets, $688,938 (M); gifts received, $1,508,030; expenditures, $510,484; qualifying distributions, $500,000; giving activities include $500,000 for grants.
Fields of interest: Human services; Children.
Limitations: Applications not accepted. Giving primarily in New York, NY.
Application information: Unsolicited requests for funds not accepted.
Officers: George Vary,* Secy.; Dawn Raymond, Treas.; Steven Wilkinston, Exec. Dir.
EIN: 272477476

NORTH DAKOTA

7350
The Barry Foundation ✧
15 N. Broadway, Ste. 600
Fargo, ND 58102-4908

Established in 1986.
Foundation type: Independent foundation.
Financial data (yr. ended 12/31/13): Assets, $44,764,961 (M); gifts received, $88,000; expenditures, $2,104,251; qualifying distributions, $1,971,501; giving activities include $1,525,390 for 169 grants (high: $500,000; low: $50), and $86,652 for foundation-administered programs.
Fields of interest: Arts; Education; Environment; Health care; Social entrepreneurship; Spirituality.
Limitations: Applications not accepted.
Application information: Contributes only to pre-selected organizations.
Officer and Director:* Marty Hoffmann, Secy. and Exec. Dir.
EIN: 205767275

7351
Fargo-Moorhead Area Foundation ✧
502 1st Ave. N., Ste. 202
Fargo, ND 58102-4804 (701) 234-0756
Contact: Lexi Oestreich, Admin. Asst.; For grants and scholarships: Cher Hersrud, Prog. Off.
FAX: (701) 234-9724;
E-mail: lexi@areafoundation.org; Additional grant and scholarship info.: cher@areafoundation.org; Main URL: http://www.areafoundation.org

Established in 1960 in ND.
Foundation type: Community foundation.
Financial data (yr. ended 12/31/13): Assets, $66,228,545 (M); gifts received, $5,346,108; expenditures, $2,660,145; giving activities include $1,137,429 for 71+ grants (high: $95,000), and $238,270 for 153 grants to individuals.
Purpose and activities: The foundation seeks to enrich the quality of life of the people in the Clay County, MN, and Cass County, ND, area by encouraging philanthropy and developing permanent endowment, assessing and responding to emerging and changing community needs, providing flexibility for donors with varied interests and levels of giving capabilities, and serving as a resource and catalyst for other organizations.
Fields of interest: Arts; Education; Environment; Animals/wildlife; Health care; Health organizations, association; Employment; Agriculture/food; Housing/shelter; Safety/disasters; Recreation; Youth development; Children/youth, services; Human services; Community/economic development; Government/public administration; Public affairs; Youth.
Type of support: Scholarships—to individuals; Management development/capacity building; Capital campaigns; Building/renovation; Equipment; Emergency funds; Program development; Scholarship funds; Technical assistance; In-kind gifts; Matching/challenge support.
Limitations: Applications accepted. Giving limited to Clay County, MN, and Cass County, ND. No support for religious purposes. No grants to individuals (except for scholarships), or for operating expenses (except for limited experimental or start-up periods), annual appeals or membership drives, capital debt reduction, or organizations which have outstanding reports from previous Fargo-Moorhead Foundation grants.
Publications: Application guidelines; Annual report; Newsletter; Program policy statement.
Application information: Visit foundation web site for application form and guidelines. Application form required.
Initial approach: Submit application form and attachments
Copies of proposal: 1
Deadline(s): Apr. 18
Board meeting date(s): Quarterly
Final notification: 6 weeks
Officers and Directors:* Carol Schlossman,* Chair.; Morrie Lanning,* Vice-Chair.; Laine Brantner,* Secy.; Dorwin Marquardt,* Treas.; Tim Beaton, Exec. Dir.; Tom Dawson; Corey Elmer; Bruce Furness; Thomas Jefferson; Susan E. Johnson-Drenth; Neil Jordheim; Dr. Joel Jorgenson; Joan Justesen; Matthew Mohr; Lisa Vatnsdal.
Trustee Banks: Alerus Financial; Bank of the West; Bremer Bank, N.A.; Heartland Trust Co.; State Bank & Trust Co.; U.S. National Bank; Wells Fargo Bank, N.A.
Number of staff: 3 full-time professional; 1 full-time support; 1 part-time support.
EIN: 456010377

7352
Edson & Margaret Larson Foundation ✧
406 Main Ave.
Fargo, ND 58126-0002
E-mail: grantadministration@wellsfargo.com; Main URL: https://www.wellsfargo.com/privatefoundationgrants/larson

Established in ND.
Donor: Margaret Larson.
Foundation type: Independent foundation.
Financial data (yr. ended 12/31/12): Assets, $16,062,665 (M); expenditures, $756,433; qualifying distributions, $858,612; giving activities include $588,000 for 5 grants (high: $380,000; low: $25,000).
Fields of interest: Performing arts, education; Higher education; Community/economic development; Public affairs.
Limitations: Applications accepted. Giving primarily in ND. No grants to individuals.
Application information: See foundation website for complete application guidelines. Application form required.
Deadline(s): Sept. 30
Officers: Douglas A. Christensen, Pres.; Andrew B. Kjos, Secy.-Treas.
Trustees: Julie A. Barner; Harold Newman; Drew Wrigley.
EIN: 271507358

7353
The Tom and Frances Leach Foundation Inc. ✧
(also known as Leach Foundation)
1720 Burn Boat Dr.
P.O. Box 1136
Bismarck, ND 58502-1136 (701) 255-0479
E-mail: leachfoundation@midconetwork.com; Main URL: http://www.leachfoundation.org

Established in 1955 in ND.
Donors: Thomas W. Leach†; Frances V. Leach†.
Foundation type: Independent foundation.
Financial data (yr. ended 12/31/12): Assets, $16,393,131 (M); expenditures, $704,027; qualifying distributions, $556,654; giving activities include $491,750 for 62 grants (high: $160,000; low: $1,250).
Purpose and activities: Primary areas of interest include the arts and humanities, education, human services, medical sciences and health, and the social sciences.
Fields of interest: Visual arts; Performing arts; Arts; Education, early childhood education; Child development, education; Higher education; Public health school/education; Medicine/medical care, public education; Hospitals (general); Health care; Human services; Children/youth, services; Child development, services; Children/youth; Youth; Adults; Disabilities, people with; Physically disabled; Blind/visually impaired; Mentally disabled; Native Americans/American Indians; Substance abusers; Crime/abuse victims; Homeless.
Type of support: General/operating support; Continuing support; Capital campaigns; Building/renovation; Equipment; Emergency funds; Program development; Curriculum development; Scholarship funds; Technical assistance; Matching/challenge support.
Limitations: Applications accepted. Giving primarily in ND, particularly in Bismarck and Mandan, and the upper Midwest. No grants for travel, or for fellowships or conferences; generally, limited grants for capital expenditures or endowments.
Publications: Application guidelines; Annual report; Informational brochure.
Application information: Application guidelines and form available on foundation web site. Submitted material should not be stapled. Application form required.
Initial approach: Cover letter and application form
Copies of proposal: 1
Deadline(s): June 30
Board meeting date(s): May and Nov.
Final notification: Dec.
Officers: Frank Bavendick, Chair.; Brian Bjella, Pres.; William Daniel, V.P.; Todd Steinwand, Secy.-Treas.
Directors: Don K. Clement; John T. Roswick; Paul D. Schliesman.
Number of staff: 1 full-time support.
EIN: 456012703

7354
MDU Resources Foundation ✧
P.O. Box 5650
Bismarck, ND 58506-5650
Contact: Rita O'Neill, Fdn. Mgr.
FAX: (701) 530-1737;
E-mail: rita.o'neill@MDUResources.com; Main URL: http://www.mdu.com/integrity/foundation

Established in 1983 in ND.
Donors: MDU Resources Group, Inc.; WBI Energy, Inc.; Knife River Corp.; Montana Dakota Utilities Co.; WBI Energy Transmission, Inc.; MDU Construction Services Grp.; Fidelity Exploration & Production Co.; Great Plains Natural Gas Co.; Cascade Natural Gas Corp.; Intermountain Gas Co.; WBI Energy Midstream, LLC.
Foundation type: Company-sponsored foundation.
Financial data (yr. ended 12/31/13): Assets, $5,012,090 (M); gifts received, $1,613,244; expenditures, $1,658,953; qualifying distributions, $1,657,953; giving activities include $1,652,570 for 593 grants (high: $50,000; low: $50).
Purpose and activities: The foundation supports organizations involved with arts and culture, education, the environment, health, human services, community development, civic affairs, and senior citizens.
Fields of interest: Arts councils; Museums; Performing arts, theater; Arts; Secondary school/education; Higher education; Business school/education; Libraries (public); Education; Environment, natural resources; Environment; Hospitals (general); Health care; Youth, services; Human services; Community/economic development; Aging.
Type of support: General/operating support; Continuing support; Annual campaigns; Capital campaigns; Building/renovation; Equipment; Program development; Scholarship funds; Employee volunteer services; Employee matching gifts; Employee-related scholarships.
Limitations: Applications accepted. Giving primarily in areas of company operations. No support for athletic, labor, fraternal, political, lobbying, organizations or regional or national organizations without local affiliation. No grants to individuals (except for employee-related scholarships), or for economic development; no loans or venture capital requests.
Publications: Application guidelines; Annual report; Program policy statement.
Application information: Application form required.
Initial approach: Download application form and mail to local MDU Resources office
Copies of proposal: 1
Deadline(s): Oct. 1
Board meeting date(s): Jan.
Officers and Directors:* Cynthia J. Norland,* Pres.; Paul K. Sandness,* V.P.; Rita R. O'Neill, Secy. and Mgr.; Douglas A. Mahowald,* Treas.; Steven L. Bietz; Nancy K. Christenson; K. Frank Morehouse; Thomas D. Nosbusch; J. Kent Wells.
Number of staff: 1 full-time professional.
EIN: 450378937
Selected grants: The following grants are a representative sample of this grantmaker's funding activity:
$5,000 to Mountain States Legal Foundation, Lakewood, CO, 2012. For civic/community grans.
$5,000 to Young Life, Colorado Springs, CO, 2012. For Health and Human Services Grants.
$3,000 to YMCA of Metropolitan Denver, Denver, CO, 2012. For civic/community grants.
$2,500 to Washakie Museum, Worland, WY, 2012. For culture/arts grants.
$1,000 to Montana Raptor Conservation Center, Bozeman, MT, 2012. For environmental grants.
$1,000 to Yakima Valley Community College, Yakima, WA, 2012. For education grants.
$500 to Nampa Christian Schools, Nampa, ID, 2012. For education grants.

7355
Myra Foundation ✧ ☆
P.O. Box 13536
Grand Forks, ND 58208-3536 (701) 795-3414
Contact: John V. Botsford, Pres.
E-mail: jbotsford@myrafoundation.org; Main URL: http://myrafoundation.org/index.html
Grants List: http://myrafoundation.org/current_receipients.html

Incorporated in 1941 in ND.
Donor: John E. Myra†.
Foundation type: Independent foundation.
Financial data (yr. ended 12/31/13): Assets, $7,190,699 (M); expenditures, $710,659; qualifying distributions, $587,868; giving activities include $257,742 for 93 grants (high: $36,000; low: $100).
Fields of interest: Education; Agriculture/food; Human services.
Type of support: General/operating support; Building/renovation; Equipment; Scholarship funds.
Limitations: Applications accepted. Giving primarily in Grand Forks County, ND. No grants to individuals, or for endowment funds, research, or matching gifts; no loans.
Publications: Informational brochure (including application guidelines).
Application information: See foundation web site for complete application guidelines. Application form not required.
Initial approach: Proposal
Copies of proposal: 1
Deadline(s): Nov. 1
Board meeting date(s): Quarterly
Officers: John Botsford, Pres.; Donna J. Gillig, Secy.-Treas.
Director: Kent Cronquist.
EIN: 450215088

7356
The R. B. Nordick Foundation ✧
675 12th Ave. N.E.
West Fargo, ND 58078-3500

Established in 1995 in ND.
Donor: Ralph B. Nordick.
Foundation type: Independent foundation.
Financial data (yr. ended 12/31/12): Assets, $42,016,335 (M); expenditures, $2,170,062; qualifying distributions, $2,124,921; giving activities include $2,113,300 for 23 grants (high: $380,000; low: $9,000).
Fields of interest: Christian agencies & churches.
Limitations: Applications not accepted. Giving in the U.S., with emphasis on CA, GA, MN, and PA. No grants to individuals.
Application information: Contributes only to pre-selected organizations.
Officers: Ralph B. Nordick, Pres.; Brett A. Nordick, V.P.; Douglas R. Geeslin, Secy.-Treas.
EIN: 450442920

7357
North Dakota Community Foundation ✧
(also known as NDCF)
309 N. Mandan St., Ste. 2
P.O. Box 387
Bismarck, ND 58502-0387 (701) 222-8349
Contact: Kevin J. Dvorak, C.E.O.; Kara Geiger, Devel. Dir.-West; Jordan J. Neufeld, Admin. and Acct.
E-mail: jordan@ndcf.net; Grand Forks Office: P.O. Box 5155, Grand Forks, ND 58206-5155; Additional e-mails: amy@ndcf.net, kara@ndcf.net, and jordan@ndcf.net; Main URL: http://www.ndcf.net
Facebook: http://www.facebook.com/NDCommunityFoundation

Established in 1977 in ND.
Foundation type: Community foundation.
Financial data (yr. ended 12/31/12): Assets, $46,925,453 (M); gifts received, $3,991,052; expenditures, $2,464,185; giving activities include $1,420,836 for 47 grants (high: $146,045), and $471,784 for 306 grants to individuals.
Purpose and activities: The foundation seeks to improve the quality of life for North Dakota's citizens through charitable giving and promoting philanthropy. Unrestricted funds largely for aid to the elderly and disadvantaged; support also for health services, including mental health, youth agencies, parks and recreation, and arts and cultural programs in ND.
Fields of interest: Historical activities; Arts; Higher education; Education; Environment; Health care; Mental health/crisis services; Recreation; Children/youth, services; Aging, centers/services; Human services; Community/economic development; Children/youth; Youth; Aging; Economically disadvantaged; Homeless.
Type of support: General/operating support; Annual campaigns; Building/renovation; Equipment; Endowments; Program development; Conferences/seminars; Publication; Seed money; Scholarship funds; Research; Scholarships—to individuals; Matching/challenge support.
Limitations: Applications accepted. Giving primarily in North Dakota and organizations supporting North Dakota. No support for sectarian projects or national organizations (generally). No grants to individuals (except for scholarships), or for multi-year commitments.
Publications: Application guidelines; Annual report; Annual report (including application guidelines); Financial statement; Grants list; Informational brochure; Informational brochure (including application guidelines); Newsletter; Occasional report.
Application information: Visit foundation web site for application guidelines. If the foundation's board is interested in additional information, formal application materials are sent in late September. Requests not continuing through the process will be notified by the first of October. Grants do not exceed $5,000. Application form not required.
Initial approach: Letter of Inquiry (not exceeding 2 pages)
Copies of proposal: 1
Deadline(s): Aug. 15 for letter of inquiry
Board meeting date(s): Mid-Sept.
Final notification: End of Dec.
Officers and Directors:* Aaron Schmit,* Chair.; Kevin J. Dvorak,* C.E.O. and Pres.; Jordan J. Neufeld,* C.F.O.; Nancy Johnson; Dawn Keeley; Christie Obenauer; Donald Oppegard; Steve Ottmar; Chad Peterson; Diane Peyerl; Douglass Prchal; Jennifer Rasch; Scott Swenson; Becky Thatcher-Keller; David Trottier; LouAnn Waliser.
Number of staff: 3 full-time professional; 1 full-time support.
EIN: 450336015
Selected grants: The following grants are a representative sample of this grantmaker's funding activity:

$122,031 to United Way, Souris Valley, Minot, ND, 2012. To be used by The Souris River Basin Unmet Needs Committee to support flood victims.
$61,000 to North Valley Career and Technology Center, Grafton, ND, 2012. For the purchase of the first digital projector for the Save Our Strand project.
$50,000 to Northern Cass School District, Hunter, ND, 2012. For school gymnasium commitment.
$50,000 to Northern Cass School District, Hunter, ND, 2013. For school gymnasium commitment.
$48,159 to Job Development Authority of Arthur, Arthur, ND, 2013. For project support.
$47,060 to Ellendale Public School Foundation, Ellendale, ND, 2013. To close out the Alternative Projects Fundraising Fund.
$46,699 to Cavalier Arts and Crafts Society, Cavalier, ND, 2013. For the purchase of the required digital projector equipment.
$37,680 to Job Development Authority of Arthur, Arthur, ND, 2012. For improvements to community projects.
$30,000 to HIT Foundation Plus, Mandan, ND, 2012.
$20,000 to Killdeer Area Ambulance Service, Killdeer, ND, 2013. For emergency medical equipment.
$19,158 to Oakes Park Board, Oakes, ND, 2012. For Flood Mitigation Costs in Dickey County.
$16,380 to Carrington Health Center, Carrington, ND, 2012.
$10,085 to Larimore Public School District No. 44, Larimore, ND, 2012.
$10,000 to Pembina Community Center, Pembina, ND, 2013. For the renovation project.
$6,305 to Oakes Park Board, Oakes, ND, 2013. For flood mitigation costs in Dickey County.
$6,000 to Bismarck-Mandan Orchestral Association, Bismarck, ND, 2013. For annual income distribution.
$5,000 to Cass County Historical Society, West Fargo, ND, 2012. For the Arthur Town Hall Building Project.
$5,000 to Dollars for Scholars - Northern Cass, Arthur, ND, 2013. For scholarships.
$4,947 to New Rockford Golf Course, New Rockford, ND, 2012. To distribute funds to Pay for NR Golf Building Project.
$2,500 to Salvation Army of Grand Forks, Grand Forks, ND, 2013. For the Sox For Kids Program.

7358
Ronald D. Offutt Family Foundation ✧
700 S. 7th St.
Fargo, ND 58103-2704

Donors: Ronald D. Offutt; Karen Offutt.
Foundation type: Independent foundation.
Financial data (yr. ended 12/31/13): Assets, $124,144 (M); gifts received, $996,188; expenditures, $982,016; qualifying distributions, $982,016; giving activities include $980,982 for 27 grants (high: $657,038; low: $500).
Fields of interest: Higher education, university; Education; Youth development; Religion.
Limitations: Applications not accepted. Giving primarily in ND.
Application information: Unsolicited requests for funds not accepted.
Officer and Trustees:* Thomas K. Espel,* Admin.; Allan F. Knoll; Rondi McGovern; Shelly Neal; Karen Offutt; Ronald D. Offutt.
EIN: 266574983
Selected grants: The following grants are a representative sample of this grantmaker's funding activity:
$582,038 to Concordia College, Moorhead, MN, 2012. For $250,000 Stadium Fund $332,038 School Endowment.
$50,000 to University of Mary, Bismarck, ND, 2012. For student center.
$25,000 to University of Puget Sound, Tacoma, WA, 2012. For Center for Health.
$5,000 to Red Willow Ministries, Binford, ND, 2012. For camp ministry.
$2,000 to Lakes Area Community Center, Battle Lake, MN, 2012. To upgrade heating.
$1,250 to Dakota Stage Limited, Bismarck, ND, 2012. For Community Theater.

7359
Scheels All Sports Foundation ✧
4550 15th Ave. S.
Fargo, ND 58103-8959

Established in ND.
Donors: Fred B. Scheel; Community Foundation of Johnson County.
Foundation type: Independent foundation.
Financial data (yr. ended 12/31/13): Assets, $29,180,812 (M); expenditures, $2,830,811; qualifying distributions, $2,800,811; giving activities include $2,788,800 for 24 grants (high: $100,000; low: $9,000).
Fields of interest: Economic development; Business/industry; Foundations (private grantmaking); Science, reform.
Type of support: General/operating support.
Limitations: Applications not accepted. Giving primarily in ND. No grants to individuals.
Application information: Unsolicited requests for funds not acknowledged or accepted under any circumstances.
Officers: Steve D. Scheel, Pres.; Steve M. Scheel, V.P.; Michelle Killoran, Secy.-Treas.
Directors: Matt R. Hanson; Karen S. Jones; Kevin J. Lambley; Bill D. Nelson.
EIN: 450447707

7360
Alex Stern Family Foundation ✧
4141 28th Ave. S.
Fargo, ND 58104-8468
Contact: Donald L. Scott, Exec. Dir.
FAX: (701) 271-0408; E-mail: donlscott@yahoo.com

Established in 1964 in ND.
Donors: William Stern†; Sam Stern†; Edward A. Stern†.
Foundation type: Independent foundation.
Financial data (yr. ended 12/31/13): Assets, $9,767,194 (M); expenditures, $502,208; qualifying distributions, $454,527; giving activities include $428,250 for 50 grants (high: $75,000; low: $1,000).
Purpose and activities: Primary areas of interest include the arts, child welfare, the elderly, alcohol abuse programs, and community funds. Support also for family and social services, including legal services, and welfare for the homeless and disabled; community organizations; higher, business, minority, and other education; and hospices and cancer research.
Fields of interest: Museums; Performing arts; Performing arts, dance; Performing arts, theater; Historic preservation/historical societies; Arts; Child development, education; Higher education; Substance abuse, services; Alcoholism; Legal services; Housing/shelter, development; Human services; Children/youth, services; Child development, services; Family services; Residential/custodial care, hospices; Aging, centers/services; Homeless, human services; Aging; Disabilities, people with; Minorities; Native Americans/American Indians; Economically disadvantaged; Homeless.
Type of support: General/operating support; Continuing support; Annual campaigns; Capital campaigns; Building/renovation; Equipment; Emergency funds; Program development; Scholarship funds; Research; Technical assistance; Matching/challenge support.
Limitations: Applications accepted. Giving limited to the Moorhead, MN, and Fargo, ND areas. No grants to individuals, or for endowment funds; no loans.
Publications: Application guidelines; Annual report.
Application information: Application form required.
Initial approach: Letter requesting application and guidelines
Copies of proposal: 3
Deadline(s): Mar. 31 for spring consideration and Aug. 31 for fall consideration
Board meeting date(s): Varies
Final notification: Within a few months
Officer and Trustees:* Donald L. Scott,* Exec. Dir.; Dan Carey; H. Michael Hardy.
Number of staff: 1 full-time professional.
EIN: 456013981
Selected grants: The following grants are a representative sample of this grantmaker's funding activity:
$10,000 to Daily Bread, Fargo, ND, 2012. For Daily Bread and Backpack Program.
$5,000 to CHARISM, Fargo, ND, 2012. For Living, Learning, and Leading Project.
$5,000 to Hospice of the Red River Valley, Fargo, ND, 2012. For Update Resource Library.
$3,000 to Impact Foundation, Fargo, ND, 2012. For 25 Sets Golf Clubs for Low Income.
$1,500 to Learning Bank, Fargo, ND, 2012. For Fine Art Series Project.

7361
Wanzek Family Foundation ✧
c/o Jon Wanzek
421 Harwood Dr. S.
Fargo, ND 58104-6229

Donor: Jon Wanzek.
Foundation type: Independent foundation.
Financial data (yr. ended 12/31/13): Assets, $7,529,540 (M); expenditures, $833,377; qualifying distributions, $799,554; giving activities include $792,967 for 23 grants (high: $275,500; low: $150).
Fields of interest: Education; Human services; Catholic agencies & churches.
Limitations: Applications not accepted. Giving primarily in Fargo, ND.
Application information: Contributes only to pre-selected organizations.
Officer: Jon Wanzek, Pres. and Secy.-Treas.
Directors: Anna Wanzek; Lori Wanzek.
EIN: 263854153

Selected grants: The following grants are a representative sample of this grantmaker's funding activity:

$65,000 to Dakota Medical Foundation, Fargo, ND, 2011.
$50,000 to Diocese of Fargo, Fargo, ND, 2011.
$15,000 to Real Presence Radio, Grand Forks, ND, 2011.

OHIO

7362
58 Partners Foundation ✧ ☆
2500 Farmers Dr., Ste. 140
Columbus, OH 43235-5706

Donors: Charley Shin; Gosh Enterprises.
Foundation type: Independent foundation.
Financial data (yr. ended 12/31/12): Assets, $2,420,587 (M); gifts received, $1,034,570; expenditures, $558,395; qualifying distributions, $515,176; giving activities include $515,176 for grants.
Fields of interest: Agriculture/food; Human services; Christian agencies & churches.
Limitations: Applications not accepted. Giving in the U.S.; funding also internationally, particularly in China and the U.K.
Application information: Unsolicited requests for funds not accepted.
Officers: Charley Shin, Pres.; Candra Alisiswanto, V.P.; Ines Lee, Secy.
EIN: 274199218

7363
A Good Neighbor Foundation ✧
414 Walnut St., Ste. 1014
Cincinnati, OH 45202-3913 (513) 651-9333
Contact: T. Hunley

Established in 2002 in OH.
Donor: Gloria J. Fehr.
Foundation type: Independent foundation.
Financial data (yr. ended 06/30/13): Assets, $27,779,855 (M); expenditures, $3,855,363; qualifying distributions, $3,591,784; giving activities include $3,311,831 for grants.
Fields of interest: Human services; Foundations (private grantmaking).
Type of support: General/operating support; Grants to individuals.
Limitations: Giving primarily in Cincinnati, OH.
Application information:
Initial approach: Letter
Deadline(s): None
Officers and Directors:* James Minutolo,* Pres.; Betty Bassett,* V.P.; Donald Feldman,* Treas.; Gary Salquist; Emily K. Uhl.
EIN: 223885976

7364
Abar Foundation ✧
Plaza South Two
7261 Engle Rd., Ste. 202
Cleveland, OH 44130-3479

Established in 2000 in NJ.
Donors: Robert A. Hoff; Mrs. Robert A. Hoff; Robert A. & Ann W. Hoff Family Trust.
Foundation type: Independent foundation.
Financial data (yr. ended 07/31/13): Assets, $19,790,458 (M); expenditures, $1,884,273; qualifying distributions, $1,649,500; giving activities include $1,649,500 for 23 grants (high: $300,000; low: $9,500).
Fields of interest: Human services; Foundations (private grantmaking).
Limitations: Applications not accepted. Giving primarily in CA; some funding also in UT. No grants to individuals.
Application information: Contributes only to pre-selected organizations.
Officers: Robert A. Hoff, Pres. and C.F.O.; Ann W. Hoff, Secy.
EIN: 330928475

7365
The Abington Foundation ✧
c/o Foundation Mgmt. Svcs., Inc.
1422 Euclid Ave., Ste. 966
Cleveland, OH 44115-2001 (216) 621-2901
Contact: Cristin Slesh, Consultant
FAX: (216) 621-8198;
E-mail: abington@fmscleveland.com; Main URL: http://www.fmscleveland.com/abington
Grants List: http://www.fmscleveland.com/abington/grants.cfm

Established in 1983 in OH.
Donors: David Knight Ford†; Elizabeth Brooks Ford†.
Foundation type: Independent foundation.
Financial data (yr. ended 12/31/13): Assets, $31,109,559 (M); expenditures, $1,537,002; qualifying distributions, $1,434,874; giving activities include $1,244,100 for 90 grants (high: $75,000; low: $3,000).
Purpose and activities: The foundation was established to support organizations that promote education, health care, economic independence and cultural activities in Cuyahoga County, Ohio. The current priority is urban education.
Fields of interest: Education; Health care; Human services; Children/youth; Youth; Aging; Economically disadvantaged.
Type of support: Management development/capacity building; Capital campaigns; Building/renovation; Program development.
Limitations: Applications accepted. Giving primarily in Cuyahoga County, OH. No grants to individuals; no support for endowments, sponsorships, seminars, or general operating support.
Publications: Financial statement.
Application information: The foundation has adopted an online application form for all grant requests. Application guidelines and procedures available on foundation web site. Mass mailings not accepted. Application form required.
Initial approach: Use online application form on foundation web site
Deadline(s): May 1, Sept. 1, and Dec. 1. When a deadline falls on a weekend or a holiday, the proposal must be submitted by 4:00 p.m. the following business day. See foundation web site for any updates on deadlines
Board meeting date(s): Jan., June, and Nov.
Final notification: 2 weeks after board meeting
Officers and Trustees:* Allen H. Ford,* Pres.; Charles Ford,* V.P.; Alex Ford; David Ford, Jr.; David Kingsley Ford; Lise Ford; Ned Ford; Sarah Ford Whitener.
EIN: 341404854
Selected grants: The following grants are a representative sample of this grantmaker's funding activity:
$200,000 to Cleveland Metropolitan School District, Cleveland, OH, 2011. For PATHS program, which provides social/emotional skills for students to improve academic achievement, payable over 2.00 years.
$50,000 to Cleveland Play House, Cleveland, OH, 2011. To build Allen Theatre Complex, three theatre center for performing arts and arts education, in partnership with Playhouse Square and Cleveland State University.
$30,000 to College Now Greater Cleveland, Cleveland, OH, 2011. To provide advisory services program in Cleveland Metropolitan School District.
$25,000 to Family Promise of Greater Cleveland, Cleveland, OH, 2011. For operating support for work to help homeless families achieve self-sufficiency.
$20,000 to Great Lakes Museum of Science, Environment and Technology, Great Lakes Science Center, Cleveland, OH, 2011. For summer programming for low-income students.
$20,000 to Literacy Cooperative of Greater Cleveland, Cleveland, OH, 2011. For SPARK (Supporting Partnerships to Assure Ready Kids), pre-school intervention program.
$15,000 to America SCORES Cleveland, Cleveland, OH, 2011. For after-school health and literacy programming in the Cleveland Metropolitan School District.
$15,000 to Salvation Army of Greater Cleveland, Cleveland, OH, 2011. For after-school and summer programming.
$10,000 to Eleanor B. Rainey Memorial Institute, Cleveland, OH, 2011. For after-school and Saturday arts programming.
$10,000 to Suicide Prevention Education Alliance of Northeast Ohio, Cleveland, OH, 2011. For suicide prevention education.

7366
AK Steel Foundation ✧
9227 Centre Pointe Dr.
West Chester, OH 45069-4822 (513) 425-5038
Main URL: http://www.aksteel.com/company/corporate-citizenship/
Application address for scholarships: c/o Middletown Community Foundation, 36 Donham Plaza, Middletown, OH 45042, tel.: (513) 424-7369; URL: http://www.mcfoundation.org

Established in 1989 in OH.
Donors: AK Steel Corp.; Kawasaki Steel Investments, Inc.
Foundation type: Company-sponsored foundation.
Financial data (yr. ended 12/31/13): Assets, $12,956,938 (M); expenditures, $1,499,044; qualifying distributions, $1,487,720; giving activities include $1,279,645 for 51 grants (high: $390,000; low: $500), and $169,349 for 431 employee matching gifts.
Purpose and activities: The foundation supports museums and community foundations and organizations involved with health, Down syndrome, cancer, heart disease, diabetes, human services, and international relief and awards college scholarships to the children of employees of AK Steel and to African-American high school seniors attending high schools in Butler and Warren counties, Ohio.
Fields of interest: Museums; Health care, volunteer services; Hospitals (general); Health care, clinics/centers; Health care; Down syndrome; Cancer; Cancer, leukemia; Heart & circulatory diseases; Diabetes; Cancer research; Boy scouts; American Red Cross; YM/YWCAs & YM/YWHAs; Children/youth, services; Aging, centers/services; Developmentally disabled, centers & services; Human services; International relief; Foundations

(community); United Ways and Federated Giving Programs; African Americans/Blacks.
Type of support: General/operating support; Continuing support; Annual campaigns; Employee matching gifts; Employee-related scholarships; Scholarships—to individuals.
Limitations: Applications accepted. Giving primarily in areas of company operations, with emphasis on OH.
Application information: The Louis F. Cox Memorial AK Steel African-American Scholarships are administered by the Middletown Community Foundation.
Initial approach: Contact application address for application form for Louis F. Cox Memorial AK Steel African-American Scholarships
Deadline(s): Dec. 31 for Louis F. Cox Memorial AK Steel African-American Scholarships
Officers and Trustees:* James L. Wainscott,* Chair.; Sarah Cunningham, Secy. and Exec. Dir.; Doug Mitterholzer, Treas.; Alan H. McCoy; Albert E. Ferrara, Jr.; David C. Horn; John F. Kaloski.
Number of staff: 1 part-time professional.
EIN: 311284344

7367
Akron Community Foundation ✧
345 W. Cedar St.
Akron, OH 44307 (330) 376-8522
Contact: John T. Petures, Jr., C.E.O.
FAX: (330) 376-0202;
E-mail: acfmail@akroncommunityfdn.org; Main URL: http://www.akroncf.org/
Facebook: http://www.facebook.com/pages/Akron-Community-Foundation/107558384403
Twitter: https://twitter.com/AkronCF

Incorporated in 1955 in OH.
Foundation type: Community foundation.
Financial data (yr. ended 03/31/14): Assets, $180,986,117 (M); gifts received, $20,159,760; expenditures, $10,020,062; giving activities include $7,214,932 for 470+ grants (high: $246,200; low: $100).
Purpose and activities: To improve the quality of life in greater Akron by building permanent endowments and providing philanthropic leadership that enables you to make a lasting investment in the community. To fulfill this mission, the foundation is committed to: 1) serving Akron and surrounding areas with creative, visionary and sensitive grants that address the evolving needs of an area experiencing rapid economic and social change; 2) devoting special emphasis to programs that enrich the community in the following distinct areas: arts and culture, education, health and human services, and civic affairs; 3) advising fundholders in areas of charitable concern and helping them achieving the highest likelihood of beneficial results; and 4) demonstrating community leadership by designing innovative programs and acting as a catalyst in identifying problems and sharing information with other funders.
Fields of interest: Media, film/video; Museums; Performing arts; Historic preservation/historical societies; Arts; Education; Environment; Health care; Mental health/crisis services; Health organizations, association; Medical research, institute; Medical research; Employment; Disasters, fire prevention/control; Disasters, Hurricane Katrina; Recreation; Children/youth, services; Children, day care; Family services; Aging, centers/services; Human services; Civil/human rights, advocacy; Community/economic development; Consumer protection; Public affairs; Aging; Disabilities, people with; African Americans/Blacks; Women; AIDS, people with; Immigrants/refugees; Economically disadvantaged; Homeless; LGBTQ.
Type of support: Program development; Seed money; Scholarship funds; Research; Matching/challenge support.
Limitations: Applications accepted. Giving primarily in Summit County, OH. No support for religious organizations for religious purposes. No grants for endowment funds, capital campaigns, or fellowships; no loans.
Publications: Application guidelines; Annual report (including application guidelines); Newsletter.
Application information: Visit foundation web site for online pre-application form and application guidelines. The foundation accepts full proposals based on pre-application form. No more than 1 grant to an organization in a 12-month period. Application form required.
Initial approach: Complete online pre-application form
Deadline(s): Full proposals are due: Apr. 1 for Arts and Culture, July 1 for Civic Affairs, and Oct. 1 for Health and Human Services and Dec. 15 for Education and Early Education
Board meeting date(s): Generally Feb., May, Aug., and Nov.
Final notification: 8 weeks
Officers and Trustees:* Mark Allio,* Chair.; Steven Cox,* Vice-Chair.; John T. Petures, Jr., C.E.O. and Pres.; Tina Boyes, V.P., Mktg. and Comms.; John Garofalo, V.P., Community Investment; Margaret Medzie, V.P., Devel. and Donor Engagement; Steven Schloenbach, V.P. and C.F.O.; Rev. Sandra F. Selby,* Secy.; Paul Belair,* Treas.; Dennis Jansky, Cont.; Virginia Albanese; F. Steven Albrecht; Nick Browning; Tommy Bruno; Marilyn Myers Buckey; Robert Cooper; Olivia Demas; Samuel DeShazior; Edward Eliopoulos; Rick Fedorovich; Sarah Friebert, M.D.; Tom Knoll; Mark Krohn; Dee Lowery; Rob Malone; Vivian Neal; Steve Strayer; Mike Sweeney; Mike Zeleznik.
Trustee Banks: Brandes Investment Partners; Clover Capital Mgmt.; FirstMerit Bank, N.A.; Frontier Capital Mgmt.; JPMorgan Chase Bank, N.A.; National City Bank; Oak Assocs.; Osprey Investment Partners.
Number of staff: 4 full-time professional; 1 part-time professional; 3 full-time support.
EIN: 341087615
Selected grants: The following grants are a representative sample of this grantmaker's funding activity:
$95,000 to Building for Tomorrow, Akron, OH, 2012. For the Early Childhood Initiative.
$95,000 to Building for Tomorrow, Akron, OH, 2013. For the Early Childhood Initiative.
$70,000 to Akron, City of, Akron, OH, 2013. For the Neighborhood Partnership Program.
$70,000 to Boys and Girls Clubs of Summit County, Akron, OH, 2012. For after-school and summer programming at the Eller Club and iStrive Outreach program.
$70,000 to Boys and Girls Clubs of Summit County, Akron, OH, 2013. For capacity building and outreach in Summit County.
$65,000 to Akron, City of, Akron, OH, 2012. For the Neighborhood Partnership Program.
$65,000 to Child Guidance and Family Solutions, Akron, OH, 2012. For Toddlers and Preschoolers Succeeding Program which evaluates, supports and enhances social-emotional well-being in childcare settings.
$65,000 to Child Guidance and Family Solutions, Akron, OH, 2013. For the Toddlers and Preschoolers Succeeding Program which evaluates, supports and enhances social-emotional well-being in childcare settings.
$50,000 to Akron Art Museum, Akron, OH, 2012. For general operating support.
$50,000 to Akron Art Museum, Akron, OH, 2013. For general operating support.
$50,000 to Akron-Canton Regional Foodbank, Akron, OH, 2013. For the Direct Distribution program and capacity building initiatives in Summit County.
$35,000 to Mobile Meals, Akron, OH, 2012. For free and subsidized meals and medically prescribed supplements for children, disabled and elderly individuals.
$25,000 to Access, Akron, OH, 2012. To shelter homeless women and children.
$25,000 to Conservancy for Cuyahoga Valley National Park, Peninsula, OH, 2012. For general operating support.
$20,000 to Bridges Out of Poverty Summit County Collaborative, Akron, OH, 2013. For the Getting Ahead program.
$15,000 to Akron Public Schools, Akron, OH, 2013. For the Destination College Summer Experience.
$15,000 to Good Neighbors, Akron, OH, 2012. For food.
$12,000 to Mental Health America of Summit County, Cuyahoga Falls, OH, 2013. For the PEERS Project to help parents and caregivers of children with mental health diagnoses.
$10,000 to Ballet Theater of Ohio, Munroe Falls, OH, 2012. For the Take Me Out to the Ballet program.
$10,000 to Cleveland Restoration Society, Cleveland, OH, 2013. For the Heritage Home program.

7368
American Electric Power Foundation
1 Riverside Plz.
Columbus, OH 43215 (614) 716-1000
Contact: Beth Smail
E-mail: Educate@aep.com; Additional application addresses: Ronn Robinson, c/o Kentucky Power, 101 Enterprise Dr., P.O. Box 5190, Frankfort, KY 40602, e-mail: rgrobinson@aep.com; Tina Salazar, c/o AEP Texas, 539 N. Carancahua, 17th FL, Corpus Christi, TX 78478, e-mail: tmsalazar@aep.com; Linda Riddle, c/o PSO, 1601 N.W. Expressway, Ste. 1400, Oklahoma City, OK 73118, e-mail: lkriddle@aep.com; Jeri Matheney, c/o Appalachian Power, P.O. Box 1986, Charleston, WV 25327, e-mail: jhmatheney@aep.com; Brian Bond c/o SWEPCO, 428 Travis St., Shreveport, LA 71101, e-mail: tbbond@aep.com; Jim Riggle, c/o Indiana Michigan Power, 110 East Waye St., Fort Wayne, IN 46802, e-mail: jariggle@aep.com; Main URL: http://www.aep.com/community/AEPFoundation/

Established in 2005 in OH.
Donor: American Electric Power Service Corp.
Foundation type: Company-sponsored foundation.
Financial data (yr. ended 12/31/13): Assets, $61,160,513 (M); gifts received, $2,500,000; expenditures, $9,119,616; qualifying distributions, $8,997,993; giving activities include $8,997,993 for 29+ grants (high: $500,000).
Purpose and activities: The foundation supports programs designed to improve lives through

education from early childhood through higher education; protect the environment; provide basic human services in the areas of hunger, housing, health, and safety; and enrich the quality of life of communities through art, music, and cultural heritage.
Fields of interest: Arts, cultural/ethnic awareness; Museums (art); Performing arts, music; Arts; Elementary/secondary education; Education, early childhood education; Higher education; Education; Environment, natural resources; Environmental education; Environment; Hospitals (general); Health care; Food services; Food banks; Housing/shelter, development; Housing/shelter; Safety/disasters; Boys & girls clubs; Big Brothers/Big Sisters; Human services; Community/economic development.
Type of support: General/operating support; Continuing support; Capital campaigns; Building/renovation; Endowments; Program development; Scholarship funds.
Limitations: Applications not accepted. Giving primarily in areas of company operations in AR, IN, KY, LA, MI, OH, OK, TN, TX, VA, and WV. No support for religious, fraternal, athletic or veterans' organizations. No grants to individuals.
Publications: Annual report; IRS Form 990 or 990-PF printed copy available upon request.
Application information: Organizations must be invited to apply by their local AEP Operating Company. Proposals should be submitted using organization letterhead and should include an executed IRS Form W-9. Proposals for multi-state or national projects should be limited to a one-page synopsis and submitted via email.
Trustees: Nicholas K. Akins; Carl L. English; Teresa L. McWain; Michael G. Morris; Robert P. Powers; Brian X. Tierney; Susan Tomasky; Dennis E. Welch.
EIN: 203886453
Selected grants: The following grants are a representative sample of this grantmaker's funding activity:
$1,000,000 to Boy Scouts of America National Council, Irving, TX, 2012. To help and improve AEP communities.
$1,000,000 to Ohio State University Medical Center, Columbus, OH, 2012. To help and improve AEP communities.
$375,000 to Marshall University Foundation, Huntington, WV, 2012. To help and improve AEP communities.
$250,000 to Ohio State University Medical Center, Columbus, OH, 2012. To help and improve AEP communities.
$231,000 to Christian Appalachian Project, Hagerhill, KY, 2012. To help and improve AEP communities.
$200,000 to University of Arkansas Foundation, Fayetteville, AR, 2012. To help and improve AEP communities.
$166,667 to Science Central, Fort Wayne, IN, 2012. To help and improve AEP communities.
$166,666 to Ohio Northern University, Ada, OH, 2012. To help and improve AEP communities.
$125,000 to Big Brothers Big Sisters of Central Ohio, Columbus, OH, 2012. To help and improve AEP communities.
$125,000 to Greater Columbus Arts Council, Columbus, OH, 2012. To help and improve AEP communities.

7369
The American Foundation Corporation ✧
200 Public Sq., Ste. 2940
Cleveland, OH 44114-2309

Incorporated in 1974 as successor to trust established in 1944 in OH.
Donors: Members of the Corning family; and members of the Murfey family.
Foundation type: Independent foundation.
Financial data (yr. ended 12/31/13): Assets, $29,323,209 (M); expenditures, $1,387,802; qualifying distributions, $1,290,532; giving activities include $1,230,333 for 138 grants (high: $326,340; low: $10).
Purpose and activities: Giving primarily for education, health associations, animal welfare, youth and family services, and to an arboretum.
Fields of interest: Museums (natural history); Education; Botanical/horticulture/landscape services; Animal welfare; Health organizations, association; Youth development; Human services; Children/youth, services; Family services.
Type of support: General/operating support; Continuing support; Annual campaigns.
Limitations: Applications not accepted. Giving in the U.S., with emphasis in the Cleveland, OH and Seattle, WA areas. No grants to individuals, or for capital or endowment funds, special projects, research, scholarships, fellowships, or matching gifts; no loans.
Publications: Annual report.
Application information: Contributes only to pre-selected organizations.
Board meeting date(s): As necessary
Officers and Trustees:* Mary M. Fernandez,* Pres.; Maria G. Muth, Secy.; Maria M. Muth, Treas.; Dwight B. Corning.
EIN: 237348126

7370
American Greetings Foundation, Inc. ✧
(formerly Gibson Foundation, Inc.)
1 American Rd.
Cleveland, OH 44144-2301 (216) 252-7300
Contact: Mary Kay Incandela, Dir.
Application address: 10500 American Rd., Cleveland, OH 44144, tel.:(216) 252-7300

Established in 1988 in OH.
Foundation type: Company-sponsored foundation.
Financial data (yr. ended 12/31/13): Assets, $9,631,414 (M); expenditures, $509,105; qualifying distributions, $470,195; giving activities include $469,995 for 31 grants (high: $131,500; low: $175).
Purpose and activities: Giving primarily for organizations supporting visual or graphic arts activities.
Fields of interest: Visual arts; Higher education; Foundations (public); Jewish federated giving programs.
Type of support: General/operating support.
Limitations: Applications accepted. Giving primarily in Cleveland, OH. No grants to individuals.
Application information: Application form required.
Initial approach: Letter
Deadline(s): None
Officers and Directors:* Morry Weiss,* Chair.; Zev Weiss,* Pres.; Jeffrey Weiss,* V.P.; Christopher Haffke,* Secy.; Gregory M. Steinberg, Treas.; Mary Kay Incandela; Erwin Weiss.
EIN: 311264728

Selected grants: The following grants are a representative sample of this grantmaker's funding activity:
$10,000 to Tulane University, New Orleans, LA, 2012. For community support.

7371
B. Charles and Jay G. Ames Foundation ✧
(formerly The Ames Family Foundation)
c/o Cornerstone Family Office
5885 Landerbrook Dr., Ste. 300
Mayfield Heights, OH 44124-4031

Established in 1995 in OH.
Donors: B. Charles Ames; Mrs. B. Charles Ames; Joyce G. Ames; Ripacy Ltd.
Foundation type: Independent foundation.
Financial data (yr. ended 12/31/13): Assets, $28,056,855 (M); gifts received, $5,869,963; expenditures, $1,902,596; qualifying distributions, $1,262,890; giving activities include $1,262,890 for 31 grants (high: $500,000; low: $100).
Purpose and activities: Giving primarily for education, health care, and human services.
Fields of interest: Higher education; Education; Health care; Human services; Residential/custodial care, hospices.
Type of support: General/operating support.
Limitations: Applications not accepted. Giving primarily in OH, with emphasis on Cleveland. No grants to individuals.
Application information: Contributes only to pre-selected organizations.
Officers: B. Charles Ames, Pres.; Cynthia Ames, V.P.; Richard S. Ames, V.P.; Paula A. Redman, V.P.; Joyce G. Ames, Secy.-Treas.
EIN: 341809978

7372
Anderson Foundation ✧ ☆
480 W. Dussel Dr.
P.O. Box 119
Maumee, OH 43537-0119 (419) 891-6353
Contact: Julie Payeff, Community Commitment Mgr.
FAX: (419) 891-6695;
E-mail: julie_payeff@andersonsinc.com

Trust established in 1949 in OH.
Donor: Partners in The Andersons, Inc.
Foundation type: Independent foundation.
Financial data (yr. ended 12/31/13): Assets, $11,367,352 (M); expenditures, $642,505; qualifying distributions, $517,400; giving activities include $515,000 for 83 grants (high: $50,000; low: $200).
Purpose and activities: Grants primarily for community funds, higher and secondary education, and cultural programs; support also for social service and youth agencies, civic and community efforts, educational and research associations, and religion.
Fields of interest: Arts; Education, association; Secondary school/education; Higher education; Education; Environment; Agriculture; Human services; Children/youth, services; Community/economic development; United Ways and Federated Giving Programs; Government/public administration; Religion.
Type of support: General/operating support; Annual campaigns; Capital campaigns; Building/renovation; Emergency funds; Program

development; Conferences/seminars; Publication; Seed money; Scholarship funds; Research; Matching/challenge support.
Limitations: Applications accepted. Giving primarily in the greater Toledo, OH, area, including Maumee and Columbus. Giving also to organizations located within the areas of the Anderson plants in the following cities: Champaign, IL, Delphi and Dunkirk, IN, and Albion, Potterville, Webberville, and White Pigeon, MI. No support for private foundations, public high schools or elementary schools. No grants to individuals, or for endowment funds, travel, or building or operating funds for churches or elementary schools.
Publications: Application guidelines.
Application information: Applications from outside the Toledo, OH area will require written support from the local manager of the nearest Anderson facility. Application form not required.
Initial approach: Typewritten proposal not exceeding 5 pages
Copies of proposal: 1
Deadline(s): Feb. 10, Apr. 20, July 20, and Oct. 19
Board meeting date(s): Mar., June, Sept., and Dec., usually the 3rd Mon. of the month
Final notification: Generally 3 months; depends on completeness of proposal
Officer and Trustees:* Matthew C. Anderson,* Chair.; Jeffrey W. Anderson; Michael J. Anderson; Richard M. Anderson; Richard P. Anderson; John P. Kraus; Lu Stauffer.
EIN: 346528868
Selected grants: The following grants are a representative sample of this grantmaker's funding activity:
$75,000 to United Way of Greater Toledo, Toledo, OH, 2011.
$61,800 to United Way of Greater Toledo, Toledo, OH, 2011.
$16,000 to Ohio Foundation of Independent Colleges, Columbus, OH, 2011.
$10,000 to Saint Johns Jesuit High School, Toledo, OH, 2011.
$9,333 to Toledo School for the Arts, Toledo, OH, 2011.
$5,000 to Read for Literacy, Toledo, OH, 2011.
$2,500 to Toledo School for the Arts, Toledo, OH, 2011.
$2,000 to Bowling Green State University Foundation, Bowling Green, OH, 2011.
$2,000 to Mercy College of Northwest Ohio, Toledo, OH, 2011.
$1,000 to Applied Research and Collaboration Promoting Advocacy and Resources for Children, Toledo, OH, 2011.

7373
Annie Wallingford Anderson Foundation ✧ ☆
c/o Christine A. Buttress
P.O. Box 1118, ML-CN-OH-W10X
Cincinnati, OH 45201-1118

Established in 1998 in OH.
Donors: Annie Wallingford Anderson; Elizabeth Mendenhall Anderson Foundation.
Foundation type: Independent foundation.
Financial data (yr. ended 12/31/13): Assets, $4,121,146 (M); gifts received, $1,716,487; expenditures, $1,045,055; qualifying distributions, $1,000,237; giving activities include $980,000 for 13 grants (high: $500,000; low: $15,000).
Fields of interest: Arthritis; Medical research, association; Blind/visually impaired.
Type of support: General/operating support.
Limitations: Applications not accepted. Giving primarily in Cincinnati, OH. No grants to individuals.
Application information: Unsolicited requests for funds not accepted.
Officers: Joseph Krabbe, Pres.; James Wellinghoff, V.P.
Trustee: Christine Buttress.
EIN: 311608632

7374
The Andersons Inc. Charitable Foundation ✧ ☆
480 W. Dussel Dr.
Maumee, OH 43537-1639

Established in 2007 in OH.
Donor: The Andersons, Inc.
Foundation type: Independent foundation.
Financial data (yr. ended 12/31/13): Assets, $6,915,835 (M); expenditures, $1,191,941; qualifying distributions, $1,106,197; giving activities include $1,103,597 for 147 grants (high: $50,000; low: $250).
Fields of interest: Higher education; Education; Human services; American Red Cross; YM/YWCAs & YM/YWHAs; Children/youth, services.
Limitations: Applications not accepted. Giving primarily in Washington, DC, IN, MI and OH.
Application information: Unsolicited requests for funds not accepted.
Officers: Tamara S. Sparks, Pres.; Tom Waggoner, V.P.; Catherine M. White, Secy.-Treas.
Trustees: Michael J. Anderson; Tasha Hussain Black; Cheryl Vion-Hasenaur.
EIN: 261665008

7375
The Androse Foundation ✧ ☆
c/o Richard A. Kovach
P.O. Box 277
Jefferson, OH 44047-0277

Established in 2007 in OH.
Donor: Richard A. Kovach.
Foundation type: Independent foundation.
Financial data (yr. ended 12/31/13): Assets, $5,512,758 (M); gifts received, $2,000,000; expenditures, $1,247,449; qualifying distributions, $1,229,150; giving activities include $1,228,950 for 30 grants (high: $1,000,000; low: $1,000).
Fields of interest: Education; Human services; Christian agencies & churches.
Limitations: Applications not accepted. Giving primarily in OH. No grants to individuals.
Application information: Unsolicited requests for funds not accepted.
Officers: Richard A. Kovach, Pres. and Treas.; Joann Whetsell, Secy.
Director: Kenneth Kovach.
EIN: 261624973
Selected grants: The following grants are a representative sample of this grantmaker's funding activity:
$25,000 to Kent State University, Kent, OH, 2011.

7376
Ar-Hale Family Foundation, Inc. ✧ ☆
(formerly Ar-Hale Foundation, Inc.)
P.O. Box 210
Lima, OH 45802-0210
Contact: Arlene F. Hawk, Pres.
E-mail: dprueter@cox.net

Established in 1990 in OH.
Donors: Superior Metal Products, Inc.; American Trim.
Foundation type: Company-sponsored foundation.
Financial data (yr. ended 12/31/13): Assets, $2,244,723 (M); gifts received, $801,213; expenditures, $501,249; qualifying distributions, $467,561; giving activities include $467,561 for 52 grants (high: $75,000; low: $250).
Purpose and activities: The foundation supports philanthropic and religious initiatives that personally impact the lives of families and children. Support is given primarily to communities where American Trim does business and in the communities where American Trim shareholders reside.
Fields of interest: Performing arts, orchestras; Secondary school/education; Higher education; Education; Health care; Athletics/sports, baseball; YM/YWCAs & YM/YWHAs; Family services; Human services; Christian agencies & churches; Catholic agencies & churches.
Type of support: General/operating support; Continuing support; Management development/capacity building; Annual campaigns; Capital campaigns; Building/renovation; Endowments; Emergency funds; Program development; Film/video/radio; Seed money; Curriculum development; Fellowships; Technical assistance; Consulting services; Scholarships—to individuals; Matching/challenge support.
Limitations: Applications accepted. Giving primarily in communities where the foundation shareholders reside, with emphasis on Louisville, KY; Allen, Auglaize, and Shelby counties, and the cities of Dayton and Lima, OH, Shawnee, OK, and Erie, PA. No support for political organizations. No grants to individuals (except for scholarships).
Application information: Application form required.
Initial approach: Proposal; e-mail dprueter@cox.net for application and information regarding next meeting date
Copies of proposal: 2
Deadline(s): None
Board meeting date(s): Last Sunday in July; others as necessary
Final notification: within 1 week after board meeting
Officers: Bryan Hawk,* Chair.; Arlene F. Hawk,* Pres.; Timothy Hawk,* V.P.; Beverly Prueter, Secy. and Exec. Dir.; Mark McKinley, Treas.
Number of staff: 1 part-time professional.
EIN: 341644337

7377
The Ariel Foundation ✧
101 E. Gambier St.
Mount Vernon, OH 43050-3509 (740) 392-0364
Contact: Jan Reynolds, Secy.-Treas.
FAX: (740) 392-0370;
E-mail: jreynolds@ariel-foundation.org; Main URL: http://www.ariel-foundation.org/
Grants Database: http://www.ariel-foundation.org/support.asp

Established in 2009 in OH.
Donors: Karen Buchwald Wright; Ariel Corporation.
Foundation type: Company-sponsored foundation.
Financial data (yr. ended 12/31/13): Assets, $31,235,159 (M); gifts received, $10,175,139; expenditures, $4,953,495; qualifying distributions, $4,749,779; giving activities include $4,707,729 for 39 grants (high: $1,750,000; low: $1,086).
Purpose and activities: The foundation supports programs designed to improve quality of life. Special emphasis is directed toward arts and culture, education, parks, and the pursuit of happiness.
Fields of interest: Arts; Higher education; Engineering school/education; Libraries (public); Education; Recreation, parks/playgrounds; YM/YWCAs & YM/YWHAs; Human services; Community/economic development; United Ways and Federated Giving Programs; Engineering; Science.
Type of support: Capital campaigns; General/operating support; Building/renovation; Equipment; Scholarship funds; Scholarships—to individuals.
Limitations: Applications accepted. Giving primarily in the Mount Vernon, OH area. No support for non-501(c)(3) organizations, or for religious organizations not of direct benefit to the entire community, or fraternal and veterans' organizations. No grants for athletic events or political campaigns.
Publications: Application guidelines; Grants list.
Application information: Letters of inquiry should be short and concise. Full grant applications may be requested at a later date.
Initial approach: E-mail, fax, or mail letter of inquiry; download application form and mail to foundation for scholarships
Deadline(s): None; July 7 for scholarships
Board meeting date(s): Quarterly
Officers and Directors:* Karen Buchwald Wright,* Chair. and Pres.; Thomas Rastin,* Vice-Chair. and V.P.; Janet L. Reynolds,* Secy.-Treas.
EIN: 270226408

7378
Ashland County Community Foundation ✧
300 College Ave.
Ashland, OH 44805-3803 (419) 281-4733
Contact: James M. Cutright, Exec. Dir.
FAX: (419) 289-5540;
E-mail: accf@accommunityfoundation.org; Main URL: http://www.accommunityfoundation.org
Facebook: http://www.facebook.com/pages/Ashland-County-Community-Foundation/136737142028
LinkedIn: https://www.linkedin.com/company/ashland-county-community-foundation
Twitter: http://twitter.com/ashlandcountycf
YouTube: http://www.youtube.com/user/accfashland?feature=watch

Established in 1995 in OH.
Foundation type: Community foundation.
Financial data (yr. ended 06/30/13): Assets, $28,519,998 (M); gifts received, $7,969,573; expenditures, $875,698; giving activities include $410,431 for 18 grants (high: $67,634), and $126,115 for 139 grants to individuals.
Purpose and activities: The mission of the foundation is to advance philanthropy and improve the quality of life in Ashland County by supporting charitable activities in the community, providing and administering a variety of planned giving programs, and serving as responsible stewards of scholarship, as well as individual and organizational funds for specific charities.
Fields of interest: Arts; Education; Environment; Health care; Human services; Community/economic development.
Type of support: Seed money; Capital campaigns; Building/renovation; Equipment; Program development; Scholarship funds; Scholarships—to individuals; Matching/challenge support; Student loans—to individuals.
Limitations: Applications accepted. Giving limited to Ashland County, OH. No support for religious organizations for religious purposes. No grants to individuals (except for designated scholarship funds and educational loans), or for ongoing operating expenses, annual campaigns, endowment funds, cash reserves, or debt reduction.
Publications: Application guidelines; Annual report; Grants list; Informational brochure; Newsletter.
Application information: Interview to discuss a grant proposal is available. Visit foundation web site for application form and guidelines. Call or e-mail foundation for an ACCF Scholarship Guide. Application form required.
Initial approach: Letter, telephone, or e-mail
Copies of proposal: 9
Deadline(s): Sept. 15 for Community grants; May 15 for Women's Fund grants; and Sept. 8 for Teacher Mini-Grants
Board meeting date(s): Last Mon. of Jan., Apr., July, and Oct.
Final notification: Nov. 1 for Community grants and Teacher Mini-Grants; and July 1 for Women's Fund grants
Officers and Trustees:* Anne K. Cowen,* Secy.; Dr. Andrew M. Stein,* Vice-Chair.; James M. Cutright, C.E.O.; Kristin Aspin,* V.P., Opers.; Patricia A. Byerly,* Secy.; Kenneth E. Milligan,* Treas.; Ann Guthrie,* Recording Secy.; Lucille G. Ford, Ph.D.*, Pres. Emerita; Keith Boales; James H. Hess; Charles A. Holdren; Michael C. Huber; John E. Miller; Susan Shafer; Donald G. Stump; Peggy L. Yoder.
Number of staff: 2 full-time professional; 1 full-time support; 1 part-time support.
EIN: 341812908
Selected grants: The following grants are a representative sample of this grantmaker's funding activity:
$15,000 to Ashland County Airport Authority, Ashland, OH, 2012. To renovate north end of Taxiway System.
$12,500 to Nankin Youth League, OH, 2012. To complete concession stand, storage and restroom project.
$10,000 to Perrysville Economic Development, `, OH, 2012. For seed money to purchase materials, equipment for annual fundraising events and for community improvement projects.
$7,500 to Mission to Amish People, OH, 2012. For GED classes, counseling room, life skill classes and computer training.
$6,000 to Ashland Christian Health Center, Ashland, OH, 2012. To waterproof basement.
$5,898 to Ashland Christian School, Ashland, OH, 2012. To purchase technology for 10th and 11th grade classrooms.
$5,800 to WZLP Radio, Loudonville, OH, 2012. To move antenna to current site.
$5,771 to Chamber of Commerce of Ashland, Ashland, OR, 2012. To employ consultant.
$5,128 to Ashland Community Breakfast Center, Ashland, OH, 2012. To purchase and install dishwasher with hot water sterilization.
$5,000 to Kidney Foundation of Ohio, Cleveland, OH, 2012. For Direct Assistance Program in Ashland City.

7379
The Ashtabula Foundation, Inc. ✧
4510 Collins Blvd., Ste. 6
Ashtabula, OH 44004-6954 (440) 992-6818
E-mail: ashtabulafdn@suite224.net; Additional e-mail: ashtabulafdn@gmail.com; Main URL: http://www.ashtabulafoundation.org

Incorporated in 1922 in OH.
Foundation type: Independent foundation.
Financial data (yr. ended 12/31/13): Assets, $16,984,157 (M); expenditures, $1,088,306; qualifying distributions, $924,637; giving activities include $855,617 for 65 grants (high: $145,518; low: $100).
Purpose and activities: The mission of the foundation is for the betterment of Ashtabula County, OH, through the administration of funds consistent with the intent of donors to address the significant needs of Ashtabula County. The foundation's current priority is assistance to the humanitarian needs of those in crisis. Additional areas of interest include, recreation, conservation, education, human services, arts and culture, historical activities, religion and community development.
Fields of interest: Higher education, university; Human services; YM/YWCAs & YM/YWHAs; Community/economic development; United Ways and Federated Giving Programs; Christian agencies & churches.
Type of support: Annual campaigns; Building/renovation; Equipment; Land acquisition; Debt reduction; Emergency funds; Program development; Curriculum development; Scholarships—to individuals; Matching/challenge support.
Limitations: Applications accepted. Giving limited to Ashtabula County, OH. No support for capital improvements or programs.
Publications: Application guidelines; Informational brochure.
Application information: Application guidelines and forms available on foundation web site. Applicants should include their e-mail in all correspondence. Application form required.
Initial approach: Letter of Intent (250 words maximum) via e-mail, or, if the application cannot be sent electronically, 1 copy should be sent via U.S. mail
Deadline(s): See foundation web site for current deadline
Board meeting date(s): 2nd Tues. of each month
Officers and Trustees:* Rick Coblitz,* Pres.; Roger Corlett,* V.P.; William W. Hill,* Secy.-Treas.; Roy H. Bean; Jerome R. Brockway; Cheryle Chiaramonte; Robert G. David; John D. Dolan; Andrew M. McElory; Joseph A. Misinec, Jr.; Glen W. Warner.
Number of staff: 1 part-time support.
EIN: 346538130
Selected grants: The following grants are a representative sample of this grantmaker's funding activity:
$48,398 to Ashtabula County Medical Center, Ashtabula, OH, 2011.
$15,000 to Fund for Our Economic Future, Cleveland, OH, 2011.
$13,553 to University of the Sciences in Philadelphia, Philadelphia, PA, 2011.
$1,000 to Philanthropy Ohio, Columbus, OH, 2011.

7380
The Austin Memorial Foundation ✧
3900 Key Ctr., 127 Public Sq.
Cleveland, OH 44114-1291

Incorporated in 1961 in OH.
Donor: Members of the Austin family.
Foundation type: Independent foundation.
Financial data (yr. ended 12/31/13): Assets, $14,238,504 (M); expenditures, $706,102; qualifying distributions, $590,332; giving activities include $531,800 for 58 grants (high: $48,000; low: $500).
Purpose and activities: Giving primarily for education, the environment, health and hospitals, human services, and to United Methodist churches.
Fields of interest: Education; Environment; Hospitals (general); Health care; Human services; Protestant agencies & churches.
Type of support: General/operating support; Continuing support; Capital campaigns; Building/renovation; Seed money; Matching/challenge support.
Limitations: Applications not accepted. Giving limited to the U.S., with emphasis on CA, CO, MI, OH and TN. No support for political organizations. No grants to individuals.
Application information: Contributes only to pre-selected organizations. Unsolicited requests for funds not accepted.
Board meeting date(s): Semiannually
Officers and Trustees:* Donald G. Austin, Jr.,* Pres.; David A. Rodgers,* V.P. and Treas.; Stewart G. Austin, Jr.,* Secy.; Donald G. Austin III; James W. Austin; John C. Austin; Paul Austin; Samuel H. Austin; Stewart G. Austin, Sr.; Thomas G. Austin; Margaret C. Chiles; Gretchen Cole; Sarah R. Cole; Sarah C. Kingston; Winnie Lerner; Ann R. Loeffler; Alexander Loeffler Prothero; Charles Rodgers; Lynn Rodgers; Ellen Austin Smith.
Number of staff: 1 part-time professional.
EIN: 346528879

7381
Cornelia T. Bailey Charitable Trust
c/o PNC Bank, N.A.
P.O. Box 94651
Cleveland, OH 44101-4651
Application address: c/o PNC Bank, N.A., 231 Royal Palm Way, Palm Beach, FL 33480; tel.: (561) 650-1411

Foundation type: Independent foundation.
Financial data (yr. ended 12/31/13): Assets, $48,628,136 (M); expenditures, $2,356,119; qualifying distributions, $2,151,614; giving activities include $1,962,416 for 43 grants (high: $250,000; low: $100).
Fields of interest: Performing arts; Libraries (public); Education; Health care, single organization support; Hospitals (general); Human services.
Limitations: Applications accepted. Giving primarily in CT, FL, NY, and OH.
Application information: Application form required.
Initial approach: Letter
Deadline(s): None
Trustee: Cornelia Bailey.
EIN: 656474256

7382
Barberton Community Foundation ✧
460 W. Paige Ave.
Barberton, OH 44203-2564 (330) 745-5995
Contact: Jim Stonkus, Exec. Dir.
FAX: (330) 745-3990;
E-mail: jstephenson@barbertoncf.org; Additional e-mail: jstonkus@barbertoncf.org; Main URL: http://www.barbertoncf.org
E-Newsletter: http://www.barbertoncf.org/enews-signup
Facebook: https://www.facebook.com/barbertoncommunityfoundation
Flickr: http://www.flickr.com/photos/bcfcharity/
LinkedIn: http://www.linkedin.com/company/barberton-community-foundation

Established in 1996 in OH.
Foundation type: Community foundation.
Financial data (yr. ended 12/31/13): Assets, $88,161,751 (M); gifts received, $211,654; expenditures, $3,458,158; giving activities include $2,245,021 for 13+ grants (high: $771,593), and $293,507 for 237 grants to individuals.
Purpose and activities: The foundation supports projects that benefit the citizens of Barberton, OH.
Fields of interest: Education; Health organizations, association; Recreation; Urban/community development.
Type of support: Capital campaigns; Building/renovation; Equipment; Land acquisition; Program development; Conferences/seminars; Curriculum development; Scholarship funds; Technical assistance; Program-related investments/loans; Matching/challenge support.
Limitations: Applications accepted. Giving limited to Barberton, OH. No support for religious organizations for religious purposes. No grants to individuals (except for scholarships), or for debt reduction, deficits or previous obligations, annual fundraising drives, ongoing operational expenses, sabbatical leaves or scholarly research, or for endowments housed at institutions other than the foundation.
Publications: Application guidelines; Annual report; Financial statement; Grants list; Informational brochure; Informational brochure (including application guidelines); Newsletter; Quarterly report.
Application information: Visit foundation web site for application forms and additional guidelines per grant type; number of copies vary per grant type. The Small Grants program accepts applications for grants of up to $1,000. Application form required.
Initial approach: Letter or telephone
Copies of proposal: 10
Deadline(s): Jan. 2, Apr. 1, July 1, and Oct. 1 for quarterly grants; last Fri. of each month for small grants
Board meeting date(s): 3rd Thurs. of each month
Final notification: Within 3 to 4 weeks for Small Grants program; within 7 to 8 weeks for quarterly grants
Officers and Trustees:* Thomas Harnden,* Chair.; Michael Chisnell,* Vice-Chair.; Mary Jo Goss,* Secy.; Ryan Pendleton,* Treas.; Jim Stonkus,* Exec. Dir.; Thomas Anders; Edna Boyle; Josh Gordon; Brett Haverlick; William Judge; Steve Kelleher; Tina Linton; Frederick Maurer; Bruce May; Michael Vinay; Richard R. Wiley.
Number of staff: 5 full-time professional; 1 full-time support.
EIN: 341846432
Selected grants: The following grants are a representative sample of this grantmaker's funding activity:
$2,329,814 to Barberton City Schools, Barberton, OH, 2012. For high school debt service payment.
$500,000 to Summa Hospitals Foundation, Akron, OH, 2012. For capital campaign.
$78,900 to Barberton, City of, Barberton, OH, 2012. For parks and recreations.
$35,286 to Barberton, City of, Barberton, OH, 2012. For senior center interest payment.

7383
The BASF Foundation USA ✧ ☆
(formerly Cognis Foundation)
23700 Chagrin Blvd.
Beachwood, OH 44122
Contact: Maureen Paukert, Secy.
Application address: 100 Park Ave., Florham Park, NJ 07932

Established in 2003 in OH.
Donors: Cognis Corp.; BASF Corp.
Foundation type: Operating foundation.
Financial data (yr. ended 12/31/13): Assets, $0 (M); gifts received, $1,233,116; expenditures, $1,233,116; qualifying distributions, $1,233,116; giving activities include $1,233,116 for 114 grants (high: $123,000; low: $1,000).
Purpose and activities: The foundation supports services clubs and organizations involved with arts and culture, education, cancer, and chemistry.
Fields of interest: Arts; Elementary/secondary education; Higher education; Higher education, college (community/junior); Scholarships/financial aid; Education; Cancer; Community development, service clubs; United Ways and Federated Giving Programs; Chemistry.
Type of support: General/operating support; Scholarship funds.
Limitations: Applications accepted. Giving primarily in IL, OH, PA, and SC. No support for religious or political organizations. No grants for capital campaigns or brick or mortar projects.
Application information: Application form required.
Initial approach: Proposal
Copies of proposal: 1
Deadline(s): None
Officers: Robert Malone, Pres. and Treas.; Maureen Paukert, Secy.
Directors: Robin Rotenberg; Judy Zagorski.
EIN: 562312894

7384
Louis and Sandra Berkman Foundation ✧
330 N. 7th St.
P.O. Box 820
Steubenville, OH 43952-5576 (740) 283-3722
Contact: Linda L. Pirkle, Secy.

Incorporated in 1952 in OH.
Donors: Louis Berkman†; Mrs. Louis Berkman; The Louis Berkman Co.; Follansbee Steel Corp.
Foundation type: Independent foundation.
Financial data (yr. ended 12/31/12): Assets, $17,301,167 (M); expenditures, $1,133,169; qualifying distributions, $1,133,169; giving activities include $748,040 for 61 grants (high: $110,000; low: $100).

Purpose and activities: Giving primarily for higher education, medical research, and Jewish organizations.
Fields of interest: Education; Health care; Religion.
Limitations: Applications accepted. Giving primarily in OH and PA. No grants to individuals.
Application information: Application form required.
Initial approach: Proposal
Deadline(s): July 1 of year prior to year of grant
Officers and Trustees:* Robert A. Paul,* Pres. and Treas.; Linda L. Pirkle,* Secy.
EIN: 346526694

7385
Berlin Family Foundation, Inc. ✧
(formerly Berlin Family Charitable Corporation)
c/o Judi Roman
1795 Brookwood Dr.
Akron, OH 44313-5070 (330) 867-2490
Contact: Robin Berlin Kane

Established in 1990 in FL and OH.
Donor: James Berlin Charitable Lead Annuity Trust.
Foundation type: Independent foundation.
Financial data (yr. ended 10/31/13): Assets, $10,720,910 (M); gifts received, $1,074,543; expenditures, $827,653; qualifying distributions, $736,361; giving activities include $736,361 for 50 grants (high: $200,100; low: $100).
Purpose and activities: Giving for Jewish organizations and health associations.
Fields of interest: Health organizations, association; Medical research, institute; United Ways and Federated Giving Programs; Jewish agencies & synagogues.
Limitations: Applications not accepted. Giving primarily in Miami, FL, and Akron and Cleveland, OH. No grants to individuals.
Application information: Unsolicited requests for funds not accepted.
Officers: Madeline Berlin, Pres.; Robin Berlin Kane, V.P.
EIN: 650230453
Selected grants: The following grants are a representative sample of this grantmaker's funding activity:
$80,000 to United Way of Summit County, Akron, OH, 2011.
$6,000 to North Coast Community Homes, Cleveland, OH, 2011.
$5,953 to Laurel School, Shaker Heights, OH, 2011. For Annual Fund.
$5,000 to Massachusetts General Hospital, Boston, MA, 2011.
$5,000 to Mount Sinai Medical Center Foundation, Miami Beach, FL, 2011.
$5,000 to Stewarts Caring Place, Akron, OH, 2011.
$5,000 to Temple Israel, Akron, OH, 2011.
$1,800 to Living Beyond Breast Cancer, Haverford, PA, 2011.
$1,000 to Aspen Community Foundation, Aspen, CO, 2011.
$1,000 to Dana-Farber Cancer Institute, Boston, MA, 2011. For research.

7386
Berry Family Foundation ✧
(formerly Loren M. Berry Foundation)
3445 S. Dixie Dr.
Dayton, OH 45439-2328
Contact: William T. Lincoln, Treas.

Incorporated in 1960 in OH.
Donors: Loren M. Berry†; George W. Berry; John W. Berry, Jr.; Charles D. Berry.
Foundation type: Independent foundation.
Financial data (yr. ended 12/31/12): Assets, $21,376,133 (M); expenditures, $1,301,808; qualifying distributions, $1,190,300; giving activities include $1,190,300 for 82 grants (high: $80,000; low: $150).
Purpose and activities: Giving primarily for education.
Fields of interest: Arts; Higher education; Education; Hospitals (general); Health organizations, association; Human services; Public policy, research.
Limitations: Applications not accepted. Giving primarily in Dayton, OH; giving on a national basis for education. No grants to individuals.
Application information: Unsolicited requests for funds not accepted.
Board meeting date(s): June and Dec.
Officers and Trustees:* John W. Berry, Jr.,* Pres.; William T. Lincoln,* Treas.; Charles D. Berry; David L. Berry; George W. Berry; Martha B. Fraim; William L. Fraim; Leland W. Henry; James O. Payne.
Number of staff: 1 part-time professional.
EIN: 316026144
Selected grants: The following grants are a representative sample of this grantmaker's funding activity:
$2,500 to Heritage Foundation, Washington, DC, 2012. For patriotic.

7387
The William Bingham Foundation
1111 Superior Ave., Ste. 700
Cleveland, OH 44114-2540 (216) 344-5200
Contact: Laura H. Gilbertson, Chief Admin.
E-mail: info@WBinghamFoundation.org; Additional contact: Daniel L. Horn, Secy., tel.: (216) 781-7800, e-mail: hornoffice@att.net; Main URL: http://www.wbinghamfoundation.org

Incorporated in 1955 in OH.
Donor: Elizabeth B. Blossom†.
Foundation type: Independent foundation.
Financial data (yr. ended 12/31/13): Assets, $18,399,940 (M); expenditures, $1,183,534; qualifying distributions, $964,866; giving activities include $773,578 for 26 grants (high: $65,000; low: $444).
Purpose and activities: The foundation furthers the philanthropic intent of its founder, Elizabeth Bingham Blossom. It supports organizations in the fields of education, science, health and human services, and the arts. It works for a world that is environmentally self-sustaining; seeks to strengthen civil society and its institutions; educates family members and others in the values and practice of philanthropy, community service, and stewardship; and it seeks to build a sense of community.
Fields of interest: Education; Environment; Health care; Human services.
Type of support: General/operating support; Continuing support; Management development/capacity building; Capital campaigns; Building/renovation; Equipment; Endowments; Program development; Conferences/seminars; Curriculum development; Technical assistance; Matching/challenge support.
Limitations: Giving on a national basis, with focus on areas in which the foundation trustees reside; see foundation web site. No support for foreign organizations. No grants to individuals; no loans.
Publications: Application guidelines; Financial statement; Grants list.
Application information: Unsolicited applications not accepted unless specific focus is posted on web site. Applications generally are accepted by invitation only. The foundation issues an RFP approximately once per year for organizations with which it does not have a relationship. Application form is provided to invited applicants. Application form required.
Initial approach: See foundation web site for current submission policy
Copies of proposal: 1
Deadline(s): Varies, see foundation web site for current deadline
Board meeting date(s): Usually Feb. and Aug.
Final notification: Varies.
Officers and Trustees:* C. Perry Blossom,* Pres.; Virginia Blossom Kruntorad,* V.P.; Daniel L. Horn,* Secy.; C. Bingham Blossom,* Treas.; David B. Blossom; Jonathan B. Blossom; Laurel Blossom; Robin Dunn Blossom; James B. Heffernan; Elizabeth B. Meers.
Number of staff: 1 full-time professional.
EIN: 346513791
Selected grants: The following grants are a representative sample of this grantmaker's funding activity:
$99,000 to Yale University, New Haven, CT, 2012. For development of exhibits in the museum of Machu Picchu and Inca Culture in Cusco, Peru.
$75,000 to Natural Resources Defense Council, New York, NY, 2012. For program to assist the united states military to advance renewable energy and energy efficiency in U.S. military operations.
$45,000 to Literacy Services of Indian River County, Vero Beach, FL, 2012. For literacy program serving the northern part of Indian river county.
$40,000 to Wings for Kids, Charleston, SC, 2012. For after-school program that develops life skills.
$30,000 to Childrens Museum of Sonoma County, Santa Rosa, CA, 2012. For general operating support.
$30,000 to Community Preparatory School, Providence, RI, 2012. For scholarship fund of independent, urban, co-educational middle school.
$30,000 to Waianae Community Redevelopment Corporation, Waianae, HI, 2012. For ma 'o organic farms.
$30,000 to Washington Jesuit Academy, Washington, DC, 2012. For operating support.
$25,000 to Das Deutsch Center for Special Needs Children, Middlefield, OH, 2012. For operating support for facility providing primary care and research on genetic disorders.
$25,000 to Institute for the Study and Practice of Nonviolence, Providence, RI, 2012. For youth programs.
$25,000 to Poets House, New York, NY, 2012. For operating support.
$25,000 to Reading Partners, Oakland, CA, 2012. For literacy tutoring program in the Washington, D.C. Region 40.
$25,000 to Spoleto Festival USA, Charleston, SC, 2012. For general operating support.
$25,000 to Young of Heart Workshop, Honolulu, HI, 2012. For development of traveling exhibit of contemporary Hawaiian Art.
$15,000 to American Philatelic Society, Bellefonte, PA, 2012. For endowment of annual prize in memory of Thomas F. Allen for best article in philatelic literature review.

7388
Boutell Memorial Fund ✧
(formerly Arnold and Gertrude Boutell Memorial Fund)
106 S. Main St., 16th Fl.
Akron, OH 44308-1412
Application address: c/o Helen James, Citizens Bank Wealth Mgmt., N.A., 101 N. Washington Ave., Saginaw, MI 48607-1207, tel.: (989) 776-7368

Established in 1961 in MI.
Donors: Arnold Boutell†; Gertrude Boutell†.
Foundation type: Independent foundation.
Financial data (yr. ended 03/31/14): Assets, $12,730,233 (M); expenditures, $838,180; qualifying distributions, $691,819; giving activities include $676,579 for 21 grants (high: $233,334; low: $5,495).
Purpose and activities: Giving primarily for human services.
Fields of interest: Environment; Youth development, services; Human services; Children/youth, services; Urban/community development.
Type of support: Equipment; Program development.
Limitations: Giving limited to Saginaw County, MI. No grants to individuals, or for endowment funds.
Application information: Application form required.
Initial approach: Letter
Copies of proposal: 1
Deadline(s): None
Board meeting date(s): 3rd Wed. of Mar., June, Sept., and Dec.
Trustee: FirstMerit Bank.
EIN: 386040492
Selected grants: The following grants are a representative sample of this grantmaker's funding activity:
$125,000 to Saginaw Valley State University, University Center, MI, 2013. For Greenhouse Project.
$110,000 to United Way of Saginaw County, Saginaw, MI, 2013. For Christmas Basket and Annual Fundraising Campaign.
$45,000 to Saginaw Future, Saginaw, MI, 2013. For CRM System.
$35,000 to Hidden Harvest, Saginaw, MI, 2013. To expand Food Distribution Initiative and Christmas Basket.
$23,000 to Emmaus House of Saginaw, Saginaw, MI, 2013. For Christmas Basket and Guest Needs.
$10,000 to Old Town Soup Kitchen, Saginaw, MI, 2013. For Christmas Baskets.
$10,000 to Underground Railroad, Saginaw, MI, 2013. For Christmas Basket.
$9,900 to Teen Challenge of Saginaw, Saginaw, MI, 2013. For Men's Refurbishing of Furniture.

7389
Broussard Charitable Foundation ✧
P.O. Box 630858
Cincinnati, OH 45263-0858

Established in 1996 in IN.
Donors: Jerome T. Broussard; Broussard No. 2 LP; Jerome T. Broussard Pledged Trust; Rebecca C. Broussard IRR Trust.
Foundation type: Independent foundation.
Financial data (yr. ended 12/31/13): Assets, $17,616,799 (M); expenditures, $756,828; qualifying distributions, $642,883; giving activities include $642,500 for 16 grants (high: $400,000; low: $5,000).
Fields of interest: Higher education; Business school/education; Animals/wildlife, sanctuaries; Athletics/sports, equestrianism; Human services; United Ways and Federated Giving Programs.
Limitations: Applications not accepted. Giving primarily in MT; some funding also in CO, KY, and NJ.
Application information: Contributes only to pre-selected organizations.
Trustee: Fifth Third Bank, N.A.
EIN: 356634227

7390
Constance W. & James W. Brown Jr. Family Foundation, Inc. ✧
1 Propeller Pl.
Piqua, OH 45356-2655

Established in 2005 in OH.
Donors: James W. Brown, Jr.; Constance W. Brown; James W. Brown III.
Foundation type: Independent foundation.
Financial data (yr. ended 12/31/12): Assets, $904,096 (M); gifts received, $127,452; expenditures, $630,649; qualifying distributions, $618,865; giving activities include $611,169 for 7 grants (high: $228,000; low: $3,500).
Fields of interest: Health care; Medical research, institute; Human services.
Limitations: Applications not accepted. Giving primarily in OH. No grants to individuals.
Application information: Unsolicited requests for funds not accepted.
Officers: Constance W. Brown, Pres.; James W. Brown, Jr., Secy.- Treas.
EIN: 203289903

7391
Eva L. and Joseph M. Bruening Foundation
c/o Foundation Management Services
1422 Euclid Ave., Ste. 966
Cleveland, OH 44115-1952 (216) 621-2632
Contact: Cristin N. Slesh, Consultant
FAX: (216) 621-8198; Main URL: http://www.fmscleveland.com/bruening

Established in 1987 in OH.
Donors: Joseph M. Bruening†; Eva L. Bruening†.
Foundation type: Independent foundation.
Financial data (yr. ended 12/31/13): Assets, $58,248,208 (M); expenditures, $3,036,382; qualifying distributions, $2,743,565; giving activities include $2,319,700 for 105 grants (high: $100,000; low: $4,000).
Purpose and activities: The mission of the foundation is to reduce the impact of poverty and enhance the quality of life of those most in need in Cuyahoga County. New priorities include Learning and Safety Net Services.
Fields of interest: Education, early childhood education; Education; Human services; Children/youth, services; Aging, centers/services; Catholic agencies & churches; Aging; Disabilities, people with; Physically disabled; Mentally disabled; Women; Economically disadvantaged; Homeless.
Type of support: Capital campaigns; Building/renovation; Equipment; Program development; Seed money.
Limitations: Applications accepted. Giving limited to Cuyahoga County, OH. No grants to individuals, or for endowment funds, general operating budgets, research, symposia or seminars, mass mailings, or annual campaigns.
Publications: Financial statement.
Application information: The foundation does not respond to mass mailings or annual campaign appeals. See foundation web site for application information. Application form required.
Initial approach: Use online application form on foundation web site
Deadline(s): Mar. 1, June 1, and Oct. 1
Board meeting date(s): May, Aug., and Dec.
Final notification: Within several weeks of board meeting
Officer and Distribution Committee:* William R. Plato,* Chair.; Marilyn A. Cunin; Diane Downing; Jane M. Harris; Thomas E. Wagner.
Trustee: KeyBank N.A.
EIN: 341584378
Selected grants: The following grants are a representative sample of this grantmaker's funding activity:
$100,000 to Sisters of Charity Foundation of Cleveland, Cleveland, OH, 2012. For the Cleveland Central Promise Neighborhood project which will develop a system of family and community supports for residents.
$50,000 to College Now Greater Cleveland, Cleveland, OH, 2012. For college advising services in the Garfield Heights and Warrensville Heights school districts.
$47,977 to Rose-Mary, the Johanna Grasselli Rehabilitation and Education Center, Euclid, OH, 2012. To upgrade the security system at the main campus.
$35,000 to Guidestone Ohio, Berea, OH, 2012. For mobile computing devices for case managers.
$32,000 to North Coast Community Homes, Cleveland, OH, 2012. To develop one home for indigent adults with MR/DD.
$30,000 to Scranton Road Ministries Community Development Corporation, Cleveland, OH, 2012. For the Youth Jobs Partnership program at Lincoln West and James F. Rhodes high schools.
$25,000 to Center for Arts-Inspired Learning, Cleveland, OH, 2012. For Art is Education, arts-integrated program within the CMSD.
$20,000 to Burten, Bell, Carr Development, Cleveland, OH, 2012. For the Bridgeport Market, Cafe and Community Kitchen, which will provide healthy foods and nutrition programming.
$20,000 to Esperanza, Cleveland, OH, 2012. To help high schoolers prepare for the OGT.
$20,000 to Family Promise of Greater Cleveland, Cleveland, OH, 2012. For family stability services.
$20,000 to Linking Employment, Abilities and Potential, Cleveland, OH, 2012. For peer support services.
$10,000 to Playhouse Square Foundation, Cleveland, OH, 2012. For programming for CMSD students.

7392
The Otto M. Budig Family Foundation ✧
1100 Gest St.
Cincinnati, OH 45203-1114
Contact: Otto M. Budig, Jr., Pres.

Established in 1994 in OH.
Donor: Otto M. Budig, Jr.
Foundation type: Independent foundation.
Financial data (yr. ended 12/31/13): Assets, $309 (M); gifts received, $1,275,050; expenditures, $1,274,774; qualifying distributions, $1,273,955;

giving activities include $1,273,205 for 43 grants (high: $270,757; low: $100).
Purpose and activities: Giving primarily to the performing arts and arts/cultural programs, especially art museums, ballet, opera and symphony.
Fields of interest: Performing arts; Arts; United Ways and Federated Giving Programs.
Type of support: General/operating support; Continuing support; Annual campaigns; Capital campaigns; Building/renovation; Endowments; Program development; Seed money.
Limitations: Applications not accepted. Giving primarily in Cincinnati, OH. No grants to individuals.
Application information: Unsolicited requests for funds not accepted.
Board meeting date(s): Quarterly
Officer and Trustees:* Otto M. Budig, Jr.,* Pres.; David H. Budig; Mark E. Budig; Sandra F. Budig; Julie B. Held.
Number of staff: 2 part-time professional.
EIN: 311411132
Selected grants: The following grants are a representative sample of this grantmaker's funding activity:
$10,000 to Greater Cincinnati Television Educational Foundation, Cincinnati, OH, 2012. For unrestricted contribution.

7393
Clement and Ann Buenger Foundation ✧
P.O. Box 630858
Cincinnati, OH 45263-0858
Contact: Dave Garber

Established in 1988 in OH.
Donors: Clement L. Buenger; Ann M. Buenger.
Foundation type: Independent foundation.
Financial data (yr. ended 09/30/13): Assets, $18,576,661 (M); expenditures, $531,994; qualifying distributions, $430,567; giving activities include $430,034 for 20 grants (high: $100,000; low: $500).
Purpose and activities: Giving primarily for secondary and higher education; some funding also for the arts.
Fields of interest: Arts; Secondary school/education; Higher education; Education.
Limitations: Applications not accepted. Giving primarily in the greater Cincinnati, OH, area. No support for religious or political purposes. No grants to individuals.
Application information: Unsolicited requests for funds not accepted.
Directors: Michael K. Keating; Nancy N. Keating; William J. Keating.
EIN: 311259480

7394
Building Healthy Lives Foundation ✧ ☆
625 Eden Park Dr., Ste. 200
Cincinnati, OH 45202-6057 (513) 419-6587
Contact: Dianne Dunkelman, Pres.
FAX: (513) 241-2888;
E-mail: kclark@clevercrazes.com; Main URL: http://www.clevercrazes.com/

Donors: Duke Energy; Carol Ann and Ralph V. Haile Jr. Foundation; JRO Charitable Lead Annuity Trust; The Kurzrok Foundation; National Speaking of Women's Health; The Selz Foundation, Inc.; Jodi Geiser.
Foundation type: Independent foundation.
Financial data (yr. ended 12/31/12): Assets, $43,945,859 (M); gifts received, $341,883; expenditures, $3,107,664; qualifying distributions, $430,425; giving activities include $430,425 for grants.
Fields of interest: Health care; Youth development; Human services.
Limitations: Applications accepted. Giving primarily in Cincinnati, OH.
Application information: Application form required.
Initial approach: Proposal
Deadline(s): None
Officers: Dianne Dunkelmann, Pres.; Lorrence Kellar, Secy.
Directors: Guy M. Hild; Sandra Lobert; Patricia Smitson.
EIN: 300214078

7395
Burleigh Family Foundation ✧ ☆
105 E. 4th St., Ste. 300
Cincinnati, OH 45202-3007

Established in 1996 in OH.
Donors: William R. Burleigh; Catherine Anne Husted Burleigh; David W. Burleigh.
Foundation type: Independent foundation.
Financial data (yr. ended 12/31/13): Assets, $4,161,128 (M); gifts received, $254,600; expenditures, $507,683; qualifying distributions, $475,458; giving activities include $458,050 for 57 grants (high: $40,000; low: $500).
Purpose and activities: Giving primarily to Roman Catholic organizations, churches, and schools.
Fields of interest: Arts; Education; Human services; Catholic agencies & churches.
Type of support: General/operating support.
Limitations: Applications not accepted. Giving primarily in OH; giving also in KY. No grants to individuals.
Application information: Contributes only to pre-selected organizations.
Trustees: Margaret W. Brecount; Catherine Anne Husted Burleigh; David W. Burleigh; William R. Burleigh.
EIN: 316543121

7396
The Butler Foundation ✧
(formerly Robert M. Butler Memorial Foundation)
P.O. Box 75020
Cincinnati, OH 45275-0020 (859) 292-5500
Contact: Barbara Schaefer, Tr.
FAX: (859) 292-5599;
E-mail: bschaefer@corporex.com

Established in 1979 in OH.
Donors: Corporex Cos., Inc.; Commonwealth Hotels, LLC; Corporex Companies, LLC; CPX Commercial Development, LLC; CPX Development & Construction Management, LLC; Five Seasons Country Clubs, LLC; William P. Butler; WM P. Butler Trust.
Foundation type: Independent foundation.
Financial data (yr. ended 09/30/13): Assets, $4,286,433 (M); gifts received, $241,050; expenditures, $470,174; qualifying distributions, $460,857; giving activities include $454,622 for 44 grants (high: $100,000; low: $540).
Purpose and activities: Giving primarily for the basic needs of the poor in northern Kentucky.
Fields of interest: Education; Health organizations, association; Human services; Youth, services; Catholic agencies & churches.
Type of support: General/operating support; Emergency funds; Scholarship funds; Matching/challenge support.
Limitations: Applications accepted. Giving limited to northern KY. No support for private foundations or for veterans', fraternal or labor organizations. No grants for event sponsorships, capital campaigns or endowment funds.
Application information: Application form required.
Initial approach: Letter
Copies of proposal: 7
Deadline(s): Oct. 1 and Mar. 1
Board meeting date(s): Semiannually
Final notification: 6 to 9 months
Trustees: Tom Banta; Christa Butler; Kevin Butler; Marty Butler; Mary Sue Butler; William P. Butler; Barbara Schaefer.
EIN: 310981683
Selected grants: The following grants are a representative sample of this grantmaker's funding activity:
$25,000 to Newport Central Catholic High School, Newport, KY, 2011. For scholarship support.
$22,970 to Brighton Center, Newport, KY, 2011.
$20,434 to Welcome House of Northern Kentucky, Covington, KY, 2011. For operating support.
$17,731 to Northern Kentucky Community Action Commission, Covington, KY, 2011. For program support.
$10,000 to Be Concerned, Covington, KY, 2011. For operating support.
$10,000 to Emergency Cold Shelter of Northern Kentucky, Covington, KY, 2011. For operating support.
$5,129 to Saint Elizabeth Medical Center, Covington, KY, 2011. For program support.
$5,000 to Cincinnati Works, Cincinnati, OH, 2011. For operating support.
$3,000 to Northern Kentucky Harvest, Covington, KY, 2011. For program support.
$2,349 to Legal Aid of the Bluegrass, Covington, KY, 2011. For program support.

7397
The William M. & A. Cafaro Family Foundation ✧
c/o The Cafaro Co.
2445 Belmont Ave.
P.O. Box 2186
Youngstown, OH 44504-0186
Contact: Ruthanne Brown

Established in 1998 in OH.
Donors: Anthony M. Cafaro; Alyce Cafaro Charitable Lead Trust; William M. Cafaro Charitable Lead Trust.
Foundation type: Independent foundation.
Financial data (yr. ended 03/31/13): Assets, $28,588,382 (M); gifts received, $1,403,185; expenditures, $1,345,469; qualifying distributions, $1,270,571; giving activities include $1,218,605 for 235 grants (high: $250,000; low: $50), and $28,000 for grants to individuals.
Purpose and activities: Giving primarily for education, including college and university scholarships; funding also for health associations,

children, youth and social services, and Roman Catholic organizations and churches.
Fields of interest: Elementary/secondary education; Higher education; Health organizations, association; Cancer; Human services; Children/youth, services; Catholic agencies & churches.
Type of support: General/operating support; Scholarships—to individuals.
Limitations: Applications accepted. Giving primarily in northeastern OH.
Application information: Application form not required.
Initial approach: Proposal
Deadline(s): None
Board meeting date(s): Monthly
Trustees: Anthony M. Cafaro; Flora M. Cafaro; Phyllis C. Cafaro.
EIN: 311550874
Selected grants: The following grants are a representative sample of this grantmaker's funding activity:
$250,000 to Youngstown State University, Youngstown, OH, 2012. For general support.
$125,000 to Ursuline High School, Youngstown, OH, 2012. For general support.
$50,000 to Animal Welfare League of Trumbull County, Warren, OH, 2012. For general support.
$50,000 to Niles Frontliners, Niles, OH, 2012. For general support.
$25,000 to Saint Rose School, Girard, OH, 2012. For general support.
$25,000 to Ursuline High School, Youngstown, OH, 2012. For general support.
$10,000 to Duquesne University, Pittsburgh, PA, 2012. For general support.
$10,000 to Niles Historical Society, Niles, OH, 2012. For general support.
$5,000 to Kent State University, College of Technology, Kent, OH, 2012. For general support.
$5,000 to Kent State University, College of the Arts, Kent, OH, 2012. For general support.

7398
Cardinal Health Foundation ✧
c/o Community Rels.
7000 Cardinal Pl.
Dublin, OH 43017-1091 (614) 757-7481
Contact: Dianne Radigan, Dir., Community Rels.
E-mail: communityrelations@cardinalhealth.com; E-mail for Dianne Radigan: Dianne.Radigan@cardinalhealth.com; Main URL: http://www.cardinal.com/
Cardinal Health Foundation: https://www.youtube.com/watch?feature=player_embedded&v=JAKMxibZ7VU
Facebook: http://www.facebook.com/CardinalHealthFoundation

Established in 2000 in OH.
Donors: The Baxter Allegiance Foundation; Cardinal Health, Inc.; World Reach.
Foundation type: Company-sponsored foundation.
Financial data (yr. ended 06/30/13): Assets, $56,596,715 (M); gifts received, $4,000,000; expenditures, $8,505,722; qualifying distributions, $8,388,505; giving activities include $7,109,580 for 472 grants (high: $250,000; low: $63), and $829,342 for employee matching gifts.
Purpose and activities: The foundation supports healthcare programs designed to improve efficiency, enhance quality, and enable cost-effectiveness; increase awareness of prescription drug abuse; and build healthy communities.
Fields of interest: Education; Medical care, community health systems; Hospitals (general); Health care, clinics/centers; Pharmacy/prescriptions; Public health; Public health, physical fitness; Health care, patient services; Health care; Disasters, preparedness/services; Safety/disasters; Children; Youth; Aging.
Type of support: Continuing support; Program development; Conferences/seminars; Scholarship funds; Research; Employee volunteer services; Employee matching gifts; Employee-related scholarships; Donated products; In-kind gifts; Matching/challenge support.
Limitations: Applications accepted. Giving primarily in areas of company operations, with emphasis on Little Rock, AR, northern Chicago, Lake, and McHenry County, IL, Radcliff, KY, Albuquerque, NM, central OH, LaVergne, TN, El Paso, TX, PR, Kenosha County, WI; giving also to national organizations and internationally in China, Dominican Republic, and Mexico. No support for fraternal, athletic, or social clubs, member-based organizations, including chambers of commerce, rotary clubs, or IRS 501(c)(4) legions or associations, municipalities, including fire departments or police departments, organizations classified as IRS 509(a)(3), discriminatory organizations, organizations with divisive or litigious public agendas, religious organizations not of direct benefit to the entire community, sport teams, veterans', labor, or political organizations, private foundations or deferred giving trusts, marching bands, or youth clubs. No grants to individuals (except for employee-related scholarships), or for advertising, capital campaigns outside of Ohio, endowments, general operating support, debt reduction, political campaigns, athletic competitions, memberships, subscriptions, club dues, or travel; no loans.
Publications: Application guidelines; IRS Form 990 or 990-PF printed copy available upon request; Program policy statement.
Application information: Organizations receiving E3 Grants are asked to submit a mid-year progress report and a final report. Organizations receiving support for Prescription Drug Abuse and Misuse Prevention Grant Program are asked to participate in webinars or conference calls, submit a program/project evaluation, and submit a year-end summary report. Application form not required.
Initial approach: Complete online proposal for E3 Grants, Prescription Drug Abuse and Misuse Prevention Grant Program, and Essential to Wellness Grants
Deadline(s): Dec. 7 for E3 Grants; Apr. 25 for Prescription Drug Abuse and Misuse Prevention Grant Program; Jan. 17 for Essential to Wellness Grants
Final notification: Apr. for E3 Grants; May for Prescription Drug Abuse and Misuse Prevention Grant Program; Apr. for Essential to Wellness Grants
Officers and Directors:* Shelley Bird,* Chair.; Tony Caprio,* Vice-Chair.; Stephen Falk,* Secy.; Sam Samad, Treas.; Lisa Ashby; Jon Giacomin; Jorge Gomez; Carole Watkins; Connie Woodburn.
EIN: 311746458
Selected grants: The following grants are a representative sample of this grantmaker's funding activity:
$250,000 to Columbus Museum of Art, Columbus, OH, 2013. For Capital campaign.
$250,000 to Nationwide Childrens Hospital Foundation, Columbus, OH, 2013. For Capital campaign.
$185,600 to Scholarship America, Saint Peter, MN, 2013. For EE Scholarship.
$150,000 to Wounded Warrior Project, Jacksonville, FL, 2013.
$100,000 to Ohio State University Foundation, Columbus, OH, 2013. For Rx abuse/misuse.
$18,450 to Brockton Health Corporation, Brockton, MA, 2013. For E3 - Effectiveness, Efficiency, Excellence.
$14,000 to Drug Free America Foundation, Saint Petersburg, FL, 2013. For Rx abuse/misuse.
$5,000 to Kohl Children's Museum of Greater Chicago, Glenview, IL, 2013. For Essential to Wellness.
$3,500 to Haddonfield School District Scholarship and Education Fund, Haddonfield, NJ, 2013. For Volunteer leadership grant.
$3,500 to Parents and Friends of Children and Adults, Little Rock, AR, 2013. For Volunteer leadership grant.

7399
Castellini Foundation ✧
312 Elm St., Ste. 2600
Cincinnati, OH 45202-2728 (513) 651-9400
Contact: Christopher L. Fister, Secy.-Treas.

Established in 1991 in OH.
Donors: Robert H. Castellini; Susan F. Castellini.
Foundation type: Independent foundation.
Financial data (yr. ended 03/31/13): Assets, $6,303,471 (M); gifts received, $2,351,748; expenditures, $1,769,176; qualifying distributions, $1,749,132; giving activities include $1,749,132 for grants.
Purpose and activities: Giving primarily for education, health care, and the arts.
Fields of interest: Museums; Arts; Higher education; Education; Health organizations, association; Human services; Children/youth, services; United Ways and Federated Giving Programs.
Limitations: Applications accepted. Giving limited to the greater Cincinnati, OH, area. No support for religious or political purposes. No grants to individuals.
Application information: Application form not required.
Initial approach: Letter
Deadline(s): None
Officers and Trustees:* Robert H. Castellini,* Chair. and Pres.; Christopher L. Fister,* Secy.-Treas.; Susan F. Castellini.
Agent: Fifth Third Bank.
EIN: 316429763
Selected grants: The following grants are a representative sample of this grantmaker's funding activity:
$62,000 to African-American Chamber of Commerce of Greater Cincinnati and Northern Kentucky, Cincinnati, OH, 2011.
$25,000 to UGive.org, Cincinnati, OH, 2011.

7400
Charities Foundation ✧
c/o Kathleen Matzinger
1 Michael Owens Way Plz. 1, 3rd Fl.
Perrysburg, OH 43551-2999

Established in 1937 in OH.

Donors: Owens-Illinois Inc.; William E. Levis†; Harold Boeschenstein†.
Foundation type: Company-sponsored foundation.
Financial data (yr. ended 12/31/13): Assets, $470,950 (M); gifts received, $2,050,000; expenditures, $1,736,550; qualifying distributions, $1,735,679; giving activities include $1,721,776 for 192 grants (high: $446,146; low: $25).
Purpose and activities: The foundation supports organizations involved with arts and culture, education, the environment, health, and human services.
Fields of interest: Visual arts; Museums (art); Performing arts, orchestras; Arts; Secondary school/education; Higher education; Scholarships/financial aid; Education, reading; Education; Environment, natural resources; Environment, beautification programs; Health care, clinics/centers; Health care; Children/youth, services; Homeless, human services; Human services; United Ways and Federated Giving Programs.
Type of support: General/operating support; Scholarship funds; Employee matching gifts; Matching/challenge support.
Limitations: Applications not accepted. Giving primarily in OH, with emphasis on Toledo. No grants to individuals, or for scholarships.
Application information: Contributes only to pre-selected organizations.
Trustees: James E. Adams; Jim Baehren; Kimberly Meneilly.
Number of staff: 1 part-time support.
EIN: 346554560

7401
Children's Family Care, Inc. ✧ ☆
c/o Grant Committee
245 Locust St.
Akron, OH 44302-1817

Established in 1999 in OH.
Donor: Maxene D. Darrah Revocable Trust.
Foundation type: Independent foundation.
Financial data (yr. ended 12/31/13): Assets, $7,802,473 (M); expenditures, $573,213; qualifying distributions, $519,000; giving activities include $519,000 for 1 grant.
Fields of interest: Hospitals (general); Human services; Children/youth, services; Family services; Children/youth; Children; Young adults, male.
Limitations: Applications not accepted. Giving primarily in OH. No support for public school programs, or for community foundations, campaigns funded by tax initiatives; no grants for religious or political organizations. No grants to individuals, or for teams or events.
Application information: Contributes only to pre-selected organizations.
Officers: Dana Zahuranec, Pres.; Sheldon W. Barlette, Jr., V.P.; Mary Yanko, Secy.; Rick Archer, Treas.
Trustees: John Blickle; Steve Cox; Dale G. Freygang; Keith Kilgore; Emily B. Petrarca; John Shaffer; Steve Shriber; Michael G. Soful; Jim Stroble; and 2 additional trustees.
EIN: 341405958

7402
Christ Foundation ✧ ☆
P.O. Box 1180
Hartville, OH 44632-1180
Contact: Patricia P. Moore, Secy.
Established in 1971 in OH.
Donors: Jerry Moore; Sara C. Gibbs; Gerald H. Moore; Patricia P. Moore.
Foundation type: Independent foundation.
Financial data (yr. ended 12/31/13): Assets, $4,773,346 (M); gifts received, $993,053; expenditures, $689,123; qualifying distributions, $689,123; giving activities include $674,295 for 40 grants (high: $500,000; low: $100).
Purpose and activities: Giving limited to persons, projects, programs, and institutions affiliated with the Church of Christ.
Fields of interest: Higher education; Human services; American Red Cross; Christian agencies & churches.
Type of support: General/operating support; Building/renovation.
Limitations: Applications accepted. Giving primarily in OH.
Application information: Application form required.
Initial approach: Proposal
Deadline(s): None
Officers: Jerry Moore, Pres.; Patricia Moore, Secy.; Lewis Yoder, Treas.
EIN: 237121546
Selected grants: The following grants are a representative sample of this grantmaker's funding activity:
$56,265 to Louisville Church of Christ, Louisville, OH, 2012. For Building Fund and Operating.

7403
Anne Kilcawley Christman Foundation ✧
c/o Farmers Trust Co.
42 McClurg Rd.
Youngstown, OH 44512

Established in 2002 in OH.
Donor: Anne Christman Irrevocable Trust.
Foundation type: Independent foundation.
Financial data (yr. ended 12/31/13): Assets, $48,473,766 (M); expenditures, $2,397,438; qualifying distributions, $2,170,664; giving activities include $2,079,840 for 7 grants (high: $297,120; low: $297,120).
Fields of interest: Museums; Performing arts; Historic preservation/historical societies; Higher education; Housing/shelter, aging; Human services; Residential/custodial care, hospices; Protestant agencies & churches.
Limitations: Applications not accepted. Giving primarily in OH, with emphasis on Youngstown. No grants to individuals.
Application information: Contributes only to pre-selected organizations.
Trustees: Herbert H. Pridham; Farmers Trust Co.
EIN: 356735706

7404
The Greater Cincinnati Foundation ✧
200 W. 4th St.
Cincinnati, OH 45202-2775
Contact: Shiloh Turner, V.P., Community Investment; For grants: Kay Pennington, Community Investment Coord.
E-mail: info@gcfdn.org; Grant application e-mail: penningtonk@gcfdn.org; Main URL: http://www.gcfdn.org
Facebook: http://www.facebook.com/pages/The-Greater-Cincinnati-Foundation/107439465485
Flickr: http://www.flickr.com/photos/14141531@N08/sets/
LinkedIn: http://www.linkedin.com/companies/the-greater-cincinnati-foundation
Pinterest: http://www.pinterest.com/gcfdn/pins/
Twitter: http://twitter.com/GrCinciFdn/
YouTube: http://www.youtube.com/user/GCFonline
Established in 1963 in OH by bank resolution and declaration of trust.
Foundation type: Community foundation.
Financial data (yr. ended 12/31/13): Assets, $539,645,114 (M); gifts received, $75,478,707; expenditures, $76,142,312; giving activities include $69,133,479 for grants.
Purpose and activities: Grants for a broad range of existing activities in general categories of arts and culture, community progress, environmental needs, education, health, and social and human services, including youth agencies. The foundation actively seeks to promote access, equity and diversity, and to end discrimination based on race, ethnicity, gender, disability and age.
Fields of interest: Arts; Education, early childhood education; Education; Environment; Health care; Housing/shelter, home owners; Disasters, Hurricane Katrina; Children/youth, services; Human services; Community/economic development; Voluntarism promotion; Children/youth; Children; Youth; Adults; Aging; Young adults; Disabilities, people with; Physically disabled; Blind/visually impaired; Deaf/hearing impaired; Mentally disabled; Minorities; African Americans/Blacks; Hispanics/Latinos; Women; Men; Economically disadvantaged; Homeless.
Type of support: Capital campaigns; Building/renovation; Equipment; Emergency funds; Program development; Seed money; Technical assistance; Matching/challenge support.
Limitations: Applications accepted. Giving limited to southeastern IN, northern KY, and the greater Cincinnati, OH area. No support for private or parochial religious purposes, units of government or government agencies, schools, hospitals, nursing homes, playgrounds, sports teams, or sports activities, or retirement centers. No grants to individuals (except for scholarships), or for operating budgets, fundraising drives, event sponsorship, or underwriting, equipment, stand-alone publications or videos, annual campaigns, deficit financing, endowments, travel, fellowships, internships, exchange programs, or scholarly or medical research; no loans.
Publications: Application guidelines; Annual report (including application guidelines); Grants list; Informational brochure (including application guidelines); Newsletter.
Application information: Visit foundation web site for online application and guidelines per grant type. Application form required.
Initial approach: Visit web site or telephone
Copies of proposal: 1
Deadline(s): Varies
Board meeting date(s): Mar., June, Sept., and Dec.
Final notification: Varies
Officers and Governing Board:* Peter S. Strange,* Chair.; Dianne M. Rosenberg,* Vice-Chair.; Kathryn

E. Merchant, C.E.O. and Pres.; Elizabeth Reiter Benson, V.P., Comms. and Mktg.; Amy L. Cheney, V.P., Giving Strategies; J. Scott McReynolds, V.P., Finance and Admin.; Shiloh Turner, V.P., Community Investment; Melissa Krabbe, Cont.; Ronald C. Christian, Legal Counsel; Calvin D. Buford; Neil Comber; Alva Jean Crawford; Thomas D. Croft; David Ellis III; Linda C. Fath; Christopher L. Fister; Wijdan Jreisat; Dr. Molly Katz; Janet B. Reid, Ph.D.; Ryan M. Rybolt; Charles R. Scheper; Ann M. Schwister; Patricia Mann Smitson.
Trustee Banks: Fifth Third Bank; The Huntington National Bank; JPMorgan Chase Bank, N.A.; KeyBank N.A.; LCNB National Bank; North Side Bank & Trust Co.; PNC Bank, N.A.; The Provident Bank; U.S. Bank, N.A.
Number of staff: 19 full-time professional; 10 full-time support; 1 part-time support.
EIN: 310669700
Selected grants: The following grants are a representative sample of this grantmaker's funding activity:
$600,000 to Cincinnati Public Schools, Cincinnati, OH, 2012.
$225,000 to Chamber of Commerce Foundation of Greater Cincinnati, Cincinnati, OH, 2012. For MBA (Minority Business Accelerator).
$150,000 to Center for Closing the Health Gap in Greater Cincinnati, Cincinnati, OH, 2012.
$100,000 to ArtsWave, Cincinnati, OH, 2012.
$100,000 to United Way of Greater Cincinnati, Cincinnati, OH, 2012. For Place Matters Initiative.
$90,000 to Children Inc., Covington, KY, 2012.
$75,000 to United Way of Greater Cincinnati, Cincinnati, OH, 2012. For Success by Six.
$45,000 to MUSE Cincinnati Womens Choir, Cincinnati, OH, 2012.
$27,112 to Hamilton County Jobs and Family Services, Cincinnati, OH, 2012.
$25,000 to Downtown Cincinnati, Cincinnati, OH, 2012.

7405
The Cincinnati Foundation for the Aged ✧

2100 4th and Vine Tower
5 W. 4th St.
Cincinnati, OH 45202-3604 (513) 381-6859
Contact: Heather Jansen

Established in 1891 in OH.
Donors: Oscar Cohrs†; Otto Luedeking†; William Meyer†; Oscar Cohrs Trust.
Foundation type: Independent foundation.
Financial data (yr. ended 03/31/13): Assets, $26,201,744 (M); gifts received, $260,420; expenditures, $1,187,341; qualifying distributions, $1,137,283; giving activities include $1,117,020 for 15 grants (high: $300,000; low: $4,000).
Purpose and activities: The sole purpose of the foundation is to assist indigent persons in the greater Cincinnati, OH, area, to gain admission to nonprofit nursing homes.
Fields of interest: Aging, centers/services; Aging.
Limitations: Giving primarily in the greater Cincinnati, OH, area; some funding also in KY. No grants to individuals.
Application information: Disbursements limited to the foundation's single mission described in Purpose & Activities; funding requests for studies or any other activity not eligible for consideration. Application form required.

Deadline(s): None
Board meeting date(s): Mar., June, Sept., and Dec.

Officers and Trustees:* Robert Porter III,* Pres.; Sr. Jean Marie Hoffman, 1st V.P.; Gene Weber,* 2nd V.P.; Heather Jansen, Secy.-Treas.; Jon Blohm; Boyd Colglazier; Thomas L. Finn; Jack Greer; Richard Hoefinghoff; Vince Hopkins; James Kemp; Robert C. Porter, Jr.; William H. Strietmann.
Number of staff: 1 full-time support.
EIN: 310536971
Selected grants: The following grants are a representative sample of this grantmaker's funding activity:
$5,000 to Our Lady of the Woods, Cincinnati, OH, 2013. To Pay for the Cost of Nursing Home Care.

7406
The Cleveland Foundation ✧

1422 Euclid Ave., Ste. 1300
Cleveland, OH 44115-2001 (216) 861-3810
Contact: Ronald B. Richard, C.E.O.
FAX: (216) 861-1729; E-mail: hello@clevefdn.org; TTY: (216) 861-3810; Main URL: http://www.clevelandfoundation.org
Advanced Energy Blog: http://advancedenergyblog.clevelandfoundation.org/
arts&ideas Blog: http://artsandcultureblog.clevelandfoundation.org/
CEP Study: http://www.clevelandfoundation.org/grants/grantee-perception-report/
Cleveland Foundation's Philanthropy Promise: http://www.ncrp.org/philanthropys-promise/who
Facebook: http://www.facebook.com/clevelandfoundation
Grantmaking Blog: http://grantmakingblog.clevelandfoundation.org/
LinkedIn: http://www.linkedin.com/companies/the-cleveland-foundation
Twitter: http://twitter.com/CleveFoundation
YouTube: http://www.youtube.com/clevelandfoundation
Scholarship e-mail: mBaker@CleveFdn.org

Established in 1914 in OH by bank resolution and declaration of trust.
Foundation type: Community foundation.
Financial data (yr. ended 12/31/13): Assets, $2,132,806,744 (M); gifts received, $37,653,516; expenditures, $100,794,968; giving activities include $81,368,990 for grants.
Purpose and activities: Established in 1914, the Cleveland Foundation is the world's first community foundation and one of the largest today. Through the generosity of donors, the foundation improves the lives of Greater Clevelanders by building community endowment, addressing needs through grantmaking, and providing leadership on vital issues. The foundation tackles the community's priority areas - economic transformation, public school improvement, youth development, neighborhood revitalization, and arts advancement - and responds to the community's needs.
Fields of interest: Arts education; Visual arts; Performing arts; Arts; Elementary school/education; Secondary school/education; Higher education; Medical school/education; Education; Environment; Health care; Health organizations, association; AIDS; Medical research, institute; AIDS research; Housing/shelter, development; Disasters, Hurricane Katrina; Youth, services; Family services; Aging, centers/services; Human services; Economic development; Urban/community development; Community/economic development; Economics; Government/public administration; Youth; Aging.
Type of support: Capital campaigns; Program development; Seed money; Scholarship funds; Research; Technical assistance; Consulting services; Program-related investments/loans; Scholarships—to individuals; Matching/challenge support; Mission-related investments/loans.
Limitations: Applications accepted. Giving limited to the greater Cleveland, OH, area, with primary emphasis on Cleveland, Cuyahoga, Lake, and Geauga counties, unless specified by donor. No support for sectarian or religious activities, community services such as fire and police protection, government staff positions, or library and welfare services. No grants to individuals (except for scholarships), or for endowment funds, operating costs, debt reduction, fundraising campaigns, publications, films and audiovisual materials (unless they are an integral part of a program already being supported), memberships, travel for bands, sports teams, classes and similar groups; no capital support for planning, construction, renovation, or purchase of buildings, equipment and materials, land acquisition, or renovation of public space unless there is strong evidence that the program is of priority to the foundation.
Publications: Annual report; Informational brochure; Newsletter; Occasional report.
Application information: The foundation now requires organizations to submit inquiries and applications electronically; visit web site for application instructions. Applicants will be notified as to whether to submit a full proposal based on Grant Inquiry Form. Application form required.

Initial approach: Establish or update online organization profile
Deadline(s): None
Board meeting date(s): Mar., June, Sept., and Dec.
Final notification: Within a few weeks for notification of Grant Inquiry Form results; varies for full proposals

Officers and Directors:* James A. Ratner, Chair.; Paul J. Dolan,* Vice-Chair.; Ronald B. Richard, C.E.O. and Pres.; Robert E. Eckardt, Exec. V.P.; Kate A. Asbeck, Sr. V.P. and C.F.O.; Kaye Ridolfi, Sr. V.P. of Advancement; Leslie A. Dunford, V.P., Corp. Gov. and Admin.; Kathy S. Parker, Cont.; Teresa Metcalf Beasley; Inajo Davis Chappell; Jenniffer D. Deckard; Hiroyuki Fujita; Sally Gries; Bernie Moreno; Frederick R. Nance; Michael Petras, Jr.; Larry Pollock; Beth O. Rankin; Stephen Rowan; Ratanjit S. Sondhe; Ernest L. Wilkerson, Jr.
Trustees: FirstMerit Bank, N.A.; The Huntington National Bank; JPMorgan Chase Bank, N.A.; KeyBank N.A.; National City Bank.
Number of staff: 42 full-time professional; 2 part-time professional; 20 full-time support; 1 part-time support.
EIN: 340714588
Selected grants: The following grants are a representative sample of this grantmaker's funding activity:
$10,000,000 to Musical Arts Association, Cleveland, OH, 2013. For bridge funding, payable over 5.00 years.
$5,000,000 to Neighborhood Progress, Cleveland, OH, 2013. To implement strategic plan, payable over 3.00 years.
$918,405 to Center for Families and Children, Cleveland, OH, 2013. For Cleveland Courage Fund.

$917,000 to Cleveland Foundation Inc., Cleveland, OH, 2013. For The Cleveland Plan for Transforming Schools.
$750,000 to Playhouse Square Foundation, Cleveland, OH, 2013. For reconfiguration of the RJF President's Club and modernization of the food and beverage concession areas throughout all the theaters.
$710,000 to College Now Greater Cleveland, Cleveland, OH, 2013. For Postsecondary Access Initiative.
$25,000 to Neighborhood Progress, Cleveland, OH, 2013. For LiveCLEVELAND! Southeast Neighborhood project.
$5,000 to Cuyahoga Valley Preservation and Scenic Railway Association, Peninsula, OH, 2013. For general support.
$5,000 to Ohio Presbyterian Retirement Services Foundation, Columbus, OH, 2013. For Beautification and Capital Campaign for Breckenridge Village.
$3,000 to Miami University, Oxford, OH, 2013. For TCF scholarship.

7407
The Cliffs Foundation ✧
(formerly The Cleveland-Cliffs Foundation)
200 Public Sq., Ste. 3300
Cleveland, OH 44114-2315 (216) 694-5700
Contact: Kimberly Regan, Mgr., Public Affairs
E-mail: kimberly.regan@cliffsnr.com; Main URL: http://www.cliffsnaturalresources.com/EN/CorpResponsibility/philanthropy/Pages/default.aspx

Established in 1962 in OH.
Donors: Cleveland-Cliffs Inc.; Tilden Mining Co.; Empire Iron Mining Partnership; Hibbing Taconite Co.; Northshore Mining Co.; Cliffs Natural Resources.
Foundation type: Company-sponsored foundation.
Financial data (yr. ended 12/31/13): Assets, $4,927,062 (M); gifts received, $1,500,000; expenditures, $1,958,284; qualifying distributions, $1,958,284; giving activities include $1,903,276 for 122 grants (high: $200,000; low: $500), and $54,274 for 42 employee matching gifts.
Purpose and activities: The foundation supports programs designed to promote healthy communities and vibrant communities through economic development, environmental stewardship, community services, and arts and culture. Special emphasis is directed toward education programs associated with mining and related technology.
Fields of interest: Museums (science/technology); Performing arts, theater; Performing arts, orchestras; Arts; Secondary school/education; Higher education; Education; Hospitals (general); Health care; Boys & girls clubs; American Red Cross; Children/youth, services; Human services; United Ways and Federated Giving Programs; Geology; Engineering/technology; Public affairs; Economically disadvantaged.
Type of support: General/operating support; Annual campaigns; Capital campaigns; Building/renovation; Scholarship funds; Employee matching gifts; Employee-related scholarships.
Limitations: Applications accepted. Giving primarily in areas of company operations, with emphasis on northwest AL, the upper MI peninsula, northeastern MN, Cleveland, OH, and southern WV. No support for political candidates or organizations, for-profit organizations, or discriminatory organizations. No grants to individuals, or for membership drives, or travel; no loans.
Publications: Application guidelines.
Application information: No solicitations made by telephone or in person will be accepted. Organizations receiving support are asked to submit interim reports and a final report. Support is limited to 1 contribution per organization during any given year. Application form not required.
Initial approach: Download application form and mail or e-mail application and proposal to foundation or local public affairs representative
Copies of proposal: 1
Deadline(s): June 1
Board meeting date(s): Annually
Officers and Trustees:* P. Kelly Tompkins,* Pres.; Raga S. Elim, V.P.; Traci L. Forrester, Secy.-Treas.; Gary B. Halverson; James R. Michaud.
EIN: 346525124
Selected grants: The following grants are a representative sample of this grantmaker's funding activity:
$50 to Bemidji State University, Bemidji, MN, 2012. For Education - Matching Gifts.

7408
August Clouse Trust ✧
P.O. Box 1118, ML CN-OH-W10X
Cincinnati, OH 45201-1118

Foundation type: Independent foundation.
Financial data (yr. ended 12/31/13): Assets, $10,855,500 (M); expenditures, $654,727; qualifying distributions, $489,767; giving activities include $474,540 for 10 grants (high: $47,454; low: $47,454).
Fields of interest: Human services; Christian agencies & churches.
Limitations: Applications not accepted.
Application information: Contributes only to pre-selected organizations.
Trustee: U.S. Bank, N.A.
EIN: 316021973
Selected grants: The following grants are a representative sample of this grantmaker's funding activity:
$24,285 to Boys Town, Boys Town, NE, 2011.
$24,285 to Divine Word Missionaries, Techny, IL, 2011.
$24,285 to Mission of Our Lady of Mercy, Chicago, IL, 2011.
$24,285 to Society for the Propagation of the Faith, New York, NY, 2011.

7409
The George W. Codrington Charitable Foundation ✧
Key Center, 39th Fl.
127 Public Sq.
Cleveland, OH 44114-1291 (216) 566-8674
Contact: Craig R. Martahus, Chair.
E-mail: tommie.robertston@thompsonhine.com

Trust established in 1955 in OH.
Donor: George W. Codrington‡.
Foundation type: Independent foundation.
Financial data (yr. ended 12/31/13): Assets, $17,591,330 (M); expenditures, $1,299,084; qualifying distributions, $1,166,580; giving activities include $1,133,500 for 81 grants (high: $110,000; low: $1,000).
Purpose and activities: Giving primarily for higher education, hospitals, arts groups, and youth.
Fields of interest: Museums; Performing arts; Arts; Higher education; Education; Hospitals (general); Children/youth, services.
Type of support: General/operating support; Continuing support; Annual campaigns; Capital campaigns; Equipment; Program development; Research.
Limitations: Applications accepted. Giving limited to Cuyahoga County, OH, and the surrounding area. No grants to individuals, or for endowment funds; no loans.
Publications: Annual report (including application guidelines).
Application information: Application form not required.
Initial approach: Full proposal
Copies of proposal: 3
Deadline(s): Submit proposal preferably the month before board meetings
Board meeting date(s): Apr., June, Sept., and Dec.
Final notification: Promptly after board meeting
Officers and Supervisory Board:* Craig R. Martahus,* Chair.; William R. Seelbach,* Vice-Chair.; Raymond T. Sawyer,* Secy.
Trustee: BNY Mellon, N.A.
EIN: 346507457

7410
Helen C. Cole Charitable Trust ✧
200 Public Sq., Ste. 2800
Cleveland, OH 44114-2316

Established in 2004 in OH.
Donors: Helen C. Cole‡; Helen C. Cole Trust.
Foundation type: Independent foundation.
Financial data (yr. ended 12/31/13): Assets, $26,073,422 (M); expenditures, $1,550,629; qualifying distributions, $1,225,200; giving activities include $1,225,000 for 15 grants (high: $612,500; low: $36,607).
Purpose and activities: Giving primarily for the arts, education, a community foundation, and social services, including a hearing and speech center, and services for the blind.
Fields of interest: Museums; Arts; Elementary/secondary education; Higher education; Education; Human services; Foundations (community).
Limitations: Applications not accepted. Giving primarily in Cleveland, OH. No grants to individuals.
Application information: Contributes only to pre-selected organizations.
Trustee: Mark F. Swary.
EIN: 347178399

7411
The Columbus Foundation and Affiliated Organizations ✧
(formerly The Columbus Foundation)
1234 E. Broad St.
Columbus, OH 43205-1453 (614) 251-4000
Contact: Raymond J. Biddiscombe, Sr. V.P., Finance
FAX: (614) 251-4009;
E-mail: tcfinfo@columbusfoundation.org; Additional e-mail: rbiddisc@columbusfoundation.org; Main URL: http://www.columbusfoundation.org
E-Newsletter: http://columbusfoundation.org/newsletter/

Facebook: http://www.facebook.com/pages/The-Columbus-Foundation/32684550098
Flickr: http://www.flickr.com/photos/7984224@N08/
Knowledge Center: http://columbusfoundation.org/resources/
LinkedIn: http://www.linkedin.com/companies/the-columbus-foundation
Twitter: http://twitter.com/colsfoundation
YouTube: http://www.youtube.com/user/columbusfoundation

Established in 1943 in OH by resolution and declaration of trust.
Foundation type: Community foundation.
Financial data (yr. ended 12/31/12): Assets, $1,520,768,529 (M); gifts received, $326,258,172; expenditures, $104,801,566; giving activities include $95,963,350 for grants.
Purpose and activities: The foundation seeks to assist donors and others in strengthening and improving the community for the benefits of all its citizens. Grants are made to strengthen existing agencies or to initiate new programs in the following categories: arts and humanities, urban affairs, conservation and environmental protection, education, health, mental health and the developmentally disabled, and social service agencies.
Fields of interest: Performing arts; Humanities; Historic preservation/historical societies; Arts; Education, association; Child development, education; Adult education—literacy, basic skills & GED; Education, reading; Education; Environment, natural resources; Environment, energy; Environment; Animal welfare; Reproductive health, family planning; Health care; Mental health/crisis services; Health organizations, association; AIDS; AIDS research; Employment, training; Housing/shelter; Disasters, Hurricane Katrina; Youth, services; Child development, services; Women, centers/services; Homeless, human services; Human services; Civil rights, race/intergroup relations; Economic development; Community/economic development; Voluntarism promotion; Philanthropy/voluntarism; Government/public administration; Public affairs; Disabilities, people with; Women; Economically disadvantaged; Homeless.
Type of support: Continuing support; Capital campaigns; Building/renovation; Land acquisition; Program development; Publication; Seed money; Scholarship funds; Technical assistance; Matching/challenge support; Mission-related investments/loans.
Limitations: Applications accepted. Giving limited to central OH. No support for religious purposes, or for projects normally the responsibility of a public agency. No grants to individuals, or generally for budget deficits, conferences, scholarly research, or endowment funds.
Publications: Application guidelines; Annual report; Informational brochure (including application guidelines); Newsletter.
Application information: Visit the foundation's web site for more information: http://columbusfoundation.org/grants/columbus-foundation/. Application form required.
Initial approach: Register and create a GO! Grants Online account through the foundation's web site
Deadline(s): Varies
Board meeting date(s): Feb., Apr., May, July, Sept., Oct., and Dec.
Final notification: Varies
Officers and Governing Committee:* Michael R. Fiorile,* Chair.; Robert C. Kidder, Vice-Chair.; Douglas F. Kridler,* C.E.O. and Pres.; Raymond J. Biddiscombe, Sr. V.P., Finance and Admin.; Lisa Schweitzer Courtice, Ph.D., Exec. V.P., Community Research and Grants Mgmt.; Tamera "Tami" Durrence, V.P., Supporting Fdns.; Beth Fisher, V.P., Donor Svcs. and Devel.; Carol Harmon, V.P., Comms. and Mktg.; Cathy Vrenna, Cont.; David P. Blom; Joseph A. Chlapaty; Lisa A. Hinson; Jerry Jurgensen; Barbara Siemer; Dwight E. Smith; Matthew D. Walter.
Number of staff: 23 full-time professional; 14 full-time support; 3 part-time support.
EIN: 316044264
Selected grants: The following grants are a representative sample of this grantmaker's funding activity:
$3,600,000 to United Way of Central Ohio, Columbus, OH, 2012. For funding for the current Family Stability Initiative sites and expansion of the program to new sites through the Siemer Institute for Family Stability.
$2,630,504 to Mennonite Foundation, Goshen, IN, 2012.
$1,227,078 to Ohio State University Foundation, Columbus, OH, 2012.
$917,578 to United Way Worldwide, Alexandria, VA, 2012.
$900,000 to Nationwide Childrens Hospital Foundation, Columbus, OH, 2012. For the Opening Gala for the new facility.
$750,000 to COSI Columbus, Columbus, OH, 2012. For general operating support.
$5,000 to Kent State University Foundation, Kent, OH, 2012. For the Fashion School's 2012 student fashion show.
$5,000 to Newark-Granville Symphony Orchestra, Granville, OH, 2012. For unrestricted support.
$4,000 to Deaf Services Center, Worthington, OH, 2012. To teach middle school deaf and hard-of-hearing students about educational and career choices.
$3,000 to First United Methodist Church, Troy, OH, 2012. For Christmas Charity to support the First Place Food Pantry.

7412
The Community Foundation of Lorain County ✧

(formerly The Community Foundation of Greater Lorain County)
9080 Leavitt Rd.
Elyria, OH 44035 (440) 984-7390
Contact: Brian R. Frederick, C.E.O.; For grants: Linda Ong Styer, Sr. Prog. Off.
FAX: (440) 984-7399;
E-mail: foundation@peoplewhocare.org; Additional e-mail: bfrederick@peoplewhocare.org; Grant inquiry e-mail: lsyter@peoplewhocare.org; Main URL: http://www.peoplewhocare.org
Facebook: http://www.facebook.com/pages/Community-Foundation-of-Lorain-County/260644913281
Flickr: http://www.flickr.com//photos/peoplewhocare/
LinkedIn: http://www.linkedin.com//company/community-foundation-of-lorain-county
Twitter: https://twitter.com/connectcarematr
YouTube: http://www.youtube.com/user/ConnectCareMatter

Incorporated in 1980 in OH.
Foundation type: Community foundation.
Financial data (yr. ended 12/31/13): Assets, $113,851,274 (M); gifts received, $14,766,094; expenditures, $5,461,919; giving activities include $4,854,237 for grants.
Purpose and activities: The foundation seeks to improve the quality of life and to instill a greater sense of unity in the Greater Lorain County community by mobilizing individuals to become active partners in building a better community; providing a permanent instrument for receiving and managing charitable gifts and bequests; supporting innovative programs and acting as a catalyst in identifying problems and sharing information with individuals, other foundations, corporations, and organizations; and exercising and promoting leadership in meeting the changing needs and opportunities of the entire community.
Fields of interest: Arts; Education; Environment; Health care; Health organizations, association; Human services; Community development, neighborhood development; Economic development; Children/youth; Youth; Asians/Pacific Islanders; African Americans/Blacks; Hispanics/Latinos; Women.
Type of support: General/operating support; Program development; Seed money; Scholarship funds; Technical assistance; Scholarships—to individuals; Matching/challenge support.
Limitations: Applications accepted. Giving primarily in Lorain County, OH. No support for religious purposes, street repair, government services, public or non-public school services required by law, or self-help clubs that meet the needs of a small population. No grants to individuals (except for scholarships), or for annual campaigns, medical research, deficit financing, membership fees, tickets for benefits, tours, equipment, group travel, or capital campaigns; no loans.
Publications: Application guidelines; Annual report (including application guidelines); Financial statement; Informational brochure (including application guidelines); Newsletter; Program policy statement.
Application information: Grantseekers should contact the Sr. Prog. Off. to discuss the proposal before submitting an application. Visit foundation web site for application form and guidelines. Application form required.
Initial approach: Letter or telephone
Copies of proposal: 2
Deadline(s): Feb. 1 and July 1 for general grants
Board meeting date(s): Bimonthly
Final notification: July and Dec. for general grants
Officers and Directors:* Jim Vandemark,* Chair.; Tim Harris,* Vice-Chair.; Brian R. Frederick,* C.E.O. and Pres.; Sandhya Subramanian,* Secy.; Susan J. Bowers,* Treas.; Cheryl McKenna,* C.F.O.; Farnaz Ansari-Berna,* Chair., Grants Comm.; Sharon Furcron,* Chair., Governance Comm.; Karen Wells,* Chair., Advancement Comm.; Joel Arrendondo; J. Lawry Babitt; Raymond L. Cushing; Chris Bellamy; Kevin Donovan; Joseph F. Miclat; Ruth Miller; Morgan Parsons; Kris Putnam-Walkerly; Margarita Quinones; Samuel Speck III; Eric Woidke.
Number of staff: 7 full-time professional; 3 full-time support.
EIN: 341322781

7413
Community Foundation of Mount Vernon & Knox County ✧
(formerly The Mount Vernon/Knox County Community Trust)
c/o The First-Knox National Bank
1 S. Main St.
P.O. Box 1270
Mount Vernon, OH 43050-3223 (740) 392-3270
Contact: Samuel Barone, Exec. Dir.
FAX: (740) 399-5296;
E-mail: sbarone@mvkcfoundation.org; Main URL: http://www.mvkcfoundation.org
Facebook: https://www.facebook.com/mvkcfoundation
YouTube: http://www.youtube.com/user/mvkcfoundationvideo?feature=guide

Established in 1944 in OH by declaration of trust.
Foundation type: Community foundation.
Financial data (yr. ended 12/31/13): Assets, $45,557,087 (M); gifts received, $5,443,729; expenditures, $2,646,077; giving activities include $2,171,720 for grants.
Purpose and activities: The foundation seeks to assist public, educational, charitable or benevolent enterprises. Grants, in accordance with the donors' wishes, for student loan and scholarship funds, community funds, youth agencies, nursing and the health profession, and museums.
Fields of interest: Museums; Humanities; Arts; Education; Environment, natural resources; Nursing care; Health care; Health organizations, association; Recreation, parks/playgrounds; Recreation; Children/youth, services; Human services; Community/economic development; United Ways and Federated Giving Programs.
Type of support: Capital campaigns; Building/renovation; Equipment; Program development; Conferences/seminars; Seed money; Scholarship funds; Program evaluation; Scholarships—to individuals; Matching/challenge support.
Limitations: Applications accepted. Giving primarily in Mount Vernon and Knox County, OH. No support for religious purposes, or police and fire protection. No grants to individuals (except for scholarships), or for ongoing operating expenses, equipment, existing obligations, liabilities, debt reduction, endowment funds, staff positions for government agencies, or research; no loans.
Publications: Application guidelines; Annual report; Informational brochure; Occasional report.
Application information: Visit foundation web site for application form, deadlines, and additional guidelines per grant type. Application form required.
Initial approach: Submit application form and attachments
Copies of proposal: 1
Deadline(s): Varies
Board meeting date(s): Feb., Apr., June, Aug., Oct., and Dec.
Final notification: Following next board meeting
Officers and Board Members:* Bruce E. Hawkins,* Chair.; Karen Buchwald Wright,* Vice-Chair.; Robert L. Rauzi,* Secy.; Kurt E. Schisler,* Treas.; Samuel Barone, Exec. Dir.; R. Leroy Bumpus; Terry L. Divelbiss; Marc C. Hawk; Gene Jackson; Dr. Amy D. Murnen; Marsha Rinehart; Kim Rose; Gordon E. Yance.
Investment Manager: The First-Knox National Bank.
Number of staff: 1 part-time professional; 1 part-time support.
EIN: 311768219

7414
The Community Foundation of Shelby County ✧
(formerly The Community Foundation of Sidney and Shelby County)
100 S. Main Ave., Ste. 202
Sidney, OH 45365-2771 (937) 497-7800
Contact: Marian Spicer, Exec. Dir.
FAX: (937) 497-7799;
E-mail: mspicer@commfoun.com; Additional e-mail: info@commfoun.com; Main URL: http://www.commfoun.com
Facebook: https://www.facebook.com/CommunityFoundationofShelbyCountyOhio

Incorporated in 1952 in OH.
Foundation type: Community foundation.
Financial data (yr. ended 12/31/13): Assets, $24,704,857 (M); gifts received, $2,338,900; expenditures, $1,103,003; giving activities include $883,428 for grants.
Purpose and activities: The foundation seeks to cultivate, administer, and distribute legacy gifts for the benefit of the community. Primary areas of giving include: Arts and Culture, Family and Community, Education, Environment, and Health.
Fields of interest: Arts; Education; Environment, natural resources; Environment, beautification programs; Environment; Health care; Health organizations, association; Recreation; Family services; Human services; Community/economic development.
Type of support: Capital campaigns; Equipment; Program development; Seed money; Scholarship funds; Scholarships—to individuals.
Limitations: Applications accepted. Giving limited to Shelby County, OH, and surrounding areas. No support for religious organizations for religious purposes. No grants to individuals (except for scholarships), or for endowments, fundraising campaigns from existing organizations, specific scientific, medical, or academic research, or general operating expenses.
Publications: Annual report; Informational brochure; Newsletter.
Application information: Visit foundation web site for preliminary grant proposal form and guidelines. Preliminary grant proposal form and proposals will not be accepted if applicant has not discussed grant request with foundation staff. Application form required.
Initial approach: Telephone
Copies of proposal: 7
Deadline(s): Mar. 20 for preliminary grant proposal and scholarships; May 15 for full proposal
Board meeting date(s): Bimonthly
Final notification: June
Officers and Trustees:* Priscilla Wilt,* Chair.; Rudy Keister,* Vice-Chair.; Ken Monnier,* Secy.; Andy Counts,* Treas.; Marian Spicer, Exec. Dir.; Carol Bennett; Doug Borchers; Jerry Doerger; Aaron Koenig; Mardie Milligan; Norm Smith.
Number of staff: 1 part-time professional; 1 part-time support.
EIN: 346565194

7415
Community Foundation of the Mahoning Valley ✧
201 E. Commerce St., Ste. 150
Youngstown, OH 44503 (330) 743-5555
Contact: Shari Harrell, Pres.
FAX: (330) 743-1802; E-mail: info@cfmv.org; Additional e-mail: sharrell@cfmv.org; Main URL: http://www.cfmv.org

Established in 1999 in OH.
Foundation type: Community foundation.
Financial data (yr. ended 06/30/13): Assets, $14,151,580 (M); gifts received, $1,375,584; expenditures, $1,373,771; giving activities include $981,345 for 51+ grants (high: $50,000), and $26,837 for 20 grants to individuals.
Purpose and activities: The mission of the foundation is to attract and invest permanent resources, with the purpose of enhancing the quality of life for the residents of the Mahoning Valley and future generations, in accordance with the charitable intentions of its donors.
Fields of interest: Humanities; Historic preservation/historical societies; Arts; Education; Environment; Animals/wildlife; Health care; Recreation; Children/youth, services; Aging, centers/services; Human services; Economic development; Science, research; Religion.
Type of support: General/operating support; Continuing support; Capital campaigns; Building/renovation; Equipment; Endowments; Program development; Technical assistance; Matching/challenge support.
Limitations: Applications accepted. Giving limited to Mahoning County and Trumbull County, OH.
Publications: Application guidelines; Annual report; Financial statement; Grants list; Informational brochure; Newsletter.
Application information: Visit foundation web site for additional information. Application form required.
Initial approach: Create online profile
Deadline(s): Jan. 1, Apr. 1, July 1, and Oct. 1
Board meeting date(s): Mar., June, Sept., and Dec.
Final notification: 2 months
Officers and Directors:* Shelley Taylor Odille,* Chair.; Jerry Bryan,* Vice-Chair.; Shari Harrell, Pres.; Julie Scarsella, V.P.; Gordon B. Wean,* Secy.; Trinette Simon,* Treas.; Bruce R. Beeghly; Gloria Cagigas; Kevin Y.T. Chiu; Brian R. Corbin; Phillip Dennison; Hon. Douglas Franklin; David J. Kostolansky; Patrice Kouvas; Diane Sauer; Hon. Diane S. A. Vettori.
Number of staff: 3 part-time professional; 1 full-time support.
EIN: 341904353

7416
Community Foundation of Union County, Inc. ✧
(also known as Union County Foundation)
126 N. Main St.
P.O. Box 608
Marysville, OH 43040-0608 (937) 642-9618
Contact: David A. Vollrath, Exec. Dir.
FAX: (937) 642-7376;
E-mail: info@unioncountyfoundation.org; Main URL: http://www.unioncountyfoundation.org
Facebook: http://www.facebook.com/pages/Union-County-Foundation/138721636147097?sk=wall

Established in 1993 in OH.
Foundation type: Community foundation.
Financial data (yr. ended 12/31/13): Assets, $7,630,805 (M); gifts received, $420,578; expenditures, $640,306; giving activities include $306,093 for 7+ grants (high: $73,386), and $119,272 for 108 grants to individuals.
Purpose and activities: The foundation seeks to enhance the quality of life for all the citizens of Union County, and to provide a vehicle whereby gifts of any size might be invested and used in perpetuity to that end.
Fields of interest: Arts; Higher education; Education; Environment; Health care; Recreation; Religion; Children/youth; Youth; Aging; Military/veterans.
Type of support: General/operating support; Continuing support; Program development; Curriculum development; Scholarships—to individuals; In-kind gifts.
Limitations: Applications accepted. Giving limited to Union County, OH. No support for sectarian religious programs. No grants to individuals (except from designated funds), or for buildings or equipment, endowments, fundraising campaigns, conferences, or annual meetings.
Publications: Application guidelines; Annual report; Grants list; Informational brochure.
Application information: Visit foundation web site for application form and guidelines. Application form required.
Initial approach: Phone or personal contact with Director
Copies of proposal: 1
Deadline(s): First business day of Jan., Apr., July, and Oct.
Board meeting date(s): 3rd Thurs. of Feb., May, Aug., and Nov.
Final notification: Quarterly
Officers and Trustees:* Jim Cox,* Chair.; Chad Hoffman,* Vice-Chair.; Dr. Victor Trianfo,* Secy.; David F. Allen,* Treas. and Counsel; David A. Vollrath, Exec. Dir.; Dr. Charlotte Agnone; Ken Boehm; Jerry Born; Bruce Daniels; Mardy Hanlon-Stolte; Eugene Mayer; Joseph Mitchell; Carroll Ormeroid; Alan Seymour; Dr. Carol Young.
Number of staff: 2 part-time professional.
EIN: 310628641

7417
The Community Foundation of West Chester/Liberty ✧

(formerly Key Community Foundation)
8366 Princeton-Glendale Rd. Ste. A2
West Chester, OH 45069 (513) 874-5450
Contact: Patti Alderson, C.E.O.
FAX: (513) 874-5472;
E-mail: info@wclfoundation.com; Additional e-mail: pattialder@aol.com; Main URL: http://www.wclfoundation.com
Facebook: https://www.facebook.com/wclfoundation
Twitter: https://twitter.com/WCLfoundation

Established in 1999 in OH.
Foundation type: Community foundation.
Financial data (yr. ended 12/31/13): Assets, $11,237,543 (M); gifts received, $1,879,119; expenditures, $1,125,464; giving activities include $413,633 for 29+ grants (high: $32,500), and $108,547 for 68 grants to individuals.
Purpose and activities: The foundation seeks to encourage, support, and facilitate philanthropy and improve the quality of life in the West Chester/Liberty area. The foundation provides support for civic affairs and community development, education (including scholarships), parks and recreation, health and human services, disaster relief, and arts and culture.
Fields of interest: Arts; Education; Health care; Disasters, preparedness/services; Recreation, parks/playgrounds; Recreation; Human services; Community/economic development; Government/public administration.
Type of support: Continuing support; Emergency funds; Program development; Scholarships—to individuals.
Limitations: Applications accepted. Giving limited to West Chester and Liberty townships, Butler County, OH.
Publications: Application guidelines; Annual report; Grants list; Informational brochure (including application guidelines); Newsletter.
Application information: Visit foundation web site for application form and guidelines. Application form required.
Initial approach: Telephone, personal contact, or attend a Grant Application Workshop
Copies of proposal: 2
Deadline(s): Mar. 13, July 17, and Oct. 16 for Community Grant Program
Board meeting date(s): 3rd Wed. of the month
Final notification: May, Sept., and Dec. for Community Grant Program
Officers and Directors:* Dan Benhase,* Chair.; Jonathan Theders,* Vice-Chair.; Patti Alderson,* C.E.O. and Pres.; Erin Clemons, V.P., Devel. and Donor Rels.; Nancy Fister, V.P., Finance; Shellie Leder,* Secy.; Craig Hudson,* Treas.; Kelly Bramel; Sandy Brueshaber; Tom Daskalakis; Marty Davis; Catherine Evans; Helen Fanz LeVay; Bob Hutsenpiller; Tim Kelly; Keith Kline; Shellie Leder; Gail Jackson Miller; Ian Murray; Karen Rolcik; Loren Schramm; Bill Schumacker; Tim Sheeran; Greg Stamp; Julie White; Tom Zenge; Dan Zieverink.
Number of staff: 3 full-time professional; 1 part-time professional.
EIN: 311661966

7418
The Conn Family Foundation ✧ ☆

11160 Kenwood Rd., Ste. 220
Cincinnati, OH 45242-1818

Established in 2001 in OH.
Donors: Raymond A. Conn; Joan D. Conn; Andrew D. Conn; Olivia D. Conn; Nicolette Conn.
Foundation type: Independent foundation.
Financial data (yr. ended 12/31/13): Assets, $1,305,701 (M); expenditures, $638,519; qualifying distributions, $635,645; giving activities include $635,000 for 7 grants (high: $300,000; low: $5,000).
Fields of interest: Higher education; Foundations (private grantmaking); Christian agencies & churches.
Limitations: Applications not accepted. No grants to individuals.
Application information: Contributes only to pre-selected organizations.
Officers: Raymond A. Conn, Pres.; Joan D. Conn, V.P.; Alan R. Trenz, Secy.-Treas.
EIN: 311784407

Selected grants: The following grants are a representative sample of this grantmaker's funding activity:
$700,000 to Lee University, Cleveland, TN, 2011.
$15,000 to Choice Ministries, Roswell, GA, 2011.
$3,000 to Chicago Hope Academy, Chicago, IL, 2011.

7419
Ruth J. & Robert A. Conway Foundation, Inc. ✧

5799 Mariemont Ave.
Cincinnati, OH 45227-4216
Contact: Robert A. Conway Sr., Treas.

Established in 1998 in OH.
Donors: Robert A. Conway, Sr.; Ruth J. Conway†.
Foundation type: Independent foundation.
Financial data (yr. ended 12/31/12): Assets, $15,317,013 (M); expenditures, $1,575,240; qualifying distributions, $1,456,639; giving activities include $1,436,611 for 105 grants (high: $425,000; low: $50).
Fields of interest: Museums; Secondary school/education; Higher education; Human services; United Ways and Federated Giving Programs; Catholic agencies & churches.
Type of support: Program development; Matching/challenge support.
Limitations: Applications accepted. Giving primarily in OH, with emphasis on the metropolitan Cincinnati area, and northern KY. No grants to individuals.
Publications: Application guidelines.
Application information: Proposals will not be accepted in person. Application form required.
Initial approach: Letter
Copies of proposal: 1
Deadline(s): 3 weeks before board meeting
Board meeting date(s): Mar., June, Sept., Dec.
Final notification: 2 weeks after board meeting
Officers and Trustees:* Robert A. Conway, Sr.,* Treas.; Kathleen Conway Bell; Sean P. Conway; Sheila Conway; Joseph A. Conway; Timothy J. Conway; William J. Keating; Judith Wimberg.
EIN: 311575184

7420
Mary S. & David C. Corbin Foundation ✧

c/o Akron Centre Plz.
50 S. Main St., Ste. 703
Akron, OH 44308-1830 (330) 762-6427
Contact: Erika J. May, Office and Grants Admin.
FAX: (330) 762-6428; E-mail: corbin@nls.net; Main URL: http://foundationcenter.org/grantmaker/corbin/

Established about 1968.
Donor: David C. Corbin†.
Foundation type: Independent foundation.
Financial data (yr. ended 12/31/13): Assets, $21,109,694 (M); expenditures, $1,186,619; qualifying distributions, $1,015,382; giving activities include $927,832 for 81 grants (high: $75,000; low: $500).
Purpose and activities: Giving primarily in Akron and Summit County, OH, for arts and culture, civic and community issues, education, environment, health care, housing, human and social services, medical research, and youth issues.

Fields of interest: Arts; Hospitals (general); Health care, home services; Housing/shelter; Recreation; Human services; Children/youth, services.
Type of support: General/operating support; Building/renovation; Equipment; Seed money; Research; Matching/challenge support.
Limitations: Applications accepted. Giving limited to Akron and Summit County, OH. No support for organizations which in turn make grants to others. No grants to individuals, or for annual fundraising campaigns, ongoing requests for general operating support, or operating deficits.
Publications: Application guidelines.
Application information: Guidelines and coversheet available on foundation web site. Application form required.
Initial approach: Cover letter, with application cover sheet, full proposal, and attachments
Copies of proposal: 2
Deadline(s): Mar. 1 for consideration in May; Sept. 1 for consideration in Nov.
Board meeting date(s): Quarterly, usually in Feb., May, Aug., and Nov.
Officers and Trustees:* Roger T. Read,* Pres. and Secy.; Robert M. Bonchack, Treas.; James S. Hartenstein, Tr. Emeritus; Sophie E. Albrecht; Robert C. Berk; Louis A. Maglione; Michael A. Sweeney; Raymond R. Wernig.
Number of staff: 1 part-time support.
EIN: 237052280
Selected grants: The following grants are a representative sample of this grantmaker's funding activity:
$40,000 to Cleveland Orchestra, Cleveland, OH, 2012. For 2012 Blossom Festival.
$25,000 to Akron Zoological Park, Akron, OH, 2012. For Grizzly Ridge.
$25,000 to International Soap Box Derby, Akron, OH, 2012. For 75th All American Soap Box Derby World Championship.
$25,000 to Rotary Camp for Children with Special Needs, Akron, OH, 2012. For Sailing the Course Together Capital Campaign.
$25,000 to Stan Hywet Hall and Gardens, Akron, OH, 2012. For Greenhouse Reinterpretation of Corbin Conservatory.
$22,000 to Access, Akron, OH, 2012. For HVAC system upgrade.
$20,000 to International Institute, Akron, OH, 2012. For 2013 citizenship and immigration services outreach.
$15,000 to Opportunity Parish Ecumenical Neighborhood Ministry, Akron, OH, 2012. For general operating support.
$15,000 to Summit County Historical Society of Akron, Akron, OH, 2012. For stone wall repair.
$15,000 to United Way of Summit County, Akron, OH, 2012. For campaign.

7421
Coshocton Foundation ✧
220 S. 4th St.
P.O. Box 55
Coshocton, OH 43812-2019 (740) 622-0010
Contact: Kathy Thompson, Exec. Dir.
FAX: (740) 622-1660;
E-mail: kthompson@coshoctonfoundation.org; Main URL: http://www.coshoctonfoundation.org

Established in 1966 in OH.
Donors: Adolph Golden†; Fred Johnston; Edward E. Montgomery†; Edith Schooler†; Seward Schooler†; Mary F. Taylor; Robert M. Thomas; Willard Baughman†; Willard S. Breon; James E. Wilson†; Herbert E. Carlson†; Ralph Wisenburg; Richard Barthebaug; Mrs. Richard Barthebaug; Ed Mulligan; Marion Mulligan Sutton.
Foundation type: Community foundation.
Financial data (yr. ended 09/30/13): Assets, $28,134,047 (M); gifts received, $1,356,221; expenditures, $1,028,267; giving activities include $788,064 for 42+ grants (high: $126,787).
Purpose and activities: The mission of the foundation is to provide a community controlled organization dedicated to the betterment and long term development of Coshocton County's natural, community, and human resources.
Fields of interest: Museums; Performing arts, dance; Arts; Child development, education; Secondary school/education; Higher education; Education; Hospitals (general); Health care; Substance abuse, services; Mental health/crisis services; Alcoholism; Crime/law enforcement; Safety/disasters; Athletics/sports, water sports; Youth development, services; Youth development, citizenship; Children/youth, services; Child development, services; Community/economic development; Government/public administration; Public affairs, citizen participation; Leadership development.
Type of support: Continuing support; Capital campaigns; Building/renovation; Equipment; Program development; Conferences/seminars; Seed money; Curriculum development; Scholarship funds; Employee matching gifts; Scholarships—to individuals; Matching/challenge support.
Limitations: Applications accepted. Giving limited to Coshocton County, OH.
Publications: Application guidelines; Annual report; Financial statement; Informational brochure (including application guidelines); Newsletter; Occasional report.
Application information: Visit foundation web site for application form, guidelines, and specific deadlines. Application form required.
Initial approach: Complete online application
Copies of proposal: 7
Deadline(s): One week before quarterly meeting
Board meeting date(s): Quarterly
Final notification: 45 days after receipt
Officers and Trustees:* Catherine Miller,* Pres.; Joe Skelton,* V.P.; Beccy Porteus,* Secy.; Kathy Thompson,* Treas. and Exec. Dir.; Sally Bullens; Barbara Brooks Emmons; Bruce Wallace.
Distribution Committee: William Brown, Chair., Distrib. Comm.; Greg Coffman; Steve Foster; Lisa Gibson; Rex Snyder.
Investment Committee: Steve Nelson, Chair., Investment Comm.; Preston Bair; Michael Baker; Richard Tompkins; Tim Vance.
Number of staff: 1 full-time professional; 1 full-time support.
EIN: 316064567

7422
Covenant Foundation, Inc. ✧
3777 W. Fork Rd.
Cincinnati, OH 45247-7575

Established in 1987 in OH.
Donors: Fairview Partners; Johnson Charitable Remainder Trust.
Foundation type: Independent foundation.
Financial data (yr. ended 12/31/13): Assets, $69,506,383 (M); gifts received, $44,144,132; expenditures, $1,140,268; qualifying distributions, $1,127,230; giving activities include $1,121,000 for 37 grants (high: $247,500; low: $2,000).
Purpose and activities: Giving to organizations that further Christian missions with a meaningful evangelical component.
Fields of interest: Christian agencies & churches.
Type of support: General/operating support; Continuing support; Capital campaigns; Building/renovation; Equipment; Land acquisition; Debt reduction; Emergency funds; Program development; Research; Program-related investments/loans; Matching/challenge support.
Limitations: Applications not accepted. Giving in the U.S., with some emphasis on CO, IL, and OH. No grants to individuals.
Application information: Unsolicited requests for grants not accepted. Grants only to organizations known to trustees.
Board meeting date(s): Mar.
Directors: Timothy C. Gehner; Janet L. Johnson; Timothy E. Johnson; Susan R. Pagliaro.
Number of staff: None.
EIN: 311225037
Selected grants: The following grants are a representative sample of this grantmaker's funding activity:
$100,000 to Crossroads Community Church of Hyde Park, Cincinnati, OH, 2011. For operating fund.
$6,000 to Underground Zone Ministries, Cincinnati, OH, 2011. For operating fund.

7423
CPB Foundation ✧
c/o PNC Bank N.A.
3550 Lander Rd.
Pepper Pike, OH 44124-5727 (216) 910-0460
Contact: Georgia A. Froelich, Sr. V.P., PNC Bank, N.A., Hawthorn

Established in 2002 in OH.
Donors: Susan Donnell Konkel; Susan Konkel; James Donnell Konkel.
Foundation type: Independent foundation.
Financial data (yr. ended 12/31/12): Assets, $34,834,651 (M); gifts received, $757,228; expenditures, $2,008,750; qualifying distributions, $1,802,622; giving activities include $1,764,565 for 44 grants (high: $425,000; low: $1,000).
Fields of interest: Museums (art); Performing arts, theater; Arts; Animals/wildlife, preservation/protection; Cancer research.
Limitations: Applications not accepted. Giving primarily in ME; some funding also in Memphis, TN. No grants to individuals.
Application information: Contributes only to pre-selected organizations.
Board meeting date(s): Nov.
Trustees: Harry W. Konkel; James Donnell Konkel; Susan Konkel; Susan Donnell Konkel; PNC Bank N.A.
EIN: 347151671
Selected grants: The following grants are a representative sample of this grantmaker's funding activity:
$425,000 to Ducks Unlimited, Memphis, TN, 2012. For Wetlands and Waterfowl Conservation.
$225,000 to Portland Museum of Art, Portland, ME, 2012. For Charles Shipman Payson Building Maintenance Endowment; Staff Salary Increase Endowment; Susan.
$146,120 to University of Wyoming Foundation, Laramie, WY, 2012. For Harry Wagner Knokel Fund for Teton County Students.

$131,500 to Maine Medical Center, Portland, ME, 2012. For Construction of the New Patient and Family Solarium and General Fund.
$10,000 to Friends of the Kotzschmar Organ, Portland, ME, 2012. For Campaign for the King of Instruments.
$10,000 to Pine Manor College, Chestnut Hill, MA, 2012. For Susan Knonkel Book Fund; Annual Fund.
$5,000 to Teton County Library Foundation, Jackson, WY, 2012. For endowment challenge.
$4,000 to Greater Portland Landmarks, Portland, ME, 2012. For Preservation and Revitalization of Portland and Surrounding Communities.
$3,000 to Maine Historical Society, Portland, ME, 2012. For Richard D'Abate Endowment Fund for Scholarship and Special Programs and Annual Fund.
$2,500 to Buffalo Bill Historical Center, Cody, WY, 2012. For Help Preserve the Spirit of the American West.

7424
Danaher Foundation ✧ ☆
6095 Parkland Blvd., Ste. 310
Mayfield Heights, OH 44124-6140

Established in 1952 in IL.
Donors: Joslyn Corp.; Steven M. Rales; Danher Corp.
Foundation type: Company-sponsored foundation.
Financial data (yr. ended 12/31/13): Assets, $1,859,742 (M); gifts received, $151; expenditures, $476,128; qualifying distributions, $466,974; giving activities include $466,974 for 23 grants (high: $155,000; low: $150).
Purpose and activities: The foundation supports organizations involved with arts and culture, higher education, health, cancer, kidney disease, international relief, philanthropy, and women.
Fields of interest: Arts; Health care; International affairs.
Type of support: General/operating support.
Limitations: Applications not accepted. Giving primarily in areas of company operations, with emphasis on Washington, DC, MD, PA, and VA. No grants to individuals.
Application information: Contributes only to pre-selected organizations.
Officers and Director:* Robert S. Lutz,* Pres.; James F. O'Reilly, V.P. and Secy.; Frank T. McFaden, V.P. and Treas.
EIN: 366042871
Selected grants: The following grants are a representative sample of this grantmaker's funding activity:
$150,000 to American Red Cross National Headquarters, Washington, DC, 2011.
$37,260 to Network for Good, Washington, DC, 2011.
$13,900 to National Kidney Foundation of the National Capital Area, Washington, DC, 2011.
$10,000 to Boys and Girls Clubs of Greater Washington, Washington, DC, 2011.
$5,000 to California State University at Northridge Foundation, Northridge, CA, 2011.
$5,000 to National Braille Press, Boston, MA, 2011.
$2,842 to Susan G. Komen for the Cure, Dallas, TX, 2011.
$2,400 to Washington Humane Society, Washington, DC, 2011.

7425
Dance Ready, Inc. ✧
625 Woods Hollow Ln.
Powell, OH 43065-7647 (614) 848-7827
Contact: Simone Sodano, Pres.

Established in 2009 in OH.
Donors: Vivian Chen; Celia Yuk Chun Tiu; Woodruff Law Firm; Alice G. Gosfield; Robert R. McComsey; Jane Ellen Parker; Susan F. Sordoni; Elaina S. Spilove; Raymond L. Walden; Julia H. Wang; TTC, LLC; Mary Hannah; Richard Wineberg; Roger Sachs, M.D.; Marilyn Palley; Beatrice Wang; Michael M. Puno; Janice Stanley Sussman; Bessemer Trust; Carolyn Woodruff; Robert McComsey; Dance Consultants Unlimited Inc.; Nancy Politzer; Celia Yuk Chun Tiu; Susan F. Sordoni; Fordney Foundation; Sussman Sessel Family Foundation; David Polinger; Suzanne Hittman; Heidi L. Steiger; Julia C. Stadler; Debroah Baronofsky; Marcia J. Wagaman; Julia H. Wang; Woodruff Law Firm PA.
Foundation type: Operating foundation.
Financial data (yr. ended 12/31/13): Assets, $345,828 (M); gifts received, $715,450; expenditures, $644,432; qualifying distributions, $640,610; giving activities include $640,610 for 24 grants (high: $230,000; low: $100).
Fields of interest: Performing arts, dance.
Application information: Application form required.
Initial approach: Letter
Deadline(s): None
Officers: Simone Sodano, Pres.; Wendy Burger, V.P. and Treas.; William Sparks, Secy.
EIN: 263691620

7426
Charles H. Dater Foundation, Inc. ✧
302 Gwynne Bldg.
602 Main St., Ste. 302
Cincinnati, OH 45202-2534 (513) 241-2658
Contact: Bruce A. Krone, Secy.
FAX: (513) 241-2731;
E-mail: info@DaterFoundation.org; E-mail for Grants Coordinator, Beth Broomall: bb@DaterFoundation.org; Main URL: http://www.daterfoundation.org
E-Newsletter: http://www.daterfoundation.org/newsletter.php

Established in 1985 in OH.
Donor: Charles H. Dater†.
Foundation type: Independent foundation.
Financial data (yr. ended 08/31/13): Assets, $44,474,427 (M); expenditures, $2,091,994; qualifying distributions, $1,893,762; giving activities include $1,501,026 for 111 grants (high: $50,000; low: $1,000).
Purpose and activities: The foundation makes grants to private, nonprofit organizations and public agencies in Greater Cincinnati, Ohio, for programs that benefit children in the region in the areas of arts/culture, education, health care, social services and other community needs.
Fields of interest: Historic preservation/historical societies; Arts; Child development, education; Higher education; Libraries/library science; Education; Hospitals (general); Medical care, rehabilitation; Crime/violence prevention, youth; Recreation; Human services; Children/youth, services; Child development, services; Family services; Christian agencies & churches; Disabilities, people with; Economically disadvantaged.
Type of support: General/operating support; Continuing support; Annual campaigns; Building/renovation; Equipment; Program development; Seed money; Scholarship funds; Consulting services.
Limitations: Giving primarily in the greater Cincinnati, OH, area. No grants to individuals, or for scholarships, debt reduction, or for capital projects.
Publications: Application guidelines; Annual report; Multi-year report.
Application information: Application guidelines and form available on foundation web site. Application form required.
Initial approach: Refer to online application process on foundation web site
Copies of proposal: 6
Deadline(s): None
Board meeting date(s): Monthly
Final notification: Within 2 months
Officers and Directors:* Bruce A. Krone,* Pres. and Secy.; Roger L. Ruhl,* V.P.; Stanley J. "Jack" Frank, Jr.,* Treas.; Dorothy G. Krone, Dir. Emeritus; Amanda Prebble Lenhart.
EIN: 311150951
Selected grants: The following grants are a representative sample of this grantmaker's funding activity:
$132,500 to Cincinnati Zoo and Botanical Garden, Cincinnati, OH, 2011.
$50,000 to Cincinnati Scholarship Foundation, Cincinnati, OH, 2011.
$40,000 to Greater Cincinnati Foundation, Cincinnati, OH, 2011.
$37,000 to Josh Cares, Cincinnati, OH, 2011.
$35,000 to Ensemble Theater of Cincinnati, Cincinnati, OH, 2011.
$35,000 to Inner-City Youth Opportunities, Cincinnati, OH, 2011.
$30,000 to Assistance League of Greater Cincinnati, Cincinnati, OH, 2011.
$15,000 to Childhood Food Solutions, Cincinnati, OH, 2011.
$15,000 to Cincinnati Nature Center, Milford, OH, 2011.
$10,000 to American Diabetes Association, Alexandria, VA, 2011.

7427
The Paul & Carol David Foundation ✧
(formerly The David Family Foundation)
4048 Dressler Rd. N.W., Ste. 200
Canton, OH 44718-2784 (330) 479-0200
Contact: Jeffrey David, Pres.
FAX: (330) 479-0222;
E-mail: info@davidfoundation.org; E-mail for Becky Duplain, Exec. Asst.: bduplain@davidfoundation.org; Main URL: http://www.davidfoundation.org
Scholarship contact: Becky Duplain

Established in 1980 in OH.
Donors: Paul David†; Paul David Charitable Lead Trust No. 1; Paul David Charitable Lead Trust No. 2.
Foundation type: Independent foundation.
Financial data (yr. ended 12/31/13): Assets, $63,844,121 (M); gifts received, $1,169,920; expenditures, $2,417,958; qualifying distributions, $1,886,646; giving activities include $646,567 for 55 grants (high: $75,000; low: $89), and $1,015,667 for grants to individuals (high: $5,500).
Purpose and activities: Giving primarily for the improvement of educational, community and health opportunities for underprivileged and/or disadvantaged children in Stark County, OH; the

foundation also awards college scholarships to high school students in Stark County, OH.
Fields of interest: Children/youth, services.
Type of support: Capital campaigns; Building/renovation; Equipment; Program development; Research; Scholarships—to individuals.
Limitations: Giving limited to Stark County, OH. No support for corporations, private foundations or government agencies. No grants for general support expenses, endowments or for grants to individuals (except for the foundation's scholarship program).
Application information: Additional application requirements and forms available on foundation web site. Application form required.
Initial approach: Proposal or application form
Copies of proposal: 6
Deadline(s): See foundation web site for deadlines
Board meeting date(s): Feb., June, Sept. and Nov.
Officers and Trustees:* Carol David,* Chair.; Jeffrey David,* Pres.; Tom Knoll, Esq.; Scott F. Whetstone.
EIN: 341319236
Selected grants: The following grants are a representative sample of this grantmaker's funding activity:
$50,000 to Community Services of Stark County, Canton, OH, 2012. For Family Living Center-Massillon 2 of 2 payments.
$10,000 to Stark Education Partnership, Canton, OH, 2012. For Year 3 of 3 - Capital Campaign.
$5,000 to Canton Central Catholic High School, Canton, OH, 2012. For annual auction.
$5,000 to Stark Development Board, Canton, OH, 2012. For Tri-Annual Fund Drive (Year 1).
$4,000 to Arts in Stark, Canton, OH, 2012. For SmArts in Massillon City Schools.
$3,000 to YMCA of Central Stark County, Canton, OH, 2012. For BBBS in Massillon.
$1,000 to Canton Country Day School, Canton, OH, 2012. For Year 3 of 3 PD Memorial Outdoor Classroom.

7428
The Dayton Foundation ✧
40 N. Main St., Ste. 500
Dayton, OH 45423 (937) 222-0410
Contact: Diane Timmons, V.P., Grants and Progs.
FAX: (937) 222-0636;
E-mail: info@daytonfoundation.org; Additional tel.: (877) 222-0410; Grants inquiry e-mail: dtimmons@daytonfoundation.org@daytonfoundation.org; Main URL: http://www.daytonfoundation.org
Facebook: http://www.facebook.com/pages/The-Dayton-Foundation/169118668484
Twitter: http://twitter.com/DaytonFdn
YouTube: http://www.youtube.com/TheDaytonFoundation

Established in 1921 in OH by resolution and declaration of trust.
Foundation type: Community foundation.
Financial data (yr. ended 06/30/13): Assets, $416,534,296 (M); gifts received, $29,009,166; expenditures, $31,669,338; giving activities include $21,906,024 for grants.
Purpose and activities: The foundation seeks to empower others through philanthropy and community leadership.
Fields of interest: Humanities; Arts; Education; Environment; Animal welfare; Health care; Youth development; Children/youth, services; Human services; Public affairs.
Type of support: Management development/capacity building; Capital campaigns; Building/renovation; Equipment; Land acquisition; Program development; Publication; Seed money; Technical assistance; Consulting services.
Limitations: Applications accepted. Giving limited to the greater Dayton and Miami Valley, OH, area. No support for religious organizations for religious purposes, or public or private schools. No grants to individuals (except for specific scholarships and award programs), or for operating budgets, exchange programs, professorships, continuing support, travel, fundraising drives, special events, annual campaigns, deficit financing, endowments, or scientific, medical, or academic research; no loans or program-related investments.
Publications: Application guidelines; Annual report; Financial statement; Grants list; Informational brochure; Newsletter; Program policy statement.
Application information: Visit foundation web site for application guidelines. The foundation highly recommends attending a free discretionary grants program orientation before applying for funding; online registration is required. Application form required.
Initial approach: Submit online Letter of Intent
Copies of proposal: 1
Deadline(s): Two grant cycles per year, see web site for specific dates
Board meeting date(s): Mar., June, Sept., and Dec.
Final notification: 8 weeks
Officers and Governing Board:* Ellen S. Ireland,* Chair.; Joseph B. Baldasare, V.P., Devel.; Stephen D. Darnell, V.P., Finance; Deborah Dulaney, V.P., Opers.; Christine Smith,* V.P., Mktg. and Public Rels.; Barbra Stonerock, V.P., Community Engagement; Diane K. Timmons, V.P., Grants and Progs.; Craig J. Brown; J. Norman Eckstein; William L. Gillispie; Lisa E. Hanauer; Helen E. Jones-Kelley; Maureen A. Lynch; David T. Miller; Anita J. Moore; Richard J. Omlor; Ratna Palakodeti, M.D.; James R. Pancoast; Colleen M. Ryan; Charles G. Schroeder; Jerome F. Tatar.
Trustees: Fifth Third Bank; JPMorgan Chase Bank, N.A.; KeyBank N.A.; Merrill Lynch Pierce Fenner & Smith; National City Bank; PNC Bank, N.A.
Number of staff: 16 full-time professional; 1 part-time professional; 7 full-time support; 5 part-time support.
EIN: 316027287
Selected grants: The following grants are a representative sample of this grantmaker's funding activity:
$30,000 to Human Race Theater Company, Dayton, OH, 2012. For new market strategies.
$25,000 to Good Neighbor House, Dayton, OH, 2012. For capital campaign.
$25,000 to YMCA of Greater Dayton, Dayton, OH, 2012. For Soccer for Success Program.
$15,000 to House of Bread, Dayton, OH, 2012. For kitchen renovations.
$10,000 to Dayton Crayons to Classrooms, Dayton, OH, 2012. For teacher resource center expansion.
$10,000 to Film Dayton, Kettering, OH, 2012. For LA Film Liaison.
$10,000 to Hospice of Dayton, Dayton, OH, 2012. For refresh and enhancement program.
$10,000 to Kettering Parks Foundation, Kettering, OH, 2012. For Kettering Veterans and Innovators Campaign.

7429
The Dayton Power and Light Company Foundation ✧
1065 Woodman Dr.
Dayton, OH 45432-1423 (937) 259-7925
Main URL: http://www.dpandl.com/about-dpl/who-we-are/community-investments/

Established in 1985 in OH.
Donor: The Dayton Power and Light Co.
Foundation type: Company-sponsored foundation.
Financial data (yr. ended 12/31/12): Assets, $27,084,620 (M); expenditures, $1,275,644; qualifying distributions, $1,244,380; giving activities include $1,190,295 for 95 grants (high: $135,000; low: $50).
Purpose and activities: The foundation supports food banks and festivals and organizations involved with arts and culture, health, human services, community economic development, civic affairs, and youth.
Fields of interest: Performing arts; Arts; Secondary school/education; Higher education; Education; Health care; Food banks; Recreation, fairs/festivals; Big Brothers/Big Sisters; Boy scouts; Girl scouts; American Red Cross; Salvation Army; Human services; Community development, business promotion; Community/economic development; United Ways and Federated Giving Programs; Public affairs; Youth.
Type of support: General/operating support; Continuing support; Program development; Employee volunteer services.
Limitations: Applications accepted. Giving in areas of company operations in west central OH. No support for religious, fraternal, labor, or veterans' organizations, national organizations, or sports leagues. No grants to individuals, or for capital campaigns, endowments or development campaigns, general operating support for hospitals, or telephone or mass mail solicitations.
Publications: Application guidelines; Informational brochure (including application guidelines).
Application information: Application form not required.
Initial approach: Proposal
Copies of proposal: 1
Deadline(s): None
Board meeting date(s): Quarterly
Officers and Directors:* Daniel J. McCabe, Pres.; Joe Mulpas, Treas.; Tom Raga, Exec. Dir.; Paul R. Bishop; Scott J. Kelly; Tim Rice; Ned J. Sifferlen.
Number of staff: 1 full-time professional.
EIN: 311138883

7430
DBJ Foundation ✧
(formerly The David H. and Barbara M. Jacobs Foundation)
1301 E. 9th St., Ste. 3500
Cleveland, OH 44114
Application address: c/o Matthew Conroy, P.O. Box 441596, Indianapolis, IN, 46244, tel.: (317) 426-0214, e-mail: mmconroy@dbjfoundation.org; Foundation headquarters: 235 Entrada, Santa Monica, CA 90402; Main URL: http://www.dbjfoundation.org

Established in 1990 in OH.
Donors: David H. Jacobs; Barbara M. Jacobs.
Foundation type: Independent foundation.

Financial data (yr. ended 12/31/13): Assets, $23,933,137 (M); gifts received, $44,000; expenditures, $1,220,782; qualifying distributions, $1,142,043; giving activities include $1,049,000 for 14 grants (high: $240,000; low: $10,000).
Purpose and activities: Giving primarily for health organizations and human services.
Fields of interest: Arts; Higher education; Education; Health organizations, association; Human services.
Type of support: General/operating support.
Limitations: Applications accepted. Giving primarily in CA, IN and OH. No grants to individuals.
Application information: Application form required.
Initial approach: Letter
Deadline(s): None
Trustee: David H. Jacobs, Jr.
EIN: 341661482
Selected grants: The following grants are a representative sample of this grantmaker's funding activity:
$50,000 to Cleveland Metropolitan School District, Cleveland, OH, 2012. For contribution to Tax-Exempt Org General Fund.

7431
Delaware County Foundation ✧
(formerly Community Fdn. of Delaware County)
3954 N. Hampton Dr.
Powell, OH 43065-8430 (614) 764-2332
FAX: (614) 764-2333;
E-mail: foundation@delawarecf.org; Main URL: http://www.delawarecf.org
Facebook: https://www.facebook.com/pages/Delaware-County-Foundation/191663982236
Flickr: http://www.flickr.com/photos/communityfoundationofdelawarecounty/

Established in 1995 in OH.
Foundation type: Community foundation.
Financial data (yr. ended 12/31/12): Assets, $8,169,147 (M); gifts received, $573,841; expenditures, $934,567; giving activities include $493,440 for 8 grants (high: $354,137), and $159,300 for 94 grants to individuals.
Purpose and activities: The foundation seeks to provide for various charitable, cultural, educational and community purposes in Delaware County, OH. Also provides scholarships to college students.
Fields of interest: Arts; Scholarships/financial aid; Education; Environment; Health care; Human services; Community/economic development; Public affairs.
Type of support: Continuing support; Capital campaigns; Building/renovation; Equipment; Program development; Seed money; Scholarship funds; Scholarships—to individuals; Matching/challenge support.
Limitations: Applications accepted. Giving limited to Delaware County, OH. No support for religious purposes. No grants to individuals (except for scholarships), or for deficit reduction, internships, operating expenses, or special fundraising events.
Publications: Application guidelines; Financial statement; Grants list; Informational brochure; Newsletter; Occasional report.
Application information: Visit foundation web site for grant application Cover Sheet and guidelines. Application form required.
Initial approach: Letter and proposal
Copies of proposal: 2
Deadline(s): Oct. 29 for Grants; Apr. 1 for Scholarship.
Board meeting date(s): 2nd Wed. of every other month
Final notification: 60-90 days
Officers and Directors:* Michael Tarullo,* Chair.; Skip Weiler,* Vice-Chair.; Marlene A. Casini,* C.E.O. and Pres.; Jane Martin,* Secy.; Rev. Dr. Norman Dewire,* Treas.; Stephen D. Martin, Emeritus; E. Jane Van Fossen, Emeritus; Mark Bergstedt; Susan Hatcher; Wayne Jenkins, Esq.; Rockwell Jones; Thomas Louden; Sue Mahler; Traci Martinez, Esq.; Susan Robenalt; David Smith, M.D.; Matt Weller.
Number of staff: 1 full-time professional; 2 part-time support.
EIN: 311450786
Selected grants: The following grants are a representative sample of this grantmaker's funding activity:
$70,000 to Delaware City Schools, Delaware, OH, 2012. For program support.
$19,000 to People in Need, Delaware, OH, 2012. For forklift.
$5,000 to Central Ohio Symphony, Delaware, OH, 2012. For concert.
$3,000 to Delaware Speech and Hearing Center, Delaware, OH, 2012. For summer literacy.
$2,500 to Cancer Support Community Central Ohio, Powell, OH, 2012.
$2,000 to Andrews House, Delaware, OH, 2012. For free meals program.
$1,500 to Family Promise of Delaware County, Delaware, OH, 2012. For job readiness and employment program.

7432
Jeanette Dermitt Hospital ✧ ☆
c/o KeyBank N.A.
4900 Tiedeman Rd., OH-01-49-0
Brooklyn, OH 44144-2302

Foundation type: Independent foundation.
Financial data (yr. ended 12/31/13): Assets, $5,605,435 (M); expenditures, $574,345; qualifying distributions, $528,884; giving activities include $517,191 for 2 grants (high: $344,791; low: $172,400).
Fields of interest: Hospitals (general); Health care.
Limitations: Applications not accepted.
Application information: Unsolicited requests for funds not accepted.
Trustee: KeyBank N.A.
EIN: 166110717
Selected grants: The following grants are a representative sample of this grantmaker's funding activity:
$344,791 to Olean General Hospital, Olean, NY, 2013. For general support.
$172,400 to Jones Memorial Hospital, Wellsville, NY, 2013. For general support.

7433
The George H. Deuble Foundation ✧
5757 Mayfair Rd.
P.O. Box 2288
North Canton, OH 44720-1546 (330) 494-0494
Contact: Andrew H. Deuble, Secy. and Tr.

Established in 1995 in OH.
Foundation type: Independent foundation.
Financial data (yr. ended 12/31/13): Assets, $23,335,518 (M); expenditures, $1,479,617; qualifying distributions, $1,360,110; giving activities include $1,134,519 for 144 grants (high: $117,000; low: $75).
Purpose and activities: Giving primarily for arts, education, health care, and human services.
Fields of interest: Arts; Education; Hospitals (general); Youth development; Human services; United Ways and Federated Giving Programs.
Limitations: Applications accepted. Giving primarily in Canton, OH. No grants to individuals.
Application information: Application form required.
Initial approach: Letter
Copies of proposal: 1
Deadline(s): None
Officers and Trustees:* Stephen G. Deuble,* Pres.; Andrew H. Deuble,* Secy.; Walter J. Deuble.
Board Member: Maxwell F. Deuble.
Number of staff: 3 part-time professional.
EIN: 341806245

7434
DeWine Family Foundation, Inc. ✧
3030 Griest Ave.
Cincinnati, OH 45208-2430

Established in 1996 in OH.
Donors: Jean L. DeWine; Richard L. DeWine.
Foundation type: Independent foundation.
Financial data (yr. ended 07/31/13): Assets, $16,611,532 (M); expenditures, $738,120; qualifying distributions, $684,518; giving activities include $684,518 for grants.
Fields of interest: Human services; Children/youth, services; Residential/custodial care.
Limitations: Applications not accepted. Giving primarily in MA and OH. No grants to individuals.
Application information: Contributes only to pre-selected organizations.
Officers: R. Michael DeWine, Pres.; Frances Dewine, V.P.; Karen DeWine, Secy.-Treas.
Trustees: Jill E. DeWine Darling; John Dewine.
EIN: 311483132
Selected grants: The following grants are a representative sample of this grantmaker's funding activity:
$415,005 to Hands Together, Springfield, MA, 2013. For funding for School in Haiti.
$15,000 to Cedarville University, Cedarville, OH, 2013. For Fund College Scholarships.
$10,390 to Wright State University, Dayton, OH, 2013. For funding college scholarships.
$5,000 to Miami University, Hamilton, OH, 2013. For Alumni Giving General Funding.
$4,934 to Ohio University, Athens, OH, 2013. For funding college scholarship.
$3,661 to Clark State Community College, Springfield, OH, 2013. For funding scholarships.
$2,500 to Spring Hill College, Mobile, AL, 2013. For Cross Country Program Funding.
$2,142 to University of North Carolina, Greensboro, NC, 2013. For college scholarship.
$300 to Eblen Charities, Asheville, NC, 2013. For Medical Energy Emergency Assistance.
$250 to Lighthouse Youth Services, Cincinnati, OH, 2013. For Youth and Family Services.

7435
Jon & Susan Diamond Family Foundation ✧
2 Miranova Pl., Ste. 600
Columbus, OH 43215-7052 (614) 253-4455
Contact: Susan Diamond, Pres.

Established in 1997 in OH.
Donors: Susan Diamond; Jon Diamond; Schottenstein Stores Corp.
Foundation type: Independent foundation.
Financial data (yr. ended 12/31/12): Assets, $9,897,786 (M); expenditures, $717,144; qualifying distributions, $694,500; giving activities include $694,500 for 7 grants (high: $525,000; low: $500).
Fields of interest: Jewish federated giving programs; Jewish agencies & synagogues.
Type of support: General/operating support; Continuing support; Annual campaigns; Capital campaigns; Building/renovation; Endowments; Emergency funds; Curriculum development; Scholarship funds; Research; Program-related investments/loans; Grants to individuals; Scholarships—to individuals; Matching/challenge support.
Limitations: Applications accepted. Giving primarily in Washington, DC and Columbus, OH.
Application information: Application form required.
Initial approach: Letter
Deadline(s): None
Officers: Susan Diamond, Pres.; Jon Diamond, V.P.; Ann Deshe, Secy.; Geraldine Schottenstein, Treas.
EIN: 311523574
Selected grants: The following grants are a representative sample of this grantmaker's funding activity:
$313,000 to Columbus Jewish Foundation, Columbus, OH, 2011.
$125,000 to American Israel Education Foundation, Washington, DC, 2011.
$20,000 to Hope for Haiti, Naples, FL, 2011.
$15,000 to Colel Chabad, Brooklyn, NY, 2011.

7436
Dicke Family Foundation ✧ ☆
40-44 S. Washington St.
New Bremen, OH 45869

Established in 1984 in OH.
Donors: Crown Equipment Corp.; James F. Dicke II; James Dicke, Sr.; Eileen W. Dicke; Jennifer D. Prewitt; Members of the Dicke family.
Foundation type: Independent foundation.
Financial data (yr. ended 11/30/13): Assets, $1,857,613 (M); gifts received, $2,000,000; expenditures, $2,067,972; qualifying distributions, $2,011,180; giving activities include $2,010,000 for 4 grants (high: $750,000; low: $10,000).
Fields of interest: Higher education; Education; Health care.
Type of support: General/operating support; Building/renovation.
Limitations: Applications not accepted. Giving primarily in Washington, DC, IN, OH and TX. No grants to individuals.
Application information: Unsolicited requests for funds not accepted.
Trustees: James Dicke; James F. Dicke II; James F. Dicke III; Jennifer D. Prewitt.
EIN: 341446513
Selected grants: The following grants are a representative sample of this grantmaker's funding activity:
$13,000 to Smithsonian American Art Museum, Washington, DC, 2011.

7437
Diebold Foundation ✧
c/o Tax Dept.
P.O. Box 3077
North Canton, OH 44720-8077 (330) 490-6973
Contact: Sheila Rutt, Tr.
Application address: 5995 Mayfair Rd., North Canton, OH 44720, tel.: (330) 490-6973

Established in 1993 in OH.
Donor: Diebold, Inc.
Foundation type: Company-sponsored foundation.
Financial data (yr. ended 12/31/13): Assets, $7,497,983 (M); expenditures, $558,211; qualifying distributions, $508,279; giving activities include $508,279 for 56 grants (high: $250,000; low: $30).
Purpose and activities: The foundation supports food banks and organizations involved with arts and culture, education, human services, and community development.
Fields of interest: Education; Human services; Religion.
Limitations: Applications accepted. Giving primarily in OH. No support for religious, political, or fraternal organizations, athletic teams, or discriminatory organizations. No grants to individuals, or for sponsorships of conventions or conferences, or athletic fundraising events not associated with schools.
Application information: Application form required.
Initial approach: Letter
Deadline(s): None
Trustees: Chad Hesse; Jamie Lambo; Sheila Rutt; Steve Wolgamott.
EIN: 341757351
Selected grants: The following grants are a representative sample of this grantmaker's funding activity:
$245,000 to United Way of Greater Stark County, Canton, OH, 2011. For general operations.
$38,650 to Scholarship America, Saint Peter, MN, 2011. For general operations.
$25,000 to Goodwill Industries of Greater Cleveland and East Central Ohio, Canton, OH, 2011. For general operations.
$25,000 to Stark State College Foundation, Canton, OH, 2011. For general operations.
$18,334 to Stark Development Board, Canton, OH, 2011. For general operations.
$10,375 to American Heart Association, Canton, OH, 2011. For general operations.
$8,000 to Urban League, Greater Stark County, Canton, OH, 2011. For general operations.
$7,500 to Arts in Stark, Canton, OH, 2011. For general operations.
$5,000 to Akron-Canton Regional Foodbank, Akron, OH, 2011. For general operations.
$1,140 to Miami University, Oxford, OH, 2011. For general operations.

7438
Corinne L. Dodero Trust for the Arts and Sciences ✧ ☆
P.O. Box 127
Rome, OH 44085-0127

Established in 1998 in FL.
Donor: Samuel J. Frankino.
Foundation type: Independent foundation.
Financial data (yr. ended 03/31/13): Assets, $10,630,715 (M); expenditures, $661,929; qualifying distributions, $547,489; giving activities include $475,730 for 92 grants (high: $75,000; low: $75).
Purpose and activities: Giving primarily for health organizations and human services; funding also for education, and children and youth services.
Fields of interest: Arts; Secondary school/education; Education; Hospitals (general); Health organizations, association; Medical research, institute; Human services; American Red Cross; Children/youth, services.
Type of support: General/operating support; Building/renovation; Program development; Research.
Limitations: Applications not accepted. No grants to individuals.
Application information: Contributes only to pre-selected organizations.
Trustees: Corinne L. Dodero; Lorraine C. Dodero; William Dodero.
EIN: 656239071

7439
Randolph J. & Estelle M. Dorn Foundation ✧
165 E. Washington Row
Sandusky, OH 44870-2610 (419) 625-8324
Contact: M.J. Stauffer, Pres.

Established around 1971.
Donor: Estelle M. Dorn.
Foundation type: Independent foundation.
Financial data (yr. ended 04/30/13): Assets, $24,614,035 (M); expenditures, $1,154,133; qualifying distributions, $936,774; giving activities include $936,774 for grants.
Purpose and activities: Giving to organizations which operate as public charities in northern OH, including arts, education, health, youth development, and social service organizations.
Fields of interest: Arts, multipurpose centers/programs; Arts education; Museums; Performing arts, orchestras; Arts; Elementary/secondary education; Higher education; Libraries/library science; Education; Health organizations, association; Cancer; Boys & girls clubs; Big Brothers/Big Sisters; Human services; Community/economic development; Christian agencies & churches.
Type of support: General/operating support; Equipment; Endowments; Program development; Employee matching gifts.
Limitations: Applications accepted. Giving limited to northern OH, with strong emphasis on Sandusky. No grants to individuals.
Application information: Application form not required.
Initial approach: Proposal
Deadline(s): None
Officers and Trustees:* M.J. Stauffer,* Pres.; Mary Jane Hill,* V.P. and Secy.; David F. Reid,* V.P.; Bobbie J. Hummel,* Treas.; John O. Bacon.
EIN: 237099592
Selected grants: The following grants are a representative sample of this grantmaker's funding activity:
$20,000 to Safe Harbour Domestic Violence Shelter, Sandusky, OH, 2013. For First Response Program/Violence No More Program.
$5,000 to Boy Scouts of America, Heart of Ohio Council, Ashland, OH, 2013. For At-Risk Scoutreach Programs in Erie County.
$5,000 to Sandusky Concert Association, Sandusky, OH, 2013. For 2012/2013 season.

$2,500 to Second Harvest Food Bank of North Central Ohio, Lorain, OH, 2013. For General Operating/Harvest for Hunger Program to benefit Erie County residents.

7440
Helen G., Henry F. & Louise T. Dornette Foundation ✧
c/o Fifth Third Bank
P.O. Box 630858
Cincinnati, OH 45263-0858

Established in 1991 in OH.
Donor: Helen G. Dornette†.
Foundation type: Independent foundation.
Financial data (yr. ended 03/31/13): Assets, $11,868,759 (M); expenditures, $967,467; qualifying distributions, $870,860; giving activities include $870,000 for 16 grants (high: $250,000; low: $10,000).
Fields of interest: Arts; Botanical gardens; Zoos/zoological societies; Health organizations, association; Human services; American Red Cross; Salvation Army.
Limitations: Applications not accepted. Giving primarily in OH. No grants to individuals.
Application information: Contributes only to pre-selected organizations.
Trustee: Fifth Third Bank.
EIN: 316425317
Selected grants: The following grants are a representative sample of this grantmaker's funding activity:
$150,000 to Childrens Hospital Medical Center, Cincinnati, OH, 2012.
$100,000 to Cincinnati Zoo and Botanical Garden, Cincinnati, OH, 2012.
$100,000 to Greater Cincinnati Television Educational Foundation, Cincinnati, OH, 2012.
$50,000 to Cincinnati Nature Center, Milford, OH, 2012.
$50,000 to Cincinnati Parks Foundation, Cincinnati, OH, 2012.
$25,000 to World Wildlife Fund, Washington, DC, 2012.
$22,500 to Public Library of Cincinnati and Hamilton County, Friends of the, Cincinnati, OH, 2012.
$10,000 to American Printing House for the Blind, Louisville, KY, 2012.
$10,000 to Ohio Valley Voices, Loveland, OH, 2012.
$10,000 to Sunrock Farm, Friends of, Wilder, KY, 2012.

7441
The George Edward Durell Foundation ✧
128 County Line Rd. W., Ste. D
Westerville, OH 43082-7205

Established in 1985 in VA.
Donor: George Edward Durell†.
Foundation type: Independent foundation.
Financial data (yr. ended 12/31/13): Assets, $30,808,693 (M); expenditures, $1,608,796; qualifying distributions, $1,427,826; giving activities include $720,000 for 34 grants (high: $75,000; low: $500).
Purpose and activities: Giving primarily for education, and to Christian schools and organizations.
Fields of interest: Higher education; Education; Human services; Youth, services; Christian agencies & churches.
Type of support: General/operating support; Program development; Conferences/seminars.
Limitations: Applications not accepted. Giving in the U.S., primarily in Denver, CO, Washington, DC, GA, Indianapolis, IN, MI, and OH. No grants to individuals.
Application information: Contributes only to pre-selected organizations. Unsolicited requests for funds not considered.
Board meeting date(s): Jan., Apr., July, and Oct.
Officer: David A. Durell, Chair.
Trustees: Anne B. Durell; James A. Landaker, C.P.A.; Lisle H. Smith; William S. Weiant.
EIN: 311111800

7442
The Eaton Charitable Fund ✧
c/o Eaton Corp.
1000 Eaton Blvd.
Cleveland, OH 44122-6058 (440) 523-4944
Contact: William B. Doggett, Sr. V.P., Public and Community Affairs
FAX: (216) 479-7013;
E-mail: barrydoggett@eaton.com; Main URL: http://www.eaton.com/Eaton/OurCompany/Sustainability/SustainablePractices/Community/index.htm
RSS Feed: http://www.eaton.com/EatonCom/OurCompany/NewsandEvents/NewsList/index.htm?category=Community

Trust established in 1953 in OH.
Donor: Eaton Corp.
Foundation type: Company-sponsored foundation.
Financial data (yr. ended 12/31/13): Assets, $2,224,379 (M); gifts received, $8,000,000; expenditures, $7,636,625; qualifying distributions, $7,635,252; giving activities include $7,629,594 for 1,451 grants (high: $200,000; low: $25).
Purpose and activities: The fund supports organizations involved with arts and culture, education, health, cancer, housing, disaster relief, human services, and community development. Special emphasis is directed toward organizations with which employees of Eaton are involved.
Fields of interest: Museums (art); Performing arts, theater; Performing arts, orchestras; Arts; Secondary school/education; Higher education; Education; Hospitals (general); Health care, patient services; Health care; Cancer; Housing/shelter, development; Housing/shelter; Disasters, preparedness/services; Youth development, business; American Red Cross; Salvation Army; YM/YWCAs & YM/YWHAs; Children/youth, services; Family services; Human services; Community/economic development; United Ways and Federated Giving Programs.
Type of support: General/operating support; Continuing support; Capital campaigns; Building/renovation; Equipment; Program development; Scholarship funds; Employee volunteer services; Employee matching gifts; In-kind gifts; Matching/challenge support.
Limitations: Applications accepted. Giving on a national and international basis in areas of company operations. No support for religious organizations not of direct benefit to the entire community; fraternal or labor organizations. No grants to individuals, or for endowments, medical research, general operating support for United Way agencies or hospitals, or debt reduction, fundraising events, or sponsorships; no loans.
Publications: Application guidelines; Corporate giving report; Informational brochure (including application guidelines).
Application information: Cover letter should be submitted using organization letterhead. Proposals should be no longer than 1 to 3 pages. Support is limited to 1 contribution per organization during any given year. Multi-year funding is not automatic. Video and audio submissions are not encouraged. Application form not required.
Initial approach: Cover letter and proposal to nearest company facility or human resources manager
Copies of proposal: 1
Deadline(s): None
Board meeting date(s): Bimonthly
Final notification: 2 to 3 months
Directors: Cynthia Brabander; William B. Doggett; Trent M. Meyerhoefer.
Trustee: KeyBank N.A.
Number of staff: None.
EIN: 346501856
Selected grants: The following grants are a representative sample of this grantmaker's funding activity:
$200,000 to Cleveland Orchestra, Cleveland, OH, 2012. For Center for Future.
$200,000 to Friends of Breakthrough Schools, Cleveland, OH, 2012. For Breakthrough Vision.
$166,194 to United Way of Greater Cleveland, Cleveland, OH, 2012. For United Way match.
$166,194 to United Way of Greater Cleveland, Cleveland, OH, 2012. For United Way match.
$128,260 to National Merit Scholarship Corporation, Evanston, IL, 2012. For scholarships.
$60,003 to YWCA of Van Wert, Van Wert, OH, 2012. For playground and transitional support.
$20,000 to Great Lakes Theater Festival, Cleveland, OH, 2012. For Young Adult Subscription.
$10,000 to Allegiance Health, Hospice Home, Jackson, MI, 2012. For automatic blood pressure.
$9,500 to North Carolina State University, Raleigh, NC, 2012. To support engineering.
$6,022 to United Way of White County, Searcy, AR, 2012. For United Way match.

7443
The Thomas J. Emery Memorial ✧
200 W. 4th St.
Cincinnati, OH 45202-2775 (513) 241-2880
Contact: Jennie Geisheimer
Facebook: http://www.facebook.com/gcfdn
RSS Feed: http://www.gcfdn.org/DesktopModules/DNNArticle/DNNArticleRSS.aspx?moduleid=691&tabid=163&categoryid=4
Twitter: http://twitter.com/grcincifdn

Incorporated in 1925 in OH.
Donor: Mary Muhlenberg Emery†.
Foundation type: Independent foundation.
Financial data (yr. ended 12/31/13): Assets, $28,426,649 (M); expenditures, $1,370,461; qualifying distributions, $1,168,312; giving activities include $1,076,000 for 52 grants (high: $101,500; low: $500).
Purpose and activities: The purpose of the foundation is to secure a citizenry which shall be more sane, sound and effective because of more satisfactory initial conditions of environment and education. The foundation is used for the physical,

social, civic and educational betterment of individuals.
Fields of interest: Performing arts; Arts; Elementary/secondary education; Higher education; Health care; Human services.
Type of support: Equipment; Capital campaigns; Building/renovation; Program development.
Limitations: Applications accepted. Giving primarily in the greater Cincinnati area, including Hamilton, Butler, Clermont and Warren counties in OH, and Boone, Campbell and Kenton counties in KY. No support for non 501(c)(3) organizations. No grants to individuals, or for continuing support or conferences; no loans.
Publications: Application guidelines.
Application information: For application information, see the Memorial page on The Greater Cincinnati Foundation web site www.gcfdn.org. Application form required.
Board meeting date(s): Apr. and Nov.
Officers and Trustees:* Lee A. Carter,* Pres.; John F. Barrett,* V.P.; Michael A. Hirschfeld,* Secy.; Thomas L. Williams,* Treas.; John T. Lawrence III.
EIN: 310536711
Selected grants: The following grants are a representative sample of this grantmaker's funding activity:
$80,000 to United Way of Greater Cincinnati, Cincinnati, OH, 2012. For 2011 campaign.
$30,000 to United Way of Greater Cincinnati, Cincinnati, OH, 2012. For Social Innovation Fund.
$20,000 to Cincinnati Works, Cincinnati, OH, 2012. For Initiative to Increase and Strengthen Its Employer Bas.
$15,000 to Boy Scouts of America, Cincinnati, OH, 2012. For Dan Beard Council.
$15,000 to Kennedy Heights Arts Center, Cincinnati, OH, 2012. For Our Face to the Community: You Are Welcome Project.
$15,000 to Legal Aid Society of Greater Cincinnati, Cincinnati, OH, 2012. For Child Help: A Medical-Legal Partnership Program.
$10,000 to Jobs for Cincinnati Graduates, Cincinnati, OH, 2012. For Connect2Success Project.
$10,000 to United Way of Greater Cincinnati, Cincinnati, OH, 2012. For 2011-2012 Campaign-Trustee Match.
$2,500 to Greater Cincinnati Foundation, Cincinnati, OH, 2012. For Nelson Schwab Distinguished Trustee Match.

7444
Erie County Community Foundation ✧
(formerly Sandusky/Erie County Community Foundation)
135 E. Washington Row
Sandusky, OH 44870-2609 (419) 621-9690
Contact: Anna J. Oertel, Exec. Dir.; For grants: Randall J. Wagner, Dir., Finance
FAX: (419) 621-8420;
E-mail: info@eriefoundation.org; Grant application email: executivedirector@sanduskyfoundation.org; Grant inquiry email: randyw@eriefoundation.org; Main URL: http://www.eriefoundation.org/
E-Newsletter: http://www.sanduskyfoundation.org/contact-us/newsletter-signup/
Facebook: http://www.facebook.com/pages/SanduskyErie-County-Community-Foundation/145979392120013
Twitter: https://twitter.com/erieccf

Established in 1996 in OH.
Foundation type: Community foundation.
Financial data (yr. ended 12/31/13): Assets, $18,213,106 (M); gifts received, $2,171,756; expenditures, $928,905; giving activities include $490,174 for 26+ grants (high: $26,201), and $55,569 for 46 grants to individuals.
Purpose and activities: The mission of the foundation is to develop a permanent endowment to identify and respond to community needs, and to facilitate charitable giving.
Fields of interest: Arts; Education; Environment; Health care; Human services; Economic development; Community/economic development; Children/youth.
Type of support: Management development/capacity building; Capital campaigns; Building/renovation; Equipment; Program development; Seed money; Scholarship funds; Program evaluation; Matching/challenge support.
Limitations: Applications accepted. Giving limited to Erie County, OH. No support for sectarian religious purposes, or medical or other research organizations. No grants to individuals (except for scholarships), or for advertising or sponsorships, annual campaigns, debt reduction, salaries/benefits of organization staff, or tickets or advertising for fundraising events.
Publications: Application guidelines; Annual report; Financial statement; Grants list; Informational brochure; Newsletter.
Application information: Visit foundation web site for application form and guidelines per grant type. Incomplete applications, faxed applications, or applications submitted after the deadline will not be considered. Application form required.
Initial approach: Submit application form and attachments
Copies of proposal: 15
Deadline(s): Feb. 1 and Aug. 1 for Community Grants
Board meeting date(s): Apr., June, Sept., and Dec.
Final notification: Within 60 days for Community Grants
Officers and Directors:* Mary Jane Hill,* Chair.; Paula J. Rengel,* Vice-Chair.; Roger Gundlach,* Secy.; Eugene A. Koby,* Treas.; Thomas M. Wolf,* Investment Adv.; Anna J. Oertel, Exec. Dir.; Jeanette Henry, Dir. Emeritus; M.J. Stauffer, Dir. Emeritus; John O. Bacon; Laurence A. Bettcher; Richard R. Brady; Eileen Bulan; Faith Denslow; Marcia Goff; Judith Kinzel; Donald G. Koch; Carole Kuhns; Darlene Lowery; George L. Mylander; Ruth F. Parker; Charles W. Rainger; Patrecia Sizemore; J. William Springer; Sparky Weilnau; Andy White.
Number of staff: 2 full-time professional; 1 full-time support; 1 part-time support.
EIN: 341792862

7445
Fairfield County Foundation ✧
162 E. Main St.
P.O. Box 159
Lancaster, OH 43130-3712 (740) 654-8451
Contact: Amy Eyman, Exec. Dir.
FAX: (740) 654-3971;
E-mail: aeyman@fairfieldcountyfoundation.org; Main URL: http://www.fairfieldcountyfoundation.org
Scholarship inquiry e-mail: mfarrow@fairfieldcountyfoundation.org

Established in 1989 in OH.
Foundation type: Community foundation.
Financial data (yr. ended 12/31/13): Assets, $37,397,176 (M); gifts received, $1,364,037; expenditures, $2,166,915; giving activities include $794,760 for 28+ grants (high: $60,000), and $562,855 for 298 grants to individuals.
Purpose and activities: The foundation was created to receive and administer charitable gifts that will provide long-term, continuing benefits to Fairfield County and its residents by supporting educational, scientific, cultural, social, environmental, medical and other charitable purposes.
Fields of interest: Arts; Education, early childhood education; Elementary/secondary school reform; Education, continuing education; Education; Environment, beautification programs; Environment; Hospitals (general); Health care; Mental health/crisis services; Health organizations, association; Employment; Housing/shelter; Recreation; Children/youth, services; Aging, centers/services; Human services; Community/economic development; Infants/toddlers; Children/youth; Children; Youth; Adults; Aging; Young adults; Disabilities, people with; Physically disabled; Blind/visually impaired; Deaf/hearing impaired; Mentally disabled; Minorities; Women; Infants/toddlers, female; Girls; Adults, women; Young adults, female; Men; Infants/toddlers, male; Boys; Adults, men; Young adults, male; Military/veterans; Substance abusers; Single parents; Crime/abuse victims; Terminal illness, people with; Economically disadvantaged; Homeless.
Type of support: Management development/capacity building; Land acquisition; General/operating support; Endowments; Employee-related scholarships; Emergency funds; Continuing support; Capital campaigns; Building/renovation; Equipment; Program development; Publication; Seed money; Curriculum development; Scholarship funds; Technical assistance; Scholarships—to individuals; Matching/challenge support.
Limitations: Applications accepted. Giving limited to Fairfield County, OH. No support for religious organizations for religious purposes, or for specific scientific, medical or academic research. No grants to individuals (except for scholarships), or for general operating expenses of existing organizations, endowments, annual fundraising campaigns, debt retirement, or vehicles.
Publications: Application guidelines; Annual report; Financial statement; Grants list; Informational brochure; Informational brochure (including application guidelines); Newsletter.
Application information: Visit foundation web site for preliminary grant proposal form and guidelines. Based on the preliminary application, the foundation's Grants Committee will confirm if project fits within the foundation's guidelines and invite the applicant to submit a full proposal. Applications submitted by e-mail or fax not accepted. Application form required.
Initial approach: Telephone
Copies of proposal: 2
Deadline(s): 2nd Mon. in Mar. or Aug. for preliminary application; 2nd Mon. in May or Oct. for full proposal
Board meeting date(s): 3rd Thurs. in Jan., Mar., May, July, Sept., and Nov.
Final notification: 2 weeks for preliminary application response
Officers and Trustees:* Judy Root,* Chair.; James Barrett, M.D.*, Vice-Chair.; Matthew E. Johnson,* Secy.; Sheila Heath,* Treas.; Amy Eyman, Exec. Dir.; John Baughman; Jonathan Clark; Terry McGhee; Andrew Ogilvie; Brian Shonk; Kamilla

Sigafoos; James Smith; Howard Sniderman; Gary Taylor; Richard Warner; Penny Wasem.
Number of staff: 1 full-time professional; 2 part-time professional; 1 part-time support.
EIN: 341623983

7446
The Fairmount Minerals Foundation ✧
8834 Mayfield Rd.
Chesterland, OH 44026-2690
Contact: Beth Lestock

Established in 2007 in OH.
Donors: Charles D. Fowler; Jenniffer D. Deckard; Jerry Clancey; Maureen Lynn; Robert Cicigoi; Fairmount Minerals, Ltd.; Chaolley; Grand Sand.
Foundation type: Operating foundation.
Financial data (yr. ended 12/31/12): Assets, $12,169,380 (M); gifts received, $4,550,000; expenditures, $2,036,959; qualifying distributions, $2,034,958; giving activities include $1,981,134 for 875 grants (high: $100,000; low: $5).
Fields of interest: Education; Environment; Health care; Health organizations, association; Human services.
Limitations: Applications accepted. Giving primarily in the Midwest.
Application information: Application form required.
Initial approach: Letter
Deadline(s): None
Directors: William E. Conway; Jenniffer D. Deckard; Charles D. Fowler; Bruce A. McBrian.
EIN: 261428733

7447
Farmer Family Foundation ✧
6847 Cintas Blvd. Ste. 120
Mason, OH 45040-9152

Established in 1988 in OH.
Donors: Brynne F. Coletti; Richard T. Farmer; Amy F. Joseph; Scott D. Farmer.
Foundation type: Independent foundation.
Financial data (yr. ended 12/31/12): Assets, $208,596,984 (M); gifts received, $10,035,000; expenditures, $9,907,748; qualifying distributions, $9,252,681; giving activities include $8,923,499 for 55 grants (high: $2,131,375; low: $500), and $5,986 for foundation-administered programs.
Purpose and activities: To provide funding for charities that will assist and protect primarily children through education, health care, and assistance to the handicapped; giving also to fund programs to assist individuals to enter the work force.
Fields of interest: Education; Medical research; Human services.
Type of support: General/operating support; Capital campaigns; Building/renovation; Program development; Scholarship funds; Research; Matching/challenge support.
Limitations: Applications accepted. Giving primarily in Cincinnati, OH. No grants to individuals.
Application information: Application form not required.
Initial approach: Letter
Copies of proposal: 1
Deadline(s): None
Board meeting date(s): As needed
Officer and Trustees:* Richard T. Farmer,* Chair. and Pres.; Brynne F. Coletti; Robert E. Coletti; Joyce E. Farmer; Mary J. Farmer; Scott D. Farmer; Amy F. Joseph; George R. Joseph.
Number of staff: 1 full-time professional.
EIN: 311256614
Selected grants: The following grants are a representative sample of this grantmaker's funding activity:
$2,179,000 to Miami University, Oxford, OH, 2011.
$2,131,375 to Miami University Foundation, Oxford, OH, 2012.
$1,750,000 to Donors Trust, Alexandria, VA, 2012.
$1,385,647 to Greater Cincinnati Foundation, Cincinnati, OH, 2012.
$1,200,000 to SEED Foundation, Washington, DC, 2012.
$500,000 to Intrepid Fallen Heroes Fund, New York, NY, 2012.
$333,333 to Memorial Sloan-Kettering Cancer Center, New York, NY, 2011.
$333,333 to Memorial Sloan-Kettering Cancer Center, New York, NY, 2012.
$333,333 to Ocean Reef Medical Center Foundation, Key Largo, FL, 2012.
$333,333 to University of Texas Medical Foundation, Houston, TX, 2011.
$333,333 to University of Texas Medical Foundation, Houston, TX, 2012.
$246,357 to United Way of Greater Cincinnati, Cincinnati, OH, 2011.
$50,000 to Purcell Marian High School, Cincinnati, OH, 2012.
$44,369 to Catholic Inner-City Schools Educational Fund, Cincinnati, OH, 2011.
$35,000 to Lighthouse Youth Services, Cincinnati, OH, 2012.
$30,000 to Boys Hope Girls Hope of Greater Cincinnati, Cincinnati, OH, 2011.
$25,000 to Freestore/Foodbank, Cincinnati, OH, 2011.

7448
Richard J. Fasenmyer Foundation ✧
c/o Deborah Vesy
7575 Northcliff Ave., Ste. 203
Brooklyn, OH 44144-3205
FAX: (216) 741-6042;
E-mail: dvesy@fasenmyerfoundation.org

Established in 1989 in OH.
Foundation type: Independent foundation.
Financial data (yr. ended 12/31/13): Assets, $41,583,762 (M); expenditures, $1,950,370; qualifying distributions, $1,875,707; giving activities include $1,769,450 for 70 grants (high: $500,000; low: $500).
Purpose and activities: The foundation supports significant, innovative, and collaborative efforts in clinical immunology, particularly those that relate to patient support, education and research in the areas of HIV/AIDS and its attendant illnesses; fosters business entrepreneurship and promotes the free enterprise spirit; and encourages economic development in partnership with the arts. The foundation is committed to continuing and strengthening the passions and legacy of its founder, Richard J. Fasenmyer.
Fields of interest: Human services.
Limitations: Applications not accepted. Giving primarily in northeastern OH. No grants to individuals.
Application information: Contributes only to pre-selected organizations.
Trustees: John L. Baechle; Walter R. Collins, Jr.; Gordon Harnett; Haven J. Hood.
EIN: 341627457

7449
Fenn S P No. 1 ✧
c/o KeyBank, N.A.
4900 Tiedman Rd., OH-01-49-0150
Brooklyn, OH 44144-2302

Foundation type: Independent foundation.
Financial data (yr. ended 12/31/13): Assets, $29,012,117 (M); expenditures, $1,366,176; qualifying distributions, $1,276,117; giving activities include $1,251,888 for 3 grants (high: $417,296; low: $417,296).
Fields of interest: YM/YWCAs & YM/YWHAs; Protestant agencies & churches.
Limitations: Applications not accepted. Giving primarily in Cleveland, OH.
Application information: Unsolicited requests for funds not accepted.
Trustee: KeyBank, N.A.
EIN: 346506790
Selected grants: The following grants are a representative sample of this grantmaker's funding activity:
$421,895 to Old Stone Church, Cleveland, OH, 2012. To support of Activities to Benefit Humanity.

7450
Leonard C. & Mildred F. Ferguson Foundation ✧
7 Easton Oval, EA4E86
Columbus, OH 43219-6010 (330) 258-2362
Application address: c/o Irene Gray, Huntington Bank, 4767 Munson St. N.W., Canton OH 44718, tel.: (330) 258-2362

Established in 1998 in FL.
Donors: Nancy Seeley; Mildred F. Ferguson Irrevocable Trust.
Foundation type: Independent foundation.
Financial data (yr. ended 01/31/14): Assets, $13,492,274 (M); expenditures, $768,175; qualifying distributions, $710,476; giving activities include $687,315 for 62 grants (high: $100,000; low: $1,000).
Purpose and activities: The foundation's primary focus is to make a difference in young people's lives and in the environment in which they live.
Fields of interest: Arts; Education; Environment; Health care; Human services; Youth.
Type of support: Program development; Seed money; Scholarship funds; Matching/challenge support.
Limitations: Applications accepted. Giving primarily in the Atherton and Menlo Park areas of CA, and in FL, ME, and VT. No grants for endowments.
Application information: Application form not required.
Initial approach: Proposal
Deadline(s): None
Trustees: Lynne A. Seeley; Dana G. Seeley Hayse; Nancy Seeley; Huntington National Bank, N.A.
EIN: 656245247
Selected grants: The following grants are a representative sample of this grantmaker's funding activity:
$20,000 to Highland Community College, Freeport, IL, 2013. For new nursing wing.

$16,000 to Androscoggin Land Trust, Auburn, ME, 2013. For Youth Reconnecting with Androscoggin.
$10,000 to Aroostook Mental Health Services, Caribou, ME, 2013. For Teen Leadership Camp.
$10,000 to Greater Portland Landmarks, Portland, ME, 2013. For Historic Preservation Grant.
$5,000 to Frederic Remington Art Museum, Ogdensburg, NY, 2013. For Kid's Place.
$5,000 to Hope for Haiti, Naples, FL, 2013. For children without schools.
$5,000 to Prevent Blindness Ohio, Columbus, OH, 2013. For vision loss prevention.
$3,000 to Maine Philanthropy Center, Portland, ME, 2013. For Environmental Funders Network.
$2,300 to Canal Fulton Public Library, Canal Fulton, OH, 2013. For juvenile programs.
$2,000 to Beacon Journal Charity Fund, Akron, OH, 2013. For dental health education.

7451
The Ferry Family Foundation ✧ ☆
1422 Euclid Ave., Ste. 1030
Cleveland, OH 44115-2001

Established in 2002 in OH.
Foundation type: Independent foundation.
Financial data (yr. ended 12/31/13): Assets, $4,218,938 (M); expenditures, $507,018; qualifying distributions, $446,501; giving activities include $435,500 for 21 grants (high: $105,000; low: $500).
Fields of interest: Arts; Higher education; Law school/education; Botanical gardens; Food banks; Human services.
Limitations: Applications not accepted. Giving primarily in OH, with emphasis on Cleveland. No grants to individuals.
Application information: Contributes only to pre-selected organizations.
Trustees: Carol Colangelo; William Culbertson; Carolyn P. Ferry.
EIN: 326000096
Selected grants: The following grants are a representative sample of this grantmaker's funding activity:
$80,000 to Case Western Reserve University, Cleveland, OH, 2012. For Research Fellowship at Law/Medicine Center.
$70,000 to Ohio Wesleyan University, Delaware, OH, 2012. For Summer Science Research Programs.
$50,000 to Cleveland Botanical Garden, Cleveland, OH, 2012. For internship endowment.
$50,000 to Hattie Larlham Foundation, Mantua, OH, 2012. For 4th Pledge Payment on Capital Campaign.
$2,000 to Cuyahoga County Public Library, Parma, OH, 2012. For After School Homework Centers.

7452
The Fifth Third Foundation ✧
38 Fountain Square Plz., M.D. 1090CA
Cincinnati, OH 45263 (513) 534-4397
Contact: Heidi B. Jark, Managing Dir.
FAX: (513) 534-0960; Additional tel.: (513) 534-7001; Main URL: https://www.53.com/site/about/in-the-community/

Trust established in 1948 in OH.
Donor: Fifth Third Bank.
Foundation type: Company-sponsored foundation.
Financial data (yr. ended 09/30/13): Assets, $9,652,581 (M); gifts received, $3,000,000; expenditures, $4,010,330; qualifying distributions, $3,940,154; giving activities include $3,912,253 for 599 grants (high: $500,000; low: $25).
Purpose and activities: The foundation supports organizations involved with arts and culture, education, health, human services, and community development.
Fields of interest: Arts; Higher education; Business school/education; Education; Health care; Housing/shelter; American Red Cross; Family services; Human services; Community/economic development; United Ways and Federated Giving Programs.
Type of support: General/operating support; Continuing support; Management development/capacity building; Annual campaigns; Capital campaigns; Building/renovation; Equipment; Program development; Scholarship funds; Employee-related scholarships.
Limitations: Applications accepted. Giving primarily in areas of company operations in FL, GA, IL, IN, KY, MI, MO, NC, OH, PA, TN, and WV. No support for individual churches or publicly-supported organizations or government agencies; generally, no support for elementary or middle schools; no support for United Way and Fine Arts Funds. No grants to individuals (except for employee-related scholarships), or for start-up funds.
Publications: Application guidelines; Corporate giving report.
Application information: Visit website for nearest company facility address. A full proposal may be requested. A site visit may be requested. Support is limited to 1 contribution per organization during any given year. Applicants seeking multi-year funding must meet additional requirements. A waiting period of three years is required for prior grant recipients receiving $10,000 or more. Organizations receiving support are asked to submit a written evaluation. Application form not required.
Initial approach: Letter of inquiry to nearest company facility; contact foundation for major campaign requests
Deadline(s): None
Board meeting date(s): Jan., Mar., June, and Sept.
Final notification: 6 months
Trustee: Fifth Third Bank.
EIN: 316024135
Selected grants: The following grants are a representative sample of this grantmaker's funding activity:
$500,000 to Eskenazi Health Foundation, Indianapolis, IN, 2013. For capital fund.
$125,000 to ArtsWave, Cincinnati, OH, 2013. For project/program support.
$100,000 to United Way, Heart of West Michigan, Grand Rapids, MI, 2013. For annual fund.
$100,000 to Xavier University, Cincinnati, OH, 2013. For program support.
$30,000 to Culture Works: The Arts and Cultural Alliance of the Miami Valley, Dayton, OH, 2013. For program support.
$30,000 to Philanthropy Ohio, Columbus, OH, 2013. For general operating support.
$15,000 to United Way, Greater Ottawa County, Holland, MI, 2013. For annual fund.
$10,000 to 2016 Olympics Fund for Chicago Neighborhoods, Chicago, IL, 2013. For project/program support.
$9,000 to Good Samaritan Ministries, Holland, MI, 2013. For program support.
$1,000 to Duke University, Durham, NC, 2013. For annual support.

7453
The Findlay Hancock County Community Foundation ✧
101 W. Sandusky St., Ste. 207
Findlay, OH 45840-3276 (419) 425-1100
Contact: Karen Smith, C.F.O.; Katherine Kreuchauf, Pres.
FAX: (419) 425-9339;
E-mail: info@community-foundation.com; Main URL: http://www.community-foundation.com
Blog: http://community-foundation.com/category/blog/
Facebook: http://www.facebook.com/pages/The-Findlay-Hancock-County-Community-Foundation/109824349061442
Twitter: https://twitter.com/tcffindlay
YouTube: https://www.youtube.com/channel/UCJlHzLdDjENjIYARTzvfDQg
Scholarship tel.: 419-425-1100; Scholarship e-mail: sjoseph@community-foundation.com

Established in 1992 in OH as a supporting organization of the Cleveland Foundation; became a community foundation independent of the Cleveland Foundation in Feb. 1999.
Foundation type: Community foundation.
Financial data (yr. ended 12/31/12): Assets, $70,959,790 (M); gifts received, $3,145,824; expenditures, $3,033,930; giving activities include $1,296,218 for 40+ grants (high: $107,952), and $3,400 for grants to individuals.
Purpose and activities: The foundation is dedicated to improving the quality of life in the Hancock County area through collaborative leadership, responsible grantmaking, and development of philanthropic giving. The foundation seeks to facilitate philanthropic efforts through the development and stewardship of donor funds. The foundation builds permanent endowed funds contributed by individuals, corporations and institutions, provides grants and assistance to develop and strengthen organizations located in the community, encourages partnerships with other foundations, businesses and government entities to increase funds distributed to the community, and inspires philanthropic and community involvement.
Fields of interest: Arts; Adult education—literacy, basic skills & GED; Education; Health care; Youth development; Human services; Economic development; Public affairs.
Type of support: General/operating support; Endowments; Management development/capacity building; Capital campaigns; Building/renovation; Program development; Seed money; Scholarship funds; Technical assistance; Consulting services; Program evaluation; Program-related investments/loans.
Limitations: Applications accepted. Giving limited to the greater Hancock County, OH, area. No support for religious organizations for religious purposes, community services such as the police and fire protection, or for staff positions for government agencies. No grants to individuals (except for scholarships), or for endowment campaigns. Generally no grants for ongoing operating expenses, annual appeals or membership drives, sponsoring or attending conferences, fundraising projects or advertisements, travel, existing obligations, debts or liabilities, or for the printing of publications,

audiovisual projects or video productions. Support for capital requests are seldom considered.
Publications: Application guidelines; Annual report; Financial statement; Informational brochure; Informational brochure (including application guidelines).
Application information: Visit foundation web site for application forms and requirements. Proposals submitted by fax or e-mail are not accepted. Application form required.
Initial approach: Submit letter of intent
Copies of proposal: 2
Deadline(s): 1st Fri. of Jan., Apr., July and Oct. for letter of intent; 1st Fri. of Mar., June, Sept. and Dec. for full proposal
Board meeting date(s): Feb., Apr., May, July, Sept., and Nov.
Final notification: Within 3 months
Officers and Trustees:* Patricia J. Brown,* Chair.; Michael S. Needler,* Vice-Chair.; Katherine Kreuchauf,* Pres.; Sherri Garner Brumbaugh,* Secy.; Garry L. Peiffer,* Treas.; Karen Smith, C.F.O.; Gwen Kuenzli; J. Alec Reinhardt; Ralph D. Russo; Gene Stevens; Gary Wilson.
Number of staff: 6 full-time professional; 1 full-time support.
EIN: 341713261
Selected grants: The following grants are a representative sample of this grantmaker's funding activity:
$200,000 to Findlay-Hancock County Community Foundation, Findlay, OH, 2011. For debt service on Family Center.
$130,190 to Findlay-Hancock County Community Foundation, Findlay, OH, 2011. For capacity building program.
$100,000 to City Mission of Findlay, Findlay, OH, 2011. To create Day Center for local homeless.
$100,000 to Northwest Ohio Flood Mitigation Partnership, Findlay, OH, 2011. For general support.
$69,543 to Alzheimers Association, Toledo, OH, 2011. For services in Findlay, Ohio.
$65,000 to Special Kids Therapy, Findlay, OH, 2011. To hire Executive Director.
$57,000 to Findlay Hope House for the Homeless, Findlay, OH, 2011.
$43,774 to United Way of Hancock County, Findlay, OH, 2011. For general support.
$26,716 to Hancock County Center for Safe and Healthy Children, Findlay, OH, 2011. For general support.
$22,219 to Hancock Historical Museum Association, Findlay, OH, 2011. For capital campaign.

7454
Firman Fund ✧
1422 Euclid Ave., Ste. 1030
Cleveland, OH 44115-2001

Incorporated in 1951 in OH.
Donor: Pamela H. Firman†.
Foundation type: Independent foundation.
Financial data (yr. ended 12/31/13): Assets, $9,144,792 (M); expenditures, $550,952; qualifying distributions, $500,224; giving activities include $488,167 for 27 grants (high: $125,000; low: $500).
Fields of interest: Arts; Education; Environment; Health care; Human services.
Type of support: General/operating support; Annual campaigns; Capital campaigns; Building/renovation; Scholarship funds.
Limitations: Applications not accepted. Giving primarily in Denver, CO, Tallahassee, FL, Thomasville, GA, and Cleveland, OH. No grants to individuals, or for research; no loans.
Application information: Unsolicited requests for funds not accepted.
Board meeting date(s): Apr. and Nov.
Officers: Neil A. Brown, Secy.; Carole M. Nowak, Treas.
Trustees: Royal Firman III; Stephanie Firman; Cynthia F. Webster.
EIN: 346513655
Selected grants: The following grants are a representative sample of this grantmaker's funding activity:
$25,000 to Boca Grande Health Clinic, Boca Grande, FL, 2012. For capital gift.
$25,000 to Tall Timbers Research, Tallahassee, FL, 2012. For Research Fund.
$1,500 to Boca Grande Health Clinic, Boca Grande, FL, 2012. For capital campaign.

7455
FirstEnergy Foundation ✧
76 S. Main St.
Akron, OH 44308-1890 (330) 384-5022
Contact: Dolores J. Lowery, Pres.; Terry Gilman, Mgr., Community Initiatives and Contribs.
For PA and WV, call: (724) 838-3082; for NJ and MD, call (732) 212-4147.; Main URL: https://www.firstenergycorp.com/community/firstenergy_foundation.html

Incorporated in 1961 in OH.
Donors: Centerior Energy Corp.; The Cleveland Electric Illuminating Co.; FirstEnergy Corp.; GPU Service, Inc.; Jersey Central Power & Light Co.; Metropolitan Edison Co.; Ohio Edison Co.; Pennsylvania Electric Co.; Potomic Edison; The Toledo Edison Co.; West Penn Power; UM Power.
Foundation type: Company-sponsored foundation.
Financial data (yr. ended 12/31/12): Assets, $43,782,988 (M); expenditures, $4,384,317; qualifying distributions, $4,384,927; giving activities include $3,869,161 for 340 grants (high: $500,000; low: $340), and $136,766 for 493 employee matching gifts.
Purpose and activities: The foundation supports programs designed to improve the vitality of the community and promote key safety initiatives; promote local and regional economic development and revitalization efforts; assist programs designed to support FirstEnergy employees' community leadership and volunteer interests; and advance an educated workforce by supporting professional development and literacy, and science, technology, and mathematics education initiatives.
Fields of interest: Arts; Higher education; Education; Health care; Employment; Youth, services; Human services; Community/economic development; United Ways and Federated Giving Programs; Mathematics; Engineering/technology; Science; Public affairs.
Type of support: General/operating support; Annual campaigns; Building/renovation; Program development; Employee matching gifts.
Limitations: Giving primarily in areas of company operations in MD, NJ, OH, PA, and WV. No support for largely tax-supported organizations, fraternal, religious, labor, athletic, social, or veterans' organizations not of direct benefit to the entire community, national or international organizations, United Way-supported organizations, or public or private Pre-K, elementary, or secondary schools. No grants to individuals, or for political or legislative activities, research, equipment, endowments, or debt reduction; no loans.
Publications: Informational brochure.
Application information: Unsolicited grant applications are not accepted at this time. Grant inquiries should be discussed with the local management of FirstEnergy companies and the staff of the foundation.
Board meeting date(s): Annually
Officers and Trustees:* Leila L. Vespoli, Chair.; Dolores J. Lowery, Pres.; Rhonda S. Ferguson, Secy.; James F. Pearson, Treas.; Mark T. Clark; Charles E. Jones.
Number of staff: 1 full-time professional; 3 part-time professional; 1 part-time support.
EIN: 346514181

7456
FirstMerit Foundation ✧
III Cascade Plz., CAS 50
Akron, OH 44308-1124 (330) 996-6444
Contact: Jane Litz

Donor: FirstMerit Bank, N.A.
Foundation type: Company-sponsored foundation.
Financial data (yr. ended 12/31/13): Assets, $82,228 (M); gifts received, $668,240; expenditures, $698,740; qualifying distributions, $698,740; giving activities include $698,740 for 114 grants (high: $100,000; low: $500).
Purpose and activities: The foundation supports organizations involved with performing arts, education, health, and community economic development.
Fields of interest: Education; Health care; Religion.
Limitations: Applications accepted. Giving primarily in areas of company operations in OH.
Application information: Application form required.
Initial approach: Completed Application form
Deadline(s): None
Officers and Directors:* Nancy H. Worman,* Pres.; Judith Steiner,* Secy.; Michael E. Miller,* Treas.
EIN: 205608263
Selected grants: The following grants are a representative sample of this grantmaker's funding activity:
$100,000 to University of Akron Foundation, Akron, OH, 2012. For Capital Campaign pledge No. 4 of 10.
$60,000 to Hospice of the Western Reserve, Cleveland, OH, 2012. For Capital support of Building Renovation Children's Playroom.
$15,000 to Cleveland Botanical Garden, Cleveland, OH, 2012. For Sponsorship support of Glow Winter show 2012 and Fall 2013 events.
$10,000 to Downtown Akron Partnership, Akron, OH, 2012. To sponsor First Night Akron 2013.
$10,000 to East Akron Neighborhood Development Corporation, Akron, OH, 2012. For contribution to Annual Campaign.
$5,000 to Lorain County Community College Foundation, Elyria, OH, 2012. For Supporting the Midpoint Campus Scholarship Fund.
$3,500 to College Now Greater Cleveland, Cleveland, OH, 2012. To support General Operations Fund.
$3,000 to Big Shoulders Fund, Chicago, IL, 2012. For Stock Market Project financial education for inner-city 8th grade students.
$2,500 to YMCA of Central Ohio, Columbus, OH, 2012. For Supporting 2012 'People Helping People' annual giving campaign.

$1,750 to Blessing House, Lorain, OH, 2012. For Supporting childcare Programs.

7457
Fleischmann Foundation ✧ ☆

7811 Laurel Ave., Ste. B
Cincinnati, OH 45243 (513) 621-1384
Contact: Noah Fleischmann, Pres. and Tr.

Incorporated in 1931 in OH.
Donors: Julius Fleischmann†; Charles Fleischmann III†.
Foundation type: Independent foundation.
Financial data (yr. ended 12/31/13): Assets, $8,242,507 (M); gifts received, $2,465,186; expenditures, $1,053,509; qualifying distributions, $997,955; giving activities include $997,955 for 21 grants (high: $760,005; low: $100).
Fields of interest: Museums (art); History/archaeology; Historic preservation/historical societies; Arts; Education; Environment; Foundations (community).
Type of support: General/operating support.
Limitations: Applications accepted. Giving primarily in OH. No grants to individuals.
Application information: Application form required.
Initial approach: Proposal
Deadline(s): None
Officers and Trustees:* Noah Fleischmann,* Pres.; Blair S. Fleischmann,* Secy.; Charles Fleischmann IV; Louisa Fleischmann; Burd B. Schlessinger.
EIN: 316025516
Selected grants: The following grants are a representative sample of this grantmaker's funding activity:
$5,000 to Kestrel Land Trust, Amherst, MA, 2011. For general charitable purposes.

7458
Fleming Family Foundation ✧

P.O. Box 1558, Dept. EA4E86
Columbus, OH 43216-1558
Application address: c/o Lynnette Pedensky, 127 W. Spring St., Titusville, PA 16354; tel.: (866) 398-5072

Established in FL.
Foundation type: Independent foundation.
Financial data (yr. ended 12/31/13): Assets, $32,351,728 (M); expenditures, $1,505,549; qualifying distributions, $1,407,295; giving activities include $1,300,000 for 36 grants (high: $120,000; low: $2,000).
Fields of interest: Environment; Animals/wildlife; Human services.
Limitations: Applications accepted. Giving primarily in FL and PA.
Application information: Application form required.
Initial approach: Letter
Deadline(s): None
Trustee: Huntington National Bank.
EIN: 266214365
Selected grants: The following grants are a representative sample of this grantmaker's funding activity:
$630,000 to YMCA, Titusville, Titusville, PA, 2010.
$539,159 to Conservation Force, Metairie, LA, 2011.
$60,000 to Billfish Foundation, Fort Lauderdale, FL, 2010.
$50,000 to Conservation Force, Metairie, LA, 2010.
$50,000 to Don Hawley Foundation, Islamorada, FL, 2011.
$50,000 to Stephens College, Columbia, MO, 2011.
$48,000 to Friends of Drake Well, Titusville, PA, 2011.
$33,500 to Palm Beach County Fishing Foundation, West Palm Beach, FL, 2011.
$33,500 to Palm Beach County Fishing Foundation, West Palm Beach, FL, 2010.
$32,500 to Friends of Drake Well, Titusville, PA, 2010.
$30,000 to Billfish Foundation, Fort Lauderdale, FL, 2011.
$30,000 to Busch Wildlife Sanctuary, Jupiter, FL, 2011.
$30,000 to Don Hawley Foundation, Islamorada, FL, 2010.
$25,000 to Busch Wildlife Sanctuary, Jupiter, FL, 2010.
$10,000 to Zoological Society of the Palm Beaches, West Palm Beach, FL, 2011.
$5,000 to Adopt a Cat Foundation, Lake Park, FL, 2011.
$5,000 to United Way, Titusville Area, Titusville, PA, 2010.

7459
S.N. & Ada Ford Fund ✧

c/o KeyBank
4900 Tiedeman Rd, OH-01-49-0150
Brooklyn, OH 44144-2302 (419) 525-7665
Contact: Dana Hammond, Tr.
*Application address:*C/o. KeyBank, N.A., 42 N. Main St., Mansfield, OH 44902, tel.: (419) 525-7665

Established in 1947 in OH.
Donors: Ada Ford, M.D.†; James F. Jolley†.
Foundation type: Independent foundation.
Financial data (yr. ended 12/31/12): Assets, $11,551,827 (M); expenditures, $553,730; qualifying distributions, $497,902; giving activities include $483,500 for 5 grants (high: $316,000; low: $12,500).
Purpose and activities: Assistance to the aged and the sick, and scholarships for the youth of Richland County, OH.
Fields of interest: Education; Catholic federated giving programs; Aging; Economically disadvantaged.
Type of support: Building/renovation; Grants to individuals; Scholarships—to individuals.
Limitations: Applications accepted. Giving primarily in Richland County, OH. No grants for endowment funds, or for operating budgets, special projects, general support, research, or matching gifts; no loans.
Publications: Annual report.
Application information: Application form required.
Initial approach: Proposal
Deadline(s): None
Board meeting date(s): Monthly
Distribution Committee: Eric Behnke; Deborah M. Schenk; Jack Welsh.
Trustee: KeyBank, N.A.
EIN: 340842282

7460
The Char and Chuck Fowler Family Foundation ✧

(formerly Charles and Charlotte Fowler Family Foundation)
c/o Cornerstone Family Offices
5885 Landerbrook Dr., Ste. 300
Mayfield Heights, OH 44124-4031 (440) 460-0460
FAX: (440) 460-0420;
E-mail: grants@fowlerfamilyfdn.org; Main URL: http://fowlerfamilyfdn.org/

Established in 2003 in OH.
Donors: Charles D. Fowler; Charlotte Fowler; Grandsand LLC; Chaolley Limited Partnership.
Foundation type: Independent foundation.
Financial data (yr. ended 12/31/13): Assets, $46,377,213 (M); expenditures, $8,078,605; qualifying distributions, $7,780,000; giving activities include $7,780,000 for 50 grants (high: $5,000,000; low: $3,000).
Purpose and activities: Giving primarily for education, health and the arts.
Fields of interest: Arts; Education; Health care.
Type of support: Program development; Management development/capacity building; General/operating support; Equipment; Curriculum development; Continuing support; Building/renovation.
Limitations: Applications accepted. Giving primarily in the greater Cleveland, OH, area. No support for political groups, annual fund raising events or event sponsorships. No grants to individuals.
Application information: See foundation web site for online letter of intent form. Application form required.
Initial approach: Online letter of intent
Deadline(s): Spring Grant Cycle: Feb. 10 for LOI, April 11 for application; Fall Grant Cycle: Aug. 29 for LOI, Oct. 20 for application
Board meeting date(s): Twice yearly
Final notification: Spring Grant Cycle: May 12; Fall Grant Cycle: Nov. 17
Officers and Trustees:* Charlotte A. Fowler,* Pres.; Chann Fowler-Spellman,* Secy.; Charles D. Fowler, Treas.; Holley Fowler Martens.
EIN: 900035660
Selected grants: The following grants are a representative sample of this grantmaker's funding activity:
$5,000,000 to University Hospitals Cleveland Medical Center, Cleveland, OH, 2011. For general support.
$500,000 to Das Deutsch Center for Special Needs Children, Middlefield, OH, 2011. For general support.
$400,000 to Positive Education Program, Cleveland, OH, 2011. For general support.
$350,000 to Flying Horse Farms, Columbus, OH, 2010. For general support.
$300,000 to Flying Horse Farms, Columbus, OH, 2011. For general support.
$250,000 to Case Western Reserve University, Cleveland, OH, 2011. For general support.
$166,667 to Cleveland Institute of Art, Cleveland, OH, 2010. For general support.
$60,000 to Drug-Free Action Alliance, Columbus, OH, 2011. For general support.
$50,000 to Hathaway Brown School, Shaker Heights, OH, 2011. For general support.
$28,000 to Family Connections, Shaker Heights, OH, 2011. For general support.

$28,000 to Progressive Arts Alliance, Cleveland, OH, 2011. For general support.
$10,000 to Open Doors, Cleveland, OH, 2010. For general support.
$5,000 to Progressive Arts Alliance, Cleveland, OH, 2010. For general support.

7461
Fox Foundation, Inc. ✧
1445 Cincinnati Zanesville Rd. S.W.
Lancaster, OH 43130-8327
Contact: Robert L. Fox, Tr.

Established in 1953 in OH.
Donor: Robert K. Fox.
Foundation type: Independent foundation.
Financial data (yr. ended 11/30/13): Assets, $19,482,211 (M); expenditures, $744,106; qualifying distributions, $730,746; giving activities include $730,000 for 32 grants (high: $100,000; low: $1,000).
Fields of interest: Arts; Education; Health organizations, association; Human services; Foundations (private grantmaking); Foundations (community); Protestant agencies & churches.
Type of support: Annual campaigns; Capital campaigns; Professorships; Exchange programs.
Limitations: Applications accepted. Giving primarily in OH; some funding in Columbia, SC. No grants to individuals.
Application information: Application form not required.
Initial approach: Proposal
Deadline(s): None
Board meeting date(s): Feb.
Trustees: Donald R. Sutton; Elizabeth Q. Fox; Robert L. Fox.
EIN: 316023906
Selected grants: The following grants are a representative sample of this grantmaker's funding activity:
$2,000 to Princeton University, Princeton, NJ, 2013. For annual giving, athletics.

7462
France Stone Foundation ✧
4 Seagate, Ste. 400
Toledo, OH 43604-2622 (419) 252-6268
Contact: James C. Anderson, Secy.-Treas. and Exec. Dir.

Established in 1952 in OH.
Donors: George A. France†; The France Stone Co.; and subsidiaries.
Foundation type: Independent foundation.
Financial data (yr. ended 12/31/13): Assets, $12,057,426 (M); expenditures, $642,833; qualifying distributions, $531,505; giving activities include $521,604 for 40 grants (high: $45,104; low: $2,000).
Fields of interest: Health organizations, association; Human services; Children/youth, services.
Type of support: General/operating support; Continuing support; Annual campaigns; Scholarship funds; Research.
Limitations: Applications accepted. Giving primarily in Toledo, OH. No grants to individuals, or for operating budgets or special projects.
Application information: Application form required.
Initial approach: Letter
Copies of proposal: 1
Deadline(s): None
Officers and Trustees:* B. Gary McBride,* Pres.; James C. Anderson, Secy.-Treas. and Exec. Dir.; Ken Bishop; Stacy Hammer.
Number of staff: 1 part-time support.
EIN: 346523033
Selected grants: The following grants are a representative sample of this grantmaker's funding activity:
$15,000 to Legal Aid of Western Ohio, Toledo, OH, 2012. For high quality legal assistance in civil matters to help eligible low-income individuals and groups in western Ohio.
$11,209 to Toledo School for the Arts, Toledo, OH, 2012. For a college preparatory academic curriculum and intense visual and performing arts environment.
$10,000 to Aurora Project, Toledo, OH, 2012. For resources and learning opportunities in a supportive and safe environment to homeless women and their children.
$10,000 to Victory Center, Toledo, OH, 2012. For needed, free services and special Programs to cancer patients and their families.
$5,000 to Diabetes Youth Services, Maumee, OH, 2012. For Teaching local children to manage their diabetes until there is a cure and supporting families, preventing complications and improving lives.
$5,000 to Toledo Opera, Toledo, OH, 2012. To enhance the cultural fabric of the region by creating opera experiences.
$5,000 to Toledo-Lucas County CareNet, Toledo, OH, 2012. For access to coordinated healthcare services for low-income residents of Lucas County who do not have health insurance and do not qualify for government healthcare.
$3,000 to Ohio Foundation of Independent Colleges, Columbus, OH, 2012. For Promotes student diversity through recruitment and retention Programming and provides college readiness Programming for underserved populations with a focus on workforce development.

7463
Friedlander Family Fund ✧
600 Vine St., Ste. 2100
Cincinnati, OH 45202-2400
Contact: William A. Friedlander, Pres. and Dir.

Established in 1968 in OH.
Donors: William A. Friedlander; Susan S. Friedlander; Jane K. Steinfirst†; Ellen S. Friedlander.
Foundation type: Independent foundation.
Financial data (yr. ended 12/31/13): Assets, $5,436,350 (M); gifts received, $82,859; expenditures, $787,020; qualifying distributions, $773,875; giving activities include $773,875 for 166 grants (high: $300,000; low: $50).
Purpose and activities: Giving primarily for the arts, education, health, Jewish organizations, and human services.
Fields of interest: Arts; Education; Environment; Health care; Human services; Family services; Jewish federated giving programs.
Type of support: General/operating support.
Limitations: Applications accepted. Giving limited to the greater Cincinnati, OH, area. No grants to individuals.
Application information: Application form required.
Initial approach: 1-page letter
Copies of proposal: 1
Deadline(s): None
Board meeting date(s): Mar., June, Sept. and Dec.
Officers and Directors:* William A. Friedlander,* Pres.; Susan S. Friedlander,* V.P.; Melissa M. LaCorte,* Secy.-Treas.; Andrea Friedlander; David Friedlander; Ellen Friedlander; Lynne Friedlander.
Number of staff: 1 part-time support.
EIN: 316023791
Selected grants: The following grants are a representative sample of this grantmaker's funding activity:
$25,000 to Cincinnati Symphony and Pops Orchestra, Cincinnati, OH, 2011. For general fund.
$20,000 to Jewish Federation of Cincinnati, Cincinnati, OH, 2011. For general fund.
$12,500 to Ensemble Theater of Cincinnati, Cincinnati, OH, 2011. For general fund.
$10,000 to Cincinnati Art Museum, Cincinnati, OH, 2011. For general fund.
$5,000 to American Jewish Committee, New York, NY, 2011. For general fund.
$5,000 to Cincinnati Museum Center, Cincinnati, OH, 2011. For general fund.
$2,500 to American Friends Service Committee, Philadelphia, PA, 2011. For general fund.
$2,500 to International Rescue Committee, New York, NY, 2011. For general fund.
$2,000 to International Rescue Committee, New York, NY, 2011. For general fund.
$2,000 to W G U C-FM, Cincinnati, OH, 2011. For general fund.

7464
The Frost-Parker Foundation ✧ ☆
165 E. Washington Row
Sandusky, OH 44870-2610 (419) 625-8324
Contact: Melvyn J. Stauffer, Secy.

Established in 1986 in OH.
Donors: Ruth F. Parker; Ruth F. Parker Trust.
Foundation type: Independent foundation.
Financial data (yr. ended 04/30/13): Assets, $101,369 (M); gifts received, $382,000; expenditures, $444,819; qualifying distributions, $444,077; giving activities include $419,780 for 52 grants (high: $90,000; low: $400).
Purpose and activities: Giving primarily for higher education and the arts.
Fields of interest: Performing arts; Arts; Higher education; Education; Human services; Community/economic development.
Type of support: General/operating support; Capital campaigns; Building/renovation; Equipment; Scholarship funds.
Limitations: Giving primarily in northern OH, with emphasis on Sandusky. No grants to individuals.
Application information: Application form not required.
Deadline(s): None
Officers and Trustees:* Ruth F. Parker,* Pres. and Treas.; Mary Jane S. Hill,* V.P.; Melvyn J. Stauffer,* Secy.
EIN: 341515319
Selected grants: The following grants are a representative sample of this grantmaker's funding activity:
$7,500 to Merry-Go-Round Museum, Sandusky, OH, 2011.

7465
GAR Foundation ✧
c/o Andrew Jackson House
277 E. Mill St.
Akron, OH 44308-1735 (330) 576-2926
Contact: Christine Amer Mayer, Pres.
FAX: (330) 330-437-2843; E-mail: info@garfdn.org; E-mail for Christine Amer Mayer: cmayer@garfdn.org; Main URL: http://www.garfoundation.org
Facebook: http://www.facebook.com/GARFoundation
Flickr: http://www.flickr.com/photos/60471463@N08
Grants Database: http://www.garfdn.org/awarded-grant-archive
LinkedIn: http://www.linkedin.com/company/gar-foundation
Pinterest: http://pinterest.com/garfoundation/
Twitter: http://twitter.com/garfoundation
YouTube: http://www.youtube.com/garfoundation

Trust established in 1967 in OH.
Donors: Ruth C. Roush†; Galen Roush†.
Foundation type: Independent foundation.
Financial data (yr. ended 12/31/12): Assets, $136,333,904 (M); expenditures, $9,412,774; qualifying distributions, $8,509,211; giving activities include $6,039,541 for 210 grants (high: $216,000; low: $50).
Purpose and activities: Grants for education, arts and arts education, health and social services, civic enhancement, and for nonprofit enhancement.
Fields of interest: Arts; Education, early childhood education; Secondary school/education; Higher education; Human services; Youth, services; Economics; Infants/toddlers; Children/youth; Children; Youth; Adults; Aging; Young adults; Minorities; Asians/Pacific Islanders; African Americans/Blacks; Hispanics/Latinos; Women; Young adults, female; Boys; Young adults, male; Crime/abuse victims; Immigrants/refugees; Economically disadvantaged; Homeless.
Type of support: Annual campaigns; Building/renovation; Continuing support; Curriculum development; Debt reduction; Employee matching gifts; Endowments; Equipment; General/operating support; Land acquisition; Management development/capacity building; Matching/challenge support; Program development; Scholarship funds; Seed money.
Limitations: Applications accepted. Giving primarily in the Akron-Summit County area and secondarily in Cuyahoga, Stark, Medina, Portage and Wayne counties, OH. No support for private non-operating foundations, health care institutions (except for collaborative efforts designed to reduce costs and promote efficient delivery of services), or national organizations. No grants to individuals, or for medical research, capital funding for churches or synagogues, or computers for schools.
Publications: Application guidelines; Newsletter.
Application information: If you are a past grantee and your current request is for the same purpose as previously awarded, complete a full online application. Paper applications not accepted. Application form required.
Initial approach: Online letter of inquiry
Copies of proposal: 1
Deadline(s): See foundation web site for current deadlines
Board meeting date(s): Feb., May, Aug., and Nov.
Officers and Trustees:* Christine Amer Mayer, Pres.; Kirstin S. Toth, Sr. V.P.; Douglas A. Wilson; PNC Bank N.A.
Number of staff: 5 full-time professional.
EIN: 346577710
Selected grants: The following grants are a representative sample of this grantmaker's funding activity:
$650,000 to Akron Public Schools, Akron, OH, 2012. For challenge grant.
$575,500 to United Way of Summit County, Akron, OH, 2010. For Northeast Ohio United Way Reg Task Force Plan.
$500,000 to Fund for Our Economic Future, Cleveland, OH, 2010. For Phase Three of the Project.
$308,000 to Akron Public Schools, Akron, OH, 2010.
$300,000 to Stan Hywet Hall and Gardens, Akron, OH, 2010. For general support.
$299,841 to Educator Initiative Grants Program, Summit County, OH, 2012. For teacher initiated classroom-based projects.
$150,000 to Akron Public Schools, Akron, OH, 2012. For STEM High School.
$120,000 to Greenleaf Family Center, Akron, OH, 2012. For SPARK (kindergarten readiness program).
$110,000 to Akron Art Museum, Akron, OH, 2012. For operating support.
$100,000 to Salvation Army of Summit County, Akron, OH, 2010. For Learning Zone Program.
$70,000 to Akron Community Foundation, Akron, OH, 2010. For Chenoweth Endowment Funds.
$70,000 to Akron Public Schools, Akron, OH, 2012. For Great Leaders Program.
$40,000 to All-American Soap Box Derby, Akron, OH, 2012. For operations and curriculum development.
$35,000 to Info Line, Akron, OH, 2010. For Project Connect Operations.
$25,000 to Service Corps of Retired Executives Association, SCORE Chapter 18, Akron, OH, 2010. For Marketing and Administrative Support.
$17,000 to Childrens Concert Society of Akron, E. J. Thomas Performing Arts Hall, Akron, OH, 2010. For Concert Hall Series and Outreach Program.
$17,000 to Educational Service Center of Cuyahoga County, Valley View, OH, 2012. For Learning Leaders of Summit County: A Principals' Academy II.
$10,000 to International Institute, Akron, OH, 2010. For Educational Programming.

7466
The James J. and Joan A. Gardner Family Foundation ✧
(formerly Gardner Family Foundation)
6847 Cintas Blvd., Ste. 120
Mason, OH 45040-9152 (513) 459-1085

Established in 1994 in OH.
Donors: Joan A. Gardner; Margaret M. Johns; Linda G. Mueller; Lorraine G. Sommer; Spencer J. Gardner; Patricia F. Gardner; James J. Gardner; Gardner Family 2000 Charitable Trust; Gardner 1992 Charitable Trust.
Foundation type: Independent foundation.
Financial data (yr. ended 12/31/13): Assets, $74,514,777 (M); gifts received, $151,128; expenditures, $2,918,445; qualifying distributions, $2,726,499; giving activities include $2,700,000 for 40 grants (high: $742,000; low: $1,000).
Purpose and activities: Giving primarily for education, including higher, Christian and Roman Catholic churches and organizations, social services, and health organizations.
Fields of interest: Higher education; Education; Health organizations; Human services; Civil liberties, right to life; Christian agencies & churches; Catholic agencies & churches.
Limitations: Applications accepted. Giving primarily in Cincinnati, OH; some funding also in FL.
Application information: Application form required.
Initial approach: Letter
Deadline(s): None
Officers and Trustees:* Gary D. Johns,* Chair.; Lorraine G. Sommer,* Vice-Chair.; James J. Gardner,* Pres.; Joan A. Gardner,* V.P.; Margaret M. Jones,* Secy.; Linda G. Mueller,* Treas.; Spencer J. Gardner; Blaire A. Johns; Kyle J. Jones; Adam T. Mueller; Eric G. Mueller; Jonathan J. Mueller; Laura K. Mueller; Thomas J. Mueller.
EIN: 311397164

7467
The Erwin & Katherine Geis Charitable Foundation ✧ ☆
10020 Aurora Hudson Rd.
Streetsboro, OH 44241-1621

Established in 2001 in OH.
Donors: Katherine Geis; Gregory Geis; Geis Construction, Inc.; Alfred Geis; Walter and Haverfield, LLP.
Foundation type: Independent foundation.
Financial data (yr. ended 12/31/13): Assets, $31,655 (M); gifts received, $1,320,485; expenditures, $1,759,811; qualifying distributions, $1,751,198; giving activities include $1,749,514 for 13 grants (high: $1,709,829; low: $75).
Fields of interest: Education; Human services; Community/economic development; Foundations (community).
Limitations: Applications not accepted. Giving primarily in Akron and Cleveland, OH. No grants to individuals.
Application information: Unsolicited requests for funds not accepted.
Trustees: Alfred Geis; Jeff Martin; James Mirgliotta.
EIN: 912127296

7468
John F. and Mary A. Geisse Foundation ✧
(formerly The Geisse Foundation)
38050 Jackson Rd.
Chagrin Falls, OH 44022-2025
Contact: Timothy F. Geisse, Exec. Dir. and Tr.

Established in 1969 in MO.
Donors: John F. Geisse†; Mary A. Geisse†.
Foundation type: Independent foundation.
Financial data (yr. ended 12/31/13): Assets, $11,274,469 (M); expenditures, $788,451; qualifying distributions, $717,184; giving activities include $659,586 for 46 grants (high: $150,000; low: $50).
Purpose and activities: Giving for economic development in the developing world, rural development, and water development.
Fields of interest: International development; Economically disadvantaged.
International interests: Central America; Developing Countries.
Type of support: General/operating support; Continuing support; Annual campaigns; Equipment;

Program-related investments/loans; Matching/challenge support.
Limitations: Applications accepted. Giving to U.S. organizations that work internationally, in the developing world. No support for purely religious or environmental protection purposes, or for arts and culture. No grants or scholarships to individuals.
Publications: Informational brochure; Informational brochure (including application guidelines).
Application information: Application form required.
Initial approach: 1-2-page letter
Copies of proposal: 1
Deadline(s): None
Board meeting date(s): As needed
Officer and Trustees:* Timothy F. Geisse,* Exec. Dir.; Lawrence J. Geisse, M.D.
Number of staff: 1 full-time professional.
EIN: 237049780

7469
Frank & Pearl E. Gelbman Charitable Trust ✧
P.O. Box 1558, Dept. EA4E86
Columbus, OH 43216-1558

Established in 2005 in OH.
Donors: Gelbman Charitable Trust; Frank Gelbman Trust; Pearl Gelbman Trust.
Foundation type: Independent foundation.
Financial data (yr. ended 12/31/13): Assets, $10,119,320 (M); expenditures, $508,193; qualifying distributions, $465,649; giving activities include $430,143 for 33 grants (high: $115,000; low: $193).
Fields of interest: Historic preservation/historical societies; Arts; Higher education; Human services; United Ways and Federated Giving Programs.
Limitations: Applications not accepted. Giving primarily in Youngstown, OH.
Application information: Contributes only to pre-selected organizations.
Trustee: Huntington National Bank.
EIN: 206609204

7470
The Generation Trust ✧
c/o Fifth Third Bank
P.O. Box 1868
Toledo, OH 43603-1868 (419) 259-6880
Contact: Marsha A. Manahan

Established in 1985 in OH.
Donors: John D. Beckett; Carolyn J. Beckett; Catherine E. Beckett; Joel D. Beckett; Jonathan M. Beckett; Jeffrey Coors; Liz Coors; The R.W. Beckett Corp.; Beckett Air, Inc.; Beckett Family; K. Carter; M. Carter.
Foundation type: Independent foundation.
Financial data (yr. ended 12/31/13): Assets, $30,730,352 (M); gifts received, $1,760,300; expenditures, $3,092,071; qualifying distributions, $2,981,582; giving activities include $2,965,000 for 50 grants (high: $150,000; low: $4,000).
Purpose and activities: Support limited to organizations with a Christian purpose, including churches and ministries.
Fields of interest: Christian agencies & churches.
Type of support: Emergency funds; Program development; Seed money; Technical assistance.
Limitations: Applications accepted. Giving primarily in CA, CO, FL, MS, NC, NY, and VA. No grants to individuals.
Application information:
Initial approach: Letter
Copies of proposal: 1
Deadline(s): None
Trustees: John D. Beckett; Fifth Third Bank.
EIN: 346850815
Selected grants: The following grants are a representative sample of this grantmaker's funding activity:
$200,000 to Campus Crusade for Christ, 2011.
$60,000 to Derek Prince Ministries, Charlotte, NC, 2011.
$55,000 to EndPoverty.org, Bethesda, MD, 2011.
$50,000 to Campus Crusade for Christ, 2011.
$50,000 to Intercessors for America, Purcellville, VA, 2011.
$20,000 to Campus Crusade for Christ, 2011.
$20,000 to Care Net, Lansdowne, VA, 2011.
$20,000 to Charles Simpson Ministries, Mobile, AL, 2011.
$20,000 to Persecution Project Foundation, Culpeper, VA, 2011.
$20,000 to Young Life North Coast, Seaside, OR, 2011.

7471
Gerlach Foundation, Inc. ✧
37 W. Broad St., 5th Fl.
Columbus, OH 43215-4132 (614) 224-7141

Incorporated in 1953 in OH.
Donors: Pauline Gerlach†; John J. Gerlach; John B. Gerlach.
Foundation type: Independent foundation.
Financial data (yr. ended 11/30/13): Assets, $46,675,418 (M); expenditures, $1,619,540; qualifying distributions, $1,521,170; giving activities include $1,515,000 for 3 grants (high: $1,500,000; low: $5,000).
Fields of interest: Arts; Higher education; Hospitals (specialty); Health care; Human services; Foundations (private grantmaking).
Type of support: General/operating support.
Limitations: Applications not accepted. Giving primarily in Columbus, OH. No grants to individuals.
Application information: Contributes only to pre-selected organizations.
Officers: Susan Douglass, V.P.; David P. Gerlach, V.P.; John B. Gerlach, Jr., Treas.
EIN: 316023912

7472
The Goatie Foundation ✧
c/o KeyBank N.A.
4900 Tiedman Rd., OH-01-49-050
Brooklyn, OH 44144-2302 (216) 689-5834
Contact: Michael Sim
Application address: Keybank, N.A., 127 Public Sq., Cleveland, OH 44113; tel.: (216) 689-5834

Established in 2001 in OH.
Donors: Louise Gund; Women's Project Foundation.
Foundation type: Independent foundation.
Financial data (yr. ended 12/31/12): Assets, $36,587 (M); gifts received, $3,227,500; expenditures, $3,850,501; qualifying distributions, $3,847,500; giving activities include $3,847,500 for 26 grants (high: $1,000,000; low: $5,000).
Purpose and activities: Giving primarily for educational purposes including, but not limited to, the welfare of children, women, and families, the expansion of opportunities for women, and the elimination of prejudice and discrimination against women.
Fields of interest: Environment; Animals/wildlife; Human services; Women.
Limitations: Applications accepted. Giving primarily in CA, NJ and NY, with some giving in MD.
Application information: Application form required.
Initial approach: Proposal
Deadline(s): None
Trustee: KeyBank, N.A.
EIN: 347158309
Selected grants: The following grants are a representative sample of this grantmaker's funding activity:
$1,000,000 to San Francisco Opera Association, San Francisco, CA, 2012. For general support.
$420,000 to CAL Performances, Berkeley, CA, 2012. For general support and matching grant.
$300,000 to Metropolitan Opera, New York, NY, 2012. For challenge grant.
$250,000 to Metropolitan Opera, New York, NY, 2012. For general operating support.
$200,000 to Philharmonia Baroque Orchestra, San Francisco, CA, 2012. For endowment.
$150,000 to K Q E D, San Francisco, CA, 2012. For general operating support.
$140,000 to Cleveland Play House, Cleveland, OH, 2012. For arts and education programs.
$125,000 to International Center of Photography, New York, NY, 2012. For general operating support.
$75,000 to Brooklyn Academy of Music, Brooklyn, NY, 2012. For annual fund.

7473
The Roe Green Foundation ✧
1301 E. 9th St., Ste. 1900
Cleveland, OH 44114-1862

Established in 1999 in OH.
Donors: Roe Green; Sylvia E. Green Charitable Lead Trust.
Foundation type: Independent foundation.
Financial data (yr. ended 12/31/13): Assets, $2,164,643 (M); gifts received, $1,573,827; expenditures, $2,576,298; qualifying distributions, $2,509,516; giving activities include $2,434,509 for 24 grants (high: $500,000; low: $1,000).
Fields of interest: Performing arts, theater; Human services.
Limitations: Applications not accepted. Giving primarily in OH; funding also in CO and FL. No grants to individuals.
Application information: Contributes only to pre-selected organizations.
Trustees: Eugene A. Kratus; Roe Green.
EIN: 341886405
Selected grants: The following grants are a representative sample of this grantmaker's funding activity:
$20,000 to Chautauqua Institution, Chautauqua, NY, 2012. For New Play Workshop.
$15,000 to Palm Beach County Cultural Council, Lake Worth, FL, 2012. For Building for Our Future Campaign.
$10,000 to Palm Beach County Cultural Council, Lake Worth, FL, 2012. For annual sponsorship.

7474
Greene County Community Foundation ✧
(doing business as Greene Giving)
941 W. 2nd. St.
Xenia, OH 45385 (937) 458-2064
Contact: Edward Marrinan, Exec. Dir.
FAX: (937) 458-2063;
E-mail: friend@greenegiving.org; Main URL: http://www.greenegiving.org

Established in 2001 in OH.
Foundation type: Community foundation.
Financial data (yr. ended 12/31/12): Assets, $8,757,185 (M); gifts received, $1,952,527; expenditures, $1,541,058; giving activities include $960,571 for 8+ grants (high: $29,500), and $401,475 for grants to individuals.
Purpose and activities: The foundation seeks to promote philanthropy and provide stewardship and leadership to enhance the use of regional resources to meet charitable needs.
Fields of interest: Arts; Education, public education; Health care; Agriculture; Recreation; Family services; Aging, centers/services; Community development, neighborhood development; Economic development.
Type of support: Building/renovation; Equipment; Scholarship funds.
Limitations: Applications accepted. Giving limited to Greene County, OH.
Publications: Informational brochure.
Application information: Application form required.
Initial approach: Letter, telephone, or e-mail
Copies of proposal: 1
Board meeting date(s): Bi-monthly
Officers and Directors:* Mark Schutter,* Pres.; Anne Gerard,* Secy.; Greg Devilbiss,* Treas.; Robert Baird; David Bartlett; Chuck Bechtel; Phil Cunningham; Michael Cusak; John Dautel; Paul Dillaplain; Jack Gayheart; Mark Guess; Joe Harkleroad; Jamie Hensley; Don Hollister; Gussie Jones; Shannon Martin; Herman N. Menapace; Paul Newman; Jane Newton; Shaun Nicholson; Mary Nutter; Fran O'Shaughnessy; Matt Pauley; Jerry Pfeifer; Dennis Phillips.
EIN: 311751001

7475
Gordon & Llura Gund 1993 Charitable Foundation ✧
25201 Chagrin Blvd., No. 370
Beachwood, OH 44122-5637

Established in 1993 in OH.
Donors: Gordon and Llura Liggett Gund Trust; Gordon and Llura Liggett Gund Charitable Lead Trust 3; Gordon and Llura Liggett Gund Charitable Lead Trust 5; Gordon and Llura Liggett Gund Charitable Lead Trust 6; Gordon and Llura Liggett Gund Charitable Lead Trust 7; Gordon and Llura Liggett Gund Charitable Lead Trust 8.
Foundation type: Independent foundation.
Financial data (yr. ended 12/31/13): Assets, $895,060 (M); gifts received, $2,481,291; expenditures, $3,820,200; giving activities include $3,750,000 for 8 grants (high: $2,000,000; low: $50,000).
Purpose and activities: Giving primarily to an art museum, as well as for health care.
Fields of interest: Museums (art); Higher education; Health care; Blind/visually impaired.
Limitations: Applications not accepted. Giving primarily in PA; some giving in MD and NJ. No grants to individuals.
Application information: Contributes only to pre-selected organizations.
Trustees: Theodore W. Baker; Rebecca H. Dent; Grant Gund; G. Zachary Gund.
EIN: 341730494

7476
The Agnes Gund Foundation ✧
c/o Agnes Gund
517 Broadway, 3rd Fl.
East Liverpool, OH 43920-3167 (330) 385-3400

Established in 1988 in OH.
Donors: Agnes Gund; The Domani Trust.
Foundation type: Independent foundation.
Financial data (yr. ended 12/31/13): Assets, $87,353 (M); gifts received, $4,953,881; expenditures, $7,164,422; qualifying distributions, $7,164,124; giving activities include $7,026,226 for 300 grants (high: $400,000; low: $500).
Purpose and activities: Support primarily for the arts and higher education.
Fields of interest: Museums; Performing arts, dance; Performing arts, music; Arts; Higher education; Health care; Health organizations, association.
Type of support: General/operating support.
Limitations: Applications not accepted. Giving primarily in New York, NY. No grants to individuals.
Application information: Contributes only to pre-selected organizations.
Trustees: Agnes Gund; Catherine Gund; Anna L. Traggio.
EIN: 341606084
Selected grants: The following grants are a representative sample of this grantmaker's funding activity:
$457,614 to Association of Art Museum Curators Foundation, Center for Curatorial Leadership, New York, NY, 2012. For general support.
$289,853 to Studio in a School Association, Studio in a School, New York, NY, 2012. For general support.
$162,681 to P.S. 1 Contemporary Art Center, Long Island City, NY, 2012. For general support.
$157,000 to Frick Collection, New York, NY, 2012. For general support.
$150,000 to Museum of Chinese in the Americas, New York, NY, 2012. For general support.
$150,000 to Museum of Modern Art, Department of Painting and Sculpture, New York, NY, 2012. For general support.
$119,620 to Museum of Modern Art, New York, NY, 2012. For general support for awards and events.
$107,600 to Museum of Contemporary Art Cleveland, MOCA Cleveland, Cleveland, OH, 2012. For general support.
$102,750 to Drawing Center, New York, NY, 2012. For general support.
$30,000 to Force Film Foundation, New York, NY, 2012. For general support.

7477
Geoffrey Gund Foundation ✧
c/o KeyBank N.A.
4900 Tiedeman Rd., OH01
Brooklyn, OH 44144-2338
Application address: c/o Geoffrey Gund, 40 E. 94th St., Apt. 28E, New York, NY 10128-0740

Established in 1987 in DC.
Donor: Geoffrey Gund.
Foundation type: Independent foundation.
Financial data (yr. ended 06/30/13): Assets, $38,293,711 (M); gifts received, $2,000,000; expenditures, $1,560,899; qualifying distributions, $1,342,815; giving activities include $1,342,815 for grants.
Purpose and activities: Giving primarily for the arts, including a museum, and education; funding also for social services.
Fields of interest: Museums (art); Arts; Elementary/secondary education; Higher education; Education; Hospitals (general); Human services; Foundations (public); Philanthropy/voluntarism.
Type of support: General/operating support; Annual campaigns; Endowments; Scholarship funds.
Limitations: Giving primarily in the Bronx and New York, NY; some funding also in MA. No grants to individuals.
Application information: Application form not required.
Initial approach: Letter
Deadline(s): None
Trustees: Geoffrey Gund; Donald Kozuskp; James O'Hara; KeyBank N.A.
EIN: 521509128
Selected grants: The following grants are a representative sample of this grantmaker's funding activity:
$180,000 to Sarah Lawrence College, Bronxville, NY, 2013. For 2013 contribution.
$80,000 to Swarthmore College, Swarthmore, PA, 2013. For 2013 Contribution - Arabic Lang Program.
$60,000 to Swarthmore College, Swarthmore, PA, 2013. For Final Pledged Payment for Parents Fund.
$50,000 to Child Mind Institute, New York, NY, 2013. For Annual Child Advocacy Benefit Contribution.
$30,000 to Cleveland Orchestra, Cleveland, OH, 2013. For 2013 annual campaign.
$25,000 to Wave Hill, Bronx, NY, 2013. For 2013 Spring Garden Gala.
$20,000 to Kingsbridge Heights Community Center, Bronx, NY, 2013. For 2013 contribution - Bernice Stern Community Services.
$5,000 to Riverdale Neighborhood House, Bronx, NY, 2013. For Benefactor Annual Benefit Contribution.
$4,400 to THIRTEEN, New York, NY, 2013. For 50th Anniversary Gala Salute 11/15/12 Contribution.
$2,500 to Wave Hill, Bronx, NY, 2013. For 2013 Benefit - Gardener's Party.

7478
The George Gund Foundation ✧
1845 Guildhall Bldg.
45 Prospect Ave. W.
Cleveland, OH 44115-1018 (216) 241-3114
Contact: David T. Abbott, Exec. Dir.; For Fellowships:: Robert B. Jaquay, Assoc. Dir.
FAX: (216) 241-6560; E-mail: info@gundfdn.org; Main URL: http://gundfoundation.org
CEP Study: http://gundfoundation.org/forms-resources/2010-grantee-perception-report/

E-Newsletter: http://www.gundfoundation.org/contact-us/join-our-email-list
Grants Database: http://gundfoundation.org/grants-awarded/search-grants-archives/

Incorporated in 1952 in OH.
Donor: George Gund†.
Foundation type: Independent foundation.
Financial data (yr. ended 12/31/13): Assets, $530,341,218 (M); expenditures, $30,695,188; qualifying distributions, $25,474,238; giving activities include $22,425,190 for 315 grants (high: $2,000,000; low: $2,000), and $500,051 for 2 loans/program-related investments (high: $500,000; low: $51).
Purpose and activities: Priority to education projects, with emphasis on new concepts and methods of teaching and learning, and on increasing educational opportunities for the disadvantaged; programs advancing economic revitalization and job creation; projects promoting neighborhood development; projects for improving human services, employment opportunities, housing for minority and low-income groups; support also for ecology, civic affairs, and the arts. Preference is given to pilot projects and innovative programs which present prospects for broad replication.
Fields of interest: Arts; Education, research; Education, early childhood education; Elementary school/education; Secondary school/education; Higher education; Education; Environment, natural resources; Environment; AIDS; AIDS research; Crime/law enforcement; Employment; Housing/shelter, development; Human services; Children/youth, services; Women, centers/services; Minorities/immigrants, centers/services; Civil rights, race/intergroup relations; Urban/community development; Community/economic development; Government/public administration; Public affairs; Minorities; Women; Economically disadvantaged.
Type of support: General/operating support; Continuing support; Land acquisition; Emergency funds; Program development; Conferences/seminars; Publication; Seed money; Internship funds; Scholarship funds; Research; Technical assistance; Program-related investments/loans; Matching/challenge support; Mission-related investments/loans.
Limitations: Applications accepted. Giving primarily in northeastern OH and the greater Cleveland, OH, area. No support for political groups, services for the physically, mentally or developmentally disabled, or the elderly. Generally, no grants to individuals, or for building or endowment funds, political campaigns, debt reduction, equipment, renovation projects, or to fund benefit events. No capital grants to projects that have not adopted green building principles.
Publications: Grants list; Newsletter; Quarterly report.
Application information: The foundation has moved to an online proposal process. Mailed grant requests will not be considered. Application form required.
Initial approach: Following review of eligibility on foundation web site, complete online application process
Copies of proposal: 1
Deadline(s): Mar. 15, July 15 and Nov. 15
Board meeting date(s): Feb., July and Nov.
Final notification: Generally three months
Officers and Trustees:* Geoffrey Gund,* Pres. and Treas.; Ann L. Gund,* V.P.; Catherine Gund, Secy.; David T. Abbott, Exec. Dir.; George Gund IV; Zachary Gund; Randell McShepard; Robyn Minter Smyers; Anna Traggio.
Number of staff: 8 full-time professional; 4 full-time support.
EIN: 346519769

7479
H.C.S. Foundation ✧
1801 E. 9th St., Ste. 1105
Cleveland, OH 44114-3103 (216) 781-3502
Contact: L. Thomas Hiltz, Tr.

Trust established in 1959 in OH.
Donor: Harold C. Schott†.
Foundation type: Independent foundation.
Financial data (yr. ended 12/31/13): Assets, $119,426,547 (M); expenditures, $5,504,295; qualifying distributions, $5,291,512; giving activities include $4,382,545 for 45 grants (high: $400,000; low: $10,000).
Purpose and activities: Grants primarily for health care, education, the arts, and the United Way.
Fields of interest: Arts; Education; Health care; Human services; United Ways and Federated Giving Programs; Catholic agencies & churches.
Type of support: General/operating support; Capital campaigns; Building/renovation; Endowments; Program development; Scholarship funds.
Limitations: Applications accepted. Giving limited to OH. No grants to individuals.
Application information: Application form not required.
Initial approach: Letter
Copies of proposal: 1
Deadline(s): Sept. 1
Board meeting date(s): Annually
Final notification: Dec.
Trustees: Francie S. Hiltz; L. Thomas Hiltz; Betty Jane Mulcahy; Elizabeth S. Saal; Milton B. Schott, Jr.
Number of staff: 1 full-time professional.
EIN: 346514235

7480
Carol & Ralph Haile, Jr./U.S. Bank Foundation ✧
(formerly Carol & Ralph Haile, Jr. Foundation)
c/o U.S. Bank, N.A.
425 Walnut St., CN-OH-W11F
Cincinnati, OH 45202-3956
E-mail: chad.mccarter@haileusb.org; Main URL: http://www.haileusb.org

Established in 2003 in OH.
Donors: Ralph V. Haile; Ralph V. Haile Trust.
Foundation type: Independent foundation.
Financial data (yr. ended 12/31/12): Assets, $229,104,157 (M); expenditures, $13,669,608; qualifying distributions, $12,253,011; giving activities include $10,842,887 for 199 grants (high: $3,000,000; low: $500).
Purpose and activities: Giving primarily for arts and culture, community development, education, and human services.
Fields of interest: Performing arts; Higher education; Education; Health organizations; Cancer research; Human services; YM/YWCAs & YM/YWHAs; Community/economic development; Foundations (community); United Ways and Federated Giving Programs.
Limitations: Applications not accepted. Giving primarily in the Greater Cincinnati, OH, area, including Dearborn and Franklin in IN, and Boone, Campbell and Kenton in KY. No grants to individuals.
Application information: Contributes only to pre-selected organizations.
Officers: Timothy Maloney, C.E.O. and Pres.; Leslie Maloney, Sr. V.P., Prog. Mgr., Education; Eric Avner, V.P. and Sr. Prog. Mgr., Community Devel.; Christine A. Bochenek, V.P., Admin. and Sr. Prog. Mgr.; Jake Hodesh, V.P., Opers.
Trustee: U.S. Bank, N.A.
EIN: 542135984
Selected grants: The following grants are a representative sample of this grantmaker's funding activity:
$3,000,000 to Northern Kentucky University, Highland Heights, KY, 2012. For Unrestricted Support.
$300,000 to Greater Cincinnati Foundation, Cincinnati, OH, 2012. For Unrestricted Support.
$250,000 to Cincinnati Center City Development, Cincinnati, OH, 2012. For Unrestricted Support.
$250,000 to Cincinnati Museum Association, Cincinnati, OH, 2012. For Unrestricted Support.
$250,000 to Cincinnati Playhouse in the Park, Cincinnati, OH, 2012. For Unrestricted Support.
$165,000 to KnowledgeWorks Foundation, Cincinnati, OH, 2012. For Unrestricted Support.
$30,360 to Northern Kentucky University, Highland Heights, KY, 2012. For Unrestricted Support.
$25,000 to Hillforest Historical Foundation, Aurora, IN, 2012. For Unrestricted Support.
$25,000 to Kentucky Philanthropy Initiative, Georgetown, KY, 2012. For Unrestricted Support.
$25,000 to Venture for America, New York, NY, 2012. For Unrestricted Support.

7481
The Hamilton Community Foundation, Inc. ✧
319 N. 3rd St.
Hamilton, OH 45011-1624 (513) 863-1717
Contact: John J. Guidugli, C.E.O.
FAX: (513) 863-2868;
E-mail: info@hamiltonfoundation.org; Main URL: http://www.hamiltonfoundation.org
Facebook: http://www.facebook.com/pages/Hamilton-Community-Foundation-OH/119062244714
YouTube: http://www.youtube.com/user/HamiltonFoundation?feature=mhee

Incorporated in 1951 in OH.
Foundation type: Community foundation.
Financial data (yr. ended 12/31/12): Assets, $76,188,512 (M); gifts received, $5,472,589; expenditures, $7,776,126; giving activities include $5,006,428 for 65+ grants (high: $800,000), and $515,883 for 329 grants to individuals.
Purpose and activities: Entrusted with the responsibility to improve quality of life, the foundation has a four-part mission: 1) to serve as a leader, catalyst, and resource for philanthropy; 2) to build and permanently hold a growing endowment for the community's changing needs and opportunities; 3) to strive for excellence through strategic grant-making in such fields as the arts, education, housing, social services, civic beautification, community development, and recreation; and 4) to provide a flexible and cost-effective way for donors to improve their community now and in the future.

Fields of interest: Arts; Elementary school/education; Education; Environment, beautification programs; Health care; Substance abuse, services; Health organizations, association; Alcoholism; Housing/shelter, development; Recreation; Children/youth, services; Human services; Community/economic development.
Type of support: Emergency funds; Program development; Conferences/seminars; Seed money; Scholarship funds; Program-related investments/loans.
Limitations: Applications accepted. Giving limited to Butler County, OH. No support for individual religious organizations, including churches and parochial schools. No grants to individuals (except for scholarships), or for operating budgets, continuing support, annual campaigns, deficit financing, capital or endowment funds, matching gifts, research, demonstration projects, equipment, or publications; no loans (except for program-related investments).
Publications: Application guidelines; Annual report; Informational brochure (including application guidelines); Newsletter.
Application information: Visit foundation web site for application form and guidelines. Application form not required.
Initial approach: Telephone
Copies of proposal: 12
Deadline(s): Jan. 1, Mar. 1, May 1, Sept. 1, and Nov. 1 for general grantmaking program; May 1 for capital grants; varies for scholarships
Board meeting date(s): Feb., Apr., June, Oct., and Dec.
Final notification: Immediately following each Board meeting for general grantmaking program; Following June Board meeting for capital grants
Officers and Trustees:* Kathleen Klink,* Chair.; Herman R. Sanders,* Vice-Chair.; John J. Guidugli,* C.E.O. and Pres.; Katie E. Braswell,* V.P.; Betsy Hope,* V.P., Comms.; Daniel J. Sander,* V.P., Finance; Craig Wilks,* Secy.; Heather Lewis,* Treas.; Lee H. Parrish, Legal Counsel; David L. Belew, Tr. Emeritus; Sara P. Carruthers; Michael P. Dingeldein; James K. Fitton; Scott Hartford; Butch Hubble; John Kirsch; Cynthia V. Parrish; Thomas Rentschler, Jr.; Steve Timmer.
Trustee Banks: First Financial Bank; U.S. Bank, N.A.
Number of staff: 2 full-time professional; 2 part-time professional; 2 full-time support; 1 part-time support.
EIN: 316038277
Selected grants: The following grants are a representative sample of this grantmaker's funding activity:
$600,000 to Center for the Performing Arts, Greenville, SC, 2012. For capital grant for renovation of center.
$400,000 to Fort Hamilton Healthcare Foundation, Hamilton, OH, 2012.
$240,000 to Christ Church of Glendale, Cincinnati, OH, 2012.
$216,490 to Butler, County of, Board of Commissioners, Hamilton, OH, 2012. For construction/bike path.
$200,000 to Miami University Foundation, Oxford, OH, 2012.
$132,507 to Butler, County of, Board of Commissioners, Hamilton, OH, 2012. For phase 1 - Great Miami River Recreation Trail.
$7,500 to Water for People, Denver, CO, 2012. For Race for Global Water Benefitting Water for People.
$5,000 to Fitton Center for Creative Arts, Hamilton, OH, 2012. For Mad Anthony Theatre/Sara Carruthers Solicitor.
$4,260 to First Baptist Church, 2012.
$2,000 to Miami University, Oxford, OH, 2012. For scholarship.

7482
Sandra L. and Dennis B. Haslinger Family Foundation, Inc. ✧
2524 Ira Rd.
Akron, OH 44333-1910 (330) 761-1040
Contact: Sandra L. Haslinger, Pres.
E-mail: lseikel@seikel.com; Application address: 686 W. Market St., Akron, OH 44303,

Established in 1997 in OH.
Donor: Sandra L. Haslinger.
Foundation type: Independent foundation.
Financial data (yr. ended 12/31/12): Assets, $5,682,199 (M); expenditures, $473,620; qualifying distributions, $438,000; giving activities include $438,000 for 15 grants (high: $202,500; low: $5,000).
Purpose and activities: Giving primarily for education, hospitals, human services and the arts.
Fields of interest: Museums (art); Education; Hospitals (specialty); Human services; Community/economic development.
Type of support: General/operating support; Building/renovation; Equipment; Endowments; Program development; Scholarship funds.
Limitations: Applications accepted. Giving primarily in Akron, OH.
Application information: Application form required.
Initial approach: Letter
Deadline(s): Aug. 1
Officers and Trustees:* Sandra L. Haslinger, Pres.; Douglas S. Haslinger,* Secy.; Jennifer S. Haslinger,* Treas.; Benjamin G. Haslinger; Kimberly M. Haslinger; Melissa A. Haslinger; Myriam Eve Haslinger.
EIN: 341848698

7483
Hatton Foundation ✧
(formerly E. Kenneth & Esther Marie Hatton Foundation)
1776 Mentor Ave., Ste. 260
Cincinnati, OH 45212-3661 (513) 351-1945
Contact: Susan Ingmire

Established in 1997 in OH.
Donors: Esther Marie Hatton†; Kenneth Hatton†.
Foundation type: Independent foundation.
Financial data (yr. ended 12/31/13): Assets, $28,614,551 (M); expenditures, $1,655,803; qualifying distributions, $1,313,550; giving activities include $1,280,453 for 49 grants (high: $150,000; low: $1,000).
Purpose and activities: The focus of the foundation is on medical organizations, youth, disabled persons, as well as research in families with disabled children, and mentoring programs.
Fields of interest: Hospitals (general); Health organizations, association; Human services; Homeless, human services; Children/youth; Youth; Disabilities, people with; Physically disabled; Military/veterans; Homeless.
Type of support: General/operating support; Building/renovation; Program development; Conferences/seminars; Research.
Limitations: Giving primarily in northern KY, and southeast OH. No grants to individuals.
Application information: Application form not required.
Board meeting date(s): Jan., March, May, July, Sept., Nov. and Dec.
Officers: Steve Scherzinger, Pres.; Jeffrey Holtmeier, V.P.; Robert Robinson, Secy.; Margaret Lunsford, Treas.; Walter Lunsford, Exec. Dir.
Trustee: Kim Beach.
EIN: 311533046
Selected grants: The following grants are a representative sample of this grantmaker's funding activity:
$80,000 to Healthy Beginnings, Cincinnati, OH, 2012. For Centering Program Support and Mortgage Assistance.
$56,368 to Good Samaritan Hospital Foundation, Cincinnati, OH, 2012. For Harp Vibration Therapy Program and Gala Support.
$47,144 to Marvin Lewis Community Fund, Cincinnati, OH, 2012. For programs and scholarships.
$30,000 to Citylink Center, Cincinnati, OH, 2012. For Dental Program and Unrestricted Operating Support.
$20,000 to ProKids, Cincinnati, OH, 2012. To foster Care Program and General Program Support.
$10,000 to Cincinnati Parks Foundation, Cincinnati, OH, 2012. For Krohn Conservatory Admission for Disabled Children.
$10,000 to Every Child Succeeds, Cincinnati, OH, 2012. To support Home Visits.
$5,800 to Cincinnati Parks Foundation, Cincinnati, OH, 2012. For event support.
$3,000 to Supporting Riley Children, Indianapolis, IN, 2012. To support Indiana University Dance Marathon.
$1,000 to Assistance League of Greater Cincinnati, Cincinnati, OH, 2012. For New Beginnings Program.

7484
The Hauss-Helms Foundation, Inc. ✧
P.O. Box 25
Wapakoneta, OH 45895-0025 (419) 738-4911
E-mail: information@hauss-helmsfoundation.org; Main URL: http://www.hauss-helmsfoundation.org

Incorporated in 1965 in OH.
Donors: Besse Hauss Helms†; W.B. Helms†.
Foundation type: Independent foundation.
Financial data (yr. ended 07/31/13): Assets, $19,698,373 (M); expenditures, $1,137,350; qualifying distributions, $1,025,253; giving activities include $859,470 for 161 grants to individuals (high: $7,500; low: $1,000).
Purpose and activities: Scholarships for graduating high school students who are residents of Auglaize and Allen counties, OH. However, students may attend any accredited institution in the U.S.
Fields of interest: Higher education; Adults; Adults, women; Adults, men.
Type of support: Scholarships—to individuals.
Limitations: Applications accepted. Giving limited to graduates of Auglaize and Allen counties, OH, high schools.
Application information: Application form must be sent via U.S. mail. Application form required.

Initial approach: Letter or telephone requesting application form, or download form from foundation web site
Copies of proposal: 1
Deadline(s): Jan. 1 through Apr. 15
Board meeting date(s): May and June
Final notification: July

Officer and Trustees:* Douglas Jauert,* Pres.; Michael A. Burton; N. Thomas Cornell; John C. Haehn; John D. Johnson, C.P.A.; James S. West.
Number of staff: 1 part-time professional; 1 part-time support.
EIN: 340975903

7485
Hayfields Foundation ✧ ☆

7811 Laurel Ave., Ste. B
Cincinnati, OH 45243-2608 (513) 621-1384
Contact: Eric B. Yeiser, Pres.

Established in 1946.
Donors: Louise F. Tate†; Charles F. Yeiser.
Foundation type: Independent foundation.
Financial data (yr. ended 12/31/13): Assets, $54,885 (M); expenditures, $6,039,927; qualifying distributions, $6,015,300; giving activities include $6,015,300 for 10 grants (high: $1,800,000; low: $300).
Purpose and activities: Giving primarily for the arts, education and health services.
Fields of interest: Performing arts; Arts; Education; Reproductive health, family planning; Health care; Health organizations; Human services.
Type of support: General/operating support.
Limitations: Applications accepted. Giving primarily in the greater Cincinnati, OH, area. No grants to individuals.
Application information: Application form required.
Initial approach: Letter
Deadline(s): None

Officers: Eric B. Yeiser, Pres.; Charles F. Yeiser, V.P.; Robert E. Rich, Secy.
EIN: 316025518
Selected grants: The following grants are a representative sample of this grantmaker's funding activity:
$40,000 to Cincinnati Symphony and Pops Orchestra, Cincinnati, OH, 2011. For general support.
$20,000 to Cancer Family Care, Cincinnati, OH, 2011. For general support.
$15,000 to Springer School and Center, Cincinnati, OH, 2011. For general support.
$12,000 to Indian Hill Church, Cincinnati, OH, 2011. For general support.
$10,000 to Cincinnati Association for the Blind and Visually Impaired, Cincinnati, OH, 2011. For general support.
$10,000 to Cincinnati Museum Center, Cincinnati, OH, 2011. For general support.
$10,000 to Living Arrangements for the Developmentally Disabled, Cincinnati, OH, 2011. For general support.
$6,000 to Little Miami, Milford, OH, 2011. For general support.
$5,000 to ArtsWave, Cincinnati, OH, 2011. For general support.
$5,000 to Freestore/Foodbank, Cincinnati, OH, 2011. For general support.

7486
The Kim and Gary Heiman Family Foundation ✧

c/o Edward M. Frankel
P.O. Box 371805
Cincinnati, OH 45222-1805

Established in 1998 in OH.
Donors: Gary Heiman; Kim Heiman; Standard Textile Co., Inc.; Seed the Dream Foundation; Bradley M. Bloom.
Foundation type: Independent foundation.
Financial data (yr. ended 12/31/13): Assets, $688,504 (M); gifts received, $38,800; expenditures, $580,376; qualifying distributions, $579,251; giving activities include $564,723 for 34 grants (high: $226,250; low: $100).
Purpose and activities: Giving primarily for Jewish federated giving programs, and to Jewish organizations and temples.
Fields of interest: Education; Health organizations, association; Human services; Jewish federated giving programs; Jewish agencies & synagogues.
Limitations: Applications not accepted. Giving primarily in OH. No grants to individuals.
Application information: Contributes only to pre-selected organizations.
Officers: Gary Heiman, Pres.; Kim Heiman, V.P.; Edward M. Frankel, Secy.-Treas.
EIN: 316605176

7487
The Hershey Foundation ✧

10229 Prouty Rd.
Concord Township, OH 44077-2104 (440) 256-6003
Contact: Debra Hershey Guren, Pres.
FAX: (440) 256-0233;
E-mail: thehersheyfoundation@gmail.com; Main URL: http://fdnweb.org/hershey
Grants List: http://fdnweb.org/hershey/grants-awarded/

Established in 1986 in OH.
Donors: Jo Hershey Selden†; Loren W. Hershey; Debra Hershey Guren; Carole Hershey Walters.
Foundation type: Independent foundation.
Financial data (yr. ended 12/31/12): Assets, $18,494,890 (M); expenditures, $1,366,514; qualifying distributions, $1,236,700; giving activities include $1,236,700 for 45 grants (high: $110,000; low: $1,500).
Purpose and activities: The foundation is dedicated to providing children in northeastern Ohio, from all socio-economic and cultural backgrounds, with special opportunities for personal growth and development. Support from the foundation helps schools, museums, cultural institutions, and other non-profit organizations develop and implement innovative programs that make the future brighter for children by improving quality of life, building self-esteem, enhancing learning, increasing exposure to other cultures and ideas, and encouraging the development of independent thinking and problem-solving skills.
Fields of interest: Arts education; Education, early childhood education; Child development, education; Elementary school/education; Education; Children/youth, services; Child development, services; Infants/toddlers; Children; Infants/toddlers, female; Girls; Infants/toddlers, male; Boys.
Type of support: Capital campaigns; Building/renovation; Equipment; Endowments; Program development; Seed money; Curriculum development.
Limitations: Applications accepted. Giving primarily in northeastern OH. No grants to individuals, or for annual campaigns, operating budgets, computer systems, technology or research, or feasibility studies.
Publications: Application guidelines; Annual report; Grants list; Informational brochure (including application guidelines); Multi-year report.
Application information: See foundation Web site for application guidelines and procedures. Application form not required.
Initial approach: 1-page letter or telephone
Copies of proposal: 1
Deadline(s): Dec. 1 and June 1
Board meeting date(s): Feb. and Aug.
Final notification: Feb. and Aug.

Officers and Trustees:* Debra Hershey Guren,* C.E.O. and Pres.; Adam M. Guren,* V.P. and Treas.; Carole Hershey Walters,* Secy.; Georgia A. Froelich; Loren W. Hershey.
Number of staff: None.
EIN: 341525626
Selected grants: The following grants are a representative sample of this grantmaker's funding activity:
$90,000 to Hershey Montessori School, Painesville, OH, 2012. For capital and anuual giving support.
$55,000 to Lake Erie College, Painesville, OH, 2012. For Hershey Montessori Institute.
$50,000 to Cleveland Botanical Garden, Cleveland, OH, 2012. For endowment and capital improvements for Hershey Children's Garden.
$50,000 to Cleveland Zoological Society, Cleveland, OH, 2012. For African Elephant Crossing.
$31,500 to Ohio Association of Independent Schools, Sunbury, OH, 2012. For endowed scholarship fund for Early Childhood Education students.
$27,500 to Ideastream, Cleveland, OH, 2012. For educational program.
$25,000 to Youth Challenge, Westlake, OH, 2012. For capital campaign for new operating facility.
$20,000 to Shaker Lakes Regional Nature Center, Cleveland, OH, 2012. For Children's Tree House Project.
$10,000 to Cleveland Reads, Cleveland, OH, 2012. For parent education program to improve children's literacy through reading.
$8,500 to America SCORES Cleveland, Cleveland, OH, 2012. For equipment.

7488
Home is the Foundation ✧

1751 N. Barron St.
Eaton, OH 45320-9277 (937) 472-0500
Contact: Bill Hutton
FAX: (937) 472-0501; Main URL: http://www.hitfoundation.org/

Established in 2003 in OH. Classified as a private operating foundation in 2004.
Donors: Franklin Steet; Mary Bullen.
Foundation type: Operating foundation.
Financial data (yr. ended 12/31/12): Assets, $1,461,328 (M); gifts received, $866,074; expenditures, $918,742; qualifying distributions, $763,357.
Fields of interest: Housing/shelter.

Application information: Application form required.
Initial approach: Apply in person or contact foundation for application form
Deadline(s): None
Officers: Mary Bullen, Pres.; Chip Christman, Treas.; Billy J. Hutton, Jr., Exec. Dir.
Directors: Joan Kreitzer; Teresa McCown; Sharon Shute; Mike Simpson.
EIN: 421580792

7489
Home Savings Charitable Foundation ✧
P.O. Box 1111
Youngstown, OH 44501-1111 (330) 742-0571
Contact: Darlene Pavlock, Exec. Dir.
FAX: (330) 742-0532;
E-mail: dpavlock@homesavings.com; Additional fax: (330) 742-0499; Main URL: https://www.homesavings.com/foundation

Established in 1991 in OH.
Donors: Home Savings and Loan Co.; United Community Financial Corp.
Foundation type: Company-sponsored foundation.
Financial data (yr. ended 12/31/13): Assets, $14,185,496 (M); expenditures, $760,604; qualifying distributions, $681,114; giving activities include $645,222 for 121 grants (high: $50,000; low: $250).
Purpose and activities: The foundation supports programs designed to promote education and address the needs of economically disadvantaged children and adults.
Fields of interest: Higher education; Education; Health care; YM/YWCAs & YM/YWHAs; Human services; United Ways and Federated Giving Programs; Children; Economically disadvantaged.
Type of support: Annual campaigns; Capital campaigns; Equipment; Program development; Scholarship funds; Sponsorships.
Limitations: Applications accepted. Giving primarily in areas of company operations in northeastern, north central, and northwestern OH, with emphasis on Columbiana, Mahoning, and Trumbull counties. No grants to individuals.
Publications: Application guidelines.
Application information: Additional information may be requested at a later date. Application form required.
Initial approach: Telephone foundation; download application form and mail to foundation
Copies of proposal: 2
Deadline(s): None
Officer: Darlene Pavlock, Exec. Dir.
Trustee: Farmers Trust Co.
Number of staff: 1 full-time professional.
EIN: 341695319

7490
Honda of America Foundation ✧
24000 Honda Pkwy.
Marysville, OH 43040 (937) 642-5000
Contact: Caroline Ramsey, Exec. Dir.

Established in 1981 in OH.
Donor: Honda of America.
Foundation type: Company-sponsored foundation.
Financial data (yr. ended 12/31/13): Assets, $10,057,335 (M); gifts received, $300,000; expenditures, $795,154; qualifying distributions, $664,836; giving activities include $628,000 for 35 grants (high: $50,000; low: $1,000).
Purpose and activities: The foundation supports organizations involved with arts and culture, education, the environment, safety, community development, and civic responsibility.
Fields of interest: Arts; Education; Environment; Safety, automotive safety; Human services; Community/economic development; Public affairs.
Type of support: General/operating support; Building/renovation; Program development; Scholarship funds.
Limitations: Applications accepted. Giving primarily in areas of company operations in west central OH, with emphasis on Allen, Auglaize, Champaign, Clark, Darke, Delaware, Franklin, Hardin, Logan, Madison, Marion, Mercer, Miami, Shelby and Union counties. No support for religious organizations, national health, fraternal, lobbying, political, or veterans' organizations, or sports teams. No grants to individuals, or for courtesy advertisements, legal advocacy, memberships, conferences, workshops, seminars, pageants, or extracurricular school activities.
Publications: Application guidelines.
Application information: Application form required.
Initial approach: Letter
Copies of proposal: 1
Deadline(s): None
Officers: Shaun McCloskey, C.F.O. and Secy.; Caroline Ramsey, Exec. Dir.
Directors: Steve Francis; Jan Gansheimer; Pam Heminger; John Spoltman; Jim Wehrman; Laura Yaroma.
Number of staff: 1 full-time professional.
EIN: 311006130
Selected grants: The following grants are a representative sample of this grantmaker's funding activity:
$70,000 to YWCA Columbus, Columbus, OH, 2012. For Women of Achievement 2013.
$40,000 to Community Shelter Board, Columbus, OH, 2012. For Transition from Homelessness to Housing Programming.
$35,000 to Ohio Association of Community Colleges, Columbus, OH, 2012. For All Ohio Team Scholar Program.
$30,000 to Columbus Federation of Settlements, Columbus, OH, 2012. For Summer Program for Disadvantaged Youth.
$25,000 to Columbus Museum of Art, Columbus, OH, 2012. For Innovation Day at CMA.
$25,000 to YWCA Columbus, Columbus, OH, 2012. For Family Center Safe and Sound Programming.
$15,000 to Alpha Community Center, Sidney, OH, 2012. For Alpha Meals.
$15,000 to New Directions Career Center, Columbus, OH, 2012. For core programming.
$10,000 to Columbus Literacy Council, Columbus, OH, 2012. For English for Speakers of Other Languages.
$10,000 to Mid-Ohio Foodbank, Grove City, OH, 2012. For Operation Feed.

7491
Herbert W. Hoover Foundation ✧
4900 Tiedman Rd. OH-01-49-0150
Brooklyn, OH 44144-2302 (330) 818-1300
E-mail: contacthwh@hwhfoundation.org; Main URL: http://www.hwhfoundation.org

Established in 1990 in OH.
Donor: The Hoover Foundation.
Foundation type: Independent foundation.
Financial data (yr. ended 12/31/12): Assets, $21,307,155 (M); expenditures, $1,418,562; qualifying distributions, $1,341,515; giving activities include $761,282 for 23 grants (high: $150,000; low: $250).
Purpose and activities: Giving primarily for education, the environment, and human services.
Fields of interest: Higher education; Education; Environment; Human services.
Type of support: Continuing support; Equipment; Program development; Scholarship funds; Research; Matching/challenge support.
Limitations: Applications accepted. Giving primarily in Stark County, OH. No support for political organizations. No grants to individuals, or for annual campaigns, fundraisers, endowments, start-up funds, or for grassroots.
Publications: Application guidelines.
Application information: Application form required.
Initial approach: Use application process on foundation web site along with the submission of a Letter of Inquiry
Deadline(s): The last business days of Jan., May and Sept. for Letters of Inquiry. The last business days of Feb., June, and Oct. for formal applications (which are by invitation only)
Board meeting date(s): 2-3 times per year
Officers and Board Members:* Elizabeth Lacey Hoover,* Chair.; Colton Hoover Chase; Jeff Congeni; Jacqueline Degarmo; Gary Smith.
Trustee: KeyBank, N.A.
Number of staff: 1 full-time professional; 1 full-time support.
EIN: 346905388

7492
The Hoover Foundation ✧
400 Market Ave. N., Ste. 210
Canton, OH 44702-1557 (330) 458-0143
Contact: Lawrence R. Hoover, Chair.

Trust established in 1945 in OH.
Donor: Members of the Hoover family.
Foundation type: Independent foundation.
Financial data (yr. ended 12/31/13): Assets, $52,516,205 (M); expenditures, $2,826,045; qualifying distributions, $2,733,861; giving activities include $2,574,610 for 64 grants (high: $342,300; low: $100).
Purpose and activities: Giving primarily to hospitals and health agencies, colleges and universities, and community organizations.
Fields of interest: Arts; Education, early childhood education; Elementary school/education; Secondary school/education; Higher education; Libraries (public); Hospitals (general); Food services; Youth development, services; YM/YWCAs & YM/YWHAs; Children/youth, services; United Ways and Federated Giving Programs.
Type of support: General/operating support; Annual campaigns; Capital campaigns; Equipment; Seed money; Curriculum development; Scholarship funds; Employee matching gifts; Matching/challenge support.
Limitations: Applications accepted. Giving primarily in Stark County, OH. No grants to individuals.
Application information: Application form not required.
Initial approach: Letter
Copies of proposal: 1
Deadline(s): None

Board meeting date(s): As required
Final notification: 1 to 4 months
Trust Committee: Lawrence R. Hoover, Chair.; Charles H. Hoover; Timothy R. Hoover; Timothy D. Schlitz.
Trustee: The Huntington National Bank.
EIN: 346510994
Selected grants: The following grants are a representative sample of this grantmaker's funding activity:
$400,000 to YMCA, Canton Area - North Canton Community Building, North Canton, OH, 2012.
$300,000 to United Way of Greater Stark County, Canton, OH, 2012.
$250,000 to Boy Scouts of America, Buckeye Council, Canton, OH, 2012.
$150,000 to Arts in Stark, Canton, OH, 2012.
$150,000 to Canton Symphony Orchestra Association, Canton, OH, 2012.

7493
Richard Horvitz and Erica Hartman-Horvitz Foundation ✧
(formerly The Richard A. Horvitz Foundation)
6095 Parkland Blvd., Ste. 300
Mayfield Heights, OH 44124-6140

Established in 1997 in OH.
Donors: Marcy R. Horvitz‡; Richard A. Horvitz; RAH Limited Partnership; Erica Hartman-Horvitz.
Foundation type: Independent foundation.
Financial data (yr. ended 12/31/13): Assets, $1,014,573 (M); expenditures, $1,895,285; qualifying distributions, $1,892,471; giving activities include $1,889,458 for 185 grants (high: $400,000; low: $50).
Fields of interest: Arts; Elementary/secondary education; Higher education; Education; Hospitals (general); Health organizations, association; Medical research, institute; Human services; Children/youth, services; Jewish federated giving programs; Jewish agencies & synagogues.
Limitations: Applications not accepted. Giving primarily in CA, Durham, NC, NY and OH. No grants to individuals.
Application information: Contributes only to pre-selected organizations.
Officers and Trustees:* Richard A. Horvitz,* Pres.; Paul A. Williams, Secy.; Diane O. Malarik, Treas.; Erica Hartman-Horvitz; Ranch Fiduciary Corp.
EIN: 311533634

7494
The Howley Family Foundation ✧
9725 Lakeshore Blvd.
Bratenahl, OH 44108-1063
E-mail: HowleyScholars@gmail.com

Established in 2003 in OH.
Donors: W. Nicholas Howley; Mrs. W. Nicholas Howley; Lauralee V. Howley.
Foundation type: Independent foundation.
Financial data (yr. ended 12/31/12): Assets, $17,154,999 (M); gifts received, $7,000,318; expenditures, $696,390; qualifying distributions, $649,275; giving activities include $649,275 for 29 grants (high: $202,700; low: $100).
Purpose and activities: Giving in support of educational organizations, as well as scholarship and tuition help to incoming 9th grade students.
Fields of interest: Arts; Elementary/secondary education; Higher education; Youth development; Youth; Young adults.
Type of support: General/operating support; Scholarships—to individuals.
Limitations: Applications not accepted. Giving primarily in northeastern OH.
Application information: Contributes only to pre-selected organizations.
Trustees: Lauralee V. Howley; W. Nicholas Howley.
EIN: 300193364

7495
Ed & Joann Hubert Family Foundation, Inc. ✧ ☆
6170 W. Fork Rd.
Cincinnati, OH 45247-5766

Established in 2003 in OH.
Donors: Ed Hubert; Joann Hubert; Hubert Foundation.
Foundation type: Independent foundation.
Financial data (yr. ended 12/31/12): Assets, $15,264,549 (M); expenditures, $635,726; qualifying distributions, $578,624; giving activities include $575,330 for 52 grants (high: $150,000; low: $85).
Purpose and activities: Support for low-income housing through grants and loans; grants also for community development, church projects, and education.
Fields of interest: Education; Housing/shelter, development; Community/economic development; Christian agencies & churches; Economically disadvantaged.
Type of support: General/operating support; Program-related investments/loans.
Limitations: Applications not accepted. Giving primarily in Cincinnati, OH. No grants to individuals.
Application information: Contributes only to pre-selected organizations.
Officer: Ed Hubert, Pres.
EIN: 223883114

7496
Hudson Community Foundation ✧
49 E. Main St.
P.O. Box 944
Hudson, OH 44236
Contact: Lisa Drew, Exec. Dir.; For grants: Richard Warfield, V.P., Grants
E-mail: support@myhcf.org; Grant inquiry e-mail: rwarfield@warfieldandcompany.com; Main URL: http://www.myhcf.org/

Established in 2000 in OH.
Foundation type: Community foundation.
Financial data (yr. ended 12/31/13): Assets, $9,968,491 (M); gifts received, $1,371,263; expenditures, $1,111,529; giving activities include $808,322 for 23+ grants (high: $246,800).
Purpose and activities: The foundation exists to preserve and enhance the quality of life for all citizens of Hudson, OH now and for generations to come.
Fields of interest: Historic preservation/historical societies; Arts; Environment; Recreation; Human services; Community/economic development; Children/youth.
Limitations: Applications accepted. Giving primarily in Hudson, OH. No support for religious organizations or events, or for private foundation. No grants to individuals, or for debt retirement, testimonial dinners or advertising, capital campaigns, or endowments.
Publications: Application guidelines; Annual report.
Application information: Visit foundation web site for application guidelines. Application form required.
Initial approach: Submit proposal
Copies of proposal: 5
Deadline(s): Mar. 15, June 15, Sept. 15, and Dec. 15
Board meeting date(s): Quarterly
Officers and Board of Trustees:* Donald Tharp,* Chair.; Philip Tobin,* C.E.O. and Pres.; Jill Bacon Madden,* Pres., Opers.; Brian Bishop,* V.P., Investments; Drew Forhan,* V.P., Devel.; Janice Gusich,* V.P., Mktg.; Richard Warfield,* V.P., Grants; Gail Tobin,* Treas.; Lisa Drew,* Exec. Dir.; Jim Hackney,* Chair. Emeritus; William D. Wooldredge,* Chair. Emeritus; William Currin; Michael Lewis; Shawn Lyden; Kent McMath; David Schweighoefer; Bill Sedlacek.
EIN: 341935499

7497
George M. and Pamela S. Humphrey Fund ✧
c/o MN Advisory Svcs. LLC
1111 Superior Ave., Ste. 700
Cleveland, OH 44114-2540 (216) 363-6489
Contact: Pamela B. Keefe, Pres.

Incorporated in 1951 in OH.
Donors: George M. Humphrey‡; Pamela S. Humphrey‡.
Foundation type: Independent foundation.
Financial data (yr. ended 12/31/13): Assets, $19,485,315 (M); expenditures, $1,046,512; qualifying distributions, $942,317; giving activities include $924,500 for 24 grants (high: $400,000; low: $500).
Purpose and activities: Giving primarily for hospitals, education and community funds.
Fields of interest: Arts; Education; Hospitals (general); Health care.
Type of support: General/operating support; Continuing support; Annual campaigns; Building/renovation; Equipment; Endowments; Emergency funds; Professorships; Internship funds; Research; Technical assistance; Matching/challenge support.
Limitations: Applications accepted. Giving primarily in OH, with emphasis on Cleveland. No grants to individuals; no loans.
Publications: Annual report.
Application information: Application form not required.
Initial approach: Letter
Copies of proposal: 1
Deadline(s): Prior to board meeting
Board meeting date(s): Oct.
Final notification: 1 month
Officers and Trustees:* Pamela B. Keefe,* Pres.; Stephen T. Keefe,* V.P.; Jennifer Tome, Secy.; Joseph P. Kovalcheck, Jr., Treas.; Alice B. Burnham; Sarah Dimling.
EIN: 346513798

7498
Margaretta W. Hunt Trust ✧
P.O. Box 1118, ML CN-OH-W10X
Cincinnati, OH 45201-1118

Foundation type: Independent foundation.
Financial data (yr. ended 12/31/12): Assets, $9,037,070 (M); expenditures, $543,672; qualifying distributions, $465,399; giving activities include $465,399 for grants.
Fields of interest: Philanthropy/voluntarism.
Limitations: Applications not accepted. Giving primarily in Covington, KY.
Application information: Contributes only to pre-selected organizations.
Trustee: U.S. Bank, N.A.
EIN: 316021586

7499
The John Huntington Fund for Education ✧
20620 N. Park Blvd., Ste. 215
Cleveland, OH 44118-4523 (216) 321-7185
Contact: Ann P. Ranney, Treas.
E-mail: jhfe@sbcglobal.net

Incorporated in 1954 in OH.
Donor: John Huntington†.
Foundation type: Independent foundation.
Financial data (yr. ended 12/31/13): Assets, $33,279,178 (M); gifts received, $10,000; expenditures, $2,458,171; qualifying distributions, $2,366,762; giving activities include $2,324,733 for 11 grants (high: $694,600; low: $10,000).
Purpose and activities: To provide grants to Cuyahoga County, OH institutions to be administered for scientific and technological scholarships to Cuyahoga students.
Fields of interest: Higher education; Engineering/technology; Science.
Type of support: Scholarship funds.
Limitations: Giving limited to Cuyahoga County, OH, for Cuyahoga County students. No grants to individuals.
Application information: Application form not required.
Initial approach: Letter
Copies of proposal: 1
Deadline(s): Apr. 15
Board meeting date(s): Usually in May
Officers and Trustees:* Peter W. Adams,* Pres.; Oakley Andrews,* Secy.; Ann P. Ranney,* Treas.; Chandler Everett; Bruce T. Goode; Robert G. McCreary III; Karen R. Nestor; Leigh H. Perkins.
Number of staff: 1 part-time professional.
EIN: 340714434
Selected grants: The following grants are a representative sample of this grantmaker's funding activity:
$661,500 to Case Western Reserve University, Cleveland, OH, 2012. For scholarships.
$592,850 to College Now Greater Cleveland, Cleveland, OH, 2012. For scholarships.
$33,333 to Fund for Our Economic Future, Cleveland, OH, 2012.

7500
The Edward L. Hutton Foundation ✧
255 E. 5th St., Ste. 2600
Cincinnati, OH 45202-4726
E-mail: sandra.laney@chemed.com

Established in 1991 in OH.
Donors: Edward L. Hutton†; Kathryn Jane Hutton.
Foundation type: Independent foundation.
Financial data (yr. ended 12/31/13): Assets, $12,252,572 (M); expenditures, $598,083; qualifying distributions, $579,950; giving activities include $568,000 for 11 grants (high: $112,000; low: $10,000).
Purpose and activities: Giving for health associations, the arts, and education.
Fields of interest: Arts; Higher education; Education; Health organizations, association; Human services.
Type of support: General/operating support; Scholarship funds; Scholarships—to individuals.
Limitations: Applications not accepted. Giving on a national basis, with emphasis on IN and OH. No support for political organizations.
Publications: Annual report.
Application information: Unsolicited requests for funds not accepted.
Board meeting date(s): Mar., June, Sept., and Dec.
Officers: Jennie Hutton Jacoby, Pres.; Edward A. Hutton, V.P.; Thomas C. Hutton, Secy.-Treas.
Number of staff: 6 part-time support.
EIN: 311334189

7501
IHS Foundation ✧
(formerly Skestos Family Foundation)
2700 E. Dublin-Granville Rd., Ste. 300
Columbus, OH 43231-4089 (614) 898-7200
Contact: Terrie L. Rice, Secy.

Established in 2000 in OH.
Donors: George A. Skestos; Jason Skestos; Alexandra Skestos Block; Stephanie K. Skestos Gabriele; Justine Skestos; Alexandra Skestos Holmes.
Foundation type: Independent foundation.
Financial data (yr. ended 12/31/12): Assets, $26,159,356 (M); expenditures, $1,668,716; qualifying distributions, $1,627,396; giving activities include $1,604,017 for 31 grants (high: $798,117; low: $1,000).
Purpose and activities: Giving primarily for higher education; some funding also for the arts, Lutheran churches, organizations, missions and ministries, health associations, and children, youth, and social services, including recordings for the blind.
Fields of interest: Arts education; Museums (art); Performing arts; Higher education; Education; Health organizations, association; Cancer; Human services; Children/youth, services; Protestant agencies & churches; Economically disadvantaged.
Limitations: Giving primarily in OH, with emphasis on Columbus.
Application information: Application form not required.
Initial approach: Letter
Deadline(s): None
Officers: Justine A. Skestos, Pres.; Terrie L. Rice, Secy.; Adam N. Scott, Treas.
Trustees: Stephanie Skestos Gabriele; Alexandra Skestos Holmes; James W. Phieffer; George Anthony Skestos; Jason J. Skestos.
EIN: 311721314

7502
Ima/Mickey Family Foundation ✧ ☆
P.O. Box 630858
Cincinnati, OH 45263-0858 (513) 534-7240
Application address: c/o Carol Schneider, Fifth Third Bank, 38 Fountain Square Plz., Cincinnati, OH 45263, tel.: (513) 534-7240

Established in OH.
Donor: R. Bruce Mickey.
Foundation type: Independent foundation.
Financial data (yr. ended 12/31/13): Assets, $618,240 (M); gifts received, $43,659; expenditures, $1,506,271; qualifying distributions, $1,500,613; giving activities include $1,500,000 for 1 grant.
Purpose and activities: Giving to a hospital in support of a Rheumatology program.
Fields of interest: Hospitals (general).
Limitations: Applications accepted. Giving primarily in Boston, MA.
Application information: Application form required.
Initial approach: Letter
Deadline(s): Sept. 30 or as determined by the Trustee
Officers: R. Bruce Mickey, Pres.; Joan Mickey, V.P.; Amy Mickey, Secy.; Elizabeth Dvorak, Treas.
EIN: 461484743

7503
The Louise H. and David S. Ingalls Foundation, Inc. ✧
20600 Chagrin Blvd., Ste., 430
Shaker Heights, OH 44122-5334 (216) 921-6000
Contact: Gary Lombardo

Incorporated in 1953 in OH.
Donors: Louise H. Ingalls†; Edith Ingalls Vignos; Louise Ingalls Brown†; David S. Ingalls†; David S. Ingalls, Jr.†; Jane I. Davison; Anne I. Lawrence.
Foundation type: Independent foundation.
Financial data (yr. ended 12/31/13): Assets, $32,884,031 (L); expenditures, $1,858,440; qualifying distributions, $1,763,162; giving activities include $1,705,500 for 39 grants (high: $215,000; low: $5,000).
Purpose and activities: Support mainly to organizations known to the trustees for the improvement of the physical, educational, mental, and moral condition of humanity primarily in the Cleveland, OH area; grants largely for education, fine arts and culture, music, historical preservation, archaeology and anthropology, the environment and conservation, health programs, and hospital building funds, rehabilitation programs, the disadvantaged, and child development.
Fields of interest: Museums; Performing arts; Historic preservation/historical societies; Arts; Higher education; Environment, natural resources; Hospitals (general); Medical care, rehabilitation; Medical research, institute.
Type of support: Capital campaigns; Building/renovation; Program development; Research.
Limitations: Applications accepted. Giving in the U.S., with emphasis on Cleveland, OH. No grants to individuals; or for annual giving.
Application information: Application form required.
Initial approach: Proposal
Copies of proposal: 1
Deadline(s): None
Board meeting date(s): As required
Officers and Trustees:* Barbara Brown,* Pres.; Caren V. Sturges, V.P.; Willard W. Brown, Jr., Recording Secy.; John T. Lawrence III,* Treas.
Number of staff: 2 part-time support.
EIN: 346516550
Selected grants: The following grants are a representative sample of this grantmaker's funding activity:

$195,000 to Yale University, Department of Athletics, New Haven, CT, 2012. For Sports.

7504
Joanie J. & H. Bernard Foundation ✧
c/o Fifth Third Bank
P.O. Box 630858
Cincinnati, OH 45263-0858

Donor: Jeanne K. Bernard Trust.
Foundation type: Independent foundation.
Financial data (yr. ended 12/31/13): Assets, $90,237,159 (M); gifts received, $12,983,600; expenditures, $5,647,053; qualifying distributions, $5,055,863; giving activities include $4,856,800 for grants.
Fields of interest: Animal welfare.
Limitations: Applications not accepted. Giving primarily in Cincinnati and Cleveland, OH.
Application information: Contributes only to pre-selected organizations.
Trustee: Fifth Third Bank.
EIN: 371547019
Selected grants: The following grants are a representative sample of this grantmaker's funding activity:
$50,000 to United Coalition for Animals, Cincinnati, OH, 2011.

7505
Carl Jacobs Foundation ✧
c/o Fifth Third Bank
P.O. Box 630858
Cincinnati, OH 45263-0858
Application address: c/o Fifth Third Bank, Agent, 38 Fountain Square Plz., Cincinnati, OH 45263, tel.: (513) 579-5324

Established in OH.
Foundation type: Independent foundation.
Financial data (yr. ended 12/31/12): Assets, $15,127,436 (M); expenditures, $740,420; qualifying distributions, $591,357; giving activities include $590,000 for 42 grants (high: $125,000; low: $2,500).
Fields of interest: Arts; Libraries (public); Health care; Human services.
Limitations: Applications accepted. Giving primarily in New York, NY.
Application information: Application form required.
Initial approach: Letter
Deadline(s): None
Officers: Robert M. Erickson, Pres.; Heidi Jark, V.P.; Susan Mendlein, Secy.; Michael Kennedy, Treas.
EIN: 800604309

7506
The Jamestown Area Foundation, Inc. ✧
133 E. Market St.
Xenia, OH 45385-3110

Established in 2002 in OH.
Donor: Bruce E. Higman.
Foundation type: Independent foundation.
Financial data (yr. ended 12/31/13): Assets, $10,687,298 (M); expenditures, $656,814; qualifying distributions, $531,653; giving activities include $2,500 for 1 grant, and $440,993 for 25 grants to individuals (high: $52,739; low: $200).
Purpose and activities: Support for higher education, including scholarship awards for high school graduates from Jamestown and Green County, Ohio.
Fields of interest: Higher education; Foundations (community).
Type of support: Scholarship funds; Scholarships—to individuals.
Limitations: Applications not accepted. Giving primarily in Jamestown and Green County, OH.
Application information: Unsolicited requests for funds not accepted.
Officer: Sheila R. Hoag, Secy.-Treas.
Tustees: Edward W. Brill; Marcia A. Brill; David L. Pendry; Pamela Pendry.
EIN: 311148328

7507
The Jegs Foundation ✧ ☆
(formerly Jeg's Quarter Mile Charities)
101 Jegs Pl.
Delaware, OH 43015-9279
Main URL: http://www.jegs.com/s/customercare/foundation.html

Established in 2000 in OH.
Donors: Jeg's Automotive, Inc.; Crown Group Ltd.
Foundation type: Company-sponsored foundation.
Financial data (yr. ended 12/31/13): Assets, $1,585,256 (M); gifts received, $77,250; expenditures, $4,031,127; qualifying distributions, $4,025,200; giving activities include $4,025,200 for 2 grants (high: $4,025,000; low: $200).
Purpose and activities: The foundation supports organizations involved with cancer and human services.
Fields of interest: Cancer; Cancer research; Human services.
Type of support: General/operating support; Research.
Limitations: Applications not accepted. Giving primarily in OH, with emphasis on Columbus. No grants to individuals.
Application information: Unsolicited requests for funds not accepted.
Officers and Trustees:* Phillip Troy Coughlin,* Pres.; Edward John Coughlin,* Secy.-Treas.; Jeg Anthony Coughlin; Michael Allen Coughlin.
EIN: 311731261

7508
The Tom H. and Anne H. Jenkins Charitable Trust ✧ ☆
26228 Lake Rd.
Bay Village, OH 44140-2567
Contact: Stephen H. Jenkins, Tr.

Donors: Tom H. Jenkins; Anne H. Jenkins.
Foundation type: Independent foundation.
Financial data (yr. ended 12/31/13): Assets, $1,782,631 (M); gifts received, $500,000; expenditures, $870,190; qualifying distributions, $855,000; giving activities include $855,000 for 4 grants (high: $450,000; low: $2,500).
Fields of interest: Education; Hospitals (specialty); Health care; Human services.
Limitations: Applications accepted. Giving primarily in OH.
Application information: Application form required.
Initial approach: Proposal sent one hundred and twenty days before funds are needed
Deadline(s): None
Trustees: Stephen H. Jenkins; Timothy J. Jenkins.
EIN: 456545911

7509
The Martha Holden Jennings Foundation ✧
The Halle Bldg.
1228 Euclid Ave., Ste. 710
Cleveland, OH 44115-1846 (216) 589-5700
Contact: Daniel J. Keenan, Jr., Exec. Dir.
FAX: (216) 589-5730; Business office: 20620 N. Park Blvd., No. 215, Cleveland, OH 44118, tel.: (216) 932-7337; Main URL: http://www.mhjf.org

Incorporated in 1959 in OH.
Donor: Martha Holden Jennings†.
Foundation type: Independent foundation.
Financial data (yr. ended 12/31/13): Assets, $70,840,063 (M); gifts received, $4,394; expenditures, $3,932,046; qualifying distributions, $3,845,293; giving activities include $2,854,765 for grants.
Purpose and activities: Giving to foster development of the capabilities of young people through improving the quality of teaching in secular elementary and secondary schools; program includes awards in recognition of outstanding teaching; special educational programs for teachers in the fields of the humanities, the arts, and the sciences; curriculum development projects; school evaluation studies; and educational television programs. Preference is given to programs that target underserved student populations and districts with fewer available resources.
Fields of interest: Education, association; Elementary school/education; Secondary school/education; Mathematics; Science.
Type of support: Program evaluation; Continuing support; Program development; Seed money; Curriculum development; Matching/challenge support.
Limitations: Applications accepted. Giving limited to OH. No grants to individuals or operating budgets, annual campaigns, travel, emergency funds, deficit financing, capital or endowment funds, research, or publications; no loans; teacher stipends; school supplies; substitute coverage; school bus transportation or graduate study.
Publications: Application guidelines; Annual report; Newsletter; Program policy statement.
Application information: Application form required for Grants-to-Educators Program, and is available on web site. Applicants must submit an original form, and nine copies signed by the principal and superintendent. Follow criteria on foundation web site for Open Grants. Open Grant requests must not exceed ten pages. Application form not required.
Initial approach: 1-page project summary with cover letter and proposal
Copies of proposal: 1
Deadline(s): 15th of each month preceding month in which application is to be considered
Board meeting date(s): Distrib. Comm. meets monthly, except July and Dec.; Board of directors meet monthly, except Feb., July, Oct., and Dec.
Final notification: 6 to 8 weeks
Officers and Directors:* George B. Milbourn,* Chair. and Pres.; Daniel J. Keenan, Jr., Exec. Dir.; Dr. Mark Collier; Rev. Jawanza Colvin; Debra H.

Guren; Anne Conway Juster; Mary Lynn Laughlin; Jon H. Outcalt; Peter E. Raskind.
Distribution Committee: Yvonne L. Allen; Lorenzo T. Carlisle; Leigh H. Carter; James V. Connell; Jane M. Neubauer; Doreen E. Osmun; Joanne Rand Schwartz; Michael R. Sheppard; John H. Wilharm, Jr.
Number of staff: 2 full-time professional; 1 part-time professional; 1 full-time support; 1 part-time support.
EIN: 340934478
Selected grants: The following grants are a representative sample of this grantmaker's funding activity:
$47,500 to Great Lakes Museum of Science, Environment and Technology, Cleveland, OH, 2012. For Excellent Teaching Initiatives.
$38,300 to Austintown Local Schools, Austintown, OH, 2012. For Re-Thinking How Children Learn Mathematics.
$30,000 to Case Western Reserve University, Cleveland, OH, 2012. For STEM Initiative.
$21,900 to Willoughby-Eastlake City School District, Willoughby, OH, 2012. For GET Science Project.
$17,850 to Kent State University, Kent, OH, 2012. For Keep Academy.
$15,440 to Akron Public Schools, Akron, OH, 2012. For Teacher as Learner.
$15,105 to Ohio Northern University, Ada, OH, 2012. For Summer Honors Institute.
$8,000 to Tri-County Educational Service Center, Wooster, OH, 2012. For IB Diploma Program.

7510
The Andrew Jergens Foundation ✧
c/o The Greater Cincinnati Foundation
200 W. 4th St.
Cincinnati, OH 45202-2775 (513) 241-2880
Contact: Jennie Geisheimer, Grants Mgr.
E-mail: geisheimerj@gcfdn.org; Main URL: http://www.gcfdn.org

Incorporated in 1962 in OH.
Donor: Andrew N. Jergens†.
Foundation type: Independent foundation.
Financial data (yr. ended 08/31/13): Assets, $11,305,056 (M); expenditures, $1,099,018; qualifying distributions, $1,050,649; giving activities include $1,006,300 for 60 grants (high: $65,000; low: $300).
Purpose and activities: Giving to programs directly serving children in the greater Cincinnati, OH, area, with emphasis on organizations serving minority, low-income, and/or disadvantaged children.
Fields of interest: Child development, education; Children/youth, services; Children/youth; Children; Economically disadvantaged.
Type of support: Program development.
Limitations: Applications accepted. Giving limited to the greater Cincinnati, OH, area, including Butler, Clermont, Hamilton, and Warren counties in OH, and Boone, Campbell and Kenton counties in KY. No grants to individuals, or for continuing support, annual campaigns, endowment funds, deficit financing, scholarships, fellowships, research, or emergency requests (unless they involve disaster and human suffering); no loans.
Publications: Application guidelines; Grants list.
Application information: See http://www.gcfdn.org under Grants/Types of Grants/Private Foundation Grants/Jergens Foundation for submission and other information pertaining specifically to The Andrew Jergens Foundation. Formal applications are by invitation only, upon review of Letter of Inquiry. Application form required.
Initial approach: E-mail online Letter of Inquiry which can be downloaded from foundation web site
Deadline(s): See foundation web site for current deadlines
Board meeting date(s): Mar./Apr., June/July, and Oct.
Final notification: 1 month after meetings
Officers and Trustees:* Michael B. Hays,* Chair.; Peter H. Dine-Jergens,* Pres.; Eric H. Kearney,* V.P.; Consuelo W. Harris,* Secy.; Thomas C. Hays,* Treas.; Mary Ann Hays; Rev. Andrew M. Jergens; Linda Busken Jergens; Joyce J. Keeshin.
EIN: 316038702

7511
The Jewish Foundation of Cincinnati ✧
4555 Lake Forest Dr., Ste. 645
Cincinnati, OH 45242-3785 (513) 214-1200
Contact: Brian Jaffee, Exec.Dir.
FAX: (513) 792-2716;
E-mail: info@thejewishfoundation.org; Main URL: http://www.thejewishfoundation.org

Established in 1995 in OH; created when the Jewish Hospital of Cincinnati's entry into the Health Alliance of Cincinnati produced assets in excess of what was required by each participating entity.
Donor: Orla Mieziner†.
Foundation type: Independent foundation.
Financial data (yr. ended 06/30/13): Assets, $84,538,665 (M); gifts received, $1,000; expenditures, $2,557,626; qualifying distributions, $2,371,728; giving activities include $2,127,352 for 13 grants (high: $974,646; low: $3,200), and $4,775 for foundation-administered programs.
Purpose and activities: Giving primarily in the following areas: 1) Unmet Basic Needs (coordinating with the Jewish Federation of Cincinnati and other local Jewish agencies to identify unique ways to help ensure that the basic needs of all Jews are met, including housing, food, medical, transportation, and jobs); 2) Jewish Education Opportunities (promoting excellence in all forms of Jewish education in Cincinnati by investing in institutional leadership, educators, institutions, materials, tools and programs); 3) Leadership Development (Enhancing all components of Jewish life by developing volunteer and professional Jewish communal leadership within organizations of all kinds); 4) Continuity of Jewish Involvement (facilitating system-wide integration of services and programs to enable lifelong involvement in Jewish life); and 5) Israel Connection (promoting meaningful connections with Israel in order to deepen Jewish identity and involvement in Jewish life).
Fields of interest: Jewish agencies & synagogues.
International interests: Israel.
Type of support: Capital campaigns; Building/renovation; Equipment; Emergency funds; Matching/challenge support.
Limitations: Giving primarily in Cincinnati, OH, and to health organizations benefiting Israel. No grants to individuals, or for general operating support, or for debt reduction or for endowments.
Application information:
Initial approach: Letter
Deadline(s): None
Board meeting date(s): Varies
Officers and Trustees:* Gary Heiman,* Chair.; Michael Oestreicher,* Pres.; J. David Rosenberg,* V.P.; Jeffrey Zipkin, M.D.*, Secy.; Beth Guttman,* Treas.; Brian Jaffee,* Exec. Dir.; Robert Brant; Bret Caller; Michael Fisher; Gloria S. Haffer; Robert Kanter; Leslie Newman.
Number of staff: 1 part-time professional.
EIN: 311451489

7512
Conrad & Caroline Jobst Foundation ✧
c/o KeyBank, N.A.
P.O. Box 10099
Toledo, OH 43699-0099 (419) 259-6197
Contact: Alyce Juby

Established in 1986 in OH.
Foundation type: Independent foundation.
Financial data (yr. ended 12/31/13): Assets, $10,311,062 (M); expenditures, $744,293; qualifying distributions, $679,877; giving activities include $660,000 for 4 grants (high: $310,000; low: $70,000).
Purpose and activities: Giving primarily for health associations and medical education; funding also for an Episcopal church, and the symphony.
Fields of interest: Performing arts, orchestras; Higher education; Medical research, institute; Protestant agencies & churches.
Limitations: Applications accepted. Giving primarily in Toledo, OH; funding also in Ann Arbor, MI. No grants to individuals.
Application information: Application form required.
Initial approach: Proposal
Deadline(s): July 31
Trustees: John M. Curphey, Esq.; Adam Barcroft; Douglas Metz, Esq.; KeyBank, N.A.
EIN: 346872214

7513
The Jochum-Moll Foundation ✧
P.O. Box 368022
Cleveland, OH 44136-9722

Incorporated in 1961 in OH.
Donors: MTD Products, Inc.; A.F. Holding Co.
Foundation type: Company-sponsored foundation.
Financial data (yr. ended 07/31/13): Assets, $35,429,169 (M); expenditures, $1,863,937; qualifying distributions, $1,708,845; giving activities include $1,652,000 for 57 grants (high: $400,000; low: $1,000).
Purpose and activities: The foundation supports food banks and organizations involved with education, health, employment, agriculture, human services, business and industry, and Christianity.
Fields of interest: Arts; Education; Human services.
Type of support: General/operating support; Annual campaigns; Capital campaigns; Building/renovation; Equipment; Program development.
Limitations: Applications not accepted. Giving primarily in OH. No grants to individuals.
Application information: Contributes only to pre-selected organizations.
Officers and Trustees:* Carol M. Manning,* Pres.; Theodore S. Moll,* V.P.; David J. Hessler,* Secy.; Curtis E. Moll,* Treas.; Emma E. Jochum; Curtis David Moll; Darrell Moll.
EIN: 346538304

Selected grants: The following grants are a representative sample of this grantmaker's funding activity:
$62,000 to United Way of Greater Cleveland, Cleveland, OH, 2011.
$30,000 to Salvation Army of Greater Cleveland, Cleveland, OH, 2010.
$30,000 to Salvation Army of Greater Cleveland, Cleveland, OH, 2011.
$25,000 to Cleveland Foodbank, Cleveland, OH, 2011.
$25,000 to Manufacturing Advocacy and Growth Network, Cleveland, OH, 2011.
$20,000 to Lutheran Chaplaincy Service, Cleveland, OH, 2011.
$20,000 to Valparaiso University, Valparaiso, IN, 2011.
$12,500 to Cleveland Institute of Art, Cleveland, OH, 2011.
$10,000 to Building Hope in the City, Cleveland, OH, 2011.
$10,000 to Youth Opportunities Unlimited, Cleveland, OH, 2011.
$8,000 to Cleveland Orchestra, Cleveland, OH, 2011.

7514
The Kim Jordan Foundation ✧
20820 Chagrin Blvd., Ste. 300
Shaker Heights, OH 44122-5323

Established in TX.
Donor: Kathryn H. Jordan.
Foundation type: Independent foundation.
Financial data (yr. ended 12/31/12): Assets, $8,158,576 (M); expenditures, $534,860; qualifying distributions, $420,031; giving activities include $420,031 for grants.
Fields of interest: Health care; Human services; Protestant agencies & churches.
Limitations: Applications not accepted.
Application information: Unsolicited requests for funds not accepted.
Trustee: Kathryn H. Jordan.
EIN: 266579229

7515
The Walter and Jean Kalberer Foundation ✧ ☆
1259 W. Hill Dr.
Gates Mills, OH 44040-9636

Established in 1995 in OH.
Donors: Walter E. Kalberer; Jean C. Kalberer; Peter Scheid.
Foundation type: Independent foundation.
Financial data (yr. ended 12/31/13): Assets, $3,286,507 (M); expenditures, $673,132; qualifying distributions, $672,932; giving activities include $672,932 for 12 grants (high: $300,000; low: $3,000).
Fields of interest: Arts; Education; Human services.
Limitations: Applications not accepted. Giving primarily in Cleveland, OH. No grants to individuals.
Application information: Contributes only to pre-selected organizations.
Trustees: Jean C. Kalberer; Lori Kalberer; Walter E. Kalberer; Gwenn S. Winkhaus.
EIN: 341817179

7516
The Kaplan Foundation ✧
9435 Waterstone Blvd., Ste. 390
Cincinnati, OH 45249-8227 (513) 721-5086
Contact: Steven J. Kaplan, Tr.

Established in 1994 in OH.
Foundation type: Independent foundation.
Financial data (yr. ended 12/31/13): Assets, $9,229,567 (M); expenditures, $478,007; qualifying distributions, $443,300; giving activities include $443,100 for 14 grants (high: $100,000; low: $500).
Purpose and activities: Giving primarily for religion, education, and medical and community projects.
Fields of interest: Museums; Performing arts; Education; Human services; United Ways and Federated Giving Programs; Jewish federated giving programs; Jewish agencies & synagogues; Religion.
Type of support: General/operating support.
Limitations: Applications accepted. Giving primarily in the greater Cincinnati, OH, area. No grants to individuals.
Application information: Application form required.
Initial approach: Letter
Deadline(s): None
Officer: Barbara S. Kaplan, M.D., Pres.
Trustees: Richard M. Kaplan; Steven J. Kaplan.
EIN: 311423392

7517
Robert T. Keeler Foundation ✧ ☆
425 Walnut St., Ste. 1800
Cincinnati, OH 45202-3957

Established in 2001 in OH.
Donor: Robert T. Keeler†.
Foundation type: Independent foundation.
Financial data (yr. ended 12/31/13): Assets, $28,380,179 (M); expenditures, $1,254,632; qualifying distributions, $1,009,085; giving activities include $937,100 for 17 grants (high: $140,000; low: $10,000).
Fields of interest: Arts; Education; Hospitals (specialty); Health care; Children.
Limitations: Applications not accepted. Giving primarily in CA and OH. No grants to individuals.
Application information: Contributes only to pre-selected organizations.
Officers and Trustees:* Peter P. Mithoefer,* Pres.; Heather M. Mithoefer,* V.P.; Mary L. Rust,* Secy.-Treas.
Number of staff: None.
EIN: 311420552

7518
Joseph and Nancy Keithley Foundation ✧
c/o Chess Financial Corp.
1100 Superior Ave. E., Ste. 700
Cleveland, OH 44114-2518

Established in 2000 in OH.
Donor: Joseph P. Keithley.
Foundation type: Independent foundation.
Financial data (yr. ended 12/31/13): Assets, $5,181,800 (M); expenditures, $653,537; qualifying distributions, $609,250; giving activities include $609,250 for 29 grants (high: $225,000; low: $500).
Fields of interest: Museums (art); Performing arts, orchestras; Arts; Higher education; Environment, natural resources.
Limitations: Applications not accepted. Giving primarily in Cleveland, OH; some giving in NY. No grants to individuals.
Application information: Contributes only to pre-selected organizations.
Officers and Trustees:* Joseph P. Keithley,* Pres.; Nancy F. Keithley,* Secy.-Treas.
EIN: 341926208

7519
Dorothy M. M. Kersten Charitable Trust ✧
c/o U.S. Bank, N.A.
P.O. Box 1118, ML CN-OH-W10X
Cincinnati, OH 45201-1118

Established in 1986; supporting organization of Cincinnati Children's Hospital, Cincinnati Institute of Fine Arts, Zoological Society of Cincinnati, Church of the Advent, Cincinnati Museum of Natural History, American Heart Association, United Way, Shriners Hospital for Children, Cincinnati Art Museum, Cincinnati Preservation Association, National Trust for Historic Preservation, Historic Southwest Ohio, Public Library of Cincinnati, The Salvation Army, Shakertown at Pleasant Hill, Inc., American Cancer Society, Greater Cincinnati Television, and Little Sisters of the Poor, OH.
Foundation type: Independent foundation.
Financial data (yr. ended 06/30/13): Assets, $23,088,517 (M); expenditures, $864,664; qualifying distributions, $620,852; giving activities include $594,107 for 18 grants (high: $84,136; low: $7,705).
Purpose and activities: Giving primarily for the arts, human services and health organizations, including a children's hospital.
Fields of interest: Museums; Museums (art); Historic preservation/historical societies; Arts; Libraries (public); Hospitals (specialty); Health organizations, association; Human services.
Limitations: Applications not accepted. Giving in the U.S., with emphasis on Cincinnati, OH. No grants to individuals.
Application information: Contributes only to pre-selected organizations; unsolicited requests for funds not considered or acknowledged.
Trustee: U.S. Bank, N.A.
EIN: 316258173
Selected grants: The following grants are a representative sample of this grantmaker's funding activity:
$17,568 to Church of the Advent, Cincinnati, OH, 2013. For Chicago.

7520
The Kettering Family Foundation ✧
1480 Kettering Twr.
Dayton, OH 45423-1160
Contact: Judith M. Thompson, Exec. Dir.
FAX: (937) 228-2399;
E-mail: info@Ketteringfamilyfoundation.org; Main URL: http://kff.cfketteringfamilies.com/
Grants List: https://www.cfketteringfamilies.com/kff/grants-history/2013

Incorporated in 1956 in IL; reincorporated in 1966 in OH.

Donors: E.W. Kettering‡; Virginia W. Kettering‡; Jane K. Lombard; S.K. Williamson; Richard D. Lombard‡; B. Weiffenbach‡; Charles F. Kettering III; Lisa S. Kettering, M.D.; Leslie G. Williamson; Douglas E. Williamson, M.D.; Susan S. Kettering; Kyle W. Kim; Mark A. Cox; Douglas J. Cushnie; Karen W. Cushnie; Linda K. Danneberg; William H. Danneberg; Jean S. Kettering; Richard J. Lombard; Debra L. Williamson; Nathalie R. Lombard.
Foundation type: Independent foundation.
Financial data (yr. ended 12/31/13): Assets, $21,925,152 (M); gifts received, $2,000; expenditures, $918,718; qualifying distributions, $876,726; giving activities include $837,540 for 46 grants (high: $80,000; low: $1,000).
Purpose and activities: Giving primarily for arts, culture, and humanities, education, the environment, health care and human services.
Fields of interest: Visual arts; Performing arts; Arts; Higher education; Education; Environment, natural resources; Environment; Health care; Medical research, institute; Human services.
Type of support: General/operating support; Annual campaigns; Capital campaigns; Equipment; Endowments; Program development; Conferences/seminars; Publication; Curriculum development; Research; Technical assistance; Matching/challenge support.
Limitations: Applications accepted. Giving on a national basis. No support for foreign purposes, religious organizations for religious purposes, public elementary or secondary schools, or local chapters of national organizations, or conduit organizations. No grants to individuals, or for scholarships, fellowships, memberships, multi-year grants, capital construction, travel expenses, or community drives; no loans.
Publications: Financial statement; Grants list.
Application information: E-mails preferred. Unsolicited proposals considered after trustee-endorsed requests. Trustee-endorsed requests get priority. Trustees may endorse requests from generally excluded areas. Only trustee-endorsed requests will be considered for international giving. Grants list available on the foundation's web site.
Initial approach: Submission through on-line application process only. The foundation strongly recommends contacting its office to discuss proposal prior to application. See foundation web site for application procedures
Copies of proposal: 1
Deadline(s): Jan. 31 and July 31 for request summary. If approved, Mar. 15 and Sept. 15, for full proposals
Board meeting date(s): Mid-May and mid-Nov.
Final notification: 2 weeks after board meetings
Officers and Trustees:* Charles F. Kettering III, Pres.; Susan S. Kettering,* V.P.; Debra L. Williamson,* V.P.; Karen W. Cushnie,* Secy.-Treas.; Judith Thompson, Exec. Dir.; Linda K. Danneberg; Lisa S. Kettering, M.D.; Kyle W. Kim; Jane K. Lombard; Richard J. Lombard; Douglas E. Williamson, M.D.; Susan K. Williamson.
Number of staff: None.
EIN: 310727384
Selected grants: The following grants are a representative sample of this grantmaker's funding activity:
$54,100 to Craig Hospital Foundation, Englewood, CO, 2012. For Therapeutic Recreation/Operating Support.
$50,000 to Sherman Library Association, Sherman, CT, 2012. For Capital Campaign and Operating Support.
$45,000 to CEC ArtsLink, New York, NY, 2012. For Global Arts Lab.
$20,000 to Vermont Institute of Natural Science, Quechee, VT, 2012. For General Operating Support and Scholarships.
$15,000 to Montshire Museum of Science, Norwich, VT, 2012. For Pavilion Project.
$10,000 to Case Western Reserve University, Cleveland, OH, 2012. For Urea Cycle Disorders Research.
$10,000 to Vital Communities, White River Junction, VT, 2012. For Valley Quest Operating Support.
$6,500 to Dayton Performing Arts Alliance, Dayton, OH, 2012. For Dayton Ballet.
$5,000 to Brooklyn Botanic Garden, Brooklyn, NY, 2012. For children's education programs.

7521
The Virginia W. Kettering Foundation ✧

1480 Kettering Twr.
Dayton, OH 45423 (937) 228-1021
Contact: Judith M. Thompson, Exec. Dir.
E-mail: info@ketteringfamilyphilanthropies.org; Main URL: http://vwk.cfketteringfamilies.com/
Grants List: http://kff.cfketteringfamilies.com/vwk/grants-history

Established in 2003 in OH.
Donors: Virginia W. Kettering‡; 1988 Kettering Tower Trust.
Foundation type: Independent foundation.
Financial data (yr. ended 12/31/13): Assets, $28,383,871 (M); expenditures, $1,378,794; qualifying distributions, $1,240,484; giving activities include $1,214,181 for 49 grants (high: $185,000; low: $1,618).
Purpose and activities: Giving to support charitable activities within Montgomery County, Ohio and counties contiguous to it. The foundation's primary areas of support are arts, culture and humanities, education, the environment, medical and health, human services and programs that benefit the public and society.
Fields of interest: Arts; Education; Environment; Health care; Human services.
Type of support: General/operating support; Management development/capacity building; Annual campaigns; Capital campaigns; Equipment; Program development; Scholarship funds; Research.
Limitations: Applications accepted. Giving primarily in Butler, Clark, Darke, Greene, Miami, Montgomery, Preble, and Warren counties in OH. No support for religious organizations for religious purposes or for individual public elementary or secondary schools or public school districts. No grants or loans to individuals or for multi-year grants, tickets, advertising or sponsorship of fundraising events.
Publications: Application guidelines; Financial statement; Grants list.
Application information: Full proposals are by invitation only, upon review of request summary. All applications are to be submitted through the web site's on-line process. Faxed, mailed or hand-delivered request summaries and full proposals will not be accepted except under unusual circumstances, and solely at the discretion of foundation staff.
Initial approach: Create (or return to) online account on foundation web site, then access online request summary form. The foundation strongly recommends that applicants contact the office to discuss the proposed program before the application process begins
Copies of proposal: 1
Deadline(s): Jan. 31 and July 31 for request summary
Board meeting date(s): Spring and fall
Final notification: 3 weeks after submission of request summary
Officer: Judith Thompson, Exec. Dir.
Trustee: JPMorgan Chase Bank, N.A.
EIN: 316570701
Selected grants: The following grants are a representative sample of this grantmaker's funding activity:
$50,000 to Kettering University, Flint, MI, 2010. For general support.
$40,000 to AIDS Resource Center Ohio, Dayton, OH, 2010. For general support.
$25,000 to Boys and Girls Club of Dayton, Dayton, OH, 2013.
$25,000 to Zoological Society of Cincinnati, Cincinnati, OH, 2010. For general support.
$15,000 to Boys and Girls Club of Dayton, Dayton, OH, 2010. For general support.

7522
The Kettering Fund ✧

1480 Kettering Twr.
Dayton, OH 45423-1020 (937) 228-1021
Contact: Judith Thompson, Exec. Dir.
FAX: (937) 228-2399;
E-mail: info@ketteringfamilyphilanthropies.org; Main URL: http://fund.cfketteringfamilies.com/

Established in 1958 in OH.
Donor: Charles F. Kettering‡.
Foundation type: Independent foundation.
Financial data (yr. ended 12/31/13): Assets, $84,887,221 (M); expenditures, $1,095,479; qualifying distributions, $673,779; giving activities include $626,946 for 12 grants (high: $356,000; low: $4,000).
Purpose and activities: Grants for scientific, medical, social, and educational studies and research.
Fields of interest: Performing arts; Arts; Higher education; Education; Health care; Human services.
Type of support: Capital campaigns; Building/renovation; Equipment; Endowments; Program development; Seed money; Scholarship funds; Research; Technical assistance; Program evaluation.
Limitations: Applications accepted. Giving limited to OH. No support for religious purposes, public elementary or secondary schools, or for efforts to carry on propaganda or otherwise attempt to influence legislation. No grants to individuals, or for travel, deficit reduction, or benefit events; no loans.
Publications: Financial statement; Grants list.
Application information: The fund is not accepting Request Summaries until further notice.
Initial approach: E-mail or telephone. All applications are through the on-line application process
Deadline(s): Request Summaries: Jan. 31 or July 31
Board meeting date(s): Usually in early May and Nov.
Officer: Judith Thompson, Exec. Dir.

Distribution Committee: Susan S. Kettering; Jane K. Lombard; Debra Williamson; Susan K. Williamson.
Trustee: JPMorgan Chase Bank, N.A.
Number of staff: 1 part-time professional.
EIN: 316027115
Selected grants: The following grants are a representative sample of this grantmaker's funding activity:
$100,000 to University of Dayton, Dayton, OH, 2012. For scholarships.
$40,000 to Ohio Arts Council, Columbus, OH, 2012. For CEC ArtsLink.
$25,000 to Greater Dayton Public Television, Dayton, OH, 2012. For Educational Resource Guide.
$6,000 to Loudonville Agricultural Society, Loudonville, OH, 2013. For awards and scholarships.

7523
KeyBank Foundation ✧
(formerly Key Foundation)
800 Superior Ave., 1st Fl.
M.C. OH-01-02-0126
Cleveland, OH 44114-2601 (216) 828-7349
Contact: Lorraine Vega, Sr. Prog. Off.
FAX: (216) 828-7845;
E-mail: key_foundation@keybank.com; Philanthropic Contacts: Civic, Health, and Human Services: Lorraine, Vega, tel.: (216) 828-7402, e-mail: Lorraine_Vega@KeyBank.com; Education: Eric S. Brown, tel.: (216) 828-7396, e-mail eric_s_brown@keybank.com; Arts and Culture and sponsorships: Karen White, tel.: (216) 828-8539, e-mail: Karen_A_White@KeyBank.com; Main URL: https://www.key.com/about/community/key-foundation-philanthropy-banking.jsp

Established about 1969 in OH.
Donors: Society Corp.; Society Capital Corp.; KeyBank N.A.; KeyCorp.
Foundation type: Company-sponsored foundation.
Financial data (yr. ended 12/31/12): Assets, $37,019,359 (M); gifts received, $9,250,000; expenditures, $12,936,466; qualifying distributions, $12,839,816; giving activities include $12,839,816 for 4,468 grants (high: $1,000,000; low: $25).
Purpose and activities: The foundation supports organizations involved with arts and culture, education, health, human services, and civic affairs. Special emphasis is directed toward programs designed to enhance economic self-sufficiency through financial education, workforce development, and diversity.
Fields of interest: Arts; Vocational education; Education; Health care; Employment, services; Employment, training; Employment; Human services, financial counseling; Human services; Civil/human rights, equal rights; Community development, small businesses; United Ways and Federated Giving Programs; Public affairs; Physically disabled; Minorities; Economically disadvantaged; LGBTQ.
Type of support: General/operating support; Continuing support; Annual campaigns; Capital campaigns; Program development; Curriculum development; Scholarship funds; Employee volunteer services; Sponsorships; Employee matching gifts; Matching/challenge support.
Limitations: Applications accepted. Giving primarily in areas of company operations in AK, CO, ID, IN, KY, ME, MI, NY, OH, OR, UT, VT, and WA; giving also to national organizations. No support for organizations outside geographic footprint, athletic teams, fraternal organizations, or discriminatory organizations. No grants to individuals, or for memberships, lobbying or political activities, or advertising.
Publications: Application guidelines; Corporate report; Occasional report.
Application information: Full proposals must include a proposal summary form. Proposals are evaluated by funding committees in KeyBank district offices. Visit website for nearest district office address. Organizations receiving support are asked to provide a final report 3 months after the completion of the project.
Initial approach: Letter of inquiry, proposal summary form, or telephone for preliminary inquiries; full proposals to foundation for organizations located in northeast OH; full proposal to closest key district office for organizations located outside of northeast, OH
Copies of proposal: 1
Deadline(s): None
Board meeting date(s): Quarterly
Final notification: Within 3 months
Officers and Trustees:* Margot James Copeland,* Chair.; Christopher M. Gorman, Pres.; James Hoffman, V.P.; Paul N. Harris, Secy.; Mark Whitham, Treas.; Cindy P. Crotty; Bruce D. Murphy; Elizabeth J. Oliver.
Number of staff: 4 full-time professional.
EIN: 237036607
Selected grants: The following grants are a representative sample of this grantmaker's funding activity:
$1,000,000 to United Way of Greater Cleveland, Cleveland, OH, 2012. For Program Support.
$200,000 to Cleveland Clinic Foundation, Cleveland, OH, 2012. For Scholarships.
$200,000 to Cleveland Metropolitan School District, Cleveland, OH, 2012. For Program Support.
$189,286 to Playhouse Square Foundation, Cleveland, OH, 2012. For Capital Campaign.
$50,000 to Girl Scouts of the U.S.A., Macedonia, OH, 2012. For Program Support.
$50,000 to Hospice of the Western Reserve, Cleveland, OH, 2012. For Program Support.
$5,000 to Bridge Meadows, Portland, OR, 2012. For Operating Support.
$5,000 to College of Idaho, Caldwell, ID, 2012. For Program Support.
$5,000 to Lake George Opera Festival Association, Saratoga Springs, NY, 2012. For Program Support.
$5,000 to United Jewish Federation of Northeastern New York, Albany, NY, 2012. For Program Support.

7524
Walter & Olivia Kiebach Foundation ✧
8964 Little Mountain Rd., Ste. 1000
Kirtland Hills, OH 44060-7946

Foundation type: Independent foundation.
Financial data (yr. ended 12/31/12): Assets, $9,199,124 (M); gifts received, $4,806; expenditures, $583,789; qualifying distributions, $475,020; giving activities include $470,000 for 40 grants (high: $50,000; low: $1,000).
Fields of interest: Education; Human services; Religion.
Limitations: Applications not accepted.
Application information: Unsolicited requests for funds not accepted.
Board Members: Dett P. Hunter; Joseph P. Keller; Blakely C. Page; Andrew Quinn.
EIN: 364631948

7525
Kikel Charitable Foundation ✧
c/o Farmers Trust Co.
42 McClurg Rd.
Youngstown, OH 44512-6700

Foundation type: Independent foundation.
Financial data (yr. ended 12/31/12): Assets, $13,852,763 (M); expenditures, $890,910; qualifying distributions, $793,228; giving activities include $758,176 for 2 grants (high: $379,096; low: $379,080).
Fields of interest: Health care.
Limitations: Applications not accepted. Giving primarily in Boardman and Youngstown, OH.
Application information: Contributes only to pre-selected organizations.
Trustee: Farmers Trust Co.
EIN: 341893970

7526
Doris & Floyd Kimble Foundation ✧
(formerly The Foundation for the Continuity of Mankind)
3596 State Rte. 39NW
Dover, OH 44622-7232 (330) 343-1226
Contact: Doris J. Kimble, Tr.

Established in 1989 in OH.
Donors: Floyd E. Kimble†; Doris Kimble.
Foundation type: Independent foundation.
Financial data (yr. ended 12/31/12): Assets, $46,599,981 (M); expenditures, $2,282,911; qualifying distributions, $2,113,979; giving activities include $1,957,575 for 56 grants (high: $400,000; low: $1,000), and $30,943 for foundation-administered programs.
Purpose and activities: Giving primarily for arts, education, hospitals and human services.
Fields of interest: Arts; Higher education; Education; Hospitals (general); Human services; United Ways and Federated Giving Programs.
Type of support: General/operating support; Building/renovation.
Limitations: Applications accepted. Giving primarily in OH. No grants to individuals.
Application information:
Initial approach: Letter
Deadline(s): None
Trustees: Doris Kimble; Greg Kimble; Phillip Raber.
EIN: 341622273

7527
Knight Charitable Trust ✧
c/o Mark F. Swary
200 Public Sq., Ste. 2800
Cleveland, OH 44114-2315

Established in 2003 in OH.
Donors: Floyd C. Knight†; Virginia Knight†; Knight Charitable Remainder Trust.
Foundation type: Independent foundation.
Financial data (yr. ended 12/31/12): Assets, $10,069,767 (M); expenditures, $699,683; qualifying distributions, $514,203; giving activities

include $514,203 for 3 grants (high: $257,101; low: $128,551).
Purpose and activities: Giving primarily to a college, a Baptist church, and a retirement community.
Fields of interest: Higher education; Residential/custodial care, senior continuing care; Protestant agencies & churches.
Limitations: Applications not accepted. Giving primarily in OH and OK. No grants to individuals.
Application information: Contributes only to pre-selected organizations.
Trustee: Mark F. Swary.
EIN: 436907987

7528
Austin E. Knowlton Foundation Inc. ✧
414 Walnut St., Ste. 1205
Cincinnati, OH 45202-3957 (513) 381-2400
Contact: Sherri L. Calk, C.A.O.
FAX: (513) 381-7666; E-mail address for Sherri L. Calk, C.A.O.: scalk@aekfoundation.org; Main URL: http://www.aekfoundation.org

Established in 1982 in OH.
Donor: Austin E. Knowlton†.
Foundation type: Independent foundation.
Financial data (yr. ended 12/31/12): Assets, $161,151,522 (M); gifts received, $128,550,541; expenditures, $7,277,411; qualifying distributions, $7,273,261; giving activities include $6,735,000 for 28 grants (high: $2,000,000; low: $5,000).
Fields of interest: Higher education.
Type of support: General/operating support.
Limitations: Applications accepted. Giving primarily in IL and OH. No grants to individuals.
Application information: Application form not required.
Initial approach: Proposal
Copies of proposal: 1
Deadline(s): None
Officers: John C. Lindberg, Pres.; Eric V. Lindberg, V.P.; Sherri L. Calk, C.A.O.
Trustees: Edward D. Diller; Robert A. Pitcairn, Jr.
EIN: 311044475

7529
Milton A. & Charlotte R. Kramer Charitable Foundation ✧ ☆
c/o North Point Tower
1001 Lakeside Ave., Ste. 900
Cleveland, OH 44114-1177

Established in 1984 in OH.
Donor: Charlotte R. Kramer.
Foundation type: Independent foundation.
Financial data (yr. ended 12/31/13): Assets, $5,163,448 (M); expenditures, $551,505; qualifying distributions, $523,516; giving activities include $519,169 for 59 grants (high: $162,250; low: $125).
Purpose and activities: Giving for the arts, education, human services and Jewish agencies.
Fields of interest: Education; Health care; Jewish agencies & synagogues.
Type of support: General/operating support; Annual campaigns; Endowments; Program development; Scholarship funds; Program evaluation; Matching/challenge support.
Limitations: Applications not accepted. Giving primarily in the Cleveland, OH, area; funding also in NY. No grants to individuals.
Application information: Contributes only to pre-selected organizations.
Board meeting date(s): Varies
Directors: Michael J. Horvitz; Joseph Kartiganer; Benjamin Kramer; Charlotte R. Kramer; Elizabeth Kramer; Mark R. Kramer; Toby Kramer.
EIN: 341467089

7530
The Krause Family Foundation ✧ ☆
3333 Richmond Rd., No. 350
Beachwood, OH 44122-4196

Established in 1968 in OH.
Donors: Harold Krause; Alan M. Krause.
Foundation type: Independent foundation.
Financial data (yr. ended 12/31/13): Assets, $660,256 (M); gifts received, $800,000; expenditures, $613,408; qualifying distributions, $610,858; giving activities include $610,858 for 34 grants (high: $200,000; low: $53).
Fields of interest: Museums; Arts; Education; Jewish agencies & synagogues; Religion.
Type of support: General/operating support.
Limitations: Applications not accepted. Giving primarily in Cleveland, OH; funding also in FL and NY. No grants to individuals.
Application information: Unsolicited requests for funds not accepted.
Officer: Alan M. Krause, Mgr.
EIN: 346611350

7531
The Kroger Co. Foundation
1014 Vine St.
Cincinnati, OH 45202-1148 (513) 762-4441
Contact: Lynn Marmer, Pres.
FAX: (513) 762-1295; Main URL: http://www.thekrogerco.com/community/kroger-foundation

Established in 1987 in OH.
Donor: The Kroger Co.
Foundation type: Company-sponsored foundation.
Financial data (yr. ended 01/31/14): Assets, $37,395,363 (M); gifts received, $5,750,777; expenditures, $9,351,693; qualifying distributions, $9,099,847; giving activities include $9,099,847 for 1,172 grants (high: $138,166; low: $41).
Purpose and activities: The foundation supports organizations involved with education, women's health, breast cancer, hunger, minorities, and women.
Fields of interest: Elementary/secondary education; Education; Health care; Breast cancer; Food services; Food banks; Women, centers/services; Minorities/immigrants, centers/services; United Ways and Federated Giving Programs; Minorities; Women.
Type of support: Capital campaigns; Program development; Seed money; Employee volunteer services.
Limitations: Applications accepted. Giving primarily in areas of company operations in AL, AR, AZ, CA, CO, GA, IL, IN, KS, KY, MI, MS, NV, OH, OR, TN, TX, UT, VA, WA, and WV. No support for national or international organizations, non-educational foundations, medical research organizations, or religious organizations or institutions not of direct benefit to the entire community. No grants to individuals, or for conventions or conferences, dinners or luncheons, endowments, general operating support, sports event sponsorships, program advertisements, or membership dues.
Publications: Application guidelines; Financial statement.
Application information: Application form not required.
Initial approach: Proposal to nearest company division
Deadline(s): None
Officers and Trustees: Lynn Marmer, Pres.; Paul W. Heldman, Secy.; Scott M. Henderson, Treas.; David B. Dillon; Dennis Hackett; Marnette Perry; Pete Williams.
Number of staff: 1 part-time professional.
EIN: 311192929
Selected grants: The following grants are a representative sample of this grantmaker's funding activity:
$689,354 to USO World Headquarters, Arlington, VA, 2013.
$309,500 to Scholarship America, Saint Peter, MN, 2013.
$133,651 to Oregon Food Bank, Portland, OR, 2013.
$100,000 to Nationwide Childrens Hospital, Columbus, OH, 2013.
$97,410 to California Science Center Foundation, Los Angeles, CA, 2013.
$75,000 to Junior Achievement of Oregon and SW Washington, Portland, OR, 2013.
$62,500 to United Way of Greater Cincinnati, Cincinnati, OH, 2013.
$50,000 to American Cancer Society, California Division, San Diego, CA, 2013.
$10,000 to Christian Helping Hands, Pearland, TX, 2013.
$7,804 to Target Hunger, Houston, TX, 2013.

7532
Kulas Foundation ✧
50 Public Sq., Ste. 600
Cleveland, OH 44113-2267 (216) 623-4770
Contact: Nancy W. McCann, Pres.
FAX: (216) 623-4773; Main URL: http://fdnweb.org/kulas

Incorporated in 1937 in OH.
Donors: Fynette H. Kulas†; E.J. Kulas†.
Foundation type: Independent foundation.
Financial data (yr. ended 12/31/13): Assets, $40,326,384 (M); expenditures, $3,027,838; qualifying distributions, $2,830,370; giving activities include $2,379,700 for 100 grants (high: $210,000; low: $200).
Purpose and activities: Grants largely to music institutions and for higher education; support also for local performing arts and social services.
Fields of interest: Museums; Performing arts; Performing arts, music; Arts; Education, association; Education, fund raising/fund distribution; Higher education; Education; Human services.
Type of support: General/operating support; Continuing support; Annual campaigns; Capital campaigns; Building/renovation; Equipment; Land acquisition; Program development; Conferences/seminars; Professorships; Research; Consulting services; Matching/challenge support.
Limitations: Applications not accepted. Giving limited to Cuyahoga County, OH, and its contiguous counties. No support for mental health

organizations. No grants to individuals, or for endowment funds; no loans or scholarships.
Publications: Financial statement.
Application information: The foundation currently is not accepting applications from new grantseekers. See foundation web site for further details.
Board meeting date(s): 4 times per year
Officers and Trustees:* Richard W. Pogue,* Chair. and V.P.; Nancy W. McCann,* Pres. and Treas.; Richard J. Clark, V.P. and Secy.; Patrick F. McCartan, Esq.*, V.P.; Ellen E. Halfon, Esq.
Number of staff: 1 full-time professional; 2 full-time support.
EIN: 340770687
Selected grants: The following grants are a representative sample of this grantmaker's funding activity:
$150,000 to Oberlin College, Oberlin, OH, 2011.
$140,000 to Musical Arts Association, Cleveland, OH, 2011.
$20,000 to Cleveland State University Foundation, Cleveland, OH, 2011.

7533
Lancaster Lens, Inc. ✧
37 W. Broad St., Ste. 530
Columbus, OH 43215-4132

Established in 1953.
Foundation type: Independent foundation.
Financial data (yr. ended 07/31/13): Assets, $12,791,009 (M); expenditures, $485,421; qualifying distributions, $453,390; giving activities include $450,000 for 13 grants (high: $125,000; low: $10,000).
Fields of interest: Higher education, university; Hospitals (specialty); Children/youth, services; Family services; Community/economic development; Foundations (private grantmaking).
Limitations: Applications not accepted. Giving primarily in Columbus, OH. No grants to individuals.
Application information: Contributes only to pre-selected organizations.
Officers: Bruce L. Rosa, Pres.; Clarence Clapham, Secy.
EIN: 316023927

7534
Elma M. Lapp Foundation ✧
38 Fountain Square Plz.
Cincinnati, OH 45202-3102

Established in OH; supporting organization of the University of Cincinnati and the University of Cincinnati College of Medicine.
Foundation type: Independent foundation.
Financial data (yr. ended 09/30/13): Assets, $56,728,142 (M); expenditures, $2,808,739; qualifying distributions, $2,621,725; giving activities include $2,614,895 for 4 grants (high: $1,743,263; low: $290,544).
Purpose and activities: Giving primarily for higher education; funding also for the performing arts.
Fields of interest: Museums; Performing arts, orchestras; Performing arts, opera; Higher education.
Limitations: Applications not accepted. Giving limited to Cincinnati, OH.
Application information: Unsolicited requests for funds not considered or acknowledged.
Trustee: The Fifth Third Bank.
EIN: 316229734
Selected grants: The following grants are a representative sample of this grantmaker's funding activity:
$1,584,976 to University of Cincinnati, College of Medicine, Cincinnati, OH, 2011.
$264,161 to Cincinnati Museum Association, Cincinnati, OH, 2011.
$264,161 to Cincinnati Opera Association, Cincinnati, OH, 2011.
$264,161 to Cincinnati Symphony and Pops Orchestra, Cincinnati, OH, 2011.

7535
The LaValley Foundation ✧
5800 Monroe St., Bldg. F
Sylvania, OH 43560-2263

Established in 1992 in OH.
Donor: Richard G. LaValley.
Foundation type: Independent foundation.
Financial data (yr. ended 12/31/13): Assets, $21,965,873 (M); expenditures, $1,232,903; qualifying distributions, $1,119,100; giving activities include $1,119,100 for 47 grants (high: $127,500; low: $1,000).
Fields of interest: Education; Human services; Catholic agencies & churches.
Type of support: General/operating support; Scholarship funds.
Limitations: Applications not accepted. Giving primarily in Toledo, OH. No grants to individuals.
Application information: Contributes only to pre-selected organizations.
Trustees: Daniel J. LaValley; Richard G. LaValley, Jr.
EIN: 341722402
Selected grants: The following grants are a representative sample of this grantmaker's funding activity:
$62,000 to University of Toledo Foundation, Toledo, OH, 2012. For donee's exempt purposes.
$10,000 to Boy Scouts of America, Erie Shores, Toledo, OH, 2012. For donee's exempt purposes.

7536
Lehner Family Foundation ✧
344 Inverness Rd.
Akron, OH 44313-4516 (330) 867-3729
Contact: Robin Compton, Exec. Dir.

Established in 1989 in OH.
Donors: Marie Lehner†; Jane Lehner†; Charles Lehner†.
Foundation type: Independent foundation.
Financial data (yr. ended 12/31/13): Assets, $21,142,225 (M); expenditures, $1,446,371; qualifying distributions, $1,182,952; giving activities include $1,077,495 for 66 grants (high: $100,000; low: $500).
Purpose and activities: Giving primarily for the arts, human services, and Roman Catholic agencies and churches; funding also for a zoological park.
Fields of interest: Museums (art); Arts; Higher education; Zoos/zoological societies; Youth development; Human services; Community/economic development; Foundations (private grantmaking); Catholic agencies & churches.
Type of support: Capital campaigns; Building/renovation; Equipment; Matching/challenge support.
Limitations: Applications accepted. Giving limited to Summit County, OH. No support for public schools. No grants to individuals.
Application information: Application form required.
Initial approach: 1-page summary
Copies of proposal: 1
Deadline(s): Mar. 31, June 30, Sept. 30, and Dec. 31
Officers: Richard W. Burke, Fdn. Mgr.; David M. Koly, Fdn. Mgr.; Michael R. Stark, Fdn. Mgr.
Number of staff: 1 full-time professional.
EIN: 346927210

7537
The Fred A. Lennon Charitable Trust ✧
29425 Chagrin Blvd., Ste. 201
Cleveland, OH 44122-4602
Contact: Chris Hitchcock

Established in 1993 in OH.
Donor: Fred A. Lennon†.
Foundation type: Independent foundation.
Financial data (yr. ended 12/31/13): Assets, $79,648,060 (M); expenditures, $3,847,510; qualifying distributions, $3,523,146; giving activities include $3,255,500 for 134 grants (high: $400,000; low: $1,000).
Purpose and activities: Giving primarily for health and economic development.
Fields of interest: Higher education; Health care; Economic development.
Type of support: General/operating support; Continuing support; Income development; Management development/capacity building; Annual campaigns; Capital campaigns; Building/renovation; Equipment; Program development; Seed money; Internship funds; Scholarship funds; Research; Matching/challenge support.
Limitations: Applications accepted. Giving primarily in northeast OH. No grants to individuals; no loans.
Publications: Informational brochure (including application guidelines).
Application information: Application form not required.
Initial approach: Letter
Copies of proposal: 1
Deadline(s): Apr. 1 and Sept. 1
Board meeting date(s): May and Oct.
Final notification: Up to 6 months
Trustees: A. Anton; T. Janoch; E.A. Lozick; T. Ryan; N. Tobbe.
Number of staff: 1 part-time professional.
EIN: 341761181

7538
The Lerner Foundation ✧
26500 Curtiss Wright Pkwy.
Highland Heights, OH 44143-1438 (440) 891-5000
Contact: Douglas C. Jacobs

Established in 1993 in OH.
Donors: Alfred Lerner†; Norma Lerner.
Foundation type: Independent foundation.
Financial data (yr. ended 12/31/13): Assets, $12,072,851 (M); expenditures, $2,309,121; qualifying distributions, $2,287,431; giving activities include $2,285,231 for 33 grants (high: $625,000; low: $100).

Purpose and activities: Support primarily for medical care, Jewish agencies and temples and Jewish federated giving programs.
Fields of interest: Museums (art); Higher education; Health care, single organization support; Hospitals (general); Jewish federated giving programs; Jewish agencies & synagogues.
Limitations: Applications accepted. Giving primarily in NY, OH and VA. No grants to individuals.
Application information: Application form not required.
Initial approach: Letter
Deadline(s): None
Officers and Trustees:* Norma Lerner,* Pres. and Treas.; Nancy Fisher,* V.P.; Randolph Lerner,* V.P.; James H. Berick,* Secy.
EIN: 341744726
Selected grants: The following grants are a representative sample of this grantmaker's funding activity:
$625,000 to Jewish Community Federation of Cleveland, Cleveland, OH, 2013. For general operating support.
$400,000 to Cleveland Museum of Art, Cleveland, OH, 2013. For general operating support.
$250,000 to Cleveland Clinic, Cleveland, OH, 2013. For Lerner Research Institute.
$238,331 to Cleveland Clinic Childrens Hospital, Center for Autism, Cleveland, OH, 2013. For general operating support.
$218,000 to Cleveland Orchestra, Cleveland, OH, 2013. For general operating support.
$200,000 to Cleveland Clinic, Cleveland, OH, 2013. For general operating support.
$100,000 to Memorial Sloan-Kettering Cancer Center, New York, NY, 2013. For general operating support.
$50,000 to United Way of Greater Cleveland, Cleveland, OH, 2013. For general operating support.
$30,000 to United States Holocaust Memorial Museum, Washington, DC, 2013. For general operating support.
$10,000 to Cleveland Clinic Foundation, Cleveland, OH, 2013. For general operating support.

7539
Levin Family Foundation ✧
7812 McEwen Rd., Ste. 100
Dayton, OH 45459-4069
E-mail: debbie@levinfamilyfoundation.org; Main URL: http://www.levinfamilyfoundation.org
Grants List: http://levinfamilyfoundation.org/past-grant-recipients.cfm

Established in 1990 in OH.
Donors: Allen Levin; Louis Levin; Barbara Levin‡; Karen Levin; Ryan Levin; Darrell Murphy; Howard Michaels; Peter Wells; LCNB; Sinclair Community College.
Foundation type: Independent foundation.
Financial data (yr. ended 12/31/13): Assets, $23,024,365 (M); gifts received, $215,771; expenditures, $1,427,088; qualifying distributions, $1,063,722; giving activities include $569,494 for 229 grants (high: $50,000; low: $50), and $75,338 for 1 foundation-administered program.
Purpose and activities: Giving primarily for health, human services, civic and community organizations, education, the underserved, and arts and culture.
Fields of interest: Arts; Education; Human services; Children, services; Jewish federated giving programs; Jewish agencies & synagogues; Women; AIDS, people with; Crime/abuse victims; Economically disadvantaged; Homeless.
Type of support: Capital campaigns; Building/renovation; Equipment; Emergency funds; Program development; Conferences/seminars; Publication; Seed money; Internship funds; Research; Program evaluation; Matching/challenge support.
Limitations: Applications accepted. Giving primarily in the Montgomery County, OH, area. The foundation also considers projects on a case-by-case basis outside this area and internationally if the projects reflect its priorities of interest. No support for political or advocacy groups, or for fiscal agents and other umbrella organizations that provide funding to non-profits. No grants to individuals, or for endowment funds.
Publications: Application guidelines.
Application information: After contacting foundation, submit a letter of intent (approx. 1 page). After review of letter of intent, foundation may invite a full proposal. Application guidelines differ depending upon amount of funds requested. See foundation web site for complete application guidelines and procedures. Application form required.
Initial approach: Contact foundation and speak with the Exec. Dir.
Deadline(s): See foundation web site for current deadlines
Officers and Board Members:* Allen Levin,* Pres.; Louis Levin,* V.P. and Treas.; Karen Levin,* Secy. and Exec. Dir.; Debbie Fox, Dir., Grants and Opers.; Ryan Levin; Howard Michaels; Peter Wells.
Number of staff: 1 full-time professional; 1 part-time support.
EIN: 311327847

7540
Licking County Foundation ✧
30 N. Second St.
P.O. Box 4212
Newark, OH 43058-4212 (740) 349-3863
Contact: Connie Hawk, Dir.
FAX: (740) 322-6260;
E-mail: lcf@thelcfoundation.org; Grant Inquiry Form e-mail: grants@thelcfoundation.org; Main URL: http://www.thelcfoundation.org
Scholarship inquiry e-mail: scholarships@thelcfoundation.org

Established in 1956 in OH.
Foundation type: Community foundation.
Financial data (yr. ended 12/31/12): Assets, $52,615,693 (M); gifts received, $809,612; expenditures, $2,095,113; giving activities include $1,283,293 for 29+ grants (high: $251,400).
Purpose and activities: The foundation seeks to improve the quality of life for the citizens of Licking County, OH. Giving primarily for arts, education, health care, recreation, human services, and children and youth services.
Fields of interest: Performing arts, music; Arts; Education; Environment, beautification programs; Health care; Mental health/crisis services; Medical research, institute; Diabetes research; Recreation; Children/youth, services; Human services; Children/youth; Disabilities, people with; Blind/visually impaired.
Type of support: Capital campaigns; Building/renovation; Equipment; Conferences/seminars; Seed money; Curriculum development; Scholarship funds; Matching/challenge support.
Limitations: Applications accepted. Giving limited to Licking County, OH. No support for religious or sectarian purposes. No grants to individuals (except for scholarships), or for annual campaigns, debt retirement or restructuring, national fundraising drives or events, feasibility studies, tickets for benefits, regranting organizations, or endowments.
Publications: Application guidelines; Annual report; Informational brochure; Newsletter.
Application information: Visit foundation web site for Grant Inquiry Form and application guidelines. Application form required.
Initial approach: E-mail Grant Inquiry Form
Copies of proposal: 5
Deadline(s): Aug. 27 for Grant Inquiry Form; Dec. 10 for Full Grant Proposal
Board meeting date(s): Feb., May, Aug., and Nov.
Final notification: Early Mar.
Officers and Governing Committee:* David Trautman,* Chair.; Frank Murphy,* Chair., Emeritus; J. Gilbert Reese,* Chair., Emeritus; Jeff Cox,* Vice-Chair.; Judy Pierce,* Secy.-Treas.; Mike Cantlin; Eschol Curl; Michael Kennedy; Jerry McClain; William McConnell; Cynthia Menzer; Sue Moore; Janine Mortellaro; Stu Parsons.
Trustee Banks: Merrill Lynch Trust Co.; National City Bank; The Park National Bank.
Number of staff: 2 full-time professional; 1 part-time professional.
EIN: 316018618

7541
Lincoln Electric Foundation
c/o KeyBank
4900 Tiedeman Rd., OH-01-49-0150
Brooklyn, OH 44144-2302 (216) 689-0416
Contact: Agnes Marountas
Application address: c/o Keybank, 127 Public Sq., Cleveland, OH 44114

Trust established in 1952 in OH.
Donors: The Lincoln Electric Co.; Lincoln Electric.
Foundation type: Company-sponsored foundation.
Financial data (yr. ended 12/31/13): Assets, $3,007,030 (M); gifts received, $1,200,000; expenditures, $1,313,804; qualifying distributions, $1,308,476; giving activities include $1,305,250 for 88 grants (high: $200,000; low: $1,500).
Purpose and activities: The foundation supports charter schools and hospitals and organizations involved with arts and culture, higher education, lung diseases, human services, the welding industry, and community development.
Fields of interest: Media, television; Arts; Charter schools; Higher education; Education; Hospitals (general); Lung diseases; Human services; Business/industry; Community/economic development; United Ways and Federated Giving Programs.
Type of support: General/operating support; Program development; Scholarship funds.
Limitations: Applications accepted. Giving primarily in areas of company operations, with emphasis on Cleveland, OH. No loans or program-related investments.
Application information: Application form not required.
Initial approach: Letter
Deadline(s): Sept. 20
Trustee: KeyBank N.A.
Number of staff: 1
EIN: 346518355

Selected grants: The following grants are a representative sample of this grantmaker's funding activity:
$100,000 to American Welding Society, Miami, FL, 2011.
$25,000 to Challenged Child and Friends, Gainesville, GA, 2011.
$25,000 to Cleveland Clinic Foundation, Cleveland, OH, 2011.
$25,000 to Manufacturing Advocacy and Growth Network, Cleveland, OH, 2011.
$12,500 to Cleveland Museum of Natural History, Cleveland, OH, 2011.
$10,000 to Hospice of the Western Reserve, Cleveland, OH, 2011.
$8,000 to Baldwin-Wallace College, Berea, OH, 2011.
$5,000 to Great Lakes Museum of Science, Environment and Technology, Cleveland, OH, 2011.
$5,000 to MetroHealth Foundation, Cleveland, OH, 2011.
$3,000 to Center for Families and Children, Cleveland, OH, 2011.

7542
Lippman Kanfer Family Foundation ✧
(formerly Jerome Lippman Family Foundation)
P.O. Box 991
Akron, OH 44309-0991
Contact: Dara Weinerman Steinberg, Project Dir.
FAX: (330) 255-6050;
E-mail: info@lippmankanfer.org; Main URL: http://www.lippmankanfer.org

Founded in 1966.
Donors: Jerome Lippman†; GOJO Industries, Inc.
Foundation type: Independent foundation.
Financial data (yr. ended 12/31/12): Assets, $43,286,579 (M); gifts received, $80,000; expenditures, $3,867,387; qualifying distributions, $3,305,430; giving activities include $3,305,430 for 15 grants (high: $900,610; low: $1,207).
Purpose and activities: The foundation gives primarily for Jewish education, and Jewish organizational capacity building. The foundation's mission is to repair and enrich the world through thriving Jewish life.
Fields of interest: Religion.
Type of support: General/operating support; Program development.
Limitations: Applications not accepted. Giving to organizations that serve the national U.S. Jewish communities; local initiatives are limited to Akron, OH. No grants to individuals, or for endowments, capital campaigns or scholarships.
Application information: Unsolicited requests for funds not accepted. However, organizations may introduce themselves via Letter of Introduction link on foundation web site.
Board meeting date(s): Annually, (Fourth quarter)
Officers and Directors:* Marcella Kanfer Rolnick,* Chair. and Pres.; Mamie Kanfer Stewart,* Secy.; Louis Colella, Treas.; Joseph Kanfer; Pamela Kanfer; Joshua N.K. Rolnick; Donny Zigdon; Ketti Zigdon.
Number of staff: 1 full-time professional.
EIN: 340974875

7543
The Llewellyn Foundation ✧
c/o Cynthia Barnett
P.O. Box 1488
Springfield, OH 45501-1488
Main URL: http://llewellynfoundation.org/

Established in 1997 in OH.
Donor: Sarah H. Lupfer.
Foundation type: Independent foundation.
Financial data (yr. ended 02/28/13): Assets, $13,383,699 (M); expenditures, $708,697; qualifying distributions, $636,250; giving activities include $636,250 for 42 grants (high: $50,000; low: $5,000).
Fields of interest: Higher education; Education; Human services; Children/youth, services.
Limitations: Giving in the U.S., with emphasis on MA. No grants to individuals.
Application information: The foundation will only request more information from an applicant upon consideration of initial contact form. Application form required.
Initial approach: Use contact form on foundation web site
Deadline(s): Apr. 30 and Sept. 30, for new inquires via foundation web site; May 31 and Oct. 31, for invited grants
Board meeting date(s): Varies
Officers and Trustees:* Sarah H. Lupfer,* Pres.; Caroline Lupfer Kurtz,* Secy.; Jonathan B. Lupfer,* Treas.; Willis O. Kurtz.
EIN: 311534056
Selected grants: The following grants are a representative sample of this grantmaker's funding activity:
$10,000 to homeWORD, Missoula, MT, 2013. For program support.

7544
Loeb Foundation ✧ ☆
c/o LCNB National Bank
P.O. Box 59
Lebanon, OH 45036-0059 (513) 932-1414
Contact: B.H. Wright, Jr., Tr.
FAX: (513) 932-1492; E-mail: bwright@lcnb.com

Established in 1992 in OH.
Donor: Justus H. Loeb†.
Foundation type: Independent foundation.
Financial data (yr. ended 09/30/13): Assets, $7,368,307 (M); expenditures, $625,997; qualifying distributions, $532,495; giving activities include $485,580 for grants.
Purpose and activities: Giving primarily for fire and police protection.
Fields of interest: Crime/law enforcement, police agencies; Disasters, fire prevention/control; Aging.
Type of support: Loans—to individuals; Equipment; Grants to individuals.
Limitations: Applications accepted. Giving limited to Warren County, OH.
Publications: Annual report.
Application information: Application form not required.
Initial approach: Letter
Copies of proposal: 3
Deadline(s): Aug. 15
Board meeting date(s): Early Sept.
Final notification: Late Sept.
Trustees: Michael E. Foley; Bernard H. Wright, Jr.; LCNB National Bank.
Number of staff: None.
EIN: 316225986

7545
The Edward A. & Catherine L. Lozick Foundation ✧
(formerly Edward A. Lozick Foundation)
29425 Chagrin Blvd., Ste. 201
Beachwood, OH 44122-4639

Established in 1983 in OH.
Donors: Edward A. Lozick; Catherine Lozick; Swagelok Manufacturing Company.
Foundation type: Independent foundation.
Financial data (yr. ended 12/31/13): Assets, $24,855,227 (M); gifts received, $3,000,000; expenditures, $2,194,884; qualifying distributions, $2,159,270; giving activities include $2,159,270 for 287 grants (high: $1,000,000; low: $100).
Purpose and activities: Giving primarily for education and human services.
Fields of interest: Museums; Education; Health care; Human services.
Type of support: Research.
Limitations: Applications not accepted. Giving primarily in Cleveland, OH. No grants to individuals.
Application information: Contributes only to pre-selected organizations.
Officers and Trustees:* Edward A. Lozick,* Pres.; Catherine L. Lozick,* Secy.; Thomas J. Janoch,* Treas.
Number of staff: 1 part-time professional.
EIN: 341386776
Selected grants: The following grants are a representative sample of this grantmaker's funding activity:
$258,334 to Notre Dame-Cathedral Latin School, Chardon, OH, 2011.
$5,000 to Great Lakes Museum of Science, Environment and Technology, Cleveland, OH, 2011.
$1,000 to Ronald Reagan Presidential Foundation, Simi Valley, CA, 2011.

7546
The Lubrizol Foundation ✧
29400 Lakeland Blvd.
Wickliffe, OH 44092-2298 (440) 347-1797
Contact: Karen A. Lerchbacher, Grants Mgr.
FAX: (440) 347-1858;
E-mail: karen.lerchbacher@lubrizol.com; Main URL: http://www.lubrizol.com/CorporateResponsibility/Lubrizol-Foundation.html

Incorporated in 1952 in OH.
Donor: The Lubrizol Corp.
Foundation type: Company-sponsored foundation.
Financial data (yr. ended 12/31/12): Assets, $22,330,894 (M); gifts received, $5,000,000; expenditures, $2,646,768; qualifying distributions, $2,646,768; giving activities include $1,902,455 for 188 grants (high: $192,500; low: $703), and $744,313 for 1,530 employee matching gifts.
Purpose and activities: The foundation makes grants in support of education, health care, human services, civic, cultural, youth development, and environmental activities. Strong emphasis on STEM (Science, Technology, Engineering and Mathematics) education.
Fields of interest: Museums; Charter schools; Higher education; Education; Environmental

education; Environment; Youth development; Human services; Chemistry; Engineering; Youth.
Type of support: General/operating support; Continuing support; Annual campaigns; Capital campaigns; Building/renovation; Equipment; Fellowships; Scholarship funds; Employee volunteer services; Employee matching gifts.
Limitations: Applications accepted. Giving primarily in areas of major company operations, with emphasis on the greater Cleveland, OH and Houston, TX, areas. No support for religious or political organizations. No grants to individuals, or for start-up needs, debt reduction, demonstration projects, publications, or conferences; generally, no grants for endowments; no loans.
Publications: Application guidelines; Annual report (including application guidelines); Financial statement; Grants list; IRS Form 990 or 990-PF printed copy available upon request.
Application information: Additional information may be requested at a later date. A site visit may be requested. Application form not required.
Initial approach: Proposal
Copies of proposal: 1
Deadline(s): None
Board meeting date(s): As required, usually 4 times per year
Final notification: 2 weeks following board meetings
Officers and Trustees:* James L. Hambrick,* Chair.; David J. Enzerra,* Pres.; Karen A. Lerchbacher,* Secy. and Grants Mgr.; Brian A. Valentine,* Treas.; Robert T. Graf; K. L. Jethrow.
Number of staff: 1 part-time professional; 1 full-time support.
EIN: 346500595
Selected grants: The following grants are a representative sample of this grantmaker's funding activity:
$192,500 to United Way of Greater Cleveland, Cleveland, OH, 2012.
$64,000 to Ohio State University, Columbus, OH, 2012. For scholarships.
$50,000 to American Red Cross, Greater Cleveland Chapter, Cleveland, OH, 2012. For Hurricane Sandy Disaster Relief Fund.
$50,000 to Cleveland Museum of Natural History, Cleveland, OH, 2012. For exhibit.
$30,000 to Cleveland Orchestra, Cleveland, OH, 2012. For general operating support.
$30,000 to Cleveland State University, Cleveland, OH, 2012. Toward purchase of laboratory equipment.

7547
Otto Luedeking Trust ✧
P.O. Box 630858
Cincinnati, OH 45263-0858

Foundation type: Independent foundation.
Financial data (yr. ended 12/31/13): Assets, $12,055,519 (M); expenditures, $599,246; qualifying distributions, $545,559; giving activities include $545,029 for 16 grants (high: $278,294; low: $7,731).
Fields of interest: Human services; Salvation Army; YM/YWCAs & YM/YWHAs; Children/youth, services; Residential/custodial care, hospices.
Limitations: Applications not accepted. Giving primarily in Cincinnati, OH.
Application information: Unsolicited requests for funds not accepted.
Trustee: Fifth Third Bank.
EIN: 316019731

7548
The Frances R. Luther Charitable Trust ✧
P.O. Box 630858
Cincinnati, OH 45263-0858
Application address: c/o Fifth Third Bank, Attn.: Paula Wharton, 38 Fountain Square Plz., Cincinnati, OH 45263, tel.: (513) 534-5498

Established in 2000 in OH.
Donor: Frances R. Luther Trust.
Foundation type: Independent foundation.
Financial data (yr. ended 12/31/13): Assets, $42,208,014 (M); expenditures, $2,109,240; qualifying distributions, $1,918,228; giving activities include $1,830,000 for 46 grants (high: $150,000; low: $5,000).
Purpose and activities: Giving primarily for the arts, children services, including a children's hospital, social services, and community development.
Fields of interest: Arts; Hospitals (specialty); Health care; Human services; Children/youth, services; Community/economic development.
Type of support: Annual campaigns; Program development; Matching/challenge support.
Limitations: Giving primarily in Cincinnati, OH.
Application information: Application form required.
Initial approach: Letter
Deadline(s): None
Trustees: Narley L. Haley; Fifth Third Bank.
EIN: 316646985
Selected grants: The following grants are a representative sample of this grantmaker's funding activity:
$250,000 to Childrens Hospital Medical Center, Cincinnati, OH, 2011. For project/program support.
$100,000 to Ronald McDonald House Charities of Greater Cincinnati, Cincinnati, OH, 2011. For project/program support.

7549
LZ Francis Foundation ✧ ☆
c/o Catherine Petrunia
3550 Lander Rd., Ste. 200
Pepper Pike, OH 44124-5727

Established in 1992 in OH as partial successor to the Nason Foundation.
Donors: The Nason Foundation; Katharine Nason Tipper; Charles F. Tipper.
Foundation type: Independent foundation.
Financial data (yr. ended 12/31/13): Assets, $10,777,278 (M); expenditures, $656,782; qualifying distributions, $536,638; giving activities include $501,500 for 39 grants (high: $75,000; low: $2,000).
Purpose and activities: Giving primarily for historic preservation, education, the environment, and human services.
Fields of interest: Historic preservation/historical societies; Education; Environment, natural resources; Human services.
Limitations: Applications not accepted. Giving primarily in VT, with some emphasis on Burlington; giving also in Fort Pierce and Vero Beach, FL. No grants to individuals.
Application information: Contributes only to pre-selected organizations.
Officers: Katharine Nason Tipper, Pres. and Treas.; Charles F. Tipper, V.P. and Secy.; Jessica A. Oski, V.P.
EIN: 341721860
Selected grants: The following grants are a representative sample of this grantmaker's funding activity:
$90,000 to Vermont Land Trust, Montpelier, VT, 2012. For Focus on Conserving Vital and in Vermont.
$30,000 to Nature Conservancy, Montpelier, VT, 2012. To promote Conservation of Land and Water.
$16,000 to Oxfam America, Boston, MA, 2012. To prevent Poverty and Injustice.
$15,000 to Vermont Sustainable Jobs Fund, Montpelier, VT, 2012. To promote Vermont's Green Economy.
$10,000 to Intervale Center, Burlington, VT, 2012. To strengthen Community Food Systems.
$10,000 to Lake Champlain Land Trust, Burlington, VT, 2012. To preserve Lake Champlain.
$8,000 to 350.org, Washington, DC, 2012. To support Global Grassroots Movement to Solve the Climate Crisis.
$8,000 to Audubon Vermont, Huntington, VT, 2012. For Protection of Birds, Other Wildlife and Their Habitat.
$8,000 to Center for Whole Communities, Fayston, VT, 2012. To Strengthen the Capacities of Environmental and Social Sectors.
$4,000 to Chittenden Emergency Food Shelf, Burlington, VT, 2012. For Food Relief Services to Low-Income Individuals.

7550
M/I Homes Foundation ✧
(formerly M/I Schottenstein Homes Foundation)
3 Easton Oval, Ste. 500
Columbus, OH 43219-6011 (614) 418-8041
Contact: Robert H. Schottenstein, Pres. and Dir.

Established in 1989 in OH.
Donors: M/I Homes, Inc.; M/I Schottenstein Homes, Inc.
Foundation type: Company-sponsored foundation.
Financial data (yr. ended 12/31/13): Assets, $275,834 (M); gifts received, $250,200; expenditures, $446,886; qualifying distributions, $445,267; giving activities include $445,267 for 35 grants (high: $150,000; low: $500).
Purpose and activities: The foundation supports community foundations and organizations involved with arts and culture, education, health, housing, human services, and community development.
Fields of interest: Arts; Health care; Recreation.
Limitations: Applications accepted. Giving primarily in Columbus, OH.
Application information: Application form required.
Initial approach: Letter
Copies of proposal: 1
Deadline(s): None
Officers and Directors: Robert H. Schottenstein,* Pres.; Phillip G. Creek,* V.P.; J. Thomas Mason,* Secy.; Ann Marie Hunker, Treas.
Number of staff: None.
EIN: 311254013

7551
The Macbea Foundation ✧ ☆
52 E. Gay St.
Columbus, OH 43215-3108 (614) 464-8295
Contact: Mark E. Vannatta, Secy.-Treas.

Established in 2010 in OH.
Donors: Joseph Gernert; Margaret Gernert.
Foundation type: Independent foundation.
Financial data (yr. ended 12/31/13): Assets, $26,187,312 (M); expenditures, $3,041,398; qualifying distributions, $2,906,528; giving activities include $2,892,000 for 25 grants (high: $1,000,000; low: $2,000).
Fields of interest: Arts; Education; Community/economic development.
Limitations: Applications accepted. Giving primarily in OH.
Application information: Application form required.
Initial approach: Proposal
Deadline(s): None
Officers: George M. Hoffman, Pres.; Mark E. Vannatta, Secy.-Treas.
Director: Robert M. Hetterscheidt.
EIN: 273409621

7552
Macy's Foundation ✧
(formerly Federated Department Stores Foundation)
c/o Macy's Corp. Svcs., Inc.
7 W. 7th St.
Cincinnati, OH 45202-2424 (513) 579-7000
FAX: (513) 579-7185; Main URL: http://www.federated-fds.com/community/

Established in 1995 in OH.
Donors: Federated Department Stores, Inc.; The May Department Stores Foundation.
Foundation type: Company-sponsored foundation.
Financial data (yr. ended 02/01/14): Assets, $102,994 (M); gifts received, $11,109,000; expenditures, $12,168,250; qualifying distributions, $12,164,680; giving activities include $11,931,489 for 6,412 grants (high: $809,095; low: $25).
Purpose and activities: The foundation supports programs designed to promote arts and culture, education, the environment, HIV/AIDS awareness and research, and women issues and domestic violence.
Fields of interest: Arts; Education; Environment; Breast cancer; AIDS; AIDS research; Food services; Food banks; Youth development, intergenerational programs; Aging, centers/services; United Ways and Federated Giving Programs; Minorities; Women.
Type of support: General/operating support; Continuing support; Annual campaigns; Capital campaigns; Program development; Seed money; Scholarship funds; Employee volunteer services; Employee matching gifts; Employee-related scholarships; Matching/challenge support.
Limitations: Applications accepted. Giving on a national basis in areas of company operations, with emphasis on CA, FL, GA, MO, NY, and OH. No support for private foundations, fraternal organizations, political or advocacy groups, athletic teams, religious organizations not of direct benefit to the entire community, charities whose focus and operations are primarily international, or fiscal agents or other umbrella organizations providing funding to nonprofit organizations. No grants to individuals, or for event or program sponsorships, or salaries for nonprofit staffing.
Publications: Application guidelines.
Application information: The foundation utilizes an invitation only process for general corporate grants. My Macy's District Grants are reviewed by local District Grants Committee's. Application form not required.
Initial approach: Complete online eligibility quiz and application for My Macy's District Gants
Copies of proposal: 1
Deadline(s): None for My Macy's District Gants
Board meeting date(s): Quarterly
Final notification: 4 to 8 weeks for My Macy's District Grants
Officers and Trustees:* James A. Sluzewski,* Pres.; Ann Munson Steines, Secy.; Matt Stautberg, Treas.; Timothy M. Adams; David W. Clark; Julie Greiner; Karen M. Hoguet.
EIN: 311427325
Selected grants: The following grants are a representative sample of this grantmaker's funding activity:
$1,000,000 to OASIS Institute, Saint Louis, MO, 2012. For Enriching the Lives of Mature Adults.
$912,590 to United Way of Metropolitan Atlanta, Atlanta, GA, 2013. For Corporate Gift.
$893,568 to United Way of Metropolitan Atlanta, Atlanta, GA, 2012. For corporate gift.
$415,000 to United Way of Greater Cincinnati, Cincinnati, OH, 2013. For Corporate Gift.
$415,000 to United Way of Greater Cincinnati, Cincinnati, OH, 2012. For corporate gift.
$380,000 to ArtsWave, Cincinnati, OH, 2012. For ArtWave Community Campaign.
$350,000 to United Way of Greater Cincinnati, Cincinnati, OH, 2013. For Winning Beginnings for Kindergarten Readiness.
$336,000 to ArtsWave, Cincinnati, OH, 2013. For Annual Community Campaign.
$250,000 to Lincoln Center for the Performing Arts, New York, NY, 2012.
$250,000 to OASIS Institute, Saint Louis, MO, 2013. For general support.
$200,000 to Xavier University, Hebrew Union College, Cincinnati, OH, 2012.
$50,000 to San Francisco Symphony, San Francisco, CA, 2013. For general education (in honor of the Black and White Ball) and Music for Families program.
$23,360 to United Way of Metropolitan Dallas, Dallas, TX, 2013. For Corporate Gift.
$17,800 to United Way for Southeastern Michigan, Detroit, MI, 2012. For corporate gift.
$10,000 to Brooklyn Academy of Music, Brooklyn, NY, 2013. For Ignite Gala which benefits BAM education programs.
$10,000 to Hebrew College, Newton Centre, MA, 2013. For student financial aid.
$5,000 to Coalition for the Homeless, New York, NY, 2013. For First Step Job Training Program.
$5,000 to Museum of Arts and Design, New York, NY, 2012. For Visionaries.
$3,000 to Lambs Farm, Libertyville, IL, 2012. For Quest/Life Skills.
$2,500 to Harvard University, Cambridge, MA, 2012.

7553
The Milton and Tamar Maltz Family Foundation ✧
3333 Richmond Rd., Ste. 460
Beachwood, OH 44122-4199
Contact: Jason Fishman, Exec. Dir.
E-mail: jfishman@maltzfamilyfoundation.org; Main URL: http://maltzfoundation.org/

Established in 1989 in FL.
Donors: Milton S. Maltz; Tamar Maltz; Daniel Maltz; David Maltz; Julie E. Konigsberg.
Foundation type: Independent foundation.
Financial data (yr. ended 12/31/13): Assets, $94,132,810 (M); gifts received, $6,076,498; expenditures, $4,317,836; qualifying distributions, $3,700,000; giving activities include $3,700,000 for 93 grants (high: $500,000).
Purpose and activities: The foundation supports programs in the areas of the arts, health and human services, medical research, education, and the environment.
Fields of interest: Arts; Education; Environment, natural resources; Environment; Animals/wildlife; Health care; Medical research; Human services.
International interests: Israel.
Type of support: General/operating support; Management development/capacity building; Annual campaigns; Capital campaigns; Building/renovation; Land acquisition; Endowments; Professorships; Scholarship funds; Research; Matching/challenge support.
Limitations: Applications not accepted. Giving on a national basis, with emphasis on AZ, FL, and Cleveland, OH. No support for lobbying. No grants to individuals.
Application information: Contributes only to pre-selected organizations. Unsolicited proposals, grant requests, or letters of inquiry are not accepted.
Officers: Milton S. Maltz, Pres.; Julie E. Konigsberg, V.P.; Daniel Maltz, V.P.; Tamar Maltz, Secy.; David Maltz, Treas.
Number of staff: 2 full-time professional.
EIN: 650164300

7554
The Joseph and Florence Mandel Family Foundation ✧
(formerly The Joseph and Florence Mandel Foundation)
1000 Lakeside Ave. E.
Cleveland, OH 44114-1117 (216) 875-6523
Contact: JoAnn White, Tr.
FAX: (216) 875-6550; Main URL: http://www.mandelfoundation.org

Established in 1963 in OH.
Donors: Florence Mandel†; Joseph C. Mandel.
Foundation type: Independent foundation.
Financial data (yr. ended 12/31/12): Assets, $124,452,068 (M); expenditures, $8,459,360; qualifying distributions, $5,910,979; giving activities include $5,271,696 for 319+ grants (high: $3,042,712; low: $15).
Purpose and activities: Giving primarily to a Jewish community fund and other Jewish organizations, including Jewish museums.
Fields of interest: Museums (art); Museums (ethnic/folk arts); Arts; Higher education; Health organizations; United Ways and Federated Giving Programs; Jewish federated giving programs; Jewish agencies & synagogues.
Type of support: General/operating support.
Limitations: Giving primarily in OH; giving also in FL and NY. No grants to individuals.
Application information: Application form not required.
Initial approach: Proposal
Deadline(s): None
Officers and Trustees:* Bradley S. Smith,* Pres.; Karen A. Vereb, Secy.; JoAnn White, Treas.; Michele Beyer; Morton L. Mandel; Penni M. Weinberg.
EIN: 346546419

7555
The Morton and Barbara Mandel Family Foundation ✧
(formerly Morton and Barbara Mandel Foundation)
1000 Lakeside Ave.
Cleveland, OH 44114-1117 (216) 875-6523
Contact: JoAnn White, Treas.
FAX: (216) 875-6550; Israel office: 15 Graetz St., Jerusalem 93111, Israel; tel.: (972) (2) 539-9666; fax: (972) (2) 566-2837; Main URL: http://www.mandelfoundation.org

Established in 1963 in OH.
Donors: Morton L. Mandel; Barbara A. Mandel.
Foundation type: Independent foundation.
Financial data (yr. ended 12/31/12): Assets, $159,702,295 (M); gifts received, $5,389,892; expenditures, $11,086,752; qualifying distributions, $7,832,412; giving activities include $7,150,073 for 179+ grants (high: $150,000).
Purpose and activities: Support primarily for leadership, management of nonprofits, higher education, Jewish education and continuity, and for urban neighborhood renewal.
Fields of interest: Higher education; Education; Urban/community development; Nonprofit management; Community/economic development; United Ways and Federated Giving Programs; Jewish federated giving programs; Leadership development; Jewish agencies & synagogues.
International interests: Israel.
Type of support: General/operating support.
Limitations: Applications not accepted. Giving primarily in Cleveland, OH; and the U.S. & Israel. No grants to individuals.
Application information: Contributes only to pre-selected organizations.
Officers and Trustees:* Morton L. Mandel,* Pres.; Barbara A. Mandel,* V.P.; Karen A. Vereb, Secy.; JoAnn White, Treas.; Amy C. Mandel; Stacy L. Mandel; Thomas A. Mandel; Bradley S. Smith.
Number of staff: 1 full-time professional; 1 part-time professional; 2 full-time support.
EIN: 346546420
Selected grants: The following grants are a representative sample of this grantmaker's funding activity:
$5,549,993 to Simon Charitable Private, Cleveland, OH, 2012. For general support.
$150,000 to National Council of Jewish Women, New York, NY, 2012. For general support.
$42,500 to Jewish Community Board of Akron, Akron, OH, 2012. For general support.
$37,500 to Jewish Community Board of Akron, Akron, OH, 2012. For general support.
$30,000 to National Council of Jewish Women, Washington, DC, 2012. For general support.
$16,667 to Midtown Cleveland, Cleveland, OH, 2012. For general support.
$15,000 to National Council of Jewish Women, New York, NY, 2012. For general support.

7556
Jack, Joseph, and Morton Mandel Foundation ✧
(formerly Jack N. and Lilyan Mandel Foundation)
1000 Lakeside Ave.
Cleveland, OH 44114-1117 (216) 875-6523
FAX: (216) 875-6570; Additional address: 15 Graetz St., Jerusalem 93111, Israeltel.: (972) (2) 539-9669fax: (972) (2) 566-2837; Main URL: http://www.mandelfoundation.org

Established in 1963 in OH.
Donors: Jack N. Mandel†; Lilyan Mandel†.
Foundation type: Independent foundation.
Financial data (yr. ended 12/31/12): Assets, $347,274,968 (M); gifts received, $26,077,303; expenditures, $23,152,602; qualifying distributions, $16,295,588; giving activities include $15,656,109 for 93+ grants (high: $15,145,150).
Purpose and activities: Giving primarily to Jewish agencies, temples and schools.
Fields of interest: Elementary/secondary education; Jewish federated giving programs; Jewish agencies & synagogues.
Limitations: Applications accepted. Giving primarily in Cleveland, OH. No grants to individuals.
Application information: Application form not required.
Initial approach: Proposal
Deadline(s): None
Officers and Trustees:* Morton L. Mandel,* Pres.; JoAnn White, Treas.; Karen A. Vereb, Secy.; Joseph C. Mandel; Bradley Smith.
EIN: 346546418
Selected grants: The following grants are a representative sample of this grantmaker's funding activity:
$15,145,150 to Simon Charitable Private, Cleveland, OH, 2012. For general support.
$16,667 to Midtown Cleveland, Cleveland, OH, 2012. For general support.

7557
Marietta Community Foundation ✧
100 Putnam St.
P.O. Box 77
Marietta, OH 45750-0077 (740) 373-3286
Contact: Carol B. Wharff, Pres. and C.E.O.
FAX: (740) 373-3937;
E-mail: info@mariettacommunityfoundation.org; Additional e-mail: carol@mcfohio.org; Main URL: http://www.mariettacommunityfoundation.org
Facebook: https://www.facebook.com/mcfohio

Established in 1974 in OH.
Donors: Lillian Strecker Smith†; Mrs. William Mildren, Sr.†; William Mildren, Sr.†; Carl L. Broughton†; Susan Marsch; Jane McCoy Peterson†; Ida Zimmer.
Foundation type: Community foundation.
Financial data (yr. ended 12/31/13): Assets, $18,285,503 (M); gifts received, $804,445; expenditures, $792,943; giving activities include $489,912 for 30+ grants (high: $50,442), and $31,152 for 18 grants to individuals.
Purpose and activities: The foundation is committed to building a strong foundation for the community and making life better for all citizens of Washington County, OH and the surrounding communities. The foundation seeks to respond to a wide variety of needs in the community.
Fields of interest: Arts; Education; Health care; Children/youth, services; Aging, centers/services; Community/economic development.
Type of support: General/operating support; Building/renovation; Equipment; Endowments; Program development; Conferences/seminars; Seed money; Scholarship funds; Research; Technical assistance; Program-related investments/loans; Grants to individuals; Scholarships—to individuals; Matching/challenge support.
Limitations: Applications accepted. Giving limited to the Marietta, OH, area, including Washington County, OH, and Wood County, WV. No grants for annual funds or continuing support.
Publications: Application guidelines; Annual report; Grants list; Informational brochure (including application guidelines); Newsletter.
Application information: Visit foundation web site for application form and guidelines. Application form required.
Initial approach: Telephone
Copies of proposal: 1
Deadline(s): Feb. 7, June 7, and Oct. 7
Board meeting date(s): 3rd Tues. of each month
Final notification: 60 to 90 days following deadlines
Officers and Directors:* Eric Erb,* Chair.; Jonathan Dehmlow,* Vice-Chair.; Carol B. Wharff,* C.E.O. and Pres.; Arlene Archer,* Secy.; Doug Robinson,* Treas.; Jennifer Christy; Dr. Bret Frye; Louise Holmes; Karen Osborne; Mark Schwendeman; Marcy Wesel; Teri Ann Zide.
Number of staff: 1 full-time professional; 1 part-time professional; 2 part-time support.
EIN: 743054287

7558
Marion Community Foundation, Inc. ✧
(formerly Ohio MedCenter Foundation, Inc.)
504 S. State St.
Marion, OH 43302-5036 (740) 387-9704
Contact: Dean L. Jacob, C.E.O.
FAX: (740) 375-0665;
E-mail: info@marioncommunityfoundation.org; Additional e-mail: deanjacob@marioncommunityfoundation.org; Main URL: http://www.marioncommunityfoundation.org

Established in 1998 in OH; converted from the sale of MedCenter Hospital.
Foundation type: Community foundation.
Financial data (yr. ended 06/30/13): Assets, $39,364,362 (M); gifts received, $648,750; expenditures, $1,906,197; giving activities include $1,317,006 for 31+ grants (high: $265,193).
Purpose and activities: The foundation is dedicated to enhancing the quality of life for the greater Marion area through fostering philanthropy consistent with community values by providing a vehicle for planned giving through acceptance management and distribution of endowed funds in accordance with the wishes of their donors.
Fields of interest: Public health, obesity; Health care; Eye diseases; Arthritis; Parkinson's disease; Food services; Food banks; Recreation, adaptive sports; Youth development; Human services, transportation; Disabilities, people with; Economically disadvantaged; Homeless.
International interests: Dominican Republic.
Type of support: General/operating support; Annual campaigns; Capital campaigns; Building/renovation; Equipment; Endowments; Program development; Conferences/seminars; Publication; Seed money; Curriculum development; Scholarship funds; Research; Technical assistance; Program evaluation; Scholarships—to individuals.
Limitations: Applications accepted. Giving limited to the greater Marion County, OH, area.
Publications: Application guidelines; Annual report; Financial statement; Grants list; Informational brochure; Newsletter.
Application information: Visit foundation web site for application forms and guidelines. Application form required.

Initial approach: Submit application form and attachments
Copies of proposal: 1
Deadline(s): July 26
Board meeting date(s): Monthly
Officers and Trustees:* Susie Brown,* Chair.; Dr. Charles Garvin,* Vice-Chair.; Dean L. Jacob,* C.E.O. and Pres.; Nicole Workman,* Secy.; Megan Queen,* Treas.; Dr. James Barney; John C. Bartram; Larry Geissler; Ted Graham; Kathy Goodman; Hon. Thomas K. Jenkins; Rev. Daniel Kiger; Rex Parrott; Dr. Kimberly Stark; Lowell Thurston; Dr. Scott Yancey.
Number of staff: 1 full-time professional; 1 part-time professional; 1 full-time support.
EIN: 314446189

7559
Elizabeth Ring Mather and William Gwinn Mather Fund

1111 Superior Ave., Ste. 1000
Cleveland, OH 44114-2568 (216) 696-4200
Contact: Lucy I. Weller, Pres.

Incorporated in 1954 in OH.
Donors: Elizabeth Ring Mather‡; James D. Ireland; Lucy I. Weller; Cornelia Hallinan; George R. Ireland; United States Trust Co.
Foundation type: Independent foundation.
Financial data (yr. ended 12/31/13): Assets, $17,763,076 (M); gifts received, $1,082,046; expenditures, $1,431,579; qualifying distributions, $1,327,144; giving activities include $1,246,836 for 79 grants (high: $173,500; low: $1,000).
Fields of interest: Arts; Higher education; Education; Human services.
Type of support: General/operating support; Annual campaigns; Building/renovation; Endowments; Publication.
Limitations: Applications accepted. Giving primarily in OH, with emphasis on the greater Cleveland area; some funding also in MA and NY. No grants to individuals, or for scholarships or fellowships; no loans.
Application information: Application form required.
Initial approach: Letter
Copies of proposal: 1
Deadline(s): Oct. 1
Board meeting date(s): June and Dec.
Officers: Lucy I. Weller, Pres.; Cornelia I. Hallinan, Secy.; George R. Ireland, Treas.
Trustees: Tess Ireland Hallinan; James D. Ireland III; James D. Ireland IV; Katherine R. Ireland.
Number of staff: 1 part-time professional.
EIN: 346519863
Selected grants: The following grants are a representative sample of this grantmaker's funding activity:
$107,500 to Phillips Academy, Andover, MA, 2012. For Repair and replacement of Addison Gallery of American Art roof.
$100,000 to Regis High School, New York, NY, 2012. For Second Century Campaign.
$50,000 to Fund for Our Economic Future, Cleveland, OH, 2012. For economic development and stimulating economy.
$33,333 to Holden Arboretum, Kirtland, OH, 2012. For New Leaf campaign and Unrestricted operating support.
$10,000 to Harcourt Parish Episcopal Church, Gambier, OH, 2012. For Parish ministry to Kenyon students.

7560
Mathile Family Foundation

6450 Sand Lake Rd., Ste. 100
Dayton, OH 45414-2679 (937) 264-4600
Contact: Emily Lewis, Opers. Coord.
FAX: (937) 264-4805;
E-mail: mffinfo@mathilefamilyfoundation.org; Mailing address: P.O. Box 13615, Dayton, OH 45413-0615; E-mail for letter of inquiry: grants@mathilefamilyfoundation.org; Main URL: http://www.mathilefamilyfoundation.org/
E-Newsletter: http://www.mathilefamilyfoundation.org/contact/

Established in 1989 in OH.
Donors: Clayton Lee Mathile; MaryAnn Mathile.
Foundation type: Independent foundation.
Financial data (yr. ended 11/30/13): Assets, $290,020,854 (M); expenditures, $47,983,279; qualifying distributions, $31,577,772; giving activities include $28,620,294 for 165 grants (high: $18,000,000; low: $1,500).
Purpose and activities: The mission of the foundation is transforming the lives of children and its vision is sharing God's blessings by perpetuating a multi-generational foundation committed to philanthropic excellence. The foundation believes in fostering hope and inspiring change, impacting children in need, the strength of family, and being a servant of God's work.
Fields of interest: Education; Food services; Children/youth, services; Family services; Homeless, human services; Infants/toddlers; Children/youth; Children; Youth; Economically disadvantaged.
Type of support: General/operating support; Equipment; Program development; Matching/challenge support.
Limitations: Applications accepted. Giving primarily in the Dayton and Montgomery County, OH, areas. No support for political organizations. No grants to individuals or for sponsorships, endowment funds, advertising for fundraising events/tickets, or mass appeals for funding.
Publications: Application guidelines; Annual report (including application guidelines).
Application information: See foundation web site for more application information. Application form required.
Initial approach: Letter of inquiry must be e-mailed. Proposal must be submitted online
Copies of proposal: 1
Deadline(s): Feb. 1, May 1, Aug. 1, and Nov. 1
Final notification: Within 100 days after the deadline
Officers and Trustees:* MaryAnn Mathile,* Chair., C.E.O., and Treas.; Clayton Lee Mathile,* Pres.; Richard J. Chernesky,* Secy.; Gregory Edwards, Exec. Dir.; Francis J. Butler; Timothy Mathile; John C. Vatterott; Mary E. Walsh.
Number of staff: 8 full-time professional.
EIN: 311257219
Selected grants: The following grants are a representative sample of this grantmaker's funding activity:
$9,100,000 to Mathile Philanthropic Trust, Dayton, OH, 2012. For general operating.
$1,500,000 to Glen at Saint Joseph, Dayton, OH, 2012. For general operating.
$1,471,855 to Parents Advancing Choice in Education, Dayton, OH, 2012. For general operating and project support.
$1,400,000 to Chaminade Julienne High School, Dayton, OH, 2012. For capital support.
$868,278 to University of Dayton, Dayton, OH, 2012. For project support.
$750,000 to Dayton Foundation, Dayton, OH, 2012. For project support.
$250,000 to Catholic Social Services of the Miami Valley, Dayton, OH, 2012. For project support.
$35,000 to Comprehensive Community Child Care Organization, Miami Valley Regional Office, Dayton, OH, 2012. For project support.
$33,000 to Ohio Association of Nonprofit Organizations, Columbus, OH, 2012. For general operating and project support.
$21,658 to University of Dayton, Dayton, OH, 2012. For scholarship - individual student.

7561
Manuel D. & Rhoda Mayerson Foundation ✧

312 Walnut St., Ste. 3600
Cincinnati, OH 45202-4029 (513) 621-7500
Contact: Jeff Seibert, Grants Off.
FAX: (513) 621-2864; E-mail for Jeff Seibert, Grants Off.: jeffs@mayersonfoundation.org; additional e-mail: info@mayersonfoundation.org; Main URL: http://www.mayersonfoundation.org

Established in 1986 in FL.
Donors: Manuel D. Mayerson‡; Rhoda Mayerson; Manuel D. Mayerson Charitable Annuity Lead Trust; The 2002 Arlene and Neal Mayerson Charitable Lead Trust.
Foundation type: Independent foundation.
Financial data (yr. ended 10/31/13): Assets, $30,094,016 (M); expenditures, $2,395,920; qualifying distributions, $1,908,256; giving activities include $1,908,256 for 78 grants (high: $869,505; low: $18).
Purpose and activities: Giving primarily for Judaism, health and well-being, basic needs, inclusion, civic engagement, and the arts.
Fields of interest: Arts; Health care; Human services; Jewish federated giving programs; Jewish agencies & synagogues.
Type of support: General/operating support; Management development/capacity building; Annual campaigns; Capital campaigns; Building/renovation; Emergency funds; Program development; Seed money; Technical assistance; Matching/challenge support.
Limitations: Applications accepted. Giving primarily in the Greater Cincinnati, OH, area, with limited grantmaking in other areas where foundation trustees reside, and at the initiative of those trustees. No support for political organizations. No grants to individuals, or for travel or study.
Publications: Grants list; Informational brochure (including application guidelines); Multi-year report.
Application information: Letters of intent or full proposals are by invitation only, after initial correspondence with Jeff Seibert. Application form required.
Initial approach: Tel. or e-mail Jeff Seibert, Grants Off. to determine eligibility
Copies of proposal: 1
Deadline(s): Ongoing
Board meeting date(s): Quarterly
Final notification: One quarter after full proposal is received
Officers and Trustees:* Neal H. Mayerson, Ph.D.*, Pres. and Treas.; Arlene B. Mayerson,* V.P.; Donna Mayerson, Ph.D.*, Secy.; Frederic H. Mayerson, J.D.; Manuel D. Mayerson; Rhoda Mayerson.

Number of staff: 3 full-time professional; 2 part-time professional; 1 full-time support.
EIN: 311310431

7562
The Arthur B. McBride, Sr. Family Foundation ✧ ☆

2069 W. 3rd St.
Cleveland, OH 44113-2502

Established in 1989 in OH.
Donors: Arthur B. McBride, Jr.; Rita McBride Charitable Lead Annuity Trust; Brian A. McBride.
Foundation type: Independent foundation.
Financial data (yr. ended 12/31/13): Assets, $6,373,491 (M); gifts received, $53,760; expenditures, $448,806; qualifying distributions, $444,711; giving activities include $444,511 for 87 + grants (high: $100,000).
Purpose and activities: Giving primarily to Roman Catholic agencies and churches, and for health care, education, and social services.
Fields of interest: Higher education; Education; Hospitals (general); Medical research, institute; Human services; YM/YWCAs & YM/YWHAs; Catholic agencies & churches.
Type of support: General/operating support.
Limitations: Applications not accepted. Giving primarily in the Cleveland, OH, area. No grants to individuals.
Application information: Contributes only to pre-selected organizations.
Trustees: Brian A. McBride; Maureen McBride; Rita McBride; Kathleen McBride Plum.
EIN: 341612197
Selected grants: The following grants are a representative sample of this grantmaker's funding activity:
$5,000 to University of Miami, Coral Gables, FL, 2011. For unrestricted operating funds.

7563
The McConnell Educational Foundation ✧ ☆

200 W. Nationwide Blvd.
Columbus, OH 43215-2563

Established in 1992 in OH.
Donors: John P. McConnell; John H. McConnell†; Ohiohealth Parent; Worthington Industries; Billy Prim; Peter Karmanos, Jr.; James Mason; Mark Ayers; Stephen Kimpel; William Burgett; John Blystone; Vorys, Sater, Seymour & Pease; Michael Endres; Dave Probst; Anthony Ciafardini; Michael Denver; John Surma.
Foundation type: Independent foundation.
Financial data (yr. ended 12/31/13): Assets, $41,976,266 (M); gifts received, $203,600; expenditures, $1,516,140; qualifying distributions, $1,404,400; giving activities include $1,404,400 for 26 grants (high: $1,022,700; low: $2,000).
Purpose and activities: Giving primarily for education.
Fields of interest: Elementary/secondary education; Education.
Type of support: Scholarship funds.
Limitations: Applications not accepted. Giving primarily in CO, OH, and WV. No grants to individuals.
Application information: Contributes only to pre-selected organizations.
Officers and Trustees:* John P. McConnell,* Pres.; Michael A. Priest,* V.P. and Treas.; Kimberly R. Sievers, Secy.; Daniel J. Minor.
EIN: 311365344

7564
The McGregor Foundation

c/o Foundation Management Svcs.
1422 Euclid Ave., Ste. 627
Cleveland, OH 44115-1952 (216) 621-2901
Contact: Susan O. Althans
FAX: (216) 621-8198;
E-mail: info@fmscleveland.com; Main URL: http://www.mcgregorfoundation.org

Established in 2003 in OH from an initial endowment from The A.M. McGregor Home.
Donors: Robert Rhodes†; Mary B. Donahue†.
Foundation type: Independent foundation.
Financial data (yr. ended 04/30/13): Assets, $21,720,117 (M); gifts received, $100; expenditures, $1,148,635; qualifying distributions, $979,576; giving activities include $784,860 for 37 grants (high: $60,000; low: $3,000).
Purpose and activities: The foundation's Board of Directors favors grant requests that meet the needs of the economically disadvantaged and frail elderly in the following priority areas: 1) Home and community based care, particularly programs such as affordable housing with services; 2) Workforce development, especially related to providing ongoing educational and training opportunities for workers engaged in direct contact with, or providing services for, seniors in home and community based settings; and 3) Total quality of life programming for seniors in all settings.
Fields of interest: Geriatrics; Human services; Residential/custodial care, hospices; Aging, centers/services; Aging.
Limitations: Applications accepted. Giving limited to Cuyahoga County, OH, with emphasis on the areas served by the A.M. McGregor Home. No support for long-term residential care facilities (for capital projects). No grants to individuals, or for scholarships, debt reduction, annual funds, research, symposia, fundraising events, or for endowments.
Publications: Application guidelines; Annual report; Grants list.
Application information: First time applicants and returning applicants should refer to foundation web site for specific application instructions and forms.
Initial approach: Submit application online via foundation web site only
Deadline(s): Feb. 1 and Sept. 1
Board meeting date(s): Apr. and Nov.
Officers and Directors:* Jane K. Meyer,* Chair.; R. Robertson Hilton,* Secy.; William D. Buss II; Marcia Egbert; Andrew L. Fabens III; David P. Handke, Jr.; Sharon Milligan, Ph.D; Bruce D. Murphy; D. Kirk Neiswander; David N. Smith; Linda M. Warren.
EIN: 352166848
Selected grants: The following grants are a representative sample of this grantmaker's funding activity:
$50,000 to Cleveland Housing Network, Cleveland, OH, 2011. For renovations to Rainbow Place, low-income housing for seniors.
$45,000 to Cleveland, City of, Cleveland, OH, 2011. For the National Council on Aging Economic Security Service Centers.
$30,000 to Cleveland Hearing and Speech Center, Cleveland, OH, 2011. For the Audiology Patient Assistance program to provide services and devices to economically disadvantaged seniors.
$25,000 to Center for Community Solutions, Cleveland, OH, 2011. For the Council on Older Persons.
$25,000 to Cleveland TOPS Swingband Foundation, Westlake, OH, 2011. For senior outreach programming.
$25,000 to Cuyahoga County Public Library, Parma, OH, 2011. For the Library2You program, providing library materials by mail to Cuyahoga County seniors.
$25,000 to Harvard Community Services Center, Cleveland, OH, 2011. For the senior services program.
$25,000 to Ideastream, Cleveland, OH, 2011. For in-depth coverage related to aging issues.
$18,000 to Western Reserve Historical Society, Cleveland, OH, 2011. For senior outreach programming.
$11,750 to Bellaire-Puritas Development Corporation, Cleveland, OH, 2011. To conduct a study of elderly housing needs.

7565
John McIntire Educational Fund ✧

c/o Huntington National Bank
422 Main St.
P.O. Box 2307
Zanesville, OH 43702-2307 (740) 455-7060
Contact: Kaleen Blosser, Acct. Relationship Assoc.

Established about 1937.
Donor: John McIntire†.
Foundation type: Independent foundation.
Financial data (yr. ended 06/30/13): Assets, $12,059,230 (M); expenditures, $645,851; qualifying distributions, $608,690; giving activities include $49,200 for 3 grants (high: $40,000; low: $1,200), and $521,324 for 162 grants to individuals (high: $6,008; low: $140).
Purpose and activities: Awards college scholarships to residents of Zanesville, OH, who are single and under 21 years of age. Applicants must have at least a 2.0 or better GPA.
Fields of interest: Higher education.
Type of support: Scholarships—to individuals.
Limitations: Applications accepted. Giving limited to residents of Zanesville, OH.
Publications: Annual report.
Application information: Application form required.
Initial approach: Proposal
Deadline(s): May 1
Officers and Directors:* Milman H. Linn III, Pres.; William Stewart, V.P.; Frederic Grant, Secy.; Michael Laplante, Treas; Craig Ballas; Marion Gilliland; Jack Joseph; Timothy H. Linn; Brent A Stubbins.
EIN: 316021239

7566
George and Margaret McLane Foundation ✧

30 E. Central Pkwy., Ste. 1202
Cincinnati, OH 45202
Contact: James Wellinghoff, Tr.

Established in 2007 in OH.
Donor: Wilhelmina McLane Vinnell†.
Foundation type: Operating foundation.
Financial data (yr. ended 12/31/13): Assets, $11,024,675 (M); expenditures, $658,875;

qualifying distributions, $568,232; giving activities include $477,332 for 36 grants (high: $50,000; low: $1,000).
Fields of interest: Arts; Libraries/library science; Education; Human services.
Limitations: Applications accepted. Giving primarily in Cincinnati and Franklin, OH.
Application information: Application form not required.
Initial approach: Proposal
Deadline(s): None
Officer: Christopher Wheeler, Mgr.
Trustee: James Wellinghoff.
EIN: 207373591
Selected grants: The following grants are a representative sample of this grantmaker's funding activity:
$24,997 to Franklin City Schools, Franklin, OH, 2012. For City Schools.
$20,000 to Cincinnati Works, Cincinnati, OH, 2012. For Prepare Poor People for Work.
$10,000 to Cincinnati Memorial Hall Society, Cincinnati, OH, 2012. For Operate Memorial Hall As Venue.
$10,000 to Haven House Emergency Shelter, Hamilton, OH, 2012. For Family Emergency Center.
$10,000 to Lower Price Hill Community School, Cincinnati, OH, 2012. For GED School.
$5,000 to Cincinnati Chamber Orchestra, Cincinnati, OH, 2012. To perform music.
$5,000 to Cincinnati Union Bethel, Cincinnati, OH, 2012. For Social Service - at Risk Population.

7567
The Mercer County Civic Foundation, Inc. ✧
119 W. Fulton St.
P.O. Box 439
Celina, OH 45822-1620 (419) 586-9950
Contact: Glenn H. Hux, Exec. Dir.
E-mail: mccf@bright.net; Main URL: http://www.mercercountycivicfdn.org

Incorporated in 1960 in OH.
Foundation type: Community foundation.
Financial data (yr. ended 12/31/13): Assets, $11,981,881 (M); gifts received, $1,715,180; expenditures, $697,494; giving activities include $590,148 for 4+ grants.
Purpose and activities: The foundation seeks to enhance the quality of life for the people of Mercer County, OH, by cultivating, managing, and disbursing charitable resources.
Fields of interest: Arts; Education; Environment; Health care; Human services; Community/economic development; Children; Aging; Disabilities, people with; Mentally disabled; Crime/abuse victims; Economically disadvantaged; Homeless.
Type of support: General/operating support; Continuing support; Scholarship funds; Scholarships—to individuals; Matching/challenge support; Student loans—to individuals.
Limitations: Applications accepted. Giving limited to Mercer County, OH. No grants to individuals (except for scholarships), or for capital campaigns; no multi-year commitments.
Publications: Application guidelines; Annual report (including application guidelines); Informational brochure; Newsletter.
Application information: Visit foundation web site for application form. Application form required.
Initial approach: Submit application form and attachments
Copies of proposal: 1
Deadline(s): Sept. 15
Board meeting date(s): Quarterly
Final notification: Nov. 1
Officers and Directors:* Maurice Cron,* Pres.; Jane Stuckman,* V.P.; Glenn H. Hux, Exec. Dir.; Jim Dippold; Deb Gibson; Barbara Hamilton; David Kaiser; Ken Kremer; Thomas Lammers; David Pax.
Number of staff: 1 part-time professional; 1 part-time support.
EIN: 346539139

7568
Meshewa Farm Foundation ✧
c/o Cors & Bassett, LLC, Attn.: Robert G. Edmiston, Esq.
537 E. Pete Rose Way, Ste. 400
Cincinnati, OH 45202-3578

Established in 1993 in OH.
Donors: Mary C. LeBlond; Mary Elizabeth Mitsui.
Foundation type: Independent foundation.
Financial data (yr. ended 12/31/13): Assets, $14,672,586 (M); gifts received, $2,008,342; expenditures, $658,595; qualifying distributions, $608,700; giving activities include $608,500 for 38 grants (high: $125,000; low: $1,000).
Fields of interest: Human services.
Limitations: Applications not accepted. Giving primarily in OH. No grants to individuals.
Application information: Unsolicited requests for funds not accepted.
Trustees: Robert Gray Edmiston; Francis R. Grebe; Charles T. Mitsui; Mary Elizabeth Mitsui.
EIN: 237748707

7569
Miami County Foundation ✧ ☆
(formerly Piqua-Miami County Foundation)
317 N. Wayne St.
P.O. Box 1526
Piqua, OH 45356-1526 (937) 773-9012
Contact: Cheryl Stiefel-Francis, Exec. Dir.
FAX: (937) 773-9012; E-mail: mcf@woh.rr.com; Main URL: http://www.miamicountyfoundation.org

Established in 1985 in OH.
Donor: Richard E. Hunt‡.
Foundation type: Independent foundation.
Financial data (yr. ended 12/31/13): Assets, $12,909,346 (M); gifts received, $58,140; expenditures, $781,824; qualifying distributions, $640,518; giving activities include $77,574 for grants, and $501,286 for grants to individuals.
Purpose and activities: The mission of the foundation is to effectively assist, encourage and promote the health, education, and welfare of the citizens of Miami County, OH, by soliciting, receiving, and administering assets exclusively for the charitable needs of the community. The Miami County Foundation endeavors to focus on "People Helping People" within the community.
Fields of interest: Education; Hospitals (general); Human services.
Type of support: Management development/capacity building; Capital campaigns; Building/renovation; Equipment; Program development; Conferences/seminars; Publication; Seed money; Curriculum development; Scholarship funds; Program evaluation.
Limitations: Applications accepted. Giving limited to Miami County, OH. No support for organizations that limit their services to members of any one religious group, political organizations or those whose primary purpose is to influence legislation, political viewpoint or promotion of a particular candidate.
Publications: Application guidelines; Informational brochure; Newsletter.
Application information: Application guidelines and forms available on foundation web site. Application form required.
Copies of proposal: 5
Deadline(s): For grants Feb. 28 and Aug. 31; See foundation web site for scholarship deadlines
Board meeting date(s): Apr. and Oct.
Final notification: 7 weeks
Officers and Directors:* Leesa Baker,* Pres.; Joe Duncan,* V.P.; Donna Favorite,* Secy.; Douglas R. Murray,* Treas.; Cheryl Stiefel-Francis, Exec. Dir.; Richard N. Adams, Ph.D.; D. Ann Baird; Carol Coate; Dan Dickerson; Ginger Godfrey; Candace Goodall; Joanna Hill Heitzman; Christine Hulme; David Larson; Lowell Nees; Jim Oda; Andy Pratt; Bradley Vath.
Number of staff: 1 part-time professional.
EIN: 311142558

7570
Middletown Community Foundation ✧
300 N. Main St., Ste. 300
Middletown, OH 45042 (513) 424-7369
Contact: T. Duane Gordon, Exec. Dir.
FAX: (513) 424-7555;
E-mail: info@mcfoundation.org; Main URL: http://www.mcfoundation.org/
Foundation Matters: http://www.mcfoundation.org/e_media.html

Incorporated in 1976 in OH.
Foundation type: Community foundation.
Financial data (yr. ended 12/31/12): Assets, $24,783,419 (M); gifts received, $1,639,760; expenditures, $2,774,336; giving activities include $1,237,162 for 49+ grants (high: $167,509), and $871,826 for 344 grants to individuals.
Purpose and activities: The mission of the foundation is to: 1) serve as a leader, catalyst and resource for philanthropy; 2) serve as a permanent and growing endowment for the community's changing needs and opportunities; 3) strive for excellence through strategic grantmaking in the areas of the arts, education, health, social services, recreation and community development; 4) provide a flexible and cost-effective way for donors to improve their community.
Fields of interest: Performing arts; Arts; Elementary/secondary education; Education, early childhood education; Elementary school/education; Higher education; Libraries/library science; Education; Health care; Recreation; Youth development, services; Youth development, citizenship; Youth, services; Family services; Human services; Community/economic development; Public affairs, citizen participation; Leadership development; Aging.
Type of support: Capital campaigns; Building/renovation; Equipment; Emergency funds; Program development; Seed money; Curriculum development; Scholarship funds; Employee matching gifts; Scholarships—to individuals; Matching/challenge support.
Limitations: Applications accepted. Giving limited to the greater Middletown, OH area. No support for

religious organizations other than religious schools, medical or other research organizations, or national or regional organizations (unless program addresses local needs). No grants to individuals (except for scholarships), or for endowments or general operating budgets of established organizations.
Publications: Application guidelines; Annual report; Financial statement; Informational brochure (including application guidelines); Newsletter.
Application information: Visit foundation web site for application guidelines. Common Grant Application may be submitted for grant requests. Application form not required.
Initial approach: Submit application form and attachments
Copies of proposal: 1
Deadline(s): Mar. 1 and Sept. 1 for Recreation, Arts, Festivals, and Community Devel. grants and June 1 and Dec. 1 for Education and Human Needs grants; varies for scholarships
Board meeting date(s): Quarterly
Final notification: 60 to 90 days
Officers and Trustees:* Cathie Mulligan,* Pres.; Richard Isroff,* V.P. and Pres.-Elect.; Robin Dennis,* Secy.; John Venturella,* Treas.; T. Duane Gordon, Exec. Dir.; Cathy Bishop-Clark; Kee Edwards; Karen Halsey; Wendy Kissel; Gina Miltenberger; Hon. Larry Mulligan; Rick Pearce; G. Michael Pratt; Tom Scott; Carole Schul; Terrence Sherrer; Andy Singer; Verlena Stewart; Joan Stonitsch; Mike Wallner; Tom Wiley; Scott Zollett; and 6 additional trustees.
Number of staff: 1 full-time professional; 1 full-time support.
EIN: 310898380

7571
Samuel H. & Maria Miller Foundation ✧
(formerly Samuel H. Miller Family Fund, Inc.)
c/o Eleanor Fanslau
1170 Terminal Tower
50 Public Sq.
Cleveland, OH 44113

Established in 1989 in OH.
Donor: Samuel H. Miller.
Foundation type: Independent foundation.
Financial data (yr. ended 12/31/13): Assets, $35,647,462 (M); expenditures, $1,451,650; qualifying distributions, $1,272,933; giving activities include $1,272,933 for 81 grants (high: $300,000; low: $250).
Purpose and activities: Giving primarily for education, the arts, health organizations, children, and social services, and Jewish organizations; some funding also for Roman Catholic and Lutheran churches and organizations.
Fields of interest: Arts; Elementary/secondary education; Higher education; Education; Health care, clinics/centers; Health organizations, association; Medical research, institute; Human services; United Ways and Federated Giving Programs; Jewish federated giving programs; Protestant agencies & churches; Catholic agencies & churches; Jewish agencies & synagogues.
Type of support: General/operating support.
Limitations: Applications not accepted. Giving primarily in Cleveland, OH. No grants to individuals.
Application information: Contributes only to pre-selected organizations.
Officers and Trustees:* Samuel H. Miller,* Pres.; Eleanor Fanslau,* Secy.-Treas.; Maria Miller.
EIN: 341482231

7572
Clement O. Miniger Memorial Foundation ✧
709 Madison Ave., Rm. 205
P.O. Box 1985
Toledo, OH 43603-1985 (419) 241-3124

Incorporated in 1952 in OH.
Donors: George M. Jones, Jr.†; Eleanor Miniger Jones†.
Foundation type: Independent foundation.
Financial data (yr. ended 12/31/13): Assets, $14,515,474 (M); expenditures, $653,617; qualifying distributions, $597,961; giving activities include $572,000 for 24 grants (high: $115,000; low: $5,000).
Purpose and activities: Giving primarily for the arts and human services.
Fields of interest: Performing arts; Arts; Environment, natural resources; Human services.
Type of support: Capital campaigns; Equipment; Emergency funds; Matching/challenge support.
Limitations: Applications accepted. Giving primarily in OH, with emphasis on Toledo. No grants to individuals.
Application information: Application form not required.
Initial approach: Proposal
Deadline(s): None
Officers and Trustees:* George M. Jones III,* Pres. and Treas.; John H. Burson, Secy.; Sara Bowen; William F. Buckley; Justice Johnson; Marna Ramnath; Steve Staelin; Edward Weber.
EIN: 346523024

7573
MJH Foundation ✧
1001 Lakeside Ave., Ste. 900
Cleveland, OH 44114-1151 (216) 479-2200

Established in 1998 in OH as a follow-up to the Lois U. Horvitz Foundation.
Donors: Lois U. Horvitz Foundation; Michael I. Horvitz.
Foundation type: Independent foundation.
Financial data (yr. ended 12/31/13): Assets, $9,313,231 (M); expenditures, $912,253; qualifying distributions, $891,631; giving activities include $871,875 for 6 grants (high: $625,000; low: $1,875).
Purpose and activities: Giving primarily for educational and charitable purposes.
Fields of interest: Higher education; Education; Human services.
Type of support: Professorships.
Limitations: Applications accepted. Giving primarily in OH, with some emphasis on Cleveland, VA and VT.
Application information: Application form required.
Initial approach: Letter
Deadline(s): None
Officers and Trustees:* Michael J. Horvitz,* Pres.; Jane R. Horvitz,* V.P.; Peter A. Kuhn, Secy. and Exec. Dir.
EIN: 341853843

7574
The Montei Foundation ✧
c/o William K. Burton
4608 Sawmill Rd.
Columbus, OH 43220-2247

Established in 2000 in OH.
Foundation type: Independent foundation.
Financial data (yr. ended 12/31/13): Assets, $21,071,383 (M); expenditures, $1,187,350; qualifying distributions, $959,058; giving activities include $959,058 for 60 grants (high: $50,000; low: $1,000).
Fields of interest: Crime/violence prevention, child abuse; Human services; Children, services.
Limitations: Applications not accepted. Giving primarily in Columbus, OH. No grants to individuals.
Application information: Contributes only to pre-selected organizations.
Trustees: Julia K. Boyer; William K. Burton; Todd Ross Montei.
EIN: 311736155
Selected grants: The following grants are a representative sample of this grantmaker's funding activity:
$25,000 to Angel Flight Mid-Atlantic, Virginia Beach, VA, 2012. For Utilize volunteer pilots to transport patients to specialized medical care.
$25,000 to Franklin County Children Services, Columbus, OH, 2012. For Serves abused, neglected, dependent, and troubled children.
$25,000 to Lutheran Social Services of Central Ohio, Worthington, OH, 2012. To provide Programs to address issues of hunger, housing, healing, and hope.
$25,000 to Operation Finally Home, New Braunfels, TX, 2012. To provide custom made mortgage free homes to wounded and disabled veterans and the windows of the fallen.
$25,000 to Special Operations Warrior Foundation, Tampa, FL, 2012. To provide support and assistance to families of fallen or wounded special forces troops.
$25,000 to YWCA Columbus, Columbus, OH, 2012. To provide Programs to eliminate racism, empowering women and promoting peace, justice, freedom, and dignity for all.
$23,000 to Gift of Adoption Fund, Techny, IL, 2012. For Inspires adoption by providing grants to qualified parents.
$20,000 to Global Soap Project, Norcross, GA, 2012. For Recovers discarded soap from hotels, reprocesses it into new bars and distributes it to vulnerable populations throughout the world.
$20,000 to Lifecare Alliance, Columbus, OH, 2012. To provide health care and nutrition services to older adults, chronically ill, and homebound Central Ohio residents.
$20,000 to Sunshine Kids Foundation, Houston, TX, 2012. To provide support for children with cancer.

7575
Montgomery Foundation ✧
Roscoe Village
Coshocton, OH 43812-1088
Contact: Linda M. Scott, Tr.
Application address: 365 N. Whitewoman St., Coshocton, OH 43812

Established in 1972 in OH.
Donors: Edward E. Montgomery†; Frances B. Montgomery†.
Foundation type: Independent foundation.

Financial data (yr. ended 12/31/13): Assets, $15,850,820 (M); expenditures, $835,475; qualifying distributions, $640,075; giving activities include $579,797 for 14 grants (high: $463,197; low: $100).
Purpose and activities: Grants primarily for local charities in Coshocton County, OH.
Fields of interest: Historic preservation/historical societies; Education; Community/economic development.
Type of support: Scholarship funds; Annual campaigns; Capital campaigns; Building/renovation; Equipment; Seed money; Matching/challenge support.
Limitations: Applications accepted. Giving primarily in Coshocton, OH. No support for religious or political organizations. No grants to individuals.
Publications: Application guidelines.
Application information: Application form not required.
Initial approach: Letter or proposal
Copies of proposal: 4
Deadline(s): None
Board meeting date(s): Board of Trustees meets as needed to review requests
Final notification: 90 days
Officers and Trustees:* Richard E. Corbett,* Pres.; William Dutton,* V.P.; Linda M. Scott,* Secy.; Randy Kreuter,* Treas.; Michael Manning; Joseph S. Montgomery; Scott Montgomery.
Number of staff: 1 full-time professional; 1 part-time professional.
EIN: 237165768
Selected grants: The following grants are a representative sample of this grantmaker's funding activity:
$416,697 to Roscoe Village Foundation, Coshocton, OH, 2012. For Restoration of Historic Site.

7576
Harry C. Moores Foundation ✧
100 S. 3rd St.
Columbus, OH 43215-4236 (614) 227-8884
Contact: Mary B. Cummins

Trust established in 1961 in OH.
Donor: Harry C. Moores†.
Foundation type: Independent foundation.
Financial data (yr. ended 09/30/13): Assets, $30,730,864 (M); expenditures, $1,802,347; qualifying distributions, $1,658,363; giving activities include $1,644,243 for 118 grants (high: $40,000; low: $2,500).
Purpose and activities: Grants largely for rehabilitation of the handicapped, as well as for hospitals, higher education, cultural programs, and social service agencies concerned with the aged, child welfare, and the developmentally disabled.
Fields of interest: Arts; Higher education; Education; Hospitals (general); Health organizations, association; Food banks; Human services; Children/youth, services.
Type of support: General/operating support; Annual campaigns; Capital campaigns; Seed money; Scholarship funds.
Limitations: Giving limited to Franklin County, OH and contiguous counties. No support for private foundations. No grants to individuals, or for endowment funds or matching gifts; no loans.
Publications: Application guidelines.
Application information: The foundation will not review or return video tapes. Application form required.
Initial approach: Letter requesting proposal cover sheet
Copies of proposal: 1
Deadline(s): June 1 (however, the foundation urges applicants to submit prior to Apr. 1)
Board meeting date(s): Aug.
Final notification: Sept. 15
Trustees: John P. Beavers; Neil B. Distelhorst; David T. Fenner; Kristen J. Sydney; Robert A. Wiseman.
EIN: 316035344

7577
Morgan Family Foundation
130 Glen St., Unit 6
P.O. Box 561
Yellow Springs, OH 45387-1844 (937) 767-9208
Contact: Lori Kuhn, Exec. Dir.
FAX: (937) 767-9308;
E-mail: info@morganfamilyfdn.org; Main URL: http://www.morganfamilyfdn.org

Established in 2003 in OH.
Donors: Lee M. Morgan; Victoria A. Morgan.
Foundation type: Independent foundation.
Financial data (yr. ended 12/31/13): Assets, $50,528,870 (M); expenditures, $2,412,670; qualifying distributions, $2,412,670; giving activities include $2,151,834 for grants (average: $33,000–$44,329).
Purpose and activities: The foundation will be a vehicle of change and instill hope for a bright future by fostering individual human potential and the desire of communities to seek out and optimize that potential, and a movement toward a healthier, more just, more caring and sustainable society.
Fields of interest: Media, radio; Performing arts; Elementary/secondary education; Higher education; Environment; Housing/shelter, development; Youth development; Human services; Foundations (community); Children/youth; Youth; Minorities; Women.
Type of support: General/operating support; Income development; Management development/capacity building; Capital campaigns; Building/renovation; Equipment; Program development; Technical assistance; Matching/challenge support.
Limitations: Applications accepted. Giving primarily in Yellow Springs OH, and St. Cloud, MN. Through 2015, the foundation will consider unsolicited grant requests only from the St. Cloud, MN area, and will also award grants to pre-selected public charities in Yellow Springs, OH and Portland, OR. Generally, no support for medical research, animal rights, animal welfare causes or to promote any particular religious doctrine. No grants to individuals.
Publications: Application guidelines; Grants list.
Application information: Full applications are by invitation only, upon review of Letter of Inquiry and narrative. Application form required.
Initial approach: Letter of Inquiry on foundation web site, and a 1-page narrative via e-mail
Copies of proposal: 2
Deadline(s): Jan. and Aug.
Board meeting date(s): Apr. and Nov.
Final notification: Within three weeks of board meeting
Officers and Directors:* Lee M. Morgan,* Pres.; Victoria A. Morgan,* V.P. and Treas.; Lori Kuhn, Exec. Dir.; Stephen T. Williams, C.F.O.; Asha Morgan Moran; Marty Moran; Karla Morgan.
Number of staff: 1 full-time professional; 1 full-time support; 1 part-time support.
EIN: 300205024
Selected grants: The following grants are a representative sample of this grantmaker's funding activity:
$500,000 to Antioch University, Yellow Springs, OH, 2011.
$100,000 to Quiet Oaks Hospice House, Saint Cloud, MN, 2011.
$33,334 to Artemis Center for Alternatives to Domestic Violence, Dayton, OH, 2011.

7578
The Burton D. Morgan Foundation ✧
22 Aurora St.
Hudson, OH 44236-2947 (330) 655-1660
Contact: Deborah D. Hoover, Pres.
FAX: (330) 655-1673;
E-mail: admin@bdmorganfdn.org; Contact for application guidelines: Leslie Nelson, email: lnelson@bdmorganfdn.org; Main URL: http://www.bdmorganfdn.org
e-Spirit Newsletter: http://www.bdmorganfdn.org/espirit
Flickr: https://www.flickr.com/photos/burtondmorgan/
Grants List: http://www.bdmorganfdn.org/grants-awarded
Twitter: http://twitter.com/bdmorganfdn
Venture Adventure Newsletter: http://www.bdmorganfdn.org/venture-adventure

Established in 1967 in OH.
Donor: Burton D. Morgan†.
Foundation type: Independent foundation.
Financial data (yr. ended 12/31/13): Assets, $152,371,400 (M); expenditures, $6,956,900; qualifying distributions, $4,752,000; giving activities include $4,752,000 for grants.
Purpose and activities: Giving to strengthen the free enterprise system by investing in organizations and institutions that foster the entrepreneurial spirit. The foundation is interested in supporting projects that nurture creativity, invention, entrepreneurship, and innovation. The foundation seeks to support educational programs and projects at the adult, collegiate, and youth levels that are designed to build competencies in entrepreneurship, free enterprise, and innovation; nonprofit organizations and programs that directly assist entrepreneurs in business planning, start-up and acceleration, and access to capital; and selected initiatives aimed at rejuvenating economic competitiveness within Northeast Ohio.
Fields of interest: Higher education; Business school/education; Education; Economics.
Type of support: General/operating support; Endowments; Program development; Conferences/seminars; Seed money; Curriculum development; Internship funds; Scholarship funds; Matching/challenge support.
Limitations: Applications accepted. Giving primarily in northeastern OH. No support for non 501(c)(3) public charities, or for governmental units, or to organizations or institutions that are primarily taxpayer-supported including state universities. No giving for arts or social services organizations outside of Hudson, OH. No grants to individuals or for multi-year grants or annual fund drives.

Publications: Application guidelines; Annual report (including application guidelines); Grants list; Newsletter.
Application information: Before submitting a full proposal, organizations should submit a letter of inquiry to the foundation regarding a request. The Pres. will then determine if the organization should proceed with a formal grant application. Organizations may only submit one grant proposal within a 12-month period. Please visit the foundation web site for additional information. Application form not required.
Initial approach: Letter of inquiry (1 page)
Copies of proposal: 1
Deadline(s): Sept. 1, Feb. 1 and May 1 for Letter of Inquiry; Oct. 1, Mar. 1 and June 1 for grant requests
Board meeting date(s): Jan., June, and Sept.
Officers: Deborah D. Hoover, C.E.O. and Pres.; Denise M. Griggs, C.F.O.
Trustees: Keith A. Brown; J. Martin Erbaugh; Patrick T. Finley; J. Michael Hochwender; Stanley C. Gault; Mark D. Robeson; Richard N. Seaman.
Number of staff: 3 full-time professional; 3 part-time professional; 2 full-time support.
EIN: 346598971
Selected grants: The following grants are a representative sample of this grantmaker's funding activity:
$1,000,000 to JumpStart, Cleveland, OH, 2013. For mentoring support services for early-stage entrepreneurs in Northeast Ohio, payable over 4.00 years.
$407,000 to Western Reserve Historical Society, Hale Farm and Village, Cleveland, OH, 2013. For Youth Entrepreneurship Education Experiences for CMSD Students, payable over 3.00 years.
$350,000 to Fund for Our Economic Future, Cleveland, OH, 2013. For additional contribution for phase 4, over 3 years.
$200,000 to BioEnterprise Corporation, Cleveland, OH, 2013. For business development and entrepreneurial assistance and graduate internship program.
$100,000 to Austen BioInnovation Institute in Akron, Akron, OH, 2013. For entrepreneurship graduate internship program and the Technology Development Fund.
$100,000 to Kent State University Foundation, Kent, OH, 2013. For the Margaret Clark Morgan Endowed Scholarship Fund.
$75,000 to Junior Achievement of North Central Ohio, Akron, OH, 2013. For Entrepreneurship Programs.
$27,000 to Junior Achievement of East Central Ohio, Canton, OH, 2013. For entrepreneurship education.
$20,000 to JumpStart, Cleveland, OH, 2013. For Gazelle Capital Initiative.
$15,000 to Old Trail School, Bath, OH, 2013. For Organic Garden Program.

7579
The Margaret Clark Morgan Foundation
10 W. Streetsboro St., Ste. 200
Hudson, OH 44236-2851 (330) 655-1366
Contact: Rick Kellar, Pres.
FAX: (330) 655-1696; E-mail: inquiry@mcmfdn.org; Main URL: http://www.mcmfdn.org
Grants List: http://www.mcmfdn.org/past-grants
Twitter: https://www.twitter.com/mcmfoundation
YouTube: http://www.youtube.com/user/MCMFFDN

Established in 2001 in OH.
Donors: Margaret Clark Morgan†; Burton D. Morgan†.
Foundation type: Independent foundation.
Financial data (yr. ended 12/31/13): Assets, $88,451,400 (M); gifts received, $205,700; expenditures, $4,319,600; qualifying distributions, $3,270,800; giving activities include $2,541,000 for 70 grants, and $228,112 for 4 foundation-administered programs.
Purpose and activities: Giving to improve the lives of people with serious mental illness by investing in innovative projects in Northeast Ohio having national transformational impact.
Fields of interest: Arts; Education; Mental health/crisis services.
Type of support: General/operating support; Continuing support; Management development/capacity building; Program development; Conferences/seminars; Curriculum development; Fellowships; Technical assistance; Consulting services; Program evaluation; Program-related investments/loans; Matching/challenge support.
Limitations: Applications accepted. Giving primarily in northeast OH counties: Ashland, Ashtabula, Carroll, Columbiana, Cuyahoga, Geauga, Holmes, Jefferson, Lake, Lorain, Mahoning, Medina, Portage, Stark, Summit, Trumbull, Tuscarwas and Wayne. No grants to individuals, or for lobbying or legislative activities.
Publications: Annual report; Grants list.
Application information: See foundation Web site for application guidelines and procedures. Application form required.
Initial approach: 1-page Letter of Inquiry
Copies of proposal: 1
Deadline(s): Letter of inquiry deadlines: Nov. 1 and May 1
Board meeting date(s): Varies
Final notification: June and Nov.
Officers and Trustees:* A. William McGraw,* Chair.; Rick Kellar, Pres.; Jeffrey Knoll, Secy.; Jonathan Pavloff, Treas.; William H. Fellows,* Tr. Emeritus; Penelope Frese; Bob Kallstrom; Suzanne Morgan; Theresa Proenza; Keith Riley.
Number of staff: 4 full-time professional; 1 part-time professional.
EIN: 341948246
Selected grants: The following grants are a representative sample of this grantmaker's funding activity:
$5,500,000 to Northeast Ohio Medical University, Rootstown, OH, 2013. For BeST Center Phase 2.
$125,500 to MetroHealth System, Cleveland, OH, 2013. For Integrated Care Reentry Project.
$48,000 to Mental Health and Recovery Board of Wayne and Holmes Counties, Wooster, OH, 2013. For tele-psychiatry partnership with Summa.
$46,500 to National Alliance on Mental Illness, Canton, OH, 2013. For support and education programs.
$35,500 to National Alliance on Mental Illness of Summit County, Cuyahoga Falls, OH, 2013. For operating support.
$35,000 to Ideastream, Cleveland, OH, 2013. For mental illness media coverage.
$30,000 to Help Hotline Crisis Center, Youngstown, OH, 2013. For program support.
$30,000 to Tuesday Musical Association, Akron, OH, 2013. For administrative assistance staff support.
$20,000 to Salvation Army of Summit County, Akron, OH, 2013. For Learning Zone.
$20,000 to Suicide Prevention Education Alliance of Northeast Ohio, Cleveland, OH, 2013. For teen depression and suicide prevention.

7580
Robert S. Morrison Foundation ✧
355 Prospect Rd., Ste. 110
P.O. Box 580
Ashtabula, OH 44005-5830 (440) 992-7674
Contact: Louise Raffa, Exec. Dir.
Main URL: http://www.robertsmorrisonfoundation.org

Established in OH.
Donor: Robert S. Morrison†.
Foundation type: Independent foundation.
Financial data (yr. ended 12/31/13): Assets, $13,668,471 (M); expenditures, $694,207; qualifying distributions, $602,983; giving activities include $479,209 for 28 grants (high: $158,000; low: $500).
Purpose and activities: The mission of the foundation is to improve the lives of people in the Ashtabula, OH area.
Fields of interest: Education; Animal welfare; Human services; Community/economic development.
Type of support: General/operating support.
Limitations: Applications accepted. Giving limited to within 100 miles of Ashtabula, OH.
Application information: Application form available on foundation web site. Application form required.
Initial approach: See foundation web site
Deadline(s): None
Officer: Louise M. Raffa, Exec. Dir.
Trustees: Richard Coblitz; John Palo; Alec J. Raffa; Richard Rowley.
EIN: 237246162
Selected grants: The following grants are a representative sample of this grantmaker's funding activity:
$135,000 to Kent State University, Ashtabula, OH, 2011. For operations.
$68,000 to Grand River Academy, Austinburg, OH, 2011. For operations.
$25,000 to Ashtabula Arts Center, Ashtabula, OH, 2011. For operations.
$15,000 to Cleveland Clinic Foundation, Cleveland, OH, 2011. For operations.
$10,000 to Beatitude House, Youngstown, OH, 2011. For operations.
$10,000 to Homesafe, Ashtabula, OH, 2011. For operations.
$1,500 to Cleveland Museum of Natural History, Cleveland, OH, 2011. For operations.
$1,000 to Cleveland Botanical Garden, Cleveland, OH, 2011. For operations.

7581
The Motorists Insurance Group Foundation ✧ ☆
(formerly The Motorists Insurance Companies Foundation)
471 E. Broad St., 21st Fl.
Columbus, OH 43215-3861 (614) 225-3861
Contact: David Kaufman, Tr.

Established in 2000 in OH.
Donor: Motorists Mutual Insurance Co.
Foundation type: Company-sponsored foundation.

Financial data (yr. ended 12/31/13): Assets, $77,037 (M); gifts received, $690,915; expenditures, $1,117,443; qualifying distributions, $1,106,767; giving activities include $1,106,767 for 53 grants (high: $266,353; low: $250).
Purpose and activities: The foundation supports organizations involved with arts and culture, education, health, cancer, law enforcement, youth development, and the insurance industry.
Fields of interest: Education; Mental health/crisis services; Human services.
Limitations: Applications accepted. Giving primarily in OH, with emphasis on Columbus. No grants to individuals.
Application information: Application form required.
Initial approach: Letter
Deadline(s): None
Trustees: Susan E. Haack; David Kaufman; Michael L. Wiseman.
EIN: 311712343
Selected grants: The following grants are a representative sample of this grantmaker's funding activity:
$150,000 to Ohio State University, Columbus, OH, 2011.
$125,000 to United Way of Central Ohio, Columbus, OH, 2011.
$40,000 to Columbus Museum of Art, Columbus, OH, 2011.
$30,000 to Buckeye Ranch Foundation, Grove City, OH, 2011.
$25,000 to Columbus Downtown Development Corporation, Columbus, OH, 2011.
$15,000 to Griffith Foundation for Insurance Education, Worthington, OH, 2011.
$10,000 to Cystic Fibrosis Foundation, Worthington, OH, 2011.
$10,000 to Law Enforcement Foundation, Dublin, OH, 2011.
$10,000 to YMCA Camp Coniston, Grantham, NH, 2011.
$1,744 to United Way, Greater Twin Cities, Minneapolis, MN, 2011.

7582
The Murch Foundation ✧
830 Hanna Bldg.
Cleveland, OH 44115-2001

Incorporated in 1956 in OH.
Donor: Maynard H. Murch†.
Foundation type: Independent foundation.
Financial data (yr. ended 12/31/13): Assets, $23,099,755 (M); expenditures, $2,653,569; qualifying distributions, $2,586,000; giving activities include $2,586,000 for grants.
Purpose and activities: Giving primarily for museums and cultural institutions, including a natural history museum and arboretum, education, and medical and health care.
Fields of interest: Museums (natural history); Arts; Higher education; Hospitals (general); Health care; Medical research, institute; Human services.
Type of support: General/operating support; Annual campaigns; Capital campaigns; Building/renovation; Endowments; Scholarship funds.
Limitations: Applications not accepted. Giving primarily in OH. No grants to individuals.
Application information: Contributes only to pre-selected organizations.
Officers: Creighton B. Murch, Pres.; Robert B. Murch, V.P. and Secy.; Maynard H. Murch V, V.P. and Treas.
Number of staff: 1 part-time support.
EIN: 346520188
Selected grants: The following grants are a representative sample of this grantmaker's funding activity:
$110,000 to Holden Arboretum, Kirtland, OH, 2011.

7583
Murdough Foundation ✧
(formerly Thomas G. & Joy P. Murdough Foundation)
102 1st St., Ste. 205
Hudson, OH 44236-5386 (330) 656-9331
Contact: James R. Miller, Exec. Dir.

Established in 1986 in OH.
Donors: Thomas G. Murdough, Jr.; William M. Oldham.
Foundation type: Independent foundation.
Financial data (yr. ended 12/31/12): Assets, $5,415,334 (M); expenditures, $3,667,560; qualifying distributions, $3,583,070; giving activities include $3,582,855 for 11 grants (high: $2,716,855; low: $1,000).
Purpose and activities: Support for organizations whose core values include belief in God, family, and community and country.
Fields of interest: Arts; Education; Human services; Community/economic development.
Type of support: General/operating support; Annual campaigns; Building/renovation.
Limitations: Applications accepted. Giving primarily in OH, with emphasis on northeastern OH. No grants to individuals.
Application information: Application form not required.
Initial approach: Proposal
Copies of proposal: 1
Deadline(s): None
Board meeting date(s): May and Nov.
Officers and Trustees:* Thomas G. Murdough, Jr.,* Pres. and Treas.; Joy P. Murdough,* Secy.; James R. Miller, Exec. Dir.; Jody P. Murdough; Marshall C. Murdough; Peter R. Murdough; Thomas G. Murdough, III; William M. Oldham.
Number of staff: 1 part-time professional.
EIN: 341454379
Selected grants: The following grants are a representative sample of this grantmaker's funding activity:
$20,000 to Ocean Reef Cultural Center, Key Largo, FL, 2011. For endowment fund.
$10,000 to Ocean Reef Foundation, Key Largo, FL, 2011.
$10,000 to United Way of Summit County, Akron, OH, 2011.
$5,000 to Cato Institute, Washington, DC, 2011. For general support.
$5,000 to Reason Foundation, Los Angeles, CA, 2011. For general support.
$2,500 to Flying Horse Farms, Columbus, OH, 2011. For general support.
$1,000 to Childrens Hospital Foundation, Akron, OH, 2011.
$1,000 to Cleveland Orchestra, Cleveland, OH, 2011.
$1,000 to Downtown Akron Partnership, Akron, OH, 2011.
$1,000 to Hudson Community First, Hudson, OH, 2011.

7584
John P. Murphy Foundation ✧
Terminal Tower
50 Public Sq., Ste. 600
Cleveland, OH 44113-2203 (216) 623-4770
Contact: Richard J. Clark, Exec. V.P.
FAX: (216) 623-4773;
E-mail: rclark@johnpmurphy.org; Additional tel.: (216) 623-4771; Main URL: http://fdnweb.org/jpmurphy

Incorporated in 1960 in OH.
Donor: John P. Murphy†.
Foundation type: Independent foundation.
Financial data (yr. ended 12/31/13): Assets, $51,014,926 (M); expenditures, $3,729,455; qualifying distributions, $3,387,861; giving activities include $2,694,000 for 128 grants (high: $150,000; low: $500).
Purpose and activities: Giving primarily for higher education, civic affairs, the performing arts, community development and health; support also for social services and youth. The foundation's board identified the subject of economic development in Northeastern Ohio as a special interest.
Fields of interest: Visual arts; Museums; Performing arts; Performing arts, dance; Performing arts, theater; History/archaeology; Historic preservation/historical societies; Arts; Vocational education; Higher education; Libraries/library science; Education; Hospitals (general); Medical care, rehabilitation; Nursing care; Health care; Health organizations, association; Alcoholism; Youth development, services; Human services; Children/youth, services; Women, centers/services; Urban/community development; Community/economic development; United Ways and Federated Giving Programs; Economics; Government/public administration; Leadership development; Public affairs; Disabilities, people with; Women.
Type of support: General/operating support; Continuing support; Annual campaigns; Capital campaigns; Building/renovation; Equipment; Program development; Publication; Curriculum development; Research; Consulting services; Program-related investments/loans; Exchange programs; Matching/challenge support.
Limitations: Applications not accepted. Giving primarily in Cuyahoga County, OH, and the surrounding counties. No support for K-12 education or mental health. No grants to individuals, scholarships, or for endowment funds; no loans (except for program-related investments).
Publications: Financial statement; Informational brochure.
Application information: The grantmaker is not accepting applications from new grant seekers. See foundation web site for latest application updates.
Board meeting date(s): 4 times a year
Officers and Trustees:* Nancy W. McCann,* Pres. and Treas.; Richard J. Clark,* Exec. V.P. and Secy.; Robert R. Broadbent,* V.P.; Patricia Brownell,* V.P.; John F. O'Brien,* V.P.; Leslie Resnik,* V.P.; Frederick G. Stueber,* V.P.
Number of staff: 1 full-time professional; 2 full-time support.
EIN: 346528308

7585
Muskingum County Community Foundation ✧
534 Putnam Ave.
Zanesville, OH 43701-4933 (740) 453-5192
Contact: David P. Mitzel, Exec. Dir.
FAX: (740) 453-5734; E-mail: giving@mccf.org; Main URL: http://www.mccf.org
Facebook: http://www.facebook.com/pages/Muskingum-County-Community-Foundation/80469432596
Scholarship Central e-mail: scholarshipcentral@mccf.org; Scholarship Central tel.: (740) 453-5192

Established in 1985 in OH.
Foundation type: Community foundation.
Financial data (yr. ended 12/31/13): Assets, $27,632,045 (M); gifts received, $838,055; expenditures, $1,634,376; giving activities include $689,322 for grants.
Purpose and activities: The foundation seeks to improve the quality of life and to serve the charitable needs of the community by attracting and administering charitable funds.
Fields of interest: Performing arts; Performing arts, music; Arts; Elementary/secondary education; Libraries/library science; Education; Animal welfare; Animals/wildlife, preservation/protection; Hospitals (general); Health care; Recreation; Youth development, services; Children/youth, services; Residential/custodial care, hospices; Human services; Community/economic development; Leadership development; Aging.
Type of support: General/operating support; Capital campaigns; Building/renovation; Equipment; Land acquisition; Endowments; Program development; Conferences/seminars; Publication; Seed money; Fellowships; Internship funds; Scholarship funds; Research; Technical assistance; Consulting services; Program-related investments/loans; Scholarships—to individuals; In-kind gifts; Matching/challenge support.
Limitations: Applications accepted. Giving limited to Muskingum County, OH.
Publications: Application guidelines; Annual report; Grants list; Informational brochure; Newsletter.
Application information: Visit foundation web site for application form and guidelines. Application form required.
Initial approach: Submit application and attachments
Copies of proposal: 11
Deadline(s): Mar. 7 and Nov. 1 for grant proposals
Board meeting date(s): 4th Wed. of Jan., Apr., July, and Oct.
Final notification: Within 30 days
Officers and Trustees:* Tim McLain,* Pres.; Greg Adams,* V.P.; Steven G. Randles,* Secy.; Michael Steen,* Treas.; David P. Mitzel, Exec. Dir.; Jamie Thomas, Cont.; Thomas Holdren; Monica Martinelli; Susan Montgomery McDonald; Michael Micheli; D. Scott Moyer; Dr. Doug Ramsay; Dan Sylvester; Beth Upton; Brian Wagner.
Number of staff: 2 full-time professional; 1 full-time support; 1 part-time support.
EIN: 311147022

7586
National Machinery Foundation Inc. ✧
P.O. Box 747
Tiffin, OH 44883-0747 (419) 443-2306
Contact: Larry F. Baker, Pres.

Incorporated in 1948 in OH.
Donors: National Machinery Co.; National Machinery LLC.
Foundation type: Company-sponsored foundation.
Financial data (yr. ended 12/31/13): Assets, $17,340,598 (M); gifts received, $240; expenditures, $907,000; qualifying distributions, $811,863; giving activities include $805,732 for 216 grants (high: $100,000; low: $30).
Purpose and activities: The foundation supports organizations involved with theater, education, health, child welfare, housing development, animal welfare, human services, and community development; and awards grants for good citizenship to high school students and relief assistance to needy individuals in Seneca County, OH.
Fields of interest: Performing arts, theater; Elementary/secondary education; Higher education; Education; Animal welfare; Hospitals (general); Health care; Crime/violence prevention, child abuse; Housing/shelter, development; Salvation Army; YM/YWCAs & YM/YWHAs; Youth, services; Human services; Community/economic development; United Ways and Federated Giving Programs.
Type of support: General/operating support; Annual campaigns; Capital campaigns; Equipment; Emergency funds; Program development; Scholarship funds; Sponsorships; Employee-related scholarships; Grants to individuals; Scholarships—to individuals.
Limitations: Applications accepted. Giving limited to the Seneca County, OH, area.
Application information: Application form required.
Initial approach: Letter
Deadline(s): None
Officer: Larry F. Baker, Pres.
Number of staff: 1 part-time professional.
EIN: 346520191

7587
Nationwide Insurance Foundation ✧
(formerly Nationwide Foundation)
1 West Nationwide Blvd., 1-2-16
Columbus, OH 43215-2220 (614) 249-4310
Contact: Karen Blickley, Sr. Dir.
FAX: (866) 212-7960;
E-mail: corpcit@nationwide.com; Main URL: http://www.nationwide.com/about-us/corporate-philanthropy.jsp

Incorporated in 1959 in OH.
Donors: Nationwide Mutual Insurance Co.; Nationwide Corp.; Nationwide Life Insurance Co. of America.
Foundation type: Company-sponsored foundation.
Financial data (yr. ended 12/31/12): Assets, $79,347,875 (M); gifts received, $9,623,022; expenditures, $25,960,284; qualifying distributions, $25,832,050; giving activities include $24,590,160 for 594 grants (high: $7,554,983; low: $100), and $968,762 for 386 employee matching gifts.
Purpose and activities: The foundation supports programs designed to address emergency and basic needs; crisis stabilization; personal and family empowerment; and community enrichment.
Fields of interest: Hospitals (general); Health care; Substance abuse, services; Food services; Food banks; Housing/shelter, temporary shelter; Housing/shelter; Disasters, preparedness/services; Boys & girls clubs; Big Brothers/Big Sisters; American Red Cross; Youth, services; Family services; Homeless, human services; Human services; Community/economic development; Economically disadvantaged.
Type of support: General/operating support; Continuing support; Annual campaigns; Capital campaigns; Emergency funds; Program development; Seed money; Employee volunteer services; Employee matching gifts; Matching/challenge support.
Limitations: Applications accepted. Giving primarily in areas of company operations in Sacramento, CA, Denver, CO, Gainesville, FL, Atlanta, GA, Baltimore, MD, Lincoln, NE, Durham and Raleigh, NC, Syracuse, NY, Canton and Cleveland, OH, Harrisburg and Philadelphia, PA, Nashville, TN, Dallas, TX, and Lynchburg and Richmond, VA, with emphasis on Scottsdale, AZ, Des Moines, IA, and Columbus, OH. No support for athletic teams, public or private primary or secondary schools, pass-through organizations (except United Way), veterans', labor, religious, or fraternal organizations not of direct benefit to the entire community, lobbying or political organizations, or bands or choirs; generally, no support for hospitals, hospital foundations, or national organizations (except local branches or chapters). No grants to individuals, or for fundraising events, sponsorships, athletic events, debt reduction, retirement campaigns, research, travel, or endowments.
Publications: Application guidelines.
Application information: Videos, albums, and binder submissions are not accepted. Grants for capital support are limited and considered on a case-by-case basis. Application form required.
Initial approach: Complete online application
Deadline(s): Sept. 1
Board meeting date(s): Feb., May, and Nov.
Final notification: Mar. 31
Officers and Trustees:* Stephen S. Rasmussen, Chair. and C.E.O.; Chad A. Jester, Pres.; Mark R. Thresher, Exec. V.P. and C.F.O.; Harry H. Hollowell, Sr. V.P.; Pamela A. Biesecker, Sr. V.P., Taxation; Robert W. Horner III, V.P. and Secy.; Carol L. Dove, V.P. and Treas.; James B. Bachman; Timothy J. Corcoran; Daniel T. Kelley; M. Diane Koken; Lydia M. Marshall.
Number of staff: 1 part-time professional; 1 full-time support.
EIN: 316022301
Selected grants: The following grants are a representative sample of this grantmaker's funding activity:
$7,554,984 to United Way of the Bay Area, Oakland, CA, 2012.
$5,000,000 to Nationwide Childrens Hospital Foundation, Columbus, OH, 2012.
$1,485,000 to American Red Cross National Headquarters, Washington, DC, 2012.
$1,250,000 to Feeding America, Chicago, IL, 2012.
$1,000,000 to COSI Columbus, Columbus, OH, 2012.
$500,000 to United Way Worldwide, Alexandria, VA, 2012.
$50,000 to Community Arts Project, Columbus, OH, 2012.

$30,000 to Childrens Hunger Alliance, Columbus, OH, 2012.
$25,000 to South County Community Clinic, Conroe, TX, 2012.
$15,000 to Salvation Army of Canton, Canton, OH, 2012.

7588
The Needmor Fund

42 S. St. Clair St.
Toledo, OH 43604-8736 (419) 255-5560
Contact: Mary Sobecki, Grants Mgr.
FAX: (419) 255-5561;
E-mail: msobecki@needmorfund.org; Additional e-mail: moreinfo@needmorfund.org; Main URL: http://www.needmorfund.org/
Online insructional application video: https://www.youtube.com/watch?v=_oPa0E3V7uU
The Needmor Fund's Philanthropy Promise: http://www.ncrp.org/philanthropys-promise/who

Trust established in 1956 in OH.
Donor: Members of the Stranahan family.
Foundation type: Independent foundation.
Financial data (yr. ended 12/31/12): Assets, $23,974,238 (M); gifts received, $857,103; expenditures, $2,419,588; qualifying distributions, $2,210,648; giving activities include $1,559,769 for 74 grants (high: $40,000; low: $250).
Purpose and activities: The mission of The Needmor Fund is to work with others to bring about social justice. It supports groups that work together to change the social, economic, or political conditions that bar access to participation in a democratic society. Needmor has identified grassroots community organizing as the most effective process by which low- and moderate-income people can build power, address the systemic barriers to the practice of democracy, hold public and corporate officials accountable for their actions, and begin to participate in shaping public policy. Its grantmaking is focused exclusively on providing support for multi-issue, democratically controlled, membership-based community organizations.
Fields of interest: Community development, citizen coalitions.
Type of support: General/operating support.
Limitations: Applications accepted. Giving limited to the U.S. No support for public or private schools. No grants to individuals, or for capital or endowment funds, scholarships, fellowships, matching gifts, deficit financing, operating support for traditional community services, replacement of lost government funding, land acquisition, purchase of buildings or equipment, or publications, media, computer projects or research.
Publications: Application guidelines; Biennial report (including application guidelines); Financial statement; Grants list.
Application information: Application form required.
Initial approach: Use online grantmaking system on foundation web site
Deadline(s): See foundation web site for current deadlines
Board meeting date(s): May and Nov.
Officers and Directors:* Abby Stranahan,* Chair.; Ken Rolling,* Vice-Chair.; Daniel Stranahan, Secy.-Treas.; Frank I. Sanchez, Exec. Dir.; Susan Chinn; Louis Delgado; James Dickson; Ana Guerrero; Virginia Parry; Ann Stranahan; Mary C. Stranahan; Patti Stranahan.
Number of staff: 3 full-time professional; 1 full-time support.
EIN: 346504812

7589
New Albany Community Foundation ✧ ☆

220 Market St., Ste. 205
New Albany, OH 43054-9031 (614) 939-8150
Contact: J. Craig Mohre, Exec. Dir.
FAX: (614) 939-8155;
E-mail: craigmohre@newalbanyfoundation.org; Main URL: http://www.newalbanyfoundation.org
Facebook: http://www.facebook.com/pages/The-New-Albany-Community-Foundation/111921911896
YouTube: https://www.youtube.com/user/newalbanycf?feature=watch

Established in 1994 in OH.
Foundation type: Community foundation.
Financial data (yr. ended 06/30/14): Assets, $12,677,154 (M); gifts received, $3,804,100; expenditures, $3,088,690; giving activities include $1,998,451 for 12+ grants (high: $1,500,000; low: $250).
Purpose and activities: The foundation's mission is to assist donors and others in strengthening and improving New Albany, OH, for the benefit of all of its residents. The scope of the foundation's charitable grantmaking includes both capital and program grants.
Fields of interest: Humanities; Arts; Education; Environment; Health care; Human services; Community/economic development.
Limitations: Applications accepted. Giving limited to New Albany, OH. No support for religious organizations or religious purposes. No grants to individuals (except for scholarships), or for operating expenses, deficit financing for programs or capital expenditures, endowment funds, annual appeals, membership contributions, conferences, or recognition events.
Publications: Application guidelines; Annual report.
Application information: Visit foundation web site for application form and guidelines. Application form required.
Initial approach: Contact foundation
Copies of proposal: 3
Board meeting date(s): Apr., July, and Oct.
Officers and Trustees:* Michael J. DeAscentis, Jr.,* Chair.; Dennis E. Welch,* Vice-Chair.; J. Craig Mohre,* Pres.; Patti Steinour,* Secy.; Kirt A. Walker,* Treas.; J. Craig Mohre, Exec. Dir.; Keith R. Berend, M.D.; Scott Bracale; Philip Heit, Ph.D.; Cindy Hilsheimer; Richard P. Lavin; Michael Marx; Ira Sharfin; Sanjay Singh.
Number of staff: 1 full-time professional; 1 part-time support.
EIN: 311409264

7590
L. and L. Nippert Charitable Foundation, Inc. ✧

c/o The Randolph Co.
8255 Spooky Hollow Rd.
Cincinnati, OH 45242-6518
Contact: Carter Randolph Ph.D., V.P.
E-mail: info@lnlcharitable.org; Contact for grantmaking process: Peggy Schatz, tel.: (513) 891-4227; Main URL: http://www.lnlcharitable.org

Established in 1992 in OH as successor to L. and L. Nippert Charitable Foundation.
Donors: Louis Nippert†; Louise D. Nippert†; Louise Dieterle Nippert Trust.
Foundation type: Independent foundation.
Financial data (yr. ended 12/31/12): Assets, $18,680,682 (M); gifts received, $5,526,007; expenditures, $741,432; qualifying distributions, $631,982; giving activities include $630,000 for 16 grants (high: $120,000; low: $5,000).
Purpose and activities: Giving primarily for education, human services, and to a children's hospital as well as a YMCA.
Fields of interest: Education; Hospitals (specialty); Human services; YM/YWCAs & YM/YWHAs; Children/youth, services.
Type of support: General/operating support; Continuing support; Annual campaigns; Capital campaigns; Building/renovation; Program development; Curriculum development; Internship funds; Scholarship funds; Research.
Limitations: Giving primarily in the greater Cincinnati, OH area; some funding also in MO and TN. No grants to individuals, or for endowments.
Publications: Application guidelines; IRS Form 990 or 990-PF printed copy available upon request.
Application information: Applicants must use 12-point type and 1 inch margins all around. Applicants may use the Ohio Common Grant Application Short Form (which can be downloaded from foundation web site) to submit a proposal. All applications must be received on a USB flash drive in Microsoft Word format with one original hard copy. The Summary of Grant Request and application should be separate files on the disk. See foundation web site for additional application information. Application form required.
Initial approach: Use Summary of Grant Request (which can be downloaded from foundation web site) and an application
Deadline(s): Sept. 15
Board meeting date(s): Annual
Officers and Directors:* Dr. Carter Randolph,* V.P. and Treas.; Lawrence Kyte, Secy.; Marie Eberhard; Dr. Timothy Johnson; Guy Randolph, Jr.; Jane R. Randolph; Nancy Walker.
EIN: 311351011

7591
NiSource Charitable Foundation ✧

(formerly Columbia Gas Foundation)
200 Civic Center Dr.
Columbus, OH 43215-4138 (219) 647-6209
Contact: Jennifer L. Moench, Exec. Dir.
E-mail: jmoench@nisource.com; Additional address: NiSource Corp. Citizenship, 801 E. 86th Ave., Merrillville, IN 46410-6271; Main URL: http://www.nisource.com/en/sustainability/communities/corporate-giving.aspx

Established in 1990 in DE.
Donors: The Columbia Gas System, Inc.; Columbia Energy Group; Columbia Gas of Ohio, Inc.; NiSource Corporate Services Co.
Foundation type: Company-sponsored foundation.
Financial data (yr. ended 12/31/12): Assets, $19,821,130 (M); expenditures, $2,780,036; qualifying distributions, $2,702,789; giving activities include $2,702,789 for 210 grants (high: $1,004,700; low: $50).
Purpose and activities: The foundation supports programs designed to promote community vitality and development; environmental and energy

sustainability; learning and science education; and public safety and human services.
Fields of interest: Education; Environment, energy; Environment; Safety/disasters; Salvation Army; Human services; Community/economic development; United Ways and Federated Giving Programs; Science, formal/general education; Science.
Type of support: Continuing support; Annual campaigns; Building/renovation; Program development.
Limitations: Applications accepted. Giving on a national basis in areas of company operations, with some emphasis on IN and OH. No support for religious organizations, political candidates or organizations, or discriminatory organizations. No grants to individuals, or for sports sponsorships, goodwill advertising, fundraising benefits, or program books.
Publications: Application guidelines.
Application information: Application form required.
Initial approach: Contact local community relations representative or e-mail foundation for application form
Copies of proposal: 1
Deadline(s): Varies
Board meeting date(s): May and Oct.
Officers and Trustees:* Robert E. Smith, Secy.; David J. Vadja, Treas.; Julie Wozniak, Cont.; Jennifer L. Moench,* Exec. Dir.; Robert D. Campbell; Joseph Hamrock; Christopher A. Helms; Carrie J. Hightman; Glen L. Kettering; Kathleen O'Leary; Robert C. Skaggs, Jr.; S Stephen P. Smith; Jimmy D. Staton; Jim L. Stanley.
EIN: 510324200

7592
Donald and Alice Noble Foundation, Inc. ✧
(formerly Donald E. and Alice M. Noble Charitable Foundation, Inc.)
1061 Venture Blvd.
Wooster, OH 44691-9358 (330) 264-8066
Contact: David D. Noble, Pres.

Established in 1990 in OH.
Donors: Donald E. Noble†; Alice M. Noble.
Foundation type: Independent foundation.
Financial data (yr. ended 12/31/12): Assets, $37,611,595 (M); expenditures, $3,978,777; qualifying distributions, $2,481,548; giving activities include $2,276,494 for 81 grants (high: $501,300; low: $50).
Purpose and activities: Giving for education and human services.
Fields of interest: Education, public education; Secondary school/education; Human services; Foundations (community); Children/youth; Youth; Economically disadvantaged.
International interests: Ghana; Honduras; Kenya; Namibia; Nicaragua; South Africa.
Type of support: General/operating support; Capital campaigns; Program development.
Limitations: Giving primarily in Wooster, OH and in Ghana and Honduras. No grants to individuals.
Application information: Application form not required.
Initial approach: Letter
Copies of proposal: 1
Deadline(s): None
Board meeting date(s): Spring and fall
Final notification: 2 weeks
Officer: David D. Noble, Pres.
Trustees: Nancy L. Holland; Steve Matthew; Donald Noble II; Matthew Noble; Chris Schmid.
Number of staff: 1 full-time professional; 1 full-time support.
EIN: 341665641

7593
The Frederick E. and Julia G. Nonneman Foundation ✧
26202 Detroit Rd., Ste. 100-D
Westlake, OH 44145-2480

Established in 1998 in OH.
Donors: Frederick E. Nonneman†; Lois Nonneman.
Foundation type: Independent foundation.
Financial data (yr. ended 12/31/13): Assets, $32,332,135 (M); gifts received, $25,000; expenditures, $2,127,575; qualifying distributions, $1,705,364; giving activities include $1,700,002 for 21 grants (high: $165,750; low: $11,050).
Fields of interest: Higher education; Legal services; Human services; American Red Cross; Salvation Army; United Ways and Federated Giving Programs; Catholic agencies & churches.
Limitations: Applications not accepted. Giving primarily in Cleveland, OH; giving also in VA and Washington, DC. No grants to individuals.
Application information: Contributes only to pre-selected organizations.
Officers: Anita C. Nonneman, Pres.; Lois E. Nonneman, Secy.-Treas.
EIN: 341881601

7594
The Nord Family Foundation
747 Milan Ave.
Amherst, OH 44001-1310 (440) 984-3939
Contact: John Mullaney, Exec. Dir.
FAX: (440) 984-3934; E-mail: johnm@nordff.org; Additional tel.: (800) 745-8946; E-mail: info@nordff.org or execdir@nordff.org; Main URL: http://www.nordff.org
Grants Database: http://www.nordff.org/meet_grantees

Trust established in 1952 in OH; reorganized in 1988 under current name.
Donors: Walter G. Nord†; Mrs. Walter G. Nord†; Nordson Corp.
Foundation type: Independent foundation.
Financial data (yr. ended 12/31/13): Assets, $129,345,575 (M); gifts received, $25,000; expenditures, $7,250,517; qualifying distributions, $6,628,540; giving activities include $5,828,672 for 365 grants (high: $200,000; low: $25).
Purpose and activities: Emphasis on projects to assist the disadvantaged and minorities, including giving for early childhood, secondary, and higher education, social services, health, cultural affairs, and civic activities. Initiatives included a project to establish a common agenda to address factors which inhibit social and economic progress within the county and a program to strengthen nonprofit organizations which address family issues.
Fields of interest: Arts; Education, early childhood education; Child development, education; Secondary school/education; Higher education; Education; Environment; Health care; Health organizations, association; Human services; Children/youth, services; Child development, services; Minorities/immigrants, centers/services; Urban/community development; Children/youth; Children; Youth; Minorities; Economically disadvantaged; Homeless.
Type of support: General/operating support; Continuing support; Capital campaigns; Building/renovation; Program development; Conferences/seminars; Publication; Seed money; Technical assistance; Program-related investments/loans; Employee matching gifts; Matching/challenge support.
Limitations: Applications accepted. Giving primarily in the Lorain and Cuyahoga County, OH, areas; also gives secondarily in Denver, CO, Boston, MA, and Columbia, SC. No support for religious or political organizations. No grants to individuals, or for deficit financing, research, capital campaigns, tickets, or advertising for fundraising activities.
Publications: Application guidelines; Annual report (including application guidelines); Financial statement; Grants list; Informational brochure (including application guidelines); Occasional report.
Application information: Colorado Common Grant Application form accepted. Application form required.
Initial approach: Online grant application and eligibility quiz on foundation web site
Copies of proposal: 1
Deadline(s): Apr. 1, Aug. 1, and Dec. 1
Board meeting date(s): Feb., June, and Oct.
Final notification: 1 to 3 months
Officers and Trustees:* Kathleen Nord Peterson,* Pres.; Virginia Barbato,* V.P.; T.K. McClintock, Secy.; Brian Ignat,* Treas; Sharon White, Cont.; John J. Mullaney, Exec. Dir.; J. Mac Bennett; Richard Berk; Caprice Bragg; Nick McLintock; Cindy Nord; Shannon Nord; Donald Sheldon; Allyson Wandtke.
Number of staff: 3 full-time professional; 1 part-time professional; 1 full-time support; 1 part-time support.
EIN: 341595929
Selected grants: The following grants are a representative sample of this grantmaker's funding activity:
$150,000 to Historical Properties Initiative, Oberlin, OH, 2012. For maintenance and repair of charitable use properties.
$135,000 to Cleveland Public Theater, Cleveland, OH, 2012. To expand new play development program into regional program with geographically diverse group of artists.
$100,000 to Columbia Film Society, Columbia, SC, 2012. For Phase II of Nickelodeon Capital Project.
$75,000 to Second Harvest Food Bank of North Central Ohio, Lorain, OH, 2012. To increase resources to hunger-relief network in Lorain County.
$60,000 to Case Western Reserve University, Cleveland, OH, 2012. For Summer Health and Academic Enrichment Program, in partnership with Lorain City Schools.
$55,000 to Ohio Dance Theater, Oberlin, OH, 2012. For continued support of general operations.
$50,000 to Colorado Coalition for the Homeless, Denver, CO, 2012. For capital support for Stout Street Integrated Health Center.
$50,000 to LightHouse on a Hill, Highlands Ranch, CO, 2012. For pilot program for Colorado to study and test effectiveness of using Khan Academy software in math classroom.
$48,000 to Boys and Girls Clubs of the Midlands, Columbia, SC, 2012. For continued support of Project Learn.
$41,000 to Sistercare, Columbia, SC, 2012. For Early Intervention Counseling Program.

$25,000 to Girl Scouts of the U.S.A., Northeast Ohio Council, Lorain, OH, 2012. For programs in Lorain County.
$25,000 to YWCA of Cleveland, Cleveland, OH, 2012. For NIA program (Nurturing Independence and Aspirations).
$20,000 to MIRCI Group Homes, Columbia, SC, 2012. For Homeless Recovery Center.
$10,000 to Beck Center for the Arts, Lakewood, OH, 2012. Toward fundraising challenge.
$10,000 to Catholic Diocese of Cleveland, Cleveland, OH, 2012. For Keys to Success intervention and remedial services program.
$10,000 to More Than Words, Waltham, MA, 2012. For general operating support for transformational model and expansion to reach additional youth.

7595
The Eric and Jane Nord Family Fund ✧

(formerly The Eric and Jane Nord Foundation)
P.O. Box 546
Oberlin, OH 44074-0546
Main URL: http://ericjanenordfnd.org/

Established in 1984 in OH.
Donors: Eric T. Nord‡; Jane B. Nord.
Foundation type: Independent foundation.
Financial data (yr. ended 06/30/14): Assets, $46,641,928 (M); gifts received, $1,500,000; expenditures, $2,467,182; qualifying distributions, $2,216,504; giving activities include $2,200,000 for 10 grants (high: $650,000; low: $700).
Purpose and activities: Giving primarily for the arts, and higher education.
Fields of interest: Arts, association; Museums; Arts; Higher education; Human services; Community/economic development.
Type of support: General/operating support.
Limitations: Applications not accepted. Giving primarily in north central OH and NY. No support for religious organizations. No grants to individuals.
Application information: Contributes only to pre-selected organizations.
Officers and Trustees:* Virginia N. Barbato,* Pres. and Treas.; Emily N. McClintock,* V.P.; Richard E. Nord,* Secy.
EIN: 341465569

7596
The Nordson Corporation Foundation ✧

28601 Clemens Rd.
Westlake, OH 44145-1119 (440) 892-1580
Contact: Cecilia H. Render, Exec. Dir.
E-mail: crender@nordson.com; Contact for Lorain County, OH: Kathy Ladiner, Grants Mgr., e-mail: kladiner@nordson.com; Mahoning County, OH and PA: Johanna Friedrich, e-mail: j.friedrich@us.xaloy.com; GA: Cindy Baumgardner, Prog. Off., tel.: (770) 497-3672, e-mail: cindy.baumgardner@nordson.com; CO: Marcus Kincaid, tel.: (970) 2675200, e-mail: marcus.kincaid@nordson.com; CA: Ray McHenry, Dir., HR, tel.: (760) 930-7258, e-mail: ray.mchenry@nordson.com; NJ: Jennifer Kuhn, tel.: (609) 772-8462, e-mail: jennifer.kuhn@nordson.com; RI and southern MA: Shannon Aiton, Exec. Asst., tel.: (401) 431-7094; and WI: Wendy Crotteau, e-mail: wcrotteau@extrusiondies.com; Main URL: http://www.nordson.com/en-us/about-nordson/community/Pages/NordsonCorporationFoundationWelcomePage1.aspx
Grants List: http://www.nordson.com/en-us/about-nordson/community/Pages/2008-Foundation-Annual-Report.aspx

Established in 1988 in OH as successor to the Nordson Foundation, established in 1952.
Donor: Nordson Corp.
Foundation type: Company-sponsored foundation.
Financial data (yr. ended 10/31/13): Assets, $23,678,161 (M); gifts received, $12,425,394; expenditures, $4,180,899; qualifying distributions, $4,087,865; giving activities include $4,087,865 for 217 grants (high: $560,000; low: $2,100).
Purpose and activities: The foundation supports organizations involved with education. Special emphasis is directed toward programs that cultivate educational curriculum and experiences that foster self-sufficiency, job readiness, and goals to aspire to higher education.
Fields of interest: Arts, cultural/ethnic awareness; Visual arts; Performing arts; Historic preservation/historical societies; Arts; Education, reform; Elementary/secondary education; Education, reading; Education; Environment; Employment, training; Housing/shelter; Human services, alliance/advocacy; Human services, reform; Children/youth, services; Family services; Human services, personal services; Human services; Economic development; Voluntarism promotion; Science, formal/general education; Mathematics; Public affairs, citizen participation; Accessibility/universal design; Public affairs; Youth; Economically disadvantaged; Homeless.
Type of support: Continuing support; Annual campaigns; Capital campaigns; Building/renovation; Equipment; Emergency funds; Seed money; Curriculum development; Scholarship funds; Technical assistance; Employee volunteer services; Employee matching gifts.
Limitations: Applications accepted. Giving primarily in areas of company operations, with emphasis on North San Diego County, CA, Larimer County, CO, Dawson County, Gwinnett County, and Emanuel County, GA, Mahoning County, OH, southeastern, MA, Mercer County, NJ, Lawrence County, PA, Providence, RI, VA, Chippewa County, WI. No support for political organizations or candidates or discriminatory organizations. No grants to individuals (except for Nordson BUILDS Scholarships), or for loans, endowments, membership drives, or travel.
Publications: Application guidelines; Annual report; Grants list; Program policy statement.
Application information: Applicants are encouraged to contact the Foundation staff member who represents their geographic area before applying. Organizations receiving support are asked to provide a final report. Application form required.
Initial approach: Complete online application
Copies of proposal: 1
Deadline(s): Feb. 15 for Mahoning County, OH, PA, and VA; Feb. 15, and May 15 for CA; Feb. 15, May 15, Aug. 15, and Nov. 15 for Lorain County, OH; May 15 for CO; Aug. 15 for NJ and RI; Aug. 15, May 15, and Nov. 15 for GA; and Nov. 15 for WI
Board meeting date(s): Feb., Apr., July, and Oct.
Final notification: Within 3 months of application
Officers and Directors:* Michael F. Hilton, Pres. and C.E.O.; John J. Keane, Sr. V.P.; Peter Lambert, Sr. V.P.; Doug Bloomfield, V.P.; Shelly Peet, V.P.; Greg Thaxton, C.F.O.; Beverly J. Coen,* Chief Tax and Risk Off.; Cecilia H. Render, Exec. Dir.
Number of staff: 3 full-time professional; 1 full-time support.
EIN: 341596194
Selected grants: The following grants are a representative sample of this grantmaker's funding activity:
$100,000 to Boys and Girls Club of Lorain County, Oberlin, OH, 2011. For general support.
$100,000 to College Now Greater Cleveland, Cleveland, OH, 2011. For general support.
$10,000 to 21st Century Leaders, Decatur, GA, 2011. For general support.

7597
Northern Ohio Golf Charities Foundation, Inc. ✧

440 E. Warner Rd.
Akron, OH 44319-1925 (330) 644-2299
Contact: Glenda Buchanan, Admin.
E-mail: glendab@neo.rr.com; Main URL: http://www.nogcf.org

Established in 1984.
Donor: Northern Ohio Golf Charities, Inc.
Foundation type: Operating foundation.
Financial data (yr. ended 10/31/13): Assets, $364,460 (M); gifts received, $1,028,075; expenditures, $988,873; qualifying distributions, $987,628; giving activities include $962,712 for 54 grants (high: $75,000; low: $1,000).
Purpose and activities: Giving primarily to advance education, health, human services, civic organizations, and arts and culture.
Fields of interest: Arts; Health care; Human services; Community/economic development.
Limitations: Applications accepted. Giving limited to northern OH. No grants for endowments, operating expenses, or programming.
Publications: Application guidelines; Grants list; Newsletter; Program policy statement (including application guidelines).
Application information: Application form required.
Initial approach: Download application form from foundation web site
Copies of proposal: 14
Deadline(s): July to Sept.
Board meeting date(s): July and Dec.
Final notification: Feb. of year following submission of application
Officers and Board Members:* Gini Paige,* Pres.; Lee DiCola,* V.P.; Cheryl Schlosser,* Secy.; Rick Burke,* Treas.; Chuck Abraham; Bernie Antonino; Barbara Dieterich; Leonard Foster; Connie Hesske; Karen Keasling; Joyce Lagios; Brian J. Moore; Pam Williams.
Number of staff: 1 full-time support.
EIN: 341712857

7598
Jim & Vanita Oelschlager Foundation ✧

3875 Embassy Pkwy.
Akron, OH 44333-8330

Established in 1997 in OH.
Donor: James Oelschlager.
Foundation type: Independent foundation.
Financial data (yr. ended 12/31/13): Assets, $13,576,379 (M); expenditures, $451,563;

qualifying distributions, $420,000; giving activities include $420,000 for 1 grant.
Purpose and activities: Giving primarily to Oak Clinic and to the University of Akron in OH.
Fields of interest: Higher education; Health care, clinics/centers.
Type of support: Endowments.
Limitations: Applications not accepted. Giving primarily in Akron, OH. No grants to individuals.
Application information: Unsolicited requests for funds not accepted.
Trustees: Robert Briggs; Jim Oelschlager; Vanita Oelschlager.
EIN: 311528866
Selected grants: The following grants are a representative sample of this grantmaker's funding activity:
$600,000 to Oak Clinic for Multiple Sclerosis, Uniontown, OH, 2011. For endowment.

7599
The Ohio National Foundation ✧
1 Financial Way
Cincinnati, OH 45242-5851 (513) 794-6100
Contact: Anthony G. Esposito, Tr.
Main URL: https://www.ohionational.com/portal/site/client/ON_Foundation/

Established in 1987 in OH.
Donors: The Ohio National Life Insurance Co.; Ohio National Financial Svcs.
Foundation type: Company-sponsored foundation.
Financial data (yr. ended 12/31/13): Assets, $4,791,700 (M); gifts received, $2,000,219; expenditures, $1,312,830; qualifying distributions, $1,310,632; giving activities include $1,295,682 for 101 grants (high: $242,000; low: $50), and $14,950 for 40 employee matching gifts.
Purpose and activities: The foundation supports hospitals and organizations involved with arts and culture, education, housing development, and human services.
Fields of interest: Arts, association; Museums; Museums (art); Performing arts, orchestras; Performing arts, opera; Arts; Education, early childhood education; Higher education; Libraries (public); Education; Hospitals (general); Housing/shelter, development; Boy scouts; American Red Cross; Children/youth, services; Residential/custodial care; Aging, centers/services; Developmentally disabled, centers & services; Human services; United Ways and Federated Giving Programs.
Type of support: General/operating support; Annual campaigns; Capital campaigns; Building/renovation; Sponsorships; Employee matching gifts.
Limitations: Applications accepted. Giving primarily in Cincinnati, OH. No grants to individuals.
Application information: Application form required.
Initial approach: Proposal
Deadline(s): None
Trustees: Howard C. Becker; Joseph Campanella; Christopher A. Carlson; Ronald J. Dolan; Anthony G. Esposito; Diane S. Hagenbuch; Gary T. Huffman; David B. O'Maley.
EIN: 311230164
Selected grants: The following grants are a representative sample of this grantmaker's funding activity:
$4,000 to Cancer Support Community, Cincinnati, OH, 2012. For sponsorship.
$1,300 to People Working Cooperatively, Cincinnati, OH, 2012. For sponsorship.

7600
The Oliver Family Foundation ✧
c/o U.S. Bank, N.A.
P.O. Box 1118, ML- CN-OH-W10X
Cincinnati, OH 45201-1118 (513) 632-4292

Established in 1992 in OH.
Donors: Gertrude M. Oliver; Richard D. Oliver; Oliver Charitable Lead Trust 1.
Foundation type: Independent foundation.
Financial data (yr. ended 12/31/13): Assets, $15,134,499 (M); gifts received, $1,362,541; expenditures, $1,056,403; qualifying distributions, $1,008,294; giving activities include $999,000 for 50 grants (high: $250,000; low: $1,000).
Purpose and activities: Giving to youth services, civic organizations, the arts and federated giving programs.
Fields of interest: Arts, fund raising/fund distribution; Museums; Residential/custodial care, hospices; United Ways and Federated Giving Programs.
Limitations: Applications accepted. Giving primarily in Cincinnati, OH.
Application information: Application form not required.
Initial approach: Proposal
Deadline(s): None
Trustees: Christine A. Buttress, Esq.; Vere W. Gaynor; Debra Oliver; John C. Oliver; Richard D. Oliver.
EIN: 311365209

7601
OMNOVA Solutions Foundation, Inc. ✧
175 Ghent Rd.
Fairlawn, OH 44333-3300 (330) 869-4289
Contact: Theresa Carter, Pres.
Main URL: http://www.omnova.com/about/community/community.aspx

Established in 1999 in OH.
Donor: GenCorp Foundation Inc.
Foundation type: Company-sponsored foundation.
Financial data (yr. ended 11/30/13): Assets, $26,638,667 (M); expenditures, $1,792,008; qualifying distributions, $1,707,327; giving activities include $1,550,000 for 493 grants (high: $118,000).
Purpose and activities: The foundation supports programs designed to create educational opportunities; connect people to health and social services; energize civic pride; and create access to the arts.
Fields of interest: Arts, cultural/ethnic awareness; Performing arts; Arts; Elementary/secondary education; Adult education—literacy, basic skills & GED; Education, services; Education, reading; Education; Hospitals (general); Crime/violence prevention; Disasters, preparedness/services; Safety/disasters; Family services, parent education; Human services; Economic development; Urban/community development; Mathematics; Science; Public affairs.
International interests: Canada; China; France; India; Thailand.
Type of support: General/operating support; Continuing support; Annual campaigns; Capital campaigns; Building/renovation; Endowments; Program development; Scholarship funds; Employee volunteer services; Employee matching gifts; Employee-related scholarships; In-kind gifts.
Limitations: Applications accepted. Giving primarily in areas of company operations in GA, MA, MS, NC, OH, PA, SC, WI, and in Canada, China, France, India, and Thailand; giving on a limited basis to national organizations. No support for private foundations, fraternal, social, labor, or veterans' organizations, discriminatory organizations, organizations not of direct benefit to the entire community, political parties or candidates, organizations posing a conflict of interest with OMNOVA, or churches or religious organizations. No grants to individuals (except for employee-related scholarships), or for lobbying activities, local athletic or sports programs or sports equipment, travel, advertising, benefits, raffles, or similar fundraising events, or research or conferences.
Publications: Application guidelines; Annual report.
Application information: Multi-year funding is not automatic. Telephone solicitations will not be considered. Application form not required.
Initial approach: Proposal
Copies of proposal: 1
Deadline(s): None
Board meeting date(s): As required
Final notification: 4 to 6 weeks
Officers: Michael E. Hicks, Chair.; S. Theresa Carter, Pres.; Kristine G. Syrvalin,* Secy.; Frank P. Robers,* Treas.
Trustees: Sandi Noah; Nick Triantafillopoulos.
Number of staff: 1 full-time professional; 1 part-time support.
EIN: 341909350
Selected grants: The following grants are a representative sample of this grantmaker's funding activity:
$118,000 to United Way, 2011.
$111,860 to Akron Public Schools, Akron, OH, 2011.
$110,000 to University of Akron, Akron, OH, 2011.
$45,000 to Western Michigan University, Kalamazoo, MI, 2011.
$20,000 to Case Western Reserve University, Cleveland, OH, 2011.
$17,500 to Habitat for Humanity of Summit County, Akron, OH, 2011.
$17,300 to Mogadore Local School District, Mogadore, OH, 2011.
$15,000 to Akron-Canton Regional Foodbank, Akron, OH, 2011.
$15,000 to Greater Akron Chamber, Akron, OH, 2011.
$5,500 to Mogadore Fire Department, Mogadore, OH, 2011.
$5,000 to YWCA Chester County, West Chester, PA, 2011.
$3,000 to Tuesday Musical Association, Akron, OH, 2011.

7602
The William J. and Dorothy K. O'Neill Foundation, Inc. ✧
30195 Chagrin Blvd., Ste. 106
Cleveland, OH 44124-5703 (216) 831-4134
Contact: Leah S. Gary, Pres. and C.E.O.; Cynthia Drennan, Grants Mgr.; Catherine T. Abbott, Dir.
FAX: (216) 378-0594;
E-mail: info@oneill-foundation.org; Contact for letter of inquiry: Timothy M. McCue, Sr. Prog. Off., tel.: (216) 831-4136, e-mail: mccuetmm@oneill-foundation.org; For questions regarding the application process or submission of application form: Symone McClain, Mgr. Grants and

Office Opers., tel.: (216) 831-4135, e-mail: smcclain@oneill-foundation.org; Main URL: http://www.oneillfdn.org
Facebook: https://www.facebook.com/oneillfoundation
Twitter: https://twitter.com/oneillfdn

Established in 1987 in OH.
Donor: Dorothy K. O'Neill†.
Foundation type: Independent foundation.
Financial data (yr. ended 12/31/12): Assets, $78,967,608 (M); gifts received, $103,969; expenditures, $4,599,449; qualifying distributions, $3,606,582; giving activities include $3,019,893 for 179 grants (high: $150,000; low: $100).
Purpose and activities: The foundation's philosophy is rooted in the shared values, sentiments and beliefs of members of the O'Neill family. The foundation exists to serve our fellow human beings. The foundation believes they can best serve by maximizing all their resources and deploying them under well thought-out strategies, developed in partnership with others, in important areas of large beneficial impact. The foundation's vision is for strong communities where families thrive. The foundation's mission is to partner with nonprofits to improve the quality of life for families and communities, in places where O'Neill family members live.
Fields of interest: Family services; Children/youth; Children; Youth; Adults; Aging; Young adults; Disabilities, people with; Physically disabled; Blind/visually impaired; Deaf/hearing impaired; Mentally disabled; Minorities; Asians/Pacific Islanders; African Americans/Blacks; Hispanics/Latinos; Women; Girls; Adults, women; Young adults, female; Men; Boys; Adults, men; Young adults, male; Offenders/ex-offenders; Substance abusers; Single parents; Crime/abuse victims; Terminal illness, people with; Economically disadvantaged; Homeless.
Type of support: Income development; Management development/capacity building; Program development; Conferences/seminars; Curriculum development; Technical assistance; Consulting services; Program evaluation; Matching/challenge support.
Limitations: Applications accepted. Giving primarily in areas where family members reside: the Washington, DC metropolitan area (including Prince George and Montgomery counties in MD), Bonita Springs, Greater Orlando, and Naples, FL, Big Island, HI, Annapolis, Anne Arundel, and Baltimore City, MD, New York, NY, Cleveland, Columbus, and Licking County, OH, Austin and Houston, TX, and Alexandria, Arlington, Richmond and Virginia Beach, VA. No support for organizations operating outside the U.S., or for agencies engaging in lobbying or evangelization. No grants to individuals, or for annual campaigns, general operating costs, debt retirement, fundraising events, lobbying activities, capital campaigns or scholarships.
Publications: Application guidelines; Annual report (including application guidelines); Financial statement; Grants list; Occasional report.
Application information: Application form required.
Initial approach: Letter of inquiry via form on foundation web site
Copies of proposal: 3
Deadline(s): See foundation web site for current deadlines
Board meeting date(s): Mar. 13, July 17 and Oct. 30
Final notification: By e-mail and letter
Officers and Trustees:* Kelly Sweeney McShane,* Chair.; Dennis W. Bower,* Chair., Grantmaking Comm.; Leah S. Gary,* C.E.O. and Pres.; Sara O'Neill Sullivan, Secy.; Robert W. Donahey,* Treas.; William J. O'Neill, Jr., Tr. Emeritus; Linda M. Clifford; John H. O'Neill.
Number of staff: 3 full-time professional.
EIN: 341560893

7603
The Ormond Family Charitable Foundation ✧

(formerly The Ormond Family Charitable Foundation)
333 N. Summit St.
Toledo, OH 43604-1531

Established in 1993 in OH.
Foundation type: Independent foundation.
Financial data (yr. ended 12/31/13): Assets, $1,305,344 (M); expenditures, $1,244,165; qualifying distributions, $1,243,925; giving activities include $1,243,925 for 13 grants (high: $1,212,000; low: $125).
Fields of interest: Higher education; Foundations (community); United Ways and Federated Giving Programs.
Limitations: Applications not accepted. Giving primarily in CA, IL, OH, and WI.
Application information: Contributes only to pre-selected organizations.
Trustees: Chase A. Ormond; Neal Ormond III; Nicholas A. Ormond; Paul A. Ormond; Susan E. Ormond.
EIN: 346991542

7604
Robert O. and AnnaMae Orr Family Foundation ✧

1817 Brookwood Dr.
Akron, OH 44313-5061
Contact: Karen Murray, Exec. Dir.
E-mail: karenmurray45@yahoo.com; Main URL: http://www.orrfamilyfoundation.org

Established in 1998 in OH.
Donor: Robert O. Orr†.
Foundation type: Independent foundation.
Financial data (yr. ended 12/31/13): Assets, $8,378,981 (M); gifts received, $20; expenditures, $789,705; qualifying distributions, $616,973; giving activities include $507,661 for 29 grants (high: $55,000; low: $1,000).
Fields of interest: Arts; Education; Youth development; Human services; Community/economic development; Christian agencies & churches.
Type of support: General/operating support; Equipment; Program development.
Limitations: Applications accepted. Giving limited to Summit and Stark counties, OH, with emphasis on Akron. No support for political organizations. No grants to individuals.
Publications: Application guidelines.
Application information: Application form required.
Initial approach: Complete application form on foundation web site or request form from foundation
Copies of proposal: 1
Deadline(s): None
Officer and Board Members:* Karen Murray,* Exec. Dir.; Kate Baker; Karen Stevens; Mary Stark; Michael Stark.
Number of staff: 1 part-time professional.
EIN: 341867983
Selected grants: The following grants are a representative sample of this grantmaker's funding activity:
$5,000 to Western Reserve Historical Society, Cleveland, OH, 2012. For Hale Farm.

7605
Osteopathic Heritage Foundations ✧

1500 Lake Shore Dr., Ste. 230
Columbus, OH 43204-3800 (614) 737-4370
Contact: Richard Vincent, Pres.
FAX: (614) 737-4371;
E-mail: heritage@ohf-ohio.org; Toll-free tel.: (866) 737-4370; Main URL: http://www.osteopathicheritage.org/
E-Newsletter: http://www.osteopathicheritage.org/News/eNewsletter.aspx
Grants Database: http://www.osteopathicheritage.org/FundingPriorities/fundingawards.aspx
Knowledge Center: http://www.osteopathicheritage.org/newsandreports.aspx

Redesigned in 1998 in OH.
Donors: Doctors Hospital; The Columbus Foundation and Affiliated Organizations.
Foundation type: Independent foundation.
Financial data (yr. ended 12/31/12): Assets, $228,414,402 (M); gifts received, $2,410; expenditures, $13,774,808; qualifying distributions, $11,863,738; giving activities include $9,902,690 for 31 grants (high: $6,400,000).
Purpose and activities: Comprised of two private foundations that share a common mission and vision, while maintaining separate boards and funding concentration: 1) the Osteopathic Heritage Foundation supports community health and quality of life - primarily in central Ohio - as well as osteopathic medical education and research throughout the nation, and 2) the Osteopathic Heritage Foundation of Nelsonville directs its funding support primarily to improving community health and quality of life in southeastern Ohio. The foundations' focus on health and quality of life is broad and concentrated primarily on mission-related, target priorities, including the following: improving access to oral health care; reducing the prevalence of overweight/obesity in central Ohio; resolving healthcare workforce shortages; enhancing access to healthcare services; enhancing osteopathic medical education; and medical research. In addition, the foundations have made reducing homelessness a recent funding priority.
Fields of interest: Health care, information services; Health care, formal/general education; Medical care, community health systems; Public health; Health care; Housing/shelter, homeless; Homeless, human services; Homeless.
Type of support: Management development/capacity building; Endowments; Program development.
Limitations: Applications not accepted. Giving primarily in the following OH counties: Athens, Delaware, Fairfield, Fayette, Franklin, Hocking, Jackson, Knox, Licking, Madison, Meigs, Morgan,

Perry, Pickaway, Ross, Union, Vinton, and Washington.
Publications: Informational brochure.
Application information: Unsolicited requests for funds generally not accepted. Grant requests are considered through a Request for Proposals (RFP) process. See foundation web site for RFP summary and application forms.
Officers and Directors:* Robert A. Palma, D.O.*, Chair., Osteopathic Heritage Fdn.; Frederick L. Oremus,* Chair., Osteopathic Heritage Fdn. of Nelsonville; Jane W. Cunningham,* Vice-Chair., Osteopathic Heritage Foundation; Joseph A. Holtel, D.O.*, Vice-Chair., Osteopathic Heritage Fdn. of Nelsonville; Richard A. Vincent,* C.E.O. and Pres.; Terri Donlin Huesman, V.P., Progs.; George O. Faerber, D.O.*, Secy., Osteopathic Heritage Fdn.; Mark R. Seckinger,* Secy., Osteopathic Heritage Fdn. of Nelsonville; Richard A. Mitchell,* Treas.; Theodore M. Ofat, Cont.; Thomas M. Anderson, D.O.; J. Michael Brooks; Steven E. Cox; Rebecca deVillers, D.O.; Susan L. Hunter; Jeffrey Hutchison, D.O.; Peter E. Johnston, D.O.; Kathy Krendl, Ph.D.; Edward Schreck, D.O.
Selected grants: The following grants are a representative sample of this grantmaker's funding activity:
$4,800,000 to Ohio University, College of Osteopathic Medicine, Athens, OH, 2013. For programs determined to be of significant value to community-at-large and of the highest priority to Foundation to help advance OU_COM to national prominence in training of primary care physicians, focused research and service to Ohio citizens, especially those within central and southeast Ohio.
$2,126,004 to OhioHealth, Columbus, OH, 2013. To enhance and secure the future of postgraduate osteopathic medical education. Enhancements to current program include orthopedic clinic, online learning program, internal medicine program director, orthopedics faculty, intensivist, clinical medicine service, salaries for additional program directors, skills laboratory, objective structured clinical examination program, research support, and emergency medicine faculty.
$251,142 to University of North Texas Health Science Center, Fort Worth, TX, 2013. To continue funding of the Osteopathic Heritage Foundation Research Chairs and Teams at national Osteopathic Research Center to achieve the research objectives of the osteopathic profession.
$49,957 to American Association of Colleges of Osteopathic Medicine, Chevy Chase, MD, 2013. To increase number of educationally-related research projects, expand program to include institutional projects and increase number of collaborative research proposals.

7606
Jane and Jon Outcalt Foundation ✧
(formerly Outcalt Charitable Fund)
c/o Jon H. Outcalt
14505 Hartwell Trail
Novelty, OH 44072-9775

Established in OH.
Donors: Jon H. Outcalt; Jane Q. Outcalt.
Foundation type: Independent foundation.
Financial data (yr. ended 12/31/13): Assets, $18,514,724 (M); gifts received, $300,000; expenditures, $473,247; qualifying distributions, $453,213; giving activities include $453,013 for 49 grants (high: $205,500; low: $100).
Fields of interest: Museums (art); Education; Hospitals (general); Human services; United Ways and Federated Giving Programs.
Limitations: Applications not accepted. Giving primarily in Cleveland, OH. No grants to individuals.
Application information: Contributes only to pre-selected organizations.
Officers: Jon H. Outcalt, Jr., Pres.; Kenneth W. Outcalt, V.P.; Jon H. Outcalt, Secy.; David B. Outcalt, Treas.
EIN: 311194069

7607
Owens Corning Foundation, Inc. ✧
c/o Tax Dept.
1 Owens Corning Pkwy., Ste. 2G/4
Toledo, OH 43659-0001 (419) 248-8000
Contact: Don Retting, Pres.

Established around 1960.
Donor: Owens Corning.
Foundation type: Company-sponsored foundation.
Financial data (yr. ended 12/31/13): Assets, $11,341,788 (M); gifts received, $360; expenditures, $1,052,965; qualifying distributions, $1,008,897; giving activities include $1,008,897 for 122 grants (high: $200,000; low: $50).
Purpose and activities: The foundation supports programs designed to provide access to education and affordable housing for those most in need, and organizations involved with arts and culture and civic betterment. Special emphasis is directed toward projects and organizations that promote diversity and social welfare; serve a broad sector of the community; and have a proven record of success.
Fields of interest: Education; Human services; Religion.
Limitations: Applications accepted. Giving on a national basis in areas of company operations, with emphasis on OH. No support for religious, political, or discriminatory organizations or United Way supported agencies. No grants for travel, capital campaigns, general operating support, or special events, conferences, or sports competitions.
Publications: Program policy statement.
Application information: Application form required.
Initial approach: Letter
Deadline(s): None
Board meeting date(s): Quarterly
Officers: Michael McMurray, Chair.; Don Retting,* Pres.; Raj Dave, Secy.; Michelle DeMarco, Treas.
Directors: Lauren Hornberger; Kim Howard; Gary Niemen; Steven Vermeulen.
Number of staff: 1 part-time professional; 1 part-time support.
EIN: 341270856

7608
Parents Advancing Choice in Education ✧
(also known as PACE)
40 S. Perry St., Ste. 120
Dayton, OH 45402-1439 (937) 228-7223
Contact: George E. Loney, Exec. Dir.
FAX: (937) 226-1887;
E-mail: dariastone@pacedayton.org; Main
URL: http://www.pacedayton.org
Facebook: http://www.facebook.com/PACEDayton

Established in 1997 in OH.
Donors: Mathile Family Foundation; Children's Scholarship Fund; Thomas B. Fordham Foundation.
Foundation type: Independent foundation.
Financial data (yr. ended 06/30/13): Assets, $575,236 (M); gifts received, $1,487,949; expenditures, $1,372,268; qualifying distributions, $1,133,918; giving activities include $915,567 for 46 grants to individuals (high: $267,713; low: $236).
Purpose and activities: The organization seeks to help families make quality education choices so that more children can successfully complete a post-secondary education.
Fields of interest: Higher education; Infants/toddlers; Children/youth; Children; Youth; Adults; Young adults; Disabilities, people with; Physically disabled; Minorities; Asians/Pacific Islanders; African Americans/Blacks; Hispanics/Latinos; Native Americans/American Indians; Women; Infants/toddlers, female; Girls; Adults, women; Young adults, female; Men; Infants/toddlers, male; Boys; Adults, men; Young adults, male; Single parents; Economically disadvantaged.
Type of support: Use of facilities; Scholarships—to individuals.
Limitations: Applications not accepted. Giving primarily in Dayton, OH.
Publications: Annual report; Informational brochure; Newsletter.
Application information: Unsolicited requests for funds not accepted.
Officers and Directors:* Thomas A. Holton,* Chair.; George E. Loney, Exec. Dir.; Dixie Allen; Vicki S. Giambrone; Ronita Hawes-Saunders; Thomas Lasley; William T. Lincoln; Clayton L. Mathile; Toni Moore; Rev. Dr. Daryl Ward; Joseph Zehenny.
Number of staff: 5 full-time professional; 1 part-time professional; 3 part-time support.
EIN: 311809977
Selected grants: The following grants are a representative sample of this grantmaker's funding activity:
$88,482 to Wright State University, Dayton, OH, 2013. To Assist Students Attend School of Choice and Improve Academic Achievement.

7609
The Park Foundation ✧
6200 Riverside Dr.
Cleveland, OH 44135-3132

Established in 2004 in OH.
Donors: Georgia Financial, LLC; Park Corp.; Piper A. Park; Raymond P. Park; Dan K. Park; Kelly C. Park.
Foundation type: Company-sponsored foundation.
Financial data (yr. ended 12/31/12): Assets, $55,157,459 (M); expenditures, $2,748,747; qualifying distributions, $2,709,414; giving activities include $2,709,050 for 59 grants (high: $377,500; low: $1,000).
Purpose and activities: The foundation supports community foundations and organizations involved with education, health, cancer, learning disorders, human services, Christianity, and economically disadvantaged people.
Fields of interest: Education, special; Education; Health care, clinics/centers; Health care; Cancer; Learning disorders; Disasters, fire prevention/control; Children, services; Human services; Foundations (community); Christian agencies & churches; Economically disadvantaged.
Type of support: General/operating support; Capital campaigns; Program development; Scholarship funds.

Limitations: Applications not accepted. Giving primarily in CA, FL, NV, OH, OR, PA, TX, and WV. No grants to individuals.
Application information: Contributes only to pre-selected organizations.
Officers: Raymond P. Park, Pres.; Kelly C. Park, V.P. and Treas.; Dan K. Park, V.P.; Patrick M. Park, V.P.; Piper A. Park, V.P.; Ricky L. Bertram, Secy.
EIN: 200791170
Selected grants: The following grants are a representative sample of this grantmaker's funding activity:
$371,000 to Park Academy, Marylhurst, OR, 2011.

7610
Park National Corporation Foundation ✧
(formerly The Park National Bank Foundation)
P.O. Box 3500
Newark, OH 43058-3500

Established in 1983 in OH.
Donors: The Park National Bank; Fairfield National Bank; The Richland Trust Co.; Park National Corp.; C. Daniel Delawder; William McConnell.
Foundation type: Company-sponsored foundation.
Financial data (yr. ended 12/31/13): Assets, $9,713,562 (M); gifts received, $30,385; expenditures, $1,782,076; qualifying distributions, $1,768,475; giving activities include $1,768,475 for 339 grants (high: $130,008).
Purpose and activities: The foundation supports community foundations and organizations involved with arts and culture, education, health, and human services.
Fields of interest: Arts councils; Performing arts; Arts; Elementary/secondary education; Higher education; Education; Hospitals (general); Health care; Salvation Army; YM/YWCAs & YM/YWHAs; Human services; Foundations (community); United Ways and Federated Giving Programs.
Type of support: General/operating support; Scholarship funds.
Limitations: Applications not accepted. Giving primarily in OH, with emphasis on Columbus, Newark, and Springfield. No grants to individuals.
Application information: Contributes only to pre-selected organizations.
Officers: Dan DeLawder, Chair.; David L. Trautman, Pres.; Cheryl L. Snyder, Secy.-Treas.
Trustees: Brady T. Burt; Thomas M. Cummiskey; Laura B. Lewis.
EIN: 316249406
Selected grants: The following grants are a representative sample of this grantmaker's funding activity:
$50,000 to Denison University, Granville, OH, 2011.
$47,200 to United Way of Knox County, Mount Vernon, OH, 2011.
$36,000 to United Way, Licking County, Newark, OH, 2011.
$25,000 to Kenyon College, Gambier, OH, 2011.
$20,000 to Community Mercy Foundation, Springfield, OH, 2011.
$12,000 to Lancaster Festival, Lancaster, OH, 2011.
$5,000 to Newark Catholic High School Foundation, Newark, OH, 2011.
$5,000 to United Way of Baldwin County, Foley, AL, 2011.
$2,500 to Decorative Arts Center of Ohio, Lancaster, OH, 2011.
$2,500 to Fairfield Medical Center Foundation, Lancaster, OH, 2011.

7611
The Parker-Hannifin Foundation ✧
6035 Parkland Blvd.
Cleveland, OH 44124-4186
Main URL: http://www.parker.com/

Incorporated in 1953 in OH.
Donor: Parker-Hannifin Corp.
Foundation type: Company-sponsored foundation.
Financial data (yr. ended 06/30/12): Assets, $2,267,130 (M); gifts received, $1,277,711; expenditures, $4,930,223; qualifying distributions, $4,930,223; giving activities include $4,544,759 for 719 grants (high: $364,350; low: $25), and $361,051 for 411 employee matching gifts.
Purpose and activities: The foundation supports organizations involved with arts and culture, education, health, sports, human services, community economic development, and civic affairs.
Fields of interest: Performing arts, theater; Performing arts, orchestras; Arts; Secondary school/education; Higher education; Libraries (public); Education; Hospitals (general); Health care, clinics/centers; Health care; Athletics/sports, amateur leagues; Boy scouts; Girl scouts; Youth development, business; Salvation Army; YM/YWCAs & YM/YWHAs; Children/youth, services; Residential/custodial care, hospices; Aging, centers/services; Human services; Community/economic development; United Ways and Federated Giving Programs; Public affairs.
Type of support: General/operating support; Annual campaigns; Capital campaigns; Building/renovation; Endowments; Scholarship funds; Employee matching gifts.
Limitations: Applications not accepted. Giving primarily in areas of company operations, with emphasis on Cleveland, OH. No support for fraternal or labor organizations.
Application information: Contributes only to pre-selected organizations.
Board meeting date(s): Jan. and July
Officers and Trustees:* Donald E. Washkewicz,* Pres.; Daniel S. Serbin, V.P.; Thomas A. Piraino,* Secy.
EIN: 346555686
Selected grants: The following grants are a representative sample of this grantmaker's funding activity:
$56,000 to American Heart Association, Dallas, TX, 2011.
$9,067 to Purdue University, West Lafayette, IN, 2011.
$9,000 to Purdue University, West Lafayette, IN, 2011.
$7,000 to American Heart Association, Dallas, TX, 2011.
$5,500 to Pennsylvania State University, University Park, PA, 2011.
$5,200 to Miami University, Oxford, OH, 2011.
$5,000 to American Heart Association, Dallas, TX, 2011.
$5,000 to University of Cincinnati, Cincinnati, OH, 2011.
$2,800 to American Cancer Society, Atlanta, GA, 2011.
$2,300 to Michigan State University, East Lansing, MI, 2011.

7612
The Partridge Foundation ✧
c/o Kozusko Harris Duncan
25201 Chagrin Blvd., Ste. 370
Cleveland, OH 44122-5637

Established in 1992 in NY.
Donors: Polly Guth; P.W. Guth Charitable Lead Unitrust; P. Guth Charitable Trusts 17; P. Guth Charitable Trusts 16.
Foundation type: Independent foundation.
Financial data (yr. ended 11/30/13): Assets, $35,784,988 (M); gifts received, $1,992,442; expenditures, $3,367,473; qualifying distributions, $2,509,206; giving activities include $2,509,206 for 18 grants (high: $600,000; low: $10,000).
Fields of interest: Arts, cultural/ethnic awareness; Performing arts; Performing arts, opera; Environment, land resources; Reproductive health, family planning; Cancer research; International affairs, goodwill promotion; International affairs; Public affairs; Women.
Limitations: Applications not accepted. Giving primarily in NY, with some giving in MA and ME. No grants to individuals.
Application information: Contributes only to pre-selected organizations.
Trustees: Virginia Montgomery; Winthrop Rutherfurd, Jr.
EIN: 341742512
Selected grants: The following grants are a representative sample of this grantmaker's funding activity:
$1,725,000 to Independent Production Fund, New York, NY, 2012. For general support.
$1,250,000 to Fair Food Network, Ann Arbor, MI, 2012. For general support.
$853,997 to Centre Hospitalier Universitaire Vaudois, Lausanne, Switzerland, 2012. For general support.
$800,000 to Asia Society, New York, NY, 2012. For general support.
$525,000 to Open Space Institute, New York, NY, 2012. For general support.
$375,000 to Planned Parenthood of New York City, New York, NY, 2012. For general support.
$300,000 to Maine Coast Heritage Trust, Topsham, ME, 2012. For general support.
$260,000 to Eastern Maine Medical Center, Bangor, ME, 2012. For general support.
$100,000 to Glimmerglass Opera, Cooperstown, NY, 2012. For general support.
$50,000 to Maine Organic Farmers and Gardeners Association, Unity, ME, 2012. For general support.

7613
Proctor Patterson Foundation ✧
c/o PNC Bank, N.A.
P.O. Box 94651
Cleveland, OH 44101-4651
Application address: c/o Kevin McManamon, 1900 E. 9th St., B7-YB13-13-2, Cleveland, OH 44114, tel.: (216) 222-5853

Established in 2004 in OH.
Donor: Proctor Patterson Trust.
Foundation type: Independent foundation.
Financial data (yr. ended 12/31/13): Assets, $13,706,271 (M); expenditures, $1,144,464; qualifying distributions, $1,091,193; giving activities include $996,992 for 31 grants (high: $436,728; low: $3,500).

Purpose and activities: Giving grants to needy individuals and for medicare reimbursement; funding also for student scholarships for higher education.
Fields of interest: Education; Human services; Economically disadvantaged.
Type of support: Grants to individuals; Scholarships —to individuals.
Limitations: Applications accepted. Giving primarily in NC, SC, and Canada; some funding also in NY, OH and Glasgow, Scotland.
Application information: Application form required.
Initial approach: Request application form
Deadline(s): None
Trustee: PNC Bank, N.A.
EIN: 306081504

7614
The Payne Fund ✧
50 Public Sq., Ste. 4100
Cleveland, OH 44113-2266

Incorporated in 1929 in OH.
Donors: Frances P. Bolton†; F.P. Bolton for Payne Fund Inc.
Foundation type: Independent foundation.
Financial data (yr. ended 12/31/12): Assets, $3,792,472 (M); gifts received, $668,756; expenditures, $853,077; qualifying distributions, $787,850; giving activities include $682,082 for 46 grants (high: $50,000; low: $500).
Purpose and activities: Giving primarily for higher education and cultural programs.
Fields of interest: Museums (art); Performing arts; Arts; Higher education; Education.
Type of support: General/operating support; Capital campaigns; Building/renovation.
Limitations: Applications not accepted. Giving primarily in FL, Asheville, NC, and Cleveland and Gambier, OH. No grants to individuals.
Application information: Contributes only to pre-selected organizations.
Board meeting date(s): Nov.
Officers: Barbara Bolton Gratry, Pres.; John B. Bolton, V.P.; Kenyon C. Bolton III, V.P.; Phillip P. Bolton, V.P.; Thomas C. Bolton, V.P.; William B. Bolton, V.P.; Mary Bolton Hooper, V.P.; Charles P. Bolton, Secy.-Treas.
Number of staff: 1 full-time professional.
EIN: 135563006

7615
The Perkins Charitable Foundation ✧
1030 Hanna Bldg.
1422 Euclid Ave.
Cleveland, OH 44115-2001 (216) 621-0465
Contact: Marilyn Best, Secy.-Treas.

Trust established in 1950 in OH.
Donors: Leigh H. Perkins; Sallie Sullivan; Members of the Perkins family.
Foundation type: Independent foundation.
Financial data (yr. ended 12/31/13): Assets, $27,985,612 (M); expenditures, $1,201,356; qualifying distributions, $1,082,040; giving activities include $1,065,080 for 145 grants (high: $52,000; low: $250).
Purpose and activities: Giving primarily for education, the arts, environmental conservation, animals, wildlife, health and medical care, and children, youth and social services.
Fields of interest: Museums; Arts; Elementary/secondary education; Higher education; Education; Environment, natural resources; Animals/wildlife, preservation/protection; Reproductive health, family planning; Health care; Human services; Children/youth, services; United Ways and Federated Giving Programs.
Limitations: Applications accepted. Giving in the U.S., primarily in CA, CT, FL, MA, MT, OH, RI, VA, and VT. No grants to individuals.
Application information: Application form not required.
Initial approach: Proposal
Deadline(s): None
Officer: Marilyn Best, Secy.-Treas.
Trustees: George Oliva III; Leigh H. Perkins; Sallie P. Sullivan.
EIN: 346549753
Selected grants: The following grants are a representative sample of this grantmaker's funding activity:
$86,350 to Connecticut College, New London, CT, 2011.
$50,000 to Property and Environment Research Center, Bozeman, MT, 2011.
$32,000 to Planned Parenthood of Northeast Florida, Jacksonville, FL, 2011.
$27,000 to American Museum of Fly Fishing, Manchester, VT, 2011.
$21,200 to World Wildlife Fund, Washington, DC, 2011.
$12,000 to United Way of Greater Cleveland, Cleveland, OH, 2011.
$12,000 to Vocational Guidance Services, Cleveland, OH, 2011.
$10,000 to Geauga Park District Foundation, Chardon, OH, 2011.
$10,000 to Nature Conservancy of Idaho, Hailey, ID, 2011.
$5,150 to West Point Fund, West Point, NY, 2011.

7616
Lovett & Ruth Peters Foundation ✧
1500 Chiquita Center
250 E. 5th St.
Cincinnati, OH 45202-4119

Established in 2007 in OH.
Donors: Lovett C. Peters†; Ruth Scott Peters 2007 Trust; Lovett C. Peters Trust.
Foundation type: Independent foundation.
Financial data (yr. ended 12/31/13): Assets, $17,036,729 (M); gifts received, $5,222,794; expenditures, $2,451,679; qualifying distributions, $1,737,450; giving activities include $1,440,000 for 26 grants (high: $150,000; low: $5,000).
Fields of interest: Scholarships/financial aid; Education; Social sciences; Economics; Public policy, research; Public affairs, finance.
Limitations: Applications not accepted. Giving primarily in CA, Washington, DC, IL, OH, and VA, with emphasis on Arlington. No grants to individuals.
Application information: Contributes only to pre-selected organizations.
Officer: Daniel S. Peters, Pres.
Trustees: Kathleen Peters; Jeff Sandefer; Stephanie Saroki.
EIN: 208934367

7617
Thomas F. Peterson Foundation ✧
c/o Bernard L. Karr
600 Superior Ave. E., Ste. 2100
Cleveland, OH 44114-2690

Established in 1953 in OH.
Donor: Ethel B. Peterson†.
Foundation type: Independent foundation.
Financial data (yr. ended 10/31/13): Assets, $2,585,202 (M); expenditures, $771,779; qualifying distributions, $750,200; giving activities include $750,000 for 2 grants (high: $500,000; low: $250,000).
Purpose and activities: Giving primarily for education, including arts education.
Fields of interest: Education.
Type of support: General/operating support.
Limitations: Applications not accepted. Giving primarily in Shaker Heights and Cleveland, OH. No support for private foundations. No grants to individuals.
Application information: Contributes only to pre-selected organizations.
Officers and Trustees:* Barbara P. Ruhlman,* Pres.; Randall M. Ruhlman,* V.P.; Robert G. Ruhlman,* V.P.; Bernard L. Karr,* Secy.
EIN: 346524958
Selected grants: The following grants are a representative sample of this grantmaker's funding activity:
$1,000,000 to Laurel School, Shaker Heights, OH, 2011.
$515,288 to University Hospitals Cleveland Medical Center, Cleveland, OH, 2011.

7618
The Daniel and Susan Pfau Foundation ✧
c/o The Greater Cincinnati Foundation
200 W. 4th St.
Cincinnati, OH 45202-2775 (513) 241-2880
Contact: Jennie Geisheimer, Grants Mgr.
E-mail: geisheimerj@gcfdn.org; Main URL: http://www.pfaufoundation.org

Established in 1994 in OH.
Donors: Daniel A. Pfau; Susan L. Pfau.
Foundation type: Independent foundation.
Financial data (yr. ended 12/31/13): Assets, $24,165,643 (M); gifts received, $5,005,000; expenditures, $967,448; qualifying distributions, $908,695; giving activities include $857,564 for 43 grants (high: $40,000; low: $4,500).
Purpose and activities: The foundation's primary focus is on the education, health, cultural experience, and social welfare of disabled and disadvantaged children, adolescents, and young adults (to age 30) and their families. There is a special interest in programs that help clients realize their full potential. An additional area of interest for the foundation is the support of arts and cultural organizations as well as recreation areas.
Fields of interest: Children/youth, services; Children/youth; Children; Disabilities, people with; Physically disabled; Economically disadvantaged.
Type of support: Program development.
Limitations: Applications accepted. Giving primarily in the greater Cincinnati area including Hamilton, Butler, Clermont and Warren counties, OH, and Boone, Campbell, and Kenton counties, KY. No grants to individuals.
Publications: Application guidelines.
Application information: Application form required.

Initial approach: E-mail Letter of Inquiry form on foundation web site to Jennie Geisheimer, Grants Mgr.
Deadline(s): Jan. 15 and May 15 for Letter of Inquiry; Mar. 1 and July 1 for applications
Board meeting date(s): May/June and Oct./Nov.
Final notification: June and Nov.

Advisory Board: Daniel A. Pfau, Chair.; David Brill; Steve Brill; Mary D. LeRoy; Ann Pfau; Susan L. Pfau.
Trustee: PNC Bank, N.A.
EIN: 311411794
Selected grants: The following grants are a representative sample of this grantmaker's funding activity:
$50,000 to Cincinnati Works, Cincinnati, OH, 2012. For the Next Step Network Project.
$30,000 to ProKids, Cincinnati, OH, 2012. For the Casa University.
$25,000 to Capital District Community Gardens, Troy, NY, 2012. For the Produce Project.
$25,000 to MindPeace, Cincinnati, OH, 2012. For the Improving Access to Mental Health Care for Underserved Children Program.
$25,000 to People Working Cooperatively, Cincinnati, OH, 2012. For the Modifications for Mobility Program.
$20,000 to Cincinnati Recreation Commission Foundation, Cincinnati, OH, 2012. For Memberships for Disadvantaged Youth and the I Can Swim Programs.
$20,000 to CincySmiles Foundation, Cincinnati, OH, 2012. For the Dental Road Crew Program.
$15,000 to Cincinnati Musical Festival Association, Cincinnati, OH, 2012. For the May Festival and Vocal Arts Ensemble Strategic Partnership.
$15,000 to Santa Maria Community Services, Cincinnati, OH, 2012. For the Building Youth Assets in Price Hill Program.
$10,000 to Literacy Center West, Cincinnati, OH, 2012. For the Urban Center Development Project.

7619
The Jesse and Caryl Philips Foundation ✧
3870 Honey Hill Ln.
Dayton, OH 45405-1826

Established in 1990 in OH.
Donor: Jesse Philips†.
Foundation type: Independent foundation.
Financial data (yr. ended 06/30/13): Assets, $11,341,313 (M); expenditures, $1,552,820; qualifying distributions, $1,457,917; giving activities include $1,262,239 for 44 grants (high: $665,000; low: $119).
Fields of interest: Museums; Performing arts, theater; Arts; Medical research, institute; Athletics/sports, equestrianism; Human services; YM/YWCAs & YM/YWHAs; Foundations (private grantmaking); Jewish federated giving programs.
Limitations: Applications not accepted. Giving primarily in Dayton, OH. No grants to individuals.
Application information: Contributes only to pre-selected organizations.
Officer and Trustees:* Caryl Philips,* Pres.; Benjamin M. Beatty; Mary Beatty.
EIN: 341656718
Selected grants: The following grants are a representative sample of this grantmaker's funding activity:
$750,000 to Salk Institute for Biological Studies, La Jolla, CA, 2011. For general expenses.

7620
The Piqua Community Foundation ✧
126 W. High St.
P.O. Box 226
Piqua, OH 45356-2310 (937) 615-9080
Contact: Karen S. Wendeln, Exec. Dir.
FAX: (937) 615-9981;
E-mail: kwendeln@piquacommunityfoundation.org;
Main URL: http://
www.piquacommunityfoundation.org

Established in 1993 in OH.
Foundation type: Community foundation.
Financial data (yr. ended 12/31/13): Assets, $8,251,331 (M); gifts received, $561,531; expenditures, $667,232; giving activities include $505,051 for 17+ grants (high: $72,730), and $56,500 for 39 grants to individuals.
Purpose and activities: The foundation encourages charitable giving to benefit the citizens of Piqua, and provides a variety of methods for donors to help fulfill their charitable giving wishes.
Fields of interest: Arts; Secondary school/education; Education; Health care; Cystic fibrosis; Health organizations; Athletics/sports, school programs; Human services; Community/economic development; United Ways and Federated Giving Programs; Science; Christian agencies & churches.
Type of support: Capital campaigns; Building/renovation; Equipment; Program development; Seed money; Scholarships—to individuals.
Limitations: Applications accepted. Giving limited to the greater Piqua, OH, area. No grants for general operating support or wages and salaries.
Publications: Application guidelines; Annual report; Grants list; Informational brochure; Newsletter.
Application information: Visit foundation web site for application information. Faxed or e-mailed applications are not accepted. Applicants are invited to contact the executive director with any questions or concerns, at Piquacf@sbcglobal.net. Application form required.
Initial approach: Letter, telephone, or e-mail
Copies of proposal: 8
Deadline(s): Mar. 31 and Sept. 30 for Standard Grants; Mar. 15 and Sept. 15 for mini-grants
Board meeting date(s): Varies
Final notification: Within 30 days of deadline

Officers and Directors:* Daniel E. Ramer,* Pres.; L. Edward Fry,* V.P.; Neill H. Haas,* Secy.-Treas.; Karen S. Wendeln,* Exec. Dir.; Jack L. Neuenschwander, Legal Counsel; John S. Alexander; Cheryl L. Burkhardt; Mimi A. Crawford; Daniel P. French; David K. Galbreath, Jr.; Michael E. Gutmann; Christine J. Hulme; Nancy K. Johnston; Craig M. Mullenbrock; Kathryn M. Patten; Stacy P. Scott; Steven K. Staley; Tony Wendeln; Michael P. Yannucci.
Number of staff: 1 part-time professional.
EIN: 311391908

7621
The Elisabeth Severance Prentiss Foundation ✧
c/o PNC Bank, N.A.
1900 E. 9th St., M.S.: B7-YB13-03-1
Cleveland, OH 44114-3404
Contact: Richard Mack, Secy.
FAX: (216) 222-2410; E-mail: john.baco@pnc.com;
Main URL: http://www.esprentissfoundation.org/

Trust established in 1944 in OH.
Donors: Elisabeth Severance Prentiss†; Luther L. Miller†; Kate W. Miller†.
Foundation type: Independent foundation.
Financial data (yr. ended 12/31/13): Assets, $86,521,123 (M); expenditures, $3,316,036; qualifying distributions, $3,237,132; giving activities include $3,180,812 for 40 grants (high: $1,000,000; low: $2,800).
Purpose and activities: Support primarily for the following five objectives: 1) to promote medical and surgical research and to assist in the acquisition, advancement and dissemination of knowledge of medicine and surgery, and of means to maintain health; 2) to promote public health; 3) to aid hospitals and health institutions in Cuyahoga County, OH, that are organized and operated exclusively for public charitable purposes by contributions for capital improvements or equipment, purchase of rare and expensive drugs, and expenses of operation or maintenance; 4) to improve methods of hospital management and administration; and 5) to aid in establishment and support of plans and programs designed to make hospital and medical care available to all, especially those of low-income.
Fields of interest: Hospitals (general); Health care; Health organizations, association; Medical research, institute.
Type of support: General/operating support; Continuing support; Building/renovation; Equipment; Program development; Seed money; Research; Matching/challenge support.
Limitations: Applications accepted. Giving primarily in the greater Cleveland, OH, area. No support for national fundraising campaigns. No grants to individuals, or for scholarships, or generally for surveys, assessments, studies, planning activities, or endowment funds; no loans.
Publications: Annual report (including application guidelines).
Application information: Each grant application must include a cover letter. Please see foundation web site for further details. Application form not required.
Initial approach: Proposal or letter
Copies of proposal: 6
Deadline(s): Apr. 15 (for May meeting) and Oct. 15 (for Nov. meeting)
Board meeting date(s): May and Nov.
Final notification: Shortly after board meeting

Officers and Managers:* Quentin Alexander,* Pres.; Richard Mack, Secy.; Elisabeth H. Alexander; Pamela A. Homsher; Harry J. Bolwell; William R. Robertson.
Trustee: PNC Bank, N.A.
EIN: 346512433

7622
Laura E. Price Briggs Charitable Trust ✧
c/o PNC Bank, N.A.
P.O. Box 94651
Cleveland, OH 44101-4651

Established in OH.
Foundation type: Independent foundation.
Financial data (yr. ended 05/31/13): Assets, $33,318,492 (M); expenditures, $1,702,875; qualifying distributions, $1,530,385; giving activities include $1,530,385 for grants.
Fields of interest: Higher education; Hospitals (general); Human services; Aging.
Limitations: Applications not accepted. Giving primarily in Cleveland, OH.

Application information: Unsolicited requests for funds not accepted.
Trustee: PNC Bank, N.A.
EIN: 346511114
Selected grants: The following grants are a representative sample of this grantmaker's funding activity:
$307,398 to Benjamin Rose Institute, Cleveland, OH, 2012. For general support.
$307,398 to Case Western Reserve University, Cleveland, OH, 2012. For general support.
$307,398 to Center for Community Solutions, Cleveland, OH, 2012. For general support.
$307,398 to Hiram College, Hiram, OH, 2012. For general support.

7623
The Progressive Insurance Foundation ✧
6300 Wilson Mills Rd.
Mayfield Village, OH 44143-2109
Main URL: http://www.progressive.com/progressive-insurance/foundation.aspx

Established in 2001 in OH.
Donors: Progressive Specialty Insurance Company; Progressive Casualty Insurance Co.
Foundation type: Company-sponsored foundation.
Financial data (yr. ended 12/31/12): Assets, $1,174,769 (M); gifts received, $5,338,851; expenditures, $5,362,880; qualifying distributions, $5,312,387; giving activities include $5,268,930 for 2,601 grants (high: $1,957,554; low: $16).
Purpose and activities: The foundation supports the Insurance Institute for Highway Safety to reduce human traumas and the economic cost of auto accidents; and matches employee giving to nonprofit organizations.
Fields of interest: Safety, automotive safety.
Type of support: General/operating support; Annual campaigns; Employee matching gifts.
Limitations: Applications not accepted. Giving primarily in areas of company operations, with emphasis on OH and VA.
Application information: Contributes only to a pre-selected organization and through employee-matching gifts.
Officers and Trustees:* Glenn M. Renwick, Pres.; Brian Domeck, V.P.; Michael J. Moroney, Secy.; James Kusmer, Treas.; W. Thomas Forrester; R. Steven Kestner.
EIN: 300013138
Selected grants: The following grants are a representative sample of this grantmaker's funding activity:
$1,846,219 to Indian Institute for Human Settlements, New Delhi, India, 2011.
$34,605 to New Community Bible Fellowship, Cleveland Heights, OH, 2011.
$25,388 to Willoughby Hills Evangelical Friends Church, Willoughby Hills, OH, 2011.
$22,481 to Saint Gabriel Church and School, Norwood, PA, 2011.
$21,465 to Saint Francis of Assisi, Cartersville, GA, 2011.
$20,608 to Saint John Vianney Parish, Flint, MI, 2011.
$18,652 to Prince of Peace Church, Mentor, OH, 2011.
$17,972 to Campus Crusade for Christ International, Orlando, FL, 2011.
$17,366 to Hudson Community Chapel, Hudson, OH, 2011.
$14,133 to Saint Barnabas Episcopal Church, Bay Village, OH, 2011.

7624
Pulley Foundation ✧
(formerly L. L. Browning Memorial Fund)
c/o U.S. Bank, N.A.
P.O. Box 1118, ML CN-OH-W10X
Cincinnati, OH 45201-1118

Established in 1969 in OH.
Donor: L.L. Browning, Jr. Charitable Lead Unitrust.
Foundation type: Independent foundation.
Financial data (yr. ended 12/31/13): Assets, $16,064,159 (M); expenditures, $1,242,068; qualifying distributions, $1,182,180; giving activities include $1,175,000 for 14 grants (high: $600,000; low: $2,000).
Purpose and activities: Giving primarily for the arts, particularly to a symphony orchestra and an opera house.
Fields of interest: Museums (science/technology); Performing arts, theater; Performing arts, orchestras; Performing arts, opera; Arts; Higher education; Education; Health organizations, association; Human services; Children/youth, services; Deaf/hearing impaired.
Type of support: Annual campaigns.
Limitations: Applications not accepted. Giving primarily in Maysville, KY, and St. Louis, MO. No grants to individuals.
Application information: Contributes only to pre-selected organizations.
Officers and Trustees:* Janet L. Houston,* Pres.; Dorothy W. Browning,* Secy.-Treas.; Kathryn B. Hendrickson; Virginia B. Illick; James A. McNeal.
EIN: 237009545

7625
R.T. Foundation ✧
(formerly Tomsich Foundation)
6140 Parkland Blvd.
Mayfield Heights, OH 44124-4187

Donors: Robert J. Tomsich; NES Group, Inc.
Foundation type: Independent foundation.
Financial data (yr. ended 12/31/13): Assets, $162,608 (M); gifts received, $778,000; expenditures, $992,067; qualifying distributions, $989,754; giving activities include $988,025 for 27 grants (high: $358,000; low: $250).
Purpose and activities: Giving primarily for the arts, education, health organizations and human services.
Fields of interest: Arts; Elementary/secondary education; Higher education; Health care, clinics/centers; Health organizations, association; Cancer research; Human services.
Limitations: Applications not accepted. Giving primarily in Cleveland, OH. No grants to individuals.
Application information: Contributes only to pre-selected organizations.
Officer: Robert J. Tomsich, Pres.
EIN: 341537777

7626
The Albert B. & Audrey G. Ratner Family Foundation ✧
(formerly Albert B. Ratner Family Foundation)
c/o RMS Investment Group
50 Public Sq.
Cleveland, OH 44113

Donors: Albert Ratner; Audrey Ratner.
Foundation type: Independent foundation.
Financial data (yr. ended 07/31/13): Assets, $2,002,300 (M); expenditures, $702,166; qualifying distributions, $680,024; giving activities include $680,024 for grants.
Purpose and activities: Giving primarily for education and Jewish organizations; some funding also for health organizations and to a musical arts association.
Fields of interest: Arts, association; Performing arts, music; Education; Health organizations; Jewish agencies & synagogues.
Limitations: Applications not accepted. Giving primarily in OH; some funding also in NY. No grants to individuals.
Application information: Contributes only to pre-selected organizations.
Officers and Trustees:* Albert B. Ratner,* Pres.; Deborah Ratner Salzberg,* Secy.; Brian Ratner,* Treas.; Audrey Ratner.
EIN: 237218805
Selected grants: The following grants are a representative sample of this grantmaker's funding activity:
$100,000 to Cleveland Clinic Foundation, Cleveland, OH, 2013. For Dr. Richard S. Lang Distinguished Chair Fund.
$100,000 to Maltz Museum of Jewish Heritage, Beachwood, OH, 2013. For Campaign for Our Future.
$50,000 to Cleveland Clinic Foundation, Cleveland, OH, 2013. For Arnold Sydell Miller Family Pavilion.
$50,000 to Tulane University, New Orleans, LA, 2013. For Ratner Family Professorship in Social Entrepreneurship/Ratner Changemakers Fund.
$50,000 to United States Holocaust Memorial Museum, Washington, DC, 2013. For Ruth Ratner Miller Leadership Endowment Fund.
$25,000 to Piano International Association of Northern Ohio, Cleveland, OH, 2013. For Bravo Piano Campaign.
$7,125 to Saint Martin de Porres High School, Cleveland, OH, 2013. For recapitalization initiative.
$6,000 to Cleveland Clinic Foundation, Cleveland, OH, 2013. For The harry R Horvitz Center for Palliative Medicine.
$1,000 to Cleveland Clinic Foundation, Cleveland, OH, 2013. For Leukemia Research.
$200 to Hawken School, Gates Mills, OH, 2013. For Sally Bob Gries Center for Experiential Service Learning.

7627
Reeves Foundation ✧
232 W. 3rd St.
P.O. Box 441
Dover, OH 44622-0441 (330) 364-4660
Contact: H. Donald Patterson, Exec. Dir.

Established in 1966 in OH.
Donors: Margaret J. Reeves†; Helen F. Reeves†; Samuel J. Reeves†.
Foundation type: Independent foundation.

Financial data (yr. ended 12/31/13): Assets, $24,794,118 (M); gifts received, $1,000; expenditures, $1,177,476; qualifying distributions, $1,001,103; giving activities include $908,143 for 32 grants (high: $150,000; low: $3,000).
Purpose and activities: Emphasis on health agencies, including hospitals; grants also for youth agencies, education, and public administration. Priority given to capital improvement projects, and requests within Tuscarawas County, OH.
Fields of interest: Education; Hospitals (general); Health care; Health organizations, association; Human services; Children/youth, services; Government/public administration.
Type of support: Continuing support; Capital campaigns; Building/renovation; Equipment; Matching/challenge support.
Limitations: Applications accepted. Giving primarily in OH, with emphasis on the Dover area and Tuscarawas County. No grants to individuals, or for annual campaigns, seed money, emergency funds, deficit financing, land acquisition, endowment funds, fellowships, special projects, publications, or conferences; no loans.
Application information: Application form not required.
Initial approach: Proposal
Copies of proposal: 1
Deadline(s): 21 days prior to those months when board meets
Board meeting date(s): Bimonthly starting in Feb.
Final notification: 1 month
Officers and Trustees:* Ronald L. Pissocra,* Pres.; Thomas J. Patton,* V.P.; Peter F. Wagner,* Secy.-Treas.; H. Donald Patterson,* Exec. Dir.; Terry A. Pennington; Don A. Ulrich; Jeffry Wagner.
Number of staff: 1 part-time professional.
EIN: 346575477
Selected grants: The following grants are a representative sample of this grantmaker's funding activity:
$55,000 to Dover Historical Society, Dover, OH, 2012. For General Fund and supplement.
$31,025 to Tuscarawas County Agricultural Society, Dover, OH, 2012. For EleCenterical Project.
$10,000 to Dennison Railroad Depot Museum, Dennison, OH, 2012. For Railroad Car Restoration.

7628
The Reinberger Foundation ✧
30000 Chagrin Blvd., No. 300
Cleveland, OH 44124-5721 (216) 292-2790
Contact: Sara Dyer, V.P.; Karen R. Hooser, Pres.
FAX: (216) 292-4466;
E-mail: info@reinbergerfoundation.org; E-mail for Letters of Inquiry:
request@reinbergerfoundation.org; Main URL: http://www.reinbergerfoundation.org

Established in 1968 in OH.
Donors: Clarence T. Reinberger†; Louise F. Reinberger†.
Foundation type: Independent foundation.
Financial data (yr. ended 12/31/13): Assets, $71,932,914 (M); expenditures, $3,605,948; qualifying distributions, $3,174,246; giving activities include $2,885,619 for 118 grants (high: $125,000; low: $5,000).
Purpose and activities: Support for the arts, social service, education, and health care.
Fields of interest: Media/communications; Visual arts; Museums; Performing arts; Humanities; Arts; Elementary/secondary education; Education, early childhood education; Higher education; Adult education—literacy, basic skills & GED; Libraries/library science; Education; Zoos/zoological societies; Hospitals (general); Health care, home services; Health care; Substance abuse, prevention; Substance abuse, treatment; Mental health, treatment; Medical research; Offenders/ex-offenders, rehabilitation; Employment, vocational rehabilitation; Food banks; Housing/shelter, temporary shelter; Recreation; Youth development; Children/youth, services; Family services, domestic violence.
Type of support: Management development/capacity building; General/operating support; Annual campaigns; Capital campaigns; Building/renovation; Equipment; Program development; Research; Matching/challenge support.
Limitations: Applications accepted. Giving primarily in Columbus and in northeastern OH. No grants to individuals, or for seed money, emergency funds, land acquisition, demonstration projects, or conferences; no loans.
Publications: Application guidelines; Informational brochure (including application guidelines).
Application information: The foundation does not accept unsolicited full proposals, after review of the letter of inquiry the foundation will request a proposal if desired. Complete application guidelines available on foundation web site. Application form not required.
Initial approach: Letter of inquiry via online application process on foundation web site
Copies of proposal: 1
Deadline(s): See foundation web site for current deadlines
Board meeting date(s): Feb., May, Aug., and Nov.
Final notification: Within 1 month of deadline
Officers and Trustees:* Karen R. Hooser,* Pres.; Sara R. Dyer,* V.P. and Treas.; Richard H. Oman,* Secy.; William C. Reinberger.
Number of staff: 1 full-time professional.
EIN: 346574879
Selected grants: The following grants are a representative sample of this grantmaker's funding activity:
$250,000 to Neighborhood Progress, Cleveland, OH, 2012. For St. Luke's Manor phase III, payable over 2.00 years.
$150,000 to Das Deutsch Center for Special Needs Children, DDC Clinic for Special Needs Children, Middlefield, OH, 2012. To be CLIA certified Clinical Genetics Lab, payable over 3.00 years.
$100,000 to Cleveland Foodbank, Cleveland, OH, 2012. To increase cold storage space, payable over 2.00 years.
$100,000 to Ronald McDonald House Charities of Central Ohio, Columbus, OH, 2012. For Capital Campaign, payable over 5.00 years.
$75,000 to Cuyahoga Community College Foundation, Cleveland, OH, 2012. For human patient simulator for Westshore Campus, payable over 2.00 years.
$75,000 to W O S U, Columbus, OH, 2012. For capital campaign to purchase Classical 101, payable over 3.00 years.
$40,000 to Community Shelter Board, Columbus, OH, 2012. For general support.
$25,000 to Saint Vincent Charity Medical Center Foundation, Cleveland, OH, 2012. For general support of palliative care services.
$17,500 to WomenSafe, Chardon, OH, 2012. For general support for shelter.
$15,000 to College Now Greater Cleveland, Cleveland, OH, 2012. For adult learner services.

7629
The Marion G. Resch Foundation ✧
c/o Farmers Trust Co.
42 McClurg Rd.
Youngstown, OH 44512-6700
Contact: James H. Sisek, Farmers Trust Co.

Established in 1997 in OH.
Donor: Marion G. Resch.
Foundation type: Independent foundation.
Financial data (yr. ended 12/31/13): Assets, $25,367,936 (M); expenditures, $1,159,201; qualifying distributions, $1,001,006; giving activities include $961,481 for 6 grants (high: $198,000; low: $120,000).
Purpose and activities: Giving primarily for high school early intervention programs and for college scholarships.
Fields of interest: Higher education; Youth; Young adults, female; Young adults, male.
Type of support: Program development; Scholarship funds.
Limitations: Applications not accepted. Giving limited within 100 miles of Youngstown, OH.
Application information: Unsolicited requests for funds not accepted.
Officers and Trustees:* George R. Berlin, Pres.; Ingrid Lundquist,* V.P.; Neil H. Maxwell,* Secy.; Eldon S. Wright, Secy.; James H. Sisek,* Treas.; Brian J. Wolf, Exec. Dir.; Kathleen Brown.
Agent: Farmers Trust Company.
Number of staff: 1 part-time professional.
EIN: 341853367

7630
Richland County Foundation ✧
(formerly The Richland County Foundation of Mansfield, Ohio)
24 W. 3rd St., Ste. 100
Mansfield, OH 44902-1209 (419) 525-3020
Contact: Bradford Groves, Pres.
FAX: (419) 525-1590;
E-mail: info@rcfoundation.org; Additional e-mail: bgroves@rcfoundation.org; Main URL: http://www.richlandcountyfoundation.org/
E-Newsletter: http://www.richlandcountyfoundation.org/surveys/newsletter-signup
Facebook: https://www.facebook.com/RichlandCountyFoundation

Incorporated in 1945 in OH.
Foundation type: Community foundation.
Financial data (yr. ended 12/31/13): Assets, $136,600,233 (M); gifts received, $13,432,629; expenditures, $3,984,538; giving activities include $2,855,781 for 63+ grants (high: $365,000), and $415,950 for 428 grants to individuals.
Purpose and activities: The foundation seeks to improve and enhance the quality of life in Richland County through strategic philanthropy and community leadership. The foundation accomplishes this mission by: 1) providing leadership and acting as a catalyst in identifying and addressing emerging community needs; 2) distributing grants for charitable purposes in the areas of Health, Economic Development, Basic Human Needs, Education, Cultural Activities, Environment, and Community Services; 3) prudently managing the Foundation's resources to achieve the maximum benefit for Richland County in perpetuity; 4) identifying and cultivating donors of all economic means and charitable interests; and 5) assisting

donors in establishing funds to meet community needs and distribute proceeds in accordance with the donor's intent.
Fields of interest: Historic preservation/historical societies; Arts; Education, early childhood education; Child development, education; Elementary school/education; Secondary school/ education; Vocational education; Higher education; Adult/continuing education; Adult education—literacy, basic skills & GED; Libraries/library science; Education, reading; Education; Environment; Hospitals (general); Health care; Substance abuse, services; Mental health/crisis services; Health organizations, association; Employment; Children/youth, services; Child development, services; Family services; Aging, centers/services; Women, centers/services; Human services; Civil rights, race/intergroup relations; Economic development; Community/ economic development; Government/public administration; Children/youth; Children; Aging; Disabilities, people with; Physically disabled; Minorities; Women; Girls; Economically disadvantaged.
Type of support: General/operating support; Management development/capacity building; Capital campaigns; Building/renovation; Equipment; Land acquisition; Endowments; Emergency funds; Program development; Seed money; Scholarship funds; Technical assistance; Program-related investments/loans; Scholarships—to individuals; Matching/challenge support.
Limitations: Applications accepted. Giving primarily in Richland County, OH. No support for sectarian religious purposes. No grants to individuals (except for scholarships), or annual campaigns, operating expenses, computer systems, fellowships, highly technical or specialized research, maintenance funds, travel, debt, or medical, scientific or academic research.
Publications: Application guidelines; Annual report (including application guidelines); Informational brochure; Newsletter.
Application information: Visit foundation web site for grant guidelines; scholarship applications also available on web site. Application form required.
Initial approach: Telephone for appointment
Copies of proposal: 1
Deadline(s): Jan. 3, Apr. 11, Aug. 22, and Oct. 17 for Competitive Grants
Board meeting date(s): 2nd Mon. of Feb., Apr., June, Aug., Oct., and Dec.; annual meeting in May
Final notification: Feb. 10, June 9, Oct. 13, and Dec. 8
Officers and Trustees:* John C. Roby,* Chair.; Beth DeLaney,* Chair.-Elect; Bradford Groves,* Pres.; Mark Masters,* Secy.; Bruce Cummins,* Treas.; Chris E. Harris,* Treas.; Patricia Addeo; Glenna Cannon; Michael Bennett; David D. Carto; Michael Chambers; Bruce Jackson, M.D.; Jason B. Murray; Justin Marotta; W. Chandler Stevens; Cathy Stimpert; Sam VanCura.
Number of staff: 4 full-time professional; 1 full-time support.
EIN: 340872883

7631
Ridgecliff Foundation Inc. ✧
P.O. Box 26167
Fairview Park, OH 44126-0167
Contact: Michael A. Minelli, 2nd V.P.
E-mail: minelli.michael01@gmail.com; Main URL: http://www.ridgecliff.org

Established in 1991 in OH; converted from sale of Laurelwood Hospital to Mount Sinai Medical Center.
Donors: Mount Sinai Medical Center; Laurelwood Hospital.
Foundation type: Independent foundation.
Financial data (yr. ended 12/31/13): Assets, $8,862,511 (M); expenditures, $495,633; qualifying distributions, $453,763; giving activities include $438,313 for 33 grants (high: $35,000; low: $2,000).
Purpose and activities: Giving to promote research, patient care and charity care in the field of mental health and chemical dependency, and activities that promote health care generally.
Fields of interest: Health care; Substance abuse, services; Mental health/crisis services; Health organizations, association; Children/youth, services; Psychology/behavioral science; Children/ youth; Children; Adults; Young adults; Mentally disabled; Substance abusers; Crime/abuse victims.
Type of support: Program development.
Limitations: Applications accepted. Giving primarily in Ashtabula, Cuyahoga, Geauga, Lake, Lorain, Mahoning, Medina, Portage, Summit, and Trumbull counties, OH. No grants to individuals, or for construction projects, feasibility studies, ongoing projects beyond one year, or equipment which is not an integral part of a program.
Publications: Application guidelines; Grants list.
Application information: Awards limited to 1 grant per organization in a 12-month period. Application form not required.
Copies of proposal: 9
Deadline(s): Mar. 31 and Sept. 30 for funding in Feb. and Aug.
Board meeting date(s): Jan., May, Aug., and Nov.
Final notification: Jan. 31 and July 31
Officers and Trustees:* Thomas TS Kaung,* Pres.; Gregory J. Malafarina, 1st V.P. and Treas.; Michael A. Minelli, 2nd V.P. and Grant Review Comm. Chair.; J. David Ingersoll, Secy.; Paul McHugh,* Investment Comm. Chair.; Donna Bonvissuto, Program Evaluator; Blanche Dortch; Hollie Gallagher; Elena Lidrbauch; Mary Therese Matousek; Roberta Taliaferro.
Number of staff: None.
EIN: 341671405
Selected grants: The following grants are a representative sample of this grantmaker's funding activity:
$40,000 to Free Medical Clinic of Greater Cleveland, Cleveland, OH, 2012. For Behavioral Health Department.
$35,000 to Womens Recovery Center, Xenia, OH, 2012. For alcohol and drug treatment for medically indigent clients.
$30,000 to Magnolia Clubhouse, Cleveland, OH, 2012. For annual support.
$30,000 to Salvation Army of Greater Cleveland, Cleveland, OH, 2012. For Harbor Light Substance Abuse Recovery Program.
$25,000 to Cleveland Rape Crisis Center, Cleveland, OH, 2012. For trauma and addiction program.
$25,000 to Hospice of the Western Reserve, Cleveland, OH, 2012. For School Crisis Response Program.
$25,000 to Saint Vincent Charity Medical Center, Cleveland, OH, 2012. For Rosary Hall Intensive Outpatient Program for uninsured battling addiction.
$25,000 to West Side Catholic Center, Cleveland, OH, 2012. For psychiatric treatment counselor for minorities with mh/sa or dual diagnosis.
$21,750 to National Alliance on Mental Illness Greater Cleveland, Cleveland, OH, 2012. For family and consumer support and education programs.
$20,000 to Suicide Prevention Education Alliance of Northeast Ohio, Cleveland, OH, 2012. To recognize teen depression and prevent suicide program.

7632
George B. Riley Trust ✧
411 Terrace Pl.
P.O. Box 356
Terrace Park, OH 45174-1164 (513) 621-5017

Established in 2003 in OH.
Foundation type: Independent foundation.
Financial data (yr. ended 12/31/13): Assets, $29,469,901 (M); expenditures, $1,393,704; qualifying distributions, $1,322,974; giving activities include $1,237,600 for 44 grants (high: $90,000; low: $10,000).
Fields of interest: Education; Health care; Food services; Human services; Children/youth, services; Aging, centers/services; Protestant agencies & churches.
Limitations: Applications accepted. Giving primarily in Cincinnati, OH.
Application information: Application form not required.
Initial approach: Proposal
Deadline(s): None
Trustees: Hubert C. Auburn; James R. Hall; Stephen M. Winhusen.
EIN: 310654315

7633
George W. & Mary F. Ritter Charitable Trust ✧
c/o KeyBank, N.A.
P.O. Box 10099
Toledo, OH 43699-0099

Established in 1982 in OH.
Donor: George W. Ritter†.
Foundation type: Independent foundation.
Financial data (yr. ended 11/30/13): Assets, $11,546,151 (M); expenditures, $487,985; qualifying distributions, $471,032; giving activities include $464,394 for 26 grants (high: $75,960; low: $131).
Purpose and activities: Giving primarily for hospitals, higher education, and Protestant churches. Student aid limited to male graduates of Ottawa Hills High School and Vermillion High School attending Baldwin-Wallace College.
Fields of interest: Museums (art); Higher education; Hospitals (general); Youth development, scouting agencies (general); Human services; YM/YWCAs & YM/YWHAs; Protestant agencies & churches.
Type of support: General/operating support; Scholarships—to individuals.
Limitations: Applications not accepted. Giving primarily in the Toledo, OH, area.
Application information: Contributes only to pre-selected organizations.
Trustee: KeyBank, N.A.
EIN: 346781636

Selected grants: The following grants are a representative sample of this grantmaker's funding activity:
$17,627 to YMCA of Greater Toledo, Toledo, OH, 2013. For social programs.

7634
The Rockwern Charitable Foundation ✧
30 Garfield Pl., Ste. 1030
Cincinnati, OH 45202-4357 (513) 621-2850
Contact: Benjamin Gettler, Exec. Dir.

Established in 1998 in OH.
Donor: S. Sumner Rockwern†.
Foundation type: Independent foundation.
Financial data (yr. ended 05/31/13): Assets, $11,702,696 (M); expenditures, $532,527; qualifying distributions, $450,000; giving activities include $450,000 for grants.
Purpose and activities: Giving primarily to Jewish organizations, including a Jewish school.
Fields of interest: Education; Jewish federated giving programs.
Limitations: Applications accepted. Giving primarily in Cincinnati, OH.
Application information: Application form required.
Initial approach: Proposal
Deadline(s): None
Officer: Benjamin Gettler, Exec. Dir.
Trustees: Stephanie R. Amlung; Deliaan A. Gettler; Gloria S. Haffer.
EIN: 311590504
Selected grants: The following grants are a representative sample of this grantmaker's funding activity:
$300,000 to Jewish Federation of Cincinnati, Cincinnati, OH, 2011.

7635
Roggecora Memorial Foundation ✧
P.O. Box 425
Zanesville, OH 43702-0425

Established in OH.
Foundation type: Independent foundation.
Financial data (yr. ended 12/31/13): Assets, $12,558,591 (M); expenditures, $774,143; qualifying distributions, $682,651; giving activities include $571,002 for 17 grants (high: $213,100; low: $956).
Fields of interest: Elementary/secondary education; Higher education; Community/economic development; Catholic agencies & churches.
Limitations: Applications not accepted. Giving primarily in Zanesville, OH. No grants to individuals.
Application information: Unsolicited requests for funds not accepted.
Trustees: Gerald A. Erhard; Frederic J. Grant III; Albert H. Hendley; Albert F. Iacovone; Charles E. White; PNC Bank, N.A.
EIN: 316183600

7636
Stuart Rose Family Foundation ✧ ☆
2875 Needmore Rd.
Dayton, OH 45414-4301

Established in 1988 in OH.
Donors: Stuart A. Rose; Christy Rose.
Foundation type: Independent foundation.
Financial data (yr. ended 11/30/13): Assets, $20,272,703 (M); gifts received, $791,100; expenditures, $3,005,321; qualifying distributions, $2,967,300; giving activities include $2,967,300 for 2 grants (high: $2,243,700; low: $723,600).
Fields of interest: Jewish federated giving programs.
Limitations: Applications not accepted. Giving primarily in Dayton, OH. No grants to individuals.
Application information: Contributes only to pre-selected organizations.
Officers: Stuart A. Rose, Pres.; Jacqueline T. Rose, Secy.; Eugene S. Rose, Treas.
EIN: 311274967

7637
Leighton A. Rosenthal Family Foundation ✧
c/o Parkland Mgmt. Co.
1001 Lakeside Ave., No. 900
Cleveland, OH 44114-1177 (216) 479-2200
Contact: Jane R. Horvitz, Tr.; Cynthia R. Boardman, Tr.

Established in 1986 in OH.
Donor: Leighton A. Rosenthal†.
Foundation type: Independent foundation.
Financial data (yr. ended 10/31/13): Assets, $3,551,159 (M); expenditures, $462,451; qualifying distributions, $448,206; giving activities include $435,150 for 11 grants (high: $187,500; low: $650).
Purpose and activities: Giving primarily for medical research and Jewish agencies and temples.
Fields of interest: Arts; Medical research, institute; Foundations (public); Philanthropy/voluntarism; Jewish agencies & synagogues.
Limitations: Applications accepted. Giving primarily in OH, with some emphasis on Cleveland.
Application information: Application form required.
Initial approach: Letter
Deadline(s): None
Trustees: Cynthia R. Boardman; Jane R. Horvitz.
EIN: 136877098
Selected grants: The following grants are a representative sample of this grantmaker's funding activity:
$950,000 to Park Synagogue, Cleveland Heights, OH, 2011.
$750,000 to Cleveland Clinic Foundation, Cleveland, OH, 2011.
$350,000 to Musical Arts Association, Cleveland, OH, 2011.
$300,000 to Cleveland Museum of Art, Cleveland, OH, 2011.
$187,500 to Cleveland Clinic Foundation, Cleveland, OH, 2011.
$100,000 to Park Synagogue, Cleveland Heights, OH, 2011.
$55,500 to Cleveland Museum of Art, Cleveland, OH, 2011.
$5,000 to Preservation Foundation of Palm Beach, Palm Beach, FL, 2011.
$2,000 to School of American Ballet, New York, NY, 2011.

7638
Safelite Charitable Foundation ✧
2400 Farmers Dr.
Columbus, OH 43235-2762 (614) 210-9000
Contact: James R. Randolph, V.P.

Donors: Safelite Group Inc.; Bank of America; Carlite; Central Mouldings Corp.; Crystal Glass; Equalizer Industries; Fifth Third Bank; FirstGiving; Glass Medic; Gold Glass Group; Installer Edge; McKenna Long Aldridge LLP; MH Equipment; Mygrant Glass Co.; National Football League Alumni, Inc.; Premier Radio; Raining Data US, Inc.; Safety Today; Saint-Gobain Autover USA, Inc.; Sunroof Express; VF Services, Inc.; Vorys Sater Seymour and Please, LLP; Truist; Carlex; Aetna; Ford Motor Co.; United Way of Central Ohio; Belron World Conference Foundation; ATT; Baker Hostetler; Cardinal Solutions Group; Wells Fargo Bank, N.A.; Dow Automotive.
Foundation type: Independent foundation.
Financial data (yr. ended 12/31/13): Assets, $515,971 (M); gifts received, $668,596; expenditures, $1,602,426; qualifying distributions, $1,186,681; giving activities include $1,186,681 for 54 grants (high: $226,000; low: $2,520).
Fields of interest: Human services; Children/youth, services.
Limitations: Applications accepted. Giving in the U.S., with emphasis on OH.
Application information: Application form required.
Initial approach: Letter
Deadline(s): None
Officers: Thomas M. Feeney, Pres.; James R. Randolph, V.P.; Brian M. Dimasi, Secy.
EIN: 203683768

7639
Saint Luke's Foundation of Cleveland, Ohio ✧
11327 Shaker Blvd., Ste. 600 W.
Cleveland, OH 44104 (216) 431-8010
Contact: Anne C. Goodman, C.E.O. and Pres.
FAX: (216) 431-8015;
E-mail: dzeman@saintlukesfoundation.org; Main URL: http://www.saintlukesfoundation.org/
Facebook: http://www.facebook.com/pages/Saint-Lukes-Foundation/130812285054?ref=ts
Flickr: http://www.flickr.com/photos/27371974@N04/
Saint Luke's Foundation of Cleveland, Ohio's Philanthropy's Promise: http://www.ncrp.org/files/Philanthropys-Promise/Statements/Saint_Lukes_Foundation_Public_Statement.pdf
Twitter: http://www.twitter.com/saintlukesfdn
Video Presentation: http://www.saintlukesfoundation.org/focus-and-funding/grantmaking-philosophy/
YouTube: http://www.youtube.com/user/saintlukesfoundation

Established in 1997 in OH; converted from the Saint Luke's Medical Center.
Foundation type: Independent foundation.
Financial data (yr. ended 12/31/12): Assets, $173,547,118 (M); gifts received, $135,995; expenditures, $12,645,544; qualifying distributions, $12,046,088; giving activities include $10,184,154 for 79 grants (high: $1,561,503; low: $2,500).
Purpose and activities: The foundation reinvests its resources to provide leadership and support for the improvement and transformation of the health and well-being of individuals, families and communities of Greater Cleveland. grantmaking revolves around three core areas: 1) Healthy People; 2) Strong Communities; 3) Resilient Families.

Fields of interest: Health care; Family services; Human services; Community development, neighborhood development; Infants/toddlers; Children; Youth; Adults; Aging; Young adults; Disabilities, people with; Physically disabled; Deaf/hearing impaired; Mentally disabled; Minorities; African Americans/Blacks; Hispanics/Latinos; Women; Substance abusers; AIDS, people with; Crime/abuse victims; Terminal illness, people with; Economically disadvantaged; Homeless.
Type of support: General/operating support; Management development/capacity building; Capital campaigns; Building/renovation; Equipment; Emergency funds; Program development; Publication; Seed money; Curriculum development; Scholarship funds; Research; Technical assistance; Consulting services; Program evaluation; Program-related investments/loans; Matching/challenge support.
Limitations: Applications accepted. Giving limited to northeastern OH. No support for for-profit organizations or for religious purposes. No grants to individuals or fundraising events, endowments, biomedical research, lobbying, or debt retirement.
Publications: Application guidelines; Annual report; Annual report (including application guidelines); Grants list; Informational brochure; Informational brochure (including application guidelines).
Application information: See web site for additional application information. Application form required.
Initial approach: Online proposal
Copies of proposal: 1
Deadline(s): Apr. 1, July 1 and Oct. 1
Board meeting date(s): Mar., June, Sept. and Dec.
Final notification: 3 months after receipt of application
Officers and Trustees:* Douglas Wang,* Chair.; Arthur Lavin, M.D.,* Vice-Chair.; Anne C. Goodman,* C.E.O. and Pres.; LaTida Smith, V.P., Program, Outcomes and Learning; Belva Denmark Tibbs, Secy.; Robert Monitello, C.F.O.; John P. O'Brien, Treas. and Chair., Finance/Aud. Comm.; Francis Afram-Gyening; April Miller Boise; Janet E. Burney; Geraldine H. Burns; Luis Cartagena; Diana Centeno-Gomez; John R. Corlett; Colleen M. Cotter; Claudia J. Coulton; Edgar B. Jackson, M.D.; Sandra Kiely Kolb; J. Christopher Manners; George Mateyo; Lori McClung; Ann O'Brien; Ashley Basile Oeken; Ken Okeson; Sally J. Staley.
Number of staff: 6 full-time professional; 2 part-time professional; 2 full-time support.
EIN: 340714513
Selected grants: The following grants are a representative sample of this grantmaker's funding activity:
$1,500,000 to Neighborhood Progress, Cleveland, OH, 2012. For Saint Luke's Manor Phase III: Turning a Vision Into Reality, payable over 3.00 years.
$1,125,000 to Neighborhood Progress, Cleveland, OH, 2012. For Creating Neighborhoods of Choice in the Buckeye-Shaker Square Area, payable over 1.50 years.
$750,000 to Neighborhood Progress, Cleveland, OH, 2012. For Creating Neighborhoods of Choice in the Buckeye, Shaker Square Area.
$550,000 to Case Western Reserve University, School of Dental Medicine, Cleveland, OH, 2012. For operating support for Healthy Smiles program.
$550,000 to Case Western Reserve University, School of Dental Medicine, Cleveland, OH, 2012. For operating support for Healthy Smiles program.
$450,000 to Free Medical Clinic of Greater Cleveland, Cleveland, OH, 2012. For operating support ($150,000)and for the electronic health records project ($300,000), payable over 3.00 years.
$350,000 to Cleveland Department of Public Health, Cleveland, OH, 2012. For Lead-Safe Living - 2012.
$301,543 to Pew Charitable Trusts, Washington, DC, 2012. For Health Impact Assessment - Greater Cleveland, payable over 2.25 years.
$225,000 to FrontLine Service, Cleveland, OH, 2012. For Operating Support to Implement Primary and Behavioral Health Services.
$220,000 to Mental Health and Addiction Advocacy Coalition, Cleveland, OH, 2012. For Operating Support, payable over 2.00 years.
$150,000 to Case Western Reserve University, Cleveland, OH, 2012. For Collaborative Cuyahoga County Community Health Improvement Data Surveillance: Behavioral Risk Factor Surveillance System and Youth Risk Behavior Surveillance System, payable over 2.00 years.
$150,000 to Case Western Reserve University, Cleveland, OH, 2012. For Cuyahoga County Community Health Data Dashboard at Case Western Reserve University.
$150,000 to Legal Aid Society of Cleveland, Cleveland, OH, 2012. For Community Advocacy Program.
$100,000 to Cleveland Housing Network, Cleveland, OH, 2012. For Strengthening the Success of Low-income Families.
$100,000 to Health Policy Institute of Ohio, Columbus, OH, 2012. For Advancing the Health of All Ohioans Through Informed Policy Decisions.
$100,000 to Western Reserve Land Conservancy, Moreland Hills, OH, 2012. For Thriving Communities Institute.
$60,000 to Esperanza, Cleveland, OH, 2012. For Family Engagement for Student Success.
$59,032 to Cuyahoga County Board of Health, Cleveland, OH, 2012. For Advancing Health Impact Assessment Through Capacity Building and Practice.
$50,000 to Neighborhood Progress, Cleveland, OH, 2012. For Accessing and Building Capacity in the Mt. Pleasant Neighborhood.

7640
Salem Community Foundation, Inc. ✧
P.O. Box 553
Salem, OH 44460-2911 (330) 332-4021
Contact: John E. Tonti, Pres.
FAX: (330) 332-4021;
E-mail: Info@salemcommunityfoundation.org; Main URL: http://www.salemcommunityfoundation.org

Established in 1966 in OH.
Donors: Joseph Sedzmak; Donna Sedzmak; A. Franklin Hubert‡; Albert Morris Family; Bernice Melitschka; Corinne Mackall‡.
Foundation type: Community foundation.
Financial data (yr. ended 12/31/13): Assets, $18,051,074 (M); gifts received, $800,655; expenditures, $903,990; giving activities include $823,416 for 12+ grants (high: $496,120).
Purpose and activities: The foundation seeks to improve the quality of life in Salem, OH, and the immediate area. The foundation, through special grants, supports charitable, educational, scientific, literary, artistic, and civic efforts, as well as public safety, welfare, and recreational programs in Salem.
Fields of interest: Arts; Education; Children/youth, services; Government/public administration; Disabilities, people with; Economically disadvantaged.
Type of support: Continuing support; Annual campaigns; Building/renovation; Equipment; Land acquisition; Scholarship funds.
Limitations: Applications accepted. Giving primarily in Salem City and Perry Township, OH. No support for religious purposes or to federal agencies. No grants to individuals (except for scholarships), or for operating budgets of established organizations or programs, budget deficits, endowments, conferences, or scholarly research.
Publications: Application guidelines; Annual report; Newsletter; Quarterly report.
Application information: Visit foundation web site for application form and guidelines. Application form required.
Initial approach: Submit application form and attachments
Copies of proposal: 2
Deadline(s): 1 month prior to quarterly board meeting
Board meeting date(s): Quarterly
Final notification: Immediately following quarterly board meetings
Officers and Directors:* John E. Tonti,* Pres.; Rob McCulloch III,* V.P.; Salvatore C. Apicella, M.D.*, Secy.; Gary E. Moffett,* Treas.; Steven J. Bailey; Larry G. Cecil; Rev. Meta S. Cramer; Mark C. Equizi; Karl Getzinger; George W.S. Hays; Joseph Julian; Deb McCulloch; Frederic E. Naragon; Audrey C. Null; Lou Ramunno; Connie Rowe; Joseph P. Sedzmak.
Number of staff: 1 part-time support.
EIN: 341001130

7641
Salem Lutheran Foundation ✧ ☆
2700 E. Dublin-Granville Rd., Ste. 300
Columbus, OH 43231-4089 (614) 898-7200
Contact: Terrie L. Rice, Secy.

Established in 1968 in OH.
Donors: Homewood Corp.; George A. Skestos.
Foundation type: Company-sponsored foundation.
Financial data (yr. ended 12/31/12): Assets, $73,536 (M); expenditures, $3,832,646; qualifying distributions, $3,824,513; giving activities include $3,822,583 for 1 grant.
Purpose and activities: The foundation awards college scholarships to men entering the pastoral ministry and attending Martin Lutheran College in Minnesota and Wisconsin Lutheran Seminary in Wisconsin.
Fields of interest: Human services.
Type of support: Scholarships—to individuals.
Limitations: Applications accepted. Giving limited to MN and WI.
Application information: Application form required.
Initial approach: Contact foundation for application form
Deadline(s): July 1
Officers: William A. Goldman, Pres.; Terrie L. Rice, Secy.; James W. Phieffer, Treas.
Trustees: Hagop Mekhjian; Adam N. Scott.
EIN: 316084166

7642
Samaritan Foundation ✧ ☆
P.O. Box 97
Haviland, OH 45851-0097 (419) 622-4611
Contact: Todd Stoller, Secy.-Treas.; Craig Stoller, V.P.

Established in 2002 in OH.
Donor: Haviland Plastic Products Co.
Foundation type: Company-sponsored foundation.
Financial data (yr. ended 12/31/13): Assets, $6,167,633 (M); gifts received, $1,156,531; expenditures, $1,428,250; qualifying distributions, $1,427,200; giving activities include $1,410,229 for 43 grants (high: $500,000; low: $1,000), and $16,194 for 6 grants to individuals (high: $5,000; low: $1,200).
Purpose and activities: The foundation supports food banks and organizations involved with education, patient services, disaster relief, human services, and Christianity; awards grants and loans to indigent individuals in economic distress; and awards college scholarships to students located in Paulding County, Ohio.
Fields of interest: Secondary school/education; Education; Health care, patient services; Food banks; Disasters, preparedness/services; American Red Cross; Children/youth, services; Human services; Christian agencies & churches; Economically disadvantaged.
Type of support: General/operating support; Grants to individuals; Scholarships—to individuals; Loans—to individuals.
Limitations: Applications accepted. Giving primarily in IN, KY, and OH.
Publications: Application guidelines.
Application information: Application form required.
Initial approach: Completed application form
Deadline(s): None
Officers: Russell Stoller, Pres.; Craig Stoller, V.P.; Todd Stoller, Secy.-Treas.
EIN: 341957355

7643
Sankey Family Foundation ✧
c/o Alan J. Tobin
4040 Embassy Pkwy., Ste. 100
Akron, OH 44333-8354

Established in 1999 in OH.
Donors: James K. Sankey; Invue Security Products, Inc.
Foundation type: Independent foundation.
Financial data (yr. ended 12/31/13): Assets, $13,202,355 (M); gifts received, $3,670,092; expenditures, $1,513,070; qualifying distributions, $1,444,560; giving activities include $1,444,560 for 11 grants (high: $592,000; low: $200).
Purpose and activities: Giving primarily for children and social services.
Fields of interest: Human services; Children, services; United Ways and Federated Giving Programs; Christian agencies & churches.
Type of support: General/operating support; Program development.
Limitations: Applications not accepted. Giving primarily in NC and OH. No grants to individuals.
Application information: Contributes only to pre-selected organizations.
Officers: James K. Sankey, Pres.; Beth H. Sankey, V.P and Treas.; Alan J. Tobin, Secy.
EIN: 341909797

7644
Sapirstein-Stone-Weiss Foundation ✧ ☆
(formerly The Jacob Sapirstein Foundation of Cleveland)
c/o Mary Kay Incandela
10500 American Rd.
Cleveland, OH 44144 (216) 252-7300
Contact: Gary Weiss

Incorporated in 1952 in OH.
Donor: Jacob Sapirstein†.
Foundation type: Independent foundation.
Financial data (yr. ended 12/31/13): Assets, $1,963,597 (M); expenditures, $2,150,677; qualifying distributions, $2,076,404; giving activities include $2,069,354 for 12 grants (high: $2,021,446; low: $100).
Purpose and activities: Giving primarily for Jewish welfare funds and secondary and higher religious education.
Fields of interest: Elementary/secondary education; Theological school/education; Human services; Jewish federated giving programs; Jewish agencies & synagogues.
Type of support: General/operating support.
Limitations: Applications accepted. Giving primarily in OH and NY; some giving in Jerusalem, Israel. No grants to individuals or for scholarships or fellowships; no loans.
Application information: Application form required.
Initial approach: Letter
Copies of proposal: 1
Deadline(s): Jan. 15
Board meeting date(s): Quarterly
Officers and Trustees:* Steven Tatar,* V.P.; Elie Weiss,* V.P.; Jeffrey Weiss,* V.P.; Judith Weiss,* V.P.; Zev Weiss,* Secy.-Treas.
EIN: 346548007

7645
Lee and Patti Schear Family Foundation Inc. ✧ ☆
1130 Harmon Ave.
Dayton, OH 45419-3023

Established in 2002 in OH.
Donor: Lee Schear.
Foundation type: Independent foundation.
Financial data (yr. ended 12/31/12): Assets, $2,231,309 (M); gifts received, $500,000; expenditures, $591,857; qualifying distributions, $580,348; giving activities include $580,348 for grants.
Fields of interest: Hospitals (specialty); Jewish federated giving programs; Jewish agencies & synagogues.
Type of support: Building/renovation; General/operating support.
Limitations: Applications not accepted. Giving primarily in Dayton, OH. No grants to individuals.
Application information: Contributes only to pre-selected organizations.
Officer: Lee Schear, Pres.
Directors: L. Keith Brunner; John M. Cloud; Barkat Ferar; Patricia Schear; Peggy Stoler.
EIN: 320015483

7646
Charles E. Schell Foundation for Education ✧
P.O. Box 630858, MD 1090CA
Cincinnati, OH 45263-0858
Application Address: Fifth Third Bank Foundation Office, 38 Fountain Square Plz., MD1090CA, Cincinnati, OH 45263, tel.: (513) 534-4397

Established in 1939 in OH.
Donor: Charles E. Schell†.
Foundation type: Independent foundation.
Financial data (yr. ended 09/30/13): Assets, $8,490,695 (M); gifts received, $769,104; expenditures, $722,570; qualifying distributions, $683,349; giving activities include $667,248 for grants.
Purpose and activities: Awards given to colleges to set up student loan programs to provide interest free loans to men and women, ages 15-25, who are living in IN, KY, OH, or in adjoining states.
Fields of interest: Education.
Limitations: Applications accepted. Giving limited to IN, KY, OH, and adjoining states. No grants to individuals directly.
Publications: Application guidelines; Annual report.
Application information: Application form required.
Initial approach: Request application form
Copies of proposal: 1
Deadline(s): None
Board meeting date(s): Mar., June, Sept. and Dec.
Trustee: Fifth Third Bank.
EIN: 316019720

7647
The Schiewetz Foundation, Inc. ✧
3110 Kettering Blvd.
Dayton, OH 45439-1924

Established in 2001 in OH.
Donor: Richard F. Schiewetz†.
Foundation type: Independent foundation.
Financial data (yr. ended 12/31/13): Assets, $88,008,304 (M); expenditures, $3,748,857; qualifying distributions, $2,832,813; giving activities include $2,721,419 for 14 grants (high: $1,150,000; low: $5,000).
Fields of interest: Historic preservation/historical societies; Arts; Education; Boy scouts; YM/YWCAs & YM/YWHAs; Youth, services.
Limitations: Applications not accepted. Giving primarily in Dayton, OH. No grants to individuals.
Application information: Contributes only to pre-selected organizations.
Officers: Richard W. Schwartz, Pres.; Amy C. Kress, V.P.; Jennifer L. Schmidt, Secy.-Treas.
Director: Jane E. Schwartz.
EIN: 311812245

7648
Robert C. & Adele R. Schiff Family Foundation ✧
c/o U.S. Bank, N.A.
P.O. Box 1118, ML CN-OH-W10X
Cincinnati, OH 45201-1118 (513) 632-2018

Established in 2002 in OH.
Donors: Robert C. Schiff; Robert C. Schiff Charitable Lead Annuity Trust Accounts.
Foundation type: Independent foundation.

Financial data (yr. ended 11/30/13): Assets, $233,468,030 (M); gifts received, $9,211,446; expenditures, $9,630,968; qualifying distributions, $8,641,530; giving activities include $8,539,569 for 64 grants (high: $1,050,089; low: $1,000).
Purpose and activities: Giving primarily for the arts, education, health organizations, human services, children and youth services, including a children's hospital, and social services.
Fields of interest: Museums; Arts; Elementary/secondary education; Higher education; Education; Hospitals (specialty); Health organizations; Human services; Children/youth, services.
Limitations: Applications not accepted. Giving primarily in OH. No grants to individuals.
Application information: Contributes only to pre-selected organizations.
Directors: James A. Schiff; Robert C. Schiff, Jr.
EIN: 300206688
Selected grants: The following grants are a representative sample of this grantmaker's funding activity:
$1,002,540 to Community Learning Center Institute, Cincinnati, OH, 2012. For grant made in form of stock.
$902,334 to Duke University, Durham, NC, 2012. For grant made in form of stock.
$500,000 to YMCA of Greater Cincinnati, Cincinnati, OH, 2012. For grant made in form of stock.
$300,818 to Childrens Hospital Foundation, Cincinnati, OH, 2012. For grant made in form of stock.
$275,707 to Cincinnati Cancer Center, Cincinnati, OH, 2012. For grant made in form of stock.
$260,000 to John Updike Society, Bloomington, IL, 2012.
$160,425 to Cincinnati Early Learning Centers, Cincinnati, OH, 2012. For grant made in form of stock.
$65,000 to Catholic Inner-City Schools Educational Fund, CISE, Cincinnati, OH, 2012.
$65,000 to Greater Cincinnati Television Educational Foundation, CET, Cincinnati, OH, 2012.
$25,000 to Lighthouse Youth Services, Cincinnati, OH, 2012.

7649
John J. and Mary R. Schiff Foundation ✧
P.O. Box 145496
Cincinnati, OH 45250-5496 (513) 870-2580

Established in 1983 in OH.
Donors: John J. Schiff; Mary R. Schiff.
Foundation type: Independent foundation.
Financial data (yr. ended 06/30/13): Assets, $283,607,702 (M); gifts received, $13,408,877; expenditures, $10,828,597; qualifying distributions, $10,630,047; giving activities include $10,514,000 for 29 grants (high: $3,525,000; low: $5,000).
Fields of interest: Museums (art); Historic preservation/historical societies; Higher education; Animal welfare; Hospitals (general).
Limitations: Applications not accepted. Giving primarily in Cincinnati, OH. No grants to individuals.
Application information: Contributes only to pre-selected organizations.
Officer and Trustees:* John J. Schiff,* Chair.; Suzanne Reid; Thomas R. Schiff.
EIN: 311077222
Selected grants: The following grants are a representative sample of this grantmaker's funding activity:
$3,525,000 to Cincinnati Museum Association, Cincinnati, OH, 2013. For general support.
$2,500,000 to Cincinnati Art Museum, Cincinnati, OH, 2012. For renovations to Art Academy Building.
$2,100,000 to Xavier University, Cincinnati, OH, 2013. For general support.
$1,900,000 to Deaconess Hospital of Cincinnati, Cincinnati, OH, 2012. For general support.
$1,900,000 to Deaconess Hospital of Cincinnati, Cincinnati, OH, 2013. For general support.
$1,000,000 to Xavier University, Cincinnati, OH, 2012. For general support.
$1,000,000 to Xavier University, Cincinnati, OH, 2012. For capital campaign.
$525,000 to Cincinnati Art Museum, Cincinnati, OH, 2012. For general support.
$450,000 to Childrens Hospital Medical Center, Cincinnati, OH, 2012. For general support.
$450,000 to Childrens Hospital Medical Center, Cincinnati, OH, 2013. For general support.
$350,000 to Cincinnati Art Museum, Mary R. Schiff Library, Cincinnati, OH, 2012. For general support.
$300,000 to U.S.S. Constitution Museum, Boston, MA, 2012. For general support.
$300,000 to U.S.S. Constitution Museum, Boston, MA, 2013. For general support.
$250,000 to Cincinnati Museum Association, Cincinnati, OH, 2013. For FotoFocus.
$200,000 to Kennedy Heights Arts Center, Cincinnati, OH, 2013. For general support.
$150,000 to United States Naval Academy Foundation, Annapolis, MD, 2012. For general support.
$145,000 to Western Hills High School, Cincinnati, OH, 2013. For general support.
$100,000 to Cultural Center of Cape Cod, South Yarmouth, MA, 2013. For general support.
$100,000 to National Underground Railroad Freedom Center, Cincinnati, OH, 2012. For general support.
$25,000 to Northern Kentucky University, Highland Heights, KY, 2013. For general support.

7650
Albert G. & Olive H. Schlink Foundation ✧
49 Benedict Ave., Ste. C
Norwalk, OH 44857-2161 (419) 668-8211
Contact: Curtis J. Koch, Pres. and Secy.
FAX: (419) 668-2813; Main URL: http://www.schlinkfoundation.org/

Established in 1966 in OH.
Donors: Albert G. Schlink†; Olive H. Schlink†.
Foundation type: Independent foundation.
Financial data (yr. ended 12/31/13): Assets, $19,149,613 (M); expenditures, $1,533,869; qualifying distributions, $1,464,999; giving activities include $1,360,700 for 61 grants (high: $230,000; low: $1,000).
Purpose and activities: Grants to organizations providing aid to the indigent, aged, including religious, educational, and health agencies and hospitals; support also for the blind and for hospice and other national agencies and charities.
Fields of interest: Museums; Education, fund raising/fund distribution; Medical school/education; Education; Nursing care; Health care; Medical research, institute; Human services; Residential/custodial care, hospices; Aging, centers/services; Biology/life sciences; Science; Aging; Disabilities, people with; Economically disadvantaged.
Type of support: Capital campaigns; Building/renovation; Equipment; Endowments; Program development; Scholarship funds; Research.
Limitations: Applications accepted. Giving primarily in OH. No grants to individuals or for operating expenses.
Publications: Application guidelines.
Application information: Application form required.
Initial approach: Proposal
Copies of proposal: 1
Deadline(s): None
Board meeting date(s): Monthly
Officers: Curtis J. Koch, Pres. and Secy.; John D. Allton, V.P. and Treas.
Trustees: Janet C. Koch; James O. Miller; Judith Sommers.
EIN: 346574722

7651
Jacob G. Schmidlapp Trust No. 1 and No. 2 ✧
(formerly Jacob G. Schmidlapp Trust No. 1)
c/o Fifth Third Bank
38 Fountain Sq. Plz., 1090CA
Cincinnati, OH 45263-0001 (513) 534-4397
Contact: Heidi B. Jark, Mgr., Charitable and Planned Giving Svcs.

Trust established in 1927 in OH.
Donor: Jacob G. Schmidlapp†.
Foundation type: Independent foundation.
Financial data (yr. ended 09/30/13): Assets, $59,648,714 (M); expenditures, $3,335,874; qualifying distributions, $3,015,170; giving activities include $3,014,000 for 51 grants (high: $500,000; low: $5,000).
Purpose and activities: Grants for the relief of sickness, suffering, and distress, and for care of young children and the aged, or the helpless and afflicted; support also for education, including child care training.
Fields of interest: Higher education; Education; Health care; Health organizations, association; Food services; Human services; Children/youth, services; Child development, services; Aging, centers/services.
Type of support: Equipment; Land acquisition; Endowments; Program development; Seed money; Technical assistance.
Limitations: Applications accepted. Giving primarily in the greater Cincinnati, OH, area. No support for religious or political purposes. No grants to individuals; no loans.
Publications: Application guidelines; Annual report.
Application information: Application form required.
Initial approach: Letter
Copies of proposal: 1
Deadline(s): Feb., May, Aug., and Nov.
Board meeting date(s): Mar., June, Sept., Dec.
Final notification: Immediately following meetings
Trustee: Fifth Third Bank.

7652
Joseph J. Schott Foundation ✧ ☆
1801 E. 9th St., Ste. 1105
Cleveland, OH 44114-3103
Application address: c/o L. Thomas Hiltz, 50 E. River Center Blvd., Covington, KY 41011-1648; tel.: (859) 431-5544

Established in 1960 in OH.

Donor: Joseph J. Schott‡.
Foundation type: Independent foundation.
Financial data (yr. ended 12/31/13): Assets, $14,540,996 (M); expenditures, $782,914; qualifying distributions, $687,488; giving activities include $506,000 for 25 grants (high: $100,000; low: $2,000).
Purpose and activities: Giving primarily for museums, education, and social services.
Fields of interest: Museums (art); Museums (history); Museums (specialized); Education; Health care; Human services; Children/youth, services.
Type of support: General/operating support; Equipment; Program development; Scholarship funds; Research.
Limitations: Applications accepted. Giving primarily in Cincinnati, OH and SC. No grants to individuals.
Application information: Application form not required.
Initial approach: Proposal
Deadline(s): None
Trustees: Francie S. Hiltz; L. Thomas Hiltz; Dunne Saal; Elizabeth S. Saal.
EIN: 346513748

7653
Marge & Charles J. Schott Foundation ✧
(formerly Charles J. Schott Foundation)
5084 Wooster Rd., No. 100
Cincinnati, OH 45226-2392 (513) 721-8400
Contact: Frank Crane III

Established around 1980.
Donors: Margaret U. Schott‡; Schottco Corp.
Foundation type: Independent foundation.
Financial data (yr. ended 12/31/12): Assets, $100,676,419 (M); expenditures, $5,765,231; qualifying distributions, $4,123,251; giving activities include $4,123,251 for grants.
Fields of interest: Secondary school/education; Higher education; Human services; Children/youth, services.
Limitations: Giving primarily in Cincinnati, OH. No grants to individuals.
Application information:
Initial approach: Letter
Deadline(s): None
Officers: Frank Crane III, Pres.; Carlotta Crane, V.P.; John R. Verkamp, Treas.
Trustee: Robert Martin.
EIN: 316063407

7654
The Jay and Jean Schottenstein Foundation ✧
(formerly Jay L. Schottenstein Foundation)
c/o Charles Spicer Inc.
4300 E. Fifth Ave.
Columbus, OH 43219-1816 (614) 449-4253

Established in OH.
Donors: Jay Schottenstein; Jeffrey Schottenstein; Jonathan Schottenstein; Joseph Schottenstein.
Foundation type: Independent foundation.
Financial data (yr. ended 12/31/12): Assets, $15,243,035 (M); gifts received, $1,646,089; expenditures, $9,775,925; qualifying distributions, $9,728,096; giving activities include $9,728,096 for 69 grants (high: $2,750,000; low: $54).
Purpose and activities: Support only for Jewish agencies, temples, and schools.
Fields of interest: Elementary/secondary education; Theological school/education; Jewish federated giving programs; Jewish agencies & synagogues.
Type of support: General/operating support.
Limitations: Applications not accepted. Giving limited to NY and OH. No grants to individuals.
Application information: Contributes only to pre-selected organizations.
Officer: Jay Schottenstein, Pres.
EIN: 311111955
Selected grants: The following grants are a representative sample of this grantmaker's funding activity:
$2,750,000 to Mesorah Heritage Foundation, Brooklyn, NY, 2012.
$1,050,000 to Agudath Israel of America, New York, NY, 2012.
$1,000,000 to Friends of the Israel Antiquities Authoritity, New York, NY, 2012.
$569,853 to Columbus Torah Academy, Columbus, OH, 2012.
$450,000 to Leo Yassenoff Jewish Community Center, Columbus, OH, 2012.
$364,409 to American Friends of Rabbinical College of Telzstone, Brooklyn, NY, 2012.
$200,000 to Friends of Ir David, Brooklyn, NY, 2012.
$81,320 to Columbus Community Kollel, Columbus, OH, 2012.
$75,000 to Yeshiva University, New York, NY, 2012.
$72,000 to Oae Pinsk Karlin, Brooklyn, NY, 2012.

7655
Saul Schottenstein Foundation C ✧ ☆
c/o Arshot Investment Corp.
107 S. High St., 3rd Fl.
Columbus, OH 43215-3456 (614) 463-9730
Contact: Thomas H. Schottenstein, Pres.

Foundation type: Independent foundation.
Financial data (yr. ended 12/31/12): Assets, $5,892,991 (M); gifts received, $1,000; expenditures, $557,479; qualifying distributions, $463,469; giving activities include $463,469 for grants.
Fields of interest: Jewish agencies & synagogues.
Application information: Application form required.
Initial approach: Letter
Deadline(s): None
Officer: Thomas H. Schottenstein, Pres.
EIN: 270167574

7656
Else L. Schulze Perpetual Charitable Trust ✧
P.O. Box 1118, ML CN-OH-W10X
Cincinnati, OH 45201-1118

Established in OH.
Foundation type: Independent foundation.
Financial data (yr. ended 12/31/13): Assets, $13,525,882 (M); expenditures, $685,718; qualifying distributions, $536,392; giving activities include $520,736 for 4 grants (high: $182,258; low: $104,147).
Fields of interest: Higher education; Education; Health organizations.
Limitations: Applications not accepted. Giving primarily in KY, OH, and OK.
Application information: Unsolicited requests for funds not accepted.
Trustee: US Bank, N.A.
EIN: 316664505

7657
The Scioto Foundation ✧
(formerly The Scioto County Area Foundation)
303 Chillicothe St.
P.O. Box 911
Portsmouth, OH 45662 (740) 354-4612
Contact: Kimberly E. Cutlip, Exec. Dir.
FAX: (740) 354-1912;
E-mail: kim.sciotofoundation@verizon.net; Main URL: http://www.sciotofoundation.org
Facebook: http://www.facebook.com/pages/Portsmouth-OH/The-Scioto-Foundation/307784404730

Established in 1974 in OH.
Foundation type: Community foundation.
Financial data (yr. ended 12/31/13): Assets, $32,951,288 (M); gifts received, $5,154,380; expenditures, $1,559,443; giving activities include $1,065,562 for 23+ grants (high: $211,878).
Purpose and activities: The foundation seeks to improve, enhance, and enrich the quality of life for all residents of southern Ohio and northern Kentucky.
Fields of interest: Arts; Education; Environment, natural resources; Health care; Human services; Community/economic development.
Type of support: Management development/capacity building; Capital campaigns; Equipment; Program development; Conferences/seminars; Publication; Seed money; Curriculum development; Scholarship funds; Research; Technical assistance; Consulting services; Program evaluation; Matching/challenge support.
Limitations: Applications accepted. Giving primarily in Scioto County, OH; distributions are regional depending on donor preference. No support for religious organizations for religious programs. No grants for continuing support, annual campaigns, emergency funds, deficit financing, building funds, land acquisition, endowments, foundation-managed projects, exchange programs, or program support; no loans.
Publications: Application guidelines; Annual report; Financial statement; Grants list; Informational brochure (including application guidelines); Newsletter; Occasional report.
Application information: Visit foundation web site for application form and guidelines. Application form required.
Initial approach: Submit application form and proposal
Copies of proposal: 6
Deadline(s): Mar. 31, June 31, Sept. 30, and Dec. 31
Board meeting date(s): 3rd Wed. of each month
Final notification: 1 month
Officers and Directors:* Jodi High,* Chair.; Josh Howard,* V.P.; Michael Gampp,* Treas.; Kimberly E. Cutlip, Exec. Dir.; Jonica Burke; Debra Esham.
Number of staff: 2 full-time professional; 2 part-time professional.
EIN: 510157026

7658
Kenneth A. Scott Charitable Trust ✧
c/o KeyBank N.A.
4900 Tiedeman Rd., OH 01-49-0150
Brooklyn, OH 44144-2302
Application address: c/o H. Richard Obermanns, Ph.D., 127 Public Sq., Ste. 1805, Cleveland, OH 44114, tel.: 216-752-3301; Main URL: http://kennethscottcharitabletrust.org/

Established in 1995 in OH.
Donor: Kenneth A. Scott†.
Foundation type: Independent foundation.
Financial data (yr. ended 12/31/13): Assets, $20,742,628 (M); expenditures, $1,111,142; qualifying distributions, $980,292; giving activities include $849,758 for 73 grants (high: $36,000; low: $3,400).
Purpose and activities: Giving only for organizations supporting the care and protection of animals.
Fields of interest: Animal welfare.
Limitations: Applications accepted. Giving primarily in OH. No grants to individuals.
Publications: Annual report.
Application information: Application form required.
Initial approach: Letter
Deadline(s): Quarterly
Trustee: KeyBank, N.A.
Number of staff: 1 part-time professional.
EIN: 347034544

7659
Scripps Howard Foundation ✧
P.O. Box 5380
312 Walnut St., 28th Fl.
Cincinnati, OH 45201 (513) 977-3035
Contact: Patty Cottingham, V.P., Admin.; Mike Philipps, C.E.O. and Pres.
FAX: (513) 977-3800;
E-mail: mike.philipps@scripps.com; Contact for Roy W. Howard Scripps Howard Competition, National Journalism Awards and Internships: Susan J. Porter, V.P., Progs., tel.: (800) 888-3000, ext. 3030, e-mail: sue.porter@scripps.com. See Web site for information on specific foundation programs.; Main URL: http://www.scripps.com/foundation
Facebook: https://www.facebook.com/scrippshowardfoundation
Scripps Howard Awards: http://www.shawards.org
Scripps Howard Foundation Wire: http://www.shfwire.com/
YouTube: https://www.youtube.com/watch?v=CRNS9n2DIBc

Incorporated in 1962 in OH.
Donors: The E.W. Scripps Co.; Jack R. Howard Trust; Robert P. Scripps; Robert A. Buzzelli; Julia & Robert Heidt; Alan & Beverley Horton Fund; Ken Lowe; George & Mary Ann Sanchez; Nackey & Robert Scagliotti; Cindy J. Scripps; Edward W. & Christy Scripps; Henry R. Scripps; William H. & Kathryn Scripps; Donna & Ed Spray; Felicia & Virginia Vasquez.
Foundation type: Company-sponsored foundation.
Financial data (yr. ended 12/31/12): Assets, $65,198,617 (M); gifts received, $3,405,998; expenditures, $6,300,234; qualifying distributions, $4,618,992; giving activities include $4,250,384 for 832 grants (high: $500,000; low: $25), and $368,608 for 92 grants to individuals (high: $35,000; low: $500).
Purpose and activities: The foundation strives to advance the cause of a free press through support of excellence in journalism, quality journalism education, and professional development. The foundation helps build healthy communities and improve the quality of life through support of sound educational programs, strong families, vital social services, enriching arts and culture, and inclusive civic affairs, with emphasis on areas of company operations.
Fields of interest: Media, print publishing; Arts; Journalism school/education; Education, reading; Education; Environment; Family services; Human services; Civil liberties, first amendment; Public affairs; General charitable giving.
Type of support: Emergency funds; General/operating support; Capital campaigns; Building/renovation; Equipment; Endowments; Program development; Conferences/seminars; Professorships; Seed money; Curriculum development; Fellowships; Internship funds; Research; Technical assistance; Employee volunteer services; Employee matching gifts; Employee-related scholarships; Grants to individuals; Scholarships—to individuals; Matching/challenge support.
Limitations: Applications accepted. Giving on a national basis, with emphasis on areas of company operations. No support for religious organizations not of direct benefit to the entire community, political causes or candidates, anti-business organizations, discriminatory organizations, private foundations, or veterans', fraternal, or labor organizations. No grants for courtesy advertising.
Publications: Application guidelines; Annual report.
Application information: See Foundation website for contact information on specific programs. Application form not required.
Initial approach: Send Community Fund (including Literacy Grant) proposals to your local Scripps executive; Greater Cincinnati Fund proposals to Patty Cottingham and Journalism Fund proposals to Mike Philipps
Copies of proposal: 1
Deadline(s): None
Board meeting date(s): Semiannually
Final notification: 90 days
Officers and Trustees:* Mike Philipps,* C.E.O. and Pres.; Patty Cottingham, V.P., Admin.; Susan J. Porter, V.P., Progs.; E. John Wolfzorn, Treas.; Charles Barmonde; Rebecca Scripps Brickner; Robin A. Davis; Eduardo Fernandez; Julia Scripps Heidt; Jack Howard-Potter; Lisa A. Knutson; Brian G. Lawlor; Margaret Scripps Klenzing; Paul K. Scripps; Virginia Scripps Vasquez; Timothy E. Stautberg; Adam Symson; Ellen Weiss; Timothy M. Wesolowski.
Members: Richard A. Boehne; Kelly Conlin; Anne M. La Dow; John W. Hayden; Roger Ogden; Mary Peirce; Mike Philipps; J. Marvin Quin; Paul K. Scripps; Kim Williams.
Number of staff: 6 full-time professional.
EIN: 316025114
Selected grants: The following grants are a representative sample of this grantmaker's funding activity:
$62,500 to Arizona State University, Tempe, AZ, 2012. For Scripps Howard Innovation Institute.
$50,000 to Florida International University, Miami, FL, 2012. For Scripps Howard Multimedia Center.
$25,000 to Association for Education in Journalism and Mass Communication, Columbia, SC, 2012. For externships to get faculty into newsrooms.
$20,000 to Harvesters-The Community Food Network, Kansas City, MO, 2012. For Fill the Fridge Project.
$15,000 to Carnegie Art Center, North Tonawanda, NY, 2012. For Scripps Howard ArtShop Program.
$10,000 to Rock and Roll Hall of Fame and Museum, Cleveland, OH, 2012. For On the Road Distance Learning Program.
$7,000 to Motor City Blight Busters, Detroit, MI, 2012. For Detroit 2020 Award.
$5,000 to Big Brothers Big Sisters, 2012. For Career Skills Mentoring Program.
$2,400 to Madisonville Emergency Assistance Center, Cincinnati, OH, 2012. For Family Literacy Nights.
$800 to Childrens Theater, Oriental, NC, 2012. For play performance about bullying.

7660
The Louise Taft Semple Foundation ✧
c/o Ignite Philanthropy Advisors
1776 Mentor Ave., Ste. 260
Cincinnati, OH 45212-3661 (513) 351-1945
Contact: Lyn Martin, V.P., Ignite Philanthropy Advisors
FAX: (513) 351-0610;
E-mail: lmartin@ignitephilanthropy.com

Incorporated in 1941 in OH.
Donor: Louise Taft Semple†.
Foundation type: Independent foundation.
Financial data (yr. ended 12/31/13): Assets, $25,385,941 (M); expenditures, $1,035,599; qualifying distributions, $893,037; giving activities include $839,000 for 50 grants (high: $70,000; low: $1,000).
Purpose and activities: Giving primarily for the arts, private elementary and secondary education, and for civic and social purposes.
Fields of interest: Humanities; Arts; Elementary/secondary education.
Type of support: Capital campaigns; Building/renovation; Equipment; Land acquisition; Endowments; Program development; Matching/challenge support.
Limitations: Applications accepted. Giving primarily in the Cincinnati and Hamilton County, OH, area. No grants to individuals, or for general purposes or research; no loans.
Publications: Application guidelines.
Application information: Ohio Common Grant Application Form accepted. Telephone or e-mail to request current version. Application form required.
Initial approach: Letter or telephone
Copies of proposal: 1
Deadline(s): Feb. 15, May 15, Aug. 15, and Oct. 15
Board meeting date(s): 3rd Mon. in Apr., July, Oct., and Dec.
Final notification: 3 months
Officers and Trustees:* Dudley S. Taft,* Chair.; James R. Bridgeland, Jr.,* Secy.; John T. Lawrence III,* Treas.; Robert Lawrence; Michael McGraw; Thomas Woodall Taft.
Number of staff: 2 part-time professional.
EIN: 310653526

7661
Sherwin-Williams Foundation ✧
101 Prospect Ave. N.W.
1180 Midland
Cleveland, OH 44115-1093 (216) 566-2000
Contact: Maria L. Haller

Incorporated in 1964 in OH.
Donor: The Sherwin-Williams Co.
Foundation type: Company-sponsored foundation.
Financial data (yr. ended 12/31/13): Assets, $18,755,446 (M); gifts received, $1,000,000; expenditures, $1,134,645; qualifying distributions, $997,236; giving activities include $997,236 for 82 grants (high: $201,000; low: $25).
Purpose and activities: The foundation supports organizations that provide community solutions in the areas of children's health and education leading to economic independence.
Fields of interest: Health care; Human services; Community/economic development.
Type of support: General/operating support; Annual campaigns; Capital campaigns; Emergency funds; Program development; Employee matching gifts; Employee-related scholarships.
Limitations: Applications accepted. Giving primarily in areas of company operations, with emphasis on Cleveland, OH. No support for sectarian, labor, veterans', or fraternal organizations, or tax-supported organizations. No grants to individuals, or for endowments, start-up needs, emergency needs, debt reduction, land acquisition, special projects, research, fellowships, publications, advertising, or conferences; no loans.
Application information: Application form required.
Initial approach: Proposal
Deadline(s): None
Officers and Trustees:* Christopher M. Connor,* Pres.; John G. Morikis,* V.P.; Sean P. Hennessy,* Secy.-Treas.; Catherine E. Carpenter; Thomas E. Hopkins; Robert J. Wells.
EIN: 346555476

7662
The Jeff and Jennie Sidwell Family Foundation ✧ ☆

5240 Wortman Rd.
Zanesville, OH 43701-9382 (740) 849-2422
Contact: Jeffrey Sidwell, Pres.

Established in 2006 in OH.
Donor: Sidwell Materials, Inc.
Foundation type: Company-sponsored foundation.
Financial data (yr. ended 12/31/13): Assets, $420,394 (M); gifts received, $250,000; expenditures, $499,276; qualifying distributions, $499,150; giving activities include $499,150 for 12 grants (high: $250,000; low: $200).
Fields of interest: Health care; Health organizations; Youth development.
Limitations: Applications accepted. Giving primarily in OH.
Application information: Application form not required.
Initial approach: Proposal
Deadline(s): None
Officers: Jeffrey Sidwell, Pres.; Jennie Sidwell, V.P.; Adam Sidwell, Secy.
EIN: 203991810

7663
Fred F. Silk Charitable Foundation ✧

1731 Edmar St.
Louisville, OH 44641-2749

Established in 1990 in OH.
Donor: Fred F. Silk†.
Foundation type: Independent foundation.
Financial data (yr. ended 09/30/13): Assets, $13,557,157 (M); expenditures, $633,076; qualifying distributions, $619,511; giving activities include $503,477 for 27 grants (high: $88,830; low: $100).
Purpose and activities: Giving primarily for higher education and community improvement.
Fields of interest: Higher education; Human services; YM/YWCAs & YM/YWHAs; Community/economic development.
Type of support: General/operating support; Capital campaigns; Building/renovation; Endowments; Scholarship funds.
Limitations: Applications not accepted. Giving primarily in Canton, OH. No grants to individuals.
Application information: Contributes only to pre-selected organizations.
Trustees: Dennis J. Fox, Esq.; Paul J. Helmuth, C.P.A.
EIN: 341651258
Selected grants: The following grants are a representative sample of this grantmaker's funding activity:
$100,000 to Salvation Army of Massillon, Massillon, OH, 2011. For building.
$57,355 to Walsh University, North Canton, OH, 2011.
$50,000 to Community Services of Stark County, Canton, OH, 2011.
$42,645 to Walsh University, North Canton, OH, 2011.
$24,500 to YMCA of Central Stark County, Canton, OH, 2011.
$12,500 to Canines Helping Independent People, Canton, OH, 2011.
$7,500 to Saint Johns Villa, Carrollton, OH, 2011. For equipment.
$5,000 to Arts in Stark, Canton, OH, 2011.
$5,000 to Guardian Support Services, Canton, OH, 2011. For equipment.
$5,000 to Stark Community Foundation, Canton, OH, 2011.

7664
The Sisler McFawn Foundation ✧

P.O. Box 149
Akron, OH 44309-0149 (330) 849-8887
Contact: Michael A. Ayers, Grants Mgr.

Trust established in 1959 in OH.
Donor: Lois Sisler McFawn†.
Foundation type: Independent foundation.
Financial data (yr. ended 12/31/13): Assets, $20,169,419 (M); expenditures, $1,298,879; qualifying distributions, $1,129,369; giving activities include $1,076,935 for grants.
Purpose and activities: Giving primarily for education, social services, and for special needs populations such as the elderly, children from disadvantaged families, and the disabled.
Fields of interest: Education; Health care; Human services; Children/youth, services; Youth; Aging; Disabilities, people with; Economically disadvantaged.
Type of support: General/operating support; Continuing support; Capital campaigns; Building/renovation; Equipment; Endowments; Program development; Seed money; Curriculum development; Scholarship funds; Matching/challenge support.
Limitations: Applications accepted. Giving primarily in Summit County, OH. No support for churches, or general units of government. No grants to individuals, or for computer equipment, annual support, or special events; no loans.
Publications: Application guidelines; Grants list.
Application information: Application form not required.
Initial approach: Telephone call prior to submission
Copies of proposal: 1
Deadline(s): 45 days prior to board meeting; Mar. 15, July 15, and Oct. 15
Board meeting date(s): May, Sept., and Dec.
Final notification: Within 3 weeks of board meeting
Distribution Committee: Richard H. Marsh, Chair.; Nicholas V. Browning; Patricia A. Kemph; Justin T. Rogers, Jr.
Trustee: KeyBank N.A.
Number of staff: 1 part-time professional.
EIN: 346508111
Selected grants: The following grants are a representative sample of this grantmaker's funding activity:
$25,000 to Musical Arts Association, Cleveland, OH, 2012. For Cleveland Orchestra 2012 Blossom Festival.
$25,000 to University of Akron, Akron, OH, 2012. For Scholarship Funding-College of Nursing.
$12,500 to Building for Tomorrow, Akron, OH, 2012. For early childhood initiative.
$10,000 to Akron General Development Foundation, Akron, OH, 2012. For McDowell Cancer Center Stress Reduction Classes.
$8,000 to Law Enforcement Foundation, Dublin, OH, 2012. For programming support.
$7,500 to Beacon Journal Charity Fund, Akron, OH, 2012. For orthodontia care- needy children.
$7,500 to Christ Child Society of Akron, Akron, OH, 2012. For Clothing Center Project.
$7,500 to Coleman Professional Services, Kent, OH, 2012. For Data Solutions Job Coach Summit County.
$6,000 to Conservancy for Cuyahoga Valley National Park, Peninsula, OH, 2012. For All the Rivers Run Scholarship Program.
$5,000 to Ideastream, Cleveland, OH, 2012. For WVIZ/PBS Kids Programming Support.

7665
The Slemp Foundation ✧

c/o Patricia L. Durbin, U.S. Bank, N.A. Trust Division
P.O. Box 5208, Loc. CN-OH-W7PT
Cincinnati, OH 45201-5208
Grant and scholarship application address: c/o Patricia L. Durbin, Tr. Off., U.S. Bank, N.A., Trust Div., P.O. Box 5208, ML CN-OH-W7PT, Cincinnati, OH 45201-5208; tel.: (513) 762-8878; Main URL: http://www.slempfoundation.org
Grants List: http://www.slempfoundation.org/grants/pastgrantees.aspx

Trust established in 1943 in VA.
Donors: C. Bascom Slemp†; Mary Virginia Edmonds Charitable Remainder Trust.
Foundation type: Independent foundation.
Financial data (yr. ended 06/30/13): Assets, $21,778,722 (M); expenditures, $1,391,111; qualifying distributions, $1,270,720; giving activities include $872,454 for 34 grants (high: $204,100; low: $500), and $320,000 for 130 grants to individuals (high: $2,500; low: $1,250).
Purpose and activities: Giving primarily for education and the arts for the benefit of residents of Lee and Wise counties, VA. Giving also for

scholarships to residents of Lee and Wise counties, VA, and to descendants of a resident thereof.
Fields of interest: Arts; Education; Recreation, parks/playgrounds; Youth development, centers/clubs.
Type of support: Building/renovation; Equipment; Endowments; Emergency funds; Seed money; Curriculum development; Scholarship funds; Scholarships—to individuals.
Limitations: Giving primarily in Lee and Wise counties, VA.
Publications: Application guidelines.
Application information: See foundation web site for application guidelines and procedures, and downloading of scholarship application form. Application form required.
Initial approach: Letter
Copies of proposal: 1
Deadline(s): Oct. 15 for first time scholarship applicants; Jul. 1 for continuing education applicants; no deadlines for grants
Board meeting date(s): Apr., July, and Nov.
Trustees: Pamela S. Edmonds; Melissa Smith Jensen; James Campbell Smith; Nancey Edmonds Smith.
Agent: U.S. Bank, N.A.
EIN: 316025080
Selected grants: The following grants are a representative sample of this grantmaker's funding activity:
$125,000 to Wellmont Foundation, Kingsport, TN, 2011.
$2,000 to East Tennessee State University, Johnson City, TN, 2011.

7666
Elizabeth C. Smith Charitable Trust ✧
c/o KeyBank, N.A.
4900 Tiedeman Rd., OH-01-49-0150
Brooklyn, OH 44144-2302

Established in OH.
Foundation type: Independent foundation.
Financial data (yr. ended 12/31/13): Assets, $16,379,451 (M); expenditures, $835,355; qualifying distributions, $736,359; giving activities include $713,215 for 5 grants (high: $142,643; low: $142,643).
Fields of interest: Education; Health care; Catholic agencies & churches.
Limitations: Applications not accepted. Giving primarily in OH.
Application information: Unsolicited requests for funds not accepted.
Trustee: KeyBank, N.A.
EIN: 346814043

7667
The Kent H. Smith Charitable Trust
1111 Superior Ave., Ste. 1000
Cleveland, OH 44114-2568
Contact: Phillip A. Ranney, Tr.

Established in 2005 in OH.
Donor: Thelma G. Smith‡.
Foundation type: Independent foundation.
Financial data (yr. ended 12/31/13): Assets, $29,816,852 (M); expenditures, $5,571,267; qualifying distributions, $5,339,812; giving activities include $5,105,387 for 45 grants (high: $2,100,000; low: $2,500).
Fields of interest: Education; Environment; Human services.
Limitations: Applications accepted. Giving primarily in Cuyahoga County, OH.
Application information: Application form not required.
Initial approach: Letter
Copies of proposal: 1
Deadline(s): None
Board meeting date(s): As necessary
Final notification: Within 1 month
Officers and Trustees:* William B. LaPlace,* Pres.; Phillip A. Ranney,* Secy.
Number of staff: 1 part-time professional; 1 full-time support.
EIN: 137486409
Selected grants: The following grants are a representative sample of this grantmaker's funding activity:
$308,815 to Fund for Our Economic Future, Cleveland, OH, 2011.
$150,000 to Vocational Guidance Services, Cleveland, OH, 2011.
$100,000 to Berea College, Berea, KY, 2011.
$100,000 to University Hospitals Cleveland Medical Center, Cleveland, OH, 2011.

7668
The Kelvin and Eleanor Smith Foundation ✧
30195 Chagrin Blvd., Ste. 275
Cleveland, OH 44124-5756 (216) 591-9111
Contact: Pamela M. Eichenauer, Grants Mgr.
FAX: (216) 591-9557;
E-mail: cwzett@kesmithfoundation.org; Main URL: http://www.kesmithfoundation.org

Incorporated in 1955 in OH.
Donor: Kelvin Smith‡.
Foundation type: Independent foundation.
Financial data (yr. ended 10/31/13): Assets, $157,790,495 (M); expenditures, $10,547,541; qualifying distributions, $7,932,515; giving activities include $7,859,426 for 87 grants (high: $1,000,000; low: $1,000).
Purpose and activities: The foundation's principal interests are in the fields of nonsectarian education, the performing and visual arts, and the environment.
Fields of interest: Arts; Education; Environment; Health care; Human services.
Type of support: General/operating support; Continuing support; Annual campaigns; Capital campaigns; Building/renovation.
Limitations: Applications accepted. Giving primarily in the greater Cleveland, OH, area. No grants to individuals, or for endowment funds, no loans.
Publications: Application guidelines.
Application information: Eligible organizations may submit only 1 request per year. Application guidelines available on foundation web site. Application form not required.
Initial approach: Letter of inquiry or telephone
Copies of proposal: 1
Deadline(s): Feb. 1, July 1, and Oct. 1. If these dates fall on a Saturday or Sunday, proposals will be accepted on the following Monday.
Board meeting date(s): No set time
Final notification: By mail
Officers and Trustees:* Ellen Stirn Mavec,* Chair. and Pres.; Andrew L. Fabens III, Secy.; William B. LaPlace,* Treas.; Charles P. Bolton; Trevor O. Jones; J. T. Mullen; John G. Nestor.
Number of staff: 1 full-time professional.
EIN: 346555349
Selected grants: The following grants are a representative sample of this grantmaker's funding activity:
$1,000,000 to Cleveland Museum of Art, Cleveland, OH, 2012. For capital campaign.
$1,000,000 to Cleveland Museum of Art, Cleveland, OH, 2012. For capital campaign.
$500,000 to Case Western Reserve University, Cleveland, OH, 2012. For capital campaign.
$500,000 to Case Western Reserve University, Cleveland, OH, 2012. For capital campaign.
$333,333 to Fund for Our Economic Future, Cleveland, OH, 2012. For general operating support.
$300,000 to Cleveland Botanical Garden, Cleveland, OH, 2012. For general operating support.
$50,000 to Saint Martin de Porres High School, Cleveland, OH, 2012. For general operating support.
$40,000 to Western Reserve Land Conservancy, Moreland Hills, OH, 2012. For general operating support.
$35,000 to Downtown Cleveland Alliance, Cleveland, OH, 2012. For general operating support.
$35,000 to Music Settlement, Cleveland, OH, 2012. For general operating support.

7669
Willard E. Smucker Foundation ✧
Strawberry Ln.
Orrville, OH 44667-1298

Established in 1968 in OH.
Donor: The J.M. Smucker Co.
Foundation type: Company-sponsored foundation.
Financial data (yr. ended 12/31/13): Assets, $24,877,211 (M); expenditures, $495,082; qualifying distributions, $484,587; giving activities include $482,762 for 57 grants (high: $25,000; low: $595).
Purpose and activities: The foundation supports food banks and organizations involved with arts and culture, education, health, Alzheimer's disease, human services, and Christianity.
Fields of interest: Education; Health care; Human services.
Limitations: Applications not accepted. Giving primarily in AZ, CA, and OH. No grants to individuals.
Application information: Contributes only to pre-selected organizations.
Officers and Trustees:* Timothy P. Smucker,* Pres.; Marcella S. Clark,* Exec. V.P.; Richard K. Smucker,* V.P.; Jeanette L. Knudson, Secy.
EIN: 346610889
Selected grants: The following grants are a representative sample of this grantmaker's funding activity:
$30,000 to Monterey Bay Aquarium, Monterey, CA, 2011. For general operations.
$25,000 to Institute for American Values, New York, NY, 2011. For general operations.
$15,000 to Chautauqua Institution, Chautauqua, NY, 2011. For general operations.
$15,000 to Chestnut Hill Benevolent Association, Chestnut Hill, MA, 2011. For general operations.
$10,000 to Arden Wood Benevolent Association, San Francisco, CA, 2011. For general operations.
$10,000 to Glenmont, Hilliard, OH, 2011. For general operations.
$10,000 to Ohio Wesleyan University, Delaware, OH, 2011. For scholarship fund.
$10,000 to Phoenix Symphony Association, Phoenix, AZ, 2011. For general operations.

$5,000 to Valley of the Sun Hospice Association, Phoenix, AZ, 2011. For general operations.
$5,000 to Western Reserve Historical Society, Cleveland, OH, 2011.

7670
The Spaulding Foundation ✧
(formerly Joseph H. Spaulding Foundation)
8260 Northcreek Dr., Ste. 340
Cincinnati, OH 45236-6114 (513) 936-0101
Contact: Laura Dunderman, Grant Admin.
FAX: (513) 936-6042;
E-mail: spaulding_laurad@fuse.net

Established in 1997 in OH.
Donor: Ruth E. Spaulding Trust.
Foundation type: Independent foundation.
Financial data (yr. ended 02/28/14): Assets, $33,590,469 (M); expenditures, $1,688,932; qualifying distributions, $1,416,753; giving activities include $1,173,336 for 48 grants (high: $450,000; low: $5,000).
Purpose and activities: Giving to organizations that improve the quality of life in the Hamilton County, OH community in the areas of mental and physical disabilities, substance abuse prevention, and care for women and children subjected to violence or abuse.
Fields of interest: Health care; Mental health/crisis services; Human services; Children/youth, services; Family services; Children/youth; Youth; Adults; Disabilities, people with; Physically disabled; Blind/visually impaired; Deaf/hearing impaired; Mentally disabled; Women; Substance abusers; Crime/abuse victims; Economically disadvantaged.
Type of support: Building/renovation; Capital campaigns; Continuing support; Emergency funds; Equipment; General/operating support; Management development/capacity building; Program development.
Limitations: Applications accepted. Giving limited to Hamilton County, OH, and the contiguous counties. No support for religious or political purposes. No grants to individuals.
Publications: Application guidelines.
Application information: Application form required.
Initial approach: Letter requesting application
Copies of proposal: 1
Deadline(s): Mar. 1, June 1, Sept. 1, and Dec. 1
Board meeting date(s): Quarterly
Final notification: Two months
Officers and Trustees:* John E. Prather,* Pres. and Treas.; James R. Marlow,* Secy.; Linda K. Marlow; Lisa L. Prather.
Number of staff: 1 full-time professional; 1 part-time professional.
EIN: 311096254
Selected grants: The following grants are a representative sample of this grantmaker's funding activity:
$30,000 to Ronald McDonald House Charities of Greater Cincinnati, Cincinnati, OH, 2013.
$25,000 to Assistance League of Greater Cincinnati, Cincinnati, OH, 2013.
$25,000 to Childrens Home of Cincinnati, Cincinnati, OH, 2013.
$25,000 to Cincinnati Association for the Blind and Visually Impaired, Cincinnati, OH, 2013.
$25,000 to Cincinnati Therapeutic Riding and Horsemanship, Milford, OH, 2013.
$25,000 to Interfaith Hospitality Network of Greater Cincinnati, Cincinnati, OH, 2013.
$25,000 to Tender Mercies, Cincinnati, OH, 2013.
$20,000 to Child Advocacy Center of Warren County, Franklin, OH, 2013.
$20,000 to Stepping Stones Center for the Handicapped, Cincinnati, OH, 2013.
$18,000 to Mercy Neighborhood Ministries, Cincinnati, OH, 2013.

7671
The Springfield Foundation ✧
333 N. Limestone St., Ste. 201
Springfield, OH 45503 (937) 324-8773
Contact: Ted Vander Roest, Exec. Dir.; For grants: Susan Carey, Dir., Grants and Scholarships
FAX: (937) 324-1836;
E-mail: info@springfieldfoundation.org; Grant application e-mail:
susan@springfieldfoundation.org; Main
URL: http://www.springfieldfoundation.org
Facebook: http://www.facebook.com/pages/Springfield-Foundation/181879671843571

Incorporated in 1948 in OH.
Foundation type: Community foundation.
Financial data (yr. ended 12/31/13): Assets, $67,910,614 (M); gifts received, $1,798,917; expenditures, $3,169,178; giving activities include $1,714,023 for 95+ grants, and $681,022 for 301 grants to individuals.
Purpose and activities: The foundation raises, strengthens, and distributes permanent charitable funds to benefit Clark County, OH.
Fields of interest: Arts; Education; Environment; Animals/wildlife; Health care; Human services; Public affairs; Infants/toddlers; Children/youth; Youth; Disabilities, people with; Physically disabled; Blind/visually impaired; Deaf/hearing impaired; Mentally disabled; African Americans/Blacks; Crime/abuse victims; Homeless.
Type of support: General/operating support; Equipment; Program development; Publication; Seed money; Curriculum development; Research; Technical assistance; Program evaluation; Scholarships—to individuals.
Limitations: Applications accepted. Giving limited to Clark County, OH. No support for sectarian worship, instruction, or proselytizing, fraternal, labor, athletic, and social or veterans' groups, or private or parochial schools. No grants to individuals (except for designated scholarships), or for annual memberships or dues, grants management or consultant fees, debt retirements, deficit financing, annual fund drives or fundraising activities, or school bands and school choral groups, drill teams, or color guards.
Publications: Application guidelines; Annual report; Financial statement; Grants list; Informational brochure (including application guidelines); Newsletter; Program policy statement.
Application information: Visit foundation web site for online application. Application form required.
Initial approach: Submit online application
Deadline(s): Aug. 15 for discretionary grant letters of inquiry; Mar. 1 for scholarship applications
Board meeting date(s): Mar., June, Sept., and Dec.
Final notification: Approx. 6 weeks for initial response; Mid-Dec. for grant determination
Officers and Trustees:* Andy Bell,* Pres.; Plato Pavlatos,* V.P.; Randall Comer,* Secy.; Kim Nedelman Fish,* Treas.; Ted Vander Roest, Exec. Dir.; Tamimi Angle; Dean Blair; Bill Brougher; Bob Burton; Lula Cosby; Cathy Crompton; William Fralick; Gus Geil; Debbie Hill; Robyn Koch-Schumaker; Edward Leventhal; Tom Loftis; Mel Marsh; Maureen Messaro; Dan O'Keefe; David Sanders; Bill Scarff; Jagdish Singh; Les Smithers; Michelle Sweeney.
Number of staff: 5 full-time professional.
EIN: 316030764

7672
St. Marys Community Foundation ✧ ☆
146 E. Spring St.
St. Marys, OH 45885 (419) 394-5693
Contact: Michael Makley, Admin. and Treas.
FAX: (419) 394-7694; E-mail: smcf@bright.net; Main URL: http://www.thesmcf.org/
Facebook: https://www.facebook.com/pages/St-Marys-Community-Foundation/207781502573493

Established in 1974 in OH.
Foundation type: Community foundation.
Financial data (yr. ended 06/30/14): Assets, $5,853,464 (M); gifts received, $382,536; expenditures, $510,423; giving activities include $463,027 for 6,410 grants to individuals.
Purpose and activities: The foundation serves to distribute funds to help the community meet religious, scientific, literary, education, recreational and charitable goals.
Fields of interest: Higher education; Education; Health care; Recreation; Government/public administration; Children/youth; Children; Youth; Adults; Young adults; Women; Girls; Men; Boys.
Type of support: General/operating support; Annual campaigns; Capital campaigns; Debt reduction; Program development; Seed money; Curriculum development; Scholarship funds; Research; Program-related investments/loans; Employee matching gifts; Grants to individuals; Scholarships—to individuals; Student loans—to individuals.
Limitations: Applications accepted. Giving limited to the St. Marys, OH, area.
Publications: Annual report; Financial statement; Informational brochure; Occasional report.
Application information: The foundation accepts applications for student loans and scholarships only; contact the foundation for more information. Application form not required.
Initial approach: Letter
Copies of proposal: 1
Deadline(s): Varies
Board meeting date(s): 2nd Wed. of odd-numbered months
Final notification: Varies
Officers and Trustees:* Calvin Caywood,* Pres.; Jeff Vossler, V.P.; Robert Howard, Secy.; Michael Makley, Treas. and Admin. Off.; Kevin Glass; Edward S. Noble; Kraig Noble; Edwin A. Pierce; Diane Shaner; MaryAnn Sheaks.
Number of staff: 1 part-time professional.
EIN: 237372270

7673
Stark Community Foundation ✧
(formerly The Stark County Foundation, Inc.)
400 Market Ave. N., Ste. 200
Canton, OH 44702-2107 (330) 454-3426
Contact: Mark J. Samolczyk, Pres.; For scholarship inquiries: Jackie Gilin, Donor Svcs./Prog. Off.

FAX: (330) 454-5855; E-mail: info@starkcf.org; Scholarship inquiries: jgilin@starkcf.org; Main URL: http://www.starkcf.org/
E-Newsletter: http://www.starkcf.org/news/newsletters
Facebook: http://www.facebook.com/pages/Stark-Community-Foundation/381913043984
YouTube: http://www.youtube.com/user/starkcomfoundation

Established in 1963 in OH by resolution and declaration of trust.
Foundation type: Community foundation.
Financial data (yr. ended 12/31/13): Assets, $215,211,851 (M); gifts received, $11,955,279; expenditures, $8,490,009; giving activities include $6,615,741 for grants.
Purpose and activities: The foundation seeks to enhance the sound health and general welfare of Stark County, OH, citizens through support for civic improvement programs and educational institutions. Primary areas of interest include the arts, education, community development, health and wellness, youth, and social services.
Fields of interest: Visual arts; Performing arts; Historic preservation/historical societies; Arts; Education, early childhood education; Child development, education; Elementary school/education; Higher education; Business school/education; Law school/education; Education; Environment, natural resources; Environment; Health care; Substance abuse, services; AIDS; AIDS research; Crime/law enforcement; Food services; Housing/shelter, development; Recreation; Youth development, services; Children/youth, services; Child development, services; Family services; Aging, centers/services; Minorities/immigrants, centers/services; Homeless, human services; Human services; Urban/community development; Community/economic development; Government/public administration; Leadership development; Youth; Aging; Disabilities, people with; Minorities; Homeless.
Type of support: In-kind gifts; General/operating support; Capital campaigns; Building/renovation; Equipment; Land acquisition; Emergency funds; Program development; Seed money; Scholarship funds; Research; Technical assistance; Consulting services; Scholarships—to individuals; Matching/challenge support; Student loans—to individuals.
Limitations: Applications accepted. Giving limited to Stark County, OH. No support for religious organizations for religious purposes. No grants for endowment funds, operating expenses of well-established organizations, continuing support, endowments, vehicles, annual appeals or membership contributions, publications, vehicles, conferences or deficit financing; no grants or loans to individuals (except to college students who are permanent residents of Stark County, OH).
Publications: Application guidelines; Annual report (including application guidelines); Financial statement; Grants list; Informational brochure; Newsletter; Program policy statement.
Application information: Visit foundation web site for application cover sheet and guidelines per grant type. Application form required.
Initial approach: Submit proposal and attachments
Copies of proposal: 1
Deadline(s): Mar. 7 and Sept. 5 for discretionary grants
Board meeting date(s): 8 to 10 times per year
Final notification: May and Nov. for discretionary grants
Officers and Board of Trustees:* Thomas W. Schervish,* Chair.; E. Lang D'Atri,* Vice-Chair.; Mark J. Samolczyk, Pres.; Bridgette Neisel, V.P., Advancement; Patricia C. Quick, V.P. and C.F.O.; William Cook; Charles Dix II; Thomas V. Ferrero; Nancy Gessner; Gregory W. Luntz; Stephen A. Perry; Nancy A. Varian.
Trustee Banks: FirstMerit Bank, N.A.; The Huntington National Bank; KeyBank N.A.; PNC Bank; Premier Bank.
Number of staff: 12 full-time professional; 1 part-time professional; 3 full-time support; 1 part-time support.
EIN: 340943665
Selected grants: The following grants are a representative sample of this grantmaker's funding activity:
$20,000 to Hospice of Tuscarawas County, Dover, OH, 2013. For Pet Services Volunteer Coordinator.
$15,000 to Arts in Stark, Canton, OH, 2013. For Birth of the NFL Public Artwork.
$15,000 to Massillon Museum, Massillon, OH, 2013. For SNAP! In the Photobooth with Warhol and Friends.
$15,000 to Meals on Wheels of Stark and Wayne Counties, Massillon, OH, 2013. For under 60 assistance program.
$15,000 to Multi-Development Services of Stark County, Canton, OH, 2013. For Career Club.
$11,272 to Stark County Community Mental Health Board, Canton, OH, 2013. For Family and Community Resource Center for Fetal Alcohol Spectrum Disorders.
$10,000 to Invent Now, North Canton, OH, 2013. For Camp Invention.
$7,000 to Buckeye Career Center Foundation, New Philadelphia, OH, 2013. For Buckeye Newsletter and Scholarship Awards.
$6,250 to Holly Hills Little League of Canton, Canton, OH, 2013. For permanent outfield fencing for Challenger Division Field.
$4,000 to Navarre Bethlehem Township Historical Society, Navarre, OH, 2013. For furnace for Schmidt House.

7674
The State Auto Foundation ✧
(formerly Paul R. Gingher State Auto Insurance Companies Foundation)
518 E. Broad St.
Columbus, OH 43215-3901

Established in 1989 in OH.
Donor: State Automobile Mutual Insurance Co.
Foundation type: Company-sponsored foundation.
Financial data (yr. ended 12/31/13): Assets, $1,757,144 (M); gifts received, $250,500; expenditures, $604,233; qualifying distributions, $606,020; giving activities include $603,120 for 177 grants (high: $88,126; low: $100).
Purpose and activities: The foundation supports community foundations and organizations involved with arts and culture, education, human services, and insurance.
Fields of interest: Arts education; Museums; Museums (art); Performing arts, ballet; Arts; Higher education; Education; Youth development, business; Salvation Army; Children/youth, services; Residential/custodial care; Human services; Business/industry; Foundations (community); United Ways and Federated Giving Programs.
Type of support: General/operating support.
Limitations: Applications not accepted. Giving primarily in Columbus, OH. No grants to individuals.
Application information: Contributes only to pre-selected organizations.
Trustees: Robert P. Restrepo; Errica Rivera; Lorranine M. Segworth; James A. Yano.
EIN: 311257265

7675
The Marc A. and Rhonda L. Stefanski Charitable Foundation ✧ ☆
(formerly Ben S. & Gerome R. Stefanski Charitable Foundation)
7007 Broadway Ave.
Cleveland, OH 44105-1490 (216) 441-7318
Contact: Marc A. Stefanski, Pres. and Tr.

Established in 1991 in OH.
Donors: Monica Martines; Paul Stefanik; Third Federal Savings and Loan Association, MHC; TFS Key Trust Donations.
Foundation type: Independent foundation.
Financial data (yr. ended 12/31/13): Assets, $9,975,292 (M); gifts received, $1,600; expenditures, $591,431; qualifying distributions, $524,850; giving activities include $524,850 for 12 grants (high: $150,000; low: $250).
Purpose and activities: Giving primarily for education and human services, including a children's hospital and a Roman Catholic diocese.
Fields of interest: Elementary/secondary education; Higher education; Hospitals (specialty); Human services; Foundations (public); Catholic agencies & churches.
Limitations: Applications accepted. Giving primarily in the greater Cleveland, OH, area.
Application information: Application form not required.
Initial approach: Proposal
Deadline(s): Sept. 30
Officers and Trustees:* Marc A. Stefanski,* Pres.; Rhonda I. Stefanski,* V.P.; Ashley Stefanski, Secy.
EIN: 341691023

7676
The Stocker Foundation ✧
201 Burns Rd.
Elyria, OH 44035-1654 (440) 366-4884
Contact: Patricia O'Brien, Exec. Dir.
FAX: (440) 366-4656;
E-mail: contact@stockerfoundation.org; Additional e-mails: pobrien@stockerfoundation.org (Patricia O'Brien); mwilson@stockerfoundation.org (Melanie R. Wilson); Main URL: http://www.stockerfoundation.org
Blog: http://allaboutliteracy.posterous.com/

Incorporated in 1979 in OH.
Donor: Beth K. Stocker†.
Foundation type: Independent foundation.
Financial data (yr. ended 12/31/13): Assets, $49,141,816 (M); expenditures, $2,809,380; qualifying distributions, $2,291,759; giving activities include $2,291,759 for 167 grants (high: $184,800; low: $100).
Purpose and activities: Giving to programs and services that positively affect children, youth, and families. The foundation has identified services for

public school students in Kindergarten through 5th grade as its primary funding interest.
Fields of interest: Education, early childhood education; Child development, education; Elementary school/education; Family services; Children/youth.
Type of support: General/operating support; Building/renovation; Equipment; Endowments; Emergency funds; Program development; Seed money; Curriculum development; Technical assistance; Matching/challenge support.
Limitations: Giving primarily in Pima County, AZ, Alameda and San Francisco counties, CA, Bernalillo and Dona Ana counties, NM, Lorain and Cuyahoga counties, OH, and King County, WA. No support for religious organizations for religious purposes, private or parochial schools, governmental services, or public school services required by law. No grants to individuals, or for annual campaigns, conferences, deficit financing/debt reduction, mass mailings, research projects and tickets or advertising for fundraising activities; no loans. Generally no grants for capital requests except when specific criteria is met.
Publications: Annual report; Grants list.
Application information: See foundation web site for latest application information.
Initial approach: Letter of Inquiry (using the format indicated on foundation web site)
Copies of proposal: 3
Deadline(s): Oct.; Letter of Inquiries are accepted through July 1st
Board meeting date(s): Spring, summer, and fall
Final notification: 5 months
Officers and Trustees:* Brenda Norton,* Pres.; Ryan Humble,* Secy.; Dawn Dobras,* Treas.; Patricia O'Brien, Exec. Dir.; Amy Dobras; Mary Ann Dobras; Jerry Humble; Brad Norton; Brent Norton; Jane Norton; Melanie R. Wilson; Nancy Elizabeth Woodling.
Corporate Trustee: KeyBank N.A.; The Huntington National Bank.
Number of staff: 2 full-time professional; 1 full-time support.
EIN: 341293603

7677
Irving I. Stone Foundation ✧
c/o Mary Kay Incandela
1 American Rd.
Cleveland, OH 44144-2301

Established in 1999 in OH.
Donors: Irving I. Stone; Irving I. Stone Irrevocable Trust; Irving Stone Oversight Trust.
Foundation type: Independent foundation.
Financial data (yr. ended 12/31/13): Assets, $38,306,398 (M); gifts received, $345,454; expenditures, $1,683,655; qualifying distributions, $1,608,492; giving activities include $1,599,650 for 52 grants (high: $400,000; low: $500).
Fields of interest: Higher education, university; Jewish federated giving programs; Jewish agencies & synagogues.
Limitations: Applications not accepted. Giving primarily in New York, NY, and Cleveland, OH. No grants to individuals.
Application information: Contributes only to pre-selected organizations.
Officers and Trustees:* Gary Weiss, Pres.; Judith Stone Weiss,* Secy.; Hensha Gansbourg; Helen Stone; Myrna Tatar; Elie Weiss; Jeffrey Weiss; Morry Weiss; Zev Weiss.
EIN: 341892327

7678
Stranahan Foundation ✧
4169 Holland-Sylvania Rd., Ste. 201
Toledo, OH 43623-2590 (419) 882-5575
Contact: Pamela G. Roberts, Grants Mgr.
FAX: (419) 882-2072;
E-mail: proberts@stranahanfoundation.org;
Additional e-mail: mail@stranahanfoundation.org;
Main URL: http://www.stranahanfoundation.org

Trust established in 1944 in OH.
Donors: Robert A. Stranahan†; Frank D. Stranahan†; Ms. Troubetzkoy Trust.
Foundation type: Independent foundation.
Financial data (yr. ended 12/31/13): Assets, $98,032,836 (M); gifts received, $1,000; expenditures, $4,203,664; qualifying distributions, $3,906,024; giving activities include $3,305,434 for 81 grants (high: $325,000; low: $916).
Purpose and activities: Giving primarily for: 1) Education, particularly to support initiatives that will increase the quality of education for students at the pre-school, primary and secondary levels, and/or promote access to quality educational programs; learning institutions that value independent thinking, artistic appreciation, cultural, economic and ethnic diversity, and community service; provide access to programs that offer alternatives to traditional educational opportunities (e.g.: career-oriented or vocational training, etc.); and small manageable programs within institutions of higher learning; 2) Physical and Mental Health, particularly programs that create better access to care, educate people to take better care of themselves and their families, as well as support alternative care methods, preventive measures, and research to eradicate health crises; 3) Ecological Well-Being, particularly programs that preserve or return to healthy, sustainable communities for both current and future generations, conserve and restore the natural environment, as well as educate community members about the natural environment; 4) Arts and Culture, particularly programs that communicate, delight and educate, motivate and build self esteem, build and reinforce communities, and have therapeutic value; and 5) Human Services, particularly programs that offer disadvantaged families and individuals of all ages access to services that meet basic human needs, opportunities to work, recreate and fully participate in community life, and provide avenues for achieving self-sufficiency and making positive contributions to their community.
Fields of interest: Arts; Education; Human services; Youth, services; Community/economic development.
Type of support: Continuing support; Program development; Program evaluation; Matching/challenge support; Mission-related investments/loans.
Limitations: Giving in Toledo and northwestern OH; giving in other regions is by invitation only. No support for religious purposes, projects located outside the U.S., or government sponsored or controlled projects. No grants to individuals.
Publications: Annual report; Grants list.
Application information: Unsolicited requests for funds accepted only from Toledo, OH, area applicants; giving in other geographic areas is by invitation only. Before an applicant begins their letter of inquiry, they must select a grant type from the choices in the Application Instructions on foundation web site. Full applications are by invitation only, upon review of initial letter of inquiry. E-mailed, faxed or mailed inquires are not accepted. Application information and form available on foundation web site. Application form required.
Initial approach: Letter of inquiry (no more than 2 pages) to be submitted online, via foundation's e-grant system on web site
Deadline(s): See foundation web site for current deadlines
Board meeting date(s): May and Nov.
Final notification: 3 weeks after board meetings
Officers and Trustees:* Pam Howell, C.E.O.; Patrick Stranahan,* Pres.; Robert Stranahan,* V.P.; Page Armstrong,* Secy.; William Foster,* Treas.; Paget Ferrell; Timothy Foster; Trevor Foster; Julie Higgins; Easter Page; Frances Parry; Mark Stranahan; Sarah Stranahan.
Number of staff: 1 full-time professional; 1 full-time support; 3 part-time support.
EIN: 346514375

7679
The Sutphin Family Foundation ✧
c/o PNC Bank, N.A.
201 E. 5th St.
Cincinnati, OH 45202-4117 (513) 651-8327
Contact: Louis Valker

Established in 1994 in OH.
Donors: Jean Webber Sutphin; Richard H. Sutphin†; Jean W. Sutphin Trust; Jean W. Sutphin Charitable Lead Remainder Trust; Jean Sutphin Charitable Lead Annuity Trust.
Foundation type: Independent foundation.
Financial data (yr. ended 12/31/12): Assets, $15,893,726 (M); gifts received, $1,485,208; expenditures, $664,542; qualifying distributions, $601,500; giving activities include $600,600 for 47 grants (high: $90,000; low: $2,500).
Purpose and activities: Giving primarily for education, health, and human services.
Fields of interest: Education; Health care; Human services; Family services.
Type of support: Capital campaigns; Building/renovation; Equipment; Program development.
Limitations: Applications accepted. Giving primarily in Cincinnati, OH. No grants to individuals.
Publications: Application guidelines.
Application information: Application form required.
Initial approach: Request guidelines by telephone or letter
Copies of proposal: 6
Board meeting date(s): Dec.
Trustees: Christine S. Kohnen; Richard H. Sutphin; Stuart B. Sutphin III.
Agent: N.A. PNC Bank.
EIN: 311423164
Selected grants: The following grants are a representative sample of this grantmaker's funding activity:
$30,000 to Cincinnati Art Museum, Cincinnati, OH, 2012. For Eternal Summer.
$15,000 to Cincinnati Nature Center, Milford, OH, 2012. For the Outdoor Learning Center Renovation.
$15,000 to ProKids, Cincinnati, OH, 2012. For Casa University.
$10,000 to Cincinnati Playhouse in the Park, Cincinnati, OH, 2012. For the Playhouse Outreach Tour.

$10,000 to Cincinnati Works, Cincinnati, OH, 2012. For the Phoenix Program.
$10,000 to Down Syndrome Association of Greater Cincinnati, Cincinnati, OH, 2012. For the Promoting Healthy Relationships.
$10,000 to FamiliesForward, Cincinnati, OH, 2012. For the Carson After School Programs.
$10,000 to Good Samaritan Hospital Foundation, Cincinnati, OH, 2012. For the Free Health Center of Price Hill.
$10,000 to Living Arrangements for the Developmentally Disabled, Cincinnati, OH, 2012. For Different Like You.
$10,000 to Santa Maria Community Services, Cincinnati, OH, 2012. For Building Youth Assets in Price Hill.

7680
Talmage Family Foundation ✧
c/o Ralph W. Talmage
P. O. Box 12490
Columbus, OH 43212-0490

Established in OH.
Donor: Ralph W. Talmage.
Foundation type: Independent foundation.
Financial data (yr. ended 12/31/13): Assets, $8,148,720 (M); expenditures, $474,606; qualifying distributions, $444,000; giving activities include $444,000 for 22 grants (high: $185,000; low: $1,000).
Fields of interest: Higher education; Human services; Christian agencies & churches; Protestant agencies & churches.
Limitations: Applications not accepted.
Application information: Unsolicited requests for funds not accepted.
Officers: Ralph W. Talmage, Pres.; Joan S. Talmage, V.P.
Trustees: Daniel B. Talmage; Scott W. Talmage.
EIN: 453630423

7681
Third Federal Foundation ✧
7007 Broadway Ave.
Cleveland, OH 44105-1441 (216) 641-7270
Contact: Kurt Karakul, Pres.

Established in 2007 in OH.
Donors: Third Federal Savings and Loan Association, MHC; TFS Financial Corp.
Foundation type: Company-sponsored foundation.
Financial data (yr. ended 12/31/13): Assets, $49,682,362 (M); expenditures, $2,649,859; qualifying distributions, $2,257,000; giving activities include $2,257,000 for 101 grants (high: $201,012; low: $250).
Purpose and activities: The foundation supports nonprofit organizations involved with education and community development. Special emphasis is directed toward programs designed to raise the aspirations of students in the community and enhance knowledge of specific areas, including economics, communications, business, and public speaking.
Fields of interest: Elementary school/education; Secondary school/education; Higher education; Business school/education; Boys & girls clubs; Youth development; Community development, neighborhood development; Economic development; Community/economic development; Economics; Economically disadvantaged.
Type of support: General/operating support; Program development.
Limitations: Applications accepted. Giving primarily in areas of company operations in OH, with emphasis on Cleveland. No grants to individuals.
Application information: Application form required.
Initial approach: Letter
Deadline(s): None
Final notification: Following review
Officers and Directors:* Marc A. Stefanski,* C.E.O.; Kurt Karakul, Pres.; Ralph M. Betters, Secy.-Treas.; Robert A. Fiala; John Marino.
EIN: 208467212

7682
The Tiffin Charitable Foundation ✧
68 S. Washington St.
Tiffin, OH 44883-2350
E-mail: adm@tiffinfoundation.org; Main URL: http://www.tiffinfoundation.org

Established in 1983 in OH.
Foundation type: Community foundation.
Financial data (yr. ended 12/31/12): Assets, $12,637,005 (M); gifts received, $134,633; expenditures, $960,784; giving activities include $877,902 for grants to individuals.
Purpose and activities: The foundation supports charitable purposes that promote the well-being of the citizens of the city of Tiffin and Seneca County, Ohio.
Fields of interest: Arts, cultural/ethnic awareness; Humanities; Arts; Higher education; Education; Environment; Animals/wildlife; Health care; Human services.
Type of support: Annual campaigns; Capital campaigns; Conferences/seminars; Emergency funds; Equipment; Matching/challenge support; Program development; Scholarship funds; Technical assistance.
Limitations: Applications accepted. Giving limited to the Tiffin and Seneca County, OH, area. No support for religious or sectarian purposes. No grants to individuals (except for scholarships), or for construction projects for routine maintenance, normal operating expenses, loan payments, endowments, multi-year funding, or re-granting in any of the next three year if the original grant was $10,000 or more.
Publications: Application guidelines; Annual report; Financial statement; Informational brochure; Newsletter.
Application information: Visit foundation web site for application guidelines. Application form required.
Initial approach: Telephone, e-mail, or online
Copies of proposal: 1
Deadline(s): Mar. 12, Jun. 4, Sept. 3, and Dec. 3
Board meeting date(s): Quarterly
Final notification: 1 to 3 months
Directors: Laura Brickner; Jeannine Curns; Charles Ervin; Thomas J. Gordon; Dr. Robert H. Huntington; Allen Schultz; Dr. Lillian Schumacher; Eric Shook; Jerry Weininger.
Number of staff: 1 full-time professional.
EIN: 341405286

7683
The Timken Company Charitable and Educational Fund, Inc. ✧
(formerly The Timken Company Educational Fund, Inc.)
4500 Mt. Pleasant St. N.W.
North Canton, OH 44720

Established in 1957.
Donors: The Timken Co.; Timken Company Charitable Trust of NH.
Foundation type: Company-sponsored foundation.
Financial data (yr. ended 12/31/13): Assets, $2,223,782 (M); gifts received, $187,622; expenditures, $1,558,239; qualifying distributions, $1,557,866; giving activities include $1,492,515 for grants.
Purpose and activities: The foundation awards college scholarships to children of associates and retirees of the Timken Company, its subsidiaries, and joint ventures.
Fields of interest: Higher education.
International interests: Asia; Brazil; China; Eastern Europe; India; Latin America; Poland; Romania; South Africa.
Type of support: Employee-related scholarships.
Limitations: Applications not accepted. Giving primarily in areas of company operations, with emphasis on Brazil, China, Poland, and Romania.
Application information: Contributes only through employee-related scholarships.
Board meeting date(s): Quarterly
Officers: W. J. Timken, Jr., Pres.; R. J. Lapp,* Secy.; P. D. Fracassa,* Treas.
Trustees: W. R. Burkhart; D. L. Walker.
EIN: 346520257
Selected grants: The following grants are a representative sample of this grantmaker's funding activity:
$750 to Boy Scouts of America, Buckeye Council, Canton, OH, 2012. For general operations.
$230 to Boy Scouts of America, Old North State Council, Greensboro, NC, 2012. For general operations.

7684
Timken Foundation of Canton ✧
200 Market Ave. N., Ste. 210
Canton, OH 44702-1437
Contact: Ward J. Timken, Tr.

Incorporated in 1934 in OH.
Donor: Members of the Timken family.
Foundation type: Independent foundation.
Financial data (yr. ended 09/30/13): Assets, $358,898,128 (M); expenditures, $13,656,276; qualifying distributions, $13,357,649; giving activities include $12,909,204 for 109 grants (high: $1,000,000; low: $10,000).
Purpose and activities: Giving to promote broad civic betterment by capital fund grants; support largely for colleges, schools, hospitals, cultural centers, social services and recreation, and other charitable institutions.
Fields of interest: Historic preservation/historical societies; Arts; Education, early childhood education; Child development, education; Elementary school/education; Secondary school/education; Higher education; Adult education—literacy, basic skills & GED; Libraries/library science; Education, reading; Education; Hospitals (general); Health care; Health organizations, association; Crime/violence prevention, abuse

prevention; Recreation; Youth development, services; Child development, services; Community/economic development; Computer science; Leadership development; Economically disadvantaged.
International interests: Brazil; Canada; China; Czech Republic; France; Germany; India; Italy; Poland; Romania; South Africa; United Kingdom.
Type of support: Capital campaigns; Building/renovation; Equipment; Land acquisition; Matching/challenge support.
Limitations: Applications not accepted. Giving primarily in local areas of Timken Co. domestic operations in Manchester, CT; Bucyrus, Canton, Eaton, New Philadelphia, OH; Ashboro, Columbus, and Lincolnton, NC; Keene, and Lebanon, NH; Honea Path, Union, and Gaffney, SC; Altavista, VA; and Mascot and Pulaski, TN. Giving also in local areas in Canada, China, France, Great Britain, India, Italy, Poland, Romania, and South Africa where Timken Co. has manufacturing facilities. No support for projects for religious or political purposes. No grants to individuals. Generally, no grants for operating budgets, endowments, or program development.
Application information: Unsolicited requests for funds not accepted.
Board meeting date(s): As required
Officers and Trustees:* Ward J. Timken,* Pres.; Jeffrey Halm,* Secy. and Exec. Dir.; W. R. Timken, Jr.,* Treas.; Joy A. Timken; W.J. Timken, Jr.
Number of staff: 1 full-time professional; 1 part-time professional; 1 full-time support.
EIN: 346520254
Selected grants: The following grants are a representative sample of this grantmaker's funding activity:
$476,186 to Stark State College Foundation, Canton, OH, 2011. To construct and equip classrooms and common areas in the Wind Energy Research and Development Center.
$400,000 to University of Akron Foundation, Akron, OH, 2011. To construct a new engineering building.
$327,000 to Habitat for Humanity Romania, Bucharest, Romania, 2011. To Build 12 Houses in Ploiesti.
$300,000 to George W. Bush Foundation, Dallas, TX, 2011. To Provide Funding for the George W. Bush Presidential Library.
$250,000 to Aultman Health Foundation, Canton, OH, 2011. To construct the Compassionate Care Center, Stark County's first inpatient hospice center.
$250,000 to Goodwill Industries of Greater Cleveland and East Central Ohio, Canton, OH, 2011. To provide funds for Community Campus.
$250,000 to Union, City of, Union, SC, 2011. To fund the purchase of theater equipment such as performance lighting and audio.
$200,000 to University of Mount Union, Alliance, OH, 2011. To Renovate and Expand the Health Education and Campus Community Wellness Facility.
$100,000 to John Wesley Community Centre, Etwatwa West, South Africa, 2011. To Construct and Equip New Building to House a Portion of the Pre-School Program.
$100,000 to Salvation Army of Massillon, Massillon, OH, 2011. To construct a new facility in Massillon.

7685
The C. Carlisle and Margaret M. Tippit Charitable Trust ✧ ☆
925 Euclid Ave., Ste. 2000
Cleveland, OH 44115-1496

Established in 1989 in OH.
Donor: Tippit 1992 Charitable Lead Trust.
Foundation type: Independent foundation.
Financial data (yr. ended 08/31/13): Assets, $5,240,573 (M); expenditures, $730,614; qualifying distributions, $692,500; giving activities include $658,500 for 30 grants (high: $60,000; low: $4,000).
Purpose and activities: Giving primarily for education, health and human services.
Fields of interest: Higher education; Education; Environment; Health care; Human services.
Limitations: Applications not accepted. Giving primarily in OH, with emphasis on Cleveland. No grants to individuals.
Application information: Contributes only to pre-selected organizations.
Trustees: James R. Bright; Carl J. Tippit.
EIN: 341627297
Selected grants: The following grants are a representative sample of this grantmaker's funding activity:
$60,000 to Cleveland Clinic Foundation, Cleveland, OH, 2011.
$27,500 to Laurel School, Shaker Heights, OH, 2011.
$25,000 to Orlando Regional Medical Center, Orlando, FL, 2011.
$25,000 to University School, Hunting Valley, OH, 2011.
$12,000 to Hattie Larlham Foundation, Mantua, OH, 2011.
$10,000 to Cleveland Botanical Garden, Cleveland, OH, 2011.
$5,000 to Cleveland Foodbank, Cleveland, OH, 2011.
$5,000 to Human Rights Watch, New York, NY, 2011.
$5,000 to Vocational Guidance Services, Cleveland, OH, 2011.
$4,000 to Cleveland Music School Settlement, Cleveland, OH, 2011.

7686
Toledo Community Foundation, Inc. ✧
300 Madison Ave., Ste. 1300
Toledo, OH 43604-1583 (419) 241-5049
Contact: For grants: Anneliese Grytafey, Sr. Prog. Off.
FAX: (419) 242-5549;
E-mail: toledocf@toledocf.org; Grant inquiry e-mail: anneliese@toledocf.org; Main URL: http://www.toledocf.org/
E-Newsletter: http://www.toledocf.org/forms/email-sign-up/
Facebook: https://www.facebook.com/ToledoCF
Toledo Community Foundation's Philanthropy Promise: http://www.ncrp.org/philanthropys-promise/who

Established in 1924 in OH by trust agreement; reactivated in 1973.
Foundation type: Community foundation.
Financial data (yr. ended 12/31/12): Assets, $172,192,517 (M); gifts received, $13,278,013; expenditures, $14,045,707; giving activities include $10,158,370 for grants.
Purpose and activities: The foundation provides support for projects which promise to affect a broad segment of the citizens of northwestern OH or which tend to help those living in an area not being adequately served by local community resources. Areas of interest include social services and youth programs, arts and culture, education, natural resources, government and urban affairs, and physical and mental health.
Fields of interest: Arts; Child development, education; Education; Environment, natural resources; Health care; Mental health/crisis services; Health organizations, association; Children/youth, services; Child development, services; Aging, centers/services; Homeless, human services; Human services; Community/economic development; Public affairs; Aging; Homeless.
Type of support: Mission-related investments/loans; Program development; Seed money; Matching/challenge support.
Limitations: Applications accepted. Giving primarily in northwestern OH, with emphasis on the greater Toledo area. No support for sectarian activities of religious organizations. No grants to individuals (except for scholarships), or for annual campaigns, capital campaigns, operating budgets, film, video, or TV productions, equipment purchase, or endowment funds.
Publications: Annual report (including application guidelines); Newsletter.
Application information: Visit foundation web site for online grant application and guidelines. Application form required.
Initial approach: Telephone
Copies of proposal: 1
Deadline(s): Jan. 15 and Sept. 15 for community grants; varies for others
Board meeting date(s): Apr., Sept., and Dec.
Final notification: Approx. 3 and a half months
Officers and Trustees:* Mary C. Werner,* Chair.; David F. Waterman,* Vice-Chair.; Keith Burwell,* Pres.; Patricia J. Appold,* Secy.; Kim Cryan, C.F.O.; Scott A. Estes,* Treas.; Mike Anderson; Dr. Anthony J. Armstrong; William Fall; James A. Hoffman; Mark D. Luetke; Rita N.A. Mansour; Beverly J. McBride; Geoffrey G. Meyers; Granger Souder, Jr.; Mark Zyndorf.
Number of staff: 12 full-time professional; 2 part-time professional; 1 full-time support.
EIN: 237284004

7687
V.B. Toulmin Charitable Foundation III ✧
10 W. 2nd St., 26th Fl.
Dayton, OH 45402-1791

Established in 2003 in OH.
Donor: Virginia B. Toulmin†.
Foundation type: Independent foundation.
Financial data (yr. ended 10/31/13): Assets, $141,701,783 (M); expenditures, $8,583,397; qualifying distributions, $6,641,427; giving activities include $6,273,558 for 61 grants (high: $1,271,000; low: $5,000).
Fields of interest: Performing arts; Education; Human services; Children/youth, services; Foundations (community).
Limitations: Applications not accepted. Giving primarily in FL, NJ, and NY. No grants to individuals.
Application information: Contributes only to pre-selected organizations.

Trustees: Alexander C. Sanger; William S. Villafranco; KeyBank, N.A.
EIN: 137385769

7688
The Troy Foundation ✧
216 W. Franklin St.
Troy, OH 45373-2846 (937) 339-8935
Contact: Melissa A. Kleptz, Exec. Dir.
FAX: (937) 339-8992;
E-mail: info@thetroyfoundation.org; Main URL: http://thetroyfoundation.org/
E-mail for Lisa Reynolds: lreynolds@thetroyfoundation.org

Established in 1924 in OH by bank resolution and declaration of trust.
Donors: Nannie Kendall†; A.G. Stouder†; J.M. Spencer†.
Foundation type: Community foundation.
Financial data (yr. ended 12/31/13): Assets, $68,331,999 (M); gifts received, $3,423,295; expenditures, $3,060,585; giving activities include $2,024,831 for 209+ grants (high: $155,204; low: $30), and $331,976 for 57 grants to individuals.
Purpose and activities: The foundation seeks to improve the quality of life for the community served by promoting philanthropy and stewardship for a better tomorrow.
Fields of interest: Museums; Historic preservation/historical societies; Arts; Elementary/secondary education; Child development, education; Elementary school/education; Vocational education; Business school/education; Libraries/library science; Education; Environment, natural resources; Environment; Hospitals (general); Health care; Substance abuse, services; Recreation; Children/youth, services; Child development, services; Residential/custodial care, hospices; Human services; Community/economic development; Youth.
Type of support: Capital campaigns; Building/renovation; Equipment; Emergency funds; Program development; Seed money; Curriculum development; Scholarship funds; Matching/challenge support.
Limitations: Applications accepted. Giving limited to the Troy City, OH. No support for religious organizations. No grants to individuals (except for scholarships), or for endowment funds, operating budgets, continuing support, deficit financing, research, demonstration projects, publications, conferences, or fellowships; no loans.
Publications: Application guidelines; Annual report; Informational brochure; Informational brochure (including application guidelines); Newsletter.
Application information: Visit foundation web site for application form and guidelines. Application form required.
Initial approach: Submit grant application and attachments
Copies of proposal: 7
Deadline(s): 15th of the month preceding board meeting
Board meeting date(s): 3rd Thurs. of Mar., June, Sept., and Dec.
Final notification: Within 10 days of the grant review meeting
Officers and Trustees:* Wanda C. Lukens,* Pres.; Brian R. Williamson,* V.P.; Robert N. Schlemmer,* Secy.; Melissa A. Kleptz, Exec. Dir.; Susan J. Behm; Brent J. Black; Mark Douglas; David J. Dippold; William J. Fulker; Arthur D. Haddad; Judith K. Hartman; James M. Johnson; Thomas E. Robinson; David Selsor; Craig E. Wise.
Number of staff: 2 full-time professional.
EIN: 316018703

7689
The Trzcinski Foundation ✧
8050 Corporate Cir., No.2
North Royalton, OH 44133-1280

Established in 1997 in OH.
Donors: Ronald Trzcinski; Cheryl Trzcinski.
Foundation type: Independent foundation.
Financial data (yr. ended 06/30/13): Assets, $26,721,507 (M); gifts received, $100,000; expenditures, $1,351,358; qualifying distributions, $1,241,000; giving activities include $1,241,000 for 22 grants (high: $385,000; low: $1,000).
Purpose and activities: Giving primarily to Roman Catholic education.
Fields of interest: Elementary/secondary education; Catholic agencies & churches.
Type of support: General/operating support.
Limitations: Applications not accepted. Giving primarily in OH and TN. No grants to individuals.
Application information: Unsolicited requests for funds not accepted.
Officer: Ronald Trzcinski, Pres.
EIN: 341852993
Selected grants: The following grants are a representative sample of this grantmaker's funding activity:
$20,000 to Atlas Economic Research Foundation, Washington, DC, 2013. For Furtherance of Charitable Activities.
$5,000 to West Side Catholic Center, Cleveland, OH, 2013. For Furtherance of Charitable and Religious Activities.

7690
The TSF ✧
(formerly The Smith Foundation)
2071 N. Bechtle Ave., Ste. 203
Springfield, OH 45504-1503

Established in 2000 in MO.
Donors: E. Smith; GHTP LLC; G.S. Revocable Living Trust.
Foundation type: Independent foundation.
Financial data (yr. ended 12/31/13): Assets, $45,967,152 (M); expenditures, $1,955,624; qualifying distributions, $1,752,239; giving activities include $1,752,239 for 146 grants (high: $160,000; low: $460).
Purpose and activities: Giving primarily for education, health organizations, children and youth services, including children's hospitals, and social services.
Fields of interest: Elementary/secondary education; Hospitals (specialty); Health organizations, association; Human services; Children/youth, services.
Limitations: Applications not accepted. Giving primarily in MO, with emphasis on St. Louis. No grants to individuals.
Application information: Contributes only to pre-selected organizations.
Trustee: E. Smith.
EIN: 436855044
Selected grants: The following grants are a representative sample of this grantmaker's funding activity:
$636,662 to Westminister Christian Academy, Saint Louis, MO, 2011.
$20,000 to Family Resource Center, Saint Louis, MO, 2011.
$18,000 to Saint Louis Childrens Hospital, Saint Louis, MO, 2011.
$15,000 to BackStoppers, Saint Louis, MO, 2011.
$15,000 to Friends of Kids With Cancer, Saint Louis, MO, 2011.
$10,000 to Lydias House, Saint Louis, MO, 2011.
$10,000 to Muscular Dystrophy Association, Saint Louis, MO, 2011.
$10,000 to Operation Food Search, Saint Louis, MO, 2011.
$10,000 to Saint Louis Zoo, Saint Louis, MO, 2011.
$10,000 to University of Missouri, Columbia, MO, 2011. For capital campaign.

7691
The Turner Foundation ✧
(formerly Harry and Violet Turner 95 Charitable Trust)
4 W. Main St., Ste. 800
Springfield, OH 45502-2302 (937) 325-1300
Contact: John Landess, Exec. Dir.
FAX: (937) 325-0100;
E-mail: email@hmturnerfoundation.org; Main URL: http://www.hmturnerfoundation.org

Established in 2001 in OH.
Donors: Harry M. Turner 97 Trust; Sara Landess.
Foundation type: Independent foundation.
Financial data (yr. ended 12/31/12): Assets, $48,354,871 (M); gifts received, $414,288; expenditures, $7,510,318; qualifying distributions, $6,434,834; giving activities include $3,296,136 for 87 grants (high: $561,242; low: $1), and $224,078 for loans/program-related investments.
Purpose and activities: The foundation's mission is to enhance the quality of life in the greater Springfield/Clark County community through artistic, educational, environmental, recreational, family, healthcare, historic preservation, community beautification and revitalization initiatives.
Fields of interest: Historic preservation/historical societies; Arts; Education; Environment; Health care; Children/youth, services; Community/economic development.
Type of support: Program-related investments/loans; General/operating support; Building/renovation; Program development; Matching/challenge support.
Limitations: Applications accepted. Giving primarily in Springfield and Clark County, OH. No support for individual churches, fraternal organizations, legislative action groups or political groups and issues. No grants to individuals, or for scholarships or annual fundraising campaigns.
Publications: Application guidelines.
Application information: Application form required.
Initial approach: Online application via foundation web site
Copies of proposal: 1
Deadline(s): See foundation web site for current deadline
Final notification: Dec.
Officers: John Landess, Exec. Dir.; Charlie McFarland, Cont.

Directors: Elizabeth Coffman; Mary Emerson; Larry Landess; William Landess; and 5 additional directors.
Number of staff: 6 full-time professional; 1 part-time professional.
EIN: 311711190

7692
The Twenty First Century Foundation ✧
P.O. Box 543
Norwalk, OH 44857-0543

Established in 1997 in OH.
Donors: John A. Bores; Mary L. Bores; Underground Utilities, Inc.
Foundation type: Independent foundation.
Financial data (yr. ended 06/30/13): Assets, $13,826,421 (M); gifts received, $354,884; expenditures, $598,056; qualifying distributions, $512,755; giving activities include $460,705 for 71 grants (high: $102,000; low: $105), and $5,550 for 5 grants to individuals (high: $1,500; low: $1,000).
Purpose and activities: Giving primarily for human services and Roman Catholic schools; grants also (by nomination only) to economically disadvantaged parents of Erie, Huron, or Seneca counties in OH for emergencies, disasters and medical expenses.
Fields of interest: Education; Human services; Children/youth, services; Catholic agencies & churches; Economically disadvantaged.
Type of support: General/operating support; Continuing support; Capital campaigns; Building/renovation; Emergency funds; Grants to individuals.
Limitations: Applications not accepted. Giving primarily in northwest and north central OH, with emphasis on Erie, Huron, and Seneca counties.
Application information: Unsolicited requests for funds not accepted.
Trustees: John A. Bores; Mary L. Bores.
EIN: 341852806
Selected grants: The following grants are a representative sample of this grantmaker's funding activity:
$75,000 to Immaculate Conception Church, Bellevue, OH, 2011. For operations.
$5,000 to Norwalk Catholic Schools, Norwalk, OH, 2011. For scholarships.
$1,200 to Immaculate Conception Church, Bellevue, OH, 2011.

7693
Frances Bean Vair Trust ✧ ☆
c/o PNC Bank, N.A.
P.O. Box 94651
Cleveland, OH 44101-4651

Established in OH.
Foundation type: Independent foundation.
Financial data (yr. ended 12/31/13): Assets, $37,800,849 (M); expenditures, $1,852,888; qualifying distributions, $1,736,991; giving activities include $1,664,737 for 1 grant.
Fields of interest: Higher education, university.
Limitations: Applications not accepted. Giving primarily in Cleveland, OH.
Application information: Unsolicited requests for funds not accepted.
Trustee: PNC Bank, N.A.
EIN: 346752642

7694
The Veale Foundation
(formerly V and V Foundation)
30195 Chagrin Blvd., Ste. 310-N
Pepper Pike, OH 44124-5703

Established in 1964 in OH.
Donors: Tinkham Veale II†; Harriet Ernst Veale†.
Foundation type: Independent foundation.
Financial data (yr. ended 12/31/13): Assets, $129,075,907 (M); gifts received, $72,313,825; expenditures, $9,934,436; qualifying distributions, $9,556,789; giving activities include $9,556,789 for 55 grants (high: $8,000,000; low: $2,789).
Fields of interest: Elementary/secondary education; Higher education; Education; Health care; Human services; International affairs, foreign policy.
Type of support: General/operating support.
Limitations: Applications not accepted. Giving primarily in OH, with emphasis on Cleveland and Northeast OH. No grants to individuals.
Application information: Contributes only to pre-selected organizations.
Officers and Trustees:* Daniel P. Harrington,* Chair.; Jane Kober,* Vice-Chair.; Richard K. Harr,* Secy.; William J. Culbertson.
Number of staff: 1 full-time professional.
EIN: 346565830

7695
Vesper Foundation ✧
8223 Brecksville Rd., Ste. 100
Brecksville, OH 44141-3184

Established in 1961 in OH.
Donors: Vesper Corp.; Industrial Manufacturing Co.; James Beneson, Jr.; Summa Holdings.
Foundation type: Company-sponsored foundation.
Financial data (yr. ended 12/31/13): Assets, $10,026,770 (M); gifts received, $300,000; expenditures, $1,021,474; qualifying distributions, $1,007,754; giving activities include $1,004,054 for 61 grants (high: $310,000; low: $250).
Purpose and activities: The foundation supports hospitals and organizations involved with arts and culture, education, the environment, and religion.
Fields of interest: Museums; Performing arts, theater; Arts; Elementary school/education; Secondary school/education; Higher education; Libraries (public); Education; Environment, water resources; Environment, land resources; Botanical gardens; Environment; Hospitals (general); Religion.
Type of support: General/operating support; Scholarship funds.
Limitations: Applications not accepted. Giving primarily in CT, MA, ME, NY, and OH. No grants to individuals.
Application information: Contributes only to pre-selected organizations.
Officers: James Beneson, Jr., Pres.; Clement C. Beneson, V.P.; James Beneson III, V.P.; Nancy S. Lenhart, Secy.; John V. Curci, Treas.
EIN: 236251198
Selected grants: The following grants are a representative sample of this grantmaker's funding activity:
$250,000 to Tulane University, New Orleans, LA, 2011.
$50,000 to Grace Church School, New York, NY, 2011.
$15,000 to Connecticut Public Broadcasting, Hartford, CT, 2011.
$11,000 to Di Capo Opera Theater, New York, NY, 2011.
$10,000 to Battery Conservancy, New York, NY, 2011.
$5,000 to Metropolitan Opera Association, New York, NY, 2011.
$2,500 to Solo Foundation, New York, NY, 2011.
$2,000 to Midtown Management Group, New York, NY, 2011.
$2,000 to Roundabout Theater Company, New York, NY, 2011.
$1,000 to Wellesley College, Wellesley, MA, 2011.

7696
Vortex Foundation ✧ ☆
(formerly Diana K. and Lawrence T. Foster Charitable Foundation)
132 W. 2nd St.
Perrysburg, OH 43551-1482
Contact: Amy Steele, Treas.

Established in 1988 in OH.
Donors: Diana K. Foster; Lawrence T. Foster.
Foundation type: Independent foundation.
Financial data (yr. ended 12/31/13): Assets, $8,521,015 (M); expenditures, $481,582; qualifying distributions, $446,500; giving activities include $446,500 for 35 grants (high: $302,000; low: $500).
Purpose and activities: Giving primarily for hospitals, recreation, and Christian organizations.
Fields of interest: Hospitals (general); Recreation, parks/playgrounds; Foundations (community); Christian agencies & churches.
Limitations: Applications not accepted. Giving primarily in OH and SC. No grants to individuals.
Application information: Contributes only to pre-selected organizations.
Officer: Amy Steele, Treas.
Trustees: Diana K. Foster; Lawrence T. Foster.
Number of staff: 1 part-time support.
EIN: 346883855

7697
Ellen Garretson Wade Memorial Fund ✧
c/o KeyBank N.A.
4900 Tiedman Rd., OH-01-49-0150
Brooklyn, OH 44144-2338

Established in 1944; supporting organization of A.M. McGregor Home, American Lung Association of Ohio, Applewood Centers Inc., Beech Brook, Boy Scouts of America, Center for Community Solutions, Center for Families and Children, Cleveland Clinic Children's Hospital, Cleveland Society for the Blind, First Church of Christ Scientist, Goodrich Social Settlement, Hiram House, Holy Cross House, Meridia Huron Hospital, Rainbow Babies and Children's Corporation, Salvation Army of Cleveland, University of Hospitals of Cleveland, Visiting Nurse Association, Vocational Guidance Services, and Young Women's Christian Association.
Foundation type: Independent foundation.
Financial data (yr. ended 12/31/13): Assets, $40,433,887 (M); expenditures, $1,876,183; qualifying distributions, $1,753,972; giving activities include $1,740,298 for 22 grants (high: $523,712; low: $6,930).
Fields of interest: Hospitals (general); Health care; Youth development; Human services; Children/youth, services; Protestant agencies & churches.

Limitations: Applications not accepted. Giving primarily in OH, with emphasis on the Cleveland area.
Application information: Contributes only to pre-selected organizations.
Trustee: KeyBank, N.A.
EIN: 346505729

7698
Wadsworth Golf Charities Foundation ✧
3201 Milton Rd.
Middletown, OH 45042-3679 (513) 424-3701
Contact: Richard S. Slagle, Exec. Dir.
FAX: (513) 217-6676; Main URL: http://www.wadsworthgolffoundation.org

Established in 1995 in IL.
Donors: Brenton H. Wadsworth; Jean Wadsworth; Wadsworth Golf Construction Company-Midwest; The Bruce Company of Wisconsin, Inc.; Amanda Charles; Arthur Hills; Fred L. Frus; Jamie Knudsen; Kate Rooni; Bryan Street; Charles J. Szoke; Benjamin Williams; United States Golf Association.
Foundation type: Independent foundation.
Financial data (yr. ended 12/31/13): Assets, $11,277,674 (M); gifts received, $5,775; expenditures, $626,868; qualifying distributions, $525,000; giving activities include $525,000 for grants.
Purpose and activities: Giving primarily to programs related to golf and recreation that offers positive alternatives for the disadvantaged or handicapped.
Fields of interest: Higher education; Health organizations; Athletics/sports, golf; Human services.
Type of support: Program development.
Limitations: Applications accepted. Giving primarily in the U.S., with some emphasis on IL and OH.
Publications: Annual report; Informational brochure.
Application information: Grant requests arriving via e-mail or fax will not be given consideration. Application form required.
Initial approach: Letter of no more than 2 typewritten pages.
Copies of proposal: 1
Deadline(s): Oct. 1
Board meeting date(s): As necessary
Officers and Directors:* Brenton H. Wadsworth,* Chair.; Leon McNair,* Pres.; Leslie Wadsworth,* Secy.-Treas.; Richard Slagle, Exec. Dir.; John Cotter.
EIN: 364028075
Selected grants: The following grants are a representative sample of this grantmaker's funding activity:
$101,000 to Copperhead Charities, Palm Harbor, FL, 2011.
$75,000 to Youth Golf of Northwest Arkansas, Rogers, AR, 2011.
$45,000 to Fort Worth, City of, Fort Worth, TX, 2011.
$1,000 to Miami University, Middletown, OH, 2011.

7699
The Phil Wagler Charitable Foundation ✧
3710 Tabs Dr.
Uniontown, OH 44685

Established in 1988 in OH.
Donors: Phil Wagler; Wagler Homes of Akron, Inc.; Wagler Homes of Cleveland, Inc.
Foundation type: Independent foundation.
Financial data (yr. ended 12/31/12): Assets, $7,762,576 (M); expenditures, $614,218; qualifying distributions, $419,800; giving activities include $419,800 for grants.
Purpose and activities: Giving primarily to Christian organizations and for human services.
Fields of interest: Food services; Housing/shelter, homeless; Human services; Salvation Army; Christian agencies & churches.
Type of support: General/operating support.
Limitations: Applications not accepted. Giving primarily in OH; some funding also in FL and MD. No grants to individuals.
Application information: Contributes only to pre-selected organizations.
Trustee: Phil Wagler.
EIN: 346886145

7700
Fred & Alice Wallace Charitable Memorial Foundation, Inc. ✧ ☆
130 W. 2nd St., Ste. 924
Dayton, OH 45402-1501 (937) 223-8194
Contact: Dennis Hanaghan, Exec. Dir.
FAX: (937) 223-6967;
E-mail: jucelenhochwalt@yahoo.com

Established in 1978 in OH.
Foundation type: Independent foundation.
Financial data (yr. ended 12/31/13): Assets, $9,752,225 (M); expenditures, $553,893; qualifying distributions, $468,229; giving activities include $424,063 for 19 grants (high: $75,000; low: $5,063).
Fields of interest: Education; Health organizations, association.
Type of support: Continuing support; Capital campaigns; Equipment; Emergency funds; Conferences/seminars; Curriculum development.
Limitations: Applications accepted. Giving limited to OH, with emphasis on the Miami Valley area. No grants to individuals.
Publications: Financial statement; Informational brochure (including application guidelines); Program policy statement.
Application information: Application form required.
Initial approach: Letter of intent
Copies of proposal: 4
Deadline(s): None
Board meeting date(s): July and Dec.
Final notification: As appropriate
Officers: Dennis Hanaghan, Pres. and Exec. Dir.; Jacob Worner, V.P.; J.R. Hochwalt, Secy.-Treas.
Number of staff: 1 full-time professional; 3 part-time professional.
EIN: 310944135

7701
Warmenhoven Family Foundation ✧
c/o Charitable Trust Administration Company
7261 Engle Rd., Ste. 202
Cleveland, OH 44130-3479

Established in 2006 in CA.
Donors: Daniel J. Warmenhoven; Charmaine A. Warmenhoven.
Foundation type: Independent foundation.
Financial data (yr. ended 12/31/13): Assets, $25,855,653 (M); expenditures, $1,247,194; qualifying distributions, $1,232,000; giving activities include $1,232,000 for 45 grants (high: $200,000; low: $5,000).
Fields of interest: Education; Alzheimer's disease; Autism; Cancer research; Human services; Catholic agencies & churches; Children.
Limitations: Applications not accepted. No grants to individuals.
Application information: Contributes only to pre-selected organizations.
Officers: Daniel J. Warmenhoven, Pres.; Charmaine Warmenhoven, V.P.
Directors: Eric Warmenhoven; Laura Warmenhoven.
EIN: 205834839
Selected grants: The following grants are a representative sample of this grantmaker's funding activity:
$100,000 to Ocean Exploration Trust, Old Lyme, CT, 2011. For general support.

7702
Warren County Foundation ✧
118 E. Main Street
P.O. Box 495
Lebanon, OH 45036-0495 (513) 934-1001
Contact: Henry Brockman, Pres.
FAX: (513) 934-3001;
E-mail: info@warrencountyfoundation.org; Additional e-mail: hfbrockman@ohiocpa.net; Main URL: http://www.warrencountyfoundation.org
Blog: http://www.warrencountyfoundation.org/pages/blog/
Facebook: https://www.facebook.com/WarrenCountyFoundation
Twitter: https://twitter.com/WarrenCountyFDN

Established in 1996 in OH.
Foundation type: Community foundation.
Financial data (yr. ended 06/30/13): Assets, $10,090,969 (M); gifts received, $1,372,744; expenditures, $924,658; giving activities include $669,350 for 15+ grants (high: $80,000).
Purpose and activities: The foundation seeks to make it easy for people to be charitable and to build an endowment to meet changing community needs over time.
Fields of interest: Community/economic development.
Type of support: General/operating support; Building/renovation; Program development; Seed money.
Limitations: Applications accepted. Giving limited to Warren County, OH. No support for organizations not exempt under IRS 501(c)3 guidelines or religious organizations for religious purposes. No grants to individuals, or for ongoing operating expenses of existing institutions, endowments, annual fundraising drives, travel grants, or scholarly or medical research.
Publications: Financial statement; Grants list; Informational brochure; Newsletter; Occasional report.
Application information: Visit foundation web site for application form and guidelines. Application form required.
Initial approach: Submit application and attachments
Copies of proposal: 12
Deadline(s): 15th of the month preceding a Grants Committee meeting
Board meeting date(s): Grants committee meets Jan., Mar., May, July, Sept., and Nov.
Officers and Trustees:* Stephen Wilson,* Chair.; Jonathan McCann,* Vice-Chair.; Henry Brockman,*

Pres. and C.A.O.; James W. Bliss,* V.P., Devel.; Richard A. Yost,* Secy.; Derek Tinnin,* Treas.; James Aumann; Barbara J. Bronson; Michael Carroll; Spencer S. Cropper; Daniel B. Cunningham; Charles K. Dilgard; Michael Geygan; James L. Gross, Jr.; Maggie Hess; Anne Krehbiel; George Leasure; Robert B. Morgan; Kenneth Natorp; Erik Peters; William G. Thornton.
Number of staff: 2 full-time professional; 1 part-time support.
EIN: 311565086

7703
The Warrington Foundation ✧
c/o Fifth Third Bank
P.O. Box 630858
Cincinnati, OH 45263-0858
Application address: c/o Fifth Third Bank, 38 Fountain Sq. Plz., MD 1090 FA, Cincinnati, OH 45263; tel.: (513) 579-5440

Established in 1997 in OH.
Donor: Elsie H. Warrington.
Foundation type: Independent foundation.
Financial data (yr. ended 12/31/13): Assets, $10,165,623 (M); expenditures, $585,479; qualifying distributions, $505,120; giving activities include $504,782 for 89 grants (high: $30,000; low: $500).
Purpose and activities: Giving primarily for the arts, education, the environment, medical research, including juvenile diabetes, and to Christian churches, as well as for children, youth and family services.
Fields of interest: Museums (art); Performing arts, orchestras; Arts; Higher education; Education; Environment, natural resources; Environment; Medical research, institute; Diabetes research; Human services; YM/YWCAs & YM/YWHAs; Children/youth, services; Protestant agencies & churches.
Limitations: Applications accepted. Giving primarily in OH.
Application information: Application form required.
Initial approach: Letter
Deadline(s): None
Trustees: Dan Bailey; John Warrington Bailey; Sam Bailey; Leslie Warrington Bailey Hardy.
EIN: 311582067

7704
Wayne County Community Foundation ✧
(formerly Greater Wayne County Foundation, Inc.)
517 N. Market St.
Wooster, OH 44691-3405 (330) 262-3877
Contact: Sara L. Patton, Exec. Dir.
FAX: (330) 262-8057; E-mail: wccf@sssnet.com; Additional e-mail: gwcf@gwcf.net; Main URL: http://www.waynecountycommunityfoundation.org
E-Newsletter: http://www.waynecountycommunityfoundation.org/about-us/wccf-newsletters
Facebook: http://www.facebook.com/pages/Wayne-County-Community-Foundation/328152980611795

Established in 1978 in OH.
Foundation type: Community foundation.
Financial data (yr. ended 06/30/13): Assets, $51,607,267 (M); gifts received, $4,580,935; expenditures, $6,089,296; giving activities include $5,087,446 for 54+ grants (high: $3,619,812), and $437,478 for grants to individuals.
Purpose and activities: The foundation seeks to: 1) encourage individuals who have prospered in Wayne County to leave part of their estates for the good of the community in which they lived; 2) assist community nonprofit organizations in the creation and management of endowments to meet future financial needs; and 3) provide oversight of investment and disbursement of funds devoted to charitable purposes.
Fields of interest: Humanities; Arts; Education; Environment; Health care; Human services; Community/economic development.
Type of support: Continuing support; Management development/capacity building; Capital campaigns; Building/renovation; Equipment; Land acquisition; Endowments; Emergency funds; Program development; Seed money; Scholarship funds; Research; Matching/challenge support.
Limitations: Applications accepted. Giving limited to Wayne County, OH. No support for religious organizations for religious purposes. No grants for deficit financing, endowment funds, annual appeals or membership contributions, conferences, field trips, travel, recognition events, or general operating expenses of well-established organizations including computers and office equipment.
Publications: Application guidelines; Annual report; Financial statement; Informational brochure (including application guidelines).
Application information: Application process has moved entirely online. Visit foundation web site for online application and guidelines. Application form required.
Initial approach: Create online profile
Copies of proposal: 1
Deadline(s): Mar. 1 and Sept. 1
Board meeting date(s): Quarterly
Final notification: June 1 and Dec. 1
Officers and Trustees:* J.C. Johnston III,* Pres.; Steve Matthew,* V.P.; Mark A. Auble,* Secy.; Mary Alice Streeter,* Treas.; Sara L. Patton, Exec. Dir.; Michael D. Agnoni; Marlene Barkheimer; Maribeth Burns; William J. DeRodes; Glenda Lehman Ervin; Cheryl M. Kirkbride; Larry Markley; William J. Robertson; Stephen L. Shapiro; Rod Steiger; Brent Steiner; Deanna Troutman; Bala Venkataraman; Howard Wenger.
Number of staff: 1 full-time professional; 1 full-time support; 1 part-time support.
EIN: 341281026

7705
The Raymond John Wean Foundation
147 W. Market St.
Warren, OH 44481-1022 (330) 394-5600
Contact: Jennifer Roller, Pres.
FAX: (330) 394-5601; E-mail: info@rjweanfdn.org; Main URL: http://www.rjweanfdn.org
The Raymond John Wean Foundation's Philanthropy Promise: http://www.ncrp.org/philanthropys-promise/who

Established in 1949 in OH.
Donor: Raymond John Wean, Sr.‡.
Foundation type: Independent foundation.
Financial data (yr. ended 12/31/13): Assets, $80,350,284 (M); gifts received, $10,000; expenditures, $3,858,666; qualifying distributions, $3,257,142; giving activities include $2,227,560 for 174 grants (high: $425,000; low: $500).
Purpose and activities: To enhance community well-being and vitality in the Mahoning Valley through strategic grant making intended to support people living in the Valley's economically disadvantaged communities and neighborhoods in adherence to the following principles: to explore new innovative approaches to addressing issues, to seek inclusion and broad community involvement; to build on the considerable assets of the Mahoning Valley; to strive for equity and support social justice; to leverage additional resources, partners and ideas; to support the development of human assets and capital; to cultivate leadership in the community; and to provide support to people and communities which are often overlooked or insufficiently funded.
Fields of interest: Education, early childhood education; Child development, services; Community/economic development.
Type of support: Income development; Management development/capacity building; Program development; Technical assistance; Program evaluation; Program-related investments/loans.
Limitations: Applications accepted. Giving limited to the Mahoning and/or Trumbull Counties in OH. No support for sectarian religious activities, veterans' or fraternal organizations, or local or national offices of organizations combating a particular disease or family of diseases. No grants to individuals; or for endowment funds, debt reduction, foreign operations, national fundraising campaigns or film or video production.
Publications: Application guidelines; Annual report; Financial statement; Grants list; Newsletter.
Application information: Applications accepted only after letter of inquiry. Letter of inquiry form is available of foundation's web site. The foundation also accepts the Ohio Grantmakers Forum's letter of inquiry, application and final evaluation forms. Application form required.
Initial approach: Complete letter of inquiry form
Copies of proposal: 2
Deadline(s): See foundation web site for current deadlines
Board meeting date(s): Mar., Jun., Sept. and Dec.
Final notification: Following board meeting
Officers and Administrators:* Gordon B. Wean,* Chair.; Jennifer Roller, Pres.; Germaine Bennett; Don Emerson; Suzanne Fleming; Paul Hagman; Michael Harrison; William Mullane; John L. Pogue; Janis Sanfrey.
Trustee: The Glenmede Trust Company.
Number of staff: 4 full-time professional; 1 full-time support.
EIN: 346505038

7706
The Weary Family Foundation ✧
c/o Gifford Weary
2731 Elginfield Rd.
Columbus, OH 43220-4289

Established in 2000 in KS.
Donors: Robert K. Weary; Mrs. Dale J. Weary; Robert K. Weary Trust; Dale J. Weary Trust.
Foundation type: Independent foundation.
Financial data (yr. ended 12/31/13): Assets, $20,777,050 (M); expenditures, $1,109,823; qualifying distributions, $1,004,558; giving activities include $999,000 for 30 grants (high: $311,000; low: $2,500).
Fields of interest: Education, single organization support; Higher education; Health care, home services; Human services; YM/YWCAs & YM/

YWHAs; United Ways and Federated Giving Programs.
Type of support: General/operating support.
Limitations: Applications not accepted. Giving primarily in CO, KS, and OH. No grants to individuals.
Application information: Contributes only to pre-selected organizations.
Officers and Directors:* Robert K. Weary, Jr.,* Pres.; Gifford Weary,* Secy.; Dale Ann Clore,* Treas.
EIN: 481224093
Selected grants: The following grants are a representative sample of this grantmaker's funding activity:
$290,000 to Ohio State University Foundation, Columbus, OH, 2011.
$200,000 to YMCA of the Rockies, Estes Park, CO, 2011.
$70,000 to YMCA, Junction City Family, Junction City, KS, 2011.
$50,000 to Homecare and Hospice Foundation, Manhattan, KS, 2011.
$45,000 to Kansas State University Foundation, Manhattan, KS, 2011.
$30,000 to Four-H Foundation, Kansas, Manhattan, KS, 2011.
$25,000 to United Way, Mile High, Denver, CO, 2011.
$18,500 to Kansas State University Foundation, Manhattan, KS, 2011.
$10,000 to National Intercollegiate Rodeo Association Alumni, Laramie, WY, 2011.
$5,000 to United Way of Riley County, Manhattan, KS, 2011.

7707
The Weatherhead Foundation ✧
5910 Landerbrook Dr., Ste. 210
Mayfield Heights, OH 44124-6500

Incorporated in 1953 in OH; foundation is income beneficiary of a perpetual trust; assets reflect assets of both feeder trust and foundation.
Donors: Albert J. Weatherhead, Jr.†; Weatherhead Charitable Trust.
Foundation type: Independent foundation.
Financial data (yr. ended 12/31/12): Assets, $5,655,799 (M); gifts received, $2,456,282; expenditures, $3,860,603; qualifying distributions, $3,607,421; giving activities include $3,607,421 for 4 grants (high: $2,522,505; low: $56,367).
Purpose and activities: Grants for endowments or programs, principally to universities and research organizations.
Fields of interest: Higher education; Foundations (community).
Type of support: General/operating support; Endowments; Program development; Research.
Limitations: Applications not accepted. Giving primarily in TX; some giving also in NY and OH. No support for religious purposes or for general support of church or denominational institutions. No grants to individuals.
Publications: Informational brochure.
Application information: Contributes only to pre-selected organizations. Grants are initiated by the trustees.
Board meeting date(s): Spring, fall, and as required
Officers and Trustees:* Celia J. Weatherhead,* Pres.; Terri Lacy,* Secy.; Prof. Jorge I. Dominguez; Carol Gluck; Dr. Eamon M. Kelly.
Number of staff: 1 full-time professional.
EIN: 132711998

7708
Robert and Mary Weisbrod Foundation ✧
c/o PNC Bank, N.A.
P.O. Box 94651
Cleveland, OH 44101-4651
Application address: c/o R & M Weisbrod Distribution Comm., P.O. Box 837, Pittsburgh, PA 15230, tel.: (412) 644-8114

Established in 1968 in PA.
Donors: Mary E. Weisbrod†; Mary Weisbrod Unitrust.
Foundation type: Independent foundation.
Financial data (yr. ended 12/31/13): Assets, $13,977,931 (M); expenditures, $674,682; qualifying distributions, $606,077; giving activities include $557,000 for 36 grants (high: $100,000; low: $5,000).
Purpose and activities: Giving primarily for education, the arts, health care, and children, youth, and social services.
Fields of interest: Arts; Libraries/library science; Education; Health care; Food services; Human services; Children/youth, services; Family services; United Ways and Federated Giving Programs.
Type of support: General/operating support; Continuing support.
Limitations: Applications accepted. Giving primarily in the Pittsburgh, PA, area. No grants to individuals.
Application information: Application form required.
Initial approach: Letter
Copies of proposal: 1
Deadline(s): None
Board meeting date(s): As required
Trustee: PNC Bank, N.A.
EIN: 256105924
Selected grants: The following grants are a representative sample of this grantmaker's funding activity:
$135,000 to Greater Pittsburgh Community Food Bank, Duquesne, PA, 2011. For general support.
$50,000 to Community College of Allegheny County Educational Foundation, Pittsburgh, PA, 2011. For general support.
$50,000 to East End Cooperative Ministry, Pittsburgh, PA, 2011. For general support.
$50,000 to Senator John Heinz History Center, Pittsburgh, PA, 2011. For general support.
$25,000 to Womansplace, McKeesport, PA, 2011. For general support.
$20,000 to FamilyLinks, Pittsburgh, PA, 2011. For general support.
$20,000 to Manchester Youth Development Center, Pittsburgh, PA, 2011. For general support.
$5,000 to Alzheimers Association, Harrisburg, PA, 2011. For general support.
$5,000 to Center of Life, Pittsburgh, PA, 2011. For general support.
$5,000 to Western Pennsylvania Conservancy, Pittsburgh, PA, 2011. For general support.

7709
The S. K. Wellman Foundation ✧
P.O. Box 32554
Euclid, OH 44132-0554 (216) 621-1180
Contact: Laurence A. Bartell, Secy.

Incorporated in 1951 in OH.
Donor: S.K. Wellman†.
Foundation type: Independent foundation.
Financial data (yr. ended 12/31/13): Assets, $4,740,092 (M); expenditures, $629,194; qualifying distributions, $548,742; giving activities include $510,000 for 78 grants (high: $25,000; low: $1,000).
Purpose and activities: The foundation's areas of funding are the following: animals/wildlife, preservation/protection (only in Cleveland, OH); the arts; children, youth, and human services; elementary/secondary/higher education; the environment/natural resources; government/public administration and health care.
Fields of interest: Arts; Elementary/secondary education; Higher education; Nursing school/education; Environment, natural resources; Environment; Animals/wildlife; Hospitals (general); Health care; Human services; Children/youth, services; Government/public administration.
Limitations: Applications accepted. Giving primarily in OH. No grants to individuals.
Publications: Application guidelines; Grants list.
Application information: Any requests or proposals for grants must follow the foundation's guidelines. Application guidelines are available on foundation web site. Application form required.
Initial approach: Written proposal, following foundation's guidelines
Copies of proposal: 1
Deadline(s): May 31
Board meeting date(s): June
Final notification: 1 week
Officers and Trustees:* Susanne W. Erikson,* Pres.; Laurence A. Bartell, Secy.
Number of staff: 1 part-time professional.
EIN: 346520032
Selected grants: The following grants are a representative sample of this grantmaker's funding activity:
$18,000 to Cleveland Foodbank, Cleveland, OH, 2012. For food for needy.
$9,000 to Hospice of the Western Reserve, Cleveland, OH, 2012. For Aid to the Dying.
$8,000 to Achievement Centers for Children, Highland Hills, OH, 2012. For Educational Services to Needy Children.
$8,000 to Cleveland Orchestra, Cleveland, OH, 2012. For preforming arts.
$6,000 to Bluecoats, Cleveland, OH, 2012. For Police Support Organization.
$5,000 to Youth Opportunities Unlimited, Cleveland, OH, 2012. For Aid to Needy Children.
$4,000 to Hiram House, Chagrin Falls, OH, 2012. For shelter for needy.

7710
Western & Southern Financial Fund, Inc. ✧
(formerly Western-Southern Foundation, Inc.)
400 Broadway, MS 28
Cincinnati, OH 45202-3312 (513) 629-1464
Contact: Edward J. Babbit, Secy.-Treas.
Main URL: http://www.westernsouthernlife.com/aboutUs/wsfg/communityinvolvement.asp

Established in 1988 in OH.
Donors: The Western & Southern Life Insurance Co.; Columbus Life Insurance Co.
Foundation type: Company-sponsored foundation.
Financial data (yr. ended 12/31/12): Assets, $4,175,726 (M); expenditures, $2,949,655;

qualifying distributions, $2,939,655; giving activities include $2,937,426 for 252+ grants (high: $481,676).
Purpose and activities: The fund supports organizations involved with arts and culture, education, health, mental health, cancer, multiple sclerosis, human services, and community development.
Fields of interest: Museums; Arts; Higher education; Business school/education; Education; Health care, patient services; Health care; Mental health/crisis services; Cancer; Multiple sclerosis; Boy scouts; American Red Cross; Salvation Army; Children/youth, services; Human services; Community development, neighborhood development; Business/industry; Community/economic development; United Ways and Federated Giving Programs.
Type of support: General/operating support; Continuing support; Annual campaigns; Capital campaigns; Building/renovation; Program development; Scholarship funds; Sponsorships; Employee matching gifts.
Limitations: Applications accepted. Giving primarily in Cincinnati, OH.
Publications: Application guidelines.
Application information: Application form not required.
Initial approach: Proposal
Deadline(s): None
Officers and Trustees:* Thomas L. Williams,* Chair.; John Finn Barrett,* Pres.; Edward J. Babbit, Secy.-Treas.
EIN: 311259670

7711
The Westfield Insurance Foundation ✧
(doing business as Westfield Group Foundation)
P.O. Box 5001
Westfield Center, OH 44251-5001
E-mail: robertkoszkalda@westfieldgrp.com

Established in 2005 in OH.
Donors: Old Guard Insurance Company; Westfield Insurance Co.; Westfield National Insurance Co.; Westfield Group Foundation.
Foundation type: Company-sponsored foundation.
Financial data (yr. ended 12/31/13): Assets, $21,365,717 (M); gifts received, $5,002,155; expenditures, $754,728; qualifying distributions, $708,000; giving activities include $708,000 for 100 grants (high: $300,000; low: $36).
Purpose and activities: The foundation supports programs designed to promote community revitalization, safety, education, and human services.
Fields of interest: Arts; Higher education; Education; Housing/shelter, development; Housing/shelter; Safety, automotive safety; Human services; Community/economic development; United Ways and Federated Giving Programs.
Type of support: General/operating support; Capital campaigns; Building/renovation; Equipment; Program development; Employee volunteer services.
Limitations: Applications accepted. Giving limited to areas where Westfield conducts business, with emphasis on IN, OH, and PA. No support for organizations outside of Westfield operating territories, annual operating budgets for United Way agencies, membership organizations (unless they benefit the public), religious, fraternal or labor organizations, or for youth and adult athletic teams and associations. No grants to individuals, or for scholarship/student exchange programs, advertising, fundraising benefits or events, or conferences or seminars.
Application information: Application form required.
Initial approach: Proposal
Deadline(s): None
Directors: Frank Carrino; James Clay; Jani Groza; Edward Largent; Jon Park; Marianne Parkinson; Stuart Rosenberg.
EIN: 203816760
Selected grants: The following grants are a representative sample of this grantmaker's funding activity:
$300,000 to Playhouse Square Foundation, Cleveland, OH, 2012. For building of broadcast theatre for public TV and radio.
$33,000 to Fund for Our Economic Future, Cleveland, OH, 2012. For economic development efforts in Northeast Ohio.
$5,000 to Habitat for Humanity of Summit County, Akron, OH, 2012. For home construction.
$3,000 to Neighborhood Housing Services of Cleveland, Cleveland, OH, 2012. For the Home Ownership Center - Homebuyer Education.
$2,500 to Habitat for Humanity of Kent County, Grand Rapids, MI, 2012. For educational partnership program.
$2,000 to Junior Achievement of North Central Ohio, Akron, OH, 2012. For Medina County Programs.
$1,000 to Spanish American Committee, Cleveland, OH, 2012. For the housing counseling Program.

7712
The Wexner Family Charitable Fund ✧
(formerly Leslie H. Wexner Charitable Fund)
c/o Delson Assocs.
8000 Walton Parkway, Ste. 100
New Albany, OH 43054-7075

Established in 1990 in OH.
Donor: Leslie H. Wexner.
Foundation type: Independent foundation.
Financial data (yr. ended 12/31/12): Assets, $168,927,019 (M); gifts received, $46,900,000; expenditures, $18,996,218; qualifying distributions, $18,023,439; giving activities include $18,012,500 for 17 grants (high: $8,000,000; low: $10,000).
Purpose and activities: Giving primarily to Jewish organizations, with an emphasis on Jewish education.
Fields of interest: Education; Reproductive health, family planning; United Ways and Federated Giving Programs; Jewish agencies & synagogues.
Limitations: Applications not accepted. Giving primarily in OH; some giving in NY and MA. No grants to individuals.
Application information: Contributes only to pre-selected organizations.
Officers: Leslie H. Wexner, Pres.; Dennis Hersch, Secy.; Peggy Ugland, Treas.
Director: Abigail S. Wexner.
EIN: 311318013
Selected grants: The following grants are a representative sample of this grantmaker's funding activity:
$8,000,000 to Wexner Foundation, New Albany, OH, 2012.
$2,900,000 to Jewish Federation, Columbus, Columbus, OH, 2012.
$2,470,000 to Columbus Foundation, Columbus, OH, 2012.
$1,500,000 to Harvard University, Cambridge, MA, 2012.
$1,000,000 to Wexner Heritage Village, Columbus, OH, 2012.
$690,500 to Nationwide Childrens Hospital, Columbus, OH, 2012.
$325,000 to United Way of Central Ohio, Columbus, OH, 2012.
$250,000 to New Albany Community Foundation, New Albany, OH, 2012.
$250,000 to Ohio State University Foundation, Columbus, OH, 2012.
$120,000 to Pelotonia, Columbus, OH, 2012.

7713
Wexner Foundation ✧
8000 Walton Pkwy., Ste. 110
New Albany, OH 43054-7074 (614) 939-6060
FAX: (614) 939-6066; E-mail: info@wexner.net; New York address: 599 Lexington Ave., Ste. 27A, New York, NY 10022, tel.: (212) 355-6115; Israel address: 37 Derech Beit Lechem, Jerusalem, Israel 93553, tel.: 02 563-7035, fax: 02 561-2002; MA address: c/o Center for Public Leadership, Harvard Kennedy School, 79 JFK St., Cambridge, MA 02139, tel.: (617) 496-7113; Main URL: http://www.wexnerfoundation.org
Fellowship address: The Wexner Israel Fellowship Program, c/o Center for Public Leadership, Harvard Kennedy School, Attn.: Abbey Onn, Coord., Wexner Israel Fellowship Prog. at Harvard University, 79 JFK St., Cambridge, MA 02138, tel.: (617) 496-7113, fax: (617) 495-4988

Established in 1973.
Donors: Abigail Wexner; Leslie H. Wexner; The Leslie H. Wexner Charitable Fund; Wexner Family Charitable Fund; The New Albany Company; Guardian Industries Corp.; Jewish Community Federation; Jewish Federation of South Palm Beach County; United Jewish Appeal; Rose Foundation; United Jewish Federation of Greater Pittsburgh; United Jewish Communities of Metrowest, NJ.
Foundation type: Independent foundation.
Financial data (yr. ended 12/31/13): Assets, $4,756,669 (M); gifts received, $10,793,903; expenditures, $10,848,639; qualifying distributions, $10,765,296; giving activities include $2,185,205 for 35 grants (high: $881,550; low: $2,088), and $4,002,961 for 3 foundation-administered programs.
Purpose and activities: The foundation focuses its giving on the arena of Jewish leadership. The fellowship programs address constituencies that the foundation believes are essential to the revitalization of Jewish life: North American Jewish professional leaders and Israeli public sector leaders.
Fields of interest: Youth development, services; Human services; Jewish federated giving programs; Leadership development; Jewish agencies & synagogues.
Type of support: Fellowships; Grants to individuals; Scholarships—to individuals.
Limitations: Applications accepted. Giving primarily in North America and Israel.
Publications: Informational brochure; Program policy statement.
Application information: Contributes to pre-selected organizations for grants; applications accepted for fellowship programs. Contact the foundation for complete application information or

refer to foundation web site. Application form required.

Initial approach: Letter

Deadline(s): See foundation web site for current deadlines

Officers and Trustees:* Leslie H. Wexner,* Chair.; Rabbi B. Elka Abrahamson, Pres.; Cindy Chazan, V.P.; Dennis S. Hersch, Secy.

Number of staff: 5 full-time professional; 6 full-time support.

EIN: 237320631

7714

Sherman White, Jr. and Virginia H. White Charitable Trust ✧

c/o KeyBank N.A.
P.O. Box 10099
Toledo, OH 43699-0099

Established in 2005 in OH.

Foundation type: Independent foundation.

Financial data (yr. ended 12/31/13): Assets, $13,527,005 (M); expenditures, $670,327; qualifying distributions, $613,225; giving activities include $594,584 for 5 grants (high: $237,834; low: $59,458).

Fields of interest: Higher education; Libraries/library science; Health organizations; Foundations (private independent); Protestant agencies & churches.

Limitations: Applications not accepted. Giving primarily in Tiffin, OH. No grants to individuals.

Application information: Contributes only to pre-selected organizations.

Trustee: KeyBank N.A.

EIN: 203970395

Selected grants: The following grants are a representative sample of this grantmaker's funding activity:

$232,615 to Tiffin Charitable Foundation, Tiffin, OH, 2011.

$145,384 to Heidelberg University, Tiffin, OH, 2011.

7715

The Thomas H. White No. 1 Trust ✧

(also known as Thomas H. White Foundation)
c/o Foundation Mgmt. Svcs., Inc.
1422 Euclid Ave., Ste. 966
Cleveland, OH 44115-1952 (216) 621-2901
Contact: Susan Althans, Consultant
FAX: (216) 621-8198;
E-mail: salthans@fmscleveland.com; Additional e-mail: info@fmscleveland.com; Main URL: http://www.fmscleveland.com/thomaswhite/

Trust established in 1913 in OH; became active in 1939.

Donor: Thomas H. White†.

Foundation type: Independent foundation.

Financial data (yr. ended 12/31/13): Assets, $24,308,433 (M); expenditures, $1,274,212; qualifying distributions, $1,214,786; giving activities include $1,112,548 for 90 grants (high: $30,000; low: $2,500).

Purpose and activities: The foundation will consider requests from tax-exempt, non-profit charitable and educational institutions located within Cuyahoga County, Ohio, if such organizations and their services and facilities primarily serve residents of the city of Cleveland. The foundation will focus its grantmaking on two major areas: education and human services. Specifically, the foundation is interested in supporting programs that address three critical areas: Workforce readiness: programs that emphasize science and technology education, adequate employment preparation, support systems, and the relationship to earning potential. School retention: programs that emphasize the critical transition issues that occur during early teenage years and affect family relationships and school attendance. Early childhood enrichment: programs that enhance the learning environment; provide support, training, and ancillary services to parents; and/or the recruitment and training of daycare providers. Organizations and programs that contribute generally to the quality of life in Greater Cleveland may also be considered at the foundation's discretion.

Fields of interest: Education, early childhood education; Elementary school/education; Secondary school/education; Education; Crime/violence prevention, domestic violence; Employment; Human services; Children/youth, services; Family services; Homeless, human services; Disabilities, people with; Minorities; Women; AIDS, people with; Economically disadvantaged; Homeless.

Type of support: Capital campaigns; Building/renovation; Equipment; Emergency funds; Program development; Seed money.

Limitations: Applications accepted. Giving limited to nonprofit charitable organizations located within Cuyahoga County, OH, if such organizations, and their services and facilities, primarily serve residents of the City of Cleveland. No grants to individuals, or for annual campaigns, general operating support, scholarships, endowments, research, symposia, seminars, deficit financing, or land acquisition; no loans.

Publications: Application guidelines; Annual report (including application guidelines); Financial statement.

Application information: Mass mailings not accepted. All applications must be submitted online. Application guidelines and form available on trust's website. Application form required.

Initial approach: Proposal

Copies of proposal: 1

Deadline(s): Apr. 1, Aug. 1, and Dec. 1

Board meeting date(s): Distribution Committee meets in Jan., May, and Sept.

Final notification: Within several weeks

Distribution Committee: Margot James Copeland; Robin Cottingham; Jan Culver; Michael S. Galland; Catherine O'Malley Kearney.

Trustee: KeyBank N.A.

EIN: 346505722

Selected grants: The following grants are a representative sample of this grantmaker's funding activity:

$75,000 to Cleveland Metropolitan School District, Cleveland, OH, 2012. For upgrades to the Fabrication Laboratories at the Mc2 Stem High School.

$35,000 to Center for Arts-Inspired Learning, Cleveland, OH, 2012. For Art is Education, arts-integrated program within the CMSD.

$25,000 to Neighborhood Progress, Cleveland, OH, 2012. For the Saint Luke's Manor Project.

$22,000 to United Way of Greater Cleveland, Cleveland, OH, 2012. For the Youth Development and Family Support Programs.

$20,000 to Towards Employment, Cleveland, OH, 2012. For NetWorks 4 Success, employment program.

$15,000 to Achievement Centers for Children, Highland Hills, OH, 2012. For the Help Me Grow Program, which provides health and developmental services to parents, newborns, infants and toddlers.

$15,000 to Boys and Girls Clubs of Cleveland, Cleveland, OH, 2012. For after-school and summer programming.

$15,000 to Minds Matter of Cleveland, Cleveland, OH, 2012. For program Support.

$10,000 to Retired and Senior Volunteer Program of Greater Cleveland, Greater Cleveland Volunteers, Cleveland, OH, 2012. For the Experience Corps Program.

$7,500 to Musical Arts Association, Cleveland, OH, 2012. For education Concerts for Cmsd Students.

7716

Harry T. Wilks Family Foundation ✧

1763 Hamilton Cleves Rd.
Hamilton, OH 45013

Donor: Harry T. Wilks.

Foundation type: Independent foundation.

Financial data (yr. ended 12/31/13): Assets, $291,402,531 (M); expenditures, $571,001; qualifying distributions, $569,755; giving activities include $558,748 for 11 grants (high: $375,000; low: $300).

Fields of interest: Arts; Education; Human services.

Limitations: Applications not accepted. Giving primarily in OH and WI. No grants to individuals.

Application information: Unsolicited requests for funds not accepted.

Trustees: Nanci Lanni; Barbara Wilks.

EIN: 273046060

7717

Wodecroft Foundation ✧

255 E. 5th St., Ste. 1900
Cincinnati, OH 45202-4720 (513) 977-8236
Contact: J. Michael Cooney Esq., Tr.

Established in 1958 in OH.

Donor: Roger Drackett†.

Foundation type: Independent foundation.

Financial data (yr. ended 12/31/13): Assets, $17,887,005 (M); expenditures, $782,721; qualifying distributions, $710,000; giving activities include $710,000 for 56 grants (high: $200,000; low: $1,000).

Purpose and activities: Giving primarily for the arts, particularly a performing arts center; funding also for higher education, health and hospitals, including a children's hospital, and youth and social services.

Fields of interest: Museums; Performing arts centers; Performing arts, orchestras; Arts; Higher education; Environment, natural resources; Hospitals (general); Hospitals (specialty); Mental health/crisis services; Health organizations, association; Medical research, institute; Human services; Children/youth, services; Foundations (private grantmaking).

Type of support: Annual campaigns; Capital campaigns; Building/renovation; Equipment.

Limitations: Applications accepted. Giving primarily in southwestern FL, and southwestern OH. No grants to individuals.

Application information: Few unsolicited applications granted. Application form not required.
Initial approach: Proposal
Deadline(s): June 30
Board meeting date(s): As required
Final notification: Prior to Dec. 31
Trustees: Cecile Drackett Allyn; William Bahl; J. Michael Cooney.
EIN: 316047601
Selected grants: The following grants are a representative sample of this grantmaker's funding activity:
$200,000 to Greater Cincinnati Arts and Education Center, Cincinnati, OH, 2011.
$70,000 to Cold Spring Harbor Laboratory, Cold Spring Harbor, NY, 2011.
$70,000 to Sun Valley Summer Symphony, Ketchum, ID, 2011.
$50,000 to Christ Church Cathedral, Cincinnati, OH, 2011.
$20,000 to Childrens Hospital Medical Center, Cincinnati, OH, 2011.
$10,000 to Dexter School, Brookline, MA, 2011.
$10,000 to Harbor House of Central Florida, Orlando, FL, 2011.
$6,000 to American Cancer Society, Cincinnati, OH, 2011.
$3,000 to Animal Shelter of Wood River Valley, Hailey, ID, 2011.
$3,000 to Nature Conservancy of Idaho, Hailey, ID, 2011.

7718
The Wohlgemuth Herschede Foundation ✧ ☆
c/o Fifth Third Bank
P.O. Box 630858
Cincinnati, OH 45263-0858
Application address: Fifth Third Bank, 38 Fountain Square Plz., MD 1090 HB, Cincinnati, OH 45236, tel.: (513) 534-7086

Established in 1994 in OH.
Foundation type: Independent foundation.
Financial data (yr. ended 12/31/13): Assets, $10,175,409 (M); expenditures, $536,082; qualifying distributions, $434,363; giving activities include $424,500 for 68 grants (high: $20,000; low: $1,000).
Fields of interest: Performing arts; Arts; Education; Human services; Catholic agencies & churches.
Limitations: Applications accepted. Giving primarily in the greater Cincinnati, OH, area.
Application information: Application form required.
Initial approach: Letter
Deadline(s): None
Trustees: Allison Herschede; Holly Herschede; Joseph P. Rouse.
EIN: 311409317
Selected grants: The following grants are a representative sample of this grantmaker's funding activity:
$500 to Christ the King Church, Cincinnati, OH, 2012. For Program support - Operating Grant.

7719
Wolfe Associates ✧
34 S. 3rd St.
Columbus, OH 43215-4201 (614) 460-3782
Contact: Rita J. Wolfe, V.P. and Tr.

Incorporated in 1973 in OH.
Donors: The Dispatch Printing Co.; The Ohio Co.; WBNS-TV, Inc.; RadiOhio, Inc.; Video Indiana, Inc.
Foundation type: Company-sponsored foundation.
Financial data (yr. ended 12/31/13): Assets, $19,000,713 (M); gifts received, $2,210,177; expenditures, $1,987,720; qualifying distributions, $1,893,106; giving activities include $1,893,106 for 129 grants (high: $730,000; low: $50).
Purpose and activities: The foundation supports organizations involved with arts and culture, education, health, youth development, human services, community development, and religion.
Fields of interest: Arts; Elementary/secondary education; Higher education; Education; Hospitals (general); Health care; Goodwill Industries; Youth development; Children/youth, services; Human services; Business/industry; Community/economic development; United Ways and Federated Giving Programs; Religion.
Type of support: General/operating support; Continuing support; Annual campaigns; Building/renovation; Equipment; Scholarship funds; Matching/challenge support.
Limitations: Applications accepted. Giving primarily in Columbus, OH. No grants to individuals, or for research, demonstration projects, publications, or conferences.
Publications: Application guidelines; Program policy statement.
Application information: Application form required.
Initial approach: Letter
Copies of proposal: 1
Deadline(s): None
Board meeting date(s): Mar., June, Sept., and Dec.
Officers and Trustees:* John F. Wolfe,* Chair.; Michael J. Fiorile,* Pres.; Poe A. Timmons,* V.P. and Treas.; Joseph Y. Gallo,* V.P.; Nancy Wolfe Lane,* V.P.; Sara Wolfe Perrini,* V.P.; Katherine I Wolfe,* V.P.; Rita J. Wolfe,* V.P.; Sherry L. Lewis, Secy.
EIN: 237303111
Selected grants: The following grants are a representative sample of this grantmaker's funding activity:
$600,000 to Nationwide Childrens Hospital, Columbus, OH, 2010.
$100,000 to Columbus College of Art and Design, Columbus, OH, 2010.
$100,000 to Mid-Ohio Foodbank, Grove City, OH, 2010.
$100,000 to Mid-Ohio Foodbank, Grove City, OH, 2011.
$50,000 to COSI Columbus, Columbus, OH, 2011.
$30,000 to Friends of Green Lawn Cemetery, Columbus, OH, 2010.
$25,000 to Columbus Foundation, Columbus, OH, 2011.
$25,000 to COSI Columbus, Columbus, OH, 2010.
$25,000 to Franklin Park Conservatory, Columbus, OH, 2011.
$25,000 to Wexner Center Foundation, Columbus, OH, 2011.
$24,200 to Ohio State University, Columbus, OH, 2011.
$20,286 to Ohio State University, Columbus, OH, 2011.
$20,000 to Columbus State Community College, Columbus, OH, 2011.
$15,000 to Goodwill Industries of Central Ohio, Columbus, OH, 2010.
$10,000 to Just Think, Columbus, OH, 2011.
$4,000 to Ohio Northern University, Ada, OH, 2011.
$3,750 to Columbus Academy, Gahanna, OH, 2010.

7720
Women's Project Foundation ✧
c/o KeyBank N.A.
4900 Tiedman Rd., OH-01-49-0150
Brooklyn, OH 44144-2302
Application address: c/o KeyBank N.A., Attn.: Michael Simmons, 127 Public Sq., 17th Fl., Cleveland, OH 44114-1221; tel.: (216) 689-2834

Established in 1986 in OH.
Donor: Louise Gund.
Foundation type: Independent foundation.
Financial data (yr. ended 11/30/13): Assets, $33,439,714 (M); expenditures, $7,408,576; qualifying distributions, $7,249,636; giving activities include $7,218,845 for 2 grants (high: $7,208,845; low: $10,000).
Purpose and activities: Giving primarily to: 1) enhance the role of women artists, including, but not limited to: writers, painters, sculptors, filmmakers, photographers and dancers, 2) encourage the use of art as a tool to educate the public regarding social problems and accomplishments, 3) promote equal rights and opportunities for women, 4) study and deal with the problems of violence in the family, child abuse, and adult survivors of child abuse, and 5) educate the public about issues affecting the social welfare of all people.
Fields of interest: Arts; Crime/violence prevention, child abuse; Women, centers/services; Foundations (private independent); Women.
Type of support: Program development; Research.
Limitations: Applications accepted. Giving primarily in CA, Washington, DC, NY and OH. No grants to individuals.
Application information: Application form not required.
Initial approach: Proposal
Deadline(s): None
Trustee: KeyBank N.A.
EIN: 133417304
Selected grants: The following grants are a representative sample of this grantmaker's funding activity:
$150,000 to Ms. Foundation for Women, Brooklyn, NY, 2011.
$130,000 to Women's Foundation of California, San Francisco, CA, 2011.
$100,000 to Planned Parenthood of Northeast Ohio, Akron, OH, 2011.
$100,000 to Preterm Cleveland, Cleveland, OH, 2011.
$25,000 to Womens Media Center, New York, NY, 2011.
$20,000 to Mothers Against Drunk Driving, Cleveland, OH, 2011.

7721
Woodruff Foundation ✧ ☆
1422 Euclid Ave., Ste. 966
Cleveland, OH 44115-2001 (216) 566-1853
Contact: Allison Rand, Consultant
FAX: (216) 621-8198;
E-mail: arand@fmscleveland.com; Main URL: http://www.fmscleveland.com/woodruff
Grants List: http://www.fmscleveland.com/woodruff/grants.cfm

Established in 1986 in OH; converted with proceeds from the sale of Woodruff Hospital.
Foundation type: Independent foundation.
Financial data (yr. ended 12/31/13): Assets, $11,934,797 (M); expenditures, $577,820; qualifying distributions, $708,141; giving activities include $432,450 for 25 grants (high: $68,000; low: $1,000).
Purpose and activities: Giving primarily to support the development and delivery of mental health services in Cuyahoga County, OH. Specifically, the foundation seeks to fund projects that will foster and enhance: the treatment of persons affected by mental disorders and chemical dependency; educational programs related to mental health, the coordination of mental health resources in the community; research into the causes, nature and recurrence of mental illness. High priority areas of interest include encouraging the implementation of innovative prevention and treatment programs and strengthening the effectiveness of existing service delivery systems.
Fields of interest: Substance abuse, services; Mental health/crisis services; Alcoholism.
Type of support: Emergency funds; Program development; Seed money; Research.
Limitations: Applications accepted. Giving limited to Cuyahoga County, OH. No grants for scholarships or fellowships, operating expenses, endowments, or annual fundraising campaigns.
Publications: Application guidelines; Financial statement; Grants list.
Application information: Online applications are available 1 month prior to deadlines. See foundation web site for necessary application details. Mass mailings are not accepted. Application form required.
Initial approach: Use online application process
Deadline(s): Jan. 1, May 1, and Sept. 1
Board meeting date(s): Feb., June, and Oct.
Officers: Ann Reischman, Pres.; Richard A. Paulson, V.P.; Valerie Bradley Hicks, Secy.-Treas.
Trustees: Mark Bonhard; Frank Fecser; Franklin J. Hickman; Valerie Raines; Robert J. Ronis.
EIN: 237425631
Selected grants: The following grants are a representative sample of this grantmaker's funding activity:
$25,000 to Beech Brook, Cleveland, OH, 2011. For the Assertive Community Treatment team to help young people with severe mental illness transition to independent adulthood.
$20,000 to Salvation Army of Greater Cleveland, Cleveland, OH, 2011. For detoxification and intensive outpatient drug abuse treatment.
$19,399 to MetroHealth Foundation, Cleveland, OH, 2011. For integration of depression screening and treatment at the MetroHealth Broadway Health Center.
$10,000 to Achievement Centers for Children, Highland Hills, OH, 2011. For the early childhood mental health program.

7722
The Wuliger Foundation, Inc. ✧
20 Basswood Ln.
Moreland Hills, OH 44022-1377 (216) 999-8922
Contact: Timothy F. Wuliger, Secy.-Treas.

Incorporated in 1956 in OH.
Donors: Ernest M. Wuliger†; Patricia Wuliger Charitable Lead Unitrust.
Foundation type: Independent foundation.
Financial data (yr. ended 12/31/13): Assets, $19,988,474 (M); gifts received, $132,026; expenditures, $1,033,966; qualifying distributions, $926,534; giving activities include $921,250 for 41 grants (high: $540,000; low: $1,000).
Purpose and activities: Giving for Jewish community organizations; support also for education, health care, and social services for disadvantaged persons.
Fields of interest: Arts; Education; Health organizations, association; Human services; Children/youth, services; United Ways and Federated Giving Programs; Jewish federated giving programs; Jewish agencies & synagogues; Economically disadvantaged.
Type of support: General/operating support; Annual campaigns; Capital campaigns; Building/renovation; Emergency funds.
Limitations: Giving primarily in OH, with some emphasis on Cleveland. No grants to individuals.
Application information: Application form not required.
Initial approach: Letter of request (no more than 2 pages)
Copies of proposal: 1
Deadline(s): None
Board meeting date(s): As necessary
Final notification: Within 2 months if possible
Officers and Directors:* E. Jeffrey Wuliger,* Pres.; Gregory Wuliger,* V.P.; Timothy F. Wuliger,* Secy.-Treas.
Number of staff: 1 part-time support.
EIN: 346527281
Selected grants: The following grants are a representative sample of this grantmaker's funding activity:
$8,500 to United Way of Greater Cleveland, Cleveland, OH, 2012. For annual support for operations.
$5,000 to Muscular Dystrophy Association, San Diego, CA, 2012. For Augie's Quest — Annual Support for Operations.

7723
The Youngstown Foundation ✧
City Centre One Bldg., 1st Fl.
P.O. Box 1162
Youngstown, OH 44501-1162 (330) 744-0320
Contact: Janice E. Strasfeld, Exec. Dir.
FAX: (330) 744-0344;
E-mail: info@youngstownfoundation.org; Additional e-mail: jan@youngstownfoundation.org; Main URL: http://www.youngstownfoundation.org
Facebook: https://www.facebook.com/TheYoungstownFoundation

Established in 1918 in OH by bank resolution.
Foundation type: Community foundation.
Financial data (yr. ended 12/31/13): Assets, $102,818,799 (M); gifts received, $2,761,214; expenditures, $4,253,908; giving activities include $3,576,064 for 74+ grants (high: $707,665).
Purpose and activities: The foundation seeks to support local charitable and educational agencies for the betterment of the community; grants for capital purposes, with emphasis on aid to crippled children, community funds, youth agencies, music and cultural programs, and hospitals.
Fields of interest: Visual arts; Museums; Performing arts; Performing arts, music; Historic preservation/historical societies; Arts; Education, association; Child development, education; Education; Environment; Health care; Alcoholism; Recreation; Youth development, services; Children/youth, services; Child development, services; Family services; Residential/custodial care, hospices; Aging, centers/services; Women, centers/services; Human services; Urban/community development; Community/economic development; Leadership development; Children/youth; Children; Youth; Adults; Aging; Disabilities, people with; Physically disabled; Mentally disabled; Girls; Military/veterans; Single parents; Crime/abuse victims; Economically disadvantaged.
Type of support: General/operating support; Management development/capacity building; Capital campaigns; Building/renovation; Equipment; Emergency funds; Program development.
Limitations: Applications accepted. Giving limited to Youngstown, OH and vicinity. No support for religious groups for religious purposes. No grants to individuals (except for scholarships), or for endowment funds, seed money, deficit financing, land acquisition, demonstration projects, publications, fellowships, travel, tours or trips, underwriting of conferences, debt reduction, projects normally the responsibility of government, sabbatical leaves, scholarly research organizations not tax exempt, or matching gifts.
Publications: Application guidelines; Annual report; Financial statement; Grants list; Informational brochure.
Application information: Visit foundation web site for application guidelines. Application form not required.
Initial approach: Proposal
Copies of proposal: 3
Deadline(s): Jan. 31, Apr. 25, July 25, and Oct. 15
Board meeting date(s): Mar., June, Sept., and Dec.
Final notification: 6 weeks
Officers and Distribution Committee:* George Berlin,* Chair.; Jude Nohra,* Vice-Chair.; Janice E. Strasfeld, Exec. Dir.; Eugenia Atkinson; Dr. Randy J. Dunn; John MacIntosh; Jeffrey Simon.
Number of staff: 2 part-time professional; 1 part-time support.
EIN: 346515788
Selected grants: The following grants are a representative sample of this grantmaker's funding activity:
$100,000 to United Way of Youngstown and the Mahoning Valley, Youngstown, OH, 2011. For program support.
$50,000 to Compass Family Services, San Francisco, CA, 2011. To merge two organizations.
$30,000 to Mahoning Valley Historical Society, Youngstown, OH, 2011. For building renovations.
$25,000 to Chamber of Commerce, Youngstown-Warren Regional, Youngstown, OH, 2011. For community development.
$25,000 to WMHP, 2011. For new breast cancer center.
$25,000 to YMCA of Youngstown, Youngstown, OH, 2011. For building repairs.
$25,000 to Youngstown Business Incubator, Youngstown, OH, 2011. For building renovations.
$20,000 to Butler Institute of American Art, Youngstown, OH, 2011. For air-conditioning system.
$15,000 to Second Harvest Food Bank of the Mahoning Valley, Youngstown, OH, 2011. To purchase equipment.

7724
Zembrodt Family Foundation, Inc. ✧
3023 E. Kemper Rd., Bldg. 9
Cincinnati, OH 45241-1509

Established in 1986 in OH and KY.
Donors: Cyril C. Zembrodt; Joseph A. Zembrodt; John A. Zembrodt; Gerald L. Zembrodt.
Foundation type: Independent foundation.
Financial data (yr. ended 12/31/13): Assets, $12,281,248 (M); gifts received, $9,489,278; expenditures, $525,448; qualifying distributions, $498,624; giving activities include $498,400 for 39 grants (high: $155,000; low: $1,000).
Purpose and activities: Giving primarily for human services, education, and Roman Catholic organizations.
Fields of interest: Secondary school/education; Human services; Catholic agencies & churches.
Type of support: General/operating support; Building/renovation; Scholarship funds.
Limitations: Applications not accepted. Giving primarily in KY. No grants to individuals.
Application information: Unsolicited requests for funds not accepted.
Officers and Directors:* Joseph A. Zembrodt,* Pres.; John A. Zembrodt,* Secy.; Gerald L. Zembrodt,* Treas.
EIN: 611108902
Selected grants: The following grants are a representative sample of this grantmaker's funding activity:
$1,000 to Dominican Sisters of Mary, Mother of the Eucharist, Ann Arbor, MI, 2011. For general fund.

OKLAHOMA

7725
The Judith and Jean Pape Adams Charitable Foundation ✧
7030 S. Yale Ave., Ste. 600
Tulsa, OK 74136-5749 (830) 997-7347
Contact: Marcia Manhart, Exec. Dir.
FAX: (830) 997-9888;
E-mail: mmanhart@jjpafoundation.com; Main URL: http://www.jjpafoundation.com/
ALS Research Grants: http://www.adamsfoundation.org/annual-report/recently-awarded-als-grants/
Tulsa Grants: http://www.adamsfoundation.org/annual-report/recently-awarded-tulsa-grants/

Established in 2003 in OK.
Donor: Jean Pape Adams Trust.
Foundation type: Independent foundation.
Financial data (yr. ended 12/31/13): Assets, $16,807,283 (M); expenditures, $1,121,318; qualifying distributions, $819,811; giving activities include $772,723 for 33 grants (high: $200,000; low: $1,000).
Purpose and activities: One-third of giving is reserved for national ALS research. Two-thirds of giving is reserved for Tulsa-area grants for arts/culture, social services, education and health.
Fields of interest: Arts; Education; Environment; Health organizations; ALS research; Human services.
Type of support: General/operating support; Annual campaigns; Capital campaigns; Building/renovation; Program development; Research; Matching/challenge support.
Limitations: Applications accepted. Giving limited to the Tulsa, OK area, except for ALS grants, which are made on a national basis. No support for political organizations. No grants to individuals.
Publications: Application guidelines; Annual report.
Application information: Application guidelines available on foundation web site. Application form not required.
Initial approach: Use online application process on foundation web site
Copies of proposal: 1
Deadline(s): See foundation web site for current deadline
Board meeting date(s): May and Nov. or as needed
Final notification: Mid-Dec.
Officer and Trustees:* Marcia Y. Manhart,* Exec. Dir.; Katherine G. Coyle; INTRUST Bank, N.A.
Number of staff: 1 full-time professional; 1 part-time support.
EIN: 200189630

7726
Ellen G. Adelson Family Foundation ✧
15 E. 5th St., Ste. 3200
Tulsa, OK 74103-4313

Established in 2007 in OK.
Donor: Ellen G. Adelson.
Foundation type: Independent foundation.
Financial data (yr. ended 12/31/13): Assets, $11,582,038 (M); gifts received, $26,875; expenditures, $1,291,649; qualifying distributions, $1,214,285; giving activities include $1,214,285 for 2 grants (high: $714,285; low: $500,000).
Fields of interest: Higher education, university.
Limitations: Applications not accepted. Giving primarily in Tulsa, OK, and Ithaca, NY. No grants to individuals.
Application information: Unsolicited requests for funds not accepted.
Trustee: Ellen G. Adelson.
EIN: 260638885
Selected grants: The following grants are a representative sample of this grantmaker's funding activity:
$914,286 to University of Tulsa, Tulsa, OK, 2011.
$5,000 to Cornell University, Ithaca, NY, 2011.

7727
Allen Family Charitable Foundation ✧
7301 N. Broadway Extension, Ste. 225
Oklahoma City, OK 73116 (580) 233-4455
Contact: Mark Allen, V.P.

Established in 2007 in OK.
Donors: Paul Allen; Amy Gray; Beth Doty; Paul Allen; Mark Allen.
Foundation type: Independent foundation.
Financial data (yr. ended 06/30/13): Assets, $11,076,454 (M); gifts received, $1,597,715; expenditures, $931,201; qualifying distributions, $926,185; giving activities include $926,185 for 56 grants (high: $205,000; low: $25).
Fields of interest: Historic preservation/historical societies; Higher education, university; Foundations (public); Public affairs.
Limitations: Applications accepted. Giving primarily in OK.
Application information: Application form not required.
Initial approach: Proposal
Deadline(s): None
Officers: Joan Allen, Pres.; Mark Allen, V.P.; John Wynne, Secy.; Greg Allen, Treas.
Director: Paul Allen.
EIN: 205490143
Selected grants: The following grants are a representative sample of this grantmaker's funding activity:
$100,000 to Oklahoma Council of Public Affairs, Oklahoma City, OK, 2011.
$100,000 to Peppers Ranch, Edmond, OK, 2011.
$20,200 to Heritage Hall, Oklahoma City, OK, 2011.
$12,500 to Oklahoma City, City of, Oklahoma City, OK, 2011.
$12,480 to Oklahoma State University Foundation, Stillwater, OK, 2011.

7728
American Fidelity Foundation ✧
(formerly American Fidelity Corporation Founders Fund, Inc.)
2000 N. Classen., Ste. 7N
Oklahoma City, OK 73106-6092
E-mail: JoElla.Ramsey@af-group.com; Main URL: http://www.americanfidelityfoundation.org
Grants List: http://www.americanfidelityfoundation.org/projects/funded_projects.HTM

Established in 1984 in OK.
Donor: American Fidelity Assurance Co.
Foundation type: Company-sponsored foundation.
Financial data (yr. ended 12/31/13): Assets, $19,254,702 (M); gifts received, $2,000,000; expenditures, $820,580; qualifying distributions, $761,526; giving activities include $761,526 for 199 grants (high: $200,000; low: $25).
Purpose and activities: The foundation supports organizations involved with arts and culture, education, heath, human services, community economic development, and civic affairs.
Fields of interest: Museums; Arts; Education, early childhood education; Higher education; Education; Health care; Children/youth, services; Family services; Human services; Community/economic development; United Ways and Federated Giving Programs; Public affairs.
Type of support: General/operating support; Annual campaigns; Program development; Seed money; Research; Employee volunteer services; Sponsorships; Program evaluation; Employee matching gifts.
Limitations: Applications accepted. Giving primarily in areas of company operations in OK. No support for private clubs, religious, fraternal, or sectarian organizations, or for organizations that seek to influence or initiate legislation, political candidates, political parties, or political campaigns. No grants to individuals, or for capital campaigns, endowments (except to fund scholarships or for other specific education projects), or for travel expenses.
Publications: Application guidelines; Grants list; Quarterly report.
Application information: Grants range from $500 to $5,000. A formal application may be requested at a later date. Support is limited to one contribution per organization during any given year. Application form not required.
Initial approach: E-mail or mail letter of interest
Copies of proposal: 1
Deadline(s): None
Board meeting date(s): Quarterly
Final notification: 2 weeks
Officers and Directors:* William M. Cameron,* Chair.; Tom J. McDaniel,* Pres.; Robert D. Brearton,* Exec. V.P. and Treas.; Stephen P. Garrett,* Secy.; Jo Carol Cameron; David R. Carpenter; William E. Durrett.
EIN: 731236059
Selected grants: The following grants are a representative sample of this grantmaker's funding activity:
$5,500 to YMCA of Greater Oklahoma City, Oklahoma City, OK, 2012. For Urban/Civic.
$3,100 to YWCA of Tulsa, Tulsa, OK, 2012. For health/welfare.
$1,000 to Oklahomans for the Arts, Oklahoma City, OK, 2012. For culture/arts.

7729
Asbjornson Foundation ✧ ☆
2202 S. Troost Ave.
Tulsa, OK 74114-1320 (918) 583-2266
Contact: Norman H. Asbjornson, Tr.

Established in 1999 in OK.
Donor: Norman H. Asbjornson.
Foundation type: Independent foundation.
Financial data (yr. ended 12/31/13): Assets, $7,883,134 (M); gifts received, $170,000; expenditures, $634,398; qualifying distributions, $632,728; giving activities include $628,415 for 4 grants (high: $567,415; low: $1,000).
Fields of interest: Education, services; Community/economic development.

Type of support: General/operating support.
Limitations: Applications accepted. Giving primarily in Winifred, MT. No grants to individuals.
Application information: Application form not required.
Initial approach: Proposal
Deadline(s): None
Trustee: Norman H. Asbjornson.
EIN: 731582633
Selected grants: The following grants are a representative sample of this grantmaker's funding activity:
$50,000 to Rotary Club of Tulsa, Tulsa, OK, 2012. For operating/building funds.

7730
Barthelmes Foundation, Inc. ✧
1717 S. Cheyenne Ave.
Tulsa, OK 74119-4611 (918) 592-7996
FAX: (918) 582-7830;
E-mail: info@thebarthelmesfoundation.org; Main URL: http://www.thebarthelmesfoundation.org

Established in OK.
Foundation type: Independent foundation.
Financial data (yr. ended 12/31/13): Assets, $8,955,125 (M); expenditures, $878,393; qualifying distributions, $660,307; giving activities include $460,486 for 5 grants (high: $448,285; low: $145).
Fields of interest: Performing arts, music; Arts; Education.
Limitations: Applications accepted. Giving primarily in Tulsa, OK.
Application information: Application form not required.
Initial approach: Proposal
Deadline(s): None
Officer: Joseph L. Hull III, Pres.
Directors: Dr. Anthony Brown; Jim Hawkins.
EIN: 201326155
Selected grants: The following grants are a representative sample of this grantmaker's funding activity:
$411,689 to Barthelmes Conservatory, Tulsa, OK, 2011.
$1,600 to Oklahoma Aquarium Foundation, Jenks, OK, 2011.

7731
The Bartlesville Community Foundation ✧
208 E. 4th St.
Bartlesville, OK 74003 (918) 337-2287
Contact: Shawn Crawford Ph.D., Exec. Dir.
FAX: (918) 337-2298;
E-mail: shawn.crawford@bartlesvillecf.org;
Additional e-mail: aswearingin@bartlesvillecf.org;
Main URL: http://www.bartlesvillecf.org
Facebook: https://www.facebook.com/pages/Bartlesville-Community-Foundation/500072663414269
Twitter: https://twitter.com/bartlesvillecf/
YouTube: http://www.youtube.com/user/bartlesvillecf

Established in 1999 in OK.
Foundation type: Community foundation.
Financial data (yr. ended 06/30/13): Assets, $3,773,582 (M); gifts received, $814,429; expenditures, $711,437; giving activities include $586,239 for 4+ grants (high: $37,100).
Purpose and activities: The Bartlesville Community foundation helps donors create funds for the continued success of Bartlesville non-profits and their projects. The foundation also makes grants in areas determined by the board of directors from its unrestricted funds.
Fields of interest: Performing arts; Arts; Education; Environment; Health care; Mental health/crisis services; Food services; Housing/shelter; Recreation; Youth development; Human services; Community/economic development.
Type of support: Program development; Building/renovation; Equipment; Continuing support; General/operating support.
Limitations: Applications accepted. Giving primarily in Bartlesville, OK. No support for sectarian purposes. No grants to individuals, or for annual fundraising, organizational endowment funds, or deficit financing.
Application information: Visit foundation web site for application form and guidelines. Application form required.
Initial approach: Query Letter
Copies of proposal: 7
Deadline(s): February and September (consult website for dates), Mar. 13 for Scholarships.
Final notification: 1 month
Officers and Directors:* Debbie Mueggenborg,* Chair.; Dan Gilliam,* Vice-Chair.; Beth Heaton,* Secy.; Spencer King,* Treas.; Shawn Crawford, Exec. Dir.; Jim Bohnsack; Charlie Bowerman; Mark Headley; Jason Hopkins; David King; Mike May; Bob Pomeroy; Kevin Potter; Earl Sears; Donna Skelly; Clent Stewart; Kent Stroman; Guy Sutherland.
EIN: 731575838

7732
Edward & Helen Bartlett Foundation ✧
(formerly Edward E. Bartlett & Helen Turner Bartlett Foundation)
c/o The Trust Company of Oklahoma
P.O. Box 3627
Tulsa, OK 74101-3627 (918) 744-0553

Established in 1961 in OK.
Donor: Edward E. Bartlett†.
Foundation type: Independent foundation.
Financial data (yr. ended 12/31/13): Assets, $30,015,915 (M); expenditures, $1,507,470; qualifying distributions, $1,387,181; giving activities include $1,149,707 for 22 grants (high: $243,350; low: $3,250), and $191,000 for grants to individuals.
Purpose and activities: Giving primarily for education, particularly public schools, community programs and services, healthcare, and children, youth and social services; giving also for student scholarships limited to Oklahoma State University, University of Oklahoma, Oklahoma State University Institute of Technology, and the University of Tulsa, Oklahoma.
Fields of interest: Higher education; Education; Health organizations, association; Human services; Children/youth, services.
Type of support: Scholarships—to individuals.
Limitations: Applications accepted. Giving limited to OK. No grants to individuals directly.
Application information: Scholarship applicants should contact the financial aid office at Oklahoma State University, University of Oklahoma, Oklahoma State University Institute of Technology and the University of Tulsa. Application form not required.
Initial approach: Letter
Deadline(s): None
Trustees: Harrison I. Bartlett III; Harry C. Freeman; The Trust Company of Oklahoma.
EIN: 736092250
Selected grants: The following grants are a representative sample of this grantmaker's funding activity:
$534,000 to Sapulpa Public School Foundation, Sapulpa, OK, 2010. For program services.
$235,000 to Boy Scouts of America, Tulsa, OK, 2011. For program services.
$105,000 to Caring Community Friends, Sapulpa, OK, 2011. For program services.
$100,000 to Autism Center of Tulsa, Tulsa, OK, 2011. For program services.
$65,000 to American Red Cross, Tulsa, OK, 2011. For program services.
$48,000 to Oklahoma State University Foundation, Stillwater, OK, 2011. For scholarship.
$38,500 to University of Oklahoma, Norman, OK, 2011. For scholarship.
$38,500 to University of Tulsa, Tulsa, OK, 2011. For scholarship.
$31,000 to Creek County Literacy Program, Sapulpa, OK, 2011. For program services.
$5,000 to Youth Services of Creek County, Sapulpa, OK, 2011. For program services.

7733
Grace & Franklin Bernsen Foundation ✧
15 W. 6th St., Ste. 1308
Tulsa, OK 74119-5407 (918) 584-4711
Contact: Trustees
FAX: (918) 584-4713; E-mail: info@bernsen.org;
E-mail for grant application correspondence: gfbernsen@aol.com; Main URL: http://www.bernsen.org
Grants List: http://www.bernsen.org/pdfs/FYE_Report_2012.pdf

Established 1968.
Donors: Grace Bernsen†; Franklin Bernsen†.
Foundation type: Independent foundation.
Financial data (yr. ended 09/30/13): Assets, $30,184,011 (M); expenditures, $2,005,367; qualifying distributions, $1,888,397; giving activities include $1,616,734 for 66 grants (high: $250,000; low: $2,500).
Purpose and activities: Giving primarily for the arts, education, health, children and youth services, and to Protestant churches. Elementary or secondary education institutions will be considered if they involve programs for at-risk, handicapped or learning-disabled children, or if they are innovative and apply to all schools in the system.
Fields of interest: Arts; Higher education; Zoos/zoological societies; Mental health/crisis services; Health organizations, association; Human services; Children/youth, services; Protestant agencies & churches.
Type of support: Capital campaigns; Building/renovation; Equipment; Emergency funds; Program development; Conferences/seminars; Matching/challenge support.
Limitations: Applications accepted. Giving primarily within the metropolitan area of Tulsa, OK. No support for continuing or additional support for the same programs (although a single grant may cover a period of several years). No grants to individuals, or for debt reduction.

Publications: Application guidelines; Annual report; Grants list; Informational brochure (including application guidelines).
Application information: Application guidelines available on foundation web site. Applicants should not use paragraph subtitles in their summary, or it will be returned. Proposals submitted in plastic covers, binders or sheet protectors will not be considered. Do not include DVDs, CDs, bound books or bulky leaflets, or letters of support. OK tax documents, certificate of incorporation or Bylaws are also not needed with application. Application form not required.
Initial approach: Letter (no more than 3 pages with type no smaller than 10.5 point); a copy of the letter must also be e-mailed in Word format immediately to application correspondence address and received in the foundation's office before the grant request is received. (Only letter should be e-mailed, not the full grant request)
Copies of proposal: 1
Deadline(s): No later than 12 o'clock noon on the 1st day of the month prior to that month's board meeting
Board meeting date(s): Monthly
Final notification: Generally within 1-week following board meeting
Officers and Trustees:* W. Bland Williamson,* Secy.; Barbara H. Pray; Donald E. Pray; John D. Strong, Jr.
Number of staff: 1 full-time professional.
EIN: 237009414

7734
The Bezalel Foundation ✧
110 W. 7th St., Ste. 2000
Tulsa, OK 74119-1076
Contact: Alana Hughes

Established in 2003 in OK.
Donors: Stacy H. Schusterman; Stacy Schusterman Revocable Trust; Stacy Family Trust; Charles and Lynn Schusterman Family Foundation.
Foundation type: Independent foundation.
Financial data (yr. ended 12/31/13): Assets, $21,342,226 (M); gifts received, $35,482; expenditures, $2,227,047; qualifying distributions, $2,190,400; giving activities include $2,190,400 for 24 grants (high: $1,000,000; low: $1,000).
Purpose and activities: Giving primarily for higher education, and to children's hospitals.
Fields of interest: Higher education; Education; Hospitals (specialty); Jewish agencies & synagogues.
Limitations: Applications accepted. Giving primarily in NY, OK and TX.
Application information: Application form not required.
Initial approach: Letter
Deadline(s): None
Officers: Stacy H. Schusterman, Pres. and Treas.; Steven Dow, V.P. and Secy.
EIN: 050578856

7735
The Mervin Bovaird Foundation ✧
401 S. Boston Ave., Ste. 2120
Tulsa, OK 74103-4070 (918) 592-3300
Contact: R. Casey Cooper, Pres.

Established in 1955.
Donor: Mabel W. Bovaird†.
Foundation type: Independent foundation.
Financial data (yr. ended 12/31/13): Assets, $45,343,951 (M); expenditures, $2,627,329; qualifying distributions, $2,033,732; giving activities include $1,640,350 for 88 grants (high: $150,000; low: $900), and $279,000 for 93 grants to individuals (high: $3,000; low: $3,000).
Purpose and activities: Support for social services, health, and education; also funds a scholarship program for Tulsa County High School graduating seniors and graduates of Tulsa Community College at the University of Tulsa (not for graduate or professional study). The recipients of these scholarships are selected by the schools, and not by the trustees of the foundation. The scholarship program is for undergraduate study only. Each scholarship is limited to $6,000 per academic year. Any high school student interested in a foundation scholarship should contact his or her high school principal. A TCC student should contact the student financial aid office of TCC. The foundation has nothing to do with the selection of the scholarship recipients.
Fields of interest: Arts; Education; Environment; Health care; Health organizations, association; Human services; Community/economic development.
Type of support: General/operating support; Continuing support; Annual campaigns; Capital campaigns; Building/renovation; Equipment; Endowments; Program development; Conferences/seminars; Curriculum development; Scholarship funds; Research; Matching/challenge support.
Limitations: Giving limited to the Tulsa, OK, area. No loans.
Publications: Program policy statement.
Application information: Scholarship recipients are chosen by Tulsa public high schools and Tulsa Community College based on need and ability to attend Tulsa University. Application form not required.
Initial approach: Brief letter
Copies of proposal: 1
Deadline(s): Between May 1 and Aug. 1 (or date established by schools selecting a recipient for scholarships); Nov. 15 for grants
Board meeting date(s): Quarterly
Final notification: Dec. 15-20
Officers: R. Casey Cooper,* Pres.; P. David Newsome, Jr., V.P., Fin.; Lance Stockwell, V.P., Fin.; Janice L. Pierce, Secy.
Trustee: Christopher K. Woosley.
Number of staff: 2 part-time professional; 1 part-time support.
EIN: 736102163
Selected grants: The following grants are a representative sample of this grantmaker's funding activity:
$10,000 to Boy Scouts of America, Indian Nations Council, Tulsa, OK, 2012. For Payment of Grants and Scholarships, all to unrelated recipients. Payment of tuition to The University of Tulsa (600 South College, Tulsa, Oklahoma) for graduates from Tulsa public high schools and Tulsa Community College.
$10,000 to Youth Services of Tulsa, Tulsa, OK, 2012. For Payment of Grants and Scholarships, all to unrelated recipients. Payment of tuition to The University of Tulsa (600 South College, Tulsa, Oklahoma) for graduates from Tulsa public high schools and Tulsa Community College.
$4,000 to University of Tulsa, Athletic Department , general, Tulsa, OK, 2012. For Payment of Grants and Scholarships, all to unrelated recipients. Payment of tuition to The University of Tulsa (600 South College, Tulsa, Oklahoma) for graduates from Tulsa public high schools and Tulsa Community College.
$3,000 to Volunteer Central of Greater Tulsa, Tulsa, OK, 2012. For Payment of Grants and Scholarships, all to unrelated recipients. Payment of tuition to The University of Tulsa (600 South College, Tulsa, Oklahoma) for graduates from Tulsa public high schools and Tulsa Community College Payment of Grants and Scholarships.

7736
Charles and Cassandra Bowen Charitable Foundation ✧ ☆
7300 N. Country Club Dr.
Oklahoma City, OK 73116-4316

Established in 2008 in OK.
Donors: Cassandra Bowen; Charles Bowen.
Foundation type: Independent foundation.
Financial data (yr. ended 09/30/13): Assets, $7,663,749 (M); gifts received, $2,255,940; expenditures, $774,957; qualifying distributions, $600,480; giving activities include $600,480 for 51 grants (high: $264,251; low: $100).
Fields of interest: Health care; Human services.
Limitations: Applications not accepted. Giving primarily in OK.
Application information: Unsolicited requests for funds not accepted.
Officers: Cassandra C. Bowen, Pres. and Treas.; Charles K. Bowen, V.P. and Secy.
EIN: 263871656

7737
Brown Foundation ✧ ☆
c/o William C. Brown
1707 Elmhurst Ave.
Oklahoma City, OK 73120-1011

Established in 1986 in OK.
Donors: William C. Brown; Carolyn M. Brown.
Foundation type: Independent foundation.
Financial data (yr. ended 12/31/13): Assets, $11,874,816 (M); expenditures, $553,581; qualifying distributions, $540,687; giving activities include $540,000 for 9 grants (high: $120,000; low: $20,000).
Fields of interest: Higher education; Human services; United Ways and Federated Giving Programs; Catholic agencies & churches.
Type of support: General/operating support.
Limitations: Applications not accepted. Giving primarily in CO, NY, OK, and PA. No grants to individuals.
Application information: Contributes only to pre-selected organizations.
Trustee: William C. Brown.
EIN: 736230335
Selected grants: The following grants are a representative sample of this grantmaker's funding activity:
$100,000 to Papal Foundation, Bala Cynwyd, PA, 2011.

7738
Browning-Kimball Foundation ✧
c/o Foundation Management, Inc.
2932 N.W. 122nd St., Ste. D
Oklahoma City, OK 73120-1955 (405) 755-5571
Contact: Kari Koster, Representative

Established in 1981 in UT.
Donors: Barbara K. Browning; Barbara Browning Cowan; Matt S. Browning.
Foundation type: Independent foundation.
Financial data (yr. ended 12/31/12): Assets, $17,363,704 (M); expenditures, $882,824; qualifying distributions, $733,187; giving activities include $725,778 for 34 grants (high: $140,000; low: $2,500).
Purpose and activities: Giving primarily for health care including mental health associations, and for children, youth, and social services.
Fields of interest: Museums; Education; Mental health, association; Health organizations; Human services; Children/youth, services.
Limitations: Applications accepted. Giving primarily in MT. No grants to individuals.
Application information: Application form required.
Initial approach: Request application package
Officer: William B. Cowan, Pres.
Directors: Barbara Cowan; Lisa Cowan; William Cowan; William B. Cowan.
EIN: 942766079

7739
H. A. and Mary K. Chapman Charitable Trust ✧
c/o Chapman Foundations Management, LLC
6100 S. Yale Ave., Ste. 1816
Tulsa, OK 74136-1928 (918) 496-7882
Contact: J. Jerry Dickman, Tr.; Donne W. Pitman, Tr.; Andrea Doyle, Prog. Off.
FAX: (918) 496-7887;
E-mail: grants@chapmantrusts.com; E-mail for Letters of inquiry: grants@chapmantrusts.com; Contact for general inquiries regarding grant programs and procedures, Andie Doyle, Prog. Off., tel.: (719) 465-5977, ext. 3, e-mail: andie@chapmantrusts.com. Additional address: c/o Chapman Foundations Management, LLC, 121 S. Tejon St., Ste. 1105, Colorado Springs, CO 80903; fax: (719) 465-5979; e-mail for Jerry Dickman, Tr.: jerry@chapmantrusts.com; e-mail for Donne Pitman, Tr.: donne@chapmantrusts.com; Main URL: http://www.chapmantrusts.org

Trust established in 1976 in OK.
Donors: H.A. Chapman†; Mary K. Chapman†.
Foundation type: Independent foundation.
Financial data (yr. ended 12/31/13): Assets, $97,396,487 (M); gifts received, $5,669,034; expenditures, $5,034,342; qualifying distributions, $4,429,690; giving activities include $4,201,250 for 86 grants (high: $500,000; low: $1,000).
Purpose and activities: Grants largely for education, particularly higher education, health, social services, and cultural programs.
Fields of interest: Arts; Higher education; Education; Environment; Animals/wildlife; Health care; Health organizations, association; Human services.
Type of support: General/operating support; Annual campaigns; Capital campaigns; Building/renovation; Program development; Research; Program evaluation; Matching/challenge support.
Limitations: Applications accepted. Giving primarily in OK, AR, and TX for colleges and universities and in OK for elementary and secondary education and for health care. No support for political campaigns, religious programs of religious organizations, or purposes normally funded by taxation or governmental agencies. No grants to individuals, or for endowments, scholarships, deficit financing, debt retirement, projects for which the foundation would be the sole source of support, for travel, conferences, conventions, group meetings, seminars, or camp programs and other seasonal activities.
Publications: Application guidelines; IRS Form 990 or 990-PF printed copy available upon request.
Application information: Application guidelines available on foundation web site. Proposal form will be sent upon approval of letter of inquiry. Application form required.
Initial approach: E-mail letter of inquiry, no more than 3 pages and in .pdf format to Prog. Off.
Copies of proposal: 3
Deadline(s): None for Letters of Inquiry; 1st day of the month preceding quarterly meeting for invited proposal
Board meeting date(s): March, June, Sept. and Dec.
Trustees: J. Jerry Dickman; Donne W. Pitman.
Number of staff: None.
EIN: 736177739

7740
Mary K. Chapman Foundation ✧
6100 S. Yale Ave., Ste. 1816
Tulsa, OK 74136-1928 (918) 496-7882
Contact: Andrea Doyle, Prog. Off.
FAX: (918) 496-7887;
E-mail: grants@chapmantrusts.com; E-mail for Andrea Doyle: andie@chapmantrusts.com; Main URL: http://www.chapmantrusts.org

Established in 1996 in OK.
Donor: Mary K. Chapman†.
Foundation type: Independent foundation.
Financial data (yr. ended 12/31/13): Assets, $19,797,333 (M); expenditures, $9,198,536; qualifying distributions, $8,135,170; giving activities include $7,787,940 for 69 grants (high: $1,000,000; low: $1,000).
Purpose and activities: Giving for education, health care, and medical research.
Fields of interest: Education; Health care; Medical research.
Type of support: Annual campaigns; Capital campaigns; Building/renovation; Equipment; Land acquisition; Research; Matching/challenge support.
Limitations: Applications accepted. Giving primarily in Tulsa and northeastern OK. No support for No grants to political or religions organizations. No grants to individuals or for endowments, debt financing, travel, conferences, conventions, group meetings or seminars, or for project or program planning.
Publications: Application guidelines.
Application information: If approved, the applicant will be invited to submit a written grant proposal. See web site for additional information. Application form required.
Initial approach: E-mail a letter of inquiry no more than 3-pages to the program officer
Copies of proposal: 3
Deadline(s): None
Board meeting date(s): Quarterly and as needed
Trustees: J. Jerry Dickman; Donne W. Pitman.
EIN: 731499528
Selected grants: The following grants are a representative sample of this grantmaker's funding activity:
$1,000,000 to University of Texas M.D. Anderson Cancer Center, Houston, TX, 2013. To create Integrative Bioinformatics Program.
$800,000 to Salk Institute for Biological Studies, La Jolla, CA, 2013. For gene sequencer.
$500,000 to Atlas Preparatory School, Colorado Springs, CO, 2013. For high school expansion phase one.
$500,000 to Tulsa Zoo Management, Tulsa, OK, 2013. For African Plains: Rhino Exhibit.
$500,000 to University of Texas M.D. Anderson Cancer Center, Houston, TX, 2013. To create Integrative Bioinformatics Program.
$500,000 to YMCA of Greater Tulsa, Tulsa, OK, 2013. For YMCA Healthy Living Center.
$125,000 to Tulsa Boys Home, Sand Springs, OK, 2013. For Bridge to the Future Campaign.
$125,000 to University of Oklahoma Foundation, Norman, OK, 2013. For Stephenson Cancer Center Collaboration with MDA/OUCI.
$50,000 to Pikes Peak Library District Foundation, Colorado Springs, CO, 2013. For Tri-Building Project.
$20,000 to DaySpring Villa Women and Childrens Shelter, Sand Springs, OK, 2013. For window replacement.

7741
Fulton & Susie Collins Foundation ✧
1924 S. Utica Ave., Ste. 800
Tulsa, OK 74104-6516 (918) 748-9860
Contact: Suzanne M. Collins, Tr.

Established in 1987 in OK.
Donors: G. Fulton Collins III; Suzanne M. Collins.
Foundation type: Independent foundation.
Financial data (yr. ended 12/31/13): Assets, $20,151,631 (M); expenditures, $1,042,918; qualifying distributions, $1,001,715; giving activities include $1,001,715 for 30 grants (high: $900,000; low: $50).
Purpose and activities: Giving primarily for higher education and human services.
Fields of interest: Museums (art); Higher education; Education; Human services; United Ways and Federated Giving Programs; Catholic agencies & churches.
Type of support: General/operating support.
Limitations: Applications accepted. Giving primarily in Tulsa, OK. No grants to individuals.
Application information: Application form not required.
Initial approach: Proposal
Deadline(s): None
Trustees: Suzanne M. Collins; Catherine C. Mantzuranis; Suzanne C. Yonkers.
EIN: 731273053
Selected grants: The following grants are a representative sample of this grantmaker's funding activity:
$625,000 to University of Tulsa, Tulsa, OK, 2012. For Softball Building.
$90,000 to University of Tulsa, Tulsa, OK, 2012. For Endowment Collins College of Business.
$1,925 to University of Tulsa, Tulsa, OK, 2012. For McFarlin Fellows.

$500 to Central High School, Tulsa, OK, 2012. For Girls Softball Program.
$100 to University of Tulsa, Tulsa, OK, 2012. For Dean Bellovich Memorial Scholarship Fund.

7742
Communities Foundation of Oklahoma ✧
(formerly Oklahoma Communities Foundation, Inc.)
2932 N.W. 122nd St., Ste. D
Oklahoma City, OK 73120-1955 (405) 488-1450
Contact: Susan R. Graves, Exec. Dir.
FAX: (405) 755-0938; E-mail: sgraves@cfok.org; Additional tel.: (877) 689-7726; Main URL: http://www.cfok.org
Scholarship inquiry e-mail: lgarey@cfok.org

Established in 1992 in OK.
Foundation type: Community foundation.
Financial data (yr. ended 06/30/13): Assets, $81,226,418 (M); gifts received, $8,222,313; expenditures, $9,579,534; giving activities include $6,355,233 for 124+ grants (high: $443,348), and $1,773,252 for 542 grants to individuals.
Purpose and activities: The foundation supports Oklahoma communities by meeting the needs of charitable organizations and donors statewide.
Fields of interest: Historic preservation/historical societies; Arts; Education; Animal welfare; Health care; Recreation, community; Human services; Science, research; Women.
Type of support: General/operating support; Endowments; Seed money; Scholarship funds; Technical assistance; Consulting services; Matching/challenge support.
Limitations: Applications accepted. Giving primarily in OK. No grants to individuals (except for scholarships), or for endowments, capital campaigns, debt retirement, fundraising events, annual appeals and membership campaigns, or budget deficits.
Publications: Annual report; Financial statement; Grants list; Informational brochure.
Application information: Visit foundation website for application and guideline information. Application form required.
Deadline(s): Jan. 15
Board meeting date(s): Quarterly
Officers and Board Members:* Mary Marks Jenkins,* Chair.; Richard Ryerson,* Vice-Chair.; Frank Merrick, Pres.; Will Merrick, Exec. V.P.; Kari Blakley, V.P., Opers.; Sherrie Schroeder, V.P., Acctg.; Leslie Rainbolt-Forbes,* Secy.; Robert Merrick, C.F.O.; DJ Thompson, C.O.O.; Susan R. Graves, Exec. Dir.; Randy Macon, Exec. Dir.; Tom McCasland III, Treas.; Bill Burgess; Roberta Burrage; Tripp Hall; April Stobbe.
Board of Governors: Rudy Alvarado; Ed Apple; Steve Beebe; Ron Beer; Lou Christian; Julie Cohen; Jimmy Cooper; Kathie Coyle; Malinda Berry Fischer; Nancy Ford; Laurie Fuller; Mary Beth Glass; Ernest Godlove; Terry Graham; Lou Hall; Jean Harbison; Joe Anna Hibler; James Howard; Sandy Ingraham; Melinda Johnson; Hilary Kitz; Craig Knutson; Tom McCasland, Jr.; James Menzer; Melvin Moran; Anne Morgan; Marilyn Murrell; Susan Paddack; Ann Powell; H.E. Gene Rainbolt; Richard Ratcliffe; Larry Roberts; Jim Rodgers; Claudia San Pedro; Jeri Towler; Pam Treadwell; Arlen Williams.
Number of staff: 2 full-time professional; 2 part-time professional; 2 full-time support; 1 part-time support.
EIN: 731396320

Selected grants: The following grants are a representative sample of this grantmaker's funding activity:
$500,000 to Oklahoma Baptist University, School of Nursing, Shawnee, OK, 2012.
$500,000 to Southern Nazarene University, Bethany, OK, 2012.
$500,000 to University of Oklahoma Health Sciences Center, Oklahoma City, OK, 2012.
$90,000 to City Care, Oklahoma City, OK, 2012. For outsourcing and professional services.
$62,500 to Homeless Alliance, Oklahoma City, OK, 2012. For Skirvin Centennial.
$57,764 to Chisholm Trail Heritage Association, Duncan, OK, 2012. For annual distribution.
$50,000 to Dallas Summer Musicals, Dallas, TX, 2012. For general support grant.
$32,293 to Willow Springs Boys Ranch, Chandler, OK, 2012. For annual distribution.
$20,000 to Chickasha Public School Foundation, Chickasha, OK, 2012.
$9,293 to Jasmine Moran Childrens Museum, Seminole, OK, 2012. For annual distribution.

7743
Community Foundation of Ardmore, Inc. ✧
P.O. Box 2597
Ardmore, OK 73402-2597 (580) 223-3883
Contact: Larry A. Pulliam, C.E.O. and Pres.
E-mail: lapulliam@sbcglobal.net

Established in 2003 in OK.
Foundation type: Independent foundation.
Financial data (yr. ended 02/28/14): Assets, $13,378,552 (M); expenditures, $642,081; qualifying distributions, $590,650; giving activities include $525,900 for 22 grants (high: $125,000; low: $1,250).
Fields of interest: Education; Health care; Human services.
Type of support: General/operating support; Continuing support; Management development/capacity building; Capital campaigns; Building/renovation; Equipment; Land acquisition; Emergency funds; Program development; Scholarship funds; Research; Program evaluation.
Limitations: Applications accepted. Giving primarily in Carter County, OK and adjacent areas, with emphasis on Ardmore. No support for churches and public schools. No grants to individuals.
Application information: Application form required.
Initial approach: Letter
Copies of proposal: 1
Deadline(s): Feb. 1, May. 1, Aug. 1 and Nov. 1
Board meeting date(s): Mar., Jun., Sept., and Dec.
Officers and Trustees:* Charles F. Williams,* Chair.; J. Robert Dexter,* Vice-Chair.; Larry A. Pulliam, C.E.O. and Pres.; Samuel J. Veazey,* Secy.-Treas.; Bill Goddard; Keith R. Gray; Milliard Ingram; Leon Simms; Alison Smalley; Mary K. Wilson.
Number of staff: 2 full-time professional; 1 full-time support.
EIN: 200514419

7744
Coretz Family Foundation ✧ ☆
2675 S. Birmingham Pl.
Tulsa, OK 74114-4320

Established in 2004 in OK.
Donor: Robert Coretz.
Foundation type: Independent foundation.
Financial data (yr. ended 12/31/13): Assets, $12,313,593 (M); gifts received, $500,000; expenditures, $688,293; qualifying distributions, $581,372; giving activities include $581,372 for 39 grants (high: $113,747; low: $18).
Fields of interest: Education; Human services; United Ways and Federated Giving Programs; Jewish federated giving programs; Philanthropy/voluntarism.
Type of support: General/operating support.
Limitations: Applications not accepted. Giving primarily in Tulsa, OK. No grants to individuals.
Application information: Unsolicited requests for funds not accepted.
Officers: Robert Coretz, Pres. and Treas.; Kim Coretz, V.P.
EIN: 201813311

7745
Kathleen S. Craft Foundation ✧
4401 Oak Rd.
Tulsa, OK 74105-4222

Established in 2012.
Donor: Kathleen S. Craft.
Foundation type: Independent foundation.
Financial data (yr. ended 12/31/13): Assets, $27,675,458 (M); gifts received, $13,750,000; expenditures, $1,017,493; qualifying distributions, $1,000,000; giving activities include $1,000,000 for 3 grants (high: $500,000; low: $250,000).
Fields of interest: Christian agencies & churches.
Limitations: Applications not accepted.
Application information: Unsolicited requests for funds not accepted.
Trustees: Kathleen S. Craft; A. Wellford Tabor.
EIN: 455153443

7746
Crawley Family Foundation ✧
105 N. Hudson Ave., Ste. 800
Oklahoma City, OK 73102-4803

Established in OK.
Donors: James B. Crawley; Mary W. Crawley; JBC Investment Co.; Crawley Petroleum Corp.; Sara B. Crawley; Linda C. Shirley; Martha C. Tracey.
Foundation type: Independent foundation.
Financial data (yr. ended 12/31/13): Assets, $8,483,500 (M); gifts received, $475,000; expenditures, $658,518; qualifying distributions, $572,000; giving activities include $572,000 for 36 grants (high: $100,000; low: $1,000).
Fields of interest: Performing arts, orchestras; Arts; Higher education; Theological school/education; Education; Human services; Foundations (private grantmaking); Protestant agencies & churches.
Limitations: Applications not accepted. Giving primarily in Norman, OK and in TX. No grants to individuals.
Application information: Contributes only to pre-selected organizations.
Officers: James B. Crawley, Pres.; Mary W. Crawley, Secy.; Sara B. Crawley, Treas.
Director: Linda C. Shirley.
EIN: 731463271

7747
Dobson Family Foundation ✧
5001 N. Gaillardia Corporate Pl., Ste. A
Oklahoma City, OK 73142-1868
Contact: Everett R. Dobson, Pres.

Established in 2007 in OK.
Donors: Everett R. Dobson; Stephen T. Dobson; Robbin L. Dobson.
Foundation type: Operating foundation.
Financial data (yr. ended 12/31/13): Assets, $9,805,296 (M); expenditures, $484,603; qualifying distributions, $448,600; giving activities include $448,600 for 39 grants (high: $110,000; low: $1,000).
Fields of interest: Museums (specialized); Education; Human services; Children/youth, services.
Limitations: Applications accepted. Giving primarily in OK, with emphasis on Oklahoma City.
Application information:
Initial approach: Letter
Deadline(s): None
Officers: Everett R. Dobson, Pres.; Stephen T. Dobson, V.P.; Phillip J. Giachino, Secy.
EIN: 261301254

7748
The Dotson Family Foundation ✧ ☆
1918 E. 30th Pl.
Tulsa, OK 74114-5414
Contact: George S. Dotson, Tr.; Phyllis N. Dotson, Tr.

Established in 1998 in OK.
Donors: George S. Dotson; Phyllis N. Dotson.
Foundation type: Independent foundation.
Financial data (yr. ended 12/31/13): Assets, $3,377,110 (M); expenditures, $1,118,794; qualifying distributions, $1,101,677; giving activities include $1,099,427 for 27 grants (high: $280,000; low: $250).
Fields of interest: Education; Mental health/crisis services; Community/economic development.
Limitations: Applications accepted. Giving primarily in Boston, MA, and OK.
Application information: Application form not required.
Initial approach: Proposal
Deadline(s): None
Trustees: George S. Dotson; Phyllis N. Dotson.
EIN: 746443176

7749
Ethics & Excellence in Journalism Foundation
210 Park Ave., Ste. 3150
Oklahoma City, OK 73102-5604 (405) 604-5388
Contact: Nancy Hodgkinson, Sr. Prog. Off.
FAX: (405) 604-0297;
E-mail: nancy.hodgkinson@journalismfoundation.org; Main URL: http://www.journalismfoundation.org
Grants Database: http://www.journalismfoundation.org/grants.htm

Established in 1982 in OK.
Donor: Edith Kinney Gaylord†.
Foundation type: Independent foundation.
Financial data (yr. ended 06/30/13): Assets, $100,278,358 (M); expenditures, $6,184,250; qualifying distributions, $3,750,823; giving activities include $3,240,500 for 78 grants (high: $100,000; low: $25,000), $58,346 for 62 employee matching gifts, and $11,995 for 2 foundation-administered programs.
Purpose and activities: The foundation invests in the future of journalism by building the ethics, skills and opportunities needed to advance principled, probing news and information.
Fields of interest: Media/communications; Journalism school/education.
Type of support: Capital campaigns; Program development; Conferences/seminars; Seed money; Curriculum development; Technical assistance.
Limitations: Applications accepted. Giving on a national basis, with some emphasis on OK. No support for international organizations, equipment, book publishing, literacy programs or documentaries. No grants to individuals or for scholarships, endowments, or personal research projects.
Publications: Grants list.
Application information: The foundation has a two-stage application process. Submit a Letter of Inquiry through the foundation's web site (use Application button on the home page). Link to online application provided for those invited to apply. Applications accepted from media institutions and journalism schools nationwide, primarily in the areas of investigative reporting, professional development, youth education and special opportunities. Within these areas, particular emphasis is placed on ethics and new media. Application form required.
Initial approach: Letters of Inquiry submitted online through the foundation's web site
Deadline(s): May 15 and Nov. 15 for letters of inquiry; June 15 and Dec. 15 for approved applications
Board meeting date(s): Jan. and July
Final notification: 2 months
Officers and Directors:* William J. Ross,* Chair.; Robert J. Ross,* C.E.O. and Pres.; Richard A. Davis, C.F.O.; David O. Hogan; Andrew W. Roff; J. Hugh Roff, Jr.; Patrick T. Rooney.
Advisory Committee Members: John A. Rieger, Chair.; Andrew C. Barth; Janet Cromley; Marian Cromley; Kay Dyer; John T. Greiner, Jr.; Ed Kelley; Jan Schaffer; Vivian Vahlberg.
Number of staff: 6 full-time professional; 3 full-time support.
EIN: 731167175
Selected grants: The following grants are a representative sample of this grantmaker's funding activity:
$100,000 to Florida Center for Investigative Reporting Corp, Tampa, FL, 2012. For investigative journalism in the public interest.
$100,000 to Investigatewest, Seattle, WA, 2012. For Pacific Northwest Network to increase number of media partners providing investigative and public service news coverage in the region, diversify funding sources, and examining new strategies to support and expand journalism.
$100,000 to Iowa Center for Public Affairs Journalism, Coralville, IA, 2012. For startup support of IowaWatch.org emphasizes investigative reporting, transparency, high ethics, collaboration with new outlets, mentoring of student journalists, and distribution of content.
$100,000 to Maine Center for Public Interest Reporting, Hallowell, ME, 2012. To expand website, make effective use of new technology and social network tools, and build wider base of financial support.
$100,000 to Rocky Mountain Investigative News Network, Denver, CO, 2012. For general support of I-News, including valuation of services by setting price points and sharing what's learned with others.
$100,000 to Wisconsin Center for Investigative Journalism, Madison, WI, 2012. To expand leadership roles in transparency, ethics, training and high standards of accuracy and to share learnings with other nonprofit investigative centers.
$85,000 to University of Oklahoma Foundation, Norman, OK, 2012. For Oklahoma Scholastic Media Initiative to disburse grants for equipment, software and training to high schools starting or improving newspapers.
$75,000 to American University, Washington, DC, 2012. For J-Lab, incubator for hyper local news entrepreneurs, to train journalists and citizens to use digital technologies, and to convene, summit for new journalism school new initiatives from which best-practices online learning module will be created.
$75,000 to Boston University, Boston, MA, 2012. For New England Center for Investigative Reporting (NECIR) to expand capacity of Public Eye, subscription service that offers investigative stories and training to small news outlets in Massachusetts.
$25,000 to Associated Press Media Editors Association Foundation, New York, NY, 2012. For NewsTrain, traveling training program designed for frontline editors and reporters, to provide sessions on the road and to branch into online training.

7750
Flint Family Foundation ✧
P.O. Box 490
Tulsa, OK 74101-0490

Donors: Flint Resources Company, LLC; Charles W. Flint Jr. 1990 Family Trust.
Foundation type: Independent foundation.
Financial data (yr. ended 12/31/13): Assets, $33,361,855 (M); gifts received, $800,000; expenditures, $2,070,277; qualifying distributions, $1,500,000; giving activities include $1,500,000 for 52 grants (high: $100,000; low: $350).
Fields of interest: Health care; Youth development; Human services.
Limitations: Applications not accepted.
Application information: Unsolicited requests for funds not accepted.
Trustees: Kelley F. Ballenger; Robin F. Ballenger; Charles W. Flint III; Susan F. Seay.
EIN: 300582777
Selected grants: The following grants are a representative sample of this grantmaker's funding activity:
$20,000 to All Souls Unitarian Church, Tulsa, OK, 2012. For Partners in Education - Jackson SOARS Camp.
$20,000 to Cherokee Nation Education Corporation, Tahlequah, OK, 2012. For Early Edge and ACT College Readiness Initiative.
$20,000 to Tulsa Library Trust, Tulsa, OK, 2012. For Library Services for Children.
$10,000 to A New Leaf, Broken Arrow, OK, 2012. For employment training.
$10,000 to Tulsa Advocates for the Protection of Children, Tulsa, OK, 2012. For CARE Program.
$10,000 to Tulsa Community Foundation, Tulsa, OK, 2012. For Tulsa County Child Protection Designated Fund.

$10,000 to Tulsa Metropolitan Ministry, Tulsa, OK, 2012. For Tulsa Metro Mechanic.
$10,000 to University of Oklahoma Foundation, Norman, OK, 2012. For Helping Families Help Themselves: EduCareers.
$5,000 to Community Action Project of Tulsa County, Tulsa, OK, 2012. For Comprehensive Health Program.
$350 to Tulsa Community Foundation, Tulsa, OK, 2012. For Funders Roundtable.

7751
The Nancy Taylor Foundation for Chronic Diseases Inc. ✧
2448 E. 81st St., Ste. 3711
Tulsa, OK 74137-4250 (918) 392-9968
Contact: Edward L. Taylor M.D.

Donor: Edward L. Taylor III.
Foundation type: Independent foundation.
Financial data (yr. ended 12/31/13): Assets, $9,711,366 (M); gifts received, $1,154,150; expenditures, $1,369,810; qualifying distributions, $1,287,060; giving activities include $1,119,074 for 9 grants (high: $162,654; low: $100,000).
Purpose and activities: Giving primarily for research involving chronic diseases.
Fields of interest: Medical research, institute; Arthritis research.
Limitations: Applications accepted. Giving primarily in CT, GA , MI, and PA.
Application information: Application form required.
Initial approach: Proposal
Deadline(s): None
Directors: Rebecca Keegan Dixon; Selman Kremer; Harvey Ruben; Edward L. Taylor IV; Stephen J. Taylor; Suzanne Taylor.
EIN: 262343375
Selected grants: The following grants are a representative sample of this grantmaker's funding activity:
$118,539 to Yale University, New Haven, CT, 2012. For Nav 1.7 and Chronic Pain: Generation of a Model of Human Inherited Erythromelalgia In.
$115,000 to Yale University, New Haven, CT, 2012. For Targeted Neurofeedback, a Novel Nonpharmacological Treatment for Obsessive-Compulsive.
$115,000 to Yale University, New Haven, CT, 2012. For Discovering Genetic Variations in Human Inflammatory Diseases Using High Throughput Robotic Platforms.
$109,020 to Yale University, New Haven, CT, 2012. For Pet Imaging to Determine Fpeb Binding and Glutamate Receptor Subtype 5 Availability in Depression, Irina.
$50,000 to Arthritis Foundation, Atlanta, GA, 2012. For Cd4+Foxp3+ Regulatory T Cell Analysis By Anatomical Location.

7752
The Sharna and Irvin Frank Foundation ✧
(formerly Frank Family Foundation)
3125 S. Yale Ave., Ste. B
Tulsa, OK 74135-8007
Main URL: http://sifrankfoundation.org/

Established in 1996 in OK.
Donor: Irvin E. Frank†.
Foundation type: Independent foundation.
Financial data (yr. ended 06/30/13): Assets, $28,026,761 (M); expenditures, $1,892,296; qualifying distributions, $1,623,520; giving activities include $1,514,950 for 145 grants (high: $200,000; low: $500).
Fields of interest: Health care; Human services.
Limitations: Applications not accepted. Giving primarily in Tulsa, OK. No grants to individuals.
Application information: Contributes only to pre-selected organizations.
Officers and Trustees:* May Sheehan, Pres. and Treas.; Coleman Robinson,* V.P. and Secy.; Sanford Cardin; Jacob Howland; Jon Stopler; Daniel Zeligson.
EIN: 731503704
Selected grants: The following grants are a representative sample of this grantmaker's funding activity:
$80,000 to San Miguel Middle School of Tulsa, Tulsa, OK, 2011.
$32,500 to Tristesse Healing Hearts Grief Center, Tulsa, OK, 2011.
$11,000 to Meals on Wheels of Metro Tulsa, Tulsa, OK, 2011. For general purpose.

7753
E. L. and Thelma Gaylord Foundation ✧
6305 Waterford Blvd., Ste. 350
Oklahoma City, OK 73118-1176
Contact: Christy Gaylord Everest, Tr.
Email address for Linda Walker Brown, Dir. Admin.: lbrown@gaylordfoundation.org; Main URL: http://www.gaylordfoundation.org/

Established in 1994 in OK.
Donors: Edward L. Gaylord; Thelma F. Gaylord.
Foundation type: Independent foundation.
Financial data (yr. ended 12/31/12): Assets, $215,847,570 (M); gifts received, $8,943,158; expenditures, $7,140,059; qualifying distributions, $6,762,330; giving activities include $6,516,447 for 91 grants (high: $1,000,000; low: $300).
Purpose and activities: Funding primarily for education. Some funding also for the Red Cross, and arts and culture.
Fields of interest: Museums (history); Arts; Elementary/secondary education; Higher education; Education; Medical research, institute; Human services; American Red Cross; Christian agencies & churches.
Type of support: Building/renovation.
Limitations: Applications accepted. Giving primarily in the greater metropolitan Oklahoma City, OK area. No grants to individuals.
Application information: Application form required.
Initial approach: Online letter of inquiry
Copies of proposal: 1
Deadline(s): Jan. 15 and July 15
Board meeting date(s): Mar., June, Sept. and Dec.
Trustees: Louise Gaylord Bennett; Christine Gaylord Everest; David O. Hogan; Mary Gaylord McClean.
EIN: 731463569
Selected grants: The following grants are a representative sample of this grantmaker's funding activity:
$1,000,000 to Oklahoma Medical Research Foundation, Oklahoma City, OK, 2012. For general operating support.
$1,000,000 to YWCA of Oklahoma City, Oklahoma City, OK, 2012. For general operating support.
$533,659 to United Way of Central Oklahoma, Oklahoma City, OK, 2012. For general operating support.
$525,000 to Casady School, Oklahoma City, OK, 2012. For general operating support.
$250,000 to Dean A. McGee Eye Institute, Oklahoma City, OK, 2012. For general operating support.
$250,000 to Smithsonian Institution, Washington, DC, 2012. For general operating support of traveling exhibit.
$225,000 to Childrens Medical Research, Childrens Hospital Foundation, Oklahoma City, OK, 2012. For general operating support.
$50,000 to Allied Arts Foundation, Oklahoma City, OK, 2012. For general operating support.
$50,000 to Little Light House, Tulsa, OK, 2012. For general operating support.
$20,000 to Parent Child Center of Tulsa, Tulsa, OK, 2012. For general operating support.

7754
Grace Living Centers Foundation, Inc. ✧
709 Fox Tail Dr.
Edmond, OK 73034-7343

Established in 2000 in OK.
Donors: K. Don Greiner; Shellie Greiner.
Foundation type: Independent foundation.
Financial data (yr. ended 12/31/13): Assets, $2,915,288 (M); gifts received, $904,197; expenditures, $637,819; qualifying distributions, $614,700; giving activities include $614,700 for 21 + grants (high: $200,000).
Fields of interest: Education; Catholic agencies & churches.
Limitations: Applications not accepted. Giving primarily in OK and Bala Cynwyd, PA. No grants to individuals.
Application information: Contributes only to pre-selected organizations.
Directors: K. Don Greiner; Shellie Greiner.
EIN: 731596382

7755
Herbert and Roseline Gussman Foundation ✧
15 E. 5th St., Ste. 3200
Tulsa, OK 74103-4340

Established in 1951 in OK.
Donors: Herbert Gussman†; Roseline Gussman†; Barbara Gussman; Ellen Jane Adelson.
Foundation type: Independent foundation.
Financial data (yr. ended 12/31/13): Assets, $8,936,673 (M); expenditures, $522,504; qualifying distributions, $492,000; giving activities include $492,000 for 16 grants (high: $100,000; low: $1,000).
Fields of interest: Arts; Higher education; Health organizations, association; Jewish agencies & synagogues.
Limitations: Applications not accepted. Giving primarily in Tulsa, OK; some giving in NY. No grants to individuals.
Application information: Contributes only to pre-selected organizations.
Trustees: Ellen G. Adelson; Barbara G. Heyman.
EIN: 736090063
Selected grants: The following grants are a representative sample of this grantmaker's funding activity:
$100,000 to Saint John Medical Center Foundation, Tulsa, OK, 2011.

$87,000 to Cornell University, Ithaca, NY, 2011.
$81,000 to Philbrook Museum of Art, Tulsa, OK, 2011.
$50,000 to Jewish Federation of Tulsa, Tulsa, OK, 2011.
$50,000 to Tulsa Symphony Orchestra, Tulsa, OK, 2011.
$35,000 to University of Pennsylvania, Philadelphia, PA, 2011.
$19,500 to University of Tulsa, Tulsa, OK, 2011.
$10,000 to East Hampton Healthcare Foundation, East Hampton, NY, 2011.
$10,000 to Tulsa Community Foundation, Tulsa, OK, 2011.
$10,000 to United Way, Tulsa Area, Tulsa, OK, 2011.
$5,000 to Tulsa Congregation Bnai Emunah, Tulsa, OK, 2010.

7756
The Hardesty Family Foundation, Inc. ✧
c/o United States Aviation Bldg.
4141 N. Memorial Dr.
Tulsa, OK 74115-1400
Contact: Michelle Hardesty, Exec. Dir.
E-mail: mhardesty@hardestyco.com; Additional contact: Dana Wilkes, Grants Mgr., tel.: (918) 560-9260, e-mail: dana@hardestyco.com; Main URL: http://www.hardestyfamilyfoundation.org

Established in OK.
Donor: F. Roger Hardesty.
Foundation type: Independent foundation.
Financial data (yr. ended 11/30/13): Assets, $109,273,129 (M); gifts received, $7,900,000; expenditures, $1,613,086; qualifying distributions, $4,493,965; giving activities include $1,065,194 for 44 grants (high: $500,000; low: $50), and $3,233,058 for 2 loans/program-related investments.
Fields of interest: Humanities; Education; Health organizations, association; Human services; Children/youth, services; Infants/toddlers; Children/youth; Children; Youth; Adults; Young adults; Disabilities, people with; Physically disabled; Blind/visually impaired; Deaf/hearing impaired; Mentally disabled; Minorities; Women; Infants/toddlers, female; Girls; Adults, women; Young adults, female; Men; Infants/toddlers, male; Boys; Adults, men; Young adults, male; Military/veterans; Offenders/ex-offenders; Substance abusers; Single parents; Terminal illness, people with; Economically disadvantaged; Homeless.
Type of support: Research; Program evaluation; Program development; Matching/challenge support; Equipment; Capital campaigns; Program-related investments/loans.
Limitations: Applications not accepted. Giving primarily in Tulsa, OK. No support for religious organizations. No grants to individuals.
Application information: Applications are by invitation only. See foundation web site for information.
Board meeting date(s): Quarterly
Officers and Directors:* F. Roger Hardesty,* Pres.; Donna J. Hardesty,* V.P.; Marilyn Cox,* Secy.; Alan Lister, Cont.; Michelle Hardesty, Exec. Dir.; Alex Cristo.
Number of staff: 2 full-time professional; 1 full-time support.
EIN: 204094088

Selected grants: The following grants are a representative sample of this grantmaker's funding activity:
$100,000 to Tulsa Boys Home, Sand Springs, OK, 2012.
$75,000 to Domestic Violence Intervention Services, Tulsa, OK, 2012.
$75,000 to Mental Health Association in Tulsa, Tulsa, OK, 2012.
$65,000 to Fab Lab Tulsa, Tulsa, OK, 2012.
$60,000 to Parent Child Center of Tulsa, Tulsa, OK, 2012.
$50,000 to Youth Services of Tulsa, Tulsa, OK, 2012.
$40,000 to Community Food Bank of Eastern Oklahoma, Tulsa, OK, 2012.
$35,000 to Emergency Infant Services, Tulsa, OK, 2012.
$27,850 to Tulsa Library Trust, Tulsa, OK, 2012.
$25,000 to Center for Individuals with Physical Challenges, Tulsa, OK, 2012.

7757
Harris Foundation, Inc. ✧
2932 N.W. 122nd St.
Oklahoma City, OK 73120 (405) 749-5117

Incorporated in 1938 in OK.
Donor: Vernon V. Harris†.
Foundation type: Independent foundation.
Financial data (yr. ended 12/31/13): Assets, $3,693,439 (M); expenditures, $692,538; qualifying distributions, $692,538; giving activities include $616,400 for 75 grants (high: $100,000; low: $500).
Purpose and activities: Funding primarily for arts, education and human services.
Fields of interest: Arts; Education; Human services; Children/youth, services.
Type of support: Continuing support; Equipment; Endowments; Matching/challenge support.
Limitations: Applications accepted. Giving limited to OK, with emphasis on Oklahoma City. No support for political organizations. No grants to individuals.
Application information: Application form not required.
Initial approach: Proposal
Copies of proposal: 1
Deadline(s): None
Officers: William V. Harris, Pres.; Bryan Garrett, V.P.; Judith H. Garrett, V.P.; Neil Harris, V.P.; Patsy D. Harris, V.P.; Malinda Harris-Silk, V.P.; Andrew Silk, V.P.; Jimi Davidson, Secy.-Treas.
Number of staff: 1 part-time professional.
EIN: 736093072
Selected grants: The following grants are a representative sample of this grantmaker's funding activity:
$12,500 to White Fields, Piedmont, OK, 2011.
$10,000 to Norman Community Foundation, Norman, OK, 2011.
$10,000 to Oklahoma Center for Community and Justice, Tulsa, OK, 2011. For general purposes.
$7,000 to Edmond Memorial High School, Edmond, OK, 2011.
$5,000 to Cherokee Strip Regional Heritage Center, Enid, OK, 2011. For general purposes.
$5,000 to Southwestern Diabetic Foundation, Gainesville, TX, 2011. For general purposes.
$3,000 to United Way of Norman, Norman, OK, 2011.

7758
The Helmerich Foundation ✧
1437 S. Boulder Ave., No. 1400
Tulsa, OK 74119-3609

Established in 1965 in OK.
Donors: W.H. Helmerich†; Walter H. Helmerich III†.
Foundation type: Independent foundation.
Financial data (yr. ended 09/30/13): Assets, $110,331,272 (M); expenditures, $5,603,045; qualifying distributions, $5,342,808; giving activities include $4,993,243 for 56 grants (high: $500,000; low: $644).
Purpose and activities: Limited to large capital needs in the Tulsa, OK, area for charitable, and educational purposes. Primary areas of interest include community development, higher education, health services, museums, and the performing arts.
Fields of interest: Museums; Performing arts; Arts; Higher education; Education; Health care; Mental health, association; Youth, services; Community/economic development.
Type of support: Capital campaigns; Building/renovation; Equipment; Land acquisition.
Limitations: Applications not accepted. Giving limited to the Tulsa, OK, area. No grants to individuals, or for general support, continuing support, annual campaigns, seed money, emergency funds, deficit financing, matching gifts, scholarships, fellowships, program support, operating budgets, research, demonstration projects, publications, or conferences; generally, no support for endowment funds; no loans.
Publications: Program policy statement.
Application information: Unsolicited requests for funds not accepted.
Board meeting date(s): As required
Trustees: Dow Zachary Helmerich; Hans C. Helmerich; Jonathan D. Helmerich; Matthew G. Helmerich; Walter H. Helmerich IV.
Number of staff: 2 part-time support.
EIN: 736105607

7759
Hille Family Charitable Foundation ✧
624 S. Boston Ave., Ste. 710
Tulsa, OK 74119-1222
Contact: Margaret Hille Yar, Exec. Dir.
FAX: (918) 592-4185;
E-mail: smartin@hillefoundation.org; Main URL: http://www.hillefoundation.org
Grants List: http://www.hillefoundation.org/2013grants.html

Established in 1997 in OK.
Donors: Jo Bob Hille†; Mary Ann Hille.
Foundation type: Independent foundation.
Financial data (yr. ended 12/31/13): Assets, $55,536,102 (M); expenditures, $3,578,186; qualifying distributions, $2,203,039; giving activities include $1,805,692 for 102 grants (high: $300,000; low: $100).
Purpose and activities: The foundation was born out of the Christian principle that it is a privilege to serve others. Raising the educational, spiritual, and physical well-being of those helpless or ignored in society and promoting projects which benefit and revitalize the Tulsa, Oklahoma community at large are primary aims of the foundation. Consideration is also given to funding research and programs aimed at those affected by Alzheimer's disease and juvenile diabetes.

Fields of interest: Education; Environment; Alzheimer's disease research; Diabetes research; Recreation, camps; Human services; Children, services; Community/economic development; Infants/toddlers; Children/youth; Children; Youth; Adults; Aging; Young adults; Disabilities, people with; Physically disabled; Blind/visually impaired; Deaf/hearing impaired; Mentally disabled; Minorities; African Americans/Blacks; Hispanics/Latinos; Indigenous peoples; Women; Girls; Men; Infants/toddlers, male; Boys; Offenders/ex-offenders; Substance abusers; AIDS, people with; Terminal illness, people with; Immigrants/refugees; Economically disadvantaged; Homeless; LGBTQ.
Type of support: Consulting services; General/operating support; Continuing support; Management development/capacity building; Annual campaigns; Capital campaigns; Building/renovation; Equipment; Land acquisition; Endowments; Emergency funds; Program development; Curriculum development; Fellowships; Scholarship funds; Research; Technical assistance; Matching/challenge support.
Limitations: Giving primarily in the Tulsa, OK, area. No grants to individuals.
Publications: Application guidelines; Program policy statement (including application guidelines).
Application information: Please check foundation web site for updated funding opportunities.
Copies of proposal: 1
Board meeting date(s): Feb., July, and Oct.
Officers and Trustees:* Mary Ann Hille,* Pres.; Margaret Hille Yar,* Exec. Dir.; Leslie Hille Hamrick,* Grant Report Off.; Sheila Hille Lequerica,* Grant Report Off.; Shirley Moyers Martin,* Grant Off.
Number of staff: 2 full-time professional; 1 part-time professional; 1 full-time support; 2 part-time support.
EIN: 731521975
Selected grants: The following grants are a representative sample of this grantmaker's funding activity:
$52,900 to Tulsa Community Foundation, Tulsa, OK, 2012. To promote and Support Organization's Exempt Purposes.

7760
Inasmuch Foundation
210 Park Ave., Ste. 3150
Oklahoma City, OK 73102-5604 (405) 604-5292
Contact: Nancy Hodgkinson, Sr. Prog. Off.
FAX: (405) 604-0297; Additional contact inf. for Nancy Hodgkinson, e-mail: nancy.hodgkinson@inasmuchfoundation.org or for Sarah Roberts, e-mail: sarah.roberts@inasmuchfoundation.org; Main URL: http://www.inasmuchfoundation.org

Established in 1982 in OK.
Donor: Edith Kinney Gaylord†.
Foundation type: Independent foundation.
Financial data (yr. ended 06/30/13): Assets, $297,813,373 (M); expenditures, $14,504,283; qualifying distributions, $12,121,017; giving activities include $10,754,202 for 221 grants (high: $1,000,000; low: $100; average: $25,000–$100,000), $230,909 for 134 employee matching gifts, and $141,367 for 4 foundation-administered programs.
Purpose and activities: Grants are made in the following areas: education, health and human services, and community enhancement.
Fields of interest: Education; Human services; Community/economic development.
Type of support: Program-related investments/loans; General/operating support; Management development/capacity building; Capital campaigns; Equipment; Land acquisition; Program development; Conferences/seminars; Seed money; Curriculum development; Technical assistance.
Limitations: Applications accepted. Giving primarily in Oklahoma, OK, with some giving in Colorado Springs, CO. No grants to individuals, or endowments.
Publications: Grants list.
Application information: The foundation has a two-stage application process. A LOI must be submitted and approved prior to submitting a full application online. Full application by invitation only. Application form required.
Initial approach: Letters of Inquiry submitted online through the Application tab on the foundation's web site
Deadline(s): Feb. 15 and Aug. 15 for letter of inquiry; Mar. 15 and Sept. 15 for application
Board meeting date(s): Apr. and Oct.
Final notification: 2 months
Officers and Trustees:* William J. Ross,* Chair.; Robert J. Ross,* C.E.O. and Pres.; David O. Hogan; Andrew W. Roff; J. Hugh Roff, Jr.; Patrick T. Rooney.
Advisory Committee: Tricia Everest, Comm. Chair.; Christine Gaylord Everest; Cathy Robbins; Jeanne Hoffman Smith; Barbara L. Yalich.
Number of staff: 6 full-time professional; 3 full-time support.
EIN: 731167188
Selected grants: The following grants are a representative sample of this grantmaker's funding activity:
$500,000 to Variety Care Foundation, Oklahoma City, OK, 2011. For capital campaign.
$250,000 to Family and Childrens Services, Tulsa, OK, 2011. For capital campaign.

7761
The Stephen E. and Shelley S. Jackson Family Foundation ✧
6655 S. Lewis Ave., Ste. 222
Tulsa, OK 74136-1031 (918) 481-6366
Contact: Stephen E. Jackson, Tr.; Shelley S. Jackson, Tr.

Established in 2004 in OK.
Donors: Stephen E. Jackson; Shelly S. Jackson.
Foundation type: Independent foundation.
Financial data (yr. ended 12/31/13): Assets, $50,236 (M); gifts received, $450,000; expenditures, $505,970; qualifying distributions, $503,900; giving activities include $502,650 for 18 grants (high: $200,000; low: $1,000).
Purpose and activities: Giving primarily to health and human service organizations, as well as to Episcopal agencies and churches.
Fields of interest: Health organizations; Human services; Foundations (community); Protestant agencies & churches.
Limitations: Applications accepted. Giving primarily in Tulsa, OK; some giving in Rochester, MN.
Application information: Application form not required.
Initial approach: Proposal
Deadline(s): None
Trustees: Shelley S. Jackson; Stephen E. Jackson.
EIN: 206276419
Selected grants: The following grants are a representative sample of this grantmaker's funding activity:
$200,000 to Mayo Clinic, Rochester, MN, 2012. For Jackson Family Professorship in Individualized Medicine.
$101,000 to University of Tulsa, Tulsa, OK, 2012. For Send a Student Fund/Lorton Performance Center.
$10,000 to Arts and Humanities Council of Tulsa, Tulsa, OK, 2012. For Hardesty Arts Center.
$10,000 to Gilcrease Museum, Tulsa, OK, 2012. For Gilcrease Council.

7762
Fred Jones Family Foundation ✧
(formerly The Fred and Mary Eddy Jones Foundation)
9225 Lake Hefner Pkwy., Ste. 200
Oklahoma City, OK 73120-2061 (405) 231-2415
Contact: Wendy Smith, V.P.
FAX: (405) 231-2406;
E-mail: wsmith@fredjonesfamilyfoundation.com; Main URL: http://www.fredjonesfamilyfoundation.com
Grants List: http://www.fredjonesfamilyfoundation.com/grant_history.html

Donors: Fred Jones†; Mary Eddy Jones†; Hall Capital, LLC.
Foundation type: Independent foundation.
Financial data (yr. ended 06/30/13): Assets, $10,872,752 (M); expenditures, $631,986; qualifying distributions, $558,100; giving activities include $526,525 for 129 grants (high: $75,000; low: $200), and $31,575 for 5 employee matching gifts.
Purpose and activities: The foundation is dedicated to supporting organizations that increase the quality of life in central Oklahoma through projects dedicated to cultural growth and beautification.
Fields of interest: Arts; Education; Community/economic development; Christian agencies & churches.
Limitations: Applications accepted. Giving primarily in central OK.
Application information: Application form required.
Initial approach: Letter
Deadline(s): None
Officers and Directors:* Kirkland Hall,* Chair. and Pres.; Brooks Hall, Jr.,* V.P.; Fred Jones Hall,* V.P.; Wendy Smith, V.P.; Vicki Schilling, Secy.; Debra Melott, Treas.; Marilyn Upsher.
EIN: 203110536
Selected grants: The following grants are a representative sample of this grantmaker's funding activity:
$50,000 to Oklahoma Zoological Society, Oklahoma City, OK, 2011.
$50,000 to University of Oklahoma Foundation, Norman, OK, 2011.
$35,000 to United Way of Central Oklahoma, Oklahoma City, OK, 2011.
$25,000 to Oklahoma City Museum of Art, Oklahoma City, OK, 2011.
$20,000 to Oklahoma City Economic Development Foundation, Oklahoma City, OK, 2011.

$20,000 to University of Oklahoma Foundation, Norman, OK, 2011.
$5,000 to Claremont Graduate University, Claremont, CA, 2011.
$3,000 to Humane Society, Central Oklahoma, Oklahoma City, OK, 2011.
$2,000 to Oklahoma City Museum of Art, Oklahoma City, OK, 2011.
$1,500 to Neighborhood Alliance of Oklahoma City, Oklahoma City, OK, 2011.

7763
Herman G. Kaiser Foundation ✧
1350 S. Boulder Ave., Ste. 400
Tulsa, OK 74119-3224
Contact: Sheryl Green, Admin. Asst.
FAX: (918) 582-6156;
E-mail: sheryl.green@swbell.net

Established around 1976.
Donor: Herman Kaiser†.
Foundation type: Independent foundation.
Financial data (yr. ended 06/30/13): Assets, $22,955,035 (M); expenditures, $2,954,706; qualifying distributions, $2,727,600; giving activities include $2,727,600 for 51 grants (high: $700,000; low: $1,000).
Purpose and activities: Giving primarily to Jewish and Oklahoma organizations for education, health and human services.
Fields of interest: Education; Health organizations, association; Human services; Jewish federated giving programs; Jewish agencies & synagogues.
Type of support: Continuing support; Annual campaigns; Capital campaigns; Building/ renovation; Equipment.
Limitations: Applications not accepted. Giving limited to OK. No grants to individuals.
Application information: Contributes only to pre-selected organizations. Applications accepted only from organizations that the foundations is already familiar with.
Board meeting date(s): Thanksgiving weekend
Trustees: Michael S. Nelson; Pamela B. Nelson; Randolph M. Nelson; Timothy B. Nelson.
Number of staff: None.
EIN: 510173653
Selected grants: The following grants are a representative sample of this grantmaker's funding activity:
$500,000 to Tulsa Community Foundation, Tulsa, OK, 2011.
$325,000 to University of Oklahoma, Norman, OK, 2011.
$75,000 to LIFE Senior Services, Tulsa, OK, 2011.
$25,000 to Oklahoma Center for Nonprofits, Oklahoma City, OK, 2011.
$25,000 to Tulsa Community College, Tulsa, OK, 2011.
$20,000 to Clarehouse, Tulsa, OK, 2011.
$15,000 to Philbrook Museum of Art, Tulsa, OK, 2011.
$15,000 to Tulsa Boys Home, Sand Springs, OK, 2011.
$10,000 to Philbrook Museum of Art, Tulsa, OK, 2011.
$5,000 to Ner Israel Rabbinical College, Baltimore, MD, 2011.

7764
The Kerr Foundation Inc. ✧ ☆
c/o ASC
5101 N. Classen Blvd., No. 600
Oklahoma City, OK 73118-1948 (405) 749-7991
Contact: Lou C. Kerr, Pres.
FAX: (405) 749-2877;
E-mail: ccastle@thekerrfoundation.org; Application address: 12501 N. May Ave. Oklahoma City, OK 73120; Main URL: http://www.thekerrfoundation.org/

Incorporated in 1963 in OK, and reincorporated in 1985.
Donor: Grayce B. Kerr Flynn†.
Foundation type: Independent foundation.
Financial data (yr. ended 12/31/12): Assets, $23,492,867 (M); expenditures, $1,782,217; qualifying distributions, $422,640; giving activities include $422,640 for grants.
Purpose and activities: Giving primarily for 1) education, particularly higher learning and pre-collegiate organizations, including health science centers and medical research done by educational institutions, 2) arts and culture, particularly organizations in the visual and performing arts areas, as well as museums and libraries, 3) health, particularly institutions providing health care, medical research, or outreach organizations employing primarily professionals from the allied health area, 4) human services, particularly organizations providing services in diverse areas to the public, and specifically to the disadvantaged, people with special needs and the elderly, and 5) public affairs-related programs. Generally all grants are challenge grants.
Fields of interest: Visual arts; Museums; Performing arts; Arts; Education; Health care; Medical research, institute; Human services; Youth, services; Government/public administration.
Type of support: Building/renovation; Equipment; Program development; Professorships; Curriculum development; Fellowships; Internship funds; Research; Program evaluation; In-kind gifts; Matching/challenge support.
Limitations: Applications accepted. Giving primarily in AR, CO, Washington, DC, KS, MO, NM, OK, and TX. No grants to individuals, or generally for continuing support.
Publications: Application guidelines; Grants list.
Application information: See foundation web site for full guidelines and downloadable application form. Application form required.
Initial approach: Application form on web site
Copies of proposal: 3
Deadline(s): See web site for current deadline
Board meeting date(s): Quarterly
Final notification: Next day following receipt of application
Officers and Trustees:* Lou C. Kerr, Pres.; Laura Kerr Ogle,* V.P. and Secy.; Steven. S. Kerr,* V.P.; Cody T. Kerr; Ruth Leebron Levenson.
Number of staff: 4 full-time professional; 1 part-time professional.
EIN: 731256122

7765
Ketchum Charitable Foundation Inc. ✧ ☆
5100 E. Skelly Dr., Ste. 1040
Tulsa, OK 74135 (918) 491-4036
Contact: Kent H. Ketchum, Chair.
Application address: 31 Hallbrook Way, Spring, TX 77389

Donors: Betts, LLC; McJunkin Red Man Corp.; Red Man Charitable Trust; Ketchum Charitable Lead Annuity Trust.
Foundation type: Company-sponsored foundation.
Financial data (yr. ended 12/31/13): Assets, $18,991,241 (M); gifts received, $2,600,000; expenditures, $518,570; qualifying distributions, $449,380; giving activities include $449,380 for 12 grants (high: $100,000; low: $3,000).
Purpose and activities: The foundation supports organizations involved with higher education and school athletics.
Fields of interest: Higher education; Education; Health organizations; Athletics/sports, school programs; Human services; United Ways and Federated Giving Programs.
Type of support: General/operating support; Management development/capacity building; Program development.
Limitations: Applications accepted. Giving primarily in MO, OK, and TX.
Application information: Application form required.
Initial approach: Letter
Copies of proposal: 1
Deadline(s): None
Officers: Kent H. Ketchum, Chair.; Kevin B. Ketchum, Pres.; Brian C. Ketchum, V.P.
Director: Lewis Craig Ketchum.
EIN: 262189909
Selected grants: The following grants are a representative sample of this grantmaker's funding activity:
$20,000 to American Heart Association, Tulsa, OK, 2011.
$20,000 to Missouri State University, Springfield, MO, 2011.
$6,656 to Oklahoma State University Foundation, Stillwater, OK, 2011.

7766
Kirkpatrick Foundation ✧
1001 W. Wilshire Blvd., No. 201
Oklahoma City, OK 73116-7025 (405) 608-0934
Contact: Meaghan Hunt Wilson, Prog. Assoc.; Paulette Black, Prog. Off.
FAX: (405) 608-0942;
E-mail: pblack@kirkpatrickfoundation.com; Main URL: http://www.kirkpatrickfoundation.com
Facebook: https://www.facebook.com/kirkpatrickfdn
Twitter: https://twitter.com/kirkpatrickfdn

The foundation was founded by John and Eleanor Kirkpatrick in 1955 in OK.
Donors: Eleanor B. Kirkpatrick†; John E. Kirkpatrick†; Kirkpatrick Oil Co.; Joan E. Kirkpatrick†; Kathryn T. Blake†.
Foundation type: Independent foundation.
Financial data (yr. ended 12/31/13): Assets, $63,150,501 (M); gifts received, $132,566; expenditures, $3,141,473; qualifying distributions, $2,790,478; giving activities include $2,169,950 for 72 grants (high: $800,000; low: $1,000), and $221,209 for foundation-administered programs.
Purpose and activities: The foundation's mission is to support arts and culture, education, animal concerns, and environmental conservation, primarily in central Oklahoma.

Fields of interest: Arts, cultural/ethnic awareness; Arts education; Museums; Performing arts; Historic preservation/historical societies; Arts; Elementary/secondary education; Education; Environmental education; Environment; Animal welfare; Animals/wildlife, preservation/protection; Veterinary medicine.
Type of support: General/operating support; Continuing support; Management development/capacity building; Equipment; Program development; Conferences/seminars; Publication; Seed money; Curriculum development; Consulting services.
Limitations: Applications accepted. Giving primarily in central OK. No support for medical and health-related causes, social welfare projects or for lobbying organizations. No grants to individuals or for school trips or athletic programs.
Publications: Application guidelines; Annual report.
Application information: Application form available on foundation web site. Application form required.
Initial approach: Telephone or e-mail to Paulette Black, Prog. Off.
Copies of proposal: 1
Deadline(s): Deadlines for letters of inquiry (preceding large grants) fall on June 1 and Dec. 1 of each year. Small grant applications are accepted on a rolling basis.
Board meeting date(s): Board meetings are typically held quarterly in Mar., June, Sept., and Dec.
Final notification: 60 days
Officers and Trustees:* Christian K. Keesee,* Chair.; Robert Clements,* Pres.; Dr. Joe Howell,* V.P.; Louisa McCune-Elmore, Secy. and Exec. Dir.; David Rainbolt,* Treas.; Liz Eickman,* Advisor; George Back; Mischa Gorkuscha; Rebecca McCubbin; Dr. Anne H. Morgan; George Records; Mark Robertson; Meg Salyer; Jeanne Hoffman Smith; Max Weitzenhoffer.
Number of staff: 4 full-time professional.
EIN: 730701736
Selected grants: The following grants are a representative sample of this grantmaker's funding activity:
$300,000 to Oklahoma City Community Foundation, Oklahoma City, OK, 2012. For Joan Kirkpatrick Animal Hospital.
$150,000 to Oklahoma City Community Foundation, Oklahoma City, OK, 2012. For Kirkpatrick Foundation Express Fund.
$10,000 to Operation Catnip Stillwater, Stillwater, OK, 2012. For Trap, Neuter, Return Program.

7767
Robert Clay Liddell Foundation ✧ ☆
3000 Berry Rd.
Norman, OK 73072-7472 (405) 310-3103

Established in 2004 in OK.
Donors: Richard D. Liddell; Kelly Rose; Suzanne Rose; Commercial Brick Corp.; Doris Dahl.
Foundation type: Company-sponsored foundation.
Financial data (yr. ended 12/31/12): Assets, $1 (M); gifts received, $556,050; expenditures, $558,676; qualifying distributions, $553,534; giving activities include $553,534 for grants.
Fields of interest: Mental health, addictions; Residential/custodial care; Christian agencies & churches.
Application information: Application form required.
Initial approach: Letter
Deadline(s): None
Officers: Richard D. Liddell, Pres.; Larry Pruitt, Secy.
Director: Lloyd R. Trenary.
EIN: 200420550

7768
Lobeck Taylor Family Foundation ✧
(formerly Lobeck-Taylor Foundation)
c/o Elizabeth Frame Ellison
1124 S. Lewis Ave.
Tulsa, OK 74104-3906

Established in 1997 in OK.
Donors: Kathy Taylor Lobeck; William E. Lobeck, Jr.; William E. Lobeck, Jr. Trust.
Foundation type: Independent foundation.
Financial data (yr. ended 12/31/13): Assets, $40,850,231 (M); expenditures, $1,442,049; qualifying distributions, $1,202,547; giving activities include $1,202,547 for 37 grants (high: $199,986; low: $500).
Purpose and activities: Giving primarily for higher education, as well as for the arts, with emphasis on museums.
Fields of interest: Museums; Museums (art); Arts; Education, single organization support; Higher education; Education; Health organizations, association; Human services; Foundations (community); Christian agencies & churches.
Limitations: Applications not accepted. Giving primarily in Tulsa, OK. No grants to individuals.
Application information: Contributes only to pre-selected organizations.
Officer: Elizabeth Frame Ellison, Exec. Dir.
Directors: Kathy Taylor Lobeck; William E. Lobeck, Jr.; Margaret Lobeck Pellegrini.
EIN: 731519836

7769
The Lyon Foundation ✧
(formerly E. H. and Melody Lyon Foundation, Inc.)
P.O. Box 546
Bartlesville, OK 74005-0546
Contact: John F. Kane, Pres.
E-mail: lyonfoundation@sbcglobal.net

Established in 1975 in OK.
Donors: E.H. Lyon†; Melody Lyon†; Charles W. Selby†.
Foundation type: Independent foundation.
Financial data (yr. ended 12/31/13): Assets, $44,593,139 (M); expenditures, $2,125,216; qualifying distributions, $1,875,548; giving activities include $1,759,633 for 57 grants (high: $250,000; low: $1,200).
Purpose and activities: Giving primarily for the aged and for education as well as for civic projects, particularly parks and recreation.
Fields of interest: Arts; Education; Hospitals (general); Recreation; Human services; Children/youth, services; Aging, centers/services; Government/public administration.
Type of support: Capital campaigns.
Limitations: Applications accepted. Giving limited to the Bartlesville, OK, area. No grants to.
Publications: Application guidelines.
Application information: Application form required.
Initial approach: Letter
Copies of proposal: 1
Deadline(s): None
Board meeting date(s): Quarterly
Final notification: 3 to 5 months
Officers: John F. Kane, Pres.; Walter W. Allison, V.P.; Larry G. Markel, V.P.; Thomas Janer, Secy.; Bruce Robinett, Treas.
Director: John B. Kane.
Number of staff: 1 full-time support; 1 part-time support.
EIN: 237299980
Selected grants: The following grants are a representative sample of this grantmaker's funding activity:
$90,000 to Price Tower Arts Center, Bartlesville, OK, 2012. For water remediation.
$57,750 to Washington County Elder Care, Bartlesville, OK, 2012. For bus.
$30,880 to Mary Martha Outreach, Bartlesville, OK, 2012. For exterior building work.
$30,000 to Westside Community Center, Bartlesville, OK, 2012. For HVAC.
$19,232 to Bartlesville Civic Ballet, Bartlesville, OK, 2012. For Portable Ballet Floor.
$12,500 to Bartlesville Community Foundation, Bartlesville, OK, 2012. For Hopestone Cancer Center.
$11,996 to Bartlesville Area Friends of the Parks, Bartlesville, OK, 2012. For playground.
$7,000 to Bartlesville Community Foundation, Bartlesville, OK, 2012. For Bark Park.
$5,000 to Bartlesville Community Foundation, Bartlesville, OK, 2012. For art mural.
$4,667 to Washington County Senior Citizens, Dewey, OK, 2012. For Light Fixtures.

7770
The J. E. and L. E. Mabee Foundation, Inc.
401 S. Boston, Ste. 3001
Tulsa, OK 74103-4017
Contact: Raymond L. Tullius, Jr., Vice-Chair. and Secy.-Treas.
Additional tel. (for Midland, TX): (432) 682-5902;
Main URL: http://www.mabeefoundation.com

Incorporated in 1948 in DE.
Donors: J.E. Mabee†; L.E. Mabee†.
Foundation type: Independent foundation.
Financial data (yr. ended 08/31/14): Assets, $1,015,687,642 (M); expenditures, $49,599,052; qualifying distributions, $46,757,358; giving activities include $46,240,322 for grants.
Purpose and activities: Giving to aid religious organizations, charitable organizations, and institutions of higher learning; and to support hospitals and other agencies and institutions engaged in the discovery, treatment, and care of diseases. Grants are limited to building projects and purchase of major medical equipment.
Fields of interest: Higher education; Hospitals (general); Youth development, services; Human services; Youth, services.
Type of support: Capital campaigns; Building/renovation; Equipment.
Limitations: Applications accepted. Giving limited to AR, KS, MO, NM, OK, and TX. No support for secondary or elementary education, or tax-supported institutions. No grants to individuals, or for research, endowment funds, scholarships, fellowships, or operating expenses; no loans.
Publications: Application guidelines; Program policy statement.
Application information: Summary statement, found on foundation's Web site, is required as cover page to all grant proposals. Application form not required.
Initial approach: Proposal

Copies of proposal: 1
Deadline(s): Mar. 1, June 1, Sept. 1, and Dec. 1
Board meeting date(s): Jan., Apr., July, and Oct.
Final notification: After board meetings
Officers and Directors:* Joe Mabee, Sr.,* Chair.; Raymond L. Tullius, Jr.,* Vice-Chair. and Secy.-Treas.; Thomas R. Brett; Ed Jones; Joseph Guy Mabee, Jr.
Number of staff: 2 full-time professional; 1 part-time professional; 2 full-time support; 1 part-time support.
EIN: 736090162
Selected grants: The following grants are a representative sample of this grantmaker's funding activity:
$2,000,000 to Scott and White Healthcare Foundation, Temple, TX, 2013. For building renovations.
$2,000,000 to Texas Biomedical Research Institute, San Antonio, TX, 2013. For building renovations.
$2,000,000 to Tulsa Jewish Retirement and Health Care Center, Tulsa, OK, 2013. For building renovations.
$2,000,000 to University of Mary Hardin-Baylor, Belton, TX, 2013. For building renovations.
$2,000,000 to YMCA, Ozarks Regional, Springfield, MO, 2012. For new building.
$1,872,093 to Truman Medical Center Charitable Foundation, Kansas City, MO, 2013. For building renovations.
$1,700,000 to Harding University, Searcy, AR, 2013. For building renovations.
$1,500,000 to Arts and Humanities Council of Tulsa, Tulsa, OK, 2012. For Building Renovation.
$1,500,000 to Shawnee Mission Medical Center, Shawnee Mission, KS, 2012. For new building.
$1,080,500 to Central Methodist University, Fayette, MO, 2012. For Building Renovation.
$1,000,000 to Mental Health Association in Tulsa, Tulsa, OK, 2012. For Building Renovation.
$751,800 to Camp Fire USA, Fort Worth, TX, 2012. For new building.
$750,000 to Baker University, Baldwin City, KS, 2012. For Building Renovation.
$750,000 to Monarch School, Houston, TX, 2013. For building renovations.
$500,000 to Saint Luke's Health System Home Care and Hospice, Kansas City, MO, 2012. For new building.
$338,708 to Oklahoma Baptist Homes for Children, Oklahoma City, OK, 2012. For new building.
$300,000 to Hill Country Memorial Hospital, Fredericksburg, TX, 2013. For equipment.
$190,000 to Boysville, Converse, TX, 2013. For building renovations.
$150,000 to Boys and Girls Club of the Columbia Area, Columbia, MO, 2012. For new building.
$65,000 to Methodist Childrens Home, Waco, TX, 2013. For building renovations.

7771
Masonic Charity Foundation of Oklahoma ✧

P.O. Box 2406
Edmond, OK 73083-2406 (405) 348-7500
Contact: John Logan, Exec. Dir.
FAX: (405) 348-9031;
E-mail: information@mcfok.org; Street address: 3424 French Park Dr., Edmond, OK 73034; Toll-free tel.: (877) 562-7667; Main URL: http://www.mcfok.org
Facebook: https://www.facebook.com/masoniccharityok?ref=ts&fref=ts

Established in 1930 in OK.
Foundation type: Independent foundation.
Financial data (yr. ended 12/31/13): Assets, $83,813,732 (M); gifts received, $1,148,193; expenditures, $4,936,462; qualifying distributions, $4,518,081; giving activities include $3,770,913 for grants, and $165,303 for grants to individuals.
Purpose and activities: The foundation is the primary charitable and educational organization of Oklahoma Freemasonry, and provides support for members of the Masonic Fraternity and other local organizations.
Fields of interest: Higher education; Human services; Community/economic development; Aging.
Type of support: Scholarships—to individuals; Program development; Matching/challenge support; General/operating support; Endowments; Emergency funds; Capital campaigns; Annual campaigns.
Limitations: Applications accepted. Giving primarily in OK. No support for religious or political organizations.
Publications: Application guidelines; Annual report; Informational brochure.
Application information: Application form not required.
Initial approach: Use online application forms on foundation web site
Board meeting date(s): Quarterly
Officers and Board Members:* Charles L. Stuckey,* Pres.; Elwood M. "Ike" Isaacs,* 1st V.P.; William J. Cloud,* 2nd V.P.; Robert G. Davis,* Secy.; Gary A. Davis,* Treas.; John L. Logan, Exec. Dir.; David W. Allen; Glenn E. Almy; Charles R. Belknap; Charles Kent Callahan; Ronald J. Chambers; Ronald S. Coppedge; Robert M. Davis; Bobby L. Laws; Warren L. McConnell; Johnny D. Onkst; Randall L. Rogers; Lanny Sanders.
Number of staff: 4 full-time professional.
EIN: 736097262
Selected grants: The following grants are a representative sample of this grantmaker's funding activity:
$720,586 to Oklahoma Area Agency on Aging, OK, 2012. For elderly services.
$250,000 to University of Oklahoma Foundation, Norman, OK, 2012. For endowment.
$160,000 to Prevent Blindness Oklahoma, Oklahoma City, OK, 2012. For program support.
$100,000 to Rogers State University Foundation, Claremore, OK, 2012. For endowment.
$50,000 to Sulphur Veterans Center, Sulphur, OK, 2012. For facility improvements.

7772
McCasland Foundation ✧

P.O. Box 400
Duncan, OK 73534-0400
Application address: c/o Barbara Braught, Exec. Dir., 905 Peach Ave., Duncan, OK 73534, tel.: (580) 252-6559

Established in 1952 in OK.
Donors: T.H. McCasland, Jr.; Mary Frances Michaelis; Barbara M. Braught; Mack Oil Co.; Jath Oil Co.; and members of the McCausland family.
Foundation type: Independent foundation.
Financial data (yr. ended 12/31/12): Assets, $40,026,012 (M); expenditures, $1,942,404; qualifying distributions, $1,505,335; giving activities include $1,459,427 for 81 grants (high: $302,000; low: $40).
Purpose and activities: Support for higher education, cultural organizations, social services, and community improvement.
Fields of interest: Arts; Elementary/secondary education; Higher education; Health organizations; Human services; Community/economic development; Foundations (community).
Type of support: General/operating support; Building/renovation; Employee matching gifts; Matching/challenge support.
Limitations: Giving primarily in OK.
Application information:
Initial approach: Request application packet requirements
Copies of proposal: 1
Deadline(s): None
Board meeting date(s): Varies; usually quarterly
Final notification: After board meetings
Officer: Barbara M. Braught, Exec. Dir.
Trustees: T.H. McCasland, Jr.; Mary Frances Michaelis; W.H. Phelps.
EIN: 736096032

7773
J. Lyndall, Robert Fulton and Montie Ray McCrory Foundation ✧

303 E St. N.W.
Ardmore, OK 73401-4303 (580) 223-0112
Contact: J. Larry Wilkes C.P.A., Tr.

Established in 1993 in OK.
Donor: J. Lyndall McCrory.
Foundation type: Independent foundation.
Financial data (yr. ended 12/31/13): Assets, $17,015,827 (M); expenditures, $670,899; qualifying distributions, $574,274; giving activities include $458,277 for 31 grants (high: $56,000; low: $500).
Fields of interest: Higher education, university; Education; Hospitals (general); Health care, clinics/centers; Food banks; Boys & girls clubs; Human services; YM/YWCAs & YM/YWHAs; Family services; United Ways and Federated Giving Programs.
Type of support: Building/renovation; General/operating support.
Limitations: Applications accepted. Giving primarily in Carter County, OK. No grants to individuals.
Application information: Application form required.
Initial approach: Letter
Deadline(s): None
Trustees: Mary Strawn; J. Larry Wilkes, C.P.A.
EIN: 731439304
Selected grants: The following grants are a representative sample of this grantmaker's funding activity:
$66,000 to Regional Food Bank of Oklahoma, Oklahoma City, OK, 2012. For Food 4 Kids Program.
$15,000 to United Way of South Central Oklahoma, Ardmore, OK, 2012. For Fall Campaign.
$10,000 to Ardmore Animal Care, Ardmore, OK, 2012. For crematory repair.
$5,000 to Ardmore Day Nursery, Ardmore, OK, 2012. For Storm Shelter Construction.
$5,000 to Cameron University, Lawton, OK, 2012. For KCCU Public Radio Support.

$3,000 to Grace Center of Southern Oklahoma, Ardmore, OK, 2012. For cribs.
$750 to Ardmore City Schools, Ardmore, OK, 2012. For Band Support.
$500 to Prevent Blindness Oklahoma, Oklahoma City, OK, 2012. For screening children.

7774
The McGee Foundation, Inc. ✧
P.O. Box 18127
Oklahoma City, OK 73154-0127

Incorporated in 1963 in OK.
Donor: Dean A. McGee†.
Foundation type: Independent foundation.
Financial data (yr. ended 06/30/13): Assets, $11,962,961 (M); expenditures, $589,292; qualifying distributions, $579,000; giving activities include $577,000 for 18 grants (high: $120,000; low: $5,000).
Fields of interest: Historic preservation/historical societies; Arts; Education; Reproductive health, family planning; Foundations (community).
Type of support: General/operating support; Annual campaigns; Capital campaigns; Building/renovation; Equipment; Land acquisition; Endowments; Professorships; Scholarship funds; Research; Matching/challenge support.
Limitations: Applications accepted. Giving primarily in CA and Oklahoma City, OK. No grants to individuals.
Application information: Application form not required.
Initial approach: Proposal
Deadline(s): None
Board meeting date(s): Early May
Officers and Directors:* Marcia McGee Bieber,* Pres.; Patricia McGee Maino,* V.P.; Charles Bieber, M.D.*, Secy.-Treas.; Paula Love.
Number of staff: 1 part-time support.
EIN: 736099203
Selected grants: The following grants are a representative sample of this grantmaker's funding activity:
$120,000 to Planned Parenthood Mar Monte, San Jose, CA, 2011.
$87,000 to Oklahoma City Community Foundation, Oklahoma City, OK, 2011.
$60,000 to Planned Parenthood Los Angeles, Los Angeles, CA, 2011.
$60,000 to Planned Parenthood of Central Oklahoma, Oklahoma City, OK, 2011.
$50,000 to Wildlife of the American West, Jackson, WY, 2011.
$20,000 to Court Appointed Special Advocates of Oklahoma County, Oklahoma City, OK, 2011.
$15,000 to Peppers Ranch, Edmond, OK, 2011.
$7,000 to HeartLine, Oklahoma City, OK, 2011.
$5,000 to Free to Live, Edmond, OK, 2011.
$5,000 to Oklahoma Caring Foundation, Tulsa, OK, 2011.

7775
Ralph and Frances McGill Foundation ✧
c/o The Trust Co. of Oklahoma
P.O. Box 3627
Tulsa, OK 74101-3627
Application address: c/o Tom Wilkins, 6120 S. Yale Ave., Ste. 1900, Tulsa, OK 74136-4218, tel.: (918) 744-0553

Established in 2000 in OK.
Foundation type: Independent foundation.
Financial data (yr. ended 12/31/13): Assets, $7,791,704 (M); expenditures, $505,071; qualifying distributions, $467,115; giving activities include $441,883 for 57 grants (high: $33,333; low: $1,000).
Purpose and activities: Giving primarily for the arts, education, health organizations, and children, youth, and social services.
Fields of interest: Arts; Elementary/secondary education; Higher education; Health organizations, association; Human services; Children/youth, services; Protestant agencies & churches; Catholic agencies & churches.
Limitations: Applications accepted. Giving primarily in Tulsa, OK. No grants to individuals.
Application information: Application form required.
Initial approach: Letter
Deadline(s): None
Trustee: The Trust Co. of Oklahoma.
EIN: 731590898
Selected grants: The following grants are a representative sample of this grantmaker's funding activity:
$5,000 to Neighbor for Neighbor, Tulsa, OK, 2011.
$5,000 to Tristesse Healing Hearts Grief Center, Tulsa, OK, 2011. For general operations.

7776
The McMahon Foundation
P.O. Box 2156
Lawton, OK 73502-2156 (580) 355-4622
Contact: Dana Parrish, Exec. Secy.

Incorporated in 1940 in OK.
Donors: Eugene D. McMahon†; Louise D. McMahon†.
Foundation type: Independent foundation.
Financial data (yr. ended 03/31/14): Assets, $57,949,324 (M); expenditures, $2,783,509; qualifying distributions, $2,526,398; giving activities include $2,453,039 for 22 grants (high: $850,000; low: $1,500).
Purpose and activities: Giving primarily for education, human services, the arts, and youth programs.
Fields of interest: Arts; Higher education; Education; Housing/shelter, development; Human services; Youth, services; Community/economic development; United Ways and Federated Giving Programs.
Type of support: Annual campaigns; Capital campaigns; Building/renovation; Equipment; Land acquisition; Emergency funds; Scholarship funds; Matching/challenge support.
Limitations: Applications accepted. Giving limited to Comanche County, OK. No support for religious or political organizations. No grants to individuals.
Publications: Application guidelines.
Application information: Application form required.
Initial approach: Letter requesting application guidelines
Copies of proposal: 7
Deadline(s): 10 days prior to the first Mon. of each month
Board meeting date(s): Monthly
Final notification: 2 to 3 days after board meeting
Officers and Trustees:* Kenneth Bridges, Chair.; Kenneth E. Easton,* Vice-Chair.; Michael Mayhall,* Secy.-Treas.; Ronald E. Cagle, M.D.; Charles S. Graybill, M.D.; Gale Sadler; Orville D. Smith.
Number of staff: 1 full-time professional; 1 full-time support; 2 part-time support.
EIN: 730664314
Selected grants: The following grants are a representative sample of this grantmaker's funding activity:
$270,000 to Lawton Food Bank, Lawton, OK, 2013. To purchase facility.
$125,000 to Cameron University, Lawton, OK, 2013. For Capital improvements and scholarships.
$60,391 to Lawton Public Schools, Lawton, OK, 2013. To support special Program.
$9,499 to On the Chisholm Trail Association, Duncan, OK, 2013. For Admission for Comanche County students.
$1,000 to Prevent Blindness Oklahoma, Oklahoma City, OK, 2013. For vision screenings for children.

7777
The Meinders Foundation ✧ ☆
14001 McAuley Blvd., Ste. 100
Oklahoma City, OK 73134-7005 (405) 749-2422
Contact: Mo Grotjohn, Treas. and Exec. Dir.

Established in 1993 in OK.
Donor: Herman Meinders.
Foundation type: Independent foundation.
Financial data (yr. ended 12/31/13): Assets, $3,495,562 (M); gifts received, $633,988; expenditures, $1,130,673; qualifying distributions, $1,102,242; giving activities include $1,102,242 for 24+ grants (high: $250,000).
Fields of interest: Secondary school/education; Higher education; Education; Health organizations, association; Boy scouts; Human services.
Type of support: General/operating support; Annual campaigns; Professorships.
Limitations: Applications accepted. Giving primarily in OK. No grants to individuals.
Application information: Application form required.
Initial approach: Proposal
Deadline(s): None
Officers and Trustees:* Herman Meinders,* Pres.; LaDonna Meinders,* V.P.; Robert Meinders,* Secy.; Mo Grotjohn, Treas. and Exec. Dir.; Linda Rice.
EIN: 731438459
Selected grants: The following grants are a representative sample of this grantmaker's funding activity:
$50,000 to Lyric Theater of Oklahoma, Oklahoma City, OK, 2011. For capital campaign.
$9,000 to Allied Arts Foundation, Oklahoma City, OK, 2011. For operating support.

7778
Lou and Connie Miller Charitable Foundation ✧ ☆
4821 S. Sheridan Rd., Ste. 225
Tulsa, OK 74145-5716 (918) 236-3477
Contact: Max R. Vowel, Pres.

Established in 2005 in OK.
Donor: Louis H. Miller Trust.
Foundation type: Independent foundation.
Financial data (yr. ended 11/30/13): Assets, $8,027,685 (M); gifts received, $2,312,113; expenditures, $499,633; qualifying distributions, $445,718; giving activities include $445,718 for 41 grants (high: $75,000; low: $100).

Fields of interest: Performing arts, ballet; Botanical gardens; Human services; Foundations (community).
Type of support: General/operating support.
Limitations: Applications accepted. Giving primarily in Tulsa, OK. No grants to individuals.
Application information: Application form required.
Initial approach: Letter
Deadline(s): None
Officers: Max R. Vowel, Pres.; W. Kirk Clausing, V.P.; Madeline K. Gilmore, Secy.-Treas.
EIN: 134222602

7779
Ruth Nelson Family Foundation ✧
1350 S. Boulder Ave., Ste. 400
Tulsa, OK 74119-3224 (918) 582-8083

Established in 1983 in OK.
Donors: Michael S. Nelson; Pamela B. Nelson; Randolph M. Nelson; Ruth Kaiser Nelson; Timothy B. Nelson.
Foundation type: Independent foundation.
Financial data (yr. ended 12/31/13): Assets, $43,037,366 (M); gifts received, $2,000; expenditures, $2,704,988; qualifying distributions, $2,300,000; giving activities include $2,300,000 for 1 grant.
Fields of interest: Hospitals (general); Mental health/crisis services, association; Protestant agencies & churches.
Type of support: General/operating support; Continuing support; Annual campaigns; Capital campaigns.
Limitations: Applications accepted. Giving primarily in Tulsa, OK. No support for denominational religious organizations. No grants to individuals.
Application information: Application form not required.
Initial approach: Proposal
Deadline(s): None
Trustees: Thomas W. Murphy; Michael Stewart Nelson; Pamela Blair Nelson; Randolph Miles Nelson; Ruth Kaiser Nelson; Timothy B. Nelson.
EIN: 731210115
Selected grants: The following grants are a representative sample of this grantmaker's funding activity:
$500,000 to Mental Health Association in Tulsa, Tulsa, OK, 2011.
$120,000 to Oklahoma State University Medical Center, Tulsa, OK, 2011.

7780
The Samuel Roberts Noble Foundation, Inc.
2510 Sam Noble Pkwy.
P.O. Box 2180
Ardmore, OK 73401-2124 (580) 223-5810
Contact: William Buckner, C.E.O. and Pres.
FAX: (580) 224-6212;
E-mail: Admin-Granting@noble.org; Letters of Inquiry may be sent to Mary Kate Wilson, Dir. of Philanthropy, Engagement and Project Mgmt., e-mail: granting@noble.org; Mary Kate Wilson's contact for questions concerning granting-related matters: tel.: (580) 224-6246, e-mail: mkwilson@noble.org; Main URL: http://www.noble.org
Facebook: https://www.facebook.com/noblefoundation#!/noblefoundation
LinkedIn: http://www.linkedin.com/company/noble-foundation
Pinterest: http://pinterest.com/noblefoundation/
RSS Feed: http://www.noble.org/rss/index.html
Twitter: https://twitter.com/noblefoundation
YouTube: http://www.youtube.com/user/thenoblefoundation

Trust established in 1945 in OK; incorporated in 1952.
Donor: Lloyd Noble†.
Foundation type: Independent foundation.
Financial data (yr. ended 12/31/13): Assets, $1,322,307,756 (M); gifts received, $1,345; expenditures, $26,947,269; qualifying distributions, $40,574,330; giving activities include $1,669,981 for 218 grants (high: $150,000; low: $25), $288,750 for 75 grants to individuals (high: $10,000; low: $2,500), $30,418 for 1 employee matching gift, and $35,933,416 for foundation-administered programs.
Purpose and activities: The Noble Foundation conducts its operations through the work of three operating divisions: 1) Agricultural Division - assists more than 1,700 regional farmers and ranchers in achieving their individual financial, production, stewardship and quality-of life goals; 2) Plant Biology Division - conducts basic biochemical, genetic and genomic plant research for the purpose of improving crop productivity and value, and enhancing animal and human health; and 3) Forage Improvement Division - translates basic plant science research into tangible plant varieties. Within the institution, the Forage Improvement Division serves as a link between the discoveries in the laboratory and the field, where such discoveries are intended to enhance agricultural outcomes in Oklahoma and around the world. Through its grantmaking program, the Noble Foundation assists community service, health research and delivery systems, educational and other nonprofit organizations through grants and employee involvement. The foundation also administers a matching gift program for employees of the Samuel Roberts Noble Foundation, Noble Corporation and Noble Energy, Inc.
Fields of interest: Higher education; Health care; Medical research, institute; Human services.
Type of support: General/operating support; Capital campaigns; Building/renovation; Equipment; Professorships; Seed money; Research; Employee matching gifts; Employee-related scholarships; Matching/challenge support.
Limitations: Applications accepted. Giving primarily in OK. No grants to individuals (except through the Noble Educational Fund and the Sam Noble Scholarship Program).
Publications: Application guidelines; Annual report; Grants list; Informational brochure; Quarterly report.
Application information: Application guidelines available on foundation web site. Application form required.
Initial approach: Letter of inquiry
Copies of proposal: 1
Deadline(s): See foundation web site for current deadlines
Board meeting date(s): Jan., Apr., July, Oct. and Dec.
Final notification: 2 weeks after board meetings
Officers and Trustees:* William Buckner,* C.E.O. and Pres.; Billy Cook,* Sr. V.P. and Dir., Agricultural Division; Michael Udvardi, Sr. V.P. and Dir., Plant Biology; Steven Rhines, V.P., General counsel and Dir. of Public Affairs; Diane Pinsker, V.P., Business Development; Jill Wallace, V.P. and C.F.O.; Elizabeth A. Aldridge, Corp. Secy.; Sarah Richardson, Cont.; Ginger DuBose, Advisory Tr.; Cody Noble, Advisory Tr.; D. Randolph Brown, Jr.; Susan Brown; James C. Day; Sam Dubose; Vivian N. Dubose; William R. Goddard, Jr.; Shelley Dru Mullins; Jessie Nance; Russell Noble; Marianne Rooney; Patrick Rooney; Stephen F. Young.
Number of staff: 272 full-time professional; 1 part-time professional; 99 full-time support; 46 part-time support.
EIN: 730606209
Selected grants: The following grants are a representative sample of this grantmaker's funding activity:
$59,626 to Greater Ardmore Scholarship Foundation, Ardmore, OK, 2012. For Pettitt Educational Fund.
$40,000 to YMCA of Ardmore, Ardmore, OK, 2012. For operating support.
$38,748 to United Way of South Central Oklahoma, Ardmore, OK, 2012. For matching grant.
$30,000 to Arbuckle Life Solutions, Ardmore, OK, 2012. For general operating support.
$30,000 to Good Shepherd Medical and Dental Clinic Foundation, Ardmore, OK, 2012. For operating support and electronic system upgrade.
$25,000 to Charles B. Goddard Center for Visual and Performing Arts, Ardmore, OK, 2012. For general support and art education outreach program.
$25,000 to Stanford University, Hoover Institution, Stanford, CA, 2012.
$20,000 to Oklahoma State University Foundation, Stillwater, OK, 2012. For Oklahoma Agricultural Leadership.
$10,000 to Education and Employment Ministry, Oklahoma City, OK, 2012. For operating support.
$10,000 to Texas A & M Foundation, College Station, TX, 2012. For Mary Anne and J.W. Kornegay Scholarship.

7781
Oklahoma City Community Foundation, Inc. ✧
P.O. Box 1146
Oklahoma City, OK 73101-1146 (405) 235-5603
Contact: Nancy B. Anthony, Pres.; Cathy Nestlen, Dir., Comms.
FAX: (405) 235-5612; E-mail: info@occf.org; Additional address: 1000 N. Broadway Ave., Oklahoma City, OK 73102; Additional e-mails: n.anthony@occf.org and c.nestlen@occf.org; Main URL: http://occf.org/
Facebook: http://www.facebook.com/occf.org
GiveSmart OKC: http://givesmartokc.guidestar.org/profile/1126778/oklahoma-city-community-foundation.aspx
LinkedIn: http://www.linkedin.com/companies/oklahoma-city-community-foundation
Twitter: http://twitter.com/occforg
YouTube: http://www.youtube.com/occforg

Incorporated in 1968 in OK.
Foundation type: Community foundation.
Financial data (yr. ended 06/30/13): Assets, $706,850,493 (M); gifts received, $37,685,620; expenditures, $29,463,331; giving activities include $25,867,694 for grants.
Purpose and activities: The foundation seeks to serve the charitable needs of the Oklahoma City, OK, area through the development and administration of endowment funds with the goal of

preserving capital and enhancing its value for the benefit of the area.
Fields of interest: Arts; Scholarships/financial aid; Education; Environment, beautification programs; Health care; Health organizations, association; Aging, centers/services; Human services; Nonprofit management; Community/economic development.
Type of support: General/operating support; Continuing support; Management development/capacity building; Equipment; Program development; Conferences/seminars; Scholarship funds; Consulting services.
Limitations: Applications accepted. Giving primarily in the greater Oklahoma City, OK, area. No grants to individuals, or for endowment funds, deficit financing, debt reduction, capital campaigns, development or fundraising campaigns, or academic research projects; no loans.
Publications: Annual report; Financial statement; Grants list; Newsletter; Program policy statement; Program policy statement (including application guidelines).
Application information: Visit foundation web site for application form and guidelines. Faxed or e-mailed proposals are not accepted. Application form required.
Initial approach: Telephone or e-mail
Copies of proposal: 15
Deadline(s): Varies
Board meeting date(s): Feb., May, Sept., and Nov.
Final notification: 6 weeks following board meeting
Officers and Trustees:* Tony J. Tyler,* Chair.; Nancy B. Anthony, Pres.; Rhonda Godwin,* Secy.; Cathy Lippard, Cont.; Harry Merson,* Treas.; Dr. Steve Agee; Mary Ann Bauman, M.D.; Steven C. Davis; Mark W. Funke; Leslie Hudson; Oscar B. Jackson, Jr.; Ann Johnstone; Jenny Love Meyer; Vicki Miles-LaGrange; P.B. Odom III; Bond Payne; David E. Rainbolt; T. Scott Spradling.
Number of staff: 22 full-time professional; 3 part-time professional; 5 full-time support; 3 part-time support.
EIN: 237024262
Selected grants: The following grants are a representative sample of this grantmaker's funding activity:
$1,177,000 to Kirkpatrick Science and Air Space Museum at Omniplex, Oklahoma City, OK, 2012. For distribution from Affiliated Fund to support operations of Kirkpatrick Center.
$350,000 to Oklahoma Zoological Society, Oklahoma City, OK, 2012. For Joan Kirkpatrick Zoo Hospital.
$309,000 to Bishop McGuinness Catholic High School, Oklahoma City, OK, 2012. For concession stand and fence.
$259,000 to Variety Care Foundation, Oklahoma City, OK, 2012. For Espera Mas.
$203,000 to Planned Parenthood of Central Oklahoma, Oklahoma City, OK, 2012. For Teen Pregnancy Prevention Initiative.
$5,000 to All Souls Episcopal Church, Oklahoma City, OK, 2012. For general support.
$5,000 to Oklahoma Philharmonic Society, Oklahoma City, OK, 2012. For general support.
$4,474 to Oklahoma Institute for Child Advocacy, Oklahoma City, OK, 2012. For general support.
$1,500 to University of Central Oklahoma, Edmond, OK, 2012. For scholarships.

7782
Oklahoma Gas and Electric Company Foundation, Inc. ✧

(also known as OGE Energy Corp. Foundation)
P.O. Box 321, M.C. 1100
Oklahoma City, OK 73101-0321 (405) 553-3203
Contact: Peter B. Delaney, Pres.
Additional tel.: (405) 553-3397; Main URL: http://www.oge.com/community/OGEFoundation/Pages/OGEFoundation.aspx

Incorporated in 1957 in OK.
Donor: Oklahoma Gas and Electric Co.
Foundation type: Company-sponsored foundation.
Financial data (yr. ended 12/31/13): Assets, $12,703,297 (M); expenditures, $2,521,203; qualifying distributions, $2,466,077; giving activities include $2,459,426 for 126 grants (high: $238,796; low: $30).
Purpose and activities: The foundation supports organizations involved with arts and culture, human services, and community development. Special emphasis is directed toward early education, primarily math and science.
Fields of interest: Museums (art); Arts; Elementary/secondary education; Higher education; Education; Recreation; Salvation Army; Human services; United Ways and Federated Giving Programs; Mathematics; Science.
Type of support: General/operating support; Continuing support; Annual campaigns; Building/renovation; Equipment; Program development; Scholarship funds; Sponsorships; Employee matching gifts.
Limitations: Applications accepted. Giving limited to areas of company operations in OK. No support for religious or faith-based organizations not of direct benefit to the entire community or political parties or candidates. No grants to individuals or families, or for sporting events, golf tournaments, dinners, luncheons, or other forms of indirect support, or capital campaigns; no loans.
Publications: Application guidelines.
Application information: Grants range from $500 to $5,000. Organizations receiving support are asked to submit a final report. Application form not required.
Initial approach: Proposal
Copies of proposal: 1
Deadline(s): Mar. 15, June 15, Sept. 15, and Dec. 15
Board meeting date(s): Mar., June, Sept., and Dec.
Final notification: 30 days
Officers and Directors:* Peter B. Delaney,* Pres.; Susie White, Secy.-Treas.; Brian Alford; Max Myers.
EIN: 736093572

7783
ONEOK Foundation, Inc. ✧

P.O. Box 871
Tulsa, OK 74102-0871 (918) 588-7000
Contact: Terri A. Pirtle, Exec. Dir.
FAX: (918) 588-7490;
E-mail: CommunityInvestments@oneok.com; Main URL: http://www.oneok.com/CorporateResponsibility/CommunityInvestments/ONEOKFoundation.aspx

Established in 1997 in OK.
Donor: ONEOK, Inc.
Foundation type: Company-sponsored foundation.
Financial data (yr. ended 12/31/13): Assets, $39,678,572 (M); expenditures, $3,049,896; qualifying distributions, $2,945,615; giving activities include $2,945,615 for 141 grants (high: $500,000; low: $100).
Purpose and activities: The foundation supports organizations involved with arts and culture, education, health, human services, and community development. Special emphasis is directed toward programs designed to help people gain skills for self-sufficiency.
Fields of interest: Performing arts, theater; Historic preservation/historical societies; Arts; Elementary/secondary education; Higher education; Education; Hospitals (general); Health care; Children/youth, services; Family services; Human services; Community/economic development; Foundations (community); United Ways and Federated Giving Programs; Utilities; Economically disadvantaged.
Type of support: General/operating support; Capital campaigns; Building/renovation; Equipment; Curriculum development; Employee volunteer services; Employee matching gifts; Matching/challenge support.
Limitations: Applications accepted. Giving primarily in areas of company operations in KS, OK, and TX. No support for churches or religious organizations not of direct benefit to the entire community, private foundations, tax-supported organizations, disease-specific organizations, or college preparatory schools or their foundations. No grants to individuals or for fundraising walks or runs.
Publications: Application guidelines.
Application information: Requests for capital campaigns generally should not exceed one percent of the total capital campaign goal. Application form required.
Initial approach: Complete online application
Copies of proposal: 1
Deadline(s): None for grant requests of $5,000 or less; 4 weeks prior to quarterly board meetings for grant requests over $5,000
Board meeting date(s): Feb., May, Aug., and Nov.
Final notification: 1 month
Officers and Directors:* John W. Gibson, Chair. and Pres.; Curtis L. Dinan, Sr. V.P., C.F.O., and Treas.; Stephen W. Lake, Sr. V.P. and Genl. Counsel; Eric Grimshaw, Secy.; Terri A. Pirtle, Exec. Dir.; Caron A. Lawhorn; Robert F. Marinovich; Pierce H. Norton II; David E. Roth; Terry K. Spencer.
EIN: 731503823

7784
Mary K. Oxley Foundation ✧ ☆

1437 S. Boulder Ave., Ste. 770
Tulsa, OK 74119-3642

Established in OK.
Foundation type: Independent foundation.
Financial data (yr. ended 12/31/13): Assets, $23,770,113 (M); expenditures, $1,287,571; qualifying distributions, $1,022,807; giving activities include $931,500 for 54 grants (high: $250,000; low: $500).
Fields of interest: Higher education; Human services.
Limitations: Applications not accepted.
Application information: Unsolicited requests for funds not accepted.
Trustees: Debby M. Oxley; John C. Oxley; R.H. Harbaugh.
EIN: 270577885

Selected grants: The following grants are a representative sample of this grantmaker's funding activity:
$10,000 to Grayson-Jockey Club Research Foundation, Lexington, KY, 2011.

7785
The Oxley Foundation ✧
1437 S. Boulder, Ste. 770
Tulsa, OK 74119-3642
FAX: (918) 582-9419;
E-mail: kboulter@oxleyfdn.com

Established in 1986 in OK.
Donor: John T. Oxley‡.
Foundation type: Independent foundation.
Financial data (yr. ended 12/31/12): Assets, $55,445,149 (M); expenditures, $4,090,218; qualifying distributions, $3,331,200; giving activities include $3,073,710 for 32 grants (high: $2,000,000; low: $300).
Purpose and activities: Giving primarily for the arts, education, the environment, health associations, recreation, and religion.
Fields of interest: Museums; Museums (art); Arts; Elementary/secondary education; Higher education; Theological school/education; Education; Environment, natural resources; Hospitals (general); Hospitals (specialty); Health organizations, association; Medical specialties; Athletics/sports, equestrianism; Recreation; Human services; Children/youth, services; United Ways and Federated Giving Programs; Christian agencies & churches; Jewish agencies & synagogues.
Type of support: General/operating support; Annual campaigns; Capital campaigns; Endowments; Scholarship funds.
Limitations: Applications not accepted. Giving primarily in OK, with emphasis on Tulsa; some giving nationally. No grants to individuals.
Application information: Contributes only to pre-selected organizations.
Board meeting date(s): Twice a year
Trustees: Russell H. Harbaugh, Jr.; John C. Oxley; Mary Jane Tritsch.
EIN: 736224031

7786
The Puterbaugh Foundation ✧
P.O. Box 1206
McAlester, OK 74502-1206 (918) 426-1591
Contact: Steven W. Taylor, Pres. and Tr.

Trust established in 1949 in OK.
Donors: Jay Garfield Puterbaugh‡; Leela Oliver Puterbaugh‡.
Foundation type: Independent foundation.
Financial data (yr. ended 12/31/13): Assets, $15,678,402 (M); expenditures, $820,933; qualifying distributions, $761,290; giving activities include $740,798 for 28 grants (high: $20,000; low: $250).
Purpose and activities: Giving primarily for education, medical research, and youth and social services.
Fields of interest: Higher education; Education; Medical research, institute; Boys & girls clubs; Human services; Children/youth, services.
Type of support: Continuing support; Annual campaigns; Capital campaigns; Building/renovation; Equipment; Endowments; Professorships; Scholarship funds; Exchange programs; Matching/challenge support.
Limitations: Applications accepted. Giving primarily in southeastern OK. No support for religious or political organizations. No grants to individuals.
Application information: Application form required.
Initial approach: Letter
Copies of proposal: 1
Deadline(s): None
Officers and Trustees:* Steven W. Taylor,* Pres.; Cara Bland,* Treas.; Lucy Smith.
Number of staff: None.
EIN: 736092193
Selected grants: The following grants are a representative sample of this grantmaker's funding activity:
$254,000 to University of Oklahoma Foundation, Norman, OK, 2011.
$85,000 to Boys and Girls Club of McAlester, McAlester, OK, 2011. For general program support.
$34,845 to McAlester Public Schools, McAlester, OK, 2011.
$25,000 to Oklahoma Medical Research Foundation, Oklahoma City, OK, 2011.
$15,000 to Eastern Oklahoma State College, Wilburton, OK, 2011.
$11,200 to Oklahoma Heritage Association, Oklahoma City, OK, 2011.
$10,000 to Oklahoma Educational Television Authority, Oklahoma City, OK, 2011.
$5,000 to Oklahoma City University, Oklahoma City, OK, 2011.
$2,000 to Oklahoma Historical Society, Oklahoma City, OK, 2011. For general program support.

7787
Robert Glenn Rapp Foundation ✧
5400 N. Grand Blvd., Ste. 545
Oklahoma City, OK 73112-5672
Contact: Trustees

Trust established in 1952 in OK.
Donor: Florence B. Clark‡.
Foundation type: Independent foundation.
Financial data (yr. ended 12/31/12): Assets, $31,002,937 (M); expenditures, $1,775,626; qualifying distributions, $1,282,354; giving activities include $1,168,000 for grants.
Purpose and activities: Giving emphasis is on primary, secondary, and higher education.
Fields of interest: Education, research; Secondary school/education; Higher education; Education.
Type of support: Capital campaigns; Building/renovation; Equipment; Endowments; Seed money; Scholarship funds; Matching/challenge support.
Limitations: Applications accepted. Giving primarily in OK, with emphasis on Oklahoma City. No grants to individuals, or for operating funds.
Publications: Application guidelines; Informational brochure (including application guidelines).
Application information: Must use application form provided by foundation. Application form required.
Initial approach: Call or write for proposal guidelines
Copies of proposal: 6
Deadline(s): Aug. 31
Board meeting date(s): Annually, usually in the latter part of the year
Final notification: Dec. 31
Trustees: Jilene K. Boghetich; Tony Boghetich; Merry L. Knowles; James H. Milligan; Lois Darlene Milligan; Michael J. Milligan.
Number of staff: 1 part-time support.
EIN: 730616840
Selected grants: The following grants are a representative sample of this grantmaker's funding activity:
$55,500 to Arthritis Foundation, Oklahoma City, OK, 2012. For Camp and Walk.
$25,000 to John Brown University, Siloam Springs, AR, 2012. For scholarship.
$25,000 to Nature Conservancy, Oklahoma City, OK, 2012. For housing.

7788
The Records-Johnston Family Foundation, Inc. ✧
(formerly Willard Johnston Foundation, Inc.)
c/o George J. Records
P.O. Box 54390
Oklahoma City, OK 73154-1390 (405) 767-7627

Established in 1951 in OK.
Donors: Kathryn Ryan; Martha Records; Nancy Records; Jeff Records; Claire Ryan.
Foundation type: Independent foundation.
Financial data (yr. ended 12/31/11): Assets, $45,594,709 (M); expenditures, $3,192,524; qualifying distributions, $3,009,361; giving activities include $3,009,361 for 182 grants (high: $250,000; low: $100).
Fields of interest: Arts; Education; Health care; Human services.
Type of support: General/operating support; Annual campaigns; Capital campaigns; Endowments; Scholarship funds.
Limitations: Applications not accepted. Giving primarily in CO and OK. No grants to individuals.
Application information: Contributes only to pre-selected organizations. Unsolicited requests for funds not considered.
Officer: Dana Reindl, Treas.
EIN: 736093829

7789
The Robinson Foundation ✧
1127 E. 33rd Pl.
Tulsa, OK 74105-2501 (918) 877-2200
Contact: Anne M. Roberts, Tr.

Established in 1976 in OK.
Donor: James A. Robinson‡.
Foundation type: Independent foundation.
Financial data (yr. ended 10/31/13): Assets, $21,323,932 (M); expenditures, $1,206,569; qualifying distributions, $1,067,141; giving activities include $993,705 for 28 grants (high: $357,525; low: $3,000).
Purpose and activities: The foundation focuses on Catholic education and the homeless.
Fields of interest: Performing arts, ballet; Health organizations, association; Crime/violence prevention, domestic violence; Human services; Homeless, human services; Catholic agencies & churches; Homeless.
Type of support: Emergency funds; Building/renovation.
Limitations: Applications accepted. Giving primarily in Tulsa, OK. No grants to individuals.
Application information: Application form required.
Initial approach: Letter
Deadline(s): None

Trustees: Anne M. Roberts; Gary L. Smith.
EIN: 731014526
Selected grants: The following grants are a representative sample of this grantmaker's funding activity:
$88,583 to Holy Family Cathedral School, Tulsa, OK, 2011.
$58,763 to Cascia Hall Preparatory School, Tulsa, OK, 2011.
$30,000 to Catholic Charities, Tulsa, OK, 2011.
$20,000 to Habitat for Humanity, Tulsa, Tulsa, OK, 2011.
$20,000 to John 3:16 Mission, Tulsa, OK, 2011.
$10,000 to Church of Saint Mary, Tulsa, OK, 2011.
$10,000 to LIFE Senior Services, Tulsa, OK, 2011.
$10,000 to Tulsa Boys Home, Sand Springs, OK, 2011.
$10,000 to United Way, Tulsa Area, Tulsa, OK, 2011.
$10,000 to Youth Services of Tulsa, Tulsa, OK, 2011.

7790
Edward D. & Janet K. Robson Foundation ✧
7136 S. Yale Ave., Ste. 208
Tulsa, OK 74136-6356
Contact: Cindy Burchett, Tr.

Established in 2000 in OK.
Donors: Cindy Burchett; Edward D. Robson; Janet K. Robson.
Foundation type: Independent foundation.
Financial data (yr. ended 12/31/13): Assets, $13,130,207 (M); expenditures, $651,349; qualifying distributions, $546,860; giving activities include $520,888 for 5 grants (high: $410,888; low: $10,000).
Fields of interest: Education; Hospitals (general).
Limitations: Applications accepted. Giving primarily in FL and OK. No grants to individuals.
Application information: Application form required.
Initial approach: Letter
Deadline(s): None
Trustees: Cindy Burchett; Edward D. Robson; Janet K. Robson.
EIN: 731589395
Selected grants: The following grants are a representative sample of this grantmaker's funding activity:
$260,486 to Nowata Public Schools, Nowata, OK, 2011.
$150,000 to Jupiter Medical Center Foundation, Jupiter, FL, 2011. For general operating fund.
$25,000 to Safenet Services, Claremore, OK, 2011.
$1,613 to Boys and Girls Club of Green Country, Pryor, OK, 2011.

7791
ROI Community, Inc. ✧
(formerly Center for Leadership Initiatives, Inc.)
110 W. 7th St., Ste. 2000
Tulsa, OK 74119-1076
Canada address: 425 W. 8th Ave., Ste. 324, Vancouver, British Columbia, Canada V5Y 3Z5, tel.: (604) 737-3676, fax: (604) 737-3686. Israel address: 1 Ben-Maimon St., Jerusalem, Israel 92262, tel.: 972-2-566-7772, fax: 972-2-566-6744
Facebook: http://www.facebook.com/group.php?gid=5319338077&ref=nf

Donors: Lynn Schusterman; Aaron Edelheit; LJS Revocable Trust; Morris B. Squire Trust; Samburg Family Foundation; Russell Berrie Foundation; Dallas Jewish Community Foundation; Howard & Leslie Schultz Family Foundation; Jewish Funders Network; The David and Minnie Meyerson Foundation.
Foundation type: Operating foundation.
Financial data (yr. ended 12/31/12): Assets, $10,566 (M); gifts received, $5,266,245; expenditures, $5,269,259; qualifying distributions, $3,659,721; giving activities include $3,379,471 for grants, and $894,500 for foundation-administered programs.
Purpose and activities: Giving for the development of Jewish leaders and promoting managerial excellence throughout the Jewish community.
Fields of interest: Jewish federated giving programs; Jewish agencies & synagogues.
Limitations: Applications not accepted. Giving primarily in CA, and Jerusalem, Israel. No grants to individuals.
Publications: Newsletter.
Application information: Contributes only to pre-selected organizations.
Officers and Directors:* Mira Oreck,* Chair.; Sanford Cardin,* Pres.; Victoria Smith,* Secy.; Adam D. Grossman,* Treas.; Rabbi Yonatan Gordis, Managing Dir.; Jonathan Gordis; Lynn Schusterman; Stacy Schusterman.
EIN: 205344753

7792
The Francis and Kathleen Rooney Foundation ✧
5601 S. 122nd East Ave.
Tulsa, OK 74146-6912

Established in 2006 in OK.
Donors: L. Francis Rooney III; Rooney Holdings, Inc.
Foundation type: Independent foundation.
Financial data (yr. ended 12/31/13): Assets, $25,878,107 (M); expenditures, $1,450,414; qualifying distributions, $1,158,027; giving activities include $1,158,027 for 12 grants (high: $325,000; low: $27).
Fields of interest: Higher education; Foundations (community).
Limitations: Applications not accepted. Giving in the U.S., with emphasis on Washington, DC; some emphasis also on Notre Dame, IN, and Tulsa, OK. No grants to individuals.
Application information: Contributes only to pre-selected organizations.
Directors: Francis Rooney; Kathleen Rooney; Kathleen Daly Rooney; Laurence Francis Rooney IV; Michael Collins Rooney.
EIN: 205524633

7793
Sarkeys Foundation ✧
530 E. Main St.
Norman, OK 73071-5823 (405) 364-3703
FAX: (405) 364-8191; E-mail: sarkeys@sarkeys.org; E-mail contact for questions: Angela Holladay, Dir., Grants Mgmt., angela@sarkeys.org; Main URL: http://www.sarkeys.org
E-Newsletter: http://www.sarkeys.org/pages/newsletter
Facebook: http://www.facebook.com/#!/pages/Norman-OK/Sarkeys-Foundation/139638042731774?ref=search
RSS Feed: http://www.sarkeys.org/blogs/in_the_news/feed

Established in 1962 in OK.
Donor: S.J. Sarkeys†.
Foundation type: Independent foundation.
Financial data (yr. ended 11/30/13): Assets, $104,421,489 (M); expenditures, $5,051,576; qualifying distributions, $4,321,285; giving activities include $3,169,704 for grants, and $184,610 for foundation-administered programs.
Purpose and activities: Giving primarily to improve the quality of life in Oklahoma.
Fields of interest: Arts; Education; Health care; Medical research; Human services.
Type of support: Consulting services; Management development/capacity building; Capital campaigns; Building/renovation; Equipment; Endowments; Emergency funds; Program development; Professorships; Scholarship funds; Research; Technical assistance; Program evaluation; Matching/challenge support.
Limitations: Applications accepted. Giving limited to OK. No support for direct-to-government agencies or individual public or private elementary or secondary schools, unless they are serving the needs of a special population which are not met elsewhere; generally, no support for hospitals or local programs appropriately financed within the community or for religious institutions and their subsidiaries, or for out of state institutions. No grants to individuals, or for operating support, permanent financing, profitmaking programs, grants which trigger expenditure responsibility, direct mail solicitations, start-up funding for new organizations, feasibility studies, vehicles or for annual campaigns.
Publications: Application guidelines; Annual report (including application guidelines).
Application information: See foundation web site for application information. Application form required.
Initial approach: Telephone a foundation program officer and inquire about submitting a Letter of Inquiry. Successful applicants will receive a password for the online application
Deadline(s): See foundation web site for current Letter of Inquiry deadlines. Feb. 1 and Aug. 1, for proposals
Board meeting date(s): Jan., Apr., July, and Oct.; grants considered at Apr. and Oct. meetings
Final notification: Varies
Officers and Trustees:* Fred Gipson,* Pres.; Dan Little, V.P.; Joseph W. Morris, Secy.-Treas.; Kim Henry, Exec. Dir.; Teresa B. Adwan; Elizabeth Base; Dr. John Bell; Clay Christensen; Jim Loftis; Terry W. West.
Number of staff: 4 full-time professional; 4 full-time support.
EIN: 730736496

7794
Charles and Lynn Schusterman Family Foundation ✧
P.O. Box 51
Tulsa, OK 74101-0051 (918) 879-0209
Contact: Sanford "Sandy" R. Cardin, Pres.

Additional address: Washington, DC Office: 1250 Eye St., Ste. 700, Washington, DC 20005; Main URL: http://www.schusterman.org
Blog: http://www.schusterman.org/blog
Facebook: http://www.facebook.com/schustermanfamilyfoundation?ref=sgm
Flickr: http://www.flickr.com/photos/schustermanfoundation/
Lynn Schusterman's Giving Pledge Profile: http://glasspockets.org/philanthropy-in-focus/eye-on-the-giving-pledge/profiles/schusterman
Twitter-DC: http://www.twitter.com/schustermanfoun
Twitter-Tulsa: http://twitter.com/clsff
YouTube: http://www.youtube.com/user/SchustermanFoun

Established in 1987 in OK.
Donors: Charles Schusterman†; Lynn Schusterman; LJS Revocable Trust.
Foundation type: Independent foundation.
Financial data (yr. ended 12/31/13): Assets, $2,291,018,311 (M); gifts received, $67,335,695; expenditures, $73,796,140; qualifying distributions, $69,904,673; giving activities include $64,025,508 for 429 grants (high: $10,282,306; low: $180).
Purpose and activities: The foundation is dedicated to helping the Jewish people flourish by supporting programs throughout the world that spread Jewish living, giving and learning. The foundation also provides assistance to non-sectarian charitable organizations dedicated to enhancing the quality of life in Tulsa, Oklahoma, especially in the areas of education, child development, and community service.
Fields of interest: Arts; Education; Crime/violence prevention, child abuse; Human services; Children/youth, services; Voluntarism promotion.
International interests: Israel.
Type of support: General/operating support; Continuing support; Annual campaigns; Capital campaigns; Building/renovation; Emergency funds; Program development; Conferences/seminars; Professorships; Publication; Seed money; Curriculum development; Fellowships; Internship funds; Scholarship funds; Research; Technical assistance; Consulting services; In-kind gifts; Matching/challenge support.
Limitations: Applications not accepted. Giving primarily to nonsectarian organizations in OK; giving on a local, national, and international basis for Jewish organizations. No grants to individuals, or for endowment funds, deficit funds, media based projects, or programs that require expenditure responsibility.
Publications: Grants list.
Application information: Unsolicited requests for funds not accepted.
Officers and Directors:* Lynn Schusterman,* Co-Chair.; Stacy H. Schusterman,* Co-Chair.; Sanford "Sandy" R. Cardin, Pres.; Lisa B. Eisen, V.P.; Gaila Gross, C.F.O., Israel; Alana Hughes, C.O.O., Tulsa.
Number of staff: 5 full-time professional.
EIN: 731312965
Selected grants: The following grants are a representative sample of this grantmaker's funding activity:
$7,370,286 to Schusterman Foundation - Israel, Jerusalem, Israel, 2012. For program support.
$5,110,000 to Center for Leadership Initiatives, Tulsa, OK, 2012. For program support.
$3,000,000 to Bnai Brith Youth Organization, Washington, DC, 2012. For general support.
$2,416,344 to Birthright Israel Foundation, New York, NY, 2012. For program support.
$1,272,500 to Teach for America, New York, NY, 2012. For program support.
$86,250 to Washington Institute for Near East Policy, Washington, DC, 2012. For program support.
$45,000 to Tulsa Community College Foundation, Tulsa, OK, 2012. For general support.
$19,894 to Jewish Federation of Tulsa, Tulsa, OK, 2012. For program support.
$12,500 to Hillel: The Foundation for Jewish Campus Life, Washington, DC, 2012. For program support.
$10,000 to Search Institute, Minneapolis, MN, 2012. For program support.

7795
Charles Morton Share Trust ✧

c/o Heritage Trust Co.
P.O. Box 21708
Oklahoma City, OK 73156-1708
Application addresses: c/o Dean Linder, 1718 S. 11th St., Alva, OK 73717; c/o Darrell Kline, Northwest Electric, 508 Flynn St., Alva, OK 73717; c/o Jim Holder, Holder Drug Co., 513 Barnes Ave., Alva, OK 73717; and c/o Johnny C. Jones, Rialto Theatre, 516 Flynn St., Alva, OK 73717

Trust established in 1959 in OK.
Donor: Charles Morton Share†.
Foundation type: Independent foundation.
Financial data (yr. ended 06/30/13): Assets, $21,441,208 (M); expenditures, $1,486,095; qualifying distributions, $1,028,925; giving activities include $1,007,879 for 9 grants (high: $250,000; low: $10,000).
Fields of interest: Education; Hospitals (general); Human services; Community/economic development; Foundations (private grantmaking).
Type of support: Building/renovation; Equipment; Scholarship funds.
Limitations: Giving primarily in Alva, OK. No grants to individuals, or for operating budgets, continuing support, annual campaigns, seed money, emergency or endowment funds, deficit financing, land acquisition, renovations, matching gifts, special projects, research, publications, or conferences; no loans.
Application information: Send copy of application to each trustee. Application form not required.
Initial approach: Letter
Copies of proposal: 5
Deadline(s): None
Trustees: J.R. Holder; Johnny C. Jones; Darrell Kline; Dean Linder; Heritage Trust Co.
EIN: 736090984

7796
The Simmons Charitable Foundation of Oklahoma ✧

P.O. Box 307
Oklahoma City, OK 73101-0307

Established in 1993 in OK.
Donor: Marjorie Simmons Gray.
Foundation type: Independent foundation.
Financial data (yr. ended 12/31/12): Assets, $16,055,996 (M); gifts received, $445,000; expenditures, $768,695; qualifying distributions, $665,262; giving activities include $665,262 for grants.
Purpose and activities: Giving primarily for the arts, education, including a music school foundation, medical research and human services.
Fields of interest: Arts, formal/general education; Museums; Arts; Education; Medical research, institute; Human services; Foundations (private grantmaking).
Type of support: General/operating support.
Limitations: Applications not accepted. Giving primarily in Oklahoma City, OK. No grants to individuals.
Application information: Unsolicited requests for funds not accepted.
Officers: Michael A. Scears, Pres.; Paul A. Cox, V.P.; Marcia Burrows, Secy.
Directors: Ann Simmons Alspaugh; Holly C. Farabee.
EIN: 731436667

7797
Sherman E. Smith Family Charitable Foundation ✧

Mid-Continent Tower
401 S. Boston Ave., Ste. 205
Tulsa, OK 74103 (918) 488-0404

Established in 2005 in OK.
Donors: Sherman E. Smith Charitable Trust; Sherman E. Smith Charitable Lead Trust.
Foundation type: Independent foundation.
Financial data (yr. ended 12/31/13): Assets, $2,435,044 (M); gifts received, $1,409,459; expenditures, $1,562,645; qualifying distributions, $1,555,486; giving activities include $1,361,950 for 26 grants (high: $250,000; low: $4,400).
Fields of interest: Arts; Higher education; Health organizations, association; Foundations (private grantmaking).
Limitations: Applications accepted. Giving primarily in Tulsa, OK.
Application information: Application form required.
Initial approach: Letter
Deadline(s): None
Trustees: Susan Smith Burghart; William Sherman Smith.
EIN: 206616936

7798
Southern Oklahoma Memorial Foundation ✧

P.O. Box 1409
Ardmore, OK 73402-1409 (580) 226-0700
Contact: Larry A. Pulliam, Pres.
FAX: (580) 226-0223;
E-mail: lapulliam@sbcglobal.net; Main URL: http://www.somfardmore.org

Established in 1950 in Ardmore, OK.
Donor: Citizens of Southern Oklahoma.
Foundation type: Independent foundation.
Financial data (yr. ended 06/30/13): Assets, $97,585,321 (M); expenditures, $5,390,203; qualifying distributions, $4,505,233; giving activities include $4,280,408 for 58 grants (high: $1,148,869; low: $100).
Purpose and activities: Giving primarily for community development, education and health care.

Fields of interest: Education; Hospitals (general); Youth development; Human services; Community/economic development.
Type of support: General/operating support; Continuing support; Annual campaigns; Capital campaigns; Building/renovation; Equipment; Program development; Scholarship funds; Matching/challenge support.
Limitations: Applications accepted. Giving limited to OK organizations within a 50-mile radius of Ardmore. No support for churches or political organizations. No grants to individuals.
Publications: Application guidelines; Annual report; Annual report (including application guidelines); Multi-year report; Multi-year report (including application guidelines).
Application information: Application form required.
Initial approach: Letter to President with brief statement
Copies of proposal: 1
Deadline(s): Mar. 1, June 1, Sept. 1, and Dec. 1
Board meeting date(s): Feb., May, Aug., and Nov.
Final notification: Within 30 days of meeting date
Officers: Larry A. Pulliam, Pres.; Jean Hattensty, Cont.
Trustees: Donald J. Chaffin; G. Bridger Cox; Ron J. Crosby; Sam Daube; Jessie Nance; Bill Owen; Keith Troop, M.D.; Mark Riesen; Gil Wallace.
Number of staff: 2 full-time professional; 1 full-time support.
EIN: 731300662
Selected grants: The following grants are a representative sample of this grantmaker's funding activity:
$5,000,000 to Southern Oklahoma Higher Education Foundation, Ardmore, OK, 2013. For Health, Science and Math Building (Phase 1).
$1,185,500 to Mercy Memorial Health Center Foundation, Ardmore, OK, 2013. For da Vinci Surgery Robot.
$355,000 to Mental Health Services of Southern Oklahoma, Ardmore, OK, 2013. For operating support.
$200,000 to Greater Ardmore Scholarship Foundation, Ardmore, OK, 2013. For Carter County Graduates excl Ard and Plain.
$148,129 to Good Shepherd Medical and Dental Clinic Foundation, Ardmore, OK, 2013. For mammogram program.
$75,000 to Salvation Army of Ardmore, Ardmore, OK, 2013. For feeding programs and homeless shelter.
$50,000 to Gloria S. Ainsworth Day Care Center, Ardmore, OK, 2013. For operating support.
$40,000 to Arbuckle Life Solutions, Ardmore, OK, 2013. For general operating support.
$40,000 to YW8, Ardmore, OK, 2013. For operating support.
$28,000 to Dickson School District No. 1-77, Ardmore, OK, 2013. For School Cafeteria Excellence Institute.

7799
The Charles and Peggy Stephenson Family Foundation ✧
(formerly Stephenson Family Foundation)
2225 E. 30th St.
Tulsa, OK 74114-5427

Established in 1997 in OK.
Donors: Charles C. Stephenson, Jr.; Peggy C. Stephenson; Stephenson Equity Co.
Foundation type: Independent foundation.
Financial data (yr. ended 12/31/13): Assets, $168,632,037 (M); gifts received, $65,600; expenditures, $5,808,007; qualifying distributions, $5,770,862; giving activities include $5,710,378 for 39 grants (high: $5,001,438; low: $500).
Fields of interest: Museums (art); Higher education; Human services; Salvation Army; Children/youth, services; Protestant agencies & churches; Native Americans/American Indians.
Limitations: Applications not accepted. Giving primarily in OK. No grants to individuals.
Application information: Contributes only to pre-selected organizations.
Manager: Cynthia A. Field.
Trustees: Charles C. Stephenson, Jr.; Peggy C. Stephenson.
EIN: 736301100

7800
Jess L. and Miriam B. Stevens Foundation ✧
4000 1 Williams Ctr.
Tulsa, OK 74172-0148 (918) 586-5711
Contact: Joseph J. McCain, Jr., Tr.

Established in 1999 in OK.
Foundation type: Independent foundation.
Financial data (yr. ended 07/31/13): Assets, $13,324,131 (M); expenditures, $1,024,899; qualifying distributions, $864,980; giving activities include $801,440 for 33 grants (high: $149,500; low: $2,000), and $45,000 for 9 grants to individuals (high: $7,500; low: $2,500).
Purpose and activities: Giving primarily to organizations that benefit education and medical research, and that contribute to the welfare of needy persons.
Fields of interest: Higher education; Human services; Salvation Army.
Type of support: General/operating support; Continuing support; Capital campaigns; Building/renovation; Endowments; Scholarship funds; Scholarships—to individuals.
Limitations: Applications accepted. Giving primarily in Tulsa and northeastern OK.
Application information: Application form not required.
Initial approach: Letter
Copies of proposal: 2
Deadline(s): None
Trustee: Joseph J. McCain, Jr.
EIN: 731557364
Selected grants: The following grants are a representative sample of this grantmaker's funding activity:
$149,500 to Salvation Army of Tulsa, Tulsa, OK, 2011.
$75,000 to Easter Seals Oklahoma, Oklahoma City, OK, 2011.
$7,000 to Tulsa Kiwanis Club Foundation, Tulsa, OK, 2011.

7801
Stone Family Foundation ✧
320 S. Boston Ave., 19th Fl.
Tulsa, OK 74103-3706 (918) 583-1178
Contact: Samuel C. Stone, Pres.

Established in 1997 in KS.
Donor: Clifford W. Stone.
Foundation type: Independent foundation.
Financial data (yr. ended 12/31/13): Assets, $9,052,697 (M); expenditures, $480,962; qualifying distributions, $431,836; giving activities include $429,586 for 42 grants (high: $40,000; low: $2,000).
Purpose and activities: Giving primarily for the arts, particularly museums, education, hospitals, and to a rowing association.
Fields of interest: Museums (art); Arts; Education; Hospitals (general); Health care; Recreation, single organization support; Protestant agencies & churches.
Type of support: Continuing support; Annual campaigns; Equipment; Land acquisition; Scholarship funds; In-kind gifts; Matching/challenge support.
Limitations: Applications accepted. Giving primarily in KS, MO, and OK. No support for political organizations.
Application information: Application form not required.
Initial approach: Proposal
Deadline(s): None
Officers: Samuel C. Stone, Pres.; Sue Stone Hunter, V.P. and Secy.
Trustees: Britton Hunter; Sara Stone Laughren.
EIN: 431773536
Selected grants: The following grants are a representative sample of this grantmaker's funding activity:
$25,000 to Sooner Rowing Association, Tulsa, OK, 2011. For operations.
$15,000 to Butler County Historical Society, El Dorado, KS, 2011. For operations.
$15,000 to Liberty Memorial Association, Kansas City, MO, 2011. For operations.
$15,000 to Nature Conservancy, Oklahoma Chapter, Tulsa, OK, 2011. For operations.
$15,000 to Oklahoma School of Science and Mathematics Foundation, Oklahoma City, OK, 2011. For operations.
$10,000 to Botanica, Wichita, KS, 2011. For operations.
$10,000 to Oklahoma Centennial Botanical Garden, Tulsa, OK, 2011. For operations.
$10,000 to Wichita Art Museum, Wichita, KS, 2011. For operations.
$10,000 to Wichita Center for the Arts, Wichita, KS, 2011. For operations.
$5,000 to Street School, Tulsa, OK, 2011. For operations.

7802
Stuart Family Foundation ✧
(formerly Harold C. Stuart Foundation)
2431 E. 61st St., Ste. 600
Tulsa, OK 74136-1244 (918) 744-5222
Contact: Jon R. Stuart, Tr.

Established in 1969 in OK.
Donors: Harold C. Stuart; Joan S. Stuart†; Harold C. Stuart Revocable Trust.
Foundation type: Independent foundation.
Financial data (yr. ended 12/31/13): Assets, $24,029,827 (M); expenditures, $1,563,331; qualifying distributions, $1,172,000; giving activities include $1,172,000 for 19 grants (high: $903,000; low: $500).
Fields of interest: Museums; Higher education; Human services; Foundations (private grantmaking).
Type of support: General/operating support.
Limitations: Giving primarily in the Tulsa, OK, area.

Application information: Application form not required.
Initial approach: Proposal
Deadline(s): None
Board meeting date(s): Varies
Trustee: Jon R. Stuart; John B. Turner.
EIN: 237052187
Selected grants: The following grants are a representative sample of this grantmaker's funding activity:
$909,000 to University of Oklahoma Foundation, Norman, OK, 2011.
$87,500 to Gilcrease Museum, Tulsa, OK, 2011.
$68,500 to Philbrook Museum of Art, Tulsa, OK, 2011.
$20,000 to Ducks Unlimited, Memphis, TN, 2011.
$16,500 to University of Tulsa, Tulsa, OK, 2011.
$15,000 to Arts and Humanities Council of Tulsa, Tulsa, OK, 2011.
$12,500 to Oklahoma State University Foundation, Stillwater, OK, 2011.
$7,500 to Cameron University Foundation, Lawton, OK, 2011.
$5,000 to Oklahoma Aquarium, Jenks, OK, 2011.
$5,000 to Tulsa Historical Society, Tulsa, OK, 2011.

7803
A. R. & Marylouise Tandy Foundation ✧
P.O. Box 3627
Tulsa, OK 74101-3627 (918) 744-0553
Application address: c/o The Trust Company of Oklahoma, Attn.: Paul G. Giehm, Sr. V.P., 6120 S. Yale Ave., Ste. 1900, Tulsa, OK 74136, tel.: (918) 744-0553

Established in 1985 in OK.
Donors: Marylouise Tandy Cowan; Marylouise Cowan Trust; Marylouise Cowan Irrevocable Trust.
Foundation type: Independent foundation.
Financial data (yr. ended 12/31/12): Assets, $63,871,571 (M); expenditures, $6,457,511; qualifying distributions, $6,124,500; giving activities include $6,124,500 for 6 grants (high: $4,000,000; low: $2,500).
Fields of interest: Arts; Higher education, university; Human services.
Type of support: General/operating support; Continuing support; Annual campaigns; Capital campaigns; Building/renovation; Emergency funds.
Limitations: Giving primarily in the Boothbay Harbor, ME, and Tulsa, OK, regions. No grants to individuals.
Application information: Application form not required.
Initial approach: Letter
Deadline(s): Jan. 1, Apr. 1, July 1, and Oct. 1
Board meeting date(s): Quarterly
Trustee: The Trust Company of Oklahoma.
EIN: 731254985
Selected grants: The following grants are a representative sample of this grantmaker's funding activity:
$8,000,000 to University of Tulsa, School of Computer Science, Tulsa, OK, 2011. For two Chairs.
$1,000,000 to University of Tulsa, Tulsa, OK, 2010.
$200,000 to Mental Health Association in Tulsa, Tulsa, OK, 2011. For general support.
$114,600 to San Miguel Middle School of Tulsa, Tulsa, OK, 2011. For general support.
$100,000 to Bigelow Laboratory for Ocean Sciences, West Boothbay Harbor, ME, 2011. For Annual Fund.
$100,000 to YMCA of Boothbay Region, Boothbay Harbor, ME, 2011. For Annual Fund.
$47,000 to YMCA of Boothbay Region, Boothbay Harbor, ME, 2011. For general support.
$45,000 to Oklahoma Methodist Manor, Tulsa, OK, 2011. For renovations and new construction.
$30,998 to Southport United Methodist Church, Southport, ME, 2011. For general support.
$18,650 to Coastal Maine Botanical Gardens, Boothbay, ME, 2011. For general support.
$15,000 to YMCA of Boothbay Region, Boothbay Harbor, ME, 2010. For annual fund drive.
$11,500 to University of Tulsa, Tulsa, OK, 2010.
$10,000 to University of Maine, Bangor, ME, 2010.
$10,000 to University of Maine, Bangor, ME, 2011. For Museum of Art.
$5,000 to Connecticut College, New London, CT, 2010. For Annual Fund.
$2,000 to American Red Cross, Topsham, ME, 2010. For general fund.
$2,000 to American Red Cross, Tulsa, OK, 2010. For general fund.
$1,000 to Holland Hall School, Tulsa, OK, 2010. For Annual Fund.

7804
Herman P. and Sophia Taubman Foundation ✧ ☆
c/o Bank of Oklahoma, N.A.
P.O. Box 1620
Tulsa, OK 74101-1620 (918) 588-6407
Application address: c/o Bank of Oklahoma, N.A., P.O. Box 1620, Tulsa, OK 74101-1620, tel.: (918) 588-6407

Trust established in 1955 in OK.
Donors: Herman P. Taubman†; Sophia Taubman†.
Foundation type: Independent foundation.
Financial data (yr. ended 12/31/13): Assets, $7,610,350 (M); expenditures, $522,639; qualifying distributions, $473,330; giving activities include $456,896 for 9 grants (high: $120,000; low: $10,000).
Fields of interest: Museums (children's); Arts; Higher education; Education; Hospitals (general); Health organizations, association; Children/youth, services; Family services; Jewish federated giving programs; Jewish agencies & synagogues.
Type of support: General/operating support; Building/renovation; Program development; Research.
Limitations: Applications accepted. Giving primarily in CA, HI, NY, TX, and WA. No grants to individuals.
Application information: Application form required.
Initial approach: Letter
Copies of proposal: 3
Deadline(s): None
Board meeting date(s): As required
Trustees: Kaaren P. Shalom; Anne C. Taubman; Deborah Taubman; H. Perry Taubman; Hilary L. Taubman; Lawrence Taubman; Bank of Oklahoma, N.A.
EIN: 736092820

7805
The David E. and Cassie L. Temple Foundation ✧
(also known as Temple Foundation)
P.O. Box 35362
Tulsa, OK 74153-0362 (918) 743-9861
Contact: Dr. C. Wayne Bland, Chair.
E-mail: templefoundation@cox.net

Established in 1995 in OK.
Donors: Cassie L. Temple†; David E. Temple†.
Foundation type: Independent foundation.
Financial data (yr. ended 06/30/13): Assets, $17,938,501 (M); expenditures, $958,144; qualifying distributions, $810,558; giving activities include $699,000 for 52 grants (high: $70,000; low: $500).
Purpose and activities: Giving primarily for the needs of educational service organizations as determined by the foundation founders.
Fields of interest: Higher education; Education; Youth development; Human services; Children/youth, services; Christian agencies & churches.
Limitations: Applications accepted. Giving primarily in the Tulsa, OK, metropolitan area.
Application information: Application form required.
Initial approach: Proposal
Copies of proposal: 3
Deadline(s): Oct. 1
Final notification: Requests for additional information & approvals/denials will be made from Nov. through May following the Oct. 1st submission deadline.
Officers and Trustees:* Dr. C. Wayne Bland,* Chair.; Betty L. Stephenson,* Secy.; Timothy L. Lyons,* Treas.
EIN: 731452166
Selected grants: The following grants are a representative sample of this grantmaker's funding activity:
$5,000 to Tulsa Ballet Theater, Tulsa, OK, 2011.

7806
C. W. Titus Foundation ✧
427 S. Boston Ave., Ste. 950
Tulsa, OK 74103-4114 (918) 582-8095
Contact: Timothy T. Reynolds, Tr.

Established in 1968 in OK.
Foundation type: Independent foundation.
Financial data (yr. ended 12/31/13): Assets, $39,273,877 (M); expenditures, $1,988,757; qualifying distributions, $1,831,583; giving activities include $1,820,000 for 56 grants (high: $500,000; low: $1,000).
Purpose and activities: Giving primarily for health, and children and social services; support also for the arts and cultural programs.
Fields of interest: Arts; Education; Hospitals (general); Health care; Health organizations, association; Youth development, centers/clubs; Human services; Children/youth, services; Residential/custodial care, senior continuing care.
Type of support: General/operating support; Building/renovation.
Limitations: Applications accepted. Giving primarily in MO and OK. No grants to individuals.
Application information:
Initial approach: Proposal
Deadline(s): None
Directors: Megan Crowder; Michael E. Davison.
Trustee: Timothy T. Reynolds.
EIN: 237016981
Selected grants: The following grants are a representative sample of this grantmaker's funding activity:
$37,500 to Gilcrease Museum, Tulsa, OK, 2012. For Help fund George Washington Exhibit.
$30,000 to Drury University, Springfield, MO, 2012. To study Abroad Scholarship Program.

$15,000 to American Lung Association, Tulsa, OK, 2012. For General Operating Expenses of the Tulsa office only.
$11,000 to Crosstown Learning Center, Tulsa, OK, 2012. For classroom supplies.

7807
Tulsa Community Foundation ✧
7030 S. Yale, Ste. 600
Tulsa, OK 74136 (918) 494-8823
Contact: Phil Lakin, Jr., C.E.O.
FAX: (918) 494-9826; E-mail: info@tulsacf.org; Additional e-mail: plakin@tulsacf.org; Main URL: http://www.tulsacf.org

Established in 1998 in OK.
Foundation type: Community foundation.
Financial data (yr. ended 12/31/12): Assets, $3,729,789,000 (M); gifts received, $173,718,000; expenditures, $145,095,000; giving activities include $110,512,000 for grants.
Purpose and activities: The foundation seeks to facilitate, assist, and support participating organizations to the fullest extent possible by growing philanthropy primarily in northeastern OK.
Fields of interest: Education; Health care; Disasters, preparedness/services; Human services; Community/economic development.
Type of support: General/operating support; Annual campaigns; Capital campaigns; Building/renovation; Equipment; Endowments; Emergency funds; Program development; Curriculum development; Fellowships; Scholarship funds; Technical assistance; Consulting services; Program evaluation; Program-related investments/loans; Employee-related scholarships; Scholarships—to individuals; Matching/challenge support.
Limitations: Applications not accepted. Giving limited to northeastern OK through discretionary funds; donor-advised and additional giving is nationwide.
Publications: Annual report; Financial statement; Informational brochure; Occasional report.
Application information: In general, TCF itself does not make discretionary grants. However, the foundation's staff does maintain contact with donors who may be interested in funding a cause. Contact the foundation as an initial approach or visit the foundation's web site for more information.
Board meeting date(s): 2nd Tues. of Feb., May, Sept., and Nov.
Officers and Trustees:* Hans Helmerich,* Chair.; Phil Lakin, Jr., C.E.O.; Jeff Stava, C.O.O.; Debbie C. Allen, Cont.; James Adelson; Dewey Bartlett; Sharon J. Bell; Chester Cadieux; Joseph Craft III; Barry Davis; Duminda De Silva; Fred Dorwart; Steven Dow; Dan Ellinor; Robyn Ewing; Jerry Goodwin; Mark Graham; Dan Harrison; Jake Henry; Michael Johnson, Sr.; Marcia MacLeod; Sanjay D. Meshri; Charles Monroe; Hillary A. Parkhurst; Julius Pegues; Molly Pellegrini; Eric Richards; Scott Thompson; Steadman Upham; Steve Walton.
Number of staff: 11 full-time professional; 1 full-time support; 1 part-time support.
EIN: 731554474
Selected grants: The following grants are a representative sample of this grantmaker's funding activity:
$2,336,500 to Midway USA Foundation, Scholastic Shooting Trust (SST) Fund, Columbia, MO, 2012. For general operating support.
$2,285,423 to United Way, Tulsa Area, Tulsa, OK, 2012. For general operating support.
$1,137,700 to Children's Hospital Foundation at Saint Francis, Tulsa, OK, 2012. For general operating support.
$821,618 to Community Service Council of Greater Tulsa, Tulsa, OK, 2012. For general operating support.
$448,000 to Harvard Avenue Christian Church, Tulsa, OK, 2012. For general operating support.
$36,000 to Medical Development for Israel, New York, NY, 2012. For general operating support.
$25,000 to Diocese of Rochester, Rochester, NY, 2012. For general operating support.
$25,000 to Greater Cornerstone Community Development Project, Tulsa, OK, 2012. For general operating support.
$24,103 to United Way of Southwest Colorado, Durango, CO, 2012. For general operating support.
$7,500 to Wright State University, Dayton, OH, 2012. For scholarship.

7808
Sam Viersen Family Foundation, Inc. ✧
c/o Lisa R. Rhynes
P.O. Box 702708
Tulsa, OK 74170-2708 (918) 742-1979

Established in 1988 in OK.
Donor: Sam K. Viersen, Jr.†.
Foundation type: Independent foundation.
Financial data (yr. ended 12/31/12): Assets, $21,090,064 (M); expenditures, $1,354,285; qualifying distributions, $1,130,356; giving activities include $1,054,564 for grants.
Fields of interest: Arts; Higher education; Libraries/library science; Education; Human services; YM/YWCAs & YM/YWHAs; Children/youth, services.
Type of support: General/operating support; Continuing support; Management development/capacity building; Capital campaigns; Building/renovation; Equipment; Land acquisition; Endowments; Emergency funds; Program development.
Limitations: Applications accepted. Giving limited to Tulsa and Okmulgee counties, OK. No support for religious or tax funded organizations. No grants to individuals.
Application information: Application form not required.
Initial approach: Telephone
Copies of proposal: 1
Deadline(s): None
Board meeting date(s): Apr. and Oct.
Officers and Directors:* Maralynn V. Sant,* Pres.; Lisa Rhynes, Mgr.; Robert English; Brian C. Johnson; Jill Johnson; Jennifer Miller; Margaret Robinson; Leo M. Sant; Julie Schenk.
Number of staff: 1 full-time professional.
EIN: 731295358

7809
The William K. Warren Foundation ✧
P.O. Box 470372
Tulsa, OK 74147-0372
Contact: M. Ross, Secy.
Main URL: http://www.williamkwarrenfoundation.org/

Incorporated in 1945 in OK.
Donors: William K. Warren†; Mrs. William K. Warren†; N.W. Bryant; P.W. Swindle.
Foundation type: Independent foundation.
Financial data (yr. ended 12/31/13): Assets, $418,807,645 (M); gifts received, $574,348; expenditures, $26,520,703; qualifying distributions, $20,744,499; giving activities include $20,218,482 for 36 grants (high: $9,988,932; low: $2,000), and $42,023 for 2 loans/program-related investments (high: $38,611; low: $3,412).
Purpose and activities: Grants for local Catholic healthcare facilities, education, and social services; substantial support for a medical research program.
Fields of interest: Education; Health care; Medical research, institute; Human services; Catholic federated giving programs.
Type of support: General/operating support; Building/renovation; Endowments; Program development; Research; Program-related investments/loans.
Limitations: Applications accepted. Giving primarily in Tulsa, OK. No support for political organizations or parties, candidates for political office, and organizations whose primary purpose is to influence legislation; labor unions, fraternal orders or veteran's organizations; foreign-based institutions or organizations' programs for use outside the United States. No grants to individuals, or for film or video productions, book, or publishing projects; business development or investments; local athletic or sports programs, including competitions, travel, and/or sponsorships.
Application information: Cover letter not exceeding two pages and a narrative not exceeding three pages. See foundation web site for additional cover letter and narrative guidelines. Application form not required.
Initial approach: Letter. E-mail not accepted
Deadline(s): None
Board meeting date(s): Semiannually
Final notification: 3 months
Officers and Directors:* John-Kelly C. Warren,* Chair. and C.E.O.; W.R. Lissau,* Vice-Chair.; Stephen K. Warren,* Sr. V.P.; M. Ross, Secy.; M.A. Buntz, C.F.O. and Treas.; L. Glenn, Cont.; W.K. Warren, Jr.,* Chair. Emeritus; Peter P. Aran; Elizabeth Warren Blankenship; John A. Gaberino, Jr.; J. Frederick McNeer, M.D.; Jean M. Warren.
Number of staff: 10
EIN: 730609599
Selected grants: The following grants are a representative sample of this grantmaker's funding activity:
$11,885,874 to William K. Warren Medical Research Center, Tulsa, OK, 2012. For general support.
$4,846,130 to Laureate Institute for Brain Research, Tulsa, OK, 2012. For general support.
$1,050,000 to Children's Hospital Foundation at Saint Francis, Tulsa, OK, 2012. For general support.
$50,000 to Saint Francis Health Systems, Tulsa, OK, 2012. For general support.

7810
Waters Charitable Foundation ✧
6846 S. Trenton Ave.
Tulsa, OK 74136-4106

Established in 1988 in OK.
Donors: Thomas J. Carson; Mary L. Carson; Feron Waters; Barbara Waters; Judy Gayle Waters; Cherokee 2000 Investments, LLC.
Foundation type: Independent foundation.
Financial data (yr. ended 06/30/13): Assets, $12,753,252 (M); expenditures, $599,125;

qualifying distributions, $476,600; giving activities include $476,600 for grants.
Purpose and activities: Giving primarily for youth and human services.
Fields of interest: Libraries/library science; Health care; Human services; Youth, services; Christian agencies & churches.
Limitations: Applications not accepted. Giving primarily in Tulsa, OK. No grants to individuals.
Application information: Contributes only to pre-selected organizations.
Trustees: Pete Adamson III; Barbara Waters; Judy Gayle Waters; Joe Wyatt.
EIN: 731323325
Selected grants: The following grants are a representative sample of this grantmaker's funding activity:
$10,000 to Smile Train, New York, NY, 2011.
$10,000 to Special Olympics Oklahoma, Tulsa, OK, 2011.
$5,000 to American Diabetes Association, Alexandria, VA, 2011.
$5,000 to Disabled American Veterans, Cold Spring, KY, 2011.

7811
Westerman Foundation ✧

P.O. Box 7327
Edmond, OK 73083-7327 (405) 748-4230
Contact: Catherine E. Belden, Pres.
E-mail for Catherine Belden: catherinebelden@aol.com; Main URL: http://www.thewestermanfoundation.org

Established in 2000 in TX.
Donor: Laura J. Westerman†.
Foundation type: Independent foundation.
Financial data (yr. ended 12/31/13): Assets, $25,681,847 (M); gifts received, $9,492,641; expenditures, $836,232; qualifying distributions, $673,654; giving activities include $521,275 for 74 grants (high: $25,000; low: $250).
Purpose and activities: Giving primarily to educational institutions with emphasis on Catholic education; Christian based organizations, which promote family unity and values; and programs, which provide assistance to the poor and the abused.
Fields of interest: Secondary school/education; Higher education; Catholic agencies & churches.
Limitations: Applications accepted. Giving on a national basis. No support for political organizations, or for bricks and mortar projects. No grants to individuals, or for salaries, or multi-year requests.
Publications: Application guidelines.
Application information: Application form required.
Initial approach: See foundation web site
Deadline(s): Aug. 1
Officers and Directors:* Catherine Belden,* Pres. and Exec. Dir.; Lene Westerman,* V.P.; Sandra Zita Pratt,* Secy.; Lindsey Thompson,* Treas.; Celeste W. Ahern; John Settich.
Number of staff: 1 part-time professional.
EIN: 752897679

7812
Jerome Westheimer Family Foundation, Inc. ✧

Colston Bldg.
218 W. Washington St.
Ardmore, OK 73401-6926

Established in 1986 in OK.
Donor: Jerome M. Westheimer.
Foundation type: Independent foundation.
Financial data (yr. ended 12/31/13): Assets, $38,661,627 (M); gifts received, $1,656,227; expenditures, $1,767,091; qualifying distributions, $1,615,219; giving activities include $1,615,219 for 47 grants (high: $160,583; low: $1,500).
Purpose and activities: Giving primarily for art and cultural programs.
Fields of interest: Arts; Higher education; Education; Health care; Medical research.
Type of support: General/operating support; Endowments.
Limitations: Applications not accepted. Giving primarily in OK. No grants to individuals.
Application information: Contributes only to pre-selected organizations.
Officers: Jerome M. Westheimer, Jr., Pres.; Larry Pulliam, V.P.; Joel F. Wellnitz, Secy.; Charles F. Williams, Treas.
Trustee: Christian O'Donnell.
EIN: 731267603

7813
The Whitwell-Meyer Foundation ✧ ☆

11122 S. Yale Ave.
Tulsa, OK 74137-7620
Application address: c/o Thomas D. Whitwell, 5904 W. Orlando Cir., Broken Arrow, OK 74011, tel.: (918) 492-4209

Donors: Thomas D. Whitwell; Sara E. Whitwell; Robert D. Meyer; Linda L. Meyer.
Foundation type: Independent foundation.
Financial data (yr. ended 12/31/13): Assets, $127,469 (M); gifts received, $299,255; expenditures, $438,651; qualifying distributions, $436,785; giving activities include $436,785 for 5 grants (high: $311,785; low: $10,000).
Fields of interest: Religion.
Limitations: Applications accepted. Giving primarily in OK.
Application information: Application form required.
Initial approach: Letter
Deadline(s): None
Trustees: Linda L. Meyer; Robert D. Meyer; Sara E. Whitwell; Thomas D. Whitwell.
EIN: 272546121

7814
The Williams Companies Foundation, Inc. ✧

1 Williams Ctr., M.D. 45
Tulsa, OK 74172-0140 (918) 573-9676
Contact: Alison Anthony, Pres.
FAX: (918) 573-6006;
E-mail: communityrelationstulsa@williams.com

Incorporated in 1974 in OK.
Donor: The Williams Cos., Inc.
Foundation type: Company-sponsored foundation.
Financial data (yr. ended 12/31/12): Assets, $14,206,370 (M); gifts received, $2,850,000; expenditures, $5,233,000; qualifying distributions, $5,223,000; giving activities include $5,223,000 for grants.
Purpose and activities: The foundation supports organizations involved with arts and culture, education, health, human services, community development, and civic affairs.
Fields of interest: Media/communications; Museums; Humanities; Arts; Libraries (public); Education; Health care; Family services; Human services; Economic development; Community/economic development; United Ways and Federated Giving Programs; Public affairs.
Type of support: General/operating support; Capital campaigns; Building/renovation; Scholarship funds; Research; Employee-related scholarships; Matching/challenge support.
Limitations: Giving primarily in areas of company operations, with emphasis on Tulsa, OK; giving also to statewide and national organizations. No grants to individuals (except for employee-related scholarships).
Application information: The majority of giving is administered by the Tulsa Community Foundation.
Officers and Directors:* Robyn L. Ewing,* Chair.; Alison Anthony, Pres.; Sarah C. Miller, Secy.; Alan S. Armstrong; Donald R. Chappel; Rory L. Miller; Craig L. Rainey; James E. Scheel.
EIN: 237413843
Selected grants: The following grants are a representative sample of this grantmaker's funding activity:
$5,223,000 to Tulsa Community Foundation, Tulsa, OK, 2012. For health, welfare, and scholarships.

7815
Wilshire Charitable Foundation ✧

5619 N. Classen Blvd.
Oklahoma City, OK 73118-4015 (405) 254-5400
Contact: Paul G. Heafy, Pres.

Established in OK.
Donors: Paul G. Heafy; Better Days Foundation.
Foundation type: Independent foundation.
Financial data (yr. ended 12/31/13): Assets, $4,955,370 (M); gifts received, $365,000; expenditures, $1,022,677; qualifying distributions, $1,000,013; giving activities include $1,000,013 for 39 grants (high: $250,000; low: $500).
Fields of interest: Higher education; Medical research; United Ways and Federated Giving Programs.
Limitations: Applications accepted. Giving primarily in OK; some funding also in MA.
Application information: Application form not required.
Initial approach: Proposal
Deadline(s): None
Officers: Paul G. Heafy, Pres.; Andria Heafy, V.P.
EIN: 203873060
Selected grants: The following grants are a representative sample of this grantmaker's funding activity:
$240,000 to Oklahoma City University, Oklahoma City, OK, 2012. For Private Education.
$98,980 to Oklahoma Honor Flights, Midwest City, OK, 2012. For veteran services.
$5,000 to Lifewater International, San Luis Obispo, CA, 2012. For Water and Sanitation Development.
$2,500 to Love Hope Strength Foundation, Denver, CO, 2012. For cancer support services.

$2,500 to Novo Ministries, Oklahoma City, OK, 2012. For children's programs.
$2,500 to Union Theological Seminary, New York, NY, 2012. For Religious Education and Training.
$1,000 to Free to Live, Edmond, OK, 2012. For animal sanctuary.
$1,000 to Special Olympics Oklahoma, Tulsa, OK, 2012. For athletic competition.

7816
Wisdom Family Foundation, Inc ✧
P.O. Box 37
Alva, OK 73717-0037 (580) 327-2215
Contact: Jim Pfeiffer, Exec. Dir.

Donor: Grace Wisdom†.
Foundation type: Independent foundation.
Financial data (yr. ended 02/28/13): Assets, $18,601,103 (M); expenditures, $914,913; qualifying distributions, $775,000; giving activities include $775,000 for grants.
Fields of interest: Foundations (private grantmaking).
Application information: Application form required.
Initial approach: Letter
Deadline(s): Sept. 30
Directors: Lee Brandt; Robert Boeckman; Nancy Hall; Jeanne Anne King; Ken Schultz; Douglas Voth; Peggy Wisdom; Jim Pfeiffer.
EIN: 262151892

7817
Yot Full Circle Foundation ✧ ☆
1437 S. Boulder Ave., Ste. 770
Tulsa, OK 74119-3642

Established in OK.
Foundation type: Independent foundation.
Financial data (yr. ended 12/31/13): Assets, $23,711,939 (M); expenditures, $1,293,290; qualifying distributions, $1,027,350; giving activities include $936,000 for 50 grants (high: $110,000; low: $5,000).
Fields of interest: Education; Health care; Human services; Children/youth, services; Foundations (community); Christian agencies & churches.
Limitations: Applications not accepted. Giving in the U.S., with some emphasis on OH, particularly Cincinnati. No grants to individuals.
Application information: Unsolicited requests for funds not accepted.
Trustees: R.H. Harbaugh; Mary Jane Tritsch; Robert C. Tritsch.
EIN: 270578014
Selected grants: The following grants are a representative sample of this grantmaker's funding activity:
$100,000 to Cincinnati Reds Community Fund, Cincinnati, OH, 2011.
$50,000 to Trout Unlimited, Arlington, VA, 2011.
$25,000 to Cincinnati Works, Cincinnati, OH, 2011.
$10,000 to Assistance League of Greater Cincinnati, Cincinnati, OH, 2011.
$10,000 to Billy Graham Evangelistic Association, Charlotte, NC, 2011.
$10,000 to Trout Unlimited, Arlington, VA, 2011.
$5,000 to Federation of Fly Fishers, Livingston, MT, 2011.

7818
Zarrow Families Foundation ✧
401 S. Boston Ave., Ste. 900
Tulsa, OK 74103-4012 (918) 295-8004
Contact: Bill Major, Exec. Dir.
FAX: (918) 295-8049; E-mail: bmajor@zarrow.com; Main URL: http://www.zarrow.com/zff.htm

Established in 1987 in OK.
Donors: Henry H. Zarrow; Jack C. Zarrow.
Foundation type: Independent foundation.
Financial data (yr. ended 12/31/13): Assets, $10,437,637 (M); expenditures, $2,970,045; qualifying distributions, $2,925,596; giving activities include $2,885,738 for grants.
Purpose and activities: Giving primarily for Jewish causes and charities' fundraising events.
Fields of interest: Arts; Elementary/secondary education; Health care; Mental health/crisis services; Health organizations, association; Human services; Youth, services; United Ways and Federated Giving Programs.
Type of support: General/operating support; Conferences/seminars.
Limitations: Applications not accepted. Giving primarily in the Tulsa, OK, area. No grants to individuals.
Publications: Financial statement; Grants list.
Application information: Contributes only to pre-selected organizations.
Board meeting date(s): May and Nov.
Trustees: Judy Kishner; Gail Richards; Stuart Zarrow.
Number of staff: 1 full-time professional.
EIN: 731332141
Selected grants: The following grants are a representative sample of this grantmaker's funding activity:
$150,000 to Tulsa Congregation Bnai Emunah, Tulsa, OK, 2011. For Building Capital Fund and the Building Renewal Endowment Fund, payable over 5.00 years.
$100,000 to Jewish Federation of Tulsa, Tulsa, OK, 2011. For annual campaign.
$25,000 to Mental Health Association in Tulsa, Tulsa, OK, 2011. For Carnivale.
$16,000 to Temple Israel, Tulsa, OK, 2011. For operating support.
$15,000 to Brain and Behavior Research Foundation, New York, NY, 2011. For research on Schizophrenia and Depression.
$10,000 to Center for Individuals with Physical Challenges, Tulsa, OK, 2011. For Barlett Regatta.
$10,000 to Tulsa Historical Society, Tulsa, OK, 2011. For Tulsa Hall of Fame Dinner.
$3,500 to Sherwin Miller Museum of Jewish Art, Tulsa, OK, 2011. For operating support.
$1,200 to Jewish Funders Network, New York, NY, 2011. For contribution.
$1,000 to Parent Child Center of Tulsa, Tulsa, OK, 2011. For Toyland Ball.

7819
The Maxine and Jack Zarrow Family Foundation ✧
(formerly The Maxine and Jack Zarrow Foundation)
c/o Zarrow Family Office, LLC
401 S. Boston Ave., Ste. 900
Tulsa, OK 74103-4012 (918) 295-8004
Contact: Bill Major, Exec. Dir.
FAX: (918) 295-8049; E-mail: bmajor@zarrow.com; Main URL: http://www.zarrow.com

Established in 1988 in OK.
Donor: Jack C. Zarrow†.
Foundation type: Independent foundation.
Financial data (yr. ended 12/31/13): Assets, $47,233,636 (M); expenditures, $3,337,788; qualifying distributions, $3,142,832; giving activities include $2,997,450 for 206 grants (high: $400,000; low: $100).
Purpose and activities: The foundation is committed to helping support education, social services, Jewish causes, health programs, medical research and mental health programs. The foundation is also very interested in helping to provide food, clothing, and shelter for the challenged, disadvantaged and homeless, with a geographical preference for the Tulsa, OK, area.
Fields of interest: Higher education; Health care; Mental health/crisis services; Human services; Jewish agencies & synagogues.
Type of support: General/operating support; Program development.
Limitations: Applications accepted. Giving primarily in the Tulsa, OK, area.
Application information: See foundation web site for application requirements. Proposals received after due date will be held until next quarter's meeting. Application form required.
Initial approach: Use online grant application
Deadline(s): Jan. 15, Apr. 15, July 15, and Oct. 15
Board meeting date(s): Quarterly in Feb., May, Sept., and Nov.
Officers and Trustees:* Gail Richards,* Pres.; Rebecca Richards,* V.P. and Treas.; Eric Richards,* V.P.; Maxine Zarrow,* V.P.; Bill Major, Exec. Dir.
Number of staff: 1 full-time professional.
EIN: 316640903
Selected grants: The following grants are a representative sample of this grantmaker's funding activity:
$258,293 to GI Health Foundation, Clark, NJ, 2013. For operating support for a conference to develop clinical practice guidelines for colorectal neoplasia in IBD patients.
$100,000 to Domestic Violence Intervention Services, Tulsa, OK, 2013. For Rebuilding Lives Capital Campaign, payable over 5.00 years.
$30,000 to Town and Country School, Tulsa, OK, 2013. For Financial Aid Program.
$25,000 to Planned Parenthood of Eastern Oklahoma and Western Arkansas, Tulsa, OK, 2013. For general operating support.
$25,000 to University of Tulsa, Tulsa, OK, 2013. For Anne Morand Endowment Fund to conserve, care for and study the collection at Gilcrease Museum, payable over 2.00 years.
$15,000 to Tulsa Project Woman, Tulsa, OK, 2013. For funds for breast healthcare for uninsured women in the Tulsa area.
$10,000 to Dean A. McGee Eye Institute Foundation, Oklahoma City, OK, 2013. For general operating support.
$10,000 to Family Safety Center, Tulsa, OK, 2013. For general operating support.
$5,000 to University of Texas, University Development Office, Austin, TX, 2013. For College of Education Deans Associates Fund.
$3,000 to American Theater Company, Tulsa, OK, 2013. For free passes to clients of Mental Health Assoc. for season and replacement costumes.

7820

The Anne and Henry Zarrow Foundation ✧
401 S. Boston Ave., Ste. 900
Tulsa, OK 74103-4012 (918) 295-8004
Contact: Bill Major, Exec. Dir.
FAX: (918) 295-8049; E-mail: Bmajor@zarrow.com; Main URL: http://www.zarrow.com/foundations/anne-henry-zarrow-foundation/

Established in 1986 in OK.
Donor: Henry H. Zarrow†.
Foundation type: Independent foundation.
Financial data (yr. ended 12/31/13): Assets, $103,996,854 (M); gifts received, $2,681,800; expenditures, $8,298,958; qualifying distributions, $7,970,895; giving activities include $7,703,138 for 316 grants (high: $600,000; low: $500).
Purpose and activities: Giving primarily for education, social services, Jewish causes, health programs, medical research and mental health programs. The foundation is also very interested in helping to provide food, clothing, and shelter for the challenged, disadvantaged and homeless. The foundation also funds scholarships at selected universities in OK.
Fields of interest: Arts; Education; Health care; Human services; Aging, centers/services; United Ways and Federated Giving Programs; Disabilities, people with.
Type of support: General/operating support; Annual campaigns; Scholarship funds.
Limitations: Applications accepted. Giving primarily in the Tulsa, OK, area. No grants to individuals.
Publications: Application guidelines.
Application information: See foundation's web site for detailed application information and guidelines.The foundation will no longer take scholarship applications from students who are not already receiving scholarship assistance from the foundation. Application form not required.
Initial approach: Letter
Copies of proposal: 1
Deadline(s): Jan. 15, Apr. 15, Aug. 15, and Oct. 15 for grants.
Board meeting date(s): Feb., Apr., Sept., and Nov.
Officers and Directors:* Judith Z. Kishner,* Pres.; Stuart A. Zarrow,* V.P.; Bill Major, Exec. Dir.; Julie W. Cohen; Jay Wohlgemuth; Edward Zarrow.
Number of staff: 1 full-time professional; 2 part-time professional.
EIN: 731286874
Selected grants: The following grants are a representative sample of this grantmaker's funding activity:
$1,000,000 to Tulsa Community Foundation, Tulsa, OK, 2013. For A Gathering Place for Tulsa Fund, payable over 5.00 years.
$750,000 to Domestic Violence Intervention Services, Tulsa, OK, 2013. For Rebuilding Lives Capital Campaign, payable over 5.00 years.
$500,000 to LIFE Senior Services, Tulsa, OK, 2013. For LIFE Senior Services PACE (program of all-inclusive care for the elderly), payable over 4.00 years.
$500,000 to Oklahoma Medical Research Foundation, Oklahoma City, OK, 2013. To underwrite endowed chair in biomedical research, payable over 5.00 years.
$375,000 to Crosstown Learning Center, Tulsa, OK, 2013. For new learning center, payable over 3.00 years.
$300,000 to United Way, Tulsa Area, Tulsa, OK, 2013. For general operating support.
$100,000 to Community Service Council of Greater Tulsa, Tulsa, OK, 2013. For Conexiones, 2-1-1 Helpline, and TACSI.
$15,000 to Education and Employment Ministry, Oklahoma City, OK, 2013. For general operating funds.
$10,000 to Foundation for Tulsa Schools, Tulsa, OK, 2013. For Designer Showcase Gala.
$5,000 to Tulsa Community Foundation, Tulsa, OK, 2013. For the Cherry Street Famers Market Double Up Food Bucks Program.

7821

John Steele Zink Foundation ✧
P.O. Box 1620
Tulsa, OK 74101-1620
Contact: Tamera Sheaffer
Application address: c/o Tamera Sheaffer, 22151 E. 91st St., Broken Arrow, OK 74014, tel.: (918) 286-0244

Established in 1972.
Donors: John Steele Zink†; Jacqueline A. Zink†.
Foundation type: Independent foundation.
Financial data (yr. ended 10/31/13): Assets, $45,043,825 (M); expenditures, $2,250,030; qualifying distributions, $2,109,591; giving activities include $2,059,753 for 61 grants (high: $400,000; low: $1,000).
Purpose and activities: Support for higher education and cultural programs.
Fields of interest: Performing arts; Arts; Higher education; Philanthropy/voluntarism; Children/youth; Disabilities, people with; Physically disabled.
Type of support: General/operating support; Continuing support; Annual campaigns; Capital campaigns; Building/renovation; Program development; Curriculum development; Scholarship funds; In-kind gifts; Matching/challenge support.
Limitations: Applications accepted. Giving primarily in Tulsa, OK. No grants to individuals.
Application information: Application form required.
Initial approach: Telephone or Letter
Copies of proposal: 1
Deadline(s): None for written requests; verbal requests should be presented at the Board meeting in Oct.
Final notification: 3 months
Trustees: Caroline H. Abbott; Darton J. Zink; Jamie Zink.
Number of staff: 1 part-time professional.
EIN: 237246964

OREGON

7822
Leo Adler Community Trust ✧
(formerly Leo Adler Trust)
c/o U.S. Bank, N.A.
P.O. Box 3168
Portland, OR 97208-3168
Application address: c/o Michael Sullivan, U.S. Bank, N.A., P.O. Box 7928, Boise, ID 83707, tel.: (208) 383-7217

Established in 1993 in OR.
Donor: Leo Adler†.
Foundation type: Independent foundation.
Financial data (yr. ended 06/30/13): Assets, $24,022,013 (M); expenditures, $1,612,810; qualifying distributions, $1,344,928; giving activities include $1,245,441 for 143 grants (high: $118,684; low: $100).
Purpose and activities: Giving limited to Baker County, 1) 60 percent scholarships to students who are graduates of high schools located in Baker County, OR, or 2) for North Powder High School in Union County, OR; 40 percent of giving is in the form of community grants to organizations supported by Mr. Adler during his lifetime, primarily in Baker County.
Fields of interest: Education; Community/economic development.
Type of support: Building/renovation; Equipment; Program development; Scholarships—to individuals; Matching/challenge support.
Limitations: Giving limited to North Powder School District or a school district of Baker County, OR (for scholarships); grants for organizations primarily in Baker County, OR.
Publications: Informational brochure.
Application information: Application forms can be obtained at the counseling offices of eligible high schools or at U.S. Bank, Baker City Branch, between Jan. 1 and Mar. 30. Application form required.
Deadline(s): Apr. 1 for first time applicants; Mar. 1 for renewals. Oct. 1 for community grant application
Final notification: Aug.
Trustee: U.S. Bank, N.A.
EIN: 936289087

7823
The Autzen Foundation ✧
P.O. Box 3709
Portland, OR 97208-3709 (503) 226-6051
Contact: Kim Freed, Admin.
E-mail: autzen@europa.com

Incorporated in 1951 in OR.
Donor: Thomas J. Autzen†.
Foundation type: Independent foundation.
Financial data (yr. ended 12/31/13): Assets, $26,231,022 (M); expenditures, $1,290,895; qualifying distributions, $1,239,762; giving activities include $1,180,348 for 233 grants (high: $53,000; low: $1,000).
Purpose and activities: Giving primarily for youth services, education, the arts, and nature.
Fields of interest: Performing arts; Arts; Higher education; Environment; Health care; Boys & girls clubs; Human services; Children/youth, services.
Type of support: Scholarship funds; Continuing support; Building/renovation; Equipment; Program development; Seed money; Matching/challenge support.
Limitations: Applications accepted. Giving primarily in OR, with some emphasis on Portland. Giving limited to the Pacific Northwest region. No grants to individuals; no loans.
Publications: Application guidelines.
Application information: Application form required.
Initial approach: Letter or e-mail requesting application
Copies of proposal: 1
Deadline(s): Mar. 15, Aug. 15, and Nov. 15
Board meeting date(s): May, Sept., and Dec.
Final notification: 3 to 4 months
Officers: Wendy Ulman, Pres.; Christina Grady, Secy.
Directors: Thomas J. Autzen; Phillip Patton; Robert W. Patton III.
Number of staff: 1 part-time professional.
EIN: 936021333
Selected grants: The following grants are a representative sample of this grantmaker's funding activity:
$54,000 to Friends of Grant Athletics, Portland, OR, 2011.
$30,000 to Oregon State University Foundation, Corvallis, OR, 2011.
$10,000 to Salvation Army, Cascade Division, Happy Valley, OR, 2011.
$10,000 to Young Life North Coast, Seaside, OR, 2011.
$5,000 to Boys and Girls Aid Society of Oregon, Portland, OR, 2011.
$5,000 to Caldera, Portland, OR, 2011.
$4,704 to Boys and Girls Clubs of Central Oregon, Bend, OR, 2011.
$4,585 to Portland State University Foundation, Portland, OR, 2011.
$3,500 to Community Cycling Center, Portland, OR, 2011.
$2,500 to Nature of Words, Bend, OR, 2011.

7824
William H. & Mary L. Bauman Foundation ✧
7991 S.W. Edgewater Dr. E.
Wilsonville, OR 97070-9483

Established in 1991 in OR.
Donor: William H. Bauman†.
Foundation type: Independent foundation.
Financial data (yr. ended 12/31/13): Assets, $9,836,348 (M); expenditures, $665,892; qualifying distributions, $560,447; giving activities include $550,000 for 15 grants (high: $137,000; low: $5,000).
Purpose and activities: Giving primarily for education, and children, youth and social services; funding also to an evangelical Christian church.
Fields of interest: Arts; Higher education; Eye research; Human services; Children/youth, services; Christian agencies & churches.
Limitations: Applications not accepted. Giving primarily in Portland, OR. No grants to individuals.
Application information: Unsolicited requests for funds not accepted.
Officer: Paul Schwindt, Mgr.
Trustees: Clarence Knoepfle; Bill Vermillion; Rod Vermillion.
EIN: 936234071
Selected grants: The following grants are a representative sample of this grantmaker's funding activity:
$110,000 to Pacific Conference of the Evangelical Church, Milwaukie, OR, 2010.
$110,000 to Pacific Conference of the Evangelical Church, Milwaukie, OR, 2011.
$100,000 to George Fox University, Newberg, OR, 2011. For student scholarships.
$50,000 to Dougy Center, Portland, OR, 2011.
$35,000 to Salvation Army Portland, Portland, OR, 2010.
$30,000 to George Fox Evangelical Seminary, Portland, OR, 2011.
$30,000 to Trillium Family Services, Portland, OR, 2011.
$25,000 to Salvation Army, Cascade Division, Happy Valley, OR, 2011.

7825
Benton County Foundation ✧ ☆
660 N.W. Harrison Blvd.
Corvallis, OR 97330 (541) 753-1603
Contact: Paula M. Grace J.D., Pres. and C.E.O.
FAX: (541) 230-1621; E-mail: bcf@peak.org; Mailing Address: P. O. Box 911, Corvallis, OR 97339; Main URL: http://bentoncountyfoundation.org
Scholarship e-mail: sue@bentoncountyfoundation.org

Established in 1953 in OR.
Foundation type: Community foundation.
Financial data (yr. ended 12/31/13): Assets, $17,916,548 (M); gifts received, $916,679; expenditures, $1,112,728; giving activities include $557,706 for 19+ grants (high: $192,651), and $179,455 for 102 grants to individuals.
Purpose and activities: The foundation provides a service to individuals, families, and organizations to establish endowments, manage the funds received, and distribute a portion of the earnings each year to benefit the youth and community.
Fields of interest: Performing arts; Arts; Education, reading; Education; Health care; Health organizations, association; Athletics/sports, water sports; Recreation; Youth, services; Aging, centers/services; Community/economic development; Children/youth; Youth; Disabilities, people with; Physically disabled; Mentally disabled; Minorities; Hispanics/Latinos; Native Americans/American Indians; Military/veterans; Economically disadvantaged; Homeless.
Type of support: General/operating support; Continuing support; Annual campaigns; Capital campaigns; Building/renovation; Equipment; Endowments; Internship funds; Scholarship funds; Scholarships—to individuals.
Limitations: Applications accepted. Giving limited to Benton County, OR.
Publications: Application guidelines; Annual report; Grants list; Informational brochure; Newsletter.
Application information: Visit foundation web site for grant application form. Application form required.
Initial approach: Submit application form and attachments
Copies of proposal: 1
Deadline(s): Mar. 13
Board meeting date(s): 3rd Thurs. of each month
Officers and Directors:* Dave Gazeley,* Chair.; Pat Lampton,* V.P.; Paula M. Grace, J.D.*, Pres. and C.E.O.; Gerry Kosanovic,* Secy.; Jon Nelson,* Treas.; Beth Heaney; Jim Jordan; Alan Lanker, J.D.,

CPA; Cam W. Little; Yema Measho, J.D.; Alice Mills Morrow, J.D.; John Turman.
Number of staff: 1 part-time professional; 1 part-time support.
EIN: 936022916

7826
Braemar Charitable Trust ✧
P.O. Box 25442
Portland, OR 97298-0442
Contact: Martha B. Cox, Tr.
E-mail: MaryL@trustmanagementservices.net; Application address: c/o Mary Lanthrum, Trust Mgmt. Svcs., P.O. Box 1990, Waldport, OR 97394-1990, tel.: (541) 563-7279; fax: (541) 563-7216

Established in 1993 in OR.
Donors: Hobart M. Bird; Marian A. Bird.
Foundation type: Independent foundation.
Financial data (yr. ended 09/30/13): Assets, $20,693,810 (M); expenditures, $799,328; qualifying distributions, $643,865; giving activities include $526,314 for 64 grants (high: $10,000; low: $2,802).
Fields of interest: Arts; Education; Human services; Children/youth, services.
Type of support: General/operating support; Building/renovation; Equipment; Program development; Curriculum development.
Limitations: Applications accepted. Giving limited to OR. No support for political organizations. No grants to individuals; or for scholarships, capital campaigns, endowments or debt retirement.
Publications: Application guidelines.
Application information: Applications sent by fax are not accepted. Application form required.
Initial approach: Request application guidelines from Waldport address, or download from web site: http://www.trustmanagementservices.net
Copies of proposal: 1
Deadline(s): Varies by region, refer to web site: http://www.trustmanagementservices.net. Applications should not be submitted more than 30 days prior to deadline date
Trustees: Hobart M. Bird; Martha B. Cox; Melanie A. Dawson.
EIN: 936272124
Selected grants: The following grants are a representative sample of this grantmaker's funding activity:
$5,000 to Multiple Sclerosis Society, National, New York, NY, 2011.

7827
The Burning Foundation ✧
715 S.W. Morrison St., Ste. 901
Portland, OR 97205-3105 (503) 419-8454
Contact: Sybil Ackerman-Munson, Fdn. Advisor
FAX: (206) 784-5987;
E-mail: BurningFoundation@gmail.com; Main URL: http://fdnweb.org/burning
Grants List: http://fdnweb.org/burning/grant-examples/

Established in 1997 in WA.
Donor: David Weise.
Foundation type: Independent foundation.
Financial data (yr. ended 12/31/13): Assets, $12,738,563 (M); expenditures, $699,335; qualifying distributions, $636,508; giving activities include $613,000 for 48 grants (high: $20,000; low: $5,000).
Purpose and activities: Giving primarily to organizations whose environmental programs address issues in WA and OR. Priority areas include protecting threatened rivers and forests, nurturing native fish populations, and conserving land and open space for ecological and recreational purposes. Preference will be given to requests from local groups working to improve their immediate environment and from statewide groups addressing general conservation and protection issues, rather than national organizations with projects in the Pacific Northwest. The foundation also supports teen pregnancy prevention projects which may include school-based health and education programs, mentoring projects, and community clinic programs providing information and services on birth control, choice, and sex education.
Fields of interest: Environment, natural resources; Environment, water resources; Environment, land resources; Environment, forests; Environmental education; Animals/wildlife, fisheries; Youth, pregnancy prevention; Youth, services.
Type of support: General/operating support; Program development.
Limitations: Giving limited to OR and WA for environmental requests, and the Puget Sound area for conservation programs for youth and teen pregnancy prevention programs. No support for private schools, universities, gardening programs, the creation or renovation of community parks, environmental education programs, or for programs related to energy conservation, alternative energy, nuclear waste, toxics, or global warming. No grants to individuals for research or scholarships, or for capital campaigns for building construction or renovations, computer, software, or office equipment purchases, or book, video, film, or home-page productions, unless the production is an essential component of the funded project.
Publications: Application guidelines; Grants list.
Application information: See foundation web site for complete application guidelines.
Deadline(s): Spring cycle: 3rd Wed. of Jan. for letter, 1st Wed. of Mar. for invited proposal; fall cycle: 3rd Wed. of Aug. for letter, 1st Wed. of Oct. for invited proposal
Final notification: 1st Wed. of May and 4th Wed. of Nov.
Officers: David N. Weise, Pres.; Daniel W. Weise, V.P.; Alisa K. F. Weise, Secy.
EIN: 911815335
Selected grants: The following grants are a representative sample of this grantmaker's funding activity:
$20,000 to Hells Canyon Preservation Council, La Grande, OR, 2012. For Wildlife Connectivity Campaign.
$20,000 to Oregon Natural Desert Association, Bend, OR, 2012. For Wilderness Stewardship and Restoration.
$20,000 to Skagit Land Trust, Mount Vernon, WA, 2012. For conservation strategy.
$15,000 to Neighborcare Health, Seattle, WA, 2012. For School-Based Health Centers.
$15,000 to Planned Parenthood of the Great Northwest, Seattle, WA, 2012. For Teen Pregnancy Prevention 'someone You Know'.
$12,000 to American Rivers, Washington, DC, 2012. For Restoring the Yakima River.
$12,000 to Bark, Portland, OR, 2012. For Monitoring Program.
$12,000 to Cascadia Wildlands Project, Eugene, OR, 2012. For Protecting Oregon's Forests and Rivers.
$12,000 to Columbia Land Trust, Vancouver, WA, 2012. For Central Willapa Bay Conservation Project.
$12,000 to Inland Northwest Land Trust, Spokane, WA, 2012. For Latah Creek Watershed Restoration.

7828
Caddock Foundation, Inc. ✧
17271 N. Umpqua Hwy.
Roseburg, OR 97470-9422
Application address: c/o Sue E. Brinkman, 1717 Chicago Ave., Riverside, CA 92507-2208, tel.: (541) 672-1716

Incorporated in 1968 in CA.
Foundation type: Independent foundation.
Financial data (yr. ended 12/31/13): Assets, $1,802,789 (M); expenditures, $740,119; qualifying distributions, $731,700; giving activities include $731,700 for 16 grants (high: $544,000; low: $1,600).
Purpose and activities: Grants to Evangelical Christian religious associations and activities, including Bible studies.
Fields of interest: Christian agencies & churches.
Type of support: General/operating support; Continuing support; Program evaluation.
Limitations: Applications accepted. Giving primarily in CA, IL, TX and OR. No grants to individuals.
Application information: Application form required.
Initial approach: Letter
Deadline(s): None
Officers: John B. Caddock, Pres.; Richard E. Caddock, Jr., V.P.; Sue E. Brinkman, Secy.-Treas.
EIN: 952559728

7829
Cambia Health Foundation ✧
(formerly The Regence Foundation)
P.O. Box 1271, M.S. E12C
Portland, OR 97207-1271 (503) 276-1965
Contact: Monique Barton, Exec. Dir.
FAX: (503) 276-1996;
E-mail: RegenceFoundation@regence.com; Main URL: http://www.regencefoundation.org/index.html
Twitter: http://twitter.com/RegenceGives

Established in 2007 in OR.
Donor: The Regence Group.
Foundation type: Company-sponsored foundation.
Financial data (yr. ended 12/31/12): Assets, $67,503,727 (M); gifts received, $8,000,161; expenditures, $4,651,902; qualifying distributions, $2,528,442; giving activities include $1,823,597 for 20 grants (high: $142,350; low: $50,000).
Purpose and activities: The foundation supports programs designed to increase access to medical care for those who cannot afford it; and promote innovating methods that improve outcomes and address disparities in care.
Fields of interest: Medical care, in-patient care; Medical care, community health systems; Hospitals (general); Health care, clinics/centers; Public health; Health care; Health care, insurance; Health care, patient services; End of life care; Palliative care.
Type of support: Management development/capacity building; Technical assistance; Research; Program development.

Limitations: Applications accepted. Giving limited to ID, OR, UT, and WA. No support for political organizations, or for religious organizations not of direct benefit to the entire community. No grants to individuals (except for Sojourns Awards), or capital construction, award dinners, athletic events, competitions, special events, or tournaments, or conferences or seminars.
Publications: Application guidelines; Program policy statement.
Application information: Unsolicited applications for Sojourns Pathway planning grants are not accepted. Organizations receiving support are asked to submit a final report. Application form required.
Initial approach: Complete online eligibility quiz and letter of inquiry for Building Healthier Communities; complete online application for Sojourns Pathways; complete online nomination form for Sojourns Award
Deadline(s): None for Building Healthier Communities; Jan. 8 to Aug. 6 for Sojourns Pathways implementation grants; None for Sojourns Pathways innovation grants; Dec. 3 for Sojourns Awards
Board meeting date(s): Quarterly
Final notification: 60 days for Building Healthier Communities; 45 days for Sojourns Pathways; Mar. for Sojourns Award
Officers and Directors: Michael C. Alexander,* Chair.; Kieren Porter, Pres.; Kerry Barnett, Secy.; Lynn Harden, Exec. Dir.; Jennifer Cannaday; Vivian Chi; Mark Ganz; Scott Kreiling; John Stellmon.
Number of staff: 3 full-time professional.
EIN: 320200578

7830
The Campbell Foundation ✧
260 S.W. Birdshill Rd.
Portland, OR 97219-8504
Contact: Cynthia A. Campbell, Dir.

Established in 1993 in OR.
Donors: J. Duncan Campbell, Jr.; Cynthia A. Campbell; Birdshill, Inc.; United Asset Mgmt.; The Campbell Group.
Foundation type: Independent foundation.
Financial data (yr. ended 12/31/12): Assets, $16,235,872 (M); expenditures, $2,056,236; qualifying distributions, $859,861; giving activities include $681,885 for 137 grants (high: $100,000; low: $100).
Purpose and activities: Giving primarily to youth organizations and programs; funding also for human services, and to museums.
Fields of interest: Museums; Higher education; Human services; Children/youth, services; Foundations (private grantmaking).
Limitations: Applications accepted. Giving primarily in Portland, OR. No grants to individuals directly.
Publications: Financial statement.
Application information: Application form required.
Initial approach: Letter
Copies of proposal: 1
Deadline(s): Dec. 1st
Officer: J. Duncan Campbell, Jr., Chair.
Directors: Cynthia A. Campbell; John Gilleland.
EIN: 931133917

7831
The Carpenter Foundation ✧
824 E. Main St., Ste. 102
Medford, OR 97504-7139 (541) 772-5732

Incorporated in 1957 in OR.
Donors: Helen Bundy Carpenter†; Alfred S.V. Carpenter†; Helene Salade Ogle Trust.
Foundation type: Independent foundation.
Financial data (yr. ended 06/30/13): Assets, $18,009,845 (M); gifts received, $219,032; expenditures, $977,394; qualifying distributions, $734,615; giving activities include $734,615 for grants.
Purpose and activities: The primary purpose of the foundation is to add opportunity, choice, inclusiveness, enrichment, and a climate for change for those living in the Rogue Valley, Oregon. Primary areas of interest include the arts, education, public interest, regional planning, and human services, including child welfare and youth.
Fields of interest: Visual arts; Performing arts; Performing arts, theater; Arts; Education, early childhood education; Child development, education; Secondary school/education; Higher education; Adult/continuing education; Adult education—literacy, basic skills & GED; Libraries/library science; Education, reading; Education; Environment, natural resources; Environment; Health care; Substance abuse, services; Mental health/crisis services; Legal services; Housing/shelter, development; Human services; Children/youth, services; Child development, services; Family services; Rural development; Community/economic development; Government/public administration; Public affairs; Disabilities, people with; Physically disabled; Blind/visually impaired; Mentally disabled; Hispanics/Latinos; Substance abusers; Economically disadvantaged; Homeless; LGBTQ.
Type of support: Management development/capacity building; Annual campaigns; Building/renovation; Capital campaigns; Conferences/seminars; Consulting services; Continuing support; Curriculum development; Equipment; General/operating support; Land acquisition; Matching/challenge support; Program development; Program evaluation; Publication; Scholarship funds; Seed money; Technical assistance.
Limitations: Applications accepted. Giving limited to Jackson and Josephine counties, OR. No grants to individuals, or for deficit financing.
Publications: Application guidelines; Annual report (including application guidelines); Financial statement; Grants list; Informational brochure (including application guidelines).
Application information: Application form required.
Initial approach: Letter
Copies of proposal: 1
Deadline(s): Telephone for current deadlines
Board meeting date(s): Quarterly
Officers and Trustees:* Emily C. Mostue,* Pres.; Karen C. Allan,* V.P. and Secy.; William R. Moffat,* Treas.
Number of staff: 2 part-time professional; 1 part-time support.
EIN: 930491360

7832
Chambers Family Foundation ✧
P.O. Box 7009
Springfield, OR 97475-0009 (541) 484-2419
FAX: (541) 342-2695;
E-mail: chambersfamilyfoundation@cmc.net; Main URL: http://www.chambersfamilyfoundation.com/

Established in 1999 in OR.
Donor: Carolyn Silva Chambers†.
Foundation type: Independent foundation.
Financial data (yr. ended 12/31/12): Assets, $16,474,906 (M); expenditures, $971,245; qualifying distributions, $835,149; giving activities include $817,092 for 32 grants (high: $270,000; low: $760).
Purpose and activities: Giving primarily to support and further the arts, education, medical health, and human needs in Lane, Benton, and Deschutes counties in Oregon.
Fields of interest: Arts; Education; Human services; Children/youth.
Type of support: General/operating support; Continuing support; Management development/capacity building; Building/renovation; Equipment; Emergency funds; Program development; Film/video/radio; Seed money; Curriculum development; Scholarship funds; Research; Matching/challenge support.
Limitations: Applications accepted. Giving primarily in Lane, Benton and Deschutes counties, OR. No support for pass through agencies or environmental projects. No grants or scholarships to individuals or for capital campaigns.
Publications: Informational brochure (including application guidelines).
Application information: Application guidelines available on foundation web site; e-mailed proposals not accepted. Application form required.
Initial approach: Proposal
Copies of proposal: 1
Deadline(s): Mar. 31 and Sept. 30
Board meeting date(s): Late May and late Nov.
Final notification: 3 months following deadline
Trustees: Elizabeth Chambers; Scott D. Chambers; Silva L. Chambers.
Number of staff: 1 part-time professional.
EIN: 931266648
Selected grants: The following grants are a representative sample of this grantmaker's funding activity:
$270,000 to Pleasant Hill Booster Club, Pleasant Hill, OR, 2012. For funds for the Track and Field Project.
$250,000 to Pleasant Hill Foundation, Pleasant Hill, OR, 2012. For funds for the Community Center.
$2,500 to Pleasant Hill Foundation, Pleasant Hill, OR, 2012. For funds for the selection of five families in need at Christmas.
$1,755 to Marist High School Foundation, Eugene, OR, 2012. For funds for income based tuition assistance.

7833
Chiles Foundation ✧
111 S.W. 5th Ave., Ste. 4050
Portland, OR 97204-3643 (503) 222-2143
E-mail: cf@uswest.net

Incorporated in 1949 in OR.
Donors: Eva Chiles Meyer†; Earle A. Chiles†; Virginia H. Chiles†.
Foundation type: Independent foundation.

Financial data (yr. ended 12/31/13): Assets, $3,066,771 (M); expenditures, $1,219,665; qualifying distributions, $947,723; giving activities include $626,300 for 34 grants (high: $100,000; low: $500).
Purpose and activities: Primary focus is to assist and support educational and medical advancement.
Fields of interest: Arts; Higher education; Medical research, institute.
Type of support: Scholarship funds; Research.
Limitations: Applications accepted. Giving primarily in OR and the Pacific Northwest; some funding also CA and Munich, Germany. No support for projects involving litigation. No grants to individuals, or for deficit financing, mortgage retirement, no loans.
Application information: Application form required.
Initial approach: Contact foundation for application form
Deadline(s): Between July 1 and July 15
Officers and Trustees:* Earle M. Chiles,* Pres.; J. Kenneth Menges, Jr.,* Secy.; Pedro Garcia.
Number of staff: 2 full-time professional; 2 part-time professional; 1 full-time support.
EIN: 936031125

7834
Clark Foundation ✧ ☆

9770 S.W. Sunshine Ct.
Beaverton, OR 97005-4100 (503) 627-9978
Contact: Richard M. Clark, Pres.

Established in 1968 in OR.
Donors: Maurie D. Clark†; Mary H. Clark.
Foundation type: Independent foundation.
Financial data (yr. ended 12/31/13): Assets, $28,835,679 (M); expenditures, $1,508,794; qualifying distributions, $1,259,650; giving activities include $1,259,650 for 66 grants (high: $130,000; low: $750).
Fields of interest: Arts; Education; Zoos/zoological societies; Animals/wildlife; Human services.
Type of support: Building/renovation.
Limitations: Applications accepted. Giving primarily in the Portland, OR, metropolitan area. No grants to individuals, or for endowment funds, research, or matching gifts; no loans.
Publications: Grants list.
Application information: Application form required.
Initial approach: Letter
Copies of proposal: 1
Deadline(s): None
Board meeting date(s): Bimonthly
Officers: Richard M. Clark, Pres. and Treas.; Brittney Clark, V.P.; Steven A. Nicholes, Secy.
Directors: Patrick E. Becker, Sr.; Christopher Brooks; Tracy A. Clark; Candace Holzgrafe; Jon Holzgrafe; Janeen McAninch.
Number of staff: 1 part-time professional.
EIN: 237423789

7835
The Clemens Foundation ✧

P.O. Box 24
Alsea, OR 97324-0024 (541) 487-4100
Contact: Susie Sapp
E-mail: clemensfound@peak.org

Incorporated in 1959 in OR.
Donors: Rex Clemens†; Ethel M. Clemens†; Rex Veneer Co.; Karl Corbin†; Stan Lowther/Wells Fargo Advisors, LLC.
Foundation type: Independent foundation.
Financial data (yr. ended 12/31/13): Assets, $30,484,593 (M); gifts received, $300; expenditures, $2,080,115; qualifying distributions, $2,003,405; giving activities include $1,948,429 for grants.
Purpose and activities: Tuition grants for high school graduates of Alsea, Crane, Eddyville and Philomath, OR, to attend college or an accredited vocational school on a full-time basis.
Fields of interest: Education.
Type of support: Scholarship funds; Scholarships—to individuals.
Limitations: Giving limited to residents (of at least 8 years) of Alsea, Crane, Eddyville and Philomath, OR.
Application information: Application form required for scholarships. Application form required.
Deadline(s): June 30 for scholarships
Officers and Board Members:* David Lowther,* Pres.; Steven Lowther,* V.P.; Ronald Edwards,* Secy.; Fred Lowther,* Treas.; Kelly D. Howard,* Exec. Dir.; Elwood Berklund; Wayne L. Howard; Thad Springer.
Number of staff: 1 full-time professional.
EIN: 936023941

7836
The Collins Foundation

1618 S.W. 1st Ave., Ste. 505
Portland, OR 97201-5706 (503) 227-7171
Contact: Cynthia G. Addams, Exec. V.P.
FAX: (503) 295-3794;
E-mail: information@collinsfoundation.org; Main URL: http://www.collinsfoundation.org

Incorporated in 1947 in OR.
Donor: Members of the Collins family.
Foundation type: Independent foundation.
Financial data (yr. ended 12/31/13): Assets, $214,370,936 (M); expenditures, $10,988,819; qualifying distributions, $9,894,492; giving activities include $9,113,297 for 268 grants (high: $504,805; low: $1,500).
Purpose and activities: To improve, enrich, and give greater expression to humanitarian endeavors in the state of Oregon, and to assist in improving the quality of life in the state.
Fields of interest: Humanities; Arts; Education; Environment; Health care; Human services; Children/youth, services; Religion; Children/youth; Adults; Aging; Physically disabled; Mentally disabled; Minorities; Immigrants/refugees; Economically disadvantaged; Homeless; LGBTQ.
Type of support: Program development; Management development/capacity building; Land acquisition; General/operating support; Curriculum development; Continuing support; Capital campaigns; Building/renovation; Equipment; Program-related investments/loans; Matching/challenge support.
Limitations: Applications accepted. Giving limited to OR. No support for individual religious congregations, elementary, secondary or public higher educational institutions. No grants to individuals, or for endowments, operational deficits, financial emergencies, debt retirement, or annual fundraising activities.
Publications: Annual report; Annual report (including application guidelines); Grants list.
Application information: Do not send proposals electronically; if applicant's program/project is time sensitive submitting two months in advance of a particular trustee meeting is recommended; a complete description of the application process is available in the submission guidelines section of the foundation web site. Application form not required.
Initial approach: Call, rather than write, if you have questions, otherwise just send complete proposal
Copies of proposal: 1
Deadline(s): None
Board meeting date(s): Feb., Apr., June, Aug., Oct. and Dec.
Final notification: 2 to 4 months
Officers and Trustees:* Truman W. Collins, Jr.,* Pres.; Cynthia G. Addams, Exec. V.P.; Ralph Bolliger,* V.P.; Cherida C. Smith,* V.P.; Lee Diane Collins Vest, V.P.; Cindy J. Knowles, Secy. and Dir., Prog(s).; Timothy R. Bishop, Treas.; Maribeth W. Collins, Tr. Emeritus; Jerry E. Hudson; Alayna Luria.
Number of staff: 3 full-time professional; 2 part-time professional; 1 full-time support.
EIN: 936021893
Selected grants: The following grants are a representative sample of this grantmaker's funding activity:
$250,000 to Willamette University, Salem, OR, 2012. To renovate the Lestle J. Sparks Center athletic facility.
$213,000 to Foundations for a Better Oregon, Portland, OR, 2012. To support the Chalkboard Project for calendar years 2013 and 2014.
$100,000 to Oregon Community Foundation, Oregon Parenting Education Collaborative Fund, Portland, OR, 2012. To expand the number of parenting education hubs serving Oregon communities.
$100,000 to Self Enhancement, Inc., Portland, OR, 2012. To provide academic and personal achievement program to low-income students in grades 3-12 at Humboldt School and Jefferson High School.
$50,000 to Virginia Garcia Memorial Foundation, Cornelius, OR, 2012. To construct a new comprehensive wellness facility and headquarters for a Federally Qualified Health Center providing healthcare to low-income individuals.
$30,000 to Elevate Oregon, Portland, OR, 2012. To support school-based mentoring for low-income at-risk high school students in the Parkrose School District.
$25,000 to Umatilla-Morrow County Head Start, Hermiston, OR, 2012. To construct a facility for Head Start and Women, Infant, Children programs serving low-income families in Milton-Freewater.
$20,000 to Society of Saint Vincent de Paul Rogue Valley Council, Medford, OR, 2012. To support operations and programs serving low-income and homeless individuals and families.
$15,000 to Northwest Professional Dance Project, Portland, OR, 2012. To support operations and programs.

7837
Collins Medical Trust ✧ ☆

1618 S.W. 1st Ave., Ste. 500
Portland, OR 97201-5706 (503) 227-1219
Contact: Nancy L. Helseth, Admin.
FAX: (503) 227-5349;
E-mail: nhelseth@collinsmedicaltrust.org; Tel. for applications: (503) 471-2223; Main URL: http://www.collinsmedicaltrust.org

Established in 1956 in OR.
Donor: Truman W. Collins†.

Foundation type: Independent foundation.
Financial data (yr. ended 09/30/13): Assets, $8,190,870 (M); expenditures, $435,431; qualifying distributions, $431,355; giving activities include $429,538 for 13 grants (high: $70,000; low: $29,760).
Purpose and activities: Grants limited to medical research and medical education within the state of Oregon.
Fields of interest: Higher education; Medical school/education; Nursing school/education; Cancer; Biomedicine; Medical research, institute; Cancer research.
Type of support: Equipment; Program development; Seed money; Scholarship funds; Research; Matching/challenge support.
Limitations: Applications accepted. Giving limited to OR.
Publications: Application guidelines; Annual report.
Application information: Complete application guidelines available on trust web site. Application form not required.
Initial approach: Letter or e-mail (e-mail preferred)
Copies of proposal: 2
Deadline(s): Last business day of the month preceding board meetings
Board meeting date(s): Jan., May, and Sept.
Officers: Timothy R. Bishop, Treas.; Nancy L. Helseth, Admin.
Trustees: Truman W. Collins, Jr.; Elizabeth Eckstrom, M.D., M.P.H.; Walter J. McDonald, M.D.
EIN: 936021895

7838
Crabby Beach Foundation ✧
P.O. Box 280
Lake Oswego, OR 97034-0280

Established in 2003 in OR.
Donor: Sue D. Cooley.
Foundation type: Independent foundation.
Financial data (yr. ended 12/31/13): Assets, $65,727,935 (M); expenditures, $2,835,172; qualifying distributions, $2,833,796; giving activities include $2,826,574 for 28 grants (high: $350,892; low: $10,000).
Fields of interest: Arts; Elementary/secondary education; Education; Environment; Health organizations, association; Housing/shelter, development.
Limitations: Applications not accepted. Giving primarily in WA. No grants to individuals.
Application information: Contributes only to pre-selected organizations.
Officers: Caroline Cooley Browne, Pres.; Jeanne Becker, Treas.
Directors: David Browne; Sue D. Cooley.
EIN: 300179374

7839
Bob and Evelyn Dieringer Family Foundation ✧
10505 S.E. 44th Ave.
Milwaukie, OR 97222-5202

Established in OR.
Donor: Victoria Evelyn Dieringer Trust.
Foundation type: Independent foundation.
Financial data (yr. ended 12/31/13): Assets, $7,585,638 (M); expenditures, $464,473; qualifying distributions, $432,026; giving activities include $428,144 for 6 grants (high: $240,000; low: $25,000).
Fields of interest: Human services; Christian agencies & churches.
Limitations: Applications not accepted. Giving primarily in Portland, OR.
Application information: Unsolicited requests for funds not accepted.
Trustee: Eugene Dieringer.
EIN: 273650979

7840
Jack and Marie Eiting Foundation ✧
(formerly Eiting Foundation)
707 S.W. Washington St., Ste. 1500
Portland, OR 97205-3532

Established in 2002 in OR.
Donors: Jack R. Eiting; Marie E. Eiting; Precision Strip, Inc.
Foundation type: Independent foundation.
Financial data (yr. ended 12/31/12): Assets, $124,865 (M); gifts received, $1,783,904; expenditures, $1,906,921; qualifying distributions, $1,900,500; giving activities include $1,900,500 for 19 grants (high: $932,091; low: $240).
Fields of interest: Education; Human services; Catholic agencies & churches.
Limitations: Applications not accepted. Giving primarily in FL, OH, and Portland, OR; funding also in WA; some funding also in Guatemala. No grants to individuals.
Application information: Contributes only to pre-selected organizations.
Officers and Directors:* John R. Eiting,* Pres.; Robert J. Preston, Secy.; Marie E. Eiting,* Treas.
EIN: 010614397

7841
The Esco Foundation ✧
(formerly The Swigert Foundation)
P.O. Box 3121
Portland, OR 97208-3121 (503) 225-2935
Contact: Robyn E. Brewer

Established in 1990 in OR.
Donors: Ernest C. Swigert‡; Henry T. Swigert.
Foundation type: Independent foundation.
Financial data (yr. ended 12/31/13): Assets, $13,956,422 (M); gifts received, $50,233; expenditures, $697,494; qualifying distributions, $600,750; giving activities include $600,750 for 54 grants (high: $131,250; low: $500).
Fields of interest: Arts, formal/general education; Museums (art); Performing arts, dance; Elementary/secondary education; Higher education, university; Medical school/education; Boys & girls clubs.
Type of support: General/operating support; Continuing support; Annual campaigns; Capital campaigns; Building/renovation; Equipment; Land acquisition; Emergency funds; Program development; Professorships; Curriculum development; Research; Matching/challenge support.
Limitations: Applications accepted. Giving primarily in OR and southwest WA. No grants to individuals.
Application information: Application form required.
Initial approach: Request application form
Copies of proposal: 1
Deadline(s): None
Board meeting date(s): Jan, Apr., Aug. and Dec.
Officers: Henry T. Swigert, Pres.; George C. Spencer, Secy.
Directors: Addison Gronquist; Kate Warren Hall; Dorn Swigert; Elizabeth K. Warren; Wendy Warren.
EIN: 943122667
Selected grants: The following grants are a representative sample of this grantmaker's funding activity:
$50,000 to Oregon Zoo Foundation, Portland, OR, 2012. For elephant/forest enrichment.
$35,000 to Blanchet House of Hospitality, Portland, OR, 2012. For kitchen remodel.
$7,500 to Growing Gardens, Portland, OR, 2012. For Youth Grow Project.
$7,000 to Oregon State Parks Foundation, Portland, OR, 2012. For Year End Request Various Projects.
$5,000 to Food Roots, Tillamook, OR, 2012. To Help End Hunger in Tilamook Cnty.
$5,000 to Human Solutions, Portland, OR, 2012. For Ongoing After School Program.
$1,000 to World Forestry Center, Portland, OR, 2012. For Memberships.

7842
Fjarli Foundation ✧
670 Mason St.
Medford, OR 97501-1340

Established in 2003 in OR.
Donors: Merlin Fjarli; Joann Fjarli.
Foundation type: Independent foundation.
Financial data (yr. ended 12/31/13): Assets, $5,863,553 (M); expenditures, $784,542; qualifying distributions, $610,106; giving activities include $589,723 for 6 grants (high: $350,000; low: $25,480).
Purpose and activities: Giving primarily for radio evangelism, and to other ministries.
Fields of interest: Human services; Religion.
Limitations: Applications not accepted. Giving primarily in the U.S., with some emphasis on IL. No grants to individuals.
Application information: Contributes only to pre-selected organizations.
Officers: Merlin Fjarli, Pres.; Bruce Fjarli, V.P.; Joann Fjarli, Secy.
EIN: 571186466
Selected grants: The following grants are a representative sample of this grantmaker's funding activity:
$27,220 to Rogue Valley Adventist School, Medford, OR, 2011.
$25,000 to Gospel Outreach, College Place, WA, 2011.
$20,000 to Southern Adventist University, Collegedale, TN, 2010.

7843
The Merlin and Jo Ann Fjarli Foundation, Inc. ✧
670 Mason Way
Medford, OR 97501-1340

Established in 2007 in OR.
Donors: Merlin Fjarli; Joann Fjarli; Clint Fjarli; Lola Fjarli.
Foundation type: Independent foundation.
Financial data (yr. ended 12/31/13): Assets, $5,416,109 (M); expenditures, $926,222; qualifying distributions, $551,837; giving activities

include $551,837 for 7 grants (high: $250,000; low: $3,876).
Fields of interest: Human services; Christian agencies & churches.
Limitations: Applications not accepted. Giving primarily in CA, ID, MD, OR, and WA.
Application information: Contributes only to pre-selected organizations.
Officers: Merlin Fjarli, Pres.; Clint Fjarli, V.P.; Joann Fjarli, Secy.
EIN: 830501956
Selected grants: The following grants are a representative sample of this grantmaker's funding activity:
$50,000 to Gospel Outreach, College Place, WA, 2012. To sponsor Gospel Workers in India.
$22,000 to Maranatha Volunteers International, Roseville, CA, 2012. For Construction of Christian School in India.

7844
Fohs Foundation ✧

P.O. Box 1001
Roseburg, OR 97470-0232 (541) 440-1587
Contact: Stefani Faunce, Amin.
Main URL: http://thefohsfoundation.com/

Established in 1937 in NY.
Donors: F. Julius Fohs‡; Cora B. Fohs‡; Fred & Frances Sohn Charitable Lead Trust.
Foundation type: Independent foundation.
Financial data (yr. ended 12/31/12): Assets, $16,505,071 (M); gifts received, $303,544; expenditures, $1,092,423; qualifying distributions, $848,417; giving activities include $730,000 for 20 grants (high: $165,000; low: $5,000).
Purpose and activities: Giving to ensure the viability of a Jewish homeland in Israel by improving relations between the Jewish majority and Arab minority within the state.
Fields of interest: Education; Civil/human rights; Community/economic development; Social sciences, research; Public affairs; Jewish agencies & synagogues; Minorities; Economically disadvantaged.
International interests: Israel.
Type of support: General/operating support; Income development; Management development/capacity building; Program development; Seed money; Curriculum development; Research.
Limitations: Applications accepted. Giving primarily in the U.S. and Israel. No support for programs that do not address majority-minority issues in Israel.
Application information: Application form required.
Initial approach: Letter
Copies of proposal: 1
Deadline(s): Mar. 31
Officers: Frances F. Sohn, Chair.; Howard F. Sohn, Vice-Chair.
Trustees: Ruth Sohn; Barbara Tint.
Number of staff: 1 part-time support.
EIN: 746003165

7845
The Ford Family Foundation

1600 N.W. Stewart Pkwy.
Roseburg, OR 97471-1957 (541) 957-5574
Contact: Anne C. Kubisch, Pres.
FAX: (541) 957-5720; E-mail: info@tfff.org; Main URL: http://www.tfff.org
Scholarship application address: The Ford Family Foundation Scholarship Office, 440 E. Broadway, Ste., 200, Eugene, OR 97401, tel.: (541) 485-6211, toll free: (877) 864-2872, e-mail: fordscholarships@tfff.org, fax: (541) 485-6223

Incorporated in 1957 in OR.
Donors: Kenneth W. Ford‡; Hallie E. Ford‡.
Foundation type: Independent foundation.
Financial data (yr. ended 12/31/13): Assets, $877,924,758 (M); expenditures, $35,105,702; qualifying distributions, $33,749,798; giving activities include $5,850,630 for 2 foundation-administered programs.
Purpose and activities: The foundation makes grants to public charities that pre-dominantly benefit small communities in rural Oregon and Siskiyou County, California. It is committed to investing in the capacities of individuals and communities through scholarships, grants and the Ford Institute of Community Building.
Fields of interest: Arts, administration/regulation; Visual arts; Libraries/library science; Health care, clinics/centers; Dental care; Crime/violence prevention, child abuse; Youth development; Children/youth, services; Community/economic development; Infants/toddlers; Children/youth; Children; Youth; Infants/toddlers, female.
Type of support: General/operating support; Management development/capacity building; Capital campaigns; Building/renovation; Equipment; Program development; Fellowships; Technical assistance; Employee matching gifts; Scholarships—to individuals; Matching/challenge support.
Limitations: Applications accepted. Giving primarily in rural OR, with special interest in Douglas and Coos counties; giving also in Siskiyou County, CA, or for populations less than 30,000 not adjacent to or part of an urban area. No support for projects or programs that are indirectly funded through a fiscal agent, or for lobbying or propaganda. No grants to individuals (except for scholarships or fellowships), or for endowment/reserve funds, general fund drives, debt retirement, deficits, or for indirect or overhead expenses.
Publications: Informational brochure (including application guidelines); Newsletter.
Application information: The foundation only accepts requests for funding through an on-line application process. Full proposals are accepted by invitation only. Application form required.
Initial approach: Review application guidelines to determine eligibility
Copies of proposal: 1
Deadline(s): None for responsive and technical assistance grants
Board meeting date(s): Four times per year
Final notification: 3-4 weeks
Officers and Directors:* Karla S. Chambers,* Chair.; Toby Luther,* Vice-Chair.; Anne Kubisch, C.E.O. and Pres.; Allyn C. Ford,* Secy.-Treas.; Deborah Millsap, C.F.O.; Dr. Knute Buehler; Joe Robertson; Wesley Sand; Carrie Thompson.
Number of staff: 7 full-time professional; 11 full-time support.
EIN: 936026156
Selected grants: The following grants are a representative sample of this grantmaker's funding activity:
$1,900,000 to Oregon Community Foundation, Portland, OR, 2012. For Advised Fund - 2012 Payout.
$800,000 to Oregon University System, Eugene, OR, 2012. For GEAR UP Sustainability Grants, payable over 5.25 years.
$595,000 to Siskiyou Community Services Council, Mount Shasta, CA, 2012. For Siskiyou Strong Families Strong Communities, payable over 3.00 years.
$400,000 to Boys and Girls Clubs of the Umpqua Valley, Roseburg, OR, 2012. For New Teen Center Development/Parking Redesign and Expansion, payable over 3.50 years.
$150,000 to Columbia River Maritime Museum, Astoria, OR, 2012. For Astoria Railroad Depot Convening Space.
$131,145 to Umpqua Community Health Center, Roseburg, OR, 2012. For Got Smile? Dental Program, payable over 2.00 years.
$130,000 to Pacific Northwest College of Art, Portland, OR, 2012. For Lee Kelly Memory 99.
$25,000 to Court Appointed Special Advocates of Douglas County, Roseburg, OR, 2012. For CASA Organizational Capacity Building.
$10,000 to Oregon Social Learning Center Foundation, Eugene, OR, 2012. For Kids in Transition to School (KITS) Program.
$5,000 to Monmouth-Independence Community Foundation, Monmouth, OR, 2012. For Monmouth/Independence Class 3: MICycles.

7846
Foreign Mission Foundation ✧

10875 S.W. 89th St.
Tigard, OR 97223-8323

Established around 1982 in OR.
Donors: John Cooner; Eugene L. Davis; Harold Kent; JoAnn Kent; Joanne Kendall; Kyle Strickland; Harry Lloyd Charitable Trust; Ralph Lloyd; Miriam Larson; Teresa Lloyd; Ralph Nordick; Calvary Church; Galcom International USA; Gill Services, Inc.; WF Foundation; Living Water Foundation; GTI Services, Inc.; NW Christian Community Foundation; Oak Hills Church; Synergy Resource Group; South Asian Advocates; Tyndale House Foundation; Strategic Resources Group; The RB Nordick Foundation; Cornerstone Trust.
Foundation type: Independent foundation.
Financial data (yr. ended 02/28/13): Assets, $7,627,060 (M); gifts received, $886,261; expenditures, $1,687,625; qualifying distributions, $1,011,903; giving activities include $1,011,903 for grants.
Purpose and activities: Giving primarily for missionary programs in the U.S. and India.
Fields of interest: Education; Human services; Religion.
International interests: India.
Limitations: Applications not accepted. Giving primarily in India; some funding in the U.S. No grants to individuals.
Application information: Contributes only to pre-selected organizations.
Officers: Eugene L. Davis, Pres.; Vivian Davis, Secy.
Directors: Don Chapman; Loren Davis.
Number of staff: 1 full-time professional; 1 part-time professional.
EIN: 930763215

7847
Glory Foundation ✧
P.O. Box 230939
Tigard, OR 97281-0939

Donor: Katherine A. Eiting.
Foundation type: Independent foundation.
Financial data (yr. ended 12/31/13): Assets, $1,563,385 (M); expenditures, $1,807,532; qualifying distributions, $1,773,922; giving activities include $1,773,922 for 18 grants (high: $50,322; low: $5,000).
Fields of interest: Education; Health care; Human services; Children, services; Catholic federated giving programs.
Limitations: Applications not accepted. Giving primarily in CA, OH, OR, and VA; some funding also in MD.
Application information: Contributes only to pre-selected organizations.
Officers: Katherine A. Eiting, Pres.; Robert J. Preston, Secy.-Treas.
EIN: 721574570

7848
Greater Hart-Sheldon Conservation Fund ✧
15 S.W. Colorado Ave., Ste. 300
Bend, OR 97702-1149

Established in 2010 in OR.
Donor: Ruby Pipeline, LLC.
Foundation type: Independent foundation.
Financial data (yr. ended 12/31/13): Assets, $2,957,068 (M); gifts received, $750,000; expenditures, $670,542; qualifying distributions, $554,547; giving activities include $554,547 for 6 grants (high: $285,318; low: $2,500).
Fields of interest: Education; Environment.
Limitations: Applications not accepted.
Application information: Unsolicited requests for funds not accepted.
Officers: Brent Fenty, Pres.; Michael Brennan, V.P.; David Dobkin, Exec. Dir.
Directors: David Bobzien.
EIN: 273442560
Selected grants: The following grants are a representative sample of this grantmaker's funding activity:
$50,000 to Oregon Natural Desert Association, Bend, OR, 2012. To study of Environmental Effects.

7849
Rosaria P. Haugland Foundation ✧
P.O. Box 40190
Eugene, OR 97404-0027

Established in 2003 in WA.
Donors: Alexander D. Haugland; Rosaria P. Haugland; Marina E. Haugland Martin.
Foundation type: Independent foundation.
Financial data (yr. ended 09/30/13): Assets, $19,589,374 (M); gifts received, $27,000; expenditures, $1,315,854; qualifying distributions, $1,163,570; giving activities include $1,163,570 for 34 grants (high: $276,000; low: $200).
Purpose and activities: Giving for support of the arts, education and community institutions to help women and children.
Fields of interest: Performing arts; Higher education; Children; Women; Girls.
Type of support: Capital campaigns; Building/renovation; Professorships; Fellowships; Scholarship funds.
Limitations: Applications not accepted. Giving primarily in OR. No support for religious or political organizations. No grants to individuals.
Publications: Annual report.
Application information: Contributes only to pre-selected organizations. Unsolicited requests for funds not accepted.
Board meeting date(s): Annually
Officer and Directors:* Rosaria P. Haugland,* Pres.; Alexander D. Haugland; Marina E. Haugland Martin.
Number of staff: None.
EIN: 200270777
Selected grants: The following grants are a representative sample of this grantmaker's funding activity:
$50,000 to University of Oregon Foundation, Eugene, OR, 2013. For Doctoral Student Support.

7850
The Bill Healy Foundation ✧
P.O. Box 4525
Portland, OR 97208-4525 (503) 222-1899
Contact: Diane Hall, Exec. Dir.
FAX: (503) 222-1861;
E-mail: info@billhealyfoundation.org; Office address: 721 N.W. 9th Ave., Ste. 229, Portland, OR 97209; Main URL: http://www.billhealyfoundation.org
Grants List: http://www.billhealyfoundation.org/recipients2013.html

Established in 1995 in OR.
Donor: Cameron Healy.
Foundation type: Independent foundation.
Financial data (yr. ended 12/31/13): Assets, $29,925,809 (M); expenditures, $1,372,640; qualifying distributions, $1,208,179; giving activities include $918,438 for 78 grants (high: $50,000; low: $1,000).
Purpose and activities: Giving primarily for environmental conservation and the well-being of children. The foundation is committed to responsible grant making through thoughtful choices by recognizing the fragile interdependence between the environment and human beings.
Fields of interest: Education; Environment; Children.
Limitations: Applications accepted. Giving primarily in HI and OR. No grants to individuals.
Publications: Application guidelines.
Application information: See foundation web site for application policies and form. Application form required.
Initial approach: Submit grant consideration application
Deadline(s): See foundation web site for current deadlines
Officers: Cameron Healy, Chair.; Diane Hall, Exec. Dir.
Directors: Marc Cramer; Kathleen Healy; Tim Healy; Laney Patrick; Susan Snow.
EIN: 931208721
Selected grants: The following grants are a representative sample of this grantmaker's funding activity:
$15,000 to Rogue Valley Farm to School, Ashland, OR, 2012. For children/environment.

7851
Hedinger Family Foundation ✧
1750 N.W. NAITO Pkwy., Ste. 106
Portland, OR 97209-2532

Established in 1998 in OR.
Donor: American Industries, Inc.
Foundation type: Company-sponsored foundation.
Financial data (yr. ended 12/31/12): Assets, $487,243 (M); gifts received, $1,000,000; expenditures, $1,774,909; qualifying distributions, $1,757,847; giving activities include $1,757,847 for 46 grants (high: $200,000; low: $500).
Purpose and activities: The foundation supports science museums and organizations involved with education, animals and wildlife, health, cancer, youth development, and human services.
Fields of interest: Education; Animals/wildlife; Youth development.
Type of support: General/operating support; Building/renovation; Program development; Scholarship funds.
Limitations: Applications not accepted. Giving primarily in the greater Portland, OR, area. No grants to individuals.
Application information: Contributes only to pre-selected organizations.
Directors: Hillary Hedinger Guelfi; Blake H. Hedinger; Howard H. Hedinger.
EIN: 931255431

7852
Ralph Hull Foundation ✧
P.O. Box 1084
Corvallis, OR 97339-1084 (541) 754-4944
Contact: Nancy Hull, Treas.

Established in OR.
Foundation type: Independent foundation.
Financial data (yr. ended 06/30/13): Assets, $19,926,821 (M); expenditures, $1,460,304; qualifying distributions, $1,038,643; giving activities include $1,038,643 for grants.
Fields of interest: Education; Human services.
Limitations: Applications accepted. Giving primarily in OR.
Application information:
Initial approach: Letter
Deadline(s): None
Officers: Herbert R. Hull, Chair.; Nancy Hull, Treas.
Directors: Con Lynch; Nathan Nystrom; Todd W. Nystrom; Dennis Olson; Edward Parker.
EIN: 931247987

7853
Intel Foundation ✧
5200 NE Elam Pkwy.
Hillsboro, OR 97124
Contact: Wendy Ramage Hawkins, Exec. Dir.
E-mail: intel.foundation@intel.com; Main URL: http://www.intel.com/foundation

Established in 1988 in OR.
Donors: Intel Corp.; Intel Capital Corp.
Foundation type: Company-sponsored foundation.
Financial data (yr. ended 12/31/12): Assets, $66,021,758 (M); gifts received, $45,528,000; expenditures, $45,557,799; qualifying distributions, $45,542,799; giving activities include $45,318,315 for grants.

Purpose and activities: The foundation supports programs designed to advance education and improve communities worldwide. Special emphasis is directed toward programs designed to advance education in math, science, and engineering; promote the entrance of women and under-represented minorities into careers in science and engineering; and enable Intel employees to improve quality of life in their communities.
Fields of interest: Elementary/secondary education; Elementary/secondary school reform; Higher education; Higher education, college; Business school/education; Teacher school/education; Engineering school/education; Education, computer literacy/technology training; Education; Disasters, preparedness/services; Youth development, business; United Ways and Federated Giving Programs; Science, formal/general education; Mathematics; Engineering/technology; Engineering; Science; Youth; Minorities; African Americans/Blacks; Hispanics/Latinos; Native Americans/American Indians; Women.
Type of support: General/operating support; Program development; Conferences/seminars; Curriculum development; Scholarship funds; Research; Employee volunteer services; Sponsorships; Employee matching gifts; Matching/challenge support.
Limitations: Applications not accepted. Giving primarily in areas of company operations in Phoenix, AZ, Folsom and Santa Clara, CA, Hudson, MA, Albuquerque, NM, Portland, OR, and DuPont, WA, Sao Paulo, Brazil, China, San Jose, Costa Rica, Egypt, India, Israel, Mexico, Russia, Taiwan, and Istanbul, Turkey; limited giving to select national organizations. No support for religious, sectarian, fraternal, or political organizations, arts or healthcare organizations, environmental organizations, private schools, or sports teams. No grants to individuals, or for endowments, capital campaigns, general fund drives, annual campaigns, fundraising events, sporting events, television or radio production costs, creation of personal/organization websites, travel or tours, or equipment.
Publications: Annual report; Corporate giving report.
Application information: Unsolicited applications are not accepted.
Board meeting date(s): Semiannually
Officers and Directors:* Richard G. A. Taylor, Chair.; Shelly M. Esque, Pres.; Suzan A. Miller, Secy.; Ravi Jacob, Treas.; Wendy Ramage Hawkins,* Exec. Dir.; Deborah S. Conrad; Justin Rattner.
Number of staff: 2 part-time professional; 1 full-time support.
EIN: 943092928
Selected grants: The following grants are a representative sample of this grantmaker's funding activity:
$6,550,000 to Society for Science and the Public, Washington, DC, 2012. For Intel International Science and Engineering Fair (ISEF) Foundation.
$5,150,000 to Society for Science and the Public, Washington, DC, 2012. For Intel Science Talent Search (STS).
$3,222,011 to United Way, Valley of the Sun, Phoenix, AZ, 2012. For matching grant.
$1,083,113 to Scholarship America, Saint Peter, MN, 2012. For student support.

7854
J.F.R. Foundation ✧
1211 S.W. 5th Ave., Ste. 2840
Portland, OR 97204-3736 (503) 552-3535
Contact: Jeff Rippey
FAX: (503) 241-0839; E-mail: jeff@jrippey.com

Established in 1993 in OR.
Donors: James F. Rippey; Jeffrey L. Rippey.
Foundation type: Independent foundation.
Financial data (yr. ended 12/31/13): Assets, $17,162,003 (M); gifts received, $1,019,552; expenditures, $1,124,014; qualifying distributions, $1,120,854; giving activities include $1,110,000 for 37 grants (high: $100,000; low: $5,000).
Purpose and activities: Giving primarily for education, children and youth services, particularly a boys and girls club, and for social services.
Fields of interest: Arts; Higher education; Education; Boys & girls clubs; Human services; Children/youth, services; Infants/toddlers; Children/youth; Children; Youth; Young adults; Physically disabled; Women; Infants/toddlers, female; Girls; Young adults, female; Infants/toddlers, male; Boys; Young adults, male; Single parents; Crime/abuse victims; Homeless.
Limitations: Giving primarily in OR, with emphasis on Portland. No support for religious or political organizations. No grants to individuals.
Publications: Application guidelines.
Application information:
Initial approach: Letter of intent
Deadline(s): May 1 for new applicants; Sept. 1 for existing clients
Board meeting date(s): Annually—in late Oct.
Officer and Directors:* Jan Dimick,* Secy.; Robin R. Holman; Jack McMurchie; James F. Rippey; Jeffrey L. Rippey; Shirley K. Rippey; Timothy M. Rippey.
EIN: 943192331
Selected grants: The following grants are a representative sample of this grantmaker's funding activity:
$80,000 to Boys and Girls Club, 2010. For general support.
$65,000 to Saint Marys Home for Boys, Beaverton, OR, 2010. For general support.
$60,000 to Albertina Kerr Centers, Portland, OR, 2011. For general support.
$50,000 to Library Foundation, 2010. For general support.
$35,000 to New Avenues for Youth, Portland, OR, 2010. For general support.
$35,000 to Oregon Zoo, Portland, OR, 2010. For general support.
$30,000 to Oregon Childrens Foundation, Portland, OR, 2010. For general support.
$25,000 to Oregon Museum of Science and Industry, Portland, OR, 2010. For general support.
$25,000 to Pearl Buck Center, Eugene, OR, 2010. For general support.
$10,000 to Court Appointed Special Advocates, 2010. For general support.

7855
The Jackson Foundation ✧
P.O. Box 3168
Portland, OR 97208-3168 (503) 275-6564
Main URL: http://www.thejacksonfoundation.com

Trust established in 1960 in OR; Philip Ludwell Jackson Charitable and Residual Trusts were merged into The Jackson Foundation in 1981.
Donor: Maria C. Jackson†.
Foundation type: Independent foundation.
Financial data (yr. ended 06/30/13): Assets, $12,875,185 (M); expenditures, $718,831; qualifying distributions, $629,147; giving activities include $542,500 for 157 grants (high: $15,000; low: $1,000).
Purpose and activities: Giving primarily for the arts, education, health, and children, youth and social services.
Fields of interest: Performing arts; Arts; Education; Health care; Human services; Children/youth, services.
Type of support: Continuing support; Capital campaigns; Endowments; Research.
Limitations: Applications accepted. Giving limited to OR, with emphasis on Portland; requests for projects located outside the Portland metropolitan area are accepted, provided that the project is of statewide appeal, rather than of local concern. No support for churches or temples. No grants to individuals, or for matching gifts, scholarships, fellowships, or building or equipment funds for religious organizations; no loans to individuals.
Publications: Application guidelines; Annual report.
Application information: Refer to foundation web site for specific application information. Telephone calls are not accepted. Application form required.
Initial approach: Use application form on foundation web site
Deadline(s): Mar. 31, June 30, Sept. 30, and Dec. 31
Board meeting date(s): Jan., Apr., July, and Oct.
Final notification: Approximately 2-3 weeks after Board meeting date
Trustees: Julie Vigeland; U.S. Bank, N.A.
Number of staff: 3 part-time professional.
EIN: 936020752
Selected grants: The following grants are a representative sample of this grantmaker's funding activity:
$10,000 to Medical Teams International, Tigard, OR, 2011. For general support.
$7,500 to Nonprofit Association of Oregon, Portland, OR, 2011. For general support.

7856
The Jeld-Wen Foundation ✧
(formerly Jeld-Wen, Wenco Foundation)
3250 Lakeport Blvd.
Klamath Falls, OR 97601-1036 (541) 880-2185
Contact: Robert Kingzett, Exec. Dir.
Klamath Falls Office: 3250 Lakeport Blvd., Klamath Falls, OR 97601, tel.: (541) 880-2185; Main URL: http://www.jeld-wenfoundation.org/

Established in 1969.
Donors: Jeld-Wen, Inc.; Jeld-Wen Fiber Products, Inc. of Iowa; Jeld-Wen Co. of Arizona; Wenco, Inc. of North Carolina; Wenco, Inc. of Ohio; Jeld-Wen Holding, Inc.
Foundation type: Company-sponsored foundation.
Financial data (yr. ended 12/31/13): Assets, $19,568,436 (M); gifts received, $600,000; expenditures, $684,259; qualifying distributions, $672,633; giving activities include $472,742 for 53 grants (high: $100,000; low: $150).
Purpose and activities: The foundation supports organizations involved with arts and culture, education, health, human services, community development, and civic affairs. Special emphasis is directed toward programs designed to strengthen

families, improve neighborhoods, and build better communities.
Fields of interest: Humanities; Arts; Education; Hospitals (general); Health care; Human services; Community/economic development; United Ways and Federated Giving Programs; Public policy, research; Public affairs.
Type of support: Matching/challenge support; General/operating support; Capital campaigns; Building/renovation; Equipment; Endowments; Program development; Scholarship funds.
Limitations: Applications accepted. Giving on a national basis in areas of company operations, with emphasis on OR. No support for private or religious schools. No grants to individuals, or for religious activities or programs that duplicate services provided by other government or private agencies; no annual support.
Publications: Application guidelines.
Application information: The foundation requests that applicants involve a Jeld-Wen manager in the application process. A site visit may be requested. Support is limited to 1 contribution per organization during any given year. Application form required.
Initial approach: Contact foundation or nearest general manager for application form
Deadline(s): Varies, but are scheduled around quarterly meetings
Board meeting date(s): Quarterly
Officers and Trustees:* Roderick C. Wendt,* Secy.; Robert Kingzett, Exec. Dir.; W. B. Early; Robert F. Turner; Nancy J. Wendt.
EIN: 936054272

7857
B. P. Lester & Regina John Foundation ✧
(formerly B. P. John Foundation)
1000 S.W. Vista Ave., Ste. 116
Portland, OR 97205-1131

Established in 1971.
Donors: Lester M. John†; Regina M. John†; Lester M. John Marital Trust.
Foundation type: Independent foundation.
Financial data (yr. ended 12/31/13): Assets, $36,395,427 (M); gifts received, $125,359; expenditures, $1,690,095; qualifying distributions, $1,384,709; giving activities include $1,274,083 for grants.
Purpose and activities: Support for Roman Catholic missionary and international relief organizations, Catholic education, and for local church-sponsored and secular health and welfare agencies.
Fields of interest: Education; Health care; Human services; Christian agencies & churches; Catholic agencies & churches; Homeless.
Type of support: Capital campaigns; Endowments; Scholarship funds.
Limitations: Applications not accepted. Giving primarily in Portland, OR. No support for political organizations. No grants to individuals.
Application information: Unsolicited requests for funds are not accepted.
Officers: Patricia J. Abraham, Pres. an Treas.; Melissa Hartnell, Secy.
Directors: Mary Amstad; Joan Hansen; Suzann Baricevic Murphy.
Number of staff: 1 part-time support.
EIN: 237110263

7858
The Samuel S. Johnson Foundation ✧
P.O. Box 356
Redmond, OR 97756-0079 (541) 548-8104
FAX: (541) 548-2014; E-mail: mary@tssjf.org

Incorporated in 1948 in CA.
Donors: Samuel S. Johnson†; Elizabeth Hill Johnson†; Robert W. Hill†.
Foundation type: Independent foundation.
Financial data (yr. ended 05/31/13): Assets, $12,501,779 (M); expenditures, $604,322; qualifying distributions, $457,590; giving activities include $457,590 for grants.
Purpose and activities: Giving for formal education programs in nursing which are geared toward preparation of RNs qualified to serve as faculty members in college and university schools of nursing or, alternatively, which qualify RNs for independent advanced practice nursing (e.g. as a licensed CRNA, Nurse Midwife, Family Nurse Practitioner, etc.); development or operation of technical or vocational education and training programs (including apprenticeships) for high school and college-age students and out-of-work adults; emergency food assistance; and rural mobile health screening/care projects benefitting the uninsured medically needy.
Fields of interest: Nursing school/education; Adult education—literacy, basic skills & GED; Reproductive health, family planning; Nursing care; Children/youth, services; Rural development; Voluntarism promotion.
Type of support: Continuing support; Emergency funds; Equipment; General/operating support; Matching/challenge support; Program development; Seed money.
Limitations: Applications accepted. Giving primarily in OR, and Clark County, WA. No support for foreign organizations. No grants or scholarships to individuals, or for leadership training or staff development, campaigns to retire debt, annual campaigns, deficit financing, construction, sole underwriting of major proposals or projects, demolition or endowments.
Publications: Application guidelines.
Application information: The foundation no longer accepts individual scholarship or grant applications. Application form not required.
Initial approach: Contact foundation for current areas of focus and guidelines
Copies of proposal: 1
Deadline(s): Anytime
Board meeting date(s): July and Nov.
Final notification: 2 to 3 weeks after board meeting
Officers and Directors:* Elizabeth K. Johnson-Helm,* Pres.; John C. Helm, V.P.; Patricia C. Johnson,* C.F.O.; Mary A. Krenowicz, Exec. Dir.; Karen K. Creason.
Number of staff: 1 full-time professional.
EIN: 946062478
Selected grants: The following grants are a representative sample of this grantmaker's funding activity:
$25,000 to Community Transitional School, Portland, OR, 2011.
$25,000 to Oregon Health and Science University, Portland, OR, 2011.
$10,000 to High Desert Museum, Bend, OR, 2011.
$10,000 to Oregon Public Broadcasting, Portland, OR, 2011.
$5,000 to Assistance League of the Columbia Pacific, Astoria, OR, 2011.
$5,000 to Astoria Music Festival, Astoria, OR, 2011.
$5,000 to Oregon Center for Nursing, Portland, OR, 2011.
$5,000 to Planned Parenthood of the Columbia-Willamette, Portland, OR, 2011.
$2,500 to Providence Saint Vincent Medical Foundation, Portland, OR, 2011.
$2,500 to Saint Helens Senior Center, Saint Helens, OR, 2011.

7859
Jubitz Family Foundation ✧
221 N.W. 2nd Ave., Ste. 204
Portland, OR 97209-3982 (503) 274-6255
Contact: Raymond Jubitz, Exec. Dir.
FAX: (503) 274-6256; E-mail: info@jubitz.org; Main URL: http://www.jubitzff.org

Established in 2001 in OR.
Donors: Jubitz Investments, LP; Saybrook, Inc.; M. Albin Jubitz, Jr.; Mike Caruso.
Foundation type: Independent foundation.
Financial data (yr. ended 12/31/13): Assets, $13,232,868 (M); gifts received, $170,000; expenditures, $978,459; qualifying distributions, $852,680; giving activities include $594,185 for 96 grants (high: $25,000; low: $1,500), and $160,478 for 2 foundation-administered programs.
Purpose and activities: The foundation supports projects and organizations that enhance the communities in which its officers live by strengthening families, by respecting the natural environment, and by fostering peace. Areas of interest include early childhood development and education, with an emphasis on children at-risk; environmental stewardship, with an emphasis on rivers and their watershed ecosystems; and peacemaking activities, with an emphasis on teaching peace and conflict resolution.
Fields of interest: Elementary/secondary education; Higher education; Education; Environment, natural resources; Environment; Animals/wildlife; Youth development; Human services; Children/youth, services; Family services.
Limitations: Applications accepted. Giving primarily in OR. No grants for capital expenditures.
Publications: Application guidelines; Grants list.
Application information: See foundation web site for application guidelines and procedures, and application form. Application form required.
Initial approach: First time applicants: 1-page letter of request to Exec. Dir. via form on foundation web site; previously funded applicants should submit a grant request via foundation web site
Deadline(s): First time applicants: Jan 1 (for Apr. 1 grant deadline), and July 1 (for Oct. 1 grant deadline); for previously funded applicants: Apr. 1 and Oct. 1
Officers: M. Albin Jubitz, Jr., Pres.; Elizabeth Jubitz Sayler, V.P.; Katherine H. Jubitz, Secy.; Sarah C. Jubitz, Treas.; Raymond G. Jubitz, Exec. Dir.
EIN: 931324016
Selected grants: The following grants are a representative sample of this grantmaker's funding activity:
$20,000 to Morrison Child and Family Services, Portland, OR, 2011. For general operations.
$15,000 to Portland Childrens Museum, Portland, OR, 2011. For general operations.
$15,000 to Portland Public Schools, Portland, OR, 2011. For general operations.

$10,000 to Columbia Land Trust, Vancouver, WA, 2011. For general operations.
$7,000 to Trout Unlimited, Arlington, VA, 2011. For general operations.
$5,000 to Court Appointed Special Advocates for Children, Portland, OR, 2011. For general operations.
$5,000 to Friends of Forest Park, Portland, OR, 2011. For general operations.
$5,000 to Northwest Youth Corps, Eugene, OR, 2011. For general operations.
$5,000 to United Way of Lane County, Springfield, OR, 2011. For general operations.
$5,000 to World Affairs Council of Oregon, Portland, OR, 2011. For general operations.

7860
Kinsman Foundation ✧

3727 S.E. Spaulding Ave.
Milwaukie, OR 97267-3938 (503) 654-1668
Contact: Keith Kinsman, C.E.O.
FAX: (503) 654-1759;
E-mail: grants@kinsmanfoundation.org; Main URL: http://www.kinsmanfoundation.org/

Established in 1983 in OR.
Donors: Elizabeth T. Kinsman†; John W. Kinsman†; Mary S. Mitchell†.
Foundation type: Independent foundation.
Financial data (yr. ended 12/31/13): Assets, $26,651,880 (M); expenditures, $1,869,233; qualifying distributions, $1,334,798; giving activities include $1,108,079 for 99 grants (high: $75,000; low: $500).
Purpose and activities: Giving for historic preservation, native wildlife rehabilitation and wildlife appreciation, and arts, culture and the humanities.
Fields of interest: Humanities; Historical activities; Historic preservation/historical societies; Arts; Animals/wildlife.
Type of support: General/operating support; Continuing support; Income development; Management development/capacity building; Annual campaigns; Capital campaigns; Building/renovation; Equipment; Land acquisition; Endowments; Debt reduction; Emergency funds; Program development; Conferences/seminars; Publication; Seed money; Curriculum development; Internship funds; Research; Technical assistance; Consulting services; Program evaluation; Matching/challenge support.
Limitations: Applications accepted. Giving primarily in OR and southern WA. No grants to individuals, or for scholarships.
Publications: Application guidelines; Grants list.
Application information: Application guidelines available on foundation web site. The foundation's Health Care Policy area has been discontinued. Application form not required.
Initial approach: Use online application process through foundation web site, or letter of inquiry (1-2 pages) via U.S. mail, e-mail or fax only
Copies of proposal: 1
Deadline(s): Feb. 15 for arts, culture and humanities Apr. grants meeting; Aug. 1 for all others at Sept. grants meeting
Board meeting date(s): Apr. for arts, culture and humanities applicants; Sept. for all others
Final notification: 7 days to acknowledge receipt; 1-6 weeks for substantive response
Officers and Directors:* Keith Kinsman,* C.E.O. and Pres.; Pamela Reynolds,* V.P., Treas. and C.F.O.; Jack Schwab,* Secy.; Shelley Bailey; Paige Kinsman.
Number of staff: 3 full-time professional.
EIN: 930861885
Selected grants: The following grants are a representative sample of this grantmaker's funding activity:
$80,000 to Oregon Health and Science University Foundation, Portland, OR, 2012. For Health Care Training Program.
$35,000 to Oregon Public Broadcasting, Portland, OR, 2012. For artistic media programming.
$33,350 to Marylhurst University, Marylhurst, OR, 2012. For Historic Building Reconstruction.
$15,000 to Oregon Council for the Humanities, Portland, OR, 2012. For artistic meetings.
$10,000 to Film Action Oregon, Portland, OR, 2012. For Historic Building Restoration.
$10,000 to Oregon Rail Heritage Foundation, Portland, OR, 2012. For historic preservation.
$10,000 to Portland Art Museum, Portland, OR, 2012. For Artistic Works Exhibition.
$10,000 to Triangle Productions, Portland, OR, 2012. For artistic performance.
$10,000 to Washington State University Foundation, Pullman, WA, 2012. For wildlife rehabilitation.
$10,000 to Western Seminary, Portland, OR, 2012. For Historic Building Preservation.

7861
Knight Foundation ✧

c/o Lisa McKillips
1 Bowerman Dr.
Beaverton, OR 97005-0979 (503) 671-3500
Contact: Lisa Mckillips

Established in 1997 in OR.
Donors: Philip H. Knight; Phight LLC.
Foundation type: Independent foundation.
Financial data (yr. ended 12/31/12): Assets, $208,747,724 (M); gifts received, $75,000,014; expenditures, $5,574,105; qualifying distributions, $5,008,576; giving activities include $5,000,000 for 1 grant.
Purpose and activities: Giving primarily for higher and other education, including a graduate school of business.
Fields of interest: Higher education; Health care; Medical research.
Limitations: Applications not accepted. Giving primarily in Portland, OR. No grants to individuals.
Application information: Contributes only to pre-selected organizations.
Officers and Director:* Philip H. Knight, Pres. and Treas.; Penelope P. Knight,* V.P.; Travis A. Knight, Secy.
EIN: 911791788
Selected grants: The following grants are a representative sample of this grantmaker's funding activity:
$5,000,000 to Oregon Health and Science University, Portland, OR, 2012. For OHSU Knight Cardiovascular Institute.

7862
Dale Krueger Scholarship Fund ✧

P.O. Box 3168
Portland, OR 97208-3168 (503) 275-5929
Contact: William Dolan
FAX: (503) 275-4177;
E-mail: sheri.hopkins@usbank.com

Established in 1999 in OR.
Donor: Dale W. Krueger†.
Foundation type: Independent foundation.
Financial data (yr. ended 07/31/13): Assets, $9,752,377 (M); expenditures, $654,433; qualifying distributions, $494,002; giving activities include $494,002 for grants.
Purpose and activities: The foundation awards scholarships to graduates of public high schools located in Gresham-Barlow, Reynolds and Centennial school districts in Oregon, who at the time of receiving their diploma, are residents of these school districts. Applicants must be graduating seniors, or previous graduates under the age of 21, and must attend a full-time program at an accredited college, university, or trade school. Students must maintain a 2.0 GPA or better in their first year of post high school study, and a 2.5 GPA or better, in their second or third year of post high school study.
Fields of interest: Education.
Limitations: Applications accepted. Giving primarily in OR.
Application information: Application form available on foundation web site. Application form required.
Initial approach: Proposal
Copies of proposal: 1
Deadline(s): Apr. 1
Final notification: May
Trustee: U.S. Bank, N.A.
EIN: 936331222
Selected grants: The following grants are a representative sample of this grantmaker's funding activity:
$86,002 to Oregon State University, Corvallis, OR, 2011. For scholarships.
$70,001 to Portland State University, Portland, OR, 2011. For scholarships.
$67,000 to Mount Hood Community College, Gresham, OR, 2011. For scholarship.
$61,334 to University of Oregon, Eugene, OR, 2011. For scholarships.
$39,333 to Western Oregon University, Monmouth, OR, 2011. For scholarships.
$38,000 to University of Portland, Portland, OR, 2011. For scholarships.
$33,000 to Concordia University, Portland, OR, 2011. For scholarship.
$19,000 to George Fox University, Newberg, OR, 2011. For scholarship.
$16,000 to Linfield College, McMinnville, OR, 2011. For scholarship.
$2,000 to University of Washington, Seattle, WA, 2011. For scholarships.

7863
Marie Lamfrom Charitable Foundation ✧ ☆

9685 S.W. Ridder Rd., Ste. 100
Wilsonville, OR 97070

Established in 1998 in OR.
Donors: Gertrude Boyle; Gert Boyle; David C. Bany; Sarah A. Bany.
Foundation type: Independent foundation.
Financial data (yr. ended 12/31/13): Assets, $12,659,050 (M); gifts received, $5,858,976; expenditures, $2,107,733; qualifying distributions, $2,071,898; giving activities include $1,606,116 for 36 grants (high: $1,323,166; low: $450).

Purpose and activities: Giving primarily for children and youth, and for local community-based programs.
Fields of interest: Education; Children/youth, services; Community/economic development; Infants/toddlers; Children/youth; Children; Youth; Young adults; Girls; Young adults, female; Young adults, male; Economically disadvantaged.
Type of support: General/operating support; Equipment; Program development.
Limitations: Applications not accepted. Giving primarily in OR. No grants to individuals.
Application information: Contributes only to pre-selected organizations.
Board meeting date(s): Quarterly
Trustees: David C. Bany; Sarah A. Bany.
Number of staff: 2 part-time professional.
EIN: 931254171
Selected grants: The following grants are a representative sample of this grantmaker's funding activity:
$10,000 to Family Stepping Stones Relief Nursery, Gladstone, OR, 2012. For child advocacy.
$5,000 to Portland Youth Philharmonic Association, Portland, OR, 2012. For arts/culture.

7864
The Lazar Foundation ✧
715 S.W. Morrison St., Ste. 901
Portland, OR 97205-3105 (503) 225-0265
Contact: Sybil Ackerman, Exec. Dir.
FAX: (503) 225-9620;
E-mail: info@lazarfoundation.org; Sybil Ackerman's e-mail: sybil@lazarfoundation.org; Main URL: http://fdnweb.org/lazar

Incorporated in 1956 in DE.
Donors: Jack Lazar†; Helen B. Lazar†.
Foundation type: Independent foundation.
Financial data (yr. ended 12/31/12): Assets, $22,489,000 (M); gifts received, $197,420; expenditures, $1,281,604; qualifying distributions, $1,088,135; giving activities include $826,845 for 50 grants (high: $100,000; low: $1,000).
Purpose and activities: The foundation focuses on preservation of biological diversity and ecosystems; broadening the environmental movement, and message development.
Fields of interest: Environment.
Type of support: General/operating support; Program development; Seed money.
Limitations: Giving primarily in ID, OR, and WA. No support for environmental education, civic projects, urban issues, suburban projects, or conservation-based scientific research, unless it directly supports a project that the foundation is currently funding. No grants to individuals, or for endowments, land acquisition, film or video projects, capital campaigns or for computer-related expenses.
Publications: Application guidelines; Grants list.
Application information: Full proposal is by invitation only, upon review of initial letter. Telephone calls are not accepted. Application form required.
Initial approach: Letter only (no more than 1-page) via e-mail to Sybil Ackerman with "LOI" in the subject bar
Copies of proposal: 1
Deadline(s): Feb. 15, June 15, and Oct. 15
Board meeting date(s): Mar., July, and Nov.
Final notification: Applicants who do not receive a reply to their LOI within 1-month will not be asked to submit a proposal
Officers and Trustees:* William B. Lazar,* Pres.; Jeanne L. Morency,* Secy.; Sybil Ackerman, Exec. Dir.; Michael Morency.
Number of staff: 1 part-time professional; 1 part-time support.
EIN: 136088182
Selected grants: The following grants are a representative sample of this grantmaker's funding activity:
$100,000 to Pew Charitable Trusts, Philadelphia, PA, 2012. For Forest Conservation in Oregon and California.
$50,000 to Association of Northwest Steelheaders, Milwaukie, OR, 2012. For Tillamook and Clatsop State Forest Program.
$45,000 to Catlin Gabel School, Portland, OR, 2012. For Innovation Center.
$45,000 to Piedmont Environmental Council, Warrenton, VA, 2012. For Virginia Land Conservation.
$30,000 to Surfrider Foundation, San Clemente, CA, 2012. For Ocean Conservation in Oregon and Washington.
$25,000 to Wild Salmon Center, Portland, OR, 2012. For Tillamook Forest Program.
$20,000 to Advocates for the West, Boise, ID, 2012. For Sagebrush Sea Program.
$20,000 to Defenders of Wildlife, Washington, DC, 2012. For Oregon and California Forest Conservation.
$20,000 to Wild Salmon Center, Portland, OR, 2012. For National Forests Protection Program.
$15,000 to Resource Media, San Francisco, CA, 2012. For Pacific Northwest Ocean Conservation.

7865
The Lemelson Foundation ✧
45 S.W. Ankeny St., Ste. 200
Portland, OR 97204-3500 (503) 827-8910
E-mail: webmaster@lemelson.org; Main URL: http://www.lemelson.org/
E-Newsletter: http://lemelson.us1.list-manage.com/subscribe?u=de855f63e59f43c6bce8afdd2&id=eb6afc211b
Facebook: http://www.facebook.com/TheLemelsonFoundation?ref=ts
Twitter: http://twitter.com/LemelsonFdn
YouTube: http://www.youtube.com/lemelsonfoundation

Established in 1994 in NV.
Donors: Dorothy Lemelson; Eric Lemelson; Jerome Lemelson†; Robert B. Lemelson.
Foundation type: Independent foundation.
Financial data (yr. ended 12/31/12): Assets, $343,785,771 (M); expenditures, $18,986,244; qualifying distributions, $16,602,891; giving activities include $11,940,587 for 36 grants (high: $1,626,840; low: $1,000), and $1,188,703 for 2 loans/program-related investments.
Purpose and activities: The foundation uses the power of invention to improve lives, by inspiring and enabling the next generation of inventors and invention based enterprises to promote economic growth in the U.S. and social and economic progress for the poor in developing countries. Established by prolific U.S. inventor Jerome Lemelson and his wife Dorothy in 1992. To date the foundation has provided or committed more than $175 million in grants and PRIs in support of its mission.
Fields of interest: Higher education; Economic development; Business/industry; Engineering/technology.
International interests: Developing Countries.
Type of support: Program-related investments/loans.
Limitations: Applications not accepted. Giving primarily in the United States and internationally in Africa, Asia and Latin America. No grants to individuals.
Application information: Contributes only to pre-selected organizations.
Officers and Directors:* Dorothy Lemelson,* Chair and Pres.; Robert Lemelson, Ph.D.*, V.P. and Secy.; Eric Lemelson,* V.P. and Treas.; Philip Varnum, C.F.O. and C.A.O.; Carol Dahl, Exec. Dir.; Jennifer Bruml Lemelson; Susan Morse.
EIN: 880391959
Selected grants: The following grants are a representative sample of this grantmaker's funding activity:
$12,253,679 to Massachusetts Institute of Technology, Cambridge, MA, 2012. For Lemelson-MIT Prize, Student Prize Program, Global Innovation Prize, National InvenTeam Initiative, evaluation of prize program and communications and to support new Invention Education Program that includes launching a geographically focused InventTeam Initiative, MakerTeams, Grassroots Coordination and local EurekaFest events, payable over 4.00 years.
$12,034,659 to National Collegiate Inventors and Innovators Alliance, Hadley, MA, 2012. For grant making and programming which support educational, E-Team and VentureWell activities, payable over 4.00 years.
$2,200,086 to Nonprofit Enterprise and Self-Sustainability Team, San Francisco, CA, 2013. To incubate and launch high-impact, highly scalable, invention-based enterprises in Peru that improve lives of the poor.
$2,200,000 to Villgro, Chennai, India, 2013. To incubate and launch high-impact, highly scalable, invention-based enterprises in India that improve lives of the poor.
$1,999,890 to Yayasan Inovasi Teknologi, Jakarta, Indonesia, 2013. To incubate and launch high-impact, highly scalable, invention-based enterprises in Indonesia that improve lives of the poor.
$1,062,643 to American Association for the Advancement of Science, Washington, DC, 2013. For the launch and development of the AAAS-Lemelson Invention Ambassadors Program.
$991,934 to Bogor Agricultural University, Bogor, Indonesia, 2013. To continue support of the student invention and entrepreneurship program.
$735,770 to Yayasan Inovasi Teknologi, Jakarta, Indonesia, 2012. To incubate and launch high-impact, highly scalable, invention-based enterprises in Indonesia that improve lives of the poor.
$600,000 to National Public Radio, Washington, DC, 2012. To support a radio and web series that explores the minds and motivations of scientists and inventors and how their discoveries translate into inventions that have the potential to change lives, payable over 3.00 years.
$400,000 to Norbu Limited, Hong Kong, China, 2013. For grant to be used by Norbu to contribute as registered capital to Norlha for Norlha to use to operate a yak wool production workshop in impoverished area of the Tibetan Plateau (the Workshop) and to distribute yak wool products in China in order to (1) support the economic development of the Tibetan Plateau, (2) develop a viable economic alternative to grazing, and (3)

provide a model that can be replicated in a franchise style in other impoverished areas of the Tibetan Plateau, bringing employment and opportunities for development.
$216,000 to Portland State University Foundation, Portland, OR, 2012. For Oregon Mathematics Engineering Science Achievement (MESA) program activities, payable over 2.00 years.
$209,573 to Oregon State University, Corvallis, OR, 2013. To be used for the Advancing STEM, Creativity and Invention Learning through SYNERGIES project which includes collecting data and evidence on how underserved youth in the Parkrose neighborhood of Portland, Oregon, engage in invention education.
$98,171 to Villgro, Chennai, India, 2013. For the Entrepreneurship Residence Program to foster the growth of young invention entrepreneurs by providing Fellows with a safe space to pilot new innovations without the pressure of raising funds.
$90,000 to National Public Radio, Washington, DC, 2012. To support a radio and web series that explores the minds and motivations of scientists and inventors and how their discoveries translate into inventions that have the potential to change lives.
$50,000 to Smithsonian Institution, Washington, DC, 2013. For project to support a joint collaboration with Smithsonian Magazine to support The Future is Here conference.
$50,000 to Yayasan Inovasi Teknologi, Jakarta, Indonesia, 2013. For a business plan competition for invention enterprises focusing in renewable energy and green technology.
$25,000 to T2 Institute, Los Altos Hills, CA, 2012. To sponsor Global Innovation Summit in Silicon Valley, CA.

7866
Maybelle Clark Macdonald Fund ✧
P.O. Box 1496
Bend, OR 97709-1496
E-mail: information@mcmfundgiving.org; Main URL: http://www.mcmfundgiving.org/

Established in 1970 in OR.
Donor: Maybelle Clark Macdonald†.
Foundation type: Independent foundation.
Financial data (yr. ended 06/30/13): Assets, $127,198,117 (M); expenditures, $5,694,362; qualifying distributions, $4,645,510; giving activities include $4,350,829 for 142 grants (high: $350,000; low: $1,000).
Purpose and activities: The mission of the foundation is to relieve the misfortune and promote the well being of mankind. Grantmaking priorities are: 1) Cultural Arts; 2) Education; 3) Human Services; 4) Medical Research; and 5) Public Benefit.
Fields of interest: Arts; Elementary/secondary education; Health care; Medical research; Human services; Aging, centers/services.
Type of support: General/operating support; Annual campaigns; Capital campaigns; Building/renovation; Endowments; Internship funds; Scholarship funds; Matching/challenge support.
Limitations: Applications accepted. Giving primarily in OR. No grants to individuals.
Application information: Full proposals by invitation after review of LOI.
Initial approach: Online letter of inquiry through foundation web site
Deadline(s): Letter of inquiry: Feb. 15 and Aug. 15
Officers and Directors:* Clark C. Munro, Sr.,* Chair.; Monique M. McCleary,* Pres.; Maurie M. Munro,* Secy.; Gary R. Branden; Gene d'Autremont; Janeen McAninch; Christopher R. Munro; Clark C. Munro, Jr.; Warner R. Munro.
Number of staff: 1 part-time professional; 1 full-time support; 1 part-time support.
EIN: 237108002
Selected grants: The following grants are a representative sample of this grantmaker's funding activity:
$343,000 to Pacific Northwest College of Art, Portland, OR, 2012. For Main Campus Center Campaign.
$275,000 to Catholic Charities, Portland, OR, 2012. For Center for Hope capital campaign.
$250,000 to Catholic Charities, Portland, OR, 2013. For Center for Hope capital campaign.
$250,000 to Providence Saint Vincent Medical Foundation, Portland, OR, 2012. For Cancer Research.
$170,000 to University of Oregon Foundation, Eugene, OR, 2012. For Academic and Athletic Scholarships.
$150,000 to Oregon State University Foundation, Corvallis, OR, 2013. For Teaching Excellence in Forestry Professor Fund.
$150,000 to University of Oregon Foundation, Eugene, OR, 2013. For academic and athletic scholarships.
$100,000 to Concordia University Foundation, Portland, OR, 2013. For Community Athletic Complex.
$100,000 to Dougy Center, Portland, OR, 2013. For capital campaign.
$100,000 to Oregon State University Foundation, Corvallis, OR, 2012. For Teaching Excellence in Forestry Professor Fund.
$100,000 to Virginia Garcia Memorial Foundation, Cornelius, OR, 2013. For Cornelius Wellness Center.
$63,800 to Salvation Army Salem, Salem, OR, 2013. To feed Marion-Polk Counties.
$53,000 to Archdiocese of Portland, Portland, OR, 2013. For general operating support.
$50,000 to Boys and Girls Aid Society of Oregon, Portland, OR, 2013. For endowment.
$50,000 to Caldera, Portland, OR, 2012. For General operating support.
$50,000 to Deschutes Land Trust, Bend, OR, 2012. For General operating support.
$50,000 to Portland Art Museum, Portland, OR, 2013. For general operating support.
$30,000 to R. E. Jewell Elementary Parent Teacher Organization, Bend, OR, 2012. For Computers for First Grade.
$27,500 to Bridge Meadows, Portland, OR, 2012. For General operating support.
$20,000 to Young Audiences of Oregon and Southwest Washington, Portland, OR, 2012. For Capacity Building.

7867
MDEKFSE Family Foundation ✧
1500 N.E. Irving St., Ste. 440
Portland, OR 97232-4208 (503) 233-1133

Established in 2008 in OR.
Donors: Michael D. Elton; Kay F.S. Elton.
Foundation type: Independent foundation.
Financial data (yr. ended 06/30/13): Assets, $19,747,462 (M); gifts received, $10,003,898; expenditures, $718,492; qualifying distributions, $696,511; giving activities include $696,511 for grants.
Fields of interest: Mormon agencies & churches.
Limitations: Applications accepted. Giving primarily in UT.
Application information: Application form required.
Initial approach: Letter
Deadline(s): None
Trustees: Aaron B. Elton; Kay F.S. Elton; Michael D. Elton.
EIN: 261489585
Selected grants: The following grants are a representative sample of this grantmaker's funding activity:
$50,000 to Southern Virginia University, Buena Vista, VA, 2013. For contribution to be used for the benefit of University.

7868
Merrill Family Foundation Inc. ✧
17952 S.W. Parrish Ln.
Sherwood, OR 97140-8857

Established in 1995 in OR.
Donors: Lenore Merrill; Charles Merrill†; Kay Merrill.
Foundation type: Independent foundation.
Financial data (yr. ended 12/31/12): Assets, $8,531,240 (M); expenditures, $693,862; qualifying distributions, $638,395; giving activities include $638,395 for grants.
Purpose and activities: Giving primarily for scholarships, and for Christian organizations and churches.
Fields of interest: Higher education; Christian agencies & churches.
Type of support: Scholarship funds; Scholarships—to individuals.
Limitations: Applications not accepted. Giving primarily in OR, some giving in NY.
Application information: Unsolicited requests for funds not accepted.
Officers: Charles Merrill, Pres.; Kay Merrill, Secy.-Treas.
Directors: Anthony C. Merrill; Lisa K. Sickler.
EIN: 931191941

7869
The Metolius Trust ✧
5665 SW Meadows Rd., Ste. 125
Lake Oswego, OR 97035-3130 (503) 265-0030
Contact: Lloyd R. Summers, Tr.

Established in 2002 in OR.
Donors: Terrence Patrick Welch; Teresa K. Welch.
Foundation type: Independent foundation.
Financial data (yr. ended 12/31/13): Assets, $14,921,344 (L); expenditures, $946,491; qualifying distributions, $795,500; giving activities include $795,500 for 25 grants (high: $200,000; low: $1,500).
Fields of interest: Education, reading; Food distribution, groceries on wheels; Protestant agencies & churches.
Type of support: Annual campaigns; Building/renovation.
Limitations: Applications accepted. Giving primarily in OR, with emphasis on Corvallis and Portland.
Application information: Application form required.
Initial approach: Letter
Copies of proposal: 1

Deadline(s): None
Final notification: 30 days
Trustee: Lloyd R. Summers.
EIN: 276000960

7870
Meyer Memorial Trust
(formerly Fred Meyer Charitable Trust)
425 N.W. 10th Ave., Ste. 400
Portland, OR 97209-3128 (503) 228-5512
Contact: Doug Stamm, C.E.O.
E-mail: mmt@mmt.org; Main URL: http://www.mmt.org
Connectipedia: http://connectipedia.org
E-Newsletter: http://www.mmt.org/newsletters
Flickr: http://www.flickr.com/photos/meyermemorialtrust/
Foundation Blogs: http://www.mmt.org/blogs
Grants Database: http://www.mmt.org/awards
Knowledge Center: http://www.mmt.org/program-analysis
LinkedIn: http://www.linkedin.com/companies/meyer-memorial-trust
Meyer Discussion Forums: http://www.mmt.org/forum
Meyer Memorial Trust's Philanthropy Promise: http://www.ncrp.org/philanthropys-promise/who
Multimedia: http://www.mmt.org/stories
PRI Awards: http://www.mmt.org/awards-by-program/14
Slideshare: http://www.slideshare.net/MeyerMT
Twitter: http://www.twitter.com/meyermt
YouTube: http://www.youtube.com/meyertrust

Trust established by will in 1978; obtained IRS status in 1982 in OR.
Donor: Fred G. Meyer‡.
Foundation type: Independent foundation.
Financial data (yr. ended 03/31/14): Assets, $791,974,273 (M); expenditures, $39,675,919; qualifying distributions, $37,259,956; giving activities include $28,578,422 for grants, and $4,350,000 for loans/program-related investments.
Purpose and activities: The trust works with and invest in organizations, communities, ideas and efforts that contribute to a flourishing and equitable Oregon.
Fields of interest: Performing arts; Humanities; Arts; Child development, education; Higher education; Education; Environment, natural resources; Environment; Health care; Health organizations; Crime/violence prevention, youth; Housing/shelter, development; Youth development; Human services; Children/youth, services; Child development, services; Family services; Aging, centers/services; Community/economic development; Leadership development.
Type of support: General/operating support; Income development; Management development/capacity building; Capital campaigns; Building/renovation; Equipment; Emergency funds; Program development; Seed money; Technical assistance; Program-related investments/loans; Employee matching gifts; Matching/challenge support; Mission-related investments/loans.
Limitations: Applications accepted. Giving limited to programs operating in the state of OR and Clark County, WA. No support for sectarian or religious organizations for religious purposes, for animal welfare organizations, animal-assisted therapy programs, or projects that primarily benefit students of a single K-12 school (unless the school is an independent alternative school primarily serving low-income and/or special needs populations). No grants to individuals or for endowment funds, annual campaigns, general fund drives, special events, sponsorships, direct replacement funding for activities previously supported by federal, state, or local public sources, deficit financing, acquisition of land for conservation purposes (except through Program Related Investments), or hospital capital construction projects (except through Program Related Investments).
Publications: Application guidelines; Financial statement; Grants list; Newsletter.
Application information: All applications online using GrantIS, an application system developed by MMT. Responsive Grants/PRIs use two-step process: Online Initial Inquiry with online Full Proposal if invited. Grassroots Grants program is a one-step online proposal process. Applications at this time are invited only from the state of OR and Clark County, WA. Please see the foundation's web site for additional details. Application form required.
Initial approach: Online application form
Deadline(s): None for Responsive Grants and PRIs; Grassroots Grants program: Mar. 15, July 15, Oct. 15
Board meeting date(s): Monthly
Final notification: 4 to 6 months for Responsive Grants proposals that pass first screening; 1 to 2 months for those that do not; 3 to 4 months for Grassroots Grants
Officers and Trustees:* Debbie F. Craig, Chair.; Doug Stamm, C.E.O.; John Emrick; Orcilla Zuniga Forbes; George J. Puentes; Charles Wilhoite.
Number of staff: 17 full-time professional; 9 full-time support.
EIN: 930806316
Selected grants: The following grants are a representative sample of this grantmaker's funding activity:
$300,000 to Court Appointed Special Advocates of Douglas County, Roseburg, OR, 2013. To implement a new system of coordinated care for at-risk children designed to prevent foster care placement, payable over 3.00 years.
$300,000 to Portland Community College Foundation, Portland, OR, 2013. To build capacity of PCC's Future Connect initiative which supports low-income, first-generation college students to graduate from college, payable over 3.00 years.
$175,505 to Adelante Mujeres, Forest Grove, OR, 2013. To help strengthen organization's internal management systems to ensure strong program outcomes for Latino families.
$125,000 to United Community Action Network, Roseburg, OR, 2013. To help construct and operate a 10-unit affordable housing complex for low-income residents in recovery from substance abuse.
$120,000 to Coalition of Oregon Land Trusts, Portland, OR, 2013. To hire the organization's first staff and establish office, payable over 3.00 years.
$50,000 to Dental Foundation of Oregon, Wilsonville, OR, 2013. For free dental care and education to underserved children in public schools throughout Oregon.
$50,000 to Newport Symphony Orchestra, Newport, OR, 2013. For operating support for the only year-round professional symphony orchestra on the Oregon coast.
$40,000 to Crag Law Center, Portland, OR, 2013. For services to grassroots organizations working to preserve Oregon's natural resources.
$25,000 to Center for Intercultural Organizing, Portland, OR, 2013. To conduct multicultural, multilingual, inter-generational and community-led engagement process to create a strategic plan for this organization that works for immigrant and refugee rights.
$4,848 to Joint Forces Dance Company, Eugene, OR, 2013. For performances of this dance troupe that includes artists with disabilities.

7871
James F. & Marion L. Miller Foundation ✧
520 S.W. Yahmill St., Ste. 520
Portland, OR 97204-1328 (503) 546-3191
E-mail: info@millerfound.org; Main URL: http://millerfound.org/
Grants List: http://www.millerfound.org/grants/2010-grants/

Established in 2002 in OR.
Donor: James F. Miller.
Foundation type: Independent foundation.
Financial data (yr. ended 12/31/12): Assets, $165,659,087 (M); expenditures, $10,388,152; qualifying distributions, $9,708,877; giving activities include $9,054,768 for 180 grants (high: $1,250,000; low: $1,000).
Purpose and activities: Giving to enhance the quality of life of Oregonians through support of the arts and education.
Fields of interest: Arts; Education.
Limitations: Applications accepted. Giving primarily in OR. Generally no support for propagandizing or influencing elections or legislation or projects of religious organizations that principally benefit their own members; no grants for private foundations. Generally no grants or loans to individuals, or for endowments, general fund drives, annual appeals, debt retirement, operation deficits, or emergency needs.
Publications: Application guidelines.
Application information: Using the foundation's online application system is required. If a proposal is declined, a subsequent request from that organization will normally not be considered within a 12-month period. An organization that has received a grant may submit another proposal two or three months prior to the end of that grant period, but no decision will be made on the new request until a final report on the prior grant has been received and approved. Application form required.
Initial approach: Online application
Copies of proposal: 1
Deadline(s): See web site for current deadlines
Final notification: 6 months
Officer: Martha S. Richards, Exec. Dir.
Directors: Alice P. McCartor; Charles H. Putney; Charles S. Rooks; William R. Swindells; Charles U. Walker.
EIN: 030373895
Selected grants: The following grants are a representative sample of this grantmaker's funding activity:
$1,833,000 to Oregon Symphony Association, Portland, OR, 2013. For general operating support, payable over 2.00 years.
$875,000 to Portland Opera Association, Portland, OR, 2013. For general operating support, payable over 2.00 years.
$725,000 to Portland Art Museum, Portland, OR, 2013. For general operating support, payable over 2.00 years.

$725,000 to Portland Center Stage, Portland, OR, 2013. For general operating support, payable over 2.00 years.
$619,500 to Chalkboard Project, Portland, OR, 2012. For the CLASS Project, payable over 3.00 years.
$300,000 to Chalkboard Project, Portland, OR, 2013. For the Teach Oregon project, payable over 3.00 years.
$300,000 to Chalkboard Project, Portland, OR, 2013. For TeachOregon program, payable over 3.00 years.
$150,000 to Oregon Museum of Science and Industry, Portland, OR, 2012. For general operating support, payable over 2.00 years.
$150,000 to White Bird, Portland, OR, 2012. For general operating support, payable over 2.00 years.
$125,000 to Northwest Academy, Portland, OR, 2012. To facilitate a move to a new facility.
$100,000 to Chamber Music Northwest, Portland, OR, 2012. For general operating support, payable over 2.00 years.
$100,000 to College Possible, Saint Paul, MN, 2012. To launch a program helping low-income students earn admission to and graduate from college, payable over 2.00 years.
$100,000 to De La Salle North Catholic High School, Portland, OR, 2012. For scholarships, payable over 2.00 years.
$100,000 to Open Meadow Alternative Schools, Portland, OR, 2013. For expansion of the Step-Up Academy.
$100,000 to Portland Schools Foundation, Portland, OR, 2013. For a community-wide collective impact project, payable over 2.00 years.
$60,000 to Columbia River Maritime Museum, Astoria, OR, 2012. For program start up costs specific to marketing and staff.
$50,000 to Artists Repertory Theater, Portland, OR, 2012. For general operating support, payable over 2.00 years.
$45,000 to Mount Scott Park Center for Learning, Portland, OR, 2013. For operating support of Transitions Program, payable over 3.00 years.
$20,000 to K B P S Public Radio Foundation, Portland, OR, 2012. For general operating support.

7872
Phillip S. Miller Foundation ✧
(formerly Phillip S. Miller Charitable Trust)
P.O. Box 3168
Portland, OR 97208-3168
Contact: Deborah J. Smith

Established in 1995 in CO.
Donor: Phillip S. Miller‡.
Foundation type: Independent foundation.
Financial data (yr. ended 12/31/13): Assets, $32,179,491 (M); expenditures, $1,678,277; qualifying distributions, $1,426,115; giving activities include $1,400,000 for 9 grants (high: $280,000; low: $28,000).
Purpose and activities: Support primarily for education and to children's hospitals.
Fields of interest: Education; Hospitals (specialty); Community/economic development.
Limitations: Applications not accepted. Giving primarily in CO. No grants to individuals.
Application information: Contributes only to pre-selected organizations. Unsolicited requests not considered.
Trustee: U.S. Bank, N.A.
Number of staff: 9 full-time professional.
EIN: 846290472

7873
Mission Increase Foundation ✧
7357 S.W. Beveland St., Ste. 200
Tigard, OR 97223-9074
FAX: (503) 210-0283;
E-mail: info@missionincrease.org; Main URL: http://www.missionincrease.org
Blog: http://www.missionincrease.org/blog/
Grants List: http://www.missionincrease.org/index.cfm?action=general.grantHistory

Established 2001 in OR.
Donors: Fidelity Charitable Gift Fund; Pearson Financial Group; Northwest Christian Community Foundation; The Christian Foundation of the Triangle; Marketplace One Foundation; Sacred Harvest Foundation.
Foundation type: Operating foundation.
Financial data (yr. ended 12/31/12): Assets, $30,240,393 (M); gifts received, $12,725; expenditures, $1,815,641; qualifying distributions, $1,580,619; giving activities include $1,502,265 for 57 grants (high: $100,000; low: $1,000).
Purpose and activities: Provides grants and targeted training to Christian ministries in the Portland, OR, Seattle, WA, Phoenix, AZ, Los Angeles and San Francisco, CA, and Denver, CO, metropolitan areas, and Raleigh, NC, Dallas, TX, Kansas City, KS, and Springfield and Columbus, OH.
Fields of interest: Human services; Children/youth, services; Christian agencies & churches; Religion.
Type of support: General/operating support; Income development; Management development/capacity building; Capital campaigns; Equipment; Program development; Consulting services; Employee matching gifts; Matching/challenge support.
Limitations: Applications not accepted. Giving primarily in the greater metro areas of Phoenix AZ, Los Angeles and San Francisco CA, Denver CO, Kansas City, KS, Raleigh, NC, Columbus and Springfield, OH, Portland OR, Dallas, TX, and Seattle WA. No grants to individuals.
Publications: Grants list; Informational brochure.
Application information: Contributes only to pre-selected organizations.
Board meeting date(s): Quarterly
Officers and Board Members:* Dale R. Stockamp,* Chair.; David Farquhar, Pres.; Ron Post,* Secy.; Daniel Davis, C.F.O.; Gail Stockamp.
Number of staff: 15 full-time professional; 1 part-time professional; 3 full-time support; 3 part-time support.
EIN: 810618279
Selected grants: The following grants are a representative sample of this grantmaker's funding activity:
$600 to Latin America Mission, Miami, FL, 2012. For general support and Grant Funds.

7874
Morris Family Foundation ✧ ☆
839 Alder Creek Dr.
Medford, OR 97504-8900
Application address: c/o Gary Rosenberger, Pres., 437 De Barr Ave., Medford, OR 97501-1661, tel.: (541) 779-1869

Established in 1998 in OR.
Donor: Earl W. Morris.
Foundation type: Independent foundation.
Financial data (yr. ended 06/30/13): Assets, $9,033,606 (M); expenditures, $561,209; qualifying distributions, $466,534; giving activities include $444,715 for 1 grant.
Purpose and activities: Scholarship awards to students in Jackson County, Oregon, School Districts No. 6, No. 35, No. 91 and No. 9, who are enrolled at Rogue Community College, Oregon, and are engaged in technical vocational education programs; giving also for orphans and victims of disasters.
Fields of interest: Education.
Type of support: General/operating support; Scholarship funds.
Limitations: Applications accepted. Giving limited to residents of Jackson County, OR.
Application information: Application form required.
Initial approach: Letter or scholarship application form
Deadline(s): None
Officers: Gary Rosenberger, Pres.; Jean Miller, V.P.; Erick Lieder, Secy.; Richard Entinger, Treas.; Pam Murphy, Exec. Dir.
EIN: 931230039
Selected grants: The following grants are a representative sample of this grantmaker's funding activity:
$329,678 to Rogue Community College Foundation, Grants Pass, OR, 2011.

7875
NIKE Foundation ✧
(formerly NIKE P.L.A.Y. Foundation)
1 Bowerman Dr.
Beaverton, OR 97005-6453
E-mail: nike.foundation@nike.com; E-mail for the Girl Effect: info@girleffect.org; Main URL: http://nikeinc.com/pages/the-nike-foundation
The Girl Effect on Facebook: http://www.facebook.com/girleffect
The Girl Effect on Twitter: http://twitter.com/girleffect
The Girl Effect on YouTube: http://www.youtube.com/girleffect

Established in 1994 in OR.
Donors: NIKE, Inc.; NoVo Foundation.
Foundation type: Company-sponsored foundation.
Financial data (yr. ended 05/31/13): Assets, $71,495,610 (M); gifts received, $6,775,807; expenditures, $30,028,172; qualifying distributions, $26,861,625; giving activities include $10,143,661 for 37 grants (high: $1,997,970; low: $15,000), and $1,997,970 for foundation-administered programs.
Purpose and activities: The foundation supports programs designed to empower adolescent girls in the developing world. Special emphasis is directed toward programs directed at reducing early marriage and delayign first birth; ensuring health and safety; secondary school completion and transitions to employment; and expanding direct access to economic assets.
Fields of interest: Secondary school/education; Education; Health care; Employment; Safety/disasters; Youth development, adult & child programs; Human services, financial counseling; Economic development; Social entrepreneurship; Microfinance/microlending; Girls; Economically disadvantaged.

International interests: Africa; Brazil; Developing Countries; India.
Type of support: General/operating support; Management development/capacity building; Program development; Seed money.
Limitations: Applications not accepted. Giving primarily in CA, Washington, DC, NY; giving on an international basis in Africa, Bangladesh, Brazil, India, Kenya, Nigeria, Paraguay, Tanzania, Uganda, and Zambia. No support for discriminatory organizations. No grants to individuals, or for general operating support for established programs, research or travel, films, television, or radio programs that are not an integral part of a project, religious programs, endowments or fundraising campaigns, lobbying or political activities, or depreciation or debt reduction.
Application information: Contributes only to pre-selected organizations. The foundation utilizes an invitation only Request for Proposal (RFP) process.
Officers and Directors:* Maria S. Eitel,* C.E.O. and Pres.; Collette Hemmings, C.O.O.; Howard Taylor, V.P. and Managing Dir.; Donald W. Blair; Trevor Edwards; Hannah Jones; Hilary Krane.
EIN: 931159948
Selected grants: The following grants are a representative sample of this grantmaker's funding activity:
$2,000,000 to International Bank for Reconstruction and Development, Washington, DC, 2012. To support World Bank Multi-Donor Trust Fund for Adolescent Girls Initiative.
$916,475 to TechnoServe, Washington, DC, 2012. To provide safe income generation opportunities for girls in harsh urban slums.
$832,950 to Stichting Mama Cash, Amsterdam, Netherlands, 2012. To build a global movement of adolescent girls and young women.
$624,770 to Grameen America, New York, NY, 2012. To develop and implement a scalable, group-based savings program with impact on health and social assets for low-income adolescent girls in new York city.
$520,672 to Girl Hub-London, London, England, 2012. To raise awareness and incite action to help girls through health, education, economic opportunity and justice programs.
$515,602 to CARE USA, Atlanta, GA, 2012. To ground sexual and reproductive health programs in economic empowerment in the south Gondar zone of the Amhara region of Ethiopia.
$415,476 to Academia para o Desenvolvimento da Educacao-Brasil, Recife, Brazil, 2012. For training and employment skills program in slums of Recife.
$307,922 to Rural Development Institute, Landesa, Seattle, WA, 2012. For work to leverage land rights in India to build girls' assets.
$252,054 to BRAC USA, New York, NY, 2012. To create Youth Learning Network.
$246,993 to Global Fund for Women, San Francisco, CA, 2012. To build the next generation of the women's movement.

7876
The Oregon Community Foundation ✧

(also known as OCF)
1221 S.W. Yamhill, Ste. 100
Portland, OR 97205-2108 (503) 227-6846
Contact: Megan Schumaker, Prog. Off., Community Grants and Funds
FAX: (503) 274-7771;
E-mail: mschumaker@oregoncf.org; Main URL: http://www.oregoncf.org
Facebook: http://www.facebook.com/pages/The-Oregon-Community-Foundation/350555908783
Flickr: http://www.flickr.com/photos/oregoncf/
Strategic Plan 2010-2015: http://www.oregoncf.org/Templates/media/files/publications/ocf_strategic_plan_2010.pdf
Twitter: http://twitter.com/TheOregonCF
YouTube: http://www.youtube.com/user/OregonCF

Established in 1973 in OR.
Foundation type: Community foundation.
Financial data (yr. ended 12/31/13): Assets, $1,698,892,336 (M); gifts received, $109,284,019; expenditures, $78,143,749; giving activities include $66,052,201 for grants.
Purpose and activities: The mission of The Oregon Community Foundation is to improve life in Oregon and promote effective philanthropy.
Fields of interest: Arts; Adult education—literacy, basic skills & GED; Education, reading; Education; Health care; Health organizations, association; Youth development, services; Children/youth, services; Family services; Aging, centers/services; Human services; Community/economic development; Voluntarism promotion; Government/public administration; Leadership development; Aging; Economically disadvantaged.
Type of support: General/operating support; Capital campaigns; Building/renovation; Equipment; Land acquisition; Program development; Seed money; Fellowships; Scholarship funds; Technical assistance; Scholarships—to individuals; Matching/challenge support.
Limitations: Applications accepted. Giving limited to OR. No support for religious organizations for religious purposes or projects in individual schools. No grants to individuals (except for scholarships), or for annual fund appeals, sponsorship of one-time events or performances or regular events or performances, emergency funding, endowments, annual campaigns, deficit financing, scientific research, publications, films, or conferences, unless so designated by a donor.
Publications: Application guidelines; Annual report; Newsletter.
Application information: Visit foundation web site for application forms, guidelines, and deadlines per grant type. Number of application copies varies by grant program; applications sent by fax are not accepted. Application form required.
Initial approach: Submit application form and required attachments (no letters of inquiry or pre-applications)
Copies of proposal: 2
Deadline(s): Jan. 15 and July 15 for Community Grant Program; varies for others
Board meeting date(s): Feb., May, Aug., and Nov.
Final notification: 6 to 14 weeks
Officers and Directors:* Sue Miller,* Chair.; Tim Mabry,* Vice-Chair.; Hal Snow,* Vice-Chair.; Max Williams, C.E.O. and Pres.; Jeff Anderson, Exec. V.P. and C.O.O.; Elizabeth Carey, V.P. and C.F.O.; Kathleen Cornett, V.P., Grants and Progs.; Laura Winter, V.P., Advised Funds; Ray Klinke, Assoc. V.P., for Finance and Fund Svcs.; Kirby Dyess,* Secy.; Jim Mark,* Treas.; Michael Coughlin; Roman Hernandez; Duane McDougall; Sue Naumes; Corrine Oishi; Trish Smith; Kay Toran; Duncan Wyse.
Investment Managers: Columbia Management Co.; CommonSense Partners; GMO City of London; Harris Associates; Iridian Asset Mgmt.; Pinnacle Associates; Wellington Management; Wells Capital Management.
Number of staff: 27 full-time professional; 3 part-time professional.
EIN: 237315673
Selected grants: The following grants are a representative sample of this grantmaker's funding activity:
$96,501 to Jackson County Childrens Relief Nursery, Family Nurturing Center, Medford, OR, 2012. For a second and final year of support to expand and strengthen mental health and family support services.

7877
PacifiCorp Foundation ✧

(doing business as Pacific Power/Rocky Mountain Power Foundation)
(also known as PacifiCorp Foundation For Learning)
825 N.E. Multnomah St., Ste. 2000
Portland, OR 97232-4116 (503) 813-7257
Contact: Lilisa Hall, Exec. Dir.
FAX: (503) 813-7249;
E-mail: pacificorpfoundation@pacificorp.com; Main URL: http://www.pacificorpfoundation.org
Grants List: http://www.pacificpower.net/about/itc/foundation/gr.html

Established in 1988 in OR.
Donor: PacifiCorp.
Foundation type: Company-sponsored foundation.
Financial data (yr. ended 12/31/12): Assets, $39,503,793 (M); expenditures, $1,952,258; qualifying distributions, $1,781,309; giving activities include $1,572,500 for 670 grants (high: $10,000; low: $25).
Purpose and activities: The foundation supports programs designed to promote education; civic and community betterment; culture and arts; and health, welfare, and social services.
Fields of interest: Arts, cultural/ethnic awareness; Arts councils; Visual arts; Museums; Performing arts; Historic preservation/historical societies; Arts; Elementary/secondary education; Education, early childhood education; Higher education; Education, reading; Education; Environment; Health care; Substance abuse, services; Courts/judicial administration; Crime/law enforcement; Children/youth, services; Family services, domestic violence; Aging, centers/services; Human services; Urban/community development; Community/economic development; United Ways and Federated Giving Programs; Public affairs.
Type of support: Building/renovation; General/operating support; Continuing support; Annual campaigns; Emergency funds; Program development; Curriculum development; Scholarship funds; Employee matching gifts; Matching/challenge support.
Limitations: Applications accepted. Giving primarily in areas of company operations in northern CA, southeastern, ID, OR, UT, central and southeastern WA, and WY. No support for religious organizations not of direct benefit to the entire community, political organizations or candidates for public office, discriminatory organizations, veterans' or fraternal organizations, or memberships in chambers of commerce, service clubs, or taxpayer associations. No grants to individuals, or for ballot measuring campaigns, endowments, debt reduction, capital campaigns, computers, software,

or related items, maintenance of existing facilities, or conferences, conventions, or events.
Publications: Application guidelines; Grants list.
Application information: Organizations receiving support are asked to provide a final report. Application form required.
Initial approach: Complete online application form and mail proposal and application form to foundation
Copies of proposal: 1
Deadline(s): Mar. 15 for Education, June 15 for Civic and Community, Sept. 15 for Culture and Arts, and Dec. 15 for Health, Welfare, and Social Service
Board meeting date(s): Mar., June, Sept., and Dec.
Final notification: 3 months following deadlines
Officers and Directors:* A. Richard Walje,* Chair.; Mark C. Moench, Secy.; Bruce Williams, Treas.; Karen Gilmore; Lilisa Hall, Exec. Dir.; Pat Reiten; Sara Schillinger.
Number of staff: 1 full-time professional; 2 part-time support.
EIN: 943089826

7878
PacificSource Foundation for Health Improvement ✧
(doing business as Pacific Source Health Plan)
(formerly PacificSource Charitable Foundation, Inc.)
P.O. Box 7068
Eugene, OR 97401-0068 (541) 684-5221
E-mail: CharitableFoundation@pacificsource.com; Toll-free tel.: (800) 624-6052; Main URL: http://www.pacificsource.com/CharitableFoundation/

Established in 1992 in OR.
Donors: Pacific Hospital Assn.; PacificSource Health Plans.
Foundation type: Independent foundation.
Financial data (yr. ended 12/31/12): Assets, $5,734,552 (M); gifts received, $600,000; expenditures, $910,226; qualifying distributions, $903,410; giving activities include $902,702 for 42 grants (high: $51,602; low: $10,000).
Fields of interest: Public health; Health care; Human services.
Type of support: General/operating support.
Limitations: Applications accepted. Giving limited to OR and ID.
Application information: Application form available on foundation web site. Applications are only accepted electronically. Application form required.
Initial approach: See foundation web site for guidelines and forms
Copies of proposal: 1
Deadline(s): At least 1 month prior to board meetings
Board meeting date(s): Semi-annually
Officers: Kenneth Provencher, Pres.; Marian Blankenship, Exec. Dir.
Trustees: David Abel, M.D.; Patricia Buchanan, M.D.; Fletcher Little; Mary McCauley-Burrows.
EIN: 931100080

7879
Mario and Alma Pastega Family Foundation ✧☆
2595 N.E. Belvue St.
Corvallis, OR 97330-4202 (541) 753-1214
Contact: Ken Pastega, Pres.

Established in 1997 in OR.
Donors: Mario Pastega†; Pastega Trust; Pepsi-Cola Bottling Co. of Corvallis, Inc.
Foundation type: Independent foundation.
Financial data (yr. ended 12/31/13): Assets, $19,528,062 (M); expenditures, $1,021,600; qualifying distributions, $891,624; giving activities include $798,049 for 105 grants (high: $280,000; low: $100).
Fields of interest: Education; Health care; Human services.
Limitations: Applications accepted. Giving primarily in Benton, Linn, Josephine and Tillamook counties, OR. No grants to individuals.
Application information: Application form required.
Initial approach: Letter
Deadline(s): None
Officer: Kenneth Pastega, Pres.
Directors: Lisa Pastega Altig; Dennis Pastega; Gary Pastega.
EIN: 931232789
Selected grants: The following grants are a representative sample of this grantmaker's funding activity:
$20,000 to George W. Bush Foundation, Dallas, TX, 2011.
$5,000 to Boys and Girls Club of Corvallis, Corvallis, OR, 2011.
$3,500 to Community Outreach, Corvallis, OR, 2011.
$3,000 to Abbey Foundation of Oregon, Saint Benedict, OR, 2011.
$2,500 to Fanconi Anemia Research Fund, Eugene, OR, 2011.
$1,500 to Knights of Columbus, Corvallis, OR, 2011.
$1,250 to Saint Jude Childrens Research Hospital, Memphis, TN, 2011.
$1,000 to Assistance League of Corvallis, Corvallis, OR, 2011.
$1,000 to Oregon Museum of Science and Industry, Portland, OR, 2011.
$1,000 to Oregon State Police Foundation, Salem, OR, 2011.

7880
Chris & Mary L. Peterson Memorial Fund ✧
P.O. Box 3168
Portland, OR 97208-3168 (503) 275-4327

Established in 1989 in OR; supporting organization of the Good Samaritan Foundation.
Foundation type: Independent foundation.
Financial data (yr. ended 06/30/13): Assets, $14,812,118 (M); expenditures, $853,771; qualifying distributions, $712,109; giving activities include $712,109 for grants.
Fields of interest: Nursing school/education; Health care.
Limitations: Applications not accepted. Giving limited to Portland, OR. No grants to individuals.
Application information: Unsolicited requests for funds not accepted.
Trustee: U.S. Bank, N.A.
EIN: 936226027
Selected grants: The following grants are a representative sample of this grantmaker's funding activity:
$937,659 to Good Samaritan Foundation, Portland, OR, 2011.

7881
PGE Foundation ✧
(formerly PGE-Enron Foundation)
One World Trade Center, 3rd Fl.
121 W. Salmon St.
Portland, OR 97204-2901 (503) 464-8818
Contact: Melissa Sircy, Grant Admin.
FAX: (503) 464-2929;
E-mail: pgefoundation@pgn.com; Additional contact: Rachel DeRosia, Prog. Off., tel.: (503) 464-8599, e-mail: rachel.derosia@pgn.com; Main URL: http://www.pgefoundation.org/

Established in 1994 in OR.
Donor: Portland General Electric Co.
Foundation type: Company-sponsored foundation.
Financial data (yr. ended 12/31/12): Assets, $22,884,117 (M); gifts received, $97,129; expenditures, $1,027,729; qualifying distributions, $1,001,495; giving activities include $874,933 for 113 grants (high: $85,133; low: $200).
Purpose and activities: The foundation supports programs designed to promote education, healthy families, and arts and culture. Special emphasis is directed toward education programs and basic needs services.
Fields of interest: Arts education; History/archaeology; Arts; Elementary/secondary education; Higher education; Education, drop-out prevention; Education, reading; Education; Health care; Employment; Food services; Food banks; Children/youth, services; Family services; Family services, parent education; Family services, domestic violence; Aging, centers/services; Developmentally disabled, centers & services; Homeless, human services; Human services; United Ways and Federated Giving Programs; Mathematics; Engineering/technology; Science; Minorities.
Type of support: General/operating support; Continuing support; Program development; Curriculum development; Scholarship funds; Sponsorships.
Limitations: Applications accepted. Giving primarily in areas of company operations in OR. No support for political entities or candidates for political office, discriminatory organizations, or fraternal, sectarian, or religious organizations not of direct benefit to the entire community. No grants to individuals, or for bridge grants, debt retirements, or operational deficits, endowments, general operating support, annual campaigns, ballot measure campaigns, travel, conferences, symposiums, festivals, events, team sponsorships, or user fees, or salaries of employees (unless costs relate directly to the funded project); generally no capital campaigns that include building improvements, equipment purchases, or anything considered an asset of the organization.
Publications: Application guidelines; Annual report.
Application information: Grants range from $2,500 to $10,000. A full application may be requested at a later date. Support is limited to 1 contribution per organization during any given year. Organizations receiving support are asked to submit a final report. Application form not required.
Initial approach: Complete online letter of inquiry
Deadline(s): Feb. 7, May 3, and Nov. 21
Board meeting date(s): May, Sept., and Feb.
Final notification: 30 days
Officers and Directors:* Gwyneth Gamble-Booth,* Chair.; Carole E. Morse, Pres.; Rosalie Duron, Secy.; James Lobdell, Treas.; David K. Carboneau; Carol

Dillin; Peggy Y. Fowler; Randolph L. Miller; James J. Piro; David Robertson; DeAngeloa Wells.
EIN: 931138806

7882
Poznanski Foundation ✧
7700 Arbor Lake Ct.
Wilsonville, OR 97070-8472 (503) 694-5463
Contact: Robert Poznanski, Pres.

Established in 1992 in OR.
Donors: Robert Poznanski; Dorothy Poznanski.
Foundation type: Independent foundation.
Financial data (yr. ended 12/31/13): Assets, $4,529,578 (M); expenditures, $576,868; qualifying distributions, $552,213; giving activities include $552,213 for 34 grants (high: $110,150; low: $60).
Purpose and activities: Giving primarily for human services and to Christian organizations.
Fields of interest: Performing arts, theater; Health care; Medical research, institute; Human services; Christian agencies & churches; Aging; Physically disabled; Women; Adults, women; Substance abusers.
Limitations: Applications accepted. Giving primarily in OR, with some giving in CA. No grants to individuals.
Application information: Application form not required.
Initial approach: Proposal
Deadline(s): None
Board meeting date(s): Yearly
Officers: Robert Poznanski, Pres.; Dorothy Poznanski, Secy.
Directors: Roberta Keller; Suanne Kottmeier; Linda Merrihew.
EIN: 943157812

7883
The Robert D. and Marcia H. Randall Charitable Trust ✧
9500 S.W. Barbur Blvd., Ste. 300
Portland, OR 97219-5436
Contact: Brenda Randall, Exec. Dir.

Established in 2001 in OR.
Donors: Robert D. Randall†; Marcia H. Randall; Randall Realty Corp.; The Randall Group, Inc.
Foundation type: Independent foundation.
Financial data (yr. ended 12/31/13): Assets, $3,093,947 (M); gifts received, $4,079,008; expenditures, $4,207,167; qualifying distributions, $4,144,863; giving activities include $4,054,443 for 73 grants (high: $3,333,000; low: $1,000).
Purpose and activities: Giving to improve and enrich the lives of people in the Pacific Northwest by supporting organizations that provide opportunity to the underprivileged and promote personal responsibility and initiative through programs which are values-based. It also focuses on improving education with challenging and stimulating instruction and social well-being, all of which reflect and are intended to strengthen the economic, political and cultural institutions upon which the American heritage of constitutional government and private enterprise is based, helping to create, with God's help, a better world.
Fields of interest: Education; Youth development; Human services.
Type of support: General/operating support; Capital campaigns; Equipment.
Limitations: Applications accepted. Giving primarily in the Pacific Northwest, with emphasis on OR. No grants to individuals.
Publications: Application guidelines.
Application information: Application form required.
Initial approach: Request pre-application form
Copies of proposal: 4
Deadline(s): Jun. 15 and Dec. 15
Board meeting date(s): Quarterly
Final notification: 3-6 months
Officer: Brenda Randall, Exec. Dir.
Trustees: Kirk A. Bass; John Emrick; Ronald L. Koos; Randall E. Norgart; Marcia H. Randall.
Number of staff: 1 part-time professional.
EIN: 931318923

7884
The Renaissance Foundation ✧
(formerly The Levin Family Foundation)
P.O. Box 80516
Portland, OR 97280-1516
Main URL: http://www.trfwebsite.org
Application address: Renaissance Scholarship Applications, Attn: The Renaissance Foundation, 8405 SW Nimbus Ave., Ste. D, Beaverton, OR 97008, tel.: (971) 722-6119, e-mail: josh.laurie@pcc.edu

Established in 2000 in OR.
Donors: Irving J. Levin; Frenda Levin.
Foundation type: Independent foundation.
Financial data (yr. ended 12/31/13): Assets, $14,738,001 (M); expenditures, $747,035; qualifying distributions, $645,639; giving activities include $641,666 for 68 grants (high: $167,999; low: $500).
Purpose and activities: Giving primarily for education, human services, and the environment. The foundation also offers a renewable scholarship awarded to first generation college freshmen and sophomores who demonstrate financial need, a passion for their field of study, and who have shown academic achievement. Scholarships are renewable for up to 4 years provided the recipient maintains a 3.0 GPA or better and completes 12 or more credits each term.
Fields of interest: Arts; Higher education; Education; Environment; Human services; Children/youth, services; Jewish agencies & synagogues.
Type of support: General/operating support; Scholarship funds.
Limitations: Giving primarily in Portland, OR. No grants to individuals (directly).
Publications: Application guidelines.
Application information: See foundation web site for scholarship application information. Scholarships paid directly to educational institutions.
Initial approach: For first-time applicants: Letter of Inquiry (no more than 2 pages in font size 12); for previous grant recipients: proposal
Final notification: Within 3-6 months for proposals
Officer: Diana Hoff, Mgr.
Trustees: Stephanie J. Fowler; Irving J. Levin.
EIN: 931306116

7885
The Salem Foundation ✧
c/o Pioneer Trust Bank, N.A.
P.O. Box 2305
Salem, OR 97308-2305 (503) 363-3136
Contact: Carol Herman, Trust Off.
E-mail: salemfoundation@pioneertrustbank.com; Main URL: http://www.salemfoundation.org

Established in 1930 in OR.
Foundation type: Community foundation.
Financial data (yr. ended 04/30/14): Assets, $21,379,376 (M); gifts received, $732,083; expenditures, $2,170,905; giving activities include $1,836,304 for 33+ grants (high: $291,356), and $6,810 for 19 grants to individuals.
Purpose and activities: The foundation provides scholarships to local students and distributions for the benefit of the community.
Fields of interest: Elementary/secondary education; Education; Botanical gardens; Health care; Recreation, parks/playgrounds; Youth development; Family services; Human services; Protestant agencies & churches; Catholic agencies & churches.
Limitations: Applications accepted. Giving limited to the Salem, OR, area. No grants for capital campaigns (generally).
Publications: Application guidelines; Financial statement; Grants list; Informational brochure.
Application information: Visit foundation web site for application information. Application form required.
Initial approach: Letter of intent, telephone, or e-mail
Copies of proposal: 7
Deadline(s): May 1 and Dec. 1
Board meeting date(s): 3rd week in Jan. and June
Final notification: 8 to 10 weeks
Trustee: Pioneer Trust Bank, N.A.
EIN: 936018523

7886
Sanders Family Foundation ✧
1800 Blankenship Rd., Ste 450
West Linn, OR 97068-4198

Established in 2006 in OR.
Donors: Robert C. Sanders; Olive Jane Sanders†.
Foundation type: Independent foundation.
Financial data (yr. ended 12/31/13): Assets, $36,344,567 (M); gifts received, $127,925; expenditures, $1,903,267; qualifying distributions, $1,731,160; giving activities include $1,725,000 for 11 grants (high: $500,000; low: $25,000).
Fields of interest: Secondary school/education; Higher education.
Limitations: Applications not accepted. Giving primarily in OR; some funding also in WA.
Application information: Contributes only to pre-selected organizations.
Officers: Robert C. Sanders, Chair.; Daniel Sanders, Pres.; Robert T. Sanders, Secy.
Directors: Susan J. Mobley; Molly Sanders; Samuel Sanders.
EIN: 205679987
Selected grants: The following grants are a representative sample of this grantmaker's funding activity:
$50,000 to Partners in Health, Boston, MA, 2012. For unrestricted general fund.

7887
Harold & Arlene Schnitzer CARE Foundation ✧
1121 S.W. Salmon St.
Portland, OR 97205-2000
Contact: Barbara Hall, V.P.

Established in 1994 in OR.
Donors: Harold J. Schnitzer; Arlene Schnitzer.
Foundation type: Independent foundation.
Financial data (yr. ended 12/31/12): Assets, $42,404,316 (M); gifts received, $1,340; expenditures, $5,330,779; qualifying distributions, $5,069,155; giving activities include $4,738,556 for 227 grants (high: $1,000,000; low: $100), and $231,668 for 2 foundation-administered programs.
Purpose and activities: Giving to arts and culture, education, health and human services, and Jewish organizations; funding also for programs to aid the needy, and to serve youth.
Fields of interest: Arts, multipurpose centers/programs; Museums; Education; Health organizations, association; Boys & girls clubs; Human services; Jewish agencies & synagogues.
Type of support: General/operating support; Continuing support; Annual campaigns; Capital campaigns; Building/renovation; Equipment; Emergency funds; Scholarship funds; Program-related investments/loans; Matching/challenge support.
Limitations: Applications accepted. Giving primarily in OR and Clark County, WA, with preference given to the Portland, OR metropolitan area. No grants to individuals.
Publications: Application guidelines; Grants list.
Application information: Grant proposals not accepted from organizations that the foundation has not previously supported. Application form not required.
Initial approach: Letter
Copies of proposal: 1
Deadline(s): Feb. 28, May 31, Aug. 31, and Nov. 30
Board meeting date(s): Quarterly
Final notification: Within 2 months of deadline
Officers and Directors:* Jordan D. Schnitzer,* Sr. V.P.; Theodore P. Malaska, V.P.; Thomas E. Eyer,* Treas.; Barbara Hall, Exec. Dir.; Arlene Schnitzer,* Grants Dir.; Joe Voboril.
Number of staff: 1 full-time professional; 1 part-time professional.
EIN: 931159884
Selected grants: The following grants are a representative sample of this grantmaker's funding activity:
$1,000,000 to Japanese Garden Society of Oregon, Portland, OR, 2012. For Endowment for Curator Position.
$400,000 to Northwest Academy, Portland, OR, 2012. For Capital Campaign.
$400,000 to Portland Art Museum, Portland, OR, 2012. For Curator Endowment.
$300,000 to Oregon School of Arts and Crafts, Portland, OR, 2012. For Craft Lives Here.
$250,000 to Oregon Public Broadcasting, Portland, OR, 2012. For New Millenium Fund Endowment.
$250,000 to Oregon Symphony Association, Portland, OR, 2012. For Annual Fund.
$83,333 to Lewis and Clark College, Portland, OR, 2012. For JDS Scholar.
$10,000 to Japanese Garden Society of Oregon, Portland, OR, 2012. For Golden Crane Society.
$5,000 to Oregon Jewish Museum, Portland, OR, 2012. For Let's Have A Ball Gala.
$5,000 to Vanderbilt University, Nashville, TN, 2012. For General Program Support.

7888
Schnitzer/Novack Foundation ✧
P.O. Box 10047
Portland, OR 97296-0047

Established in 1996 in OR.
Donors: Gilbert Schnitzer; Thelma Schnitzer; Schnitzer Investment Corp.
Foundation type: Independent foundation.
Financial data (yr. ended 12/31/13): Assets, $14,463,048 (M); gifts received, $60,000; expenditures, $735,861; qualifying distributions, $646,930; giving activities include $643,000 for 8 grants (high: $500,000; low: $1,000).
Purpose and activities: Primary focus on education and health care in the Pacific Northwest.
Fields of interest: Arts; Higher education; Hospitals (general); Human services; Jewish agencies & synagogues.
Type of support: Annual campaigns; Capital campaigns; Building/renovation; Program development; Professorships; Research.
Limitations: Applications not accepted. Giving limited to the West Coast, with emphasis on Portland, OR, and southern CA. No grants to individuals.
Application information: Unsolicited requests for funds not accepted.
Trustees: Deborah S. Novack; Kenneth M. Novack; Melanie Piziali; Gary Schnitzer.
EIN: 931220522

7889
Simple Actions Family Foundation ✧ ☆
8045 N.W. Skillings Dr.
Corvallis, OR 97330-2724
Main URL: http://simpleactionsfamilyfoundation.org/
Grants List: http://www.simpleactionsfamilyfoundation.org/archive

Established in 2008 in OR.
Donors: Eric Helpenstell; Bonnie Helpenstell.
Foundation type: Independent foundation.
Financial data (yr. ended 12/31/13): Assets, $1,034,064 (M); gifts received, $480,000; expenditures, $444,226; qualifying distributions, $444,226; giving activities include $436,640 for 91 grants (high: $26,640; low: $500).
Fields of interest: Education; Mental health/crisis services; Housing/shelter.
Limitations: Applications not accepted. Giving primarily in OR.
Application information: Unsolicited requests for funds not accepted.
Officers: Bonnie Helpenstell, Pres.; Lily Helpenstell, V.P.; Emily Helpenstell, Secy.; Eric Helpenstell, Treas.
EIN: 263209131

7890
Sky View Foundation ✧
P.O. Box 280
Lake Oswego, OR 97034-0280

Established in 2003 in OR.
Donor: Sue D. Cooley.
Foundation type: Independent foundation.
Financial data (yr. ended 12/31/12): Assets, $12,494,114 (M); expenditures, $1,053,302; qualifying distributions, $640,000; giving activities include $640,000 for grants.
Fields of interest: Environment, land resources; Community/economic development; Foundations (community).
Limitations: Applications not accepted. Giving primarily in CA and MA. No grants to individuals.
Application information: Contributes only to pre-selected organizations.
Officers: Robert Cooley-Gilliom, Pres.; Jeanne Becker, Treas.
Directors: Sue D. Cooley; Brian Charles Cooley-Gilliom.
EIN: 470927354

7891
Stoller Family Foundation ✧
7401 S.W. Washo Ct., Ste. 200
Tualatin, OR 97062-8343

Established in 2002 in OR.
Donors: William H. Stoller; Cathy A. Stoller.
Foundation type: Independent foundation.
Financial data (yr. ended 12/31/13): Assets, $0 (M); gifts received, $750,000; expenditures, $532,051; qualifying distributions, $530,503; giving activities include $530,503 for 30 grants (high: $240,000; low: $100).
Fields of interest: Higher education, university; Hospitals (general); Athletics/sports, football.
Limitations: Applications not accepted. Giving primarily in OR. No grants to individuals.
Application information: Contributes only to pre-selected organizations.
Officer and Directors:* William H. Stoller,* Pres.; Arthur C. Ramill, Jr., C.P.A.
EIN: 421566765

7892
Ann and Bill Swindells Charitable Trust ✧
1221 S.W. Yamhill St., Ste. 100
Portland, OR 97205-2108 (503) 222-0689
Contact: Donna Wecker, Admin.
FAX: (503) 222-0726;
E-mail: dwecker@swindellstrust.org; Main URL: http://www.swindellstrust.org

Established in 1998 in OR.
Donors: Ann Swindells; William Swindells.
Foundation type: Independent foundation.
Financial data (yr. ended 12/31/13): Assets, $48,902,558 (M); expenditures, $6,150,972; qualifying distributions, $5,787,828; giving activities include $5,680,345 for 68 grants (high: $1,000,000; low: $1,000).
Purpose and activities: Giving primarily to organizations whose principal mission is to improve the quality of life of the citizens of Oregon and to assist and sustain the educational, cultural, and scientific endeavors of the state.
Fields of interest: Humanities; Historical activities; Arts; Higher education; Medical school/education; Human services.
Type of support: Capital campaigns; Building/renovation; Equipment; Land acquisition; Program development; Professorships; Scholarship funds; Research; Matching/challenge support.

Limitations: Applications accepted. Giving limited to OR. No support for religious organizations or their capital fund drives or for activist organizations. No grants to individuals, or for annual operating budgets, development office personnel, annual fund raising activities, endowments, operational deficits, financial emergencies or for debt retirements.
Publications: Grants list; Informational brochure (including application guidelines).
Application information: Application form not required.
Initial approach: Letter (no more than 2 pages)
Copies of proposal: 1
Deadline(s): 30 days prior to board meetings
Board meeting date(s): Feb. 1, May 1, Aug. 1, and Nov. 1
Final notification: 15 days after board meetings
Trustees: William Swindells, Managing Tr.; Leslie Ann Ballinger; Charles Swindells; William R. Swindells III.
Number of staff: 1 full-time support.
EIN: 931246433
Selected grants: The following grants are a representative sample of this grantmaker's funding activity:
$10,000,000 to Oregon State University Foundation, Corvallis, OR, 2012. For capital support for College of Engineering.
$1,000,000 to Emanuel Medical Center Foundation, Portland, OR, 2012. For Legacy Emanuel Medical Center Critical Care Services.
$1,000,000 to Portland State University Foundation, Portland, OR, 2012. For capital support for new Viking Pavilion, multi-purpose campus facility which will host events ranging from lecture series, traveling artists, charity auctions, banquets, graduations and sports events.
$1,000,000 to University of Oregon Foundation, Eugene, OR, 2012. For American Judicature Society (AJS) Pledge.
$250,000 to Western Oregon University Development Foundation, Monmouth, OR, 2012. To construct new DeVolder Family Science Center.
$200,000 to Eisenhower Medical Center Foundation, Rancho Mirage, CA, 2012. For general support.
$155,000 to University of Oregon Foundation, Eugene, OR, 2012. For Willamette Presidential Scholars Program.
$50,000 to Marylhurst University, Marylhurst, OR, 2012. For HVAC upgrades and renovations to B.P. John Administration Building.
$50,000 to Portland Community College, Portland, OR, 2012. For scholarships.
$25,000 to Oregon Rehabilitation Association, Salem, OR, 2012. To remodel Oregon Disabilities Collaborative Center.

7893
TeamCFA Foundation ✧
311B Ave., Ste. M
Lake Oswego, OR 97034
Main URL: http://teamcfa.org/
Twitter: https://twitter.com/teamcfa

Donors: Challenge Foundation, Inc.; Louis Calder Foundation; Kenneth Levy.
Foundation type: Operating foundation.
Financial data (yr. ended 12/31/12): Assets, $558,166 (M); gifts received, $2,609,439; expenditures, $2,067,949; qualifying distributions, $1,772,381; giving activities include $871,200 for 11 grants (high: $187,618; low: $3,900).
Fields of interest: Secondary school/education.
Limitations: Applications not accepted.
Application information: Unsolicited requests for funds not accepted.
Officers and Directors:* Alfred C. Eckert III, Chair.; Joseph A. Maimone,* Pres.; Joan Lange, Secy.; William M. Steinbrook, Jr.,* Treas.; Ruppert Reinstadler; Ryan Stowers; Abigail Thernstrom.
EIN: 262778821

7894
Tektronix Foundation ✧
P.O. Box 500, M.S. 50-LAW
Beaverton, OR 97077-0001 (503) 627-7088
Contact: Anne Koopman, Admin.

Incorporated in 1952 in OR.
Donor: Tektronix, Inc.
Foundation type: Company-sponsored foundation.
Financial data (yr. ended 12/31/13): Assets, $191,406 (M); gifts received, $480,000; expenditures, $460,295; qualifying distributions, $460,295; giving activities include $449,260 for 24 + grants (high: $87,500).
Purpose and activities: The foundation supports organizations involved with arts and culture, education, conservation, and human services.
Type of support: General/operating support; Continuing support; Annual campaigns; Equipment; Program development; Employee matching gifts.
Limitations: Applications accepted. Giving primarily in OR. No grants to individuals, or for emergency needs or endowments, demonstration projects, debt reduction, research, publications, or conferences; no loans; no challenge grants.
Application information: Application form required.
Initial approach: Letter or e-mail
Deadline(s): None
Officer: Amie Aghdaei, Chair.
Trustees: Curt Bludworth; Robin Burnham.
EIN: 936021540
Selected grants: The following grants are a representative sample of this grantmaker's funding activity:
$76,000 to Oregon State University, Corvallis, OR, 2011.
$50,000 to Oregon Food Bank, Portland, OR, 2010.
$45,000 to Oregon Food Bank, Portland, OR, 2011.
$35,000 to Portland State University, Portland, OR, 2010.
$35,000 to University of Oklahoma, Norman, OK, 2010.
$25,000 to University of Texas at Dallas, Richardson, TX, 2010.
$10,000 to Library Foundation, 2010.
$10,000 to Oregon Childrens Foundation, Portland, OR, 2010.
$10,000 to Oregon Childrens Foundation, Portland, OR, 2010.
$10,000 to Portland State University, Portland, OR, 2010.

7895
Herbert A. Templeton Foundation ✧
0650 S.W. Gaines St., Ste. 1102
Portland, OR 97239 (503) 223-0036
Contact: Ruth B. Richmond, Pres.

Incorporated in 1955 in OR.
Donors: Herbert A. Templeton†; Herbert A. Templeson Trust for Robert Templeson.
Foundation type: Independent foundation.
Financial data (yr. ended 12/31/13): Assets, $23,594,796 (M); expenditures, $1,277,809; qualifying distributions, $1,117,637; giving activities include $1,013,850 for 135 grants (high: $25,000; low: $1,900).
Purpose and activities: Grants for youth, cultural, and social service organizations operating in Oregon, or having programs significantly affecting Oregon residents; present emphasis on program and direct services.
Fields of interest: Arts; Education, early childhood education; Human services; Children/youth, services; Children/youth; Youth.
Type of support: General/operating support; Continuing support; Emergency funds; Program development; Seed money.
Limitations: Applications accepted. Giving limited to OR. No support for medical services, the aged, or parochial education. No grants to individuals, or for fellowships, building or endowment funds, scientific research or technology, matching gifts, or medical or medically-related programs; no loans or program-related investments.
Publications: Application guidelines; Program policy statement.
Application information: Application form required.
Initial approach: Letter
Copies of proposal: 1
Deadline(s): Mar. 15 and Sept. 15 (no later than 5:00pm on deadline days)
Board meeting date(s): Feb., May, Sept. and Nov.
Officers and Trustees:* Ruth B. Richmond,* Pres.; Henry R. Richmond,* V.P.; Terrence R. Pancoast,* Secy.; Jimmie Perkins,* Treas.; Margaret Eickmann; Linda McKinley Girard; Christian T. Richmond.
Number of staff: 2 part-time professional.
EIN: 930505586

7896
Rose E. Tucker Charitable Trust ✧
900 S.W. 5th Ave., Ste. 2600
Portland, OR 97204-1229
Contact: Milo E. Ormseth, Tr.; Terrence R. Pancoast, Tr.; Sherri Gold
E-mail: Tuckertrust@stoel.com

Trust established in 1976 in OR.
Donors: Rose E. Tucker†; Max and Rose Tucker Foundation.
Foundation type: Independent foundation.
Financial data (yr. ended 06/30/13): Assets, $20,502,698 (M); expenditures, $1,428,088; qualifying distributions, $1,274,054; giving activities include $1,198,900 for 112 grants (high: $175,000; low: $500).
Fields of interest: Arts; Higher education; Education; Environment; Health care; Human services; Children/youth, services; Community/economic development; Disabilities, people with; Economically disadvantaged.
Type of support: General/operating support; Capital campaigns; Building/renovation; Equipment; Land acquisition; Program development; Scholarship funds; Matching/challenge support.
Limitations: Applications accepted. Giving limited to organizations and projects in OR, with emphasis on the metropolitan Portland area. No support for religious purposes, private foundations, or conduit organizations. No grants to individuals, or for fellowships; no loans or program-related investments.
Publications: Application guidelines; Grants list.

Application information: Organizations may only apply once within a 12 month period. Application form not required.
Initial approach: Proposal
Copies of proposal: 2
Deadline(s): None
Board meeting date(s): Approximately every 2 months
Final notification: Within 15 days of board meetings
Trustees: Milo E. Ormseth; Terrence R. Pancoast; U.S. Bank, N.A.
Number of staff: None.
EIN: 936119091
Selected grants: The following grants are a representative sample of this grantmaker's funding activity:
$150,000 to Tucker-Maxon Oral School, Portland, OR, 2011. For general support.
$50,000 to Oregon Public Broadcasting, Portland, OR, 2011. For general support.
$45,000 to Natural Resources Defense Council, San Francisco, CA, 2011. For general support.
$20,000 to Mercy Corps, Portland, OR, 2011. For general support.
$15,000 to Oregon Food Bank, Portland, OR, 2011. For general support.
$15,000 to Sisters of the Road, Portland, OR, 2011. For general support.
$13,000 to Friends of the Children-Portland, Portland, OR, 2011. For general support.
$10,000 to Emanuel Childrens Hospital Foundation, Portland, OR, 2011. For general support.
$7,500 to Court Appointed Special Advocates for Children, Portland, OR, 2011. For general support.
$6,000 to Trillium Family Services, Portland, OR, 2011. For general support.

7897
Tykeson Family Charitable Trust ✧
1144 Willagillespie Rd., Ste. 33
Eugene, OR 97401-6722

Established in 2004 in OR and funded through the transferred assets of the liquidated Donald E.Tykeson Foundation.
Donor: Donald E. Tykeson.
Foundation type: Independent foundation.
Financial data (yr. ended 12/31/13): Assets, $23,138,596 (M); gifts received, $80,996; expenditures, $1,224,010; qualifying distributions, $1,187,417; giving activities include $1,187,417 for 71 grants (high: $369,962; low: $25).
Purpose and activities: Giving primarily to hospitals and health organizations; funding also for the arts, education, and social services.
Fields of interest: Arts; Higher education; Hospitals (general); Health organizations, association; Human services; Children/youth, services; Foundations (community).
Limitations: Applications not accepted. Giving primarily in OR, with emphasis on Eugene. No grants to individuals.
Application information: Unsolicited requests for funds not accepted.
Trustees: Amy C. Tykeson; Donald E. Tykeson.
EIN: 367428977

7898
The Vibrant Village Foundation ✧ ☆
1737 N.E. Alberta St., Ste. 207
Portland, OR 97211-5890
E-mail: info@vibrantvillage.org; Main URL: http://www.vibrantvillage.org/
Blog: http://www.vibrantvillage.org/blog
Facebook: https://www.facebook.com/pages/The-Vibrant-Village-Foundation/229178943809497

Donors: Kathleen De Laski Grubb; Donald De Laski; The De Laski Family Foundation.
Foundation type: Independent foundation.
Financial data (yr. ended 12/31/12): Assets, $76,214,370 (M); gifts received, $32,643,056; expenditures, $1,991,713; qualifying distributions, $1,676,323; giving activities include $1,148,932 for 26 grants (high: $230,295; low: $5,000), and $558,750 for foundation-administered programs.
Purpose and activities: The foundation invests in the potential of communities around the world, and provides support in the areas of nutrition and health, clean water, agriculture, education, arts and economic development.
Fields of interest: Arts; Environment; Human services; International development.
International interests: Ecuador; Ghana; Guatemala; Haiti; Indonesia; Niger.
Limitations: Giving primarily in Washington, DC, and Portland, OR.
Publications: Annual report.
Application information: See foundation web site for updates in grant cycles.
Officers and Directors:* Kenneth E. deLaski,* Pres.; Sarah Goracke,* Secy.; Carolyn T. Standing,* Treas.; Kathleen deLaski.
EIN: 270745672

7899
The Woodard Family Foundation ✧
(also known as Woodard Family Foundation)
P.O. Box 10666
Eugene, OR 97440 (541) 343-9402
Contact: Tyson Woodard, Dir.
FAX: (541) 343-0122;
E-mail: wffstaff@woodardff.com; Main URL: http://www.woodardff.com

Incorporated in 1952 in OR.
Donors: Walter A. Woodard†; Carlton Woodard.
Foundation type: Independent foundation.
Financial data (yr. ended 06/30/13): Assets, $8,676,276 (M); expenditures, $783,509; qualifying distributions, $636,675; giving activities include $636,675 for grants.
Purpose and activities: It is the desire of the foundation to assist charitable organizations in developing the internal capacity to meet present and future needs; not to remove responsibilities from people.
Fields of interest: Arts; Higher education; Business school/education; Education; Human services; Community/economic development.
Type of support: General/operating support; Annual campaigns; Capital campaigns; Building/renovation; Land acquisition; Program development; Professorships; Seed money; Consulting services.
Limitations: Applications accepted. Giving limited to local organizations in the greater Cottage Grove/Eugene, OR, area.
Publications: Application guidelines.
Application information: See foundation web site for complete application guidelines. Application form required.
Initial approach: Letter request, or contact foundation for application form
Copies of proposal: 1
Board meeting date(s): Quarterly
Officers and Directors:* Tod Woodard,* Pres.; Andrew Woodard,* V.P. and Treas.; Pepper Woodard Bridgens,* Secy.; Dena Woodard McCoy; Carlton Woodard; Joy Woodard; Kim Woodard; Kristen A. Woodard; Tyson Woodard.
Number of staff: 1 part-time professional; 1 part-time support.
EIN: 936026550
Selected grants: The following grants are a representative sample of this grantmaker's funding activity:
$25,000 to Indian Mountain School, Lakeville, CT, 2013. For Education 2013 Impact Grant Recipient.
$15,000 to Indian Mountain School, Lakeville, CT, 2013. For education capital campaign.
$15,000 to Sacred Heart Medical Center Foundation, Eugene, OR, 2013. For Health Kokkino Oregon Neuroscience Institute Endowment.
$8,000 to South Lane School District, Cottage Grove, OR, 2013. For Education Cottage Grove High School Football Equipment.
$6,000 to South Lane School District, Cottage Grove, OR, 2013. For Education London School.
$5,000 to Grace Church School, New York, NY, 2013. For education annual giving campaign.
$2,750 to Sacred Heart Medical Center Foundation, Eugene, OR, 2013. For Health Children's Miracle Network.
$2,000 to Sacred Heart Medical Center Foundation, Eugene, OR, 2013. For Health Courageous Kids.
$2,000 to Sacred Heart Medical Center Foundation, Eugene, OR, 2013. For Health: Courageous Kids.
$1,500 to South Lane School District, Cottage Grove, OR, 2013. For Education Baseball Team Equipment Cottage Grove High School.

7900
Yarg Foundation ✧
3805 N. Colonial Ave.
Portland, OR 97227-1005

Established in OR.
Donor: John Gray.
Foundation type: Independent foundation.
Financial data (yr. ended 12/31/13): Assets, $22,659,808 (M); gifts received, $20,294,360; expenditures, $780,909; qualifying distributions, $780,342; giving activities include $775,000 for 1 grant.
Fields of interest: Environment, land resources; Environment.
Limitations: Applications not accepted. Giving primarily in Washington, DC.
Application information: Contributes only to pre-selected organizations.
Officers: Jack Gray, Chair.; Joan Gray, Vice-Chair.; Nicholas Walrod, Secy.-Treas.
EIN: 364708840
Selected grants: The following grants are a representative sample of this grantmaker's funding activity:
$935,819 to Land Trust Alliance, Washington, DC, 2012. To Fund a Needs Assessment, and the Oregon Advancing Conservation Excellence Program.

7901
Juan Young Trust ✧
c/o Western Division
P.O. Box 91429
Portland, OR 97291-0429
Contact: Antoinette Kienow Arenz, Tr.
E-mail: juanyoungtrust@msn.com; Eastern Division address: c/o Scott G. Klusmann, Tr., 1980 Willamette Falls Dr., Ste. 230/252, West Linn, OR 97068-4675; tel.: (503) 722-7080; fax: (503) 513-9259; e-mail: edjyt@ipns.com; Main URL: http://www.gosw.org/juanyoungtrust

Established in 1996 in OR under the will of Juan Young; funded in 1999.
Donor: Juan Young†.
Foundation type: Independent foundation.
Financial data (yr. ended 12/31/12): Assets, $17,576,439 (M); expenditures, $1,760,787; qualifying distributions, $1,669,640; giving activities include $1,400,000 for 230 grants (high: $20,000; low: $800).
Purpose and activities: Giving primarily for the education, health and welfare of children under the age of 21, who reside in OR. The foundation also awards grants to colleges and universities in OR to provide scholarships to lineal descendants of former employees of Kienow's Food Stores Inc. and/or Kienow's Wholesale Grocery Company, as well as to the general student population. Recipients must be at the time of application: 1) under the age of 21 years old; 2) a resident of OR; and 3) acceptable to the college or university as a full-time student.
Fields of interest: Education; Health care; Children/youth, services.
Type of support: Capital campaigns; Building/renovation; Equipment; Program development.
Limitations: Applications accepted. Giving limited to OR, with emphasis on Portland. No support for religious purposes, propaganda or to influence legislation, or private foundations. No grants to individuals, or for operating budgets, fund appeals, debt retirement, or to defray deficits; no loans or program-related investments.
Publications: Application guidelines; Informational brochure (including application guidelines).
Application information: Application materials must remain unstapled. See foundation web site for additional information. Application form required.
Initial approach: Request application form
Copies of proposal: 2
Deadline(s): Mar. 31, June 30, Sept. 30, and Dec. 31
Board meeting date(s): Jan., Apr., July, and Oct.
Final notification: First week of Feb., May, Aug., and Nov.
Trustees: Antoinette Kienow Arenz; Scott G. Klusmann.
Number of staff: 2 full-time professional.
EIN: 931245000

7902
Jay and Diane Zidell Charitable Foundation ✧
3121 S.W. Moody Ave.
Portland, OR 97239-4505 (503) 937-2236
Contact: Larry Richards, Dir.

Established in 2005 in OR.
Donors: Jay Zidell; Diane Zidell.
Foundation type: Independent foundation.
Financial data (yr. ended 12/31/13): Assets, $21,515,235 (M); gifts received, $1,000,000; expenditures, $824,048; qualifying distributions, $791,400; giving activities include $791,400 for 63 grants (high: $167,000; low: $180).
Fields of interest: Arts; Health care; Jewish federated giving programs; Jewish agencies & synagogues.
Limitations: Applications accepted. Giving primarily in OR.
Application information:
Initial approach: Letter
Deadline(s): None
Directors: Larry Richards; Diane Zidell; Jay Zidell.
EIN: 203912349
Selected grants: The following grants are a representative sample of this grantmaker's funding activity:
$137,840 to Portland Jewish Academy, Portland, OR, 2010.
$20,000 to Oregon Food Bank, Portland, OR, 2011.
$2,500 to Pacific Legal Foundation, Sacramento, CA, 2011.
$1,000 to Jewish National Fund, Rockville Centre, NY, 2011.
$1,000 to Muscular Dystrophy Association, Tucson, AZ, 2011.
$1,000 to National Jewish Health, Denver, CO, 2011.

PENNSYLVANIA

7903
1675 Foundation
16 E. Lancaster Ave., Plz. 16, Ste. 102
Ardmore, PA 19003-2228 (610) 896-3868
Contact: Marge Brennan, Grants Mgr.
FAX: (610) 896-3869;
E-mail: mbrennan@1675foundation.org; Main URL: http://www.1675foundation.org

Established in 2004 in PA from the reorganization of The Oxford Foundation into 4 distinct entities.
Foundation type: Independent foundation.
Financial data (yr. ended 12/31/13): Assets, $17,173,311 (M); gifts received, $32,446; expenditures, $1,286,837; qualifying distributions, $1,140,795; giving activities include $813,500 for 49 grants (high: $300,000; low: $2,000).
Purpose and activities: The mission of the 1675 Foundation is to fortify the key elements of a healthy community: health; human services; education; the environment; and the arts; particularly as they relate to under-served and vulnerable populations. The foundation makes grants in Chester County, Pennsylvania.
Fields of interest: Arts; Education; Environment; Health care; Human services.
Type of support: General/operating support; Annual campaigns; Building/renovation; Program development; Research; Matching/challenge support.
Limitations: Applications accepted. Giving primarily in Chester County, PA. No funding outside the U.S. No support for political organizations. No grants to individuals; no loans.
Publications: Application guidelines.
Application information: Delaware Valley Grantmakers Common Grant Application Form accepted (along with foundation cover sheet). Application form required.
Initial approach: Proposal
Copies of proposal: 1
Deadline(s): Mar. 1, and Oct. 1
Board meeting date(s): May and Dec.
Final notification: Within 2 months
Officers and Directors:* Carol E. Ware,* Pres.; Daphne C. Rowe,* Exec. Dir.
Number of staff: 2 part-time professional.
EIN: 201083951
Selected grants: The following grants are a representative sample of this grantmaker's funding activity:
$25,000 to Lighthouse Youth Center, Oxford, PA, 2013.
$20,000 to Decade to Doorways, West Chester, PA, 2013.
$15,000 to ChesPenn Health Services, Chester, PA, 2013.
$15,000 to Chester County Community Dental Center, Coatesville, PA, 2013.
$15,000 to Clinic, The, Phoenixville, PA, 2013.
$10,000 to Legal Aid of Southeastern Pennsylvania, Norristown, PA, 2013.
$8,000 to CHOICE: Concern for Health Options-Information, Care and Education, Philadelphia, PA, 2013.
$8,000 to Womens Medical Fund, Philadelphia, PA, 2013.
$7,000 to Safe Harbor of Chester County, West Chester, PA, 2013.
$5,000 to PennEnvironment Research and Policy Center, Philadelphia, PA, 2013.

7904
Abessinio Family Foundation, Inc. ✧
P.O. Box 159
Concordville, PA 19331-1322

Established in 2001.
Donors: Rocco A. Abessinio; Applied Card Systems, Inc.
Foundation type: Independent foundation.
Financial data (yr. ended 12/31/13): Assets, $10,921,139 (M); gifts received, $1,000,000; expenditures, $737,884; qualifying distributions, $717,626; giving activities include $715,629 for 26 grants (high: $250,000; low: $100).
Fields of interest: Arts; Education; Religion.
Limitations: Applications not accepted. Giving primarily in PA. No grants to individuals.
Application information: Contributes only to pre-selected organizations.
Directors: Mary F. Abessinio; Peter G. Abessinio; Rocco A. Abessinio; Vincent T. Abessinio; Mary D. Cool; Joanne F. Fabrizio.
EIN: 540413298
Selected grants: The following grants are a representative sample of this grantmaker's funding activity:
$200,000 to Archdiocese of Philadelphia, St Rocco Catholic Church, Philadelphia, PA, 2010.
$125,000 to Archdiocese of Philadelphia, St Rocco Catholic Church, Philadelphia, PA, 2010.
$125,000 to Archdiocese of Philadelphia, St Rocco Catholic Church, Philadelphia, PA, 2010.
$20,000 to Salesianum School, Wilmington, DE, 2010.
$10,000 to Historical Society of Delaware, Wilmington, DE, 2011. For general operating fund.
$5,000 to Archmere Academy, Claymont, DE, 2011. For general operating fund.
$5,000 to Saint Edmonds Academy, Wilmington, DE, 2011. For general operating fund.
$5,000 to Ursuline Academy, Wilmington, DE, 2011. For general operating fund.
$2,000 to Unicorn Childrens Foundation, Boca Raton, FL, 2011. For general operating fund.
$1,500 to Sojourners Place, Wilmington, DE, 2011. For general operating fund.

7905
ACE Charitable Foundation ✧
(formerly ACE INA Foundation)
436 Walnut St., WA 08G
Philadelphia, PA 19106-3786
Contact: Eden Kratchman, Exec. Dir.
E-mail: acecharitablefoundation@acegroup.com; Main URL: http://www.acegroup.com/About-ACE/Philanthropy/Philanthropy.html

Established in 2007 in PA.
Donor: ACE American Insurance Co.
Foundation type: Company-sponsored foundation.
Financial data (yr. ended 12/31/12): Assets, $2,961,688 (M); gifts received, $1,370,441; expenditures, $1,950,246; qualifying distributions, $1,940,651; giving activities include $1,379,674 for 66 grants (high: $250,000; low: $75), and $560,977 for 1,104 employee matching gifts.
Purpose and activities: The foundation supports organizations involved with education, poverty and health, and the environment. Special consideration is given to opportunities where ACE employees' time and expertise can be utilized in addition to financial support.
Fields of interest: Museums; Higher education; Education; Environment, water resources; Environment, land resources; Environment; Health care; Food services; Food banks; Disasters, preparedness/services; American Red Cross; International development; International relief; United Ways and Federated Giving Programs; Economically disadvantaged.
Type of support: Scholarship funds; General/operating support; Program development; Employee volunteer services; Employee matching gifts.
Limitations: Giving on a national and international basis in areas of company operations (outside of Bermuda), with some emphasis on Philadelphia, PA.
Application information:
Initial approach: E-mail foundation for application guidelines
Deadline(s): None
Officers and Directors:* Evan Greenberg,* Chair. and C.E.O.; Brian Dowd,* Exec. V.P.; John Keogh,* Exec. V.P.; Lori Samson,* V.P.; Kathryn Schneider, Secy.; Joseph Jordan, Treas.; Eden M. Kratchman, Exec. Dir.; Robert Hernandez.
EIN: 262456949
Selected grants: The following grants are a representative sample of this grantmaker's funding activity:
$50,000 to Saint Johns University, School of Risk Management, New York, NY, 2012.
$75 to Temple University, Department of Risk Insurance and Health Care Mngmt, Philadelphia, PA, 2012.
$50 to Temple University, Fox School of Business, Philadelphia, PA, 2012.

7906
E. Reginald Adam and Rhea H. Adam Trust ✧ ☆
c/o BNY Mellon, N.A.
P.O. Box 185
Pittsburgh, PA 15230-0185

Donor: Eva Reth Trust.
Foundation type: Independent foundation.
Financial data (yr. ended 12/31/13): Assets, $8,409,895 (M); expenditures, $693,976; qualifying distributions, $653,227; giving activities include $635,326 for 6 grants (high: $632,526; low: $100).
Fields of interest: Arts; Health care; Community/economic development.
Limitations: Applications not accepted. Giving primarily in Akron, OH.
Application information: Unsolicited requests for funds not accepted.
Trustee: BNY Mellon, N.A.
EIN: 136192599

7907
The Air Products Foundation ✧
7201 Hamilton Blvd.
Allentown, PA 18195-1501 (610) 481-7020
Contact: Timothy J. Holt, Pres.
E-mail: corprela@airproducts.com; Tel. for Timothy J. Holt: (610) 481-4911; Main URL: http://www.airproducts.com/company/sustainability/

corporate-citizenship/
charitable-giving-and-philanthropy.aspx

Incorporated in 1979 in PA.
Donor: Air Products and Chemicals, Inc.
Foundation type: Company-sponsored foundation.
Financial data (yr. ended 09/30/12): Assets, $97,695,969 (M); gifts received, $27,231,185; expenditures, $4,987,781; qualifying distributions, $4,734,571; giving activities include $4,371,673 for 500 grants (high: $250,000; low: $100), and $313,910 for 421 employee matching gifts.
Purpose and activities: The foundation supports organizations involved with arts and culture, education, the environment, health, safety and sustainability, human services, and community economic development.
Fields of interest: Arts; Higher education; Education; Environment; Health care; Safety/disasters; Human services; Civil/human rights, fund raising/fund distribution; Civil/human rights, equal rights; Community/economic development; United Ways and Federated Giving Programs.
Type of support: General/operating support; Continuing support; Annual campaigns; Employee volunteer services; Employee matching gifts; In-kind gifts.
Limitations: Applications accepted. Giving on a national basis in areas of major company operations. No support for sectarian religious organizations, political or veterans' organizations, labor groups, service clubs, elementary or secondary schools, or United Way-supported organizations. No grants to individuals, or for capital campaigns or general operating support for health organizations or hospitals; no loans.
Publications: Application guidelines.
Application information: Organizations receiving support are asked to submit an impact report. Application form not required.
Initial approach: E-mail proposal to foundation
Copies of proposal: 1
Deadline(s): June 1
Board meeting date(s): Monthly
Final notification: Sept. or Oct.
Officers and Trustees:* John D. Stanley,* Chair.; Timothy J. Holt, Pres.; George G. Bitto, V.P. and Treas.; Charles G. Stinner, V.P.; Gregory E. Weigard, V.P.; Benjamin M. Hussa, Secy.; Paul E. Huck; Lynn C. Minella.
EIN: 232130928

7908
Alcoa Foundation ✧
Alcoa Corporate Ctr.
201 Isabella St.
Pittsburgh, PA 15212-5858
Main URL: http://www.alcoa.com/global/en/community/foundation.asp
E-Newsletter: http://www.alcoa.com/global/en/community/foundation/info_page/newsletters.asp
Facebook: http://www.facebook.com/alcoamonthofservice
Grants Database: http://www.alcoa.com/global/en/community/foundation/grants.asp
Twitter: https://twitter.com/alcoafoundation
YouTube: http://www.youtube.com/alcoatv

Trust established in 1952 in PA; incorporated in 1964.
Donors: Alcoa Corp.; Aluminum Co. of America; Alcoa Inc.
Foundation type: Company-sponsored foundation.
Financial data (yr. ended 12/31/12): Assets, $460,142,329 (M); gifts received, $500,000; expenditures, $24,816,126; qualifying distributions, $23,143,326; giving activities include $21,517,932 for 1,070 grants.
Purpose and activities: The foundation supports programs designed to engage people to improve the environment, educate tomorrow's leaders, and enhance communities where Alcoa operates around the world.
Fields of interest: Higher education; Teacher school/education; Adult/continuing education; Education, services; Education; Environment, public policy; Environment, pollution control; Environment, waste management; Environment, recycling; Environment, climate change/global warming; Environment, natural resources; Environment, water resources; Environment, land resources; Environment, energy; Environment, forests; Environmental education; Environment; Employment, services; Employment, training; Employment; Disasters, preparedness/services; Safety/disasters; Recreation, parks/playgrounds; Girl scouts; Youth development, business; Youth development; American Red Cross; Children/youth, services; Urban/community development; Mathematics; Engineering/technology; Science; Transportation; Minorities; Women; Girls.
International interests: Africa; Asia; Australia; Caribbean; Central America; Europe; Mexico; South America.
Type of support: Continuing support; Management development/capacity building; Annual campaigns; Building/renovation; Equipment; Emergency funds; Program development; Conferences/seminars; Curriculum development; Scholarship funds; Research; Employee volunteer services; Sponsorships; Employee matching gifts; Employee-related scholarships; Matching/challenge support.
Limitations: Applications accepted. Giving on a national and international basis in areas of company operations, with emphasis on New York, NY, Pittsburgh, PA, Africa, Asia, Australia, Brazil, Canada, Caribbean, China, Central America, Europe, Mexico, Russia, and South America. No support for political or lobbying organizations, sectarian or religious organizations not of direct benefit to the entire community, discriminatory organizations, social clubs or organizations, sports teams, private foundations, or trust funds. No grants to individuals (except for employee-related scholarships), or for endowments, capital campaigns, debt reduction, operating costs or reserves, indirect or overhead costs, fundraising events or sponsorships including walks/runs, golf tournaments, tickets, tables, benefits, raffles, souvenir programs, advertising, or fundraising dinners, trips, conferences, seminars, festivals, one-day events, documentaries, videos, or research projects/programs.
Publications: Application guidelines; Corporate giving report; Grants list; Newsletter; Program policy statement.
Application information: The minimum grant request is $15,000. Selected applicants will be invited to submit an online application. Organizations receiving support are asked to submit interim reports and a final report.
Initial approach: Proposal to nearest company facility
Copies of proposal: 1
Deadline(s): Contact nearest company facility
Board meeting date(s): Monthly
Officers and Directors:* Esra Ozer,* Pres.; Dean Will, Cont. and Business Mgr.; Micheal T. (Mike) Barriere; John (Jack) D. Bergen; Alan Cransberg; Franklin L. (Frank) Feder; Shauna Huang; Lysane Martel; Tim D. Myers; William J. O'Rourke; William F. (Bill) Oplin; Shannon Parks; Rosa Garcia Pineiro; Vitaliy V. Rusakov; Maxim Smirnov.
Corporate Trustee: The Bank of New York Mellon, N.A.
Number of staff: 6 full-time professional; 1 full-time support.
EIN: 251128857
Selected grants: The following grants are a representative sample of this grantmaker's funding activity:
$750,000 to Girl Scouts of the U.S.A. National Headquarters, New York, NY, 2012. For Girl Scouts Forever Green program.
$713,000 to Alcoa Institute, Instituto Alcoa, Sao Paulo, Brazil, 2012. For grants in Brazil.
$250,000 to Junior Achievement Worldwide, Colorado Springs, CO, 2012. For Science, Technology, Engineering and Mathematics (STEM) Career Program Enhancements.
$200,000 to Engineers Without Borders USA, Boulder, CO, 2012. For creation of a Global Engineer position.
$190,000 to Institute of International Education, New York, NY, 2012. To advance a Sustainability Academic Partnership as the Managing Partner.
$25,000 to Brookings Institution, Washington, DC, 2012. For China Center Clean Energy Research Project.
$20,000 to Engineers Society of Western Pennsylvania, Pittsburgh, PA, 2012. For Pittsburgh Regional Design Lives Here Event.
$18,000 to StrongLand Chamber Foundation, Vandergrift, PA, 2012. For Invention Convention Showcase.
$15,000 to Dodge County Certified Literate Community Program, Eastman, GA, 2012. For Heart Connection Mentoring Project for 4th and 5th grade students in Dodge County. Heart Connection matches students with a trained mentor at an age when they are on the verge of independence and personal decision making.
$750 to Duquesne University, Pittsburgh, PA, 2012. For matching gift.

7909
Alderbaugh Foundation ✧ ☆
c/o Bee Bergvall & Co.
444 S. State St.
Newtown, PA 18940-1945 (215) 968-4224

Established in 1982.
Donor: Clarence E. Denoon, Jr.
Foundation type: Independent foundation.
Financial data (yr. ended 12/31/13): Assets, $2,702,511 (M); expenditures, $881,766; qualifying distributions, $877,500; giving activities include $876,000 for 6 grants (high: $800,000; low: $1,000).
Fields of interest: Arts; Higher education; Education.
Limitations: Applications accepted. Giving primarily in PA.
Application information: Application form required.
Initial approach: Letter
Deadline(s): None
Officer: Ashby Denoon, Mgr.
Director: David B.H. Denoon.
EIN: 232173929

7910
Joseph Alexander Foundation, Inc. ✧
P.O. Box 433
Ft. Washington, PA 19034-0433 (813) 902-2691
Contact: Harvey Mackler, Dir.

Established in 1960 in NY.
Donor: Joseph Alexander†.
Foundation type: Independent foundation.
Financial data (yr. ended 10/31/13): Assets, $15,302,991 (M); gifts received, $379,354; expenditures, $938,637; qualifying distributions, $811,345; giving activities include $722,000 for 62 grants (high: $100,000; low: $1,500).
Purpose and activities: Giving primarily for higher education, health organizations and medical research, particularly optic nerve research, social services, and Jewish organizations.
Fields of interest: Higher education; Education; Human services; Jewish agencies & synagogues.
Type of support: General/operating support; Annual campaigns; Capital campaigns; Building/renovation; Equipment; Endowments; Program development; Conferences/seminars; Curriculum development; Scholarship funds; Research; Exchange programs.
Limitations: Applications accepted. Giving primarily in New York, NY; funding also in PA.
Publications: Financial statement.
Application information: Application form required.
Initial approach: Letter
Copies of proposal: 1
Deadline(s): None
Board meeting date(s): Jan., Apr., July, and Oct.
Officers and Directors:* Harvey Mackler,* Pres.; Randi Windheim,* Secy.; Alexander Mackler; Jessica Rosenberg; Justin Windheim.
EIN: 510175951
Selected grants: The following grants are a representative sample of this grantmaker's funding activity:
$50,000 to University of Pennsylvania, Perelman School of Medicine, Philadelphia, PA, 2011.
$50,000 to Western Wall Heritage Foundation, New York, NY, 2011.
$50,000 to Yeshiva University, New York, NY, 2011.
$30,000 to Amyotrophic Lateral Sclerosis Association, Ambler, PA, 2011.
$25,000 to Albert Einstein College of Medicine of Yeshiva University, Bronx, NY, 2010.
$25,000 to Chamah, New York, NY, 2011.
$20,000 to Dorot, New York, NY, 2011.
$15,000 to Jewish Museum, New York, NY, 2011.
$10,000 to American Friends of the Israel Museum, New York, NY, 2011.
$5,000 to International Center of Photography, New York, NY, 2011.
$5,000 to National Down Syndrome Society, New York, NY, 2011.

7911
Allegheny Foundation ✧
1 Oxford Ctr.
301 Grant St., Ste. 3900
Pittsburgh, PA 15219-6401 (412) 392-2900
Contact: Matthew A. Groll, Exec. Dir.
Main URL: http://www.scaife.com/alleghen.html

Incorporated in 1953 in PA.
Donor: Richard M. Scaife†.
Foundation type: Independent foundation.
Financial data (yr. ended 12/31/13): Assets, $67,210,520 (M); expenditures, $2,833,843; qualifying distributions, $2,607,441; giving activities include $2,128,400 for 36 grants (high: $200,000; low: $5,000).
Purpose and activities: Giving primarily for historic preservation, education, and community development.
Fields of interest: Historic preservation/historical societies; Education; Youth development; Community development, neighborhood development.
Type of support: General/operating support; Program development; Seed money.
Limitations: Applications accepted. Giving primarily in western PA, with emphasis on Pittsburgh. No grants to individuals, or for endowment funds, event sponsorship, capital campaigns, renovations, government agencies, scholarships, or fellowships; no loans.
Publications: Application guidelines; Annual report.
Application information: Application form not required.
Initial approach: Letter
Copies of proposal: 1
Deadline(s): None
Board meeting date(s): Nov.
Final notification: 4-6 weeks
Officer and Trustees:* Matthew A. Groll,* Exec. Dir.; Joanne B. Beyer; Ralph H. Goettler; Doris O'Donnell; Jane Roesch; George Weymouth; Arthur P. Ziegler, Jr.
Number of staff: 1 part-time professional; 1 full-time support.
EIN: 256012303

7912
The Allerton Foundation, Inc. ✧
(formerly The Diane Lenfest Myer Foundation, Inc.)
5 Tower Bridge
300 Barr Harbor Dr., Ste. 460
West Conshohocken, PA 19428
Contact: Bruce Melgary, Exec. Dir.
Application address: 2 Logan Sq., 100 N. 18th St., Ste. 800, Philadelphia, PA 19103, tel.: (215) 239-9003

Established in 1999 in PA.
Donor: Diane Lenfest Myer.
Foundation type: Independent foundation.
Financial data (yr. ended 06/30/13): Assets, $58,435,984 (M); expenditures, $3,430,080; qualifying distributions, $3,158,071; giving activities include $3,101,500 for 26 grants (high: $1,000,000; low: $5,000).
Purpose and activities: Giving for animal welfare, and land conservation to preserve animal habitat.
Fields of interest: Environment, land resources; Animal welfare; Animals/wildlife; Autism research.
Type of support: General/operating support; Continuing support; Annual campaigns; Capital campaigns; Building/renovation; Seed money.
Limitations: Applications accepted. Giving primarily in New York, NY and southeastern PA. No grants to individuals, or for event tickets, tables, or sponsorships.
Application information: Brochures, newsletters, videos or any other materials should not be submitted with the initial letter. Application form not required.
Initial approach: 2- to 3-page letter
Copies of proposal: 1
Deadline(s): None
Board meeting date(s): As necessary
Final notification: 3 to 6 months
Officers and Directors:* Diane Lenfest Myer,* Pres.; Grahame Richards, Secy.; Joy Tartar, C.F.O.; Marguerite Lenfest,* Treas.; L. Bruce Melgary,* Exec. Dir.
EIN: 233035225
Selected grants: The following grants are a representative sample of this grantmaker's funding activity:
$1,000,000 to Autism Speaks, New York, NY, 2011.
$500,000 to Becker College, Worcester, MA, 2011.
$500,000 to Childrens Hospital of Philadelphia Foundation, Philadelphia, PA, 2011.
$100,000 to Family Service Association of Bucks County, Langhorne, PA, 2011.
$50,000 to Philadelphia Museum of Art, Philadelphia, PA, 2011. For operating support.
$25,000 to Academy of Natural Sciences of Philadelphia, Philadelphia, PA, 2011. For operating support.
$25,000 to Franklin Institute Science Museum, Philadelphia, PA, 2011.
$25,000 to Teach for America, Philadelphia, PA, 2011. For general operating support.
$25,000 to Woodmere Art Museum, Philadelphia, PA, 2011. For operating support.
$20,000 to Norristown Zoological Society, Norristown, PA, 2011. For operating support.

7913
Ametek Foundation, Inc. ✧
1100 Cassatt Rd.
Berwyn, PA 19312-1177 (610) 647-2121
Contact: Kathryn E. Sena, Secy.-Treas.

Incorporated in 1960 in NY.
Donor: Ametek, Inc.
Foundation type: Company-sponsored foundation.
Financial data (yr. ended 12/31/13): Assets, $3,709,897 (M); expenditures, $1,219,890; qualifying distributions, $1,219,890; giving activities include $1,204,434 for 86 grants (high: $104,112; low: $1,000).
Purpose and activities: The foundation supports hospitals and organizations involved with arts and culture, education, the environment, cancer, diabetes, human services, international affairs, and community economic development.
Fields of interest: Museums; Arts; Elementary school/education; Higher education; Scholarships/financial aid; Education; Environment, natural resources; Environment; Hospitals (general); Cancer; Diabetes; American Red Cross; Youth, services; Human services; International affairs; Business/industry; Community/economic development; United Ways and Federated Giving Programs.
Type of support: Program development; General/operating support; Annual campaigns; Building/renovation; Equipment; Endowments; Scholarship funds; Research; Technical assistance; Exchange programs; Matching/challenge support.
Limitations: Applications accepted. Giving primarily in areas of company operations, with emphasis on PA. No support for organizations lacking significant employee interest or involvement. No grants to individuals; no loans.
Application information: Application form not required.
Initial approach: Proposal
Copies of proposal: 1

Deadline(s): None
Board meeting date(s): Apr. and Oct.
Officers and Directors:* Frank S. Hermance,* Chair. and Pres.; Elizabeth R. Varet,* V.P.; Kathryn E. Sena, Secy.-Treas.; Dennis K. Williams.
EIN: 136095939
Selected grants: The following grants are a representative sample of this grantmaker's funding activity:
$1,000 to Temple University, Fox School, Philadelphia, PA, 2012. For education.

7914
Angelakis Family Foundation ✧
1250 Lafayette Rd.
Gladwyne, PA 19035-1110

Established in 2006 in RI.
Donors: Michael J. Angelakis; Christine B. Angelakis.
Foundation type: Independent foundation.
Financial data (yr. ended 12/31/13): Assets, $3,627,915 (M); gifts received, $1,077,064; expenditures, $723,432; qualifying distributions, $692,750; giving activities include $692,750 for 26 grants (high: $200,000; low: $100).
Fields of interest: Education; Human services.
Type of support: General/operating support.
Limitations: Applications not accepted. Giving primarily in PA. No grants to individuals.
Application information: Unsolicited requests for funds not accepted.
Trustees: Christine B. Angelakis; Michael J. Angelakis.
EIN: 207011268
Selected grants: The following grants are a representative sample of this grantmaker's funding activity:
$502,242 to Babson College, Babson Park, MA, 2011.
$92,709 to William Penn Charter School, Philadelphia, PA, 2011.
$43,500 to YMCA of Philadelphia and Vicinity, Philadelphia, PA, 2011.
$20,000 to YMCA, Bayside Family, Barrington, RI, 2011.
$5,000 to Meeting Street, Providence, RI, 2011.
$5,000 to Steppingstone Scholars, Philadelphia, PA, 2011.

7915
AO North America, Inc. ✧
1700 Russell Rd.
Paoli, PA 19301-1224 (610) 993-5100
FAX: (610) 695-2420; Course Info.: c/o AO North America Continuing Medical Education, 1690 Russell Rd., Paoli, PA 19301, tel.: (800) 769-1391 or (610) 695-2459; e-mail: registrar@aona.org; Main URL: http://www.aona.org

Established in 1992 in PA.
Donors: AO/ASIF Foundation; Synthes, Inc.
Foundation type: Independent foundation.
Financial data (yr. ended 06/30/13): Assets, $10,488,966 (M); gifts received, $16,503,747; expenditures, $13,054,842; qualifying distributions, $10,518,346; giving activities include $602,275 for 15 grants (high: $50,000; low: $7,275), and $13,055,332 for foundation-administered programs.
Purpose and activities: The organization is dedicated to the advancement of patient care in orthopedic, craniomaxillofacial, spine, and veterinary surgery. Its mission is to improve the care of patients with musculo-skeletal injuries and their sequelae in North America, through education and research in the principles, practice and results of treatment. Recipients chosen on the basis of their knowledge of orthopedic medicine for their research ability. Support given to trauma research projects, training in the management and care of teachers, and to visiting professors in the teaching of orthopedic, maxillofacial, spine or veterinary trauma treatment. The organization has also established The Kathryn Cramer Memorial Fellowship to foster medical students, young orthopedic residents, orthopedic trauma fellows, and junior orthopedic trauma faculty who are interested in educational and research endeavors in orthopedics (preferably orthopedic trauma).
Fields of interest: Higher education; Medical school/education; Hospitals (general); Medical research, institute; Nerve, muscle & bone research; Orthopedics research.
Type of support: Research.
Limitations: Giving primarily in North America. No grants for purchase of instruments or implants for research, equipment, salaries or travel expenses.
Application information: Grants rarely exceed $5,000 for research projects. Maximum funding for visiting professor program: $3,000 per professor from North America, $6,000 per professor from abroad. Application form required.
Initial approach: Letter, telephone, or fax for application guidelines, or refer to foundation Web site for guidelines
Copies of proposal: 10
Deadline(s): None
Board meeting date(s): Jan. 15, Apr. 15, July 15, and Oct. 15
Officers: John Wilber, Chair.; Michael Baumgaertner, Pres.; John Frodel, Secy.; Michael J. Lewis, Treas.; Nancy Holmes, Exec. Dir.
Members: James E. Gerry; Ziya Gokaslan; Dean Richardson; Peter Trafton.
EIN: 232701788

7916
Aospine North America Inc. ✧
1700 Russell Rd.
P.O. Box 1755
Paoli, PA 19301-1224

Donors: Aospine International; Synthes; Orthopaedic Research & Education Foundation.
Foundation type: Independent foundation.
Financial data (yr. ended 12/31/12): Assets, $1,417,739 (M); gifts received, $5,180,147; expenditures, $4,544,516; qualifying distributions, $4,397,624; giving activities include $1,225,842 for 29 grants (high: $90,000; low: $5,842).
Fields of interest: Medical school/education; Education; Health care; Neuroscience; Orthopedics; Spine disorders research; Medical research.
Limitations: Applications not accepted.
Application information: Contributes only to pre-selected organizations.
Officers: Jens R. Chapman, M.D., Chair.; Nancy H. Holmes, Exec. Secy.; Robert A. McGuire, Jr., Treas.
Directors: Paul M. Arnold, M.D.; Darrel Brodke; Michael D. Daubs, M.D.; Michael G. Fehlings, M.D.; Roger A. Hartl, M.D.; Alexander R. Vaccaro, M.D.
EIN: 270411158

7917
Aqua Charitable Trust ✧
(formerly PSC Charitable Foundation)
762 W. Lancaster Ave.
Bryn Mawr, PA 19010-3402
Main URL: https://www.aquaamerica.com/

Donor: Aqua Pennsylvania, Inc.
Foundation type: Company-sponsored foundation.
Financial data (yr. ended 12/31/13): Assets, $424,674 (M); gifts received, $900,500; expenditures, $493,720; qualifying distributions, $493,720; giving activities include $489,220 for 275 grants (high: $37,000; low: $50).
Purpose and activities: Giving primarily for the arts, education, health associations, human services, and YMCAs.
Fields of interest: Performing arts; Arts; Education; Environment; Health organizations, association; Human services; YM/YWCAs & YM/YWHAs; United Ways and Federated Giving Programs.
Limitations: Applications not accepted. Giving primarily in the Philadelphia, PA, area. No grants to individuals.
Application information: Contributes only to pre-selected organizations.
Officers: Nicholas DeBenedictis, Chair. and C.E.O.; Christopher Luning, Exec. V.P. and C.O.O.; David P. Smeltzer, Exec. V.P. and C.F.O.; Karl Kyriss, Exec. V.P.
EIN: 232985234

7918
The Arcadia Foundation ✧
105 E. Logan St.
Norristown, PA 19401-3058

Incorporated in 1964 in PA.
Donors: Edith C. Steinbright†; Marilyn Lee Steinbright.
Foundation type: Independent foundation.
Financial data (yr. ended 09/30/13): Assets, $27,663,561 (M); expenditures, $965,716; qualifying distributions, $796,500; giving activities include $796,500 for 20 grants (high: $250,000; low: $2,000).
Purpose and activities: Emphasis on hospitals and hospital building funds, health agencies and services, nursing, hospices, early childhood, adult and higher education, libraries, child development and welfare agencies, youth organizations, and social service and general welfare agencies, including care of the handicapped, aged, and hungry; support also for family services, the environment and conservation, wildlife and animal welfare, religious organizations, historical preservation, and music organizations.
Fields of interest: Performing arts, music; Historic preservation/historical societies; Education, early childhood education; Child development, education; Higher education; Nursing school/education; Adult/continuing education; Libraries/library science; Education; Environment, natural resources; Environment; Animal welfare; Animals/wildlife, preservation/protection; Hospitals (general); Nursing care; Health care; Health organizations, association; Food services; Human services; Children/youth, services; Child development, services; Family services; Residential/custodial care, hospices; Aging, centers/services; Christian agencies & churches; Protestant agencies & churches; Religion; General charitable giving; Aging;

Disabilities, people with; Economically disadvantaged.
Type of support: General/operating support; Continuing support; Annual campaigns; Capital campaigns; Building/renovation; Equipment; Endowments; Program development; Scholarship funds; Research.
Limitations: Applications not accepted. Giving limited to eastern PA organizations whose addresses have zip codes beginning with 18 and 19. Generally, low support for cultural programs. No grants to individuals, or for deficit financing, land acquisition, fellowships, demonstration projects, publications, or conferences; no loans.
Publications: Annual report.
Application information: Contributes only to pre-selected organizations.
Board meeting date(s): Nov.
Officers: Marilyn Lee Steinbright, Pres.; David P. Sandler, Secy.; Harvey S.S. Miller, Treas.
Number of staff: None.
EIN: 236399772

7919
Arete Foundation ✧

1845 Walnut St., 10th Fl.
Philadelphia, PA 19103-4709
Contact: Sue Taylor, Exec. Dir.

Established in 1986 in PA.
Donors: Edward E. Cohen; Betsy Z. Cohen; Jonathan Z. Cohen; Solomon Investment Partnership.
Foundation type: Independent foundation.
Financial data (yr. ended 11/30/12): Assets, $102,148,629 (M); gifts received, $1,130,400; expenditures, $6,574,990; qualifying distributions, $5,931,087; giving activities include $5,931,087 for 54 grants (high: $2,475,460; low: $250).
Purpose and activities: Giving primarily for higher education; giving also for the arts and to Jewish organizations.
Fields of interest: Museums (art); Performing arts; Arts; Higher education; Education; Human services; Jewish federated giving programs; Jewish agencies & synagogues.
Type of support: Continuing support; Annual campaigns; Conferences/seminars; Publication; Scholarship funds; Research.
Limitations: Giving primarily in Philadelphia, PA; some giving in NY.
Application information: Application form not required.
Initial approach: Detailed letter
Copies of proposal: 1
Deadline(s): None
Board meeting date(s): Annually
Officer: Sue Taylor, Exec. Dir.
Trustees: Betsy Z. Cohen; Daniel G. Cohen; Edward E. Cohen; Jonathan Z. Cohen.
EIN: 236779271
Selected grants: The following grants are a representative sample of this grantmaker's funding activity:
$3,225,000 to Metropolitan Opera Association, New York, NY, 2011. For production campaign and general support.
$754,564 to American Academy in Rome, New York, NY, 2011. For general support, matching grant and Centenary Celebration membership.
$335,000 to Asia Society, New York, NY, 2011. For task force report, gala fundraising, annual fund, and membership.
$255,078 to Jewish Theological Seminary of America, New York, NY, 2010.
$247,322 to Metropolitan Opera Association, New York, NY, 2010.
$224,200 to Jewish Theological Seminary of America, New York, NY, 2011. For dinner fundraising and fellowship program.
$181,919 to National Museum of American Jewish History, Philadelphia, PA, 2011. For capital campaign and annual gala.
$174,663 to Yale University, Law School, New Haven, CT, 2011.
$160,047 to Brearley School, New York, NY, 2011. For 125th Anniversary Campaign, annual fund and benefit.
$123,727 to American Academy in Rome, New York, NY, 2010.
$100,509 to Roundabout Theater Company, New York, NY, 2010.
$100,000 to Washington University, School of Medicine, Saint Louis, MO, 2011. For Research Fund.
$98,949 to Asia Society, New York, NY, 2010.
$98,916 to University of Pennsylvania, Philadelphia, PA, 2010.
$85,000 to Asia Society, New York, NY, 2010.
$60,000 to Metropolitan Museum of Art, New York, NY, 2010.
$50,000 to New York City Opera, New York, NY, 2011. For general operating support.
$25,145 to Columbia University, New York, NY, 2010.
$25,000 to FotoFest, Houston, TX, 2010.
$25,000 to United States Department of State, Washington, DC, 2011. For US Diplomatic Reception Rooms.

7920
The Argus Fund ✧

501 Office Center Dr., Ste. 2
Fort Washington, PA 19034

Established in 2006 in PA.
Donors: Mark Dibner; Rachel Zax Dibner; The Dibner Fund, Inc.
Foundation type: Independent foundation.
Financial data (yr. ended 12/31/13): Assets, $22,265,754 (M); expenditures, $1,469,242; qualifying distributions, $1,208,464; giving activities include $1,020,692 for 34 grants (high: $209,667; low: $500).
Purpose and activities: The fund will be dedicated, within its financial ability, to provide leadership and supportive funding to organizations, programs and institutions that provide individuals and families with opportunities to help themselves improve the quality of their lives. The fund will also serve to initiate and assist a broad range of activities and projects which tend to improve the human condition, bringing better health, education, self-sufficiency, and cross-cultural understanding to individuals and groups worldwide. To this end, initially, the fund will make local, national, and international grants related but not restricted to: 1) The Arts and Humanities; 2) Humanitarian Aid; 3) Environmental Protection & Conservation; 4) Peaceful Coexistence; 5) Social Reform & Progressive problem solving; 6) Educational Access; 7) Health Care Advocacy; 8) Technological Accessibility & Empowerment; 9) Historical Preservation; and 10) Multi-Cultural Awareness Legacy Giving.
Fields of interest: Arts, cultural/ethnic awareness; Humanities; Historic preservation/historical societies; Arts; Education; Environment; Health care; International relief; International democracy & civil society development; International peace/security; Civil/human rights.
Limitations: Applications not accepted. Giving primarily in NY and Washington, DC.
Application information: Unsolicited requests for funds not accepted.
Officers: Mark Dibner, Pres.; Rachel Zax Dibner, V.P.
EIN: 205045447

7921
The Armstrong County Community Foundation ✧

220 S. Jefferson St., Ste. B
Kittanning, PA 16201 (724) 548-5897
Contact: Mindy Knappenberger, Exec. Dir.
FAX: (724) 548-4275;
E-mail: accfound@windstream.net; Main URL: http://www.accfound.org
Facebook: https://www.facebook.com/ArmstrongCountyCommunityFoundation
Flickr: http://www.flickr.com/people/25001158@N02/
RSS Feed: http://feeds.feedburner.com/makingchange
Twitter: http://twitter.com/accf

Established in 1998 in PA.
Foundation type: Community foundation.
Financial data (yr. ended 12/31/13): Assets, $8,276,219 (M); gifts received, $1,594,840; expenditures, $811,746; giving activities include $244,742 for 6+ grants (high: $69,805), and $404,136 for 566 grants to individuals.
Purpose and activities: The foundation serves the people of Armstrong County to enhance the quality of life by: 1) giving grants, scholarships and organizational support to address the changing needs of our community; 2) building a permanent endowment for our community and helping our donors create a legacy for the future through this endowment; 3) promoting informed philanthropy and volunteerism to increase charitable resources for the region; 4) providing leadership and building partnerships to identify and solve community issues.
Fields of interest: Visual arts; Performing arts; Historic preservation/historical societies; Arts; Libraries/library science; Education; Health care; Mental health/crisis services; Employment, training; Human services; Economic development; Community/economic development; Aging; Disabilities, people with.
Type of support: Management development/capacity building.
Limitations: Applications accepted. Giving primarily in Armstrong County, PA. No grants to individuals (except for scholarships).
Publications: Grants list.
Application information: Visit foundation web site for application guidelines. Based on letter of inquiry, if the request is deemed appropriate to the foundation's guidelines, the agency will receive a full grant application packet. Application form required.
Initial approach: Mail, fax, or e-mail letter of inquiry (no longer than 2 pages)
Copies of proposal: 1
Deadline(s): July 1
Board meeting date(s): 2nd Thurs. of each month
Final notification: Sept. 30

Officers and Director:* Chase McClister,* Pres.; Christine Moss,* V.P.; Autumn Volpe-Seyler,* Secy.-Treas.; Mindy Knappenberger, Exec. Dir.; Richard G. Snyder, Dir., Emeritus; Frank Baker; Sandy Bradigan; Kristen Samosky; Lance Whiteman.
Number of staff: 2 full-time professional; 1 part-time support.
EIN: 311625798

7922
Armstrong Foundation ✧
2500 Columbia Ave.
Lancaster, PA 17603-4117
Main URL: http://www.armstrongfoundation.com/

Established in 1985 in PA.
Donor: Armstrong World Industries, Inc.
Foundation type: Company-sponsored foundation.
Financial data (yr. ended 12/31/13): Assets, $1,498,389 (M); gifts received, $1,000,000; expenditures, $1,046,188; qualifying distributions, $1,031,328; giving activities include $1,031,328 for 228 grants (high: $375,000; low: $50).
Purpose and activities: The foundation supports organizations involved with education, health, substance abuse, hunger, housing development, human services, and community development.
Fields of interest: Higher education; Education; Hospitals (general); Health care; Substance abuse, services; Substance abuse, treatment; Food services; Food banks; Food distribution, meals on wheels; Housing/shelter, development; Boys & girls clubs; Boy scouts; Youth development, business; American Red Cross; Children/youth, services; Family services; Human services; Community/economic development.
Type of support: General/operating support; Annual campaigns; Building/renovation; Scholarship funds; Employee volunteer services; Employee matching gifts; Employee-related scholarships; Grants to individuals.
Limitations: Applications accepted. Giving primarily in areas of company operations. No grants to individuals (except for employee-related scholarships and hardship grants), or for legislative or political activities.
Publications: Application guidelines; Program policy statement.
Application information: Application form required.
Initial approach: Complete online application form
Deadline(s): July 1
Officers and Directors: David S. Cookson,* Pres.; Thomas J. Waters, V.P. and Treas.; Christopher Parisi, V.P.; Leslie J. Kulis; Stephen H. Poole; Ellen R. Romano.
EIN: 232387950
Selected grants: The following grants are a representative sample of this grantmaker's funding activity:
$10,000 to American Red Cross, Des Moines, IA, 2012. To improve quality of life in communities.
$500 to York College of Pennsylvania, York, PA, 2012. To improve quality of American education.

7923
Asplundh Foundation ✧
708 Blair Mill Rd.
Willow Grove, PA 19090-1701

Incorporated in 1953 in PA.
Donors: Carl H. Asplundh†; Lester Asplundh†; Asplundh Tree Expert Co.; Asplundh Family Public Foundation inc.
Foundation type: Independent foundation.
Financial data (yr. ended 12/31/13): Assets, $68,993,615 (M); gifts received, $45,900; expenditures, $5,045,385; qualifying distributions, $5,043,340; giving activities include $1,803,000 for 77 grants (high: $500,000; low: $250).
Purpose and activities: Giving primarily to Christian agencies, churches, and schools, as well as for the arts, education and health organizations.
Fields of interest: Arts; Education; Environment; Hospitals (general); Health organizations; Human services; Christian agencies & churches.
Limitations: Applications not accepted. Giving primarily in PA. No grants to individuals.
Application information: Unsolicited requests for funds not accepted.
Trustees: Christopher B. Asplundh; Edward K. Asplundh; Kurt H. Asplundh.
EIN: 236297246

7924
Avs Foundation ✧
1000 Gamma Dr., No. 106
Pittsburgh, PA 15238-2929

Established in PA.
Donor: The David Henry Charitable Trust.
Foundation type: Independent foundation.
Financial data (yr. ended 06/30/13): Assets, $37,861,395 (M); gifts received, $120,872; expenditures, $1,871,995; qualifying distributions, $1,504,217; giving activities include $1,477,201 for 8 grants (high: $537,201; low: $10,000).
Fields of interest: Education; Human services; Children/youth, services; Disabilities, people with.
Limitations: Applications not accepted. Giving primarily in FL and PA.
Application information: Contributes only to pre-selected organizations.
Officers: Patricia Miller Duggan, Pres. and C.E.O.; John K. Duggan, Jr., Secy.-Treas.
Trustees: Edward Bash; Regis G. Champ; Robert Cornell.
EIN: 320243951
Selected grants: The following grants are a representative sample of this grantmaker's funding activity:
$877,050 to Allegheny Valley School, Coraopolis, PA, 2010.
$860,131 to Allegheny Valley School, Coraopolis, PA, 2011.
$100,000 to Mount Sinai Medical Center, New York, NY, 2011.
$100,000 to University of Florida Foundation, Gainesville, FL, 2011.
$100,000 to University of Florida Foundation, Gainesville, FL, 2010.
$45,000 to Canine Companions for Independence, Santa Rosa, CA, 2011.
$30,000 to Mount Sinai Medical Center, New York, NY, 2010.
$30,000 to Western Pennsylvania School for Blind Children, Pittsburgh, PA, 2010.
$20,000 to Sharp Visions, Pittsburgh, PA, 2010.
$10,000 to Special Olympics Pennsylvania, Pittsburgh, PA, 2011.
$5,000 to Autism Society of Pittsburgh, Monroeville, PA, 2010.
$3,500 to Northwestern Human Services Foundation, Lafayette Hill, PA, 2010.

7925
Michael Baker Corporation Foundation ✧
100 Airside Dr.
Moon Township, PA 15108

Established in 2006 in PA.
Donor: Michael Baker Corporation.
Foundation type: Company-sponsored foundation.
Financial data (yr. ended 12/31/13): Assets, $322,015 (M); gifts received, $75,771; expenditures, $455,113; qualifying distributions, $455,113; giving activities include $441,242 for 193 grants (high: $52,400; low: $25).
Purpose and activities: The foundation supports hospitals and organizations involved with education, children services, community economic development, and engineering.
Fields of interest: Higher education; Education; Hospitals (general); Health care; Children, services; Human services; Community/economic development; United Ways and Federated Giving Programs; Engineering/technology.
Type of support: General/operating support; Continuing support; Program development; Scholarship funds; Sponsorships; Employee matching gifts.
Limitations: Applications not accepted. Giving primarily in areas of company operations in PA. No grants to individuals.
Application information: Contributes only to pre-selected organizations.
Officers and Directors:* David G. Higie, Pres. and Exec. Dir.; H. James McKnight,* Secy.; James M. Kempton,* Treas.; Jeffrey S. Hill.
EIN: 830448116
Selected grants: The following grants are a representative sample of this grantmaker's funding activity:
$60,000 to United Way of Beaver County, Monaca, PA, 2012. For Member Agencies Support.
$20,500 to American Red Cross, Des Moines, IA, 2012. For Program support (Hurricane Sandy Relief).
$13,650 to Allegheny Conference on Community Development, Pittsburgh, PA, 2012. For Regional Growth Initiative.
$5,000 to Beaver County Foundation, Beaver, PA, 2012. For operating support (Baker Blkhs and Cemetery).
$1,000 to United Way of Wyoming Valley, Wilkes Barre, PA, 2012. For Program support (Williams Campaign).
$150 to Community Foundation of Utah, Salt Lake City, UT, 2012. For Memorial Gift (J Mcminimee Memorial).
$100 to Hospice of Central Pennsylvania, Harrisburg, PA, 2012. For Memorial Gift (J Wilson Memorial).

7926
Dexter F. and Dorothy H. Baker Foundation ✧
3440 Lehigh St.
P.O. Box 290
Allentown, PA 18103-7001 (610) 533-2837
Contact: Ellen B. Ghelardi, Exec. Dir.
FAX: (610) 481-5450; E-mail: baker1ebb@aol.com

Established in 1986 in PA.
Donors: Dexter F. Baker; Dorothy H. Baker.
Foundation type: Independent foundation.
Financial data (yr. ended 12/31/12): Assets, $16,978,703 (M); expenditures, $880,132; qualifying distributions, $853,672; giving activities

include $783,375 for 35 grants (high: $125,000; low: $500).
Purpose and activities: Giving primarily for arts and culture, youth, education, and social service initiatives.
Fields of interest: Arts education; Visual arts; Performing arts; Higher education; Social entrepreneurship; United Ways and Federated Giving Programs; Youth.
Type of support: General/operating support; Continuing support; Management development/capacity building; Annual campaigns; Capital campaigns; Equipment; Program development; Conferences/seminars; Film/video/radio; Curriculum development; Scholarship funds; Technical assistance; Matching/challenge support.
Limitations: Applications accepted. Giving primarily in Lehigh, and Northampton counties, PA, trustee endorsed grants in Collier, County FL, Hilton Head, SC, Syracuse, NY, Dallas, TX, San Francisco, CA, and Philadelphia, PA, only. No support for non-Presbyterian religious organizations, for government or for political organizations. No grants to individuals, or for endowment funds or for debt reduction.
Publications: Application guidelines.
Application information: Application form required.
Initial approach: Contact Ellen Baker Ghelardi to request guidelines
Copies of proposal: 1
Deadline(s): Letter of intent deadline: Mar. 15th; Invited applicants, July 15th
Board meeting date(s): Nov.
Final notification: Dec. 1
Officers and Trustees:* Dorothy H. Baker,* Chair.; Leslie Baker Boris,* Secy.; Ellen Baker Ghelardi,* Exec. Dir.; Carolyn Baker; Susan B. Royal.
Number of staff: 1 full-time professional; 1 part-time support.
EIN: 232453230
Selected grants: The following grants are a representative sample of this grantmaker's funding activity:
$50,000 to Lehigh University, Bethlehem, PA, 2012. For Baker Creativity Professor.
$33,000 to Muhlenberg College, Allentown, PA, 2012. For Baker Scholars - 2013.
$30,000 to Muhlenberg College, Allentown, PA, 2012. For Baker Artists - 2013.
$25,000 to Syracuse University, Syracuse, NY, 2012. For Baker Artists - 2013.
$15,000 to Bach Choir of Bethlehem, Bethlehem, PA, 2012. For School Outreach Program.
$10,000 to Community Music School, Allentown, PA, 2012. For Baker Scholarships.
$10,000 to Koresh Dance Company, Philadelphia, PA, 2012. For I school Dance Education.
$8,000 to Lafayette College, Easton, PA, 2012. For Guest Dance Series.
$5,500 to Syracuse University, Syracuse, NY, 2012. For Baker Scholars.
$3,500 to Baum School of Art, Allentown, PA, 2012. For Fashion Design Program.

7927
The Ball Family Foundation ✧
(formerly Russell C. Ball Foundation)
555 Croton Rd., Ste. 200
King of Prussia, PA 19406-3171

Donors: Philadelphia Gear Corp.; American Manufacturing Corp.; Lehigh Consumer Products Corp.; Goddard Systems, Inc.; Wind River Holdings, LP.
Foundation type: Company-sponsored foundation.
Financial data (yr. ended 12/31/13): Assets, $14,347 (M); gifts received, $525,000; expenditures, $518,708; qualifying distributions, $518,500; giving activities include $518,500 for 12 grants (high: $187,500; low: $1,000).
Purpose and activities: The foundation supports hospitals and organizations involved with arts and culture and education.
Fields of interest: Arts; Education; Health care.
Type of support: General/operating support; Annual campaigns; Capital campaigns; Program development.
Limitations: Applications not accepted. Giving limited to PA.
Application information: Contributes only to pre-selected organizations.
Officers and Directors:* Russell C. Ball III,* Pres. and Treas.; Andrew L. Ball,* V.P.; Robert H. Strouse, V.P.; Paul F. Brennan, Secy.
EIN: 516017780

7928
Barra Foundation, Inc. ✧
200 W. Lancaster Ave., Ste. 202
Wayne, PA 19087-4046 (610) 964-7601
Contact: Kristina Wahl, Pres.
FAX: (610) 964-0155;
E-mail: kwahl@barrafoundation.org; E-mail address for Kristi Poling, Prog. Off.: kpoling@barrafoundation.org; e-mail address for Kate Houstoun, Prog. Off.: khoustoun@barrafoundation.org; e-mail address for Stephanie Mullen, Admin. Asst.: smullen@barrafoundation.org; Main URL: http://www.barrafoundation.org/

Incorporated in 1963 in DE.
Donor: Robert L. McNeil, Jr.
Foundation type: Independent foundation.
Financial data (yr. ended 12/31/12): Assets, $88,047,212 (M); gifts received, $1,853,507; expenditures, $5,172,006; qualifying distributions, $4,768,145; giving activities include $4,241,196 for 423 grants (high: $800,000; low: $1,000).
Purpose and activities: The foundation seeks to support and encourage innovation, a key element to discovering new and more effective ways to serve the ever-changing needs in communities. It funds organizations and projects that enable the foundation to achieve greater social impact in the Philadelphia five-county region through strategic grantmaking in the areas of arts and culture, education, health, and human services. The foundation pursues two goals in its grantmaking: 1) to advance the health, education, well-being, achievement, and life prospects of low-income, underserved individuals and communities, and 2) to enrich the quality of life for all by promoting the sustainability of a vibrant arts and cultural community.
Fields of interest: Arts; Education; Human services.
Type of support: General/operating support; Management development/capacity building; Program development; Consulting services; Program evaluation.
Limitations: Applications accepted. Giving limited to organizations in the 5 county Philadelphia, PA, area (Bucks, Chester, Delaware, Montgomery and Philadelphia). No support for religious organizations, or for environmental or preservation groups. No grants to individuals, or for annual or capital campaigns, building or endowment funds, operating budgets, deficit drives, scholarships, fellowships, ongoing programs, publications, catalogues or exhibitions; no loans.
Application information: See foundation web site for complete policies, guidelines and application form. Application form required.
Initial approach: Proposal
Copies of proposal: 1
Deadline(s): None
Board meeting date(s): Dec. and as appropriate
Final notification: 3 to 6 months
Officers and Directors:* Seymour S. Preston III,* Chair.; Kristina Wahl, Pres.; Victoria M. LeVine,* Secy.; Eric C. Andersen; Patrick P. Coyne; A. Louis Denton; William Harral III; Frazierita D. Klasen; Joanna M. Lewis; Collin F. McNeil; Robert L. McNeil III.
Number of staff: 3 full-time professional; 1 part-time support.
EIN: 236277885

7929
The Barrist Family Foundation ✧ ☆
P.O. Box 513
Gwynedd Valley, PA 19437-0513

Established in 2003 in PA.
Donor: Michael Barrist.
Foundation type: Operating foundation.
Financial data (yr. ended 10/31/13): Assets, $4,605,836 (M); expenditures, $542,560; qualifying distributions, $512,000; giving activities include $512,000 for 5 grants (high: $312,000; low: $5,000).
Fields of interest: Education; Children/youth, services; Jewish federated giving programs.
Limitations: Applications not accepted. Giving primarily in PA. No grants to individuals.
Application information: Contributes only to pre-selected organizations.
Trustees: Michael Barrist; Natalie Barrist.
EIN: 200383922
Selected grants: The following grants are a representative sample of this grantmaker's funding activity:
$75,000 to Saint Marys Villa for Children, Ambler, PA, 2011. For annual campaign.
$50,000 to University of Pennsylvania, Philadelphia, PA, 2011.
$15,000 to Drexel University, Philadelphia, PA, 2011. For annual campaign.

7930
Bayard Cutting Arboretum Endowment Fund ✧ ☆
c/o BNY Mellon, N.A.
P.O. Box 185
Pittsburgh, PA 15230-0185

Established in NY.
Foundation type: Independent foundation.
Financial data (yr. ended 12/31/13): Assets, $12,669,170 (M); expenditures, $600,144; qualifying distributions, $553,381; giving activities include $530,000 for 1 grant.
Fields of interest: Environment.
Limitations: Applications not accepted.
Application information: Unsolicited requests for funds not accepted.

Trustee: BNY Mellon, N.A.
Board Member: Barbara M. Schaedler, Prof.
EIN: 136080826
Selected grants: The following grants are a representative sample of this grantmaker's funding activity:
$250,000 to Natural Heritage Trust, Albany, NY, 2011.

7931
Bayer U.S. Patient Assistance Foundation ✧ ☆
100 Bayer Rd., Tax Dept.
Pittsburgh, PA 15205-9741 (877) 744-5615
Application address: Betaseron Assistance Prog., P.O. Box 221349, Charlotte, NC 28222-1349

Donor: Bayer Healthcare Pharmaceuticals Inc.
Foundation type: Company-sponsored foundation.
Financial data (yr. ended 11/30/13): Assets, $2,730,764 (M); gifts received, $37,658,676; expenditures, $34,927,912; qualifying distributions, $34,927,912; giving activities include $34,927,912 for grants to individuals.
Purpose and activities: Giving to provide Betaseron free of charge to ill and needy individuals nationwide.
Fields of interest: Health care; Economically disadvantaged.
Type of support: Donated products; Grants to individuals.
Limitations: Applications accepted. Giving on a national basis.
Application information: Application form required.
Initial approach: Contact foundation for application form
Deadline(s): None
Officers: Srah Toulouse, Pres.; Franky Pauwels, V.P. and C.A.O.; Tracy E. Spagnol, V.P. and Treas.; Keith R. Abrams, Secy.; William Goodson, V.P., Patient Assistance.
Directors: Daniel Apel; Robert S. Meece; Alex Santini.
EIN: 900918808

7932
Bayer USA Foundation ✧
(formerly Bayer Foundation)
100 Bayer Rd.
Pittsburgh, PA 15205-9741 (412) 777-2000
Contact: Sarah Toulouse, Exec. Dir.
Main URL: http://www.bayerus.com/Foundation/Foundation_Home.aspx

Established in 1985 in PA.
Donor: Bayer Corp.
Foundation type: Company-sponsored foundation.
Financial data (yr. ended 12/31/12): Assets, $42,552,317 (M); gifts received, $9,145,127; expenditures, $6,825,690; qualifying distributions, $6,768,060; giving activities include $6,456,590 for 137 grants (high: $3,000,000; low: $100).
Purpose and activities: The foundation supports programs designed to promote education and workforce development; and the environment and sustainability.
Fields of interest: Museums; Museums (science/technology); Arts; Higher education; Engineering school/education; Education; Environment, energy; Environmental education; Environment; Cancer; Diabetes; Employment, services; Food banks; Housing/shelter; American Red Cross; Youth, services; Human services; Economic development; Community/economic development; Mathematics; Engineering/technology; Science; Youth; Minorities; Women.
Type of support: Continuing support; Capital campaigns; Equipment; Program development; Conferences/seminars; Curriculum development; Scholarship funds.
Limitations: Applications accepted. Giving primarily in areas of company operations in Berkeley and northern CA, Shawnee, KS, Kansas City, MO, Raleigh-Durham, NC, northern NJ, Newark, OH, Allegheny county and Pittsburgh, PA, and Baytown and Houston, TX; giving also to national organizations. No support for discriminatory, political, or religious organizations, primary or secondary schools, or organizations outside of the U.S. No grants to individuals, or for general operating support for United Way affiliated organizations, endowments, debt reduction or operating reserves, charitable dinners, events, sponsorships, conferences, or seminars, community or event advertising, research projects, student trips or exchange programs, athletic sponsorships or scholarships, or telephone solicitations.
Publications: Application guidelines; Program policy statement.
Application information: A full proposal may be requested at a later date. The Bayer USA Foundation application follows the Common Grant application process. Collateral materials including books, binders, videos, CDs, DVDs, programs, brochures, etc. will not be accepted unless specifically requested by the foundation. Application form not required.
Initial approach: Complete online application
Copies of proposal: 1
Deadline(s): None
Board meeting date(s): Feb. and Oct.
Final notification: Following board meetings
Officers and Directors:* Richard K. Heller, V.P., Tax; Robert J. Koch, Secy.; James Martin, Treas.; Sarah Toulouse, Exec. Dir.; Lars Benecke; Andrew J. Diana; Micheal J. McDonald; Elizabeth Roden.
EIN: 251508079

7933
Helen D. Groome Beatty Trust ✧ ☆
c/o BNY Mellon, N.A.
P.O. Box 185
Pittsburgh, PA 15230-0185

Trust established in 1951 in PA.
Donor: Helen D. Groome Beatty‡.
Foundation type: Independent foundation.
Financial data (yr. ended 12/31/13): Assets, $12,503,917 (M); expenditures, $509,294; qualifying distributions, $460,627; giving activities include $436,000 for 40 grants (high: $20,000; low: $5,000).
Fields of interest: Arts; Education; Human services.
Type of support: General/operating support; Capital campaigns; Building/renovation; Scholarships—to individuals.
Limitations: Applications not accepted. Giving primarily in PA, with emphasis on the Philadelphia area, and Harrisburg. No grants to individuals, (except for scholarships), or for endowment funds, or operating budgets.
Application information: Unsolicited requests for funds not accepted.
Board meeting date(s): Nov. 15
Trustee: BNY Mellon, N.A.
EIN: 236224798
Selected grants: The following grants are a representative sample of this grantmaker's funding activity:
$10,000 to Brandywine Health Foundation, Coatesville, PA, 2012. For general operating purposes.

7934
The Beaver County Foundation ✧
P.O. Box 569
Beaver, PA 15009-0569 (724) 728-1331
Contact: Charles O'Data, Pres.
FAX: (724) 773-0964; E-mail: cnodata@aol.com; Main URL: http://www.beavercountyfoundation.com

Established in 1992 in PA.
Foundation type: Community foundation.
Financial data (yr. ended 12/31/13): Assets, $7,694,902 (M); gifts received, $178,754; expenditures, $622,460; giving activities include $397,323 for 18+ grants (high: $34,000), and $51,500 for 30 grants to individuals.
Purpose and activities: The mission of the Beaver County Foundation is to create an atmosphere for and an understanding of philanthropy, the love of humankind, in order to preserve and encourage the development of organizations and programs that meet human needs. This has been accomplished by enabling individuals and organizations to build endowments, which, in turn, produce revenues designed to strengthen programs, and events which serve to benefit the people of Beaver County and the surrounding geographic region.
Fields of interest: Arts; Education; Health care; Human services; Community development, neighborhood development; Economic development; Christian agencies & churches; Children/youth; Children.
Type of support: General/operating support; Program development; Scholarship funds; Research; Scholarships—to individuals.
Limitations: Applications accepted. Giving limited to Beaver County, PA; support for pharmacological research or addiction interdiction given nationwide. No grants to individuals (except for scholarships).
Publications: Informational brochure.
Application information: Visit the foundation's web site for more information. Application form required.
Initial approach: Contact foundation by letter, phone or e-mail
Copies of proposal: 1
Deadline(s): Apr. 1 and Oct. 1
Board meeting date(s): May, July, Oct., and Dec.
Final notification: generally during the last week of April and the last week of October.
Officers and Directors:* Charles N. O'Data,* Chair. and Pres.; Yvonne Connor,* Vice-Chair.; Toni L. Sadecky,* Treas.; Theresa M. Laderer, Exec. Dir.; Jessica Briggs, Genl. Counsel; Joseph Bauman; Richard Blackwood; Thomas J. Bryan; George Juba; John Lehman, M.D.; Susan R. McCormick; Thomas Reed; Paul Sweeney; Richard Shaw; Melvin H. Steals, Ph.D.; Joseph N. Tosh II; Keith M. Wing.
Number of staff: 1 part-time professional.
EIN: 251660309

7935
Claude Worthington Benedum Foundation ✧
223 4th Ave.
1400 Benedum-Trees Bldg.
Pittsburgh, PA 15222-1713 (412) 288-0360
Contact: William P. Getty, Pres.
FAX: (412) 288-0366; E-mail: info@benedum.org; Tel. for Grants Admin.: (412) 246-3636; Main URL: http://www.benedum.org
Grants Database: http://www.benedum.org/grants/grants.shtml
Knowledge Center: http://www.benedum.org/pages.cfm?id=17

Incorporated in 1944 in PA.
Donors: Michael Late Benedum‡; Sarah N. Benedum‡.
Foundation type: Independent foundation.
Financial data (yr. ended 12/31/13): Assets, $377,249,868 (M); expenditures, $20,572,277; qualifying distributions, $18,140,752; giving activities include $15,276,350 for 163 grants (high: $500,000; low: $5,000), $154,652 for 2 foundation-administered programs and $650,000 for 1 loan/program-related investment.
Purpose and activities: The foundation makes grants in three program areas that spans its geographic areas of interest, West Virginia, and in Southwestern Pennsylvania: education, civic engagement, and economic development. In addition, the Foundation supports community development and health & human services grants programs in West Virginia, and in Southwestern Pennsylvania supports the major performing arts organizations within the cultural district. The Foundation recognizes that economic regions do not follow political boundaries, and therefore, the foundation both encourages projects that cross state lines, and supports economic initiatives that benefit the multi-state economy centered on Pittsburgh.
Fields of interest: Education; Health care; Human services; Economic development; Community/economic development.
Type of support: Management development/capacity building; Program development; Seed money; Technical assistance; Matching/challenge support.
Limitations: Applications accepted. Giving limited to southwestern PA and WV. No support for biomedical research, national organizations, or individual elementary or secondary schools. No grants to individuals, or for student aid, fellowships, travel, ongoing operating expenses, annual appeals, membership drives, conferences, films, books, or audio-visual productions (unless an integral part of a foundation supported program), or for construction, equipment, religious activities or endowments.
Publications: Annual report (including application guidelines).
Application information: Applicants should submit applications using the foundation's online grant application process found on the foundation's web site.If one does not have the ability to submit online, please contact the Grants Admin. Application form not required.
Initial approach: Online application
Copies of proposal: 1
Deadline(s): None
Board meeting date(s): Mar., June, Sept., and Dec.
Final notification: Within 60 days
Officers and Trustees:* Lloyd G. Jackson II,* Chair.; William P. Getty,* Pres.; Dwight M. Keating, V.P. and C.I.O.; James V. Denova, V.P.; Rose A. McKee, Secy. and Dir., Admin.; Lori Lordo, Treas.; Ralph J. Bean, Jr., Tr. Emeritus; Gaston Caperton, Honorary Tr.; L. Newton Thomas, Tr. Emeritus; G. Randolph Worls, Tr. Emeritus; Esther L. Barazzone; G. Nicholas Beckwith III; Paul G. Benedum, Jr.; Thomas A. Heywood; Parween S. Mascari; Robert B. Walker, M.D.
Number of staff: 7 full-time professional; 2 part-time professional; 3 full-time support.
EIN: 251086799
Selected grants: The following grants are a representative sample of this grantmaker's funding activity:
$415,000 to Natural Capital Investment Fund, Shepherdstown, WV, 2012. For an amount not to exceed $415,000, to support the Agricultural Value-Chain Clusters in Rural West Virginia over three years, payable over 3.25 years.
$267,000 to Carnegie Institute, The Andy Warhol Museum, Pittsburgh, PA, 2012. For Employ Andy Warhol silkscreen techniques in a variety of courses and educational settings over two years, payable over 2.25 years.
$250,000 to Intermediate Unit One, Coal Center, PA, 2012. For a collaborative career education project based at a public housing community center over two years, payable over 2.00 years.
$250,000 to Marshall University Research Corporation, WV School-Based Health Technical Assistance Center, Huntington, WV, 2012. For School Partnerships for Oral Health and WV Home Visitor Oral Health.
$250,000 to West Liberty University Foundation, College of Education, West Liberty, WV, 2012. For a regional teaching-artist professional development program in partnership with Gateway to the Arts, payable over 1.50 years.
$250,000 to West Virginia Community Development Hub, Stonewood, WV, 2012. For the work plan of the West Virginia Community Development Hub, including matching funds for the USDA Rural Community Development Initiative, payable over 1.25 years.
$100,000 to OSM VISTA Team, Friends of the, Beckley, WV, 2012. For training program for volunteers for rural nonprofit organizations, payable over 2.00 years.
$100,000 to Wheeling Health Right, Wheeling, WV, 2012. To improve patient outcomes and reduce hospital charity care through a medical home model over two years, payable over 2.00 years.
$75,000 to Carnegie Mellon University, CREATE Lab, Pittsburgh, PA, 2012. To develop evaluation protocol and teachers guide for Carnegie Mellon/Marshall University CREATE Lab educational technology products, payable over 1.25 years.
$75,000 to Pittsburgh Opera, Pittsburgh, PA, 2012. For operating support.

7936
The Beneficial Foundation ✧
1818 Beneficial Bank Pl., 1818 Market
Philadelphia, PA 19103 (267) 519-5747
Contact: Robert J. Juliano, Dir.
Main URL: https://www.thebeneficial.com/foundation-mission.asp

Established in 2007 in PA.
Donor: Beneficial Mutual Bancorp, Inc.
Foundation type: Company-sponsored foundation.
Financial data (yr. ended 12/31/13): Assets, $6,926,130 (M); expenditures, $552,665; qualifying distributions, $548,583; giving activities include $546,050 for 158 grants (high: $50,000; low: $500).
Purpose and activities: The foundation supports programs designed to address children in crisis; youth and education; and human service programs designed to improve the needs of low- and moderate income communities.
Fields of interest: Education; Health care; Medical research; Human services; Community/economic development; Religion; Children/youth; Children; Youth; Adults; Aging; Young adults; Disabilities, people with; Physically disabled; Blind/visually impaired; Mentally disabled; Minorities; Asians/Pacific Islanders; African Americans/Blacks; Hispanics/Latinos; Women; Infants/toddlers, female; Girls; Adults, women; Young adults, female; Men; Infants/toddlers, male; Boys; Adults, men; Young adults, male; Military/veterans; Substance abusers; AIDS, people with; Single parents; Crime/abuse victims; Immigrants/refugees; Economically disadvantaged; Homeless.
Type of support: Annual campaigns; Capital campaigns; Building/renovation; Equipment; Emergency funds; Program development; Scholarship funds; Technical assistance.
Limitations: Applications accepted. Giving primarily in areas of company operations in NJ and PA. No support for political or fraternal organizations. No grants to individuals.
Publications: Application guidelines; Annual report; Program policy statement (including application guidelines); Quarterly report.
Application information: Application form required.
Initial approach: Letter
Copies of proposal: 1
Deadline(s): Jan. 1st to Dec. 31st
Board meeting date(s): Quarterly
Final notification: 2-3 weeks
Officers and Directors:* Gerard P. Cuddy,* Pres.; William J. Kline, Jr., Secy.; Thomas D. Cestare,* Treas.; Karen Dougherty Buchholz; Pamela M. Cyr; Robert J. Juliano; Joseph J. McLaughlin; George W. Nise; Marcy C. Panzer; Joanne Ryder.
Number of staff: 3 full-time professional; 3 full-time support.
EIN: 260542636
Selected grants: The following grants are a representative sample of this grantmaker's funding activity:
$3,000 to Alexs Lemonade Stand Foundation, Wynnewood, PA, 2011.

7937
The Benter Foundation ✧
c/o William Benter
4 Smithfield St., 9th Fl.
Pittsburgh, PA 15222-2226

Established in 2007 in PA.
Donor: William F. Benter.
Foundation type: Independent foundation.
Financial data (yr. ended 12/31/12): Assets, $95,147 (M); gifts received, $1,850,000; expenditures, $1,801,727; qualifying distributions, $1,800,008; giving activities include $1,613,500 for 39 grants (high: $200,000; low: $5,000).
Purpose and activities: Giving primarily for higher education, as well as for international and cultural affairs.

Fields of interest: Arts, cultural/ethnic awareness; Performing arts, ballet; Higher education; Education; Boy scouts; International affairs; Foundations (public).
Limitations: Applications not accepted. Giving primarily in PA, with emphasis on Pittsburgh. No grants to individuals.
Application information: Contributes only to pre-selected organizations.
Officers and Directors:* William F. Benter,* Pres.; Bruce Benter,* Secy.; Bruce Pyle,* Treas.
EIN: 208807953
Selected grants: The following grants are a representative sample of this grantmaker's funding activity:
$150,000 to Propel Schools Foundation, Pittsburgh, PA, 2012. For Launch of a Children's Savings Account Pilot at Three Schools in Spring 2013 and System-Wide in Fall 2013.
$80,000 to World Affairs Council of Pittsburgh, Pittsburgh, PA, 2012. For the 80th Anniversary Speaker Series and Other Programming Initiatives Designed to Encourage Discussion of International Issues.
$52,000 to University of Pittsburgh, Pittsburgh, PA, 2012. For Directed to the University of Pittsburgh's Human Engineering Research Lab to Support the Final Phase of Development and Testing of a Model for Increasing the Mobility of People with Disabilities in Mexico.
$40,000 to Pittsburgh Trust for Cultural Resources, Pittsburgh, PA, 2012. For the Second Season of Cabaret Series.
$35,000 to Pittsburgh Trust for Cultural Resources, Pittsburgh, PA, 2012. For the Launch of a Headliner Cabaret Series in 2012.
$30,000 to Propel Schools Foundation, Pittsburgh, PA, 2012. To design Work on Prize Linked Children's Savings Accounts.
$25,000 to Pittsburgh Promise Foundation, Pittsburgh, PA, 2012. For Executive Experience Program.
$25,000 to World Affairs Council of Pittsburgh, Pittsburgh, PA, 2012. For funding for Competitive Fellowships for Pittsburgh Nonprofit Leaders to Attend One Young World Summit.
$20,000 to Pittsburgh Trust for Cultural Resources, Pittsburgh, PA, 2012. For Continuation of Parkpgh Through Patent License Agreement.
$15,000 to August Wilson Center for African American Culture, Pittsburgh, PA, 2012. For Three Concerts in Duet Series.

7938
Sybiel B. Berkman Foundation ✧
850 Poplar St.
Pittsburgh, PA 15220-2828

Established in 1965.
Donors: Myles P. Berkman; Jack N. Berkman†.
Foundation type: Independent foundation.
Financial data (yr. ended 12/31/13): Assets, $12,240,842 (M); expenditures, $1,417,085; qualifying distributions, $1,408,535; giving activities include $1,408,535 for 57 grants (high: $317,000; low: $240).
Purpose and activities: Giving primarily for the arts, education, health organizations, human services, and Jewish organizations.
Fields of interest: Museums; Museums (ethnic/folk arts); Arts; Higher education; Education; Hospitals (general); Health organizations; Human services; Jewish federated giving programs.
Limitations: Applications not accepted. Giving primarily in FL, New York, NY, and PA. No grants to individuals.
Application information: Contributes only to pre-selected organizations.
Officers and Trustees:* Myles P. Berkman,* Pres.; David J. Berkman,* V.P. and Secy.; William H. Berkman,* V.P. and Treas.; Monroe E. Berkman,* V.P.; Stephen L. Berkman,* V.P.
EIN: 346566801
Selected grants: The following grants are a representative sample of this grantmaker's funding activity:
$333,000 to University of Pennsylvania, Philadelphia, PA, 2011. For general purpose.
$300,000 to Harvard University, Cambridge, MA, 2011. For general purpose.
$75,000 to Florida Orchestra, Saint Petersburg, FL, 2011. For general purpose.
$55,000 to Grace Church School, New York, NY, 2011. For general purpose.
$25,000 to Peer Health Exchange, New York, NY, 2011. For general purpose.
$14,950 to Jewish Federation of Greater Philadelphia, Philadelphia, PA, 2011. For general purpose.
$10,000 to Academy in Manayunk, Conshohocken, PA, 2011. For general purpose.
$10,000 to Childrens Home, Tampa, FL, 2011. For general purpose.
$10,000 to New York-Presbyterian Hospital, New York, NY, 2011. For general purpose.
$4,183 to Museum of Science and Industry, Tampa, FL, 2011. For general purpose.

7939
Berks County Community Foundation
237 Court St.
Reading, PA 19601 (610) 685-2223
Contact: Kevin K. Murphy, Pres.; For grants: Heidi Williamson, V.P., Grantmaking and Comms.
FAX: (610) 685-2240; E-mail: info@bccf.org; Grant program e-mail: heidiw@bccf.org; Finance e-mail: frankia@bccf.org; Main URL: http://www.bccf.org
E-Newsletter: http://www.bccf.org/index.php?option=com_content&view=article&id=371&Itemid=248
LinkedIn: http://www.linkedin.com/companies/berks-county-community-foundation
YouTube: http://www.youtube.com/user/bccfor

Established in 1994 in PA.
Foundation type: Community foundation.
Financial data (yr. ended 06/30/14): Assets, $61,988,066 (M); gifts received, $2,146,026; expenditures, $4,216,255; giving activities include $3,273,686 for grants.
Purpose and activities: The mission of the foundation is to promote philanthropy and improve the quality of life for the residents of Berks County, PA.
Fields of interest: Arts, cultural/ethnic awareness; Historic preservation/historical societies; Arts; Higher education; Education; Environment; Animals/wildlife; Health care; Youth development; Community development, neighborhood development; Economic development; Community/economic development; Aging.
Type of support: Fellowships; Capital campaigns; Program development; Conferences/seminars; Seed money; Scholarship funds; Research; Consulting services; Program-related investments/loans; Employee-related scholarships; Grants to individuals; Scholarships—to individuals; Matching/challenge support.
Limitations: Applications accepted. Giving limited to Berks County, PA for discretionary funds. No support for religious organizations from discretionary funds. No grants for operational support.
Publications: Application guidelines; Annual report; Financial statement; Grants list; Newsletter.
Application information: Visit foundation web site for additional information. Application form required.
Initial approach: Telephone or e-mail
Copies of proposal: 1
Deadline(s): Varies
Board meeting date(s): Feb., Apr., June, Aug., Oct., and Dec.
Officers and Directors:* J. William Widing III, Esq.*, Chair.; P. Sue Perrotty,* Vice-Chair.; Kevin K. Murphy,* Pres.; Frances A. Aitken,* Sr. V.P., Finance and Opers. and Treas.; Heidi Williamson, V.P., Comms. and Grantmaking; Jay R. Wagner, Esq.,* Secy.; Latisha Bernard Schuenemann,* Asst. Treas.; James S. Boscov; Eric Burkey; P. Michael Ehlerman; James A. Gilmartin; Charles Haddad, Esq.; Kathleen D. Herbein; Thomas D. Leidy, Esq.; Chris Pruitt, CPA; Al Weber.
Number of staff: 3 full-time professional; 2 part-time professional; 4 full-time support.
EIN: 232769892
Selected grants: The following grants are a representative sample of this grantmaker's funding activity:
$157,592 to Diakon Lutheran Social Ministries, Allentown, PA, 2013. For the exclusive benefit of The Lutheran Home at Topton.
$100,000 to Alvernia University, Reading, PA, 2014. For Olivet-Alvernia Scholarship Program.
$100,000 to Carnegie Mellon University, Pittsburgh, PA, 2013. For University Center Expansion Fund to honor the Cohon Presidency.
$100,000 to Saint Joseph Medical Center Foundation, Reading, PA, 2013. For implementation and support of the Palliative Care Program.
$90,000 to Berks County Women in Crisis, Reading, PA, 2014. For Bilingual Legal Advocacy.
$85,500 to Berks Community Television, Reading, PA, 2013. For Voice of Berks County Engagement Coordinator for Free Flow.
$85,285 to Gilmore Henne Community Fund, Reading, PA, 2013. For distribution of balance of fund.
$72,000 to Visiting Nurse Association, Berks, Wyomissing, PA, 2014. For Berks VNA Community Health and Wellness Program.
$50,000 to Reading Symphony Orchestra Association, Reading, PA, 2014. For 4th of July Concert.
$45,000 to Building a Better Boyertown, Boyertown, PA, 2014. For Sustainability Program.
$20,000 to Jewish Federation of Reading Pennsylvania, Wyomissing, PA, 2014. For Local Community Fund.
$20,000 to Jewish Federation of Reading Pennsylvania, Wyomissing, PA, 2013. For Community Emergency Fund.
$15,000 to YMCA of Boyertown, Boyertown, PA, 2013. For renovations and equipment for youth fitness center.
$10,581 to YMCA of Reading and Berks County, Reading, PA, 2014. For Y-Haven: Child Care and Transportation Funding.
$8,150 to City of Reading Police Department, Reading, PA, 2014. For Updated equipment for Training Center.

$5,000 to Berks Business Education Coalition, Reading, PA, 2014. For Students Interacting with Business.
$5,000 to Berks County Conservancy, Reading, PA, 2014. For Boyertown Water Supply - Public Education.
$3,819 to Saint Margaret's School, Reading, PA, 2013. For scholarship.
$3,175 to Boyertown Area Multi-Service, Boyertown, PA, 2013. For Computer Server.
$1,500 to W G C U Public Media, Fort Myers, FL, 2013. For Radio Reading Service.

7940
Isaac W. Bernheim Trust ✧ ☆

c/o PNC Bank. N.A.
620 Liberty Ave., 10th Fl.
Pittsburgh, PA 15222-2705

Foundation type: Independent foundation.
Financial data (yr. ended 12/31/13): Assets, $32,939,088 (M); expenditures, $1,547,206; qualifying distributions, $1,413,725; giving activities include $1,410,665 for 1 grant.
Purpose and activities: Giving primarily to an arboretum.
Fields of interest: Botanical gardens.
Limitations: Applications not accepted.
Application information: Contributes only to pre-selected organizations.
Trustees: Jon M. Burnham; Marshall P. Eldred, Jr.; Debra B. Hyman; PNC Bank, N.A.
EIN: 610514702

7941
Biesecker Foundation ✧

c/o Donn Shires
P.O. Box 258
Boyertown, PA 19512-0258

Established in PA.
Donors: Frederick N. Biesecker; Lissa Biesecker Longacre; Rick Biesecker; Britta Biesecker; Suzanne K. Biesecker; Drug Plastics & Glass Co., Inc.; Drug Plastics & Glass Inc Profit Sharing Plan.
Foundation type: Independent foundation.
Financial data (yr. ended 12/31/13): Assets, $2,030,754 (M); gifts received, $3,024,777; expenditures, $1,051,407; qualifying distributions, $1,051,250; giving activities include $1,051,250 for 12 grants (high: $500,000; low: $1,000).
Purpose and activities: Giving primarily to health organizations, particularly a children's hospital and a pediatric liver center; funding also for the arts, social services, and Protestant churches.
Fields of interest: Arts; Higher education; Education; Hospitals (specialty); Health care; Liver disorders; Pediatrics; Human services; Children/ youth, services; Protestant agencies & churches.
Limitations: Applications not accepted. Giving primarily in PA. No grants to individuals.
Application information: Contributes only to pre-selected organizations.
Director: Suzanne K. Biesecker.
EIN: 251867942

7942
The Birmingham Foundation ✧

Brashear Ctr.
2005 Sarah St., 2nd Fl.
Pittsburgh, PA 15203-2021 (412) 481-2777
Contact: Mark Stephen Bibro, Exec. Dir.; Chris Mason, Admin. Asst.
FAX: (412) 481-2727; E-mail: info@bfpgh.org; Main URL: http://www.birminghamfoundation.org
Grants List: http://foundationcenter.org/grantmaker/birminghamfdn/awarded.html

Established in 1996 in PA; converted with assets from the sale of The South Side Hospital.
Foundation type: Independent foundation.
Financial data (yr. ended 06/30/13): Assets, $22,181,519 (M); gifts received, $11,581; expenditures, $1,602,653; qualifying distributions, $1,433,948; giving activities include $1,192,850 for 53 grants (high: $105,000; low: $500).
Purpose and activities: The foundation is dedicated to health and human services, and serves as a change agent for improved health and wellness in South Pittsburgh, PA, through the dynamic use of resources such as grantmaking, information-sharing, partnering and leveraging of assets. Funding priorities include health access and education, strengthening children's well being, enhancing senior safety and health, building the capacity of local organizations, and improving community life by addressing violence, substance abuse and mental health. Within these priorities, the foundation has streamlined it focus on programs that 1) deal with issues of violence, especially youth violence, 2) deal with safety net issues such as food banks and utility assistance, 3) deal with school youth, including programs that decrease drop out rates, are high quality out-of-school programs, and improve reading and educational opportunities, and 4) deal with healthcare improvements for vulnerable and underserved populations.
Fields of interest: Health care; Human services; Infants/toddlers; Children/youth; Youth; Adults; Aging; Young adults; Disabilities, people with; Minorities; African Americans/Blacks; Women; Girls; Men; Boys; Substance abusers; Crime/abuse victims; Economically disadvantaged.
Type of support: General/operating support; Program development; Technical assistance.
Limitations: Applications accepted. Giving limited to the South Pittsburgh, PA, area served by the following zip codes: 15203 (South Side), 15210 (Mt. Oliver and Hilltop), and 15211 (Mt. Washington), including in particular the neighborhoods of Allentown, Arlington, Arlington Heights, Beltzhoover, Bon Air, Carrick, Duquesne Heights, Knoxville, Mt. Oliver, Mt. Washington, St. Clair Village, and the South Side Flats and Slopes. No grants to individuals, or for operating budgets, deficits, fund-raising, general research, overhead, scholarships, political campaigns; no loans.
Publications: Application guidelines; Biennial report; Financial statement; Grants list; Multi-year report; IRS Form 990 or 990-PF printed copy available upon request.
Application information: The foundation now has an online grant application system. Application information available on foundation web site. Grantmakers of Western Pennsylvania's Common Grant Application Format accepted; see URL: http://www.gwpa.org for copies. Application form required.
Initial approach: Complete letter of intent on foundation web site
Copies of proposal: 1
Deadline(s): 2 months prior to board meetings
Board meeting date(s): Apr. and Nov.
Final notification: Letters of approval mailed following board meetings
Officers and Directors:* Terrence L. Wirginis,* Chair.; William T. Simmons, Esq.*, Vice-Chair.; Carey A. Harris,* Chair., Grants; Eileen O. Smith,* Secy.; H. Don Gordon,* Treas.; Jane H. Roesch, Dir., Emeritus; Mark S. Bibro, Exec. Dir.; Roberta Smith, Dir., Emeritus; Maurita J. Bryant; Hugo Churchill; Betty Kripp; Beth Marcello; Mihai Marcu; Kenneth McCrory; Duane Swager II.
Number of staff: 1 full-time professional; 1 full-time support.
EIN: 250965572

7943
Peter P. Blanchard III Trust- Dendroica Foundation ✧

(formerly The Dendroica Foundation)
c/o BNY Mellon, N.A.
P.O. Box 185
Pittsburgh, PA 15230-0185

Established in 1997 in PA.
Donor: Peter P. Blanchard, Jr.†.
Foundation type: Independent foundation.
Financial data (yr. ended 12/31/13): Assets, $12,564,772 (M); expenditures, $538,396; qualifying distributions, $511,502; giving activities include $500,000 for 1 grant.
Purpose and activities: Giving primarily for the environment.
Fields of interest: Environment, natural resources; Botanical gardens.
Limitations: Applications not accepted. Giving primarily in Short Hills, NJ.
Application information: Contributes only to pre-selected organizations.
Trustee: BNY Mellon, N.A.
EIN: 237912826

7944
Arthur F. Blanchard Trust ✧

c/o BNY Mellon, N.A.
P.O. Box 185
Pittsburgh, PA 15230-0185

Trust established in 1943 in MA.
Donor: Arthur F. Blanchard†.
Foundation type: Independent foundation.
Financial data (yr. ended 08/31/13): Assets, $18,033,061 (M); expenditures, $1,403,264; qualifying distributions, $1,348,694; giving activities include $1,256,800 for 102 grants (high: $55,000; low: $500).
Purpose and activities: Giving for neighborhood and economic development, health and human services, education, and cultural access. Scholarships are awarded to residents of Boxborough, MA, who had attended the Blanchard Memorial School, and are for the cost of tuition and other expenses related to education.
Fields of interest: Higher education; Education; Health care; Human services; Community development, neighborhood development; Economic development.
Type of support: General/operating support; Capital campaigns; Building/renovation; Equipment; Land acquisition; Emergency funds; Program

development; Seed money; Research; Scholarships—to individuals; Matching/challenge support.
Limitations: Applications not accepted. Giving primarily in MA, with some emphasis on Boston. No grants for endowment funds or fellowships; no loans.
Application information: Unsolicited requests for funds not accepted.
Board meeting date(s): Mar., June, Sept. and Dec.
Trustee: BNY Mellon, N.A.
EIN: 046093374
Selected grants: The following grants are a representative sample of this grantmaker's funding activity:
$50,000 to Boston Childrens Museum, Boston, MA, 2011.
$50,000 to City School, Dorchester, MA, 2011.
$50,000 to Goodwill Industries, Morgan Memorial, Boston, MA, 2011.
$50,000 to Housing Families, Malden, MA, 2011.
$50,000 to National Braille Press, Boston, MA, 2011.
$50,000 to South Boston Neighborhood House, South Boston, MA, 2011.
$50,000 to YMCA of Malden, Malden, MA, 2011.
$30,000 to City Year, Boston, MA, 2011.
$5,000 to Brandeis University, Waltham, MA, 2011.

7945
BNY Mellon Foundation, Inc. ✧
(formerly The Bank of New York Mellon Corporation Foundation)
P.O. Box 185
Pittsburgh, PA 15230-9897 (412) 234-8679
E-mail: powering.potential@bnymellon.com

Established in 1997 in NY.
Donors: The Bank of New York; BNY Capital Corp.; Bank of New York Mellon Corp. Foundation.
Foundation type: Company-sponsored foundation.
Financial data (yr. ended 12/31/13): Assets, $36,861,850 (M); expenditures, $1,796,877; qualifying distributions, $1,660,000; giving activities include $1,660,000 for 28 grants (high: $200,000; low: $10,000).
Purpose and activities: The foundation supports programs designed to address workforce development and basic needs provision.
Fields of interest: Employment, services; Employment, training; Employment; Human services, financial counseling; Human services; Economic development.
Type of support: General/operating support; Employee matching gifts.
Limitations: Applications accepted. Giving on a national basis through throughout the U.S., except for southwestern PA. No grants to individuals.
Publications: Application guidelines.
Application information: Letters of inquiry should be no longer than 2 to 3 pages. A full application may be requested at a later date.
Initial approach: E-mail letter of inquiry
Deadline(s): None
Officers and Directors:* R. Jeep Byant,* Chair.; Daisy Holmes, Pres.; Lisa Concepcion, Secy.; Michael McFadden, Treas.; Raymond Dorado; Gerald L. Hassell; Joanne Jaxtimer; David F. Lamere; James P. McDonald; Karen Peetz; Patricia Sampson; Kurt Woetzel.
EIN: 311605320

7946
BNY Mellon Foundation of Southwestern PA ✧
(formerly The BNY Mellon Charitable Foundation)
BNY Mellon Ctr., Ste. 1830
500 Grant St.
Pittsburgh, PA 15258-0001
Contact: James P. McDonald, Pres.
E-mail: powering.potential@bnymellon.com; Additional address: P.O. Box 185, Pittsburgh, PA 15230; Main URL: http://www.bnymellon.com/about/charitablegiving-howto.html

Established in 1974 in PA.
Donors: Mellon Bank; Mellon Financial Corp.
Foundation type: Company-sponsored foundation.
Financial data (yr. ended 12/31/12): Assets, $73,474,458 (M); expenditures, $3,536,352; qualifying distributions, $3,399,000; giving activities include $3,399,000 for 56 grants (high: $175,000; low: $25,000).
Purpose and activities: The foundation supports organizations involved with economic development, education, and human services. Special emphasis is directed toward programs designed to promote basic needs and workforce development.
Fields of interest: Performing arts, theater; Higher education; Education; Health care, clinics/centers; Health care; Employment, services; Employment, training; Food banks; Housing/shelter; YM/YWCAs & YM/YWHAs; Human services, financial counseling; Human services; Community/economic development; Jewish federated giving programs.
Type of support: Program development.
Limitations: Applications accepted. Giving limited to southwestern PA. No support for fraternal or religious organizations, United Way agencies, or national organizations. No grants to individuals, or for emergency needs, debt reduction, endowments, equipment, land acquisition, scholarships, fellowships, research, publications, travel, conferences, continuing support, or specialized health campaigns or other highly specialized projects with little or no positive impact on communities; no loans.
Publications: Application guidelines.
Application information: Letters of inquiry should be no longer than 3 pages. Application form not required.
Initial approach: Letter of inquiry
Copies of proposal: 1
Deadline(s): None
Board meeting date(s): Quarterly
Final notification: 2 months
Officers and Directors:* Steven G. Elliott,* Chair.; James P. McDonald,* Pres.; Barry Athol, Treas.; R. Jeep Bryant; Jared L. Cohon; Frank M. Hammond; Donald J. Heberle; Mark A. Nordenberg; Lisa B. Peters; Vincent V. Sands; David S. Shapira; William E. Strickland, Jr.
Number of staff: None.
EIN: 237423500

7947
The Dietrich W. Botstiber Foundation ✧
200 E. State St., Ste. 306-A
Media, PA 19063-3434 (610) 566-3375
Contact: Carlie Numi, Grants Mgr.
FAX: (610) 566-3376;
E-mail: varapis@botstiber.org; E-mail for Carlie Numi: Cnumi@botstiber.org; Main URL: http://www.botstiber.org/

Established in 1995 in PA.
Donors: Dietrich W. Botstiber†; Dietrich W. Botstiber Charitable Lead Annuity Trust.
Foundation type: Independent foundation.
Financial data (yr. ended 08/31/13): Assets, $30,939,640 (M); gifts received, $4,745; expenditures, $1,565,079; qualifying distributions, $1,358,182; giving activities include $974,926 for 10 grants (high: $588,757; low: $2,600), and $137,524 for 9 grants to individuals (high: $30,000; low: $4,113).
Purpose and activities: Giving in 3 major areas: 1) scholarships; 2) Austrian-U.S.A. relations; and 3) reducing poverty and malnutrition among the poorest and most marginalized of the world's people, especially those who are at particular risk because of conflict or other cruel conditions.
Fields of interest: Higher education, university; International affairs.
Type of support: Professorships; Scholarship funds; Scholarships—to individuals.
Limitations: Giving primarily in PA, and Vienna, Austria.
Publications: Financial statement; IRS Form 990 or 990-PF printed copy available upon request.
Application information: Unsolicited requests for funds not accepted, except for grant requests to the Botstiber Institute for Austrian-American Studies.
Board meeting date(s): Bimonthly
Trustees: Dorothy Boylan; Terrance A. Kline.
Number of staff: 1 part-time professional.
EIN: 237807828
Selected grants: The following grants are a representative sample of this grantmaker's funding activity:
$539,367 to Lehigh University, Bethlehem, PA, 2011. For general operating expenses.
$340,000 to CARE USA, Atlanta, GA, 2011. For general operating expenses.
$283,998 to CARE USA, Atlanta, GA, 2010.
$18,000 to Delaware Valley Science Fairs, Philadelphia, PA, 2011. For general operating expenses.
$8,983 to University of Notre Dame, Notre Dame, IN, 2011. For general operating expenses.
$6,583 to University of Chicago, Chicago, IL, 2011. For general operating expenses.
$4,970 to University of Michigan, Ann Arbor, MI, 2011. For general operating expenses.
$3,879 to University of Vienna, Vienna, Austria, 2011. For general operating expenses.
$2,890 to Council on Foundations, Arlington, VA, 2011.
$2,500 to Clemson University, Clemson, SC, 2011. For general operating expenses.
$2,000 to University of Vermont, Burlington, VT, 2011. For general operating expenses.

7948
Bozzone Family Foundation ✧
c/o Eckman & Danovitz LLC
1001 Liberty Ave., 11th Fl
Pittsburgh, PA 15222-3715

Established in 1986 in PA.
Donor: Robert P. Bozzone.
Foundation type: Independent foundation.
Financial data (yr. ended 12/31/13): Assets, $5,924,450 (M); gifts received, $3,850; expenditures, $1,084,161; qualifying distributions, $1,045,142; giving activities include $1,045,142 for grants.

Purpose and activities: Giving primarily for education, the arts, children, youth and social services, YMCAs, and to Roman Catholic churches and organizations.
Fields of interest: Museums; Arts; Higher education; Education; Health organizations, association; Human services; YM/YWCAs & YM/YWHAs; Children/youth, services; Catholic agencies & churches.
Type of support: General/operating support.
Limitations: Applications not accepted. Giving primarily in PA. No grants to individuals.
Application information: Contributes only to pre-selected organizations.
Trustee: Robert P. Bozzone.
EIN: 256277066

7949
Brickman Foundation ✧
1 Pitcairn Pl., Ste. 3000
Jenkintown, PA 19046-3543 (215) 881-6040
Contact: Matthew McCarte

Established in 1994 in PA.
Donors: Sally Brickman; Theodore Brickman; Julie B. Carr; Susan B. McGrath; Scott W. Brickman; Steven G. Brickman.
Foundation type: Independent foundation.
Financial data (yr. ended 12/31/12): Assets, $10,722,634 (M); gifts received, $2,030,377; expenditures, $2,229,007; qualifying distributions, $2,032,999; giving activities include $2,032,999 for grants.
Fields of interest: Education; Environment, land resources; Human services; Christian agencies & churches; Protestant agencies & churches.
Limitations: Giving primarily in FL and PA. No grants to individuals.
Application information: Application form not required.
Deadline(s): None
Trustees: Sally Brickman; Scott W. Brickman; Steven G. Brickman; Theodore Brickman; Julie B. Carr; Susan B. McGrath; Pitcairn Trust Co.
EIN: 237790986

7950
Margaret Briggs Foundation ✧
c/o PNC Bank, N.A.
620 Liberty Ave., 10th Fl.
Pittsburgh, PA 15222-2722
Application address: Margaret Briggs Foundation, c/o PNC Bank, P.O. Box 937, Scranton, PA 18501, tel.: (570) 961-7337

Established in 1969 in PA.
Donor: Margaret Briggs†.
Foundation type: Independent foundation.
Financial data (yr. ended 12/31/13): Assets, $12,277,014 (M); expenditures, $513,466; qualifying distributions, $450,637; giving activities include $441,250 for 46 grants (high: $50,000; low: $750).
Fields of interest: Medical school/education; Education; Medical care, rehabilitation; Health organizations, association; Housing/shelter, development; Youth development, centers/clubs; Boys & girls clubs; Human services; United Ways and Federated Giving Programs.
Limitations: Applications accepted. Giving limited to the greater Scranton/Lackawanna County, PA, area.
Publications: Application guidelines.
Application information: Application form not required.
Initial approach: Proposal
Copies of proposal: 6
Deadline(s): None
Board meeting date(s): Quarterly
Directors: William J. Calpin; James Fleming; Thomas G. Gallagher; Judith O. Graziano; Kevin E. Rogers.
EIN: 232719328

7951
Britton Fund ✧
c/o Glenmede Trust Co., N.A.
1650 Market St., Ste. 1200
Philadelphia, PA 19103-7391
Application address: c/o Wendy Louis, The Glenmede Trust Co., N.A., 25825 Science Park Dr., Ste. 110, Beechwood, OH 44122-7315; tel.: (216) 378-2900

Incorporated in 1952 in OH.
Donors: Gertrude H. Britton†; Charles S. Britton II†; Brigham Britton†.
Foundation type: Independent foundation.
Financial data (yr. ended 12/31/13): Assets, $20,070,516 (M); expenditures, $861,399; qualifying distributions, $736,674; giving activities include $673,000 for 31 grants (high: $180,000; low: $1,000).
Purpose and activities: Giving primarily for health and human services; support also for the arts and education.
Fields of interest: Arts; Education; Health care; Health organizations; Human services.
Type of support: General/operating support; Continuing support; Annual campaigns; Endowments; Emergency funds; Scholarship funds; Research.
Limitations: Giving primarily in the greater Cleveland, OH area, Cuyahoga, Geauga, and Lake counties. No grants to individuals.
Publications: Annual report.
Application information: Funds substantially committed. Application form required.
Initial approach: Letter
Copies of proposal: 1
Deadline(s): None
Board meeting date(s): May and Nov.
Officers and Trustees:* Lynda R. Britton,* Pres.; Terence B. Britton,* V.P.; Timothy C. Britton,* V.P.
EIN: 346513616
Selected grants: The following grants are a representative sample of this grantmaker's funding activity:
$45,000 to Marine Environmental Research Institute, Blue Hill, ME, 2012. For Marine Laboratory - Core Research and Monitoring Programs.
$10,000 to Hiram House, Chagrin Falls, OH, 2012. For The Campership Fund.
$10,000 to Kneisel Hall, Blue Hill, ME, 2012. To underwrite scholarship.
$2,000 to Mark Skinner Library, Manchester, VT, 2012. For the Purchase of New Land and Construction.

7952
The Julian A. and Lois G. Brodsky Foundation ✧ ☆
1701 John F. Kennedy Blvd., 52nd Fl.
Philadelphia, PA 19103-2838
Contact: Julian A. Brodsky, Dir.

Established in 1994 in PA.
Donors: Julian A. Brodsky; Lois G. Brodsky.
Foundation type: Independent foundation.
Financial data (yr. ended 12/31/13): Assets, $16,548,994 (M); gifts received, $1,511,150; expenditures, $648,970; qualifying distributions, $540,474; giving activities include $540,474 for 122 grants (high: $56,166; low: $100).
Fields of interest: Arts; Education; Zoos/zoological societies; Human services; Civil liberties, advocacy; Physics; Jewish agencies & synagogues.
Limitations: Applications accepted. Giving primarily in Philadelphia, PA. No grants to individuals.
Application information: Application form required.
Initial approach: Request application form
Deadline(s): None
Directors: Debra G. Brodsky; Ellen G. Brodsky; Julian A. Brodsky; Laura G. Brodsky; Lois G. Brodsky.
EIN: 232785280
Selected grants: The following grants are a representative sample of this grantmaker's funding activity:
$25,000 to Teach for America, New York, NY, 2011.
$5,000 to First Book, Washington, DC, 2011.
$2,000 to W H Y Y, Philadelphia, PA, 2011.
$2,000 to W H Y Y, Philadelphia, PA, 2011.
$1,000 to Sierra Club, San Francisco, CA, 2011.
$1,000 to Susan G. Komen for the Cure, Dallas, TX, 2011.

7953
Charles Brooks for Charities ✧ ☆
c/o PNC Bank
620 Liberty Ave., 10th Fl.
Pittsburgh, PA 15222-2722

Established in PA.
Foundation type: Independent foundation.
Financial data (yr. ended 12/31/13): Assets, $13,217,529 (M); expenditures, $636,880; qualifying distributions, $516,864; giving activities include $512,396 for 21 grants (high: $90,336; low: $7,532).
Fields of interest: Higher education; Health care; Human services; Salvation Army.
Limitations: Applications not accepted. Giving primarily in Pittsburgh, PA.
Application information: Unsolicited requests for funds not accepted.
Trustee: PNC Bank, N.A.
EIN: 256025151
Selected grants: The following grants are a representative sample of this grantmaker's funding activity:
$36,662 to Boy Scouts of America, Allegheny Trails Council, Pittsburgh, PA, 2012. For general use and purposes of said charity.
$36,662 to Pittsburgh Theological Seminary, Pittsburgh, PA, 2012. For general use and purposes of said charity.

7954
William & Jemima Brossman Charitable Foundation ✧
c/o Ephrata National Bank
P.O. Box 457
Ephrata, PA 17522-2713 (717) 733-6576
Contact: William Barnett

Established in 1986 in PA.
Donors: Bertha Brossman Blair‡; Anne B. Sweigart Irrevocable Trust.
Foundation type: Independent foundation.
Financial data (yr. ended 10/31/13): Assets, $7,688,685 (M); expenditures, $1,001,970; qualifying distributions, $993,975; giving activities include $957,175 for 31 grants (high: $376,175; low: $250).
Purpose and activities: Giving primarily for higher education.
Fields of interest: Arts; Higher education; Scholarships/financial aid; Education; Human services.
Type of support: General/operating support; Capital campaigns; Building/renovation; Scholarship funds.
Limitations: Applications accepted. Giving primarily in PA, with emphasis on Ephrata. No grants to individuals.
Application information: Application form required.
Initial approach: Proposal
Deadline(s): None
Trustee: Ephrata National Bank.
EIN: 236087844
Selected grants: The following grants are a representative sample of this grantmaker's funding activity:
$5,000 to Boy Scouts of America, Pa Dutch Council, Lancaster, PA, 2013. For general fund.
$4,000 to Ephrata Community Hospital, Ephrata, PA, 2013. For indigent care.
$1,000 to Lebanon Valley College, Annville, PA, 2013. For scholarships.

7955
Caroline Alexander Buck Foundation ✧ ☆
1600 Market St., Ste. 3600
Philadelphia, PA 19103-7212 (215) 751-2085
Contact: Bruce A. Rosenfield Esq., Dir.

Established in 1960.
Donors: Caroline A. Churchman‡; W. Morgan Churchman.
Foundation type: Independent foundation.
Financial data (yr. ended 12/31/13): Assets, $10,485,905 (M); expenditures, $602,305; qualifying distributions, $550,947; giving activities include $514,300 for 42 grants (high: $100,000; low: $2,500).
Purpose and activities: Giving primarily for education and social services.
Fields of interest: Elementary school/education; Education; Human services; Protestant agencies & churches.
Type of support: In-kind gifts.
Limitations: Applications accepted. Giving primarily in PA, with emphasis on the greater metropolitan Philadelphia area. No grants to individuals.
Application information: Application guidelines are available upon request. Application form not required.
Initial approach: Proposal
Deadline(s): None
Board meeting date(s): Spring and fall
Directors: J. Alexander Churchman; Lee Stirling Churchman; Leidy McIlvaine Churchman; W. Morgan Churchman; George Connell; Gordon L. Keen, Jr., Esq.; Wendy Mackey; Beverly Anne McConnell; Bruce A. Rosenfield, Esq.; Binney H.C. Wietlisbach.
EIN: 236257115
Selected grants: The following grants are a representative sample of this grantmaker's funding activity:
$15,000 to Chipping Hill Micro Farms, Glenside, PA, 2011. For general support.
$12,000 to Gesu School, Philadelphia, PA, 2011. For general support.
$10,000 to Episcopal Community Services of the Diocese of Pennsylvania, Philadelphia, PA, 2011.
$10,000 to Hope Partnership for Education, Philadelphia, PA, 2011. For general support.
$10,000 to Inn Dwelling, Philadelphia, PA, 2011. For general support.
$10,000 to Mighty Writers, Philadelphia, PA, 2011. For general support.
$10,000 to Need in Deed, Philadelphia, PA, 2011. For general support.
$10,000 to Neighbor to Neighbor, Fort Collins, CO, 2011. For general support.
$8,000 to Jubilee School, Philadelphia, PA, 2011. For general support.
$6,500 to Summer Search Philadelphia, Philadelphia, PA, 2011. For general support.

7956
The Buhl Foundation ✧
City Centre Tower
650 Smithfield St., Ste. 2300
Pittsburgh, PA 15222-3912 (412) 566-2711
Contact: Linda Weaver, Office Mgr.
FAX: (412) 566-2714;
E-mail: buhl@buhlfoundation.org; Main URL: http://www.buhlfoundation.org/

Established as a trust in 1927 in PA; reincorporated in 1992.
Donors: Henry Buhl, Jr.‡; Henry C. Frick‡.
Foundation type: Independent foundation.
Financial data (yr. ended 06/30/13): Assets, $83,120,429 (M); expenditures, $4,816,758; qualifying distributions, $4,217,319; giving activities include $3,638,772 for 138 grants (high: $500,000; low: $1,500), and $80,253 for foundation-administered programs.
Purpose and activities: Emphasis on developmental or innovative grants to regional institutions, with special interest in education, particularly K-12, and in regional concerns, particularly those related to problems of children and youth.
Fields of interest: Elementary/secondary education; Child development, education; Libraries/library science; Education; Children/youth, services; Child development, services; Economic development; Engineering/technology; Science; Children/youth; Minorities; Economically disadvantaged.
Type of support: Management development/capacity building; Program development; Seed money; Curriculum development; Research; Technical assistance; Program evaluation; Program-related investments/loans; Employee matching gifts.
Limitations: Applications accepted. Giving primarily in southwestern PA, with emphasis on the Pittsburgh area. No support for religious or political activities, or nationally funded organizations. No grants to individuals, or for building funds, overhead costs, accumulated deficits, operating budgets, scholarships, fellowships, fundraising campaigns; no loans (except for program-related investments).
Publications: Annual report; Informational brochure (including application guidelines).
Application information: Submit final proposal upon invitation only. Grantmakers of Western Pennsylvania's Common Grant Application Format accepted. Application form not required.
Initial approach: Letter of inquiry required prior to submitting a proposal. Letter of inquiry may be unsolicited but generally only invited proposals accepted.
Copies of proposal: 1
Deadline(s): If a letter of inquiry is approved, and a formal proposal invited, the proposal is due typically, at least 1 month prior to particular Board meeting
Board meeting date(s): 6 times a year (usually in Feb., Apr., June., Sept., Oct., and Dec.)
Final notification: Approximately 6 weeks
Officers and Directors:* Peter F. Mathieson,* Chair.; Saleem H. Ghubril,* Vice-Chair.; Frederick W. Thieman, Esq.*, Pres.; Diana Bucco, V.P.; Kim Tillotson Fleming, Secy.-Treas.; Jean A. Robinson; Lara E. Washington.
Number of staff: 2 full-time professional; 1 part-time professional; 1 full-time support; 1 part-time support.
EIN: 250378910
Selected grants: The following grants are a representative sample of this grantmaker's funding activity:
$100,000 to August Wilson Center for African American Culture, Pittsburgh, PA, 2013. For continued support of the Center's educational programs for Pittsburgh and its young people.
$100,000 to Community Design Center of Pittsburgh, Pittsburgh, PA, 2013. To support efforts on the North Side of Pittsburgh to encourage effective and attractive design and development.
$100,000 to W Q E D Multimedia, Pittsburgh, PA, 2013. For WQED series It's Pittsburgh and a Lot of Other Stuff produced by Rick Seback.
$75,000 to Growth Through Energy and Community Health Strategies, Pittsburgh, PA, 2013. For collaborations with multiple partners on Pittsburgh North Side to energize community revitalization through education and vacant lot reclamation.
$50,000 to Urban League of Pittsburgh, Pittsburgh, PA, 2013. To continue support of innovative recreational activities targeting at-risk populations on the North Side.
$45,000 to Carnegie Institute, Carnegie Museums of Pittsburgh, Pittsburgh, PA, 2013. Grant shared with Carnegie Science Center for students in grades 5-12 including SciTech Days, Pittsburgh Regional Science and Engineering Fair, Future City Competition and National Engineers Week.
$30,000 to Childrens Institute of Pittsburgh, Pittsburgh, PA, 2013. For strategic planning for increased organizational capacity to ensure continued outreach to children with special needs.
$20,000 to River City Brass Band, Pittsburgh, PA, 2013. For collaboration with Pittsburgh Public Schools to provide instrumental and musical enrichment programs for PPS students.
$15,000 to Big Brothers Big Sisters of Greater Pittsburgh, Pittsburgh, PA, 2013. To build capacity in this mentoring program by expanding training and outreach to adult mentors.

$15,000 to Carnegie Mellon University, Pittsburgh, PA, 2013. To improve teaching and learning of music in urban school districts.
$15,000 to World Affairs Council of Pittsburgh, Pittsburgh, PA, 2013. For Summer Institute for Teachers: Teaching Contemporary Global Issues.
$12,500 to Young Men and Womens African Heritage Association, Pittsburgh, PA, 2013. For additional support of the Education and Goals Equals Rewards (E.A.G.E.R.).
$7,500 to Blind and Vision Rehabilitation Services of Pittsburgh, Homestead, PA, 2013. To assist with business and financial analysis to improve efficiency and effectiveness of employment services for the blind and visually impaired.
$6,000 to Pittsburgh Youth Symphony Orchestra, Pittsburgh, PA, 2013. To build and grow the Chamber Music program with increased participants and increase performances.
$6,000 to Three Rivers Young Peoples Orchestras, Pittsburgh, PA, 2013. To support and grow the Youth Chamber Music Program.

7957
Jack Buncher Foundation ✧
(formerly Buncher Family Foundation)
Penn Liberty Plz. I
1300 Penn Ave., Ste. 300
Pittsburgh, PA 15222-4211 (412) 422-9900
Contact: Bernita Buncher, Pres.

Established in 1974 in PA.
Donors: Jack G. Buncher‡; The Buncher Co.; Buncher Rail Car Service Co.; Jack G. Buncher Trust.
Foundation type: Independent foundation.
Financial data (yr. ended 11/30/13): Assets, $270,089,243 (M); expenditures, $25,556,755; qualifying distributions, $25,508,994; giving activities include $25,296,164 for 240 grants (high: $3,757,174; low: $15).
Purpose and activities: Giving primarily to encourage the pursuit of ideas and innovations that unlock the potential of individuals and communities, and that enrich people's lives.
Fields of interest: Arts; Education; Health care; Medical research, institute; Human services; Jewish federated giving programs; Jewish agencies & synagogues.
Type of support: Scholarship funds; Program development; Matching/challenge support; General/operating support; Capital campaigns; Building/renovation; Annual campaigns.
Limitations: Applications accepted. Giving primarily in PA, with emphasis on Pittsburgh. No grants to individuals.
Application information: Grantmakers of Western Pennsylvania's Common Grant Application Format accepted. Application form required.
Initial approach: Letter
Deadline(s): None
Final notification: Within 3 months from receipt
Officers: Bernita Buncher, Pres.; Thomas Balestrieri, V.P.; Joseph M. Jakovic, Secy.; H. William Doring, Treas.
Number of staff: 1 part-time professional; 1 part-time support.
EIN: 237366998

7958
The Burke Family Foundation ✧
650 Smithfield St., Ste. 250
Pittsburgh, PA 15222-3907

Established in 1998 in PA.
Donors: Charles R. Burke Charitable Trust; Charles R. Burke; Charles R. Burke Charitable Lead AnnuityTrust 00; Charles R. Burke Charitable Lead AnnuityTrust 02; Charles R. Burke Charitable Lead AnnuityTrust 03; Charles R. Burke Charitable Lead AnnuityTrust 99; Charles R. Burke Charitable Lead Unitrust 08; Charles R. Burke Charitable Lead Unitrust 98; Charles R. Burke Charitable Lead Unitrust 03.
Foundation type: Independent foundation.
Financial data (yr. ended 12/31/13): Assets, $19,376,512 (M); gifts received, $1,049,511; expenditures, $924,655; qualifying distributions, $739,203; giving activities include $714,338 for 1 grant.
Purpose and activities: Giving for education.
Fields of interest: Arts; Higher education, university; Education; Human services; United Ways and Federated Giving Programs; Christian agencies & churches.
Type of support: Continuing support.
Limitations: Applications not accepted. Giving primarily in PA.
Application information: Unsolicited requests for funds not accepted.
Board meeting date(s): Semiannually
Officers: Charles R. Burke, Jr., Pres.; Patricia G. Burke, V.P. and Treas.
Trustee: Steven E. Burke.
EIN: 311583757

7959
The Burke Foundation ✧
650 Smithfield St., Ste. 250
Pittsburgh, PA 15222-3907

Established in 1981 in PA.
Donor: Charles R. Burke.
Foundation type: Independent foundation.
Financial data (yr. ended 12/31/12): Assets, $15,540,471 (M); gifts received, $1,022,925; expenditures, $748,265; qualifying distributions, $533,900; giving activities include $533,900 for grants.
Purpose and activities: Giving primarily to higher education, specifically colleges and universities.
Fields of interest: Higher education, college; Higher education, university; Human services; United Ways and Federated Giving Programs; Christian agencies & churches.
Type of support: Continuing support.
Limitations: Applications not accepted. Giving primarily in Pittsburgh, PA.
Application information: Unsolicited requests for funds not accepted.
Board meeting date(s): Semiannually
Officers: Steven E. Burke, Pres.; Patricia G. Burke, V.P. and Treas.
Trustee: Charles R. Burke, Jr.
EIN: 251407410

7960
Estelle S. Campbell Charitable Foundation ✧
c/o PNC Bank
620 Liberty Ave., 30th Fl.
Pittsburgh, PA 15222-2722 (412) 762-3502
Contact: Bruce Bickel, Sr. V.P., PNC Bank
E-mail: bruce.bickel@pnc.com

Established in 1998 in PA.
Foundation type: Independent foundation.
Financial data (yr. ended 12/31/13): Assets, $17,861,113 (M); expenditures, $873,969; qualifying distributions, $796,523; giving activities include $672,500 for 31 grants (high: $50,000; low: $5,000).
Fields of interest: Higher education; Youth development; Human services.
Type of support: General/operating support.
Limitations: Giving primarily in Birmingham, AL and Pittsburgh, PA; giving also in KY.
Application information: Application form required.
Initial approach: Letter
Copies of proposal: 1
Deadline(s): Apr. 15
Board meeting date(s): Mid-June
Trustee: National City Bank.
EIN: 251809360

7961
George H., Lillian S. & Mary S. Campbell Foundation ✧
c/o PNC Bank
620 Liberty Ave., 10th Fl., P2-PTPP-07-1
Pittsburgh, PA 15222-2705 (412) 762-2864
Contact: Robert Shaposka
FAX: (412) 762-4160;
E-mail: bruce.bickel@pnc.com

Donor: Mary S. Campbell‡.
Foundation type: Independent foundation.
Financial data (yr. ended 12/31/13): Assets, $15,461,218 (M); expenditures, $772,991; qualifying distributions, $674,487; giving activities include $607,500 for 10 grants (high: $162,500; low: $15,000).
Purpose and activities: Giving to provide care and support for the elderly in western PA.
Fields of interest: Christian agencies & churches; Adults; Aging.
Limitations: Applications accepted. Giving primarily in western PA.
Publications: Application guidelines.
Application information: Application form required.
Initial approach: Letter
Copies of proposal: 1
Deadline(s): None
Board meeting date(s): Contact foundation for dates
Final notification: 30 days
Trustee: PNC Bank, N.A.
Number of staff: None.
EIN: 256833660

7962
Julius H. Caplan Charity Foundation ✧
261 Old York Rd., Ste. 514
Jenkintown, PA 19046-3720 (215) 886-1234
Contact: Lowell H. Dubrow

Incorporated in 1944 in NY.

Donor: Helen Caplan Charitable Lead Unitrust.
Foundation type: Independent foundation.
Financial data (yr. ended 12/31/13): Assets, $10,189,204 (M); gifts received, $258,310; expenditures, $724,904; qualifying distributions, $629,601; giving activities include $534,300 for 25 grants (high: $405,000; low: $100).
Fields of interest: Higher education; Hospitals (general); Jewish agencies & synagogues.
Limitations: Applications accepted. Giving primarily in PA, with emphasis on Lebanon and Philadelphia; some giving also in NJ and NY. No grants to individuals.
Application information: Application form not required.
Initial approach: Proposal
Deadline(s): None
Directors: Eli Caplan; Perry Caplan; Sloan Caplan.
EIN: 136067379

7963
The Cardiovascular Medical Research and Education Fund, Inc. ✧

510 Walnut St., Ste. 500
Philadelphia, PA 19106-3601 (215) 413-2414
Contact: Patricia A. Wolf, Exec. Dir.
E-mail: patt.wolfe@ipahresearch.org; Main URL: http://www.ipahresearch.org/

Established in 2003 in PA.
Foundation type: Independent foundation.
Financial data (yr. ended 12/31/12): Assets, $15,250,201 (M); expenditures, $3,756,722; qualifying distributions, $3,641,703; giving activities include $3,612,675 for 15 grants (high: $697,021; low: $30,000).
Purpose and activities: The fund's mission is to support research to uncover the etiology and pathogenesis of idiopathic pulmonary arterial hypertension (IPAH, or PPH), in pursuit of the ultimate goal of its treatment and cure.
Fields of interest: Heart & circulatory research.
Type of support: Research; Grants to individuals.
Limitations: Giving on a national basis.
Publications: Application guidelines; Annual report.
Application information: Submit letter of intent in electronic format. The fund will respond within four weeks if a full application will be requested. Complete application guidelines are available on the fund web site. Application form required.
Initial approach: Online Letter of Intent (not exceeding 2 pages)
Officers and Directors:* John H. Newman, M.D.*, Pres.; Patricia A. Wolfe, Exec. Dir.; Michael Fishbein, Esq.; Peter Pantaleo, Esq.
Research Advisory Committee: Stuart Rich, M.D.
EIN: 050579911

7964
Cardone Foundation ✧

24 N. Bryn Mawr Ave., PMB 153
Bryn Mawr, PA 19010-3304
Contact: Luanne Foti

Established in 2002 in PA; as the successor to the Michael Cardone Foundation.
Donors: Michael Cardone Foundation; Cardone Industries.
Foundation type: Independent foundation.
Financial data (yr. ended 12/31/12): Assets, $6,479,472 (M); gifts received, $2,500,000; expenditures, $822,235; qualifying distributions, $804,871; giving activities include $298,000 for 17 grants (high: $50,000; low: $500), and $500,000 for 1 employee matching gift.
Fields of interest: Education; Health care; Human services; Christian agencies & churches.
Limitations: Applications not accepted. Giving on a national basis, with some emphasis on GA, NY, and PA. No grants to individuals.
Application information: Contributes only to pre-selected organizations.
Officers: Jacqueline Cardone, Pres.; Michael Cardone, Jr., V.P.
Trustees: Michael Cardone III; Ryan D. Cardone; Christin C. McClave.
EIN: 300028232
Selected grants: The following grants are a representative sample of this grantmaker's funding activity:
$50,000 to Oral Roberts University, Tulsa, OK, 2012. For Whole Person Scholarship.
$50,000 to Search Ministries, Ellicott City, MD, 2012. To Be Used for the Organization's Charitable Purposes in Its Discretion.
$20,000 to Council for Relationships, Philadelphia, PA, 2012. To support grant.

7965
Carnahan-Jackson Foundation ✧

c/o Northwest Savings Bank, N.A.
1030 State St., Ste. 1
Erie, PA 16501-1840
Application address: P.O. Box 3326, Jamestown, NY 14702-3326, tel.: (716) 483-1015

Trust established in 1972 in NY.
Donor: Katharine J. Carnahan†.
Foundation type: Independent foundation.
Financial data (yr. ended 07/31/13): Assets, $11,494,960 (M); expenditures, $580,445; qualifying distributions, $549,354; giving activities include $423,870 for 41 grants (high: $50,000; low: $1,000).
Purpose and activities: Primary areas of interest include higher and other education, libraries, hospitals, and youth; support also for the handicapped, drug abuse programs, ecology, housing, community development, dance and other performing arts groups, and church support; some support for certain prior interests of the donor.
Fields of interest: Performing arts; Higher education; Education; Hospitals (general); Human services; YM/YWCAs & YM/YWHAs; Children/youth, services; Christian agencies & churches.
Type of support: General/operating support; Continuing support; Capital campaigns; Building/renovation; Equipment; Program development; Seed money; Curriculum development; Scholarship funds; Matching/challenge support.
Limitations: Applications accepted. Giving primarily in Chautauqua County, NY, particularly in the Jamestown area. No grants to individuals.
Publications: Application guidelines; Grants list.
Application information: Application form not required.
Initial approach: Letter
Copies of proposal: 8
Deadline(s): June and Sept.
Board meeting date(s): June and Dec.
Trustee: Northwest Savings Bank, N.A.
Number of staff: 2 part-time professional; 1 part-time support.
EIN: 166151608

7966
Carnegie Hero Fund Commission ✧

436 7th Ave., Ste. 1101
Pittsburgh, PA 15219-1841
Contact: Jeffrey A. Dooley, Investigations Mgr.
FAX: (412) 281-5751;
E-mail: carnegiehero@carnegiehero.org; Toll free tel.: (800) 447-8900; Main URL: http://www.carnegiehero.org/
Awardees database: http://carnegiehero.org/search-awardees/

Established in 1904 in PA.
Donor: Andrew Carnegie†.
Foundation type: Operating foundation.
Financial data (yr. ended 12/31/12): Assets, $38,278,724 (M); gifts received, $620; expenditures, $1,775,175; qualifying distributions, $1,755,068; giving activities include $920,544 for grants to individuals.
Purpose and activities: A private operating foundation established to recognize, with the award of medals and sums of money, heroism voluntarily performed by civilians within the U.S. and Canada in saving or attempting to save the lives of others; and to grant monetary assistance, including scholarship aid, to awardees and to the dependents of those who have lost their lives or who have been disabled in such heroic manner.
Fields of interest: Human services; Voluntarism promotion.
International interests: Canada.
Type of support: Continuing support; Grants to individuals; Scholarships—to individuals.
Limitations: Applications accepted. Giving primarily in the U.S.; some giving also in Canada.
Publications: Annual report; Informational brochure; Newsletter.
Application information: Awards by nomination only. Refer to the commission web site for complete nominating guidelines and form. Application form required.
Initial approach: Use online nomination form on foundation web site, or contact the Commission to request a nomination form. Nominations may also be made by letter
Copies of proposal: 1
Deadline(s): Within 2 years of the act for nominations
Board meeting date(s): Mar., June, Sept., and Dec.
Final notification: Following board meetings
Officers and Trustees:* Mark Laskow,* Chair.; Walter F. Rutkowski, Pres. and Secy.; Priscilla J. McCrady,* V.P.; Dan D. Sandman,* Treas.; Albert H. Burchfield III; Robert J. Cindrich; Robert M. Hernandez; Thomas J. Hilliard, Jr.; David McL. Hillman; Linda T. Hills; Peter J. Lambrou; Natalie Lemieux; Christopher R. McCrady; Ann M. McGuinn; Nancy L. Rackoff; Frank Brooks Robinson; Arthur M. Scully III; Michael A. Thompson; Sybil P. Veeder, Ph.D.; Joseph C. Walton; Susanne C. Wean; Thomas L. Wentling, Jr.
Number of staff: 5 full-time professional; 2 part-time professional; 2 full-time support; 1 part-time support.
EIN: 251062730

7967
E. Rhodes & Leona B. Carpenter Foundation ✧
1735 Market St., Ste. 3420
Philadelphia, PA 19103-2921 (215) 979-3221
Contact: Joseph A. O'Connor, Jr., Exec. Dir.
FAX: (215) 979-3229;
E-mail: admin@carpenterfoundation.us; Main URL: http://www.erlbcarpenterfoundation.org

Established in 1975 in VA.
Donors: E. Rhodes Carpenter†; Leona B. Carpenter†.
Foundation type: Independent foundation.
Financial data (yr. ended 12/31/12): Assets, $218,865,841 (M); expenditures, $12,368,101; qualifying distributions, $11,016,885; giving activities include $10,321,203 for 259 grants (high: $500,000; low: $1,500).
Purpose and activities: Support for performing arts organizations in the Richmond, VA, area; education, particularly graduate theological educational institutions; museums (including museums associated with colleges and universities) for purchase, restoration, and conservation of Asian art; institutions providing education in the field of Asian art; and organizations providing health care, particularly hospices.
Fields of interest: Arts education; Museums; Performing arts; Arts; Theological school/education; Education; Residential/custodial care, hospices.
Limitations: Applications accepted. Giving primarily in MA, NC, NY, PA, TX, and Richmond, VA (for performing arts only). No support for private secondary education, or large public charities. No grants to individuals or for endowments (generally).
Application information: Application form not required.
Initial approach: Letter
Copies of proposal: 2
Deadline(s): Jan. 31 and July 31
Board meeting date(s): Spring and fall
Officers and Directors:* Ann B. Day,* Pres.; Paul B. Day, Jr.,* V.P. and Secy.; J.A. O'Connor, Jr., Exec. Dir.; M.H. Reinhart.
EIN: 510155772
Selected grants: The following grants are a representative sample of this grantmaker's funding activity:
$500,000 to Duke University, Durham, NC, 2012. For Benefit of Duke's Libraries and to endow position of Senior Conservator.
$500,000 to Hampden-Sydney College, Hampden Sydney, VA, 2012. For Creation of a Fine Arts Center.
$250,000 to Harvard University, Art Museum, Cambridge, MA, 2012. For renovation costs of a new building to house the Harvard Art Museum.
$200,000 to Vanderbilt University, Divinity School, Nashville, TN, 2012. For Scholarships and stipends for 3 Master of Divinity students.
$125,000 to Public Health Management Corporation, Philadelphia, PA, 2012. For Congreso Health Center nurse practitioner.
$100,000 to Persephone Productions, Washington, DC, 2012. To produce a PBS documentary on Christian Welcoming movement.
$40,000 to Pierpont Morgan Library, New York, NY, 2012. For general operation expenses.
$35,000 to Massachusetts Conference of the United Church of Christ, Framingham, MA, 2012. For Funding Hispanic Ministry Pastoral Development and Education project.
$28,000 to Cornell University, Ithaca, NY, 2012. For Conservation for 3 Tibetan Buddhist paintings.
$25,000 to Itawamba Community College, Fulton, MS, 2012. For Medical equipment for the health programs offered at Education Center.

7968
The Carthage Foundation ✧
1 Oxford Ctr.
301 Grant St., Ste. 3900
Pittsburgh, PA 15219-6401 (412) 392-2900
Contact: Michael W. Gleba, Pres. and Treas.
Main URL: http://www.scaife.com/carthage.html

Incorporated in 1964 in PA.
Donor: Richard M. Scaife†.
Foundation type: Independent foundation.
Financial data (yr. ended 12/31/13): Assets, $36,673,519 (M); expenditures, $1,717,490; qualifying distributions, $1,623,342; giving activities include $1,210,000 for 15 grants (high: $200,000; low: $5,000).
Purpose and activities: Grants primarily for public policy research, particularly in the areas of government and international affairs and only to U.S. 501(c)(3) organizations.
Fields of interest: Crime/law enforcement, counterterrorism; International affairs; Political science; Public policy, research; Government/public administration.
Type of support: General/operating support; Conferences/seminars.
Limitations: Applications accepted. Giving on a national basis, with emphasis on the Washington, DC, metro area. No support for nationally-organized fundraising groups. No grants to individuals. Generally, no grants for event sponsorships, endowments, capital campaigns, renovations or government agencies.
Publications: Annual report.
Application information: The foundation does not issue a separate program policy statement or grant application guidelines. The foundation acknowledges receipt of proposals. Application form required.
Initial approach: Letter
Copies of proposal: 1
Deadline(s): None
Board meeting date(s): Quarterly
Final notification: 1 to 3 weeks
Officers and Trustees:* Michael W. Gleba,* Pres. and Treas.; Yvonne Marie Bly,* Secy.; R. Daniel McMichael; Roger W. Robinson, Jr.
Number of staff: 2 part-time professional; 2 part-time support.
EIN: 256067979
Selected grants: The following grants are a representative sample of this grantmaker's funding activity:
$50,000 to Atlas Economic Research Foundation, Washington, DC, 2012. For Prague Security Studies Institute.
$40,000 to Cato Institute, Washington, DC, 2012. For Conference Support.

7969
Louis N. Cassett Foundation ✧
2001 Market St., 10th Fl.
Philadelphia, PA 19103-1834 (215) 315-7789
Contact: Malcolm B. Jacobson, Tr.

Trust established in 1946 in PA.
Donor: Louis N. Cassett†.
Foundation type: Independent foundation.
Financial data (yr. ended 12/31/13): Assets, $11,558,900 (M); expenditures, $666,921; qualifying distributions, $567,905; giving activities include $539,100 for 136 grants (high: $20,000; low: $500).
Purpose and activities: Giving primarily for cultural programs, social service and health agencies, and Jewish organizations.
Fields of interest: Arts; Health organizations; Human services; Jewish federated giving programs; Jewish agencies & synagogues.
Type of support: Annual campaigns; Building/renovation.
Limitations: Applications accepted. Giving primarily in FL and Philadelphia, PA. No grants to individuals, or for endowment funds.
Application information: Application form required.
Initial approach: Letter
Copies of proposal: 1
Deadline(s): None
Board meeting date(s): As required
Trustees: Malcolm B. Jacobson; Susan Kershnaum; Vanessa Elias Krelstein.
EIN: 236274038

7970
CentiMark Foundation ✧
12 Grandview Cir.
Canonsburg, PA 15317-8533 (724) 514-8572
Contact: Kathy Slencak, Mgr., Community Rels.
E-mail: Kathy.Slencak@CentiMark.Com

Established in 2007 in PA.
Donors: Timothy M. Dunlap; CentiMark Corp.
Foundation type: Company-sponsored foundation.
Financial data (yr. ended 12/31/13): Assets, $82,651 (M); gifts received, $1,500,000; expenditures, $1,462,671; qualifying distributions, $1,459,400; giving activities include $1,459,400 for 205 grants (high: $220,000; low: $250).
Purpose and activities: The foundation supports organizations involved with education, health, hunger, housing, human services, and Catholicism.
Fields of interest: Elementary/secondary education; Higher education; Education; Hospitals (general); Health care; Food services; Food banks; Food distribution, meals on wheels; Housing/shelter; Salvation Army; Children/youth, services; Family services; Pregnancy centers; Developmentally disabled, centers & services; Homeless, human services; Human services; Catholic agencies & churches.
Type of support: General/operating support; Capital campaigns; Program development.
Limitations: Applications not accepted. Giving primarily in PA.
Application information: Contributes only to pre-selected organizations.
Officers and Trustees:* Edward B. Dunlap, Jr.,* Pres.; Timothy M. Dunlap,* V.P.; Thor D. DiCesare, Secy.; John A. Rudzik,* Treas.; John L. Heisey.
EIN: 208911858
Selected grants: The following grants are a representative sample of this grantmaker's funding activity:
$95,000 to Washington City Mission, Washington, PA, 2011.
$64,000 to Blessings in a Backpack, Louisville, KY, 2011.
$54,355 to Washington City Mission, Washington, PA, 2011.

$25,000 to North Hills Affordable Housing Task Force, Pittsburgh, PA, 2011. For operating expenses.
$15,000 to Allegheny Valley School, Coraopolis, PA, 2011.
$15,000 to Sisters Place, Clairton, PA, 2011. For operating expenses.
$10,000 to Holy Family Foundation, Pittsburgh, PA, 2011. For operating expenses.
$5,000 to Cancer League of Colorado, Englewood, CO, 2011. For operating expenses.
$5,000 to Dialysis Clinic, Nashville, TN, 2011. For operating expenses.
$5,000 to Early Learning Institute, Pittsburgh, PA, 2011. For operating expenses.

7971
Central Pennsylvania Community Foundation ✧
(formerly Blair County Community Endowment)
1330 11th Ave.
Altoona, PA 16601-3302 (814) 944-6102
Contact: Jodi Cessna, Exec. Dir.
FAX: (814) 381-7104;
E-mail: cessna@centralpacf.org; Main URL: http://centralpagives.org/

Established in 1995 in PA.
Foundation type: Community foundation.
Financial data (yr. ended 12/31/12): Assets, $11,035,154 (M); gifts received, $2,006,155; expenditures, $1,522,909; giving activities include $958,574 for 41+ grants (high: $61,130), and $37,774 for 1 grant to an individual.
Purpose and activities: The foundation seeks to provide a permanent trust that will help the local community in the future by providing a perpetual fund to aid civic and charitable projects.
Fields of interest: Performing arts, music; Arts; Education; Health organizations, association; Recreation; Community/economic development; Science, research; Religion.
Type of support: Fellowships.
Limitations: Applications accepted. Giving limited to Blair County, PA. No grants to individuals.
Publications: Application guidelines; Informational brochure; Newsletter.
Application information: Visit foundation web site for application cover sheet and guidelines.
Initial approach: Contact foundation
Copies of proposal: 9
Deadline(s): Last business day of Apr.
Board meeting date(s): Mar., June, Sept., and Dec.
Final notification: 4 weeks
Officers and Directors:* John Kazmaier,* Chair.; Allan G. Hancock,* Pres.; Nancy Devorris,* V.P.; Randy Tarpey,* Secy.; Fred Imler, Sr.,* Treas.; Jodi Cessna, Exec. Dir.; Len Whiting, Dir. Emeritus; Gerald Wolf, Dir. Emeritus; Larry Claton; John E. Eberhardt, Jr.; Matt Garber; Michele Haas; Barry Halbritter; Ray Hess; Joseph D. Hurd, Jr.; Gail H. Irwin; Craig Kilmer; Michael Kranich, Sr.; Astride McLanahan; James Moran; Neil Port; April Ressler; Steve Sloan; Maureen Smithe.
Number of staff: 1 full-time professional.
EIN: 251761379

7972
Central Susquehanna Community Foundation ✧
(formerly Administers of the Berwick Health and Wellness Fund)
725 West Front St.
Berwick, PA 18603 (570) 752-3930
Contact: Eric DeWald, C.E.O.; For grants: Kara Seesholtz, Sr. Prog. Off.
FAX: (570) 752-7435;
E-mail: edewald@csgiving.org; Additional e-mail: kseesholtz@csgiving.org; Main URL: http://www.csgiving.org

Established in 1999 in PA; converted from the sale of Berwick Hospital.
Foundation type: Community foundation.
Financial data (yr. ended 12/31/13): Assets, $44,235,511 (M); gifts received, $994,539; expenditures, $2,160,886; giving activities include $1,236,855 for 29+ grants (high: $384,898), and $28,330 for 25 grants to individuals.
Purpose and activities: The foundation seeks to improve the quality of life for citizens of the Central Susquehanna Region.
Fields of interest: Arts; Education; Health care; Mental health/crisis services; Human services.
Type of support: General/operating support; Continuing support; Building/renovation; Equipment; Program development; Seed money; Technical assistance; Consulting services; Program-related investments/loans; Scholarships—to individuals; Matching/challenge support.
Limitations: Applications accepted. Giving limited to Columbia, Lower Luzerne, Montour, Northumberland, and Snyder counties, PA. No support for religious purposes. No grants to individuals (except for scholarships).
Publications: Application guidelines; Annual report; Financial statement; Grants list; Informational brochure; Newsletter; Occasional report (including application guidelines).
Application information: Visit foundation web site for application guidelines. Application form required.
Initial approach: Telephone
Copies of proposal: 2
Deadline(s): Varies
Board meeting date(s): Quarterly
Final notification: Within 2 months
Officers and Trustees:* M. Holly Morrison,* Chair.; Kendra Aucker,* Vice-Chair.; Eric Dewald,* C.E.O. and Pres.; Roger S. Haddon, Jr.,* Secy.; Dr. John E. DeFinnis,* Treas.; Al Meale, Cont.; Timothy Apple; Roger J. Davis; JoAnne Ferentz; Peggy Fullmer; Thomas R. Harlow; James Kishbaugh; John S. Mulka; John B. Parker; Joseph Scopelliti; Rhonda Seebold; J. Donald Steele, Jr.; Connie Tressler; Kevin D. Woodeshick.
Number of staff: 2 full-time professional; 3 part-time professional.
EIN: 232982141

7973
Centre County Community Foundation, Inc. ✧
2601 Gateway Dr., Bristol II, Ste. 175
P.O. Box 648
State College, PA 16804-0648 (814) 237-6229
Contact: Molly Kunkel, Exec. Dir.
FAX: (814) 237-2624;
E-mail: info@centre-foundation.org; Additional e-mail: mkunkel@centrecountycf.org; Main URL: http://www.centrecountycf.org
Blog: http://centrefoundation.wordpress.com/
Facebook: http://www.facebook.com/pages/Centre-County-Community-Foundation/108336539198975
LinkedIn: http://www.linkedin.com/company/centre-county-community-foundation
Twitter: http://twitter.com/CentreFNDN

Established in 1981 in PA.
Foundation type: Community foundation.
Financial data (yr. ended 12/31/12): Assets, $24,905,016 (M); gifts received, $2,832,835; expenditures, $2,324,175; giving activities include $1,374,300 for grants.
Purpose and activities: The foundation's mission is to improve the quality of life in Centre County by providing enduring support to community charities from the invested gifts of visionary donors.
Fields of interest: Arts; Education; Environment; Health care; Human services; Community/economic development.
Type of support: General/operating support; Income development; Annual campaigns; Capital campaigns; Building/renovation; Equipment; Emergency funds; Program development; Conferences/seminars; Publication; Seed money; Internship funds; Scholarship funds; Research; Technical assistance; Matching/challenge support.
Limitations: Applications accepted. Giving limited to PA, predominately in Centre County; limited funding also to immediate surrounding counties. No support for religious organizations for sectarian purposes, or government or educational entities with taxing authority. No grants for payment of debt, travel or accommodation services, or event ads or sponsorships.
Publications: Application guidelines; Annual report (including application guidelines); Informational brochure; Occasional report; Quarterly report.
Application information: Visit foundation web site for specific application forms and guidelines per grant type. Application form required.
Initial approach: Visit foundation web site to create online profile and complete eligibility quiz
Deadline(s): Oct. 27
Board meeting date(s): 3rd Wed. of Feb., May, Aug., and Nov.
Final notification: May and Dec.
Officer and Directors:* Molly Kunkel,* Exec. Dir.; Patrick Bisbey; John Conroy; Desiree Fralick; Blake Gall; Tammy Gentzel; Amos Goodall; R. Riggs Griffith; Kelly Grimes; Jack Infield; Oscar Johnston; Terrell Jones; Bill Keough; Heddy Kervandjian; Kay Kustanbauter; Heidi Nicholas; Rabbi David Ostrich; Carmine Prestia; Bob Ricketts; Todd Sloan; Chuck Witmer; Ted Ziff II; Jane Zimmerman.
Number of staff: 2 full-time professional; 1 full-time support.
EIN: 251782197

7974
The Century Fund Trust ✧
462 W. Walnut St., Ste. 202
Allentown, PA 18102-5497 (610) 434-4000
Contact: Alice A. Miller, Vice-Chair.
E-mail: centuryfund@aol.com

Established in 1985 in PA.
Foundation type: Independent foundation.

Financial data (yr. ended 12/31/13): Assets, $22,695,736 (M); expenditures, $1,696,876; qualifying distributions, $1,387,175; giving activities include $1,345,550 for 123 grants (high: $225,000; low: $300).
Purpose and activities: Giving primarily to arts and cultural programs, education, conservation, human services, and community development in the Lehigh Valley, Pennsylvania.
Fields of interest: Museums (art); Performing arts, orchestras; Historic preservation/historical societies; Arts; Higher education; Education; Environment, natural resources; Animal welfare; Human services; YM/YWCAs & YM/YWHAs; Children/youth, services; Aging, centers/services; Community/economic development; Protestant agencies & churches.
Type of support: General/operating support; Continuing support; Annual campaigns; Capital campaigns; Building/renovation; Equipment; Debt reduction; Program development; Seed money; Scholarship funds; Matching/challenge support.
Limitations: Applications accepted. Giving primarily in the greater Lehigh Valley, PA, area.
Publications: Application guidelines.
Application information: Application form not required.
Initial approach: Proposal
Copies of proposal: 6
Deadline(s): Apr. 1
Board meeting date(s): 6-10 times per year
Final notification: 1-2 months
Officers and Trustees:* Jack Leh,* Pres.; Alice Miller,* Vice-Chair.; Rev. Grant E. Harrity,* Secy.; David K. Bausch,* Treas.; Lee A. Butz.
Number of staff: 1 part-time professional; 1 part-time support.
EIN: 226404912

7975
Michele and Agnese Cestone Foundation, Inc. ✧

c/o Bruce Bickel, PNC Private Foundation
1 PNC Plz.
249 5th Ave., 3rd Fl.
Pittsburgh, PA 15222 (412) 762-3502
Contact: Bruce Bickel; Cynthia Hamorsky; Yhezzi Owen
FAX: (412) 762-4160;
E-mail: bruce.bickel@pnc.com

Established in 1990 in NJ.
Foundation type: Independent foundation.
Financial data (yr. ended 12/31/13): Assets, $17,724,532 (M); expenditures, $1,088,131; qualifying distributions, $993,096; giving activities include $879,425 for 47 grants (high: $150,000; low: $5,000).
Purpose and activities: Giving primarily for the care and welfare of animals.
Fields of interest: Animal welfare.
Type of support: General/operating support; Continuing support; Capital campaigns; Building/renovation; Equipment; Emergency funds; Program development; Seed money; Curriculum development; Scholarship funds; Research; Technical assistance; Matching/challenge support.
Limitations: Applications accepted. Giving on the East Coast of the U.S., with some emphasis on NJ and NY.
Publications: Application guidelines.
Application information: Application form required.
Initial approach: Letter
Copies of proposal: 1
Deadline(s): Contact foundation for deadlines
Board meeting date(s): June and Nov.
Final notification: 30 days
Officers and Trustees:* Michele J. Cestone,* Pres.; Maria A. Cestone II,* Secy.
Number of staff: 2 full-time professional.
EIN: 521720903
Selected grants: The following grants are a representative sample of this grantmaker's funding activity:
$40,000 to Animal Medical Center, New York, NY, 2012. For Guide Dog Program.
$16,000 to Friends of Animals, Darien, CT, 2012. For spay/neuter program.
$15,000 to Glade Run Foundation, Zelienople, PA, 2012. For care of horses.
$15,000 to National Aviary in Pittsburgh, Pittsburgh, PA, 2012. For veterinary hospital.
$15,000 to Sea Turtle Conservancy, Gainesville, FL, 2012. For Sea Turtle Protection Program.
$10,000 to Washington Animal Rescue League, Washington, DC, 2012. For assistance low-income.
$5,000 to Mylestone Equine Rescue, Phillipsburg, NJ, 2012. For horse rescue.
$5,000 to Zoological Society of New Jersey, West Orange, NJ, 2012. For zoo education Program.

7976
The Ralph M. Cestone Foundation, Inc. ✧

2 PNC Plz., 30th Fl.
620 Liberty Ave.
Pittsburgh, PA 15222-2722 (412) 762-3502
Contact: Bruce Bickel
FAX: (412) 762-4160;
E-mail: bruce.bickel@pnc.com

Established in 1997 in NJ.
Donors: Maria A. Cestone; Ralph M. Cestone.
Foundation type: Independent foundation.
Financial data (yr. ended 12/31/13): Assets, $10,490,766 (M); expenditures, $654,297; qualifying distributions, $589,005; giving activities include $477,660 for 41 grants (high: $50,000; low: $2,500).
Purpose and activities: Support for arts, education, health, religion, and social services on the East Coast of the United States.
Fields of interest: Arts; Education; Health care; Human services; Religion.
Type of support: General/operating support; Capital campaigns; Building/renovation; Equipment; Emergency funds; Curriculum development; Research; Technical assistance.
Limitations: Applications accepted. Giving primarily on the East Coast, with emphasis on NJ, OH, and PA.
Application information: Telephone foundation for board meeting and application information. Application form required.
Initial approach: Letter including necessary historical background
Copies of proposal: 1
Deadline(s): Apr. 1 and Oct. 1
Board meeting date(s): June and Dec.
Final notification: 30 days
Officers and Directors:* Michele J. Cestone,* Pres.; Maria A. Cestone,* Secy.-Treas.
Number of staff: 2 full-time professional.
EIN: 226703196
Selected grants: The following grants are a representative sample of this grantmaker's funding activity:
$25,000 to Exploring the Arts, New York, NY, 2012. For ETA Apprenticeship Program.
$20,000 to Eva's Village, Paterson, NJ, 2012. To support Homeless Shelter needs.
$16,200 to Idaho State University, Pocatello, ID, 2012. For Trackway Analysis Research Program.
$10,000 to Rider University, Lawrenceville, NJ, 2012. For Summer Apprentice Program.
$5,000 to Bergen Performing Arts Center, Englewood, NJ, 2012. For arts education program.
$5,000 to Children on the Green, Morristown, NJ, 2012. For shelter education program.
$5,000 to Morris Catholic High School, Denville, NJ, 2012. To redesign chemistry lab.

7977
The Charter Foundation ✧

640 Narcisi Ln.
Wayne, PA 19087-2238 (610) 688-9055
E-mail: info@thecharterfoundation.com; Main URL: http://thecharterfoundation.com/

Donor: The McLean Contributionship.
Foundation type: Independent foundation.
Financial data (yr. ended 12/31/12): Assets, $13,161,929 (M); gifts received, $15,000; expenditures, $717,228; qualifying distributions, $634,410; giving activities include $592,000 for 23 grants (high: $200,000; low: $2,000).
Purpose and activities: Giving primarily for education, healthcare, medical research, and other human services.
Fields of interest: Education; Hospitals (general); Health care; Human services.
Limitations: Applications accepted. Giving primarily in the Greater Philadelphia, PA, area. No grants for annual appeals, or annual event sponsorship.
Publications: Application guidelines; Grants list.
Application information: Application form required.
Initial approach: Take eligibility quiz on foundation web site to determine eligibility
Deadline(s): See foundation web site for current deadlines
Officers and Trustees:* Joseph K. Gordon, Esq.*, Pres.; Leila Gordon,* V.P. and Exec. Dir.; C. Scott Gordon; Hunter R. Gordon.
EIN: 271234570

7978
The Chatham Foundation ✧

660 Dorset Rd.
Devon, PA 19333-1843

Established in 2002 in PA.
Donors: Barbara H. Sutherland; L. Frederick Sutherland.
Foundation type: Independent foundation.
Financial data (yr. ended 12/31/13): Assets, $9,930,888 (M); expenditures, $477,115; qualifying distributions, $474,500; giving activities include $474,500 for 22 grants (high: $200,000; low: $1,000).
Fields of interest: Community/economic development; Philanthropy/voluntarism; Christian agencies & churches.
Limitations: Applications not accepted. Giving primarily in PA. No grants to individuals.

Application information: Contributes only to pre-selected organizations.
Trustees: Barbara H. Sutherland; L. Frederick Sutherland.
EIN: 300162130

7979
Chester County Community Foundation ✧
The Lincoln Bldg.
28 W. Market St.
West Chester, PA 19382-3020 (610) 696-8211
Contact: Karen A. Simmons, C.E.O.; For grants: Beth Harper Briglia, V.P., Grants and Donor Svcs.
FAX: (610) 696-8213; E-mail: info@chescocf.org; Additional e-mail: karen@chescocf.org; Grant application e-mail: grants@chescocf.org; Main URL: http://www.chescocf.org
Blog: http://chescocf.wordpress.com
Facebook: http://www.facebook.com/pages/Chester-County-Community-Foundation/89750399079
Twitter: http://twitter.com/ChesCoCF

Established in 1994 in PA.
Foundation type: Community foundation.
Financial data (yr. ended 06/30/14): Assets, $47,552,823 (M); gifts received, $4,434,228; expenditures, $3,732,548; giving activities include $2,070,377 for 26+ grants (high: $200,000), and $224,855 for 147 grants to individuals.
Purpose and activities: Grow legacy philanthropy via those who live, work and enjoy Chester County, connecting people who care with causes that matter now and forever.
Fields of interest: Arts; Libraries/library science; Scholarships/financial aid; Education, drop-out prevention; Education; Environment; Health care; Youth development; Human services; Community development, neighborhood development; Economic development; Religion.
Type of support: General/operating support; Management development/capacity building; Capital campaigns; Building/renovation; Endowments; Program development; Conferences/seminars; Scholarship funds; Research; Consulting services; Program evaluation; Scholarships—to individuals.
Limitations: Applications accepted. Giving primarily in Chester County, PA. No grants to individuals (except for scholarships).
Publications: Application guidelines; Annual report; Financial statement; Informational brochure; Newsletter.
Application information: Visit foundation web site for application form and guidelines. Proposals submitted by Sept. 15 will receive priority consideration under all grantmaking funds. Delaware Valley Grantmakers Common Grant Application Form accepted. Application form required.
Initial approach: E-mail grant Summary Sheet and proposal
Copies of proposal: 1
Deadline(s): Sept. 15 for Fund for Chester County Initiative; none for Donor-Advised and Field-of-Interest funds
Board meeting date(s): Feb., May., Sept., and Nov.
Final notification: 2 months
Officers and Directors:* L. Peter Temple, Esq.,* Chair.; J. Stoddard Hayes, Jr., Esq.,* Vice-Chair.; Meghan McVety,* Vice-Chair.; Karen A. Simmons,* C.E.O. and Pres.; Beth Harper Briglia,* V.P., Donor Svcs. and Grantmaking; Cynthia Sineath Ray,* Corp. Secy.-Treas.; Carol Clark; John H. Diederich; David Elderkin; Carl Francis; William J. Gallagher, Esq.; Sara D. Harris; Ann Hutton; Michael B. Karwic; Stacey Willits McConnell, Esq.; Anthony Morris, Esq.; Robert E. Rigg; Karen Simmons.
Number of staff: 4 full-time professional; 1 part-time professional; 8 part-time support.
EIN: 232773822

7980
The Philip Chosky Charitable & Educational Foundation ✧
330 Grant St., Ste. 1500
Pittsburgh, PA 15219

Established in 1998 in PA.
Donors: Philip Chosky†; Electronic Institutes, Inc.; Electronic Institutes Foundation.
Foundation type: Independent foundation.
Financial data (yr. ended 12/31/12): Assets, $15,301,870 (M); gifts received, $417,727; expenditures, $1,165,428; qualifying distributions, $1,004,909; giving activities include $877,753 for 17 grants (high: $310,000; low: $1,253).
Purpose and activities: Giving primarily for performing arts and theater.
Fields of interest: Performing arts, theater; Arts; Higher education; Jewish federated giving programs; Jewish agencies & synagogues.
Limitations: Applications not accepted. Giving primarily in Pittsburgh, PA. No grants to individuals.
Application information: Contributes only to pre-selected organizations.
Officer: Meryl Ainsman, Exec. Dir.
Directors: Stanley Barg; Michael O'Malley; Susan O'Malley.
EIN: 232932969
Selected grants: The following grants are a representative sample of this grantmaker's funding activity:
$100,000 to Carnegie Mellon University, School of Drama, Pittsburgh, PA, 2012. For Discretionary Fund.

7981
CIGNA Foundation ✧
1601 Chestnut St., TL15C
Philadelphia, PA 19192-1540 (215) 761-4328
Contact: David Figliuzzi, Exec. Dir.
E-mail: CommunityService@Cigna.com; Application address: CIGNA Grant Program, P.O. Box 2248, Princeton, NJ 08543-2248, tel.: 866) 865-5277; Main URL: http://www.cigna.com/about-us/corporate-responsibility/cigna-foundation

Incorporated in 1962 in PA.
Donor: CIGNA Corp.
Foundation type: Company-sponsored foundation.
Financial data (yr. ended 12/31/12): Assets, $3,669,331 (M); gifts received, $6,687,846; expenditures, $3,940,974; qualifying distributions, $3,939,478; giving activities include $3,853,023 for 1,006 grants (high: $500,000; low: $25).
Purpose and activities: The foundation supports programs designed to enable individuals and family to take responsibility for their own wealth; make heath information and services available through expanded opportunities; leverage education and life experiences to promote personal and professional growth; and encourage shared approaches to issues of local and global concern.
Fields of interest: Elementary school/education; Higher education; Education; Environment; Health care, equal rights; Health care, clinics/centers; Public health; Health care, patient services; Health care; Genetic diseases and disorders; Breast cancer; Recreation, parks/playgrounds; American Red Cross; YM/YWCAs & YM/YWHAs; Children/youth, services; Family services; Developmentally disabled, centers & services; Human services; Civil/human rights, equal rights; Civil/human rights, advocacy; Community/economic development; Foundations (public); Public policy, research; Leadership development.
Type of support: Capital campaigns; General/operating support; Annual campaigns; Program development; Conferences/seminars; Scholarship funds; Employee volunteer services; Employee matching gifts.
Limitations: Applications accepted. Giving primarily in Hartford, CT, Washington, DC, and Philadelphia, PA; giving also to national organizations. No support for fraternal organizations, social or political organizations, faith-based organizations not of direct of the entire community, or discriminatory groups. No grants to individuals, or for capital campaigns, or discriminatory projects.
Publications: Application guidelines; Annual report; Corporate giving report (including application guidelines).
Application information: Support is generally limited to 1 contribution per organization during any given year. Support for capital campaigns is extremely selective. Application form required.
Initial approach: Complete online application form
Deadline(s): None, but Oct. 15 is encouraged
Board meeting date(s): Biannually
Final notification: All funds distributed on an annual basis by Nov. 30
Officers and Directors:* John M. Murabito,* Chair.; Margaret M. Fitzpatrick,* Pres.; Thomas A. McCarthy, V.P.; David Figliuzzi, Exec. Dir.; David M. Cordani.
EIN: 236261726

7982
Claneil Foundation, Inc. ✧
2250 Hickory Rd., Ste. 450
Plymouth Meeting, PA 19462-1074 (610) 941-1131
Contact: Mailee Walker, Exec. Dir.
FAX: (610) 828-6405; For questions about Letter of Intent process or online application system, contact Karen Race, Grants Mgr. and Exec. Asst., tel.: (610) 941-1143; Main URL: http://www.claneil.org

Incorporated in 1968 in DE.
Donors: Henry S. McNeil†; Claneil Enterprises, Inc.
Foundation type: Independent foundation.
Financial data (yr. ended 12/31/12): Assets, $62,657,909 (M); expenditures, $3,265,741; qualifying distributions, $3,221,780; giving activities include $3,221,720 for 167 grants (high: $350,000; low: $1,500).
Purpose and activities: Giving to create healthy communities by supporting organizations that make a difference in the lives of individuals, families and the institutions that support them, and to develop an informed, educated and engaged citizenry, and increase the understanding and appreciation of natural, built and cultural assets.

Fields of interest: Visual arts; Performing arts; Historic preservation/historical societies; Arts; Education, early childhood education; Secondary school/education; Environment, natural resources; Environment, beautification programs; Environment; Reproductive health, family planning; Health care; Crime/violence prevention, domestic violence; Crime/violence prevention, child abuse; Housing/shelter; Youth development; Human services; Family services; Civil liberties, reproductive rights; Community/economic development; Women; Economically disadvantaged.
Type of support: General/operating support; Continuing support; Management development/capacity building; Capital campaigns; Building/renovation; Equipment; Land acquisition; Endowments; Program development; Conferences/seminars; Publication; Seed money; Curriculum development; Scholarship funds; Research; Technical assistance; Consulting services; Program evaluation; Matching/challenge support.
Limitations: Applications accepted. Giving primarily in southeastern PA, with emphasis on Chester, Delaware, Montgomery and Philadelphia counties. No support for religion-based programming. No grants to individuals.
Publications: Application guidelines; Informational brochure (including application guidelines).
Application information: Under the Community Grant Program, organizations that received funding in the past 3 years may submit a grant proposal without a letter of intent. The Emerging Leaders Fund and the Proactive Grant Program are invitation-only grant programs, unsolicited inquiries are not accepted in these areas. Only electronic submissions are accepted. See foundation web site for additional information. Application form required.
Initial approach: Letter of intent via online application system on foundation web site only
Copies of proposal: 1
Deadline(s): For Letters of Intent: June 30 (for fall cycle), and Dec. 1 (for spring cycle). Special Project Fund letters are accepted for consideration in the spring cycle only
Board meeting date(s): Nov. and June
Officers and Directors:* Marjorie M. Findlay, Chair.; Gretchen Menzies, Vice-Chair.; Jennifer McNeil, Secy.; Langhorne B. Smith,* Treas.; Mailee Walker, Exec. Dir.; Hathaway F. Jade; Geoffrey T. Freeman; Barbara M. Jordan; Duncan McFarland; Robert D. McNeil.
Number of staff: 1 full-time professional; 1 full-time support.
EIN: 236445450

7983
The Anne L. and George H. Clapp Charitable and Educational Trust ✧
c/o BNY Mellon, N.A.
P.O. Box 185
Pittsburgh, PA 15230-0185 (412) 234-1634
Contact: Annette Calgaro

Established in 1949.
Donor: George H. Clapp†.
Foundation type: Independent foundation.
Financial data (yr. ended 09/30/13): Assets, $18,455,699 (M); expenditures, $1,005,257; qualifying distributions, $894,928; giving activities include $827,480 for 88 grants (high: $25,000; low: $2,000).
Purpose and activities: Primary areas of interest include child welfare, education, social services, and community funds; limited support for arts and conservation.
Fields of interest: Arts; Education; Human services; Children/youth; Aging; Economically disadvantaged.
Type of support: General/operating support; Continuing support; Annual campaigns; Capital campaigns; Building/renovation; Endowments; Matching/challenge support.
Limitations: Applications accepted. Giving limited to southwestern PA, Richmond, VA, and southwestern NC. No grants to individuals, or for sponsorship of events or trips.
Publications: Application guidelines; Grants list.
Application information: Most grants range from $5,000-$10,000. Application form not required.
Initial approach: Proposal
Copies of proposal: 3
Deadline(s): None
Board meeting date(s): Early Sept.
Final notification: Sept.
Trustees: William Collin; Galbreath Hubbard; BNY Mellon, N.A.
EIN: 256018976

7984
The Clayman Family Foundation ✧ ☆
1 Presidential Blvd., Ste. 200
Bala Cynwyd, PA 19004-1007

Established in 1997 in PA.
Foundation type: Independent foundation.
Financial data (yr. ended 12/31/13): Assets, $10,479,282 (M); expenditures, $648,658; qualifying distributions, $635,528; giving activities include $501,161 for 76 grants (high: $100,000; low: $25).
Fields of interest: Higher education; Education; Health organizations, association; Crime/law enforcement, police agencies; Human services; Children, services; International affairs; Jewish federated giving programs; Christian agencies & churches; Catholic agencies & churches; Jewish agencies & synagogues.
Limitations: Applications not accepted. Giving primarily in NJ and PA. No grants to individuals.
Application information: Contributes only to pre-selected organizations.
Officer and Directors:* David M. Cohen,* Treas.; Bradford Clayman; Deborah Clayman; Roberta Clayman; Stephen A. Cohen.
EIN: 232893816
Selected grants: The following grants are a representative sample of this grantmaker's funding activity:
$25,000 to Lankenau Hospital Foundation, Wynnewood, PA, 2012. For Registered 501 (c) (3) Organization, Funding the Vascular Cardiology Fellow.
$10,000 to University of Nebraska Foundation, Omaha, NE, 2012. For Registered 501 (c) (3) Organization, To Be used for Lymphoma research.
$5,000 to Prostate Cancer Foundation, Santa Monica, CA, 2012. For Philadelphia Fundraiser, Registered 501 (c) (3) Organization.
$3,000 to Treatment Research Institute, Philadelphia, PA, 2012. For Registered 501 (c) (3) Organization, General Operating Expenses.
$2,000 to Aish Tamid of Los Angeles, Los Angeles, CA, 2012. For Registered 501 (c) (3) Organization.
$2,000 to Jewish Federation of Greater Philadelphia, Philadelphia, PA, 2012. For Account No. 2078575, Registered 501(c)(3) Organization.
$1,800 to Kellman Brown Academy, Voorhees, NJ, 2012. For Registered 501 (c) (3) Organization/half page ad in Tribute Book.

7985
The Cochran Family Foundation ✧
c/o Glenmede Trust Co., N.A.
1650 Market St., Ste. 1200
Philadelphia, PA 19103-7391

Established in 1998 in DE.
Donor: John R. Cochran III.
Foundation type: Independent foundation.
Financial data (yr. ended 12/31/13): Assets, $10,846,073 (M); gifts received, $500,000; expenditures, $1,829,078; qualifying distributions, $1,788,025; giving activities include $1,788,000 for 28 grants (high: $500,000; low: $2,500).
Purpose and activities: Giving primarily for education, with some emphasis on Roman Catholic education.
Fields of interest: Elementary/secondary education; Higher education; Education; Health care; Youth development; Human services; Catholic federated giving programs.
Limitations: Applications not accepted. Giving primarily in DE and MD. No grants to individuals.
Application information: Contributes only to pre-selected organizations.
Officers: John R. Cochran III, Pres.; Patricia A. Cochran, V.P.
EIN: 522084405
Selected grants: The following grants are a representative sample of this grantmaker's funding activity:
$5,000 to YMCA of Delaware, Wilmington, DE, 2012. For the Water Wise Program.

7986
Colcom Foundation
2 Gateway Ctr., Ste. 1800
Pittsburgh, PA 15222-1442
Contact: John F. Rohe, V.P., Philanthropy
FAX: (412) 765-2407;
E-mail: contact@colcomfdn.org; Main URL: http://www.colcomfdn.org/

Established in 1996 in PA.
Donor: Cordelia S. May†.
Foundation type: Independent foundation.
Financial data (yr. ended 06/30/13): Assets, $493,698,213 (M); gifts received, $30,219; expenditures, $27,637,262; qualifying distributions, $24,006,067; giving activities include $22,790,788 for 186 grants (high: $2,235,000; low: $5,000).
Purpose and activities: The primary mission of the foundation is to foster a sustainable environment to ensure quality of life for all Americans by addressing major causes and consequences of overpopulation and its adverse effects on natural resources. Regionally, the foundation supports conservation and environmental projects and cultural assets.
Fields of interest: Environment, administration/regulation; Environment, beautification programs; Environment; Recreation; Community/economic development; Population studies.
Type of support: General/operating support; Continuing support; Management development/capacity building; Annual campaigns; Capital campaigns; Equipment; Land acquisition;

Endowments; Program development; Seed money; Research; Technical assistance; Program evaluation; Matching/challenge support.
Limitations: Giving nationally in the areas of population and immigration, regionally (southwestern PA) for the environment and conservation, and locally (Pittsburgh, PA) for community and economic development. No grants to individuals, or for scholarships; no loans.
Publications: Application guidelines; Annual report; Financial statement; Grants list; Informational brochure.
Application information: Grant applications are not accepted unless in response to an invitation following a letter of inquiry. See web site for additional application information. Application form required.
Initial approach: Letter of inquiry not exceeding 2 pages
Copies of proposal: 1
Deadline(s): Varies
Board meeting date(s): Feb., May, Aug. and Nov.
Final notification: Up to 4 months
Officers and Directors:* Timothy M. Inglis,* Pres. and Treas.; John F. Rohe, V.P., Philanthropy and Secy.; John S. Barsotti,* V.P., Investments; Donna M. Panazzi; Michael M. Strueber.
Number of staff: 2 full-time professional; 1 full-time support.
EIN: 311479839
Selected grants: The following grants are a representative sample of this grantmaker's funding activity:
$2,300,000 to Federation for American Immigration Reform, Washington, DC, 2012. For public education on the causes and effects of overpopulation.
$2,235,000 to NumbersUSA Education and Research Foundation, Arlington, VA, 2012. For public education on the relationship between immigration and quality of life.
$1,300,000 to Center for Immigration Studies, Washington, DC, 2012. For research and public education on immigration.
$825,000 to US, Social Contract Press (U.S. Inc.), Petoskey, MI, 2012. For public education on the source of domestic population increase and the effect on natural resources, wages, education, infrastructure and taxes.
$700,000 to West Virginia University Foundation, West Virginia Water Research Institute, Morgantown, WV, 2012. For comprehensive multi-basin water quality monitoring network.
$500,000 to Western Pennsylvania Conservancy, Pittsburgh, PA, 2012. To protect and restore key Western Pennsylvania watersheds through direct implementation of conservation practices.
$442,200 to Carnegie Mellon University, Pittsburgh, PA, 2012. For doctoral fellowships on environmental carrying capacity.
$405,000 to Pennsylvania State University, University Park, PA, 2012. For documentary to raise public awareness of green infrastructure strategies for managing water.
$150,000 to Californians for Population Stabilization, Santa Barbara, CA, 2012. For public education on the causes and consequence of overpopulation.
$100,000 to Phipps Conservatory and Botanical Gardens, Pittsburgh, PA, 2012. For Laminar Flow Fountain.

7987
Ethel D. Colket Foundation ✧
c/o PNC Bank, N.A.
620 Liberty Ave., 10th Fl.
Pittsburgh, PA 15222-2723
Contact: Kirsten Cataldi
Application address: c/o PNC Bank, 1600 Market St., F2-F070-07-1, Philadelphia, PA 19103, tel.: (215) 585-4419

Established in 1964 in PA.
Donor: Tristram C. Colket, Jr.
Foundation type: Independent foundation.
Financial data (yr. ended 08/31/13): Assets, $4,657,709 (M); expenditures, $1,118,198; qualifying distributions, $1,094,982; giving activities include $1,094,982 for 139 grants (high: $371,189; low: $100).
Purpose and activities: Giving primarily for the arts, including an art museum, education, and to hospitals, including a children's hospital.
Fields of interest: Museums; Performing arts; Arts; Elementary/secondary education; Higher education; Hospitals (general); Hospitals (specialty); Human services.
Type of support: General/operating support; Building/renovation; Program development.
Limitations: Applications accepted. Giving primarily the Delaware Valley, PA, area; support also in ME. No grants to individuals; no loans.
Application information:
Initial approach: Letter
Copies of proposal: 1
Deadline(s): None
Board meeting date(s): Spring
Trustees: Bryan D. Colket; Tristram C. Colket, Jr.; Carolyn Colket Cullen; PNC Bank, N.A.
Number of staff: 2 part-time support.
EIN: 236292917
Selected grants: The following grants are a representative sample of this grantmaker's funding activity:
$75,046 to Philadelphia Museum of Art, Philadelphia, PA, 2011.
$50,007 to Childrens Hospital of Philadelphia, Philadelphia, PA, 2011.
$25,000 to Atlantic Salmon Federation, Brunswick, ME, 2011. For general use of the organization.
$20,044 to Maine Sea Coast Missionary Society, Bar Harbor, ME, 2011. For general use of the organization.
$15,016 to University of Pennsylvania, School of Nursing, Philadelphia, PA, 2011.
$12,500 to Schoodic Education and Research Center Institute, Winter Harbor, ME, 2011. For general use of the organization.
$5,028 to Zoological Society of Philadelphia, Philadelphia, PA, 2011. For general use of the organization.
$5,000 to Mount Desert Island Hospital, Bar Harbor, ME, 2011. For general use of the organization.
$2,800 to Philadelphia Museum of Art, Philadelphia, PA, 2011. For general use of the organization.
$2,000 to Roanoke College, Salem, VA, 2011. For general use of the organization.

7988
Colonial Oaks Foundation ✧
850 N. Wyomissing Blvd., Ste. 200
Wyomissing, PA 19610-1752 (610) 988-2400
Contact: Virginia T. Rush

Established in 1992 in PA.
Donors: Terrence J. McGlinn, Sr.; Christine M. Auman; John F. McGlinn; Margaret M. Shields.
Foundation type: Independent foundation.
Financial data (yr. ended 09/30/13): Assets, $19,610,859 (M); expenditures, $972,722; qualifying distributions, $950,000; giving activities include $950,000 for 50 grants (high: $111,000; low: $500).
Fields of interest: Education; Youth development; Human services.
Type of support: General/operating support; Continuing support; Annual campaigns; Capital campaigns; Building/renovation; Emergency funds; Program development.
Limitations: Applications accepted. Giving primarily in Berks County, PA. No grants to individuals.
Application information: Application form required.
Initial approach: Letter
Copies of proposal: 1
Deadline(s): None
Officers: Terrence J. McGlinn, Sr., Chair.; Barbara T. McGlinn, Vice-Chair.; Kristin E. McGlinn, Pres.; Margaret M. Shields, Secy.; John F. McGlinn II, Treas.
Number of staff: 1 part-time professional.
EIN: 232705277

7989
The Comcast Foundation ✧
1 Comcast Ctr., 48th Fl.
Philadelphia, PA 19103-2838 (215) 286-1700
Contact: William D. Black, V.P. and Exec. Dir.
E-mail for Leaders and Achievers Scholarships: comcast@applyists.com; Main URL: http://www.comcast.com/corporate/about/inthecommunity/foundation/comcastfoundation.html
ComcastVoices: http://corporate.comcast.com/comcast-voices?category=community-investment
Facebook: https://www.facebook.com/WePowerDreams
Leaders and Achievers Scholarship Program on Facebook: http://www.facebook.com/ComcastLeadersandAchievers?ref=mf
Twitter: https://twitter.com/comcastdreambig

Established in 1999 in DE.
Donors: Comcast CICG, LP; Comcast QVC, Inc.; MOC Holdco II, Inc.
Foundation type: Company-sponsored foundation.
Financial data (yr. ended 12/31/12): Assets, $4,508,591 (M); expenditures, $16,196,745; qualifying distributions, $16,170,519; giving activities include $14,228,519 for 1,202 grants (high: $525,000; low: $250), and $1,942,000 for 1,790 grants to individuals (high: $10,000; low: $1,000).
Purpose and activities: The foundation supports programs designed to expand digital literacy; promote community service; and build tomorrow's leaders; and awards college scholarships to high school seniors.
Fields of interest: Education, reading; Education, computer literacy/technology training; Education, e-learning; Education; Employment, training; Boys & girls clubs; Big Brothers/Big Sisters; Youth development, services; YM/YWCAs & YM/YWHAs; Children/youth, services; Voluntarism promotion; United Ways and Federated Giving Programs; Computer science; Military/veterans' organizations; Leadership development; Economically disadvantaged.

Type of support: General/operating support; Continuing support; Program development; Conferences/seminars; Publication; Scholarship funds; Employee volunteer services; Sponsorships; Scholarships—to individuals.
Limitations: Applications accepted. Giving on a national basis in areas of company operations, with emphasis on CA, MA, and PA. No support for discriminatory organizations, donor-advised funds, private foundations, political candidates or organizations, or Type III Non-Supporting organizations as defined by the IRS. No grants to individuals (except for scholarships), or for marketing sponsorships, sporting events, trips or tours, capital campaigns, endowments, research studies, or lobbying campaigns.
Publications: Application guidelines.
Application information: Contributes only to individuals nominated by high school principals for scholarships. Unsolicited applications for grants or sponsorships are not accepted. Local Comcast systems and employees identify non-profit organizations as potential grant recipients. Application form required.
Initial approach: Principals should e-mail foundation to verify school eligibility status and request nomination form for scholarships
Deadline(s): Dec. 7 for Comcast Leaders and Achievers Scholarship Program
Officers and Directors:* David L. Cohen,* Co-Chair.; Ralph J. Roberts,* Co-Chair.; Charisse Lillie, Pres.; Kristine A. Dankenbrink,* Sr. V.P. and Secy.; Joseph F. Ditrolio,* Sr. V.P. and Treas.; Tracy J. Baumgartner, Sr. V.P.; William E. Dordelman, Sr. V.P.; William D. Black, V.P. and Exec Dir.; Frederick J. Maahs, V.P.; Dave R. Breidinger; Julian A. Brodsky; Kevin M. Casey; William Connors; Elizabeth A. Colleton; Thomas J. Donnelly; A. Melissa Maxfield; Adam L. Miller; David A. Scott; Steven A. White.
EIN: 510390132
Selected grants: The following grants are a representative sample of this grantmaker's funding activity:
$525,000 to City Year, Boston, MA, 2012. For Comcast HQ Commitment to City Year.
$385,000 to National Council of La Raza, Washington, DC, 2012. For NCLR's affiliate Networks.
$385,000 to United Way of Greater Philadelphia and Southern New Jersey, Philadelphia, PA, 2012. For Employee Campaign.
$285,750 to Barnes Foundation, Philadelphia, PA, 2012. For naming rights fee indicated in our partnership agreement.
$250,000 to Urban League, National, New York, NY, 2012. For operating support.
$200,000 to Boys and Girls Clubs of America, National Headquarters, Atlanta, GA, 2012. For Matching grants and trainings for the Powered by Club Tech sites.
$15,000 to Urban League of Middle Tennessee, Nashville, TN, 2012. For National Partner Grant NULITES and Project Ready Initiative.
$13,000 to Boys and Girls Clubs of King County, Seattle, WA, 2012. For Comcast Digital Connectors 2012 2013.
$10,000 to Big Brothers Big Sisters of Mississippi, Jackson, MS, 2012. For National Partner Grant General Mentoring Program.
$4,871 to United Way of Miami-Dade, Miami, FL, 2012. For Employee Campaign.

7990
The Community Foundation for the Alleghenies ✧

(also known as The Community Foundation of Greater Johnstown)
116 Market St., Ste. 4
Johnstown, PA 15901-1644 (814) 536-7741
Contact: Michael Kane, Pres.
FAX: (814) 536-5859;
E-mail: info@cfalleghenies.org; Main URL: http://www.cfalleghenies.org
Facebook: http://www.facebook.com/pages/Johnstown-PA/Community-Foundation-for-the-Alleghenies/369858724479?ref=search

Established in 1990 in PA.
Foundation type: Community foundation.
Financial data (yr. ended 06/30/13): Assets, $54,986,653 (M); gifts received, $4,328,398; expenditures, $7,932,893; giving activities include $3,767,341 for grants.
Purpose and activities: The foundation seeks to obtain permanent endowments to provide benefits to individuals and organizations located in Bedford, Cambria, Indiana and Somerset counties, PA.
Fields of interest: Humanities; Arts; Education; Environment, natural resources; Health care; Health organizations, association; Disasters, Hurricane Katrina; Children/youth, services; Human services; Community/economic development; Public affairs; Religion; Children/youth.
Type of support: Continuing support; Equipment; Program development; Program-related investments/loans; Scholarships—to individuals.
Limitations: Applications accepted. Giving primarily in Bedford, Cambria, Indiana and Somerset counties, PA.
Publications: Annual report; Annual report (including application guidelines); Grants list; Informational brochure; Newsletter.
Application information: Visit foundation Web site for application form and guidelines; accepts Grantmakers of Western Pennsylvania Common Grant Application Format. Application form required.
Initial approach: Submit application form and attachments
Copies of proposal: 2
Deadline(s): Last Fri. in Jan. and last Fri. in Aug.
Board meeting date(s): Every 2 months
Final notification: Mid-Apr. and Mid-Nov.
Officers and Directors:* Mark E. Pasquerilla,* Chair.; Michael Kane,* Pres. and Exec. Dir.; Gary C. Horner, Esq.,* Secy.; Terry K. Dunkle,* Treas.; Robert Allen, Exec. Dir., Emeritus; Michelle Beener; John Blackburn III; Allan Cashaw; Lori Copley; Raymond DiBattista; Robert J. Eyer; Hon. Linda Rovder Fleming; Daniel Glosser; William L. Glosser, Esq.; Jerry Hudson; Sue Kiniry; John M. Kriak; Richard H. Mayer; Robin Quillon; Bill Rice; Michael Sahlaney, Esq.; Sara Ann Sargent; Thomas C. Slater; Rev. Robert Swanson; Michelle Tokarsky, Esq.; Dr. Donato Zucco.
Number of staff: 3 full-time professional; 1 part-time professional; 1 full-time support; 1 part-time support.
EIN: 251637373

7991
Community Foundation of Fayette County ✧

2 W. Main St., Ste. 101
Uniontown, PA 15401-3450 (724) 437-8600
FAX: (724) 438-3856;
E-mail: cpascoe@cffayettepa.org; Main URL: http://cffayettepa.org
Facebook: https://www.facebook.com/pages/The-Community-Foundation-of-Fayette-County/126870187383560

Established in 1999 in PA.
Donor: Emmanuel Osagie, Ph.D.†.
Foundation type: Community foundation.
Financial data (yr. ended 12/31/12): Assets, $11,747,461 (M); gifts received, $1,414,638; expenditures, $1,496,225; giving activities include $1,202,238 for 24+ grants (high: $53,902).
Purpose and activities: The foundation helps define charitable needs, connects donors with causes that matters to them, supports nonprofit organizations, and invests charitable assets to make the community a better place to live.
Fields of interest: Historic preservation/historical societies; Arts; Education; Environment; Health care; Health organizations, association; Human services; Economic development; Economic development, visitors/convention bureau/tourism promotion; Community/economic development.
Type of support: Annual campaigns; Capital campaigns; Building/renovation; Equipment; Emergency funds; Program development; Scholarship funds; Technical assistance; Scholarships—to individuals.
Limitations: Applications accepted. Giving limited to the Fayette County, PA, area.
Publications: Application guidelines; Annual report; Grants list; Informational brochure; Newsletter.
Application information: Visit foundation web site for summary request form and application guidelines. Based on information provided in the letter, selected organizations may be requested additional information that could assist in making a decision. Grantmakers of Western Pennsylvania's Common Grant Application Format accepted. Application form required.
Initial approach: Letter (2 to 3 pages)
Copies of proposal: 1
Deadline(s): Feb. 28
Board meeting date(s): Jan., Apr., July, and Oct.
Officers and Directors:* James R. Foutz,* Chair.; W. David Kerr,* Vice-Chair.; Beth Casteel,* Secy.; Clara L. Pacoe, Exec. Dir.; David M. Callahan,* Treas.; Robin Bubarth; J.D. Ewing; Joseph F. Ferens, Esq.; Dan Gearing; David R. Hughes; Joy Huston; Philip S. Rishel; Ron Sheba; John A. Sunyecz, M.D.; Joshua Swimmer; Lynda S. Waggoner.
Number of staff: 2 full-time professional; 1 part-time professional.
EIN: 251851158

7992
Community Foundation of the Endless Mountains ✧
(formerly Community Foundation of Susquehanna and Wyoming Counties)
270 Lake Ave.
Montrose, PA 18801 (570) 278-3800
FAX: (570) 278-9608;
E-mail: info@community-foundation.org; Main URL: http://www.community-foundation.org/
E-Newsletter: http://community-foundation.us4.list-manage.com/subscribe?u=a6cbebdfaba538090f4095795&id=bd51de6879
Facebook: https://www.facebook.com/CommunityFDN?ref=hl
Twitter: https://twitter.com/CommunityFDN

Established in 1998 in PA.
Foundation type: Community foundation.
Financial data (yr. ended 12/31/13): Assets, $8,895,216 (M); gifts received, $1,845,256; expenditures, $2,970,001; giving activities include $2,717,490 for grants to individuals.
Purpose and activities: The foundation assists donors in their long-range plans for the support of their favorite charities.
Fields of interest: Education; Community/economic development.
Type of support: Program development; Scholarships—to individuals.
Publications: Newsletter.
Officers and Directors: Earle Wootton,* Chair.; Peter Quigg,* Pres.; Sandra Boyle; Robert Brown; Maggie Cartwright; Thomas Chamberlain; Karl Kail IV; Jason Legg; William Lewis; Richard Lochen, Jr.; Rep. Sandra Major; Robert McNamara; Marian S. Miskell; Dr. Arthur Sherwood; Matthew Sordoni; George Stark.
EIN: 300011355

7993
Community Foundation of Warren County ✧
(formerly The Warren Foundation)
213 W. 3rd Ave.
P.O. Box 691
Warren, PA 16365-0691 (814) 726-9553
Contact: Charles E. MacKenzie M.D., Exec. Dir.
FAX: (814) 726-7099; E-mail: cfwc@westpa.net; Additional e-mail: info@communityfoundationofwarrencounty.org; Main URL: http://www.communityfoundationofwarrencounty.org
Alternate URL: http://www.warrenfoundationpa.org
Facebook: https://www.facebook.com/pages/Community-Foundation-of-Warren-County/212716675445171?sk=wall

Established in 1949 in PA by declaration of trust.
Foundation type: Community foundation.
Financial data (yr. ended 12/31/12): Assets, $59,568,829 (M); gifts received, $2,894,878; expenditures, $2,737,681; giving activities include $1,470,433 for grants, and $855,319 for grants to individuals.
Purpose and activities: The foundation seeks to promote the well-being of local inhabitants. The use of the bulk of funds has been designated by the donors, with distributions for child welfare, church building maintenance, community funds, scholarships, and delinquency and crime prevention.
Fields of interest: Crime/law enforcement; Children/youth, services; United Ways and Federated Giving Programs; Protestant agencies & churches.
Type of support: Program development; Matching/challenge support; Equipment; Building/renovation; Continuing support; Capital campaigns; Employee-related scholarships; Scholarships—to individuals.
Limitations: Applications accepted. Giving limited to Warren County, PA (except for Donor-Advised funds). No support for religious purposes (unless specified by a donor). No grants to individuals (except for scholarships), or for administrative expenses or endowment funds.
Publications: Annual report.
Application information: Visit foundation web site for application form and guidelines. Application form required.
Initial approach: Submit application form
Copies of proposal: 1
Deadline(s): None
Board meeting date(s): Monthly
Final notification: 1 to 2 months
Officers and Trustees:* John O. Hanna,* Chair.; Charles E. MacKenzie, M.D., Exec. Dir.; Robert Crowley; Bernard J. Hessley; John Lasher; Murray K. McComas; Ellen Paquette; Barbara Tubbs.
Trustee Banks: BNY Mellon, N.A.; Northwest Savings Bank; PNC Bank, N.A.
Number of staff: 1 part-time professional; 1 full-time support.
EIN: 251380549

7994
Community Foundation of Western Pennsylvania and Eastern Ohio ✧
(formerly Shenango Valley Foundation)
7 W. State St.
Sharon, PA 16146-2713 (724) 981-5882
Contact: Lawrence E. Haynes, Exec. Dir.; For grants: Amy Atkinson, Assoc. Dir.
FAX: (724) 983-9044;
E-mail: info@comm-foundation.com; Additional tel.: (866) 901-7204; Grant inquiry e-mail: amy@comm-foundation.org; Main URL: http://comm-foundation.org/
Facebook: https://www.facebook.com/TCFWPEO
YouTube: http://www.youtube.com/user/tcfwpeo?feature=watch

Established in PA in 1981.
Donors: Paul O'Brien; Tina O'Brien.
Foundation type: Community foundation.
Financial data (yr. ended 12/31/12): Assets, $51,748,231 (M); gifts received, $9,066,461; expenditures, $4,411,730; giving activities include $2,350,183 for 59+ grants (high: $100,000), and $847,543 for 791 grants to individuals.
Purpose and activities: The foundation is a public, non-profit charitable organization designed to attract and invest permanent endowment resources, with the purpose of enhancing the quality of life for the residents of western Pennsylvania and eastern Ohio, in accordance with the charitable intentions of its donors who wish to leave a legacy. To fulfill this mission, the foundation will: 1) identify and support community-based charitable purposes in the areas of health, education, economic development, human services, historical, cultural and environmental activities; 2) help to shape responses to community needs through philanthropic leadership, commitment, and compassion; and 3) demonstrate accountability and integrity in the management of resources.
Fields of interest: Education, early childhood education; Higher education; Medical care, rehabilitation; Employment; Food services; Homeless, human services; Community/economic development; Aging; Disabilities, people with; Economically disadvantaged.
Type of support: General/operating support; Building/renovation; Equipment; Emergency funds; Program development; Curriculum development; Scholarship funds; Employee-related scholarships; Grants to individuals; Scholarships—to individuals; Matching/challenge support; Student loans—to individuals.
Limitations: Applications accepted. Giving limited to the Shenango Valley area, including Trumbull and Mahoning counties, OH, and Mercer and Lawrence counties, PA. No support for sectarian religious activities or fire departments. No grants for program ads, fundraising events, more than half the cost of a vehicle, start-up organizations, school playgrounds, endowments, field trips, internships, or indirect costs.
Publications: Application guidelines; Annual report; Informational brochure.
Application information: Visit foundation web site for application information. The foundation will request full proposals based on letters of inquiry. Application form required.
Initial approach: Letter of inquiry
Copies of proposal: 1
Deadline(s): None
Board meeting date(s): Quarterly
Officers and Directors:* James A. O'Brien, Esq.,* Pres.; Karen Winner Sed,* V.P.; Ronald R. Anderson,* Secy.; James E. Feeney,* Treas.; Shelly R. Mason, C.F.O.; Lawrence E. Haynes, Exec. Dir.; Robert C. Jazwinski, Dir. Emeritus; Mel Grata; Paul E. O'Brien; Albert R. Puntureri; William J. Strimbu; James T. Weller, Sr.; Donna Winner.
Number of staff: 1 full-time professional; 2 part-time professional.
EIN: 251407396

7995
Connelly Foundation ✧
100 Front St.
1 Tower Bridge, Ste. 1450
West Conshohocken, PA 19428-2873 (610) 834-3222
Contact: E. Ann Wilcox, Assoc. V.P., Admin.
FAX: (610) 834-0866; E-mail: info@connellyfdn.org; Main URL: http://www.connellyfdn.org
Grants Database: http://www.connellyfdn.org/searchgrants.aspx

Incorporated in 1955 in PA.
Donors: John F. Connelly†; Josephine C. Connelly†.
Foundation type: Independent foundation.
Financial data (yr. ended 12/31/12): Assets, $223,101,276 (M); gifts received, $98,863; expenditures, $17,072,600; qualifying distributions, $10,915,696; giving activities include $9,199,737 for 552 grants (high: $750,000; low: $100).
Purpose and activities: The foundation seeks to foster learning and to improve the quality of life in the Greater Philadelphia area. The foundation supports local non-profit organizations in the fields

of education, health and human services, arts and culture, and civic enterprise.
Fields of interest: Arts; Elementary/secondary education; Education, early childhood education; Child development, education; Elementary school/education; Secondary school/education; Higher education; Adult/continuing education; Education; Health care; Substance abuse, services; Alcoholism; Employment, training; Youth development, citizenship; Human services; Children/youth, services; Child development, services; Aging, centers/services; Women, centers/services; Homeless, human services; Community/economic development; Protestant agencies & churches; Catholic agencies & churches; Infants/toddlers; Children/youth; Children; Youth; Adults; Aging; Young adults; Disabilities, people with; Physically disabled; Blind/visually impaired; Deaf/hearing impaired; Mentally disabled; Minorities; Hispanics/Latinos; Women; Girls; Immigrants/refugees; Economically disadvantaged; Homeless.
Type of support: Technical assistance; General/operating support; Continuing support; Capital campaigns; Building/renovation; Equipment; Program development; Scholarship funds; Employee matching gifts; Matching/challenge support.
Limitations: Applications accepted. Giving in Philadelphia, and surrounding counties of Bucks, Chester, Delaware and Montgomery, PA, and in Camden, NJ. No support for political or national organizations, or for public or charter schools, environmental programs, re-granting organizations, or for national organizations focused on a single disease. No grants to individuals, or for research, annual appeals advocacy, conferences, feasibility or planning studies, general solicitations, or for historic preservation projects.
Publications: Application guidelines; Financial statement.
Application information: Delaware Valley Grantmakers Common Grant Application Form and the Delaware Valley Grantmakers Common Report Form accepted. To access these forms (along with two other specific application instructions) please go to the "Downloadable Forms" section of the foundation website. Application form required.
Initial approach: Proposal
Copies of proposal: 1
Deadline(s): None
Board meeting date(s): Jan., Apr., Aug., Nov.
Final notification: 3 months
Officers and Trustees:* Josephine C. Mandeville,* Chair., C.E.O., and Pres.; Victoria K. Flaville,* C.O.O. and Sr. V.P., Progs.; Emily C. Riley,* Exec. V.P.; Lewis W. Bluemle,* Sr. V.P.; Thomas A. Riley, V.P., Planning; Amy M. Snyder,* C.F.O. and Treas.; Joseph D. Frangiosa, Cont.; Ira Brind; Craig R. Carnaroli; Christine C. Connelly; Daniele M. Connelly; Stephan T. Connelly; Thomas S. Connelly; Eleanor L. Davis; Brendan Delany; Mary G. Duden; James P. Gallagher; Scott M. Jenkins; Caroline Mandeville; Amelia Q. Riley; Barbara W. Riley.
Number of staff: 6 full-time professional; 6 part-time professional; 3 full-time support; 2 part-time support.
EIN: 236296825
Selected grants: The following grants are a representative sample of this grantmaker's funding activity:
$750,000 to Archdiocese of Philadelphia, Philadelphia, PA, 2012. For Josephine C. Connelly Achievement Awards.
$506,727 to Archdiocese of Philadelphia, Philadelphia, PA, 2012. For Josephine C. Connelly Achievement Awards.
$300,000 to Mann Center for the Performing Arts, Philadelphia, PA, 2012. Toward Campaign for the Future, $150,000 in capital support toward Lawn Experience and $150,000 in operating support toward Artistic/Strategic Initiatives.
$200,000 to Childrens Hospital of Philadelphia, Philadelphia, PA, 2012. Toward renovations to the Connelly Family Resource Center to maximize space and increase efficiency. Modifications to the laundry area and kitchen space will be made to create enhanced environment for families.
$150,000 to Arden Theater Company, Philadelphia, PA, 2012. For capital support toward renovating newly purchased building into a center for arts and education that will house classrooms, shop space and a new studio theatre.
$100,000 to CORA Services, Philadelphia, PA, 2012. For capital support toward construction of daycare center supporting children ages 3-5 while offering inclusion program for children born deaf or hard of hearing. Project is in partnership with LaSalle University and Clarke School.
$10,000 to Play On, Philly, Philadelphia, PA, 2012. For music education programming at Saint Francis de Sales School and to expand the program into another school.
$6,715 to College of Physicians of Philadelphia, Philadelphia, PA, 2012. For Connelly Access Program (CAP) for 420 students to participate in a Mutter Lesson discussing a particular topic of relevance to the museum specimens and includes a museum visit.
$5,000 to West Chester Area Day Care Center, West Chester, PA, 2012. To support toward renovating the Infant/Toddler Playground to create outdoor learning environment where infants and toddlers can safely play and develop their sensory, physical and social skills.
$2,500 to Visitation Blessed Virgin Mary School, Philadelphia, PA, 2012. For general support.

7996
Harry K. Constandy, Vaseleke H. Constandy, and C. Harry Constandy Memorial Trust ✧ ☆
310 Grant St., Ste. 300
Pittsburgh, PA 15219-2201

Established in 1993 in PA.
Donor: Vaseleke H. Constandy†.
Foundation type: Independent foundation.
Financial data (yr. ended 12/31/13): Assets, $0 (M); expenditures, $712,122; qualifying distributions, $669,298; giving activities include $669,298 for 6 grants (high: $638,834; low: $3,616).
Fields of interest: Education; Religion.
Limitations: Applications not accepted. Giving primarily in PA. No grants to individuals.
Application information: Unsolicited requests for funds not accepted.
Trustee: Jack G. Armstrong.
EIN: 256397698
Selected grants: The following grants are a representative sample of this grantmaker's funding activity:
$638,834 to Pittsburgh Foundation, Pittsburgh, PA, 2013.
$7,616 to Hellenic College/Holy Cross, Brookline, MA, 2013.
$7,616 to Saint Basils Academy, Garrison, NY, 2013.
$7,616 to University of Pittsburgh, School of Dental Medicine, Pittsburgh, PA, 2013.
$3,616 to Desert Ministries, Matthews, NC, 2013.

7997
The Cooper-Siegel Family Foundation ✧
c/o BNY Mellon, N.A.
P.O. Box 185
Pittsburgh, PA 15230-0185

Established in 1996 in PA.
Donors: Eric C. Cooper; Cooper-Siegel Foundation Charitable Lead Trusts; Eric C. Cooper Charitable Lead Trust; Naomi L. Siegel Charitable Lead Trust.
Foundation type: Independent foundation.
Financial data (yr. ended 04/30/13): Assets, $2,851,008 (M); gifts received, $841,528; expenditures, $928,285; qualifying distributions, $911,000; giving activities include $911,000 for grants.
Fields of interest: Education; Health organizations; Diabetes research; Human services; Children/youth, services; Jewish federated giving programs.
Limitations: Applications not accepted. Giving primarily in Pittsburgh, PA; some giving in NY. No grants to individuals.
Application information: Contributes only to pre-selected organizations.
Trustee: E. David Margolis.
EIN: 311537177
Selected grants: The following grants are a representative sample of this grantmaker's funding activity:
$375,000 to Jewish Federation of Greater Pittsburgh, Pittsburgh, PA, 2011.
$100,000 to Juvenile Diabetes Research Foundation International, New York, NY, 2011.
$100,000 to Squirrel Hill Health Center, Pittsburgh, PA, 2011.
$25,000 to Jewish Federation of Greater Pittsburgh, Pittsburgh, PA, 2012.
$10,000 to Childrens Hospital of Pittsburgh, Pittsburgh, PA, 2012.
$5,000 to Carnegie Library of Pittsburgh, Pittsburgh, PA, 2012.
$5,000 to Childrens Institute of Pittsburgh, Pittsburgh, PA, 2012.
$5,000 to Womens Center and Shelter of Greater Pittsburgh, Pittsburgh, PA, 2012.
$1,000 to Big Brothers Big Sisters of Greater Pittsburgh, Pittsburgh, PA, 2012.
$1,000 to National Aviary in Pittsburgh, Pittsburgh, PA, 2012.

7998
Copernicus Society of America ✧ ☆
1 Reiffs Mill Rd.
Ambler, PA 19002-4280

Established in 1972 in PA.
Donors: Edward J. Piszek, Sr.†; James A. Michener†.
Foundation type: Independent foundation.
Financial data (yr. ended 06/30/13): Assets, $4,868,807 (M); gifts received, $3,262,744; expenditures, $1,968,757; qualifying distributions, $1,880,516; giving activities include $1,842,263 for 34 grants (high: $1,686,000; low: $100).

Purpose and activities: Giving primarily for the support and advancement of the Polish culture and heritage. Giving also for education and Roman Catholic organizations.
Fields of interest: Higher education, university; Education; Catholic agencies & churches.
International interests: Poland.
Type of support: Continuing support; Endowments; Conferences/seminars; Publication.
Limitations: Applications not accepted. Giving primarily in PA. No grants to individuals, or for special projects, operating budgets, annual campaigns, seed money, emergency funds, deficit financing, building funds, equipment and materials, land acquisition, matching gifts, scholarships, fellowships, or research; no loans.
Application information: Unsolicited requests for funds not accepted.
Officers: Helen P. Nelson, Pres.; Francis Keenan, V.P.; Edward J. Piszek, Jr., V.P.; George W. Piszek, V.P.; William P. Piszek, V.P.; P. Erik Nelson, Exec. Dir.
Number of staff: 1 full-time professional; 3 part-time support.
EIN: 237184731
Selected grants: The following grants are a representative sample of this grantmaker's funding activity:
$23,750 to University of Iowa Foundation, Iowa City, IA, 2011.
$20,000 to Pennsylvania State University, University Park, PA, 2011.
$19,034 to Dickinson College, Carlisle, PA, 2011.
$13,044 to Public School of Germantown, Fort Washington, PA, 2011.
$10,250 to Community Partnership School, Philadelphia, PA, 2011.
$5,500 to Rodale Institute, Kutztown, PA, 2011.
$4,200 to Kelly Anne Dolan Memorial Fund, Ambler, PA, 2011.
$3,500 to Commonwealth Youthchoirs, Philadelphia, PA, 2011.
$2,500 to Ambler Theater, Ambler, PA, 2011.
$1,200 to Center for Autism, Philadelphia, PA, 2011.

7999
The Cotswold Foundation ✧
234 Broughton Ln.
Villanova, PA 19085-1914

Established in 1994 in PA.
Donors: I. Wistar Morris III; Martha Morris; Melissa H. Morris; Lydia P. Morris; Eleanor W. Morris; Eleventh Generation, LP.
Foundation type: Independent foundation.
Financial data (yr. ended 12/31/13): Assets, $42,380,056 (M); gifts received, $230,574; expenditures, $2,014,211; qualifying distributions, $1,868,625; giving activities include $1,867,425 for 34 grants (high: $400,000; low: $25).
Fields of interest: Museums (art); Higher education; Medical research; Human services; International affairs, foreign policy; Biology/life sciences.
Type of support: General/operating support.
Limitations: Applications not accepted. Giving in the U.S., particularly in PA, with emphasis on Philadelphia. No grants to individuals.
Application information: Contributes only to pre-selected organizations.
Trustees: I. Wistar Morris III; Martha H. Morris.
EIN: 237767257

8000
The Frank L. and Sarah Miller Coulson Foundation ✧
1100 Barberry Rd.
Bryn Mawr, PA 19010-1908

Established in 2000 in PA.
Donors: Frank L. Coulson, Jr.; Sarah Miller Coulson.
Foundation type: Independent foundation.
Financial data (yr. ended 10/31/13): Assets, $10,651,608 (M); expenditures, $522,071; qualifying distributions, $449,750; giving activities include $449,750 for 30 grants (high: $200,000; low: $1,000).
Purpose and activities: Giving primarily for higher education and the performing arts; funding also for social services and animal welfare.
Fields of interest: Performing arts; Arts; Higher education; Animal welfare; Human services.
Limitations: Applications not accepted. Giving primarily in Philadelphia, PA; some funding also in MA. No grants to individuals or for scholarships; no loans.
Application information: Contributes only to pre-selected organizations.
Trustee: Sarah Miller Coulson.
EIN: 134148044
Selected grants: The following grants are a representative sample of this grantmaker's funding activity:
$265,971 to Johns Hopkins University, Baltimore, MD, 2011. For general purposes.
$265,971 to Philadelphia Orchestra Association, Philadelphia, PA, 2011. For general purposes.
$50,000 to Philadelphia Orchestra Association, Philadelphia, PA, 2011. For general charitable purposes.
$5,000 to Natural Resources Defense Council, New York, NY, 2011. For general charitable purposes.
$5,000 to Pennsylvania Ballet, Philadelphia, PA, 2011. For general charitable purposes.
$3,500 to Philadelphia Orchestra Association, Philadelphia, PA, 2011. For general charitable purposes.
$3,000 to Main Line Animal Rescue, Wayne, PA, 2011. For general charitable purposes.
$2,000 to Humane Society of the United States, Washington, DC, 2011. For general charitable purposes.
$2,000 to Kimmel Center for the Performing Arts, Philadelphia, PA, 2011. For general charitable purposes.

8001
Crawford Heritage Community Foundation ✧ ☆
911 Diamond Park
P.O. Box 933
Meadville, PA 16335 (814) 336-5206
Contact: Christian Maher, Exec. Dir.
FAX: (814) 724-1407;
E-mail: executive@crawfordheritage.org; Additional Address: 415 Chestnut Street, Meadville, PA 16335; Main URL: http://www.crawfordheritage.org
Facebook: http://www.facebook.com/pages/Crawford-Heritage-Community-Foundation/147574338611417
YouTube: http://www.youtube.com/user/crawfordheritage?feature=watch

Established in 1998 in PA.
Foundation type: Community foundation.
Financial data (yr. ended 12/31/12): Assets, $12,741,847 (M); gifts received, $1,340,275; expenditures, $578,532; giving activities include $303,700 for 22 grants (high: $19,197), and $135,484 for 120 grants to individuals.
Purpose and activities: The foundation awards discretionary grants twice yearly to assist nonprofit organizations meet the changing opportunities and needs in Crawford County, PA. Grants are made county-wide from the Crawford Heritage Community Foundation Unrestricted Fund and the Ben Franklin Trust, in the Titusville area from the Fred Lintner Fund and from the Bernadene R. and John B. Cooley Fund to benefit programs for children and youth.
Fields of interest: Media, film/video; Arts; Education; Environment, beautification programs; Environment; Health care; Agriculture; Community/economic development; Science.
Type of support: Management development/capacity building; Building/renovation; Equipment; Program development; Conferences/seminars; Publication; Curriculum development; Scholarship funds; Research; Program evaluation.
Limitations: Applications accepted. Giving limited to Crawford County, PA. No support for religious or political purposes. No grants to individuals (except for scholarships), or for annual campaigns or endowments, or for routine operating expenses (i.e., salaries, rent, and/or utilities); no loans.
Publications: Application guidelines; Annual report; Grants list; Informational brochure; Newsletter.
Application information: Visit foundation web site for online application and guidelines. Application form required.
Initial approach: Complete online application
Deadline(s): June 15 and Dec. 15
Board meeting date(s): Jan. and July
Final notification: Feb. and Aug.
Officers and Directors:* Paul L. Huber,* Pres.; Rev. Barry Cressman,* 1st V.P.; Saundra Mook,* 2nd V.P.; Milosh Mamula,* 3rd V.P.; Carl E. Terry,* Secy.; John K. Hodges,* Treas.; Christian Maher, Exec. Dir.; Dwight Haas, Dir. Emeritus; Christopher A. Junker, Esq., Dir. Emeritus; Mary Alice Kirkpatrick, Dir. Emeritus; Christine B. Lang, Dir. Emeritus; Melissa Mencotti, Dir. Emeritus; Stephen P. Mizner, Dir. Emeritus; Ken Montag, Dir. Emeritus; John Nesbitt, M.D., Dir. Emeritus; Rev. William A. Smith, Dir. Emeritus; Mark Strausbaugh, C.P.A., Dir. Emeritus; Earl Yingling, Dir. Emeritus; Robert S. Bailey; Greg Bush; Robin Ernst; Charlotte Foresther; David Gagnon; Judith Griffin; Nita Hughes; Todd Ishimaru; Jeffrey S. Lang; Ken Lindberg; Mathew L. Sampson, Esq.; Samuel Spencer; Lisa Pepicelli Youngs, Esq.
Number of staff: 5 full-time professional; 1 part-time professional; 2 part-time support.
EIN: 251813245

8002
Crels Foundation ✧
5917 Main St.
East Petersburg, PA 17520-1519 (717) 581-8130

Established in 1953 in PA.
Donor: Edwin B. Nolt†.
Foundation type: Independent foundation.
Financial data (yr. ended 12/31/13): Assets, $16,633,110 (M); expenditures, $988,773; qualifying distributions, $942,283; giving activities include $900,000 for 116 grants (high: $150,000; low: $2,000).

Purpose and activities: Support for hospitals, nursing homes, Mennonite-related religious associations, and parochial elementary education.
Fields of interest: Education; Hospitals (general); Human services; Christian agencies & churches.
Type of support: General/operating support; Capital campaigns; Building/renovation; Equipment; Debt reduction.
Limitations: Giving primarily in the Lancaster County, PA, area. No grants to individuals, or for endowment funds, research programs, scholarships, fellowships, continuing support, annual campaigns, seed money, emergency funds, land acquisition, renovation projects, publications, conferences, matching gifts, or special projects; no loans.
Application information:
Initial approach: Letter
Copies of proposal: 1
Deadline(s): Sept. 15
Officers and Trustees:* Kenneth N. Burkholder,* Chair.; J Michael Burkholder,* Vice-Chair.; Leon Ray Burkholder,* Secy.; J. Michael Melbert, Treas.; Charles N. Burkholder; Eugene N. Burkholder.
Number of staff: 1 part-time professional.
EIN: 236243577
Selected grants: The following grants are a representative sample of this grantmaker's funding activity:
$10,000 to Anabaptist Foundation, New Columbia, PA, 2012. For general support of Welfare Agencies.
$7,000 to Landis Homes Retirement Community, Lititz, PA, 2012. For general support of Medical Institutions.
$5,000 to Lancaster Bible College, Lancaster, PA, 2012. For general support of Educational Institutions.
$5,000 to Parish Resource Center, Lancaster, PA, 2012. For general support of Religious Organizations.
$1,500 to Lancaster Mennonite Historical Society, Lancaster, PA, 2012. For general support of Information Agency.

8003
The Davenport Family Foundation ✧
P.O. Box 178
Pocopson, PA 19366-9998

Established in 1997 in PA.
Donor: Peter D. Davenport.
Foundation type: Independent foundation.
Financial data (yr. ended 12/31/12): Assets, $44,908,326 (M); expenditures, $2,158,969; qualifying distributions, $1,936,046; giving activities include $1,741,873 for 16 grants (high: $568,187; low: $5,000).
Purpose and activities: Giving primarily for education and human services.
Fields of interest: Arts; Higher education; Education; Hospitals (general); Human services.
Limitations: Applications not accepted. Giving primarily in NY and PA. No grants to individuals.
Application information: Contributes only to pre-selected organizations.
Trustees: Cynthia L. Borger; Peter D. Davenport; Scott D. Davenport; Elizabeth S. Woolever.
EIN: 237871419
Selected grants: The following grants are a representative sample of this grantmaker's funding activity:
$250,000 to Kalmar Nyckel Foundation, Wilmington, DE, 2012. For Historic ship repairs and equipment Facilities.
$163,875 to Associates of the University of Toronto, New York, NY, 2012. For equipment purchases.
$100,000 to Operation Warm, Chadds Ford, PA, 2012. To purchase winter coats.
$15,500 to Delaware Museum of Natural History, Wilmington, DE, 2012. For publications.
$5,000 to Philadelphia Museum of Art, Philadelphia, PA, 2012. For Special Event Every Family Party.

8004
William and Deborah Davis Family Foundation, Inc. ✧
4 Aronwold Ln.
Newtown Square, PA 19073-1419

Donor: William Davis.
Foundation type: Independent foundation.
Financial data (yr. ended 12/31/12): Assets, $11,154,540 (M); gifts received, $17,767; expenditures, $603,340; qualifying distributions, $557,361; giving activities include $557,361 for 38 grants (high: $110,100; low: $1,000).
Purpose and activities: Giving primarily for education, including Roman Catholic education.
Fields of interest: Education; Philanthropy/voluntarism.
Limitations: Applications not accepted. Giving primarily in PA.
Application information: Contributes only to pre-selected organizations.
Officers: William Davis, Pres. and Treas.; Deborah Davis, Secy.
EIN: 261595211

8005
The Hilda and Preston Davis Foundation ✧
c/o Schnader Harrison Segal and Lewis LLP
1600 Market St., Ste. 3600
Philadelphia, PA 19103-7286 (203) 629-8552
FAX: (203) 547-6112; E-mail: davis@fsllc.net; Additional address: c/o Foundation Svcs., LLC, 640 W. Putman Ave., 3rd Fl., Greenwich, CT 06830-6008; additional e-mail: info@fsllc.net; Main URL: http://www.hpdavis.org

Established in 1998 in PA.
Donors: Hilda J. Davis†; Preston Davis†.
Foundation type: Independent foundation.
Financial data (yr. ended 12/31/13): Assets, $41,165,161 (M); expenditures, $2,397,904; qualifying distributions, $2,112,886; giving activities include $1,728,175 for 52 grants (high: $174,000; low: $580).
Purpose and activities: The foundation provides funds to charitable organizations whose programs advance the development of all areas of the lives of children and young adults. The foundation places special emphasis on, and channels most of its financial resources toward, organizations whose attention is concentrated on eating disorders and education for the underprivileged.
Fields of interest: Education; Mental health, eating disorders; Children, services.
Limitations: Giving on a national basis and in areas of geographic importance to the donors including CA, CT and PA. No support for organizations lacking 501(c)(3) status, government agencies, or organizations that subsist mainly on third party funding and have demonstrated no ability or expended little effort to attract private funding. No grants to individuals, or for general fundraising drives or endowments.
Application information: Application form available on foundation web site. Application form required.
Initial approach: Fill out on-line application form
Deadline(s): None
Trustees: John D. Iskrant; Geoffrey M. Parkinson.
EIN: 237966458
Selected grants: The following grants are a representative sample of this grantmaker's funding activity:
$76,140 to Stanford University, Stanford, CA, 2012. For Post Doctoral Fellowship in Eating Disorders.
$50,000 to National Eating Disorders Association, Seattle, WA, 2012. For Proud2bme Interactive Teen Website.
$25,000 to KIPP Philadelphia Charter School, Philadelphia, PA, 2012. For North Philadelphia Campuses.
$25,000 to Overlook Hospital Foundation, Summit, NJ, 2012. For Hungry for Health Eating Disorders Program.
$10,000 to Friends of Green Chimneys, Brewster, NY, 2012. For Science and Experiential Learning Programs.
$5,000 to Stanwich Congregational Church, Greenwich, CT, 2012. For Missions Budget.
$2,000 to General Hospital Corporation, Boston, MA, 2012. For Multi-Site Eating Disorders Program.

8006
Rebecca Davis Trust ✧ ☆
c/o PNC Bank, N.A.
P.O. Box 609
Pittsburgh, PA 15230-9738

Foundation type: Independent foundation.
Financial data (yr. ended 12/31/13): Assets, $13,549,164 (M); expenditures, $664,104; qualifying distributions, $587,398; giving activities include $538,633 for 11 grants (high: $102,340; low: $16,159).
Fields of interest: Higher education; Education; Health care; Jewish agencies & synagogues; Religion.
Limitations: Applications not accepted. Giving primarily in New York, NY.
Application information: Unsolicited requests for funds not accepted.
Trustee: PNC Bank, N.A.
EIN: 256104864

8007
Mirrel Davis Trust for Charity ✧ ☆
c/o PNC Bank, N.A.
P.O. Box 609
Pittsburgh, PA 15230-9738

Foundation type: Independent foundation.
Financial data (yr. ended 12/31/12): Assets, $9,857,947 (M); expenditures, $544,992; qualifying distributions, $490,353; giving activities include $438,505 for 11 grants (high: $83,316; low: $13,155).
Fields of interest: Education; Health care; Community/economic development; Jewish agencies & synagogues.
Limitations: Applications not accepted.

Application information: Unsolicited requests for funds not accepted.
Trustee: PNC Bank, N.A.
EIN: 256064855

8008
The 1994 Charles B. Degenstein Foundation ✧
c/o BNY Mellon, N.A.
P.O. Box 185
Pittsburgh, PA 15230-0185
Application address: 43 S. 5th St., Sunbury, PA 17801-2896, tel.: (570) 286-1582; Main URL: http://www.deg-fdn.org/

Established in 1996 in PA.
Foundation type: Independent foundation.
Financial data (yr. ended 06/30/13): Assets, $86,045,552 (M); expenditures, $6,189,601; qualifying distributions, $5,310,578; giving activities include $4,852,711 for 128 grants (high: $1,000,000; low: $500).
Purpose and activities: Special consideration is given to unique, innovative, and creative projects that benefit children, promote education, improve health care, encourage business, culture, conservation of nature resources, and protection of the environment.
Fields of interest: Arts; Libraries (public); Education; Health care; Disasters, fire prevention/control; Human services; YM/YWCAs & YM/YWHAs; Children, services; Community/economic development; United Ways and Federated Giving Programs; Christian agencies & churches.
Type of support: Capital campaigns; Equipment; Program development; Matching/challenge support.
Limitations: Applications accepted. Giving within a 75-mile radius of Sunbury, PA. No support for religious or political activities. No grants to individuals, or for scholarships, annual campaigns, endowment funds, operating budgets, emergency needs, or mass mailings; no loans.
Publications: Application guidelines.
Application information: Application form pages must be stapled with one staple in the upper left corner. Do not use notebooks, folders, or bind pages together. All information submitted to the foundation shall be on recycled paper and stapled with ease of recycling in mind. Videos, cassettes, or applications submitted by fax or e-mail are not accepted. See instructions on application form for exact number of copies which need to be submitted. Application form required.
Initial approach: 1-page cover letter along with 2-page application form which can be found on foundation web site
Deadline(s): None
Trustee: BNY Mellon, N.A.
EIN: 237792979

8009
Conway Wing Dickson and Gertrude Finck Dickson Memorial Trust ✧ ☆
c/o BNY Mellon, N.A.
P.O. Box 185
Pittsburgh, PA 15230-0185

Established in 1993; supporting organization of National Foundation for Cancer Research, The Lawrenceville School, University of Pennsylvania Law School, Arthritis Foundation, American Heart Association, Berwick Health and Wellness Foundation, First Presbyterian Church, YMCA, Wilkes-Barre General Hospital, American Red Cross, and First United Methodist Church.
Foundation type: Independent foundation.
Financial data (yr. ended 12/31/13): Assets, $8,464,428 (M); expenditures, $613,498; qualifying distributions, $580,151; giving activities include $480,006 for 9 grants (high: $53,334; low: $53,334).
Fields of interest: Law school/education; Education; Health care; Cancer research; American Red Cross; YM/YWCAs & YM/YWHAs; Christian agencies & churches.
Type of support: Research.
Limitations: Applications not accepted. Giving primarily in PA.
Application information: Contributes only to pre-selected organizations; unsolicited requests for funds not considered or acknowledged.
Trustee: BNY Mellon, N.A.
EIN: 236992853
Selected grants: The following grants are a representative sample of this grantmaker's funding activity:
$36,636 to University of Pennsylvania, Law School, Philadelphia, PA, 2012. For general operating purposes.

8010
William B. Dietrich Foundation ✧
30 S. 17th St.
Philadelphia, PA 19103-4001
Application address: c/o Frank G. Cooper, P.O. Box 58177, Philadelphia, PA 19102-8177, tel.: (215) 979-1000

Established in PA.
Donors: William B. Dietrich†; William B. Dietrich Charitable Lead Annuity Trust; William B. Dietrich Trust No. 1.
Foundation type: Independent foundation.
Financial data (yr. ended 12/31/13): Assets, $38,034,880 (M); gifts received, $3,531,047; expenditures, $1,498,554; qualifying distributions, $1,332,874; giving activities include $1,153,500 for 15 grants (high: $290,000; low: $5,000).
Fields of interest: Museums (art); Human services; Community/economic development.
Limitations: Applications accepted. Giving primarily in Philadelphia, PA.
Application information: Application form required.
Initial approach: Letter
Deadline(s): None
Officers: Frank G. Cooper, Esq., Pres. and Treas.; John J. Soroko, Esq., Secy.
EIN: 900628306
Selected grants: The following grants are a representative sample of this grantmaker's funding activity:
$232,500 to Philadelphia Museum of Art, Philadelphia, PA, 2012. For Rodin Museum Restoration.
$225,000 to Philadelphia Museum of Art, Philadelphia, PA, 2012. For Cedar Grove Restoration.
$150,000 to Barnes Foundation, Philadelphia, PA, 2012. For Installation of Clerestory Windows.
$12,500 to Philadelphia Museum of Art, Philadelphia, PA, 2012. For special exhibit.
$10,000 to Main Line Art Center, Haverford, PA, 2012. For contribution to ART 75 Campaign.

8011
Sidciyo Jaamac Suldaan Diiriye Foundation, Inc. ✧ ☆
855 Waverly Rd.
Bryn Mawr, PA 19010-1928

Donor: Mustafa A. Jama.
Foundation type: Independent foundation.
Financial data (yr. ended 12/31/13): Assets, $2,643,192 (M); gifts received, $1,601,000; expenditures, $521,268; qualifying distributions, $520,000; giving activities include $520,000 for 1 grant.
Fields of interest: Community/economic development.
International interests: Somalia.
Limitations: Applications not accepted. Giving primarily in Somaliland, Somalia.
Application information: Unsolicited requests for funds not accepted.
Officers: Mustafa Jama, Pres.; Lucky Farah, Secy.
Director: Mohamed Ahmed.
EIN: 460905081

8012
The Francis J. Dixon Foundation ✧
P.O. Box 333
Lebanon, PA 17042-0333

Established in 1989 in PA.
Donors: Francis J. Dixon; Brandywine Recyclers, Inc.
Foundation type: Independent foundation.
Financial data (yr. ended 12/31/12): Assets, $12,473,608 (M); expenditures, $760,684; qualifying distributions, $585,959; giving activities include $544,900 for 22 grants (high: $200,000; low: $200).
Purpose and activities: Support for education, medical and community organizations, scholarships, and disaster relief.
Fields of interest: Education, fund raising/fund distribution; Higher education, college (community/junior); Health care; Safety/disasters; International relief; United Ways and Federated Giving Programs.
Type of support: Equipment; Emergency funds; Program development; Scholarship funds; Technical assistance.
Limitations: Applications accepted. Giving primarily in Lebanon County, PA. No support for businesses, private foundations, large community based or national charities, or religious organizations. No grants to individuals, or for endowments, capital expenditures, general operating expenses, or debt reduction.
Publications: Annual report; Financial statement; Grants list.
Application information: Application form required.
Initial approach: 1-2 page cover letter outlining grant request
Copies of proposal: 1
Deadline(s): None
Board meeting date(s): 2nd Wed. of Mar., July, & Nov.
Officers: Richard Scott, Chair.; Robert J. Phillips, Pres.; JoAnn D. White, Treas.; Frank Dixon, Chair. Emeritus.
Directors: David Dixon; Thomas Dixon; Timothy J. Huber; Thomas I. Siegel.
Number of staff: 1 full-time professional.
EIN: 251600852

8013
Dolfinger 2 Trust ✧
c/o Duane Morris, LLP
30 S. 17th St.
Philadelphia, PA 19103-4196 (215) 979-1834
Contact: David Loder Esq., Tr.
FAX: (215) 979-1020;
E-mail: renz@duanemorris.com

Trust established in 1957 in PA, and originally comprised of four separate trusts: T/W of Henry Dolfinger as modified by will of Mary McMahon; 1935 D/T of Henry Dolfinger as modified by will of Caroline D. McMahon; Residuary T/W of Caroline D. McMahon; Dolfinger-McMahon Trust for Greater Philadelphia. In 1986 the 1935 D/T of H. Dolfinger was merged with the residuary T/W of C. McMahon.
Donors: Henry Dolfinger†; Caroline D. McMahon†; Mary M. McMahon†.
Foundation type: Independent foundation.
Financial data (yr. ended 12/31/13): Assets, $20,143,267 (M); expenditures, $1,077,275; qualifying distributions, $921,581; giving activities include $804,500 for 222 grants (high: $50,000; low: $1,000).
Purpose and activities: Primary areas of interest include community development, the disadvantaged, education, the handicapped, and health. Emphasis on experimental, demonstration, or seed money projects in race relations, aid to the handicapped, higher and secondary education, social and urban programs, church programs, and health agencies. Emergency funding will be made rarely and, once made, will disqualify the agency from receiving any additional funding for the succeeding three years.
Fields of interest: Museums; Performing arts; Performing arts, dance; Performing arts, theater; Performing arts, music; Humanities; Arts; Elementary/secondary education; Education, early childhood education; Child development, education; Elementary school/education; Secondary school/education; Vocational education; Higher education; Theological school/education; Adult/continuing education; Adult education—literacy, basic skills & GED; Education, reading; Education; Environment, natural resources; Environment, energy; Environment; Animal welfare; Hospitals (general); Reproductive health, family planning; Nursing care; Health care; Substance abuse, services; Mental health/crisis services; Health organizations, association; AIDS; Alcoholism; AIDS research; Crime/violence prevention, youth; Legal services; Crime/law enforcement; Employment; Food services; Nutrition; Recreation; Youth development, services; Human services; Children/youth, services; Child development, services; Family services; Aging, centers/services; Women, centers/services; Minorities/immigrants, centers/services; Homeless, human services; Civil rights, race/intergroup relations; Urban/community development; Community/economic development; Voluntarism promotion; Religious federated giving programs; Government/public administration; Transportation; Leadership development; Public affairs; Religion; Children/youth; Children; Youth; Adults; Aging; Young adults; Disabilities, people with; Blind/visually impaired; Deaf/hearing impaired; Minorities; African Americans/Blacks; Women; Economically disadvantaged; Homeless.
Type of support: Emergency funds; Program development; Conferences/seminars; Publication; Seed money; Matching/challenge support.
Limitations: Applications accepted. Giving limited to the greater Philadelphia, PA, area. No support for private foundations or special interest advocacy through legislative lobbying or solicitation of government agencies. No grants to individuals, or for endowment funds, physical facilities, ordinary operating expenses, renovations or building repairs, building funds, scholarships, medical or scientific research, or fellowships.
Publications: Application guidelines; Annual report (including application guidelines).
Application information: Application form required.
Initial approach: Letter
Copies of proposal: 2
Deadline(s): None
Trustees: Sheldon M. Bonovitz, Esq.; David E. Loder, Esq.
Number of staff: 1 part-time professional.
EIN: 236207346

8014
Dollar Bank Foundation ✧ ☆
c/o Dollar Bank, Public Affairs Dept.
3 Gateway Ctr., Rm. 8N
Pittsburgh, PA 15222-1094

Established in 1998 in PA.
Donor: Dollar Bank, FSB.
Foundation type: Company-sponsored foundation.
Financial data (yr. ended 11/30/13): Assets, $11,013,880 (M); gifts received, $2,000,000; expenditures, $503,701; qualifying distributions, $493,986; giving activities include $427,640 for 44 grants (high: $89,763; low: $1,000), and $66,346 for 271 grants to individuals.
Purpose and activities: The foundation supports community foundations and organizations involved with arts and culture, education, water conservation, housing, human services, and community economic development.
Fields of interest: Housing/shelter; Human services; Community/economic development.
Type of support: General/operating support; Continuing support; Program development; Scholarship funds.
Limitations: Applications accepted. Giving primarily in areas of company operations in Cleveland, OH and Pittsburgh, PA. No support for political, veterans', fraternal, labor, or religious organizations, hospitals, or health care delivery facilities. No grants to individuals, or for non-academic efforts at the elementary or high school level.
Publications: Application guidelines.
Application information: Multi-year funding is not automatic. Application form required.
Initial approach: Proposal
Deadline(s): None
Officers: Thomas A. Kobus, Pres.; Joseph Smith, V.P.; C. Andrew McGhee, Secy.; James T. Jurcic, Treas.
EIN: 251822243
Selected grants: The following grants are a representative sample of this grantmaker's funding activity:
$65,000 to United Way of Allegheny County, Pittsburgh, PA, 2011.
$50,000 to Pittsburgh Partnership for Neighborhood Development, Pittsburgh, PA, 2011.
$35,000 to Pittsburgh Foundation, Pittsburgh, PA, 2011.
$25,000 to Hill House Association, Pittsburgh, PA, 2011.
$15,000 to Pittsburgh Community Reinvestment Group, Pittsburgh, PA, 2011.
$10,000 to Cleveland Housing Network, Cleveland, OH, 2011.
$10,000 to Pittsburgh Symphony, Pittsburgh, PA, 2011.
$10,000 to Western Pennsylvania School for the Deaf, Pittsburgh, PA, 2011.
$5,000 to Cleveland Public Theater, Cleveland, OH, 2011.
$5,000 to United Way of Lake County, Mentor, OH, 2011.

8015
Donahue Family Foundation, Inc. ✧
1001 Liberty Ave., Ste. 850
Pittsburgh, PA 15222-3718
Contact: William Donahue, Pres.
E-mail: bdonahue@thebeechwood.com

Established around 1990 in PA.
Donors: John F. Donahue; Rhodora J. Donahue.
Foundation type: Independent foundation.
Financial data (yr. ended 12/31/13): Assets, $7,579,160 (M); expenditures, $1,455,671; qualifying distributions, $1,446,768; giving activities include $1,361,905 for 49 grants (high: $299,386; low: $500), and $84,863 for foundation-administered programs.
Purpose and activities: Giving primarily for education and Roman Catholic organizations.
Fields of interest: Education; Human services; Catholic agencies & churches.
Limitations: Applications accepted. Giving primarily in Pittsburgh, PA. No grants to individuals.
Application information: CGAF Common Grant Application Format accepted. Application form not required.
Initial approach: 1-page letter
Copies of proposal: 2
Deadline(s): May 1
Board meeting date(s): June and Dec.
Final notification: 60 days
Officers and Directors:* John F. Donahue,* Chair.; William J. Donahue,* Pres.; James Bougher,* Secy.-Treas.; Benjamin P. Barton; Dick K. Barton; James C. Donahue; Rhodora J. Donahue; Kathleen M. Donahue-Wallach; Richard S. Donley; Thomas M. Freyvogel III; Patrick K. Moore; Rhodara Freyvogel Noethling; Rainey D. Redd.
Number of staff: 1 full-time professional.
EIN: 251619351

8016
The Drumcliff Foundation ✧
1021 W. Hortter St.
Philadelphia, PA 19119
Application address: c/o Daniel Gordon, P.O. Box 26087, Philadelphia, PA 19128, tel.: (215) 849-9080

Established in 1988 in PA.
Donor: Dauphinot Gordon Fund.
Foundation type: Independent foundation.
Financial data (yr. ended 12/31/13): Assets, $2,481,644 (M); gifts received, $511,500; expenditures, $696,992; qualifying distributions, $696,992; giving activities include $671,632 for 67 grants (high: $113,380; low: $375).

Fields of interest: Museums; Performing arts, music; Arts; Higher education; Libraries (public); Education; Recreation; Human services.
Type of support: General/operating support; Continuing support; Annual campaigns; Capital campaigns; Building/renovation; Matching/challenge support.
Limitations: Applications accepted. Giving primarily in Philadelphia, PA. No grants to individuals.
Application information: Application form required.
Initial approach: Letter
Copies of proposal: 1
Deadline(s): None
Trustee: Daniel F. Gordon.
Number of staff: 1 part-time professional.
EIN: 236957302

8017
DSF Charitable Foundation ✧
(formerly Scaife Charitable Foundation)
5840 Ellsworth Ave., Ste. 200
Pittsburgh, PA 15232-1727 (412) 362-6000
Contact: J. Nicholas Beldecos, Exec. Dir.
FAX: (412) 362-6600; E-mail: info@dsfcf.org; Main URL: http://www.dsfcf.org

Established in 2000 in PA.
Foundation type: Independent foundation.
Financial data (yr. ended 12/31/13): Assets, $103,655,848 (M); expenditures, $4,934,042; qualifying distributions, $4,387,537; giving activities include $3,734,507 for 28 grants (high: $600,000; low: $5,000).
Purpose and activities: Giving primarily for human services, health, and education.
Fields of interest: Higher education; Education; Health care; Biomedicine; Neuroscience; Medical research; Human services; Children/youth, services; Residential/custodial care, senior continuing care.
Type of support: General/operating support; Building/renovation; Equipment; Program development; Seed money; Research; Program evaluation; Matching/challenge support.
Limitations: Applications accepted. Giving primarily in southwestern PA, particularly in Pittsburgh. No grants to individuals, or for endowments.
Publications: Application guidelines.
Application information: Accepts the Common Grant Application Format of Grantmakers of Western Pennsylvania. See foundation web site for application information and guidelines. Though not required, all material may be submitted in electronic format (PDF preferred). Application form not required.
Initial approach: Letter of inquiry (with supporting material not to exceed 5 pages)
Copies of proposal: 1
Deadline(s): None
Board meeting date(s): Varies
Final notification: Following board meeting
Officers and Trustees:* David N. Scaife,* Chair.; Sanford B. Ferguson,* Vice-Chair.; Sara D. Scaife,* Secy.; Edward J. Goncz,* Treas.; J. Nicholas Beldecos, Exec. Dir.; Donald A. Collins; Frances G. Scaife.
Number of staff: 1 full-time professional; 2 part-time professional; 1 full-time support.
EIN: 251847237

8018
Lola G. Duff & William H. Duff II Scholarship Fund ✧
P.O. Box 609
Pittsburgh, PA 15230-9738

Foundation type: Independent foundation.
Financial data (yr. ended 03/31/13): Assets, $89,618,949 (M); expenditures, $3,857,943; qualifying distributions, $3,479,987; giving activities include $3,257,108 for grants.
Fields of interest: Scholarships/financial aid.
Type of support: Scholarship funds.
Limitations: Applications not accepted. Giving primarily in PA. No grants to individuals.
Application information: Unsolicited requests for funds not accepted.
Trustee: PNC Bank, N.A.
EIN: 611467176

8019
Dull Casper Trust ✧ ☆
c/o BNY Mellon, N.A.
P.O. Box 185
Pittsburgh, PA 15230-0185

Established in PA.
Foundation type: Independent foundation.
Financial data (yr. ended 09/30/13): Assets, $8,306,166 (M); expenditures, $512,851; qualifying distributions, $482,005; giving activities include $462,794 for 1 grant.
Fields of interest: Nursing home/convalescent facility.
Limitations: Applications not accepted. Giving primarily in Harrisburg, PA.
Application information: Contributes only to pre-selected organizations.
Trustee: BNY Mellon, N.A.
EIN: 236236573
Selected grants: The following grants are a representative sample of this grantmaker's funding activity:
$394,648 to Homeland Center, Harrisburg, PA, 2011.

8020
John E. DuPont Foundation ✧ ☆
13 Paoli Ct.
Paoli, PA 19301-1403 (610) 296-9900
Contact: Taras M. Wochok, Pres.

Foundation type: Independent foundation.
Financial data (yr. ended 12/31/13): Assets, $28,136 (M); gifts received, $683,832; expenditures, $655,720; qualifying distributions, $655,720; giving activities include $551,000 for 2 grants (high: $550,000; low: $1,000).
Fields of interest: Museums (natural history); Arts; Housing/shelter.
Limitations: Applications accepted. Giving primarily in DE.
Application information: Application form required.
Initial approach: Letter
Deadline(s): None
Officer and Directors:* Taras M. Wochok,* Pres.; Daniel A. Czaplicki; Joseph T. Labrum, Jr.
EIN: 357019969

8021
Eden Hall Foundation ✧
600 Grant St., Ste. 3232
Pittsburgh, PA 15219-2713 (412) 642-6697
Contact: G.C. Greer
FAX: (412) 642-6698; Main URL: http://www.edenhallfdn.org

Established in 1984 in PA.
Donor: Eden Hall Farm.
Foundation type: Independent foundation.
Financial data (yr. ended 12/31/13): Assets, $198,948,346 (M); expenditures, $10,528,411; qualifying distributions, $10,151,093; giving activities include $9,601,225 for 121 grants (high: $780,000; low: $500).
Purpose and activities: The foundation seeks to improve the quality of life in Pittsburgh and western Pennsylvania through support of organizations whose missions address the needs and concerns of the area. The foundation awards grants over four basic program areas: arts and culture; education; health; and social welfare.
Fields of interest: Arts education; Arts; Higher education; Education; Environment, beautification programs; Health care; Substance abuse, services; Multiple sclerosis; Lupus; Agriculture/food; Recreation, parks/playgrounds; Human services; American Red Cross; YM/YWCAs & YM/YWHAs; Women; Economically disadvantaged.
Type of support: Research; General/operating support; Management development/capacity building; Capital campaigns; Building/renovation; Equipment; Endowments; Program development; Scholarship funds; Program evaluation.
Limitations: Applications accepted. Giving limited to southwestern PA. No support for private foundations, sectarian or denominational religious organizations (except those providing direct educational or health care services to the public), or political or fraternal organizations. No grants to individuals, or generally for operating budgets, endowments, or deficit financing.
Publications: Application guidelines.
Application information: Interviews or visitation may be necessary for additional information. Application form not required.
Initial approach: Letter
Copies of proposal: 5
Deadline(s): None
Board meeting date(s): Quarterly
Officers and Directors:* George C. Greer,* Chair. and Pres.; Margaret P. Joy,* V.P. and Secy.; John M. Mazur,* V.P. and Treas.; Charles J. Stout,* V.P.; Laura S. Fisher,* V.P.; Sylvia V. Fields, Exec. Dir.
Number of staff: 1 full-time professional; 1 full-time support; 1 part-time support.
EIN: 251384468
Selected grants: The following grants are a representative sample of this grantmaker's funding activity:
$780,000 to Pittsburgh Trust for Cultural Resources, Pittsburgh, PA, 2012. For programming.
$750,000 to Pittsburgh Parks Conservancy, Pittsburgh, PA, 2012. For construction of Environmental Center at Frick Park.
$500,000 to Pittsburgh Botanic Garden, Pittsburgh, PA, 2012. For Phase I of the Building Plan.
$400,000 to Carnegie Mellon University, Pittsburgh, PA, 2012. To establish Energy Futures Institute and construct Bio, Energy, Nano Building.
$333,000 to Westminster College, New Wilmington, PA, 2012. For renovations to Patterson Hall.

$250,000 to Adelphoi USA, Latrobe, PA, 2012. For capital improvements to Margaret Home and Colony Home.
$250,000 to Pittsburgh Symphony, Heinz Hall for the Performing Arts, Pittsburgh, PA, 2012. For program support.
$15,000 to Dress for Success Pittsburgh, Pittsburgh, PA, 2012. For Professional Women's Group and Career Center programs.
$15,000 to Urban Impact Foundation, Pittsburgh, PA, 2012. For Performing Arts and Options Programs.
$10,000 to Partners in Progress, Ligonier, PA, 2012. For school construction in Deslandes, Haiti.

8022
Elias Family Charitable Trust ✧
P.O. Box 340
Merion, PA 19066-0340

Established in 1980.
Donor: Gabriel Elias.
Foundation type: Independent foundation.
Financial data (yr. ended 12/31/12): Assets, $16,412,094 (M); expenditures, $1,799,228; qualifying distributions, $1,279,050; giving activities include $1,279,050 for 94 grants (high: $471,240; low: $250).
Purpose and activities: Giving primarily for Delaware Valley institutions to increase public commitment to the American Ideals of Universal Egalitarian Humanism and nationalism.
Fields of interest: Human services; Jewish federated giving programs; Public affairs.
Limitations: Applications not accepted. Giving primarily in the Delaware Valley, PA, area. No support for capital expenditures. No grants to individuals.
Application information: Contributes only to pre-selected organizations. Unsolicited requests for funds not accepted.
Manager: Alma Elias.
EIN: 236749244
Selected grants: The following grants are a representative sample of this grantmaker's funding activity:
$25,000 to United Synagogue of Conservative Judaism, New York, NY, 2012. To Carry Out Charitable Purpose of Donee.

8023
Charles E. Ellis Grant and Scholarship Fund ✧
c/o PNC Bank, N.A.
1600 Market St., Tax Dept., 4th Fl.
Philadelphia, PA 19103-7240
Application address: c/o Philadelphia Futures, 230 S. Broad St., 7th Fl., Philadelphia, PA 19102-4121

Established in 1981 in PA.
Donor: Charles E. Ellis†.
Foundation type: Independent foundation.
Financial data (yr. ended 06/30/13): Assets, $39,400,839 (M); expenditures, $1,859,206; qualifying distributions, $1,737,499; giving activities include $1,442,039 for grants.
Purpose and activities: The purpose of the fund is to provide grants and scholarships for the benefit of functionally orphaned girls or for girls from single-parent families, who are living in the 5 county area of southeastern Pennsylvania, with preference given to girls who are residing in Philadelphia County.
Fields of interest: Secondary school/education; Education; Girls.
Type of support: Scholarship funds; Scholarships—to individuals.
Limitations: Giving limited to the five county area of southeastern, PA, with emphasis on Philadelphia County.
Publications: Application guidelines; Informational brochure; Program policy statement.
Application information: Funds paid directly to the educational institution the individual attends. Application form required.
Initial approach: Letter
Deadline(s): None
Board meeting date(s): Apr., May, Aug., and Nov.
Final notification: 2 weeks after each board meeting
Trustee: PNC Bank, N.A.
EIN: 236725618

8024
Elizabeth R. England Trust ✧
c/o Mellon Financial Corp.
P.O. Box 185
Pittsburgh, PA 15230-0185

Established in 1987 in PA.
Foundation type: Independent foundation.
Financial data (yr. ended 06/30/13): Assets, $18,090,269 (M); expenditures, $917,821; qualifying distributions, $890,510; giving activities include $747,688 for 2 grants (high: $374,844; low: $372,844), and $135,330 for 6 grants to individuals (high: $44,881; low: $510).
Purpose and activities: Giving primarily for education and churches. Scholarships are primarily awarded to art majors who are students at Philadelphia High School for Girls or West Philadelphia High School.
Fields of interest: Arts education; Christian agencies & churches.
Type of support: Grants to individuals; Scholarships—to individuals.
Limitations: Applications accepted. Giving limited to residents of Philadelphia, PA.
Application information: Application form not required.
Deadline(s): None
Trustee: BNY Mellon, N.A.
EIN: 236606334

8025
EQT Foundation, Inc. ✧
(formerly Equitable Resources Foundation, Inc.)
1 PNC Plaza
249 Fifth Ave., 3rd Fl.
Pittsburgh, PA 15222 (412) 762-3502
Contact: Bruce Bickel, Exec. Dir.
E-mail: bruce.bickel@pncadvisors.com; Main URL: http://www.eqt.com/ourcommunities/eqt-foundation.aspx
ASPIRE on Facebook: https://www.facebook.com/pages/ASPIRE-Area-Students-Participating-in-Rewarding-Education/214494945406237
ASPIRE Website: http://www.aspireprogram.org/
Application address: 625 Liberty Ave., Pittsburgh, PA 15222, e-mail: aspire@egt.com

Established in 2003 in PA.
Donors: Equitable Production Co.; EQD Holdings Co., LLC.
Foundation type: Company-sponsored foundation.
Financial data (yr. ended 12/31/12): Assets, $24,337,308 (M); expenditures, $3,156,514; qualifying distributions, $2,922,822; giving activities include $2,888,936 for 353 grants (high: $146,162; low: $100).
Purpose and activities: The foundation supports programs designed to promote education for children and adults; encourage the development of safe and livable communities; promote the environment and preservation of local natural resources; and foster understanding and appreciation of culture and heritage.
Fields of interest: Arts, cultural/ethnic awareness; Museums; Performing arts; Arts; Elementary/secondary education; Higher education; Adult/continuing education; Libraries (public); Education, reading; Education; Environment, recycling; Environment, natural resources; Environment, energy; Horticulture/garden clubs; Environmental education; Animal welfare; Employment, services; Housing/shelter, development; Recreation, fairs/festivals; Youth development, adult & child programs; Youth development, business; Business/industry; Community/economic development; Voluntarism promotion; Mathematics; Engineering/technology; Science; Aging; Economically disadvantaged.
Type of support: Program development; Seed money; Scholarship funds; Employee volunteer services; Sponsorships; Scholarships—to individuals; In-kind gifts; Matching/challenge support.
Limitations: Applications accepted. Giving primarily in areas of company operations in KY, Pittsburgh, PA, VA, and WV. No support for churches or religious organizations, political parties, candidates, or public policy advocates, for-profit businesses or associations, tax-supported entities (except for public schools), or fraternal, social, union, or hobby/recreational clubs or organizations. No grants to individuals (except for ASPIRE), or for capital campaigns, endowments, new construction or building renovations, mortgage/rent/insurance/utility costs, vehicle purchases or repairs, infrastructure improvements, sporting events including golf outings, travel to conferences, workshops, seminars, competitions, or emergency or stop-gap funding.
Publications: Application guidelines.
Application information: Proposals should be no longer than 6 pages. Application form required.
Initial approach: Download application form and mail proposal and application form to foundation; complete application form during enrollment period for ASPIRE
Copies of proposal: 1
Deadline(s): Feb. 1, May 1, Aug. 1, and Nov. 1; Varies for ASPIRE
Board meeting date(s): Mar., June, Sept., and Dec.
Officers and Directors:* Charlene G. Petrelli,* Pres.; Natalie Cox, V.P., Public Affairs; Ellen Donnelly, V.P., Community Rels.; Patrick J. Kane, V.P., Finance; Christopher T. Akers, V.P.; Kenneth C. Kirk, V.P.; John H. Obrist, Secy.; Thomas E. Quinlan, Treas.; Bruce Bickel, Exec. Dir.; Martin A. Fritz, Esq.; M. Elise Hyland; Lewis B. Gardner; Steven T. Schlotterbeck.
EIN: 043747289

8026
The Erie Community Foundation ✧
459 W. 6th St.
Erie, PA 16507-1215 (814) 454-0843
Contact: Michael L. Batchelor, Pres.
FAX: (814) 456-4965;
E-mail: mbatchelor@eriecommunityfoundation.org;
Grant inquiry tel.: 814-454-0843; Main URL: http://www.eriecommunityfoundation.org
E-Newsletter: http://www.eriecommunityfoundation.org/about-ecf/publications/enewsletter/
Facebook: http://www.facebook.com/pages/Erie-PA/The-Erie-Community-Foundation/72006534178
RSS Feed: http://www.eriecommunityfoundation.org/rss/
Twitter: https://twitter.com/TheECF1935
YouTube: http://www.youtube.com/ecferiepa

Established in 1935 in PA as Erie Endowment Foundation; renamed in 1970.
Foundation type: Community foundation.
Financial data (yr. ended 12/31/13): Assets, $207,903,253 (M); gifts received, $7,631,670; expenditures, $13,028,341; giving activities include $10,398,404 for grants.
Purpose and activities: The mission of the foundation is to improve the quality of life for all in the region by evaluating and addressing community issues, building permanent charitable endowments and promoting philanthropic and community leadership.
Fields of interest: Arts; Education; Health care; Human services; Community/economic development.
Type of support: Income development; Management development/capacity building; Capital campaigns; Building/renovation; Equipment; Land acquisition; Emergency funds; Program development; Publication; Curriculum development; Research; Technical assistance; Program evaluation; Scholarships—to individuals; Matching/challenge support.
Limitations: Applications accepted. Giving limited to Erie County, PA. No support for sectarian religious activities, fire departments, nursing homes, field trips, or school playgrounds. No grants to individuals (except for scholarships), or for fundraising events, programs ads, vehicles, organization start-up costs, endowments, deficit financing, or operating expenses.
Publications: Application guidelines; Annual report; Financial statement; Grants list; Informational brochure (including application guidelines); Newsletter.
Application information: Visit foundation web site for guidelines per grant type. Application form required.
Initial approach: Online grant application for Helping Today grants; Letter of Inquiry for Shaping Tomorrow grants
Deadline(s): Jan. 14, May 14, Aug. 27, and Nov. 4 for Helping Today grants; Feb. 14 and Aug. 27 for Shaping Tomorrow grants
Board meeting date(s): Mar., June, Sept., and Dec.
Final notification: Within 3 months
Officers and Trustees:* Robert G. Dwyer, Esq.,* Chair.; Michael L. Batchelor,* Pres.; George E. Espy, V.P., Community Impact; Erin D. Fessler, V.P., Comms.; Sussanah Weis Frigon, V.P., Investor Rels.; Barbara F. Sambroak, V.P., Finance and Admin.; Russell S. Warner, Esq.,* Secy.; Amanda Schantz Lincoln,* Cont.; Clemont R. Austin; Geoffrey P. Dunn, M.D.; Thomas B. Hagen; Timothy M. Hunter; Susan Kemenyffy; Lynn M. McBrier; Tim Shuttleworth; R. Anthony Snow, M.D.; Maryann C. Yochim.
Trustee Banks: Advest, Inc.; BNY Mellon, N.A.; National Bank & Trust Co.; LPL Finanacial; Merrill Lynch Trust Co.; National City Bank; PNC Bank, N.A.
Number of staff: 4 full-time professional; 1 part-time professional; 3 full-time support.
EIN: 256032032

8027
Erlbaum Family Foundation ✧
44 W. Lancaster Ave., Ste. 110
Ardmore, PA 19003-1339

Established in 1998 in PA.
Donors: Philip Youtie; Gary E. Erlbaum; Marc N. Erlbaum; Erlbaum Family Limited Partnership; Erlbaum Family 2005 Trust; Erlbaum Investments LP.
Foundation type: Independent foundation.
Financial data (yr. ended 12/31/13): Assets, $1,753,828 (M); gifts received, $574,700; expenditures, $711,458; qualifying distributions, $705,761; giving activities include $692,433 for 146 grants (high: $185,900; low: $36).
Purpose and activities: Giving primarily for Jewish organizations.
Fields of interest: Health organizations, association; Human services; Jewish federated giving programs; Jewish agencies & synagogues.
Limitations: Applications not accepted. Giving primarily in PA and NY.
Application information: Unsolicited requests for funds not accepted.
Officer: Gary E. Erlbaum, Pres.
Directors: Daniel A. Erlbaum; Jon L. Erlbaum; Marc N. Erlbaum; Vicki O. Erlbaum.
EIN: 232962563

8028
ESSA Bank & Trust Foundation ✧
200 Palmer St., P.O. Box L
Stroudsburg, PA 18360-0160 (570) 422-0182
Contact: Suzie T. Farley, V.P. and Secy.-Treas.
Main URL: https://www.essabank.com/html/essa_foundation1.html
Grants List: https://www.essabank.com/index.cfm?siteid=336&itemcategory=35757&priorId=35647&newP=35643

Established in 2007 in PA.
Donor: ESSA Bancorp, Inc.
Foundation type: Company-sponsored foundation.
Financial data (yr. ended 12/31/13): Assets, $10,492,100 (M); expenditures, $909,767; qualifying distributions, $870,899; giving activities include $866,374 for 36 grants (high: $100,000; low: $4,250).
Purpose and activities: The foundation supports fire departments and organizations involved with arts and culture, education, health, housing, recreation, human services, and community development.
Fields of interest: Arts; Higher education; Libraries (public); Education; Health care, clinics/centers; Health care; Housing/shelter; Disasters, fire prevention/control; Recreation, parks/playgrounds; Athletics/sports, baseball; Recreation; Boy scouts; YM/YWCAs & YM/YWHAs; Children/youth, services; Family services; Residential/custodial care, hospices; Human services; Community/economic development.
Type of support: General/operating support; Capital campaigns; Equipment.
Limitations: Applications accepted. Giving limited to areas of company operations in Monroe County, PA.
Publications: Application guidelines; Grants list.
Application information: Support is limited 1 contribution per organization during a three year period. Application form not required.
Initial approach: Letter of inquiry
Deadline(s): None
Officers and Directors:* John E. Burrus,* Pres.; Suzie T. Farley,* V.P. and Secy.-Treas.; Lois B. Heckman; Gary S. Olson; Elizabeth B. Weekes.
EIN: 208227643

8029
The Eustace Foundation ✧
c/o Cabrini Asset Mgmt., Inc., Attn.: Conie Gerhart
700 S. Henderson Rd., No. 202
King of Prussia, PA 19406-3530 (610) 945-1655
FAX: (610) 945-1653; Main URL: http://foundationcenter.org/grantmaker/eustace

Established in 1985 in PA.
Donors: J. Eustace Wolfington; James W. Finegan, Jr.; Richard D. Scott.
Foundation type: Independent foundation.
Financial data (yr. ended 09/30/13): Assets, $22,128,349 (M); expenditures, $1,556,818; qualifying distributions, $1,360,699; giving activities include $1,360,699 for 51 grants (high: $318,000; low: $200).
Purpose and activities: Giving primarily for religious and educational organizations that are affiliated with the Roman Catholic Church.
Fields of interest: Elementary/secondary education; Higher education; Human services; Children/youth, services; Christian agencies & churches; Catholic agencies & churches.
Limitations: Applications not accepted. Giving primarily in eastern PA. No grants to individuals or for tuition subsidy.
Publications: IRS Form 990 or 990-PF printed copy available upon request.
Application information: Contributes only to pre-selected organizations.
Trustee: J. Eustace Wolfington.
EIN: 222664349
Selected grants: The following grants are a representative sample of this grantmaker's funding activity:
$13,200 to United Way of Greater Philadelphia and Southern New Jersey, Philadelphia, PA, 2011.
$1,000 to Dominican Sisters of Mary, Mother of the Eucharist, Ann Arbor, MI, 2011.

8030
Fair Oaks Foundation ✧
(formerly AMPCO-Pittsburgh Foundation II, Inc.)
600 Grant St., Ste. 4600
Pittsburgh, PA 15219-2903 (412) 456-4418
Contact: Rose Hoover, V.P.

Established in 1988 in PA.
Donors: Pittsburgh Forgings Foundation; AMPCO-Pittsburgh Foundation.

Foundation type: Company-sponsored foundation.
Financial data (yr. ended 12/31/13): Assets, $5,392,101 (M); expenditures, $459,937; qualifying distributions, $447,850; giving activities include $447,850 for 152 grants (high: $100,000; low: $50).
Purpose and activities: The foundation supports botanical gardens, zoos, food banks, and community centers and organizations involved with orchestras, higher education, animal welfare, and human services.
Fields of interest: Education; Agriculture/food; Religion.
Limitations: Applications accepted. Giving primarily in PA and VA.
Application information: Application form not required.
Initial approach: Proposal
Deadline(s): Oct. 31
Officers and Trustees:* Robert A. Paul,* Chair.; Ernest G. Siddons,* Pres.; Rose Hoover,* V.P.
EIN: 251576560
Selected grants: The following grants are a representative sample of this grantmaker's funding activity:
$5,000 to University of Pittsburgh, Pittsburgh, PA, 2012. For General Contribution in Support of Programs.

8031
The Anthony P. Falcone Trust ✧
c/o Bryn Mawr Trust Co.
1 E. Chocolate Ave., Ste. 200
Hershey, PA 17033

Foundation type: Independent foundation.
Financial data (yr. ended 08/31/13): Assets, $16,826,097 (M); expenditures, $937,755; qualifying distributions, $828,804; giving activities include $802,072 for 17 grants (high: $57,584; low: $32,932).
Fields of interest: Health care; Catholic agencies & churches.
Limitations: Applications not accepted. Giving primarily in PA.
Application information: Unsolicited requests for funds not accepted.
Trustees: Nicholas Falcone; Bryn Mawr Trust Co.
EIN: 236743142

8032
Farber Family Foundation Inc. ✧
1845 Walnut St., Ste. 800
Philadelphia, PA 19103-4708

Incorporated in 1992 in FL.
Donors: Jack Farber; Ellen B. Farber; Vivian Farber.
Foundation type: Independent foundation.
Financial data (yr. ended 12/31/13): Assets, $18,360,995 (M); gifts received, $1,107,200; expenditures, $802,683; qualifying distributions, $2,054,600; giving activities include $615,850 for 21 grants (high: $100,000; low: $1,500).
Purpose and activities: Funding primarily for education, Jewish organizations, health and human services.
Fields of interest: Higher education; Medical research; Human services; United Ways and Federated Giving Programs; Jewish federated giving programs; Jewish agencies & synagogues.
Type of support: General/operating support; Endowments; Program development; Research.
Limitations: Applications not accepted. Giving primarily in PA. No grants to individuals.
Application information: Contributes only to pre-selected organizations.
Officers and Directors:* Jack Farber,* Chair.; Vivian Farber,* Pres.; Ellen Farber, Treas. and Exec. Dir.
EIN: 650336266

8033
Federated Investors Foundation, Inc. ✧
1001 Liberty Avenue, 21st Fl.
Pittsburgh, PA 15222-3779

Established in 1997.
Donor: Federated Investors, Inc.
Foundation type: Company-sponsored foundation.
Financial data (yr. ended 04/30/12): Assets, $650,252 (M); expenditures, $593,069; qualifying distributions, $592,900; giving activities include $592,900 for grants.
Purpose and activities: The foundation supports organizations involved with arts and culture, education, crime and law enforcement, human services, civil liberties, public affairs, and Christianity.
Fields of interest: Arts, cultural/ethnic awareness; Media/communications; Museums; Performing arts, opera; Historic preservation/historical societies; Arts; Elementary school/education; Secondary school/education; Higher education; Education; Crime/law enforcement; Children, services; Human services; Civil liberties, advocacy; Civil liberties, right to life; United Ways and Federated Giving Programs; Public affairs, alliance/advocacy; Christian agencies & churches.
Type of support: General/operating support; Annual campaigns; Capital campaigns; Building/renovation; Program development; Scholarship funds.
Limitations: Applications not accepted. Giving primarily in Pittsburgh, PA. No grants to individuals.
Application information: Contributes only to pre-selected organizations.
Officers and Directors:* J. Christopher Donahue,* Pres.; John W. McGonigle, Secy.; Thomas R. Donahue, Treas.; John F. Donahue.
EIN: 232913182
Selected grants: The following grants are a representative sample of this grantmaker's funding activity:
$3,000 to Big Brothers Big Sisters of Greater Pittsburgh, Pittsburgh, PA, 2011.
$3,000 to Epilepsy Foundation Western/Central Pennsylvania, Pittsburgh, PA, 2011.

8034
The Moses Feldman Family Foundation ✧
8 Tower Bridge
161 Washington St, Ste. 410
Conshohocken, PA 19428-2043
Main URL: http://www.tmfff.org/

Established in 2005 in PA.
Donors: The Feldman Foundation; Jacob Feldman Marital Trust; Jacob Feldman Charitable Lead Trust; Sara Feldman Charitable Lead Trust.
Foundation type: Independent foundation.
Financial data (yr. ended 12/31/13): Assets, $50,923,086 (M); gifts received, $17,788,922; expenditures, $1,803,741; qualifying distributions, $1,676,189; giving activities include $1,536,687 for 46 grants (high: $166,667; low: $5,000).
Purpose and activities: Giving primarily for Jewish organizations, higher education, and the environment, specifically an arboretum and an environmental club.
Fields of interest: Higher education; Botanical gardens; Animals/wildlife, clubs; Jewish federated giving programs; Public policy, research; Jewish agencies & synagogues.
Type of support: General/operating support.
Limitations: Applications not accepted. Giving primarily in MA, NY, PA, and Washington, DC. No grants to individuals.
Application information: Contributes only to pre-selected organizations.
Trustees: Moses Feldman; Susan Feldman.
EIN: 202086533

8035
Samuel S. Fels Fund ✧
1528 Walnut St., Ste. 1002
Philadelphia, PA 19102-3627 (215) 731-9455
Contact: Helen Cunningham, Exec. Dir.
FAX: (215) 731-9457; Main URL: http://www.samfels.org

Incorporated in 1935 in PA.
Donor: Samuel S. Fels†.
Foundation type: Independent foundation.
Financial data (yr. ended 12/31/13): Assets, $50,444,324 (M); expenditures, $2,512,833; qualifying distributions, $2,257,018; giving activities include $1,747,800 for 172 grants (high: $150,000; low: $1,000).
Purpose and activities: Grants for projects and organizations that help to prevent, lessen, or resolve contemporary social problems, or that seek to provide permanent improvements in the provision of services for the improvement of daily life; to increase the stability of arts organizations and enrich the cultural life of the city of Philadelphia, PA.
Fields of interest: Arts; Education; Community/economic development.
Type of support: General/operating support; Continuing support; Equipment; Program development; Seed money; Curriculum development; Internship funds; Technical assistance; Matching/challenge support.
Limitations: Applications accepted. Giving limited to the City of Philadelphia, PA. No support for national organizations, day or after-school care programs, routine social services or counseling, drug and alcohol addiction programs, religious education, private schools, hospitals, programs for animals, or summer recreation programs. No grants for endowment or building funds, travel, research, publications, deficit financing, scholarships, fellowships, purchase of tickets, tables, ads or sponsorships, parties, conferences, fairs and festivals, or disease research.
Publications: Application guidelines; Annual report (including application guidelines); Grants list.
Application information: Applicant must request guidelines before submitting proposals; the fund accepts Delaware Valley Grantmakers Common Grant Application and Common Report forms. Proposal Cover Sheet is available on foundation web site. Application form required.
Initial approach: Proposal or telephone requesting guidelines
Copies of proposal: 1

Deadline(s): For Arts and Humanities projects: by 5:00 p.m. on Jan. 15 or May 15; None for others
Board meeting date(s): Rolling application review, board meets 7 times a year
Final notification: Usually one or two months
Officers and Directors:* Valerie Clayton,* Pres.; Beverly Coleman,* V.P.; Helen Cunningham,* Secy. and Exec. Dir.; John Rice,* Treas.; Ida K. Chen; Sandra Featherman; Pari Hashemi; Gabriel Mandujano; Len Rieser; David H. Wice.
Number of staff: 1 full-time professional; 1 full-time support; 1 part-time support.
EIN: 231365325

8036
Ferree Foundation ✧
229 N. Duke St.
Lancaster, PA 17602-2709 (717) 735-8288, ext. 109
Contact: Phillip L. Calhoun, Exec. Dir.
FAX: (717) 735-8291;
E-mail: pcalhoun@ferree-foundation.org; Main URL: http://www.ferree-foundation.org

Established in 2004 in PA.
Foundation type: Independent foundation.
Financial data (yr. ended 12/31/12): Assets, $15,269,673 (M); gifts received, $770,044; expenditures, $1,379,614; qualifying distributions, $1,287,084; giving activities include $1,227,500 for 34 grants (high: $200,000; low: $1,000).
Purpose and activities: The foundation is dedicated to promoting and supporting excellence in the arts, culture and history, education, youth engagement, health, human services, and local economic and community development.
Fields of interest: Performing arts; Historical activities; Higher education; Education; Health care; Children/youth, services.
Type of support: Building/renovation; Endowments; Program development; Capital campaigns; Technical assistance; Research; General/operating support; Annual campaigns.
Limitations: Applications accepted. Giving primarily in Lancaster County and southeastern PA. No grants to individuals; no loans.
Publications: Application guidelines; Financial statement; Grants list; Program policy statement (including application guidelines).
Application information: Application guidelines available on foundation web site. Full proposals accepted by invitation only, following positive ruling on letter of inquiry. Delaware Valley Grantmakers Common Grant Application Form accepted. Application form not required.
Initial approach: Letter of inquiry (1-page maximum)
Copies of proposal: 1
Deadline(s): Oct. 15th
Board meeting date(s): Bi-annually
Final notification: Ruling on letter of inquiry within 1 month
Officers and Directors:* Paul W. Ware,* Pres.; Ron Frederick, V.P.; Phillip L. Calhoun, Exec. Dir.; Judy S. Ware.
Number of staff: 1 part-time professional; 1 part-time support.
EIN: 201060557
Selected grants: The following grants are a representative sample of this grantmaker's funding activity:
$100,000 to Elizabethtown College, Elizabethtown, PA, 2012. For The Ware Collo Quium on Peacemaking and Global Citizenship.
$100,000 to Lancaster Country Day School, Lancaster, PA, 2012. For Dare to Be Great Campaign.
$100,000 to Lancaster Symphony Orchestra, Lancaster, PA, 2012. For Conductors Position Fund.
$100,000 to Pennsylvania Ballet, Philadelphia, PA, 2012. For Raising the Barre the Campaign for Pennsylvania Ballet.
$60,000 to Saint James Episcopal Church, Lancaster, PA, 2012. For Gifts Across Generations.
$10,000 to Elizabethtown College, Elizabethtown, PA, 2012. For unrestricted trustee pledge.
$2,000 to Boy Scouts of America, Cradle of Liberty Council, Wayne, PA, 2012. For Thank You Gift.
$2,000 to Water for People, Denver, CO, 2012. For Office Space Renovations.

8037
Joseph and Marie Field Foundation ✧
c/o E.R. Boynton
30 Valley Stream Pkwy.
Malvern, PA 19355-1462

Established in 1999 in PA.
Donors: Joseph M. Field; Marie H. Field.
Foundation type: Independent foundation.
Financial data (yr. ended 07/31/13): Assets, $37,868,854 (M); gifts received, $2,176,750; expenditures, $1,871,653; qualifying distributions, $1,859,060; giving activities include $1,859,060 for 21 grants (high: $250,000; low: $25,000).
Fields of interest: Performing arts centers; Performing arts, music; Performing arts, orchestras; Higher education; Neuroscience research.
Limitations: Applications not accepted. Giving primarily in Philadelphia, PA. No grants to individuals.
Application information: Contributes only to pre-selected organizations.
Officers and Directors:* Joseph M. Field,* Pres. and Treas.; Marie H. Field,* V.P. and Secy.; John C. Donlevie.
EIN: 233009586
Selected grants: The following grants are a representative sample of this grantmaker's funding activity:
$250,000 to Thomas Jefferson University Hospitals, Philadelphia, PA, 2011.
$100,000 to University of Pennsylvania, Philadelphia, PA, 2011. For endowment.

8038
Fieldstone 1793 Foundation ✧
2250 Hickory Rd., Ste. 450
Plymouth Meeting, PA 19462-1037

Established in 2006 in PA.
Donor: Barbara M. Jordan.
Foundation type: Independent foundation.
Financial data (yr. ended 12/31/12): Assets, $2,952,316 (M); expenditures, $1,109,119; qualifying distributions, $1,081,906; giving activities include $1,081,500 for 63 grants (high: $200,000; low: $1,000).
Fields of interest: Historic preservation/historical societies; Arts; Medical school/education; Environment, natural resources; Breast cancer; Health organizations; Human services; Women, centers/services.
Type of support: General/operating support; Program development.
Limitations: Applications not accepted. Giving primarily in PA and VT. No grants to individuals.
Application information: Contributes only to pre-selected organizations.
Trustee: Barbara M. Jordan.
EIN: 207138983

8039
The Fine Foundation ✧
(formerly The Fine Family Foundation)
c/o FFC Capital Corp.
625 Liberty Ave., Ste. 3110
Pittsburgh, PA 15222-3115 (412) 444-3521
Contact: Susan H. Brownlee, Exec. Dir.
FAX: (412) 697-0872;
E-mail: info@thefinefoundation.org

Established in 2007 in PA.
Donors: Milton Fine; The Milton Fine Irrevocable Trust of 1998; The Milton Fine Irrevocable Trust of 2000.
Foundation type: Independent foundation.
Financial data (yr. ended 12/31/12): Assets, $1,902,419 (M); gifts received, $3,500,000; expenditures, $2,459,548; qualifying distributions, $2,454,424; giving activities include $2,089,683 for 226 grants (high: $165,000; low: $100).
Purpose and activities: Giving primarily for arts and culture, Jewish life, science and medicine, and to benefit Pittsburgh, PA.
Fields of interest: Visual arts; Museums (art); Arts; Higher education; Health care; Medical research, institute; Human services; Jewish federated giving programs; Science; Jewish agencies & synagogues.
Type of support: Program development; Film/video/radio; Publication; Seed money; Research; Program evaluation.
Limitations: Applications accepted. Giving primarily in Pittsburgh, PA.
Publications: Application guidelines.
Application information: Grantmakers of Western Pennsylvania's Common Grant Application Format accepted. Application form not required.
Initial approach: Letter of inquiry
Deadline(s): None
Board meeting date(s): Varies, 2 times per year
Final notification: Within 60 days
Officers and Directors:* Milton Fine,* Chair. and Pres.; Sheila Fine, Secy.-Treas.; Susan H. Brownlee,* Exec. Dir.; Richard Armstrong; David Fine; Carolyn Fine Friedman; Keith Kanel; Sibyl Fine King; Judy Roscow.
Number of staff: 2 full-time professional.
EIN: 256335329

8040
First Community Foundation Partnership of Pennsylvania ✧
(formerly Williamsport-Lycoming Foundation)
330 Pine St., Ste. 401
Williamsport, PA 17701-6242 (570) 321-1500
Contact: For grants and scholarships: Betty Gilmour, Dir., Grantmaking
FAX: (570) 321-6434;
E-mail: jenniferw@fcfpartnership.org; Additional tel.: (866) 901-2372; Grant and scholarship inquiry

e-mail: bettyg@fcfpartnership.org; Main URL: http://www.fcfpa.org

Established in 1916 in PA by bank resolution.
Foundation type: Community foundation.
Financial data (yr. ended 12/31/13): Assets, $80,333,056 (M); gifts received, $2,721,145; expenditures, $3,888,220; giving activities include $2,427,904 for 106+ grants (high: $150,110).
Purpose and activities: The foundation serves Central and Northcentral PA by helping donors make a difference in the community and making grants to nonprofit organizations in support of their charitable work.
Fields of interest: Historic preservation/historical societies; Arts; Higher education; Education; Environment, natural resources; Environment; Health care; Recreation; Youth development; Youth, services; Family services; Human services; Economic development; Community/economic development.
Type of support: Computer technology; General/operating support; Continuing support; Capital campaigns; Building/renovation; Equipment; Land acquisition; Program development; Conferences/seminars; Seed money; Scholarship funds; Program-related investments/loans; Matching/challenge support.
Limitations: Applications accepted. Giving primarily in Central and Northcentral PA. No support for sectarian religious programs, clubs, sports teams, cemeteries, school districts, or fire companies. No grants to individuals (except for scholarships), or generally for endowment funds, annual campaigns, event sponsorships, debt reduction, fellowships, honorary awards, travel grants, or ongoing operating support; no loans to individuals.
Publications: Application guidelines; Annual report; Financial statement; Informational brochure; Program policy statement.
Application information: Visit foundation web site for application guidelines per grant type. Based on letter of intent, nonprofit organizations will be notified of whether they will be invited to submit a full grant application or whether their proposal has been denied. Application form required.

Initial approach: Submit letter of intent
Copies of proposal: 1
Deadline(s): Varies
Board meeting date(s): Monthly
Final notification: Varies

Officers and Directors:* Marshall Welch III,* Chair.; Frank Pellegrino,* Vice-Chair.; Jennifer D. Wilson,* C.E.O. and Pres.; Dawn M. Linn,* V.P., Planned Philanthropy.; Jack Willoughby,* C.F.O.; Timothy D. Fitzgerald,* Secy.; Jay B. Alexander; Lise M. Barrick; Thomas Charles; Ronald Cimini; Davie Jane Gilmour, Ph.D.; Tim Karr; Daniel A. Klingerman; Keith S. Kuzio; George E. Logue, Jr.; Grace M. Mahon; Trisha G. Marty; Teri MacBride; R. Jack McKernan, Jr.; Gary Peck; Ted Strosser; Leslie P. Temple; Alice Trowbridge; Tammy A. Weber; Bob Wayne; Jennifer Wilson; Sue Young.
Number of staff: 4 full-time professional; 1 part-time professional; 1 full-time support; 1 part-time support.
EIN: 246013117

8041
The First Hospital Foundation ✧

230 S. Broad St., Ste. 402
Philadelphia, PA 19102-4108 (215) 546-4290
Contact: Ann Marie Healy, Exec. Dir.; Julia Boerth, Prog. Off.
FAX: (215) 546-4291;
E-mail: info@firsthospitalfdn.org; E-mail for Ann Marie Healy: amhealy@firsthospitalfdn.org; Main URL: http://www.firsthospitalfdn.org
Blog: http://firsthospitalfdn.org/news-events/
Grants List: http://firsthospitalfdn.org/grantees/

Established in 1997 in PA.
Foundation type: Independent foundation.
Financial data (yr. ended 12/31/13): Assets, $44,020,594 (M); expenditures, $1,835,002; qualifying distributions, $1,733,309; giving activities include $1,392,772 for 53 grants (high: $96,700; low: $1,650).
Purpose and activities: The foundation seeks to provide funding support for the health needs of the underserved in the communities served by the Pennsylvania Hospital.
Fields of interest: Health care; Crime/violence prevention, abuse prevention; Human services; Community/economic development; Children; Youth; Adults; Aging; Disabilities, people with; Physically disabled; Blind/visually impaired; Deaf/hearing impaired; Mentally disabled; Minorities; Asians/Pacific Islanders; African Americans/Blacks; Hispanics/Latinos; Native Americans/American Indians; Women; Substance abusers; AIDS, people with; Single parents; Terminal illness, people with; Economically disadvantaged; Homeless; LGBTQ.
Type of support: Program evaluation; Program development; Matching/challenge support; Management development/capacity building; General/operating support; Equipment; Continuing support.
Limitations: Applications accepted. Giving primarily in the greater Philadelphia region, preference to Philadelphia County. No support for fraternal organizations, political parties, candidates, veterans, labor or local civic groups, groups engaged in influencing legislation. No grants for capital campaigns or costs associated with foundation fundraising; major building projects (minor renovations that relate directly to the effectiveness of the program may be considered); no scholarships, fellowships, grants to individuals.
Publications: Application guidelines; Financial statement; Grants list; IRS Form 990 or 990-PF printed copy available upon request.
Application information: Faxed applications are not accepted. Application form required.

Initial approach: Submit application form from foundation web site via e-mail or U.S. Mail
Deadline(s): July 31
Board meeting date(s): Apr., Oct. and Dec.

Officers and Directors:* Julia Dutton, Ph.D.*, Chair.; Jane G. Pepper,* Vice-Chair.; Suzanne Sheehan Becker, Secy.; Keith Kasper, MBA*, Treas.; Ann Marie Healy, Exec. Dir.; R. Michael Buckley, Jr., M.D.; Helen L. Coons, Ph.D., ABPP; Joanne R. Denworth; Bruce W. Herdman, M.B.A., Ph.D.; Natalie Levkovich; Sueyun Pyo Locks; Lawrence T. Mangan; A. Scott McNeal, DO; Susan E. Phillips; Pamela A. Strisofksy.
Number of staff: 1 full-time professional.
EIN: 232904262

8042
Firstfruits Foundation ✧

P.O. Box 239
Elverson, PA 19520-0239

Established in 1995 in PA.
Donors: Robert L. Cone; Dawn M. Cone.
Foundation type: Independent foundation.
Financial data (yr. ended 12/31/13): Assets, $4,594,551 (M); gifts received, $50,000; expenditures, $1,033,509; qualifying distributions, $991,601; giving activities include $986,800 for 14 grants (high: $669,300; low: $3,000).
Purpose and activities: Giving primarily to Christian and Baptist churches, schools, and ministries.
Fields of interest: Higher education; Theological school/education; Education; Christian agencies & churches; Protestant agencies & churches.
Type of support: Program-related investments/loans; General/operating support.
Limitations: Applications not accepted. Giving primarily in PA, TX and WI. No grants to individuals.
Application information: Contributes only to pre-selected organizations.
Officers: Robert L. Cone, Pres. and Treas.; Edward H. Cone, V.P. and Secy.
Director: Derial H. Sanders.
EIN: 232808624

8043
FISA Foundation

535 Smithfield St., Ste. 710
Pittsburgh, PA 15222-2393 (412) 456-5550
Contact: Kristy Trautmann, Exec. Dir.
FAX: (412) 456-5551;
E-mail: info@fisafoundation.org; Main URL: http://www.fisafoundation.org/
Facebook: http://www.facebook.com/fisafoundation
FISA Foundation's Philanthropy Promise: http://www.ncrp.org/philanthropys-promise/who
Grants Database: http://fisafoundation.org/grants/grants-awarded/
YouTube: http://www.youtube.com/user/fisafoundation/feed?feature=context

Established in 1996 in PA; converted from proceeds received through the sale of Harmaville Rehabilitation Center to HEALTHSOUTH Corporation.
Foundation type: Independent foundation.
Financial data (yr. ended 06/30/13): Assets, $39,993,295 (M); gifts received, $8,676; expenditures, $2,227,332; qualifying distributions, $1,992,522; giving activities include $1,591,837 for 79 grants (high: $53,751; low: $200).
Purpose and activities: The foundation's mission is to build a culture of respect and improve the quality of life for three populations in southwestern Pennsylvania: women, girls, and people with disabilities.
Fields of interest: Medical care, rehabilitation; Health care; Mental health/crisis services, rape victim services; Mental health/crisis services; Autism; Crime/violence prevention, domestic violence; Crime/violence prevention, sexual abuse; Employment, vocational rehabilitation; Employment, sheltered workshops; Recreation; Girl scouts; Human services; Family services, domestic violence; Family services, adolescent parents; Women, centers/services; Human services; Civil/human rights, disabled; Civil/human rights;

Disabilities, people with; Mentally disabled; Women; Girls.
Type of support: General/operating support; Continuing support; Capital campaigns; Building/renovation; Equipment; Program development; Conferences/seminars; Seed money; Technical assistance; Program evaluation; Matching/challenge support.
Limitations: Applications accepted. Giving limited to a 10-county area of southwestern PA, including: Allegheny, Armstrong, Beaver, Butler, Greene, Fayette, Indiana, Lawrence, Washington, and Westmoreland counties. No support for organizations that lack tax-exempt status, or for religious purposes. No grants to individuals, or for scholarships, endowments, travel, or study.
Publications: Application guidelines; Annual report; Financial statement; Occasional report.
Application information: Unsolicited inquiries accepted, but unsolicited proposals are not. Full proposal is by invitation only; Grantmakers of Western Pennsylvania's Common Grant Application Format accepted. Application form required.
Initial approach: Letter of inquiry along with foundation application form (which can be downloaded from foundation web site), via U.S. mail or e-mail
Copies of proposal: 1
Deadline(s): 3-4 months prior to board meeting
Board meeting date(s): Feb., June and Oct.
Final notification: Within 2 weeks
Officers and Board Members:* Susan L. Chase,* Pres.; Linda Beerbower Burke, Esq.*, V.P.; Margaret Mary Kimmel, Ph.D.*, Secy.; Margaret Mary Kanaan,* Treas.; Kristy Trautmann, Exec. Dir.; Tina Calabro; Kulsum G. Davidson; Susan Davis; Susan Kirsch; Deborah W. Linhart; Carol S. MacPhail; Rosa Copeland Miller; Cheryl A. Parzych; Evelyn D. Savido; Janet Simon, Ph.D.; Bernadette Eyler Smith; Ellen Srodes; Tamiko L. Stanley; Andrea M. Williams; Elise Roby Yanders.
Number of staff: 2 full-time professional; 1 full-time support.
EIN: 250965388
Selected grants: The following grants are a representative sample of this grantmaker's funding activity:
$110,000 to National Council of Jewish Women, Pittsburgh Section, New York, NY, 2014. For STANDING FIRM: The Business Case to End Partner Violence, payable over 2.00 years.
$105,000 to Childrens Hospital of Pittsburgh Foundation, Pittsburgh, PA, 2014. For continued support for initiative to improve the transition from pediatric to adult health care for youth with disabilities, payable over 3.00 years.
$60,000 to Lifesteps, Butler, PA, 2014. For general operating support to strengthen services to people with disabilities across southwestern Pennsylvania.
$60,000 to South Hills Interfaith Ministries, Bethel Park, PA, 2014. For domestic violence prevention and response among refugee families, payable over 2.00 years.
$40,000 to Pittsburgh Promise Foundation, Pittsburgh, PA, 2014. To increase participation in the Pittsburgh Promise by Pittsburgh Public School students with disabilities, payable over 2.00 years.
$35,000 to Strong Women, Strong Girls, Pittsburgh, PA, 2014. For general operating support for this after school mentoring and skill-building program that pairs college-age women with elementary school girls to promote mutual empowerment, payable over 2.00 years.
$30,000 to Gwens Girls, Pittsburgh, PA, 2014. For Operating support for the Girls Coalition of Southwestern Pennsylvania, a network of providers, funders and community leaders who are dedicated to improving the lives of girls, payable over 2.00 years.
$28,000 to Greater Pittsburgh Arts Council, Pittsburgh, PA, 2014. For continued support to promote inclusion and accessibility in arts and cultural organizations.
$25,000 to Planned Parenthood of Western Pennsylvania, Pittsburgh, PA, 2014. For adolescent peer to peer sexuality education to prevent pregnancy and sexually transmitted infections.
$15,000 to Pittsburgh Entertainment Project, Steeltown Entertainment Project, Pittsburgh, PA, 2014. To pilot a workforce development program that trains transition age youth with and without disabilities in film production.

8044
The Jill and Mark Fishman Foundation ✧ ☆

848 Roscommon Rd.
Bryn Mawr, PA 19010-1845

Donors: Jill Fishman; Mark Fishman.
Foundation type: Independent foundation.
Financial data (yr. ended 12/31/13): Assets, $15,397,976 (M); gifts received, $6,015,000; expenditures, $1,870,129; qualifying distributions, $1,768,582; giving activities include $1,768,582 for 30 grants (high: $1,500,000; low: $1,000).
Fields of interest: Arts; Health care; Jewish federated giving programs; Jewish agencies & synagogues.
Type of support: General/operating support.
Limitations: Applications not accepted. Giving primarily in PA.
Application information: Unsolicited requests for funds not accepted.
Trustees: Jill Fishman; Mark Fishman.
EIN: 272372930

8045
Lydia J. Fitch Trust ✧

c/o BNY Mellon, N.A.
P.O. Box 185
Pittsburgh, PA 15230-0185

Donor: Lydia J. Fitch.
Foundation type: Independent foundation.
Financial data (yr. ended 12/31/13): Assets, $10,876,472 (M); gifts received, $5,486; expenditures, $532,375; qualifying distributions, $480,274; giving activities include $447,804 for 7 grants (high: $74,468; low: $1,000).
Fields of interest: Health organizations; Housing/shelter, aging; Children/youth, services; Protestant agencies & churches.
Limitations: Applications not accepted. Giving primarily in NY and PA.
Application information: Unsolicited requests for funds not accepted.
Trustee: BNY Mellon, N.A.
EIN: 236463130

8046
The Foundation for Enhancing Communities ✧

(formerly The Greater Harrisburg Foundation)
200 N. 3rd St., 8th Fl.
P.O. Box 678
Harrisburg, PA 17108-0678 (717) 236-5040
Contact: Janice R. Black, C.E.O.; For grants: Jennifer Doyle, Dir., Devel. and Community Investment
FAX: (717) 231-4463; E-mail: janice@tfec.org; Grant application e-mail: jkuntche@tfec.org; Main URL: http://www.tfec.org
Scholarship inquiry e-mail: allison@tfec.org

Established in 1920 in PA; assets first acquired in 1940; grants first made in the mid-1940's.
Foundation type: Community foundation.
Financial data (yr. ended 12/31/13): Assets, $62,195,211 (M); gifts received, $5,113,453; expenditures, $9,606,210; giving activities include $5,486,331 for 352+ grants (high: $216,530), and $499,704 for 268 grants to individuals.
Purpose and activities: The foundation seeks to stimulate philanthropy and enhance the quality of life in the community through accumulating, managing and disbursing financial assets, and to serve as a catalyst and neutral convener to meet a wide range of community needs in the south central Pennsylvania counties of Cumberland, Dauphin, Franklin, Lebanon, and Perry, and also in the Dillsburg area.
Fields of interest: Humanities; Arts; Education; Environment; Health care; Health organizations, association; Human services; Community/economic development; Religion.
Type of support: General/operating support; Equipment; Program development; Publication; Seed money; Scholarship funds; Technical assistance; Scholarships—to individuals; Matching/challenge support.
Limitations: Applications accepted. Giving primarily in Cumberland, Dauphin, Franklin, Lebanon, and Perry counties, PA. No support for religious organizations for religious purposes (except from Donor-Advised or Restricted funds), or for private foundations or discretionary funds. No grants to individuals (except for scholarships).
Publications: Application guidelines; Annual report (including application guidelines); Financial statement; Grants list; Informational brochure (including application guidelines); Newsletter; Program policy statement.
Application information: Call Prog. Off. for current application guidelines or visit foundation web site; copies of application vary per regional fdn. Application form required.
Initial approach: Contact Prog. Off.
Deadline(s): Varies
Board meeting date(s): Jan., Mar., June, Sept., and Nov.
Final notification: Approx. 8 weeks after proposal submission
Officers and Directors:* Kathy Pape,* Chair.; L. Jeffrey Mattern,* Vice-Chair.; Janice R. Black,* C.E.O. and Pres.; Neal S. West, Esq.,* Secy.; Steven M. Hoffman,* Treas.; Kirk C. Demyan,* C.F.O.; Dolly M. Lalvani, Asst. Treas.; Marilynn R. Abrams; Cate Barron; Barbara A. Darkes; Carolyn C. Dumaresq; Michael R. Gillepsie; Nancy J. Glen; Glenn P. Heisey; David Schankweiler; Karen F. Snider; Cynthia Tolsma.
Trustee Banks: BNY Mellon, N.A.; Bryn Mawr Trust Company; Citizens Bank of Southern Pennslyvania; Farmers Trust of Carlisle; Financial Trust Services;

First National Bank & Trust of Waynesboro; First National Bank of Greencastle; Fulton Financial Advisors, N.A.; GHF, Inc.; Hershey Trust Co.; Juniata Valley Bank; M&T Bank; PNC Bank, N.A.; Pennsylvania State Bank; Sentry Trust Co.; Susquehanna Bank; Valley Bank & Trust Co.; Wachovia Bank, N.A.; Wells Fargo.
Number of staff: 9 full-time professional; 1 part-time professional; 2 full-time support.
EIN: 010564355
Selected grants: The following grants are a representative sample of this grantmaker's funding activity:
$187,500 to United Way of the Capital Region, Enola, PA, 2012.
$173,500 to Central Pennsylvania Workforce Development Corporation, Lewisburg, PA, 2012.
$120,000 to Lancaster County Workforce Investment Board, Lancaster, PA, 2012.
$96,000 to NACER, USA, Bluffton, OH, 2012.
$82,000 to Lancaster-Lebanon Intermediate Unit 13, Lancaster, PA, 2012.
$80,551 to Helping a Hero, Houston, TX, 2012.
$80,317 to Perry County Council of the Arts, Newport, PA, 2012.
$75,000 to YWCA of Greater Harrisburg, Harrisburg, PA, 2012.
$56,000 to Harrisburg Area Community College Foundation, Harrisburg, PA, 2012.
$50,000 to Jewish Community Foundation of Central Pennsylvania, Harrisburg, PA, 2012.

8047
Fourjay Foundation ✧
2300 Computer Ave., Bldg. G, Ste. 1
Willow Grove, PA 19090-1753 (215) 830-1437
Contact: Ann T. Bucci, Grants Coord.
FAX: (215) 830-0157; E-mail: info@fourjay.org; Main URL: http://www.fourjay.org

Established in 1988 in PA.
Donors: Eugene W. Jackson†; Springhouse Realty Co.
Foundation type: Independent foundation.
Financial data (yr. ended 12/31/13): Assets, $16,851,922 (M); expenditures, $1,143,271; qualifying distributions, $962,794; giving activities include $828,950 for 161 grants (high: $50,000; low: $200).
Purpose and activities: The foundation supports education and human services. Its directors believe these two areas of human endeavor offer people the greatest help; education enables people to make the most of their abilities; human services offer a helping hand to the afflicted, the socially disadvantaged, and the financially handicapped.
Fields of interest: Higher education; Adult education—literacy, basic skills & GED; Medical care, rehabilitation; Nursing care; Health care; Substance abuse, services; Mental health/crisis services; Health organizations, association; Cancer; Eye diseases; Ear, nose & throat diseases; Food services; Human services; Children/youth, services; Family services; Residential/custodial care, hospices; Aging, centers/services; Homeless, human services; Disabilities, people with; Economically disadvantaged; Homeless.
Type of support: General/operating support; Continuing support; Building/renovation; Equipment; Endowments; Emergency funds; Program development; Publication; Seed money; Scholarship funds; Matching/challenge support.
Limitations: Applications accepted. Giving limited to Philadelphia, Bucks, and Montgomery counties, PA. No support for political or religious organizations, museums, musical groups, theaters, or cultural organizations, athletic groups, civic associations, alumni associations, elementary or secondary schools, foreign organizations, public broadcasting, libraries, the United Way, or the YMCA. No grants to individuals or multi-year grants.
Publications: Application guidelines; Grants list.
Application information: Telephone calls accepted. Submit 1 complete proposal and 7 copies of cover proposal letter; only 1 application per organization accepted per year. Grant requests lacking appropriate financial information will not be accepted. All requests for foundation guidelines should be submitted in writing on the grant seeking organization's letterhead, with the appropriate return mailing and contact information provided. Copies of current guidelines can be downloaded from the foundation web site. Unannounced or impromptu visits are not entertained. Delaware Valley Grantmakers Common Grant Application Form accepted. Application form not required.
Initial approach: Proposal and separate 1-page cover letter on organization letterhead
Deadline(s): See foundation web site for current deadlines
Board meeting date(s): Mar. 15, June 15, Sept. 15, and Dec. 15
Final notification: Generally within 90 days of proposal receipt
Officer and Directors:* Susan Jackson Tressider, Exec. Dir. and Managing Tr.; Geoffrey W. Jackson,* Managing Tr.; Sean E. Brinda; Diana Loukedis Doherty; Marie-Louise Jackson; Daniel O'Connell, Esq.; Jean Robinson.
Number of staff: 1 part-time professional; 1 part-time support.
EIN: 232537126

8048
Franklin St. Giving Tree Foundation ✧ ☆
(formerly Clark Family Foundation)
P.O. Box 409
Lahaska, PA 18931

Established in 2000 in PA.
Donors: Richard T. Clark Living Trust, Jr.; Angela Clark Living Trust.
Foundation type: Operating foundation.
Financial data (yr. ended 12/31/13): Assets, $5,408,219 (M); gifts received, $3,200,575; expenditures, $501,290; qualifying distributions, $500,000; giving activities include $500,000 for 3 grants (high: $250,000; low: $50,000).
Fields of interest: Higher education; Hospitals (general); Human services; Catholic agencies & churches.
Limitations: Applications not accepted. Giving in the U.S., with some emphasis on PA and VA. No grants to individuals.
Application information: Unsolicited requests for funds not accepted.
Trustees: Angela Clark; Kelly Lynn Clark; Lisa Marie Clark; Richard Clark, Jr.
EIN: 256667093

8049
Helen Clay Frick Foundation ✧
c/o BNY Mellon, N.A.
Room 151-3825
Pittsburgh, PA 15258-0001

Newly formed in 2002 in PA from The Helen Clay Frick Foundation.
Donor: The Helen Clay Frick Foundation.
Foundation type: Independent foundation.
Financial data (yr. ended 12/31/13): Assets, $24,176,690 (M); expenditures, $1,375,509; qualifying distributions, $1,308,457; giving activities include $1,255,467 for 74 grants (high: $230,000; low: $1,000).
Fields of interest: Arts; Higher education; Education; Human services.
Limitations: Applications not accepted. Giving on a national basis. No grants to individuals.
Application information: Contributes only to pre-selected organizations.
Board meeting date(s): Nov.
Officers: Adelaide F. Trafton, Chair.; I. Townsend Burden III, Secy.
Trustees: Peter P. Blanchard III; Childs Frick Burden; Dixon Frick Burden; Frances D. Burden; Henry S. Burden; Helen Clay Chace; Arabella S. Dane; Elise Frick; Frances Frick; H. Clay Frick III; Henry Clay Frick II; Mrs. Henry Clay Frick II; Martha F.S. Sanger; J. Fife Symington III.
EIN: 300091891
Selected grants: The following grants are a representative sample of this grantmaker's funding activity:
$214,000 to Frick Collection, New York, NY, 2011.
$40,000 to Santa Barbara Botanic Garden, Santa Barbara, CA, 2011.
$35,000 to Maine Coast Heritage Trust, Topsham, ME, 2011.
$35,000 to Oregon Shakespeare Festival, Ashland, OR, 2011.
$35,000 to Tanzanian Childrens Fund, Cambridge, MA, 2011.
$30,000 to Southeast Alaska Conservation Council, Juneau, AK, 2011.
$20,000 to Columbia University, New York, NY, 2011.
$8,000 to Maryland Historical Society, Baltimore, MD, 2011.
$7,500 to Garden Club of Virginia, Richmond, VA, 2011.
$5,000 to Spaulding Youth Center, Tilton, NH, 2011.
$2,500 to Boston Partners in Education, Boston, MA, 2010.

8050
Frick H C For City of PGH ✧
c/o BNY Mellon, N.A.
P. O. Box 185
Pittsburgh, PA 15230-0185

Established in PA.
Foundation type: Independent foundation.
Financial data (yr. ended 09/30/13): Assets, $16,363,172 (M); expenditures, $824,163; qualifying distributions, $783,658; giving activities include $762,288 for 1 grant.
Fields of interest: Recreation, parks/playgrounds.
Limitations: Applications not accepted. Giving primarily in Pittsburgh, PA. No grants to individuals.
Application information: Contributes only to pre-selected organizations.

Trustee: BNY Mellon, N.A.
EIN: 256018759

8051
Alexander Hamilton Fulton Trust ✧
c/o BNY Mellon, N.A.
P.O. Box 185
Pittsburgh, PA 15230-0185

Foundation type: Independent foundation.
Financial data (yr. ended 12/31/13): Assets, $22,696,843 (M); expenditures, $1,124,073; qualifying distributions, $1,040,480; giving activities include $1,002,507 for 2 grants (high: $902,256; low: $100,251).
Fields of interest: Higher education; Health care.
Limitations: Applications not accepted. Giving primarily in Burlington, VT.
Application information: Contributes only to pre-selected organizations.
Trustee: BNY Mellon, N.A.
EIN: 136882400
Selected grants: The following grants are a representative sample of this grantmaker's funding activity:
$104,339 to Fletcher Allen Health Care, Burlington, VT, 2011.

8052
The Eugene Garfield Foundation ✧ ☆
c/o Glenmede Trust Co.
1650 Market St., Ste. 1200
Philadelphia, PA 19103-7391 (215) 419-6000
Contact: Eugene Garfield, Chair., Pres. and Treas.

Established in 1988 in PA.
Donors: Eugene Garfield; Catheryne Stout.
Foundation type: Independent foundation.
Financial data (yr. ended 11/30/13): Assets, $3,694,264 (M); expenditures, $784,466; qualifying distributions, $766,064; giving activities include $761,500 for 25 grants (high: $300,000; low: $500).
Purpose and activities: Giving primarily for higher education and human services; funding also for the arts.
Fields of interest: Performing arts; Higher education; Medical school/education; Education; Human services.
Limitations: Applications accepted. Giving primarily in CA, NY, and PA. No grants to individuals.
Application information: Application form required.
Initial approach: Letter
Deadline(s): None
Officers: Eugene Garfield, Chair., Pres., and Treas.; Joshua Garfield, V.P. and Secy.
Director: Robert S. Bramson.
EIN: 232553258
Selected grants: The following grants are a representative sample of this grantmaker's funding activity:
$50,000 to University of Pennsylvania, Philadelphia, PA, 2011.
$25,000 to American Civil Liberties Union Foundation, New York, NY, 2011. For general purposes.
$25,000 to American Philosophical Society, Philadelphia, PA, 2011.
$20,000 to Center for Academic and Social Advancement, San Diego, CA, 2011.
$15,000 to Research America, Alexandria, VA, 2011.
$5,000 to American Philosophical Society, Philadelphia, PA, 2011.
$5,000 to Center for Academic and Social Advancement, San Diego, CA, 2011.
$3,000 to Chemical Heritage Foundation, Philadelphia, PA, 2011.
$1,000 to University of Pennsylvania, Philadelphia, PA, 2011.

8053
Genuardi Family Foundation ✧
470 Norristown Rd., Ste. 102
Blue Bell, PA 19422-2322 (610) 834-2030
Contact: Meredith A. Huffman, Exec. Dir.
E-mail: info@GenuardiFamilyFoundation.org; Main URL: http://www.genuardifamilyfoundation.org

Established in 2000 in PA.
Donors: Anthony D. Genuardi; Charles A. Genuardi; David T. Genuardi; Dominic S. Genuardi, Jr.; Francis L. Genuardi; Gasper A. Genuardi; James V. Genuardi; Laurence P. Genuardi; Michael A. Genuardi.
Foundation type: Independent foundation.
Financial data (yr. ended 12/31/13): Assets, $32,180,965 (M); expenditures, $1,564,154; qualifying distributions, $1,335,530; giving activities include $1,070,000 for 148 grants (high: $60,000; low: $2,000).
Purpose and activities: Giving primarily to: 1) promote the unity, health and well-being of families; 2) improve access to basic services for the most vulnerable in our communities; 3) prepare children, youth and adults for success in their schools, in the workplace and in their communities; and 4) invest in systems and sustainable change efforts to break the cycles of poverty and vulnerability, and build toward a better future for all people.
Fields of interest: Dental care; Reproductive health, prenatal care; Health care; Mental health/crisis services; Offenders/ex-offenders, transitional care; Offenders/ex-offenders, rehabilitation; Employment, training; Food distribution, meals on wheels; Housing/shelter; Youth development; Human services, self-help groups; Human services, emergency aid; Disabilities, people with; Military/veterans.
Type of support: General/operating support; Program development; Scholarship funds; Technical assistance; Program evaluation.
Limitations: Applications accepted. Giving in the foundation's core grant program limited to Montgomery, Chester, Delaware and Bucks Counties in PA, including Philadelphia-based organizations that provide services in these four counties. No support for organizations outside the Greater Philadelphia, PA area. No support for political organizations, or for public, private or parochial schools that serve the general public, fraternal and/or civic organizations, public radio or television, environmental issues or initiatives, or to other foundations or organizations which redistribute resources to beneficiaries of their own selection, including The United Way. No grants to individuals, or for capital projects, including equipment purchase or replacement, general fundraising, annual appeals or special events, endowment drives, or debt reduction.
Application information: Applications are only accepted online. Paper applications are not accepted. Initial letters of inquiry are required for all applicants regardless of prior funding. Only invited full proposals will be reviewed. Application form not required.
Initial approach: Letter of inquiry to be submitted online via foundation web site, between June 1 and June 30
Deadline(s): Sept. 1 for invited proposals
Board meeting date(s): Feb., May and Sept.
Final notification: Mar.
Officers and Directors:* Laurence P. Genuardi,* Pres.; Charles A. Genuardi,* V.P.; Meredith Huffman,* Secy. and Exec. Dir.; Tom Genuardi, Jr.,* Treas.; Beth Borrelli; Robert C. Fernandez, Esq.; Anthony D. Genuardi; David T. Genuardi; Francis L. Genuardi; Gasper A. Genuardi; James V. Genuardi; Michael A. Genuardi; Michael B. Kennedy; Joy Mears.
Number of staff: 1 full-time professional; 1 part-time support.
EIN: 233041300

8054
The Cindy & Murry Gerber Foundation ✧ ☆
c/o Metz Lewis, Larry S. Blair
535 Smithfield St., Ste. 800
Pittsburgh, PA 15222-2305

Donors: Cindy Gerber; Murray Gerber.
Foundation type: Independent foundation.
Financial data (yr. ended 12/31/13): Assets, $5,999,555 (M); gifts received, $1,505,436; expenditures, $502,542; qualifying distributions, $481,914; giving activities include $481,914 for 25 grants (high: $228,914; low: $500).
Fields of interest: Arts; Education; Human services.
Type of support: General/operating support.
Limitations: Applications not accepted. Giving primarily in PA.
Application information: Unsolicited requests for funds not accepted.
Officer: Cindy Akers Gerber, Chair.
Board Members: Larry S. Blair; Murry S. Gerber.
EIN: 452954190

8055
Giant Eagle Foundation ✧ ☆
c/o Gaint Eagle, Inc., Attn.: David S. Shapira
101 Kappa Dr.
Pittsburgh, PA 15238-2809

Established in PA.
Foundation type: Independent foundation.
Financial data (yr. ended 06/30/13): Assets, $4,344,764 (M); gifts received, $4,472,328; expenditures, $4,498,457; qualifying distributions, $4,478,743; giving activities include $4,478,743 for 172 grants (high: $2,113,577; low: $180).
Fields of interest: Arts; Education; Health organizations; Human services; Jewish agencies & synagogues.
Limitations: Applications accepted. Giving primarily in OH and PA.
Application information: Application form required.
Initial approach: Letter
Deadline(s): None
Officers: David Shapira, Chair.; Louis Plung, Vice-Chair.
Directors: Gerald Chait; Laura Karet; Edward Moravitz; Charles Porter; Norman Weizenbaum.
EIN: 320384487

8056
Addison H. Gibson Foundation ✧
1 PPG Pl., Ste. 2230
Pittsburgh, PA 15222-5401
Contact: Rebecca Wallace, Dir.
E-mail contact for loans: ldunbar@gibson-fnd.org

Foundation established in 1937 in PA.
Donor: Addison H. Gibson†.
Foundation type: Independent foundation.
Financial data (yr. ended 12/31/13): Assets, $35,033,571 (M); gifts received, $2,420,501; expenditures, $1,813,673; qualifying distributions, $2,416,397; giving activities include $505,642 for grants to individuals, and $672,908 for loans to individuals.
Purpose and activities: The purpose of the foundation is to help the people of western PA to become productive members of society (through education) or to return to productivity by receiving necessary medical treatment. To this end, the foundation provides limited grants to healthcare providers on behalf of self-supporting residents of western PA who have correctable medical conditions but do not have health insurance or the ability to pay for necessary treatment. The foundation also provides low-interest education loans to residents of western PA who have successfully completed at least one year of undergraduate or graduate study and continue to be enrolled as full-time students at an accredited college or university.
Fields of interest: Higher education; Health care.
Type of support: Student loans—to individuals.
Limitations: Applications not accepted. Giving limited to residents of western PA. No support for weekend college, distance learning or degree completion program participants, students attending for-profit universities, or for students with a recent history of poor credit. No grants for building funds, endowments, operating budgets, or special projects.
Application information: The foundation is no longer accepting applications.
Board meeting date(s): 9 times annually
Director: Rebecca Wallace.
Trustees: Douglas E. Gilbert, Esq.; Timothy M. Slavish, Esq.; PNC Bank, N.A.
Number of staff: 2 full-time professional; 1 full-time support.
EIN: 250965379

8057
Sonia Raiziss Giop Charitable Foundation ✧
c/o Bank of New York Mellon, N.A.
P.O. Box 185
Pittsburgh, PA 15230-0185

Established in 1994 in PA.
Donors: Sonia Giop†; Ines Giop Trust; Benz Charitable Remainder Unitrust.
Foundation type: Independent foundation.
Financial data (yr. ended 12/31/13): Assets, $3,645,974 (M); expenditures, $462,378; qualifying distributions, $456,964; giving activities include $455,150 for 29 grants (high: $234,150; low: $2,000).
Purpose and activities: Giving primarily for education, the arts, particularly for poetry and other literary organizations, and animal welfare.
Fields of interest: Performing arts, music; Literature; Arts; Higher education; Animal welfare.
Limitations: Applications not accepted. Giving primarily in NY. No grants to individuals.
Application information: Contributes only to pre-selected organizations.
Trustees: Alfredo De Palchi; Antoinette Denisof; Bank of New York Mellon, N.A.
EIN: 256453053
Selected grants: The following grants are a representative sample of this grantmaker's funding activity:
$15,000 to Columbia University, Department of Italian, New York, NY, 2012. For operational.

8058
The Gitlin Foundation ✧
(formerly The Harvey S. Gitlin Family Foundation)
270 Commerce Dr., Ste. 101
Fort Washington, PA 19034-2405

Established in 1999 in PA.
Donors: Harvey S. Gitlin; Amy Gitlin; Michelle Gitlin Goldstein.
Foundation type: Independent foundation.
Financial data (yr. ended 12/31/13): Assets, $26,594,622 (M); gifts received, $1,000,000; expenditures, $1,016,569; qualifying distributions, $973,000; giving activities include $973,000 for 9 grants (high: $100,000; low: $1,000).
Purpose and activities: Giving primarily for health, youth services, and Jewish organizations.
Fields of interest: Arts; Cancer; Health organizations; Medical research, institute; Jewish agencies & synagogues; Youth.
Limitations: Applications not accepted. Giving primarily in PA. No grants to individuals.
Application information: Unsolicited requests for funds not accepted.
Officers and Directors:* Michelle Gitlin Goldstein,* Pres.; Amy E. Gitlin,* Treas.; Harvey S. Gitlin.
EIN: 256645244
Selected grants: The following grants are a representative sample of this grantmaker's funding activity:
$50,000 to American Cancer Society, Philadelphia, PA, 2012. For Charitable Continue Fight for a Cure.

8059
Anne & Philip Glatfelter III Family Foundation ✧
c/o Bryn Mawr Trust Co.
1 E. Chocolate Ave., Ste. 200
Hershey, PA 17033-1314 (717) 534-3225
Contact: Lisa Piergallini

Established in 2001 in PA.
Donor: Anne M. Glatfelter Charitable Lead Trust.
Foundation type: Operating foundation.
Financial data (yr. ended 12/31/13): Assets, $17,301,635 (M); gifts received, $1,100,376; expenditures, $670,462; qualifying distributions, $601,572; giving activities include $598,635 for 42 grants (high: $50,000; low: $2,500).
Fields of interest: Arts; Higher education; Education.
Limitations: Giving limited to southeastern PA. No grants to individuals.
Application information: Application form required.
Initial approach: Contact foundation for application form
Copies of proposal: 3
Deadline(s): Refer to application form for deadlines
Board meeting date(s): Apr. and Oct.
Officers: Elizabeth Glatfelter, Pres.; Patricia G. Foulkrod, Secy.
EIN: 233094915

8060
GlaxoSmithKline Foundation ✧
(formerly SmithKline Beecham Foundation)
5 Crescent Drive, NY0200
Philadelphia, PA 19112

Established in 1967 in DE.
Donors: GlaxoSmithKline LLC F.K.A. SmithKline; SmithKline Beecham Corp.
Foundation type: Company-sponsored foundation.
Financial data (yr. ended 12/31/12): Assets, $264,653 (M); gifts received, $3,387,589; expenditures, $3,294,843; qualifying distributions, $3,294,843; giving activities include $500,000 for 1 grant, and $2,794,843 for 10,501 employee matching gifts.
Purpose and activities: The foundation matches contributions made by part-time and full-time employees, directors, and retirees of GlaxoSmithKline to nonprofit organizations.
Fields of interest: General charitable giving.
Type of support: Employee matching gifts.
Limitations: Applications not accepted. Giving primarily in Philadelphia, PA. No grants to individuals.
Application information: Contributes only through employee matching gifts.
Officers and Directors:* Lewsley A. Tewnion,* Chair.; Mary Linda Andrews,* Secy.-Treas.; Robert W. Carr; M. Judith Lynch; Nancy K. Pekarek.
EIN: 232120418

8061
GlaxoSmithKline Patient Access Programs Foundation ✧
1 Franklin Plaza, Rm. 2335
Philadelphia, PA 19101 (888) 825-5249
Additional address: Frank Barrett, 200 N. 16th St., Philadelphia, PA 19102; Tel. for Bridges to Access: (866) 728-4368; Tel. for Commitment to Access: (866) 265-6491; Main URL: http://www.gskforyou.com/

Established as a company-sponsored operating foundation in 2003 in NC.
Donor: SmithKline Beecham Corp.
Foundation type: Operating foundation.
Financial data (yr. ended 12/31/12): Assets, $47,877,145 (M); gifts received, $620,484,885; expenditures, $620,484,885; qualifying distributions, $620,484,885; giving activities include $599,953,667 for grants to individuals.
Purpose and activities: The foundation provides for non-oncology prescription medication to economically disadvantaged patients without prescription drug benefits.
Fields of interest: Health care; Economically disadvantaged.
Type of support: Grants to individuals; Donated products.
Publications: Application guidelines.
Application information: Applications should include proof of income. Application form required.

Initial approach: Download application and mail to foundation
Deadline(s): None
Officers and Directors:* Lesley A. Tewnion,* Chair.; Mary Linda Andrews,* Secy.-Treas; Frank Barrett, Exec. Dir.; Eric Dube; Nancy J. Pekarek; William Shore.
EIN: 200031992

8062
Glencairn Foundation ✧
1 Pitcairn Pl., Ste. 3000
Jenkintown, PA 19046-3593 (617) 457-8368
Contact: Laird P. Pendleton, Secy.
FAX: (215) 881-6092; Application address: 10 Liberty Sq., 3rd Fl., Boston, MA 02109, tel.: (617) 457-8368

Incorporated in 1950 in PA.
Donors: Raymond Pitcairn†; and members of the Pitcairn family.
Foundation type: Independent foundation.
Financial data (yr. ended 12/31/12): Assets, $15,048,115 (M); expenditures, $822,037; qualifying distributions, $711,960; giving activities include $711,960 for grants.
Fields of interest: Christian agencies & churches.
Type of support: General/operating support; Building/renovation.
Limitations: Applications accepted. Giving primarily in Bryn Athyn, PA. No grants to individuals.
Application information: Application form required.
Initial approach: Letter
Deadline(s): Contact foundation for deadline
Board meeting date(s): As necessary
Officers: Kenneth Schauder, Pres.; Dean Pitcairn, V.P.; Laird Pendleton, Secy.; Kean Pitcairn, Treas.
Directors: Kai Bau-Madsen; Nathaniel Brock; Beth Jewell.
EIN: 231429828

8063
Gospel Evangelism Foundation ✧ ☆
c/o PNC Bank, N.A.
620 Liberty Ave., 10th Fl.
Pittsburgh, PA 15222-2705

Established in 1999 in PA.
Donors: Joseph F. Sprankle III; Brenda Lynn Sprankle; Carolyn Ann Sprankle; Melissa F Sprankle.
Foundation type: Independent foundation.
Financial data (yr. ended 12/31/13): Assets, $11,876,177 (L); expenditures, $1,213,746; qualifying distributions, $1,137,766; giving activities include $1,130,376 for 3 grants (high: $790,828; low: $139,558).
Purpose and activities: The foundation is primarily interested in accomplishing overseas mission work via U.S. agencies.
Fields of interest: Christian agencies & churches; Religion.
Limitations: Applications not accepted. No grants to individuals.
Application information: Unsolicited requests for funds not accepted.
Board meeting date(s): Contact foundation for dates
Trustee: PNC Bank, N.A.
EIN: 256639102

8064
The Grable Foundation ✧
650 Smithfield St., Ste. 240
Pittsburgh, PA 15222-3907 (412) 471-4550
Contact: Mary Anne Mistick, Grants Admin.
FAX: (412) 471-2267; E-mail: grable@grable.org; Main URL: http://www.grable.org

Established in 1976 in PA.
Donor: Minnie K. Grable†.
Foundation type: Independent foundation.
Financial data (yr. ended 12/31/12): Assets, $264,974,279 (M); expenditures, $13,106,377; qualifying distributions, $13,052,105; giving activities include $10,883,346 for 220 grants (high: $1,000,000; low: $1,500).
Purpose and activities: Giving primarily to organizations that improve educational opportunities, strengthen families and support community efforts that create an environment in which children can succeed.
Fields of interest: Arts education; Elementary/secondary education; Child development, education; Education; Employment, training; Youth, pregnancy prevention; Youth, services.
Type of support: General/operating support; Continuing support; Program development; Conferences/seminars; Seed money; Curriculum development; Research; Technical assistance; Consulting services; Program evaluation; Program-related investments/loans; Matching/challenge support.
Limitations: Applications accepted. Giving primarily in southwestern PA. No grants to individuals, or for scholarships, endowment funds or fundraising.
Publications: Annual report; Financial statement; Grants list.
Application information: Grable Grant Inquiry Sheet required and is available on website; applicants may also use Western Pennsylvania Common Grant Application Form, but must still submit Grable Grant Inquiry Sheet. Application form required.
Initial approach: Submit grant inquiry sheet
Copies of proposal: 1
Deadline(s): Jan. 1, May 1 and Sept. 1 for inquiry
Board meeting date(s): Mar., July, and Nov.
Final notification: Generally, following board meetings
Officers and Trustees:* Charles R. Burke, Jr.,* Chair.; Jan Nicholson,* Pres.; Steven E. Burke,* Treas.; Gregg Behr, Exec. Dir.; Susan H. Brownlee; Patricia Grable Burke; William H. Isler; Barbara Nicholson McFadyen; Marion Grable Nicholson.
Number of staff: 4 full-time professional; 2 part-time professional; 5 full-time support.
EIN: 251309888
Selected grants: The following grants are a representative sample of this grantmaker's funding activity:
$1,000,000 to Pittsburgh Promise Foundation, Pittsburgh, PA, 2012. For scholarships.
$300,000 to Sprout Fund, Pittsburgh, PA, 2012. For Pittsburgh Kids+Creativity.
$164,032 to Elizabeth Forward School District, Elizabeth, PA, 2012. To create technology-rich library.
$115,000 to Arts Education Collaborative, Pittsburgh, PA, 2012. To enhance arts education across Pittsburgh region.
$100,000 to Childrens Museum of Pittsburgh, Pittsburgh, PA, 2012. For MakeShop, a space dedicated to nurturing learning opportunities at the intersection of digital media and learning and do-it yourself practices.
$80,000 to Pittsburgh Association for the Education of Young Children, Pittsburgh, PA, 2012. For professional development.
$75,000 to ASSET, Inc., Pittsburgh, PA, 2012. For professional development.
$75,000 to Education Partnership, Pittsburgh, PA, 2012.
$65,000 to Carnegie Library of Pittsburgh, Pittsburgh, PA, 2012. For digital learning librarian for teen services and online programs.
$65,000 to Mentoring Partnership of Southwestern Pennsylvania, Pittsburgh, PA, 2012.
$65,000 to Planned Parenthood of Western Pennsylvania, Pittsburgh, PA, 2012. To train peer educators to reduce teen pregnancy and prevent school dropout in local middle and high schools.
$25,000 to Smart Futures, Pittsburgh, PA, 2012. For expansion of internet-based college and career mentoring program for teens.
$15,000 to Quantum Theater, Pittsburgh, PA, 2012. For in-school residencies linking high school students with theatrical productions.
$15,000 to Urban Impact Foundation, Pittsburgh, PA, 2012. For summer camp program.
$12,500 to Pittsburgh Arts and Lectures, Pittsburgh, PA, 2012. For community outreach.

8065
The Graham Foundation ✧
P.O. Box 1104
York, PA 17405-1104 (717) 849-4001
Contact: William H. Kerlin, Jr., Tr.

Established in 1986 in PA.
Donors: Graham Engineering Corp.; Graham Capital Corp.; Donald C. Graham; Graham Packaging Co., L.P.; Graham Packaging Holdings Co.; Graham Architectural Products Corp.
Foundation type: Company-sponsored foundation.
Financial data (yr. ended 12/31/13): Assets, $20,626,985 (M); gifts received, $110,000; expenditures, $821,106; qualifying distributions, $781,475; giving activities include $781,475 for 56 grants (high: $275,000; low: $125).
Purpose and activities: The foundation supports community foundations and organizations involved with arts and culture, education, land conservation, animals and wildlife, and human services.
Fields of interest: Arts; Education; Human services.
Type of support: General/operating support; Annual campaigns; Capital campaigns; Building/renovation; Program development; Scholarship funds; Sponsorships.
Limitations: Applications accepted. Giving primarily in York, PA. No grants to individuals.
Application information: Application form not required.
Initial approach: Proposal
Deadline(s): None
Trustees: Donald C. Graham; Ingrid A. Graham; Kristin Graham; William H. Kerlin, Jr.
EIN: 236805421

8066
Grass Family Foundation ✧
P.O. Box 1426
Mechanicsburg, PA 17055-1426

Established in 1972 in PA.
Donor: Alex Grass.
Foundation type: Independent foundation.

Financial data (yr. ended 11/30/13): Assets, $5,547,983 (M); expenditures, $1,060,276; qualifying distributions, $1,049,321; giving activities include $1,030,282 for 41 grants (high: $501,500; low: $50).
Purpose and activities: Giving primarily for the arts, education, health, and Jewish agencies and temples.
Fields of interest: Arts; Education; Health care; Human services; Jewish agencies & synagogues.
Limitations: Applications not accepted. Giving primarily in FL; Baltimore, MD; New York, NY; and Harrisburg, PA. No grants to individuals.
Application information: Contributes only to pre-selected organizations.
Directors: Rachel Shapiro; Emily Staszewski; Elizabeth Grass Weese.
EIN: 237218002

8067
The Alexander Grass Foundation ✧
P.O. Box 1426
Mechanicsburg, PA 17055-1426

Established in 2010 in PA.
Donors: Alexander Grass†; Grass Charitable Lead Annuity Trust.
Foundation type: Independent foundation.
Financial data (yr. ended 12/31/13): Assets, $22,081,975 (M); gifts received, $14,689,739; expenditures, $3,965,562; qualifying distributions, $3,864,000; giving activities include $3,864,000 for 16 grants (high: $1,436,500; low: $5,000).
Fields of interest: Education; Jewish federated giving programs; Jewish agencies & synagogues.
Type of support: General/operating support.
Limitations: Applications not accepted. Giving primarily in NY and PA.
Application information: Unsolicited requests for funds not accepted.
Officer and Directors:* Elizabeth Grass Weese,* Pres.; Roger L. Grass.
EIN: 272987061
Selected grants: The following grants are a representative sample of this grantmaker's funding activity:
$30,000 to Israel Education Fund, New York, NY, 2012. For Construction the Alexander Grass Nissan Nativ Acting Studio in Jaffa.

8068
Lois Lehrman Grass Foundation ✧
(formerly Lois F. Grass Foundation)
P.O. Box 593
Harrisburg, PA 17108-0593 (717) 652-2552
Contact: Lois Lehrman Grass, Chair.

Established in 1972 in PA.
Donors: Lois Lehrman Grass; Jody Grass; Linda Grass Shapiro; Elizabeth Grass Weese.
Foundation type: Independent foundation.
Financial data (yr. ended 11/30/13): Assets, $3,106,553 (M); expenditures, $484,224; qualifying distributions, $464,014; giving activities include $464,014 for 54 grants (high: $50,000; low: $150).
Purpose and activities: Giving primarily for arts and culture, women, and Jewish interests.
Fields of interest: Arts; Human services; Jewish agencies & synagogues; Women.
Type of support: General/operating support; Continuing support; Annual campaigns; Capital campaigns; Building/renovation; Endowments.
Limitations: Applications accepted. Giving primarily in central PA. No grants to individuals.
Application information: Application form not required.
Initial approach: Proposal
Deadline(s): None
Officer: Lois Lehrman Grass, Chair.
Directors: Kristen Olewine Milke; Elizabeth Grass Weese.
EIN: 237218005
Selected grants: The following grants are a representative sample of this grantmaker's funding activity:
$40,000 to Jewish Federation of Greater Harrisburg, Harrisburg, PA, 2013. For program continuation.
$24,320 to Hospice of Central Pennsylvania, Harrisburg, PA, 2013. For Pathway to Caring.
$20,000 to United States Holocaust Memorial Museum, Washington, DC, 2013. For 20th Anniversary.
$12,000 to Market Square Concerts, Harrisburg, PA, 2013. For Parker Quarter.
$10,000 to Hamilton Health Center, Harrisburg, PA, 2013. For Phase II.
$10,000 to National Museum of Women in the Arts, Washington, DC, 2013. For Stem.
$6,000 to Cultural Enrichment Fund, Harrisburg, PA, 2013. For Arts Calendar.
$2,605 to Cultural Enrichment Fund, Harrisburg, PA, 2013. For fundraising party.
$1,000 to Downtown Daily Bread, Harrisburg, PA, 2013. For 30th Anniversary.

8069
Gray Charitable Trust ✧
c/o Kenneth Gray
1 Town Pl., Ste. 200
Bryn Mawr, PA 19010-3418
E-mail: june@graytrust.org

Established in 1998 in PA.
Donor: Kenneth B. Gray, Jr.
Foundation type: Independent foundation.
Financial data (yr. ended 12/31/12): Assets, $24,605,425 (M); gifts received, $2,000,000; expenditures, $1,147,414; qualifying distributions, $1,085,747; giving activities include $1,047,890 for 31 grants (high: $242,500; low: $500).
Purpose and activities: The foundation supports organizations in areas of interest to the Gray family.
Fields of interest: Arts; Education; Environment; Health care; Human services.
Type of support: Matching/challenge support; Capital campaigns; General/operating support; Continuing support; Building/renovation; Equipment; Research.
Limitations: Applications not accepted. Giving primarily in PA. No grants to individuals.
Application information: Contributes only to pre-selected organizations.
Board meeting date(s): Twice a year
Trustees: Samuel M. Gawthrop; Doreen H. Gray; Kenneth B. Gray, Jr.; Kimberley H. Gray; Meridith L. Gray.
Number of staff: 1 part-time professional.
EIN: 237987964
Selected grants: The following grants are a representative sample of this grantmaker's funding activity:
$50,000 to University of Pennsylvania, School of Medicine, Philadelphia, PA, 2012. For general support.
$18,000 to Lenox Hill Neighborhood House, New York, NY, 2012. For Senior Citizens Lenox Hill Program Which Provides a Broad Range of Service.
$15,000 to New York University, School of Medicine, Department of Opthalmology, New York, NY, 2012. For general support.

8070
The Daniel B. and Florence E. Green Foundation ✧ ☆
15 E. Ridge Pike, 5th Fl.
Conshohocken, PA 19428-2139
Contact: Daniel B. Green, Tr.

Established in 2005 in PA.
Donors: Rancho Santa Fe Thrift; Firstrust Bank; Daniel B. Green; Florence E. Green.
Foundation type: Independent foundation.
Financial data (yr. ended 06/30/13): Assets, $11,752,879 (M); gifts received, $1,000; expenditures, $505,285; qualifying distributions, $488,063; giving activities include $488,063 for 49 + grants (high: $81,000).
Fields of interest: Education; Health care; Religion.
Limitations: Applications accepted. Giving primarily in PA. No grants to individuals.
Application information: Application form not required.
Initial approach: Proposal
Deadline(s): None
Trustee: Daniel B. Green.
EIN: 201910865
Selected grants: The following grants are a representative sample of this grantmaker's funding activity:
$54,868 to Greater Philadelphia Film Office, Philadelphia, PA, 2011. For general fund.
$20,000 to Philadelphia Theater Company, Philadelphia, PA, 2011. For general fund.
$12,000 to Hospice of the Conejo, Thousand Oaks, CA, 2011. For general fund.
$10,000 to Har Zion Temple, Penn Valley, PA, 2011. For general fund.
$10,000 to Haverford School, Haverford, PA, 2011. For general fund.
$7,500 to Center for Literacy, Philadelphia, PA, 2011. For general fund.
$5,000 to Lankenau Hospital Foundation, Wynnewood, PA, 2011. For general fund.
$5,000 to Zoological Society of Philadelphia, Philadelphia, PA, 2011. For general fund.
$3,000 to Jewish Federation of Greater Philadelphia, Philadelphia, PA, 2011. For general fund.
$2,500 to Saint Johns College, Annapolis, MD, 2011. For general fund.

8071
The Albert M. Greenfield Foundation ✧
P.O. Box 30267
Philadelphia, PA 19103-8267 (215) 354-0604
Contact: Priscilla M. Luce, Pres.
Main URL: http://www.thealbertmgreenfieldfoundation.org/

Incorporated in 1953 in PA.
Donor: Albert M. Greenfield†.
Foundation type: Independent foundation.

Financial data (yr. ended 08/31/13): Assets, $19,569,463 (M); expenditures, $1,283,931; qualifying distributions, $1,161,871; giving activities include $1,133,417 for 13 grants (high: $166,667; low: $5,000).
Purpose and activities: Giving primarily to the arts and higher education.
Fields of interest: Performing arts, music; Arts; Higher education; Hospitals (specialty).
Type of support: Endowments; Professorships; Scholarship funds.
Limitations: Applications accepted. Giving primarily in the Philadelphia, PA, area. No grants to individuals, or for general operating funds; no loans.
Application information: Application form not required.
Initial approach: Proposal
Copies of proposal: 1
Deadline(s): None
Board meeting date(s): As required
Officers: Priscilla M. Luce, Pres.; Deborah G. DeLauro, Esq., Secy.; Juliet G. Six, Treas.
Members: Albert M. Greenfield III; Sarah E. Mark; Edward J. Montgomery, Jr.
Number of staff: 1
EIN: 236050816

8072
The Greenfield Foundation Inc. ✧
(formerly The Goldsmith-Greenfield Foundation, Inc.)
P.O. Box 187
Fort Washington, PA 19034-0187

Established in 1991 in FL; merged with The Alexis Rosenberg Foundation in 2005.
Foundation type: Independent foundation.
Financial data (yr. ended 05/31/13): Assets, $14,002,077 (M); gifts received, $1,000; expenditures, $735,460; qualifying distributions, $630,445; giving activities include $630,445 for grants.
Purpose and activities: Giving primarily for human services and the arts.
Fields of interest: Arts; Higher education; Education; Human services.
Limitations: Applications not accepted. Giving primarily in FL, MA and PA. No grants to individuals, endowments, deficit financing, debt reduction, operating expenses, conferences/seminars, workshops, travel, surveys, advertising, fundraising, research, or for annual campaigns.
Publications: Grants list; Informational brochure.
Application information: Proposals must be sponsored by a trustee. Unsolicited requests for funds not accepted.
Board meeting date(s): Varies
Officers: William Greenfield, Pres.; Charles Kahn, V.P.; Jill Feldman, Treas.
Trustees: Emily Clark; Claudia Cleary; William Epstein; Ronald Feldman; Ben Greenfield; Joan Greenfield; Michael Greenfield.
EIN: 650301946
Selected grants: The following grants are a representative sample of this grantmaker's funding activity:
$323,945 to Harvard University, Cambridge, MA, 2013. To Fund Goldsmith Investigative Awards.
$70,000 to Temple University, Philadelphia, PA, 2013. To Fund Emergency Action Corps.

8073
Robert J. Gunterberg Charitable Foundation ✧
1350 Park Rd.
Lancaster, PA 17601-5244

Established in IL.
Donor: Robert J. Gunterberg.
Foundation type: Independent foundation.
Financial data (yr. ended 12/31/13): Assets, $45,287,453 (M); expenditures, $2,325,825; qualifying distributions, $2,322,542; giving activities include $2,023,530 for 128 grants (high: $45,000; low: $400).
Fields of interest: Health care; Human services; Christian agencies & churches.
Limitations: Applications not accepted. Giving primarily in FL, IL, and PA. No grants to individuals.
Application information: Contributes only to pre-selected organizations.
Officers: Carol Culliton-Metzger, Pres.; Richard Metzger, V.P.; Michael J. Piascinski, Treas.
Directors: Diane J. Blair; Adam B. Culliton; Laurence J. Hayes.
EIN: 331176987

8074
Emily Guthrie Healthcare Trust ✧
c/o BNY Mellon, N.A.
P.O. Box 185
Pittsburgh, PA 15230-0185

Foundation type: Independent foundation.
Financial data (yr. ended 06/30/13): Assets, $24,827,443 (M); expenditures, $1,325,366; qualifying distributions, $1,167,077; giving activities include $1,105,357 for 1 grant.
Fields of interest: Health care.
Limitations: Applications not accepted. Giving in PA.
Application information: Contributes only to pre-selected organizations.
Trustee: BNY Mellon, N.A.
EIN: 236632633
Selected grants: The following grants are a representative sample of this grantmaker's funding activity:
$1,105,357 to Guthrie Healthcare System, Sayre, PA, 2013. For operational.

8075
Margaret Voorhies Haggin Trust in Memory of Her Late Husband, James Ben Ali Haggin ✧
c/o BNY Mellon, N.A.
P.O. Box 185
Pittsburgh, PA 15230-0185

Established in 1938 in NY.
Donor: Margaret Voorhies Haggin†.
Foundation type: Independent foundation.
Financial data (yr. ended 12/31/13): Assets, $24,250,079 (M); expenditures, $1,463,924; qualifying distributions, $1,367,998; giving activities include $1,320,036 for 12 grants (high: $675,776; low: $7,700).
Purpose and activities: Giving primarily for higher education and health care.
Fields of interest: Higher education; Hospitals (general).
Limitations: Applications not accepted. Giving limited to KY. No grants to individuals.
Application information: Contributes only to pre-selected organizations.
Trustee: BNY Mellon, N.A.
EIN: 136078494
Selected grants: The following grants are a representative sample of this grantmaker's funding activity:
$280,727 to James B. Haggin Memorial Hospital, Harrodsburg, KY, 2011.
$105,000 to Alice Lloyd College, Pippa Passes, KY, 2011.

8076
The Haldeman Family Foundation ✧
c/o Dechert, LLP
2929 Arch St.
Philadelphia, PA 19104-2808

Established in 2003 in PA.
Donors: Charles Haldeman; Barbara C. Haldeman; Charles Edgar Haldeman, Jr.
Foundation type: Independent foundation.
Financial data (yr. ended 12/31/13): Assets, $22,068,068 (M); gifts received, $500,000; expenditures, $899,264; qualifying distributions, $890,800; giving activities include $890,800 for 36 grants (high: $205,000; low: $250).
Fields of interest: Elementary/secondary education; Higher education; Higher education, college; Business school/education; Law school/education; Environment, natural resources; United Ways and Federated Giving Programs; Christian agencies & churches.
Limitations: Applications not accepted. Giving primarily in MA, NH, and PA. No grants to individuals.
Application information: Contributes only to pre-selected organizations.
Officers and Directors:* Matthew A. Haldeman,* Pres.; Charles Edgar Haldeman, Jr.,* V.P.; Barbara C. Haldeman,* Secy.-Treas.; Catherine J. Haldeman; Charlotte E. Haldeman.
EIN: 352218296

8077
The Hamer Foundation ✧ ☆
2470 Fox Hill Rd.
State College, PA 16803-1729 (814) 355-8004
Contact: Diane M. Kerly, Tr.

Established in 1989 in PA.
Donor: Donald W. Hamer.
Foundation type: Independent foundation.
Financial data (yr. ended 12/31/13): Assets, $52,303,179 (M); gifts received, $3,742,234; expenditures, $2,068,058; qualifying distributions, $2,010,000; giving activities include $2,010,000 for 8 grants (high: $310,000; low: $100,000).
Purpose and activities: Giving primarily for conservation and educational programs in Centre County, PA.
Fields of interest: Education; Environment; Animals/wildlife.
Type of support: General/operating support; Annual campaigns; Capital campaigns; Building/renovation.
Limitations: Applications accepted. Giving primarily in Centre County, PA. No support for religious or political organizations. No grants to individuals.
Application information: Application form not required.
Initial approach: Proposal

Copies of proposal: 1
Deadline(s): None
Trustees: Marie Bednar; Donald W. Hamer; Diane M. Kerly; C.J. Wagner.
Number of staff: None.
EIN: 251610780

8078
The Hamilton Family Foundation ✧
200 Eagle Rd., Ste. 308
Wayne, PA 19087-3115 (610) 293-2225
Contact: Nancy Brent Wingo, Exec. Dir.; Gail C. Berreitter, Off. Mgr.
FAX: (610) 293-0967;
E-mail: information@hamiltonfamilyfoundation.org; Contact for Nancy Brent Wingo, Exec, Dir.: e-mail: nwingo@218enterprises.com or nancywingo@hamiltonfamilyfoundation.org; Contact for Amy E. Benjamin, Grants Mgr., tel.: (610) 293-2228, e-mail: abenjamin@218enterprises.com; Main URL: http://www.hamiltonfamilyfoundation.org

Established in 1992 in PA.
Donor: Dorrance H. Hamilton.
Foundation type: Independent foundation.
Financial data (yr. ended 12/31/13): Assets, $31,286,747 (M); gifts received, $1,426,052; expenditures, $3,129,801; qualifying distributions, $3,062,502; giving activities include $3,047,030 for 336 grants (high: $20,000; low: $30).
Purpose and activities: Giving primarily for education, particularly quality literacy-based educational projects for underserved children and youth in Philadelphia area K-12-grade schools. Colleges and universities generally are not considered.
Fields of interest: Elementary school/education; Secondary school/education; Education.
Type of support: General/operating support; Annual campaigns; Program development; Scholarship funds; Matching/challenge support.
Limitations: Applications accepted. Giving primarily in Chester and Philadelphia, PA, and Camden, NJ. Organizations outside of these cities may apply if invited by a member of the foundation's Board of Directors or the Exec. Dir. No grants to individuals or for bricks and mortar projects or endowments.
Publications: Application guidelines.
Application information: Proposals accepted only once during a 12-month period; application form and guidelines available on foundation web site. Application form required.
Initial approach: Use application process on foundation web site
Copies of proposal: 1
Deadline(s): Feb. 1 (for summer meeting), May 1 (for fall meeting), Aug 1 (for winter meeting), and Nov. 1 (for spring meeting
Board meeting date(s): Quarterly
Final notification: Within 1 month of meeting
Officers and Directors:* Dorrance H. Hamilton,* Pres.; Nancy Brent Wingo, Exec. Dir.; Barbara R. Cobb; Margaret H. Duprey; Nathaniel P. Hamilton; S. Matthews V. Hamilton, Jr.; Francis J. Mirabello, Esq.
Number of staff: 1 full-time professional; 1 full-time support.
EIN: 232684976
Selected grants: The following grants are a representative sample of this grantmaker's funding activity:
$400,000 to Mastery Charter Schools Foundation, Philadelphia, PA, 2011.
$100,000 to United Way of Greater Philadelphia and Southern New Jersey, Philadelphia, PA, 2011.
$30,000 to Boys and Girls Clubs of Metropolitan Philadelphia, Philadelphia, PA, 2011.

8079
William Stucki Hansen Foundation ✧
(formerly Hansen Foundation)
432 Green St.
Sewickley, PA 15143-1563 (412) 771-7300

Established in 1984 in PA.
Donors: William Gregg Hansen†; Hansen, Inc.
Foundation type: Independent foundation.
Financial data (yr. ended 12/31/12): Assets, $28,354,389 (M); expenditures, $1,451,976; qualifying distributions, $1,289,250; giving activities include $1,289,250 for 25 grants (high: $250,000; low: $1,000).
Fields of interest: Arts; Higher education; Education; Family services.
Type of support: General/operating support; Endowments; Program-related investments/loans.
Limitations: Giving primarily in Pittsburgh and Sewickley, PA. No grants to individuals.
Application information: Application form not required.
Initial approach: Letter
Deadline(s): None
Directors: Gretchen Hansen; Nancy K. Hansen; David W. Lendt.
EIN: 251483674

8080
The Harding Foundation ✧
c/o The Glenmede Trust Co.
1650 Market St., Ste. 1200
Philadelphia, PA 19103-7391 (215) 419-6000
Contact: Melanie Redmond Quackenbush

Established in 1988 in MI.
Donor: C.S. Harding Mott Trust.
Foundation type: Independent foundation.
Financial data (yr. ended 06/30/13): Assets, $56,020,963 (M); expenditures, $1,735,343; qualifying distributions, $1,627,672; giving activities include $1,300,000 for 18 grants (high: $200,000; low: $10,000).
Purpose and activities: Giving primarily to organizations which are dedicated to supporting or contributing to the cause of Christian Science.
Fields of interest: Museums (history); Education, early childhood education; Protestant agencies & churches.
Limitations: Applications accepted. Giving primarily in FL, MA, and MI. No grants to individuals.
Application information: Application form required.
Initial approach: Letter
Copies of proposal: 1
Deadline(s): None
Officers: Paula K. Turrentine, Chair. and Pres.; Paula M. Switzer, V.P. and Secy.; Milo I. Mott, V.P. and Treas.
Number of staff: 1 full-time professional; 1 full-time support; 1 part-time support.
EIN: 382849003
Selected grants: The following grants are a representative sample of this grantmaker's funding activity:
$50,000 to Hillsdale College, Hillsdale, MI, 2013. For general charitable purposes.

8081
Head Family Charitable Foundation ✧ ☆
c/o Glenmede Trust Co., N.A.
1650 Market St., Ste. 1200
Philadelphia, PA 19103-7391

Established in NJ.
Donor: Carol A. Head.
Foundation type: Independent foundation.
Financial data (yr. ended 12/31/13): Assets, $30,591,483 (M); expenditures, $1,333,080; qualifying distributions, $1,268,065; giving activities include $1,247,496 for 56 grants (high: $400,000; low: $2,500).
Fields of interest: Arts; Animal welfare; Hospitals (general); Human services.
Limitations: Applications not accepted. Giving primarily in NJ.
Application information: Unsolicited requests for funds not accepted.
Trustee: Carol A. Head.
EIN: 386949833
Selected grants: The following grants are a representative sample of this grantmaker's funding activity:
$1,000,000 to Foundation for Morristown Medical Center, Morristown, NJ, 2012. For From the Head Family Charitable Foundation - To Support the Behavioral Health Unit.
$100,000 to Drew University, Madison, NJ, 2012. To endow The Head Family Scholarship for minority students at Drew University.
$2,500 to Our House, Murray Hill, NJ, 2012. To Help Purchase Generators for Homes.

8082
The Hecht-Levi Foundation, Inc. ✧
c/o PNC Bank, N.A.
620 Liberty Ave., 10th Fl.
Pittsburgh, PA 15222-2705
Application address: c/o Linda Angevine, 2 Hopkins Plz., Baltimore, MD 21201-2930, tel.: (410) 237-5551

Incorporated in 1958 in MD.
Donors: Alexander Hecht†; Selma H. Hecht†; Robert H. Levi†; Ryda H. Levi.
Foundation type: Independent foundation.
Financial data (yr. ended 12/31/13): Assets, $20,806,018 (M); expenditures, $1,311,077; qualifying distributions, $1,269,585; giving activities include $1,266,500 for 54 grants (high: $430,000; low: $2,000).
Purpose and activities: Giving primarily for education and the arts.
Fields of interest: Museums (art); Performing arts; Arts; Education; Human services; Jewish federated giving programs.
Limitations: Applications accepted. Giving primarily in the metropolitan Baltimore, MD, area. No grants to individuals.
Application information:
Initial approach: Letter
Copies of proposal: 1
Deadline(s): None
Officers and Directors:* Sandra L. Gerstung,* Pres.; Richard H. Levi,* V.P. and Treas.; Alexander H. Levi,* V.P.; Ryda H. Levi, V.P.; Wilbert H. Sirota, Esq.*, Secy.
EIN: 526035023

8083
H. J. Heinz Company Foundation ✧

P.O. Box 57
Pittsburgh, PA 15230-0057 (412) 456-5773
Contact: Tammy B. Aupperle, Chair.
FAX: (412) 442-3227;
E-mail: heinz.foundation@us.hjheinz.com; Main URL: http://www.heinz.com/sustainability/social/heinz-foundation.aspx
Heinz Micronutrient Compaign: http://www.heinz.com/media-gallery.aspx?video=26

Established in 1951 in PA.
Donor: H.J. Heinz Co.
Foundation type: Company-sponsored foundation.
Financial data (yr. ended 04/29/13): Assets, $10,857,472 (M); expenditures, $3,440,849; qualifying distributions, $3,428,128; giving activities include $2,924,120 for 474 grants (high: $209,000; low: $25).
Purpose and activities: The foundation supports organizations involved with arts and culture, education, human services, diversity, women, and economically disadvantaged people. Special emphasis is directed toward programs designed to promote the health and nutritional needs of children and families.
Fields of interest: Arts; Higher education; Education; Public health, obesity; Health care; Food banks; Nutrition; Big Brothers/Big Sisters; Children/youth, services; Family services; Human services; Civil/human rights, equal rights; Minorities; Women; Economically disadvantaged.
Type of support: General/operating support; Annual campaigns; Capital campaigns; Building/renovation; Endowments; Emergency funds; Program development; Seed money; Internship funds; Scholarship funds; Technical assistance; Employee volunteer services; Employee matching gifts; In-kind gifts.
Limitations: Applications accepted. Giving primarily in areas of company operations, with emphasis on Pittsburgh, PA; giving to Africa, Bangladesh, China, India, and Tanzania for Heinz Micronutrient Campaign; giving also to international organizations. No support for religious or political organizations. No grants to individuals (except for Heinz Scholars), or for political campaigns, debt reduction, land acquisition, equipment, conferences, travel, or unsolicited research projects; no loans.
Publications: Application guidelines; Annual report (including application guidelines); Corporate giving report.
Application information: An interview may be requested. Multi-year funding is not automatic. Organizations receiving support are asked to provide a final report. Application form not required.
Initial approach: Proposal; letter of inquiry for international organizations
Copies of proposal: 1
Deadline(s): None
Board meeting date(s): Quarterly
Final notification: Varies
Officers and Directors:* Tammy Aupperle,* Chair.; Theodore N. Bobby,* Secy.; Kristen Clark,* Treas.; Michael Okoroafor; Michael Mullen; Sonja Narcisse; John Runkel.
Number of staff: 1 full-time professional; 1 full-time support.
EIN: 300055087

8084
The Heinz Endowments ✧

30 Dominion Twr.
625 Liberty Ave., 30th Fl.
Pittsburgh, PA 15222-3115 (412) 281-5777
Contact: Robert F. Vagt, Pres.
FAX: (412) 281-5788; E-mail: info@heinz.org; Main URL: http://www.heinz.org
Grants Database: http://www.heinz.org/Interior.aspx?id=418
Knowledge Center: http://www.heinz.org/Interior.aspx?id=433
Special Initiatives: http://www.heinz.org/Interior.aspx?id=6
THE Point: http://www.heinz.org/Interior.aspx?id=480

The Heinz Endowments was formed in 2007 from the Howard Heinz Endowments, established in 1941, and the Vira I. Heinz Endowment, established in 1986.
Donors: Howard Heinz; Vira I. Heinz.
Foundation type: Independent foundation.
Financial data (yr. ended 12/31/13): Assets, $1,601,995,851 (M); expenditures, $77,981,577; qualifying distributions, $70,948,367; giving activities include $61,162,789 for 564 grants (high: $2,000,000; low: $507), $573,778 for 4 foundation-administered programs and $1,575,000 for 1 loan/program-related investment.
Purpose and activities: The Heinz Endowments is based in Pittsburgh, where it uses its region as a laboratory for the development of solutions to challenges that are national in scope. Although the majority of its giving is concentrated within southwestern Pennsylvania, it does work wherever necessary, including statewide and nationally, to fulfill its mission. That mission is to help the Endowments' region thrive as a whole community, economically, ecologically, educationally and culturally, while advancing the state of knowledge and practice in the fields in which it works. Its fields of emphasis include philanthropy in general and the disciplines represented by its five grant-making programs: Arts & Culture; Children, Youth & Families; Community & Economic Development; Education; and Environment.
Fields of interest: Arts; Education; Environment; Children/youth, services; Family services; Economic development; Children/youth; Young adults; African Americans/Blacks; Girls; Boys; Economically disadvantaged.
Type of support: Continuing support; General/operating support; Management development/capacity building; Program development; Program evaluation; Technical assistance.
Limitations: Applications accepted. Giving primarily to southwestern PA. Funding for projects outside the Commonwealth of Pennsylvania is generally only at specific request of the foundation. No support for for-profit organizations. No grants to individuals.
Publications: Annual report; Financial statement; Grants list; Occasional report.
Application information: Supporting materials can be uploaded electronically to the application. Please do not send any other paper materials unless requested by endowments' staff. Application form not required.
Initial approach: Prospective applicants should review carefully the guidelines for the grant-making program from which they anticipate seeking support.Inquiries regarding funding should demonstrate a familiarity with the program's goals and strategies. Review the eligibility requirements. Create an account and submit application online. No paper applications accepted.
Deadline(s): Mar. 1 (for spring board meeting), and Aug. 1 (for fall board meeting)
Board meeting date(s): May and Oct.
Final notification: Within several weeks of board meeting
Officers and Directors:* Teresa F. Heinz,* Chair.; James M. Walton,* Vice-Chair.; Grant Oliphant, Pres.; Edward Kolano, V.P., Finance and Admin. and C.F.O.; Ann C. Plunkett, Cont. and Dir., Payroll/Benefits Admin.; Drue Heinz, Dir. Emeritus; Damon Aherne; Carol R. Brown; Jared L. Cohon; Judith Davenport; Franco Harris; Andre T. Heinz; Christopher Heinz; H. John Heinz, IV; Sasha Heinz; Wendy Mackenzie; Shirley M. Malcom; James Rohr.
Number of staff: 20 full-time professional; 4 part-time professional; 10 full-time support.
EIN: 251721100

8085
Heinz Family Foundation ✧

625 Liberty Ave., Ste. 3200
Pittsburgh, PA 15222-3120
FAX: (412) 497-5790; Main URL: http://www.heinzfamily.org/aboutus/philanthropies.html
Facebook: http://www.facebook.com/pages/The-Heinz-Awards/303772805614
Heinz Award Recipients: http://www.heinzawards.net/recipients
Twitter: http://twitter.com/heinzawards

Established in 1984 in PA; incorporated in 1992.
Donors: Teresa F. Heinz; Teresa and H. John Heinz III Charitable Trust; H. John Heinz III Charitable and Family Trust.
Foundation type: Independent foundation.
Financial data (yr. ended 12/31/12): Assets, $117,095,904 (M); expenditures, $3,691,114; qualifying distributions, $3,442,681; giving activities include $2,007,563 for 61 grants (high: $250,000; low: $500), and $215,000 for 1 grant to an individual.
Purpose and activities: Giving primarily for the Heinz Awards, environmental organizations, arts and cultural organizations, and women's health and pension.
Fields of interest: Museums; Arts; Higher education; Education; Environment.
Type of support: Capital campaigns; Building/renovation; Equipment; Endowments; Grants to individuals.
Limitations: Applications accepted. Giving limited to the U.S. No grants to individuals (except for Heinz Awards).
Application information: Application form required.
Initial approach: Proposal
Deadline(s): None
Officers: Teresa F. Heinz, Chair. and C.E.O.; Jack E. Kime, C.F.O.; Andrew Eberhart, C.I.O.; John R. Taylor, C.I.O.; Wendy MacKenzie, Secy.
Director: Andre Heinz.
EIN: 251689382
Selected grants: The following grants are a representative sample of this grantmaker's funding activity:
$250,000 to Zagaya, Emeryville, CA, 2012. For designated payment by 2012 Heinz Awards Winner - Technology, the Economy and Employment.
$160,000 to Yale University, New Haven, CT, 2012. For the 2012-2013 undergraduate scholarships.

$75,000 to Climate Solutions, Seattle, WA, 2012. For designated payment by KC Golden, 2012 Heinz Awards Winner - Public Policy.
$42,000 to Phillips Exeter Academy, Exeter, NH, 2012. For scholarships for the 2012-2013 academic year.
$25,000 to Carnegie Institute, Pittsburgh, PA, 2012. For the 2012 Annual Giving Campaign.
$25,000 to Carnegie Mellon University, Pittsburgh, PA, 2012. For the 2011-2012 Trustee Annual Fund.
$10,000 to International Conservation Caucus Foundation, Washington, DC, 2012. For the 2012 Oceans Gala.
$10,000 to Nantucket Land Council, Nantucket, MA, 2012. For the Bartlett's Farm Project.
$10,000 to National Gallery of Art, Washington, DC, 2012. For the annual Circle Fund.
$10,000 to Seattle Art Museum, Seattle, WA, 2012. For the Special Exhibitions Fund.

8086
Drue Heinz Trust ✧
(formerly H. J. & Drue Heinz Trust)
c/o BNY Mellon, N.A.
P.O. Box 185
Pittsburgh, PA 15230-0185

Established in 1954 in PA.
Foundation type: Independent foundation.
Financial data (yr. ended 12/31/13): Assets, $37,142,990 (M); expenditures, $2,209,630; qualifying distributions, $1,732,711; giving activities include $1,665,000 for 34 grants (high: $950,000; low: $500).
Fields of interest: Museums; Arts; Higher education; Libraries/library science; Foundations (private grantmaking).
Type of support: Program development.
Limitations: Applications not accepted. Giving primarily in NY and PA.
Application information: Unsolicited requests for funds not accepted.
Trustees: Drue Heinz; Julia V. Shea; BNY Mellon, N.A.
Number of staff: 1 full-time professional; 1 part-time professional; 1 full-time support.
EIN: 256018930

8087
Helen's Hope Foundation ✧ ☆
212 Iron Works Way
Wayne, PA 19087-4213
Contact: Mallory Silva
E-mail: MallorySilva@HelensHopeFoundation.org; Main URL: http://www.helenshopefoundation.org

Established in 2007 in NJ.
Donors: Kenneth Karl; Stephanie Karl.
Foundation type: Independent foundation.
Financial data (yr. ended 12/31/13): Assets, $12,428,502 (M); expenditures, $633,262; qualifying distributions, $581,971; giving activities include $527,103 for 13 grants (high: $50,000; low: $1,500).
Purpose and activities: The foundation gives to support underprivileged youth and the programs and people that aid them. It funds programs in FL (Monroe County and the Miami area), NJ, NY (Greater NY and the Mid-Hudson Valley), and PA (Philadelphia and the surrounding area) from organizations that provide educational support, health and fitness, family support and other important areas of development for underprivileged youth.
Fields of interest: Education; Youth, services; Human services; Philanthropy/voluntarism.
Application information: The Foundation accepts requests from organizations with programs in the following locations: Florida (Monroe County and the Miami area), New Jersey, New York (Greater NY and the Mid-Hudson Valley), and Pennsylvania (Philadelphia and the surrounding areas). All applications must be emailed in the required format. See complete application guidelines on Foundation web site.
Deadline(s): Applications accepted between Jan. 1 and Apr. 1
Trustees: Kenneth Karl; Stephanie Karl.
EIN: 207410435
Selected grants: The following grants are a representative sample of this grantmaker's funding activity:
$100,000 to Childrens Aid and Family Services, Paramus, NJ, 2011.

8088
Helping Hands Foundation, Inc. ✧
(formerly Kenneth W. Hammel Foundation, Inc.)
c/o Schneider Downs & Co. Inc.
1 PPG Pl., Ste. 1700
Pittsburgh, PA 15222-4237

Established in 2003 in DE.
Donors: Kenneth W. Hammel; Linda Sue Hammel.
Foundation type: Independent foundation.
Financial data (yr. ended 12/31/13): Assets, $13,622,812 (M); expenditures, $649,649; qualifying distributions, $608,088; giving activities include $599,510 for grants.
Fields of interest: Hospitals (specialty); Youth development, services; Children/youth, services.
Limitations: Applications not accepted. Giving primarily in FL, PA, and TN.
Application information: Contributes only to pre-selected organizations.
Officers and Directors:* Kenneth W. Hammel,* Pres.; Linda Sue Hammel,* V.P.
EIN: 810636347

8089
Henkels Foundation ✧
985 Jolly Rd.
Blue Bell, PA 19422-0900

Established in 1956 in DE and PA.
Donors: Henkels & McCoy, Inc.; Liberty Mutual Group.
Foundation type: Company-sponsored foundation.
Financial data (yr. ended 06/30/13): Assets, $913,813 (M); gifts received, $2,037,598; expenditures, $1,751,078; qualifying distributions, $1,748,751; giving activities include $1,720,554 for 82 grants (high: $269,424; low: $200).
Purpose and activities: The foundation supports organizations involved with education, family planning, human services, and Christianity.
Fields of interest: Education; Health care; Human services.
Type of support: General/operating support; Program development; Scholarship funds.
Limitations: Applications not accepted. Giving primarily in PA. No grants to individuals.
Application information: Contributes only to pre-selected organizations.
Officers: Barbara B. Henkels, Pres.; Christopher B. Henkels, V.P.; Paul M. Henkels, Jr., V.P.; Angela Henkels Dale, Secy.-Treas.
EIN: 236235239
Selected grants: The following grants are a representative sample of this grantmaker's funding activity:
$4,950 to Bishop Shanahan High School, Downingtown, PA, 2013. For Charitable and Religious within Section 170(c)(2)(B).

8090
J. S. Herr Foundation ✧
P.O. Box 300
Nottingham, PA 19362-0300
Contact: James S. Herr, Pres.

Established in 1990 in PA.
Donors: James S. Herr; Herr Foods, Inc.; Guardian Exploration, LLC; Mennonite Foundation.
Foundation type: Independent foundation.
Financial data (yr. ended 12/31/13): Assets, $1,079,141 (M); gifts received, $201,254; expenditures, $619,651; qualifying distributions, $619,651; giving activities include $618,630 for 72 grants (high: $165,130; low: $1,000).
Purpose and activities: Giving primarily for education and human services.
Fields of interest: Education; Human services; Christian agencies & churches.
Limitations: Giving primarily in PA. No grants to individuals.
Application information:
Initial approach: Letter
Officers and Trustees:* James S. Herr,* Pres.; Miriam Herr,* Secy.; Gene Herr,* Treas.; June Gunden; Edwin Herr; James M. Herr; Martha Thomas.
EIN: 232531170

8091
J. Hibshman Scholarship Fund ✧
c/o Ephrata National Bank
P.O. Box 457
Ephrata, PA 17522-0457
Application address: c/o The Ephrata National Bank, 47 E. Main St., Ephrata, PA 17522; tel.: (717) 733-6576

Donor: The Hibshman Trust for Ephrata.
Foundation type: Independent foundation.
Financial data (yr. ended 12/31/13): Assets, $3,405,630 (M); gifts received, $858,682; expenditures, $875,306; qualifying distributions, $859,016; giving activities include $855,000 for grants to individuals.
Purpose and activities: Scholarships are given only to qualifying Ephrata, PA, area high school students who will be attending post-secondary school.
Fields of interest: Higher education.
Limitations: Applications accepted. Giving limited to the Ephrata, PA, area.
Application information: Application form required.
Initial approach: Letter
Deadline(s): Varies
Trustee: The Ephrata National Bank.
EIN: 236401674

8092
Highmark Foundation ✧
120 5th Ave., Ste. 1733
Pittsburgh, PA 15222-3001 (866) 594-1730
FAX: (412) 544-6120;
E-mail: info@highmarkfoundation.org; Additional tel.: (866) 594-1730; Main URL: http://www.highmarkfoundation.org/
Additional URL: http://www.highmarkhealthyhigh5.org/index.shtml
Grants List: http://www.highmarkfoundation.org/pdf/3_27_2014%20HM%20Grants%20Listing.pdf

Established in 2000 in PA.
Donors: Highmark West Virginia, Inc.; Highmark Inc.
Foundation type: Company-sponsored foundation.
Financial data (yr. ended 12/31/12): Assets, $21,908,655 (M); expenditures, $6,947,160; qualifying distributions, $5,765,267; giving activities include $4,507,735 for 66 grants (high: $598,000; low: $500).
Purpose and activities: The foundation supports programs designed to address chronic disease, family health, service delivery systems, and healthy communities. Special emphasis is directed toward programs designed to address bullying prevention; childhood obesity; and schools.
Fields of interest: Elementary/secondary education; Education; Health care, equal rights; Hospitals (general); Health care, clinics/centers; Dental care; Reproductive health, prenatal care; Public health; Public health, obesity; Public health, physical fitness; Health care, patient services; Health care; Mental health, grief/bereavement counseling; Mental health/crisis services; Cancer; Heart & circulatory diseases; Nerve, muscle & bone diseases; Diabetes; Health organizations; Crime/violence prevention, youth; Nutrition; Family services; Children; Youth; Aging; Disabilities, people with; Minorities; Economically disadvantaged.
Type of support: General/operating support; Continuing support; Management development/capacity building; Equipment; Program development; Curriculum development; Matching/challenge support.
Limitations: Applications accepted. Giving primarily in PA. No support for fraternal or civic groups, discriminatory organizations, or sports teams. No grants to individuals, or for annual fundraising campaigns, capital campaigns, endowment funds, lobbying or political causes or campaigns, debt reduction, sponsorships, clinical research, scholarships, routine operational costs, or overhead costs or direct financial subsidies of health services.
Publications: Application guidelines; Informational brochure (including application guidelines); Program policy statement.
Application information: Unsolicited proposals are considered on rare occasions. The foundation utilizes invited proposals and a request for proposals (RFP) process.
Initial approach: Proposal
Deadline(s): None
Board meeting date(s): Mar., June, Sept., and Dec.
Officers and Directors:* Doris Carson Williams,* Vice-Chair.; Yvonne Cook, Pres.; Melissa M. Anderson,* Treas.; C. Michael Blackwood; James B. Bramson; Janine Colinear; Evan S. Frazier; Don Onorato; Judy Sjostedt.
EIN: 251876666
Selected grants: The following grants are a representative sample of this grantmaker's funding activity:
$598,000 to Windber Research Institute, Windber, PA, 2012. To continue analysis of the evaluation outcomes and reporting of data related to Highmark Foundation's bullying prevention efforts.
$591,000 to Central Susquehanna Intermediate Unit, Milton, PA, 2012. To strengthen and promote sustainability of bullying prevention efforts in Pennsylvania.
$500,000 to Catholic Charities of the Diocese of Pittsburgh, Pittsburgh, PA, 2012. To increase access to primary health, dental and specialty care for underserved.
$180,126 to Pennsylvania State University, University Park, PA, 2012. For continuing support of NRG Powered by Choice Program.
$175,000 to University of Pittsburgh, School of Dental Medicine, Pittsburgh, PA, 2012. For equipment for Department of Pediatric Dentistry.
$150,000 to Butler Memorial Hospital, Butler, PA, 2012. For Maternal Services Program (MSP) which provides a variety of coordinated services to low-income and uninsured women and their children from birth through age five..
$145,860 to Monongahela Valley Hospital, Monongahela, PA, 2012. For salary of clinical pharmacist and to reduce hospital readmissions.
$125,000 to North Side Christian Health Center, Pittsburgh, PA, 2012. For salaries of medical and dental professionals to support the integration of oral health and primary care.
$60,250 to Chatham University, Pittsburgh, PA, 2012. To support the integration of patient simulation training in Chatham's academic programs.
$50,000 to Southeast Lancaster Health Services, Lancaster, PA, 2012. To support two Expanded Function Dental Hygienists (EFDH) positions in order to increase patient visits, improve efficiencies, increase dental emergency patients, improve dental visits and increase the percentage of preventive procedures.

8093
Hillman Family Foundations ✧
(formerly Henry L. Hillman Foundation)
310 Grant St., Ste. 2000
Pittsburgh, PA 15219-2309 (412) 338-3466
Contact: David K. Roger, Pres.
FAX: (412) 338-3463;
E-mail: foundation@hillmanfo.com; Main URL: http://hillmanfamilyfoundations.org/

Donors: Henry L. Hillman; J.H. Hillman, Jr.
Foundation type: Independent foundation.
Financial data (yr. ended 12/31/12): Assets, $357,584,648 (M); gifts received, $9,985,926; expenditures, $19,513,079; qualifying distributions, $18,704,422; giving activities include $17,093,300 for 588 grants (high: $2,000,000; low: $500), and $500,000 for 1 loan/program-related investment.
Purpose and activities: Hillman Family Foundations acts as the umbrella for the individual foundations listed. Prospective applicants should address grants inquiries to the appropriate individual foundations. Each foundation retains its own grantmaking focus and eligibility criteria. 1) Hillman Foundation: Arts and culture, health and medicine, education, economic development, human services, and conservation; 2) Henry L. Hillman Foundation: Arts and culture (focus on visual arts), health and medicine (research focused), education (focus on higher education), economic development, human services, conservation, and technology ; 3) Elsie L. Hillman Foundation: Education, human services (women-focused), religion, arts and culture, and community development with emphasis on civic affairs; 4) Mary Hillman Jennings Foundation: Healthcare, human services (focus on disabilities) and education; 5) Polk Foundation: Human services for individuals with intellectual and developmental disabilities; 6) Audrey Hillman Fisher Foundation: Human services (focus on woman and children), healthcare, conservation, education, arts ; 7) Juliet Lea Hillman Simonds Foundation: Arts and culture ; 8) Henry Lea Hillman, Jr. Foundation: Education, arts and culture, human services, community development, conservation, health and medicine; 9) William Talbott Hillman Foundation: Arts and culture, education, environment/conservation and human services ; 10) Dylan Todd Simonds Foundation: Environment/conservation (focus on sustainable development) arts and culture, education; 11) Talbott and Carter Simonds Foundation: Health and medicine, arts/culture, education, youth programs (focus on social enterprise and entrepreneurship); 12) Henry John Simonds Foundation: Arts/culture (focus on artist development in visual and performing arts) civic affairs, community development, education, conservation and environment; 13) Justin Brooks Fisher Foundation: Conservation/environment (focus on animal health and veterinary medicine), education, arts/culture; 14) Matthew Hillman Fisher Foundation: Arts/culture, human services, education, conservation/environment; 15) Nina Baldwin Fisher Foundation: Human services (focus on women and children) education (focus on culinary training), environment/conservation and arts/culture; 16) Lilah Hilliard Fisher Foundation: Human services (focus on early childhood development. adolescents, women and reproductive rights), education, arts/culture and environment/conservation ; 17) Juliet Ashby Hillman Foundation: Animal welfare, education and human services; 18) Summer Lea Hillman Foundation: Animal welfare, education and human services.
Fields of interest: Arts; Education; Environment; Health care; Human services.
Type of support: Program-related investments/loans; Continuing support; Capital campaigns; Endowments.
Limitations: Applications accepted. Giving primarily in the following areas: Hillman Foundation: Pittsburgh and Southwestern PA; Henry L. Hillman Foundation: Pittsburgh and Southwestern PA; Mary Hillman Jennings Foundation: Pittsburgh and Southwestern PA; Elsie H. Hillman Foundation: Pittsburgh and Southwestern PA; Polk Foundation: Pittsburgh, PA; Juliet Lea Simonds Foundation: Pittsburgh, PA and New York City, NY; Audrey Hillman Fisher Foundation: Pittsburgh, PA, Santa Barbara, CA, and central NH; Henry Lea Hillman, Jr. Foundation: Portland, OR; William Talbott Hillman Foundation: Pittsburgh, PA and New York City, NY; Dylan Todd Simonds Foundation: San Francisco, CA and Pittsburgh, PA; Talbott & Carter Simonds Foundation: New York City, NY and Pittsburgh, PA; Henry John Simonds Foundation: New York City, NY and Pittsburgh, PA; Justin Brooks Fisher Foundation: Boulder, CO and Pittsburgh, PA; Matthew Hillman Fisher Foundation: Pittsburgh, PA, New York City, NY and Los Angeles, CA; Lilah Hilliard Fisher Foundation: New York City, NY and Pittsburgh, PA; Nina Baldwin Fisher Foundation: Pittsburgh, PA, Juliet Ashby Hillman Foundation: Portland, OR, Summer Lea Hillman Foundation: Portland, OR. No

grants to individuals, or for deficit financing, publications, or conferences.
Application information: Prospective applicants should address grant requests and inquiries to one of the individual foundations.
Initial approach: Online
Board meeting date(s): Apr., June, Oct. and Dec.
Officers and Directors:* Henry L. Hillman,* Chair.; David K. Roger,* Pres.; C.G. Grefenstette,* V.P.; Bruce I. Crocker,* Secy.; Lisa R. Johns, Treas. and Prog. Mgr.; Elsie H. Hillman; Juliet L. Hillman Simonds.
Number of staff: 5
EIN: 256065959
Selected grants: The following grants are a representative sample of this grantmaker's funding activity:
$2,000,000 to Taft School, Watertown, CT, 2013. Toward Second Century Campaign, payable over 4.00 years.
$1,060,000 to Program for Offenders, Pittsburgh, PA, 2012. Toward new treatment facility property acquisition.
$1,000,000 to Carlow University, Pittsburgh, PA, 2012. Toward Capital Campaign, payable over 3.00 years.
$1,000,000 to Westmoreland Museum of American Art, Greensburg, PA, 2012. Toward changing exhibitions at the museum, payable over 9.00 years.
$750,000 to ACHIEVA, Pittsburgh, PA, 2013. Toward capital campaign for Waiting List Reduction Initiative, which will reduce waiting time for basic supportive and health care services, payable over 2.50 years.
$750,000 to Innovation Works, Pittsburgh, PA, 2013. Toward hardware for AlphaLab, payable over 3.00 years.
$575,000 to Growth Through Energy and Community Health Strategies, Pittsburgh, PA, 2013. Toward project, Scaling Community Innovation: Engage, Investigate, Act, Connect, Share.
$500,000 to Carnegie Mellon University, Pittsburgh, PA, 2013. Toward Traffic21 Scalable Urban Traffic Control (SURTRAC), smart traffic signal demonstration project. Traffic21 is a multi-disciplinary research initiative. Its goal is to design, test, deploy and evaluate information and communications technology based solutions to address the problems facing the transportation system of the Pittsburgh region. SURTRAC is designed to discover the dominant flow of vehicles through an intersection and automatically adjust the signaling. It is designed to operate within urban grids, where the volume and direction of traffic can change throughout the day, payable over 2.00 years.
$500,000 to East Liberty Development, Pittsburgh, PA, 2012. Toward the revitalization of Larimer Avenue.
$500,000 to Frick Art and Historical Center, Pittsburgh, PA, 2013. Toward capital support for Education Center, payable over 3.00 years.
$200,000 to Homewood Childrens Village, Pittsburgh, PA, 2012. Toward infrastructure/support of office of evaluation, payable over 2.00 years.
$50,000 to Center of Life, Pittsburgh, PA, 2012. Toward capital improvements to program facility.
$5,000 to Lydias Place, Pittsburgh, PA, 2012. Toward general operating support.
$3,000 to Brady Center to Prevent Gun Violence, Washington, DC, 2012. Toward gun violence preventive programs.
$3,000 to Headlands Center for the Arts, Sausalito, CA, 2013. For Unrestricted.
$2,500 to Art Connects New York, New York, NY, 2012. Toward exhibition programs.
$2,500 to Catholic Youth Association of Pittsburgh, Pittsburgh, PA, 2012. Toward the 39th Annual Art Rooney Award Dinner and Auction.
$2,500 to Mountain Institute, Washington, DC, 2013. Toward programs and operations.
$2,500 to Rutgers University Foundation, New Brunswick, NJ, 2013. Toward Founders Circle.
$2,500 to Ursuline Senior Services, Pittsburgh, PA, 2013. Toward the Good Grief Center for Bereavement Support.
$2,500 to Westminster College, New Wilmington, PA, 2012. Toward Annual Fund.

8094
The Ethel Mae Hocker Foundation Inc. ✧
c/o Richard A. Hocker, Gerald McBride
3 Crescent Dr., Ste. 400
Philadelphia, PA 19112-1017

Established in 2005 in NJ.
Donors: Richard A. Hocker; Marcia Hocker.
Foundation type: Independent foundation.
Financial data (yr. ended 06/30/13): Assets, $14,770,053 (M); gifts received, $1,850,000; expenditures, $642,086; qualifying distributions, $532,600; giving activities include $532,600 for grants.
Fields of interest: Education; Military/veterans.
Limitations: Applications not accepted. Giving primarily in PA. No grants to individuals.
Application information: Contributes only to pre-selected organizations.
Officer: Gerald McBride, Exec. Dir.
Trustees: John J. Gallagher, Jr.; Kimberly A. Hocker; Kirsten Hocker; Marcia A. Hocker; Richard A. Hocker.
EIN: 201991591
Selected grants: The following grants are a representative sample of this grantmaker's funding activity:
$229,740 to Valley Forge Military Academy, Wayne, PA, 2011. For scholarships.
$36,075 to Camden Catholic High School, Cherry Hill, NJ, 2011. For scholarships.
$35,000 to Camden Catholic High School, Cherry Hill, NJ, 2011.
$18,000 to Gesu School, Philadelphia, PA, 2011. For scholarships.
$5,000 to UrbanPromise Ministries, Camden, NJ, 2011. For scholarships.

8095
Emma Clyde Hodge Memorial Fund ✧
c/o PNC Bank
620 Liberty Ave., 10th Fl.
Pittsburgh, PA 15222-2705

Established in 1990 in PA.
Donor: Edwin Hodge, Jr.‡.
Foundation type: Independent foundation.
Financial data (yr. ended 06/30/13): Assets, $9,465,657 (M); expenditures, $492,422; qualifying distributions, $421,500; giving activities include $421,500 for grants.
Purpose and activities: Giving primarily for the arts, education, health care, and human services.
Fields of interest: Performing arts, orchestras; Arts; Education; Health care; Human services.
Type of support: Building/renovation.
Limitations: Applications not accepted. Giving primarily in the U.S., with some emphasis on Pittsburgh, PA. No grants to individuals.
Application information: Contributes only to pre-selected organizations.
Trustees: L. Van V. Dauler, Jr.; Anne Gordon Earle; Emma Sarosdy; PNC Bank, N.A.
EIN: 256227653
Selected grants: The following grants are a representative sample of this grantmaker's funding activity:
$37,500 to Pittsburgh Public Theater, Pittsburgh, PA, 2013. For $25,000 Sponsorship of Play, $13481 Board Contribution.
$35,000 to Pittsburgh Glass Center, Pittsburgh, PA, 2013. For Studio Stools, Energy Efficient Lighting and Website Rebuild.
$20,000 to Thiel College, Greenville, PA, 2013. For the Formation of the Dr. Edwin Hodge, Jr. Institute for Learning.
$11,000 to Moses Brown School, Providence, RI, 2013. For $1,500 for the Class of 1997 15th Year Reunion, $4,000 for the Nat Earle Scholarship Fund, $4,500 for the Moses Brown Fund.
$9,000 to Save the Bay, Providence, RI, 2013. For $5,000 for the Asa Messer Program, $2,000 for the Annual Fund.
$5,000 to Taft School, Watertown, CT, 2013. For $5,000 for the John Small Chair, $4,000 for the Class of 1972.
$2,000 to University of Pittsburgh, Katz School, Pittsburgh, PA, 2013. For the Dean's Excellence Fund.
$1,500 to Davidson College, Davidson, NC, 2013. To Be Used for the Endowed Book Fund Established By Cabot Earle.

8096
John M. Hopwood Charitable Trust ✧
1 PNC Plz., 3rd Fl.
249 5th Ave.
Pittsburgh, PA 15222-2719 (412) 762-3502
Contact: Bruce Bickel
FAX: (412) 705-3743;
E-mail: bruce.bickel@pnc.com

Established about 1948 in PA.
Donors: John M. Hopwood‡; Mary S. Hopwood‡; William T. Hopwood; Danforth K. Richardson; Marge Richardson.
Foundation type: Independent foundation.
Financial data (yr. ended 12/31/13): Assets, $27,332,739 (M); expenditures, $1,407,386; qualifying distributions, $1,240,287; giving activities include $1,155,848 for 55 grants (high: $100,000; low: $1,000).
Purpose and activities: Primary areas of interest include hospitals, education, and the environment.
Fields of interest: Arts; Higher education; Education; Environment, natural resources; Environment, energy; Environment; Hospitals (general); Health organizations, association; Human services; Youth, services; Religion.
Type of support: General/operating support; Continuing support; Annual campaigns; Capital campaigns; Building/renovation; Endowments; Emergency funds; Program development; Conferences/seminars; Seed money; Scholarship funds; Research; Technical assistance; Program-related investments/loans; Matching/challenge support.
Limitations: Applications not accepted. Giving primarily in western PA and New England.

Application information: Unsolicited requests for funds not accepted.
Board meeting date(s): Varies
Trustees: Anna Hopwood Blanton; William T. Hopwood; PNC Bank, N.A.
Number of staff: 2 part-time professional.
EIN: 256022634

8097
Lawrence L. and Julia Z. Hoverter Charitable Foundation ✧
4250 Crums Mill Rd., Ste. 301
P.O. Box 6991
Harrisburg, PA 17112-2889

Established in 1998 in PA.
Donors: Julia Hoverter†; Lawrence Hoverter.
Foundation type: Independent foundation.
Financial data (yr. ended 12/31/13): Assets, $11,891,241 (M); expenditures, $850,219; qualifying distributions, $724,017; giving activities include $700,501 for 20 grants (high: $249,800; low: $1,400).
Purpose and activities: Giving primarily for education, human services, and children and youth services, including a children's hospital.
Fields of interest: Higher education; Education; Hospitals (specialty); Human services; Children/youth, services; Economically disadvantaged.
Type of support: General/operating support.
Limitations: Applications not accepted. Giving primarily in PA. No grants to individuals.
Application information: Unsolicited requests for funds not accepted.
Officers and Trustees:* H. Craig Watkins,* Pres.; Joe Cecere,* V.P.; Ronald M. Katzman,* Secy.; Amos Miller,* Treas.; Rebecca Cecere; John R. Miller.
EIN: 232944271
Selected grants: The following grants are a representative sample of this grantmaker's funding activity:
$35,000 to CURE International, Lemoyne, PA, 2012. For relief of poor.
$10,000 to Nativity School of Harrisburg, Harrisburg, PA, 2012. For education of disadvantaged children.

8098
Hoyt Foundation ✧
P.O. Box 788
New Castle, PA 16103-0788 (724) 535-1280
Contact: Jaimie Kopp

Incorporated in 1962 in PA.
Donors: May Emma Hoyt†; Alex Crawford Hoyt.
Foundation type: Independent foundation.
Financial data (yr. ended 10/31/13): Assets, $18,788 (M); gifts received, $373; expenditures, $1,171,334; qualifying distributions, $1,121,284; giving activities include $951,673 for 38 grants (high: $500,000; low: $300).
Purpose and activities: Emphasis on higher education, including scholarships, and a hospital; some support also for cultural programs.
Fields of interest: Arts; Higher education; Hospitals (general); Human services; Children/youth, services; Economically disadvantaged.
Type of support: Continuing support; Annual campaigns; Capital campaigns; Building/renovation; Seed money; Scholarships—to individuals.
Limitations: Applications accepted. Giving limited to residents and organizations in Lawrence County, PA.
Application information: Application form required.
Initial approach: Completed application form
Copies of proposal: 1
Deadline(s): 3rd Fri. in Aug.
Board meeting date(s): Quarterly
Officer: Charles Y. Mansell, Pres.
Directors: Debbie Lynch; Floyd H. McElwain; Stephen R. Sant; Steven C. Warner.
Number of staff: 1 part-time support.
EIN: 256064468

8099
R. Dale and Frances M. Hughes Foundation ✧
P.O. Box 3215
Lancaster, PA 17604-3215

Established in 1997 in PA.
Donors: Frances M. Hughes†; R. Dale Hughes; R. Dale Hughes Family Non-Exe Trust.
Foundation type: Independent foundation.
Financial data (yr. ended 12/31/13): Assets, $37,024,115 (M); gifts received, $415,695; expenditures, $2,063,866; qualifying distributions, $1,738,960; giving activities include $1,738,960 for 25 grants (high: $505,000; low: $10,000).
Fields of interest: Health care, clinics/centers; Human services; Salvation Army; YM/YWCAs & YM/YWHAs; Protestant agencies & churches.
Type of support: General/operating support.
Limitations: Applications not accepted. Giving primarily in PA. No grants to individuals.
Application information: Contributes only to pre-selected organizations.
Trustees: Kevin D. Hughes; Patricia G. Hughes; Fulton Bank, N.A.
EIN: 237914215
Selected grants: The following grants are a representative sample of this grantmaker's funding activity:
$10,000 to Devereux Foundation, Villanova, PA, 2012. For Staff Training and General Use.

8100
Roy A. Hunt Foundation ✧
1 Bigelow Sq., Ste. 630
Pittsburgh, PA 15219-3030 (412) 281-8734
Contact: Tony Macklin, Exec. Dir.
FAX: (412) 255-0522; E-mail: info@rahuntfdn.org;
Main URL: http://www.rahuntfdn.org
Grants Mapping feature: http://batchgeo.com/map/bcabb381cdea3bad436c568c7a723411
LinkedIn: http://www.linkedin.com/company/roy-a.-hunt-foundation
RSS Feed: http://feeds.feedburner.com/RoyAHuntFoundation

Established in 1966 in PA.
Donor: Roy A. Hunt†.
Foundation type: Independent foundation.
Financial data (yr. ended 05/31/14): Assets, $77,965,829 (M); expenditures, $3,690,813; qualifying distributions, $3,411,977; giving activities include $2,996,333 for 384 grants (high: $75,000; low: $1,000).
Purpose and activities: Giving to improve the quality of life through grants for education, the arts and cultural programs, social services, the environment, health services, community development, and youth violence prevention.
Fields of interest: Arts; Elementary/secondary education; Higher education; Environment; Health care; Crime/violence prevention, youth; Human services; Community/economic development; Public affairs; Religion.
Type of support: Continuing support; Program evaluation; Program development; General/operating support; Annual campaigns; Capital campaigns; Building/renovation; Endowments.
Limitations: Giving primarily in the Boston, MA, and Pittsburgh, PA, areas, also in CA, ID, NH, ME, and OH. No grants to individuals.
Publications: Application guidelines; Grants list.
Application information: Applicants are encouraged to use the foundation's on-line grant-making system. Organizations that are new to the foundation complete a narrative using the Charting Impact questions and attach: past and current financials, board list, key staff list, and other optional materials. Previous Grant Recipients complete a streamlined proposal. Special Initiative Proposals require a 6-question narrative and a project budget, past financials, board and staff list. Once invited to submit a proposal, applicants will receive detailed instructions from the foundation on how to submit their proposal via the on-line system. Organizations that have received a general grant in the past three years do not need to submit a letter of inquiry, the foundation will send e-mail instructions to apply to all invited organizations in late summer. Organizations that have never received funding and special initiative applicants are required to submit a letter of inquiry and should review the "Applying for a Grant" page on the foundation's web site for more guidance.
Initial approach: Letter of inquiry via the foundation's online grantmaking system
Deadline(s): Special Initiatives: Letter of Inquiry, Jan. 20 (for June meeting), and June 23 (for Nov. meeting), Invited Proposal: Mar. 10 (for June meeting) and Aug. 11 (for Nov. meeting); For General Grants: Letter of Inquiry, Mar 31 (for June meeting), and Aug. 20 (for Nov. meeting), Invited Proposal: Apr. 15 (for June meeting), and Sept. 15 (for Nov. meeting)
Board meeting date(s): June and Nov.
Final notification: 30 days for a letter of inquiry and 1 week after board meeting for full proposal
Officer: Tony Macklin, Exec. Dir.
Trustees: India Hunt Badiner; Helen Hunt Bouscaren; Cathryn Hunt Graybill; Sophie Hunt Hollingsworth; Susan Hunt Hollingsworth; A. James Hunt; Alexandra K. Hunt; Andrew McQ. Hunt; Avery S. Hunt; Christopher M. Hunt; Daniel K. Hunt; Edward M. Hunt; Elizabeth H. Hunt; Evan McMasters Hunt; John B. Hunt; Justin Hunt; Lila C. Hunt; Marion M. Hunt; Oliver Hunt; Richard M. Hunt; Roy A. Hunt III; Torrence M. Hunt, Jr.; Torrence W.B. Hunt; Tyler B. Hunt; William E. Hunt; Rachel Hunt Knowles; Joan Hunt Maxwell; Bonnie B.K. Hunt Pierson; Caroline Hunt Zaw-Mon.
Number of staff: 1 full-time professional; 1 full-time support.
EIN: 256105162

8101
Priscilla Payne Hurd Foundation ☆
P.O. Box 399
Springtown, PA 18081-0399 (610) 346-7158
Contact: Laura Herzog Kaplus, Dir.
E-mail: pphf@foundationoffices.org

Established in 1998.
Donor: Priscilla Payne Hurd Char. Lead Annuity Trust.
Foundation type: Independent foundation.
Financial data (yr. ended 12/31/13): Assets, $14,427,171 (M); gifts received, $732,700; expenditures, $743,989; qualifying distributions, $713,125; giving activities include $573,980 for 52 grants (high: $20,000; low: $2,468).
Purpose and activities: Giving to various charitable organizations throughout the Lehigh Valley region of Pennsylvania. Grants are anonymous.
Fields of interest: Arts, association; Arts, single organization support; Arts, volunteer services; Arts, multipurpose centers/programs; Arts, cultural/ethnic awareness; Arts education; Arts councils; Visual arts; Visual arts, art conservation; Museums; Museums (art); Museums (children's); Museums (ethnic/folk arts); Museums (history); Museums (science/technology); Museums (specialized); Performing arts; Performing arts, theater; Performing arts, theater (playwriting); Performing arts, theater (musical); Performing arts, music (choral); Performing arts, music ensembles/groups; Performing arts, music composition; Performing arts, education; Performing arts (multimedia); Historic preservation/historical societies; Arts; Education, early childhood education; Teacher school/education; Adult education—literacy, basic skills & GED; Education, ESL programs; Libraries/library science; Libraries (public); Libraries (school); Education, community/cooperative; Education; Hospitals (general); Health care, EMS; Health care; Food banks; Youth development; Human services, single organization support; Human services, information services; Human services; Neighborhood centers; Children/youth, services; Children, day care; Human services, emergency aid; Women, centers/services; Homeless, human services.
Type of support: Income development; Management development/capacity building; Annual campaigns; Capital campaigns; Building/renovation; Equipment; Emergency funds; Program development; Film/video/radio; Curriculum development; Research; Technical assistance.
Limitations: Applications accepted. Giving limited to Lehigh Valley, PA. No grants to individuals or to political candidates or organizations; no multiple-year support commitments.
Application information: Grant recipients, upon receipt of award, must sign an agreement to maintain the confidentiality of the source of income. No other follow-up is required. Application form required.
Initial approach: Request application materials between Jan. 1 and June 30
Copies of proposal: 1
Deadline(s): June 30 (for application requests), July 15 (applications)
Final notification: Mid-Dec.
Director: Laura Herzog Kaplus.
Trustees: Susan Hurd Cumings; Bank of America, N.A.
Number of staff: 1 full-time professional; 5 part-time professional; 1 part-time support.
EIN: 367240364
Selected grants: The following grants are a representative sample of this grantmaker's funding activity:
$15,000 to Bethlehem Area Public Library, Bethlehem, PA, 2011.
$15,000 to Mosser Village Family Center, Allentown, PA, 2011.
$12,500 to Meals on Wheels of Lehigh County, Allentown, PA, 2011.
$10,000 to Casa Refugio, Bethlehem, PA, 2011. For general operations.
$10,000 to Moravian Academy, Bethlehem, PA, 2011.
$10,000 to Touchstone Theater, Bethlehem, PA, 2011.
$9,000 to Stephens Place, Bethlehem, PA, 2011.
$7,975 to Treatment Trends, Allentown, PA, 2011.
$6,225 to Civic Theater of Allentown, Allentown, PA, 2011.
$6,000 to ShareCare Faith in Action, Bethlehem, PA, 2011.

8102
The Stewart Huston Charitable Trust ✧
50 S. 1st Ave.
Coatesville, PA 19320-3418

Established in 1989 in PA.
Donor: Stewart Huston‡.
Foundation type: Independent foundation.
Financial data (yr. ended 12/31/13): Assets, $27,006,960 (M); expenditures, $1,175,241; qualifying distributions, $939,633; giving activities include $596,500 for 47 grants (high: $130,000; low: $1,000).
Purpose and activities: Giving primarily for religion, the arts, education, the environment, health care, substance abuse, human services, community development, public affairs, and historic preservation.
Fields of interest: Performing arts; Historic preservation/historical societies; Arts; Education, early childhood education; Environment; Medical care, rehabilitation; Health care; Substance abuse, services; Health organizations, association; Housing/shelter, development; Human services; Children/youth, services; Family services; Residential/custodial care, hospices; Aging, centers/services; Homeless, human services; Community/economic development; Christian agencies & churches; Children/youth; Youth; Disabilities, people with; Physically disabled; Deaf/hearing impaired; Mentally disabled; Minorities; African Americans/Blacks; Hispanics/Latinos; Women; Adults, women; Adults, men; Offenders/ex-offenders; Substance abusers; Crime/abuse victims; Economically disadvantaged; Homeless.
Type of support: General/operating support; Capital campaigns; Building/renovation; Equipment; Program development; Seed money; Technical assistance; Matching/challenge support.
Limitations: Applications accepted. Giving primarily in the Savannah, GA, area and Coatesville, PA. No support for political organizations or volunteer fire companies. No grants to individuals, including scholarships or for endowments.
Publications: Annual report; Annual report (including application guidelines); Informational brochure (including application guidelines).
Application information: Application form required.
Initial approach: Contact foundation for application form
Copies of proposal: 4
Deadline(s): None
Board meeting date(s): May (Trinitarian-Evangelical and Secular) and Nov. (Trinitarian-Evangelical only)
Final notification: June (Trinitarian-Evangelical and Secular) and Dec. (Trinitarian-Evangelical only)
Trustees: Alex L. Cann, Sr.; Charles L. Huston III; Shelton Sanford.
Number of staff: 1 full-time professional; 1 part-time support.
EIN: 232612599

8103
The Huston Foundation ✧
900 W. Valley Rd., Ste. 204
Wayne, PA 19087-1849 (610) 832-4955
FAX: (610) 832-4960; E-mail: hustonfndn@aol.com; For secular information contact: Susan B. Heilman, Exec. Asst., tel.: (610) 832-4955, ext. 1; for Protestant Evangelical Christian information contact: Patricia A. Jones, tel.: (610) 832-4955, ext. 4; Main URL: http://www.hustonfoundation.org

Incorporated in 1957 in PA.
Donors: Charles L. Huston, Jr.‡; Ruth Huston‡.
Foundation type: Independent foundation.
Financial data (yr. ended 12/31/12): Assets, $24,168,890 (M); expenditures, $1,543,057; qualifying distributions, $1,383,328; giving activities include $856,288 for 132 grants (high: $60,000; low: $400).
Purpose and activities: Giving primarily to Protestant evangelical ministries, health organizations, and human service organizations. Also some support for education and the arts.
Fields of interest: Arts; Education; Health care; Human services; Public policy, research; Christian agencies & churches; Protestant agencies & churches.
International interests: Africa; Italy.
Type of support: General/operating support; Annual campaigns; Equipment; Emergency funds; Program development; Seed money; Research; Technical assistance; Matching/challenge support.
Limitations: Giving primarily in southeastern PA; some funding nationally. No grants to individuals, or for research programs, endowments, fellowships, capital campaigns or salaries; no loans.
Publications: Application guidelines; Annual report.
Application information: See foundation web site for complete application guidelines. Application form required.
Initial approach: Letter of request or telephone call
Copies of proposal: 1
Deadline(s): Jan. 1 and Mar. 15 for spring, July 1 and Sept. 15 for Fall
Board meeting date(s): May and Nov.
Officers and Directors:* Elinor Huston Lashley,* Chair.; Charles L. Huston III,* C.E.O. and Pres.; Nancy Huston Hansen,* V.P.; Rebecca H. Mathews,* Secy.; Charles L. Huston IV,* Treas.; Scott G. Huston; Patricia A. Jones.
Number of staff: 4 full-time professional; 1 part-time professional.
EIN: 236284125
Selected grants: The following grants are a representative sample of this grantmaker's funding activity:
$25,000 to Bryan College, Dayton, TN, 2012. For Huston Hall renovations and projects.
$25,000 to Bryan College, Dayton, TN, 2012. For Renovations to Huston Hall including new HVAC

system and renovation of built-in furniture and woodworking.
$10,000 to Parkesburg Point Youth Center, Parkesburg, PA, 2012. For the afterschool and weekend Christian Programs for at-risk and low-income youth in Western Chester County.
$10,000 to Parkesburg Point Youth Center, Parkesburg, PA, 2012. For fundi to be used to support the Point's Programs addressing the spiritual, physical, emotional, and academic needs of at-risk youth in Chester County.
$8,000 to Far East Broadcasting Company, La Mirada, CA, 2012. For Internet Broadcasting via Mobile Devices (IBMD) to broadcast the gospel in Vietnam.
$7,500 to Chester County Food Bank, Exton, PA, 2012. For supporting costs to renovate and outfit the new Octorara area Food pantry. which will be a permanent facility, co-located with The Point Funds are needed to complete renovations so that the pantry can open by 12/1/12.
$7,000 to Water Street Ministries, Lancaster, PA, 2012. For the Water Street Women's Shelter The funding will assist with the cost of shelter for 85 beds that serve 300 to 500 homeless women and children per year.
$6,000 to Family Service of Chester County, West Chester, PA, 2012. For providing confidential counseling, child abuse prevention, and HIV/AIDS case management and prevention to vulnerable and disadvantaged people in Coatesville, PA and its surrounding townships.
$6,000 to Scripture Memory Mountain Mission, Emmalena, KY, 2012. For the ministry of Raymond and Gerry Haddix.
$5,000 to Chester County Christian Chorale, Atglen, PA, 2012. For 26th annual Messiah Sing-a-long at Upper Octorara Presbyterian Church in December 28, 2012.

8104
Hutton & Jost Memorial Trust ✧ ☆

P.O. Box 609
Pittsburgh, PA 15230-9738

Foundation type: Independent foundation.
Financial data (yr. ended 12/31/13): Assets, $11,951,736 (M); expenditures, $543,582; qualifying distributions, $496,766; giving activities include $450,000 for 12 grants (high: $37,500; low: $37,500).
Fields of interest: Health care; Youth development; Human services; Catholic agencies & churches.
Limitations: Applications not accepted. Giving primarily in St. Louis, MO.
Application information: Unsolicited requests for funds not accepted.
Trustee: PNC Bank, N.A.
EIN: 436266746

8105
II-VI Foundation ✧

(formerly II-VI Incorporated Foundation)
1370 Washington Pike, Ste. 404
Bridgeville, PA 15017-2826 (412) 206-0580
Contact: Richard W. Purnell, Exec. Dir.
FAX: (412) 206-0583;
E-mail: info@ii-vifoundation.com; Main URL: http://ii-vifoundation.com
Facebook: https://www.facebook.com/pages/II-VI-Foundation/425726714117561

Established in 2007 in PA.
Donors: Carl J. Johnson; Margot A. Johnson.
Foundation type: Independent foundation.
Financial data (yr. ended 12/31/13): Assets, $19,718,260 (M); expenditures, $3,841,856; qualifying distributions, $3,639,521; giving activities include $2,644,876 for 32 grants (high: $200,000; low: $3,500), and $528,755 for 57 grants to individuals (high: $14,000; low: $2,500).
Purpose and activities: Scholarship awards to graduating high school students in the areas where II-VI, Inc. maintains a facility. The overall mission of the foundation is to encourage and enable students to pursue a career in engineering, science and mathematics while maintaining a standard of excellence in that pursuit.
Fields of interest: Higher education.
Type of support: Scholarships—to individuals.
Limitations: Giving primarily in areas where II-VI, Inc. maintains a plant or a manufacturing facility.
Publications: Application guidelines.
Application information: Application information and forms available on foundation web site. Application form required.
Deadline(s): See application form for current deadlines
Officers and Directors:* Carl J. Johnson,* Chair.; Robert D. German, Secy.; Richard W. Purnell, Exec. Dir.; Marc Y.E. Pelaez; Peter Sognefast.
EIN: 208824719

8106
Independence Blue Cross Foundation ✧

1901 Market St., 37 Fl
Philadelphia, PA 19103-1480 (855) 422-3386
Contact: Marie Lange, Prog. Anaylst
E-mail: ibxfoundation@ibx.com; E-mail and tel. for Marie Lange: marie.lange@ibx.com; (215) 241-2817; Main URL: http://www.ibxfoundation.org/
Blue Safety Net Grant Recipients: http://www.ibxfoundation.org/grants/grantees/blue_safety_net.html
Building Healthier Communities Grant Recipients: http://www.ibxfoundation.org/grants/grantees/healthy_communities.html
Nurses for Tomorrow Grant Recipients: http://www.ibxfoundation.org/grants/grantees/nurses_for_tomorrow.html
Twitter: https://twitter.com/ibxfdn

Donor: Independence Blue Cross.
Foundation type: Company-sponsored foundation.
Financial data (yr. ended 12/31/12): Assets, $57,319,736 (M); gifts received, $15,000,000; expenditures, $5,068,145; qualifying distributions, $4,028,399; giving activities include $4,018,599 for 66 grants (high: $231,690; low: $2,226).
Purpose and activities: The foundation supports programs designed to care for the most vulnerable; enhance health care delivery; and build healthier communities.
Fields of interest: Nursing school/education; Health care, clinics/centers; Public health; Public health, obesity; Public health, physical fitness; Health care; Nutrition; Children; Economically disadvantaged.
Type of support: General/operating support; Management development/capacity building; Program development; Internship funds; Scholarship funds.
Limitations: Applications accepted. Giving primarily in southeastern PA, with emphasis on Bucks, Chester, Montgomery, and Philadelphia County. No support for political causes, candidates, organizations, or capital campaigns;. No grants to individuals or for endowments, award dinners, sponsorships or fundraising events, capital construction, conferences, seminars, trips or camps.
Publications: Application guidelines.
Application information: A site visit may be conducted.
Initial approach: Complete online application for Blue Safety Net and Building Healthier Communities
Deadline(s): Varies for Blue Safety Net; Apr. 9 and June 20 for Building Healthier Communities
Officers and Directors:* Patrick B. Gillespie,* Chair.; Lorina L. Marshall-Blake, Pres.; Lilton R. Taliaferro, Jr., Esq., Secy.; Alan Krigstein, Treas.; Chistopher Cashman; Joan Hilferty; Plato A. Marinakos; Paul A. Tufano, Esq.; I. Steven Udvarhelyi, M.D.
EIN: 364685801
Selected grants: The following grants are a representative sample of this grantmaker's funding activity:
$136,952 to University of Pennsylvania, School of Nursing, Philadelphia, PA, 2012. For Scholarships to graduate and undergraduate nursing students.
$130,625 to Project HOME, Philadelphia, PA, 2012. For Primary Health Care Expansion.
$129,673 to Thomas Jefferson University, Jefferson School of Nursing, Philadelphia, PA, 2012. For Scholarships to graduate and undergraduate nursing students.
$105,300 to La Salle University, School of Nursing and Health Sciences, Philadelphia, PA, 2012. For Scholarships to graduate nursing students.
$76,884 to Widener University, School of Nursing, Chester, PA, 2012. For Scholarships to graduate and undergraduate nursing students.
$75,000 to Bucks County Health Improvement Partnership, Langhorne, PA, 2012. For Primary Health Care.
$50,000 to Puentes de Salud, Philadelphia, PA, 2012. For NP residency Program.
$30,496 to Temple University, Department of Nursing, Philadelphia, PA, 2012. For Scholarships to graduate and undergraduate nursing students.
$30,000 to Chester County Community Dental Center, Coatesville, PA, 2012. For dental care.
$18,125 to National Nursing Centers Consortium, Philadelphia, PA, 2012. To support clinics for best practices.

8107
Independence Foundation ✧

200 S. Broad St., Ste. 1101
Philadelphia, PA 19102-3802 (215) 985-4009
Contact: Susan E. Sherman, C.E.O. and Pres.
FAX: (215) 985-3989; Main URL: http://independencefoundation.org/about-us/

Established in 1932 as International Cancer Research Foundation; incorporated as Donner Foundation in 1945 in DE; divided in 1961 into Independence Foundation and a newly formed William H. Donner Foundation.
Donor: William H. Donner†.
Foundation type: Independent foundation.
Financial data (yr. ended 12/31/13): Assets, $72,451,745 (M); expenditures, $5,501,424; qualifying distributions, $4,949,698; giving activities include $3,393,046 for grants, and $243,000 for 16 employee matching gifts.

Purpose and activities: The foundation's mission is to support organizations that provide services to people who do not ordinarily have access to them. The current funding agenda includes the following areas of interest: nurse managed health care, culture and the arts, public interest legal services, and health and human services, with special focus on food distribution, housing for the homeless, and services which help people with disabilities to lead independent lives. The foundation also has two special initiatives: Public Interest Law Fellowships and Fellowships for Visual and Performing Artists.
Fields of interest: Visual arts; Performing arts; Arts; Nursing school/education; Nursing care; Health care; Legal services; Legal services, public interest law; Human services; Children; Aging; Disabilities, people with; Physically disabled; Women; Immigrants/refugees; Economically disadvantaged; Homeless; Migrant workers.
Type of support: General/operating support; Professorships; Fellowships; Scholarship funds; Matching/challenge support.
Limitations: Applications accepted. Giving primarily in Philadelphia, PA, and Bucks, Chester, Delaware, and Montgomery counties. No grants to individuals (except for art fellowships), or for building and development funds, travel, research, publications, or matching gifts.
Publications: Application guidelines; Annual report; Grants list; Occasional report.
Application information: Unsolicited proposals are not accepted. Application form required.
Initial approach: 2-page Letter of Inquiry
Deadline(s): Contact foundation for deadline dates
Board meeting date(s): Varies
Final notification: Varies
Officers and Directors:* Hon. Phyllis W. Beck,* Chair. and Treas.; Susan E. Sherman,* C.E.O. and Pres.; Andre Dennis,* V. P.; Barton M. Silverman,* V.P.; Andrea L. Mengel, Ph.D.*, Secy.; Pedro Ramos.
Number of staff: 5 full-time professional; 2 full-time support.
EIN: 231352110

8108
Justin Ingerman Foundation ✧ ☆
837 Lafayette Rd.
Bryn Mawr, PA 19010-1816

Established in PA.
Donors: Brad Ingerman; Laurie Ingerman; MBI Development Co., Inc; MBI Equities Corp.; Pheasant Hill Construction.
Foundation type: Independent foundation.
Financial data (yr. ended 12/31/13): Assets, $1,871,871 (M); gifts received, $799,719; expenditures, $619,365; qualifying distributions, $611,000; giving activities include $611,000 for 3 grants (high: $535,000; low: $1,000).
Purpose and activities: Giving primarily to a children's hospital foundation, and for higher education.
Fields of interest: Higher education; Hospitals (specialty).
Limitations: Applications not accepted. Giving primarily in Philadelphia, PA.
Application information: Unsolicted requests for funds not accepted.
Trustee: Brad Ingerman.
EIN: 271750707

8109
The Institute for Aegean Prehistory ✧
2133 Arch St., Ste. 300
Philadelphia, PA 19103 (215) 496-9914
Contact: Karen B. Vellucci, Dir., Grants
FAX: (215) 496-9925; E-mail: instap@hotmail.com; Application e-mail: instapplications@gmail.com; Main URL: http://www.aegeanprehistory.net

Established in 1983 in NY.
Donors: Malcolm H. Wiener; Gordon & Llura Gund Foundation.
Foundation type: Operating foundation.
Financial data (yr. ended 06/30/13): Assets, $16,625,587 (M); gifts received, $8,122,618; expenditures, $6,371,043; qualifying distributions, $5,660,262; giving activities include $4,006,717 for 266 grants (high: $292,283; low: $300).
Purpose and activities: The Institute for Aegean Prehistory (INSTAP) is a private operating foundation; opportunities to participate in the organization's activities are given only for the purpose of allowing and encouraging persons to study Aegean prehistory with expectation of research publication under the direct supervision of the institute. The goal of the Institute's grant program is to promote knowledge of the Aegean region, and to support archaeological fieldwork and research in that area in the chronological span of the Paleolithic period through to the First Olympiad in 776 BC.
Fields of interest: History/archaeology.
International interests: Greece.
Type of support: Internship funds; Research; Grants to individuals.
Limitations: Applications accepted. Giving on a national and international basis, with emphasis on Greece. No grants for students obtaining degrees, travel or maintenance of children or spouses, research expenses incurred before the date of a grant, salaries for researchers, purchase of expensive individual items of equipment such as computers, cameras and video recorders, or general activities of other institutions, or entities including "overhead expenses".
Application information: Application forms are available on the institute's web site. The institute prefers applications and final reports submitted by e-mail. Faxed applications not accepted. Application form required.
Initial approach: Letter
Deadline(s): New Research Grants and Renewal Grants applications due Nov. 1
Final notification: 60 days
Officers and Directors:* Malcolm H. Wiener, Pres.; Harvey Beker,* V.P.; Phillip Betancourt, V.P.; George E. Crapple,* V.P.; Gregg Buckbinder,* Secy.-Treas.; Henry Davis; Floyd McCoy; Jeffrey Soles; Carolyn S. Wiener.
EIN: 133137391

8110
John E. & Sue M. Jackson Charitable Trust ✧
c/o PNC Bank, N.A.
P.O. Box 609
Pittsburgh, PA 15230-9738
Application address: c/o PNC Charitable Trust, Review Committee, PNC Bank, N.A., 249 5th Ave., 20th Fl., Pittsburgh, PA 15222, tel.: (412) 768-8248

Established in 1950.
Foundation type: Independent foundation.
Financial data (yr. ended 12/31/13): Assets, $11,128,929 (M); expenditures, $523,254; qualifying distributions, $451,844; giving activities include $432,362 for 81 grants (high: $37,000; low: $484).
Fields of interest: Museums; Historic preservation/historical societies; Higher education; Theological school/education; Hospitals (general); Legal services, public interest law; Employment, research; Human services; American Red Cross; Children/youth, services; Family services; Foundations (private grantmaking); Social sciences, research; Social sciences, public policy; Christian agencies & churches.
Application information: Application form required.
Initial approach: See website
Deadline(s): None
Trustees: William R. Jackson, Jr.; Polly J. Townsend; N.A. PNC Bank.
EIN: 256019484

8111
Henry Janssen Foundation ✧
c/o David F. Rick
2650 Westview Dr.
Wyomissing, PA 19610-1187

Established in 2005 in PA.
Foundation type: Independent foundation.
Financial data (yr. ended 12/31/12): Assets, $10,305,307 (M); expenditures, $589,113; qualifying distributions, $556,754; giving activities include $536,500 for grants.
Fields of interest: Historic preservation/historical societies; Higher education; Human services; YM/YWCAs & YM/YWHAs; United Ways and Federated Giving Programs.
Limitations: Applications not accepted. Giving primarily in PA. No grants for indications.
Application information: Contributes only to pre-selected organizations.
Officers: Elsa M. Hoppman, Pres.; Nancy M. Wissinger, V.P. and Treas.; Jane M. Rohrbach, Secy.
EIN: 201812511

8112
Jerlyn Foundation ✧
1740 Van Reed Rd.
Sinking Spring, PA 19608-8801
Application address: c/o T. Jerome Holleran, 1170 Cedar Hill Dr., Reading, PA 19605, tel.: (610) 378-1606

Established in 1992 in PA.
Donors: T. Jerome Holleran; Carolyn R. Holleran.
Foundation type: Independent foundation.
Financial data (yr. ended 12/31/13): Assets, $2,317,911 (M); expenditures, $848,659; qualifying distributions, $830,270; giving activities include $828,200 for 68 grants (high: $225,000; low: $500).
Purpose and activities: Giving primarily for higher and other education, and for human services.
Fields of interest: Arts; Higher education; Education; Environment; Health organizations, association; Human services.
Type of support: General/operating support; Continuing support; Capital campaigns; Program development.

Limitations: Applications accepted. Giving primarily in the Berks County, PA, area. No grants to individuals.
Application information: Application form not required.
Initial approach: Proposal
Deadline(s): None
Officers: T. Jerome Holleran, Pres.; Carolyn R. Holleran, Secy.-Treas.
Director: Patrick B. Holleran.
EIN: 232699256

8113
Jones Foundation ✧ ☆
c/o John P. Jones, III
3020 Fairfield Dr.
Allentown, PA 18103-5542

Established in 2007 in PA.
Donor: John P. Jones III.
Foundation type: Independent foundation.
Financial data (yr. ended 12/31/13): Assets, $2,216,079 (M); expenditures, $483,345; qualifying distributions, $481,435; giving activities include $481,435 for 2 grants (high: $246,435; low: $235,000).
Fields of interest: Higher education; Catholic agencies & churches.
Limitations: Applications not accepted. Giving primarily in PA. No grants to individuals.
Application information: Contributes only to pre-selected organizations.
Officers and Directors:* John P. Jones III,* Pres.; Denise Jones,* Secy.-Treas.; Jaqueline Jones Hoxie; Marcelle Jones.
EIN: 412258026

8114
Fred J. and Shirley H. Jordan Foundation ✧ ☆
20 Stanwix St., Ste. 650
Pittsburgh, PA 15222-4803

Donor: Shirley H. Jordan†.
Foundation type: Independent foundation.
Financial data (yr. ended 02/28/13): Assets, $18,730,588 (M); gifts received, $41,453; expenditures, $861,565; qualifying distributions, $672,000; giving activities include $672,000 for 12 grants (high: $56,000; low: $56,000).
Fields of interest: Animals/wildlife; Youth development; Human services.
Limitations: Applications not accepted. Giving primarily in Pittsburgh, PA. No grants to individuals.
Application information: Contributes only to pre-selected organizations.
Trustees: John Eidemueller, Jr.; Smithfield Trust Co.
EIN: 272151492
Selected grants: The following grants are a representative sample of this grantmaker's funding activity:
$26,500 to Animal Rescue League of Western Pennsylvania, Pittsburgh, PA, 2012. For general support.
$26,500 to Audubon Society of Western Pennsylvania, Pittsburgh, PA, 2012. For general support.
$26,500 to Big Brothers Big Sisters of Greater Pittsburgh, Pittsburgh, PA, 2012. For general support.
$26,500 to Blind and Vision Rehabilitation Services of Pittsburgh, Homestead, PA, 2012. For general support.
$26,500 to Guide Dog Foundation for the Blind, Smithtown, NY, 2012. For general support.
$26,500 to Humane Society of the United States, Washington, DC, 2012. For general support.
$26,500 to National Wildlife Federation, Reston, VA, 2012. For general support.
$26,500 to Pennsylvania Wildlife Federation, Harrisburg, PA, 2012. For general support.
$26,500 to Western Pennsylvania School for Blind Children, Pittsburgh, PA, 2012. For general support.
$26,500 to Western Pennsylvania School for the Deaf, Pittsburgh, PA, 2012. For general support.

8115
Robert J Kahn Foundation ✧ ☆
c/o M. Blackman, Tr.
1650 Market St., 46th Fl.
Philadelphia, PA 19103-7301

Established in PA.
Foundation type: Independent foundation.
Financial data (yr. ended 12/31/12): Assets, $10,959,420 (M); expenditures, $606,820; qualifying distributions, $476,000; giving activities include $476,000 for grants.
Fields of interest: Medical school/education; Education; Hospitals (specialty); Health care; Health organizations.
Limitations: Applications not accepted. Giving primarily in New York, NY, and PA.
Application information: Unsolicited Requests for funds not accepted.
Trustee: Murray I. Blackman.
EIN: 256667083

8116
The Karabots Foundation ✧
P.O. Box 736
Fort Washington, PA 19034-0736

Established in 1998 in PA.
Donors: Nicholas G. Karabots; Athena Karabots; Glendi Publications, Inc.; Kappa Graphics, LP; Spartan Organization, Inc.; Geopedior Assocs., LP; Kappa Media Group, Inc.
Foundation type: Independent foundation.
Financial data (yr. ended 06/30/13): Assets, $3,160,545 (M); gifts received, $89,951; expenditures, $800,394; qualifying distributions, $710,443; giving activities include $710,443 for 2 grants (high: $695,143; low: $15,300).
Fields of interest: Museums.
Type of support: General/operating support.
Limitations: Applications not accepted. Giving primarily in PA. No support for religious organizations. No grants to individuals.
Application information: Contributes only to pre-selected organizations.
Officers: Nicholas G. Karabots, Pres. and Treas.; Athena Karabots, V.P. and Secy.
EIN: 232939856
Selected grants: The following grants are a representative sample of this grantmaker's funding activity:
$1,500,000 to Childrens Hospital of Philadelphia, Philadelphia, PA, 2011.
$200,000 to Hellenic Museum and Cultural Center, Chicago, IL, 2011.
$19,875 to Philadelphia Museum of Art, Philadelphia, PA, 2011.
$5,000 to Highlands Historical Society, Fort Washington, PA, 2011.

8117
The Katz Family Foundation ✧ ☆
c/o Diamatrix
225 Lincoln Hwy.
Fairless Hills, PA 19030-1103
Contact: F. Katz

Established in 1998 in MA.
Donors: Frank L. Katz; Elise Katz.
Foundation type: Independent foundation.
Financial data (yr. ended 06/30/13): Assets, $7,935,947 (M); expenditures, $451,755; qualifying distributions, $420,000; giving activities include $420,000 for 4 grants (high: $250,000; low: $50,000).
Purpose and activities: Giving primarily for medical and health care services.
Fields of interest: Education; Hospitals (general); Health care; Human services.
Limitations: Applications not accepted. Giving primarily in IN, MA and PA. No grants to individuals.
Application information: Contributes only to pre-selected organizations.
Trustees: Benjamin A. Katz; Brooke D. Katz; Elise R. Katz; Frank L. Katz; Philip J. Katz.
EIN: 237996192
Selected grants: The following grants are a representative sample of this grantmaker's funding activity:
$100,000 to Park Center, Fort Wayne, IN, 2011.
$85,000 to Beth Israel Deaconess Medical Center, Boston, MA, 2011.
$59,720 to McLean Hospital, Belmont, MA, 2011.
$53,500 to Simmons College, Boston, MA, 2011.
$25,000 to Geisinger Medical Center, Danville, PA, 2011.
$25,000 to Project HOME, Philadelphia, PA, 2011.

8118
T. James Kavanagh Foundation Inc. ✧
P.O. Box 1667
Hermitage, PA 16148-0667
Contact: Thomas E. Kavanagh, Tr.

Established in 1968 in PA.
Donor: T. James Kavanagh†.
Foundation type: Independent foundation.
Financial data (yr. ended 12/31/13): Assets, $16,662,790 (M); expenditures, $862,656; qualifying distributions, $705,750; giving activities include $692,475 for grants.
Purpose and activities: Giving primarily to Roman Catholic churches, schools, missions, and organizations; some funding for the arts, health, and human services.
Fields of interest: Arts; Education; Human services; Children/youth, services; Community development, neighborhood development; Catholic agencies & churches.
Type of support: General/operating support; Continuing support; Annual campaigns; Equipment; Program development; Scholarship funds; Research.
Limitations: Applications accepted. Giving primarily in PA. No support for private foundations or organizations outside the U.S., including Roman

Catholic organizations with missions overseas. No grants to individuals, or for seed money, deficit financing, land acquisition, publications, conferences, fellowships, or matching gifts; no loans.
Publications: Application guidelines; Grants list.
Application information: Application form required.
Initial approach: Request application form
Copies of proposal: 1
Deadline(s): None
Trustees: Melvin L. Bandzak; Louis E. Esposito; Thomas E. Kavanagh.
Number of staff: 1 part-time professional; 2 part-time support.
EIN: 236442981

8119
Paul E. Kelly Foundation ✧
(formerly Superior-Pacific Fund)
109 Forrest Ave.
Narberth, PA 19072-2212

Trust established in 1952 in PA.
Donors: Superior Tube Co.; Pacific Tube Co.; Cawsl Enterprises, Inc.
Foundation type: Independent foundation.
Financial data (yr. ended 12/31/13): Assets, $18,770,057 (M); expenditures, $879,949; qualifying distributions, $782,351; giving activities include $679,000 for 82 grants (high: $75,000; low: $100).
Purpose and activities: Grants primarily for Roman Catholic education, community funds, and cultural/ arts organizations.
Fields of interest: Arts; Elementary school/ education; Secondary school/education; Higher education.
Type of support: General/operating support; Continuing support; Annual campaigns; Capital campaigns; Building/renovation; Endowments.
Limitations: Applications not accepted. Giving primarily in the Philadelphia, PA, area.
Application information: Contributes only to pre-selected organizations.
Officers and Directors:* Paul E. Kelly, Jr.,* Pres.; Peter J. Kelly,* V.P.; Christine K. Kieman,* V.P.; Judith K. Shea,* V.P.
Number of staff: 1 full-time professional; 1 full-time support.
EIN: 236298237

8120
Kennametal Foundation ✧
P.O. Box 231
Latrobe, PA 15650-0231 (724) 539-5000
Contact: Erica Clayton Wright, Mgr., Public Affairs
Application address: 1600 Technology Way, Latrobe, PA 15650; Main URL: http://www.kennametal.com/kennametal/en/about-us/in-the-community.html

Established in 1955 in PA.
Donor: Kennametal Inc.
Foundation type: Company-sponsored foundation.
Financial data (yr. ended 06/30/13): Assets, $351,383 (M); gifts received, $915,000; expenditures, $650,126; qualifying distributions, $642,817; giving activities include $630,555 for 112 grants (high: $75,000; low: $100).
Purpose and activities: The foundation supports organizations involved with education and science.
Fields of interest: Secondary school/education; Higher education; Science, formal/general education; Engineering/technology; Science.
Type of support: General/operating support; Continuing support; Building/renovation; Equipment; Scholarship funds; Employee volunteer services.
Limitations: Applications accepted. Giving on a global basis in areas of company operations, with some emphasis on PA. No support for sectarian or religious organizations, political organizations, private foundations, or trust funds. No grants to individuals, or for endowments, development campaigns, debt reduction, or operating reserves, fundraising events or sponsorships, trips, conferences, seminars, festivals, or one-day events, documentaries, videos, research projects/ programs, or indirect or overhead costs.
Publications: Application guidelines.
Application information: Application form required.
Initial approach: Complete online application form
Deadline(s): Last Fri. in May
Board meeting date(s): Annually
Trustees: Carlos M. Cardoso; Joy Chandler; David W. Greenfield; Frank P. Simpkins; Cathy Smith; Phil Wehl.
EIN: 256036009
Selected grants: The following grants are a representative sample of this grantmaker's funding activity:
$75,000 to Saint Vincent College, Latrobe, PA, 2011. For general purpose.
$25,000 to American Heart Association, Greensburg, PA, 2011. For general purpose.
$25,000 to New Century Careers, Pittsburgh, PA, 2011. For general purpose.
$15,000 to Childrens Institute of Pittsburgh, Pittsburgh, PA, 2011. For general purpose.
$12,000 to Tianjin University, Tianjin, China, 2011. For general purpose.
$8,250 to Seton Hill University, Greensburg, PA, 2011. For general purpose.
$7,500 to World Affairs Council of Pittsburgh, Pittsburgh, PA, 2011. For general purpose.
$5,000 to Milwaukee School of Engineering, Milwaukee, WI, 2011. For general purpose.
$5,000 to Pittsburgh Cancer Institute, Pittsburgh, PA, 2011. For general purpose.
$3,400 to Cabbage Patch Settlement House, Louisville, KY, 2011. For general purpose.

8121
The Kestenbaum Family Foundation ✧ ☆
4000 Chemical Rd., No. 401
Plymouth Meeting, PA 19462-1712

Established in PA.
Donors: Joseph Kestenbaum; Sharon Tobin Kestenbaum.
Foundation type: Independent foundation.
Financial data (yr. ended 12/31/13): Assets, $5,249,111 (M); expenditures, $561,821; qualifying distributions, $528,739; giving activities include $528,739 for 26 grants (high: $375,000; low: $25).
Fields of interest: Museums (ethnic/folk arts); Education; Health care; Jewish federated giving programs.
Limitations: Applications not accepted. Giving primarily in Philadelphia, PA.
Application information: Unsolicited requests for funds not accepted.
Directors: Joseph Kestenbaum; Sharon Tobin Kestenbaum.
EIN: 261363714
Selected grants: The following grants are a representative sample of this grantmaker's funding activity:
$385,000 to National Museum of American Jewish History, Philadelphia, PA, 2011.
$100,000 to Jewish Federation of Greater Philadelphia, Philadelphia, PA, 2011.
$100,000 to Jewish Federation of Greater Philadelphia, Philadelphia, PA, 2010. For unrestricted charitable donation.
$10,000 to Har Zion Temple, Penn Valley, PA, 2010. For unrestricted charitable donation.
$5,250 to Childrens Crisis Treatment Center, Philadelphia, PA, 2010. For unrestricted charitable donation.
$5,000 to Childrens Crisis Treatment Center, Philadelphia, PA, 2011.
$2,500 to Har Zion Temple, Penn Valley, PA, 2011.
$1,500 to University of Pennsylvania, Philadelphia, PA, 2011.
$1,000 to Arthritis Foundation, Rocky Hill, CT, 2010. For unrestricted charitable donation.

8122
Keystone Savings Foundation ✧
(formerly Keystone Nazareth Charitable Foundation)
90 Highland Ave.
Bethlehem, PA 18017-9408 (610) 861-5010
Contact: Michele Linsky, Secy.
E-mail: michele.linsky@nationalpenn.com; Main URL: http://www.nationalpenn.com/KeystoneSavingsFoundation/default.html

Established in 2004.
Donor: Keystone Nazareth Bank & Trust Co.
Foundation type: Company-sponsored foundation.
Financial data (yr. ended 12/31/13): Assets, $15,787,341 (M); expenditures, $756,536; qualifying distributions, $670,507; giving activities include $666,250 for 103 grants (high: $51,000; low: $100).
Purpose and activities: The foundation supports organizations involved with arts and culture, education, the environment, health, housing, human services, neighborhood development, leadership development, youth, senior citizens, and the disabled.
Fields of interest: Visual arts; Museums; Performing arts; Arts; Elementary/secondary education; Higher education; Libraries (public); Education, drop-out prevention; Education; Environment, natural resources; Environment; Hospitals (general); Health care; Housing/shelter; Human services; Community development, neighborhood development; Leadership development; Youth; Aging; Disabilities, people with.
Type of support: Matching/challenge support; General/operating support; Capital campaigns; Building/renovation; Equipment; Program development; Scholarship funds; Sponsorships.
Limitations: Applications accepted. Giving limited to areas of company operations in Lehigh, Northampton, and Southern Carbon counties, PA. No grants to individuals, or for golf tournaments, dinners, lunches, auction, or other similar events, endowments, or debt reduction.
Publications: Application guidelines; Program policy statement.
Application information: Grant requests less than $25,000 are reviewed quarterly. Grant requests of

$25,000 or more are reviewed once a year. E-mailed applications are not accepted. Support is limited to 1 contribution per organization during any given year. Organizations receiving support are asked to submit a report within 6 months of receiving funds. Application form required.

Initial approach: Download application form and mail to foundation

Copies of proposal: 1

Deadline(s): Feb. 15, May 15, Aug. 15, and Nov. 15; Aug 15. for grant requests of $25,000 or more

Board meeting date(s): Mar., June, Sept. and Dec.

Officers and Directors:* Jeffrey P. Feather,* Chair., Pres., and Treas.; Michele A. Linsky, Secy.; Scott V. Fainor; Daniel G. Gambet; R. Charles Stehy.

EIN: 421607170

8123
The James & Agnes Kim Foundation, Inc. ✧

c/o Siana Carr O'Connor and Lynam, LLP
1500 E. Lancaster Ave.
Paoli, PA 19301-1500

Established in 1997 in PA.

Donors: James J. Kim; Agnes C. Kim.

Foundation type: Independent foundation.

Financial data (yr. ended 12/31/13): Assets, $7,786,719 (M); gifts received, $650,000; expenditures, $3,376,558; qualifying distributions, $3,372,684; giving activities include $3,361,000 for 25 grants (high: $1,025,000; low: $1,000).

Purpose and activities: Giving primarily for education and art museums.

Fields of interest: Museums (art); Arts; Elementary/secondary education; Higher education; Cancer; Catholic agencies & churches.

Limitations: Applications not accepted. Giving primarily in Philadelphia, PA. No grants to individuals.

Application information: Contributes only to pre-selected organizations.

Officers: Agnes C. Kim, Pres.; Susan Y. Kim, Secy.; James J. Kim, Treas.

EIN: 232899799

8124
The Sidney Kimmel Foundation ✧

1900 Market St.
Philadelphia, PA 19103-3527 (215) 665-2079
Contact: Matthew H. Kamens
FAX: (215) 701-2257;
E-mail: mkamens@cozen.com; Main URL: http://www.kimmel.org
Sidney Kimmel's Giving Pledge Profile: http://glasspockets.org/philanthropy-in-focus/eye-on-the-giving-pledge/profiles/kimmel
Application address: Gary Cohen, M.D., Cancer Center GBMC, 6569 N. Charles St., Ste. 300, Baltimore, MD 21204, on-line address: kimmel@gbmc.org

Established in 1993 in PA.

Donor: Sidney Kimmel.

Foundation type: Independent foundation.

Financial data (yr. ended 07/31/13): Assets, $1,957,678 (M); gifts received, $9,802,368; expenditures, $11,647,173; qualifying distributions, $11,642,465; giving activities include $8,171,695 for 17 grants (high: $5,000,000; low: $1,500), and $3,000,000 for 45 grants to individuals.

Purpose and activities: Giving for cancer research and treatment; funding also for education and Jewish federated giving programs and causes.

Fields of interest: Higher education; Cancer; Medical research, institute; Cancer research; Jewish federated giving programs.

Type of support: Scholarships—to individuals.

Limitations: Applications not accepted. Giving in the U.S., with emphasis on Philadelphia, PA.

Application information: Unsolicited requests for funds are not accepted.

Officer: Sidney Kimmel, Pres. and Treas.

EIN: 232698492

8125
Patricia Kind Family Foundation ✧

717 Bethlehem Pike, Ste. 160
Erdenheim, PA 19038-8111 (215) 836-9536
Contact: Laura Kind McKenna, Managing Trustee; Regina Bosca, Grants Mgr.
FAX: (215) 836-9537;
E-mail: PKFFoundation@comcast.net; Main URL: http://www.PKFFoundation.net

Established in 1996 in PA.

Donors: Hedwig A. van Ameringen‡; Louis van Ameringen‡.

Foundation type: Independent foundation.

Financial data (yr. ended 12/31/12): Assets, $22,386,781 (M); expenditures, $2,338,464; qualifying distributions, $2,319,632; giving activities include $2,180,500 for 216 grants (high: $25,000; low: $2,500), and $37,000 for 1 loan/program-related investment.

Purpose and activities: Giving to organizations that help children, adults, and seniors in need to obtain physical and mental health care and related human services in the Philadelphia, PA, area.

Fields of interest: Education; Health care; Human services.

Type of support: Mission-related investments/loans; General/operating support; Continuing support; Program development; Curriculum development; Program-related investments/loans; Matching/challenge support.

Limitations: Applications accepted. Giving primarily in Bucks, Chester, Delaware, Montgomery and Philadelphia counties in PA. No grants to individuals, or for scholarships, international giving activities, or fundraising; no endowments.

Publications: Application guidelines; Financial statement; Grants list; Informational brochure (including application guidelines).

Application information: The foundation now only accepts applications made online. Paper applications are no longer accepted. See foundation web site for application guidelines. Application form required.

Initial approach: Use online application on foundation web site

Copies of proposal: 1

Deadline(s): See foundation web site for current deadlines

Board meeting date(s): Jan., Apr., and Aug.

Trustees: Laura Kind McKenna, Managing Tr.; Christina Kind; Ken Kind; Patricia Kind; Andrew Kindfuller; Valerie Kind-Rubin.

Number of staff: 1 part-time support.

EIN: 237839035

8126
The Jeffery & Cynthia King Family Foundation ✧ ☆

2062 General Alexander Dr.
Malvern, PA 19355-9799 (610) 647-2000
Contact: Jeffrey L. King; Cynthia M. King

Established in 1999 in PA.

Donors: Jeffery L. King; Cynthia M. King.

Foundation type: Independent foundation.

Financial data (yr. ended 05/31/13): Assets, $5,430,049 (M); gifts received, $1,100,000; expenditures, $1,128,154; qualifying distributions, $1,124,000; giving activities include $1,124,000 for 2+ grants (high: $1,115,000).

Fields of interest: Education; Human services.

Limitations: Applications not accepted. Giving primarily in PA. No grants to individuals.

Application information: Unsolicited requests for funds not accepted.

EIN: 256638460

8127
Kinsley Family Foundation ✧

6259 Reynolds Mill Rd.
Seven Valleys, PA 17360-8844
Contact: Anne W. Kinsley, Pres.
Application address: 2700 Water St., York, PA 17403-9306, tel.: (410) 537-5491

Established in 1997 in PA.

Donors: Robert A. Kinsley; Anne W. Kinsley; Kinsley Construction, Inc.; Walton & Co., Inc.; Gettle, Inc.; I.B. Abel, Inc.; LSC Design Inc.; Gettle Inc.

Foundation type: Independent foundation.

Financial data (yr. ended 12/31/13): Assets, $9,674,949 (M); gifts received, $2,016,616; expenditures, $1,897,732; qualifying distributions, $1,809,798; giving activities include $1,809,783 for 67 grants (high: $748,000; low: $100).

Fields of interest: Elementary/secondary education; Higher education; Education; Health care; Human services; YM/YWCAs & YM/YWHAs; Community/economic development.

Limitations: Applications accepted. Giving primarily in York, PA.

Application information: Application form required.

Initial approach: Letter

Deadline(s): None

Officers: Anne W. Kinsley, Pres.; Christopher A. Kinsley, Secy.; Timothy J. Kinsley, Treas.

EIN: 232870170

8128
Charles and Figa Kline Foundation ✧

c/o Commerce Corporate Ctr.
5050 Tilghman St., Ste. 115
Allentown, PA 18104-9114 (610) 437-4077

Incorporated in 1957 in PA.

Donors: Charles Kline‡; Figa Cohen Kline‡.

Foundation type: Operating foundation.

Financial data (yr. ended 10/31/13): Assets, $8,752,975 (M); expenditures, $494,561; qualifying distributions, $431,200; giving activities include $431,200 for 12 grants (high: $178,200; low: $1,000).

Purpose and activities: Giving largely for Jewish welfare and community service agencies, temple support, and education.

Fields of interest: Education; Human services; Jewish federated giving programs; Jewish agencies & synagogues.
Type of support: Capital campaigns; Building/renovation.
Limitations: Applications accepted. Giving primarily in Allentown, PA. No grants to individuals.
Application information: Application form not required.
Initial approach: Proposal
Deadline(s): Sept. 30
Officers: Stewart Furmansky, Pres.; Barnet H. Fraenkel, V.P.; Roberto Fischmann, Secy.
EIN: 236262315

8129
Josiah W. and Bessie H. Kline Foundation, Inc. ✧
515 S. 29th St.
Harrisburg, PA 17104-2106 (717) 561-0820
Contact: John A. Obrock C.P.A., Secy.
Main URL: http://www.kline-foundation.org/

Incorporated in 1952 in DE.
Donors: Josiah W. Kline†; Bessie H. Kline†.
Foundation type: Independent foundation.
Financial data (yr. ended 12/31/13): Assets, $23,164,665 (M); expenditures, $1,140,469; qualifying distributions, $1,028,113; giving activities include $1,019,760 for grants.
Fields of interest: Arts; Higher education; Education; Health organizations; Human services; Children/youth, services; United Ways and Federated Giving Programs.
Type of support: Continuing support; Annual campaigns; Capital campaigns; Building/renovation; Equipment; Land acquisition; Emergency funds; Curriculum development; Scholarship funds; Research; Matching/challenge support.
Limitations: Applications accepted. Giving primarily in south central PA, with emphasis on Cumberland and Dauphin counties. No grants to individuals, or for endowment funds, operating budgets, special projects, publications, conferences, or fellowships; no loans.
Publications: Application guidelines; Program policy statement.
Application information: Application form required.
Initial approach: Contact foundation for application form
Deadline(s): None
Officers and Directors:* John A. Russell,* Pres.; Paul B. Shannon,* V.P. and Treas.; John A. Obrock, Secy.; Constance B. Foster; George F. Grode; Robert S. Jones; Roger Longenderfer; Cassandra W. Pepinsky; Samuel D. Ross, Jr.
EIN: 236245783
Selected grants: The following grants are a representative sample of this grantmaker's funding activity:
$100,000 to Pinnacle Health Foundation, Harrisburg, PA, 2011.
$75,000 to United Way of the Capital Region, Enola, PA, 2011.
$50,000 to Central Pennsylvania Food Bank, Harrisburg, PA, 2011.
$50,000 to Gettysburg College, Gettysburg, PA, 2011.
$50,000 to YMCA of Harrisburg Area, Harrisburg, PA, 2011.
$22,255 to Boy Scouts of America, Mechanicsburg, PA, 2011.
$15,000 to Amyotrophic Lateral Sclerosis Association, Ambler, PA, 2011.
$15,000 to Brethren Housing Association, Harrisburg, PA, 2011.
$15,000 to Humane Society of Harrisburg Area, Harrisburg, PA, 2011.
$15,000 to Pennsylvania Coalition Against Domestic Violence, Harrisburg, PA, 2011.

8130
Airie Knipel, Harry V. and J. William Warehime Foundation ✧
c/o Bergdoll & Co., LLP
137 W. Market St.
York, PA 17401-1322

Established in 1996 in PA.
Donor: J. William Warehime†.
Foundation type: Independent foundation.
Financial data (yr. ended 12/31/13): Assets, $87,791,411 (M); expenditures, $6,853,670; qualifying distributions, $6,766,112; giving activities include $6,757,500 for 26 grants (high: $4,250,000; low: $1,000).
Purpose and activities: Giving primarily for education, including a health education center; support also for a performing arts center.
Fields of interest: Performing arts centers; Higher education; Health sciences school/education; Education; American Red Cross.
Limitations: Applications not accepted. Giving primarily in Gettysburg and York, PA. No grants to individuals.
Application information: Contributes only to pre-selected organizations.
Officers: Elizabeth W. Stick, Pres.; James K. Bergdoll, V.P.; Linda A. Lohr, Secy.-Treas.
EIN: 311481509

8131
The Kohelet Foundation ✧
822 Montgomery Ave., Ste. 201
Narbeth, PA 19072-1937 (484) 278-1328
Contact: Nancy Bonner, Office Mgr.
FAX: (484) 589-4638;
E-mail: info@koheletfoundation.org; E-mail address for Nancy Bonner, Office Mgr.: nancy@koheletfoundation.org; Main URL: http://www.koheletfoundation.org/
Blog: http://www.koheletfoundation.org/blog
Facebook: https://www.facebook.com/koheletfoundation

Donors: David M. Magerman; Kohelet Yeshiva High School.
Foundation type: Independent foundation.
Financial data (yr. ended 12/31/12): Assets, $304,595 (M); gifts received, $5,121,333; expenditures, $5,119,448; qualifying distributions, $5,005,332; giving activities include $4,019,824 for 49 grants (high: $577,134; low: $335), and $465,422 for foundation-administered programs.
Purpose and activities: Giving primarily for the healthy development of Jewish identity and the observance of Jewish laws and traditions. The foundation's interests are to: 1) promote access to Jewish education at all levels as the path to cultivating a strong Jewish identity; 2) ease the financial obstacles to families committed to day school education; 3) reinforce the value of family learning to strengthen the impact of Jewish day school education; 4) unify the educational messages at school and at home so that Jewish living and learning are fortified; and 5) inspire life-long learning and the conviction that the Jewish person's pursuit of learning, questioning and refining is never complete.
Fields of interest: Education; Jewish agencies & synagogues.
Limitations: Applications accepted. Giving primarily in the greater Philadelphia, PA, region. No support for organizations outside the U.S. No grants to individuals, or for capital campaigns, construction, debt, or endowments.
Application information:
Initial approach: Letter
Final notification: Four weeks
Officers: David Magerman, Pres.; Holly B. Cohen, Exec. Dir.
Advisors: Michael Bohnen; Lester Lipschutz; Sam Moed; Yossi Prager.
EIN: 263773063
Selected grants: The following grants are a representative sample of this grantmaker's funding activity:
$14,972,700 to Kohelet Yeshiva High School, Merion Station, PA, 2011.
$1,193,451 to Kohelet Yeshiva High School, Merion Station, PA, 2011.
$887,800 to Kellman Brown Academy, Voorhees, NJ, 2010.
$771,011 to Raymond and Ruth Perelman Jewish Day School, Wynnewood, PA, 2011.
$240,260 to Torah Academy of Greater Philadelphia, Wynnewood, PA, 2011.
$210,000 to Abrams Hebrew Academy, Yardley, PA, 2010.
$125,000 to Yeshivat Noam, Paramus, NJ, 2011.
$100,000 to OROT, Jenkintown, PA, 2011.
$93,630 to Politz Hebrew Academy of Northeast Philadelphia, Philadelphia, PA, 2011.
$80,530 to Abrams Hebrew Academy, Yardley, PA, 2011.
$61,455 to Yeshiva University, New York, NY, 2011.
$60,160 to National Society for Hebrew Day Schools - Torah Umesorah, New York, NY, 2011.
$55,000 to Albert Einstein Academy, Wilmington, DE, 2010.
$50,000 to Birthright Israel Foundation, New York, NY, 2010.
$50,000 to Schechter Institutes, Philadelphia, PA, 2010.
$25,000 to Yeshiva University, New York, NY, 2010.
$5,000 to OROT, Jenkintown, PA, 2010.

8132
Jane & Leonard Korman Family Foundation ✧
2 Neshaminy Interplex, Ste. 305
Trevose, PA 19053-6933

Established in 2006 in PA.
Donors: Jane Korman; Leonard Korman.
Foundation type: Independent foundation.
Financial data (yr. ended 12/31/13): Assets, $13,333,405 (M); gifts received, $204,841; expenditures, $1,795,445; qualifying distributions, $1,683,858; giving activities include $1,683,858 for 24 grants (high: $800,000; low: $500).
Fields of interest: Arts; Education.
Limitations: Applications not accepted. Giving primarily in FL and PA. No grants to individuals.

Application information: Contributes only to pre-selected organizations.
Officers: Jane Korman, Co-Pres.; Leonard Korman, Co-Pres.
Directors: Catherine Korman Altman; Alison Korman Feldman; Susan Korman Schurr.
EIN: 204253701
Selected grants: The following grants are a representative sample of this grantmaker's funding activity:
$117,000 to Thomas Jefferson University, Philadelphia, PA, 2012. To support the Educational Mission of the University.
$50,000 to Scripps Research Institute, Jupiter, FL, 2012. To support the Research Efforts of the Organization That Is Engaged in Biomedical Science.
$43,923 to Philadelphia Museum of Art, Philadelphia, PA, 2012. To support the Mission of the Museum.
$40,000 to Whitemarsh Foundation, Lafayette Hill, PA, 2012. To provide Assistance to the Foundation That Is Dedicated to Preserving the Whitemarsh Valley.
$5,000 to Chestnut Hill Academy, Philadelphia, PA, 2012. To support the Educational Mission of the Academy.
$5,000 to Maltz Jupiter Theater, Jupiter, FL, 2012. To provide Assistance to Performing Arts.
$1,500 to Woodmere Art Museum, Philadelphia, PA, 2012. To support the Educational Mission of the Museum.
$1,000 to Community Partnership School, Philadelphia, PA, 2012. To support the Educational Mission of School.
$1,000 to Watershed Center for the Ceramic Arts, Newcastle, ME, 2012. To provide Assistance That Supports the Site Project of the Watershed.

8133
John Crain Kunkel Foundation ✧
225 Market St., 2nd Fl.
Harrisburg, PA 17101-0658 (717) 902-9817
Contact: Nancy W. Bergert, Tr.
E-mail: info@kunkelfoundation.org; Main URL: http://www.kunkelfoundation.org

Established in 1965 in PA.
Foundation type: Independent foundation.
Financial data (yr. ended 12/31/13): Assets, $13,258,536 (M); expenditures, $860,517; qualifying distributions, $798,613; giving activities include $656,700 for 27 grants (high: $125,000; low: $1,000).
Purpose and activities: Giving primarily for human services, health care, and to a museum.
Fields of interest: Museums (specialized); Health care; Human services; YM/YWCAs & YM/YWHAs; United Ways and Federated Giving Programs.
Type of support: General/operating support.
Limitations: Applications accepted. Giving primarily in Harrisburg, PA.
Application information: See foundation website for complete application guidelines. Application form required.
Initial approach: Letter
Trustees: Nancy W. Bergert; Elizabeth K. Davis; Deborah L. Facini; John C. Kunkel II; Paul A. Kunkel; Jay W. Stark; John K. Stark; Jennifer R. Wright; William T. Wright II.
EIN: 237026914
Selected grants: The following grants are a representative sample of this grantmaker's funding activity:
$150,000 to Harrisburg Area Community College Foundation, Harrisburg, PA, 2011. For general purpose fund.

8134
James Annenberg La Vea Charitable Foundation ✧
(formerly James Annenberg Levee Charitable Foundation)
c/o PNC Bank, N.A.
1600 Market St., 29th Fl.
Philadelphia, PA 19103-7240
Contact: Lawrence J. Miller, Tr.

Established in 2000 in FL.
Donors: James Annenberg Levee Charitable Trust; James Annenberg La Vea.
Foundation type: Independent foundation.
Financial data (yr. ended 12/31/13): Assets, $44,294,127 (M); gifts received, $50,000; expenditures, $2,159,483; qualifying distributions, $2,061,023; giving activities include $2,061,023 for 31 grants (high: $82,441; low: $61,831).
Purpose and activities: Giving primarily for health and children's services.
Fields of interest: Health care; Health organizations, association; Medical research; Human services; Children/youth, services.
Limitations: Applications not accepted. Giving primarily in FL, IL, MA, and NY. No grants to individuals.
Application information: Contributes only to pre-selected organizations.
Officer: James Annenberg La Vea, Fdn. Mgr.
Trustee: Lawrence J. Miller, Esq.
EIN: 656323823
Selected grants: The following grants are a representative sample of this grantmaker's funding activity:
$59,598 to Shriners Hospitals for Children, Tampa, FL, 2012. To be used exclusively for the benefit of Shriners Hospitals for Children - BOSTON (51 Blossom St Boston, MA 02114) In honor of James Annenberg La Vea.
$59,598 to Teach for America, New York, NY, 2012. For In honor of James Annenberg La Vea.

8135
The Lancaster County Community Foundation ✧
(formerly The Lancaster County Foundation)
24 W. King St., Ste. 201
Lancaster, PA 17603 (717) 397-1629
Contact: Samuel J. Bressi, C.E.O.
FAX: (717) 397-6877;
E-mail: info@lancastercountyfoundation.org; Main URL: http://www.lancfound.org/
Blog: http://lancfound.org/blog/
Facebook: http://www.facebook.com/pages/Lancaster-County-Community-Foundation/61365582396
LinkedIn: http://www.linkedin.com/companies/lancaster-community-foundation
Twitter: https://twitter.com/lancfound

Established in 1924 in PA.
Foundation type: Community foundation.
Financial data (yr. ended 12/31/12): Assets, $71,604,558 (M); gifts received, $2,399,242; expenditures, $5,147,466; giving activities include $3,502,168 for grants.
Purpose and activities: The foundation advances the vitality and well-being of the people of Lancaster County by inspiring generosity and by being responsible stewards of gifts for today and tomorrow.
Fields of interest: Arts; Education; Environment; Health care; Housing/shelter, home owners; Children/youth, services; Human services; Community/economic development; Disabilities, people with.
Type of support: Management development/capacity building; Endowments; Program development; Scholarship funds; Mission-related investments/loans.
Limitations: Applications accepted. Giving limited to Lancaster County, PA. No support for governmental agencies, umbrella organizations for purposes of re-granting funds, cemetery associations, or sectarian religious purposes. No grants to individuals (except for scholarships), or for operating budgets, continuing support, annual campaigns, deficit financing, land acquisition, fellowships, consulting services, fundraising events, solicitations, multi-year funding for bricks and mortar projects, conferences, trips, or seminars.
Publications: Application guidelines; Annual report; Grants list; Informational brochure; Newsletter.
Application information: The foundation accepts applications on a yearly basis. Applications are posted and accepted online. Visit foundation Web site to sign up for our e-newsletter and learn about our grant opportunities. Application form required.
Initial approach: Complete online application
Copies of proposal: 1
Deadline(s): Rolling
Board meeting date(s): 6 times annually
Final notification: Within a few weeks after proposal deadline
Officers and Directors:* Samuel J. Bressi,* C.E.O. and Pres.; Tracy Cutler,* V.P., Comms. and Donor Cultivation; Wayne Groff,* V.P., Finance; Melody Keim,* V.P., Progs. and Initiatives; Kim Shorter,* V.P., Opers. and Donor Support; Vance Antonacci; Benjamin Atwater; Jan Bergen; Joe Byorick; Jennifer Craighead; Steve Geisenberger; Elizabeth Krapp; Francine McNairy; Rod Messick; Lisa Riggs; Tim Rochel, Sr.; Kim Smith; Linda Porr Sweeney.
Number of staff: 7 full-time professional; 1 full-time support; 1 part-time support.
EIN: 200874857

8136
Lehigh Valley Community Foundation ✧
(formerly Bethlehem Area Foundation)
840 W. Hamilton St., Ste. 310
Allentown, PA 18101 (610) 351-5353
Contact: Bernard J. Story, C.E.O.; For grants: Corrina Lillis, Mktg. and Grants Mgr.
FAX: (610) 351-9353;
E-mail: lvcf@lvcfoundation.org; Grant inquiry e-mail: corrina@lvcfoundation.org; Main URL: http://www.lehighvalleyfoundation.org/
Facebook: https://www.facebook.com/LVCFoundation
Twitter: https://twitter.com/LVCFoundation

Established in 1967 in PA.
Foundation type: Community foundation.
Financial data (yr. ended 06/30/13): Assets, $35,381,043 (M); gifts received, $3,094,930; expenditures, $4,412,675; giving activities include $3,705,356 for 77+ grants (high: $1,993,747).

Purpose and activities: The foundation enables donors, including individuals, families, businesses, private foundations and nonprofit agencies, to establish funds which will serve their charitable intentions temporarily or in perpetuity by providing grants to nonprofit organizations and programs. Giving for arts, culture, and heritage, community development, education, environment and science, health care, and human services.
Fields of interest: Historic preservation/historical societies; Arts; Education; Environment; Health care; Children, services; Human services; Community/economic development; Science.
Type of support: Management development/capacity building; Capital campaigns; Building/renovation; Equipment; Emergency funds; Program development; Publication; Seed money; Scholarship funds; Matching/challenge support.
Limitations: Applications accepted. Giving limited to Lehigh, Monroe, Northampton, and Upper Bucks counties, PA. No support for sectarian religious purposes. No grants for operating budgets, continuing support, annual campaigns, deficit financing, endowments, foundation scholarships, or research; no loans.
Publications: Application guidelines; Annual report; Grants list; Program policy statement.
Application information: Visit foundation web site for application form guidelines and specific deadlines. Faxed or e-mailed applications are accepted. Capital funding: must submit invoice copies when requesting release of funds. Site visits may be made. Final reports required. Application form required.

Initial approach: Complete application form
Deadline(s): July 1 for Community Partnership Grants
Board meeting date(s): Quarterly
Final notification: Dec. and Jan.

Officers and Board of Governors:* Denise M. Blew,* Chair.; Michael Stershic,* Vice-Chair.; Bernard J. Story,* Pres. and C.E.O.; Trisha R. Higgins,* V.P. and C.F.O.; Kamran Afsar, Ph.D.; Geoffrey B. Borda; Beth Williams Boyer; Greg L. Butz; Thomas L. Campbell; Bonnie S. Coyle, M.D.; Cynthia Lambert Durham; W. Beal Fowler, Ph.D.; Robert E. Gadomski; Karen R. Green; Raymond B. Holton; David Lobach; Jennifer L. Mann; L. Charles Marcon; James Margolis, Ph.D.; Robert Moffett, Esq.; William K. Murphy, Esq.; Bruce A. Palmer; Martha Phelps; Ann Haggerty Raines; Matthew R. Sorrentino, Esq.; Melinda Stumpf; J. Marshall Wolff.
Investment Management: BNY Mellon, N.A.; Comerica; Merrill Lynch Trust Co.; Morgan Stanley Smith Barney; Vanguard Group; Wells Fargo.
Number of staff: 3 full-time professional; 1 part-time professional; 1 full-time support.
EIN: 231686634

8137
The Brook J. Lenfest Foundation, Inc. ✧

2 Logan Sq.
100 N. 18th St., Ste. 800
Philadelphia, PA 19103-2707 (215) 239-9003
Contact: Bruce Melgary, Exec. Dir.
FAX: (610) 828-0390;
E-mail: lenfestfoundation@lenfestfoundation.org;
Main URL: http://www.brookjlenfestfoundation.org

Established in 2000 in PA.
Donor: Brook J. Lenfest.
Foundation type: Independent foundation.
Financial data (yr. ended 06/30/13): Assets, $29,480,787 (M); expenditures, $1,801,119; qualifying distributions, $1,702,383; giving activities include $1,648,824 for 26 grants (high: $801,391).
Purpose and activities: The foundation is dedicated to making people aware of positive life choices and providing support and opportunities for those motivated to pursue them. In keeping with its mission, the foundation will focus mainly on education, job training, mentoring programs, wellness-based health care, and the arts. The foundation also supports the Mastery Charter High School in Philadelphia, PA, whose mission is to ensure all students develop the skills they need to succeed in the 21st century economy with full preparation for college education. The foundation believes that it is important to support only organizations and programs that demonstrate effectiveness through documented outcomes.
Fields of interest: Arts; Education; Human services.
Type of support: General/operating support; Continuing support; Capital campaigns; Seed money; Scholarship funds.
Limitations: Applications accepted. Giving primarily in southeastern PA, with emphasis on Philadelphia. No support for health or religious programs, day care or pre-K education programs, or political or quasi-political organizations. No grants to individuals, or for medical research, publications or litigation.
Publications: Application guidelines.
Application information: The foundation is currently only accepting applications from organizations that it has funded in the past. Eligible organizations must have well documented positive outcomes to be competitive for funding and must show that a grant from the foundation will have a meaningful impact. See foundation web site for guidelines and updates. Applications sent by e-mail will not be accepted. Grant requests may be submitted for 1 year only, and not to exceed $25,000. Application form not required.

Initial approach: Organizations that the foundation has funded in the past may submit a short (3-5 page) letter
Copies of proposal: 1
Deadline(s): Mar. 15 for consideration at the spring meeting and Sept. 15 for consideration at the fall meeting
Board meeting date(s): Nov. or Dec.
Final notification: After board meeting

Officers and Directors:* Brook J. Lenfest,* Pres.; Marguerite B. Lenfest,* Treas.; Joy Tartar, C.F.O.; William Luterman, C.I.O.; Bruce Melgary, Exec. Dir.
EIN: 233031338

8138
The Lenfest Foundation, Inc. ✧

100 N. 18th St., Ste. 800
Two Logan Sq.
Philadelphia, PA 19103-2743 (215) 239-9003
Contact: Bruce Melgary, Exec. Dir.
FAX: (610) 828-0390;
E-mail: lenfestfoundation@lenfestfoundation.org;
Main URL: http://www.lenfestfoundation.org
Gerry and Marguerite Lenfest's Giving Pledge Profile: http://glasspockets.org/philanthropy-in-focus/eye-on-the-giving-pledge/profiles/lenfest

Established in 2000 in PA.
Donors: H.F. (Gerry) Lenfest; Mrs. H.F. Lenfest.
Foundation type: Independent foundation.
Financial data (yr. ended 06/30/13): Assets, $103,125,296 (M); gifts received, $600,000; expenditures, $8,924,842; qualifying distributions, $8,368,242; giving activities include $6,445,337 for 48 grants (high: $2,000,000; low: $5,000), and $1,031,400 for grants to individuals.
Purpose and activities: Giving primarily for the foundation's own rural education scholarship programs, major project support initiated by the foundation's founders, and approved by its Board of Directors. Limited number of grants in the areas of education, arts, and the environment.
Fields of interest: Arts; Education; Environment.
Type of support: General/operating support; Continuing support; Annual campaigns; Capital campaigns; Scholarships—to individuals.
Limitations: Applications accepted. Giving primarily in northern DE, southern NJ, and southeastern and south central PA. No support for disease research. No grants to individuals (except for Lenfest scholarships), political organizations, religious programs or activities, university presses, tickets, tables or sponsorships or conferences, or organizations that deal with health, physical or mental disabilities; no loans.
Publications: Application guidelines; Informational brochure (including application guidelines).
Application information: The foundation does not accept e-mail requests. Application guidelines available on web site. Application form not required.

Initial approach: Letter (2 - 3 pages)
Copies of proposal: 1
Deadline(s): None
Board meeting date(s): Feb., May, and Oct.
Final notification: Usually 1 - 3 months

Officers and Directors:* Keith Leaphart,* Chair.; Marguerite Lenfest,* Pres.; Grahame Richards, Secy.; Joy Tarta, C.F.O. and Treas.; Bruce Melgary, Exec. Dir.; T. Douglas Hale; Joseph F. Huber; H.F. (Gerry) Lenfest; John Strassburger.
Number of staff: 2 full-time professional; 2 full-time support.
EIN: 233031350
Selected grants: The following grants are a representative sample of this grantmaker's funding activity:
$2,000,000 to Pew Charitable Trusts, Philadelphia, PA, 2012. For Lenfest Ocean Program.
$2,000,000 to Teach for America, Philadelphia, PA, 2012. For Philadelphia Challenge Grant.
$250,000 to United Way of Greater Philadelphia and Southern New Jersey, Philadelphia, PA, 2012. For Planning and Restructuring work at the School District of Philadelphia.
$200,000 to Childrens Scholarship Fund, Philadelphia, Philadelphia, PA, 2012. For Campaign for Scholarships.
$200,000 to Fund for Philadelphia, Philadelphia, PA, 2012. For PhillyGoes2College and College Ready Data Project.
$150,000 to City Year Greater Philadelphia, Philadelphia, PA, 2012. For Whole School Whole Child.
$100,000 to Franklin and Marshall College, Lancaster, PA, 2012. For National College Advising Corps, Keystone Region.
$100,000 to Saint James School, Philadelphia, PA, 2012. For general operating support.
$30,000 to Mercy Vocational High School, Philadelphia, PA, 2012. For general operating support.

$25,000 to Free Library of Philadelphia Foundation, Philadelphia, PA, 2012. For 2012 One Book program.

8139
Leonard Family Foundation ✧
c/o S. Roth (ML&B)
1701 Market St.
Philadelphia, PA 19103-2901

Established in 2002 in PA.
Donor: William Leonard.
Foundation type: Independent foundation.
Financial data (yr. ended 12/31/13): Assets, $6,630,084 (M); gifts received, $4,422; expenditures, $585,300; qualifying distributions, $544,548; giving activities include $535,000 for 5 grants (high: $250,000; low: $10,000).
Fields of interest: Education; Hospitals (general); Human services.
Limitations: Applications not accepted. Giving primarily in CA. No grants to individuals.
Application information: Contributes only to pre-selected organizations.
Trustees: Christopher A. Leonard; Judith V. Leonard; William Leonard; Deborah A. Perez.
EIN: 256823063
Selected grants: The following grants are a representative sample of this grantmaker's funding activity:
$225,000 to Las Palmas Elementary School, San Clemente, CA, 2012. For educational supplies.

8140
Levis Trust ✧
c/o BNY Mellon, N.A.
P.O. Box 185
Pittsburgh, PA 15230-0185

Established in 2001 in PA.
Donor: Adolph Levis Trust.
Foundation type: Independent foundation.
Financial data (yr. ended 12/31/13): Assets, $3,325,169 (M); expenditures, $3,948,343; qualifying distributions, $3,936,861; giving activities include $3,922,430 for 12 grants (high: $1,000,000; low: $5,000).
Fields of interest: Hospitals (general); Jewish federated giving programs; Jewish agencies & synagogues.
Type of support: Matching/challenge support.
Limitations: Applications not accepted. Giving primarily Boca Raton, FL and PA. No grants to individuals.
Application information: Contributes only to pre-selected organizations.
Trustees: Barbara Brodsky; BNY Mellon, N.A.
EIN: 311631647

8141
The Lily Foundation ✧
200 W. Lancaster Ave., Ste. 202
Wayne, PA 19087-4046

Established in 1997 in PA.
Donors: Robert L. McNeil III; Jane McNeil; Robert L. McNeil, Jr.
Foundation type: Independent foundation.
Financial data (yr. ended 12/31/13): Assets, $12,923,933 (M); expenditures, $689,969; qualifying distributions, $624,674; giving activities include $614,500 for 23 grants (high: $250,000; low: $1,000).
Fields of interest: Elementary/secondary education; Higher education; Human services; Family services, domestic violence.
Limitations: Applications not accepted. Giving primarily in PA; funding also in Tampa, FL. No grants to individuals.
Application information: Contributes only to pre-selected organizations.
Trustees: Jane McNeil; Robert L. McNeil III.
EIN: 526854621

8142
The Lindback Foundation ✧
(also known as Christian R. and Mary F. Lindback Foundation)
c/o Duane Morris LLP
30 S. 17th St.
Philadelphia, PA 19103-4196 (215) 979-1555
Contact: Sharon M. Renz, V.P. of Admin.

Established in 1955 in NJ.
Donors: Mary F. Lindback†; Christian R. Lindback†.
Foundation type: Independent foundation.
Financial data (yr. ended 12/31/13): Assets, $30,094,248 (M); expenditures, $1,806,019; qualifying distributions, $1,495,911; giving activities include $1,272,501 for 158 grants (high: $213,500; low: $1,000).
Purpose and activities: Giving primarily to universities for distinguished teaching awards (college and high school level), and discretionary grants.
Fields of interest: Museums; Arts; Education; Environment; Animals/wildlife; Hospitals (general); Human services.
Type of support: General/operating support; Annual campaigns; Capital campaigns; Seed money; Fellowships; Matching/challenge support.
Limitations: Applications accepted. Giving primarily in southern NJ, and southeastern PA. No support for private organizations. No grants to individuals, or for building or endowment funds.
Publications: Application guidelines.
Application information: Application form not required.
Initial approach: Proposal
Copies of proposal: 4
Deadline(s): Sept. 15 and Mar. 15
Board meeting date(s): Late spring and late fall
Final notification: Approx. 4 weeks after semi-annual meeting
Trustees: Sheldon M. Bonovitz; David E. Loder; Wells Fargo Bank, N.A.
Number of staff: 1
EIN: 236290348
Selected grants: The following grants are a representative sample of this grantmaker's funding activity:
$89,458 to Free Library of Philadelphia Foundation, Philadelphia, PA, 2012. For Summer 2012 College Prep Program.
$50,000 to Philadelphia Museum of Art, Philadelphia, PA, 2012. For funding for the Student Admission and Philadelphia Student and Family Pass Program 2 year grant @$50,000.
$40,000 to Lincoln University, Lincoln University, PA, 2012. For the Lincoln-Barnes Arts and Lecture Series.
$28,724 to Free Library of Philadelphia Foundation, Philadelphia, PA, 2012. For grant commitment for funding to expand services to older adults at the Parkway Central Library.
$25,000 to Zoological Society of Philadelphia, Philadelphia, PA, 2012. For Final 2 years of 5 year commitment to fund award winning educational Programs 2 year@$25,000.
$13,932 to University of the Sciences in Philadelphia, Philadelphia, PA, 2012. For Seed funding for The CarFit Project.
$12,500 to Philadelphia Museum of Art, Philadelphia, PA, 2012. For community outreach and educational Programs in conjunction with the Jill and Sheldon Bonovitz Collection 2 year grant @ $12,500.
$5,000 to Appel Farm Arts and Music Center, Elmer, NJ, 2012. For funding for the Greater Camden/ Philadelphia Scholars Initiative of the Rising Young Artist Program.
$5,000 to Curtis Institute of Music, Philadelphia, PA, 2012. For continued support for the Curtis Student Recital Series.
$1,000 to Pennsylvania Society for the Prevention of Cruelty to Animals, Philadelphia, PA, 2012. For the development of a Humane Education initiative.

8143
Linlundh Foundation ✧
c/o Parentebeard LLC
1800 Byberry Rd., Ste. 1100
Huntingdon Valley, PA 19006-3523

Established in 2007 in PA.
Donors: Kurt H. Asplundh; Martha L. Asplundh; Peter Asplundh.
Foundation type: Independent foundation.
Financial data (yr. ended 12/31/12): Assets, $14,356,401 (M); gifts received, $1,950,000; expenditures, $694,270; qualifying distributions, $600,900; giving activities include $600,900 for grants.
Fields of interest: Human services; Christian agencies & churches.
Limitations: Applications not accepted. Giving in the U.S., with emphasis on PA. No grants to individuals.
Application information: Unsolicited requests for funds not accepted.
Trustees: Kurt H. Asplundh; Martha L. Asplundh.
EIN: 261099081

8144
Herman & Helen Lipsitz Charitable Trust ✧
1900 Murray Ave., Ste. 203
Pittsburgh, PA 15217-1657

Established around 1972 in PA.
Donors: Herman Lipsitz†; Helen Lipsitz; Helen V. Lipsitz Administrative Trust.
Foundation type: Independent foundation.
Financial data (yr. ended 11/30/13): Assets, $8,559,116 (M); expenditures, $741,636; qualifying distributions, $709,196; giving activities include $709,196 for 49 grants (high: $57,200; low: $1,000).
Fields of interest: Human services; Jewish federated giving programs; Jewish agencies & synagogues.
Type of support: General/operating support.
Limitations: Applications accepted. Giving primarily in PA. No grants to individuals.
Application information: Application form not required.

Initial approach: Proposal
Copies of proposal: 2
Deadline(s): None
Trustee: Barbara Katch.
EIN: 256134327

8145
Little Royal-Family Foundation ✧
c/o BNY Mellon, N.A.
P.O. Box 185
Pittsburgh, PA 15230-0185

Established in 1946 in RI.
Donor: Royal Little‡.
Foundation type: Independent foundation.
Financial data (yr. ended 12/31/13): Assets, $21,742,743 (M); expenditures, $1,601,821; qualifying distributions, $1,504,266; giving activities include $1,306,052 for 133 grants (high: $145,000; low: $500).
Fields of interest: Arts; Higher education; Education; Human services.
Type of support: General/operating support; Continuing support; Annual campaigns; Building/renovation; Equipment; Emergency funds; Scholarship funds; Matching/challenge support.
Limitations: Applications not accepted. Giving primarily in MA and RI in the New England region, and OR and WA in the Pacific Northwest; some funding also in Newark, DE, NY, and Nassau, Bahamas. No grants to individuals directly, or for seed money or deficit financing; no loans.
Application information: Contributes only to pre-selected organizations.
Board meeting date(s): Quarterly
Trustee: BNY Mellon, N.A.
Number of staff: 1 part-time support.
EIN: 056016740

8146
J. M. Ally Lockhart ✧
c/o BNY Mellon, N.A.
P.O. Box 185
Pittsburgh, PA 15230-0185

Foundation type: Independent foundation.
Financial data (yr. ended 09/30/13): Assets, $12,668,004 (M); expenditures, $675,619; qualifying distributions, $651,067; giving activities include $634,686 for 1 grant.
Fields of interest: Hospitals (general).
Limitations: Applications not accepted. Giving primarily in Pittsburgh, PA.
Application information: Contributes only to pre-selected organizations.
Trustee: BNY Mellon, N.A.
EIN: 256018602
Selected grants: The following grants are a representative sample of this grantmaker's funding activity:
$575,102 to Western Pennsylvania Hospital Foundation, Pittsburgh, PA, 2011.

8147
Locks Foundation ✧ ☆
(formerly Locks Family Foundation)
600 Washington Sq. S.
Philadelphia, PA 19106-4155 (215) 893-3448
Contact: Gene Locks, Pres.

Established in PA.
Donor: Gene Locks.
Foundation type: Independent foundation.
Financial data (yr. ended 06/30/13): Assets, $10,274,588 (M); expenditures, $845,818; qualifying distributions, $827,500; giving activities include $827,500 for 13 grants (high: $520,000; low: $5,000).
Fields of interest: Museums (art); Education.
Limitations: Applications accepted. Giving primarily in PA, with emphasis on Philadelphia. No grants to individuals.
Application information: Application form required.
Initial approach: Proposal
Deadline(s): None
Officers: Gene Locks, Pres.; Sueyun Locks, Secy.-Treas.
EIN: 222709744

8148
Lomax Family Foundation ✧
200 Highpoint Dr., Ste. 215
Chalfont, PA 18914-3925 (215) 822-1550
Contact: M. Claire Lomax, Tr.

Established in 2002 in PA.
Donors: Beverly H. Lomax; Walter P. Lomax, Jr.; M. Claire Lomax.
Foundation type: Independent foundation.
Financial data (yr. ended 12/31/13): Assets, $1,307,133 (M); expenditures, $596,838; qualifying distributions, $570,694; giving activities include $533,350 for 81 grants (high: $50,000; low: $300).
Purpose and activities: Giving primarily for the benefit of the African-American community.
Fields of interest: Museums; Arts; Higher education, university; Education; Human services; Salvation Army; African Americans/Blacks.
Type of support: General/operating support.
Limitations: Applications accepted. Giving primarily in Philadelphia, PA. No grants to individuals.
Application information: Application form required.
Initial approach: Letter
Deadline(s): None
Board meeting date(s): Quarterly
Trustees: Laura L. Gaines; Bennett P. Lomax; Beverly H. Lomax; Charles D. Lomax; M. Claire Lomax; W. Thomas Lomax; Walter P. Lomax, Jr.; Sara Lomax-Reese.
EIN: 166531650
Selected grants: The following grants are a representative sample of this grantmaker's funding activity:
$10,800 to Philadelphia Orchestra Association, Philadelphia, PA, 2012. For annual giving and 3 year pledge.
$10,000 to LiveConnections.org, Philadelphia, PA, 2012. For Bridge Session Programs.
$7,500 to Peirce College, Philadelphia, PA, 2012. For Parent University Program.
$7,500 to Philadelphia Education Fund, Philadelphia, PA, 2012. For Artsrising Program.
$7,500 to Philadelphia Museum of Art, Philadelphia, PA, 2012. For School and Teacher Programs.
$7,500 to Wissahickon Charter School, Philadelphia, PA, 2012. For general support for School Programs.
$6,000 to Quaker School at Horsham, Horsham, PA, 2012. For Scholarship Money for 2012 School Year.
$5,000 to Art Sanctuary, Philadelphia, PA, 2012. For Sponsorship for Passing the Baton.
$5,000 to Intercultural Family Services, Philadelphia, PA, 2012. For Music and Mentoring Program.
$5,000 to Urban League of Philadelphia, Philadelphia, PA, 2012. For Sponsorship for Empowerment Week Gala.

8149
Long Family Education Foundation ✧
300 Belvedere St.
Carlisle, PA 17013-3503

Established around 1986.
Donor: Robert F. Long.
Foundation type: Independent foundation.
Financial data (yr. ended 12/31/13): Assets, $8,898,703 (M); gifts received, $1,413,401; expenditures, $910,617; qualifying distributions, $905,512; giving activities include $905,512 for 28 grants (high: $623,727; low: $250).
Fields of interest: Elementary/secondary education; Higher education; YM/YWCAs & YM/YWHAs; Christian agencies & churches.
Limitations: Applications not accepted. Giving primarily in NY and PA. No grants to individuals.
Application information: Contributes only to pre-selected organizations.
Trustees: Benjamin James; Katherine Long; Robert F. Long.
EIN: 222719260

8150
Karen & Herbert Lotman Foundation ✧
100 Front St., Ste. 300
West Conshohocken, PA 19428-2894 (610) 234-0090
Contact: Herbert Lotman, V.P.

Established in 1982 in PA.
Donors: Shelly Lotman Fisher; Herbert Lotman; Jeffrey Lotman; Karen Lotman; Julia G. Fisher; Smaul A. Fisher; Joseph E. Fisher; Keystone Foods Corp.
Foundation type: Independent foundation.
Financial data (yr. ended 11/30/13): Assets, $5,361,346 (M); expenditures, $661,313; qualifying distributions, $650,643; giving activities include $650,643 for 21 grants (high: $164,000; low: $3,000).
Purpose and activities: Giving primarily for medical research, including juvenile diabetes research, as well as for the arts, education, and Jewish organizations.
Fields of interest: Historical activities, war memorials; Arts; Higher education; Education; Medical research, institute; Eye research; Diabetes research; Jewish federated giving programs; Jewish agencies & synagogues.
Limitations: Giving primarily in Philadelphia and West Conshohocken, PA.
Application information:
Initial approach: Letter
Deadline(s): Aug. 31
Officers: Karen Lotman, Pres.; Herbert Lotman, V.P.; Shelly Lotman Fisher, Secy.; Jeffrey Lotman, Treas.
EIN: 222429821
Selected grants: The following grants are a representative sample of this grantmaker's funding activity:

$50,000 to Willows Community School, Culver City, CA, 2011.
$30,000 to Federation Housing, Philadelphia, PA, 2011.
$12,500 to Shipley School, Bryn Mawr, PA, 2011.
$10,000 to Jefferson Foundation, Philadelphia, PA, 2011.
$10,000 to Main Line Art Center, Haverford, PA, 2011.
$5,000 to American Cancer Society, Philadelphia, PA, 2011.
$5,000 to Parkinson Council, Bala Cynwyd, PA, 2011.
$3,000 to National Organization for Hearing Research Foundation, Narberth, PA, 2011.

8151
Lutron Foundation ✧
1506 Pleasant View Rd.
Coopersburg, PA 18036-9652

Established around 1985 in PA.
Donors: Joel Spira; Lutron Electronics Co., Inc.; Davison & McCarthy, PC.
Foundation type: Independent foundation.
Financial data (yr. ended 12/31/13): Assets, $4,671,279 (M); gifts received, $675,000; expenditures, $751,175; qualifying distributions, $723,451; giving activities include $723,451 for 90 grants (high: $110,032; low: $100).
Fields of interest: Arts; Higher education; Hospitals (general); Medical research, institute; Human services; United Ways and Federated Giving Programs.
Type of support: Scholarships—to individuals.
Limitations: Applications not accepted. Giving primarily in PA.
Application information: Unsolicited requests for funds not accepted.
Directors: Joel Spira; Ruth Spira.
EIN: 232322928
Selected grants: The following grants are a representative sample of this grantmaker's funding activity:
$107,483 to United Way of the Greater Lehigh Valley, Bethlehem, PA, 2011.
$49,320 to Lehigh Valley Hospital, Allentown, PA, 2011.
$35,000 to Eisenhower Exchange Fellowships, Philadelphia, PA, 2011.
$21,304 to Lehigh University, Bethlehem, PA, 2011.
$12,934 to DeSales University, Center Valley, PA, 2011.
$10,000 to University of Pennsylvania, Philadelphia, PA, 2011.
$8,330 to Allentown Symphony Association, Allentown, PA, 2011.
$4,500 to ArtsQuest, Bethlehem, PA, 2011.
$4,000 to Fox Chase Cancer Center, Philadelphia, PA, 2011.
$2,000 to Yale University, New Haven, CT, 2011.

8152
The Luzerne Foundation ✧
140 Main St., 2nd Fl.
Luzerne, PA 18709 (570) 714-1570
Contact: Charles M. Barber, C.E.O.
FAX: (570) 300-1712; E-mail: diane@luzfdn.org; Additional tel.: (877) 589-3386; Main URL: http://www.luzfdn.org/
Blog: http://luzfdn.org/blog/
Facebook: http://www.facebook.com/luzernefoundation
Twitter: https://twitter.com/luzernefdn
YouTube: http://www.youtube.com/channel/UCthDh1BYHd4gv6ej18eTNBQ

Established in 1995 in PA.
Foundation type: Community foundation.
Financial data (yr. ended 12/31/12): Assets, $23,734,299 (M); gifts received, $11,808,207; expenditures, $12,185,930; giving activities include $11,303,725 for 128+ grants (high: $1,200,000).
Purpose and activities: The mission of the foundation is to cultivate measurable community improvement by: 1) serving as a leader, catalyst, and resource for charitable activities; 2) building and administering a permanent reserve of charitable capital for the community's present needs and future opportunities; and 3) making strategic grants in the areas of education, health and human services, the environment, and the arts.
Fields of interest: Arts; Education; Environment; Health care; Health organizations, association; Recreation; Human services; Community/economic development.
Type of support: Endowments; Program development; Scholarship funds; Technical assistance; Consulting services; Scholarships—to individuals.
Limitations: Applications accepted. Giving limited to the Luzerne County, PA, area. No grants for capital projects, technology software or hardware, annual fundraising campaigns, operating budgets or to established programs merely requiring additional maintenance funding.
Publications: Application guidelines; Annual report; Financial statement; Grants list; Informational brochure (including application guidelines); Newsletter; Program policy statement.
Application information: Visit foundation web site for application form and guidelines. Application form required.
Initial approach: Complete online survey
Copies of proposal: 10
Deadline(s): Apr. 15 and Oct. 14
Board meeting date(s): Quarterly
Final notification: Mid-May and mid-Dec.
Officer and Directors:* Thomas L. Kennedy,* Chair.; Michael D. Weaver,* Vice-Chair.; Charles M. Barber, C.E.O. and Pres.; Gertrude C. McGowan,* Secy.; Kevin Foley,* Treas.; Charie K. Aponick; Joseph F. Butcher; Terrence W. Casey; Peter J. Danchak; Philip G. Decker; John Dowd; Kathi Flack; August F. Genetti, Jr.; Louis F. Goeringer; R. Clements Gover; Scott Henry; Michael Hirthler; William M. Jones; William Joyce; Joseph E. Kluger; Melanie M. Lumia; Joseph L. Persico; Alexander Sloot; Scott W. Williams; John T. Yudichak.
Number of staff: 2 full-time professional.
EIN: 232765498

8153
Samuel P. Mandell Foundation ✧
1818 Market St., Ste. 3220
Philadelphia, PA 19103-3632 (215) 979-3400
Contact: Seymour Mandell, Tr.

Established in 1955 in PA.
Donors: Samuel P. Mandell†; Ida S. Mandell†.
Foundation type: Independent foundation.
Financial data (yr. ended 12/31/12): Assets, $22,783,207 (M); expenditures, $1,234,913; qualifying distributions, $832,263; giving activities include $813,638 for 126 grants (high: $100,000; low: $35).
Purpose and activities: Giving primarily for the arts, education, health organizations, youth and social services, as well as services for the elderly, and Jewish agencies.
Fields of interest: Museums; Performing arts; Arts; Higher education; Education; Hospitals (general); Health care; Health organizations, association; Medical research, institute; Human services; Children/youth, services; Jewish federated giving programs; Jewish agencies & synagogues.
Type of support: General/operating support; Continuing support; Annual campaigns; Capital campaigns; Building/renovation; Program development; Professorships; Research.
Limitations: Applications accepted. Giving primarily in PA, with emphasis on Philadelphia. No support for private operating foundations. No grants to individuals.
Application information: Application form required.
Initial approach: Letter
Copies of proposal: 1
Deadline(s): None
Trustees: Harold Cramer; Gerald Mandell; Judith Mandell; Morton Mandell; Ronald Mandell; Seymour Mandell.
Number of staff: 2 part-time support.
EIN: 236274709

8154
Maplewood Foundation ✧
c/o PNC Bank
620 Liberty Ave., 10th Fl.
Pittsburgh, PA 15222-2705
Contact: Susan J. Wagner

Established in 1995 in PA.
Foundation type: Independent foundation.
Financial data (yr. ended 06/30/13): Assets, $9,800,709 (M); expenditures, $571,236; qualifying distributions, $506,479; giving activities include $500,000 for 1 grant.
Fields of interest: Human services.
Limitations: Applications not accepted. Giving primarily in Pittsburgh, PA. No grants to individuals.
Application information: Contributes only to pre-selected organizations.
Trustees: G. William Bissell, Esq.; PNC Bank, N.A.
EIN: 256502637
Selected grants: The following grants are a representative sample of this grantmaker's funding activity:
$1,000,000 to Neighborhood Academy, Pittsburgh, PA, 2011.

8155
Thomas Marshall Foundation ✧
441 Division St., Ste. 202
Sewickley, PA 15143-1774 (412) 741-9032
Contact: Sue Marshall Roberts, Dir.
E-mail: jstepp@tmfound.org

Established in 1994 in PA.
Donor: Thomas Marshall†.
Foundation type: Independent foundation.

Financial data (yr. ended 12/31/13): Assets, $9,326,312 (M); expenditures, $534,415; qualifying distributions, $472,400; giving activities include $466,400 for 46 grants (high: $60,000; low: $2,000).
Purpose and activities: Support for improving the quality of life for children.
Fields of interest: Education; Hospitals (specialty); Children, services; Christian agencies & churches.
Type of support: General/operating support; Annual campaigns; Capital campaigns.
Limitations: Applications accepted. Giving primarily in PA.
Application information: Application form not required.
Initial approach: Proposal
Copies of proposal: 1
Deadline(s): None
Directors: Jeffrey A. Marshall; Theresa Marshall; Sue Marshall Roberts.
Trustee: PNC Bank, N.A.
Number of staff: 1 part-time professional.
EIN: 256479933
Selected grants: The following grants are a representative sample of this grantmaker's funding activity:
$20,000 to Vermont Center for Ecostudies, Norwich, VT, 2012. For general/charitable purpose.

8156
George & Miriam Martin Foundation ✧
1818 Market St., 35th Fl.
Philadelphia, PA 19103-3636 (215) 587-8400
Contact: George Martin, Tr.
E-mail: gmteam@paworkinjury.com; Main URL: http://www.themartinfoundation.org
Grants List: http://www.themartinfoundation.org/grantHistory.htm

Established in 1996 in PA.
Donors: George Martin; Carol Martin Strange; Matthew Wilson; Lawrence Strange.
Foundation type: Independent foundation.
Financial data (yr. ended 12/31/13): Assets, $9,723,865 (M); gifts received, $351,100; expenditures, $509,235; qualifying distributions, $495,500; giving activities include $495,500 for 37 grants (high: $200,000; low: $500).
Purpose and activities: Grants are given for charitable river or watershed protection activities, including trails, conservation easements, and wetland protection.
Fields of interest: Environment, research; Environment, water resources.
Type of support: General/operating support; Continuing support; Annual campaigns; Capital campaigns; Land acquisition; Seed money; Matching/challenge support.
Limitations: Applications accepted. Giving primarily in southeast PA.
Publications: Application guidelines; Grants list.
Application information: See foundation web site for application guidelines and procedures. Application form not required.
Initial approach: Letter
Copies of proposal: 1
Deadline(s): None
Board meeting date(s): Mar.
Directors: Glenn Emery; Christy Martin; George Martin; Rebecca Martin; Maura Shuey; Carol Martin Strange; H. Lawrence Strange.
Number of staff: None.
EIN: 232828201

8157
Martha L. Mason Trust Memorial Fund ✧
P.O. Box 609
Pittsburgh, PA 15230-9738

Foundation type: Independent foundation.
Financial data (yr. ended 12/31/13): Assets, $36,906,011 (M); expenditures, $1,588,914; qualifying distributions, $1,487,069; giving activities include $1,409,432 for 29 grants (high: $854,201; low: $7,118).
Fields of interest: Hospitals (general); Human services; YM/YWCAs & YM/YWHAs; Protestant agencies & churches.
Limitations: Applications not accepted. Giving primarily in Pittsburgh, PA.
Application information: Contributes only to pre-selected organizations.
Trustee: PNC Bank, N.A.
EIN: 256020716

8158
Massey Charitable Trust ✧
1370 Washington Pike, Ste. 306
Bridgeville, PA 15017-2839
Contact: Robert M. Connolly, Exec. Dir. and Tr.

Established in 1968 in PA.
Donors: H.B. Massey‡; Doris J. Massey‡.
Foundation type: Independent foundation.
Financial data (yr. ended 12/31/13): Assets, $39,832,112 (M); expenditures, $2,003,550; qualifying distributions, $1,799,345; giving activities include $1,680,000 for 98 grants (high: $51,500; low: $2,500).
Fields of interest: Performing arts; Arts; Higher education; Health care; Health organizations, association; Medical research, institute; Human services; Children/youth, services.
Limitations: Applications accepted. Giving primarily in southwestern PA. No support for political organizations. No grants to individuals.
Application information: Common Grant Application Cover Sheet is available at the website of Grantmakers of Western Pennsylvania-www.gwpa.org. Application form required.
Initial approach: See website
Copies of proposal: 1
Deadline(s): None
Board meeting date(s): May and Sept.
Officer and Trustees:* Robert M. Connolly, C.P.A.*, Exec. Dir.; Daniel B. Carroll; Barbara A. Dewitt; Robert M. Entwisle, Esq.; Joe B. Massey.
Number of staff: 1 full-time professional.
EIN: 237007897

8159
The McCausland Foundation ✧
P.O. Box 6675
Radnor, PA 19087-8675
Contact: Bonnie McCausland, Pres.

Established in 1994 in PA.
Donors: Bonnie McCausland; Peter McCausland.
Foundation type: Independent foundation.
Financial data (yr. ended 12/31/13): Assets, $43,680,533 (M); gifts received, $3,511,098; expenditures, $3,461,212; qualifying distributions, $3,436,737; giving activities include $3,436,737 for 51 grants (high: $1,946,035; low: $250).
Fields of interest: Museums (marine/maritime); Arts; Education; Environment; Cancer; Human services; Christian agencies & churches.
Type of support: General/operating support.
Limitations: Applications accepted. Giving primarily in Philadelphia, PA. No grants to individuals.
Application information: Application form required.
Initial approach: Letter
Deadline(s): None
Officers: Bonnie McCausland, Pres.; Peter McCausland, V.P.; Cornelia B. Gross, Secy.-Treas.
Director: Gordon L. Keen, Jr.
EIN: 232776475
Selected grants: The following grants are a representative sample of this grantmaker's funding activity:
$100,000 to Philadelphia Orchestra Association, Philadelphia, PA, 2012. For 2nd Payment of $400,000 Pledge.
$75,000 to Council for Relationships, Philadelphia, PA, 2012. For Operation Home and Healing.
$50,268 to Independence Seaport Museum, Philadelphia, PA, 2012. For funding for the War of 1812 Exhibition.
$35,000 to Philadelphia Museum of Art, Philadelphia, PA, 2012. For Chairman's Council.
$20,044 to Nantucket Land Council, Nantucket, MA, 2012. For Bartlett's Project Support.
$20,000 to Boston University, School of Law, Boston, MA, 2012. For annual fund.
$15,000 to University of South Carolina, Columbia, SC, 2012. For Thomas E. Suggs Endowed Quarterback Scholarship Fund ($75,000 Pledge - 1st payment).
$10,000 to Council for Relationships, Philadelphia, PA, 2012. For Operation Home and Healing Tribute.
$5,000 to Nantucket Historical Association, Nantucket, MA, 2012. For year-end appeal.
$4,080 to Inglis House Foundation, Philadelphia, PA, 2012. For 11th Annual Golf Outing.

8160
John R. McCune Charitable Trust ✧
P.O. Box 609
Pittsburgh, PA 15230-0609 (412) 644-7796
Contact: Jeanette Edwards, Grants Mgr.

Established in 1972 in PA.
Donor: John R. McCune IV‡.
Foundation type: Independent foundation.
Financial data (yr. ended 11/30/13): Assets, $136,917,938 (M); expenditures, $7,337,866; qualifying distributions, $7,034,836; giving activities include $6,695,500 for 207 grants (high: $100,000; low: $5,000).
Purpose and activities: Emphasis on secondary and higher education, health services, and social services.
Fields of interest: Secondary school/education; Higher education; Health care; Human services; Aging.
Type of support: General/operating support; Continuing support; Capital campaigns; Building/renovation; Endowments; Seed money.
Limitations: Applications accepted. Giving primarily in southwestern PA. No grants to individuals.
Publications: Application guidelines.
Application information: Application form not required.
Initial approach: 1-2 page letter of inquiry

Copies of proposal: 1
Deadline(s): Apr. 1
Board meeting date(s): Annually
Officer: Jeanette Edwards, Grants Mgr.
Trustee: National City Bank.
Number of staff: 1 full-time professional; 1 part-time professional.
EIN: 256160722
Selected grants: The following grants are a representative sample of this grantmaker's funding activity:
$150,000 to Colorado State University Foundation, Fort Collins, CO, 2012. For general support.
$107,500 to Discovery Science Center, Fort Collins, CO, 2012. For general support.
$100,000 to East End Cooperative Ministry, Pittsburgh, PA, 2012. For general support.
$100,000 to University of California, Davis, CA, 2012. For general support.
$90,000 to Voice of Hope Ministries, Dallas, TX, 2012. For general support.
$50,000 to Inova Alexandria Hospital, Alexandria, VA, 2012. For general support.
$25,000 to Metro Dallas Homeless Alliance, Dallas, TX, 2012. For general support.
$20,000 to Arts Council of Oklahoma City, Oklahoma City, OK, 2012. For general support.
$20,000 to Avon Old Farms School, Avon, CT, 2012. For general support.
$20,000 to Global Links, Pittsburgh, PA, 2012. For general support.

8161
McCune Foundation ✧

3 PPG Pl., Ste. 400
Pittsburgh, PA 15222-5411 (412) 644-8779
Contact: Henry S. Beukema, Exec. Dir.
E-mail: info@mccune.org; Main URL: http://www.mccune.org
Grants Database: http://www.mccune.org/foundation:Website,mccune,grants

Established in 1979 in PA.
Donor: Charles L. McCune†.
Foundation type: Independent foundation.
Financial data (yr. ended 09/30/13): Assets, $348,745,098 (M); expenditures, $28,986,956; qualifying distributions, $28,134,873; giving activities include $25,988,575 for 133 grants (high: $2,098,000; low: $1,500).
Purpose and activities: The mission of the foundation is to enable communities and nonprofit institutions to improve the quality and circumstances of life for present and future generations. In meeting these challenges, the foundation employs flexible approaches and innovative strategies that are responsive to changing needs and new opportunities. The goal is to stimulate long-lasting and sustainable progress, which contributes to community vitality and economic growth.
Fields of interest: Museums; Performing arts; Historic preservation/historical societies; Arts; Higher education; Adult education—literacy, basic skills & GED; Libraries/library science; Health care; Medical research, institute; Employment; Housing/shelter, development; Youth development, services; Human services; Economic development; Urban/community development.
Type of support: Income development; Management development/capacity building; Capital campaigns; Building/renovation; Equipment; Land acquisition; Endowments; Program development; Seed money; Technical assistance; Program-related investments/loans; Employee matching gifts.
Limitations: Applications accepted. Giving primarily in western PA, with emphasis on the Pittsburgh area. No grants to individuals.
Publications: Application guidelines; Financial statement; Grants list.
Application information: Applicants can be submitted via foundation's web site. Applicants are encouraged to wait at least 3 years after receiving a grant before reapplying. Funding is concentrated in Southwestern PA, mainly the Pittsburgh area. Unsolicited proposals from outside this region are not accepted. Application form required.
Initial approach: Inquiry letter (2 - 3 pages)
Copies of proposal: 1
Deadline(s): None
Board meeting date(s): Mar., June, Sept., and Dec.
Final notification: Minimum 90 days
Officers and Distribution Committee:* Michael M. Edwards,* Chair.; Henry S. Beukema, Exec. Dir.; Ronald R. Davenport, Jr.; Adam B. Edwards; John H. Edwards; Laura E. Ellsworth; Sarah McCune Losinger; James C. Roddey.
Trustee: National City Bank.
Number of staff: 4 full-time professional; 2 full-time support.
EIN: 256210269
Selected grants: The following grants are a representative sample of this grantmaker's funding activity:
$8,017,944 to Communities Foundation of Oklahoma, Laurie McCune Lewis Donor Advised Fund, Oklahoma City, OK, 2012. For general charitable support.
$8,017,944 to Community Foundation of Northern Colorado, Charles L. McCune Fund, Fort Collins, CO, 2012. For general charitable support.
$8,017,944 to Horizons Foundation, Janet Lockhart McCune and John Robison McCune Fund, San Francisco, CA, 2012. For general charitable support.
$8,017,944 to Rhode Island Foundation, Edwards Family Fund, Providence, RI, 2012. For general charitable support.
$2,500,000 to Carnegie Mellon University, Pittsburgh, PA, 2012. To create innovation graduate fellowships and further develop enhanced recoverable grant program.
$1,000,000 to Carnegie Mellon University, Pittsburgh, PA, 2012. To establish innovation scholars program.
$750,000 to University of Pittsburgh, Pittsburgh, PA, 2012. For inner-city entrepreneurs program.
$425,000 to Strategic Regional Development, Pittsburgh, PA, 2012. To develop the former LTV Coke Works in Hazelwood.
$125,000 to Manchester Citizens Corporation, Pittsburgh, PA, 2012. To continue real estate development in Manchester.
$100,000 to Communities in Schools of Pittsburgh-Allegheny County, Pittsburgh, PA, 2012. For Champions for Kids campaign.

8162
The McCutchen Foundation ✧

c/o PNC Bank, N.A.
1600 Market St., Tax. Dept.
Philadelphia, PA 19103-7240
Application address: c/o Charles W. McCutchen, Tr., 108 East G. St., Brunswick, MD 21716-1450

Trust established in 1956 in NJ.
Donors: Brunson S. McCutchen; Charles W. McCutchen; Margaret W. McCutchen.
Foundation type: Independent foundation.
Financial data (yr. ended 12/31/13): Assets, $26,279,816 (M); gifts received, $246,880; expenditures, $1,242,412; qualifying distributions, $1,100,700; giving activities include $1,100,000 for 52 grants (high: $75,000; low: $5,000).
Purpose and activities: Giving primarily for education, human services, and health associations.
Fields of interest: Performing arts, orchestras; Arts; Higher education; Education; Health organizations, association; Human services; Residential/custodial care, hospices.
Limitations: Giving primarily in NJ and NY; some funding also in CA and PA. No grants to individuals.
Application information:
Initial approach: Letter
Deadline(s): Dec. 1
Trustees: Anne Terry; Benson J. Chapman; Charles W. McCutchen; N.A. PNC Bank.
EIN: 226050116
Selected grants: The following grants are a representative sample of this grantmaker's funding activity:
$100,000 to Lafayette College, Easton, PA, 2011.
$60,000 to American Committee for the Weizmann Institute of Science, New York, NY, 2011. For general use of the organization.
$40,000 to Daughters of Miriam Center, Clifton, NJ, 2011. For general use of the organization.
$40,000 to Trudeau Institute, Saranac Lake, NY, 2011. For general use of the organization.
$20,000 to Cambridge in America, New York, NY, 2011. For general use of the organization.
$20,000 to Hospice Care of the District of Columbia, Washington, DC, 2011. For general use of the organization.
$20,000 to Institute for Justice, Arlington, VA, 2011. For general use of the organization.
$20,000 to National Hypertension Association, New York, NY, 2011. For general use of the organization.
$20,000 to National Sports Academy, Lake Placid, NY, 2011. For general use of the organization.
$10,000 to American Friends Service Committee, New York, NY, 2011. For general use of the organization.

8163
McFeely-Rogers Foundation ✧

816 Ligonier St., Ste. 610
P.O. Box 110
Latrobe, PA 15650-0110 (724) 537-5588
Contact: James R. Okonak, Exec. Dir.
FAX: (724) 805-0121; E-mail: main@mcfrfdn.org

Incorporated in 1953 in PA.
Donors: James H. Rogers†; Nancy K. McFeely†; Nancy M. Rogers†; Fred M. Rogers†.
Foundation type: Independent foundation.
Financial data (yr. ended 12/31/13): Assets, $17,738,637 (M); expenditures, $1,325,607; qualifying distributions, $970,795; giving activities include $680,765 for 59 grants (high: $159,000; low: $100).
Purpose and activities: Support mainly to local educational and charitable institutions, including civic affairs, community development, recreation programs, Protestant giving, cultural programs, and hospitals.
Fields of interest: Arts; Education; Hospitals (general); Recreation; Human services; Community/

economic development; Protestant agencies & churches.
Type of support: General/operating support; Continuing support; Annual campaigns; Capital campaigns; Building/renovation; Equipment; Land acquisition; Endowments; Debt reduction; Emergency funds; Program development; Seed money; Scholarship funds; Matching/challenge support.
Limitations: Applications accepted. Giving primarily in the Latrobe, PA, area, with some giving in Pittsburgh. No support for political organizations. No grants to individuals, or for scholarships, research, publications, or conferences; no loans.
Publications: Application guidelines; Program policy statement.
Application information: Common Grant application form accepted. Application form not required.
Initial approach: Letter
Copies of proposal: 2
Deadline(s): May 1 and Nov. 1
Board meeting date(s): June and Nov.
Final notification: 2 weeks after board meeting; or immediate, upon review
Officers and Trustees:* Nancy R. Crozier,* Pres.; James R. Okonak,* Secy. and Exec. Dir.; Annette M. Couch, Treas.; Daniel G. Crozier, Jr.; James Brooks Crozier; Douglas R. Nowicki; James B. Rogers; John F. Rogers.
Number of staff: 2 full-time professional.
EIN: 251120947
Selected grants: The following grants are a representative sample of this grantmaker's funding activity:
$35,000 to Saint Vincent Archabbey, Latrobe, PA, 2012. For Archabbot's Discretionary Fund.
$25,000 to Adams Memorial Library, Latrobe, PA, 2012. For Bookmobile Collection.
$25,000 to Latrobe Presbyterian Church, Latrobe, PA, 2012. For Organ Fund.
$25,000 to Saint Vincent College, Latrobe, PA, 2012. For FMR Center Archives.
$25,000 to Saint Vincent College, Latrobe, PA, 2012. For FMR Center Archivist.
$24,000 to Latrobe Presbyterian Church, Latrobe, PA, 2012. For 410 Main Street School Building.
$10,000 to Greater Latrobe School District, Latrobe, PA, 2012. For Art Trust, Preserve the Vision.
$10,000 to Rollins College, Winter Park, FL, 2012. For Rollins Fund.
$4,500 to Greater Latrobe School District, Latrobe, PA, 2012. For Multi-Sensory Room/Equipment.
$3,800 to Latrobe Presbyterian Church, Latrobe, PA, 2012. For Concert Digital Piano- Unity Chapel.

8164
Rita M. McGinley Foundation ✧

600 Grant St., Ste. 4400
Pittsburgh, PA 15219-2713 (412) 566-1984
Contact: John R. McGinley, Jr., V.P. and Secy.

Established in 2003 in PA, as the successor to the Rita M. McGinley Foundation.
Donor: Rita M. McGinley.
Foundation type: Independent foundation.
Financial data (yr. ended 12/31/13): Assets, $16,147,182 (M); expenditures, $1,243,153; qualifying distributions, $1,154,504; giving activities include $1,154,504 for 13 grants (high: $835,754; low: $3,750).
Fields of interest: Education; Health organizations; Human services; Women, centers/services.
Limitations: Applications accepted. Giving primarily in PA.
Application information:
Initial approach: Letter
Deadline(s): None
Officers and Directors:* John R. McGinley, Jr.,* Pres.; John C. McGinley,* V.P. and Treas.; Nancy Palamara, Secy.
EIN: 432024870
Selected grants: The following grants are a representative sample of this grantmaker's funding activity:
$100,000 to Little Sisters of the Poor, Pittsburgh, PA, 2012. For Campaign for Compassion.
$4,775 to Gibbs Rest Home, Pittsburgh, PA, 2012. For facilities improvements.

8165
Lalitta Nash McKaig Foundation ✧

c/o PNC Advisors
620 Liberty Ave., 10th Fl.
Pittsburgh, PA 15222-2705
Application address: Gregory H. Getty, Esq., Admin, c/o Geppert, McMullen, Paye & Getty, 21 Prospect Sq., Cumberland, MD, 21502, tel.: (301) 777-1515

Established in 1973 in PA.
Foundation type: Independent foundation.
Financial data (yr. ended 09/30/13): Assets, $11,639,782 (M); expenditures, $626,023; qualifying distributions, $551,225; giving activities include $488,650 for grants to individuals.
Fields of interest: Higher education; Higher education, university.
Type of support: Scholarships—to individuals.
Limitations: Applications accepted. Giving limited to residents who graduated from high schools in Allegany and Garrett counties, MD, Bedford and Somerset counties, PA, and Mineral and Hampshire counties, WV.
Publications: Application guidelines.
Application information: Application forms can be obtained from high school guidance offices in the Cumberland, MD, area, financial aid offices of Frostburg State College and Allegany Community College, the foundation's office in Cumberland, MD, or PNC Bank, N.A. Application form required.
Deadline(s): May 30
Board meeting date(s): June
Trustee: PNC Bank, N.A.
EIN: 256071908

8166
Katherine Mabis McKenna Foundation, Inc. ✧

P.O. Box 186
Latrobe, PA 15650-0186 (724) 537-6900
Contact: Linda McKenna Boxx, Chair.

Incorporated in 1969 in PA.
Donor: Katherine M. McKenna†.
Foundation type: Independent foundation.
Financial data (yr. ended 12/31/12): Assets, $72,400,045 (M); expenditures, $3,748,918; qualifying distributions, $3,467,698; giving activities include $3,212,166 for 62 grants (high: $500,000; low: $500).
Purpose and activities: Giving primarily for education, the arts, cultural organizations, and community development. Some support also for environmental organizations and human services.
Fields of interest: Arts; Higher education; Environment, natural resources.
Type of support: General/operating support; Annual campaigns; Capital campaigns; Building/renovation; Equipment; Land acquisition; Endowments; Program development; Seed money.
Limitations: Applications accepted. Giving primarily in Westmoreland County, PA. No grants to individuals.
Publications: Grants list; Program policy statement.
Application information: Grantmakers of Western Pennsylvania's Common Grant Application Format accepted. Application form not required.
Initial approach: Letter
Copies of proposal: 1
Deadline(s): Apr. 1 and Oct. 1
Board meeting date(s): Spring and fall
Final notification: 3 to 6 months
Officers and Directors:* Linda McKenna Boxx,* Chair.; Zan McKenna Rich,* Vice-Chair.; Nathan McKenna Boxx,* Treas.
Trustee: BNY Mellon, N.A.
Number of staff: 1 full-time professional; 1 part-time professional; 1 part-time support.
EIN: 237042752
Selected grants: The following grants are a representative sample of this grantmaker's funding activity:
$150,000 to Phipps Conservatory and Botanical Gardens, Pittsburgh, PA, 2011. For capital campaign.
$100,000 to Westmoreland Museum of American Art, Greensburg, PA, 2011. For general operating support.
$80,000 to Westmoreland Cultural Trust, Greensburg, PA, 2011. For general operating support.
$75,000 to YMCA of Ligonier Valley, Ligonier, PA, 2011. For capital improvements.
$65,000 to University of Pittsburgh at Greensburg, Greensburg, PA, 2011. For capital improvements.
$50,000 to Carnegie Institute, Pittsburgh, PA, 2011. For general operating support.
$25,000 to Latrobe Community Revitalization Inc, Latrobe, PA, 2011. For general operating support.
$25,000 to United Way of Westmoreland County, Greensburg, PA, 2011. For annual campaign.
$20,000 to Loyalhanna Watershed Association, Ligonier, PA, 2011. For general operating support.
$20,000 to Western Pennsylvania Conservancy, Pittsburgh, PA, 2011. For Fallingwater Internship Program.

8167
Philip M. McKenna Foundation, Inc. ✧

c/o BNY Mellon, N.A.
P.O. Box 185
Pittsburgh, PA 15230-0185

Incorporated in 1967 in PA.
Donor: Philip M. McKenna†.
Foundation type: Independent foundation.
Financial data (yr. ended 12/31/13): Assets, $15,904,148 (M); expenditures, $735,874; qualifying distributions, $668,265; giving activities include $505,918 for 28 grants (high: $80,000; low: $500).
Purpose and activities: Support for public policy and educational programs focused on free market economics, American constitutional government, and western civilization. Support also for the general benefit of the foundation's local area.

Fields of interest: Higher education; Economics; Public policy, research.
Type of support: General/operating support; Continuing support.
Limitations: Applications not accepted. Giving primarily in the Latrobe, Pennsylvania, area for community and civic programs; grants to PA and national organizations for public policy and educational programs. No grants to individuals, or for matching gifts; no loans.
Application information: Contributes only to pre-selected organizations.
Board meeting date(s): Apr. and Oct.
Officers: T. William Boxx, Chair. and Treas.; Charles R. Kesler, Ph.D., Vice-Chair.; Norbert J. Pail, Secy.
Directors: Jonathan C. Hall; Zan McKennarich.
Trustee: BNY Mellon, N.A.
Number of staff: 1 full-time professional.
EIN: 256082635
Selected grants: The following grants are a representative sample of this grantmaker's funding activity:
$20,000 to Heritage Foundation, Washington, DC, 2012. For First Princples Initiative.
$10,000 to American Enterprise Institute for Public Policy Research, Washington, DC, 2012. For Road to Freedom Project.
$10,000 to Federalist Society for Law and Public Policy Studies, Washington, DC, 2012. For General Support, Faculty Division, Pa Chapters.
$7,000 to Ethics and Public Policy Center, Washington, DC, 2012. For Constitution, Courts and Culture Culture Program.
$7,000 to Latrobe, City of, Latrobe, PA, 2012. For K-9 Unit.
$5,000 to Hillsdale College, Hillsdale, MI, 2012. For Kirby Center Lecture Series.
$2,000 to Service Corps of Retired Executives Association, Latrobe, PA, 2012. For General Operations and Marketing.

8168
William V. and Catherine A. McKinney Charitable Foundation ✧ ☆

c/o PNC Bank, N.A.
P.O. Box 609
Pittsburgh, PA 15230-9738

Established in 1990 in PA.
Donor: Catherine A. McKinney†.
Foundation type: Independent foundation.
Financial data (yr. ended 03/31/13): Assets, $10,879,391 (M); expenditures, $557,087; qualifying distributions, $502,890; giving activities include $433,117 for grants.
Purpose and activities: Giving limited to organizations in western PA whose activities aid the elderly, disadvantaged youth and/or the disabled and support the arts.
Fields of interest: Arts; Human services; Public affairs.
Type of support: General/operating support; Capital campaigns; Endowments; Program development; Matching/challenge support.
Limitations: Applications not accepted. Giving limited to western PA. No grants to individuals.
Application information: Contributes only to pre-selected organizations.
Board meeting date(s): 3 times per year
Trustee: PNC Bank.
EIN: 251641619
Selected grants: The following grants are a representative sample of this grantmaker's funding activity:
$13,734 to Pittsburgh Filmmakers, Pittsburgh, PA, 2012.
$10,000 to Emmaus Community of Pittsburgh, Pittsburgh, PA, 2012.
$10,000 to Pittsburgh Public Theater, Pittsburgh, PA, 2012.
$7,500 to Attack Theater, Pittsburgh, PA, 2012.
$7,500 to Society for Arts in Crafts, Pittsburgh, PA, 2012.
$5,000 to Asian American Film Festival, Pittsburgh, PA, 2012.
$5,000 to Little Sisters of the Poor, Pittsburgh, PA, 2012.
$4,500 to YouthWorks, Pittsburgh, PA, 2012.

8169
The McLean Contributionship

230 Sugartown Rd., Ste. 30
Wayne, PA 19087-6001 (610) 989-8090
Contact: Sandra L. McLean, Exec. Dir.
Main URL: http://fdnweb.org/mclean
Arts, Culture and Humanities Grants: http://fdnweb.org/mclean/grants-arts/
Education Grants: http://fdnweb.org/mclean/grants-education/
Environment and Animal Welfare Grants: http://fdnweb.org/mclean/grants-environment-animals/
Health Grants: http://fdnweb.org/mclean/grants-health/
Human Services Grants: http://fdnweb.org/mclean/grants-human-services/

Trust established in 1951 in PA.
Donors: William L. McLean, Jr.†; Robert McLean†; William L. McLean III†; William Clarke Mason†; William L. McLean IV; Sandra McLean; Lisa McLean; Elizabeth P. McLean; Elizabeth R. McLean; Wendy McLean; Richard Bove; Bulletin Co.; Independent Publications, Inc.; Independence Communications, Inc.
Foundation type: Independent foundation.
Financial data (yr. ended 12/31/13): Assets, $46,666,044 (M); gifts received, $138,766; expenditures, $2,416,214; qualifying distributions, $2,239,900; giving activities include $2,089,933 for 117 grants (high: $100,000; low: $1,000).
Purpose and activities: The grantmaker supports understanding and preservation of the environment, compassionate and cost effective health care and improving the quality of life through capital and other projects. Trustees prefer special projects rather than continuing programs and focus on capital projects: bricks and mortar, endowment, or will provide seed money for purposes falling within the contributorship's guidelines.
Fields of interest: Museums; Performing arts; Historic preservation/historical societies; Libraries/library science; Education; Environment, natural resources; Environmental education; Hospitals (general); Nursing home/convalescent facility; Health care, home services; Youth development, services; Children/youth, services; Aging, centers/services; Children/youth; Youth; Aging.
Type of support: Capital campaigns; Building/renovation; Equipment; Land acquisition; Endowments; Program development; Publication; Seed money; Research; Matching/challenge support.
Limitations: Applications accepted. Giving primarily in the greater Philadelphia, PA, area. No grants to individuals.
Publications: Application guidelines; Financial statement; Grants list; Informational brochure; Informational brochure (including application guidelines).
Application information: Philanthropy Network Greater Philadelphia Common Grant Application Form accepted, and can be downloaded via grantmaker web site. Preference is for applications to be submitted online. See foundation web site for application guidelines and procedures. Application form not required.
Initial approach: Use online application system on grantmaker web site
Copies of proposal: 1
Deadline(s): See grantmaker web site for current deadlines
Board meeting date(s): Quarterly: Mar., June, Sept., and Dec.
Officers and Trustees:* William L. McLean IV,* Chair.; Sandra L. McLean, Vice-Chair., Secy. and Exec. Dir.; Susannah McLean, Advisory Trustee; Jean G. Bodine, Trustee Emeritus; John F. Bales III; Diana McLean Liefer; Carolyn M. Raymond.
Number of staff: None.
EIN: 236396940
Selected grants: The following grants are a representative sample of this grantmaker's funding activity:
$100,000 to Academy of Natural Sciences of Philadelphia, Philadelphia, PA, 2012. Toward endowment to help post-undergraduate, post-doctoral research projects in the areas of ornithology and environmental sciences.
$100,000 to Academy of Natural Sciences of Philadelphia, Philadelphia, PA, 2012. Toward endowment in memory of William L. McLean III, to help fund post-undergraduate, post-doctoral research projects in areas of ornithology and environmental sciences.
$100,000 to Audubon Society, Valley Forge, Audubon, PA, 2012. To build new raptor enclosure.
$65,000 to Jenkins Arboretum, Devon, PA, 2012. Toward 35th Anniversary Campaign for Endowment.
$65,000 to Temple University Ambler, Ambler, PA, 2012. Toward growing the McLean Contributionship Philadelphia Evening Bulletin Endowment in order to support the purchase of equipment and storage for exciting new digitization project.
$50,000 to Bryn Mawr Rehabilitation Hospital, Malvern, PA, 2012. To establish Comprehensive Outpatient Neurorehabilitation Center.
$50,000 to Visiting Nurse Association of Greater Philadelphia, Philadelphia, PA, 2012. Toward purchase of new Fujitsu LIFEBOOK T731 Tablet PCs for daily use by nurses and other clinical staff.
$35,000 to Trust for Public Land, Morristown, NJ, 2012. Toward work this year to create health, green play spaces at two adjacent locations in Philadelphia's Strawberry Mansion neighborhood: William Dick Elementary School and Hank Gathers Recreation Center.
$30,000 to Philabundance, Philadelphia, PA, 2012. Toward acquisition and renovation of new community food center in Chester, PA.
$25,000 to College of Physicians of Philadelphia, Philadelphia, PA, 2012. Toward the replacement of the College's roof.
$25,000 to Main Line Art Center, Haverford, PA, 2012. Toward ART (Access. Renew. Transform.) 75 Campaign, to renovate the building.

$25,000 to Melmark, Berwyn, PA, 2012. Toward renovation of the indoor pool on Melmark's Berwyn campus in Delaware County.
$20,000 to Friends of the Japanese House and Garden, Philadelphia, PA, 2012. Toward construction and masonry portion of historic landscape restoration project at Shofuso Japanese House and Garden.
$15,000 to Free Library of Philadelphia, Friends of the, Philadelphia, PA, 2012. Toward equipment and furnishings for youth and teens for the Readers are Leaders initiative.
$15,000 to Free Library of Philadelphia, Friends of the, Philadelphia, PA, 2012. Toward equipment and furnishings for youth and teens for Readers and Leaders initiative.
$15,000 to Western Pennsylvania Conservancy, Pittsburgh, PA, 2012. Toward purchase of forest land from Forest Investment Associates, along the Clarion River near Ridgeway in Elk County.
$11,000 to Chestnut Hill Academy, Philadelphia, PA, 2012. Toward Outdoor Program, Natural Playspace.
$10,000 to Handi-Crafters, Thorndale, PA, 2012. Toward software necessary to comply with state funding and licensing requirements.

8170
The Benjamin and Mary Siddons Measey Foundation ✧

225 N. Olive St.
P.O. Box 258
Media, PA 19063-2810
Contact: James C. Brennan, Mgr.
E-mail: jbrennan1977@yahoo.com

Trust established in 1958 in PA.
Donor: William Maul Measey†.
Foundation type: Independent foundation.
Financial data (yr. ended 12/31/13): Assets, $61,614,408 (M); expenditures, $2,351,712; qualifying distributions, $2,191,852; giving activities include $2,160,000 for 10 grants (high: $325,000; low: $35,000).
Purpose and activities: Grants to medical schools in Philadelphia for scholarships and fellowships.
Fields of interest: Medical school/education.
Type of support: Fellowships; Scholarship funds.
Limitations: Applications accepted. Giving limited to Philadelphia, PA, region. No support for medical institutions for their distribution. No grants to individuals, or for non-medical related activities.
Publications: Informational brochure.
Application information: Accepts applications only for medical institutions. Scholarship applications should be made to the dean of the particular medical school. Application form not required.
Initial approach: Letter
Copies of proposal: 6
Deadline(s): 1 month prior to meeting
Board meeting date(s): 2nd Tues. in Mar., June, Sept., and Dec.
Final notification: 1 month following meeting
Officer: Matthew S. Donaldson, Jr., Esq., Secy.
Board of Managers: Clyde F. Barker, M.D.; Marshall E. Blume, Ph.D.; James C. Brennan, Esq.; Ronald M. Fairman, M.D.; Stanley Goldfarb, M.D.
Number of staff: None.
EIN: 236298781

8171
The Medleycott Family Foundation ✧

c/o Leon W. Marchetti
P.O. Box 189
Southampton, PA 18966-0189

Donors: Superpac, Inc.; Mary E. Medleycott.
Foundation type: Independent foundation.
Financial data (yr. ended 12/31/13): Assets, $2,679,763 (M); gifts received, $649,520; expenditures, $636,325; qualifying distributions, $636,088; giving activities include $636,000 for 18 grants (high: $70,000; low: $10,000).
Fields of interest: Hospitals (general); Health care; Christian agencies & churches.
Limitations: Applications not accepted. Giving primarily in PA. No grants to individuals.
Application information: Contributes only to pre-selected organizations.
Officers: Leon Marchetti, Pres.; Alice E. Medleycott, Secy.; Deborah Hedrick, Treas.
EIN: 743101031

8172
R. K. Mellon Family Foundation ✧

c/o BNY Mellon Center
500 Grant St., Ste. 4106
Pittsburgh, PA 15219-2502 (724) 238-5269
Contact: Scott D. Izzo, Dir.
Application address: R. K. Mellon Family Foundation, P.O. Box 690, ;igonier, PA 15658-0690

Incorporated in PA in 1978 through consolidation of Landfall, Loyalhanna, Rachelwood, and Cassandra Mellon Henderson foundations.
Donors: Seward Prosser Mellon; Richard P. Mellon; Constance B. Mellon†; Cassandra M. Milbury.
Foundation type: Independent foundation.
Financial data (yr. ended 12/31/12): Assets, $41,043,943 (M); expenditures, $2,123,132; qualifying distributions, $1,923,922; giving activities include $1,748,550 for 119 grants (high: $438,383; low: $500).
Purpose and activities: Grants largely for education, health care, social services, and conservation programs.
Fields of interest: Education; Environment, natural resources; Health care; Human services; Public affairs.
Type of support: General/operating support; Continuing support; Annual campaigns; Capital campaigns; Building/renovation; Equipment; Program development; Seed money; Research.
Limitations: Applications accepted. Giving primarily in western PA. No grants to individuals, or for endowment funds, scholarships, fellowships, or matching gifts; no loans.
Publications: Informational brochure (including application guidelines).
Application information: Application form required.
Initial approach: Proposal
Copies of proposal: 1
Deadline(s): Submit proposal preferably Jan. through Mar. or July through Sept.; deadlines Apr. 1 and Oct. 1
Board meeting date(s): June and Dec.
Final notification: 1 to 6 months
Trustees: Robert B. Burr, Jr.; Lawrence S. Busch; Alison M. Byers; Catharine Mellon Cathey; W. Russell G. Byers, Jr.; Bruce K. M. Henderson; Armour N. Mellon; Constance Elizabeth Mellon; Richard A. Mellon; Richard P. Mellon; Seward Prosser Mellon.
Number of staff: 4 part-time professional; 9 part-time support.
EIN: 251356145

8173
Richard King Mellon Foundation ✧

BNY Mellon Ctr.
500 Grant St., 41st Fl., Ste. 4106
Pittsburgh, PA 15219-2502 (412) 392-2800
Contact: Scott Izzo, Dir.
FAX: (412) 392-2837; Main URL: http://fdncenter.org/grantmaker/rkmellon
Grants List: http://foundationcenter.org/grantmaker/rkmellon/grantlist2010.html

Trust established in 1947 in PA; incorporated in 1971 in PA.
Donor: Richard K. Mellon†.
Foundation type: Independent foundation.
Financial data (yr. ended 12/31/13): Assets, $2,343,064,597 (M); expenditures, $112,292,253; qualifying distributions, $105,666,045; giving activities include $99,152,041 for 244 grants (high: $24,000,000; low: $650), and $3,703,000 for 2 loans/program-related investments (high: $2,000,000; low: $1,703,000).
Purpose and activities: Local grant programs emphasize conservation, education, families and youth, regional economic development, system reform; support also for conservation of natural areas and wildlife preservation elsewhere in the United States.
Fields of interest: Education, early childhood education; Education; Environment, natural resources; Environment; Youth development, services; Human services; Children/youth, services; Family services; Urban/community development; Community/economic development; Infants/toddlers; Children/youth; Youth; Adults; Young adults; Economically disadvantaged.
Type of support: Technical assistance; General/operating support; Continuing support; Capital campaigns; Building/renovation; Equipment; Land acquisition; Program development; Seed money; Research; Program evaluation; Program-related investments/loans; Matching/challenge support.
Limitations: Applications accepted. Giving primarily in Southwestern PA. No grants to individuals, or for fellowships or scholarships, or conduit organizations.
Publications: Annual report (including application guidelines); Grants list.
Application information: Grantmakers of Western Pennsylvania's Common Grant Application Format accepted. Application form required.
Initial approach: Proposal or letter of inquiry
Copies of proposal: 1
Deadline(s): None
Board meeting date(s): Varies
Final notification: 1 - 6 months
Officers and Trustees:* Seward Prosser Mellon,* Chair. and C.E.O.; W. Russell G. Byers, Jr.,* Pres.; Douglas L. Sisson, V.P. and Treas.; Lisa Kuzma, Secy. and Sr. Prog. Off.; Scott D. Izzo,* Dir.; John J. Turcik,* Cont.; Richard P. Mellon, Chair. and Tr. Emeritus; Lawrence S. Busch; Alison M. Byers; Catharine Mellon Cathey; Bruce King Mellon Henderson; Constance Elizabeth Mellon Kapp; Armour N. Mellon; Richard A. Mellon.
Number of staff: 1 full-time support.
EIN: 251127705

Selected grants: The following grants are a representative sample of this grantmaker's funding activity:
$22,000,000 to University of Pittsburgh, Pittsburgh, PA, 2012. Toward support of the Center for Energy at the University of Pittsburgh, with a particular focus on advance materials and energy delivery and reliability, to recruit talented faculty and researchers, to expand existing and stimulate new commercial activities, and to help make western Pennsylvania a national center for energy research and education.
$8,000,000 to Westmoreland Museum of American Art, Greensburg, PA, 2012. Toward capital and endowment support.
$7,500,000 to Chatham University, Pittsburgh, PA, 2012. Toward infrastructure development at Eden Hall Campus Sustainability Project.
$7,000,000 to Conservation Fund, Arlington, VA, 2012. Toward protection of land in northern Wisconsin.
$5,000,000 to Western Pennsylvania Conservancy, Pittsburgh, PA, 2012. Toward support for protection of land and water in western Pennsylvania.
$3,000,000 to August Wilson Center for African American Culture, Pittsburgh, PA, 2012. Toward reduction of principal on the outstanding construction note held by Dollar Bank.
$2,500,000 to RIDC Fund for Economic Growth, Pittsburgh, PA, 2012. Toward development or expansion of production facilities for manufacturing companies.
$2,000,000 to Carlow University, Pittsburgh, PA, 2012. Toward renovations for the University Learning Commons.
$1,500,000 to Pittsburgh Parks Conservancy, Pittsburgh, PA, 2012. Toward restoration of Mellon Square Park.
$1,500,000 to Renewable Manufacturing Gateway, Pittsburgh, PA, 2012. Toward support of operations and program-related investments.

8174
Glenn and Ruth Mengle Foundation ✧

c/o First Commonwealth Trust Co.
5355 Shaffer Rd.
Du Bois, PA 15801-1046 (814) 371-7730
Contact: Mary K. Kocher

Established in 1956 in PA.
Donors: Glenn A. Mengle†; Ruth E. Mengle Blake†.
Foundation type: Independent foundation.
Financial data (yr. ended 12/31/13): Assets, $22,252,066 (M); expenditures, $885,387; qualifying distributions, $666,919; giving activities include $666,919 for 26 grants (high: $95,000; low: $1,000).
Purpose and activities: Giving primarily for education, health, and children and social services.
Fields of interest: Higher education; Education; Health organizations; Human services; Children/youth, services; United Ways and Federated Giving Programs.
Type of support: General/operating support; Capital campaigns.
Limitations: Applications accepted. Giving limited to the Brockway, Du Bois, and Erie, PA, areas. No grants to individuals.
Application information: Application form required.
Initial approach: Letter
Copies of proposal: 1
Deadline(s): Sept. 1
Trustee: First Commonwealth Bank Trust.
EIN: 256067616
Selected grants: The following grants are a representative sample of this grantmaker's funding activity:
$25,000 to Shriners Hospitals for Children, Erie, PA, 2012. For Grant Distribution to Support the Synergy H.D. Video Imaging Project for the Ambulatory Surgery Center.
$2,500 to Achievement Center, Erie, PA, 2012. For Grant Distribution in Support of the Annual Appeal to Help Fund Therapeutic Service to Children from Birth to Young Adulthood with Special Needs.

8175
Merchants Fund ✧ ☆

1616 Walnut St., Ste. 802
Philadelphia, PA 19103-5308 (215) 339-1339
Contact: Patricia Blakely
FAX: (215) 399-1440;
E-mail: info@merchantsfund.org; Main URL: http://www.merchantsfund.org/
Grants List: http://www.merchantsfund.org/grantee-awards.html

Established Jan. 21, 1854 in PA.
Donors: Lewis Elkins Fund; Lewis Elkins Trust; Charles Fearon†.
Foundation type: Independent foundation.
Financial data (yr. ended 12/31/13): Assets, $15,780,004 (M); expenditures, $763,419; qualifying distributions, $662,309; giving activities include $596,587 for 46 grants (high: $122,916; low: $2,000).
Purpose and activities: The Merchants Fund is committed to providing for the economic needs of the merchant community by making modest grants to small businesses. Merchants must do business in Philadelphia, Pennsylvania and have conducted business for a minimum of three years.
Grant-making areas include: stabilization grants, loan matches, and emergency grants.
Fields of interest: Community development, business promotion; Community development, small businesses; Economically disadvantaged.
Type of support: Emergency funds; Technical assistance; Grants to individuals.
Limitations: Applications accepted. Giving primarily in Philadelphia, PA. No support for home businesses, or businesses holding an off-premise liquor license. No grants for new business ventures.
Publications: Application guidelines; Grants list.
Application information: See foundation Web site for guidelines and latest news. Application form required.
Initial approach: E-mail, telephone or letter
Copies of proposal: 1
Deadline(s): Feb., May, and Oct. Refer to foundation Web site for details
Board meeting date(s): Feb., May, Sept., and Dec.
Final notification: 6-8 weeks
Officers and Directors:* Bruce Hotaling,* Pres.; Fernando Chang-Muy, Secy.; John W. Gould, Treas.; Patricia Blakely, Exec. Dir.; Henry Winsor, Emeritus; Kira Baker-Doyle; Suzanne Cunningham; Steven King, Sr.; Elbert Sampson; Andrew Toy.
Number of staff: 1 full-time professional.
EIN: 231584975

8176
Mericle Foundation ✧ ☆

100 Baltimore Dr.
Wilkes Barre, PA 18702-7955 (570) 823-1100
Contact: Robert E. Mericle, Tr.

Established in 2011 in PA.
Donor: Robert K. Mericle.
Foundation type: Independent foundation.
Financial data (yr. ended 12/31/13): Assets, $924,464 (M); expenditures, $737,809; qualifying distributions, $733,673; giving activities include $732,520 for 16 grants (high: $195,000; low: $10,000).
Fields of interest: Youth development; Human services.
Limitations: Applications accepted. Giving primarily in Wilkes Barre, PA.
Application information: Application form required.
Initial approach: Proposal
Deadline(s): None
Trustees: Kim E. Mericle; Robert K. Mericle.
EIN: 371639789

8177
The Mertz Charitable Trust ✧

c/o BNY Mellon, N.A., Tax Dept.
P.O. Box 185
Pittsburgh, PA 15230-0185

Established in 1984; supporting organization of Alzheimer's Association, Macula Foundation, and Swarthmore College.
Foundation type: Independent foundation.
Financial data (yr. ended 01/31/14): Assets, $7,977,050 (M); expenditures, $1,539,714; qualifying distributions, $957,800; giving activities include $950,000 for grants.
Fields of interest: Higher education, college; Eye diseases; Alzheimer's disease.
Limitations: Applications not accepted. Giving primarily in IL, NY, and PA.
Application information: Contributes only to pre-selected organizations.
Trustee: BNY Mellon, N.A.
EIN: 133206669
Selected grants: The following grants are a representative sample of this grantmaker's funding activity:
$200,000 to Macula Foundation, New York, NY, 2011.
$200,000 to Swarthmore College, Development Office, Swarthmore, PA, 2011.

8178
The Dorothy A. Metcalf Charitable Foundation ✧

c/o PNC Bank, N.A., Tax Dept.
1600 Market St.-Hawthorn, 29th Fl.
Philadelphia, PA 19103-7240

Established in 1997 in MD.
Donors: Dorothy A. Metcalf†; Dorothy A. Metcalf Charitable Trust; Dorothy A. Metcalf Charitable Trust No. 1; Dorothy A. Metcalf Charitable Trust No. 2; Dorothy A. Metcalf Charitable Trust No. 3; Dorothy A. Metcalf Charitable Trust No. 4; Dorothy A. Metcalf Charitable Trust No. 5.
Foundation type: Independent foundation.
Financial data (yr. ended 12/31/13): Assets, $1,246 (M); gifts received, $494,922;

expenditures, $493,070; qualifying distributions, $493,070; giving activities include $493,000 for 19 grants (high: $150,000; low: $5,000).
Fields of interest: Higher education; Health care; Human services.
Limitations: Applications not accepted. Giving primarily in AL and MD. No grants to individuals.
Application information: Contributes only to pre-selected organizations.
Trustee: Robert A. Metcalf.
EIN: 522053820
Selected grants: The following grants are a representative sample of this grantmaker's funding activity:
$150,000 to Auburn University Foundation, Auburn, AL, 2012. For Metcalf Sports Medicine Program.
$10,000 to Clarina Howard Nichols Center, Morrisville, VT, 2012. For Charitable Use of the Organization.

8179
The Jack Miller Center for Teaching America's Founding Principles and History ✧ ☆
3 Bala Plz. W., Ste. 401
Bala Cynwyd, PA 19004-3481 (484) 436-2060
Contact: Perry M. Ratcliff
E-mail: jmc@gojmc.org; Main URL: http://www.jackmillercenter.org
Facebook: https://www.facebook.com/pages/The-Jack-Miller-Center/179231111654
Twitter: https://twitter.com/TheMillerCenter
YouTube: http://www.youtube.com/user/JMCVid?feature=watch

Foundation type: Independent foundation.
Financial data (yr. ended 12/31/13): Assets, $22,414,655 (M); gifts received, $23,900,967; expenditures, $3,080,524; qualifying distributions, $3,059,807; giving activities include $1,270,626 for 41 grants (high: $202,000; low: $2,000), and $5,876,847 for 4 foundation-administered programs.
Fields of interest: Higher education; Education; Civil/human rights; Public affairs.
Limitations: Applications accepted. Giving in the U.S., with some emphasis on Chicago, IL.
Application information: See foundation web site for complete application guidelines. Application form required.
Initial approach: Letter
Deadline(s): None
Officers: Jack Miller, Chair.; RADM. Mike Ratcliff, Pres.; Michael Andrews, V.P.; Michael Deshaies, V.P.
EIN: 261147689
Selected grants: The following grants are a representative sample of this grantmaker's funding activity:
$50,000 to Yale University, New Haven, CT, 2012. To Fund the Yale Center for the Study of Representation.
$20,000 to University of Texas, Austin, TX, 2012. To Fund the Thomas Jefferson Center for the Study Of.
$20,000 to University of Virginia, Charlottesville, VA, 2012. To Fund the Program for Constitutionalism and Democracy.
$12,500 to Ethics and Public Policy Center, Washington, DC, 2012. To Fund a Post-Doctoral Fellowship in Support of the Jack Miller Center's Mission.
$10,000 to University of Wisconsin, Madison, WI, 2012. To Fund Full Time Post-Doctoral Fellowships for Teac.

8180
The Alan B. Miller Family Foundation ✧
57 Crosby Brown Rd.
Gladwyne, PA 19035-1512
Contact: Alan B. Miller, Pres.

Established in 1998 in PA.
Donor: Alan B. Miller.
Foundation type: Independent foundation.
Financial data (yr. ended 01/31/14): Assets, $11,365,595 (M); expenditures, $594,891; qualifying distributions, $586,150; giving activities include $586,150 for 22 grants (high: $180,000; low: $250).
Purpose and activities: Giving primarily for higher education and Jewish agencies; funding also for the arts, education, and health organizations.
Fields of interest: Arts; Higher education; Education; Hospitals (general); Health organizations, association; Cancer; Human services; Jewish federated giving programs; Jewish agencies & synagogues.
Limitations: Applications accepted. Giving primarily in the Philadelphia, PA area. No grants to individuals.
Application information: Application form not required.
Initial approach: Letter
Deadline(s): None
Officers and Directors:* Alan B. Miller,* Pres. and Treas.; Jill S. Miller,* Secy.; Abby D. King; Marc D. Miller; Marni E. Spencer.
EIN: 232899896
Selected grants: The following grants are a representative sample of this grantmaker's funding activity:
$352,500 to College of William and Mary, Williamsburg, VA, 2012.
$42,645 to National Museum of American Jewish History, Philadelphia, PA, 2012.
$40,000 to Kimmel Center for the Performing Arts, Philadelphia, PA, 2012.
$20,000 to Ed Snider Youth Hockey Foundation, Philadelphia, PA, 2012.
$20,000 to Macula Vision Research Foundation, West Conshohocken, PA, 2012.
$15,000 to American Cancer Society, Hershey, PA, 2012.
$15,000 to Jewish Policy Center, Washington, DC, 2012.
$15,000 to Wounded Warrior Project, Jacksonville, FL, 2012.
$12,500 to Thomas Jefferson University, Philadelphia, PA, 2012.
$5,000 to George Washington University, Washington, DC, 2012.

8181
Marlin Miller, Jr. Family Foundation ✧
211 N. Tulpehocken Rd.
Reading, PA 19601-1024 (610) 373-5320
Contact: Marlin Miller, Jr., Tr.

Established in 1989 in PA.
Donor: Marlin Miller, Jr.
Foundation type: Independent foundation.
Financial data (yr. ended 12/31/13): Assets, $18,635,308 (M); gifts received, $50,000; expenditures, $1,076,793; qualifying distributions, $916,542; giving activities include $916,542 for 55 grants (high: $421,000; low: $250).
Fields of interest: Museums; Arts; Higher education; Education; Cancer; Human services; Foundations (private grantmaking).
Limitations: Applications accepted. Giving primarily in MA, ME, NY and PA. No grants to individuals.
Application information: Application form required.
Initial approach: Letter
Deadline(s): None
Trustees: Eric Miller; James H. Miller; Marlin Miller, Jr.; Regina Miller.
EIN: 232591890

8182
The Elinor & T. W. Miller, Jr. Foundation, Inc. ✧
P.O. Box 609
Pittsburgh, PA 15230-9738

Established in 1998 in FL.
Donors: T. W. Miller, Jr.; Thomas W. Miller Irrev. Trust.
Foundation type: Independent foundation.
Financial data (yr. ended 12/31/13): Assets, $19,163,873 (M); expenditures, $924,775; qualifying distributions, $786,533; giving activities include $710,500 for 9 grants (high: $230,000; low: $15,000).
Fields of interest: Higher education, college; Foundations (community).
Type of support: General/operating support.
Limitations: Applications not accepted. Giving primarily in FL.
Application information: Unsolicited requests for funds not accepted.
Trustees: Marilyn Becker; Donald E. Brown; Harold A. Ward, Esq.; Graham White.
EIN: 593508428
Selected grants: The following grants are a representative sample of this grantmaker's funding activity:
$200,000 to Winter Park Memorial Hospital, Winter Park, FL, 2011. For general support.
$100,000 to Rollins College, Winter Park, FL, 2011.
$30,000 to Harvest Food and Outreach Center, Fort Pierce, FL, 2011. For general support.
$25,000 to Community Foundation of Central Florida, Orlando, FL, 2011.
$25,000 to Winter Park High School Foundation, Winter Park, FL, 2011. For general support.

8183
Miller-Worley Charitable Foundation ✧
(formerly The Richard B. Worley and Leslie A. Miller Charitable Trust)
1111 Barberry Rd.
Bryn Mawr, PA 19010-1907

Established in 1996 in PA.
Donors: Richard B. Worley; Leslie A. Miller.
Foundation type: Independent foundation.
Financial data (yr. ended 12/31/13): Assets, $26,283,577 (M); expenditures, $2,067,106; qualifying distributions, $1,968,702; giving activities include $1,909,172 for 78 grants (high: $476,000; low: $250).

Purpose and activities: Funding primarily for higher education and arts and culture.
Fields of interest: Performing arts; Arts; Higher education; Education; Horticulture/garden clubs; Environment; Human services.
Limitations: Applications not accepted. Giving primarily in the Philadelphia, PA area. No grants to individuals.
Application information: Unsolicited requests for funds not accepted.
Trustees: Leslie A. Miller; Richard B. Worley.
EIN: 237862650

8184
Mine Safety Appliances Company Charitable Foundation ✧
1000 Cranberry Woods Dr.
Cranberry Township, PA 16066-5207 (724) 776-8231
Contact: Dennis L. Zeitler, V.P.
Main URL: http://us.msasafety.com/corporateGiving

Established in 1991 in PA as successor to the Mine Safety Appliances Company Charitable Trust.
Donor: Mine Safety Appliances Co.
Foundation type: Company-sponsored foundation.
Financial data (yr. ended 12/31/12): Assets, $199,075 (M); gifts received, $600,000; expenditures, $419,764; qualifying distributions, $419,670; giving activities include $419,670 for 65 grants (high: $41,433; low: $200).
Purpose and activities: The foundation supports botanical gardens and fire fighters and organizations involved with arts and culture, education, health, children, residential care, foreign policy, and engineering.
Fields of interest: Museums; Performing arts, ballet; Performing arts, orchestras; Arts; Higher education; Libraries (public); Scholarships/financial aid; Education; Botanical gardens; Hospitals (general); Health care; Disasters, fire prevention/control; Youth development, business; Children, services; Residential/custodial care, senior continuing care; International affairs, foreign policy; United Ways and Federated Giving Programs; Engineering.
Type of support: Annual campaigns; General/operating support; Continuing support; Program development; Scholarship funds.
Limitations: Applications accepted. Giving primarily in Pittsburgh, PA. No grants to individuals.
Application information: Application form not required.
Initial approach: Letter of inquiry
Deadline(s): None
Officer: Dennis L. Zeitler, V.P. and Secy.
EIN: 256023104

8185
MKM Foundation ✧ ☆
c/o Glenmede Trust Co., N.A.
1650 Market St., Ste. 1200
Philadelphia, PA 19103-7391

Established in 1998 in NJ.
Donor: James E. O'Donnell.
Foundation type: Independent foundation.
Financial data (yr. ended 12/31/13): Assets, $20,458,739 (M); gifts received, $10,000,000; expenditures, $498,385; qualifying distributions, $470,448; giving activities include $446,000 for 63 grants (high: $50,000; low: $500).
Purpose and activities: Giving primarily for elementary and secondary education.
Fields of interest: Education; Health organizations, association; Human services; American Red Cross; Salvation Army.
Limitations: Applications not accepted. Giving primarily in NJ and PA. No grants to individuals.
Application information: Unsolicited requests for funds not accepted.
Trustees: Elizabeth O'Donnell; Marie O'Donnell.
EIN: 237966478
Selected grants: The following grants are a representative sample of this grantmaker's funding activity:
$50,000 to New Venture Fund, Washington, DC, 2012. For the Founding of the Center for Disaster Philanthropy.
$20,000 to Philabundance, Philadelphia, PA, 2012. For the Philabundance Community Food Center in Chester.
$15,000 to Friends Central School, Wynnewood, PA, 2012. For the David Felsen Scholarship Fund.
$10,000 to Community Foundation of New Jersey, Morristown, NJ, 2012. For Restricted to the New Jersey Recovery Fund.
$5,000 to Elon University, Elon, NC, 2012. For the John L. Georgeo Scholarship.
$5,000 to Wounded Warrior Project, Topeka, KS, 2012. For Alumni, Caregiver Retreats, Benefits Counseling, Coping/Family Services, and Peer Mentoring.
$3,500 to Lutheran Social Ministries of New Jersey, Burlington, NJ, 2012. For Restricted for use by New Visions Homeless Day Shelter.
$1,000 to Fractured Atlas, New York, NY, 2012. For the Philadelphia Artists' Collective.
$500 to Elon University, Elon, NC, 2012. For Hillel Operating Budget.

8186
The Ruth Danley & William Enoch Moore Fund ✧
c/o PNC Bank
620 Liberty Ave., 10th Fl.
Pittsburgh, PA 15222-2705 (412) 762-3502
Contact: Bruce R. Bickel

Established in 1992 in PA.
Donor: Grace Danley Moore†.
Foundation type: Independent foundation.
Financial data (yr. ended 12/31/13): Assets, $16,328,157 (M); expenditures, $791,697; qualifying distributions, $709,152; giving activities include $663,354 for 13 grants (high: $100,000; low: $20,000).
Purpose and activities: Giving for K-12 education for Native American children on reservations.
Fields of interest: Education; Native Americans/American Indians.
Type of support: Capital campaigns; Building/renovation; Equipment; Program development; Seed money; Scholarship funds.
Limitations: Applications accepted. Giving on a national basis. No grants to individuals.
Publications: Application guidelines.
Application information: Application form not required.
Initial approach: Proposal
Copies of proposal: 1
Deadline(s): None
Trustee: PNC Bank, N.A.
EIN: 256399593

8187
The Mitchell and Hilarie Morgan Family Foundation ✧
160 Clubhouse Rd.
King of Prussia, PA 19406-3300

Established in 1999 in PA.
Donors: Mitchell L. Morgan; Hilarie L. Morgan.
Foundation type: Independent foundation.
Financial data (yr. ended 12/31/13): Assets, $29,419 (M); gifts received, $1,650,000; expenditures, $1,743,805; qualifying distributions, $1,742,365; giving activities include $1,742,365 for 34 grants (high: $1,011,000; low: $50).
Purpose and activities: Giving primarily for the arts, education, health organizations, and to Jewish organizations.
Fields of interest: Arts; Higher education; Education; Health organizations, association; Human services; Jewish federated giving programs; Jewish agencies & synagogues.
Type of support: General/operating support.
Limitations: Applications not accepted. Giving primarily in PA, with emphasis on Philadelphia. No grants to individuals.
Application information: Contributes only to pre-selected organizations.
Trustees: Hilarie L. Morgan; Mitchell L. Morgan.
EIN: 256683715
Selected grants: The following grants are a representative sample of this grantmaker's funding activity:
$5,000 to Temple University, Law School, Philadelphia, PA, 2012. For general.

8188
Charles M. Morris Charitable Trust ✧
c/o PNC Institutional Investments
1 PNC Plz., 20th Fl.
Pittsburgh, PA 15222-2707 (412) 762-8390
Contact: Mark Bezilla
FAX: (412) 705-3584;
E-mail: mark.bezilla@pnc.com; Main URL: http://www.morrisfoundation.org

Established in 1988 in PA.
Donor: Charles M. Morris†.
Foundation type: Independent foundation.
Financial data (yr. ended 12/31/13): Assets, $30,469,490 (M); expenditures, $1,439,302; qualifying distributions, $1,273,952; giving activities include $1,184,920 for 22 grants (high: $722,500; low: $5,000).
Purpose and activities: Giving for organizations that benefit the elderly, disadvantaged persons, youth, the disabled, and the performing arts, as well as for Jewish charities located in or serving Jewish people residing in Allegheny County, Pennsylvania, and certain charities located in Israel.
Fields of interest: Family services; Aging, centers/services; Homeless, human services; United Ways and Federated Giving Programs; Jewish agencies & synagogues; Religion; Aging; Homeless.
Type of support: General/operating support; Continuing support; Capital campaigns; Building/renovation; Equipment; Conferences/seminars.
Limitations: Giving primarily in Allegheny County and western PA. No grants to individuals.

Publications: Application guidelines; Grants list; Informational brochure; Multi-year report; IRS Form 990 or 990-PF printed copy available upon request.
Application information: Telephone inquiries about the status of applications are not accepted. Application form required.
Initial approach: Take eligibility quiz on foundation web site
Deadline(s): Varies, refer to foundation web site for current dates
Board meeting date(s): Varies
Final notification: Following board meetings
Distribution Committee: Arthur C. Fidel; Charles Perlow.
Trustee: PNC Bank, N.A.
EIN: 256312920
Selected grants: The following grants are a representative sample of this grantmaker's funding activity:
$33,333 to Hillel Academy of Pittsburgh, Pittsburgh, PA, 2012. For early childhood classrooms.
$20,000 to Hillel Jewish University Center, Pittsburgh, PA, 2012. For Security and Material Upgrades.

8189
Mosi Foundation ✧ ☆
c/o Gerald A. Isom
202 Valley Forge Lookout Pl.
Radnor, PA 19087-4673

Established in 2002 in PA.
Donors: Gerald A. Isom; Lucille E. Isom.
Foundation type: Operating foundation.
Financial data (yr. ended 12/31/13): Assets, $3,894,751 (M); gifts received, $324,388; expenditures, $470,507; qualifying distributions, $429,145; giving activities include $429,145 for 15 grants (high: $250,194; low: $1,500).
Fields of interest: Higher education, college; Education; Autism research; Recreation, camps; Christian agencies & churches.
Limitations: Applications not accepted. No grants to individuals.
Application information: Unsolicited requests for funds not accepted.
Officers: Gerald A. Isom, Pres.; Lucille E. Isom, V.P.; Jana L. de Leon, Secy.; Jennifer A. O'Malley, Treas.
Director: Karen M. Schmid.
EIN: 743071480
Selected grants: The following grants are a representative sample of this grantmaker's funding activity:
$100,000 to Ohio Valley University, Vienna, WV, 2010.
$15,000 to Bryn Mawr Hospital Foundation, Bryn Mawr, PA, 2010.
$10,000 to Autism Speaks, New York, NY, 2011.

8190
The Mullen Family Foundation ✧ ☆
(formerly The Mullen Family Foundation)
P.O. Box 199
Newtown Square, PA 19073-0199 (215) 265-5617
Contact: Joan J. Mullen, Dir.

Established in 1979 in PA.
Donors: John J. Mullen; Joan A. Mullen.
Foundation type: Independent foundation.
Financial data (yr. ended 09/30/13): Assets, $2,377,702 (M); expenditures, $446,072; qualifying distributions, $436,500; giving activities include $436,500 for 13 grants (high: $200,000; low: $500).
Fields of interest: Education; Health organizations; Human services.
Type of support: General/operating support; Program development; Scholarship funds.
Limitations: Applications accepted. Giving primarily in the Philadelphia, PA, area. No grants to individuals.
Application information: Application form required.
Initial approach: Completed application form
Deadline(s): None
Directors: Joan A. Mullen; John J. Mullen.
Number of staff: 3 part-time support.
EIN: 232125388
Selected grants: The following grants are a representative sample of this grantmaker's funding activity:
$25,000 to Archdiocese of Philadelphia, Philadelphia, PA, 2011.
$12,500 to Radnor A Better Chance, Radnor, PA, 2011.
$10,000 to West Philadelphia Catholic High School, Philadelphia, PA, 2011.
$2,500 to Country Day School of the Sacred Heart, Bryn Mawr, PA, 2011.
$1,500 to Monsignor Bonner High School, Drexel Hill, PA, 2011.
$1,000 to Sisters, Servants of the Immaculate Heart of Mary, Immaculata, PA, 2011.
$1,000 to West Philadelphia Catholic High School, Philadelphia, PA, 2011.

8191
Custer Musser Memorial Fund ✧
c/o BNY Mellon, N.A.
P.O. Box 185
Pittsburgh, PA 15230-0185

Foundation type: Independent foundation.
Financial data (yr. ended 06/30/13): Assets, $14,173,443 (M); expenditures, $732,097; qualifying distributions, $685,678; giving activities include $685,678 for grants.
Fields of interest: Education; Health care; Human services.
Limitations: Applications not accepted.
Application information: Unsolicited requests for funds not accepted.
Trustee: BNY Mellon, N.A.
EIN: 236226957

8192
The Mylan Charitable Foundation ✧
1500 Corporate Dr., Ste. 400
Canonsburg, PA 15317-8580
Contact: Christina Matluck, Exec. Admin.
E-mail: christina.matluck@mylanfoundation.org

Established in 2002 in PA and WV.
Donors: Mylan Laboratories Inc.; Mylan Pharmaceuticals.
Foundation type: Company-sponsored foundation.
Financial data (yr. ended 12/31/12): Assets, $10,200,441 (M); expenditures, $943,036; qualifying distributions, $862,500; giving activities include $862,500 for 11 grants (high: $250,000; low: $25,000).
Purpose and activities: The foundation supports organizations involved with education, health, human services, and community development.
Fields of interest: Arts; Education; Health care.
Type of support: General/operating support; Building/renovation.
Limitations: Applications accepted. Giving primarily in PA and WV as well as Rockford, IL, Sugar Land, TX, and St. Albans, VT. No grants to individuals.
Application information:
Copies of proposal: 1
Deadline(s): Varies
Officers and Directors: Rodney L. Piatt, Chair.; C. B. Todd, Secy.; Brian Byala, Treas.; Heather Bresch; Robert J. Coury.
Number of staff: 1 full-time professional.
EIN: 431954390

8193
The Nararo Foundation ✧
c/o Thomas I. Whitman
720 Westview St.
Philadelphia, PA 19119-0037

Established in 2002 in PA.
Donors: Thomas I. Whitman; Mira Rabin; Martin J. Whitman.
Foundation type: Independent foundation.
Financial data (yr. ended 12/31/13): Assets, $15,391,492 (M); gifts received, $500,000; expenditures, $613,669; qualifying distributions, $567,157; giving activities include $567,157 for 59 grants (high: $50,000; low: $1,000).
Fields of interest: Human services; International human rights.
Limitations: Applications not accepted. Giving primarily in NY and PA, some giving also in MA. No grants to individuals.
Application information: Contributes only to pre-selected organizations.
Trustees: Mira Rabin; Thomas I. Whitman.
EIN: 020229861

8194
Naylor Family Foundation ✧
100 Boxwood Ln.
York, PA 17402-9305

Established in 2004 in PA.
Donors: Irvin S. Naylor; Leah R. Naylor; Sarah R. Naylor.
Foundation type: Independent foundation.
Financial data (yr. ended 12/31/13): Assets, $888,330 (M); gifts received, $1,050,000; expenditures, $2,205,212; qualifying distributions, $2,201,500; giving activities include $2,200,000 for 2 grants (high: $2,000,000; low: $200,000).
Fields of interest: Higher education; Education; Athletics/sports, equestrianism.
Limitations: Applications not accepted. Giving primarily in MD. No grants to individuals.
Application information: Contributes only to pre-selected organizations.
Officers: Diane G. Naylor, Pres.; Irvin S. Naylor, V.P.; Brad Leber, Secy.; Scott W. Romberger, Treas.
Director: S. Chester Naylor II.
EIN: 421640416

8195
Grace S. & W. Linton Nelson Foundation
150 N. Radnor Chester Rd., Ste. F200
Radnor, PA 19087 (610) 977-2488
Contact: Gloria Feldman, Exec. Admin.
FAX: (610) 977-0043;
E-mail: nelson.info@nelsonfoundationpa.org; Main URL: http://nelsonfoundationpa.org

Established in 1984 in PA.
Donors: ADM. W. Linton Nelson†; Grace Nelson†; William P. Brady; Delaware Management Co.
Foundation type: Independent foundation.
Financial data (yr. ended 12/31/12): Assets, $18,953,822 (M); expenditures, $842,909; qualifying distributions, $763,312; giving activities include $502,656 for 51 grants (high: $198,906; low: $1,000).
Purpose and activities: Giving for: 1) the unmet needs of children and youth in the areas of shelter, day care, preschool, education, health care, child and drug abuse prevention, after school and summer programs, child advocacy, parenting, and foster care and adoption; 2) The Nelson Foundation Scholarship Program at the Wharton School; and 3) programs fostering leadership and citizenship in youth.
Fields of interest: Child development, education; Youth development, citizenship; Children/youth, services; Child development, services.
Type of support: General/operating support; Equipment; Program development; Seed money.
Limitations: Applications accepted. Giving primarily in Philadelphia, PA, and the surrounding counties, including Bucks, Chester, Delaware, Montgomery and Philadelphia. No support for national or umbrella organizations, religious education, public, private or charter schools, routine social services or counseling, individual daycare, disease research, hospitals or programs for animals. No grants to individuals directly, or for tickets, tables, ads, sponsorships, parties, conferences, fairs and fundraising events, fellowships, travel, or public policy research or advocacy.
Publications: Application guidelines.
Application information: Application form required.
Initial approach: Proposal cover sheet (which can be downloaded from foundation web site)
Copies of proposal: 1
Deadline(s): 6 weeks before board meetings in Jan., Apr., July, and Oct.
Board meeting date(s): 2nd week of every month; grants reviewed quarterly in Jan., Apr., July, and Oct.
Officers and Directors:* Alexandra A. Aldridge,* Pres.; Fred C. Aldridge, Jr.,* Treas.; Beth A. Coyne; Richard J. Flannery.
Number of staff: 2 part-time professional.
EIN: 222583922
Selected grants: The following grants are a representative sample of this grantmaker's funding activity:
$20,000 to Boy Scouts of America, Cradle of Liberty Council, Philadelphia, PA, 2012. For ScoutReach.
$12,500 to Steppingstone Scholars, Philadelphia, PA, 2012. For Education Access/Support Program for children/youth.
$10,000 to Chester County Futures, Exton, PA, 2012. For education enrichment.
$10,000 to Philadelphia Education Fund, Philadelphia, PA, 2012. For Education Aid for high school graduates.
$10,000 to VNA Community Services, Abington, PA, 2012. For healthcare/pre-school screening program.
$5,000 to Boy Scouts of America, Chester County, West Chester, PA, 2012. For ScoutReach.
$5,000 to Community Volunteers in Medicine, West Chester, PA, 2012. For Dental care for low-income children/youth.
$5,000 to Cradles to Crayons, West Conshohocken, PA, 2012. For Aid for homeless/low-income children/youth.
$5,000 to Settlement Music School, Philadelphia, PA, 2012. For early childhood education initiative.
$3,500 to North Light Community Center, Philadelphia, PA, 2012. For out-of-school-time Programs for children.

8196
The Neubauer Family Foundation ✧
c/o Baker Tilly LLP
1800 Byberry Rd., Ste. 1100
Huntingdon Valley, PA 19006-3523

Established in 1998 in PA.
Donor: Joseph Neubauer.
Foundation type: Independent foundation.
Financial data (yr. ended 11/30/13): Assets, $238,892,912 (M); gifts received, $9,085,758; expenditures, $12,264,997; qualifying distributions, $12,000,055; giving activities include $11,778,164 for 97 grants (high: $2,475,000; low: $150).
Purpose and activities: Giving primarily for higher education, the arts, and to Jewish organizations.
Fields of interest: Museums; Performing arts; Performing arts, orchestras; Performing arts, opera; Higher education; Theological school/education; Education; Hospitals (general); Jewish agencies & synagogues.
Type of support: Program development.
Limitations: Applications not accepted. Giving primarily in Philadelphia, PA; some funding in Chicago, IL, and New York, NY. No grants to individuals.
Application information: Contributes only to pre-selected organizations.
Trustees: Melissa Neubauer Anderson; Joseph Neubauer; Lawrence Neubauer.
EIN: 256627704
Selected grants: The following grants are a representative sample of this grantmaker's funding activity:
$3,365,000 to Barnes Foundation, Philadelphia, PA, 2012. For program support.
$2,492,500 to University of Chicago, Chicago, IL, 2012. For program support.
$1,450,000 to Metropolitan Opera, New York, NY, 2012. For program support.
$1,000,000 to Curtis Institute of Music, Philadelphia, PA, 2012. For program support.
$670,000 to Pew Charitable Trusts, Philadelphia, PA, 2012. For program support.
$291,874 to Jewish Theological Seminary of America, New York, NY, 2012. For program support.
$100,000 to University of Chicago, Oriental Institute, Chicago, IL, 2012. For program support.
$50,000 to Brandeis University, Waltham, MA, 2012. For program support.
$25,000 to Academy of Music of Philadelphia, Philadelphia, PA, 2012. For restoration fund.
$20,000 to United Way of Greater Philadelphia and Southern New Jersey, Philadelphia, PA, 2012. For program support.

8197
Nichols Foundation, Inc. ✧
c/o J. Melendez
102 Slate Ct.
Milford, PA 18337
NY tel.: (212) 632-3000, NY fax: (212) 632-3198

Incorporated in 1923 in NY.
Donors: Nichols Foundation, Inc. Trust; Members of the Nichols family.
Foundation type: Independent foundation.
Financial data (yr. ended 12/31/13): Assets, $20,476,124 (M); expenditures, $1,274,430; qualifying distributions, $1,099,588; giving activities include $1,029,083 for 153 grants (high: $100,000; low: $75).
Purpose and activities: Giving primarily for education, health care, and human services.
Fields of interest: Secondary school/education; Higher education; Education, reading; Education; Environment, natural resources; Environment; Animals/wildlife, preservation/protection; Hospitals (general); Reproductive health, family planning; Cancer; Biomedicine; Cancer research; Human services; Children/youth, services; Family services; Disabilities, people with; Economically disadvantaged.
Type of support: Continuing support; Annual campaigns; Capital campaigns; Building/renovation; Equipment; Land acquisition; Program development; Scholarship funds; Research; Matching/challenge support.
Limitations: Applications not accepted. Giving primarily in Santa Barbara, CA, Hinsdale County, CO, FL, and the metropolitan New York, NY area. No support for religious institutions. No grants to individuals, or for individual scholarships or general support; no loans.
Application information: Contributes only to pre-selected organizations. Unsolicited requests for funds not considered.
Officers: Peter C. Coxhead, Pres.; Marguerite D. R. Buttrick, V.P.; Jessica Melendez, Exec. Dir.; David H. Nichols, Treas.
Director: Sandra P. Nash.
EIN: 136400615
Selected grants: The following grants are a representative sample of this grantmaker's funding activity:
$2,500 to Willamette University, Salem, OR, 2012. For All = Sustaining Gifts.

8198
Nimick Forbesway Foundation ✧
(formerly Forbesway Foundation)
1 Oxford Ctr., 20th Fl.
Pittsburgh, PA 15219-1407
Application address: c/o Jack J. Kessler, Esq., Secy.-Treas., 301 Grant St., 20th Fl. Pittsburgh, PA 15219; tel.: (412) 562-8879

Established in 1989 in PA.
Donors: Thomas H. Nimick, Jr.†; Theresa L. Nimick Trust 1996 No. 1; Theresa L. Nimick Trust 1996 No. 2.
Foundation type: Independent foundation.
Financial data (yr. ended 06/30/13): Assets, $23,549,125 (M); expenditures, $1,320,272; qualifying distributions, $1,149,965; giving activities include $1,132,500 for 31 grants (high: $200,000; low: $2,500).

Fields of interest: Higher education; Education; Hospitals (general); Children/youth, services; Protestant agencies & churches.
Limitations: Applications accepted. Giving primarily in Pittsburgh, PA. No grants to individuals.
Application information: Application form required.
Initial approach: Letter
Deadline(s): None
Officers and Directors:* Charles L.H. Nimick,* Chair.; Cathleen Lockhart Nimick,* Vice-Chair.; Victoria Nimick Enright,* Vice-Chair.; Jack J. Kessler,* Secy.-Treas.
EIN: 251597437
Selected grants: The following grants are a representative sample of this grantmaker's funding activity:
$200,000 to American Red Cross, Pittsburgh, PA, 2011.
$162,910 to Congressional Schools of Virginia, Falls Church, VA, 2011. For scholarship fund.
$25,000 to Carnegie Institute, Pittsburgh, PA, 2011.
$25,000 to Shadyside Hospital Foundation, Pittsburgh, PA, 2011.
$25,000 to Washington National Cathedral, Washington, DC, 2011. For general operating support.
$20,000 to Saint Michaels of the Valley Episcopal Church, Ligonier, PA, 2011. For general operating support.
$16,700 to International Student Conferences, Washington, DC, 2011.
$10,000 to Franklin and Marshall College, Lancaster, PA, 2011.
$10,000 to Madison Public Library Foundation, Madison, WI, 2011.
$10,000 to United States Holocaust Memorial Museum, Washington, DC, 2011. For general operating support.

8199
North Penn Community Health Foundation ✧

2506 N. Broad St., Ste. 206
Colmar, PA 18915-9439 (215) 716-5400
Contact: Russell Johnson, C.E.O. and Pres.
FAX: (215) 716-5410; E-mail: jpedroni@npchf.org; Toll-free tel.: (888) 412-0314; Main URL: http://www.npchf.org

Established in 2002; converted from the sale of North Penn Hospital. Converted to a private foundation in 2008.
Foundation type: Independent foundation.
Financial data (yr. ended 06/30/13): Assets, $44,792,336 (M); gifts received, $527,370; expenditures, $2,027,666; qualifying distributions, $1,463,854; giving activities include $486,118 for 24 grants (high: $65,875; low: $100), and $941,880 for foundation-administered programs.
Purpose and activities: The foundation provides support to health and human service organizations that serve the residents living in the service community. The foundation is interested in building collaborative relationships with providing organizations. By establishing and strengthening these relationships, the foundation intends to identify, select and invest in programs and organizations that will improve the health, welfare and quality of life of children and families, adults and senior citizens, people with disabilities and other disadvantaged populations residing the foundation's service community.
Fields of interest: Health care, reform; Public health; Health care, patient services; Health care; Food services; Nutrition; Housing/shelter, reform; Housing/shelter, homeless; Housing/shelter, services; Housing/shelter; Human services; Aging; Disabilities, people with; Physically disabled; Mentally disabled; Economically disadvantaged; Homeless.
Type of support: Management development/capacity building; Program development; Technical assistance; Consulting services; Matching/challenge support.
Limitations: Applications accepted. Giving in Montgomery County and the North Penn region, PA. Montgomery County is a suburban county of the Philadelphia metropolitan region, in the southeastern portion of the state. The North Penn region is defined by the boundaries of the North Penn, Souderton Area, and Wissahickon School Districts. No support for No support to for-profit organizations, disease-specific charities, religious congregations, fraternal, political, or civic groups, or recreational clubs. No grants to individuals, or for fundraising, endowments, debt reduction, replacement of lost government funds, supplementation of groups, private/public insurance, clinical or academic research, student projects, athletic, or alumni activities, equipment, or publications (unless such publications are an integral component for a specific grant initiative).
Publications: Application guidelines; Annual report; Financial statement; Grants list; Occasional report.
Application information: The foundation has an online application format. Do not submit videos or electronic media unless directly related to the nature of the grant request. Do not use ringed binders or other elaborate document fasteners. Faxed or e-mailed applications are not accepted.
Initial approach: The foundation prefers to receive a phone call or letter of inquiry prior to full application
Deadline(s): Generally 6-8 weeks before board meetings
Board meeting date(s): Varies (refer to foundation web site for current dates)
Final notification: Approximately 1-week after board meeting following receipt of application
Officers and Directors:* Russel R. Hensel, Ph.D.*, Chair.; Nancy Alba Dunleavy, Vice-Chair.; Russell Johnson,* C.E.O. and Pres.; Alfredo de la Pena,* Secy.; Kenneth Amey,* Treas.; David Crosson; George E. Marks, AIA; Paul W. Pocalyko, CPA/CFF, CFE; William C. Stevens III; R. John Stubbs, Ph.D.; Elizabeth Styer; Sandra C. Vasoli.
Number of staff: 4 full-time professional.
EIN: 231352175
Selected grants: The following grants are a representative sample of this grantmaker's funding activity:
$183,000 to Visiting Nurse Association, North Penn, Lansdale, PA, 2012. For continued support of primary and preventative health care services to low-income individuals and families and in support of expenses associated with the expansion of the oral health clinic.
$120,000 to Family Service of Montgomery County, Eagleville, PA, 2012. For continued support of efforts to become a high-performing organization, payable over 2.00 years.
$99,300 to Health Promotion Council of Southeastern Pennsylvania, Philadelphia, PA, 2012. For continued support of the Wellness Initiative for the School Environment: Smart Nutrition and Activity Collaborative (WISE SNAC).
$94,000 to Manna on Main Street, Lansdale, PA, 2012. For furtherance of the Lansdale Collaboration Project.
$87,300 to Food Trust, Philadelphia, PA, 2012. For continued support of the Nutrition Coalition.
$85,000 to Health Promotion Council of Southeastern Pennsylvania, Philadelphia, PA, 2012. For Cultivating Communities Campaign, project geared toward increasing access to fresh produce for low-income families.
$80,250 to Indian Creek Foundation, Souderton, PA, 2012. For the expansion of behavioral health services to children with intellectual and developmental disabilities.
$65,000 to Greater North Penn Collaborative for Health and Human Services, Harleysville, PA, 2012. For continued support of fostering collaboration among nonprofit organizations and other community stakeholders.
$50,000 to Advanced Living Management and Development, Lansdale, PA, 2012. For legal and market research to explore the feasibility and interest of developing independent living campus for financially independent adults with intellectual and/or developmental disability.
$20,000 to VNA Community Services, Abington, PA, 2012. For Personal Navigator Program - Access to Benefits for Individuals in Need.

8200
Northwest Charitable Foundation ✧

100 Liberty St.
Warren, PA 16365-2411

Foundation type: Independent foundation.
Financial data (yr. ended 12/31/13): Assets, $20,609,721 (M); gifts received, $500; expenditures, $845,070; qualifying distributions, $818,470; giving activities include $818,346 for 98 grants (high: $150,000; low: $500).
Fields of interest: Human services; Community/economic development; Religion.
Limitations: Applications not accepted. Giving primarily in PA.
Application information: Unsolicited requests for funds not accepted.
Officers: Gregory C. Larocca, Pres.; Vicki L. Stec, V.P.; Jessie L. Thomas, Secy.; Donald E. Reed, Treas.
Directors: Richard E. McDowell; Sonia M. Probst; Phillip M. Tredway; William J. Wagner.
EIN: 271403629
Selected grants: The following grants are a representative sample of this grantmaker's funding activity:
$25,000 to Erie Community Foundation, Erie, PA, 2012. For Bayfront Project.
$25,000 to Warren General Hospital, Warren, PA, 2012. For Cancer Center (2nd Grant Check).
$10,000 to Columbia Foundation, Columbia, MD, 2012. For Grow and Maintain Critical Community R.
$8,334 to YMCA of Corry, Corry, PA, 2012. For Repair/Maintenance of YMCA Facility.
$5,000 to Erie Art Museum, Erie, PA, 2012. For Building Campaign (2nd Year of 5-Year.
$3,500 to United Way of Washington County, Washington, PA, 2012. For Contribution 2012.
$3,000 to Clearfield Educational Foundation, Clearfield, PA, 2012. For Community Education Programs.
$2,500 to United Way of the Capital Region, Enola, PA, 2012. For Contribution 2012 (Covers Cumberland.

$500 to Hospice of Warren County, Warren, PA, 2012. For Hospice Care, Bereavement Services.

8201
Noteman Memorial Fund Trust ✧
c/o BNY Mellon, N.A., Tax Dept.
P.O. Box 185
Pittsburgh, PA 15230-0185

Supporting organization of Sound Shore Medical Center.
Foundation type: Independent foundation.
Financial data (yr. ended 12/31/13): Assets, $13,282,724 (M); expenditures, $550,333; qualifying distributions, $500,991; giving activities include $493,904 for 1 grant.
Fields of interest: Medical care, community health systems.
Limitations: Applications not accepted. Giving primarily in New Rochelle, NY.
Application information: Unsolicited requests for funds not accepted.
Trustees: John A. Geoghegan; BNY Mellon, N.A.
EIN: 136063390

8202
Yetta Deitch Novotny Charitable Trust ✧ ☆
2 Penn Ctr. Plz., Ste. 803
Philadelphia, PA 19102-1723

Established in 1990 in PA.
Donor: Yetta Deitch Novotny‡.
Foundation type: Independent foundation.
Financial data (yr. ended 08/31/13): Assets, $6,509,295 (M); expenditures, $731,446; qualifying distributions, $457,790; giving activities include $457,790 for 25 grants (high: $125,000; low: $250).
Fields of interest: Education; Hospitals (general); Human services; Jewish federated giving programs; Jewish agencies & synagogues.
Limitations: Applications not accepted. Giving primarily in New York, NY, and Philadelphia, PA. No grants to individuals.
Application information: Contributes only to pre-selected organizations.
Trustees: Andrew Zolot; Stanley L. Zolot.
EIN: 237642807
Selected grants: The following grants are a representative sample of this grantmaker's funding activity:
$155,000 to Jewish Federation of Greater Philadelphia, Philadelphia, PA, 2011.
$15,000 to Har Zion Temple, Penn Valley, PA, 2011.
$10,000 to Brandeis University, Waltham, MA, 2011.
$10,000 to Carmel Academy, Greenwich, CT, 2011.
$10,000 to National Museum of American Jewish History, Philadelphia, PA, 2011.
$5,000 to Hadassah, The Womens Zionist Organization of America, New York, NY, 2011.
$3,000 to Juvenile Diabetes Research Foundation International, New York, NY, 2011.
$1,800 to Friends of the Israel Defense Forces, New York, NY, 2011.
$1,000 to Jewish Employment and Vocational Service, Philadelphia, PA, 2011.
$1,000 to Jewish Federation of Greater Philadelphia, Philadelphia, PA, 2011.

8203
Oberkotter Foundation ✧
1600 Market St., Ste. 3600
Philadelphia, PA 19103-7286 (215) 751-2601
Contact: Bruce A. Rosenfield, Exec. Dir.
FAX: (215) 751-2678;
E-mail: info@oberkotterfoundation.org; Main URL: http://www.oberkotterfoundation.org

Established in 1992 in PA.
Donors: Paul Oberkotter‡; Mildred L. Oberkotter.
Foundation type: Independent foundation.
Financial data (yr. ended 11/30/13): Assets, $161,624,373 (M); gifts received, $9,968,216; expenditures, $20,129,714; qualifying distributions, $19,174,089; giving activities include $16,297,410 for 49 grants (high: $2,832,805; low: $8,000), and $18,176,288 for 2 foundation-administered programs.
Purpose and activities: The foundation limits its grants to educational institutions and centers for the deaf that use the auditory/oral or auditory/verbal method exclusively; research in the area of hearing-impairment where interdisciplinary resources are used.
Fields of interest: Education, special; Speech/hearing centers; Diabetes; Ear, nose & throat research; Diabetes research; Infants/toddlers; Children.
Type of support: General/operating support; Research; Matching/challenge support.
Limitations: Applications not accepted. Giving on a national basis. No support for non-U.S. organizations and entities. No grants to individuals or for capital campaigns, endowments, debt reduction, fundraising events, and sponsorships.
Application information: Contributes only to pre-selected organizations.
Officer and Trustees:* Bruce A. Rosenfield,* Exec. Dir.; Mildred L. Oberkotter; David A. Pierson, Ph.D.
Number of staff: 1 full-time professional; 1 full-time support.
EIN: 232686151
Selected grants: The following grants are a representative sample of this grantmaker's funding activity:
$638,784 to Clarke School for the Deaf, Northampton, MA, 2012.
$403,868 to Alexander Graham Bell Association for the Deaf and Hard of Hearing, Washington, DC, 2012.
$335,500 to Clarke School for the Deaf, Northampton, MA, 2012.
$257,000 to Foundation for Hearing Research, Jean Weingarten Peninsula Oral School for the Deaf, Redwood City, CA, 2012.
$180,000 to Alexander Graham Bell Association for the Deaf and Hard of Hearing, Washington, DC, 2012. To provide financial aid.
$177,062 to Vanderbilt University Medical Center, Nashville, TN, 2012. For professional learning development for staff.
$175,000 to Vanderbilt University Medical Center, Nashville, TN, 2012.
$139,937 to Alexander Graham Bell Association for the Deaf and Hard of Hearing, Washington, DC, 2012.
$70,000 to Buffalo Hearing and Speech Center, Buffalo, NY, 2012.
$68,231 to New Orleans Oral School, Metairie, LA, 2012.

8204
Sharp Emma O-Parker Foundation Trust ✧
c/o BNY Mellon, N.A.
P.O. Box 185
Pittsburgh, PA 15230-0185
Contact: James Zern

Established in 1997 in PA.
Foundation type: Independent foundation.
Financial data (yr. ended 12/31/13): Assets, $191,224 (M); gifts received, $527,063; expenditures, $830,213; qualifying distributions, $819,285; giving activities include $812,000 for 8 grants (high: $305,000; low: $25,000).
Fields of interest: Arts; Education; Children/youth, services.
Limitations: Applications not accepted. Giving primarily in Pittsburgh, PA.
Application information: Unsolicited requests for funds not accepted.
Trustees: John C. Harmon; BNY Mellon, N.A.
EIN: 237883782
Selected grants: The following grants are a representative sample of this grantmaker's funding activity:
$205,000 to Shadyside Presbyterian Church, Pittsburgh, PA, 2011.
$170,000 to Pittsburgh Symphony, Pittsburgh, PA, 2011.
$117,940 to Winchester-Thurston School, Pittsburgh, PA, 2011.
$85,000 to Carnegie Library of Pittsburgh, Pittsburgh, PA, 2011.
$60,000 to Brothers Brother Foundation, Pittsburgh, PA, 2011.
$25,000 to Coalition for Christian Outreach, Pittsburgh, PA, 2011.
$10,000 to Carnegie Mellon University, Pittsburgh, PA, 2011.
$10,000 to Massachusetts Institute of Technology, Cambridge, MA, 2011.
$10,000 to Wheelock College, Boston, MA, 2011.

8205
The Robert and Angela Ortenzio Family Foundation ✧
4718 Old Gettysburg Rd., Ste. 405
Mechanicsburg, PA 17055-4380 (717) 972-1305
Contact: Robert A. Ortenzio, Tr.

Established in 2003 in PA.
Donor: Robert A. Ortenzio.
Foundation type: Independent foundation.
Financial data (yr. ended 12/31/13): Assets, $3,280,783 (M); gifts received, $899,967; expenditures, $1,058,845; qualifying distributions, $1,043,948; giving activities include $1,041,000 for 7 grants (high: $500,000; low: $1,000).
Fields of interest: Secondary school/education; Higher education.
Type of support: General/operating support.
Limitations: Applications accepted. Giving primarily in PA. No grants to individuals.
Application information:
Initial approach: Letter
Deadline(s): None
Trustees: Angela D. Ortenzio; Robert A. Ortenzio.
EIN: 256843186

8206
The Rocco and Nancy Ortenzio Foundation ✧
(formerly The Rocco and Nancy Ortenzio Family Foundation)
4718 Old Gettysburg Rd., Ste. 405
Mechanicsburg, PA 17055-4380 (717) 972-1305
Contact: Robert A. Ortenzio, Tr.

Established in 1986 in PA.
Donors: Rocco A. Ortenzio; Russell L. Carson; Martin J. Ortenzio.
Foundation type: Independent foundation.
Financial data (yr. ended 12/31/13): Assets, $16,309,313 (M); gifts received, $2,000,000; expenditures, $2,234,073; qualifying distributions, $2,165,705; giving activities include $2,162,290 for 13 grants (high: $800,000; low: $1,000).
Purpose and activities: Grants are primarily restricted to Roman Catholic educational institutions to provide scholarships or other assistance to qualified students with financial need, with first preference being given to students who are members of St. Ann's Roman Catholic Church, in Steelton, PA.
Fields of interest: Elementary school/education; Secondary school/education; Higher education; Scholarships/financial aid; Residential/custodial care, hospices; Catholic agencies & churches.
Type of support: Scholarship funds.
Limitations: Applications accepted. Giving primarily in PA. No grants to individuals.
Application information: Application form required.
Initial approach: Letter
Deadline(s): None
Trustees: John M. Ortenzio; Martin J. Ortenzio; Robert A. Ortenzio; Rocco A. Ortenzio.
EIN: 236805409

8207
Theresa and Edward O'Toole Foundation ✧
c/o Bank of New York Mellon, N.A.
P.O. Box 185
Pittsburgh, PA 15230-0185

Established in 1971.
Donor: Theresa O'Toole‡.
Foundation type: Independent foundation.
Financial data (yr. ended 06/30/13): Assets, $76,448,915 (M); expenditures, $5,059,142; qualifying distributions, $4,155,106; giving activities include $3,790,000 for 39 grants (high: $875,000; low: $10,000).
Purpose and activities: Giving primarily for education, and Roman Catholic schools and churches.
Fields of interest: Higher education; Education; Human services; Catholic agencies & churches; Blind/visually impaired.
Type of support: General/operating support; Continuing support; Annual campaigns; Capital campaigns; Building/renovation; Emergency funds; Program development; Seed money; Research; Matching/challenge support.
Limitations: Applications not accepted. Giving primarily in CA, FL, and NY; some support also in NJ. No grants to individuals, or for endowment funds, scholarships, or fellowships; no loans.
Application information: Unsolicited requests for funds not accepted.
Board meeting date(s): Apr. and Oct.
Trustees: Bert Degheri; BNY Mellon, N.A.
EIN: 136350175

8208
The Oxford Area Foundation ✧
P.O. Box 322
Oxford, PA 19363-1358 (610) 932-4627

Established in 2004 in PA.
Donors: John H. Ware, III Trust; John H. Ware III Charitable Lead Annuity Trust; Marian S. Ware Charitable Lead Annuity Trust; John H. Ware, IV Trust; John H. Ware, III Trust; Marian S. Ware Trust.
Foundation type: Independent foundation.
Financial data (yr. ended 12/31/12): Assets, $20,406,176 (M); gifts received, $5,667,879; expenditures, $937,552; qualifying distributions, $777,384; giving activities include $719,990 for 127 grants (high: $100,000; low: $90).
Fields of interest: Education; Human services; Community/economic development; Protestant agencies & churches.
Limitations: Applications accepted. Giving primarily in PA; with some emphasis on Oxford. No grants to individuals; no loans.
Application information: Application form required.
Initial approach: Letter
Deadline(s): Oct. 15
Officers and Director:* Nancy Ware Sapp,* Pres.; John H. Ware IV, V.P.; Kimberly Zuleba, Secy.; Adam Sapp, Treas.
Board Member: Brigham Faria.
EIN: 201060782

8209
A. J. & Sigismunda Palumbo Charitable Trust ✧
c/o PNC Bank, N.A.
620 Liberty Ave. N., 10th Fl.
Pittsburgh, PA 15222-2705
Application address: c/o John W. Kowach, 1659 Rt. 228, Ste. 4, Cranberry Township, PA 16066-5319; tel.: (814) 788-5093

Established in 1974 in PA.
Donors: A.J. Palumbo; Antonio J. Palumbo‡.
Foundation type: Independent foundation.
Financial data (yr. ended 03/31/13): Assets, $50,268,656 (M); gifts received, $7,558,000; expenditures, $2,746,503; qualifying distributions, $2,488,024; giving activities include $2,281,614 for 60 grants (high: $200,000; low: $5,000).
Fields of interest: Higher education; Hospitals (general); Human services; Catholic agencies & churches.
Limitations: Giving primarily in western PA.
Application information: Application form required.
Initial approach: Letter requesting application procedure
Deadline(s): Dec. 31
Board meeting date(s): Mar. 1
Trustees: Donald Fleming; Rex Knisley; Robert Y. Kopf, Jr.; John W. Kowach; Donald W. Meredith; Robert Ordiway; Joseph Palumbo; P.J. Palumbo; David A. Ricchuito; PNC Bank, N.A.
Number of staff: 1 part-time support.
EIN: 256168159
Selected grants: The following grants are a representative sample of this grantmaker's funding activity:
$150,000 to Elk County Catholic High School, Saint Marys, PA, 2011. For project support.
$50,000 to Gannon University, Erie, PA, 2011. For project support.
$50,000 to Neighborhood Academy, Pittsburgh, PA, 2011. For program support.
$50,000 to Saint Vincent College, Latrobe, PA, 2011. For project support.
$30,000 to Carlow University, Pittsburgh, PA, 2011. For program support.
$25,000 to Imani Christian Academy, Pittsburgh, PA, 2011. For project support.
$20,000 to Jubilee Association, Pittsburgh, PA, 2011. For program support.
$20,000 to Villa Saint Joseph, Baden, PA, 2011. For program support.
$10,000 to Little Sisters of the Poor, Pittsburgh, PA, 2011. For project support.
$5,000 to Bradley Center, Pittsburgh, PA, 2011. For program support.

8210
John C. Pangborn Trust ✧
c/o PNC Bank, N.A.
620 Liberty Ave., 10th Fl.
Pittsburgh, PA 15222

Foundation type: Independent foundation.
Financial data (yr. ended 12/31/13): Assets, $10,039,361 (M); expenditures, $482,871; qualifying distributions, $425,536; giving activities include $421,731 for 35 grants (high: $126,519; low: $2,126).
Fields of interest: Education; Human services; Religion.
Limitations: Applications not accepted. Giving primarily in MD.
Application information: Unsolicited requests for funds not accepted.
Trustee: PNC Bank, N.A.
EIN: 526024502

8211
Thomas W. Pangborn Trust ✧ ☆
c/o PNC Bank, N.A.
620 Liberty Ave., 10th Fl.
Pittsburgh, PA 15222-2705

Established in MD.
Foundation type: Independent foundation.
Financial data (yr. ended 12/31/13): Assets, $25,247,294 (M); expenditures, $1,102,660; qualifying distributions, $1,041,089; giving activities include $1,038,093 for 38 grants (high: $368,524; low: $5,190).
Fields of interest: Education; Health care; Human services; Catholic agencies & churches.
Limitations: Applications not accepted. Giving in the U.S., with emphasis on MD.
Application information: Unsolicited requests for funds not accepted.
Trustee: PNC Bank, N.A.
EIN: 526073332
Selected grants: The following grants are a representative sample of this grantmaker's funding activity:
$14,025 to Washington County Museum of Fine Arts, Hagerstown, MD, 2012. For general financial support.

8212
Parmer Family Foundation Inc. ✧ ☆
911 Grove Rd.
Harrisburg, PA 17111-4674

Established in 2001 in PA.
Donors: Residential Warranty Corp.; Western Pacific Mutual Insurance Co.; George A. Parmer.
Foundation type: Company-sponsored foundation.
Financial data (yr. ended 12/31/13): Assets, $2,347,818 (M); gifts received, $500,000; expenditures, $499,838; qualifying distributions, $484,733; giving activities include $484,733 for 1 grant.
Purpose and activities: The foundation supports organizations involved with K-12 and higher education and Christianity.
Fields of interest: Elementary/secondary education; Higher education; Christian agencies & churches.
Type of support: General/operating support.
Limitations: Applications not accepted. Giving limited to PA. No grants to individuals.
Application information: Unsolicited requests for funds not accepted.
Officer and Directors:* George A. Parmer,* Pres.; Barbara J. Parmer.
EIN: 251883175

8213
Frank J. & Sylvia T. Pasquerilla Foundation ✧ ☆
c/o Mark E. & Leah M. Pasquerilla
1 Pasquerilla Plz.
Johnstown, PA 15901-1999

Established in 2000 in PA.
Donor: Sylvia T. Pasquerilla‡.
Foundation type: Independent foundation.
Financial data (yr. ended 12/31/13): Assets, $395,135 (M); expenditures, $481,336; qualifying distributions, $475,623; giving activities include $473,104 for 13 grants (high: $352,500; low: $800).
Fields of interest: Arts, folk arts; Cancer research.
Limitations: Applications not accepted. Giving primarily in PA. No grants to individuals.
Application information: Unsolicited requests for funds not accepted.
Trustees: Leah M. Pasquerilla; Mark E. Pasquerilla.
EIN: 256690814
Selected grants: The following grants are a representative sample of this grantmaker's funding activity:
$263,000 to Johnstown Area Heritage Association, Johnstown, PA, 2012. For general purposes and for Flood Museum.
$17,000 to Johnstown Symphony Orchestra, Johnstown, PA, 2012. For 2011 Opera Festival Gala.

8214
Patriarch Family Foundation ✧
(formerly Harron Family Foundation)
c/o Anthony M. Imbesi
311 N. Sumneytown Pike, Ste. 1A
North Wales, PA 19454-2532

Established in 2007 in PA.
Donors: Margaret E. Harron Charitable Trust; Margaret E. Harron Charitable Lead Unitrust.
Foundation type: Independent foundation.
Financial data (yr. ended 12/31/13): Assets, $20,425,295 (M); gifts received, $2,691,110; expenditures, $767,308; qualifying distributions, $663,261; giving activities include $646,620 for 70 grants (high: $35,000; low: $20).
Fields of interest: Higher education, university.
Limitations: Applications not accepted. No grants to individuals.
Application information: Contributes only to pre-selected organizations.
Trustees: Anthony M. Imbesi; Charles L. Imbesi; Giovanna C. Imbesi; John C. Imbesi; Patricia H. Imbesi; Paul H. Imbesi.
EIN: 208353260

8215
The Peirce Family Foundation, Inc. ✧
707 Grant St., Ste. 2500
Pittsburgh, PA 15219-1919 (412) 281-7229
Contact: Robert N. Peirce, Jr., Pres.

Established in 1997 in PA.
Donors: Robert N. Peirce, Jr.; Joan Peirce.
Foundation type: Independent foundation.
Financial data (yr. ended 12/31/13): Assets, $14,135,337 (M); gifts received, $797,418; expenditures, $777,802; qualifying distributions, $615,395; giving activities include $615,395 for 63 grants (high: $150,000; low: $50).
Fields of interest: Arts; Higher education; Education; Health care; Human services; Children/youth, services.
Limitations: Applications accepted. Giving primarily in Pittsburgh and Sewickley, PA. No grants to individuals.
Application information:
Initial approach: Proposal
Deadline(s): None
Officers: Robert N. Peirce, Jr., Pres.; Joan Peirce, Secy.
EIN: 232903074

8216
The William Penn Foundation ✧
2 Logan Sq., 11th Fl.
100 N. 18th St.
Philadelphia, PA 19103-2757 (215) 988-1830
Contact: Helen Davis Picher, Interim Pres.; Laura Sparks, V.P., Phil. Prog(s)
FAX: (215) 988-1823;
E-mail: grants@williampennfoundation.org; Main URL: http://www.williampennfoundation.org
Grants Database: http://www.williampennfoundation.org/Search.aspx
Knowledge Center: http://www.williampennfoundation.org/Strategy.aspx
Twitter: https://twitter.com/WilliamPennFdn

Incorporated in 1945 in DE.
Donors: John C. Haas‡; Otto Haas‡; Phoebe W. Haas‡; Otto Haas & Phoebe W. Haas Charitable Trusts.
Foundation type: Independent foundation.
Financial data (yr. ended 12/31/13): Assets, $2,283,164,256 (M); expenditures, $103,688,660; qualifying distributions, $85,187,146; giving activities include $78,821,512 for 410 grants (high: $5,748,437; low: $1,000), and $1,277,948 for 518 employee matching gifts.
Purpose and activities: The foundation is dedicated to improving the quality of life in the Greater Philadelphia region through efforts that close the achievement gap for low-income children, ensure a sustainable environment, foster creativity that enhances civic life, and advance philanthropy in the Philadelphia region. In partnership with others, the foundation works to advance opportunity, ensure sustainability, and enable effective solutions.
Fields of interest: Performing arts; Arts; Child development, education; Elementary school/education; Secondary school/education; Elementary/secondary school reform; Environment, natural resources; Environment, beautification programs; Environment; Economically disadvantaged.
Type of support: Building/renovation; Capital campaigns; Consulting services; Employee matching gifts; Equipment; General/operating support; Land acquisition; Management development/capacity building; Matching/challenge support; Program development; Program evaluation; Program-related investments/loans; Research; Seed money; Technical assistance.
Limitations: Applications accepted. Giving limited to the greater Philadelphia region. (An expanded region for some environmental grants may be viewed on the foundation web site). No support for sectarian religious activities, political lobbying or legislative activities, or for-profit organizations. No support for institutions that discriminate on the basis of race, ethnicity, creed, gender, or sexual orientation in policy or practice. No grants to individuals, or for debt reduction, hospital capital projects, medical research, programs that replace lost government support, housing construction or rehabilitation, scholarships, or fellowships; no loans (except for program-related investments).
Publications: Application guidelines; Annual report; Grants list.
Application information: Letters of inquiry are not accepted by fax. If the LOI indicates a potential fit with the foundation's criteria, applicants will be invited to submit a formal and complete proposal. Those applicants encouraged to submit a full proposal will be directed to the appropriate site section for information on preparing a complete proposal. Unsolicited complete grant proposals are no longer accepted. Please see the foundation Web site for additional information. Application form required.
Initial approach: Complete a general inquiry form. Review program guidelines on the foundation's website and confirm that the proposed work aligns with the foundation's strategic priorities. Once an idea has been submitted, foundation staff will review the submission and notify the organization of next steps, which could include a request for more information, a request to discuss the idea further, or notification from the foundation that the idea is ineligible or not aligned with the foundation's strategic priorities
Copies of proposal: 1
Deadline(s): Deadlines have been imposed for funding through Increasing Arts Education and Advancing Arts and Cultural Organizations. Please see the foundation web site for further information
Board meeting date(s): Four times per year (Jan., Apr., July and Nov.)
Final notification: 30 days
Officers and Directors:* David W. Haas,* Chair.; Janet Haas, M.D.*, Vice-Chair.; Frederick R. Haas,*

Secy.; Laura Sparks, Exec. Dir.; MaDoe Htun, C.I.O.; Judith Freyer; James Gately; Andrew Haas; Christina Haas; Katherine Haas; Leonard C. Haas; Thomas W. Haas; Daniel Meyer, M.D.; Howard Meyers.
Number of staff: 24 full-time professional; 3 part-time professional; 6 full-time support.
EIN: 231503488
Selected grants: The following grants are a representative sample of this grantmaker's funding activity:
$15,000,000 to Philadelphia Schools Project, Philadelphia School Partnership, Philadelphia, PA, 2012. Toward the Great Schools Fund, to invest in the creation, expansion, and maintenance of high quality schools in Philadelphia, payable over 5.00 years.
$2,500,000 to Kimmel Center for the Performing Arts, Philadelphia, PA, 2012. Toward ongoing capitalization strategy for the Kimmel Center in service to its resident companies in fiscal 2012 and 2013.
$2,000,000 to Franklin Institute Science Museum, Philadelphia, PA, 2012. Toward climate control in the third-floor exhibit gallery in the new Nicholas and Athena Karabots Pavilion, allowing for safe display of the Franklin's own collections as well as traveling exhibits, payable over 2.00 years.
$1,500,000 to United Way of Greater Philadelphia and Southern New Jersey, Philadelphia, PA, 2012. Toward the design and implementation of a restructuring plan for the School District of Philadelphia.
$800,000 to Greater Philadelphia Tourism Marketing Corporation, Philadelphia, PA, 2012. Toward support for a marketing initiative expanding on Philly Homegrown's local food focus, to raise visibility of Philadelphia's creative neighborhood assets, and to increase participation and organizational capacity, payable over 2.00 years.
$660,000 to Nature Conservancy, Conshohocken, PA, 2012. Toward mapping, analysis of baseline conditions, outreach, and targeted technical assistance to advance conservation and restoration of key ecological functions in the Delaware and Susquehanna River Basins, payable over 3.00 years.
$165,000 to Brandywine Conservancy, Chadds Ford, PA, 2012. To its Environmental Management Center, toward completion of transactions to permanently protect priority lands in the Pennsylvania Highlands, and to develop a greenway and trail plan for the Brandywine Creek Regional Recreation Corridor, payable over 1.50 years.
$139,000 to Vox Populi, Philadelphia, PA, 2012. Toward staff salaries and guest artists and curators in fiscal years 2013 and 2014, payable over 2.00 years.
$137,456 to Abington Art Center, Jenkintown, PA, 2012. For strategic planning, with emphasis on a redesigned business model and leadership transition, payable over 3.75 years.
$82,500 to Community Design Collaborative of AIA Philadelphia, Philadelphia, PA, 2012. Toward pro-bono professional design services in support of a series of pilot creative placemaking efforts.
$82,500 to Friends of Saint Martin de Porres School, Philadelphia, PA, 2012. Toward strategic and business planning efforts for Philadelphia Independent Mission Schools.

8217
Penn Treaty Special Services District ✧ ☆
702 N. 3rd St., PMB 38
Philadelphia, PA 19123-2904 (267) 251-2704
Contact: Dolores Griffith, Secy.

Donor: HSP Gaming L.P.
Foundation type: Independent foundation.
Financial data (yr. ended 12/31/13): Assets, $437,569 (M); gifts received, $500,000; expenditures, $604,981; qualifying distributions, $566,102; giving activities include $566,102 for 37 grants (high: $50,000; low: $2,000).
Fields of interest: Arts; Education; Human services.
Limitations: Applications accepted. Giving primarily in Philadelphia, PA.
Application information: Application form required.
Initial approach: Proposal
Deadline(s): None
Officers: Enrico Angeli, Chair.; Tim Breslin, Vice-Chair.; Dolores Griffith, Secy.; John R. Moore, Treas.
Board Members: Kevin Kelly; Rich Levins; Anna McKenna.
EIN: 270368388

8218
Peoples Security Charitable Foundation ✧ ☆
(formerly Penseco Foundation)
150 N. Washington Ave.
Scranton, PA 18503-1843

Established in 2000.
Donor: Penn Security Bank & Trust Co.
Foundation type: Company-sponsored foundation.
Financial data (yr. ended 12/31/13): Assets, $160,809 (M); gifts received, $600,000; expenditures, $526,602; qualifying distributions, $526,500; giving activities include $526,500 for 35 grants (high: $65,000; low: $500).
Purpose and activities: The foundation supports organizations involved with higher education.
Fields of interest: Education; Human services; Religion.
Type of support: Capital campaigns; Scholarship funds.
Limitations: Applications not accepted. Giving primarily in Scranton, PA.
Application information: Contributes only to pre-selected organizations.
Trustees: William J. Calpin; Debra E. Dissinger; Patrick Scanlon.
EIN: 251886434

8219
Raymond & Ruth Perelman Education Foundation ✧
1 Bala Ave., Ste. 310
Bala Cynwyd, PA 19004-3210

Established in 1995 in PA.
Foundation type: Independent foundation.
Financial data (yr. ended 04/30/13): Assets, $44,034,977 (M); expenditures, $1,349,305; qualifying distributions, $602,800; giving activities include $602,800 for 10 grants (high: $250,000; low: $200).
Fields of interest: Higher education; Medical school/education; Human services.
Limitations: Applications not accepted. Giving primarily in PA. No grants to individuals.
Application information: Contributes only to pre-selected organizations.
Trustee: Raymond G. Perelman.
EIN: 232819735

8220
The Pew Charitable Trusts
1 Commerce Sq.
2005 Market St., Ste. 2800
Philadelphia, PA 19103-7077 (215) 575-9050
Contact: Rebecca W. Rimel, C.E.O. and Pres.
FAX: (215) 575-4939; E-mail: info@pewtrusts.org; Additional address: 901 E St. N.W., Washington, DC 20004-2037; tel.: (202) 552-2000, fax: (202) 552-2299; Main URL: http://www.pewtrusts.org
E-Newsletter: http://www.pewtrusts.org/news_room_alerts.aspx
Facebook: https://www.facebook.com/pewcharitabletrusts
News Feed: http://www.pewtrusts.org/rss_feed.aspx?category=news
Twitter: https://twitter.com/pewtrusts
YouTube: http://www.youtube.com/pew

Established in 1948; the trusts reorganized into a public charity in 2004.
Donors: Mary Ethel Pew†; Mabel Pew Myrin†; J. Howard Pew†; Joseph N. Pew, Jr.†.
Financial data (yr. ended 06/30/13): Assets, $753,245,419 (M); gifts received, $305,809,297; expenditures, $307,065,604; giving activities include $131,988,597 for grants.
Purpose and activities: The Pew Charitable Trusts support nonprofit activities in the areas of culture, education, the environment, health and human services, public policy and religion. Based in Philadelphia, the trusts make strategic investments to help organizations and citizens develop practical solutions to difficult problems. Under its Public Policy initiative, the Trusts support environmental causes including wilderness protection, conservation of living marine resources, and clean energy. Under its Government Performance, the Trusts interest include state policy, health, consumer financial stability, and fiscal and economic policy. The Trust's Philadelphia Program includes arts and culture, civic initiatives, health and human services, and the Philadelphia Research Initiative. The Pew Research Center aligns with the Trust's Informing the Public program.
Fields of interest: Media, print publishing; Visual arts; Museums; Performing arts; Performing arts, dance; Performing arts, theater; Performing arts, music; Humanities; Historic preservation/historical societies; Arts; Education, research; Child development, education; Education; Environment, natural resources; Environment, energy; Environment; Animals/wildlife, preservation/protection; Public health; Health care; Biomedicine; Employment; Housing/shelter, development; Youth development, services; Youth development, citizenship; Human services; Children/youth, services; Child development, services; Family services; Aging, centers/services; Minorities/immigrants, centers/services; Homeless, human services; Voluntarism promotion; Biology/life sciences; Science; Social sciences; Government/public administration; Public affairs, election regulation; Public affairs, citizen participation; Leadership development; Public affairs; Religion, research; Religion, public policy; Children/youth;

Adults; Aging; Physically disabled; Mentally disabled; Offenders/ex-offenders; Economically disadvantaged; Homeless.
International interests: Australia; Canada; Europe.
Type of support: Continuing support; Program development; Research; Technical assistance; Program-related investments/loans; Employee matching gifts.
Limitations: Applications accepted. Giving on an international basis, with a special commitment to the Philadelphia, PA, region. No grants to individuals, or for endowment funds, capital campaigns, construction, equipment, deficit financing, scholarships, or fellowships (except those identified or initiated by the trusts).
Publications: Application guidelines; Grants list; Occasional report.
Application information: Contact Pew for specific guidelines and limitations or visit the Trusts' web site; applicants should not send full proposals unless requested by trustee representatives. Examples of past work, articles, reports, videos or other material should not be submitted with the letter of inquiry. Application form required.
Initial approach: Letter of inquiry (2 to 3 pages)
Copies of proposal: 1
Deadline(s): See foundation web site for current deadlines
Board meeting date(s): Mar., June, Sept., and Dec.
Final notification: Approximately 4 to 6 weeks
Officer and Board Members:* Rebecca W. Rimel,* C.E.O. and Pres.; Robert H. Campbell; Susan W. Catherwood; Aristides W. Georgantas; J. Howard Pew II; J.N. Pew IV, M.D.; Mary Catherine Pew, M.D.; R. Anderson Pew; Sandy Ford Pew; Doris Pew Scott; Robert G. Williams.
Trustee: The Glenmede Trust Co.
Number of staff: 398 full-time professional; 17 part-time professional; 128 full-time support; 6 part-time support.
EIN: 562307147

8221
The Philadelphia Foundation ✧

1234 Market St., Ste. 1800
Philadelphia, PA 19107-3794 (215) 563-6417
Contact: R. Andrew Swinney, Pres.; For grants: Alyson Miksitz, Prog. Asst., Philanthropic Svcs.
FAX: (215) 563-6882;
E-mail: almiksitz@philafound.org; Main URL: http://www.philafound.org
Facebook: http://www.facebook.com/group.php?gid=123231491028641
YouTube: http://www.youtube.com/user/PhiladelphiaFound?feature=CAQQwRs%3D

Established in 1918 in PA by bank resolution.
Donor: 800 different funds.
Foundation type: Community foundation.
Financial data (yr. ended 12/31/12): Assets, $334,451,741 (M); gifts received, $23,349,324; expenditures, $30,812,696; giving activities include $24,679,393 for grants.
Purpose and activities: The Philadelphia Foundation is in the business of "building community" through: 1) building philanthropic resources; 2) managing those resources well; and 3) distributing those resources effectively. The foundation fulfills that mission by: convening, leading and supporting, and focusing on vulnerable populations, donors and the nonprofit sector.
Fields of interest: Performing arts, dance; Arts; Education; Health care; AIDS; AIDS research; Legal services; Housing/shelter, development; Family services; Minorities/immigrants, centers/services; Human services; Civil/human rights; Urban/community development; Community/economic development; Public policy, research; Public affairs; Children; Disabilities, people with; Minorities; Economically disadvantaged.
Type of support: General/operating support; Continuing support; Emergency funds; Program development; Seed money; Scholarship funds; Technical assistance; Matching/challenge support.
Limitations: Applications accepted. Giving limited to Bucks, Chester, Delaware, Montgomery, and Philadelphia counties in southeastern PA, except for designated funds. No support for religious purposes; generally, low priority given to national organizations, government agencies, large budget agencies, public or private schools, or umbrella funding organizations. No grants to individuals (except for scholarships), or for annual or capital campaigns, building funds, land acquisition, endowment funds, research, publications, tours or trips, conferences, or deficit financing; no loans.
Publications: Application guidelines; Newsletter.
Application information: Visit foundation web site for application forms and guidelines per grant type. First-time applicants should contact the Grantmaking Services Department via phone or e-mail before submitting an application. Application form required.
Initial approach: Complete online eligibility quiz
Deadline(s): None
Board meeting date(s): Apr. and Oct.
Final notification: Varies
Officers and Board Members:* Lawrence J. Beaser,* Chair.; Kathleen S. Allison,* Vice-Chair.; R. Andrew Swinney, Pres.; Pat Meller, V.P., Finance and Admin.; Beatrice F. "Bia" Viera, V.P., Philanthropic Svcs.; William Bullitt,* Treas.; Mark Froelich, Cont.; N. Nina Ahmad, Ph.D.; Kerry Benson; Anthony J. Conti; Patricia A. Coulter; Alan R. Hirsig; Frederick J.M. LaValley; Roseline H. Marston; Francis "Frank" Mirabello; Anne Morrisey; Richard Negrin; John Nihill; Daniel J. Phelan; Mindy M. Posoff; Steven L. Sanders; Betsy Leebron Tutleman, Ph.D.
Number of staff: 17 full-time professional; 9 full-time support.
EIN: 231581832
Selected grants: The following grants are a representative sample of this grantmaker's funding activity:
$858,112 to Philadelphia Ranger Corps, Philadelphia, PA, 2012. For Fairmount Park Ranger Program.
$750,000 to Philadelphia Youth Network, Philadelphia, PA, 2012. For WorkReady summer interns.
$750,000 to Weight City Productions, Emeryville, CA, 2013. For general support.
$510,000 to International Institute for Restorative Practices, Pipersville, PA, 2013. For Implementation of School Wide Climate Programs.
$500,000 to Denver Foundation, Denver, CO, 2012. For Ryan Family Fund.
$500,000 to RSF Social Investment Fund, RSF Social Finance, San Francisco, CA, 2013. For ARG Resources Fund - Cash.
$430,000 to Philadelphia Museum of Art, Philadelphia, PA, 2013. For the James Turrell project.
$427,890 to Seattle Foundation, Seattle, WA, 2013. To be granted to Seattle Foundation to support the Stoneleigh Fund to be distributed to not for profits in the Pacific Northwest.
$300,000 to University of Notre Dame, Notre Dame, IN, 2012. For Presidents circle, Glee Club, undertones, pemco.
$250,000 to B Lab Company, Wayne, PA, 2012. For general operating support.
$200,000 to Historical Society of Pennsylvania, Philadelphia, PA, 2012. For the History Making Productions.
$100,000 to Council for Relationships, Philadelphia, PA, 2012. For general operating support.
$100,000 to Delaware County Community Foundation, Radnor, PA, 2013. For four home health care grants.
$40,000 to Philadelphia Childrens Alliance, Philadelphia, PA, 2013. For general operating support Mission Impact.
$10,000 to CEOs for Cities, Washington, DC, 2013. For Talent Dividend Meeting.
$5,000 to Arts in Schools Collaborative, Philadelphia, PA, 2013. For general operating support.
$4,000 to Delaware State University, Dover, DE, 2013. For scholarship.
$3,000 to Public Citizens for Children and Youth, Philadelphia, PA, 2012. For Health Outreach Program.
$3,000 to Wilma Theater, Philadelphia, PA, 2012. For education programs.
$2,500 to KIPP Philadelphia Charter School, Philadelphia, PA, 2012. For general operating support for KIPP.

8222
Dr. & Mrs. Arthur William Phillips Charitable Trust ✧

299 Elm St.
P.O. Box 316
Oil City, PA 16301-0316
Contact: Berta Winters

Established in 1978 in PA.
Donor: Arthur William Phillips†.
Foundation type: Independent foundation.
Financial data (yr. ended 09/30/13): Assets, $15,038,387 (M); expenditures, $748,891; qualifying distributions, $625,295; giving activities include $571,384 for 17 grants (high: $100,000; low: $3,500).
Purpose and activities: Giving primarily to organizations with medical or educational purposes.
Fields of interest: Higher education; Education; Health organizations, association; Human services; YM/YWCAs & YM/YWHAs; Children/youth, services.
Type of support: Capital campaigns; Building/renovation; Equipment; Program development; Scholarship funds; Matching/challenge support.
Limitations: Applications accepted. Giving primarily in northwestern PA. No grants to individuals.
Application information: Application form required.
Initial approach: Letter
Copies of proposal: 3
Deadline(s): None
Trustees: Larry S. Adams; Edith Gilmore Letcher; Robert W. McFate.
EIN: 256201015

Selected grants: The following grants are a representative sample of this grantmaker's funding activity:
$89,000 to Meadville Medical Center Foundation, Meadville, PA, 2011.
$45,000 to Oil City Library, Oil City, PA, 2011.
$25,000 to Gannon University, Erie, PA, 2011.
$10,000 to Barrow Civic Theater, Franklin, PA, 2011.
$6,000 to United Negro College Fund, Pittsburgh, PA, 2011.

8223
Phoenixville Community Health Foundation ✧

821 Gay St.
Phoenixville, PA 19460-4410 (610) 917-9890
Contact: Louis J. Beccaria, C.E.O. and Pres.
FAX: (610) 917-9861; E-mail: pchf1@pchf1.org; Main URL: http://www.pchf1.org/
Blog: http://pchf1.blogspot.com/

Established in 1997 in PA; converted from Phoenixville Hospital.
Foundation type: Independent foundation.
Financial data (yr. ended 06/30/13): Assets, $50,203,434 (M); gifts received, $11,960; expenditures, $2,390,260; qualifying distributions, $2,180,044; giving activities include $1,624,118 for 185 grants (high: $528,500; low: $50), $45,000 for 24 grants to individuals (high: $3,000; low: $1,000), and $17,800 for 1 loan/program-related investment.
Purpose and activities: The foundation seeks to improve the health and quality of life in the greater Phoenixville, PA community.
Fields of interest: Medical care, community health systems; Optometry/vision screening; Public health; Health care; Mental health/crisis services; Housing/shelter; Children, services; Youth, services; Human services; Children/youth; Children; Youth; Adults; Aging; Young adults; Disabilities, people with; Physically disabled; Blind/visually impaired; Deaf/hearing impaired; Mentally disabled; Hispanics/Latinos; Women; Girls; Adults, women; Young adults, female; Men; Adults, men; Young adults, male; Military/veterans; Substance abusers; Single parents; Crime/abuse victims; Terminal illness, people with; Economically disadvantaged; Homeless.
Type of support: General/operating support; Continuing support; Management development/capacity building; Capital campaigns; Building/renovation; Equipment; Endowments; Program development; Seed money; Technical assistance; Program evaluation; Scholarships—to individuals; Matching/challenge support.
Limitations: Applications accepted. Giving primarily in the greater Phoenixville, PA, area. No support for fraternal organizations, political parties, or veterans, labor, or civic groups. No grants for benefits, operating deficits, or publications.
Publications: Application guidelines; Annual report; Financial statement; Grants list; Informational brochure (including application guidelines); Newsletter; Occasional report; Program policy statement.
Application information: Based on the initial telephone call or meeting, a grant request will be accepted if the proposed initiative fits within the foundation's guidelines. Application information and forms available on foundation web site. Application form required.
Initial approach: Telephone or office visit
Copies of proposal: 1
Deadline(s): See foundation web site for current deadlines
Board meeting date(s): Jan., Apr., and Sept.
Final notification: 8 weeks
Officers and Directors:* Robert Ryan,* Chair.; Maria Schwab, Ed.D.*, Vice-Chair.; Louis J. Beccaria, Ph.D.*, C.E.O. and Pres.; Carol Poinier, V.P., Admin.; Lynn Pike Hartman, V.P., Progs.; Charles Henry, Jr.,* Secy.; David Gautreau, Treas.; Frank J. Cirone; Timothy Durkin; Kathryn Evans; Anna Mae Galbraith; R. John Giannone; Anita Guzman; Andrea Hanaway, M.D.; James Kovaleski; Kenneth Krenicky; Rev. Dr. Koshy Mathews.
Number of staff: 3 full-time professional; 1 full-time support.
EIN: 232912035

8224
The Leo and Peggy Pierce Family Foundation ✧

(formerly The L. W. Pierce Family Foundation)
300 Barr Harbor Dr., Ste. 280
Five Tower Bridge
W. Conshohocken, PA 19428 (610) 862-2105
Contact: Daphne Rowe, Exec. Dir.
FAX: (610) 862-2120;
E-mail: drowe@piercefamilyfdn.org; Main URL: http://www.piercefamilyfdn.org

Established in 1997 in FL.
Donors: Leo W. Pierce, Sr.; Marjorie L. Pierce†; Mary Pierce; Sarah Quinn.
Foundation type: Independent foundation.
Financial data (yr. ended 12/31/12): Assets, $16,832,542 (M); gifts received, $745,825; expenditures, $947,864; qualifying distributions, $771,708; giving activities include $683,700 for 52 grants (high: $100,000; low: $2,000).
Purpose and activities: Giving primarily for activities that address hunger and food insecurity through direct service program and/or advocacy efforts.
Fields of interest: Food services; Human services; Aging.
Type of support: General/operating support; Capital campaigns; Building/renovation; Endowments.
Limitations: Applications accepted. Giving primarily in the 5-county Philadelphia, PA, area and in Indian River County, FL. No grants to individuals.
Publications: Application guidelines; Grants list.
Application information: Applications and supporting documentation accepted only online through foundation web site. Complete application guidelines available on foundation web site. Application form not required.
Copies of proposal: 2
Deadline(s): Jan. 15 and July 15
Board meeting date(s): Apr. and Oct.
Officers and Trustees:* Constance Buckley,* Chair. and Pres.; Molly Pierce, V.P. and Secy.; Michael Pierce,* Treas.; Kathryn Cox; Eve Pierce; J. Peter Pierce; Kathleen F. Pierce; Leo W. Pierce, Jr.; Barbara Quinn.
EIN: 597109847

8225
The Pilgrim Foundation ✧

P.O. Box 155
East Earl, PA 17519-0155 (610) 314-1967
Contact: Gary L. Pilgrim, Pres.
E-mail: info@thepilgrimfoundation.org; Main URL: http://www.thepilgrimfoundation.org
Blog: http://thepilgrimfoundation.org/blog/

Established in 1998 in PA.
Donor: Gary L. Pilgrim.
Foundation type: Independent foundation.
Financial data (yr. ended 06/30/13): Assets, $16,488,668 (M); gifts received, $1,433,195; expenditures, $814,879; qualifying distributions, $773,105; giving activities include $636,000 for 29 grants (high: $70,000; low: $5,000).
Purpose and activities: Giving primarily to Christian organizations and churches, and to Evangelical Christian organizations benefiting women and children, primarily in Chester County, PA.
Fields of interest: Education; Reproductive health; Family services; Women, centers/services; Christian agencies & churches; Infants/toddlers; Children/youth; Children; Youth; Minorities; Women; Infants/toddlers, female; Girls; Infants/toddlers, male; Boys; Single parents; Economically disadvantaged.
International interests: India; Zimbabwe.
Type of support: General/operating support; Scholarship funds.
Limitations: Applications not accepted. Giving primarily in Chester County, PA. No grants to individuals.
Application information: Unsolicited requests for funds not accepted.
Board meeting date(s): No set dates
Officers: Gary L. Pilgrim, Pres.; Karen Pennell, Exec. Dir.
Director: Suzanne T. Daniel.
Number of staff: 1 part-time support.
EIN: 232955610

8226
Pine Tree Foundation ✧

120 Righters Mill Rd.
Gladwyne, PA 19035-1531 (610) 649-4601
Contact: A. Morris Williams, Jr., Chair.; Ruth W. Williams, Pres.

Established in 1986 in PA.
Donors: A. Morris Williams, Jr.; Ruth W. Williams.
Foundation type: Independent foundation.
Financial data (yr. ended 07/31/13): Assets, $28,523,863 (M); expenditures, $1,860,649; qualifying distributions, $1,823,500; giving activities include $1,823,500 for grants.
Purpose and activities: Giving primarily for education and human services.
Fields of interest: Performing arts; Higher education; Education; Housing/shelter, development; Human services; Salvation Army; International relief.
Type of support: General/operating support.
Limitations: Applications accepted. Giving primarily in CO, GA, NC, NY, OH, and PA. No grants to individuals.
Application information:
Initial approach: Letter
Deadline(s): None
Officers and Directors:* A. Morris Williams, Jr.,* Chair. and Treas.; Ruth W. Williams,* Pres. and Secy.; Susan W. Beltz; Joanne W. Markman.
EIN: 222751187
Selected grants: The following grants are a representative sample of this grantmaker's funding activity:
$300,000 to CARE USA, Atlanta, GA, 2011.

$100,000 to Habitat for Humanity International, Americus, GA, 2011.
$100,000 to Salvation Army of Philadelphia, Philadelphia, PA, 2011.
$10,000 to Presbyterian Childrens Village, Rosemont, PA, 2011.

8227
Roy W. Piper Charitable Trust ✧
P.O. Box 460
Tunkhannock, PA 18657-0460 (570) 836-3868
Contact: William A. Petty, Mgr.

Donors: William A. Petty; Roy W. Piper†; Piper Construction, LLC.
Foundation type: Independent foundation.
Financial data (yr. ended 12/31/13): Assets, $16,888,501 (M); expenditures, $1,446,397; qualifying distributions, $825,706; giving activities include $32,500 for 4 grants (high: $20,000; low: $2,500), and $732,520 for 83 grants to individuals (high: $33,000; low: $796).
Purpose and activities: The foundation makes scholarship awards only to applicants who are members of a family with a combined household income of less than $75,000, and who have a cumulative "C" average through the first term of the student's senior year in high school. Students who reside in Lackawanna and Luzerne counties in WY will have preference. Some funding also for human services, a public library, a medical college, and to a cultural center.
Fields of interest: Arts, multipurpose centers/ programs; Medical school/education; Libraries (public); Education; Human services.
Type of support: Scholarships—to individuals.
Limitations: Applications accepted. Giving primarily in PA.
Application information: Application form required.
Initial approach: Proposal
Deadline(s): Mar. 15
Officer: William A. Petty, Mgr.
Trustees: Robert P. Browning; Ronald G. Kukuchka; Thomas P. Tulaney.
EIN: 207487500
Selected grants: The following grants are a representative sample of this grantmaker's funding activity:
$20,000 to Commonwealth Medical Education Corporation, Scranton, PA, 2011.
$20,000 to Commonwealth Medical Education Corporation, Scranton, PA, 2010. For general grant.
$20,000 to Wyoming County Cultural Center, Tunkhannock, PA, 2011.

8228
The Pittsburgh Foundation ✧
5 PPG Pl., Ste. 250
Pittsburgh, PA 15222-5414 (412) 391-5122
Contact: For grant applications: Jeanne Pearlman, V.P., Prog. and Policy
FAX: (412) 391-7259; E-mail: email@pghfdn.org; Grant application e-mail: pearlmanj@pghfdn.org; Main URL: http://www.pittsburghfoundation.org
Facebook: http://www.facebook.com/PittsburghFdn
Instagram: http://instagram.com/thepittsburghfoundation
Multimedia: http://www.pittsburghfoundation.org/media
Pinterest: http://www.pinterest.com/pittsburghfdn/
Pittsburgh Community EForum: http://blog.pittsburghfoundation.org/
Pittsburgh Community EForum Feed: http://blog.pittsburghfoundation.org/?feed=rss2
The Pittsburgh Foundation's Philanthropy Promise: http://www.ncrp.org/philanthropys-promise/who
Twitter: http://twitter.com/PittsburghFdn
Vimeo: http://vimeo.com/user2159711
YouTube: http://www.youtube.com/PittsburghFoundation
Scholarship application information, tel.: (412) 394-2649, e-mail: turnerD@pghfdn.org

Established in 1945 in PA by bank resolution and declaration of trust.
Foundation type: Community foundation.
Financial data (yr. ended 12/31/13): Assets, $1,073,171,203 (M); gifts received, $13,199,979; expenditures, $52,993,842; giving activities include $42,569,107 for grants.
Purpose and activities: The foundation promotes and champions the betterment of the greater Pittsburgh, PA, community and the quality of life for all its citizens by helping a wide variety of donors fulfill their philanthropic interests through providing leadership in identifying and addressing significant community needs. The foundation provides a vehicle to make giving easy, personally satisfying and effective. The foundation is organized for the permanent administration of funds placed in trust for public charitable and educational purposes. Funds are used for programs of regularly established agencies for organizational capacity building, systemic change, improved service delivery, planning and program development, capital and equipment, operating support and community building. Grants are made primarily in the areas of Self Sufficient Individuals and Families, Healthy Communities and Vibrant Democracy.
Fields of interest: Arts, cultural/ethnic awareness; Arts; Education; Health care; Safety/disasters; Youth development; Family services; Community development, public/private ventures; Economic development; Community/economic development.
Type of support: Management development/capacity building; Program development; Seed money; Scholarship funds; Research; Technical assistance; Program-related investments/loans.
Limitations: Applications accepted. Giving from unrestricted funds limited to Pittsburgh and Allegheny County, PA. No support for sectarian purposes, private and parochial schools, or hospitals (from unrestricted funds). No grants to individuals (from unrestricted funds except for the Isabel P. Kennedy Award) or for annual campaigns, capital costs, endowment funds, travel, operating budgets, fellowships, internships, awards, special events or research of a highly technical or specialized nature; no loans (except for program related investments).
Publications: Application guidelines; Annual report; Informational brochure (including application guidelines); Newsletter.
Application information: Visit foundation web site for application form and guidelines. Program staff will review each letter of inquiry, and contact the organization if additional information, including a complete proposal, is required. Once a full proposal is requested by the foundation, the organization may follow the application guidelines provided by the foundation. Grantmakers of Western Pennsylvania's Common Grant Application Format accepted. Application form required.
Initial approach: Letter of inquiry
Copies of proposal: 1
Deadline(s): None
Board meeting date(s): Six meetings annually
Final notification: 6 to 8 weeks for letter of inquiry review/full proposal invitation
Officers and Directors:* Edith L. Shapira, Chair.; John C. Harmon,* Vice-Chair.; Maxwell King, C.E.O. and Pres.; Molly Beerman, V.P., Finance and Admin.; Jonathan Brelsford,* V.P., Investments; Kevin Jenkins, V.P., Public Policy and Civic Leadership; Jeanne Pearlman, Ph.D., Sr. V.P., Prog. and Policy; Yvonne Maher, V.P., Devel. and Donor Svcs.; Nancy L. Rackoff, Secy.; Kim Fleming,* Treas.; Bryan Tait, Cont.; Dr. Morton Coleman; Edward J. Donnelly III, M.D.; Lee B. Foster II; Evan Frazier; David McL. Hillman; William E. Hunt; Anne Lewis; Claudette R. Lewis; David J. Malone; Vincent J. Quatrini, Jr.; James C. Roddey; Howard B. Slaughter, Jr.; Walter H. Smith; William Strickland.
Trustee Banks: BNY Mellon, N.A.; National City Bank; PNC Bank, N.A.
Number of staff: 34 full-time professional; 2 part-time professional.
EIN: 250965466
Selected grants: The following grants are a representative sample of this grantmaker's funding activity:
$2,159,500 to Pittsburgh, City of, Pittsburgh, PA, 2012. For the last two quarters of the year.
$1,357,911 to Riverlife, Pittsburgh, PA, 2012. For the Fountain Project.
$1,200,000 to Pittsburgh Public Schools, Pittsburgh, PA, 2012. For the Summer Dreamers Academy Year 4.
$520,196 to Pittsburgh Theological Seminary, Pittsburgh, PA, 2012. For general operating support.
$247,324 to Pittsburgh Symphony, Pittsburgh, PA, 2012. For general operating support.
$150,000 to Little Sisters of the Poor, Pittsburgh, PA, 2012. For the building campaign.
$6,954 to New Florence, Borough of, New Florence, PA, 2012. For a new furnace in the old school building and to replace the Community Bulletin Board.
$4,369 to Asian American Film Festival, Pittsburgh, PA, 2012. For general operating support.
$2,500 to University of Pittsburgh, Pittsburgh, PA, 2012. For scholarships.

8229
Harry Plankenhorn Foundation Inc. ✧ ☆
c/o New Covenant United Church of Christ
202 E. 3rd St.
Williamsport, PA 17701-6625

Incorporated in 1959 in PA.
Donor: Harry Plankenhorn†.
Foundation type: Independent foundation.
Financial data (yr. ended 12/31/13): Assets, $7,482,663 (M); gifts received, $5,000; expenditures, $478,157; qualifying distributions, $435,867; giving activities include $433,910 for 20 grants (high: $125,000; low: $4,000).
Purpose and activities: Giving for human services, including programs for the visually handicapped, children and youth, and emergency aid.
Fields of interest: Recreation, camps; Youth development; Human services; Children/youth, services; Human services, emergency aid.

Type of support: Annual campaigns; Building/renovation; General/operating support; Program development.
Limitations: Applications not accepted. Giving primarily in Lycoming County, PA. No grants to individuals.
Application information: Unsolicited requests for funds not accepted.
Officers: Charles F. Greevy III, Pres.; Robert Reeder, V.P.; Nancy Stearns, Secy.; Carl O. Hieber, Treas.
Directors: Barbara Ertel; Mark A. Huffman; Philip D. Landers; Dean F. Rabert; J. Michael Wiley.
EIN: 246023579

8230
The PNC Foundation ✧
(formerly PNC Bank Foundation)
1 PNC Plz.
249 5th Ave., 20th Fl.
Pittsburgh, PA 15222-1119 (412) 762-2748
Contact: Eva Tansky Blum, Chair. and Pres.
FAX: (412) 705-3584; E-mail: eva.blum@pnc.com; Additional contact: Michael Labriola, Secy., tel.: (412) 762-2803, e-mail: michael.labriola@pnc.com; contact for PNC Grow Up Great: Sally McCrady, Prog. Mgr., tel.: (412) 768-8371, e-mail: sally.mccrady@pnc.com; Main URL: https://www.pncsites.com/pncfoundation/foundation_overview.html
PNC Grow Up Great on Facebook: https://www.facebook.com/pncgrowupgreat
PNC Grow Up Great on Twitter: https://twitter.com/pncgrowupgreat
YouTube: https://www.youtube.com/playlist?list=PLD5E62F6A4812B420

Established in 1970 in PA.
Donors: PNC Equity Partners, LP; PNC Bank, N.A.; The PNC Financial Services Group, Inc.
Foundation type: Company-sponsored foundation.
Financial data (yr. ended 12/31/13): Assets, $99,267,621 (M); gifts received, $90,002,532; expenditures, $51,734,922; qualifying distributions, $52,923,896; giving activities include $45,330,260 for grants, $1,377,970 for 3,889 employee matching gifts, and $870,359 for 3 loans/program-related investments.
Purpose and activities: The foundation supports programs designed to enhance educational opportunities for children, with emphasis on underserved pre-K children; and to promote the growth of targeted communities through economic development initiatives.
Fields of interest: Arts education; Arts; Elementary/secondary education; Education, early childhood education; Child development, education; Teacher school/education; Environment; Employment, training; Housing/shelter, temporary shelter; Housing/shelter, home owners; Housing/shelter; Human services, financial counseling; Human services; Community development, neighborhood development; Economic development; Business/industry; Community development, small businesses; Community/economic development; Mathematics; Science; Children; Economically disadvantaged.
Type of support: General/operating support; Continuing support; Capital campaigns; Building/renovation; Program development; Publication; Curriculum development; Program-related investments/loans; Employee matching gifts; Matching/challenge support.
Limitations: Applications accepted. Giving primarily in areas of company operations in Washington, DC, DE, FL, IL, IN, KY, MD, MI, MO, NJ, OH, TN, VA, and WI, with emphasis on PA. No support for discriminatory organizations, churches, religious organizations, advocacy groups, or private foundations. No grants to individuals, or for endowments, conferences, seminars, tickets, or goodwill advertising, or annual campaigns for hospitals, colleges, or universities; no loans (except for program-related investments).
Publications: Application guidelines; Corporate report.
Application information: An interview may be requested. Organizations that receive support are asked to submit a grant report. Application form required.
Initial approach: Complete online application
Copies of proposal: 1
Deadline(s): None
Board meeting date(s): Quarterly
Final notification: Approximately 6 weeks
Officers and Trustees:* Eva T. Blum,* Chair. and Pres.; Michael A. Labriola,* Secy.; Thomas F. Garbe, Treas.; Peter K. Classen; William S. Demchak; Joan L. Gulley; Joseph C. Guyaux; Neil Hall; Roberta London; Donna C. Peterman; Shelley J. Seifert; PNC Bank, N.A.
EIN: 251202255
Selected grants: The following grants are a representative sample of this grantmaker's funding activity:
$600,000 to Carnegie Mellon University, Tepper School of Business, Pittsburgh, PA, 2012. To support of the current PNC Chair of Computational Finance and the construction of the new building for the Tepper School of Business.
$600,000 to United Way of Greater Cleveland, Cleveland, OH, 2012. For Annual contribution to United Way of Cleveland to support social services, health, education and other community services.
$500,000 to ACHIEVA, Pittsburgh, PA, 2012. For support of People with Disabilities: ACHIEVA'S Commitment to the Community Capital Campaign The campaign will reduce the size and duration of waiting lists for vital services, increase participation in the ACHIEVA Family.
$300,000 to Local Initiatives Support Corporation Greater Newark and Jersey City, Newark, NJ, 2012. For Excellence (CORE) Phase II Program. CORE's objective is to deliver visible improvements coupled with increased local capacity on commercial corridors in low and moderate income census tracts.
$270,000 to Wolf Trap Foundation for the Performing Arts, Vienna, VA, 2012. For Wolf Trap National Park for the Performing Arts' Summer Season, which will be enjoyed by approximately 500,000 patrons.
$245,166 to Adler Planetarium, Chicago, IL, 2012. For a collaboration project with the Shedd Aquarium, Museum of Science and Industry, the Field Museum and the Chicago Public Schools to transform early science education for preschoolers in Chicago.
$20,000 to Ideastream, Cleveland, OH, 2012. For educational outreach programming at the Fairfax Center targeted to the at-risk children and families in the area.
$11,500 to Oakland University, Rochester, MI, 2012. For English As a Second Language program for the Hispanic youth population in Pontiac, serving 30 to 40 children from homes where English is not the primary language.
$7,500 to Newark Emergency Services for Families, Newark, NJ, 2012. For Families, Inc., (NESF) mission is to stabilize Newark families and individuals in crisis as well as to empower and prepare them to achieve self-sufficiency It administers programs such as emergency services, homeless service.
$5,000 to Pittsburgh Foundation, Pittsburgh, PA, 2012. For the Live Like Lou organization that fights Amylo Lateral Sclerosis otherwise known as Lou Gehrig's Disease.

8231
The C. Northrop and Alethea Marder Pond Foundation ✧
c/o PNC Bank, N.A., Tax Dept.
1600 Market St.
Philadelphia, PA 19103-7240 (941) 363-5068
Contact: Christine Wilkinson
Application address: 240 S. Pineapple Ave., Ste. 400, Sarasota, FL 34236; tel.: (941) 363-5068

Established in 1997 in NJ.
Donor: Alethea Marder Pond†.
Foundation type: Independent foundation.
Financial data (yr. ended 04/30/13): Assets, $11,299,322 (M); expenditures, $622,178; qualifying distributions, $463,050; giving activities include $463,050 for grants.
Fields of interest: Hospitals (general); Medical research; Human services; American Red Cross; Children/youth, services; Protestant agencies & churches.
Limitations: Applications accepted. Giving primarily in NJ.
Application information: Application form not required.
Initial approach: Proposal
Deadline(s): None
Trustees: Grace Pond Fisher; Richard F. Greaves; Charles N. Pond, Jr.; Donna S. Pond; PNC Bank, N.A.
EIN: 226727894
Selected grants: The following grants are a representative sample of this grantmaker's funding activity:
$40,000 to Housing Assistance Corporation, Hyannis, MA, 2013. For Noah Program = $20,000.00 + Angel House = $ 20,000.00.
$40,000 to Summit Speech School, New Providence, NJ, 2013. For Parent/Infant Program/Itinerant Mainstream Support.
$30,000 to Children International, Kansas City, MO, 2013. For Construction of a 25,000 Gallon Water Tank.
$15,000 to Diabetes Foundation, Paramus, NJ, 2013. To support of Medical Assistance Program.
$15,000 to Hunterdon Regional Community Health, Flemington, NJ, 2013. For Adult Daycare Program.
$15,000 to Somerset Medical Center Foundation, Somerville, NJ, 2013. For fetal monitor.

8232
Poor Richard's Charitable Trust ✧
(formerly Lisa S. Roberts & David Seltzer Charitable Trust)
c/o Fairman Group LLC
899 Cassatt Rd., Ste. 115
Berwyn, PA 19312-1190

Established in 1997 in PA.
Donors: Lisa S. Roberts; Ralph Roberts; Suzanne Roberts.
Foundation type: Independent foundation.

Financial data (yr. ended 12/31/13): Assets, $12,925,925 (M); gifts received, $6,015; expenditures, $1,507,542; qualifying distributions, $1,443,400; giving activities include $1,443,400 for 39 grants (high: $500,000; low: $1,000).
Purpose and activities: Giving primarily for the arts, particularly museums, and for education.
Fields of interest: Museums; Museums (art); Arts; Education; Athletics/sports, soccer; Children, services.
Limitations: Applications not accepted. Giving primarily in Philadelphia, PA; some giving also in Crested Butte, CO. No grants to individuals.
Application information: Contributes only to pre-selected organizations.
Trustees: David Seltzer; Lisa S. Roberts.
EIN: 237909451

8233
Posner Foundation of Pittsburgh ✧
500 Greentree Commons
381 Mansfield Ave., Ste. 500
Pittsburgh, PA 15220-2754
Contact: Henry Posner III, Tr.

Established about 1965 in PA.
Donors: Henry Posner III; Henry Posner, Jr.; James T. Posner; Helen M. Posner; Paul M. Posner; Anne M. Molloy.
Foundation type: Independent foundation.
Financial data (yr. ended 12/31/13): Assets, $30,666,103 (M); expenditures, $1,412,374; qualifying distributions, $1,251,046; giving activities include $1,250,081 for 36 grants (high: $550,360; low: $180).
Fields of interest: Education; Human services; Jewish federated giving programs; Jewish agencies & synagogues.
Limitations: Applications accepted. Giving primarily in Pittsburgh, PA, with some funding in New York, NY. No grants to individuals.
Application information:
Initial approach: Letter
Deadline(s): None
Trustees: Anne M. Molloy; Helen M. Posner; Henry Posner III; James T. Posner; Paul M. Posner.
EIN: 256055022
Selected grants: The following grants are a representative sample of this grantmaker's funding activity:
$391,940 to Winchester-Thurston School, Pittsburgh, PA, 2011. For unrestricted/general use.
$251,500 to Neighborhood Academy, Pittsburgh, PA, 2011. For unrestricted/general use.
$120,000 to Kohala Center, Kamuela, HI, 2011. For unrestricted/general use.
$111,000 to World Union for Progressive Judaism, New York, NY, 2011. For unrestricted/general use.
$101,000 to Shady Side Academy, Pittsburgh, PA, 2011. For unrestricted/general use.
$52,000 to Princeton University, Princeton, NJ, 2011. For unrestricted/general use.
$50,000 to East End Cooperative Ministry, Pittsburgh, PA, 2011. For unrestricted/general use.
$50,000 to Steamship Historical Society of America, East Providence, RI, 2011. For unrestricted/general use.
$27,000 to Grand River Academy, Austinburg, OH, 2011. For unrestricted/general use.
$25,000 to Jewish Family and Childrens Service of Pittsburgh, Pittsburgh, PA, 2011. For unrestricted/general use.

8234
Pottstown Area Health & Wellness Foundation ✧
152 E. High St., Ste. 500
Pottstown, PA 19464-5400 (610) 323-2006
Contact: Anna Brendle, Prog. Off.
FAX: (610) 323-0047;
E-mail: rosecrews@pottstownfoundation.org;
Contact for large event, grant-related requests: Ashley Pultorak, e-mail: apultorak@pottstownfoundation.org; Main URL: http://pottstownfoundation.org

Established in 2003 in PA; supporting organization of PMMC Over Corp.
Foundation type: Independent foundation.
Financial data (yr. ended 06/30/13): Assets, $78,446,123 (M); gifts received, $44,192; expenditures, $4,150,299; qualifying distributions, $3,566,515; giving activities include $2,583,859 for 62 grants (high: $466,700; low: $2,500).
Purpose and activities: Giving primarily to enhance the health and wellness of area residents, providing education, funding and programs that motivate people to adopt healthy lifestyles.
Fields of interest: Education; Medical care, community health systems; Public health; Public health, physical fitness; Health care; YM/YWCAs & YM/YWHAs.
Type of support: General/operating support; Management development/capacity building; Annual campaigns; Building/renovation; Program development; Conferences/seminars; Curriculum development; Research; Consulting services; Matching/challenge support.
Limitations: Applications accepted. Giving limited to Pottstown, PA. No support for for-profit organizations, disease-related charities, art programs, or economic development. No grants to individuals, or for endowments, debt reduction, or alumni activities; no loans.
Publications: Application guidelines; Annual report; Grants list.
Application information: Application form required.
Initial approach: Letter of intent
Copies of proposal: 12
Deadline(s): See foundation web site for current deadlines
Board meeting date(s): 4th Tues. of every month
Final notification: 1-2 months
Officers and Directors:* Kenneth E. Picardi, Esq.*, Pres.; Arthur Green,* V.P.; Myra Gehert Forrest, Ed.D.*, Secy.; Matthew Cappelletti, Jr., C.P.A.*, Treas.; Laura DeFlavia, Cont.; Dave Kraybill,* Exec. Dir.; Todd Alderfer; Robert W. Boyce; James R. Bush; Philip I. Cook, M.D., J.D.; D. Scott Detar, C.P.A.; Linda Flederbach, MSW, LSW; Milton D. Martyny; Charles F. Palladino; Rev. Kerry Pidcock-Lester; Donald Silverson; William Taddonio, M.D.; B. Douglas Trainer; Sharon L. Weaver.
Number of staff: 3 full-time professional; 1 part-time professional; 1 full-time support; 1 part-time support.
EIN: 232344729

8235
PPG Industries Foundation ✧
1 PPG Pl., Ste. 7E
Pittsburgh, PA 15272-0001
Contact: Sue Sloan, Exec. Dir.
E-mail: foundation@ppg.com; Main URL: http://www.ppg.com/en/ppgfoundation/Pages/default.aspx

Incorporated in 1951 in PA.
Donor: PPG Industries, Inc.
Foundation type: Company-sponsored foundation.
Financial data (yr. ended 12/31/12): Assets, $9,337,618 (M); gifts received, $5,000,000; expenditures, $5,255,340; qualifying distributions, $5,185,281; giving activities include $4,582,454 for 301+ grants (high: $500,000), and $381,297 for employee matching gifts.
Purpose and activities: The foundation supports organizations that enhance the quality of life in communities where PPG has a presence. Special emphasis is directed toward programs designed to promote educational opportunities and access to community services.
Fields of interest: Arts, equal rights; Museums (science/technology); Performing arts; Arts; Elementary/secondary education; Higher education; Libraries (public); Scholarships/financial aid; Education; Environmental education; Zoos/zoological societies; Aquariums; Disasters, preparedness/services; Youth development, adult & child programs; American Red Cross; YM/YWCAs & YM/YWHAs; Human services, financial counseling; Human services; Economic development; Community/economic development; United Ways and Federated Giving Programs; Science, formal/general education; Chemistry; Mathematics; Engineering/technology; Science; Public affairs; Disabilities, people with; Minorities; African Americans/Blacks; Women; Economically disadvantaged.
Type of support: General/operating support; Continuing support; Annual campaigns; Capital campaigns; Building/renovation; Equipment; Emergency funds; Program development; Scholarship funds; Employee volunteer services; Employee matching gifts; Employee-related scholarships.
Limitations: Applications accepted. Giving on a national basis in areas of company operations in AL, AR, CA, CT, DE, GA, KY, IA, IL, LA, MI, NC, NV, OH, SC, TX, WA, WI, and WV, with emphasis on Pittsburgh, PA; giving also to national organizations and in Africa, Asia, Europe, and the Middle East for the Global Charitable Contributions Program. No support for lobbying organizations, political organizations, or religious organizations not of direct benefit to the entire community. No grants to individuals (except for scholarships), or for advertising or sponsorships, endowments, projects that would directly benefit PPG, special events or telephone solicitation, or general operating support for United Way-supported organizations.
Publications: Application guidelines; Annual report (including application guidelines); Financial statement.
Application information: Organizations located in the Pittsburgh area and organizations of national scope should direct inquiries to the Executive Director of the foundation. Additional information may be requested at a later date. Application form required.
Initial approach: Complete online application
Deadline(s): None
Board meeting date(s): Usually in June and Dec.
Final notification: Following board meetings
Officers and Directors:* Charles E. Bunch,* Chair. and Pres.; David B. Navikas, Vice-Chair.; Glenn E. Bost II,* V.P. and Genl. Counsel; J. Craig Jordan,*

V.P.; Lynn D. Schmidt, V.P.; Daniel Fayock, Secy.; Aziz S. Giga, Treas. and Cont.; Sue Sloan, Exec. Dir.
Number of staff: 1 full-time professional; 1 part-time professional; 1 part-time support.
EIN: 256037790

8236
The Presser Foundation ✧
385 Lancaster Ave., No. 205
Haverford, PA 19041-1576 (610) 658-9030
Contact: Mariel Frank, Exec. Dir.
E-mail: mfrank@presserfoundation.org; Main URL: http://www.presserfoundation.org

Founded in 1916; incorporated in 1939 in PA.
Donors: Theodore Presser‡; Theodore Presser Foundation.
Foundation type: Independent foundation.
Financial data (yr. ended 06/30/13): Assets, $61,712,301 (M); gifts received, $1,879,221; expenditures, $2,965,871; qualifying distributions, $2,911,914; giving activities include $1,615,134 for grants, and $1,092,800 for grants to individuals.
Purpose and activities: Giving primarily to: 1) promising undergraduate and graduate students of music through grants to accredited institutions in the U.S.; 2) enhance music education and performance by supporting the acquisition of musical equipment and instruments and the construction and renovation of suitable buildings for musical instruction and performance; 3) advance the study and appreciation of music by aiding the promotion of formal musical programs and projects; and 4) provide financial relief to worthy teachers of music in distress.
Fields of interest: Arts education; Performing arts, music; Higher education.
Type of support: Building/renovation; Equipment; Program development; Seed money; Fellowships; Scholarship funds; Grants to individuals; Matching/challenge support.
Limitations: Giving primarily to organizations located in DE, MD NJ, and PA, and are within a 100-mile radius of Philadelphia.
Publications: Application guidelines.
Application information: Application forms available for financial aid to needy music teachers and for scholarships. The participating institutions select the students to receive the awards. The foundation does not give awards directly to individuals. Faxed or e-mailed applications are not considered. Application form required.
Initial approach: Use online application process on foundation web site
Deadline(s): See foundation web site for deadline information
Officers and Trustees:* Robert Capanna, Pres.; Jeffrey Cornelius,* V.P.; Lucinda Landreth,* Secy.; William M. Davison IV,* Treas.; Mariel Frank, Exec. Dir.; Leon Bates; Peter Burwasser; Anthony P. Checchia; Robert W. Denious, Esq.; Martin A. Heckscher, Esq.; Thomas M. Hyndman, Jr., Esq.; William B. McLaughlin III; Corey R. Smith; Sharon L. Sorokin; Michael Stairs; Henderson Supplee III; Radclyffe F. Thompson; Mark Wait; Vera Wilson.
Number of staff: 1 full-time professional.
EIN: 232164013

8237
The Psalm 103 Foundation ✧
601 Pembroke Rd.
Bryn Mawr, PA 19010-3613

Established in 1987.
Donors: John M. Templeton, Jr.; J.M. Templeton Cust Trust JMT, Jr.
Foundation type: Independent foundation.
Financial data (yr. ended 09/30/13): Assets, $1,666,258 (M); gifts received, $205,785; expenditures, $613,421; qualifying distributions, $613,421; giving activities include $586,200 for 1 grant.
Purpose and activities: Giving primarily for a Christian school.
Fields of interest: Elementary/secondary education; Health care; Health organizations, association; Christian agencies & churches.
Limitations: Applications not accepted. Giving primarily in PA, some funding also in NY. No grants to individuals.
Application information: Contributes only to pre-selected organizations.
Officers: John M. Templeton, Jr., Pres. and Treas.; Josephine J. Templeton, V.P. and Secy.
EIN: 232500843

8238
PTS Foundation ✧
450 Plymouth Rd., Ste. 305
Plymouth Meeting, PA 19462-1644 (610) 825-4300

Established in 1998 in PA as a follow-up to the Lois U. Horvitz Foundation.
Donors: Lois U. Horvitz Foundation; Pam H. Schneider; Milton S. Schneider; Glenville Capital Partners, L.P.
Foundation type: Independent foundation.
Financial data (yr. ended 12/31/13): Assets, $11,867,751 (M); expenditures, $648,002; qualifying distributions, $620,074; giving activities include $601,875 for 9 grants (high: $150,000; low: $1,875).
Purpose and activities: Giving primarily for education and health, including a children's hospital foundation.
Fields of interest: Higher education; Hospitals (specialty); Human services; Community/economic development, single organization support.
Type of support: Program development.
Limitations: Applications accepted. Giving in the U.S., with emphasis on PA. No support for religious organizations. No grants for operating budgets of established agencies, recurring expenses for direct services, annual appeals, debt reduction campaigns, publications or workshops, travel, or government services.
Application information: Application form required.
Initial approach: Letter
Deadline(s): None
Officers and Directors:* Pam H. Schneider,* Chair.; Milton S. Schneider,* Pres. and Secy.-Treas.
EIN: 232930670

8239
Public Health Fund ✧
(formerly Philadelphia Health Care Trust)
260 South Broad St., Ste. 1800
Philadelphia, PA 19102-5000 (215) 985-2500

Established in 1976 in PA; assumed current name in 1998.
Foundation type: Independent foundation.
Financial data (yr. ended 06/30/13): Assets, $37,428,765 (M); gifts received, $350; expenditures, $4,192,882; qualifying distributions, $2,192,210; giving activities include $2,101,630 for 16 grants (high: $612,500; low: $25,000).
Purpose and activities: Giving primarily for education, and children and social services.
Fields of interest: Secondary school/education; Education; Health care; Human services; Children/youth, services.
Limitations: Applications not accepted. Giving primarily in the Delaware Valley and in the greater Philadelphia, PA, area.
Application information: Contributes only to pre-selected organizations.
Officers and Directors:* Richard J. Cohen,* Pres.; Michael K. Pearson,* Treas.; John D. Cacciamani; Renee Cardwell Hughes.
EIN: 231985544

8240
Quaker City Foundation ✧
c/o Collin F. McNeil
1701 Horseshoe Trail
Chester Springs, PA 19425-1814

Established in 1997 in PA.
Donor: Collin F. McNeil.
Foundation type: Independent foundation.
Financial data (yr. ended 12/31/12): Assets, $10,433,359 (M); gifts received, $10,000; expenditures, $1,021,000; qualifying distributions, $885,845; giving activities include $785,559 for 51 grants (high: $117,001; low: $16).
Fields of interest: Historic preservation/historical societies; Education; Foundations (private grantmaking); Protestant agencies & churches.
Limitations: Applications not accepted. No grants to individuals.
Application information: Unsolicited requests for funds not accepted.
Officer and Trustee:* Collin F. McNeil,* Mgr.
EIN: 526854624

8241
Quantitative Foundation ✧
c/o N. Allen
1701 Market St.
Philadelphia, PA 19103-2903

Foundation type: Independent foundation.
Financial data (yr. ended 12/31/12): Assets, $105,439,059 (M); expenditures, $5,234,455; qualifying distributions, $5,016,280; giving activities include $4,751,000 for 15 grants (high: $4,000,000; low: $3,500), and $350,000 for 1 loan/program-related investment.
Fields of interest: Higher education; Education; Hospitals (general); Boys & girls clubs.
Limitations: Applications not accepted. Giving primarily in Charlottesville, VA.
Application information: Contributes only to pre-selected organizations.
Officer: Gordon R. Giuliano, C.F.O.; William W. Foshay III, Exec. Dir.
Trustee: Jaffray P. Woodriff.
EIN: 263922404

8242
Norman Raab Foundation ✧
P.O. Box 657
Holicong, PA 18928-0657 (215) 794-5640
Contact: Stephen Raab, Tr.
FAX: (215) 794-5642;
E-mail: info@raabfoundation.org; E-mail for Letters of Inquiry: inquiries@raabfoundation.org; Main URL: http://raabfoundation.org

Established in PA in 1968.
Donors: Norman Raab†; Stephen Raab; Whitney Raab; Sara Raab.
Foundation type: Independent foundation.
Financial data (yr. ended 09/30/13): Assets, $21,194,757 (M); expenditures, $1,531,424; qualifying distributions, $1,222,218; giving activities include $1,222,218 for 77 grants (high: $64,500; low: $500).
Purpose and activities: Giving primarily for education, health and research, and human services.
Fields of interest: Education; Health care; Human services.
Type of support: General/operating support; Research.
Limitations: Applications accepted. Giving primarily in CA, MD, NY, PA, and WA. No support for political organizations. No grants to individuals.
Publications: Application guidelines.
Application information: All submissions must be filed electronically. Grant requests are by invitation only, upon review of letter of inquiry. Application form not required.
Initial approach: Letter of Inquiry via the foundation's online grant management system
Copies of proposal: 3
Deadline(s): See foundation web site for current deadlines
Board meeting date(s): Jan. 25 and Apr. 30
Officer and Trustees:* Stephen Raab,* Chair.; Stephen A. Bleyer; Marie Brickley-Raab; Emily Raab; Isabel Raab; Sara Raab; Whitney Raab.
Number of staff: 1 part-time support.
EIN: 237006390

8243
The Ranger Family Charitable Trust ✧
c/o BNY Mellon, N.A.
P. O. Box 185
Pittsburgh, PA 15230-0185

Established in 1999 in NJ.
Donors: Michael W. Ranger; Virginia R. Ranger.
Foundation type: Independent foundation.
Financial data (yr. ended 12/31/13): Assets, $1,169,776 (M); gifts received, $705,764; expenditures, $1,633,619; qualifying distributions, $1,627,381; giving activities include $1,625,000 for 3 grants (high: $1,000,000; low: $125,000).
Fields of interest: Higher education; Human services.
Limitations: Applications not accepted. Giving primarily in NJ and NY. No grants to individuals.
Application information: Contributes only to pre-selected organizations.
Trustee: BNY Mellon, N.A.
EIN: 137213551

8244
John G. Rangos Charitable Foundation ✧ ☆
1301 Grandview Ave., Ste. 230
Pittsburgh, PA 15211-1288 (412) 871-6120
Main URL: http://www.rangosfoundation.org/
Google Plus: https://plus.google.com/113826762632597248016/

Established in 1987 in PA.
Donor: John G. Rangos, Sr.
Foundation type: Independent foundation.
Financial data (yr. ended 06/30/13): Assets, $3,205,496 (M); gifts received, $3,083,580; expenditures, $2,048,471; qualifying distributions, $2,040,680; giving activities include $1,891,490 for 13 grants (high: $1,500,000; low: $200).
Purpose and activities: The foundation is dedicated to providing children with a springboard to knowledge through education and good health, so that they may build a blueprint for life.
Fields of interest: Higher education; Health care; Pediatrics; Medical research; Youth development; Children/youth, services; Christian agencies & churches; Children.
Type of support: Annual campaigns; Program development.
Limitations: Giving primarily in MD and PA. No grants to individuals.
Application information: Application form not required.
Deadline(s): None
Trustees: Alexander Rangos; Jenica Rangos; Jill Rangos; John G. Rangos, Sr.; John G. Rangos, Jr.
Number of staff: 1 full-time professional.
EIN: 251599198
Selected grants: The following grants are a representative sample of this grantmaker's funding activity:
$1,600,000 to Johns Hopkins University, Baltimore, MD, 2011.
$30,000 to American Hellenic Institute Foundation, Washington, DC, 2011.
$25,000 to Carnegie Science Center, Pittsburgh, PA, 2011. For general support.
$25,000 to Cystic Fibrosis Foundation, Bethesda, MD, 2011. For general support.
$14,939 to Congressional Medal of Honor Foundation, Arlington, VA, 2011.
$10,000 to Leukemia & Lymphoma Society, Pittsburgh, PA, 2011. For general support.
$9,500 to Duquesne University, Pittsburgh, PA, 2011.

8245
John Nesbit Rees and Sarah Henne Rees Charitable Foundation ✧
314 S. Franklin St., Ste. B
Titusville, PA 16354-0325 (814) 827-1845
Contact: Richard W. Roeder, Tr.
E-mail: rwrll@verizon.net

Established in 1989 in PA.
Donors: John Nesbit Rees†; Sarah Henne Rees†.
Foundation type: Independent foundation.
Financial data (yr. ended 12/31/13): Assets, $14,825,722 (M); expenditures, $727,117; qualifying distributions, $676,962; giving activities include $615,057 for 34 grants (high: $125,000; low: $100).
Purpose and activities: Giving primarily for local civic causes, the arts, education, health and human services.
Fields of interest: Historic preservation/historical societies; Arts; Higher education; Health care; Human services.
Type of support: General/operating support; Continuing support; Annual campaigns; Capital campaigns; Building/renovation; Equipment; Endowments; Program development; Curriculum development; Scholarship funds; Employee matching gifts; Matching/challenge support.
Limitations: Applications accepted. Giving primarily in the Titusville, PA, area, including parts of Forest, Crawford, Venango, and Warren counties. No support for private foundations or for churches. No grants to individuals directly, or for scholarships.
Publications: Application guidelines; Annual report.
Application information: Application and Grant Procedure brochure available upon request. Application form required.
Initial approach: Letter
Copies of proposal: 2
Deadline(s): None
Board meeting date(s): Monthly
Final notification: 2 months
Trustees: Richard W. Roeder; Barbara L. Smith.
Number of staff: 2 part-time professional.
EIN: 256264847
Selected grants: The following grants are a representative sample of this grantmaker's funding activity:
$12,000 to Boy Scouts of America, Erie, PA, 2012. For improvements to camp trading post and science and technology Program.

8246
Arthur H. Reeser Trust ✧
c/o BNY Mellon, N.A.
P.O. Box 185
Pittsburgh, PA 15230-0185

Foundation type: Independent foundation.
Financial data (yr. ended 05/31/13): Assets, $11,530,876 (M); expenditures, $540,697; qualifying distributions, $463,120; giving activities include $463,120 for grants.
Fields of interest: Higher education; Protestant federated giving programs.
Limitations: Applications not accepted.
Application information: Contributes only to pre-selected organizations.
Trustee: BNY Mellon, N.A.
EIN: 256389439

8247
Allene Reuss Memorial Trust ✧
c/o BNY Mellon, N.A.
P.O. Box 185
Pittsburgh, PA 15230-0185

Established in 1996 in France.
Donor: Henry Reuss†.
Foundation type: Independent foundation.
Financial data (yr. ended 12/31/13): Assets, $13,757,690 (M); expenditures, $632,630; qualifying distributions, $581,784; giving activities include $552,500 for 23 grants (high: $500,000; low: $10,000).
Purpose and activities: Giving primarily for the aiding, prevention, and cure of vision problems.

Fields of interest: Higher education; Eye diseases.
Limitations: Applications not accepted. Giving primarily in NY.
Application information: Contributes only to pre-selected organizations.
Trustees: Richard H. Pershan, Esq.; BNY Mellon, N.A.
EIN: 137086745
Selected grants: The following grants are a representative sample of this grantmaker's funding activity:
$45,000 to Jewish Guild for the Blind, New York, NY, 2011. For general support.
$25,000 to American Foundation for the Blind, New York, NY, 2011. For general support.
$25,000 to Helen Keller International, New York, NY, 2011. For general support.
$15,000 to Healthy Eyes Alliance, New Haven, CT, 2011. For general support.
$10,000 to New York Community Trust, New York, NY, 2011. For general support.

8248
Jay, Rhoads,Jr. Family Environmental Fund ✧

c/o BNY Mellon N.A.
P.O. Box 185
Pittsburgh, PA 15230-0185

Established in 2007 in PA.
Donors: Jay R. Rhoads Trust, Jr.; Jay Rhoads Jr. Charitable Lead Annuity Trust; Jay Rhoads Jr. f/b/o P.F. Young Charitable Remainder Unitrust.
Foundation type: Independent foundation.
Financial data (yr. ended 12/31/13): Assets, $20,360,495 (M); gifts received, $4,847,124; expenditures, $584,784; qualifying distributions, $530,760; giving activities include $485,658 for 6 grants (high: $165,258; low: $24,500).
Fields of interest: Environment, plant conservation; Landscaping; Environment.
Limitations: Applications not accepted. Giving primarily in ME and NH. No grants to individuals.
Application information: Contributes only to pre-selected organizations.
Trustee: Bank of New York Mellon, N.A.
EIN: 364613133
Selected grants: The following grants are a representative sample of this grantmaker's funding activity:
$130,000 to Monadnock Conservancy, Keene, NH, 2011.
$120,500 to Greater Lovell Land Trust, Center Lovell, ME, 2011.
$102,200 to Loon Echo Land Trust, Bridgton, ME, 2011.
$90,000 to Upper Saco Valley Land Trust, North Conway, NH, 2011.
$78,500 to Lakes Environmental Association, Bridgton, ME, 2011.
$60,000 to Harris Center for Conservation Education, Hancock, NH, 2011.
$17,500 to Tin Mountain Conservation Center, Albany, NH, 2011.

8249
The RJM Foundation ✧

c/o R. James MacAleer
907 Robin Dr.
West Chester, PA 19382

Established in PA.
Donor: R. James MacAleer.
Foundation type: Independent foundation.
Financial data (yr. ended 12/31/13): Assets, $14,262,481 (M); expenditures, $762,773; qualifying distributions, $713,500; giving activities include $713,500 for 46 grants (high: $67,000; low: $1,000).
Purpose and activities: Giving primarily for education and health organizations.
Fields of interest: Education; Environment; Hospitals (general); Health organizations.
Limitations: Applications not accepted. Giving primarily in PA, with some emphasis on the Philadelphia and West Chester area; some funding also in Princeton, NJ. No grants to individuals.
Application information: Unsolicited requests for funds not accepted.
Trustee: R. James MacAleer.
EIN: 236953316

8250
Gilroy & Lillian P. Roberts Charitable Foundation ✧ ☆

101 W. Elm St., Ste. 500
Conshohocken, PA 19428-2075 (610) 862-1998
Contact: Stanley Merves, Mgr.; Jennifer M. Robbins

Established in 1982 in PA.
Donors: Gilroy Roberts†; Lillian Roberts†; Segel Foundation.
Foundation type: Independent foundation.
Financial data (yr. ended 06/30/13): Assets, $11,502,123 (M); expenditures, $750,764; qualifying distributions, $702,894; giving activities include $636,727 for 112+ grants (high: $160,000).
Purpose and activities: Giving primarily for higher education, health, and the arts. The foundation is also funding the storage and exhibition of the art work of Gilroy Roberts at Philadelphia Community College.
Fields of interest: Arts; Higher education; Hospitals (general); Human services; Jewish federated giving programs; Jewish agencies & synagogues; Children/youth; Adults; Aging; Young adults; Women.
Type of support: General/operating support; Continuing support; Annual campaigns; Capital campaigns; Professorships; Scholarship funds; Program-related investments/loans; Matching/challenge support.
Limitations: Applications accepted. Giving primarily in Philadelphia, Montgomery, and Delaware counties, PA. No support for political candidates and parties. No grants to individuals.
Application information: Board of grantseeker organization must have 100 percent participation in grantmaking on a cash basis, annually. Application form not required.
Initial approach: Letter
Copies of proposal: 1
Deadline(s): None
Board meeting date(s): Apr. and May
Final notification: Varies
Officer and Trustees:* Stanley Merves,* Mgr.; Walter G. Arader; Audrey Merves; Jennifer Merves-Robbins; John T. Roberts.
Number of staff: 1 full-time support; 1 part-time support.
EIN: 232219044
Selected grants: The following grants are a representative sample of this grantmaker's funding activity:
$500,000 to Community College of Philadelphia Foundation, Philadelphia, PA, 2012. For exhibition and storage of art works of Gilroy Roberts.
$30,000 to Temple University, Fox School of Business, Philadelphia, PA, 2012. For scholarships for undergraduates.
$25,000 to Bryn Mawr Hospital, Bryn Mawr, PA, 2012. For Nursing Excellence.
$25,000 to Temple University, Philadelphia, PA, 2012. For Athletics Department.
$21,000 to Harriton Association, Bryn Mawr, PA, 2012. For historic preservation of home and land.
$20,000 to Pennsylvania Academy of the Fine Arts, Philadelphia, PA, 2012. For scholarships.
$10,000 to United Way of Greater Philadelphia and Southern New Jersey, `, Philadelphia, PA, 2012. For Community Chest.
$5,000 to Madlyn and Leonard Abramson Center for Jewish Life, North Wales, PA, 2012. For nursing home.
$4,000 to Franklin Institute Science Museum, Philadelphia, PA, 2012. For education of Philadelphia School Children.
$3,000 to Scheie Eye Institute, Philadelphia, PA, 2012. For research.

8251
The Aileen K. and Brian L. Roberts Foundation ✧

c/o Comcast Corp.
1701 John F. Kennedy Blvd., 52nd Fl.
Philadelphia, PA 19103-2838

Established in 1994 in PA.
Donor: Brian L. Roberts.
Foundation type: Independent foundation.
Financial data (yr. ended 12/31/13): Assets, $23,843,595 (M); expenditures, $2,231,504; qualifying distributions, $2,154,518; giving activities include $2,154,518 for grants.
Purpose and activities: Giving primarily for the arts, education, human services, and Jewish organizations.
Fields of interest: Arts; Higher education; Education; Hospitals (general); Human services; Foundations (private grantmaking); Jewish agencies & synagogues.
Limitations: Applications not accepted. Giving primarily in Philadelphia, PA. No grants to individuals.
Application information: Contributes only to pre-selected organizations.
Officers: Aileen K. Roberts, Pres.; Brian L. Roberts, V.P.
EIN: 232787654

8252
William G. Rohrer Charitable Foundation ✧

c/o PNC Bank, N.A.
1600 Market St., 4th Fl.
Philadelphia, PA 19103-7240
Contact: Stacey Jaskol
Application address: PNC Wealth Management, Rte. 38 at Eastgate Dr., Moorestown, NJ 08057, tel.: (856) 638-4876

Established in 1990 in NJ.
Foundation type: Independent foundation.

Financial data (yr. ended 12/31/13): Assets, $41,627,386 (M); expenditures, $2,224,733; qualifying distributions, $1,846,276; giving activities include $1,682,000 for 41 grants (high: $500,000; low: $10,000).
Purpose and activities: Giving primarily for higher education, health organizations, and human services.
Fields of interest: Higher education; Health organizations, association; Medical research, institute; Human services; Children/youth, services.
Limitations: Applications accepted. Giving primarily in NJ. No grants to individuals.
Application information: Application form required.
Initial approach: Letter
Deadline(s): None
Trustees: Thomas N. Bantivoglio, Esq.; Daniel J. Ragone; Linda Rohrerrohrer Sayers; PNC Bank, N.A.
EIN: 226455062
Selected grants: The following grants are a representative sample of this grantmaker's funding activity:
$500,000 to Rowan University Foundation, Glassboro, NJ, 2012. For The Rohrer College of Business.
$80,000 to Camden County College, Blackwood, NJ, 2012. For general use of the college.

8253
The Rorer Foundation, Inc. ✧
761 Newtown Rd.
Villanova, PA 19085-1027

Established in 1963.
Donors: Heather A. Rorer; Edward C. Rorer; Gerald B. Rorer; Herbert T. Rorer.
Foundation type: Independent foundation.
Financial data (yr. ended 11/30/13): Assets, $10,289,095 (M); gifts received, $74,357; expenditures, $540,116; qualifying distributions, $501,566; giving activities include $501,000 for 118 grants (high: $35,500; low: $500).
Purpose and activities: Giving for education, with an emphasis on higher education.
Fields of interest: Higher education, college; Education.
Limitations: Applications not accepted. Giving primarily in New Haven, CT, and the Philadelphia, PA, area. No grants to individuals.
Publications: Annual report.
Application information: Contributes only to pre-selected organizations. Unsolicited requests for funds not accepted.
Board meeting date(s): Varies
Officers: Gerald B. Rorer, Pres.; Edward C. Rorer, V.P.; Herbert T. Rorer, Secy.-Treas.
EIN: 516017981

8254
The Rosenstiel Foundation ✧
c/o John R. Latourette
1500 Market St., Ste. 3500E
Philadelphia, PA 19102-2101

Incorporated in 1950 in OH.
Donor: Lewis S. Rosenstiel†.
Foundation type: Independent foundation.
Financial data (yr. ended 12/31/13): Assets, $20,410,861 (M); expenditures, $987,286; qualifying distributions, $891,548; giving activities include $873,600 for 101 grants (high: $115,000; low: $500).
Purpose and activities: Giving primarily for the arts, including theater and music, as well as for Polish cultural programs.
Fields of interest: Performing arts, theater; Performing arts, music; Arts; Higher education; Substance abuse, treatment; Health organizations, association; Human services.
International interests: Poland.
Type of support: General/operating support; Continuing support; Seed money.
Limitations: Applications not accepted. Giving primarily in FL and NY. No grants to individuals.
Application information: Contributes only to pre-selected organizations.
Officers and Trustees:* Elizabeth R. Kabler,* Pres.; Blanka A. Rosenstiel,* V.P. and Secy.-Treas.
EIN: 066034536
Selected grants: The following grants are a representative sample of this grantmaker's funding activity:
$157,650 to Center for Living, New York, NY, 2011. For unrestricted grant.
$14,000 to Creative Time, New York, NY, 2011. For unrestricted grant.
$11,900 to Whitney Museum of American Art, New York, NY, 2011. For unrestricted grant.
$10,000 to Florida International University, Miami, FL, 2011. For unrestricted grant.
$10,000 to Fund for American Studies, Washington, DC, 2011. For unrestricted grant.
$6,500 to Foreign Policy Association, New York, NY, 2011. For unrestricted grant.
$5,000 to Hudson Institute, Washington, DC, 2011. For unrestricted grant.
$3,470 to American Cancer Society, East Syracuse, NY, 2011. For unrestricted grant.
$2,175 to El Museo del Barrio, New York, NY, 2011. For unrestricted grant.
$2,000 to Polish Assistance, New York, NY, 2011. For unrestricted grant.

8255
Ross Family Fund ✧
(formerly Lynn & George M. Ross Foundation)
c/o Cozen O'Connor
1900 Market St.
Philadelphia, PA 19103-3527

Established in 1977.
Donors: George M. Ross†; Merry Ross; Patrick Zimski; MIchael Ross.
Foundation type: Independent foundation.
Financial data (yr. ended 02/28/13): Assets, $1,860,346 (M); expenditures, $8,041,041; qualifying distributions, $7,955,186; giving activities include $7,866,205 for 111 grants (high: $7,500,000; low: $100).
Fields of interest: Museums; Arts; Higher education; Education; Health organizations, association; Cancer; Human services; Jewish federated giving programs; Jewish agencies & synagogues.
Limitations: Applications not accepted. Giving primarily in FL and PA. No grants to individuals.
Application information: Contributes only to pre-selected organizations.
Director: Lyn M. Ross.
EIN: 232049592
Selected grants: The following grants are a representative sample of this grantmaker's funding activity:
$300,286 to National Museum of American Jewish History, Philadelphia, PA, 2011. For general purpose fund.
$250,000 to National Museum of American Jewish History, Philadelphia, PA, 2011. For general purpose fund.
$50,000 to Jewish Federation of Greater Philadelphia, Philadelphia, PA, 2011. For general purpose fund.
$50,000 to Main Line Reform Temple, Wynnewood, PA, 2011. For general purpose fund.
$25,000 to Operation Understanding, Philadelphia, PA, 2011. For general purpose fund.
$10,000 to Child Mind Institute, New York, NY, 2011. For general purpose fund.
$10,000 to Ed Snider Youth Hockey Foundation, Philadelphia, PA, 2011. For general purpose fund.
$10,000 to Jewish Federation of Greater Philadelphia, Philadelphia, PA, 2011. For general purpose fund.
$7,000 to Episcopal Academy, Newtown Square, PA, 2011. For general purpose fund.
$5,000 to Metropolitan Museum of Art, New York, NY, 2011. For general purpose fund.

8256
Rossin Foundation ✧ ☆
(formerly Dynamet Foundation)
P.O. Box 1225
McMurray, PA 15317-4225 (412) 746-3401
Contact: Viola G. Taboni

Established in 1989 in PA.
Donors: Dynamet Inc.; Peter C. Rossin; Ada E. Rossin.
Foundation type: Company-sponsored foundation.
Financial data (yr. ended 12/31/13): Assets, $21,196,778 (M); gifts received, $1,045,159; expenditures, $470,922; qualifying distributions, $600,833; giving activities include $358,250 for 24 grants (high: $200,000; low: $250).
Purpose and activities: The foundation supports hospitals and organizations involved with arts and culture, patient services, and senior citizens.
Fields of interest: Museums (art); Arts; Hospitals (general); Health care, patient services; YM/YWCAs & YM/YWHAs; Aging, centers/services.
Type of support: Building/renovation; General/operating support; Program development; Research.
Limitations: Applications accepted. Giving primarily in PA, with some emphasis on Pittsburgh. No grants to individuals.
Application information: Application form required.
Initial approach: Letter
Deadline(s): None
Officers and Trustees:* Joan R. Stephans,* Chair.; Peter N. Stephans,* Pres.; John Campbell Harmon,* Secy.; Elizabeth Stephans Baker,* Treas.; Katherine Dec.
EIN: 256327217

8257
Rubin Family Foundation ✧ ☆
4201 Neshaminy Blvd.
P.O. Box 207
Bensalem, PA 19020

Donor: Michael Rubin.
Foundation type: Independent foundation.
Financial data (yr. ended 12/31/13): Assets, $4,929,740 (M); expenditures, $451,734;

qualifying distributions, $425,000; giving activities include $425,000 for 48 grants (high: $62,500; low: $500).
Fields of interest: Arts; Health care; Human services.
Limitations: Applications not accepted. Giving primarily in NY and VA.
Application information: Unsolicited requests for funds not accepted.
Officers: Paulette Rubin, Pres.; Michael Rubin, Secy.; Michele Reardon, Treas.
EIN: 452485007

8258
The Josephine Schell Russell Charitable Trust ✧

249 5th Ave.
1 PNC Plz., 20th Fl.
Pittsburgh, PA 15222-2790 (513) 651-8463
Contact: Mary Alice Koch, Admin.
E-mail: mary.koch@pnc.com; Additional address: c/o PNC Advisors Charitable Trust Committee, 201 E. 5th St., M.D. B1-BM01-02-5, Cincinnati, OH 45202; Main URL: https://www.pncsites.com/pncfoundation/charitable_trusts.html

Trust established in 1976 in OH.
Donor: Josephine Schell Russell†.
Foundation type: Independent foundation.
Financial data (yr. ended 06/30/13): Assets, $11,538,337 (M); expenditures, $583,868; qualifying distributions, $517,066; giving activities include $474,048 for 29 grants (high: $50,000; low: $1,000).
Purpose and activities: Giving primarily for the arts, health care and human services.
Fields of interest: Arts; Health care; Human services; Children/youth, services; Economically disadvantaged.
Type of support: Capital campaigns; Building/renovation; Equipment; Program development; Seed money.
Limitations: Applications accepted. Giving limited to the greater Cincinnati, OH, area. No support for private foundations, or for political, fraternal, labor or advocacy groups. No grants to individuals, or for endowment funds, operating budgets, continuing support, annual campaigns, deficit financing, scholarships, or conferences; no loans.
Application information: Submit one copy of either the Ohio Common Grant Form or the Greater Cincinnati Common Grant Form. Application form not required.
Initial approach: Telephone
Copies of proposal: 1
Deadline(s): Feb.1, May 1, Aug. 1, and Oct. 1
Trustee: PNC Bank, N.A.
EIN: 316195446
Selected grants: The following grants are a representative sample of this grantmaker's funding activity:
$50,000 to YMCA of Greater Cincinnati, Cincinnati, OH, 2011.
$30,000 to Tender Mercies, Cincinnati, OH, 2011.
$25,000 to Brighton Center, Newport, KY, 2011.
$25,000 to Urban League of Greater Cincinnati, Cincinnati, OH, 2011.
$20,000 to Jewish Family Service of the Cincinnati Area, Cincinnati, OH, 2011.
$15,000 to Dress for Success Cincinnati, Cincinnati, OH, 2011.
$15,000 to Emanuel Community Center, Cincinnati, OH, 2011.
$10,000 to Beech Acres Parenting Center, Cincinnati, OH, 2011.
$10,000 to Independent Living Options, Cincinnati, OH, 2011.

8259
S & T Bancorp Charitable Foundation ✧

c/o S&T Bank, Trust Dept.
P.O. Box 220
Indiana, PA 15701-0220 (724) 465-1443
Contact: Todd D. Brice, Pres.
Application address: P.O. Box 190, Indiana, PA 15701, tel.: (724) 465-1443

Established in 1993 in PA.
Donors: S&T Bancorp, Inc.; S&T Bank.
Foundation type: Company-sponsored foundation.
Financial data (yr. ended 12/31/13): Assets, $86,471 (M); gifts received, $500,000; expenditures, $539,615; qualifying distributions, $538,783; giving activities include $538,783 for 134 grants (high: $36,000; low: $100).
Purpose and activities: The foundation supports organizations involved with arts and culture, education, health, athletics, human services, community development, and economically disadvantaged people.
Fields of interest: Education; Health care; Youth development.
Type of support: General/operating support; Annual campaigns; Capital campaigns; Building/renovation; Program development; Scholarship funds; Sponsorships.
Limitations: Applications accepted. Giving limited to areas of company operations in Indiana, PA. No grants to individuals.
Application information: Application form required.
Initial approach: Letter
Deadline(s): None
Officers: Todd D. Brice, Pres.; Edward C. Hauck, V.P.; G. Robert Jorgenson, Treas.
Trustee: S&T Bank.
EIN: 251716950
Selected grants: The following grants are a representative sample of this grantmaker's funding activity:
$15,000 to American Heart Association, Greensburg, PA, 2012. For Go Red for Women.
$5,000 to Punxsutawney Area Hospital, Punxsutawney, PA, 2012. For Golf Outing.
$2,500 to Alice Paul House, Indiana, PA, 2012. For Women Supporting Women.
$2,500 to Grove City College, Grove City, PA, 2012. For Business Competition.
$2,500 to Indiana Healthcare Foundation, Indiana, PA, 2012. For Love of Life Campaign.
$2,000 to Westmoreland Symphony Orchestra, Greensburg, PA, 2012. For Home for the Holidays.

8260
Saint-Gobain Corporation Foundation ✧

(formerly Norton Company Foundation)
750 E. Swedesford Rd.
P.O. Box 860
Valley Forge, PA 19482-0101 (610) 341-7000
Contact: Carman Ferrigno, V.P.
Main URL: http://www.saint-gobain-northamerica.com/people/foundation.asp

Trust established in 1953 in MA; incorporated in 1975.
Donors: Norton Co.; Saint-Gobain Corporation.
Foundation type: Company-sponsored foundation.
Financial data (yr. ended 12/31/13): Assets, $0 (M); gifts received, $1,104,049; expenditures, $1,104,049; qualifying distributions, $1,104,049; giving activities include $1,098,367 for grants.
Purpose and activities: The foundation supports organizations involved with arts and culture, education, health, human services, and other areas. Special emphasis is directed toward programs designed to address housing and community development; energy conservation; and environmental concerns.
Fields of interest: Arts; Education; Environment, energy; Environment; Health care; Housing/shelter; Human services; Community/economic development; General charitable giving.
Type of support: General/operating support; Continuing support; Annual campaigns; Capital campaigns; Building/renovation; Emergency funds; Program development; Seed money; Employee matching gifts; Matching/challenge support.
Limitations: Applications accepted. Giving primarily in areas of company operations, with emphasis on MA and PA. Generally, no support for national or international organizations, national health agencies, or religious, veterans', or fraternal organizations. No grants to individuals, or for endowments, scholarships, fundraising dinners or events, chairs or professorships; no loans.
Publications: Application guidelines; Informational brochure.
Application information: Application form required.
Initial approach: Download application form and mail to foundation for Direct Grants
Copies of proposal: 1
Deadline(s): None
Board meeting date(s): Apr. and Sept.
Final notification: Within 3 weeks
Officers and Directors:* John T. Crowe, Pres.; John J. Sweeney III,* V.P. and Treas.; Timothy L. Feagans, V.P.; Carmen Ferrigno, V.P.; Steven F. Messmer, V.P.; M. Shawn Puccio, V.P.; William C. Seiberlich, Secy.; Michael Cahill; Antonuio Carlos Viela de Moaraes; Bradley Johnson; Glenn Knowlton; Susan Nutson; Darrell Williams.
Number of staff: 1 full-time professional.
EIN: 237423043
Selected grants: The following grants are a representative sample of this grantmaker's funding activity:
$10,000 to Energy Coordinating Agency of Philadelphia, Philadelphia, PA, 2012. For Habitat Fund.
$5,000 to Baker Industries, Malvern, PA, 2012. For discretionary.
$2,420 to Children's Hospital Corporation, Boston, MA, 2012. For Plant Community.
$2,000 to Tarleton State University, Department of Fine Arts, Stephenville, TX, 2012. For Plant Community.
$500 to Boy Scouts of America, Northern NJ Council, Oakland, NJ, 2012. For Plant Community.
$465 to Boy Scouts of America, Rainbow Council, Morris, IL, 2012. For Plant Community.

8261
Robert Saligman Charitable Trust ✧
c/o Isdaner & Co.
3 Bala Plz., Ste. 501 W.
Bala Cynwyd, PA 19004-3481
Application address: c/o Grant Officer, 200 Chamounix Rd., St. Davids, PA 19087, tel.: (610) 324-5500

Established in 1987 in PA.
Donor: Robert Saligman†.
Foundation type: Independent foundation.
Financial data (yr. ended 12/31/13): Assets, $16,806,050 (M); expenditures, $776,891; qualifying distributions, $722,302; giving activities include $719,588 for 30 grants (high: $192,500; low: $1,000).
Purpose and activities: Giving primarily for Jewish agencies, temples, and education; funding also for the arts, health, and human services.
Fields of interest: Museums (art); Museums (ethnic/folk arts); Arts; Higher education; Nursing school/education; Education; Health organizations; Human services; Children, services; Family services; Jewish federated giving programs; Jewish agencies & synagogues.
Limitations: Applications accepted. Giving primarily in PA. No grants to individuals.
Application information: Application form not required.
Initial approach: Proposal
Copies of proposal: 1
Deadline(s): None
Trustees: Alice Saligman; Carolyn Saligman; Ira Saligman; Laury Saligman.
EIN: 236875203
Selected grants: The following grants are a representative sample of this grantmaker's funding activity:
$35,000 to University of Pennsylvania, School of Nursing, Philadelphia, PA, 2012. For general fund.

8262
Saltsgiver Family Foundation ✧
1605 James Rd.
Williamsport, PA 17701-1757

Established in 1995 in PA.
Donors: Thomas M. Saltsgiver; Joann Saltsgiver.
Foundation type: Independent foundation.
Financial data (yr. ended 12/31/13): Assets, $7,042,540 (M); gifts received, $384,000; expenditures, $642,435; qualifying distributions, $638,000; giving activities include $638,000 for 16 grants (high: $400,000; low: $1,000).
Purpose and activities: Giving primarily to Christian evangelical organizations, including a broadcast network.
Fields of interest: Media/communications; Human services; Christian agencies & churches.
Limitations: Applications not accepted. Giving primarily in PA and Virginia Beach, VA. No grants to individuals.
Application information: Contributes only to pre-selected organizations.
Officers: Thomas M. Saltsgiver, Pres.; Willam F. Huber, C.F.O.; Joann Saltsgiver, Secy.-Treas.
EIN: 232803397

8263
Salvaggio Family Foundation ✧
c/o Norene Salvaggio
1390 Ridgeview Dr., Ste. 300
Allentown, PA 18104-9065

Established in 1998 in PA.
Donors: Norene L. Salvaggio; Anthony Salvaggio.
Foundation type: Independent foundation.
Financial data (yr. ended 12/31/13): Assets, $9,382,689 (M); expenditures, $595,919; qualifying distributions, $563,058; giving activities include $563,058 for 47 grants (high: $25,000; low: $50).
Fields of interest: Education; Human services; United Ways and Federated Giving Programs; Catholic agencies & churches.
Limitations: Applications not accepted. Giving primarily in PA. No grants to individuals.
Application information: Contributes only to pre-selected organizations.
Trustees: Christy A. Ghigiarelli; Norene L. Salvaggio; Thomas A. Salvaggio; Suzie A. Spinosa.
EIN: 256614812

8264
Sand Dollar Fund ✧
2250 Hickory Rd., Ste. 450
Plymouth Meeting, PA 19462-1074

Established in 2005 in PA.
Donor: Grace III, LLC.
Foundation type: Independent foundation.
Financial data (yr. ended 12/31/12): Assets, $7,006,353 (M); expenditures, $3,656,684; qualifying distributions, $3,618,615; giving activities include $3,618,500 for 49 grants (high: $500,000; low: $4,000).
Purpose and activities: Giving primarily for education, the environment, hospitals, and human services.
Fields of interest: Higher education; Medical school/education; Education; Environment, water resources; Hospitals (general); Cancer research; Human services; Youth, services.
Limitations: Applications not accepted. Giving primarily in FL, MA, with emphasis on Boston, and PA. No grants to individuals.
Application information: Contributes only to pre-selected organizations.
Trustees: Marjorie M. Findlay; Geoffrey T. Freeman.
EIN: 550910574
Selected grants: The following grants are a representative sample of this grantmaker's funding activity:
$810,000 to Dana-Farber Cancer Institute, Boston, MA, 2011. For Act Now Fund.
$500,000 to Health Leads National, Boston, MA, 2011. For general operating support.
$200,000 to Drexel University, Philadelphia, PA, 2011. To hire Policy Director and for Witness-to-Witness Peer Mentor Project.
$150,000 to Food Project, Lincoln, MA, 2011. For Real Food Challenge.
$150,000 to Ocean Research and Conservation Association, Fort Pierce, FL, 2011. For general operating support.
$100,000 to Citizen Schools, Boston, MA, 2011. For general operating support.
$100,000 to Nature Conservancy, Massachusetts Field Office, Boston, MA, 2011.
$80,000 to Foundation of the Massachusetts Eye and Ear Infirmary, Boston, MA, 2011. For research.
$40,000 to Food Project, Lincoln, MA, 2011. For Real Food Challenge.
$30,000 to New England Forestry Foundation, Littleton, MA, 2011. For general operating support.

8265
Sargent Foundation ✧
c/o Glenmede Trust Co., N.A.
1650 Market St., Ste. 1200
Philadelphia, PA 19103-7391
Application address: Dr. Robert Wilson, Tr., P.O. Box 3714, Greenville, SC 29608

Established in 2007 in NY.
Foundation type: Independent foundation.
Financial data (yr. ended 12/31/13): Assets, $12,709,564 (M); expenditures, $612,597; qualifying distributions, $543,800; giving activities include $533,556 for 11 grants (high: $268,556; low: $5,000).
Purpose and activities: Giving for education and the arts.
Fields of interest: Museums (art); Higher education; United Ways and Federated Giving Programs.
Limitations: Applications accepted. Giving limited to Greenville, SC.
Application information: Application form not required.
Initial approach: Letter
Deadline(s): None
Trustees: Dr. Thomas Barton; Dr. Bob Jones; Dr. Robert A. Wilson.
EIN: 562144280
Selected grants: The following grants are a representative sample of this grantmaker's funding activity:
$247,862 to Bob Jones University, Greenville, SC, 2011. For general support.
$40,000 to Boys and Girls Club, Salvation Army, Greenville, SC, 2011. For general support.
$33,500 to Greenville Technical College, Greenville, SC, 2011. For general support.
$5,000 to Greenville Literacy Association, Greenville, SC, 2011. For general support.

8266
Sarah Scaife Foundation, Inc. ✧
1 Oxford Ctr.
301 Grant St., Ste. 3900
Pittsburgh, PA 15219-6401 (412) 392-2900
Contact: Michael W. Gleba, Pres. and Treas.
Main URL: http://www.scaife.com/sarah.html

Trust established in 1941; incorporated in 1959 in PA; present name adopted in 1974.
Donor: Sarah Mellon Scaife†.
Foundation type: Independent foundation.
Financial data (yr. ended 12/31/13): Assets, $320,817,214 (M); expenditures, $16,588,969; qualifying distributions, $15,903,123; giving activities include $14,647,500 for 85 grants (high: $800,000; low: $32,500).
Purpose and activities: Grants primarily directed toward public policy programs that address major international and domestic issues.
Fields of interest: Higher education; Education; International affairs; Economics; Political science; Law/international law; International studies; Public policy, research.
Type of support: General/operating support; Continuing support; Program development;

Conferences/seminars; Publication; Seed money; Curriculum development; Fellowships; Research.
Limitations: Applications accepted. Giving primarily in Washington, DC and VA. No support for nationally organized fundraising groups or generally for government agencies. No grants to individuals, or generally for event sponsorships, endowments, capital campaigns, or renovations; no loans.
Publications: Annual report (including application guidelines).
Application information: Application form not required.
Initial approach: Letter signed by the organization's President, or authorized representative and have the approval of the board
Copies of proposal: 1
Deadline(s): None
Board meeting date(s): Feb., May, Sept., and Nov.
Final notification: 2 - 4 weeks
Officers and Trustees:* Richard M. Scaife,* Chair.; Michael W. Gleba,* Pres. and Treas.; Barbara L. Slaney, V.P.; Yvonne Marie Bly, Secy.; T. Kenneth Cribb, Jr.; Edwin J. Feulner, Jr.; Roger Kimball; Allan H. Meltzer, Ph.D.; E. Van R. Milbury; Roger W. Robinsin, Jr.; James C. Roddey; Christine J. Toretti; James M. Walton; Arthur P. Ziegler.
Number of staff: 1 full-time professional; 2 part-time professional; 2 full-time support; 4 part-time support.
EIN: 251113452
Selected grants: The following grants are a representative sample of this grantmaker's funding activity:
$600,000 to Institute for Foreign Policy Analysis, Cambridge, MA, 2012. For general operating and special projects support.
$500,000 to University of Kentucky, Lexington, KY, 2012. For The New University of Kentucky Albert B. Chandler Hospital Auditorium.
$400,000 to American Enterprise Institute for Public Policy Research, Washington, DC, 2012. For project support.
$375,000 to Center for Strategic and International Studies, Washington, DC, 2012. For Senior Advisor Post and project support.
$350,000 to Stanford University, Hoover Institution on War, Revolution and Peace, Stanford, CA, 2012. For research programs and Hoover Fellows support.
$250,000 to Landmark Legal Foundation, Kansas City, MO, 2012. For general operating support.
$150,000 to George Mason University Foundation, Fairfax, VA, 2012. For Law and Economics Center.
$140,000 to Missouri State University Foundation, Springfield, MO, 2012. For Department of Defense and Strategic Studies.
$125,000 to Federation for American Immigration Reform, Washington, DC, 2012. For general operating and project support.
$60,000 to Johns Hopkins University, Baltimore, MD, 2012. For The Paul H. Nitze School of Advanced International Studies in Washington, DC.

8267
Scattergood Behavioral Health Foundation ✧

4641 Roosevelt Blvd.
Philadelphia, PA 19124-2399 (215) 831-3000
Contact: Joe Pyle, Pres.
FAX: (215) 831-3028;
E-mail: info@scattergoodfoundation.org; Additional address: Thomas Scattergood Behavioral Health Foundation at Friends Center, 1501 Cherry St., Philadelphia, PA 19102; Main URL: http://www.scattergoodfoundation.org/
Facebook: https://www.facebook.com/pages/The-Thomas-Scattergood-Foundation/354334557958051
Twitter: https://twitter.com/ScattergoodFdn

Donors: Joseph Gaskill; Philadelphia Foundation.
Foundation type: Independent foundation.
Financial data (yr. ended 06/30/13): Assets, $21,529,249 (M); gifts received, $182,271; expenditures, $1,428,041; qualifying distributions, $1,219,202; giving activities include $691,811 for 59 grants (high: $50,000; low: $99).
Purpose and activities: This Quaker-based foundation is committed to the improvement of the system through which behavioral healthcare is delivered in the Philadelphia, PA, region.
Fields of interest: Education; Mental health/crisis services.
Publications: Application guidelines; Grants list.
Application information: Unsolicited requests for funds are not considered. Applications are by invitation only. Invited applicants should follow guidelines on foundation web site. Innovation Award nominations may be made through foundation web site.
Deadline(s): See foundation web site for Innovation Awards nomination deadlines
Officer: Joe Pyle, Pres.
Directors: Cindy Baum-Baicker, Ph.D.; David R. Fair; Bruce S. Haines, Esq.; Anne H. Matlack; N. Chiyo Moriuchi; Samuel V. Rhoads; David Roby, M.D.; Antonio Valdes; Molly Kreider Viscardi; Catherine Williams.
EIN: 231352178
Selected grants: The following grants are a representative sample of this grantmaker's funding activity:
$50,000 to Student Conservation Association, Arlington, VA, 2013. For Mental Health.

8268
Roberta and Ernest Scheller, Jr. Family Foundation ✧

1 S. Church St., 4th Fl.
Hazleton, PA 18201-6200

Established in 1995 in PA.
Donors: Ernest Scheller, Jr.; Roberta Scheller‡; Lisa Scheller.
Foundation type: Independent foundation.
Financial data (yr. ended 12/31/12): Assets, $10,954,715 (M); expenditures, $701,568; qualifying distributions, $593,137; giving activities include $593,137 for grants.
Purpose and activities: Giving for Jewish organizations and higher education.
Fields of interest: Arts; Higher education; Education; Cancer research; Human services; United Ways and Federated Giving Programs; Jewish federated giving programs; Jewish agencies & synagogues.
Limitations: Applications not accepted. No grants to individuals.
Application information: Contributes only to pre-selected organizations.
Officer: Ernest Scheller, Jr., Chair.
Trustees: Lisa Scheller; Roberta Scheller.
EIN: 237828732

8269
L. P. Schenck Fund ✧

c/o PNC Bank, N.A.
1600 Market St., Tax Dept.
Philadelphia, PA 19103-7240
Application address: c/o PNC Bank, N.A., Att.: Claudia Latorre, V.P., W. 115 Century Rd., Ste. 115, Paramus, NJ 07652, tel.: (201) 225-5004

Established in 1960 in NJ.
Donor: Lillian Pitkin Schenck‡.
Foundation type: Independent foundation.
Financial data (yr. ended 08/31/13): Assets, $10,489,685 (M); expenditures, $614,049; qualifying distributions, $537,621; giving activities include $515,000 for 88 grants (high: $65,000; low: $2,000).
Purpose and activities: Grants restricted to institutions in the NJ area, including support for youth, social service and mental health agencies, and cultural programs.
Fields of interest: Performing arts, theater; Arts; Hospitals (general); Mental health/crisis services; Human services; Children/youth, services.
Type of support: General/operating support; Building/renovation; Equipment; Program development; Curriculum development.
Limitations: Applications accepted. Giving limited to NJ. No grants to individuals, or for endowment funds.
Application information: Application form not required.
Initial approach: Letter
Copies of proposal: 3
Deadline(s): Aug. 1
Board meeting date(s): Oct.
Trustees: Marguerite Logan; Susan C. Madden; PNC Bank, N.A.
EIN: 226040581
Selected grants: The following grants are a representative sample of this grantmaker's funding activity:
$28,000 to Englewood Hospital and Medical Center, Englewood, NJ, 2013. For general use of the hospital/medical center.
$5,000 to Volunteer Center of Bergen County, Hackensack, NJ, 2013. For Superstorm Sandy.

8270
Sarah I. Schieffelin Residuary Trust ✧

c/o BNY Mellon, N.A.
P.O. Box 185
Pittsburgh, PA 15230-0185

Established in 1976.
Donor: Sarah I. Schieffelin‡.
Foundation type: Independent foundation.
Financial data (yr. ended 03/31/13): Assets, $13,986,887 (M); expenditures, $699,652; qualifying distributions, $624,873; giving activities include $589,039 for 54 grants (high: $58,904; low: $2,000).
Purpose and activities: Giving primarily for the arts, education, the environment, animals and wildlife, health organizations, children and social services, and for religious purposes.
Fields of interest: Arts; Education; Environment, natural resources; Animals/wildlife, preservation/protection; Hospitals (general); Health organizations, association; Human services; Children/youth, services; Christian agencies & churches; Protestant agencies & churches.
Type of support: Continuing support.

Limitations: Applications not accepted. Giving primarily in New York, NY. No grants to individuals.
Application information: Unsolicited requests for funds not accepted.
Trustee: BNY Mellon, N.A.
EIN: 136724459
Selected grants: The following grants are a representative sample of this grantmaker's funding activity:
$10,000 to Summer Search New York City, New York, NY, 2012.

8271
Dr. Louis A. and Anne B. Schneider Foundation Trust ✧

c/o PNC Charitbale Trusts, Margaret Sturm
249 5th Ave.
1 PNC Plz., 20th Fl.
Pittsburgh, PA 15222
E-mail: margaret.sturm@pnc.com; Application address: Jocy Muya, c/o PNC Bank, N.A., 1900 E. 9th St., Cleveland, OH 44114; tel.: (216) 222-3226

Established in 1986 in IN.
Donors: Louis Schneider‡; Louis and Anne Schneider Irrevocable Trust.
Foundation type: Independent foundation.
Financial data (yr. ended 11/30/13): Assets, $13,540,373 (M); expenditures, $743,651; qualifying distributions, $665,759; giving activities include $554,000 for 22 grants (high: $62,500; low: $7,500).
Purpose and activities: Giving primarily to religious, charitable, scientific, literary, and educational organizations, the Jewish community, and for cultural initiatives.
Fields of interest: Performing arts, opera; Libraries (public); Health care, clinics/centers; Medical research; Jewish federated giving programs; Jewish agencies & synagogues.
Limitations: Applications accepted. Giving primarily in Fort Wayne, IN. No grants to individuals.
Application information:
Initial approach: Letter
Copies of proposal: 1
Deadline(s): None
Trustee: PNC Bank, N.A.
EIN: 311193706
Selected grants: The following grants are a representative sample of this grantmaker's funding activity:
$75,000 to Neighborhood Health Clinics, Fort Wayne, IN, 2013. For medical/dental care.
$25,000 to Allen County Public Library, Fort Wayne, IN, 2013. For Ready Program.
$25,000 to Fort Wayne Zoological Society, Fort Wayne, IN, 2013. For Australian Adventure Project.
$20,000 to United Way of Allen County, Fort Wayne, IN, 2013. For early childhood training.
$10,000 to Fort Wayne Park Foundation, Fort Wayne, IN, 2013. For New Bloom Project.
$10,000 to Fort Wayne Public Television, Fort Wayne, IN, 2013. For HD Based Technology Upgrade.

8272
The Clarence Schock Foundation ✧

(formerly The SICO Foundation)
15 Mount Joy St.
P.O. Box 127
Mount Joy, PA 17552-1417
Contact: Dr. Joseph A. Caputo
E-mail: info@sicofoundation.org; Main URL: http://www.clarenceschockfoundation.org

Incorporated in 1941 in DE.
Donor: Clarence Schock‡.
Foundation type: Independent foundation.
Financial data (yr. ended 12/31/13): Assets, $16,251,515 (M); gifts received, $740; expenditures, $1,740,254; qualifying distributions, $1,705,581; giving activities include $1,149,650 for 12 grants (high: $250,000; low: $16,350).
Purpose and activities: The foundation promotes higher education through scholarships for students who are attending Cheney University, Kutztown University, Millersville University, Shippensburg University, and West Chester University, all of which are located in PA. It is the mission of the foundation to help to develop in students, the intellectual, personal, and social capabilities they need to achieve their highest potential, and to succeed as good citizens and capable professionals who contribute to the well-being of their community.
Fields of interest: Higher education.
Type of support: Scholarship funds; Scholarships—to individuals.
Limitations: Applications not accepted. Giving primarily in PA. No support for political organizations and activities. No grants to individuals (except for scholarships).
Publications: Annual report; Financial statement; Informational brochure; Newsletter; Program policy statement.
Application information: Unsolicited requests for funds not accepted. Applications are to be made directly to the participating universities, which have full responsibility for soliciting, receiving, and processing applications, and for notifying recipients.
Board meeting date(s): 4th Thurs. of Jan., Apr., July and Oct.
Officers and Directors:* Anthony F. Ceddia,* Chair.; Joseph A. Caputo,* Pres.; Darlene F. Halterman, Secy.; Harrison L. Diehl,* Treas.; Charles W. Ricedorf, Emeritus; John N. Weidman, Emeritus; David F. Eichler; Carl R. Hallgren; Helen A. Stine.
Number of staff: 1 full-time support; 3 part-time support.
EIN: 236298332

8273
The Scholler Foundation ✧

c/o MMWR
123 S. Broad St.
Philadelphia, PA 19109-1029 (215) 772-7505
Contact: William W. Keffer Esq., Chair.

Trust established in 1939 in PA.
Donor: F.C. Scholler‡.
Foundation type: Independent foundation.
Financial data (yr. ended 12/31/13): Assets, $15,313,173 (M); expenditures, $824,810; qualifying distributions, $707,460; giving activities include $669,403 for 79 grants (high: $30,000; low: $1,000).
Purpose and activities: Giving primarily for education, education, and health care.
Fields of interest: Education; Hospitals (general); Health care; Human services.
Type of support: General/operating support; Continuing support; Seed money.
Limitations: Applications accepted. Giving limited to the Delaware Valley, PA area.
Application information: Application form required.
Initial approach: Letter
Copies of proposal: 1
Deadline(s): Aug. 15
Board meeting date(s): Feb., May, Aug., and Nov.
Officer: William W. Keffer, Chair.
Trustees: David Bradley; Anthony J. Brown; E. Brooks Keffer, Jr., Esq.; Jonathan Sergeant Pepper; T. Sergeant Pepper.
EIN: 236245158
Selected grants: The following grants are a representative sample of this grantmaker's funding activity:
$33,596 to Philadelphia University, Philadelphia, PA, 2012. For a grant was made to provide scholarships for up to 16 deserving students with scholarships in majors across three colleges: The Kanbar College of Design, Engineering and Commerce; the College of Architecture and the Built Environment; and the College of S.
$23,000 to University of Pennsylvania, Penn Medicine School of Medicine, Philadelphia, PA, 2012. For a grant was made to support the Project BioEYES Program, which is a K-12 science education Program that provides classroom-based learning opportunities through the use of live zebrafish.
$22,000 to Curtis Institute of Music, Philadelphia, PA, 2012. For a grant was made to support the Curtis Student Assistance Fund, which will provide critical financial support for 12 students from Pennsylvania who lack the resources to pay for costs related to their education.
$18,000 to Lankenau Institute for Medical Research, Wynnewood, PA, 2012. For a grant was made to support the purchase of gel imaging technology known as the ChemiDoc XRS+ System. This technology provides accurate gel and blot imaging and analysis as well as comprehensive quantitative analysis of protein and DNA samples.
$15,000 to Magee Rehabilitation Hospital Foundation, Philadelphia, PA, 2012. For a grant was made to support Magee's Wheelchair Sports Program, specifically for purchase of equipment to aid in the expansion of its racing team.
$15,000 to Montgomery County Association for the Blind, North Wales, PA, 2012. For a grant was made to support their efforts to deliver Orientation and Mobility Training, Vision Rehabilitation therapy and their Prevention of Blindness Program to people with blindness and/or vision impairments.
$11,950 to Inglis House Foundation, Philadelphia, PA, 2012. For a grant was made for two pieces of therapy/exercise equipment for the Rehabilitation Department of Inglis House: a Cadillac Reformer Table and a Vitaglide Pro Wheelchair Fitness Machine.
$10,000 to Bryn Mawr Terrace, Bryn Mawr, PA, 2012. For a grant was made for painting, carpeting, significant new lighting, furniture and other major improvements to the nursing home.
$10,000 to Deborah Hospital Foundation, Browns Mills, NJ, 2012. For a grant was made to help fund the purchase or a new Portable Ultrasound Machine to be utilized at the Deborah Heart and Lung Center.
$10,000 to West Philadelphia Catholic High School, Philadelphia, PA, 2012. For a grant was made to be used for the general operating support of the school.

8274
The John A. Schroth Family Charitable Trust ✧
249 5th Ave.
1 PNC Bank, 20th Fl.
Pittsburgh, PA 15222 (216) 222-2700
E-mail: mary.koch@pnc.com; Main URL: https://www.pncsites.com/pncfoundation/charitable_trusts.html

Established in 2008 in OH.
Donor: Mary Louise Schroth Ireevocable Trust.
Foundation type: Independent foundation.
Financial data (yr. ended 12/31/13): Assets, $42,269,099 (M); expenditures, $1,988,368; qualifying distributions, $1,745,105; giving activities include $1,616,059 for 49 grants (high: $150,000; low: $5,000).
Fields of interest: Performing arts; Performing arts centers; Higher education; Health care; Human services.
Limitations: Applications accepted. Giving primarily in OH. No grants to individuals.
Application information: See PNC charitable grantmaking web site for guidelines, forms and deadlines.
Initial approach: Interested organizations must submit a preliminary letter of inquiry
Trustee: PNC Bank, N.A.
EIN: 207470868
Selected grants: The following grants are a representative sample of this grantmaker's funding activity:
$120,000 to Cincinnati Opera Association, Cincinnati, OH, 2012. For the Technology Package.
$75,000 to Ronald McDonald House Charities of Greater Cincinnati, Cincinnati, OH, 2012. For the Access Control System.
$50,000 to Cincinnati Parks Foundation, Cincinnati, OH, 2012. For the Butterfly Show.
$50,000 to Lighthouse Youth Services, Cincinnati, OH, 2012. For the Lighthouse Girls' Circle.
$50,000 to Zoological Society of Cincinnati, Cincinnati, OH, 2012. For the Living Classroom Education Access Fund.
$35,000 to People Working Cooperatively, Cincinnati, OH, 2012. For the Multi-Purpose Room.
$25,000 to Mercy Neighborhood Ministries, Cincinnati, OH, 2012. For Path to Homecare Aides.
$20,000 to Supports to Encourage Low-Income Families, Hamilton, OH, 2012. For the Circles Campaign.
$15,000 to Economics Center for Education and Research, Cincinnati, OH, 2012. For the Money Savvy Kids Program.
$10,000 to Episcopal Community Services Foundation, Cincinnati, OH, 2012. For the Strengthening Safety Net Program.

8275
The Scranton Area Foundation, Inc. ✧
615 Jefferson Ave., Ste. 102
Scranton, PA 18510 (570) 347-6203
Contact: Laura J. Ducceschi, C.E.O.; For grants: Cathy Fitzpatrick, Grants Admin.
FAX: (570) 347-7587; E-mail: safinfo@safdn.org; Grant inquiry e-mail: cathyf@sadfn.org; Main URL: http://www.safdn.org
Facebook: https://www.facebook.com/ScrantonAreaCommunityFoundation

Established in 1954 in PA by resolution and declaration of trust; reorganized in 1998.
Foundation type: Community foundation.
Financial data (yr. ended 12/31/13): Assets, $31,049,026 (M); gifts received, $1,012,248; expenditures, $1,667,849; giving activities include $514,044 for 15+ grants (high: $50,695), and $358,222 for 143 grants to individuals.
Purpose and activities: The foundation's mission is to enhance the quality of life for all people in Lackawanna County through the development of organized philanthropy. The foundation strives to carry out this mission as a steward by developing and managing permanent endowment funds, as a grant maker by awarding grants and support to enable the community to respond to emerging and changing needs and opportunities, as a charitable resource by encouraging and educating donors and providing a flexible vehicle for individual donors, non-profit organizations and the community-at-large, and as a catalyst by mobilizing community leadership in response to issues.
Fields of interest: Historic preservation/historical societies; Arts; Child development, education; Vocational education; Higher education; Libraries/library science; Education; Environment, natural resources; Environment; Animal welfare; Health care; Mental health/crisis services; Health organizations, association; Housing/shelter; Youth development, services; Children/youth, services; Child development, services; Human services; International human rights; Community/economic development; Voluntarism promotion; Leadership development; Public affairs; Religion; Aging.
Type of support: General/operating support; Continuing support; Program development; Conferences/seminars; Publication; Seed money; Curriculum development; Scholarship funds; Research; Technical assistance; Consulting services; Matching/challenge support.
Limitations: Applications accepted. Giving limited to Lackawanna County and Scranton, PA, area. No grants for building funds, annual campaigns, deficit financing, or emergency funds.
Publications: Application guidelines; Annual report; Annual report (including application guidelines); Grants list; Informational brochure; Informational brochure (including application guidelines); Newsletter; Occasional report.
Application information: Visit foundation web site for application guidelines. The foundation strongly recommends submission of letter of intent; immediate response as to the potential for the project will be provided. Application forms may be requested by calling the foundation. Application form required.
Initial approach: Submit letter of intent (1-2 pages maximum)
Copies of proposal: 1
Deadline(s): Varies
Board meeting date(s): Feb., May, Sept., and Dec.
Final notification: Applications are reviewed quarterly
Officers and Governors:* Kathleen Graff,* Chair.; David Hawk,* Vice-Chair.; Laura J. Ducceschi, M.B.A.*, C.E.O. and Pres.; William J. Calpin, Jr.,* Secy.; John P. Kearney,* Treas.; Rosemary Broderick; Ida Castro; James F. Clemente; Matthew E. Haggerty, Esq.; Cathy Ann Hardaway; Alan F. Hughes; James Gillotti, Esq.; Paula Mackarey; Jane Oppenheim; Ann Lavelle Powell, Esq.; Maryla Scranton; Mary Ann Sorokanich; Jack Tighe; Cynthia Yevich.
Investment Managers: Penn Security Bank & Trust Co.; PNC Advisors.
Number of staff: 1 full-time professional; 3 full-time support.
EIN: 232890364

8276
The Sedwick Foundation ✧
c/o Kirby J. Campbell
1 Armstrong Pl.
Butler, PA 16001-1951

Established in 1986 in PA.
Donors: Armstrong Utilities, Inc.; Jay L. Sedwick; Linda Sedwick; Armstrong Communications, Inc.; Armstrong Telephone Co. of West Virginia; Armstrong Telephone Co. of Maryland; Guardian Protection Services, Inc.; Laurie Sedwick.
Foundation type: Company-sponsored foundation.
Financial data (yr. ended 06/30/14): Assets, $43,474,332 (M); gifts received, $8,300; expenditures, $2,567,702; qualifying distributions, $2,443,850; giving activities include $2,443,850 for 64 grants (high: $525,000; low: $1,500).
Purpose and activities: The foundation supports camps and medical centers and organizations involved with higher education, human services, public policy, and Christianity.
Fields of interest: Higher education; Health care, clinics/centers; Recreation, camps; YM/YWCAs & YM/YWHAs; Human services; Public policy, research; Christian agencies & churches.
Type of support: General/operating support.
Limitations: Applications not accepted. Giving primarily in Butler, PA. No grants to individuals.
Application information: Contributes only to pre-selected organizations.
Trustees: Kirby J. Campbell; Dru A. Sedwick; Jay L. Sedwick; William C. Stewart.
EIN: 256284774
Selected grants: The following grants are a representative sample of this grantmaker's funding activity:
$500,000 to Grove City College, Grove City, PA, 2011.
$100,000 to Christian and Missionary Alliance, Colorado Springs, CO, 2011.
$100,000 to Leadership Institute, Arlington, VA, 2011.
$100,000 to Renaissance Charitable Foundation, Indianapolis, IN, 2011.
$60,000 to Pine Valley Bible Conference, Ellwood City, PA, 2011.
$50,000 to Dallas Theological Seminary, Dallas, TX, 2011.
$40,000 to Judicial Watch, Washington, DC, 2011.
$30,000 to Food for the Hungry, Phoenix, AZ, 2011.
$30,000 to Mission Aviation Fellowship, Nampa, ID, 2011.
$9,500 to Community Alliance Church, Butler, PA, 2011.

8277
Seed Foundation ✧
397 Eagleview Blvd.
Exton, PA 19341-1156

Donors: Edward Cone; Frontline Technologies.
Foundation type: Independent foundation.
Financial data (yr. ended 12/31/13): Assets, $334,109 (M); gifts received, $770,833; expenditures, $843,706; qualifying distributions,

$843,081; giving activities include $803,689 for 23 grants (high: $88,589; low: $6,000).
Fields of interest: Education; Christian agencies & churches.
Limitations: Applications not accepted. Giving primarily in FL, PA, OH, OR, and SC.
Application information: Unsolicited requests for funds not accepted.
Officers: Roland Thompson, Chair.; Todd Orlando, Secy.-Treas.
Directors: Michael Blackstone; Edward Cone.
EIN: 274194214

8278
Seed the Dream Foundation ✧
P.O. Box 768
Gladwyne, PA 19035-0768
Main URL: http://seedthedream.org/

Donors: Joel Greenberg; Marcy Gringlas.
Foundation type: Independent foundation.
Financial data (yr. ended 12/31/13): Assets, $2,654,028 (M); gifts received, $6,463,822; expenditures, $4,206,991; qualifying distributions, $4,151,946; giving activities include $4,151,946 for 87 grants (high: $1,202,500; low: $250).
Fields of interest: Arts; Education; Youth development; Jewish agencies & synagogues.
Limitations: Applications not accepted. Giving primarily in New York, NY; some giving also in PA.
Application information: Contributes only to pre-selected organizations.
Officers and Directors:* Marcy Gringlas,* Pres.; Joel Greenberg,* Secy.-Treas.
EIN: 274662369
Selected grants: The following grants are a representative sample of this grantmaker's funding activity:
$10,000 to Council for Relationships, Philadelphia, PA, 2012. For Supported a Transcending Trauma Event Held By the Charity.

8279
The Seraph Foundation ✧
c/o Glenmede Trust Co.
1650 Market St., Ste. 1200
Philadelphia, PA 19103-7391
Contact: Carol M. Drummond, Admin.

Established in 1997 in DE.
Donor: Edna Marion Davenport.
Foundation type: Independent foundation.
Financial data (yr. ended 06/30/13): Assets, $36,960,886 (M); expenditures, $2,140,850; qualifying distributions, $1,889,500; giving activities include $1,889,500 for grants.
Fields of interest: Higher education; Cancer research; Medical research.
Type of support: Capital campaigns; Building/renovation; Equipment; Land acquisition; Endowments; Professorships; Internship funds; Scholarship funds; Research; Matching/challenge support.
Limitations: Applications not accepted. Giving primarily in MD, with some funding also in the Midwest US. No grants to individuals.
Publications: Grants list.
Application information: Contributes only to pre-selected organizations.
Board meeting date(s): Sept., Dec., Mar., and June
Officers and Board Members:* Henry Spire,* Pres. and Treas.; Linda J. Spire,* V.P. and Secy.; Kimberly Spire Folts; William Bruce Spire.
EIN: 522030228
Selected grants: The following grants are a representative sample of this grantmaker's funding activity:
$500,000 to Lancaster General Hospital, Lancaster, PA, 2013. For Ann B. Barshinger Cancer Center - Conference and Educational Center.
$125,000 to Cold Spring Harbor Laboratory, Cold Spring Harbor, NY, 2013. For Start-up funding for Cancer Therapeutics.
$93,000 to Lancaster Farmland Trust, Strasburg, PA, 2013. For Fisher Family Farm.
$67,000 to Lancaster Day Care Center, Lancaster, PA, 2013. For Lower Play Yard Renovation.
$35,000 to AmeriCares, Stamford, CT, 2013. For Aid for Hurricane Sandy Relief.
$25,000 to Dickinson College, Carlisle, PA, 2013. For Addition to the Seraph Scholarship Endowment in honor of President Bill Durden.
$20,000 to Chesapeake Bay Foundation, Annapolis, MD, 2013. For Report on Angling for Healthier Rivers.

8280
The Sexauer Foundation ✧
c/o Thomas J. Abbamont, BNY Mellon, N.A.
P.O. Box 185
Pittsburgh, PA 15230-0185

Incorporated in 1961 DE.
Donors: John A. Sexauer‡; Nancy Walsh Trust.
Foundation type: Independent foundation.
Financial data (yr. ended 08/31/13): Assets, $10,699,749 (M); expenditures, $635,371; qualifying distributions, $525,787; giving activities include $471,500 for 29 grants (high: $42,000; low: $1,000).
Fields of interest: Higher education; Hospitals (general); Mental health/crisis services; Health organizations, association; Cancer; Heart & circulatory diseases; Eye research; Alzheimer's disease research; Big Brothers/Big Sisters; American Red Cross; Salvation Army; YM/YWCAs & YM/YWHAs; Christian agencies & churches.
Type of support: General/operating support; Research.
Limitations: Applications not accepted. Giving primarily in FL and NY. No grants to individuals.
Application information: Contributes only to pre-selected organizations.
Trustees: Thomas J. Abbamont; Wesley G. Cawley; Eileen Hoffman; Gil V. Silva; James R. Walsh.
EIN: 136156256
Selected grants: The following grants are a representative sample of this grantmaker's funding activity:
$100,000 to Saint Marys Hospital for Children, Bayside, NY, 2011.
$30,000 to Educational Network of Artists in Creative Theater, New York, NY, 2011.
$25,000 to Saint Christophers, Inc., Dobbs Ferry, NY, 2011.
$25,000 to Waterside School, Stamford, CT, 2011.
$20,000 to Caroline House, Bridgeport, CT, 2011.
$20,000 to Kids in Crisis, Cos Cob, CT, 2011.
$20,000 to Quantum House, West Palm Beach, FL, 2011.
$15,000 to Westchester Childrens Association, White Plains, NY, 2011.
$10,000 to Cystic Fibrosis Foundation, New York, NY, 2011.
$5,000 to Aspetuck Land Trust, Westport, CT, 2011.

8281
Shaffer Family Charitable Trust ✧
c/o David N. Shaffer
1588 Weyhill Cir.
Bethlehem, PA 18015-5253 (610) 867-7568

Established in 1987 in PA.
Donors: David Shaffer; Susan Shaffer; Jack M. Shaffer‡; Cecile Shaffer; Rose Shaffer.
Foundation type: Independent foundation.
Financial data (yr. ended 12/31/13): Assets, $10,910,023 (M); gifts received, $267,930; expenditures, $1,134,134; qualifying distributions, $1,047,000; giving activities include $1,047,000 for 34 grants (high: $250,000; low: $2,500).
Purpose and activities: Support for capital operations and special projects not funded through normal income sources to social service agencies serving the at-risk population in the Lehigh Valley, PA, area.
Fields of interest: Human services; Children/youth, services; Aging, centers/services.
Type of support: General/operating support; Capital campaigns; Endowments; Seed money.
Limitations: Applications not accepted. Giving primarily in Lehigh Valley, PA. No grants to individuals.
Application information: Contributes only to pre-selected organizations.
Board meeting date(s): Quarterly
Trustees: David Shaffer; Rose Shaffer; Susan Shaffer.
EIN: 232502319

8282
The David S. and Karen A. Shapira Foundation ✧
101 Kappa Dr.
Pittsburgh, PA 15238-2809 (412) 963-2501
Contact: David Shapira, Pres. and Treas.

Established in PA.
Donors: David S. Shapira; Karen A. Shapira.
Foundation type: Independent foundation.
Financial data (yr. ended 12/31/13): Assets, $3,638,239 (M); gifts received, $2,580,000; expenditures, $2,107,854; qualifying distributions, $2,098,476; giving activities include $1,919,770 for 59 grants (high: $825,754; low: $100).
Purpose and activities: Giving primarily for higher education and Jewish federated giving programs.
Fields of interest: Performing arts, orchestras; Higher education; Jewish federated giving programs; Jewish agencies & synagogues.
Limitations: Applications not accepted. Giving primarily in Pittsburgh, PA. No grants to individuals.
Application information: Contributes only to pre-selected organizations.
Officers: David S. Shapira, Pres. and Treas.; Cynthia Shapira, V.P.; Charles C. Cohen, Secy.; Amy Snider, Exec. Dir.
Directors: Shelia Fine; David J. Kalson; Laura M. Karet; Deborah B. Shapira; Jeremy M. Shapira; Joel Weinberg, M.D.
EIN: 251711993

8283
The Shiloh Foundation ✧ ☆
c/o David C. Paul
123 Anderson Farm Rd.
Phoenixville, PA 19460-5769

Established in 2007 in PA.
Donors: David C. Paul; Sonali Paul.
Foundation type: Independent foundation.
Financial data (yr. ended 12/31/13): Assets, $3,661,856 (M); gifts received, $500,000; expenditures, $1,055,540; qualifying distributions, $1,055,000; giving activities include $1,055,000 for 3 grants (high: $1,000,000; low: $5,000).
Fields of interest: Human services; Christian agencies & churches.
Limitations: Applications not accepted. Giving primarily in PA. No grants to individuals.
Application information: Contributes only to pre-selected organizations.
Trustees: David C. Paul; Sonali Paul.
EIN: 256915616

8284
The Thomas H. and Mary Williams Shoemaker Fund ✧ ☆
c/o Greene Street Friends School
5511 Greene St.
Philadelphia, PA 19144-2805 (215) 545-7099
Contact: Anne L. Edmunds, Admin. Asst.
E-mail: aedmunds@shoemakerfund.org; Main URL: http://www.shoemakerfund.org

Established in 1953 in PA.
Donors: Mary Williams Shoemaker†; Thomas H. Shoemaker†; Thomas H. and Mary Williams Shoemaker Trust.
Foundation type: Independent foundation.
Financial data (yr. ended 09/30/13): Assets, $8,378,088 (M); expenditures, $507,499; qualifying distributions, $457,833; giving activities include $426,000 for 13 grants (high: $206,000; low: $2,000).
Purpose and activities: Giving to organizations that are investing specifically in the growth and development of the Society of Friends.
Type of support: General/operating support; Continuing support; Capital campaigns; Building/renovation; Endowments; Program development; Publication; Seed money; Curriculum development; Scholarship funds.
Limitations: Applications accepted. Giving primarily in PA. No grants to individuals, or for matching gifts; no loans.
Publications: Application guidelines; Informational brochure (including application guidelines).
Application information: Complete application guidelines available on Fund web site. Application form required.
Board meeting date(s): May and Nov.
Officers and Trustees:* Edward W. Marshall III,* Chair.; Martha B. Bryans,* Secy.; Samuel D. Caldwell; Mary Ellen McNish; Parker Snowe; Advisory Trust Co. of Delaware.
Number of staff: 1 full-time support.
EIN: 236209783
Selected grants: The following grants are a representative sample of this grantmaker's funding activity:
$100,000 to Friends General Conference, Philadelphia, PA, 2011.
$4,000 to Friends Council on Education, Philadelphia, PA, 2011.
$4,000 to Greene Street Friends School, Philadelphia, PA, 2011.

8285
R. P. Simmons Family Foundation ✧ ☆
c/o Birchmere
79 Quaker Hollow Rd.
Sewickley, PA 15143-9353

Established in 1987 in PA.
Donors: Richard P. Simmons; Diamond Investments Corp.
Foundation type: Independent foundation.
Financial data (yr. ended 12/31/13): Assets, $4,344,062 (M); expenditures, $541,030; qualifying distributions, $518,900; giving activities include $518,900 for 17 grants (high: $60,000; low: $3,900).
Purpose and activities: Giving primarily for children and social services, including a children's hospital.
Fields of interest: Arts; Higher education; Education; Hospitals (specialty); Health organizations; Human services; Children/youth, services.
Type of support: General/operating support; Capital campaigns; Endowments; Program development; Professorships; Scholarship funds.
Limitations: Applications not accepted. Giving primarily in PA, with emphasis on Pittsburgh. No grants to individuals.
Application information: Contributes only to pre-selected organizations.
Trustee: Richard P. Simmons.
EIN: 256277068

8286
B. K. Simon Family Charitable Foundation Trust ✧
c/o BNY Mellon, N.A.
P.O. Box 185
Pittsburgh, PA 15230-0185
Application address: c/o Daniel W. Pfaff, 1 Mellon Center, Rm. 3725, Pittsburgh, PA 15258-0001, tel.: (412) 234-1584

Established in 2006 in PA.
Foundation type: Independent foundation.
Financial data (yr. ended 12/31/13): Assets, $14,194,111 (M); expenditures, $1,530,406; qualifying distributions, $1,491,229; giving activities include $1,479,000 for 24 grants (high: $343,000; low: $2,500).
Fields of interest: Higher education; Libraries (public); Education; Children/youth, services; Community/economic development; Foundations (public); Catholic agencies & churches.
Limitations: Applications accepted. Giving primarily in Washington, DC, and Pittsburgh, PA.
Application information: Application form required.
Initial approach: Proposal
Deadline(s): None
Trustee: BNY Mellon, N.A.
EIN: 206817430
Selected grants: The following grants are a representative sample of this grantmaker's funding activity:
$200,000 to Carnegie Mellon University, Pittsburgh, PA, 2011.
$200,000 to University of Pittsburgh, Pittsburgh, PA, 2011.
$100,000 to Childrens Institute, Verona, NJ, 2011.
$100,000 to Heritage Foundation, Washington, DC, 2011.
$100,000 to Institute for Justice, Arlington, VA, 2011.
$100,000 to Robert Morris University, Moon Township, PA, 2011.
$100,000 to University of Pittsburgh, Pittsburgh, PA, 2011.
$30,000 to Media Research Center, Reston, VA, 2011.
$16,000 to Bidwell Training Center, Pittsburgh, PA, 2011.
$15,000 to Fisher House Foundation, Rockville, MD, 2011.

8287
Christine and Lawrence Smith Charitable Trust ✧ ☆
1415 Kriebel Mill Rd.
Collegeville, PA 19426-1539

Established in 1999 in PA.
Donors: Lawrence S. Smith; Christine J. Smith.
Foundation type: Independent foundation.
Financial data (yr. ended 12/31/13): Assets, $2,142,643 (M); expenditures, $1,101,285; qualifying distributions, $1,078,896; giving activities include $1,078,896 for 34 grants (high: $385,000; low: $100).
Fields of interest: Higher education; Human services; YM/YWCAs & YM/YWHAs; Children/youth, services; Religion.
Limitations: Applications not accepted. Giving primarily in Philadelphia and Worchester, PA; some giving in NY. No grants to individuals.
Application information: Contributes only to pre-selected organizations.
Trustees: Christine J. Smith; Lawrence S. Smith.
EIN: 256632482
Selected grants: The following grants are a representative sample of this grantmaker's funding activity:
$100,200 to Central Schwenkfelder Church, Worcester, PA, 2011.
$4,700 to Barnes Foundation, Philadelphia, PA, 2011.

8288
W. W. Smith Charitable Trust ✧
200 Four Falls Corporate Ctr., Ste. 300
West Conshohocken, PA 19428-2958 (610) 397-1844
Contact: Michelle Montgomery, Grant Admin.
FAX: (610) 397-1680;
E-mail: mmontgomery@wwsmithcharitabletrust.org; Main URL: http://www.wwsmithcharitabletrust.org
Grants List: http://www.wwsmithcharitabletrust.org/Announcements.html

Trust established in 1977 in PA.
Donor: William Wikoff Smith†.
Foundation type: Independent foundation.
Financial data (yr. ended 06/30/13): Assets, $137,433,598 (M); expenditures, $7,284,324; qualifying distributions, $6,940,424; giving activities include $6,601,171 for 120 grants (high: $625,000; low: $5,000).

Purpose and activities: Support for college financial aid programs for qualified needy students at accredited universities and colleges in the Philadelphia, PA area; and for basic medical research programs dealing with cancer, AIDS, and heart disease; and for programs providing food and clothing for children and the elderly.
Fields of interest: Higher education; Cancer research; Heart & circulatory research; AIDS research; Medical research; Food services; Housing/shelter, development; Children/youth, services; Aging, centers/services; Women, centers/services; Homeless, human services; Infants/toddlers; Youth; Aging; Economically disadvantaged; Homeless.
Type of support: Equipment; Emergency funds; Scholarship funds; Research.
Limitations: Applications accepted. Giving limited to Bucks, Chester, Delaware, Montgomery, and Philadelphia counties, PA. No support for day care centers, or for educational institutions (other than invited colleges). No grants to individuals, or for deficit financing, capital campaigns, existing endowment funds, or retroactive funding for non-emergencies; no funding of events such as dinners, golf tournaments, or program ads.
Publications: Biennial report (including application guidelines).
Application information: Will only accept the trust's website application for proposal summary and guidelines. College financial aid programs by invitation only; applications for basic medical research grants must be submitted by the researcher's institution in quadruplicate; applications for other grants available on the trust's web site. Application form required.
Initial approach: Letter or phone call of inquiry prior to preparing a full proposal
Copies of proposal: 1
Deadline(s): Food, clothing, and Shelter, Dec. 15 and June 15; Scholarships, Apr. 1 by invitation only; Cancer and AIDS Research, June 15; and Heart Research, Sept. 15
Board meeting date(s): Food, Clothing and Shelter, Mar. and Sept.; Scholarships, May; Cancer and AIDS Research, Sept.; Heart Research, Dec.
Final notification: Usually 1 month after board meeting
Trustees: Mary L. Smith; Wells Fargo Bank, N.A.
Advisory Committee: Harry G. Dittmann; Ellen D. Harvey; Deborah J. McKenna.
Number of staff: 1 full-time professional; 1 full-time support.
EIN: 236648841
Selected grants: The following grants are a representative sample of this grantmaker's funding activity:
$169,000 to Temple University, Philadelphia, PA, 2012.
$156,000 to Fox Chase Cancer Center, Philadelphia, PA, 2012. For How do Viruses Trigger Myocarditis? Novel Lessons From the Fruitfly.
$131,000 to Drexel University, Philadelphia, PA, 2012.
$110,000 to Johns Hopkins University, Baltimore, MD, 2012. For Drivers of Inflammatory Dilated Cardiomyopathy.
$100,000 to Lankenau Institute for Medical Research, Wynnewood, PA, 2012. For Role of Myo/Nog Cells in Tumorigenesis.
$66,000 to Chestnut Hill College, Philadelphia, PA, 2012.
$64,500 to Salvation Army of Philadelphia, Philadelphia, PA, 2012. For food distribution at their Emergency Assistance Services program, lunch services at their RESTORE program for seniors, and physical improvements to their residential shelters located in Philadelphia, Norristown and Pottstown.
$53,000 to Lutheran Children and Family Service, Philadelphia, PA, 2012. For nutritional food and emergency food/shelter assistance vouchers to low-income seniors, and take-home containers of food to additional seniors.
$20,500 to Family Support Services, Upper Darby, PA, 2012. For food to low-income parents and very young children (birth to five years old), as part of their flagship program, Family School.
$20,000 to Camphill Village Kimberton Hills, Kimberton, PA, 2012. For food, shelter and clothing needs for a targeted elderly population.

8289
Hoxie Harrison Smith Foundation ✧ ☆
(formerly The Smith Foundation)
P.O. Box 665
Downingtown, PA 19335-0665 (610) 269-4802
Contact: Charles P. Barber, Pres.

Incorporated in 1920 in PA.
Donors: W. Hinckle Smith†; H. Harrison Smith†.
Foundation type: Independent foundation.
Financial data (yr. ended 12/31/13): Assets, $9,133,140 (M); expenditures, $470,026; qualifying distributions, $448,691; giving activities include $440,100 for 67 grants (high: $12,500; low: $1,250).
Purpose and activities: The purpose of the foundation is to support benevolent, charitable and educational undertakings; to further secular and religious education, and to care for the sick, aged and disabled; to minister to the poor and to improve the physical, mental, and moral condition of humanity, and to promote American patriotism.
Fields of interest: Historical activities, war memorials; Education; Hospitals (general); Children/youth, services; Aging, centers/services; Children/youth; Children; Aging; Disabilities, people with.
Type of support: General/operating support; Continuing support; Capital campaigns; Building/renovation; Equipment; Program development; Scholarship funds.
Limitations: Applications accepted. Giving limited to charities in the five counties of southeastern PA. No support for political organizations or action committees. No grants to individuals, or for emergency funds, tickets and tables, special events, multi-year awards, deficit financing, regranting through third parties, replacement of terminating government contracts, or for unfunded government mandates.
Publications: Annual report.
Application information: Eligibility to submit an unsolicited grant application is limited to charities having received at least one grant from the Foundation during the years 2009-2013 inclusive. Complete application guidelines available from the Foundation.
Initial approach: Telephone the Foundation to receive Grant Application Guidelines
Copies of proposal: 2
Deadline(s): Before Aug. 31
Board meeting date(s): Semiannually
Officers and Directors:* Charles P. Barber,* Pres.; William W. Heilig,* V.P.; Mark T. Ledger, V.P.; Joseph H. Barber; James A. Bennett; Bruce M. Brown; Philip C. Burnham; Howard W. Busch; Lee E. Daney; Jack T. Tomarchio.
Custodian: The Vanguard Group.
Number of staff: None.
EIN: 236238148
Selected grants: The following grants are a representative sample of this grantmaker's funding activity:
$10,000 to AchieveAbility, Philadelphia, PA, 2012. For Comprehensive Family Self-Sufficiency Program.
$10,000 to CityTeam Ministries, Chester, PA, 2012. For Philadelphia Rescue Mission Support.
$9,000 to Melmark, Berwyn, PA, 2012. For Indoor Pool Renovation.
$7,500 to Child Abuse Prevention Effort, Philadelphia, PA, 2012. For Emergency Family Fund.
$6,000 to Camphill Village Kimberton Hills, Kimberton, PA, 2012. For Reflective Signs.
$6,000 to Endow-A-Home, Philadelphia, PA, 2012. For Aid for Homeless Women.
$6,000 to Wagner Free Institute of Science, Philadelphia, PA, 2012. For Free Education Program.
$5,000 to Franklin Institute Science Museum, Philadelphia, PA, 2012. For Pacts Program.
$5,000 to Philadelphia Wooden Boat Factory, Philadelphia, PA, 2012. For Boating Education.
$5,000 to Support Center for Child Advocates, Philadelphia, PA, 2012. To support (No Suggestions) Youth Program.

8290
Frank L. and Laura L. Smock Foundation ✧
c/o Wells Fargo Bank, N.A.
101 N. Independence Mall E MACY 1372-062
Philadelphia, PA 19106-2112

Established in 1953 in IN.
Donor: Laura L. Smock†.
Foundation type: Independent foundation.
Financial data (yr. ended 12/31/12): Assets, $15,458,775 (M); expenditures, $800,112; qualifying distributions, $714,399; giving activities include $684,724 for grants.
Purpose and activities: Giving to promote the health, welfare and happiness of poor and elderly men and women of the Presbyterian faith throughout the state of Indiana.
Fields of interest: Human services; Aging, centers/services; Protestant agencies & churches.
Type of support: Grants to individuals.
Limitations: Applications not accepted. Giving limited to IN, with emphasis on Fort Wayne. No grants for general or operating support, capital campaigns, building or endowment funds.
Application information: Unsolicited requests for funds not accepted.
Board meeting date(s): Monthly
Trustee: Wells Fargo Bank, N.A.
EIN: 356011335
Selected grants: The following grants are a representative sample of this grantmaker's funding activity:
$149,266 to First Presbyterian Church, Fort Wayne, IN, 2011.

8291
Snee-Reinhardt Charitable Foundation
470 Streets Run Rd., Ste. 401
Pittsburgh, PA 15236-2075 (412) 884-3626
Contact: Christina Heasley-Treadwell, Chair. and Fdn. Mgr.; Jill M. Oluszak, Exec. Asst.
FAX: (412) 881-4636;
E-mail: info@snee-reinhardt.org; Main URL: http://www.snee-reinhardt.org

Established in 1987 in PA.
Donor: Katherine E. Snee‡.
Foundation type: Independent foundation.
Financial data (yr. ended 12/31/13): Assets, $21,481,390 (M); gifts received, $50,953; expenditures, $1,153,324; qualifying distributions, $984,990; giving activities include $753,801 for 56 grants (high: $50,000; low: $1,800).
Purpose and activities: The foundation believes that life is like that of an oak tree; strong and beautiful and should be given every chance to grow. As a family foundation in Pittsburgh, PA, the foundation's philanthropic traditions are well rooted in its continued support of organizations that foster transformative programs which best serve the local community as a whole in the areas of arts and culture, education, environmental, health and medical, human services, and religion.
Fields of interest: Arts; Libraries/library science; Education; Environment; Health care; Substance abuse, services; Health organizations, association; Cancer; Children/youth, services; Aging, centers/services; Community/economic development; Christian agencies & churches; Children/youth; Youth; Adults; Aging; Disabilities, people with; Physically disabled; Mentally disabled; Economically disadvantaged; Homeless.
Type of support: Building/renovation; Equipment; Program development.
Limitations: Applications accepted. Giving primarily in southwestern PA, secondly in northern WV, northern MD, and PA; some giving also throughout the U.S. No support for sectarian or religious organizations or for programs that promote, research or support the prevention of life, abortion, the practice of euthanasia, or cruelty to animals, or highly specialized health or medical programs that do not have a specific impact on the community. No grants to individuals, endowment funds, or general operating expenses, including salaries and fringe benefits, chairs or professorships. No grants for general capital campaigns (projects should be specific to a particular project or program within the overall campaign).
Publications: Application guidelines; Grants list.
Application information: Application guidelines and procedures are available on foundation web site. The amount being requested should not exceed $50,000. A request for a greater amount or a request that would be payable over a multiple-year period should not be submitted without first contacting the foundation office. All proposal pages are to be printed single-sided and unbound. Do not mail with any signature requirement for receipt. Application form required.
Initial approach: Letter of inquiry or telephone call to the office.
Copies of proposal: 1
Deadline(s): Apr. 1 and Aug. 1. (If deadline falls on a weekend then deadline is prior Friday).
Board meeting date(s): Grant review on the second Tues. of May and Sept., and annual meeting on the second Tues. of Nov.
Final notification: 2 weeks after board meeting
Officer and Directors:* Christina Heasley-Treadwell,* Chair. and Mgr.; Jeff Flick; Karen Heasley; Lucas Heasley.
Trustee: PNC Bank, N.A.
Number of staff: 1 full-time support.
EIN: 256292908
Selected grants: The following grants are a representative sample of this grantmaker's funding activity:
$25,000 to Western Pennsylvania School for Blind Children, Pittsburgh, PA, 2013. For refton chairs and standers.
$20,000 to Saint Anthony School Programs, Wexford, PA, 2013. To purchase Google Chromebooks for student use.
$16,500 to Westmoreland County Community College Educational Foundation, Youngwood, PA, 2013. For SimMan manikin for Nursing and Health Professional program.
$15,000 to Womens Center and Shelter of Greater Pittsburgh, Pittsburgh, PA, 2013. For food and supply cost associated with Emergency Shelter program.
$14,170 to Christian Laymans Corps, Greensburg, PA, 2013. To purchase beds for A Bed for Every Child program.
$11,716 to Riverquest, Pittsburgh, PA, 2013. To purchase hands-on equipment for onboard science programs.
$11,500 to Uniontown Hospital, Uniontown, PA, 2013. For fetal monitoring system.
$10,000 to Glade Run Foundation, Zelienople, PA, 2013. For undergarments, shoes and toiletries for Mercy Project.
$10,000 to Mainstay Life Services, Pittsburgh, PA, 2013. For Summer Respite and Recreation program.
$10,000 to Mount Macrina Manor Nursing Home, Uniontown, PA, 2013. To purchase Turbo Chef ovens for new country kitchens.
$10,000 to South Hills Interfaith Ministries, Bethel Park, PA, 2013. For food and household supplies for Pantry Plus program.
$10,000 to Tri-City Life Center, Lower Burrell, PA, 2013. For cribs, mattresses, and Pack N' Plays for Parent Baby program.
$9,000 to Variety-The Childrens Charity, Pittsburgh, PA, 2013. To purchase adaptive bikes for children with disabilities.
$6,800 to Light of Life Rescue Mission, Pittsburgh, PA, 2013. For chest freezers and washers and dryers set.
$5,000 to Tickets for Kids Foundation, Pittsburgh, PA, 2013. For ticket distribution program.

8292
The Snider Foundation ✧
(formerly The Ed Snider Foundation)
c/o Spectacor, Wells Fargo Ctr.
3601 S. Broad St.
Philadelphia, PA 19148-5250

Established in 1977 in PA.
Donor: Edward M. Snider.
Foundation type: Independent foundation.
Financial data (yr. ended 04/30/13): Assets, $16,060,514 (M); gifts received, $7,999,584; expenditures, $2,414,002; qualifying distributions, $1,999,850; giving activities include $1,999,850 for 82 grants (high: $600,000; low: $150).
Purpose and activities: Support primarily for Jewish organizations, education, and health; some funding also for the arts.
Fields of interest: Arts; Education; Health organizations, association; Human services; Jewish federated giving programs; Jewish agencies & synagogues.
Limitations: Applications not accepted. Giving primarily in CA and PA. No grants to individuals.
Application information: Contributes only to pre-selected organizations.
Officers: Edward M. Snider, Chair.; Fred A. Shabel, Vice-Chair.; Sanford Lipstein, Treas.; Craig Snider, Exec. Dir.
EIN: 232047668
Selected grants: The following grants are a representative sample of this grantmaker's funding activity:
$350,000 to Simon Wiesenthal Center, Los Angeles, CA, 2011. For general purpose.
$101,565 to Santa Barbara Center for the Performing Arts, Santa Barbara, CA, 2011. For general purpose.
$100,000 to National Foundation for Celiac Awareness, Ambler, PA, 2011. For general purpose.
$100,000 to Santa Barbara Cottage Hospital Foundation, Santa Barbara, CA, 2011. For general purpose.
$84,277 to David Horowitz Freedom Center, Sherman Oaks, CA, 2011. For general purpose.
$35,000 to YMCA, Kennebec Valley, Augusta, ME, 2011. For general purpose.
$20,000 to Beth David Reform Congregation, Gladwyne, PA, 2011. For general purpose.
$15,000 to Middle East Forum, Philadelphia, PA, 2011. For general purpose.
$12,500 to Macula Vision Research Foundation, West Conshohocken, PA, 2011. For general purpose.
$10,000 to Friends Central School, Wynnewood, PA, 2011. For general purpose.

8293
Springbank Foundation ✧
2250 Hickory Rd., Ste. 450
Plymouth Meeting, PA 19462-1037

Established in 2006 in PA.
Donor: Robert D. McNeil.
Foundation type: Independent foundation.
Financial data (yr. ended 12/31/12): Assets, $3,687,349 (M); expenditures, $995,464; qualifying distributions, $974,735; giving activities include $974,500 for 42 grants (high: $250,000; low: $2,000).
Fields of interest: Education; Health care; Medical research, institute; Human services.
Limitations: Applications not accepted. Giving primarily in PA; some funding also in OH. No grants to individuals.
Application information: Unsolicited requests for funds not accepted.
Trustees: James P. Lisa, Jr.; Jennifer C. McNeil; Robert D. McNeil.
EIN: 207138964

8294
Donald B. and Dorothy L. Stabler Foundation ✧
One S. Market Sq., 12th Fl.
P.O. Box 1146
Harrisburg, PA 17108-1146 (717) 231-6639
Contact: Kathleen O'Hare

FAX: (717) 238-1080;
E-mail: LHartman@StablerFoundation.org; Main URL: http://www.stablerfoundation.org/

Established in 1966 in PA.
Foundation type: Independent foundation.
Financial data (yr. ended 12/31/12): Assets, $379,786,812 (M); gifts received, $9,037,996; expenditures, $29,730,497; qualifying distributions, $27,439,435; giving activities include $27,364,000 for 168 grants (high: $9,020,000; low: $1,000).
Fields of interest: Higher education, college; Education; Health care; Human services.
Limitations: Applications accepted. Giving primarily in PA.
Application information: Application form required.
Initial approach: Letter
Deadline(s): None
Board meeting date(s): Quarterly
Officers: Cyril C. Dunmire, Jr., Pres.; Sherill T. Moyer, Esq., Secy.; Paul B. Shannon, Treas.; Larry Hartman, Exec. Dir.
Directors: Patricia H. Vance; Richard A. Zimmerman.
EIN: 263598470
Selected grants: The following grants are a representative sample of this grantmaker's funding activity:
$9,020,000 to Lehigh University, Bethlehem, PA, 2012. For operating support.
$1,000,000 to Milton S. Hershey Medical Center, Hershey, PA, 2012. For College of Medicine.
$750,000 to Harrisburg University of Science and Technology, Harrisburg, PA, 2012. For scholarships.
$750,000 to Lycoming College, Williamsport, PA, 2012. For scholarships.
$500,000 to Sacred Heart Hospital, Allentown, PA, 2012. For Come Home to Your Heart Capital Campaign.
$400,000 to Albright College, Reading, PA, 2012. For scholarships.
$400,000 to Saint Lukes University Health Network, Bethlehem, PA, 2012. For scholarships.
$300,000 to Homeland Center, Harrisburg, PA, 2012. For indigent care.
$200,000 to Leg Up Farm, Mount Wolf, PA, 2012. For matching grant for operating support.
$25,000 to Diakon Lutheran Social Ministries, Allentown, PA, 2012. For Flight Program.

8295
Stackpole-Hall Foundation ✧

44 S. Saint Marys St.
St. Marys, PA 15857-1667 (814) 834-1845
FAX: (814) 834-1869;
E-mail: stackpolehall@windstream.net; Main URL: http://www.stackpolehall.org/

Trust established in 1951 in PA.
Donors: Lyle G. Hall, Sr.†; J. Hall Stackpole†; Harrison C. Stackpole†; Lyle G. Hall, Jr.; Adelaide Stackpole†; Stackpole Carbon Co.
Foundation type: Independent foundation.
Financial data (yr. ended 12/31/13): Assets, $26,837,836 (M); expenditures, $1,349,131; qualifying distributions, $1,217,908; giving activities include $949,885 for 85 grants (high: $100,000; low: $500).
Purpose and activities: Support for higher and secondary education, and literacy and vocational projects; Christian agencies and churches; social services, including youth and child welfare agencies; the arts and cultural programs; health services, including mental health and drug abuse issues; and community development, including civic affairs and leadership development, conservation concerns, rural development, and voluntarism.
Fields of interest: Education, fund raising/fund distribution; Secondary school/education; Vocational education; Higher education; Adult/continuing education; Adult education—literacy, basic skills & GED; Libraries/library science; Education, reading; Education; Substance abuse, services; Mental health/crisis services; Alcoholism; Youth development, services; Human services; Children/youth, services; Rural development; Community/economic development; Voluntarism promotion; Leadership development; Protestant agencies & churches; Catholic agencies & churches; Disabilities, people with.
Type of support: Annual campaigns; Capital campaigns; Building/renovation; Equipment; Program development; Seed money; Matching/challenge support.
Limitations: Applications accepted. Giving primarily in Elk County, PA, and communities in which the foundation's donors, donors' families and trustees reside. No grants to individuals, or for scholarships or fellowships; generally, no grants for operating budgets or endowment funds; no loans.
Publications: Application guidelines; Annual report (including application guidelines); Financial statement; Grants list.
Application information: Grantmakers of Western Pennsylvania's Common Grant Application Format accepted; application guidelines available on foundation web site. Application form not required.
Initial approach: E-mailed grant requests preferred; supporting documentation maybe sent via U.S. mail
Copies of proposal: 1
Deadline(s): None
Board meeting date(s): Quarterly
Officers and Trustees:* R. Dauer Stackpole,* Chair.; J.M. Hamlin Johnson,* Vice-Chair.; Dennis J. Bonanno, Secy.-Treas.; William C. Conrad,* Exec. Dir.; Heather L. Conrad; Douglas R. Dobson; Francis Grandinetti; Lyle G. Hall; Megan Hall; Richard Masson; Deborah Dick Pontzer; John I. Saalfield; Alexander Sheble-Hall; Laurey Stackpole Turner; Lawrence E. Whiteman.
Number of staff: 1 full-time professional; 1 full-time support; 1 part-time support.
EIN: 256006650
Selected grants: The following grants are a representative sample of this grantmaker's funding activity:
$20,000 to Elk County Council on the Arts, Ridgway, PA, 2012. For Gallery Renovation.
$13,953 to Yale University, New Haven, CT, 2012. For Initial 2012 Distribution.
$9,172 to Yale University, New Haven, CT, 2012. For Final 2011 Distribution.
$8,689 to Ridgway Area School District, Ridgway, PA, 2012. For Summer Jobs Program.
$5,000 to Gannon University, Erie, PA, 2012. For Diversity Project.

8296
Staunton Farm Foundation ✧

650 Smithfield St., Ste. 210
Pittsburgh, PA 15222-3907 (412) 281-8020
Contact: Joni Schwager, Exec. Dir.
FAX: (412) 232-3115;
E-mail: jschwager@stauntonfarm.org; E-mail for letter of inquiry or questions regarding application process: office@stauntonfarm.org; Main URL: http://www.stauntonfarm.org
Facebook: https://www.facebook.com/stauntonfarm

Incorporated in 1937 in PA.
Donor: Mathilda Staunton Craig McCready†.
Foundation type: Independent foundation.
Financial data (yr. ended 12/31/12): Assets, $52,975,123 (M); expenditures, $2,819,294; qualifying distributions, $2,600,575; giving activities include $2,154,122 for 58 grants (high: $147,000; low: $75).
Purpose and activities: The foundation is dedicated to improving the lives of people who suffer from mental illness. It works to enhance mental health treatment and support by advancing the best practices through grant making to non profit organizations in the 10 southwestern Pennsylvania counties of Allegheny, Armstrong, Beaver, Butler, Fayette, Greene, Indiana, Lawrence, Washington, and Westmoreland. Current priorities include: 1) rural behavioral health: applicants for this grant will provide services to people in at least one rural area and will describe how the approach used will reach and engage people who face the challenges of distance and stigma; 2) access to behavioral health services and support for underserved populations: applicants for this grant will make the case that the population they are targeting does not now receive services at an expected rate and that their project will reach and engage the underserved individuals more effectively; and 3) Criminal Justice Diversion. Applicants for this grant will propose a program in collaboration with the criminal justice system that will divert youth or adults with behavioral health issues from arrest/jail to treatment and support in the community.
Fields of interest: Substance abuse, services; Substance abuse, prevention; Substance abuse, treatment; Mental health, treatment; Mental health/crisis services; Crime/violence prevention, domestic violence; Human services; Children/youth, services; Family services; Family services, counseling; Psychology/behavioral science; Infants/toddlers; Children/youth; Children; Youth; Adults; Young adults; Disabilities, people with; African Americans/Blacks; Women; Girls; Men; Military/veterans; Substance abusers; Crime/abuse victims; Homeless; LGBTQ; Lesbians.
Type of support: Management development/capacity building; Program development; Conferences/seminars; Seed money; Curriculum development; Program evaluation; Matching/challenge support.
Limitations: Giving limited to a ten-county area in southwestern PA: Allegheny, Armstrong, Beaver, Butler, Fayette, Greene, Indiana, Lawrence, Washington, and Westmoreland counties.
Publications: Application guidelines; Annual report; Grants list.
Application information: Application guidelines available on foundation web site. SWPA Common Grant Application accepted. Application form required.
Initial approach: Use letter of inquiry format and online application process on foundation web site
Copies of proposal: 1
Deadline(s): Refer to foundation web site for latest deadlines
Board meeting date(s): Quarterly
Final notification: Immediately following board meetings

Officers and Directors:* Robert B. Ferree IV, Pres.; Margaret Weaver,* V.P.; Paul "Stoney" Griffiths III, Secy.; Joni S. Schwager, Exec. Dir.; Bonni Dunlap, Ph.D.; Philip G. Gulley.
Number of staff: 3 full-time professional; 1 part-time professional.
EIN: 250965573

8297
Louis and Bessie Stein Foundation ✧
c/o Ruth Nathanson
The Fairmont
4100 Conshohocken State Rd., Ste. 308
Bala Cynwyd, PA 19004

Established in 1953 in NJ.
Donors: Louis Stein†; Walter Leventhal; Stanley Merves; Bessie Stein; Stein, Stein & Engel.
Foundation type: Independent foundation.
Financial data (yr. ended 12/31/13): Assets, $12,939,073 (M); expenditures, $687,284; qualifying distributions, $658,569; giving activities include $647,176 for 42 grants (high: $151,330; low: $50).
Purpose and activities: Giving primarily to Jewish organizations and federated giving programs and for higher education.
Fields of interest: Higher education; Cancer; Medical specialties; Human services; Jewish federated giving programs; Jewish agencies & synagogues.
Limitations: Applications not accepted. Giving primarily in NY and PA. No grants to individuals.
Application information: Contributes only to pre-selected organizations.
Officer: Ruth Leventhal Nathanson, Pres. and Treas.
EIN: 236395253
Selected grants: The following grants are a representative sample of this grantmaker's funding activity:
$201,570 to American Society for Technion-Israel Institute of Technology, New York, NY, 2011. For general support.
$100,000 to University of Pennsylvania, Philadelphia, PA, 2011. For general support.
$6,152 to Har Zion Temple, Penn Valley, PA, 2011. For general support.
$3,250 to Jewish Federation of the Berkshires, Pittsfield, MA, 2011. For general support.
$2,500 to Jewish Community Centers of Greater Philadelphia, Wynnewood, PA, 2011. For general support.

8298
Stein/Bellet Foundation, Inc. ✧
1820 Rittenhouse Sq., Ste. 902
Philadelphia, PA 19103-5824 (215) 732-7781
Contact: Sally Bellet, Pres.

Established in 2004 in PA.
Donor: Edward Bellet.
Foundation type: Independent foundation.
Financial data (yr. ended 12/31/13): Assets, $8,946,776 (M); expenditures, $544,855; qualifying distributions, $425,000; giving activities include $425,000 for 22 grants (high: $122,000; low: $100).
Fields of interest: Museums (art); Law school/education; Hospitals (specialty); Health organizations, association.
Type of support: General/operating support.
Limitations: Giving primarily in PA; funding also in NY. No grants to individuals.
Application information:
Initial approach: Letter
Deadline(s): Dec. 31
Officers and Trustees:* Sally Bellet,* Pres.; Laura Bellet,* V.P.; Matthew Kessler,* Secy.-Treas.
EIN: 562491254
Selected grants: The following grants are a representative sample of this grantmaker's funding activity:
$85,000 to Fordham University, School of Law, New York, NY, 2012. For general support.

8299
James Hale Steinman Foundation ✧
8 W. King St.
P.O. Box 128
Lancaster, PA 17608-0128 (717) 291-8676
Contact: Christine Mellinger
E-mail: cmellinger@lnpnews.com

Established in 1952 in PA.
Donors: James Hale Steinman†; Louise Steinman von Hess†; Lancaster Newspapers, Inc.; and others.
Foundation type: Independent foundation.
Financial data (yr. ended 12/31/12): Assets, $32,806,614 (M); expenditures, $2,079,162; qualifying distributions, $1,918,098; giving activities include $1,915,621 for 86 grants (high: $420,621; low: $1,000).
Purpose and activities: Giving for the arts and historic preservation, higher and other education (including scholarships to newspaper carriers and children of employees of Steinman Enterprises), youth and social services, and health.
Fields of interest: Performing arts, music; Historic preservation/historical societies; Arts; Secondary school/education; Higher education; Education; Health care; Health organizations, association; Human services; Children/youth, services; United Ways and Federated Giving Programs.
Type of support: Annual campaigns; Capital campaigns; Building/renovation; Employee-related scholarships; Scholarships—to individuals.
Limitations: Applications not accepted. Giving primarily in Lancaster, PA.
Application information: Unsolicited requests for funds not accepted. Grants restricted to newspaper carriers and employees' children.
Board meeting date(s): June and Dec.
Officers: Beverly R. Steinman, Chair.; Dennis A. Getz, Secy.; Willis W. Shenk, Treas.
Trustee: Harold E. Miller.
EIN: 236266377
Selected grants: The following grants are a representative sample of this grantmaker's funding activity:
$30,000 to Historic Preservation Trust of Lancaster County, Lancaster, PA, 2012. For Historic Site Restoration.
$25,000 to Community First Fund, Lancaster, PA, 2012. For Capital Loan Expansion.
$17,500 to Thaddeus Stevens Foundation, Lancaster, PA, 2012. For Career Prep and Training Laboratory.
$6,000 to Elizabethtown College, Elizabethtown, PA, 2012. For journalism workshop.
$2,500 to No Longer Alone Ministries, Lancaster, PA, 2012. For computer upgrades.

8300
John Frederick Steinman Foundation ✧
P.O. Box 128
Lancaster, PA 17608-0128
E-mail: cmellinger@lnpnews.com; Additional address: c/o M. Steven Weaver, Secy., Fellow, 8 W. King St., P.O. Box 1328, Lancaster, PA 17603-3824, tel.: (717) 291-8676

Trust established in 1952 in PA.
Donors: John Frederick Steinman†; Shirley W. Steinman†; Lancaster Newspapers, Inc.; and others.
Foundation type: Independent foundation.
Financial data (yr. ended 12/31/12): Assets, $31,251,661 (M); expenditures, $1,512,884; qualifying distributions, $1,362,373; giving activities include $1,359,250 for 107 grants (high: $100,000; low: $1,000).
Purpose and activities: Giving for higher and secondary education, the arts, community funds, family planning and other social services, youth, health services and hospitals, and the handicapped; support also for a fellowship program limited to graduate study in mental health or a related field.
Fields of interest: Arts; Education; Hospitals (general); Health care; Mental health, treatment; Mental health/crisis services; Human services; Children/youth, services; United Ways and Federated Giving Programs; Psychology/behavioral science; Disabilities, people with.
Type of support: General/operating support; Annual campaigns; Capital campaigns; Building/renovation; Land acquisition; Emergency funds; Fellowships.
Limitations: Giving primarily in PA, with emphasis on the Lancaster area.
Publications: Informational brochure.
Application information: Unsolicited requests for funds not accepted. Contact foundation for Fellowship application forms or refer to: http://contests.lancasteronline.com/fellowshipfund/.
Deadline(s): Feb. 1 for Fellowships
Board meeting date(s): Mar., June, Sept., and Dec.
Officers and Trustees:* Pamela M. Thye,* Chair.; Dennis A. Getz,* Secy.; Willis W. Shenk, Treas.; Henry Pildner, Jr.
EIN: 236266378
Selected grants: The following grants are a representative sample of this grantmaker's funding activity:
$25,000 to Heritage Center Museum of Lancaster County, Lancaster, PA, 2012. For Debt Relief and Building Renovations.
$20,000 to Historic Preservation Trust of Lancaster County, Lancaster, PA, 2012. For Historic Site Project.
$17,500 to Library System of Lancaster County, Lancaster, PA, 2012. For Network Installation.
$17,500 to Thaddeus Stevens Foundation, Lancaster, PA, 2012. For Career Prep and Training.
$12,500 to Lancaster Symphony Orchestra, Lancaster, PA, 2012. For education program.
$10,000 to Franklin and Marshall College, Lancaster, PA, 2012. For cultural enrichment Program.
$10,000 to Friendship Community, Lititz, PA, 2012. For Heart of Friendship Art Program.
$5,000 to Rock Ford Foundation, Lancaster, PA, 2012. For events.
$2,000 to YWCA of Lancaster, Lancaster, PA, 2012. For child abuse prevention.

8301
Lawrence and Rebecca Stern Family Foundation Inc. ✧
1540 Fox Chase Ln.
Pittsburgh, PA 15241-3148

Donors: Lawrence Stern; Rebecca Stern.
Foundation type: Independent foundation.
Financial data (yr. ended 12/31/13): Assets, $5,525,403 (M); gifts received, $250,000; expenditures, $1,099,277; qualifying distributions, $1,044,499; giving activities include $1,019,700 for 30 grants (high: $250,000; low: $50).
Fields of interest: Human services; Philanthropy/voluntarism; Religion.
Limitations: Applications not accepted.
Application information: Unsolicited requests for funds not accepted.
Officers and Directors:* Lawrence Stern,* Pres. and Treas.; Rebecca Stern,* V.P. and Secy.
EIN: 274129652

8302
The James M. and Margaret V. Stine Foundation ✧
c/o Lisa B. Petkun, Esq.
3000 Two Logan Sq.
Philadelphia, PA 19103-2799

Established in 1996 in PA.
Donors: James M. Stine; Margaret V. Stine.
Foundation type: Independent foundation.
Financial data (yr. ended 12/31/13): Assets, $21,521,320 (M); expenditures, $1,022,871; qualifying distributions, $974,116; giving activities include $968,000 for 30 grants (high: $110,000; low: $5,000).
Purpose and activities: Giving primarily to Roman Catholic agencies and churches; funding also for education and hospitals.
Fields of interest: Hospitals (general); Health organizations, association; United Ways and Federated Giving Programs; Catholic federated giving programs; Catholic agencies & churches.
Limitations: Applications not accepted. Giving primarily in MD and PA. No grants to individuals.
Application information: Contributes only to pre-selected organizations.
Officers and Directors:* Margaret V. Stine,* Pres. and Treas.; Sarah Igler,* V.P.; Martha Lee Boyd,* Secy.; Michael Boyd; Thomas Igler; David J. Stine; Lindsay Stine.
EIN: 232834787

8303
Stoneleigh Foundation ✧
(formerly A. Stoneleigh Research and Education Center Serving Children and Youth)
123 S. Broad St., Ste. 1130
Philadelphia, PA 19109-1019 (215) 735-7080
Contact: Ronnie Bloom, Exec. Dir.
FAX: (215) 735-7089;
E-mail: info@stoneleighfoundation.org; Main URL: http://www.stoneleighfoundation.org
Blog: http://stoneleighfoundation.org/blog
E-Newsletter: http://stoneleighfoundation.org/news/newsletters
Facebook: https://www.facebook.com/StoneleighFdn?ref=hl
LinkedIn: http://www.linkedin.com/company/stoneleigh-foundation
RSS Feed: http://stoneleighfoundation.org/blog/rss.xml
Twitter: http://twitter.com/StoneleighFdn
Vimeo: http://www.vimeo.com/user3587811
YouTube: http://www.youtube.com/user/StoneleighFoundation

Established in 2006 in PA.
Donors: John C. Haas; Chara C. Haas.
Foundation type: Operating foundation.
Financial data (yr. ended 06/30/13): Assets, $82,650,774 (M); gifts received, $70,912,256; expenditures, $1,925,756; qualifying distributions, $1,819,832; giving activities include $1,086,690 for 16 grants (high: $135,000; low: $1,310), and $1,818,723 for foundation-administered programs.
Purpose and activities: Giving to improve life outcomes of vulnerable children and youth (those in child welfare and juvenile justice systems).
Fields of interest: Children/youth.
Type of support: Fellowships.
Limitations: Applications accepted. Giving primarily in the Philadelphia, PA, area. No support for projects. No grants for direct service support.
Publications: Application guidelines.
Application information: Faxed or incomplete proposals not accepted. See foundation web site for complete application guidelines. Application form not required.
Initial approach: Letter of inquiry
Deadline(s): None
Board meeting date(s): Mar., June, Sept. and Dec.
Final notification: 1-month
Officers and Directors:* Carole Haas Gravagno,* Chair.; Darlyne Bailey, Ph.D.*, Secy.; Morrison C. Huston, Jr.,* Treas.; Ms. Ronnie L. Bloom, Esq., Exec. Dir.; Paul DiLorenzo; Carol Emig; David Haas; Katherine Hanrahan; Frazierita D. Klasen; David M. Rubin, M.D.; Daniel Shapiro; Larry Steinberg.
Number of staff: 2 full-time professional; 1 full-time support.
EIN: 371526458

8304
Stratton Foundation ✧ ☆
P.O. Box 100
Blue Bell, PA 19422-0100
Contact: Carol Beers

Established in 1988 in PA.
Donors: James W. Stratton; Arlene Stratton.
Foundation type: Independent foundation.
Financial data (yr. ended 12/31/13): Assets, $12,245,551 (M); expenditures, $469,475; qualifying distributions, $443,640; giving activities include $443,640 for 39 grants (high: $129,890; low: $1,000).
Fields of interest: Education, alliance/advocacy; Higher education, university; Environment, natural resources; Human services; Christian agencies & churches.
Limitations: Applications accepted. Giving primarily in PA. No grants to individuals.
Officers: Carol Stratton Beers, Pres.; Jeanne Stratton Jenkins, V.P.; Susan Stratton McGinnis, V.P.
EIN: 232508658
Selected grants: The following grants are a representative sample of this grantmaker's funding activity:
$12,500 to Wissahickon Valley Watershed Association, Ambler, PA, 2012. For Conservation Green Ribbon Trail Improvements.
$10,000 to Manna on Main Street, Lansdale, PA, 2012. For Social Services Soup Kitchen Equipment and Office Furniture for new location.
$5,000 to Pennsylvania State University, University Park, PA, 2012. For Education Earth and Mineral Sciences Future Fund.
$5,000 to Wayne Art Center, Wayne, PA, 2012. For education general Program support (annual giving campaign).
$3,000 to North Fulton Community Charities, Roswell, GA, 2012. For Social Service General Program Support.
$2,000 to Harvard University, Cambridge, MA, 2012. For Education Harvard Business School Dean's Fund.
$2,000 to Settlement Music School, Philadelphia, PA, 2012. For education general Program support.
$900 to Pitch in for Baseball, Harleysville, PA, 2012. For Social Services General Program Support.

8305
Margaret Dorrance Strawbridge Foundation of Pennsylvania I Inc. ✧
c/o Dechert
2929 Arch St.
Philadelphia, PA 19104-2808

Established in 1985 in PA.
Donors: George Strawbridge, Jr.; Margaret Dorrance Strawbridge Foundation.
Foundation type: Independent foundation.
Financial data (yr. ended 12/31/13): Assets, $7,149,202 (M); expenditures, $754,005; qualifying distributions, $690,000; giving activities include $690,000 for 8 grants (high: $350,000; low: $10,000).
Fields of interest: Environment, natural resources; Cancer.
Limitations: Applications not accepted. Giving primarily in KY, ME and PA. No grants to individuals, or for endowment funds.
Application information: Contributes only to pre-selected organizations.
Officers and Directors:* George Strawbridge, Jr.,* Pres. and Secy.; R. Stewart Strawbridge.
EIN: 232373081

8306
The Dorothy Strelsin Foundation ✧
c/o BNY Mellon, N.A.
P.O. Box 185
Pittsburgh, PA 15230-0185

Established in NY.
Foundation type: Independent foundation.
Financial data (yr. ended 12/31/13): Assets, $14,660,882 (M); expenditures, $676,806; qualifying distributions, $624,130; giving activities include $533,250 for 124 grants (high: $30,000; low: $300).
Purpose and activities: Giving primarily for theater; some funding also for museums and human services.
Fields of interest: Museums (art); Performing arts, theater; Human services.
Limitations: Applications not accepted. Giving primarily in New York, NY. No grants to individuals.
Application information: Unsolicited requests for funds not accepted.
Officers: Enid Nemy, Pres.; Shirley Boley, Co-Secy.; Corinne Nemy, Co-Secy.

Director: Gwin Joh Chin.
EIN: 133561352
Selected grants: The following grants are a representative sample of this grantmaker's funding activity:
$15,000 to New York City Center, New York, NY, 2011.
$5,000 to New York City Center, New York, NY, 2011.
$5,000 to New York City Center, New York, NY, 2011.
$4,000 to Parkinsons Disease Foundation, New York, NY, 2011.
$2,000 to Guiding Eyes for the Blind, Yorktown Heights, NY, 2011.
$2,000 to Jewish Guild for the Blind, New York, NY, 2011.
$2,000 to Parkinsons Disease Foundation, New York, NY, 2011.
$1,000 to World Wildlife Fund, Washington, DC, 2011.

8307
G. B. Stuart Charitable Foundation ✧
15 State Ave., Ste. 101
Carlisle, PA 17013-4456 (717) 243-3735
Contact: Keith D. Falconer, Exec. Dir.

Established in 1976.
Donor: George B. Stuart†.
Foundation type: Independent foundation.
Financial data (yr. ended 12/31/13): Assets, $18,756,084 (M); expenditures, $917,505; qualifying distributions, $826,234; giving activities include $612,328 for 37 grants (high: $50,000; low: $2,000).
Purpose and activities: Support for local concerns, including youth and social services, and charitable, educational and religious purposes.
Fields of interest: Education; Human services; Youth, services.
Limitations: Applications accepted. Giving to PA organizations, primarily in Cumberland County with emphasis on Carlisle. No grants to individuals.
Application information: . Application form required.
Initial approach: Completed grant application package required
Deadline(s): Oct. 1
Board meeting date(s): May and Nov.
Officers: Karen E. Faircloth,* Secy.; Keith D. Falconer, Exec. Dir.; M & T Invesment Group, Mgr.
Trustees: Alison J. Alioto; Barbara E. Falconer; Victoria J. Macauley; Mellon Bank, N.A.
Number of staff: 1 full-time professional; 1 full-time support.
EIN: 232042245
Selected grants: The following grants are a representative sample of this grantmaker's funding activity:
$75,000 to Carlisle Arts Learning Center, Carlisle, PA, 2012. For renovation costs to Pomfret St property.
$40,500 to Cumberland County Historical Society, Carlisle, PA, 2012. To support of annual McLain Celtic Festival - $500.; to update their technology and fire security systems - $40,000.
$33,070 to Employment Skills Center, Carlisle, PA, 2012. For $10,063. to replace current server; $4,000 for PC updates and maintenance; $3,250 for backup and disaster recovery solution, $8,467 to purchase a new copier/printer; $7,290 for two computers and additional cost for server.
$29,800 to Project SHARE of Carlisle, Carlisle, PA, 2012. For $4,800. - to sponsor annual holiday dinner $25,000. - maintenance items; supplies; office equipment, misc. food related items.
$25,000 to Carlisle Regional Performing Arts Center, Carlisle, PA, 2012. For Capital campaign for renovations to equipment and building.
$15,000 to Harrisburg Symphony Association, Harrisburg, PA, 2012. For Presenting sponsor for summer concerts on July 4th, 2013 and July 4th, 2014.
$13,250 to Lancaster Cleft Palate Clinic, Lancaster, PA, 2012. To support of Operatory and Laboratory Equipment project.
$10,000 to Samaritan Fellowship, Carlisle, PA, 2012. For General assistance - $5,000.00 Trust fund - $5,000.00.
$1,500 to Hospice of Central Pennsylvania, Harrisburg, PA, 2012. For general support of fundraiser.

8308
The Sunoco Foundation ✧
1735 Market St., Ste. LL
Philadelphia, PA 19103-7583
Main URL: https://online.foundationsource.com/public/home/sunoco

Established in 2005 in PA.
Donor: Sunoco, Inc.
Foundation type: Company-sponsored foundation.
Financial data (yr. ended 12/31/13): Assets, $32,526,876 (M); expenditures, $1,856,942; qualifying distributions, $1,836,755; giving activities include $1,763,869 for 29 grants (high: $750,000; low: $750).
Purpose and activities: The foundation supports programs designed to promote projects that educate and develop skills for the workforce; promote environmental stewardship and responsibility; and help communities become better places to live and work.
Fields of interest: Education; Agriculture/food; Human services.
Type of support: Program development.
Limitations: Applications accepted. Giving primarily in areas of company operations, with emphasis on Philadelphia, PA. No support for athletic teams, bands, or choirs, religious organizations, pass-through organizations, discriminatory organizations, political parties, candidates, or partisan-political groups, fraternal or war veteran organizations, or private schools. No grants to individuals, or for fundraising events or sponsorships, single diseases or disease related causes, equipment (unless part of a community outreach program), athletic events, memorial grants, or travel.
Publications: Application guidelines.
Application information: Application form required.
Initial approach: Complete online application
Deadline(s): None
Officers and Directors:* Dennis Zeleny, Chair.; Ruth A. Clauser, Pres.; John J. DiRocco, Jr., Secy.; Charmian Uy,* Treas.; Anne-Marie Ainsworth; Cynthia A. Archer; Kathleen Shea-Ballay; David C. Webster.
EIN: 203459268
Selected grants: The following grants are a representative sample of this grantmaker's funding activity:
$200,000 to Philabundance, Philadelphia, PA, 2012. For Fuel Grant to Supply Food.
$200,000 to Philabundance, Philadelphia, PA, 2012. For Innovative Programs in the Battle Against Hunger.
$100,000 to Philabundance, Philadelphia, PA, 2012. For Philabundance Vehicle Fleet Support Fund.
$10,000 to Cornell University, Ithaca, NY, 2012. For Annual Fund for Industrial and Labor Relations.
$7,689 to Bryn Mawr College, Bryn Mawr, PA, 2012. For Bryn Mawr College Fund.
$5,000 to Philabundance, Philadelphia, PA, 2012. For Dover Food Drive.
$3,000 to Arts in Schools Collaborative, Philadelphia, PA, 2012. For Dancing Classrooms Philly.
$500 to College of Charleston Foundation, Charleston, SC, 2012. For Department of Communication Advisory Council Scholarship Fund.
$500 to West Philadelphia Alliance for Children, Philadelphia, PA, 2012. For leadership project.

8309
M. J. Surgala Trust ✧
5966 Wyndemere Dr.
Erie, PA 16505-5606 (814) 868-4921
Contact: Mary Lincoln, Exec. Dir.

Established in 2001 in NY.
Donor: M.J. Surgala†.
Foundation type: Independent foundation.
Financial data (yr. ended 12/31/12): Assets, $16,333,656 (M); expenditures, $778,814; qualifying distributions, $648,350; giving activities include $648,350 for grants.
Purpose and activities: Giving primarily in the field of health care.
Fields of interest: Arts; Hospitals (general); Health care, home services; Human services; Homeless.
Limitations: Applications accepted. Giving primarily in New York, NY and Erie, PA.
Application information: Application form required.
Initial approach: Contact foundation for application form
Deadline(s): None
Officer: Mary Lincoln, Exec. Dir.
EIN: 116556638

8310
Susquehanna Pfaltzgraff Foundation ✧ ☆
140 E. Market St.
P.O. Box 2026
York, PA 17405-2026 (717) 848-5500
Contact: John L. Finlayson, Treas. and Dir.

Established in 1966 in PA.
Donors: Susquehanna Pfaltzgraff Co.; Susquehanna Radio Corp.; The Pfaltzgraff Co.; Susquehanna Cable Co.; York Cable Television Co.; Louis J. Appell, Jr.
Foundation type: Company-sponsored foundation.
Financial data (yr. ended 12/31/13): Assets, $15,513,919 (M); gifts received, $853,302; expenditures, $760,654; qualifying distributions, $652,324; giving activities include $640,000 for 4 grants (high: $265,000; low: $25,000).
Purpose and activities: The foundation supports botanical gardens and organizations involved with preservation, land conservation, mental health, youth, and residential care.
Fields of interest: Agriculture/food; Recreation; Human services.

Type of support: Capital campaigns; Program development.
Limitations: Applications accepted. Giving in the U.S., primarily in Washington, DC, ME, and York, PA; giving also in Australia.
Application information: Application form required.
Initial approach: Letter
Copies of proposal: 1
Deadline(s): None
Officers and Directors:* Louis J. Appell, Jr.,* Pres.; Josephine S. Appell,* V.P.; John L. Finlayson,* Treas.
EIN: 236420008

8311
Kenneth and Caroline Taylor Family Foundation ✧
897 Rte. 706
Wyalusing, PA 18853

Established in 2000 in PA.
Donors: Caroline E. Taylor; Kenneth H. Taylor, Jr.; Parentebeard, LLC.
Foundation type: Independent foundation.
Financial data (yr. ended 12/31/12): Assets, $10,209,783 (M); gifts received, $10,000; expenditures, $648,081; qualifying distributions, $527,088; giving activities include $518,600 for 52 grants (high: $105,000; low: $500).
Purpose and activities: Giving primarily for the arts, education, health, social services, local fire departments, and to a Presbyterian church.
Fields of interest: Arts; Higher education; Education; Environment, land resources; Health organizations, association; Disasters, fire prevention/control; Human services; United Ways and Federated Giving Programs; Protestant agencies & churches.
Limitations: Applications not accepted. No grants to individuals.
Application information: Contributes only to pre-selected organizations.
Trustees: Caroline E. Taylor; Kenneth H. Taylor, Jr.
EIN: 256742004

8312
Tecovas Foundation ✧ ☆
c/o Glenmede Trust Co.
1650 Market St., Ste. 1200
Philadelphia, PA 19103-7391 (215) 419-6000
Contact: Janet W. Havener, Treas.
Twitter: http://twitter.com/TecovasFound

Established in 1999 in TX.
Donor: Caroline Bush Emeny†.
Foundation type: Independent foundation.
Financial data (yr. ended 12/31/13): Assets, $13,286,473 (M); expenditures, $697,398; qualifying distributions, $701,088; giving activities include $600,088 for 26 grants (high: $75,000; low: $1,180), and $92,190 for 1 loan/program-related investment.
Fields of interest: Food services; Human services; Foundations (community).
Limitations: Giving on a national basis, with emphasis on OH and TX. No grants to individuals.
Application information: Application form required.
Initial approach: Letter or telephone
Copies of proposal: 1
Board meeting date(s): Semi-annually
Officers and Directors:* Mary T. Emeny,* Chair.; Mary Galeti,* Vice-Chair.; George Ingalls,* Secy.; Nina L. Cohen, Treas.; Timothy Ingalls; Alexander S. Taylor.
Number of staff: None.
EIN: 752829989
Selected grants: The following grants are a representative sample of this grantmaker's funding activity:
$50,000 to Globe-News Center for the Performing Arts, Amarillo, TX, 2012. For General Operating Support (Seven Year Grant, 2006-2012).
$33,333 to Fund for Our Economic Future, Cleveland, OH, 2012. For General Operating Support (Three Year Grant, 2011-2013).
$25,000 to Hospice of the Western Reserve, Cleveland, OH, 2012. For Capital Campaign (Five Year Grant, 2008-2012).
$20,000 to Geauga Park District Foundation, Chardon, OH, 2012. For Observatory Park Construction.
$20,000 to Reading Village, Boulder, CO, 2012. To Create Replicable Model for Literacy.
$3,200 to Search for Common Ground, Washington, DC, 2012. For Participation by Kevin and Hannah Salwen at the Nexus Youth Summit.
$3,000 to New Venture Fund, Washington, DC, 2012. For the Launch of the Global Impact Institute, July 26, 2012 at the House of Commons in London.

8313
John Templeton Foundation ✧
300 Conshohocken State Rd., Ste. 500
West Conshohocken, PA 19428-3801 (610) 941-2828
Contact: Grant Admin.
FAX: (610) 825-1730; E-mail: info@templeton.org; Main URL: http://www.templeton.org/
Facebook: http://www.facebook.com/TempletonFoundation
Twitter: http://twitter.com/templeton_fdn
YouTube: http://www.youtube.com/user/TempletonFoundation

Established in 1988 in TN.
Donors: Sir. John Marks Templeton†; Templeton Religious Trust; Templeton World Charity Foundation.
Foundation type: Independent foundation.
Financial data (yr. ended 12/31/12): Assets, $2,555,855,497 (M); gifts received, $65,303,327; expenditures, $135,931,727; qualifying distributions, $126,124,827; giving activities include $105,248,596 for grants, and $2,429,016 for foundation-administered programs.
Purpose and activities: The John Templeton Foundation serves as a philanthropic catalyst for discoveries relating to the Big Questions of human purpose and ultimate reality. It supports research on subjects ranging from complexity, evolution, and infinity to creativity, forgiveness, love, and free will. It encourages civil, informed dialogue among scientists, philosophers, and theologians and between such experts and the public at large, for the purposes of definitional clarity and new insights. Its vision is derived from the late Sir John Templeton's optimism about the possibility of acquiring "new spiritual information" and from his commitment to rigorous scientific research and related scholarship. The foundation's motto, "How little we know, how eager to learn," exemplifies its support for open-minded inquiry and its hope for advancing human progress through breakthrough discoveries.
Fields of interest: Health care; Youth development; Economic development; Science; Leadership development; Religion.
Type of support: Program development; Conferences/seminars; Publication; Curriculum development; Fellowships; Research; Grants to individuals; Matching/challenge support.
Limitations: Applications accepted. Giving on a national and international basis. No support for the development of new business ventures or the creation of for-profit companies. No grants for academic scholarships for individuals or groups, endowment funds, building funds, real estate holdings, capital campaigns, or artistic productions; no grants for the purchase of equipment, unless deemed a vital and necessary component of a larger research project falling within the foundation's funding purposes; and no grants for general operating support to universities, institutions, or organizations.
Publications: Annual report; Financial statement; Informational brochure; Newsletter.
Application information: The foundation has established a new online grantmaking process for its Core Funding and Funding Priorities areas. Grants to individuals are a tiny portion of its grant-making because the foundation focuses on making grants in its area of interest. The foundation will award a grant to an applicant, whether an individual or an organization, if the applicant establishes an ability to make a contribution in one of the foundation's areas of interest. Generally, individual applicants must be associated with a 501 (c) (3) organization and the grant will be made to the organization. Full proposals will be accepted by invitation only. Application form required.
Initial approach: Submit online funding inquiry form
Deadline(s): Deadlines for inquiries: Feb. 3 - Apr. 1 and Aug.1 - Oct. 1
Board meeting date(s): Varies
Final notification: May 2 and Nov. 5
Officers and Trustees:* John Marks Templeton, Jr., M.D.*, Chair. and Pres.; Douglas W. Scott, Exec. V.P. and C.A.O.; Dawn Bryant, Exec. V.P. and General Counsel; Michael J. Murray, Exec. V.P., Progs.; Barnaby Marsh, Sr. V.P., Management and Strategic Initiatives; Kimon Howland Sargeant, Ph.D., V.P., Human Sciences; Paul K. Wason, Ph.D., V.P., Life Sciences and Genetics; Earl D. Whipple, V.P., Comms. and Public Affairs; Harvey M. Templeton III,* Secy.; Valerie K. Martin, C.F.O.; Denis R. Alexander; Heather Templeton Dill; Nidhal Guessoum; Rory Knight; Stephen G. Post; Eric Priest; Jeffrey P. Schloss; John W. Schott, M.D.; Jane M. Siebels, Ph.D.; Josephine "Pina" Templeton.
Number of staff: 12 full-time professional; 6 full-time support.
EIN: 621322826
Selected grants: The following grants are a representative sample of this grantmaker's funding activity:
$3,500,000 to Biologos Foundation, San Diego, CA, 2012. For general support.
$1,949,049 to University of California, Davis, CA, 2012. For general support.
$75,000 to Philanthropy Roundtable, Washington, DC, 2012. For general support.
$72,000 to Center for Strategic and International Studies, Washington, DC, 2012. For general support.
$71,326 to Deutsches Archaologisches Institut, Berlin, Germany, 2012. For general support.

$56,250 to International Computer Science Institute, Berkeley, CA, 2012. For general support.
$52,499 to University of Notre Dame, Notre Dame, IN, 2012. For general support.

8314
Teva Cares Foundation ✧
(formerly Cephalon Cares Foundation)
1090 Horsham Rd.
P.O. Box 1090
North Wales, PA 19454-1505 (877) 237-4881
Application address: 6900 College Blvd., Ste. 1000, Overland Park, KS 66211, tel.: (877) 237-4881;
Main URL: http://www.tevacares.org/

Established in 2009.
Foundation type: Operating foundation.
Financial data (yr. ended 12/31/13): Assets, $10,100,246 (M); gifts received, $51,085,676; expenditures, $50,246,701; qualifying distributions, $50,951,640; giving activities include $49,164,295 for grants to individuals.
Purpose and activities: The foundation provides prescription medication to economically disadvantaged individuals who lack prescription drug coverage and who meet certain income criteria.
Fields of interest: Economically disadvantaged.
Type of support: Donated products; In-kind gifts.
Publications: Application guidelines.
Application information: Applications are accepted for Fentora, Nuvigil, Treanda, Gabitril, Tev-Tropin, and Trisenox. Application form required.
Initial approach: Telephone foundation for application form or download application form and fax or mail to application address
Deadline(s): None
Officers and Directors:* Denise Bradley,* Chair.; Laurie Thibodeau,* Pres.; Kristen Bauer,* Secy.; Felicia Ladin, Treas.; Mike Derkacz; Denise Lynch; Jim Ottinger.
EIN: 263977456

8315
Thornedge Foundation ✧
(formerly E. Newbold & Margaret duPont Smith Foundation)
Station Sq. 1, Ste. 205
Paoli, PA 19301-1319 (610) 647-5577
Contact: Henry B. duPont Smith, V.P.

Donors: Margaret D. Smith Trust; E. Newbold Smith Trust.
Foundation type: Independent foundation.
Financial data (yr. ended 11/30/13): Assets, $25,956,014 (M); gifts received, $716,041; expenditures, $1,021,064; qualifying distributions, $940,000; giving activities include $940,000 for 82 grants (high: $120,000; low: $1,000).
Fields of interest: Arts; Education; Recreation; Human services.
Limitations: Applications accepted. Giving primarily in the greater Philadelphia, PA, area, some giving also in CT, MA, and RI.
Application information: Application form required.
Initial approach: 1-page letter
Deadline(s): None
Officers: Eleuthera S. Grassi, C.E.O. and Pres.; Henry B. duPont Smith,* V.P.; Stockton N. Smith, V.P.; Michelle Hughes, Secy.-Treas.
EIN: 516015711
Selected grants: The following grants are a representative sample of this grantmaker's funding activity:
$100,000 to Eaglebrook School, Deerfield, MA, 2011.
$89,000 to Franklin and Marshall College, Lancaster, PA, 2011.
$52,000 to Pennsylvania Academy of the Fine Arts, Philadelphia, PA, 2011.
$50,000 to Rectory School, Pomfret, CT, 2011.
$45,000 to Saint James School, Saint James, MD, 2011.
$40,000 to Avon Old Farms School, Avon, CT, 2011.
$10,000 to Barnes Foundation, Philadelphia, PA, 2011.
$10,000 to Mystic Seaport - The Museum of America and the Sea, Mystic, CT, 2011.
$7,750 to National Gallery of Art, Washington, DC, 2011.
$3,000 to Woodberry Forest School, Woodberry Forest, VA, 2011.

8316
The Bruce E. and Robbi S. Toll Foundation ✧
(formerly The Bruce E. Toll Foundation)
250 Gibraltar Rd.
Horsham, PA 19044-2323

Established in 1991 in PA.
Donor: Bruce E. Toll.
Foundation type: Independent foundation.
Financial data (yr. ended 12/31/13): Assets, $24,666,588 (M); expenditures, $1,265,285; qualifying distributions, $742,123; giving activities include $742,123 for 67 grants (high: $261,000; low: $120).
Purpose and activities: Giving primarily for Jewish organizations, including a museum of Jewish history; funding also for arts and culture, higher education, and hospitals.
Fields of interest: Museums; Museums (ethnic/folk arts); Performing arts; Higher education; Hospitals (general); Health organizations, association; Cancer research; Foundations (public); Jewish federated giving programs; Jewish agencies & synagogues.
Limitations: Applications not accepted. Giving primarily in Philadelphia, PA and New York, NY; funding also in Miami, FL. No grants to individuals.
Application information: Contributes only to pre-selected organizations.
Officer: Bruce E. Toll, Pres.
EIN: 232667935

8317
The Robert and Jane Toll Foundation ✧
250 Gibraltar Rd.
Horsham, PA 19044-2323

Established in 1991 in PA.
Donors: Robert I. Toll; Sylvia S. Toll†.
Foundation type: Independent foundation.
Financial data (yr. ended 12/31/13): Assets, $10,493,234 (M); expenditures, $617,230; qualifying distributions, $584,533; giving activities include $578,707 for 57 grants (high: $130,000; low: $95).
Purpose and activities: Giving primarily for Jewish federated giving programs, art and cultural programs, higher education, and for health and human services.
Fields of interest: Arts; Higher education; Hospitals (general); Human services; Jewish federated giving programs; Jewish agencies & synagogues.
Type of support: General/operating support.
Limitations: Applications not accepted. Giving primarily in NY and PA. No grants to individuals.
Application information: Contributes only to pre-selected organizations.
Officer and Director:* Robert I. Toll,* Pres.
EIN: 232654322
Selected grants: The following grants are a representative sample of this grantmaker's funding activity:
$3,500 to Urban Stages, New York, NY, 2012. For operating budget.

8318
Jordan Torch Foundation ✧ ☆
c/o BNY Mellon, N.A.
P.O. Box 185
Pittsburgh, PA 15230-0185

Established in 1997 in MA.
Foundation type: Independent foundation.
Financial data (yr. ended 12/31/13): Assets, $0 (M); expenditures, $776,151; qualifying distributions, $768,389; giving activities include $764,000 for 7 grants (high: $284,000; low: $40,000).
Fields of interest: Performing arts, orchestras; Education; Environment, natural resources; Marine science.
Type of support: General/operating support.
Limitations: Applications not accepted. Giving primarily in MA. No grants to individuals.
Application information: Unsolicited requests for funds not accepted.
Trustee: BNY Mellon, N.A.
EIN: 043388013
Selected grants: The following grants are a representative sample of this grantmaker's funding activity:
$40,000 to Falmouth Academy, Falmouth, MA, 2011.

8319
Edith L. Trees Charitable Trust ✧
c/o PNC Bank, N.A.
620 Liberty Ave., 10th Fl.
Pittsburgh, PA 15222-2705 (412) 762-4133
Contact: M. Bradley Dean, V.P., PNC Bank, N.A.; J. Murray Egan Esq., Tr.

Established around 1976.
Donor: Edith L. Trees Trust.
Foundation type: Independent foundation.
Financial data (yr. ended 12/31/13): Assets, $192,327,199 (M); gifts received, $38,000,000; expenditures, $7,511,307; qualifying distributions, $6,282,746; giving activities include $6,176,351 for 106 grants (high: $500,000; low: $5,000).
Purpose and activities: Giving solely for the care and welfare of children with mental retardation.
Fields of interest: Children/youth, services; Youth, services; Mentally disabled.
Type of support: General/operating support; Equipment; Endowments; Debt reduction.
Limitations: Applications accepted. Giving primarily in PA. No grants to individuals.
Application information: Application form not required.

Initial approach: Proposal
Deadline(s): Oct. 1
Trustees: J. Murray Egan; PNC Bank, N.A.
EIN: 256026443

8320
Harry C. Trexler Trust ✧
33 S. 7th St., Ste. 205
Allentown, PA 18101-2406
Contact: Janet E. Roth, Exec. Dir.
FAX: (610) 437-5721; Main URL: http://www.TrexlerTrust.org

Trust established in 1934 in PA.
Donors: Harry C. Trexler†; Mary M. Trexler†.
Foundation type: Independent foundation.
Financial data (yr. ended 03/31/13): Assets, $114,463,040 (M); expenditures, $5,261,597; qualifying distributions, $4,120,080; giving activities include $3,741,975 for 104 grants (high: $1,039,598; low: $1,000).
Purpose and activities: The trust provides that one-fourth of the income shall be added to the corpus, one-fourth paid to the city of Allentown for park purposes, and the remainder distributed to such charitable organizations and objects as shall be of the most benefit to humanity, but limited to Allentown and Lehigh County, Pennsylvania, particularly for hospitals, churches, institutions for the care of the crippled and orphans, youth agencies, social services, cultural programs, and support of ministerial students at two named Pennsylvania institutions.
Fields of interest: Arts; Higher education; Education; Food banks; Recreation; Human services; Children/youth, services; Aging, centers/services; Disabilities, people with; Economically disadvantaged.
Type of support: General/operating support; Continuing support; Capital campaigns; Building/renovation; Equipment; Land acquisition; Program development; Matching/challenge support.
Limitations: Applications accepted. Giving limited to Lehigh County, PA. No grants to individuals, or for endowment funds, research, scholarships, or fellowships; no loans.
Publications: Application guidelines; Annual report; Grants list; Occasional report.
Application information: Prospective grantees are welcome to request a meeting with staff well in advance of the Dec. 1 deadline to discuss the grant application process. Questions may be directed to Janet E. Roth, Exec. Dir., at the trust office. Application form and guidelines available on foundation web site. Application form required.
Initial approach: Letter no more than 3 pages
Copies of proposal: 1
Deadline(s): Dec. 1 for consideration at annual fund distribution
Board meeting date(s): Monthly; grant distribution takes place annually after Mar. 31
Final notification: June 1
Officer: Janet E. Roth, Exec. Dir.
Trustees: Barnet H. Fraenkel; Fr. Daniel G. Gambet; Malcolm J. Gross; L. Charles Marcon; Jamie P. Musselman.
Number of staff: 1 full-time professional; 1 part-time professional; 1 full-time support.
EIN: 231162215
Selected grants: The following grants are a representative sample of this grantmaker's funding activity:
$1,601,875 to Allentown, City of, Allentown, PA, 2011. To improve, extend and maintain parks.
$425,000 to Lehigh, County of, Allentown, PA, 2011. For improvements to Trexler Nature Center.
$315,000 to Allentown Art Museum, Allentown, PA, 2011. Toward capital campaign pledge.
$250,000 to Wildlands Conservancy, Emmaus, PA, 2011. For Jordan Creek Greenway project.
$200,000 to Boy Scouts of America, Minsi Trails Council, Lehigh Valley, PA, 2011. Toward camp improvements.
$200,000 to Casa Guadalupe Center, Allentown, PA, 2011. Toward campaign for new building.
$100,000 to Allentown Symphony Association, Allentown, PA, 2011. For operating support.
$100,000 to Sacred Heart Hospital, Allentown, PA, 2011. For parish nurse program in Allentown.
$75,000 to Allentown Public Library, Allentown, PA, 2011. For operating support.
$50,000 to Family Answers, Allentown, PA, 2011. For building improvements.

8321
Turner Family Foundation ✧
(also known as Robert E. & Carolyn Turner Foundation)
9 Horseshoe Ln.
Paoli, PA 19301-1909 (610) 696-1802

Established in 1994 in PA.
Donors: Robert E. Turner, Jr.; Carolyn Turner.
Foundation type: Independent foundation.
Financial data (yr. ended 12/31/12): Assets, $8,373,774 (M); gifts received, $788,569; expenditures, $1,339,377; qualifying distributions, $1,301,050; giving activities include $1,301,050 for grants.
Fields of interest: Higher education; Education; Human services; Protestant agencies & churches.
Limitations: Applications not accepted. Giving primarily in IN and PA. No grants to individuals.
Application information: Contributes only to pre-selected organizations.
Officers: Robert E. Turner, Jr., Pres.; Carolyn Turner, Treas.
EIN: 232792012

8322
The Tyler Foundation ✧
c/o PNC Bank N.A.
1600 Market St., Tax Dept.
Philadelphia, PA 19103-7240
Application address: c/o Jayne Kredatus, PNC Wealth Mgmt., PNC Bank, N.A., 454 State Rte. 28, Bridgewater, NJ 08807-2452

Established in 1984 in NJ; funded in 1990.
Donor: Charitable Remainder Unitrust U/W/O John Tyler.
Foundation type: Independent foundation.
Financial data (yr. ended 12/31/12): Assets, $11,306,458 (M); gifts received, $379,588; expenditures, $634,307; qualifying distributions, $527,778; giving activities include $495,612 for 30 grants (high: $84,888; low: $5,000).
Purpose and activities: Giving primarily for medical services and research, education, homeless and housing services, and for the arts.
Fields of interest: Elementary/secondary education; Environment; Heart & circulatory diseases; Cancer research; Human services.
Type of support: Capital campaigns; Building/renovation; Equipment; Emergency funds.
Limitations: Applications accepted. Giving primarily in NJ, with emphasis on Plainfield. No grants to individuals.
Application information: Application form required.
Initial approach: Letter
Copies of proposal: 5
Deadline(s): None
Board meeting date(s): July and Dec.
Trustees: Norman M. Carter, Jr., Esq.; Claudia Creo; PNC Bank, N.A.
Number of staff: 1 part-time support.
EIN: 226499512
Selected grants: The following grants are a representative sample of this grantmaker's funding activity:
$57,466 to American Heart Association, Watertown, NY, 2011. For general use of the organization.
$57,466 to Memorial Sloan-Kettering Cancer Center, New York, NY, 2011.
$20,000 to Matheny School and Hospital, Peapack, NJ, 2011. For general use of the organization.
$20,000 to Saint Huberts Giralda, Madison, NJ, 2011. For general use of the organization.
$15,601 to Mylestone Equine Rescue, Phillipsburg, NJ, 2011. For general use of the organization.
$15,000 to HomeFirst Interfaith Housing and Family Services, Plainfield, NJ, 2011. For general use of the organization.
$15,000 to Last Chance Ranch, Quakertown, PA, 2011. For general use of the organization.
$15,000 to Summit Speech School, New Providence, NJ, 2011. For general use of the organization.
$12,000 to Childrens Specialized Hospital, Mountainside, NJ, 2011. For general use of the organization.
$10,000 to Somerset Home for Temporarily Displaced Children, Bridgewater, NJ, 2011. For general use of the organization.

8323
Ujala Foundation ✧ ☆
43 Sleepy Hollow Dr.
Newtown Square, PA 19073-3929

Donor: Rajiv L. Gupta.
Foundation type: Independent foundation.
Financial data (yr. ended 12/31/13): Assets, $12,993,032 (M); gifts received, $993,060; expenditures, $768,511; qualifying distributions, $768,178; giving activities include $768,178 for 22 grants (high: $325,000; low: $500).
Fields of interest: Higher education; Education; Human services.
Limitations: Applications not accepted. Giving primarily in Baltimore, MD, NY, and Philadelphia, PA.
Application information: Unsolicited requests for funds not accepted.
Directors: Kamla Gupta; Rajiv L. Gupta.
EIN: 263274193

8324
United Service Foundation Inc. ✧
P.O. Box 309
Shrewsbury, PA 17361-0309
Contact: Larry Newswanger, Secy.
E-mail: LNewswa@aol.com

Established in 1969 in PA.
Donors: Janet Weaver Newswanger; Larry Newswanger; Dale M. Weaver†; Edith M. Weaver†; Irene M. Weaver; Victor F. Weaver†; Dawn Isley; Gregory Newswanger; Kendall Newswanger; Randall Newswanger; Geof Isley; Juji Woodring.
Foundation type: Independent foundation.
Financial data (yr. ended 12/31/13): Assets, $12,697,557 (M); expenditures, $639,727; qualifying distributions, $544,753; giving activities include $496,704 for 26 grants (high: $55,000; low: $2,500).
Purpose and activities: Giving primarily to Mennonite religious and educational organizations and a camping association. Support for leadership development and microenterprise development.
Fields of interest: Elementary/secondary education; Recreation; Community/economic development; Religion.
Type of support: General/operating support; Income development; Building/renovation; Program development; Conferences/seminars; Seed money; Internship funds; Program-related investments/loans.
Limitations: Applications not accepted. No support for political organizations. No grants to individuals.
Application information: Contributes only to pre-selected organizations.
Board meeting date(s): Quarterly
Officers and Trustees:* Dawn Isley,* Pres.; Larry W. Newswanger,* Secy.; Janet Newswanger,* Treas.; Greg Newswanger,* Genl. Mgr.
Number of staff: None.
EIN: 237038781
Selected grants: The following grants are a representative sample of this grantmaker's funding activity:
$44,805 to Paxton Street Home Benevolent Society, Paxton Ministries, Harrisburg, PA, 2012. For medical and spiritual care for those without insurance.
$24,000 to Christian Peacemaker Teams, Chicago, IL, 2012. For International Peacemaker Team operations.
$20,000 to No Longer Alone Ministries, Lancaster, PA, 2012. For mental health operations.
$15,000 to Eastern Mennonite University, Harrisonburg, VA, 2012. For scholarships for international students to attend summer Peace Building Institute of the Center for Justice and Peacebuilding.

8325
United States Steel Foundation, Inc. ✧
(formerly USX Foundation, Inc.)
600 Grant St., Rm. 675
Pittsburgh, PA 15219-2800 (412) 433-5237
Contact: Susan M. Kapusta, Pres.
FAX: (412) 433-2792; Main URL: http://www.ussteel.com/uss/portal/home/aboutus/foundation

Incorporated in 1953 in DE.
Donor: United States Steel Corp.
Foundation type: Company-sponsored foundation.
Financial data (yr. ended 11/30/13): Assets, $1,981,946 (M); gifts received, $1,726,000; expenditures, $2,415,969; qualifying distributions, $2,313,354; giving activities include $2,169,251 for 237 grants (high: $336,000; low: $1,250), and $144,103 for 173 employee matching gifts.
Purpose and activities: The foundation supports organizations involved with arts and culture, higher education, the environment, health, violence prevention, legal aid, safety, human services, science, and civic affairs.
Fields of interest: Performing arts; Arts; Higher education; Business school/education; Engineering school/education; Environment; Public health; Health care; Crime/violence prevention; Legal services; Safety, education; Human services; Engineering; Science; Public policy, research; Public affairs.
Type of support: General/operating support; Capital campaigns; Scholarship funds; Employee matching gifts; Employee-related scholarships.
Limitations: Applications accepted. Giving primarily in areas of company operations, with an emphasis on AL, IL, IN, and PA. No support for religious organizations for religious purposes, hospitals or nursing homes, or grantmaking foundations. No grants to individuals (except for employee-related scholarships), or for pre-collegiate education (unless U.S. Steel employees are directly involved), individual research projects, economic development, conferences, seminars, or symposia, travel, sponsorship of special events or fundraising events, publication of papers, books, or magazines, production of films, videotapes, or other audio-visual materials, or general operating support for organizations that receive operating funds from United Ways.
Publications: Application guidelines; Program policy statement.
Application information: Support is limited to 1 contribution per organization during any given year. Application form required.
Initial approach: Complete online application
Copies of proposal: 1
Deadline(s): Apr. 13 for Education; June 1 for Public, Cultural, and Scientific Affairs and Safety, Health, and Human Services
Board meeting date(s): July and Nov.
Final notification: Following board meetings
Officers and Trustees:* David H. Lohr,* Chair.; Susan M. Kapusta, Ph.D.*, Pres.; John J. Quaid, V.P. and Treas.; William Donovan, V.P., Investments; James D. Garraux,* Secy. and Genl. Counsel; Gretchen R. Haggerty,* C.F.O.; Gregory A. Zovko, Compt.; Darin R. Hoffner, Tax Counsel; John P. Surma; Susan M. Suver.
Number of staff: 1 full-time professional; 1 part-time professional; 2 full-time support.
EIN: 136093185
Selected grants: The following grants are a representative sample of this grantmaker's funding activity:
$166,500 to United Way of Allegheny County, Pittsburgh, PA, 2011.
$166,500 to United Way of Allegheny County, Pittsburgh, PA, 2011.
$110,000 to United Way, Lake Area, Griffith, IN, 2011.
$100,000 to Robert Morris University, School of Business, Moon Township, PA, 2011.
$50,000 to Focus: HOPE, Detroit, MI, 2011.
$25,000 to Northeast Texas Community College Foundation, Mount Pleasant, TX, 2011.
$25,000 to United Way of Northeastern Minnesota, Chisholm, MN, 2011.
$20,000 to Little Sisters of the Poor, Pittsburgh, PA, 2011.
$20,000 to Saint Vincent College, Latrobe, PA, 2011.
$12,000 to Make-A-Wish Foundation of Greater Pennsylvania and Southern West Virginia, Pittsburgh, PA, 2011.

8326
The Richard Vague Foundation ✧ ☆
1807 Delancey St.
Philadelphia, PA 19103-6606

Established in PA.
Donor: Richard W. Vague.
Foundation type: Independent foundation.
Financial data (yr. ended 12/31/13): Assets, $663,483 (M); gifts received, $323,283; expenditures, $2,411,425; qualifying distributions, $2,402,536; giving activities include $1,372,128 for 26 grants (high: $500,000; low: $300).
Fields of interest: Arts; Higher education; Foundations (private grantmaking).
Limitations: Applications not accepted. Giving primarily in New York, NY, and Philadelphia, PA.
Application information: Unsolicited requests for funds not accepted.
Trustee: Richard W. Vague.
EIN: 454104509

8327
The Vanguard Group Foundation ✧
100 Vanguard Blvd.
Malvern, PA 19355-2331
Application address: c/o Tami Wise, Admin., P.O. Box 2600 (V38), Valley Forge, PA 19482; tel.: (610) 669-6331

Established in 1992 in PA.
Donor: The Vanguard Group, Inc.
Foundation type: Company-sponsored foundation.
Financial data (yr. ended 12/31/12): Assets, $13,372,221 (M); gifts received, $4,006,785; expenditures, $4,114,731; qualifying distributions, $4,103,010; giving activities include $4,095,002 for 489 grants (high: $2,210,000; low: $25).
Purpose and activities: The foundation supports organizations involved with arts and culture, education, the environment, health, employment, human services, community development, and civic affairs.
Fields of interest: Media/communications; Museums; Performing arts; Arts; Elementary/secondary education; Higher education; Libraries (public); Education; Environment, natural resources; Environment; Health care; Employment; Human services; Economic development; Community/economic development; United Ways and Federated Giving Programs; Public affairs.
Type of support: General/operating support; Employee matching gifts.
Limitations: Applications accepted. Giving primarily in areas of company operations in the Delaware Valley, PA, area, with emphasis on the greater Philadelphia, PA, metropolitan area. No grants to individuals.
Publications: Application guidelines.
Application information: Telephone calls during the application process are not encouraged. Application form required.
Initial approach: Contact foundation for application form
Deadline(s): None
Board meeting date(s): Quarterly
Final notification: Within 4 to 6 weeks
Officers and Directors:* Michael S. Miller,* Chair. and Pres.; Amy B. Cooper,* Secy.; Glenn W. Reed,* Treas.; Mortimer Buckley; F. William McNabb III; Pauline C. Scalvino.
EIN: 232699769

8328
Viropharma Charitable Foundation ✧ ☆
730 Stockton Dr.
Exton, PA 19341-1171 (877) 945-1000
FAX: (888) 281-8211;
E-mail: inquiries@cinryzesolutions.com; Additional tel.: (800) 517-2457, fax: (800) 483-6714; Main URL: http://www.cinryze.com/hae-patient-assistance.aspx

Established in 2011 in PA.
Donor: Viropharma Inc.
Foundation type: Company-sponsored foundation.
Financial data (yr. ended 12/31/12): Assets, $122,597 (M); gifts received, $14,721,998; expenditures, $14,774,016; qualifying distributions, $14,774,016; giving activities include $14,774,016 for 91 grants to individuals.
Purpose and activities: The foundation provides the pharmaceutical product CINRYZE to people in need.
Fields of interest: Pharmacy/prescriptions; Health care; Economically disadvantaged.
Type of support: Donated products.
Limitations: Applications accepted. Giving primarily on an national basis.
Publications: Application guidelines.
Application information: Patients must work with a Patient Care Coordinator from the Patient Service Center. Application form required.
Initial approach: Telephone and fax or mail prequalification form
Deadline(s): None
Officers and Directors:* Paul Firuta,* Chair.; Thomas F. Doyle,* V.P.; Bryant Lim, Secy.; David Garrett, Treas.; Brad Dickerson, Exec. Dir.; Robert C. Fletcher.
EIN: 453132103

8329
The Richard C. von Hess Foundation ✧
c/o The Glenmede Trust Co., N.A.
1650 Market St., Ste. 1200
Philadelphia, PA 19103-7391

Established in 1989 in PA.
Donor: Richard C. von Hess.
Foundation type: Independent foundation.
Financial data (yr. ended 12/31/13): Assets, $24,479,242 (M); expenditures, $1,459,976; qualifying distributions, $1,335,619; giving activities include $1,155,351 for 30 grants (high: $125,000; low: $5,000).
Purpose and activities: The foundation was created to assist the work of Wright's Ferry Museum, a historic 18th century house museum in Columbia, Pennsylvania, as well as to further art education and other charitable purposes.
Fields of interest: Arts education; Museums (art); Performing arts; Historic preservation/historical societies; Arts.
Limitations: Applications not accepted. Giving primarily in PA. No grants to individuals.
Application information: Contributes only to pre-selected organizations.
Trustees: Thomas Hills Cook; Anne Genter; Warren A. Reintzel, Esq.
EIN: 236962077

8330
The Waldorf Educational Foundation ✧ ☆
c/o The Glenmede Trust Co.
1650 Market St., Ste. 1200
Philadelphia, PA 19103-7391 (215) 419-6000
Contact: Melanie Redmond Quackenbush

Established in 1951 in PA.
Foundation type: Independent foundation.
Financial data (yr. ended 12/31/13): Assets, $12,126,797 (M); expenditures, $650,492; qualifying distributions, $602,120; giving activities include $562,981 for 44 grants (high: $100,000; low: $500).
Purpose and activities: Grants are made for the aid and benefit of the principles and developments of the Waldorf method of Education.
Fields of interest: Education, association; Elementary/secondary education; Higher education; Human services, mind/body enrichment.
Type of support: Building/renovation; Program development; Conferences/seminars; Scholarship funds; Research; Matching/challenge support.
Limitations: Applications accepted. Giving in the US, with emphasis on Ghent, NY, and CA; some funding also in Ontario, Canada. No grants to individuals.
Publications: Application guidelines.
Application information: Application form not required.
Initial approach: Proposal
Copies of proposal: 7
Deadline(s): None
Trustees: David Alsop; Erika V. Asten, Ph.D.; Mark Finser; Karin Myrin; Clemens Pietzner; The Glenmede Trust Co.
EIN: 236254206

8331
The Ralph T. & Esther L. Warburton Foundation ✧
c/o Glenmede Trust Co., N.A.
1650 Market St., Ste. 1200
Philadelphia, PA 19103-7391

Established around 1966 in OH.
Donor: Ralph T. Warburton†.
Foundation type: Independent foundation.
Financial data (yr. ended 12/31/13): Assets, $11,548,518 (M); gifts received, $13,441; expenditures, $915,542; qualifying distributions, $732,184; giving activities include $623,000 for 7 grants (high: $250,000; low: $3,000).
Fields of interest: Higher education; Health care.
Type of support: General/operating support.
Limitations: Applications not accepted. Giving primarily in Stark County, OH. No grants to individuals.
Application information: Contributes only to pre-selected organizations.
Trustees: Betsy Warburton Downs; Mike D. Downs; Alex W. Montalto; Carrie Warburton Montalto; Phillip L. Warburton; Sally Warburton.
EIN: 346574882
Selected grants: The following grants are a representative sample of this grantmaker's funding activity:
$21,000 to Mayo Clinic, Rochester, MN, 2011. For general purposes.

8332
Washington County Community Foundation, Inc. ✧
331 S. Main St.
Washington, PA 15301 (724) 222-6330
Contact: Betsie Trew, C.E.O.
FAX: (724) 222-7960; E-mail: info@wccf.net; Additional e-mail: brtrew@wccf.net; Main URL: http://www.wccf.net
Facebook: https://www.facebook.com/pages/Washington-County-Community-Foundation/221252694651719
RSS Feed: http://www.wccf.net/rss
Twitter: https://twitter.com/washcocommfdtn

Established in 1993 in PA.
Foundation type: Community foundation.
Financial data (yr. ended 12/31/13): Assets, $17,033,661 (M); gifts received, $1,611,924; expenditures, $1,157,663; giving activities include $846,976 for 40+ grants (high: $50,378).
Purpose and activities: The foundation fosters philanthropy by offering charitable gifting opportunities to donors. Its purpose includes helping donors accomplish their goals by professionally managing funds entrusted to it for today and for the future, and by distributing these funds as directed by the donor or the Board of Trustees in the areas of arts, education, the environment, health, human needs, and religion.
Fields of interest: Arts education; Visual arts; Performing arts; Humanities; Arts; Education; Environment, pollution control; Environment; Animal welfare; Health care; Human services; Community development, neighborhood development; Economic development; Urban/community development; Religion.
Type of support: Film/video/radio; Publication; Program development; General/operating support; Equipment; Continuing support; Capital campaigns; Building/renovation; Annual campaigns; Scholarship funds; Scholarships—to individuals.
Limitations: Applications accepted. Giving primarily in Washington County, PA. No support for private charities. No grants to individuals (except for scholarships), or for routine or land acquisition projects, or endowment funds; no loans.
Publications: Application guidelines; Annual report; Financial statement; Informational brochure; Newsletter.
Application information: Visit foundation web site for application forms and guidelines. Application form required.
Initial approach: Application
Copies of proposal: 1
Deadline(s): Sept. 1 for discretionary fund grants; varies for others
Board meeting date(s): 4th Thurs. of each month; annual meeting in June
Final notification: Varies
Officers and Trustees:* Deborah E. Takach,* Chair.; Edward C. Morascyzk,* Vice-Chair.; Betsie Trew,* Pres. and C.E.O.; Jarol A. DeVoge,* Secy.; Sandra Guthrie,* Treas.; Mark A. Campbell; William M. Campbell; Thomas Gladden; Tammy Hardy; Thomas Hart; Thomas F. Hoffman; Geraldine M. Jones; Charles C. Keller; William M. Kline III; John McCarthy; Barron P. McCune, Jr.; James McCune; Andrew M. McIlvaine; Thomas P. Northrup; Alex E. Paris, III; Kurt Salvatori; Gwen Simmons; Brian J. Smith; Lynne Stout; Dorothy Tecklenburg; Thomas Uram; Richard L. White.

Number of staff: 1 full-time professional; 2 part-time support.
EIN: 251726013

8333
Wells Fargo Regional Foundation ✧
(formerly Wachovia Regional Foundation)
123 S. Broad St.
MAC Y1379-030
Philadelphia, PA 19109-1029 (215) 670-4300
Contact: Denise McGregor Armbrister, Exec. Dir.
FAX: (215) 670-4313;
E-mail: communityaffairs@wachovia.com; Contact for Neighborhood Implementation and Planning Grants: Kimberly Allen, Prog. Off., tel.: (215) 670-4307, Crystal Dundas, Prog. Off., tel.: (215) 670-4311; Main URL: https://www.wellsfargo.com/about/regional-foundation/index
Grants List: https://www.wellsfargo.com/downloads/pdf/about/WFRF_Active_Grantee_Portfolio.pdf

Established in 1998.
Donors: CoreStates Financial Corp; First Union Corp.; Wachovia Corp.
Foundation type: Company-sponsored foundation.
Financial data (yr. ended 12/31/12): Assets, $77,675,043 (M); expenditures, $5,250,455; qualifying distributions, $4,974,479; giving activities include $4,861,350 for 118 grants (high: $110,000; low: $1,500).
Purpose and activities: The foundation supports organizations involved with neighborhood planning and development.
Fields of interest: Employment, job counseling; Employment, training; Housing/shelter, development; Housing/shelter; Children, services; Family services; Community development, neighborhood development; Economic development; Urban/community development.
Type of support: Equipment; Program development; Technical assistance; Program evaluation.
Limitations: Applications accepted. Giving primarily in Kent, New Castle, and Sussex, DE, Atlantic, Bergen, Burlington, Camden, Cape May, Cumberland, Essex, Hudson, Hunterdon, Gloucester, Mercer, Middlesex, Monmouth, Morris, Ocean, Passaic, Salem, Somerset, Sussex, Union, and Warren, NJ, and Adams, Berks, Bradford, Bucks, Carbon, Centre, Chester, Clinton, Columbia, Cumberland, Dauphin, Delaware, Juniata, Lackawanna, Lancaster, Lebanon, Lehigh, Lycoming, Luzerne, Mifflin, Monroe, Montgomery, Montour, Northampton, Northumberland, Perry, Philadelphia, Pike, Potter, Schuylkill, Snyder, Sullivan, Susquehanna, Tioga, Union, Wayne, Wyoming, and York, PA. No support for political organizations or national or international organizations; generally, no support for K-12 private schools, colleges or universities, veterans' or fraternal organizations, arts or cultural organizations, hospitals or medical centers, or health- or disease-related organizations. No grants to individuals, or for general operating support, strategic or business plans, "bricks and mortar" projects, political causes, endowments, capital campaigns, debt reduction, or special events; generally, no grants for religious programs or activities.
Publications: Application guidelines; Grants list; Program policy statement.
Application information: Neighborhood Planning and Implementation Grants have two phases. Phase two of the application process is by invitation only. A site visit may be requested. Application form required.
Initial approach: Complete online eligibility quiz and application form
Deadline(s): Sept. 5 for phase one and Oct. 13 for phase two for Neighborhood Planning Grants; Apr. 11 and Oct. 24 for phase one and June 23 and Jan. 16 for phase two for Neighborhood Implementation Grants
Board meeting date(s): Jan., Apr., July, and Oct.
Final notification: Jan. 31 for Neighborhood Planning Grants; Nov. 1 and Apr. 30 for Neighborhood Implementation Grants
Officers and Directors:* Austin J. Burke, Chair.; Robert Torres, Esq., Vice-Chair.; Denise McGregor Armbrister, Sr. V.P. and Exec. Dir.; Lois W. Greco, Sr. V.P. and Evaluation Off.; Kimberly Allen, V.P. and Sr. Prog. Off.; Fernando Chang-Muy, Esq.; Shinjoo Choo; Lucia Gibbons; Tom Hanlon; Stacy Holland; Maria Matos; Gabriella Morris; Greg Redden; Ralph Smith, Esq.; John Thurber, Esq.
Number of staff: 4 full-time professional; 1 full-time support.
EIN: 222625990

8334
The H. O. West Foundation ✧
(also known as The Herman O. West Foundation)
530 Heilman O. West Dr.
Exton, PA 19341 (610) 594-2945
Contact: Richard D. Luzzi, Tr.; Maureen B. Goebel, Admin.
E-mail: maureen.goebel@westpharma.com; Main URL: http://www.westpharma.com/en/about/Pages/CharitableGiving.aspx

Established in 1972 in PA.
Donors: The West Co., Inc.; West Pharmaceutical Services, Inc.
Foundation type: Company-sponsored foundation.
Financial data (yr. ended 12/31/13): Assets, $4,630,935 (M); gifts received, $1,000,000; expenditures, $755,730; qualifying distributions, $755,730; giving activities include $668,893 for 88 grants (high: $130,018; low: $875), $59,880 for 48 grants to individuals (high: $3,750; low: $912), and $25,948 for 111 employee matching gifts.
Purpose and activities: The foundation supports organizations involved with arts and culture, education, health, human services, community development, and science and technology. Support is given primarily in areas of company operations in Arizona, Florida, Michigan, North Carolina, Nebraska, and Pennsylvania.
Fields of interest: Arts; Education, fund raising/fund distribution; Higher education; Education; Hospitals (general); Health care; Human services; Community/economic development; United Ways and Federated Giving Programs; Engineering/technology; Science.
Type of support: Annual campaigns; Building/renovation; Capital campaigns; Continuing support; Emergency funds; Employee matching gifts; Employee-related scholarships; General/operating support; Matching/challenge support; Research; Scholarships—to individuals.
Limitations: Applications accepted. Giving primarily in areas of company operations in AZ, FL, MI, NC, NE, and PA.
Publications: Application guidelines.
Application information: Application form not required.
Initial approach: Proposal or letter
Copies of proposal: 1
Deadline(s): 1 week prior to board meetings
Board meeting date(s): Spring and fall
Final notification: Varies
Officer and Trustees:* George R. Bennyhoff, Chair.; Paula A. Johnson, M.D.; Richard D. Luzzi.
Number of staff: None.
EIN: 383674460
Selected grants: The following grants are a representative sample of this grantmaker's funding activity:
$50,000 to YMIC Foundation, West Chester, PA, 2012.
$46,000 to Fox Chase Cancer Center, Philadelphia, PA, 2012.
$10,000 to American Red Cross, Southeastern Pennsylvania Chapter, Philadelphia, PA, 2012. For Hurricane Sandy.
$10,000 to Franklin Institute Science Museum, Philadelphia, PA, 2012.
$5,000 to Academy of Natural Sciences of Philadelphia, Philadelphia, PA, 2012.
$5,000 to American Red Cross, Southeastern Pennsylvania Chapter, Philadelphia, PA, 2012.
$5,000 to Cancer Care, New York, NY, 2012.
$5,000 to Downingtown STEM Academy, Downingtown, PA, 2012.
$5,000 to Philadelphia Museum of Art, Philadelphia, PA, 2012.
$5,000 to Zoological Society of Philadelphia, Philadelphia Zoo, Philadelphia, PA, 2012.
$3,500 to YMIC Foundation, West Chester, PA, 2012.

8335
The Wheeler Family Charitable Foundation ✧
P.O. Box 466
Somerset, PA 15501-0466 (814) 445-8442
Contact: Barbara Davies, Dir.

Established in 1997 in PA.
Donors: Harold W. Wheeler; Joan M. Wheeler; Barbara Davies; Randy Davies; Paul Wheeler; Stacy Wheeler; Wheeler Bros., Inc.
Foundation type: Independent foundation.
Financial data (yr. ended 12/31/13): Assets, $6,152,570 (M); expenditures, $1,567,772; qualifying distributions, $1,521,634; giving activities include $1,521,634 for 29 grants (high: $750,000; low: $1,000).
Purpose and activities: Giving primarily for health care and human services.
Fields of interest: Hospitals (specialty); Medical research, institute; Food banks; Food distribution, meals on wheels; Human services; Children/youth, services.
Type of support: Continuing support; Annual campaigns; Capital campaigns; Emergency funds.
Limitations: Applications accepted. Giving primarily in Somerset County, PA. No grants to individuals.
Application information: Application form not required.
Initial approach: Proposal
Deadline(s): None
Officer: Joan M. Wheeler, Chair.
Directors: Barbara Davies; David L. Wheeler; Harold W. Wheeler III; Paul J. Wheeler.

Trustee: Somerset Trust Co.
EIN: 232938580
Selected grants: The following grants are a representative sample of this grantmaker's funding activity:
$10,000 to Boy Scouts of America, Laurel Highlands Council, Ebensburg, PA, 2012. For unrestricted contribution.

8336
Widener Memorial Foundation in Aid of Handicapped Children ✧
4060 Butler Pike, Ste. 225
Plymouth Meeting, PA 19462-1554 (215) 825-8900
Contact: Edith R. Dixon, Treas. and Tr.

Incorporated in 1912 in PA.
Donors: Peter A.B. Widener†; Widener Memorial Foundation 2; Widener Memorial School Endowment.
Foundation type: Independent foundation.
Financial data (yr. ended 12/31/13): Assets, $8,109,304 (M); gifts received, $570,613; expenditures, $1,085,358; qualifying distributions, $1,026,648; giving activities include $1,003,980 for 29 grants (high: $120,000; low: $3,000).
Purpose and activities: Support for research into the causes, treatment, and prevention of diseases and conditions which handicap children orthopedically; to aid and assist public and private charitable institutions and associations in the care, education, and rehabilitation of children so handicapped.
Fields of interest: Orthopedics; Medical research, institute; Children/youth, services; Disabilities, people with.
Type of support: Building/renovation; Equipment; Program development; Seed money; Research.
Limitations: Giving limited to the Delaware Valley area, with emphasis on Philadelphia, PA. No support for private foundations or for organizations lacking 501(c)(3) status. No grants to individuals, or for endowment funds, scholarships, fellowships, or matching gifts; no loans.
Application information:
Initial approach: Letter
Copies of proposal: 1
Deadline(s): May and Nov.
Board meeting date(s): May and Nov.
Final notification: Immediately after board meetings
Officers and Trustees:* Edith D. Miller,* Pres.; Peter M. Mattoon,* V.P.; George W. Dixon,* Secy.; Edith R. Dixon,* Treas.; Bruce L. Castor; Michael Clancy, M.D.; Mark S. DePillis; Linda Grobman; John Keleher; Peter M. Mattoon.
EIN: 236267223

8337
Wiegand Morning Star Foundation, Inc. ✧ ☆
c/o Carr & Associates
508 Allegheny River Blvd., No. 212
Oakmont, PA 15139

Established in 2004 in PA.
Donors: Phillips Wiegand; PW Financial Partners.
Foundation type: Independent foundation.
Financial data (yr. ended 12/31/13): Assets, $5,917,572 (M); expenditures, $983,723; qualifying distributions, $952,500; giving activities include $952,500 for 14 grants (high: $260,000; low: $1,000).
Fields of interest: Human services; Family services; Christian agencies & churches.
Limitations: Applications not accepted. Giving primarily in CO, LA, PA and TN. No grants to individuals.
Application information: Contributes only to pre-selected organizations.
Directors: Sara Valentine; Ben Wiegand; Phillips Wiegand; Phillips Wiegand, Jr.; Ruth Wiegand.
EIN: 562449126

8338
The C. K. Williams Foundation ✧ ☆
c/o BNY Mellon, N.A.
P.O. Box 185
Pittsburgh, PA 15230-0185

Established in 1963 in PA.
Foundation type: Independent foundation.
Financial data (yr. ended 12/31/13): Assets, $10,180,011 (M); expenditures, $485,649; qualifying distributions, $454,409; giving activities include $435,000 for 16 grants (high: $200,000; low: $5,000).
Fields of interest: Museums; Elementary/secondary education; Higher education; Protestant agencies & churches.
Type of support: General/operating support.
Limitations: Applications not accepted. Giving in the U.S., with emphasis on PA. No grants to individuals.
Application information: Contributes only to pre-selected organizations.
Board meeting date(s): Oct.
Trustee: Joan W. Rhome.
EIN: 236292772
Selected grants: The following grants are a representative sample of this grantmaker's funding activity:
$25,000 to Hamilton College, Clinton, NY, 2011.
$25,000 to Smithsonian American Art Museum, Washington, DC, 2011.
$10,000 to Garden Club of Virginia, Richmond, VA, 2011.
$10,000 to Lafayette College, Easton, PA, 2011.
$10,000 to Longwood Gardens, Kennett Square, PA, 2011.
$10,000 to Saint Stephens Episcopal Church, Boston, MA, 2011.
$5,000 to Washington Winter Show, Washington, DC, 2011.
$5,000 to Winterthur Museum, Garden and Library, Winterthur, DE, 2011.
$3,000 to Breast Cancer Network of Strength, Herndon, VA, 2011.

8339
Charles K. Williams II Trust ✧
c/o BNY Mellon, N.A.
P.O. Box 185
Pittsburgh, PA 15230-0185 (215) 553-3344

Established in 1985 in PA.
Donor: Charles K. Williams II.
Foundation type: Independent foundation.
Financial data (yr. ended 11/30/13): Assets, $134,021 (M); gifts received, $525,000; expenditures, $450,261; qualifying distributions, $450,205; giving activities include $165,000 for 3 grants (high: $90,000; low: $25,000), and $285,168 for 7 grants to individuals (high: $45,000; low: $4,000).
Purpose and activities: Scholarship awards for postgraduate studies limited to the field of scientific archaeology; also providing awards and fellowships for individuals and/or projects in specific archaeology endeavors.
Fields of interest: History/archaeology.
International interests: Greece.
Type of support: Fellowships; Scholarship funds; Research.
Limitations: Applications accepted. Giving primarily in DE and Italy.
Application information: Application form not required.
Initial approach: Proposal
Deadline(s): None
Trustee: BNY Mellon, N.A.
EIN: 236758319

8340
Hilda M. Willis Foundation ✧
c/o BNY Mellon, N.A.
P.O. Box 185
Pittsburgh, PA 15230-0185 (412) 234-1634

Established in 1981 in PA; initial endowment in fiscal 1992.
Donor: Hilda M. Willis†.
Foundation type: Independent foundation.
Financial data (yr. ended 06/30/13): Assets, $12,366,736 (M); expenditures, $767,507; qualifying distributions, $702,500; giving activities include $702,500 for grants.
Purpose and activities: Giving primarily for higher education and the arts; special interest in those organizations supported by Mrs. Willis during her lifetime.
Fields of interest: Arts; Elementary/secondary education; Higher education; Medical care, rehabilitation.
Type of support: Annual campaigns; Building/renovation; Capital campaigns.
Limitations: Applications not accepted. Giving limited to Allegheny County, PA, with the majority paid in Pittsburgh. No grants to individuals.
Application information: Unsolicited requests for funds not accepted.
Board meeting date(s): Nov. and Apr.
Trustee: BNY Mellon, N.A.
Number of staff: None.
EIN: 256371417
Selected grants: The following grants are a representative sample of this grantmaker's funding activity:
$100,000 to University of Pittsburgh, School of Medicine, Pittsburgh, PA, 2013. For general operating purposes.

8341
Edward M. Wilson Family Foundation ✧
c/o PNC Bank, N.A.
P.O. Box 609
Pittsburgh, PA 15230-0609
Application address: c/o Jocy Muya PNC Bank, 101 W. Washington St., Ste. 600E, Indianapolis, IN 46204-3494, tel.: (216) 222-3226

Established around 1980 in IN.
Donor: William Telfer.

Foundation type: Independent foundation.
Financial data (yr. ended 09/30/13): Assets, $32,532,224 (M); expenditures, $1,591,900; qualifying distributions, $1,482,591; giving activities include $1,381,200 for 87 grants (high: $85,000; low: $1,500).
Purpose and activities: Giving primarily for arts and culture, education, children, youth and social services, and to Christian organizations.
Fields of interest: Museums (art); Arts; Education; Human services; American Red Cross; YM/YWCAs & YM/YWHAs; Children/youth, services; Foundations (private grantmaking); Christian agencies & churches.
Type of support: General/operating support.
Limitations: Giving primarily in Fort Wayne, IN. No grants to individuals.
Application information:
Initial approach: Proposal
Deadline(s): None
Distribution Committee: Janet C. Chrzan; Hon. William Lee; Tom Quirk; Thomas Shoaff; Don A. Wolf.
Trustee: PNC Bank, N.A.
EIN: 310976337
Selected grants: The following grants are a representative sample of this grantmaker's funding activity:
$100,000 to Arts United of Greater Fort Wayne, Fort Wayne, IN, 2011.
$50,000 to Community Foundation of Greater Fort Wayne, Fort Wayne, IN, 2011. For general support.
$30,000 to Southeast Youth Council, Monroeville, IN, 2011. For general support.
$25,000 to Northeast Indiana Innovation Center, Fort Wayne, IN, 2011.
$25,000 to Shepherds House, Fort Wayne, IN, 2011. For general support.
$15,000 to Cancer Services of Northeast Indiana, Fort Wayne, IN, 2011.
$15,000 to Community Transportation Network, Fort Wayne, IN, 2011.
$10,000 to Blessings in a Backpack, Fort Wayne, IN, 2011.
$10,000 to Childrens Hope, Fort Wayne, IN, 2011.
$10,000 to Literacy Alliance, Fort Wayne, IN, 2011.

8342
Winstar Institute ✧

c/o BNY Mellon, N.A.
P.O. Box 185
Pittsburgh, PA 15230-0185

Established in PA.
Foundation type: Independent foundation.
Financial data (yr. ended 12/31/13): Assets, $11,996,216 (M); expenditures, $597,680; qualifying distributions, $557,896; giving activities include $543,504 for 1 grant.
Fields of interest: Anatomy (human).
Limitations: Applications not accepted. Giving primarily in Philadelphia, PA.
Application information: Contributes only to pre-selected organizations.
Trustee: BNY Mellon, N.A.
EIN: 236227265

8343
The Joan M. Wismer Foundation ✧

1600 Market St., Ste. 3600
Philadelphia, PA 19103-7286 (215) 751-2338
Contact: John D. Iskrant, Tr.
E-mail: jiskrant@schnader.com

Established in 2001 in PA.
Donor: Joan M. Wismer.
Foundation type: Independent foundation.
Financial data (yr. ended 12/31/13): Assets, $15,449,059 (M); gifts received, $749,494; expenditures, $748,047; qualifying distributions, $594,881; giving activities include $501,000 for 23 grants (high: $75,000; low: $2,500).
Fields of interest: Health organizations; Human services; YM/YWCAs & YM/YWHAs.
Limitations: Applications accepted. Giving primarily in CA and VA.
Application information: Application form not required.
Initial approach: Proposal
Deadline(s): None
Trustees: N. Jack Dilday; John D. Iskrant; Joan M. Wismer.
EIN: 233089181

8344
Withington Foundation, Inc. ✧

c/o Andrew K. Rooke
7029 Sheaf Ln.
Fort Washington, PA 19034-2005

Established in 1994 in NJ.
Donors: William W. Rooke; Robert L. Rooke†.
Foundation type: Independent foundation.
Financial data (yr. ended 12/31/12): Assets, $19,156,684 (M); expenditures, $1,274,727; qualifying distributions, $1,021,291; giving activities include $1,021,291 for 49 grants (high: $145,000; low: $500).
Purpose and activities: Giving primarily for education; funding also for health care, and human services.
Fields of interest: Higher education; Education; Hospitals (general); Medical research, institute; Human services.
Type of support: Continuing support; Capital campaigns.
Limitations: Applications not accepted. Giving in the U.S., with some emphasis on AZ and PA. No grants to individuals.
Application information: Contributes only to pre-selected organizations.
Board meeting date(s): Nov.
Officers: William W. Rooke, Pres.; Andrew K. Rooke, V.P.; Charles C. Rooke, Secy.-Treas.
EIN: 223291812
Selected grants: The following grants are a representative sample of this grantmaker's funding activity:
$10,000 to University of Denver, Denver, CO, 2012. To support the Annual Fund.
$5,000 to Fairfield University, Fairfield, CT, 2012. For general university funding support.
$5,000 to YMCA of Greenville, Greenville, SC, 2012. To support Young Men's Health and Athlete.
$2,500 to Camperdown Academy, Greenville, SC, 2012. For Dyslexia in Children.

8345
The Wolf Creek Charitable Foundation ✧

c/o PNC Bank
1600 Market St., 29th Fl.
Philadelphia, PA 19103-7240
Contact: Robert Berry, Tr.

Established in 1995 in WY.
Donor: A.W. Berry Charitable Remainder Unitrust.
Foundation type: Independent foundation.
Financial data (yr. ended 12/31/13): Assets, $83,244,535 (M); expenditures, $3,398,579; qualifying distributions, $3,151,246; giving activities include $3,148,000 for 56 grants (high: $1,000,000; low: $1,000).
Purpose and activities: Giving primarily to conserve ecologically significant land and the biodiversity of life it supports.
Fields of interest: Animals/wildlife, preservation/protection; Human services; Foundations (community).
Limitations: Applications not accepted. Giving in the U.S., with emphasis on TX and WY. No support for religious or political organizations. No grants to individuals.
Application information: Contributes only to pre-selected organizations.
Trustee: Robert Berry.
Agent: PNC Bank, N.A.
EIN: 830310959
Selected grants: The following grants are a representative sample of this grantmaker's funding activity:
$3,156,295 to Maine Community Foundation, Ellsworth, ME, 2011. For general support.
$500,000 to CLL Global Research Foundation, Houston, TX, 2011. For general support.
$500,000 to Cornell University, Laboratory of Ornithology, Ithaca, NY, 2011. For general support.
$270,000 to Peregrine Fund, Boise, ID, 2011. For general support.
$100,000 to American Bird Conservancy, Washington, DC, 2011. For general support.
$25,000 to RARE, Arlington, VA, 2011. For general support.
$10,000 to High Arctic Institute, Orion, IL, 2011. For general support.
$10,000 to International Crane Foundation, Baraboo, WI, 2011. For general support.
$10,000 to University of Washington, Seattle, WA, 2011. For Penguin Project.

8346
Woodtiger Fund ✧

P.O. Box 66
Erwinna, PA 18920-0066

Established in 2009 in PA.
Donor: Wallace Global Fund.
Foundation type: Independent foundation.
Financial data (yr. ended 12/31/12): Assets, $62,994,275 (M); expenditures, $2,855,227; qualifying distributions, $2,518,549; giving activities include $2,227,567 for 44 grants (high: $350,000; low: $1,000).
Fields of interest: Environment, water pollution; Environment, energy; Animal welfare; Animals/wildlife, preservation/protection.
Limitations: Applications not accepted. Giving primarily in DC and PA.
Application information: Contributes only to pre-selected organizations.

Officers and Directors:* Susan Wallace,* Pres.; R. Bruce Wallace,* Treas.; Damon Aherne,* Exec. Dir.
EIN: 270222692

8347
John H. Wright Etal Trust ✧
c/o BNY Mellon, N.A.
P.O. Box 185
Pittsburgh, PA 15230-0185

Foundation type: Independent foundation.
Financial data (yr. ended 12/31/13): Assets, $35,282,118 (M); expenditures, $1,829,929; qualifying distributions, $1,687,412; giving activities include $1,625,002 for 1 grant.
Fields of interest: Aging, centers/services.
Limitations: Applications not accepted. Giving primarily in Gerry, NY.
Application information: Contributes only to pre-selected organizations.
Trustees: Robert C. Muth; Larry J. Yartz; BNY Mellon, N.A.
EIN: 250989820

8348
Lucile M. Wright For Charities Trust ✧ ☆
c/o BNY Mellon, N.A.
P.O. Box 185
Pittsburgh, PA 15230-0185

Foundation type: Independent foundation.
Financial data (yr. ended 12/31/13): Assets, $10,201,528 (M); expenditures, $509,433; qualifying distributions, $473,983; giving activities include $459,447 for 2 grants (high: $393,746; low: $65,701).
Fields of interest: Youth development.
Limitations: Applications not accepted.
Application information: Unsolicited requests for funds not accepted.
Trustee: BNY Mellon, N.A.
EIN: 256034126
Selected grants: The following grants are a representative sample of this grantmaker's funding activity:
$372,220 to Girls Incorporated, New York, NY, 2010.
$59,880 to Boys and Girls Club of Jamestown, Jamestown, NY, 2011.

8349
The Wyncote Foundation ✧
1717 Arch St., 14th Fl.
Philadelphia, PA 19103-2713 (215) 557-9577
E-mail: info@wyncotefoundation.org; Main URL: http://www.wyncotefoundation.org

Established in 2009 in PA.
Donors: Otto Haas 1945 B Trust; Otto Haas 1955 B Trust; Otto Haas 1956 B Trust; Phoebe W. Haas Charitable Trust B; David W. Haas.
Foundation type: Independent foundation.
Financial data (yr. ended 12/31/12): Assets, $516,012,211 (M); expenditures, $36,169,051; qualifying distributions, $33,874,079; giving activities include $33,330,325 for 311 grants (high: $2,250,000; low: $1,750).
Fields of interest: Media/communications; Media, journalism.
Limitations: Applications not accepted.
Application information: Contributes only to pre-selected organizations.
Officers: David W. Haas, Chair. and Pres.; Frederick R. Haas, Vice-Chair. and V.P.; Duncan A. Haas, V.P.; Leonard C. Haas, Secy.
EIN: 263535044
Selected grants: The following grants are a representative sample of this grantmaker's funding activity:
$2,250,000 to Seattle Foundation, Seattle, WA, 2012. For a donor-advised fund.
$1,266,667 to Philadelphia Orchestra Association, Philadelphia, PA, 2012. For a discretionary grant for the preservation and renewal of the Philadelphia Orchestra.
$1,250,000 to Seattle Foundation, Seattle, WA, 2012. For a donor-advised fund.
$1,250,000 to Seattle Foundation, Seattle, WA, 2012. For a donor-advised fund.
$1,000,000 to Philadelphia Orchestra Association, Philadelphia, PA, 2012. For discretionary grant for the preservation and renewal of the Philadelphia Orchestra.
$1,000,000 to Philadelphia Orchestra Association, Philadelphia, PA, 2012. For discretionary grant for the preservation and renewal of the Philadelphia Orchestra.
$500,000 to Bement School, Deerfield, MA, 2012. To help redo and rename the Wright House The Haas House.
$200,000 to Open Connections, Newtown Square, PA, 2012. For general support.
$50,000 to Greater Philadelphia Association for Recovery Education, Philadelphia, PA, 2012. For a digital media program for children in rehabilitation.
$35,000 to Headlong Dance Theater, Philadelphia, PA, 2012. For general operating support.

8350
The Wyomissing Foundation, Inc. ✧
960 Old Mill Rd.
Wyomissing, PA 19610-2522 (610) 376-7494

Incorporated in 1929 in DE.
Donors: Ferdinand Thun†; and family.
Foundation type: Independent foundation.
Financial data (yr. ended 12/31/13): Assets, $33,981,608 (M); expenditures, $1,782,068; qualifying distributions, $1,603,077; giving activities include $1,330,732 for 37 grants (high: $179,000; low: $1,981).
Purpose and activities: Giving primarily for the arts, education, and human services.
Fields of interest: Arts; Higher education; Environment, natural resources; Human services; United Ways and Federated Giving Programs.
Type of support: General/operating support; Continuing support; Annual campaigns; Capital campaigns; Building/renovation; Equipment; Endowments; Emergency funds; Seed money; Matching/challenge support.
Limitations: Applications accepted. Giving primarily in Reading, PA. No grants to individuals, or for deficit financing, land acquisition, publications, conferences, scholarships, or fellowships; no loans.
Publications: Application guidelines; Program policy statement.
Application information:
Initial approach: Letter
Deadline(s): None
Officers: Glenn E. Moyer, Chair.; Karen Rightmire, Pres.; Alexena Frazee, Vice-Chair.; Cornelia St. John, Secy.; Christopher Pruitt, Treas.
Directors: Kristen Thun Dunn; Julia Landstreet; Ruth Mathews; Anna Weitz.
Number of staff: 1 full-time support; 1 part-time support.
EIN: 231980570

8351
York County Community Foundation ✧
(formerly York Foundation)
14 W. Market St.
York, PA 17401-1203 (717) 848-3733
Contact: For grants: Jane Conover, C.O.O.; For grants: Sandy Aulbach, Grants Admin.
FAX: (717) 854-7231; E-mail: info@yccf.org; Grant inquiry e-mails: jconover@yccf.org and saulbach@yccf.org; Main URL: http://www.yccf.org

Established in 1961 in PA.
Foundation type: Community foundation.
Financial data (yr. ended 12/31/13): Assets, $101,523,802 (M); gifts received, $14,363,592; expenditures, $4,341,090; giving activities include $2,604,561 for 104+ grants (high: $280,000), and $135,458 for 106 grants to individuals.
Purpose and activities: The foundation seeks to promote the betterment of York County, PA, and the enhancement of the quality of life for all its citizens by attracting and managing funds to build a permanent endowment, serving as a leader in responding to community needs, and by serving as a resource and catalyst for charitable activities.
Fields of interest: Arts; Education; Environment, land resources; Environment, energy; Environment; Health care; Child development, services; Human services; Economic development; Community/economic development; Philanthropy/voluntarism, management/technical assistance; Public affairs; Youth; Aging.
Type of support: Equipment; Program development; Conferences/seminars; Seed money; Scholarship funds; Technical assistance; Consulting services; Matching/challenge support.
Limitations: Applications accepted. Giving primarily in York County, PA. No support for sectarian religious projects. No grants to individuals (except for specific assistance in support of disaster relief from Hurricane Katrina), or for endowments, capital campaigns, budget shortfalls, debt retirement or association dues.
Publications: Application guidelines; Annual report; Informational brochure; Newsletter.
Application information: Visit foundation web site for application guidelines. Application form required.
Initial approach: Telephone
Copies of proposal: 6
Deadline(s): None for Alliance Grants; Apr. 1 for Community Support Grants
Board meeting date(s): Quarterly
Final notification: Within 2 months
Officers and Directors:* Michael Newsome,* Chair.; Paul Rudy III,* Vice-Chair.; Bill Hartman,* C.E.O. and Pres.; Jane Conover,* V.P., Community Investment; George Dvoryak,* V.P., Finance and Opers.; Bryan K. Tate,* V.P., Philanthropy; Marsha M. Everton,* Secy.; Margaret Z. Swartz,* Asst. Secy.; Henry J. Christ,* Treas.; Donna B. Jones, Cont.; Jeffrey Lobach, Esq., Legal Counsel; Carl E. Anderson, Esq.; John Bailey; Timothy J. Bupp, Esq.; Betty Carson; Charles H. Chodroff, M.D.; Joseph P. Clark II; David L. Cross; Krista S. Darr; David M. Davidson; Sally J. Dixon; Jennifer Geesey; Michael H. Hady III; Ronald L. Herrshner, Esq.; Timothy Kinsley; Susan D. Krebs; Loren H. Kroh; Erin J.

Miller, Esq.; Lori O. Mitrick; John M. Polli; Scott C. Rogers; William S. Shipley III; Jack Shorb; Patti Stirk; John J. Sygielski, Ed.D; Joseph G. Wagman; Claire S. Weaver.

Number of staff: 2 full-time professional; 1 part-time professional; 1 full-time support.
EIN: 236299868

PUERTO RICO

8352
Kinesis, Inc ✧ ☆
89 De Diego Ave., PMB-607, Ste. 105
San Juan, PR 00927

Donors: Jose E. Fernandez Bjerg; Omega Overseas Investment; Walmart Foundation.
Foundation type: Independent foundation.
Financial data (yr. ended 06/30/13): Assets, $11,255,771 (M); gifts received, $536,415; expenditures, $1,087,163; qualifying distributions, $536,601; giving activities include $536,601 for 108 grants to individuals (high: $10,000; low: $1,500).
Fields of interest: Education.
Limitations: Applications not accepted.
Application information: Unsolicted requests for funds not accepted.
Officers: Jose E. Fernandez Bjerg, Chair.; Jorge L. Fernandez Bjerg, Vice-Chair.; Milton Jimenez, Secy.; Jose E. Fernandez Richards, Treas.; Andre Muniz, Exec. Dir.
Director: Julia Socorro.
EIN: 660727042

8353
Puerto Rico Community Foundation, Inc. ✧
1719 Ponce de Leon Ave.
San Juan, PR 00909-1905 (787) 721-1037
Contact: Juan J. Reyes, Admin.
FAX: (787) 982-1673; E-mail: fcpr@fcpr.og; Mailing address: PO Box 70362, San Juan, PR 00936-8362; Main URL: http://www.fcpr.org
Facebook: https://www.facebook.com/FundacionComunitaria
Google Plus: https://plus.google.com/113780275269417199627/posts
LinkedIn: https://www.linkedin.com/company/fundaci-n-comunitaria-de-puerto-rico
Twitter: https://twitter.com/fcomunitaria
YouTube: https://www.youtube.com/channel/UCGGW21eIGw6NRinOBrylmWg

Incorporated in 1984 in PR; began operations in 1985.
Foundation type: Community foundation.
Financial data (yr. ended 12/31/13): Assets, $29,006,577 (M); gifts received, $3,283,981; expenditures, $3,601,080; giving activities include $1,202,667 for 42+ grants (high: $54,366), and $712,267 for grants to individuals.
Purpose and activities: The foundation seeks to develop the capacities of communities in Puerto Rico to accomplish their social transformation and economic self-sufficiency, stimulating investment in the communities and maximizing the yield of each contribution. The scope of the foundation's program areas, which reflect the area of interest and opportunities available to the community, are community economic development, community development and housing, education, youth, arts and health.
Fields of interest: Education; Housing/shelter; Community/economic development; Economically disadvantaged.
Type of support: General/operating support; Continuing support; Management development/capacity building; Equipment; Emergency funds; Program development; Conferences/seminars; Professorships; Publication; Curriculum development; Research; Technical assistance; Consulting services; Program-related investments/loans; Scholarships—to individuals; In-kind gifts; Matching/challenge support.
Limitations: Applications accepted. Giving limited to PR. No support for religious organizations for sectarian or proselytizing purposes. No grants for capital or trust funds, operational expenses of an already established organization, operational deficit, annual fundraising, membership fees for associations, galas, special events, travel expenses, or building funds.
Publications: Application guidelines; Annual report; Biennial report; Financial statement; Informational brochure (including application guidelines); Newsletter; Occasional report; Program policy statement.
Application information: Visit foundation web site for application guidelines. Application form required.
Initial approach: Letter
Copies of proposal: 2
Deadline(s): None
Board meeting date(s): Mar., June, Sept., Dec.
Final notification: Within 2 weeks after board meetings
Officers and Directors:* Rene Pinto Lugo,* Pres.; Dr. Nelson I. Colon,* Exec. Pres.; Cesar A. Rey-Hernandez,* V.P.; Mary A. Gabino,* Sr. V.P.; Aida Torres Cruz,* Secy.; Carlos H. del Rio,* Sub-Treas.; Antonio Escudero Viera,* Treas.; Juan J. Reyes, Admin.; Justo Mendez Aramburu; Maria D. Fernos; Victor Rivera Hernandez; Angel L. Saez Lopez; Anitza Cox Marrero; Dr. Manuel A. Morales; Vivian Neptune; Roberto Pagan; Ruben Morales Rivera; Victor Garcia San Inocencio; Nelson Colon Tarrats.
Number of staff: 10 full-time professional; 4 full-time support.
EIN: 660413230

RHODE ISLAND

8354
Hortense Acton Charitable Trust ✧
c/o US Trust, Fiduciary Tax Svcs.
P.O. Box 1802
Providence, RI 02901-1802

Foundation type: Independent foundation.
Financial data (yr. ended 12/31/13): Assets, $23,384,393 (M); expenditures, $1,247,156; qualifying distributions, $1,059,422; giving activities include $995,941 for 1 grant.
Fields of interest: Higher education.
Limitations: Applications not accepted. Giving primarily in New York, NY.
Application information: Contributes only to pre-selected organizations.
Trustee: Bank of America, N.A.
EIN: 367110976

8355
Warren Alpert Foundation ✧
27 Warren Way
P.O. Box 72743
Providence, RI 02907-2424 (401) 781-9900
Main URL: http://www.warrenalpert.org/prize
Alpert Prize inquiry: Edward Canton, Harvard Medical School, 25 Shattuck St., Rm. 101, Boston, MA 02115, tel.: (617) 432-2116,
e-mail: edward_canton@hms.harvard.edu

Established in 1986 in RI.
Donors: Warren Alpert†; Warren Equities, Inc.; Warren Alpert Trust.
Foundation type: Independent foundation.
Financial data (yr. ended 12/31/12): Assets, $198,551,435 (M); expenditures, $17,633,182; qualifying distributions, $17,406,000; giving activities include $17,150,000 for 2 grants (high: $17,000,000; low: $150,000), and $256,000 for 5 grants to individuals (high: $150,000; low: $6,000).
Purpose and activities: Support primarily for medical education and research; awards given to individuals for medical research are determined in consultation with a panel of medical experts in concert with the faculties of Harvard Medical School and Albert Einstein School of Medicine.
Fields of interest: Higher education; Medical school/education; Hospitals (general); Medical research, institute; Jewish agencies & synagogues.
Type of support: Research; Grants to individuals.
Limitations: Applications not accepted. Giving primarily in MA and RI.
Publications: Grants list.
Application information: Unsolicited applications from individuals or organizations not accepted.
Officers: Herbert Kaplan, Pres.; Jeffrey Walker, V.P. and Secy.; Edward M. Cosgrove, V.P.; John Dziedzic, Treas.
Director: Joseph B. Martin.
EIN: 050426623

8356
Amica Companies Foundation ✧
100 Amica Way
Lincoln, RI 02865-1156
Contact: Paul S. Bruno, Cash Mgr.
E-mail: amicacofoundations@amica.com; Main URL: http://www.amica.com/about_us/in_your_community/events.html

Established in 1997 in RI.
Donor: Amica Mutual Insurance Co.
Foundation type: Company-sponsored foundation.
Financial data (yr. ended 12/31/12): Assets, $22,502,956 (M); gifts received, $500,000; expenditures, $1,756,158; qualifying distributions, $1,696,069; giving activities include $864,668 for 196 grants (high: $50,000; low: $500), and $831,401 for 830 employee matching gifts.
Purpose and activities: The foundation supports organizations involved with arts and culture, education, the environment, health, youth development, human services, and civic and community development.
Fields of interest: Humanities; Arts; Education; Environment; Health care; Youth development; Human services; Community/economic development; United Ways and Federated Giving Programs.
Type of support: Employee volunteer services; General/operating support; Continuing support; Annual campaigns; Capital campaigns; Building/renovation; Endowments; Scholarship funds; Research; Employee matching gifts; Matching/challenge support.
Limitations: Applications accepted. Giving primarily in RI. No support for political, lobbying, or religious organizations, or discriminatory organizations. No grants to individuals.
Publications: Application guidelines; Financial statement.
Application information: Application form not required.
Initial approach: E-mail or mail proposal to foundation
Copies of proposal: 1
Deadline(s): None
Board meeting date(s): Bimonthly
Final notification: Up to 8 weeks
Officers and Directors:* Robert A. DiMuccio,* Pres.; Robert K. MacKenzie, Secy.; Robert P. Suglia, Genl. Counsel; James P. Loring, Treas.; Robert K. Benson, C.I.O.; Jeffrey P. Aiken; Patricia W. Chadwick; Edward F. DeGraan; Andrew M. Erickson; Barry G. Hittner; Michael D. Jeans; Ronald K. Machtley; Richard A. Plotkin; Donald J. Reaves; Cheryl W. Snead; Thomas A. Taylor.
Number of staff: None.
EIN: 050493445
Selected grants: The following grants are a representative sample of this grantmaker's funding activity:
$45,600 to Community Preparatory School, Providence, RI, 2011.
$20,325 to Bryant University, Smithfield, RI, 2011.
$15,075 to Downtown Chapel, Portland, OR, 2011.
$11,025 to McAuley Ministries, Providence, RI, 2011.
$10,000 to Dana-Farber Cancer Institute, Boston, MA, 2011.
$10,000 to Rhode Island for Community and Justice, Providence, RI, 2011.
$7,500 to Greenwich Music Festival Company, Greenwich, CT, 2011.
$6,349 to Providence Rescue Mission, Providence, RI, 2011.
$6,050 to Miriam Hospital, Providence, RI, 2011.
$2,500 to Meals on Wheels, Lexington, NC, 2011.

8357
Apple Pickers Foundation ✧
P.O. Box 1033
Westerly, RI 02891-0901

Established in 2006 in CT.
Donors: George S. Warburg; Elinor B. Warburg.
Foundation type: Independent foundation.
Financial data (yr. ended 12/31/13): Assets, $12,342,685 (M); expenditures, $747,131; qualifying distributions, $673,000; giving activities include $673,000 for 16 grants (high: $100,000; low: $2,500).
Fields of interest: Education.
Limitations: Applications not accepted. Giving primarily in CT, MA, and NY. No grants to individuals.
Application information: Contributes only to pre-selected organizations.
Trustees: Daniel S. Warburg; Elinor B. Warburg; George S. Warburg; John P. Warburg; Michael F. Warburg.
EIN: 207196513

8358
Lolita Sheldon Armour Article VII Charitable Trust ✧
P.O. Box 1802
Providence, RI 02901-1802

Established in 1979; supporting organization of the Chicago Community Trust, Rush Presbyterian-St. Luke's Medical Center, and Illinois Institute of Technology.
Donor: Lolita S. Armour.
Foundation type: Independent foundation.
Financial data (yr. ended 06/30/13): Assets, $28,784,330 (M); gifts received, $6,675; expenditures, $1,601,280; qualifying distributions, $1,398,314; giving activities include $1,398,314 for grants.
Fields of interest: Engineering school/education; Hospitals (general); Foundations (community).
Limitations: Applications not accepted. Giving primarily in Chicago, IL.
Application information: Contributes only to pre-selected organizations; unsolicited requests for funds not considered or acknowledged.
Trustee: Bank of America, N.A.
EIN: 366676138
Selected grants: The following grants are a representative sample of this grantmaker's funding activity:
$203,693 to Rush University Medical Center, Chicago, IL, 2011.

8359
Bafflin Foundation ✧
50 Kennedy Plz., Ste. 1500
Providence, RI 02903-2393 (401) 274-2000
Contact: Paul A. Silver Esq., Secy.
E-mail: psilver@haslaw.com

Established in 1990 in RI.
Donor: Lois Orswell†.
Foundation type: Independent foundation.
Financial data (yr. ended 12/31/13): Assets, $21,282,892 (M); expenditures, $816,302; qualifying distributions, $797,930; giving activities include $767,500 for 31 grants (high: $150,000; low: $1,000).

Purpose and activities: Giving primarily for the preservation of land and wildlife; some support also for art museums.
Fields of interest: Museums (art); Environment, natural resources; Animals/wildlife, preservation/protection.
Type of support: Matching/challenge support; Land acquisition; Building/renovation.
Limitations: Applications accepted. Giving primarily in southern New England. No grants to individuals, or for continuing support.
Application information: Application form not required.
Initial approach: Proposal
Copies of proposal: 2
Deadline(s): None
Officers and Directors:* Paul A. Silver,* Secy.; Michael M. Edwards,* Treas.; Joachim A. Weissfeld.
EIN: 050454795
Selected grants: The following grants are a representative sample of this grantmaker's funding activity:
$75,000 to Trust for Public Land, New Haven, CT, 2012. To support Googan Farm Campaign.
$50,000 to Rhode Island School of Design, Providence, RI, 2012. To support Renovation Project of Radeke Building.
$25,000 to Vermont Land Trust, Montpelier, VT, 2012. To support Preservation of Wildlife Habitat.
$20,000 to Sudbury Valley Trustees, Sudbury, MA, 2012. To support Land Acquisition.

8360
Avis & Clifford Barrus Medical Foundation ✧
P.O. Box 1802
Providence, RI 02901-1802

Established in 2005 in NY.
Donors: Avis B. Barrus; Clifford B. Barrus, Jr.
Foundation type: Independent foundation.
Financial data (yr. ended 12/31/13): Assets, $24,919,166 (M); expenditures, $1,087,106; qualifying distributions, $956,354; giving activities include $860,000 for 6 grants (high: $190,000; low: $100,000).
Fields of interest: Health care.
Limitations: Applications not accepted.
Application information: Unsolicited requests for funds not accepted.
Trustees: Celeste B. Cooper; Louis B. Frost; Bank of America, N.A.
EIN: 204069648
Selected grants: The following grants are a representative sample of this grantmaker's funding activity:
$150,000 to Health Resources in Action, Boston, MA, 2012. For unrestricted general support'.

8361
The Bingham Trust ✧
(formerly Mr. Bingham's Trust for Charity)
c/o Patricia F. Davidson
P.O. Box 1802
Providence, RI 02901-1802

Trust established in 1935 in NY.
Donor: William Bingham II†.
Foundation type: Independent foundation.
Financial data (yr. ended 12/31/13): Assets, $51,992,023 (M); expenditures, $2,286,446; qualifying distributions, $2,125,949; giving activities include $1,820,000 for 11 grants (high: $250,000; low: $5,000).
Purpose and activities: Since its inception, the trust has confined its grants to a small group of institutions to achieve maximum philanthropic effect. Every five years it reviews its focus and may choose new fields of interest. Two new fields of interest that have been added to the foundation's focus are the prevention and treatment of teenage obesity, and research in aging. Because its grant criteria are extremely narrow, all grantees are selected by invitation only after research by the trustees.
Fields of interest: Performing arts, music; Higher education; Environment.
Type of support: Program development; Fellowships; Research.
Limitations: Applications not accepted. Giving on a national basis. No support for religious organizations. No grants to individuals, or for scholarships or fellowships.
Publications: Multi-year report.
Application information: Contributes only to pre-selected organizations.
Board meeting date(s): Quarterly
Trustees: Donald M. Barr; Patricia F. Davidson; Bank of America, N.A.
EIN: 136069740

8362
E. P. Binney Charitable Fund ✧
(formerly Elizabeth Peters Binney Charitable Trust)
c/o Bank of America, N.A.
P.O. Box 1802
Providence, RI 02901-1802

Established in 1961 in MA; supporting organization of Lewis & Clark College & Law school, National Wildlife Federation, Western Oregon State College, Pacific University, Parry Center For Children, Parish of St. Mark, St. Paul's Episcopal Church, First Church of Christ Scientists, Boys and Girls Aid Society of Oregon, Cedars Home for Children Foundation, and Eastern Oregon University.
Foundation type: Independent foundation.
Financial data (yr. ended 05/31/13): Assets, $19,069,400 (M); expenditures, $955,962; qualifying distributions, $869,287; giving activities include $816,577 for 18 grants (high: $81,657; low: $16,332).
Purpose and activities: Giving primarily for higher education, Christian Science churches, and children's services.
Fields of interest: Higher education; Children/youth, services; Protestant agencies & churches.
Limitations: Applications not accepted. Giving primarily in OR; funding also in CT and NE. No grants to individuals.
Application information: Contributes only to pre-selected organizations.
Trustee: Bank of America, N.A.
EIN: 046020266
Selected grants: The following grants are a representative sample of this grantmaker's funding activity:
$100,695 to Boys and Girls Aid Society of Oregon, Portland, OR, 2012.
$100,695 to Cedars Home for Children Foundation, Lincoln, NE, 2012.
$100,695 to Parry Center for Children, Portland, OR, 2012.
$80,556 to Eastern Oregon University, La Grande, OR, 2012.
$80,556 to Lewis and Clark College, Law School, Portland, OR, 2012.
$80,556 to Pacific University, Forest Grove, OR, 2012.
$36,249 to Saint Pauls Episcopal Church, The Dalles, OR, 2012.
$20,139 to National Wildlife Federation, Reston, VA, 2012.

8363
Biogen Idec Foundation Incorporated ✧
(formerly Biogen Foundation, Inc.)
P.O. Box 1802
Providence, RI 02901-1802
FAX: (617) 679-3223;
E-mail: foundation@biogenidec.com; Additional address: 225 Binney St., Cambridge, MA 02142; Main URL: http://www.biogenidec.com/foundation.aspx?ID=20552

Established in 2002 in MA.
Donor: Biogen idec Foundation, Inc.
Foundation type: Company-sponsored foundation.
Financial data (yr. ended 12/31/13): Assets, $23,011,096 (M); expenditures, $5,085,307; qualifying distributions, $4,829,127; giving activities include $4,388,035 for 141 grants (high: $500,000; low: $25), and $286,953 for 333 employee matching gifts.
Purpose and activities: The foundation supports programs designed to improve quality of life for communities in which Biogen operates. Special emphasis is directed toward programs designed to promote science literacy and encourage young people to consider careers in science.
Fields of interest: Museums; Museums (science/technology); Arts; Middle schools/education; Secondary school/education; Higher education; Education; Youth, services; Human services; Mathematics; Engineering/technology; Science.
Type of support: General/operating support; Continuing support; Annual campaigns; Program development; Sponsorships; Employee matching gifts.
Limitations: Applications accepted. Giving primarily in areas of company operations in San Diego, CA, Cambridge and Greater Boston, MA, and Durham and Raleigh, NC. No support for discriminatory, religious, or political organizations, or government agencies. No grants to individuals, or for political candidates, special events, fundraising, or capital campaigns.
Publications: Application guidelines.
Application information: Application form required.
Initial approach: Complete eligibility quiz and application
Deadline(s): Nov. 1 for U.S. Grant Program
Board meeting date(s): Quarterly
Officers and Directors:* Tony Kingsley,* Chair. and Pres.; Susan Alexander, Secy.; Michael Dambach,* Treas.; Thomas Lackner; Daniel McIntyre; Machelle Sanders; Jo Viney.
Number of staff: 1 full-time professional.
EIN: 161636254

8364
Buehler Family Foundation ✧
(formerly A. C. Buehler Foundation)
P.O. Box. 1802
Providence, RI 02901-1802
Application Address: George Thorn, 231 S. Lasalle St., IL1-231-03-40, Chicago, IL, 60604, tel.: (312) 828-6763

Incorporated in 1972 in IL.
Donor: Albert C. Buehler.
Foundation type: Independent foundation.
Financial data (yr. ended 12/31/13): Assets, $14,530,259 (M); expenditures, $905,619; qualifying distributions, $859,217; giving activities include $820,000 for 4 grants (high: $250,000; low: $150,000).
Fields of interest: Higher education; Botanical gardens; Aquariums; Human services; Girls.
Type of support: General/operating support; Equipment; Research.
Limitations: Applications accepted. Giving primarily in AZ, FL, and IL.
Application information: Application form not required.
Initial approach: Proposal
Deadline(s): None
Officers and Directors:* Patricia Buehler Blankenship,* Pres.; Dale Park, Jr.,* Secy.; M. Catherine Ryan,* Treas.; A.C. Buehler; Pamela Varner.
Trustee: Bank of America, N.A.
EIN: 237166014
Selected grants: The following grants are a representative sample of this grantmaker's funding activity:
$250,000 to Northwestern University, Evanston, IL, 2011.
$25,000 to John G. Shedd Aquarium, Chicago, IL, 2011.
$15,000 to North Shore Senior Center, Northfield, IL, 2011.

8365
George J. Capewell Foundation Trust No. 3 ✧
P.O. Box 1802
Providence, RI 02901-1802

Foundation type: Independent foundation.
Financial data (yr. ended 12/31/13): Assets, $64,615,480 (M); expenditures, $3,168,820; qualifying distributions, $2,936,310; giving activities include $2,816,153 for 9 grants (high: $823,927; low: $20).
Fields of interest: Hospitals (general); Hospitals (specialty); Human services; Children/youth, services; Family services.
Limitations: Applications not accepted. Giving primarily in Hartford, CT.
Application information: Unsolicited requests for funds not accepted.
Trustee: Bank of America.
EIN: 066066755

8366
George J. Capewell Jr. Foundation Trust No. 2 ✧
P.O. Box 1802
Providence, RI 02901-1802

Foundation type: Independent foundation.
Financial data (yr. ended 12/31/13): Assets, $56,657,372 (M); expenditures, $2,844,800; qualifying distributions, $2,587,172; giving activities include $2,481,340 for 7 grants (high: $1,033,748; low: $20).
Fields of interest: Hospitals (general); Nursing home/convalescent facility; Health care; Children/youth, services; Protestant agencies & churches.
Limitations: Applications not accepted. Giving primarily in Hartford, CT.
Application information: Contributes only to pre-selected organizations.
Trustee: Bank of America.
EIN: 066030604

8367
Gar Capewell Trust ✧
P.O. Box 1802
Providence, RI 02901-1802

Foundation type: Independent foundation.
Financial data (yr. ended 12/31/13): Assets, $30,178,787 (M); expenditures, $1,509,291; qualifying distributions, $1,374,737; giving activities include $1,315,908 for 6 grants (high: $548,159; low: $325).
Fields of interest: Hospitals (general); Human services; Children/youth, services.
Limitations: Applications not accepted. Giving primarily in Hartford, CT.
Application information: Contributes only to pre-selected organizations.
Trustee: Bank of America, N.A.
EIN: 066030606
Selected grants: The following grants are a representative sample of this grantmaker's funding activity:
$407,987 to Hartford Hospital, Hartford, CT, 2011.
$203,994 to Village for Families and Children, Hartford, CT, 2011.
$203,992 to Saint Francis Hospital and Medical Center, Hartford, CT, 2011.

8368
The Carter Family Charitable Trust ✧
P.O. Box 41119
Providence, RI 02940-1119
Contact: John S. Carter, Jr., Tr.; Letitia Carter, Tr.

Established in 1991 in RI.
Donors: Letitia M. Carter; John S. Carter, Jr.
Foundation type: Independent foundation.
Financial data (yr. ended 06/30/13): Assets, $5,142,619 (M); expenditures, $989,893; qualifying distributions, $989,513; giving activities include $989,513 for 25 grants (high: $184,013; low: $3,000).
Purpose and activities: Giving primarily for community development, as well as for education, the arts, and human services.
Fields of interest: Arts; Education; Medical research; Human services; Community/economic development.
Type of support: General/operating support; Continuing support; Annual campaigns; Capital campaigns; Building/renovation; Emergency funds; Scholarship funds; Research; Matching/challenge support.
Limitations: Applications accepted. Giving primarily in RI, with emphasis on Providence. No support for religious organizations. No grants to individuals.
Application information: Application form not required.
Initial approach: Letter
Copies of proposal: 1
Deadline(s): None
Board meeting date(s): July 1
Final notification: 3 months
Trustees: John S. Carter, Jr.; Letitia M. Carter.
Number of staff: 1 part-time professional.
EIN: 056093256

8369
Harry E. Chamberlain & Adrienne S. Chamberlain Memorial Fund ✧
c/o Bank of America, N.A.
P.O Box 1802
Providence, RI 02901-1802

Established in 1986; supporting organization of the Animal Welfare League, Illinois Masonic Children's Home, The Salvation Army, Union League Foundation for Boys Club, Seeing Eye, Inc., and Damon-Runyon-Walter Winchell Cancer Fund.
Foundation type: Independent foundation.
Financial data (yr. ended 04/30/13): Assets, $14,479,414 (M); expenditures, $989,277; qualifying distributions, $895,160; giving activities include $895,160 for grants.
Fields of interest: Animal welfare; Cancer; Boys clubs; Salvation Army; Children/youth, services.
Limitations: Applications not accepted. Giving primarily in Long Beach, CA, Charlestown, Chicago and Chicago Ridge, IL, Morristown, NJ, and New York, NY. No grants to individuals.
Application information: Contributes only to pre-selected organizations.
Trustee: Bank of America, N.A.
EIN: 366836133
Selected grants: The following grants are a representative sample of this grantmaker's funding activity:
$128,558 to Animal Welfare League, Chicago Ridge, IL, 2012.
$120,243 to Damon Runyon Cancer Research Foundation, New York, NY, 2011.
$96,419 to Union League Foundation for Boys Clubs, Chicago, IL, 2012.
$80,349 to Seeing Eye, Morristown, NJ, 2012.
$57,716 to Union League Foundation for Boys Clubs, Chicago, IL, 2011.

8370
The Champlin Foundations
2000 Chapel View Blvd., Ste. 350
Cranston, RI 02920-3040 (401) 944-9200
Contact: Keith H. Lang, Exec. Dir.
FAX: (401) 944-9299; Main URL: http://www.champlinfoundations.org/
Grants List: http://www.champlinfoundations.org/annualreport/2010grantslist.html

Trusts established in 1932, 1947, and 1975 in DE.
Donors: George S. Champlin†; Florence C. Hamilton†; Hope C. Neaves†.
Foundation type: Independent foundation.
Financial data (yr. ended 12/31/13): Assets, $405,495,880 (M); expenditures, $21,969,174; qualifying distributions, $18,119,840; giving

activities include $18,119,840 for 189 grants (high: $850,000; low: $2,600).
Purpose and activities: Giving primarily for conservation; higher, secondary, and other education, including libraries; health and hospitals; and cultural activities, including historic preservation; support also for social and family services, including programs for youth.
Fields of interest: Historic preservation/historical societies; Secondary school/education; Higher education; Education; Environment; Hospitals (general); Health care; Health organizations, association; Human services; Youth, services.
Type of support: Equipment; Capital campaigns; Building/renovation; Land acquisition; Matching/challenge support.
Limitations: Applications accepted. Giving primarily in RI. No support for daycare centers, housing, mental health counseling centers or senior centers. No grants to individuals; or for program or operating expenses, administrative facilities, equipment, books, films, videos, plays, or for multi-year grants.
Publications: Application guidelines; Annual report; Grants list; Program policy statement.
Application information: No grants are awarded on a continuing basis, but applicants may qualify annually. Application form not required.
Initial approach: Brief 1-page letter. Faxed or e-mailed applications will not be accepted
Copies of proposal: 1
Deadline(s): Submit all requests between Mar. 1 and Apr. 30; June 30th for invited public schools only
Board meeting date(s): Nov.
Final notification: After Nov. meeting
Officer and Distribution Committee:* Keith H. Lang,* Exec. Dir.; Jonathan K. Farnum; John Gorham; Timothy N. Gorham, Esq.; Dione D. Kenyon; Robert W. Kenyon; Lisa P. Koelle; Marie J. Langlois; R. Kelly Sheridan; Rev. Rebecca L. Spencer; Edward B Wetherill.
Trustee: PNC Delaware Trust Company.
Number of staff: 2 full-time professional; 1 part-time professional; 1 full-time support; 1 part-time support.
Selected grants: The following grants are a representative sample of this grantmaker's funding activity:
$1,750,000 to Nature Conservancy in Rhode Island, Providence, RI, 2012. For Land Conservation Partnership and Stewardship of Francis C. Carter Preserve.
$850,000 to Emma Pendleton Bradley Hospital, East Providence, RI, 2012. To expand Outpatient Services Department.
$800,000 to YMCA of Greater Providence, Providence, RI, 2012. For locker room renovations and spray park at South County branch.
$750,000 to Tiverton Library Foundation, Tiverton, RI, 2012. For new library.
$531,125 to University of Rhode Island, Kingston, RI, 2012. For treadmill for Motion Analysis Lab, Biochemical Instrumentation to equip Advanced Biochemistry Lab, equipment for scientific program, digital recording and video teleconferencing system for Behavior Change Research Center, and to create Ocean Engineering Oceanography Teaching and Design Lab.
$250,000 to Rhode Island School of Design, Providence, RI, 2012. To complete Radeke building restoration project at Museum of Art.
$200,000 to Trinity Repertory Company, Providence, RI, 2012. For fire safety improvements to Ledener Theater.
$139,690 to Ronald McDonald House of Providence, Providence, RI, 2012. For window and door replacement.
$96,315 to Family Service of Rhode Island, Providence, RI, 2012. For carpeting and bathroom upgrades for Hope Street facility.
$95,000 to Gilbert Stuart Memorial, Saunderstown, RI, 2012. To expand and restore Welcome Center.
$80,000 to Providence Animal Rescue League, Providence, RI, 2012. To relocate dog adoption room to newly renovated space.
$58,180 to Dorcas International Institute of Rhode Island, Providence, RI, 2012. For classroom blinds and kitchen renovations.
$45,430 to Slater Junior High School, Pawtucket, RI, 2012. For musical instruments in effort to restore band program.
$29,400 to SecondStory Repertory, Redmond, WA, 2012. For pick up truck for transporting supplies and materials.
$20,000 to Providence Cityarts for Youth, Providence, RI, 2012. For physcial plant improvments at Broad Street art center.

8371
The Charlesmead Foundation, Inc. ✧ ☆
1 W. Exchange St., 4th Fl.
Providence, RI 02903-1064
Contact: Heather D. Crosby, Exec. Dir.
FAX: (401) 421-1177;
E-mail: hcrosby@matheyslane.com

Established in 1987 in MD.
Donors: Anthony W. Deering; Kathryn R. Deering.
Foundation type: Independent foundation.
Financial data (yr. ended 12/31/13): Assets, $20,576,465 (M); expenditures, $1,587,838; qualifying distributions, $1,219,082; giving activities include $1,215,350 for 95 grants (high: $140,000; low: $200), and $461,471 for loans/program-related investments.
Purpose and activities: Giving for art and cultural programs and education.
Fields of interest: Museums; Performing arts; Arts; Higher education; Education; Health organizations; Medical research, institute; Human services.
Type of support: General/operating support; Annual campaigns; Capital campaigns; Program-related investments/loans.
Limitations: Applications not accepted. Giving primarily in Baltimore, MD. No grants to individuals.
Application information: Unsolicited applications not accepted.
Officers: Anthony W. Deering, Chair.; Kathryn R. Deering, Pres.; Heather Crosby, Exec. Dir.
Trustees: Maron Deering; Spencer Deering; John Warren.
Number of staff: None.
EIN: 521550204

8372
Ida S. Charlton Charity Fund ✧
P.O. Box 1802
Providence, RI 02901-1802

Established in 1995 in MA; supporting organization of Spaulding Rehabilitation Hospital, The Volunteers in Medicine Clinic, UNR Foundation-College of Business Administration, and University of Massachusetts-Dartmouth.
Foundation type: Independent foundation.
Financial data (yr. ended 12/31/13): Assets, $18,320,106 (M); expenditures, $925,286; qualifying distributions, $816,303; giving activities include $698,500 for 8 grants (high: $300,000; low: $5,000).
Fields of interest: Higher education; Health care; Human services; United Ways and Federated Giving Programs.
Limitations: Applications not accepted. Giving primarily in MA.
Application information: Contributes only to pre-selected organizations.
Trustees: E.P. Charlton II; Stacey Charlton; Michael Garfield; Bank of America, N.A.
EIN: 046009559

8373
M. A. Chisholm Charitable Trust ✧
P.O. Box 1802
Providence, RI 02901-1802

Established in 1991 in NY.
Donors: E.G. Chisholm; M.A. Chisholm.
Foundation type: Independent foundation.
Financial data (yr. ended 12/31/13): Assets, $20,915,562 (M); expenditures, $1,000,808; qualifying distributions, $900,313; giving activities include $864,000 for 1 grant.
Purpose and activities: Giving primarily for the performing arts and higher education.
Fields of interest: Performing arts; Arts; Elementary/secondary education; Higher education; Foundations (private grantmaking); Christian agencies & churches.
Limitations: Applications not accepted. Giving primarily in MS and NY. No grants to individuals.
Application information: Contributes only to pre-selected organizations.
Trustees: John Lindsay; Nathan Saint-Amand; Bank of America, N.A.
EIN: 136984354
Selected grants: The following grants are a representative sample of this grantmaker's funding activity:
$47,000 to University of Mississippi, University, MS, 2012. For Charitable Purposes Center for the Study of Southern Culture Southern Foodways Alliance.
$35,000 to Millsaps College, Jackson, MS, 2012. For Charitable Purposes New Beginnings Fund.
$25,000 to Eudora Welty Foundation, Jackson, MS, 2012. For Charitable Purposes Welty Scholar at Millsaps.
$25,000 to Harlem Educational Activities Fund, New York, NY, 2012. For Charitable Purposes 3rd payment on $100,000 pledge to College Quest.
$25,000 to Mississippi Museum of Art, Jackson, MS, 2012. For Charitable Purposes Reinstallation of The Mississippi Story.
$20,000 to Childhaven, Seattle, WA, 2012. For Charitable Purposes 1st payment on $100,000 pledge.
$20,000 to Morris Museum of Art, Augusta, GA, 2012. For Charitable Purposes 20th Anniversary.
$10,000 to Jones County Junior College, Ellisville, MS, 2012. For Charitable Purposes Bobcat Math League.
$7,500 to French Camp Academy, French Camp, MS, 2012. For Charitable Purposes Rainwater Observatory and Planetarium.
$5,000 to Hermann-Grima/Gallier Historic Houses, New Orleans, LA, 2012. For Charitable Purposes Hermann-Grima Preservation Fund.

8374
Citizens Charitable Foundation ✧
10 Tripps Ln.
Riverside, RI 02915-7995
Main URL: http://www.citizensbank.com/community/corporate/grants.aspx

Established in 1967 in RI; reincorporated in 2005.
Donors: Citizens Savings Bank; Citizens Trust Co.; Citizens Bank of Rhode Island; Cambridgeport Bank; Charter One Bank; The Citizens Bank Mid-Atlantic Charitable Foundation; Citizens Charitable Foundation; RBS Citizens, N.A.
Foundation type: Company-sponsored foundation.
Financial data (yr. ended 12/31/12): Assets, $9,154,163 (M); gifts received, $7,164,104; expenditures, $11,248,600; qualifying distributions, $11,218,067; giving activities include $11,186,774 for 3,114 grants (high: $150,000; low: $25).
Purpose and activities: The foundation supports organizations involved with affordable housing, hunger programs, economic development activities, and financial education.
Fields of interest: Employment; Nutrition; Agriculture/food; Housing/shelter, development; Housing/shelter; Human services; Economic development; Community/economic development; Economically disadvantaged.
Type of support: Employee matching gifts; Employee volunteer services; General/operating support; Program development; Public relations services; Scholarship funds; Sponsorships.
Limitations: Applications accepted. Giving on a national basis in areas of company operations, with emphasis on CT, DE, IL, MA, MI, NH, NJ, NY, OH, PA, RI, and VT. No support for discriminatory organizations, single disease/issue information or research organizations, religious organizations, labor, fraternal, or veterans' organizations, political organizations, governmental or quasi-governmental public agencies or organizations, grantmakers, or public or private educational institutions. No grants to individuals, or for annual campaigns, political projects, debt reduction, conferences or seminars, endowments, trips or tours, advertising or fundraising activities, or historic preservation; no loans.
Publications: Application guidelines; Informational brochure.
Application information: Prospective applicants must take the charitable grant eligibility quiz on the foundation's website. A site visit and additional information may be requested at a later date. Application form not required.
Initial approach: Complete online application or submit proposal to nearest Public Relations Department
Copies of proposal: 1
Deadline(s): None
Board meeting date(s): Monthly
Final notification: 8 weeks
Officers and Directors: Robert Matthews, Pres.; Denise Leyhe, V.P.; Reza Aghamirzadeh; Heidi Brooks; Cindy Erikson; Bruce Figueroa; Quincy Miller; Tony Moscrop; Kevin Walsh.
Trustee: RBS Citizens, N.A.
Number of staff: 4 full-time professional.
EIN: 202302039
Selected grants: The following grants are a representative sample of this grantmaker's funding activity:
$250,000 to Greater Boston Food Bank, Boston, MA, 2012. For General Support.
$150,000 to United Way of Rhode Island, Providence, RI, 2012. For General Support.
$120,000 to Local Initiatives Support Corporation, New York, NY, 2012. For General Support.
$100,000 to Crossroads Rhode Island, Providence, RI, 2012. For General Support.
$75,000 to Ohio City Near West Development Corporation, Cleveland, OH, 2012. For General Support.
$73,004 to W G B H Educational Foundation, Boston, MA, 2012. For General Support.
$20,000 to Food Bank of Western New York, Buffalo, NY, 2012. For General Support.
$15,000 to Greater New Haven Community Loan Fund, New Haven, CT, 2012. For General Support.
$10,000 to Bethlehem Haven of Pittsburgh, Pittsburgh, PA, 2012. For General Support.
$10,000 to New Reach, New Haven, CT, 2012. For General Support.

8375
Combined Townsend Fund ✧
P.O. Box 1802
Providence, RI 02901-1802

Established in 1974; supporting organization of Rhode Island Hosital Foundation, St. Joseph Health Services of Rhode Island and Woman and Infants Hospital.
Foundation type: Independent foundation.
Financial data (yr. ended 12/31/13): Assets, $19,060,031 (M); expenditures, $1,015,055; qualifying distributions, $899,183; giving activities include $853,957 for 3 grants (high: $284,653; low: $284,652).
Fields of interest: Hospitals (general); Health care.
Limitations: Applications not accepted. Giving limited to RI. No grants to individuals.
Application information: Contributes only to pre-selected organizations; unsolicited requests for funds not considered or acknowledged.
Trustee: Bank of America, N.A.
EIN: 056007985

8376
John J. Corning Trust ✧
P.O. Box 1802
Providence, RI 02901-1802

Foundation type: Independent foundation.
Financial data (yr. ended 12/31/13): Assets, $20,147,168 (M); expenditures, $1,088,062; qualifying distributions, $979,151; giving activities include $924,676 for 4 grants (high: $231,169; low: $231,169).
Fields of interest: Animals/wildlife; Hospitals (general); Youth development; Human services.
Limitations: Applications not accepted. Giving primarily in CT, with emphasis on Hartford.
Application information: Unsolicited requests for funds not accepted.
Trustee: Bank of America, N.A.
EIN: 066027742

8377
David Crary, Jr. Estate Trust ✧ ☆
P.O. Box 1802
Providence, RI 02901-1802

Foundation type: Independent foundation.
Financial data (yr. ended 08/31/13): Assets, $11,164,161 (M); expenditures, $588,276; qualifying distributions, $533,138; giving activities include $501,158 for 7 grants (high: $71,594; low: $71,594).
Fields of interest: Health care; Housing/shelter; Human services.
Limitations: Applications not accepted. Giving primarily in CT.
Application information: Unsolicited requests for funds not accepted.
Trustee: Bank of America, N.A.
EIN: 066027764

8378
Cuno Foundation ✧ ☆
c/o U.S. Trust Fiduciary Tax Services
P.O. Box 1802
Providence, RI 02901-1802
Application address: c/o Secretary of the Distribution Committee, 562 Baldwin Ave., Unit 6, Meriden, CT 06450

Established in 1948 in CT.
Donor: Frank Davelia†.
Foundation type: Independent foundation.
Financial data (yr. ended 12/31/13): Assets, $10,430,142 (M); expenditures, $601,105; qualifying distributions, $522,854; giving activities include $475,997 for grants.
Purpose and activities: Giving primarily to scholarship funds to support students residing in the Meriden, Connecticut, area who will be entering a 4-year college program. Funding also for health organizations, human services and federated giving programs.
Fields of interest: Higher education; Health care; Human services; United Ways and Federated Giving Programs.
Type of support: General/operating support; Scholarship funds; Scholarships—to individuals; Student loans—to individuals.
Limitations: Giving primarily to organizations and residents of the Meriden, CT, area.
Application information: Application form required.
Trustees: Gertrude Cotton; Bank of America, N.A.
EIN: 066033040
Selected grants: The following grants are a representative sample of this grantmaker's funding activity:
$2,500 to Johnson and Wales University, Providence, RI, 2011.
$2,500 to Ohio State University, Columbus, OH, 2011.
$2,500 to Pennsylvania State University, University Park, PA, 2011.
$2,500 to Pennsylvania State University, University Park, PA, 2011.
$2,500 to University of Connecticut, Storrs, CT, 2011.
$2,500 to University of Connecticut, Storrs, CT, 2011.
$2,500 to University of Connecticut, Storrs, CT, 2011.
$2,500 to University of Connecticut, Storrs, CT, 2011.
$2,500 to University of New England, Biddeford, ME, 2011.
$2,500 to University of New England, Biddeford, ME, 2011.

8379
CVS Health Foundation ✧
(formerly CVS Caremark Charitable Trust, Inc.)
1 CVS Dr.
Woonsocket, RI 02895-6146 (401) 770-2898
Contact: Joanne Dwyer, Dir., Corporate Comms. & Community Relas.
E-mail: Joanne.Dwyer@cvscaremark.com; Main URL: http://www.cvshealth.com/social-responsibility
Charitable Trust Featured Recipients: http://info.cvscaremark.com/healthier-communities/charitable-trust-featured-grantees
CVS Caremark All Kids Can Website: http://www.cvscaremarkallkidscan.com/

Established in 1992 in DE and MA.
Donors: Melville Corp.; CVS Corp.; CVS Pharmacy, Inc.
Foundation type: Company-sponsored foundation.
Financial data (yr. ended 12/31/12): Assets, $45,651,274 (M); expenditures, $5,830,000; qualifying distributions, $5,779,242; giving activities include $5,665,193 for 487 grants (high: $375,994; low: $500).
Purpose and activities: The trust supports programs designed to promote access to health care; wellness and prevention initiatives to help people achieve their best health; and programs designed to help all kids in their path to better health.
Fields of interest: Higher education; Medical school/education; Health care, equal rights; Medicine/medical care, public education; Hospitals (general); Health care, clinics/centers; Medical care, rehabilitation; Physical therapy; Art & music therapy; Pharmacy/prescriptions; Public health, physical fitness; Health care, patient services; Health care; Heart & circulatory diseases; Asthma; Diabetes; Pediatrics; Disasters, preparedness/services; Recreation, camps; Recreation, parks/playgrounds; Athletics/sports, school programs; Recreation; Youth development; Family services, parent education; Independent living, disability; Assistive technology; Children; Disabilities, people with; Economically disadvantaged.
Type of support: Continuing support; Management development/capacity building; Building/renovation; Program development; Scholarship funds; Employee volunteer services; Employee-related scholarships.
Limitations: Applications not accepted. Giving primarily in areas of company operations in the U.S. and Puerto Rico. No grants for general operating support, direct healthcare services, staff salaries (unless it's needed to create or enhance a program or increase the number of people or geographic areas served), fundraising events, sponsorships, scholarships (except for employee-related and pharmacy scholarships), endowments, or capital campaigns.
Publications: Grants list; Program policy statement.
Application information: Unsolicited applications are currently not accepted. Giving is by invitation only.
Officers and Directors:* Eileen Howard Boone,* Pres.; David M. Denton,* V.P. and Treas.; Carol A. DeNale, V.P.
EIN: 223206973

8380
The Fred Harris Daniels Foundation, Inc.
c/o Bank of America, N.A.
P.O. Box 1802
Providence, RI 02901-1802
E-mail: info@danielsfoundation.org; Main URL: http://www.danielsfoundation.org/
Online Grants Management System: https://www.grantinterface.com/Common/LogOn.aspx?eqs=ApVvmgXCk2WSOoGBjCinoP2jEMgQfY8yTeejKK7CIns1

Incorporated in 1949 in MA.
Donors: Fred H. Daniels†; Eleanor G. Daniels†.
Foundation type: Independent foundation.
Financial data (yr. ended 10/31/13): Assets, $21,144,736 (M); expenditures, $1,302,223; qualifying distributions, $1,148,709; giving activities include $1,094,500 for 66 grants (high: $150,000; low: $1,000).
Purpose and activities: The foundation's mission is to support sustainable, creative solutions to Worcester, Massachusetts' most pressing societal challenges by funding programs and institutions that help people become more self-reliant in their lives and communities. The foundation provides annual support grants as well as capital grants. Additionally there is an invitation-only strategic grants program which focuses on girls ages 10-14.
Fields of interest: Museums; Performing arts; Historic preservation/historical societies; Arts; Education; Botanical gardens; Environment; Health care, support services; Mental health/crisis services; Offenders/ex-offenders, rehabilitation; Employment; Food services; Housing/shelter; Recreation; Youth development, services; Human services.
Type of support: Annual campaigns; Building/renovation; Capital campaigns; Continuing support; Emergency funds; Equipment; General/operating support; Land acquisition; Matching/challenge support; Program development; Scholarship funds.
Limitations: Applications accepted. Giving limited to the greater Worcester, MA, area. No grants to individuals, or for seed money or deficit financing; no loans.
Application information: Application form required.
Initial approach: Online only
Deadline(s): Generally 5 weeks prior to board meeting
Board meeting date(s): Mar., June, Sept., and Dec.
Final notification: After board meeting at which application is reviewed
Officers and Directors:* Fred H. Daniels II,* Chair. and Pres.; Meridith D. Wesby,* V.P.; David A. Nicholson,* Secy.; Jonathan D. Blake,* Treas.; Dwight C. Blake; Sarah Daignault; Christina N. Eaton; James T. Morse; Sarah D. Morse; William O. Pettit III.
EIN: 046014333
Selected grants: The following grants are a representative sample of this grantmaker's funding activity:
$10,000 to Dismas House of Massachusetts, Worcester, MA, 2014. For annual support.
$5,000 to African Community Education Program, Worcester, MA, 2014. For annual support.
$3,500 to First Night Worcester, Worcester, MA, 2014. For annual support.
$2,500 to Apple Tree Arts, Grafton, MA, 2014. For annual support.

8381
The De Ramel Foundation ✧
c/o Michael A. Orefice, Jr.
1445 Wampanoag Trail
Riverside, RI 02915-1000

Established in 2007 in RI.
Foundation type: Independent foundation.
Financial data (yr. ended 12/31/13): Assets, $13,217,511 (M); expenditures, $672,381; qualifying distributions, $593,372; giving activities include $577,500 for 68 grants (high: $100,000; low: $250).
Fields of interest: Education; Recreation; Human services.
Limitations: Applications not accepted. Giving primarily in RI. No grants to individuals.
Application information: Contributes only to pre-selected organizations.
Trustee: Guillaume De Ramel.
EIN: 266190697

8382
Henrietta F. Dexter Trust ✧ ☆
P.O. Box 1802
Providence, RI 02901-1802
Application address: c/o Bank of America, Attn.: Thea Katsounakis, 1 Monarch Pl., Springfield, MA 01144; tel.: (413) 787-8524

Established in RI.
Foundation type: Independent foundation.
Financial data (yr. ended 12/31/13): Assets, $15,262,626 (M); expenditures, $637,602; qualifying distributions, $550,609; giving activities include $501,852 for 35 grants (high: $132,452; low: $2,500).
Fields of interest: Higher education; Education; Health organizations; Human services; YM/YWCAs & YM/YWHAs; Children/youth, services; Foundations (community).
Limitations: Applications accepted. Giving limited to Springfield, MA.
Application information: Application form required.
Initial approach: Contact foundation for application form
Deadline(s): None
Trustee: Bank of America, N.A.
EIN: 046018698

8383
Diagnostic Imaging Foundation ✧
20 Catamore Blvd.
East Providence, RI 02914-1204

Established in 2006 in RI.
Donors: Gerald Abbott; Michael Atalay; James C. Bass; Michael D. Beland; Jerrold Boxerman; Jeffrey M. Brody; John Cassese; Kevin Chang; John J. Cronan, M.D.; Lawrence M. Davis; Douglas F. De Orchis; Linda Livingston Donegan; Gregory J. Dubel; Damian Dupuy; Thomas Egglin; Peter Thomas Evangelista; Holly Cresho Gil; Richard L. Gold; Daniel M. Golding; David Grand; Thaddeus Herliczek; Richard Haas; Mary M. Hillstrom; Brian Jay; Mahesh Jayaraman; Hanan Khalil; Susan L. Koelliker; Robert E. Lambiase; Elizabeth Lazarus; Scott M. Levine; Ana Lourenco; Martha B. Mainiero; William Mayo-Smith; Kathleen M. McCarten; Brian Murphy; Jonathan S. Movson; Timothy P. Murphy; David P. Neumann; Arthur W. Noel; Richard Noto,

M.D.; John A. Pezzullo III; Marcelle L. Piccolello; Mark Ridlen; Jeffrey Rogg; Michael J. Ryvicker; Sanford L. Schatz; Barbara Schepps; Gregory M. Soares; Julie Song; Patricia Spencer; Glenn Tung; Michael Wallach; Don Chan Yoo; RIMI; Sun Ho Ahn; Ethan A. Prince; Terrance T. Healey.
Foundation type: Independent foundation.
Financial data (yr. ended 12/31/13): Assets, $362,975 (M); gifts received, $1,500,000; expenditures, $1,448,028; qualifying distributions, $1,447,984; giving activities include $1,446,259 for 4 grants (high: $1,266,259; low: $30,000).
Purpose and activities: Giving primarily for a hospital.
Fields of interest: Higher education; Hospitals (general).
Limitations: Applications not accepted. Giving primarily in Providence, RI.
Application information: Contributes only to pre-selected organizations.
Officers and Directors:* John J. Cronan, M.D.*, Pres.; Richard Noto, M.D.*, Secy.-Treas.; Timothy J Babineau, M.D.; Edward J. Wing, M.D.
EIN: 204099897
Selected grants: The following grants are a representative sample of this grantmaker's funding activity:
$778,266 to Rhode Island Hospital, Providence, RI, 2011.
$100,000 to Brown University, Providence, RI, 2011.

8384
Dorot Foundation ✧
401 Elmgrove Ave.
Providence, RI 02906-3451 (401) 351-8866
Contact: Michael Hill, Exec. V.P.
FAX: (401) 351-4975; E-mail: dorotinfo@dorot.org; Main URL: http://www.dorot.org
Fellowship e-mail: dfi@dorot.org

Incorporated in 1958 in NY as Joy and Samuel Ungerleider Foundation.
Donors: Joy G. Ungerleider-Mayerson†; D.S. and R.H. Gottesman Foundation; Yesod Fund.
Foundation type: Independent foundation.
Financial data (yr. ended 03/31/13): Assets, $46,511,324 (M); gifts received, $2,012,273; expenditures, $3,519,963; qualifying distributions, $3,049,378; giving activities include $1,647,691 for 44 grants (high: $175,000; low: $3,000), and $566,930 for 10 grants to individuals (high: $57,240; low: $56,140).
Purpose and activities: Grants primarily for informal education, the Dorot Fellowship in Israel, cultural organizations with which the foundation has an existing relationship, and organizations supporting adult education for democratic participation in Israel.
Fields of interest: Arts, cultural/ethnic awareness; Education; International affairs; Public affairs, citizen participation.
International interests: Israel.
Type of support: General/operating support; Continuing support; Program development; Publication; Seed money; Fellowships; Internship funds; Technical assistance; Program evaluation; Matching/challenge support.
Limitations: Applications not accepted. Giving primarily in Washington, DC, MA, NY, and Israel. No support for acquisitions for museums or excavation phase of archaeological work. No grants for endowments, capital campaigns, equipment, debt reduction, consultants or technical assistance, or events.
Publications: Financial statement; Grants list.
Application information: Unsolicited requests for funds not accepted. See foundation web site for Fellowship application guidelines.
Board meeting date(s): Apr./May and Oct./Nov.
Officers and Director:* Dr. Ernest S. Frerichs,* Pres.; Michael Hill, Exec. V.P.; Steven M. Jackson, V.P. Strategy.
Number of staff: 3 full-time professional; 1 part-time professional.
EIN: 136116927
Selected grants: The following grants are a representative sample of this grantmaker's funding activity:
$369,239 to Dorot Fellows, Jerusalem, Israel, 2012. For Dorot Fellowship Program.
$290,000 to W. F. Albright Institute of Archaeological Research, Jerusalem, Israel, 2012. For Fellowships and Director's Fund.
$175,000 to Union for Reform Judaism, New York, NY, 2012. For Just Congregation Initiative.
$150,000 to Jewish Womens Archive, Brookline, MA, 2012. To expand educational program.
$80,000 to New Israel Fund, Washington, DC, 2012. For Social Change in Israel.
$65,000 to American Friends of the Israel Museum, New York, NY, 2012. For Director's Fund Ashrine of the Book Info.
$60,000 to Encounter, New York, NY, 2012.
$55,000 to Friends of Kol Haneshama, New York, NY, 2012. For fellowships.
$50,000 to AVODAH: The Jewish Service Corps, New York, NY, 2012. For general operating support.
$40,000 to Isabella Freedman Jewish Retreat Center, Falls Village, CT, 2012. For Adanah Fellowship.

8385
James W. Dunphy Trust ✧
P.O. Box 1802
Providence, RI 02901-1802

Foundation type: Independent foundation.
Financial data (yr. ended 12/31/13): Assets, $17,221,461 (M); expenditures, $942,832; qualifying distributions, $785,289; giving activities include $708,908 for 6 grants (high: $246,209; low: $18,500).
Fields of interest: Health care.
Limitations: Applications not accepted.
Application information: Contributes only to pre-selected organizations.
Trustees: Francis M. McLaughlin, M.D.; Bank of America.
EIN: 046024367

8386
EJMP Fund for Philanthropy ✧
(formerly Elizabeth Prince Charitable Trust)
c/o Weetamoe
2 Rovensky Ave.
Newport, RI 02840-4227

Established in 2007 in RI.
Donor: Elizabeth Prince.
Foundation type: Independent foundation.
Financial data (yr. ended 12/31/13): Assets, $13,146,673 (M); expenditures, $649,004; qualifying distributions, $571,310; giving activities include $571,000 for 15 grants (high: $65,000; low: $20,000).
Fields of interest: Foundations (private grantmaking).
Limitations: Applications not accepted.
Application information: Contributes only to pre-selected organizations.
Trustee: Elizabeth Prince.
EIN: 262485081

8387
The Elms Foundation ✧
244 Gano St.
Providence, RI 02906-4027

Established in 1989 in RI.
Donors: Stanley P. Goldstein; Merle F. Goldstein; JPMorgan Chase Bank, N.A.; First Republic Bank.
Foundation type: Independent foundation.
Financial data (yr. ended 12/31/13): Assets, $15,884,950 (M); gifts received, $709,800; expenditures, $623,091; qualifying distributions, $539,254; giving activities include $516,400 for 54 grants (high: $50,000; low: $1,000).
Purpose and activities: Funding primarily for education; some giving also for health care and the arts.
Fields of interest: Arts; Education; Health care; Community/economic development; Jewish federated giving programs; Jewish agencies & synagogues.
Limitations: Applications not accepted. Giving primarily in RI.
Application information: Unsolicited requests for funds not accepted.
Officers and Directors:* Stanley P. Goldstein,* Pres. and Treas.; Merle F. Goldstein,* Secy.; Eugene S. Goldstein; Larry M. Goldstein; Peter Karoff.
EIN: 050450051

8388
The Norman and Rosalie Fain Family Foundation ✧
(formerly Norman & Rosalie Fain Fund Trust)
505 Central Ave.
Pawtucket, RI 02861-1945

Established in 1964 in RI.
Donors: Norman M. Fain; Rosalie B. Fain; Jonathan D. Fain; Martha F. Roberts; Wendy B. Feldman; Jonathan D. Fain Charitable Lead Trust; Wendy F. Feldman Charitable Lead Trust; Martha F. Roberts Charitable Lead Trust.
Foundation type: Independent foundation.
Financial data (yr. ended 12/31/13): Assets, $11,867,292 (M); gifts received, $1,273,400; expenditures, $815,551; qualifying distributions, $805,500; giving activities include $805,500 for 23 grants (high: $200,000; low: $1,000).
Fields of interest: Higher education; Human services; Jewish federated giving programs; Jewish agencies & synagogues.
Limitations: Applications not accepted. Giving primarily in RI. No grants to individuals.
Application information: Contributes only to pre-selected organizations.
Trustees: Jonathan D. Fain; Rosalie B. Fain; Wendy F. Feldman; Martha F. Roberts.
EIN: 056022655

Selected grants: The following grants are a representative sample of this grantmaker's funding activity:
$1,000 to American Jewish Committee, New York, NY, 2011.
$1,000 to American Jewish Committee, New York, NY, 2011.

8389
Dr. Ralph and Marian Falk Medical Research Trust ✧
c/o US Trust Tax Svcs.
P.O. Box 1802
Providence, RI 02901-1802 (888) 866-3275
Application address: c/o George Thorn, Bank of America, N.A., 231 S. LaSalle St., Chicago, IL 60604, tel.: (312) 828-6763

Established in 1991 in IL.
Donor: Marian Citron Falk Trust.
Foundation type: Independent foundation.
Financial data (yr. ended 11/30/13): Assets, $150,326,031 (M); expenditures, $7,019,141; qualifying distributions, $6,311,716; giving activities include $5,692,403 for 15 grants (high: $787,403; low: $50,000).
Purpose and activities: Support for medical research in the area of diseases for which no definite cure is known.
Fields of interest: Medical research, institute.
Limitations: Applications accepted. Giving primarily in IL. No grants to individuals.
Application information: Application form not required.
Initial approach: Proposal
Deadline(s): None
Trustee: Bank of America, N.A.
EIN: 366975534
Selected grants: The following grants are a representative sample of this grantmaker's funding activity:
$787,403 to Ann and Robert H. Lurie Children's Hospital of Chicago Foundation, Chicago, IL, 2012. For medical research.
$505,000 to Loyola University Medical Center, Maywood, IL, 2012. For medical research.
$500,000 to Northwestern Memorial Foundation, Chicago, IL, 2012. For medical research.
$500,000 to Northwestern University, Evanston, IL, 2012. For medical research.
$500,000 to Rehabilitation Institute of Chicago, Chicago, IL, 2012. For medical research.
$500,000 to Thomas Jefferson University, Philadelphia, PA, 2012. For medical research.
$500,000 to University of Chicago Medical Center, Bernard Mitchell Hospital, Chicago Lying-in Hospital & Wyler Children's Hospital, Chicago, IL, 2012. For medical research.
$500,000 to University of Chicago Medical Center, Bernard Mitchell Hospital, Chicago Lying-in Hospital & Wyler Children's Hospital, Chicago, IL, 2012. For medical research.
$400,000 to Yale University, New Haven, CT, 2012. For medical research.
$250,000 to Marquette University, Milwaukee, WI, 2012. For medical research.

8390
Feinstein Family Fund ✧
41 Alhambra Cir.
Cranston, RI 02905-3416 (401) 467-5155
Contact: Alan Shawn Feinstein, Pres.

Established in RI.
Foundation type: Independent foundation.
Financial data (yr. ended 12/31/12): Assets, $1,914,428 (M); expenditures, $574,236; qualifying distributions, $568,508; giving activities include $568,508 for grants.
Purpose and activities: Giving to anti-hunger causes.
Fields of interest: Food services.
Limitations: Giving on a national basis.
Application information: Application form not required.
Initial approach: Proposal
Deadline(s): None
Officers and Directors:* Alan Shawn Feinstein,* Pres.; Ari Feinstein,* V.P.
EIN: 050474981

8391
The Feinstein Foundation, Inc. ✧
37 Alhambra Cir.
Cranston, RI 02905-3416 (401) 467-5155
Contact: Alan Shawn Feinstein, Pres.
FAX: (401) 941-0988;
E-mail: asf@feinsteinfoundation.org; Main URL: http://www.feinsteinfoundation.org
Facebook: http://www.facebook.com/pages/The-Feinstein-Foundation/310441040233?ref=search
YouTube: http://www.youtube.com/user/AlanShawnFeinstein

Established in 1991 in RI.
Donors: Alan Shawn Feinstein; Leila Feinstein; Ari Feinstein; Fidelity Charitable Gift Fund; The Rhode Island Foundation.
Foundation type: Independent foundation.
Financial data (yr. ended 12/31/12): Assets, $36,408,811 (M); gifts received, $31,812; expenditures, $2,230,759; qualifying distributions, $1,760,694; giving activities include $1,760,694 for grants.
Purpose and activities: Giving primarily for public service and fighting hunger.
Fields of interest: Elementary/secondary education; Higher education; Education; Food services; Food banks; Human services.
Limitations: Applications not accepted. Giving on a national basis.
Application information: Unsolicited requests for funds not accepted.
Board meeting date(s): Varies
Officers and Directors:* Alan Shawn Feinstein, Pres.; Edward Valenti, V.P.; Michael Finer,* Secy.; Ari Feinstein; Leila Feinstein; Richard Feinstein; Kevin Hanlon; Ofir Katz; Reza Khoyi; Edward Walton.
Number of staff: 1 full-time professional; 1 part-time professional.
EIN: 223142312
Selected grants: The following grants are a representative sample of this grantmaker's funding activity:
$2,374 to Boys Town Jerusalem Foundation of America, New York, NY, 2012. For Million Dollar Challenge.
$2,010 to Governor Pothier School, Woonsocket, RI, 2012. For T Shirts.
$1,000 to All Saints Academy, Middletown, RI, 2012. For Food Drive 2011.
$1,000 to Western Coventry School, Coventry, RI, 2012. For Newsletter Grants.
$987 to Monsignor Gadoury School, Woonsocket, RI, 2012. For Food Drive 2012.
$700 to Cluny School, Newport, RI, 2012. For Year End School Party.
$250 to Western Coventry School, Coventry, RI, 2012. For Hope Fund Match.

8392
Felicia Fund, Inc. ✧
90 Elm St.
Providence, RI 02903-4647 (401) 274-1550
Contact: Pauline C. Metcalf, Pres.

Established in 1985 in RI.
Donor: Pauline C. Metcalf.
Foundation type: Independent foundation.
Financial data (yr. ended 11/30/13): Assets, $9,654,074 (M); gifts received, $300,000; expenditures, $621,176; qualifying distributions, $550,465; giving activities include $550,465 for 54 grants (high: $200,000; low: $150).
Purpose and activities: Giving primarily to fund projects that relate to architecture, decorative art, historic preservation, conservation, and related educational pursuits.
Fields of interest: Visual arts, architecture; Museums (history); Historic preservation/historical societies; Education, formal/general education; Zoos/zoological societies.
Limitations: Applications accepted. Giving primarily in MA, NY, and RI. No grants to individuals.
Application information: Application form not required.
Initial approach: Proposal
Deadline(s): None
Officers and Trustees:* Pauline C. Metcalf,* Pres.; Frank Mauran,* Secy.; Paul W. Whyte,* Treas.; Joseph Soang III.
EIN: 050420703
Selected grants: The following grants are a representative sample of this grantmaker's funding activity:
$300,000 to Edith Wharton Restoration, Lenox, MA, 2011.
$45,000 to Mount Vernon Ladies Association, Mount Vernon, VA, 2011.
$16,600 to Salve Regina University, Newport, RI, 2011.
$15,000 to Society for the Preservation of New England Antiquities, Boston, MA, 2011.
$10,000 to Lower East Side Tenement Museum, New York, NY, 2011.
$10,000 to Olana Partnership, Hudson, NY, 2011.
$7,500 to North Bennet Street School, Boston, MA, 2011.
$5,000 to Museum of the City of New York, New York, NY, 2011.
$5,000 to Naval War College Foundation, Newport, RI, 2011.
$2,500 to Boston Athenaeum, Boston, MA, 2011.

8393
FM Global Foundation ✧
(formerly Allendale Insurance Foundation)
270 Central Ave.
P.O. Box 7500
Johnston, RI 02919-4923
Main URL: http://www.fmglobal.com/page.aspx?id=01060100

Established in 1986 in RI.
Donors: Allendale Mutual Insurance Co.; Factory Mutual Insurance Co.; Subramaniam Family Foundation.
Foundation type: Company-sponsored foundation.
Financial data (yr. ended 12/31/12): Assets, $5,787,156 (M); gifts received, $42,000; expenditures, $3,506,562; qualifying distributions, $3,480,408; giving activities include $2,183,082 for 26 grants (high: $695,390; low: $500), and $1,269,589 for 1,603 employee matching gifts.
Purpose and activities: The foundation supports museums and organizations involved with education, human services, community development, and public policy research.
Fields of interest: Museums; Elementary/secondary education; Scholarships/financial aid; Education; Human services; Economic development, visitors/convention bureau/tourism promotion; Community/economic development; United Ways and Federated Giving Programs; Public policy, research.
International interests: Canada.
Type of support: General/operating support; Scholarship funds; Employee volunteer services; Employee matching gifts.
Limitations: Applications not accepted. Giving primarily in NJ, RI, WA, and Canada. No grants to individuals.
Application information: Contributes only to pre-selected organizations.
Officers and Directors: Shivan S. Subramaniam,* Chair., C.E.O., and Pres.; Paul E. LaFleche, Sr. V.P., Investments; Roberta H. Butler,* Sr. V.P., Mktg.; Nelson G. Wester, V.P. and Secy.; William A. Mekrut,* V.P. and Treas.
Trustee: JPMorgan Chase Bank, N.A.
Number of staff: 1
EIN: 222773230

8394
Alta W. Foster Trust ✧
P.O. Box 1802
Providence, RI 02901-1802

Established in 1990; supporting organization of the Children's Hospital, American Cancer Society, Cape Cod Community College, Shriners Hospital, and Cape Cod Hospital.
Foundation type: Independent foundation.
Financial data (yr. ended 12/31/13): Assets, $29,912,347 (M); expenditures, $1,355,967; qualifying distributions, $1,168,994; giving activities include $1,124,710 for 5 grants (high: $224,942; low: $224,942).
Fields of interest: Higher education; Hospitals (general); Hospitals (specialty); Cancer; Cancer research.
Limitations: Applications not accepted. Giving primarily in MA. No grants to individuals.
Application information: Contributes only to pre-selected organizations.
Trustee: Bank of America.
EIN: 046269700
Selected grants: The following grants are a representative sample of this grantmaker's funding activity:
$243,179 to American Cancer Society, Framingham, MA, 2011.
$243,179 to Cape Cod Hospital, Hyannis, MA, 2011.

8395
Nella M. Grimm Fox Foundation Trust ✧
P.O. Box 1802
Providence, RI 02901-1802

Established in 1972; supporting organization of Rutland Regional Medical Center; Grace Congregational United Church, Rutland Free Public Library Association, and The Sunset Home.
Foundation type: Independent foundation.
Financial data (yr. ended 05/31/13): Assets, $11,530,100 (M); expenditures, $567,461; qualifying distributions, $489,968; giving activities include $489,968 for grants.
Fields of interest: Libraries (public); Hospitals (general); Protestant agencies & churches.
Limitations: Applications not accepted. Giving limited to Rutland, VT. No grants to individuals.
Application information: Contributes only to pre-selected organizations; unsolicited requests for funds not considered or acknowledged.
Trustee: Bank of America, N.A.
EIN: 046019494

8396
Samuel Freeman Charitable Trust ✧
P.O. Box 1802
Providence, RI 02901-1802

Established in 1981 in NY.
Donor: Samuel Freeman†.
Foundation type: Independent foundation.
Financial data (yr. ended 12/31/13): Assets, $44,202,398 (M); expenditures, $2,280,498; qualifying distributions, $1,927,819; giving activities include $1,736,600 for 51 grants (high: $222,500; low: $4,000).
Purpose and activities: Preferred consideration is given to cancer research and treatment; the preservation, exhibition, and operation of historical railway equipment; and secondary schools and universities.
Fields of interest: Historic preservation/historical societies; Secondary school/education; Higher education; Cancer; Cancer research.
Type of support: General/operating support; Continuing support; Annual campaigns; Seed money.
Limitations: Applications not accepted. Giving in the U.S., with some emphasis on NY and Charleston, SC. No grants to individuals or private foundations.
Application information: Proposals are accepted by invitation only. Therefore, the trust is unable to consider or respond to unsolicited proposals.
Trustees: Christopher J. Elliman; George Frampton; Elizabeth E. Murray; Pamela Murray; John Palms; Catherine Murray Smith; Bank of America, N.A.
EIN: 136803465
Selected grants: The following grants are a representative sample of this grantmaker's funding activity:
$240,000 to Medical University of South Carolina, Charleston, SC, 2011.
$100,000 to Dana-Farber Cancer Institute, Boston, MA, 2011.
$45,358 to Audubon Society, Bedford, Katonah, NY, 2011.

8397
Mary Gale Foundation, Inc. ✧ ☆
10 Tripps Ln.
Riverside, RI 02915-7995
Application Address: Tom Boucher, c/o Karr & Boucher PLLC, 16 Salmon St., Manchester, NH 03104, tel.: (603) 625-8286

Established in NH.
Donor: Gale Home.
Foundation type: Independent foundation.
Financial data (yr. ended 12/31/13): Assets, $13,228,553 (M); gifts received, $2,132; expenditures, $644,345; qualifying distributions, $563,858; giving activities include $562,225 for 33 grants (high: $44,077; low: $2,250).
Purpose and activities: Giving to organizations that provide housing and healthcare services benefiting women over age 65 in the greater Manchester, New Hampshire area.
Fields of interest: Aging, centers/services.
Limitations: Giving primarily in Manchester, NH.
Application information:
Initial approach: Proposal
Deadline(s): None
Officers: Tom Boucher, Pres.; Carol Kunz, Secy.; Jeffrey Hickok, Treas.
Directors: Eli Cochran; Fred Rusczek; Kathleen Sullivan, Esq.; Anna Thomas; Patrick Tufts.
EIN: 571171038

8398
Helen Wade Greene Charitable Trust ✧
P.O. Box 1802
Providence, RI 02901-1802

Established in 1957 in OH.
Foundation type: Independent foundation.
Financial data (yr. ended 12/31/13): Assets, $12,086,725 (M); expenditures, $467,405; qualifying distributions, $441,249; giving activities include $430,000 for 10 grants (high: $310,000; low: $5,000).
Fields of interest: Arts, association; Museums (art); Arts; Higher education; Education; Hospitals (general); Human services; Foundations (private grantmaking); United Ways and Federated Giving Programs.
Type of support: General/operating support.
Limitations: Applications not accepted. Giving primarily in Boston, MA; some funding also in Cleveland, OH. No grants to individuals.
Application information: Unsolicited requests for funds not accepted.
Trustees: Anne Hollis Perkins; E. Lee Perry; Slocumb Hollis Perry; Bank of America, N.A.
EIN: 346527172

8399
Russell Grinnell Memorial Trust ✧
P.O. Box 1802
Providence, RI 02901-1802
Contact: IRI Augusta Haydock, Bank of America, N.A.

Established in 1998 in RI.

Foundation type: Independent foundation.
Financial data (yr. ended 12/31/13): Assets, $18,953,534 (M); expenditures, $997,270; qualifying distributions, $910,605; giving activities include $823,500 for 21 grants (high: $125,000; low: $7,500).
Fields of interest: Education; Human services; Children/youth, services.
Limitations: Applications not accepted. Giving on a national basis. No grants to individuals.
Application information: Contributes only to pre-selected organizations.
Trustee: Bank of America.
EIN: 311603440

8400
Guth Foundation Charitable Trust ✧
(formerly The Guth Foundation)
P.O. Box 1802
Providence, RI 02901-1802

Established in 1993 in MO.
Donors: James Black Guth; James Black Guth Interim Trust.
Foundation type: Independent foundation.
Financial data (yr. ended 12/31/13): Assets, $14,792,313 (M); expenditures, $1,449,073; qualifying distributions, $1,350,580; giving activities include $1,282,500 for 41 grants (high: $200,000; low: $5,000).
Purpose and activities: Giving primarily for education, children and youth services, including a children's hospital, and human services.
Fields of interest: Education; Hospitals (specialty); Health organizations; Human services; Children/youth, services; Human services, emergency aid; Deaf/hearing impaired.
Limitations: Applications not accepted. Giving primarily in St. Louis, MO. No grants to individuals.
Application information: Contributes only to pre-selected organizations.
Trustees: Edward J. Costigan, III, Jr.; Mark J. Bade; Sally C. Coleman; Bank of America, N.A.
EIN: 436462823
Selected grants: The following grants are a representative sample of this grantmaker's funding activity:
$35,000 to Evans Scholars Foundation, Golf, IL, 2011. For general support.
$25,000 to Boys and Girls Town of Missouri, Saint Louis, MO, 2011. For general support.
$25,000 to Missouri Botanical Garden, Saint Louis, MO, 2011. For general support.
$20,000 to Boys and Girls Club, Herbert Hoover, Saint Louis, MO, 2011. For general support.
$20,000 to Cardinal Glennon Childrens Hospital, Saint Louis, MO, 2011. For general support.
$15,000 to Lift for Life Gym, Saint Louis, MO, 2011. For general support.
$15,000 to Our Little Haven, Saint Louis, MO, 2011. For general support.
$15,000 to Rebuilding Together Saint Louis, Webster Groves, MO, 2011. For general support.
$10,000 to Kid Smart Foundation, New Orleans, LA, 2011. For general support.
$10,000 to Lets Start, Saint Louis, MO, 2011. For general support.

8401
Emma F. Hallett Trust ✧
P.O. Box 1802
Providence, RI 02901-1802

Established in 1974; supporting organization of Steere House, RI, St. Andrews School, TN, Tockwotten Home, RI, and Berry College, Inc., GA.
Foundation type: Independent foundation.
Financial data (yr. ended 09/30/13): Assets, $12,356,671 (M); expenditures, $619,552; qualifying distributions, $543,716; giving activities include $510,087 for 4 grants (high: $127,522; low: $127,521).
Fields of interest: Higher education; Education; Health care.
Limitations: Applications not accepted. Giving primarily in Mount Berry, GA, Providence, RI and Sewanee, TN.
Application information: Contributes only to pre-selected organizations.
Trustee: Bank of America, N.A.
EIN: 166375405
Selected grants: The following grants are a representative sample of this grantmaker's funding activity:
$113,213 to Berry College, Mount Berry, GA, 2011.

8402
The Harris Family Foundation ✧ ☆
P.O. Box 1802
Providence, RI 02901-1802

Established in DE.
Donor: Joshua J. Harris.
Foundation type: Independent foundation.
Financial data (yr. ended 12/31/13): Assets, $3,878,148 (M); gifts received, $182,177; expenditures, $1,628,845; qualifying distributions, $1,621,309; giving activities include $1,621,309 for 50 grants (high: $277,500; low: $180).
Fields of interest: Arts; Education; Human services.
Limitations: Applications not accepted.
Application information: Unsolicited requests for funds not accepted.
Trustee: US Trust Company of Delaware.
EIN: 326080127

8403
Hasbro Children's Fund, Inc. ✧
(formerly Hasbro Charitable Trust, Inc.)
c/o Hasbro, Inc.
1027 Newport Ave.
Pawtucket, RI 02861-2539 (401) 727-5429
Contact: Karen Davis, V.P., Community Rels.
E-mail: kdavis@hasbro.com; Main URL: http://www.hasbro.com/corporate/en_US/community-relations/childrens-fund.cfm
Grants List: http://www.hasbro.com/corporate-2/en_US/community-relations/upload/2013-Local-Grantees-for-Internet-pdf.pdf

Established in 1984 in RI.
Donor: Hasbro, Inc.
Foundation type: Company-sponsored foundation.
Financial data (yr. ended 12/30/12): Assets, $4,728,634 (M); gifts received, $109,843; expenditures, $4,052,490; qualifying distributions, $4,052,475; giving activities include $3,991,841 for 114 grants (high: $1,104,134; low: $25).
Purpose and activities: The fund supports programs designed to provide hope to children who need it most; play for children who otherwise would not be able to experience that joy; and empowerment of youth through service.
Fields of interest: Elementary/secondary education; Zoos/zoological societies; Hospitals (general); Health care; Mental health/crisis services; Pediatrics; Food services; Food banks; Disasters, preparedness/services; Recreation, parks/playgrounds; Recreation; Philanthropy/voluntarism; Children; Economically disadvantaged.
Type of support: General/operating support; Continuing support; Capital campaigns; Building/renovation; Program development; Employee matching gifts.
Limitations: Applications not accepted. Giving primarily in Los Angeles, CA, Springfield, MA, RI, and Renton, WA; giving also to regional, national, and U.S.-based international organizations through strategic partnership program. No support for religious organizations, political organizations, or schools. No grants to individuals, or for research, scholarships, travel, endowments, advertising, sponsorship of recreational activities, fundraisers, or auctions; no loans; no cash-free grants.
Publications: Corporate giving report.
Application information: The fund awards grants through an RFP process. Visit website for updated guidelines. Unsolicited requests from regional, national, and U.S.-based international organizations are not accepted.
Board meeting date(s): Oct./Nov.
Officers: David D.R. Hargreaves, C.O.O.; Brian Goldner, Pres.; Barbara Finigan, Sr. V.P. and Secy.; Deborah Thomas, Sr. V.P. and C.F.O.; Martin Trueb, Sr. V.P. and Treas.; Jeffrey Barkan, Sr. V.P and Cont.
Number of staff: 3 full-time professional; 1 full-time support; 1 part-time support.
EIN: 222538470
Selected grants: The following grants are a representative sample of this grantmaker's funding activity:
$1,104,134 to Points of Light Institute, Atlanta, GA, 2012. For GenerationOn.
$552,762 to Rhode Island Hospital Foundation, Providence, RI, 2012. For Hasbro Children's Hospital.
$200,000 to United Way of Rhode Island, Providence, RI, 2012. For Hasbro Summer Learning Initiative.
$175,000 to Give Kids the World, Kissimmee, FL, 2012. For Winter Wonderland Program.
$175,000 to Operation Smile International, Norfolk, VA, 2012. For Smile Missions.
$50,000 to Angel Flight New England, North Andover, MA, 2012. For Mission Coordination.
$33,333 to Amos House, Providence, RI, 2012. For Mother-Child Reunification Program.
$25,000 to Big Brothers Big Sisters of Puget Sound, Seattle, WA, 2012. For general operating support.
$20,000 to First Star, Washington, DC, 2012. For First Star URI Ram Academy.

8404
Hassenfeld Foundation ✧
101 Dyer St., Ste. 401
Providence, RI 02903-3908

Established in 1944 in RI.
Donors: Sylvia Hassenfeld; Hasbro, Inc.; Stephen Hassenfeld Charitable Lead Trust; Sylvia K.

Hassenfeld Revocable Trust; and members of the Hassenfeld family.
Foundation type: Independent foundation.
Financial data (yr. ended 12/31/12): Assets, $15,887,206 (M); gifts received, $2,678,145; expenditures, $4,488,267; qualifying distributions, $4,238,469; giving activities include $4,238,469 for grants.
Purpose and activities: Giving primarily for higher education and Jewish federated giving programs.
Fields of interest: Higher education; Health organizations; Jewish federated giving programs.
Limitations: Applications not accepted. Giving primarily in MA, NY, PA, RI. No grants to individuals.
Application information: Contributes only to pre-selected organizations.
Officers and Director:* Sylvia K. Hassenfeld,* Pres.; Alan G. Hassenfeld, V.P. and Treas.; Ellen Block, Secy.
EIN: 056015373

8405
Hoche-Scofield Foundation ✧
P.O. Box 1802
Providence, RI 02901-1802
Contact: Audrey Klein-Leach

Established in 1983 in MA.
Donor: William B. Scofield†.
Foundation type: Independent foundation.
Financial data (yr. ended 12/31/13): Assets, $18,022,411 (M); expenditures, $965,476; qualifying distributions, $839,534; giving activities include $775,420 for 109 grants (high: $64,000; low: $2,000).
Purpose and activities: Giving primarily for education and community and social services in Worcester, Massachusetts.
Fields of interest: Arts; Higher education; Health care; Health organizations, association; Human services; Children/youth, services; Women, centers/services; Community/economic development; United Ways and Federated Giving Programs; Women; Economically disadvantaged.
Type of support: Continuing support; Capital campaigns; Equipment; Program development; Seed money.
Limitations: Applications accepted. Giving limited to the City and County of Worcester, MA.
Publications: Application guidelines.
Application information: Application form required.
Initial approach: Letter
Copies of proposal: 5
Deadline(s): Feb. 15, May 15, Aug. 15, and Nov. 15
Board meeting date(s): Mar. 15, June 15, Sept. 15, and Dec. 15
Final notification: Apr. 15, July 15, Oct. 15, and Jan. 15
Trustees: Henry B. Dewey, Esq.; Warner S. Fletcher; Sumner Tilton; Bank of America, N.A.
EIN: 222519554

8406
Edward Wagner and George Hosser Scholarship Fund Trust ✧ ☆
c/o Citizens Bank
10 Tripps Ln.
Riverside, RI 02915-7995 (603) 634-7752
Application address: c/o Bill Dirak, 875 Elm St., Manchester, NH 03101

Established in 1964 in NH.
Donor: Ottilie Wagner Hosser†.
Foundation type: Independent foundation.
Financial data (yr. ended 06/30/13): Assets, $5,571,405 (M); expenditures, $560,247; qualifying distributions, $469,700; giving activities include $469,700 for grants.
Purpose and activities: Scholarship grants for college or professional education to worthy boys and young men from Manchester, New Hampshire, who wish to pursue an undergraduate program at an accredited school.
Type of support: Scholarships—to individuals.
Limitations: Applications accepted. Giving limited to residents of Manchester, NH.
Application information: Application form required.
Initial approach: Letter
Copies of proposal: 1
Deadline(s): May 31
Board meeting date(s): Aug.
Final notification: Approx. the 3rd week in Aug.
Trustee: RBS Citizens, N.A.
EIN: 026005491

8407
HPB Foundation ✧
P.O. Box 1802
Providence, RI 02901-1802

Established in 2005 in NY.
Donor: Harry Payne Bingham, Jr.
Foundation type: Independent foundation.
Financial data (yr. ended 12/31/13): Assets, $15,904,083 (M); expenditures, $877,740; qualifying distributions, $848,118; giving activities include $824,831 for 15 grants (high: $240,000; low: $10,000).
Fields of interest: Higher education; Education; Health care; Mental health, depression; Food services; Human services.
Limitations: Applications not accepted. Giving primarily in MA and NY.
Application information: Contributes only to pre-selected organizations.
Trustee: Bank of America, N.A.
EIN: 202279585
Selected grants: The following grants are a representative sample of this grantmaker's funding activity:
$150,000 to New York Eye and Ear Infirmary, New York, NY, 2012. For Gerald G. Pierce MD Endowment.
$51,188 to Watkinson School, Hartford, CT, 2012. For Head Scholars Scholarship Program.
$35,000 to Bennington-Rutland Opportunity Council, Rutland, VT, 2012. For Relief from Tropical Storm Irene.
$30,000 to Boston Public Library, Boston, MA, 2012. For Children's Writer-In-Residence Program.

8408
IMA McQuade Family Foundation ✧
P.O. Box 1802
Providence, RI 02901-1802

Established in 2004 in RI.
Donors: Eugene M. McQuade; Peggy McQuade; Bank of America.
Foundation type: Independent foundation.
Financial data (yr. ended 12/31/13): Assets, $2,931,064 (M); gifts received, $979,865; expenditures, $721,129; qualifying distributions, $709,074; giving activities include $702,595 for 28 grants (high: $400,000; low: $500).
Fields of interest: Higher education; Education; Foundations (private grantmaking).
Limitations: Applications not accepted. Giving in the U.S., with emphasis on NY. No grants to individuals.
Application information: Unsolicited requests for funds not accepted.
Directors: Eugene M. McQuade; Peggy J. McQuade; Brian Wade.
Trustee: Bank of America, N.A.
EIN: 202057759
Selected grants: The following grants are a representative sample of this grantmaker's funding activity:
$28,000 to Boston College, Chestnut Hill, MA, 2012. For university advancement.
$1,000 to Villanova University, Villanova, PA, 2012. For College of Nursing.

8409
Leonard & Hilda Kaplan Charitable Foundation ✧
56 Exchange Terr.
Providence, RI 02903 (774) 206-8300
Contact: Todd Eisenberg, Tr.

Established in MA.
Donors: Hilda Kaplan†; Hilda Kaplan 1999 Revocable Trust.
Foundation type: Independent foundation.
Financial data (yr. ended 04/30/13): Assets, $12,525,964 (M); expenditures, $791,008; qualifying distributions, $722,850; giving activities include $682,000 for 28 grants (high: $57,000; low: $2,000).
Fields of interest: Museums; Education; Pediatrics; Human services; YM/YWCAs & YM/YWHAs; Children/youth, services.
Application information: Application form required.
Initial approach: Letter
Deadline(s): None
Trustees: Todd Eisenberg; George Robinson.
EIN: 046528085
Selected grants: The following grants are a representative sample of this grantmaker's funding activity:
$55,000 to New Bedford Art Museum, New Bedford, MA, 2013. For Summer Artmobile.

8410
Horace A. Kimball and S. Ella Kimball Foundation ✧ ☆
23 Broad St.
Westerly, RI 02891-1879
Application address: c/o Thomas F. Black, III, Pres., 130 Woodville Rd., Hope Valley, RI 02832-2423, tel.: (401) 364-7799; Main URL: http://www.hkimballfoundation.org

Incorporated in 1956 in DE.
Donor: H. Earle Kimball†.
Foundation type: Independent foundation.
Financial data (yr. ended 10/31/13): Assets, $9,291,649 (M); expenditures, $568,951; qualifying distributions, $537,056; giving activities include $490,325 for 48 grants (high: $50,000; low: $1,500).

Purpose and activities: Giving broadly in the areas of human services, the environment, and health care.
Fields of interest: Arts; Secondary school/education; Education; Environment, natural resources; Environment; Animal welfare; Hospitals (general); Health care; Health organizations, association; Food banks; Boys clubs; Human services; YM/YWCAs & YM/YWHAs; Children/youth, services; Aging, centers/services; Homeless, human services; Aging; Disabilities, people with; Economically disadvantaged; Homeless.
Type of support: General/operating support; Capital campaigns; Building/renovation; Emergency funds; Seed money; Matching/challenge support.
Limitations: Applications accepted. Giving primarily in RI. No support for religious organizations. No grants to individuals, or for feasibility studies, capital projects or multi-year commitments.
Publications: Financial statement; Grants list.
Application information: Application form and guidelines available on foundation web site; online application preferred. Application form required.
Copies of proposal: 3
Deadline(s): None, but preferably by July 15
Board meeting date(s): Mar., June, Aug., and Oct.
Officers and Trustees:* Thomas F. Black III,* Pres.; Norman D. Baker, Jr.,* Secy.-Treas.; Edward C. Marth.
Number of staff: 1 part-time support.
EIN: 056006130

8411
Rose Knoop Trust ✧
P.O. Box 1802
Providence, RI 02901-1802

Established in 2001 in MA.
Donor: Rose Knoop Unitrust.
Foundation type: Independent foundation.
Financial data (yr. ended 10/31/13): Assets, $11,160,551 (M); expenditures, $563,965; qualifying distributions, $485,820; giving activities include $446,304 for 12 grants (high: $37,192; low: $37,192).
Purpose and activities: Giving primarily to Christian churches and organizations including a theological seminary; giving also for human services.
Fields of interest: Higher education, college; Theological school/education; Human services; Salvation Army; Christian agencies & churches; Protestant agencies & churches; Catholic agencies & churches.
Limitations: Applications not accepted. Giving in the U.S., with emphasis on IN, MA, NC, NJ, and NY. No grants to individuals.
Application information: Contributes only to pre-selected organizations.
Trustee: Bank of America, N.A.
EIN: 046240765
Selected grants: The following grants are a representative sample of this grantmaker's funding activity:
$7,188 to Billy Graham Evangelistic Association, Charlotte, NC, 2011.
$7,188 to Billy Graham Evangelistic Association, Charlotte, NC, 2011.
$7,188 to Billy Graham Evangelistic Association, Charlotte, NC, 2011.
$7,188 to Billy Graham Evangelistic Association, Charlotte, NC, 2011.
$7,012 to Billy Graham Evangelistic Association, Charlotte, NC, 2011.

8412
Koonce Family Foundation ✧
P.O. Box 1802
Providence, RI 02901-1802

Established in 2005 in TX.
Donors: K. Terry Koonce; Beverly Koonce.
Foundation type: Independent foundation.
Financial data (yr. ended 12/31/13): Assets, $14,237,629 (M); gifts received, $288,438; expenditures, $597,596; qualifying distributions, $538,862; giving activities include $512,500 for 25 grants (high: $85,000; low: $3,750).
Fields of interest: Media/communications; Higher education, university; Human services; International development; Christian agencies & churches.
Type of support: General/operating support.
Limitations: Applications not accepted. Giving primarily in TX. No grants to individuals.
Application information: Contributes only to pre-selected organizations.
Trustees: Charlene C. Koonce; Kelly M. Koonce; Kenneth T. Koonce; Kimberly Koonce; K. Terry Koonce; Diana Koonce Walla; Richard E. Walla; Bank of America, N.A.
EIN: 766211703

8413
Edward H. Luehrmann Co Trust ✧
P.O. Box 1802
Providence, RI 02901-1802

Foundation type: Independent foundation.
Financial data (yr. ended 12/31/13): Assets, $23,412,373 (M); expenditures, $1,998,990; qualifying distributions, $1,869,123; giving activities include $1,859,450 for 1 grant.
Fields of interest: Higher education.
Limitations: Applications not accepted. Giving primarily in St. Louis, MO.
Application information: Contributes only to pre-selected organizations.
Trustee: Bank of America, N.A.
EIN: 436023541

8414
M. Capewell Trust ✧
P.O. Box 1802
Providence, RI 02901-1802

Foundation type: Independent foundation.
Financial data (yr. ended 12/31/13): Assets, $43,193,689 (M); expenditures, $2,172,678; qualifying distributions, $1,963,492; giving activities include $1,881,242 for 8 grants (high: $626,966; low: $20).
Fields of interest: Nursing home/convalescent facility; Health care; Human services; Family services; Protestant agencies & churches.
Limitations: Applications not accepted. Giving primarily in Hartford, CT.
Application information: Contributes only to pre-selected organizations.
Trustee: Bank of America.
EIN: 066030605

8415
Estelle A. Manning Residuary ✧
P.O. Box 1802
Providence, RI 02901-1802

Established in NY.
Foundation type: Independent foundation.
Financial data (yr. ended 12/31/13): Assets, $33,560,530 (M); expenditures, $1,800,591; qualifying distributions, $1,563,826; giving activities include $1,486,238 for 11 grants (high: $366,599; low: $73,319).
Fields of interest: Higher education; Health care, association; Hospitals (general); Hospitals (specialty); Lung diseases; Human services; Salvation Army; Protestant agencies & churches.
Limitations: Applications not accepted. Giving primarily in New York, NY.
Application information: Contributes only to pre-selected organizations.
Trustee: Bank of America, N.A.
EIN: 136073778

8416
McAdams Charitable Foundation ✧
320 S. Main St.
Providence, RI 02903-2911

Established in 1992 in RI.
Donors: Norman Estes McCulloch, Jr.; Dorothy McCulloch; Microfibres, Inc.
Foundation type: Independent foundation.
Financial data (yr. ended 12/31/12): Assets, $9,219,193 (M); gifts received, $28,720; expenditures, $1,924,063; qualifying distributions, $1,806,171; giving activities include $1,732,779 for grants.
Purpose and activities: Giving primarily for education, as well as for the arts, the environment and hospitals.
Fields of interest: Arts; Elementary/secondary education; Higher education; Education; Environment, natural resources; Hospitals (general); Human services; United Ways and Federated Giving Programs; Christian agencies & churches.
Type of support: General/operating support; Capital campaigns.
Limitations: Applications not accepted. Giving primarily in RI; some funding also in MA and NH. No grants to individuals.
Application information: Contributes only to pre-selected organizations.
Officers: Norman Estes McCulloch, Jr., Pres. and Treas.; Dorothy R. McCulloch, V.P.
Trustees: Stacey A. McCullough; Paul A. Silver.
EIN: 050468638

8417
McCurdy Article 2nd Charitable Trust ✧
P. O. Box 1802
Providence, RI 02901-1802

Donor: Matilda G. McCurdy.
Foundation type: Independent foundation.
Financial data (yr. ended 12/31/13): Assets, $22,745,091 (M); gifts received, $26,442; expenditures, $1,193,642; qualifying distributions, $1,033,847; giving activities include $970,996 for 6 grants (high: $161,833; low: $161,832).
Fields of interest: Higher education; Hospitals (general); Eye research; Protestant agencies & churches.
Limitations: Applications not accepted.
Application information: Unsolicited requests for funds not accepted.

Trustee: Bank of America, N.A.
EIN: 136216017

8418
Colonel Stanley R. McNeil Foundation ✧
P.O. Box 1802
Providence, RI 02901-1802
E-mail: ilgrantmaking@ustrust.com; Main
URL: http://www.bankofamerica.com/grantmaking

Established in 1993 in IL.
Donor: Stanley McNeil.
Foundation type: Independent foundation.
Financial data (yr. ended 11/30/13): Assets, $20,532,998 (M); expenditures, $1,000,939; qualifying distributions, $914,243; giving activities include $776,000 for 40 grants (high: $125,000; low: $2,500).
Purpose and activities: Giving primarily for children's causes, healthcare, and to start-up initiatives within the human services or arts and cultural arenas.
Fields of interest: Arts; Education; Health care; Human services; Children/youth, services.
Type of support: General/operating support; Building/renovation; Equipment; Program development; Curriculum development; Scholarship funds; Research; Matching/challenge support.
Limitations: Giving primarily in the Chicago, IL, area. No grants to individuals, or for endowments, capital projects, or multi-year funding requests.
Publications: Application guidelines.
Application information: The foundation will consider requests for general operations only if the organization's operating budget is less than $1 million. Application form not required.
Copies of proposal: 1
Deadline(s): Feb. 1 and June 1
Final notification: June 30 (for the Feb. deadline), Nov. 30 (for the June deadline)
Trustee: Bank of America, N.A.
Number of staff: 1 full-time professional; 3 full-time support.
EIN: 367016333
Selected grants: The following grants are a representative sample of this grantmaker's funding activity:
$35,000 to Gads Hill Center, Chicago, IL, 2011. For Teen Connection.
$29,000 to Peer Health Exchange, Chicago, IL, 2011. For general operating support.
$25,000 to Ada S. McKinley Community Services, Chicago, IL, 2011. For McKinley College Preparation and Placement Program.
$25,000 to By the Hand Club for Kids, Chicago, IL, 2011. For Education and Literacy Initiative, to provide the personalized attention, support and materials needed to assist first through twelfth graders.
$25,000 to Camp of Dreams, Chicago, IL, 2011. For general operating support.
$25,000 to Catholic Charities of the Archdiocese of Chicago, Chicago, IL, 2011. For Community Family Service Center.
$24,000 to United States Catholic Conference, Chicago, IL, 2011. For Super School Initiative.
$15,000 to Park Ridge Youth Campus, Park Ridge, IL, 2011. For Foster Care and Adoption Program.
$10,000 to Association House of Chicago, Chicago, IL, 2011. For Healthy Lifestyles Program, a renewed gift to help further efforts to educate community members, especially youth, about health, nutrition and physical fitness.
$10,000 to Vital Bridges, Chicago, IL, 2011. For Food and Nutrition Program.

8419
Martha Dana Mercer Trust ✧ ☆
P.O. Box 1802
Providence, RI 02901-1802

Established in MA.
Foundation type: Independent foundation.
Financial data (yr. ended 12/31/13): Assets, $64,225,625 (M); expenditures, $3,479,540; qualifying distributions, $3,054,235; giving activities include $2,937,149 for 6 grants (high: $963,442; low: $8,093).
Fields of interest: Museums (art); Performing arts, orchestras; Botanical gardens.
Limitations: Applications not accepted. Giving primarily in Boston, MA; some funding also in Doylestown, PA.
Application information: Unsolicited requests for funds not accepted.
Trustee: Bank of America.
EIN: 046009617
Selected grants: The following grants are a representative sample of this grantmaker's funding activity:
$18,480 to Boston Athenaeum, Boston, MA, 2012. For unrestricted general support.

8420
Middendorf Family Foundation ✧ ☆
(formerly Frank J. Middendorf Family Foundation)
P.O. Box 1802
Providence, RI 02901-1802

Established in 2001 in NY.
Donor: Frank J. Middendorf.
Foundation type: Independent foundation.
Financial data (yr. ended 12/31/13): Assets, $11,213,233 (M); gifts received, $280,581; expenditures, $634,081; qualifying distributions, $500,752; giving activities include $470,000 for 16 grants (high: $110,000; low: $5,000).
Fields of interest: Education; United Ways and Federated Giving Programs; Christian agencies & churches.
Type of support: Scholarship funds.
Limitations: Applications not accepted. Giving primarily in FL, IA, and NJ. No grants to individuals.
Application information: Contributes only to pre-selected organizations.
Trustees: Frank J. Middendorf; Patricia A. Middendorf; Bank of America, N.A.
EIN: 233069847

8421
Murray Family Charitable Foundation ✧
10 Weybosset St., Ste. 302B
Providence, RI 02903-2818 (401) 444-0818
Contact: Paula McNamara, Pres. and Treas.
E-mail: pmcnamara712@aol.com

Established in 1993 in RI.
Donors: Terrence J. Murray; Murray Family Annuity.
Foundation type: Independent foundation.
Financial data (yr. ended 12/31/13): Assets, $26,754,650 (M); gifts received, $2,061,883; expenditures, $1,358,991; qualifying distributions, $996,615; giving activities include $925,548 for 130 grants (high: $82,500; low: $100).
Purpose and activities: Giving primarily to hospitals, and for education and human services.
Fields of interest: Museums (art); Elementary/secondary education; Higher education; Education; Hospitals (general); Human services; United Ways and Federated Giving Programs.
Type of support: Scholarship funds; Matching/challenge support.
Limitations: Applications accepted. Giving primarily in MA and RI.
Application information: Application form required.
Initial approach: Letter
Deadline(s): None
Officers: Paula McNamara, Pres. and Treas.; Colleen M. Coggins, Exec. V.P.; Megan Craigen, Exec. V.P.; Christopher D. Murray, Exec. V.P.; Terrence Murray, Exec. V.P.
EIN: 050475089

8422
Jonathan M. Nelson Family Foundation ✧
c/o Providence Equity Partners, Inc.
50 Kennedy Pl., 18th Fl.
Providence, RI 02903-2393 (401) 751-0588
Contact: Jonathan M. Nelson, Tr.
Jonathan M. Nelson's Giving Pledge Profile: http://glasspockets.org/philanthropy-in-focus/eye-on-the-giving-pledge/profiles/nelson

Established in 1999 in RI.
Donor: Jonathan M. Nelson.
Foundation type: Independent foundation.
Financial data (yr. ended 12/31/13): Assets, $50,427,395 (M); gifts received, $11,516,984; expenditures, $2,559,607; qualifying distributions, $2,298,504; giving activities include $2,298,454 for 40 grants (high: $1,400,000; low: $500).
Purpose and activities: Giving primarily for higher education, the arts, health, and children, youth, and social services.
Fields of interest: Arts; Higher education, university; Health organizations, association; Human services; Children/youth, services; Foundations (private grantmaking).
Limitations: Applications accepted. Giving primarily in RI, with emphasis on Providence; some funding nationally, particularly in MA and NY. No grants to individuals.
Application information: Application form not required.
Initial approach: Proposal
Deadline(s): None
Trustees: David K. Duffell; Jane S. Nelson; Jonathan M. Nelson.
EIN: 050504814
Selected grants: The following grants are a representative sample of this grantmaker's funding activity:
$1,200,000 to Brown University, Providence, RI, 2012. For Nelson Fitness Center.
$250,000 to Brown University, Providence, RI, 2012. For Brown Annual Fund.
$50,000 to Brown University, Providence, RI, 2012. For Educational-To Support Students Needs.
$10,000 to Northfield Mount Hermon School, Mount Hermon, MA, 2012. For Funds Help Support This Coed Boarding and Day School.

8423
Newport Restoration Foundation ✧ ☆
51 Touro St.
Newport, RI 02840-2932 (401) 849-7300
Contact: Robert Foley, Dir.
FAX: (401) 849-0125; Main URL: http://www.newportrestoration.org/
Blog: https://newportrestoration.wordpress.com/2014/09/29/a-fond-farewell/
E-Newsletter: http://www.newportrestoration.org/about/contact
Facebook: http://www.facebook.com/NewportRestorationFoundation
Instagram: http://instagram.com/nptrestoration#
Pinterest: http://www.pinterest.com/NPTRestoration/
Twitter: https://twitter.com/NPTRestoration
YouTube: http://www.youtube.com/user/newportrestoration

Established in 1968 in RI.
Donors: Doris Duke†; Doris Duke Charitable Foundation; Margaretta M. Clulow Revocable Trust.
Foundation type: Operating foundation.
Financial data (yr. ended 12/31/13): Assets, $55,617,389 (M); gifts received, $2,523,392; expenditures, $5,344,562; qualifying distributions, $726,722; giving activities include $495,676 for 30 grants (high: $442,626; low: $50), and $4,208,009 for 4 foundation-administered programs.
Purpose and activities: The foundation was formed with the express purpose of preserving, interpreting, and maintaining landscape and objects reflecting Aquidneck Island's 18th- and 19th- century architectural culture. It fulfills its mission in the following ways: being a leader in historic preservation in Newport County and Rhode Island; preserving a collection of the arts of cabinetmaking and building trades of the Newport region, along with art and artifacts from Doris Duke's life in Newport, Rhode Island; and utilizing its collections for educational programs.
Fields of interest: Arts; Human services; Religion.
Limitations: Applications accepted. Giving limited to Newport County, RI. No grants to individuals.
Publications: Financial statement.
Application information: Application form required.
Initial approach: Letter
Deadline(s): Dec.
Officers: Roger Mandle, Pres.; Thomas Goddard, V.P.; Eric Hertfelder, Secy.-Treas.; Pieter N. Roos, Exec. Dir.
Board Members: Maia Farish; David Gordon; Edith McBean; Victoria Mele.
Number of staff: 3 full-time professional; 11 full-time support; 10 part-time support.
EIN: 050317816
Selected grants: The following grants are a representative sample of this grantmaker's funding activity:
$442,626 to Doris Duke Monument Foundation, Providence, RI, 2013. For creation of monument in Queen Anne Square.
$5,000 to La Farge Heritage Foundation of Newport, Newport, RI, 2013. For electrical upgrades/safety/usability.
$5,000 to Saint Mary's Roman Catholic Church, Newport, RI, 2013. For restoration of tower.
$4,000 to Newport, City of, Newport, RI, 2013. For Farewell Street Burial Ground Wall Restoration.
$3,000 to Jamestown Historical Society, Jamestown, RI, 2013. For vapor mitigation.
$2,500 to Whitehall Museum House, Middletown, RI, 2013. For improvements to drainage around house.

8424
Deborah M. Noonan Memorial Fund ✧
P.O. Box 1802
Providence, RI 02901-1802
Main URL: https://www.bankofamerica.com/philanthropic

Donor: Walter J. Noonan Trust.
Foundation type: Independent foundation.
Financial data (yr. ended 11/30/13): Assets, $16,026,777 (M); gifts received, $10,405; expenditures, $652,462; qualifying distributions, $580,391; giving activities include $490,750 for 26 grants (high: $25,000; low: $10,000).
Fields of interest: Health care; Human services; Religion.
Limitations: Applications accepted. Giving primarily in the greater Boston area.
Application information: Application form required.
Initial approach: Online application form on foundation web site
Deadline(s): Sept. 1
Final notification: End of Nov.
Trustee: Bank of America, N.A.
EIN: 306306752

8425
O'Brien Trust ✧
P.O. Box 1802
Providence, RI 02901-1802

Established in NY.
Donor: Elsa O'Brien.
Foundation type: Independent foundation.
Financial data (yr. ended 12/31/13): Assets, $63,318 (M); expenditures, $1,975,146; qualifying distributions, $1,959,990; giving activities include $1,953,034 for 1 grant.
Purpose and activities: Giving primarily to a hospital.
Fields of interest: Hospitals (general).
Limitations: Applications not accepted. Giving primarily in Little Falls, NY. No grants to individuals.
Application information: Unsolicited requests for funds not accepted.
Trustee: Bank of America, N.A.
EIN: 306310874

8426
Edward B. Osborn Charitable Trust ✧
c/o Bank of America, N.A.
P.O. Box 1802
Providence, RI 02901-1802

Trust established in 1961 in NY.
Donor: Edward B. Osborn.
Foundation type: Independent foundation.
Financial data (yr. ended 12/31/11): Assets, $0 (M); expenditures, $4,993,466; qualifying distributions, $4,971,777.
Fields of interest: Museums; Arts; Higher education; Environment; Cancer; Boys clubs; Children/youth, services; United Ways and Federated Giving Programs.
Limitations: Applications not accepted. Giving primarily in MN and NY. No grants to individuals.
Application information: Contributes only to pre-selected organizations.
Trustee: Bank of America, N.A.
EIN: 136071296

8427
John L. Patten Charitable Trust ✧
P.O. Box 1802
Providence, RI 02901-1802

Foundation type: Independent foundation.
Financial data (yr. ended 09/30/13): Assets, $20,607,102 (M); expenditures, $880,810; qualifying distributions, $830,185; giving activities include $798,072 for 2 grants (high: $399,036; low: $399,036).
Fields of interest: Health care; Foundations (community).
Limitations: Applications not accepted. Giving primarily in IL.
Application information: Contributes only to pre-selected organizations.
Trustee: Bank of America, N.A.
EIN: 366661467
Selected grants: The following grants are a representative sample of this grantmaker's funding activity:
$393,536 to Chicago Community Trust, Chicago, IL, 2011. For general support.
$393,536 to NorthShore University HealthSystem, Evanston, IL, 2011. For general support.

8428
The Rainbow Foundation ✧ ☆
50 Kennedy Plz., Ste. 1500
Providence, RI 02903
Application address: c/o JP Morgan, Attn.: Andrew Thompson, 270 Park Ave., New York, NY 10017-2014

Established in 2007 in RI.
Donors: Maurania Corp.; Massachusetts Towing Co.
Foundation type: Independent foundation.
Financial data (yr. ended 12/31/13): Assets, $0 (M); gifts received, $691; expenditures, $1,028,147; qualifying distributions, $1,023,171; giving activities include $1,023,171 for 6 grants (high: $1,014,021; low: $500).
Fields of interest: Education; Foundations (community).
Limitations: Applications accepted. Giving primarily in RI; some funding also in MA.
Application information: Application form not required.
Initial approach: Proposal
Deadline(s): None
Trustees: Marion H.M. Mariner; Hope Ives Mauran; Louise S. Mauran; Harriette M. Merrill; Louise M. Nadler; Margaret M. Zuccotti.
EIN: 260639525
Selected grants: The following grants are a representative sample of this grantmaker's funding activity:
$1,014,021 to Rhode Island Foundation, Providence, RI, 2013. For general use.
$4,650 to Saint Timothys School, Stevenson, MD, 2013. For general use.
$2,000 to Tabor Academy, Marion, MA, 2013. For general use.
$1,000 to Middlebury College, Middlebury, VT, 2013. For general use.

$1,000 to Milton Academy, Milton, MA, 2013. For general use.

8429
The Rhode Island Foundation ✧
(also known as The Rhode Island Community Foundation)
1 Union Station
Providence, RI 02903-1746 (401) 274-4564
FAX: (401) 331-8085;
E-mail: nsteinberg@rifoundation.org; Main URL: http://www.rifoundation.org
Facebook: http://www.facebook.com/rhodeislandfoundation?ref=mf
RSS Feed: http://www.rifoundation.org/DefaultPermissions/Home/tabid/36/moduleid/927/RSS.aspx
Video Directory: http://www.rifoundation.org/AboutUs/VideosOurWorkintheCommunity/tabid/509/Default.aspx

Incorporated in 1916 in RI (includes The Rhode Island Community Foundation in 1984).
Foundation type: Community foundation.
Financial data (yr. ended 12/31/12): Assets, $678,230,790 (M); gifts received, $38,467,685; expenditures, $36,048,030; giving activities include $28,267,948 for grants.
Purpose and activities: The foundation seeks to promote philanthropic activities that will improve the living conditions and well-being of the inhabitants of Rhode Island.
Fields of interest: Performing arts; Historic preservation/historical societies; Arts; Libraries/library science; Education; Environment, natural resources; Environment; Animal welfare; Health care; Health organizations, association; AIDS; Legal services; Housing/shelter; Children/youth, services; Family services; Human services, emergency aid; Minorities/immigrants, centers/services; Homeless, human services; Human services; Nonprofit management; Community/economic development; Voluntarism promotion; Government/public administration; Leadership development; Public affairs.
Type of support: General/operating support; Management development/capacity building; Capital campaigns; Building/renovation; Equipment; Land acquisition; Emergency funds; Program development; Conferences/seminars; Film/video/radio; Publication; Seed money; Fellowships; Scholarship funds; Technical assistance; Consulting services; Program evaluation; Program-related investments/loans; Grants to individuals; Scholarships—to individuals; Matching/challenge support.
Limitations: Applications accepted. Giving through discretionary funds limited to RI. No support for religious organizations for sectarian purposes (except as specified by donors). No grants for endowment funds, research, hospital equipment, capital needs of health organizations, annual campaigns, deficit financing, or educational institutions for general operating expenses.
Publications: Application guidelines; Annual report (including application guidelines); Financial statement; Grants list; Informational brochure; Informational brochure (including application guidelines); Newsletter; Occasional report; Program policy statement.
Application information: Visit foundation web site for application guidelines as well as scholarship information. Application form required.
Initial approach: Letter of intent
Copies of proposal: 1
Deadline(s): Varies
Board meeting date(s): Varies
Final notification: Varies
Officers and Directors:* Frederick K. Butler,* Chair.; Neil Steinberg,* C.E.O. and Pres.; Jessica David, V.P., Strategy and Public Affairs; Daniel Kertzner, V.P., Grants Progs.; Kathleen Malin, V.P., Technology and Opers. Mgmt.; Jill Pfitzenmayer, Ph.D., V.P., Initiative for Nonprofit Excellence; James Sanzi, V.P., Devel.; Jennifer Reid, Cont.; Michael K. Allio; Mary W.C. Daly; Jorge O. Elorza; Patricia J. Flanagan, M.D.; Ned Handy; Marie J. Langlois; Mary F. Lovejoy; H. Ronald K. Machtley; Cynthia Reed; Hon. Ernest C. Torres.
Number of staff: 30 full-time professional; 4 part-time professional; 11 full-time support.
EIN: 222604963
Selected grants: The following grants are a representative sample of this grantmaker's funding activity:
$2,832,044 to United Way of Rhode Island, Providence, RI, 2012. For community improvement.
$500,000 to Miriam Hospital Foundation, Providence, RI, 2012. For a capital campaign.
$421,456 to Teach for America, New York, NY, 2012. For Teach for America.
$196,056 to East Bay Community Action Program, Newport, RI, 2012. For East Bay Community Action Program's Care, Access, Readiness and Evolution Initiative.
$125,000 to Community MusicWorks, Providence, RI, 2012. For general support.
$90,000 to Save the Bay, Providence, RI, 2012. For Narragansett Bay Field Studies and Project Narragansett programs in urban communities.
$16,666 to Providence Plan, Providence, RI, 2012. For Rhode Island DataHUB.
$12,500 to Portsmouth United Methodist Church, Methodist Community Gardens, Portsmouth, RI, 2012. For Nicaragua Covenant Medical Clinic.
$7,500 to Wolf School, East Providence, RI, 2012. For general support.
$5,000 to Salvation Army, Rhode Island State Office, Cranston, RI, 2012. For general support.

8430
Paul K. Richter Memorial Fund ✧
P.O. Box 1802
Providence, RI 02901-1802
Application Details: Debra Grand, c/o Bank of America, 231 S. LaSalle St., Chicago, IL 60604. tel.: (312) 828-2055

Donor: J. Edward Richter Trust.
Foundation type: Independent foundation.
Financial data (yr. ended 12/31/13): Assets, $47,866,250 (M); expenditures, $1,406,996; qualifying distributions, $1,086,907; giving activities include $850,200 for 12 grants (high: $77,800; low: $50,000).
Purpose and activities: Giving to primarily Protestant-oriented educational institutions, which through substantial support by private funds, provide top-quality undergraduate or graduate school training. Such institutions should advocate a policy of maintaining small classes and a low ratio of students to teaching members of the faculty. Such institutions should encourage individual achievement and emphasize the necessity for the student's use of his or her own capacity to achieve, based on his or her own efforts and a sense of responsibility for his or her own conduct.
Fields of interest: Higher education.
Limitations: Applications accepted. Giving primarily in CA and IL; some giving also in CT, NC, NH, OR, and TX.
Application information: Application form required.
Initial approach: Proposal
Deadline(s): Sept. 30
Trustee: Bank of America, N.A.
EIN: 366208740
Selected grants: The following grants are a representative sample of this grantmaker's funding activity:
$107,226 to Wake Forest University, Winston-Salem, NC, 2011.
$107,223 to California Institute of Technology, Pasadena, CA, 2011.
$107,223 to Claremont Graduate University, Claremont, CA, 2011.
$107,223 to Dartmouth College, Hanover, NH, 2011.
$107,223 to George Fox University, Newberg, OR, 2011.
$107,223 to Knox College, Galesburg, IL, 2011.
$107,223 to Northwestern University, Evanston, IL, 2011.
$107,223 to Occidental College, Los Angeles, CA, 2011.
$107,223 to Southern Methodist University, Dallas, TX, 2011.
$53,620 to Yale University, New Haven, CT, 2011.

8431
Lewis Roraback Trust ✧
c/o Bank of America, N.A.
P.O. Box 1802
Providence, RI 02901-1802

Established in 1980; supporting organization of Hartford Hospital, St. Francis Hospital and Medical Center, Mount Sinai Hospital, and Newington Children's Hospital.
Foundation type: Independent foundation.
Financial data (yr. ended 02/28/13): Assets, $28,374,150 (M); expenditures, $1,455,058; qualifying distributions, $1,289,939; giving activities include $1,234,447 for 7 grants (high: $555,501; low: $8,044).
Purpose and activities: Giving primarily for hospitals.
Fields of interest: Hospitals (general); Hospitals (specialty); YM/YWCAs & YM/YWHAs; United Ways and Federated Giving Programs.
Limitations: Applications not accepted. Giving limited to CT. No grants to individuals.
Application information: Contributes only to pre-selected organizations; unsolicited requests for funds not considered or acknowledged.
Trustee: Bank of America, N.A.
EIN: 066233067
Selected grants: The following grants are a representative sample of this grantmaker's funding activity:
$581,498 to Saint Francis Hospital and Medical Center, Hartford, CT, 2011.
$323,054 to Hartford Hospital, Hartford, CT, 2011.

8432
E. J. & V. M. Routhier Foundation ✧
(formerly Edward J. & Virginia M. Routhier Foundation)
10 Tripps Ln.
Riverside, RI 02915-7995

Established in 1995 in RI.
Foundation type: Independent foundation.
Financial data (yr. ended 12/31/13): Assets, $18,471,800 (M); expenditures, $986,384; qualifying distributions, $909,330; giving activities include $855,813 for 25 grants (high: $251,000; low: $2,000).
Fields of interest: Education; Hospitals (general); Health organizations; Foundations (community); Christian agencies & churches.
Limitations: Applications not accepted. Giving primarily in RI, with emphasis on Providence. No grants to individuals.
Application information: Unsolicited requests for funds not accepted.
Trustee: RBS Citizens, N.A.
Distribution Committee Members: Peter Arden; Dennis DiBenedetto; James E. Murphy; Phyllis Nigris; David F. Rampone.
EIN: 050485198
Selected grants: The following grants are a representative sample of this grantmaker's funding activity:
$200,000 to Rhode Island Foundation, Providence, RI, 2012. For donor-advised fund.

8433
Ryan Charitable Trust ✧
c/o Rex Capital Advisors, LLC
50 Park Row W., Ste. 113
Providence, RI 02903-1114 (401) 383-5370
Contact: Charles E. Ryan, Tr.

Established in 2006 in RI.
Donor: Charles E. Ryan.
Foundation type: Independent foundation.
Financial data (yr. ended 12/31/12): Assets, $4,593,960 (M); expenditures, $548,189; qualifying distributions, $487,000; giving activities include $487,000 for 7 grants (high: $200,000; low: $25,000).
Purpose and activities: Giving primarily for education and international affairs.
Fields of interest: Education.
International interests: Russia.
Limitations: Applications accepted. Giving primarily in Washington, DC, MD and Moscow, Russia.
Application information: Application form required.
Initial approach: Letter
Deadline(s): None
Trustees: Caren S. Lambert; Charles E. Ryan.
EIN: 207196210

8434
The Salem Foundation ✧
(formerly Paul and Navyn Salem Charitable Trust)
c/o Providence Equity Partners
50 Kennedy Plz., 18th Fl.
Providence, RI 02903-2393 (401) 751-0588
Contact: Paul J. Salem, Tr.

Established in 2000 in RI.
Donor: Paul J. Salem.
Foundation type: Independent foundation.
Financial data (yr. ended 12/31/13): Assets, $13,640,696 (M); gifts received, $3,989,412; expenditures, $516,311; qualifying distributions, $498,250; giving activities include $498,200 for 25 grants (high: $158,000; low: $100).
Purpose and activities: Giving primarily for education, health organizations, and human services.
Fields of interest: Secondary school/education; Higher education; Education; Health organizations, association; Youth development; Human services.
Limitations: Applications accepted. Giving primarily in IN, MA and RI. No grants to individuals.
Application information: Application form not required.
Initial approach: Proposal
Deadline(s): None
Trustee: Paul J. Salem.
EIN: 137196668
Selected grants: The following grants are a representative sample of this grantmaker's funding activity:
$120,100 to Year Up Providence, Providence, RI, 2012. For Further Young Adults Technical and Professional Skills.
$44,000 to Nantucket Golf Club Foundation, Siasconset, MA, 2012. To support Local Charitable Organizations and Support Programs That Award Scholarship Grants in the Field of Education.
$5,000 to Save the Bay, Providence, RI, 2012. To preserve and Protect the Water Quality of Narragansett Bay and Its Ecological Integrity.
$5,000 to United States Fund for UNICEF, New York, NY, 2012. For Saving Children's Lives Around the World By Informing American People of the Needs of Children in Developing Countries.
$1,250 to Reach Out and Read Rhode Island, Providence, RI, 2012. To provide Children with Books in Order to Promote Literacy.
$1,050 to Plan International USA, Warwick, RI, 2012. For Funds Support Child-Centered Community Development Programs.
$1,000 to American Cancer Society, Oklahoma City, OK, 2012. To Eliminate Cancer As a Major Health Problem Through Research, Education, Advocacy, and Service.
$400 to Feeding America, Chicago, IL, 2012. For Help Feed America's Hungry Through a Nationwide Network of Food Banks and Engage Our Country in the Fight to End Hunger.

8435
The Scrooby Foundation ✧
P.O. Box 1802
Providence, RI 02901-1802

Established in 1995 in MN.
Donor: Frederick Brewster.
Foundation type: Independent foundation.
Financial data (yr. ended 06/30/13): Assets, $13,603,056 (M); expenditures, $631,319; qualifying distributions, $560,000; giving activities include $560,000 for grants.
Fields of interest: Museums (science/technology); Performing arts centers; Historic preservation/historical societies; Recreation, parks/playgrounds; Human services.
Limitations: Applications not accepted. Giving primarily in MN. No grants to individuals.
Application information: Contributes only to pre-selected organizations.
Officers and Directors:* Susan B. McCarthy,* Pres.; Priscilla Brewster,* V.P.; Marvin J. Pertzik,* Secy.-Treas.; Allison Brewster; Barbara B. Johnson; Eric L. Johnson; Edwin J. McCarthy.
EIN: 411795397
Selected grants: The following grants are a representative sample of this grantmaker's funding activity:
$100,000 to Minnesota Historical Society, Saint Paul, MN, 2013. For grant for Endowment for Education.
$35,000 to Vail Valley Foundation, Avon, CO, 2013. For Education Program for Eagle County.
$10,000 to Fisher House Foundation, Rockville, MD, 2013. To assist with Minnesota Operations.

8436
George Dudley Seymour Trust ✧ ☆
c/o Bank of America, N.A., Fdn. and Philanthropic Svcs.
P.O. Box 1802
Providence, RI 02901-1802
Application Address: c/o Bank of America, Attn.: Carmen Britt, 200 Glastonbury Blvd., Glastonbury, CT 06033

Established in 1986 in CT.
Foundation type: Independent foundation.
Financial data (yr. ended 07/31/13): Assets, $6,000,674 (M); expenditures, $521,030; qualifying distributions, $479,878; giving activities include $459,000 for 1 grant.
Purpose and activities: Grants are made primarily for purchase of lands within the state of Connecticut to be delivered as recreational centers in the towns, and secondarily for the preservation of the history of Connecticut and its cities and towns.
Fields of interest: Public affairs.
Type of support: General/operating support; Land acquisition.
Limitations: Applications accepted. Giving limited to CT. No grants to individuals.
Publications: Application guidelines.
Application information: Application form required.
Initial approach: Letter
Deadline(s): None
Board meeting date(s): June
Trustee: Bank of America, N.A.
EIN: 066021772

8437
The Sharpe Family Foundation ✧
c/o KLR
951 N. Main St.
Providence, RI 02904-5759

Established in 1966 in RI.
Donors: Mary Elizabeth Sharpe‡; Henry D. Sharpe, Jr.; Peggy Boyd Sharpe.
Foundation type: Independent foundation.
Financial data (yr. ended 12/31/13): Assets, $24,970,793 (M); expenditures, $1,440,380; qualifying distributions, $1,394,472; giving activities include $1,384,625 for 119 grants (high: $160,000; low: $500).
Purpose and activities: Giving primarily for higher and other education, nature conservation, hospitals, and human services.
Fields of interest: Museums; Arts; Elementary/secondary education; Higher education; Environment, natural resources; Zoos/zoological societies; Hospitals (general); United Ways and Federated Giving Programs.

Limitations: Applications not accepted. Giving primarily in RI; some giving in MA. No grants to individuals.
Application information: Unsolicited requests for funds not accepted.
Trustees: Douglas B. Sharpe; Henry D. Sharpe, Jr.; Henry D. Sharpe III; Peggy B. Sharpe; Sarah A. Sharpe.
EIN: 136208422
Selected grants: The following grants are a representative sample of this grantmaker's funding activity:
$1,000 to Providence Public Library, Providence, RI, 2012. For education.

8438
Shriners of Rhode Island Charities Trust ✧
(formerly Palestine Temple Charities Trust)
1 Rhodes Pl.
Cranston, RI 02905-3326 (401) 467-7100
Contact: A. Sheffield Reynolds, Treas.

Established in 1993 in RI.
Donors: Abbey Francis Lawton; Hodges-Lawton Charities; Willis F. Leach‡; Pauline Patt; Henry Stone; Af Preston.
Foundation type: Independent foundation.
Financial data (yr. ended 12/31/13): Assets, $29,189,208 (M); gifts received, $103,909; expenditures, $1,646,355; qualifying distributions, $1,596,092; giving activities include $1,386,025 for 105+ grants (high: $242,500).
Purpose and activities: Giving primarily for hospitals; funding also for children and youth services.
Fields of interest: Hospitals (general); Children/youth, services.
Type of support: General/operating support; Scholarships—to individuals.
Limitations: Applications accepted. Giving primarily in RI.
Application information: Application form required.
Initial approach: Letter with medical information
Deadline(s): None
Officer: A. Sheffield Reynolds, Treas.
Trustees: Leon Knudsen; John Takian, Jr.; Robert H. Williams.
EIN: 223191072

8439
Helen and Ritter Shumway Foundation ✧ ☆
c/o Bank of America, N.A.
P.O. Box 1802
Providence, RI 02901-1802

Established in 2002 in CT.
Donors: Helen Shumway Mayer‡; Helen Mayer Charitable Trust.
Foundation type: Independent foundation.
Financial data (yr. ended 11/30/13): Assets, $8,275,863 (M); gifts received, $127,865; expenditures, $558,680; qualifying distributions, $528,095; giving activities include $489,500 for 21 grants (high: $75,000; low: $5,000).
Fields of interest: Museums; Historic preservation/historical societies; Education; Hospitals (general).
Limitations: Applications not accepted. Giving primarily in Rochester, NY. No grants to individuals.
Application information: Contributes only to pre-selected organizations.
Trustees: Paul C. Lambert, Esq.; Frank R. Shumway, Jr.; Bank of America, N.A.
EIN: 166538147

8440
Ethel Walker Smith Fund ✧
P.O. Box 1802
Providence, RI 02901-1802

Foundation type: Independent foundation.
Financial data (yr. ended 12/31/13): Assets, $12,107,877 (M); expenditures, $611,417; qualifying distributions, $562,848; giving activities include $532,917 for 6 grants (high: $266,458; low: $26,646).
Fields of interest: Education; Health care.
Limitations: Applications not accepted. Giving primarily in CT.
Application information: Unsolicited requests for funds not accepted.
Trustee: Bank of America, N.A.
EIN: 306223450

8441
Amy Plant Statter Foundation ✧
P.O. Box 1802
Providence, RI 02901-1802

Established in 1958 in NY.
Donor: Amy Plant Statter Clark.
Foundation type: Independent foundation.
Financial data (yr. ended 12/31/13): Assets, $30,038,314 (M); gifts received, $2,094,726; expenditures, $1,228,398; qualifying distributions, $1,095,735; giving activities include $990,500 for 28 grants (high: $150,000; low: $500).
Fields of interest: Foundations (private grantmaking).
Type of support: General/operating support.
Limitations: Applications not accepted. Giving primarily in CA, CT, NY, and VA. No grants to individuals.
Application information: Contributes only to pre-selected organizations.
Trustees: Elena G. Oxman; Lee W. Oxman; Phyllis S. Oxman; Bank of America, N.A.
EIN: 136152801
Selected grants: The following grants are a representative sample of this grantmaker's funding activity:
$100,000 to Room to Read, San Francisco, CA, 2012. To support the Literacy Fund.
$36,000 to World Learning, Brattleboro, VT, 2012. For Chatham Hall Eil Scholarships.

8442
Kent D. & Mary L. Steadley Memorial Trust ✧
c/o Bank of America, N.A.
1 Financial Plz., 7th Fl.
Providence, RI 02903-2448

Established in 1970.
Donor: K.D. & M.L. Steadley Irrevocable Trust.
Foundation type: Independent foundation.
Financial data (yr. ended 12/31/13): Assets, $31,979,303 (M); gifts received, $3,716,970; expenditures, $1,537,558; qualifying distributions, $1,361,021; giving activities include $1,217,643 for 13 grants (high: $550,000; low: $3,000).
Purpose and activities: Funds shall be distributed exclusively in and near the city of Carthage, MO, to promote community well-being.
Fields of interest: Elementary/secondary education; Libraries (public); Hospitals (general); Human services; Community/economic development.
Limitations: Applications accepted. Giving limited to the Carthage, MO, area. No grants to individuals, or for national fundraising events.
Application information: Application form required.
Initial approach: Three page letter form with attachments
Deadline(s): None
Trustee: Bank of America, N.A.
EIN: 436120866
Selected grants: The following grants are a representative sample of this grantmaker's funding activity:
$250,000 to Mercy Hospital Carthage, Carthage, MO, 2013. For establishing Telemedicine services in Carthage.
$200,000 to Carthage R-9 School District, Carthage, MO, 2013. For Capital Grant for New Technical School on the New Carthage High School Grounds.
$185,402 to Carthage, City of, Carthage, MO, 2013. To assist with debt service on golf course.
$35,000 to Humane Society, Carthage, Carthage, MO, 2013. For veterinary services.
$25,000 to Lifechoices, Joplin, MO, 2013. For the purchase of needed equipment for and renovation of the Carthage, MO medical clinic.
$15,733 to Humane Society, Carthage, Carthage, MO, 2013. For veterinary services.
$13,853 to Humane Society, Carthage, Carthage, MO, 2013. For veterinary services.
$10,000 to Carthage R-9 School District, Carthage, MO, 2013. For a match for the expected fundraising effort of the Carthage 'Food for Thought Events' occurring summer, 2013, to benefit the backpack program.
$10,000 to Carthage R-9 School District, Carthage, MO, 2013. For the acquisition of concussion safety helmets for the Carthage high school football team.
$5,000 to Carthage, City of, Carthage, MO, 2013. To assist with the Parks Visioning Plan.

8443
Georgia S. Stone Trust ✧
P.O. Box 1802
Providence, RI 02901-1802

Established in CT.
Foundation type: Independent foundation.
Financial data (yr. ended 08/31/13): Assets, $12,693,983 (M); expenditures, $641,493; qualifying distributions, $599,311; giving activities include $572,150 for 5 grants (high: $114,430; low: $114,430).
Fields of interest: Animal welfare; Salvation Army; United Ways and Federated Giving Programs; Protestant agencies & churches; Blind/visually impaired.
Limitations: Applications not accepted. Giving primarily in CT and NY. No grants to individuals.
Application information: Contributes only to pre-selected organizations.
Trustee: Bank of America, N.A.
EIN: 066029757
Selected grants: The following grants are a representative sample of this grantmaker's funding activity:

$92,007 to Christ Church Cathedral, Hartford, CT, 2011.

8444
SVF Foundation ✧ ☆
152 Harrison Ave.
Newport, RI 02840-3704 (401) 848-7229
FAX: (401) 848-5515; Main URL: http://www.svffoundation.org/
E-Newsletter: http://svffoundation.org/
Facebook: http://www.facebook.com/SVFFoundation

Established in 1999 in PA.
Donor: Dorrance H. Hamilton.
Foundation type: Operating foundation.
Financial data (yr. ended 12/31/13): Assets, $9,650,045 (M); gifts received, $2,513,550; expenditures, $3,430,600; qualifying distributions, $2,779,164; giving activities include $499,632 for 3 grants (high: $409,584; low: $3,500).
Purpose and activities: Giving to preserve germplasm of rare and endangered breeds of livestock.
Fields of interest: Higher education; Animals/wildlife, preservation/protection; Animals/wildlife, endangered species.
Limitations: Applications not accepted. Giving on a national basis. No grants to individuals.
Application information: Contributes only to pre-selected organizations.
Board meeting date(s): Quarterly
Officers: Peter Borden, Pres.; Lisa Cafferty, Secy.-Treas.
Trustees: Sean Conway; Margaret H. Duprey; Dorrance H. Hamilton; Stephen MacGillivray; George W. Moore.
Number of staff: 6 full-time professional; 9 full-time support; 1 part-time support.
EIN: 142008091

8445
Gertrude and Walter E. Swanson, Jr. Foundation ✧
P.O. Box 1802
Providence, RI 02901-1802

Established in 1995 in IL.
Foundation type: Independent foundation.
Financial data (yr. ended 12/31/13): Assets, $14,067,580 (M); expenditures, $722,859; qualifying distributions, $609,367; giving activities include $573,000 for 10 grants (high: $114,600; low: $28,650).
Purpose and activities: Giving primarily to health associations and hospitals, including a children's hospital; funding also for human services, and to a Christian church.
Fields of interest: Higher education; Hospitals (general); Hospitals (specialty); Health organizations, association; American Red Cross; Salvation Army; Christian agencies & churches.
Limitations: Applications not accepted. No grants to individuals.
Application information: Contributes only to pre-selected organizations.
Trustee: Bank of America, N.A.
EIN: 363994250

8446
The Textron Charitable Trust ✧
c/o Textron Inc.
40 Westminster St.
Providence, RI 02903-2525 (401) 457-3573
Contact: Karen Warfield, Mgr., Community Affairs
E-mail: kwarfield@textron.com; Main URL: http://www.textron.com/about/commitment/corp-giving/

Trust established in 1953 in VT.
Donors: Textron Inc.; Cessna Foundation, Inc.
Foundation type: Company-sponsored foundation.
Financial data (yr. ended 12/31/12): Assets, $19,727,812 (M); expenditures, $2,927,600; qualifying distributions, $2,874,575; giving activities include $1,901,262 for 111 grants (high: $350,000; low: $1,000), and $838,611 for 1,895 employee matching gifts.
Purpose and activities: The foundation supports organizations involved with arts and culture, education, the environment, animals and wildlife, health, workforce development, hunger, housing, youth development, human services, community revitalization, minorities, women, and low-income individuals.
Fields of interest: Arts; Education, early childhood education; Higher education; Education, ESL programs; Education, services; Education, reading; Education; Environment; Animals/wildlife; Hospitals (general); Public health; Health care; Employment, training; Employment; Food services; Food banks; Housing/shelter; Youth development, adult & child programs; Youth development; Family services; Homeless, human services; Human services; Economic development; Community/economic development; United Ways and Federated Giving Programs; Engineering/technology; Minorities; Women; Economically disadvantaged.
Type of support: Sponsorships; General/operating support; Continuing support; Capital campaigns; Building/renovation; Equipment; Program development; Internship funds; Scholarship funds; Technical assistance; Employee matching gifts; Employee-related scholarships; Matching/challenge support.
Limitations: Applications accepted. Giving on a national basis in areas of company operations, with emphasis on Washington, DC, KS, NJ, RI, and VA. No support for political, fraternal, or veterans' organizations, religious institutions, or discriminatory organizations. No grants to individuals (except for employee-related scholarships), or for endowments, land acquisition, debt reduction, or demonstration projects; no loans.
Publications: Application guidelines; Program policy statement.
Application information: Proposals should be no longer than 5 pages. The Associated Grant Makers (AGM) Common Proposal Form is also accepted. Support is limited to 1 contribution per organization during any given year. Multi-year commitments will be considered but are limited. Application form required.
Initial approach: Download application form and mail proposal and application form to foundation
Copies of proposal: 1
Deadline(s): Mar. 1 and Sept. 1
Board meeting date(s): Quarterly
Charitable Contributions Committee: John D. Butler; Terry O' Donnell; Deborah Imondi; Jim Walters; Richard Yates.
Trustees: Robert Rowland; Adele J. Suddes; Keith Watson; State Street Bank & Trust Co.
Number of staff: 1 full-time professional.
EIN: 256115832
Selected grants: The following grants are a representative sample of this grantmaker's funding activity:
$350,000 to United Way of the Plains, Wichita, KS, 2011.
$100,000 to John F. Kennedy Center for the Performing Arts, Washington, DC, 2011.
$75,000 to Textron Chamber of Commerce Academy, Providence, RI, 2011.
$50,000 to American Red Cross, Providence, RI, 2011.
$35,000 to Womens Lunch Place, Boston, MA, 2011.
$15,000 to Wichita Grand Opera, Wichita, KS, 2011.
$10,000 to Family Service of Rhode Island, Providence, RI, 2011.
$10,000 to Rhode Island Community Food Bank Association, Providence, RI, 2011.
$7,500 to University of Dubuque, Dubuque, IA, 2011.
$3,375 to United Fund of Coffeyville, Coffeyville, KS, 2011.

8447
Jon L. & Beverly A. Thompson Foundation ✧
P.O. Box 1802
Providence, RI 02901-1802

Established in 2006 in FL.
Donor: Jon L. Thompson.
Foundation type: Independent foundation.
Financial data (yr. ended 12/31/13): Assets, $21,124,194 (M); gifts received, $1,562,981; expenditures, $813,463; qualifying distributions, $788,513; giving activities include $775,000 for 4 grants (high: $310,000; low: $100,000).
Fields of interest: Education; Multiple sclerosis; Christian agencies & churches.
Limitations: Applications not accepted. Giving primarily in AZ, FL and NC. No grants to individuals.
Application information: Unsolicited requests for funds not accepted.
Trustees: Beverly A. Thompson; Jon L. Thompson; Bank of America, N.A.
EIN: 204863679
Selected grants: The following grants are a representative sample of this grantmaker's funding activity:
$100,000 to Samaritans Purse, Boone, NC, 2011.
$100,000 to University of Texas, Austin, TX, 2011.
$90,000 to Alliance Defending Freedom, Scottsdale, AZ, 2011.

8448
TriMix Foundation ✧
c/o Rex Capital Advisors, LLC
50 Park Row W., Ste. 113
Providence, RI 02903-1114 (401) 383-5370
Contact: Gail S. Mixer, Pres.

Established in 1997 in RI.
Donors: David P. Mixer; Gail S. Mixer; Dalton Charitable Lead Trust.
Foundation type: Independent foundation.
Financial data (yr. ended 12/31/12): Assets, $25,341,013 (M); gifts received, $11,294,209; expenditures, $882,533; qualifying distributions,

$669,350; giving activities include $669,350 for 42 grants (high: $100,000; low: $100).
Purpose and activities: Supports programs and initiatives designed to improve the lives of children, build cohesive neighborhoods and communities, and improve animal welfare.
Fields of interest: Media, television; Arts; Education; Animal welfare; Veterinary medicine; Youth, services; Human services; Community development, neighborhood development; Community/economic development.
Type of support: General/operating support; Continuing support; Annual campaigns; Program development; Seed money; Curriculum development; Technical assistance.
Limitations: Applications accepted. Giving primarily in MA and RI. No grants to individuals.
Application information: Application form required.
Initial approach: Letter
Copies of proposal: 2
Deadline(s): None
Officers: Gail S. Mixer, Pres.; David P. Mixer, V.P.; Matthew A. Thibault, Secy.; Arthur X. Duffy, Treas.
Directors: Brian Mixer; Mark Mixer; Michael Mixer.
Number of staff: 1 part-time professional; 1 part-time support.
EIN: 050494244

8449
van Beuren Charitable Foundation, Inc.
130 Bellevue Ave., Ste. 304
Newport, RI 02840-3291 (401) 619-5910
Contact: Elizabeth R. Lynn, Exec. Dir.
FAX: (401) 619-5917;
E-mail: kdame@vbcfoundation.org; Contact for questions regarding grant application: Kim Dame, Grants Mgr., tel.: (401) 619-5910; Main
URL: http://www.vbcfoundation.org
Facebook: https://www.facebook.com/pages/Van-Beuren-Charitable-Foundation/153747571340286
Grants List: http://vbcfoundation.org/recent-recipients/
Twitter: https://twitter.com/vbcfoundation

Established in 1986 in RI.
Donor: Members of the van Beuren family.
Foundation type: Independent foundation.
Financial data (yr. ended 12/31/12): Assets, $200,930,376 (M); gifts received, $6,640,947; expenditures, $4,517,003; qualifying distributions, $3,882,263; giving activities include $3,345,963 for 146 grants (high: $261,000; low: $100), and $28,241 for foundation-administered programs.
Purpose and activities: The primary mission of the foundation is to build community value by protecting and preserving Newport County's unique quality of place, and improving the quality of life for its residents. Program areas include Health, Education, Land Use and Conservation, and for Historic Preservation.
Fields of interest: Historic preservation/historical societies; Education; Environment, land resources; Health care; Human services.
Type of support: General/operating support; Capital campaigns; Building/renovation; Land acquisition; Endowments; Program development.
Limitations: Applications accepted. Giving primarily in Newport County, RI. No grants to individuals.
Publications: Application guidelines; Annual report (including application guidelines); Grants list.
Application information: Application form required.
Initial approach: Use online application process on foundation web site
Copies of proposal: 1
Deadline(s): See foundation web site for current deadline date
Board meeting date(s): Fall
Officers and Directors:* Hope Hill van Beuren,* Chair.; Archbold D. van Beuren,* Pres.; Leonard B. Boehner, Secy.; Stephen L. Glascock, Treas.; Elizabeth R. Lynn,* Exec. Dir.; Roger E. Kass; Andrea van Beuren; Barbara van Beuren; Helene B. van Beuren.
Number of staff: 2 full-time support.
EIN: 222773769

8450
Robert C. Vance Charitable Foundation ✧
P.O. Box 1802
Providence, RI 02901-1802
Application address: c/o Herbert E. Carlson, 21 Winesap Rd., Kensington, CT 06307-2932

Established in 1960 in CT.
Donor: Robert C. Vance†.
Foundation type: Independent foundation.
Financial data (yr. ended 01/31/14): Assets, $10,269,226 (M); expenditures, $509,384; qualifying distributions, $497,378; giving activities include $485,500 for 12 grants (high: $250,000; low: $1,500).
Purpose and activities: Giving primarily for the arts, hospitals, human services, and higher education.
Fields of interest: Museums; Performing arts; Higher education; Education; Hospitals (general); United Ways and Federated Giving Programs.
Type of support: Annual campaigns; Capital campaigns; Building/renovation.
Limitations: Applications accepted. Giving limited to the New Britain, CT, area. No grants to individuals.
Publications: Application guidelines.
Application information: Application form not required.
Initial approach: Letter
Deadline(s): None
Officers and Directors:* Herbert E. Carlson, Jr.,* Chair. and Pres.; Cheryl C. Carlson,* Secy.; Rita H. Beaulieu,* Treas.
Trustee: Bank of America, N.A.
EIN: 066050188

8451
Wille Family Foundation ✧
P.O. Box 1802
Providence, RI 02901-1802
Application address: c/o Carmen Britt, Bank of America, 200 Glastonbury Rd., Glastonbury, CT 06033

Established in 2006 in CT.
Foundation type: Independent foundation.
Financial data (yr. ended 12/31/13): Assets, $10,522,053 (M); expenditures, $518,809; qualifying distributions, $500,065; giving activities include $488,000 for 26 grants (high: $55,000; low: $2,000).
Fields of interest: Education; Human services.
Application information: Application form not required.
Initial approach: Proposal
Deadline(s): None
Trustee: Bank of America.
EIN: 206639861
Selected grants: The following grants are a representative sample of this grantmaker's funding activity:
$75,000 to Remote Area Medical Foundation, Rockford, TN, 2011.
$55,000 to Prep for Prep, New York, NY, 2011.
$44,100 to Algebra Project, Cambridge, MA, 2011.
$35,000 to Food Bank for New York City, New York, NY, 2011.
$10,000 to Foodbank of Santa Barbara County, Santa Barbara, CA, 2011.
$10,000 to Santa Barbara Museum of Art, Santa Barbara, CA, 2011.
$10,000 to University of Colorado Foundation, Boulder, CO, 2011.
$8,000 to Bakehouse Art Complex, Miami, FL, 2011.
$3,100 to Duke University, Durham, NC, 2011.
$3,000 to Miami Childrens Hospital Foundation, Miami, FL, 2011.

8452
William M. Wood Foundation ✧
c/o Bank of America, N.A.
P.O. Box 1802
Providence, RI 02901-1802
Application address: c/o Emma Greene, 225 Franklin St., Boston, MA 02110

Established in 2004 in MA.
Donors: William Wood III; William M. Wood III Trust; William M. Wood 2004 Charitable Remainder Unitrust.
Foundation type: Independent foundation.
Financial data (yr. ended 11/30/13): Assets, $36,148,524 (M); gifts received, $17,885,914; expenditures, $893,947; qualifying distributions, $803,811; giving activities include $705,000 for 10 grants (high: $125,000; low: $20,000).
Purpose and activities: Giving primarily to museums and for education, particularly to a school for people who are blind.
Fields of interest: Museums (specialized); Theological school/education; Education; Biomedicine research; Blind/visually impaired.
Application information: Application form not required.
Deadline(s): None
Trustees: Edward M. Condit, Jr.; Bank of America, N.A.
EIN: 383716011

8453
Woodward Trust ✧
P.O. Box 1802
Providence, RI 02901-1802

Foundation type: Independent foundation.
Financial data (yr. ended 12/31/13): Assets, $33,620,296 (M); expenditures, $1,655,791; qualifying distributions, $1,538,408; giving activities include $1,461,340 for 20 grants (high: $219,201; low: $14,613).
Fields of interest: Higher education; Theological school/education; Education; Hospitals (general); Health organizations, association; Human services; Children/youth, services.
Limitations: Applications not accepted. Giving primarily in Hartford, CT.

Application information: Contributes only to pre-selected organizations.
Trustee: Bank of America, N.A.
EIN: 066031300
Selected grants: The following grants are a representative sample of this grantmaker's funding activity:
$80,583 to Connecticut Historical Society, Hartford, CT, 2011.
$80,583 to Wadsworth Atheneum Museum of Art, Hartford, CT, 2011.
$60,437 to Hartford Hospital, Hartford, CT, 2011.
$48,557 to Village for Families and Children, Hartford, CT, 2011.
$30,219 to Boys and Girls Clubs of Hartford, Hartford, CT, 2011.
$30,219 to Saint Francis Hospital and Medical Center, Hartford, CT, 2011.
$30,219 to Windham Community Memorial Hospital, Willimantic, CT, 2011.
$10,073 to Camp Courant, Hartford, CT, 2011.
$10,073 to Hartford HealthCare at Home, Wethersfield, CT, 2011.
$1,807 to Village for Families and Children, Hartford, CT, 2011.

SOUTH CAROLINA

8454
The Abney Foundation ✧
100 Vine St.
Anderson, SC 29621-3265
Contact: Carl T. Edwards, Vice-Chair.
E-mail: info@abneyfoundation.org; Tel. and fax: (864) 964-9201; Main URL: http://www.abneyfoundation.org

Trust established in 1957 in SC.
Donors: John S. Abney†; Susie M. Abney†.
Foundation type: Independent foundation.
Financial data (yr. ended 12/31/12): Assets, $41,269,895 (M); expenditures, $2,592,154; qualifying distributions, $2,110,444; giving activities include $1,930,000 for 42 grants (high: $400,000; low: $5,000).
Purpose and activities: The mission of the foundation is to make grants to innovative and creative projects, and to programs which are responsive to changing community needs in the areas of education, health, social services and cultural affairs. The foundation's primary focus is on higher education. The foundation also has scholarship endowments at fourteen colleges and universities across SC.
Fields of interest: Higher education; Medical school/education; Health care; Medical research, institute; Human services; Salvation Army; Children/youth, services; Residential/custodial care, hospices; Christian agencies & churches; Protestant agencies & churches.
Type of support: General/operating support; Continuing support; Annual campaigns; Building/renovation; Equipment; Land acquisition; Endowments; Emergency funds; Professorships; Seed money; Fellowships; Internship funds; Scholarship funds; Research.
Limitations: Giving primarily in SC, with emphasis on the Anderson area. No grants to individuals, or for operating expenses; no loans.
Publications: Application guidelines.
Application information: See foundation web site for application guidelines and procedures, as well as for scholarship endowment information. Application form not required.
Initial approach: Letter
Copies of proposal: 1
Deadline(s): Nov. 15
Board meeting date(s): Dec.
Officers and Trustees:* J.R. Fulp, Jr.,* Chair.; David C. King,* Vice-Chair. and Exec. Dir.; Johnnye K. Palmer,* Secy.- Treas.; Lebrena F. Campbell; Carl T. Edwards; John R. Fulp III; Edd Sheriff.
Number of staff: 1 full-time professional; 1 part-time support.
EIN: 576019445

8455
Agape Senior Foundation, Inc. ✧ ☆
1053 Center St.
West Columbia, SC 29169-6749 (803) 454-0365
Contact: Lisa K. Livingston, Exec. Dir.
E-mail: LLivingston@AgapeSenior.com; Additional Tel.: (803)-960-3675; Main URL: http://agapesenior.com/store.html

Foundation type: Independent foundation.
Financial data (yr. ended 12/31/12): Assets, $263,701 (M); gifts received, $6,342,704; expenditures, $6,429,727; qualifying distributions, $6,417,726; giving activities include $6,417,726 for grants.
Fields of interest: Aging.
Limitations: Giving primarily in West Columbia, SC.
Officer and Directors:* Lisa K. Livingston, Exec. Dir.; Danny E. Belk; Evelyn Middleton; G. Scott Middleton.
EIN: 202075089

8456
Arkwright Foundation ✧
314 S. Pine St., Bldg. 100
Spartanburg, SC 29302-2677 (864) 585-9213
Contact: Walter S. Montgomery, Jr., Vice-Chair.

Incorporated in 1945 in SC.
Donors: Members of the M.L. Cates family; members of the W.S. Montgomery family.
Foundation type: Independent foundation.
Financial data (yr. ended 12/31/13): Assets, $14,389,082 (M); expenditures, $653,791; qualifying distributions, $600,199; giving activities include $600,199 for 104 grants (high: $125,750; low: $25).
Purpose and activities: Giving primarily for education, wildlife conservation, health, social services, arts education, and Protestant education and churches.
Fields of interest: Arts education; Higher education; Education; Animals/wildlife; Health care; Health organizations, association; Human services; Protestant agencies & churches.
Limitations: Applications accepted. Giving primarily in SC. No grants to individuals.
Application information: Application form required.
Initial approach: Letter, personal visit, or telephone
Deadline(s): None
Officers: M.L. Cates, Sr., Chair.; Walter S. Montgomery, Jr., Vice-Chair.
EIN: 576000066

8457
AVX-Kyocera Foundation ✧
1 AVX Blvd.
Fountain Inn, SC 29644-9039

Established in 1996 in SC.
Donor: AVX Corp.
Foundation type: Company-sponsored foundation.
Financial data (yr. ended 03/31/14): Assets, $10,692,830 (M); expenditures, $574,126; qualifying distributions, $487,461; giving activities include $480,461 for 13 grants (high: $50,000; low: $1,000), and $7,000 for 8 grants to individuals (high: $1,000; low: $500).
Purpose and activities: The foundation supports museums and organizations involved orchestras, education, health, and heart disease and awards undergraduate scholarships to individuals.
Fields of interest: Museums; Museums (art); Performing arts, orchestras; Secondary school/education; Higher education; Education; Hospitals (general); Health care, clinics/centers; Health care; Heart & circulatory diseases; International relief.
Type of support: General/operating support; Sponsorships; Scholarships—to individuals.
Limitations: Applications not accepted. Giving primarily in the U.S., with emphasis on SC; giving also in Czech Republic, El Salvador, and Malaysia.
Application information: Unsolicited requests for funds not accepted.
Officers: John S. Gilbertson, Pres.; Kathleen M. Kelly, V.P.; Kurt P. Cummings, Treas.
EIN: 571057142
Selected grants: The following grants are a representative sample of this grantmaker's funding activity:
$55,000 to Brookgreen Gardens, Murrells Inlet, SC, 2011.
$50,000 to Alfred University, Alfred, NY, 2011.
$30,000 to Webber Hospital Association, Biddeford, ME, 2011.
$25,000 to Coastal Carolina University, Conway, SC, 2011.
$25,000 to Greenville County Museum of Art, Greenville, SC, 2011.
$25,000 to Greenville Technical College, Greenville, SC, 2011.
$25,000 to Olean General Hospital, Olean, NY, 2011.
$9,000 to Clemson University, Clemson, SC, 2011.
$4,000 to College of Charleston, Charleston, SC, 2011.
$1,500 to Florida State College, Jacksonville, FL, 2011.

8458
P. S. and Ouida C. Bailey Foundation ✧
P.O. Box 380
Clinton, SC 29325-0380

Established in SC.
Donors: Emily F. Bailey; Clinton Investment Co.
Foundation type: Independent foundation.
Financial data (yr. ended 12/31/13): Assets, $7,662,498 (M); expenditures, $649,244; qualifying distributions, $579,283; giving activities include $550,000 for 4 grants (high: $320,000; low: $20,000).
Purpose and activities: Giving primarily for the revitalization of Clinton, South Carolina's downtown area; some giving also to Anglican missions, and to a home for the aged.
Fields of interest: Human services; Community/economic development; Religion.
Limitations: Applications not accepted. Giving primarily in SC, with some emphasis on Clinton.
Application information: Unsolicited requests for funds not accepted.
Officer and Trustees:* Emily F. Bailey,* Chair.; Bishop Alex D. Dickson.
EIN: 570813063
Selected grants: The following grants are a representative sample of this grantmaker's funding activity:
$5,000 to Presbyterian College, Clinton, SC, 2012. For Scholarship Program (Champs Fund).

8459
Mary Black Foundation, Inc. ✧
349 E. Main St., Ste. 100
Spartanburg, SC 29302-1917 (864) 573-9500
Contact: Kathy Dunleavy, Pres.; Kim Stravolo, Dir., Fin.
FAX: (864) 573-5805; Main URL: http://www.maryblackfoundation.org
Blog: http://www.maryblackfoundation.org/blog

Facebook: http://www.facebook.com/pages/Spartanburg-SC/Mary-Black-Foundation/50398562097
Grants List: http://www.maryblackfoundation.org/grantmaking/grant-history
Twitter: http://twitter.com/MaryBFoundation
YouTube: http://www.youtube.com/user/MaryBFoundation

Established in 1986 in SC; converted from the proceeds from the sale of Mary Black Memorial Hospital in 1996.
Foundation type: Independent foundation.
Financial data (yr. ended 12/31/13): Assets, $81,842,005 (M); gifts received, $175; expenditures, $4,305,193; qualifying distributions, $3,614,227; giving activities include $2,529,208 for 43 grants (high: $1,020,000; low: $1,000), $3,573,935 for foundation-administered programs and $12,500 for loans/program-related investments.
Purpose and activities: The foundation's mission is to improve the health and wellness of the people and communities of Spartanburg County, South Carolina. Funding priorities are Healthy Eating and Active Living and Early Childhood Development.
Fields of interest: Public health; Health care; Health organizations, public education.
Type of support: General/operating support; Continuing support; Management development/capacity building; Program development; Seed money; Technical assistance; Program evaluation.
Limitations: Applications accepted. Giving primarily in Spartanburg County, SC. No support for political organizations or for proselytizing religious work. No grants to individuals or for general fundraising solicitations.
Publications: Application guidelines; Annual report; Financial statement; Grants list; Informational brochure (including application guidelines); Occasional report.
Application information: See foundation web site for application guidelines and procedures: www.maryblackfoundation.org. Application form required.
Initial approach: Grant Consultation is required for Healthy Eating and Active Living and Early Childhood Development applications.
Copies of proposal: 1
Deadline(s): Quarterly (Mar. 1, June 1, Sept. 1, and Dec. 1)
Board meeting date(s): 3rd Tues. of Feb., March, April, Aug., Sep., Nov., and Dec.
Final notification: Generally within 90 days
Officers and Trustees:* Ruth L. Cate,* Chair.; Kathy Dunleavy, C.E.O. and Pres.; Molly Talbot-Metz, V.P., Progs.; Ethan Burroughs; William M. Coker; Anna Converse; A. Tony Fisher; Colleen Perry Keith, Ph.D.; Dr. James A. Littlefield; Jack McBride; D. Byrd Miller III; Betsy Teter; Doris H. Tidwell.
Number of staff: 4 full-time professional; 2 full-time support.
EIN: 570843135
Selected grants: The following grants are a representative sample of this grantmaker's funding activity:
$40,000 to Urban League of the Upstate, Spartanburg, SC, 2012. For Project Ready, program provides academic and social support to students in grades 7-9 as they prepare for college enrollment.
$35,000 to Adult Learning Center, Spartanburg, SC, 2012. For Community Health through Career Readiness / GED 2014.
$25,000 to Butterfly Foundation, Spartanburg, SC, 2012. For Culinary Job Training Program.
$25,000 to Piedmont Care, Spartanburg, SC, 2012. For Community HIV Prevention Initiative.
$25,000 to Senior Centers of Spartanburg County, Spartanburg, SC, 2012. For Shop N Cart (Grocery Delivery Program).
$25,000 to Spartanburg County School District No. 7, Spartanburg, SC, 2012. For Partnerships to Progress.
$24,000 to University of South Carolina Upstate Foundation, Watershed Ecology Center, Spartanburg, SC, 2012. For Renaming Nasty Creek.
$14,300 to Ellen Hines Smith Girls Home, Spartanburg, SC, 2012. For Partnership Exploration.
$13,772 to Spartanburg Little Theater, Spartanburg, SC, 2012. For Imagine That, youth improve theater troupe.
$12,500 to University of South Carolina Upstate Foundation, Spartanburg, SC, 2013. For program support for Iron Yard, Spartanburg Accelerator Program.
$5,000 to Hope Center for Children, Spartanburg, SC, 2013. For technology and phone system upgrades.
$5,000 to Spartanburg County Foundation, Spartanburg, SC, 2012. For Behavioral Health Collaborative.
$5,000 to Spartanburg Regional Healthcare System Foundation, Spartanburg, SC, 2013. For AccessHealth Spartanburg strategic plan.
$2,093 to South Carolina Association of Nonprofit Organizations, Columbia, SC, 2013. For scholarships.
$1,000 to Mobile Meals of Spartanburg County, Spartanburg, SC, 2013. For National Philanthropy Day Luncheon.

8460
Blue Cross and Blue Shield of South Carolina Foundation ✧

I-20 at Alpine Rd., MC AX-G22
Columbia, SC 29219-0001
Contact: Harvey L. Galloway, Exec. Dir.
E-mail: info.foundation@bcbssc.com; Main
URL: http://www.bcbsscfoundation.org
Facebook: http://www.facebook.com/pages/BlueCross-BlueShield-of-South-Carolina-Foundation/379866912041426
Grants List: http://www.bcbsscfoundation.org/awards.aspx

Donors: Bluechoice Health Plan of SC, Inc.; Blue Cross and Blue Shield of South Carolina; Companion Healthcare Corp.
Foundation type: Company-sponsored foundation.
Financial data (yr. ended 12/31/13): Assets, $144,040,193 (M); gifts received, $10,500,000; expenditures, $4,630,325; qualifying distributions, $3,966,372; giving activities include $3,966,372 for 32 grants (high: $1,538,398; low: $500).
Purpose and activities: The foundation supports programs designed to the promote good health of South Carolinians and to increase access to healthcare for the economically disadvantaged. Special emphasis is directed toward programs designed to assist the uninsured and underinsured, children, and adolescents.
Fields of interest: Health care, clinics/centers; Public health; Public health, obesity; Health care, insurance; Health care, patient services; Nursing care; Health care; Mental health/crisis services; Health organizations; Children/youth, services; Children; Youth; Economically disadvantaged.
Type of support: General/operating support; Equipment; Program development; Research; Employee volunteer services.
Limitations: Applications accepted. Giving limited to areas of company operations in SC. No support for political, lobbying, or religious organizations. No grants to individuals, or for annual campaigns, capital campaigns, sports tournaments, raffles, or auctions, fundraising events, or membership drives.
Publications: Application guidelines; Grants list; Newsletter; Program policy statement.
Application information: A full application may be requested at a later date. Support is limited to 1 contribution per organization during any given year. Application form not required.
Initial approach: Complete online letter of intent
Deadline(s): Spring (Feb. 20) and Fall (Aug. 18)
Board meeting date(s): Spring and Fall
Officers and Directors:* M. Edward Sellers,* Chair.; Judith M. Davis,* Secy.; Michael J. Mizeur, Treas.; Harvey L. Galloway, Exec. Dir.; Minor M. Shaw; Joseph F. Sullivan.
EIN: 223847938

8461
Drs. Bruce and Lee Foundation ✧

201 S. Dargan St.
BTC Box 022
Florence, SC 29506-2535 (843) 664-2870
Contact: Mr. L. Bradley Callicott, Exec. Dir.
FAX: (843) 664-2815;
E-mail: blfound@bellsouth.net

Established in 1995 in SC; converted from the sale of the assets of Carolinas Hospital System to Quorum, Inc.
Foundation type: Independent foundation.
Financial data (yr. ended 12/31/13): Assets, $177,438,092 (M); expenditures, $6,402,494; qualifying distributions, $10,290,948; giving activities include $4,621,850 for 22 grants (high: $2,100,000; low: $1,000).
Purpose and activities: The foundation aims to advance the general welfare of people in the Florence, SC, area, and the surrounding region by providing economic support to qualified and nonprofit organizations. In furtherance of its mission, the foundation will support a board range of charitable purposes including, but not limited to medical, health, human services, education, arts, religion, civic affairs and the conservation, preservation and promotion of cultural, historical and environmental resources programs.
Fields of interest: Historical activities; Arts; Education; Environment; Health care; Medical research; Human services.
Type of support: Continuing support; Capital campaigns; Building/renovation; Equipment; Land acquisition; Endowments; Debt reduction; Emergency funds; Seed money; Scholarship funds; Matching/challenge support.
Limitations: Applications accepted. Giving primarily in the Florence, SC, area. No grants to individuals, or for fundraising events.
Publications: Application guidelines; Annual report; Grants list; Occasional report.
Application information: Selected applicants will be sent a formal grant proposal form requiring additional information. Application form required.
Initial approach: Telephone, then letter of no more than 3 pages

Copies of proposal: 1
Deadline(s): None
Board meeting date(s): 3rd Tues. monthly except in Dec.
Final notification: Generally within 90 days
Officers and Trustees:* C. Edward Floyd, M.D.*, Chair.; John L. Bruce, Jr., D.M.D.*, Vice-Chair.; Mark Buyck, Jr.,* Secy.; Bradley L. Callicott,* Exec. Dir.; Gordon B. Baker, Jr.; Coleman Floyd Buckhouse, M.D.; Frank B. Lee, Jr., M.D.; John W. McGinnis; Haigh Porter; Henry Swink; Kim Thomason Turner.
Number of staff: 2 full-time professional.
EIN: 570902483
Selected grants: The following grants are a representative sample of this grantmaker's funding activity:
$3,000,000 to Francis Marion University Foundation, Florence, SC, 2010.
$2,101,359 to Florence, City of, Florence, SC, 2011. For new tennis center project.
$1,800,000 to Florence, County of, Florence, SC, 2011. For Florence County Museum project.
$1,050,406 to Florence, County of, Florence, SC, 2010. For general support.
$1,050,000 to Florence County Library System, Florence, SC, 2010.
$150,000 to Lamar Library, Friends of the, Lamar, SC, 2010. For general support.
$150,000 to Teach for America, Florence, SC, 2011. To implement Teach for America program in South Carolina area.
$125,000 to Florence-Darlington Technical College Foundation, Florence, SC, 2011. For allied health scholarships.
$110,148 to Florence-Darlington Technical College, Florence, SC, 2010.
$100,000 to Boys and Girls Clubs of the Pee Dee Area, Florence, SC, 2011. To pay off portion of building improvements to facility on Roughfork Street.
$100,000 to Francis Marion University Foundation, Florence, SC, 2011. For nursing scholarships.
$100,000 to Francis Marion University Foundation, Florence, SC, 2010.
$100,000 to Medical University of South Carolina, Charleston, SC, 2010.
$50,000 to Lighthouse Ministries, Florence, SC, 2011. For general support.
$50,000 to Mercy Medicine Clinic, Florence, SC, 2011. For medical and dental supplies and equipment.
$50,000 to South Carolina Governors School for Science and Mathematics, Hartsville, SC, 2011. To establish endowed fund to cover various program expenses of Florence County students at GSSM.
$35,000 to Francis Marion University Foundation, Florence, SC, 2010.
$30,000 to Manna House, Florence, SC, 2011. For general support.
$25,000 to Francis Marion University Foundation, Florence, SC, 2010. For staff retention fund.

8462
The Byerly Foundation ✧
P.O. Drawer 1925
Hartsville, SC 29551-1925 (843) 383-2400
Contact: Richard A. Puffer, Exec. Dir.
FAX: (843) 383-0661; E-mail for Richard A. Puffer: rapuffer@byerlyfoundation.org; Main URL: http://www.byerlyfoundation.org
Facebook: https://www.facebook.com/ByerlyFoundation
YouTube: https://www.youtube.com/channel/UCENOFjTAKZKuVtaNLiPOR8Q

Established in 1995 in SC; converted from the sale of local hospital.
Foundation type: Independent foundation.
Financial data (yr. ended 09/30/13): Assets, $22,087,342 (M); expenditures, $1,446,351; qualifying distributions, $1,291,783; giving activities include $1,184,000 for 18 grants (high: $283,000; low: $1,000).
Purpose and activities: The mission of the foundation is to improve the quality of life in Hartsville, SC.
Fields of interest: Education; Economic development; Community/economic development.
Type of support: Curriculum development; General/operating support; Continuing support; Capital campaigns; Building/renovation; Equipment; Program development; Seed money; Technical assistance; Consulting services; Program evaluation; Matching/challenge support.
Limitations: Giving primarily in Hartsville, SC. No support for sectarian religious programs, or intermediate organizations. No grants to individuals, or for debt and existing obligations, lobbying or political campaigns, technical or specialized research, fundraising, teams or special events, advertising, or memorials.
Publications: Application guidelines; Annual report; Financial statement; Grants list; Occasional report.
Application information: Application form required.
Initial approach: Telephone or brief letter of inquiry
Copies of proposal: 1
Board meeting date(s): Monthly, on the last Tues.
Officer: Richard A. Puffer, Exec. Dir.
Directors: Steve Avant; Monty Bell; Harris DeLoach; Brianna Douglas; Alvin T. Heatley; Nancy McGee; Jerome Reyes; Barry Saunders; Todd Shifflett; Johnna Shirley; Rob Tiede.
Number of staff: 1 part-time professional; 1 part-time support.
EIN: 570324909
Selected grants: The following grants are a representative sample of this grantmaker's funding activity:
$250,000 to Hartsville High School, Hartsville, SC, 2013. For Public School Support.

8463
Betsy M. Campbell Foundation ✧ ☆
104 Broadus Ave.
Greenville, SC 29601-3040

Established in 1997 in SC.
Donor: Betsy McDavid Campbell Remainder Unitrust.
Foundation type: Independent foundation.
Financial data (yr. ended 12/31/13): Assets, $8,274,931 (M); expenditures, $604,949; qualifying distributions, $458,278; giving activities include $422,500 for 4 grants (high: $415,000; low: $2,000).
Fields of interest: Youth development; Protestant agencies & churches.
Type of support: General/operating support.
Limitations: Applications not accepted. Giving primarily in Greenville, SC. No grants to individuals.
Application information: Contributes only to pre-selected organizations.
Trustee: William W. Brown.
EIN: 586346237
Selected grants: The following grants are a representative sample of this grantmaker's funding activity:
$25,000 to Miracle Hill Ministries, Greenville, SC, 2012. For Harbor of Hope Program.

8464
Robert S. Campbell Foundation ✧
104 Broadus Ave.
Greenville, SC 29601-3040

Established in 1995 in SC.
Donor: RS Campbell Irrevocable Trust.
Foundation type: Independent foundation.
Financial data (yr. ended 12/31/12): Assets, $23,670,797 (M); expenditures, $5,104,682; qualifying distributions, $4,728,305; giving activities include $4,657,500 for 2 grants (high: $4,655,000; low: $2,500).
Purpose and activities: Giving primarily for youth services.
Fields of interest: Boy scouts; Youth development; Youth, services.
Limitations: Applications not accepted. Giving in SC, with emphasis on Greenville. No grants to individuals.
Application information: Contributes only to pre-selected organizations.
Trustee: William W. Brown.
EIN: 571031564

8465
Campbell Young Leaders, Inc. ✧
104 Broadus Ave.
Greenville, SC 29601-3040

Established in 1999 in SC.
Donors: William W. Brown; Betsy M. Campbell Foundation; Robert S. Campbell Foundation; Greenville Symphony Assoc.; Pellett Foundation; Alan P. Bryan Rev. Trust; The Beach Ball Foundation; Graham Foundation; Ray R. Williams, Jr.; Ameris Bank; Parker High School Alumni Association.
Foundation type: Independent foundation.
Financial data (yr. ended 12/31/13): Assets, $17,011,054 (M); gifts received, $2,065,024; expenditures, $1,614,958; qualifying distributions, $6,804,243; giving activities include $1,092,873 for 12 grants (high: $867,521; low: $1,500).
Fields of interest: Secondary school/education; Higher education; Human services.
Limitations: Applications not accepted. Giving primarily in SC. No grants to individuals.
Application information: Contributes only to pre-selected organizations.
Officer: William W. Brown, Pres.
EIN: 223670039

8466
Canal Charitable Foundation ✧
P.O. Box 7
Greenville, SC 29602-0007

Established in DE.
Donor: William R. Timmons, Jr. Testamentary Charitable Lead Annuity Trust.
Foundation type: Independent foundation.
Financial data (yr. ended 12/31/13): Assets, $152,981 (M); expenditures, $2,494,155; qualifying distributions, $2,494,155; giving

activities include $2,490,481 for 12 grants (high: $2,407,780; low: $1,000).
Fields of interest: Arts; Higher education; Hospitals (general); Health care; Human services; YM/YWCAs & YM/YWHAs; Children/youth, services; Family services; United Ways and Federated Giving Programs; Protestant agencies & churches.
Limitations: Applications not accepted. Giving primarily in SC and UT.
Application information: Contributes only to pre-selected organizations.
Officers and Directors:* William R. Timmons III,* Pres.; Christopher B. Greene,* Secy.-Treas.; David J. Firstenberg.
EIN: 203971600
Selected grants: The following grants are a representative sample of this grantmaker's funding activity:
$20,000 to University of Chicago, Booth School of Business, Chicago, IL, 2012. For general charitable activities.

8467
The Cassels Foundation ✧
420 Davega Rd.
Lexington, SC 29073

Established in SC.
Donors: Rosalie O. Cassels Charitable Lead AnnuityTrust I; Rosalie O. Cassels Charitable Lead AnnuityTrust II; Charlotte R. Cassels.
Foundation type: Independent foundation.
Financial data (yr. ended 12/31/13): Assets, $22,254,942 (M); gifts received, $4,094,338; expenditures, $4,551,863; qualifying distributions, $4,472,242; giving activities include $4,472,242 for 14 grants (high: $4,075,000; low: $1,000).
Purpose and activities: Giving primarily for higher education, Christian agencies and human services.
Fields of interest: Higher education; Housing/shelter, alliance/advocacy; Human services; Children/youth, services; Residential/custodial care; Christian agencies & churches.
Type of support: General/operating support.
Limitations: Applications not accepted. Giving primarily in Columbia, SC. No grants to individuals.
Application information: Contributes only to pre-selected organizations.
Directors: Charlotte Cassels; William Tobin Cassels, Jr.; William Tobin Cassels III; Katherine Cassels Wolfe.
EIN: 571029022
Selected grants: The following grants are a representative sample of this grantmaker's funding activity:
$15,000 to Charlotte Rescue Mission, Charlotte, NC, 2012. For 6 Beds in the New Dove's Nest Building.

8468
Central Carolina Community Foundation ✧
2711 Middleburg Dr., Ste. 213
Columbia, SC 29204-2486 (803) 254-5601
FAX: (803) 799-6663;
E-mail: info@yourfoundation.org; Main URL: http://www.yourfoundation.org
Facebook: http://www.facebook.com/pages/Central-Carolina-Community-Foundation/116968705601
Flickr: http://www.flickr.com/photos/yourfoundation/
LinkedIn: http://www.linkedin.com/company/central-carolina-community-foundation?trk=tabs_biz_home
Talk About Giving - an initiative developed by the Central Carolina Community Foundation to encourage multi-generational conversation about philanthropy: http://www.talkaboutgiving.org/
Twitter: https://twitter.com/CCCFtweets

Incorporated in 1984 in SC.
Foundation type: Community foundation.
Financial data (yr. ended 06/30/14): Assets, $106,803,692 (M); gifts received, $8,659,895; expenditures, $11,409,084; giving activities include $10,652,963 for grants.
Purpose and activities: The foundation seeks to promote, facilitate, and expand philanthropy to create a sustainable impact within the community through giving.
Fields of interest: Arts; Education, early childhood education; Child development, education; Elementary school/education; Adult education—literacy, basic skills & GED; Education, services; Education, reading; Education; Environment; Animals/wildlife; Crime/violence prevention, youth; Crime/law enforcement; Nutrition; Housing/shelter, development; Recreation; Youth development; Homeless, human services; Human services; Community/economic development.
Type of support: General/operating support; Continuing support; Management development/capacity building; Equipment; Endowments; Program development; Scholarship funds; Research; Technical assistance; Matching/challenge support.
Limitations: Applications accepted. Giving limited to Calhoun, Clarendon, Fairfield, Kershaw, Lee, Lexington, Newberry, Orangeburg, Richland, Saluda, and Sumter counties, SC. No grants to individuals (except for designated awards or prizes), or for endowments, debt reduction, fundraising projects, medical research, publications, annual campaigns, annual appeals, routine operating expenses, or conference travel, underwriting, or sponsorship.
Publications: Annual report; Financial statement; Informational brochure; Newsletter.
Application information: Visit foundation web site for application form and guidelines. Application form required.
Initial approach: Mail or e-mail application form and attachments
Copies of proposal: 1
Deadline(s): Varies
Board meeting date(s): Quarterly
Officers and Trustees:* Judith M. Davis,* Chair.; Bruce W. Hughes,* Vice-Chair.; JoAnn M. Turnquist, C.E.O. and Pres.; Jennifer Meyer,* V.P., Finance; Heather Sherwin,* V.P., Institutional Advancement; Ben Rex,* Secy.-Treas.; Scott R. Adams; Dr. William Babcock; J. Mac Bennett; Cliff Bourke, Jr.; Sharon W. Bryant; William H. Cason II; Rita Bragg Caughman; Elizabeth A. Dinndorf; Paul Duane; Dr. Sharon Reynolds Earle; Eric M. Elkins; John Garrison; L. Marion Gressette III; C. Carroll Heyward; David G. Hodges; Catherine H. Kennedy; Charlene H. Keys; David Kulbersh; Dan Lebish; Dan Mann; Cory Manning; Shannon Nord; Linda O'Bryon; Donna S. Pullen; Barbara Rackes; Terry K. Schmoyer, Jr.; Michael Schraibman; Roger Schrum; Sue-Ann Gerald Shannon; Martha Scott Smith; Stacy S. Stokes; J. Hagood Tighe; Susie H. VanHuss.
Number of staff: 8 full-time professional; 1 part-time support.
EIN: 570793960

8469
The Ceres Foundation, Inc. ✧
328 E. Bay St.
Charleston, SC 29401-1593

Established in 1999 in SC.
Donors: Diane D. Terni; Dorothy Diebold.
Foundation type: Independent foundation.
Financial data (yr. ended 12/31/13): Assets, $32,797,126 (M); expenditures, $1,650,275; qualifying distributions, $1,242,697; giving activities include $1,061,500 for 116 grants (high: $100,000; low: $1,000).
Fields of interest: Education; Environment; Health organizations; Human services; Children/youth, services.
Limitations: Applications not accepted. Giving primarily in CT, SC, and VA. No grants to individuals.
Application information: Contributes only to pre-selected organizations.
Board meeting date(s): Varies
Officers and Directors:* Stephen L. Gavel, Co-Pres.; Diane D. Terni,* Co-Pres.; Frank J. Gavel, Jr.,* V.P.; Linda Gavel Webb,* V.P.
Number of staff: 1 full-time support; 1 part-time support.
EIN: 582479387

8470
The Chester Foundation ✧
P. O. Box 832
Chester, SC 29706-0832 (803) 581-9198
Contact: Joseph M. Mcelwee, Jr., Tr.

Foundation type: Independent foundation.
Financial data (yr. ended 12/31/13): Assets, $13,074,408 (M); expenditures, $526,466; qualifying distributions, $466,371; giving activities include $453,730 for 20 grants (high: $191,465; low: $2,000).
Fields of interest: Education; Human services; Religion.
Limitations: Applications accepted. Giving primarily in Chester County, SC.
Application information: Application form required.
Initial approach: Proposal
Deadline(s): None
Trustees: Joseph M. Mcelwee, Jr.; Robert W. Moser; Dwight W. Pearson; J. Brian Singleton; Ladson F. Stringfellow; D.C. Wylie.
EIN: 576056810

8471
Childrens Cancer Cooperative, Inc. ✧
1341 College Park Rd.
Summerville, SC 29483

Donor: Music in Motion Family Fun Center.
Foundation type: Operating foundation.
Financial data (yr. ended 12/31/11): Assets, $90,245 (M); gifts received, $500,000; expenditures, $1,278,898; qualifying distributions, $1,277,461; giving activities include $1,222,186 for 34+ grants (high: $523,000).
Purpose and activities: Giving primarily for children's organizations, including children's hospitals and aid to indigent children.
Fields of interest: Hospitals (specialty); Children.
Limitations: Applications not accepted. Giving primarily in FL; some funding also in SC.

Application information: Unsolicited requests for funds not accepted.
Officers: Harold T. Dukes, Sr., Pres.; Carl Elias Bailey Dukes, V.P.; Melissa G. Barfield, Secy.; Mike Welch, Treas.
EIN: 571089273

8472
Coastal Community Foundation of South Carolina ✧

(formerly The Community Foundation Serving Coastal South Carolina)
635 Rutledge St., Ste. 201
Charleston, SC 29403 (843) 723-3635
Contact: George C. Stevens, C.E.O.
FAX: (843) 577-3671;
E-mail: info@coastalcommunityfoundation.org;
Grant application e-mail: grants@coastalcommunityfoundation.org; Main URL: http://www.coastalcommunityfoundation.org
Blog: http://www.ccfblog.org/
E-Newsletter: http://visitor.constantcontact.com/manage/optin/ea?v=001jarSHX2McaQyAf_LyS9qwQ%3D%3D
Facebook: http://www.facebook.com/CoastalCommunityFoundation
Twitter: http://www.twitter.com/georgestevens
YouTube: http://www.youtube.com/user/CoastalCommunityFdn

Incorporated in 1974 in SC.
Foundation type: Community foundation.
Financial data (yr. ended 06/30/13): Assets, $164,055,934 (M); gifts received, $15,068,690; expenditures, $15,673,717; giving activities include $12,756,639 for grants.
Purpose and activities: The Coastal Community Foundation is a public grantmaking foundation that fosters philanthropy for the lasting good of the community; giving primarily for education and human services.
Fields of interest: Arts; Child development, education; Education; Environment; Health care; Housing/shelter, development; Children/youth, services; Family services; Homeless, human services; Human services; Civil/human rights; Rural development; Community/economic development; Minorities; Homeless.
Type of support: General/operating support; Capital campaigns; Building/renovation; Equipment; Land acquisition; Emergency funds; Program development; Publication; Seed money; Scholarship funds; Technical assistance; Consulting services.
Limitations: Applications accepted. Giving in eight coastal counties of SC: Beaufort, Berkeley, Charleston, Colleton, Dorchester, Georgetown, Hampton and Jasper. No support for religious activities or private foundations. No grants to individuals (except for designated scholarship funds), or for endowments, deficit financing, dinners or other special one-time events, or generally for building funds.
Publications: Application guidelines; Biennial report; Financial statement; Grants list; Informational brochure (including application guidelines); Newsletter; Occasional report.
Application information: Visit foundation web site for application forms and additional guidelines per grant type. The foundation's Grants Committee assesses all Open Grants Letters of Intent and then recommends a full proposal be submitted, that a full proposal be submitted with suggested changes, or that the applicant not submit a proposal because the request is not likely to be funded. Faxed or e-mailed Letters of Intent are not accepted. Application form required.
Initial approach: Letter of intent (not to exceed 2 pages excluding attachments)
Copies of proposal: 1
Deadline(s): Varies
Board meeting date(s): 2nd Wed. of alternate months
Final notification: Varies
Officers and Directors:* William C. Medich,* Chair.; George C. Stevens, C.E.O. and Pres.; Brian Hussain, C.I.O. and V.P., Finance; Edie Blakeslee, Regional V.P.; Edna Crews, Regional V.P.; Raymond C. Smith, Jr.,* Secy.-Treas.; Angel Johnson-Brebner, C.O.O.; David C. Jensen,* Chair.-Elect; Todd Abedon; Amy Armstrong; J. Elizabeth Bradham; C. Michael Branham; D. Cabell Gilley; Steven E. Goldberg; Gordon Granger; Cedric F. Green; Jim Greenho; Paul Hooker; Rachel Hutchisson; Bonnie Adams Kapp; Paul Kohlheim; James L. Marks; Scott E. Phillips; Linda Plunkett; Dawn H. Robinson; Darcy Shankland; Lawton R. Smith; Bill Stanfield; Libby Steadman; Terry Stinson; Chris Volf; Anita Zucker.
Number of staff: 8 full-time professional; 1 part-time professional; 4 full-time support; 1 part-time support.
EIN: 237390313
Selected grants: The following grants are a representative sample of this grantmaker's funding activity:
$500,000 to Spring Hill College, Mobile, AL, 2013. For general operating support.
$390,000 to New Morning Foundation, Columbia, SC, 2013. For general operating support.
$300,000 to Wings for Kids, Charleston, SC, 2013. For special project support.
$250,000 to Southern Environmental Law Center, Charlottesville, VA, 2013. For general operating support.
$125,000 to Yellow Ribbon Fund, Bethesda, MD, 2013. For general operating support.
$50,000 to Gaillard Performance Hall Foundation, Charleston, SC, 2013. For general operating support.
$5,000 to Bnai Brith Youth Organization, Washington, DC, 2013. For special project support.
$5,000 to Charleston Promise Neighborhood, Charleston, SC, 2013. For general operating support.
$4,000 to South Eastern Wildlife and Environment Education Association, Mount Pleasant, SC, 2013. For special project support.
$2,000 to Communities in Schools of the Charleston Area, Charleston, SC, 2013. For special project support.

8473
Coker College Foundation ✧

c/o Edgar H. Lawton, Jr.
P.O. Box 1057
Darlington, SC 29540-1057

Established in SC.
Foundation type: Independent foundation.
Financial data (yr. ended 06/30/13): Assets, $11,755,438 (M); expenditures, $577,211; qualifying distributions, $550,234; giving activities include $550,234 for 1 grant.
Purpose and activities: Giving primarily for higher education, particularly to Coker College in Hartsville, SC.
Fields of interest: Higher education, college.
Limitations: Applications not accepted. Giving primarily in Hartsville, SC.
Application information: Unsolicited requests for funds not accepted.
Officers: Joseph J. Lawton, Pres.; Edgar H. Lawton, Jr., Treas.
Board Members: Charles W. Coker; Charles W. Coker, Jr.; James C. Fort; Hamlet Ford; Edgar H. Lawton III; Ione C. Lee; William Timberlake.
EIN: 576021383

8474
Community Foundation of Greenville, Inc. ✧

630 E. Washington St., Ste. A
Greenville, SC 29601 (864) 233-5925
Contact: Robert W. Morris, Pres.
FAX: (864) 242-9292;
E-mail: rmorris@cfgreenville.org; Main URL: http://www.cfgreenville.org
Facebook: http://www.facebook.com/pages/Community-Foundation-of-Greenville/77607907249
Scholarship inquiry e-mail: dcooper@cfgreenville.org

Established in 1956 in SC; incorporated in 1970.
Foundation type: Community foundation.
Financial data (yr. ended 12/31/13): Assets, $58,286,129 (M); gifts received, $20,249,080; expenditures, $7,760,999; giving activities include $6,733,863 for 117+ grants (high: $417,312).
Purpose and activities: The foundation exists to enhance the quality of life of citizens of Greater Greenville, SC by linking philanthropic leadership, charitable resources and civic influence with needs and opportunities in the community.
Fields of interest: Arts; Education, early childhood education; Higher education; Education; Environment; Health care; Children/youth, services; Human services; United Ways and Federated Giving Programs; Christian agencies & churches.
Type of support: Equipment; Emergency funds; Program development; Conferences/seminars; Seed money; Internship funds; Scholarship funds; Technical assistance; In-kind gifts; Matching/challenge support.
Limitations: Applications accepted. Giving limited to Greenville County, SC. No grants to individuals (except for scholarships), or for general operational expenses or existing debts; no multi-year grants.
Publications: Application guidelines; Annual report; Informational brochure; Newsletter; Program policy statement.
Application information: Visit foundation web site for application forms and guidelines. Application form required.
Initial approach: Telephone or letter
Deadline(s): Varies
Board meeting date(s): Jan., Mar., May, July, Sept., and Nov.
Final notification: Varies
Officers and Board Members:* Harriet Goldsmith,* Chair.; Dick Wilkerson,* Vice-Chair.; Robert W. Morris, Pres.; Susan Priester,* Secy.; Sharon Gibbs, C.F.O.; Doug Kroske,* Treas.; J. Tod Hyche, Legal Counsel; Perry Gilreath, Asst. Secy.; Bill Bridges, Asst. Treas.; Ann Bryan; Ben Clauss; Mark Cooter; Mark Crocker; Jon Good; Todd Harward; Lesa Kastler; Adela Mendoza; Marie Monroe; Rob Morgan; Travis Olmert; Frances Patterson; Magaly Penn; Michelle Seaver; Steve Spinks; Ralph

Sweeney; Brenda Thames; Wendy Walden; Angela Webb.
Number of staff: 5 full-time professional; 1 part-time professional.
EIN: 576019318

8475
Community Foundation of the Lowcountry ✧
(formerly Hilton Head Island Foundation, Inc.)
4 Northridge Dr., Ste. A
P.O. Box 23019
Hilton Head Island, SC 29925-3019 (843) 681-9100
Contact: Denise K. Spencer, C.E.O.; For grants: Cindy Smith, V.P., Grantmaking
FAX: (843) 681-9101;
E-mail: foundation@cf-lowcountry.org; Grant inquiry e-mail: csmith@cf-lowcountry.org; Main URL: http://www.cf-lowcountry.org
Blog: http://www.cf-lowcountry.org/About/OurBlog.aspx
Facebook: http://www.facebook.com/pages/Community-Foundation-of-the-Lowcountry/77341029228
Twitter: http://twitter.com/cflowcountry
YouTube: http://www.youtube.com/user/CFLowcountry
Scholarship inquiry e-mail: cmead@cf-lowcountry.org

Established in 1983 in SC; converted to a community foundation in 1994 from the proceeds of the sale of Hilton Head Hospital to AMI.
Foundation type: Community foundation.
Financial data (yr. ended 06/30/14): Assets, $70,183,760 (M); gifts received, $12,526,586; expenditures, $7,033,632; giving activities include $4,845,521 for grants.
Purpose and activities: The foundation strengthens the community by connecting people, resources and needs.
Fields of interest: Arts; Education; Environment; Health care; Human services; Community development, neighborhood development; Community/economic development; Religion.
Type of support: Management development/capacity building; Building/renovation; Equipment; Program development; Seed money; Curriculum development; Technical assistance; Consulting services; Program evaluation; Scholarships—to individuals; Matching/challenge support.
Limitations: Applications accepted. Giving limited to Beaufort, Colleton, Hampton and Jasper counties, SC. No support for sectarian or religious activities. No grants to individuals (except for scholarships), or for capital campaigns, endowments, or special events or fundraisers.
Publications: Application guidelines; Annual report; Financial statement; Grants list; Informational brochure; Informational brochure (including application guidelines); Newsletter.
Application information: Visit foundation Web site for application forms and guidelines. Application form required.
Initial approach: Attend a Grants Information Session
Copies of proposal: 11
Deadline(s): Apr. 1, Aug. 1, and Dec. 1
Board meeting date(s): Jan., Mar., May, July, Sept., and Nov.
Final notification: Approximately 3 months after deadline
Officers and Trustees:* Perry Washington,* Chair.; Denise K. Spencer,* C.E.O. and Pres.; Carl L. Conklin,* V.P., Finance and Admin.; Emmy Rooney,* V.P., Devel. and Donor Svcs.; Cynthia Smith, Ph.D.*, V.P., Grantmaking and Community Leadership; Carolyn Torgersen,* V.P., Mktg. and Comms.; Donna Bafundo; Rabbi Brad Bloom; Denis Bonnett; Jeff Bradley; Marva J. Brooks; Ethel Denmark; Berryman W. Edwards; Eric Esquivel; Jeff Evans; J. Dudley King, Jr.; Helen S. Mavrogordato; Elizabeth B. Mayo; Joyce Patterson; William Stinnett III; John Weymouth; J. Eric Woods.
Number of staff: 6 full-time professional; 3 part-time professional; 1 full-time support.
EIN: 570756987

8476
Daniel-Mickel Foundation ✧
(formerly The Daniel Foundation of South Carolina)
P.O. Box 9278
Greenville, SC 29604-9278
Contact: Tamara Lawson, Asst.
E-mail: info@danielmickelfoundation.org; E-mail for Tamara Lawson: tamara@thelewiscompany.org; Main URL: http://www.daniel-mickel-foundation.org

Established in 1978 in SC as partial successor to The Daniel Foundation.
Donors: Daniel International Corp.; Charles E. Daniel‡.
Foundation type: Independent foundation.
Financial data (yr. ended 12/31/13): Assets, $17,396,630 (M); expenditures, $959,396; qualifying distributions, $862,965; giving activities include $834,500 for 91 grants (high: $103,000; low: $100).
Purpose and activities: Giving primarily for higher education, art, healthcare, and upstate SC community development.
Fields of interest: Performing arts, orchestras; Higher education; Hospitals (general); Human services.
Type of support: Continuing support; Management development/capacity building; Capital campaigns; Building/renovation; Equipment; Endowments; Program development; Seed money; Curriculum development; Program evaluation; Matching/challenge support.
Limitations: Applications accepted. Giving primarily in SC. No grants to individuals, or for scholarships.
Publications: Application guidelines; Annual report; Program policy statement.
Application information: Application form required.
Initial approach: Use application system on foundation website
Deadline(s): See foundation website for current deadlines
Board meeting date(s): May, Aug., Nov., and Feb.
Final notification: 4 months
Trustees: Katie S. Howell; Charles Mickel; Minor M. Shaw.
EIN: 570673409
Selected grants: The following grants are a representative sample of this grantmaker's funding activity:
$13,510 to Christ Church Episcopal, Greenville, SC, 2012. For religion and education.
$5,000 to Urban League of the Upstate, Greenville, SC, 2012. For Wellness.

8477
First Citizens Foundation, Inc. ✧
c/o Lisa Mendenall
1230 Main St.
Columbia, SC 29201-3210 (803) 733-2020
Contact: Peter M. Bristow, Dir.

Established in 2000 in SC.
Donors: First Citizens Bancorporation of South Carolina, Inc.; First Citizens Bancorporation, Inc.
Foundation type: Company-sponsored foundation.
Financial data (yr. ended 12/31/12): Assets, $11,477,090 (M); expenditures, $546,889; qualifying distributions, $513,495; giving activities include $513,495 for 45 grants (high: $40,000; low: $1,666).
Purpose and activities: The foundation supports zoos and festivals and organizations involved with arts and culture, education, human services, and community development.
Fields of interest: Arts; Education; Religion.
Limitations: Applications accepted. Giving primarily in SC, with emphasis on Columbia.
Application information: Application form required.
Initial approach: Contact foundation for application form
Deadline(s): None
Officers and Directors:* Frank B. Holding,* Chair.; Jim B. Apple,* Pres.; Peter M. Briston; Wycliffe E. Haynes; Allen H. Mcintyre; Charles S. Mclaurin III.
EIN: 571108547
Selected grants: The following grants are a representative sample of this grantmaker's funding activity:
$40,000 to United Way of the Midlands, Columbia, SC, 2012. To provide funds for midlands homeless transition center.
$35,000 to Spoleto Festival USA, Charleston, SC, 2012. For funding for Gate Theatre's production of Noel Coward's Hay Fever.
$35,000 to United Way of the Midlands, Columbia, SC, 2012. To provide support for the community impact fund.
$25,000 to Charleston Day School, Charleston, SC, 2012. To support capital campaign for new construction.
$20,000 to Columbia College, Columbia, SC, 2012. For funding for student scholarships for low to moderate income families.
$20,000 to Columbia Museum of Art, Columbia, SC, 2012. To support educational exhibition for Mark Rothko.
$20,000 to Lancaster County Educational Foundation, Lancaster, SC, 2012. For funding for construction campaign for classrooms.
$15,000 to Wake Forest University, Winston-Salem, NC, 2012. To support capital campaign for new classrooms.
$10,000 to Fernbank Museum of Natural History, Atlanta, GA, 2012. To support Pathways to Success-Building Scientific Achievement.
$10,000 to Midlands Technical College Foundation, Columbia, SC, 2012. To provide funding for grants to needy college students.

8478
Foothills Community Foundation ✧
907 N. Main St.
P.O. Box 1228
Anderson, SC 29621-5526 (864) 222-9096
Contact: Robert M. Rainey, Pres.

FAX: (864) 222-9727;
E-mail: info@foothillsfoundation.org; Main URL: http://www.foothillscommunityfoundation.org

Established in 1999 in SC.
Foundation type: Community foundation.
Financial data (yr. ended 06/30/14): Assets, $12,535,957 (M); gifts received, $880,309; expenditures, $864,797; giving activities include $502,269 for 19+ grants (high: $39,294).
Purpose and activities: The foundation seeks to retain and nurture the charitable wealth of the community for the perpetual benefit of all in the foundation's service area.
Fields of interest: Arts; Education, public education; Higher education, college; Education; Health care; Recreation; Youth, services; Community/economic development; Foundations (community); United Ways and Federated Giving Programs.
Type of support: Continuing support; Capital campaigns; Scholarship funds.
Limitations: Applications accepted. Giving primarily in Abbeville, Anderson, Oconee, and Pickens counties, SC.
Publications: Annual report; Financial statement; Occasional report.
Application information: Visit foundation web site for application information.
Initial approach: Telephone
Officer and Directors:* Robert M. Rainey, Pres.; Lamar Bailes; James T. Boseman; Glenn D. Buddin, Jr.; Irvin L. Cauthen; Fred L. Foster; Ann D. Herbert; F. Stevon Kay; Theresa G. Knopp, M.D.; John A. Miller, Jr.; Jane W. Mudd; William B. Pickens; Edward A. Spitz; D. Gray Suggs; Joseph J. Turner, Jr.; Robert W. Wilkes; S. Smith Wham.
Number of staff: 1 full-time professional; 1 part-time support.
EIN: 582453349

8479
The Fullerton Foundation, Inc. ✧
515 W. Buford St.
Gaffney, SC 29341-1703 (864) 489-6678
Contact: Charles J. Bonner, Exec. Dir.
FAX: (864) 487-9946;
E-mail: cjbonner@fullertonfoundation.org; Application address: P.O. Box 2208, Gaffney, SC 29342-2208

Established in 1954 in NY.
Donor: Alma H. Fullerton†.
Foundation type: Independent foundation.
Financial data (yr. ended 11/30/13): Assets, $39,045,647 (M); expenditures, $2,508,263; qualifying distributions, $2,085,585; giving activities include $1,859,392 for 27 grants (high: $166,667; low: $15,000).
Purpose and activities: Giving primarily for health care and medicine; some support for higher education.
Fields of interest: Higher education; Health care.
Type of support: Program development; Seed money; Matching/challenge support.
Limitations: Applications accepted. Giving primarily in NC and SC. No grants to individuals.
Publications: Application guidelines.
Application information: Application form not required.
Initial approach: Letter or e-mail requesting guidelines
Copies of proposal: 1
Deadline(s): Apr. 1, Aug. 1 and Dec. 1
Board meeting date(s): 3 times yearly
Final notification: After each meeting of the Board of Directors
Officers and Directors:* Charles F. Hamrick II,* Chair.; Lyman W. Hamrick,* Secy.; W. Carlisle Hamrick,* Treas.; Charles J. Bonner, Exec. Dir.; Helen T. Baden; Jean H. Haas; A. Wardlaw Hamrick; Volina V. Lyons; Elaine H. Shields.
Number of staff: 1 full-time professional; 1 part-time professional; 1 full-time support.
EIN: 570847444
Selected grants: The following grants are a representative sample of this grantmaker's funding activity:
$166,667 to Mission Healthcare Foundation, Asheville, NC, 2013. For Help support the expansion of the Fullerton Genetics Center into a new building which will place under one roof the laboratory and the counseling/clinical genetics services.
$133,200 to University of South Carolina, School of Medicine, Columbia, SC, 2013. To expand the existing ultrasound multi-media production center to provide the type and amount of interactive materials, which are in demand by USCSOM and other healthcare providers.
$100,000 to Limestone College, Gaffney, SC, 2013. For Help fund construction of a new campus library.
$93,031 to Clemson University, Clemson, SC, 2013. For Development of the driving simulator applications and training tools for therapists to assist patients with autism.
$91,464 to Duke University Medical Center, Durham, NC, 2013. To train primary care providers in the Carolinas to serve as leaders of local, regional and national Programs so they may improve the health in our communities and make health care more accessible, effective and economical Project title: PHIL II.
$60,000 to Converse College, Spartanburg, SC, 2013. For Help update some outdated laboratory equipment being used by pre-medical and other medical profession students.
$50,000 to University of South Carolina, School of Medicine, Columbia, SC, 2013. To develop a prototype, referred to as ICARE, which can provide physical as well as mental health care within a primary care doctor's office via telepsychiatry.
$30,000 to Fellowship of Christian Athletes, Gaffney, SC, 2013. For Help cover three years of FCA's general operating expense in Cherokee County.
$25,000 to Gardner-Webb University, Boiling Springs, NC, 2013. For continued support for the Nursing School by helping provide simulation-based learning experiences in order to become better oriented to the real world of nursing in a healthcare setting and preparation for licensing in various nursing disciplines.
$15,000 to Spartanburg Regional Healthcare System Foundation, Spartanburg, SC, 2013. To ensure continued support for the current part-time mobile mammography patient navigator to serve Cherokee County.

8480
Gibbs Charitable Foundation ✧
P.O. Box 1727
Spartanburg, SC 29304-1727

Established in 2002 in SC.
Donors: Jimmy I. Gibbs; Marsha H. Gibbs; Gibbs International, Inc.
Foundation type: Company-sponsored foundation.
Financial data (yr. ended 12/31/13): Assets, $14,529 (M); gifts received, $925,000; expenditures, $985,278; qualifying distributions, $984,325; giving activities include $984,325 for 30 grants (high: $368,100; low: $100).
Purpose and activities: The foundation supports organizations involved with radio, higher education, health, hunger, sports, human services, and Christianity.
Fields of interest: Health care; Health organizations; Human services.
Type of support: General/operating support; Capital campaigns; Endowments; Program development; Scholarship funds.
Limitations: Applications not accepted. Giving primarily in SC, with emphasis on Spartanburg. No grants to individuals.
Application information: Contributes only to pre-selected organizations.
Trustees: Allen O. Clark; Jimmy I. Gibbs; Marsha H. Gibbs; J. Brian Honeycutt; Joe Lesesne; Sidney H. Walker.
EIN: 571111450

8481
The Graham Foundation ✧
531 S. Main St., Ste. ML-7
Greenville, SC 29601-2500
Contact: William A. Bridges, Managing Tr.
FAX: (864) 233-3667;
E-mail: bill@thegrahamfoundation.org; Additional e-mails: Eleanor B. Dunlap: eleanor@thegrahamfoundation.org, Stephen J. Lambert, Tr.: steve@thegrahamfoundation.org; Main URL: http://www.thegrahamfoundation.org

Established in 1985 in SC.
Donors: Allen J. Graham†; Frances G. MacIlwinen†; Allen J. Graham Marital Trust.
Foundation type: Independent foundation.
Financial data (yr. ended 08/31/13): Assets, $52,090,586 (M); gifts received, $5,065,500; expenditures, $2,866,639; qualifying distributions, $2,442,188; giving activities include $2,014,125 for 105 grants (high: $210,000; low: $1,000).
Purpose and activities: Giving to organizations that make a significant difference for the betterment of residents of Greenville and upstate, South Carolina, and are focused on needs that are specific and contained. The primary areas of focus are the arts, children, community welfare, education, the environment, and religion.
Fields of interest: Performing arts; Historic preservation/historical societies; Arts; Elementary/secondary education; Education; Health care; Human services; Community/economic development; Children.
Type of support: Capital campaigns; Building/renovation; Equipment; Endowments; Matching/challenge support.
Limitations: Applications accepted. Giving primarily in Greenville and upstate, SC. No support for political purposes. No grants to individuals or for scholarships.
Publications: Application guidelines.
Application information: Application guidelines, procedures, deadlines, application form available on foundation web site. Application form required.
Initial approach: Letter or telephone, or e-mail
Copies of proposal: 3
Deadline(s): See application page on foundation web site for current deadline

Board meeting date(s): Feb., May, Aug. and Nov.
Final notification: Generally within 30 days after the end of the month following the board meeting dates.
Trustees: William A. Bridges; Stephen J. Lambert; Susan R. Lambert.
Agent: Bank of America, N.A.
EIN: 570805774

8482
The Hartness Foundation ✧
P.O. Box 25309
Greenville, SC 29616-5309

Established in SC.
Donor: Thomas S. Hartness†.
Foundation type: Independent foundation.
Financial data (yr. ended 12/31/13): Assets, $10,986,787 (M); gifts received, $350; expenditures, $457,672; qualifying distributions, $452,350; giving activities include $450,000 for 1 grant.
Fields of interest: Foundations (community).
Limitations: Applications not accepted. Giving primarily in Greenville, SC. No grants to individuals.
Application information: Contributes only to pre-selected organizations.
Officers: Jo H. Guinn, Pres.; Thomas P. Hartness, V.P.; Robert G. Hartness, Secy.-Treas.
EIN: 205376522

8483
The W. Hayne Hipp Foundation ✧
135 S. Main St.
Greenville, SC 29601-2778

Established in 1987 in SC.
Donors: W. Hayne Hipp; Dorothy H. Gunter Cemetery Trust.
Foundation type: Independent foundation.
Financial data (yr. ended 12/31/13): Assets, $7,875,495 (M); expenditures, $1,704,828; qualifying distributions, $1,507,829; giving activities include $1,236,879 for 156 grants (high: $100,000; low: $59).
Purpose and activities: Giving primarily for the arts, higher education, health associations, social services, community development, and Methodist and Presbyterian churches.
Fields of interest: Arts; Higher education; Education; Health organizations, association; Human services; Community/economic development; Foundations (community); Protestant agencies & churches.
Limitations: Applications not accepted. Giving primarily in Greenville and Spartanburg, SC. No grants to individuals; no loans.
Application information: Contributes only to pre-selected organizations.
Officers: W. Hayne Hipp, Pres.; Anne Kate Hipp, V.P. and Secy.-Treas.
Trustees: F. Reid Hipp; Mary H. Hipp; Anna H. Small.
Number of staff: 1 full-time support.
EIN: 570861526
Selected grants: The following grants are a representative sample of this grantmaker's funding activity:
$35,000 to Aspen Institute, Aspen, CO, 2012. For annual trustee fund.
$30,000 to Mary Baldwin College, Staunton, VA, 2012. For Baldwin Fund.
$3,000 to Wofford College, Spartanburg, SC, 2012. For Liberty Fellowship Fund.
$200 to Greenville Airport Commission, Greenville, SC, 2012. For Par at GMU.
$100 to American Lung Association, Washington, DC, 2012. For Fight for the Climb.
$40 to University of South Carolina, Columbia, SC, 2012. For educational fund.

8484
Hopewell Foundation, Inc. ✧
P.O. Box 470
Rock Hill, SC 29731-6470

Established in 1985 in SC.
Foundation type: Independent foundation.
Financial data (yr. ended 12/31/13): Assets, $13,473,834 (M); expenditures, $664,698; qualifying distributions, $645,000; giving activities include $645,000 for 18 grants (high: $100,000; low: $5,000).
Purpose and activities: Giving primarily for higher and other education, human services, Christian organizations, as well as to Presbyterian churches and organizations, and to a United Methodist church.
Fields of interest: Higher education; Theological school/education; Education; Health care; Human services; Christian agencies & churches; Protestant agencies & churches.
Limitations: Applications not accepted. Giving primarily in SC, with emphasis on Rock Hill; some funding also in Charlotte, NC. No grants to individuals.
Application information: Contributes only to pre-selected organizations.
Officers: Ladson A. Barnes, Jr., Pres.; Edwin L. Barnes, Secy.-Treas.
Directors: Bryant G. Barnes; John M. Barnes, Jr.; Robert L. Helmly.
EIN: 570792719
Selected grants: The following grants are a representative sample of this grantmaker's funding activity:
$5,000 to Traditional Values Coalition Education and Legal Institute, Anaheim, CA, 2011.

8485
Inman-Riverdale Foundation ✧ ☆
P.O. Box 207
Inman, SC 29349-0207

Incorporated in 1946 in SC.
Donors: Inman Mills; Chapman High School.
Foundation type: Company-sponsored foundation.
Financial data (yr. ended 11/30/13): Assets, $2,177,578 (M); gifts received, $800,000; expenditures, $689,539; qualifying distributions, $664,341; giving activities include $573,160 for 50 grants (high: $473,564; low: $65), and $22,426 for grants to individuals.
Purpose and activities: The foundation supports organizations involved with arts and culture, secondary and higher education, health, hunger, human services, and Christianity.
Fields of interest: Arts; Education; Human services.
Type of support: General/operating support; Program development; Employee-related scholarships.
Limitations: Applications not accepted. Giving primarily in SC.
Application information: Contributes only to pre-selected organizations and individuals.
Officers: Robert H. Chapman, Chair.; Patricia H. Robbins, Secy.; John F. Renfro, Jr., Treas.
Trustees: Norman H. Chapman; James C. Pace, Jr.
EIN: 576019736

8486
Ellison S. and Noel P. McKissick Foundation ✧
(formerly Alice Manufacturing Company, Inc. Foundation)
P.O. Box 369
Easley, SC 29641-0369 (864) 859-6323

Established in 1983.
Donors: Alice Manufacturing Co., Inc.; Trust A U/A of Ellison S. Mckissick, Jr.
Foundation type: Company-sponsored foundation.
Financial data (yr. ended 06/30/14): Assets, $19,125,662 (M); expenditures, $883,222; qualifying distributions, $830,374; giving activities include $785,374 for 29 grants (high: $122,500; low: $1,500).
Purpose and activities: The foundation supports museums and organizations involved with education, land conservation, medical care, children, and Christianity.
Fields of interest: Museums; Elementary/secondary education; Higher education; Business school/education; Education; Environment, land resources; Medical care, rehabilitation; Boys & girls clubs; American Red Cross; Children, services; United Ways and Federated Giving Programs; Christian agencies & churches.
Type of support: Scholarship funds; General/operating support.
Limitations: Applications not accepted. Giving primarily in NC and SC. No grants to individuals.
Application information: Contributes only to pre-selected organizations.
Officer: Robert H. Thomas, Treas.
Directors: Elizabeth M. Fauntleroy; Ellison Smyth McKissick III; Caroline McKissick Young.
EIN: 570739969
Selected grants: The following grants are a representative sample of this grantmaker's funding activity:
$120,000 to United Way of Pickens County, Easley, SC, 2011.
$120,000 to United Way of Pickens County, Easley, SC, 2011.
$50,000 to Tri-County Technical College, Pendleton, SC, 2011.
$42,162 to Christ Church Episcopal School, Greenville, SC, 2011.
$25,000 to Clemson University, Clemson, SC, 2011.
$25,000 to Clemson University, Clemson, SC, 2011.
$10,000 to Peter-Paul Development Center, Richmond, VA, 2011.
$10,000 to Peter-Paul Development Center, Richmond, VA, 2011.
$5,000 to United Way of Pickens County, Easley, SC, 2011.
$1,500 to Tri-County Technical College, Pendleton, SC, 2011.

8487
Rose and Walter Montgomery Foundation ✧
314 S. Pine St., Bldg. 100
Spartanburg, SC 29302-2677 (864) 585-9213
Contact: Walter S. Montgomery, Jr., Tr.

Established in SC.
Donors: Walter S. Montgomery†; Rose C. Montgomery Trust A.
Foundation type: Independent foundation.
Financial data (yr. ended 12/31/13): Assets, $15,182,939 (M); expenditures, $1,135,375; qualifying distributions, $700,284; giving activities include $700,284 for 76 grants (high: $100,000; low: $250).
Purpose and activities: Giving primarily for the arts, education, social services, and Episcopal churches and organizations.
Fields of interest: Arts; Education; Human services; Protestant agencies & churches.
Limitations: Applications accepted. Giving primarily in Spartanburg, SC, and Memphis, TN. No grants to individuals.
Application information: Application form required.
Initial approach: Letter
Deadline(s): None
Trustees: Rose M. Johnston; Walter S. Montgomery, Jr.
EIN: 570986535

8488
Darla Moore and Richard Rainwater Foundation ✧
133-B E. Main St.
Lake City, SC 29560

Donors: Darla D. Moore; Richard E. Rainwater.
Foundation type: Independent foundation.
Financial data (yr. ended 12/31/12): Assets, $5,454,265 (M); gifts received, $5,000,000; expenditures, $2,515,033; qualifying distributions, $2,509,783; giving activities include $2,501,464 for 2 grants (high: $1,271,464; low: $1,230,000).
Fields of interest: Community/economic development.
Limitations: Applications not accepted. Giving primarily in Lake City, SC.
Application information: Contributes only to pre-selected organizations.
Officers and Trustees:* Darla D. Moore,* Pres.; Franklin B. Caggiano,* V.P.; James P. Fields, Jr.,* V.P.; Melissa T. Parrish, Secy.-Treas.
EIN: 273130736

8489
The Cissy Patterson Foundation ✧ ☆
c/o Ruth S. Flynn, Esq. PLLC
188 King St., Ste. B
Charleston, SC 29401-3208

Established in 1993 in DC.
Donor: The Cissy Patterson Trust.
Foundation type: Independent foundation.
Financial data (yr. ended 12/31/13): Assets, $1,974,590 (M); expenditures, $522,969; qualifying distributions, $510,556; giving activities include $502,500 for 15 grants (high: $80,000; low: $2,500).
Purpose and activities: Giving primarily to environmental organizations, as well as for the arts, higher education, and human services, particularly an organization which provides humanitarian assistance to refugees.
Fields of interest: Arts; Higher education; Environment, natural resources; Human services; Immigrants/refugees.
Type of support: General/operating support.
Limitations: Applications not accepted. Giving primarily in CO, Washington, DC, FL, NY and WY. No grants to individuals.
Application information: Contributes only to pre-selected organizations.
Officers: Alice Arlen, Pres.; Joseph P. Albright, V.P.; Blandina A. Rojek, Secy.; Adam Albright, Treas.
EIN: 521795554

8490
Norma F. Pfriem Foundation ✧
c/o Roger Perry
6 Planters Wood Dr.
Hilton Head, SC 29928-4404

Donor: Norma F. Pfriem†.
Foundation type: Independent foundation.
Financial data (yr. ended 12/31/13): Assets, $15,367,157 (M); expenditures, $5,635,355; qualifying distributions, $5,425,510; giving activities include $5,425,510 for 20 grants (high: $2,250,000; low: $11,500).
Fields of interest: Museums; Education; Hospitals (general); Protestant agencies & churches; Catholic agencies & churches.
Limitations: Applications not accepted. Giving primarily in CT.
Application information: Contributes only to pre-selected organizations.
Trustees: Paul S. Miller; Roger L. Perry; Matthew B. Woods.
EIN: 206776658
Selected grants: The following grants are a representative sample of this grantmaker's funding activity:
$2,000,000 to Bridgeport Hospital Foundation, Bridgeport, CT, 2012.
$1,000,000 to Fidelco Guide Dog Foundation, Bloomfield, CT, 2012. For endowment.
$700,000 to Connecticut Hospice, Branford, CT, 2012.
$366,000 to United Congregational Church, Bridgeport, CT, 2012.
$130,000 to Council of Churches of Greater Bridgeport, Bridgeport, CT, 2012.
$120,000 to Kennedy Center, Trumbull, CT, 2012.
$54,000 to Star Foundation, Norwalk, CT, 2012.
$50,000 to Bridgeport Child Advocacy Coalition, Bridgeport, CT, 2012.
$50,000 to Connecticut Braille Association, Westport, CT, 2012.
$23,480 to Norma F. Pfriem Urban Outreach, Bridgeport, CT, 2012.

8491
Phifer/Johnson Foundation ✧
P.O. Box 3524
Spartanburg, SC 29304-3524

Established in 1993 in SC.
Donor: George Dean Johnson, Jr.
Foundation type: Independent foundation.
Financial data (yr. ended 12/31/13): Assets, $14,929,493 (M); expenditures, $1,913,679; qualifying distributions, $1,797,956; giving activities include $1,797,956 for 136 grants (high: $500,000; low: $100).
Purpose and activities: Giving primarily for the arts, education, health, and human services.
Fields of interest: Museums (art); Museums (history); Arts; Elementary/secondary education; Higher education; Education; Health care; Human services; YM/YWCAs & YM/YWHAs; Protestant agencies & churches.
Limitations: Applications not accepted. Giving primarily in FL, NC, and SC. No grants to individuals.
Application information: Contributes only to pre-selected organizations.
Directors: George Dean Johnson, Jr.; George D. Johnson, III; Susan P. Johnson; Susanna P. Johnson.
EIN: 576153679

8492
Post and Courier Foundation ✧
134 Columbus St.
Charleston, SC 29403-4800 (843) 937-5605
Contact: Susan N. Sanders, Secy.

Incorporated in 1951 in SC.
Donors: Evening Post Publishing Co.; Blackbaud, Inc.; David Buchanan; Whitfield Familt Charitable Trust; Yarborough Applegate Law Firm; Colbert Family Fund of Coastal Community Foundation; Daniel Island Co.; Ronald Banks; Particia Banks; David J. Miller; Cynthia Miller; Marine Environmental Testing; Four J's Ranch; Bakker Family Fund of Coastal Community Foundation; The Schirmer Estate; Evening Post Industries.
Foundation type: Company-sponsored foundation.
Financial data (yr. ended 12/31/13): Assets, $4,467,857 (M); gifts received, $1,109,302; expenditures, $742,253; qualifying distributions, $678,281; giving activities include $678,281 for 87 grants (high: $110,214; low: $500).
Purpose and activities: The foundation supports food banks and youth development centers and organizations involved with arts and culture, education, conservation, animal welfare, human services, and the visually impaired.
Fields of interest: Human services; Community/economic development; Religion.
Limitations: Applications accepted. Giving primarily in Charleston, SC. No grants to individuals.
Application information: Application form required.
Initial approach: Letter
Deadline(s): June 30
Board meeting date(s): As needed, usually twice annually
Officers: Rebecca Gilbreth Herres, Pres.; Pierre Manigault, V.P.; Susan N. Sanders, Secy.; Joseph I. Waring, Treas.
Number of staff: 1 part-time professional.
EIN: 576020356
Selected grants: The following grants are a representative sample of this grantmaker's funding activity:
$108,825 to Star Gospel Mission, Charleston, SC, 2012. For Good Cheer Christmas Fund to purchase free food certificates and Financial Assistant for Needy.
$36,275 to Association for the Blind, Charleston, SC, 2012. To provide Food Clothing etc for Blind People at Christmas.
$36,275 to Lowcountry Food Bank, Charleston, SC, 2012. To support Homeless Shelter for Men/

Women/and Children Meals, Financial Assistant for Needy.
$36,275 to Salvation Army, Charleston, SC, 2012. To support Homeless Shelter for Men/Women/and Children, Meals Financial Assistant for Needy.
$2,500 to Drayton Hall, Charleston, SC, 2012. For restoration.
$1,000 to Moja Arts Festival, Charleston, SC, 2012. For educational outreach activities.

8493
The Reams Foundation, Inc. ✧
216 Confederate Cir.
Charleston, SC 29407-7429

Established in 1994 in IN.
Donor: Fred W. Reams.
Foundation type: Independent foundation.
Financial data (yr. ended 12/31/13): Assets, $23,720,089 (M); expenditures, $1,111,704; qualifying distributions, $971,218; giving activities include $855,300 for 23 grants (high: $360,000; low: $300).
Fields of interest: Education; Hospitals (general); Health organizations, association; Housing/shelter, development; Human services; Foundations (public); Public affairs, research.
Limitations: Applications not accepted. Giving primarily in AZ and IN. No grants to individuals.
Application information: Contributes only to pre-selected organizations.
Officers and Directors:* Fred W. Reams,* Pres.; Karen A. Reams,* V.P.; Karen E. Saboe,* Secy.; Kristen A. Carter; Kimberly A. Cole; Matthew D. Reams.
EIN: 351933846

8494
The Roe Foundation ✧
301 N. Main St., Ste. 1735
Greenville, SC 29601-2122 (864) 242-5007
Contact: Shirley W. Roe, Chair.
FAX: (864) 242-5014; E-mail: roefdn@aol.com

Incorporated in 1968 in SC.
Donor: Thomas A. Roe†.
Foundation type: Independent foundation.
Financial data (yr. ended 12/31/13): Assets, $33,070,387 (M); gifts received, $345,300; expenditures, $1,856,251; qualifying distributions, $1,724,270; giving activities include $1,655,000 for 93 grants (high: $150,000; low: $1,000).
Purpose and activities: The purpose of the foundation is to assist non-profit educational institutions whose primary mission is to promote a better understanding and appreciation of the value of human and economic freedom functioning within a moral framework. Such organizations will believe: 1) the maximum potential of a free people is achieved when they are able control their own destiny. 2) The greatest threat to these freedoms is intrusive government. 3) The Judeo-Christian tradition represents the underpinnings of a just society. Such organizations will recognize: 1) the importance of state and local organizations functioning alongside national organizations in the pursuit of free society; and 2) that their operations should be designed to educate the public at large and all public policy makers to a better understanding of these fundamental values and practical ways to achieve the goals of expanding human freedom.
Fields of interest: Education; Civil/human rights.
Type of support: General/operating support; Continuing support; Annual campaigns; Capital campaigns; Building/renovation; Equipment; Land acquisition; Program development; Conferences/seminars; Publication; Seed money; Research; Matching/challenge support.
Limitations: Applications accepted. No support for organizations that do not deal with public policy. No grants to individuals; no loans or multiple-year pledges.
Publications: Application guidelines.
Application information: The foundation only accepts applications from public policy research organizations. Application form not required.
Initial approach: Letter
Copies of proposal: 1
Deadline(s): Mar. through Oct. 31
Board meeting date(s): Jan., Feb. or Mar.
Final notification: 5 months after deadline
Officers and Trustees:* Shirley W. Roe,* Chair. and Treas.; Edwin J. Feulner, Jr.,* Vice-Chair.; Carl O. Helstrom; Byron S. Lamm; Tracie J. Sharp; Thomas L. Willcox, Jr.
Number of staff: 1 part-time professional.
EIN: 237011541
Selected grants: The following grants are a representative sample of this grantmaker's funding activity:
$225,000 to South Carolina Policy Council, Columbia, SC, 2012. For general operating support.
$125,000 to Heritage Foundation, Washington, DC, 2012. For general operating support.
$100,000 to State Policy Network, Richmond, CA, 2012. For general operating support.
$25,000 to Intercollegiate Studies Institute, Wilmington, DE, 2012. For general operating support.
$20,000 to Cascade Policy Institute, Portland, OR, 2012. For general operating support.
$20,000 to Indiana Policy Review Foundation, Fort Wayne, IN, 2012. For general operating support.
$15,000 to Buckeye Institute for Public Policy Solutions, Columbus, OH, 2012. For general operating support.
$15,000 to Institute for Humane Studies, Arlington, VA, 2012. For general operating support.
$10,000 to Mont Pelerin Society, Alexandria, VA, 2012. For general operating support.

8495
ScanSource Charitable Foundation ✧
6 Logue Ct.
Greenville, SC 29615-5725 (800) 944-2432
Contact: Mike Fuller, Pres.
E-mail: charity@scansource.com; Main URL: http://www.scansource.com/en/responsibility/scansource-charitable-foundation/

Established in 1998 in SC.
Donors: ScanSource, Inc.; Owings Family Foundation.
Foundation type: Company-sponsored foundation.
Financial data (yr. ended 12/31/13): Assets, $6,999,546 (M); gifts received, $898,493; expenditures, $2,559,024; qualifying distributions, $2,481,912; giving activities include $2,481,912 for 100 grants (high: $351,000; low: $50).
Purpose and activities: The foundation supports organizations involved with children, education, and community wellness. Special emphasis is directed toward programs designed to provide volunteer opportunities.
Fields of interest: Child development, education; Education, services; Education; Health care; Housing/shelter, development; YM/YWCAs & YM/YWHAs; Children, services; Family services; Residential/custodial care; Human services; Community/economic development; Children.
Type of support: General/operating support; Emergency funds; Scholarship funds; Employee volunteer services.
Limitations: Applications accepted. Giving primarily in areas of company operations, with some emphasis on AZ, FL, GA, KS, MS, SC, TN, WA, Canada, London, England, France, and Germany. No grants to individuals (except for employee-related scholarships).
Publications: Application guidelines; IRS Form 990 or 990-PF printed copy available upon request.
Application information: Grant requests should allow ScanSource and the ScanSource Charitable Foundation to maintain an anonymous posture. A limited number of requests for emergency funds are accepted outside of the annual application process. Application form required.
Initial approach: E-mail foundation for application form
Deadline(s): Feb. to Oct.
Officers and Directors:* Mike Fuller,* Pres.; Tinsley Maness,* V.P.; Beth Dameron,* Secy.; Camilo Franco, Treas.; Joey Altom; Carolina Arroyave; Joan Burket; Alex Ellenburg; Robin Genzy; Jessica Howard; Anna Karageorglou; Ruth Robinson; Jordan Shrack; Allean Simmonds; Zach Thrasher; Rhonda Trainor; Cate Tyson; Cendrine Vermer; Sara Wilde.
EIN: 571002959
Selected grants: The following grants are a representative sample of this grantmaker's funding activity:
$157,116 to Harvest Hope Food Bank, Columbia, SC, 2011.
$5,000 to A Childs Haven, Greenville, SC, 2011.

8496
The Self Family Foundation ✧
(formerly The Self Foundation)
120 Main St.
Greenwood, SC 29646-2763 (864) 941-4011
Contact: Mamie W. Nicholson, Prog. Off.
FAX: (864) 941-4091;
E-mail: info@selffoundation.org; E-mail and tel. for Mamie W. Nicholson:
mamienic@selffoundation.org; (864) 953-2441;
Main URL: http://www.selffoundation.org

Incorporated in 1942 in SC.
Donor: James C. Self†.
Foundation type: Independent foundation.
Financial data (yr. ended 12/31/13): Assets, $32,778,890 (M); expenditures, $1,733,279; qualifying distributions, $1,538,182; giving activities include $1,094,554 for 52 grants (high: $400,000; low: $1,000).
Purpose and activities: Primary interest is in health care, (K-12) education, and early childhood development. Support also for civic and community service, activities for youth and the elderly, and cultural and historical activities; grants mainly for programs or special purposes.
Fields of interest: Arts; Education; Health care; Children/youth, services; Aging, centers/services; Community development, neighborhood development; Aging.

Type of support: Equipment; Emergency funds; Program development; Seed money; Technical assistance; Consulting services; Matching/challenge support.
Limitations: Applications accepted. Giving limited to SC, with primary emphasis on Greenwood. No support for churches. No grants to individuals, or for endowment funds, land acquisition, operating budgets, continuing support, annual campaigns, deficit financing, publications, conferences, scholarships, fellowships, or research-related programs; no loans.
Publications: Application guidelines; Annual report (including application guidelines); Grants list; Program policy statement.
Application information: See foundation Web site for application guidelines. Application form not required.
Initial approach: E-mail or telephone
Copies of proposal: 1
Deadline(s): Mar. 1, June 1, Sept. 1, and Nov. 1
Board meeting date(s): 3rd week in Apr., July, Oct., and Dec.
Final notification: 10 days after board meeting
Officers and Trustees:* W.M. Self,* Chair.; Frank J. Wideman III, Pres.; Sally E. Self, M.D.*, Secy.; J.C. Self III,* Treas.; David Welborn Adams; Jon Holloway; Cade Brennan Jackson; Furman C. Self.
Number of staff: 2 full-time professional; 1 full-time support.
EIN: 570400594
Selected grants: The following grants are a representative sample of this grantmaker's funding activity:
$102,840 to Clemson University Foundation, Clemson, SC, 2012. For Establishment of Jim Self Center on the Future at Strom Thurmond Institute at Clemson.
$72,378 to Converse College, Spartanburg, SC, 2012. For Virginia Turner Self Scholarship.
$45,000 to Furman University, Greenville, SC, 2012. For Understanding the Impact of Montessori in South Carolina (Research Study).
$30,000 to Partnership for a Greater Greenwood County, Greenwood, SC, 2012. For workforce development efforts in Greenwood County.
$25,000 to Healthy Learners, Columbia, SC, 2012. For Annual funding to sustain the Greenwood Program.
$20,000 to Food Bank of Greenwood County, Greenwood, SC, 2012. To support operations and purchase computer equipment/software.
$15,000 to Wofford College, Spartanburg, SC, 2012. For Liberty Fellows (Community Connect Collaborative).
$1,800 to Columbia College, Columbia, SC, 2012. For Leadership Program for Girls.
$1,500 to South Carolina Future Minds, Florence, SC, 2012. For Teacher of the Year Sponsorship (2012).

8497
J. Marion Sims Foundation, Inc. ✧
800 N. White St.
Lancaster, SC 29720-2177 (803) 286-8772
Contact: James T. Morton, Pres.
FAX: (803) 286-8774; E-mail: jmorton@jmsims.org; Mailing address: P.O. Box 818, Lancaster SC 29721; Main URL: http://www.jmsims.org

Established in 1995 in SC; converted from sale of Elliott White Springs Memorial Hospital, Inc.
Foundation type: Independent foundation.
Financial data (yr. ended 12/31/13): Assets, $71,860,949 (M); expenditures, $3,908,119; qualifying distributions, $2,682,075; giving activities include $2,020,771 for 29 grants (high: $430,491; low: $5,000).
Purpose and activities: The foundation supports programs and projects of prevention and education that enhance health and wellness in Lancaster County, SC, and the communities of Great Falls and Fort Lawn.
Fields of interest: Education; Health care.
Type of support: Management development/capacity building; General/operating support; Continuing support; Capital campaigns; Building/renovation; Equipment; Program development; Seed money; Research; Matching/challenge support.
Limitations: Applications accepted. Giving primarily in Lancaster County, Great Falls, and Fort Lawn, SC. No support for political purposes, indigent care, or programs or projects generally considered to be the role of government. No grants to individuals, or for endowments, event tickets, projects of organizations that primarily benefit their own members or adherents, indirect costs (including payments of a percentage of a grant to a local organization's national affiliate), or to retire accumulated debt; no loans.
Publications: Application guidelines; Annual report.
Application information: Application forms and guidelines available on foundation web site. The foundation will acknowledge receipt of an application by telephone or letter. Application form required.
Initial approach: Letter or telephone
Copies of proposal: 1
Deadline(s): Apr. 15 and Oct. 15
Board meeting date(s): Monthly (excluding July and Dec.)
Final notification: Aug. 31 and Feb. 28
Officers and Trustees:* Malcolm Edwards, M.D.*, Chair.; Robert K. Folks,* Vice-Chair.; James T. Morton,* Pres.; E. Brown Crenshaw, Jr., CPA*, V.P., Fin. and Admin.; Pamela Y. Temple,* Secy.; Phyllis B. Bunkley,* Treas.; Miriam M. Boucher; Timothy H. Hallman; Charles M. Harrell; Polly C. Jackson; Stanley D. Johnson; Hubert F. "Hugh" Mobley; Marvin L. Starks.
Number of staff: 4 full-time professional; 1 full-time support.
EIN: 570355295

8498
John I. Smith Charities, Inc. ✧
P.O. Box 1687
Greer, SC 29652-1687 (864) 879-2455
Contact: Jefferson V. Smith, Jr., Pres.

Established in 1985 in SC.
Donor: John I. Smith‡.
Foundation type: Independent foundation.
Financial data (yr. ended 07/31/13): Assets, $25,605,901 (M); expenditures, $1,440,807; qualifying distributions, $1,297,500; giving activities include $1,297,500 for grants.
Purpose and activities: Giving primarily for higher education, human services, and the arts.
Fields of interest: Arts; Higher education; Theological school/education; Education; Human services; YM/YWCAs & YM/YWHAs; Christian agencies & churches.
Type of support: General/operating support; Capital campaigns; Endowments; Emergency funds; Scholarship funds.
Limitations: Giving primarily in SC. No grants to individuals.
Application information: Application form not required.
Initial approach: Letter
Deadline(s): None
Board meeting date(s): Quarterly
Officers: Jefferson V. Smith, Jr.,* Pres.; Elizabeth Clayton,* V.P.; Travis V. Olmert,* Treas.
EIN: 570806327
Selected grants: The following grants are a representative sample of this grantmaker's funding activity:
$100,000 to Davidson College, Davidson, NC, 2011.
$60,000 to Furman University, Greenville, SC, 2011.
$30,000 to Montreat College, Montreat, NC, 2011.
$25,000 to Gateway House, Greenville, SC, 2011.
$25,000 to Homes of Hope, Greenville, SC, 2011.
$15,000 to Greenville Symphony Orchestra, Greenville, SC, 2011.
$15,000 to Metropolitan Arts Council, Greenville, SC, 2011.
$10,000 to Mere Christianity Forum, Greenville, SC, 2011.
$10,000 to YMCA of Greenville, Greenville, SC, 2011.
$7,000 to Clarity, The Speech, Hearing and Learning Center, Greenville, SC, 2011.

8499
J.M. Smith Foundation ✧
101 W. St. John St., Ste. 305
Spartanburg, SC 29306-5150

Established in 1996 in SC.
Donor: J M Smith Corp.
Foundation type: Company-sponsored foundation.
Financial data (yr. ended 02/28/13): Assets, $435,242 (M); gifts received, $2,982,337; expenditures, $2,854,492; qualifying distributions, $2,854,492; giving activities include $2,854,090 for 392 grants (high: $146,660; low: $200).
Purpose and activities: The foundation supports organizations involved with education, hunger, human services, and Christianity.
Fields of interest: Secondary school/education; Higher education; Education; Food services; Food distribution, meals on wheels; Boys & girls clubs; YM/YWCAs & YM/YWHAs; Human services; United Ways and Federated Giving Programs; Christian agencies & churches.
Type of support: Equipment; General/operating support; Continuing support; Program development; Scholarship funds.
Limitations: Applications not accepted. Giving primarily in SC; giving also in AR, FL, GA, KY, NC, PA, and VA. No grants to individuals.
Application information: Contributes only to pre-selected organizations.
Officers: Kenneth R. Couch, Pres.; Tammy Devine, Secy.; James C. Wilson, Jr., Treas.
Directors: Henry D. Smith; Mike Webb; Russ Webber.
EIN: 571046595

8500
Sonoco Foundation ✧ ☆
1 N. 2nd St., M.S. B04
Hartsville, SC 29550
Contact: Joyce Beasley
E-mail: sonoco.foundation@sonoco.com; Main URL: http://www.sonocofoundation.com/

Established in 1983 in SC.
Donor: Sonoco Products Co.
Foundation type: Company-sponsored foundation.
Financial data (yr. ended 12/31/12): Assets, $50,169 (M); gifts received, $1,975,000; expenditures, $1,950,144; qualifying distributions, $1,950,144; giving activities include $1,950,144 for 84 grants (high: $400,000; low: $250).
Purpose and activities: The foundation supports organizations involved with arts and culture, education, the environment, health and welfare, disaster relief, community economic development, and civic affairs.
Fields of interest: Education; Human services; Community/economic development.
Type of support: General/operating support; Continuing support; Capital campaigns; Employee volunteer services; Employee matching gifts.
Limitations: Applications accepted. Giving primarily in areas of company operations, with emphasis on Hartsville, SC. No support for private foundations, sectarian or denominational religious organizations, missionary groups, organizations with local or regional chapters that are supported by Sonoco, fraternal, social, labor, or veterans' organizations, discriminatory organizations, or intermediary funding agencies (except the United Way). No grants to individuals, or for courtesy advertising, testimonial dinners, loans or investments, political or lobbying campaigns, debt reduction, memorials, endowments, memberships, or conferences, workshops, or seminars.
Publications: Application guidelines.
Application information: Multi-year funding is not automatic. Organizations receiving support are asked to submit a final report. Application form required.
Initial approach: Letter
Copies of proposal: 1
Deadline(s): None
Board meeting date(s): Quarterly, and as needed
Trustees: R.P. Schrum; Barry L. Saunders; H.E. Deloach, Jr.
Number of staff: 1 part-time professional.
EIN: 570752950

8501
The Spartanburg County Foundation ✧
424 E. Kennedy St.
Spartanburg, SC 29302-1916 (864) 582-0138
Contact: Troy M. Hanna, C.E.O.; For grants: Ashley T. Whitt, Prog. Assoc.
FAX: (864) 573-5378; E-mail: info@spcf.org; Additional e-mail: thanna@spcf.org; Grant inquiry e-mail: awhitt@spcf.org; Main URL: http://www.spcf.org
Facebook: https://www.facebook.com/pages/The-Spartanburg-County-Foundation/130298439113
LinkedIn: http://www.linkedin.com/company/the-spartanburg-county-foundation
Twitter: https://twitter.com/spcountyfdn
YouTube: http://www.youtube.com/user/SpartanburgCntyFndn?feature=mhee

Incorporated in 1943 in SC.
Foundation type: Community foundation.
Financial data (yr. ended 12/31/13): Assets, $144,985,101 (M); gifts received, $10,600,690; expenditures, $9,646,149; giving activities include $6,877,464 for 125+ grants, and $580,409 for 527 grants to individuals.
Purpose and activities: The foundation seeks to provide for the mental, moral, intellectual and physical improvement, assistance and relief of the inhabitants of Spartanburg County. Primary areas of interest include local projects in higher and other education, community development, recreation, and health.
Fields of interest: Humanities; Historic preservation/historical societies; Arts; Higher education; Adult/continuing education; Education; Environment; Health care; Health organizations, association; Recreation; Children/youth, services; Human services; Community/economic development; Children/youth.
Type of support: Continuing support; Building/renovation; Equipment; Emergency funds; Conferences/seminars; Seed money; Curriculum development; Scholarship funds; Consulting services; Employee-related scholarships; Scholarships—to individuals; In-kind gifts; Matching/challenge support.
Limitations: Applications accepted. Giving limited to the Spartanburg County, SC, area. No support for religious organizations for sectarian purposes. No grants to individuals (except designated scholarship funds), or for operating budgets, annual campaigns, deficit financing, land acquisition, film projects, publication of books or reports, or endowment funds; no loans.
Publications: Application guidelines; Annual report (including application guidelines); Informational brochure; Newsletter.
Application information: Visit foundation web site for application guidelines. Application form required.
Copies of proposal: 1
Deadline(s): Spring and Fall
Board meeting date(s): Monthly
Officers and Trustees:* Robert E. Gregory, Jr.,* Chair.; John S. Poole,* Vice-Chair.; Troy M. Hanna, C.E.O. and Pres.; Mary L. Thomas, C.O.O.; Dr. John Stockwell,* Secy.; Andrew J. Falatok,* Treas.; James W. Shaw, Genl. Council and Asst. Secy.; John E. Bauknight; Terry L. Cash; Dr. Kay E. Woodward.
Number of staff: 8 full-time professional.
EIN: 570351398

8502
Spaulding-Paolozzi Foundation ✧
14 George St.
Charleston, SC 29401

Established in SC.
Foundation type: Independent foundation.
Financial data (yr. ended 12/31/13): Assets, $5,312,056 (M); expenditures, $748,150; qualifying distributions, $686,568; giving activities include $683,333 for 3 grants (high: $500,000; low: $83,333).
Fields of interest: Women, centers/services.
Limitations: Applications not accepted. Giving primarily in Charleston, SC. No grants to individuals.
Application information: Contributes only to pre-selected organizations.
Officers: Nigel Redden, Pres.; Jennet Robinson Alterman, V.P.; Whit McMillan, Secy.; Alan W. Elzerman, Ph.D., Treas.
Board Members: John R. Feussner, M.D.; Rose Delores Gibbs, M.D.; Daniel Kelting; John W. Mills, Ph.D.; Linda Plunkett; Joseph P. Riley, Jr.; Lester S. Schwartz; Hilton C. Smith, Jr.
EIN: 311751351

8503
The Speedwell Foundation ✧
2 Gibbes St.
Charleston, SC 29401-2302
Contact: Michael G. Messner, Tr.; Jenny K. Messner, Tr.

Established in 2000 in NJ.
Donor: Michael G. Messner.
Foundation type: Independent foundation.
Financial data (yr. ended 12/31/12): Assets, $94,174,743 (M); gifts received, $4,150,000; expenditures, $4,071,568; qualifying distributions, $3,751,696; giving activities include $3,751,696 for grants.
Fields of interest: Higher education; Education; Human services; Children/youth, services.
Limitations: Applications not accepted. Giving primarily in MA, NJ and NY; some funding also in GA.
Application information: Contributes only to pre-selected organizations.
Trustees: Jenny K. Messner; Michael G. Messner.
EIN: 223764378

8504
The Springs Close Foundation, Inc. ✧
(formerly Springs Foundation, Inc.)
951 Market St., Ste. 205
Fort Mill, SC 29708-6529 (803) 548-2002
Contact: Angela H. McCrae, Pres.
FAX: (803) 548-1797;
E-mail: amccrae@springsfnd.com; Lancaster, SC, office address: 201 W. Gay St., Lancaster, SC 29720, tel.: (803) 286-2197, fax: (803) 416-4626; Chester, SC, office address: 109 Gadsden St., Chester, SC 29706, tel.: (803) 581-7874, fax: (803) 581-2431; Main URL: http://www.thespringsclosefoundation.org

Incorporated in 1942 in DE.
Donors: Elliott W. Springs†; Anne Springs Close; Frances Ley Springs†; members of the Springs and Close families.
Foundation type: Independent foundation.
Financial data (yr. ended 12/31/13): Assets, $43,862,310 (M); gifts received, $12,100; expenditures, $1,327,877; qualifying distributions, $1,244,052; giving activities include $880,900 for 102 grants (high: $100,000; low: $200).
Purpose and activities: In response to high unemployment rates and growing economic distress, the foundation shifted its charitable efforts toward helping local citizens who need basic and emergency needs, such as shelter, food, and medical assistance.
Fields of interest: Education, early childhood education; Health care; Family services; Aging, centers/services; Community/economic development; Christian agencies & churches; Economically disadvantaged.
Type of support: General/operating support; Annual campaigns; Capital campaigns; Building/renovation; Equipment; Endowments; Program development; Seed money; Matching/challenge support; Student loans—to individuals.

Limitations: Applications accepted. Giving limited to Chester, Lancaster and York Counties, SC. No grants to individuals (except for student loans), or for travel expenses.
Publications: Application guidelines; Annual report; Annual report (including application guidelines); Grants list.
Application information: Applications should be mailed or delivered to the Fort Mill, SC, office. Applications may be faxed as well to the foundation's 1797 number, or scanned and e-mailed to the foundation's main e-mail address. Application form required.
Initial approach: Use application form on foundation web site; applicants are strongly encouraged to contact foundation Pres., Angela McCrae to discuss proposals prior to submission
Copies of proposal: 1
Deadline(s): Mar. 1 and Oct. 1; none for grant requests of up to $2,500
Board meeting date(s): Apr. and Nov.
Final notification: 3 months
Officers and Directors:* Anne Springs Close,* Chair.; Angela H. McCrae, Pres.; Harry B. Emerson, Secy.; William G. Taylor,* Treas.; Chantay Bouler; Crandall C. Bowles; Bruce A. Brumfield; Derick S. Close; Elliott S. Close; Frances A. Close; H.W. Close; Katherine A. Close; M. Scott Close; Nancy Coleman; W. Dehler Hart; Robert Holcombe, Jr.
Number of staff: 1 full-time professional; 2 part-time professional; 1 full-time support.
EIN: 570426344

8505
Teach Foundation ✧ ☆
214 N. 5th St.
Hartsville, SC 29550-4136
Main URL: http://www.teachfoundation.org

Established in SC.
Donor: Sonoco Foundation.
Foundation type: Independent foundation.
Financial data (yr. ended 06/30/13): Assets, $163,838 (M); gifts received, $925,002; expenditures, $824,801; qualifying distributions, $728,665; giving activities include $728,665 for 6 grants (high: $207,697; low: $6,795).
Fields of interest: Education; Youth development.
Limitations: Applications not accepted. Giving primarily in Hartsville, SC.
Publications: Newsletter.
Application information: Unsolicited requests for funds not accepted.
Officers and Directors:* Harris E. DeLoach, Jr.,* Chair.; Dr. Tracy Parkinson,* Secy.; Gloria Bell,* Treas.; Sharman Poplava, Exec. Dir.; Dr. Murray Brockman; Tim Browne; Dr. Eddie Ingram.
EIN: 452542245

8506
TSC Foundation, Inc. ✧
104 E. Springs St.
Lancaster, SC 29720-2159

Established in 2001 in SC.
Donors: Derick S. Close; Crandall C. Bowles; Leroy S. Close; Francie Close; Springs Industries, Inc.; Patricia Close Charitable Lead Trust No. 2; Springs Window Fashions, Inc.; 09 PGC Charitable Lead Annuity Trust; Springs Creative Products Group; The Springs Company.
Foundation type: Independent foundation.
Financial data (yr. ended 12/31/13): Assets, $994,492 (M); gifts received, $2,216,295; expenditures, $2,131,778; qualifying distributions, $2,131,589; giving activities include $2,131,589 for grants.
Purpose and activities: Giving primarily for the arts, education, the environment, health organizations, children, youth and social services, and to Christian and Protestant agencies and churches.
Fields of interest: Arts; Education; Environment, natural resources; Animals/wildlife; Health organizations, association; Medical research, institute; Boy scouts; Human services; American Red Cross; Children, services; Residential/custodial care, hospices; Foundations (private grantmaking); Foundations (community); Christian agencies & churches; Protestant agencies & churches.
Limitations: Applications not accepted. Giving primarily in NC and SC; some funding nationally, particularly in NJ and RI. No grants to individuals.
Application information: Contributes only to pre-selected organizations.
Officers: William Taylor, Pres.; Harry Emerson, V.P. and Secy.; Peyton Worley, V.P. and Treas.
EIN: 571124837
Selected grants: The following grants are a representative sample of this grantmaker's funding activity:
$1,200 to YMCA of Greater Charlotte, Charlotte, NC, 2012. For distribution.

8507
Waccamaw Community Foundation ✧
3655 S. Hwy. 17 Bus.
Murrells Inlet, SC 29576-6178 (843) 357-4483
Contact: David Bishop, Chair.
FAX: (843) 357-4457; E-mail: david@mywcf.org;
Main URL: http://www.waccamawcf.org
Facebook: https://www.facebook.com/WaccamawCF

Established in 1997 in SC as an affiliate of the Foundation For The Carolinas; became an independent community foundation in 1999.
Foundation type: Community foundation.
Financial data (yr. ended 12/31/13): Assets, $20,924,539 (M); gifts received, $1,965,518; expenditures, $1,877,082; giving activities include $1,328,141 for 64+ grants (high: $105,000).
Purpose and activities: The foundation uses distributions from various funds to award grants to many of the humanitarian, educational and cultural organizations in the community.
Fields of interest: Arts; Education; Environment; Animal welfare; Community/economic development; Children.
Type of support: Scholarship funds.
Limitations: Applications accepted. Giving limited to Georgetown and Horry, SC.
Publications: Application guidelines; Annual report; Financial statement; Informational brochure; Newsletter.
Application information: Visit foundation web site for application information and guidelines. Application form required.
Initial approach: Submit Concept Letter
Deadline(s): Quarterly
Officers and Board Members:* G. David Bishop,* Chair.; Scott W. Hutto,* Vice-Chair.; Muriel Ward O'Tuel, Ph.D.*, Secy.; Ruell L. Hicks, Jr.,* Treas.; Kathryn M. Cook, Exec. Dir.; Clyde W. Port, Emeritus; Cheryl Adamson; Frank J. Bullard III; John Draughn; William F. Drew, Jr.; Dr. Hal Holmes, Jr.; Otis Allen Jeffcoat III; Dennis Wade.
EIN: 562121992

8508
The WLT Foundation ✧
(formerly Wadley R. Glenn Foundation)
P.O. Box 16613
Greenville, SC 29606-7613

Established in SC.
Donors: W. Raoul Glenn, Jr.; Wadley R. Glenn III.
Foundation type: Independent foundation.
Financial data (yr. ended 12/31/13): Assets, $13,226,099 (M); expenditures, $1,187,714; qualifying distributions, $1,043,325; giving activities include $1,042,000 for 3 grants (high: $887,000; low: $5,000).
Purpose and activities: Giving primarily for children and youth services.
Fields of interest: Children/youth, services; Christian agencies & churches.
Limitations: Applications not accepted. Giving primarily in CO; some funding also in Greenville, SC. No grants to individuals.
Application information: Contributes only to pre-selected organizations.
Officer: W. Raoul Glenn, Jr., Chair.
Trustee: Wadley R. Glenn III.
EIN: 306016104

8509
Henry and Sylvia Yaschik Foundation Inc. ✧
P.O. Box 328
Charleston, SC 29402-0328
Application address: Paul Lynch, Secy.-Treas., c/o Moore and Van Allen Law Firm, 40 Calhoun St., Ste. 300, Charleston, SC 29401-3532, tel.: (843) 723-6464

Established in SC.
Donor: Henry Yaschik†.
Foundation type: Independent foundation.
Financial data (yr. ended 12/31/13): Assets, $11,750,447 (M); expenditures, $765,970; qualifying distributions, $715,184; giving activities include $621,500 for 79 grants (high: $60,000; low: $1,000).
Fields of interest: Arts; Human services; Jewish agencies & synagogues.
Limitations: Applications accepted. Giving limited to the Charleston, SC, area.
Application information: Application form required.
Initial approach: Letter
Deadline(s): Apr. 30
Officers: Howard B. Sherman, Chair.; Martin Perlmutter, Pres.; Paul M. Lynch, Secy.-Treas.
Board Member: Thomas M. Ervin.
EIN: 582281499
Selected grants: The following grants are a representative sample of this grantmaker's funding activity:
$8,800 to Avian Conservation Center, Charleston, SC, 2011. For general support.

8510
Jerry and Anita Zucker Family Foundation, Inc. ✧
4838 Jenkins Ave.
North Charleston, SC 29405-4816 (843) 744-5174

Established in 1996 in SC.
Donors: Jerry Zucker; Anita G. Zucker.
Foundation type: Independent foundation.
Financial data (yr. ended 12/31/13): Assets, $1,955,123 (M); gifts received, $1,394,571; expenditures, $1,955,116; qualifying distributions, $2,479,526; giving activities include $1,933,705 for 83 grants (high: $250,000; low: $40).
Fields of interest: Human services; Children/youth, services; Jewish federated giving programs; Jewish agencies & synagogues.
Limitations: Applications accepted. Giving primarily in CO and SC. No grants to individuals.
Application information: Application form required.
Initial approach: Grant application
Deadline(s): None
Directors: Anita G. Zucker; Jonathan M. Zucker.
EIN: 571061131

SOUTH DAKOTA

8511
Black Hills Area Community Foundation ✧ ☆
825 St. Joseph St., 3rd Fl.
P.O. Box 231
Rapid City, SD 57709 (605) 718-0112
Contact: Erin Green, Admin. Asst.
FAX: (605) 718-0113;
E-mail: bhacf@rushmore.com; Main URL: http://bhacf.org/
Facebook: https://www.facebook.com/BlackHillsAreaCommunityFoundation

Established in 1987 in SD.
Foundation type: Community foundation.
Financial data (yr. ended 12/31/13): Assets, $15,966,624 (M); gifts received, $4,990,459; expenditures, $1,888,618; giving activities include $1,131,923 for 19+ grants (high: $496,400), and $9,000 for 16 grants to individuals.
Fields of interest: Arts; Education; Human services; Economic development; Community/economic development.
Limitations: Applications accepted. Giving primarily in Butte, Lawrence, Meade, Pennington, Custer, and Fall River and the adjacent counties of Harding, Perkins, Haakon, Ziebach, Jackson, and Shannon, SD. No grants for operating deficits or to provide long-term operating support.
Publications: Annual report.
Application information: Visit foundation website for guideline information.
Initial approach: Contact foundation
Officers and Directors:* Karen Simmons-Parks,* Chair.; Brian Boyer; Erika Campbell; Casey Derflinger; Jane Farrell; Lia Green; Mike Guilbert, O.D.; Dr. Urla Marcus; Rob Mudge; Katherine Kinsman; Anna Merrill; James Olson; Bob Paulson; Richard Wahlstrom; Dr. Roger Wilson.
EIN: 363608635

8512
Branches Foundation ✧
401 E. 8th St., Ste. 319
Sioux Falls, SD 57103-7031

Established in 1999 in MN.
Donors: David O. Christianson; Julia Christianson; Trudy Christianson; Branches Charitable Annuity Trust; Gustafson 2003 Charitable Lead Annuity Trust; Branches 1999 Charitable Lead Annuity Trust; Tessa Christianson; David Christianson.
Foundation type: Independent foundation.
Financial data (yr. ended 12/31/13): Assets, $33,884,194 (M); gifts received, $1,146,114; expenditures, $1,855,353; qualifying distributions, $1,687,505; giving activities include $1,575,900 for 26 grants (high: $375,000; low: $500).
Fields of interest: Human services; Christian agencies & churches; Protestant agencies & churches.
Limitations: Applications not accepted. Giving in the U.S., with emphasis on CO and MN. No grants to individuals.
Application information: Contributes only to pre-selected organizations.
Trustees: Todd J. Christianson; Trudy A. Christianson.
EIN: 416463939

8513
Blythe Brenden-Mann Foundation ✧
(formerly Brenden-Mann Foundation)
401 E. 8th St., Ste. 319
Sioux Falls, SD 57103-7031
Main URL: http://www.blythebrendenmannfdn.org/
Facebook: https://www.facebook.com/blythebrendenmannfdn
LinkedIn: http://www.linkedin.com/company/3155222

Established in 2005 in SD.
Donor: The Tedd & Roberts Mann Foundation of Minnesota.
Foundation type: Independent foundation.
Financial data (yr. ended 12/31/12): Assets, $24,461,369 (M); expenditures, $1,447,104; qualifying distributions, $1,311,332; giving activities include $1,174,865 for 19 grants (high: $268,500; low: $465).
Fields of interest: Arts; Hospitals (general).
Limitations: Applications not accepted.
Application information: Unsolicited requests for funds not accepted.
Trustee: Dorsey & Whitney Trust Co., LLC.
EIN: 416546887

8514
Dakota Charitable Foundation, Inc. ✧
P.O. Box 8303
Rapid City, SD 57709-8303

Established in 1992 in SD.
Donors: Margaret Lally†; Ray Hillenbrand; and members of the Hillenbrand family.
Foundation type: Independent foundation.
Financial data (yr. ended 12/31/13): Assets, $72,862,693 (M); gifts received, $18,788,059; expenditures, $6,261,678; qualifying distributions, $5,034,304; giving activities include $4,966,100 for 24 grants (high: $2,560,000; low: $1,500).
Purpose and activities: Giving primarily for education and human services.
Fields of interest: Higher education; Education; Human services; Community/economic development; United Ways and Federated Giving Programs; Catholic agencies & churches.
Limitations: Applications not accepted. Giving primarily in Rapid City, SD. No grants to individuals.
Application information: Contributes only to pre-selected organizations.
Officer: Ray Hillenbrand, Mgr.
Directors: Gretchen Hillenbrand; Heidi Hillenbrand; Margaret Hillenbrand.
EIN: 460422869

8515
John D. & Edna Hofer Trust ✧
79 2nd St., S.W.
Huron, SD 57350-1903

Established in 2002 in SD.
Foundation type: Independent foundation.
Financial data (yr. ended 12/31/13): Assets, $16,376,527 (M); expenditures, $825,746; qualifying distributions, $751,963; giving activities include $722,700 for 7 grants (high: $173,200; low: $45,000).
Fields of interest: Human services; Salvation Army; Christian agencies & churches; Protestant agencies & churches; Catholic agencies & churches.
Limitations: Applications not accepted. Giving primarily in SD; some giving also in IA and NE. No grants to individuals.
Application information: Contributes only to pre-selected organizations.
Trustee: First National Bank South Dakota.
EIN: 466088580

8516
Larson Foundation ✧
2333 Eastbrook Dr.
Brookings, SD 57006-2899 (605) 692-6115
Contact: Maree Larson, Secy.

Established in 1990 in SD.
Donors: O. Dale Larson; Patricia Larson; Maree Larson; Bridget Larson Ennevor; Carmelle Jackson; Larson Manufacturing Co. of SD, Inc.
Foundation type: Independent foundation.
Financial data (yr. ended 04/30/13): Assets, $13,460,077 (M); gifts received, $960,000; expenditures, $1,204,123; qualifying distributions, $1,156,631; giving activities include $1,156,631 for grants.
Fields of interest: Arts; Higher education; Housing/shelter, development; Recreation, parks/playgrounds; Human services; Children/youth, services; United Ways and Federated Giving Programs.
Type of support: Continuing support; Annual campaigns; Capital campaigns; Building/renovation; Endowments; Program development; Scholarship funds; Employee matching gifts; Matching/challenge support.
Limitations: Applications accepted. Giving primarily in SD, with emphasis on Brookings.
Publications: Application guidelines.
Application information: Application form required.
Initial approach: Request application form
Copies of proposal: 7
Deadline(s): Mar. 1 and Sept. 1
Board meeting date(s): Semiannually
Officers: Patricia M. Larson, Pres.; O. Dale Larson, V.P.; Maree Larson, Secy.
EIN: 460412311
Selected grants: The following grants are a representative sample of this grantmaker's funding activity:
$200,000 to Childrens Inn, Sioux Falls, SD, 2012. For construction and renovations.
$100,000 to Teach for America, Pierre, SD, 2013. For program support.
$92,000 to United Way, Brookings Area, Brookings, SD, 2013. For matching grant for Larson employee donations.
$90,000 to Boys and Girls Club of Brookings, Brookings, SD, 2012. For program support.
$90,000 to Boys and Girls Club of Brookings, Brookings, SD, 2013. For program support.
$83,301 to United Way, Brookings Area, Brookings, SD, 2012. For employee matching grant.
$75,000 to South Dakota Public Broadcasting, Vermillion, SD, 2013. For Family Reading Project.
$74,000 to Red Cloud Indian School, Pine Ridge, SD, 2013. To provide healthy meals to students.
$60,000 to Red Cloud Indian School, Pine Ridge, SD, 2012. To provide healthy meals to students.

$50,000 to Black Hills Playhouse, Custer, SD, 2013. For renovations.
$50,000 to Habitat for Humanity, Brookings Area, Brookings, SD, 2013. To construct a house.
$50,000 to Lutherans Outdoors in South Dakota, Sioux Falls, SD, 2013. For riding program and playground equipment.
$41,698 to United Way of North Central Iowa, Mason City, IA, 2012. For employee match grant.
$32,000 to Habitat for Humanity, South Dakota, Brookings, SD, 2012. For neighborhood revitalization.
$25,000 to Brookings Domestic Abuse Shelter, Brookings, SD, 2013. For facility upgrade and for outreach.
$25,000 to Girl Scouts of the U.S.A., Dakota Horizons Council, Sioux Falls, SD, 2013. For program support.
$25,000 to Somali Bantu Community Development Council of Denver, Denver, CO, 2012. For program support.
$25,000 to YMCA, Aberdeen Family, Aberdeen, SD, 2012. For Youth Development Center.
$20,000 to Habitat for Humanity, Brookings Area, Brookings, SD, 2012. For ReStore Truck.
$16,000 to ECCO, Inc., Madison, SD, 2012. For program support.

8517
The Mark and Mary Ellen Nylen Foundation, Inc. ✧ ☆
P.O. Box 649
North Sioux City, SD 57049-0649

Established in 2006 in SD.
Donors: Mark A. Nylen; Mary Ellen Nylen.
Foundation type: Independent foundation.
Financial data (yr. ended 05/31/13): Assets, $21,327 (M); gifts received, $516,000; expenditures, $516,000; qualifying distributions, $516,000; giving activities include $516,000 for 2 grants (high: $266,000; low: $250,000).
Fields of interest: Health organizations; Human services.
Limitations: Applications not accepted.
Application information: Unsolicited requests for funds not accepted.
Officers and Directors:* Mary Ellen Nylen,* Pres. and Treas.; Mark A. Nylen,* V.P. and Secy.; Irene Schrunk.
EIN: 204322232
Selected grants: The following grants are a representative sample of this grantmaker's funding activity:
$100,000 to Camp High Hopes, Sioux City, IA, 2011.
$100,000 to June E. Nylen Cancer Center, Sioux City, IA, 2011.

8518
Opus Prize Foundation ✧
(formerly Alpha & Omega Family Foundation)
c/o Adler Trust Co.
401 E. 8th St., Ste. 250A
Sioux Falls, SD 57103-7034

Established in 1994 in SD.
Foundation type: Independent foundation.
Financial data (yr. ended 12/31/12): Assets, $27,361,754 (M); expenditures, $1,535,142; qualifying distributions, $1,520,012; giving activities include $1,313,000 for 10 grants (high: $1,000,000; low: $2,500).
Purpose and activities: Giving primarily for human services.
Fields of interest: Education; Human services; Catholic federated giving programs; Economically disadvantaged.
International interests: Brazil; Colombia; Jamaica; Malawi; Mexico; Morocco.
Type of support: General/operating support; Capital campaigns; Program development.
Limitations: Applications not accepted. Giving in the U.S., as well as internationally. No grants to individuals.
Application information: Contributes only to pre-selected organizations.
Officers and Directors:* Michael Rauenhorst,* Pres.; Suzanne Flannigan,* V.P.; Loretta Rauenhorst,* Secy.; Kristine Rauenhorst,* Treas.; Janine Geske; Katherine Marshall; Jeff Turner.
EIN: 460434399

8519
Raft Charitable Foundation ✧
401 E. 8th St., Ste. 319
Sioux Falls, SD 57103-7031

Established in MN.
Donors: Raft Charitable Foundation; Raft 2003 Charitable Lead Annuity Trust; Raft 1999 Charitable Lead Annuity Trust.
Foundation type: Independent foundation.
Financial data (yr. ended 12/31/13): Assets, $26,940,225 (M); gifts received, $895,996; expenditures, $853,624; qualifying distributions, $747,305; giving activities include $661,000 for 22 grants (high: $80,000; low: $1,000).
Fields of interest: Arts; Higher education; Libraries/library science; Human services; American Red Cross; Salvation Army.
Limitations: Applications not accepted. Giving primarily in MN.
Application information: Contributes only to pre-selected organizations.
Trustees: Faye L. Youngren; Dorsey & Whitney Trust Co. LLC.
EIN: 376439235

8520
C. H. Robinson Worldwide Foundation ✧
401 E. Eighth Street, Ste. 319
Sioux Falls, SD 57103-7031 (952) 683-3432
Contact: Kristi Nichols
E-mail: foundation@chrobinson.com; Application address: 14701 Charlson Rd., Ste. 1750, Eden Prairie, MN 55347; Main URL: http://www.chrobinson.com/en/us/About-Us/Corporate-Responsibility/Foundation/

Established in 2005 in MN.
Donor: C.H. Robinson Worldwide, Inc.
Foundation type: Company-sponsored foundation.
Financial data (yr. ended 12/31/12): Assets, $10,775,360 (M); expenditures, $1,428,707; qualifying distributions, $1,375,173; giving activities include $1,325,406 for 195 grants (high: $300,050; low: $25).
Purpose and activities: The foundation supports programs designed to expand educational success for at-risk youth; prevent hunger and provide food assistance; improve access to affordable housing; support the immediate living needs of people in crisis; and promote health research, prevention, and treatment.
Fields of interest: Education; Hospitals (general); Health care, clinics/centers; Health care, patient services; Health care; Food services; Food banks; Housing/shelter; American Red Cross; YM/YWCAs & YM/YWHAs; Children/youth, services; Family services; Homeless, human services; Human services; United Ways and Federated Giving Programs; Youth.
Type of support: General/operating support; Continuing support; Capital campaigns; Building/renovation; Program development; Seed money; Technical assistance; Employee matching gifts; Employee-related scholarships.
Limitations: Applications accepted. Giving primarily in areas of company operations in MN, with emphasis on the Minneapolis-St. Paul metropolitan area. No support for political organizations or religious organizations not of direct benefit to the entire community.
Publications: Application guidelines; Grants list.
Application information: Grants range from $1,000 to $25,000. Priority is given to organizations with current C.H. Robinson employee involvement.
Initial approach: E-mail letter of inquiry
Copies of proposal: 1
Deadline(s): None
Board meeting date(s): Quarterly
Officers: Angela K. Freeman, Pres.; Ben G. Campbell, Secy.; Troy A. Renner, Treas.
EIN: 680599299

8521
Sioux Falls Area Community Foundation ✧
200 N. Cherapa Pl.
Sioux Falls, SD 57103 (605) 336-7055
Contact: Andy Patterson, Pres.; For grants: Patrick Gale, Prog. Off.
FAX: (605) 336-0038; E-mail: chanson@sfacf.org; Letter of inquiry e-mail: pgale@sfacf.org; Main URL: http://www.sfacf.org

Established in 1984 in SD.
Foundation type: Community foundation.
Financial data (yr. ended 06/30/13): Assets, $100,675,247 (M); gifts received, $13,921,843; expenditures, $9,299,722; giving activities include $7,788,003 for 136+ grants (high: $669,000), and $217,409 for 127 grants to individuals.
Purpose and activities: The foundation advances philanthropy in the 4-county area by attracting, managing & distributing charitable funds.
Fields of interest: Museums; Performing arts, dance; Performing arts, theater; Performing arts, music; Humanities; Historic preservation/historical societies; Arts; Libraries/library science; Education; Environment, pollution control; Environment, water pollution; Environment, waste management; Environment, energy; Environment; Animals/wildlife, preservation/protection; Health care; Substance abuse, prevention; Mental health/crisis services; Medical research; Employment, training; Family services; Human services; Economic development; Community/economic development; Religion; Youth; Aging; Disabilities, people with; Women.
Type of support: Management development/capacity building; Conferences/seminars; Curriculum development; Equipment; General/operating support; Matching/challenge support; Program development; Program evaluation;

Research; Scholarship funds; Scholarships—to individuals; Seed money; Technical assistance.
Limitations: Applications accepted. Giving generally limited to Lincoln, McCook, Minnehaha, and Turner counties and communities within a 75-mile radius of Sioux Falls, SD. No support for sectarian religious purposes. No grants to individuals (except for scholarships), or for capital or construction drives, ongoing operating support, reducing or eliminating organizational debts or deficits, staff salaries (except in conjunction with a new program), endowments, telephone solicitations, or national fundraising efforts.
Publications: Application guidelines; Annual report; Financial statement; Grants list; Newsletter.
Application information: Visit foundation web site for application forms, guidelines, and specific deadlines. Grant requests of under $2,500 do not require an application form. Scholarship application forms available online after Dec. 15, annually. Application form required.
Initial approach: Submit Letter of Intent
Copies of proposal: 14
Deadline(s): Jan. 1 and Mar. 1 for grants $2,500 and up; none for grants less than $2,500
Board meeting date(s): Bimonthly
Officers and Directors:* Dr. Michael Olson,* Chair.; Tom McDowell,* Vice-Chair.; Andy Patterson, Pres.; Douglas J. Hajek,* Secy.; Gina Jahr, V.P., Devel.; Martha Carlson,* Treas.; Mike Finnegan, Cont.; Holly Brunick; Greg Carmon; Scott Christensen; Sara Crosby; John Henkhaus; Jay Huizenga; Angeline Lavin; Mary Jo Murray; Susie Patrick; Jeff Strand; Jayna Voss.
Number of staff: 4 full-time professional; 4 full-time support; 1 part-time support.
EIN: 311748533

8522
South Dakota Community Foundation ✧
1714 North Lincoln Ave.
P.O. Box 296
Pierre, SD 57501 (605) 224-1025
Contact: Stephanie Judson, Pres.
FAX: (605) 224-5364;
E-mail: stephj16@sdcommunityfoundation.org; Additional tel.: (800) 888-1842; Main URL: http://www.sdcommunityfoundation.org

Incorporated in 1987 in SD.
Foundation type: Community foundation.
Financial data (yr. ended 12/31/12): Assets, $152,369,276 (M); gifts received, $11,957,731; expenditures, $4,810,805; giving activities include $3,737,662 for grants.
Purpose and activities: The foundation seeks to promote philanthropy, receive, and administer charitable gifts and invest in a wide range of programs promoting the social and economic well-being of the people of SD.
Fields of interest: Arts; Education; Health care; Health organizations, association; Youth development, citizenship; Human services; Economic development; Community/economic development; United Ways and Federated Giving Programs; Public affairs, citizen participation; Minorities; Native Americans/American Indians; Economically disadvantaged.
Type of support: Income development; Capital campaigns; Building/renovation; Endowments; Publication; Seed money; Curriculum development; Research; Technical assistance; Scholarships—to individuals; Matching/challenge support.
Limitations: Applications accepted. Giving limited to SD. No grants to individuals (except for scholarships), or for operating expenses; no loans.
Publications: Application guidelines; Annual report; Financial statement; Grants list; Informational brochure; Newsletter; Program policy statement.
Application information: Visit foundation web site application guidelines. Application form required.
Initial approach: Complete eGrant Letter of Inquiry
Copies of proposal: 1
Deadline(s): None
Board meeting date(s): May and Nov.
Final notification: Within 15 business days for letter of inquiry decision; 45-60 days for grant notification
Officers and Directors:* Al Kurtenbach,* Chair.; Stephanie Judson, Pres.; Patricia Adam; David Anderson; Beth Benning; Bruce Brandner; Muffy Christen; Dale Christensen; Janet B. Cronin; Jeff Erickson; Charles Hart; Jim Hart; Blake Hoffman; Trudy Morgan; Steve Myers; Anita Nachtigal; Stanley Porch; John Porter; Norbert Sebade; Peg Seljeskog; Curt Wischmeier.
Number of staff: 2 full-time professional; 1 part-time professional; 1 full-time support.
EIN: 460398115

8523
South Dakota Education Access Foundation ✧
115 1st Ave. S.W.
Aberdeen, SD 57401-4124 (888) 502-5902, ext. 3035
FAX: (800) 354-7070; E-mail: cwold@glhec.org; Main URL: http://www.sdeducationaccess.org

Established in 2009 in SD.
Donor: Great Lakes Higher Education Guaranty Corporation.
Foundation type: Independent foundation.
Financial data (yr. ended 12/31/12): Assets, $41,365,841 (M); gifts received, $431,203; expenditures, $2,170,775; qualifying distributions, $1,952,478; giving activities include $1,845,900 for 29 grants (high: $371,800; low: $900).
Purpose and activities: The foundation seeks to provide scholarships for postsecondary education and to donate to programs at higher education institutions and other nonprofit agencies that help people access the same.
Fields of interest: Higher education; Education.
Type of support: Scholarship funds.
Limitations: Giving limited to SD. No support for religious or political activities. No grants for capital campaigns, endowments, equipment, corporate sponsorships or fundraising events.
Publications: Application guidelines.
Application information:
Initial approach: SD colleges and universities may submit a proposal
Officers: Rod Fouberg, Co-Pres.; Clark Wold, Co-Pres.; Kae McNeil, Secy. - Treas.
Directors: Mike Duch; Kristen Fauth; Dennis Hagny; Chris Jung; Patti Mesmer; Cindi Walsh.
EIN: 263941129

8524
John T. Vucurevich Foundation ✧
2800 Jackson Blvd., Ste. 410
Rapid City, SD 57702-3477 (605) 343-3141
Contact: Sandy Diegel, Exec. Dir.; Paul Phelan, C.F.O.
FAX: (605) 343-5264; E-mail: sdiegel@jtvf.org; Main URL: http://www.jtvf.org
Grants List: http://www.jtvf.org/index.php?page=grants

Established in 1985 in SD; reincorporated in 2007.
Donor: John T. Vucurevich†.
Foundation type: Independent foundation.
Financial data (yr. ended 12/31/13): Assets, $108,879,936 (M); expenditures, $4,987,213; qualifying distributions, $4,838,294; giving activities include $4,181,032 for 78 grants (high: $500,000; low: $218), and $141,589 for foundation-administered programs.
Purpose and activities: The foundation has the following priorities: 1) To identify scholarship needs for critical shortage professions and retention of South Dakota's best students; 2) Reduce dropout rates, truancy and bullying; 3) To increase access to affordable health and dental care ; 4) To increase access to affordable mental health and substance abuse services, and to promote suicide prevention; 5) Increase affordable housing opportunities, and 6) To increase community transportation availability.
Fields of interest: Education; Health care; Mental health/crisis services; Housing/shelter, development; Human services; Children/youth, services; United Ways and Federated Giving Programs.
Type of support: General/operating support; Continuing support; Management development/capacity building; Capital campaigns; Building/renovation; Equipment; Emergency funds; Program development; Scholarship funds; Matching/challenge support.
Limitations: Applications accepted. Giving primarily in western SD, with emphasis on Rapid City and the Black Hills. No support for programs with religious content, for international organizations or to organizations that have been in existence for fewer than 5 years; no support also for museums, or for animal-related programs. No grants to individuals or for benefit events, sporting activities, publications, video and film production, camp development and infrastructure, or endowments.
Publications: Application guidelines.
Application information: Full applications are by invitation, upon review of initial Letter of Inquiry. Application form required.
Initial approach: Letter of Inquiry via e-mail or U.S. mail
Copies of proposal: 6
Deadline(s): None, for letters; Mar. 1, June 1, Sept. 1, and Dec. 1, for full applications
Board meeting date(s): Quarterly, and as needed
Final notification: Within 2 months
Officers: Paul Phelan, C.F.O.; Sandy Diegel, Exec. Dir.
Directors: Eric John Abrahamson; Dale Clement; Steven Flanery; Renee Parker; Lawrence Piersol; Thomas Vucurevich; Steve Zellmer.
Number of staff: 4 full-time professional.
EIN: 203326026
Selected grants: The following grants are a representative sample of this grantmaker's funding activity:
$500,000 to Feeding South Dakota, Sioux Falls, SD, 2013. For Hand in Hand Campaign.

$475,000 to Compass Point, Sturgis, SD, 2012. For building and renovations.
$400,000 to Main Street Square, Rapid City, SD, 2012. For Main Street Square Granite Sculpture Project.
$275,000 to Behavior Management Systems, Rapid City, SD, 2013. For New Start Program.
$250,000 to Community Health Center of the Black Hills, Rapid City, SD, 2013. For New Facility.
$250,000 to Habitat for Humanity, Black Hills Area, Rapid City, SD, 2013. For Volunteer Training and Administration Facility.
$250,000 to Teach for America, Mission, SD, 2012. For work of South Dakota Corps.
$215,000 to Rapid City Regional Hospital, Rapid City, SD, 2013. For Outpatient Palliative Care Team.
$200,000 to Rapid City Area Schools, Rapid City, SD, 2013. For Library Civil Discourse Project.
$150,000 to Cornerstone Rescue Mission, Rapid City, SD, 2012. For kitchen remodeling.
$150,000 to Wellspring, Rapid City, SD, 2013. For Boys Residential Treatment Program.
$104,750 to Rapid City Fire Department, Rapid City, SD, 2013. For Rapid City Community Paramedic Program.
$100,000 to Youth and Family Services, Rapid City, SD, 2013. For Intensive Family Services Program.
$82,500 to Catholic Social Services, Rapid City, SD, 2012. For Lakota Circles of Hope, culturally specific prevention curriculum that teaches elementary school students how to use their culture to deal more effectively with risky behaviors such as drugs, alcohol, tobacco usage, bullying and suicide. The curriculum is intended to foster a positive Lakota identity and enhance students understanding of Lakota culture.
$50,000 to Action for the Betterment of Our Community, Sturgis, SD, 2012. For ABC Afterschool Program.
$50,000 to Boys Club of Rapid City, Rapid City, SD, 2012. For general operating support.
$50,000 to YMCA of Rapid City, Rapid City, SD, 2012. For Jump Start Day Care.
$39,604 to Northern Hills Alliance for Children, Deadwood, SD, 2013. For First Step Child Care Center.
$18,500 to Belle Fourche School District Foundation, Belle Fourche, SD, 2012. For Career and Technical Education Program.
$16,000 to Allied Arts Fund Drive, Rapid City, SD, 2012. For Allied Arts Fund Drive.

TENNESSEE

8525
Adams Family Foundation I ✧
2217 Battleground Dr.
Murfreesboro, TN 37129-6006 (615) 890-2020
Contact: Robert G. Adams, Tr.

Established in 1993.
Donors: Carl E. Adams; Jennie Mae Adams; W. Andrew Adams; Gerald Coggin.
Foundation type: Independent foundation.
Financial data (yr. ended 12/31/13): Assets, $8,503,991 (M); expenditures, $423,679; qualifying distributions, $423,679; giving activities include $419,750 for 43 grants (high: $136,000; low: $500).
Fields of interest: Arts; Elementary/secondary education; Higher education, university; Human services; Children/youth, services; Christian agencies & churches.
Type of support: General/operating support.
Limitations: Applications accepted. Giving primarily in TN.
Application information: Application form required.
Initial approach: Letter
Deadline(s): None
Trustees: Alan B. Adams; Carl Adams; Fred Adams; W. Andrew Adams; Joanne Coggin.
EIN: 621515107

8526
Adams Family Foundation II ✧
801 Mooreland Ln.
Murfreesboro, TN 37128-4634 (615) 848-0171
Contact: W. Andrew Adams, Tr.

Established in 1993 in TN.
Donors: W. Andrew Adams; East Main Assoc.
Foundation type: Independent foundation.
Financial data (yr. ended 12/31/13): Assets, $17,872,092 (M); expenditures, $1,138,493; qualifying distributions, $1,133,592; giving activities include $1,132,923 for 44 grants (high: $313,000; low: $150).
Fields of interest: Secondary school/education; Education; Boys & girls clubs; Boy scouts; Human services; Children/youth, services; Christian agencies & churches.
Limitations: Applications accepted. Giving limited to the southeast, primarily in TN.
Application information: Application form required.
Initial approach: Letter
Deadline(s): None
Trustees: Andrew Adams; Anthony A. Adams; Dorothy Adams; W. Andrew Adams.
EIN: 621515108

8527
Alumni Achievement Awards, Inc. ✧ ☆
7201 Shallowford Rd., Ste. 200
Chattanooga, TN 37421-2780 (423) 308-1855
Contact: Melanie Litchfield
E-mail: info@alumniawards.org; Main URL: http://alumniawards.org
Facebook: https://www.facebook.com/AlumniAwardsFoundation

Established in 2004 in TN.
Donors: I.M. Feldkemp; Arpad Soo; Gary Wilt; George T. Herding; Versa Cace Inc.; McKee Foods Corp.; Byron DeFoor; Dr. C.H. Dehaan; Dave Briscoe.
Foundation type: Operating foundation.
Financial data (yr. ended 06/30/13): Assets, $131,084 (M); gifts received, $1,041,171; expenditures, $990,551; qualifying distributions, $723,796; giving activities include $505,000 for 2 grants (high: $285,833; low: $219,167), and $40,000 for 20 grants to individuals (high: $2,000; low: $2,000).
Purpose and activities: Giving to inspire and reward excellence in Adventist K-12 schools, educators and alumni.
Fields of interest: Education.
Type of support: General/operating support; Scholarships—to individuals.
Limitations: Applications not accepted. Giving primarily in AZ.
Application information: Unsolicited requests for funds not accepted.
Officers: Dr. Robert B. Summerour, M.D., Chair.; Dave Briscoe, Treas.
Board Members: Dr. Joan Coggin; Byron DeFoor; Dr. Greg Gerard; Jeff Londis; John O'Brien; Kathy Proffitt; Arpad Soo; Keith White; Gary Wilt.
Director: Melanie Litchfield.
EIN: 592413171

8528
American Snuff Charitable Trust ✧
(formerly Conwood Charitable Trust)
c/o Regions Morgen Keegan
1100 Ridgeway Loop, Ste. 100
Memphis, TN 38120-4053 (901) 761-2050
Contact: Ed Roberson, Dir.
Additional address: 813 Ridgelake Blvd., Memphis, TN 38119, tel.: (901) 761-2050

Established in 1952 in TN.
Donors: American Snuff Co.; Conwood Co.
Foundation type: Company-sponsored foundation.
Financial data (yr. ended 12/31/13): Assets, $4,683,882 (M); expenditures, $498,675; qualifying distributions, $477,466; giving activities include $458,000 for 82 grants (high: $28,000; low: $500).
Purpose and activities: The trust supports food banks and organizations involved with education, health, housing development, human services, and religion.
Fields of interest: Higher education; Education; Health care, clinics/centers; Health care; Food banks; Housing/shelter, development; Children/youth, services; Family services; Residential/custodial care, hospices; Aging, centers/services; Developmentally disabled, centers & services; Human services; Christian agencies & churches; Religion.
Type of support: General/operating support; Capital campaigns; Building/renovation; Scholarship funds; Sponsorships.
Limitations: Applications accepted. Giving primarily in areas of company operations in Memphis, TN; limited giving in NC. No grants to individuals.
Application information: Application form required.
Initial approach: Proposal
Deadline(s): None
Director: Ed Roberson.
Trustee: Regions Bank.
EIN: 626036034
Selected grants: The following grants are a representative sample of this grantmaker's funding activity:
$5,000 to Boy Scouts of America, Chickasaw Council, Memphis, TN, 2012. For charitable donations.
$5,000 to Youth Villages, Memphis, TN, 2012. For charitable donations.
$3,500 to Boy Scouts of America, Middle Tn Council, Memphis, TN, 2012. For charitable donations.

8529
The Aslan Foundation ✧
4800 Old Kingston Pike, Ste. 100
Knoxville, TN 37919-6478 (865) 524-6360
Contact: Debbie Black, Admin. Dir.; Jeff Mansour, Exec. Dir.
FAX: (865) 588-4496; E-mail: debbie@tn-cf.org; Additional e-mail:Jeff@tn-cf.org

Established in 1995 in TN.
Donor: Lindsay Young.
Foundation type: Independent foundation.
Financial data (yr. ended 12/31/12): Assets, $95,687,327 (M); gifts received, $563,640; expenditures, $3,583,387; qualifying distributions, $4,518,283; giving activities include $2,407,357 for 43+ grants (high: $517,224), and $1,354,299 for foundation-administered programs.
Purpose and activities: Giving for child and family welfare, health care, literacy programs, and environmental preservation.
Fields of interest: Adult education—literacy, basic skills & GED; Environment, natural resources; Animal welfare; Health care; Children/youth, services; Family services.
Limitations: Applications accepted. Giving primarily in east TN.
Application information: Application form required.
Initial approach: Completed application form
Copies of proposal: 1
Deadline(s): 30 days before meeting
Board meeting date(s): June and Nov.
Officers and Directors:* Robert S. Young III,* Pres.; Lindsay Y. McDonough,* V.P.; Mark K. Williams,* Secy.; Jeff Mansour, Exec. Dir.; Debbie Black; Jim McDonough; Rachel P. Young.
Number of staff: 2 full-time professional.
EIN: 621520208

8530
The Assisi Foundation of Memphis, Inc. ✧
(formerly Assisi Foundation)
515 Erin Dr.
Memphis, TN 38117-4211 (901) 684-1564
Contact: Jan Young, Exec. Dir.
FAX: (901) 684-1997;
E-mail: jyoung@assisifoundation.org; Main URL: http://www.assisifoundation.org/

Established in 1994 in TN; converted from the sale of St. Francis Hospital.
Foundation type: Independent foundation.
Financial data (yr. ended 12/31/13): Assets, $228,227,005 (M); expenditures, $12,107,971; qualifying distributions, $10,444,883; giving activities include $9,780,971 for 63+ grants (high: $550,250).
Purpose and activities: The foundation supports health, lifelong learning, social justice and

responsible use of resources with respect and compassion for all.
Fields of interest: Education; Health care; Human services; Community/economic development; Social sciences, ethics; Social sciences, equal rights.
Type of support: General/operating support; Management development/capacity building; Capital campaigns; Equipment; Endowments; Emergency funds; Program development; Conferences/seminars; Publication; Curriculum development; Research; Technical assistance; Consulting services; Program evaluation; Matching/challenge support.
Limitations: Applications accepted. Giving primarily in the Greater Memphis area of Shelby, Fayette and Tipton Counties, TN; Crittenden County, AR and Desoto County, MS. No grants to individuals, fundraising, tickets for benefits, lobbying, budget deficits, or for tournament fees and/or travel for athletic competitions, scholarships or for replacement of government funding cuts.
Publications: Application guidelines.
Application information: See foundation's web site for additional information. Application form required.
Copies of proposal: 8
Deadline(s): Feb. 13, May 15, Aug. 14 and Nov. 13
Board meeting date(s): 4th Thurs. of Jan., Apr., July, and Oct.
Final notification: First week of Apr., July., Oct. and Jan.
Officers and Directors:* Lee J. Chase III,* Chair.; Martin F. Thompson,* Vice-Chair; Ronald Belz,* Secy.; Gary Joffe,* C.F.O.; William L. Zoccola, Treas.; Dr. Jan Young, Exec. Dir.; Dr. Susan M. Aguillard; Jack A. Belz; Michael J. Bruns; Fred L. Davis; Joseph Evangelisti; William E. Frulla; James J. Gattas; Art Gilliam; Harry Goldsmith; Robert D. Gooch III; Forrest N. Jenkins; Nancy C. Lanigan; Deborah O. Schadt, Ph.D.; Charles D. Schaffler; Thomas W. Scherer; Peggy I. Veeser, Ed.D.; C. Thomas Whitman; Philip R. Zanone, Jr.
Number of staff: 4 full-time professional; 1 part-time professional; 1 full-time support; 1 part-time support.
EIN: 621558722
Selected grants: The following grants are a representative sample of this grantmaker's funding activity:
$1,000,000 to Christian Brothers University, Memphis, TN, 2012. For capital campaign.
$878,585 to Saint Jude Childrens Research Hospital, Memphis, TN, 2012.
$520,000 to Streets Ministries, Memphis, TN, 2012.
$501,000 to Saint Louis Catholic Church, Memphis, TN, 2012.
$500,000 to Youth Villages, Memphis, TN, 2012.
$325,000 to Christ Community Health Services, Memphis, TN, 2012.
$300,000 to Opera Memphis, Memphis, TN, 2012.
$300,000 to Synergy Foundation, Memphis, TN, 2012.
$275,000 to Alliance for Nonprofit Excellence, Memphis, TN, 2012. For operating support.
$205,000 to University of Tennessee, Knoxville, TN, 2012.

8531
Atticus Trust ✧
(formerly The Atticus Foundation)
c/o Martin S. Brown, Jr., Tr.
424 Church St., Ste. 2800
Nashville, TN 37219-2386

Established in 1986 in TN.
Donor: Sara S. Brown.
Foundation type: Independent foundation.
Financial data (yr. ended 12/31/13): Assets, $17,676,497 (M); expenditures, $765,743; qualifying distributions, $628,000; giving activities include $628,000 for 64 grants (high: $100,000; low: $1,000).
Purpose and activities: Giving primarily for the arts, education, conservation, and to Episcopal organizations and churches; support also for a law center.
Fields of interest: Media, television; Media, radio; Visual arts; Museums (art); Performing arts; Historic preservation/historical societies; Arts; Education, public education; Higher education; Education; Environment, legal rights; Environment, natural resources; Environment; Animals/wildlife; Girl scouts; Human services; Children/youth, services; Family services; Residential/custodial care, hospices; United Ways and Federated Giving Programs; Protestant agencies & churches.
Limitations: Applications not accepted. Giving primarily in TN. No grants to individuals.
Application information: Contributes only to pre-selected organizations.
Trustee and Committee Members:* Elizabeth M. Brown; Martin S. Brown*; Martin S. Brown, Sr.; Margaret DeClercq; Susannah Scott-Barnes.
EIN: 581796390

8532
Ayers Foundation ✧
450 Tennessee Ave., Ste. 101
P.O. Box 217
Parsons, TN 38363-4615 (731) 847-4962
Contact: Janet Ayers, Pres.

Established in 1999 in TN.
Donors: James W. Ayers; Nancy Sharon Ayers; Jon Ayers; Sarah K. Givens; Tennessee Higher Education Assn.; Oasis Center.
Foundation type: Independent foundation.
Financial data (yr. ended 12/31/13): Assets, $3,268,563 (M); gifts received, $5,646,002; expenditures, $2,620,904; qualifying distributions, $2,105,985; giving activities include $2,105,985 for 51 grants (high: $990,000; low: $50).
Fields of interest: Higher education; Human services; Foundations (community).
Limitations: Applications accepted. Giving limited to Decatur and Henderson counties, TN. No grants to individuals.
Application information: Application form not required.
Initial approach: Proposal
Deadline(s): None
Officers: James W. Ayers, Chair.; Janet Ayers, Pres.; Clay Petrey, Secy.
Directors: Jon Ayers; Kristy Ayers; Agenia Clark; Lee Ann Ingram; Cassie Lynn; Joann Lynn.
EIN: 621773033

8533
Baptist Healing Hospital Trust ✧
(also known as Baptist Healing Trust)
2928 Sidco Dr.
Nashville, TN 37204-3758 (615) 284-8271
Contact: Kristen Keely-Dinger, V.P., Progs. & Grants
FAX: (615) 284-2683;
E-mail: info@healinghospital.org; Main URL: http://www.baptisthealingtrust.org
LinkedIn: http://www.linkedin.com/company/baptist-healing-trust

Established in 2002; converted from the sale of the Baptist Hospital System to Ascension Health Systems.
Foundation type: Independent foundation.
Financial data (yr. ended 12/31/12): Assets, $117,384,024 (M); expenditures, $5,115,661; qualifying distributions, $5,710,997; giving activities include $3,961,350 for 144 grants (high: $323,860; low: $100).
Purpose and activities: The trust supports organizations that offer a holistic and loving approach to health care. It seeks to increase the access of underprivileged populations to appropriate and affordable health care and to support and enhance the success of the nonprofit organizations it funds by offering funding and consulting to organizations to promote cultures centered on compassionate care.
Fields of interest: Holistic medicine; Health care; Mental health/crisis services; Infants/toddlers; Children/youth; Youth; Adults; Aging; Young adults; Disabilities, people with; Physically disabled; Deaf/hearing impaired; Mentally disabled; Minorities; African Americans/Blacks; Hispanics/Latinos; Native Americans/American Indians; Military/veterans; Offenders/ex-offenders; Substance abusers; AIDS, people with; Crime/abuse victims; Terminal illness, people with; Immigrants/refugees; Economically disadvantaged; Homeless.
Type of support: General/operating support; Continuing support; Emergency funds; Program development; Technical assistance.
Limitations: Applications accepted. Giving limited to middle TN, and serve at least one of the forty counties in Middle TN (list of counties available on foundation web site). No support for fraternal organization or political parties. No grants to individuals.
Publications: Application guidelines; Grants list; Informational brochure.
Application information: Application form required.
Initial approach: New applicants are required to attend an introduction workshop. See foundation web site for specific details
Deadline(s): Jan., Apr., July, and Oct.
Board meeting date(s): June and Dec.
Final notification: 2 months
Officers: Catherine Self, P.T., Ph.D., C.E.O. and Pres.; Kristen Keely-Dinger, V.P., Progs. and Grants; Matt Deeb, C.F.O.
Number of staff: 6 full-time professional.
EIN: 522362225

8534
Alvin and Sally Beaman Foundation ✧
c/o Larry T. Thrailkill
P.O. Box 2408
Brentwood, TN 37024-2408

Established in 1998 in TN.
Donor: Sally M. Beaman.

Foundation type: Independent foundation.
Financial data (yr. ended 12/31/13): Assets, $20,653,024 (M); expenditures, $1,086,079; qualifying distributions, $931,000; giving activities include $931,000 for 43 grants (high: $250,000; low: $2,500).
Purpose and activities: Giving primarily for children, youth, and social services; funding also for higher education, and health.
Fields of interest: Performing arts, orchestras; Higher education; Health organizations, association; Boy scouts; Youth development; Human services; American Red Cross; Children/youth, services; Family services; Christian agencies & churches.
Type of support: General/operating support; Continuing support; Annual campaigns; Capital campaigns; Building/renovation.
Limitations: Applications not accepted. Giving primarily in Nashville, TN. No grants to individuals.
Application information: Unsolicited requests for funds not accepted.
Board meeting date(s): Quarterly
Officers and Trustees:* Lee A. Beaman,* Pres.; Kelley S. Beaman,* V.P.; Larry T. Thrailkill,* Secy.
EIN: 621743008
Selected grants: The following grants are a representative sample of this grantmaker's funding activity:
$100,000 to Baptist Hospital Foundation, Nashville, TN, 2011.

8535
Benwood Foundation, Inc. ✧
736 Market St., Ste. 1600
Chattanooga, TN 37402-4807
Contact: Sarah H. Morgan, Pres.
FAX: (423) 267-9049;
E-mail: smorgan@benwood.org; Main URL: http://www.benwood.org
Facebook: http://www.facebook.com/pages/Chattanooga-TN/The-Benwood-Foundation/35114638807
Gaining Ground Facebook: http://www.facebook.com/pages/Gaining-Ground-Chattanooga/403992784713
Gaining Ground Twitter: http://twitter.com/GainGroundCHA
Grants List: http://www.benwood.org/pages/Grants-Awarded/

Incorporated in 1944 in DE, and 1945 in TN.
Donor: George Thomas Hunter‡.
Foundation type: Independent foundation.
Financial data (yr. ended 12/31/12): Assets, $105,162,018 (M); expenditures, $6,583,538; qualifying distributions, $5,934,381; giving activities include $4,209,144 for 129 grants (high: $1,000,000; low: $1,000).
Purpose and activities: The foundation seeks to stimulate creative and innovative efforts to build and strengthen the Chattanooga, TN community.
Fields of interest: Performing arts; Humanities; Arts; Education, early childhood education; Secondary school/education; Environment; Economic development; Urban/community development.
Type of support: Program-related investments/loans; Management development/capacity building; Land acquisition; Continuing support; Capital campaigns; Building/renovation; Equipment; Program development; Conferences/seminars; Seed money; Scholarship funds; Technical assistance; Matching/challenge support.
Limitations: Applications not accepted. Giving primarily in the Chattanooga, TN, area. No support for political organizations or causes. No grants to individuals, financial deficits, fundraising, or endowments, no loans (except for program-related investments).
Application information: Contributes only to selected organizations.
Board meeting date(s): Jan., Apr., July, and Oct.
Officers and Trustees:* Robert J. Sudderth, Jr.,* Chair.; Sebert Brewer, Jr.,* Vice-Chair.; Sarah H. Morgan, Pres.; Martha T. Robinson,* Secy.; Paul K. Brock, Jr.,* Treas.; William H. Chapin.
Number of staff: 4 full-time professional; 2 full-time support.
EIN: 620476283
Selected grants: The following grants are a representative sample of this grantmaker's funding activity:
$1,000,000 to University of Chattanooga Foundation, Chattanooga, TN, 2012. For SimCenter.
$500,000 to Open Space Conservancy, New York, NY, 2012. For Protecting Wildlife of Southern Cumberland Plateau Initiative.
$250,000 to Hamilton County Department of Education, Chattanooga, TN, 2012. For implementation of strategic plan.
$157,000 to Community Foundation of Greater Chattanooga, Chattanooga, TN, 2012. For Challenges and Opportunities Fund.
$100,000 to Chamber Foundation of Chattanooga, Chattanooga, TN, 2012. For Regional Growth Initiative.
$100,000 to Lula Lake Land Trust, Lookout Mountain, GA, 2012. For Revolving Land Acquisition Fund.
$50,000 to Co.Lab, Chattanooga, TN, 2012. For program support.
$40,000 to Trust for Public Land, National Office, San Francisco, CA, 2012. For information to complete North and South Chickamauga Creek Greenways.
$34,775 to Community Foundation of Greater Chattanooga, Chattanooga, TN, 2012. For Normal Park Museum Magnet Fund Great Start at Normal Park Summer Program.
$15,000 to Community Foundation of Southern New Mexico, Las Cruces, NM, 2012. For Grant County Education Fund.

8536
Blankemeyer Foundation Inc. ✧
190 Bay Pointe Dr.
Vonore, TN 37885-5383
Application address: c/o Mary Brinkman, Secy., 3034 Legacy Pointe Way, Apt. 93B, Knoxville, TN 37921; tel.: (864) 884-5891

Established in 1994 in OH.
Donors: James C. Blankemeyer; National Christian Foundation.
Foundation type: Independent foundation.
Financial data (yr. ended 12/31/12): Assets, $18,671 (M); gifts received, $1,300,000; expenditures, $1,379,731; qualifying distributions, $1,287,434; giving activities include $1,287,434 for grants.
Purpose and activities: Giving primarily to Christian organizations and ministries.
Fields of interest: Christian agencies & churches.
Limitations: Applications accepted. Giving primarily in IN, MD, MI, and PA. No grants to individuals.
Application information: Application form required.
Initial approach: Letter
Deadline(s): None
Officers: James C. Blankemeyer, Pres.; Carolyn Blankemeyer, V.P.; Mary Brinkman, Secy.
Director: Julie Bridenbaugh.
EIN: 582086417

8537
The Bridgestone Americas Trust Fund ✧
(formerly The Bridgestone/Firestone Trust Fund)
535 Marriott Dr.
Nashville, TN 37214-5092 (615) 937-1415
Contact: Bernice Csaszar, Admin.
FAX: (615) 937-1414;
E-mail: bfstrustfund@bfusa.com; Main URL: http://www.bridgestone-firestone.com/community/trustfund/index.html

Trust established in 1952 in OH.
Donors: The Firestone Tire and Rubber Co.; Bridgestone/Firestone, Inc.; Bridgestone Americas Holding, Inc.; Bridgestone Americas, Inc.
Foundation type: Company-sponsored foundation.
Financial data (yr. ended 12/31/13): Assets, $21,961,928 (M); expenditures, $2,702,507; qualifying distributions, $2,589,796; giving activities include $2,478,743 for 788 grants (high: $69,955; low: $49).
Purpose and activities: The foundation supports organizations involved with arts and culture, agriculture, housing development, disaster relief, automotive safety, human services, and the automotive industry. Special emphasis is directed towards programs designed to address education; the environment and conservation; and children.
Fields of interest: Media, television; Media, radio; Performing arts, orchestras; Performing arts, opera; Arts; Higher education; Scholarships/financial aid; Education; Environment, natural resources; Environment; Agriculture; Housing/shelter, development; Disasters, preparedness/services; Safety, automotive safety; YM/YWCAs & YM/YWHAs; Children, services; Human services; Business/industry; United Ways and Federated Giving Programs; Children.
Type of support: General/operating support; Continuing support; Annual campaigns; Capital campaigns; Building/renovation; Endowments; Emergency funds; Program development; Scholarship funds; Research; Sponsorships; Employee matching gifts; Employee-related scholarships; Matching/challenge support.
Limitations: Applications accepted. Giving on a national basis, with emphasis on areas of company operations in AR, IN, OH, and TN; giving also to regional and national organizations. No support for partisan political organizations, discriminatory organizations, or religious organizations not of direct benefit to the entire community. No grants to individuals (except for employee-related scholarships), or for debt reduction, equipment, land acquisition, or publications; no loans.
Publications: Application guidelines; Grants list.
Application information: Proposals should be no longer than 2 pages. Application form not required.
Initial approach: Proposal to nearest company facility; proposal to foundation for national organizations
Copies of proposal: 1

Deadline(s): None
Board meeting date(s): As required
Officer and Committee Members:* Christine Karbowiak,* Chair.; David Dumas; Truman Hyde; Eugene Stephens.
Trustee: KeyBank N.A.
Number of staff: 1 full-time support.
EIN: 346505181
Selected grants: The following grants are a representative sample of this grantmaker's funding activity:
$195,050 to National Merit Scholarship Corporation, Evanston, IL, 2011.
$61,200 to National FFA Foundation, Indianapolis, IN, 2011.
$50,020 to United Way of Summit County, Akron, OH, 2011.
$34,210 to Lost Boys Foundation of Nashville, Nashville, TN, 2011.
$29,135 to Nashville Public Radio, Nashville, TN, 2011.
$9,000 to Tennessee Performing Arts Center, Nashville, TN, 2011.
$6,000 to New England Institute of Technology, Warwick, RI, 2011.
$3,000 to Boy Scouts of America, Caddo Area Council, Texarkana, TX, 2011.
$2,500 to Main Street Community Foundation, Bristol, CT, 2011.
$2,500 to Youth Villages, Nashville, TN, 2011.

8538
Thomas W. Briggs Foundation, Inc. ✧
c/o The Cresent Ctr.
6075 Poplar Ave., Ste. 330
Memphis, TN 38119-0114 (901) 680-0276
Contact: Margaret Craddock, Exec. Dir.
E-mail: twbriggs@aol.com; Main URL: http://www.thomaswbriggsfoundation.com

Established in 1957.
Donors: Thomas W. Briggs Residuary Trust; Isabell Bateman†.
Foundation type: Independent foundation.
Financial data (yr. ended 09/30/13): Assets, $15,531,145 (M); expenditures, $984,190; qualifying distributions, $775,245; giving activities include $688,025 for 47 grants (high: $75,000; low: $25).
Purpose and activities: The focus of the foundation's funding includes youth projects and programs, education, social services, arts and cultural organizations and civic organizations that promote quality of life.
Fields of interest: Museums; Museums (children's); Arts; Education; Human services; Children/youth, services.
Type of support: General/operating support; Capital campaigns; Building/renovation.
Limitations: Applications accepted. Giving primarily in the Memphis, TN, area. No support for nationally affiliated organizations, or for public and private schools, or churches and synagogues. No grants for seminars or special events.
Publications: Application guidelines.
Application information: The information that is to be included in the initial letter, must appear in the order indicated on foundation web site. New applicants and those that have not received funding from the foundation in the past 10 years, must arrange for a site visit by the foundation's Exec. Dir., well in advance of the funding deadlines. Application form not required.
Initial approach: Letter (no more than 3 pages, and typed in a 12 point font)
Copies of proposal: 1
Deadline(s): Aug. 1 and Feb. 1
Board meeting date(s): Spring and fall
Final notification: May and Nov.
Officers and Directors:* James D. Witherington, Jr.,* Chair.; Lawrence Jenson,* Pres.; Gwen P. Owen,* V.P.; Hunter Witherington,* Treas.; Margaret Craddock, Secy. and Exec. Dir.; Kathleen D. Blair; V. Lynn Evans; Bernice H. Hussey; Dr. Kenneth S. Robinson; Spence Wilson.
Number of staff: 1 full-time professional.
EIN: 626039986
Selected grants: The following grants are a representative sample of this grantmaker's funding activity:
$25,000 to Teach for America, New York, NY, 2011. For program support.
$6,000 to Young Life, Colorado Springs, CO, 2011. For program support.
$6,000 to Youth Villages, Memphis, TN, 2011. For program support.

8539
Elizabeth Turner Campbell Foundation ✧
P.O. Box 1628
Franklin, TN 37065-1628

Established in TN.
Donors: Elizabeth Turner Campbell; 1994 Elizabeth Turner Campbell Trust.
Foundation type: Independent foundation.
Financial data (yr. ended 12/31/13): Assets, $13,834,627 (M); expenditures, $1,144,808; qualifying distributions, $1,080,144; giving activities include $1,070,000 for 5 grants (high: $1,000,000; low: $5,000).
Purpose and activities: Giving primarily for children and social services, including to a free camp for children with medical problems.
Fields of interest: Recreation, camps; Human services; Children/youth, services.
Limitations: Applications not accepted. Giving primarily in FL and KY. No grants to individuals.
Application information: Contributes only to pre-selected organizations.
Officers and Directors:* Joseph W. Harwell,* Pres.; Diane H. Green,* V.P.; Dana Spencer,* Secy.
EIN: 621833493

8540
The Ann and Monroe Carell Foundation ✧
(formerly The Monroe Carell, Jr. Foundation)
95 White Bridge Rd., Ste. 514
Nashville, TN 37205-1490

Established in 1983 in TN.
Donors: Monroe Carell, Jr.; Ann Scott Carell; Ann & Monroe Carell 2002 Trust; Monroe Carell, Jr. 1995 Trust; Monroe Carell Jr. Testmentary Q-Tip Trust.
Foundation type: Independent foundation.
Financial data (yr. ended 12/31/13): Assets, $21,277,714 (M); gifts received, $5,300,000; expenditures, $1,888,014; qualifying distributions, $1,783,528; giving activities include $1,776,899 for 6 grants (high: $1,209,899; low: $15,000).
Purpose and activities: Giving primarily for education and Catholic agencies.
Fields of interest: Arts; Elementary/secondary education; Higher education; Education; Botanical gardens; Catholic agencies & churches.
Limitations: Applications not accepted. Giving primarily in Nashville, TN. No grants to individuals.
Application information: Unsolicited requests for funds not accepted.
Officers: Kathryn C. Brown, Pres.; Julie Carell Stadler, Secy.; Edith C. Johnson, Treas.
EIN: 581537831
Selected grants: The following grants are a representative sample of this grantmaker's funding activity:
$146,128 to Vanderbilt University, Nashville, TN, 2012. To further charitable activities.
$55,000 to Nashville Symphony, Nashville, TN, 2012. To further charitable activities.
$20,000 to Ensworth School, Nashville, TN, 2012. To further charitable activities.
$100 to American Council of Trustees and Alumni, Washington, DC, 2012. To further charitable activities.

8541
Andrea Waitt Carlton Family Foundation ✧
(also known as AWC Family Foundation)
(formerly Messengers of Healing Winds Foundation)
P.O. Box 58389
Nashville, TN 37205-8389 (615) 873-4142
Contact: Steven Rasmussen, Exec. Dir.

Established in 1998 in DE and NM.
Donor: Andrea Waitt Carlton.
Foundation type: Independent foundation.
Financial data (yr. ended 12/31/12): Assets, $54,259,236 (M); expenditures, $3,611,704; qualifying distributions, $2,709,800; giving activities include $2,709,800 for 94 grants (high: $333,000; low: $1,000).
Purpose and activities: Giving primarily in four major areas: 1) environmental concerns, with emphasis on programs that strive to preserve the land and educate our children on the importance of protecting and caring for our natural heritage; 2) animal welfare, with emphasis on the protection and humane treatment of both wild and domestic animals; 3) social concerns, with emphasis on helping Native Americans help themselves; and 4) the fine arts, with emphasis on renovation or the visual and performing arts. The foundation may also fund other charitable organizations or programs as deemed appropriate by the board of directors.
Fields of interest: Performing arts centers; Environment, natural resources; Environmental education; Animal welfare; Animals/wildlife, preservation/protection; Zoos/zoological societies.
Type of support: Annual campaigns; Capital campaigns; Building/renovation; Land acquisition; Endowments; Program development; Technical assistance; Consulting services; Matching/challenge support.
Limitations: Applications accepted. Giving primarily in the lake region of northwest IA, selected parts of FL, and in SD, and Santa Fe, NM. Giving on a national basis for environmental concerns. No grants to individuals, or for political lobbying.
Application information: Application form required.
Initial approach: Telephone
Copies of proposal: 4
Deadline(s): Varies, but usually 1-month prior to each board meeting date

Board meeting date(s): 5 times per year
Final notification: Within 60 days of receipt of proposal
Officers and Directors:* Andrea Waitt Carlton,* Pres.; Jennifer Kronebusch,* Secy.-Treas.; Steven Rasmussen, Exec. Dir.; Jason Gant; Charles Mosley.
Number of staff: 1 full-time professional; 1 part-time support.
EIN: 860910220
Selected grants: The following grants are a representative sample of this grantmaker's funding activity:
$333,000 to Montgomery Bell Academy, Nashville, TN, 2012. For Capital Campaign Request - Construction.
$250,000 to Montgomery Bell Academy, Nashville, TN, 2012. For Wallace Dining Hall.
$250,000 to Nashville Symphony, Nashville, TN, 2012. For Sustaining Greatness Campaign.
$150,000 to Belmont University, Nashville, TN, 2012. For New Concert Hall Campaign.
$100,000 to Land Trust for Tennessee, Nashville, TN, 2012. For infrastructure support.
$50,000 to Hillsdale College, Hillsdale, MI, 2012. For Kirby Center Fellows and Lecture Programs.
$50,000 to Nashville Zoo, Nashville, TN, 2012. For Option 1: sponsorship of the landscaping project or Option 2: A new signage project for orientation, direction, information, identification and interpretation.
$25,000 to Hillsdale College, Hillsdale, MI, 2012. For Online Constitution Course.
$15,000 to South Dakota Humanities Council, Brookings, SD, 2012. For Festival of Books $15,000 - Book Festival Operations.
$10,000 to Sea Turtle Conservancy, Gainesville, FL, 2012. For General Operations for research, education, and habitat conservation Programs.

8542
Charis Foundation Inc. ✧
c/o Steiner & Ellis, PLLC
5516 Lonas Dr., Ste. 260
Knoxville, TN 37909-3243 (865) 212-3800
Contact: J. Todd Ellis, Secy.-Treas.
Application address: P.O. Box 52206, Knoxville, TN 37950-2206, tel.: (865) 212-3800

Established in 2001 in TN.
Donors: Cristen G. Haslam; William E. Haslam.
Foundation type: Independent foundation.
Financial data (yr. ended 12/31/12): Assets, $15,068,362 (M); expenditures, $969,507; qualifying distributions, $760,750; giving activities include $760,750 for grants.
Purpose and activities: Giving primarily for higher education, federated giving programs, health care, and children and social services.
Fields of interest: Higher education; Education; Health care; Human services; Children/youth, services; United Ways and Federated Giving Programs.
Limitations: Applications accepted. Giving primarily in the eastern TN area, with emphasis on Knoxville. No grants to individuals.
Application information: Application form required.
Initial approach: Letter
Deadline(s): June 30 and Dec. 31
Officers and Directors:* William E. Haslam,* Pres.; Cristen G. Haslam,* V.P.; J. Todd Ellis,* Secy.-Treas.
EIN: 621867423

8543
The Children's Foundation of Memphis ✧
(formerly Crippled Children's Foundation)
700 Colonial Rd., Ste. 227
Memphis, TN 38117-5190
Contact: Lindsay Boggan
FAX: (901) 762-0093; E-mail: cfom@comcast.net

Established in 1982.
Donors: Le Bonheur Health Systems Foundation; Edward H. Little Memorial Trust Fund.
Foundation type: Independent foundation.
Financial data (yr. ended 12/31/12): Assets, $28,965,864 (M); gifts received, $92,517; expenditures, $1,286,962; qualifying distributions, $1,223,390; giving activities include $1,178,895 for 12 grants (high: $487,500; low: $2,000).
Purpose and activities: Giving primarily for children's services, with emphasis on health care and medical research.
Fields of interest: Hospitals (specialty); Medical research, institute; Human services; Children, services.
Limitations: Applications accepted. Giving primarily in the Memphis, TN, area. No grants to individuals.
Application information: Application form required.
Initial approach: Request application
Deadline(s): Within 6 weeks of grant notification to the public- generally in Sept.
Board meeting date(s): Sept., Nov., Jan., and Apr.
Officers and Directors:* Peggy McClure,* Pres.; Holly McGehee,* V.P.; Linda Mallory,* Community Grant Chair.; Martha Horton.
Number of staff: 1 part-time professional; 1 part-time support.
EIN: 620560292
Selected grants: The following grants are a representative sample of this grantmaker's funding activity:
$30,000 to Overton Park Conservancy, Memphis, TN, 2012. For playground equipment.
$23,000 to Streets Ministries, Memphis, TN, 2012. For children's assistance.

8544
Christian Education Charitable Trust ✧
820 Broad St., Ste. 300
Chattanooga, TN 37402-2604 (423) 755-1366
Contact: Jan Purdy
FAX: (423) 755-1640;
E-mail: support@maclellan.net; Main URL: http://www.maclellan.net/family-foundations/CECT

Established in 1974; supporting organization of Chattanooga Christian Community Foundation, Chattanooga Christian School, Covenant College, Covenant Theological Seminary, King College, Psychological Studies Institute - Chattanooga Bible Institute, Public School Bible Study Committee, and Reformed Theological Seminary.
Foundation type: Independent foundation.
Financial data (yr. ended 12/31/12): Assets, $21,327,727 (M); expenditures, $1,637,472; qualifying distributions, $1,120,442; giving activities include $1,046,650 for 7 grants (high: $500,000; low: $55,000).
Fields of interest: Higher education; Education; Christian agencies & churches.
Limitations: Applications accepted. Giving limited to within a 500-mile radius of Hamilton County, TN. No support for for-profit organizations. No grants to individuals.
Publications: Application guidelines.
Application information: Application form required.
Initial approach: Submit online application
Board meeting date(s): Spring and fall
Officers and Trustees:* Hugh O. MacLellan, Jr.,* Pres.; Robert H. MacLellan,* V.P.; Ralph S. Paden,* Secy.-Treas.; Lawrence B. Austin III; Hugh D. Huffaker, Jr.
EIN: 237412895

8545
Christy-Houston Foundation, Inc. ✧
1296 Dow St.
Murfreesboro, TN 37130-2413
Contact: Robert B. Mifflin, Pres.

Established in 1986 in TN; converted from the sale of Middle Tennessee Medical Center to Mid-State Baptist and Saint Thomas Hospitals.
Foundation type: Independent foundation.
Financial data (yr. ended 12/31/13): Assets, $93,474,011 (M); expenditures, $4,646,613; qualifying distributions, $4,099,415; giving activities include $3,858,842 for 27 grants (high: $800,000; low: $2,000).
Purpose and activities: Giving to enhance the quality of life in Rutherford County, TN, with emphasis on health care.
Fields of interest: Hospitals (general); Nursing care; Health care; Health organizations, association; Nutrition; Residential/custodial care, hospices; Community/economic development.
Type of support: Building/renovation; Equipment; Matching/challenge support.
Limitations: Applications accepted. Giving limited to Rutherford County, TN. No support for religious, political, or veterans' organizations or historical societies. No grants to individuals, operating expenses or endowments.
Publications: Application guidelines; Grants list.
Application information: Application form not required.
Initial approach: Proposal (less than 5 pages)
Copies of proposal: 1
Deadline(s): None
Board meeting date(s): Varies
Officers and Directors:* Newton F. Molloy, Chair.; George W. White, Vice-Chair.; Robert B. Mifflin,* Pres.; Kent Coleman, Secy.-Treas.; James R. Arnhart, Dir. Emeritus; Granville S.R. Bouldin, Dir. Emeritus; David C. Davis, Dir. Emeritus; Thomas E. Hord III, Dir. Emeritus; William Henry Huddleston III, Dir. Emeritus; Hubert L. McCullough, Jr., Dir. Emeritus; Edward E. Miller, Jr., Dir. Emeritus; Myers B. Parsons, Dir. Emeritus; Herbert D. Young, Jr., Dir. Emeritus; Henry King Butler, M.D.; Ed Elam; Larry N. Haynes; William S. Jones; Michael Jordan; Ed C. Loughry, Jr.; Matt B. Murfree III.
Number of staff: 1 part-time professional; 1 full-time support.
EIN: 621280998

8546
CIC Foundation, Inc. ✧
139 Lake Harbor Dr.
Hendersonville, TN 37075 (615) 386-2296
Main URL: http://www.cicfoundationinc.org/

Established in 2003 in TN.
Donor: Credit Bureau of Nashville, Inc.
Foundation type: Company-sponsored foundation.

Financial data (yr. ended 12/31/12): Assets, $0 (M); expenditures, $6,355,437; qualifying distributions, $5,493,203; giving activities include $3,268,121 for 61 grants (high: $350,000; low: $200), and $2,211,300 for 254 grants to individuals (high: $60,000; low: $1,250).
Purpose and activities: The foundation supports organizations involved with health, substance abuse, human services, and Christianity and awards college scholarships to students located in Kentucky and Tennessee.
Fields of interest: Education; Human services; Religion.
Type of support: General/operating support; Building/renovation; Program development; Scholarship funds; Scholarships—to individuals.
Limitations: Applications accepted. Giving primarily in KY and TN.
Application information: Application form required.
Initial approach: Contact foundation for scholarship application
Deadline(s): Apr. 1 for scholarships
Officers: William D. Maxfield, Chair.; Garry V. Forsythe, Pres.; Charles C. Martin, Secy.; Donna Tilley, Treas.
Directors: Leslie B. Enoch II; W. Dale Maxfield, Sr.; J. Terry Olive; M. Terry Turner.
EIN: 562348880
Selected grants: The following grants are a representative sample of this grantmaker's funding activity:
$85,000 to Tennesseans for Alternatives to the Death Penalty, Nashville, TN, 2012. To provide food and clothing for the needy and homeless.
$60,000 to Nashville Rescue Mission, Nashville, TN, 2012. To support services for indigent children.
$30,000 to Nashville Zoo, Nashville, TN, 2012. For A 200 acre zoo and historic farmhouse.
$25,175 to Our Kids, Nashville, TN, 2012. For medical assistance for families of the ill.
$25,000 to Sexual Assault Center, Nashville, TN, 2012. To facilitate development of Christ-centered relationships between individuals of different backgrounds.
$20,000 to Siloam Family Health Center, Nashville, TN, 2012. For services for needy blind people.
$15,000 to Hospital Hospitality House, Nashville, TN, 2012. For rehabilitation and lifestyle training for substance abuse victims.
$10,000 to Madison Christian Medical Clinic, Madison, TN, 2012. For Faith based health center providing affordable, quality primary medical care for working, uninsured, and low income residents of North Davidson County.
$5,000 to Cumberland Crisis Pregnancy Center, Hendersonville, TN, 2012. To provide ready-to-eat meals and personal contact to persons over 60 and others unable to prepare for themselves.

8547
The Clayton Family Foundation ✧
520 W. Summit Hill Dr., Ste. 801
Knoxville, TN 37902-2006
Contact: Grant Officer
E-mail: CFF.mail@Clayton.org; E-mail for grant requests: Grant.Request@Clayton.org; E-mail to request copy of application process: Grants@Clayton.org; Main URL: http://www.clayton.org

Established in 1991 in TN.
Donor: James L. Clayton.
Foundation type: Independent foundation.
Financial data (yr. ended 12/31/12): Assets, $91,816,291 (M); expenditures, $4,946,625; qualifying distributions, $4,634,350; giving activities include $4,634,350 for 287 grants (high: $850,000; low: $500).
Purpose and activities: Giving primarily for higher education, health associations, youth development, the arts, health organizations, social services, and Protestant churches.
Fields of interest: Arts; Elementary/secondary education; Higher education; Education; Health care; Health organizations, association; Boys & girls clubs; Human services; YM/YWCAs & YM/YWHAs; Children/youth, services; Community/economic development; Foundations (public); United Ways and Federated Giving Programs; Protestant agencies & churches.
Limitations: Giving limited to areas of company operations, particularly where Clayton Banks and other family businesses are located in TN. No support for private or supporting foundations, non-US charities, or political activities. No grants to individuals, or for fundraisers, social or sporting events, advertising, conferences, trips, tours, or seed money.
Publications: Application guidelines; IRS Form 990 or 990-PF printed copy available upon request.
Application information: One grant request per calendar year. Resumes or staff bios, letters of support, photographs, news articles, videos or DVDs, or 990 forms should not be initially sent with application. Incomplete grant requests will not be processed. See foundation web site for application information. Application form not required.
Deadline(s): None
Final notification: Up to 3 months following receipt of grant request
Officers and Directors:* James L. Clayton,* Pres.; Janice K. Clayton,* V.P.; Jeanne C. Campbell,* Secy.-Treas. and Managing Dir.; Kay Clayton, Exec. Dir.; B. Joe Clayton; Kevin T. Clayton.
EIN: 581970851

8548
The Community Foundation of Greater Chattanooga, Inc. ✧
1270 Market St.
Chattanooga, TN 37402-2713 (423) 265-0586
Contact: Peter T. Cooper, Pres.; For grants: Robin Posey, Prog. Off.
FAX: (423) 265-0587; E-mail: info2@cfgc.org; Additional e-mail: pcooper@cfgc.org; Grant application e-mail: rposey@cfgc.org; Main URL: http://www.cfgc.org
Facebook: http://www.facebook.com/pages/Community-Foundation-of-Greater-Chattanooga/90899078728
RSS Feed: http://www.cfgc.org/index.php?format=feed&type=rss
Twitter: http://www.twitter.com/WEAREGREATER
Scholarship e-mail: rsmith@cfgc.org

Incorporated in 1963 in TN.
Foundation type: Community foundation.
Financial data (yr. ended 12/31/12): Assets, $104,192,001 (M); gifts received, $21,557,574; expenditures, $15,312,011; giving activities include $12,668,443 for 308+ grants (high: $600,000; low: $75), and $1,430,226 for 741 grants to individuals.
Purpose and activities: The foundation seeks to promote and enhance the well-being of the inhabitants of the greater Chattanooga, TN area.
Fields of interest: Child development, education; Higher education; Education; Health care; Human services; Community development, neighborhood development; Community/economic development; Children/youth; Youth; Adults; Disabilities, people with; Women; Immigrants/refugees; Economically disadvantaged.
Type of support: Technical assistance; Management development/capacity building; Capital campaigns; Building/renovation; Equipment; Land acquisition; Program development; Seed money; Scholarship funds; Scholarships—to individuals.
Limitations: Applications accepted. Giving limited to the Hamilton County, TN, area. No support for private schools, religious causes, or veterans' or fraternal organizations, public agencies, state, national or regional organizations. No grants to individuals (except for scholarship programs), endowment campaigns, operating support for existing programs, conferences, advertising, telephone solicitations, needs assessments, comprehensive program evaluations, feasibility studies for capital campaigns, fundraising expenses, or federated fund drives; no loans.
Publications: Application guidelines; Annual report; Biennial report (including application guidelines); Grants list; Informational brochure; Informational brochure (including application guidelines).
Application information: Visit foundation web site for online application form and guidelines. Applicants are required to submit a Letter of Intent form and receive written approval from the foundation to continue the application process. Application form required.
Initial approach: Submit Letter of Intent form. See web site for details
Copies of proposal: 1
Deadline(s): Jan. 9, May 8, and Sept. 11 for letter of intent; Jan. 23, May 22, and Sept. 25 for full application
Board meeting date(s): Quarterly; Prog. Comm. meets 3 times per year
Final notification: Apr., Aug., and Dec.
Officers and Directors:* Michelle Ruest,* Chair.; Cliff Cleaveland,* Vice-Chair.; Tim Kelly,* Vice-Chair.; Peter T. Cooper, Pres.; Marty Robinson, V.P., Donor Rels.; Rebecca Underwood, V.P., Finance and Admin.; Ansley Moses,* Secy.; Linda Mosley,* Treas.; Mike Berry; Richard Brown; Lakweshia Ewing; Tom Glenn; Tom Greenholtz; Stacy Johnson; James McKissic; Hugh Moore; Ward Nelson; Rachel Schulson; Alfred Smith; Lacie Stone; Julie Stowe.
Number of staff: 8 full-time professional; 2 full-time support.
EIN: 626045999
Selected grants: The following grants are a representative sample of this grantmaker's funding activity:
$20,000 to Co.Lab, Chattanooga, TN, 2013. For core, urban, and rural entrepreneurship curriculum.
$20,000 to Hixson High School, Hixson, TN, 2013. For greenhouse for school agriculture program.
$19,040 to Creative Discovery Museum, Chattanooga, TN, 2013. For early childhood interventions, family interactions, and school experiences.
$14,000 to Rivermont Elementary, Chattanooga, TN, 2013. For fitness trail for students and the community.

$10,000 to Caldsted Foundation, Chattanooga, TN, 2013. To upgrade low-cost senior living facility.
$10,000 to Chattanoogas Kids on the Block, Chattanooga, TN, 2013. For educational programs focus on personal safety.
$10,000 to East Lake Academy of Fine Arts, Chattanooga, TN, 2013. For community-based learning for students.
$10,000 to Stop the Madness National, Chattanooga, TN, 2013. For summer enrichment camp for at risk youth.
$7,000 to Greenspaces Chattanooga, Chattanooga, TN, 2013. For Green business certification program.
$6,580 to Wallys Friends, Chattanooga, TN, 2013. For spay/neuter for low-income residents.

8549
Community Foundation of Greater Memphis ✧

1900 Union Ave.
Memphis, TN 38104-4029 (901) 728-4600
Contact: Robert M. Fockler, Pres.; For grants and scholarships: Vanessa Langston, Grants and Initiatives Assoc.
FAX: (901) 722-0010; E-mail: rfockler@cfgm.org; Grants and scholarship inquiry tel.: (901) 722-0032, e-mail: vlangston@cfgm.org; Main URL: http://www.cfgm.org
Facebook: https://www.facebook.com/CommunityFoundationGreaterMemphis?ref=hl
LinkedIn: http://www.linkedin.com/company/2253239?trk=tyah
Twitter: http://twitter.com/GiVE365Memphis
YouTube: http://www.youtube.com/user/cfgreatermemphis

Established in 1969 in TN; combined operations with The Memphis-Plough Community Foundation in 1989.
Foundation type: Community foundation.
Financial data (yr. ended 04/30/13): Assets, $314,940,599 (M); gifts received, $76,819,617; expenditures, $64,205,129; giving activities include $58,341,057 for grants.
Purpose and activities: The foundation seeks to provide support for the benefit of the geographic area that the foundation serves, and to strengthen the community through philanthropy.
Fields of interest: Arts; Education; Environment; Health care; Human services; Community development, neighborhood development; Philanthropy/voluntarism; Religion.
Type of support: Research; Management development/capacity building; Program development; Seed money; Scholarship funds; Technical assistance.
Limitations: Applications accepted. Giving limited to Crittenden County, AR, DeSoto, Marshall, Tate, and Tunica counties, MS, and Fayette, Shelby, and Tipton counties, TN. No grants to individuals (except for scholarships), or for endowments, capital or building funds, annual campaigns, code enforcement, or core operating costs; no loans.
Publications: Application guidelines; Annual report; Newsletter.
Application information: Nonprofit Capacity Building Grant applicants are notified whether or not they are invited to submit a full proposal based on Letter of Intent. The foundation holds a mandatory pre-application workshop every Feb.; see foundation web site for specific dates and additional application guidelines. Application form required.
Initial approach: Pre-Application Workshop
Copies of proposal: 1
Deadline(s): July 31 for letter of intent and Sept. 30 for full proposals for Nonprofit Capacity Building grants; varies for others
Board meeting date(s): Mar., May, Sept., and Dec.
Final notification: Dec.
Officers and Governors:* Meg Crosby,* Chair.; Robert M. Fockler, Pres.; Sutton Mora Hayes, V.P.; Mack E. McCaul, Jr., V.P., Finance; Sudhir K. Agrawal; Bert E. Barnett; Larry Bryan; G. Rice Byars; Gale Jones Carson; Marshall Clark; Kathy W. Cowan; Susan H. Foster; Hugh P. Fraser; Katina Gaines; J.W. Gibson; George M. Griesbeck; Fred D. Johnson; Ellen Cooper Klyce; Steve Leib; Duncan L. Miller; Jacqueline L. Nesbit; Carol W. Prentiss; Kenneth Robinson; Paulo L. Teixeira; N. Gordon Thompson; Lashell Vaughn; James L. Vining.
Number of staff: 14 full-time professional; 3 full-time support.
EIN: 581723645
Selected grants: The following grants are a representative sample of this grantmaker's funding activity:
$7,000,000 to Southern College of Optometry, Memphis, TN, 2013. For wire transfer.
$1,150,000 to Childrens Bureau, Porter-Leath Children's Center, Memphis, TN, 2013. For anonymous-Purchase Pre-K Facility in Frayser.
$600,000 to Memphis Symphony Orchestra, Memphis, TN, 2013. For wire transfer.
$425,000 to Calvary Episcopal Church, Memphis, TN, 2013. For anonymous - annual contribution.
$336,000 to A Step Ahead Foundation, Memphis, TN, 2013. For anonymous.
$5,000 to Harvest United Methodist Church, Missouri City, TX, 2013. For general fund.
$3,000 to Hope Works, Memphis, TN, 2013. For A Morning of Hope.
$2,500 to Haiti Medical Missions of Memphis, Memphis, TN, 2013.
$2,500 to Memphis University School, Memphis, TN, 2013. For Thorn Society.
$2,500 to Tennessee Shakespeare Company, Germantown, TN, 2013.

8550
Community Foundation of Middle Tennessee, Inc. ✧

(formerly Nashville Community Foundation, Inc.)
3833 Cleghorn Ave., No. 400
Nashville, TN 37215-2519 (615) 321-4939
Contact: Ellen E. Lehman, Pres.
FAX: (615) 327-2746; E-mail: mail@cfmt.org; Additional tel.: (888) 540-5200; Main URL: http://www.cfmt.org
E-Newsletter: http://www.cfmt.org/newsletter/subscribe/
Facebook: http://www.facebook.com/pages/Nashville-TN/The-Community-Foundation-of-Middle-Tennessee/55356141327
Google+: https://plus.google.com/106900481091008609401/posts
Grants List: http://www.cfmt.org/request/grants/grantees/
LinkedIn: http://www.linkedin.com/companies/the-community-foundation-of-middle-tennessee
Twitter: http://twitter.com/CFMT

Established in 1991 in TN.
Foundation type: Community foundation.
Financial data (yr. ended 12/31/13): Assets, $382,262,416 (M); gifts received, $24,791,249; expenditures, $51,949,370; giving activities include $44,904,846 for 550+ grants, and $1,702,569 for 295 grants to individuals.
Purpose and activities: The foundation is dedicated to enriching the quality of life in middle Tennessee. It serves as a leader, catalyst and resource for philanthropy, and strives to build a permanent endowment for the community for now and all time.
Fields of interest: Humanities; Historic preservation/historical societies; Arts; Education; Environment, natural resources; Environment; Animal welfare; Animals/wildlife; Health care; Health organizations, association; Employment; Housing/shelter, development; Aging, centers/services; Human services; Community development, neighborhood development; Community/economic development; Aging.
Type of support: Program development.
Limitations: Applications accepted. Giving limited to serving the 40 counties comprising the middle TN area. No support for private foundations, religious or sectarian purposes, private schools, biomedical or clinic studies (other than those related to breast cancer), or fundraising feasibility studies. No grants for fundraising events, debt retirement, annual and capital campaigns, endowment campaigns, equipment and technology for general operations, fundraising events, receptions, advertising, sponsorships, trips, conferences, computers or equipment.
Publications: Annual report; Informational brochure; Newsletter.
Application information: Visit foundation web site for application forms and guidelines. Faxed or e-mailed applications are not accepted. Application form required.
Initial approach: Create online profile
Deadline(s): Aug. 1 for grants; Mar. 15 for scholarships
Board meeting date(s): Feb., Apr., June, Sept., Nov., and Dec.
Final notification: Mid-Nov. for grants; Mid-May for scholarships
Officers and Directors:* Jerry B. Williams,* Chair.; Kerry Graham,* Vice-Chair.; Ellen E. Lehman,* Pres.; Leilani S. Boulware,* Secy.; Charles W. Cook, Jr.,* Treas.; Melisa Currey, Compt.; Ronald L. Corbin; Jana J. Davis; Rod Essig; Irwin E. Fisher; Dr. Stephen F. Flatt; Jay L. Frank; Ben G. Freeland; Gary A. Garfield; Hon. Alberto R. Gonzales; Jose D. Gonzalez; Mark R. Gwyn; Carl T. Haley; Henry B. Hicks, III; Carol Hudler; Decosta E. Jenkins; Hon. William C. Koch, Jr.; Robert S. Lipman; Don MacLachlan; Bert Mathews; Stephen F. Moore; Joelle J. Phillips; Deborah Taylor Tate; Dr. Stephanie H. Walker; Kevin J. Wheeler; David Williams II.
Trustees: Judy Liff Barker; Jack O. Bovender, Jr.; Ben Cundiff; Kitty Moon Emery; Richard J. Eskind; Farzin Ferdowsi; John D. Ferguson; Dr. Thomas F. Frist, Jr.; Joel C. Gordon; Francis Guess; James S. Gulmi; Mr. Aubrey B. Harwell, Jr.; Catherine T. Jackson; Kevin P. Lavender; Dr. John E. Maupin, Jr.; Ralph W. Mosley; Donna D. Nicely; Ben R. Rechter; Michael D. Shmerling; Susan W. Simons; Howard L. Stringer; Charles A. Trost; Deborah F. Turner; Jack B. Turner; Betsy Walkup.
Number of staff: 20 full-time professional.
EIN: 621471789
Selected grants: The following grants are a representative sample of this grantmaker's funding activity:

$1,000,000 to Currey Ingram Academy, Brentwood, TN, 2012. For general support.
$1,000,000 to Currey Ingram Academy, Brentwood, TN, 2012. For general support.
$1,000,000 to Harpeth Hall School, Nashville, TN, 2012. To benefit the Athletic and Wellness Building.
$1,000,000 to United Way of Metropolitan Nashville, Nashville, TN, 2012. For capacity building funding.
$750,000 to Nashville Symphony Association, Nashville, TN, 2012. For unrestricted funding.
$750,000 to Nashville Symphony Association, Nashville, TN, 2012. For unrestricted funding.
$8,100 to United Way of Metropolitan Nashville, Nashville, TN, 2012.
$5,000 to Friends of Warner Park, Nashville, TN, 2012. For the Hill Property campaign.
$3,180 to Nashville Symphony Association, Nashville, TN, 2012.
$2,968 to Columbia State Community College, Columbia, TN, 2012. For scholarship.

8551
Compton Family Foundation, Inc. ✧
6750 Poplar Ave., Ste. 118
Memphis, TN 38138-7407

Established in 2000 in IN.
Donors: Janice A. Compton; Robert A. Compton.
Foundation type: Independent foundation.
Financial data (yr. ended 12/31/11): Assets, $0 (M); expenditures, $755,602; qualifying distributions, $752,929; giving activities include $752,929 for 3 grants (high: $423,047; low: $148,628).
Fields of interest: Education; Diabetes; Health organizations; Orthopedics research.
Limitations: Applications not accepted. Giving primarily in NY and TN.
Application information: Unsolicited requests for funds not accepted.
Officers and Directors:* Robert A. Compton,* Pres.; Janice A. Compton,* Secy.-Treas.; Steve Phillips.
EIN: 352105286
Selected grants: The following grants are a representative sample of this grantmaker's funding activity:
$148,628 to Saint Georges Independent Schools Foundation, Germantown, TN, 2011.

8552
The Judith E. & Joseph C., Jr. Cook Foundation, inc. ✧
1600 Division St., Ste. 580
Nashville, TN 37203-2777

Established in 1997 in IN.
Donors: Joseph C. Cook; Judith E. Cook, Jr.
Foundation type: Independent foundation.
Financial data (yr. ended 12/31/12): Assets, $9,523,510 (M); expenditures, $599,535; qualifying distributions, $530,053; giving activities include $522,500 for 25 grants (high: $107,500; low: $33).
Fields of interest: Human services; Children/youth, services; Christian agencies & churches.
Type of support: General/operating support; Annual campaigns; Capital campaigns; Building/renovation; Scholarship funds.
Limitations: Applications not accepted. Giving primarily in NC and TN. No grants to individuals.
Application information: Contributes only to pre-selected organizations.
Officers: Joseph C. Cook, Jr., Pres.; Joseph C. Cook III, V.P.; Christine Cook Singleton, V.P.; Steven D. Singleton, Secy.; Judith E. Cook, Treas.
EIN: 352006656
Selected grants: The following grants are a representative sample of this grantmaker's funding activity:
$35,000 to Montreat Presbyterian Church, Montreat, NC, 2012. For Mission and Outreach.
$10,000 to Montreat College, Montreat, NC, 2012. For education and scholarship.

8553
Deborah and C. A. Craig II Family Foundation ✧
(formerly C. A. Craig II Family Foundation)
206 Paddock Pl.
Nashville, TN 37205-3337

Established in 1993 in IN.
Donor: C.A. Craig II†.
Foundation type: Independent foundation.
Financial data (yr. ended 12/31/13): Assets, $6,541,695 (M); expenditures, $3,036,642; qualifying distributions, $2,926,144; giving activities include $2,926,144 for 4 grants (high: $2,870,144; low: $1,000).
Purpose and activities: Giving for youth services, Methodist churches and federated giving programs.
Fields of interest: Health care; Recreation; Youth development.
Limitations: Applications not accepted. Giving primarily in the middle TN area. No grants to individuals.
Application information: Contributes only to pre-selected organizations.
Trustees: Deborah Ann Craig; Elizabeth Weaver Lane; Emilie Robinson Rick; Pamela Wallace Rowan.
EIN: 621550883

8554
Mike Curb Family Foundation ✧
48 Music Sq. E.
Nashville, TN 37203-4323

Established in 1998 in TN.
Donors: Mike Curb; Leanne Rimes.
Foundation type: Independent foundation.
Financial data (yr. ended 07/31/13): Assets, $23,832,891 (M); gifts received, $1,600,000; expenditures, $3,612,339; qualifying distributions, $3,181,834; giving activities include $3,112,059 for 10 grants (high: $1,428,571; low: $40,000).
Purpose and activities: Giving primarily for higher and other education, as well as for social services, and to a Baptist church.
Fields of interest: Performing arts; Arts; Higher education; Human services; Protestant agencies & churches.
Type of support: General/operating support; Program-related investments/loans.
Limitations: Applications not accepted. Giving primarily in Nashville, TN; some giving also in CA and TX. No grants to individuals.
Application information: Contributes only to pre-selected organizations.
Officers and Directors:* Mike Curb,* Pres.; Tracy Moore,* Secy.; Linda Curb.
EIN: 954686920

8555
Joe C. Davis Foundation ✧
3022 Vanderbilt Pl.
Nashville, TN 37212-2516
Contact: Angela Moretti Goddard, Assoc. Dir.
E-mail: agoddard@joecdavisfoundation.org; Main URL: http://www.joecdavisfoundation.org

Established in 1976 in TN.
Donor: Joe C. Davis†.
Foundation type: Independent foundation.
Financial data (yr. ended 09/30/13): Assets, $121,660,795 (M); expenditures, $6,147,616; qualifying distributions, $4,772,964; giving activities include $4,700,000 for 55 grants (high: $1,501,000; low: $2,500).
Purpose and activities: Support for all levels of education; grants also for health, medical research, and human services.
Fields of interest: Education, early childhood education; Elementary school/education; Education; Health care; Substance abuse, services; Health organizations, association; Cancer; Alcoholism; Medical research, institute; Cancer research; Housing/shelter, development.
Type of support: Program development; Seed money; Scholarship funds; Research; Matching/challenge support.
Limitations: Applications accepted. Giving primarily in the Nashville, TN, area; funding also in Boston, MA. No grants to individuals.
Publications: Application guidelines.
Application information: Organizations may only submit one grant request per calendar year. Requests should not exceed $25,000 for the Feb./Mar. grant cycle. Application form not required.
Initial approach: Letter (2-3 pages) sent via e-mail
Copies of proposal: 1
Deadline(s): Feb. 15 and Aug. 1
Board meeting date(s): Mar. 20 and Sept. 20
Final notification: Mar. 31 and Sept. 30
Trustees: Nancy Graves Beveridge; Delta Anne Davis; William R. DeLoache, Jr.; Frances D. Ellison.
Number of staff: 1 part-time support.
EIN: 626125481

8556
The Day Foundation ✧
5100 Wheelis Dr., No. 300
Memphis, TN 38117-4554

Established in 1960 in MS.
Donors: Clarence C. Day†; Day Cos., Inc.
Foundation type: Independent foundation.
Financial data (yr. ended 12/31/12): Assets, $155,827,281 (M); expenditures, $8,696,680; qualifying distributions, $8,193,400; giving activities include $8,193,400 for 17 grants (high: $7,000,000; low: $100).
Purpose and activities: Funding for education and for community projects in the arts and social services.
Fields of interest: Arts; Education; Youth development, centers/clubs; Children/youth, services.
Type of support: Seed money; Matching/challenge support.
Limitations: Applications not accepted. Giving primarily in the Memphis, TN, area. No grants to individuals, or for endowment funds, scholarships, fellowships, capital funds, or operating budgets; no loans.

Application information: Contributes only to pre-selected organizations.
Trustees: J. Richard Buchignani; William G. Griesbeck; C. Thomas Whitman.
Number of staff: 1 part-time support.
EIN: 646025122

8557
Peter Hawkins Dobberpuhl Foundation ✧
12 Cadillac Dr., Ste. 280
Brentwood, TN 37027-5360

Established in 2007 in TN.
Donor: Joel E. Dobberpuhl.
Foundation type: Independent foundation.
Financial data (yr. ended 12/31/13): Assets, $164,281,738 (M); gifts received, $2,010,950; expenditures, $6,186,261; qualifying distributions, $4,227,080; giving activities include $4,189,027 for 31 grants (high: $1,000,000; low: $5,000).
Fields of interest: Education; Children/youth, services; Christian agencies & churches.
Limitations: Applications not accepted. Giving primarily in TN. No grants to individuals.
Application information: Contributes only to pre-selected organizations.
Officers and Directors:* Joel E. Dobberpuhl,* Pres.; Holly S. Dobberpuhl,* Secy.; Mark Ezell.
EIN: 261454348
Selected grants: The following grants are a representative sample of this grantmaker's funding activity:
$306,709 to YMCA of Middle Tennessee, Brentwood Family Branch, Brentwood, TN, 2012.
$175,000 to Mercy Health Services, Franklin, TN, 2012.
$150,000 to Leadership International, Brentwood, TN, 2012.
$100,000 to Standing With Hope, Nashville, TN, 2012.
$40,000 to Campus Crusade for Christ International, Orlando, FL, 2012.
$25,000 to Brightstone, Franklin, TN, 2012.
$25,000 to Nashville Rescue Mission, Nashville, TN, 2012.
$20,000 to Siloam Family Health Center, Nashville, TN, 2012.
$10,000 to Kindred Spirits, Nashville, TN, 2012.
$10,000 to Saddle Up!, Franklin, TN, 2012.

8558
Dollar General Employee Assistance Foundation ✧
c/o Denine Torr
100 Mission Ridge
Goodlettsville, TN 37072-2171 (615) 855-5208
Contact: Denie Torr

Established in 2006 in TN.
Donors: Dollar General Corp.; William Bass.
Foundation type: Operating foundation.
Financial data (yr. ended 01/31/13): Assets, $1,265,940 (M); gifts received, $824,215; expenditures, $641,884; qualifying distributions, $621,972; giving activities include $621,972 for 411 grants to individuals (high: $2,500; low: $89).
Purpose and activities: The foundation provides grants to general employees and their families who are experiencing financial hardship due to circumstances beyond their control.
Fields of interest: Economically disadvantaged.
Type of support: Emergency funds; Grants to individuals.
Application information: Application form not required.
Initial approach: Proposal
Deadline(s): None
Officers: Susan S. Lanigan, Pres.; Anita C. Elliott, Treas.
Directors: Bill Clark; Greg Sparks; Rod Wesr.
EIN: 611492355

8559
Dugas Family Foundation, Inc. ✧
138 2nd Ave. N., Ste. 200
Nashville, TN 37201-1927 (615) 846-2053
Contact: Cabot Pyle

Donors: Laura Jo Dugas; Wayne F. Dugas, Sr.
Foundation type: Independent foundation.
Financial data (yr. ended 12/31/12): Assets, $23,798,078 (M); gifts received, $1,278,000; expenditures, $3,983,740; qualifying distributions, $3,646,934; giving activities include $3,580,051 for 24 grants (high: $615,000; low: $5,000).
Fields of interest: Education; Environment, natural resources; Human services; Children/youth, services.
Limitations: Applications accepted. Giving primarily in FL. No grants to individuals, or for travel, seminars, dinner events, or telethons; no loans.
Application information: Application form required.
Initial approach: Letter requesting application form
Deadline(s): None
Officers: Laura Jo Dugas, Pres.; Wayne F. Dugas, Sr., V.P.; Lynn King Dugas, Secy.; Stephen H. Dugas, Treas.
Directors: Pam Dugas; Wayne F. Dugas, Jr.
EIN: 263847853

8560
East Tennessee Foundation ✧
625 Market St., Ste. 1400
Knoxville, TN 37902-2219 (865) 524-1223
Contact: Michael T. McClamroch, C.E.O. and Pres.
FAX: (865) 637-6039; E-mail: etf@etf.org; Toll free tel.: (877) 524-1223; Main URL: http://www.easttennesseefoundation.org
Facebook: http://www.facebook.com/pages/East-Tennessee-Foundation/133730519976308?ref=ts
RSS Feed: http://www.easttennesseefoundation.org/RSS.aspx?pid=2&eid=3
Twitter: https://twitter.com/etfoundation
YouTube: http://www.youtube.com/user/easttennfoundation
Scholarship inquiry e-mail: bheller@etf.org

Incorporated in 1986 in TN.
Foundation type: Community foundation.
Financial data (yr. ended 12/31/13): Assets, $206,679,710 (M); gifts received, $7,746,236; expenditures, $11,232,447; giving activities include $7,824,137 for grants.
Purpose and activities: Giving to organizations which strengthen the capacity of existing institutions to reach a broader segment of the community, encourage cooperation, decrease duplication of services, and develop partnerships that can have a synergistic effect; address diversity and positive change; encourage citizen participation in meeting community challenges; demonstrate vision, action, effectiveness, good management and quality; focus on prevention and education; and provides models for replication.
Fields of interest: Arts; Education; Housing/shelter; Children/youth, services; Community/economic development.
Type of support: General/operating support; Building/renovation; Equipment; Program development; Conferences/seminars; Publication; Seed money; Scholarship funds; Technical assistance; Consulting services; Program evaluation; Program-related investments/loans; Matching/challenge support.
Limitations: Applications accepted. Giving limited to Knoxville, TN, and its 25 surrounding counties. No support for religious organizations which limit their services to any one religious group. No grants for annual campaigns, capital fund drives, endowment or general fundraising campaigns, research projects, debt retirement, or general operating budgets.
Publications: Application guidelines; Annual report; Informational brochure (including application guidelines); Newsletter.
Application information: Visit foundation web site for application guidelines. Application form required.
Initial approach: E-mail or telephone
Copies of proposal: 1
Deadline(s): Varies
Board meeting date(s): 5 times per year
Final notification: Varies
Officers and Directors:* Fred D. Womack,* Chair.; Keith D. Goodwin,* Vice-Chair.; Michael T. McClamroch,* C.E.O. and Pres.; Carolyn Schwenn,* Exec. V.P. and Secy.; Sherri Alley, V.P., Advancement; Jackie Lane, V.P., Comms.; John T. Worden,* Treas.; Dan M. Bechtol; Jeffrey M. Becker; Martha E. Begalla; Howard Z. Blum; Mary Ellen Brewington; Cynthia Burnley; Keith Burroughs; Patsy Q. Carson; Jefferson Chapman; Joan C. Cronan; Jed Dance; Larry R. Estepp; Ellen B. Fowler; Richard T. Fox; John T. Geppi; David Haynes; Christine Hayworth; Richard E. Jacobstein; David P. Jones; Cheryl Massingale; Jan McNally; Phyllis Y. Nichols; Pat Postma; Will J. Pugh; Patricia Robledo; Mitch Steenrod; Nita Summers; Dwight Tarwater; Dennis R. Upton; Mary Beth West.
Number of staff: 8 full-time professional; 2 part-time professional; 2 full-time support.
EIN: 620807696

8561
Eastman Chemical Company Foundation, Inc. ✧
c/o Bank One Trust Co.
P.O. Box 511
Kingsport, TN 37662-5075 (423) 229-1413
Contact: Paul Montgomery, Dir.
Application address: Pennsylvania: Gerald Kuhn, Jefferson Site Mgr., Eastman Chemical Co., P.O. Box 567, West Elizabeth, PA 15088, fax: (412) 384-7311, e-mail: gkuhn@eastman.com; Tennessee and National Organizations: Angie Jobe, Eastman Chemical Co., P.O. Box 431, Kingsport, TN 37662, fax: (423) 229-8280, e-mail: angieb@eastman.com; and Texas: Sally Azbell, Eastman Chemical Co., P.O. Box 7444, Longview, TX 75607, fax: (903) 237-5799, e-mail: sazbell@eastman.com; Main URL: http://www.eastman.com/Company/Sustainability/

Social_Responsibility/communities/Eastman_Foundation/Pages/Eastman_Foundation.aspx

Established in 1996 in TN.
Donor: Eastman Chemical Co.
Foundation type: Company-sponsored foundation.
Financial data (yr. ended 12/31/13): Assets, $4,146,343 (M); gifts received, $929,900; expenditures, $2,641,149; qualifying distributions, $2,625,324; giving activities include $2,625,324 for 393 grants (high: $400,000; low: $300).
Purpose and activities: The foundation supports programs designed to promote arts and culture, education, health, human services, community development, and civic affairs. Special emphasis is directed toward programs designed to improve the quality of life in communities where Eastman employees live and work.
Fields of interest: Arts councils; Performing arts; Arts; Higher education; Education, reading; Health care; Human services; Community development, neighborhood development; Business/industry; Community/economic development; United Ways and Federated Giving Programs; Mathematics; Engineering/technology; Science; Public affairs.
Type of support: General/operating support; Continuing support; Capital campaigns; Endowments; Program development; Scholarship funds.
Limitations: Applications accepted. Giving in areas of company operations, with emphasis on PA, TN and TX; giving also to national organizations. No support for athletic teams, choirs, bands, drill teams, labor, veterans', fraternal, social, or political organizations, United Way-supported agencies (except for capital fund drives), discriminatory organizations, or religious organizations not of direct benefit to the entire community. No grants to individuals, or for travel, student trips, or tours.
Publications: Application guidelines.
Application information: Multi-year funding is not automatic. Support is limited to 1 contribution per organization during any given year. Multi-year funding is not automatic. Application form required.
Initial approach: Complete online application or download application form and mail or fax to nearest application address
Deadline(s): July 31
Final notification: 12 weeks
Officers and Directors:* David Golden,* Pres.; Etta Clark,* V.P.; Elizabeth Twomey, Secy.; Mary Hall,* Treas.; Paul Montgomery; Perry Stuckey.
EIN: 621614800

8562
Elgin Foundation ✧ ☆
4624 Chambliss Ave., Ste. 200
Knoxville, TN 37919-5118

Established in 2003 in TN.
Donor: The B.R. Thompson Charitable Trust.
Foundation type: Independent foundation.
Financial data (yr. ended 06/30/13): Assets, $33,719,156 (M); expenditures, $1,733,535; qualifying distributions, $1,385,344; giving activities include $1,267,395 for 8 grants (high: $642,943; low: $400).
Fields of interest: Education; Human services; Christian agencies & churches.
Limitations: Applications not accepted. Giving primarily in GA and TN. No grants to individuals.
Application information: Contributes only to pre-selected organizations.
Officers and Directors:* B. Ray Thompson, Jr.,* Pres.; Sarah T. Tarver,* Secy.; Rebekah T. Palmer; Adella S. Thompson; B. Ray Thompson III; Juanne J. Thompson; C. Vance Thompson.
EIN: 200337919

8563
The Jane and Richard Eskind and Family Foundation ✧
104 Lynnwood Blvd.
Nashville, TN 37205-2904

Established in 1986 in TN.
Donors: Jane Eskind; Richard Eskind.
Foundation type: Independent foundation.
Financial data (yr. ended 06/30/13): Assets, $3,122,108 (M); expenditures, $1,388,543; qualifying distributions, $1,380,750; giving activities include $1,380,750 for grants.
Fields of interest: Arts; Higher education; Human services; Foundations (community); Jewish agencies & synagogues.
Limitations: Applications not accepted. Giving primarily in Nashville, TN. No grants to individuals.
Application information: Contributes only to pre-selected organizations.
Officers: Jane Eskind, Pres.; Richard Eskind, Secy.
Trustees: William H. Eskind; Ellen E. Lehman.
EIN: 621289998
Selected grants: The following grants are a representative sample of this grantmaker's funding activity:
$500,000 to Community Foundation of Middle Tennessee, Nashville, TN, 2011.
$20,020 to American Civil Liberties Union Foundation of Tennessee, Nashville, TN, 2011.
$7,500 to Meharry Medical College, Nashville, TN, 2011.
$5,020 to Nashville Symphony Association, Nashville, TN, 2011.
$5,000 to University of Louisville, Louisville, KY, 2011.
$1,000 to Humanities Tennessee, Nashville, TN, 2011.

8564
Ezell Foundation, Inc. ✧
P.O. Box 100957
Nashville, TN 37224-0957
Contact: F. Miles Ezell Jr., Pres.

Established in 1964.
Donors: F. Miles Ezell, Sr.†; and members of the Ezell family.
Foundation type: Independent foundation.
Financial data (yr. ended 12/31/13): Assets, $13,166,704 (M); gifts received, $250; expenditures, $875,527; qualifying distributions, $756,419; giving activities include $753,450 for 66 grants (high: $228,450; low: $500).
Purpose and activities: Giving primarily to the Church of Christ and related educational programs.
Fields of interest: Education; Protestant agencies & churches.
International interests: Guatemala; Honduras; Nigeria.
Type of support: General/operating support; Continuing support; Capital campaigns; Equipment.
Limitations: Applications accepted. Giving primarily in TN.
Application information: Application form required.
Initial approach: Letter
Deadline(s): None
Board meeting date(s): Annually
Officers: F. Miles Ezell, Jr., Pres.; John W. Ezell, 1st V.P.; Roy C. Ezell, 2nd V.P.; David Thomas, Secy.
EIN: 626046865

8565
First Horizon Foundation ✧
(formerly First Tennessee Foundation)
c/o First Horizon National Corp.
165 Madison Ave., 8th. Fl.
Memphis, TN 38103-2723 (901) 523-4207
Contact: Melissa Duong, Mgr.
FAX: (901) 523-4354;
E-mail: MDuong@FirstTennessee.com; Contact for Leadership Grants Program: Erica Wilkins, e-mail: EEWilkins@firsthorizon.com; Additional tel.: (901) 523-4291; Contact for Award for Innovation in the Arts: Lizzy Haymond, Corp. Comms., tel.: (901) 523-4291, e-mail: emhaymond@firsthorizon.com; Main URL: http://www.firsttennesseefoundation.com/

Established in 1993 in TN.
Donors: First Tennessee National Corp.; First Horizon National Corp.
Foundation type: Company-sponsored foundation.
Financial data (yr. ended 12/31/12): Assets, $46,311,463 (M); expenditures, $5,454,714; qualifying distributions, $5,228,724; giving activities include $5,228,724 for 1,035 grants (high: $391,000; low: $25).
Purpose and activities: The foundation supports programs designed to promote arts and culture; education and youth; financial literacy and economic development; and health and human services.
Fields of interest: Visual arts; Museums; Performing arts, orchestras; Arts; Elementary/secondary education; Higher education; Education; Environment, natural resources; Environment, land resources; Environment; Hospitals (general); Health care, clinics/centers; Health care; Athletics/sports, amateur leagues; Salvation Army; Youth, services; Human services, financial counseling; Human services; Economic development; United Ways and Federated Giving Programs.
Type of support: General/operating support; Annual campaigns; Capital campaigns; Building/renovation; Equipment; Endowments; Program development; Conferences/seminars; Professorships; Scholarship funds; Employee volunteer services; Sponsorships; Employee matching gifts.
Limitations: Applications accepted. Giving primarily in areas of company operations in TN. No support for bank clearinghouse organizations, charities sponsored solely by a single civic organization, pass through organizations, religious, veterans', social, or fraternal organizations, or political organizations. No grants to individuals, or for trips or tours, or debt reduction.
Publications: Application guidelines.
Application information:
Initial approach: E-mail or mail cover letter and proposal to nearest community investment manager
Deadline(s): Nov. 1
Final notification: End of Feb.

Officers and Directors:* Charles G. Burkett, Chair.; Gregg I. Lansky,* Pres., C.F.O, and Treas.; Clyde A. Billings, Jr.,* V.P. and Secy.; Kimberley C. Cherry; Charles T. Tuggle, Jr.; William C. Losch III.
EIN: 621533987
Selected grants: The following grants are a representative sample of this grantmaker's funding activity:
$391,000 to ArtsMemphis, Memphis, TN, 2012. For general operating funds.
$225,000 to United Way of the Mid-South, Memphis, TN, 2012. For general operating funds.
$185,000 to University of Memphis Foundation, Memphis, TN, 2012. For general operating funds.
$100,000 to Saint Jude Childrens Research Hospital, Memphis, TN, 2012. For general operating funds.
$50,000 to Shelby Residential and Vocational Services, Memphis, TN, 2012. For general operating funds.
$6,585 to United Way of Greater Kingsport, Kingsport, TN, 2012. For general operating funds.
$5,000 to Lifeblood, Memphis, TN, 2012. For general operating funds.
$3,000 to Miss Tennessee Scholarship Foundation, Jackson, TN, 2012. For general operating funds.
$2,500 to Dixon Gallery and Gardens, Memphis, TN, 2012. For general operating funds.
$2,500 to Operation Stand Down Nashville, Nashville, TN, 2012. For general operating funds.

8566
Formanek Foundation ✧
6075 Poplar Ave., Ste. 726
Memphis, TN 38119-4750 (901) 797-9500
Contact: Peter R. Formanek, Pres. and Dir.

Established in TN.
Donor: Peter R. Formanek.
Foundation type: Independent foundation.
Financial data (yr. ended 12/31/12): Assets, $14,481,516 (M); gifts received, $1,435,884; expenditures, $1,396,988; qualifying distributions, $1,003,450; giving activities include $1,003,450 for 29 grants (high: $301,000; low: $100).
Fields of interest: Arts; Education; Environment.
Application information: Application form required.
Initial approach: Proposal
Deadline(s): None
Officers and Directors:* Peter R. Formanek,* Pres.; Walter W. Rotchild,* Secy.-Treas.
EIN: 261565007

8567
The Dorothy Cate & Thomas F. Frist Foundation ✧
(formerly The Frist Medical Foundation)
95 White Bridge Rd., Ste. 505
Nashville, TN 37205
E-mail: dctffoundation@bellsouth.net

Established in 1989 in TN.
Donors: Dr. Thomas F. Frist, Sr.†; Dorothy Cate Frist†.
Foundation type: Independent foundation.
Financial data (yr. ended 11/30/13): Assets, $46,643,026 (M); expenditures, $2,246,589; qualifying distributions, $1,945,125; giving activities include $1,875,000 for 327 grants (high: $375,000; low: $100).
Fields of interest: Education; Human services.
Type of support: Annual campaigns; Capital campaigns; Building/renovation; Scholarship funds; Research.
Limitations: Applications not accepted. Giving primarily in TN. No grants to individuals.
Application information: Contributes only to pre-selected organizations.
Board meeting date(s): Mar. and Oct.
Officers: Thomas F. Frist, Jr., M.D., Pres.; Mary F. Barfield, V.P.; Dorothy Cate Frist, V.P.; Robert A. Frist, M.D., V.P.; William H. Frist, M.D., Secy.
Number of staff: 1 part-time professional.
EIN: 621103568
Selected grants: The following grants are a representative sample of this grantmaker's funding activity:
$3,000 to Oasis Center, Nashville, TN, 2011. For general support.

8568
The Frist Foundation ✧
(formerly The HCA Foundation)
3100 West End Ave., Ste. 1200
Nashville, TN 37203-1348 (615) 292-3868
Contact: Peter F. Bird, Jr., C.E.O. and Pres.
FAX: (615) 292-5843;
E-mail: askfrist@fristfoundation.org; Main
URL: http://www.fristfoundation.org
Grants List: http://www.fristfoundation.org/Grant_Recpients_2

Established in 1982 in TN.
Donors: Hospital Corp. of America; Lee, Danner & Bass, Inc.
Foundation type: Independent foundation.
Financial data (yr. ended 12/31/12): Assets, $239,569,212 (M); expenditures, $9,953,876; qualifying distributions, $8,505,690; giving activities include $7,767,725 for 202 grants, and $154,700 for 30 employee matching gifts.
Purpose and activities: The foundation supports organizations involved with arts and culture, education, health, human services, youth leadership training, community development, and civic affairs.
Fields of interest: Visual arts; Performing arts; Arts; Education; Health care; Youth development; Human services; Community/economic development; Philanthropy/voluntarism, management/technical assistance; Voluntarism promotion; United Ways and Federated Giving Programs.
Type of support: General/operating support; Management development/capacity building; Capital campaigns; Building/renovation; Equipment; Emergency funds; Program development; Technical assistance; Consulting services; Employee matching gifts; Matching/challenge support.
Limitations: Applications accepted. Giving primarily in Nashville, TN. No support for national disease-specific organizations, private foundations, religious organizations not of direct benefit to the entire community, hospitals, nursing homes, or retirement homes. No grants to individuals, or for endowments, biomedical or clinical research, social events or similar fundraising events, goodwill advertising, telethons, sponsorships, publications, trips, tours, political activities, or start up needs.
Publications: Application guidelines; Grants list.
Application information: An application form is available online. Application form required.
Initial approach: Complete online application form or download application form and mail to foundation
Copies of proposal: 1
Deadline(s): Apr. 1 for Technology Grants Program
Board meeting date(s): Jan., Apr., July, and Oct.
Final notification: Usually within 1 month
Officers and Directors:* Thomas F. Frist, Jr.,* Chair.; Peter F. Bird, Jr.,* C.E.O. and Pres.; Barbara W. Baker, Corp. Secy. and Prog. Asst.; Colette R. Easter, Treas.; Kenneth L. Roberts,* Pres. Emeritus; Frank F. Drowota III; Patricia Frist Elcan; Patricia C. Frist; Thomas F. Frist III; William R. Frist.
Number of staff: 1 full-time professional; 1 part-time professional; 1 full-time support; 1 part-time support.
EIN: 621134070
Selected grants: The following grants are a representative sample of this grantmaker's funding activity:
$200,000 to Safe Haven Family Shelter, Nashville, TN, 2012. For program expansion.

8569
Herbert A. Fritch Family Foundation ✧
1 Morningside Dr.
Nashville, TN 37215-5831

Established in 2006 in TN.
Foundation type: Independent foundation.
Financial data (yr. ended 12/31/12): Assets, $1,224,655 (M); gifts received, $4,983,686; expenditures, $3,801,775; qualifying distributions, $3,801,775; giving activities include $3,801,775 for 7 grants (high: $1,899,775; low: $1,000).
Fields of interest: Performing arts, ballet; Higher education; Health care; Food banks; Recreation, centers.
Limitations: Applications not accepted. Giving primarily in MN and TN. No grants to individuals.
Application information: Contributes only to pre-selected organizations.
Trustees: Barbara A. Fritch; Herbert A. Fritch.
EIN: 626404383

8570
Eldon and Emma Belle Gardner Charitable Foundation ✧ ☆
c/o Cumberland Trust
40 Burton Hills Blvd., Ste. 300
Nashville, TN 37215-6292

Established in TN.
Foundation type: Independent foundation.
Financial data (yr. ended 12/31/13): Assets, $1,317,415 (M); gifts received, $1,500,000; expenditures, $544,108; qualifying distributions, $541,919; giving activities include $534,247 for 3 grants (high: $400,000; low: $34,247).
Fields of interest: Higher education; Christian agencies & churches.
Limitations: Applications not accepted. Giving primarily in TN. No grants to individuals.
Application information: Unsolicited requests for funds not accepted.
Trustee: Cumberland Trust.
EIN: 466336914

8571
The Bill Gatton Foundation ✧
P.O. Box 1147
Bristol, TN 37621-1147
Application address: c/o Frank Winston, 1000 W. State St., Bristol, TN 37620, tel.: (423) 764-5121

Donors: C.M. Gatton; Customer 1 One, Inc.
Foundation type: Independent foundation.
Financial data (yr. ended 11/30/13): Assets, $67,821,558 (M); gifts received, $1,829,028; expenditures, $2,669,886; qualifying distributions, $2,438,221; giving activities include $2,426,221 for 9 grants (high: $1,828,900; low: $15).
Purpose and activities: Giving primarily for higher education.
Fields of interest: Higher education; Human services.
Limitations: Applications accepted. Giving primarily in KY, TN, and VA. No grants to individuals.
Application information: Application form not required.
Initial approach: Proposal
Deadline(s): None
Trustees: C.M. Gatton; Frank Winston.
EIN: 621266284

8572
The Glenn Family Foundation ✧ ☆
45 S. Pisgah
Eads, TN 38028-8018

Donor: T. Michael Glenn.
Foundation type: Independent foundation.
Financial data (yr. ended 12/31/13): Assets, $1,914,626 (M); gifts received, $965,213; expenditures, $658,500; qualifying distributions, $658,500; giving activities include $658,500 for 11 grants (high: $506,500; low: $1,000).
Fields of interest: Higher education, university; Christian agencies & churches.
Limitations: Applications not accepted. Giving primarily in MS and TN. No grants to individuals.
Application information: Unsolicited requests for funds not accepted.
Directors: Donna Glenn; T. Michael Glenn.
EIN: 203867226

8573
The Elliott & Harriet Goldstein Private Foundation ✧ ☆
(doing business as Highland Vineyard Foundation)
40 Burton Hills Blvd., Ste. 300
Nashville, TN 37215-6292

Donor: Elliott Goldstein†.
Foundation type: Independent foundation.
Financial data (yr. ended 12/31/13): Assets, $8,458,287 (M); expenditures, $819,281; qualifying distributions, $683,552; giving activities include $657,500 for 24 grants (high: $455,000; low: $500).
Fields of interest: Education; Environment; Housing/shelter.
Limitations: Applications not accepted. Giving primarily in FL, GA and NC.
Application information: Unsolicited requests for funds not accepted.
Trustees: Lil Friedlander; Burton Goldstein; Cumberland Trust & Investment Co.
EIN: 376456099

8574
The Goodfriend Foundation ✧
P.O. Box 22726
Knoxville, TN 37933-0726

Established in 2005 in TN.
Donor: Robert M. Goodfriend.
Foundation type: Independent foundation.
Financial data (yr. ended 12/31/13): Assets, $7,175,970 (M); expenditures, $529,993; qualifying distributions, $464,900; giving activities include $464,000 for 18 grants (high: $200,000; low: $500).
Purpose and activities: Giving primarily to Jewish organizations, as well as to federated giving programs and to a children's hospital.
Fields of interest: Hospitals (specialty); Foundations (community); United Ways and Federated Giving Programs; Jewish agencies & synagogues.
Limitations: Applications not accepted. Giving primarily in Knoxville, TN. No grants to individuals.
Application information: Contributes only to pre-selected organizations.
Directors: Harold I. Apolisky; Jeffrey A. Goodfriend; Robert M. Goodfriend; Stacey A. Goodfriend; Wendy S. Goodfriend; Leigh A. Kaylor.
EIN: 203791086
Selected grants: The following grants are a representative sample of this grantmaker's funding activity:
$50,000 to Eisenhower Medical Center, Rancho Mirage, CA, 2012. For Building and Improvements to Facilities.
$25,000 to Webb School of Knoxville, Knoxville, TN, 2012. For Change the Campus to Ensure Outstanding Programs Con.
$10,000 to United Way of McMinn and Meigs Counties, Athens, TN, 2012. For general support for Mission.
$300 to AIDS Assistance Program, Palm Springs, CA, 2012. To support Dance-For-Life Palm Springs.

8575
Great Oaks Foundation ✧
(formerly Martha and Robert Fogelman Foundation)
744 S. White Station Rd.
Memphis, TN 38117-4577

Established in 1981 in TN.
Donor: Robert F. Fogelman.
Foundation type: Independent foundation.
Financial data (yr. ended 12/31/13): Assets, $4,708,473 (M); expenditures, $611,176; qualifying distributions, $583,502; giving activities include $583,502 for 54 grants (high: $142,000; low: $52).
Fields of interest: Arts; Higher education; Foundations (private grantmaking); Foundations (community); Jewish federated giving programs.
Limitations: Applications not accepted. Giving primarily in Memphis, TN. No grants to individuals.
Application information: Contributes only to pre-selected organizations.
Officers and Trustees:* Catherine S. Fogelman,* Pres.; Martha H. Fogelman,* Secy.; Robert F. Fogelman II; Fran Hyde.
EIN: 586163005

8576
Hamico, Inc. ✧
1715 W. 38th St.
Chattanooga, TN 37409-1248

Incorporated in 1956 in TN.
Donor: Chattem, Inc.
Foundation type: Company-sponsored foundation.
Financial data (yr. ended 12/31/12): Assets, $53,181,342 (M); expenditures, $4,358,024; qualifying distributions, $3,734,246; giving activities include $3,427,310 for 131 grants (high: $1,000,000; low: $50).
Purpose and activities: The foundation supports community foundations and festivals and organizations involved with arts and culture, education, health, athletics, and human services.
Fields of interest: Arts; Elementary/secondary education; Higher education; Education; Zoos/zoological societies; Medical care, community health systems; Hospitals (general); Health care; Athletics/sports, school programs; Recreation, fairs/festivals; Athletics/sports, amateur leagues; Athletics/sports, racquet sports; Children/youth, services; Developmentally disabled, centers & services; Human services; Foundations (community); United Ways and Federated Giving Programs.
Type of support: General/operating support; Continuing support.
Limitations: Applications not accepted. Giving limited to Chattanooga, TN. No grants to individuals.
Application information: Contributes only to pre-selected organizations.
Officers and Directors:* Zan Guerry,* Pres.; Robert E. Bosworth,* Secy.; Herbert Barks; Alexis G. Bogo; John P. Guerry.
EIN: 626040782

8577
Helen and Jabie Hardin Charitable Trust ✧
4385 Poplar Ave.
Memphis, TN 38117-3715 (901) 681-2349
Contact: Leigh Lawler

Established in 2009 in TN.
Donor: Helen E. Hardin Trust.
Foundation type: Independent foundation.
Financial data (yr. ended 10/31/13): Assets, $15,259,900 (M); expenditures, $6,615,541; qualifying distributions, $6,550,103; giving activities include $6,502,500 for 18 grants (high: $4,300,000; low: $2,500).
Fields of interest: Higher education; Education; Health care.
Limitations: Applications accepted. Giving primarily in TN.
Application information:
Initial approach: Letter
Deadline(s): None
Trustee: First Tennessee Bank.
EIN: 266754597
Selected grants: The following grants are a representative sample of this grantmaker's funding activity:
$300,000 to University of Memphis Foundation, Memphis, TN, 2011.
$100,000 to Salvation Army, Atlanta, GA, 2011.
$50,000 to Montefiore Medical Center, Bronx, NY, 2011.
$10,000 to Memphis Child Advocacy Center, Memphis, TN, 2011.
$10,000 to Rachels Kids, Memphis, TN, 2011.

8578
Patricia and Rodes Hart Foundation ✧
3001 Hillsboro Rd.
Brentwood, TN 37027-4863

Established in 1988 in TN.
Donors: Rodes Hart; Patricia I. Hart.
Foundation type: Operating foundation.
Financial data (yr. ended 12/31/13): Assets, $5,553,179 (M); gifts received, $5,508,349; expenditures, $1,759,820; qualifying distributions, $1,757,370; giving activities include $1,757,370 for 52 grants (high: $520,750; low: $25).
Fields of interest: Performing arts, orchestras; Higher education; Cancer; Aging, centers/services; United Ways and Federated Giving Programs.
Type of support: General/operating support.
Limitations: Applications not accepted. Giving primarily in Nashville, TN. No grants to individuals.
Application information: Contributes only to pre-selected organizations.
Trustees: H. Rodes Hart; Patricia I. Hart.
EIN: 621355032
Selected grants: The following grants are a representative sample of this grantmaker's funding activity:
$505,000 to Vanderbilt University, Nashville, TN, 2011.
$170,600 to Metropolitan Museum of Art, New York, NY, 2011.

8579
The Hartwell Foundation ✧
6000 Poplar Ave. Ste. 250
Memphis, TN 38119-3974
Main URL: http://www.thehartwellfoundation.org/

Established in 1996 in CT.
Donors: Laurence H. Smead; Transnetyx; Larry H. Smead.
Foundation type: Operating foundation.
Financial data (yr. ended 06/30/13): Assets, $87,477,656 (M); expenditures, $11,142,281; qualifying distributions, $9,107,610; giving activities include $2,260,212 for 36 grants (high: $326,345; low: $900).
Purpose and activities: Giving primarily to universities for medical research.
Fields of interest: Higher education, university; Medical research, institute.
Type of support: Fellowships; Research.
Limitations: Applications not accepted. Giving primarily in the San Francisco Bay Area, CA, Baltimore, MD, Ann Arbor, MI, Durham, NC, Ithaca, NY, PA, Memphis, TN, Dallas, TX, Charlottesville, VA, and Madison, WI. No grants to individuals.
Application information: Contributes only to pre-selected organizations.
Officers and Directors:* Larry H. Smead, Chair.; Preston J. Smead, Vice-Chair. and V.P.; Russell J. Hensley,* C.E.O. and Secy.; Fred Dombrose,* Pres.; Milton Greene,* C.F.O. and Treas.
EIN: 061468749
Selected grants: The following grants are a representative sample of this grantmaker's funding activity:
$326,345 to University of Michigan, Ann Arbor, MI, 2013. For fellowship.
$250,000 to Tragedy Assistance Program for Survivors, Washington, DC, 2013. For Children's Good Grief Camps.
$150,000 to Tragedy Assistance Program for Survivors, Washington, DC, 2013. For children of KIA soldiers.
$100,000 to Land of the Free Foundation, City of Industry, CA, 2013. For Veteran's Day Golf Classic.
$70,000 to Woodland Presbyterian School, Memphis, TN, 2013. For tuition assistance for children.
$66,667 to Avon Old Farms School, Avon, CT, 2013. For GMT Scholar.
$50,000 to Saint Jude Childrens Research Hospital, Memphis, TN, 2013. For fellowship.
$50,000 to University of California, Davis, CA, 2013. For fellowship.
$50,000 to University of Texas Southwestern Medical Center, Dallas, TX, 2013. For fellowship.
$33,634 to Avon Old Farms School, Avon, CT, 2013.

8580
The Haslam 3 Foundation, Inc. ✧
(formerly The Sycamore Foundation, Inc.)
P.O. Box 10573
Knoxville, TN 37919-0573 (865) 384-4178
Contact: Susan B. Haslam, Pres.

Established in 2001 in TN.
Donors: James A. Haslam III; Susan B. Haslam.
Foundation type: Independent foundation.
Financial data (yr. ended 12/31/12): Assets, $5,006,925 (M); gifts received, $771,000; expenditures, $1,279,544; qualifying distributions, $1,155,580; giving activities include $1,145,309 for 31 grants (high: $312,500; low: $1,000).
Fields of interest: Arts; Higher education; Education; Human services; United Ways and Federated Giving Programs; Christian agencies & churches.
Limitations: Giving primarily in Knoxville, TN.
Application information:
Initial approach: Letter
Deadline(s): June 30 and Dec. 31
Officers and Directors:* Susan B. Haslam,* Pres.; James A. Haslam III,* V.P.; James E. Oakley III,* Secy.-Treas.; Cynthia Haslam Arnholt; Whitney H. Johnson.
EIN: 621867421
Selected grants: The following grants are a representative sample of this grantmaker's funding activity:
$76,928 to Legacy Parks Foundation, Knoxville, TN, 2012. To Assure That Our Community Enjoys Exceptional Recreational Opportunities, Natural Beauty and Open Spaces, and That Those Assets Exist for Generations to Come.
$57,957 to Emerald Youth Foundation, Knoxville, TN, 2012. To Develop Christian Leaders Who Use Their Knowledge, Skills, and Gifts to Renew Their Neighborhoods.
$45,000 to Maryville College, Maryville, TN, 2012. For the Civic/Fine Arts Center of Maryville College.
$25,000 to American Heart Association, Saint Petersburg, FL, 2012. To Build Healthier Lives, Free of Cardiovascular Diseases and Stroke.
$20,000 to Knoxville Museum of Art, Knoxville, TN, 2012. To Present Art Displays Which Represent Diverse Cultures, Periods, Styles and Medias.
$20,000 to Youth Villages, Memphis, TN, 2012. To Help Children and Families Live Successfully.
$12,500 to Webb School of Knoxville, Knoxville, TN, 2012. For Maintenance of Educational Institution Properties.
$10,000 to Nantucket Dreamland Foundation, Nantucket, MA, 2012. To Develop and Run a Community, Arts and Cultural Center in Nantucket, Ma.
$9,269 to Knoxville Family Justice Center, Knoxville, TN, 2012. For a Safe Harbor for Domestic Abuse Victims.
$5,000 to Breakthrough Corporation, Knoxville, TN, 2012. For Specialized Services for Adults with Autism in East Tennessee.

8581
The Haslam Family Foundation, Inc. ✧
c/o Steiner & Ellis, PLLC
P.O. Box 10146
Knoxville, TN 37939-0146
Application address: c/o Todd Ellis, Asst. Secy., P.O. Box 52206, Knoxville, TN 37950-2206; tel.: (865) 212-3800

Established in 1998 in TN.
Donors: James A. Haslam III; Cynthia A. Haslam Bailey; William E. Haslam; James A. Haslam II.
Foundation type: Independent foundation.
Financial data (yr. ended 12/31/12): Assets, $91,045,018 (M); gifts received, $3,850,000; expenditures, $5,066,337; qualifying distributions, $4,342,651; giving activities include $4,342,651 for grants.
Purpose and activities: Giving primarily for education, children, youth and social services, health care, the arts, and human services.
Fields of interest: Historic preservation/historical societies; Arts; Higher education; Education; Health care; Human services; Children/youth, services; Community/economic development; Foundations (private grantmaking).
Limitations: Giving primarily in the eastern TN area. No grants to individuals.
Application information:
Initial approach: Letter
Deadline(s): June 30 and Dec. 31
Officers and Directors:* James A. Haslam II,* Pres.; Ann Haslam Bailey,* V.P.; Natalie L. Haslam,* Secy.; J. Todd Ellis,* Treas.; James A. Haslam III; William E. Haslam.
EIN: 621692007

8582
The HCA Foundation ✧
(formerly Columbia/HCA Healthcare Foundation, Inc.)
1 Park Plz., 4th Fl. East
Nashville, TN 37203-6527 (615) 344-2390
Contact: Lois Abrams, Grants Mgr.
FAX: (615) 344-5722;
E-mail: lois.abrams@hcahealthcare.com; Tel.: (615) 344-2343; e-mail: Corp.FoundationsGifts@HCAHealthcare.com; Main URL: http://hcacaring.org/
Grants List: http://hcacaring.org/supporting/agency-list.dot

Established in 1992 in KY.
Donors: Columbia/HCA Healthcare Corp.; HCA—The Healthcare Co.; HCA Inc.
Foundation type: Company-sponsored foundation.
Financial data (yr. ended 12/31/12): Assets, $76,555,046 (M); expenditures, $5,238,547; qualifying distributions, $4,753,498; giving activities include $4,650,965 for 756 grants (high: $300,000; low: $1).

Purpose and activities: The foundation supports organizations involved with education, health, mental health, hunger, housing, family services, and economic development. Special emphasis is directed toward programs designed to promote health and well-being; support childhood and youth development; and foster the arts in middle Tennessee.
Fields of interest: Arts education; Visual arts; Performing arts, opera; Historical activities; Arts; Education; Health care, clinics/centers; Health care; Food services; Housing/shelter, development; Housing/shelter; Youth development, community service clubs; Youth development, business; Youth development; YM/YWCAs & YM/YWHAs; Family services; Economic development; United Ways and Federated Giving Programs.
Type of support: General/operating support; Annual campaigns; Capital campaigns; Building/renovation; Equipment; Program development; Scholarship funds; Employee volunteer services; Employee matching gifts; Matching/challenge support.
Limitations: Applications accepted. Giving primarily in middle TN. No support for political organizations, individual churches or schools, organizations established less than 3 years ago, or research, sports, environmental, wildlife, civic or international affairs organizations. No grants to individuals, or for advertising or sponsorships or social events or similar fundraising activities.
Publications: Corporate giving report; Grants list; Newsletter.
Application information: Letters of inquiry should be no longer than 1 to 2 pages. A full application may be requested at a later date. Organizations must have a full updated GivingMatters.com profile to be considered for funding. General operations and program grants range from $1,500 - $25,000. Basic need and primary health grants range from $25,000 - $50,000.Organizations receiving support of $5,000 or more are asked to submit semi-annual and final progress reports. Application form not required.
Initial approach: Letter of inquiry to foundation for new applicants; complete online application for returning grantees
Deadline(s): Mar. 14, June 13, Sept. 12, and Dec. 13
Board meeting date(s): Mar., May, Aug., and Nov.
Officers and Directors:* Richard M. Bracken,* Chair.; R. Milton Johnson, Vice-Chair.; Joanne Pulles,* Pres.; Gary Pack, Secy.; David G. Anderson, Treas.; Peter F. Bird, Jr.; Jana Davis; Ray Monroe; Bruce Moore, Jr.; Cheryl Read; John M. Steele; John Steakley; Noel Brown Williams.
Number of staff: 1 full-time professional; 1 full-time support.
EIN: 611230563

8583
Orion L. & Emma B. Hurlbut Memorial Fund ✧

701 Market St.
Chattanooga, TN 37402-4828
Application address: c/o Kathy Wood, 975 E. 3rd St., Chattanooga, TN 37403-2147; tel.: (423) 778-7503

Established in 1937 in TN.
Foundation type: Independent foundation.
Financial data (yr. ended 04/30/13): Assets, $21,088,208 (M); expenditures, $747,071; qualifying distributions, $721,179; giving activities include $581,429 for 2 grants (high: $550,000; low: $31,429).
Purpose and activities: Giving primarily to a tumor clinic; support also for treatment of indigent cancer patients outside of Hamilton County, TN.
Fields of interest: Cancer; Cancer research; Foundations (community); Economically disadvantaged.
Type of support: Grants to individuals.
Limitations: Giving primarily in Chattanooga, TN.
Application information: Applicants should include physicians' detailed expense voucher.
Initial approach: Letter
Deadline(s): None
Directors: Dr. John F. Boxell; Dr. Frank C. Kimsey; Harold G. Robertson.
Trustee: First Tennessee Bank, N.A.
EIN: 626034546

8584
Hyde Family Foundations ✧

17 W. Pontotoc Ave., Ste. 200
Memphis, TN 38103-3826 (901) 685-3400
Contact: Teresa Sloyan, Exec. Dir.
FAX: (901) 683-7478;
E-mail: info@hydefoundation.org; Main URL: http://www.hydefoundation.org
E-Newsletter: http://feedburner.google.com/fb/a/mailverify?uri=hydefoundation/zjaC
GiveSmart: http://www.givesmart.org/Stories/Donors/Barbara-and-Pitt-Hyde
Knowledge Center: http://www.hydefoundation.org/news?xtags=knowledge

J.R. Hyde Senior Family Foundation and J.R. Hyde III Family Foundation established in TN in 1961 and 1993, respectively.
Donors: J.R. Hyde, Sr.‡; J.R. Hyde III; Barbara R. Hyde.
Foundation type: Independent foundation.
Financial data (yr. ended 12/31/12): Assets, $119,208,601 (M); gifts received, $16,488,803; expenditures, $24,209,283; qualifying distributions, $23,137,054; giving activities include $21,574,968 for 306 grants (high: $2,504,943; low: $25).
Purpose and activities: The Hyde Family Foundations are committed to building a better Memphis. Through active, engaged philanthropy, their mission is to empower the people and programs that are making measurable differences in the community, and to provide leadership on public policy issues that will help Memphis become a world-class, 21st century city. The foundation is passionate about supporting high-impact initiatives in Memphis, focusing on three distinct areas of influence: 1) Transforming Education; 2) Positioning Authentic Assets; and 3) Livable Communities.
Fields of interest: Arts; Education, reform; Education; Recreation, parks/playgrounds; Community development, neighborhood development; Public affairs, alliance/advocacy; Leadership development.
Type of support: General/operating support; Capital campaigns; Building/renovation; Program development; Seed money; Technical assistance; Consulting services; Program evaluation; Employee matching gifts; Matching/challenge support; Pro bono services - advocacy.
Limitations: Applications accepted. Giving primarily in Memphis, TN. No support for political organizations. No grants to individuals.
Publications: Application guidelines.
Application information: Applications accepted via website, e-mail or mail. Application form required.
Initial approach: Submit application following review of foundation eligibility criteria
Copies of proposal: 1
Deadline(s): Mar. 1, June 1, Sept. 1 and Dec. 1
Board meeting date(s): Feb., May, Aug. and Nov.
Final notification: Within 6 to 8 weeks of submission
Officers and Directors:* Barbara R. Hyde,* Pres.; Jeanne Varnell,* Secy.; John Pontius, Treas.; Teresa Sloyan, Exec. Dir.; Ruth Bernabe; Allen B. Hyde; J.R. Hyde III; Margaret Hyde; Henry Varnell.
Number of staff: 5 full-time professional; 1 part-time professional; 4 full-time support.

8585
International Paper Company Foundation ✧

6400 Poplar Ave.
Memphis, TN 38197-0100 (800) 236-1996
Contact: Deano C. Orr, Exec. Dir.
E-mail: IPFoundation@ipaper.com; E-mail for Coins 4 Kids Program: coins4kids@ipaper.com; Main URL: http://www.internationalpaper.com/US/EN/Company/IPGiving/IPFoundation.html

Incorporated in 1952 in NY.
Donor: International Paper Co.
Foundation type: Company-sponsored foundation.
Financial data (yr. ended 12/31/12): Assets, $55,611,033 (M); expenditures, $2,913,305; qualifying distributions, $2,654,995; giving activities include $2,654,995 for 484 grants (high: $600,000; low: $30).
Purpose and activities: The foundation supports organizations involved with literacy, environmental education, and critical community needs.
Fields of interest: Museums; Education, ESL programs; Education, reading; Education; Environment, air pollution; Environment, water pollution; Environment, recycling; Environment, forests; Environmental education; Food services; Human services; Science; Children; Youth.
International interests: Africa.
Type of support: General/operating support; Equipment; Program development; Seed money; Curriculum development; Employee volunteer services; Employee matching gifts; In-kind gifts.
Limitations: Applications accepted. Giving on a national basis in areas of company operations, with some emphasis on Memphis, TN; giving also in Africa through the World Food Program. No support for veterans' or labor groups, religious or political groups, lobbying organizations, discriminatory organizations, or private foundations. No grants to individuals, or for scholarships, salaries, stipends, or other forms of compensation, mortgage, rent, or utilities, endowments, capital campaigns, multi-year commitments, sponsorships, advertising, travel or lodging expenses, national conferences, sporting events, or other one-time events; no loans.
Publications: Application guidelines; Corporate giving report; IRS Form 990 or 990-PF printed copy available upon request; Program policy statement.
Application information: All applications are routed to a local IP facility. Please contact the facility for local submission deadlines. Multi-year funding is not automatic. Application form required.
Initial approach: Complete online eligibility quiz and application

Copies of proposal: 1
Deadline(s): Varies per location, but generally reviewed Feb. 1, Apr. 1, Aug. 1, and Oct. 1
Board meeting date(s): Sept.
Officers and Directors:* Patricia Neuhoff, Pres.; Marla Adair, Secy.; Carol Tusch, Treas.; Deano C. Orr, Exec. Dir.; Terri Herrington; Paul J. Karre; Franz Marx; Carol L. Roberts; Mark Sutton; Fred Towler.
Number of staff: 3 full-time professional; 1 part-time support.
EIN: 136155080
Selected grants: The following grants are a representative sample of this grantmaker's funding activity:
$10,000 to Feeding America, Chicago, IL, 2011.
$10,000 to Nature Conservancy, Arlington, VA, 2011.
$7,500 to Pennsylvania State University, University Park, PA, 2011.
$5,000 to Junior Achievement Worldwide, Colorado Springs, CO, 2011.
$5,000 to Leukemia & Lymphoma Society, White Plains, NY, 2011.
$5,000 to Muscular Dystrophy Association, Tucson, AZ, 2011.
$4,000 to Special Olympics South Carolina, Columbia, SC, 2011.
$3,000 to Dress for Success Cincinnati, Cincinnati, OH, 2011.
$3,000 to Learning for Life, Irving, TX, 2011.
$2,500 to Crohns and Colitis Foundation of America, New York, NY, 2011.

8586
The Jeckyl Charitable Foundation ✧ ☆
c/o Sussman & Associates
700 12th Ave. S., Ste. 201
Nashville, TN 37203-2926

Established in CA.
Donors: Bette Midler; The Carole & Robert Daly Charitable Foundation; The Tomorrow Foundation; The City of New York.
Foundation type: Independent foundation.
Financial data (yr. ended 07/31/13): Assets, $2,460 (M); gifts received, $473,421; expenditures, $476,901; qualifying distributions, $476,711; giving activities include $476,711 for grants.
Fields of interest: Education.
Limitations: Applications not accepted. No grants to individuals.
Application information: Unsolicited requests for funds not accepted.
Officers: Bette Midler, Pres.; Charles Sussman, Mgr.
EIN: 954385689

8587
The Jeniam Foundation ✧
(also known as The Jeniam Clarkson Foundation)
270 Bremington Pl.
Memphis, TN 38111-6007
Contact: Tripp Killin, Exec. Dir.

Established in 1992 in TN.
Donors: Andrew M. Clarkson; Carole G. Clarkson.
Foundation type: Independent foundation.
Financial data (yr. ended 12/31/12): Assets, $18,660,695 (M); expenditures, $1,098,946; qualifying distributions, $898,112; giving activities include $754,689 for 46 grants (high: $79,500; low: $1).
Purpose and activities: The mission of the foundation is to provide venture philanthropy to the arts in Memphis, Tennessee, elder care and education in New Canaan, Connecticut, and national and international conservation.
Fields of interest: Arts, association; Arts, administration/regulation; Museums; Museums (children's); Performing arts, theater; Arts; Higher education; Environment, research; Animals/wildlife, preservation/protection; Foundations (community); Philanthropy/voluntarism.
Type of support: Capital campaigns; Building/renovation; Equipment; Seed money; Curriculum development; Research; Consulting services; Program-related investments/loans; Matching/challenge support.
Limitations: Applications accepted. Giving primarily in CT and TN. No grants to individuals, or for ongoing operating support.
Publications: Informational brochure (including application guidelines).
Application information: Contact Exec. Dir. for application guidelines. Application form not required.
Initial approach: 1- to 2-page letter
Copies of proposal: 1
Deadline(s): None
Board meeting date(s): Varies
Officer: Tripp Killin, Exec. Dir.
Trustees: Andrew M. Clarkson; Carole G. Clarkson; William M. Clarkson; Jennifer Clarkson Killin.
Number of staff: 1 full-time professional; 1 part-time professional.
EIN: 621516244
Selected grants: The following grants are a representative sample of this grantmaker's funding activity:
$79,500 to American Bird Conservancy, The Plains, VA, 2012. For Welcome Center, Iba, Dominican Republic; iPads, Scholarships Funds, Reserve Expansion, Mosquito Netting, Donor Relations Specialist.
$50,000 to Audubon Connecticut, Greenwich, CT, 2012. For General Operating Funds; Bird Program Support; Computers, Repairs.
$29,750 to Stamford Symphony Orchestra, Stamford, CT, 2012. For Scholarship Program; Sponsorship Recitals; Callalis Concert.
$25,000 to Connecticut Fund for the Environment, New Haven, CT, 2012. For Feasibility Study, Plum Island Conservation.
$23,500 to Americans for Oxford, New York, NY, 2012. For St Edmund Hall, Oxford, University.
$19,750 to Silvermine Guild Arts Center, New Canaan, CT, 2012. For Remodel Classroom; Online Registration; Computer Equipment.
$15,000 to Northern Jaguar Project, Tucson, AZ, 2012. For Tractor and Other Equipment.
$15,000 to RARE, Arlington, VA, 2012. For funding initiative.
$10,000 to Oceanites, Chevy Chase, MD, 2012. For Film Trailer on Penguins.
$10,000 to Wellesley College, Wellesley, MA, 2012. For environmental study; internship.

8588
George R. Johnson Family Foundation ✧
P.O. Box 4558
Cleveland, TN 37320-4558 (423) 614-2393
Contact: Janice L. Wilson

Established in 2004 in TN.
Donors: George R. Johnson†; Janice J. Wilson; Beverly P. Johnson; George R. Johnson Charitable Trust.
Foundation type: Independent foundation.
Financial data (yr. ended 12/31/12): Assets, $23,307,540 (M); expenditures, $1,426,226; qualifying distributions, $1,280,286; giving activities include $1,199,500 for 67 grants (high: $60,000; low: $500).
Purpose and activities: Giving primarily for education, youth, social services, and federated giving programs.
Fields of interest: Arts; Higher education; Health organizations; Youth development; Human services; United Ways and Federated Giving Programs.
Type of support: General/operating support; Building/renovation; Equipment; Endowments; Scholarship funds.
Limitations: Giving primarily in Catoosa, Dade, Murray, Walker, and Whitfield counties in GA, and in Bradley, Hamilton, Loudon, Marion, McMinn, Meigs, Monroe, Polk, Rhea, and Sequatchie counties in TN. No grants to individuals.
Application information: Application form not required.
Initial approach: Letter of no more than 2 pages
Deadline(s): None
Officer and Trustees:* Janice J. Wilson,* Exec. Dir.; Beverly P. Johnson; R. Mark Johnson; Julia Johnson Scoggins.
Agent: First Tennessee Bank, N.A.
EIN: 626401641
Selected grants: The following grants are a representative sample of this grantmaker's funding activity:
$30,000 to Chattanooga Area Food Bank, Chattanooga, TN, 2012. For Sak Pack Program.
$20,000 to Creative Discovery Museum, Chattanooga, TN, 2012. For Play Gym Program.
$15,000 to Ballet Tennessee, Chattanooga, TN, 2012. For Dance Alive Program.

8589
The Keith & Nancy Johnson Foundation ✧ ☆
(formerly Johnson Custody Foundation)
c/o L. Thompson, Merrill Lynch Trust Co.
5121 Maryland Way
Brentwood, TN 37027-7516

Established in 1999 in TN.
Donor: H. Keith Johnson, M.D.
Foundation type: Independent foundation.
Financial data (yr. ended 09/30/13): Assets, $9,683,361 (M); expenditures, $521,238; qualifying distributions, $460,974; giving activities include $420,800 for 57 grants (high: $179,000; low: $1,000).
Fields of interest: Higher education; Cancer.
Type of support: General/operating support.
Limitations: Applications not accepted. Giving primarily in Nashville, TN. No grants to individuals.
Application information: Contributes only to pre-selected organizations.
Trustee: H. Keith Johnson, M.D.
EIN: 626369110
Selected grants: The following grants are a representative sample of this grantmaker's funding activity:
$5,000 to Georgetown University, Washington, DC, 2011.

$5,000 to Georgetown University, Washington, DC, 2011.
$5,000 to Tufts University, Medford, MA, 2011.

8590
Willis and Reba Johnson's Foundation ✧ ☆
1301 Moran Rd.
Franklin, TN 37069-6310

Donors: Willis Johnson; Reba Johnson; The WJ Foundation.
Foundation type: Independent foundation.
Financial data (yr. ended 12/31/13): Assets, $5,893,085 (M); expenditures, $2,739,500; qualifying distributions, $2,739,500; giving activities include $2,739,500 for 10 grants (high: $2,600,000; low: $500).
Fields of interest: Human services; Christian agencies & churches; Religion.
Limitations: Applications not accepted. Giving primarily in TN.
Application information: Unsolicited requests for funds not accepted.
Officer: Willis Johnson, Pres.
Director: Reba Johnson.
EIN: 461306623

8591
Kharis Foundation ✧ ☆
401 Church St., Ste. 2323
Nashville, TN 37219-2211

Foundation type: Independent foundation.
Financial data (yr. ended 06/30/13): Assets, $15,801,865 (M); expenditures, $847,697; qualifying distributions, $632,580; giving activities include $453,650 for 14 grants (high: $100,000; low: $1,500).
Fields of interest: Arts; Human services; Protestant agencies & churches.
Limitations: Applications not accepted. Giving primarily in Nashville, TN.
Application information: Unsolicited requests for funds not accepted.
Officers: George Crawford III, Chair.; Beth Chiles, Vice-Chair.; Melinda Lawrence Sanders, Pres.; Kathy Corlew, Secy.; Terry Rappuhn, Treas.
Board Members: Lawson A. Allen; Tom Frye; Charles Higgins; Fred Kirchner; John Lagrasse.
EIN: 620640228

8592
Robert E. and Jenny D. Kirkland Foundation ✧
624 E. Reelfoot Ave.
Union City, TN 38261-5739

Established in 2003 in TN.
Donors: Robert Kirkland; Kirkland 2004 Charitable Trust; Kirkland 2005 Charitable Trust; Kirkland 2007 Charitable Trust.
Foundation type: Independent foundation.
Financial data (yr. ended 12/31/12): Assets, $82,447,043 (M); gifts received, $7,539,195; expenditures, $1,912,503; qualifying distributions, $1,826,566; giving activities include $1,756,214 for 23 grants (high: $1,665,773; low: $100).
Fields of interest: Elementary/secondary education; Children/youth, services.
Type of support: Scholarship funds.
Limitations: Applications not accepted. Giving primarily in TN. No grants to individuals.
Application information: Contributes only to pre-selected organizations.
Officers and Directors:* Jenny D. Kirkland,* Pres.; Christopher Kirkland,* Secy.; Bedford F. Kirkland; Macy D. Swensson.
EIN: 134228589

8593
Lura-Lee G. & William E. Lange Foundation ✧
161 Harris Hill Rd.
Maryville, TN 37804

Established in 2006 in TX.
Donor: William E. Lange.
Foundation type: Independent foundation.
Financial data (yr. ended 12/31/13): Assets, $20,090,332 (M); expenditures, $915,636; qualifying distributions, $812,005; giving activities include $810,000 for 15 grants (high: $100,000; low: $10,000).
Fields of interest: Higher education.
Limitations: Applications not accepted. Giving primarily in NM and TN.
Application information: Unsolicited requests for funds not accepted.
Officers: William E. Lange, Pres.; Margaret Young, Secy.
Directors: Bradford C. Denning; Lisa Lange-Fitzinger.
EIN: 208002817

8594
Irvin Lansky Foundation ✧
5400 Poplar Ave.
Memphis, TN 38119-3669 (901) 683-3526
Contact: Robert K. Alvarez, Dir.

Established in 2002 in TN.
Foundation type: Independent foundation.
Financial data (yr. ended 12/31/13): Assets, $11,773,720 (M); expenditures, $698,469; qualifying distributions, $566,253; giving activities include $458,150 for 11 grants (high: $119,500; low: $3,650).
Fields of interest: Human services; Community/economic development; Religion, interfaith issues; Religion.
Limitations: Applications accepted. Giving primarily in Memphis, TN.
Application information: Application form required.
Initial approach: Request application form
Deadline(s): None
Directors: Robert K. Alvarez, Dir.; Wilson Barton, Jr., Dir.; Roger Fakes, Jr., Dir.; Thomas L. Lamb, Dir.; Mark D. Puckett, Dir.; Tim Russell, Dir.; Monte Weaver, Dir.
EIN: 621859941
Selected grants: The following grants are a representative sample of this grantmaker's funding activity:
$50,000 to Advance Memphis, Memphis, TN, 2012. For Jobs for Life Program.

8595
The Bill and Carol Latimer Charitable Foundation
201 W. Main St., Ste. E
Union City, TN 38261-2132 (731) 885-2888
Contact: William H. Latimer III, Pres.
FAX: (731) 885-3888;
E-mail: bill@latimerfoundation.org; Main URL: http://www.latimerfoundation.org/

Established in 2005 in TN.
Donor: William H. Lattimer III.
Foundation type: Independent foundation.
Financial data (yr. ended 12/31/12): Assets, $133,188,510 (M); expenditures, $11,949,503; qualifying distributions, $11,949,503; giving activities include $11,490,129 for 29+ grants (high: $7,000,000), and $26,705 for 8 loans to individuals (high: $9,259; low: $427).
Purpose and activities: Giving primarily to Christian churches and organizations, including a seminary, as well as for human services; student loans also available to students graduating from Obion, Weakly and Lake County, TN, high schools to secure a college or technical education.
Fields of interest: Theological school/education; Education; Human services; Christian agencies & churches.
Type of support: Student loans—to individuals.
Limitations: Applications not accepted.
Application information: Unsolicited requests for funds not accepted.
Officers and Trustees:* John L. Warner, Jr.,* Chair.; William H. Latimer III,* Pres.; Carol Rogers Latimer,* Secy.; Al Creswell; Barry Duncan; John Harney; Douglas N. Latimer; Mark M. Layne; Alan G. Oliver.
EIN: 203450991

8596
The Lazarus Foundation, Inc. ✧
340 Martin Luther King Blvd.,Ste. 200
Bristol, TN 37620-2313

Established in 1992 in VA.
Donors: John M. Gregory; Joan P. Gregory.
Foundation type: Operating foundation.
Financial data (yr. ended 12/31/12): Assets, $387,259 (M); gifts received, $835,000; expenditures, $817,083; qualifying distributions, $677,352; giving activities include $677,352 for 12 grants (high: $333,333; low: $1,489).
Purpose and activities: Giving primarily to Christian organizations for family financial distress.
Fields of interest: Food services; Human services; International development; Christian agencies & churches; Economically disadvantaged.
International interests: Developing Countries.
Type of support: Grants to individuals.
Limitations: Applications not accepted. Giving primarily in Bristol, TN, and surrounding communities.
Application information: Unsolicited requests for funds not accepted.
Officers: John M. Gregory, Pres.; Joan P. Gregory, V.P. and Secy.; Mary Ann Blessing, Treas.
Board Member: James Gregory.
Number of staff: 1 part-time professional.
EIN: 541654943
Selected grants: The following grants are a representative sample of this grantmaker's funding activity:

$81,126 to Church of God World Missions, Cleveland, TN, 2012. For family financial distress.
$15,000 to T.L. Lowery Global Foundation, Cleveland, TN, 2012. For ministry donations.
$2,000 to People for Care and Learning, Cleveland, TN, 2012. For Other Christian Programs.

8597
Lebovitz Family Charitable Trust ✧

(formerly Moses and Leba Lebovitz Charitable Trust)
2030 Hamilton Place Blvd., Ste. 500
Chattanooga, TN 37421-6000 (423) 855-0001
Contact: Charles B. Lebovitz, Tr.

Established in 1991 in TN.
Donor: Charles B. Lebovitz.
Foundation type: Independent foundation.
Financial data (yr. ended 12/31/13): Assets, $10,624,431 (M); expenditures, $630,751; qualifying distributions, $570,477; giving activities include $526,370 for 34 grants (high: $150,000; low: $250).
Purpose and activities: Giving primarily to Jewish organizations.
Fields of interest: Human services; Jewish federated giving programs; Jewish agencies & synagogues.
Limitations: Applications accepted. Giving primarily in Chattanooga, TN. No grants to individuals.
Application information:
Initial approach: Letter
Deadline(s): None
Trustees: Beth Lebovitz Backer; Alan Cates; Alan Lebovitz; Charles B. Lebovitz; Michael Lebovitz; Stephen Lebovitz; Faye L. Peterken.
EIN: 626247365
Selected grants: The following grants are a representative sample of this grantmaker's funding activity:
$5,000 to Camp Ramah Darom, Atlanta, GA, 2012. For educational and cultural.
$5,000 to Community Foundation of Greater Chattanooga, Chattanooga, TN, 2012. For Financial and Social Services.
$1,000 to Bright School, Chattanooga, TN, 2012. For educational and cultural.
$900 to Jewish Community Housing for the Elderly, Brighton, MA, 2012. For Financial and Social Services.
$500 to American Cancer Society, Nashville, TN, 2012. For public charity.

8598
Lewis Foundation ✧ ☆

9274 Exton Ln.
Brentwood, TN 37027-1402

Established in TN.
Donor: Thomas A. Vallett.
Foundation type: Independent foundation.
Financial data (yr. ended 12/31/13): Assets, $21,572,961 (M); expenditures, $1,511,370; qualifying distributions, $1,400,000; giving activities include $1,400,000 for 7 grants (high: $600,000; low: $50,000).
Fields of interest: Human services; Children/youth, services; Protestant agencies & churches.
Limitations: Applications not accepted. Giving primarily in TN; some funding also in Colorado Springs, CO. No grants to individuals.
Application information: Unsolicited requests for funds not accepted.
Trustee: Thomas A. Vallett.
Committee Members: Jeff Baumgartner; Elizabeth Privett; Wade C. Privett; Jane E. Vallett; Sara J. Vallett; Paul T. Vallett.
EIN: 456628772

8599
Lyndhurst Foundation ✧

517 E. 5th St.
Chattanooga, TN 37403-1826 (423) 756-0767
Contact: Benic M. Clark III, Pres.
FAX: (423) 756-0770; E-mail for proposals: Krudolph@lyndhurstfoundation.org; Main URL: http://www.lyndhurstfoundation.org
Grants List: http://www.lyndhurstfoundation.org/page/grant-list/

Incorporated in 1938 in DE.
Donors: T. Cartter Lupton‡; Central Shares Corp.
Foundation type: Independent foundation.
Financial data (yr. ended 12/31/12): Assets, $109,622,109 (M); expenditures, $4,900,181; qualifying distributions, $4,114,537; giving activities include $3,079,267 for 30 grants (high: $750,000; low: $2,500).
Purpose and activities: The mission of the foundation is to invest in initiatives, institutions, people and programs that contribute to the long-term livability and resilience of the greater Chattanooga region. It will accomplish this by focusing its efforts on education, conservation, arts, culture, economy, urban design and development, neighborhood revitalization, and physical health.
Fields of interest: Arts; Elementary school/education; Secondary school/education; Environment; Housing/shelter, development; Community/economic development.
Type of support: General/operating support; Continuing support; Capital campaigns; Building/renovation; Land acquisition; Program development; Seed money; Technical assistance; Employee matching gifts; Matching/challenge support.
Limitations: Applications not accepted. Giving primarily in the metropolitan Chattanooga, TN, area and the surrounding three-state region. No support for political organizations. No grants to individuals.
Publications: Financial statement; Grants list.
Application information: Unsolicited requests for funds not accepted.
Board meeting date(s): Feb., May, Aug., and Nov.
Officers and Trustees:* Robert C. Taylor, Jr., Chair.; Benic M. Clark III, Pres. and Treas.; Katherine N. Currin,* Secy.; Margaret Stakely, Cont.; Stephen A. Culp; Kathlee S. Hunt, M.D.; James O. Kennedy; Alison G. Lebovitz; James J. McGinness; Robert K. Mills; Margaret W. Townsend.
Number of staff: 4 full-time professional; 1 full-time support.
EIN: 626044177
Selected grants: The following grants are a representative sample of this grantmaker's funding activity:
$750,000 to University of Chattanooga Foundation, Chattanooga, TN, 2012. For expansion and commercialization activities at SimCenter: National Center for Computational Engineering.
$500,000 to Hamilton, County of, Chattanooga, TN, 2012. For Downtown Riverwalk project, which will connect Ross Landing to base of Lookout Mountain.
$350,000 to River City Company, Chattanooga, TN, 2012. To enhance exterior facade of former Bijou Theater building in downtown Chattanooga.
$282,000 to River City Company, Chattanooga, TN, 2012. For revitalization activities on Main Street.
$225,000 to Co.Lab, Chattanooga, TN, 2012. For Gig Tank, Entrepreneurs-In-Residence program and full-time event coordinator.
$120,000 to ArtsBuild, Chattanooga, TN, 2012. For artistic landscaping elements in new Main Terrain Park.
$105,000 to Chattanooga-Hamilton County Regional Planning Commission, Chattanooga, TN, 2012. For design consulting services to improve pedestrian and bicycle links on Chattanooga's North Shore and mitigate stormwater runoff at Manufacturers Road Interchange.
$75,000 to Trust for Public Land, Chattanooga, TN, 2012. To purchase land and for related improvements in the vicinity of Spears Avenue to facilitate trail access at Stringer's Ridge Park.
$70,000 to RiverRocks, Chattanooga, TN, 2012. For demonstration project held during RiverRocks Festival to promote performing arts and Chattanooga's fiber optic network.
$35,000 to Georgia Land Trust, Savannah, GA, 2012. For land protection efforts in northwest Georgia and northeast Alabama.

8600
Hugh and Charlotte MacLellan Charitable Trust ✧

820 Broad St., Ste. 300
Chattanooga, TN 37402-2604

Established in 2008 in TN.
Foundation type: Independent foundation.
Financial data (yr. ended 06/30/13): Assets, $20,806,458 (M); expenditures, $1,439,219; qualifying distributions, $973,925; giving activities include $938,102 for 3 grants (high: $908,102; low: $10,000).
Fields of interest: Education; Christian agencies & churches; Protestant agencies & churches.
Limitations: Applications not accepted. Giving primarily in CO, GA and TN.
Application information: Contributes only to pre-selected organizations.
Officers: Daniel O. MacLellan, Pres.; Catherine M. Heald, V.P.; Elizabeth M. Lindquist, V.P.; Christopher H. MacLellan, V.P.; Hugh O. MacLellan, Jr., Secy.-Treas.
EIN: 626268981
Selected grants: The following grants are a representative sample of this grantmaker's funding activity:
$908,102 to Chattanooga Christian Community Foundation, Chattanooga, TN, 2013. For charitable projects.

8601
The Maclellan Foundation, Inc. ✧

820 Broad St., Ste. 300
Chattanooga, TN 37402-2604 (423) 755-1366
Contact: Hugh O. Maclellan, Jr., Pres.
FAX: (423) 755-1640; E-mail: info@maclellan.net; Additional e-mail: support@maclellan.net; Main URL: http://www.maclellan.net/family-foundations/maclellan

Incorporated in 1945 in DE; reincorporated in TN in 1992.
Donors: Robert J. Maclellan†; and members of the Maclellan family.
Foundation type: Independent foundation.
Financial data (yr. ended 12/31/13): Assets, $313,291,997 (M); expenditures, $31,834,860; qualifying distributions, $25,284,303; giving activities include $19,749,096 for 2+ grants (high: $19,745,000).
Purpose and activities: The purpose of the foundation in the Chattanooga area is to provide financial and leadership resources to foster biblical Christian values in the community and meet practical and spiritual needs. This is primarily accomplished through faith-based ministries. On a national basis, the foundation's vision is to see strong families worshipping in healthy churches, influencing culture, and seeking to serve God above all else. The focus is on nationwide strategies that deliver faith-based solutions.On an international basis, the foundation's vision is to see a vibrant, disciplined, reproducing church. The focus is on establishing and strengthening the church, discipleship and leadership development, promoting community transformation, and increasing access to Scripture.
Fields of interest: Religion, association; Christian agencies & churches; Protestant agencies & churches; Children; Youth; Adults; Young adults; Hispanics/Latinos; Indigenous peoples.
International interests: Africa; Asia; Eastern Europe; Middle East.
Type of support: Consulting services; Matching/challenge support; Program development; Program evaluation.
Limitations: Applications accepted. Giving nationally, with emphasis on the Chattanooga, TN, area; giving internationally in Asia, Africa, Europe and Eurasia and the Middle East. No grants to individuals, or for emergency funds, deficit financing, land acquisition, endowment funds, health services, medical research, publications scholarships, or for renovations.
Application information: See foundation's website for granting guidelines, LOI, and explanation of application process. Only online LOI's will be considered. Application form not required.
Initial approach: Online application required
Copies of proposal: 1
Deadline(s): Ongoing through out the year.
Board meeting date(s): 3-4 times per year
Final notification: Within 60 days of LOI submission
Officers and Trustees:* Hugh O. Maclellan, Jr.,* Exec. Chair. and Treas.; Robert H. Maclellan,* Vice-Chair.; Sandy Barber, Compt.; David Denmark, Exec. Dir.; Tom Lowe, C.I.O.; Mrs. R.L. Maclellan, Tr. Emeritus; Ronald W. Blue; Mrs. Catherine Maclellan Heald; Christopher Maclellan; A.S. Pat MacMillan; Niel Nielson, Ph.D.; Laurence Powell; W. Miller Welborn.
Number of staff: 17 full-time professional; 5 full-time support.
EIN: 626041468
Selected grants: The following grants are a representative sample of this grantmaker's funding activity:
$17,660,000 to National Christian Foundation, Alpharetta, GA, 2012.
$3,350,000 to Chattanooga Christian Community Foundation, Chattanooga, TN, 2012.

8602
Robert L. and Kathrina H. Maclellan Foundation ✧

820 Broad St., Ste. 300
Chattanooga, TN 37402-2604 (423) 755-1366
Contact: Jan Purdy
FAX: (423) 755-1640;
E-mail: support@maclellan.net; Main URL: http://www.maclellan.net/family-foundations/rlkhm

Established in 1972 in TN.
Donor: Kathrina H. MacLellan.
Foundation type: Independent foundation.
Financial data (yr. ended 12/31/13): Assets, $58,096,500 (M); gifts received, $1,440,879; expenditures, $2,870,209; qualifying distributions, $2,554,337; giving activities include $1,969,566 for 25 grants (high: $1,219,116; low: $2,000).
Purpose and activities: The foundation exists to support the Church as it expands by word and deed to provide the blessings of shalom. The foundation works primarily in the Greater Chattanooga, Tennessee community, primarily supporting Evangelical Christian ministries with an emphasis on: youth and children, family, education, leadership, and redemption.
Fields of interest: Elementary/secondary education; Theological school/education; Education; Children/youth, services; Christian agencies & churches.
Limitations: Giving primarily in the greater Chattanooga, TN area.
Application information: The foundation will primarily send application invitations to ministries of interest. It will also review the letters of inquiry submitted online (www.maclellan.net); however it will only contact those of potential interest. If you do not hear directly from the foundation, you should assume that your project is not a good match for its giving priorities. Application form required.
Initial approach: Refer to foundation web site
Deadline(s): None
Board meeting date(s): Quarterly
Officers and Trustees:* Kathrina H. Maclellan,* Chair.; Robert H. Maclellan,* Pres. and Treas.; Thomas H. McCallie III,* Secy.; Robert Bosworth; Robert Divine; Donald J. Holwerda; Albert MacMillan; Lara Munford; N. Carter Newbold.
EIN: 237159802
Selected grants: The following grants are a representative sample of this grantmaker's funding activity:
$90,000 to Chalmers Center for Economic Development At Covenant College, Lookout Mountain, GA, 2012. For Community Development/Social Services.
$45,000 to Young Life, Colorado Springs, CO, 2012. For Youth and Children.
$25,000 to Mastermedia International, Redlands, CA, 2012. For leadership development.
$15,000 to United Way of Greater Chattanooga, Chattanooga, TN, 2012. For general charitable funding.

8603
The Dan and Margaret Maddox Charitable Fund ✧

(formerly The Dan and Margaret Maddox Charitable Trust)
P.O. Box 58493
Nashville, TN 37205-8493 (615) 385-1006
Contact: Kaki Friskics-Warren, Dir.
E-mail: kaki@maddoxcharitablefund.org; E-mail for Kaki Friskics-Warren: kaki@maddoxcharitablefund.org; Main URL: http://www.maddoxcharitablefund.org/
Facebook: https://www.facebook.com/MaddoxCharitableFund

Established in 1968.
Donors: Dan W. Maddox†; Margaret Maddox.
Foundation type: Independent foundation.
Financial data (yr. ended 12/31/12): Assets, $46,210,960 (M); expenditures, $1,944,937; qualifying distributions, $1,891,700; giving activities include $1,891,700 for grants (high: $169,000; low: $1,000; average: $15,000–$75,000).
Purpose and activities: The purpose of the fund is to make a positive difference in the lives of young people and promote the conservation of wildlife habitat.
Fields of interest: Elementary/secondary education; Middle schools/education; Secondary school/education; Higher education, college; Animals/wildlife, preservation/protection; Youth, services.
Type of support: Program development.
Limitations: Applications accepted. Giving limited to forty-one counties in middle Tennessee. No support for congregations and religious organizations for projects that primarily benefit their own members or for evangelical purposes (exception: programs that are: 1) receiving broad community support, 2) keeping separate financial statements, and 3) primarily benefiting persons outside of their congregational members) or for organizations incorporated for fewer than 3 years, 501(c)(3) organizations that are government or government affiliates, supporting organizations or private foundations. No grants to individuals or for operating expenses, endowment, debt reduction, depreciation, advocacy efforts (defined as lobbying or attempting to impact legislation), and personal travel (Staff).
Publications: Grants list.
Application information: See web site for application form and to submit an online proposal. Application form required.
Initial approach: Telephone or e-mail
Deadline(s): On or about Jan. 15
Final notification: 3-months
Officers and Directors:* Shirley Zeitlin,* Chair.; Tommye Maddox,* Secy.; Joe Russell,* Treas.; The Rev. Mary K. "Kaki" Friskics-Warren, Exec. Dir.; Robert S. Brandt; Lauren Briskey; Greg Burns; Michael Carter; David Esquivel; LeShane Greenhill; Becky Harrell; Will Martin; Kay Simmons; Lisa Wiltshire; Brenda Wynn.
EIN: 237017790

8604
The Albert Jay Martin Family Foundation ✧

140 Crescent Dr.
Collierville, TN 38017

Established in 1997 in TN.
Donor: Albert Jay Martin.
Foundation type: Independent foundation.
Financial data (yr. ended 11/30/13): Assets, $2,816,940 (M); gifts received, $398,801; expenditures, $1,274,274; qualifying distributions, $1,255,227; giving activities include $1,255,227 for 27 grants (high: $536,427; low: $500).

Purpose and activities: Giving primarily for education and human services.
Fields of interest: Education; Health care; Boys & girls clubs; Human services; United Ways and Federated Giving Programs; Protestant agencies & churches.
Limitations: Applications not accepted. Giving primarily in TN; funding also in NC. No grants to individuals.
Application information: Unsolicited requests for funds not accepted.
Trustee: Albert Jay Martin.
EIN: 626345910

8605
R. Brad Martin Family Foundation ✧
(formerly R. Brad & Jean L. Martin Family Foundation)
1025 Cherry Rd.
Memphis, TN 38117-5423

Established in 1994 in TN.
Donors: R. Brad Martin; RBM Shopping Centers, Inc.
Foundation type: Independent foundation.
Financial data (yr. ended 09/30/13): Assets, $10,141,056 (M); gifts received, $1,007,760; expenditures, $892,127; qualifying distributions, $856,691; giving activities include $855,296 for 53 grants (high: $580,000; low: $250).
Purpose and activities: Giving primarily for human services; funding also for education, and United Methodist churches.
Fields of interest: Arts; Education; Hospitals (specialty); Health organizations, association; Human services; Children/youth, services; Protestant agencies & churches.
Limitations: Applications not accepted. Giving primarily in Memphis, TN. No grants to individuals.
Application information: Unsolicited requests for funds not accepted.
Officers and Directors:* R. Brad Martin,* Pres.; Rawleigh B. Martin, V.P.; Scott Imorde,* Secy.; C.T. Courtenay,* Treas.; Brian J. Martin; Dina M. Martin.
EIN: 621548977
Selected grants: The following grants are a representative sample of this grantmaker's funding activity:
$110,000 to Presbyterian Day School, Memphis, TN, 2011.
$100,000 to Christ United Methodist Church, Memphis, TN, 2011.
$50,000 to Prince of Wales Foundation, Washington, DC, 2011.
$50,000 to Saint Jude Childrens Research Hospital, Memphis, TN, 2011.
$25,000 to Hazelden Foundation, Center City, MN, 2011.
$25,000 to LArche USA, Portland, OR, 2011.
$25,000 to Saint Johns United Methodist Church, Memphis, TN, 2011.
$10,000 to American Friends of the Louvre, New York, NY, 2011.
$10,000 to Christ Methodist Day School, Memphis, TN, 2011.
$5,000 to My Memphis Charitable Foundation, Memphis, TN, 2011.

8606
The Martin Foundation ✧
P.O. Box 1869
Brentwood, TN 37024-1869
Main URL: http://martinfoundationnashville.com/

Established in 1996 in TN.
Donor: Charles N. Martin, Jr.
Foundation type: Independent foundation.
Financial data (yr. ended 12/31/13): Assets, $3,418,266 (M); expenditures, $1,194,622; qualifying distributions, $1,113,333; giving activities include $1,113,333 for 11 grants (high: $583,333; low: $5,000).
Purpose and activities: Giving primarily for the arts, education, and children and social services in middle Tennessee.
Fields of interest: Arts; Education; Health organizations, association; Human services; Children/youth, services.
Type of support: General/operating support; Continuing support; Annual campaigns; Capital campaigns; Building/renovation; Equipment; Debt reduction; Seed money; Matching/challenge support.
Limitations: Applications accepted. Giving primarily in middle TN. No grants to individuals, or for endowments.
Application information: Application form required.
Initial approach: See website
Copies of proposal: 1
Deadline(s): None
Board meeting date(s): Annual
Officers: Charles N. Martin, Jr., Chair.; Shannon Presley Martin, Exec. Dir.
Trustee: Leslie Wilkinson.
Number of staff: 1 full-time professional.
EIN: 621679129

8607
Jack C. Massey Foundation ✧
(formerly JCM Foundation)
5123 Virginia Way, Ste. B-22
Brentwood, TN 37027-7598

Reincorporated in 1998 in TN.
Foundation type: Independent foundation.
Financial data (yr. ended 12/31/13): Assets, $49,225,808 (M); expenditures, $1,571,611; qualifying distributions, $1,122,250; giving activities include $1,120,100 for 43 grants (high: $225,000; low: $100).
Purpose and activities: Giving primarily for the arts, education, particularly higher education, as well as for health care, and children, youth, and social services,.
Fields of interest: Performing arts; Arts; Elementary/secondary education; Higher education; Education; Health care; Health organizations, association; Medical research, institute; Human services; Children/youth, services.
Limitations: Applications not accepted. Giving primarily in FL and TN. No grants to individuals.
Application information: Contributes only to pre-selected organizations.
Officers and Directors:* Leonard H. Armistead III, Co-Chair.; Barbara Massey Rogers, Co-Chair.; Clarence Edmonds,* Pres.; J. Brad Reed,* V.P.
EIN: 621649826

8608
The Master's Table Inc. ✧
620 Shelby St.
Bristol, TN 37620-2241

Established in 2001 in TN.
Donors: Joseph R. Gregory; Lucinda Gregory.
Foundation type: Independent foundation.
Financial data (yr. ended 12/31/13): Assets, $2,181,601 (M); gifts received, $853,945; expenditures, $2,818,797; qualifying distributions, $2,801,187; giving activities include $2,801,187 for 14 grants (high: $1,920,087; low: $1,650).
Fields of interest: Higher education, university; Human services.
Limitations: Applications not accepted. Giving primarily in TN. No grants to individuals.
Application information: Contributes only to pre-selected organizations.
Officers: Joseph R. Gregory, Pres.; Lucinda J. Gregory, Secy.-Treas.
EIN: 621874715
Selected grants: The following grants are a representative sample of this grantmaker's funding activity:
$500,000 to Regent University, Virginia Beach, VA, 2012. For Chapel Building Fund.
$10,000 to Tennessee Sports Hall of Fame, Nashville, TN, 2012. For Jeff Byrd Memorial Scholarship.

8609
The Melkus Family Foundation ✧
102 Woodmont Blvd., Ste. 110
Nashville, TN 37205-5248

Established in 1993 in TN.
Donors: Kenneth J. Melkus; Barbara L. Melkus; Lauren E. Melkus; Melkus Partners, Ltd.
Foundation type: Independent foundation.
Financial data (yr. ended 12/31/13): Assets, $38,082,239 (M); gifts received, $1,415,290; expenditures, $1,164,247; qualifying distributions, $1,026,264; giving activities include $1,025,389 for 58 grants (high: $102,994; low: $500).
Purpose and activities: Giving primarily to the United Way as well as for the arts, health associations, health care, and for children, youth, and social services.
Fields of interest: Arts; Hospitals (general); Hospitals (specialty); Health organizations, association; Crime/violence prevention, sexual abuse; Food services; Human services; Children/youth, services; United Ways and Federated Giving Programs.
Limitations: Applications not accepted. Giving primarily in Nashville, TN. No grants to individuals.
Application information: Contributes only to pre-selected organizations.
Officers: Kenneth J. Melkus, Pres.; Barbara L. Melkus, Secy.; Lauren E. Melkus, Treas.
EIN: 621518285
Selected grants: The following grants are a representative sample of this grantmaker's funding activity:
$50,000 to Habitat for Humanity of Greater Nashville, Nashville, TN, 2012. For Further Exempt Purposes of Organization.

8610
Memphis Grizzlies Charitable Foundation ✧
191 Beale St.
Memphis, TN 38103-3715 (901) 205-8326
Contact: Jenny Koltnow, Exec. Dir.
FAX: (901) 205-1444;
E-mail: foundation@grizzlies.com; E-mail for Tickets for Kids: ticketsforkids@grizzlies.com; Contact for Honoring Our Military Families: Eric Bleier, tel.: (901) 205-1249; Main URL: http://www.teamupmemphis.org/
RSS Feed: http://teamupmemphis.org/index.php/site/rss_2.0
Team Up Memphis Blog: http://teamupmemphis.org/index.php/blog/

Established in 2004 in TN.
Donors: The Poplar Foundation; Hope Christian Community Foundation; Helco Holding, Inc.
Foundation type: Company-sponsored foundation.
Financial data (yr. ended 12/31/12): Assets, $429,546 (M); gifts received, $1,171,719; expenditures, $306,676; qualifying distributions, $1,264,177; giving activities include $1,071,510 for 22 grants (high: $300,000; low: $1,000).
Purpose and activities: The foundation supports programs designed to serve youth through education and mentoring. Special emphasis is directed toward organizations that operate a youth mentoring program; recruit or promote the retention of youth mentors; and organizations that provide specialized or significant expertise to mentoring programs.
Fields of interest: Secondary school/education; Education; Athletics/sports, amateur leagues; Athletics/sports, basketball; Boys & girls clubs; Youth development, adult & child programs; Youth development; Human services.
Type of support: General/operating support; Program development; Technical assistance; Donated products; In-kind gifts.
Limitations: Applications accepted. Giving limited to AR, MS, and the Memphis, TN, area.
Publications: Application guidelines.
Application information: Letter of intent should be submitted on organization letterhead. Application form required.
Initial approach: Letter of intent; download application form and e-mail or fax to foundation for Tickets for Kids
Deadline(s): June 4; None for Tickets for Kids
Officers and Directors:* Staley Cates,* Pres.; Elliot Perry, V.P.; Stanley Meadows,* Secy.-Treas.; Jennifer Koltnow, Exec. Dir.; Andy Cates; Michael Conley; Charles Ewing, Sr.; Michael Heisley; Barbara Hyde; J. R. Hyde III; Fred Jones, Jr.; Pete Prancia; Sean Tuohy.
EIN: 201356702

8611
Midler Family Foundation ✧
c/o Sussman & Associates
700 12th Avenue S., Ste. 201
Nashville, TN 37203

Established in 2004 in TN.
Donor: Bette Midler.
Foundation type: Operating foundation.
Financial data (yr. ended 11/30/12): Assets, $4,024,447 (M); gifts received, $25,000; expenditures, $505,322; qualifying distributions, $487,070; giving activities include $487,070 for 48 grants.
Purpose and activities: Giving primarily for medical research, as well as for education, including a music education program benefiting underserved New York City public school students, and social services.
Fields of interest: Arts; Education; Medical research, institute; Human services; Children/youth, services; Urban/community development; Economically disadvantaged.
Limitations: Applications not accepted. Giving primarily in New York, NY and ME. No grants to individuals.
Application information: Contributes only to pre-selected organizations.
Trustee: Bette Midler.
EIN: 137437183

8612
Msb Cockayne Fund, Inc ✧
424 Church St., Ste. 2800
Nashville, TN 37219-2386

Established in UT.
Donor: Cockayne Fund.
Foundation type: Independent foundation.
Financial data (yr. ended 12/31/13): Assets, $33,513,309 (M); expenditures, $1,672,798; qualifying distributions, $1,600,659; giving activities include $1,583,387 for 58 grants (high: $125,000; low: $1,000).
Fields of interest: Arts; Higher education; Botanical gardens; Medical research.
Limitations: Applications not accepted. Giving primarily in Nashville, TN.
Application information: Contributes only to pre-selected organizations.
Officers: Martin S. Brown, Sr., Chair.; Martin S. Brown, Jr., Pres.; Susannah Scott-Barnes, Secy.-Treas.
EIN: 452806883

8613
The Nissan Foundation ✧
P.O. Box 685001, M.S. B5B
Franklin, TN 37068-5001 (615) 725-1501
E-mail: nissanfoundation@nissan-usa.com; Main URL: http://www.nissanusa.com

Established in 1993 in CA.
Donors: Nissan Motor Corp. U.S.A.; Nissan North America, Inc.
Foundation type: Company-sponsored foundation.
Financial data (yr. ended 06/30/14): Assets, $13,705,104 (M); expenditures, $734,315; qualifying distributions, $718,088; giving activities include $715,000 for 31 grants (high: $65,000; low: $10,000).
Purpose and activities: The foundation supports educational programs designed to promote diverse cultural heritage.
Fields of interest: Arts, cultural/ethnic awareness; Museums; Performing arts; Education.
Type of support: General/operating support; Program development.
Limitations: Applications not accepted. Giving limited to areas of company operations in southern CA, the Atlanta, GA, metropolitan area, Detroit, MI, south central MS, the New York, NY, metropolitan area, middle TN, and Dallas and Forth Worth, TX. No support for disease advocacy, research, or religious organizations. No grants to individuals, or for fundraising events, sponsorships, or political activities or capital campaigns.
Application information: Unsolicited requests for funds not accepted.
Officers and Directors:* Scott Becker,* Pres.; David Reuter,* V.P.; John M. Dab,* Secy.; William H. Scott, Jr.,* Treas.; Holly Bracco; Bradley D. Thacker; Allesandra Tharp; George Vazquez; Jun Watnabe; Jeffrey Webster; Paula Wells; Robert Wilson.
EIN: 954413799
Selected grants: The following grants are a representative sample of this grantmaker's funding activity:
$60,000 to Nashville Public Television, Nashville, TN, 2011.
$50,000 to Oasis Center, Nashville, TN, 2011.
$30,000 to 100 Black Men of Jackson, Jackson, MS, 2011.
$30,000 to Brooklyn Childrens Museum, Brooklyn, NY, 2011.
$30,000 to International Museum of Muslim Cultures, Jackson, MS, 2011.
$30,000 to Jobs for Mississippi Graduates, Jackson, MS, 2011.
$25,000 to Global Education Center, Nashville, TN, 2011.
$20,000 to National Black Arts Festival, Atlanta, GA, 2011.
$15,000 to Bayside Community Center, San Diego, CA, 2011.
$10,000 to New York University, New York, NY, 2011.

8614
Weldon F. Osborne Foundation, Inc. ✧
Krystal Bldg.
1 Union Sq., Ste. 210
Chattanooga, TN 37402-2501 (423) 267-0931
Contact: Barbara Marter, Exec. Dir.
FAX: (423) 402-8040;
E-mail: wosborne@comcast.net; Main URL: http://www.wfosbornefoundation.org/
Grants List: http://www.wfosbornefoundation.org/grant-history/

Established in 1959.
Donors: Osborne Enterprises, Inc.; Osborne Building Corp.
Foundation type: Independent foundation.
Financial data (yr. ended 06/30/13): Assets, $18,534,890 (M); expenditures, $1,545,008; qualifying distributions, $1,122,362; giving activities include $998,024 for 116 grants (high: $100,000; low: $500).
Purpose and activities: Giving for civic, community, education and youth services.
Fields of interest: Education; Human services; Children/youth, services; Foundations (community); United Ways and Federated Giving Programs; Christian agencies & churches.
Type of support: Capital campaigns; Building/renovation; Seed money; Scholarship funds; Matching/challenge support.
Limitations: Giving primarily in the Chattanooga and Hamilton County, TN, areas. No grants to individuals.
Publications: Application guidelines; Annual report; Financial statement.
Application information: Application video tutorials and application policies and guidelines available on foundation web site. Application form required.

Initial approach: Letter of Inquiry to be submitted online through foundation web site after creating a user ID and password
Deadline(s): Nov. 1 - Jan. 31 (for Feb. meeting); Mar. 1 - May 31 (for June meeting); and July 1 - Sept. 30 (for Oct. meeting)
Board meeting date(s): 2nd Tues. each quarter; after annual meeting 2nd Tues. in June
Final notification: After next board meeting
Officers and Directors:* Glenn C. Stophel,* Pres.; H.E. "Gene" Burnett,* V.P., Progs.; Arch E. Trimble III,* Secy.; Barbara J. Marter, Exec. Dir.; C. Duffy Franck, Jr.; W. Scott Mattice; Dr. Christine B. Smith.
Number of staff: 1 part-time professional.
EIN: 626026442
Selected grants: The following grants are a representative sample of this grantmaker's funding activity:
$100,000 to Chattanooga Christian Community Foundation, Chattanooga, TN, 2010.
$100,000 to Chattanooga Christian Community Foundation, Chattanooga, TN, 2011.
$76,102 to Community Foundation of Greater Chattanooga, Chattanooga, TN, 2011.
$68,578 to Community Foundation of Greater Chattanooga, Chattanooga, TN, 2010.
$35,000 to First Things First, Chattanooga, TN, 2011. For general support.
$35,000 to Little Miss Mag Child Care Center, Chattanooga, TN, 2011.
$31,250 to Siskin Childrens Institute, Chattanooga, TN, 2011.
$25,000 to Boyd-Buchanan School, Chattanooga, TN, 2010. For general support.
$25,000 to Memorial Health Care System Foundation, Chattanooga, TN, 2010. For general support.
$25,000 to Memorial Health Care System Foundation, Chattanooga, TN, 2011. For general support.
$25,000 to T. C. Thompson Childrens Hospital, Chattanooga, TN, 2010. For general support.
$20,000 to Bryan College, Dayton, TN, 2010. For general support.
$20,000 to Bryan College, Dayton, TN, 2011. For general support.
$20,000 to Hospice of Chattanooga, Chattanooga, TN, 2010.
$20,000 to Volunteers in Medicine, Chattanooga, Chattanooga, TN, 2010. For general support.
$10,000 to Contact of Chattanooga, Chattanooga, TN, 2010. For general support.
$10,000 to Southern Adventist University, Collegedale, TN, 2010.
$5,000 to Contact of Chattanooga, Chattanooga, TN, 2011. For general support.
$4,000 to Memorial Health Care System Foundation, Chattanooga, TN, 2011. For general support.
$2,000 to Chattanooga-Hamilton County Public Education Fund, Chattanooga, TN, 2011. For general support.

8615
Plough Foundation ✧
62 N. Main St., Ste. 201
Memphis, TN 38103-2110
Contact: Barbara Jacobs, Prog. Dir.
FAX: (901) 529-4063; E-mail: mail@plough.org

Established in 1972 in TN.
Donors: Abe Plough‡; Jocelyn P. Rudner; Patricia R. Burnham; Diane R. Rudner; Sharon D. Eisenberg; William Rudner.
Foundation type: Independent foundation.
Financial data (yr. ended 12/31/12): Assets, $112,125,038 (M); gifts received, $237,649; expenditures, $11,366,347; qualifying distributions, $10,560,749; giving activities include $9,499,414 for 40 grants (high: $2,000,000; low: $500).
Purpose and activities: Grants to community projects, early childhood and elementary education, crime, health care, economic development, social service agencies, housing and homelessness, and the arts.
Fields of interest: Arts; Education, public education; Education, early childhood education; Health care; Crime/violence prevention; Housing/shelter, homeless; Human services; Youth, services; Family services; Economic development.
Type of support: Management development/capacity building; Capital campaigns; Building/renovation; Equipment; Land acquisition; Endowments; Program development; Professorships; Seed money; Program evaluation; Program-related investments/loans; Matching/challenge support.
Limitations: Giving in Shelby County, TN, with an emphasis on Memphis. No grants to individuals, and generally no grants for annual operating funds.
Publications: Informational brochure (including application guidelines).
Application information: Receipt of concept letters is acknowledged. Foundation will invite full application and supply forms only to those applicants whose proposals are deemed to match the foundation's focuses. Interviews with applicants are granted only after receipt of the written proposal and at the invitation of the foundation. The applicant organization should be aware that most grants carry a stipulation that other contributed amounts must be obtained by the organization as matching funds. Application form required.
Initial approach: Letter describing project, no more than 3 pages; full application by invitation only
Copies of proposal: 3
Deadline(s): 10th of month prior to board meeting for full application
Board meeting date(s): Feb., May, Aug., and Nov.
Final notification: Generally within two week
Officers and Trustees:* Diane R. Rudner,* Chair.; Patricia R. Burnham; Eugene J. Callahan; Sharon Eisenberg; Rick Masson; Johnny B. Moore; Peter R. Pettit; Jocelyn P. Rudner; James Springfield; Steve Wishnia; SunTrust Bank.
Number of staff: 4 full-time professional; 1 full-time support.
EIN: 237175983
Selected grants: The following grants are a representative sample of this grantmaker's funding activity:
$2,000,000 to University of Memphis, Memphis, TN, 2012. For new Community Health Building on Park Avenue campus.
$500,000 to Memphis Museums, Memphis, TN, 2012. For Pink Palace Capital Campaign for restoration and new space for Clyde Parks Miniature Circus.
$500,000 to Saint Jude Childrens Research Hospital, Memphis, TN, 2012. For Global Education and Communication Center in new Tower II Building.
$250,000 to Knowledge Quest, Memphis, TN, 2012. To expand Knowledge Quest Kids Zone, and afterschool program to children in South Memphis.
$150,000 to Soulsville Foundation, Memphis, TN, 2012. For startup support for afterschool program for middle school students.

8616
The Poplar Foundation ✧
(formerly The Longleaf Foundation)
6410 Poplar Ave., Ste. 720
Memphis, TN 38119-4843 (901) 818-5195
Contact: Thomas M. Marino, Exec. Dir.

Established in 1994 in TN.
Donors: O. Mason Hawkins; Joseph L. Ott; Southeastern Asset Management, Inc.
Foundation type: Independent foundation.
Financial data (yr. ended 12/31/12): Assets, $228,106,440 (M); gifts received, $15,200,000; expenditures, $13,822,218; qualifying distributions, $12,192,553; giving activities include $12,192,553 for 38 grants (high: $2,435,000; low: $350).
Purpose and activities: Funding primarily for youth services and education.
Fields of interest: Arts; Education; Health care; Human services; Children/youth, services; Christian agencies & churches.
Limitations: Giving primarily in Memphis, TN.
Application information:
Initial approach: Letter
Deadline(s): None
Officers and Directors:* G. Staley Cates,* Pres.; Andrew R. McCarroll,* Secy.-Treas.; Dallas M. Greer, C.F.O.; Thomas M. Marino, Exec. Dir.
EIN: 621586727
Selected grants: The following grants are a representative sample of this grantmaker's funding activity:
$2,435,000 to Collegiate School of Memphis, Memphis, TN, 2012.
$1,474,601 to Catholic Memphis Urban Schools, Memphis, TN, 2012.
$937,500 to Teach for America, Memphis, TN, 2012.
$930,000 to Hope Christian Community Foundation, Memphis, TN, 2012.
$740,000 to Memphis Teacher Residency, Memphis, TN, 2012.
$675,000 to New Leaders for New Schools, Memphis Office, Memphis, TN, 2012.
$591,160 to Salvation Army, Memphis, Memphis, TN, 2012.
$562,500 to Charter Fund, Broomfield, CO, 2012.
$433,000 to Memphis Leadership Foundation, Memphis, TN, 2012.
$125,000 to Stand for Children Memphis, Memphis, TN, 2012.

8617
Elizabeth Craig Weaver Proctor Charitable Foundation ✧ ☆
215 Evelyn Ave.
Nashville, TN 37205-3307

Established in 2000 in TN.
Donors: Elizabeth C. Proctor; E.C.W. Proctor Trust.
Foundation type: Independent foundation.
Financial data (yr. ended 12/31/13): Assets, $6,023,143 (M); gifts received, $108,813;

expenditures, $534,544; qualifying distributions, $479,000; giving activities include $479,000 for 10 grants (high: $300,000; low: $5,000).
Fields of interest: Education; Health care; Multiple sclerosis; Recreation, parks/playgrounds; Boy scouts; Religious federated giving programs; Christian agencies & churches.
Type of support: General/operating support; Endowments.
Limitations: Applications not accepted. Giving primarily in Nashville, TN. No grants to individuals.
Application information: Unsolicited requests for funds not accepted.
Officer: Elizabeth Craig Weaver Proctor, Chair.
Trustees: Kathryn L. Berschback; Craig W. Friedrich; Collins W. Hooper; Elizabeth W. Lane; Elizabeth McAlister; Margaret A. Robinson; William C. Weaver IV.
EIN: 621819464
Selected grants: The following grants are a representative sample of this grantmaker's funding activity:
$103,500 to Time to Rise, Nashville, TN, 2012. For operating and endowment.

8618
Promethean Foundation ✧
206 E. Reelfoot Ave., Ste. 23
Union City, TN 38261-5739 (731) 884-0088
FAX: (888) 884-0237;
E-mail: promethean@bellsouth.net; Application address: c/o Cathy Waggoner, 115 W. Main St., Union City, TN 38261-3223; Main URL: http://www.unioncityrotary.org/serviceProjects/promethean.asp

Established in 2004 in TN.
Donor: Robert E. & Jenny D. Kirkland Foundation.
Foundation type: Independent foundation.
Financial data (yr. ended 12/31/12): Assets, $149,179 (M); gifts received, $1,665,773; expenditures, $1,713,377; qualifying distributions, $1,543,454; giving activities include $1,543,454 for grants.
Purpose and activities: The foundation provides scholarships for qualifying day care to newborns throughout school age, with the requirement that their progress be monitored throughout their school years. The applicants must live in Obion County, Tennessee, and scholarships are only paid to day cares which are approved and monitored by the foundation. The qualifying daycare facility must meet the moral, social, and educational values that the foundation feels are necessary to provide an excellent background for a successful life.
Fields of interest: Children, day care.
Type of support: Scholarship funds.
Limitations: Giving limited to Obion County, TN.
Application information: Application form required.
Initial approach: Letter or telephone requesting application form
Deadline(s): Prior to the birth of the child for which the scholarship is being requested
Officers and Directors:* Henry Clay Woods III,* Chair.; Todd Stone,* Vice-Chair.; Gary Houston,* Secy.; Clint Joiner,* Treas.; David Huss; Robert E. Kirkland; Martin Sisco.
EIN: 201690784

8619
Provision Trust Inc. ✧
2095 Lakeside Center Way, Ste. 10
Knoxville, TN 37922-6634

Established in TN.
Donor: Provision Trust.
Foundation type: Independent foundation.
Financial data (yr. ended 12/31/12): Assets, $15,580,242 (M); expenditures, $3,505,795; qualifying distributions, $3,097,225; giving activities include $3,097,225 for grants.
Fields of interest: Education; Human services; Christian agencies & churches.
Limitations: Applications not accepted. Giving primarily in Knoxville, TN. No grants to individuals.
Application information: Unsolicited requests for funds not accepted.
Directors: Rosann B. Douglas; Terry D. Douglas; Anne Sale.
EIN: 272029644

8620
The Pyramid Peak Foundation ✧
6410 Poplar Ave., Ste.710
Memphis, TN 38119-4863

Donors: O. Mason Hawkins; Katherine D. Hawkins; Sidney H. Gargiulo; Southeastern Asset Mgmt., Inc.
Foundation type: Independent foundation.
Financial data (yr. ended 12/31/13): Assets, $433,124,006 (M); gifts received, $5,000,000; expenditures, $34,117,825; qualifying distributions, $30,859,942; giving activities include $29,975,438 for 1 grant.
Fields of interest: Foundations (community).
Limitations: Applications not accepted. Giving primarily in Memphis, TN.
Application information: Contributes only to pre-selected organizations.
Officers and Directors:* Andrew R. McCarroll,* Secy.; Melissa R. Russell, Treas.; James R. Ryod,* Exec.Dir; Lee Harper; O. Mason Hawkins.
EIN: 453444341

8621
Ramsey Family Foundation Trust ✧ ☆
1749 Mallory Ln.
Brentwood, TN 37027

Donors: David L. Ramsey III; Sharon Ramsey.
Foundation type: Independent foundation.
Financial data (yr. ended 12/31/13): Assets, $2,050,328 (M); gifts received, $502,359; expenditures, $548,240; qualifying distributions, $548,192; giving activities include $448,415 for 36 grants (high: $95,750; low: $300).
Fields of interest: Health care, clinics/centers; Religion; Children.
Type of support: General/operating support.
Limitations: Applications not accepted. Giving primarily in TN.
Application information: Unsolicited requests for funds not accepted.
Officer: Denise Whittemore, Exec. Dir.
Trustees: David L. Ramsey III; Sharon Ramsey.
EIN: 274314234

8622
Regal Foundation ✧
7132 Regal Ln.
Knoxville, TN 37918-5803 (865) 925-9435
Main URL: http://www.regmovies.com/About-Regal/Community-Affairs

Established in 2003.
Donor: Regal Entertainment Group.
Foundation type: Company-sponsored foundation.
Financial data (yr. ended 12/31/12): Assets, $7,450,049 (M); gifts received, $5,226,353; expenditures, $3,561,793; qualifying distributions, $3,561,362; giving activities include $3,339,671 for 179 grants (high: $1,006,950; low: $100).
Purpose and activities: The foundation supports food banks and organizations involved with arts and culture, education, health, cancer, multiple sclerosis, diabetes, child welfare, human services, and children. Special emphasis is directed toward programs designed to benefit economically disadvantaged people or persons suffering economic, social, physical, or educational hardship.
Fields of interest: Media, film/video; Museums (art); Performing arts, theater; Arts; Secondary school/education; Higher education; Education; Hospitals (general); Health care, patient services; Health care; Cancer; Multiple sclerosis; Diabetes; Crime/violence prevention, child abuse; Food banks; Boys & girls clubs; American Red Cross; YM/YWCAs & YM/YWHAs; Human services, gift distribution; Human services; United Ways and Federated Giving Programs; Children; Economically disadvantaged.
Type of support: Capital campaigns; General/operating support; Program development; Scholarship funds; Sponsorships; In-kind gifts.
Limitations: Applications not accepted. Giving primarily in areas of company operations in CA and Knoxville, TN. No support for political or discriminatory organizations. No grants for travel, operating, or advertising expenses.
Officers and Directors: Michael L. Campbell,* Pres.; Richard S. Westerling, Secy.; Gregory W. Dunn; Neal D. Pinsker; Amy E. Miles; Raymond L. Smith, Jr.
EIN: 134249812
Selected grants: The following grants are a representative sample of this grantmaker's funding activity:
$268,513 to United Way of Greater Knoxville, Knoxville, TN, 2011.
$255,000 to Boys and Girls Clubs of America, Atlanta, GA, 2011.
$125,000 to Jimmy Fund, Brookline, MA, 2011.
$100,000 to Multiple Sclerosis Society, National, Los Angeles, CA, 2011.
$45,000 to Adoption Exchange, Aurora, CO, 2011.
$42,609 to Will Rogers Motion Picture Pioneers Foundation, Toluca Lake, CA, 2011.
$32,500 to Fort Sanders Foundation, Knoxville, TN, 2011.
$10,000 to Junior Achievement Rocky Mountain, Denver, CO, 2011.
$5,205 to Northern New York Community Foundation, Watertown, NY, 2011.
$5,000 to Edgewood Childrens Ranch, Orlando, FL, 2011.

8623
Sasco Foundation Corporation ✧ ☆
6000 Poplar Ave., Ste. 250
Memphis, TN 38119-3974

Established in CT.
Donor: Larry H. Smead.
Foundation type: Independent foundation.
Financial data (yr. ended 06/30/13): Assets, $9,028,681 (M); expenditures, $565,666; qualifying distributions, $436,880; giving activities include $427,863 for 12 grants (high: $125,000; low: $1,009).
Fields of interest: Health organizations; Human services; Children/youth, services; Foundations (private grantmaking); Foundations (public).
Limitations: Applications not accepted. Giving primarily in CA and WA.
Application information: Unsolicited requests for funds not accepted.
Officers: Larry H. Smead, Chair.; Preston Smead, Vice-Chair.
EIN: 452286657

8624
Scarlett Family Foundation ✧
4117 Hillsboro Pike, Ste. 103255
Nashville, TN 37215-2728
Contact: Tom Parrish, Exec. Dir.
E-mail: tomparrish@scarlettfoundation.org; Main URL: http://www.scarlettfoundation.org/
E-Newsletter: https://app.e2ma.net/app2/audience/signup/1744548/1726359/?v=a
Facebook: https://www.facebook.com/pages/Scarlett-Family-Foundation/165267570180614
LinkedIn: http://www.linkedin.com/company/scarlett-family-foundation?goback=.cps_1290558041631_1&trk=co_search_results
Twitter: https://twitter.com/ScarlettFndt
Scholarship application address: c/o International Scholarship Tuition Services, Inc., 1321 Murfreesboro Rd., Ste. 800, Nashville, TN 37217, tel.: (615) 777-3750, fax: (615) 320-3151, e-mail: info@applyists.com

Established in 2004 in TN.
Donor: Joseph H. Scarlett, Jr.
Foundation type: Independent foundation.
Financial data (yr. ended 06/30/13): Assets, $53,260,252 (M); gifts received, $24,730,551; expenditures, $2,221,891; qualifying distributions, $1,863,333; giving activities include $1,314,891 for 27 grants (high: $260,000; low: $4,576), and $397,204 for 57 grants to individuals (high: $15,000; low: $2,462).
Purpose and activities: Giving primarily for education, including scholarship awards to high school seniors and college freshmen, sophomores, and juniors from Middle Tennessee for full-time enrollment in a 4-year not-for-profit business studies program at a college or university within the U.S. Grants to Middle Tennessee-based organizations that support education for students of all ages.
Fields of interest: Higher education; Education; Children; Adults; Young adults; Girls; Boys.
Type of support: General/operating support; Continuing support; Management development/capacity building; Program development; Seed money; Curriculum development; Internship funds; Program evaluation; Scholarships—to individuals.
Limitations: Giving primarily in middle TN (the 39 counties are available on foundation web site). No support for political programs or purposes. No grants to individuals (except for scholarships), or for news letters or magazines, tickets to charitable events or dinners, sponsor special events, productions, or performances, legislative lobbying or to retire debt.
Publications: Application guidelines; Grants list.
Application information: Application form required for scholarships and grants. Grant applications are accepted by invitation only. See web site for application information. Application form required.
Initial approach: E-mail
Copies of proposal: 1
Board meeting date(s): Four times a year.
Officers and Directors:* Tara Anne Scarlett, Pres.; Jennifer Scarlett, Secy.; Andrew S. Scarlett, Treas.; Tom Parrish, Exec. Dir.; Dorothy F. Scarlett; Joseph H. Scarlett, Jr.
Number of staff: 1 part-time professional.
EIN: 201980932
Selected grants: The following grants are a representative sample of this grantmaker's funding activity:
$88,706 to United Way of Metropolitan Nashville, Nashville, TN, 2011.
$75,000 to LEAD Academy, Nashville, TN, 2011.
$60,000 to Conexion Americas, Nashville, TN, 2011.
$50,000 to Creating an Environment of Success, Nashville, TN, 2011.
$50,000 to Nashville Adult Literacy Council, Nashville, TN, 2011.
$43,316 to KIPP Academy Nashville, Nashville, TN, 2011.
$35,000 to Backfield in Motion, Nashville, TN, 2011.
$33,333 to Oasis Center, Nashville, TN, 2011.
$25,000 to Books from Birth of Middle Tennessee, Nashville, TN, 2011.
$15,000 to Girl Scouts of the U.S.A., Nashville, TN, 2011.

8625
Scheidt Family Foundation, Inc. ✧
54 S. White Station Rd.
Memphis, TN 38117-3430 (901) 682-8371
Contact: Helen H. Scheidt, Pres.

Established in 1976 in TN.
Donors: Rudi E. Scheidt; Helen H. Scheidt.
Foundation type: Independent foundation.
Financial data (yr. ended 10/31/13): Assets, $7,911,509 (M); expenditures, $813,331; qualifying distributions, $767,200; giving activities include $767,200 for 26 grants (high: $350,000; low: $500).
Purpose and activities: Giving for Jewish organizations, higher education, and the arts.
Fields of interest: Performing arts; Arts; Higher education; Jewish agencies & synagogues.
Limitations: Applications accepted. Giving primarily in Memphis, TN. No grants to individuals.
Application information: Application form required.
Initial approach: Proposal
Deadline(s): None
Officers: Helen H. Scheidt, Pres.; Susan Scheidt Arney, V.P.; Helen Scheidt Gronauer, V.P.; E. Elkan Scheidt, V.P.; Rudi E. Scheidt, Jr., V.P.; Rudi E. Scheidt, Secy.-Treas.
EIN: 620989531
Selected grants: The following grants are a representative sample of this grantmaker's funding activity:
$350,000 to University of Memphis, School of Music, Memphis, TN, 2013. For educational.
$50,000 to University of Memphis, School of Music, Memphis, TN, 2013. For educational.

8626
Seme Foundation, Inc. ✧ ☆
455 Security Pl.
Cookeville, TN 38506-4941

Established in 2002 in TN.
Donors: Lisa L. Jones; Thomas H. Jones.
Foundation type: Independent foundation.
Financial data (yr. ended 06/30/13): Assets, $3,784,713 (M); gifts received, $1,500,000; expenditures, $427,637; qualifying distributions, $427,637; giving activities include $427,350 for 14 grants (high: $181,000; low: $350).
Fields of interest: Education; Children, services; Family services; Christian agencies & churches; Children.
Type of support: General/operating support.
Limitations: Applications not accepted. Giving primarily in OH and TN. No grants to individuals.
Application information: Contributes only to pre-selected organizations.
Officers and Directors:* Thomas H. Jones,* Pres.; Lisa L. Jones,* Secy.; Bruce R. Barsumian.
EIN: 383656678
Selected grants: The following grants are a representative sample of this grantmaker's funding activity:
$40,000 to International Justice Mission, Arlington, VA, 2012.
$40,000 to International Justice Mission, Arlington, VA, 2011.
$5,000 to Doctors Without Borders USA, New York, NY, 2012.

8627
George Shinn Foundation, Inc. ✧ ☆
725 Cool Springs Blvd., Ste. 600
Franklin, TN 37067 (615) 732-6076
Contact: George Shinn, V.P. and Dir.

Established in 1973 in NC.
Donors: The Charlotte Hornets; George Shinn; George Shinn & Assocs., Inc.; Denise Shinn.
Foundation type: Company-sponsored foundation.
Financial data (yr. ended 12/31/13): Assets, $31,740 (M); expenditures, $660,547; qualifying distributions, $660,547; giving activities include $655,500 for 5 grants (high: $500,000; low: $3,500).
Fields of interest: Education; Crime/law enforcement; Youth, services; Community/economic development; United Ways and Federated Giving Programs; Christian agencies & churches.
Type of support: General/operating support; Scholarship funds.
Limitations: Applications accepted. Giving primarily in Charlotte, NC.
Application information: Application form required.
Initial approach: Letter
Deadline(s): None
Board meeting date(s): Varies
Officers and Directors:* Denise Shinn,* Pres.; George Shinn,* V.P.; Hugh Weber,* Secy.; Harold Bouillion,* Treas.; Chad Shinn; Chris Shinn; Susan Shinn.
EIN: 561083525

8628
Henry Laird Smith Foundation ✧
4400 Harding Rd., Ste. 310
Nashville, TN 37205-5215

Established in 1993 in TN.
Donor: Margaret Thompson Smith†.
Foundation type: Independent foundation.
Financial data (yr. ended 12/31/13): Assets, $12,221,112 (M); expenditures, $602,703; qualifying distributions, $594,014; giving activities include $537,500 for 67 grants (high: $102,000; low: $500).
Fields of interest: Higher education; Education; Health care; Boys & girls clubs; Human services; Children/youth, services.
Limitations: Applications not accepted. Giving primarily in Nashville, TN. No grants to individuals.
Application information: Contributes only to pre-selected organizations.
Trustees: Overton T. Smith; Russell O. Stewart; Margaret S. Warner; Equitable Trust Co.
EIN: 626271796
Selected grants: The following grants are a representative sample of this grantmaker's funding activity:
$200,000 to Vanderbilt University, Nashville, TN, 2011.
$52,000 to Friends of Warner Park, Nashville, TN, 2010.
$27,000 to Nashville Public Television, Nashville, TN, 2010.
$15,000 to Christ Church Cathedral, Nashville, TN, 2011.
$13,838 to Salvation Army of Nashville, Nashville, TN, 2010.
$12,500 to Harpeth Hall School, Nashville, TN, 2011.
$10,000 to Monroe Carell Jr. Childrens Hospital at Vanderbilt, Nashville, TN, 2010.
$7,000 to Lexington School, Lexington, KY, 2011.
$5,000 to Nashville Public Library, Nashville, TN, 2011.
$5,000 to Nashville Symphony, Nashville, TN, 2010.
$2,000 to Kent Denver Country Day School, Englewood, CO, 2011.
$1,250 to Columbia University, New York, NY, 2011.
$1,000 to Montgomery Bell Academy, Nashville, TN, 2011.

8629
The Sparks Foundation ✧ ☆
743 Eventide Dr.
Memphis, TN 38120-9473 (901) 766-4412
Contact: Robert D. Sparks, Tr.

Established in 2001 in TN.
Donors: Willard D. Sparks; Gerard Miller.
Foundation type: Independent foundation.
Financial data (yr. ended 12/31/13): Assets, $4,033,527 (M); expenditures, $9,215,114; qualifying distributions, $9,154,754; giving activities include $9,154,754 for 16 grants (high: $4,046,790; low: $1,000).
Purpose and activities: Giving primarily for the arts, education, causes for the handicapped, and religion.
Fields of interest: Education; Human services; Religion.
Limitations: Applications accepted. Giving limited to MS, OK and TN. No grants to individuals, or for federated campaigns.
Application information: Application form required.
Initial approach: Proposal
Deadline(s): Mar. 31 and Oct. 31
Board meeting date(s): Apr. and Nov.
Final notification: Within 30 days
Trustee: Robert D. Sparks.
EIN: 237029788

8630
Speer Charitable Trust ✧
P.O. Box 240368
Memphis, TN 38124-0368

Established in 1987 in TN.
Donor: R. Wayne Speer.
Foundation type: Independent foundation.
Financial data (yr. ended 11/30/13): Assets, $46,430,090 (M); gifts received, $11,465,996; expenditures, $2,355,348; qualifying distributions, $1,871,452; giving activities include $1,863,931 for 35 grants (high: $500,225; low: $1,000).
Purpose and activities: Giving primarily for Christian churches and agencies, education, hospitals, health associations, and human services.
Fields of interest: Higher education; Hospitals (general); Health organizations, association; Food services; Food banks; Human services; Christian agencies & churches.
Type of support: General/operating support.
Limitations: Applications not accepted. Giving primarily in Memphis, TN. No grants to individuals.
Application information: Contributes only to pre-selected organizations.
Officers and Trustees: Stephen W. Vescovo,* Pres.; Kate Watkins,* Secy.-Treas.; C.T. Courtenay; Chris Koch.
EIN: 621338941

8631
The William B. Stokely, Jr. Foundation ✧
620 Campbell Station Rd., Ste. 27
Knoxville, TN 37934-1624 (865) 966-4878
Contact: William B. Stokely III, Pres. and Dir.

Incorporated in 1951 in IN.
Donor: William B. Stokely III†.
Foundation type: Independent foundation.
Financial data (yr. ended 12/31/12): Assets, $4,688,373 (M); expenditures, $667,283; qualifying distributions, $600,744; giving activities include $536,550 for 29 grants (high: $107,500; low: $200).
Purpose and activities: Giving primarily for education, health, youth services, the arts, and to Baptist churches and organizations.
Fields of interest: Museums; Arts; Higher education; Health care; Health organizations, association; Children/youth, services; Protestant agencies & churches.
Type of support: General/operating support; Continuing support; Annual campaigns; Capital campaigns; Endowments; Scholarship funds.
Limitations: Applications accepted. Giving primarily in eastern TN, with emphasis on Knoxville. No grants to individuals.
Application information: Application form not required.
Initial approach: Proposal
Copies of proposal: 1
Deadline(s): None
Officers and Directors:* William B. Stokely III,* Pres.; Kay H. Stokely,* Exec. V.P.; Andrea A. White, V.P. and Secy.-Treas.; Stacy S. Byerly; Clayton F. Stokely; Shelley S. Przewrocki; William B. Stokely IV.
Number of staff: 1 full-time professional.
EIN: 356016402

8632
T & T Family Foundation ✧
P.O. Box 101444
Nashville, TN 37224-1444 (615) 360-3698
Contact: Lester L. Turner, Jr., Tr.

Established in 1998 in TN.
Donor: Betty M. Turner†.
Foundation type: Independent foundation.
Financial data (yr. ended 12/31/13): Assets, $10,731,900 (M); expenditures, $532,041; qualifying distributions, $465,587; giving activities include $465,587 for 126 grants (high: $100,000; low: $500).
Fields of interest: Health organizations, association; Human services; Children/youth, services.
Type of support: Annual campaigns.
Limitations: Applications accepted. Giving primarily in Nashville, TN; funding also in Abilene, TX.
Application information: Application form required.
Initial approach: Letter
Copies of proposal: 1
Deadline(s): Oct.
Board meeting date(s): Oct.
Trustees: Curry Turner Thornton; Lester L. Turner, Jr.
EIN: 626324206
Selected grants: The following grants are a representative sample of this grantmaker's funding activity:
$2,000 to Happy Tales Humane, Franklin, TN, 2012. For Rescuing Dogs and Finding homes for them.
$2,000 to Hollins University, Roanoke, VA, 2012. For general funds.
$1,000 to Cornell University, Department of Ornithology, Ithaca, NY, 2012. For NEST Box Cam Gits.
$1,000 to Harpeth River Watershed Association, Franklin, TN, 2012. For Protecting Harpeth River.
$1,000 to Nashville Humane Association, Nashville, TN, 2012. For Pet Care Operations.
$1,000 to Nashville Rescue Mission, Nashville, TN, 2012. For Helping the Homeless of Nashville.

8633
Temple-Inland Foundation ✧
6400 Poplar Ave.
Memphis, TN 38197-0100 (512) 434-3160
FAX: (512) 434-2566; Application address: c/o Karen Lee, 1300 S. Mopac Expwy., Fl. 3N, Austin, TX 78746, tel.: (512) 434-3160.; Main URL: http://www.templeinland.com/OurMission/CorporateCitizenship/social.asp

Established in 1985 in TX.
Donors: Temple-Inland Inc.; Temple-Inland Forest Products Corp.
Foundation type: Company-sponsored foundation.
Financial data (yr. ended 06/30/12): Assets, $24,995 (M); gifts received, $1,444,454; expenditures, $1,427,189; qualifying distributions, $1,422,669; giving activities include $1,422,669 for 824 grants (high: $80,610; low: $25).
Purpose and activities: The foundation supports organizations involved with arts and culture, education, health, youth development, and human services.

Fields of interest: Museums; Performing arts; Arts; Elementary/secondary education; Higher education; Education; Medical care, rehabilitation; Health care; Youth development, centers/clubs; Boys & girls clubs; Children/youth, services; Human services.
Type of support: General/operating support; Research; Employee-related scholarships.
Limitations: Applications accepted. Giving primarily in areas of company operations, with emphasis on TX. No grants to individuals (except for employee-related scholarships).
Application information:
Initial approach: Proposal
Copies of proposal: 1
Deadline(s): None
Board meeting date(s): Quarterly
Officers and Directors:* Patricia Neuhoff, Pres.; Deano Orr, V.P.; Maria F. Adair, Secy.; Carol Tusch, Treas.; Terri L. Herrington; Paul J. Karre; Franz J. Marx; Carol L. Roberts; Mark S. Sutton; Fred A. Towler.
EIN: 751977109

8634
Tennessee Health Foundation, Inc. ✧
1 Cameron Hill Cir.
Chattanooga, TN 37402-9815 (423) 535-7163
Contact: Kathy Bingham, Mgr.
FAX: (423) 535-7173;
E-mail: Kathy_Bingham@bcbst.com; Additional address: 801 Pine St., Chattanooga, TN 37402-2555; Main URL: http://www.bcbst.com/about/community/TN-health-foundation/
Foundation in Action: Discovery Museum "Good For You" Exhibit Video: http://www.bcbst.com/about/community/video/cdm.shtml
Foundation in Action: Tennessee Center for Patient Safety Video: http://www.bcbst.com/about/community/video/safety.shtml

Established in 2003 in TN.
Donor: Blue Cross and Blue Shield of Tennessee.
Foundation type: Company-sponsored foundation.
Financial data (yr. ended 12/31/12): Assets, $164,070,865 (M); gifts received, $28,000,000; expenditures, $6,713,846; qualifying distributions, $6,294,493; giving activities include $5,717,471 for grants.
Purpose and activities: The foundation supports programs designed to improve health, public education, and economic development for Tennesseans. Special emphasis is directed towards programs designed to address healthcare workforce needs; health disparities and at-risk populations; infant mortality and childhood obesity; and patient safety and quality.
Fields of interest: Higher education; Medical school/education; Hospitals (general); Health care, clinics/centers; Health care, infants; Public health; Public health, obesity; Health care, insurance; Health care, patient services; Health care; Disasters, preparedness/services; American Red Cross; Human services; Economic development; Children; Economically disadvantaged.
Type of support: General/operating support; Program development.
Limitations: Applications accepted. Giving primarily in areas of company operations in TN. No support for private clubs, private schools, organizations not eligible for tax deductible support, religious organizations, political candidates or organizations, hospitals or hospital building funds, or sports facilities or sports teams. No grants to individuals, or for political causes or campaigns, or special occasion or commemorative advertising.
Publications: Application guidelines; Informational brochure.
Application information: Letter of inquiry must be submitted using organization letterhead and should be no longer than 2 pages. A full proposal may be requested at a later date.
Initial approach: Download letter of inquiry cover sheet and mail letter of inquiry and cover sheet to foundation
Deadline(s): Last day of Jan., May 1, and Sept. 1
Officers and Directors:* Lamar J. Partridge,* Chair.; Betty De Vinney,* Vice-Chair.; Vicky B. Gregg,* C.E.O.; William M. Gracey, Pres. and C.O.O.; Sheila Clemons, Secy.; John Giblin, C.F.O.; Danny Timblin, Treas.; Calvin Anderson,* Exec. Dir.; James B. Baker; Hulet Chaney; Reginald W. Coopwood; Gus B. Denton; Herbert H. Hilliard; James M. Phillips; Gloria S. Ray; Emily J. Reynolds; Paul E. Stanton.
EIN: 200298456
Selected grants: The following grants are a representative sample of this grantmaker's funding activity:
$1,392,261 to University of Memphis, Memphis, TN, 2012. For Phase III of Blues Project, research project seeking to reduce the infant mortality rate.
$944,993 to University of Tennessee Health Science Center, Memphis, TN, 2012. For Teamwork Focused Interdisciplinary Simulations Program.
$935,050 to Tennessee Hospital Education and Research Foundation, Nashville, TN, 2012. For Tennessee Surgical Quality Improvement Project.
$507,885 to Tennessee Hospital Education and Research Foundation, Nashville, TN, 2012. For Tennessee Patient Safety Program.
$357,042 to Regional Obstetrical Consultants, Chattanooga, TN, 2012. For Solutions to Obstetrics in Rural Counties (STORC) Program.
$263,996 to Tusculum College, Greeneville, TN, 2012. For Nursing Simulation Center.
$195,969 to Tennessee Pharmacists Research and Education Foundation, Nashville, TN, 2012. For Diabetes Care Program.
$100,000 to Friends in Need Health Center, Kingsport, TN, 2012. For matching grant.
$60,000 to Knoxville News Sentinel Charities, Knoxville, TN, 2012. For Free Flu Shot Saturday Program.
$50,000 to Methodist Healthcare Foundation, Memphis, TN, 2012. For Sickle Cell Center of Memphis.

8635
The Thompson Charitable Foundation ✧
4800 Old Kingston Pike, Ste. 100
Knoxville, TN 37919-6478 (865) 588-0491
Contact: Debbie Black, Exec. Dir.
FAX: (865) 588-4496; E-mail: debbie@cf.org

Established in 1987 in TN.
Donor: B.R. Thompson, Sr.‡.
Foundation type: Independent foundation.
Financial data (yr. ended 06/30/13): Assets, $37,014,012 (M); expenditures, $1,915,821; qualifying distributions, $1,631,517; giving activities include $1,608,000 for grants.
Purpose and activities: Giving primarily for education, health, and human services, including funding for capital and building improvements for human service organizations and educational institutions; funding also for youth and Christian organizations.
Fields of interest: Graduate/professional education; Education; Environment, water resources; Health care; Cancer; Autism research; Food services; Housing/shelter, development; Housing/shelter; Disasters, fire prevention/control; Human services; YM/YWCAs & YM/YWHAs; Children/youth, services; Family services, adolescent parents; Residential/custodial care, hospices; Community development, neighborhood development; Economically disadvantaged.
Type of support: General/operating support; Capital campaigns; Building/renovation; Program development; Scholarship funds.
Limitations: Applications accepted. Giving limited to Bell, Clay, Laurel, and Leslie counties, KY; Anderson, Blount, Knox, and Scott counties, TN; and Buchanan and Tazewell counties, VA. No support for religious or political organizations. No grants for budget deficits or endowments.
Publications: Informational brochure.
Application information:
Initial approach: Letter (no more than 2 pages)
Deadline(s): Mar. 15, Sept. 1
Board meeting date(s): Apr. and Oct.
Officers and Directors:* Merle D. Wolfe,* Pres.; Debbie Black, Exec. Dir.; Kyle Derham; Matthew Derham; Greg Erickson; JoAnne Manofksy; Ginny Thompson; Jessie Thompson; Sylvia M. Thompson.
EIN: 581754763
Selected grants: The following grants are a representative sample of this grantmaker's funding activity:
$100,000 to YMCA of Buchanan County, Grundy, VA, 2011.
$80,000 to Breakthrough Corporation, Knoxville, TN, 2011.
$50,000 to Alice Lloyd College, Pippa Passes, KY, 2011.
$50,000 to Appalachia Service Project, Johnson City, TN, 2011.
$37,000 to Good Samaritan Food Pantry, Richlands, VA, 2011.
$30,000 to East Tennessee Childrens Hospital, Knoxville, TN, 2011.
$25,000 to Helen Ross McNabb Center, Knoxville, TN, 2011.
$20,000 to Richlands Athletic League, Richlands, VA, 2011.
$15,000 to Tennessee Archive of the Moving Image and Sound, Knoxville, TN, 2011.
$9,000 to Panco Youth Center, Oneida, KY, 2011.

8636
Lucille S. Thompson Family Foundation ✧
P.O. Box 11146
Knoxville, TN 37939-1146
Contact: Lila K. Pfleger
E-mail: lpfleger@ltff.org

Established in 1988 in TN.
Donor: Lucille S. Thompson.
Foundation type: Independent foundation.
Financial data (yr. ended 02/28/13): Assets, $7,260,911 (M); expenditures, $1,130,763; qualifying distributions, $841,973; giving activities include $703,630 for 81 grants (high: $100,000; low: $200).
Purpose and activities: Support primarily for human services, youth services, education, medical services, and arts and culture for individuals and families of the east TN region.
Fields of interest: Museums; Arts; Elementary/secondary education; Higher education; Education;

Health care; Food services; Disasters, Hurricane Katrina; Human services; Children/youth, services; Christian agencies & churches; Children/youth; Youth; Physically disabled; Economically disadvantaged; Homeless.
Type of support: General/operating support; Annual campaigns; Equipment; Matching/challenge support.
Limitations: Applications accepted. Giving primarily in the east TN region; some funding in CO. No grants to individuals, or for endowment funds, deficit operating budgets or capital projects.
Publications: Application guidelines.
Application information: Application form not required.
Initial approach: Letter or proposal
Copies of proposal: 1
Deadline(s): Jan. 31, Apr. 30, July 31, and Oct. 31
Board meeting date(s): 1
Final notification: Within 2 weeks after board meeting
Officer and Trust Committee:* Kristin Bishop MacDermott,* Chair.; John W. Baker, Jr.; Archer W. Bishop, Jr.; Archer W. Bishop III; Baker O'Neil Bishop; Sandra K. Bishop; Thompson A. Bishop.
Trustee: Cumberland Trust & Investment.
Director: Lila K. Pfleger.
Number of staff: 1 full-time professional; 2 part-time support.
EIN: 581788548
Selected grants: The following grants are a representative sample of this grantmaker's funding activity:
$100,000 to Aspen Music Festival and School, Aspen, CO, 2011.
$100,000 to Christ Episcopal Church of Aspen, Aspen, CO, 2011.

8637
Jeanette Travis Foundation ✧ ☆
P.O. Box 340025
Nashville, TN 37203-0025
Application address: c/o Richard Warren, Jr., 1600 Division St., Ste. 700, Nashville, TN 37203-2771

Established in 2003 in TN.
Donors: Jeanette Travis; Anthony Anglin, Jr; Kimberly Anglin.
Foundation type: Independent foundation.
Financial data (yr. ended 12/31/13): Assets, $17,524,485 (M); gifts received, $20,997; expenditures, $995,598; qualifying distributions, $909,393; giving activities include $875,000 for 7 grants (high: $500,000; low: $10,000).
Purpose and activities: Giving primarily to educational institutions for their nursing scholarship programs.
Fields of interest: Media, television; Nursing school/education.
Type of support: Scholarship funds.
Limitations: Applications accepted. Giving primarily in TN.
Application information: Application form not required.
Initial approach: Letter
Deadline(s): None
Officers and Directors:* Richard F. Warren, Jr,* Pres.; Barbara Kimmins,* Secy.; Thomas Baker,* Treas.
EIN: 710907506

8638
Tucker Foundation
600 Krystal Bldg.
100 W. MLK Blvd.
Chattanooga, TN 37402-2514 (423) 756-1202
Contact: M. Hayne Hamilton, Pres.
E-mail: hhamilton@johnsouth.com; Additional e-mail: amoore@johnsouth.com; Main URL: http://www.thetuckerfoundation.org/

Established in 1996.
Donor: S.K. Johnston, Jr.
Foundation type: Independent foundation.
Financial data (yr. ended 12/31/13): Assets, $33,510,106 (M); expenditures, $1,551,763; qualifying distributions, $1,339,982; giving activities include $1,231,054 for 64 grants (high: $200,000; low: $250).
Purpose and activities: The primary objective of The Tucker Foundation is to provide financial support to non-profit organizations to produce in young people the character and skills required to live a productive and happy life. It also supports organizations that conserve essential elements of our natural environment forever.
Fields of interest: Arts, public education; Performing arts, education; Humanities; Education; Environment; Human services.
Type of support: Scholarship funds; Program-related investments/loans; Land acquisition; Internship funds; General/operating support; Endowments; Capital campaigns; Building/renovation; Annual campaigns.
Limitations: Applications accepted. Giving primarily in the Chattanooga/Hamilton County metro area and the Cleveland/Bradley County, area, TN, Sheridan County and Johnson County, WY, and Palm Beach County, FL. No support for political or lobbying activities, churches and purely religious activities, start-ups or organizations without 501 (c) (3) status. No grants to individuals, or for seed money, capacity building, film, video, or radio or for institutional startup or reorganization, marketing and public relations activities or for requests containing any benefit to family members, trustees, and officers of the foundation.
Application information: Unsolicited applications are accepted from organizations within the foundation's geographic concentration. Application form not required.
Initial approach: Online application process
Copies of proposal: 1
Deadline(s): Apr. 15th for June meeting; Oct. 15th for Dec. meeting
Board meeting date(s): June and Dec.
Final notification: July and Dec.
Officers and Trustees:* M. Hayne Hamilton,* Pres.; Pamela K. Cuzzort,* Treas.; Andrew G. Cope; Gillian Johnston; Lavinia Johnston; Robert T. Johnston; Katherine J. Tudor.
Number of staff: 2 full-time professional.
EIN: 621603398

8639
Laura G. Turner Charitable Foundation, Inc. ✧
138 2nd Ave. N., Rm. 200
Nashville, TN 37201-1927 (615) 846-2053
Contact: Cabot Pyle

Established in 1989 in KY.
Donors: Laura Jo Turner Dugas; Cal Turner, Sr.; Dollar General Corp.
Foundation type: Independent foundation.
Financial data (yr. ended 12/31/12): Assets, $15,304,810 (M); gifts received, $1,000,000; expenditures, $2,225,531; qualifying distributions, $1,993,937; giving activities include $1,879,715 for 27 grants (high: $495,160; low: $1,000).
Purpose and activities: Giving primarily for education, community development, and social services.
Fields of interest: Higher education; Education; Human services; Community/economic development.
Limitations: Applications accepted. Giving primarily in Bowling Green and Scottsville, KY. No support for government agencies, political organizations, or to other private foundations. No grants to individuals, or for travel, seminars, dinner events or telethons; no loans.
Application information: Application form required.
Initial approach: Letter or telephone requesting application form
Deadline(s): None
Board meeting date(s): Annually
Officers and Directors:* Laura Jo Turner Dugas,* Chair.; Laura Turner, Vice-Chair.; Katherine Sikora, Vice-Chair.; John Newman, Secy.-Treas.
EIN: 611170828
Selected grants: The following grants are a representative sample of this grantmaker's funding activity:
$40,000 to United Way of Southern Kentucky, Bowling Green, KY, 2012. For continued support of programs.
$7,000 to United Way of Southern Kentucky, Bowling Green, KY, 2012. For Dolly Parton Imaging Program.

8640
Cal Turner Family Foundation, Inc.
138 2nd Ave. N., No. 200
Nashville, TN 37201-1927 (615) 846-2053
Contact: Cabot Pyle
Tel. for Cabot Pyle: (615) 846-2053

Established in 2008 in TN.
Donor: H. Callister Turner, Jr.
Foundation type: Independent foundation.
Financial data (yr. ended 12/31/12): Assets, $47,444,683 (M); gifts received, $2,316,550; expenditures, $5,321,119; qualifying distributions, $4,755,500; giving activities include $4,661,004 for 109 grants (high: $600,000; low: $1,000).
Fields of interest: Education; Human services; YM/YWCAs & YM/YWHAs; Children/youth, services; Foundations (community).
Limitations: Applications accepted. Giving primarily in Nashville, TN. No support for political organizations. No grants to individuals, or for travel, seminars, dinners, or telethons; no loans.
Application information: Application form provided by the foundation. Application form required.
Deadline(s): None
Officers: H. Callister Turner, Jr., Pres.; Margaret B. Turner, V.P.; Hurley C. Turner III, Secy.-Treas.
Directors: Hal Cato; Mark Ezell; Jennifer L. Turner.
EIN: 262886973

8641
James Stephen Turner Family Foundation, Inc. ✧
138 2nd Ave., N., Ste. 200
Nashville, TN 37201-1926 (615) 846-2053
Contact: Cabot Pyle

Donor: James Stephen Turner, Sr.
Foundation type: Independent foundation.
Financial data (yr. ended 12/31/12): Assets, $19,429,135 (M); gifts received, $10,052,882; expenditures, $2,052,462; qualifying distributions, $1,831,450; giving activities include $1,791,000 for 19 grants.
Fields of interest: Museums (science/technology); Education; Human services.
Limitations: Applications accepted. Giving primarily in TN. No support for government agencies, political purposes or other private foundations. No grants to individual or for travel, seminars, dinner events or telethons; no loans.
Application information: Application form required.
Initial approach: Proposal
Deadline(s): None
Officers: James Stephen Turner, Sr., Pres.; Judith Payne Turner, V.P.; Laura Turner, Secy.; James Stephen Turner, Jr., Treas.
Director: Christi Turner.
EIN: 264386453

8642
Louise B. Wallace Foundation ✧
c/o Equitable Trust Co.
4400 Harding Rd., Ste. 310
Nashville, TN 37205-5215

Established in 1989 in TN.
Donor: George Newton Bullard Foundation.
Foundation type: Independent foundation.
Financial data (yr. ended 12/31/13): Assets, $15,902,270 (M); expenditures, $1,166,641; qualifying distributions, $980,200; giving activities include $980,200 for 54 grants (high: $450,000; low: $1,000).
Fields of interest: Arts; Education; Youth development; Human services; Protestant agencies & churches.
Limitations: Applications not accepted. Giving primarily in Nashville, TN. No grants to individuals.
Application information: Contributes only to pre-selected organizations.
Board meeting date(s): Biannually
Trustees: Elizabeth W. Caldwell; Elena W. Graves; Anne B. Nesbitt; J. Bransford Wallace, Jr.
EIN: 581797048

8643
Washington Foundation ✧
(formerly Church of Christ Foundation, Inc.)
P.O. Box 159057
Nashville, TN 37215-9057

Incorporated in 1946 in TN.
Donor: G.L. Comer.
Foundation type: Independent foundation.
Financial data (yr. ended 12/31/13): Assets, $12,087,804 (M); expenditures, $650,292; qualifying distributions, $610,357; giving activities include $600,000 for 68 grants (high: $42,000; low: $1,000).
Purpose and activities: Giving primarily to Church of Christ churches, and to other Christian organizations and schools; funding also for higher education and social services.
Fields of interest: Higher education; Education; Human services; Christian agencies & churches; Protestant agencies & churches.
Type of support: General/operating support.
Limitations: Applications not accepted. Giving primarily in Nashville, TN. No grants to individuals.
Application information: Contributes only to pre-selected organizations.
Directors: James N. Denton III; Miles Ezell, Jr.; James Gooch; Harold Hazelip.
Number of staff: 1
EIN: 620649477

8644
Westwood Endowment, Inc. ✧
P.O. Box 4268
Chattanooga, TN 37405-0268 (423) 755-3964
Contact: Thomas H. McCallie III, Pres.
FAX: (423) 755-1640;
E-mail: mccallie60@gmail.com

Established in 1986 in IN.
Donors: Richard A. West; Florence G. West; Marie G. Byers‡; West Baking Co.; Single Family Residential Property.
Foundation type: Independent foundation.
Financial data (yr. ended 12/31/13): Assets, $10,034,854 (M); expenditures, $717,263; qualifying distributions, $635,130; giving activities include $594,000 for 21 grants (high: $60,000; low: $5,000).
Purpose and activities: Support for various needs of the Third World through organizations with tax-exempt status.
International interests: Africa; Asia; India.
Type of support: General/operating support.
Limitations: Applications not accepted. Giving primarily to U.S.-based organizations for benefit of third world countries.
Application information: The foundation initiates funding for service opportunities in its target fields. Unsolicited requests for funds not considered or acknowledged.
Board meeting date(s): As necessary
Officers and Directors:* Thomas H. McCallie III,* Pres.; Craig Hammon,* Secy.-Treas.; Robert Martin; Richard A. West.
Number of staff: 2 part-time support.
EIN: 311197125

8645
Blair J. Wilson Charitable Trust ✧ ☆
(formerly Sunnyside Foundation)
3022 Vanderbilt Pl.
Nashville, TN 37212-2516 (615) 352-2080
Contact: Blair J. Wilson, Tr. and Mgr.

Established in 1992 in TN.
Donors: Blair J. Wilson; Linde B. Wilson.
Foundation type: Independent foundation.
Financial data (yr. ended 12/31/13): Assets, $9,466,792 (M); gifts received, $975,000; expenditures, $463,851; qualifying distributions, $459,650; giving activities include $459,000 for 18 grants (high: $250,000; low: $1,000).
Fields of interest: Arts education; Higher education; Education; Human services; Protestant agencies & churches.
Limitations: Applications accepted. Giving primarily in CO and Nashville, TN. No grants to individuals.
Application information: Application form required.
Initial approach: Letter
Deadline(s): None
Officer and Trustee:* Blair J. Wilson,* Mgr.
EIN: 621498117

8646
The Kemmons Wilson Family Foundation ✧
1027 Cherry Rd.
Memphis, TN 38117-5423 (901) 328-5037
Contact: Lauren Wilson-Young, Exec. Dir.
FAX: (901) 396-3570; E-mail: lyoung@kwilson.com; Additional e-mail for Lee Morris: lmorris@kwilson.com, e-mail for Libby Wilson, Dir., Comm.: lwilson@kwilson.com; Main URL: http://www.kwilsonff.com

Established about 1961 in TN.
Foundation type: Independent foundation.
Financial data (yr. ended 12/31/13): Assets, $37,373,635 (M); gifts received, $1,301; expenditures, $1,840,223; qualifying distributions, $1,804,315; giving activities include $1,626,468 for 149 grants (high: $238,700; low: $75).
Purpose and activities: The foundation intends to positively impact and transform the Memphis, Tennessee community through grantmaking in the following categories: community outreach, and development advancement of youth, enriching education, faith-based ministries, and health and research related organizations.
Fields of interest: Museums; Elementary/secondary education; Higher education; Hospitals (general); Children/youth, services; Community/economic development; United Ways and Federated Giving Programs; Protestant agencies & churches; Infants/toddlers; Children/youth; Children; Youth; Adults; Aging; Young adults; Disabilities, people with; Physically disabled; Deaf/hearing impaired; Mentally disabled; Minorities; African Americans/Blacks; Women; Infants/toddlers, female; Girls; Adults, women; Young adults, female; Men; Infants/toddlers, male; Boys; Adults, men; Young adults, male; Military/veterans; Substance abusers; Single parents; Crime/abuse victims; Terminal illness, people with; Economically disadvantaged; Homeless.
Type of support: General/operating support; Continuing support; Annual campaigns; Capital campaigns; Building/renovation; Endowments; Emergency funds; Program development; Seed money; Curriculum development; Scholarship funds; Research; Program evaluation; Matching/challenge support.
Limitations: Applications accepted. Giving primarily in the greater Memphis area, TN. No grants to individuals.
Publications: Application guidelines.
Application information: Complete application guidelines available on foundation web site. Application form required.
Initial approach: Use grant application system on foundation web site
Copies of proposal: 1
Deadline(s): Jan. 15 and Aug. 15
Board meeting date(s): Mar., Aug. and Nov.

Officers and Directors:* Spence L. Wilson,* Pres.; Charles K. Wilson, Jr.,* V.P.; Robert A. Wilson,* V.P.; Elizabeth Wilson-Moore; Carol Wilson-West.
Number of staff: 3 part-time professional.
EIN: 626046687
Selected grants: The following grants are a representative sample of this grantmaker's funding activity:
$200,250 to Baptist Memorial Health Care Foundation, Memphis, TN, 2012. For Donation for the Baptist Trinity Center for Good.
$30,000 to Rhodes College, Memphis, TN, 2012. For Donation to Service Scholarship.
$10,000 to Vanderbilt University, Nashville, TN, 2012. For Donation to Department of Special Education, Champion's Circle, and.
$7,500 to Presbyterian Day School, Memphis, TN, 2012. For Donation to the Annual Fund.
$5,000 to Memphis University School, Memphis, TN, 2012. For Donation for Wilson Society.

TEXAS

8647
The 1687 Foundation ✧
P.O. Box 11283
Midland, TX 79702

Donors: Patti Jo Peck Wood; Danny Lee Wood.
Foundation type: Independent foundation.
Financial data (yr. ended 10/31/13): Assets, $13,463,406 (M); gifts received, $5,050,548; expenditures, $3,933,804; qualifying distributions, $3,477,956; giving activities include $3,150,715 for 14 grants (high: $2,625,715; low: $10,000).
Fields of interest: Athletics/sports, equestrianism; Human services; Children/youth, services; Military/veterans.
Limitations: Applications not accepted. Giving primarily in TX.
Application information: Unsolicited requests for funds not accepted.
Officers and Directors:* Danny Lee Wood,* Pres.; Patti Jo Peck Wood,* V.P. and Secy.-Treas.; Herbert L. Cartwright III; Debbie Galloway; Mindy Johnson; Don L. Parks.
EIN: 263772474
Selected grants: The following grants are a representative sample of this grantmaker's funding activity:
$50,000 to American Quarter Horse Foundation, Amarillo, TX, 2011.
$50,000 to Make-A-Wish Foundation of North Texas, Irving, TX, 2011.

8648
80/20 Fund ✧ ☆
112 E. Pecan St., Ste. 175
San Antonio, TX 78205-1522 (210) 775-2370
Contact: Lorenzo Gomez III, Exec. Dir.
Main URL: http://8020foundation.com/

Established in 2004 in TX.
Donor: Trout, Ltd.
Foundation type: Independent foundation.
Financial data (yr. ended 12/31/13): Assets, $703,647 (M); expenditures, $1,956,645; qualifying distributions, $1,956,645; giving activities include $1,917,491 for 21 grants (high: $801,006; low: $500).
Fields of interest: American Red Cross; Foundations (public).
Type of support: General/operating support.
Limitations: Applications accepted. Giving primarily in TX. No grants to individuals.
Application information: Application form required.
Initial approach: See website
Deadline(s): None
Officer: Lorenzo Gomez III, Exec. Dir.
Trustee: James E. Irwine.
EIN: 200683200

8649
A Glimmer of Hope Foundation ✧
3600 N. Capital of TX Hwy, Bldg. B, Ste. 330
Austin, TX 78746-3209 (512) 328-9944
Contact: Kendra Beach, Dir., Comms.
FAX: (512) 328-8872;
E-mail: inquiries@aglimmerofhope.org; Main URL: http://www.aglimmerofhope.org
A Glimmer of Hope Foundation's Philanthropy's Promise: http://www.ncrp.org/philanthropys-promise/who
Facebook: http://www.facebook.com/pages/A-Glimmer-of-Hope-Foundation/102487557749
Founder's Blog: http://aglimmerofhopefoundation.blogspot.com/
Multimedia: http://www.aglimmerofhope.org/success-stories
Pinterest: http://www.pinterest.com/aglimmerofhope/
Twitter: http://twitter.com/aglimmerofhope
Vimeo: http://www.vimeo.com/aglimmerofhope
YouTube: http://www.youtube.com/aglimmerofhopeorg

Established in 2000 in TX.
Donors: Donna Berber; Philip Berber; Eric Schmidhauser; Lucie Schmidhauser; Leslie Moore; Kathy Moore; Neil Webber; Ronnie Morgan; Bill Parrish; Margaret Parrish; Neil Webber; Ernst & Young; Tim Brosnan; Tony Gannon; Berberfam, Ltd.; Operation Days Work; Berberfam, Ltd.; Austin Ethiopian Women Assn.; Lee Portnoi; Mark Stryker; Oregon Ethiopian Community Organization; Robert Epstein; Preston Ctr.; The Andrew S. Roddick Foundation.
Foundation type: Independent foundation.
Financial data (yr. ended 12/31/12): Assets, $50,557,929 (M); gifts received, $10,250,911; expenditures, $11,950,582; qualifying distributions, $11,560,671; giving activities include $8,738,503 for 14 grants (high: $5,750,412; low: $9,926).
Purpose and activities: The foundation serves to ease some of the pain and suffering on the planet. It currently operates a national aid program in Ethiopia as well as programs for excluded youth in the U.S. and the U.K.
Fields of interest: Business school/education; Human services; Children/youth, services; International relief; International affairs; Economically disadvantaged.
International interests: England; Ethiopia; Ireland.
Limitations: Applications not accepted. Giving primarily in Austin, TX, London, England, and Ethiopia.
Application information: Contributes only to pre-selected organizations.
Officers and Director: Donna Berber, Co-Chair. and Pres.; Philip Berber, Co-Chair.; Stephanie Fast, C.F.O.; David Porter III, Exec. Dir.; Carla Power, Cont.; Brian Cooper.
EIN: 311758218
Selected grants: The following grants are a representative sample of this grantmaker's funding activity:
$5,750,412 to Relief Society of Tigray, Addis Ababa, Ethiopia, 2012.
$1,218,144 to Oromia Development Association, Addis Ababa, Ethiopia, 2012.
$631,160 to Tigray Development Association, Mek'ele, Ethiopia, 2012.
$330,574 to Organization for Rehabilitation and Development in Amhara, Bahir Dar, Ethiopia, 2012.
$118,127 to Amhara Development Association, Bahir Dar, Ethiopia, 2012.
$90,363 to Dawro Development Association, Tercha, Ethiopia, 2012.
$56,827 to Bench Maji Development Association, Mizan Teferi, Ethiopia, 2012.
$46,064 to Sidama Development Association, Kelle, Ethiopia, 2012.

8650
Abell-Hanger Foundation ✧
P.O. Box 430
Midland, TX 79702-0430
Contact: David L. Smith, Exec. V.P. and Exec. Dir.
FAX: (432) 684-4474;
E-mail: AHF@abell-hanger.org; Main URL: http://www.abell-hanger.org

Incorporated in 1954 in TX.
Donors: George T. Abell†; Gladys H. Abell†.
Foundation type: Independent foundation.
Financial data (yr. ended 06/30/13): Assets, $155,772,456 (M); expenditures, $8,871,669; qualifying distributions, $8,701,554; giving activities include $6,702,316 for 186 grants (high: $1,500,000; low: $85), and $407,647 for 157 employee matching gifts.
Purpose and activities: Support primarily for higher education, youth activities, cultural programs, health services, the handicapped, and social welfare agencies.
Fields of interest: Arts; Higher education; Business school/education; Nursing school/education; Nursing care; Health care; Substance abuse, services; Human services; Children/youth, services; Family services; Aging, centers/services; Community/economic development; Voluntarism promotion; Government/public administration; Children/youth; Young adults; Disabilities, people with; Physically disabled; Blind/visually impaired; Deaf/hearing impaired; Mentally disabled; Hispanics/Latinos; Substance abusers; AIDS, people with; Crime/abuse victims; Economically disadvantaged; Homeless; Migrant workers.
Type of support: General/operating support; Continuing support; Annual campaigns; Capital campaigns; Building/renovation; Equipment; Program development; Seed money; Scholarship funds; Research; Employee matching gifts; Matching/challenge support.
Limitations: Applications accepted. Giving limited to West TX, especially the Midland and Ector counties. No support for individuals, or for individual scholarships or fellowships; no loans.
Publications: Annual report (including application guidelines); Financial statement; Grants list.
Application information: The foundation supplied grant application forms are required. The foundation does not acknowledge the receipt of proposals, and only grants interviews with applicants at the final stage of the application process. Application form required.
Copies of proposal: 1
Deadline(s): Feb., May, Aug., and Nov. 15.
Board meeting date(s): Mar., June, Sept., and Dec.
Final notification: 1 month
Officers and Trustees:* Tevis Herd,* Pres.; David L. Smith,* Exec. V.P. and Exec. Dir.; Herbert L. Cartwright, V.P., Secy.-Treas., and Comp.; John D. Bergman; Jake Harper; Robert C. Leibrock; Elaine Magruder; Clarence Scharbauer III; Wes Perry; James C. Trott; Charles M. Younger, M.D.
Number of staff: 4 full-time professional; 1 full-time support.
EIN: 756020781
Selected grants: The following grants are a representative sample of this grantmaker's funding activity:

$1,500,000 to Midland Shared Spaces, Midland, TX, 2013. For charitable forgiveness of promissory note installment on MSS building.
$500,000 to Permian Basin Petroleum Museum, Library and Hall of Fame, Midland, TX, 2013. For the capital campaign.
$250,000 to Midland College, Midland, TX, 2013. For funding of the Legacy Scholarship program for four years.
$200,000 to Manor Park, Midland, TX, 2013. For final challenge grant for the Household Capital and Training Campaign.
$170,000 to United Way of Midland, Midland, TX, 2013. For fundraising campaign to underwrite administrative costs.
$100,000 to UMC Foundation, Lubbock, TX, 2013. For renovation and expansion of the Timothy J. Harner Regional Burn Center.
$40,000 to Midland Community Development Corporation, Midland, TX, 2013. For the 100th Home Project.
$20,000 to Midland Community Theater, Midland, TX, 2013. For Les Miserables performance at Wagner Noel Performing Arts Center in April 2014.
$20,000 to Texas Hearing and Service Dogs, Dripping Springs, TX, 2013. To rescue, train and place a service dog for a Permian Basin resident.
$6,250 to University of Texas of the Permian Basin, Odessa, TX, 2013. For Spring 2013 Individual Student Scholarships.

8651
Edward & Wilhelmina Ackerman Foundation ✧
5956 Sherry Ln., Ste. 1600
Dallas, TX 75225-8027

Established in 1996 in TX.
Donors: Edward M. Ackerman; Wilhelmina Ackerman.
Foundation type: Independent foundation.
Financial data (yr. ended 12/31/13): Assets, $12,950,619 (M); expenditures, $1,123,410; qualifying distributions, $1,107,885; giving activities include $1,105,450 for 35 grants (high: $326,000; low: $50).
Purpose and activities: Giving primarily for education, religion, and community services.
Fields of interest: Education; Medical research, institute; Community/economic development; Foundations (community); Jewish agencies & synagogues.
Limitations: Applications not accepted. Giving in the U.S., with emphasis on TX and Washington, DC; some giving also in CA and OH. No grants to individuals.
Application information: Contributes only to pre-selected organizations.
Officers and Directors:* Edward M. Ackerman,* Pres.; David B. Ackerman,* Secy.; Samantha Ackerman Simons,* Treas.; Edward W. Ackerman; Paul Ackerman Menendez.
EIN: 752681488
Selected grants: The following grants are a representative sample of this grantmaker's funding activity:
$1,000,000 to University of Texas at Dallas, Richardson, TX, 2011.
$276,500 to Hockaday School, Dallas, TX, 2011.
$50,000 to Media Research Center, Reston, VA, 2011.
$25,500 to Saint Marks School of Texas, Dallas, TX, 2011.
$25,000 to Heritage Foundation, Washington, DC, 2011.
$15,000 to Fund for American Studies, Washington, DC, 2010.
$10,000 to American Council of Trustees and Alumni, Washington, DC, 2011.
$10,000 to Cato Institute, Washington, DC, 2011.
$10,000 to National Journalism Center, Washington, DC, 2011.
$10,000 to Parents Television Council, Los Angeles, CA, 2010.
$10,000 to Parents Television Council, Los Angeles, CA, 2011.
$10,000 to Young Americas Foundation, Herndon, VA, 2011.

8652
Susie and John L. Adams Family Foundation ✧
(formerly The Adams Foundation)
c/o John L. Adams
4011 Miramar Ave.
Dallas, TX 75205-3129

Established in 1997 in TX.
Donors: John L. Adams; Suzanne L. Adams.
Foundation type: Independent foundation.
Financial data (yr. ended 12/31/12): Assets, $505,704 (M); gifts received, $4,995; expenditures, $477,411; qualifying distributions, $464,624; giving activities include $464,624 for grants.
Fields of interest: Higher education; Human services.
Type of support: General/operating support.
Limitations: Applications not accepted. Giving primarily in Dallas and Richardson, TX. No grants to individuals.
Application information: Contributes only to pre-selected organizations.
Officers: John L. Adams, Pres. and Treas.; Suzanne L. Adams, V.P. and Secy.
Directors: John R. Adams; Elise Adams Harper.
EIN: 752738717

8653
The John and Patricia Adams Foundation ✧ ☆
2350 Airport Freeway, Ste. 160
Bedford, TX 76022-6026

Established in 2006 in TX.
Donors: John Adams; Patricia Adams.
Foundation type: Independent foundation.
Financial data (yr. ended 12/31/13): Assets, $6,084,601 (M); gifts received, $500,000; expenditures, $788,277; qualifying distributions, $737,093; giving activities include $729,520 for 5 grants (high: $500,000; low: $10,000).
Fields of interest: Higher education.
Limitations: Applications not accepted. No grants to individuals.
Application information: Contributes only to pre-selected organizations.
Officers: John Adams, Pres.; Patricia Adams, Secy.
Trustees: Sam P. Burford, Jr.; Larry Snodgrass; Sherri Adams Steinford.
EIN: 204480039

8654
The Albany Foundation ✧
807 Las Cimas Pkwy., Ste. 370
Austin, TX 78746-6183

Established in 2003 in TX.
Donors: Jon Rex Jones; Ann M. Jones.
Foundation type: Independent foundation.
Financial data (yr. ended 12/31/13): Assets, $14,778,436 (M); expenditures, $748,913; qualifying distributions, $635,237; giving activities include $625,000 for 16 grants (high: $200,000; low: $1,000).
Fields of interest: Higher education, university; Christian agencies & churches.
Type of support: General/operating support.
Limitations: Applications not accepted. Giving primarily in IN and TX. No grants to individuals.
Application information: Contributes only to pre-selected organizations.
Officers and Directors:* Jon Rex Jones,* Pres.; Ann M. Jones,* Secy.
EIN: 770594694

8655
The Alcon Foundation, Inc. ✧
6201 S. Freeway
Fort Worth, TX 76134-2099 (800) 222-8103
Contact: Matthew Head, Dir., Corp. Giving
FAX: (817) 615-3811; Main URL: http://www.alcon.com/en/corporate-responsibility/alcon-foundation.asp

Established in 1962 in TX.
Donor: Alcon Laboratories, Inc.
Foundation type: Company-sponsored foundation.
Financial data (yr. ended 12/31/12): Assets, $30,000 (M); gifts received, $6,379,485; expenditures, $6,398,990; qualifying distributions, $6,398,990; giving activities include $6,379,485 for 155 grants (high: $600,000; low: $677).
Purpose and activities: The Alcon Foundation supports programs designed to improve the quality of eye care and patient access to eye care; advance eye health education, research, and awareness; and enhance and create sound communities where Alcon has a facility presence.
Fields of interest: Medical school/education; Education; Hospitals (specialty); Optometry/vision screening; Eye diseases; Eye research; Human services; Community/economic development; Blind/visually impaired; Economically disadvantaged.
Type of support: Management development/capacity building; Program development; Curriculum development; Research.
Limitations: Applications accepted. Giving primarily in areas of company operations in Irvine, CA, Atlanta, GA, Sinking Spring, PA, Fort Worth and Houston, TX, and Huntington, WV. No support for fraternal, labor, political, or veterans' organizations, discriminatory organizations, or private K-12 schools. No grants to individuals, or for family requests for scholarships, fellowships, religious activities, endowments, capital or building campaigns, matching gifts, university administrative, management, or indirect fees, golf tournaments, athletic events, league or team sponsorships, school-affiliated orchestras, bands, choirs, student trips or tours, unrestricted grants, books, research papers, articles in professional journals, travel, fundraising activities, or advertising sponsorships.

Publications: Application guidelines; Corporate giving report.
Application information: Application form required.
Initial approach: Complete online eligibility quiz and application
Deadline(s): None; Feb. 1 to July 31 for requests of $50,000 or more
Board meeting date(s): 4th quarter
Final notification: Final notification for large grant requests is 1st quarter of the following year.
Officers and Directors:* Kevin J. Buehler,* Chair.; Bettina Maunz, Pres.; Christina Ackerman; Robert Kim; Merrick McCracken; Steven Wilson.
EIN: 200166600

8656
The Stanford & Joan Alexander Foundation ✧
1400 Post Oak Blvd., Ste. 900
Houston, TX 77056-6657

Established in 1986 in TX.
Donors: Stanford Alexander; Joan Alexander.
Foundation type: Independent foundation.
Financial data (yr. ended 12/31/13): Assets, $18,812,929 (M); expenditures, $6,769,071; qualifying distributions, $6,740,666; giving activities include $6,693,511 for 57 grants (high: $3,761,319; low: $1,000).
Fields of interest: Elementary school/education; Secondary school/education; Higher education; Medical school/education; Health care; Mental health/crisis services; Health organizations, association; Medical research, institute; Civil/human rights; Community/economic development; Government/public administration; Jewish agencies & synagogues; Religion.
Type of support: General/operating support; Research.
Limitations: Applications not accepted. Giving primarily in TX, with emphasis on Houston; some funding nationally. No grants to individuals.
Application information: Contributes only to pre-selected organizations.
Officers and Directors:* Stanford Alexander,* Chair.; Joan Alexander,* C.E.O., Pres., and Treas.; Andrew M. Alexander, Secy.; Kevin B. Alexander; Melvin Dow; Benjamin Warren.
Number of staff: 1 part-time professional; 1 part-time support.
EIN: 760204170

8657
The Alkek and Williams Foundation ✧
1100 Louisiana St., Ste. 5250
Houston, TX 77002-5100 (713) 652-6600
Contact: Charles A. Williams, Tr.

Established in 1996 in TX.
Donor: Margaret M. Alkek.
Foundation type: Independent foundation.
Financial data (yr. ended 12/31/12): Assets, $8,127,534 (M); expenditures, $1,762,699; qualifying distributions, $1,732,900; giving activities include $1,732,900 for 81 grants (high: $850,000; low: $100).
Purpose and activities: Giving primarily for higher education, the performing arts, including the symphony, and medical research.
Fields of interest: Performing arts, orchestras; Elementary/secondary education; Higher education; Health organizations; Medical research, institute; Human services.
Limitations: Applications accepted. Giving limited to TX, with emphasis on Houston.
Application information: Application form required.
Initial approach: Contact foundation for application form
Deadline(s): None
Trustees: Charles A. Williams; Margaret V. Williams; Randa Duncan Williams.
EIN: 766122587

8658
Albert and Margaret Alkek Foundation ✧
1100 Louisiana St., Suite 5250
Houston, TX 77002-5227 (713) 652-6601
Contact: Sandra Bacak, Cont.
FAX: (713) 652-6621; E-mail: info@alkek.org; Main URL: http://www.alkek.org

Established in 1995 in TX.
Donors: Albert B. Alkek†; Margaret M. Alkek†.
Foundation type: Independent foundation.
Financial data (yr. ended 12/31/12): Assets, $215,818,397 (M); gifts received, $1,563,036; expenditures, $14,595,988; qualifying distributions, $10,673,048; giving activities include $10,400,000 for 25 grants (high: $6,710,000; low: $10,000).
Purpose and activities: Giving primarily for higher education and medical research.
Fields of interest: Higher education; Medical school/education; Medical research, institute.
Type of support: General/operating support; Capital campaigns; Building/renovation; Endowments; Scholarship funds; Research.
Limitations: Applications accepted. Giving limited to TX. No support for political purposes or organizations. No grants to individuals, or for fundraising events or student organizations; no loans.
Publications: Application guidelines; Financial statement; Multi-year report; IRS Form 990 or 990-PF printed copy available upon request.
Application information: The foundation primarily makes grants to organizations supported by the Alkek Family during their lifetimes. Grants are limited to non-profits in the state of Texas. Letter of inquiry should be submitted by U.S. mail only. Faxed or e-mailed applications will not be accepted. The letter of inquiry should not include copies of budgets, tax returns, or financial statements. Application form not required.
Initial approach: Brief letter of inquiry (1-2 pages)
Copies of proposal: 1
Deadline(s): None
Board meeting date(s): Quarterly
Final notification: Varies
Officers and Directors:* Margaret Alkek Williams,* Chair.; Charles A. Williams,* Pres.; Randa Duncan Williams,* V.P.; Scott B. Seaman,* Treas. and Exec. Dir.; Sandra Bacak, Cont.; Bobby R. Alford, M.D.; Daniel C. Arnold; Joe M. Bailey; Dan B. Jones, M.D.; Paul Klotman, M.D.
Number of staff: 1 full-time professional; 1 part-time professional.
EIN: 760491186
Selected grants: The following grants are a representative sample of this grantmaker's funding activity:
$6,710,000 to Baylor College of Medicine, Houston, TX, 2012. For medical research and educational programs.
$1,000,000 to University of Texas M.D. Anderson Cancer Center, Houston, TX, 2012. For construction.
$411,000 to Houston Ballet Foundation, Houston, TX, 2012. For capital campaign.
$220,000 to Houston Symphony Society, Houston, TX, 2012. For program support.
$200,000 to Texas State University, San Marcos, TX, 2012. For library repository construction.
$150,000 to Saint Marys University, San Antonio, TX, 2012. For scholarships.
$130,000 to TMI-The Episcopal School of Texas, San Antonio, TX, 2012. For scholarships.
$47,000 to Episcopal High School, Bellaire, TX, 2012. For scholarships.
$25,000 to Saint Pius X High School, Houston, TX, 2012. For capital campaign.
$20,000 to Arthur Nagel Community Clinic, Bandera, TX, 2012. For program support.

8659
The Carolyn J. and Robert J. Allison, Jr. Family Foundation ✧
Chasewood Crossing 1
19500 State Hwy. 249, Ste. 760
Houston, TX 77070

Established in 1997 in TX.
Donors: Carolyn J. Allison; Robert J. Allison; Robert J. Allison, Jr.
Foundation type: Independent foundation.
Financial data (yr. ended 12/31/13): Assets, $26,220,801 (M); gifts received, $2,947,330; expenditures, $1,380,595; qualifying distributions, $1,242,590; giving activities include $1,237,355 for 19 grants (high: $500,000; low: $1,000).
Fields of interest: Human services; Protestant agencies & churches.
Limitations: Applications not accepted. Giving primarily in TX. No grants to individuals.
Application information: Unsolicited requests for funds not accepted.
Officers: Robert J. Allison, Jr., Pres.; Jane S. Allison, Secy.; Carolyn J. Allison, Treas.
Directors: Ann A. Stanislaw; Amy A. Watkins.
EIN: 760539246

8660
Amarillo Area Foundation, Inc. ✧
801 S. Fillmore, Ste. 700
Amarillo, TX 79101-3537 (806) 376-4521
Contact: For grants: Kathie Grant, Grants Coord.
FAX: (806) 373-3656; E-mail: haf@aaf-hf.org; Grant application e-mail: kathie@aaf-hf.org; Main URL: http://www.amarilloareafoundation.org
E-Newsletter: http://www.amarilloareafoundation.org/page.aspx?pid=528

Established as a trust in 1957 in TX.
Foundation type: Community foundation.
Financial data (yr. ended 12/31/12): Assets, $205,986,892 (M); gifts received, $8,409,849; expenditures, $9,851,923; giving activities include $5,378,320 for 174+ grants (high: $479,621), and $827,475 for 783 grants to individuals.
Purpose and activities: The foundation seeks to improve the quality of life in the TX Panhandle through effective philanthropic efforts. The foundation is currently focused on four areas of

particular priority: 1) Education; 2) Health; 3) Human Services; and 4) Youth and Families.
Fields of interest: Arts; Education; Health care; Disasters, preparedness/services; Recreation, centers; Recreation; Children/youth, services; Family services; Aging, centers/services; Human services; Youth; Economically disadvantaged.
Type of support: Management development/ capacity building; Building/renovation; Equipment; Land acquisition; Emergency funds; Program development; Seed money; Scholarship funds; Matching/challenge support.
Limitations: Applications accepted. Giving limited to the 26 northernmost counties of the Texas Panhandle region. No support for private or parochial schools, national, state, or local fundraising activities, or religious activities or programs that serve or appear to serve specific religious groups, or denominations. No grants to individuals (except for the scholarship program), or generally for operating budgets, annual campaigns, deficit financing, endowment funds, publications, conferences, travel, research projects, or historic preservation; no loans.
Publications: Annual report; Informational brochure; Newsletter.
Application information: Visit foundation web site for application form and guidelines. Proposals should be submitted a minimum of 3-4 months before funds are needed. Application form required.
Initial approach: Mail or e-mail application form and attachments
Copies of proposal: 1
Deadline(s): None
Board meeting date(s): Feb., Apr., June, Aug., Oct., and Dec.; Exec. Comm. meets bimonthly: Mar., May, July, Sept., and Nov.
Officers and Directors:* Julie Mitchell,* Chair.; Cliff Bickerstaff,* 1st Vice-Chair.; Puff Niegos,* 2nd Vice-Chair.; Clay Stribling,* C.E.O. and Pres.; Angela Lust,* Sr. V.P.; Charlotte Rhodes,* V.P., Regional Svcs.; Linda Rasor,* Secy.; Jason Herrick,* Treas.; Roy Bara; Jeri Bezner; Vanessa Buzzard; Terry Caviness; Paul Clark; Kathy Cornett; LeRayne Donelson; Mike Engler; Steve Hoard; Steve Hoard; Larry Johnson; Ken Kelley; Sharon Miner; Alice O'Brien; Jackie Pearson; Dyke Rogers; Rod Schroder; Edward Scott; Nancy Seliger; Caroline Smith; Roy Urrutia.
Number of staff: 10 full-time professional.
EIN: 750978220
Selected grants: The following grants are a representative sample of this grantmaker's funding activity:
$75,000 to Cal Farleys Boys Ranch, Amarillo, TX, 2013. For renovation of the facility at 10th and Monroe in order to expand the NoLimitsNoExcuses and Neighborhood Navigator programs.
$75,000 to Kids, Inc. of Amarillo, Amarillo, TX, 2013. To replace the poligrass field turf and purchase bleachers for the Bus and Freda Dugger Sportsplex.
$68,000 to Panhandle Twenty/20, Amarillo, TX, 2013. For program support.
$63,275 to Baptist Community Services, Amarillo, TX, 2013. To purchase delivery truck for Amarillo Snack Pak 4 Kids.
$60,000 to New Horizons Ranch and Center, Abilene, TX, 2013. For residential, therapeutic treatment for Panhandle foster children.
$51,880 to Catholic Charities of the Texas Panhandle, Amarillo, TX, 2013. To install a fire sprinkler system and related repairs, including supplies, at the Pearl Longbine Emergency Youth Shelter.
$50,000 to Victory Tree Foundation, Dumas, TX, 2013. To construct duplex.
$35,000 to Panhandle AIDS Support Organization, Amarillo, TX, 2013. For roof replacement and ceiling repairs at 1501 SW 10th Avenue.
$18,836 to YMCA of Moore County, Dumas, TX, 2013. To create a Teen Center at the Dumas Y.

8661
Anadarko Foundation ✧
1201 Lake Robbins Dr.
The Woodlands, TX 77380-1181 (832) 636-1000
Contact: R.K. Reeves, Sr. V.P.

Established in 2007 in TX.
Foundation type: Independent foundation.
Financial data (yr. ended 12/31/13): Assets, $3,978,430 (M); expenditures, $1,383,783; qualifying distributions, $1,356,668; giving activities include $1,356,668 for 7 grants (high: $333,334; low: $40,000).
Fields of interest: Higher education; Cancer; Medical research, institute.
Limitations: Applications accepted. Giving primarily in CO, OK, and TX. No grants for Limited to public charities.
Application information: Application form required.
Initial approach: Letter
Deadline(s): None
Officers: James T. Hackett, Chair., C.E.O., and Pres.; Robert G. Gwin, Sr. V.P. and C.FO.; Robert K. Reeves, Sr. V.P.; R.A. Walker, Sr. V.P.; Amanda M. McMillian, V.P. and Corp. Secy.; Bruce Busmire, V.P. and Treas.; Margaret C. Douglas, Cont.
EIN: 262113030
Selected grants: The following grants are a representative sample of this grantmaker's funding activity:
$520,000 to American Association of Petroleum Geologists Foundation, Tulsa, OK, 2011. For general operating budget.
$200,000 to Colorado School of Mines Foundation, Golden, CO, 2011. For general operating budget.
$200,000 to Greater Houston Partnership, Houston, TX, 2011. For general operating budget.
$200,000 to Houston Grand Opera, Houston, TX, 2011. For general operating budget.
$166,667 to Texas Heart Institute, Houston, TX, 2011. For general operating budget.
$75,000 to Oklahoma City University, Oklahoma City, OK, 2011. For general operating budget.
$75,000 to Oklahoma City University, Oklahoma City, OK, 2011. For general operating budget.
$20,000 to Oklahoma Medical Research Foundation, Oklahoma City, OK, 2011. For general operating budget.

8662
Anchorage Foundation of Texas ✧
10 Waverly Ct.
Houston, TX 77005-1842

Established in 1979 in TX.
Donors: Anne S. Bohnn; Anne S. Brown; Godfather Charitable Trust.
Foundation type: Independent foundation.
Financial data (yr. ended 06/30/13): Assets, $8,960,694 (M); gifts received, $436,731; expenditures, $1,150,885; qualifying distributions, $1,108,601; giving activities include $1,063,565 for 22 grants (high: $639,065; low: $1,000), and $41,497 for 2 foundation-administered programs.
Fields of interest: Arts; Education; Recreation, centers; Children/youth, services.
Type of support: General/operating support; Program development; Fellowships; Research.
Limitations: Applications not accepted. Giving primarily in Houston, TX. No grants to individuals.
Application information: Contributes only to pre-selected organizations.
Officers: Marc C. Melcher, Pres.; C. LeRoy Melcher, Secy.; Jody Blazek, C.P.A., Treas.
Director: Pierre S. Melcher.
EIN: 742071804
Selected grants: The following grants are a representative sample of this grantmaker's funding activity:
$96,734 to Houston Grand Opera, Houston, TX, 2011. For program support.
$35,000 to Houston Public Library Foundation, Houston, TX, 2011.
$25,000 to Houston Tomorrow, Houston, TX, 2011.
$25,000 to Menil Foundation, Houston, TX, 2011.
$20,000 to Childrens Museum of Houston, Houston, TX, 2011. For capital campaign.
$20,000 to Fort Worth Country Day School, Fort Worth, TX, 2011. For general support.
$20,000 to Houston Artists Fund, Houston, TX, 2011.
$20,000 to Saint Johns School, Houston, TX, 2011. For general support.
$10,000 to Orange Show Center for Visionary Art, Houston, TX, 2011. For charitable event.
$2,500 to Houston Tomorrow, Houston, TX, 2011.

8663
Carl C. Anderson, Sr. and Marie Jo Anderson Charitable Foundation ✧
114 W. 7th St., Ste. 1200
Austin, TX 78701-3048 (512) 458-2285

Donors: Carl C. Anderson, Sr.†; Marie Jo Anderson†.
Foundation type: Independent foundation.
Financial data (yr. ended 12/31/13): Assets, $87,126,200 (M); expenditures, $3,800,571; qualifying distributions, $2,959,217; giving activities include $2,231,997 for 138 grants (high: $200,000; low: $1,000).
Purpose and activities: The mission of the foundation is: to support medical research seeking the cure and prevention of catastrophic disease; to assist in meeting the essential needs of children; and to enhance the quality of life for elderly persons and those with mental and physical disabilities.
Fields of interest: Child development, education; Education, special; Health care, clinics/centers; Medical research; Food distribution, groceries on wheels; Food distribution, meals on wheels; Children/youth, services; Aging, centers/services; Developmentally disabled, centers & services; Independent living, disability; Children; Aging; Disabilities, people with.
Type of support: General/operating support; Continuing support; Emergency funds; Matching/ challenge support.
Limitations: Giving primarily in NM, OK, and TX. No support for government agencies or municipalities, or advocacy/similar indirect support of organizations. No grants to individuals, or for events, seed money, endowments, staff development or for debt reduction.

Application information: Acknowledgment will be sent immediately upon receipt of application. Application form required.
Initial approach: Letter of interest outlining your request
Deadline(s): None
Final notification: 3- to 6-months after receipt of application
Officer and Trustees:* Brad Robb,* Exec. Dir.; Carl C. Anderson III; Jennifer J. Bird; R. Russell Rager.
EIN: 746078530
Selected grants: The following grants are a representative sample of this grantmaker's funding activity:
$50,000 to Junior League of Austin, Austin, TX, 2012. For matching grant for Hillcrest F.I.T. Program.
$25,000 to University of Texas, Austin, TX, 2012. For Acellular Peripheral Nerve Graft As a Bridge After Spinal Cord Surgery.
$20,000 to Daughters of Charity of Canossa, Albuquerque, NM, 2012. For Casa Angelica Operations.
$20,000 to Gethsemane Lutheran Church, Austin, TX, 2012. For Children's and Senior's Program.
$20,000 to La Vida Felicidad, Los Lunas, NM, 2012. For Homecare/Personal Care Program.
$15,000 to LIFE Senior Services, Tulsa, OK, 2012. For Adult Day Services for Low-Income Seniors.
$10,000 to High Plains Food Bank, Amarillo, TX, 2012. For Kid's Cafe.
$10,000 to Northwest Assistance Ministries, Houston, TX, 2012. For funding for the Children's Clinic.
$5,000 to Dallas Community Lighthouse, Garland, TX, 2012. For Kid's Campus Tutoring Program.
$5,000 to El Pasoans Fighting Hunger, El Paso, TX, 2012. For general operations/food bank.

8664
M. D. Anderson Foundation ✧
c/o JPMorgan Chase
P. O. Box 2558
Houston, TX 77252-8037 (713) 216-8138
Contact: Karla Dominguez

Established in 2003 in TX as a successor foundation to the first M.D. Anderson Foundation.
Donors: M.D. Anderson‡; Linda K. Finger Trust.
Foundation type: Independent foundation.
Financial data (yr. ended 12/31/12): Assets, $114,363,888 (M); gifts received, $52,139; expenditures, $7,006,985; qualifying distributions, $5,951,213; giving activities include $5,670,000 for 120 grants (high: $250,000; low: $2,500).
Purpose and activities: Giving for: 1) the improvement of working class conditions among workers generally, as well as among particular classes of unskilled, skilled, and agricultural workers; 2) the establishment, support, and maintenance of hospitals, homes, and institutions for the care of the sick, the young, the aged, the incompetent, and the helpless; 3) the improvement of living conditions among people generally, as well as in particular sections or localities; and 4) the promotion of health, science, education, and advancement and diffusion of knowledge and understanding among people.
Fields of interest: Education; Hospitals (general); Health care; Medical specialties; Employment, alliance/advocacy; Employment; Youth, services; Aging, centers/services; Human services; Public policy, research; Government/public administration.
Type of support: Building/renovation; Equipment; Seed money; Research; Matching/challenge support.
Limitations: Applications accepted. Giving primarily in TX, with emphasis on the Houston area. No grants to individuals, or for operating funds or endowments.
Publications: Application guidelines; Multi-year report.
Application information: Application form required.
Initial approach: Letter
Copies of proposal: 5
Deadline(s): None
Board meeting date(s): 3rd Tues. monthly
Final notification: Within 1 month
Officers: Gibson Gayle, Jr., Pres.; Uriel E. Dutton, V.P.; Charles W. Hall, V.P.; Leo Linbeck, Jr., V.P.
EIN: 300129656

8665
Rose-Marie and Jack R. Anderson Foundation ✧
5000 Legacy Dr., Ste. 140
Plano, TX 75024-3186

Established in 1994 in TX.
Donors: Jack R. Anderson; Rose-Marie Anderson; Brian Childs Trust.
Foundation type: Independent foundation.
Financial data (yr. ended 12/31/13): Assets, $57,461,796 (M); expenditures, $2,321,543; qualifying distributions, $2,239,579; giving activities include $2,128,590 for 28 grants (high: $464,471; low: $59).
Fields of interest: Higher education; Education; Human services; Foundations (public).
Limitations: Applications not accepted. Giving primarily in IN, NY, and PA; some funding also in CA. No grants to individuals.
Application information: Contributes only to pre-selected organizations.
Officers and Directors:* Jack R. Anderson,* Pres.; Neil R. Anderson,* Treas.; Rose-Marie Anderson; Gail Anderson Canizares; Barbara Anderson McDonald.
EIN: 752542403

8666
The Andras Foundation ✧
412 Timberwilde Ln.
Houston, TX 77024-6928 (713) 822-3512
Contact: Oscar S. Andras, Pres.

Established in 2004 in TX.
Donor: Oscar S. Andras.
Foundation type: Independent foundation.
Financial data (yr. ended 12/31/13): Assets, $13,480,998 (M); expenditures, $647,463; qualifying distributions, $645,937; giving activities include $644,500 for 15 grants (high: $200,000; low: $1,000).
Fields of interest: Elementary/secondary education; Higher education; Hospitals (specialty); Boys & girls clubs.
Limitations: Applications accepted. Giving primarily in TX. No grants to individuals.
Application information: Application form required.
Initial approach: Proposal
Deadline(s): None
Final notification: Within one month
Officers: Oscar S. Andras, Pres.; Louis J. Andras, V.P. and Secy.; David S. Andras, V.P. and Treas.
EIN: 202025934
Selected grants: The following grants are a representative sample of this grantmaker's funding activity:
$20,000 to Wounded Warrior Project, Jacksonville, FL, 2012. To fund charitable activities.

8667
Selma E. Andrews Trust ✧
c/o Bank of America, N.A.
P.O. Box 831041
Dallas, TX 75283-1041

Established in 2010 in TX.
Foundation type: Independent foundation.
Financial data (yr. ended 12/31/13): Assets, $40,099,595 (M); expenditures, $9,099,036; qualifying distributions, $7,580,879; giving activities include $7,570,900 for 6 grants (high: $1,262,069; low: $1,261,312).
Fields of interest: Education; Health organizations, association; Human services.
Limitations: Applications not accepted. Giving primarily in CA.
Application information: Contributes only to pre-selected organizations.
Trustee: Bank of America, N.A.
EIN: 756327536

8668
Paul E. Andrews, Jr. Foundation ✧
(formerly Andrews Family Fund)
P.O. Box 1290
Fort Worth, TX 76101-1290

Established in 2007 in TX.
Donors: Paul E. Andrews; Judith E. Andrews.
Foundation type: Independent foundation.
Financial data (yr. ended 12/31/12): Assets, $70,055,400 (M); expenditures, $4,035,610; qualifying distributions, $3,718,500; giving activities include $3,710,000 for 13 grants (high: $1,000,000; low: $15,000).
Fields of interest: Museums; Health care; Children/youth, services.
Limitations: Applications not accepted. Giving primarily in TX.
Application information: Contributes only to pre-selected organizations.
Officers: Paul E. Andrews, Pres. and Treas.; Judith E. Andrews, V.P. and Secy.
Directors: Christopher Andrews; Emelie Andrews-Graham; Jennifer Moore.
EIN: 261516686

8669
The Angela Foundation ✧
1132 Indian Pass
Salado, TX 76571-6158 (254) 947-3148
Contact: Joy Lavale Beiler

Established in 1998 in PA.
Donors: Anne Beiler; Jonas Z. Beiler; The Coca-Cola Co.
Foundation type: Independent foundation.
Financial data (yr. ended 12/31/13): Assets, $2,317,149 (M); expenditures, $569,506; qualifying distributions, $548,558; giving activities

include $538,134 for 4 grants (high: $304,002; low: $2,400).
Purpose and activities: The foundation was established to provide financial support for programs and ministries assisting children and families. Giving primarily to Christian counseling centers that provide services free of charge to women and children.
Fields of interest: Human services; Christian agencies & churches.
Type of support: General/operating support.
Limitations: Applications accepted. Giving primarily in PA, with emphasis on Gap. No grants to individuals, or for capital campaigns, equipment, endowments, direct services, or for media productions.
Application information: Application form required.
Initial approach: Letter
Deadline(s): None
Officers: Jonas Z. Beiler, Chair.; LaWonna Goedhart, Pres.; Mary Trego, Secy.-Treas.
Directors: Jeff Blevins; Doris Swaim.
EIN: 232985480

8670
The Arena Energy Foundation ✧
4200 Research Forest Dr., Ste. 500
The Woodlands, TX 77381-4224

Donors: Don Metz; Larry Hoelscher; Arena Energy, LLC; William Companies, Inc.
Foundation type: Independent foundation.
Financial data (yr. ended 12/31/12): Assets, $150,676 (M); gifts received, $60,000; expenditures, $448,692; qualifying distributions, $444,633; giving activities include $444,633 for 46 grants (high: $213,408; low: $375).
Fields of interest: Health care; Crime/violence prevention, child abuse; Children/youth, services; Human services.
Limitations: Applications not accepted. Giving primarily in LA, MI and TX.
Application information: Unsolicited requests for funds not accepted.
Directors: Renee Kelly; Don Metz; Jane C. Minarovic; Jennifer Stone.
EIN: 261636123

8671
William E. Armentrout Foundation ✧
c/o Lee C. Ritchie
P.O. Box 190407
Dallas, TX 75219-0407

Established in 1998 in TX.
Donor: William E. Armentrout†.
Foundation type: Independent foundation.
Financial data (yr. ended 12/31/13): Assets, $18,526,595 (M); expenditures, $903,394; qualifying distributions, $885,000; giving activities include $810,000 for 8 grants (high: $405,000; low: $40,500).
Fields of interest: Higher education; Nursing care; Youth development; Human services; Protestant agencies & churches.
Type of support: General/operating support; Scholarship funds; Research.
Limitations: Applications not accepted. Giving primarily in Dallas and University Park, TX. No grants to individuals.
Application information: Contributes only to pre-selected organizations.
Officers and Directors:* Lee C. Ritchie, Chair. and Pres.; Elizabeth R. Kaye, V.P. and Treas.; Dennis L. Lutes,* Secy.; Richard Hanschen.
EIN: 752750535

8672
Laura and John Arnold Foundation ✧
2800 Post Oak Blvd., Ste. 225
Houston, TX 77056-8809 (713) 554-1349
E-mail: info@arnoldfoundation.org; Main
URL: http://www.arnoldfoundation.org/
GiveSmart: http://www.givesmart.org/Stories/Donors/John-and-Laura-Arnold
Laura and John Arnold's Giving Pledge
Profile: http://glasspockets.org/philanthropy-in-focus/eye-on-the-giving-pledge/profiles/arnold
The Giving Library: http://www.givinglibrary.org/

Established in 2008 in TX.
Donors: John D. Arnold; Laura E. Arnold.
Foundation type: Independent foundation.
Financial data (yr. ended 12/31/13): Assets, $1,648,587,004 (M); gifts received, $233,865,444; expenditures, $104,564,215; qualifying distributions, $93,865,784; giving activities include $80,519,024 for 114 grants (high: $18,000,000; low: $2,587), $7,839,467 for foundation-administered programs and $2,004,788 for 1 loan/program-related investment.
Purpose and activities: The foundation's core objective is to produce substantial, widespread and lasting reforms that will maximize opportunities and minimize injustice in our society. To do this, the foundation identifies challenges and address their root causes through innovative, multi-disciplinary solutions. The foundation aims to foster a culture in which individuals have the best chance to succeed and prosper, while encouraging a sense of responsibility, compassion and reinvestment toward their communities and society as a whole.
Fields of interest: Education, reform; Education, public education; Elementary/secondary education; Middle schools/education; Health organizations, research; Medical research; Crime/law enforcement, reform; Courts/judicial administration; Social sciences; Government/public administration; Public affairs, citizen participation; Pensions.
Type of support: Program-related investments/loans; General/operating support; Management development/capacity building; Program development; Seed money; Research; Technical assistance.
Limitations: Applications not accepted. Giving on a national basis. No grants to individuals.
Application information: Contributes only to pre-selected organizations.
Officers and Directors:* John D. Arnold,* Co-Chair.; Laura E. Arnold,* Co-Chair.; Denis Calabrese,* Pres.; Lesley Briones, J.D.*, V.P., Fdn. Mgmt. and General Counsel and Secy.; Josh B. McGee, Ph.D.*, V.P., Public Accountability; Anne Milgram, J.D., V.P., Criminal Justice; Caprice Young, Ed.D., V.P., Education; Elizabeth Banks,* Treas., Cont. and Grants Mgr.
Number of staff: 19 full-time support; 6 part-time support.
EIN: 263241764
Selected grants: The following grants are a representative sample of this grantmaker's funding activity:
$35,500,000 to Nutrition Science Initiative, San Diego, CA, 2013. To reduce the economic and social burden of obesity and obesity-related chronic disease by improving the quality of science in nutrition and obesity research, payable over 4.75 years.
$15,000,000 to MDRC, New York, NY, 2013. To address the root causes of poverty by advancing evidence-based policies that support concrete, measurable, and lasting improvements in society.
$9,847,418 to Massachusetts Institute of Technology, Cambridge, MA, 2013. For the development of the Abdul Latif Jameel Poverty Action Lab's regional office in North America.
$6,130,243 to Stanford University, Stanford, CA, 2013. For the development of a center that is focused on improving the quality of medical research in order to improve patient health.
$6,000,000 to Computers for Youth Foundation, New York, NY, 2013. For blended learning.
$6,000,000 to Rice University, Houston, TX, 2013. For the OpenStax College project to create free, high-quality online textbooks.
$3,250,000 to Education Reform Now, New York, NY, 2013. To improve K-12 public education.
$950,000 to Coalition for Evidence-Based Policy, Washington, DC, 2013. To demonstrate the feasibility of low-cost randomized controlled trials in order to advance evidence-based policy-making.
$399,993 to Behavioral Ideas Laboratory, ideas42, New York, NY, 2013. To determine what the most important components of cognitive behavioral therapy are and to design a more robust version of cognitive behavioral therapy to help reduce crime and violence.
$300,000 to Alliance for School Choice, Washington, DC, 2013. To educate families about and assist them with available educational options.

8673
Truman and Anita Arnold Foundation ✧
2900 St. Michael Dr., 5th Fl.
Texarkana, TX 75503-2388 (903) 794-3835
Contact: Truman Arnold, Tr.; Anita Arnold, Tr.

Established in 1998 in TX.
Donors: Truman Arnold; Anita Arnold.
Foundation type: Independent foundation.
Financial data (yr. ended 12/31/13): Assets, $7,308,902 (M); gifts received, $5,004,700; expenditures, $3,102,221; qualifying distributions, $3,058,383; giving activities include $3,058,383 for 13 grants (high: $1,100,526; low: $5,000).
Fields of interest: Higher education, university; Cancer; Human services; Children/youth, services; Youth, services; Christian agencies & churches.
Limitations: Applications accepted. Giving primarily in Texarkana, TX; some giving also in AR and CA.
Application information: Application form not required.
Initial approach: Proposal
Deadline(s): None
Trustees: Anita Arnold; Truman Arnold.
EIN: 710811364
Selected grants: The following grants are a representative sample of this grantmaker's funding activity:
$845,262 to Texas A & M University, Texarkana, TX, 2011.

8674
Astros in Action Foundation—Fielding the Dreams of Houston ✧

501 Crawford St., Ste. 500
Houston, TX 77002-2113
E-mail: foundation@astros.com; Additional address: P.O. Box 288, Houston, TX 77001; Additional tel.: (713) 259-8956; Main URL: http://houston.astros.mlb.com/NASApp/mlb/hou/community/foundation_mission.jsp
Grand Slam for Youth Baseball Website: http://www.gsfyb.com/
E-mail for Grand Slam for Youth Baseball Scholarships: scholarships@gsfyb.org

Established in 2000 in TX.
Donors: Houston McLane Co., Inc.; William L. Berkman; Lance Berkman; Carlos Lee; Drayton McLane, Jr.; Roy Oswalt.
Foundation type: Company-sponsored foundation.
Financial data (yr. ended 12/31/12): Assets, $2,327,880 (M); gifts received, $3,011,011; expenditures, $955,531; qualifying distributions, $953,531; giving activities include $819,792 for 9 grants (high: $759,590; low: $2,000), and $62,500 for 25 grants to individuals (high: $2,500; low: $2,500).
Purpose and activities: The foundation supports programs designed to promote literacy; education; scholarship; health; faith-based organizations; and programs designed to revive baseball in the inner city.
Fields of interest: Education, reading; Education; Health care; Cancer; Heart & circulatory diseases; Athletics/sports, baseball; Boys & girls clubs; United Ways and Federated Giving Programs; Christian agencies & churches; Religion.
Type of support: Scholarships—to individuals; General/operating support; Capital campaigns; Building/renovation; Program development; Scholarship funds; Sponsorships; Grants to individuals.
Limitations: Applications accepted. Giving primarily in Houston, TX.
Publications: Application guidelines.
Application information: A personal interview may be requested for Grand Slam for Youth Baseball Scholarships. Application form required.
Initial approach: Download application form and mail to foundation for Grand Slam for Youth Baseball Fundraising and Scholarships; download nomination form for Hometown Heroes
Deadline(s): None for Grand Slam for Youth Baseball Fundraising; May 14 for Grand Slam for Youth Baseball Scholarships; None for Hometown Heroes
Final notification: 4 weeks for Grand Slam for Youth Baseball Fundraising; June 17 for Grand Slam for Youth Baseball Scholarships
Officers and Directors:* Drayton McLane, Jr.,* Pres.; Pamela J. Gardner, V.P.; Marian Harper, V.P.; Robert S. McClaren, V.P.; G.W. Sanford, Jr.,* V.P.; Webster F. Stickney, Jr.,* Secy.-Treas.
EIN: 742793078

8675
AT&T Foundation
(formerly SBC Foundation)

208 S. Akard, Ste. 100
Dallas, TX 75202-4206
Additional e-mail: questions@aspirerfp.com; Main URL: http://www.att.com/gen/landing-pages?pid=7735
AT&T Aspire Local Impact Initiative Recipients: http://www.att.com/gen/press-room?pid=23079
AT&T Aspire on Twitter: https://twitter.com/attaspire/
AT&T Aspire on YouTube: https://www.youtube.com/playlist?list=PL804D2528577ACFAC
AT&T Aspire RFP website: http://www.aspirerfp.com
AT&T Military/Veterans Program Funding Inquiry: http://about.att.com/content/csr/home/people/serving-our-communities/supporting-our-troops/at-t-military-veterans-program-survey.html
RSS Feed: http://www.att.com/gen/press-room?pid=21287
The People| Planet| Possibilities Blog: http://about.att.com/content/csr/home/blog.html

Established in 1984 in MO.
Donors: Southwestern Bell Corp.; SBC Communications Inc.; AT&T Inc.; Network for Good.
Foundation type: Company-sponsored foundation.
Financial data (yr. ended 12/31/12): Assets, $9,768,836 (M); gifts received, $261,703; expenditures, $11,312,889; qualifying distributions, $11,464,285; giving activities include $8,745,039 for 57 grants (high: $1,124,494; low: $10,000), $153,200 for 753 grants to individuals (high: $3,000; low: $100), and $2,114,471 for 452 employee matching gifts.
Purpose and activities: The foundation supports programs designed to advance education. Through its community initiatives, AT&T has a long history of investing in projects that create learning opportunities; promote academic and economic achievement; or address community needs.
Fields of interest: Arts; Secondary school/education; Higher education; Scholarships/financial aid; Education, drop-out prevention; Education; Health care; Employment, training; Employment; Disasters, preparedness/services; Human services; Community development, neighborhood development; Community/economic development; Mathematics; Engineering/technology; Science; Leadership development; Public affairs; Children/youth; Youth; Young adults; Minorities; Military/veterans; Economically disadvantaged.
Type of support: Curriculum development; Employee matching gifts; Employee volunteer services; Matching/challenge support; Program development; Scholarship funds.
Limitations: Applications accepted. Giving on a national basis in areas of company operations. No support for religious organizations not of direct benefit to the entire community, or for political, discriminatory, or disease-specific organizations, or medical clinics or research. No grants to individuals (except for employee-related disaster grants) or for capital campaigns, endowment funds, goodwill ads, ticket or dinner purchases, sports programs or events, or cause-related marketing; no product donations.
Publications: Corporate giving report; Program policy statement.
Application information: Company facility addresses can be found on the 990. Multi-year funding is not automatic. AT&T Aspire applications are accepted on an invitation-only basis. Visit website for RFP announcements.
Initial approach: Contact nearest statewide facility for general funding; proposal to application address for general national funding; complete online pre-qualification for AT&T Aspire RFP
Copies of proposal: 1
Deadline(s): None for general funding; Jan. 17 for AT&T Aspire RFP
Board meeting date(s): Twice per year
Final notification: Mid-June for AT&T Aspire, 4-6 weeks for all other applications
Officers and Directors:* James W. Cicconi,* Chair.; Nicole Anderson, Pres. and Exec. Dir., Philanthropy; Thomas R. Giltner, V.P. and Secy.; Jonathan P. Klug, V.P. and Treas.; Charlene Lake, V.P.; William A. Blase, Jr.; Catherine Coughlin; Ralph De La Vega; John Stephens; Wayne Watts.
Number of staff: 11 full-time professional; 1 full-time support.
EIN: 431353948
Selected grants: The following grants are a representative sample of this grantmaker's funding activity:
$1,124,494 to Scholarship America, Saint Peter, MN, 2012. For scholarship awards for the first half of 2012 under the AT&T Foundation Scholarship Program designed to help eligible employees defray a portion of the costs of college education for their children or stepchildren.
$1,124,493 to Scholarship America, Saint Peter, MN, 2012. For scholarship awards for the second half of 2012 under the AT&T Foundation Scholarship Program designed to help eligible employees defray a portion of the costs of college education for their children or stepchildren.
$1,000,000 to Bexar County Performing Arts Center Foundation, San Antonio, TX, 2012. For the Bexar County Performing Arts Center Foundation in the creation of a world-class performance facility that will serve as a permanent home for the major performing and cultural arts organizations of San Antonio and Bexar County.
$750,000 to Roadtrip Nation Experience, Costa Mesa, CA, 2012. For the expansion of Roadtrip Nation (RTN) programming into AVID and Continuation Schools in five states, Florida, Georgia, New York, Tennessee, and Texas, serving specific needs of 8,000 at-risk youth, empowering them to explore what's possible and make better, more sound choices about their education and careers.
$500,000 to George W. Bush Presidential Center, George W. Bush Institute, Dallas, TX, 2012. For Network Programming, sharing of best practices and research, and the development and testing of a Principal Preparation Program (PPP) Evaluation tool for the Alliance To Reform Education Leadership (AREL).
$300,000 to Alliance for Excellent Education, Washington, DC, 2012. For the Alliance's 2013 Digital Learning Day and Project 24 implementation that focuses on the effective use of technology in secondary schools.
$250,000 to Achieve, Inc., Washington, DC, 2012. For creation of the Business Center for a College- and Career-Ready America, providing STEM education that will have a positive impact on student success in high school, college and the workforce.
$250,000 to Arc of the United States, Washington, DC, 2012. For The Arc's School-to-Community

Transition Initiative, assisting and supporting youth with intellectual and developmental disabilities to transition from high school to post-secondary education and employment.
$250,000 to Girls Incorporated, New York, NY, 2012. For the development phase in year one of a three-year national career development and college prep program, with emphasis on STEM, for underserved girls. The pilot phase of this project will serve 50 girls ages 15-18 in grades 11 and 12, expanding on the important work they are doing to increase the number of girls graduating high school under their existing Eureka! Project.
$50,000 to House of Grace, Sparks, GA, 2012. For the Cook County School Success Initiative designed to support and expand existing retention efforts for 250 struggling 9th grade students at Cook High School. The program is designed around six different components to improve school success.

8676
Austin Community Foundation for the Capital Area, Inc. ✧

(formerly Austin Community Foundation)
4315 Guadalupe St., Ste. 300
Austin, TX 78751 (512) 472-4483
Contact: MariBen Ramsey, V.P.
FAX: (512) 472-4486; E-mail: info@austincf.org; Additional e-mail: mbramsey@austincommunityfoundation.org; Main URL: http://www.austincommunityfoundation.org
E-Newsletter: http://www.austincommunityfoundation.org/?nd=email
Facebook: http://www.facebook.com/pages/Austin-Community-Foundation/250561989784?ref=ts
LinkedIn: http://www.linkedin.com/groups?about=&gid=2640460&trk=anet_ug_grppro
Twitter: http://twitter.com/austincommfound
YouTube: https://www.youtube.com/channel/UCfEu8nYi4QiPoqJlhftE7Xg
Scholarship inquiry e-mail: amyallen@austincommunityfoundation.org

Established in 1977 in TX.
Foundation type: Community foundation.
Financial data (yr. ended 12/31/12): Assets, $140,587,100 (M); gifts received, $36,417,268; expenditures, $34,251,100; giving activities include $22,509,920 for grants.
Purpose and activities: The foundation promotes philanthropy in Central Texas to improve the quality of life now and in the future. The foundation provides support for arts and culture, education and training, community development and community services, the environment, health, human services, recreation, and animal-related services.
Fields of interest: History/archaeology; Arts; Child development, education; Education; Environment; Animal welfare; Medical care, rehabilitation; Health care; Disasters, Hurricane Katrina; Recreation; Child development, services; Human services; Community/economic development.
Type of support: Continuing support; Annual campaigns; Capital campaigns; Building/renovation; Equipment; Land acquisition; Program development; Conferences/seminars; Professorships; Publication; Seed money; Research; Technical assistance; Consulting services; Matching/challenge support.
Limitations: Applications accepted. Giving limited to Travis County, TX, for discretionary grants. No support for religious organizations for religious purposes. No grants to individuals (except for scholarships), or for endowments, unrestricted general operating expenses, fundraising activities or events; no loans.
Publications: Application guidelines; Annual report; Informational brochure; Newsletter; Program policy statement.
Application information: Visit foundation web site for Agency Information Sheet and application guidelines. Faxed proposals are not accepted. Application form required.
Initial approach: Submit online Agency Information Sheet and attachments
Copies of proposal: 1
Deadline(s): None
Board meeting date(s): At least 9 times per year
Final notification: 4 to 6 months
Officers and Board of Governors:* William Volk,* Chair.; Mike Nellis, C.E.O. and Pres.; Susan Finfer, V.P., Finance; MariBen Ramsey,* V.P. and C.O.O.; Gigi Bryant,* Secy.; Rob Repass,* Treas.; Ray Benson; Carmel Borders; Graciela Cigarroa; Sandy Gottesman; Chris Harte; Dan Herd; Jan Lehman; Lew Little, Jr.; Hal Peterson; David Porter; Steve Saunders; Steve Shook; Evan Smith.
Number of staff: 3 full-time professional; 1 part-time professional; 1 full-time support.
EIN: 741934031
Selected grants: The following grants are a representative sample of this grantmaker's funding activity:
$1,000,000 to Harvard University, Cambridge, MA, 2012. For general support.
$965,589 to University of Texas, Austin, TX, 2012. For general support.
$907,228 to Presbyterian Home for Children, Amarillo, TX, 2012. For general support.
$582,192 to Youth and Family Alliance, Austin, TX, 2012. For general support.
$254,000 to Lyndon Baines Johnson Foundation, Austin, TX, 2012. For general support.
$188,475 to Zachary Scott Theater Center, Austin, TX, 2012. For general support.
$147,457 to Texas Tribune, Austin, TX, 2012. For general support.
$20,500 to Conspirare, Austin, TX, 2012. For general support.
$20,000 to Blue School, New York, NY, 2012. For general support.
$17,670 to Behive Youth Development, Austin, TX, 2012. For general support.

8677
The B.E.L.I.E.F. Foundation ✧ ☆

(formerly Janet Jarie Jensen Foundation)
130 E. John Carpenter Fwy.
Irving, TX 75062-2708 (972) 999-4564
FAX: (972) 999-4568;
E-mail: info@thebelieffoundation.com; Main URL: http://www.thebelieffoundation.org
Grants List: http://www.thebelieffoundation.org/recipients.php

Established in 1996 in TX.
Donor: Janet Jarie Jensen.
Foundation type: Independent foundation.
Financial data (yr. ended 12/31/12): Assets, $9,326,007 (M); expenditures, $792,077; qualifying distributions, $637,712; giving activities include $637,712 for grants.
Purpose and activities: The philosophy of the B.E.L.I.E.F. Foundation's Scholarship Program is to give financial assistance to deserving college, vocational or technical school students as well as provide encouragement and support to the students and their families.
Fields of interest: Higher education; Scholarships/financial aid; Education; Youth.
Type of support: Scholarship funds.
Limitations: Applications not accepted. Giving limited to 22 zip codes within the Dallas, TX area. No grants to individuals.
Application information: Contributes only to pre-selected organizations.
Trustee: Janet Jarie Jensen.
EIN: 752707934

8678
William A. Badger Foundation ✧

c/o Wells Fargo Bank, N.A.
P.O. Box 41629
Austin, TX 78704-0028

Established in 1968; supporting organization of Baylor University; Waco Methodist Home; City of Waco, Texas; City of Edinburg, Indiana; Paul Quinn College; Edinburg Methodist Episcopal Church; St. Paul's Episcopal Church.
Foundation type: Independent foundation.
Financial data (yr. ended 03/31/13): Assets, $53,169,878 (M); expenditures, $2,726,067; qualifying distributions, $2,572,871; giving activities include $2,526,044 for 7 grants (high: $1,010,418; low: $126,302).
Purpose and activities: The foundation gives grants to cities, churches, and colleges and universities to promote education and community awareness.
Fields of interest: Higher education; Community/economic development; Protestant agencies & churches.
Limitations: Applications not accepted. Giving limited to IN, and Dallas and Waco, TX.
Application information: Unsolicited requests for funds not considered or acknowledged.
Trustee: Wells Fargo Bank, N.A.
EIN: 746087935
Selected grants: The following grants are a representative sample of this grantmaker's funding activity:
$1,024,973 to Baylor University, Waco, TX, 2011.
$128,122 to Paul Quinn College, Dallas, TX, 2011.
$128,121 to Saint Pauls Episcopal Church, Waco, TX, 2011.
$128,121 to Waco, City of, Waco, TX, 2011.

8679
Baker Hughes Foundation ✧

P.O. Box 3045
Houston, TX 77253-3045 (713) 439-8662
Contact: Sandra E. Alford, Secy.-Treas. and Exec. Dir.
E-mail: bakerhughesfoundation@bakerhughes.com; Main URL: http://www.bakerhughes.com/company/corporate-social-responsibility/people-and-society/

Established in 1994 in TX.
Donor: Baker Hughes Inc.
Foundation type: Company-sponsored foundation.
Financial data (yr. ended 12/31/12): Assets, $5,311,235 (M); gifts received, $3,768,532; expenditures, $3,105,045; qualifying distributions, $3,103,447; giving activities include $3,095,122 for 311 grants (high: $1,051,650; low: $100).

Purpose and activities: The foundation supports nonprofit organizations on a case by case basis in areas of company operations.
Fields of interest: Arts; Education; Health care; Youth, services; Human services.
Type of support: Scholarship funds; Employee matching gifts.
Limitations: Applications accepted. Giving in areas of company operations in the greater Tulsa, OK, and Houston, TX, areas; and on an international basis in Angola. No support for religious or political organizations or secondary schools.
Application information: Application form required.
Initial approach: E-mail or mail proposal
Copies of proposal: 1
Deadline(s): None
Officers and Trustees:* Chad C. Deaton,* Chair. and Pres.; Didier Charreton,* V.P.; Alan R. Crain, Jr.,* V.P.; Martin Craighead,* V.P.; Peter A. Ragauss,* V.P.; Sandra E. Alford, Secy.-Treas. and Exec. Dir.
Number of staff: 1 full-time professional.
EIN: 760441292
Selected grants: The following grants are a representative sample of this grantmaker's funding activity:
$10,000 to Boy Scouts of America, South Houston Area Council, Houston, TX, 2012. For general support.

8680
The Ballard Foundation ✧ ☆
4403 Perdido Bay
Katy, TX 77450-8656 (281) 451-2351

Established in TX.
Donor: Triumph MC LP.
Foundation type: Independent foundation.
Financial data (yr. ended 12/31/12): Assets, $6,680,428 (M); gifts received, $8,000,800; expenditures, $1,634,387; qualifying distributions, $1,664,689; giving activities include $1,590,289 for 9 grants (high: $1,000,000; low: $40), and $1,601,802 for 4 foundation-administered programs.
Fields of interest: Education; Health care; Community/economic development.
Limitations: Applications not accepted. Giving primarily in TX.
Application information: Unsolicited requests for funds not accepted.
Directors: Edwin Lee Ballard; Rachel Maria Ballard; Duval Meade McDaniels.
EIN: 454077080

8681
Joe Barnhart Foundation ✧
5615 Kirby Dr., Ste. 520
Houston, TX 77005-1714
Main URL: http://www.thejoebarnhartfoundation.org/

Established in 1988 in TX.
Foundation type: Independent foundation.
Financial data (yr. ended 12/31/13): Assets, $49,387,353 (M); expenditures, $2,091,941; qualifying distributions, $1,774,384; giving activities include $712,637 for 32 grants (high: $250,000; low: $201).
Purpose and activities: Giving primarily for education.
Fields of interest: Museums (art); Libraries (public); Education.
Limitations: Applications not accepted. Giving primarily in Beeville, TX. No grants to individuals.
Application information: Unsolicited requests for funds not accepted.
Trustees: Walter S. Baker, Jr.; Lou Adele May; Margaret Price; George Tallichet; V. Richard Viebig, Jr.
EIN: 760261675

8682
Baron & Blue Foundation ✧
P.O. Box 25464
Dallas, TX 75225-1464 (214) 692-5789
E-mail: info@baronandbluefoundation.org; Main URL: http://www.baronandbluefoundation.org
Facebook: https://www.facebook.com/pages/The-Baron-and-Blue-Foundation/316486968410248
Twitter: https://twitter.com/baronbluefdn

Established in 2001 in TX.
Donors: Frederick M. Baron†; Lisa A. Blue Baron.
Foundation type: Independent foundation.
Financial data (yr. ended 12/31/12): Assets, $4,417,706 (M); expenditures, $726,368; qualifying distributions, $587,883; giving activities include $587,883 for grants.
Purpose and activities: The foundation strives to enhance the function of non-profit organizations in the Dallas, TX community by assisting to maintain existing programs and further opportunities for grassroots organizations focusing on homelessness, transitional housing and the needs of the underserved.
Fields of interest: Education; Housing/shelter; Human services; Family services; Homeless.
Type of support: Program development; General/operating support.
Limitations: Applications accepted. Giving limited to Dallas County, TX.
Publications: Application guidelines.
Application information: Application form required.
Initial approach: Submit online form via foundation web site
Deadline(s): Apr. 1st and Oct. 1st
Officers and Directors:* Lisa A. Blue Baron,* Pres. and Treas.; Robert M. Greenberg,* V.P. and Secy.; Lara Ashmore, Exec. Dir.; Robert M. Greenberg; Laura Miller.
Number of staff: 1 full-time professional.
EIN: 752965720

8683
Melza M. and Frank Theodore Barr Foundation, Inc. ✧
952 Echo Ln., Ste. 300
Houston, TX 77024-2790

Established in 2003 in TX.
Donors: Frank Theodore Barr; Melza M. Barr.
Foundation type: Independent foundation.
Financial data (yr. ended 12/31/13): Assets, $1,741,803 (M); expenditures, $1,377,425; qualifying distributions, $1,377,425; giving activities include $1,377,425 for 9 grants (high: $1,100,000; low: $10,000).
Purpose and activities: Giving primarily to a ballet foundation and for medical research related to the treatment of glaucoma; funding also to support programs in education and the environment worldwide.
Fields of interest: Performing arts, ballet; Environment; Eye research; Human services.
Limitations: Applications not accepted. Giving primarily in Houston, TX and San Francisco, CA; some funding nationally. No grants to individuals.
Application information: Contributes only to pre-selected organizations.
Officers and Directors:* Frank Theodore Barr,* Pres. and Treas.; Melza M. Barr,* V.P. and Secy.; Christopher Michael Barr; Terence David Barr; Marilyn Beach; Patricia Shanley.
EIN: 200301511
Selected grants: The following grants are a representative sample of this grantmaker's funding activity:
$1,000,000 to Houston Ballet Foundation, Houston, TX, 2012. For foundation endowment.
$800,000 to Glaucoma Research Foundation, San Francisco, CA, 2012. To support of medical research related to treatment of glaucoma.
$20,000 to Raptor Trust, Millington, NJ, 2012. For the care and rehabilitation of wildlife, primarily birds of prey.

8684
James Purdy Barrow Foundation ✧ ☆
2200 Ross Ave., 31st Fl.
Dallas, TX 75201-2708

Donor: James P. Barrow.
Foundation type: Independent foundation.
Financial data (yr. ended 12/31/13): Assets, $6,746,654 (M); gifts received, $2,954,473; expenditures, $442,167; qualifying distributions, $440,410; giving activities include $438,653 for 4 grants (high: $205,561; low: $51,301).
Fields of interest: Arts; Education; Catholic agencies & churches.
Limitations: Applications not accepted.
Application information: Unsolicited request for funds not accepted.
Officers: James P. Barrow, Pres.; Jean S. Barrow, Secy.
Director: Ray Nixon.
EIN: 461638136

8685
The Bass Charitable Corporation ✧
(formerly Perry and Nancy Lee Bass Corporation)
201 Main St., Ste. 2300
Fort Worth, TX 76102-3127

Established in 1989 in TX.
Donor: Perry R. Bass†.
Foundation type: Independent foundation.
Financial data (yr. ended 06/30/13): Assets, $49,111,220 (M); expenditures, $2,119,612; qualifying distributions, $2,100,000; giving activities include $2,100,000 for 4 grants (high: $1,000,000; low: $100,000).
Fields of interest: Environment, plant conservation; Foundations (public).
Limitations: Applications not accepted. Giving primarily in New York, NY and Fort Worth, TX. No grants to individuals.
Application information: Contributes only to pre-selected organizations.
Officers and Directors:* William P. Hallman, Jr., Chair. and Pres.; Nancy Lee Bass,* Vice-Chair. and

V.P.; Gary W. Reese, V.P.; Thomas W. White, V.P.; Valleau Wilkie, Jr.,* V.P.; Lee M. Bass,* Secy.-Treas.
EIN: 752308846
Selected grants: The following grants are a representative sample of this grantmaker's funding activity:
$333,333 to Botanical Research Institute of Texas, Fort Worth, TX, 2010. For general purpose.
$333,333 to Botanical Research Institute of Texas, Fort Worth, TX, 2011. For general purpose.
$100,000 to Amon Carter Museum of Western Art, Fort Worth, TX, 2011. For general purpose.

8686
Bass Foundation ✧
c/o Valleau Wilkie, Jr.
309 Main St.
Fort Worth, TX 76102-4006 (817) 336-0494

Established in 1963 in TX.
Donors: Perry R. Bass†; Lee M. Bass; Edward P. Bass; Sid Richardson Carbon and Gasoline Co.; Perry R. Bass, Inc.
Foundation type: Independent foundation.
Financial data (yr. ended 12/31/13): Assets, $17,043,780 (M); expenditures, $1,743,198; qualifying distributions, $1,596,898; giving activities include $1,563,000 for 7 grants (high: $600,000; low: $30,000).
Purpose and activities: Giving primarily for the arts and cultural institutions; some support for conservation.
Fields of interest: Arts; Environment, natural resources.
Type of support: General/operating support; Capital campaigns; Building/renovation.
Limitations: Applications not accepted. Giving primarily in Fort Worth, TX.
Application information: Contributes only to pre-selected organizations.
Board meeting date(s): Feb.
Officers and Directors:* Lee M. Bass,* Pres.; Edward P. Bass,* V.P.; Ardon E. Moore, V.P.; Cynthia K. Alexander, Secy.-Treas.; Pete Geren, Exec. Dir.
Number of staff: 3 part-time professional.
EIN: 756033983
Selected grants: The following grants are a representative sample of this grantmaker's funding activity:
$250,000 to New York Botanical Garden, Bronx, NY, 2012. To support science operating needs.

8687
Anne T. & Robert M. Bass Foundation ✧
201 Main St., Ste. 2300
Fort Worth, TX 76102-3137 (817) 390-8400

Established in 1984 in TX.
Donors: Robert M. Bass; Anne T. Bass; WAMU II Partners, LLC; Keystone, LP.
Foundation type: Independent foundation.
Financial data (yr. ended 12/31/12): Assets, $81,614,681 (M); expenditures, $4,044,855; qualifying distributions, $3,563,032; giving activities include $3,563,032 for 23 grants (high: $1,800,000; low: $1,201).
Fields of interest: Historic preservation/historical societies; Elementary/secondary education; Higher education; Education; Health organizations; Human services.
Type of support: General/operating support.
Limitations: Applications not accepted. Giving primarily MA, ME, and Fort Worth, TX; some funding also in Washington, DC. No grants to individuals.
Application information: Contributes only to pre-selected organizations.
Officers and Directors:* Anne T. Bass,* Pres.; Robert M. Bass,* V.P.; J. Taylor Crandall, Secy.-Treas.
EIN: 752001892

8688
Lee and Ramona Bass Foundation ✧
309 Main St.
Fort Worth, TX 76102-4006 (817) 336-0494
Contact: Pete Geren, Exec. Dir.
FAX: (817) 332-2176;
E-mail: cjohns@sidrichardson.org; Main URL: http://www.leeandramonabass.org

Established in 1994 in TX.
Donor: Lee M. Bass.
Foundation type: Independent foundation.
Financial data (yr. ended 12/31/13): Assets, $57,068,589 (M); expenditures, $2,460,081; qualifying distributions, $2,330,308; giving activities include $2,250,000 for 11 grants (high: $500,000; low: $50,000).
Purpose and activities: The foundation funds grants in the following categories: 1) Schools, colleges and universities within Texas, with emphasis placed upon faculty development and liberal arts programs. 2) Community programs and projects, particularly related to the arts and the environment, such as museums, zoos, and educational/research institutions. 3) National and regional conservation programs.
Fields of interest: Arts; Higher education; Environment; Community/economic development.
Type of support: Scholarship funds; General/operating support; Building/renovation; Endowments; Curriculum development.
Limitations: Applications not accepted. Giving primarily in DE, ID, and TX. No grants to individuals.
Publications: Annual report; Grants list.
Application information: Unsolicited requests for funds not accepted.
Board meeting date(s): Varies
Officers and Directors:* Lee M. Bass,* Pres. and Treas.; Ramona S. Bass,* V.P.; Gary W. Reese, V.P.; Thomas W. White, Secy.; Preston M. Geren III,* Exec. Dir.
Number of staff: 3 full-time professional.
EIN: 752495163
Selected grants: The following grants are a representative sample of this grantmaker's funding activity:
$250,000 to Intercollegiate Studies Institute, Wilmington, DE, 2012. To support Western Civilization Program.
$200,000 to All Saints Episcopal School of Fort Worth, Fort Worth, TX, 2012. To establish endowment to be used for performing arts Programming and/or securing/retaining faculty leadership.
$100,000 to Taking Care of Texas, Austin, TX, 2012. For establishment of the Program.
$100,000 to Texas Agricultural Land Trust, San Antonio, TX, 2012. For the establishment of the Land Transactions Program.
$50,000 to Amon Carter Museum of Western Art, Fort Worth, TX, 2012. To support the museum's 50th Anniversary in Excellence in Education campaign.
$25,000 to Lower Rio Grande Valley Nature Center, Weslaco, TX, 2012. For matching grant for support of the production of a documentary film on the endangered ocelot.

8689
Richard D. Bass Foundation ✧
(formerly The Bass Foundation)
4516 Wildwood Rd.
Dallas, TX 75209-1926

Established in 1945 in TX; in 1983, foundation split up into The Bass Foundation and Harry Bass Foundation.
Donors: Harry W. Bass, Sr.†; Mrs. Harry W. Bass, Sr.†.
Foundation type: Independent foundation.
Financial data (yr. ended 12/31/13): Assets, $81,111 (M); expenditures, $433,164; qualifying distributions, $428,150; giving activities include $427,000 for 22 grants (high: $200,000; low: $1,000).
Purpose and activities: Giving primarily for cultural programs, including music and dance companies; support also for universities, health associations, and religious organizations.
Fields of interest: Performing arts, dance; Performing arts, music; Arts; Higher education; Education; Health organizations, association; Community/economic development; Protestant agencies & churches; Catholic agencies & churches.
Type of support: General/operating support; Annual campaigns; Capital campaigns; Building/renovation.
Limitations: Giving primarily in TX and UT. No support for private foundations. No grants to individuals; no loans.
Application information:
Board meeting date(s): As required
Trustees: Alice W. Bass; Richard D. Bass; Barbara B. Moroney; Bonnie B. Smith.
Number of staff: None.
EIN: 756013540
Selected grants: The following grants are a representative sample of this grantmaker's funding activity:
$1,000 to Dallas Morning News Charities, Dallas, TX, 2012. For community.

8690
Harry W. Bass, Jr. Foundation ✧
4809 Cole Ave., Ste. 250
Dallas, TX 75205-3553 (214) 599-0300
Contact: F. David Calhoun, Exec. Dir.
FAX: (214) 599-0405; E-mail: dcalhoun@hbrf.org; Grant correspondence should be addressed to: Grants Dept.; Main URL: http://www.harrybassfoundation.org

Established in 1983 in TX.
Donor: Harry W. Bass, Jr.†.
Foundation type: Independent foundation.
Financial data (yr. ended 12/31/13): Assets, $76,255,444 (M); expenditures, $1,845,040; qualifying distributions, $1,478,194; giving activities include $1,184,123 for 69 grants (high: $295,000; low: $50).
Purpose and activities: Primary focus is in the areas of youth and education.

Fields of interest: Arts education; Museums; Performing arts centers; Arts; Education, early childhood education; Child development, education; Secondary school/education; Education; Environment, public education; Botanical gardens; Animals/wildlife; Health care; Medical research; Crime/violence prevention, abuse prevention; Food banks; Food distribution, meals on wheels; Human services; American Red Cross; YM/YWCAs & YM/YWHAs; Children/youth, services; Children, services; Youth, services; Child development, services; Family services; Aging, centers/services; Science; Infants/toddlers; Children/youth; Children; Youth; Adults; Aging; Physically disabled; Women; Infants/toddlers, female; Girls; Adults, women; Young adults, female; Infants/toddlers, male; Boys; Adults, men; Young adults, male; Economically disadvantaged.
Type of support: General/operating support; Continuing support; Building/renovation; Equipment; Program development; Research; Matching/challenge support.
Limitations: Applications accepted. Giving exclusively in the greater Dallas, TX area. No support for seminaries or private foundations. No grants to individuals, or for capital campaigns, fundraisers or conferences.
Publications: Application guidelines; Financial statement; Grants list.
Application information: Application form not required.

Initial approach: Letter with full grant application via e-mail followed by a printed copy
Copies of proposal: 1
Deadline(s): None
Board meeting date(s): Quarterly
Final notification: 3 months

Officers and Trustees:* Doris L. Bass,* Pres.; Michael Calhoun,* V.P.; F. David Calhoun,* Secy. and Exec. Dir.; J. Michael Wylie.
Number of staff: 1 full-time professional; 1 part-time support.
EIN: 751876307
Selected grants: The following grants are a representative sample of this grantmaker's funding activity:
$486,450 to Southwestern Medical Foundation, Dallas, TX, 2011.

8691
Ruth & Ted Bauer Family Foundation ✧
4400 Post Oak Pkwy., Ste. 2160
Houston, TX 77027-3416
E-mail: ckatrana@bauerfoundation.org

Established in 1997 in TX.
Donors: Charles T. Bauer; Ruth J. Bauer.
Foundation type: Independent foundation.
Financial data (yr. ended 12/31/13): Assets, $10,400,693 (M); expenditures, $570,986; qualifying distributions, $554,762; giving activities include $544,500 for 20 grants (high: $100,000; low: $2,000).
Purpose and activities: Giving primarily for education, and to address the needs of children.
Fields of interest: Education.
Type of support: General/operating support; Continuing support; Annual campaigns; Building/renovation; Scholarship funds.
Limitations: Applications not accepted. Giving primarily in TX. No grants to individuals.
Application information: Contributes only to pre-selected organizations.
Officers: C. Douglas Bauer, Pres. and Treas.; Jeffrey C. Lamberth, Secy.
Directors: Jay C. Houren; Ted Pulsifer.
EIN: 760537473
Selected grants: The following grants are a representative sample of this grantmaker's funding activity:
$30,000 to Boys and Girls Harbor, Houston, TX, 2012. For Harbor's Program.
$30,000 to Small Steps Nurturing Center, Houston, TX, 2012. For funding of Teachers' Salaries.
$25,000 to Houston Grand Opera Association, Houston, TX, 2012. For High School Voice Studio.
$20,000 to Chinquapin School, Highlands, TX, 2012. To underwrite Salary of Science Teacher.
$15,000 to Houston Symphony Society, Houston, TX, 2012. For Symphony Explorer Concert Series.
$5,000 to Collaborative for Children, Houston, TX, 2012. For College Bound from Birth.

8692
Charles T. Bauer Foundation ✧
11 Greenway Plz., Ste. 2600
Houston, TX 77046-1100

Established in 2004 in TX.
Donor: Charles T. Bauer†.
Foundation type: Independent foundation.
Financial data (yr. ended 12/31/12): Assets, $145,449,706 (M); gifts received, $851,313; expenditures, $8,134,785; qualifying distributions, $6,757,875; giving activities include $6,542,742 for 49 grants (high: $1,857,500; low: $5,000).
Fields of interest: Higher education; Education.
Limitations: Applications not accepted. Giving primarily in MD and TX. No grants to individuals.
Application information: Contributes only to pre-selected organizations.
Trustees: Theodore Wingate Bauer; Janet Bauer Hartman; Darren Wolfman.
EIN: 206284839
Selected grants: The following grants are a representative sample of this grantmaker's funding activity:
$1,742,500 to University of Houston-University Park, Houston, TX, 2011. For general support.
$1,525,000 to University of Houston-University Park, Houston, TX, 2010. For general support.
$500,000 to Notre Dame Preparatory School, Towson, MD, 2010. For general support.
$400,000 to Johns Hopkins University, Baltimore, MD, 2010. For general support.
$400,000 to Johns Hopkins University, Baltimore, MD, 2011. For general support.
$325,000 to National Aquarium in Baltimore, Baltimore, MD, 2011. For general support.
$300,000 to Baltimore Jesuit Educational Initiative, Cristo Rey Jesuit High School, Baltimore, MD, 2010. For general support.
$300,000 to Baltimore Jesuit Educational Initiative, Cristo Rey Jesuit High School, Baltimore, MD, 2011. For general support.
$300,000 to Living Classrooms Foundation, Baltimore, MD, 2011. For general support.
$262,000 to Maryland Food Bank, Baltimore, MD, 2010. For general support.
$250,000 to Biotechnical Institutes of Maryland, Baltimore, MD, 2010. For general support.
$250,000 to Biotechnical Institutes of Maryland, Baltimore, MD, 2011. For general support.
$250,000 to Boys Latin School of Maryland, Baltimore, MD, 2011. For general support.
$200,000 to Johns Hopkins University, Mood Disorder Center, Baltimore, MD, 2011. For general support.
$200,000 to National Kidney Foundation, New York, NY, 2010. For general support.
$150,000 to Pathfinders for Autism Resource Center, Cockeysville, MD, 2010. For general support.
$50,000 to Johns Hopkins University, Wilmer Eye Institute, Baltimore, MD, 2011. For general support.
$50,000 to Paul's Place, Baltimore, MD, 2010. For general support.
$40,000 to Johns Hopkins University, Wilmer Eye Institute, Baltimore, MD, 2010. For general support.
$20,000 to Houston Zoo, Houston, TX, 2011. For general support.

8693
Eula Mae and John Baugh Foundation ✧
15329 Clevedon Ln.
Jersey Village, TX 77040-1314

Established in 1995 in TX.
Donors: Eula Mae Baugh†; John F. Baugh†; Barbara Baugh Charitable Lead Trust.
Foundation type: Independent foundation.
Financial data (yr. ended 12/31/13): Assets, $171,556,520 (M); gifts received, $100,000; expenditures, $7,980,264; qualifying distributions, $7,357,581; giving activities include $7,259,690 for 47 grants (high: $500,000; low: $2,090).
Purpose and activities: Giving primarily to Baptist organizations, as well as for higher education.
Fields of interest: Higher education; Theological school/education; Education; Protestant agencies & churches.
Type of support: General/operating support; Program-related investments/loans.
Limitations: Applications not accepted. Giving primarily in TX; funding also in Atlanta, GA, Washington, DC, and Kansas City, KS. No grants to individuals.
Application information: Contributes only to pre-selected organizations.
Officers: Barbara N. Baugh, Pres.; Jacqueline B. Moore, V.P.; Julia B. Cloud, Secy.; Douglas C. Chiles, Treas. and Exec. Dir.
EIN: 760457820
Selected grants: The following grants are a representative sample of this grantmaker's funding activity:
$500,000 to Central Baptist Theological Seminary, Shawnee, KS, 2013. For operating support.
$500,000 to Mercer University, Macon, GA, 2013. For Baugh Leadership Center.
$500,000 to University of Mary Hardin-Baylor, Belton, TX, 2013. For capital support.
$400,000 to Baptist Joint Committee, Washington, DC, 2013. For operating support.
$320,000 to Windermere Baptist Conference Center, Roach, MO, 2013. For operating support.
$250,000 to Religious Herald, Richmond, VA, 2013. For operating support.
$225,000 to Youth Choirs, San Antonio, TX, 2013. For operating support.
$200,000 to Baylor University Alumni Association, Waco, TX, 2013. For operating support.
$100,000 to Baptist History and Heritage Society, Manhattan, MT, 2013. For operating support.
$60,000 to Baptists Today, Macon, GA, 2013. For operating support.

8694
Baumberger Endowment ✧
7201 Broadway, Ste. 300
San Antonio, TX 78209-3774

Trust established in 1979 in TX.
Donor: Charles Baumberger, Jr.†.
Foundation type: Independent foundation.
Financial data (yr. ended 12/31/13): Assets, $30,506,630 (M); gifts received, $225; expenditures, $1,561,370; qualifying distributions, $1,427,854; giving activities include $1,243,297 for 18 grants (high: $448,300; low: $5,000).
Purpose and activities: Scholarship awards paid directly to the institution for graduating high school seniors from Bexar County, Texas, to attend Texas colleges and universities.
Fields of interest: Higher education.
Type of support: Scholarship funds; Scholarships—to individuals.
Limitations: Applications accepted. Giving limited to residents of Bexar County, TX.
Publications: Application guidelines; Program policy statement.
Application information: Contact Bexar County high schools' counselors to pick up application form. Application form required.
Initial approach: Obtain application from Bexar County high school counselor only. Applications are not mailed.
Deadline(s): Feb. 15 for filing financial aid form, high school transcript, and application form
Board meeting date(s): Mar., June, Sept., and Dec.
Final notification: May
Officers: Ronald Schmidt, Chair.; Frank W. Burk, Secy.; Cynde Zietlow, Exec. Dir.
Trustees: Nancy F. May; Kenneth M. Taggart; Albert J. Tietze, Jr.
Number of staff: 1 full-time professional; 1 full-time support.
EIN: 237225925

8695
The Baxter Trust ✧
c/o Private Foundation Services, Inc.
4265 San Felipe, Ste. 1100
Houston, TX 77027-2913

Donors: Murphy H. Baxter; Murphy Baxter†.
Foundation type: Independent foundation.
Financial data (yr. ended 12/31/13): Assets, $44,638,735 (M); expenditures, $2,382,542; qualifying distributions, $2,164,452; giving activities include $2,041,957 for 50 grants (high: $100,000; low: $4,565).
Fields of interest: Mental health/crisis services, suicide; Children, services; Christian agencies & churches; Children/youth; Children; Aging; Disabilities, people with; Deaf/hearing impaired; Mentally disabled; Economically disadvantaged; Homeless.
Limitations: Applications not accepted. Giving primarily in TX. No grants to individuals.
Application information: Contributes only to pre-selected organizations.
Trustees: Blair Baxter; J. Greg Crow; John Fenoglio; Thomas G. Hambrick, Jr.; David Hessel; Heidi Kelsey; Tobias T. Mongan; David Welsh; David D. Welsh.
Number of staff: 1 part-time professional.
EIN: 760174893

8696
The Beal Foundation ✧
104 S. Pecos
Midland, TX 79701-5021 (432) 682-3753
Contact: Spencer E. Beal

Incorporated in 1962 in TX.
Donors: Carlton Beal; Keleen H. Beal; W.R. Davis; Barry Beal, Jr.
Foundation type: Independent foundation.
Financial data (yr. ended 12/31/12): Assets, $19,785,503 (M); expenditures, $1,866,925; qualifying distributions, $1,434,000; giving activities include $1,434,000 for grants.
Fields of interest: Education; Human services; Children/youth, services.
Type of support: General/operating support.
Limitations: Applications accepted. Giving primarily in the Midland, TX, area.
Application information: First time applicants must complete longer application form. Application form required.
Initial approach: Request application
Deadline(s): 1 month prior to board meetings
Board meeting date(s): Apr. 1 and Nov. 1
Officers: Carlton Beal, Jr., Chair.; Bryan Limmer, Secy.-Treas.
Trustees: Barry Beal, Jr.; Kelly S. Beal; Spencer E. Beal; Stuart Beal; Larry Bell; Elizabeth Beal Davenport; Karlene Beal Garber; Steven C. Hofer; Ray Poage; Laura Buckner.
EIN: 756034480

8697
David T. Beals, III Charitable Trust ✧
c/o Bank of America, N.A.
P.O. Box 831041
Dallas, TX 75283-1041
Application address: c/o Bank of America, N.A., Attn.: Spence Heddens, P.O. BOX 219119, Kansas City, MO 64121-9119, tel.: (816) 292-4300

Established in 2006 in MO.
Donor: David Beals, III Residuary Trust.
Foundation type: Independent foundation.
Financial data (yr. ended 06/30/13): Assets, $17,057,549 (M); expenditures, $1,080,380; qualifying distributions, $948,100; giving activities include $948,100 for grants.
Fields of interest: Museums (art); Performing arts, ballet; Arts; Environment, natural resources.
Type of support: General/operating support; Capital campaigns; Program development.
Limitations: Applications accepted. Giving primarily in the greater Kansas City, MO, area.
Application information:
Initial approach: Letter, no more than 3 pages
Deadline(s): None
Trustee: Bank of America, N.A.
EIN: 597272524
Selected grants: The following grants are a representative sample of this grantmaker's funding activity:
$100,000 to Nelson-Atkins Museum of Art, Kansas City, MO, 2013. For Director of Education Position.
$75,000 to Kansas City Ballet Association, Kansas City, MO, 2013. To support Artistic Director/Capital Campaign.
$50,000 to Ducks Unlimited, Ann Arbor, MI, 2013. To support Wetlands Conservation in Mo.
$30,000 to Kansas City Chorale, Kansas City, MO, 2013. To support of the Arts Stabilization Campaign.
$25,000 to Powell Gardens, Kingsville, MO, 2013. To support Summer Art Exhibition/Nature Connects.

8698
Theodore and Beulah Beasley Foundation, Inc. ✧
3811 Turtle Creek Blvd., Ste. 940
Dallas, TX 75219-4490

Incorporated in 1957 in TX.
Donors: Theodore P. Beasley; Mary Evans Beasley†.
Foundation type: Independent foundation.
Financial data (yr. ended 12/31/13): Assets, $30,754,217 (M); expenditures, $1,622,187; qualifying distributions, $1,292,433; giving activities include $1,178,738 for 48 grants (high: $225,000; low: $1,500).
Fields of interest: Arts; Education; Health care; Human services; YM/YWCAs & YM/YWHAs; Children/youth, services.
Type of support: General/operating support; Capital campaigns; Building/renovation.
Limitations: Applications not accepted. Giving primarily in the Dallas, TX, area. No grants to individuals.
Application information: Contributes only to pre-selected organizations.
Officers: Robert R. Beasley, Pres. and Treas.; Vicki Vanderslice, V.P. and Secy.
Directors: Samuel Dashefsky; Linda Tinney; Michael Vanderslice.
EIN: 756035806

8699
Belin Foundation ✧ ☆
c/o Mary Ann Belin
2438 Windmill Dr.
Richmond, TX 77406-1256

Established in 1985 in TX.
Donors: J.B. Land Co., Inc.; James Bruce Belin, Jr.; Mary Ann Belin.
Foundation type: Independent foundation.
Financial data (yr. ended 10/31/13): Assets, $2,166,444 (M); expenditures, $3,068,248; qualifying distributions, $3,042,707; giving activities include $3,039,239 for 20 grants (high: $3,000,000; low: $40).
Fields of interest: Higher education; Human services.
Limitations: Applications not accepted. Giving primarily in Houston, TX.
Application information: Unsolicited requests for funds not accepted.
Officers: Mary Ann Belin, Pres.; Chad Mahlmann, V.P. and Secy.; Laurie Mahlmann, V.P.
EIN: 760163560
Selected grants: The following grants are a representative sample of this grantmaker's funding activity:
$3,550 to Trees of Hope Festival, Houston, TX, 2011.
$3,000 to Trees of Hope Festival, Houston, TX, 2011.

8700
Bell Trust ✧
11700 Preston Rd., Ste. 660-545
Dallas, TX 75230-6112 (972) 788-4151
Contact: Barry D. Packer, Exec. Tr.

FAX: (972) 788-4181;
E-mail: barrypacker@belltrust.org; Main URL: http://www.belltrust.org

Trust established in 1956 in TX.
Donors: R.S. Bell‡; Katharine Bell‡.
Foundation type: Independent foundation.
Financial data (yr. ended 12/31/12): Assets, $13,364,066 (M); expenditures, $854,249; qualifying distributions, $589,651; giving activities include $494,640 for 54 grants (high: $21,000; low: $1,500).
Purpose and activities: Giving limited to congregations that are associated with the Church of Christ.
Fields of interest: Christian agencies & churches.
Type of support: General/operating support.
Limitations: Applications accepted. Giving on a national and international basis. No grants to individuals, or for building or endowment funds, scholarships, fellowships, or matching gifts; no loans.
Application information: Application guidelines available on the trust's web site. Application form not required.
Initial approach: Letter from Church of Christ
Copies of proposal: 1
Deadline(s): Feb. 15, May 15, Aug. 15, and Nov. 15
Board meeting date(s): The 1st Tues. of Mar., June, Sept., and Dec.
Trustees: Barry D. Packer, Exec. Tr.; Betty Bell Muns; James N. Muns; John B. Muns; Barbara Bell Packer; C. Philip Slate; Harold G. Taylor; Robert T. Waldron.
Number of staff: 1 full-time professional.
EIN: 756020180
Selected grants: The following grants are a representative sample of this grantmaker's funding activity:
$18,000 to Park Plaza Church of Christ, Tulsa, OK, 2012. For Lynn and Carol Stringfellow - Campus Ministry United.
$14,400 to Monterey Church of Christ, Lubbock, TX, 2012. For Ivan and Stefanie Ponce de Leon - Lazaro Cardenas, Mexico.
$10,000 to Homewood Church of Christ, Birmingham, AL, 2012. For Jonathan and Deborah Strasser - Tanzania.
$10,000 to Monterey Church of Christ, Lubbock, TX, 2012. For Jim and Phyllis Beck - Malindi, Kenya.
$6,640 to Collingswood Church of Christ, Collingswood, NJ, 2012. For Matt Fortunato - work there.
$6,000 to Round Rock Church of Christ, Round Rock, TX, 2012. For Jason and Nicole Whaley - Wollongong, Australia.

8701
The Ted and Laurie Beneski Foundation ✧
6405 Cutter Ridge Ct.
Colleyville, TX 76034-6545

Established in 2007 in TX.
Donors: Ted W. Beneski; Laurie M. Beneski.
Foundation type: Independent foundation.
Financial data (yr. ended 12/31/12): Assets, $4,273,881 (M); gifts received, $1,003,000; expenditures, $1,102,342; qualifying distributions, $1,102,337; giving activities include $1,102,337 for 4 grants (high: $1,000,000; low: $500).
Fields of interest: Higher education.
Type of support: Building/renovation.
Limitations: Applications not accepted. Giving primarily in Amherst, MA, as well as in CT and Tarrant County, TX. No grants to individuals.
Application information: Contributes only to pre-selected organizations.
Directors: Kristin M. Beneski; Laurie M. Beneski; Ted W. Beneski.
EIN: 562640822

8702
Gayle and Tom Benson Charitable Foundation ✧
100 Sandau, Ste. 210
San Antonio, TX 78216-3635 (210) 349-6200
Contact: R. Tom Roddy, Tr.

Established in 2007 in TX.
Donors: Tom Benson; Gayle Benson; Grace and Tom Benson Charitable Foundation; Benson Football; NFL Charities.
Foundation type: Independent foundation.
Financial data (yr. ended 12/31/12): Assets, $16,826,442 (M); gifts received, $8,545,000; expenditures, $6,868,671; qualifying distributions, $6,866,792; giving activities include $6,866,792 for 29 grants (high: $2,200,000; low: $1,000).
Fields of interest: Higher education; Catholic agencies & churches.
Limitations: Giving primarily in San Antonio, TX; some funding also in New Orleans, LA, and Nashville, TN.
Application information: Application form not required.
Initial approach: Letter
Deadline(s): None
Trustees: Gayle Benson; Tom Benson; R. Tom Roddy; Stanley Rosenberg.
EIN: 260221908
Selected grants: The following grants are a representative sample of this grantmaker's funding activity:
$2,200,000 to Archdiocese of New Orleans, New Orleans, LA, 2012.
$1,000,000 to Brother Martin High School, New Orleans, LA, 2012.
$800,000 to Loyola University, New Orleans, LA, 2012.
$600,000 to University of the Incarnate Word, San Antonio, TX, 2012.
$500,000 to Oblate School of Theology, San Antonio, TX, 2012.
$500,000 to Ochsner Clinic Foundation, New Orleans, LA, 2012.
$400,000 to Central Catholic High School, San Antonio, TX, 2012.
$200,000 to Shirley Landry Benson PACE Center, New Orleans, LA, 2012.
$200,000 to Society of Jesus, New Orleans Province, New Orleans, LA, 2012.
$161,894 to Dominican Sisters of Saint Cecilia, Nashville, TN, 2012.

8703
Bergman-Davison-Webster Charitable Trust ✧
P.O. Box 1617
Livingston, TX 77351-0029
Application address: c/o Floyd Bush, 306 N. Washington Ave., Livingston, TX 77351-3240; tel.: (936) 327-7181

Established in 1996 in TX.
Foundation type: Independent foundation.
Financial data (yr. ended 06/30/13): Assets, $9,288,238 (M); expenditures, $576,722; qualifying distributions, $503,345; giving activities include $462,744 for 7 grants (high: $200,000; low: $10,000), and $18,000 for 8 grants to individuals (high: $3,000; low: $1,000).
Purpose and activities: Giving to promote, assist, and further the cultural, artistic, educational, literary, recreational, charitable, and historical activities and facilities carried on, or maintained by, the cities of Corrigan and Livingston, TX, and Polk County, TX, for their residents.
Fields of interest: Arts; Education; Human services.
Type of support: Scholarships—to individuals.
Limitations: Applications accepted. Giving limited to the cities of Corrigan and Livingston as well as Polk County, TX.
Application information: Application form not required.
Initial approach: Proposal
Deadline(s): None
Trustees: Gene Bush; Carolyn Davison Nixon; Anthony Page.
EIN: 760521612

8704
Henry & Eileen Beyer Foundation ✧
c/o Kenwood & Associates PC
P.O. Box 1104
Sugar Land, TX 77487-1104

Donors: Henry T. Beyer III; Juliette E. Beyer.
Foundation type: Independent foundation.
Financial data (yr. ended 12/31/13): Assets, $13,582,441 (M); expenditures, $1,260,101; qualifying distributions, $1,250,178; giving activities include $1,250,178 for 5 grants (high: $300,000; low: $178).
Fields of interest: International relief; Christian agencies & churches.
Limitations: Applications not accepted. Giving primarily in TX.
Application information: Contributes only to pre-selected organizations.
Directors: Darren R. Beyer; Henry T. Beyer III; Juliette E. Beyer.
EIN: 203905824
Selected grants: The following grants are a representative sample of this grantmaker's funding activity:
$400,000 to Texas Baptist Missions Foundation, Dallas, TX, 2012. To support ministry.

8705
Bickel & Brewer Foundation ✧
(formerly Bickel & Brewer Legal Foundation)
4800 Comerica Bank Tower
1717 Main Street
Dallas, TX 75201 (214) 653-4026
Contact: Andrea Burnett
E-mail: aburnett@bickelbrewer.com; Main URL: http://www.bickelbrewer.com/#/thefoundation

Established in 1995 in TX.
Donor: Bickel & Brewer.
Foundation type: Company-sponsored foundation.
Financial data (yr. ended 12/31/12): Assets, $43,928 (M); gifts received, $3,016,008;

expenditures, $2,967,334; qualifying distributions, $2,992,334; giving activities include $758,098 for 33 grants (high: $132,348; low: $500), and $1,731,426 for 3 foundation-administered programs.
Purpose and activities: The foundation supports organizations involved with health, community reinvestment, and public policy. Special emphasis is directed toward programs designed to promote law and education.
Fields of interest: Higher education; Law school/education; Education; Health care; Legal services; Crime/law enforcement; Community/economic development; Public policy, research.
Type of support: General/operating support; Annual campaigns; Program development; Scholarship funds.
Limitations: Applications accepted. Giving primarily in New York, NY, and TX, with some emphasis on the Dallas area. No grants to individuals.
Publications: Application guidelines.
Application information: Application form not required.
Initial approach: Download application form and mail to foundation
Copies of proposal: 1
Deadline(s): None
Officers: William A. Brewer III, Chair.; John W. Bickel II, Pres.; James S. Renard, Secy.; Mike McCormack, Treas.; Travis J. Carter, Exec. Dir.
EIN: 752625364

8706
BNSF Railway Foundation ✧
(formerly BNSF Foundation)
2650 Lou Menk Dr.
Fort Worth, TX 76131-2830 (817) 867-6458
Contact: Deanna Dugas, Mgr., BNSF Railway Fdn.
FAX: (817) 352-7925;
E-mail: BNSFFoundation@bnsf.com; Main URL: http://www.bnsffoundation.org/giving.html
Contact for Diversity Scholarship Program: Teresa Beman, E-mail: teresa.beman@bnsf.com

Donors: BNSF Railway; Burlington Northern Santa Fe Corp.
Foundation type: Company-sponsored foundation.
Financial data (yr. ended 12/31/12): Assets, $281,406 (M); gifts received, $8,200,000; expenditures, $8,256,585; qualifying distributions, $8,256,585; giving activities include $7,059,138 for 658 grants (high: $625,000; low: $250), and $1,149,563 for 1,126 employee matching gifts.
Purpose and activities: The foundation supports organizations involved with arts and culture, higher education, the environment, health, substance abuse services, crime and violence prevention, recreation, human services, diversity, community development, children and youth, minorities, women, and economically disadvantaged people, and awards college scholarships to high school seniors, college sophomores, and Native Americans.
Fields of interest: Visual arts; Museums; Performing arts; Arts; Vocational education; Higher education; Education; Environment; Hospitals (general); Health care; Substance abuse, services; Crime/violence prevention, domestic violence; Crime/violence prevention, child abuse; Recreation, parks/playgrounds; Recreation; Boys & girls clubs; Boy scouts; Camp Fire; Youth development, business; American Red Cross; YM/YWCAs & YM/YWHAs; Residential/custodial care; Human services; Civil/human rights, equal rights; Business/industry; Community/economic development; United Ways and Federated Giving Programs; Children/youth; Minorities; Hispanics/Latinos; Native Americans/American Indians; Women; Economically disadvantaged.
Type of support: Management development/capacity building; Annual campaigns; Building/renovation; Program development; Scholarship funds; Employee matching gifts; Employee-related scholarships; Scholarships—to individuals; Matching/challenge support.
Limitations: Applications accepted. Giving limited to communities located on main BNSF Railway operating lines. No support for religious organizations, veterans' or fraternal organizations, national health organizations, corporate memberships, taxpayer associations or other bodies whose activities are expected to directly benefit the corporation, or political organizations or candidates. No grants to individuals (except for scholarships), or for general operating support, endowments, national health programs, loans, travel, corporate memberships, political campaigns, computers or computer-related projects, benefit tickets or courtesy advertising, tables and/or tickets to gala fundraisers, salaries, wages, or administrative expenses, or capital campaigns.
Publications: Application guidelines.
Application information: Support is limited to 1 contribution per organization during any given year. Telephone calls during the application process are not encouraged. Additional information may be requested at a later date. Priority is given to organizations that have an established relationship with the BNSF Foundation. Grants range between $1,000 and $10,000. Application form required.
Initial approach: Complete online application
Deadline(s): None
Board meeting date(s): Monthly
Final notification: 3 months to one year
Officers and Directors:* John O. Ambler,* Pres.; Michael R. Annis, V.P.; C. Alec Vincent, Treas.; Amy Hawkins; Carl R. Ice; Andrew Johnsen; Roger Nober; Matthew K. Rose.
EIN: 261635887
Selected grants: The following grants are a representative sample of this grantmaker's funding activity:
$625,000 to Texas Christian University, Fort Worth, TX, 2012. For general purpose.
$500,000 to Texas Christian University, Fort Worth, TX, 2012. For general purpose.
$359,131 to United Way of Tarrant County, Fort Worth, TX, 2012. For general purpose.
$150,000 to USO World Headquarters, Arlington, VA, 2012. For general purpose.
$100,000 to USO World Headquarters, Arlington, VA, 2012. For general purpose.
$100,000 to Van Cliburn Foundation, Fort Worth, TX, 2012. For general purpose.
$7,000 to United Way of the Black Hills, Rapid City, SD, 2012. For general purpose.
$5,000 to Fort Morgan Heritage Foundation, Fort Morgan, CO, 2012. For general purpose.
$5,000 to Independent Colleges of Washington, Seattle, WA, 2012. For general purpose.
$3,000 to Saint Josephs Childrens Home, Torrington, WY, 2012. For general purpose.

8707
The Boeckman Family Foundation ✧ ☆
2911 Turtle Creek Blvd., Ste. 1240
Dallas, TX 75219-6256 (214) 522-8292
Contact: Elizabeth Mayer Boeckman, Pres.

Established in 1998 in TX.
Donors: Elizabeth Mayer Boeckman; Duncan E. Boeckman.
Foundation type: Independent foundation.
Financial data (yr. ended 12/31/13): Assets, $123,544 (M); expenditures, $581,840; qualifying distributions, $576,100; giving activities include $576,100 for 51 grants (high: $175,000; low: $1,000).
Purpose and activities: Giving primarily for education and the arts, including grant awards to art students.
Fields of interest: Museums; Performing arts; Elementary/secondary education; Education; Environment, natural resources; Community/economic development.
Type of support: General/operating support; Annual campaigns; Capital campaigns; Building/renovation; Program development; Curriculum development; Grants to individuals.
Limitations: Applications accepted. Giving primarily in Santa Fe, NM and Dallas, TX.
Application information: Application form required.
Initial approach: Proposal
Deadline(s): None
Officers: Elizabeth Mayer Boeckman, Pres.; Kathryn Boeckman Howd, Secy.-Treas.
EIN: 752766894

8708
Simon Bolivar Foundation, Inc. ✧
P.O. Box 4689
Houston, TX 77210-4689
Contact: Dario Merchan, Pres.
E-mail: sbf@citgo.com; Additional address: 1293 Eldridge Pkwy, N5033, Houston, TX 77077; Main URL: http://www.simonbolivarfoundation.org/

Established in 2007 in TX.
Donor: CITGO Petroleum Corporation.
Foundation type: Company-sponsored foundation.
Financial data (yr. ended 12/31/12): Assets, $4,540,592 (M); expenditures, $8,461,223; qualifying distributions, $8,354,459; giving activities include $2,815,141 for 39 grants (high: $2,000,000; low: $7,500), and $5,338,616 for 3 foundation-administered programs.
Purpose and activities: The foundation supports programs designed to expand access to healthcare to underprivileged individuals who are affected by critical illness and poverty.
Fields of interest: Environment; Hospitals (general); Health care, clinics/centers; Speech/hearing centers; Health care, support services; Health care, organ/tissue banks; Health care, patient services; Health care; Disasters, preparedness/services; Human services; Economically disadvantaged.
International interests: Venezuela.
Type of support: Building/renovation; Equipment; Program development.
Limitations: Applications accepted. Giving primarily in Washington, DC, New York, NY, Argentina, Italy, and Venezuela.
Publications: Application guidelines; Program policy statement.
Application information: Application form required.

Initial approach: Complete online application for medical assistance and Bronx Social Programs
Deadline(s): None for medical assistance; Mar. 27 for Bronx Social Programs
Officers and Directors:* Maritza Rojas de Villanueva,* Chair.; Dario Merchan, Pres.; Arnaldo Arcay, Secy.; Fatima Romero, Treas.; David Diaz; Richard Gooley; Orestes Parilli; Eladio Perez; Fernando Valera.
EIN: 205787382
Selected grants: The following grants are a representative sample of this grantmaker's funding activity:
$99,294 to New Orleans, City of, New Orleans, LA, 2011.
$80,000 to Mothers on the Move, Bronx, NY, 2011.
$70,000 to Point Community Development Corporation, Bronx, NY, 2011.
$70,000 to Rocking the Boat, Bronx, NY, 2011.
$50,000 to Mary Mitchell Family and Youth Center, Bronx, NY, 2011.
$45,000 to Bronx Childrens Museum, Bronx, NY, 2011.
$40,000 to Abraham House, Bronx, NY, 2011.
$40,000 to Legal Information for Families Today, New York, NY, 2011.
$40,000 to Mercy Center, Bronx, NY, 2011.
$25,000 to Bronx River Art Center, Bronx, NY, 2011.

8709
The Bookout Family Foundation ✧ ☆

P.O. Box 61309
Houston, TX 77208-1309

Established in 1996 in TX.
Donors: John F. Bookout, Jr.; Carolyn C. Bookout; John F. Brookout III; Ann H. Brookout.
Foundation type: Independent foundation.
Financial data (yr. ended 12/31/12): Assets, $1,937,768 (M); gifts received, $275,000; expenditures, $607,708; qualifying distributions, $549,863; giving activities include $549,863 for grants.
Fields of interest: Museums (art); Arts; Education; Hospitals (general); Human services; United Ways and Federated Giving Programs; Women.
Limitations: Applications not accepted. Giving primarily in Houston, TX. No grants to individuals.
Application information: Unsolicited requests for funds not accepted.
Officers and Directors:* John F. Bookout, Jr.,* Pres.; John F. Bookout III, V.P.; Beverly Von Kurnatowski, Secy.-Treas.; Carolyn C. Bookout; Adair Stevenson.
EIN: 760508684

8710
The Boone Family Foundation ✧

5949 Sherry Ln., Ste. 1010
Dallas, TX 75225-8076
E-mail: info@theboonefamilyfoundation.org; Main URL: http://www.theboonefamilyfoundation.org

Established in 2007 in TX.
Donors: Garrett Boone; Cecilia Boone; Aimee Brooks Boone; Katherine Nancy Boone; Daniel Guthrie Boone.
Foundation type: Independent foundation.
Financial data (yr. ended 12/31/12): Assets, $44,821,788 (M); expenditures, $2,830,484; qualifying distributions, $2,613,993; giving activities include $2,336,905 for 39 grants (high: $300,000; low: $1,500).
Purpose and activities: Giving primarily to advance equity for women and girls, improve quality of life for children, and promote environmental stewardship.
Fields of interest: Environment, natural resources; Reproductive health, family planning; Children/youth, services; Family services; Homeless, human services; Christian agencies & churches.
Type of support: Capital campaigns; Building/renovation; Program development.
Limitations: Applications not accepted. Giving primarily in TX and in communities where the directors have an interest. No grants to individuals.
Application information: Contributes only to pre-selected organizations.
Officers and Directors:* Cecilia Boone,* Pres.; Cynthia Yung, V.P. and Secy.; James F. Adams, V.P. and Treas.; Aimee Brooks Boone; Daniel Guthrie Boone; Garrett Boone; Katherine Nancy Boone.
EIN: 261407294

8711
Booth Ferris Foundation ✧

c/o JPMorgan Private Bank, Philanthropic Svcs.
P.O. 227237 TX1-2963
Dallas, TX 75222-7237
Contact: Contact for Parks and Gardens, Arts and Culture: Jonathan Horowitz, Prog. Off.; Contact for Education: Casey Castaneda, V.P. and Prog. Off.; Contact for Strengthening NYC's Nonprofit Sector: Connie Giampapa, Prog. Off.
FAX: (212) 464-2304;
E-mail: jonathan.g.horowitz@jpmorgan.com; E-mail for jonathan.g.horowitz@jpmchase.com; e-mail for Connie Giampapa:
connie.a.giampapa@jpmorgan.com; e-mail for Casey Castaneda:
casey.b.castaneda@jpmchase.com; Main URL: http://fdnweb.org/boothferris

Trusts established in 1957 and 1958 in NY; merged in 1964.
Donors: Chancie Ferris Booth†; Willis H. Booth†.
Foundation type: Independent foundation.
Financial data (yr. ended 12/31/13): Assets, $226,931,028 (M); expenditures, $10,704,587; qualifying distributions, $9,346,306; giving activities include $9,038,075 for 95 grants (high: $250,000; low: $725).
Purpose and activities: Grants primarily for education, smaller colleges, and independent secondary schools; limited support also for urban programs, social service agencies, and cultural activities.
Fields of interest: Museums; Arts; Education, association; Secondary school/education; Higher education; Adult education—literacy, basic skills & GED; Education, reading; Education; Human services; Children/youth, services; Community/economic development; Government/public administration; Public affairs.
Type of support: Management development/capacity building; Capital campaigns.
Limitations: Applications accepted. Giving limited to the New York, NY, metropolitan area for the arts, K-12 education, and civic and urban affairs; a broader geographic scope for higher education. No support for federated campaigns, community chests, social services and cultural institutions from outside the New York metropolitan area, or for work with specific diseases or disabilities. No grants to individuals, or for research; generally no grants to educational institutions for scholarships, fellowships, or unrestricted endowments; no loans.
Publications: Annual report; Annual report (including application guidelines).
Application information: Interviews will not be granted prior to the submission of a proposal. After proposals are received interviews will be granted only in those cases in which the trustees feel it will be helpful to their decision. The foundation will make every effort to inform applicants promptly if their proposal will not be successful. At least three years must pass between grant awards. Proposals from social services and cultural institutions from outside the metropolitan New York area will not be considered. Do not mail applications. Only submit information online at http://www.jpmorgan.com/pages/jpmorgan/private_banking/foundations/online_grant_application/guidelines_to_apply. Application form not required.
Initial approach: Proposals for funding should be submitted to the appropriate contact person
Copies of proposal: 1
Deadline(s): Feb. 1 for Strengthening NYC, Education and Arts/Culture grants; May 31, Parks Gardens grants
Board meeting date(s): Approximately 4 times per year
Final notification: 5 months
Trustee: JPMorgan Chase Bank, N.A.
EIN: 136170340
Selected grants: The following grants are a representative sample of this grantmaker's funding activity:
$250,000 to Education Pioneers, Brooklyn, NY, 2012. For capacity building associated with program expansion in New York City.
$225,000 to Turnaround for Children, New York, NY, 2012. For First installment of a $450,000 grant to develop communications and policy capacity to improve education in high-poverty schools.
$200,000 to Allegheny College, Meadville, PA, 2012. For Grant of $200,000 for the Carr Hall renovation project.
$200,000 to Carnegie Hall Society, New York, NY, 2012. For the expansion of its Carnegie Hall Online Resource Center.
$200,000 to New York Shakespeare Festival, New York, NY, 2012. For the capital campaign to renovate the organization's historic building.
$200,000 to Teachers College Columbia University, New York, NY, 2012. For Final installment of a $400,000 grant for the Safeguarding A Sound Basic Education project.
$200,000 to Theater for a New Audience, New York, NY, 2012. For the capital campaign for a new building.
$150,000 to Drawing Center, New York, NY, 2012. For capital campaign to renovate and expand its building.
$100,000 to PENCIL, New York, NY, 2012. For First installment of a $200,000 grant for technology and communications assistance to enlarge business sector in education.
$75,000 to W N Y C Radio, New York, NY, 2012. For First installment of a $150,000 grant for the Cultural Partnership Programming Fund.

8712
Booth Heritage Foundation, Inc. ✧

4107 Lakeplace Ln.
Austin, TX 78746-1623

Established in 2000 in CA.

Donors: David Booth; Suzanne Deal Booth.
Foundation type: Independent foundation.
Financial data (yr. ended 01/31/12): Assets, $8,664,554 (M); expenditures, $2,808,629; qualifying distributions, $2,785,838; giving activities include $2,781,660 for 49 grants (high: $1,180,000; low: $250).
Purpose and activities: Giving primarily for higher education and the arts.
Fields of interest: Museums (art); Arts; Higher education; Education; Human services.
Limitations: Applications not accepted. Giving primarily in CA. No grants to individuals.
Application information: Contributes only to pre-selected organizations.
Officers and Directors:* Suzanne Deal Booth,* Pres.; David Booth,* Secy. and C.F.O.
EIN: 954785406
Selected grants: The following grants are a representative sample of this grantmaker's funding activity:
$1,180,000 to Rice University, Houston, TX, 2012. For operating support.
$427,000 to Saint Stephens Episcopal School, Austin, TX, 2012. For operating support.
$310,000 to University of Texas, Austin, TX, 2012. For operating support.
$150,000 to Museum Associates, Los Angeles County Museum of Art, Los Angeles, CA, 2012. For operating support.
$100,000 to American Academy in Rome, New York, NY, 2012. For operating support.
$62,800 to New York University, New York, NY, 2012. For operating support.
$50,000 to Menil Foundation, Houston, TX, 2012. For operating support.
$40,000 to Arthouse at the Jones Center, Austin, TX, 2012. For operating support.
$30,000 to Austin Achieve Public Schools, Austin, TX, 2012. For operating support.
$25,000 to Texas Tribune, Austin, TX, 2012. For operating support.

8713
Suzanne Deal and David G. Booth Inc. ✧ ☆
4107 Lakeplace Ln.
Austin, TX 78746-1623

Established in TX.
Donors: Suzanne Deal Booth; David G. Booth.
Foundation type: Independent foundation.
Financial data (yr. ended 01/31/14): Assets, $427,748 (M); expenditures, $6,595,226; qualifying distributions, $6,540,261; giving activities include $6,537,200 for 58 grants (high: $3,393,000; low: $250).
Fields of interest: Arts; Higher education; Education; Human services.
Limitations: Applications not accepted. Giving primarily in New York, NY, and Austin and Houston, TX.
Application information: Unsolicited requests for funds not accepted.
Officers: Suzanne Deal Booth, Pres.; David G. Booth, V.P. and Secy.; Beverly G. Irick, V.P.
EIN: 454364494

8714
Louis L. Borick Foundation
2707 Kipling St.
Houston, TX 77098-1214 (213) 278-0855
Contact: Lauren Johnson, Grants Mgr.
Main URL: http://louislborickfoundation.org/
Grants Database: http://louislborickfoundation.org/past-grants

Established in 1997 in CA.
Donors: Louis L. Borick; Steven Borick.
Foundation type: Independent foundation.
Financial data (yr. ended 12/31/13): Assets, $88,055,066 (M); gifts received, $63,503,537; expenditures, $4,920,555; qualifying distributions, $4,097,250; giving activities include $4,097,250 for grants.
Purpose and activities: The vision of the foundation is to create opportunity for people to reach their full potential, positively contribute to society and participate in a culturally rich community by supporting education, youth and leadership development, and the arts. Concurrently, the foundation supports furthering animal welfare through conservation and protection efforts.
Fields of interest: Arts education; Arts; Education; Animals/wildlife, preservation/protection; Youth development; Children/youth, services.
Type of support: General/operating support; Program development.
Limitations: Applications accepted. Giving primarily in CA, particularly the Los Angeles County, and San Francisco Bay Area, and in MT and TX. No grants to individuals.
Publications: Application guidelines.
Application information: Full applications by invitation only, upon consideration on Letter of Inquiry. Application form required.
Initial approach: Letter of Inquiry via online portal on foundation web site
Deadline(s): See foundation web site for current deadline
Officers and Directors:* Steven J. Borick,* Pres.; Robert Borick,* V.P.; Linda Borick,* Secy.-Treas.
EIN: 954635770

8715
The Bosarge Family Foundation ✧
4203 Yoakum Blvd., Ste. 200
Houston, TX 77006-5455
Contact: Darla Tollefson, Treas.

Donors: The Southport Trust; The Leopard Delaware Trust; Spotted Leopard Trust; Mid-Coast Trust; South Pacific Trust.
Foundation type: Independent foundation.
Financial data (yr. ended 12/31/12): Assets, $1,010,041 (M); gifts received, $7,127,198; expenditures, $6,127,157; qualifying distributions, $6,121,809; giving activities include $6,118,000 for 11 grants (high: $3,000,000; low: $5,000).
Fields of interest: Arts; Human services; Public affairs.
Limitations: Applications accepted. Giving primarily in ME.
Application information: Application form required.
Initial approach: Proposal
Deadline(s): None
Officers and Directors:* W.E. Bosarge, Pres.; Marie Bosarge, V.P.; David J. Houston, Secy.; Darla Tollefson, Treas.
EIN: 273139347

8716
Harry E. Bovay, Jr. Foundation ✧ ☆
c/o Michael L. Patrick
3355 W. Alabama St., Ste. 1140
Houston, TX 77098-1863

Established in 2001 in TX.
Donors: H.E. Bovay, Jr.; Mid-South Telecommunications Trust; Mid-South Telecommunications Company.
Foundation type: Independent foundation.
Financial data (yr. ended 12/31/12): Assets, $36,313,252 (M); gifts received, $1,437,551; expenditures, $1,678,732; qualifying distributions, $1,396,253; giving activities include $1,396,253 for grants.
Purpose and activities: Giving to colleges and universities for their scholarship programs.
Fields of interest: Education; Human services.
Type of support: General/operating support.
Limitations: Applications not accepted. Giving on a national basis. No grants to individuals.
Application information: Unsolicited requests for funds not accepted.
Directors: H.E. Bovay, Jr.; C. Ronald Dorchester; Peggy L. Kelly; Michael L. Patrick; Travis Traylor, Jr.
EIN: 760343221

8717
Bowling Family Charitable Foundation ✧ ☆
4655 Cohen Ave.
El Paso, TX 79924-4415 (915) 821-3550
Contact: Robert L. Bowling III, Pres.

Donors: Robert L. Bowling III; Robert L. Bowling IV; Randall J. Bowling; Gregory B. Bowling.
Foundation type: Independent foundation.
Financial data (yr. ended 12/31/13): Assets, $6,116 (M); gifts received, $436,625; expenditures, $439,428; qualifying distributions, $438,502; giving activities include $438,502 for 20 grants (high: $180,112; low: $200).
Fields of interest: Youth development; Human services.
Limitations: Applications accepted. Giving primarily in El Paso, TX.
Application information: Application form required.
Initial approach: Letter
Deadline(s): None
Officers and Directors:* Robert L. Bowling III,* Pres.; Gregory B. Bowling,* Secy.; Randall J. Bowling,* Treas.; Robert L. Bowling IV.
EIN: 272955506
Selected grants: The following grants are a representative sample of this grantmaker's funding activity:
$75 to Clint High School, Clint, TX, 2012. For 2013 High School Football Support.

8718
BP Foundation, Inc. ✧
(formerly BP Amoco Foundation, Inc.)
501 Westlake Park Blvd., 25th Fl
Houston, TX 77079-2604
Main URL: http://www.bp.com/en/global/corporate/sustainability/society/Supporting-development-in-societies-where-we-work/community-investment.html

Incorporated in 1952 in IN.

Donors: Amoco Corp.; BP Amoco Corp.; BP Corp. North America Inc.; BP America Inc.; Amoco Production Co.; Atlantic Richfield Co.; BP Products North America, Inc.
Foundation type: Company-sponsored foundation.
Financial data (yr. ended 12/31/13): Assets, $25,714,939 (M); expenditures, $19,230,326; qualifying distributions, $19,211,498; giving activities include $18,152,126 for 32 grants (high: $7,714,444; low: $38,565).
Purpose and activities: The foundation supports programs designed to promote science, engineering, and math education, economic development, practical approaches to environmental need, and provide humanitarian relief.
Fields of interest: Higher education; Education; Environment, natural resources; Environment; Disasters, preparedness/services; American Red Cross; Human services; International relief; Community/economic development; Foundations (community); Mathematics; Engineering/technology; Science; Economically disadvantaged.
Type of support: General/operating support; Emergency funds; Program development; Scholarship funds; Research; Employee volunteer services; Sponsorships; Employee matching gifts.
Limitations: Applications not accepted. Giving primarily in AK, AL, CA, Washington, DC, GA, Chicago, IL, IN, NY, and OH; giving also in Australia, China, Europe, Germany, Japan, Philippines and the United Kingdom. No support for religious, fraternal, political, social, or athletic organizations; generally, no support for organizations already receiving general operating support through the United Way. No grants to individuals, or for endowments, medical research, publications, or conferences.
Application information: Contributes only to pre-selected organizations.
Board meeting date(s): Apr., July, and Nov.
Officers and Directors:* Andrew P. Hopwood,* Chair.; Ray C. Dempsey,* Pres.; Don Eldred,* C.F.O.; Mark E. Thompson, Treas.; Hans Boas, Legal Counsel; Lori Wittlin, Genl. Tax Off.; Sherry L. Strasner, Assoc. Dir.; Benjamin E. Cannon, Exec. Dir.; Iris M. Cross; Elodie Grant Goodey; Anshul Mathur; Luis Sierra; Marta Vasel.
Number of staff: 4 full-time professional; 1 full-time support.
EIN: 366046879
Selected grants: The following grants are a representative sample of this grantmaker's funding activity:
$7,714,444 to JK Group, Plainsboro, NJ, 2013.
$5,982,574 to JK Group, Plainsboro, NJ, 2012.
$2,467,856 to Charities Aid Foundation America, Alexandria, VA, 2012.
$2,460,000 to Museum Associates, Los Angeles County Museum of Art, Los Angeles, CA, 2012.
$2,460,000 to Museum Associates, Los Angeles County Museum of Art, Los Angeles, CA, 2013.
$2,194,057 to Charities Aid Foundation America, Alexandria, VA, 2013.
$1,508,822 to Maecenata Management, Munich, Germany, 2013. To provide matching grants to schools, community, health and human services organizations in Germany.
$1,020,399 to Maecenata Management, Munich, Germany, 2012. To provide matching grants to schools, community, health and human services organizations in Germany.
$500,000 to Tsinghua University, Beijing, China, 2012. For School of Economics and Management.
$395,880 to National Merit Scholarship Corporation, Evanston, IL, 2012.
$383,439 to National Merit Scholarship Corporation, Evanston, IL, 2013.
$350,000 to National Action Council for Minorities in Engineering, White Plains, NY, 2013.
$275,000 to Fletcher Community College Foundation, Schriever, LA, 2012.
$209,787 to Canadian Red Cross Society, Calgary, Canada, 2013. For disaster relief efforts which will provide humanitarian aid to victims of Alberta floods. Grant includes matching gifts from employee contributions ($9,787).
$200,000 to National Action Council for Minorities in Engineering, White Plains, NY, 2012.
$167,500 to Plan International India Chapter, New Delhi, India, 2013. For disaster relief efforts which will provide humanitarian aid to victims of Northern India floods.
$150,431 to Teach First, London, England, 2013. To support seventeen college graduates as Science Fellows in schools located in disadvantaged areas of London.
$150,000 to Delgado Community College, New Orleans, LA, 2012.
$50,000 to COSI Toledo, Toledo, OH, 2012.

8719
George W. Brackenridge Foundation ✧
700 N. Saint Mary's St., Ste. 875
San Antonio, TX 78205-3507 (210) 693-0819
Contact: Karen Matyear, Opers. Mgr.
FAX: (210) 226-1715;
E-mail: info@brackenridgefoundtion.org; Main URL: http://www.brackenridgefoundation.org

Trust established in 1920 in TX.
Donor: George W. Brackenridge‡.
Foundation type: Independent foundation.
Financial data (yr. ended 12/31/12): Assets, $26,541,299 (M); expenditures, $1,552,251; qualifying distributions, $1,319,772; giving activities include $829,550 for 15 grants (high: $515,550; low: $5,000).
Purpose and activities: The foundation's current focus is assisting best-in-class CMOs (charter management organizations) to create high performing public charter schools in the San Antonio, TX, area.
Fields of interest: Charter schools; Education.
Type of support: Endowments; Program development; Scholarship funds; Research.
Limitations: Giving primarily in San Antonio, TX, and the surrounding area. No grants to individuals, or for general purposes, continuing support, seed money, emergency funds, land acquisition, renovation projects, building funds, operating budgets, annual campaigns, deficit financing, or matching gifts; no loans.
Application information: Applications are currently by invitation only. See foundation web site for updates in this area.
Board meeting date(s): Mar., June, Sept., and Dec.
Officer and Trustee:* Victoria B. Rico,* Chair.; Randy J. Boatright; David H.O. Roth.
EIN: 746034977
Selected grants: The following grants are a representative sample of this grantmaker's funding activity:
$30,000 to San Antonio Area Foundation, San Antonio, TX, 2012. For Educational Purposes Or Programs.

8720
C. B. and Anita Branch Trust ✧
c/o Anita Branch
103 Ranger Creek Rd.
Boerne, TX 78006-5624

Established in 1995 in TX.
Donors: C.B. Branch‡; Anita Branch.
Foundation type: Independent foundation.
Financial data (yr. ended 12/31/12): Assets, $11,906,896 (M); expenditures, $745,515; qualifying distributions, $730,433; giving activities include $730,433 for grants.
Purpose and activities: Giving primarily for education, human services, and to Roman Catholic agencies and churches, including missionary work, and schools.
Fields of interest: Education; Human services; Children/youth, services; Catholic agencies & churches.
Limitations: Applications not accepted. Giving primarily in TX, with emphasis on Boerne. No grants to individuals.
Application information: Unsolicited requests for funds not accepted.
Trustee: Anita Branch.
EIN: 746431994

8721
Brass Family Foundation ✧ ☆
11 Greenway Plz., Ste. 2950
Houston, TX 77046-1107

Established in 2008 in TX.
Donors: Ned Davenport; Matthew Johnson; Lou Anne Kellman; Joseph Mattingly; Michael Mithoff; Philip Laak; Ernest Scalamandre; Brad Scott; Lester Smith; Chris Wilbratte; Gulf Coast Asphalt Company; Mithoff Family Foundation.
Foundation type: Independent foundation.
Financial data (yr. ended 12/31/12): Assets, $76,726 (M); gifts received, $393,625; expenditures, $472,854; qualifying distributions, $469,779; giving activities include $469,779 for grants.
Fields of interest: Arts; Health care; Health organizations.
Limitations: Applications not accepted. Giving primarily in TX.
Application information: Unsolicited requests for funds not accepted.
Officers and Directors:* Catherine M. Brass,* Pres. and Treas.; Arthur J. Brass,* V.P. and Secy.; Joyce Brass.
EIN: 263882953

8722
The Bratton Family Foundation ✧ ☆
201 Main St., Ste. 1900
Fort Worth, TX 76102-3134

Established in 1993 in TX.
Donors: Douglas K. Bratton; Bratton Family Partners, L.P.
Foundation type: Independent foundation.
Financial data (yr. ended 12/31/13): Assets, $4,861,998 (M); gifts received, $205,000; expenditures, $474,456; qualifying distributions, $455,350; giving activities include $455,350 for 23 grants (high: $250,000; low: $500).

Fields of interest: Museums; Performing arts; Higher education; Education; Boys clubs; Protestant agencies & churches.
Limitations: Applications not accepted. Giving in the U.S., primarily in Fort Worth, TX. No grants to individuals.
Application information: Contributes only to pre-selected organizations.
Director: Douglas K. Bratton.
EIN: 752513615

8723
Brentwood Foundation ✧
3198 Parkwood Blvd., Ste. 11076
Frisco, TX 75034-9518

Donors: Thomas Teague; Syd Teague; George Allen; Holt Lunsford; Michael Ording; Elizabeth Ording; Donal Berg.
Foundation type: Independent foundation.
Financial data (yr. ended 12/31/13): Assets, $305,270 (M); gifts received, $1,668,150; expenditures, $2,208,934; qualifying distributions, $2,079,350; giving activities include $2,079,350 for 42 grants (high: $995,000; low: $50).
Fields of interest: Human services; Christian agencies & churches.
Limitations: Applications not accepted. Giving primarily in TX. No grants to individuals.
Application information: Contributes only to pre-selected organizations.
Officer: Michael G. Jaccar, Pres.
Director: Thomas Teague.
EIN: 752032865

8724
The Bridge Foundation, Inc. ✧
c/o Bruce Petty
201 Main St., Ste. 600
Fort Worth, TX 76102-3110 (817) 339-1156
Contact: Marguerite M. Gordon, Pres.

Established in NM.
Donor: Anna Melissa Gordon.
Foundation type: Independent foundation.
Financial data (yr. ended 12/31/13): Assets, $10,038,692 (M); expenditures, $437,909; qualifying distributions, $420,000; giving activities include $420,000 for 3 grants (high: $315,000; low: $5,000).
Fields of interest: Animal welfare.
Limitations: Giving in the U.S., with emphasis on NM and VA. No grants to individuals.
Application information:
Initial approach: Letter
Deadline(s): None
Officers: Marguerite M. Gordon, Pres.; Anna Melissa Gordon, V.P. and Treas.; Bruce Petty, Secy.
EIN: 850476426
Selected grants: The following grants are a representative sample of this grantmaker's funding activity:
$100,000 to People for the Ethical Treatment of Animals, Norfolk, VA, 2011.

8725
Bridges Evangelical Foundation ✧ ☆
331 W. Alkire Lake Dr.
Sugar Land, TX 77478-3511

Established in TX.
Donor: Waterstone Foundation.
Foundation type: Independent foundation.
Financial data (yr. ended 12/31/12): Assets, $868,876 (M); gifts received, $467,690; expenditures, $825,183; qualifying distributions, $732,721; giving activities include $732,421 for 12 grants (high: $359,690; low: $1,825).
Fields of interest: Human services.
Limitations: Applications not accepted. Giving primarily in IN and TX; funding also in MI.
Application information: Unsolicited requests for funds not accepted.
Trustees: James W. Briges; R. Darlene Bridges.
EIN: 266528682

8726
The J. S. Bridwell Foundation ✧
807 8th St., 2nd Fl.
Wichita Falls, TX 76301-3365

Incorporated in 1949 in TX.
Donors: J.S. Bridwell†; Margaret B. Bowdle; Brian Lee Bowdle Trust No. 2.
Foundation type: Independent foundation.
Financial data (yr. ended 12/31/13): Assets, $52,027,017 (M); expenditures, $1,815,373; qualifying distributions, $1,531,500; giving activities include $1,471,800 for 106 grants (high: $250,000; low: $250).
Purpose and activities: Giving primarily for the arts, health, and volunteer fire departments; funding also for children, youth, and social services.
Fields of interest: Arts; Higher education; Health care; Health organizations, association; Disasters, fire prevention/control; Human services; Children/youth, services; Residential/custodial care, hospices.
Type of support: General/operating support; Capital campaigns; Building/renovation; Equipment; Program development.
Limitations: Applications not accepted. Giving primarily in TX, with emphasis on Wichita Falls. No grants to individuals.
Application information: Contributes only to pre-selected organizations.
Officers: Mac W. Cannedy, Jr., Pres. and Treas.; Thomas E. Knight, Jr., Secy.
Directors: Ralph S. Bridwell; Bobby Henry; Paul Schoppa, Jr.; Terry M. Walker.
EIN: 756032988
Selected grants: The following grants are a representative sample of this grantmaker's funding activity:
$250,000 to Midwestern State University, Wichita Falls, TX, 2012. For museum construction.
$250,000 to Presbyterian Manor, Wichita Falls, TX, 2012. For Good Samaritan Fund.
$120,000 to United Regional Health Care Foundation, Wichita Falls, TX, 2012. For Simulation Mannequins.
$100,000 to Hands to Hands Community Fund, Wichita Falls, TX, 2012. For Community Trust.
$25,000 to United Regional Health Care Foundation, Wichita Falls, TX, 2012. For Circle of Friends Lecture.
$15,000 to Child Advocates, Wichita Falls, TX, 2012. For Development Director's Salary.
$10,000 to Wichita Falls Area Community Foundation, Wichita Falls, TX, 2012. For Revitalize Olney Campaign.
$5,000 to Inheritance Adoptions, Wichita Falls, TX, 2012. For Healthy Beginnings.

8727
The Todd Brock Family Foundation ✧
P.O. Box 3528
Beaumont, TX 77704-3528 (409) 833-6226
Contact: Todd O. Brock, Pres.

Established in 2007 in TX.
Donor: Todd O. Brock.
Foundation type: Independent foundation.
Financial data (yr. ended 12/31/12): Assets, $3,696,221 (M); expenditures, $1,026,599; qualifying distributions, $919,550; giving activities include $919,550 for grants.
Fields of interest: Education; Protestant agencies & churches.
Limitations: Applications accepted. Giving primarily in TX.
Application information: Application form not required.
Initial approach: Proposal
Deadline(s): None
Officers: Todd Brock, Pres.; Brennin Brock, V.P.; Diana Brock, Secy.-Treas.
EIN: 262049780

8728
William A. Brookshire Foundation ✧ ☆
c/o Charles Reid
7825 Park Place Blvd.
Houston, TX 77087-4639

Established in 1998 in TX.
Donor: William A. Brookshire.
Foundation type: Independent foundation.
Financial data (yr. ended 06/30/13): Assets, $22,081,763 (M); gifts received, $6,000,000; expenditures, $476,091; qualifying distributions, $470,000; giving activities include $470,000 for 33 grants to individuals (high: $15,000; low: $10,000).
Fields of interest: Higher education; Education.
Type of support: Scholarships—to individuals.
Limitations: Applications not accepted.
Application information: Unsolicited requests for funds not accepted.
Officers and Directors:* William A. Brookshire,* Pres.; Lori Brookshire-Garrison,* V.P.; Dean Quinn,* Secy.-Treas.
EIN: 760594307

8729
G. C. Broughton Foundation Trust ✧
P.O. Box 2197
Big Spring, TX 79721-2197
Contact: Jean Broughton, Fdn. Mgr. and Tr.

Donor: G.C. Broughton†.
Foundation type: Independent foundation.
Financial data (yr. ended 12/31/13): Assets, $15,482,481 (M); expenditures, $1,157,271; qualifying distributions, $585,607; giving activities include $585,607 for 5 grants (high: $530,607; low: $10,000).
Purpose and activities: Giving primarily for higher education.
Fields of interest: Higher education; Human services.
Limitations: Applications accepted. Giving in TX, with emphasis on Big Spring.
Application information: Application form not required.

Initial approach: Proposal
Deadline(s): None
Officer and Trustees:* Jean Broughton,* Fdn. Mgr.; John Grant; John Marshall; Cliff Talbot; Jim Weaver.
EIN: 756395131
Selected grants: The following grants are a representative sample of this grantmaker's funding activity:
$685,000 to Howard College, Big Spring, TX, 2011.
$10,000 to Retina Foundation of the Southwest, Dallas, TX, 2011. For operations.

8730
T. J. Brown and C. A. Lupton Foundation, Inc. ✧
P.O. Box 1629
Fort Worth, TX 76101-1629 (817) 738-1804
Contact: Charles Lupton Geren, Dir.

Incorporated in 1942 in TX.
Donors: T.J. Brown†; C.A. Lupton†; V.J. Earnhart; J.A. Gooch; John V. Halick†.
Foundation type: Independent foundation.
Financial data (yr. ended 12/31/13): Assets, $40,300,183 (M); expenditures, $1,946,218; qualifying distributions, $1,685,440; giving activities include $1,637,500 for 26 grants (high: $1,000,000; low: $2,500).
Purpose and activities: Giving primarily for the arts, health, and human services.
Fields of interest: Museums (science/technology); Arts; Higher education; Libraries/library science; Zoos/zoological societies; Health organizations, association; Agriculture, livestock issues; Human services.
Limitations: Applications accepted. Giving primarily in Fort Worth, TX. No grants to individuals, or for scholarships, prizes, or similar benefits; no loans.
Application information:
Initial approach: Letter
Deadline(s): None
Board meeting date(s): Quarterly
Directors: Tav Holmes Berry; Charles Lupton Geren; Kit Tennison Moncrief; Lee Lupton Tennison; William E. Tucker.
Number of staff: 1 full-time professional; 1 part-time professional.
EIN: 750992690
Selected grants: The following grants are a representative sample of this grantmaker's funding activity:
$800,000 to Texas Christian University, Fort Worth, TX, 2012. For Scholarships, Student Center and Baseball Stadium.
$10,000 to Humane Society of North Texas, Fort Worth, TX, 2012. For Prevention of Cruelty and Abuse.

8731
The Brown Foundation, Inc. ✧
2217 Welch Ave.
Houston, TX 77019-5617 (713) 523-6867
Contact: Nancy Pittman, Exec. Dir.
FAX: (713) 523-2917;
E-mail: bfi@brownfoundation.org; Application address: P.O. Box 130646, Houston, TX 77219-0646; Main URL: http://www.brownfoundation.org

Incorporated in 1951 in TX.
Donors: Herman Brown†; Margarett Root Brown†; George R. Brown†; Alice Pratt Brown†.
Foundation type: Independent foundation.
Financial data (yr. ended 06/30/14): Assets, $1,375,012,451 (M); expenditures, $82,116,230; qualifying distributions, $75,807,636; giving activities include $73,502,532 for 593 grants (high: $10,007,562; low: $2,000), and $985,092 for 201 employee matching gifts.
Purpose and activities: Support principally for the encouragement of and assistance to education, the arts and community service. The projects selected for funding most likely will have the potential for long-lasting significant impact in the community. The foundation's current emphasis is in the field of public education at the primary and secondary levels. It will focus on finding and supporting nontraditional and innovative approaches designed to improve public education primarily within the state of Texas. Other areas of interest continue to be the visual and performing arts, and also include community service projects focused upon the needs of children and youth, especially in the Houston area.
Fields of interest: Arts; Education; Human services; Science; Public affairs.
Type of support: General/operating support; Continuing support; Annual campaigns; Capital campaigns; Building/renovation; Land acquisition; Program development; Professorships; Curriculum development; Scholarship funds; Research; Employee matching gifts; Matching/challenge support.
Limitations: Applications accepted. Giving primarily in TX, with emphasis on Houston. No support for political organizations, private foundations, or religious organizations for religious purposes. No grants to individuals, or for operating deficits, debt retirement, testimonial dinners, marketing or fundraising events; no loans.
Publications: Application guidelines; Annual report (including application guidelines); Informational brochure (including application guidelines).
Application information: Grant proposal guidelines and proposal summary form are available upon request. Will consider one grant proposal per 12-month period from an organization. See foundation web site for downloadable proposal summary form. Application form required.
Initial approach: Proposal should be submitted a minimum of 4 months before funds are needed
Copies of proposal: 1
Deadline(s): None
Board meeting date(s): Feb., May, Sept., and Nov.
Final notification: 3 months
Officers and Trustees:* Nancy Brown Negley,* Chair.; Herman L. Stude,* Pres.; Louisa Stude Sarofim,* V.P. and Secy.; William N. Mathis,* Treas.; Jacklyn Tatge, C.F.O.; Carla Knobloch, C.I.O.; Nancy Abendshein; Holbrook Dorn; John O'Connor; Elisa Stude Pye; Christopher B. Sarofim.
Number of staff: 3 full-time professional; 2 part-time professional; 4 full-time support.
EIN: 746036466
Selected grants: The following grants are a representative sample of this grantmaker's funding activity:
$1,250,000 to Houston Grand Opera Association, Houston, TX, 2012. For Comprehensive Development Campaign.
$1,000,000 to Buffalo Bayou Partnership, Houston, TX, 2012. For Buffalo Bayou Park Shepherd to Sabine Project.
$1,000,000 to Houston Zoo, Houston, TX, 2012. For African Forest Phase 11 Capital Campaign.
$800,000 to Menil Foundation, Houston, TX, 2012. For operating support.
$600,000 to Teach for America, Houston, TX, 2012. For Empower Houston: Teach for America-Houston's 2015 Growth Plan.
$500,000 to Hermann Park Conservancy, Houston, TX, 2012. For Centennial Gardens.
$500,000 to Menninger Clinic, Houston, TX, 2012. For Research Institute and Outpatient Center.
$250,000 to Collaborative for Children, Houston, TX, 2012. For operating support.
$200,000 to Institute for Rehabilitation and Research Foundation, Houston, TX, 2012. For Mission Connect: The Knowledge to Heal, collaborative neurotrauma research project created to translate scientific knowledge, the product of research, into pioneering medical treatments to help people who have sustained a neurological injury.
$200,000 to Planned Parenthood Gulf Coast, Houston, TX, 2012. For operating support.

8732
H.L. Brown, Jr. Family Foundation ✧
P.O. Box 2237
Midland, TX 79702-2237
Application address: c/o Hubert L. Brown, III, Exec. Dir., 300 W. Louisiana Ave., Midland, TX 79701-3401

Established in 2009 in TX.
Donor: H.L. Brown Charitable Lead Annuity Trust, Jr.
Foundation type: Independent foundation.
Financial data (yr. ended 12/31/13): Assets, $13,569,204 (M); gifts received, $2,302,383; expenditures, $792,019; qualifying distributions, $670,549; giving activities include $567,000 for 47 grants (high: $50,000; low: $500).
Fields of interest: Arts; Education; Health care; Protestant agencies & churches; Catholic agencies & churches.
Limitations: Applications accepted. Giving primarily in NY and TX.
Application information: Application form not required.
Initial approach: Proposal
Deadline(s): None
Officers: Hubert L. Brown III, Exec. Dir.; Annabelle B. Fowlkes, Exec. Dir.
Director: Q. Peter Courtney III.
EIN: 261223638
Selected grants: The following grants are a representative sample of this grantmaker's funding activity:
$50,000 to Permian Basin Petroleum Museum, Library and Hall of Fame, Midland, TX, 2011.
$45,000 to Mount Sinai Medical Center, New York, NY, 2011.
$20,000 to Groundwork, Inc., Brooklyn, NY, 2010.
$20,000 to Midland Childrens Rehabilitation Center, Midland, TX, 2011.
$20,000 to Midland Memorial Foundation, Midland, TX, 2011.
$20,000 to Midland Memorial Foundation, Midland, TX, 2010.
$20,000 to Spence School, New York, NY, 2011.
$20,000 to University of Texas, Austin, TX, 2011.
$15,000 to Nantucket Dreamland Foundation, Nantucket, MA, 2011. For general operations.
$10,000 to Permian Basin Petroleum Museum, Library and Hall of Fame, Midland, TX, 2010.
$10,000 to University of Texas, Austin, TX, 2010.

$10,000 to University of Texas M.D. Anderson Cancer Center, Houston, TX, 2011.
$5,000 to American Museum of Natural History, New York, NY, 2010.
$5,000 to Buckley School, New York, NY, 2011.
$5,000 to Buckley School, New York, NY, 2010.
$5,000 to George W. Bush Presidential Center, Dallas, TX, 2010.
$5,000 to Museum of the Southwest, Midland, TX, 2010.
$5,000 to New Mexico Military Institute, Roswell, NM, 2011. For endowment fund.
$5,000 to New York-Presbyterian Fund, New York, NY, 2010.
$2,500 to First Presbyterian Church, Midland, TX, 2010.

8733
Brownsville Foundation for Health and Education ✧ ☆
c/o Wells Fargo
P.O. Box 41629
Austin, TX 78704-9926
Application address: c/o United Way, 634 E. Levee, Brownsville, TX 78520

Foundation type: Independent foundation.
Financial data (yr. ended 05/31/13): Assets, $7,275,350 (M); expenditures, $596,739; qualifying distributions, $545,828; giving activities include $533,328 for 26 grants (high: $125,000; low: $1,152).
Fields of interest: Arts; Education; Human services; United Ways and Federated Giving Programs; Public affairs.
Limitations: Applications accepted. Giving primarily in TX.
Application information: Application form required.
Initial approach: Proposal
Deadline(s): Jan. 31
Officers: David Garza, Chair.; Renato E. Cardenas, Vice-Chair.; Antonio M. Diaz, M.D., Secy.-Treas.
EIN: 741818930

8734
The Brumley Foundation ✧
P.O. Box 9294
Amarillo, TX 79105-9294 (806) 376-1555
Contact: Marilyn C. Ault, Secy.-Treas.
Grants List: http://www.brumleyfoundation.org/media/2008_Grants.pdf

Established in 1986 in TX.
Donors: Dixie Holland†; Frank J. Warren†; Vivian Warren†.
Foundation type: Independent foundation.
Financial data (yr. ended 12/31/12): Assets, $19,739,996 (M); expenditures, $1,065,024; qualifying distributions, $971,850; giving activities include $955,899 for 42 grants (high: $75,000; low: $1,000).
Purpose and activities: Giving primarily for human services. Scholarship requests are accepted only from 501(c)(3) organizations. The preference is to help persons to help themselves: needy, students, aged, ill or disabled, day care, and youth programs.
Fields of interest: Food banks; Recreation, community; Youth development; Human services; YM/YWCAs & YM/YWHAs; Children/youth, services; Family services; Economically disadvantaged.
Type of support: General/operating support; Capital campaigns; Equipment; Scholarship funds; Matching/challenge support.
Limitations: Giving limited to the upper 26 counties of the Texas Panhandle, with preference to the population centers of Potter and Randall counties, as well as Moore County. No grants to individuals, directly.
Publications: Grants list.
Application information: Application form not required.
Initial approach: Letter of inquiry
Copies of proposal: 1
Deadline(s): None
Board meeting date(s): As necessary
Final notification: Letter following board meeting
Officers and Directors:* Dayle Tipton,* Pres.; G. Bruce Burnett,* V.P.; Marilyn C. Ault,* Secy.-Treas.; Dennis Beene; Kurt Gehring.
EIN: 752089705
Selected grants: The following grants are a representative sample of this grantmaker's funding activity:
$75,000 to High Plains Food Bank, Amarillo, TX, 2012. For Rural delivery for feeding entities.
$45,000 to Frank Phillips College, Borger, TX, 2012. For Scholarships for low-income students.
$35,000 to Amarillo Opera, Amarillo, TX, 2012. For 2013 Summer mentoring program.
$33,750 to Ronald McDonald House Charities of Amarillo, Amarillo, TX, 2012. For Purchase vehicle for transporting children obtaining medical care.
$30,000 to Amarillo Opera, Amarillo, TX, 2012. For Summer mentoring program.
$25,000 to Frank Phillips College, Borger, TX, 2012. For Acquire equipment for cosmetology program.
$25,000 to Frank Phillips College, Borger, TX, 2012. For Scholarships for cosmetology program.
$25,000 to High Plains Food Bank, Amarillo, TX, 2012. For grant to assist food bank agencies with operating/fees.
$15,000 to Texas Panhandle Heritage Foundation, Canyon, TX, 2012. To build dressing rooms for children at the Pioneer Theatre.
$10,690 to YMCA of Moore County, Dumas, TX, 2012. For Drown-proof Program for local school children.

8735
James & Catherine Buck Charitable Trust ✧
c/o Bank of America, N.A.
P.O. Box 831041
Dallas, TX 75283-1041

Donor: James Wallace Buck, Jr.†.
Foundation type: Independent foundation.
Financial data (yr. ended 06/30/13): Assets, $17,991,261 (M); gifts received, $243; expenditures, $857,823; qualifying distributions, $700,000; giving activities include $700,000 for grants.
Fields of interest: Higher education.
Limitations: Applications not accepted. Giving primarily in Wichita, KS. No grants to individuals.
Application information: Unsolicited requests for funds not accepted.
Trustee: Bank of America, N.A.
EIN: 597250952
Selected grants: The following grants are a representative sample of this grantmaker's funding activity:
$490,000 to Wichita State University Foundation, Wichita, KS, 2013. For Scholarships (95%) and French Department Support (5%).

8736
Buford Foundation ✧
2626 Cole Ave., Ste. 910
Dallas, TX 75204-1078

Established in 1998 in TX.
Donors: Linda C. Buford; Robert P. Buford; Communities Foundation of Texas; Wallestad Foundation; OneHundredX.
Foundation type: Operating foundation.
Financial data (yr. ended 12/31/13): Assets, $1,993,624 (M); gifts received, $244,731; expenditures, $3,010,607; qualifying distributions, $2,973,595; giving activities include $2,544,673 for 8 grants (high: $2,168,673; low: $1,000).
Fields of interest: Higher education; Nonprofit management; Leadership development; Christian agencies & churches.
Type of support: General/operating support.
Limitations: Applications not accepted. Giving in the U.S., primarily in IL, New York, NY, and Dallas, TX. No grants to individuals.
Application information: Contributes only to pre-selected organizations.
Officers: Robert P. Buford, Chair.; Gayle Carpenter, Secy.; Diane Reynolds, Treas.
Directors: Linda C. Buford; Robert Lewis.
EIN: 752791126

8737
The Burnett Foundation ✧
(formerly The Burnett-Tandy Foundation)
801 Cherry St., Ste. 1585
Fort Worth, TX 76102-6881 (817) 877-3344
Contact: V. Neils Agather, Exec. Dir.

Established in 1978 in TX.
Donors: Anne Burnett Tandy†; Dee Kelly Foundation.
Foundation type: Independent foundation.
Financial data (yr. ended 12/31/12): Assets, $269,560,726 (M); expenditures, $22,842,105; qualifying distributions, $16,372,549; giving activities include $15,989,810 for 28 grants (high: $10,000,000; low: $7,500), and $6,561 for 1 foundation-administered program.
Purpose and activities: Support primarily for major museum projects and other cultural institutions, social service agencies, community development groups, and educational institutions.
Fields of interest: Museums; Arts; Education; AIDS; Human services; Community development, neighborhood development.
Type of support: General/operating support; Capital campaigns; Program development; Seed money; Technical assistance; Program-related investments/loans.
Limitations: Applications not accepted. Giving primarily in the Fort Worth, TX, area.
Application information: Unsolicited requests not accepted.
Board meeting date(s): Generally in June and Nov.
Officers and Trustees:* Anne W. Marion,* Pres.; Edward R. Hudson, Jr.,* V.P. and Secy.; V. Neils Agather, V.P. and Treas.; Benjamin J. Fortson,* V.P.; John L. Marion,* V.P.; Anne W. Grimes.

Number of staff: 1 full-time professional; 2 full-time support.
EIN: 751638517
Selected grants: The following grants are a representative sample of this grantmaker's funding activity:
$5,000,000 to Harris Methodist Health Foundation, Fort Worth, TX, 2012.
$2,900,000 to Georgia OKeeffe Museum, Santa Fe, NM, 2012. For operating support.
$1,250,000 to Fort Worth Art Association, Modern Art Museum of Fort Worth, Fort Worth, TX, 2012.
$1,050,000 to Safe City Commission, Fort Worth, TX, 2012.
$1,000,000 to All Saints Episcopal School of Fort Worth, Fort Worth, TX, 2012.
$1,000,000 to George W. Bush Foundation, Dallas, TX, 2012.
$575,000 to Fort Worth Museum of Science and History, Fort Worth, TX, 2012.
$433,812 to Georgia OKeeffe Museum, Santa Fe, NM, 2012.
$300,000 to Site Santa Fe, Santa Fe, NM, 2012.
$200,000 to Fort Worth Symphony Orchestra Association, Fort Worth, TX, 2012.

8738
H. E. Butt Foundation ✧
P.O. Box 290670
Kerrville, TX 78029-0670
Contact: Jennifer D. Hargrave, Cont.
FAX: (830) 257-3137; Tel. for Jennifer Hargrave: (830) 792-1246; Main URL: http://www.laityrenewal.org/aboutFoundation.php

Incorporated as a company-sponsored operating foundation in 1933 in TX.
Donors: Howard E. Butt, Sr.†; Howard E. Butt, Jr.; H.E. Butt Grocery Co.
Foundation type: Operating foundation.
Financial data (yr. ended 12/31/12): Assets, $227,363,262 (M); gifts received, $15,776,139; expenditures, $9,521,495; qualifying distributions, $12,677,365; giving activities include $589,360 for 16 grants (high: $243,810; low: $80), and $7,839,544 for 4 foundation-administered programs.
Purpose and activities: The foundation supports camps in Texas used by qualifying organizations related to church renewal, summer Christian youth camps, and organizations involved with lay theological education and mental health.
Fields of interest: Theological school/education; Mental health/crisis services; Recreation, camps; Christian agencies & churches; Children/youth; Youth; Adults.
Type of support: General/operating support.
Limitations: Applications not accepted. Giving limited to TX. No grants to individuals, or for building or endowments.
Publications: Newsletter.
Application information: Contributes only to pre-selected organizations. The foundation's giving is limited to its own giving programs, including a Christian adult retreat center, a youth camp, a family camp, and camping facilities administered through Foundations for Laity Renewal.
Board meeting date(s): Dec.
Officers and Directors:* Howard E. Butt, Jr.,* Pres.; David M. Rogers,* Exec. V.P. and C.O.O.; F. Dwight Lacy,* Sr. V.P.; Barbara Dan Butt,* V.P. and Secy.-Treas.; Deborah Butt Rogers,* V.P.; Jennifer D. Hargrave, Cont.
Number of staff: 25 full-time professional; 20 full-time support; 1 part-time support.
EIN: 741239819

8739
Faith P. & Charles L. Bybee Foundation - A Trust ✧ ☆
(also known as Texas Pioneer Arts Foundation)
207 W. Mill St.
Round Top, TX 78954-5278

Established in 1970 in TX.
Donors: Faith P. Bybee†; Charles L. Bybee†.
Foundation type: Independent foundation.
Financial data (yr. ended 12/31/12): Assets, $4,177,746 (M); expenditures, $664,751; qualifying distributions, $430,000; giving activities include $430,000 for grants.
Purpose and activities: Preservation of historic buildings in Round Top, Texas, and maintenance of houses open for public tours about the architecture and furnishings of 19th Century Texas. Also provides a living laboratory for students from the University of Houston to study architectural preservation.
Fields of interest: Education.
Limitations: Applications not accepted. Giving primarily in TX. No grants to individuals.
Application information: Contributes only to pre-selected organizations.
Officers and Trustees:* Barry Moore,* Pres.; Jacqueline Ditsler,* V.P. and Secy.; Ernesto Caldeira; Steve Ditsler; Gabrielle Hale; Joe N. Westerlage.
EIN: 741917686

8740
C.I.O.S. ✧
P.O. Box 20815
Waco, TX 76702-0815 (254) 752-5551

Incorporated about 1952 in TN; corporation liquidated into a charitable trust in 1987.
Donors: Paul P. Piper, Sr.; Mrs. Paul P. Piper; Paul P. Piper, Jr.; Piper Industries, Inc.
Foundation type: Independent foundation.
Financial data (yr. ended 06/30/13): Assets, $112,535,310 (M); gifts received, $2,725; expenditures, $7,088,124; qualifying distributions, $6,483,075; giving activities include $6,094,462 for 47 grants (high: $500,000; low: $1,000), and $25,000 for 1 loan/program-related investment.
Purpose and activities: Grants for Protestant church support and religious programs, including Christian education, evangelism, welfare, and support for foreign missions.
Fields of interest: Theological school/education; Human services; Christian agencies & churches; Protestant agencies & churches.
Type of support: Program-related investments/loans.
Limitations: Applications not accepted. Giving primarily in TX. No grants to individuals.
Application information: Contributes only to pre-selected organizations.
Board meeting date(s): Monthly
Trustees: Jill Piper Lawrence; Lynn Piper; Paul Piper, Jr.; Shirley Piper; Polly Piper Rickard.
EIN: 742472778
Selected grants: The following grants are a representative sample of this grantmaker's funding activity:
$2,000,000 to Baptist Child and Family Services, San Antonio, TX, 2012. For facilities.
$600,000 to Mission Society for United Methodists, Norcross, GA, 2012.
$500,000 to Buckner Children and Family Services, Lubbock, TX, 2012.
$490,000 to Cooperative Baptist Fellowship, Atlanta, GA, 2012.
$480,000 to One By One, Seattle, WA, 2012.
$333,333 to Baptist Standard Publishing Company, Dallas, TX, 2012. For operating support.
$250,000 to B. H. Carroll Theological Institute, Arlington, TX, 2012.
$250,000 to Judson College, Marion, AL, 2012.
$93,000 to Council for Christian Colleges and Universities, Washington, DC, 2012. For operating support.
$62,500 to John Wood Ministries, Waco, TX, 2012.

8741
Kathleen Cailloux Family Foundation ✧
c/o Centennial Bank
1145 Junction Hwy.
Kerrville, TX 78028-4903 (830) 896-2142
Contact: Penny J. van Shoubrouek

Established in 1998 in TX.
Donors: Kathleen C. Cailloux; Kathleen C. Cailloux 1997 Charitable Remainder Unitrust.
Foundation type: Independent foundation.
Financial data (yr. ended 12/31/13): Assets, $17,367,013 (M); expenditures, $966,499; qualifying distributions, $875,000; giving activities include $875,000 for 3 grants (high: $437,500; low: $218,750).
Purpose and activities: Giving primarily for higher education, hospitals, and health associations; support also for social service agencies and youth organizations.
Fields of interest: Education; Animal welfare; Hospitals (general); Health organizations, association; Human services.
Limitations: Applications accepted. Giving primarily in Galveston and Kerr counties, TX.
Application information: Application form required.
Initial approach: Letter
Deadline(s): None
Trustees: Robert S. Andresakis; Kenneth F. Cailloux; Paula L. Heileman; Centennial State Banking Assn.
EIN: 742857513

8742
The Cailloux Foundation ✧
(also known as Floyd A. & Kathleen C. Cailloux Foundation)
P.O. Box 291276
Kerrville, TX 78029-1276 (830) 895-5222
Contact: Barbara Gaither, Exec. Asst.
FAX: (830) 895-5212;
E-mail: info@caillouxfoundation.org; Main URL: http://www.caillouxfoundation.org

Established in 1994 in TX.
Donors: Floyd A. Cailloux†; Kathleen C. Cailloux†.
Foundation type: Independent foundation.
Financial data (yr. ended 12/31/13): Assets, $94,143,109 (M); gifts received, $80,000; expenditures, $7,555,521; qualifying distributions, $6,925,079; giving activities include $5,560,914 for 51 grants (high: $2,300,322; low: $4,000).

Purpose and activities: Giving primarily to civic, community service, cultural, educational, child development, health and rehabilitation and animal welfare organizations.
Fields of interest: Education; Animal welfare; Health care; Health organizations; Children/youth, services; Family services; Community/economic development.
Type of support: General/operating support; Continuing support; Annual campaigns; Capital campaigns; Building/renovation; Equipment; Land acquisition; Emergency funds; Program development; Seed money; Scholarship funds; Technical assistance; Program evaluation; Matching/challenge support.
Limitations: Applications accepted. Giving limited to Kerr County, TX, and its surrounding communities of Bandera, Edwards, Gillespie, Kimble and Real counties for grants. Giving is limited to residents of selected Texas Hill Country communities for scholarships. No support for seminaries for construction, projects normally funded by governmental entities or church-related entities that do not meet foundation guidelines. No grants to individuals, or for fund raisers, conferences, membership drives or competitions; no loans.
Publications: Application guidelines; Financial statement; Program policy statement (including application guidelines).
Application information: The foundation only reviews grant proposals from applicants whose online letter of inquiry has been approved. Application available on foundation web site. Application form required.
Initial approach: Use letter of inquiry form on foundation web site
Copies of proposal: 1
Deadline(s): None for grants; see web site for Scholarship Program
Board meeting date(s): Quarterly
Final notification: Within 4 weeks
Officers and Directors:* Kenneth F. Cailloux,* Chair. and Pres.; Robert Andresakis,* V.P.; Paula Heilemann,* V.P.; Sandra Cailloux,* Secy. and Exec. Dir.; Hon. Steve Ables; Summer Andresakis; Blackie Heilemann; David Jackson; Cori Modisett; Leslie Modisett; Mark Moore.
Number of staff: 3 full-time professional; 1 part-time professional; 1 full-time support.
EIN: 746422979

8743
The Effie and Wofford Cain Foundation ✧
(doing business as The Cain Foundation)
4131 Spicewood Springs Rd., Ste. A-1
Austin, TX 78759-8658 (512) 346-7490
Contact: Lynn Fowler, Secy.-Treas. and Exec. Dir.
FAX: (512) 346-7491;
E-mail: info@cainfoundation.org

Incorporated in 1952 in TX.
Donors: Effie Marie Cain†; R. Wofford Cain†.
Foundation type: Independent foundation.
Financial data (yr. ended 10/31/13): Assets, $124,295,893 (M); expenditures, $6,085,119; qualifying distributions, $5,393,355; giving activities include $4,711,700 for 98 grants (high: $1,000,000; low: $300).
Purpose and activities: Giving primarily to scientific, medical, and educational institutions.
Fields of interest: Elementary/secondary education; Secondary school/education; Higher education; Health care; Medical research, institute; Protestant agencies & churches.
Type of support: Endowments; Professorships; Scholarship funds; Research.
Limitations: Applications not accepted. Giving primarily in TX. No grants to individuals or organizations on behalf of specific individuals.
Application information: The foundation provides grants and contributions, on a highly selective basis, primarily to scientific, medical, and educational institutions. Substantially all of the grants and contributions are dedicated for purposes that fulfill the foundation's philanthropic goals and are made to organizations with which the foundation has an existing historical relationship. The foundation's general policy is to not accept unsolicited grant applications and no grants are made to or for the benefit of specific individuals.
Board meeting date(s): Oct. (annual meeting); 6 to 8 interim meetings (dates vary)
Officers and Directors:* Franklin W. Denius,* Pres.; John C. Cain,* V.P.; F. Wofford Denius,* V.P.; Charmaine D. McGill,* V.P. and Grants Admin.; Lynn Fowler, Secy.-Treas. and Exec. Dir.
Number of staff: 3 full-time professional.
EIN: 756030774

8744
The Gordon A. Cain Foundation ✧
8 Greenway Plz., Ste. 606
Houston, TX 77046-0892 (713) 840-7896
Contact: James D. Weaver, Chair., Pres. and Dir.

Established in 2007 in TX.
Donor: The Gordon A. and Mary Cain Foundation.
Foundation type: Independent foundation.
Financial data (yr. ended 12/31/13): Assets, $16,355,951 (M); expenditures, $794,499; qualifying distributions, $665,500; giving activities include $665,500 for 64 grants (high: $68,000; low: $1,000).
Fields of interest: Museums; Education; Human services; Foundations (private grantmaking).
Limitations: Applications accepted. Giving primarily in Houston, TX; some funding also in Columbus, GA.
Application information: Do not use presentation or display binders, report covers, or folders. Application form required.
Initial approach: Proposal
Deadline(s): None
Board meeting date(s): Apr., Sept., and Dec.
Officers and Directors:* James D. Weaver,* Chair. and Pres.; John M. Sullivan,* Secy.-Treas.; Alyson A. Weaver; James K. Weaver; Sharyn A. Weaver.
EIN: 208483773
Selected grants: The following grants are a representative sample of this grantmaker's funding activity:
$125,000 to Houston Museum of Natural Science, Houston, TX, 2011.
$50,000 to Good Samaritan Foundation of Texas, Houston, TX, 2011.
$50,000 to National Infantry Foundation, Columbus, GA, 2011.
$50,000 to Saint Martins Episcopal Church, Houston, TX, 2011.
$25,000 to Citizens Against Government Waste, Washington, DC, 2011.
$20,000 to Depression and Bipolar Support Alliance - Greater Houston, Houston, TX, 2011.
$20,000 to Museum of Fine Arts, Houston, Houston, TX, 2011.
$20,000 to National Center for Policy Analysis, Dallas, TX, 2011.
$10,000 to American Heritage Education Foundation, Houston, TX, 2011.
$5,000 to Teach for America, Houston, TX, 2011.

8745
The Mary H. Cain Foundation ✧
8 Greenway Plz., Ste. 606
Houston, TX 77046-0801 (713) 840-7896
Contact: Margaret W. Weaver, Chair. and Pres.

Established in 2007 in TX.
Foundation type: Independent foundation.
Financial data (yr. ended 12/31/13): Assets, $17,454,610 (M); expenditures, $828,421; qualifying distributions, $716,100; giving activities include $716,000 for 15 grants (high: $150,000; low: $5,000).
Fields of interest: Education; Human services; Foundations (private grantmaking).
Limitations: Applications accepted. Giving primarily in Houston, TX. No grants to individuals.
Application information: Proposals in binders, report covers, or folders are not accepted. Application form required.
Initial approach: Formal proposal
Deadline(s): Nov. 1 for Dec. board meeting
Board meeting date(s): Dec.
Officers and Directors:* Margaret W. Weaver,* Chair. and Pres.; Pam Woods, Secy.; John M. Sullivan,* Treas.
EIN: 208483925
Selected grants: The following grants are a representative sample of this grantmaker's funding activity:
$150,000 to Institute for Rehabilitation and Research Foundation, Houston, TX, 2011.
$150,000 to Linville Foundation, Linville, NC, 2011.
$75,000 to Saint Thomas High School, Houston, TX, 2011.
$60,000 to Saint Martins Episcopal Church, Houston, TX, 2011.
$50,000 to Memorial Park Conservancy, Houston, TX, 2011.
$35,000 to Humble Independent School District, Humble, TX, 2011.
$25,000 to Sheldon Independent School District, Houston, TX, 2011.
$18,000 to W. Oscar Neuhaus Memorial Foundation, Bellaire, TX, 2011.
$12,500 to Lauren Rogers Museum of Art, Laurel, MS, 2011.
$7,500 to Westview School, Houston, TX, 2011.

8746
The Callaway Foundation ✧
(formerly Central Texas Scholarship Foundation)
605 W. Park Ave.
Temple, TX 76501-1641 (254) 771-7409
Contact: Kevin J. Koch, Tr.

Established in 2002 in TX.
Donor: J.L. Callaway, Jr.
Foundation type: Independent foundation.
Financial data (yr. ended 12/31/13): Assets, $11,887,791 (M); expenditures, $573,745; qualifying distributions, $505,054; giving activities include $473,601 for 19 grants (high: $200,000; low: $820).
Fields of interest: Higher education.

Limitations: Applications accepted. Giving primarily in TX. No grants to individuals.
Application information: Application form not required.
Initial approach: Proposal
Deadline(s): None
Trustee: Kevin J. Koch.
EIN: 331010957

8747
Harry S. and Isabel C. Cameron Foundation ✧
c/o Bank of America, N.A.
P.O. Box 831041
Dallas, TX 75283-1041
Contact: Diane Guiberteau

Established in 1966 in TX.
Donors: Isabel C. Cameron†; Charlotte Cameron†; Estelle Cameron Maloney†.
Foundation type: Independent foundation.
Financial data (yr. ended 06/30/13): Assets, $33,796,981 (M); gifts received, $374,707; expenditures, $1,546,998; qualifying distributions, $1,329,298; giving activities include $1,247,825 for 104 grants (high: $200,000; low: $325).
Purpose and activities: Giving primarily for education, health, and human services.
Fields of interest: Elementary/secondary education; Higher education; Hospitals (general); Health organizations, association; Human services; Children/youth, services; Catholic agencies & churches.
Type of support: General/operating support; Building/renovation; Equipment; Research.
Limitations: Applications accepted. Giving primarily in TX, with emphasis on Houston, Galveston, and The Woodlands. No support for organizations or programs involving abortion. No grants to individuals, or for operating support, endowment funds, or matching gifts; no loans.
Application information: Application form required.
Initial approach: Request guideline letter
Copies of proposal: 6
Deadline(s): 1 month prior to meeting date
Board meeting date(s): Mar., June, Sept., and Dec.
Final notification: 2 weeks after meeting date
Trustees: David Cameron; Sylvia Joan Cameron; Shirley Cameron Davis; Eva Langley; Frances Cameron Miller; Bank of America, N.A.
EIN: 746073312
Selected grants: The following grants are a representative sample of this grantmaker's funding activity:
$154,000 to Memorial Hermann Hospital System, Houston, TX, 2011.
$5,000 to Center Foundation, Houston, TX, 2011.

8748
Ina T. Campbell Trust ✧
c/o Bank of America, N.A.
P.O. Box 831041
Dallas, TX 75283-1041

Foundation type: Independent foundation.
Financial data (yr. ended 08/31/13): Assets, $12,239,469 (M); expenditures, $653,085; qualifying distributions, $589,866; giving activities include $552,692 for 2 grants (high: $276,346; low: $276,346).
Fields of interest: Museums (art); Education.
Limitations: Applications not accepted. Giving primarily in CA.
Application information: Unsolicited requests for funds not accpeted.
Trustee: Bank of America, N.A.
EIN: 956025008
Selected grants: The following grants are a representative sample of this grantmaker's funding activity:
$276,346 to Santa Barbara Museum of Art, Santa Barbara, CA, 2013. For unrestricted general support.

8749
Caris Foundation ✧
(formerly Halbert Walling Family Foundation)
55 Main St., Ste. 200
Colleyville, TX 76034-2956 (817) 514-7411
FAX: (817) 514-7404; Additional U.S. contact: Caris Foundation - Medical Missions: Dr. John Bailey, tel.: (817) 480-2156, e-mail: john.bailey@carisfoundation.org; International contacts: Caris Foundation International - Kenya, P.O. Box 1965, Malindi, Kenya, tel.: +254 734-014832, e-mails: Jim Reppart jim.reppart@carisfoundation.org, and Laura Reppart: laura.reppart@carisfoundation.org; Caris Foundation International - Haiti, e-mails: Nathaniel Segaren: nat.segaren@carisfoundation.org, and Tessa Lewis: tessa.lewis@carisfoundation.org; Main URL: http://www.carisfoundation.org

Established in 2002 in TX.
Donors: David D. Halbert; Kathryn Ann Halbert; JoAnn Walling Halbert Trust; JWH Testamentary Trust.
Foundation type: Independent foundation.
Financial data (yr. ended 12/31/12): Assets, $42,127,212 (M); gifts received, $494,495; expenditures, $2,318,118; qualifying distributions, $2,277,886; giving activities include $1,824,873 for 12 grants (high: $943,783; low: $500).
Purpose and activities: Giving primarily for aid to impoverished people in the areas of medical services, housing, nutrition, and to empower people to enhance the standard of living in their community.
Fields of interest: Higher education; Education; Human services; Christian agencies & churches; Economically disadvantaged.
Type of support: General/operating support.
Limitations: Applications not accepted. Giving primarily in TX; some funding also for projects in Belize, China, the Democratic Republic of Congo, Ecuador, Ethiopia, Guatemala, Haiti, Indonesia, Kenya, the Philippines, and Zambia. No grants to individuals.
Application information: Contributes only to pre-selected organizations.
Officers and Directors:* Kathryn Ann Halbert,* Pres. and Exec. Dir.; Christopher Harmon, V.P. and Secy.; Kristen S. Halbert,* Treas.; David D. Halbert; Patrick Halbert; Michael D. Halbert.
EIN: 460510753
Selected grants: The following grants are a representative sample of this grantmaker's funding activity:
$12,125 to Health Talents International, Searcy, AR, 2012. For Payments for General Support.

8750
The Carlson Foundation ✧
c/o Clint D. Carlson
2100 McKinney Ave., Ste. 1800
Dallas, TX 75201-6929

Established in 2002 in TX.
Donors: Clint D. Carlson; Nancy Carlson.
Foundation type: Independent foundation.
Financial data (yr. ended 12/31/13): Assets, $7,761,308 (M); expenditures, $2,037,295; qualifying distributions, $1,991,000; giving activities include $1,991,000 for 19 grants (high: $1,075,000; low: $5,000).
Purpose and activities: Giving primarily for the arts and education.
Fields of interest: Performing arts centers; Performing arts, ballet; Arts; Higher education; Zoos/zoological societies; Children/youth, services.
Limitations: Applications not accepted. Giving primarily in TX.
Application information: Unsolicited requests for funds not accepted.
Directors: Keith T. Anderson; Clint D. Carlson; Nancy Packer Carlson.
EIN: 270005700

8751
The Carruth Foundation Inc. ✧
2727 Allen Pkwy., Ste. 1570
Houston, TX 77019-2125

Established in 1994 in TX.
Donors: Allen H. Carruth; Ethel G. Carruth†.
Foundation type: Independent foundation.
Financial data (yr. ended 01/31/13): Assets, $12,287,996 (M); expenditures, $711,641; qualifying distributions, $589,462; giving activities include $585,000 for 8 grants (high: $330,000; low: $20,000).
Fields of interest: Museums (natural history); Child development, education; Elementary school/education; Education; Recreation, parks/playgrounds.
Limitations: Applications not accepted. Giving primarily in Houston, TX. No grants to individuals.
Application information: Contributes only to pre-selected organizations.
Officers: Brady F. Carruth, Pres.; William V.H. Clarke, Secy.-Treas.
Trustees: Gentry Lee; Alan Schubert.
EIN: 760439576
Selected grants: The following grants are a representative sample of this grantmaker's funding activity:
$187,500 to Houston Museum of Natural Science, Houston, TX, 2011.
$150,000 to Houston Zoo, Houston, TX, 2011.
$75,000 to Buffalo Bayou Partnership, Houston, TX, 2011.
$75,000 to Parish School, Houston, TX, 2011. For scholarships.
$25,000 to Menil Foundation, Houston, TX, 2011. For operations.
$15,000 to Museum of Fine Arts, Houston, Houston, TX, 2011.

8752
Amon G. Carter Foundation ✧
201 Main St., Ste. 1945
Fort Worth, TX 76102-3114 (817) 332-2783
Contact: John H. Robinson, Exec. V.P., Grant Admin.
FAX: (817) 332-2787; E-mail: jrobinson@agcf.org; Application address: P.O. Box 1036, Fort Worth, TX 76101; Main URL: http://www.agcf.org/
Grants List: http://www.agcf.org/documents/Grants_2009.pdf

Incorporated in 1945 in TX.
Donors: Amon G. Carter†; N.B. Carter†; Star-Telegram Employees Fund; Carter Foundation Production Co.
Foundation type: Independent foundation.
Financial data (yr. ended 12/31/13): Assets, $599,861,530 (M); expenditures, $32,829,625; qualifying distributions, $30,362,018; giving activities include $25,056,249 for 185 grants (high: $9,576,239; low: $780).
Purpose and activities: Grants primarily for arts, education, health care and medical services, social service and youth agencies, programs for youth and the elderly, and civic and community endeavors that enhance the quality of life. The foundation sponsors and largely supports the Amon Carter Museum.
Fields of interest: Museums; Performing arts; Arts; Higher education; Education; Hospitals (general); Health care; Human services; Youth, services; Aging, centers/services; Government/public administration; Aging.
Type of support: General/operating support; Continuing support; Annual campaigns; Capital campaigns; Building/renovation; Equipment; Land acquisition; Endowments; Emergency funds; Program development; Professorships; Seed money; Scholarship funds; Research; Matching/challenge support.
Limitations: Applications accepted. Giving largely restricted to Fort Worth and Tarrant County, TX. No grants to individuals, or for ongoing operating budgets, deficit financing, publications, or conferences; no loans.
Publications: Application guidelines; Financial statement; Grants list; Program policy statement.
Application information: Grants outside local geographic area usually initiated by board. The foundation does not currently accept grant applications via e-mail. Application form not required.
Initial approach: Letter
Copies of proposal: 1
Deadline(s): None
Board meeting date(s): Feb., May and Nov.
Final notification: Within 10 days of board meeting
Officers and Directors:* Mark L. Johnson,* Pres.; W. Patrick Harris, Exec. V.P., Investments; John H. Robinson, Exec. V.P., Grant Admin.; Robert W. Brown, M.D.*, V.P.; Sheila B. Johnson,* Secy.; Kate Johnson,* Treas.; Kathy A. King, Cont.
Number of staff: 3 full-time professional; 2 full-time support.
EIN: 756000331
Selected grants: The following grants are a representative sample of this grantmaker's funding activity:
$8,118,244 to Amon Carter Museum of Western Art, Amon Carter Museum of American Art, Fort Worth, TX, 2012. For operating support.
$3,000,000 to Texas Christian University, Fort Worth, TX, 2012. For stadium renovation.
$750,000 to Ronald McDonald House of Fort Worth, Fort Worth, TX, 2012. For Capital support.
$500,000 to All Saints Episcopal School of Fort Worth, Fort Worth, TX, 2012. For Capital support.
$125,000 to Fort Worth Chamber Development Foundation, Fort Worth, TX, 2012. For park enhancements.
$100,000 to Fort Worth Symphony Orchestra Association, Fort Worth, TX, 2012. For operating support.
$50,000 to Christs Haven for Children, Keller, TX, 2012. For facility improvement.
$25,000 to Performing Arts Fort Worth, Fort Worth, TX, 2012. For Children's Educational Program.
$25,000 to Southwestern Baptist Theological Seminary, Fort Worth, TX, 2012. For Event underwriting.
$20,000 to Texas Christian University, Fort Worth, TX, 2012. For Special program.
$10,000 to Little League Baseball, Rookie League Baseball, Fort Worth, TX, 2012. For special program.

8753
Amon G. Carter Star-Telegram Employees Fund ✧
306 W. 7th St., Ste. 440
Fort Worth, TX 76102-0480 (817) 332-3535
Contact: Nenetta Carter Tatum, Pres.

Established in 1945 in TX.
Donors: Fort Worth Star-Telegram; Amon G. Carter†; KXAS-TV; WBAP Radio.
Foundation type: Company-sponsored foundation.
Financial data (yr. ended 04/30/13): Assets, $32,170,263 (M); expenditures, $1,360,859; qualifying distributions, $1,306,825; giving activities include $886,500 for 59 grants (high: $250,000; low: $2,500), and $301,107 for 200 grants to individuals (high: $5,000; low: $94).
Purpose and activities: The foundation supports organizations involved with arts and culture, education, health, breast cancer, housing development, and human services and awards pension, medical, and hardship assistance to employees and scholarships to children of employees.
Fields of interest: Museums; Performing arts; Performing arts, opera; Secondary school/education; Higher education; Education; Health care, blood supply; Health care; Breast cancer; Housing/shelter, development; Camp Fire; YM/YWCAs & YM/YWHAs; Children, services; Homeless, human services; Human services.
Type of support: General/operating support; Employee-related scholarships; Grants to individuals.
Limitations: Applications accepted. Giving primarily in Arlington, Bedford, Burleson, Cleburne, and Fort Worth, TX. No grants to individuals (except for employee-related scholarships and employee assistance grants).
Application information: Application form required.
Initial approach: Letter, One copy of Proposal
Copies of proposal: 1
Deadline(s): None
Officers: Nenetta Carter Tatum, Pres.; Mark L. Johnson, V.P.; John H. Robinson, Secy.-Treas.
Number of staff: 1 part-time professional; 1 part-time support.
EIN: 756014850
Selected grants: The following grants are a representative sample of this grantmaker's funding activity:
$5,000 to Volunteer Center of North Texas, Dallas, TX, 2011.

8754
The Don-Kay-Clay Cash Foundation ✧
5201 18th Pl.
Lubbock, TX 79416
Contact: Roy Don Cash, Pres.

Established in 1997 in UT.
Donors: Roy Don Cash; Sondra Kay Cash; Triple C Securities & Investment Ltd.
Foundation type: Independent foundation.
Financial data (yr. ended 12/31/13): Assets, $25,029,441 (M); expenditures, $1,262,622; qualifying distributions, $1,246,787; giving activities include $1,210,450 for 22+ grants (high: $850,000).
Fields of interest: Arts; Higher education; Health organizations, association; Human services; Foundations (public).
Type of support: General/operating support.
Limitations: Applications accepted. Giving primarily in Lubbock, TX. No grants to individuals.
Application information: Application form required.
Initial approach: Letter
Deadline(s): None
Officers: Roy Don Cash, Pres.; Clay Collin Cash, V.P.; Sondra Kay Cash, Secy.-Treas.
Director: Ashley B. Cash.
EIN: 841381970
Selected grants: The following grants are a representative sample of this grantmaker's funding activity:
$126,500 to Ranching Heritage Association, Lubbock, TX, 2011.
$17,500 to Trinity School of Midland, Midland, TX, 2011.
$7,500 to Lubbock Symphony Orchestra, Lubbock, TX, 2011.
$5,800 to Junior League of Midland, Midland, TX, 2011.
$2,000 to Big Brothers Big Sisters of Midland, Midland, TX, 2011.
$1,000 to American Cancer Society, Lubbock, TX, 2011.
$1,000 to Buckner Foundation, Dallas, TX, 2011.

8755
Castex Foundation ✧
333 Clay St., Rm. 2000
Houston, TX 77002-2569

Established in 2001 in TX.
Donors: John R. Stoika; Lisa A. Stoika.
Foundation type: Independent foundation.
Financial data (yr. ended 12/31/13): Assets, $14,313,156 (M); gifts received, $800,000; expenditures, $1,652,709; qualifying distributions, $1,615,045; giving activities include $1,615,045 for 8 grants (high: $1,009,450; low: $20,000).
Fields of interest: Human services; Children/youth, services.
Limitations: Applications not accepted. Giving primarily in Houston, TX. No grants to individuals.
Application information: Unsolicited requests for funds not accepted.
Officers: John R. Stoika, Pres.; Ronald E. Rinard, V.P.; Laura P. Holeman, Secy.-Treas.
EIN: 760699169

8756
Castle Hills Schools Foundation, Inc. ✧
2520 King Arthur Blvd., Ste. 200
Lewisville, TX 75056

Donors: Castle Hills Development Corp.; Weekley Homes, L.P.; Wyndsor Custom Homes; Highland Homes; Darling Homes; Lewis and Early; Landstar Homes; Shelly Malone Custom Builders; Garvey Homes; American Legend Homes; David Weekley Homes; Sanders; Hungtington Homes; Mercedes; Shaddock/Sotherby Homes; Bright Realty, LLC.
Foundation type: Independent foundation.
Financial data (yr. ended 12/31/12): Assets, $2,386,720 (M); gifts received, $715,858; expenditures, $1,023,776; qualifying distributions, $997,267; giving activities include $990,189 for 22 grants (high: $640,000; low: $189).
Purpose and activities: Giving primarily for education, including to Catholic and Protestant religious schools.
Fields of interest: Education.
Type of support: Scholarships—to individuals.
Limitations: Applications not accepted. Giving primarily in TX; some emphasis on Dallas. No grants to.
Application information: Unsolicited requests for funds not accepted.
Officers: Christopher R. Bright, Pres. and Treas.; Clay V.N. Bright, V.P.
Directors: Carol Bright Hunter; Margaret Bright Vonder Hoya.
EIN: 752732689

8757
CEMEX Foundation ✧
(formerly Southdown Foundation)
c/o Cemex Inc.
P.O. Box 1500
Houston, TX 77251-1500 (713) 650-6200
Application address: c/o CEMEX Inc., 929 Gessner Rd., Ste. 1900, Houston, TX 77024

Established in 1993.
Donors: Medusa Corp.; CEMEX Corp.
Foundation type: Company-sponsored foundation.
Financial data (yr. ended 12/31/12): Assets, $6,145,404 (M); expenditures, $505,057; qualifying distributions, $497,888; giving activities include $497,888 for 16+ grants (high: $105,000).
Purpose and activities: The foundation supports organizations involved with education, birth defects, human services, and the masonry trade.
Fields of interest: Education; Human services.
Type of support: General/operating support.
Limitations: Applications accepted. Giving primarily on FL, NY, and OH. No grants to individuals.
Application information: Application form required.
Initial approach: Letter
Deadline(s): None
Officers: Karl H. Watson, Jr., Chair. and Pres.; Mike F. Egan, Secy.; Frank E. Angelle, Treas.
EIN: 346505254

8758
CFP Foundation ✧
11 Greenway Plz., No. 2600
Houston, TX 77046-1100

Established in 1997 in TX.
Donors: Gary T. Crum; Sylvie P. Crum.
Foundation type: Independent foundation.
Financial data (yr. ended 12/31/13): Assets, $44,570,907 (M); gifts received, $7,874,500; expenditures, $1,844,960; qualifying distributions, $1,477,872; giving activities include $1,300,000 for 61 grants (high: $100,000; low: $2,500).
Purpose and activities: Giving primarily for education.
Fields of interest: Arts; Elementary/secondary education; Higher education; Education; Human services; Foundations (community).
Type of support: General/operating support; Continuing support; Annual campaigns; Capital campaigns; Building/renovation.
Limitations: Applications not accepted. Giving primarily in TX.
Application information: Unsolicited requests for funds not accepted.
Officers: Gary T. Crum, Pres. and Treas.; Sylvie P. Crum, Exec. V.P.; Carol L. Drawe, V.P. and Secy.
EIN: 760537479
Selected grants: The following grants are a representative sample of this grantmaker's funding activity:
$100,000 to Ex-Students Association of the University of Texas, Austin, TX, 2011. For general support.
$100,000 to Saint Johns School, Houston, TX, 2011. For general support.
$100,000 to Southern Methodist University, Dallas, TX, 2011. For general support.
$25,000 to Aspen Community Foundation, Aspen, CO, 2011. For general support.
$25,000 to Chinquapin School, Highlands, TX, 2011. For general support.
$20,000 to Casa de Esperanza de los Ninos, Houston, TX, 2011. For general support.
$20,000 to Dress for Success Houston, Houston, TX, 2011. For general support.
$15,000 to Saint Johns School, Houston, TX, 2011. For general support.
$15,000 to United Way of Greater Houston, Houston, TX, 2011. For general support.
$12,500 to Houston Hospice and Palliative Care System, Houston, TX, 2011. For general support.

8759
The CH Foundation ✧
P.O. Box 94038
Lubbock, TX 79493-4038 (806) 792-0448
Contact: Kay Sanford, Exec. Dir.
FAX: (806) 792-7824; E-mail for Kay Sanford: ksanford@chfoundation.com; Main URL: http://www.chfoundationlubbock.com/

Established in 1976 in TX.
Donor: Christine DeVitt†.
Foundation type: Independent foundation.
Financial data (yr. ended 12/31/13): Assets, $200,192,789 (M); expenditures, $11,793,104; qualifying distributions, $9,151,769; giving activities include $8,967,142 for 107 grants (high: $2,000,000; low: $3,500).
Purpose and activities: To significantly improve human services and cultural and educational opportunities for the residents of the South Plains of Texas.
Fields of interest: Museums; Elementary/secondary education; Higher education; Medical school/education; Nursing school/education; Hospitals (general); Crime/violence prevention, domestic violence; Human services; Aging; Disabilities, people with; Women; Economically disadvantaged.
Type of support: General/operating support; Annual campaigns; Capital campaigns; Building/renovation; Equipment; Publication; Curriculum development; Scholarship funds; Research; Matching/challenge support.
Limitations: Applications accepted. Giving primarily in Lubbock, TX and surrounding counties. No grants to individuals.
Publications: Application guidelines; Grants list.
Application information: Application guidelines available on foundation web site. Application form not required.
Initial approach: Proposal
Copies of proposal: 1
Deadline(s): May 1
Board meeting date(s): As necessary
Final notification: July
Officers and Trustees:* Kathy Gilbreath,* V.P.; Don Graf,* Secy.; Kevin G. McMahon,* Treas.; Kay Sanford,* Exec. Dir.; Carol McWhorter.
Number of staff: 1 full-time professional; 1 part-time professional.
EIN: 751534816
Selected grants: The following grants are a representative sample of this grantmaker's funding activity:
$2,019,918 to Texas Tech Foundation, Lubbock, TX, 2012. For Tier 1 Advancement.
$227,436 to United Way, Lubbock Area, Lubbock, TX, 2012. For operating expenses.
$210,000 to YWCA of Lubbock, Lubbock, TX, 2012. For renovation of exterior of land complex.
$203,289 to Covenant Health System Foundation, Lubbock, TX, 2012. For 1st of 2 years, cardiac catheterization.
$150,000 to Chamber of Commerce, Lubbock, Lubbock, TX, 2012. For Performing Arts Center A.
$110,000 to United Way, Lubbock Area, Lubbock, TX, 2012. For Annual Campaign.
$100,000 to Texas Tech University Health Sciences Center, Lubbock, TX, 2012. Toward IVIS Lumina XR Series II.
$81,050 to South Plains College Foundation, Levelland, TX, 2012. For 1St of 3 Years, Retain Nursing Progr.
$61,500 to Museum of Texas Tech University Association, Lubbock, TX, 2012. For docent program.
$50,000 to Salvation Army of Lubbock, Lubbock, TX, 2012. For 1st of 3 years - Red Shield Transition.

8760
Chaparral Foundation ✧
P.O. Box 130
Midland, TX 79702-0130 (4432) 684-5591
Application address: c/o H. Tevis Herd, Pres., 413 W. Wall St., Ste. 300, Midland, TX 79701, tel.: (432) 684-5591

Established in 1997 in TX.
Donors: J. Harvey Herd; Harriet D. Herd†; J.H. Herd 2005 Charitable Trust.
Foundation type: Independent foundation.
Financial data (yr. ended 12/31/12): Assets, $15,951,183 (M); gifts received, $272,805; expenditures, $682,682; qualifying distributions, $629,040; giving activities include $629,040 for 39 grants (high: $110,000; low: $1,000).
Fields of interest: Higher education; Human services; Children/youth, services; Foundations (private grantmaking).

Type of support: General/operating support.
Limitations: Applications accepted. Giving primarily in Midland, TX.
Application information: Application form required.
Initial approach: Proposal
Deadline(s): May 15 and Nov. 15
Officers: H. Tevis Herd, Pres.; Dan Herd, Secy.-Treas.
EIN: 752707574

8761
Mark A. Chapman Foundation ✧
c/o Lois Krenek
1205 Silliman St.
Sealy, TX 77474-3513

Established in 2001 in TX.
Donors: Mark A. Chapman; Broughton Petroleum Inc.; Otter Creek, LLC; Mark A. Chapman Royalty; Mark A. Chapman Nebraska Land.
Foundation type: Operating foundation.
Financial data (yr. ended 07/31/13): Assets, $81,813 (M); gifts received, $1,412,765; expenditures, $1,557,735; qualifying distributions, $1,557,118; giving activities include $1,557,118 for 1 grant.
Purpose and activities: Giving primarily for higher education, including scholarships; funding also for medical research, and children and social services.
Fields of interest: Arts; Higher education; Environment; Animal population control; Medical research, institute; Human services; Children/youth, services; Christian agencies & churches.
Type of support: General/operating support; Scholarships—to individuals.
Limitations: Applications not accepted. Giving primarily in TX; some giving in KS.
Application information: Unsolicited requests for funds not accepted.
Officer: Lois Krenek, Mgr.
Director: Mark A. Chapman.
EIN: 364460345
Selected grants: The following grants are a representative sample of this grantmaker's funding activity:
$485,000 to Kansas State University Foundation, Manhattan, KS, 2011.
$175,000 to Kansas State University Foundation, Manhattan, KS, 2011.
$45,000 to Kansas State University Foundation, Manhattan, KS, 2011.
$40,000 to Kansas State University Foundation, Manhattan, KS, 2011.
$25,000 to Kansas State University Foundation, Manhattan, KS, 2011.
$13,000 to Kansas State University Foundation, Manhattan, KS, 2011.
$5,000 to Kansas State University Foundation, Manhattan, KS, 2011.
$2,000 to Kansas State University Foundation, Manhattan, KS, 2011.

8762
The Chasdrew Fund ✧
130 E. John Carpenter Fwy.
Irving, TX 75062
Facebook: https://www.facebook.com/sharer/sharer.php?u=http%3A%2F%2Fchasdrew.org%2Fcontact%2F&t=Contact
Twitter: http://twitter.com/intent/tweet?source=webclient&text=Contact+-+http%3A%2F%2Fchasdrew.org%2Fcontact%2F

Established in 1997 in MD.
Donor: Julie Jensen.
Foundation type: Operating foundation.
Financial data (yr. ended 12/31/11): Assets, $3,325,472 (M); expenditures, $940,000; qualifying distributions, $920,767; giving activities include $750,830 for 7+ grants (high: $455,000).
Fields of interest: Human services; LGBTQ.
Type of support: Technical assistance.
Limitations: Applications not accepted. No grants to individuals.
Publications: Occasional report; Program policy statement.
Application information: Contributes only to pre-selected organizations.
Officer and Trustees:* Julie Jensen,* Chair.; Scott Letier; Jane Smith.
Number of staff: None.
EIN: 526854447

8763
Christian Mission Concerns ✧
P.O. Box 20815
Waco, TX 76702-0815

Established in 1984 in TX.
Donors: Paul Piper, Sr.; Paul Piper, Jr.; Kent Reynolds; Mrs. Kent Reynolds.
Foundation type: Independent foundation.
Financial data (yr. ended 12/31/13): Assets, $17,199,670 (M); expenditures, $1,019,885; qualifying distributions, $894,779; giving activities include $789,900 for 64 grants (high: $100,000; low: $1,000).
Purpose and activities: Giving primarily to Baptist churches and organizations.
Fields of interest: Human services; Protestant agencies & churches.
Type of support: Program-related investments/loans.
Limitations: Applications not accepted. Giving primarily in Waco, TX. No grants to individuals.
Application information: Contributes only to pre-selected organizations.
Officers and Directors:* Kent Reynolds,* Pres.; Paul Piper, Jr.,* V.P.; Jonathan Reynolds,* Secy.; J.D. Hudson,* Treas.
EIN: 742317938

8764
The Robert & Jane Cizik Foundation ✧
8839 Harness Creek Ln.
Houston, TX 77024-7044

Established in 1997 in TX.
Donors: Robert Cizik; Jane Morin Cizik.
Foundation type: Independent foundation.
Financial data (yr. ended 12/31/13): Assets, $1,447,713 (M); gifts received, $1,000,000; expenditures, $718,040; qualifying distributions, $667,780; giving activities include $667,780 for 12 grants (high: $305,000; low: $1,000).
Fields of interest: Arts; Higher education; Animals/wildlife; Women.
Limitations: Applications not accepted. Giving primarily in Houston, TX. No grants to individuals.
Application information: Contributes only to pre-selected organizations.
Directors: Jane Morin Cizik; Paula J. Cizik; Robert Cizik.
Number of staff: 1 part-time professional.
EIN: 760528683

8765
The Clayton Fund, Inc. ✧
c/o Chase Bank of Texas, Inc.
707 Travis St., 11th Fl.
Houston, TX 77252-3232 (713) 216-1453

Trust established in 1952 in TX.
Donors: William L. Clayton‡; Susan V. Clayton‡.
Foundation type: Independent foundation.
Financial data (yr. ended 12/31/12): Assets, $38,276,073 (M); expenditures, $2,287,227; qualifying distributions, $1,933,812; giving activities include $1,883,525 for 50 grants (high: $200,000; low: $5,000).
Purpose and activities: Giving primarily for aid to the needy, especially children, the environment, family planning, education, agriculture, and arts and culture.
Fields of interest: Arts; Elementary/secondary education; Higher education; Education; Environment, natural resources; Reproductive health, family planning; Health organizations, association; Human services; Children/youth, services; Foundations (private grantmaking).
Type of support: General/operating support; Continuing support; Building/renovation; Program development; Scholarship funds.
Limitations: Applications accepted. Giving primarily in TX; some funding also in MD and NY. No grants to individuals; generally no giving for building or endowment funds.
Publications: Application guidelines.
Application information: Applications should include a 1-page summary of the request and a narrative of 3-5 typewritten pages. Application form not required.
Initial approach: Proposal
Copies of proposal: 3
Deadline(s): Feb. 1, June 1, and Oct. 1
Board meeting date(s): Mar., June, Sept., and Dec.
Final notification: In writing
Officers: William L. Garwood, Jr., Pres.; William Baker, V.P.
Trustee: Burdine C. Johnson.
Number of staff: 1 full-time professional; 1 full-time support.
EIN: 760285764

8766
Clements Foundation ✧ ☆
1901 N. Akard St.
Dallas, TX 75201-2305 (214) 549-3175
Contact: Pauline S. Neuhoff, Pres.

Established in 1968 in TX.
Donors: B. Gill Clements Foundation; Pauline Austin Neuhoff Foundation; New Convnant Foundation; Catherine Elizabeth Clements; Bill Clements Foundation; Gigi Clements Foundation; Margaret Gill Clements Napier; George E. Eay III Foundation; William P. Clements, Jr.‡.
Foundation type: Independent foundation.

Financial data (yr. ended 12/31/13): Assets, $31,254,240 (M); gifts received, $11,058,788; expenditures, $1,787,525; qualifying distributions, $1,036,493; giving activities include $1,036,493 for 5 grants (high: $627,200; low: $293).
Purpose and activities: Support primarily for youth groups and higher education; giving also for cultural institutions. The foundation supports courses of study involving the history of the state of TX, the greater Southwest, and related matters of historical value.
Fields of interest: Museums; History/archaeology; Historic preservation/historical societies; Arts; Elementary/secondary education; Higher education; Theological school/education; Health care; Human services; Children/youth, services.
Type of support: General/operating support.
Limitations: Applications accepted. Giving primarily in the Dallas, TX, area. No grants to individuals.
Application information: Application form required.
Initial approach: Proposal
Deadline(s): None
Officers: Pauline S. Neuhoff, Pres.; Nancy Clements Seay, V.P.; Margaret Napier, Secy.; George E. Seay III, Treas.
EIN: 756065076

8767
The B. Gill Clements Foundation ✧ ☆
1901 N. Akard St.
Dallas, TX 75201-2305

Established in 2002 in TX.
Donor: Pauline G. Sullivan Trust.
Foundation type: Independent foundation.
Financial data (yr. ended 12/31/13): Assets, $14,841,924 (M); expenditures, $759,455; qualifying distributions, $673,419; giving activities include $641,500 for 26 grants (high: $130,000; low: $500).
Purpose and activities: Giving primarily for human services, and for health care, including a children's hospital.
Fields of interest: Hospitals (specialty); Health care; Human services.
Type of support: General/operating support; Capital campaigns.
Limitations: Applications not accepted. Giving in the U.S., with emphasis on TX. No grants to individuals.
Application information: Unsolicited requests for funds not accepted.
Officers and Trustees:* Patricia L. Clements,* Pres.; Margaret Gill Clements Napier,* V.P.; Frank Martin Wood,* Secy.; William Mems Rohde, Jr.,* Treas.
EIN: 731645566

8768
Coastal Bend Community Foundation ✧
615 N. Upper Broadway, Ste. 1950
Corpus Christi, TX 78401 (361) 882-9745
Contact: Karen W. Selim, C.E.O.
FAX: (361) 882-2865;
E-mail: kselim@cbcfoundation.org; Main URL: http://www.cbcfoundation.org
Scholarship inquiry e-mail: kwesson@cbcfoundation.org

Established in 1981 in TX.
Foundation type: Community foundation.
Financial data (yr. ended 12/31/12): Assets, $52,932,112 (M); gifts received, $5,811,192; expenditures, $4,643,473; giving activities include $1,944,927 for 80 grants (high: $91,130), and $1,034,507 for 997 grants to individuals.
Purpose and activities: The foundation seeks to help meet the charitable and educational needs and enhance and improve the quality of life in the Coastal Bend area of Texas through grants to charitable organizations; serve a wide variety donors by providing a vehicle for the establishment of various types of funds designed to serve their charitable wishes; exercise leadership on charitable issues and advance the cause of philanthropy throughout the area; and solicit others to partner with the foundation to provide for increased giving to address the ever-growing needs of the Coastal Bend.
Fields of interest: Museums; History/archaeology; Arts; Higher education; Adult education—literacy, basic skills & GED; Libraries/library science; Education, reading; Education; Environment; Animal welfare; Zoos/zoological societies; Hospitals (general); Health care, patient services; Health care; Substance abuse, services; Alcoholism; Diabetes; Food services; Food banks; Housing/shelter; Disasters, preparedness/services; Safety/disasters; Recreation, parks/playgrounds; Children/youth, services; Family services; Aging, centers/services; Homeless, human services; Human services; Community/economic development; Children/youth; Aging; Economically disadvantaged; Homeless.
Type of support: General/operating support; Equipment; Program development; Seed money; Fellowships; Scholarship funds.
Limitations: Applications accepted. Giving limited to Aransas, Bee, Jim Wells, Kleberg, Nueces, Refugio, and San Patricio counties, TX. No support for religious purposes, athletic teams, school groups, school districts, or academic or scientific research projects. No grants to individuals (except for scholarships), or for annual fund drives, social or special events, debt retirement, travel expenses, office or playground equipment (unless for efficiency or safety), or trips.
Publications: Application guidelines; Annual report; Grants list; Informational brochure.
Application information: Visit foundation web site for application guidelines. Application form required.
Initial approach: Complete application online
Copies of proposal: 1
Deadline(s): June 15
Board meeting date(s): Feb., May, Aug., and Nov.
Officers and Directors:* Dr. Robert Furgason,* Chair.; Jean Claire Turcotte,* Vice-Chair.; Karen W. Selim,* Pres. and C.E.O.; Leah Pagan Olivarri,* Secy.; Kathleen M. White,* Treas.; Larry D. Aduddell; Jan G. Anderson; Judge Bobby Galvan; Ralph Gomez; Joe Henkel; Jonathan M. Hornblower; Susan E. Hutchinson; Nancy Bellows Johnson; Rumaldo Z. Juarez, Ph.D.; Omar J. Leal; Robert W. Maxwell; Lou Adele May; Laura M. Miller; Fred J. Nemec; Henry Nuss; Karen O'Connor Urban; Jon Whatley; William B. Whitworth; Clare Atkinson Wonders; Jack W. Wright.
Number of staff: 3 full-time professional; 1 part-time professional; 1 full-time support.
EIN: 742190039

8769
Elizabeth Huth Coates Charitable Foundation of 1992 ✧
P.O. Box 17001
San Antonio, TX 78217-0001
Main URL: http://broadwaybank.com/wealthmanagement/FoundationElizabethHuthCoates.html

Established in 1993 in TX.
Donor: Elizabeth Huth Coates‡.
Foundation type: Independent foundation.
Financial data (yr. ended 12/31/12): Assets, $35,238,082 (M); expenditures, $1,779,761; qualifying distributions, $1,686,364; giving activities include $1,645,400 for 48 grants (high: $263,700; low: $4,900).
Purpose and activities: Giving primarily for the arts and education.
Fields of interest: Museums; Arts; Higher education; Education; Zoos/zoological societies; Medical research, institute; Protestant agencies & churches; Catholic agencies & churches.
Type of support: General/operating support; Continuing support; Annual campaigns; Capital campaigns; Building/renovation; Program development; Curriculum development; Research.
Limitations: Applications accepted. Giving primarily in San Antonio, TX. No grants to individuals.
Application information: See foundation website for complete application guidelines. Application form required.
Board meeting date(s): Feb.
Distribution Committee: Betty Ann Stieren Kelso; Amy Stieren.
Trustee: Broadway National Bank.
Number of staff: 2
EIN: 746399782

8770
The Cockrell Foundation ✧
1000 Main St., Ste. 3250
Houston, TX 77002-7348 (713) 209-7500
Contact: M. Nancy Williams, Exec. V.P.
E-mail: foundation@cockrell.com; Main URL: http://www.cockrell.com/foundation

Trust established in 1957 in TX; incorporated in 1966.
Donors: Dula Cockrell‡; Ernest Cockrell, Jr.‡; Virginia H. Cockrell‡.
Foundation type: Independent foundation.
Financial data (yr. ended 12/31/12): Assets, $154,737,146 (M); expenditures, $7,952,323; qualifying distributions, $6,477,315; giving activities include $6,412,088 for 50 grants (high: $2,557,805; low: $500).
Purpose and activities: The foundation gives only one higher education grant to the University of Texas Engineering Foundation. Giving primarily for cultural programs, social services, youth services, and health care.
Fields of interest: Museums; Arts; Higher education; Hospitals (general); Crime/violence prevention, domestic violence; Human services; Children/youth, services; Christian agencies & churches; Youth; Aging; Disabilities, people with; Women; Economically disadvantaged.
Type of support: General/operating support; Annual campaigns; Capital campaigns; Building/renovation; Land acquisition; Endowments; Program development; Professorships; Fellowships;

Scholarship funds; Research; Matching/challenge support.
Limitations: Applications accepted. Giving primarily in Houston, TX. No support for medical or scientific research projects. No grants to individuals, or mass appeal solicitations.
Publications: Application guidelines; Grants list; Informational brochure (including application guidelines).
Application information: The foundation does not accept grant requests via fax or e-mail. Application form not required.
Initial approach: Brief proposal
Copies of proposal: 1
Deadline(s): None
Board meeting date(s): Spring and fall
Final notification: 6 weeks
Officers and Directors:* Ernest H. Cockrell,* Pres.; M. Nancy Williams, Exec. V.P.; Milton T. Graves,* V.P. and Assoc. Dir.; David A. Cockrell; Ernest D. Cockrell II; Janet S. Cockrell; Carol Cockrell Curran; Richard B. Curran; J. Webb Jennings; Laura Jennings Turner.
EIN: 746076993
Selected grants: The following grants are a representative sample of this grantmaker's funding activity:
$2,557,805 to University of Texas Engineering Foundation, Austin, TX, 2012. For endowment for scholarships and professorships.
$653,344 to M. D. Anderson Cancer Center Outreach Corporation, Houston, TX, 2012. For endowment and physician-scientist program.
$628,344 to Methodist Hospital Foundation, Houston, TX, 2012. For Virginia and Ernest Cockrell Junior Center for Advanced Therapeutics.
$411,229 to Houston Museum of Natural Science, Houston, TX, 2012. For endowment, gems and minerals, and Cockrell Butterfly Center.
$358,000 to Boy Scouts of America, Sam Houston Area Council, Houston, TX, 2012. For general support.
$250,000 to Greater Houston Community Foundation, Houston, TX, 2012. For general support.
$250,000 to Greater Houston Community Foundation, Houston, TX, 2012. For Reasoning Mind.
$250,000 to Greater Houston Community Foundation, Houston, TX, 2012. For general support.
$205,615 to Houston Museum of Natural Science, Houston, TX, 2012. For endowment, facilities, and Virginia and Ernest Cockrell Junior Opp Fund.
$25,000 to Methodist Hospital Foundation, Houston, TX, 2012. For Virginia and Ernest Cockrell Junior Center for Advanced Therapeutics.

8771
Calvert K. Collins Family Foundation, Inc. ✧
(formerly Calvert K. Collins Foundation, Inc.)
c/o Kuprion-Thomas, PC
8510 N. Central Expwy., Ste. 1900
Dallas, TX 75206
E-mail: sthomas@kuprionthomas.com; Main URL: http://www.calvertkcollins.com

Incorporated in 1962 in TX.
Donor: Carr P. Collins.
Foundation type: Independent foundation.
Financial data (yr. ended 12/31/12): Assets, $16,644,807 (M); expenditures, $985,673; qualifying distributions, $831,687; giving activities include $686,551 for 34 grants (high: $246,551; low: $200), and $116,492 for foundation-administered programs.
Purpose and activities: Giving primarily to federated giving programs and for philanthropy; funding also for the arts, education, and children, youth, and social services. The foundation also has an investment in an 1872 registered historic property, the House of the Seasons, in Jefferson, TX. The foundation is involved in preserving this historic property, promoting and increasing the visibility of Jefferson, TX, and other historic homes, buildings and monuments, while providing information and education to the public regarding the historic city of Jefferson.
Fields of interest: Historic preservation/historical societies; Arts; Elementary/secondary school reform; Higher education; Human services; Children/youth, services; Community/economic development.
Type of support: General/operating support; Building/renovation; Research.
Limitations: Applications not accepted. Giving primarily in Dallas, TX; some funding also in Jefferson, TX. No grants to individuals.
Application information: Contributes only to pre-selected organizations.
Board meeting date(s): April
Officers and Directors:* Calvert K. Collins,* Pres.; Sandra R. Kuprion-Thomas, V.P. and Secy.; Richard H. Collins,* V.P. and Treas.
Number of staff: 1 full-time professional.
EIN: 756011615

8772
The James M. Collins Foundation ✧
8115 Preston Rd., Ste. 680
Dallas, TX 75225-6335 (214) 691-2032

Established in 1964 in TX.
Donors: James M. Collins†; Michael Collins; Dorothy Dann Collins Torbert; Dorothy Collins Weaver.
Foundation type: Independent foundation.
Financial data (yr. ended 12/31/13): Assets, $18,329,401 (M); expenditures, $832,683; qualifying distributions, $803,678; giving activities include $803,678 for 131 grants (high: $100,000; low: $100).
Fields of interest: Museums; Performing arts centers; Arts; Higher education; Health organizations, association; Human services; Salvation Army; United Ways and Federated Giving Programs.
Limitations: Applications accepted. Giving primarily in TX. No grants to individuals; no loans.
Application information: Application form not required.
Initial approach: Proposal
Deadline(s): None
Officers: Dorothy Dann Collins Torbert, Pres.; Michael J. Collins, V.P.; Dorothy Collins Weaver, Secy.
EIN: 756040743

8773
Communities Foundation of Texas, Inc. ✧
5500 Caruth Haven Ln.
Dallas, TX 75225-8146 (214) 750-4222
FAX: (214) 750-4210;
E-mail: donorservices@cftexas.org; Grant inquiry e-mail: grants@cftexas.org; Main URL: http://www.cftexas.org
Facebook: https://www.facebook.com/CFTexas
Twitter: https://twitter.com/givewisely
Scholarship enquiry e-mail: scholarships@cftexas.org

Established in 1953 in TX; incorporated in 1960.
Foundation type: Community foundation.
Financial data (yr. ended 06/30/13): Assets, $982,331,000 (M); gifts received, $120,500,000; expenditures, $103,454,000; giving activities include $82,493,000 for grants.
Purpose and activities: CFT stimulates creative solutions to key challenges in the community. The foundation thoughtfully and effectively supports diverse donors and grantees by providing exemplary service and by demonstrating accountability, improving lives through an unwavering commitment to lasting impact. The foundation's vision is to enhance the experience and impact of giving through: 1) exemplary service; 2) wise stewardship of resources; and 3) as a Trusted partner for community knowledge and collaboration.
Fields of interest: Arts; Higher education; Education; Environment, natural resources; Animals/wildlife; Hospitals (general); Health care; Health organizations, association; Disasters, Hurricane Katrina; Youth, services; Aging, centers/services; Human services.
Type of support: Capital campaigns; Building/renovation; Equipment; Land acquisition; Emergency funds; Program development; Seed money; Scholarship funds; Research; Technical assistance; Scholarships—to individuals; Matching/challenge support.
Limitations: Applications accepted. Giving primarily in the Dallas, TX, area (for grants from unrestricted funds). No support for religious purposes from general fund or organizations which redistribute funds to other organizations. No grants to individuals (except for scholarships), or for continuing support, media projects or publications, deficit financing, endowment funds, fellowships, salaries, annual campaigns, or operational expenses of well-established organizations.
Publications: Application guidelines; Annual report; Financial statement; Newsletter; Program policy statement.
Application information: Visit foundation web site for application information for Donor-Advised grants. LOIs are initially reviewed by a staff subcommittee; applicants will be notified if staff or a donor would like more information about the funding request. Application form not required.
Initial approach: Submit letter of inquiry via mail or e-mail
Copies of proposal: 1
Deadline(s): Apr. 1 for Donor-Advised grants letter of inquiry; varies for others
Board meeting date(s): Distribution committee for unrestricted funds meets in Mar. and Nov.
Officers and Trustees:* Frank A. Risch,* Chair.; Terdema L. Ussery II,* Vice-Chair.; Brent E. Christopher, C.E.O. and Pres.; Elizabeth W. Bull, Sr. V.P. and C.F.O.; J. Steven Orr, V.P., Investments; Kristine Thomas, V.P., Acctg.; Vester T. Hughes, Jr., Legal Counsel; James E. Bass; Becky Bright; Jeanne T. Cox; Judith W. Gibbs; Frederick B. Hegi, Jr.; Kenneth Hersh; Jack M. Kinnebrew; Chris Kleinert; Bobby B. Lyle; John McStay; Harold Montgomery; Carlos Gonzalez Pena; Hon. Florence Shapiro; Karen L. Shuford; Nicole G. Small.

Number of staff: 28 full-time professional; 13 full-time support; 2 part-time support.
EIN: 750964565
Selected grants: The following grants are a representative sample of this grantmaker's funding activity:
$5,000,000 to George W. Bush Foundation, Dallas, TX, 2012. For construction of George W. Bush Presidential Center.
$1,063,252 to Hope for the Heart, Dallas, TX, 2012. For staff wages and benefits.
$1,000,000 to University of North Texas Foundation, Denton, TX, 2012. To purchase and renovate building to house the UNT Autism Center, which will provide comprehensive, research-based interventions and services to positively impact and improve outcomes for individuals with autism spectrum disorders.
$500,000 to Cooper Institute for Aerobics Research, Dallas, TX, 2012. For Cooper Legacy Campaign.
$300,000 to Texas A & M Foundation, College Station, TX, 2012. For Safety Center.
$225,000 to Big Thought, Dallas, TX, 2012. To create and implement High Impact Learning Institute professional development program.
$100,000 to Salvation Army of Dallas, Dallas, TX, 2012. For general support.
$3,000 to Creede Community Church, Creede, CO, 2012. For 1st Quarter 2012 donation.
$2,500 to Grace Museum, Abilene, TX, 2012. For general support.
$2,500 to Invisible Children, San Diego, CA, 2012. For unrestricted support for the 13 Lengths Campaign.
$1,500 to University of Texas, Arlington, TX, 2012. For scholarship for the spring 2012 semester.
$1,500 to University of Texas, Austin, TX, 2012. For scholarship for the spring 2012 semester.

8774
Community Foundation of Abilene ✧

500 Chestnut, Ste. 1634
Abilene, TX 79602-1434
Contact: Katie Alford, C.E.O.
FAX: (325) 676-4206; E-mail: cfainfo@cfabilene.org; Mailing address: P.O. Box 1001, Abilene, TX 79604; Grant application e-mail: cvletas@cfabilene.org; Main URL: http://www.cfabilene.org
Facebook: http://www.facebook.com/pages/Community-Foundation-of-Abilene/368906421394

Incorporated in 1985 in TX.
Foundation type: Community foundation.
Financial data (yr. ended 06/30/13): Assets, $89,839,830 (M); gifts received, $5,612,472; expenditures, $5,415,980; giving activities include $5,032,238 for grants.
Purpose and activities: The mission of the foundation is to provide charitable endowments to promote local philanthropy, and to address local challenges and opportunities.
Fields of interest: Arts; Education; Animals/wildlife; Health care; Children/youth, services; Human services; Community/economic development; Infants/toddlers; Children/youth; Children; Youth; Adults; Aging; Young adults; Disabilities, people with; Physically disabled; Blind/visually impaired; Deaf/hearing impaired; Mentally disabled; Minorities; African Americans/Blacks; Hispanics/Latinos; Indigenous peoples; Women; Adults, women; Men; Adults, men; Military/veterans; Substance abusers; Single parents; Crime/abuse victims; Terminal illness, people with; Immigrants/refugees; Economically disadvantaged; Homeless.
Type of support: General/operating support; Management development/capacity building; Capital campaigns; Building/renovation; Equipment; Endowments; Emergency funds; Program development; Conferences/seminars; Publication; Seed money; Curriculum development; Scholarship funds; Technical assistance; Consulting services; Scholarships—to individuals; Matching/challenge support.
Limitations: Applications accepted. Giving limited to the Abilene, TX, area and adjacent counties. No support for sectarian religious purposes. No grants to individuals (except for scholarships), or for continuing support, capital debt reduction, medical or scholar research, fundraising events, travel, maintenance expenses, membership fees, or endowment funds; no loans or program-related investments, or multi-year grants (generally).
Publications: Application guidelines; Annual report; Informational brochure; Newsletter; Occasional report.
Application information: Visit foundation web site for grant guidelines. The foundation's Grant Distribution Committee reviews Letters of Intent and determines which organizations are invited to submit a grant proposal. Application form required.
Initial approach: Letter of Intent via online grants process
Deadline(s): Feb. 6 and Sept. 5 for Letters of Intent
Board meeting date(s): 1st Tues. of Feb., Apr., June, Aug., Oct., and Dec.
Final notification: Approx. 6 weeks after proposal submission
Officers and Trustees:* Jack Rich,* Secy.; Katie Alford,* C.E.O. and Pres.; Ken Burgess, Sr.; Joe Crawford; Laura Dyer; Sarah Ferguson; Scott Hibbs; Jill Bailey Hoebelheinrich; Fred Lee Hughes; Bobby Melson; Ken P. Musgrave; Buddy Napier; Danna Oliver; Becky Rentz; Kim Snyder; Anthony Williams.
Number of staff: 6 full-time professional; 1 part-time professional.
EIN: 752045832
Selected grants: The following grants are a representative sample of this grantmaker's funding activity:
$542,721 to Grace Museum, Abilene, TX, 2012. For general operating support and program support.
$229,702 to Historic Paramount Theater, Abilene, TX, 2012. For general operating support and program support.
$206,000 to Manasseh Ministries, Ben Wheeler, TX, 2012. For general operating support and program support.
$144,997 to Kenley School, Abilene, TX, 2012. For scholarships and general operating support.
$127,404 to First Christian Church, Abilene, TX, 2012. For general operating support.
$42,511 to Abilene Boys Ranch, Abilene, TX, 2012. For general operating support and program support.
$39,600 to Regional Crime Victim Crisis Center, Abilene, TX, 2012. For program support.
$34,760 to McMurry University, Abilene, TX, 2012. For scholarships, programs and general operating support.
$11,719 to Sacred Heart Catholic Church, Abilene, TX, 2012. For general operating support.
$10,000 to Restorative Justice Ministries Network of North America, Huntsville, TX, 2012. For program support.

8775
The Community Foundation of Brazoria County, Texas ✧

104 W. Myrtle, Ste. 204
P.O. Box 2392
Angleton, TX 77515 (979) 848-2628
Contact: Barbara Franklin, Exec. Dir.
FAX: (979) 848-0031; E-mail: cfbr@sbcglobal.net; Main URL: http://www.cfbr.org
Facebook: http://www.facebook.com/pages/Community-Foundation-of-Brazoria-County/199647567486

Established in 1994 in TX.
Foundation type: Community foundation.
Financial data (yr. ended 06/30/13): Assets, $1,638,249 (M); gifts received, $439,919; expenditures, $555,527; giving activities include $504,909 for 24+ grants (high: $119,340).
Purpose and activities: The Community Foundation of Brazoria County aspires to significantly enhance the quality of life of the local community by providing outstanding service to donors, producing significant asset growth, strengthening community collaboration and managing an exemplary grants program.
Fields of interest: Performing arts, theater; Arts; Elementary/secondary education; Higher education; Education; Environment; Health care; Human services; Community/economic development; Religion.
Type of support: Annual campaigns; Capital campaigns; Building/renovation; Endowments; Emergency funds; Program development; Seed money; Scholarship funds; Employee-related scholarships.
Limitations: Applications accepted. Giving primarily in Brazoria County, TX. No support for religious organizations for sectarian purposes. No grants for endowments or foundations.
Publications: Informational brochure; Newsletter.
Application information: See web site for RFPs.
Deadline(s): Varies
Board meeting date(s): 4th Tues. of each month
Officers and Directors:* Val Walleck,* Chair.; Norman Wood,* Pres.; Paul Sofka,* V.P., Finance; Sarah vonRosenberg,* V.P., Devel.; Val Walleck,* V.P., Disbursement; Jackie King,* Secy.; Ron Jones,* Treas.; Barbara Franklin, Exec. Dir.; Gabe Adame; Debs Cofer; Chad Dudley; Martha Eighme; Barbara Fratila; Vicki Melass; Barbara Monical; Evelyn Moore; Lucy Pendon; Anita Rau; Tabitha Ray; Rudy Santos; Ravi Singhania; Jennifer Wehrly.
Number of staff: 1 part-time professional; 1 part-time support.
EIN: 760427068

8776
Community Foundation of North Texas ✧

(formerly The Community Foundation of Metropolitan Tarrant County)
306 W. 7th St., Ste. 850
Fort Worth, TX 76102 (817) 877-0702
Contact: Nancy E. Jones, C.E.O.
FAX: (817) 877-1215; E-mail: nancyjones@cfntx.org; Main URL: http://www.cfntx.org
Blog: http://cfntx.typepad.com/blog/
E-Newsletter: http://www.cfntx.org/signupforenews
Facebook: http://www.facebook.com/pages/Community-Foundation-of-North-Texas/108993399124254
Grants List: http://www.cfntx.org/toolboxgrants

Twitter: http://twitter.com/cf_northtexas
For scholarship inquiries: lmund@cfntx.org

Established in 1981 in TX as a program of the United Way; status changed to independent community foundation in 1989.
Foundation type: Community foundation.
Financial data (yr. ended 12/31/12): Assets, $155,874,668 (M); gifts received, $16,795,185; expenditures, $12,951,949; giving activities include $11,348,788 for 1,225 grants (high: $500,000; low: $30), and $645,407 for 213 grants to individuals (high: $44,000; low: $250).
Purpose and activities: The foundation provides stewardship for many individual charitable funds. With its specialized services, the foundation gives donor efficient charitable fund administration. Support for community development, social services, education, youth, health, and arts and cultural programs; emphasis on one-time grants to new and innovative programs. The foundation's mission is to: 1) establish permanent charitable endowments; 2) provide a vehicle for donors' varied interests; 3) promote local philanthropy; and 4) provide leadership and resources in addressing challenges and opportunities facing North Texas.
Fields of interest: Arts; Health care; Health organizations, association; Children/youth, services; Human services; Community/economic development; Infants/toddlers; Children/youth; Children; Youth; Adults; Aging; Young adults; Disabilities, people with; Women; Economically disadvantaged; Homeless.
Type of support: Equipment; Technical assistance; Consulting services; Program evaluation.
Limitations: Applications accepted. Giving limited to Tarrant County, TX for discretionary grants. Currently serve an 11-county region in North Texas. No grants to individuals (except for scholarships), or for deficit financing, endowments or emergency funds, matching grants, publications, research, continuing support, or conferences and seminars.
Publications: Application guidelines; Annual report; Financial statement; Grants list; Informational brochure; Newsletter; IRS Form 990 or 990-PF printed copy available upon request.
Application information: Visit foundation web site for application form, guidelines and specific deadlines. Based on letter of intent, approved applicants are invited to submit a full proposal. Application form required.
Initial approach: Submit letter of intent
Copies of proposal: 9
Deadline(s): Early July
Board meeting date(s): Jan., Mar., May, Aug., and Oct.
Officers and Directors:* Phillip W. McCrury,* Chair.; Chris Huckabee,* Vice-Chair.; Nancy E. Jones,* Pres.; Elaine J. Petrus,* V.P., Distributions; Bill Dismuke,* Corp. Secy.; Larry Autrey,* Treas.; Cynthia Adams; Dave Deison; James Demoss; Liz Fleischer; Ralph Heath; Joan Katz; John Kuelbs; Mike Reese; J. Russell Reid; Beth Rivers; Alfred Saenz; Scott Sankary.
Number of staff: 6 full-time professional; 3 part-time professional; 2 part-time support.
EIN: 752267767
Selected grants: The following grants are a representative sample of this grantmaker's funding activity:
$500,000 to Princeton University, Princeton, NJ, 2012. For Annual Giving - Class of 1987.
$250,000 to All Saints Episcopal School of Fort Worth, Fort Worth, TX, 2012. For the addition to the gym.
$180,000 to Empowering Church Healthcare Outreach, Fort Worth, TX, 2012. For general operating support.
$167,979 to Salvation Army of Dallas, Dallas, TX, 2012. For annual distribution.
$100,000 to First United Methodist Church of Keller, Keller, TX, 2012. For general operating support.
$77,199 to United Way of Tarrant County, Fort Worth, TX, 2012. For the United Way Legacy I Fund.
$30,000 to Kimbell Art Foundation, Fort Worth, TX, 2012. For Building.
$3,000 to New Key School, Fort Worth, TX, 2012. For Changing Lives Campaign.
$1,918 to American Red Cross, Fort Worth, TX, 2012.
$1,500 to Cook Childrens Medical Center, Fort Worth, TX, 2012. For Neuroblastoma Fund, Annual Neuroblastoma 5K Run and Walk.

8777
Community Foundation of the Texas Hill Country ✧

(formerly Kerrville Area Community Trust)
301 Junction Highway, Suite 346-B
Kerrville, TX 78028 (830) 896-8811
Contact: Paul D. Urban; Amy Rector, Business Mgr.
FAX: (830) 792-5956;
E-mail: paul@communityfoundation.net; Mailing address: P.O. Box 291354, Kerrville TX 78029-1354; Main URL: http://www.communityfoundation.net
Facebook: https://www.facebook.com/pages/The-Community-Foundation-of-the-Texas-Hill-Country/153272534718916
Twitter: https://twitter.com/#!/CommFoundTX

Established in 1981 in TX.
Foundation type: Community foundation.
Financial data (yr. ended 12/31/13): Assets, $11,559,357 (M); gifts received, $1,687,947; expenditures, $943,812; giving activities include $561,999 for 8+ grants (high: $13,100), and $64,033 for 35 grants to individuals.
Purpose and activities: The foundation seeks to respond to area needs by providing stewardship of donations, and funding worthwhile community projects.
Fields of interest: Arts; Education; Health care; Children/youth, services; Family services; Human services; Community/economic development; Infants/toddlers; Children/youth; Youth; Aging; Disabilities, people with; Physically disabled; Blind/visually impaired; Deaf/hearing impaired; Mentally disabled; Minorities; Asians/Pacific Islanders; African Americans/Blacks; Hispanics/Latinos; Native Americans/American Indians; Indigenous peoples; Women; Girls; Adults, women; Young adults, female; Men; Adults, men; Young adults, male; Military/veterans; Substance abusers; Single parents; Crime/abuse victims; Terminal illness, people with; Immigrants/refugees; Economically disadvantaged; Homeless; Migrant workers.
Type of support: General/operating support; Continuing support; Management development/capacity building; Capital campaigns; Building/renovation; Equipment; Endowments; Program development; Conferences/seminars; Film/video/radio; Publication; Curriculum development; Internship funds; Scholarship funds; Research; Technical assistance; Consulting services; Program evaluation; Matching/challenge support.
Limitations: Applications accepted. Giving limited to the area generally known as the Texas Hill Country, including Kerr, Kendall, Gillespie and Bandera counties. No support for religious activities.
Publications: Application guidelines; Annual report; Financial statement; Grants list; Informational brochure; Newsletter.
Application information: Visit foundation web site for application form and guidelines. Application form required.
Initial approach: Submit application form and attachments
Copies of proposal: 1
Deadline(s): Varies, see web site
Board meeting date(s): 4 to 5 times annually, as required
Final notification: Varies, see web site
Officers and Trustees:* Robert Kelly,* Pres.; John Carlson,* V.P.; Dave Weekley,* Secy.; Catherine Schulte,* Treas.; Paul D. Urbano, Exec. Dir.; Wes Dorman; Chaille Hawkins; John Hutcherson; Jim McAfee; Roy Thompson; Chris Wallendorf; Mindy Wendele.
Number of staff: 2 full-time professional; 1 part-time professional.
EIN: 742225369

8778
The Constantin Foundation, Inc. ✧

4809 Cole Ave., LB 127, Ste. 346
Dallas, TX 75205-3654 (214) 522-9300
Contact: Angie Burch, Exec. Dir.
FAX: (214) 521-7025;
E-mail: constantinfdn@sbcglobal.net

Trust established in 1947 in TX; reincorporated under current IRS identification number in 2007.
Donors: E. Constantin, Jr.†; Mrs. E. Constantin, Jr.†.
Foundation type: Independent foundation.
Financial data (yr. ended 12/31/13): Assets, $55,001,776 (M); expenditures, $2,780,047; qualifying distributions, $2,243,728; giving activities include $2,213,064 for 11 grants (high: $544,082; low: $25,000).
Purpose and activities: Emphasis on higher and other education; some support for cultural programs, social service and youth agencies, and hospitals and health, including alcohol and drug abuse programs.
Fields of interest: Museums; Humanities; Arts; Secondary school/education; Vocational education; Higher education; Adult/continuing education; Libraries/library science; Education; Hospitals (general); Medical care, rehabilitation; Health care; Substance abuse, services; Crime/violence prevention, youth; Housing/shelter, development; Human services; Children/youth, services; Children/youth; Youth; Disabilities, people with; Economically disadvantaged.
Type of support: Capital campaigns; Building/renovation; Equipment; Land acquisition; Endowments; Program development; Scholarship funds; Matching/challenge support.
Limitations: Applications accepted. Giving limited to Dallas County, TX. No support for tax-supported institutions, theater groups, churches, debt retirement, political organizations or second party requesters. No grants to individuals, or for debt retirement, operations, research, special events, fundraisers, or second party requests; no loans.
Publications: Application guidelines.

Application information: Application form not required.
Initial approach: Letter (up to 3 pages)
Copies of proposal: 1
Deadline(s): Sept. 15 for letters of inquiry; grants reviewed at quarterly meetings; grant meeting in Dec.
Board meeting date(s): Feb., May, Aug., and Dec.
Final notification: Following Dec. meeting, and only if applicant is a recipient of a grant
Officers: Roy Gene Evans, Chair.; Gene H. Bishop, Pres.; Patrick McEvoy, Secy.-Treas.; Angie Burch, Exec. Dir.; Joel T. Williams, Jr., Chair. Emeritus.
Directors: Harvey Berryman Cash; Joseph Boyd Neuhoff.
Number of staff: 1 full-time professional.
EIN: 205150433

8779
Kelly Gene Cook, Sr. Charitable Foundation, Inc. ✧

230 Kilts Dr.
Houston, TX 77024-6214
Contact: Robert Knеppler, V.P.
E-mail: cookfoundation@sbcglobal.net; Application address: c/o Kathy Pacelli, 1675 Lakeland Dr. S., No. 507, Jackson, MS 39216-4841, tel.: (601) 981-1116, e-mail: kathy@kgccf.com

Incorporated in 1986 in TX.
Donors: Kelly G. Cook‡; Peggy Cook Pool.
Foundation type: Independent foundation.
Financial data (yr. ended 12/31/13): Assets, $34,278,682 (M); expenditures, $1,573,260; qualifying distributions, $1,315,945; giving activities include $1,124,235 for grants.
Purpose and activities: Support primarily for higher education, including student aid provided through scholarship funds at Millsaps College, the University of Mississippi, Mississippi State University, Mississippi College, and the University of Southern Mississippi.
Fields of interest: Higher education; Children/youth; Children; Deaf/hearing impaired; Economically disadvantaged.
Type of support: General/operating support; Capital campaigns; Endowments; Matching/challenge support; Professorships; Scholarship funds; Scholarships—to individuals.
Limitations: Giving primarily in LA, MS, and TX.
Application information: Apply to the financial aid office at Millsaps College, the University of Mississippi, Mississippi State University, Mississippi College, or the University of Southern Mississippi; the foundation makes final selection of recipients for scholarships. Application form required.
Initial approach: Letter
Copies of proposal: 6
Deadline(s): Oct. 1
Board meeting date(s): Nov.
Officers and Directors:* Deborah Rochelle,* Pres.; Robert Knеppler, Jr.,* V.P.; JoAnn Mikell,* Secy.; Ron Page,* Treas.; Kathy Pacelli, Exec. Dir.; Peggy Cook Pool,* Pres. Emeritus.
Number of staff: 1 full-time professional.
EIN: 760201807
Selected grants: The following grants are a representative sample of this grantmaker's funding activity:
$35,000 to University of Southern Mississippi, Hattiesburg, MS, 2012. For fall scholarships.
$30,000 to Briarwood School, Houston, TX, 2012. For Scholarships and Teacher Intensive Program.
$24,479 to University of Southern Mississippi, Hattiesburg, MS, 2012. For Spring Scholarships.
$13,874 to University of Mississippi, University, MS, 2012. For additional spring scholarships.
$10,530 to Mississippi State University, Mississippi State, MS, 2012. For additional spring scholarships.
$8,000 to University of Southern Mississippi, Hattiesburg, MS, 2012. For Spring Graduate Assistantships.
$8,000 to University of Southern Mississippi, Hattiesburg, MS, 2012. For Summer Graduate Assistantships.
$8,000 to University of Southern Mississippi, Hattiesburg, MS, 2012. For Fall Graduate Assistantships.
$6,018 to University of Mississippi, University, MS, 2012. For additional spring scholarship.
$4,000 to Mississippi State University, Mississippi State, MS, 2012. For GRAD Spring.

8780
The Cornerstone Project ✧

301 Commerce St., Ste. 3300
Fort Worth, TX 76102-4133

Donor: David Bonderman.
Foundation type: Independent foundation.
Financial data (yr. ended 12/31/13): Assets, $7,092,310 (M); gifts received, $130,000; expenditures, $722,019; qualifying distributions, $652,829; giving activities include $564,892 for 6 grants (high: $290,000; low: $30,000).
Fields of interest: Housing/shelter; Youth development; Christian agencies & churches.
Limitations: Applications not accepted. Giving primarily in CA; some giving nationally.
Application information: Contributes only to pre-selected organizations.
Officers: Jesse D. Bonderman, Pres.; David Belena Quinones, Secy.; Fred Makana Noa, Treas.
Board Member: Adrian L. Koehler.
EIN: 273409935

8781
Covenant Foundation, Inc. ✧

18615 Tuscany Stone, Ste. 200
San Antonio, TX 78258-3502 (210) 614-7051
Contact: David Craven, Pres.

Established in 1991 in TX.
Donors: James R. Leininger; Cecelia A. Leininger.
Foundation type: Independent foundation.
Financial data (yr. ended 12/31/12): Assets, $28,213,596 (M); expenditures, $13,286,762; qualifying distributions, $13,131,108; giving activities include $13,131,108 for 63 grants (high: $3,000,000; low: $200).
Purpose and activities: Giving primarily to Christian agencies and churches.
Fields of interest: Elementary/secondary education; Public affairs; Christian agencies & churches.
Type of support: General/operating support; Continuing support; Publication; Seed money; Internship funds.
Limitations: Applications accepted. Giving primarily in TX. No grants to individuals.
Application information: Application form required.
Initial approach: Letter
Copies of proposal: 1
Board meeting date(s): Quarterly
Final notification: 3 months
Officers and Directors:* James R. Leininger,* Chair.; David Craven,* Pres.; Thomas W. Lyles, Jr., Secy.-Treas.; Tracy M. Craven; Brian C. Leininger; Cecelia A. Leininger; Kelly C. Welch.
Number of staff: 1 full-time professional.
EIN: 742622129
Selected grants: The following grants are a representative sample of this grantmaker's funding activity:
$3,000,000 to Patrick Henry College, Purcellville, VA, 2012. For general support.
$2,800,000 to Texas Public Policy Foundation, Austin, TX, 2012. For general support.
$2,490,000 to Christian Academy of San Antonio, San Antonio, TX, 2012. For general support.
$1,562,053 to Shelby Kennedy Foundation, Bible Bee, Wilmington, OH, 2012. For general support.
$1,347,155 to Christian Academy of San Antonio, San Antonio, TX, 2012. For general support.
$1,000,000 to Family Talk, Colorado Springs, CO, 2012. For general support.
$90,000 to Living Waters Publications, Bellflower, CA, 2012. For general support.
$50,000 to San Antonio Symphony, San Antonio, TX, 2012. For general support.
$26,700 to Family Educators Alliance of South Texas, FEAST, San Antonio, TX, 2012. For general support.
$15,000 to Whetstone Ministries, Farmington, AR, 2012. For general support.

8782
Faye L. and William L. Cowden Charitable Foundation ✧

c/o Broadway National Bank, Trust Dept.
P.O. Box 17001
San Antonio, TX 78217-0001 (210) 283-6500
Contact: David White, Trust Off., Broadway National Bank
Main URL: http://broadwaybank.com/wealthmanagement/FoundationFayeLWilliamLCowden.html

Established in 1988 in TX.
Foundation type: Operating foundation.
Financial data (yr. ended 03/31/13): Assets, $12,297,354 (M); expenditures, $647,906; qualifying distributions, $569,629; giving activities include $561,000 for 62 grants (high: $20,000; low: $2,000).
Purpose and activities: Giving to Texas organizations which direct their activities toward the health, medical care and treatment of children, the education of children and young adults, the prevention of cruelty to children or animals, and the protection and preservation of wildlife and natural areas.
Fields of interest: Arts; Education; Environment; Animal welfare; Human services; Children/youth, services.
Limitations: Applications accepted. Giving limited to TX, with emphasis on San Antonio. No grants to individuals.
Application information: See foundation website for complete application guidelines. Application form required.
Initial approach: Application form on foundation web site

Deadline(s): Mar. 31
Final notification: Aug.
Trustee: Broadway National Bank.
EIN: 746359520
Selected grants: The following grants are a representative sample of this grantmaker's funding activity:
$10,000 to University of Texas Foundation, Austin, TX, 2013. To support Uthscsa.

8783
Louetta M. Cowden Foundation ✧
c/o Bank Of America, N.A.
P. O. Box 831041
Dallas, TX 75283-1041
Application address: P.O. Box 219119, Kansas City, MO 64121-9119, tel.: 816-292-4300

Trust established in 1964 in MO.
Donor: Louetta M. Cowden†.
Foundation type: Independent foundation.
Financial data (yr. ended 12/31/13): Assets, $11,288,887 (M); expenditures, $543,761; qualifying distributions, $465,814; giving activities include $446,950 for 11 grants (high: $50,000; low: $8,950).
Purpose and activities: The foundation was established in 1964 to support and promote quality educational, cultural, human services, and health care programming.
Fields of interest: Performing arts, orchestras; Arts; Education; Food banks; Human services; YM/YWCAs & YM/YWHAs; Children/youth, services.
Type of support: Capital campaigns; Building/renovation; Equipment; Land acquisition; Emergency funds; Program development; Seed money.
Limitations: Applications accepted. Giving limited to MO, with an emphasis on the metropolitan Kansas City area. No grants to individuals, or for endowment funds, scholarships, fellowships, or matching gifts; no loans.
Application information: Application form required.
Initial approach: Letter
Copies of proposal: 2
Deadline(s): None
Trustee: Bank of America, N.A.
Number of staff: 1 full-time professional.
EIN: 436052617
Selected grants: The following grants are a representative sample of this grantmaker's funding activity:
$50,000 to Childrens Mercy Hospital, Kansas City, MO, 2011. For the Children's Mercy Hospital EAST capital campaign.
$50,000 to Harvesters-The Community Food Network, Kansas City, MO, 2011. For operations.
$50,000 to Saint Lukes Hospital Foundation, Kansas City, MO, 2011. For St. Luke's Senior Center (year two of three).
$50,000 to YMCA of Greater Kansas City, Kansas City, MO, 2011. For the Challenger Complex Phase II.
$25,000 to Boys and Girls Clubs of Greater Kansas City, Kansas City, MO, 2011. For Deepening Impact initiative.
$25,000 to Liberty Memorial Association, National World War I Museum at Liberty Memorial, Kansas City, MO, 2011. For general operating support.
$25,000 to Mid-America Arts Alliance, Kansas City, MO, 2011. For the $5 million integrated campaign.
$20,000 to Child Advocacy Services Center, Childrens Place, Kansas City, MO, 2011. For the clinical services provided to child survivors of abuse, neglect and trauma.
$10,000 to Shepherds Center, Kansas City, MO, 2011. For Meals on Wheels.
$2,500 to Pets for Life, Kansas City, MO, 2011. For operations.

8784
Berry R. Cox Family Foundation ✧
2100 McKinney Ave., Ste. 1700
Dallas, TX 75201-6975

Established in 2000 in TX.
Donor: Berry R. Cox.
Foundation type: Independent foundation.
Financial data (yr. ended 12/31/13): Assets, $8,942,576 (L); expenditures, $576,381; qualifying distributions, $464,501; giving activities include $459,451 for 9 grants (high: $446,101; low: $50).
Fields of interest: Elementary/secondary education; Higher education; Human services; Foundations (private grantmaking); Protestant agencies & churches.
Type of support: General/operating support; Program development.
Limitations: Applications not accepted. Giving primarily in Dallas, TX. No grants to individuals.
Application information: Contributes only to pre-selected organizations.
Officers: David S. Boylan, Pres. and Treas.; Cindy Wolf, Secy.
Trustees: Berry R. Cox; Jeanne T. Cox; John G.T. Cox; Justin B. Cox.
EIN: 752864400
Selected grants: The following grants are a representative sample of this grantmaker's funding activity:
$120,000 to Communities Foundation of Texas, Dallas, TX, 2012. For Berry R. Cox Family Fund.
$54,487 to Southern Methodist University, Dallas, TX, 2012. For Medal of Freedom Event.
$10,000 to Greenhill School, Addison, TX, 2012. For Building Community Campaign.
$5,000 to Southern Methodist University, Dallas, TX, 2012. For SMU Mustang Bank Hall Project.
$2,500 to Southern Methodist University, Dallas, TX, 2012. For Central University Libraries Fund.
$565 to Family Legacy Missions International, Irving, TX, 2012. For Child Sponsorship-Father's Heart.
$200 to Communities Foundation of Texas, Dallas, TX, 2012. For Saving Hope Foundation Fund.
$150 to Southern Methodist University, Dallas, TX, 2012. For The Dr. Jim Caswell Endowment for Leadership Development and Training.
$100 to Texas Tech Foundation, Lubbock, TX, 2012. For Sam Montgomery Scholarship Fund.

8785
John and Maurine Cox Foundation ✧
P.O. Box 2217
Midland, TX 79702-2217

Established in 1994 in TX.
Donors: John L. Cox; Maurine T. Cox.
Foundation type: Independent foundation.
Financial data (yr. ended 12/31/13): Assets, $21,305,440 (M); gifts received, $875,000; expenditures, $1,006,512; qualifying distributions, $826,492; giving activities include $826,492 for 33 grants (high: $291,000; low: $1,000).
Purpose and activities: Giving primarily for education, health, children and social services, and to a golf organization.
Fields of interest: Museums; Higher education; Cancer; Health organizations; Athletics/sports, golf; Children/youth, services.
Limitations: Applications not accepted. Giving primarily in TX. No grants to individuals.
Application information: Contributes only to pre-selected organizations.
Trustees: Kelly Cox; Maurine T. Cox.
EIN: 752536459
Selected grants: The following grants are a representative sample of this grantmaker's funding activity:
$50,000 to Gladney Center for Adoption, Fort Worth, TX, 2011.
$50,000 to Texas Christian University, Fort Worth, TX, 2011.
$50,000 to United Way of Midland, Midland, TX, 2011.
$40,000 to Midland Childrens Rehabilitation Center, Midland, TX, 2011.
$30,000 to American Cancer Society, Midland, TX, 2011.
$25,000 to Southwestern University, Georgetown, TX, 2011.
$20,000 to Aphasia Center of West Texas, Midland, TX, 2011.
$20,000 to Briarwood-Brookwood, Brookshire, TX, 2011.
$20,000 to High Sky Childrens Ranch, Midland, TX, 2011.
$10,000 to Petroleum Museum, Midland, TX, 2011.

8786
The T.E. Craig, S.D. Heard and L.D. Heard Memorial Trust ✧
P.O. Box 831041
Dallas, TX 75283-1041

Established in TX.
Foundation type: Independent foundation.
Financial data (yr. ended 12/31/13): Assets, $9,189,406 (M); expenditures, $610,612; qualifying distributions, $517,806; giving activities include $486,172 for 6 grants (high: $121,543; low: $40,514).
Purpose and activities: Giving primarily for higher education, as well as to Presbyterian organizations, including churches; funding also for a children's home.
Fields of interest: Higher education; Children, services; Residential/custodial care; Women, centers/services; Protestant agencies & churches.
Limitations: Applications not accepted. Giving primarily in TX.
Application information: Contributes only to pre-selected organizations.
Trustee: Bank of America, N.A.
EIN: 597279007

8787
The Crain Foundation ✧
P.O. Box 2146
Longview, TX 75606-2146 (903) 758-8276
Contact: Ann Lacy Crain, Pres.

Established in 1997 in TX.

Donors: Lacy Holdings Ltd.; Crain Resources.
Foundation type: Independent foundation.
Financial data (yr. ended 12/31/12): Assets, $30,167,203 (M); gifts received, $1,500,000; expenditures, $1,429,537; qualifying distributions, $1,351,510; giving activities include $1,285,740 for 100 grants (high: $200,000; low: $50), and $65,770 for 9 employee matching gifts.
Fields of interest: Secondary school/education; Education; Health care; Children/youth, services; Protestant agencies & churches.
Limitations: Applications accepted. Giving primarily in TX, with emphasis on Houston and Longview.
Application information:
Initial approach: Proposal
Deadline(s): None
Final notification: Within 2 months of request
Officers and Directors:* Ann Lacy Crain,* Pres.; Rogers L. Crain,* V.P. and Secy.; Susan Mincey, V.P. and Treas.; Ann Lacy Crain II,* V.P.; B. Walter Crain III,* V.P.; Darren Croce, V.P.; Terri Downing, Cont.
EIN: 752698267

8788
James R. Crane Foundation ✧
4409 Montrose Blvd., Ste. 200
Houston, TX 77006-5859

Established in 1999 in TX.
Donor: James R. Crane.
Foundation type: Independent foundation.
Financial data (yr. ended 12/31/12): Assets, $6,142,236 (M); gifts received, $2,000,000; expenditures, $2,187,702; qualifying distributions, $2,140,536; giving activities include $2,140,536 for 62 grants (high: $1,000,000; low: $250).
Purpose and activities: Giving primarily for higher education, and a private foundation; support also for the arts.
Fields of interest: Museums; Arts; Higher education; Hospitals (specialty); Human services; Foundations (private independent).
Limitations: Applications not accepted. Giving primarily in Monterey, CA and TX, with emphasis on Houston. No grants to individuals.
Application information: Contributes only to pre-selected organizations.
Directors: James R. Crane; Ronald Franklin; Douglas Seckel.
EIN: 760626224

8789
W.A. Criswell Foundation, Inc. ✧
2000 McKinney Ave., Ste. 975
Dallas, TX 75201-2084

Donors: Blake Pogue; Ann Pogue; Jack Brady; Dan Hall; Evelyn Johnson; W.A. Criswell‡; Clifford E. Winkler; Don Hodges; Harriet Miers; The Pogue Foundation; Virginia Fay Gross Trust; The Simpson Charitable Trust; Premier Designs.
Foundation type: Independent foundation.
Financial data (yr. ended 12/31/12): Assets, $25,646,985 (M); gifts received, $165,460; expenditures, $1,935,583; qualifying distributions, $1,747,907; giving activities include $1,428,487 for 8 grants (high: $1,338,707; low: $713), and $319,420 for foundation-administered programs.
Purpose and activities: Giving primarily for education, including support for a Southern Baptist theological seminary, and to a Christian radio station.
Fields of interest: Media, radio; Elementary/secondary education; Higher education; Theological school/education; Christian agencies & churches; Protestant agencies & churches.
Limitations: Applications not accepted. Giving primarily in Arlington and Dallas, TX.
Application information: Contributes only to pre-selected organizations.
Officers and Directors:* Jack Pogue,* Chair.; Darrell Lafitte,* Pres.; Curtis Baker; Randy Bradley; Jack Brady; Dean Childress; Brian Hermes; Don Hodges; Garry Kinder; Michael Lafitte; Blake Pogue; Dr. Steve Washburn.
EIN: 237226473

8790
Eleanor Crook Foundation ✧ ☆
c/o Joye Blankenship
227 N. Mitchell St.
San Marcos, TX 78666-4217 (512) 392-5205
Contact: Eleanor Crook, Pres. and Treas.

Established in TX.
Donors: Eleanor Butt Crook; William H. Crook; Caryl Crook; Elizabeth Crook; Marc Lewis; Richard Moore; Noel Moore.
Foundation type: Independent foundation.
Financial data (yr. ended 12/31/13): Assets, $32,970,885 (M); gifts received, $2,315,900; expenditures, $2,187,099; qualifying distributions, $2,004,750; giving activities include $2,004,750 for 54 grants (high: $1,750,000; low: $100).
Fields of interest: Education; Health care; Human services.
Limitations: Applications accepted. Giving primarily in TX; funding also in Washington, DC.
Application information: Application form required.
Initial approach: Letter
Deadline(s): None
Officers: Eleanor Crook, Pres. and Treas.; William H. Crook, Jr., V.P. and Secy.; Mary Elizabeth Crook, V.P.; Noel C. Moore, V.P.
EIN: 742857866

8791
Renee C. Crowell Trust f/b/o Charities ✧
c/o Bank of America, N.A.
P.O. Box 831041
Dallas, TX 75283-1041

Established in 1973; supporting organization of Alphapointe Association for the Blind, Grace and Holy Trinity Cathedral, the Humane Society of Greater Kansas City, Kansas University Endowment Association, St. Luke's Hospital, St. Paul's Episcopal Church, and the Unity School of Christianity.
Foundation type: Independent foundation.
Financial data (yr. ended 12/31/13): Assets, $20,080,487 (M); expenditures, $1,044,579; qualifying distributions, $942,175; giving activities include $900,000 for 7 grants (high: $257,139; low: $32,148).
Fields of interest: Higher education, university; Animal welfare; Hospitals (general); Christian agencies & churches; Protestant agencies & churches; Blind/visually impaired.
Limitations: Applications not accepted. Giving primarily in KS and MO.
Application information: Contributes only to pre-selected organizations; unsolicited requests for funds not considered or acknowledged.
Trustee: Bank of America, N.A.
EIN: 436113386
Selected grants: The following grants are a representative sample of this grantmaker's funding activity:
$214,282 to Grace and Holy Trinity Cathedral, Kansas City, MO, 2011. For unrestricted contribution.
$214,282 to Saint Pauls Episcopal Church, Kansas City, MO, 2011. For unrestricted contribution.
$107,145 to Kansas University Endowment Association, Lawrence, KS, 2011. For unrestricted contribution.
$80,355 to Saint Lukes Hospital of Kansas City, Kansas City, MO, 2011. For unrestricted contribution.
$53,572 to Alphapointe Association for the Blind, Kansas City, MO, 2011. For unrestricted contribution.
$53,572 to Humane Society of Greater Kansas City, Kansas City, KS, 2011. For unrestricted contribution.
$26,790 to Unity School of Christianity, Unity Village, MO, 2011. For unrestricted contribution.

8792
The Cullen Foundation ✧
601 Jefferson St., 40th Fl.
Houston, TX 77002-7900 (713) 651-8837
Contact: Alan M. Stewart, Treas.
E-mail for Alan M. Stewart: astewart@cullenfdn.org; e-mail for Sue A.
Alexander: salexander@cullenfdn.org; Main
URL: http://www.cullenfdn.org
Grants List: http://www.cullenfdn.org/frame.htm

Trust established in 1947 in TX.
Donors: Hugh Roy Cullen‡; Lillie Cullen‡.
Foundation type: Independent foundation.
Financial data (yr. ended 12/31/12): Assets, $230,689,000 (M); expenditures, $13,320,061; qualifying distributions, $11,493,242; giving activities include $11,136,500 for 58 grants (high: $5,000,000; low: $10,000).
Purpose and activities: Giving for charitable, educational, medical, and other eleemosynary purposes; grants for hospitals, medical research, including eye research, and higher education; support also for music, the performing arts, social services, drug abuse prevention, community funds, and conservation.
Fields of interest: Arts; Education; Hospitals (general); Health care; Health organizations, association; Medical research, institute; Human services; Homeless.
Type of support: General/operating support; Annual campaigns; Capital campaigns; Building/renovation; Equipment; Land acquisition; Endowments; Debt reduction; Program development; Professorships; Curriculum development; Fellowships; Scholarship funds; Research; Matching/challenge support.
Limitations: Applications accepted. Giving limited to TX, with emphasis on Houston. No support for religious organizations directly. No grants to individuals, or for underwriting or sponsorship of fundraising events; no loans.
Publications: Application guidelines.
Application information: Application form not required.

Initial approach: Proposal, letter, or telephone
Copies of proposal: 1
Deadline(s): None
Board meeting date(s): As required
Final notification: Varies
Officers and Directors:* Roy Henry Cullen,* Pres.; Isaac Arnold, Jr.,* V.P.; Wilhelmina E. Robertson,* Secy.; Alan M. Stewart, Treas. and Exec. Dir.; Bert L. Campbell; William H. Drushel, Jr.
Number of staff: 3 full-time professional.
EIN: 760647361
Selected grants: The following grants are a representative sample of this grantmaker's funding activity:
$5,000,000 to Baylor College of Medicine, Houston, TX, 2012. To build-out of outpatient facility on McNair Campus.
$1,000,000 to Houston Zoo, Houston, TX, 2012. For Phase II of African Forest Master Plan.
$750,000 to Lone Star Flight Museum, Galveston, TX, 2012. For capital campaign.
$500,000 to Houston Hospice and Palliative Care System, Houston, TX, 2012. For build-out of 3rd floor of Margaret Cullen Marshall Patient Care Center.

8793
The Cultural Heritage Preservation Fund ✧
800 Gessner Rd., Ste. 1260
Houston, TX 77024-4273

Established in 2004 in TX.
Donors: Laurans Trust; Blue Ridge Wealth Mgmt.
Foundation type: Independent foundation.
Financial data (yr. ended 12/31/13): Assets, $7,605,088 (M); expenditures, $1,768,730; qualifying distributions, $1,735,000; giving activities include $1,735,000 for grants (high: $1,000,000; low: $10,000).
Fields of interest: Media, film/video; Arts; Foundations (private grantmaking).
International interests: France.
Limitations: Applications not accepted. Giving primarily in Paris, France; some giving also in the U.S., primarily in New York, NY. No grants to individuals.
Application information: Contributes only to pre-selected organizations.
Officers: Francois Letaconnoux, Pres.; Jacques Le Blevennec, V.P.; Marvin A. Wurzer, Secy.-Treas.
EIN: 201442065
Selected grants: The following grants are a representative sample of this grantmaker's funding activity:
$12,500 to Museum of Modern Art, New York, NY, 2011. For general support.

8794
The Dahan Family Foundation, Inc. ✧ ☆
c/o Marcus Rowan
200 Crescent Ct., Ste. 1325
Dallas, TX 75201-3270

Established in 2004 in FL.
Donors: Rene Dahan; Elisabeth Dahan.
Foundation type: Independent foundation.
Financial data (yr. ended 12/31/13): Assets, $6,503,932 (M); gifts received, $316,960; expenditures, $1,557,764; qualifying distributions, $1,534,000; giving activities include $1,534,000 for 3 grants (high: $834,000; low: $300,000).
Purpose and activities: Giving primarily to organizations that provide medical and social services to people in developing countries.
Fields of interest: Animal welfare; Health care; Food services; Economically disadvantaged.
Limitations: Applications not accepted. Giving primarily in AZ and TX; some funding also in NY. No grants to individuals.
Application information: Contributes only to pre-selected organizations.
Officers and Directors:* Rene Dahan,* Pres. and Treas.; Elisabeth Dahan,* V.P. and Co-Secy.; Brian G. Cheslack, Co-Secy.; Marcus Rowan.
EIN: 201959792
Selected grants: The following grants are a representative sample of this grantmaker's funding activity:
$200,000 to MediSend International, Dallas, TX, 2012. For Health care and supplies for developing countries.

8795
The Dallas Foundation
Reagan Place at Old Parkland
3963 Maple Ave., Ste. 390
Dallas, TX 75219 (214) 741-9898
Contact: Mary M. Jalonick, Pres.; For grants: Laura J. Ward, Dir., Community Philanthropy
FAX: (214) 741-9848;
E-mail: info@dallasfoundation.org; Additional e-mail: mjalonick@dallasfoundation.org; Grant request e-mail: lward@dallasfoundation.org; Main URL: http://www.dallasfoundation.org
Facebook: http://www.facebook.com/dallasfoundation

Established in 1929 in TX.
Foundation type: Community foundation.
Financial data (yr. ended 12/31/12): Assets, $237,683,349 (M); gifts received, $39,607,136; expenditures, $34,447,583; giving activities include $33,204,208 for grants.
Purpose and activities: The foundation serves as a resource, leader, and catalyst for philanthropy by providing donors with flexible means of making gifts to charitable causes that enhance the community.
Fields of interest: Arts; Education; Animal welfare; Health care; Health organizations, association; Crime/violence prevention, child abuse; Recreation, parks/playgrounds; Human services; Community development, neighborhood development; Infants/toddlers; Aging; Disabilities, people with; Physically disabled; Blind/visually impaired; Deaf/hearing impaired; Mentally disabled; African Americans/Blacks; Military/veterans; AIDS, people with; Crime/abuse victims; Immigrants/refugees; Economically disadvantaged; Homeless; LGBTQ.
Type of support: General/operating support; Management development/capacity building; Capital campaigns; Building/renovation; Equipment; Emergency funds; Program development; Scholarship funds; Employee-related scholarships; Matching/challenge support.
Limitations: Applications accepted. Giving primarily to the City and County of Dallas, TX. No support for religious purposes from discretionary funds. No grants to individuals from discretionary funds, or for endowments, research, operating budgets, annual fund campaigns, debt retirement, or underwriting of fundraising events or marketing campaigns; generally no multi-year grants.
Publications: Application guidelines; Annual report; Financial statement; Grants list; Newsletter.
Application information: Visit foundation web site for application guidelines per grant type. Application form required.
Initial approach: Attend Grantmaking Seminar
Copies of proposal: 1
Deadline(s): Aug. 1 for letters of inquiry for full proposals for Community Impact grants; Mar. 3 for Field-of-Interest fund grants; rolling basis for Safety Net Fund grants
Board meeting date(s): Mar., June, Sept., and Dec.
Final notification: Mid-Dec. for Unrestricted fund grants; Mid-June for Field-of-Interest fund grants; within 30 days for Safety Net fund grants
Officers and Governors:* John P. Puckett III,* Chair.; Anne B. Motsenbocker,* Vice-Chair.; Mary M. Jalonick, Pres.; Nita Clark,* Secy.; William T. Solomon, Jr., C.F.O.; Torrey B. Littleton, Cont.; Liz Cedillo-Perez; David R. Corrigan; Don W. Crisp; Valerie Freeman; Stephanie E. Hunt; Carol Levy; James M. "Jim" Moroney III; Amirali Rupani; Jere W. Thompson, Jr.; W. Kelvin Walker.
Trustee Banks: Bank of America, N.A.; Compass Bank.
Number of staff: 7 full-time professional; 5 full-time support.
EIN: 752890371
Selected grants: The following grants are a representative sample of this grantmaker's funding activity:
$6,873,000 to Dallas, City of, Dallas, TX, 2013. For Continental Avenue Bridge project.
$1,874,800 to Harvard University, Cambridge, MA, 2013. For the Harvard Art Museums.
$1,350,000 to Educational First Steps, Dallas, TX, 2012. For operating budget.
$1,250,000 to Educational First Steps, Dallas, TX, 2013. For operating budget.
$900,000 to Teach for America, Dallas, TX, 2012. For Dallas Fort Worth 2015 Expansion Campaign.
$800,000 to Southwestern Medical Foundation, Dallas, TX, 2013. For construction of the Clements University Hospital.
$500,000 to Dallas Theater Center, Dallas, TX, 2012. For Advancement Campaign.
$486,763 to SPCA of Texas, Dallas, TX, 2012. For Big Fix.
$335,000 to University of Texas, Arlington, TX, 2012. For Innovative Community-Academic Partnership program (iCAP) in Dallas County.
$335,000 to University of Texas, Arlington, TX, 2013. For Innovative Community-Academic Partnership program (iCAP) in Dallas County.
$330,039 to Catholic Charities of Dallas, Dallas, TX, 2012. For year 4 programming in the Bachman Lake area.
$5,000 to American Academy of Family Physicians Foundation, Leawood, KS, 2013. For general operating fund.
$5,000 to Buckner Foundation, Dallas, TX, 2013. For annual gift.
$5,000 to Crystal Charity Ball, Dallas, TX, 2013. Toward funding of the beneficiaries.
$5,000 to Focus on the Family, Colorado Springs, CO, 2012. For general operating support.
$5,000 to Hermann-Grima/Gallier Historic Houses, New Orleans, LA, 2012. For Hermann-Grima.
$5,000 to Humane Society of the United States, Washington, DC, 2012. For general support.
$5,000 to Lamplighter School, Dallas, TX, 2012. For Campaign For the Future, Land Fund.

$5,000 to University of Chicago, Booth School of Business, Chicago, IL, 2013. For Booth Graduate School of Business.
$3,000 to Dallas Symphony Association, Dallas, TX, 2013. For general operating support.

8796
Milton E. Daniel Trust ✧
P.O. Box 831041
Dallas, TX 75283-1041

Foundation type: Independent foundation.
Financial data (yr. ended 03/31/13): Assets, $60,222,460 (M); expenditures, $2,910,386; qualifying distributions, $2,411,870; giving activities include $2,411,870 for grants.
Fields of interest: Higher education.
Limitations: Applications not accepted. Giving primarily in Fort Worth, TX.
Application information: Contributes only to pre-selected organizations.
Trustee: Bank of America, N.A.
EIN: 750989260
Selected grants: The following grants are a representative sample of this grantmaker's funding activity:
$2,793,861 to Texas Christian University, Fort Worth, TX, 2012. For unrestricted contribution.

8797
James A. "Buddy" Davidson Charitable Foundation ✧
P.O. Box 494
Midland, TX 79702-0494 (432) 682-6482
Contact: Sandra L. Davidson, Pres.
E-mail: director@jadfoundation.com; Additional e-mail addresses: Denise Newton, V.P., Medical, Nursing, and Religious Svcs.: denise@jadfoundation.com; Gail McCall, Dir., Children, Family, and Community Svcs: gail@jadfoundation.com; Elaine Greenshaw, Dir., Animals, Wildlife, and Soil Conservation: elaine@jadfoundation.com

Established in 2002 in TX.
Donor: James A. Davidson†.
Foundation type: Independent foundation.
Financial data (yr. ended 12/31/12): Assets, $85,590,973 (M); expenditures, $4,003,889; qualifying distributions, $3,441,885; giving activities include $3,266,054 for 77 grants (high: $350,000; low: $50).
Purpose and activities: The foundation's spending policy is as follows: Children - 25 percent, Family and Community Services - 10 percent; Animals, wildlife, environmental - 25 percent; Nursing - percent; Religious - 15 percent.
Fields of interest: Higher education; Environment; Animals/wildlife; Nursing care; Human services; Foundations (public); Religion.
Limitations: Applications accepted. Giving limited to TX. No grants for capital projects, salaries or employee benefits.
Application information: Application form available upon request. Application form required.
Deadline(s): Nov. 1 for nursing projects and religious organizations; March 1 for children, family and community-related organizations; and July 1 for wildlife, animals and environmental organizations
Board meeting date(s): Jan., May, and Sept.
Officers and Directors:* Sandra L. Davidson,* Pres.; Denise Newton, V.P.; Doug Tull,* V.P.; Elaine Greenhaw,* Secy.; Karen Melton,* Treas.; Gail McCall; Doyle Snow; Jerry Zant.
EIN: 731627705

8798
The Carl A. and Lois E. Davis Foundation ✧ ☆
2700 Post Oak Blvd., Ste. 1050
Houston, TX 77056-5709

Established in 2011 in TX.
Donors: Carl A. Davis; Lois E. Davis.
Foundation type: Independent foundation.
Financial data (yr. ended 12/31/13): Assets, $73,572,196 (M); expenditures, $4,190,851; qualifying distributions, $4,000,000; giving activities include $4,000,000 for 1 grant.
Fields of interest: Catholic agencies & churches.
Limitations: Applications not accepted. Giving primarily in Houston, TX.
Application information: Contributes only to pre-selected organizations.
Directors: Carl A. Davis; Lois E. Davis; Charlotte Davis Laker.
EIN: 371648116

8799
Ken W. Davis Foundation ✧
P.O. Box 3419
Fort Worth, TX 76113-3419
Main URL: http://foundationcenter.org/grantmaker/davis/

Incorporated in 1954 in TX.
Donors: Ken W. Davis, Jr.; T.C. Davis.
Foundation type: Independent foundation.
Financial data (yr. ended 12/31/13): Assets, $12,546,351 (M); expenditures, $908,103; qualifying distributions, $793,694; giving activities include $787,624 for 269 grants (high: $20,000; low: $30).
Purpose and activities: Primary areas of interest are human health and welfare.
Fields of interest: Hospitals (general); Medical care, rehabilitation; Health care; Health organizations, association; Agriculture/food; Housing/shelter; Human services; Children, services; Homeless, human services; Disabilities, people with; Homeless.
Type of support: Technical assistance; Matching/challenge support; General/operating support; Continuing support; Management development/capacity building; Capital campaigns; Building/renovation; Equipment; Program development; Consulting services.
Limitations: Applications accepted. Giving limited to Fort Worth and Midland, TX. No support for religious programs. No grants to individuals, or for annual appeals, debt retirement, research, dinners and special events, media productions or publications, scholarships, start-ups or multi-year grants; no loans.
Publications: Application guidelines; Annual report; Financial statement; IRS Form 990 or 990-PF printed copy available upon request.
Application information: Application form required.
Initial approach: Letter
Copies of proposal: 1
Deadline(s): Dec. 31
Board meeting date(s): Varies
Officers: Ken W. Davis, Jr., Pres.; T.C. Davis, V.P.; Lorene Smith, Secy.; E.K. Kaufmann, Treas.
Director: Alana Marsh.
Number of staff: 1 part-time professional.
EIN: 756012722
Selected grants: The following grants are a representative sample of this grantmaker's funding activity:
$300 to Wycliffe Bible Translators, Orlando, FL, 2012. For fund general operating expenses.

8800
Carl A. Davis & Lois E. Davis Religious & Charitable Trust ✧
8822 Stable Crest Blvd.
Houston, TX 77024-7034

Established in 1990 in TX.
Donors: Carl A. Davis; Lois E. Davis.
Foundation type: Independent foundation.
Financial data (yr. ended 12/31/13): Assets, $6,644,548 (M); gifts received, $505,120; expenditures, $4,604,205; qualifying distributions, $4,598,230; giving activities include $4,597,255 for 48 grants (high: $2,950,100; low: $50).
Purpose and activities: Giving primarily for human services and religious organizations.
Fields of interest: Human services; Religion, single organization support; Catholic agencies & churches.
Limitations: Applications not accepted. Giving primarily in Houston, TX. No grants to individuals.
Application information: Contributes only to pre-selected organizations.
Trustee: Carl A. Davis.
EIN: 766066429

8801
James C. and Teresa K. Day Foundation ✧ ☆
2277 Plaza Dr., Ste. 630
Sugar Land, TX 77478-6608

Donors: James C. Day; Teresa K. Day.
Foundation type: Independent foundation.
Financial data (yr. ended 11/30/13): Assets, $7,208,477 (M); expenditures, $499,766; qualifying distributions, $465,650; giving activities include $436,900 for 22 grants (high: $100,000; low: $1,500).
Fields of interest: Arts; Education; Human services.
Limitations: Applications not accepted.
Application information: Unsolicited requests for funds not accepted.
Officers: James C. Day, Pres.; Andrew Kanaly, Secy.; James C. Day, Jr., Treas.
EIN: 061742265

8802
Matias De Llano Charitable Trust ✧ ☆
c/o International Bank of Commerce
1200 San Bernardo Ave.
Laredo, TX 78042-1359

Established in 2003 in TX.
Donor: Matias De Llano†.
Foundation type: Independent foundation.
Financial data (yr. ended 12/31/12): Assets, $9,999,714 (M); expenditures, $1,276,408;

qualifying distributions, $1,167,500; giving activities include $1,167,500 for grants.
Purpose and activities: Giving primarily for education, and children, youth, and social services.
Fields of interest: Higher education; Education; Boys & girls clubs; Human services; Children/youth, services.
Limitations: Applications not accepted. Giving primarily in Laredo, TX.
Application information: Contributes only to pre-selected organizations.
Trustee: International Bank of Commerce.
EIN: 743013012

8803
Dean Foods Foundation ✧
2711 N. Haskell Ave., 34th Fl.
Dallas, TX 75204-2911
E-mail: giving@deanfoods.com; Main URL: http://responsibility.deanfoods.com/

Established in 1993 in IL.
Donors: Dean Foods Corporation; Dean Management Corp.
Foundation type: Company-sponsored foundation.
Financial data (yr. ended 12/31/13): Assets, $2,010,042 (M); expenditures, $623,062; qualifying distributions, $623,062; giving activities include $617,500 for 21 grants (high: $107,500; low: $5,000).
Purpose and activities: The foundation supports programs designed to promote childhood nutrition; youth leadership; dairy stewardship; and disaster response.
Fields of interest: Education; Health care, clinics/centers; Agriculture; Agriculture, farmlands; Food services; Food banks; Nutrition; Disasters, preparedness/services; American Red Cross; Leadership development; Children/youth.
Type of support: General/operating support; Continuing support; Program development.
Limitations: Applications accepted. Giving primarily in areas of company operations in Dallas, TX; giving also to national organizations. No support for religious or faith-based organizations not of direct benefit to the entire community, athletic teams, fraternal, veterans', social, alumni, or labor organizations, political or lobbying organizations, or disease-focused organizations. No grants to individuals, or for travel, film, music, television, video or media productions, or broadcast underwriting, capital campaigns, endowments, general operating support for schools, colleges, or universities, sponsorship of fundraising events, benefit dinners, auctions, sports competitions, or goodwill advertising; no product donations.
Publications: Application guidelines.
Application information: A full proposal may be requested at a later date. Organizations applying for support must have been operating and providing relevant services for a least 3 years. Unsolicited applications for disaster relief grants are not accepted. Telephone calls during the application process are not encouraged.
Initial approach: Download letter of inquiry form and e-mail to foundation
Deadline(s): Mar. 31 and Sept. 30
Final notification: Apr. 15 and Oct. 15
Officers and Directors:* Gregg L. Engles,* Chair.; Liliana M. Esposito, Pres.; Timothy A. Smith, Sr. V.P. and Treas.; Deborah E. Sutton,* V.P. and Secy.; Amy N. Barker,* V.P.; Sayeda Mahler, V.P.; Stuart R. Hueber,* V.P.
EIN: 363845182
Selected grants: The following grants are a representative sample of this grantmaker's funding activity:
$215,725 to North Texas Food Bank, Dallas, TX, 2012. For Supporting Childhood Hunger and Nutrition Programs.
$20,250 to National FFA Foundation, Indianapolis, IN, 2012. For Supporting the Career Development Event at the National FFA Convention.
$13,500 to American Red Cross, Dallas, TX, 2012. For Supporting Disaster Relief.
$9,915 to Promise House, Dallas, TX, 2012. For Product Donations to Support Homeless and Runaway Youths.
$2,500 to Michigan State University, East Lansing, MI, 2012. For Supporting Animal Welfare Research and Development Program.

8804
The DeBakey Medical Foundation ✧
3355 W. Alabama, No. 500
Houston, TX 77098-1717

Incorporated in 1961 in TX.
Donors: Michael E. DeBakey, M.D.; James F. Breuil; Eugene C. Pulliam; Rosa Taub Kahn; and others.
Foundation type: Independent foundation.
Financial data (yr. ended 04/30/13): Assets, $45,980,755 (M); gifts received, $50; expenditures, $2,112,757; qualifying distributions, $1,525,000; giving activities include $1,525,000 for grants.
Purpose and activities: Giving primarily for education and research in medicine.
Fields of interest: Medical school/education; Medical research, institute.
Limitations: Applications not accepted. Giving primarily in Houston, TX and New York, NY. No grants to individuals.
Application information: Contributes only to pre-selected organizations.
Officers and Trustees:* Dr. George P. Noon, Pres.; Gale L. Galloway,* V.P.; Oscar S. Wyatt, Jr., Secy.-Treas.; Dr. Bobby Alford; Lois DeBakey, Ph.D.
EIN: 746053822
Selected grants: The following grants are a representative sample of this grantmaker's funding activity:
$500,000 to Baylor College of Medicine, Houston, TX, 2013. For Construction and Support of Library.
$25,000 to Baylor College of Medicine, Houston, TX, 2013. For Michael E. DeBakey Excellence in Research Award.

8805
The Michael and Susan Dell Foundation ✧
P.O. Box 163867
Austin, TX 78716-3867
FAX: (512) 600-5501; E-mail: info@msdf.org; Main URL: http://www.msdf.org/
Blog: http://www.msdf.org/blog/
Facebook: http://www.facebook.com/dellfamilyfoundation?v=info
Grants Database: http://www.msdf.org/Grants/Master_Grant_List.aspx
Twitter: http://twitter.com/msdf_foundation

Established in 1999 in TX.
Donors: Michael Dell; Susan Dell.
Foundation type: Independent foundation.
Financial data (yr. ended 12/31/13): Assets, $841,658,316 (M); gifts received, $25,094,436; expenditures, $118,669,258; qualifying distributions, $116,728,588; giving activities include $66,675,040 for 562 grants (high: $5,000,000; low: $25), $6,110,000 for 1,110 grants to individuals (high: $20,000; low: $60), $19,765,349 for 4 foundation-administered programs and $6,872,048 for 10 loans/program-related investments (high: $1,500,000; low: $218,548).
Purpose and activities: The foundation's mission is to fund initiatives that seek to foster active minds, healthy bodies and a safe environment where children can thrive. It proactively seeks out opportunities to support or develop programs that address five essential focus areas: children's health, education, safety, youth development and early childhood care.
Fields of interest: Elementary/secondary education; Elementary/secondary school reform; Education; Health care, HMOs; Health care, clinics/centers; Health care, infants; Health care; Health care, patient services; Crime/violence prevention, abuse prevention; Crime/violence prevention, child abuse; Youth development; Children/youth, services; Children, day care; Community/economic development.
Limitations: Applications accepted. Giving on a local (central TX) , regional, national and international basis (international emphasis is on India). No support for medical research. No grants to individuals except for scholarship program, or for fundraisers, sponsorships, lobbying or endowments.
Publications: Grants list.
Application information: See foundation web site for guidelines and requirements. To begin, use the foundation's "Check Your Eligibility" section on its web site.
Initial approach: Submit preliminary grant request online
Officers and Directors:* Michael Dell,* Pres.; Susan Dell,* 1st V.P.; Alexander Dell,* 2nd V.P.; Marc Lisker, Secy.; Lorenzo Tellez, C.F.O.; Janet Mountain, Exec. Dir.
Number of staff: 35
EIN: 364336415
Selected grants: The following grants are a representative sample of this grantmaker's funding activity:
$4,342,107 to Dell Childrens Medical Center Foundation of Central Texas, Austin, TX, 2012. For Dell Children's Medical Center Third Bed Tower project.
$1,500,000 to New Schools Fund, New Schools Venture Fund, Oakland, CA, 2012. For DC Schools Fund II.
$1,500,000 to Saint Andrews Episcopal School, Austin, TX, 2012. For Saint Andrew's Performing and Visual Arts Center.
$1,125,000 to Charter Fund, Broomfield, CO, 2012. For efforts of Fund II to expand emerging Charter Management Organizations (CMO).
$1,125,000 to Charter Fund, Broomfield, CO, 2012. For efforts of Fund II to expand emerging Charter Management Organizations (CMO).
$1,001,710 to National Academy of Sciences, Washington, DC, 2012. For The Weight of the Nation, obesity program to be broadcast on HBO.

$874,162 to National Academy of Sciences, Washington, DC, 2012. For The Weight of the Nation, obesity program to be broadcast on HBO.
$510,849 to University of Texas Health Science Center, Houston, TX, 2012. For Michael and Susan Dell Center for the Advancement of Healthy Living.
$138,249 to Krishnamurti Foundation India, Chennai, India, 2012. For Project Delta (Phase I) Core group for Content Development and Teacher Training.
$128,162 to Andhra Pradesh Mahila Abhivruddhi Society, Hyderabad, India, 2012. For Integrated Access to Clean Water and Sanitation in urban slums through the Microfinance Delivery Channel.

8806
Dickson-Allen Foundation ✧

(formerly The Raymond Dickson Foundation)
P.O. Box 406
Hallettsville, TX 77964-0406 (361) 798-2531

Established in 1958 in TX.
Donors: Raymond Dickson†; Alton C. Allen†; Wilbur H. Baber, Jr.†.
Foundation type: Independent foundation.
Financial data (yr. ended 12/31/12): Assets, $32,542,282 (M); expenditures, $2,082,566; qualifying distributions, $1,708,460; giving activities include $1,708,460 for 71 grants (high: $300,000; low: $1,000).
Purpose and activities: Giving primarily for education, social services, and community development.
Fields of interest: Museums; Arts; Elementary/secondary education; Higher education; Education; Human services; Children/youth, services; Community/economic development.
Type of support: General/operating support; Building/renovation; Scholarship funds.
Limitations: Giving limited to TX, with emphasis on Hallettsville and San Antonio. No grants to individuals, or for building funds.
Publications: Application guidelines; Program policy statement.
Application information: Application form not required.
Initial approach: Proposal
Copies of proposal: 1
Board meeting date(s): Oct. or Nov.
Trustees: Jessie L. Allen; Curtis Gunn, Jr.; Dunham F. Jewett; Curtis T. Vaughan III.
EIN: 746052983
Selected grants: The following grants are a representative sample of this grantmaker's funding activity:
$130,000 to Shiner Catholic School, Shiner, TX, 2012. For equipment purchase.
$30,000 to Lavaca County Rescue Service, Hallettsville, TX, 2012. For equipment purchase.
$15,000 to Saint Marys University, School of Law, San Antonio, TX, 2012. For unrestricted operating funds.

8807
Robert and Michelle Diener Foundation ✧

3010 LBJ Freeway, Ste. 748
Dallas, TX 75234
Application address: c/o Robert Diener, Michelle Diener, 5521 Greenville Ave., Ste. 104-540, Dallas, TX 75206; tel.: (305) 865-9300

Established in 2001 in TX.
Donors: Robert B. Diener; Michelle S. Diener.
Foundation type: Independent foundation.
Financial data (yr. ended 12/31/13): Assets, $30,611,073 (M); expenditures, $1,884,660; qualifying distributions, $1,843,789; giving activities include $1,840,917 for 37 grants (high: $1,200,000; low: $100).
Purpose and activities: Giving primarily for Jewish education, agencies and temples; funding also for human services.
Fields of interest: Museums (children's); Education; Human services; Jewish federated giving programs; Jewish agencies & synagogues.
Limitations: Applications accepted. Giving primarily in FL and NY.
Application information: Application form not required.
Initial approach: Proposal
Deadline(s): None
Directors: Michelle S. Diener; Robert B. Diener; David S. Litman.
EIN: 752919060

8808
The Discovery Foundation ✧

6060 N. Central Expwy., Ste. 560
Dallas, TX 75206-5272

Established in TX.
Donors: Clint W. Josey, Jr.; Roger M. Dixon†.
Foundation type: Independent foundation.
Financial data (yr. ended 12/31/13): Assets, $12,888,159 (M); expenditures, $702,031; qualifying distributions, $535,388; giving activities include $504,001 for 9 grants (high: $75,788; low: $39,000).
Fields of interest: Medical care, community health systems.
Limitations: Applications not accepted. Giving primarily in Dallas, TX. No grants to individuals.
Application information: Unsolicited requests for funds not accepted.
Officers and Directors:* Clint Josey,* Chair.; David Winter, Pres. and C.E.O.; Nina Radford,* V.P.; Isabelle Moro,* Secy.; Amy Anderson,* Treas.; Christie Columbus; Paul Neubach.
EIN: 752625743

8809
The Dixon Water Foundation ✧

(formerly The Dixon Foundation)
4528 County Rd., Ste. 398
Decatur, TX 76234
Application address: c/o Robert J. Potts, P.O. Box 177, Marfa, TX 79843; tel.: (432) 729-4600

Established in TX.
Donor: Roger M. Dixon†.
Foundation type: Independent foundation.
Financial data (yr. ended 12/31/13): Assets, $53,849,225 (M); expenditures, $2,038,062; qualifying distributions, $1,463,650; giving activities include $608,542 for 19 grants (high: $50,000; low: $7,950).
Purpose and activities: Giving limited to land management, watershed protection and education.
Fields of interest: Higher education, university; Environment, land resources.
Type of support: General/operating support.
Limitations: Applications accepted. Giving primarily in TX. No grants to individuals.
Application information: Application form required.
Initial approach: Letter no more than 3 pages
Deadline(s): None
Officers: Clinton W. Josey, Jr., Chair. and V.P.; Kathy Smith, Vice-Chair. and V.P.; Robert J. Potts, Pres. and C.E.O.; Janet Samford, Secy.; Melissa Bookhout, Treas.
Directors: Jerry Addison; Hugh Aljoe; Walt Davis; Leslie C. Rauscher; Laura L. Whiting.
EIN: 752521176

8810
Dodge Jones Foundation ✧

P.O. Box 176
Abilene, TX 79604-0176 (325) 673-6429
Contact: Lawrence E. Gill, V.P. and Grants Admin.

Incorporated in 1954 in TX.
Donors: Ruth Leggett Jones†; and others.
Foundation type: Independent foundation.
Financial data (yr. ended 12/31/12): Assets, $62,809,944 (M); expenditures, $4,827,046; qualifying distributions, $3,832,686; giving activities include $3,743,288 for 141 grants (high: $1,000,000; low: $1,000), and $10,000 for 1 employee matching gift.
Purpose and activities: Support for education, the arts, health, community funds, and youth programs.
Fields of interest: Arts; Education; Animal welfare; Health care; Health organizations, association; Youth, services; Civil liberties, right to life; United Ways and Federated Giving Programs.
Type of support: General/operating support.
Limitations: Applications accepted. Giving primarily in Abilene, TX. No grants to individuals.
Application information: Application form not required.
Initial approach: Letter
Copies of proposal: 1
Deadline(s): None
Board meeting date(s): Varies
Final notification: Varies; negative responses are immediate
Officers and Directors:* Kade L. Matthews,* Chair. and Pres.; Joseph E. Canon,* Exec. V.P. and Exec. Dir.; Thomas R. Allen, V.P. and C.F.O.; Lawrence E. Gill, V.P. and Grants Admin.; Linda Buckner, Secy.-Treas.; Julia Jones Matthews, Pres. Emeritus; John A. Matthews, Jr.; Jill Matthews Wilkinson.
Number of staff: 1 full-time professional; 1 part-time professional; 3 part-time support.
EIN: 756006386

8811
The Dogwood Foundation ✧

201 Sweetwater Springs Dr.
Poolville, TX 76487-2413

Established in 1994 in FL.
Donors: Dorothy Scott Merrill†; Dorothy Scott Merrill Charitable Lead Unitrust.
Foundation type: Independent foundation.
Financial data (yr. ended 12/31/13): Assets, $18,937,762 (M); gifts received, $188,540; expenditures, $1,012,783; qualifying distributions, $837,600; giving activities include $768,000 for 29 grants (high: $120,000; low: $5,000).

Fields of interest: Historic preservation/historical societies; Arts; Education; Athletics/sports, equestrianism; Foundations (community).
Limitations: Applications not accepted. Giving primarily in FL, MI, OK, TX, and WI. No grants to individuals.
Application information: Unsolicited requests for funds not accepted.
Officers and Trustees:* Susan Meyers, Secy.; Frank G. Merrill,* Mgr.; Kyle Merrill Converse; Danielle Merrill; Holly S. Merrill.
EIN: 650499552

8812
James & Dorothy Doss Foundation, Inc. ✧
6300 Ridglea Pl., Ste. 1107
Fort Worth, TX 76116-5737

Established in 1972 in TX.
Donors: James Doss; Bill Knight; John Doss.
Foundation type: Independent foundation.
Financial data (yr. ended 12/31/13): Assets, $21,754,116 (M); expenditures, $912,121; qualifying distributions, $848,284; giving activities include $842,474 for 62 grants (high: $400,000; low: $100).
Fields of interest: Arts, multipurpose centers/programs; Higher education; Libraries/library science; Education; Health organizations; Protestant agencies & churches.
Type of support: General/operating support; Building/renovation.
Limitations: Applications not accepted. Giving primarily in TX. No grants to individuals.
Application information: Contributes only to pre-selected organizations.
Officers: Bill Knight, Pres.; Nancy Knight, Secy.-Treas.
Trustees: Jim Doss; John Doss.
EIN: 756170120
Selected grants: The following grants are a representative sample of this grantmaker's funding activity:
$100,000 to Grace First Presbyterian Church, Weatherford, TX, 2011. For building fund.
$25,000 to Howard Payne University, Brownwood, TX, 2011. For scholarship.
$19,000 to Grace First Presbyterian Church, Weatherford, TX, 2010.
$18,750 to Grace First Presbyterian Church, Weatherford, TX, 2011.
$15,000 to Manna Storehouse, Weatherford, TX, 2010.
$10,000 to Alzheimers Association, Fort Worth, TX, 2011.
$10,000 to Happy Hill Farm Childrens Home and Academy, Granbury, TX, 2010.
$10,000 to Weatherford Public Library, Friends of the, Weatherford, TX, 2010.
$5,000 to Brownwood ISD, Brownwood, TX, 2011. For scholarship.
$5,000 to TSTC Regents Circle, Waco, TX, 2011. For scholarship.
$1,000 to Weatherford Christian School, Weatherford, TX, 2011.

8813
The M. S. Doss Foundation, Inc. ✧
P.O. Box 1677
Seminole, TX 79360-1677 (432) 758-2770
Contact: Joe K. McGill, Pres.

Established in 1985 in TX.
Donors: M.S. Doss†; Meek Lane Doss†.
Foundation type: Independent foundation.
Financial data (yr. ended 12/31/13): Assets, $112,322,792 (M); expenditures, $2,479,845; qualifying distributions, $1,587,892; giving activities include $1,226,482 for 47 grants (high: $151,847; low: $159), and $143,795 for 4 foundation-administered programs.
Purpose and activities: Support primarily for family and youth services, clubs, and centers; support also for scholarships for higher education.
Fields of interest: Higher education; Youth development, centers/clubs; Children/youth, services; Family services; Residential/custodial care; Community/economic development.
Type of support: General/operating support; Building/renovation; Equipment; Endowments; Scholarship funds.
Limitations: Giving primarily in the eastern NM and western TX area; giving limited to Gaines County, TX, for scholarships. No grants to individuals directly.
Application information: Scholarship payments made directly to the college on behalf of named recipient. Application form required.
Initial approach: Letter of inquiry
Copies of proposal: 1
Deadline(s): None
Board meeting date(s): Feb. and as required
Final notification: Following board meeting
Officers and Trustees:* Joe K. McGill,* Chair. and Pres.; Stuart Robertson,* V.P.; Julia Narvarte Romanow,* Secy.; Karla Morton,* Treas.
Number of staff: 1 full-time professional; 1 full-time support; 1 part-time support.
EIN: 751945227
Selected grants: The following grants are a representative sample of this grantmaker's funding activity:
$500,000 to Abilene Boys Ranch, Abilene, TX, 2012. For building renovations.
$500,000 to UMC Foundation, Lubbock, TX, 2012. For building renovations.
$250,000 to Childrens Hospital Association, Aurora, CO, 2012. For operating support.
$250,000 to Cook Childrens Medical Center, Fort Worth, TX, 2012. For operating support.
$150,000 to Texas A & M Foundation, College Station, TX, 2012. For scholarships.
$150,000 to Texas Tech Foundation, Lubbock, TX, 2012. For scholarships.
$110,000 to University of Texas, El Paso, TX, 2012. For scholarships.
$100,000 to Camp Fire USA, First Texas Council, Fort Worth, TX, 2012. For building renovations.
$84,374 to YMCA of Hereford, Hereford, TX, 2012. For building renovations and equipment.
$50,000 to Big Brothers Big Sisters of Midland, Midland, TX, 2012. For capital campaign.

8814
H. J. & Florence A. Doswell Foundation ✧
6211 W. Nothwest Hwy., No. 507
Dallas, TX 75225-3422

Established in 2008 in TX.
Donor: Florence A. Doswell.
Foundation type: Independent foundation.
Financial data (yr. ended 12/31/12): Assets, $10,216,355 (M); expenditures, $665,044; qualifying distributions, $500,000; giving activities include $500,000 for 14 grants (high: $200,000; low: $5,000).
Fields of interest: Food banks; Human services; Salvation Army; Residential/custodial care.
Limitations: Applications not accepted. Giving primarily in TX. No grants to individuals.
Application information: Contributes only to pre-selected organizations.
Officers and Directors:* Florence A. Doswell,* Pres.; A. Carl Johnston,* Secy.; Kenneth E. Fricke,* Treas.; Dial H. Anderson; John B. Mills.
EIN: 262767135
Selected grants: The following grants are a representative sample of this grantmaker's funding activity:
$200,000 to North Texas Food Bank, Dallas, TX, 2012. To purchase food supplies.

8815
The Duda Family Foundation ✧
c/o James F. Tabor
5950 Berkshire Ln., No. 800
Dallas, TX 75225-5836 (972) 616-8777

Established in 1997.
Donors: Fritz L. Duda; Mrs. Fritz L. Duda; Mary L. Duda.
Foundation type: Independent foundation.
Financial data (yr. ended 12/31/12): Assets, $19,353,129 (M); expenditures, $1,307,821; qualifying distributions, $1,031,007; giving activities include $1,008,012 for 112 grants (high: $200,000; low: $100).
Purpose and activities: Giving primarily for education, health organizations, and children, youth, and social services.
Fields of interest: Elementary/secondary education; Higher education; Education; Health organizations, association; Human services; Children/youth, services.
Limitations: Applications accepted. Giving primarily in CA and TX. No grants to individuals.
Application information: Application form required.
Initial approach: Letter
Deadline(s): Sept. 30
Trustees: Fritz L. Duda; Fritz L. Duda, Jr.; James F. Duda; Mary L. Duda; Leigh A. Duda Scott; Lendy D. Duda Vail.
EIN: 436765664

8816
John S. Dunn Research Foundation
3355 W. Alabama St., Ste. 990
Houston, TX 77098-1863 (713) 626-0368
Contact: Donna Nasso, Office Mgr.
FAX: (713) 626-3866; E-mail: jsdrf@swbell.net; Main URL: http://johnsdunnfoundation.org/

Established in 1985 in TX.
Donor: John S. Dunn, Sr.†.
Foundation type: Independent foundation.
Financial data (yr. ended 12/31/12): Assets, $88,488,650 (M); expenditures, $6,137,912; qualifying distributions, $5,278,584; giving activities include $5,010,250 for 32 grants (high: $400,000; low: $35,000).
Purpose and activities: Giving limited to institutions in the State of Texas and the foundation's grants are generally approved for nursing programs, healthcare clinics for the underserved, mental health programs, and medical research and education in the greater Houston, TX, area.

Fields of interest: Hospitals (general); Health care; Health organizations, association; Cancer; Medical research, institute; Cancer research; Biology/life sciences.
Type of support: Endowments; Matching/challenge support; Professorships; Research.
Limitations: Applications accepted. Giving generally limited to TX. No grants to individuals, or for multi-year or seed money grants.
Publications: Application guidelines; Informational brochure (including application guidelines).
Application information: Application form not required.
Initial approach: Letter
Copies of proposal: 1
Deadline(s): None
Board meeting date(s): Full board meets monthly and quarterly; 4th Wed. of each month
Final notification: Written notice 1 week following meeting
Officers and Trustees:* J. Dickson Rogers,* Pres.; Dan S. Wilford,* 1st V.P.; John S. Dunn, Jr.,* V.P. and Secy.-Treas.; Mrs. Dagmar Dunn Pickens Gipe,* V.P.; David G. Key,* V.P.; Charles M. Lusk III,* V.P.; John R. Wallace,* V.P.
Number of staff: 1 full-time professional; 2 full-time support.
EIN: 741933660
Selected grants: The following grants are a representative sample of this grantmaker's funding activity:
$500,000 to CHRISTUS Foundation for Healthcare, Houston, TX, 2012.
$500,000 to Texas Childrens Hospital, Cancer Center, Houston, TX, 2012.
$500,000 to University of Texas Health Science Center, School of Nursing, Houston, TX, 2012.
$400,000 to Memorial Hermann Foundation, Houston, TX, 2012.
$140,000 to San Jose Clinic, Houston, TX, 2012.
$100,000 to Council on Alcohol and Drugs Houston, Houston, TX, 2012.
$100,000 to Depression and Bipolar Support Alliance - Greater Houston, Houston, TX, 2012.
$100,000 to El Centro de Corazon, Houston, TX, 2012.
$100,000 to Rice University, Houston, TX, 2012.
$100,000 to University of Texas Health Science Center, Department of Psychiatry, Houston, TX, 2012.

8817
Steven H. Durham Family Charitable Foundation ✧ ☆
(formerly Margre & Charles Durham Foundation I)
5944 Luther Ln., Ste. 600
Dallas, TX 75225-5918

Established in 2000 in NE; Dec. 2008 absorbed assets of the Durham Foundation.
Donors: Charles W. Durham Charitable Lead Annuity Trust; Charles W. Durham Charitable Lead Annuity Trust no. 2; Charles W. W. Durham‡.
Foundation type: Independent foundation.
Financial data (yr. ended 12/31/12): Assets, $22,520,882 (M); gifts received, $500,000; expenditures, $974,847; qualifying distributions, $438,788; giving activities include $438,788 for grants.
Fields of interest: Arts; Human services; United Ways and Federated Giving Programs.
Type of support: General/operating support.
Limitations: Applications not accepted. Giving primarily in NE. No grants to individuals.
Application information: Unsolicited requests for funds not accepted.
Directors: Steven H. Durham; Barbara Durham; Carol Cashman.
EIN: 470830375

8818
J. Tom Eady Charitable Trust ✧
c/o Community National Bank & Trust
P.O. Box 624
Corsicana, TX 75151-9004
Contact: Les Leskoven, Sr. V.P. and Trust Off., Community National Bank & Trust
Tel. and e-mail for L. Leskoven: (903) 654-4528, e-mail: lleskoven@cbhot.com

Established in 2000 in TX.
Donor: John Thomas Eady‡.
Foundation type: Independent foundation.
Financial data (yr. ended 12/31/13): Assets, $10,955,389 (M); expenditures, $482,353; qualifying distributions, $449,307; giving activities include $378,192 for 23 grants (high: $95,000; low: $425), and $66,418 for 20 grants to individuals (high: $7,500; low: $1,000).
Purpose and activities: Giving primarily for the arts, education, youth and social services, and community development. Scholarships are also made to selected students to help cover the cost of education beyond high school. Students should be a current year graduate of a Navarro County, Texas, high school, and have been accepted into an accredited college, university or technical college. Applicants should also have an SAT (math and reading portions only) minimum total score of 1,000 or ACT minimum total score of 21.
Fields of interest: Arts; Education; Youth development; Human services; Community/economic development; Christian agencies & churches.
Type of support: General/operating support; Continuing support; Annual campaigns; Capital campaigns; Building/renovation; Equipment; Program development; Scholarships—to individuals; Matching/challenge support.
Limitations: Applications accepted. Giving limited to Navarro County, TX.
Application information: Application required for scholarships. Application form not required.
Initial approach: Letter
Deadline(s): None
Board meeting date(s): Jan., Apr., July, and Oct.
Final notification: 3 month or less, depending on time of receipt
Board Members: George Burrell; Les Leskoven; Eric Meyers; B.F. Risinger.
Trustee: Community National Bank & Trust.
EIN: 756604134

8819
East Texas Communities Foundation, Inc. ✧
(formerly East Texas Area Foundation)
315 N. Broadway, Ste. 210
Tyler, TX 75702-5757 (903) 533-0208
Contact: Kyle L. Penney, Pres.; For grants: Mary Lynn Smith, Prog. Off.
FAX: (903) 533-0258; E-mail: etcf@etcf.org; Grant inquiry e-mail: mlsmith@etcf.org; Additional tel.: (866) 533-3823; Main URL: http://www.etcf.org

Established in 1989 in TX.
Foundation type: Community foundation.
Financial data (yr. ended 12/31/12): Assets, $52,992,326 (M); gifts received, $6,443,366; expenditures, $5,566,763; giving activities include $4,608,968 for 129+ grants (high: $281,000), and $238,400 for 96 grants to individuals.
Purpose and activities: The foundation supports philanthropy by offering simple ways for donors to achieve their long-term charitable goals. The foundation does this by: 1) serving as a flexible and cost-effective vehicle for donors to invest in the community; 2) promoting philanthropy in all its forms; and 3) building permanent endowments for the region's changing issues and opportunities. Primary areas of grantmaking include arts and humanities, education, health, and human services.
Fields of interest: Humanities; Historic preservation/historical societies; Arts; Education; Hospitals (general); Health care; Youth, services; Human services; Community/economic development; Engineering/technology.
Limitations: Applications accepted. Giving primarily in eastern TX. No grants to individuals (except for scholarships), or for budget deficits, debt retirement, or restructuring, conferences, or travel, capital campaigns, general operating expenses, endowments or reserve funds, or scholarly research, biomedical, or clinical studies.
Publications: Annual report; Informational brochure; Newsletter.
Application information: Visit foundation web site for grant application information from various funds.
Deadline(s): Varies
Board meeting date(s): 3rd Tues., monthly
Officers and Directors:* Shannon Dacus,* Chair.; Richard W. Jett, Jr.,* Vice-Chair.; Kyle L. Penney, Pres.; Craig S. Adams,* Secy.; John W. Ferguson, Jr.,* Treas. and Chair., Support Committee; Michael Bosworth, Chair., Policy; Steve Dement, Chair., Grants; Tony Morgan, Chair., Audit; Laura Koenig Young, Chair., Mktg. and Devel.; Allen Burt, Dir. Emeritus; F. William Martin, Dir. Emeritus; H.T. Smith, Dir. Emeritus; Jon Alexander; James Richard Allen; Michael D. Allen; Douglas G. Bolles; Mark Boon; Michelle Brookshire; Tom Brown; Roe Buckley; Bob Dyer; Dawn Franks; Tiffany Kirgan; Lisa Lujan; Fritter McNally; John Minton; Gordon L. Northcutt; John G. Payne; Kristen Seeber; Thomas Smith; W. Fred Smith, Jr.; Scott Terry; Thomas M. Woldert.
Number of staff: 3 full-time professional; 1 part-time professional.
EIN: 752309138

8820
George Eby Foundation ✧ ☆
2109 Paramount Ave.
Austin, TX 78704-3935
Contact: George A. Eby, Pres.

Established in 1998 in TX.
Donors: George Eby; Patsy Ann Eby.
Foundation type: Independent foundation.
Financial data (yr. ended 12/31/12): Assets, $400,738 (M); expenditures, $482,830; qualifying distributions, $431,460; giving activities include $431,460 for 3 grants (high: $231,112; low: $37,087).

Purpose and activities: Giving limited to research and projects in the scientific field.
Fields of interest: Foundations (community).
Limitations: Applications accepted. Giving primarily in TX.
Application information: Application form required.
Initial approach: Proposal
Deadline(s): None
Officer: George Eby, Pres.
EIN: 742860396

8821
John R. Eckel Jr. Foundation ✧
c/o C. Slack (GHCF)
5120 Woodway, No. 6000
Houston, TX 77056-1723

Donor: John R. Eckel, Jr.†.
Foundation type: Independent foundation.
Financial data (yr. ended 12/31/13): Assets, $46,697,297 (M); gifts received, $49,862,575; expenditures, $2,386,007; qualifying distributions, $2,175,415; giving activities include $2,120,000 for 10 grants (high: $1,000,000; low: $25,000).
Fields of interest: Arts; Agriculture/food; Human services.
Limitations: Applications not accepted. Giving primarily in Houston, TX.
Application information: Unsolicited requests for funds not accepted.
Officers and Directors:* Douglas L. Lawing,* Pres. and Treas.; Jeffrey A. Casey,* V.P. and Secy.; T. Randolph Harris.
EIN: 272818091
Selected grants: The following grants are a representative sample of this grantmaker's funding activity:
$1,360,950 to Whitney Museum of American Art, New York, NY, 2012. For capital campaign/general support.
$100,000 to Menil Foundation, Houston, TX, 2012. For exhibition fund.
$95,000 to Elton John AIDS Foundation, New York, NY, 2012. For Purpose for the Enduring Vision Event.
$25,000 to Columbia University, New York, NY, 2012. For general support in honor of 100th Anniversary.
$25,000 to Lawndale Art and Performance Center, Houston, TX, 2012. To design Fair.

8822
Ed Foundation ✧
(formerly The Jeff D. Sandefer Foundation)
1606 Niles Rd.
Austin, TX 78703 (512) 495-9925

Established in 1997 in TX.
Donors: Jeff D. Sandefer; Sandefer Capital Partners, LP.
Foundation type: Independent foundation.
Financial data (yr. ended 12/31/12): Assets, $95,030,188 (M); expenditures, $5,009,555; qualifying distributions, $4,973,909; giving activities include $4,954,200 for 18 grants (high: $3,250,000; low: $1,500).
Fields of interest: Business school/education; Education; Human services; Foundations (private grantmaking); Christian agencies & churches.
Limitations: Applications not accepted. Giving in the U.S., with emphasis on Austin, TX. No grants to individuals.
Application information: Contributes only to pre-selected organizations.
Officers and Directors:* Jeff D. Sandefer,* Pres.; Laura Sandefer,* Secy.; John B. Lawson; John R. Rutherford.
EIN: 742804730

8823
Bryant Edwards Foundation, Inc. ✧
807 8th St., 2nd Fl.
Wichita Falls, TX 76301-3381

Established in 1959.
Donors: Bryant Edwards†; Dorothy B. Edwards†.
Foundation type: Independent foundation.
Financial data (yr. ended 10/31/13): Assets, $23,936,091 (M); expenditures, $1,698,355; qualifying distributions, $1,434,520; giving activities include $1,380,695 for 55 grants (high: $31,000; low: $182).
Purpose and activities: Giving primarily for the arts, education, and youth.
Fields of interest: Historic preservation/historical societies; Arts; Higher education; Hospitals (general); Health organizations; Human services.
Type of support: Capital campaigns; Building/renovation; Equipment; Endowments; Internship funds.
Limitations: Applications not accepted. Giving primarily in Wichita Falls, TX. No grants to individuals.
Application information: Contributes only to pre-selected organizations.
Officers and Directors:* Mac W. Cannedy, Jr.,* Pres. and Treas.; Dennis D. Cannedy,* V.P.; Erwin Davenport,* Secy.
EIN: 756012973

8824
J. E. S. Edwards Foundation ✧
P.O. Box 122297
Fort Worth, TX 76121-2297 (817) 737-6924
Contact: Jareen E. Schmidt, Pres.

Established in 1976 in TX.
Donors: Jareen E. Schmidt; Jareen E. Schmidt Irrevocable Charitable Lead Annuity Trust; Jareen E. Schmidt Revocable Trust.
Foundation type: Independent foundation.
Financial data (yr. ended 07/31/13): Assets, $15,132,723 (M); gifts received, $589,778; expenditures, $724,909; qualifying distributions, $621,000; giving activities include $621,000 for 41 grants (high: $50,000; low: $2,350).
Purpose and activities: Grants largely for social services, including programs for women, hunger, the disadvantaged, and child welfare; support also for health and at-risk youth agencies, and Christian missionary programs.
Fields of interest: Child development, education; Adult/continuing education; Health care; Cancer; Medical research, institute; Cancer research; Food services; Human services; Youth, services; Child development, services; Women, centers/services; Christian agencies & churches; Religion; Women; Economically disadvantaged.
Type of support: Technical assistance; General/operating support; Capital campaigns; Equipment; Emergency funds; Research; Matching/challenge support.
Limitations: Applications accepted. Giving primarily in Fort Worth, TX. No support for individual churches. No grants to individuals, or for scholarships.
Application information: Application form required.
Initial approach: Letter
Copies of proposal: 1
Deadline(s): May 31
Board meeting date(s): June
Officers: Jareen E. Schmidt, Pres.; Stace Sewell, V.P.; Sheryl E. Bowen, Secy.-Treas.
Director: Stan Sewell.
EIN: 510173260

8825
El Paso Community Foundation ✧
333 N. Oregon, 2nd Fl.
P.O. Box 272
El Paso, TX 79901 (915) 533-4020
Contact: Richard E. Pearson, Pres.
FAX: (915) 532-0716; E-mail: info@epcf.org; Main URL: http://www.epcf.org
Facebook: https://www.facebook.com/ElPasoCommunityFoundation
Twitter: https://twitter.com/ElPasoCF

Incorporated in 1977 in TX.
Foundation type: Community foundation.
Financial data (yr. ended 12/31/13): Assets, $4,310,390 (M); gifts received, $1,965,155; expenditures, $6,181,535; giving activities include $2,823,329 for grants.
Purpose and activities: The foundation seeks to: 1) establish permanent charitable endowments; 2) provide a vehicle for donors' varied interests; 3) promote local philanthropy; and 4) provide leadership and resources in addressing local challenges and opportunities. Primary areas of interest include education, human services, health and disabilities, arts and humanities, the environment and animals, and community development.
Fields of interest: Humanities; Arts; Education; Environment; Animal welfare; Health care; Independent living, disability; Human services; Community/economic development.
International interests: Mexico.
Type of support: General/operating support; Management development/capacity building; Equipment; Program development; Seed money; Scholarship funds; Technical assistance; Matching/challenge support.
Limitations: Applications accepted. Giving limited to the El Paso, TX region: far west Texas, southern NM, and northern Chihuahua, Mexico. No support for medical or academic research, or religious purposes. No grants to individuals (except for scholarships), or for deficit financing, annual campaigns, travel, capital campaigns, fundraising events, endowments, or ongoing support.
Publications: Application guidelines; Annual report; Financial statement; Grants list; Informational brochure; Newsletter; Occasional report.
Application information: Visit foundation web site for application form and guidelines. Application form required.
Initial approach: Submit application
Copies of proposal: 1
Deadline(s): Feb. 1 and Aug. 1
Board meeting date(s): Feb. May, Sept., and Nov.
Final notification: Following board consideration
Officers and Directors:* Leigh V. Bloss,* Chair.; Marylee Warwick Jurecky,* Vice-Chair.; Eric Pearson,* C.E.O. and Pres.; Carmen M. Vargas,*

C.F.O.; Jonathan Rogers, Jr.,* Secy.-Treas.; Joe Alcantar, Jr.; Frances R. Axelson; Jack Eisenberg; Ruth E. Gillett; Tom Hussman; Laura Karam; Chris Lane; Betty MacGuire; James Magee; John S. McKee, Jr.; Dorothy Murray; Dr. Roger G. Ortiz, D.D.S.; Mary Carmen Saucedo.
Number of staff: 8 full-time professional; 4 full-time support; 1 part-time support.
EIN: 741839536
Selected grants: The following grants are a representative sample of this grantmaker's funding activity:
$425,400 to University of Texas, El Paso, TX, 2011.
$175,000 to El Pasoans Fighting Hunger, El Paso, TX, 2011.
$163,500 to Diocese of El Paso, El Paso, TX, 2011.
$158,017 to University Medical Center Foundation of El Paso, El Paso, TX, 2011.
$130,000 to Archdiocese of Galveston-Houston, Houston, TX, 2011.
$100,000 to Paso Del Norte Childrens Development Center, El Paso, TX, 2011.
$100,000 to Paso Del Norte Childrens Development Center, El Paso, TX, 2011.
$54,000 to Assistance League of El Paso, El Paso, TX, 2011.
$40,000 to Creative Kids, El Paso, TX, 2011.

8826
The Elkins Foundation ✧
(formerly Margaret & James A. Elkins, Jr. Foundation)
1166 First City Twr.
1001 Fannin St.
Houston, TX 77002-6706
Contact: Larry Medford

Established in 1956 in TX.
Donor: Elkins Family Charitable Lead Annuity Trust.
Foundation type: Independent foundation.
Financial data (yr. ended 10/31/13): Assets, $209,160,859 (M); gifts received, $3,540,031; expenditures, $9,639,997; qualifying distributions, $8,660,000; giving activities include $8,660,000 for 54 grants (high: $2,150,000; low: $5,000).
Purpose and activities: Giving primarily for charitable, religious, scientific, or educational and literacy programs, including public safety testing, and the prevention of cruelty to children and animals.
Fields of interest: Child development, education; Higher education; Medical school/education; Education; Hospitals (general); Health organizations, association; Medical research, institute; Safety/disasters; Children/youth, services; Child development, services; Engineering/technology; Biology/life sciences; Science; Christian agencies & churches; Religion.
Type of support: Capital campaigns; Building/renovation; Equipment; Endowments; Emergency funds; Program development; Research.
Limitations: Applications accepted. Giving primarily in the metropolitan Houston, TX area, support also in Princeton, NJ. No grants to individuals, or for deficit financing; generally no grants for continuing operating support.
Application information: Application form not required.
Initial approach: Letter
Copies of proposal: 1
Deadline(s): None
Board meeting date(s): Varies

Officers and Trustees:* Leslie E. Sasser,* Pres.; Elise E. Joseph,* V.P.; William L. Medford, Secy.-Treas.; Virginia A. Elkins.
EIN: 746051746
Selected grants: The following grants are a representative sample of this grantmaker's funding activity:
$100,000 to Asia Society Texas Center, Houston, TX, 2011.
$50,000 to Salvation Army of Alexandria, Alexandria, VA, 2011.

8827
The Ellwood Foundation ✧
P.O. Box 550049
Houston, TX 77255-0049 (713) 785-5507
Contact: H. Wayne Hightower, Jr., Tr.

Trust established in 1958 in TX.
Donors: D.C. Ellwood†; Irene L. Ellwood†.
Foundation type: Independent foundation.
Financial data (yr. ended 09/30/13): Assets, $40,761,241 (M); expenditures, $2,188,093; qualifying distributions, $1,860,000; giving activities include $1,860,000 for 65 grants (high: $120,000; low: $5,000).
Purpose and activities: Giving primarily for medical research and education.
Fields of interest: Education, special; Medical school/education; Education; Health organizations; Medical research, institute; Cancer research; Human services; Children/youth, services.
Type of support: General/operating support; Scholarship funds; Research.
Limitations: Applications accepted. Giving primarily in the Houston, TX, area.
Application information:
Initial approach: Letter
Deadline(s): None
Trustees: Raymond L. Brown; H. Wayne Hightower, Jr.; Raybourne Thompson, Jr.
EIN: 746039237
Selected grants: The following grants are a representative sample of this grantmaker's funding activity:
$100,000 to Briarwood School, Houston, TX, 2013. For special educational needs.
$50,000 to Child Advocates, Houston, TX, 2013. For Advocate through courts for abused children.
$40,000 to Texas Heart Institute, Houston, TX, 2013. For Cardiology Research.
$25,000 to Holly Hall, Houston, TX, 2013. For Home for Aged and Infirmed.
$25,000 to Texas Christian University, Fort Worth, TX, 2013. For Upgrade Pre - Medical Program.

8828
Embrey Family Foundation ✧
3625 N. Hall St., Ste. 720
Dallas, TX 75219-5106 (214) 206-3577
Contact: Jackie Robertson, Grants Admin.
FAX: (214) 599-9203;
E-mail: jrobertson@embreyfdn.org; E-mail for Jackie Robertson: jrobertson@embreyfdn.org; Main URL: http://www.embreyfdn.org
Facebook: https://www.facebook.com/EmbreyFamilyFoundation
Twitter: https://twitter.com/embreyfdn
WordPress: http://www.embreyfoundation.wordpress.com
YouTube: http://www.youtube.com/user/EmbreyFoundation

Established in 2004.
Donor: James L. Embrey, Jr.†.
Foundation type: Independent foundation.
Financial data (yr. ended 12/31/12): Assets, $24,216,297 (M); gifts received, $2,318,294; expenditures, $5,479,684; qualifying distributions, $4,956,292; giving activities include $4,300,436 for 40+ grants (high: $500,000), and $28,268 for loans/program-related investments.
Purpose and activities: The foundation's mission champions the well-being and rights of all people by supporting programs that advance human rights, healthy communities, the environment, education, and creativity.
Fields of interest: Arts; Education; Animal welfare; Human services; Civil/human rights; Community/economic development; Infants/toddlers; Children/youth; Adults; Aging; Minorities; Hispanics/Latinos; Women; Girls; Adults, women; Young adults, female; Adults, men; AIDS, people with; Single parents; Crime/abuse victims; Immigrants/refugees; Economically disadvantaged; Homeless.
Type of support: General/operating support; Continuing support; Capital campaigns; Building/renovation; Equipment; Emergency funds; Program development; Seed money; Matching/challenge support.
Limitations: Applications not accepted. Giving primarily in the North TX area. No support for religious, political or medical organizations, or for youth sports programs and activities. No grants to individuals or for individual scholarship awards, or for operating deficits, debt retirement, research, media production or publications, conferences, school trips or other educational events.
Application information: All grant requests are via invitation only. If you believe your program aligns with the foundation's priorities, please contact the foundation to discuss the possibility of receiving an invitation.
Board meeting date(s): Jan., Apr., July, and Oct.
Officers and Directors:* Lauren Embrey,* Chair., C.E.O., and Pres.; Gayle Embrey,* Vice-Chair. and V.P.; Ben Ablon,* Secy.; Michael Magers,* Treas.; Bobbie Embrey; Jeffery Harwell, Jr.; Bryan Marquis.
EIN: 200215399
Selected grants: The following grants are a representative sample of this grantmaker's funding activity:
$513,035 to Colonnades Theater Lab, Los Angeles, CA, 2011.
$500,000 to Planned Parenthood of Greater Texas, Dallas, TX, 2011.
$450,000 to Dallas Womens Foundation, Dallas, TX, 2011.
$332,000 to Southern Methodist University, Dallas, TX, 2011.
$300,000 to Amnesty International USA, New York, NY, 2011.
$300,000 to Education is Freedom Foundation, Dallas, TX, 2011.
$250,000 to Washington Area Womens Foundation, Washington, DC, 2011.
$250,000 to Womens Campaign Forum Foundation, Washington, DC, 2011.
$98,000 to Booker T. Washington High School for the Performing and Visual Arts, Dallas, TX, 2011.
$25,000 to Dallas Film Society, Dallas, TX, 2011.

8829
Endowment for Regional Sustainability Science ✧
24 Waterway Ave., Ste. 300
The Woodlands, TX 77380-3289 (713) 377-5085
Contact: John B. Planchard, V.P. and Secy.- Treas.
George Mitchell's Giving Pledge Profile: http://glasspockets.org/philanthropy-in-focus/eye-on-the-giving-pledge/profiles/mitchell

Established in 2004 in TX.
Donors: Cynthia W. Mitchell; George P. Mitchell‡.
Foundation type: Independent foundation.
Financial data (yr. ended 12/31/12): Assets, $27,340,300 (M); expenditures, $1,365,606; qualifying distributions, $1,353,897; giving activities include $1,350,000 for 2 grants (high: $750,000; low: $600,000).
Purpose and activities: Giving primarily for advanced research dedicated to improving human and ecosystem well-being through the application of sustainability science and principles of sustainable development.
Fields of interest: Environment.
Limitations: Giving primarily in TX.
Application information: The foundation generally contributes to pre-selected organizations.
Officers and Directors:* Barry E. Leavitt,* Pres.; John B. Planchard, V.P. and Secy.-Treas; Marilu Hestings; Katherine Lorenz; Dietrich Scheder-Bieschien; Jonathan Zonis.
EIN: 202028290

8830
Paul F. and Virginia J. Engler Foundation ✧
P.O. Box 2010
Amarillo, TX 79105-2010

Established in 1990 in TX.
Donors: Members of the Engler family; Paul F. Engler.
Foundation type: Independent foundation.
Financial data (yr. ended 12/31/12): Assets, $36,585,508 (M); gifts received, $134,243; expenditures, $2,490,145; qualifying distributions, $2,044,281; giving activities include $2,044,281 for 38 grants (high: $2,000,000; low: $37).
Fields of interest: Higher education; Education; Health organizations, association; Human services.
Limitations: Applications not accepted. Giving primarily in Lincoln, NE, and TX. No grants to individuals.
Application information: Contributes only to pre-selected organizations.
Officers and Directors:* Paul F. Engler,* Chair.; Peggy McGuire, Exec. Dir.; Jerry D. Miller; Richard C. Ware III.
EIN: 752356449

8831
The Roger and Rosemary Enrico Foundation ✧
3831 Turtle Creek Blvd., No. 23B
Dallas, TX 75219-4480

Established in 2000 in TX.
Donor: Roger A. Enrico.
Foundation type: Independent foundation.
Financial data (yr. ended 12/31/12): Assets, $28,306,644 (M); gifts received, $2,545,866; expenditures, $2,301,722; qualifying distributions, $1,773,872; giving activities include $1,773,872 for grants.
Fields of interest: Human services; Catholic federated giving programs.
Type of support: General/operating support.
Limitations: Applications not accepted. Giving primarily in Washington, DC, and Dallas, TX; giving also in CA, FL, MT, and NY. No grants to individuals.
Application information: Contributes only to pre-selected organizations.
Officer: Terence C. Sullivan, Treas.
Directors: Aaron J. Enrico; Roger A. Enrico; Rosemary Enrico.
EIN: 752871636

8832
The Eugene McDermott Foundation ✧
5018 Antoine Dr., Ste. B-153
Houston, TX 77092-3357
Application address: c/o Mary McDermott Cook, Pres., 3808 Euclid, Dallas, TX, 75205; tel.: (214) 521-2924

Established in 2006 in TX.
Donor: Eugene McDermott.
Foundation type: Independent foundation.
Financial data (yr. ended 12/31/12): Assets, $92,299,293 (M); expenditures, $6,570,335; qualifying distributions, $6,333,644; giving activities include $6,239,000 for 118 grants (high: $1,000,000; low: $1,000).
Fields of interest: Arts; Education; Health organizations.
Limitations: Giving primarily in TX.
Application information: Application form not required.
Initial approach: Proposal
Deadline(s): None
Officer and Trustees:* Mary McDermott Cook,* Pres.; J. H. Cullum Clark; Liza Lee; Mrs. Eugene McDermott; Sam Self.
EIN: 237237818

8833
ExxonMobil Foundation ✧
5959 Las Colinas Blvd.
Irving, TX 75039-2298
Contact: Patrick McCarthy, Exec. Dir.
Main URL: http://www.exxonmobil.com/Corporate/community_foundation.aspx

Incorporated in 1955 in NJ as Esso Education Foundation; name changed to Exxon Education Foundation in 1972; name changed to ExxonMobil Foundation in 1999.
Donors: Exxon Corp.; Exxon Mobil Corp.
Foundation type: Company-sponsored foundation.
Financial data (yr. ended 12/31/13): Assets, $106,013,353 (M); gifts received, $110,654,768; expenditures, $73,602,542; qualifying distributions, $73,002,542; giving activities include $40,196,645 for 322+ grants, and $32,551,321 for employee matching gifts.
Purpose and activities: The foundation supports organizations involved with education, the environment, endangered species and habitats, health, medical research, human services, community development, civic affairs, and women. Special emphasis is directed toward programs designed to provide mathematics, engineering, science, and technology education. Support is given primarily in areas of company operations; giving also to national and international organizations.
Fields of interest: Higher education; Engineering school/education; Education; Environment, natural resources; Environment; Animals/wildlife, endangered species; Health care; Parasitic diseases; Medical research; Human services; Economic development; Business/industry; Community/economic development; Science, formal/general education; Mathematics; Public policy, research; Public affairs; Women.
International interests: Africa; Developing Countries.
Type of support: Employee matching gifts; Employee volunteer services; General/operating support; Program development.
Limitations: Applications not accepted. Giving on national and international basis, primarily in areas of company operations in Baldwin and Mobile counties, AL, Anchorage, Fairbanks, and North Slope, AK, Santa Barbara County and Torrance, CA, Cortez and Rio Blanco County, CO, Washington, DC, LaGrange, GA, Joliet, IL, Baton Rouge, Chalmette, and Grand Isle, LA, Billings, MT, Clinton and Paulsboro, NJ, Rochester, NY, Akron, OH, Shawnee and Texas County, OK, Baytown, Beaumont, Dallas, Fort Worth, Houston, Midland, Odessa, and Tyler, TX, San Juan County, UT, Fairfax County and northern VA, and Lincoln, Sublette, and Sweetwater counties, WY; giving also to national and international organizations. No support for political or religious organizations or youth sports organizations. No grants to individuals, or for institutional scholarship or fellowship programs, capital campaigns, land acquisition, equipment, renovation projects, endowments, athletics, or scholarships; no loans.
Publications: Annual report; Corporate giving report; Grants list.
Application information: Contributes only to pre-selected organizations.
Officers and Trustees:* K. P. Cohen,* Chair.; Suzanne M. McCarron, Pres.; N. H. Jenkins, Secy.; L. M. Rubin, Treas.; B. A. Babock, Cont.; Patrick McCarthy, Exec. Dir.; L. M. Lachenmyer; J. M. Spellings; E. White; J. J. Woodbury.
Number of staff: 5 part-time professional; 3 part-time support.
EIN: 136082357
Selected grants: The following grants are a representative sample of this grantmaker's funding activity:
$2,670,000 to Vital Voices Global Partnership, Washington, DC, 2013. For Business Women's Network as part of Women's Economic Opportunity Initiative.
$1,836,872 to National Science Teachers Association, Arlington, VA, 2013. For Mickelson ExxonMobil (EM) Teachers Academies designed to provide third- through fifth-grade teachers with the knowledge and skills necessary to motivate students to pursue careers in science and math.
$1,500,000 to Malaria No More, New York, NY, 2013. For malaria advocacy and prevention work in Chad and Nigeria.
$750,000 to Global Health Service Corps, Seed Global Health, Boston, MA, 2013. For ExxonMobil Fellowships in Global Health.
$600,000 to Harris Foundation, Houston, TX, 2013. For administration of ExxonMobil Bernard Harris Science Camps.

$500,000 to Africare, Washington, DC, 2013. For Phase II of Economic Empowerment of Women Entrepreneurs in Chad as part of Women's Economic Opportunity Initiative.
$300,000 to Norges Rode Kors, Oslo, Norway, 2013. For Mobile Phone Malaria Survey.
$195,000 to George Washington University, Trachtenberg School of Public Policy and Public Administration, Washington, DC, 2013. For Regulatory Studies Center.
$80,000 to Prairie View A & M University, Prairie View, TX, 2013. For ExxonMobil Bernard Harris Summer Science Camp.
$25,000 to National Academy Foundation, New York, NY, 2013. For Academies of Engineering.

8834
Ezcorp Foundation ✧ ☆

1901 Capital Pkwy.
Austin, TX 78746-7613 (214) 651-4418

Donors: Datamax System Solutions Inc.; Marketing Response Solutions; ASG Security; United Healthcare Services; Office Depot; Precision Signs Lighting Inc.; Technology Media Group; Surdellpartners LLC; United Precious Metals; Trandotcom Solutions; R. Baker Associates LLC; Scott General Contracting Co.; Mexico Vendor Casa Deb; Results Direct Marketing; Miner Fleet Management Group; Rolland Safe And Lock; Corelogic Real Estate Solutions; Strasburger Price; Advanced Systems Inc; Patrick Quinn; Haden Construction; Sungard; Unifirst; Potricinos Mexico; Eric Fosse; Corporacion Agga Sa De Cv Mexico; Grupo Aliades Sa De Cv Mexico; Grupo Outhelping Sc Mexico; Isabella Edificaciones Sa De Cv Mex; Technologia Tecnomet Sa De Cv Mexic; Vh Arquitectos Asociados Sa De Cv M.
Foundation type: Independent foundation.
Financial data (yr. ended 12/31/12): Assets, $1,404,266 (M); gifts received, $800,063; expenditures, $730,920; qualifying distributions, $546,525; giving activities include $546,525 for grants.
Fields of interest: Arts; Health care; Human services.
Limitations: Applications accepted. Giving primarily in TX.
Application information: Application form required.
Initial approach: Letter or Telephone
Officers and Directors:* Gabrielle Adams,* Co-Chair. and Treas.; Anthony Sanders,* Co-Chair.; Thomas H. Welch, Jr., Pres.; Ellen Bryant, Secy.; Leigh Ann Lindsey; Paul E. Rothamel; Mike Volpe.
EIN: 272894858

8835
The Fain Foundation ✧

807 8th St., 2nd Fl.
Wichita Falls, TX 76301-3381

Established in 1942 in TX.
Donors: Minnie Rhea Wood†; Martha Fain.
Foundation type: Independent foundation.
Financial data (yr. ended 12/31/13): Assets, $17,188,482 (M); expenditures, $776,848; qualifying distributions, $628,000; giving activities include $580,500 for 52 grants (high: $50,000; low: $1,000).
Fields of interest: Arts; Higher education; Youth development; Human services; Foundations (community); United Ways and Federated Giving Programs.
Type of support: General/operating support; Capital campaigns; Program development.
Limitations: Applications not accepted. Giving primarily in Wichita Falls, TX. No grants to individuals.
Application information: Contributes only to pre-selected organizations.
Officers and Directors:* Martha Fain,* Pres. and Treas.; Mac W. Cannedy, Jr.,* V.P. and Secy.; Ann K. Kouri; Dennis D. Cannedy; John M. Kelly.
EIN: 756016679
Selected grants: The following grants are a representative sample of this grantmaker's funding activity:
$112,500 to Wichita Falls Area Community Foundation, Wichita Falls, TX, 2012. For Hands to Hands Fund.
$15,000 to Wichita Falls Area Community Foundation, Wichita Falls, TX, 2012. For Pride in the Falls Fund.
$10,000 to Midwestern State University, Wichita Falls, TX, 2012. For women's athletics.
$2,000 to Midwestern State University, Wichita Falls, TX, 2012. For Fantasy of Lights.

8836
Watson Family Foundation ✧

P.O. Box 56389
Houston, TX 77256-6389 (713) 690-4848
Contact: Charles L. Watson, Pres.

Established in 1994 in TX.
Donors: Charles L. Watson; Kim R. Watson; Wincrest Ventures LP.
Foundation type: Independent foundation.
Financial data (yr. ended 12/31/13): Assets, $110,379 (M); expenditures, $1,536,719; qualifying distributions, $1,533,511; giving activities include $1,533,511 for 67 grants (high: $540,848; low: $250).
Purpose and activities: Giving primarily for education, as well as for the arts, health, and children, youth and social services.
Fields of interest: Arts; Education; Health organizations, association; Human services; Children/youth, services; United Ways and Federated Giving Programs; Protestant agencies & churches.
Limitations: Applications accepted. Giving primarily in Houston, TX and Stillwater, OK.
Application information: Application form required.
Initial approach: Proposal
Deadline(s): End of 3rd quarter
Officers: Charles L. Watson, Pres.; Kim R. Watson, V.P. and Secy.-Treas.
EIN: 760420732

8837
The Fant Foundation ✧

1322 N. Post Oak
Houston, TX 77055-1597

Established in 1994 in TX.
Donors: Alta Fay Fant†; Fant Properties; Land and Gravel Pit; New Process Steel; Fant Energy.
Foundation type: Operating foundation.
Financial data (yr. ended 12/31/13): Assets, $703,027 (M); gifts received, $845,000; expenditures, $955,724; qualifying distributions, $938,847; giving activities include $813,817 for 41 grants (high: $150,000; low: $1,000), and $125,030 for 21 grants to individuals (high: $30,000; low: $750).
Purpose and activities: Giving for support and assistance to impoverished, distressed, and disadvantaged individuals and families who seek to improve their present living conditions.
Fields of interest: Economically disadvantaged.
Type of support: Scholarships—to individuals.
Limitations: Applications accepted. Giving primarily to residents of TX.
Application information: Application form required.
Initial approach: Letter
Deadline(s): None
Directors: Jana Fant; Richard E. Fant; Stephen Swan.
EIN: 760443413

8838
The William Stamps Farish Fund ✧

1100 Louisiana St., Ste. 2200
Houston, TX 77002-5245
Contact: William Stamps Farish, Pres.

Incorporated in 1951 in TX.
Donor: Libbie Rice Farish†.
Foundation type: Independent foundation.
Financial data (yr. ended 06/30/13): Assets, $238,930,758 (M); expenditures, $12,258,871; qualifying distributions, $11,959,581; giving activities include $11,800,000 for 111 grants (high: $500,000; low: $10,000).
Purpose and activities: Giving primarily for basic education and basic medical research.
Fields of interest: Education; Medical research; Human services.
Type of support: Equipment; Program development; Research.
Limitations: Applications accepted. Giving primarily in Houston, TX. No support for political organizations. No grants to individuals, or for annual campaigns, deficit financing, operating budgets, exchange programs, consulting services, or endowment funds; no loans.
Publications: Application guidelines.
Application information: Application form not required.
Initial approach: Proposal
Copies of proposal: 1
Deadline(s): July 1- Apr. 1
Board meeting date(s): Annually
Final notification: 1 year
Officers and Trustees:* William Stamps Farish,* Pres.; Larry L. Shryock, V.P. and Treas.; Laura Farish Chadwick, V.P.; Cornelia Gerry Corbett, V.P.; Caroline P. Rotan, Secy.
Number of staff: 1 full-time professional.
EIN: 746043019
Selected grants: The following grants are a representative sample of this grantmaker's funding activity:
$500,000 to Boca Grande Health Clinic Foundation, Boca Grande, FL, 2013. For program support at the clinic.
$400,000 to Tampa Museum of Art, Tampa, FL, 2013. For annual giving.
$400,000 to University of Texas, Austin, TX, 2013. For collaboration of post-doctorate work with Texas Heart Institute on plaque detection.
$350,000 to Crisis Center of Tampa Bay, Tampa, FL, 2013. For program support for families in crisis.

$300,000 to Escuela Bilingue Internacional, Oakland, CA, 2013. For school expansion.
$150,000 to Juvenile Diabetes Research Foundation International, New York, NY, 2013. For developing one-a-day insulin and collaborating with Baylor College of Medicine.
$100,000 to Neighborhood Centers, Sheltering Arms, Bellaire, TX, 2013. For merged programs to assist young and old.
$75,000 to Johann Fust Community Library of Boca Grande, Boca Grande, FL, 2013. For community library.
$50,000 to Museum of Fine Arts, Houston, Houston, TX, 2013. For annual giving.
$50,000 to Periwinkle Foundation, Houston, TX, 2013. For golf carts for terminally-ill cancer patients at camp.

8839
The Fasken Foundation ✧

P.O. Box 2024
Midland, TX 79702-2024 (432) 683-5401
Contact: Jeff Alsup, Exec. Dir.
FAX: (432) 683-5402;
E-mail: jeff@faskenfoundation.org; Main URL: http://www.faskenfoundation.org

Incorporated in 1955 in TX.
Donors: Andrew A. Fasken†; Helen Fasken House†; Vickie Mallison†; Howard Marshall Johnson†; Ruth Shelton†.
Foundation type: Independent foundation.
Financial data (yr. ended 12/31/13): Assets, $20,609,402 (M); expenditures, $1,751,284; qualifying distributions, $1,064,130; giving activities include $863,801 for 71 grants (high: $110,000; low: $1,000), and $93,875 for 41 grants to individuals (high: $3,300; low: $128).
Purpose and activities: Giving primarily for youth, health, human services, and education, including scholarships to the Texas students of: Midland High School, Midland Robert Lee High School, Midland Greenwood High School, and Ft. Stockton High School. Also, nursing educational scholarships are available through Midland College.
Fields of interest: Arts; Hospitals (general); Health organizations; Human services; Children/youth, services.
Type of support: General/operating support; Program development; Curriculum development; Scholarship funds; Scholarships—to individuals; Matching/challenge support.
Limitations: Applications accepted. Giving limited to TX. Eighty percent of the giving is in the Midland area; 20 percent of the giving is to communities where foundation directors reside. No support for political or religious organizations. No grants to individuals (except scholarships limited to graduates of Midland County, TX, public high schools and junior college); no loans.
Publications: Application guidelines.
Application information: Application form required.
Initial approach: Letter, with appropriate application forms, which can be downloaded from foundation web site
Copies of proposal: 1
Deadline(s): Mar. 31, June 30, Sept. 30, and Dec. 31
Board meeting date(s): Jan., Apr., July, and Oct.
Officers and Directors:* Steve Fasken,* Pres.; John W. Wilkins, Jr.,* V.P.; Paula Fasken,* Secy.-Treas.; Jeff Alsup, Jr.,* Exec. Dir.; Tracy Elms; Susan F. Hartin; Tevis Herd; Bobby Jones; Thomas E. Kelly.
Number of staff: 1 full-time professional; 1 part-time support.
EIN: 756023680
Selected grants: The following grants are a representative sample of this grantmaker's funding activity:
$110,000 to Midland Memorial Foundation, Midland, TX, 2011.
$30,000 to United Way of Midland, Midland, TX, 2011.
$25,000 to High Sky Childrens Ranch, Midland, TX, 2011.
$20,000 to Fine Arts for Children and Teens, Santa Fe, NM, 2011.
$20,000 to Midland College Foundation, Midland, TX, 2011.
$15,000 to Christmas in Action, Midland, TX, 2011.
$15,000 to Court Appointed Special Advocates of West Texas, Midland, TX, 2011.
$15,000 to Springboard Center, Midland, TX, 2011.
$12,000 to Big Brothers Big Sisters of Midland, Midland, TX, 2011.
$5,000 to West Texas Food Bank, Odessa, TX, 2011.

8840
Creekmore and Adele Fath Charitable Foundation ✧

P.O. Box 300910
Austin, TX 78703-0016 (512) 474-8627
Contact: Mandy Dealey, Secy.-Treas.
Application address: 5401 Ridge Oak Dr., Austin, TX 78731

Established in 2007 in TX.
Donor: Creekmore Fath†.
Foundation type: Independent foundation.
Financial data (yr. ended 12/31/12): Assets, $3,866,388 (M); expenditures, $1,698,321; qualifying distributions, $1,647,700; giving activities include $1,647,700 for grants.
Fields of interest: Reproductive health; Pregnancy centers.
Type of support: Advocacy.
Limitations: Applications accepted. Giving primarily in NY and TX. No grants to individuals.
Application information: Application form required.
Initial approach: Proposal
Deadline(s): None
Officers: Larry Morning Star, Chair.; Mandy Dealey, Secy.-Treas.
Directors: Moyra Byrne; Besty Faith Hiller.
EIN: 261634020

8841
The Faulconer Scholarship Programs ✧

611 Chase Dr.
Tyler, TX 75701-9431
Contact: Ron Gleason, V.P. , Secy. and Dir., Scholarship Prog.
E-mail: info@faulconerscholars.org; Main URL: http://www.faulconerscholars.org
E-mail address for Ron Gleason.: rgleason@faulconerscholars.org

Donor: Vernon E. Faulconer.
Foundation type: Independent foundation.
Financial data (yr. ended 12/31/12): Assets, $0 (M); gifts received, $1,075,000; expenditures, $1,256,848; qualifying distributions, $1,255,224; giving activities include $880,628 for 14 grants (high: $289,750; low: $7,000).
Purpose and activities: The programs award scholarships to African-American and Hispanic-American graduating seniors who have earned at least a 2.5 GPA while in high school and who are enrolled in schools within the Tyler Junior College District in East Texas. The Tyler Junior College District includes the Independent School Districts in Chapel Hill, Grand Saline, Lindale, Tyler, Van, and Winona, Texas.
Fields of interest: Higher education; African Americans/Blacks; Hispanics/Latinos.
Type of support: Scholarships—to individuals.
Limitations: Applications accepted. Giving limited to TX.
Application information: Application form available on foundation web site. See foundation web site for application guideline procedures, and downloading of application form. Applications must be mailed. E-mailed, faxed or hand-delivered applications will not be accepted. Application form required.
Deadline(s): Mar. 1
Officers: Vernon E. Faulconer, Pres.; Ron Gleason, V.P. , Secy. and Dir., Scholarship Prog.; Tom Markel, Treas.
EIN: 010752611

8842
The Favrot Fund ✧

1770 Saint James Pl., Ste. 510
Houston, TX 77056-3405
Contact: Julie Richardson

Established in 1952 in TX.
Foundation type: Independent foundation.
Financial data (yr. ended 12/31/13): Assets, $21,370,219 (M); expenditures, $1,164,510; qualifying distributions, $927,802; giving activities include $891,100 for 49 grants (high: $40,000; low: $1,100).
Fields of interest: Arts; Education; Animals/wildlife; Human services; Children/youth; Youth; Aging; Economically disadvantaged.
Type of support: General/operating support; Management development/capacity building; Building/renovation; Program development; Conferences/seminars; Research; Program evaluation.
Limitations: Giving primarily in CA and TX.
Application information: Unsolicited requests for funds are generally not accepted. Application form not required.
Initial approach: Letter
Copies of proposal: 1
Deadline(s): May 31
Board meeting date(s): 3rd quarter
Final notification: 6-8 weeks
Officers and Trustees:* Laurence Favrot,* Pres.; Leo M. Favrot,* Secy.; Romelia Favrot,* Treas.; Celestine Favrot Arndt; Lenior M. Josey; Jeanette F. Peterson.
Number of staff: 1 part-time professional.
EIN: 760638639
Selected grants: The following grants are a representative sample of this grantmaker's funding activity:
$90,000 to Museum of Fine Arts, Houston, Houston, TX, 2012. For Portrait of Spain: Masterpieces from the Prado and to underwrite One Great Night.
$50,000 to Metropolitan Museum of Art, New York, NY, 2012. For exhibition, The Interwoven Globe.

$40,000 to University of California at Santa Barbara Foundation, Department of History of Art and Architecture, Santa Barbara, CA, 2012. For Graduate Enrichment Fund.
$30,850 to Girl Scouts of the U.S.A., San Diego, CA, 2011.
$30,000 to Friends of Balboa Park, San Diego, CA, 2012. To make Balboa Park water-wise by 2020.
$30,000 to San Antonio Area Foundation, San Antonio, TX, 2012. For Bamberger Ranch Preserve including field trips and workshops at schools in Austin, San Antonio and Hill Country School Districts.
$30,000 to Teach for America, Houston, TX, 2012. For Sponsor a Teacher campaign.
$30,000 to Volcan Mountain Preserve Foundation, Julian, CA, 2012. To establish Volcan Mountain Gateway Nature Education Center.
$30,000 to Zoological Society of San Diego, San Diego, CA, 2011.
$30,000 to Zoological Society of San Diego, San Diego, CA, 2012. For Peruvian Andean Bear Project.
$25,000 to San Antonio Area Foundation, San Antonio, TX, 2011.
$20,000 to Chad Relief Foundation, Santa Barbara, CA, 2012. For school materials and teacher training to improve education of children in camps.
$20,000 to San Diego Opera Association, San Diego, CA, 2011.
$20,000 to University of California at San Diego Foundation, La Jolla, CA, 2011.
$15,000 to Sharp Healthcare Foundation, San Diego, CA, 2011.
$10,000 to Community Partners, Los Angeles, CA, 2011.
$10,000 to Hope Stone, Houston, TX, 2012. For Kids Play program to reach out to at-risk youth in Houston and New Orleans.
$5,000 to Doctors Without Borders USA, New York, NY, 2011.

8843
The Feldman Family Foundation ✧
1431 Greenway Dr., No. 360
Irving, TX 75038-2442
Contact: Robert L. Feldman, V.P.

Established in 2005 in TX as successor foundation to The Feldman Foundation.
Donor: The Feldman Foundation.
Foundation type: Independent foundation.
Financial data (yr. ended 12/31/13): Assets, $73,929,405 (M); gifts received, $7,905,275; expenditures, $4,054,798; qualifying distributions, $3,560,094; giving activities include $3,034,933 for 40 grants (high: $1,283,333; low: $2,000).
Fields of interest: Education; Human services; Jewish federated giving programs; Jewish agencies & synagogues.
International interests: Israel.
Limitations: Applications accepted. Giving primarily in CA and TX.
Application information: Application form not required.
Initial approach: Letter
Copies of proposal: 1
Deadline(s): None
Board meeting date(s): Late summer/early fall
Officers and Directors:* Daniel E. Feldman,* Pres.; Robert L. Feldman,* V.P.
Number of staff: 1 part-time support.
EIN: 202098529

Selected grants: The following grants are a representative sample of this grantmaker's funding activity:
$150,000 to American Friends of the Reut Institute, Beverly Hills, CA, 2012. For non-specific religious purposes.
$100,000 to Dallas Jewish Community Foundation, Dallas, TX, 2012. For non-specific religious and charitable purpose.
$37,500 to Tufts University, Medford, MA, 2012. For non-specific education purpose.
$30,000 to New Israel Fund, Washington, DC, 2012. For non-specific educational purpose.
$25,000 to Jewish Community Center of Dallas, Dallas, TX, 2012. For specific educational purpose.
$15,000 to University of California San Francisco Foundation, San Francisco, CA, 2012. For specific education purposes.
$1,680 to Jewish Federation of Greater Dallas, Dallas, TX, 2012. For non-specific charitable purpose.

8844
Leland Fikes Foundation ✧
500 N. Akard St., Ste. 1919
Dallas, TX 75201-3322 (214) 754-0144
Contact: Risa Gross

Incorporated in 1952 in DE.
Donors: Leland Fikes†; Catherine W. Fikes†.
Foundation type: Independent foundation.
Financial data (yr. ended 12/31/13): Assets, $99,466,911 (M); expenditures, $6,702,678; qualifying distributions, $5,079,254; giving activities include $4,930,522 for 49 grants (high: $1,000,000; low: $5,000).
Purpose and activities: Giving primarily for medical research, health, and social services, family planning, public interest groups, and education and cultural programs.
Fields of interest: Museums; Performing arts; Performing arts, music; Higher education; Medical school/education; Education; Environment; Reproductive health, family planning; Health care; Mental health/crisis services; Medical research, institute; Crime/violence prevention, domestic violence; Legal services; Food services; Housing/shelter, development; Human services; Children/youth, services; Family services; Homeless, human services; Civil/human rights, advocacy; Civil liberties, reproductive rights; Community development, neighborhood development; Science; Public policy, research; Public affairs.
Type of support: General/operating support; Continuing support; Annual campaigns; Capital campaigns; Building/renovation; Equipment; Endowments; Emergency funds; Program development; Seed money; Research; Program evaluation; Matching/challenge support.
Limitations: Applications accepted. Giving primarily in the Dallas, TX, area. No grants to individuals; no loans.
Publications: Application guidelines.
Application information: Application form not required.
Initial approach: Letter on organization letterhead
Copies of proposal: 1
Deadline(s): None
Board meeting date(s): Bimonthly
Final notification: By letter, usually within 1-3 months

Officers and Trustees:* Lee Fikes,* Pres. and Treas.; Nancy J. Solana, Exec. V.P.; Amy L. Fikes,* V.P.; Brendan J. Fikes; Catherine F. Lavie.
Number of staff: 1 full-time professional; 1 part-time professional; 1 part-time support.
EIN: 756035984

8845
Marvy Finger Family Foundation ✧
99 Detering St., Ste. 200
Houston, TX 77007-8259

Established in 1999 in TX.
Donors: Marvy A. Finger Interests, Ltd.; Marvy A. Finger.
Foundation type: Independent foundation.
Financial data (yr. ended 12/31/13): Assets, $16,424,795 (M); gifts received, $1,903,539; expenditures, $815,785; qualifying distributions, $704,500; giving activities include $701,187 for 21 grants (high: $200,000; low: $1,000).
Purpose and activities: Giving primarily to a community foundation; giving also to a hospital, a Jewish temple and a Catholic church.
Fields of interest: Hospitals (general); Human services; Foundations (community); Catholic agencies & churches; Jewish agencies & synagogues.
Limitations: Applications not accepted. No grants to individuals.
Application information: Unsolicited requests for funds not accepted.
Officers: Marvy A. Finger, Pres.; Edward Finger, V.P.; Elaine W. Finger, V.P.; Jill F. Jewett, V.P.
EIN: 760625865

8846
Ben & Maytee Fisch Foundation
821 E. Southeast Loop 323, Ste. 590
Tyler, TX 75701-9735
Contact: Dawn Franks, Exec. Dir.
E-mail: info@fischfoundation.org; Main URL: http://www.fischfoundation.org

Established in 1997 in TX.
Donors: Ben Fisch†; Maytee R. Fisch†.
Foundation type: Independent foundation.
Financial data (yr. ended 12/31/13): Assets, $56,548,833 (M); gifts received, $199,112; expenditures, $3,719,407; qualifying distributions, $2,970,231; giving activities include $2,953,308 for 102 grants (high: $1,000,000; low: $1,000).
Purpose and activities: The foundation is focused on human needs and strives to help people help themselves.
Fields of interest: Higher education; Adult education—literacy, basic skills & GED; Education; Mental health/crisis services; Food banks; Housing/shelter; Human services; Children/youth, services; Residential/custodial care, hospices.
Type of support: General/operating support; Continuing support; Annual campaigns; Capital campaigns; Building/renovation; Equipment; Program development; Scholarship funds; Matching/challenge support.
Limitations: Applications accepted. Giving primarily in East TX; national organizations with significant operations in or providing material benefits to the citizens of East Texas will be considered based on the degree of benefits. No support for public or private elementary or secondary schools. No grants

for debt retirement, reserve funding, endowments or conferences.
Publications: Application guidelines.
Application information: Application form required.
Initial approach: On-line application
Copies of proposal: 1
Deadline(s): Check for deadlines
Board meeting date(s): 3 times per year.
Final notification: 60-90 days
Officers: Martee F. Fuerst, Pres.; Stephanie Fisch, V.P.; Mandy Fuerst, Secy.
Directors: Sandra Fisch; David Fuerst; Jan F. Fuerst.
Number of staff: 1 part-time support.
EIN: 752732192

8847
Jill and Charles Fischer Foundation ✧
P.O. Box 83
Fort Worth, TX 76101-0083

Established in 2007 in TX.
Donors: Charles K. Fischer; Jill A. Fischer.
Foundation type: Independent foundation.
Financial data (yr. ended 12/31/13): Assets, $21,100,824 (M); expenditures, $980,215; qualifying distributions, $906,662; giving activities include $906,500 for 11 grants (high: $575,000; low: $500).
Fields of interest: Performing arts, ballet.
Limitations: Applications not accepted. Giving primarily in Fort Worth, TX. No grants to individuals.
Application information: Contributes only to pre-selected organizations.
Officers and Directors:* Charles K. Fischer,* Pres.; Jill A. Fischer,* Secy.; Charles K. Fischer, Jr.; David G. Fischer; Patrick N. Fischer; Teresa F. Howard.
EIN: 260247855

8848
Ray C. Fish Foundation ✧
2001 Kirby Dr., Ste. 1005
Houston, TX 77019-6081
Contact: Catherine Daniel Kaldis, Pres.
FAX: (713) 529-4033;
E-mail: sarahg.young@outlook.com; Main URL: http://www.raycfishfoundation.org

Incorporated in 1957 in TX.
Donors: Raymond Clinton Fish†; Mirtha G. Fish†; Ray C. Fish and Mirtha G. Fish Trust.
Foundation type: Independent foundation.
Financial data (yr. ended 06/30/13): Assets, $22,985,967 (M); gifts received, $69,998; expenditures, $1,831,781; qualifying distributions, $1,463,109; giving activities include $1,180,430 for 71 grants (high: $250,000; low: $1,000).
Purpose and activities: Giving to support, establish or advance educational, scientific or other charitable activities.
Fields of interest: Performing arts; Arts; Higher education; Libraries (special); Education; Hospitals (general); Medical research, institute; Human services; Children/youth, services.
Type of support: General/operating support; Continuing support; Annual campaigns; Capital campaigns; Building/renovation; Endowments; Program development; Professorships; Seed money; Scholarship funds; Research; Matching/challenge support.
Limitations: Giving primarily in TX, with emphasis on Houston. No grants to individuals.
Publications: Application guidelines; Informational brochure (including application guidelines).
Application information: See foundation web site for updates regarding grantmaking procedures.
Board meeting date(s): Quarterly
Officers and Trustees:* Catherine Daniel Kaldis, Pres.; Robert J. Cruikshank,* V.P. and Treas.; Christopher J. Daniel,* V.P.; James L. Daniel, Jr.,* V.P.; Paula Hooton,* Secy.
Number of staff: 1 full-time professional; 1 part-time professional.
EIN: 746043047
Selected grants: The following grants are a representative sample of this grantmaker's funding activity:
$10,000 to Nature Conservancy of Texas, Houston, TX, 2011.

8849
Fleming Endowment ✧ ☆
2800 Post Oak Blvd., No. 4000
Houston, TX 77056-6109

Established in 1997 in TX.
Donor: George M. Fleming.
Foundation type: Independent foundation.
Financial data (yr. ended 10/31/13): Assets, $8,078,077 (M); expenditures, $615,805; qualifying distributions, $583,850; giving activities include $583,850 for 15 grants (high: $312,500; low: $1,000).
Fields of interest: Higher education; Libraries (law); Education; Health organizations; Human services; Christian agencies & churches.
Limitations: Applications not accepted. Giving primarily in Houston, TX. No grants to individuals.
Application information: Unsolicited requests for funds not accepted.
Officers and Trustees:* George M. Fleming,* Pres. and Secy.; Raymond E. Kinzer,* Treas.; Scott Fleming.
EIN: 760555849
Selected grants: The following grants are a representative sample of this grantmaker's funding activity:
$500,000 to University of Texas, Austin, TX, 2011.
$80,000 to University of Texas M.D. Anderson Cancer Center, Houston, TX, 2011.
$50,000 to Saint Agnes Academy, Houston, TX, 2011.
$12,500 to Briarwood School, Houston, TX, 2011.
$8,500 to University of Texas, Austin, TX, 2011.
$5,000 to University of Texas M.D. Anderson Cancer Center, Houston, TX, 2011.
$3,500 to University of Houston Law Foundation, Houston, TX, 2011.
$1,630 to Star of Hope Mission, Houston, TX, 2011.
$1,000 to Houston Livestock Show and Rodeo, Houston, TX, 2011. For scholarship fund.
$1,000 to Magnificat House, Houston, TX, 2011.

8850
Fleming Foundation ✧
500 W. 7th St., Ste. 1007
Fort Worth, TX 76102-4732
Contact: G. Malcolm Louden C.P.A., Pres.

Incorporated in 1936 in TX.
Donor: William Fleming†.
Foundation type: Independent foundation.
Financial data (yr. ended 12/31/13): Assets, $5,785,213 (M); expenditures, $944,083; qualifying distributions, $855,000; giving activities include $855,000 for 3 grants (high: $565,000; low: $10,000).
Purpose and activities: Giving limited to the promotion of health, education, the performing arts, and general welfare.
Fields of interest: Performing arts.
Type of support: General/operating support; Continuing support; Annual campaigns; Emergency funds; Program development; Professorships; Research.
Limitations: Applications accepted. Giving primarily in TX, with emphasis on Fort Worth. No grants to individuals, or for deficit financing, building or endowment funds, land acquisition, matching or challenge grants, scholarships, fellowships, exchange programs, publications, or conferences; single-year grants only; no loans.
Application information: Application form required.
Initial approach: Letter
Copies of proposal: 1
Deadline(s): None
Officers: G. Malcolm Louden, Pres.; Gary F. Goble, Secy.-Treas.
Directors: J. Robert Green, Jr.; Robert Lombardi; F. Howard Walsh.
EIN: 756022736

8851
The Fluor Foundation ✧
6700 Las Colina Blvd.
Irving, TX 75039-2902 (469) 398-7000
Contact: Terence H. Robinson, Pres.
E-mail: community.relations@fluor.com; Main URL: http://www.fluor.com/sustainability/community/Pages/default.aspx

Incorporated in 1952 in CA.
Donor: Fluor Corp.
Foundation type: Company-sponsored foundation.
Financial data (yr. ended 12/31/12): Assets, $12,476,435 (M); gifts received, $3,158,038; expenditures, $4,348,321; qualifying distributions, $4,327,953; giving activities include $4,327,951 for 443 grants (high: $544,943; low: $50).
Purpose and activities: The foundation supports programs designed to promote education; social services; community and economic development; and the environment.
Fields of interest: Elementary/secondary education; Middle schools/education; Higher education; Business school/education; Engineering school/education; Education; Environment, natural resources; Environmental education; Environment; Employment, services; Employment, training; Employment, retraining; Food services; Housing/shelter; Disasters, preparedness/services; Youth development, adult & child programs; Youth, services; Family services; Human services, emergency aid; Homeless, human services; Human services; Economic development; Community/economic development; Science, formal/general education; Mathematics; Engineering/technology; Science; Crime/abuse victims; Homeless.
Type of support: General/operating support; Annual campaigns; Capital campaigns; Building/renovation; Equipment; Endowments; Program development; Curriculum development; Scholarship funds; Research; Employee volunteer services; Employee matching gifts; Employee-related scholarships.

Limitations: Applications accepted. Giving primarily in areas of company operations, with some emphasis on AK, Aliso Viejo, CA, FL, KY, MS, NM, Greenville, SC, Irving and Sugar Land, TX, and Richland, WA. No support for sectarian or denominational religious organizations, political organizations or candidates, fraternal or labor organizations, or school-related bands. No grants to individuals (except for employee scholarships), or for entertainment events, school-related events, freelance films, video tapes, or audio productions, or courtesy advertising, program books, or yearbooks.
Publications: Application guidelines; Financial statement; Informational brochure; IRS Form 990 or 990-PF printed copy available upon request; Program policy statement.
Application information: Proposals should be no longer than 2 to 3 pages. Additional information may be requested at a later date. Application form not required.
Initial approach: Proposal to nearest company facility
Copies of proposal: 1
Deadline(s): None
Board meeting date(s): Apr. and Oct.
Final notification: Within 2 months
Officers and Directors:* David T. Seaton, Chair.; Torrence H. Robinson, Pres.; Carlos M. Hernandez, Secy.; E. J. Kowalchuk, Treas.; Ray F. Barnard; S. B. Dobbs; Glenn C. Gilkey; Kirk Grimes; Biggs C. Porter; Dwayne A. Wilson.
EIN: 510196032

8852
FMH Foundation ✧
P.O. Box 51310
Midland, TX 79710-1370

Donor: F. Marie Hall.
Foundation type: Independent foundation.
Financial data (yr. ended 12/31/13): Assets, $17,103,584 (M); gifts received, $6,000,000; expenditures, $870,401; qualifying distributions, $754,470; giving activities include $754,470 for 19 grants (high: $150,000; low: $5,000).
Fields of interest: Education; Human services.
Limitations: Applications not accepted. Giving primarily in TX.
Application information: Unsolicited requests for funds not accepted.
Officers: Florence Marie Hall, Pres.; Kristi Elsom, Secy.; Laura Buckner, Treas.; Eileen Piwetz, Exec. Dir.
Directors: Laura McCabe; Glenn A. Rogers.
EIN: 272504803

8853
The Fondren Foundation ✧
c/o JPMorgan Chase Trust Dept.
P.O. Box 2558
Houston, TX 77252-2558
Contact: Martie Herrick
E-mail: Fondren_Foundation@jpmorgan.com

Established in 1948 in TX.
Donor: Mrs. W.W. Fondren, Sr.†.
Foundation type: Independent foundation.
Financial data (yr. ended 10/31/13): Assets, $213,951,470 (M); expenditures, $12,306,227; qualifying distributions, $10,903,299; giving activities include $10,680,629 for 95 grants (high: $720,000; low: $10,000).
Purpose and activities: Emphasis on higher and secondary education, social service and youth agencies, cultural organizations, and health.
Fields of interest: Arts; Secondary school/education; Higher education; Health care; Human services; Youth, services.
Type of support: Continuing support; Capital campaigns; Building/renovation; Program development.
Limitations: Applications accepted. Giving primarily in TX, with emphasis on Houston. No support for Type III supporting organizations. No grants to individuals, or for annual fund drives or fundraising events, annual gifts for operational support; nor to an organization which is currently receiving installment payments on a previous grant.
Publications: Application guidelines.
Application information: Do not submit videotapes, DVDs, or CDs. Grant requests for endowments must provide the spending policy. Application form not required.
Initial approach: Proprosal
Copies of proposal: 1
Deadline(s): Feb. 1, May 1, Aug. 1, Nov. 1
Board meeting date(s): Mar., June, Sept., and Dec.
Final notification: 3 to 6 months
Officers and Trustees:* Michael E. Hanson, Jr.,* Chair.; David M. Underwood, Jr.,* Vice-Chair.; Doris Fondren Allday; R. Edwin Allday; Laura Trammell Baird; Bradley Beard; Ellanor Allday Camberg; Celia Whitfield Crank; Ashley Fondren; Bentley B. Fondren; Brittany Fondren; Frances Fondren; Lauren Fondren; Leland T. Fondren; Lindsey Fondren; Robert E. Fondren; Marie Fondren Hall; Walter W. Fondren IV; Burton M. Hanson; Catherine Underwood Murray; Michael W. Springer; Ann Gordon Trammell; Harper B. Trammell; David M. Underwood; Duncan K. Underwood; Lynda Knapp Underwood; Sue Trammell Whitfield; W. Trammell Whitfield; William F. Whitfield, Jr.; Ellanor Yates; Emily Yates.
EIN: 746042565
Selected grants: The following grants are a representative sample of this grantmaker's funding activity:
$720,000 to Saint Johns School, Houston, TX, 2013. For Campaign for Center/Great Hall Project and Taub Land Acquisition.
$400,000 to Methodist Hospital Foundation, Houston, TX, 2013. For Walter W. Fondren III Distinguished Endowed Chair for Medical Director of Methodist Debakey Heart and Vascular Center.
$400,000 to University of Texas, Athletics Department, Austin, TX, 2012. For Walter W. Fondren, III Athletics Leadership Center.
$400,000 to University of Texas, Athletics Department, Austin, TX, 2013. For Walter W. Fondren III Athletics Leadership Center.
$325,000 to Menninger Clinic, Houston, TX, 2013. For mental health Epicenter, for education, treatment and research.
$325,000 to Menninger Foundation, Houston, TX, 2012. For Mental Health Epicenter dedicated to mental health education, treatment, and research.
$250,000 to Buffalo Bayou Partnership, Houston, TX, 2013. For Buffalo Bayou Park Shepherd to Sabine Greenway Project.
$250,000 to Galveston Historical Foundation, Galveston, TX, 2012. For capital campaign focusing on Elissa (official tall ship of Texas) and Bishop's Palace.
$250,000 to Houston Independent School District Foundation, Houston, TX, 2012. For Apollo 20 project to transform district's lowest-performing schools.
$250,000 to Nau Center for Texas Cultural Heritage, Houston, TX, 2013. To build Nau Center.
$250,000 to Neighborhood Centers, Bellaire, TX, 2012. For 2010 endowment for funding community based initiatives.
$250,000 to Salvation Army of Houston, Houston, TX, 2013. For Giving for Living Campaign to develop and renovate facilities.
$250,000 to University of Texas Medical Branch, Galveston, TX, 2013. For Jennie Sealy Hospital as part of Working Wonders Campaign.
$166,664 to Camp for All Foundation, Houston, TX, 2012. For Reaching for the Stars capital campaign.
$150,000 to Institute for Spirituality and Health at the Texas Medical Center, Houston, TX, 2012. For endowment fund.
$113,333 to Cornerstone Recovery, Houston, TX, 2012. For program expansion project.
$100,000 to Cristo Rey Jesuit College Preparatory School of Houston, Houston, TX, 2012. For Campaign to Transform Houston's Future.
$100,000 to Evelyns Park Conservancy, Bellaire, TX, 2013. To design, develop and transform former Texas nursery site into a park.
$80,000 to Saint Edwards University, Austin, TX, 2013. To preserve and repair main building.
$66,664 to Catholic Charities of the Archdiocese of Galveston-Houston, Houston, TX, 2012. For Reaching Out in Faith capital campaign.

8854
Gerald J. Ford Family Foundation ✧
(formerly Ford Family Foundation)
200 Crescent Ct., Ste. 1350
Dallas, TX 75201-6988

Established in 2005 in TX.
Donors: Gerald J. Ford; Hunter's Glen/Ford, Ltd.
Foundation type: Independent foundation.
Financial data (yr. ended 12/31/11): Assets, $8,249,109 (M); expenditures, $1,672,857; qualifying distributions, $1,672,758; giving activities include $1,672,758 for 33 grants (high: $1,000,000; low: $50).
Purpose and activities: Giving primarily for medical research and human services.
Fields of interest: Museums (art); Performing arts; Higher education; Health care; Medical research; Human services; Children/youth, services.
Limitations: Giving primarily in TX and NY.
Officers: Gerald J. Ford, Pres.; Gary Shultz, V.P.; Jeremy B. Ford, Secy.-Treas.
EIN: 203966400

8855
Ershel Franklin Charitable Trust ✧
P.O. Box 790
Post, TX 79356-0790

Established in 1985 in TX.
Foundation type: Independent foundation.
Financial data (yr. ended 12/31/13): Assets, $12,104,635 (M); expenditures, $576,394; qualifying distributions, $575,810; giving activities include $512,379 for 52 grants (high: $75,000; low: $250).

Fields of interest: Education, research; Higher education; Business school/education; Medical school/education; Education; Hospitals (general); Nursing care; Cancer; Alcoholism; Biomedicine; Medical research, institute; Cancer research; Government/public administration; Religion.
Type of support: Endowments; Scholarship funds; Research.
Limitations: Applications not accepted. No grants to individuals.
Application information: Contributes only to pre-selected organizations.
Trustee: Mary L. McCrary.
EIN: 756305761

8856
Franklin Family Foundation ✧
12500 San Pedro Ave., Ste. 404
San Antonio, TX 78216

Established in 1999 in TX.
Donors: Larry D. Franklin; Charlotte A. Franklin.
Foundation type: Independent foundation.
Financial data (yr. ended 12/31/13): Assets, $853,638 (M); gifts received, $605,820; expenditures, $793,654; qualifying distributions, $792,268; giving activities include $760,050 for 14 grants (high: $478,250; low: $500).
Purpose and activities: Giving primarily for medical research, including juvenile diabetes research, as well as for social services.
Fields of interest: Education; Medical research; Human services; Children/youth, services; Religion.
Limitations: Applications not accepted. Giving primarily in IN, TX; some funding also in Washington, DC. No grants to individuals.
Application information: Contributes only to pre-selected organizations.
Officers and Directors:* Larry D. Franklin,* Pres. and Treas.; Charlotte A. Franklin,* V.P. and Secy.; Kristi Borchardt; Kelly Hardwick.
EIN: 742921587
Selected grants: The following grants are a representative sample of this grantmaker's funding activity:
$13,000 to Young Life, Colorado Springs, CO, 2012. For youth ministry.

8857
The Frees Foundation ✧
1770 St. James Pl., Ste. 616
Houston, TX 77056-3500
E-mail: nancy@freesfoundation.org; Main URL: http://www.freesfoundation.org
Grants List: http://www.freesfoundation.org/index_granthistoryff.htm

Established in 1983 in TX.
Donors: C. Norman Frees‡; Shirley B. Frees.
Foundation type: Independent foundation.
Financial data (yr. ended 12/31/13): Assets, $11,690,593 (M); expenditures, $924,173; qualifying distributions, $845,465; giving activities include $599,924 for 41 grants (high: $55,000; low: $1,000).
Purpose and activities: The grantmaker's mission is to assist vulnerable and underserved populations in achieving self-sufficiency.
Fields of interest: Education; Health care; Housing/shelter, development; Children/youth, services; Family services; Aging, centers/services; Community/economic development; Aging; Minorities; Hispanics/Latinos; Women; Girls; Immigrants/refugees; Economically disadvantaged; Homeless.
Type of support: General/operating support; Continuing support; Program development.
Limitations: Applications not accepted. Giving primarily in Houston, TX. No support for art programs, the environment, animals, and political organizations. No grants to individuals, or for deficit financing, endowments, capital campaigns, or fundraising events.
Application information: Unsolicited requests for funds not accepted.
Board meeting date(s): Apr. 15 and Oct. 15
Officers: Edmund M. Fountain, Jr., Pres. and Treas.; Esther M. Perrine, V.P.; Nancy Frees Fountain, Managing Dir.
Number of staff: 1 full-time professional; 1 full-time support.
EIN: 760053200
Selected grants: The following grants are a representative sample of this grantmaker's funding activity:
$26,000 to Houston Police Foundation, Houston, TX, 2012. For Homeless Outreach Program.
$20,000 to Memorial Assistance Ministries, Houston, TX, 2012. For ESL Coordinator Salary.
$20,000 to Mona Foundation, Kirkland, WA, 2012. For Children's Develop Center Mongolia.
$15,000 to Alliance of Community Assistance Ministries, Houston, TX, 2012. For Homeless Prevention Coordinator.
$15,000 to Harmony House, Houston, TX, 2012. For emergency response homeless.
$10,000 to Santa Maria Hostel, Houston, TX, 2012. For Transitional Housing-Women and Child.
$5,000 to Camp for All Foundation, Houston, TX, 2012. For Scholarship for Special Needs Campers.
$5,000 to United Way of King County, Seattle, WA, 2012. For National Homeless Youth Count.
$1,000 to Bread for the World Institute, Washington, DC, 2012. For Community Education.

8858
Leo & Rhea Fay Fruhman Foundation ✧
P.O. Box 835786
Richardson, TX 75083-5786

Established in 1989 in TX; funded in 1990.
Donor: Rhea Fay Fruhman‡.
Foundation type: Independent foundation.
Financial data (yr. ended 12/31/13): Assets, $14,372,985 (M); expenditures, $777,829; qualifying distributions, $642,358; giving activities include $520,175 for 74 grants (high: $44,075; low: $1,000).
Fields of interest: Medical research; Human services; Jewish agencies & synagogues.
Limitations: Applications not accepted. Giving primarily in TX. No grants to individuals.
Application information: Contributes only to pre-selected organizations.
Officers: Beverly T. Goldman, Pres.; Ronald Goldman, V.P.; Timothy P. Tehan, Secy.; Joe Goldman, Treas. and Exec. Dir.
Trustee: Michael Goldman.
EIN: 752302749
Selected grants: The following grants are a representative sample of this grantmaker's funding activity:
$10,000 to Ronald McDonald House of Dallas, Dallas, TX, 2012. For Health - Child Welfare.
$7,500 to Learning Ally, Austin, TX, 2012. For Health - Disability Services.
$7,000 to Preble Street, Portland, ME, 2012. For community assistance.
$5,000 to Greene Family Camp, Bruceville, TX, 2012. For religion - camp.
$5,000 to Southern Poverty Law Center, Montgomery, AL, 2012. For education - legal.

8859
The Gale Foundation ✧
2615 Calder St., Ste. 630
Beaumont, TX 77702-1937

Donor: Edwin Gale.
Foundation type: Independent foundation.
Financial data (yr. ended 04/30/13): Assets, $10,472,373 (M); expenditures, $534,477; qualifying distributions, $473,185; giving activities include $473,185 for grants.
Purpose and activities: Giving primarily to Jewish organizations, as well as for education and human services.
Fields of interest: Media/communications; Higher education; Education; Human services; Jewish federated giving programs; Jewish agencies & synagogues.
Limitations: Applications not accepted. No grants to individuals.
Application information: Unsolicited requests for funds not accepted.
Trustee: Rebecca S. Gale.
EIN: 760009604
Selected grants: The following grants are a representative sample of this grantmaker's funding activity:
$100,000 to Commentary, New York, NY, 2011.
$60,000 to Donors Trust, Alexandria, VA, 2011.
$50,000 to Ner Israel Rabbinical College, Baltimore, MD, 2011.
$18,860 to Temple Emanuel, Beaumont, TX, 2011.
$8,000 to Family Services of Southeast Texas, Beaumont, TX, 2011.
$5,000 to National Yiddish Book Center, Amherst, MA, 2011.
$2,500 to Baylor College of Medicine, Houston, TX, 2011.
$2,000 to University of Texas, Austin, TX, 2011.
$2,000 to University of Texas, Austin, TX, 2011.
$1,000 to American Society for Technion-Israel Institute of Technology, New York, NY, 2011.

8860
The Gallagher Foundation ✧ ☆
2905 Sackett Blvd.
Houston, TX 77098-1127

Established in 2000 in TX.
Donor: Michael T. Gallagher.
Foundation type: Independent foundation.
Financial data (yr. ended 11/30/13): Assets, $765,630 (M); gifts received, $200,000; expenditures, $843,782; qualifying distributions, $836,350; giving activities include $836,350 for 25 grants (high: $500,000; low: $1,000).
Fields of interest: Recreation; Human services; Christian agencies & churches.
Limitations: Applications not accepted. Giving primarily in TX; some giving in AR and NY. No grants to individuals.

Application information: Contributes only to pre-selected organizations.
Officer: Michael T. Gallagher, Pres.
Directors: Joan D. Gallagher; Michael D. Gallagher; Sean Gallagher; Shannon G. Smith.
EIN: 760662307

8861
Gayden Family Foundation ✧
13727 Noel Rd., Ste. 1200
Dallas, TX 75240-7312

Established in 1999 in TX.
Donors: William K. Gayden; Mrs. William Gayden; Cynthia N. Gayden.
Foundation type: Independent foundation.
Financial data (yr. ended 12/31/13): Assets, $33,368,039 (M); gifts received, $240,850; expenditures, $1,596,961; qualifying distributions, $1,557,250; giving activities include $1,554,750 for 48 grants (high: $370,000; low: $1,000).
Purpose and activities: Giving primarily for education, health associations, human services, and to a Presbyterian church.
Fields of interest: Education; Health organizations, association; Human services; United Ways and Federated Giving Programs; Protestant agencies & churches.
Limitations: Applications not accepted. Giving primarily in Dallas, TX and Washington, DC. No grants to individuals.
Application information: Contributes only to pre-selected organizations.
Trustees: Cynthia N. Gayden; William K. Gayden; Katherine G. Keenan; Elizabeth G. Williams.
EIN: 756563143

8862
A. S. Genecov Foundation ✧ ☆
P.O. Box 132450
Tyler, TX 75713-2450 (903) 509-8844
E-mail: freedy@genecov.com

Established in 1955 in TX.
Donors: A.S. Genecov†; Hilda J. Genecov†; Terry Muntz Darryl; Linda Lynn; Debra Janelle; Martin Muntz.
Foundation type: Independent foundation.
Financial data (yr. ended 12/31/12): Assets, $5,163,336 (M); gifts received, $16,395; expenditures, $656,043; qualifying distributions, $610,500; giving activities include $610,500 for grants.
Purpose and activities: Giving primarily for public service organizations, including support for the aged and education.
Fields of interest: Scholarships/financial aid; Education; Human services; Foundations (community); Jewish agencies & synagogues; Aging.
Type of support: Scholarship funds; Continuing support; Annual campaigns.
Limitations: Applications accepted. Giving primarily in TX. No grants to individuals.
Application information: Application form required.
Initial approach: Letter
Copies of proposal: 1
Deadline(s): None
Officers: Dennis D. Darryl, Mgr.; Terry Muntz Darryl, Mgr.; Maurine Genecov Muntz, Mgr.
Number of staff: None.
EIN: 756023698

8863
The George Foundation ✧
215 Morton St.
Richmond, TX 77469-3116 (281) 342-6109
Contact: Theresa Kopnicky, Grant Assoc.
FAX: (281) 341-7635; Mailing address: 310 Morton St., PMB, Ste. C, Richmond, TX 77469-3119;
E-mail: scholarships@thegeorgefoundation.org;
Main URL: http://www.thegeorgefoundation.org
Grants List: http://www.thegeorgefoundation.org/grants/approved-grants/

Trust established in 1945 in TX.
Donors: A.P. George†; Mamie E. George†.
Foundation type: Independent foundation.
Financial data (yr. ended 12/31/13): Assets, $307,799,478 (M); expenditures, $14,033,792; qualifying distributions, $11,039,907; giving activities include $7,436,746 for 110 grants (high: $1,000,000; low: $450), $901,125 for 2 employee matching gifts, and $1,235,458 for 1 foundation-administered program.
Purpose and activities: Giving primarily for human services, education, health care and for community enhancement.
Fields of interest: Historic preservation/historical societies; Education, early childhood education; Child development, education; Elementary school/education; Adult education—literacy, basic skills & GED; Education, reading; Education; Health care; AIDS; Human services; Children/youth, services; Child development, services; Family services; Economically disadvantaged.
Type of support: General/operating support; Capital campaigns; Program development; Seed money; Scholarship funds; Matching/challenge support.
Limitations: Applications accepted. Giving primarily in Fort Bend County, TX. No support for religious, fraternal or regranting organizations, religious or private schools or individual K-12 public schools. No grants to individuals; or for travel, conferences, conventions, group meetings, or seminars, research or studies, films, videos, books or other media projects, direct mail campaigns, no loans.
Publications: Application guidelines; Grants list; Informational brochure.
Application information: The foundation acknowledges receipt of proposals within two weeks. During the review process, interviews and site visits are requested to better evaluate the proposal. The foundation will not consider a grant application from the same applicant, whether granted or denied, more frequently than once every twelve month period. Application form not required.
Initial approach: Letter
Copies of proposal: 1
Deadline(s): Jan. 15, Apr. 15, July 15, and Oct. 15 (for capital proposals)
Board meeting date(s): Monthly; grants reviewed quarterly
Final notification: Approximately 6 months
Officers and Trustees:* Roger Adamson, C.E.O.; Sandra G. Thompson, C.F.O.; Bill Jameson; Pat McDonald; Tom McNutt; John Null; Don Wenzel.
Number of staff: 3 full-time professional; 9 full-time support.
EIN: 746043368
Selected grants: The following grants are a representative sample of this grantmaker's funding activity:
$2,000,000 to Fort Bend, County of, Richmond, TX, 2012. To restore historic Fort Bend Courthouse.
$1,000,000 to Fort Bend Independent School District, Sugar Land, TX, 2012. To develop Teaching and Learning Science Platform for students in Kindergarten through 8th grade.
$840,000 to Memorial Hermann Foundation, Houston, TX, 2012. For Lamar Conroe Independent School District school-based health center which will provide uninsured students access to medical care.
$630,000 to Fort Bend County Museum Association, Richmond, TX, 2012. For public programming at George Ranch Historical Park.
$500,000 to Girl Scouts of the U.S.A., San Jacinto Council, Houston, TX, 2012. For matching grant to support Phase I of capital campaign to create Ranch complex at Camp Pryor.
$423,898 to Scholarship America, Saint Peter, MN, 2012. For continuing and new scholarships to graduating seniors of Fort Bend County public high schools.
$379,284 to Fort Bend, County of, Richmond, TX, 2012. To purchase digital equipment and signage for Fort Bend County Libraries.
$229,153 to Fort Bend Family Health Center, Richmond, TX, 2012. To provide integrated behavioral health care programs to serve Fort Bend County residents.
$125,000 to YMCA of Greater Houston Area, Houston, TX, 2012. To support outreach recreational and after-school programming in ten underserved communities in Fort Bend County.
$78,000 to University of Houston System, Houston, TX, 2012. For scholarships to two bi-lingual Spanish speaking Fort Bend County residents seeking a master level social work degree.

8864
Harry A. and Rose Getz Foundation ✧ ☆
1717 St. James Pl., Ste. 245
Houston, TX 77056-3407

Established in TX.
Foundation type: Independent foundation.
Financial data (yr. ended 12/31/13): Assets, $0 (M); expenditures, $530,597; qualifying distributions, $530,597; giving activities include $524,372 for 2 grants (high: $305,000; low: $219,372).
Fields of interest: Family services; Jewish agencies & synagogues; Religion.
Limitations: Applications not accepted. Giving primarily in Houston, TX.
Application information: Unsolicited requests for funds not accepted.
Trustee: Judy Weiser.
EIN: 760678230

8865
GHS Foundation ✧
2900 Weslayan St., Ste. B
Houston, TX 77027-5150

Established in 2000 in TX.
Donors: Gerald H. Smith; Fidelity Charitable Gift Trust.
Foundation type: Independent foundation.
Financial data (yr. ended 02/28/13): Assets, $9,195,602 (M); gifts received, $1,157,220; expenditures, $971,850; qualifying distributions, $957,351; giving activities include $942,850 for 4 grants (high: $776,500; low: $2,500).
Fields of interest: Higher education, university; Zoos/zoological societies; Human services.
Type of support: Scholarship funds.

Limitations: Applications accepted. Giving primarily in TX. No grants to individuals; no loans or scholarships.
Application information: Application form not required.
Initial approach: Proposal
Deadline(s): Sept. 30
Officers: Gerald H. Smith, Pres.; Nancy Hamlin Cooke, V.P. and Secy.-Treas.; Robert E. Hutson, V.P.
EIN: 760628970
Selected grants: The following grants are a representative sample of this grantmaker's funding activity:
$613,632 to Sam Houston State University, Huntsville, TX, 2012. For scholarships.
$100,000 to Houston Zoo, Houston, TX, 2012. For general funds.
$3,000 to Angel Flight, Carrollton, TX, 2012. For general funds.

8866
Mary Rodes Gibson Hemostasis-Thrombosis Foundation ✧
1707 Broadmoor, Ste. 103
Bryan, TX 77802-5219

Established in 2001 in TX.
Donor: Mary R. Gibson†.
Foundation type: Independent foundation.
Financial data (yr. ended 12/31/12): Assets, $9,197,108 (M); expenditures, $635,527; qualifying distributions, $521,699; giving activities include $500,000 for 2 grants (high: $250,000; low: $250,000).
Purpose and activities: Giving primarily for medical research.
Fields of interest: Higher education, university; Medical research, institute.
Limitations: Applications not accepted. No grants to individuals.
Application information: Contributes only to pre-selected organizations.
Officer: Larry G. Holt, Chair.
Trustees: Jeff Harris; William Price.
EIN: 743015534

8867
Melbern G. & Susanne M. Glasscock Foundation ✧ ☆
3555 Timmons, Ste. 700
Houston, TX 77027-6450
Application address: c/o S.M. Glasscock, P.O. Box 22143, Houston, TX 77227, tel.: (713) 520-2902

Established in 1992 in TX.
Donors: Melbern G. Glasscock; Susanne M. Glasscock.
Foundation type: Independent foundation.
Financial data (yr. ended 12/31/13): Assets, $18,637,832 (M); expenditures, $482,509; qualifying distributions, $471,331; giving activities include $471,331 for 22 grants (high: $68,831; low: $7,500).
Fields of interest: Museums; Arts; Education; Girl scouts; Human services.
Limitations: Applications accepted. Giving primarily in Houston, TX. No grants to individuals.
Application information: Application form not required.
Initial approach: Letter
Deadline(s): None
Officers and Trustees:* Melbern G. Glasscock,* Pres.; Susanne M. Glasscock,* V.P.; M.M. Bass,* Secy.; R.E. Bean,* Treas.; B.A. Baring, Jr.; R.R. Casey III; S. Lindley.
EIN: 760380195

8868
The Goldsbury Foundation ✧
P.O. Box 460567
San Antonio, TX 78246-0567 (210) 582-2074
Contact: Suzanne Mead Feldmann, Exec. Dir.
FAX: (210) 930-2482;
E-mail: info@goldsbury-foundation.org; Main URL: http://www.goldsbury-foundation.org

Established in 1996 in TX.
Donors: Christopher Goldsbury, Jr.; Goldsbury Charitable Trust.
Foundation type: Independent foundation.
Financial data (yr. ended 12/31/12): Assets, $49,135,190 (M); gifts received, $24,861,108; expenditures, $3,295,032; qualifying distributions, $3,246,461; giving activities include $3,010,756 for 36 grants (high: $1,000,000; low: $100).
Purpose and activities: The foundation is committed to providing meaningful philanthropic support that stimulates positive and lasting change for the children and families of San Antonio, Texas. Reflecting its historic funding focus on the prevention of substance abuse, the foundation remains strongly committed to providing positive healthy and transformational experiences and opportunities for the children and families of San Antonio. On a going forward basis, it is specifically interested in addressing the issues contributing to young people dropping out of school in its community.
Fields of interest: Arts; Elementary/secondary education; Education; Substance abuse, prevention; Heart & circulatory research; Crime/violence prevention, child abuse; Children/youth, services; Homeless, human services.
Type of support: General/operating support; Program development; Matching/challenge support.
Limitations: Applications not accepted. Giving primarily in San Antonio, TX. No support for research, or for political or religious organizations. No grants to individuals, or for capital campaigns, conferences, dinners, special events, sponsorships, or advertising.
Publications: Grants list.
Application information: Unsolicited requests for funds are currently not accepted.
Board meeting date(s): Quarterly
Officers and Directors:* Christopher Goldsbury, Jr.,* Pres.; Angela Aboltin Goldsbury,* V.P.; William Scanlan, Jr.,* Secy.; Suzanne Mead Feldmann, Exec. Dir.
Number of staff: 1 part-time professional.
EIN: 742780083

8869
The Gonsoulin Charitable Trust ✧
c/o Al A. Gonsoulin
P.O. Box 16757
Sugar Land, TX 77479

Established in 1998 in TX.
Foundation type: Independent foundation.
Financial data (yr. ended 12/31/12): Assets, $2,878,342 (M); expenditures, $539,629; qualifying distributions, $511,500; giving activities include $511,500 for 30 grants (high: $165,000; low: $1,000).
Purpose and activities: Giving primarily to Roman Catholic agencies, churches, and schools, and for human services.
Fields of interest: Elementary school/education; Human services; Catholic agencies & churches.
Limitations: Applications not accepted. Giving primarily in LA and TX. No grants to individuals.
Application information: Contributes only to pre-selected organizations.
Trustees: Al A. Gonsoulin; Gene J. Gonsoulin.
EIN: 766106726

8870
Goodman-Abell Foundation ✧
1721 Hollister St.
Houston, TX 77055-3126

Established in 1998 in TX.
Donors: G. Hughes Abell; Betsy G. Abell; Nelson Abell Foundation.
Foundation type: Independent foundation.
Financial data (yr. ended 02/28/13): Assets, $20,645,379 (M); gifts received, $1,995,153; expenditures, $1,374,558; qualifying distributions, $1,374,558; giving activities include $1,169,981 for 42 grants (high: $261,968; low: $250).
Fields of interest: Museums; Arts; Elementary/secondary education; Children/youth, services; United Ways and Federated Giving Programs.
Type of support: General/operating support.
Limitations: Applications not accepted. Giving primarily in Austin, TX. No grants to individuals.
Application information: Contributes only to pre-selected organizations.
Officers: Betsy G. Abell, Pres.; G. Hughes Abell, V.P.
EIN: 742869876
Selected grants: The following grants are a representative sample of this grantmaker's funding activity:
$200,000 to Saint Andrews Episcopal School, Austin, TX, 2011.
$60,000 to Austin Recovery, Austin, TX, 2011.
$50,000 to Hill Country Conservancy, Austin, TX, 2011.
$30,000 to Texas State History Museum Foundation, Austin, TX, 2011.
$25,000 to Seton Fund of the Daughters of Charity of Saint Vincent de Paul, Austin, TX, 2011.
$25,000 to Texas State History Museum Foundation, Austin, TX, 2011.
$20,000 to Texas Water Foundation, Austin, TX, 2011.
$19,877 to University of Texas Elementary School, Austin, TX, 2011.
$12,500 to Saint Davids Episcopal Church, Austin, TX, 2011.
$4,000 to Austin Community Foundation for the Capital Area, Austin, TX, 2011.

8871
Vijay and Marie Goradia Charitable Foundation ✧ ☆
16800 Imperial Valley Dr., Ste. 499
Houston, TX 77060-3134

Established in 2006 in TX.
Donors: Vijay P. Goradia; Marie G. Goradia.
Foundation type: Independent foundation.

Financial data (yr. ended 12/31/13): Assets, $27,741,769 (M); gifts received, $3,852,861; expenditures, $522,302; qualifying distributions, $485,606; giving activities include $481,574 for 20 grants (high: $135,644; low: $75).
Fields of interest: Minorities/immigrants, centers/services; International development; United Ways and Federated Giving Programs.
Limitations: Applications not accepted. Giving primarily in NY and TX. No grants to individuals.
Application information: Contributes only to pre-selected organizations.
Officers: Sapphira Goradia, Pres. and Treas.; Vijay P. Goradia, V.P.; Marie G. Goradia, Secy.
EIN: 205835715

8872
The Gorman Foundation ✧
7373 Broadway, Ste. 508
San Antonio, TX 78209-3269 (210) 821-7041
Contact: Frances M. Coker, Secy.

Established in 1997.
Foundation type: Independent foundation.
Financial data (yr. ended 12/31/12): Assets, $6,016,276 (M); expenditures, $483,364; qualifying distributions, $447,500; giving activities include $447,500 for grants.
Purpose and activities: Giving primarily for education and to a Christian evangelistic fund, as well as for health and children's and social services.
Fields of interest: Education; Health care; Human services; Children, services; Christian agencies & churches.
Limitations: Applications accepted. Giving primarily in San Antonio, TX.
Application information: Application form not required.
Initial approach: Proposal
Deadline(s): None
Officers: James W. Gorman, Jr., Pres.; Rowena C. Gorman, V.P.; Frances M. Coker, Secy.; David A. Gorman, Treas.
Director: Michael A. Schott.
EIN: 742822598

8873
Greater Round Rock Community Foundation ✧ ☆
206 E. Main St.
Round Rock, TX 78664 (512) 514-0046
Contact: Jerry Bradley, Exec. Dir.
E-mail: info@rrcommunityfoundation.org; Main URL: http://www.rrcommunityfoundation.org
Facebook: https://www.facebook.com/rrcommunityfoundation
Twitter: http://twitter.com/RRFoundation

Established in 2004 in TX.
Foundation type: Community foundation.
Financial data (yr. ended 09/30/13): Assets, $8,291,065 (M); gifts received, $4,724,829; expenditures, $957,757; giving activities include $737,158 for 12+ grants (high: $303,218).
Purpose and activities: The foundation seeks to enrich the quality of life in the Greater Round Rock, TX area.
Fields of interest: Arts; Education; Crime/violence prevention; Human services; Community/economic development.
Limitations: Applications accepted. Giving primarily in the Greater Round Rock area, TX.
Application information: Visit foundation web site for online application. Application form required.
Initial approach: Complete online application
Deadline(s): None
Officer and Board Members:* Jerry Bradley, Exec. Dir.; John S. Avery, Sr.; Bruce Bessner; Ashley Blake; Jim Boles; Holly Coe; Mark Fritz; Chaz Glace; Keith Hickman; Jay Latham; Frank Leffingwell; T. Nyle Maxwell; Deanna Miller; John C. Nelson; Nancy Rabb; Shari Ramming; Jon E. Sloan; Tim Timmerman; Shevawn Walzel; George White.
EIN: 432043188

8874
Helen Greathouse Charitable Trust ✧
c/o Wells Fargo Bank, N.A.
P.O. Box 41629
Austin, TX 78704-9926
Application address: c/o Wells Fargo Bank, N.A., Attn.: Trust Department, P.O. Box 1959, Midland, TX 79702 tel.: (432) 685-5300

Established in 1997 in TX.
Foundation type: Independent foundation.
Financial data (yr. ended 12/31/13): Assets, $36,764,315 (M); expenditures, $1,561,977; qualifying distributions, $1,257,728; giving activities include $1,185,000 for 58 grants (high: $125,000; low: $2,000).
Fields of interest: Higher education; Education; Human services; Children/youth, services.
Type of support: General/operating support; Building/renovation; Program development; Scholarship funds.
Limitations: Applications accepted. Giving primarily in Midland County, TX. No grants to individuals.
Application information: Application form required.
Initial approach: Grant application form
Deadline(s): Apr. 15 and Oct. 15
Final notification: June and Dec.
Advisory Committee: Joan Baskin; Dona Bradley; Frank K. Cahoon; Becky Ferguson; Richard Folger; Christine Foreman; Vicky Jay; Paul Morris; Mike Talley.
Trustee: Wells Fargo Bank Texas, N.A.
EIN: 752691859

8875
Greathouse Foundation ✧
P.O. Box 3739
Abilene, TX 79604-3739
Contact: Dewayne E. Chitwood, V.P. and Exec. Dir.

Established in 1997 in TX.
Donor: Wes-Tex Drilling Co.
Foundation type: Independent foundation.
Financial data (yr. ended 12/31/13): Assets, $13,569,736 (M); expenditures, $588,626; qualifying distributions, $543,332; giving activities include $540,000 for 81 grants (high: $50,000; low: $500).
Purpose and activities: Giving primarily for education, and children, youth and social services.
Fields of interest: Scholarships/financial aid; Education; Human services; Children/youth, services; Family services; Economically disadvantaged.
Type of support: General/operating support; Continuing support; Emergency funds; Program development.
Limitations: Applications accepted. Giving primarily in Abilene, TX; some funding also in Norman, OK.
Application information: Application form required.
Initial approach: Letter
Deadline(s): None
Board meeting date(s): Quarterly
Officers and Directors:* Sharon McDonald, Pres.; Dewayne E. Chitwood,* V.P. and Exec. Dir.; Micah Greathouse, V.P.; Paul Cannon, Secy.; Carl S. Cook,* Treas.
EIN: 752710208
Selected grants: The following grants are a representative sample of this grantmaker's funding activity:
$50,000 to University of Oklahoma, Norman, OK, 2012. For the University of Oklahoma.
$30,000 to Fellowship of Christian Athletes, Abilene, TX, 2012. To support of the All Star Classic Fundraiser.
$10,000 to Lake Brownwood Christian Retreat, Brownwood, TX, 2012. For Christian Camps Ropes Course.
$3,500 to Abilene Arts Alliance, Abilene, TX, 2012. For performance series.
$3,000 to Abilene Education Foundation, Abilene, TX, 2012. For foundations campaign.
$2,250 to Grace Museum, Abilene, TX, 2012. For general support for the Museum.
$2,000 to Hendrick Home for Children, Abilene, TX, 2012. For Funds for Operational Support of a Residential Facility for Children Who Cannot Live with Their Parents.
$1,000 to YMCA of Abilene, Abilene, TX, 2012. For Funds to Support Programs for Youth.

8876
Mary K. and Clifford Grum Foundation ✧
(formerly Janelle and Clifford Grum Foundation)
P.O. Box 368
Diboll, TX 75941-0368 (936) 829-1334
Contact: Clifford J. Grum, Tr.; Mary K. Grum, Tr.

Established in 1993 in TX.
Donors: Clifford J. Grum; Dona Janelle Grum.
Foundation type: Independent foundation.
Financial data (yr. ended 06/30/13): Assets, $358,612 (M); expenditures, $2,011,584; qualifying distributions, $2,006,150; giving activities include $2,005,000 for 2 grants (high: $2,000,000; low: $5,000).
Fields of interest: Higher education; Theological school/education; Protestant agencies & churches.
Limitations: Applications accepted. Giving primarily in eastern TX. No grants to individuals.
Application information: Application form required.
Initial approach: Letter
Deadline(s): None
Trustees: Clifford J. Grum; Mary K. Grum.
EIN: 756454067

8877
The Jack & Valerie Guenther Foundation ✧
(formerly The Charles and Betty Urschel Foundation)
153 Treeline Park, Ste. 300
San Antonio, TX 78209-1880

Established in 1960 in TX.

Donors: Elizabeth H. Urschel†; Jack Guenther; Valerie Urschel Guenther.
Foundation type: Independent foundation.
Financial data (yr. ended 07/31/13): Assets, $35,626,994 (M); gifts received, $2,595,460; expenditures, $1,304,057; qualifying distributions, $1,801,849; giving activities include $1,203,828 for 27 grants (high: $530,082; low: $100).
Purpose and activities: Giving primarily for the arts.
Fields of interest: Museums (art); Arts; Cancer.
Type of support: General/operating support; Building/renovation.
Limitations: Applications not accepted. Giving primarily in San Antonio, TX, area. No grants to individuals.
Application information: Contributes only to pre-selected organizations.
Officers: Valerie Urschel Guenther, Pres.; Abigail G. Kampmann, V.P.; Jack Guenther, Secy.; Jack E. Guenther, Jr., Treas.
EIN: 746053172
Selected grants: The following grants are a representative sample of this grantmaker's funding activity:
$1,000,000 to National Western Art Foundation, San Antonio, TX, 2011.
$50,000 to Texas Biomedical Research Institute, San Antonio, TX, 2011. For capital campaign.
$10,000 to Cancer Therapy and Research Center, San Antonio, TX, 2011.
$3,000 to Charity Ball Association of San Antonio, San Antonio, TX, 2011.

8878
Gulf Coast Medical Foundation ✧
P.O. Box 30
Wharton, TX 77488-0030
E-mail: mburnham@gulfcoastmedfndn.org; Tel./fax: (979) 532-0904

Established in 1983 in TX; converted from Caney Valley Memorial Hospital and Gulf Coast Medical Center.
Foundation type: Independent foundation.
Financial data (yr. ended 12/31/13): Assets, $18,243,802 (M); gifts received, $1,000; expenditures, $1,052,686; qualifying distributions, $783,425; giving activities include $707,609 for 32 grants (high: $162,000; low: $77).
Purpose and activities: The Gulf Coast Medical Foundation is a private foundation which aims to make a meaningful and significant difference in the quality of life for residents of Fort Bend, Matagorda, and Wharton counties in Texas. To achieve this aim, grants are awarded to qualified non-profit organizations primarily in the following areas: medical/health, human services, education, civic and arts & culture with priority given to medical/health projects.
Fields of interest: Higher education; Medical school/education; Nursing care; Health care; Mental health/crisis services; Children/youth, services.
Type of support: General/operating support; Capital campaigns; Building/renovation; Equipment; Endowments; Program development; Matching/challenge support.
Limitations: Applications accepted. Giving primarily in Fort Bend, Matagorda and Wharton counties, TX. No support for national fundraising organizations. No grants to individuals; no loans.
Publications: Application guidelines; Grants list.
Application information: Application form required.
Copies of proposal: 1
Deadline(s): Dec. 15, Mar. 15, June 15, and Sept. 15
Board meeting date(s): Quarterly
Officers: Robert Michael Farrell, Pres.; Melissa M. Burnham, Exec. V.P.; Janet Peden, V.P.; Jack Moore, Secy.; Charles Davis, Treas.
Directors: Laurance H. Armour III; Jeffrey D. Blair; Sam Golden; Joe Gurecky; Kent Hill; Clive Runnells III; Guy F. Stovall III; Robert M. Taylor.
Number of staff: 1 part-time professional.
EIN: 741285242
Selected grants: The following grants are a representative sample of this grantmaker's funding activity:
$100,000 to Just Do It Now, Wharton, TX, 2012. For operating support 2012-2013.
$50,000 to Just Do It Now, Wharton, TX, 2012. For matching grant for Operations.
$22,500 to Northside Center, El Campo, TX, 2012. For Certified Nurse Program - 3 Semesters.
$10,000 to Palacios Community Medical Center, Palacios, TX, 2012. To purchase hematology analyzer.
$10,000 to Palacios Library, Palacios, TX, 2012. For Blessing Library Technology.

8879
H.E.B. Tournament of Champions Charitable Trust ✧
646 S. Main Ave.
San Antonio, TX 78204-1210
Contact: Dir. of Public Affairs

Established in TX.
Foundation type: Independent foundation.
Financial data (yr. ended 12/31/13): Assets, $6,139,605 (M); gifts received, $6,550,367; expenditures, $6,120,727; qualifying distributions, $4,843,117; giving activities include $4,843,117 for 206 grants (high: $500,000; low: $150).
Purpose and activities: Giving primarily for the arts, education, health, and children, youth and social services.
Fields of interest: Arts; Education; Health care; Athletics/sports, Special Olympics; Human services; Children/youth, services; Community/economic development.
Limitations: Giving primarily in TX.
Application information:
Initial approach: Letter
Deadline(s): None
Trustees: Winell I. Heron; Robert D. Loeffler; Martin H. Otto.
EIN: 766187819

8880
D. D. Hachar Charitable Trust Fund ✧
2200 Post Oak Blvd., 19th Fl.
Houston, TX 77056-4700 (956) 764-2811
FAX: (956) 764-1592; Application address: c/o BBVA Compass Bank, 700 San Bernardo Ave., Laredo, TX 78042, tel.: (956) 727-9311

Established in 1980 in TX.
Donor: Lamar Bruni Vergara Trust.
Foundation type: Independent foundation.
Financial data (yr. ended 04/30/13): Assets, $25,257,202 (M); expenditures, $1,626,472; qualifying distributions, $1,344,391; giving activities include $1,306,818 for 17 grants (high: $268,250).
Purpose and activities: Giving primarily for higher education, particularly scholarships to financially needy residents (of at least 3 years) of Laredo, Webb County, and surrounding counties in TX, who must maintain a GPA of 2.75. Students planning to attend a technical or vocational school will be considered on an individual basis as far as grade point average is concerned.
Fields of interest: Higher education.
Type of support: General/operating support; Scholarships—to individuals; Student loans—to individuals.
Limitations: Giving limited to Laredo and Webb County, TX, and surrounding areas.
Publications: Application guidelines; Annual report; Informational brochure; Program policy statement.
Application information: Application form required for scholarships. Grants to organizations are limited. Application form required.
Initial approach: Letter or telephone requesting application guidelines
Deadline(s): Refer to application guidelines
Trustee: BBVA Compass Bank.
Number of staff: 2 full-time professional.
EIN: 742093680
Selected grants: The following grants are a representative sample of this grantmaker's funding activity:
$200,000 to Laredo Community College, Laredo, TX, 2011.
$26,500 to United Day School, Laredo, TX, 2011.

8881
Patrick & Beatrice Haggerty Foundation ✧
(formerly Haggerty Foundation)
4712 Shadywood Ln.
Dallas, TX 75209-2020

Established in 1968 in TX.
Donors: Patrick E. Haggerty†; Beatrice M. Haggerty†.
Foundation type: Independent foundation.
Financial data (yr. ended 12/31/13): Assets, $14,675,306 (M); expenditures, $708,199; qualifying distributions, $607,907; giving activities include $561,000 for 25 grants (high: $373,500; low: $2,000).
Purpose and activities: Giving primarily for the arts, education, and health and human services.
Fields of interest: Arts; Education; Health care; Human services; Catholic agencies & churches.
Type of support: General/operating support; Capital campaigns; Building/renovation; Equipment; Scholarship funds; Research; Matching/challenge support.
Limitations: Applications not accepted. Giving primarily in Dallas County, TX. No grants to individuals.
Application information: Unsolicited requests for funds not accepted.
Board meeting date(s): Nov.
Officers: Patrick E. Haggerty, Chair. and C.E.O.; Michael G. Haggerty, Secy.-Treas.
Directors: Robert Moosey; Teresa Haggerty Parravano; Shella Haggerty Turner.
Number of staff: 1 part-time professional; 1 part-time support.
EIN: 752076387
Selected grants: The following grants are a representative sample of this grantmaker's funding activity:

$317,500 to Childrens Medical Center of Dallas, Dallas, TX, 2011.
$130,000 to Cistercian Preparatory School, Irving, TX, 2011.
$50,000 to University of Dallas, Irving, TX, 2011.
$14,500 to Childrens Medical Center of Dallas, Dallas, TX, 2011.
$7,250 to Saint Michaels Catholic Academy, Austin, TX, 2011.
$7,250 to University of Dallas, Irving, TX, 2011.

8882
Jon and Linda Halbert Family Foundation ✧

4245 N. Central Expwy., Ste. 505
Dallas, TX 75205-4581 (214) 526-6494
Contact: Carol Cashman

Donors: Jon S. Halbert; Linda M. Halbert; Jo Ann Walling Halbert†; Jo Ann Walling Halbert Trust.
Foundation type: Independent foundation.
Financial data (yr. ended 12/31/13): Assets, $16,118,871 (M); gifts received, $149,131; expenditures, $1,452,022; qualifying distributions, $1,375,614; giving activities include $1,353,333 for 8 grants (high: $500,000; low: $2,000).
Fields of interest: Human services; Protestant agencies & churches.
Limitations: Applications accepted. Giving primarily in TX. No grants to individuals.
Application information: Application form required.
Initial approach: Proposal
Deadline(s): None
Officers: Jon S. Halbert, Pres. and Treas.; Linda M. Halbert, V.P. and Secy.
Director: Lindsay M. Halbert.
EIN: 470929091

8883
Craig and Kathryn Hall Foundation ✧

(formerly Hall Foundation for Individual Opportunity)
6801 Gaylord Pkwy., Ste. 100
Frisco, TX 75034-8557 (972) 377-1100
Contact: Brijetta Hall Waller, Pres. and Tr.

Established in 1979 in MI and TX.
Donors: Craig Hall; Hall Financial Group; Brijetta Lynn Hall; Craig and Kathryn Hall Charitable Lead Annuity Trust.
Foundation type: Independent foundation.
Financial data (yr. ended 08/31/13): Assets, $2,758,039 (M); expenditures, $627,309; qualifying distributions, $627,004; giving activities include $545,518 for 54 grants (high: $125,000; low: $500).
Fields of interest: Education; Health organizations, association; Human services; Jewish federated giving programs; Jewish agencies & synagogues; Women.
Type of support: Capital campaigns.
Limitations: Applications accepted. Giving primarily in north TX and the Napa Valley, CA. No grants to individuals.
Application information: Application form required.
Initial approach: Letter
Deadline(s): None
Officers and Trustees:* Brijetta Waller Hall,* Pres.; Bryan Toblert, V.P., Finance and Treas.; David H. Cain,* Secy.; Jennifer Cain; Kristina Hahsler; Craig Hall; Kathryn Walt Hall.
EIN: 382275211
Selected grants: The following grants are a representative sample of this grantmaker's funding activity:
$100,000 to Jewish Federation of Greater Dallas, Dallas, TX, 2011.
$20,000 to North Texas Food Bank, Dallas, TX, 2011.
$10,000 to Clinic Ole Foundation, Napa, CA, 2011.
$5,000 to Friendship Shelter, Laguna Beach, CA, 2011.
$5,000 to Napa County Land Trust, Napa, CA, 2011.
$5,000 to Shakespeare Festival of Dallas, Dallas, TX, 2011.
$3,100 to Dallas Womens Foundation, Dallas, TX, 2011.
$2,500 to American Red Cross, Napa, CA, 2011.
$1,800 to Legal Aid of Napa Valley, Napa, CA, 2011.
$1,000 to La Reunion TX, Dallas, TX, 2011.

8884
Halliburton Foundation, Inc. ✧

P.O. Box 42806
Houston, TX 77242-2806 (281) 575-3558
Contact: Brinda Maxwell, Prog. Admin.
Application address: 10200 Bellaire Blvd., Houston, TX 77072-5206; Additional address: P.O. Box 4574, Houston, TX 77072-4574; Main URL: http://www.halliburton.com/AboutUs/default.aspx?navid=992&pageid=2347

Incorporated in 1965 in TX.
Donors: Halliburton Co.; Brown & Root, Inc.
Foundation type: Company-sponsored foundation.
Financial data (yr. ended 12/31/12): Assets, $19,014,892 (M); gifts received, $2,850,000; expenditures, $2,701,234; qualifying distributions, $2,660,372; giving activities include $2,660,372 for 140 grants (high: $244,594; low: $100).
Purpose and activities: The foundation supports organizations involved with education, health, and health-related social services.
Fields of interest: Elementary/secondary education; Higher education; Education; Health care; Human services.
Type of support: General/operating support; Continuing support; Annual campaigns; Equipment; Program development; Conferences/seminars; Curriculum development; Employee volunteer services; Employee matching gifts; Employee-related scholarships.
Limitations: Applications accepted. Giving primarily in areas of company operations, with emphasis on KS, LA, OK, PA, and TX. No support for religious, fraternal, or veterans organizations, athletic organizations, or political or union organizations. No grants to individuals (except for employee-related scholarships), or for trips, sporting events, tours, or transportation, advertising, film, or video projects; no loans.
Publications: Application guidelines.
Application information: Application form not required.
Initial approach: Proposal
Copies of proposal: 1
Deadline(s): None
Board meeting date(s): Quarterly
Final notification: 3 months
Officers and Trustees: David J. Lesar, Pres.; Cathy Mann, V.P. and Secy.; Craig W. Nunez, Treas.; Lawrence J. Pope; Tim Probert.
EIN: 751212458

8885
The Ewing Halsell Foundation ✧

711 Navarro St., Ste. 737
San Antonio, TX 78205-1711 (210) 223-2640
Contact: Jackie J. Moczygemba, Fdn. Mgr.
FAX: (210) 271-9089; E-mail for Jackie J. Moczygemba: Jackie@ewinghalsell.org; Main URL: http://www.ewinghalsell.org

Trust established in 1957 in TX.
Donors: Ewing Halsell†; Mrs. Ewing Halsell†; Grace F. Rider†.
Foundation type: Independent foundation.
Financial data (yr. ended 06/30/11): Assets, $154,114,916 (M); expenditures, $8,562,739; qualifying distributions, $7,551,603; giving activities include $7,000,500 for 40 grants (high: $1,000,000; low: $3,500).
Purpose and activities: Grants primarily for education, cultural programs, health organizations, and social service and youth agencies.
Fields of interest: Museums (art); Performing arts, orchestras; Arts; Higher education; Libraries (public); Education; Health organizations, association; Medical research, institute; Girl scouts; Human services; Youth, services.
Type of support: Annual campaigns; Building/renovation; Equipment; Land acquisition; Publication; Seed money; Research; Technical assistance.
Limitations: Giving limited to TX, with emphasis on southwestern TX, particularly San Antonio. No grants to individuals, or for deficit financing, emergency funds, general endowments, matching gifts, scholarships, fellowships, demonstration projects, general purposes, or conferences; no loans.
Publications: Biennial report (including application guidelines); Program policy statement.
Application information: If the program/project is appropriate, the foundation manager will schedule a meeting and/or site visit to learn more about the applicant organization. Application form not required.
Initial approach: Telephone
Copies of proposal: 1
Deadline(s): Varies
Board meeting date(s): Quarterly
Final notification: 3 months
Officers and Trustees: Edward H. Austin, Jr.,* Co-Chair.; Hugh A. Fitzsimmons, Jr.; William Harte; William Scanlon.
Number of staff: 1 full-time professional; 2 part-time support.
EIN: 746063016
Selected grants: The following grants are a representative sample of this grantmaker's funding activity:
$1,005,000 to IDEA Public Schools, Weslaco, TX, 2012. For expansion in San Antonio.
$850,000 to Texas Biomedical Research Institute, San Antonio, TX, 2012. For program support.
$700,000 to Bexar County Performing Arts Center, San Antonio, TX, 2012. For general support.
$700,000 to Saint Marys Hall, San Antonio, TX, 2012. For capital campaign.
$500,000 to Reasoning Mind, Houston, TX, 2012. For program support.
$500,000 to San Antonio Childrens Museum, San Antonio, TX, 2012. For capital campaign.
$333,000 to Southwest School of Art and Craft, San Antonio, TX, 2012. For program support.
$300,000 to Teach for America, New York, NY, 2012. For program support.

$300,000 to University of the Incarnate Word, San Antonio, TX, 2012. For Fine Arts Center Capital Campaign.
$272,000 to Generation TX San Antonio, San Antonio, TX, 2012. For in-school curriculum project expansion.

8886
The Ewing Halsell Foundation ✧
711 Navarro St., Ste. 737
San Antonio, TX 78205-1711 (210) 223-2640
Contact: Jackie Moczygemba, Mgr.

Foundation type: Independent foundation.
Financial data (yr. ended 06/30/13): Assets, $159,426,713 (M); expenditures, $9,365,869; qualifying distributions, $8,058,932; giving activities include $7,816,000 for 29 grants (high: $2,000,000; low: $5,000).
Fields of interest: Museums; Arts; Education; Biomedicine research; Agriculture/food; Human services; Children/youth, services.
Limitations: Giving primarily in TX.
Application information:
Initial approach: Telephone foundation mgr. to discuss project/program and set up a meeting, then submit 1-5 page proposal letter.
Officer: Jackie Moczygemba, Fdn. Mgr.
Directors: Edward H. Austin, Jr.; Hugh A. Fitzsimons, Jr.; William Harte; William Scanlan.
EIN: 300654055

8887
The Hamill Foundation ✧
1160 Dairy Ashford, Ste. 250
Houston, TX 77079-3014
Contact: Charlie H. Read, C.E.O.
FAX: (281) 556-0456;
E-mail: cread_hamill@sbcglobal.net

Established in 1969 in TX.
Donors: Marie G. Hamill†; Claud B. Hamill†.
Foundation type: Independent foundation.
Financial data (yr. ended 12/31/12): Assets, $199,724,148 (M); expenditures, $11,661,191; qualifying distributions, $9,185,977; giving activities include $8,816,000 for 102 grants.
Purpose and activities: Giving primarily to education, health associations, medical research, human services, children and youth services, and Christian agencies and churches.
Fields of interest: Museums; Higher education; Education; Health organizations, association; Medical research, institute; Human services; Children/youth, services; Christian agencies & churches.
Type of support: General/operating support; Annual campaigns; Capital campaigns; Emergency funds; Scholarship funds; Research.
Limitations: Applications not accepted. Giving primarily in Houston, TX. No grants to individuals.
Application information: Contributes only to pre-selected organizations.
Board meeting date(s): Four or five times a year
Officers and Directors:* Charlie H. Read,* C.E.O., Pres., and Treas.; Thomas H. Brown,* V.P., Secy., and Dir., Grants; Charles W. Snider,* V.P.; Charles D. McMurrey, Emeritus; William T. Miller; Barbara Strobel.
Number of staff: 2 full-time professional; 2 full-time support.
EIN: 237028238
Selected grants: The following grants are a representative sample of this grantmaker's funding activity:
$400,000 to Houston Museum of Natural Science, Houston, TX, 2012. For capital campaign.
$300,000 to Rice University, Houston, TX, 2012. For capital campaign and research.
$275,000 to Council on Alcohol and Drugs Houston, Houston, TX, 2012. For operating support.
$250,000 to YMCA of Greater Houston Area, Houston, TX, 2012. For capital campaign and operating support.
$225,000 to Memorial Hermann Hospital System, Houston, TX, 2012. For program support.
$200,000 to University of Texas Foundation, Austin, TX, 2012. For medical research.
$125,000 to Menninger Clinic, Houston, TX, 2012. For capital campaign.
$100,000 to Saint Martins Episcopal Church, Houston, TX, 2012. For capital campaign.
$75,000 to Chinquapin School, Highlands, TX, 2012. For general operating support.
$50,000 to Small Steps Nurturing Center, Houston, TX, 2012. For operating support or capital campaign.

8888
George and Mary Josephine Hamman Foundation ✧
3336 Richmond, Ste. 310
Houston, TX 77098-3022 (713) 522-9891
Contact: D. Troy Derouen CPA, Exec. Dir.
FAX: (713) 522-9693;
E-mail: HammanFdn@aol.com; Main URL: http://www.hammanfoundation.org

Incorporated in 1954 in TX.
Donors: Mary Josephine Hamman†; George Hamman†.
Foundation type: Independent foundation.
Financial data (yr. ended 12/31/13): Assets, $101,453,950 (M); expenditures, $5,586,843; qualifying distributions, $6,710,800; giving activities include $3,534,000 for grants, and $1,001,875 for grants to individuals.
Purpose and activities: Giving for construction and operation of hospitals, medical treatment, and research organizations and programs; grants to churches and affiliated religious organizations (nondenominational); grants to building programs or special educational projects at colleges and universities, mostly local; contributions also to cultural programs, social services, youth agencies, and ecological causes. Each spring, the foundation also awards 70 scholarships to Houston area high school seniors for undergraduate study. The award is $16,000, disbursed over 4 years. Applicants must have a minimum SAT score of 1,000 (on the Math and Critical Reading portions combined), and/or ACT score of 21. The recipient may select any major at any four year college or university.
Fields of interest: Arts; Higher education; Education; Hospitals (general); Health care; Medical research, institute; Human services; Children/youth, services; Religion.
Type of support: General/operating support; Continuing support; Annual campaigns; Capital campaigns; Building/renovation; Equipment; Scholarship funds; Research; Scholarships—to individuals; Matching/challenge support.
Limitations: Applications accepted. Giving only in the state of TX for grants. Scholarships to high school seniors is limited to the immediate Houston area, particularly Brazoria, Chambers, Fort Bend, Galveston, Harris, Liberty, Montgomery and Waller counties. No support for postgraduate education. No grants to individuals (except for scholarships).
Publications: Application guidelines; Financial statement; Grants list.
Application information: Grant Application form and Grant follow-up reports must be completed for grantseekers. Application and financial qualification statement must be completed for scholarships. Forms can also be downloaded from foundation web site. Requests by fax or e-mail will not be accepted. For applicants who have received a prior grant from the foundation, complete the one-page "Follow-up Report" on the prior grant. Do not expand beyond the foundation's 1-page report. Application form required.
Initial approach: Application
Copies of proposal: 1
Deadline(s): Feb. 22 for scholarships, none for grants
Board meeting date(s): Bi-monthly
Final notification: 60 days
Officers and Directors:* Henry R. Hamman,* Pres.; Anne H. Shepherd,* Secy.; Charles D. Milby, Jr.,* Treas.; D. Troy Derouen, CPA, Exec. Dir.; Russell R. Hamman; Mary J. Milby.
Number of staff: 1 full-time professional; 1 full-time support.
EIN: 746061447
Selected grants: The following grants are a representative sample of this grantmaker's funding activity:
$190,000 to Texas Heart Institute, Houston, TX, 2011.
$100,000 to Foundation for Hope Village, Friendswood, TX, 2011.
$100,000 to Houston Museum of Natural Science, Houston, TX, 2011.
$100,000 to University of Texas Medical Branch, Galveston, TX, 2011.
$75,000 to Briarwood-Brookwood, Brookshire, TX, 2011.
$60,000 to Wildlife Habitat Federation, Mountain City, TX, 2011.
$50,000 to Camp for All Foundation, Houston, TX, 2011.
$50,000 to Houston Museum of Natural Science, Houston, TX, 2011.
$50,000 to Monarch School, Houston, TX, 2011.
$50,000 to Rice University, Houston, TX, 2011.

8889
Hamon Charitable Foundation ✧
1925 Lincoln Plz.
500 N. Akard St.
Dallas, TX 75201-3329 (214) 922-9850
Contact: Kelly Roach, Pres.

Established in 1998 in TX.
Donor: Nancy B. Hamon†.
Foundation type: Independent foundation.
Financial data (yr. ended 12/31/13): Assets, $139,528,554 (M); gifts received, $200,000; expenditures, $20,511,335; qualifying distributions, $19,191,500; giving activities include $19,191,500 for 19 grants (high: $6,000,000; low: $10,000).

Fields of interest: Museums (art); Performing arts, opera; Higher education; Libraries (special); Environment.
Limitations: Giving primarily in TX. No grants to individuals.
Application information:
Initial approach: Letter
Deadline(s): None
Officers and Directors:* Kelly Roach,* Pres.; John L. Roach,* V.P.; Linda J. Dunavant, Secy.; Nancy Halbreicht; Ray M. Poage; Tom M. Souers; Kern Wildenthal, M.D., Ph.D.
EIN: 752734057
Selected grants: The following grants are a representative sample of this grantmaker's funding activity:
$5,000,000 to Children's Medical Foundation of Texas, Dallas, TX, 2012. For general support.
$2,000,000 to Texas A & M Foundation, College Station, TX, 2012. For general support.
$350,000 to University of Texas at Dallas, Richardson, TX, 2012. To endow UTEACH Dallas.
$50,000 to Educational First Steps, Dallas, TX, 2012. For general support.
$50,000 to Wesley-Rankin Community Center, Dallas, TX, 2012. For after-school programs helping children with math, reading and homework.

8890
Curtis & Doris K. Hankamer Foundation ✧
9039 Katy Freeway, Ste. 530
Houston, TX 77024-1656

Established in 1981 in TX.
Donors: Doris K. Hankamer‡; Earl Curtis Hankamer, Jr.‡.
Foundation type: Independent foundation.
Financial data (yr. ended 12/31/13): Assets, $17,820,216 (M); expenditures, $1,152,095; qualifying distributions, $1,013,130; giving activities include $986,230 for 21 grants (high: $182,080; low: $8,000).
Purpose and activities: Giving primarily for services for the elderly, particularly in the areas of medical research and Christian ministry programs.
Fields of interest: Medical school/education; Medical research, institute; Aging, centers/services; Christian agencies & churches.
Type of support: General/operating support; Fellowships.
Limitations: Applications not accepted. Giving primarily in Houston, TX. No grants to individuals.
Application information: Contributes only to pre-selected organizations.
Trustees: S. Terry Bracken; Earl Curtis Hankamer III; H. Scott Hunsaker.
EIN: 760022687

8891
Elisabeth Katte Harris Foundation Trust ✧
c/o Wells Fargo Bank, N.A.
P.O. Box 41629
Austin, TX 78704-0028

Established in 2005 in CA.
Donor: Elizabeth Katte Harris Trust.
Foundation type: Independent foundation.
Financial data (yr. ended 12/31/13): Assets, $58,278,317 (M); expenditures, $3,191,889; qualifying distributions, $2,983,542; giving activities include $2,795,267 for 5 grants (high: $972,529; low: $93,166).
Fields of interest: Arts; Education; Health care.
Limitations: Applications not accepted. Giving primarily in CA. No grants to individuals.
Application information: Contributes only to pre-selected organizations.
Trustee: Wells Fargo Bank, N.A.
EIN: 206769125

8892
Harte Charitable Foundation ✧ ☆
20742 Stone Oak Pkwy., Ste. 107
San Antonio, TX 78258-7538

Established in 2002 in TX.
Donor: Edward Harte.
Foundation type: Independent foundation.
Financial data (yr. ended 06/30/13): Assets, $5,168,183 (M); expenditures, $801,213; qualifying distributions, $756,895; giving activities include $592,284 for 3 grants (high: $322,284; low: $25,000).
Fields of interest: Higher education, university.
Limitations: Applications not accepted. Giving primarily in TX. No grants to individuals.
Application information: Contributes only to pre-selected organizations.
Officers and Directors:* William S. Harte,* Co-Pres.; Julia H. Widdowson,* Co-Pres.; David L. Sinak,* Secy.-Treas.; Christopher M. Harte; Elizabeth H. Owens.
EIN: 450489907
Selected grants: The following grants are a representative sample of this grantmaker's funding activity:
$336,396 to Texas A & M University, Corpus Christi, TX, 2011.

8893
The Gordon Hartman Family Foundation ✧
c/o Gordon Hartman Family Foundation
1202 W. Bitters Bldg. 1, Ste. 1200
San Antonio, TX 78216-7851 (210) 479-2811
FAX: (210) 493-7828;
E-mail: becky@gordonhartman.com; Main URL: http://hartmansa.org
E-Newsletter: http://hartmansa.org/About/newsletter-sign-up.asp
Facebook: http://www.facebook.com/HartmanFoundation
Grants List: http://www.hartmansa.org/grants/previously-awarded
Twitter: http://twitter.com/GHFF

Established in 2005 in TX.
Donors: Gordon Hartman; RAD Investments Inc.; Meh Holding Company, Ltd; Margaret M. Hartman; Ruth Eaton; Joseph Eaton.
Foundation type: Independent foundation.
Financial data (yr. ended 12/31/12): Assets, $10,757,911 (M); gifts received, $486,513; expenditures, $1,050,924; qualifying distributions, $621,972; giving activities include $621,972 for grants.
Purpose and activities: The foundation supports programs, projects and collaborative efforts of Bexar County, TX, organizations that serve individuals with cognitive and physical disabilities, with a particular focus on serving children's needs in this area.
Fields of interest: Children; Disabilities, people with; Physically disabled; Mentally disabled.
Limitations: Giving limited to the Bexar County, TX, area. No support for for-profit organizations, or for religious organizations for sectarian purposes. No grants to individuals, or for economic development, annual fund drives, events, fundraisers or sponsorships.
Publications: Application guidelines.
Application information: Applications are by invitation only, upon the selection committee's review of the Letter of Inquiry. Complete application guidelines and policies are available on foundation web site.
Initial approach: Letter of Inquiry
Deadline(s): See foundation web site for current deadlines
Officers: Gordon V. Hartman, Pres.; Margaret M. Hartman, Secy.-Treas.
EIN: 203537281

8894
J. H. Harvey Trust ✧
c/o Wells Fargo Bank, N.A.
P.O. Box 41629
Austin, TX 78704-9926

Established in 1973; supporting organization of Masonic Home and School, Methodist Home of Waco, TX, Rice University, and Texas Scottish Rite Hospital for Crippled Children.
Foundation type: Independent foundation.
Financial data (yr. ended 11/30/13): Assets, $23,396,304 (M); expenditures, $882,415; qualifying distributions, $564,325; giving activities include $564,325 for 4 grants (high: $288,163; low: $92,054).
Fields of interest: Higher education, university; Hospitals (specialty); Children/youth, services.
Type of support: General/operating support.
Limitations: Applications not accepted. Giving limited to TX.
Application information: Contributes only to pre-selected organizations.
Trustee: Wells Fargo Bank, N.A.
EIN: 746031695
Selected grants: The following grants are a representative sample of this grantmaker's funding activity:
$453,171 to Texas Scottish Rite Hospital for Children, Dallas, TX, 2011. For general support.
$147,056 to Masonic Home and School of Texas, Hurst, TX, 2011. For general support.

8895
Russell and Diana Hawkins Family Foundation ✧ ☆
18 West Ln.
Houston, TX 77019-1008

Donors: Russell B. Hawkins; Diana M. Hawkins.
Foundation type: Independent foundation.
Financial data (yr. ended 12/31/13): Assets, $3,365,891 (M); expenditures, $1,218,449; qualifying distributions, $1,204,800; giving activities include $1,204,800 for 25 grants (high: $300,000; low: $1,000).
Fields of interest: Higher education; Libraries (special); Education; Human services.

Limitations: Applications not accepted. Giving primarily in Houston, TX; some giving in MA and New York, NY.
Application information: Unsolicited requests for funds not accepted.
Directors: Diana M. Hawkins; Laura B. Hawkins; Russell B. Hawkins.
EIN: 271475361
Selected grants: The following grants are a representative sample of this grantmaker's funding activity:
$25,000 to Discovery Green Conservancy, Houston, TX, 2011. For general fund.
$25,000 to New York University, New York, NY, 2011. For general fund.
$17,050 to Trees for Houston, Houston, TX, 2011. For general fund.
$15,000 to Community Foundation of Jackson Hole, Jackson, WY, 2011. For general fund.
$15,000 to Houston Parks Board, Houston, TX, 2011. For general fund.
$15,000 to Menil Collection, Houston, TX, 2011. For general fund.
$15,000 to Saint Johns School, Houston, TX, 2011. For general fund.
$10,000 to Medical Bridges, Houston, TX, 2011. For general fund.
$5,000 to University of Houston Foundation, Houston, TX, 2011. For general fund.
$2,500 to Scenic Texas, Houston, TX, 2011. For general fund.

8896
Hawn Foundation, Inc. ✧
5949 Sherry Ln., Ste. 775
Dallas, TX 75225-8043 (214) 696-6595
Contact: Joe V. Hawn, Jr., Pres.
Main URL: http://www.hawnfoundation.org/

Incorporated in 1962 in TX.
Donors: Mildred Hawn†; W.R. Hawn†; Mary C. Hawn†.
Foundation type: Independent foundation.
Financial data (yr. ended 08/31/13): Assets, $44,438,394 (M); expenditures, $2,378,561; qualifying distributions, $2,081,458; giving activities include $1,924,215 for 59 grants (high: $200,000; low: $250).
Purpose and activities: Giving primarily for health care, and to organizations providing direct assistance to needy individuals.
Fields of interest: Arts; Education; Hospitals (general); Health care; Health organizations, association; Medical research, institute; Human services; Children/youth, services; Christian agencies & churches; Protestant agencies & churches.
Limitations: Applications accepted. Giving primarily in the metropolitan area of Dallas, TX.
Application information:
Initial approach: Letter
Copies of proposal: 1
Deadline(s): Mar. 15
Board meeting date(s): Aug. and as necessary
Final notification: Aug. 31
Officers and Directors:* Joe V. Hawn, Jr., Pres.; Edward A. Copley,* Secy.; Shannon Bair; Sarah Hawn; Doug Kelley; Margaret Hawn Kelley.
Number of staff: 2 part-time professional.
EIN: 756036761
Selected grants: The following grants are a representative sample of this grantmaker's funding activity:
$300,000 to Southwestern Medical Foundation, Dallas, TX, 2010.
$100,000 to Parkland Foundation, Dallas, TX, 2010. For capital campaign.
$100,000 to Presbyterian Healthcare Foundation, Albuquerque, NM, 2010. For capital campaign.
$25,000 to Wounded Warrior Project, Jacksonville, FL, 2011.
$15,000 to Gladney Center for Adoption, Fort Worth, TX, 2011.
$10,000 to Children's Center for Self-Esteem, Houston, TX, 2011.

8897
Heavenly Father's Foundation ✧
425 Country Rd. 168
Cisco, TX 76437-6413

Donors: Dan H. Wilks; Staci Wilks.
Foundation type: Independent foundation.
Financial data (yr. ended 12/31/12): Assets, $120,430,587 (M); expenditures, $4,551,852; qualifying distributions, $4,319,100; giving activities include $4,319,100 for 11 grants (high: $1,699,000; low: $500).
Fields of interest: Health care; Substance abuse, treatment; Health organizations; Human services; Christian agencies & churches.
Limitations: Applications not accepted. Giving primarily in TX.
Application information: Unsolicited requests for funds not accepted.
Trustees: Dan H. Wilks; Staci Wilks.
EIN: 276987913

8898
Gary & Diane Heavin Community Fund ✧
(formerly The Curves Community Fund, Inc.)
c/o Ronnie Glaesmann
100 Ritchie Rd.
Waco, TX 76712-8544

Established in 2001 in TX.
Donors: Curves International, Inc.; Gary Heavin; Diane Heavin.
Foundation type: Company-sponsored foundation.
Financial data (yr. ended 12/31/12): Assets, $36,099,714 (M); gifts received, $20,000,000; expenditures, $1,943,814; qualifying distributions, $1,754,886; giving activities include $1,754,886 for 53 grants (high: $263,271; low: $250).
Purpose and activities: The fund supports organizations involved with television, radio, education, health, human services, and Christianity.
Fields of interest: Media, television; Media, radio; Higher education; Education; Hospitals (general); Health care; Salvation Army; Family services; Family services, domestic violence; Aging, centers/services; Developmentally disabled, centers & services; Human services; Christian agencies & churches.
Type of support: General/operating support.
Limitations: Applications not accepted. Giving primarily in Waco, TX.
Application information: Contributes only to pre-selected organizations.
Officers: Gary H. Heavin, Pres.; Diane Heavin, V.P.
EIN: 743003293

8899
Wilton and Effie Hebert Foundation ✧
P.O. Box 908
Port Neches, TX 77619
Application address: c/o Black & Black Attorneys, 3535 Calder Ave., Ste. 300, Beaumont, TX 77706, tel.: (409) 982-9433

Established in 1992 in TX.
Donors: Wilton P. Hebert†; Effie Mae Hebert†; Concert Association of Southeast Tex.
Foundation type: Independent foundation.
Financial data (yr. ended 12/31/13): Assets, $13,819,755 (M); expenditures, $807,739; qualifying distributions, $620,408; giving activities include $616,507 for 40 grants (high: $65,140; low: $1,000).
Purpose and activities: Giving primarily for children and youth services, as well as for hospitals and health associations; funding also for education, social services, and Roman Catholic organizations and churches.
Fields of interest: Higher education; Education; Hospitals (general); Substance abuse, prevention; Health organizations, association; Muscular dystrophy; Human services; Children/youth, services; Catholic agencies & churches.
Type of support: General/operating support; Building/renovation.
Limitations: Applications accepted. Giving primarily in TX. No grants to individuals.
Application information: Application form required.
Initial approach: Proposal
Deadline(s): None
Directors: James Black; Catherine Hughes Bruney; Joe Vernon.
Number of staff: 1 full-time professional; 1 part-time professional.
EIN: 760065521
Selected grants: The following grants are a representative sample of this grantmaker's funding activity:
$102,760 to Lamar University Foundation, Beaumont, TX, 2011. For scholarships.
$15,000 to YMCA of Port Arthur, Port Arthur, TX, 2011. For operations.
$5,000 to Retina Research Foundation, Houston, TX, 2011. For operations.

8900
Simon & Louise Henderson Foundation ✧
P.O. Box 1365
Lufkin, TX 75902-1365 (936) 634-2448

Established in 1958 in TX.
Donor: Louise Henderson†.
Foundation type: Independent foundation.
Financial data (yr. ended 12/31/12): Assets, $9,436,791 (M); expenditures, $644,030; qualifying distributions, $637,823; giving activities include $631,618 for 61 grants (high: $272,175; low: $200).
Fields of interest: Arts; Elementary/secondary education; Higher education; Hospitals (general); Human services; Protestant agencies & churches.
Type of support: General/operating support; Building/renovation.
Limitations: Applications accepted. Giving primarily in eastern TX. No grants to individuals.
Application information: Application form not required.
Initial approach: Proposal
Deadline(s): None

Officers: Simon W. Henderson III, Pres.; Honea H. Rothermel, V.P.; Virginia L. Henderson, Secy.; Holly Henderson, Treas.
EIN: 756022769

8901
Henderson-Wessendorff Foundation ☆
611 Morton St.
Richmond, TX 77469-3083 (281) 342-2044
Main URL: http://www.hw-foundation.com

Established in 1956 in TX.
Donor: Loise J. Henderson†.
Foundation type: Independent foundation.
Financial data (yr. ended 12/31/12): Assets, $186,538,479 (M); gifts received, $74,383,631; expenditures, $7,856,638; qualifying distributions, $5,163,832; giving activities include $3,485,461 for 44 grants (high: $1,000,000; low: $200).
Fields of interest: Elementary/secondary education; Theological school/education; Animal welfare; Mental health/crisis services; Health organizations, association; Human services; Protestant agencies & churches; Religion.
Limitations: Applications accepted. Giving primarily in TX. No grants to individuals.
Application information:
Initial approach: Letter
Deadline(s): None
Officers and Directors:* Charles Pat McDonald, C.E.O. and Pres.; Ben Jones, C.F.O.; Jack Moore,* Secy.; Barbara R. Bleil; Seth Deleery; Will Robertson; Lane Ward.
EIN: 746047149

8902
Bob L. Herd Foundation ✧
P.O. Box 9340
Tyler, TX 75711-9340
Application address: c/o Janice Thompson, 3901 Manhattan Dr., Tyler, TX 75701, tel.: (903) 509-3456

Established in 1994 in TX.
Donor: Bob L. Herd.
Foundation type: Independent foundation.
Financial data (yr. ended 12/31/13): Assets, $31,219,794 (M); expenditures, $1,572,814; qualifying distributions, $1,423,009; giving activities include $1,163,185 for 44 grants (high: $470,000; low: $500).
Purpose and activities: Giving primarily for higher education, health and human services, and to a United Methodist church.
Fields of interest: Arts; Higher education; Medical research, institute; Human services; Children/youth, services; United Ways and Federated Giving Programs; Protestant agencies & churches.
Limitations: Applications accepted. Giving primarily in Tyler, TX. No grants to individuals.
Application information:
Initial approach: Letter
Deadline(s): None
Officers: Bob L. Herd, Pres.; Janice Thompson, Secy.-Treas.
Director: Michael Herd.
EIN: 752530305
Selected grants: The following grants are a representative sample of this grantmaker's funding activity:
$30,000 to Texas Tech University, Lubbock, TX, 2012. To provide for Scholarships.
$25,000 to East Texas Crisis Center, Tyler, TX, 2012. To assist Victims of Family and Other Violent Crimes.
$20,000 to United Way of Abilene, Abilene, TX, 2012. To Local Agencies Providing Human Services Needs.
$5,000 to Hospice of East Texas, Tyler, TX, 2012. For Care and Comfort of the Terminally Ill and Their Families.
$5,000 to Shackelford County Community Resource Center, Albany, TX, 2012. To Provide Food, Health Education and Human Services.
$5,000 to West Texas Rehabilitation Center, Abilene, TX, 2012. For services for disabled.
$2,000 to Literacy Council of Tyler, Tyler, TX, 2012. For Improvement of Adult Literacy Skills.
$1,000 to Texas Chest Foundation, Tyler, TX, 2012. For Asthma Camp for Children.
$500 to Tyler Rose Museum, Tyler, TX, 2012. To preserve and Display History of Tyler's Rose Growing Industry.

8903
The Hersh Foundation ✧
5221 N. O'Connor Blvd., Ste. 1200
Irving, TX 75039-3754

Established in 1997 in TX.
Donors: Julie K. Hersch; Kenneth A. Hersch; Richard Rainwater.
Foundation type: Independent foundation.
Financial data (yr. ended 12/31/12): Assets, $23,298,448 (M); gifts received, $14,500,000; expenditures, $1,794,140; qualifying distributions, $1,733,225; giving activities include $1,721,617 for 50 grants (high: $600,000; low: $50).
Fields of interest: Performing arts, theater; Higher education; Education; Cancer research; Human services; Jewish agencies & synagogues.
Limitations: Applications not accepted. Giving primarily in the greater Dallas, TX, area. No grants to individuals.
Application information: Contributes only to pre-selected organizations.
Officers: Kenneth A. Hersh, Pres. and Treas.; Julie K. Hersh, V.P. and Secy.
Trustee: Richard L. Covington.
EIN: 752720646
Selected grants: The following grants are a representative sample of this grantmaker's funding activity:
$333,333 to Stanford University, Stanford, CA, 2012. For GSB New Campus Fund.
$100,000 to Dallas Theater Center, Dallas, TX, 2012. For Salary Support for MI Club Program to Support Child and Family Counseling Program.
$33,333 to Letot Center Capital Foundation, Dallas, TX, 2012. For Letot Girls' Residential Treatment Center Construction Campaign.
$25,000 to Harvard University, Cambridge, MA, 2012. For HKS Fund Grant.
$25,000 to Suicide and Crisis Center, Dallas, TX, 2012. For SOS Program.
$10,000 to Educational First Steps, Dallas, TX, 2012. For assistance for childcare centers.
$10,000 to Galaxy Counseling Center, Garland, TX, 2012. For Child and Family Counseling Program.
$10,000 to Stanford University, Stanford, CA, 2012. For Dean's Fund Donation.
$5,000 to Princeton University, Princeton, NJ, 2012. For Annual Giving Campaign for Bendheim Center for Finance.
$1,000 to CONTACT Crisis Line, Dallas, TX, 2012. For 45th anniversary campaign.

8904
Jacob and Terese Hershey Foundation ✧ ☆
2121 San Felipe., Ste. 122
Houston, TX 77019-5600 (713) 529-7611
Contact: Terese T. Hershey, Pres.
E-mail: judyboyce@jthershey.org

Foundation type: Independent foundation.
Financial data (yr. ended 12/31/13): Assets, $3,696,867 (M); expenditures, $438,534; qualifying distributions, $425,261; giving activities include $420,100 for 83 grants (high: $30,250; low: $100).
Fields of interest: Environment; Animals/wildlife; Human services.
Limitations: Applications accepted. Giving primarily in TX.
Application information: Application form not required.
Initial approach: Proposal
Deadline(s): None
Officers: Terese T. Hershey, Pres.; Amie Rodnick, Secy.; Andrew H. Sansom, Treas.
Directors: Jeffrey Hershey; Olive Hershey.
EIN: 746039126
Selected grants: The following grants are a representative sample of this grantmaker's funding activity:
$2,000 to Writers in the Schools, Houston, TX, 2012. For Furthering Purpose of Respective Donee.

8905
Albert & Ethel Herzstein Charitable Foundation ✧
6131 Westview Dr.
Houston, TX 77055-5421 (713) 681-7868
Contact: L. Michael Hajtman, Pres.
FAX: (713) 681-3652;
E-mail: mail@herzsteinfoundation.org; Main URL: http://www.herzsteinfoundation.org
Grants List: http://www.herzsteinfoundation.org/Grant_History.html

Established in 1965 in TX.
Donors: Albert H. Herzstein†; Ethel Avis Herzstein†; Sadie Herzstein Smith†; and members of the Herzstein family.
Foundation type: Independent foundation.
Financial data (yr. ended 12/31/12): Assets, $97,836,563 (M); expenditures, $5,337,202; qualifying distributions, $4,499,365; giving activities include $4,046,550 for 258 grants (high: $500,000; low: $1,000).
Purpose and activities: The trust was organized and shall be operated exclusively for religious, charitable, scientific, literary and/or educational purposes.
Fields of interest: Historic preservation/historical societies; Arts; Education, community/cooperative; Education; Environment; Health care; Youth development; Human services; Community development, civic centers; Community/economic development.

Type of support: General/operating support; Continuing support; Annual campaigns; Capital campaigns; Building/renovation; Equipment; Land acquisition; Endowments; Debt reduction; Scholarship funds.
Limitations: Applications accepted. Giving primarily in TX, with emphasis on the greater Houston-Galveston area. No grants to individuals.
Publications: Application guidelines; Annual report; Grants list; Informational brochure (including application guidelines).
Application information: Only one proposal may be submitted in any twelve month period. All proposals must be submitted via U.S. mail, and must be unbound. E-mails are not accepted. Application form not required.
Initial approach: Letter or proposal
Copies of proposal: 1
Deadline(s): None
Final notification: 90 days
Officers and Directors:* George W. Strake,* Chair.; L. Michael Hajtman,* Pres.; Steven Goodman; Richard Loewenstern; Bryan Miller; Nathan H. Topek, M.D.
Number of staff: 1 full-time professional; 3 full-time support.
EIN: 746070484

8906
The Higgins Family Charitable Foundation ✧

c/o Bank of America, N.A.
P.O. Box 831041
Dallas, TX 75283-1041

Established in 2005 in CA.
Donors: Dr. S. Daniels Higgins; Sam Higgins; Betty M. Higgins; Margaret E. Higgins.
Foundation type: Independent foundation.
Financial data (yr. ended 06/30/13): Assets, $11,381,036 (M); gifts received, $1,000,000; expenditures, $537,763; qualifying distributions, $523,287; giving activities include $512,000 for 8 grants (high: $350,000; low: $2,000).
Fields of interest: Higher education; Health care; Autism research.
Limitations: Applications not accepted. Giving primarily in AZ, CA, and NY. No grants to individuals.
Application information: Contributes only to pre-selected organizations.
Officers and Directors:* S. Daniel Higgins, Pres. and C.E.O.; Margaret E. Higgins, C.F.O. and Treas.; Andrew Higgins,* V.P.; Samantha Higgins-Moss,* V.P.; Harvey Moss,* V.P.
EIN: 030569654
Selected grants: The following grants are a representative sample of this grantmaker's funding activity:
$350,000 to Autism Speaks, New York, NY, 2011.
$13,500 to Power Paws Assistance Dogs, Scottsdale, AZ, 2011.
$10,000 to Pediatric Therapy Network, Torrance, CA, 2011.
$10,000 to Stop Cancer, Los Angeles, CA, 2011.

8907
Hildebrand Foundation ✧

P.O. Box 1308
Houston, TX 77251-1308 (713) 965-9177
Contact: Jennifer Gibson, Grant Coord.
FAX: (713) 622-2732;
E-mail: myrawilliams@hilhouse.com; Main URL: http://www.hildebrandfoundation.com

Established in 2001 in TX.
Donors: Jeffrey D. Hildebrand; Melinda B. Hildebrand.
Foundation type: Independent foundation.
Financial data (yr. ended 12/31/13): Assets, $156,484,487 (M); gifts received, $42,403; expenditures, $28,776,560; qualifying distributions, $28,302,604; giving activities include $28,296,250 for 57 grants (high: $24,500,000; low: $250).
Purpose and activities: Giving for the poor and needy through faith-based organizations.
Fields of interest: Religion.
Limitations: Applications accepted. Giving primarily in Houston, TX. No support for trips for school-related organizations or amateur sports teams. No grants to individuals, or for the purchase of uniforms, or equipment; no loans.
Application information: Application form not required.
Initial approach: Written request on organization's letterhead
Copies of proposal: 1
Deadline(s): Ongoing
Board meeting date(s): Several times each year
Final notification: Two weeks after board meeting
Officers: Jeffrey D. Hildebrand, Pres.; Melinda B. Hildebrand, V.P.
Director: Jean-Paul Budinger.
EIN: 760699250

8908
The Lyda Hill Foundation ✧ ☆

2001 Ross Ave., Ste. 4600
Dallas, TX 75201-8007 (214) 922-1100
Main URL: http://lydahillfoundation.org/
Lyda Hill's Giving Pledge Profile: http://glasspockets.org/philanthropy-in-focus/eye-on-the-giving-pledge/profiles/hill

Established in 1997 in TX.
Donor: Lyda Hill.
Foundation type: Independent foundation.
Financial data (yr. ended 11/30/13): Assets, $7,674,007 (M); expenditures, $1,054,785; qualifying distributions, $1,034,392; giving activities include $1,034,142 for 2 grants (high: $1,000,809; low: $33,333).
Purpose and activities: Support for efforts that advance transformational research in the foundation's primary interest areas of early stage bio-medical, environment, and alternative energy.
Fields of interest: Environment; Biomedicine.
Limitations: Applications not accepted. Giving primarily in CO and TX. No support for religious organizations. No grants to individuals, or for scholarships.
Application information: Unsolicited requests for funds not accepted.
Officers: Nicole Small, Pres.; Frank Mackey, V.P. and Secy.-Treas.; Leslie Carlson, V.P.
Directors: Lyda Hill; Mary Jalonick; Nancy Lewis.
EIN: 752708838
Selected grants: The following grants are a representative sample of this grantmaker's funding activity:
$1,000,000 to Pew Charitable Trusts, Philadelphia, PA, 2011.

8909
Hillcrest Foundation ✧

c/o US Trust, Philanthropic Solutions
901 Main St., 19th Fl., TX1-492-19-11
Dallas, TX 75283-1041 (214) 209-1965
Contact: David T. Ross, US Trust, Philanthropic Solutions
E-mail for David T. Ross: david.ross@baml.com; Additional e-mail for Debi Allen: debi.allen@baml.com; additional e-mail for questions about the application process or the foundation: tx.philanthropic@ustrust.com (indicate the foundation name in e-mail subject line); Main URL: http://www.bankofamerica.com/grantmaking

Trust established in 1959 in TX.
Donor: Mrs. W.W. Caruth, Sr.‡.
Foundation type: Independent foundation.
Financial data (yr. ended 05/31/13): Assets, $143,498,239 (M); expenditures, $7,036,684; qualifying distributions, $6,481,981; giving activities include $5,947,000 for 151 grants (high: $250,000; low: $1,000).
Purpose and activities: To relieve poverty, advance education, and promote health; support for higher and other education, health and hospitals, social services, including programs for youth and child welfare, drug abuse, rehabilitation and housing. Grant requests for capital and program support are strongly encouraged.
Fields of interest: Secondary school/education; Vocational education; Higher education; Business school/education; Adult/continuing education; Education; Hospitals (general); Dental care; Medical care, rehabilitation; Health care; Substance abuse, services; Health organizations, association; Cancer; Medical research, institute; Food services; Housing/shelter, development; Human services; Children/youth, services; Aging, centers/services; Aging; Disabilities, people with.
Type of support: Capital campaigns; Building/renovation; Equipment; Land acquisition; Program development; Matching/challenge support.
Limitations: Applications accepted. Giving limited to TX, with emphasis on Dallas County. No grants to individuals or for general operating support; no loans.
Publications: Application guidelines; Informational brochure (including application guidelines).
Application information: The majority of grants are 1 year in duration. On occasion, multi-year support is awarded. An organization that receives a one-year grant must skip a year before submitting a subsequent application. An organization that receives a multi-year grant is not eligible to apply until one year after the close of its grant cycle. Application form required.
Initial approach: Letter
Copies of proposal: 2
Deadline(s): Rolling for proposals; Applications: Feb. 28, July 31 and Nov. 30
Board meeting date(s): As required, usually 3 times annually; Feb., May, and Oct.
Final notification: Feb. deadline applicants will be notified by June 30; July applicants will be notified by Nov. 30; Nov. applicants will be notified by Mar. 31 of the following year
Trustees: George W. Bramblett, Jr.; D. Harold Byrd, Jr.; W.W. Caruth III; Sandra Estess; Charles P. Storey; Bank of America, N.A.
Number of staff: 1 part-time professional; 2 part-time support.
EIN: 756007565

Selected grants: The following grants are a representative sample of this grantmaker's funding activity:
$400,000 to Southern Methodist University, Dallas, TX, 2012. For multi pledge to construct new Caruth Hall of Engineering and Amphitheater.
$250,000 to Momentous Institute, Dallas, TX, 2012. For Capital Campaign for family service center.
$250,000 to Volunteer Center of North Texas, Dallas, TX, 2013. For Technology Upgrade.
$200,000 to Austin College, Sherman, TX, 2012. To construct a Science Center; provide modern space for academic classes, research and laboratories.
$200,000 to Austin College, Sherman, TX, 2013. To construct a Science Center; provide modern space for academic classes, research and laboratories.
$200,000 to Childrens Medical Center of Dallas, Dallas, TX, 2013. For funding in support of the renovation and expansion of Children's Center for Cancer and Blood Disorders; integrate outpatient clinic.
$200,000 to Girl Scouts of the U.S.A., Dallas, TX, 2012. To upgrade communication equipment.
$200,000 to Parkland Foundation, Dallas, TX, 2013. For funding in support of the I Stand for Parkland capital campaign; construct new 862 bed hospital acorss from the present Parkland facility.
$170,000 to Perot Museum of Nature and Science, Dallas, TX, 2012. For Expansion Project Campaign. For completion of the new Museum of Nature and Science building in Victory Park; to improve science literacy, science process skills and awareness of natural world; and to encourage children to pursue careers in science.
$150,000 to Communities Foundation of Texas, Dallas, TX, 2013. For 50th Anniversary Commemoration.
$125,000 to Texas Health Presbyterian Foundation, Dallas, TX, 2012. For renovation, construction and outfitting of the Safe Healing Suites.
$100,000 to American Red Cross, Dallas Area Chapter, Dallas, TX, 2013. For Install equipment and technology at 22 office locations.
$100,000 to Special Camps for Special Kids, Dallas, TX, 2013. For capital campaign - create new housing for Camp John Marc medical team members, volunteers and families.
$100,000 to University of Dallas, Irving, TX, 2013. For renovation and equipment for the Haggar University Center.
$90,000 to North Texas Winds, Dallas, TX, 2012. For concerts to nursing homes in Dallas County over the next three years.
$40,000 to Dallas County Heritage Society, Dallas Heritage Village, Dallas, TX, 2012. For technology and communication upgrades; integrate phone system and replace aging server.
$30,000 to GREAT Kids with ADHD, Plano, TX, 2012. For Smart Boards for classrooms.
$25,000 to Foundation for the Education of Young Women, Dallas, TX, 2013. To support 2013 Summer for Success! Program.
$25,000 to Mosaic, Carrollton, TX, 2012. For extended cab box truck and to purchase industrial shredder.
$3,000 to Salvation Army of Dallas, Dallas, TX, 2013. For Humanitarian Grant to purchase food, clothing and other essential items for the underserved in the DFW area.

8910
Hirsch Family Foundation ✧

3811 Turtle Creek Blvd., Ste. 250
Dallas, TX 75219-4504
Contact: Rachel Gallini

Established in 2004 in TX.
Donors: Laurence Hirsch; Susan Hirsch.
Foundation type: Independent foundation.
Financial data (yr. ended 12/31/12): Assets, $32,460,531 (M); expenditures, $2,902,165; qualifying distributions, $2,548,730; giving activities include $2,401,350 for 43 grants (high: $650,000; low: $250).
Fields of interest: Arts; Elementary/secondary education; Higher education; Education; Human services; Children/youth, services; United Ways and Federated Giving Programs; Jewish federated giving programs; Public policy, research; Jewish agencies & synagogues.
Type of support: Research; Professorships; Continuing support; Capital campaigns; Annual campaigns.
Limitations: Applications accepted. Giving primarily in Washington, DC, and Dallas, TX.
Application information: Application form not required.
Initial approach: Letter
Copies of proposal: 2
Deadline(s): None
Board meeting date(s): Quarterly
Directors: Bradford Hirsch; Daria Lee Hirsch; Laurence Hirsch; Susan Hirsch.
EIN: 201225862

8911
Hobby Family Foundation ✧

2131 San Felipe
Houston, TX 77019-5620

Established in 1995 in TX.
Donors: Oveta Culp Hobby 1985 Grantor Trust; W.P. Hobby.
Foundation type: Independent foundation.
Financial data (yr. ended 12/31/13): Assets, $18,038,434 (M); gifts received, $55,000; expenditures, $2,233,142; qualifying distributions, $2,142,192; giving activities include $2,141,300 for 73 grants (high: $500,000; low: $500).
Purpose and activities: Giving primarily for education, the environment, hospitals, and human services.
Fields of interest: Elementary/secondary education; Higher education; Medical school/education; Education; Environment, natural resources; Hospitals (general); Human services.
Limitations: Applications not accepted. Giving primarily in TX, with emphasis on Austin and Houston, and VA. No grants to individuals.
Application information: Contributes only to pre-selected organizations.
Officers and Trustees:* W.P. Hobby,* Pres.; Laura H. Beckworth,* V.P.; Diana P. Hobby,* V.P.; Paul W. Hobby, V.P.; Pamela George, Secy.; Cathy Leeson, Treas.
EIN: 760489862

8912
Hoblitzelle Foundation ✧

5556 Caruth Haven Ln., Ste. 200
Dallas, TX 75225-8146 (214) 373-0462
Contact: Paul W. Harris, C.E.O. and Pres.
FAX: (214) 750-7412;
E-mail: pharris@hoblitzelle.org; E-mail address for Kathy Shannon Stone for general inquiries: kstone@hoblitzelle.org; Main URL: http://www.hoblitzelle.org

Trust established in 1942 in TX; incorporated in 1953.
Donors: Karl St. John Hoblitzelle†; Esther T. Hoblitzelle†; Karl Hoblitzelle Trust.
Foundation type: Independent foundation.
Financial data (yr. ended 04/30/13): Assets, $119,487,983 (M); gifts received, $38,717; expenditures, $5,700,717; qualifying distributions, $5,448,155; giving activities include $5,142,049 for 87 grants (high: $425,000; low: $500).
Purpose and activities: Grants for higher, secondary, vocational, scientific and medical education, hospitals and health services, youth agencies, cultural programs, social services, and community development.
Fields of interest: Visual arts; Performing arts; Historic preservation/historical societies; Arts; Secondary school/education; Vocational education; Higher education; Medical school/education; Adult/continuing education; Adult education—literacy, basic skills & GED; Education, reading; Education; Hospitals (general); Medical care, rehabilitation; Health care; AIDS; Alcoholism; Housing/shelter, development; Human services; Children/youth, services; Aging, centers/services; Community/economic development; Science; Children/youth; Youth; Aging; Disabilities, people with; Mentally disabled; Minorities; Substance abusers; Economically disadvantaged; Homeless.
Type of support: Capital campaigns; Building/renovation; Equipment; Land acquisition; Program development; Seed money; Matching/challenge support.
Limitations: Applications accepted. Giving limited to TX, primarily within the Dallas Metroplex. No support for religious organizations (except for sectarian purposes). No grants to individuals; only occasional board-initiated support for operating budgets, debt reduction, research, scholarships, media productions, publications, or endowments; no loans (except for program-related investments).
Publications: Application guidelines; Annual report (including application guidelines); Grants list; Newsletter; Program policy statement.
Application information: Submitted application material must be unbound without folders or binders. Application form not required.
Initial approach: Letter
Copies of proposal: 1
Deadline(s): Dec. 15, Apr. 15 and Aug. 15
Board meeting date(s): Latter part of Jan, May, and Sept.
Final notification: After next board meeting
Officers and Directors:* William T. Solomon,* Chair.; Caren H. Prothro,* Vice-Chair.; Paul W. Harris, C.E.O. and Pres.; J. McDonald Williams,* Treas.; Rafael M. Anchia; Linda P. Custard; John Dayton; Karen L. Shuford; Deedie Rose; Jere W. Thompson, Jr.; Kern Wildenthal, M.D., Ph.D.
Number of staff: 1 full-time professional; 1 full-time support.
EIN: 756003984

8913
The Hoglund Foundation ✧
5910 N. Central Expwy., Ste. 255
Dallas, TX 75206-1106 (214) 987-3605
Contact: Kelly H. Compton, Secy.-Treas.
FAX: (214) 363-6507;
E-mail: info@hoglundfoundation.org; Main URL: http://www.hoglundfoundation.org
Grants List: http://www.hoglundfoundation.org/grants_prior.html

Established in 1989 in TX.
Donor: Forrest E. Hoglund.
Foundation type: Independent foundation.
Financial data (yr. ended 12/31/13): Assets, $61,789,039 (M); expenditures, $3,514,782; qualifying distributions, $3,246,614; giving activities include $2,884,000 for 142 grants (high: $1,000,000; low: $500).
Purpose and activities: The primary focus of the foundation is to promote interests and entities in education, health science and services, social services and children's health and development.
Fields of interest: Education; Health care; Health organizations, association; Human services; Child development, services; Infants/toddlers; Children/youth; Adults; Young adults; Mentally disabled; Adults, women; Adults, men; Single parents; Crime/abuse victims; Economically disadvantaged.
Type of support: General/operating support; Annual campaigns; Capital campaigns; Building/renovation; Equipment; Endowments; Program development; Scholarship funds; Research; Matching/challenge support.
Limitations: Applications accepted. Giving primarily to organizations that are located in and focused on the city of Dallas, TX. No grants to individuals.
Publications: Application guidelines.
Application information: Inclusion of videos or CDs with application is discouraged. See foundation web site for specific application guidelines. Application form not required.
Initial approach: Letter
Copies of proposal: 1
Deadline(s): 75 days prior to meeting date.
Board meeting date(s): Apr., Aug., and Dec.
Final notification: Within 4 months
Officers and Trustees:* Forrest E. Hoglund,* Chair. and Pres.; Sally R. Hoglund,* V.P.; Kelly H. Compton,* Secy.-Treas. and Exec. Dir.; Shelly H. Dee; Kristy H. Robinson.
Number of staff: 2 full-time professional; 1 part-time professional; 1 part-time support.
EIN: 752300978
Selected grants: The following grants are a representative sample of this grantmaker's funding activity:
$550,000 to Perot Museum of Nature and Science, Dallas, TX, 2012. For capital support.
$400,000 to Reasoning Mind, Houston, TX, 2012. For program support.
$25,000 to North Texas Food Bank, Dallas, TX, 2012. For program support.
$25,000 to Our Friends Place, Dallas, TX, 2012. For capital support.
$25,000 to Teach for America, Dallas, TX, 2012. For general operating support.
$15,000 to Austin Street Center, Dallas, TX, 2012. For general operating support.
$10,000 to Aberg Center for Literacy, Dallas, TX, 2012. For program support.
$10,000 to Promise House, Dallas, TX, 2012. For program support.
$10,000 to Services of Hope, Dallas, TX, 2012. For program support.
$5,000 to Attitudes and Attire, Dallas, TX, 2012. For general operating support.

8914
Hollomon-Price Foundation ✧ ☆
c/o Gloria Arecchi
130 Crofton Ave.
San Antonio, TX 78210-1127

Established in 1999 in TX.
Donors: Wayne Hollomon Price†; South Texas Money Management.
Foundation type: Independent foundation.
Financial data (yr. ended 09/30/13): Assets, $14,064,946 (M); gifts received, $45,000; expenditures, $1,139,917; qualifying distributions, $952,576; giving activities include $909,000 for 20 grants (high: $250,000; low: $8,000).
Fields of interest: Environment, natural resources; Environment, energy; Animal welfare; Animals/wildlife, preservation/protection; Indigenous peoples.
Limitations: Applications not accepted. Giving primarily in DC, NY and TX. No grants to individuals.
Application information: Unsolicited requests for funds not accepted.
Officers and Directors:* Michael Casey,* Pres.; Thaddeus Hollomon,* V.P.; John R. Bauer,* Secy.; Gloria P. Arecchi,* Treas.; John Bellett, Exec. Dir.; Nancy Bellett; Wayne Bellet; Rita Braeutigam; Michael John Deppe; Ann Edwards; Jack Murray; Jacob Scherr; Robert "Bob" Werner.
EIN: 752850527
Selected grants: The following grants are a representative sample of this grantmaker's funding activity:
$20,000 to Cibolo Nature Center, Boerne, TX, 2011.
$20,000 to Earth Island Institute, Berkeley, CA, 2011.
$20,000 to Natural Resources Defense Council, New York, NY, 2011.
$20,000 to Natural Resources Defense Council, New York, NY, 2011.
$20,000 to Ocean Conservancy, Washington, DC, 2011.
$15,000 to ECOLIFE Foundation, Escondido, CA, 2011.
$5,000 to Last Chance Forever, San Antonio, TX, 2011. For general operating expenses.

8915
The Holthouse Foundation for Kids ✧
1800 West Loop S., Ste. 1875
Houston, TX 77027-3209 (713) 626-5511
Contact: Lisa Holthouse, Dir.
E-mail: lisa@holthouse.net; Additional e-mail: info@holthouse.net; Main URL: http://www.holthousefoundationforkids.org
Blog: http://blog.hffk.org/
Twitter: http://twitter.com/holthouseffk

Established in 2000 in TX.
Donors: Colleen Holthouse; Michael H. Holthouse.
Foundation type: Independent foundation.
Financial data (yr. ended 12/31/12): Assets, $18,978,733 (M); expenditures, $1,119,030; qualifying distributions, $977,051; giving activities include $911,677 for 68 grants (high: $185,000; low: $250).
Purpose and activities: The foundation engages in proactive initiatives to improve opportunities for at-risk children, by developing and implementing programs that will teach them set goals, build character, become self-reliant, and establish positive direction in their lives.
Fields of interest: Education; Health organizations, association; Boys & girls clubs; Human services; Children/youth, services; Family services.
Limitations: Applications accepted. Giving primarily in Houston, TX. No support for political or legislative causes. No grants to individuals, or for lobbying, or debt.
Application information: Proposals are by invitation, only after consideration of initial letter of inquiry. The foundation will not grant funds to the same organization for more than 5 consecutive years. Application guidelines available on foundation web site.
Initial approach: Letter of inquiry (no more than 3 pages)
Deadline(s): None
Board meeting date(s): Jan., Apr., July, and Oct.
Final notification: 1 month (for letter)
Officers and Directors:* Michael H. Holthouse,* Pres.; Lisa Holthouse,* V.P.; Richard H. Stein,* Secy.-Treas.; Colleen M. Holthouse.
EIN: 760620426

8916
Greater Houston Community Foundation
5120 Woodway Dr., Ste. 6000
Houston, TX 77056 (713) 333-2200
Contact: Linda Gardner, Dir., Opers.; Nelson Hernandez, Acct. Mgr.
FAX: (713) 333-2220; E-mail: lgardner@ghcf.org; Main URL: http://www.ghcf.org
E-Newsletter: http://www.ghcf.org/Resources/News/Publications/
Facebook: http://www.facebook.com/pages/Greater-Houston-Community-Foundation/147438280341

Established in 1971 in TX.
Foundation type: Community foundation.
Financial data (yr. ended 12/31/13): Assets, $438,701,314 (M); gifts received, $118,518,630; expenditures, $108,171,184; giving activities include $98,934,435 for grants.
Purpose and activities: The foundation grows effective philanthropy by connecting donors to the causes they care about, provides excellent stewardship of assets entrusted to them, and convenes resources to address important community needs.
Fields of interest: Arts; Education; Environment; Health care; Human services; Public affairs; Religion.
Type of support: General/operating support; Continuing support; Income development; Management development/capacity building; Annual campaigns; Capital campaigns; Building/renovation; Equipment; Land acquisition; Endowments; Debt reduction; Emergency funds; Program development; Conferences/seminars; Professorships; Film/video/radio; Publication; Seed money; Curriculum development; Fellowships; Internship funds; Scholarship funds; Research; Technical assistance; Consulting services; Program evaluation; Program-related investments/loans; Employee matching gifts; Employee-related

scholarships; Exchange programs; In-kind gifts; Matching/challenge support.
Limitations: Applications not accepted. Giving primarily in Houston, TX. Also gives nationally and internationally. No grants to individuals (except for disaster relief funds).
Publications: Annual report; Financial statement; Grants list; Informational brochure; Newsletter; Occasional report; IRS Form 990 or 990-PF printed copy available upon request.
Application information: The foundation does not issue requests for proposals or take grant applications.
Board meeting date(s): 4 times a year
Officers and Directors:* Bruce R. Bilger,* Chair.; Stephen D. Maislin, C.E.O. and Pres.; Renee Wizig-Barrios, V.P. and Chief Philanthropy Off.; Ed Padar, Cont.; William J. Bryan; Ric Campo; Martha Carnes; Ernie D. Cockrell II; Michael R. Dumas; Rob Galtney; Melanie Gray; Terri Lacy; Leo Linbeck III; Barry H. Margolis; Gasper Mir III; Dave Pruner; Gavin H. Smith; Elizabeth A. Tilney.
Number of staff: 12 full-time professional; 10 full-time support.
EIN: 237160400
Selected grants: The following grants are a representative sample of this grantmaker's funding activity:
$2,100,000 to University of Houston-Downtown, Houston, TX, 2012. For Fund Endowment Agreement: The CJ Fund for Graduate Creative Writing Program Student Grants.
$2,000,000 to Dallas Baptist University, Dallas, TX, 2012. For the construction of the Pilgrim Chapel.
$2,000,000 to First Baptist Church, Pittsburg, TX, 2012. For the construction of the Children and Pre-School Building.
$1,500,000 to Methodist Hospital Foundation, Houston, TX, 2012. For the J.C. Walter, Jr. Transplant Center and the J.C. Walter Distinguished Chair.
$948,270 to Bank of America Charitable Gift Fund, Providence, RI, 2012.
$500,000 to Young Life, Colorado Springs, CO, 2012. For the Campership Legacy Fund.
$150,000 to Laity Renewal Foundation, Laity Lodge, Kerrville, TX, 2012. For Family Camp.
$5,000 to Memorial Drive Presbyterian Church, Houston, TX, 2012. For the Good Housekeeping Capital Campaign.
$3,250 to Kinkaid School, Houston, TX, 2012. For matching gift.
$3,000 to Krist Samaritan Center for Counseling and Education, Houston, TX, 2012. For the Krist Samaritan Center and its annual gala, A Samaritan Celebration.

8917
Houston Endowment Inc. ✧

600 Travis, Ste. 6400
Houston, TX 77002-3003 (713) 238-8100
Contact: Lydia Hickey, Grant Mgr.
FAX: (713) 238-8101;
E-mail: info@houstonendowment.org; E-mail and tel. for Lydia Hickey: online@houstonendowment.org; (713) 238-8134; Main URL: http://www.houstonendowment.org
Grants Database: http://www.houstonendowment.org/GrantHistory/Search.aspx

Incorporated in 1937 in TX.
Donors: Jesse H. Jones†; Mrs. Jesse H. Jones†.
Foundation type: Independent foundation.
Financial data (yr. ended 12/31/13): Assets, $1,727,247,300 (M); expenditures, $97,914,262; qualifying distributions, $64,484,305; giving activities include $64,484,305 for grants.
Purpose and activities: Support primarily for nonprofit organizations and educational institutions that improve life for the people of the greater Houston, TX area. Funding for programs in the arts, community enhancement, education, health, human services, the environment and neighborhood development.
Fields of interest: Arts; Education; Environment; Health care; Human services; Community development, neighborhood development.
Type of support: General/operating support; Continuing support; Annual campaigns; Capital campaigns; Building/renovation; Equipment; Land acquisition; Endowments; Program development; Conferences/seminars; Publication; Curriculum development; Fellowships; Scholarship funds; Research; Employee matching gifts.
Limitations: Applications accepted. Giving primarily in the greater Houston, TX area, with some funding throughout the state for projects central to TX history. No support for religious organizations for religious purposes, or organizations that are the responsibility of the government. No grants to individuals (except for scholarships); or generally for fundraising activities including galas, lobbying or for individual memorials, or for scholarship programs other than the Jones Scholars.
Publications: Application guidelines; Annual report; Financial statement; Grants list; Informational brochure (including application guidelines).
Application information: The foundation has recently implemented a comprehensive online Grant Management System. Applicants should go to the program area that matches their request, select the result area and type of investment that matches their request. The foundation will contact applicants to request any additional information needed. In some cases, organizations will need to complete a pre-application. Scholarship applicants should contact their high school college counselor for an application. Application form not required.
Initial approach: Online submission
Copies of proposal: 1
Deadline(s): None
Board meeting date(s): 9 to 10 times per year
Final notification: Online submissions receive e-mail response within 2 weeks
Officers and Directors:* Linnet F. Deily,* Chair.; Ann B. Stern,* Pres.; Sheryl L. Johns, Exec. V.P.; Lisa Hall, V.P., Prog(s).; Anne S. Chao; Anthony Chase; Douglas L. Foshee; Anthony W. Hall, Jr.; Jesse H. Jones II; David Louis Mendez; Paul B. Murphy, Jr.
Number of staff: 16 full-time professional; 10 full-time support.
EIN: 746013920
Selected grants: The following grants are a representative sample of this grantmaker's funding activity:
$6,000,000 to Match Midtown Arts & Theater Center Houston, Houston, TX, 2012. Toward development of a new art center and cultural destination in Midtown Houston.
$5,200,000 to Rice University, Houston, TX, 2012. Toward the Rice Education Entrepreneurship Program, a regional public school principal leadership academy in the Jesse H. Jones Graduate School of Business.
$5,000,000 to Houston Zoo, Houston, TX, 2012. Toward construction of Gorilla Habitat in the African Forest exhibit, payable over 2.00 years.
$5,000,000 to Museum of Fine Arts, Houston, Houston, TX, 2013. Toward expansion of the facility, payable over 2.00 years.
$4,000,000 to Childrens Assessment Center Foundation, Houston, TX, 2013. Toward building expansion.
$3,000,000 to Hermann Park Conservancy, Houston, TX, 2012. Toward the Centennial Gardens project, to enhance and reconfigure the 15-acre area surrounding the Garden Center.
$3,000,000 to University of Texas Health Science Center, Houston, TX, 2012. Toward a comprehensive community-wide approach to adolescent sexual health, payable over 3.00 years.
$2,100,000 to National College Access Network, Washington, DC, 2013. Toward project to increase effectiveness of college access services offered by community-based organizations in greater Houston, payable over 3.00 years.
$2,000,000 to Houston Parks Board, Houston, TX, 2012. Toward the renovation and restoration of the existing Emancipation Park Community Center.
$1,400,000 to Neighborhood Centers, Bellaire, TX, 2013. Toward increasing the financial well-being of low income residents in the greater Houston area through free tax preparation, payable over 3.00 years.
$1,125,000 to National Wildlife Federation, Austin, TX, 2013. Toward continued implementation of new state policies on environmental flows protection, groundwater management and water conservation as they impact Harris and contiguous counties, payable over 3.00 years.
$325,000 to United Way of Baytown, Baytown, TX, 2013. Toward a kindergarten readiness program for children in Baytown, Highlands and West Chambers County, payable over 3.00 years.
$300,000 to Fourth Ward Clinic, Good Neighbor Healthcare Clinic, Houston, TX, 2012. Toward general operating support, payable over 2.00 years.
$200,000 to Nature Discovery Center, Bellaire, TX, 2013. Toward renovations.
$175,000 to Literacy Advance of Houston, Houston, TX, 2012. Toward strengthening infrastructure and diversifying the agency's funding portfolio, payable over 2.00 years.
$160,000 to Crisis Intervention of Houston, Houston, TX, 2013. Toward general operating support, payable over 2.00 years.
$120,000 to West Houston Assistance Ministries, Houston, TX, 2012. For general operating support, payable over 2.00 years.
$100,000 to University of Houston-Downtown, Houston, TX, 2013. Toward All Kids Alliance, a Cradle to Career Continuum for improving the lives of children and youth in the greater Houston area.
$90,000 to Musiqa, Houston, TX, 2012. Toward general operating support, payable over 2.00 years.
$80,000 to Aurora Picture Show, Houston, TX, 2013. Toward general operating support, payable over 2.00 years.

8918
Laverne and Thomas Howell Foundation ✧

P.O. Box 2003
Rockport, TX 78381-2003 (361) 729-3441
E-mail: info@howellfoundationtx.org; Letter of Inquiry e-mail: grantrequests@HowellFoundationTx.org; Main URL: http://www.howellfoundationtx.org/public/

Established in 2003 in TX.
Donor: Laverne Howell†.
Foundation type: Independent foundation.
Financial data (yr. ended 12/31/12): Assets, $11,516,480 (M); expenditures, $610,079; qualifying distributions, $541,373; giving activities include $479,655 for 18 grants (high: $147,000; low: $10,000).
Purpose and activities: Giving primarily for Christian religious activities, impoverished individuals in need of financial or health care assistance, or other similar charitable purposes.
Fields of interest: Health organizations, association; Human services; Christian agencies & churches; Economically disadvantaged.
Limitations: Giving limited to Nueces County, TX. No grants to individuals.
Application information: Full proposals are by invitation only, upon review of Letter of Inquiry.
Initial approach: Letter of Inquiry (1-2 pages) via U.S. mail or e-mail
Deadline(s): May 1
Officers and Directors:* Martin C. Davis,* Mgr.; Sandra L. Garrison,* Mgr.; Gary B. Pearce.
EIN: 460501821
Selected grants: The following grants are a representative sample of this grantmaker's funding activity:
$147,000 to First United Methodist Church, Corpus Christi, TX, 2012. For windows replacement.
$34,826 to Del Mar College Foundation, Corpus Christi, TX, 2012. For direct scholarships.
$25,000 to Food Bank of Corpus Christi, Corpus Christi, TX, 2012. For Food Products and Storage.
$24,829 to American Cancer Society, Corpus Christi, TX, 2012. For patient transportation.
$20,000 to Coastal Bend Community Foundation, Corpus Christi, TX, 2012. To Match 501(c)(3) Program Grants.
$10,000 to Family Outreach of Corpus Christi, Corpus Christi, TX, 2012. For Abuse Prevention Programs.

8919
The M. R. & Evelyn Hudson Foundation ✧
P.O. Box 2110
Keller, TX 76244-2110
Contact: Jesse S. Larson, V.P., Grant Analysis
FAX: (817) 431-4830;
E-mail: FourSticks@thehudsonfoundation.org; Main URL: http://thehudsonfoundation.org/aboutus.html

Established in 1992 in KS.
Donors: M.R. Hudson; Murdock Hudson†.
Foundation type: Independent foundation.
Financial data (yr. ended 12/31/13): Assets, $105,335,354 (M); gifts received, $25,212,215; expenditures, $4,622,715; qualifying distributions, $3,958,688; giving activities include $3,099,014 for 65 grants (high: $450,000; low: $500).
Purpose and activities: Giving primarily for community development; funding also for the arts, education, and children, youth and family services.
Fields of interest: Visual arts; Museums; Museums (art); Performing arts; Arts; Elementary/secondary education; Higher education; Medical school/education; Libraries (public); Education; Hospitals (general); Health care, support services; Cancer research; Human services; Children/youth, services.
Type of support: Management development/capacity building; Emergency funds; Program development; Conferences/seminars; Curriculum development; Research; Program evaluation; Matching/challenge support.
Limitations: Applications not accepted. Giving primarily in North TX and the bi-state Kansas City metropolitan area. No support for nonprofit pass-through organizations. No endowments or grants to individuals, or for tickets for dinners, benefits, conferences, and sports events, advertisements, debt reduction or the underwriting of deficits, or for endowments.
Publications: Informational brochure.
Application information: Unsolicited requests for funds not accepted. Check foundation web site for current grant process status.
Board meeting date(s): Quarterly
Officers and Directors:* Frank Merrick, Chair.; Marshall K. Larson,* C.E.O. and Pres.; John D. Hooser, V.P., Special Projects; Jesse Larson, V.P., Grant Analysis; Amy Coopman; Amy Meadows.
Number of staff: 4 full-time professional; 1 full-time support.
EIN: 481107753

8920
Huffington Foundation
5555 San Felipe St., Ste. 840
Houston, TX 77056-2701 (713) 753-1000
Contact: Paulo Cantu, Exec. Dir.
FAX: (713) 651-0119;
E-mail: PCantu@huffingtonfdn.org; Additional address: P.O. Box 4337, Houston, TX 77210-4337

Established in 1987 in Houston, TX.
Donors: Michael Huffington; Phyllis Gough Huffington; Roy M. Huffington†; Terry L. Huffington.
Foundation type: Independent foundation.
Financial data (yr. ended 12/31/12): Assets, $156,189,108 (M); expenditures, $8,672,465; qualifying distributions, $7,744,532; giving activities include $7,742,500 for 62 grants (high: $3,100,000; low: $1,500).
Purpose and activities: Giving primarily for education, particularly a medical school, as well as for the arts and human services.
Fields of interest: Arts; Higher education; Medical school/education; Education; Human services.
Type of support: General/operating support; Annual campaigns; Capital campaigns; Building/renovation; Endowments; Scholarship funds.
Limitations: Applications not accepted. Giving primarily in Houston, TX. No grants to individuals.
Application information: Contributes only to pre-selected organizations.
Board meeting date(s): Quarterly
Officer: Paulo Cantu, Exec. Dir.
Trustees: Ralph E. Dittman, M.D.; Terry L. Huffington.
EIN: 766040840
Selected grants: The following grants are a representative sample of this grantmaker's funding activity:
$2,000,000 to Baylor College of Medicine, Houston, TX, 2011. For Huffington Center on Aging Chair.
$1,000,000 to Texas Wesleyan University, College of Environment, Fort Worth, TX, 2011.
$500,000 to Texas Wesleyan University, College of Environment, Fort Worth, TX, 2011.
$500,000 to University of Texas Health Science Center, School of Nursing, San Antonio, TX, 2011. For endowment.
$370,000 to Texas Childrens Hospital, Houston, TX, 2011.
$250,000 to River Oaks Baptist School, Houston, TX, 2011.
$100,000 to Baylor College of Medicine, Houston, TX, 2011. For Brinkley Lab.
$50,000 to CHRISTUS Foundation for Healthcare, Houston, TX, 2011. For Saint Mary's Clinic.
$15,000 to Houston Community Health Centers, Vecino Health Centers, Houston, TX, 2011. For healthcare for uninsured.
$10,000 to Healthcare for the Homeless, Houston, Houston, TX, 2011.

8921
Humphreys Foundation ✧
P.O. Box 550
Liberty, TX 77575-0550 (936) 336-3321
Contact: Doris Peters, Mgr.

Incorporated in 1957 in TX.
Donor: Geraldine Davis Humphreys†.
Foundation type: Independent foundation.
Financial data (yr. ended 09/30/13): Assets, $20,014,333 (M); expenditures, $1,062,576; qualifying distributions, $1,023,006; giving activities include $1,005,000 for 17 grants (high: $325,000; low: $7,000).
Purpose and activities: Giving for production costs of plays and performances in the field of dramatic arts. The foundation also makes some of its grants to colleges and universities which, in turn, use the grant money to award scholarships to students studying drama or dance under the supervision of the grantee educational institutions.
Fields of interest: Performing arts; Performing arts, ballet; Performing arts, theater; Performing arts, opera.
Limitations: Applications accepted. Giving limited to TX. No grants to individuals, or for building funds; no loans.
Publications: Application guidelines.
Application information: Application form required.
Initial approach: Letter
Copies of proposal: 4
Deadline(s): Applications accepted between July 1 and Aug. 15
Board meeting date(s): Sept.
Officers: Linda Bertman, Pres.; Louis B. Paine, V.P. and Secy.; Robert Wall, V.P. and Treas.
Number of staff: 1 full-time support.
EIN: 746061381
Selected grants: The following grants are a representative sample of this grantmaker's funding activity:
$175,000 to Houston Grand Opera, Houston, TX, 2011.
$160,000 to Theater Under the Stars, Houston, TX, 2011.
$125,000 to Alley Theater, Houston, TX, 2011.
$50,000 to Society for the Performing Arts, Houston, TX, 2011.
$40,000 to A.D. Players, Houston, TX, 2011.
$15,000 to Houston Ballet, Houston, TX, 2011.
$10,000 to Lamar University, Beaumont, TX, 2011.
$10,000 to Lee College, Baytown, TX, 2011.
$10,000 to Texas Christian University, Fort Worth, TX, 2011.
$10,000 to University of Saint Thomas, Houston, TX, 2011.

8922
The Hunt Family Foundation ✧
(formerly The Cimarron Foundation)
P.O. Box 12667
El Paso, TX 79913-0667
Application address: c/o Mariana Benavides, 4401 N. Mesa St., El Paso, TX 79902, tel.: (915) 747-4294; Main URL: http://www.huntfamilyfoundation.com/

Established in 1987 in TX.
Donors: Woody L. Hunt; Gayle G. Hunt.
Foundation type: Independent foundation.
Financial data (yr. ended 12/31/13): Assets, $1,108,127 (M); gifts received, $610,635; expenditures, $3,974,897; qualifying distributions, $3,974,897; giving activities include $3,927,760 for 85 grants (high: $700,000; low: $250).
Purpose and activities: Giving primarily for the arts, education, hospitals, including a cancer center, community development, and children and social services.
Fields of interest: Arts; Elementary/secondary education; Higher education; Hospitals (general); Human services; Children/youth, services; Community/economic development; Foundations (community).
Type of support: General/operating support; Capital campaigns; Building/renovation; Research.
Limitations: Applications not accepted. Giving primarily in El Paso, TX. No grants to individuals.
Application information: Contributes only to pre-selected organizations.
Officers and Directors: Woody L. Hunt,* Chair.; Joshua W. Hunt,* Pres.; Gayle G. Hunt,* V.P.; William C. Sanders, V.P.; Susanne Smith, Secy.; Claudia Ivey, Treas.
EIN: 742489868

8923
Nancy Ann Hunt and Ray L. Hunt Philanthropic Fund ✧
(formerly Nancy Ann Hunt and Ray L. Hunt Foundation)
1900 N. Akard St.
Dallas, TX 75201-2300

Established in 1983 in TX.
Donors: Ray L. Hunt; Nancy Ann Hunt.
Foundation type: Independent foundation.
Financial data (yr. ended 12/31/12): Assets, $8,148,386 (M); expenditures, $2,146,096; qualifying distributions, $2,139,900; giving activities include $2,124,900 for 5 grants (high: $550,000; low: $250,000).
Fields of interest: Foundations (public).
Type of support: General/operating support.
Limitations: Applications not accepted. Giving primarily in Dallas, TX. No grants to individuals.
Application information: Contributes only to pre-selected organizations.
Officers and Directors:* Ray L. Hunt,* Pres. and Treas.; David Hernandez,* V.P. and Secy.; Nancy Ann Hunt,* V.P.; Heather Hunt; Ashlee Hunt Kleinert.
EIN: 751903084

8924
Impetus Foundation ✧
4114 Pond Hill, Ste. 201
San Antonio, TX 78231-1273 (210) 404-2211

Established in TX.
Donors: Carlos E. Alvarez; Maria G. Alvarez.
Foundation type: Independent foundation.
Financial data (yr. ended 12/31/13): Assets, $68,110,515 (M); gifts received, $7,000,000; expenditures, $2,452,845; qualifying distributions, $2,120,000; giving activities include $2,120,000 for 7 grants (high: $1,000,000; low: $50,000).
Fields of interest: Museums (children's); Higher education; Education; Children/youth, services.
Limitations: Applications accepted. Giving primarily in San Antonio, TX.
Application information: Application form not required.
Initial approach: Proposal
Deadline(s): None
Trustee: Carlos Alvarez.
EIN: 271602489
Selected grants: The following grants are a representative sample of this grantmaker's funding activity:
$25,000 to San Antonio Zoological Society, San Antonio, TX, 2012. For San Antonio Zoo.

8925
Joe Ingram Trust ✧
c/o Bank of America, N.A.
P.O. Bank 831041
Dallas, TX 75283-1041 (816) 388-5555

Established in 1960 in MO.
Donor: Joe Ingram†.
Foundation type: Independent foundation.
Financial data (yr. ended 12/31/12): Assets, $16,011,867 (M); expenditures, $342,102; qualifying distributions, $1,043,843; giving activities include $127,250 for 29 grants (high: $24,900; low: $50), and $783,269 for 352 grants to individuals (high: $20,000; low: $105).
Purpose and activities: Giving primarily for student loans to residents of Chariton County Missouri, only; some support for local civic projects and valedictorian awards.
Fields of interest: Education; Community/economic development; Government/public administration.
Type of support: General/operating support; Grants to individuals; Student loans—to individuals.
Limitations: Giving limited to residents of Chariton County, MO.
Application information: Application form required.
Initial approach: Proposal
Deadline(s): None
Board meeting date(s): 2nd Thur. of each month
Trustees: David Sturm; Bank of America, N.A.
Number of staff: 1 part-time professional; 1 part-time support.
EIN: 446006475

8926
Inspiration Charitable Foundation ✧
915 Franklin St., Ste. 8C
Houston, TX 77002-1735

Donors: Ann Marie Cover; Mark Allen Cover.
Foundation type: Independent foundation.
Financial data (yr. ended 12/31/12): Assets, $94,845 (M); gifts received, $577,424; expenditures, $505,204; qualifying distributions, $503,920; giving activities include $503,920 for 14 grants (high: $400,000; low: $600).
Fields of interest: Education; Health care; Religion.
Limitations: Applications not accepted. Giving primarily in SC.
Application information: Unsolicited requests for funds not accepted.
Directors: Allen Michael Cover; Angela Marie Cover; Ann Marie Cover; Jonathan Mark Cover; Mark Allen Cover; William Randall Cover.
EIN: 264223774

8927
International Medical Outreach, Inc. ✧
915 Gessner Rd., Ste. 620
Houston, TX 77024-2551 (713) 935-9057
Contact: Todd Price, C.E.O. and Pres.
Main URL: http://www.imoutreach.com
Twitter: https://twitter.com/imoutreach

Established in 1997 in TX.
Donors: Todd Price, M.D.; William Lee; Donna Greer; Ingrid Sharon, M.D.; Leticia J. Dizov; Lakewood Church; Christian Alliance for Humanitarian Aid; Medical Bridges, Inc.; Feed the Children.
Foundation type: Operating foundation.
Financial data (yr. ended 12/31/12): Assets, $788,111 (M); gifts received, $249,408,395; expenditures, $247,561,196; qualifying distributions, $247,416,601; giving activities include $247,416,601 for 12 grants (high: $120,248,725; low: $1,100).
Purpose and activities: The grantmaker provides health care for those in need on a worldwide basis. It concentrates on efforts towards the relief of infectious diseases, including malaria, HIV/AIDS, tuberculosis, pneumonia, and diarrhea in addition to other diseases. It also establishes and assists existing medical clinics, orphanages, feeding centers, drug rehabilitation projects and teaching centers among other humanitarian efforts.
Fields of interest: Health care, clinics/centers; Health care, support services; Public health; Health care; Substance abuse, treatment; AIDS; Diseases (rare); Food services; Children, adoption; Children, services; International relief.
Type of support: General/operating support.
Limitations: Giving primarily on an international basis.
Application information: Applicants must also include the need for medical supplies and equipment, as well as the Christian-related organization with which they are affiliated.
Initial approach: Letter
Deadline(s): None
Officers: Todd Price, M.D., C.E.O. and Pres.; Andrew Francis Price, C.O.O.; Susan Price, V.P. and Exec. Dir.
EIN: 760392915

8928
David & Sharon Jamail Family Foundation ✧
2303 River Hills Rd.
Austin, TX 78733-2130

Established in 1997 in TX.
Donors: David G. Jamail; Sharon Jamail.
Foundation type: Independent foundation.
Financial data (yr. ended 12/31/12): Assets, $555,390 (M); gifts received, $610,000; expenditures, $748,633; qualifying distributions, $742,629; giving activities include $742,629 for 65 grants (high: $179,100; low: $100).

Purpose and activities: Giving primarily to Protestant organizations, churches, missions, and ministries.
Fields of interest: Human services; Children/youth, services; Protestant agencies & churches.
Limitations: Applications not accepted. Giving in the U.S., with emphasis on TX, particularly Austin. No grants to individuals.
Application information: Unsolicited requests for funds not accepted.
Officers: David G. Jamail, Pres. and Treas.; Sharon Jamail, V.P. and Secy.
Trustee: Brian M. Wallace.
EIN: 742854045

8929
The Lee and Joseph D. Jamail Foundation ✧
(formerly The Joseph D. and Lillie H. Jamail Foundation)
1200 Smith St., Ste. 1135
Houston, TX 77002-4592 (713) 650-8544
Contact: Robert L. Jamail, Secy.-Treas.

Established in 1986 in TX.
Donors: Joseph D. Jamail; Lillie H. Jamail.
Foundation type: Independent foundation.
Financial data (yr. ended 12/31/13): Assets, $3,727,033 (M); expenditures, $651,282; qualifying distributions, $628,167; giving activities include $628,167 for 21 grants (high: $166,667; low: $1,500).
Purpose and activities: Giving primarily for higher education; funding also for the arts and human services.
Fields of interest: Performing arts, theater; Arts; Higher education; Education; Human services.
Type of support: General/operating support; Capital campaigns; Endowments; Scholarship funds.
Limitations: Giving primarily in Houston, TX. No grants to individuals or to organizations which are professional fundraisers.
Application information: No videos accepted. Application form not required.
Initial approach: Letter on organization letterhead
Deadline(s): None
Board meeting date(s): Dec.
Officers: Joseph D. Jamail III, Pres.; Randall Hage Jamail, V.P.; Robert Lee Jamail, Secy.-Treas.; Denise S. Davidson, Secy.
EIN: 760181247
Selected grants: The following grants are a representative sample of this grantmaker's funding activity:
$4,000,000 to University of Texas, Austin, TX, 2011.
$1,000,000 to San Marcos Baptist Academy, San Marcos, TX, 2011.
$166,667 to Rice University, Houston, TX, 2011.
$75,000 to Kinkaid School, Houston, TX, 2011.
$70,000 to Saint Johns School, Houston, TX, 2011.
$12,500 to Southern Methodist University, Dallas, TX, 2011.

8930
The Janszen Charitable Trust ✧ ☆
4831 Merlot Ave., Ste. 320
Grapevine, TX 76051-7384

Established in 1992 in TX.
Foundation type: Independent foundation.
Financial data (yr. ended 12/31/13): Assets, $25,966 (M); gifts received, $315,100; expenditures, $436,610; qualifying distributions, $435,650; giving activities include $435,650 for 34 grants (high: $159,000; low: $250).
Purpose and activities: Giving primarily for evangelical Christian churches and agencies.
Fields of interest: Human services; Christian agencies & churches.
Limitations: Applications not accepted. Giving primarily in TX. No grants to individuals.
Application information: Contributes only to pre-selected organizations.
Trustee: Ronald D. Ray.
EIN: 756423830

8931
Julietta Jarvis Foundation ✧
100 E. Ferguson, Ste. 1005
Tyler, TX 75702-5706

Established in 1989 in TX.
Donor: Julietta Jarvis‡.
Foundation type: Independent foundation.
Financial data (yr. ended 11/30/13): Assets, $14,057,056 (M); expenditures, $1,110,576; qualifying distributions, $837,930; giving activities include $584,738 for 18 grants (high: $273,738; low: $2,500).
Fields of interest: Museums (art); Community/economic development; United Ways and Federated Giving Programs.
Limitations: Applications not accepted. Giving primarily in TX. No grants to individuals.
Application information: Unsolicited requests for funds not accepted.
Officers: Eleanor Cameron, Pres.; H.B. Cameron, Jr., Secy.; William L. Long, Treas.
EIN: 752303424

8932
The Jenesis Group ✧
130 E. John Carpenter Fwy.
Irving, TX 75062-2708
Contact: Kim Tanner
E-mail: ktanner@jenesis.org; Main URL: http://www.jenesis.org

Established in 1986 in TX.
Donor: R.J. Jensen.
Foundation type: Independent foundation.
Financial data (yr. ended 12/31/12): Assets, $46,732,994 (M); expenditures, $2,294,930; qualifying distributions, $1,904,770; giving activities include $1,458,347 for 16 grants (high: $1,000,000; low: $2,000).
Purpose and activities: Support limited to grass-roots organizations with annual budgets below $500,000 that sponsor programs which serve children under 18 years of age, provide some type of leadership training, teach entrepreneurial skills, and/or help children develop self-esteem and self reliance. Provides funds for development of preventive social service programs, their expansion, and materials needed.
Fields of interest: Education, early childhood education; Child development, education; Youth development, services; Human services; Children/youth, services; Child development, services; Minorities/immigrants, centers/services; Leadership development; Children/youth; Children; Young adults; Minorities.
Type of support: General/operating support; Continuing support; Program development; Seed money; Technical assistance; Matching/challenge support.
Limitations: Applications not accepted. Giving on a national basis. No grants to individuals, or for buildings or building maintenance, transportation of clients to programs, refreshments, or media presentations.
Application information: Unsolicited requests for funds not accepted.
Board meeting date(s): Varies
Officer: Kim Tanner.
EIN: 756349718

8933
Jiv Daya Foundation ✧
5420 Lyndon B. Johnson Fwy., Ste. 410
Dallas, TX 75240-6279 (214) 593-0500
FAX: (214) 593-1902;
E-mail: coordinators@jivdayafound.org; Main URL: http://www.jivdayafound.org
Facebook: https://www.facebook.com/pages/Jiv-Daya-Foundation/100438146673008
Twitter: http://twitter.com/JivDaya

Established in 2002 in TX.
Donors: Vinay K. Jain; Kanika Virmani Jain.
Foundation type: Independent foundation.
Financial data (yr. ended 12/31/13): Assets, $79,224,701 (M); expenditures, $7,152,680; qualifying distributions, $7,075,639; giving activities include $6,657,523 for 86 grants (high: $6,000,000; low: $1,200).
Purpose and activities: Giving primarily for pediatric oncology, palliative care, amputee assistance, kala-azar/tropical disease eradication, and maternal and neonatal health.
Fields of interest: Education; Reproductive health; Palliative care; Health care; Tropical diseases; Pediatrics; Human services; Foundations (public).
International interests: India.
Limitations: Applications accepted. Giving primarily in MA, TX and India.
Publications: Application guidelines.
Application information:
Initial approach: Letter of inquiry form on foundation web site
Officers and Directors:* Vinay K. Jain,* Pres. and Treas.; Kanika Virmani Jain,* V.P. and Secy.; Yash Paul Virmani.
EIN: 320045123

8934
JKJ Charitable Foundation ✧ ☆
(formerly John and Linda Knox Family Foundation)
1330 Post Oak Blvd., Ste. 1100
Houston, TX 77056-3309

Established in 1998 in TX.
Donors: John T. Knox; John T. Knox, Jr.; Linda S. Knox.
Foundation type: Independent foundation.
Financial data (yr. ended 12/31/13): Assets, $5,659,537 (M); gifts received, $1,500,000; expenditures, $940,574; qualifying distributions, $923,350; giving activities include $923,350 for 14 grants (high: $270,000; low: $1,250).

Fields of interest: Education; Health care; Human services.
Type of support: General/operating support.
Limitations: Applications not accepted. Giving primarily in TX. No grants to individuals.
Application information: Unsolicited requests for funds not accepted.
Officer: John T. Knox, Jr., Pres.
Trustees: John T. Knox; Steven M. Rakofsky.
EIN: 760573833

8935
The JKL Foundation ✧
15950 N. Dallas Pkwy., Ste. 725
Dallas, TX 75248-6692

Established in 2005 in TX.
Donors: Judy Burleson; Kathi Yeager.
Foundation type: Independent foundation.
Financial data (yr. ended 12/31/12): Assets, $4,367,158 (M); gifts received, $54,285; expenditures, $665,522; qualifying distributions, $606,432; giving activities include $606,432 for grants.
Purpose and activities: Giving primarily to Baptist and other Christian agencies and churches.
Fields of interest: Human services; Christian agencies & churches; Protestant agencies & churches.
Limitations: Applications not accepted. Giving primarily in TX. No grants to individuals.
Application information: Contributes only to pre-selected organizations.
Trustees: Judy Burleson; Ron Murff; Kathi Yeager.
EIN: 386835410

8936
JLH Foundation ✧
11555 Dairy Ashford, Ste. 725
Houston, TX 77079-4024

Established in 2001 in TX.
Donors: Donna L. Sheppard-Hern; Paula Hern; Trigeant, Ltd.
Foundation type: Independent foundation.
Financial data (yr. ended 12/31/12): Assets, $15,476,906 (M); gifts received, $2,500,000; expenditures, $607,666; qualifying distributions, $520,000; giving activities include $520,000 for 5 grants (high: $300,000; low: $20,000).
Fields of interest: Hospitals (general); Health care.
Limitations: Giving primarily in TX.
Officers and Directors:* Paula A. Hern,* Chair.; Ellis Tudzin,* Secy.-Treas.; Tom Barbour.
EIN: 760668991

8937
The Willard and Ruth Johnson Charitable Foundation ✧
P.O. Box 27727
Houston, TX 77227-7727

Established in 1992 in TX.
Donors: Ruth Johnson†; Willard Johnson†.
Foundation type: Independent foundation.
Financial data (yr. ended 12/31/12): Assets, $22,268,275 (M); expenditures, $1,290,225; qualifying distributions, $1,095,050; giving activities include $1,095,050 for 66 grants (high: $200,000; low: $200).
Purpose and activities: Giving primarily for education, children and youth services, social services, and to a United Methodist church.
Fields of interest: Elementary/secondary education; Higher education; Education; Human services; Children/youth, services; Protestant agencies & churches.
Limitations: Applications not accepted. Giving primarily in Houston and Midland, TX. No grants to individuals.
Application information: Contributes only to pre-selected organizations.
Officers: John W. Johnson, Pres.; David M. Johnson, V.P.; Steven J. Lindley, V.P.; Christopher B. Johnson, Secy.
EIN: 760386599

8938
Joe & Nan Johnson Family Foundation ✧ ☆
P.O. Box 2249
Wichita Falls, TX 76307-2249
Application address: c/o Nan H. Johnson, 811 6th St., Ste. 300, Wichita Falls, TX 76301, tel.: (940) 723-2166

Established in 2005 in TX.
Donors: Joe L. Johnson, Jr.; Nan H. Johnson.
Foundation type: Independent foundation.
Financial data (yr. ended 12/31/13): Assets, $2,055,179 (M); gifts received, $2,200,000; expenditures, $458,644; qualifying distributions, $454,350; giving activities include $451,397 for 68 grants (high: $50,000; low: $500).
Fields of interest: Education, alumni groups; Education; Health organizations; Food banks; Human services; Children/youth, services; Protestant agencies & churches.
Type of support: General/operating support.
Limitations: Applications accepted. Giving primarily in TX.
Application information: Application form required.
Initial approach: Request application form
Deadline(s): None
Officers and Directors:* Joe L. Johnson III,* Pres.; Nan H. Johnson,* V.P. and Secy.; Nancy Isom; Jeannie Ralston.
EIN: 202784844
Selected grants: The following grants are a representative sample of this grantmaker's funding activity:
$25,000 to Senior Citizens Services of North Texas, Wichita Falls, TX, 2011. For general operations.
$15,000 to Texas Tech Alumni Association, Lubbock, TX, 2011. For general operations.
$10,000 to United Regional Health Care Foundation, Wichita Falls, TX, 2011.
$7,500 to Hospice of Wichita Falls, Wichita Falls, TX, 2011.
$5,000 to Grace Church, Wichita Falls, TX, 2011. For building fund.
$3,000 to Junior League of Wichita Falls, Wichita Falls, TX, 2011. For general operations.
$2,500 to University Little League, Fort Worth, TX, 2011. For general operations.
$2,000 to Texas Tech Alumni Association, Lubbock, TX, 2011. For general operations.
$1,000 to Wichita Falls Area Community Foundation, Wichita Falls, TX, 2011.
$1,000 to Young Life, Colorado Springs, CO, 2011. For general operations.

8939
The Burdine Johnson Foundation ✧
P.O. Box 1230
Buda, TX 78610-1230 (512) 312-1336
Contact: Robert C. Giberson, Tr.; Lisa Giberson, Fin. Mgr.

Established in 1960 in TX.
Donors: Burdine C. Johnson; J.M. Johnson.
Foundation type: Independent foundation.
Financial data (yr. ended 12/31/13): Assets, $33,773,412 (M); expenditures, $1,824,555; qualifying distributions, $1,610,845; giving activities include $1,610,845 for 54 grants (high: $130,000; low: $2,200).
Purpose and activities: Giving primarily for the performing arts, education, human services, historic preservation, the environment and health.
Fields of interest: Performing arts; Performing arts, music; Historic preservation/historical societies; Elementary/secondary education; Higher education; Education; Environment, natural resources; Health care; Human services.
Limitations: Applications accepted. Giving primarily in TX, with emphasis on Austin and Hays County. No grants to individuals.
Application information: Application form not required.
Initial approach: Proposal
Deadline(s): None
Board meeting date(s): 3 to 4 times annually
Final notification: Approximately 3-4 months
Officer and Trustees:* William T. Johnson, Exec. Dir.; Robert C. Giberson; Katherine A. Johnson.
EIN: 746036669
Selected grants: The following grants are a representative sample of this grantmaker's funding activity:
$100,000 to Historic Bridge Foundation, Austin, TX, 2012. For operational support to advocate and educate for preservation of US historical bridges.
$50,000 to Planned Parenthood of the Texas Capital Region, Austin, TX, 2012. To support ongoing Programs in year 2012.
$50,000 to Texas State University, San Marcos, TX, 2012. To support visiting Author Series at the Katherine Porther House.
$25,000 to Jeremiah Program, Austin, TX, 2012. For construction assistance of twenty, 2 bedroom apartments which will be affordable housing and support for approved single parent applicants who are attending college.
$25,000 to Literacy Coalition of Central Texas, Austin, TX, 2012. To assist in expanding the Literacy Illuminates Program in Hays County.
$25,000 to Sustainable Food Center, Austin, TX, 2012. For assistance in construction costs of the new SFC Training Facility.
$20,000 to Austin Steam Train Association, Cedar Park, TX, 2012. To purchase vintage Rippling Stream railroad passenger car.
$20,000 to West Tennessee Healthcare Foundation, Jackson, TN, 2012. To assist MD Anderson Memorial Fund for construction and site preparation of a memorial honoring Monoe Dunaway Anderson.
$15,000 to Texas Land Conservancy, Austin, TX, 2012. To fund strategic conservation of Pedernales, Llano and Medina River watersheds.
$10,000 to Texas Land Trust Council, Austin, TX, 2012. For update/reproduction of conservation Easement Guidebook, support Land Trust Assembly and costs of conservation.

8940
The Carl J. and Margot A. Johnson Foundation ✧
18 Windsor Ridge
Frisco, TX 75034-6858

Established in 1991 in PA.
Donors: Carl J. Johnson; Margot A. Johnson.
Foundation type: Independent foundation.
Financial data (yr. ended 12/31/13): Assets, $14,126,499 (M); expenditures, $876,230; qualifying distributions, $872,351; giving activities include $816,295 for 11 grants (high: $200,010; low: $10,000).
Fields of interest: Performing arts, music (choral); Arts; Higher education; Higher education, university; Health care; Athletics/sports, school programs; Community/economic development; Christian agencies & churches.
Limitations: Applications not accepted. Giving primarily in TX. No grants to individuals.
Application information: Contributes only to pre-selected organizations.
Officer: J.D. Brookhart, Exec. Dir.
Trustees: Carl J. Johnson; Margot A. Johnson.
EIN: 251675809
Selected grants: The following grants are a representative sample of this grantmaker's funding activity:
$146,001 to Insight for Living, Frisco, TX, 2011.
$99,993 to China Ministries International, Pasadena, CA, 2011.
$79,995 to Stonebriar Community Church, Frisco, TX, 2011.
$24,005 to Athletes in Action, Xenia, OH, 2011.
$5,008 to University of Illinois Foundation, Urbana, IL, 2011.

8941
M. G. and Lillie A. Johnson Foundation, Inc. ✧
P.O. Box 2269
Victoria, TX 77902-2269 (361) 575-7970
Contact: Robert Halepeska, Exec. V.P.
E-mail: mgljf@sbcglobal.net

Incorporated in 1958 in TX.
Donors: M.G. Johnson‡; Lillie A. Johnson‡.
Foundation type: Independent foundation.
Financial data (yr. ended 11/30/13): Assets, $101,119,330 (M); expenditures, $4,827,737; qualifying distributions, $3,817,775; giving activities include $3,799,292 for 32 grants (high: $1,000,000; low: $3,630).
Purpose and activities: Primary emphasis on medical and allied health purposes and institutions of higher education located on the Texas Gulf Coast in the 14 counties surrounding Victoria County.
Fields of interest: Higher education; Nursing school/education; Education; Hospitals (general); Nursing care; Health care; Health organizations, association; Human services; Aging, centers/services; Community/economic development.
Type of support: Endowments; Building/renovation; Capital campaigns; Equipment; Land acquisition; Scholarship funds.
Limitations: Applications accepted. Giving limited to TX. Recent giving exclusively to the Texas Gulf Coast area, including Matagorda, Wharton, Colorado, Lavaca, Jackson, Calhoun, Victoria, DeWitt, Gonzales, Karnes, Bee, Goliad, Refugio, Aransas, and Waller counties. No support for most religious and political organizations, and national charities, or for arts, museums or renovations to historic buildings. No grants to individuals, or for general support, operating budgets, endowment funds, fellowships, research, special projects, publications, or conferences; no loans.
Publications: Application guidelines.
Application information: Application form not required.
Initial approach: Proposal
Copies of proposal: 1
Deadline(s): Submit proposal 1 month before meetings; no set deadline
Board meeting date(s): Mar., July, Oct.
Final notification: Following board meetings
Officers and Trustees:* M.H. Brock,* Pres.; Robert Halepeska, Exec. V.P.; James Bouligny,* V.P.; Jack R. Morrison, Secy.-Treas.; Dick Koop; Terrell Mullins; Rosemary Rust; Munson Smith.
Number of staff: 1 full-time professional; 1 part-time support.
EIN: 746076961

8942
Jones Family Fund ✧
P.O. Box 129
La Pryor, TX 78872-0129

Established in 2007 in TX.
Donor: D. Paul Jones, Jr.
Foundation type: Independent foundation.
Financial data (yr. ended 12/31/13): Assets, $10,724,866 (M); gifts received, $285,000; expenditures, $674,896; qualifying distributions, $622,725; giving activities include $622,725 for 54 grants (high: $306,675; low: $100).
Fields of interest: Higher education; Hospitals (specialty); Health organizations, association; Human services; Foundations (community); United Ways and Federated Giving Programs; Protestant agencies & churches.
Limitations: Applications not accepted.
Application information: Contributes only to pre-selected organizations.
Officers: D. Paul Jones, Jr., Pres. and Secy.-Treas.; Allison J. Holt, V.P.; Holly J. Terrell, V.P.
EIN: 260426186

8943
Gene and Jerry Jones Family/Dallas Cowboys Charities ✧
1 Cowboys Pkwy.
Irving, TX 75063-4924 (972) 556-9367
Contact: Charlotte Jones Anderson, Pres.
Main URL: http://www.dallascowboys.com/community/jones-family-charities.html

Established in TX as a public charity. Status changed to a company-sponsored foundation in 2006.
Donors: Dallas Cowboys Football Club, Ltd.; Texas Stadium Corp; NFL Charities; NFL Youth Football; Dallas Cowboys Merchandising; Cowboys Wives Association.
Foundation type: Company-sponsored foundation.
Financial data (yr. ended 12/31/13): Assets, $157,721 (M); gifts received, $2,712,375; expenditures, $2,733,880; qualifying distributions, $2,733,880; giving activities include $2,731,624 for 137 grants (high: $500,000; low: $110).
Purpose and activities: The foundation supports programs designed help those who don't have the strength, resources, or the means to help themselves.
Fields of interest: Museums (art); Performing arts; Performing arts, theater; Arts; Elementary/secondary education; Higher education; Education, reading; Education; Athletics/sports, amateur leagues; Recreation; Boys & girls clubs; Salvation Army; YM/YWCAs & YM/YWHAs; Children/youth, services; Family services; Human services; Christian agencies & churches.
Type of support: In-kind gifts; General/operating support.
Limitations: Applications accepted. Giving primarily in Dallas, TX.
Publications: Application guidelines.
Application information: Support is limited 1 contribution per organization during any given year.
Initial approach: Complete online donation form for auction or raffle fundraisers
Deadline(s): None
Officers: Charlotte Jones Anderson,* Pres.; Jerral W. Jones, V.P.; John Stephen Jones,* V.P.; Jerral W. Jones, Jr.,* Secy.; David Frey, Treas.
EIN: 752808490

8944
Helen Jones Foundation, Inc. ✧
P.O. Box 53665
Lubbock, TX 79453-3665
Contact: James C. Arnold, Pres.

Established about 1984 in TX.
Donor: Helen DeVitt Jones.
Foundation type: Independent foundation.
Financial data (yr. ended 12/31/12): Assets, $153,651,602 (M); expenditures, $8,988,971; qualifying distributions, $6,994,739; giving activities include $6,842,650 for 83 grants (high: $550,000; low: $2,400).
Purpose and activities: Giving primarily for charitable, scientific, literary or educational purposes.
Fields of interest: Museums; Arts; Higher education; Youth development; Human services; Children/youth; Youth; Adults; Young adults.
Type of support: General/operating support; Equipment; Scholarship funds; Research.
Limitations: Applications accepted. Giving primarily in Lubbock, TX. No support for religious or political organizations. No grants to individuals.
Publications: Application guidelines; Informational brochure.
Application information: Application form required.
Initial approach: Letter
Copies of proposal: 1
Deadline(s): Jan. 1 thru. Apr. 30
Board meeting date(s): June
Final notification: Aug. 1
Officers and Directors:* James C. Arnold,* Pres.; Marianna Markham,* V.P.; Barbara Bush,* Secy.; Randy L. Wright,* Treas.; Stephen Michael Briggs.
Number of staff: 1 full-time professional.
EIN: 751977748

8945
Walter S. and Evan C. Jones Testamentary Trust ✧
c/o Bank of America, N.A.
P.O. Box 831041
Dallas, TX 75283-1041
Application address: c/o James J. Mueth, Trust Off., Bank of America, N.A., P.O. Box 219119, Kansas City, MO 64121-9119, tel.: (816) 292-4342

Established in KS and MO.
Foundation type: Independent foundation.
Financial data (yr. ended 06/30/13): Assets, $86,864,091 (M); expenditures, $7,082,103; qualifying distributions, $6,336,861; giving activities include $6,042,910 for 23 grants (high: $2,282,500; low: $5,000).
Purpose and activities: Giving for the improvement of recreational or governmental services to the public in the cities, towns, and other government subdivisions within Lyon, Coffey, and Osage Counties, Kansas.
Fields of interest: Arts councils; Higher education; Education; Health care; Youth development, centers/clubs; Foundations (private grantmaking).
Limitations: Giving limited to Lyon, Coffey and Osage counties, KS. No grants to individuals.
Application information: Application form not required.
Initial approach: Letter, no more than 3 pages
Deadline(s): None
Board meeting date(s): 2nd Tues. quarterly
Advisory Committee: Gregory A. Bachman; Max Stewart, Jr.; Thomas D. Thomas.
Trustee: Bank of America, N.A.
EIN: 480674648

8946
Jonesville Foundation ✧ ☆
P.O. Box 84
Jonesville, TX 75659-0084

Established in TX.
Donor: Patricia A. Vaughan.
Foundation type: Independent foundation.
Financial data (yr. ended 12/31/13): Assets, $12,151,068 (M); expenditures, $751,225; qualifying distributions, $670,692; giving activities include $669,280 for 6 grants (high: $250,000; low: $50,000).
Fields of interest: Human services; Children/youth, services; Residential/custodial care; Women; Girls.
Limitations: Applications not accepted. Giving primarily in TX.
Application information: Unsolicited requests for funds not accepted.
Officers and Directors:* Patricia A. Vaughan, Chair., Pres. and Treas.; Kim V. Scrivener,* V.P.; Barbara Turner,* Secy.; Jill Turner; Shirley Vaughan.
EIN: 263242289
Selected grants: The following grants are a representative sample of this grantmaker's funding activity:
$100,000 to Audubon Texas, Dallas, TX, 2012. Toward the year-round school kids Program.

8947
Jane and John Justin Foundation ✧
1300 S. University Dr., Ste. 400
Fort Worth, TX 76107-5726

Donor: Jane C. Justin†.
Foundation type: Independent foundation.
Financial data (yr. ended 12/31/12): Assets, $108,484,281 (M); expenditures, $5,823,010; qualifying distributions, $5,080,553; giving activities include $4,943,336 for 10 grants (high: $2,201,518; low: $20,000).
Fields of interest: Higher education; Hospitals (specialty); Cancer; Human services; Christian agencies & churches.
Limitations: Applications not accepted. Giving primarily in TX. No grants to individuals.
Application information: Contributes only to pre-selected organizations.
Officers: J.T. Dickenson, Pres.; Roy B. Topham, Secy.-Treas. and Exec. Dir.
Directors: Mary C. Justin; Dee J. Kelly; Robert Watt.
EIN: 752442749
Selected grants: The following grants are a representative sample of this grantmaker's funding activity:
$2,201,518 to Texas Christian University, Fort Worth, TX, 2012. For Building Fund for Stadium, Locker Room and Weight Room.
$750,000 to Cook Childrens Medical Center, Fort Worth, TX, 2012. For Building Fund.
$515,000 to Child Study Center, Fort Worth, TX, 2012. For capacity building.
$500,000 to Ronald McDonald House of Fort Worth, Fort Worth, TX, 2012. For building improvements.
$350,000 to Marbridge Foundation, Manchaca, TX, 2012. For general support.
$301,136 to Helping Other People Excel Farm, Fort Worth, TX, 2012. To furnish building.
$125,000 to Womens Center of Tarrant County, Fort Worth, TX, 2012. For Play it Safe, videos about child abuse prevention.
$100,000 to Downtown Fort Worth Initiatives, Fort Worth, TX, 2012. For construction of John F. Kennedy Memorial.
$80,682 to Special Olympics Texas, Fort Worth, TX, 2012. To furnish medals for games.
$20,000 to Texas Christian University, Athletics Department, Fort Worth, TX, 2012.

8948
Kahng Foundation ✧
c/o Stephen Kahng
2106 Cliff Edge Dr.
Austin, TX 78733

Established in 1998 in TX.
Donors: Choonja Kahng; Stephen Kahng.
Foundation type: Independent foundation.
Financial data (yr. ended 12/31/13): Assets, $12,646,498 (M); expenditures, $586,062; qualifying distributions, $460,700; giving activities include $460,700 for 10 grants (high: $200,000; low: $500).
Purpose and activities: Giving for education and religion, with an emphasis on Korean culture and interests.
Fields of interest: Museums (art); Higher education, university; Education; Human services; Christian agencies & churches.
Limitations: Applications not accepted. Giving primarily in CA, Washington, DC, and MA.
Application information: Contributes only to pre-selected organizations.
Officers: Choonja Kahng, Pres.; Stephen Kahng, Treas.
EIN: 742883492
Selected grants: The following grants are a representative sample of this grantmaker's funding activity:
$100,000 to Hoover Institution on War, Revolution and Peace, Stanford, CA, 2011.
$60,000 to Harvard University, Cambridge, MA, 2011.
$32,000 to Asian Art Museum of San Francisco, San Francisco, CA, 2010.
$10,000 to Asia Foundation, San Francisco, CA, 2011.
$1,500 to California College of the Arts, San Francisco, CA, 2011.

8949
KDK-Harman Foundation ✧
1000 Westbank Dr., Bldg. 3
Austin, TX 78746-6687 (512) 328-9400
FAX: (512) 328-9402; E-mail: info@kdk-harman.org; Main URL: http://www.kdk-harman.org
Blog: http://blog.kdk-harman.org/
Facebook: https://www.facebook.com/KDKHarman
Knowledge Center: http://www.kdk-harman.org/summer-learning.html
Twitter: https://twitter.com/kdkharman
YouTube: http://www.youtube.com/user/KDKHarman

Established in 2004 in Austin, TX.
Donor: Janet E. Harman.
Foundation type: Independent foundation.
Financial data (yr. ended 12/31/12): Assets, $24,477,125 (M); gifts received, $500,000; expenditures, $1,235,783; qualifying distributions, $1,137,740; giving activities include $928,000 for 27 grants (high: $60,000; low: $10,000).
Purpose and activities: The foundation's mission is to break the cycle of poverty through education in Central Texas. It focuses strictly on academic education. The foundation funds educational programs across the age spectrum from pre-kindergarten through adult. Its program interests include early and family literacy, college access, GED certification, academically rigorous out-of-school-time programs, traditional pre-K-12 education, and postsecondary education. It also supports workforce development programs that are academically rigorous, allow individuals to obtain college credit, and open doors for them to acquire living-wage jobs. In addition, KDK-Harman will favor those programs in the areas of science, technology, engineering, and math (STEM).
Fields of interest: Education, public policy; Education, formal/general education; Education, services; Science, formal/general education; Economically disadvantaged.
Type of support: Mission-related investments/loans; General/operating support; Continuing support; Management development/capacity building; Program development; Technical assistance.
Limitations: Applications accepted. Giving primarily in central TX: Travis, Williamson, Hays, Bastrop, Caldwell, Burnet, and Llano counties. No support for arts or athletic education, tax-generating entities for services, political campaigns, or pregnancy prevention programs. No grants to individuals, or for loans to individuals, research, scholarships, purchase of tickets for events, or school fundraisers.
Publications: Application guidelines; Annual report; Financial statement; Grants list.

Application information: Electronic application is required. Upon review of letter of inquiry, the foundation will send an e-mail either inviting an application, or declining the request. Following approval of application by the board, the grant contract and evaluation is developed. Once executed, the grant funds are released. This process takes 30-45 days after the board meeting. Central Texas Education Funders Common Application Form accepted. Application form required.

Initial approach: Letter of inquiry. Instructions, grant guidelines and form available on foundation web site.
Deadline(s): Throughout the year
Board meeting date(s): Apr., Sept., and Nov.
Final notification: Applications approved by the board are notified within a week of the board meeting

Officers and Trustees:* Janet E. Harman,* Pres.; Eugene Sepulveda,* V.P.; Mark Williams,* Secy.-Treas.; Melanie Moore, Exec. Dir.; Kent Mayes.
Number of staff: 2 part-time professional; 1 full-time support.
EIN: 611478157
Selected grants: The following grants are a representative sample of this grantmaker's funding activity:
$60,000 to University of Texas Foundation, Austin, TX, 2012. For UT Elementary School.
$50,000 to Austin Partners in Education, Austin, TX, 2012. For Austin Partners in Education.
$50,000 to Children at Risk, Houston, TX, 2012. For children at risk.
$50,000 to E3 Alliance, Austin, TX, 2012. For E3 Alliance Operating Grant_STEM Pipeline.
$50,000 to Foundation Communities, Austin, TX, 2012. For PATHS After School and Summer Youth Program.
$50,000 to Girlstart, Austin, TX, 2012. For Girlstart.
$50,000 to Texas Tribune, Austin, TX, 2012. For Texas Tribune Hot Seat Statewide Event Series.
$35,000 to Breakthrough, Austin, TX, 2012. For Breakthrough General Program.
$25,000 to Ann Richards School Foundation, Austin, TX, 2012. For Ann Richards School STEM Focused Enhancement Programs.
$25,000 to University of Texas Foundation, Austin, TX, 2012. For Uteach Outreach/UT PREP Summer Pre-Freshman Engineering Program.

8950
Steven J. and Melissa C. Kean Charitable Foundation Inc. ✧ ☆

3631 Meadowlake Ln.
Houston, TX 77027-4110

Established in TX.
Donors: Steven J. Kean; Melissa C. Kean.
Foundation type: Independent foundation.
Financial data (yr. ended 07/31/13): Assets, $26,267,268 (M); gifts received, $24,414,500; expenditures, $1,031,338; qualifying distributions, $1,030,000; giving activities include $1,030,000 for 8 grants (high: $500,000; low: $10,000).
Fields of interest: Higher education; Education.
Limitations: Applications not accepted. Giving primarily in TX; some funding also in Omaha, NE.
Application information: Unsolicited requests for funds not accepted.
Directors: Melissa C. Kean; Nora K. Kean; Steven J. Kean; Margaret Kean Wissink.
EIN: 371701236

8951
Joan and Herb Kelleher Charitable Foundation ✧

P.O. Box 12170
San Antonio, TX 78212-0829
E-mail: tina.pawelek@paisanocattle.com;
Application address: c/o Tina A. Pawelek, 405 N. St. Mary's St., Ste. 700, San Antonio, TX 78205, tel.: (210) 229-1975

Established in 1997 in TX.
Donors: Herbert D. Kelleher; Joan N. Kelleher.
Foundation type: Independent foundation.
Financial data (yr. ended 12/31/13): Assets, $14,860,943 (M); expenditures, $913,043; qualifying distributions, $750,605; giving activities include $690,750 for 45 grants (high: $110,000; low: $1,500).
Fields of interest: Historic preservation/historical societies; Arts; Environment; Youth development; Human services.
Type of support: General/operating support; Capital campaigns; Building/renovation.
Publications: Application guidelines.
Application information: Application form not required.

Initial approach: Request application guidelines
Copies of proposal: 1
Deadline(s): None
Board meeting date(s): Varies

Trustees: Ruth K. Agather; David N. Kelleher; Herbert D. Kelleher; J. Michael Kelleher; Joan N. Kelleher; Julia K. Stacy.
EIN: 742833381
Selected grants: The following grants are a representative sample of this grantmaker's funding activity:
$15,000 to Witte Museum, San Antonio, TX, 2012. For Darwin Exhibit.
$10,000 to Cibolo Nature Center, Boerne, TX, 2012. For Herff Farm Purchase (4 of 5).
$10,000 to University of Texas, Austin, TX, 2012. For McDonald Observatory Workshops.
$5,000 to Boy Scouts of America, Alamo Area Council, San Antonio, TX, 2012. For Capital Campaign (4 of 5).
$5,000 to National Trust for Historic Preservation, Washington, DC, 2012. For White Grass Dude Ranch Restoration.
$5,000 to San Antonio Zoological Society, San Antonio, TX, 2012. For School Field Trip Admissions.
$5,000 to University of Texas, School of Law, Austin, TX, 2012. For general funding.
$2,500 to Guide Dogs of Texas, San Antonio, TX, 2012. For Training Pavilion Project.

8952
Harris and Eliza Kempner Fund ✧

(formerly Harris and Eliza Kempner Fund, Inc.)
2201 Market St., Ste. 1250
Galveston, TX 77550-1527 (409) 762-1603
Contact: Anne Brasier, Exec. Dir.
FAX: (409) 762-5435;
E-mail: information@kempnerfund.org; Main URL: http://www.kempnerfund.org

Established in 1946 in TX; incorporated in 2001.
Donor: Various interests and members of the Kempner family.
Foundation type: Independent foundation.
Financial data (yr. ended 12/31/12): Assets, $42,786,341 (M); gifts received, $366,889; expenditures, $2,293,865; qualifying distributions, $1,965,181; giving activities include $1,617,141 for 387 grants (high: $254,740; low: $25).
Purpose and activities: Support primarily for human services, arts and humanities, education, community development, and health in the Galveston, TX, area.
Fields of interest: Visual arts; Museums; Performing arts; Performing arts, dance; Performing arts, theater; Humanities; History/archaeology; Historic preservation/historical societies; Arts; Education, early childhood education; Child development, education; Elementary school/education; Secondary school/education; Higher education; Medical school/education; Adult education—literacy, basic skills & GED; Education, reading; Education; Environment, natural resources; Environment; Reproductive health, family planning; Health care; Substance abuse, services; Mental health/crisis services; Crime/law enforcement; Food services; Housing/shelter, development; Youth development, services; Human services; Youth, services; Child development, services; Residential/custodial care, hospices; Minorities/immigrants, centers/services; Homeless, human services; Civil rights, race/intergroup relations; Community/economic development.
Type of support: General/operating support; Continuing support; Annual campaigns; Capital campaigns; Building/renovation; Equipment; Emergency funds; Program development; Conferences/seminars; Professorships; Publication; Seed money; Curriculum development; Fellowships; Scholarship funds; Research; Program-related investments/loans; Matching/challenge support.
Limitations: Applications accepted. Giving primarily in Galveston County, TX. No support for non-U.S. based organizations. No grants to individuals, or for fundraising benefits or direct mail solicitations.
Publications: Application guidelines; Financial statement; Grants list; Program policy statement.
Application information: Electronic proposals only; application guidelines available on foundation web site. Computerized solicitations not considered. Application form required.

Deadline(s): For grant program: Mar. 15 and Oct. 15
Board meeting date(s): May, Sept., Dec., and as required
Final notification: 8 weeks

Officers and Directors:* Robert L.K. Lynch,* Pres.; Eliza Kempner Quigley, V.P.; Armin Cantini,* Secy.; Daniel K. Thorne,* Treas.; Anne Brasier, Exec. Dir.; Barbara Sasser, Honorary Dir.; Lynda Ann Thomas, Honorary Dir.; Lisa Allen; Hetta Towler Kempner; Randall T. Kempner; Victoria Marchand; Andrew Mytelka; Carol Roberts.
Number of staff: 1 full-time professional; 1 full-time support.
EIN: 760680130
Selected grants: The following grants are a representative sample of this grantmaker's funding activity:
$50,000 to Galveston College Foundation, Galveston, TX, 2012. For Cecile Kempner Vocational Technical Scholarship Fund.
$50,000 to Galveston Historical Foundation, Galveston, TX, 2012. For Restoration of Elissa.

$50,000 to Rosenberg Library, Galveston, TX, 2012. For Renovation of 1st Floor (Phase V).
$30,000 to Family Service Center of Galveston County, Galveston, TX, 2012. For Project Community Mental Health Services Outreach Program.
$20,000 to Galveston Island Tree Conservancy, Galveston, TX, 2012. For Professional Arborist for Agalveston Reforestation.
$17,500 to Galveston Arts Center, Galveston, TX, 2012. For operations and Programs.
$12,500 to Planned Parenthood Gulf Coast, Houston, TX, 2012. For Operations Galveston County Clinic.
$7,500 to Advocacy Center for Children of Galveston County, Galveston, TX, 2012. For Forensic Interviewing Project.
$2,500 to Justin-Siena High School, Napa, CA, 2012. For Sports expansion Program.
$1,500 to Palacios Area Historical Association, Palacios, TX, 2012. For Capital Improvements to Museum.

8953
Dr. and Mrs. Hugh A. Kennedy Foundation ✧

c/o Martin C. Davis
802 N. Carancahua St., Ste. 1270
Corpus Christi, TX 78401-0400

Established in 2001 in TX.
Donors: Hugh A. Kennedy†; Margaret T. Kennedy†.
Foundation type: Independent foundation.
Financial data (yr. ended 12/31/13): Assets, $11,574,638 (M); expenditures, $656,826; qualifying distributions, $523,424; giving activities include $446,350 for 11 grants (high: $116,600; low: $5,000).
Fields of interest: Higher education; Health care; Human services; Catholic agencies & churches; Homeless.
Limitations: Applications not accepted. Giving limited to Nueces County, TX. No grants to individuals.
Application information: Unsolicited requests for funds not accepted.
Officers: Martin C. Davis, Pres.; Patricia Williams, V.P.; Karen Bonner, Secy.; Barbara Little, Treas.
EIN: 742983794

8954
Carl E. Kessler Family Foundation ✧

P.O. Box 121579
Fort Worth, TX 76121-1579

Established in 1994 in TX.
Donors: Carl E. Kessler; Kenneth R. Kessler.
Foundation type: Independent foundation.
Financial data (yr. ended 12/31/13): Assets, $7,681,493 (M); gifts received, $100,000; expenditures, $737,417; qualifying distributions, $422,324; giving activities include $421,835 for 104 grants (high: $120,000; low: $5).
Fields of interest: Higher education; Community/economic development; Christian agencies & churches; Children/youth.
Limitations: Applications not accepted. Giving primarily in Bloomington, IN; giving also in TX, with some emphasis on Mineral Wells. No grants to individuals.
Application information: Contributes only to pre-selected organizations.
Officers: Kenneth R. Kessler, Pres.; David R. Kessler, V.P.; Carla Kay Kessler, Secy.-Treas.
EIN: 752567397
Selected grants: The following grants are a representative sample of this grantmaker's funding activity:
$30,000 to Community Renewal International, Shreveport, LA, 2012. For Community Service-fuller Center House Project.
$5,000 to Small Steps Nurturing Center, Houston, TX, 2012. For Helps at risk children - education and feed.
$2,500 to Amazon Conservation Association, Washington, DC, 2012. For Jet Memorial.
$2,500 to Animal Welfare Institute, Washington, DC, 2012. For Star lights for children's cancer units.
$2,500 to Puppies Behind Bars, New York, NY, 2012. For Community Service - Animals.
$2,500 to Smile Train, New York, NY, 2012. For Helps children with dental costs.
$1,000 to Humane Society of North Texas, Fort Worth, TX, 2012. For Community Service - Animal Shelter.

8955
Kickapoo Springs Foundation ✧

P.O. Box 176
Abilene, TX 79604-0176 (325) 673-6429
Contact: John A. Matthews, Jr., Pres.

Established in 1997 in TX.
Donors: John A. Matthews, Jr.; Dodge Jones Foundation.
Foundation type: Independent foundation.
Financial data (yr. ended 12/31/12): Assets, $63,729,055 (M); gifts received, $36,085; expenditures, $3,809,417; qualifying distributions, $3,115,117; giving activities include $3,043,983 for 44 grants (high: $1,000,000; low: $1,000).
Fields of interest: Human services.
Type of support: General/operating support.
Limitations: Applications accepted. Giving primarily in San Angelo, TX. No grants to individuals.
Application information: Application form required.
Initial approach: Letter
Deadline(s): None
Officers and Directors:* John A. Matthews, Jr.,* Chair. and C.E.O.; Kade L. Matthews,* Pres.; Joseph E. Canon,* Exec. V.P. and Exec. Dir.; Thomas R. Allen,* V.P. and C.F.O.; Lawrence E. Gill, V.P.; Linda S. Buckner, Secy.-Treas.; Jill Matthews Wilkinson.
EIN: 752684716
Selected grants: The following grants are a representative sample of this grantmaker's funding activity:
$750,000 to Hendrick Medical Center Foundation, Abilene, TX, 2012. For Educational/Texas Tech School of Nursing.
$400,000 to Texas Tech Foundation, Lubbock, TX, 2012. For Educational/to Establish the Free Market Economics Institute.
$67,840 to Angelo State University, San Angelo, TX, 2012. For Welding and Engine Cubicles for Agriculture Education Training Center.
$27,239 to Washington Legal Foundation, Washington, DC, 2012. For Charitable/Judge K.K. Legett Fellows for 2011-2015.
$25,000 to Legacy Foundation, Merrillville, IN, 2012. For Charitable/Operating Support - Military Voter Protection Project.
$20,000 to Shannon Medical Center, San Angelo, TX, 2012. For Charitable/Construction of Garden of Hope.
$5,000 to Foundation for Teaching Economics, Davis, CA, 2012. For educational/operating support.
$5,000 to Regional Crime Victim Crisis Center, Abilene, TX, 2012. For Charitable/Support the Who Program.
$5,000 to Texas Public Policy Foundation, Austin, TX, 2012. For Charitable/Policy Primer Series.
$1,000 to State Policy Network, Arlington, VA, 2012. For charitable/operating support.

8956
William S. & Lora Jean Kilroy Foundation ✧

4400 Post Oak Pkwy, Ste. 2280
Houston, TX 77027-3421 (713) 621-8221

Established in 1985 in TX.
Donors: William S. Kilroy†; Lora Jean Kilroy.
Foundation type: Independent foundation.
Financial data (yr. ended 12/31/13): Assets, $12,384,794 (M); gifts received, $4,800; expenditures, $571,204; qualifying distributions, $504,734; giving activities include $502,399 for 28 grants (high: $150,000; low: $500).
Fields of interest: Museums; Performing arts; Higher education; Education; Community/economic development.
Type of support: General/operating support; Annual campaigns; Capital campaigns.
Limitations: Applications accepted. Giving primarily in TX, with emphasis on Houston. No grants to individuals.
Application information: Application form required.
Initial approach: Letter
Deadline(s): None
Trustees: Lora Jean Kilroy; Mari Angela Kilroy; William S. Kilroy, Jr.
EIN: 760169904

8957
Kimberly-Clark Foundation, Inc. ✧

351 Phelps Dr.
Irving, TX 75038-6507 (972) 281-1200
Application address: P.O. Box 619100, Dallas, TX 75261-9100; Main URL: http://www.kimberly-clark.com/ourcompany/community/kc_foundation.aspx
Bright Futures Scholarship Program Recipients: http://www.cms.kimberly-clark.com/UmbracoImages/UmbracoFileMedia/BrightFutures2011Recipients_umbracoFile.pdf

Incorporated in 1952 in WI.
Donors: Kimberly-Clark Corp.; P.D. and Tracy Parsons Trust.
Foundation type: Company-sponsored foundation.
Financial data (yr. ended 12/31/12): Assets, $14,395 (M); gifts received, $4,632,524; expenditures, $4,317,002; qualifying distributions, $4,312,513; giving activities include $1,455,495 for grants, $1,318,075 for grants to individuals, and $1,466,831 for employee matching gifts.
Purpose and activities: The foundation supports organizations involved with arts and culture, education, the environment, health, and human services. Special emphasis is directed toward

programs designed to strengthen families around the world.
Fields of interest: Arts; Higher education; Education; Environment, natural resources; Environment; Hospitals (general); Health care; Disasters, preparedness/services; Boys & girls clubs; American Red Cross; Salvation Army; Children/youth, services; Family services; Human services; United Ways and Federated Giving Programs.
Type of support: General/operating support; Continuing support; Capital campaigns; Program development; Curriculum development; Employee volunteer services; Sponsorships; Employee matching gifts; Employee-related scholarships.
Limitations: Applications accepted. Giving primarily in areas of company operations, with emphasis on CA and TX; giving also to national organizations. No support for religious or political organizations. No grants to individuals (except for employee-related scholarships), or for non-disaster relief product donations, or sports or athletic activities; no loans.
Publications: Corporate giving report.
Application information: Unsolicited requests from national or international organizations are not accepted. Application form not required.
Initial approach: Proposal to application address
Deadline(s): None
Officers and Directors:* Anthony J. Palmer,* Pres.; Mark A. Buthman,* V.P.; Jennifer L. Lewis, V.P.; John W. Wesley, Secy.; Steven E. Voskuil, Treas.; Thomas J. Falk.
Number of staff: 1 full-time professional; 1 full-time support.
EIN: 396044304

8958
Kinder Foundation ✧
(formerly Richard D. Kinder Foundation, Inc.)
P.O. Box 130776
Houston, TX 77219-0776
Contact: Nancy G. Kinder, Pres.
Main URL: http://www.kinderfoundation.org
Richard D. and Nancy Kinder's Giving Pledge Profile: http://glasspockets.org/philanthropy-in-focus/eye-on-the-giving-pledge/profiles/kinder

Established in 1994 in TX.
Donors: Richard D. Kinder; Nancy G. Kinder.
Foundation type: Independent foundation.
Financial data (yr. ended 12/31/13): Assets, $138,622,283 (M); gifts received, $69,816,443; expenditures, $33,993,241; qualifying distributions, $33,374,261; giving activities include $33,214,714 for 83 grants (high: $9,899,042; low: $500).
Purpose and activities: Giving primarily for the arts, education, health associations, social services, children services, including a children's hospital, community development and federated giving programs.
Fields of interest: Museums; Arts; Education; Environment; Hospitals (specialty); Health organizations, association; Human services; Children, services; Community/economic development; Catholic agencies & churches.
Type of support: Matching/challenge support; Scholarship funds; Emergency funds; Land acquisition; General/operating support; Continuing support; Annual campaigns; Capital campaigns; Building/renovation; Endowments; Program development; Professorships.
Limitations: Applications not accepted. Giving primarily in TX, with emphasis on the Greater Houston area. No grants to individuals.
Application information: Contributes only to pre-selected organizations.
Board meeting date(s): Unscheduled
Officers and Board Members:* Richard D. Kinder,* Chair.; Nancy G. Kinder, Pres. and Treas.; James V. Derrick, Jr., Secy.; Gary C. Dudley; David D. Kinder; Roxann S. Neumann; Kara K. Vidal.
Advisory Board: Todd V. Adam; Ginger A. Corley; Polly K. Whittle.
Number of staff: None.
EIN: 760519073
Selected grants: The following grants are a representative sample of this grantmaker's funding activity:
$6,498,335 to Buffalo Bayou Partnership, Houston, TX, 2012. For Buffalo Bayou Park Construction.
$2,584,893 to Rice University, Houston, TX, 2012. For Urban Studies at Rice University.
$1,992,810 to Archdiocese of Galveston-Houston, Houston, TX, 2012. To support of Inner-City Catholic Schools.
$1,613,261 to Archdiocese of Galveston-Houston, Houston, TX, 2012. To support of Inner-City Catholic Schools.
$502,282 to Houston Parks Board, Emancipation Park, Houston, TX, 2012. For Renovation of Emancipation Park.
$400,000 to Museum of Fine Arts, Houston, Houston, TX, 2012. To support of Art Education.
$299,101 to Buffalo Bayou Partnership, Houston, TX, 2012. For Buffalo Bayou Park Final Design.
$150,000 to Rice University, Houston, TX, 2012. For Urban Studies at Rice University.
$76,589 to Archdiocese of Galveston-Houston, Houston, TX, 2012. To support of Inner-City Catholic Schools.
$28,750 to Jack Miller Center for Teaching Americas Founding Principles and History, Bala Cynwyd, PA, 2012. For Education - American History, University of Missouri.

8959
Carl B. and Florence E. King Foundation
2301 Cedar Springs Rd., Ste. 330
Dallas, TX 75201-7886 (214) 750-1884
Contact: Michelle D. Monse, Pres.
FAX: (214) 750-1651;
E-mail: michellemonse@kingfoundation.com; Main URL: http://www.kingfoundation.com
Grants List: http://www.kingfoundation.com/Grants/Grants-By-Year.aspx

Incorporated in 1966 in TX.
Donors: Carl B. King†; Florence E. King†; Dorothy E. King†.
Foundation type: Independent foundation.
Financial data (yr. ended 12/31/13): Assets, $74,556,988 (M); expenditures, $3,470,958; qualifying distributions, $2,847,528; giving activities include $2,135,561 for 90 grants (high: $100,000; low: $5,000), and $40,951 for 1 foundation-administered program.
Purpose and activities: The foundation is committed to the highest standards of philanthropy and to honoring the intent of the founders, Carl B. and Florence E. King. The foundation's work is guided by the following principles: commitment to high ethical standards, adherence to strict financial guidelines, selection of appropriate and mission-focused grantees, evaluation and assessment of the grants, and clear and timely communications with all constituents. Grants are made in five counties in North Texas in specific areas. Grants are made in defined areas of West Texas and Arkansas in the following areas: aging; arts, culture, and history; children and youth; education; the indigent; and nonprofit capacity, including nonprofit management.
Fields of interest: Arts education; Performing arts; Historical activities; Arts; Education, early childhood education; Child development, education; Adult education—literacy, basic skills & GED; Libraries (public); Education; Health care, clinics/centers; Health care, rural areas; AIDS; Alzheimer's disease; Crime/violence prevention, abuse prevention; Crime/violence prevention, domestic violence; Crime/violence prevention, child abuse; Employment, job counseling; Food banks; Food distribution, groceries on wheels; Food services, congregate meals; Agriculture/food; Housing/shelter; Youth development; Children/youth, services; Family services; Aging, centers/services; Human services; Rural development; Nonprofit management; Children/youth; Aging; Economically disadvantaged; Homeless.
Type of support: Management development/capacity building; Building/renovation; Equipment; Program development.
Limitations: Applications accepted. Giving in 28 counties in eastern and southern Arkansas, 5 counties in the Dallas-Fort Worth area, and 38 counties in West Texas; please see foundation web site for a list of the specific counties. No support for religious organizations, or to non-exempt organizations. The foundation will, however, support social service programs conducted by faith-based organizations. No grants to individuals directly, or for construction of churches or seminaries, or for religious programs (except for social service programs available to the community at large) or for ongoing operating expenses or funds to offset operating losses. No grants for loan financing; endowments; professional conferences or symposia; or balls, events, or for galas benefiting charitable organizations.
Publications: Financial statement; Grants list.
Application information: Complete application and grant guidelines available on foundation web site. Application form required.
Initial approach: Letter of inquiry to be submitted online via foundation web site. The foundation no longer accepts applications in hard copy
Deadline(s): Fall cycle: letter of inquiry due June 15; invited proposals due Aug. 31. Spring cycle: letter of inquiry due Dec. 15; invited proposals due Feb. 28. If the deadline falls on a weekend or holiday, the deadline rolls to the next business day.
Board meeting date(s): June and Dec.
Final notification: 6 weeks for letters of inquiry; 3-4 months for proposals.
Officers and Directors:* Teresa D. Wilkinson,* Chair.; Robert E. Weiss, Vice-Chair.; Michelle D. Monse, Pres.; Kimberly H. Evans,* V.P.; John Martin Davis, V.P.; Robert I. Fernandez,* V.P.; Michael Phillips, V.P.; Patricia A. Porter, V.P.; Ann C. Fielder, Secy.
Number of staff: 4 full-time professional.
EIN: 756052203
Selected grants: The following grants are a representative sample of this grantmaker's funding activity:
$100,000 to Dallas Foundation, Dallas, TX, 2013. For program support for Year 5 of the Zero to Five

Funder's Collaborative promoting school readiness in Bachman Lake area.
$50,000 to West Texas Food Bank, Odessa, TX, 2013. For capital support to build new food bank facilities in Odessa, Midland, and Alpine, Texas.
$40,000 to Arkansas Food Bank Network, Little Rock, AR, 2013. For program support of Local Partner Development Initiative which assists rural communities in developing local food pantries.
$30,000 to CitySquare, Dallas, TX, 2013. For program support for TRAC, Transition Resource Action Center, supports young adults aging out of foster care as they transition to independent adult life.
$30,000 to Family Compass, Dallas, TX, 2013. For program support for Healthy Families, intervention program to prevent child abuse and promote healthy child development.
$25,000 to Alliance for Children, Fort Worth, TX, 2013. For program support for group counseling for children who have experience child abuse or neglect.
$25,000 to Communities in Schools of Greater Tarrant County, Fort Worth, TX, 2013. For program support of case management services at elementary school in Tarrant County.
$25,000 to Dallas Theater Center, Dallas, TX, 2013. For program support for Project Discovery, program using live theater as vehicle for teaching low-income high school students.
$25,000 to Daughters of Charity of Arkansas, Dumas, AR, 2013. For program support of Diabetes Self-Management Education Program which teaches adults who are pre-diabetic or diabetic how to maintain optimal health.
$20,000 to Dallas Concilio of Hispanic Service Organizations, Dallas, TX, 2013. For program support for PASE (Parents Advocating for Student Excellence) parent engagement program.
$15,000 to Casa de Amigos of Midland, Midland, TX, 2013. For program support for Senior Services program which provides socialization, health screenings, meals, and activities for low-income seniors.

8960
Klabzuba Family Foundation ✧

100 Lexington Ave., Ste. 050
Fort Worth, TX 76102-2742 (817) 339-1657
Contact: John R. Brown

Established in 2002 in TX.
Donor: Robert Klabzuba†.
Foundation type: Independent foundation.
Financial data (yr. ended 12/31/12): Assets, $178,973 (M); expenditures, $493,850; qualifying distributions, $491,850; giving activities include $491,850 for grants.
Purpose and activities: The mission of the foundation is to enhance the quality of life through education, health care, and culture. The foundation seeks to recognize and support organizations and programs that serve others through generosity, compassion, good citizenship, and philanthropy.
Fields of interest: Arts; Education; Health care.
Type of support: Capital campaigns; Building/renovation; Equipment; Endowments; Program development; Professorships; Scholarship funds; Research; Scholarships—to individuals; Matching/challenge support.
Limitations: Applications accepted. Giving primarily in cities in which Klabzuba family members or businesses are located, with emphasis on TX and OK.
Application information: Application form required.
Initial approach: See Website
Copies of proposal: 1
Deadline(s): See Website
Officers and Directors:* Doris Klabzuba,* Pres.; Hank Akin,* V.P.; Judith Park,* V.P.; Janet Stevens,* V.P.; Jane Korman,* Secy.; John Klabzuba,* Treas.; Melinda Klabzuba; Josh Korman; Alice Park; Byron Searcy; E.R. Sidwell; Jackie Stevens.
EIN: 912136476

8961
The KLE Foundation ✧

P.O. Box 163991
Austin, TX 78716-3991

Established in 1997 in TX.
Donors: Lorraine Clasquin; Eric Harslem.
Foundation type: Independent foundation.
Financial data (yr. ended 12/31/13): Assets, $27,289,647 (M); gifts received, $860,280; expenditures, $1,059,069; qualifying distributions, $933,843; giving activities include $863,000 for 12 grants (high: $384,000; low: $1,500).
Fields of interest: Education; Health care; Religion, interfaith issues.
Limitations: Applications not accepted. Giving primarily in TX. No grants to individuals.
Application information: Contributes only to pre-selected organizations.
Officers and Directors:* Lorraine Clasquin,* Pres.; Eric Harslem,* V.P. and Secy.; Kate Harslem; Andrew S. White.
EIN: 742860436
Selected grants: The following grants are a representative sample of this grantmaker's funding activity:
$535,000 to Advanced Placement Strategies, Austin, TX, 2012. For advanced placement curriculum.
$51,000 to Foundation Communities, Austin, TX, 2012. For after-school programming.
$20,000 to Girlstart, Austin, TX, 2012. For STEM instruction.
$16,500 to English at Work, Austin, TX, 2012. For adult basic literacy education.
$9,000 to Interfaith Action of Central Texas, Austin, TX, 2012. For summer school instruction.
$5,000 to WeViva, Austin, TX, 2012. For health and wellness.

8962
Robert J. Kleberg, Jr. and Helen C. Kleberg Foundation ✧

700 N. St. Mary's St., Ste. 1200
San Antonio, TX 78205-3510
Contact: Cathy Friese, Grants Admin.
FAX: (210) 299-1541; E-mail for Cathy Friese: cathyf@alexventures.com; Main URL: http://www.klebergfoundation.org/

Incorporated in 1950 in TX.
Donors: Helen C. Kleberg†; Robert J. Kleberg, Jr.†.
Foundation type: Independent foundation.
Financial data (yr. ended 12/31/13): Assets, $259,551,031 (M); expenditures, $12,773,687; qualifying distributions, $11,082,903; giving activities include $11,010,325 for 41 grants (high: $2,000,000; low: $10,000).
Purpose and activities: Giving on a national basis for medical research, veterinary and animal sciences, wildlife research and preservation, health services, higher education, and arts and humanities; support also for local community organizations.
Fields of interest: Arts; Higher education; Animals/wildlife, preservation/protection; Health care; Medical research, institute; Biology/life sciences.
Type of support: Scholarship funds; Program development; Research; Matching/challenge support.
Limitations: Applications accepted. Giving primarily in south TX. No support for organizations limited by race or religion or for community organizations outside TX. No grants to individuals, or for endowments, general operating expenses, deficit financing, capital for construction, or for indirect costs or overhead for research projects.
Publications: Application guidelines; Annual report.
Application information: Application form not required.
Initial approach: Letter on organization letterhead
Copies of proposal: 1
Deadline(s): Apr. 15 and Oct. 15. Should the deadline fall on a weekend, it will be extended to the following Monday. Should the deadline fall on a weekend and the following Monday is a holiday, it will be extended to the following Tuesday.
Board meeting date(s): Usually in early June and early Dec.
Final notification: 6 months
Officers and Directors:* Helen K. Groves,* Pres.; John D. Alexander, Jr.,* V.P. and Secy.; Emory A. Hamilton,* V.P. and Treas.; Helen C. Alexander,* V.P.; Henrietta K. Alexander; Caroline A. Forgason; Dorothy A. Matz.
Number of staff: 1 full-time professional.
EIN: 746044810
Selected grants: The following grants are a representative sample of this grantmaker's funding activity:
$1,300,000 to Texas Biomedical Research Institute, San Antonio, TX, 2012. For monodelphis breeding and construction of lab.
$1,000,000 to University of Texas M.D. Anderson Cancer Center, Houston, TX, 2012. For research.
$1,000,000 to Vanderbilt-Ingram Cancer Center, Nashville, TN, 2012. For imaging advances for early detection of cancer.
$875,000 to King High Historical Foundation, Kingsville, TX, 2012. For King School Project.
$600,000 to Teach for America, New York, NY, 2012. For Lower Rio Grande Valley.
$600,000 to Witte Museum, San Antonio, TX, 2012. For South Texas Heritage Center.
$500,000 to CHRISTUS Spohn Hospital Kleberg, Kingsville, TX, 2012. For renovations to emergency department.
$400,000 to Memorial Sloan-Kettering Cancer Center, New York, NY, 2012. For brain tumor research.
$250,000 to Foxcroft School, Middleburg, VA, 2012. For STEM Program.
$25,000 to Texas State Historical Association, Denton, TX, 2012. For operating support.

8963
Caesar Kleberg Foundation for Wildlife Conservation ✧
P.O. Box 911
Kingsville, TX 78364-0911 (361) 592-8501
Contact: Stephen J. Kleberg, Tr.

Trust established about 1951 in TX.
Donor: Caesar Kleberg†.
Foundation type: Independent foundation.
Financial data (yr. ended 12/31/12): Assets, $53,268,834 (M); gifts received, $4,000; expenditures, $2,726,988; qualifying distributions, $2,244,849; giving activities include $2,113,000 for 3 grants (high: $2,098,000; low: $5,000).
Purpose and activities: Giving primarily for wildlife conservation and studies.
Fields of interest: Higher education; Animals/wildlife, research; Animals/wildlife, preservation/protection.
Limitations: Giving in the U.S., with emphasis on TX. No grants to individuals, or for building or endowment funds, scholarships, fellowships, or matching gifts; no loans.
Application information: Application form not required.
Initial approach: Letter on organization's letterhead
Copies of proposal: 3
Deadline(s): None
Board meeting date(s): As required
Final notification: 3 months
Trustees: Chris Kleberg; Stephen J. Kleberg; Dr. Duane M. Leach.
EIN: 746038766

8964
Kleinheinz Family Endowment for the Arts ✧
301 Commerce St., Ste. 1900
Fort Worth, TX 76102-3021
Application address: c/o James K. Phillips, 209 W. 2nd St., Ste. 308, Fort Worth, TX 76102, tel.: (682) 747-5656

Established in TX.
Donors: John B. Kleinheinz; Marsha Kleinheinz.
Foundation type: Independent foundation.
Financial data (yr. ended 12/31/13): Assets, $129,202,435 (M); gifts received, $16,155,314; expenditures, $8,349,584; qualifying distributions, $6,804,700; giving activities include $6,650,000 for 17 grants (high: $2,000,000; low: $20,000).
Fields of interest: Arts, cultural/ethnic awareness; Higher education, university; Education; Catholic agencies & churches.
Limitations: Applications accepted. Giving primarily in OR and TX. No grants to individuals.
Application information:
Initial approach: Proposal
Deadline(s): June 1 or Nov. 1
Officers and Directors:* Marsha Kleinheinz,* Pres.; James K. Phillips, C.F.O.; Peter Philpott,* V.P.; Jay Herd; Peter Mesrobian.
EIN: 261631057
Selected grants: The following grants are a representative sample of this grantmaker's funding activity:
$100,000 to Van Cliburn Foundation, Fort Worth, TX, 2012. For Cash Grant for the Endowment.
$30,000 to Jesuit High School, Portland, OR, 2012. For Cash Grant for the Jesuit Endowment.

8965
Knobloch Family Foundation ✧
2411 Stanmore Dr.
Houston, TX 77019-3423

Established in TX.
Donors: Carl W. Knobloch, Jr.; Carla Knobloch; Emily Knobloch; Eleanor Knobloch Ratchford.
Foundation type: Independent foundation.
Financial data (yr. ended 12/31/12): Assets, $73,245,693 (M); expenditures, $5,479,641; qualifying distributions, $4,858,291; giving activities include $4,858,291 for grants.
Fields of interest: Education; Environment, natural resources; Environment, land resources; Environment; Hospitals (general); Medical research, institute.
Limitations: Applications not accepted. Giving primarily in CT, Washington, DC, MA, and WY. No grants to individuals.
Application information: Contributes only to pre-selected organizations.
Officers: Carl W. Knobloch, Jr., Pres. and Treas.; Emily C. Knobloch, V.P. and Secy.
Directors: Carla Knobloch; Emily J. Knobloch; Eleanor Knobloch Ratchford; Stevens Sharkey.
EIN: 760538135
Selected grants: The following grants are a representative sample of this grantmaker's funding activity:
$2,725,000 to Yale University, School of Forestry and Environment, New Haven, CT, 2011.
$1,021,000 to Brigham and Women's Hospital, Boston, MA, 2011. For research.
$410,000 to Atlanta International School, Atlanta, GA, 2011.
$250,000 to Nature Conservancy of Montana, Helena, MT, 2011.
$250,000 to Trust for Public Land, San Francisco, CA, 2011.
$116,000 to Trust for Public Land, Tallahassee, FL, 2011.
$100,000 to University of Wyoming, Laramie, WY, 2011.
$100,000 to Yale University, New Haven, CT, 2011.
$50,000 to Sand County Foundation, Madison, WI, 2011.
$20,000 to Saint Johns Medical Center Foundation, Jackson, WY, 2011.

8966
The Kodosky Foundation ✧
22 Cousteau Ln.
Austin, TX 78746-3126

Established in 1996 in TX.
Donors: Gail T. Kodosky; Jeffrey L. Kodosky.
Foundation type: Independent foundation.
Financial data (yr. ended 12/31/13): Assets, $7,120,915 (M); expenditures, $1,593,286; qualifying distributions, $1,559,861; giving activities include $1,557,836 for 30 grants (high: $535,000; low: $1,000).
Fields of interest: Museums (children's); Performing arts; Arts; Higher education.
Type of support: General/operating support; Continuing support; Annual campaigns; Capital campaigns; Building/renovation; Endowments; Program development; Conferences/seminars; Seed money; Curriculum development; Scholarship funds; Matching/challenge support.
Limitations: Applications not accepted. Giving primarily in TX, with great emphasis on Austin; some giving also in NY. No grants to individuals.
Application information: Contributes only to pre-selected organizations.
Officers and Directors:* Jeffrey L. Kodosky,* Pres. and Treas.; Gail T. Kodosky,* V.P. and Secy.; Karen Kodosky Tips; Laura L. Walterman.
EIN: 742802674

8967
The Kohl Family Foundation ✧
(formerly The Nicole F. and Atlee M. Kohl Family Foundation)
4400 State Hwy. 360
Grapevine, TX 76051-6754

Established in 1982.
Donors: Atlee Kohl; Nicole F. Kohl; Stewart Siebens; Clayton Kohl; Barbara Kohl; Carol Fullinwider†; Carol Fullinwider Trust.
Foundation type: Independent foundation.
Financial data (yr. ended 11/30/13): Assets, $31,012,551 (M); gifts received, $70,790; expenditures, $1,348,031; qualifying distributions, $1,089,571; giving activities include $645,490 for 57 grants (high: $45,000; low: $3,000).
Purpose and activities: Giving primarily for Christian organizations and missions, as well as for the arts and education.
Fields of interest: Museums; Performing arts, orchestras; Arts; Education; Christian agencies & churches.
Type of support: General/operating support; Continuing support.
Limitations: Applications not accepted. Giving primarily in the Dallas, TX, area. No grants to individuals.
Application information: Contributes only to pre-selected organizations.
Board meeting date(s): Mar. and Nov.
Officers and Directors:* Nicole F. Kohl, Pres.; Caroline Kohl,* V.P.; Clayton Kohl,* V.P.; Marian Kohl, V.P.; Atlee Kohl,* Treas.
EIN: 363214720
Selected grants: The following grants are a representative sample of this grantmaker's funding activity:
$86,000 to Covenant Church, Carrollton, TX, 2011. For general support.
$45,000 to Junior League of Dallas, Dallas, TX, 2011. For general support.
$20,000 to Baylor Health Care System, Dallas, TX, 2011. For general support.
$17,000 to Austin Street Center, Dallas, TX, 2011. For general support.
$16,000 to North Dallas Shared Ministries, Dallas, TX, 2011. For general support.
$15,000 to Bread Basket Ministries, Fort Worth, TX, 2011. For general support.
$15,000 to Dallas Symphony Orchestra, Dallas, TX, 2011. For general support.
$15,000 to Educational Concerns for Hunger Organization, North Fort Myers, FL, 2011. For general support.
$13,500 to National Center for Policy Analysis, Dallas, TX, 2011. For general support.
$11,000 to Mission Arlington, Arlington, TX, 2011. For general support.

8968
Kolitz Foundation Inc. ✧ ☆
425 W. Bitters
San Antonio, TX 78216-1604 (210) 493-7743
Contact: Robert Kolitz, Dir.

Established in 2005 in TX.
Donors: Robert Kolitz; Sandora Kolitz.
Foundation type: Independent foundation.
Financial data (yr. ended 12/31/13): Assets, $10,490 (M); gifts received, $430,000; expenditures, $440,307; qualifying distributions, $440,307; giving activities include $429,862 for 20 grants (high: $15,000; low: $5,000).
Purpose and activities: Giving primarily to Jewish agencies and temples, including a Jewish day school; funding also for health organizations and children, youth, and social services.
Fields of interest: Museums (art); Elementary/secondary education; Health organizations, association; Children/youth, services; Jewish federated giving programs; Jewish agencies & synagogues.
Limitations: Applications accepted. Giving primarily in San Antonio, TX.
Application information: Application form not required.
Initial approach: Proposal
Deadline(s): None
Directors: Robert Kolitz; Sandora Kolitz.
EIN: 412181211

8969
Harlan and Amy Korenvaes Family Foundation ✧
c/o Harlan B. Korenvaes
5423 Park Ln.
Dallas, TX 75220-2149

Established in 2000 in TX.
Donors: Harlan B. Korenvaes; Amy B. Korenvaes.
Foundation type: Independent foundation.
Financial data (yr. ended 12/31/12): Assets, $7,652,459 (M); expenditures, $553,343; qualifying distributions, $545,474; giving activities include $545,474 for grants.
Purpose and activities: Giving primarily for higher education.
Fields of interest: Higher education, university; Hospitals (specialty); Cancer.
Limitations: Applications not accepted. Giving primarily in NY, with emphasis on Ithaca; giving also in Dallas, TX. No grants to individuals.
Application information: Contributes only to pre-selected organizations.
Officers and Directors:* Harlan B. Korenvaes,* Chair. and Pres.; Amy B. Korenvaes,* Secy.; Harold Ames.
EIN: 752902691
Selected grants: The following grants are a representative sample of this grantmaker's funding activity:
$131,520 to Jewish Federation of Greater Dallas, Dallas, TX, 2011.
$110,000 to Southern Methodist University, Dallas, TX, 2011.
$25,000 to Capital for Kids, Dallas, TX, 2011.
$20,000 to Jewish Community Center of Dallas, Dallas, TX, 2011.
$10,000 to Cornell University, Ithaca, NY, 2011.
$1,000 to Dallas Jewish Community Foundation, Dallas, TX, 2011.

8970
Albert & Bessie Mae Kronkosky Charitable Foundation ✧
112 E. Pecan, Ste. 830
San Antonio, TX 78205-1574 (210) 475-9000
Contact: Palmer Moe, Managing Dir.
FAX: (210) 354-2204;
E-mail: kronfndn@kronkosky.org; Additional tel.: (888) 309-9001; Main URL: http://www.kronkosky.org
Evaluation: http://www.kronkosky.org/pages/evaluation-main.html
Grants Database: http://www.kronkosky.org/grants
Research: http://www.kronkosky.org/pages/research.html

Established in 1991 in TX.
Donors: Albert Kronkosky, Jr.†; Bessie Mae Kronkosky†.
Foundation type: Independent foundation.
Financial data (yr. ended 12/31/12): Assets, $335,330,549 (M); gifts received, $9,663; expenditures, $17,784,650; qualifying distributions, $16,000,175; giving activities include $14,966,107 for 166 grants (high: $1,000,000; low: $2,150), and $125,892 for 2 foundation-administered programs.
Purpose and activities: To produce profound good that is tangible and measurable in Bandera, Bexar, Comal, and Kendall counties in Texas by implementing the Kronkosky's charitable purposes.
Fields of interest: Arts, multipurpose centers/programs; Museums; Libraries (public); Animal welfare; Animals/wildlife, sanctuaries; Zoos/zoological societies; Medical research, institute; Crime/violence prevention, child abuse; Recreation, parks/playgrounds; Youth development, centers/clubs; Family services, parent education; Aging.
Type of support: General/operating support; Continuing support; Management development/capacity building; Building/renovation; Equipment; Land acquisition; Endowments; Debt reduction; Emergency funds; Program development; Seed money; Research; Technical assistance; Consulting services; Program evaluation; Matching/challenge support.
Limitations: Applications accepted. Giving limited to Bandera, Bexar, Comal, and Kendall counties, TX. No support for religious or political activities, private or public education, or for economic development. No grants to individuals, scholarships, capital grants annual funds, or for galas and other events.
Publications: Application guidelines; Annual report; Grants list.
Application information: Letters of Inquiry are only accepted from 501(c)(3) nonprofit organizations that are GuideStar Exchange Program Members, a free service of GuideStar www.guidestar.org The foundation has currently suspended awarding any capital grants, and will focus on program operations grants. Proposal package supplied with acceptance of letter of inquiry. See foundation's web site for more detailed information. Application form required.
Initial approach: Letter of Inquiry
Copies of proposal: 2
Deadline(s): See foundation website for current details
Board meeting date(s): 6 times annually
Final notification: Within 10 days of receipt of letter of inquiry and within 1 week of Dist. Comm. meeting, upon decision
Officer: Palmer Moe, Managing Dir.
Trustee: Bank of America, N.A.
Number of staff: 2 full-time professional; 1 part-time professional; 2 full-time support; 1 part-time support.
EIN: 746385152
Selected grants: The following grants are a representative sample of this grantmaker's funding activity:
$1,000,000 to San Antonio Food Bank, San Antonio, TX, 2012. For Facility Expansion.
$750,000 to Texas Biomedical Research Institute, San Antonio, TX, 2012. For Enhancing the Vision campaign.
$550,000 to San Antonio Area Foundation, San Antonio, TX, 2012. For Human Services Fund.
$500,000 to Haven for Hope of Bexar County, San Antonio, TX, 2012. For Prospect Courtyard infirmary.
$500,000 to University of Texas Foundation, Austin, TX, 2012. For CTRC's Cancer Prevention and Population Science Research Program.
$250,000 to Guadalupe Cultural Arts Center, San Antonio, TX, 2012. For Center Operations.
$75,000 to San Antonio Family Endeavors, San Antonio, TX, 2012. For Fairweather Family Lodge.
$50,000 to Medical Equipment Network for the Disabled, San Antonio, TX, 2012. For operations.
$50,000 to San Antonio Little Theater, San Antonio, TX, 2012. For Theater Operations.

8971
Ernest L. Kurth, Jr. Charitable Foundation ✧
P.O. Box 831041
Dallas, TX 75283-1041
Application address: c/o Wyatt Leinart, P.O. Box 1506, Lufkin, TX 75902-1506, tel.: (936) 632-6450

Established in 1983.
Donors: Ernest L. Kurth†; Lynn Fisher.
Foundation type: Independent foundation.
Financial data (yr. ended 12/31/13): Assets, $44,719,966 (M); expenditures, $2,545,450; qualifying distributions, $2,256,900; giving activities include $2,106,053 for 29 grants (high: $228,262; low: $8,000).
Purpose and activities: The foundation supports institutions and organizations that give promise of producing significant advances in the areas of education, health, community and social service, and cultural arts and the humanities.
Fields of interest: Museums; Education; Human services; Family services; Community/economic development; Government/public administration.
Limitations: Applications accepted. Giving primarily in Angelina County, TX. No grants to individuals.
Application information: Application form required.
Initial approach: Contact foundation for application form
Deadline(s): None
Advisors: Bob Brown; J.C. Clement, Jr.; Lynn Fisher; Sandra G. Kurth; Thomas Moore; Charles W. Perry; Mary Ann Whitaker.
Trustees: Wyatt Leinart; Bank of America, N.A.
EIN: 751862248

8972
Mary Potishman Lard Trust ✧
c/o Walker Friedman
604 E. 4th St., Ste. 200
Fort Worth, TX 76102-4074 (817) 334-0144
Contact: Walker C. Friedman, Tr.

Trust established in 1968 in TX.
Donor: Mary P. Lard‡.
Foundation type: Independent foundation.
Financial data (yr. ended 12/31/13): Assets, $34,451,143 (M); expenditures, $1,505,815; qualifying distributions, $1,279,532; giving activities include $1,254,500 for 85 grants (high: $100,000; low: $1,000).
Fields of interest: Performing arts, orchestras; Arts; Higher education; Education; Health care; Youth development; Human services; Children/youth, services; Christian agencies & churches.
Limitations: Applications accepted. Giving primarily in TX, with emphasis on Fort Worth. No grants to individuals.
Application information: Application form required.
Initial approach: Proposal
Deadline(s): None
Trustees: Alan D. Friedman; Walker C. Friedman.
Number of staff: 1 full-time professional.
EIN: 756210697
Selected grants: The following grants are a representative sample of this grantmaker's funding activity:
$5,000 to Camp Fire USA, Fort Worth, TX, 2012. For program support.

8973
Lawrence Family Foundation ✧
P.O. Box 1343
Houston, TX 77251-1343

Established in 2003 in TX.
Donors: Charles Berdon Lawrence, Jr.; Rolanette Lawrence.
Foundation type: Independent foundation.
Financial data (yr. ended 12/31/13): Assets, $4,023,627 (M); expenditures, $1,059,418; qualifying distributions, $1,025,648; giving activities include $1,025,648 for 23 grants (high: $500,000; low: $250).
Fields of interest: Museums (art); Higher education; Business school/education; Education; Medical research; Community/economic development; Foundations (private grantmaking).
Limitations: Applications not accepted. Giving primarily in Houston, TX. No grants to individuals.
Application information: Contributes only to pre-selected organizations.
Officers: Charles Berdon Lawrence, Pres.; Rolanette Lawrence, Exec. V.P.; Heather L. Mitchell, V.P.
EIN: 200054871
Selected grants: The following grants are a representative sample of this grantmaker's funding activity:
$5,000 to Texas Heart Institute, Houston, TX, 2012. For The Cooley Circle.
$3,000 to American Diabetes Association, Houston, TX, 2012. For Per Mark Lawrence.
$2,250 to Houston Arboretum and Nature Center, Houston, TX, 2012. For Rachel and Mark Lawrence.
$1,000 to Galveston Bay Foundation, Webster, TX, 2012. For annual dues.
$1,000 to Katy Prairie Conservancy, Houston, TX, 2012. For Donating to 20th Anniversary Gala - Charles.
$1,000 to Museum of Fine Arts, Houston, Houston, TX, 2012.
$1,000 to Texas A & M Foundation, College Station, TX, 2012. For In honor of Rudy Teichman.
$1,000 to Yellowstone Academy, Houston, TX, 2012. For Per Heather Mitchell in honor of Ann Marie Wood.
$500 to Still Water Christian Ministries, Boerne, TX, 2012. For Charles and Megan Lawrence.

8974
Geraldine G. Lawson Charitable Trust ✧
7809 Broadway St.
San Antonio, TX 78209-2558

Foundation type: Independent foundation.
Financial data (yr. ended 12/31/13): Assets, $34,553,346 (M); expenditures, $3,272,244; qualifying distributions, $2,429,919; giving activities include $2,429,919 for 2 grants (high: $1,943,935; low: $485,984).
Fields of interest: Museums (art); Zoos/zoological societies.
Limitations: Applications not accepted. Giving primarily in San Antonio, TX.
Application information: Contributes only to pre-selected organizations.
Trustee: Herbert H. Hahn, Jr.
EIN: 742802237
Selected grants: The following grants are a representative sample of this grantmaker's funding activity:
$455,807 to San Antonio Zoological Society, San Antonio, TX, 2011.
$375,792 to San Antonio Zoological Society, San Antonio, TX, 2010.

8975
Lebowitz-Aberly Family Foundation ✧
P.O. Box 670504
Dallas, TX 75367-0504

Donors: Laurence H. Lebowitz; Naomi D. Aberly.
Foundation type: Independent foundation.
Financial data (yr. ended 12/31/12): Assets, $34,441,323 (M); gifts received, $50,000; expenditures, $1,302,995; qualifying distributions, $1,140,000; giving activities include $1,140,000 for 8 grants (high: $500,000; low: $5,000).
Fields of interest: Elementary/secondary education; Higher education; Human services.
Limitations: Applications not accepted. Giving primarily in MA and TX.
Application information: Contributes only to pre-selected organizations.
Officers and Directors:* Laurence H. Lebowitz,* Pres. and Treas.; Naomi D. Aberly,* V.P. and Secy.; Kathleen J. Wu.
EIN: 263931946

8976
Leducq Foundation for Cardiovascular Research ✧ ☆
800 Gessner Rd., Ste. 1260
Houston, TX 77024-4273

Established in 2012 in TX.
Donor: Harrisville Enterprises SA.
Foundation type: Independent foundation.
Financial data (yr. ended 12/31/12): Assets, $35,017,116 (M); gifts received, $53,177,775; expenditures, $18,960,651; qualifying distributions, $18,492,500; giving activities include $18,492,500 for 1 grant.
Purpose and activities: Giving primarily to combat cardiovascular and neurovascular disease.
Fields of interest: Heart & circulatory research; Neuroscience research.
Limitations: Applications not accepted. Giving primarily in Paris, France.
Application information: Contributes only to pre-selected organizations.
Officers: David Tancredi, Pres.; Martin Landaluce, V.P.; James Floyd, Secy.-Treas.
EIN: 454696263

8977
Quincy and Estine Lee Charitable Fund ✧ ☆
P.O. Box 2950, Tax Dept. T-8
San Antonio, TX 78299-2950

Established in TX.
Donor: Estine Lee‡.
Foundation type: Independent foundation.
Financial data (yr. ended 06/30/13): Assets, $6,409,781 (M); gifts received, $3,313; expenditures, $1,159,125; qualifying distributions, $1,115,180; giving activities include $1,097,650 for 10 grants (high: $400,000; low: $1,250).
Fields of interest: Education; Health care; Human services.
Limitations: Applications not accepted. Giving primarily in MA and TX.
Application information: Unsolicited requests for funds not accepted.
Trustee: Frost Bank.
EIN: 616434862

8978
The Legett Foundation ✧
P.O. Box 176
Abilene, TX 79604-0176 (325) 673-6429
Contact: Kade L. Matthews, Chair. and Pres.

Established in 1996 in TX.
Donors: Kade L. Matthews; Julia Jones Matthews; Dodge Jones Foundation.
Foundation type: Independent foundation.
Financial data (yr. ended 12/31/12): Assets, $64,420,377 (M); gifts received, $36,085; expenditures, $3,689,760; qualifying distributions, $3,000,093; giving activities include $2,931,197 for 83 grants (high: $750,000; low: $250).
Fields of interest: Education, management/technical assistance; Higher education; Education; Human services.
Limitations: Applications accepted. Giving primarily in TX.
Application information: Application form required.
Initial approach: Letter
Deadline(s): None
Officers and Directors:* Kade L. Matthews,* Chair. and Pres.; Joseph E. Cannon,* Exec. V.P. and Exec. Dir.; Thomas R. Allen, V.P. and C.F.O.; Lawrence E. Gill, V.P.; Linda S. Buckner, Secy.-Treas.; John A. Matthews, Jr.
EIN: 752696419
Selected grants: The following grants are a representative sample of this grantmaker's funding activity:
$210,000 to Texas Christian University, Fort Worth, TX, 2012. For Educational/Scholarship Ranch Management Consult Pram K.
$150,000 to Hendrick Medical Center Foundation, Abilene, TX, 2012. For Educational/Texas Tech School of Nursing.

$100,000 to Texas Christian University, Fort Worth, TX, 2012. For Educational/Endowed Scholarship for Middle Income Students.
$50,000 to Texas Tech University, Lubbock, TX, 2012. For Educational/Institute for the Study of Western Civilization.
$35,000 to Texas Christian University, Fort Worth, TX, 2012. For Educational/Student-At Scholarship Program.
$25,000 to Wayland Baptist University, Plainview, TX, 2012. For educational/volleyball program.
$10,000 to Texas Tech University, Lubbock, TX, 2012. For educational/football program.
$5,000 to Johns Hopkins University, Baltimore, MD, 2012. For Education/Brady Urological Institute Operating Support.
$5,000 to Texas Christian University, Fort Worth, TX, 2012. For Educational/Leap-Frog for Kinderfrogs.
$5,000 to Texas Tech University Health Sciences Center, Lubbock, TX, 2012. For Educational/Power of the Purse.

8979
Martha, David & Bagby Lennox Foundation ✧

P.O. Box 188
Paris, TX 75461-0188
Contact: William P. Streng, Pres.
Application email: submit@mdblf.org; Main URL: http://www.mdblf.org

Established in 1985 in TX.
Donors: Martha Lennox†; David Lennox†; Bagby Lennox†.
Foundation type: Independent foundation.
Financial data (yr. ended 12/31/12): Assets, $15,612,997 (M); expenditures, $906,363; qualifying distributions, $608,018; giving activities include $530,661 for 27 grants (high: $113,500; low: $5,000).
Purpose and activities: Giving primarily for education, the environment, and children, youth and social services.
Fields of interest: Higher education; Education; Environment, natural resources; Human services; Children/youth, services.
Limitations: Applications accepted. Giving primarily in the northeast TX area. No grants to individuals.
Publications: Application guidelines.
Application information: See foundation web site for complete application guidelines. Application form required.
Initial approach: Letter or e-mail
Deadline(s): Oct. 31
Board meeting date(s): Varies
Officers and Directors:* William P. Streng,* Pres. and Treas.; Sam L. Hocker,* V.P. and Secy.; Mary W. Clark, V.P.
EIN: 760157945

8980
Lesley Family Foundation, Inc. ✧

c/o Bank of America, N.A.
P.O. Box 831041
Dallas, TX 75283-1041
Application address: c/o Debra Phares, Bank of America, N.A., 901 Main St., 19 Fl., Dallas, TX 75202-3714

Established in 2001 in TX.
Donors: Sarah A. Lesley Charitable Trust; Hattie Mae Lesley†.
Foundation type: Independent foundation.
Financial data (yr. ended 12/31/13): Assets, $12,006,102 (M); gifts received, $847,380; expenditures, $487,385; qualifying distributions, $471,151; giving activities include $460,000 for 6 grants (high: $130,000; low: $20,000).
Fields of interest: Higher education; Animals/wildlife; Food banks; Youth development, centers/clubs.
Limitations: Applications accepted. Giving primarily in TX. No grants to individuals.
Application information: Application form required.
Initial approach: Contact foundation for application form
Deadline(s): None
Directors: Sarah A. Keeyes; Joseph D. Lesley; Sammy Joe Ramsey.
Trustee: Bank of America, N.A.
EIN: 752936755
Selected grants: The following grants are a representative sample of this grantmaker's funding activity:
$200,000 to Texas Christian University, Fort Worth, TX, 2012. For TBRI Evaluation Study-Institute/Child Development.
$30,000 to North Texas Food Bank, Dallas, TX, 2012. To support Food 4 Kids ' Backpack Program'.
$20,000 to Promise House, Dallas, TX, 2012. For Project Bed Night - Emergency Youth Shelter.

8981
The Levant Foundation ✧

c/o JPMorgan Chase Tower
600 Travis St., Ste. 6800
Houston, TX 77002-3010 (713) 222-6900
FAX: (713) 222-1614; Main URL: http://www.thelevantfoundation.org/

Established in 1999 in TX.
Donors: Jamal Daniel; Rania Daniel.
Foundation type: Independent foundation.
Financial data (yr. ended 12/31/13): Assets, $9,124 (M); gifts received, $8,235,000; expenditures, $8,262,371; qualifying distributions, $8,262,371; giving activities include $8,080,665 for 8 grants (high: $7,000,000; low: $5,000).
Fields of interest: Arts, cultural/ethnic awareness; Higher education, university; Education; Foundations (community).
Limitations: Applications not accepted. Giving primarily in Washington, DC, New York, NY, and Houston, TX; some giving in Geneva, Switzerland. No grants to individuals.
Application information: Contributes only to pre-selected organizations.
Officers and Directors:* Pamela E. Powers,* Chair. and Pres.; Michelle Upton, V.P.; Bernice Holland, Secy.; Deb Loscuito, Treas.; Sonny Hudson, Exec. Dir.; Toufic Chahine; John M. Howland.
EIN: 311637973

8982
Joe Levit Family Foundation ✧

P.O. Box 14200
Houston, TX 77221-4200

Established in 1968 in TX.
Donors: Max S. Levit; Milton H. Levit; The Grocers Supply Co., Inc.
Foundation type: Independent foundation.
Financial data (yr. ended 12/31/13): Assets, $21,881,659 (M); expenditures, $1,158,682; qualifying distributions, $982,183; giving activities include $982,183 for 28 grants (high: $25,000; low: $100).
Purpose and activities: Support primarily for Jewish organizations and temples; funding also for higher and other education, children and family services, the arts, social services, and health associations.
Fields of interest: Arts; Elementary/secondary education; Higher education; Education; Hospitals (general); Health organizations, association; Human services; Children/youth, services; Family services; Aging, centers/services; Jewish federated giving programs; Jewish agencies & synagogues.
Limitations: Applications not accepted. Giving primarily in Houston, TX. No grants to individuals.
Application information: Contributes only to pre-selected organizations.
Directors: Leah S. Levit; Max S. Levit; Rochelle Levit; Jan Levit Silver.
EIN: 746103403

8983
Liatis Foundation ✧

c/o Steven J. Borick
2707 Kipling St.
Houston, TX 77098-1214

Established in 1993 in TX.
Donor: Juanita A. Borick.
Foundation type: Independent foundation.
Financial data (yr. ended 12/31/13): Assets, $10,588,379 (M); expenditures, $635,592; qualifying distributions, $580,000; giving activities include $580,000 for 53 grants (high: $50,000; low: $1,000).
Fields of interest: Arts; Education; Hospitals (specialty); Human services; Children/youth, services; Religion.
Type of support: Annual campaigns; Capital campaigns; Building/renovation; Professorships; Fellowships; Scholarship funds; Matching/challenge support.
Limitations: Applications not accepted. Giving primarily in CA, CO, NV, and TX. No grants to individuals.
Application information: Unsolicted requests for funds not accepted.
Officers: Steven James Borick, Pres.; Linda Susan Borick, Secy.
Directors: Juanita A. Borick; Robert Allen Borick; Lauren B. Davidson.
Number of staff: 1 part-time professional; 1 part-time support.
EIN: 760420275

8984
Jack H. & William M. Light Charitable Trust ✧

P.O. Box 17001-Trust
San Antonio, TX 78217-0001
Main URL: http://broadwaybank.com/wealthmanagement/FoundationWilliamMLight.html

Established in 1998 in TX.
Donors: Jack H. Light†; William M. Light†; William M. Light Community Property Trust.
Foundation type: Independent foundation.

Financial data (yr. ended 12/31/12): Assets, $9,730,605 (M); expenditures, $547,514; qualifying distributions, $499,296; giving activities include $460,000 for 42 grants (high: $35,000; low: $2,500).
Purpose and activities: Giving primarily for health and human services for the benefit of children.
Fields of interest: Human services.
Type of support: Continuing support; Annual campaigns; Capital campaigns; Building/renovation; Equipment; Endowments; Emergency funds; Program development; Curriculum development; Research.
Limitations: Applications accepted. Giving primarily in Houston and San Antonio, TX. No grants to individuals.
Application information: See foundation website for complete application guidelines. Application form required.
Deadline(s): Apr. 30 and Oct. 31
Final notification: June and Dec.
Trustee: Broadway National Bank, N.A.
EIN: 742874941
Selected grants: The following grants are a representative sample of this grantmaker's funding activity:
$40,000 to Cal Ripken, Sr. Foundation, Baltimore, MD, 2011.

8985
Larry Lightner Sams Foundation, Inc. ✧
16800 Dallas Pkwy., Ste. 218
Dallas, TX 75248-6796 (972) 458-8811
Contact: Larry Lightner, Tr.

Established in 1994 in TX.
Foundation type: Independent foundation.
Financial data (yr. ended 12/31/12): Assets, $12,385,955 (M); expenditures, $796,840; qualifying distributions, $621,653; giving activities include $505,580 for 42 grants (high: $40,000; low: $500).
Fields of interest: Education; Health organizations, association; Medical research, institute; Human services; Children/youth, services; Community/economic development; Children/youth; Aging; Women.
Type of support: General/operating support; Annual campaigns; Capital campaigns; Building/renovation; Equipment; Debt reduction; Program development; Research; Matching/challenge support.
Limitations: Applications not accepted. Giving primarily in Dallas, TX. No support for political organizations. No grants to individuals, or for fundraisers.
Application information: Unsolicited requests for funds not accepted; applications are by trustee invitation only.
Board meeting date(s): Late Mar., late July, and late Nov.
Trustees: Charles Derek Adleta; Larry Lightner; Sue B. Lightner; Kamala Lightner Scammahorn.
Number of staff: 1 full-time professional; 1 part-time professional; 1 full-time support.
EIN: 752555622
Selected grants: The following grants are a representative sample of this grantmaker's funding activity:
$40,000 to Southern Methodist University, Department of Physics, Dallas, TX, 2012. For Graduate Fellowships; Distinguished Physics Professors Visitor Program; Research; 2012 Lecture; Outreach Programs.
$30,000 to Brook Hill School, Bullard, TX, 2012. For Purchase of Interactive Whiteboard technology systems and teacher training for academic classrooms.
$20,000 to Galaxy Counseling Center, Garland, TX, 2012. For Child and Family Counseling Program expenses.
$20,000 to Mental Health America of Greater Dallas, Dallas, TX, 2012. For education and advocacy Programs.
$15,000 to Family Place, Dallas, TX, 2012. For Operating expenses of Children's Educational Services at Safe Campus.
$15,000 to Senior Source, Dallas, TX, 2012. For Senior companions and/or Ombudsmen Program expenses.
$12,000 to Gleaning Network of Texas, Dallas, TX, 2012. For programs' expenses.
$10,000 to Crossroads Community Services, Dallas, TX, 2012. For Operating costs of Community Distribution Partners sites for food distribution and health education workshops.
$10,000 to Metrocare Services, Dallas, TX, 2012. For Renovations at Career Design and Development Services Center in Dallas, TX.
$10,000 to Wilkinson Center, Dallas, TX, 2012. For Food Pantry Program expenses.

8986
The Link Foundation ✧ ☆
401 Congress Ave., Ste. 2424
Austin, TX 78701-3711 (512) 480-0010
Contact: Joe W. Bratcher III, Pres. and Treas.

Established in 1985 in TX.
Donors: Joe W. Bratcher III; Joe W. Bratcher, Jr.
Foundation type: Independent foundation.
Financial data (yr. ended 12/31/13): Assets, $4,448,632 (M); expenditures, $466,238; qualifying distributions, $429,259; giving activities include $425,195 for 19 grants (high: $66,666; low: $5,000).
Purpose and activities: Giving primarily for human services, health care, and relief organizations.
Fields of interest: Arts; Health care; Human services.
Limitations: Applications accepted. Giving primarily in Austin, TX. No grants to individuals.
Application information: Application form required.
Initial approach: Proposal
Deadline(s): Sept. 30
Officers: Joe W. Bratcher III, Pres. and Treas.; Brigid Anne Cockrum, V.P. and Secy.
Director: Wendy Albrecht.
EIN: 742387802

8987
The Litman Foundation ✧
3010 Lyndon B. Johnson Freeway, Ste. 712
Dallas, TX 75234-7006
Contact: David S. Litman, Dir.; Malia A. Litman

Established in 2000 in TX.
Donors: David S. Litman; Malia A. Litman.
Foundation type: Independent foundation.
Financial data (yr. ended 12/31/13): Assets, $34,045,893 (M); expenditures, $2,169,592; qualifying distributions, $2,045,307; giving activities include $2,042,300 for 4 grants (high: $2,035,000; low: $400).
Fields of interest: Health organizations; Human services; Foundations (community); Jewish agencies & synagogues.
Limitations: Applications accepted. Giving primarily in TX.
Application information: Application form not required.
Initial approach: Proposal
Deadline(s): None
Directors: Robert B. Diener; David S. Litman; Malia A. Litman.
EIN: 752892769

8988
Helen Irwin Littauer Educational Trust ✧ ☆
c/o Bank of America, N.A.
P.O. Box 831041
Dallas, TX 75283-1041
Contact: Mark J. Smith
E-mail: tx.philanthropic@ustrust.com; Main URL: http://www.bankofamerica.com/grantmaking

Established in 1969 in TX.
Foundation type: Independent foundation.
Financial data (yr. ended 04/30/13): Assets, $8,692,417 (M); expenditures, $688,688; qualifying distributions, $644,126; giving activities include $585,000 for 25 grants (high: $75,000; low: $5,000).
Purpose and activities: The trust is particularly interested in, but not limited to charitable organizations that focus on: scholarships that enable needy, but worthy boys and girls and young adults to attend school, college, or university, with a particular emphasis on making scholarships available for attending schools of journalism; promotion of art, education, and good citizenship; alleviating human suffering; medical care and treatment for all needy persons, including hospitals and clinics; providing care, education, recreation and/or physical training for needy, orphaned or disabled children; care of needy persons who are sick, aged or disabled; and improvement of living and working conditions of all persons.
Fields of interest: Performing arts; Performing arts, opera; Arts; Education; Health care; Housing/shelter; Youth development; Human services; Children/youth, services.
Type of support: General/operating support; Income development; Building/renovation; Program development; Matching/challenge support.
Limitations: Applications accepted. Giving primarily in Tarrant County, TX. No grants to individuals.
Application information: Application guidelines on Trust web site. Application form required.
Deadline(s): Mar. 31 and Sept. 30
Trustee: Bank of America, N.A.
EIN: 237029857
Selected grants: The following grants are a representative sample of this grantmaker's funding activity:
$30,000 to Harris Methodist Health Foundation, Fort Worth, TX, 2011. For the Puttin' on the Pink Presenting Sponsorship.
$30,000 to Presbyterian Night Shelter of Tarrant County, Fort Worth, TX, 2011. For the purpose of underwriting the PNS Christmas Gala.
$25,000 to CASA of Tarrant County, Fort Worth, TX, 2011. To recruit, supervise and train CASA volunteers.

$25,000 to Fort Worth Opera Association, Fort Worth, TX, 2011. For the purpose of being a Production Sponsor for Fort Worth Opera Festival. The purpose of this grant would be for the Fort Worth Opera to secure funding.
$25,000 to Helping Other People Excel Farm, Fort Worth, TX, 2011. For building a family life center.
$25,000 to River Legacy Foundation, Arlington, TX, 2011. For general operating support.
$25,000 to Texas Christian University, Fort Worth, TX, 2011. For a new convergence newsroom equipped with the latest technology at the Schieffer School of Journalism.
$25,000 to Texas Christian University, Fort Worth, TX, 2011. For a new convergence newsroom equipped with the latest technology at the Schieffer School of Journalism.
$20,000 to C.R. Smith Aviation Museum Foundation, Fort Worth, TX, 2011. For expansion of the children's area.
$10,000 to Junior Achievement of the Chisholm Trail, Fort Worth, TX, 2011. To support and maintenance of program services for students in the Fort Worth Independent School District.

8989
Live Oak Foundation ✧ ☆
1315 W. 10th St.
Fort Worth, TX 76102-3437

Established in TX.
Donors: Andrew Rector; Linda Rector; Jane Rector.
Foundation type: Independent foundation.
Financial data (yr. ended 12/31/12): Assets, $1,215,505 (M); gifts received, $449,849; expenditures, $548,764; qualifying distributions, $515,711; giving activities include $515,711 for grants.
Purpose and activities: Giving primarily for education, human services, and to a United Methodist church.
Fields of interest: Education; Human services; Community development, service clubs; Protestant agencies & churches.
Limitations: Applications not accepted. Giving primarily in Azle and Fort Worth, TX.
Application information: Unsolicited requests for funds not accepted.
Officer: Andrew Rector, Pres.
EIN: 300519320

8990
The Looper Foundation ✧
11757 Katy Freeway, Ste. 1400
Houston, TX 77079-1725

Established in 1997 in TX.
Donors: Doris Looper; Terry L. Looper; Kirkwood Realty.
Foundation type: Independent foundation.
Financial data (yr. ended 12/31/12): Assets, $53,274,874 (M); gifts received, $1,200,000; expenditures, $1,763,336; qualifying distributions, $1,392,822; giving activities include $1,296,870 for 39 grants (high: $229,000; low: $100).
Fields of interest: Theological school/education; Education; Recreation, camps; Youth development, religion; Human services; Children/youth, services; Christian agencies & churches; Protestant agencies & churches.
Limitations: Applications not accepted. Giving primarily in CO, FL, MO, PA and TX. No grants to individuals.
Application information: Unsolicited requests for funds not accepted.
Officers: Terry L. Looper, Pres.; Jeannie Looper Able, V.P.; Tanya Jean Pitre, Treas.; Doris Looper, Secy.
EIN: 760330594

8991
Carrie J. Loose Trust ✧
c/o Bank of America, N.A.
P.O. Box 831041
Dallas, TX 75283-1041

Trust established in 1927 in MO.
Donors: Harry Wilson Loose‡; Carrie J. Loose‡.
Foundation type: Independent foundation.
Financial data (yr. ended 12/31/13): Assets, $16,370,979 (M); expenditures, $859,339; qualifying distributions, $747,830; giving activities include $645,000 for 5 grants (high: $300,000; low: $25,000).
Purpose and activities: Grants to established local educational, health, and welfare institutions; support for research into the community's social and cultural needs and for experimental and demonstration projects.
Fields of interest: Arts education; Higher education; Libraries (public); Hospitals (general); Human services; Foundations (community).
Limitations: Giving limited to Kansas City, MO. No grants to individuals, business start-up or reduction, or annual appeals.
Application information:
Board meeting date(s): Quarterly
Trustee: Bank of America, N.A.
Number of staff: 43
EIN: 446009246
Selected grants: The following grants are a representative sample of this grantmaker's funding activity:
$140,000 to Kansas City Public Library, Kansas City, MO, 2012. For Raising a Community of Readers' Program.

8992
Grogan Lord Foundation ✧ ☆
P.O. Box 649
Georgetown, TX 78627-0649 (512) 863-2594
Contact: R. Griffin Lord, Pres.

Established in 1992 in TX.
Donors: Sharon Lord Daggett; R. Griffin Lord; W. Grogan Lord‡; Ruth Joyce Hite; Grogan Lord Irrevocable Trust.
Foundation type: Independent foundation.
Financial data (yr. ended 12/31/13): Assets, $7,309,130 (M); expenditures, $1,950,023; qualifying distributions, $1,937,910; giving activities include $1,937,910 for 6 grants (high: $1,712,910; low: $25,000).
Fields of interest: Higher education; Human services.
Limitations: Applications accepted. Giving primarily in TX.
Application information: Application form required.
Initial approach: Contact foundation for application form
Deadline(s): None
Officers: R. Griffin Lord, Pres.; Sharon Lord Daggett, V.P. and Secy.-Treas.
EIN: 742623948

8993
Lowe Foundation ✧
2630 Exposition Blvd., Ste. G-14
Austin, TX 78703-1757 (512) 322-0041
Contact: Clayton Maebius, Tr.
FAX: (512) 322-0061;
E-mail: info@thelowefoundation.org; Main URL: http://www.thelowefoundation.org

Established in 1988 in TX.
Donors: Erma Lowe‡; Maralo, Inc.; Mary Ralph Lowe; Erma Lowe Charitable Trust.
Foundation type: Independent foundation.
Financial data (yr. ended 12/31/13): Assets, $55,649,105 (M); gifts received, $1,315,167; expenditures, $2,423,071; qualifying distributions, $2,214,000; giving activities include $2,214,000 for 91 grants (high: $250,000; low: $1,000).
Purpose and activities: Grant requests are limited to programs and projects benefitting the critical needs of at-risk women and children in TX.
Fields of interest: Human services; Children/youth, services; Family services; Women, centers/services; Women.
Type of support: General/operating support; Capital campaigns; Building/renovation; Professorships; Research.
Limitations: Applications accepted. Giving limited to the Dallas-Fort Worth and Austin-San Antonio, TX, areas. No grants to individuals.
Publications: Application guidelines; Grants list.
Application information: Application guidelines and pre-proposal form available on foundation web site. All requests are pre-screened to evaluate whether the project falls within the foundation's guidelines. If a project meets the criteria, then a full written proposal will be requested by the foundation. Application form required.
Initial approach: Submit pre-proposal application
Copies of proposal: 1
Deadline(s): Pre-proposal by Dec. 1; full application by Dec. 31
Board meeting date(s): Apr.
Final notification: Funding occurs in May
Officers and Trustees:* Mary Ralph Lowe,* Pres.; Diana Strauss,* V.P.; Clayton Yost, Secy.; Geoffrey Perrin, Treas.; Patricia Morrison; Samantha Pace.
Number of staff: None.
EIN: 760262645

8994
Lubbock Area Foundation, Inc. ✧
2509 80th St.
Lubbock, TX 79423 (806) 762-8061
Contact: For grants: Michelle Tosi-Stephens, Dir., Grants and Scholarships
FAX: (806) 762-8551;
E-mail: contact@lubbockareafoundation.org; Grant inquiry e-mail: michelle@lubbockareafoundation.org; Main URL: http://www.lubbockareafoundation.org
Facebook: http://www.facebook.com/pages/Lubbock-Area-Foundation/171261678910
Google Plus: https://plus.google.com/+LubbockAreaFoundationOrg/about?hl=en
Pinterest: http://www.pinterest.com/LubbockAreaFdn/

Twitter: https://twitter.com/LubbockAreaFdn
YouTube: https://www.youtube.com/channel/UCwjoh29CMtmkUvfoWhZPSzA/feed

Incorporated in 1980 in TX.
Foundation type: Community foundation.
Financial data (yr. ended 12/31/12): Assets, $28,748,043 (M); gifts received, $2,526,048; expenditures, $1,239,684; giving activities include $582,028 for 38+ grants (high: $70,000), and $109,613 for 64 grants to individuals.
Purpose and activities: The foundation is a permanent charitable institution dedicated to the South Plains community. Giving primarily for education, arts, environment, health, civic affairs, and social services.
Fields of interest: Historic preservation/historical societies; Arts; Adult education—literacy, basic skills & GED; Education, reading; Education; Environment; Animal welfare; Health care; Health organizations, association; Children/youth, services; Family services; Human services; Community/economic development.
Type of support: General/operating support; Continuing support; Capital campaigns; Building/renovation; Equipment; Emergency funds; Program development; Seed money; Scholarship funds; Matching/challenge support.
Limitations: Applications accepted. Giving limited to Lubbock, TX, and the surrounding South Plains counties. No grants to individuals (except for scholarships), or for debt retirement; no loans.
Publications: Application guidelines; Annual report; Financial statement; Grants list; Informational brochure; Newsletter.
Application information: Visit foundation web site for application form and guidelines. Application form required.
Initial approach: Submit application form
Copies of proposal: 12
Deadline(s): Feb. 1, May 1, Sept. 1 and Nov. 1 for Community Fund grants
Board meeting date(s): Jan., Mar., May, July, Sept., and Nov.
Final notification: 2 months
Officers and Directors:* Jeff Klotzman,* Chair.; Chad Grant, Chair.-Elect; Sheryl Cates,* Pres.; John Tye,* Secy.-Treas.; Cindy Whitehead, V.P., Donor Rels.; Rodney Cates; Abel Castro; James Conwright; Shirley Edwards; Linda Gaither; Christy Hartin; Robert Kollman; Eric McDonald; Mark Meurer; Mary Meyers; Tania Moody; Carlos Morales; Mack Owen; Jim Phillips; Norval Pollard; Tim Pridmore; Tony Privett; Don Rushing; Ted Rushing; Tim Sampson; Gwen Stafford; Ray Thornton; Cindy Whitehead; Diann Windham; Karen Worley.
Number of staff: 2 full-time professional; 2 part-time professional.
EIN: 751709180

8995
Rachel Lyman Charitable Trust ✧
c/o Bank of America, N.A.
P.O. Box 831041
Dallas, TX 75283-1041

Established in 2000 in TX.
Donor: Rachel Lyman†.
Foundation type: Independent foundation.
Financial data (yr. ended 07/31/13): Assets, $14,585,393 (M); expenditures, $738,451; qualifying distributions, $677,154; giving activities include $637,373 for 30 grants (high: $95,606; low: $1,275).
Purpose and activities: Giving primarily for health associations and human services, including services for people who are blind; funding also for higher education, children and youth services, including a children's hospital, and to Episcopal churches.
Fields of interest: Higher education; Hospitals (general); Hospitals (specialty); Health care; Health organizations, association; Medical research; Human services; Children, services; Independent living, disability; Protestant agencies & churches; Blind/visually impaired.
Type of support: General/operating support; Endowments; Scholarship funds.
Limitations: Applications not accepted. Giving primarily in TX, with emphasis on Midland. No grants to individuals.
Application information: Contributes only to pre-selected organizations.
Trustee: Bank of America, N.A.
EIN: 527114493
Selected grants: The following grants are a representative sample of this grantmaker's funding activity:
$89,760 to University of the South, Sewanee, TN, 2011. For unrestricted contribution.
$59,840 to Guide Dogs for the Blind, San Rafael, CA, 2011. For unrestricted contribution.
$59,840 to High Sky Childrens Ranch, Midland, TX, 2011. For unrestricted contribution.
$59,840 to Saint Jude Childrens Research Hospital, Memphis, TN, 2011. For unrestricted contribution.
$59,840 to West Texas Boys Ranch, San Angelo, TX, 2011.
$35,904 to Saint Lukes Episcopal Hospital, Houston, TX, 2011. For unrestricted contribution.
$24,534 to Midland College Foundation, Midland, TX, 2011.
$16,755 to Gladney Fund, Fort Worth, TX, 2011.
$12,566 to American Cancer Society, Oklahoma City, OK, 2011. For unrestricted contribution.
$2,992 to Scott and White Memorial Hospital, Temple, TX, 2011.

8996
The Lyons Foundation ✧
1202A Dairy Ashford Rd.
Houston, TX 77079-3004

Established in 1961 in TX.
Donors: Richard T. Lyons†; Sammie Lyons†; Magalou W. Hestand Trust; Sammie W. Lyons.
Foundation type: Independent foundation.
Financial data (yr. ended 12/31/13): Assets, $14,448,685 (M); expenditures, $711,595; qualifying distributions, $559,500; giving activities include $557,000 for 53 grants (high: $30,000; low: $5,000).
Purpose and activities: Giving primarily for education, health and human services.
Fields of interest: Education; Health care; Human services; Children/youth, services; Family services; Catholic agencies & churches.
Type of support: General/operating support; Continuing support; Annual campaigns; Capital campaigns; Building/renovation; Equipment; Endowments; Emergency funds; Program development; Professorships; Internship funds; Exchange programs; Matching/challenge support.
Limitations: Applications accepted. Giving limited to Harris, Fort Bend, Montgomery and Galveston counties, TX. No grants to individuals.
Publications: Application guidelines.
Application information: Application form required.
Initial approach: Letter
Copies of proposal: 2
Deadline(s): Nov. 1
Board meeting date(s): Dec.
Officers: R.A. Seale, Jr., Pres.; Flo McGee, V.P.; John W. Storms, V.P.; James S. Prentice, Secy.-Treas.
EIN: 746038717
Selected grants: The following grants are a representative sample of this grantmaker's funding activity:
$40,000 to Episcopal High School, Bellaire, TX, 2011. For capital campaign.

8997
Madison Charitable Foundation, Inc. ✧
121 FM 359 Rd.
Richmond, TX 77406-2401 (281) 344-9455

Established in 2007 in TX.
Donor: Wiley Hatcher.
Foundation type: Independent foundation.
Financial data (yr. ended 12/31/12): Assets, $26,820,744 (M); expenditures, $4,370,481; qualifying distributions, $4,230,865; giving activities include $4,230,865 for grants.
Purpose and activities: Giving primarily for the arts, education, health and hospitals, including a children's hospital, as well as for other children and social services.
Fields of interest: Performing arts; Arts; Higher education; Hospitals (general); Hospitals (specialty); Health organizations; Human services; Children/youth, services; Christian agencies & churches.
Limitations: Applications accepted. Giving primarily in MS and TX.
Application information:
Initial approach: Letter
Deadline(s): None
Directors: James O. Carpenter; Wiley Hatcher; Lorinda Beth Madison; Norma Montalvo Petrosewicz.
EIN: 261147137

8998
The Mankoff Family Foundation ✧
(formerly The Mankoff Charitable Foundation)
5950 Berkshire Ln., Ste. 810
Dallas, TX 75225-5861

Established in 1997 in TX.
Donors: Joy S. Mankoff; Ronald M. Mankoff; Douglas F. Mankoff; Jeffrey W. Mankoff; Green Pass Investments, G.P.
Foundation type: Independent foundation.
Financial data (yr. ended 12/31/13): Assets, $6,168,764 (M); gifts received, $336,552; expenditures, $631,326; qualifying distributions, $565,435; giving activities include $550,026 for grants.
Purpose and activities: Giving primarily for the arts, education, and Jewish organizations and temples.
Fields of interest: Performing arts, opera; Arts; Higher education; Health organizations; Jewish federated giving programs; Jewish agencies & synagogues.

Type of support: Annual campaigns; Capital campaigns; Building/renovation; Matching/challenge support.
Limitations: Applications not accepted. Giving primarily in Dallas, TX, and New London, CT.
Application information: Contributes only to pre-selected organizations.
Directors: Douglas F. Mankoff; Jeffrey W. Mankoff; Joy S. Mankoff; Ronald M. Mankoff.
EIN: 752739184

8999
Tom and Charlene Marsh Family Foundation ✧

P.O. Box 460
Dallas, TX 75221-0460

Established in 2007 in TX.
Donors: Marsh Foundation, Inc.; Estelle Fariss Marsh‡.
Foundation type: Independent foundation.
Financial data (yr. ended 12/31/13): Assets, $7,758,429 (M); expenditures, $489,781; qualifying distributions, $470,200; giving activities include $470,200 for 26 grants (high: $100,000; low: $1,000).
Fields of interest: Museums (art); Performing arts; Performing arts, orchestras; Elementary/secondary education; Higher education; Hospitals (general); Human services; International affairs, foreign policy; International affairs; Christian agencies & churches; Protestant agencies & churches.
Type of support: General/operating support; Endowments; Program development.
Limitations: Applications not accepted. Giving primarily in NJ, New York, NY, and Dallas and San Antonio, TX. No grants to individuals.
Application information: Contributes only to pre-selected organizations.
Officers and Directors:* Tom F. Marsh,* Chair.; Charlene Marsh,* Pres.; Joe Coffman, V.P. and Secy.; William E. Allen, Treas.; Tennessee E. Kellogg; Charlene C. Marsh; Charles A. Marsh.
EIN: 260177017
Selected grants: The following grants are a representative sample of this grantmaker's funding activity:
$7,500 to Southern Methodist University, Dallas, TX, 2012. For Meadows School of the Arts.

9000
Douglas B. Marshall, Jr. Family Foundation ✧

600 Jefferson St., Ste. 310
Houston, TX 77002-7324 (713) 651-8806
Contact: Robert Carter, Secy.
FAX: (713) 651-2387;
E-mail: rcarter@legacytrust.com; Main URL: http://www.dbmjr.org

Established in 2001 in TX.
Donors: Douglas B. Marshall, Jr.‡; Douglas B. Marshall III.
Foundation type: Independent foundation.
Financial data (yr. ended 12/31/12): Assets, $29,836,157 (M); expenditures, $1,654,558; qualifying distributions, $1,366,873; giving activities include $1,342,464 for 19 grants (high: $400,000; low: $2,000).
Purpose and activities: The mission of the foundation is to support education and research on all levels. This includes supporting cutting edge research at universities, laboratories, and other such institutions. It also includes the support of basic education, especially in areas of literacy, numeracy, and science. Since education and research are impossible without food, shelter, clothing, or medicine, it is within the bounds of the foundation's mission to provide these when necessary.
Fields of interest: Education; Human services; Poverty studies.
Type of support: General/operating support; Continuing support; Income development; Annual campaigns; Capital campaigns; Building/renovation; Equipment; Emergency funds; Program development; Seed money; Curriculum development; Scholarship funds; Research; In-kind gifts; Matching/challenge support.
Limitations: Applications not accepted. Giving on a national basis. No grants to individuals.
Application information: Grant applications are by invitation only.
Board meeting date(s): As necessary
Officers and Directors:* Douglas B. Marshall III,* Pres.; Robert T. Arnold,* V.P.; Robert Carter, Secy.; Carla Chaney, Treas.; J.K. Jones; Wilhelmina B. Traylor.
EIN: 760664812
Selected grants: The following grants are a representative sample of this grantmaker's funding activity:
$400,000 to Innovations for Poverty Action, New Haven, CT, 2012. For Deworm School Children in Kenya.
$100,898 to Massachusetts Institute of Technology, Cambridge, MA, 2012. For Post Primary Education in Development Countries.
$73,064 to CARE, Merrifield, VA, 2012. For Project Kawsay 11 Fight Global Poverty.
$46,284 to Wellesley College, Wellesley, MA, 2012. For Micronutrient Fortification Strategies in India's Midday Meal Program.
$16,000 to Houston Parks Board, Houston, TX, 2012. For Trees for Tanglewood Park.
$10,000 to University of Texas, Austin, TX, 2012. For Center for Students in Recovery.
$4,000 to Houston Zoo, Houston, TX, 2012. For animal support.

9001
Marti Foundation ✧

1501-D N. Main St.
Cleburne, TX 76033-3876 (817) 558-0079
Contact: Hoylene Harris, Mgr.

Established in 1988 in TX.
Donors: George W. Marti; Jo C. Marti; Wesley Marti; John Barger; Chesapeake Energy Corp.; Hill College; Regal Energy LLC; Chesapeake Operating Co.
Foundation type: Independent foundation.
Financial data (yr. ended 12/31/13): Assets, $17,042,082 (M); gifts received, $49,200; expenditures, $597,012; qualifying distributions, $583,735; giving activities include $1,921 for 1 grant, and $581,814 for 269 grants to individuals (high: $3,750; low: $750).
Purpose and activities: Giving primarily for educational scholarships and loans to residents of Texas.
Fields of interest: Scholarships/financial aid.
Type of support: Scholarship funds; Scholarships—to individuals; Student loans—to individuals.
Limitations: Applications accepted. Giving in TX, primarily to residents of Johnson County.
Application information: Application form required.
Deadline(s): 60 days prior to beginning of semester
Officers and Directors:* Michelle Marti,* Pres.; Justin Hewlett,* 1st V.P.; Rebee Brockett,* 2nd V.P.; Michael K. Lilly,* Secy.; George W. Marti, Treas.; Tom O'Neil.
EIN: 752265837

9002
The Don and Faith Martin Family Foundation, Inc. ✧ ☆

17404 Pauma Valley Cir.
Dallas, TX 75287-7419

Donors: D. & F. Martin Family Foundation, Ltd.; Don Martin; Faith Martin.
Foundation type: Independent foundation.
Financial data (yr. ended 12/31/13): Assets, $5,288,229 (M); gifts received, $500,000; expenditures, $566,620; qualifying distributions, $531,400; giving activities include $531,400 for 6 grants (high: $515,000; low: $1,000).
Fields of interest: Christian agencies & churches.
Limitations: Applications not accepted. Giving primarily in TX.
Directors: Don W. Martin, Jr.; Faith S. Martin; Chris Schultz.
EIN: 460882496

9003
The Guadalupe and Lilia Martinez Foundation ✧

361 Pine Valley Dr.
Fairview, TX 75069-1915 (972) 549-1605
Contact: Shirley S. Gonzalez, Pres.
E-mail: glmfoundation@grandecom.net; E-mail for questions concerning funding: funding@glmfoundation.org; Main URL: http://www.glmfoundation.org

Established in 2001 in TX.
Donors: Guadalupe Martinez‡; Lilia Martinez‡; Guadalupe Martinez 2001 Trust.
Foundation type: Independent foundation.
Financial data (yr. ended 12/31/13): Assets, $41,468,375 (M); expenditures, $2,774,727; qualifying distributions, $1,991,967; giving activities include $1,991,967 for 41 grants (high: $255,000; low: $1,000).
Purpose and activities: Giving primarily for charitable and religious organizations and for scientific testing for public safety, literacy, health, and education primarily for the benefit of the people of Webb and Zapata counties in Texas.
Fields of interest: Elementary/secondary education; Higher education; Human services; Christian agencies & churches.
Type of support: General/operating support; Continuing support; Annual campaigns; Capital campaigns; Building/renovation; Equipment; Program development; Scholarship funds.
Limitations: Applications accepted. Giving primarily in Webb and Zapata counties in TX. No grants to individuals.
Application information: Application form not required.
Initial approach: Letter of request via foundation web site

Copies of proposal: 1
Deadline(s): None
Board meeting date(s): 3-4 times annually, as determined by board
Final notification: After the next board meeting
Officers and Directors:* Shirley Gonzalez,* Pres.; Robert J. Gonzalez, Jr., V.P.; Larry Sandlin,* V.P.; Maria Louisa Sandlin,* V.P.; Ana Gonzalez,* Secy.; Robert Gonzalez,* Treas.
EIN: 743005930

9004
The Masters Foundation Inc. ✧
4 Savannah Cir.
Frisco, TX 75034 (214) 472-5000
Contact: Charles A. Loper, Jr., Chair.

Established in 1999 in TX.
Donors: Charles A. Loper, Jr.; Charles Loper III; Feed the Children.
Foundation type: Independent foundation.
Financial data (yr. ended 12/31/11): Assets, $1,904,954 (M); gifts received, $920,557; expenditures, $743,833; qualifying distributions, $1,009,164; giving activities include $717,489 for 9+ grants (high: $421,326; low: $670), and $14,851 for grants to individuals (high: $14,851).
Purpose and activities: Giving to Baptist faith-based organizations that provide aid to the community.
Fields of interest: Religion.
Limitations: Applications accepted. Giving primarily in Dallas County, TX.
Application information: Application form required.
Initial approach: Proposal
Deadline(s): None
Officers: James Bradshaw, Co-Chair.; Charles A. Loper, Jr., Co-Chair.; Charles A. Loper III, Co-Chair.
Board Member: Carol D. Loper.
EIN: 752883327

9005
Maverick Capital Foundation ✧
300 Crescent Ct., 18th Fl.
Dallas, TX 75201-1836

Established in 2002 in TX.
Donors: Brian L. Zied; Erika Long; Carter Creech; Glenn Engel; Keith Hennington; Winston Holt; Andrew Homan; Steven H. Kapp; Katherine Neufeld; Gunnar Overstrom; Michelle Perrin; Alex Rafal; Elena Ridloff; Vinay Saqi; Natalie Shea; David Singer; Sean Walsh; Christy Wyskiel; Pedro Zevallos; Maverick Capital Charities, Ltd.; Cohasset Ltd.; Marmalade, Inc.; Lee S. Ainslie III; Evan A. Wyly; Michael A. Pausic.
Foundation type: Company-sponsored foundation.
Financial data (yr. ended 12/31/13): Assets, $9,777,093 (M); gifts received, $915,010; expenditures, $2,382,857; qualifying distributions, $2,358,343; giving activities include $2,357,939 for 328 grants (high: $150,000; low: $30).
Purpose and activities: The foundation supports organizations involved with education, health, medical research, child welfare, legal aid, hunger, youth development, human services, and economically disadvantaged people.
Fields of interest: Elementary school/education; Secondary school/education; Charter schools; Higher education; Education, services; Education; Health care, clinics/centers; Public health, obesity; Health care; Medical research; Crime/violence prevention, child abuse; Legal services; Food services; Food banks; Youth development; Children/youth, services; Family services; Human services; Economically disadvantaged.
Type of support: Scholarship funds; General/operating support; Program development.
Limitations: Applications not accepted. Giving in the U.S., with emphasis on NY and TX. No grants to individuals.
Application information: Contributes only to pre-selected organizations.
Trustees: Lee S. Ainslie III; Carter Creech; Bates Brown; Donald Devine; Steve Galbraith; William Goodell; Keith Hennington; Winston Holt IV; Steven H. Kapp; John McCafferty; Gunnar Overstrom; Michael A. Pausic; Alex Rafal; David Singer; Andrew Warford; Evan A. Wyly; Brian L. Zied.
EIN: 710917626

9006
The Frank W. & Sue Mayborn Foundation ✧
(formerly The Frank and Anyse Sue Mayborn Foundation)
10 S. 3rd St.
Temple, TX 76501-7619

Established in 1965 in TX.
Donors: Anyse Sue Mayborn; Anyse Sue Mayborn Charitable Lead Annuity Trust.
Foundation type: Independent foundation.
Financial data (yr. ended 12/31/13): Assets, $24,290,519 (M); gifts received, $1,900,000; expenditures, $1,274,065; qualifying distributions, $1,272,970; giving activities include $1,271,650 for 20 grants (high: $1,000,000; low: $250).
Fields of interest: Arts; Higher education; Nursing school/education; Boys & girls clubs; Youth development.
Type of support: General/operating support; Capital campaigns; Building/renovation; Endowments; Scholarship funds.
Limitations: Applications not accepted. Giving primarily in the central TX area. No grants to individuals.
Application information: Contributes only to pre-selected organizations.
Officers and Directors:* Anyse Sue Mayborn,* Pres. and Treas.; Jerry L. Arnold,* Secy.; Vance K. Maultsby, Jr.
EIN: 746067859

9007
Oliver Dewey Mayor Foundation ✧
P.O. Box 1088
Sherman, TX 75091-1088
Contact: Regina D. Pruitt, Asst. V.P.
FAX: (903) 813-5121;
E-mail: rpruitt@bankoftexas.com

Established in 1983 in TX.
Donor: Oliver Dewey Mayor†.
Foundation type: Independent foundation.
Financial data (yr. ended 06/30/13): Assets, $14,856,306 (M); expenditures, $1,545,113; qualifying distributions, $900,632; giving activities include $793,695 for 25 grants (high: $337,750; low: $364).
Purpose and activities: Support for education, community development, and youth and social services.
Fields of interest: Education; Human services; Youth, services; Community/economic development.
Type of support: General/operating support; Building/renovation; Research; Matching/challenge support.
Limitations: Applications accepted. Giving limited to Mayes County, OK and Grayson County, TX. No grants to individuals.
Publications: Application guidelines.
Application information: Application form required.
Initial approach: Proposal
Copies of proposal: 9
Deadline(s): Mar. 15, June 15, Sept. 15 and Dec. 15
Board meeting date(s): Mar. 15, Jun. 15, Sept. 15, and Dec. 15
Board of Governors: Tracey L. Dean; Samuel W. Graber; Nash Lamb; Dr. James E. Pledger; Marion Stinson; Gail Utter; Vickie White.
Trustee: Bank of Texas, N.A.
EIN: 751864630

9008
Mays Family Foundation ✧
200 E. Basse Rd.
San Antonio, TX 78209-8328

Established around 1994 in TX.
Donors: L. Lowry Mays; Mark Mays; Randall Mays; Mays Family 2000 Charitable Lead Annuity Trust; Clear Channel Communication Foundation.
Foundation type: Independent foundation.
Financial data (yr. ended 12/31/12): Assets, $249,503,618 (M); expenditures, $9,218,003; qualifying distributions, $7,103,456; giving activities include $7,103,456 for 108 grants (high: $1,200,000; low: $79).
Purpose and activities: Giving primarily for education, health, human services, and Christian organizations and ministries.
Fields of interest: Museums (art); Education; Health organizations; Human services; Foundations (private grantmaking); Christian agencies & churches.
Limitations: Applications not accepted. Giving primarily in TX, with emphasis on San Antonio. No grants to individuals.
Application information: Contributes only to pre-selected organizations.
Officers and Directors:* Kathryn M. Johnson,* Pres.; Mark P. Mays,* V.P.; Randall T. Mays,* V.P.; L. Lowry Mays,* Treas.; Peggy P. Mays; Linda Mays McCaul.
EIN: 742691624

9009
McCombs Foundation, Inc. ✧
755 E. Mulberry, Ste. 600
San Antonio, TX 78212-6013 (210) 821-6523
Contact: Gary V. Woods, Secy.-Treas.
Red and Charline McCombs's Giving Pledge Profile: http://glasspockets.org/philanthropy-in-focus/eye-on-the-giving-pledge/profiles/mccombs

Established in 1981 in TX.
Donors: Gary V. Woods; McCombs Family Charitable Lead Trust; and members of the McCombs family.
Foundation type: Independent foundation.

Financial data (yr. ended 12/31/13): Assets, $41,776,354 (M); expenditures, $4,800,484; qualifying distributions, $4,689,029; giving activities include $4,688,375 for 169 grants (high: $2,000,000; low: $150).
Purpose and activities: Giving primarily for higher education, athletic programs, and historic preservation.
Fields of interest: Historic preservation/historical societies; Arts; Higher education; Medical research, institute; Athletics/sports, school programs; Recreation; Youth development, centers/clubs; Philanthropy/voluntarism.
Limitations: Applications accepted. Giving primarily in TX. No grants to individuals.
Publications: Annual report.
Application information: Application form not required.
Initial approach: Letter
Copies of proposal: 1
Deadline(s): None
Final notification: 2 weeks
Officers: Marsha M. Shields, Pres.; Gary V. Woods, Secy.-Treas.
Directors: Lynda G. McCombs; Connie M. McNab.
EIN: 742204217
Selected grants: The following grants are a representative sample of this grantmaker's funding activity:
$2,000,000 to University of Texas Longhorn Foundation, Austin, TX, 2013.
$300,000 to Bexar County Performing Arts Center Foundation, San Antonio, TX, 2013.
$300,000 to Saint Marys Hall, San Antonio, TX, 2013.
$250,000 to George W. Bush Foundation, Dallas, TX, 2013.
$250,000 to National Western Art Foundation, San Antonio, TX, 2013.
$250,000 to Southwestern University, Georgetown, TX, 2013.
$150,000 to Roadrunner Foundation, San Antonio, TX, 2013.
$50,000 to Southwestern University, Georgetown, TX, 2013.
$25,000 to Paisano Educational Trust, San Antonio, TX, 2013.
$20,000 to Sports, Outdoor and Recreation SOAR Park, San Antonio, TX, 2013.

9010
James N. McCoy Foundation ✧
5001 Ditto Ln.
Wichita Falls, TX 76302-3501 (940) 767-4334
Contact: Vicki D. McCoy, Pres. and Tr.

Established in 1995 in TX.
Donor: James N. McCoy.
Foundation type: Independent foundation.
Financial data (yr. ended 12/31/13): Assets, $31,084,596 (M); gifts received, $1,445,065; expenditures, $1,147,426; qualifying distributions, $1,045,040; giving activities include $1,035,425 for 39 grants (high: $300,000; low: $3,000).
Fields of interest: Higher education; Education; Health care; Human services; Foundations (community); Christian agencies & churches.
Limitations: Applications accepted. Giving primarily in OK and TX. No grants to individuals.
Application information: Application form required.
Initial approach: Letter
Deadline(s): None
Officers and Trustees:* Vicki D. McCoy,* Pres.; R. Ken Hines,* V.P. and Secy.-Treas.; Mark McCoy,* V.P.; Robert W. Goff, Jr.
EIN: 752587034
Selected grants: The following grants are a representative sample of this grantmaker's funding activity:
$300,000 to United Regional Health Care Foundation, Wichita Falls, TX, 2011. For capital improvements.
$85,750 to Wichita Falls Area Community Foundation, Wichita Falls, TX, 2011.
$25,000 to Hospice of Wichita Falls, Wichita Falls, TX, 2011. For general operations.
$20,000 to Genesis Place, Wichita Falls, TX, 2011. For capital improvements.
$10,000 to Camp Fire USA, Wichita Falls, TX, 2011. For capital improvements.
$10,000 to United Way of North Texas Area, Wichita Falls, TX, 2011.
$5,000 to Inheritance Adoptions, Wichita Falls, TX, 2011.
$5,000 to Mary Abbott Childrens House, Norman, OK, 2011.
$5,000 to Patsys House Childrens Advocacy Center, Wichita Falls, TX, 2011.

9011
The Ralph H. & Ruth J. McCullough Foundation ✧
c/o Joseph W. Royce
1300 Post Oak Blvd., Ste. 2000
Houston, TX 77056-8000

Established in 1981 in TX.
Donors: Ralph H. McCullough†; Ruth J. McCullough†.
Foundation type: Independent foundation.
Financial data (yr. ended 12/31/13): Assets, $15,340,539 (M); expenditures, $822,714; qualifying distributions, $699,797; giving activities include $605,000 for 51 grants (high: $36,000; low: $1,500).
Purpose and activities: Support primarily for higher education; some support also for medical services, welfare, religion and the arts.
Fields of interest: Higher education; Health care; Human services.
Type of support: General/operating support; Endowments; Scholarship funds.
Limitations: Applications not accepted. Giving primarily in TX. No support for political organizations. No grants to individuals.
Publications: Annual report.
Application information: Contributes only to pre-selected organizations.
Board meeting date(s): Quarterly
Officers and Trustees:* Joe E. Coleman,* Pres.; Anne M. Shallenberger,* V.P.; Joseph W. Royce,* Secy.; James T. McCullough; Dee S. Osborne; H. Michael Tyson; Katherine M. Wade.
EIN: 742177193

9012
McDaniel Charitable Foundation ✧
P.O. Box 2968
Texas City, TX 77592-2968
FAX: (409) 944-0120;
E-mail: contactus@mcdanielcharitablefoundation.org; Main URL: http://mcdanielcharitablefoundation.org/
Established in 1999 in TX.
Donors: Lola McDaniel†; Mark A. Lyons; Melissa Lyons-Gardner; Michelle Spier; Jene M. Moseley.
Foundation type: Independent foundation.
Financial data (yr. ended 12/31/12): Assets, $7,550,582 (M); gifts received, $248,017; expenditures, $1,420,875; qualifying distributions, $1,299,952; giving activities include $603,100 for 7 grants (high: $357,000; low: $500), $86,500 for 38 grants to individuals (high: $6,000; low: $1,000), and $462,375 for 1 foundation-administered program.
Purpose and activities: Giving to support programs, projects, and education that enhance the quality of life within the local community and State of Texas.
Fields of interest: Higher education; Scholarships/financial aid.
Limitations: Applications not accepted. Giving primarily in TX.
Application information: Unsolicited requests for funds not accepted.
Officers: Mark A. Lyons, Pres.; Michelle Lyons-Spier, V.P.; Melissa Lyons-Gardner, Secy.
Directors: R. Stewart Campbell; Randall Harris; Robert Harris.
EIN: 760538313

9013
The Eugene McDermott Foundation ✧
3808 Euclid Ave.
Dallas, TX 75205-3102 (214) 521-2924
Contact: Mary McDermott Cook, Pres.

Incorporated in 1972 in TX; absorbed The McDermott Foundation in 1977.
Donors: Eugene McDermott†; Mrs. Eugene McDermott.
Foundation type: Independent foundation.
Financial data (yr. ended 08/31/13): Assets, $91,279,437 (M); expenditures, $6,353,496; qualifying distributions, $6,090,917; giving activities include $6,000,500 for 65 grants (high: $1,000,000; low: $1,500).
Purpose and activities: Support primarily for cultural programs, higher and secondary education, health, and general community interests.
Fields of interest: Museums; Historic preservation/historical societies; Arts; Education, early childhood education; Elementary school/education; Secondary school/education; Higher education; Education; Hospitals (general); Health care; Health organizations, association; Medical research, institute; Children/youth, services; International human rights; Community/economic development; United Ways and Federated Giving Programs; Government/public administration; Children/youth; Children; Youth; Adults; Aging; Young adults; Disabilities, people with; Physically disabled; Blind/visually impaired; Deaf/hearing impaired; Mentally disabled; Minorities; African Americans/Blacks; Hispanics/Latinos; Native Americans/American Indians; Indigenous peoples; Women; Girls; Young adults, female; Men; Boys; Young adults, male; Substance abusers; AIDS, people with; Single parents; Crime/abuse victims; Terminal illness, people with; Economically disadvantaged; Homeless.
Type of support: General/operating support; Continuing support; Annual campaigns; Capital campaigns; Building/renovation; Equipment; Land acquisition; Endowments; Program development; Professorships; Seed money; Curriculum

development; Scholarship funds; Research; Matching/challenge support.
Limitations: Applications accepted. Giving primarily in Dallas, TX. No grants to individuals.
Application information: No printed material available. Application form not required.
Initial approach: Letter
Copies of proposal: 1
Deadline(s): None
Board meeting date(s): Quarterly
Final notification: Prior to Aug. 31
Officers and Trustees:* Mary McDermott Cook,* Pres.; J.H. Cullum Clark; Mrs. Eugene McDermott.
Agent: Bank of America, N.A.
Number of staff: 2 part-time professional.
EIN: 237237919
Selected grants: The following grants are a representative sample of this grantmaker's funding activity:
$1,000,000 to Dallas Symphony Association, Dallas, TX, 2012. For Operations.
$1,000,000 to University of Texas at Dallas, Richardson, TX, 2012. For Landscaping Project.
$750,000 to Perot Museum of Nature and Science, Dallas, TX, 2012. To Endow a CEO ($1,500,000 over two years).
$500,000 to Dallas Opera, Dallas, TX, 2012. To Underwrite a New Opera by Jake Heggie.
$200,000 to Southern Methodist University, Dallas, TX, 2012.
$100,000 to Trinity Trust Foundation, Dallas, TX, 2012. For Operations.
$80,000 to Communities in Schools Dallas Region, Dallas, TX, 2012. For Program Services.
$25,000 to University of Texas, Austin, TX, 2012. For Lady Bird Johnson Wildflower Center.
$10,000 to Dallas Childrens Theater, Dallas, TX, 2012. For Operations.
$10,000 to West Dallas Initiative, Dallas, TX, 2012. For Tuition.

9014
John P. McGovern Foundation ✧
2211 Norfolk St., Ste. 900
Houston, TX 77098-4044
Contact: Kathrine McGovern, Pres. and V.P.

Established in 1961 in TX.
Donor: John P. McGovern, M.D.†.
Foundation type: Independent foundation.
Financial data (yr. ended 12/31/13): Assets, $175,871,084 (M); gifts received, $5,850,300; expenditures, $10,824,337; qualifying distributions, $14,948,551; giving activities include $9,551,000 for 305 grants (high: $1,500,000; low: $500).
Purpose and activities: To carry on the charitable interests of the donor to support the activities of established nonprofit organizations, which are of importance to human welfare with special focus on children and family health education and promotion, treatment and disease prevention.
Fields of interest: Education; Health care; Children/youth, services; Family services; Community development, neighborhood development.
Type of support: General/operating support; Continuing support; Building/renovation; Endowments; Emergency funds; Conferences/seminars; Professorships; Publication; Curriculum development; Scholarship funds; Research; Matching/challenge support.
Limitations: Applications not accepted. Giving primarily in TX, with emphasis on Houston; giving also in the Southwest. No grants to individuals.
Application information: Unsolicited requests for funds not accepted.
Board meeting date(s): Monthly
Officers and Directors:* Kathrine G. McGovern,* Pres. and V.P.; Julia Mitchell, Secy.; Sheila Lewis,* Treas.
Number of staff: 1 part-time professional; 4 part-time support.
EIN: 746053075
Selected grants: The following grants are a representative sample of this grantmaker's funding activity:
$1,000,000 to John P. McGovern Museum of Health and Medical Science, Houston, TX, 2010. For capital campaign.
$1,000,000 to John P. McGovern Museum of Health and Medical Science, Houston, TX, 2011. For capital campaign.
$500,000 to Houston Zoo, Houston, TX, 2010. For program support for the John P. McGovern Children's Zoo.
$400,000 to Houston Community College System Foundation, Houston, TX, 2010. For Opportunity 14, need-based scholarship for entering HCC freshmen who qualify for some financial aid, but not enough to cover the costs of their tuition, fees and textbooks.
$300,000 to Friends of Mandell Park, Houston, TX, 2011. For the Meadow's Curvilinear Wall.
$200,000 to Houston Community College System Foundation, Houston, TX, 2011. For Opportunity 14 Scholarship Endowment Fund.
$155,000 to Council on Alcohol and Drugs Houston, Houston, TX, 2010. For John P. McGovern Education Center, which offers basic alcohol and drug education, family education about the effects and consequences of the disease of addiction and alcohol and drug awareness education for the community.
$150,000 to Salvation Army of Houston, Houston, TX, 2010.
$150,000 to Salvation Army of Houston, Houston, TX, 2011. For Program Support.
$150,000 to University of Texas Health Science Center, Houston, TX, 2011. For John P. McGovern, M.D Center for Health Humanities and the Human Spirit.
$35,000 to Alcohol and Drug Abuse Womens Center, Galveston, TX, 2010. For program support.
$25,000 to Camp for All Foundation, Houston, TX, 2011. For CampFest Gala.
$20,000 to Houston Zoo, Houston, TX, 2010. For Feed Your Wildlife Conservation Luncheon.
$20,000 to Ronald McDonald House of Galveston, Galveston, TX, 2010. For Birthday Party.
$15,000 to Sheltering Arms Senior Services, Houston, TX, 2011. For Luncheon.
$15,000 to Texas Childrens Hospital, Houston, TX, 2011. For Legends Gala.
$15,000 to Theta Charity Antiques Show, Houston, TX, 2011.
$12,500 to Literacy Advance of Houston, Houston, TX, 2011.
$10,000 to American Festival for the Arts, Houston, TX, 2010. For Gala.
$10,000 to University of Texas Medical Branch, Galveston, TX, 2010.

9015
Callie D. McGrath Charitable Trust ✧
c/o Bank of America, N.A.
P.O. Box 831041
Dallas, TX 75283-1041

Established in 1995 in California.
Foundation type: Independent foundation.
Financial data (yr. ended 12/31/13): Assets, $13,885,492 (M); expenditures, $810,314; qualifying distributions, $703,273; giving activities include $624,772 for 35 grants (high: $75,000; low: $1,000).
Purpose and activities: Giving primarily for hospitals, health organizations, human services, and to Christian organizations.
Fields of interest: Hospitals (general); Hospitals (specialty); Health organizations, association; Human services; Children/youth, services; Christian agencies & churches.
Limitations: Applications not accepted. Giving primarily in CA. No grants to individuals.
Application information: Contributes only to pre-selected organizations.
Trustee: Bank of America, N.A.
EIN: 956995594
Selected grants: The following grants are a representative sample of this grantmaker's funding activity:
$5,000 to Campus Crusade for Christ International, Orlando, FL, 2011.

9016
Shirley & William S. McIntyre Foundation ✧ ☆
c/o William S. McIntyre, V.P.
12222 Merit Dr., Ste. 1450
Dallas, TX 75251-3212

Established in 2000 in TX.
Donors: Shirley C. McIntyre; William S. McIntyre; International Risk Management; McIntyre Financial Svcs.; American Contractors Insurance Group.
Foundation type: Independent foundation.
Financial data (yr. ended 06/30/13): Assets, $2,293,223 (M); gifts received, $1,381,397; expenditures, $670,348; qualifying distributions, $591,354; giving activities include $585,292 for 46 grants (high: $200,000; low: $50).
Fields of interest: Performing arts; Arts; Hospitals (general); Human services.
Limitations: Applications not accepted. Giving primarily in Dallas, TX. No grants to individuals.
Application information: Contributes only to pre-selected organizations.
Officers: Shirley C. McIntyre, Pres.; William S. McIntyre, V.P.
EIN: 752910339
Selected grants: The following grants are a representative sample of this grantmaker's funding activity:
$200,000 to Southwestern Medical Foundation, Dallas, TX, 2011. For general operations.
$52,798 to Dallas Arboretum and Botanical Society, Dallas, TX, 2011. For general operations.
$27,500 to Dallas Symphony Orchestra, Dallas, TX, 2011. For general operations.
$25,000 to George W. Bush Presidential Center, Dallas, TX, 2011. For general operations.
$20,000 to AT&T Performing Arts Center, Dallas, TX, 2011. For general operations.
$20,000 to Bravo! Colorado Music Festival at Vail, Vail, CO, 2011. For general operations.

$11,000 to Episcopal Church of the Transfiguration, Vail, CO, 2011. For general operations.
$10,250 to Saint Michael and All Angels Episcopal Church, Dallas, TX, 2011. For general operations.
$2,500 to Episcopal School of Dallas, Dallas, TX, 2011. For general operations.
$1,500 to Saint Paul Medical Foundation, Dallas, TX, 2011. For general operations.

9017
The Robert and Janice McNair Foundation ✧

109 N. Post Oak Ln., Ste. 600
Houston, TX 77024-7753
Contact: Joanie Haley, Exec. Dir.
FAX: (713) 336-7757;
E-mail: jhaley@mcnairfoundation.org; Main URL: http://mcnairfoundation.org/

Established in 1988 in TX.
Donors: Robert C. McNair; Janice McNair.
Foundation type: Independent foundation.
Financial data (yr. ended 12/31/12): Assets, $65,391,752 (M); gifts received, $46,323,235; expenditures, $13,115,323; qualifying distributions, $12,614,128; giving activities include $12,310,604 for 161 grants (high: $2,000,000; low: $250).
Purpose and activities: The mission of the foundation is to help find cures for breast and pancreatic cancer, diabetes and neurological problems by funding research by outstanding McNair Scholars and to prepare youth through educational means for productive and enriched lives with respect to work, family and service to others.
Fields of interest: Performing arts, opera; Arts; Higher education; Education; Cancer research; Breast cancer research; Brain research; Diabetes research; Medical research; Safety/disasters; Community/economic development.
Type of support: Program development; Curriculum development; Scholarship funds; Research.
Limitations: Applications not accepted. Giving primarily in Houston, TX. No support for political organizations. No grants to individuals.
Publications: Grants list; Occasional report.
Application information: Contributes only to pre-selected organizations.
Board meeting date(s): Varies, usually quarterly
Officer: Joanie Haley, Exec. Dir.
Trustees: Daniel Calhoun McNair; Janice S. McNair; Robert C. McNair; Robert Cary McNair, Jr.; Melissa McNair Reichert; Ruth McNair Smith.
Number of staff: 1 full-time professional; 1 full-time support.
EIN: 766050185
Selected grants: The following grants are a representative sample of this grantmaker's funding activity:
$2,000,000 to Baylor College of Medicine, Houston, TX, 2012. For the Improvements to the new Specialty Care Center on the McNair Campus.
$1,554,500 to Lexicon Pharmaceuticals, The Woodlands, TX, 2012. For funding research of efficacy of protein LX4211 as a cure of Type 1 Diabetes.
$1,500,000 to University of South Carolina, Columbia, SC, 2012. For McNair Scholars Program for Honor Students at USC.
$850,000 to Columbia College, Columbia, SC, 2012. For McNair Scholarship Funds for Deserving Students, Landscape Project and College Dorm Renovations.
$500,000 to Baylor College of Medicine, Houston, TX, 2012. For McNair Scholar at Baylor College of Medicine pursuing research in the Area of Juvenile Diabetes.
$400,000 to A.D. Players, Houston, TX, 2012. For the First of Five Payments to Support the Capital Campaign.
$125,000 to Texas Heart Institute, Houston, TX, 2012. For Research Grant for Texas Heart Institute McNair Scholar in areas of Cardiovascular Disease and Stem Cell Research.
$10,000 to Education Foundation of Harris County, Houston, TX, 2012. For Innovative Educational Programs for 800,000+ K-12 Public Education Students in the Greater Houston/Harris County Region.
$10,000 to Living Water International, Sugar Land, TX, 2012. To demonstrate the Love of God by helping communities acquire desperately needed Clean Water and experience the Living Water Of The Gospel of Jesus Christ, which alone satisfies the deepest thirst.
$10,000 to Museum of Fine Arts, Houston, Houston, TX, 2012. For Summer Exhibit at the Museum and Visitor Center at Bayou Bend.

9018
Amy Shelton McNutt Charitable Trust ✧

c/o Trust Secretary
153 Treeline Park, Ste. 300
San Antonio, TX 78209-1880

Established about 1983 in TX.
Donor: Amy Shelton McNutt‡.
Foundation type: Independent foundation.
Financial data (yr. ended 09/30/13): Assets, $17,285,053 (M); expenditures, $809,789; qualifying distributions, $759,537; giving activities include $722,342 for 145 grants (high: $150,000; low: $100).
Fields of interest: Museums (art); Arts; Higher education; Education; Environment, natural resources; Animal welfare; Health care; Human services; Foundations (private grantmaking); Christian agencies & churches.
Type of support: General/operating support; Capital campaigns; Building/renovation; Matching/challenge support.
Limitations: Applications accepted. Giving primarily in MO and TX. No grants to individuals.
Application information: Unsolicited applications from outside of the San Antonio, TX, metropolitan area are not considered. Contact the Trust for complete application guidelines. Application form required.
Initial approach: Letter of application, not to exceed 3 pages
Deadline(s): Feb. 28 and July 31
Board meeting date(s): Mar. and Aug.
Trustees: Jack Guenther; Courtney J. Walker.
EIN: 742298675

9019
The Meadows Foundation, Inc.

Wilson Historic District
3003 Swiss Ave.
Dallas, TX 75204-6049 (214) 826-9431
Contact: Bruce H. Esterline, V.P., Grants
FAX: (214) 827-7042;
E-mail: webgrants3003@mfi.org; Additional tel.: (800) 826-9431; Main URL: http://www.mfi.org
Customer Feedback Study: http://www.mfi.org/display.asp?link=ETMAOD
Grants Database: http://www.mfi.org/display.asp?link=GSRCH1

Incorporated in 1948 in TX.
Donors: Algur Hurtle Meadows‡; Virginia Meadows‡.
Foundation type: Independent foundation.
Financial data (yr. ended 12/31/13): Assets, $750,972,129 (M); expenditures, $47,911,233; qualifying distributions, $35,791,388; giving activities include $27,287,441 for 172 grants (high: $6,000,000; low: $10,000), $653,395 for foundation-administered programs and $205,277 for 1 loan/program-related investment.
Purpose and activities: The foundation strives to exemplify the principles of its founder in addressing basic human needs by working toward the elimination of ignorance, hopelessness and suffering, protecting the environment, providing cultural enrichment, encouraging excellence and promoting understanding and cooperation among people. It exists to assist people and institutions of Texas improve the quality and circumstances of life for themselves and future generations.
Fields of interest: Media/communications; Visual arts, architecture; Museums; Humanities; History/archaeology; Historic preservation/historical societies; Arts; Education, public education; Education, early childhood education; Child development, education; Medical school/education; Adult/continuing education; Adult education—literacy, basic skills & GED; Libraries/library science; Education, reading; Education; Environment, natural resources; Environment; Animals/wildlife, preservation/protection; Dental care; Medical care, rehabilitation; Nursing care; Health care; Substance abuse, services; Mental health/crisis services; AIDS; Alcoholism; AIDS research; Crime/violence prevention, abuse prevention; Crime/violence prevention, domestic violence; Crime/violence prevention, child abuse; Crime/law enforcement; Employment; Agriculture; Nutrition; Housing/shelter, development; Housing/shelter, homeless; Safety/disasters; Recreation; Youth development, services; Human services; Children/youth, services; Child development, services; Family services; Residential/custodial care, hospices; Aging, centers/services; Homeless, human services; Civil rights, race/intergroup relations; Urban/community development; Rural development; Community/economic development; Voluntarism promotion; Government/public administration; Transportation; Leadership development; Public affairs; Aging; Economically disadvantaged; Homeless.
Type of support: General/operating support; Continuing support; Income development; Management development/capacity building; Capital campaigns; Building/renovation; Equipment; Land acquisition; Debt reduction; Emergency funds; Program development; Film/video/radio; Publication; Seed money; Curriculum development; Research; Technical assistance; Consulting services; Program evaluation; Program-related investments/loans; Employee matching gifts; Matching/challenge support.
Limitations: Applications accepted. Giving limited to TX. No grants to individuals; generally, no grants for annual campaigns, fundraising events, professional

conferences and symposia, travel expenses for groups to perform or compete outside of TX, construction of churches and seminaries, scholarships, or support of single artistic events or performances.
Publications: Application guidelines; Annual report (including application guidelines); Financial statement.
Application information: An online grant application form is available on the foundation's web site. Please do not attempt to attach files to online applications. Please mail attachments and grant correspondence to the foundation main address. Applications are acknowledged within a week, but are usually processed within three to four months. Grants staff is available by phone or email to respond to inquiries at any time and may schedule pre-grant interviews with applicants as time permits. After receiving an application, a face-to-face meeting may be scheduled as needed. Applicants seeking funding for construction and renovations should review the foundation's Green Building Guidelines, and for projects incorporating human-animal connection they should see the foundation's Animal Welfare Plan. Application form not required.
Initial approach: Proposal
Copies of proposal: 1
Deadline(s): None
Board meeting date(s): Grants review committee meets monthly; full board meets 2 or 3 times a year
Final notification: 3 to 4 months
Officers and Directors:* Robert A. Meadows,* Chair. and V.P.; Linda P. Evans,* C.E.O. and Pres.; Paula Herring, V.P. and Treas.; Tom Gale, V.P. and C.I.O.; Bruce H. Esterline, V.P., Grants; John W. Broadfoot, Dir. Emeritus; Judy Broadfoot Culbertson, Dir. Emeritus; Sally R. Lancaster, Dir. Emeritus; Curtis W. Meadows, Jr., Dir. Emeritus; Sally Cheney Miller, Dir. Emeritus; Eloise Meadows Rouse, Dir. Emeritus; Dorothy Cheney Wilson, Dir. Emeritus; Holli Leigh Broadfoot; John Broadfoot, Jr.; Daniel H. Chapman; Linda P. Evans; John A. Hammack; Virginia Hanson; P. Mike McCullough; Karen L. Meadows; Julie Lancaster Morris; William A. Nesbitt; Jason Ritzen; Dudley L. Rouse, Jr.; Elizabeth Meadows Rouse; Amy Whiting.
Number of staff: 25 full-time professional; 1 part-time professional; 18 full-time support; 2 part-time support.
EIN: 756015322
Selected grants: The following grants are a representative sample of this grantmaker's funding activity:
$1,000,000 to George W. Bush Foundation, Dallas, TX, 2011. Toward developing the Middle School Matters technical assistance and training program to better prepare middle school students for high school and college success.
$1,000,000 to Perot Museum of Nature and Science, Dallas, TX, 2011. Toward support to ensure student access to the new Perot Museum of Nature and Science.
$350,000 to National Wildlife Federation, Austin, TX, 2011. Toward continuing the Texas Living Waters Project as a means for ensuring Texas has adequate water supplies in the future.
$348,000 to Texas Department of State Health Services, Austin, TX, 2011. Toward continuing the Texas Self-Directed Care Program pilot program for individuals with severe mental illness.
$300,000 to Metro Dallas Homeless Alliance, Dallas, TX, 2011. Toward providing mental health services to homeless individuals during a time of increased demand and reduced public funding.
$300,000 to Texas Health Institute, Austin, TX, 2011. Toward implementing the Benefit Bank of Texas, a statewide web-based system to increase access to public benefits by low-income families in Texas.
$150,000 to Green Doors, Austin, TX, 2011. Toward renovating substandard multi-family units into energy efficient affordable housing for low-income residents.
$100,000 to E3 Alliance, Austin, TX, 2011. Toward implementing a demonstration model to transform teaching and learning practices in selected middle schools in Central Texas.
$67,000 to El Paso Symphony Orchestra Association, El Paso, TX, 2011. Toward emergency funding to complete the current season without a budget deficit.
$64,000 to Spaulding for Children, Houston, TX, 2011. Toward emergency operating support for a special needs adoption program.

9020
Medallion Foundation, Inc. ✧
1407 Fannin St.
Houston, TX 77002-7613 (713) 654-0144

Established in 1984 in TX.
Donors: Hubert S. Finkelstein†; Finkelstein Partners, Ltd.
Foundation type: Independent foundation.
Financial data (yr. ended 09/30/12): Assets, $21,483,950 (M); expenditures, $2,035,120; qualifying distributions, $746,473; giving activities include $727,473 for 39 grants (high: $121,718; low: $210).
Purpose and activities: Giving primarily for education, health organizations, and children, youth, and social services.
Fields of interest: Medical school/education; Education; Health organizations, association; Human services; Children/youth, services; Foundations (private grantmaking).
Limitations: Applications accepted. Giving primarily in Houston, TX. No grants to individuals.
Application information: Application form required.
Initial approach: Letter or telephone requesting application form
Deadline(s): None
Directors: Philip A. Donisi; Mark L. Entmann; Jereld E. McQueen; Robert J. Pilegge.
EIN: 760141071
Selected grants: The following grants are a representative sample of this grantmaker's funding activity:
$50,000 to Aishel House, Houston, TX, 2012. For expansion and improvements.
$45,750 to Beth Yeshurun Day School, Houston, TX, 2012. For technology infrastructure.
$5,000 to Be The Match Foundation, Minneapolis, MN, 2012. For Hosuton Patients.
$5,000 to El Centro de Corazon, Houston, TX, 2012. For Diabetic Self-Management Program.
$5,000 to Houston Hospice, Houston, TX, 2012. For Charity Care Program.
$210 to East Carolina University, Greenville, NC, 2012. For employee match grant.

9021
The Mehta Family Foundation ✧
(formerly Bhupat and Jyott Mehta Family Foundation)
20018 Chateau Bend Dr.
Katy, TX 77450-5149
Contact: Bernard Luksich, Exec. Dir.
E-mail: Bernie@MehtaFamilyFoundation.Org
Application address: c/o Janet Bertolino, U.S. National Bank, 2201 Market St., Galveston, TX 77553, tel.: (409) 770-7165

Established in 1996 in TX.
Donors: Rahul Mehta; Nisha B. Mehta; Jay Mehta; Nirajadh, LP.
Foundation type: Independent foundation.
Financial data (yr. ended 09/30/13): Assets, $21,060,532 (M); gifts received, $360,000; expenditures, $953,827; qualifying distributions, $913,574; giving activities include $824,671 for 20 grants (high: $340,000; low: $500).
Purpose and activities: The foundation works to improve access to education as a way to improve the economics of under-served populations. In addition, it works to support targeted leading edge cancer research.
Fields of interest: Education; Cancer research; Economics.
Limitations: Giving primarily in Houston, TX.
Application information: Application form required.
Initial approach: Write or telephone to request application
Deadline(s): Jan. 1 to Mar. 31
Directors: Dharmesh Mehta; Jainesh Mehta; Nisha B. Mehta; Rahul B. Mehta.
EIN: 760522455
Selected grants: The following grants are a representative sample of this grantmaker's funding activity:
$5,000 to Rice University, Houston, TX, 2011.
$4,400 to Bo's Place, Houston, TX, 2011.
$2,400 to Multiple Sclerosis Society, National, Houston, TX, 2011.
$1,000 to River Oaks Chamber Orchestra, Houston, TX, 2011.

9022
The Shirin Pandju Merali Foundation ✧
1 Ocommor Plz., Ste. 200
Victoria, TX 77901

Established in TX.
Donor: Pandju Merali.
Foundation type: Independent foundation.
Financial data (yr. ended 12/31/12): Assets, $159,518 (M); gifts received, $712,953; expenditures, $555,751; qualifying distributions, $551,353; giving activities include $551,353 for 2 grants (high: $529,753; low: $21,600).
Purpose and activities: Giving primarily to finance education for women in developing countries.
Fields of interest: Education; International development; Women.
Limitations: Applications not accepted. Giving primarily in CA and Washington, DC; some funding also in Bangladesh and Tajikistan. No grants to individuals.
Application information: Unsolicited requests for funds not accepted.
Officers and Directors:* Karim Merali,* Pres.; Mehdi Merali,* V.P.; Gary Worsham,* Secy.-Treas.
EIN: 260875013

9023
Meredith Foundation ✧
P.O. Box 117
Mineola, TX 75773-0117

Trust established in 1958 in TX.
Donor: Harry W. Meredith†.
Foundation type: Independent foundation.
Financial data (yr. ended 12/31/13): Assets, $27,619,245 (M); expenditures, $1,583,214; qualifying distributions, $1,404,936; giving activities include $1,360,220 for 12 grants (high: $310,000; low: $2,000).
Purpose and activities: Giving primarily for civic projects; support also for children, youth, and social services, cultural projects, and a library.
Fields of interest: Performing arts, theater; Arts; Libraries/library science; Education; Health care; Human services; Children/youth, services; Community/economic development.
Type of support: General/operating support; Equipment; Scholarship funds.
Limitations: Applications not accepted. Giving limited to the Mineola, TX, area. No grants to individuals.
Publications: Program policy statement.
Application information: Contributes only to pre-selected organizations.
Board meeting date(s): Monthly
Officers: J. Carl Norris, Chair.; Lou Wagner, Vice-Chair.; Bob Smith, Secy.-Treas.
Trustees: Freda Madsen; Jerry Phillips.
EIN: 756024469
Selected grants: The following grants are a representative sample of this grantmaker's funding activity:
$221,939 to Mineola Civic Center, Mineola, TX, 2012. For Charitable - Operating Budget; Maintenance; Equipment.
$125,886 to Mineola Memorial Library, Mineola, TX, 2012. For Charitable - Operating Budget.
$111,964 to Lake Country Playhouse, Mineola, TX, 2012. For Charitable - Promote Theatre Arts; Salaries and Operations.
$41,474 to Addie E. McFarland Foundation, Mineola, TX, 2012. For charitable - operations.

9024
Paul & Jane Meyer Family Foundation ✧
(formerly Paul J. Meyer Family Foundation)
P.O. Box 7411
Waco, TX 76714-7411 (254) 776-0034

Established in 1984 in TX.
Donors: Paul J. Meyer, Sr.†; Jane Meyer; Japale, Ltd.; SMI International, Inc.; L-K Marketing; Cayhesse; Darrell Helton; Terry Irwin; Centre Island Properties.
Foundation type: Independent foundation.
Financial data (yr. ended 12/31/12): Assets, $32,210,132 (M); gifts received, $200,000; expenditures, $2,976,983; qualifying distributions, $1,976,904; giving activities include $1,852,586 for grants.
Purpose and activities: Giving primarily to Protestant organizations, schools, and churches, with emphasis on Baptist churches; some funding also for education, camps, and human services.
Fields of interest: Higher education; Education; Health organizations, association; Recreation, camps; Human services; Protestant agencies & churches.
Limitations: Giving primarily in TX, with emphasis on Waco; some funding nationally. No grants to individuals.
Application information:
Initial approach: Typed statement
Deadline(s): None
Officers and Directors:* Alice Jane Meyer,* Pres.; Terry Irwin,* V.P.; Georgetta Duncan, Secy.-Treas.; Christie Johnson; Janna Slechta.
EIN: 742357421

9025
MFI Foundation ✧
(formerly Meredith Private Foundation)
P.O. Box 2146
Austin, TX 78768-3597

Established in 1998 in TX.
Donors: Lynn M. Meredith; Thomas J. Meredith.
Foundation type: Independent foundation.
Financial data (yr. ended 12/31/12): Assets, $20,395,073 (M); expenditures, $1,689,228; qualifying distributions, $1,562,213; giving activities include $1,561,965 for 45 grants (high: $500,000; low: $250).
Purpose and activities: Giving primarily for the arts, education, children and youth services, including a children's hospital, and for human services.
Fields of interest: Performing arts centers; Arts; Elementary/secondary education; Higher education; Education; Hospitals (specialty); Human services; Children/youth, services.
Limitations: Applications not accepted. Giving primarily in TX. No grants to individuals.
Application information: Contributes only to pre-selected organizations.
Directors: Lynn M. Meredith; Thomas J. Meredith; Scott M. Mullen.
EIN: 742882442

9026
The Miles Foundation, Inc. ✧
2821 W. 7th St., Ste. 200
Fort Worth, TX 76107-8914 (817) 420-9914
Contact: Jay McCall

Established in 1999 in TX.
Donors: Ellison Miles†; Miles Production, Co., Inc.; The Ellison Miles EM Trust; The Ellison Miles Production Co. Trust.
Foundation type: Independent foundation.
Financial data (yr. ended 12/31/13): Assets, $43,112,286 (M); gifts received, $1,040,000; expenditures, $3,392,765; qualifying distributions, $2,106,200; giving activities include $1,440,890 for 44 grants (high: $270,000; low: $250).
Purpose and activities: Giving primarily for higher education and human services.
Fields of interest: Elementary/secondary education; Higher education; Human services.
Limitations: Applications accepted. Giving primarily in TX, with emphasis on Dallas. No grants to individuals.
Application information: Application form required.
Initial approach: Proposal
Deadline(s): Spring: Letters of Inquiry due Apr. 1; Full Applications due May 15, Fall: Letters of Inquiry due Sept. 1; Full Applications due Oct. 15
Officers and Directors:* C. Grant Coates,* C.E.O.; Sherry A. Wilson,* C.O.O.; Jack L. Burdett,* C.F.O.
EIN: 752739180

9027
The David B. Miller Family Foundation ✧
3811 Turtle Creek Blvd., Ste. 1000
Dallas, TX 75219-4533

Established in 2006 in TX.
Donor: David B. Miller.
Foundation type: Independent foundation.
Financial data (yr. ended 12/31/13): Assets, $339,850 (M); gifts received, $4,238,183; expenditures, $5,149,812; qualifying distributions, $5,139,601; giving activities include $5,139,601 for 63 grants (high: $2,212,072; low: $500).
Fields of interest: Higher education; Human services; Foundations (private grantmaking); United Ways and Federated Giving Programs; Protestant agencies & churches.
Limitations: Applications not accepted. Giving primarily in TX, with emphasis on Dallas. No grants to individuals.
Application information: Contributes only to pre-selected organizations.
Officers: David B. Miller, Pres.; Meredith Miller Bebee, V.P. and Secy.; Kyle David Miller, V.P. and Treas.; Carolyn Lacy Miller, V.P.
EIN: 208103224
Selected grants: The following grants are a representative sample of this grantmaker's funding activity:
$131,690 to Make-A-Wish Foundation of North Texas, Irving, TX, 2011.
$110,000 to Salvation Army of Dallas, Dallas, TX, 2011.

9028
Steven and Sheila Miller Foundation ✧
10000 Memorial Dr., Ste. 660
Houston, TX 77024-3411
FAX: (713) 259-8864;
E-mail: Steve.Miller@SLMDV.com

Established in 2002 in TX.
Donors: Sheila M. Miller; Steven L. Miller.
Foundation type: Independent foundation.
Financial data (yr. ended 12/31/13): Assets, $3,857,163 (M); expenditures, $708,062; qualifying distributions, $681,344; giving activities include $676,650 for 23 grants (high: $270,000; low: $250).
Fields of interest: Arts; Higher education, university; Education; Human services; Youth, services; United Ways and Federated Giving Programs.
Type of support: General/operating support; Annual campaigns; Capital campaigns; Professorships; Scholarship funds; Research.
Limitations: Applications not accepted. Giving primarily in Houston, TX. No grants to individuals.
Application information: Contributes only to pre-selected organizations.
Officers and Directors:* Steven L. Miller,* Pres. and Treas.; Sheila M. Miller,* V.P.; Steven L. Miller, Jr.,* Secy.; Ashley M. Ranton.
EIN: 820576089
Selected grants: The following grants are a representative sample of this grantmaker's funding activity:

$25,000 to Points of Light Institute, Atlanta, GA, 2011.

9029
The Cynthia & George Mitchell Foundation
P.O. Box 8937
The Woodlands, TX 77387-8937 (713) 377-5060
Contact: Katherine Lorenz, Pres.; Marilu Hastings, Dir., Sustainability Prog.
Main URL: http://www.cgmf.org/p/home.html
Cynthia and George Mitchell Foundation
Blog: http://www.cgmf.org/blog/rss.php
Facebook: https://www.facebook.com/MitchellFoundation
George Mitchell's Giving Pledge Profile: http://glasspockets.org/philanthropy-in-focus/eye-on-the-giving-pledge/profiles/mitchell
Google Plus: https://www.plus.google.com/111250604816631864539/posts
Twitter: https://twitter.com/MitchFound
YouTube: https://www.youtube.com/user/CGMFoundation

Established in 1981 in TX.
Donors: Cynthia W. Mitchell†; George P. Mitchell†.
Foundation type: Independent foundation.
Financial data (yr. ended 12/31/12): Assets, $133,156,145 (M); gifts received, $24,700,630; expenditures, $14,855,243; qualifying distributions, $15,092,777; giving activities include $12,871,500 for 128 grants (high: $2,500,000; low: $500).
Purpose and activities: The foundation is a mission-driven grantmaking foundation that seeks innovative, sustainable solutions for human and environmental problems. The foundation works as an engine of change in both policy and practice in Texas, supporting high-impact projects at the nexus of environmental protection, social equity, and economic vibrancy.
Fields of interest: Science; Science.
Limitations: Giving limited to TX. No support for political candidates or support to influence legislation, or for research, development, commercialization or demonstration of technology, and no support for demonstration projects or local community projects. No grants for for-profit organizations and generally no support for general operating support.
Application information: The foundation does not review unsolicited proposals. If you are confident that your project fits within the priorities of a particular foundation program, you may complete the online Letter of Inquiry form available on foundation website without discussing your project with foundation staff.
Initial approach: Online letter of inquiry
Officers and Directors:* Katherine Lorenz,* Pres. and Treas.; Carleton Grant Mitchell,* V.P. and Secy.; Meredith Mitchell Dreiss,* Pres. Emeritus; Meredith Heimburger; Pamela Mitchell Maguire; Brian Gregory Mitchell; George Scott Mitchell; John Kirk Mitchell; Mark Douglas Mitchell; Michael Kent Mitchell; Sarah Scott Mitchell.
EIN: 742170127
Selected grants: The following grants are a representative sample of this grantmaker's funding activity:
$2,500,000 to Carnegie Institution of Washington, Washington, DC, 2012. For Giant Magellan Telescope Consortium.
$2,500,000 to Texas A & M Foundation, College Station, TX, 2012. For Giant Magellan Telescope Consortium.
$1,750,000 to Texas A & M Foundation, College Station, TX, 2012. For MIFPA consultancy fee.
$1,000,000 to Texas A & M Foundation, College Station, TX, 2012. For Giant Magellan Telescope.
$500,000 to University of Texas Health Science Center, Houston, TX, 2012. To compete for NIH Recognition.
$400,000 to Environmental Defense Fund, New York, NY, 2012. For Getting Natural Gas on Right Path.
$350,000 to Novim Group, Santa Barbara, CA, 2012. For analysis of hydrocarbon emissions.
$250,000 to University of Texas, Austin, TX, 2012. For Sustainability in Higher Education.
$125,000 to Baylor College of Medicine, Houston, TX, 2012.
$100,000 to Texas Tribune, Austin, TX, 2012. For energy and water reporting budget.

9030
The Mitchell Foundation ✧
12400 Coit Rd., No. 800
Dallas, TX 75251-2009 (214) 751-8183
Contact: Gary D. Witherspoon, V.P.

Established in 1998 in TX.
Donors: Lee Roy Mitchell; Tandy Mitchell.
Foundation type: Independent foundation.
Financial data (yr. ended 12/31/12): Assets, $40,753,666 (M); expenditures, $2,324,400; qualifying distributions, $1,793,667; giving activities include $1,793,667 for 30 grants (high: $350,000; low: $5,000).
Fields of interest: Education; Animal welfare; Human services; Children, services; Christian agencies & churches.
Limitations: Applications accepted. Giving primarily in TX. No grants to individuals.
Application information: Application form required.
Initial approach: Letter
Deadline(s): None
Officers: Lee Roy Mitchell, Pres.; Gary D. Witherspoon, V.P.; Tandy Mitchell, Secy.
EIN: 752769798

9031
William A. and Elizabeth B. Moncrief Foundation ✧
950 Commerce St.
Fort Worth, TX 76102-5418
Contact: W.A. Moncrief, Jr., Pres. and Fdn. Mgr.

Established in 1954 in TX.
Donors: William A. Moncrief†; Elizabeth B. Moncrief†; William A. Moncrief, Jr.; Moncrief Corporation.
Foundation type: Independent foundation.
Financial data (yr. ended 09/30/13): Assets, $2,390,869 (M); gifts received, $29,249; expenditures, $672,720; qualifying distributions, $672,500; giving activities include $672,500 for 33 grants (high: $125,000; low: $1,000).
Fields of interest: Museums (art); Museums (specialized); Arts; Higher education; Education; Animal welfare; Hospitals (general); Human services; United Ways and Federated Giving Programs.
Type of support: General/operating support.
Limitations: Applications accepted. Giving primarily in TX. No grants to individuals.
Application information: Application form required.
Initial approach: Letter
Deadline(s): None
Officers: William A. Moncrief, Jr., Pres. and Fdn. Mgr.; R.W. Moncrief, V.P.; C.B. Moncrief, Secy.-Treas.
EIN: 756036329

9032
Moneygram Foundation, Inc ✧ ☆
2828 N. Harwood St., Ste. 1500
Dallas, TX 75201

Donor: Moneygram Payment Systems, Inc.
Foundation type: Company-sponsored foundation.
Financial data (yr. ended 12/31/13): Assets, $60,038 (M); gifts received, $525,030; expenditures, $464,922; qualifying distributions, $464,922; giving activities include $464,922 for 13 grants (high: $75,000; low: $10,000).
Limitations: Applications not accepted.
Application information: Unsolicited requests for funds not accepted.
Directors: Juan Agualimpia; Larry Angelilli; Michael Engelmeyer; Patricia Sullivan; Corinna Ulrich.
EIN: 454157335

9033
The Moody Foundation ✧
2302 Post Office St., Ste. 704
Galveston, TX 77550-1936 (409) 797-1500
Contact: Allan Matthews, Grants Dir.
FAX: (409) 763-5564; E-mail: info@themoodyf.org; Additional tel. (for Dallas office): (866) 742-1133. E-mail for Allan Matthews: Amatthews@moodyf.org; Main URL: http://www.moodyf.org
For scholarships: Samantha Seale, Scholarship Admin., tel.: (409) 797-1511, e-mail: Samanthas@moodyf.org

Trust established in 1942 in TX.
Donors: William Lewis Moody, Jr.†; Libbie Shearn Moody†.
Foundation type: Independent foundation.
Financial data (yr. ended 12/31/13): Assets, $1,530,491,198 (M); gifts received, $25,328,000; expenditures, $62,643,810; qualifying distributions, $58,919,621; giving activities include $54,015,543 for 58 grants (high: $13,938,065; low: $5,000), and $781,000 for grants to individuals.
Purpose and activities: Funds to be used for historic restoration projects, performing arts organizations, and cultural programs; promotion of health, science, and education; community and social services; and the field of religion.
Fields of interest: Performing arts; Arts; Medical school/education; Education; Environment; Health care; AIDS; Medical research, institute; AIDS research; Youth development; Human services; Community/economic development; Engineering/technology; Science; Religion; Aging; Disabilities, people with; Economically disadvantaged.
Type of support: Capital campaigns; Building/renovation; Equipment; Land acquisition; Program development; Conferences/seminars; Publication; Seed money; Scholarship funds; Research; Technical assistance; Matching/challenge support.

Limitations: Applications accepted. Giving limited to TX, with a primary emphasis on foundation-initiated projects in Galveston. No grants to individuals (except for students covered by scholarship programs in Galveston and Dallas Counties), or for operating budgets (except for start-up purposes), continuing support, annual campaigns, or deficit financing; no loans or program-related investments.
Publications: Application guidelines; Annual report; Grants list.
Application information: Foundation will send application guidelines if project is of interest. For scholarship application form and submission deadlines contact Samantha Seale, Scholarship Admin. Application form required.
Initial approach: Letter of inquiry or through web site on an ongoing basis
Copies of proposal: 1
Deadline(s): 6 weeks prior to board meetings
Board meeting date(s): Quarterly
Final notification: 3 weeks after board meetings
Officers and Trustees:* Robert L. Moody, Sr.,* Chair.; Garrick Addison, C.F.O.; Frances A. Moody-Dahlberg,* Exec. Dir.; Ross R. Moody.
Number of staff: 10 full-time professional; 4 full-time support.
EIN: 741403105
Selected grants: The following grants are a representative sample of this grantmaker's funding activity:
$12,000,000 to Southern Methodist University, Dallas, TX, 2012. For assistance in renovating Moody Coliseum, multi-purpose arena on SMU campus and home to SMU Mustangs, basketball team.
$6,872,254 to Transitional Learning Center at Galveston, Galveston, TX, 2012. For assistance in continuing programs at the Transitional Learning Center of Galveston-Post Office Division.
$6,061,935 to Moody Gardens, Galveston, TX, 2012. For assistance with guest room and public areas renovations.
$4,000,000 to College Baseball Foundation, Lubbock, TX, 2012. For assistance in constructing and endowing the College Baseball Hall of Fame.
$4,000,000 to OConnell High School Foundation, Galveston, TX, 2012. For assistance in repairing aging facilities, upgrading curriculum and faculty, and increasing the operating endowment.
$100,000 to Holy Family Catholic School, Galveston, TX, 2012. For assistance with improvements to the early childhood and middle-school wings, and enhancing the appearance of the facility.
$75,000 to Camp for All Foundation, Houston, TX, 2012. To support the Reaching the Stars campaign to build improvements to Camp For All, including a multi-purpose center.
$37,500 to Saint Vincents House, Galveston, TX, 2012. For assistance in providing clinic care, including specialty clinics in vision, psychiatry, nephrology and dermatology to uninsured, underinsured and indigent patients.

9034
Allen Lovelace Moore and Blanche Davis Moore Foundation ✧
(doing business as The Blanche Davis Moore Foundation)
700 Everhart Rd., Ste. J-21
Corpus Christi, TX 78411-1941 (361) 814-6700
Contact: Gary J. Leach
FAX: (361) 814-6701; Main URL: http://www.moorefoundationcc.com

Established in 1993 in TX.
Donor: Blanche Davis Moore†.
Foundation type: Independent foundation.
Financial data (yr. ended 12/31/13): Assets, $12,353,838 (M); expenditures, $935,916; qualifying distributions, $539,063; giving activities include $539,063 for 54 grants (high: $75,000; low: $63).
Purpose and activities: Support primarily for projects benefiting children and youth under 18 years of age, in Neuces County, TX, and the immediately surrounding counties.
Fields of interest: Higher education; Athletics/sports, training; Human services; Salvation Army; YM/YWCAs & YM/YWHAs; Children/youth, services; Christian agencies & churches; Infants/toddlers; Children/youth; Children; Youth; Young adults; Disabilities, people with; Physically disabled; Blind/visually impaired; Deaf/hearing impaired; Mentally disabled; Minorities; African Americans/Blacks; Hispanics/Latinos; Infants/toddlers, female; Girls; Young adults, female; Infants/toddlers, male; Boys; Young adults, male; Substance abusers; Crime/abuse victims; Immigrants/refugees; Economically disadvantaged; Homeless.
Type of support: General/operating support; Continuing support; Annual campaigns; Equipment; Emergency funds; Program development; Conferences/seminars; Film/video/radio; Publication; Scholarship funds; Research; Technical assistance.
Limitations: Applications accepted. Giving primarily in the Corpus Christi, TX area. No grants to individuals.
Publications: Application guidelines; Grants list.
Application information: Application form and complete application guidelines available on foundation web site. Application form required.
Initial approach: Fax or mail application
Deadline(s): July 1
Board meeting date(s): Oct.
Officer and Directors:* Rev. J. Homer Davis,* Chair.; Gary J. Leach,* Pres.; Paul Davis,* Treas.; Robyn Abernathy; Ira Gillum; Brandon Leach.
Number of staff: 1 full-time professional; 1 full-time support.
EIN: 742675281
Selected grants: The following grants are a representative sample of this grantmaker's funding activity:
$14,250 to Del Mar College Foundation, Corpus Christi, TX, 2012. For child care.
$14,250 to Laity Renewal Foundation, Kerrville, TX, 2012. For summer recreation.
$14,250 to Palmer Drug Abuse Program of Corpus Christi, Corpus Christi, TX, 2012. For youth outreach.

9035
Wayne & Jo Ann Moore Charitable Foundation ✧
403 N. Marienfeld St.
Midland, TX 79701-7323

Established in 2006 in TX.
Donor: Lee Wayne Moore†.
Foundation type: Independent foundation.
Financial data (yr. ended 12/31/12): Assets, $36,998,743 (M); gifts received, $728,000; expenditures, $2,903,970; qualifying distributions, $1,985,419; giving activities include $1,910,633 for 84 grants (high: $135,000; low: $5,000).
Fields of interest: Human services.
Limitations: Applications not accepted. Giving primarily in TX, with emphasis on Midland. No grants to individuals.
Application information: Contributes only to pre-selected organizations.
Officer: Tom Moore, Pres. and Exec. Dir.
Directors: Emily Gilmer; Stuart Gilmer; Dauphen Jackson; Ann Jensen; James Moore.
EIN: 204808454

9036
The W. T. & Louise J. Moran Foundation ✧
3843 N. Braeswood Blvd., Ste. 200
Houston, TX 77025-3001
Contact: R. Robert Mullins, Tr.

Established in 1997 in TX.
Donor: Mrs. W.T. Moran.
Foundation type: Independent foundation.
Financial data (yr. ended 12/31/12): Assets, $41,855,825 (M); gifts received, $1,300,000; expenditures, $2,742,310; qualifying distributions, $2,063,847; giving activities include $1,982,800 for 50 grants (high: $600,000; low: $1,000).
Fields of interest: Museums; Health organizations, association; United Ways and Federated Giving Programs; Children.
Type of support: Continuing support; Capital campaigns.
Limitations: Applications not accepted. Giving primarily in Houston, TX. No grants to individuals.
Application information: Contributes only to pre-selected organizations.
Trustees: Randall E. Evans; Allen L. Jogerst; R. Robert Mullins; C.W. Sunday.
Number of staff: None.
EIN: 760513027

9037
Morgan Charitable Foundation, Inc. ✧
801 Laurel St.
Beaumont, TX 77701-2228
Contact: Glen W. Morgan, Pres.

Established in 1998 in TX.
Donor: Glen W. Morgan.
Foundation type: Independent foundation.
Financial data (yr. ended 12/31/13): Assets, $2,101,798 (M); gifts received, $750,000; expenditures, $1,018,483; qualifying distributions, $1,017,933; giving activities include $1,017,933 for 16 grants (high: $550,000; low: $400).
Fields of interest: Higher education; Human services; Children/youth, services; Protestant agencies & churches.
Limitations: Applications accepted. Giving primarily in Beaumont, TX.
Application information: Application form not required.
Initial approach: Proposal
Deadline(s): None
Officer: Glen W. Morgan, Pres.
EIN: 760589391
Selected grants: The following grants are a representative sample of this grantmaker's funding activity:

$102,000 to Garth House-Mickey Mehaffy Childrens Advocacy Program, Beaumont, TX, 2011.

9038
Morgan Foundation ✧
11 Greenway Plz., Ste. 2000
Houston, TX 77046

Established in 2002 in TX.
Donor: Portcullis Partners, L.P.
Foundation type: Company-sponsored foundation.
Financial data (yr. ended 12/31/13): Assets, $18,501,656 (M); expenditures, $3,365,857; qualifying distributions, $3,055,000; giving activities include $3,055,000 for 6 grants (high: $1,600,000; low: $5,000).
Purpose and activities: The foundation supports community foundations and organizations involved with folk arts, secondary and higher education.
Fields of interest: Arts, folk arts; Secondary school/ education; Higher education; Foundations (community).
Type of support: Scholarship funds; General/ operating support; Program development.
Limitations: Applications not accepted. Giving limited to CA and Houston, TX. No grants to individuals.
Application information: Contributes only to pre-selected organizations.
Officers and Directors:* William V. Morgan,* Pres. and Treas.; Sara S. Morgan,* V.P. and Secy.; Catherine A. Morgan; Christine R. Morgan; Michael C. Morgan.
Number of staff: None.
EIN: 223886549

9039
Morian Foundation ✧ ☆
300 Jackson Hill St.
Houston, TX 77007-7430

Established in TX.
Donor: S. Reed Morian.
Foundation type: Independent foundation.
Financial data (yr. ended 12/31/13): Assets, $11,460,423 (M); gifts received, $2,000,000; expenditures, $595,114; qualifying distributions, $500,000; giving activities include $500,000 for 1 grant.
Fields of interest: Museums (science/technology).
Limitations: Applications not accepted. Giving primarily in Houston, TX. No grants to individuals.
Application information: Unsolicited requests for funds not accepted.
Trustee: S. Reed Morian.
EIN: 461580212

9040
Morning Star Family Foundation ✧
3628 Beverly Dr.
Dallas, TX 75205-2868

Established in 1996 in TX.
Donors: Ellen McStay; Mrs. John D. McStay; The Morning Star Family Limited Partnership.
Foundation type: Independent foundation.
Financial data (yr. ended 12/31/13): Assets, $7,325,316 (M); expenditures, $785,805; qualifying distributions, $779,464; giving activities include $761,000 for 31 grants (high: $100,000; low: $5,000).
Purpose and activities: Giving for education, youth programs, social services, and Christian and Protestant organizations, churches and ministries.
Fields of interest: Education; Human services; Children/youth, services; Christian agencies & churches; Protestant agencies & churches.
Limitations: Applications not accepted. Giving primarily in Dallas, TX. No grants to individuals.
Application information: Contributes only to pre-selected organizations.
Officers and Trustees:* Ellen McStay,* Pres.; John McStay,* Secy.; Dee Devlin; Eric Devlin; Judge McStay.
EIN: 752682211

9041
The Morris Foundation ✧
3707 Camp Bowie Blvd., Ste. 260
Fort Worth, TX 76107-3328 (817) 882-8100

Established in 1986 in TX.
Donors: Jack B. Morris†; Linda C. Morris.
Foundation type: Independent foundation.
Financial data (yr. ended 12/31/13): Assets, $143,350,651 (M); expenditures, $7,460,677; qualifying distributions, $7,127,494; giving activities include $6,803,205 for 95 grants (high: $500,000; low: $1,000).
Purpose and activities: Giving primarily for social services, including child development and welfare; support also for educational programs, health associations, and to Protestant churches and organizations.
Fields of interest: Child development, education; Education; Hospitals (specialty); Health organizations; Human services; Children/youth, services; Child development, services; Protestant agencies & churches.
Limitations: Applications not accepted. Giving primarily in Fort Worth, TX. No grants to individuals.
Application information: Contributes only to pre-selected organizations.
Officer: Joseph A. Monteleone, Exec. Dir.
Trustee: Linda C. Elsey.
EIN: 752137184
Selected grants: The following grants are a representative sample of this grantmaker's funding activity:
$1,000,000 to Child Study Center Foundation, Fort Worth, TX, 2011. For Developmental Pediatrics Chair.
$1,000,000 to Cook Childrens Medical Center, Fort Worth, TX, 2011. For Capital Campaign.
$500,000 to Union Gospel Mission of Tarrant County, Fort Worth, TX, 2011. For God's Healthy Place Capital Campaign.
$300,000 to Ronald McDonald House of Fort Worth, Fort Worth, TX, 2011. For Making More Rooms Capital Campaign - Inst 1.
$150,000 to Cook Childrens Medical Center, Fort Worth, TX, 2011. For Charity Care Community Clinics.
$125,000 to Camp Fire USA, First Texas Council, Fort Worth, TX, 2011. For Kindergarten Readiness Program.
$40,000 to Gill Childrens Services, Fort Worth, TX, 2011. For Critically Needed Children's Services.
$40,000 to Harris Methodist Health Foundation, Fort Worth, TX, 2011. For Indigent Mammography Program.
$30,000 to Harris Methodist Health Foundation, Fort Worth, TX, 2011. For Indigent Pharmacy Program.
$20,000 to Learning Center of North Texas, Fort Worth, TX, 2011. For Schools Attuned Teacher Training Program.

9042
Luke And Lori Morrow Family Foundation ✧ ☆
P.O. Box 61447
Midland, TX 79711-1447

Established in TX.
Foundation type: Independent foundation.
Financial data (yr. ended 12/31/13): Assets, $18,841,237 (M); expenditures, $1,107,372; qualifying distributions, $1,005,000; giving activities include $1,005,000 for 34 grants (high: $150,000; low: $5,000).
Fields of interest: Human services; Christian agencies & churches.
Limitations: Giving in the U.S., with emphasis on TX.
Directors: Lori Morrow; Luke Morrow.
EIN: 453982079

9043
Harry S. Moss Heart Trust ✧
c/o Bank of America, N.A.
P.O. Box 831041
Dallas, TX 75283-1041 (214) 209-6477
Contact: Jenae Guillory

Trust established in 1973 in TX.
Donors: Harry S. Moss†; Florence M. Moss†.
Foundation type: Independent foundation.
Financial data (yr. ended 09/30/13): Assets, $42,025,990 (M); expenditures, $2,802,210; qualifying distributions, $2,154,232; giving activities include $1,904,067 for 7 grants (high: $1,200,000; low: $50,000).
Purpose and activities: Support for the cure and research of heart disease.
Fields of interest: Heart & circulatory diseases; Medical research, institute; Heart & circulatory research.
Type of support: Annual campaigns; Capital campaigns; Building/renovation; Equipment; Endowments; Research.
Limitations: Applications accepted. Giving limited to TX, with emphasis on Dallas County.
Application information: Application form not required.
Initial approach: Letter
Copies of proposal: 1
Deadline(s): None
Board meeting date(s): As required
Trustee: Bank of America, N.A.
Number of staff: 1 part-time professional; 1 part-time support.
EIN: 756147501

9044
The Mulva Family Foundation ✧
11603 Versailles Lakes Ln.
Houston, TX 77082-6843

Established in 2005 in TX.
Donors: James J. Mulva; Miriam B. Mulva.
Foundation type: Independent foundation.

Financial data (yr. ended 12/31/13): Assets, $216,408,959 (M); gifts received, $4,290,556; expenditures, $6,225,954; qualifying distributions, $5,711,088; giving activities include $5,692,500 for 20 grants (high: $3,000,000; low: $2,500).
Fields of interest: Higher education; Health care; Catholic agencies & churches.
Limitations: Applications not accepted. Giving primarily in OK, TX, and WI.
Application information: Unsolicited requests for funds not accepted.
Officers: James J. Mulva, Pres.; Adelaide M. Debow, Secy.
Directors: John A. Carrig; Miriam B. Mulva.
EIN: 203221183
Selected grants: The following grants are a representative sample of this grantmaker's funding activity:
$100,000 to University of Texas, Austin, TX, 2011.
$50,000 to Green Country Free Clinic, Bartlesville, OK, 2011.
$50,000 to Norbertine Community of New Mexico, Albuquerque, NM, 2011.
$50,000 to Pontifical North American College, Washington, DC, 2011.
$25,000 to Birthright of Bartlesville, Bartlesville, OK, 2011.
$25,000 to Texas Heart Institute, Houston, TX, 2011.

9045
The Ginger Murchison Foundation ✧
c/o Don Wills, Pres.
5949 Sherry Ln., Ste. 1225
Dallas, TX 75225-8067

Established in 1993 in TX.
Donor: Virginia L. Murchison†.
Foundation type: Independent foundation.
Financial data (yr. ended 12/31/13): Assets, $41,299,026 (M); expenditures, $2,452,270; qualifying distributions, $1,765,087; giving activities include $1,634,675 for 69 grants (high: $405,675; low: $1,000).
Purpose and activities: Giving primarily for education, health care, and human services; support also for Christian organizations.
Fields of interest: Arts; Elementary/secondary education; Higher education; Medical care, community health systems; Health organizations, association; Human services; Children/youth, services; Family services; Community/economic development; Christian agencies & churches.
Limitations: Applications not accepted. Giving primarily in TX, with emphasis on Athens. No grants to individuals.
Application information: Contributes only to pre-selected organizations.
Officers: Don Wills, Pres. and Treas.; Don Jackson, V.P.; Rusty Workman, Secy.
Director: Charles Wills.
EIN: 752482261
Selected grants: The following grants are a representative sample of this grantmaker's funding activity:
$461,850 to Athens Independent School District, Athens, TX, 2012. For Staff development, purchase of laptops, mentoring Program and other Programs.
$55,000 to Henderson County Food Pantry, Athens, TX, 2012. For General operating support of Programs for indigent.
$35,000 to Mercy Street, Dallas, TX, 2012. For General operating support for local meals for seniors.
$25,000 to Baylor University, School of Nursing, Waco, TX, 2012. For endowed scholarships.
$20,000 to Dallas Theological Seminary, Dallas, TX, 2012. For General operating support of Christian education.
$10,000 to Barbara Bush Texas Fund for Family Literacy, Houston, TX, 2012. Toward literacy programs.
$10,000 to Henderson County HELP Center, Athens, TX, 2012. For Teen education Programs.
$10,000 to Preston Hollow Presbyterian Church, Dallas, TX, 2012. To support of Angel Tree and Malawi Tree Programs.
$6,000 to Fairhill School, Dallas, TX, 2012. Toward general operating support of education of students with learning differences.
$2,000 to K-Life Ministries, Branson, MO, 2012. To support of youth ministry.

9046
The Lupe Murchison Foundation ✧
c/o J.V. Smith Professional Corp.
16250 Knoll Trail Dr., Ste. 110
Dallas, TX 75248-2863 (972) 248-2200
Contact: Jerry V. Smith, Tr.

Established in 2001 in TX.
Donor: Lucille G. Murchison†.
Foundation type: Independent foundation.
Financial data (yr. ended 12/31/12): Assets, $46,752,459 (M); expenditures, $3,259,962; qualifying distributions, $2,331,990; giving activities include $2,230,053 for 22+ grants (high: $500,000).
Purpose and activities: Focusing primarily on support to qualified organizations that administer the funding of programs that provide educational and medical benefits to children, higher and other education; support also for hospitals, including a children's hospital.
Fields of interest: Higher education; Education; Hospitals (general); Hospitals (specialty); Health care; Medical research, institute; Human services; Christian agencies & churches.
Type of support: General/operating support; Scholarship funds.
Limitations: Giving primarily in North TX, with emphasis on Dallas. No grants to individuals.
Application information:
Initial approach: Letter
Deadline(s): None
Trustees: Robert McCulloch; D. Michael Redden; Jerry V. Smith.
EIN: 752953224

9047
The NAH Foundation ✧
1900 N. Akard St.
Dallas, TX 75201-2300

Established in 2001 in TX.
Donors: Ray L. Hunt; Nancy Ann Hunt.
Foundation type: Independent foundation.
Financial data (yr. ended 12/31/12): Assets, $1,357,970 (M); gifts received, $1,000,000; expenditures, $1,210,100; qualifying distributions, $1,210,100; giving activities include $1,208,402 for 17 grants (high: $220,000; low: $10,000).
Purpose and activities: Giving primarily for education and human services.
Fields of interest: Education; Substance abuse, services; Mental health/crisis services, hot-lines; Human services; Protestant agencies & churches; Women.
Limitations: Applications not accepted. Giving primarily in Dallas, TX. No grants to individuals.
Application information: Unsolicited requests for funds not accepted.
Officers and Directors:* Nancy Ann Hunt,* Pres.; Christopher W. Kleinert,* Secy.; Hunter L. Hunt,* Treas.
EIN: 752945062

9048
Harvey E. Najim Family Foundation ✧
613 N.W. Loop 410, Ste. 875
San Antonio, TX 78216-5507 (210) 369-0666
Contact: Melissa Bauman, Exec. Dir.
FAX: (210) 918-1860;
E-mail: melissa.bauman@najimfoundation.org;
E-mail for Stephanie Sanders, Grants Admin.: stephanie.sanders@najimfoundation.org, tel.: (210) 255-8435, ext. 18002; Main URL: http://www.najimfoundation.org/
Facebook: http://www.facebook.com/pages/San-Antonio-TX/The-Harvey-E-Najim-Family-Foundation/83493988379

Established in 2006 in TX.
Donor: Harvey E. Najim.
Foundation type: Independent foundation.
Financial data (yr. ended 12/31/12): Assets, $71,843,534 (M); gifts received, $16,000; expenditures, $4,766,339; qualifying distributions, $4,448,271; giving activities include $4,448,271 for grants.
Purpose and activities: The foundation's mission is to help 501(c)(3) public charities in the greater San Antonio, Texas, area to advance children's education, children's medical treatment, medical research for illnesses and diseases affecting children, and other children's charitable purposes.
Fields of interest: Education; Health care; Medical research; Crime/violence prevention, child abuse; Youth development, services; Children/youth, services; Children; Disabilities, people with.
Limitations: Applications accepted. Giving primarily in the greater San Antonio, TX area. No support for organizations lacking 501(c)(3) status. No grants to individuals, or for multi-year projects.
Application information: Once the Letter of Inquiry and IRS determination letter have been completed and uploaded to the foundation web site, applicants must e-mail Stephanie Sanders, Grants Admin., stating that these materials have been uploaded. See foundation web site for full guidelines and requirements. A letter of inquiry (no more than 3 pages), must be submitted to the foundation for consideration to be invited for a full application. Articles, reports, videos, or other material are to be submitted upon the request of the foundation if needed.
Initial approach: Online Letter of Inquiry format on foundation web site
Copies of proposal: 9
Deadline(s): See funding schedule on foundation web site for current deadlines
Board meeting date(s): Apr., July, and Oct.
Final notification: Within 60 days following deadline dates

Directors: Don Harris; Jim House; Carrie N. Matthiesen; Nancy May; Harvey E. Najim; Christine N. Ray; Roy Terracina.
EIN: 208060391

9049
Nape Charities Fund ✧ ☆
4100 Fossil Creek Blvd.
Fort Worth, TX 76137-2723

Donors: Alamo Resources; American Oil & Gas Reporter; Harold J. Anderson, Inc.; BP American Producation Co.; Cabot Oil & Gas Corp.; Exco Resources, Inc.; Forestar; Foundation Energy Company, Inc.; G&G, Ltd.; Helis Oil & Gas Co., LLC; Indigo; Kare-Sue Energy; Jackson Kelly, PLLC; McClure Oil Company, Inc.; Oasis Petroleum North America, LLC; Qep Energy Company; Shell Offshore, Inc.; Roger A. Soupe, Inc.; Ted W. Walters & Associates, LP; The Kilburn Law Firm, PLLC.
Foundation type: Independent foundation.
Financial data (yr. ended 06/30/13): Assets, $211,082 (M); gifts received, $553,010; expenditures, $500,689; qualifying distributions, $500,000; giving activities include $500,000 for 6 grants (high: $100,000; low: $50,000).
Fields of interest: Human services.
Limitations: Applications not accepted.
Application information: Unsolicited requests for funds not accepted.
Directors: Roger Soape; Steve Wentworth; Brooks Yates.
EIN: 453791212

9050
The Margaret Gill Clements Napier Foundation ✧
1901 N. Akard St.
Dallas, TX 75201-2305

Established in 2002 in TX.
Foundation type: Independent foundation.
Financial data (yr. ended 12/31/13): Assets, $11,212,126 (M); expenditures, $730,956; qualifying distributions, $698,604; giving activities include $698,604 for 15 grants (high: $470,000; low: $1,000).
Fields of interest: Arts; Elementary/secondary education; Protestant agencies & churches.
Type of support: General/operating support.
Limitations: Applications not accepted. Giving primarily in TX, with emphasis on Dallas and Rockwell. No grants to individuals.
Application information: Contributes only to pre-selected organizations.
Officers and Trustees:* Margaret Gill Clements Napier,* Pres. and Treas.; Jeff Napier,* V.P. and Secy.; Nancy Clements Seay.
EIN: 731645120
Selected grants: The following grants are a representative sample of this grantmaker's funding activity:
$10,000 to Pregnancy Resource Council, Dallas, TX, 2011.
$5,000 to Fuller Theological Seminary, Pasadena, CA, 2011.

9051
The Nasher Foundation ✧
500 S. Center St.
Forney, TX 75126-9783

Established in 1996 in TX.
Donors: Raymond D. Nasher‡; Raymond D. Nasher Mgmt. Trust Estate.
Foundation type: Operating foundation.
Financial data (yr. ended 09/30/13): Assets, $155,245,060 (M); expenditures, $8,613,798; qualifying distributions, $6,082,519; giving activities include $5,790,000 for 2 grants (high: $5,750,000; low: $40,000), and $5,750,000 for 1 foundation-administered program.
Purpose and activities: Giving primarily to a sculpture center.
Fields of interest: Visual arts, sculpture.
Limitations: Applications not accepted. Giving primarily in TX. No grants to individuals.
Application information: Contributes only to pre-selected organizations.
Officers and Directors:* Stephen Stamas,* Chair.; David Haemissegger,* Pres.; Byron A. Parker, CPA, Treas.; Elliot R. Cattarulla,* Exec. Dir.; Nancy N. Haemissegger; John G. Heimann; William Jordan; Andrea Nasher.
EIN: 752674048

9052
Natem Foundation Inc. ✧
3555 Timmons Ln., Ste. 800
Houston, TX 77027-6498

Donor: Linda Pritzker.
Foundation type: Independent foundation.
Financial data (yr. ended 12/31/12): Assets, $52,952,450 (M); expenditures, $4,460,519; qualifying distributions, $4,382,828; giving activities include $4,188,038 for 18 grants (high: $1,000,000; low: $25,000).
Fields of interest: Human services; Community/economic development.
Limitations: Applications not accepted. Giving primarily in CA, MA, and NM and in Schwarzwald, Germany.
Application information: Contributes only to pre-selected organizations.
Officers and Directors:* Linda Pritzker,* Pres.; Aaron Stern,* V.P.; Mary Jo Sandlin,* Secy.-Treas.
EIN: 271345897
Selected grants: The following grants are a representative sample of this grantmaker's funding activity:
$1,030,928 to Tides Foundation, San Francisco, CA, 2012. For Mind and Life Institute.
$360,825 to Tides Foundation, San Francisco, CA, 2012. For Positive Futures Network.
$150,000 to University of Wisconsin Foundation, Madison, WI, 2012. For Epigenetics Project.
$100,000 to Institute for Policy Studies, Washington, DC, 2012. For New Economy Working Group Project.
$100,000 to Rudolf Steiner Foundation, San Francisco, CA, 2012. For Small Planet Fund Strategic Grants Program.
$100,000 to Santa Fe Community Foundation, Santa Fe, NM, 2012. For Hai Donor Advised Fund.
$100,000 to Tides Foundation, San Francisco, CA, 2012. For Solpo Donor Advised Fund.
$90,500 to Institute for Policy Studies, Washington, DC, 2012. For Jamaica Plain New Economy Transition Project.
$67,010 to Tides Foundation, San Francisco, CA, 2012. For The People Centered Development Forum.
$36,500 to Tides Foundation, San Francisco, CA, 2012. For Blue Mountain Clinic.

9053
Natural Gas Partners Foundation ✧ ☆
5221 N O'Connor Blvd., Ste. 1100
Irving, TX 75039-3788

Established in 2004 in TX.
Donors: Petne Parkman & Co., Inc.; Mark Doenng; Rising Starr Energy, LLC; Action Energy, Inc.; Bravo Natural Resources; Fleet; NGP Energy Capital Management, LLC; and 24 additional donors.
Foundation type: Company-sponsored foundation.
Financial data (yr. ended 12/31/13): Assets, $1,560,473 (M); expenditures, $573,597; qualifying distributions, $547,653; giving activities include $539,650 for 5 grants (high: $490,000; low: $900).
Purpose and activities: The foundation supports museums and food banks and organizations involved with theater, higher education, children services, and economically disadvantaged people.
Fields of interest: Museums; Performing arts, theater; Higher education, college; Food banks; Children, services; Economically disadvantaged.
Type of support: General/operating support.
Limitations: Applications not accepted. Giving primarily in CT, NM, TX, and WA. No grants to individuals.
Application information: Contributes only to pre-selected organizations.
Officers: Kenneth A. Hersh,* Pres.; David R. Albin,* V.P.; Christopher Ray, Secy.; Stacie Moore, Treas.
EIN: 770620172

9054
Navarro Community Foundation ✧
401 N. 14th St.
Corsicana, TX 75110-4509 (903) 874-4301
Contact: Bruce Robinson, Secy.-Treas.

Established in 1938 in TX.
Donor: Frank N. Drane‡.
Foundation type: Independent foundation.
Financial data (yr. ended 12/31/13): Assets, $22,979,758 (M); gifts received, $60,000; expenditures, $1,365,552; qualifying distributions, $1,284,410; giving activities include $1,275,897 for 35 grants (high: $200,000; low: $3,000).
Purpose and activities: Giving primarily for education, community development and human services.
Fields of interest: Education; Human services; Community/economic development.
Type of support: General/operating support; Annual campaigns; Capital campaigns; Building/renovation; Seed money; Scholarship funds; Matching/challenge support.
Limitations: Applications accepted. Giving limited to Navarro County, TX. No grants to individuals, or for research, conferences, endowment funds, publications, or special projects; no loans.
Application information: Application form required.
Initial approach: Letter
Copies of proposal: 2

Deadline(s): Requests must be received by the first of each quarter
Board meeting date(s): Jan., Apr., July, and Oct.
Officers: C. David Campbell, Chair.; C.L. Brown III, 2nd Vice-Chair.; Bruce Robinson, Secy.-Treas.
Trustees: Lloyd Huffman; John Jackson; Bill Maupin; Billie Love McFerran; Ellen McKeown; Scott Middleton; B.F. Risinger; Kim Wyatt.
Number of staff: 1 full-time professional; 1 part-time professional.
EIN: 750800663

9055
The Charles and Dana Nearburg Foundation ✧
P.O. Box 823085
Dallas, TX 75382-3085
Contact: Charles E. Nearburg, Pres.

Established in 1996 in TX.
Donors: Charles E. Nearburg; Dana E. Nearburg.
Foundation type: Operating foundation.
Financial data (yr. ended 12/31/13): Assets, $2,636,475 (M); gifts received, $39,534; expenditures, $1,775,306; qualifying distributions, $1,753,477; giving activities include $1,753,477 for 4 grants (high: $1,500,000; low: $31,250).
Purpose and activities: Giving primarily for the arts, health, and education, including assistance to children of Nearburg Producing Co. employees, or to those who have been accepted to a private middle or secondary school approved by the Corporation's scholarship committee.
Fields of interest: Performing arts; Education; Health care; Recreation, camps; Children/youth; Disabilities, people with.
Type of support: General/operating support; Building/renovation; Scholarships—to individuals.
Limitations: Giving primarily in Hanover, NH; some giving also in MD and in Dallas, TX. No support for religious or political organizations.
Application information: Application form required.
Initial approach: Letter
Deadline(s): Aug. 1
Officers and Directors:* Charles E. Nearburg,* Pres.; Duane A. Davis, Secy.; Bryan C. Birkeland; Anna A. Reischman.
EIN: 752658947
Selected grants: The following grants are a representative sample of this grantmaker's funding activity:
$750,000 to Dartmouth College, Hanover, NH, 2012. For Visual Arts Center - Nearburg Gallery and Arts Forum.
$100,000 to Maryland Institute College of Art, Baltimore, MD, 2012. For Rett Nearburg '07 Scholarship Endowment.

9056
Nestle Scholarship Foundation ✧
(formerly Carnation Company Scholarship Foundation)
c/o Bank of America, N.A.
P.O. Box 831041
Dallas, TX 75283-1041 (800) 537-4180
Contact: Kelly Voss

Established in 1952 in CA.
Donors: Carnation Co.; Nestle USA, Inc.
Foundation type: Company-sponsored foundation.
Financial data (yr. ended 12/31/13): Assets, $12,217,370 (M); expenditures, $657,621; qualifying distributions, $577,767; giving activities include $540,300 for 180 grants to individuals (high: $3,600; low: $300).
Purpose and activities: The foundation awards college scholarships to children of employees of Nestle USA. The program is administered by Scholarship America, Inc.
Fields of interest: Higher education.
Type of support: Employee-related scholarships.
Limitations: Applications not accepted. Giving primarily in areas of company operations.
Application information: Contributes only through employee-related scholarships.
Trustee Bank: Bank of America, N.A.
Advisory Committee: Paul Grimwood; Judy Cascapara; Steven Presley.
EIN: 956118622

9057
New Beginning Resources, Inc. ✧ ☆
P.O. Box 509
Porter, TX 77365-0509 (713) 494-0596
Contact: Russell Leatherman, C.O.O.
FAX: (281) 354-2110; E-mail: nbri@earthlink.net; Main URL: http://www.nbri.net

Established in 2004 in TX.
Donors: Perry L. Shaw; Patricia Shaw.
Foundation type: Operating foundation.
Financial data (yr. ended 12/31/13): Assets, $1,059,198 (M); gifts received, $557,320; expenditures, $714,419; qualifying distributions, $600,861; giving activities include $427,180 for grants, and $554,546 for 4 foundation-administered programs.
Purpose and activities: Grants primarily for Christian missionary work and human services.
Fields of interest: Human services; Christian agencies & churches.
Type of support: General/operating support; Grants to individuals.
Limitations: Applications accepted. Giving primarily in TX.
Application information: Application form not required.
Initial approach: Letter
Deadline(s): None
Officer: Russell Leatherman, C.O.O.
Board Members: Matthew P. Brouwer; Perry L. Shaw.
EIN: 200432677

9058
New Hope Foundation ✧ ☆
6230 Stichter Ave.
Dallas, TX 75230-5110
Main URL: http://www.newhopefoundation.com/

Established in 2007 in TX.
Donors: Kip A. Petroff; Frame House Press; Chris Canfield.
Foundation type: Independent foundation.
Financial data (yr. ended 06/30/13): Assets, $27,756 (M); gifts received, $52,187; expenditures, $767,752; qualifying distributions, $751,227; giving activities include $751,227 for 9 grants (high: $736,280; low: $200).
Purpose and activities: The foundation is dedicated to improving the living conditions of underprivileged families living in North Central Texas who are seeking assistance to help them escape poverty.
Fields of interest: Education; Housing/shelter; Safety/disasters.
Limitations: Applications not accepted. Giving primarily in Dallas, TX. No grants to individuals.
Application information: Unsolicited requests for funds not accepted.
Officers and Directors:* Kip A. Petroff, Pres.; Suzi Petroff,* Secy.; Donna Mitchell, Treas.; Johnny Flowers.
EIN: 061831240
Selected grants: The following grants are a representative sample of this grantmaker's funding activity:
$5,000 to Prairie View American University, Prairie View, TX, 2013. For education scholarship.
$1,054 to Mountain View College, Dallas, TX, 2013.

9059
New Hope Initiative Inc. ✧
P.O. Box 5071
Kingwood, TX 77325
Application address: Sandy Baird, 1042 Shorewood Dr., Seabrook, TX 77586

Donors: Sandy Baird; David Dorsett; Dorsett Family Foundation; Robert Baird; Sagemont Church; North Metro Church; Metropolitan Baptist Church; Calvary Baptist Church; Midway Baptist Church; Chrystal Hancock; Grace Community Baptist Church; Gerard Monsivaiz; Michael Prendergast; Beth Snyder; Beacon Baptist Church; Life Point Baptist Church; North Metro Church; North Park Baptist Church; Kyle Davis; McLean Bible Church; James Nobilini; Sondra Fox; Campbell United Methodist Church; Grace Baptist Church; Timothy Larson; James Hancock; Kyle Baird; Gerald Roper; Andrew Gallo; Timothy Shelby.
Foundation type: Operating foundation.
Financial data (yr. ended 12/31/12): Assets, $190,219 (M); gifts received, $969,167; expenditures, $1,029,882; qualifying distributions, $1,029,882; giving activities include $869,591 for 27 grants (high: $432,052; low: $100).
Fields of interest: Housing/shelter; Human services; Religion.
Limitations: Applications accepted. Giving primarily in MO.
Application information: Application form not required.
Initial approach: Proposal
Deadline(s): None
Officers: Sandy Baird, Pres.; Karen Baird, V.P.; Roy Guel, Secy.; David Dorsett, Treas.
Trustee: Sondra Fox.
EIN: 273984784
Selected grants: The following grants are a representative sample of this grantmaker's funding activity:
$111,200 to Baptist Bible Fellowship International, Springfield, MO, 2012. For Construction and Support of Medical Clinic in Arusha, Tanzania.
$26,400 to Baptist Bible Fellowship International, Springfield, MO, 2012. To support of School in Kibera, Kenya.
$12,000 to Baptist Bible Fellowship International, Springfield, MO, 2012. For Construction of Church in Kibera, Kenya.
$9,005 to Baptist Bible Fellowship International, Springfield, MO, 2012. For Secondary/University Scholarships in Kibera, Kenya.

$8,746 to Baptist Bible Fellowship International, Springfield, MO, 2012. For Jobs Program for women in Kibera, Kenya.
$7,605 to Baptist Bible Fellowship International, Springfield, MO, 2012. To support of School in Arusha, Tanzania.
$5,345 to Baptist Bible Fellowship International, Springfield, MO, 2012. For general support to Missionary Work in Arusha, Tanzania.
$2,400 to Baptist Bible Fellowship International, Springfield, MO, 2012. For Medical Support in Kibera, Kenya.
$2,000 to Baptist Bible Fellowship International, Springfield, MO, 2012. For general support to Missionary Work in Manila, Philippines.
$100 to Baptist Bible Fellowship International, Springfield, MO, 2012. For general support to Missionary Work in Kibera, Kenya.

9060
Newfield Foundation ✧
4 Waterway Square Pl., Ste. 100
The Woodlands, TX 77380 (281) 210-2100
Contact: Rita Dennis, Secy.

Established in 2001 in TX.
Donor: Newfield Exploration Co.
Foundation type: Company-sponsored foundation.
Financial data (yr. ended 12/31/13): Assets, $18,293,624 (M); gifts received, $900,000; expenditures, $921,115; qualifying distributions, $855,100; giving activities include $855,100 for 109 grants (high: $38,500; low: $500).
Purpose and activities: The foundation supports programs designed to promote the environment, medical, cultural arts, and community services.
Fields of interest: Animals/wildlife; Health care; Religion.
Limitations: Applications accepted. Giving primarily in areas of company operations in Tulsa, OK and Houston, TX. No grants to individuals.
Application information: Application form required.
Initial approach: Online application request
Deadline(s): August 1 - September 15
Officers: Lee K. Boothby,* Pres.; Susan G. Riggs, V.P. and Treas.; Terry W. Rathert,* V.P.; Rita Dennis, Secy.; Dolores Vasquez, Exec. Dir.
Directors: Lee Boothby; Clay Gaspar; Daryll T. Howard; John Jasek; Larry Massaro; Terry W. Rathert.
EIN: 760663978
Selected grants: The following grants are a representative sample of this grantmaker's funding activity:
$38,000 to Habitat for Humanity, Tulsa, Tulsa, OK, 2010.
$25,000 to Big Brothers Big Sisters Lone Star, Houston, TX, 2010.
$25,000 to Denver Rescue Mission, Denver, CO, 2010.
$25,000 to Denver Rescue Mission, Denver, CO, 2011.
$17,000 to Utah Wildlife and Conservation Foundation, Salt Lake City, UT, 2010.
$15,000 to Brent Eley Foundation, Aurora, CO, 2010.
$15,000 to Rape Assistance and Awareness Program, Denver, CO, 2010.
$15,000 to Tulsa Advocates for the Protection of Children, Tulsa, OK, 2010.
$11,000 to Houston Food Bank, Houston, TX, 2011.
$10,000 to Houston Food Bank, Houston, TX, 2010.
$10,000 to Houston Hospice and Palliative Care System, Houston, TX, 2010.
$10,000 to Little Light House, Tulsa, OK, 2010.
$7,000 to Houston Area Womens Center, Houston, TX, 2011.
$5,000 to Houston Zoo, Houston, TX, 2011.
$3,000 to Denver Museum of Nature and Science, Denver, CO, 2011.
$3,000 to Houston Museum of Natural Science, Houston, TX, 2011.
$1,000 to Houston Area Parkinson Society, Houston, TX, 2011.

9061
John & Florence Newman Foundation ✧
112 E. Pecan St., Ste. 1330
San Antonio, TX 78205-1536

Established in 1988 in TX.
Donor: Florence B. Newman.
Foundation type: Independent foundation.
Financial data (yr. ended 12/31/13): Assets, $18,513,501 (M); expenditures, $1,048,662; qualifying distributions, $754,750; giving activities include $669,300 for 29 grants (high: $130,000; low: $200).
Purpose and activities: Giving primarily for education and the environment; funding also for a community foundation and human services.
Fields of interest: Higher education; Education; Environment; Biomedicine research; Human services; Foundations (community).
Type of support: General/operating support; Equipment; Scholarship funds.
Limitations: Applications not accepted. Giving primarily in San Antonio, TX. No grants to individuals.
Application information: Contributes only to pre-selected organizations.
Directors: Ann J. Newman; John E. Newman, Jr.; Thomas R. Semmes.
EIN: 742525348
Selected grants: The following grants are a representative sample of this grantmaker's funding activity:
$115,000 to San Antonio Area Foundation, San Antonio, TX, 2012. For JEN Family Charitable Fund.
$10,000 to San Antonio Public Library Foundation, San Antonio, TX, 2012. For Copywrite Texas Gala.
$5,000 to San Antonio Public Library Foundation, San Antonio, TX, 2012. For Board Builder Luncheon.
$2,500 to San Anto Cultural Arts, San Antonio, TX, 2012. For Huevos Rancheros Gala.

9062
The Nightingale Code Foundation ✧
1001 McKinney St., Ste. 1900
Houston, TX 77002-6411 (713) 265-0266
Contact: Michael Zilkha, Pres.

Established in 1998 in TX.
Donors: Michael Zilkha; Cornelia O'Leary Zilkha.
Foundation type: Independent foundation.
Financial data (yr. ended 12/31/13): Assets, $1,423,646 (M); gifts received, $1,975,729; expenditures, $1,019,286; qualifying distributions, $1,017,923; giving activities include $1,017,923 for 69 grants (high: $200,000; low: $100).
Purpose and activities: Giving primarily for higher education and the arts.
Fields of interest: Museums (art); Arts; Higher education; Education; Health organizations, association; Human services; Jewish agencies & synagogues.
Limitations: Applications accepted. Giving primarily in Houston, TX; some funding also in NY.
Application information:
Initial approach: Letter
Deadline(s): None
Officers: Michael Zilkha, Pres.; Joseph Romano, V.P. and Treas.; Susanne Tatum, Secy.
Director: Cornelia O'Leary Zilkha.
EIN: 760574572
Selected grants: The following grants are a representative sample of this grantmaker's funding activity:
$150,000 to Menil Foundation, Houston, TX, 2011.
$100,000 to New York Shakespeare Festival, New York, NY, 2011. For general support.
$60,000 to Menil Foundation, Houston, TX, 2011.
$50,000 to Julia Ideson Library Preservation Partners, Houston, TX, 2011. For general support.
$50,000 to Menil Foundation, Houston, TX, 2011.
$25,000 to Williams College, Williamstown, MA, 2011.
$10,000 to Discovery Green Conservancy, Houston, TX, 2011. For general support.
$10,000 to Jewish Family Service of Colorado, Denver, CO, 2011. For general support.
$5,000 to Dance Source Houston, Houston, TX, 2011. For general support.
$4,000 to Maine College of Art, Portland, ME, 2011. For general support.

9063
Mary Moody Northen Endowment
2618 Broadway
Galveston, TX 77550-4427 (409) 765-9770
Contact: Betty Massey, Exec. Dir.
FAX: (409) 762-7055;
E-mail: b.massey@northenendowment.org; Main URL: http://www.northenendowment.org

Established in 1964.
Donor: Mary Moody Northen‡.
Foundation type: Independent foundation.
Financial data (yr. ended 12/31/13): Assets, $73,805,754 (M); expenditures, $6,216,075; qualifying distributions, $4,351,738; giving activities include $1,812,500 for 12 grants (high: $1,317,000; low: $1,000), and $1,933,804 for foundation-administered programs.
Purpose and activities: Support for educational institutions, community development and civic affairs, and wildlife and the environment. The foundation has completed restoration of the W.L. Moody residence and currently operates it as a house museum. The foundation also conducts research of the history of 20th century Texas, and gives to an organization that provides affordable space for artists and art organizations.
Fields of interest: Museums; History/archaeology; Historic preservation/historical societies; Arts, artist's services; Arts; Education, research; Education; Environment, natural resources; Environment; Animals/wildlife, preservation/protection; Community/economic development.
Type of support: General/operating support; Continuing support; Capital campaigns; Building/renovation; Program development; Curriculum development; Consulting services.
Limitations: Applications accepted. Giving limited to TX and VA.

Publications: Grants list.
Application information: See Endowment web site for complete application guidelines.
Board meeting date(s): Monthly
Officers and Directors:* Edward L. Protz,* Pres.; G. William Rider,* V.P. and Treas.; Robert L. Moody,* Secy.; Betty Massey, Exec. Dir.
Number of staff: 1 full-time professional; 2 full-time support.
EIN: 751171741

9064
The Notsew Orm Sands Foundation ✧
c/o Connie McClure
2470 S. Dairy Ashford St., Ste. 802
Houston, TX 77077-5716 (281) 497-0744

Established around 1995.
Donor: Charles Burnett III.
Foundation type: Independent foundation.
Financial data (yr. ended 12/31/12): Assets, $2,424,437 (M); gifts received, $5,694,291; expenditures, $3,318,039; qualifying distributions, $3,286,172; giving activities include $3,286,172 for grants.
Fields of interest: Higher education; Hospitals (general); Medical research, institute; Human services; Protestant agencies & churches.
Limitations: Giving on a national and international basis, with some emphasis on Houston, TX, and the United Kingdom. No grants to individuals.
Application information:
Initial approach: Letter
Deadline(s): None
Final notification: Usually within 90 days
Officer: Charles Burnett III, Pres. and Secy.
Directors: Pilar Bauta; Garfield Mitchell; Melissa Baron Murdock; Graham Weston.
EIN: 760455176

9065
NuStar Foundation ✧
19003 IH-10 W.
San Antonio, TX 78257-9518 (210) 918-2000
Contact: Cynthia Pena
Application address: c/o Cynthia Pena, P.O. Box 781609, San Antonio, TX 78269, tel.: (210) 918-2000

Donor: NuStar Logistics, L.P.
Foundation type: Company-sponsored foundation.
Financial data (yr. ended 12/31/12): Assets, $1,435,877 (M); gifts received, $5,025,440; expenditures, $3,622,891; qualifying distributions, $3,174,988; giving activities include $3,174,988 for 557 grants (high: $450,000; low: $48).
Purpose and activities: The foundation supports organizations involved with arts and culture, education, medical research, golf, youth development, human services, and community development.
Fields of interest: Arts education; Arts; Higher education; Education; Heart & circulatory diseases; Medical research; Athletics/sports, golf; Youth development; Homeless, human services; Human services; Community/economic development; United Ways and Federated Giving Programs.
Type of support: Employee matching gifts; General/operating support.
Limitations: Applications accepted. Giving in the U.S., primarily in TX; with some emphasis on San Antonio.
Application information: Application form required.
Initial approach: Proposal
Deadline(s): None
Directors: Curtis V. Anastasio; Mary Rose Brown; William E. Greehey.
EIN: 260629473

9066
The O'Connor & Hewitt Foundation ✧
(formerly Dorothy O'Connor Foundation)
P.O. Box 400
Victoria, TX 77902-0400 (361) 578-6271
Contact: Robert J. Hewitt, Pres.

Established in 1989 in TX.
Donors: Dorothy Hanna O'Connor‡; Dennis O'Connor‡; Robert J. Hewitt.
Foundation type: Independent foundation.
Financial data (yr. ended 12/31/13): Assets, $37,108,922 (M); expenditures, $1,990,448; qualifying distributions, $1,685,858; giving activities include $1,685,858 for 93 grants (high: $446,366; low: $250).
Purpose and activities: Giving primarily for the arts, education, health organizations, children, youth and social services, and to Protestant agencies and churches.
Fields of interest: Arts; Education; Animal welfare; Health organizations, association; Human services; Children/youth, services; Protestant agencies & churches.
Type of support: General/operating support; Continuing support; Annual campaigns; Building/renovation.
Limitations: Giving generally limited to the south TX area. No grants to individuals or for matching gifts; no loans.
Publications: Annual report.
Application information: Application form not required.
Initial approach: Letter
Copies of proposal: 2
Deadline(s): None
Board meeting date(s): As required
Officers: Robert J. Hewitt, Pres.; Robert J. Hewitt, Jr., V.P.; Joe B. Bland, Secy.-Treas.
EIN: 742527227
Selected grants: The following grants are a representative sample of this grantmaker's funding activity:
$10,000 to Citizens Medical Foundation, Victoria, TX, 2012. For Private Found.

9067
O'Donnell Foundation ✧
100 Crescent Ct., Ste. 1660
Dallas, TX 75201-1884
Contact: Carolyn B. Dickson, Exec. Dir.
E-mail: info@odf.org

Incorporated in 1957 in TX.
Donors: Peter O'Donnell, Jr.; Edith Jones O'Donnell.
Foundation type: Independent foundation.
Financial data (yr. ended 12/31/13): Assets, $63,676,146 (M); gifts received, $2,000,000; expenditures, $25,315,895; qualifying distributions, $23,737,472; giving activities include $22,871,295 for 27 grants (high: $6,839,733; low: $1,000).
Purpose and activities: The foundation primarily supports engineering, science, and mathematics education at the graduate level. The foundation also supports Advanced Placement programs (math, science, English, art) and arts education.
Fields of interest: Arts; Higher education; Education; Mathematics; Engineering; Science.
Limitations: Applications accepted. Giving primarily in TX. No grants to individuals, or for scholarships, fellowships, or prizes; no loans.
Application information: Application form not required.
Initial approach: Letter with brief proposal
Deadline(s): None
Board meeting date(s): As required
Officers and Directors:* Peter O'Donnell, Jr.,* Chair.; Rita Clements,* V.P.; Edith Jones O'Donnell,* Secy.-Treas.; Carolyn B. Dickson, Exec. Dir.; Edward A. Copley; Bob Dedman, Jr.; Larry Faulkner; Ruth O'Donnell Mutch; Caren Prothro.
Number of staff: 4 full-time professional.
EIN: 756023326
Selected grants: The following grants are a representative sample of this grantmaker's funding activity:
$10,000,000 to Perot Museum of Nature and Science, Dallas, TX, 2012. For operating support.
$8,538,101 to University of Texas, Austin, TX, 2012. For operating support.
$6,839,733 to National Math and Science Initiative, Dallas, TX, 2013. For operating support.
$4,600,000 to University of Texas Southwestern Medical Center, Dallas, TX, 2013. For operating support.
$3,661,000 to University of Texas, Austin, TX, 2013. For operating support.
$3,000,000 to Dallas Museum of Art, Dallas, TX, 2013. For operating support.
$2,300,000 to Southwestern Medical Foundation, Dallas, TX, 2012. For operating support.
$1,743,750 to University of Texas Southwestern Medical Center, Dallas, TX, 2013. For endowment.
$1,250,000 to Southern Methodist University, Dallas, TX, 2013. For operating support.
$640,381 to Advanced Placement Strategies, Dallas, TX, 2012. For operating support.
$375,879 to Laying the Foundation, Dallas, TX, 2013. For operating support.
$256,420 to Laying the Foundation, Dallas, TX, 2012. For operating support.
$250,000 to Monuments Men Foundation for the Preservation of Art, Dallas, TX, 2012. For operating support.
$210,000 to Big Thought, Dallas, TX, 2012. For operating support.
$149,806 to University of Colorado, Boulder, CO, 2012. For operating support.
$100,000 to Distance Learning Center, Philadelphia, PA, 2013. For operating support.
$100,000 to University of Texas Law School Foundation, Austin, TX, 2012. For operating support.
$60,000 to Center for Media and Public Affairs, Arlington, VA, 2012. For operating support.
$60,000 to Center for Media and Public Affairs, Arlington, VA, 2013. For operating support.

9068
The O'Hare Family Private Foundation ✧ ☆
c/o W. Scott O'Hare
2905 Popano Cove
Austin, TX 78746-1974

Established in 1999 in TX.
Donor: W. Scott O'Hare.
Foundation type: Independent foundation.
Financial data (yr. ended 12/31/13): Assets, $435,448 (M); gifts received, $199,159; expenditures, $431,668; qualifying distributions, $429,750; giving activities include $429,750 for 21 grants (high: $133,000; low: $500).
Purpose and activities: Giving primarily for education and to Protestant churches; funding also for social services.
Fields of interest: Elementary/secondary education; Higher education; Health care; Human services; Protestant agencies & churches; Children.
Limitations: Applications not accepted. Giving primarily in Austin, TX. No grants to individuals.
Application information: Unsolicited requests for funds not accepted.
Officers: W. Scott O'Hare, Pres.; Kathryn Angell Sackett O'Hare, V.P. and Secy.
Director: Jody Cole.
EIN: 752802946

9069
Oldham Little Church Foundation ✧
24 Greenway Plz., Ste. 1202
Houston, TX 77046-2445 (713) 275-1050
Contact: Paul Sanders
FAX: (713) 275-1051; E-mail: info@oldhamlcf.org; Main URL: http://www.oldhamlcf.org/

Trust established in 1949 in TX.
Donor: Morris Calvin Oldham†.
Foundation type: Independent foundation.
Financial data (yr. ended 12/31/13): Assets, $29,632,719 (M); expenditures, $1,572,835; qualifying distributions, $1,244,618; giving activities include $903,379 for 123 grants (high: $20,000; low: $2,000).
Purpose and activities: Giving limited to small Protestant churches and organizations with emphasis on Baptist churches.
Fields of interest: Protestant agencies & churches.
Type of support: Building/renovation; Equipment; Program development.
Limitations: Applications accepted. Giving primarily in the U.S., with some emphasis on TX; very limited funding internationally. No grants to individuals, or for operating budgets, endowments, or deficit financing; no loans.
Publications: Application guidelines.
Application information: Applications sent by U.S. mail, fax or e-mail are not accepted. Application form required.
Initial approach: Use online application process on foundation web site
Copies of proposal: 1
Deadline(s): See foundation web site for current deadlines
Officers and Directors:* Stewart Morris, Jr.,* Chair.; Paul Sanders,* C.E.O. and Pres.; Louis E. "Ed" Finlay,* V.P.; Ralph Hull,* V.P.; Kay Parker,* V.P.; David Stutts,* V.P.; David Taylor,* V.P.; Stewart Morris, Sr.,* Secy.
Number of staff: 1 part-time professional; 1 full-time support; 1 part-time support.
EIN: 760465633

9070
Once Upon A Time Foundation ✧
(formerly Will E. Coyote Foundation)
301 Commerce St., Ste. 3200
Fort Worth, TX 76102-4175

Established in 1998 in TX.
Donor: Geoffrey P. Raynor.
Foundation type: Independent foundation.
Financial data (yr. ended 12/31/12): Assets, $39,400,853 (M); gifts received, $30,000,000; expenditures, $3,378,134; qualifying distributions, $3,285,514; giving activities include $3,130,518 for 128 grants (high: $250,000; low: $25).
Purpose and activities: Giving primarily for the arts, education, hospitals and medical research, and children and social services.
Fields of interest: Museums; Arts; Education; Zoos/zoological societies; Hospitals (general); Hospitals (specialty); Health care; Medical research, institute; Human services; Children/youth, services; Community/economic development.
Type of support: General/operating support; Income development; Annual campaigns; Equipment; Debt reduction; Program development; Matching/challenge support.
Limitations: Applications not accepted. Giving primarily in the Fort Worth/Dallas, TX, area. No grants to individuals.
Application information: Contributes only to pre-selected organizations.
Officers: Sam Lett, Pres. and Treas.; Noel Nesser, Secy.
Directors: William Cunningham; Adam Davidson; Edward Nelson, Jr., M.D.; Geoffrey P. Raynor; Kim Raynor; Tom Rogers, Jr., M.D.
EIN: 752765224

9071
Robert R. & Kay M. Onstead Foundation ✧
5298 Memorial Dr.
Houston, TX 77007-8260

Established in 1993 in TX.
Donors: Robert R. Onstead; Kay M. Onstead.
Foundation type: Independent foundation.
Financial data (yr. ended 12/31/13): Assets, $31,826,336 (M); gifts received, $200,000; expenditures, $1,791,056; qualifying distributions, $1,587,829; giving activities include $1,587,829 for 24 grants (high: $1,000,000; low: $1,000).
Purpose and activities: Giving primarily for education, social services, zoos, and Christian organizations.
Fields of interest: Higher education; Education; Zoos/zoological societies; Human services; Christian agencies & churches.
Limitations: Applications accepted. Giving primarily in Houston, TX. No grants to individuals.
Application information: Application form required.
Initial approach: Letter
Deadline(s): None
Officers and Trustees:* Kay M. Onstead,* Pres.; Charles M. Onstead,* V.P. and Secy.-Treas.; Lee E. Straus, Exec. Dir.; Ann Onstead Hill; Mary Onstead; R. Randall Onstead, Jr.
EIN: 760417998

9072
John M. O'Quinn Foundation ✧
(formerly The O'Quinn Foundation)
1300 Post Oak Blvd., Ste. 1200
Houston, TX 77056-3088 (713) 871-5860
Contact: Brittany Meyn, Exec. Asst.
E-mail: meyn@oquinnfoundation.org; Application address: c/o Brittany Meyn, P.O. Box 27501, Houston, TX 27501, tel.: (713) 871-5860; Main URL: http://www.oquinnfoundation.org

Established in 1986 in TX.
Donors: John M. O'Quinn†; Robert C. Wilson III.
Foundation type: Independent foundation.
Financial data (yr. ended 12/31/12): Assets, $22,894,098 (M); gifts received, $20,332,531; expenditures, $6,230,630; qualifying distributions, $5,894,883; giving activities include $5,505,000 for 48 grants (high: $2,000,000; low: $2,500).
Purpose and activities: Giving primarily for education, health care, the environment and the lives of underprivileged youth in Houston, Texas and the surrounding area.
Fields of interest: Higher education; Law school/education; Mental health, treatment; Mental health, association; Health organizations, association; Autism; Cancer research; Lupus research; Athletics/sports, Special Olympics; Recreation; Human services; Children/youth, services; Women, centers/services.
Limitations: Applications accepted. Giving primarily in TX, with emphasis on Houston. No grants to individuals.
Application information: Application form not required.
Initial approach: Cover letter on the organization's letterhead
Deadline(s): Feb. 28, May 30, Sept. 1, and Nov. 1
Board meeting date(s): Mar. 25, June 24, Sept. 23, and Dec. 9
Officers and Trustees:* Robert C. Wilson III,* Pres.; David A. Ott, M.D.*, V.P.; Anette Edens, Ph.D.*, Secy.; Corbin J. Robertson III,* Treas.
EIN: 760206844

9073
Genevieve and Ward Orsinger Foundation ✧
(formerly Genevieve McDavitt Orsinger Foundation)
P.O. Box 90987
San Antonio, TX 78209-9094
Contact: Linda McDavitt, C.E.O. and Pres.
E-mail: lmcd@orsingerfoundation.org; Tel./fax: (210) 590-0535; mobile phone: (210) 378-6614; Main URL: http://www.orsingerfoundation.org

Established in 1997 in TX.
Donor: Genevieve McDavitt Orsinger†.
Foundation type: Independent foundation.
Financial data (yr. ended 12/31/13): Assets, $11,237,576 (M); expenditures, $812,879; qualifying distributions, $745,400; giving activities include $657,238 for 71 grants (high: $100,000; low: $250).
Purpose and activities: Giving in Bexar County includes: 1) programs related to early childhood that emphasize health and wellness, the fine arts, outdoor activities and/or literacy; 2) community service learning projects planned and operated by youth; 3) programs for adults that support self-sufficiency and/or enhance their capacity to

care for their families; and 4) programs for elderly persons that use the fine arts to enhance quality of life and/or support health and wellness. Giving in the Central Texas counties of Comal, Guadalupe, Hays, Kendall and Travis consists of programs delivered to children ages 0 to 5 years old that utilize fine arts in curriculum.
Fields of interest: Arts; Education; Human services; Infants/toddlers; Children/youth; Children; Youth; Adults; Aging; Young adults; Disabilities, people with; Physically disabled; Mentally disabled; Minorities; Indigenous peoples; Women; Infants/toddlers, female; Girls; Adults, women; Men; Boys; Adults, men; Military/veterans; Offenders/ex-offenders; Substance abusers; Single parents; Terminal illness, people with; Economically disadvantaged; Homeless.
Type of support: General/operating support; Continuing support; Management development/capacity building; Equipment; Program development; Curriculum development; Technical assistance; Program evaluation; Program-related investments/loans; Matching/challenge support.
Limitations: Applications accepted. Giving primarily in Bexar County, TX; outside Bexar County, the foundation will only consider requests for programs in Comal, Guadalupe, Hays, Kendall and/or Travis Counties delivered to children aged 0 to 5 years old that utilize fine arts in the curriculum. No support for political organizations. No grants to individuals; no grants for start up funds or seed money, capital campaigns, endowments, fundraising events or sponsorships, long term commitments, salaries, reduction of debts or scholarships.
Publications: Application guidelines; Grants list; IRS Form 990 or 990-PF printed copy available upon request.
Application information: Must submit letter of inquiry first and then be asked to submit a full application. Letter of inquiry and application available on foundation web site. Strong preference will be given to existing programs/projects or general operating support that have funding from other sources, rather than new programs or the expansion of existing programs. Application form required.
Initial approach: Electronic letter of inquiry from foundation web site
Copies of proposal: 1
Deadline(s): See foundation web site for current deadline
Board meeting date(s): Mid-Mar.
Final notification: Letter of inquiry response by Dec. 1 to ask for full application. Grants reviewed results by Apr. 1
Officers and Directors:* Linda McDavitt, C.E.O. and Pres.; Clarence Bray, Secy.-Treas.; Megan Kromer; Nancy May; Patricia Meyer.
Number of staff: 1 part-time professional.
EIN: 742832873
Selected grants: The following grants are a representative sample of this grantmaker's funding activity:
$10,000 to Assistance League of San Antonio, San Antonio, TX, 2012. For Togs for Tots and Operation School Bell.
$10,000 to Clarity Child Guidance Center, San Antonio, TX, 2012. For Providing Access to Treatment for Children with Mental Illnesses.
$10,000 to Haven for Hope of Bexar County, San Antonio, TX, 2012. For General operating support for Transformational Services for the homeless.
$10,000 to Mainspring Schools, Austin, TX, 2012. For Fine Arts for Little Ones.
$10,000 to Texas Ramp Project, Richardson, TX, 2012. For Texas Ramp Project - San Antonio Project.
$10,000 to Witte Museum, San Antonio, TX, 2012. For Health and Wellness Demonstrations at the Witte Museum.
$9,360 to Guide Dogs of Texas, San Antonio, TX, 2012. For Guide Dog Advanced Training Program.
$7,500 to Unicorn Centers, San Antonio, TX, 2012. For Ensuring a Balance Between Programs and Resources.
$5,275 to Morningside Ministries, San Antonio, TX, 2012. For Chandler House Players.
$5,000 to E3 Alliance, Austin, TX, 2012. For Central Texas Attendance Challenge.

9074
Oshman Foundation ✧ ☆
P.O. Box 27969
Houston, TX 77227-7969

Established in 1958.
Donors: Oshman's Sporting Goods, Inc.; Jeanette Oshman Efron.
Foundation type: Company-sponsored foundation.
Financial data (yr. ended 11/30/13): Assets, $3,581,607 (M); expenditures, $3,555,441; qualifying distributions, $3,546,974; giving activities include $3,535,552 for 11 grants (high: $3,485,052; low: $500).
Purpose and activities: The foundation supports hospitals and organizations involved with arts and culture, education, cancer, human services, and Judaism.
Fields of interest: Education; Environment; Religion.
Limitations: Applications not accepted. Giving limited to Houston, TX. No grants to individuals.
Application information: Contributes only to pre-selected organizations.
Officers: Marilyn Oshman, Pres. and Treas.; Karen Desenberg, V.P. and Secy.; Andrew Lubetkin, V.P.
EIN: 746039864
Selected grants: The following grants are a representative sample of this grantmaker's funding activity:
$62,000 to Congregation Emanu-El, Houston, TX, 2010.
$40,000 to Baylor College of Medicine, Houston, TX, 2011.
$35,506 to Congregation Emanu-El, Houston, TX, 2011.
$25,000 to Menil Foundation, Houston, TX, 2011.
$20,000 to Memorial Park Conservancy, Houston, TX, 2011.
$20,000 to Orange Show Center for Visionary Art, Houston, TX, 2011.
$6,500 to Houston Ballet, Houston, TX, 2011.
$5,000 to Houston Food Bank, Houston, TX, 2010.
$5,000 to Houston Public Media Foundation, Houston, TX, 2011.
$5,000 to Methodist Hospital Foundation, Houston, TX, 2011.
$5,000 to Periwinkle Foundation, Houston, TX, 2011.
$3,500 to Houston Zoo, Houston, TX, 2010.
$2,500 to Menninger Clinic, Houston, TX, 2010.
$2,500 to Saint Johns School, Houston, TX, 2011.
$2,000 to Child Advocates, Houston, TX, 2010.
$2,000 to Houston Arboretum and Nature Center, Houston, TX, 2010.

9075
The Louis and Peaches Owen Family Foundation ✧
P.O. Box 132648
Tyler, TX 75713-2648

Established in 2006 in TX.
Donors: Louis Owen; Alberta M. Owen.
Foundation type: Independent foundation.
Financial data (yr. ended 12/31/12): Assets, $15,914,299 (M); expenditures, $1,079,056; qualifying distributions, $839,774; giving activities include $839,774 for grants.
Fields of interest: Higher education; Education; Youth development; Human services; Children/youth, services; Christian agencies & churches; Catholic agencies & churches.
Limitations: Applications not accepted. Giving primarily in TX, with emphasis on Tyler. No grants to individuals.
Application information: Unsolicited requests for funds not accepted.
Officers: Louis W. Owen, Pres.; Marie G. Owen, V.P.; Louis P. Owen, Secy.
EIN: 205919770

9076
Dian Graves Owen Foundation ✧
400 N. Pine St., Ste. 1000
Abilene, TX 79601-5142
Contact: Jane Verner Beard, Grants Admin.

Established in 1996 in TX.
Donor: Dian Graves Owen Stai.
Foundation type: Independent foundation.
Financial data (yr. ended 12/31/12): Assets, $128,484,531 (M); gifts received, $2,906,815; expenditures, $8,521,197; qualifying distributions, $6,143,692; giving activities include $6,007,523 for 229 grants (high: $1,000,000; low: $200).
Purpose and activities: Giving primarily for the arts, education, health, and human services.
Fields of interest: Performing arts; Performing arts, opera; Historic preservation/historical societies; Arts; Higher education; Education; Hospitals (general); Hospitals (specialty); Health care; Health organizations, association; Cancer; Boys & girls clubs; Human services; Children/youth, services; Family services; Social sciences, public policy; Christian agencies & churches.
Type of support: General/operating support; Continuing support; Annual campaigns; Capital campaigns; Building/renovation; Program development; Conferences/seminars; Scholarship funds; Consulting services; Program evaluation; Matching/challenge support.
Limitations: Applications not accepted. Giving primarily in Abilene, TX. No grants to individuals.
Application information: Contributes only to pre-selected organizations.
Board meeting date(s): Quarterly
Officers and Directors:* Dian Graves Owen Stai,* Chair. and Treas.; Tucker S. Bridwell,* Pres.; Diane K. Nichols, Secy.; Deborah O. Carson.
Number of staff: 1 part-time professional.
EIN: 752682536

9077
B. B. Owen Trust ✧
P.O. Box 832350
Richardson, TX 75083-2350
Contact: Monty J. Jackson, Tr.

Established in 1974 in TX.
Donor: B.B. Owen†.
Foundation type: Independent foundation.
Financial data (yr. ended 09/30/13): Assets, $10,981,967 (M); expenditures, $1,053,278; qualifying distributions, $991,784; giving activities include $951,784 for 25 grants (high: $200,000; low: $5,000).
Purpose and activities: Giving primarily for education and human services, with emphasis on children and youth, and for local government facilities.
Fields of interest: Education; Hospitals (specialty); Health organizations, association; Boy scouts; Human services; Salvation Army; Children/youth, services; Public affairs, government agencies; Christian agencies & churches.
Type of support: General/operating support; Capital campaigns; Building/renovation; Equipment; Program development.
Limitations: Applications accepted. Giving primarily in the Dallas, TX, area. No grants to individuals.
Application information: Application form required.
Initial approach: Letter
Deadline(s): None
Trustees: Monty J. Jackson; Wendell W. Judd.
Number of staff: 1 full-time professional.
EIN: 751385809

9078
Alvin & Lucy Owsley Foundation ✧
1600 Post Oak Blvd., Apt. 802
Houston, TX 77056-2905 (713) 622-1352
Contact: Alvin M. Owsley, Jr., Tr.

Trust established in 1950 in TX.
Donors: Alvin M. Owsley†; Lucy B. Owsley†.
Foundation type: Independent foundation.
Financial data (yr. ended 12/31/13): Assets, $9,840,435 (M); expenditures, $546,522; qualifying distributions, $470,986; giving activities include $451,430 for 54 grants (high: $125,955; low: $100).
Purpose and activities: Giving primarily for the arts, education and human services.
Fields of interest: Museums (art); Arts; Elementary/secondary education; Higher education; Libraries (public); Education; Medical research, institute; Human services; Children/youth, services; United Ways and Federated Giving Programs.
Type of support: General/operating support; Continuing support; Annual campaigns; Building/renovation; Emergency funds; Seed money; Scholarship funds; Matching/challenge support.
Limitations: Applications accepted. Giving limited to TX. No grants to individuals, or for endowment funds; no loans.
Publications: Application guidelines.
Application information: Application form required.
Initial approach: Letter not exceeding 2 pages (no enclosures)
Copies of proposal: 1
Deadline(s): None
Trustees: Sophia Garrett; Alvin M. Owsley, Jr.; David T. Owsley.
EIN: 756047221

9079
Linda Pace Foundation ✧
c/o Rick Moore
P.O. Box 830607
San Antonio, TX 78283-0607
FAX: (210) 226-6669;
E-mail: rmoore@pacefound.org; Main URL: http://www.lindapacefoundation.org
Facebook: http://www.facebook.com/pages/Linda-Pace-Foundation/164522646938918

Established in 2003 in TX.
Donors: Linda M. Pace†; Pace 2005 Charitable Lead Annuity Trust.
Foundation type: Independent foundation.
Financial data (yr. ended 12/31/12): Assets, $86,426,661 (M); gifts received, $4,765,198; expenditures, $2,390,377; qualifying distributions, $2,045,913; giving activities include $897,000 for 6 grants (high: $810,000; low: $2,000).
Purpose and activities: The foundation fosters the creation, presentation, and understanding of innovative expression through contemporary art. Grants support the operation of Artspace, CHRISpark, the public exhibition of Pace's contemporary arts collection, and the work of contemporary artists.
Fields of interest: Museums (art).
Type of support: General/operating support.
Limitations: Applications not accepted. Giving primarily in TX. No support for organizations not related to contemporary art. No grants to individuals.
Application information: Contributes only to pre-selected organizations.
Board meeting date(s): Usually 4 times per year
Officers and Trustees:* Rick R. Moore,* Pres.; Jan Jarboe Russell,* V.P.; Steven Evans, Exec. Dir.; Kathryn Kanjo; Anne Hodges Morgan; Dennis Scholl.
Number of staff: 3 full-time professional; 2 full-time support.
EIN: 043757853
Selected grants: The following grants are a representative sample of this grantmaker's funding activity:
$20,000 to Americans for the Arts, Washington, DC, 2012. For annual operating expenses.
$20,000 to San Antonio Museum of Art, San Antonio, TX, 2012. For contemporary art exhibits.

9080
Paloheimo Foundation ✧
c/o Wells Fargo Bank, N.A.
P.O. Box 41629, MAC A0330-011
Austin, TX 78704-9926

Established in 2000 in CA.
Donor: Leonora Curtin Paloheimo Trust.
Foundation type: Independent foundation.
Financial data (yr. ended 12/31/13): Assets, $21,914,428 (M); expenditures, $1,158,340; qualifying distributions, $962,859; giving activities include $820,687 for 7 grants (high: $234,672; low: $50,000).
Purpose and activities: Giving primarily for education and to Finnish organizations.
Fields of interest: Arts, cultural/ethnic awareness; Historic preservation/historical societies; Higher education; Education.
Type of support: Continuing support; Program development; Publication; Seed money; Matching/challenge support.
Limitations: Applications not accepted. Giving primarily in CA and NM; some giving also in Helsinki, Finland. No grants to individuals.
Application information: Contributes only to pre-selected organizations.
Board Members: Morgan Halme; Paul Halme; George Paloheimo; George Paloheimo, Jr.; Martti Paloheimo.
Trustee: Wells Fargo Bank, N.A.
EIN: 946752361
Selected grants: The following grants are a representative sample of this grantmaker's funding activity:
$107,591 to Pasadena Historical Society, Pasadena, CA, 2012. For matching grants.

9081
Fred & Mabel R. Parks Foundation ✧
12926 Dairy Ashford Rd., Ste. 130
Sugar Land, TX 77478-3102 (281) 313-6464
Contact: James G. McClellan, Pres.
E-mail: jimmcclellan@windstream.net

Established in 1984 in TX.
Donor: Fred Parks†.
Foundation type: Independent foundation.
Financial data (yr. ended 12/31/13): Assets, $56,297,003 (M); gifts received, $15,435; expenditures, $11,733,313; qualifying distributions, $2,600,583; giving activities include $2,548,600 for 69 grants (high: $400,000; low: $5,000).
Purpose and activities: Giving primarily for health and education.
Fields of interest: Higher education; Education; Health care; Medical research, institute; Diabetes research.
Type of support: General/operating support; Continuing support; Emergency funds; Research; Matching/challenge support.
Limitations: Applications accepted. Giving primarily in the Houston, TX area. No support for political organizations. No grants to individuals.
Application information: Application form required.
Initial approach: Letter requesting application form
Copies of proposal: 1
Deadline(s): None
Board meeting date(s): Fall
Final notification: 3 months
Officers: James G. McClellan, Pres.; Ann Parks Stallings, V.P.; Virginia McClintock, Secy.; Debra Marfin, Treas.
Number of staff: 1 part-time professional; 4 part-time support.
EIN: 760122692
Selected grants: The following grants are a representative sample of this grantmaker's funding activity:
$100,000 to Texas Heart Institute, Houston, TX, 2012. For Adult Stem Cell Research.
$49,000 to South Texas College of Law, Houston, TX, 2012. For scholarship/financial aid program.
$10,000 to Casa de Esperanza de los Ninos, Houston, TX, 2012. For Program for Children in Crisis.
$3,000 to Houston Bar Foundation, Houston, TX, 2012. For Houston Attorney Bar's Night Court.

9082
The Partnership Foundation ✧ ☆
6031 Woodland Dr.
Dallas, TX 75225-2834

Established in 1999 in TX.
Foundation type: Independent foundation.
Financial data (yr. ended 12/31/13): Assets, $10,800,502 (M); expenditures, $475,154; qualifying distributions, $431,242; giving activities include $425,000 for 32 grants (high: $35,000; low: $1,000).
Fields of interest: Arts; Education; Environment; Human services.
Limitations: Applications not accepted. Giving primarily in Berkeley and Alameda County, CA, Providence, RI, and Dallas, TX. No grants to individuals.
Application information: Contributes only to pre-selected organizations.
Officers: Anne Paxton Wagley, Pres.; B. Allyn Copp, V.P.; James F.P. Wagley, V.P.; Mary Wagley Copp, Secy.; Sue Wagley, Treas.
EIN: 752796975

9083
Paso del Norte Health Foundation ✧
221 N. Kansas St., Ste. 1900
El Paso, TX 79901-1428 (915) 544-7636
Contact: Myrna Deckert, C.E.O. and Pres.
FAX: (915) 544-7713; E-mail: health@pdnhf.org; Additional E-mail: mdeckert@pdnhf.org; Main URL: http://www.pdnhf.org
Blog: http://www.pdnhf.org/Blog.asp
Facebook: https://www.facebook.com/PdNHFoundation
Grants Database: http://www.pdnhf.org/searchgrantdb.asp
RSS Feed: http://www.pdnhf.org/index.php?option=com_content&view=category&id=60&Itemid=83&lang=us
Twitter: https://twitter.com/PdNHFoundation
YouTube: https://www.youtube.com/user/PDNHFoundation?feature=CEgQwRs%3D

Established in 1995 in TX; converted from sale of the assets of Providence Memorial Hospital.
Foundation type: Independent foundation.
Financial data (yr. ended 12/31/12): Assets, $204,802,919 (M); gifts received, $1,460; expenditures, $6,928,522; qualifying distributions, $5,527,498; giving activities include $3,373,607 for 66 grants (high: $331,709; low: $1,500), and $254,223 for 1 foundation-administered program.
Purpose and activities: The foundation's mission is to promote health and prevent disease in the region through leadership in health education, research, and advocacy.
Fields of interest: Education, public education; Health care, support services; Health care; Mental health/crisis services; Nutrition; Youth development; Human services; Children/youth; Children; Youth; Hispanics/Latinos.
International interests: Mexico.
Type of support: Technical assistance; Program evaluation; Program development.
Limitations: Applications not accepted. Giving limited to Dona Ana, Luna, and Otero Counties in Southern NM, Hudspeth and El Paso Counties in West TX, and Ciudad Juarez, Chihuahua, Mexico. No support for political organizations. No grants to individuals, or for building/renovation, capital campaigns, or research.
Publications: Annual report.
Application information: Unsolicited applications not accepted. However, when launching a new request for proposals, a grant workshop will be hosted by the foundation for nonprofit organizations so that they may better understand the purpose of the initiative and how to respond to the Request For Proposal (RFP).
Board meeting date(s): Jan., Mar., May, July, Sept., and Nov.
Officers and Directors:* Robert Ash,* Chair.; Carolyn Mora,* Vice-Chair.; Myrna Deckert, C.E.O. and Pres.; Marcela Garcia, C.F.O.; John Law, C.O.O.; Alan Abbott; Sandra Sanchez Almanzan; Sharon Butterworth; Allan Goldfarb; Christopher Lopez; Michael Miles; Jose Prieto, M.D.; Hector Retta; Judy Robinson; Benjamin Torres-Barron.
Number of staff: 11 full-time professional; 3 full-time support.
EIN: 741143071
Selected grants: The following grants are a representative sample of this grantmaker's funding activity:
$1,239,429 to University of Texas, El Paso, TX, 2013. To continue to develop and assess media messaging for adult tobacco cessation, youth tobacco prevention, and regional and campus smoke free campaigns, to provide strong leadership to and assessment of the El Paso / Cd. Juarez Tobacco Control Network, to provide technical assistance to A Smoke Free Paso del Norte grantees, and to educate and promote regional Clean Indoor Air Ordinances and campus smoke free policies. Through these and multiple other objectives, the OA plans to work in a coordinated fashion with regional tobacco control stakeholders to significantly reduce tobacco use prevalence in the region.
$680,000 to Paso del Norte Foundation, El Paso, TX, 2013. For the PDNF's operations costs for fiscal year 2014 and manage a project to recruit community partners from throughout the region to participate in a matching fund initiative.
$663,418 to University of Texas, El Paso, TX, 2012. To continue to develop and assess media messaging for adult tobacco cessation, youth tobacco prevention, and regional and campus smoke free campaigns, to provide strong leadership to and assessment of the El Paso / Cd. Juarez Tobacco Control Network, to provide technical assistance to A Smoke Free Paso del Norte grantees, and to educate and promote regional Clean Indoor Air Ordinances and campus smoke free policies. Through these and multiple other objectives, the OA plans to work in a coordinated fashion with regional tobacco control stakeholders to significantly reduce tobacco use prevalence in the region.
$574,729 to University of Texas, El Paso, TX, 2013. To establish a Center of Excellence for healthy eating and active living in the Paso del Norte region.
$506,895 to University of Texas, El Paso, TX, 2012. To establish a Center of Excellence for healthy eating and active living in the Paso del Norte region.
$245,700 to Paso del Norte Health Information Exchange, El Paso, TX, 2013. For a HIE patient portal, a secure messaging using the DIRECT protocol. Patients will be able to access data from their providers and track the accuracy of information For expanding HIE to include all of PdNHF's service area, including Dona Ana, Luna, and Otero Counties, as well as Ciudad Juarez, To Negotiate with New Mexico's statewide HIE and Mexico's federal system to attempt to work with these systems To Maximize relationships with providers and government systems in New Mexico and Ciudad Juarez.
$216,260 to YMCA of Metropolitan El Paso, El Paso, TX, 2013. To reduce early onset of alcohol use before the age of 15. To reduce alcohol use and binge drinking among high school students and adults.
$137,692 to Child Crisis Center of El Paso, El Paso, TX, 2012. To implement the Teen Talk Sexuality Education Curriculum for youth 16-24 years of age at multiple sites including: David L. Carrasco Job Corps, Boys and Girls Clubs, and Housing Authority communities. Programming includes peer mentor presentations for middle and high school youth in El Paso and Hudspeth County Districts.
$135,993 to El Paso, City of, El Paso, TX, 2012. For tobacco prevention lessons to elementary, middle, and high school students and parents in El Paso County to prevent youth from initiating tobacco use and to encourage current smokers to stop, to provide tobacco prevention in-services to El Paso high school educators to build capacity at the school district level, and support smoke free policy initiatives to improve the quality of life for all El Pasoans.
$132,000 to El Paso, City of, El Paso, TX, 2013. For tobacco prevention lessons to elementary school students and their parents, provide prevention and awareness materials and in-services to middle and high school teachers and college-level health education students, and continue to advocate for smoke-free policies in El Paso, Texas.
$117,293 to El Paso, City of, El Paso, TX, 2013. To improve healthy family dining options in El Paso, TX by increasing from 24 to 100 the number of restaurants with healthy children's meals, offering 20 currently participating restaurants the opportunity to improve adult entrees, and training 200 cook/wait staff on child nutrition.
$117,251 to El Paso, City of, El Paso, TX, 2012. For sexual health education for prevention of sexually transmitted infections and unintended second pregnancy in women under the age of 25 in El Paso County Women, Infants and Children Centers.
$95,736 to Children in Need of Services, Alamogordo, NM, 2012. To conduct a tobacco prevention curriculum for middle school youth in Alamogordo, Tularosa, and Cloudcroft schools. To implement Breathe Smart from the Start with pregnant teenage youth, coordinate youth coalition and the Paso del Norte region's Youth Empowerment Summit, monitor retail compliance with New Mexico state law, and conduct presentations on the risks of secondhand smoke exposure to multiple audiences promote tobacco control in Otero County.
$84,850 to Families and Youth, Las Cruces, NM, 2013. To implement the Safer Choices sex education curriculum for youth and their parents, hosting the Next Rainbow Generation Lesbian, Gay, Bisexual, Transgendered, and Queer (GBTQ) youth support group in Dona Ana County, New Mexico.
$74,953 to University of Texas, El Paso, TX, 2013. To assess cessation program effectiveness in smokers highly motivated to quit smoking as well as individual and group interventions in adult light and intermittent smokers in El Paso, Texas, to reduce, and eventually eliminate, tobacco prevalence in the border region.
$73,700 to Families and Youth, Las Cruces, NM, 2012. To facilitate prevention education for elementary and middle school students, empower youth through action teams, engage members of the

Lesbian, Gay, Bisexual, Transgendered and Queer (LGBTQ) community to empower them toward community change, and provide cessation services for high school-aged youth and LGBTQ adults interested in quitting in Las Cruces, New Mexico, to reduce cigarette smoking among youth and adults.
$58,058 to El Paso, City of, El Paso, TX, 2012. To reduce childhood obesity by improving children's menus at locally owned restaurants, coordinating a National Food Day Celebration, and marketing online nutrition course to parents, day care providers, and restaurant employees in El Paso, TX.
$52,645 to New Mexico State University, Las Cruces, NM, 2012. To increase family purchases of fresh fruits and vegetables in select El Paso County, TX and Dona Ana County, NM grocery stores and advancing policy for the same.
$40,000 to FEMAP Foundation, El Paso, TX, 2012. To assess nutritional status of elementary school age children in Cuidad Juarez, Mexico and offer nutrition services for children and their families.
$40,000 to FEMAP Foundation, El Paso, TX, 2013. To improve the health of 700 children in Cd. Juarez, MX by offering a wide array of nutritional and physical activity workshops and services.

9084
George W. & Mary B. Patton Foundation ✧

c/o Bank of America, N.A.
P.O. Box 831041
Dallas, TX 75283-1041

Established in 1978 in CA; supporting organization of Boys and Girls Club of Pasadena, Boys Republic of Chino, Minnesota Peoples Home Fund, San Gabriel Valley Learning Center, and Seabury Western Church Seminary.
Foundation type: Independent foundation.
Financial data (yr. ended 12/31/13): Assets, $13,367,860 (M); expenditures, $729,355; qualifying distributions, $618,773; giving activities include $580,305 for 8 grants (high: $115,261; low: $1,000).
Fields of interest: Higher education; Theological school/education; Education; Boys & girls clubs; Human services.
Limitations: Applications not accepted. Giving primarily in CA and MN. No grants to individuals.
Application information: Unsolicited requests for funds not accepted.
Trustee: Bank of America, N.A.
EIN: 953382952

9085
George William Patton Trust ✧ ☆

c/o Bank of America N.A.
P.O. Box 831041
Dallas, TX 75283-1041

Established in CA.
Foundation type: Independent foundation.
Financial data (yr. ended 12/31/13): Assets, $11,933,250 (M); expenditures, $656,550; qualifying distributions, $555,555; giving activities include $519,446 for 15 grants (high: $72,778; low: $1,000).
Fields of interest: Health organizations; Youth development; Christian agencies & churches.
Limitations: Applications not accepted. Giving primarily in IL, MN, NY, OH, and OK.
Application information: Unsolicited requests for funds not accepted.
Trustee: Bank of America, N.A.
EIN: 956017501

9086
David D. & Nona S. Payne Foundation, Inc. ✧

P.O. Box 174
Pampa, TX 79066-0174 (806) 665-0063
Contact: Rebecca L. Holmes, V.P. and Treas.
FAX: (806) 665-2882;
E-mail: bholmes@bl-supply.com; Main URL: http://davidandnonapaynefoundation.com

Established in 1980 in TX.
Donor: Nona S. Payne†.
Foundation type: Independent foundation.
Financial data (yr. ended 06/30/13): Assets, $18,198,752 (M); expenditures, $1,154,292; qualifying distributions, $914,084; giving activities include $914,084 for 59 grants (high: $100,000; low: $800).
Purpose and activities: Giving primarily for the arts, education, youth and social services.
Fields of interest: Performing arts; Higher education; Education; Human services; Youth, services; Christian agencies & churches.
Type of support: General/operating support; Capital campaigns; Building/renovation; Equipment; Emergency funds; Publication; Scholarship funds; Matching/challenge support.
Limitations: Applications accepted. Giving limited to the TX Panhandle area. No grants to individuals.
Publications: Financial statement; Grants list.
Application information: See foundation web site for additional application requirements. Application form required.
Initial approach: Register on foundation web site to gain access to application form
Copies of proposal: 3
Deadline(s): Mar. 23 and Sept. 23; grant awards are made semiannually in Apr. and Oct.
Board meeting date(s): 1st Tues. of each calendar quarter
Final notification: 4 weeks
Officers and Trustees:* Vanessa G. Buzzard,* Pres.; Rick B. Leverich,* V.P.; Rebecca L. Holmes,* Secy.-Treas.
EIN: 751736339
Selected grants: The following grants are a representative sample of this grantmaker's funding activity:
$100,000 to Texas Tech University Health Sciences Center, Amarillo, TX, 2013. For Medical Plaza Students Center.
$25,000 to Amarillo Opera, Amarillo, TX, 2013. For Production of Gaetano Donizettis.
$25,000 to Spearhead Corporation, Spearman, TX, 2013. For O'Loughlin Center Renovations.
$10,000 to Opportunity School, Amarillo, TX, 2013. For family care program.

9087
Pediatric Epilepsy Research Foundation ✧ ☆

7777 Forest Ln.
Dallas, TX 75230-2571 (972) 566-8439
Contact: Roy D. Elterman M.D., Pres.

Foundation type: Independent foundation.
Financial data (yr. ended 12/31/13): Assets, $7,750,837 (M); expenditures, $731,646; qualifying distributions, $580,965; giving activities include $580,965 for 5 grants (high: $345,515; low: $12,450).
Purpose and activities: Giving for research in the fields of pediatric epilepsy and neurology.
Fields of interest: Health organizations; Epilepsy research; Neuroscience research; Pediatrics research; Children.
Limitations: Applications accepted. Giving in the U.S., with some emphasis on Chicago, IL, and Minneapolis, MN.
Application information: Application form required.
Initial approach: Contact foundation to request application material
Deadline(s): None
Officer: Roy D. Elterman, M.D., Pres.
Directors: Stephen Ashwal, M.D.; Alicia Freysinger; Lawrence Madigan; David McLaughlin; Cynthia Morriss; W. Donald Shields, M.D.; Herbert Winokur.
EIN: 201779737

9088
Pema Foundation ✧

3555 Timmons Ln., Ste. 800
Houston, TX 77027-6498

Established in 2002 in IL.
Donors: Pritzker's Foundation; Pritzker's Cousin Foundation; Colson Trust; N-1 Trust.
Foundation type: Independent foundation.
Financial data (yr. ended 12/31/12): Assets, $14,573,485 (M); gifts received, $17,463,849; expenditures, $3,797,487; qualifying distributions, $3,743,926; giving activities include $3,713,677 for 4 grants (high: $3,512,182; low: $10,000).
Purpose and activities: The foundation supports initiatives that are socially constructive.
Fields of interest: Human services; Community development, real estate; Foundations (community); Philanthropy/voluntarism; Financial services.
Limitations: Applications not accepted. Giving primarily in San Francisco, CA; some funding nationally. No grants to individuals.
Application information: Contributes only to pre-selected organizations.
Officers and Directors:* Linda Pritzker,* Pres.; Mary Jo Sandlin, V.P. and Secy.-Treas.; Roland B. Pritzker; Rosemary Pritzker.
EIN: 300039844

9089
J. C. Penney Company Fund, Inc. ✧

6501 Legacy Dr., MS 1205
Plano, TX 75024-3612 (972) 431-1431
FAX: (972) 431-1355; Main URL: http://www.jcpenney.com/jsp/browse/marketing/promotion.jsp?&pageId=pg40037900007

Established in 1984 in NY.
Donors: J.C. Penney Co., Inc.; J.C. Penney Corp., Inc.
Foundation type: Company-sponsored foundation.
Financial data (yr. ended 02/02/13): Assets, $10,355,909 (M); gifts received, $3,505,362; expenditures, $4,847,149; qualifying distributions, $4,847,149; giving activities include $4,846,275 for grants.
Purpose and activities: The fund supports organizations involved with arts and culture, education, health and welfare, cancer, disaster

relief, youth development, human services, the retail industry, and civic betterment.
Fields of interest: Arts; Elementary/secondary education; Higher education; Scholarships/financial aid; Education; Health care; Cancer; Disasters, preparedness/services; Youth development, business; Youth development; American Red Cross; Developmentally disabled, centers & services; Human services; Business/industry; United Ways and Federated Giving Programs; Public affairs.
Type of support: General/operating support; Annual campaigns; Equipment; Program development; Scholarship funds; Employee volunteer services; Sponsorships; Grants to individuals.
Limitations: Applications accepted. Giving on a national basis in areas of company operations. No support for individual K-12 schools lacking a community partnership with J.C. Penney, PTO's or PTA's, higher education institutions lacking a business or recruiting relationship with J.C. Penney, or membership, religious, political, labor, or fraternal organizations. No grants to individuals (except for disaster relief grants), or for door prizes, gift certificates, or other giveaways, fundraising or special events, proms or graduations, scholarships for colleges lacking a recruiting relationship with J.C. Penney, conferences or seminars, capital campaigns, multi-year or long-term support, or film or video projects or research projects; no merchandise donations; no employee matching gifts.
Publications: Application guidelines; Corporate giving report.
Application information: Additional information may be requested at a later date. Telephone calls are not encouraged. Application form not required.
Initial approach: Letter of inquiry
Copies of proposal: 1
Deadline(s): None
Final notification: 6 to 8 weeks
Officers and Directors: Darcie Brossart, V.P.; Brandy Treadway, Secy.; Windon Chau, Treas.; Susan Fournier, Cont.; Michael Dastugue; Janet Dhillon; Kenneth Hannah; Michael Kramer; Daniel Walker.
EIN: 133274961
Selected grants: The following grants are a representative sample of this grantmaker's funding activity:
$2,500,000 to J. C. Penney Afterschool Fund, Plano, TX, 2012. For general program support.
$887,452 to United Way Worldwide, Alexandria, VA, 2012. For general program support.
$876,621 to United Way Worldwide, Alexandria, VA, 2012. For general program support.
$873,715 to United Way Worldwide, Alexandria, VA, 2012. For general program support.
$661,154 to United Way Worldwide, Alexandria, VA, 2012. For general program support.
$400,000 to Salvation Army of Rochester, Rochester, NY, 2012. For general program support.
$200,000 to American Red Cross, Greater Ozarks Chapter, Springfield, MO, 2012. For general program support.
$200,000 to United Way of Metropolitan Dallas, Dallas, TX, 2012. For general program support.
$100,000 to American Red Cross, Greater Ozarks Chapter, Springfield, MO, 2012. For general program support.
$25,000 to USO World Headquarters, Arlington, VA, 2012. For general program support.

9090
Perkins-Prothro Foundation ✧
2304 Midwestern Pkwy., Ste. 200
Wichita Falls, TX 76308-2334

Established in 1967.
Donors: Lois Perkins†; Charles N. Prothro; Elizabeth P. Prothro; Joe N. Prothro; Kathryn P. Yeager; Mark H. Prothro.
Foundation type: Independent foundation.
Financial data (yr. ended 12/31/13): Assets, $26,945,534 (M); gifts received, $15,058; expenditures, $3,092,271; qualifying distributions, $2,613,303; giving activities include $2,573,185 for 157 grants (high: $255,750; low: $100).
Purpose and activities: Giving primarily for the arts, education, health, human services, and to United Methodist churches.
Fields of interest: Arts; Higher education; Education; Health care; Health organizations, association; Boys & girls clubs; Human services; Protestant agencies & churches.
Type of support: General/operating support; Building/renovation; Endowments.
Limitations: Applications not accepted. Giving primarily in TX, with emphasis on Dallas and Wichita Falls; funding also in UT. No grants to individuals.
Application information: Contributes only to pre-selected organizations.
Officers: Joe N. Prothro, Pres.; Kathryn Prothro Yeager, V.P.; K. Elizabeth Yeager, Secy.; Mark H. Prothro, Treas.
Director: Charlotte P. Philbin.
EIN: 751247407

9091
Permian Basin Area Foundation ✧
200 N. Loraine St., Ste. 500
Midland, TX 79701-4711 (432) 617-3213
Contact: Guy McCrary, C.E.O.
FAX: (432) 617-0151; E-mail: gmccrary@pbaf.org;
Main URL: http://www.pbaf.org

Incorporated in 1989 in TX.
Foundation type: Community foundation.
Financial data (yr. ended 12/31/13): Assets, $108,144,057 (M); gifts received, $8,896,501; expenditures, $12,033,073; giving activities include $9,914,934 for 113+ grants (high: $3,057,800), and $295,442 for 198 grants to individuals.
Purpose and activities: The foundation seeks to provide a vehicle through which donors may make gifts for charitable, religious, scientific, and educational uses. The ultimate goals are to improve the quality of life of the communities' residents, promote equality of opportunity, and assist those in need or at risk in the Permian Basin.
Fields of interest: Humanities; Arts; Education; Health care; Housing/shelter; Human services; Community/economic development; Public affairs; Aging.
Type of support: Emergency funds; Program development; Seed money; Scholarship funds; Matching/challenge support.
Limitations: Applications accepted. Giving primarily in the Permian Basin area of western TX, with consideration to southeastern NM. No grants to individuals (except for scholarships), or for ongoing operating expenses, basic research, endowment funds, deficit financing, or fundraising campaigns; generally no multi-year grants.
Publications: Application guidelines; Annual report; Newsletter.
Application information: Visit foundation web site for application form and guidelines. Based on Pre-Application Summary form, applicants will be notified that they are encouraged to submit a full application or that their project is unlikely to be funded. Application form required.
Initial approach: Submit Pre-Application Summary form
Copies of proposal: 1
Deadline(s): Apr. 1 and Oct. 1 for pre-application summary
Board meeting date(s): Feb., Apr., June, Aug., Oct., and Dec.
Final notification: Approx. 30 days from pre-application submission for full application request; July and Dec. for grant determination
Officers and Governors:* Mike Canon,* Chair.; Trey Grafa,* Vice-Chair.; Guy McCrary,* C.E.O. and Pres.; Mark Nicholas,* Secy.; Stacey Gerig,* Treas.; Kathy Clark; Cathy Eastham; Larry Edgerton; Cal Hendrick; Patty Herd; Scott Kidwell; Jerry Morales; Carolyn Stone.
Number of staff: 6 full-time professional; 3 full-time support.
EIN: 752295008

9092
The Perot Foundation ✧
P.O. Box 269014
Plano, TX 75026-9014 (972) 535-1900
Contact: Carolyn P. Rathjen, V.P.

Established in 1969 in TX.
Donor: H. Ross Perot.
Foundation type: Independent foundation.
Financial data (yr. ended 12/31/12): Assets, $75,553,806 (M); gifts received, $20,182,921; expenditures, $13,354,276; qualifying distributions, $13,256,753; giving activities include $12,925,084 for 204 grants (high: $2,000,000; low: $100).
Purpose and activities: Support primarily for higher education, a Salvation Army training school, and a Presbyterian church.
Fields of interest: Higher education; Human services; Religious federated giving programs; Protestant agencies & churches.
Type of support: Grants to individuals.
Limitations: Applications accepted. Giving primarily in TX.
Application information:
Initial approach: Letter
Officers and Directors:* H. Ross Perot,* Pres.; Carolyn P. Rathjen,* V.P. and Exec. Dir.; J. Thomas Walter,* Secy.; J.Y. Robb III, Treas.; Katherine P. Reeves; Suzanne P. McGee; Nancy P. Mulford; Bette Perot; H. Ross Perot, Jr.; Margot B. Perot.
EIN: 756093258
Selected grants: The following grants are a representative sample of this grantmaker's funding activity:
$2,000,000 to University of Texas M.D. Anderson Cancer Center, Houston, TX, 2012. For cancer research.
$1,000,000 to Dallas Symphony Association, Dallas, TX, 2012. For the performing arts.
$1,000,000 to Texarkana College, Texarkana, TX, 2012. For TC Tomorrow Community Challenge.
$735,000 to Command and General Staff College Foundation, Fort Leavenworth, KS, 2012. For

Colonel Arthur D. Simons Center for the Study of Interagency Cooperation.
$666,667 to Cooper Institute for Aerobics Research, Dallas, TX, 2012. To prevent illness and obesity in children and adults.
$200,000 to Ronald McDonald House of Dallas, Dallas, TX, 2012. For housing for families of children receiving medical treatment.
$80,000 to Mary Crowley Medical Research Center, Dallas, TX, 2012. For Contribution to Urschel Cardia Stem Cell Fund.
$25,000 to Texas Scottish Rite Hospital for Children, Dallas, TX, 2012. For Healthcare to children.
$20,833 to Reasoning Mind, Houston, TX, 2012. For online and face-to-face instruction in order for students to learn math.
$5,000 to Westmoreland Symphony Orchestra, Greensburg, PA, 2012. To promote musical enrichment through quality performance and education.

9093
The Sarah and Ross Perot, Jr. Foundation ✧

P.O. Box 269014
Plano, TX 75026-9014 (972) 535-1900
Application address: c/o Kristen Garcia, 5500 Preston Rd., Ste. 365 Dallas, TX 75205; tel.: (214) 528-2225

Established in 2002 in TX.
Donors: Henry Ross Perot, Jr.; Sarah F. Perot; SFP, Inc.
Foundation type: Independent foundation.
Financial data (yr. ended 12/31/12): Assets, $14,012,454 (M); gifts received, $1,363,620; expenditures, $4,319,688; qualifying distributions, $4,246,890; giving activities include $4,246,890 for grants.
Purpose and activities: Giving primarily for the arts, education, social services, and to Protestant organizations.
Fields of interest: Performing arts; Arts; Higher education; Education; Human services; Protestant agencies & churches.
Type of support: General/operating support; Capital campaigns; Building/renovation.
Limitations: Giving primarily in TX.
Application information:
Initial approach: Letter
Deadline(s): None
Officers and Trustees:* Sarah F. Perot,* Pres. and Secy.; Henry Ross Perot, Jr.,* V.P. and Treas.; Darcy Glen Anderson; J.Y. Robb III.
EIN: 431964344
Selected grants: The following grants are a representative sample of this grantmaker's funding activity:
$1,250,000 to Saint Marks School of Texas, Dallas, TX, 2012. For building campaign.
$500,000 to Global Fund for Children, Washington, DC, 2012. For program support.
$500,000 to Southern Methodist University, Perkins School of Theology, seminary of United Methodist Church, Dallas, TX, 2012. For educational support.
$333,334 to George W. Bush Foundation, Dallas, TX, 2012. To provide education and promote the advancement of public service in today's youth.
$333,333 to AT&T Performing Arts Center, Dallas, TX, 2012. For the performing arts.
$200,000 to Global Fund for Children, Washington, DC, 2012. For program support.
$100,000 to Dallas Symphony Orchestra, Dallas, TX, 2012. For the performing arts.
$50,000 to Global Fund for Children, Washington, DC, 2012. For program support.
$50,000 to Southern Methodist University, Perkins School of Theology, seminary of United Methodist Church, Dallas, TX, 2012. For educational support.
$25,000 to AT&T Performing Arts Center, Dallas, TX, 2012. For the performing arts.

9094
Joseph & Evelyn Pertusati Chartitable Trust ✧

c/o Bank of America, N.A.
P.O. Box 831041
Dallas, TX 75283-1041

Established in 1999 in CA.
Donor: Joseph Pertusati†.
Foundation type: Independent foundation.
Financial data (yr. ended 06/30/13): Assets, $13,729,237 (M); expenditures, $789,794; qualifying distributions, $607,784; giving activities include $607,784 for grants.
Fields of interest: Hospitals (general); Human services; Salvation Army; Children/youth, services.
Limitations: Applications not accepted. Giving primarily in CA. No grants to individuals.
Application information: Contributes only to pre-selected organizations.
Trustee: Bank of America, N.A.
EIN: 957088381

9095
Hal & Charlie Peterson Foundation ✧

P.O. Box 293870
Kerrville, TX 78029-3871
Contact: Brian Oehler, Gen. Mgr.
FAX: (830) 896-2283;
E-mail: info@hcpetersonfoundation.org; Additional address: 515 Jefferson St., Kerrville, TX 78028; Main URL: http://www.hcpetersonfoundation.org/

Established in 1944 in TX.
Donors: Hal Peterson†; Charlie Peterson†.
Foundation type: Independent foundation.
Financial data (yr. ended 12/31/13): Assets, $55,981,247 (M); gifts received, $1,433; expenditures, $2,609,527; qualifying distributions, $2,410,043; giving activities include $2,178,745 for 66 grants (high: $150,000; low: $425).
Purpose and activities: Giving primarily for education and health care.
Fields of interest: Elementary school/education; Secondary school/education; Higher education; Health care.
Type of support: General/operating support; Building/renovation; Equipment; Seed money; Matching/challenge support.
Limitations: Applications accepted. Giving limited to Kerr, Bandera, Edwards, Gillespie, Kendall, Kimble and Real counties, TX, and to state or national organizations with a local chapter in this area. No support for religious purposes. No grants to individuals, or for operating budgets, debt retirement, media productions, lobbying, publications, or endowments; no loans.
Publications: Application guidelines; Grants list; Informational brochure (including application guidelines); Program policy statement.
Application information: Application form required.
Initial approach: Letter or telephone requesting application form
Copies of proposal: 1
Deadline(s): See foundation web site for current deadlines
Board meeting date(s): Monthly
Officers and Directors:* Scott Parker,* Pres.; W.H. Cowden, Jr.,* V.P.; John Mosty,* Secy.-Treas.; Lynn Lemeilleur; Nowlin McBryde; Kyle Priour; James Stehling.
Number of staff: 1 full-time professional; 1 full-time support.
EIN: 741109626
Selected grants: The following grants are a representative sample of this grantmaker's funding activity:
$100,000 to Schreiner University, Kerrville, TX, 2012. For Fund Support for Nursing Program.
$50,000 to Raphael Community Free Clinic, Kerrville, TX, 2012. To assist Heart Disease Program.
$30,000 to Bandera Sports Complex, Bandera, TX, 2012. For Fund Baseball Field Improv.
$30,000 to Playhouse 2000, Kerrville, TX, 2012. To fund program/operating support.
$25,000 to Admiral Nimitz Foundation, Fredericksburg, TX, 2012. For Fund Rest/Creation Visitors Center.
$19,000 to Schreiner University, Kerrville, TX, 2012. For Landers Fund for 2012.
$17,766 to Frio Canyon EMS, Leakey, TX, 2012. To fund equip/conference.
$10,000 to Peterson Regional Medical Center, Kerrville, TX, 2012. For Lapham FD Distribution.
$10,000 to Special Olympics Texas, Austin, TX, 2012. To fund operating support.

9096
Petrello Family Foundation ✧

515 W. Greens Rd., Ste. 1200
Houston, TX 77067-4536

Established in 2001 in DE.
Donor: Anthony G. Petrello.
Foundation type: Independent foundation.
Financial data (yr. ended 06/30/13): Assets, $7,478,683 (M); gifts received, $3,506,843; expenditures, $664,506; qualifying distributions, $641,482; giving activities include $641,482 for 63 grants (high: $98,905; low: $71).
Purpose and activities: Giving primarily for the arts and health care, particularly a children's hospital.
Fields of interest: Performing arts; Arts; Hospitals (specialty); Human services.
Limitations: Applications not accepted. Giving primarily in TX, with emphasis on Houston. No grants to individuals.
Application information: Contributes only to pre-selected organizations.
Directors: Anthony G. Petrello; Cynthia A. Petrello.
EIN: 010559509
Selected grants: The following grants are a representative sample of this grantmaker's funding activity:
$60,750 to Houston Grand Opera, Houston, TX, 2013. To support of Artistic Endeavors.
$26,000 to Memorial Park Conservancy, Houston, TX, 2013. For Memorial Park.

$6,000 to Holocaust Museum Houston, Houston, TX, 2013. For the Holocaust Museum.
$6,000 to Inprint, Houston, TX, 2013. To Promote Literary Arts.
$4,300 to Houston Center for Contemporary Craft, Houston, TX, 2013. To Advance Education of Craft.

9097
Phillips Family Foundation ✧
P.O. Box 17149
Sugar Land, TX 77496-7149

Established in 2001 in TX.
Donors: D. Martin Phillips; Liane M. Phillips.
Foundation type: Independent foundation.
Financial data (yr. ended 12/31/13): Assets, $12,724,404 (M); gifts received, $4,023,383; expenditures, $1,579,968; qualifying distributions, $1,438,467; giving activities include $1,438,467 for 42 grants (high: $500,300; low: $50).
Fields of interest: Children/youth, services; Human services; Protestant agencies & churches.
Limitations: Applications not accepted. Giving primarily in Houston, TX. No grants to individuals.
Application information: Contributes only to pre-selected organizations.
Trustees: D. Martin Phillips; Gary R. Petersen; Liane M. Phillips.
EIN: 750590214

9098
The PHM Foundation ✧
4817 N FM 1417
Sherman, TX 75092-6605
Main URL: http://phmfoundation.org/

Established in 2006 in TX.
Donors: Care Now; Dura Medical Inc.; Primary Health Management, Ltd.; Primary Health, Inc.
Foundation type: Operating foundation.
Financial data (yr. ended 12/31/12): Assets, $7,202,529 (M); gifts received, $8,100,000; expenditures, $6,166,778; qualifying distributions, $6,166,091; giving activities include $6,151,549 for 14 grants (high: $2,145,000; low: $20,000).
Purpose and activities: The foundation supports religious ministries and organizations involved with print publishing, reproductive health, and youth. The foundation also operates an economic development program to promote entrepreneurship and development in developing countries.
Fields of interest: Media, print publishing; Reproductive health; Youth, services; International economic development; Social entrepreneurship; Christian agencies & churches; Jewish agencies & synagogues; Religion, interfaith issues; Religion.
International interests: Developing Countries.
Type of support: General/operating support; Program-related investments/loans.
Limitations: Applications not accepted. Giving primarily in CA, Washington, DC, FL, MO, NM, NV, and TX; giving also to developing countries through program-related investments. No grants to individuals.
Application information: Unsolicited applications are not accepted. The foundation utilizes an invitation only process for giving.
Officers and Directors:* David Walter,* Pres.; Jennifer L. Walter,* Secy.; Daniel E. Walter,* Exec. Dir.
EIN: 204948182
Selected grants: The following grants are a representative sample of this grantmaker's funding activity:
$2,145,000 to International House of Prayer, Kansas City, MO, 2012.
$1,500,000 to International Justice Mission, Arlington, VA, 2012. For advocacy for victims of violence.
$1,016,000 to Friends of India Christian Ministries, Dana Point, CA, 2012. For education, evangelism, nutrition.
$416,650 to General Council of the Assemblies of God, Springfield, MO, 2012. For aftercare for child and teen survivors of sexual abuse; education, evangelism, nutrition.
$259,100 to Hosanna, Albuquerque, NM, 2012. For audio bibles.
$110,000 to Antioch Oasis International, Grand Prairie, TX, 2012. For pastoral care.
$105,000 to Messianic Jewish Bible Institute, Euless, TX, 2012. For training.
$60,000 to Deep Water Ministries, Washburn, MO, 2012. For training.
$50,000 to Agape International Missions, Roseville, CA, 2012. For aftercare for child survivors of sexual abuse.
$40,000 to Metro Family Ministries, Garland, TX, 2012. For outreach to at-risk teens.

9099
The T. Boone Pickens Foundation ✧
8117 Preston Rd., Ste. 260 W.
Dallas, TX 75225-6321
Main URL: http://www.tboonepickensfoundation.org
T. Boone Pickens's Giving Pledge Profile: http://glasspockets.org/philanthropy-in-focus/eye-on-the-giving-pledge/profiles/pickens

Established in 2006 in TX.
Donors: T. Boone Pickens; Dick Grant.
Foundation type: Independent foundation.
Financial data (yr. ended 12/31/12): Assets, $328,709 (M); gifts received, $1,453,650; expenditures, $1,137,153; qualifying distributions, $1,134,903; giving activities include $1,125,000 for 6 grants (high: $600,000; low: $10,000).
Purpose and activities: The foundation improves lives through grants supporting education, medical research/development and services, athletics and corporate wellness, at-risk youths, the entrepreneurial process, conservation and wildlife programs and a wide range of public policy initiatives.
Fields of interest: Environment, natural resources; Health care; Medical research; Human services.
Limitations: Applications not accepted. Giving primarily in OK and TX.
Application information: Contributes only to pre-selected organizations.
Officers: T. Boone Pickens, Chair.; Ronald D. Bassett, Pres.; Robert L. Stillwell, V.P. and Secy.-Treas.; Andrew Littlefair, V.P.; Marti Carlin, Mgr., Community Rels.
EIN: 205892962

9100
Pinon Foundation ✧
P.O. Box 1989
Addison, TX 75001-1989

Established in TX.
Donors: N. Malone Mitchell III; Amy E. Mitchell.
Foundation type: Independent foundation.
Financial data (yr. ended 12/31/12): Assets, $19,269,861 (M); expenditures, $853,516; qualifying distributions, $846,542; giving activities include $846,542 for grants.
Fields of interest: Higher education; Education; Children/youth, services; Christian agencies & churches.
Limitations: Applications not accepted. Giving primarily in TX.
Application information: Contributes only to pre-selected organizations.
Officers: Amy E. Mitchell, Pres. and Secy.; N. Malone Mitchell III, V.P.
Directors: Alexandria M. Jacobs; Noah M. Mitchell.
EIN: 205688587

9101
Minnie Stevens Piper Foundation ✧
1250 N.E. Loop 410, Ste. 810
San Antonio, TX 78209-1539 (210) 525-8494
Contact: Joyce M. Ellis, Secy. and Exec. Dir.
FAX: (210) 341-6627; E-mail: mspf@mspf.org; Main URL: http://www.everychanceeverytexan.org/about/scholars/
Additional URL: http://www.everychanceeverytexan.org/about/scholars/

Incorporated in 1950 in TX.
Donors: Randall G. Piper‡; Minnie Stevens Piper‡.
Foundation type: Independent foundation.
Financial data (yr. ended 12/31/13): Assets, $25,367,815 (M); gifts received, $798; expenditures, $1,917,044; qualifying distributions, $1,547,595; giving activities include $469,770 for 42+ grants, $154,000 for loans to individuals, and $433,953 for foundation-administered programs.
Purpose and activities: Giving especially to contribute toward the education of worthy students. The foundation administers a student loan fund, annual Piper Professor Awards to recognize teaching excellence at the college level, Piper Scholar Awards of four-year college scholarships to outstanding high school graduates in TX, a student aid library and information center, and a scholarship clearinghouse. Grants to individuals as educational loans, scholarships, and teaching awards are made only through the programs operated by the foundation.
Fields of interest: Higher education; Education.
Type of support: Scholarships—to individuals; Student loans—to individuals.
Limitations: Giving limited to TX; student loans limited to U.S. citizens residing in TX and attending TX educational institutions. No grants for building or endowment funds.
Publications: Application guidelines; Occasional report; Program policy statement.
Application information: Recipients of scholarship and professorship award programs must be nominated; nomination not necessary for student loans. See foundation web site for current information. Application form not required.
Initial approach: Letter
Copies of proposal: 1
Deadline(s): None
Board meeting date(s): Mar., June, Sept., and Dec.; student loan committee meets monthly
Officers and Directors:* Lewis M. Fox,* Pres.; Paul T. Curl,* V.P.; Joyce M. Ellis,* Secy. and Exec. Dir.;

Martin R. Harris,* Treas.; Kenneth Shumate; J. Burleson Smith; John H. Wilson II; Joyce A. Yanta.
Number of staff: 4 full-time professional; 4 full-time support; 1 part-time support.
EIN: 741292695
Selected grants: The following grants are a representative sample of this grantmaker's funding activity:
$3,000 to Cancer Therapy and Research Center, San Antonio, TX, 2012. To support Grant for Calendar Year 2012 - Surviving and Thriving Conference.
$3,000 to Texas Public Radio, San Antonio, TX, 2012. To support Grant for Calendar Year 2012 - McClain Circle.
$2,500 to Youth Orchestras of San Antonio, San Antonio, TX, 2012. To support Grant for Calendar Year 2012.
$1,000 to Musical Bridges Around the World, San Antonio, TX, 2012. For general support grant for calendar year 2012.
$1,000 to UNAM Foundation, San Antonio, TX, 2012. To support Grant - San Antonio ESL for Calendar Year.

9102
Pleroma, Inc. ✧
P.O. Box 1796
Glen Rose, TX 76043-1796

Established in 2004 in DE and TX; funded in 2006 with assets from the Alfred Jurzykowski Foundation.
Donor: M. Christine Jurzykowski.
Foundation type: Independent foundation.
Financial data (yr. ended 12/31/12): Assets, $15,151,111 (M); expenditures, $612,089; qualifying distributions, $500,000; giving activities include $500,000 for 1 grant.
Fields of interest: Philanthropy/voluntarism, management/technical assistance; Philanthropy/voluntarism.
Limitations: Applications not accepted. Giving primarily in San Francisco, CA. No grants to individuals.
Application information: Contributes only to pre-selected organizations.
Directors: Claude Del Pepin; Mark Finser; M. Christine Jurzykowski.
EIN: 200622367

9103
Pollock Foundation ✧
2626 Howell St., Ste. 166
Dallas, TX 75204-0802
Contact: Robert G. Pollock, Tr.

Established in 1955 in TX.
Donors: Lawrence S. Pollock, Sr.†; Lawrence S. Pollock, Jr.†.
Foundation type: Independent foundation.
Financial data (yr. ended 12/31/13): Assets, $19,492,962 (M); gifts received, $120,420; expenditures, $1,171,514; qualifying distributions, $948,000; giving activities include $948,000 for 21 grants (high: $300,000; low: $1,000).
Fields of interest: Arts; Public health school/education; Libraries/library science; Nursing care; Youth development, centers/clubs; Human services; Jewish agencies & synagogues.
Limitations: Applications accepted. Giving primarily in Dallas, TX.
Application information: Application form required.
Initial approach: Letter
Copies of proposal: 1
Deadline(s): None
Board meeting date(s): Apr. and Oct.
Trustees: Lawrence S. Pollock III; Richard Pollock; Robert G. Pollock.
EIN: 756011985

9104
Posey Family Foundation ✧ ☆
2804 Swiss Ave.
Dallas, TX 75204-5955

Established in 1998 in TX.
Donors: Lee Posey†; Sally Posey.
Foundation type: Independent foundation.
Financial data (yr. ended 12/31/13): Assets, $16,164,554 (M); expenditures, $877,488; qualifying distributions, $807,819; giving activities include $805,319 for 11 grants (high: $264,319; low: $25,000).
Purpose and activities: Giving primarily for education.
Fields of interest: Education.
Limitations: Applications not accepted. Giving primarily in TX, with emphasis on Dallas; some giving nationally. No grants to individuals.
Application information: Unsolicited requests for funds not accepted.
Officers: Tim Smith, Pres.; Gina Betts, Secy.
Directors: Dan Ahearn; Jennifer P. Ahearn; Donald Key; Jill M. Posey; Sally Posey; Todd Williams.
EIN: 752768325

9105
The Powell Foundation ✧
2121 San Felipe St., Ste. 110
Houston, TX 77019-5600 (713) 523-7557
Contact: Caroline J. Sabin, Exec. Dir.
FAX: (713) 523-7553;
E-mail: info@powellfoundation.org; Main URL: http://www.powellfoundation.org
Grants List: http://www.powellfoundation.org/grantsbyyear.html

Established in 1967 in TX.
Donors: Ben H. Powell, Jr.†; Kitty King Powell.
Foundation type: Independent foundation.
Financial data (yr. ended 12/31/13): Assets, $30,009,000 (M); gifts received, $450,000; expenditures, $1,354,590; qualifying distributions, $1,220,731; giving activities include $1,004,600 for 131 grants (high: $35,000; low: $50).
Purpose and activities: The foundation distributes funds for public charitable purposes, principally for the support, encouragement, and assistance to education, health, conservation, and the arts with a direct impact within the foundation's geographic zone of interest: Harris, Travis, and Walker counties in TX.
Fields of interest: Arts; Education, public education; Education, early childhood education; Environment; Health care; Human services; Children/youth; Children; Youth; Minorities; Economically disadvantaged.
Type of support: General/operating support; Management development/capacity building; Program development; Curriculum development; Scholarship funds; Matching/challenge support.
Limitations: Applications accepted. Giving primarily in Harris, Travis and Walker counties, TX. No support for private foundations, or religious organizations for religious purposes. No grants to individuals or for testimonial dinners, building funds, fundraising events, advertising, or for debt retirement or operating deficits.
Publications: Application guidelines; Annual report (including application guidelines); Grants list.
Application information: See foundation web site for complete application policies and guidelines. Application form required.
Initial approach: Proposal
Copies of proposal: 1
Deadline(s): None
Board meeting date(s): Spring and fall
Officers and Directors:* Nancy Powell Moore,* Pres. and Treas.; Albert S. Tabor,* V.P. and Secy.; Ben H. Powell V,* V.P.; Caroline J. Sabin, Exec. Dir.; Kitty King Powell, Founding Dir.; Charles F. Caldwell; Marian M. Casey; Marian P. Harrison; Katherine P. Hill; Ben H. Powell VI; Jan L. Redford; Katherine Osborn Valdez.
Number of staff: 1 full-time professional; 1 part-time professional; 1 part-time support.
EIN: 746104592
Selected grants: The following grants are a representative sample of this grantmaker's funding activity:
$25,000 to Teach for America, Houston, TX, 2012. To support of the recruitment and training of Houston teacher corps.
$20,000 to Citizen Schools, Houston, TX, 2012. To deepen and expand high-quality, high-impact after-school Programs - Extended Learning Times.
$20,000 to Collaborative for Children, Houston, TX, 2012. To support of the College Bound-Beginning at Birth initiative. Last of 3 yr pledge.
$20,000 to Project GRAD Houston, Houston, TX, 2012. For continued support of the Fine Arts Program in elementary and middle schools.
$15,000 to Hermann Park Conservancy, Houston, TX, 2012. For First of three year capital pledge for the Centennial Gardens Project.
$10,000 to American Festival for the Arts, Houston, TX, 2012. For the AFA Scholarship/Enrichment Fund to provide need-based scholarships.
$10,000 to Bayou Land Conservancy, Houston, TX, 2012. For Programs for the Watershed Protection education Program for middle school students.
$10,000 to Boys and Girls Clubs of Greater Houston, Houston, TX, 2012. For the Summer Learning Camp Program to help at-risk children prevent the summer slide.
$10,000 to Great Expectations Foundation, Tahlequah, OK, 2012. To support of Teacher Professional Development Program in Houston area schools.
$10,000 to Texans Care for Children, Austin, TX, 2012. For continued support for policies and advocacy work begun by Texas Early Childhood Education Coalition.

9106
The Prairie Foundation ✧ ☆
6101 Holiday Hill Rd.
Midland, TX 79701-1631 (432) 683-1777
Contact: Deborah Williams

Established in 1957 in TX.
Donors: David Fasken Special Trust; Barbara Fasken.
Foundation type: Independent foundation.

Financial data (yr. ended 12/31/13): Assets, $8,393,852 (M); expenditures, $545,653; qualifying distributions, $488,289; giving activities include $455,250 for 44 grants (high: $60,000; low: $1,000).
Fields of interest: Arts; Education; Health organizations, association; Youth development, scouting agencies (general); Human services; Children/youth, services.
Limitations: Applications accepted. Giving primarily in the San Francisco Bay Area, CA; and Midland, Laredo, and Odessa, TX.
Publications: Application guidelines.
Application information: Application form required.
Initial approach: Letter
Copies of proposal: 1
Deadline(s): None
Board meeting date(s): As needed
Officers and Directors:* Robert T. Dickson,* Pres.; Norbert J. Dickman,* V.P.; Charles F. Hedges, Jr.,* Secy.; Lynda James,* Treas.
EIN: 756012458
Selected grants: The following grants are a representative sample of this grantmaker's funding activity:
$5,000 to West Texas Food Bank, Odessa, TX, 2012. To assist named recipient to carry out its exempt purpose.

9107
The Prentice Foundation ✧ ☆
52 Arnold Palmer
San Antonio, TX 78257-1723 (210) 698-9773
Contact: Cynthia R. Prentice, V.P.

Established in 1994 in TX.
Donors: F. David Prentice; Mrs. F. David Prentice.
Foundation type: Independent foundation.
Financial data (yr. ended 11/30/13): Assets, $1,391,789 (M); gifts received, $2,282; expenditures, $582,839; qualifying distributions, $564,500; giving activities include $564,500 for 5 grants (high: $500,000; low: $12,500).
Purpose and activities: Giving primarily for animal care.
Fields of interest: Animals/wildlife.
Limitations: Applications accepted. Giving primarily in TX.
Application information: Application form not required.
Initial approach: Proposal
Deadline(s): None
Officers: F. David Prentice, Pres. and Treas.; Cynthia R. Prentice, V.P. and Secy.
Director: Robert J. Fumagalli.
EIN: 760455526

9108
Presbyterian Village North Foundation ✧
8600 Skyline Dr.
Dallas, TX 75243-4198

Donors: James Clutts; Erik Vohtz; Craig Millis; Mrs. Craig Millis; Presbyterian Communities and Svcs. Fdn.; Louis T. and Bobbie M. Pope Revocable Trust; C. Maxine Morrison†; Lucille Amen Storey†; Betty Rogers; Bob Symon; Jeanne Dodds†; Ruth M. Gruennert†; Wynne Miller; Betty Miller; David Streitmatter; LaCava Gift Annuity; John Funk†.
Foundation type: Independent foundation.
Financial data (yr. ended 12/31/13): Assets, $39,168,397 (M); gifts received, $778,100; expenditures, $2,392,063; qualifying distributions, $2,085,099; giving activities include $1,955,822 for 1 grant.
Fields of interest: Residential/custodial care.
Limitations: Applications not accepted. Giving primarily in TX.
Application information: Contributes only to pre-selected organizations.
Officers and Trustees:* Billye Miars,* Chair.; Bob Maier,* Vice-Chair.; Harvey Cragon,* Secy.; Bob Symon,* Treas.; Margaret Zagurski, Exec. Dir.; Jim Clutts; Roger Green; Jack Holmes; Joe Roach; Jim Wiley.
EIN: 752022746
Selected grants: The following grants are a representative sample of this grantmaker's funding activity:
$1,150,116 to Presbyterian Village North, Dallas, TX, 2011.
$909,198 to Presbyterian Village North, Dallas, TX, 2010.
$96,000 to Texas Presbyterian Foundation, Irving, TX, 2011.

9109
The Priddy Foundation ✧
807 8th St., Ste. 1010
Wichita Falls, TX 76301-3310 (940) 723-8720
Contact: Debbie C. White, Dir., Grants; Pat Myers, Secy. and Admin.
FAX: (940) 723-8656;
E-mail: debbiecw@priddyfdn.org; Main URL: http://www.priddyfdn.org
Grants List: http://www.priddyfdn.org/grants/

Established in 1963 in TX.
Donors: Ashley H. Priddy†; Robert T. Priddy; Swannanoa H. Priddy†; Walter M. Priddy†.
Foundation type: Independent foundation.
Financial data (yr. ended 12/31/13): Assets, $171,226,978 (M); expenditures, $5,708,870; qualifying distributions, $4,654,539; giving activities include $3,803,738 for 85+ grants (high: $350,000).
Purpose and activities: The foundation is dedicated to the support of programs in human services, education, the arts, and health, which offer significant potential for individual development and community improvement.
Fields of interest: Arts; Education; Health care; Youth development; Human services; Community/economic development.
Type of support: General/operating support; Management development/capacity building; Capital campaigns; Building/renovation; Equipment; Program development; Scholarship funds; Technical assistance; Matching/challenge support.
Limitations: Applications accepted. Giving primarily in Archer, Baylor, Childress, Clay, Cottle, Foard, Hardeman, Haskell, Jack, King, Knox, Montague, Stonewall, Throckmorton, Wichita, Wilbarger, Wise, and Young counties, TX; and Comanche, Cotton, Jackson, Jefferson, Stephens, and Tillman counties, OK. No support for individual public elementary or secondary schools, or religious institutions (except for non-sectarian, human service programs offered on a non-discriminatory basis). No grants to individuals, or for endowments, operating deficits, debt retirement, start-up funding, basic or applied research, fundraising programs or events, conferences or other educational events (except through an organizational development grant), media productions or publications, or school trips.
Publications: Application guidelines; Financial statement; Grants list; Informational brochure (including application guidelines); Program policy statement.
Application information: See foundation's web site for more application information. The preliminary and formal applications must be submitted online at the foundation's web site. Application form required.
Initial approach: Brief preliminary application online through the web site
Copies of proposal: 1
Deadline(s): Feb. 1 and Aug. 1 for preliminary applications; Mar. 1 and Sept. 1 for formal grant application
Board meeting date(s): May and Nov.
Final notification: Within two weeks of board meeting
Officer and Trustees:* David Wolverton,* Pres.; Berneice R. Leath, Tr. Emeritus; Robert T. Priddy, Tr. Emeritus; Doug Armstrong; Paul Clark; Murphy Davis; David Flack; Alice Huang; Jerry Johnson; Nancy Marks; Liz Martin; Gale Richardson; Sara Jane Snell; Patty Young.
Number of staff: 3 full-time professional; 1 full-time support.
EIN: 756029882
Selected grants: The following grants are a representative sample of this grantmaker's funding activity:
$900,000 to Wichita Falls Faith Mission, Wichita Falls, TX, 2011. For Faith Refuge Capital Campaign.
$673,389 to United Way of North Texas Area, Wichita Falls, TX, 2011. For Early Childhood Development Initiative.
$558,371 to University of North Texas Foundation, Denton, TX, 2011. For Rural Library Initiative.
$426,822 to Center for Reform of School Systems, Houston, TX, 2011. For Reform Governance in Action.
$300,000 to Graham, City of, Graham, TX, 2011. For Memorial Auditorium Renovation and Expansion.
$120,000 to Communities in Schools of Greater Wichita Falls, Wichita Falls, TX, 2011. For Program Operations.
$100,000 to Boys Club of Wichita Falls, Wichita Falls, TX, 2011. For Central Building Preservation.
$90,000 to Vernon College, Vernon, TX, 2011. For New Beginnings.
$50,000 to Boys and Girls Club of Burkburnett, Burkburnett, TX, 2011. For Program Operation.
$29,000 to Child Care, Wichita Falls, TX, 2011. For Agency Minivan.

9110
The Jay Pritzker Foundation ✧
3555 Timmons Ln., Ste. 800
Houston, TX 77027-6498 (713) 961-1600

Established in 2002 in IL.
Donor: Daniel F. Pritzker.
Foundation type: Independent foundation.
Financial data (yr. ended 12/31/12): Assets, $14,970,188 (M); gifts received, $14,892,714; expenditures, $3,867,994; qualifying distributions, $3,833,191; giving activities include $3,830,150 for 19 grants (high: $3,012,654; low: $496).
Fields of interest: Elementary school/education; Higher education; Higher education, university; Education.

Limitations: Applications not accepted. Giving primarily in CA and MA; some funding also in Chicago, IL. No grants to individuals.
Application information: Contributes only to pre-selected organizations.
Officers and Directors:* Daniel F. Pritzker,* Pres.; Karen M. Pritzker,* Secy.; Michele Tayler,* Treas.
EIN: 020550210
Selected grants: The following grants are a representative sample of this grantmaker's funding activity:
$3,012,654 to Providence Saint Mel School, Chicago, IL, 2012. For general operating support.
$250,000 to San Francisco Jazz Organization, San Francisco, CA, 2012. For The World is Listening Campaign.
$200,000 to Northwestern University, Evanston, IL, 2012. For work at Center for Wrongful Convictions at School of Law in Chicago.
$100,000 to Katherine Branson School, Ross, CA, 2012. For general support.
$50,000 to Dartmouth College, Hanover, NH, 2012. For Conway Scholarship Fund.
$25,000 to California Film Institute, San Rafael, CA, 2012. For general support.
$25,000 to University of California San Francisco Foundation, San Francisco, CA, 2012. For general support.
$20,000 to Kentfield Schools Foundation, Kentfield, CA, 2012. For Annual Fund.
$1,000 to Lycee Francais La Perouse, San Francisco, CA, 2012. For Annual Fund.
$1,000 to Tufts University, Medford, MA, 2012. For general support.

9111
Pritzker Innovation Fund ✧
c/o M. Jo Sandlin
3555 Timmons Ln., Ste. 800
Houston, TX 77027-6498
Main URL: http://www.lotusfdn.org/

Established in 2004 in IL.
Donors: Linda Pritzker; The N-1 Trust; Festus Bahamas Trust; Scorpion Nassau Trust; Rachel Pritzker; Roland Pritzker.
Foundation type: Independent foundation.
Financial data (yr. ended 12/31/12): Assets, $3,692,309 (M); gifts received, $50,000; expenditures, $1,134,209; qualifying distributions, $1,121,222; giving activities include $1,065,872 for 5 grants (high: $683,672; low: $10,000).
Fields of interest: Elementary/secondary education; Philanthropy/voluntarism, management/technical assistance; Public affairs.
Limitations: Applications not accepted. Giving primarily to national organizations in CA, Washington, DC, and NY. No grants to individuals.
Application information: Contributes only to pre-selected organizations.
Officers and Directors:* Rachel Pritzker,* Pres.; Mary Jo Sandlin,* V.P. and Treas.; Roland Pritzker; Jeffrey Rusnak.
EIN: 201252591

9112
Vin & Caren Prothro Foundation ✧
2501 N. Harwood St., No. 2400
Dallas, TX 75201-1607

Established in 2000 in TX.
Donors: Caren H. Prothro; Microsoft Corp.
Foundation type: Independent foundation.
Financial data (yr. ended 12/31/13): Assets, $12,970,866 (M); expenditures, $973,479; qualifying distributions, $925,879; giving activities include $881,650 for 112 grants (high: $250,000; low: $500).
Fields of interest: Arts; Education; Human services.
Limitations: Applications not accepted. Giving primarily in TX. No grants to individuals.
Application information: Contributes only to pre-selected organizations.
Officers: Caren H. Prothro, Pres.; Vincent H. Prothro, V.P.; Nita C. Clark, Secy.; J.H. Cullum Clark, Treas.
EIN: 752911958
Selected grants: The following grants are a representative sample of this grantmaker's funding activity:
$100,000 to Southern Methodist University, Dallas, TX, 2012. For 5th payment on $500K pledge to Perkins School of Theology.
$100,000 to Trinity Trust Foundation, Dallas, TX, 2012. For 5th payment on $500K pledge toward naming part of the trail system in honor of Margaret McDermott and Mary McDermott Cook.
$50,000 to Episcopal School of Dallas, Dallas, TX, 2012. For 5th payment on $250K pledge toward the Wellness for Life capital campaign.
$30,000 to Dallas Theater Center, Dallas, TX, 2012. For 3rd payment on $150K pledge toward the capital campaign.
$25,000 to Communities Foundation of Texas, Dallas, TX, 2012. For 1st payment on $50K pledge toward the 50th Anniversary JFK Commemoration Fund.
$25,000 to North Texas Food Bank, Dallas, TX, 2012. For 2nd payment on $75K pledge for general operating support.
$20,000 to Parkland Foundation, Dallas, TX, 2012. For 4th payment on $100K pledge toward the new hospital construction capital campaign.
$10,000 to Teach for America, Dallas, TX, 2012. For 1st payment on $30K pledge toward operating support.
$10,000 to Visiting Nurse Association of Texas, Dallas, TX, 2012. Toward Meals on Wheels event.
$5,000 to Sammons Center for the Arts, Dallas, TX, 2012. Toward capital repairs donation.

9113
Myra Stafford Pryor Charitable Trust ✧
P.O. Box 2950, Tax Dept T-8
San Antonio, TX 78299-2950
Application address: c/o Melissa Adams, Frost Bank, 100 W. Houston, San Antonio, TX 78210, tel.: (210) 220-4353

Established in 1993.
Foundation type: Independent foundation.
Financial data (yr. ended 12/31/13): Assets, $25,619,864 (M); expenditures, $1,248,276; qualifying distributions, $1,116,887; giving activities include $1,077,501 for 86 grants (high: $50,000; low: $50).
Fields of interest: Arts; Education; Hospitals (general); Human services; Religion.
Type of support: Capital campaigns; Building/renovation; Equipment.
Limitations: Applications accepted. Giving primarily in San Antonio, TX.
Application information: Application form required.
Initial approach: Letter on organization's letterhead
Copies of proposal: 1
Deadline(s): None
Trustee: Frost National Bank.
EIN: 746417499
Selected grants: The following grants are a representative sample of this grantmaker's funding activity:
$25,000 to United Way of San Antonio and Bexar County, San Antonio, TX, 2012. To Boysville.
$20,000 to United Way of San Antonio and Bexar County, San Antonio, TX, 2012. To Catholic Charities Archdiocese of Sa.
$17,000 to United Way of San Antonio and Bexar County, San Antonio, TX, 2012. To Sa Metropolitan Ministry, Inc.
$15,000 to United Way of San Antonio and Bexar County, San Antonio, TX, 2012. To Boy Scouts of America - Alamo Area Council.
$15,000 to United Way of San Antonio and Bexar County, San Antonio, TX, 2012. To Family Service Association.
$15,000 to United Way of San Antonio and Bexar County, San Antonio, TX, 2012. To Healy-Murphy Center, Inc.
$15,000 to United Way of San Antonio and Bexar County, San Antonio, TX, 2012. To Good Samaritan Center of San Antonio.
$12,735 to United Way of San Antonio and Bexar County, San Antonio, TX, 2012. To Any Baby Can, Inc.
$12,500 to United Way of San Antonio and Bexar County, San Antonio, TX, 2012. To Goodwill Industries of Sa.
$10,000 to United Way of San Antonio and Bexar County, San Antonio, TX, 2012. To Brighton School, Inc.

9114
Nelson Puett Foundation ✧
P.O. Box 9038
Austin, TX 78766-9038
Contact: Nelson Harwood Puett, Pres.

Established in 1955 in TX.
Donors: Nelson Harwood Puett; Nelson Puett Mortgage Co.; Cardwell Family Limited Partnership.
Foundation type: Independent foundation.
Financial data (yr. ended 02/28/13): Assets, $21,904,502 (M); expenditures, $1,261,115; qualifying distributions, $1,125,390; giving activities include $1,125,390 for 62 grants (high: $500,000; low: $200).
Purpose and activities: Giving primarily for education, religion, and social services.
Fields of interest: Education; Health organizations, association; Housing/shelter; Boy scouts; Human services; Religion.
Type of support: Annual campaigns; Capital campaigns; Building/renovation; Equipment; Program development; Fellowships; Scholarship funds; Research.
Limitations: Applications accepted. Giving primarily in TX. No grants to individuals.
Publications: Financial statement.
Application information: Information on scholarships available from individual high schools. Application form not required.
Initial approach: Letter
Deadline(s): None
Board meeting date(s): Varies

Officers: Nelson Harwood Puett, Pres.; Ruth B. Puett, V.P.; T.H. Worthington, V.P.; Caroline C. Puett, Secy.-Treas.
EIN: 746062365
Selected grants: The following grants are a representative sample of this grantmaker's funding activity:
$350,000 to Boy Scouts of America, Atlanta, GA, 2011.
$150,000 to Schreiner University, Kerrville, TX, 2011.

9115
The QuadW Foundation ✧
(also known as What Would Willie Want Foundation)
100 Crescent Ct., Ste. 700
Dallas, TX 75201-2112 (214) 459-3330
Contact: Lisa Tichenor, Tr.
E-mail: info@QuadW.org; Main URL: http://www.quadw.org
Facebook: https://www.facebook.com/pages/QuadW-Foundation/195619433811221

Established in 2006 in TX.
Donor: McHenry "Taylor" T. Tichenor III.
Foundation type: Independent foundation.
Financial data (yr. ended 12/31/13): Assets, $12,487,044 (M); gifts received, $773,565; expenditures, $710,135; qualifying distributions, $641,252; giving activities include $549,111 for 15 grants (high: $103,512; low: $1,000).
Purpose and activities: Giving primarily for higher education, sarcoma research, and transforming mission experiences.
Fields of interest: Higher education; Cancer research; Spirituality.
Type of support: Internship funds; Research; Program development; General/operating support; Fellowships; Scholarship funds.
Publications: Application guidelines; Multi-year report.
Application information: Application guidelines available for each program on foundation web site. Application form required.
Initial approach: E-mail
Deadline(s): 1 month before each board meeting
Board meeting date(s): Aug. and Dec.
Officer: McHenry "Mac" T. Tichenor, Jr., Exec. Dir.
Directors: Bret Alexander; Charlie Haggard; Laureen Hayden; Johnny Peters; Elizabeth Trieu; Ross Vick; Mary Katherine Vigness.
Trustees: Lisa Tichenor; Taylor Tichenor.
EIN: 204750916
Selected grants: The following grants are a representative sample of this grantmaker's funding activity:
$70,000 to Baylor College of Medicine, Houston, TX, 2012. For Fund the Production of a T-Cell Reagent for Use in a Pediatric Cancer Immunotherapy Clinical Trial Conducted By the National Cancer Institute.
$2,000 to 826 Valencia, San Francisco, CA, 2012. For Discretionary Grant for This Organization, Which Supports Children 6-18 and Their Teachers to Develop the Students' Creative and Expository Writing Skills.

9116
Allen and Kelli Questrom Foundation ✧
c/o Henderson Edwards Wilson Evetts LLP
16660 Dallas Pkwy., Ste. 2400
Dallas, TX 75248-2698

Donors: Allen I. Questrom; Kelli Questrom.
Foundation type: Independent foundation.
Financial data (yr. ended 12/31/13): Assets, $29,349,252 (M); gifts received, $3,737,867; expenditures, $3,097,693; qualifying distributions, $2,327,068; giving activities include $2,325,014 for 8 grants (high: $1,875,000; low: $7).
Fields of interest: Museums (art); Arts.
Limitations: Applications not accepted. Giving primarily in New York, NY and Dallas, TX.
Application information: Unsolicited requests for funds not accepted.
Officers and Directors:* Allen I. Questrom,* Pres.; Carol L. Questrom,* Secy.-Treas.; Ben Beavers.
EIN: 272598904

9117
Ed Rachal Foundation ✧
500 N. Shoreline Blvd., Ste. 606
Corpus Christi, TX 78401-0323
Contact: Paul D. Altheide, C.E.O.
FAX: (361) 881-9885; E-mail: info@edrachal.org; Main URL: http://www.edrachal.org

Established in 1965 in TX.
Donor: Ed Rachal†.
Foundation type: Independent foundation.
Financial data (yr. ended 08/31/13): Assets, $208,323,946 (M); expenditures, $12,703,386; qualifying distributions, $11,608,756; giving activities include $9,321,508 for 154 grants (high: $2,000,000; low: $500), and $683,665 for foundation-administered programs.
Purpose and activities: The combination of commitments to education and youth, and to the land and its resources, is the cornerstone of the foundation.
Fields of interest: Higher education; Libraries/library science; Health organizations, association; Human services; Children/youth, services; Christian agencies & churches.
Type of support: General/operating support; Capital campaigns; Building/renovation; Equipment; Emergency funds; Employee matching gifts.
Limitations: Applications accepted. Giving limited to TX. No grants to individuals, or for multi-year commitments.
Publications: Application guidelines; Annual report; Grants list.
Application information: Applications sent by fax will not be accepted. It is not necessary to place application in folder or binder. Application guidelines available on foundation web site. Application form required.
Initial approach: Use application form on foundation web site
Copies of proposal: 1
Deadline(s): None
Board meeting date(s): Jan., Apr., July, and Oct.
Officers and Directors:* John D. White,* Chair.; Robert L. Walker,* Vice-Chair.; Paul D. Altheide,* C.E.O. and Secy.; Richard Schendel,* Treas.; David Hoyer; John J. Johnson; Ken W. Trawick.
Number of staff: 1 full-time professional; 1 full-time support.
EIN: 741116595

9118
The Radler Foundation ✧
3131 W. 7th St., Ste. 400
Fort Worth, TX 76107-8702 (817) 632-5200
Contact: Casey Leiber
E-mail: info@radlerfoundation.org; Main URL: http://www.radlerfoundation.org

Established in 2009 in TX.
Donors: Michael G. Radler; Chief Oil & Gas, LLC; Christ Church; Drop in the Bucket; Radler 2000; The Water Project, Inc.; Helfen Wir; Jeremiah Project; Lenexa Baptist Church; Neverthirst; Villages of Hope Africa; Salinas Valley Community Church; A to Z Mud Co., Inc.; Alliance for the Lost Boys of Sudan; Aqua-Africa; Baker Hughes; Brooke Point High School; Covenant Church of Pittsburgh; Diq Deep; Frost Bank; Geoff Radler; Rosario Garcia; Greg Garcia; Jeff Jordan; Leon Laubscher; Loadcraft Industries, Ltd.; Nikki Mildren; Matt Mildren; Radler 2000 Limited Partnership; Randy Wolsey; Tim Ellsworth; U. S. Trust; Villages of Hope Africa; Mary Frank.
Foundation type: Independent foundation.
Financial data (yr. ended 12/31/12): Assets, $1,329,637 (M); gifts received, $453,970; expenditures, $3,546,689; qualifying distributions, $3,211,417; giving activities include $3,184,059 for 24 grants (high: $2,618,767; low: $538).
Purpose and activities: The foundation is a private, Christian foundation that supports organizations serving the local community and around the world, with a special focus on East Africa.
Fields of interest: Education; Health organizations; Housing/shelter.
Limitations: Applications not accepted. Giving primarily in TX; with some giving in Eastern Africa and South Sudan.
Application information: Unsolicited requests for funds not accepted.
Officers and Directors:* Michael G. Radler,* Pres.; Graham C. Radler,* Secy.; Michael Evan Radler,* Treas.; Gail Andrae-Pianta, Cont.; B.J. Goergen; Reinke Radler.
EIN: 264582178

9119
The Rainwater Charitable Foundation ✧
c/o Jeremy Smith
777 Main St., Ste. 2250
Fort Worth, TX 76102-5308 (817) 820-6622
E-mail for Jeremy Smith: jsmith@rwtrine.com

Established in 1990 in TX.
Donor: Richard E. Rainwater.
Foundation type: Independent foundation.
Financial data (yr. ended 12/31/12): Assets, $0 (M); gifts received, $112,000; expenditures, $828,778; qualifying distributions, $824,038; giving activities include $647,000 for 16 grants, and $45,946 for 3 foundation-administered programs.
Purpose and activities: Giving primarily for education; funding also for health organizations and human services.
Fields of interest: Education, early childhood education; Education; Health organizations; Human services.
Limitations: Applications not accepted. Giving primarily in TX; some funding also in SC. No grants to individuals.
Application information: Contributes only to pre-selected organizations.

Officers and Directors:* Richard E. Rainwater,* Pres.; Darla D. Moore,* Secy.; Courtney E. Rainwater; Matthew J. Rainwater; R. Todd Rainwater; Walter James Rainwater, Jr.
EIN: 752356333
Selected grants: The following grants are a representative sample of this grantmaker's funding activity:
$300,000 to Real School Gardens, Fort Worth, TX, 2012. For school gardens program in Fort Worth.
$150,000 to Palmetto Institute, Columbia, SC, 2012.
$50,000 to Community Museum Society, Lake City, SC, 2012. For general support.
$50,000 to South Carolina Council on Competitiveness, Columbia, SC, 2012. For program support.
$27,500 to University of North Texas Health Science Center, Fort Worth, TX, 2012. For Alzheimer's research.
$20,000 to United Way of Tarrant County, Fort Worth, TX, 2012. For Fort Worth Early Childhood Collaborative.
$10,000 to Paschal High School Booster Club, Fort Worth, TX, 2012. To improve infrastructure for athletics and extracurricular activities.
$10,000 to Tarrant Area Food Bank, Fort Worth, TX, 2012.

9120
Ram Foundation ✧
P.O. Box 6519
Paris, TX 75461-6519 (903) 517-7032
Contact: Tanis Hager, Exec. Dir.

Established in TX.
Foundation type: Independent foundation.
Financial data (yr. ended 12/31/12): Assets, $21,355,801 (M); expenditures, $1,455,598; qualifying distributions, $903,664; giving activities include $887,739 for 41 grants (high: $129,592; low: $300).
Fields of interest: Higher education; Human services; Children/youth, services; Christian agencies & churches; Protestant agencies & churches.
Limitations: Applications accepted. Giving primarily in the Northeast TX area.
Publications: Application guidelines.
Application information: E-mailed applications are not accepted. Application form required.
Initial approach: Use application form from the foundation's sister foundation at http://www.faskenfoundation.org and send via U.S. mail to Ram Foundation
Deadline(s): None
Officers: F. Andrew Fasken, Pres.; Andrew C. Elliott, Jr., V.P.; Tanis Hager, Secy. and Exec. Dir.
Board Members: John R. Elliott; Dede E. Faskin; Helen T. Faskin.
EIN: 263541160

9121
Rapier Family Foundation ✧ ☆
119 E. Kings Hwy.
San Antonio, TX 78212

Established in TX.
Donors: George M. Rapier III; Kymberly Ann Rapier.
Foundation type: Independent foundation.
Financial data (yr. ended 12/31/13): Assets, $34,965,295 (M); gifts received, $7,600; expenditures, $1,786,202; qualifying distributions, $1,574,207; giving activities include $1,567,382 for 34 grants (high: $250,000; low: $3,400).
Fields of interest: Education; Environment; Human services; Children/youth, services.
Limitations: Applications not accepted. Giving primarily in MT and TX. No grants to individuals.
Application information: Unsolicited requests for funds not accepted.
Officers and Directors:* George M. Rapier III,* Pres.; Kymberly Ann Rapier,* V.P.; Hutson Hardwick Rapier,* Secy.-Treas.
EIN: 273894167

9122
Bernard and Audre Rapoport Foundation ✧
5400 Bosque Blvd., Ste. 304
Waco, TX 76710-4446 (254) 741-0510
Contact: Tom Stanton, Exec. Dir.
FAX: (254) 741-0092; E-mail: tom@rapoportfdn.org; Additional e-mail: Casey Sadler, Foundation Coord.: casey@rapoportfdn.org; Main URL: http://www.rapoportfdn.org
Grants Database: http://www.rapoportfdn.org/grants.php

Established in 1986 in TX.
Donors: Audre Rapoport; Bernard Rapoport; Patricia Rapoport; Ronald B. Rapoport.
Foundation type: Independent foundation.
Financial data (yr. ended 12/31/13): Assets, $54,271,497 (M); expenditures, $3,783,800; qualifying distributions, $2,807,883; giving activities include $2,466,069 for 34 grants (high: $399,366; low: $250).
Purpose and activities: To meet basic human needs while building individual and social resiliency.
Fields of interest: Arts; Education; Health care; Civil/human rights; Community/economic development; Jewish federated giving programs.
Type of support: General/operating support; Equipment; Program development; Seed money; Matching/challenge support.
Limitations: Applications accepted. Giving primarily within a 30 mile radius of Waco, TX. No support for political or religious organizations. No grants to individuals.
Publications: Annual report.
Application information: Application form required.
Initial approach: Use online application form on foundation web site
Board meeting date(s): Three times per year
Officers and Trustees:* Ronald B. Rapoport,* Chair.; Audre Rapoport,* Pres.; William A. Nesbitt, Secy.-Treas.; Tom Stanton, Exec. Dir.; Rick Battistoni; James D. Chesney; Lyndon Olson, Jr.; Emily Rapoport; Patricia Rapoport; Joel Schwartz.
Number of staff: 2 full-time professional.
EIN: 742479712

9123
Rea Charitable Trust ✧
P.O. Box 41629
Austin, TX 78701
Application address: c/o Trust Dept., P.O. Box 1959, Midland, TX 79702, tel.: (432) 685-5300; Main URL: http://reacharitabletrust.org/

Established in 2009 in TX.
Foundation type: Independent foundation.
Financial data (yr. ended 09/30/13): Assets, $38,458,535 (M); expenditures, $2,198,877; qualifying distributions, $1,256,234; giving activities include $1,180,700 for 27 grants (high: $300,000; low: $5,000).
Fields of interest: Media, television; Arts; Higher education; Education; United Ways and Federated Giving Programs.
Limitations: Applications accepted. Giving primarily in TX, with emphasis on Midland.
Application information: Application form required.
Initial approach: Completed application form
Deadline(s): April 15 and Oct. 15
Final notification: June and Dec.
Advisors: Dona Bradley; Becky Ferguson; Richard Folger; Vicky Jay; Paul Morris; Mike Talley.
Trustee: Wells Fargo Bank, N.A.
EIN: 263671567
Selected grants: The following grants are a representative sample of this grantmaker's funding activity:
$100,000 to Permian Basin Public Telecommunications, Midland, TX, 2011.

9124
The Reaud Charitable Foundation, Inc. ✧
801 Laurel St.
Beaumont, TX 77701-2228 (409) 838-1000
Contact: Jon Reaud, Exec. Dir.

Established in 1989 in TX.
Donors: Wayne A. Reaud; Daylight Motors.
Foundation type: Independent foundation.
Financial data (yr. ended 12/31/13): Assets, $34,497,854 (M); gifts received, $1,700,000; expenditures, $1,710,209; qualifying distributions, $1,504,942; giving activities include $1,504,942 for 50 grants (high: $138,000; low: $100).
Purpose and activities: Giving primarily for education, Christian organizations and churches, and social services.
Fields of interest: Higher education; Education; Health organizations; Human services; Children/youth, services; Christian agencies & churches.
Limitations: Applications accepted. Giving primarily in Beaumont, TX. No grants to individuals directly.
Application information: Application form not required.
Initial approach: Proposal
Deadline(s): None
Officers: Jon A. Reaud, Exec. Dir.; Wayne A. Reaud, Mgr.
EIN: 760291657
Selected grants: The following grants are a representative sample of this grantmaker's funding activity:
$100,000 to Catholic Charities of Southeast Texas, Beaumont, TX, 2011.
$100,000 to Memorial Hermann Baptist Hospital, Orange, TX, 2011.
$25,000 to Beaumont Family Shelter, Beaumont, TX, 2011.

9125
The Rees-Jones Foundation
5956 Sherry Ln., Ste. 1603
Dallas, TX 75225-6531 (214) 751-2977
Contact: Thornton Hardie III, Pres.

FAX: (214) 751-2978;
E-mail: info@rees-jonesfoundation.org; Main URL: http://www.rees-jonesfoundation.org/

Established in 2006 in TX.
Donors: Janice M. Rees-Jones; Trevor Rees-Jones.
Foundation type: Independent foundation.
Financial data (yr. ended 12/31/13): Assets, $562,944,755 (M); expenditures, $47,263,730; qualifying distributions, $23,066,907; giving activities include $21,779,611 for grants.
Purpose and activities: The foundation's mission is to serve God by serving others, sharing His resources in ways that provide opportunities for the disadvantaged, relief for the suffering, and encouragement in the growth and wellbeing of children and families in our community.
Fields of interest: Education; Health care; Mental health/crisis services; Employment; Housing/shelter; Children/youth, services; Family services; Human services; Community/economic development; Christian agencies & churches; Infants/toddlers; Children/youth; Youth; Disabilities, people with; Physically disabled; Mentally disabled; Minorities; Economically disadvantaged; Homeless.
International interests: Ethiopia; India; Uganda.
Type of support: Building/renovation; Capital campaigns; Employee matching gifts; General/operating support; Management development/capacity building; Matching/challenge support; Program development; Program-related investments/loans; Scholarship funds.
Limitations: Applications accepted. Giving primarily in Dallas and North TX. No support for organizations lacking 501(c)(3) status. No grants to individuals, or for fundraising events, professional conferences, symposiums, performances or competition expenses, or toward general sustentation drives; generally limited grants for general operating expenses or annual campaigns.
Publications: Application guidelines; Annual report; Grants list.
Application information: All grant requests must be submitted via the foundation's online application format. See foundation web site for full application guidelines and requirements. Application form required.
Initial approach: See "How to Apply" section of web site
Copies of proposal: 1
Deadline(s): No set deadline, but proposals should be submitted several months before the funding is needed
Board meeting date(s): 10 times annually
Final notification: Within 3 to 4 months
Officers and Directors:* Trevor Rees-Jones,* Chair.; Janice M. Rees-Jones,* Vice-Chair.; Thornton Hardie III,* Pres.; David Hundley, Secy.; Cissy Moses, Treas.; Petere Collins, C.I.O.
Number of staff: 6 full-time professional; 1 full-time support.
EIN: 205132900
Selected grants: The following grants are a representative sample of this grantmaker's funding activity:
$10,000,000 to Perot Museum of Nature and Science, Dallas, TX, 2012. Toward Perot Museum of Nature and Science, which will fulfill museum's mission to inspire minds through nature and science with dynamic exhibits that bring natural world to life.
$5,000,000 to Parkland Foundation, Dallas, TX, 2012. For construction of new hospital through Campaign for a New Parkland.
$1,750,000 to Dallas Childrens Advocacy Center, Dallas, TX, 2012. Toward the capital campaign for a new facility that will better meet the needs of abused children in the Dallas community by expanding capacity for child-focused forensic and treatment services.
$1,000,000 to Texas Christian University, Institute of Child Development, Fort Worth, TX, 2012. For the Institute's operations, and support for the Child Institute TBRI Evaluation Study which seeks to demonstrate the efficacy of Trust-Based Relational Intervention (TBRI) as a therapeutic model for abused/neglected children.
$500,000 to Living Water International, Sugar Land, TX, 2012. For the Water, Sanitation and Hygiene program which provides clean water, sanitation, and hygiene services to communities in Southern Uganda and will serve as a sustainable, community-based model for Living Water world-wide.
$280,000 to CURE International, Lemoyne, PA, 2012. For operating expenses for the CURE Ethiopia Children's Hospital which provides orthopedic and spiritual care for disabled children.
$250,000 to Teach for America, Dallas, TX, 2012. For multi-year funding for the 2015 Growth Plan which will greatly increase the number of Teach For America teachers serving at-risk students in Dallas-Fort Worth area schools.
$50,000 to Trinity River Mission, Dallas, TX, 2012. To provide low-income, at-risk West Dallas students with high quality afterschool and summer programs.
$40,000 to Disability Rights Texas, Austin, TX, 2012. For The Legal Advocacy for Dually Managed Children Project, which provides legal representation to foster youth in the state juvenile justice or mental health systems.
$40,000 to Rise School of Dallas, Dallas, TX, 2012. For tuition assistance for children with developmental delays to attend a preschool with quality academic and therapeutic services.

9126
Reliant Energy Charitable Foundation ✧

1201 Fannin St.
Houston, TX 77002-6929
Contact: Misty White

Established in TX.
Foundation type: Independent foundation.
Financial data (yr. ended 12/31/13): Assets, $2,304,057 (M); expenditures, $2,619,296; qualifying distributions, $2,616,261; giving activities include $2,616,261 for 171 grants (high: $383,000; low: $250).
Fields of interest: Education; Medical research, institute; Human services.
Limitations: Applications accepted. Giving primarily in communities where Reliant Energy operates.
Application information: Application form required.
Initial approach: Proposal
Deadline(s): None
Officers and Directors:* Elizabeth Killinger,* Pres.; Karen Jones,* V.P.; John Ragan,* V.P.; Genora Boykins,* Co-Secy.; Christopher O'Hara,* Co-Secy.; Sherrie Martin,* Treas.; William Harmon.
EIN: 273283754

9127
Alice Kleberg Reynolds Foundation ✧

(also known as Alice Kleberg Reynolds Meyer Foundation)
c/o Frost National Bank
P.O. Box 2127
Austin, TX 78768-2127
Contacts for questions: Mary Haught, V.P., Frost National Bank, tel.: (512) 473-4838, e-mail: mary.haught@frostbank.com, and Beverly Scott, Trust Officer, tel.: (512) 473-4803, e-mail: beverly.scott@frostbank.com; Main URL: http://www.akrfoundation.org

Established in 1978 in TX.
Donor: Alice K. Meyer†.
Foundation type: Independent foundation.
Financial data (yr. ended 12/31/13): Assets, $28,906,074 (M); expenditures, $1,323,598; qualifying distributions, $1,209,000; giving activities include $1,209,000 for 106 grants (high: $144,500; low: $1,000).
Purpose and activities: Grants to qualified non-profit organizations for arts and culture, charitable, educational, literary, medical, and scientific purposes.
Fields of interest: Visual arts; Performing arts; Arts; Education; Medical research, institute.
Type of support: General/operating support; Capital campaigns; Building/renovation; Equipment; Endowments; Program development; Curriculum development; Fellowships; Research.
Limitations: Applications accepted. Giving limited to 50 specified counties in south central TX, (Aransas, Atascosa, Bandera, Bee, Bexar, Blanco, Brooks, Caldwell, Calhoun, Cameron, Colorado, Comal, DeWitt, Dimmit, Duval, Fayette, Frio, Goliad, Gonzalez, Guadalupe, Harris, Hays, Hidalgo, Jackson, Jim Hogg, Jim Wells, Karnes, Kendall, Kenedy, Kleberg, LaSalle, Lavaca, Live Oak, Matagorda, Maverick, McMullen, Medina, Nueces, Rufugio, San Patricio, Starr, Travis, Uvalde, Victoria, Webb, Wharton, Willacy, Wilson, Zapata and Zavala). No support for religious organizations. No grants to individuals, or for scholarships or salaries.
Publications: Application guidelines; Grants list.
Application information: Brochures, DVD's or other printed materials are not accepted. Application guidelines and form available on foundation web site. Application form required.
Initial approach: Use only online application format on foundation web site. Questions should be e-mailed to both Mary Haught and Beverly Scott
Copies of proposal: 1
Deadline(s): Throughout the year
Board meeting date(s): Varies
Final notification: Nov. 30
Trustee: Frost National Bank.
EIN: 742847652
Selected grants: The following grants are a representative sample of this grantmaker's funding activity:
$30,000 to Gazelle Foundation, Austin, TX, 2012. For Austin Operations.
$25,000 to Hispanas Unidas, San Antonio, TX, 2012. For Escuelitas Leadership and Mentoring Pr.
$25,000 to Planned Parenthood of the Texas Capital Region, Austin, TX, 2012. For Core Programs and Services.
$25,000 to Planned Parenthood Trust of South Texas, San Antonio, TX, 2012. For Family Planning/Women's Health Care.

$20,000 to Useful Wild Plants of Texas, Austin, TX, 2012. For UWP VA Completion.
$20,000 to Waller Creek Conservancy, Austin, TX, 2012. For Phase One Design Competition.
$15,000 to Greater Austin Performing Arts Center, Austin, TX, 2012. For Armed Forces Program.
$11,000 to Planned Parenthood Trust of South Texas, San Antonio, TX, 2012. For abortion care.
$10,000 to San Antonio Museum of Art, San Antonio, TX, 2012. For Sylvie Blocher/Living Pictures Program.
$5,000 to Ballet Austin, Austin, TX, 2012. For Stay Awake Presentation.

9128
RGK Foundation ✧

1301 W. 25th St., Ste. 300
Austin, TX 78705-4236 (512) 474-9298
Contact: Suzanne Haffey, Grants Assoc.
FAX: (512) 474-7281; E-mail: shaffey@rgkfoundation.org; Main URL: http://www.rgkfoundation.org
Grants List: http://www.rgkfoundation.org/public/grants

Incorporated in 1966 in TX.
Donors: George Kozmetsky‡; Ronya Kozmetsky‡.
Foundation type: Independent foundation.
Financial data (yr. ended 12/31/12): Assets, $144,634,722 (M); expenditures, $8,456,682; qualifying distributions, $6,737,755; giving activities include $6,209,812 for 138 grants (high: $537,500; low: $1,500).
Purpose and activities: Grants to education, community, and medicine/health.
Fields of interest: Education, formal/general education; Health care; Medical research; Crime/violence prevention, abuse prevention; Crime/violence prevention, domestic violence; Crime/violence prevention, child abuse; Family services, domestic violence; Children/youth; Children; Women; Economically disadvantaged.
Type of support: Management development/capacity building; Program development; Conferences/seminars; Matching/challenge support.
Limitations: Applications accepted. Giving on a national basis. No support for organizations limited by race or religion. No grants to individuals, or for deficit financing, capital campaigns, building renovations or endowment funds, indirect costs, special events, disaster relief funds, student research projects, political lobbying, or equipment; no loans.
Publications: Application guidelines; Grants list.
Application information: Unsolicited full proposals will not be accepted. Proposals will be invited by the foundation following positive response to Letter if Inquiry. Central Texas Education Funders Common Grant Application Form accepted for those invited. Application form required.
Initial approach: Submit an electronic letter of inquiry form available on foundation web site
Copies of proposal: 1
Deadline(s): None
Board meeting date(s): Mar., June, Sept. and Dec.
Final notification: Decision on Letter of Inquiry within two weeks
Officers and Trustees:* Gregory A. Kozmetsky,* Chair., Pres. and Treas.; Nadya Kozmetsky Scott,* Vice-Chair.; Christina C. Collier, Exec. V.P.; Cynthia H. Kozmetsky,* V.P. and Secy.; Beth Sexworth, C.I.O.; Caroline Avery; Douglas Bryant; Daniel A. Kozmetsky; Chris Miller; Sarah K. Miller; Laila P. Scott; Martha Smiley; F. Gary Valdez.
Number of staff: 7 full-time professional; 1 full-time support.
EIN: 746077587
Selected grants: The following grants are a representative sample of this grantmaker's funding activity:
$250,000 to Texas State University, San Marcos, TX, 2011. To establish endowment to provide permanent support to summer math programs for K-12 students, teacher training, and curriculum development.
$200,000 to Downtown Womens Center, Los Angeles, CA, 2011. For domestic violence support program providing counseling, case management, outreach, and prevention education to homeless survivors of domestic violence.
$50,000 to Huntsville Hospital Foundation, Huntsville, AL, 2011. To operate new mobile medical unit to serve 14 county region.
$50,000 to MIND Research Institute, Irvine, CA, 2011. For Los Angeles and North Central Texas math initiatives to elevate math performance in low-performing schools.
$50,000 to Youth and Family Alliance, LifeWorks, Austin, TX, 2011. For literacy programs including adult basic education, English as a second language, GED classes, and literacy services for youth.
$45,000 to All Our Kin, New Haven, CT, 2011. To expand Toolkit Licensing Program for home-base child care providers to additional cities in Connecticut.
$40,000 to Break the Cycle, Los Angeles, CA, 2011. To pilot Girl Scouts Edition of violence prevention curriculum in Texas and California.
$40,000 to Childrens Advocacy Center of Hidalgo County, Edinburg, TX, 2011. To expand mental health services to child victims of abuse in Rio Grande Valley.
$35,000 to Capital Area Dental Foundation, Austin, TX, 2011. To expand dental services program.
$25,000 to Commerce City Community Health Services, Commerce City, CO, 2011. To provide mental health services at school-based health centers.

9129
Ann L. Rhodes and Carol Greene Rhodes Charitable Trust ✧

P.O. Box 831041
Dallas, TX 75283-1041
Application address: c/o Mark J. Smith, P.O. Box 1479, Fort Worth, TX 76101, tel.: (817) 390-6028; Main URL: https://www.bankofamerica.com/philanthropic/grantmaking.go

Established in 2009 in TX.
Foundation type: Independent foundation.
Financial data (yr. ended 12/31/13): Assets, $26,915,773 (M); expenditures, $1,687,243; qualifying distributions, $1,202,571; giving activities include $1,039,000 for 30 grants (high: $129,000; low: $2,500).
Fields of interest: Arts; Education; Human services.
Limitations: Applications accepted. Giving limited to Tarrant County, TX.
Application information: Application form required.
Deadline(s): Mar. 31 and Sept. 30
Trustee: Bank of America, N.A.
EIN: 266660796
Selected grants: The following grants are a representative sample of this grantmaker's funding activity:
$90,000 to Circle Theater, Fort Worth, TX, 2012. For general operating support.
$78,000 to Hip Pocket Theater, Fort Worth, TX, 2012. For general operating support.
$75,000 to Amphibian Productions, Fort Worth, TX, 2012. For general operating support.
$75,000 to Arlington Heights High School All Sports Booster Club, Fort Worth, TX, 2012. For school improvement project - Turf Field Project.
$75,000 to Casa Manana, Fort Worth, TX, 2012. For Buckley Awards and Student Matinee Performances.
$65,000 to Youth Orchestra of Greater Fort Worth, Fort Worth, TX, 2012. For renovation and restoration of the Auditorium at Orchestra Hall 4401 Trail Lake Drive.
$40,000 to Womens Center of Tarrant County, Fort Worth, TX, 2012. For general operating support for the three major programs of The Women's Center (Rape Crisis, Employment, and Counseling) with special funding for the Play It Safe! child sexual abuse prevention program.
$25,000 to Amphibian Productions, Fort Worth, TX, 2012. For Capital Campaign- to assist in the acquisition of theatre.
$25,000 to Cornerstone Assistance Network, Fort Worth, TX, 2012. For general operating support.
$10,000 to Southwestern Exposition and Livestock Show, Fort Worth, TX, 2012. For supporting sponsorship of the Stock Show Art Contest.

9130
Sid W. Richardson Foundation ✧

309 Main St.
Fort Worth, TX 76102-4006 (817) 336-0494
Contact: Pete Geren, Pres.
FAX: (817) 332-2176;
E-mail: cjohns@sidrichardson.org; E-mail for Pete Geren: pgeren@sidrichardson.org; Main URL: http://www.sidrichardson.org

Established in 1947 in TX.
Donors: Sid W. Richardson‡; and associated companies.
Foundation type: Independent foundation.
Financial data (yr. ended 12/31/13): Assets, $556,633,727 (M); gifts received, $31,422; expenditures, $18,541,111; qualifying distributions, $17,126,632; giving activities include $14,331,618 for 129 grants (high: $1,000,000; low: $2,500), and $1,227,726 for 1 foundation-administered program.
Purpose and activities: Giving primarily for education, health, the arts, and social service programs.
Fields of interest: Performing arts; Arts; Higher education; Education; Health care; Health organizations, association; Human services.
Type of support: Program-related investments/loans; General/operating support; Continuing support; Building/renovation; Equipment; Land acquisition; Endowments; Program development; Conferences/seminars; Publication; Seed money; Research; Matching/challenge support.
Limitations: Applications accepted. Giving limited to TX, with emphasis on Fort Worth for the arts and human services, and statewide for health and education. No support for religious organizations. No grants to individuals, or for scholarships or fellowships; no loans (except for program-related investments).

Publications: Annual report (including application guidelines); Financial statement; Grants list.
Application information: Formal proposals are by invitation, only after review of letter. Application form required.
Initial approach: Letter
Copies of proposal: 1
Deadline(s): Jan. 15
Board meeting date(s): Spring and fall
Final notification: Varies
Officers and Directors:* Edward P. Bass,* Chair.; Pete Geren, C.E.O. and Pres.; Lee M. Bass,* V.P.; Sid R. Bass,* V.P.
Number of staff: 5 full-time professional.
EIN: 756015828
Selected grants: The following grants are a representative sample of this grantmaker's funding activity:
$1,000,000 to Safe City Commission, Fort Worth, TX, 2012. To support construction of One Safe Place - matching grant.
$750,000 to Fort Worth Art Association, Modern Art Museum of Fort Worth, Fort Worth, TX, 2012. For general support.
$600,000 to George W. Bush Foundation, Dallas, TX, 2012. To support two education programs.
$150,000 to Harris Methodist Health Systems, Fort Worth, TX, 2012. To support the Nursing Excellence Fund.
$150,000 to University of North Texas Foundation, Denton, TX, 2012. To support Morningside Children's Zone.
$50,000 to Green Oaks School, Arlington, TX, 2012. To support education and life skills program for adults with Down Syndrome in Tarrant County.
$50,000 to James L. West Presbyterian Special Care Center, Fort Worth, TX, 2012. To support the Family Caregiver Education program.
$50,000 to Kids Who Care, Fort Worth, TX, 2012. For general operational support for the performing arts education program.
$50,000 to Learning Center of North Texas, Fort Worth, TX, 2012. To support educational services for children and adults with learning differences.
$30,000 to Texas Inmate Services, Fort Worth, TX, 2012. To support program assisting formerly incarcerated persons seeking reintegration into society.

9131
Anne S. Richardson Fund ✧
(formerly Anne S. Richardson Charitable Trust)
c/o JPMorgan Chase Bank, Philanthropic Svcs.
P.O. Box 227237 TX1-2963
Dallas, TX 75222-7237
Contact: Carolyn O'Brien, Prog. Off.
E-mail: carolyn.r.obrien@jpmorgan.com; Main URL: http://fdnweb.org/richardson
Grants List: http://fdnweb.org/richardson/grants/year/2013-contributions/

Trust established in 1965 in CT.
Donor: Anne S. Richardson‡.
Foundation type: Independent foundation.
Financial data (yr. ended 07/31/13): Assets, $12,556,904 (M); expenditures, $693,725; qualifying distributions, $597,440; giving activities include $570,000 for 21 grants (high: $100,000; low: $5,000).
Purpose and activities: Funding interests include: 1) eight organizations recommended by the donor; 2) programs in Ridgefield, Connecticut, that assist lower-income people or that are of broad interest to the community; and 3) programs in Fairfield County, Connecticut, that promote the independence of women, support the lesbian and gay community, foster youth development, or enhance the natural beautification of communities through parks or gardens.
Fields of interest: Botanical/horticulture/landscape services; Recreation, parks/playgrounds; Youth development; Children/youth, services; Women; LGBTQ.
Type of support: General/operating support; Capital campaigns; Program development.
Limitations: Giving primarily in CT, with emphasis on the town of Ridgefield and Fairfield County. No support for private foundations or organizations lacking 501(c)(3) status. No grants to individuals; no loans.
Publications: Application guidelines; Grants list.
Application information: Application guidelines available on foundation web site.
Initial approach: Use proposal format on foundation web site
Deadline(s): Mar. 1
Final notification: July 31
Trustee: JPMorgan Chase Bank, N.A.
Number of staff: None.
EIN: 136192516
Selected grants: The following grants are a representative sample of this grantmaker's funding activity:
$75,000 to Mill River Collaborative, Stamford, CT, 2011. For the Mill River Park and Greenway project.
$45,000 to Hartford Gay and Lesbian Health Collective, Hartford, CT, 2011. For first installment of a $90,000 grant for Health Collective East.
$45,000 to Ridgefield High School Parent Teacher School Association, Ridgefield, CT, 2011. For first installment of a $90,000 grant for student mailings and the Anne S. Richardson Memorial Scholarship Fund.
$40,000 to Connecticut Fund for the Environment, New Haven, CT, 2011. To install a river-edge buffer in Old Mine Park.
$40,000 to Pro Bono Partnership, White Plains, NY, 2011. For first installment of $80,000 grant to provide services to nonprofit organizations in Fairfield County.
$30,000 to Mercy Learning Center of Bridgeport, Bridgeport, CT, 2011. For first installment in a $60,000 grant for the organization's expansion project.
$25,000 to Ridgefield Symphony Orchestra, Ridgefield, CT, 2011. For general operating support.
$20,000 to Ridgefield High School Parent Teacher School Association, Ridgefield, CT, 2011. For final installment of a $120,000 grant to repair the auditorium stage and improve the black box theatre at Ridgefield High School.
$20,000 to Ridgefield Playhouse for Movies and the Performing Arts, Ridgefield, CT, 2011. For the auditorium renovation project.
$15,000 to Memorial Sloan-Kettering Cancer Center, New York, NY, 2011. For general operating support.

9132
The Roach Foundation Inc. ✧
Fort Worth Club
777 Taylor St., PH-11J
Fort Worth, TX 76102-4919

Established in 1999 in TX.
Donors: John V. Roach; Jean W. Roach.
Foundation type: Independent foundation.
Financial data (yr. ended 12/31/13): Assets, $7,519,055 (M); expenditures, $859,619; qualifying distributions, $795,611; giving activities include $789,602 for 90 grants (high: $440,500; low: $100).
Purpose and activities: Giving primarily for education, particularly higher education; some funding for the arts, health associations, children, youth, and social services, including health and medical care for children.
Fields of interest: Arts; Higher education; Education; Health care; Health organizations, association; Human services; Children/youth, services; United Ways and Federated Giving Programs; Christian agencies & churches.
Limitations: Applications not accepted. Giving primarily in TX, with emphasis on Fort Worth. No grants to individuals.
Application information: Contributes only to pre-selected organizations.
Officers: John V. Roach, Pres.; Jean W. Roach, V.P.; Amy Roach Callaway, Secy.; Lori Anne Roach, Treas.; Lou Ann Blaylock, Exec. Dir.
EIN: 752848244

9133
Velma Lee & John Harvey Robinson Charitable Foundation ✧
P.O. Box 924
Edna, TX 77957-0924 (361) 782-5737
Contact: John J. Shutt, V.P.

Donor: Velma Lee Robinson.
Foundation type: Independent foundation.
Financial data (yr. ended 09/30/13): Assets, $27,254,588 (M); expenditures, $1,413,780; qualifying distributions, $1,200,000; giving activities include $1,200,000 for grants.
Purpose and activities: Giving primarily for Baptist agencies, churches, and schools, as well as for community development. Scholarships are also made to Jackson County, TX, students who will attend a Texas college, university or trade school, and maintain a 2.75 GPA.
Fields of interest: Higher education; Human services; Children/youth, services; Community/economic development; Protestant agencies & churches.
Type of support: Scholarship funds.
Limitations: Giving limited to TX.
Application information: Scholarship applications become available to the high school counselors of the three high schools in Jackson County, TX, by Apr. 1. Application form required.
Deadline(s): May 1 for scholarships
Officers and Directors:* M.H. Brock,* Pres.; John J. Shutt,* V.P.; Mary H. Thedford,* Secy.; Bobby Bell; Jan McClanahan; Travis R. Phillips; Henry C. Whitley.
EIN: 742300129
Selected grants: The following grants are a representative sample of this grantmaker's funding activity:
$221,250 to San Marcos Baptist Academy, San Marcos, TX, 2011.
$130,000 to South Texas Childrens Home, Beeville, TX, 2011.
$5,000 to Jesus Film Project, Orlando, FL, 2011.

9134
The Rockjensen Foundation, Inc. ✧
7 Grand Regency Cir.
The Woodlands, TX 77382-1607

Established in 2004 in TX.
Donors: Douglas Rock; Julie Rock.
Foundation type: Independent foundation.
Financial data (yr. ended 12/31/13): Assets, $14,413,714 (M); expenditures, $783,800; qualifying distributions, $783,800; giving activities include $783,800 for 33 grants (high: $300,000; low: $1,000).
Fields of interest: Human services; Christian agencies & churches.
Limitations: Applications not accepted. Giving primarily in TX. No grants to individuals.
Application information: Contributes only to pre-selected organizations.
Directors: Gary M. Howell; Douglas Rock; Julie Rock.
EIN: 201823029

9135
Rockwell Fund, Inc. ✧
770 S. Post Oak Ln., Ste. 525
Houston, TX 77056-6660 (713) 629-9022
Contact: Judy Ahlgrim, Grants Admin.
FAX: (713) 629-7702; E-mail: info@rockfund.org; Main URL: http://www.rockfund.org

Trust established in 1931; incorporated in 1949 in TX; merged with Rockwell Brothers Endowment, Inc. in 1981.
Donor: Members of the James M. Rockwell family.
Foundation type: Independent foundation.
Financial data (yr. ended 12/31/13): Assets, $85,426,576 (M); gifts received, $500; expenditures, $4,387,710; qualifying distributions, $3,672,321; giving activities include $2,700,141 for 42 grants (high: $490,000; low: $1), and $23,058 for foundation-administered programs.
Purpose and activities: The foundation's grantmaking priorities focus on tackling issues in a comprehensive and coordinated manner to provide the best outcomes for low-income individuals, families and communities. Its current Issue Areas are: Education: Dropout prevention strategies that target the intermediate and middle school years; Health: Community-based health services, including physical, mental and behavioral health; Housing: Supportive housing, defined as affordable housing coupled with on-site support services needed to achieve self-sufficiency; Workforce Development: Job training/placement and jobs creation/small business development opportunities.
Fields of interest: Secondary school/education; Public health; Mental health/crisis services, association; Mental health, treatment; Mental health, counseling/support groups; Mental health, disorders; Employment, services; Employment, training; Housing/shelter, services; Human services; Children/youth, services; Family services; Community development, neighborhood development; Nonprofit management; Community/economic development; Children/youth; Children; Youth; Adults; Young adults; Mentally disabled; Minorities; Hispanics/Latinos; Women; Girls; Adults, women; Young adults, female; Men; Boys; Adults, men; Young adults, male; Single parents; Economically disadvantaged; Homeless.
Type of support: Continuing support; Curriculum development; General/operating support; Income development; Management development/capacity building; Matching/challenge support; Program development; Program evaluation; Program-related investments/loans; Seed money; Technical assistance.
Limitations: Giving primarily in Houston, TX. No support for houses of worship, organizations that target a specific disease, or for parochial, private primary or secondary schools. No grants to individuals or for medical or scientific research projects, underwriting benefits, dinners, galas, golf tournaments, and fundraising special events, or mass appeal solicitations.
Publications: Application guidelines; Financial statement; Grants list.
Application information: Ann on-line letter of inquiry must be submitted first. Please refer to the foundation web site. Applicants should not submit more than 1 proposal per year. Application form required.
Initial approach: On-line inquiry form
Copies of proposal: 1
Deadline(s): None
Board meeting date(s): Quarterly
Final notification: After each quarterly meeting
Officers and Trustees:* R. Terry Bell,* C.E.O. and Pres.; Margaret E. McConn,* V.P., C.F.O., and C.I.O.; Barbara W. Bellatti,* Secy.; Whitney Randolph, Treas.; Domingo Barrios; Sharon Edwards; William "Billy" Granville III.
Number of staff: 4 full-time professional; 2 full-time support.
EIN: 746040258
Selected grants: The following grants are a representative sample of this grantmaker's funding activity:
$575,000 to Alliance of Community Assistance Ministries, Houston, TX, 2012. For general operating support.
$317,000 to South Texas College of Law, Houston, TX, 2012. For general civil clinic's battered and homeless women's program.
$75,000 to Houston Community Health Centers, Vecino Health Centers, Houston, TX, 2012. For Airline Clinic.
$75,000 to New Hope Housing, Houston, TX, 2012. For general operating support.
$65,000 to Depression and Bipolar Support Alliance - Greater Houston, Houston, TX, 2012. For general operating support.
$25,000 to National Alliance on Mental Illness Gulf Coast, Alvin, TX, 2012. For general operating support.

9136
Roddy-Holden Foundation Inc. ✧
901 W. 9th St., Ste. 205
Austin, TX 78703
Contact: Lee A. Kintzel, Pres., Clerk and Dir.
E-mail: lhkintzel44@aol.com

Foundation type: Independent foundation.
Financial data (yr. ended 12/31/13): Assets, $9,610,910 (M); expenditures, $663,413; qualifying distributions, $635,505; giving activities include $635,000 for 14 grants (high: $200,000; low: $5,000).
Fields of interest: Higher education, university; Education; Health care; Human services.
Limitations: Applications not accepted. Giving primarily in RI and TN.
Application information: Contributes only to pre-selected organizations.
Officers and Directors:* Lee A. Kintzel,* Pres. and Clerk; Roger S. Kintzel,* Treas.
EIN: 830490627
Selected grants: The following grants are a representative sample of this grantmaker's funding activity:
$100,000 to University of Tennessee Foundation, Knoxville, TN, 2012. For grant for Roddy-Holden Scholarship Endowment.
$50,226 to Austin Child Guidance Center, Austin, TX, 2012. To support the Sliding Fee Scale Rates for Mental Health Services to Underserved, Lower Income and Working Poor Families.
$40,000 to Peoples Community Clinic, Austin, TX, 2012. For the Purchase of New Ultrasound Equipment and Related Maintenance Warranty to Serve Prenatal Patients.
$20,000 to Rhode Island Free Clinic, Providence, RI, 2012. To support Expansion of Primary Care Access for Uninsured, Working Poor and Low-Income Residents By Increasing Volunteer Medical Providers and Community Partners Throughout Rhode Island.
$10,000 to Family Service of Rhode Island, Providence, RI, 2012. To support Renovation of New Office Location.
$10,000 to Homefront Health Care, Providence, RI, 2012. To support the Volunteer Visitor Program.

9137
Ralph B. Rogers Foundation ✧
4848 Lemmon Ave., Ste. 100-402
Dallas, TX 75219-1400

Established in 2005 in TX.
Foundation type: Independent foundation.
Financial data (yr. ended 12/31/13): Assets, $10,931,380 (M); expenditures, $1,170,557; qualifying distributions, $1,134,444; giving activities include $1,126,000 for 37 grants (high: $250,000; low: $250).
Fields of interest: Arts; Education; Hospitals (general); Human services.
Limitations: Applications not accepted. Giving primarily in the greater Dallas, TX, area.
Application information: Unsolicited requests for funds not accepted.
Officers: William B. Rogers, Pres.; William E. Rogers II, Secy.; David Rogers, Treas.
Directors: Mary Rhoades; Katherine Roberts; John B. Rogers; John B. Rogers, Jr.; Michael Rogers; Richard G. Rogers; Buff Strickland.
EIN: 203452395

9138
The Rogers Foundation ✧
P.O. Box 8799
Tyler, TX 75711-8799
Application address: c/o Robyn Rogers, C.E.O., 2335 Oak Alley, Tyler, TX 75703, tel.: (903) 561-4041

Established in 1986 in TX.
Donors: Robert M. Rogers†; Rogers Children's Heritage Trust One; Rogers Children's Heritage Trust Two; Rogers Granchildren's Heritage Trust.
Foundation type: Independent foundation.
Financial data (yr. ended 12/31/12): Assets, $43,779,751 (M); gifts received, $60,000; expenditures, $1,636,457; qualifying distributions,

$1,358,622; giving activities include $1,271,490 for 67 grants (high: $100,000; low: $1,000).
Purpose and activities: Giving to promote education by providing funds for schools, educational programs, scholarships, and scholarship funds; support also for Protestant organizations.
Fields of interest: Arts; Education, fund raising/fund distribution; Elementary/secondary education; Elementary school/education; Higher education; Health care; Protestant agencies & churches; Religion.
Type of support: General/operating support; Building/renovation; Scholarship funds; Matching/challenge support.
Limitations: Applications accepted. Giving primarily in ID and TX. No grants to individuals.
Publications: Informational brochure (including application guidelines).
Application information: Application form required.
Initial approach: Letter
Copies of proposal: 1
Deadline(s): Oct. 1
Officers and Directors:* Robyn M. Rogers,* C.E.O. and Pres.; Sheryl Rogers Palmer,* V.P.; Paul W. Powell,* Secy.-Treas.
Number of staff: 1 part-time professional.
EIN: 752143064
Selected grants: The following grants are a representative sample of this grantmaker's funding activity:
$40,000 to East Texas Crisis Center, Tyler, TX, 2012. For Donation Sponsor Events for Fundraising.
$35,000 to Boy Scouts of America, East Tx Council, Tyler, TX, 2012. For donation for operations.
$25,000 to East Texas Baptist University, Marshall, TX, 2012. For donation for capital project.
$20,000 to Tyler Day Nursery, Tyler, TX, 2012. For Donation - Capital Project.
$15,000 to Discovery Science Place, Tyler, TX, 2012. For Donation for Summer Camp.
$7,000 to Tyler Rose Museum, Tyler, TX, 2012. For donation for operations.
$5,000 to Cystic Fibrosis Foundation, Tyler, TX, 2012. For donation for fundraiser.

9139
Russell H. Rogers Fund for the Arts ✧
(formerly Russell Hill Rogers Fund for the Arts)
4040 Broadway, Ste. 605
San Antonio, TX 78209 (210) 826-8781
Contact: Jean Winchell, Tr.

Established in 1986 in TX.
Foundation type: Independent foundation.
Financial data (yr. ended 12/31/13): Assets, $15,770,276 (M); expenditures, $846,847; qualifying distributions, $697,626; giving activities include $692,626 for 24 grants (high: $200,000; low: $2,000).
Purpose and activities: Support for the encouragement and preservation of the creative and performing arts.
Fields of interest: Museums; Performing arts; Arts.
Limitations: Applications accepted. Giving limited to the San Antonio, TX metropolitan area.
Application information: Application form not required.
Initial approach: Proposal
Deadline(s): None
Trustees: Frank P. Christian; Barbara S. Condos; Robert R. Lende; Allan G. Paterson, Jr.; Jean Rogers Winchell; Bank of America, N.A.
EIN: 742403914

9140
The Rosewood Foundation ✧
2101 Cedar Springs Rd., Ste. 1600
Dallas, TX 75201-7861

Established in 2000 in TX.
Donor: The Rosewood Corp.
Foundation type: Independent foundation.
Financial data (yr. ended 12/31/12): Assets, $23,297 (M); gifts received, $554,033; expenditures, $533,081; qualifying distributions, $533,081; giving activities include $533,081 for 286 grants (high: $35,000; low: $50).
Fields of interest: Performing arts; Arts; Higher education; Education; Environment; Youth development; Human services; Children/youth, services.
Type of support: General/operating support; Continuing support; Annual campaigns; Capital campaigns; Building/renovation; Program development; Research; Program evaluation; Employee matching gifts; Matching/challenge support.
Limitations: Applications not accepted. Giving primarily in TX. No support for direct funding of churches or schools. No grants to individuals.
Application information: Contributes only to pre-selected organizations.
Board meeting date(s): Quarterly
Officers and Trustees:* Patrick B. Sands,* Pres.; Don W. Crisp,* V.P. and Treas.; Laurie Sands Harrison,* V.P.; Haven S. Heinrichs,* V.P.; J. Clayton Sands,* V.P.; Stephen Sands,* Secy.; Schuyler B. Marshall IV.
Number of staff: 1 part-time professional.
EIN: 752827470

9141
Rowling Foundation ✧
600 E. Las Colinas Blvd., Ste. 1900
Irving, TX 75039-5626

Established in 2003 in TX.
Donors: Robert B. Rowling; Terry H. Rowling; TRT Holdings, Inc.; TRT Equity Advisors, LLC.
Foundation type: Independent foundation.
Financial data (yr. ended 12/31/12): Assets, $8,895,950 (M); gifts received, $5,377,685; expenditures, $5,705,464; qualifying distributions, $5,705,464; giving activities include $5,705,464 for grants.
Fields of interest: Higher education; Human services; Christian agencies & churches; Protestant agencies & churches.
Limitations: Applications not accepted. Giving primarily in TX, with some emphasis on Dallas. No grants to individuals.
Application information: Contributes only to pre-selected organizations.
Trustees: James D. Caldwell; William C. Dunlap; Robert B. Rowling; Robert B. Rowling, Jr.; Terry H. Rowling; Travis Blake Rowling.
EIN: 736351612

9142
Saada Foundation ✧ ☆
8383 Preston Center Plaza Dr., 5th Fl.
Dallas, TX 75225

Established in 2003 in TX.
Donors: Jean-Claude Saada; Elizabeth Ann Saada; Cambridge Real Estate Holdings, Inc.
Foundation type: Independent foundation.
Financial data (yr. ended 12/31/12): Assets, $402,304 (M); gifts received, $1,700,000; expenditures, $1,300,000; qualifying distributions, $1,300,000; giving activities include $1,300,000 for 3 grants (high: $1,000,000; low: $100,000).
Fields of interest: Education; Hospitals (specialty); Religious federated giving programs.
Type of support: General/operating support; Equipment.
Limitations: Applications not accepted. Giving in San Diego, CA and Dallas, TX. No grants to individuals.
Application information: Unsolicited requests for funds not accepted.
Officers and Directors:* Jean-Claude Saada,* Pres.; Elizabeth Ann Saada,* Secy.-Treas.; Robert J. Brill.
EIN: 421592648

9143
Sadler Family Foundation ✧ ☆
P.O. Box 1746
Henderson, TX 75653-1088 (903) 657-5581
Contact: Harold J. Sadler, Mgr. and Dir.

Established in 2001 in TX.
Donors: Harold Sadler; New Life Church.
Foundation type: Independent foundation.
Financial data (yr. ended 06/30/13): Assets, $5,975,385 (M); gifts received, $312,799; expenditures, $710,155; qualifying distributions, $698,331; giving activities include $617,645 for 15 grants (high: $444,645; low: $400).
Purpose and activities: Giving primarily for Christian education organizations and for youth or elderly in financial need.
Fields of interest: Elementary/secondary education; Theological school/education; Christian agencies & churches.
Type of support: General/operating support.
Limitations: Applications accepted. Giving primarily in TX. No grants to individuals.
Application information: Application form required.
Initial approach: Letter
Deadline(s): None
Officer and Directors:* Harold J. Sadler,* Mgr.; Jason Flanagan; Mildred Sadler; Randy Sadler; Ricky Sadler; Robin Sadler.
EIN: 752918989

9144
Saint Susie Charitable Foundation ✧
800 Navarro St., Ste. 210
San Antonio, TX 78205-1877 (210) 226-9249
Contact: John R. Hannah, Tr.
Main URL: http://www.saintsusie.org

Established in 2004 in TX.
Foundation type: Independent foundation.
Financial data (yr. ended 12/31/13): Assets, $10,738,847 (M); expenditures, $730,674; qualifying distributions, $645,775; giving activities include $637,500 for 43 grants (high: $130,000; low: $1,500).
Purpose and activities: The foundation's goal is to support organizations that contribute to medicine, education and religion.

Fields of interest: Arts; Education; Health care; Human services; Children/youth, services; Family services.
Limitations: Applications accepted. Giving primarily in San Antonio, TX. No grants to individuals.
Publications: IRS Form 990 or 990-PF printed copy available upon request.
Application information:
Initial approach: Concise proposal via U.S. mail
Deadline(s): None
Officer: Cory Albracht, Exec. Dir.
Trustees: Dr. Fernando Guerra; John R. Hannah.
EIN: 200404671
Selected grants: The following grants are a representative sample of this grantmaker's funding activity:
$15,000 to Friends of Hospice San Antonio, San Antonio, TX, 2012. For Poinsettia Ball 2011.
$10,000 to Healy-Murphy Center, San Antonio, TX, 2012. For Spirituality Center.
$10,000 to Medical Institute for Sexual Health, Austin, TX, 2012. For science department.
$10,000 to Mission Road Ministries, San Antonio, TX, 2012. For Soar and More Program.
$10,000 to University of Texas Medical Branch, Galveston, TX, 2012. For Jennie Sealy Hospital Construction.
$5,000 to Trinity University, San Antonio, TX, 2012. For Saisd Math and Science Improvement.
$1,250 to George Gervin Youth Center, San Antonio, TX, 2012. For Urban Leadership Council.

9145
Earl C. Sams Foundation, Inc. ✧
101 N. Shoreline Dr., Ste. 602
Corpus Christi, TX 78401-2824 (361) 888-6485
Contact: Bruce S. Hawn, Pres. and C.E.O.
FAX: (361) 884-4241; E-mail: sueo@ecsams.org; Main URL: http://www.ecsams.org

Incorporated in 1946 in NY; reincorporated in 1988 in TX.
Donor: Earl C. Sams†.
Foundation type: Independent foundation.
Financial data (yr. ended 12/31/13): Assets, $22,617,215 (M); expenditures, $1,403,954; qualifying distributions, $1,037,044; giving activities include $701,251 for grants.
Purpose and activities: Giving support for health care, youth and community development, and the environment.
Fields of interest: Environment; Health care; Children/youth, services; Community/economic development.
Type of support: General/operating support; Continuing support; Annual campaigns; Building/renovation; Equipment; Program development; In-kind gifts; Matching/challenge support.
Limitations: Applications accepted. Giving primarily in southern TX. No grants to individuals.
Publications: Application guidelines; Grants list; Program policy statement (including application guidelines).
Application information: Electronic submissions are preferred. Application should be scanned and e-mailed in PDF format. Application form required.
Initial approach: Use application form on foundation web site
Copies of proposal: 1
Deadline(s): Mar., June, Nov.
Board meeting date(s): Mar., June, and Nov.
Officers and Directors:* Susan G. Hawn,* Chair. and V.P.; Bruce Sams Hawn,* C.E.O. and Pres.; Susan Ohnmacht, Secy.; Candace Coutinho; Caitlyn J. Hawn; Nancy E. Hawn; Sydney E. Thames; Michael T. Yuras.
Number of staff: 4 full-time professional.
EIN: 741463151
Selected grants: The following grants are a representative sample of this grantmaker's funding activity:
$20,000 to Corpus Christi Metro Ministries, Corpus Christi, TX, 2012. For Loaves and Fishes free Cafeteria.
$15,000 to Citizens for Animal Protection, Houston, TX, 2012. For Onsite Veterinary Services.
$15,000 to Coastal Bend Kidney Foundation, Corpus Christi, TX, 2012. For Pediatric Nephrology Program.
$15,000 to Good Samaritan Rescue Mission, Corpus Christi, TX, 2012. For Good Sam 203-bed Homeless Shelter and Diner.
$10,000 to Art Center of Corpus Christi, Corpus Christi, TX, 2012. For Air Conditioner Replacement/Energy Efficient Upgrades Program.
$10,000 to Camp Aranzazu, Rockport, TX, 2012. For Sustain Nature Pond Through Use of Renewable Energy Source.
$10,000 to Coastal Bend Community Foundation, Corpus Christi, TX, 2012. For Coastal Bend Day of Giving.
$10,000 to Food Bank of Corpus Christi, Corpus Christi, TX, 2012. For Kids Cafe.
$10,000 to Spaulding for Children, Houston, TX, 2012. For South TX Special Needs Adoption Program.
$5,000 to South Texas Institute for the Arts, Corpus Christi, TX, 2012. For youth education Program.

9146
San Angelo Area Foundation ✧
221 S. Irving St.
San Angelo, TX 76903-6421 (325) 947-7071
Contact: Matt Lewis, C.E.O.
FAX: (325) 947-7322;
E-mail: infosaaf@saafound.org; Additional e-mail: mlewis@saafound.org; Main URL: http://www.saafound.org

Established in 2002 in TX by the San Angelo Health Foundation, a private foundation.
Foundation type: Community foundation.
Financial data (yr. ended 12/31/13): Assets, $94,652,501 (M); gifts received, $17,814,485; expenditures, $6,449,432; giving activities include $4,810,136 for 72 grants (high: $590,717), and $720,203 for 593 grants to individuals.
Purpose and activities: The foundation seeks to improve quality of life in the San Angelo, Texas, area by awarding grants to nonprofits and scholarships to individuals.
Fields of interest: Arts; Elementary/secondary education; Higher education; Human services; Community/economic development.
Type of support: Program development; General/operating support; Capital campaigns; Building/renovation; Scholarships—to individuals.
Limitations: Applications accepted. Giving limited to the 17-county San Angelo, TX, area: Concho, Coke, Crockett, Glasscock, Irion, Kimble, Llano, Mason, McCullough, Menard, Reagan, Runnels, San Saba, Schleicher, Sterling, Sutton, and Tom Green. No support for umbrella funding organizations for distribution of the requested funds at their own discretion. No grants for endowments, debt retirement, deficit financing, reduction of an operating deficit or liquidation of debt, or replenishment of resources used to pay for such purposes; or for courtesy advertising, benefit tickets, telephone solicitations.
Publications: Annual report; Grants list; Informational brochure; Newsletter.
Application information: Visit foundation web site for full application guidelines and requirements. Application form required.
Initial approach: Submit online application
Copies of proposal: 1
Deadline(s): Sept. 1 for grants
Board meeting date(s): Quarterly, 1st Thurs. of 2nd month of quarter
Final notification: Dec. 1
Officers and Board Members:* Allen L. Price,* Chair.; Matt Lewis, C.E.O. and Pres.; Patti May, Cont.; Liz Bates; Jay Boyd; Susan Brooks; Gary Cox; Al Elliott; Brenda Gunter; Fred Hernandez; Deanna Mayfield; Jim W. Raymond; Patrick Shannon; Camille Yale.
Number of staff: 5 full-time professional; 1 full-time support.
EIN: 731634145
Selected grants: The following grants are a representative sample of this grantmaker's funding activity:
$734,437 to West Texas Boys Ranch, San Angelo, TX, 2012.
$467,000 to Cornerstone Christian School, San Angelo, TX, 2012.
$439,100 to Boy Scouts of America, Texas Southwest Council, San Angelo, TX, 2012.
$244,000 to San Angelo Museum of Fine Arts, San Angelo, TX, 2012.
$173,000 to First Presbyterian Church, San Angelo, TX, 2012.
$80,521 to House of Faith, San Angelo, TX, 2012.
$38,000 to Concho Valley Home for Girls, San Angelo, TX, 2012.
$27,590 to Angelo State University Foundation, San Angelo, TX, 2012.
$15,940 to Trinity Lutheran Church, San Angelo, TX, 2012.
$10,000 to Green Apple Art Center, Eden, TX, 2012.

9147
San Angelo Health Foundation ✧
P.O. Box 3550
San Angelo, TX 76902-3550 (325) 486-0185
Contact: Tom Early, Pres.; Vicki Ford, Admin. Off.
FAX: (325) 486-1125;
E-mail: tomearly@sahfoundation.org; Main URL: http://www.sahfoundation.org

Established in 1995 in TX.
Foundation type: Independent foundation.
Financial data (yr. ended 12/31/13): Assets, $61,261,123 (M); expenditures, $3,374,306; qualifying distributions, $2,684,689; giving activities include $2,327,961 for 36 grants (high: $1,000,000; low: $1,500).
Purpose and activities: The foundation seeks to enhance the quality of life for the people of the San Angelo, TX, area.
Fields of interest: Arts; Education; Health care; Human services; Community/economic development.
Type of support: Consulting services; General/operating support; Management development/capacity building; Capital campaigns; Building/renovation; Equipment; Land acquisition; Emergency funds; Program development;

Conferences/seminars; Seed money; Research; Technical assistance; Program evaluation; Matching/challenge support.
Limitations: Applications accepted. Giving limited to San Angelo and the Concho Valley, TX, area. No support for religious organizations for religious purposes. No grants to individuals, or for fundraising events, operating deficits or debt retirement.
Publications: Application guidelines; Annual report.
Application information: See foundation web site for application guidelines. Application form not required.
Initial approach: Proposal
Copies of proposal: 2
Deadline(s): 3 to 4 months prior to when funds are needed
Board meeting date(s): Quarterly
Final notification: 1 to 3 months
Officers: Mike Boyd, Chair.; Marilyn Aboussie, Vice-Chair.; Tom Early, Pres.; Mary Jane Steadman, Secy.; David Lupton, Treas.
Trustees: Devin Bates; Jim Cummings; Rick DeHoyos; Sande Vincent Harrison; T. Richey Oliver; Robert S. Patyrak, M.D.; Karen Pfluger; Joanne Rice; Hugh Lamar Stone III; Joe B. Wilkinson, M.D.
Number of staff: 2 full-time professional.
EIN: 751315145
Selected grants: The following grants are a representative sample of this grantmaker's funding activity:
$200,000 to Rust Street Ministries, San Angelo, TX, 2012. For Renovation of Donated Warehouse to Expand Programming.
$100,000 to San Angelo Museum of Fine Arts, San Angelo, TX, 2012. For transitional funding.
$80,506 to House of Faith, San Angelo, TX, 2012. For EAM Step Forward Scholarship Funding for Higher Education Opportunities for Qualifying Students.
$60,000 to Christoval Volunteer Fire Department, Christoval, TX, 2012. For EMS response vehicle and a building.
$20,000 to Adult Enrichment Center, San Angelo, TX, 2012. For marketing plan.
$15,000 to San Angelo Museum of Fine Arts, San Angelo, TX, 2012. To establish outdoor public art exhibition.
$10,000 to San Angelo Museum of Fine Arts, San Angelo, TX, 2012. For Cultural District Planning Study.
$5,350 to Council on Foundations, Arlington, VA, 2012. For membership organization.
$2,500 to Concho Valley Home for Girls, San Angelo, TX, 2012. For seasonal grant.
$2,000 to Conference of Southwest Foundations, Dallas, TX, 2012. For Philanthropic Membership Organization.

9148
San Antonio Area Foundation ✧

303 E. Pearl Pkwy., Ste. 114
San Antonio, TX 78215 (210) 225-2243
Contact: For grant applications: Lydia Saldana, Prog. Off., Community and Research Grants
FAX: (210) 225-1980; E-mail: info@saafdn.org; Grant application tel.: (210) 228-3753 and e-mail: lsaldana@saafdn.org; Main URL: http://www.saafdn.org
Facebook: http://www.facebook.com/pages/San-Antonio-Area-Foundation/75337284062
Flickr: http://www.flickr.com/photos/saafdn/
Pinterest: http://pinterest.com/saafdn/
Twitter: http://twitter.com/SAAFdn
YouTube: http://www.youtube.com/user/saafdn

Established in 1964 in TX.
Foundation type: Community foundation.
Financial data (yr. ended 12/31/13): Assets, $259,936,270 (M); gifts received, $16,849,092; expenditures, $21,035,491; giving activities include $11,748,778 for grants.
Purpose and activities: The foundation seeks to help donors achieve their charitable goals for the greater benefit of the community.
Fields of interest: Media/communications; Visual arts; Museums; Performing arts; Performing arts, dance; Performing arts, theater; Historic preservation/historical societies; Arts; Education, research; Education, early childhood education; Child development, education; Higher education; Medical school/education; Nursing school/education; Adult/continuing education; Adult education—literacy, basic skills & GED; Education, reading; Education; Environment, natural resources; Environment; Animal welfare; Animals/wildlife, preservation/protection; Reproductive health, family planning; Medical care, rehabilitation; Health care; Substance abuse, services; Health organizations, association; Cancer; Heart & circulatory diseases; AIDS; Alcoholism; Diabetes; Medical research, institute; Cancer research; Heart & circulatory research; AIDS research; Crime/violence prevention, domestic violence; Disasters, Hurricane Katrina; Children/youth, services; Child development, services; Family services; Residential/custodial care, hospices; Aging, centers/services; Homeless, human services; Human services; Community/economic development; Computer science; Religion; Children/youth; Aging; African Americans/Blacks; Hispanics/Latinos; Women; Military/veterans.
Type of support: General/operating support; Continuing support; Annual campaigns; Building/renovation; Equipment; Land acquisition; Emergency funds; Program development; Professorships; Publication; Seed money; Curriculum development; Scholarship funds; Research; Program-related investments/loans; Scholarships—to individuals; Matching/challenge support.
Limitations: Applications accepted. Giving limited to Bexar County, TX, and surrounding counties, except when otherwise specified by donor. No support for individual churches, congregations, or parishes (unless projects benefit community at large). No grants to individuals (except for designated scholarship funds), or for debt reduction, operating deficits, endowment funds, or indirect costs.
Publications: Application guidelines; Annual report; Financial statement; Grants list; Informational brochure; Newsletter; Quarterly report.
Application information: Visit foundation web site for applications and specific guidelines per grant type. The foundation offers grant information meetings; reservations must be made via e-mail. Faxed applications are not accepted. Application form required.
Initial approach: Complete online account via foundation's web site
Deadline(s): Feb. for Community Grants; varies for others
Board meeting date(s): Bimonthly
Final notification: May for Community Grants
Officers and Directors:* David Hennessee,* Chair.; G.P. Singh, Ph.D.*, Vice-Chair.; Dennis E. Noll, C.E.O. and Pres.; Carrie Gray, V.P., Devel. and Donor Svcs.; Susan Steves Thompson, V.P., Grants, Progs. and Nonprofit Support Svcs.; Sue Turner,* Secy.; Luis de la Garza,* Treas.; Dee-Ann Calderon, C.F.O.; Janie Barrera; Harold Berg; Laura Ehrenberg-Chesler; Theodore Guidry II; John Hayes; Edward B. Kelley; William G. Moll; Brad Parman; Jane Phipps; Knox Pitts II; Michelle R. Scarver; Richard T. Schlosberg, III; Marie Smith; Bruce Tilley.
Trustee Banks: Bank of America, N.A.; Bank One, Texas, N.A.; Broadway National Bank; Frost National Bank; Jefferson State Bank; JPMorgan Chase Bank, N.A.; Wells Fargo Bank, N.A.; Merrill Lynch Trust Co.
Number of staff: 16 full-time professional; 7 full-time support.
EIN: 746065414
Selected grants: The following grants are a representative sample of this grantmaker's funding activity:
$61,397 to Austin Pets Alive, Austin, TX, 2012. For SAPA! Service Learning Project.
$40,000 to I Care San Antonio, San Antonio, TX, 2012. For I Care Vision Center.
$40,000 to University of Texas at San Antonio, San Antonio, TX, 2012. For Role of CX3CR1 in the Regulation of Microglial Function and its Effects in Neuronal Pathology During Diabetic Retinopathy.
$33,800 to University of Texas Health Science Center, San Antonio, TX, 2012. For Proinflammatory Cytokines and Depression in Mexican Americans with Diabetes and End-stage Renal Disease.
$25,000 to San Antonio Lighthouse for the Blind, San Antonio, TX, 2012. For Seniors' Program, which promotes individual independence among blind and visually-impaired senior citizens and older in San Antonio and the surrounding area.
$20,000 to Hill Country Animal League, Boerne, TX, 2012. For Spay/Neuter Program Expansion.
$20,000 to McNay Art Museum, San Antonio, TX, 2012. For Estampas de la Raza: Contemporary Prints from the Romo Collection.
$15,680 to Arthur Nagel Community Clinic, Bandera, TX, 2012. For RiskBusters Program.
$8,000 to Cactus Pear Music Festival, Converse, TX, 2012. For Cactus Pear Music Festival.
$8,000 to Rainbow Senior Center, Boerne, TX, 2012. For Nutritional Programs for Kendall County Senior Citizens.

9149
San Antonio Foundation for Excellence in Education ✧ ☆

141 Lavaca St.
San Antonio, TX 78210-1039
Main URL: http://www.saisdfoundation.com/

Established in 1998 in TX.
Donors: H.E. Butt Grocery Co.; AT&T Foundation; Zachry Group, Inc.; Douglas J. Dever†; State Farm; Valero Energy Foundation; 8020 Foundation; BBVA Compass Bank; Brighter Sky Foundation; C.H. Guenther & Sons Inc.; Carol E. Jones Educational and Cultural Fund; CPS Energy; David Zachry; Karen Zachry; Escamilla Poneck & Cruz LLP; Frost Bank; G.E. Rodriguez & Associates; Genesis Concepts & Consultants LLC; The GEO Group Foundation Inc.; Health Care Service Corp; HEB; IBM; RICOH; Waste Mangement; Koch Companies; Lionel Sosa; Katherine Sosa; Lockheed Martin; Morganti Tedas Casias A Joint Venture; Mullen Pension & Benefits Group; Harvey E. Nijim Family Foundation; SAISD; Silver & Black Give Back; Spurs Sports & Entertainment; The Gambrinus Co.; The Greehey Family & Sons Inc.; The Tobin Endowment; The

Zachary Foundation; Valero Services Inc.; Wellmed Medical Management Inc.
Foundation type: Independent foundation.
Financial data (yr. ended 12/31/13): Assets, $1,125,962 (M); gifts received, $730,432; expenditures, $822,604; qualifying distributions, $629,953; giving activities include $629,953 for 4 grants (high: $452,054; low: $20,314).
Fields of interest: Elementary/secondary education.
Limitations: Applications not accepted. Giving primarily in San Antonio, TX. No grants to individuals.
Application information: Unsolicited requests for funds not accepted.
Officers: Carri Baker Wells, Chair. and Pres.; Leo Gomez, Vice-Chair.; Joe Bernal, Secy.; Bob Raymond, Treas.; Judy Geelhoed, Exec. Dir.
Trustees: Shari Albright; Mario Barrera; Geoff Bley; Patrick Carrier; Trish Deberry; Steve Delahaya; Laura Dixon; Greg Garcia; Margaret Garcia; Andrew Grove; Kimberly Harle; Jesus Hernandez; Derrick Howard; Javier Leal; Brandon Logan; and additional 5 Trustees.
EIN: 742861587

9150
A.R. "Tony" and Maria J. Sanchez Family Foundation ✧
(formerly Sanchez Family Foundation)
1920 Sandman St.
Laredo, TX 78041-3819

Donors: Antonio R. Sanchez, Jr.; Alicia M. Sanchez†; Alicia M. Sanchez Charitable Lead Annuity Trust.
Foundation type: Independent foundation.
Financial data (yr. ended 12/31/13): Assets, $69,440,890 (M); gifts received, $7,625,892; expenditures, $4,602,206; qualifying distributions, $3,407,276; giving activities include $3,208,880 for 16 grants (high: $1,000,000; low: $10,000).
Fields of interest: Secondary school/education; Higher education; Education; Hospitals (general); Human services.
Type of support: General/operating support.
Limitations: Applications not accepted. Giving primarily in TX. No grants to individuals.
Application information: Contributes only to pre-selected organizations.
Officers: Antonio R. Sanchez, Jr., Pres.; Maria J. Sanchez, Sr. V.P.; Ana Lee Sanchez, V.P. and Mgr.; Antonio R. Sanchez III, V.P.; Eduardo Sanchez, V.P.; Patricio Sanchez, V.P.; Frank A. Guerra, Secy.-Treas.
EIN: 742835977

9151
Sand Dollar Foundation ✧
(doing business as Autobahn Motorcar Group Youth Scholarship Tour)
3000 White Settlement Rd.
Fort Worth, TX 76107-1338 (817) 988-6110
Contact: Larry Barker, Dir.
E-mail: lbarker@abahn.com; Additional contact: Stacie Williams, Morgan Stanley, (314) 889-9842, (800) 488-9880, e-mail: Stacie.Williams@mssb.com; Main URL: http://www.autobahnyouthtour.com/

Established in 2001 in TX.
Donors: Autobahn Imports, Inc.; Texas Longhorn Breeders Association of America.
Foundation type: Company-sponsored foundation.
Financial data (yr. ended 12/31/13): Assets, $7,587 (M); gifts received, $549,350; expenditures, $562,008; qualifying distributions, $477,215; giving activities include $449,600 for 226 grants to individuals (high: $11,075; low: $100).
Purpose and activities: The foundation awards college scholarships to winners of Texas Longhorn Breeders Association qualifying shows.
Fields of interest: Education; Athletics/sports, equestrianism; Youth development.
Type of support: Scholarships—to individuals.
Limitations: Applications accepted. Giving primarily in Fort Worth, TX.
Publications: Application guidelines.
Application information: Applicants are selected through the Texas Longhorn Breeders Association's world show qualifying circuit for youth. Scholarships are publicized as part of each show and the winners of each class in the show are eligible.
Initial approach: Download entry form and mail to foundation
Deadline(s): Varies
Directors: Larry W. Barker; Chad Chase; Diann Chase; John S. Chase; Tim Karr.
EIN: 752957772

9152
Don A. Sanders Family Foundation ✧ ☆
600 Travis St.
Houston, TX 77002-3009

Established in 1997 in TX.
Donors: Don A. Sanders; Chris Sanders.
Foundation type: Independent foundation.
Financial data (yr. ended 12/31/13): Assets, $112,918 (M); gifts received, $424,021; expenditures, $739,138; qualifying distributions, $732,145; giving activities include $732,145 for 46 grants (high: $250,000; low: $300).
Purpose and activities: Giving for Christian churches and organizations, children's services, education, and for health and human services.
Fields of interest: Environment; Animals/wildlife; Human services.
Limitations: Applications not accepted. Giving primarily in Houston, TX. No grants to individuals.
Application information: Unsolicited requests for funds not accepted.
Officers: Don A. Sanders, Pres.; Ben T. Morris, V.P.; Walter P. Zivley, Secy.
EIN: 760537031

9153
The Sangreal Foundation ✧
3502 Sacred Moon Cove
Austin, TX 78746
Contact: Brian Sheth, V.P.; Adria Sheth, Pres.; Andrew Geller, Secy.

Donors: Adria Sheth; Brian Sheth.
Foundation type: Independent foundation.
Financial data (yr. ended 12/31/13): Assets, $144,746 (M); gifts received, $1,057,838; expenditures, $937,525; qualifying distributions, $933,592; giving activities include $909,831 for 10 grants (high: $486,331; low: $7,500).
Fields of interest: Education; Animals/wildlife; Human services.
Limitations: Applications not accepted.
Application information: Unsolicited requests for funds not accepted.
Officers: Adria Sheth, Pres.; Brian Sheth, V.P.; Andrew Geller, Secy.
EIN: 453779543

9154
Sarofim Foundation ✧
P.O. Box 52830
Houston, TX 77052-2830
Application address: Fayez Sarofim, Tr., 2 Houston Ctr., Ste. 2907, Houston, TX 77010; tel.: (713) 654-4484

Established in 1968 in TX.
Donors: Fayez Sarofim; Louisa Stude Sarofim.
Foundation type: Independent foundation.
Financial data (yr. ended 06/30/13): Assets, $30,050,098 (M); expenditures, $848,512; qualifying distributions, $820,458; giving activities include $820,000 for 6 grants (high: $500,000; low: $25,000).
Fields of interest: Museums (art); Education; Heart & circulatory research.
Type of support: Building/renovation.
Limitations: Applications accepted. Giving primarily in Newport, RI and Houston, TX. No grants to individuals, or for scholarships programs.
Application information: Application form not required.
Initial approach: Requests application form
Deadline(s): None
Trustees: Christopher B. Sarofim; Fayez Sarofim; Raye G. White.
EIN: 237065248

9155
Scaler Foundation, Inc. ✧
800 Gessner Rd., Ste. 1260
Houston, TX 77024-4273

Incorporated in 1954 in TX.
Donors: Eric Boissonnas; Blue Bridge Wealth Management.
Foundation type: Independent foundation.
Financial data (yr. ended 12/31/13): Assets, $20,647,781 (M); expenditures, $990,182; qualifying distributions, $856,063; giving activities include $824,482 for 17 grants (high: $139,289; low: $7,929).
Purpose and activities: Giving primarily for arts and culture, social services, and to French Protestant federated giving programs.
Fields of interest: Visual arts; Performing arts, music; Human services; United Ways and Federated Giving Programs; Protestant federated giving programs.
International interests: France.
Type of support: General/operating support; Continuing support; Income development; Building/renovation; Program development; Seed money.
Limitations: Applications not accepted. Giving primarily in Paris, France; some giving in the U.S., primarily in Brooklyn and New York, NY and in Houston, TX. No grants to individuals, or for building or endowment funds, research, scholarships, fellowships, or matching gifts; no loans.
Application information: Contributes only to pre-selected organizations.

Officers and Directors:* Nicolas H. Boissonnas,* Pres.; Jacques C. Boissonnas,* V.P.; Marvin A. Wurzer, Secy.-Treas.; Catherine B. Coste.
EIN: 746036684
Selected grants: The following grants are a representative sample of this grantmaker's funding activity:
$284,988 to Fondation de France, Paris, France, 2011. For general support.
$66,031 to Federation Protestante de France, Paris, France, 2011. For general support.
$42,551 to La Petite Bibliotheque Ronde, Clamart, France, 2011.
$30,000 to Center for Khmer Studies, New York, NY, 2011. For general support.
$25,000 to American Library in Paris, Paris, France, 2011.
$15,000 to Museum of Fine Arts, Houston, Houston, TX, 2011.
$1,000 to Architectural League of New York, New York, NY, 2011. For general support.

9156
William & Salome McAllen Scanlan Foundation ✧
(formerly William and Salome Scanlan Foundation)
112 E. Pecan St., Ste. 3000
San Antonio, TX 78205-1512 (210) 224-4491
Contact: William Scanlan, Jr., Tr.

Established in TX.
Donors: John McAllen Scanlan; William Scanlan, Jr.; Wilson M. Scanlan; Ken Cho.
Foundation type: Independent foundation.
Financial data (yr. ended 12/31/12): Assets, $994,937 (M); gifts received, $766,865; expenditures, $1,147,538; qualifying distributions, $1,134,890; giving activities include $1,134,890 for grants.
Purpose and activities: Giving primarily for environmental and educational concerns.
Fields of interest: Arts; Education; Environment; Human services; Children/youth, services; Christian agencies & churches.
Limitations: Applications accepted. Giving primarily in TX, with emphasis on Austin and San Antonio.
Application information: Application form required.
Initial approach: Letter
Deadline(s): None, but preferably before Oct.
Trustees: John McAllen Scanlan; William Scanlan, Jr.
EIN: 742697713

9157
Scharbauer Foundation Inc ✧
300 N. Marienfeld St., Ste. 850
Midland, TX 79701-4387 (432) 683-2222
Contact: Grant A. Billingsley, Exec. Dir.
E-mail: gbillingsley@scharbauerfoundation.org; Main URL: http://www.scharbauerfoundation.org

Established in TX.
Donor: Clarence Scharbauer, Jr.
Foundation type: Independent foundation.
Financial data (yr. ended 12/31/12): Assets, $122,917,413 (M); gifts received, $27,457,297; expenditures, $3,146,657; qualifying distributions, $2,289,002; giving activities include $2,204,000 for 16 grants (high: $1,000,000; low: $1,500).
Fields of interest: Arts; Education; Health care; Human services; Public affairs; Religion.
Limitations: Applications accepted. Giving primarily in TX, with emphasis on Midland, the Permian Basin region, and the Panhandle region. No support for lobbying organizations. No grants or loans to individuals.
Publications: Application guidelines; Grants list.
Application information: Pre-applications are not generally considered out-of-cycle. Only hard-copy Pre-application forms will be accepted and no electronic, fax, or handwritten Pre-application forms will be accepted. Pre-applications must be received by the foundation by 5:00 p.m. on the day of the deadline. Pre-application form and guidelines available on foundation web site.
Initial approach: Pre-application
Deadline(s): See foundation web site for current deadlines
Officers: Clarence Scharbauer, Jr., Pres.; Clarence Scharbauer, III, V.P.; James M. Alsup, V.P.; Allen McGuire, Treas.; Cynthia Y. Benson, Cont.; Grant Billingsley, Exec. Dir.
EIN: 262527362

9158
A. I. and Manet Schepps Foundation ✧
(formerly Schepps Charitable Foundation, Inc.)
P. O. Box 539
Bellaire, TX 77402-0539

Established in 1962 in TX.
Donors: A.I. Schepps; Manet Schepps†.
Foundation type: Independent foundation.
Financial data (yr. ended 12/31/12): Assets, $5,481,970 (M); gifts received, $5,445,219; expenditures, $6,680,798; qualifying distributions, $6,635,831; giving activities include $6,496,461 for 48 grants (high: $5,474,061; low: $46).
Fields of interest: Education; Human services; United Ways and Federated Giving Programs; Jewish federated giving programs; Jewish agencies & synagogues.
Type of support: General/operating support.
Limitations: Applications not accepted. No grants to individuals.
Application information: Contributes only to pre-selected organizations.
Officer: Nancy Brand, Pres.
Directors: Jennifer Brand; Gilda Sprung.
EIN: 746050262

9159
Schollmaier Foundation ✧
2501 Museum Way, Ste. 823
Fort Worth, TX 76107

Established in 1978.
Donors: Edgar H. Schollmaier; Rama L. Schollmaier.
Foundation type: Independent foundation.
Financial data (yr. ended 12/31/13): Assets, $8,807,068 (M); expenditures, $1,549,965; qualifying distributions, $1,542,773; giving activities include $1,542,748 for 40 grants (high: $218,400; low: $500).
Purpose and activities: Giving primarily for education, arts and culture, and health care.
Fields of interest: Arts; Higher education; Education; Hospitals (general); Human services; Children/youth, services.
Limitations: Applications not accepted. Giving primarily in Fort Worth, TX. No grants to individuals.
Application information: Contributes only to pre-selected organizations.
Officers and Directors:* Rama L. Schollmaier,* Pres. and Treas.; Edgar H. Schollmaier,* V.P.; Harry Brants,* V.P.; Taylor Schollmaier,* V.P.
EIN: 751577328
Selected grants: The following grants are a representative sample of this grantmaker's funding activity:
$2,500 to Wings of Hope Equitherapy, Cleburne, TX, 2012. For Help Crippled Children.

9160
Victor E. & Caroline E. Schutte Foundation ✧
c/o Bank of America, N.A.
P.O. Box 831041
Dallas, TX 75283-1041
Application address: c/o Anthony Twyman, Bank of America, N.A., P.O. Box 219119, Kansas City, MO 64121-9119, tel.: (816) 292-4342

Established in 1993 in MO.
Donor: Caroline Schutte†.
Foundation type: Independent foundation.
Financial data (yr. ended 12/31/13): Assets, $16,167,270 (M); expenditures, $857,670; qualifying distributions, $728,974; giving activities include $638,333 for 14 grants (high: $240,000; low: $8,333).
Fields of interest: Arts; Education; Health organizations, association.
Type of support: Capital campaigns; Building/renovation; Endowments.
Limitations: Applications accepted. Giving primarily in Kansas City, MO; some funding also in KS.
Application information: Application form required.
Initial approach: Letter of no more than 3 pages
Deadline(s): None
Trustees: Stinson Morrison Hecker, LLP; Bank of America, N.A.
EIN: 431661684
Selected grants: The following grants are a representative sample of this grantmaker's funding activity:
$50,000 to Boy Scouts of America, Heart of America Council, Kansas City, MO, 2012. To support 'shelter Our Scouts' Capital Campaign.
$50,000 to Kauffman Center for the Performing Arts, Kansas City, MO, 2012. For Purchase Compact Hydraulic Aerial Lift.
$25,000 to Leukemia & Lymphoma Society, White Plains, NY, 2012. To support Learning Collaborative.
$20,000 to Avila University, Kansas City, MO, 2012. For Campus Monument Markers.
$10,000 to Avila University, Kansas City, MO, 2012. For Scholarship Fund for Books and Tuition.
$5,000 to Kansas University Endowment Association, Lawrence, KS, 2012. To support Lung Cancer Program.

9161
William E. Scott Foundation ✧
801 Cherry St., Ste. 2000
Fort Worth, TX 76102-6882 (817) 336-2400
Contact: Raymond B. Kelly III, Pres.

Incorporated in 1960 in TX.
Donor: William E. Scott†.
Foundation type: Independent foundation.

Financial data (yr. ended 05/31/14): Assets, $21,890,282 (M); expenditures, $1,091,963; qualifying distributions, $944,430; giving activities include $932,250 for 40 grants (high: $105,000; low: $2,000).
Purpose and activities: Giving for the arts, special, elementary, and secondary education, health care, and human services.
Fields of interest: Arts; Child development, education; Elementary school/education; Secondary school/education; Health care.
Type of support: Continuing support; Annual campaigns; Capital campaigns; Building/renovation; Equipment; Program development.
Limitations: Applications accepted. Giving limited to Fort Worth-Tarrant County, TX. No grants to individuals or for endowments, debt reduction, or memorial or permanently restricted funds.
Publications: Application guidelines.
Application information: Application form not required.
Initial approach: Letter
Copies of proposal: 1
Deadline(s): None
Board meeting date(s): As required
Final notification: By mail, within 60-90 days
Officer: Raymond B. Kelly III, Pres.
Number of staff: 1 part-time support.
EIN: 756024661
Selected grants: The following grants are a representative sample of this grantmaker's funding activity:
$200,000 to All Saints Health Foundation, Fort Worth, TX, 2011.
$100,000 to W. I. Cook Foundation, Fort Worth, TX, 2011.
$40,000 to Fort Worth Symphony Orchestra Association, Fort Worth, TX, 2011.
$30,000 to Davey OBrien Educational and Charitable Trust, Fort Worth, TX, 2011.
$25,000 to Camp Fire USA, Fort Worth, TX, 2011.
$25,000 to Carter BloodCare, Bedford, TX, 2011.
$25,000 to Fort Worth Museum of Science and History, Fort Worth, TX, 2011.
$25,000 to Fort Worth Opera, Fort Worth, TX, 2011.
$25,000 to Imagination Celebration of Fort Worth, Fort Worth, TX, 2011.
$10,000 to Big Brothers and Sisters of Tarrant County, Fort Worth, TX, 2011.

9162
Scurlock Foundation ✧

3355 W. Alabama St., Ste. 630
Houston, TX 77098-1799
Contact: Kathy Munger, Admin.
FAX: (713) 222-2419; E-mail: kmunger@swbell.net; Main URL: http://www.scurlockfoundation.org

Incorporated in 1954 in TX.
Donors: E.C. Scurlock†; Mrs. E.C. Scurlock†; Scurlock Oil Co.; D.E. Farnsworth†; Jack S. Blanton, Sr.; Mrs. Jack S. Blanton†; and other members of the Blanton family.
Foundation type: Independent foundation.
Financial data (yr. ended 12/31/12): Assets, $34,112,155 (M); expenditures, $2,418,185; qualifying distributions, $2,067,943; giving activities include $1,870,383 for 160 grants (high: $300,000; low: $100).
Purpose and activities: Giving primarily for the arts, education, health, children and social services, and to Christian and Protestant agencies and churches.
Fields of interest: Performing arts; Arts; Higher education; Education; Hospitals (general); Health organizations, association; Human services; Children/youth, services; Public affairs; Christian agencies & churches; Protestant agencies & churches.
Type of support: General/operating support; Continuing support; Annual campaigns; Capital campaigns; Building/renovation; Land acquisition; Endowments; Emergency funds; Research; Matching/challenge support.
Limitations: Giving primarily in TX, with emphasis on the Houston area. No grants to individuals, or for scholarships or fellowships; no loans.
Publications: Application guidelines; Financial statement.
Application information: Unsolicited grant requests are not accepted. Funds are heavily committed. Application guidelines available on foundation web site.
Initial approach: Pre-selected organizations may submit a letter or e-mail of inquiry
Copies of proposal: 1
Deadline(s): Aug. 1, Nov. 1, Jan. 1, and Apr. 1
Board meeting date(s): Feb., May, Sept. and Nov.
Directors: Eddy S. Blanton; Jack S. Blanton, Sr.; Jack S. Blanton, Jr.; Elizabeth Blanton Wareing; Kathleen (Kathy) Dies Munger.
Number of staff: 1 part-time professional.
EIN: 741488953
Selected grants: The following grants are a representative sample of this grantmaker's funding activity:
$300,000 to Methodist Hospital Foundation, Houston, TX, 2012. For Endowment for JSB Chair.
$200,000 to University of Texas Foundation, Austin, TX, 2012. For Blanton Endowment.
$80,000 to Laity Renewal Foundation, Kerrville, TX, 2012. For Capital for Family Camp.
$25,000 to Rice University, Jones School of Management, Houston, TX, 2012. For Leslie and Jack Blanton Scholarship Endowment.
$10,000 to Houston Hospice, Houston, TX, 2012. For LLB Award.
$10,000 to Memorial Hermann Foundation, Houston, TX, 2012. For Operating Atilla Ertan.
$5,000 to Community of the Streets Outreach Corporation, Houston, TX, 2012. For crisis management.
$5,000 to Teach for America, New York, NY, 2012. To sponsor a teacher.
$5,000 to YMCA of Greater Houston Area, Houston, TX, 2012. For In Honor of John Duncan.
$1,000 to Memorial Hermann Foundation, Houston, TX, 2012. For spinal cord research.

9163
George E. Seay III Foundation ✧

325 N. St. Paul, Ste. 3500
Dallas, TX 75201-3869

Established in 2002 in TX.
Donors: Pauline Allen Gill Foundation; The New Covenant Foundation; The Legacy Education Fund; George E. Seay III.
Foundation type: Independent foundation.
Financial data (yr. ended 12/31/12): Assets, $9,985,105 (M); expenditures, $750,066; qualifying distributions, $442,787; giving activities include $442,787 for 48 grants (high: $123,650; low: $250).
Fields of interest: Education; Christian agencies & churches.
Limitations: Applications not accepted. No grants to individuals.
Application information: Contributes only to pre-selected organizations.
Officer: David Epperson, Secy.
Directors: George E. Seay III; Nancy Clements Seay.
EIN: 731645127

9164
Seegers Foundation ✧

12720 Hillcrest Rd., Ste. 530
Dallas, TX 75230-2000

Established in 1984 in TX.
Donors: Paul Ray Seegers; Phyllis Ann Seegers; Steven P. Seegers; Scott R. Seegers.
Foundation type: Independent foundation.
Financial data (yr. ended 12/31/13): Assets, $6,431,418 (M); gifts received, $802,680; expenditures, $641,650; qualifying distributions, $621,230; giving activities include $619,142 for 38 grants (high: $400,000; low: $1,000).
Fields of interest: Higher education; Theological school/education; Health organizations, association; Human services; Children/youth, services; Christian agencies & churches.
International interests: Mexico.
Type of support: General/operating support.
Limitations: Applications not accepted. Giving primarily in TX. No grants to individuals.
Application information: Unsolicited requests for funds not accepted.
Officers: Phyllis Ann Seegers, Pres. and Treas.; Paul Ray Seegers, V.P.; Scott R. Seegers, V.P.; Pamela Seegers Gaulding, Secy.
Directors: David G. Glickman; Jacob P. Seegers.
EIN: 752001868
Selected grants: The following grants are a representative sample of this grantmaker's funding activity:
$5,000 to Liberty Institute, Plano, TX, 2012. For Strengthens Family Values.
$4,000 to Union Gospel Mission, Dallas, TX, 2012. To promote Christian Values.
$2,000 to Dallas Life, Dallas, TX, 2012. To assist homeless.
$2,000 to Feed My Starving Children, Coon Rapids, MN, 2012. To assist Neglected Children.
$2,000 to Smile Train, Washington, DC, 2012. For children's facial surgery.
$2,000 to Wet Mountain Fire Protection District, Westcliffe, CO, 2012. To improve community.
$1,000 to Dallas Pregnancy Resource Center, Dallas, TX, 2012. To assist Unwed Mothers.

9165
The Abe and Annie Seibel Foundation ✧

c/o Frost National Bank
P.O. Box 179
Galveston, TX 77553-0179 (409) 770-7100
Contact: Janet L. Bertiolino, V.P. and Trust Off., Frost National Bank

Trust established in 1960 in TX.
Donors: Abe Seibel†; Annie Seibel†.
Foundation type: Independent foundation.
Financial data (yr. ended 07/31/13): Assets, $37,848,774 (M); gifts received, $500; expenditures, $5,177,422; qualifying distributions, $4,865,410; giving activities include $500,000 for

3 grants (high: $375,000; low: $62,500), and $4,046,935 for loans to individuals.
Purpose and activities: Interest-free loans to needy and worthy full-time undergraduate students enrolled in four-year higher educational institutions.
Fields of interest: Economically disadvantaged.
Type of support: Student loans—to individuals.
Limitations: Applications accepted. Giving limited to graduates of TX high schools attending TX colleges and universities.
Publications: Application guidelines; Informational brochure (including application guidelines).
Application information: Application form required.
Initial approach: Telephone or letter requesting application form
Deadline(s): Feb. 28
Directors: Ellen Druss; Temple B'nai Israel.
Trustee: Frost National Bank.
EIN: 746035556

9166
Semmes Foundation, Inc. ✧
800 Navarro St., Ste. 210
San Antonio, TX 78205-1877
Contact: Thomas R. Semmes, Pres.
Main URL: http://www.semmesfoundation.org
Grants List: http://www.semmesfoundation.org/recipients.htm

Incorporated in 1952 in TX.
Donors: Douglas R. Semmes†; Julia Yates Semmes†.
Foundation type: Independent foundation.
Financial data (yr. ended 12/31/13): Assets, $43,953,194 (M); gifts received, $45,739; expenditures, $1,909,636; qualifying distributions, $1,316,046; giving activities include $1,274,359 for 14 grants (high: $500,000; low: $2,000).
Purpose and activities: Support for museums and nonprofit organizations involved with education and health.
Fields of interest: Museums; Education; Health care.
Limitations: Applications accepted. Giving primarily in the San Antonio, TX, area. No grants to individuals; no loans.
Publications: IRS Form 990 or 990-PF printed copy available upon request.
Application information: Application guidelines available on foundation web site. The overwhelming majority of grants are initiated by the directors of the foundation. Application form not required.
Initial approach: Proposal via regular mail
Copies of proposal: 1
Deadline(s): None
Board meeting date(s): Annually, and as required
Final notification: Within 6 months
Officers and Directors:* Thomas R. Semmes,* Pres.; Douglas R. Semmes, Jr.,* V.P.; Carol Duffell, Secy.-Treas.; John R. Hannah; Patricia A. Semmes.
Number of staff: 1 part-time professional.
EIN: 746062264
Selected grants: The following grants are a representative sample of this grantmaker's funding activity:
$800,000 to Trinity University, San Antonio, TX, 2011. For scholarship fund.
$100,000 to Morningside Ministries, San Antonio, TX, 2011.
$100,000 to National Western Art Foundation, San Antonio, TX, 2011.
$100,000 to Southwest School of Art and Craft, San Antonio, TX, 2011.
$75,000 to San Antonio Public Library Foundation, San Antonio, TX, 2011.
$25,000 to McNay Art Museum, San Antonio, TX, 2011.
$25,000 to United Way of San Antonio and Bexar County, San Antonio, TX, 2010. For general support.
$20,000 to McNay Art Museum, San Antonio, TX, 2011.
$16,000 to McNay Art Museum, San Antonio, TX, 2011.
$10,000 to YMCA of Greater San Antonio, San Antonio, TX, 2010. For general support.
$10,000 to YMCA of Greater San Antonio, San Antonio, TX, 2011. For general support.
$2,000 to University of Texas, Austin, TX, 2011. For general support.

9167
Ruth C. and Charles S. Sharp Foundation, Inc. ✧
P.O. Box 560397
The Colony, TX 75056-0397

Incorporated in 1965 in TX.
Donors: Charles S. Sharp; Ruth Collins Sharp; Henry J. Smith; Carr P. Collins Foundation.
Foundation type: Independent foundation.
Financial data (yr. ended 12/31/13): Assets, $13,702,963 (M); expenditures, $1,783,768; qualifying distributions, $1,646,297; giving activities include $1,603,083 for 141 grants (high: $350,933; low: $100).
Purpose and activities: Giving primarily for higher education; historic preservation, human services; and the arts.
Fields of interest: Museums; Historic preservation/historical societies; Arts; Higher education; Hospitals (general); Health organizations; Human services; Children/youth, services; Community/economic development; Foundations (public); United Ways and Federated Giving Programs; Protestant agencies & churches.
Type of support: General/operating support.
Limitations: Applications not accepted. Giving primarily in Dallas, TX; some funding also in MA. No grants to individuals.
Application information: Contributes only to pre-selected organizations.
Officers and Directors:* Ruth Sharp Altshuler,* Pres.; Sally S. Harris,* V.P.; Susan F. Sharp.
EIN: 756045366
Selected grants: The following grants are a representative sample of this grantmaker's funding activity:
$250 to Educational First Steps, Dallas, TX, 2012. To support Organizations in Achieving Its Objective.

9168
Shell Oil Company Foundation ✧
(formerly Shell Companies Foundation, Inc.)
1 Shell Plz., P.O. Box 4749
Houston, TX 77210-4749
FAX: (713) 241-3329;
E-mail: scofoundation@shellus.com

Incorporated in 1953 in NY.
Donors: Shell Oil Co.; Shell Exploration & Production; Motiva.
Foundation type: Company-sponsored foundation.
Financial data (yr. ended 12/31/12): Assets, $127,428,662 (M); gifts received, $226,754; expenditures, $3,060,299; qualifying distributions, $2,319,879; giving activities include $2,319,879 for 1,138 grants (high: $88,147; low: $25).
Purpose and activities: The foundation supports organizations involved with community development and through an employee matching gift program.
Fields of interest: Community/economic development; United Ways and Federated Giving Programs.
Type of support: General/operating support; Employee matching gifts.
Limitations: Applications not accepted. Giving primarily in areas of company operations with emphasis on Houston, TX. No support for religious organizations not of direct benefit to the entire community, fraternal or labor organizations, private foundations, or organizations located outside the U.S. No grants to individuals, or for endowments, capital campaigns, or general operating support, or conferences and seminars.
Application information: Contributes only to pre-selected organizations.
Officers and Directors: Bruce Culpepper, Pres.; Frazier Wilson, V.P.; Lynn S. Borgmeier, Secy.; Anothy M. Nolte, Cont. and Treas.; Cynthia A. P. Deere; Christopher B. Rice.
Number of staff: 7
EIN: 136066583

9169
Shelton Family Foundation ✧
P.O. Box 2791
Abilene, TX 79604-2791 (325) 676-7724
Contact: David L. Copeland, Pres.

Established in 1997 in TX.
Donor: Andrew B. Shelton†.
Foundation type: Independent foundation.
Financial data (yr. ended 06/30/14): Assets, $42,098,562 (M); expenditures, $2,180,569; qualifying distributions, $2,041,063; giving activities include $1,815,073 for 81 grants (high: $500,000; low: $250).
Purpose and activities: Giving primarily for the arts, education, health, children, youth and social services, and to Christian and Protestant organizations.
Fields of interest: Arts; Higher education; Education; Health organizations, association; Human services; Salvation Army; Children/youth, services; Foundations (private grantmaking); Christian agencies & churches; Protestant agencies & churches.
Limitations: Applications accepted. Giving primarily in the west central TX area. No grants to individuals.
Application information: Application form not required.
Initial approach: Letter requesting guidelines
Deadline(s): None
Officers and Directors:* David L. Copeland,* Pres. and Treas.; C. Christine Nicols, Advisory Dir.; Andrew D. Durham; David R. Durham; Sindy Shelton Durham; Wendy H. Durham; Leonard R. Hoffman; Shay Shelton Hoffman; Ruby W. Shelton.
EIN: 752655885
Selected grants: The following grants are a representative sample of this grantmaker's funding activity:
$54,250 to United Way of Abilene, Abilene, TX, 2013. For IDA Program plus Operating Funds.
$50,000 to Abilene Boys Ranch, Abilene, TX, 2013. For Corner Post Project-additional funding.

$50,000 to Noah Project, Abilene, TX, 2013. For 2010 capital campaign.
$30,000 to Day Nursery of Abilene, Abilene, TX, 2013. For Security System and Operating Funds.
$20,000 to Connecting Caring Communities, Abilene, TX, 2013. For 4 Year Operating Grant.
$20,000 to Rescue the Animals, Abilene, TX, 2013. For 2013 operating expenses.
$12,500 to United Way of Abilene, Abilene, TX, 2013. For United Way 2013 Campaign.
$10,000 to Community Foundation of Abilene, Abilene, TX, 2013. For Endowments for VFDs.
$10,000 to San Antonio Area Foundation, San Antonio, TX, 2013. For Franklin Family Charitable Fund.
$1,000 to Day Nursery of Abilene, Abilene, TX, 2013. For Putt Fore Children.

9170
Shield-Ayres Foundation ✧

3101 Bee Caves Rd., Ste. 260
Austin, TX 78746-5574 (512) 476-4816
Contact: Patricia Shield Ayres, Tr.
E-mail: info@shield-ayresfoundation.org; Main URL: http://www.shield-ayresfoundation.org/

Established in 1977 in TX.
Donors: Fred W. Shield†; Robert M. Ayres, Jr.; Patricia Shield Ayres.
Foundation type: Independent foundation.
Financial data (yr. ended 12/31/13): Assets, $21,760,060 (M); expenditures, $2,207,534; qualifying distributions, $1,909,756; giving activities include $1,909,756 for 141 grants (high: $50,000; low: $11).
Purpose and activities: Giving primarily for health, human services, environment, education and the arts.
Fields of interest: Arts; Education; Environment, public education; Environment, water resources; Environment, land resources; Environment; Health care; Food services; Human services; Social sciences, public policy.
Type of support: Endowments; General/operating support; Annual campaigns; Capital campaigns; Building/renovation; Land acquisition; Emergency funds; Program development; Matching/challenge support.
Limitations: Applications accepted. Giving primarily in the Austin and San Antonio, TX, area. No grants to individuals.
Publications: Application guidelines; Annual report (including application guidelines).
Application information: Only those applicants who have received a favorable response to their Letter of Inquiry will be able to access the application to submit a full grant proposal. Application form required.
Initial approach: Use online Letter of Inquiry format on foundation web site
Deadline(s): Feb. 15 and Aug. 15
Board meeting date(s): Generally in Mar. and Sept.
Officers and Directors:* Vera Ayres Bowen,* Pres.; Margaret Ayres,* V.P.; Marshall Ayres Bowen,* Secy.; Robert Atlee Ayres,* Treas.; Patricia Shield Ayres; Robert Moss Ayres, Jr.
EIN: 741938157
Selected grants: The following grants are a representative sample of this grantmaker's funding activity:
$50,000 to Land Trust Alliance, Washington, DC, 2012. For Conservation Initiatives in Texas.
$30,000 to YMCA of Austin, Austin, TX, 2012. For East Communities Branch.
$25,000 to National Wildlife Federation, Austin, TX, 2012. For Texas Living Waters project.
$25,000 to Regents School of Austin, Austin, TX, 2012. For Capital Campaign for the Vision 20/20 Building Fund.
$25,000 to Sustainable Food Center, Austin, TX, 2012. For Capital Campaign for the Sustainable Food Center training.
$20,000 to Texas A & M University, College Station, TX, 2012. For Capital Campaign for Renovation of Memorial Student Center.
$15,000 to Autism Community Network, San Antonio, TX, 2012. For Expansion of services and technology network support.
$15,000 to Hill Country Conservancy, Austin, TX, 2012. For USDA Farm and Ranchland Protection Program.
$10,000 to American Cancer Society, San Antonio, TX, 2012. For Cancer patient transportation Program.
$10,000 to Manos de Cristo, Austin, TX, 2012. For affordable dental health services.

9171
Shivers Cancer Foundation ✧

P.O. Box 98
Austin, TX 78767-0098

Donor: The Davis Charitable Trust.
Foundation type: Independent foundation.
Financial data (yr. ended 12/31/13): Assets, $12,049,779 (M); gifts received, $12,261; expenditures, $623,564; qualifying distributions, $519,863; giving activities include $512,184 for 7 grants (high: $155,000; low: $15,000).
Fields of interest: Health care, blood supply; Medical research, institute; Cancer research; Foundations (private grantmaking); Foundations (community).
Limitations: Applications not accepted. Giving primarily in Austin, TX. No grants to individuals.
Application information: Contributes only to pre-selected organizations.
Officers: Clarke Heidrick, Chair.; Arthur Dilly, Vice-Chair.; Britt Steffensen, Secy.
Directors: Mary Lou Adams, R.N., Ph.D.; Robert E. Askew, M.D.; Robert E. Askew, Jr.; Charles E. Lemaistre, M.D.; Lew Little; Barbara Jean Olsen.
EIN: 741715889
Selected grants: The following grants are a representative sample of this grantmaker's funding activity:
$150,000 to Planned Parenthood of the Texas Capital Region, Austin, TX, 2011.
$125,000 to Lance Armstrong Foundation, Austin, TX, 2011.
$100,000 to Daughters of Charity Health Services of Austin, Austin, TX, 2011.

9172
The Sidhu-Singh Family Foundation ✧

5001 Spring Valley Rd., Apt. 600W
Dallas, TX 75244

Established in 1999 in TX.
Donors: Sanjiv Sidhu; Lekha Singh.
Foundation type: Independent foundation.
Financial data (yr. ended 12/31/12): Assets, $3,784,516 (M); gifts received, $3,000,000; expenditures, $987,000; qualifying distributions, $984,400; giving activities include $984,400 for grants.
Fields of interest: Arts; Human services; Women, centers/services.
Limitations: Applications not accepted. Giving primarily in Washington, DC, and NY. No grants to individuals.
Application information: Contributes only to pre-selected organizations.
Directors: Michael Held; Sanjiv Sidhu; Lekha Singh.
EIN: 752849866

9173
The Virginia and L. E. Simmons Family Foundation ✧

6600 JPMorgan Chase Twr.
Houston, TX 77002-3007

Established in 1994 in TX.
Donors: L.E. Simmons; Virginia W. Simmons; Elizabeth E. Simmons†.
Foundation type: Independent foundation.
Financial data (yr. ended 12/31/13): Assets, $15,681,959 (M); gifts received, $1,061,142; expenditures, $1,282,047; qualifying distributions, $1,255,036; giving activities include $1,252,109 for 39 grants (high: $627,434; low: $100).
Purpose and activities: Giving primarily for health associations, and children and youth services; funding also for human services.
Fields of interest: Arts; Higher education; Environment; Hospitals (general); Health organizations, association; Cancer research; Boy scouts; Human services; Children/youth, services; Family services; Community development, women's clubs; Foundations (private grantmaking).
Limitations: Applications not accepted. Giving primarily in Houston, TX. No grants to individuals.
Application information: Contributes only to pre-selected organizations.
Officers: L.E. Simmons, Pres.; Virginia W. Simmons, V.P.; Anthony F. DeLuca, Secy.-Treas.
EIN: 760453177
Selected grants: The following grants are a representative sample of this grantmaker's funding activity:
$600,000 to Rice University, Houston, TX, 2010.
$75,000 to Texas Heart Institute, Houston, TX, 2011.
$50,000 to Rice University, Houston, TX, 2011.
$50,000 to University of Utah, Salt Lake City, UT, 2011.
$47,120 to Woodrow Wilson Center, Houston, TX, 2011.
$40,000 to Grand Teton National Park, Moose, WY, 2010.
$40,000 to Grand Teton National Park Foundation, Jackson, WY, 2011.
$32,500 to George Bush Presidential Library Foundation, College Station, TX, 2011.
$25,000 to Kinkaid School, Houston, TX, 2011.
$25,000 to United Way of Greater Houston, Houston, TX, 2011.
$20,000 to Rice University, Houston, TX, 2011.
$20,000 to Texas A & M Foundation, College Station, TX, 2011.

9174
Harold Simmons Foundation ✧
3 Lincoln Centre
5430 LBJ Fwy., Ste. 1700
Dallas, TX 75240-2697 (972) 233-1700
Contact: Lisa Simmons Epstein, Pres.
Main URL: http://www.haroldsimmonsfoundation.org/
Annette and Harold Simmons's Giving Pledge Profile: http://glasspockets.org/philanthropy-in-focus/eye-on-the-giving-pledge/profiles/simmons

Incorporated in 1988 in TX.
Donors: Contran Corp.; NL Industries, Inc.; Harold Simmons†.
Foundation type: Company-sponsored foundation.
Financial data (yr. ended 12/31/13): Assets, $81,435,144 (M); gifts received, $30,965,075; expenditures, $31,419,718; qualifying distributions, $31,398,545; giving activities include $31,398,545 for 203 grants (high: $15,000,000; low: $1,750).
Purpose and activities: The foundation supports programs designed to promote education; health care; social welfare including human rights; civic improvement; and culture and the arts.
Fields of interest: Museums (art); Performing arts, dance; Performing arts, theater; Arts; Elementary/secondary education; Higher education; Education, services; Education; Environment, natural resources; Zoos/zoological societies; Hospitals (general); Health care, clinics/centers; Health care; Disasters, preparedness/services; YM/YWCAs & YM/YWHAs; Children/youth, services; Youth, services; Women, centers/services; Homeless, human services; Human services; Civil/human rights; Community/economic development; United Ways and Federated Giving Programs; Public affairs.
Type of support: General/operating support; Continuing support; Annual campaigns; Capital campaigns; Building/renovation; Equipment; Emergency funds; Program development; Conferences/seminars; Publication; Curriculum development; Scholarship funds; Research; Employee matching gifts; In-kind gifts; Matching/challenge support.
Limitations: Applications accepted. Giving primarily in the Dallas, TX. No support for discriminatory organizations. No grants to individuals, or for endowments, or debt reduction; no loans.
Publications: Application guidelines.
Application information: Grants range from $5,000 to $20,000 for first time applicants. Collaborations with other agencies and public entities are encouraged. Proposals should be printed double-sided. Support is limited to 1 contribution per organization during any given year. Application form not required.
Initial approach: Proposal
Copies of proposal: 1
Deadline(s): None
Board meeting date(s): As needed
Final notification: 3 months
Officers and Directors:* Lisa K. Simmons,* Pres.; Serena Simmons Connelly, Exec. V.P. and Dir. of Philanthropy; A. Andrew R. Louis, V.P., Secy., and Genl. Counsel; John A. St. Wrba, V.P. and Treas.
Number of staff: 2 full-time professional; 1 part-time professional; 1 full-time support.
EIN: 752222091
Selected grants: The following grants are a representative sample of this grantmaker's funding activity:
$5,000,000 to Parkland Foundation, Dallas, TX, 2012. For challenge grant for construction of new Women and Infants' Specialty Health Hospital.
$1,000,000 to Crystal Charity Ball, Dallas, TX, 2012. To support Jubilee Park and Community Center, Letot Girl's Residential Treatment Center, Our Lady Of Perpetual Help School, Retina Foundation of the Southwest, Voice of Hope Ministries and Wilkinson Center.
$1,000,000 to Dallas Arboretum and Botanical Society, Dallas, TX, 2012. For Children's Exploration Garden.
$500,000 to Dallas Summer Musicals, Music Hall at Fair Park, Dallas, TX, 2012. For matching grant for operating support.
$500,000 to Uplift Education, Irving, TX, 2012. To expand new Pinnacle Preparatory School and Hampton Preparatory School, both in Dallas, TX.
$25,000 to PediPlace, Lewisville, TX, 2012. To establish pediatric clinic in Northeast Dallas.
$25,000 to Real School Gardens, Fort Worth, TX, 2012. For operating support.
$20,000 to North Dallas Shared Ministries, Dallas, TX, 2012. For Clothes Closet, which provides casual, business casual and work clothing for men, women and children.
$20,000 to Reading Partners, Oakland, CA, 2012. For operating support for early intervention program in Dallas schools during school year.
$12,000 to Dallas Theater Center, Dallas, TX, 2012. For Project Discovery, outreach and educational program.

9175
The Simmons Foundation ✧
109 N. Post Oak Ln., Ste. 220
Houston, TX 77024-7750 (713) 268-8099
Contact: Linda K. May, Pres.
FAX: (713) 580-1850;
E-mail: kdavis@thesimmonsfoundation.org;
Additional e-mail: info@thesimmonsfoundation.org;
Main URL: http://www.thesimmonsfoundation.org
Facebook: https://www.facebook.com/TheSimmonsFdn
LinkedIn: http://www.linkedin.com/groups?trk=hb_side_g&gid=4709034
Twitter: https://twitter.com/TheSimmonsFdn

Established in 1993 in TX.
Donors: Gay A. Roane; Marjorie S. Gray†.
Foundation type: Independent foundation.
Financial data (yr. ended 12/31/12): Assets, $8,681,270 (M); expenditures, $3,888,786; qualifying distributions, $3,840,907; giving activities include $3,433,465 for 213 grants (high: $37,500; low: $236).
Purpose and activities: The foundation's mission is to invest in the community so lives can be improved by helping people help themselves. The foundation focuses its funding in one of 5 areas: health, education, civic/community, capacity building, and humans services. In each quarter the foundation pays particular attention to the following: advocacy, empowering vulnerable communities, prevention and intervention, and women and children.
Fields of interest: Education; Health care; Human services; Children/youth, services; Women, centers/services; Community/economic development.
Type of support: General/operating support; Continuing support; Management development/capacity building; Capital campaigns; Building/renovation; Equipment; Emergency funds; Program development; Seed money; Technical assistance; Employee-related scholarships; Matching/challenge support.
Limitations: Applications accepted. Giving primarily in Harris County and the Greater Houston, TX area; the foundation may fund in other TX cities when the purpose of the grant directly benefits and/or affects Greater Houston. No support for religious organizations for religious purposes, (though the foundation funds faith-based organizations, unless they require clients to participate in religious worship or practices as a condition of service), major arts organizations, political organizations, major medical research projects, international organizations, local, national or international organizations' annual giving or holiday campaigns, 509(a)(3) Type III supporting organizations, disease-related organizations, or adoption agencies. No grants for individual scholarships (except for The Simmons Foundation/Redstone Scholarship Program), or for galas/social fundraisers, annual giving campaigns, luncheons, medical research, seniors, substance abuse, people with disabilities, or endowments.
Publications: Application guidelines; Annual report; Grants list.
Application information: Proposals are by invitation only, upon review of Letter of Inquiry.
Initial approach: Letter of Inquiry to be submitted through online application system on foundation web site
Copies of proposal: 1
Deadline(s): See foundation web site for current deadlines
Board meeting date(s): Quarterly
Final notification: Within 10 business days for letters of inquiry
Officers and Directors:* Linda K. May,* Pres. and Exec. Dir.; Bob Henricksen,* V.P.; Amanda Cloud, Secy.; John Durie; Gay A. Roane; Betty K. Mathis; Jim T. Mills.
Number of staff: 2 full-time professional; 1 full-time support.
EIN: 760398915

9176
Sam and Sylva Simonian Foundation ✧ ☆
5423 Willow Wood Ln.
Dallas, TX 75252

Established in TX.
Donors: Sam Simonian; Sylva Simonian.
Foundation type: Independent foundation.
Financial data (yr. ended 12/31/13): Assets, $0 (M); gifts received, $3,732,328; expenditures, $3,731,433; qualifying distributions, $3,731,433; giving activities include $3,710,414 for 5 grants (high: $2,083,320; low: $10,000).
Fields of interest: Education; Human services.
Limitations: Applications not accepted. Giving primarily in Armenia, and New York, NY.
Application information: Unsolicited requests for funds not accepted.
Officers: Sam Simonian, Pres.; Sylva Simonian, Secy.
Directors: Annie Ghannoum; Boghos Kirazian; William Mina; Aida Kantzabedian Nanikian; Zapur Ohanian; Sevahn Simonian.
EIN: 452130686

9177

Simpson Charitable Trust ✧

P.O. Box 100
Avinger, TX 75630-0100

Established in 2000 in TX.
Donors: Phil Simpson; Lorraine Hammerich Simpson.
Foundation type: Independent foundation.
Financial data (yr. ended 12/31/13): Assets, $3,128,306 (M); expenditures, $506,612; qualifying distributions, $460,601; giving activities include $460,600 for 62 grants (high: $100,000; low: $500).
Purpose and activities: Giving primarily to support Christian ministries and Christian missionary organizations.
Fields of interest: Theological school/education; Human services; Children/youth, services; Christian agencies & churches.
Limitations: Applications not accepted. Giving primarily in TX. No grants to individuals.
Application information: Contributes only to pre-selected organizations.
Officer and Trustees:* Marimon Nettleton,* Admin.; David Philip Simpson; Lorraine Hammerich Simpson; Michael W. Dirks; Phil Simpson.
EIN: 756583001
Selected grants: The following grants are a representative sample of this grantmaker's funding activity:
$100,000 to Dallas Theological Seminary, Dallas, TX, 2012. To support Christian Ministry Education.
$36,000 to Child Evangelism Fellowship, Warrenton, MO, 2012. To support Christian Missions.
$15,000 to LeTourneau University, Longview, TX, 2012. For Center for Faith and Work.
$10,000 to Crown Financial Ministries, Gainesville, GA, 2012. For Financial Christian Ministry Support.
$5,000 to West Dallas Initiative, Dallas, TX, 2012. For Inner-City Christian Education.
$4,000 to Focus on the Family, Colorado Springs, CO, 2012. For family ministry support.
$3,000 to Joni and Friends, Dallas, TX, 2012. For Christian Ministry for Disabled Support.
$2,000 to Insight for Living, Anaheim, CA, 2012. For Christian Radio Ministry Support.
$2,000 to Trans World Radio, Cary, NC, 2012. For Worldwide Christian Radio Support.
$2,000 to Voice of the Martyrs, Bartlesville, OK, 2012. For Overseas Christian Ministry Support.

9178

The Six Four Foundation ✧

(formerly The Sixty Four Foundation)
2850 Lake Vista Dr., Ste. 150
Lewisville, TX 75067-4297

Established in 2002 in DE.
Donor: Crum & Forster Holdings Corporation.
Foundation type: Independent foundation.
Financial data (yr. ended 12/31/13): Assets, $4,360,943 (M); expenditures, $4,457,031; qualifying distributions, $4,381,200; giving activities include $4,381,200 for 36 grants (high: $2,000,000; low: $200).
Fields of interest: Arts; Education; Health care; Human services.
Type of support: General/operating support; Scholarship funds; Research.
Limitations: Applications not accepted. Giving primarily in CA and NY and in Toronto, Canada. No grants to individuals.
Application information: Contributes only to pre-selected organizations.
Officers and Directors:* V. Prem Watsa,* Pres.; Ronald Schokking, V.P. and Treas.; Anthony F. Griffiths; Eric P. Salsberg.
EIN: 980364976
Selected grants: The following grants are a representative sample of this grantmaker's funding activity:
$2,000,000 to SickKids Foundation, Toronto, Canada, 2012. For program support.
$1,000,000 to Dakshana Foundation, Irvine, CA, 2012. For program support.
$600,000 to University of Western Ontario Foundation, Jericho, NY, 2012. For program support.
$475,900 to Horatio Alger Association of Distinguished Americans, Alexandria, VA, 2012. For program support.
$200,000 to University of Waterloo, Waterloo, Canada, 2012. For program support.
$75,000 to Brigham Young University, Provo, UT, 2012. For program support.
$61,500 to University of Hawaii Foundation, Honolulu, HI, 2012. For program support.
$60,000 to Saint Johns University, School of Risk Management, New York, NY, 2012. For program support.
$50,000 to Arkansas Childrens Hospital Foundation, Little Rock, AR, 2012. For program support.
$25,000 to Halter, Inc, Katy, TX, 2012. For program support.

9179

Clara Blackford Smith & W. Aubrey Smith Charitable Foundation ✧

c/o US Trust, Philanthropic Solutions
901 Main St., 19th Fl., TX1-492-19-11
Dallas, TX 75202-3714
Contact: David T. Ross, Sr. V.P.
E-mail: tx.philanthropic@ustrust.com; Main URL: http://www.bankofamerica.com/grantmaking

Established in 1985 in TX.
Donor: Clara Blackford Smith†.
Foundation type: Independent foundation.
Financial data (yr. ended 06/30/13): Assets, $15,848,598 (M); expenditures, $1,052,332; qualifying distributions, $977,982; giving activities include $865,425 for 78 grants (high: $157,925; low: $500).
Purpose and activities: The foundation was established to support and promote quality education, health care, and human services programming for underserved populations. Special consideration is given to charitable organizations that serve the people of Grayson County, TX.
Fields of interest: Elementary school/education; Higher education; Health care; Youth development; Human services; Children/youth, services; Community/economic development; Economically disadvantaged.
Type of support: Capital campaigns; Building/renovation; Equipment; Program development.
Limitations: Giving primarily in Grayson County, TX, and its surrounding areas.
Publications: Application guidelines.
Application information: Application form required.
Initial approach: See foundation web site
Copies of proposal: 6
Deadline(s): Mar. 1, June 1, Sept. 1 and Dec. 1
Board meeting date(s): Quarterly
Final notification: June 30, Sept. 30, Dec. 31 and Mar. 31
Directors: Ronnie Cole; Jerry Culpepper; Wayne E. Delaney, M.D.; Jack B. Lilley.
Trustee: Bank of America, N.A.
EIN: 756314114
Selected grants: The following grants are a representative sample of this grantmaker's funding activity:
$60,000 to University of Texas Health Science Center, M.D. Anderson Cancer Center, Houston, TX, 2011. For stipends for five Social Services Students, with the remainder to pay the services of a Pediatric Social Service Counselor.
$55,000 to Denison Independent School District, Denison, TX, 2011. For Smart Boards for DISD classrooms.
$50,000 to Grayson County Shelter, Denison, TX, 2011. For shelter operations.
$36,000 to Loy Park Improvement Association, Denison, TX, 2011. To install ceiling fans in the Mayor Arena at Loy Park.
$32,000 to Denison Independent School District, Denison, TX, 2011. To assist economically disadvantaged 5th grade students attending Camp Goddard, a science and environmental camp in the Arbuckle Wilderness.
$25,000 to Denison Community Foundation, Denison, TX, 2011. For Crusin' Texoma benefit supporting mentally and physically handicapped children in Grayson.
$20,500 to New Beginning Fellowship Church, Denison, TX, 2011. For the Care Ministry to purchase food and food storage equipment for low income citizens of Denison.
$4,000 to Denison Independent School District, Denison, TX, 2011. For emergency support for fire victim. Board directed distribution.
$4,000 to Little League Baseball, Denison, TX, 2011. To assist low-income little league players who cannot afford the registration fee.
$2,500 to Southwestern Oklahoma State University, Weatherford, OK, 2011. For scholarship. Board directed distribution.

9180

The Mary Alice Smith Charitable Foundation ✧

c/o Harrison Interests Ltd.
712 Main St., Ste. 1900
Houston, TX 77002-3220 (713) 632-1300
Contact: Brenda Straube

Established in 2003 in TX.
Foundation type: Independent foundation.
Financial data (yr. ended 05/31/13): Assets, $15,275,003 (M); expenditures, $752,148; qualifying distributions, $710,000; giving activities include $710,000 for 8 grants (high: $455,000; low: $10,000).
Fields of interest: Historic preservation/historical societies; Health care; Alzheimer's disease; Aging, centers/services.
Limitations: Giving primarily in TX.
Application information: Application form not required.
Initial approach: Letter
Deadline(s): None
Director and Trustee:* Dan J. Harrison III*.
EIN: 200532337

Selected grants: The following grants are a representative sample of this grantmaker's funding activity:
$50,000 to Caesar Kleberg Wildlife Research Institute, Kingsville, TX, 2013. For charitable contribution to qualified organization.
$25,000 to Forge for Families, Houston, TX, 2013. For charitable contribution to qualified organization.

9181
Linda and Mark Smith Family Foundation ✧
5949 Sherry Ln., Ste. 800
Dallas, TX 75225-5815

Established in 2006 in TX.
Donor: Linda J. Smith.
Foundation type: Independent foundation.
Financial data (yr. ended 12/31/12): Assets, $798,916 (M); gifts received, $3,006,397; expenditures, $2,962,083; qualifying distributions, $2,943,000; giving activities include $2,943,000 for 8 grants (high: $1,500,000; low: $5,000).
Fields of interest: Higher education; Community/economic development.
Limitations: Applications not accepted. Giving primarily in Huntsville, AL, and Nashville, TN. No grants to individuals.
Application information: Contributes only to pre-selected organizations.
Officers: Linda J. Smith, Pres.; Cynthia S. McKernan, V.P.; Mark Clay Smith, Treas.
EIN: 203919012
Selected grants: The following grants are a representative sample of this grantmaker's funding activity:
$1,500,000 to Georgia Tech Foundation, Atlanta, GA, 2012. For Endowed Chair in School of Electrical and Computer Engineering.
$10,000 to Telluride Mountain School, Telluride, CO, 2012. For Movie Night Fundraiser.

9182
The Smith Family Foundation ✧
c/o Thomas & Evonne Smith
5227 Tortuga Trail
Austin, TX 78731-4501

Donors: Evonne E. Smith; Tom Smith.
Foundation type: Independent foundation.
Financial data (yr. ended 12/31/13): Assets, $2,790,453 (M); expenditures, $656,055; qualifying distributions, $642,530; giving activities include $640,000 for 5 grants (high: $600,000; low: $10,000).
Fields of interest: Arts; Education.
Limitations: Applications not accepted. Giving primarily in IA; some giving also in OK and SD.
Application information: Unsolicited requests for funds not accepted.
Officers and Directors:* Thomas A. Smith,* Pres.; Kyle T. Smith,* V.P.; Evonne E. Smith,* Secy.-Treas.
EIN: 331211325

9183
Bob and Vivian Smith Foundation ✧
1900 W. Loop S., Ste. 1050
Houston, TX 77027-3207 (713) 986-8030
Contact: Amy M. Meckel, Secy.-Treas.

Established about 1969.
Donors: R.E. Smith†; Vivian L. Smith†.
Foundation type: Independent foundation.
Financial data (yr. ended 12/31/12): Assets, $0 (M); expenditures, $591,641; qualifying distributions, $498,422; giving activities include $487,036 for 41 grants (high: $73,876; low: $1,000).
Purpose and activities: Giving primarily for health and medical research, as well as for education.
Fields of interest: Education; Hospitals (general); Hospitals (specialty); Medical research, institute.
Type of support: General/operating support; Continuing support; Annual campaigns; Capital campaigns.
Limitations: Applications accepted. Giving primarily in Houston and Harris County, TX. No grants to individuals; no program-related investments.
Publications: Application guidelines.
Application information: Application form not required.
Initial approach: Proposal
Copies of proposal: 1
Deadline(s): Oct. 25
Officers and Trustees:* Suzanne R. Benson,* Pres.; H. Devon Graham, Jr.,* V.P.; Amy M. Meckel,* Secy.-Treas.; Sandra Smith Dompier; Courtney Cohn Hopson.
EIN: 237029052

9184
Dr. Bob and Jean Smith Foundation ✧
(formerly Bob Smith, M.D. Foundation)
3811 Turtle Creek Blvd., Ste. 200
Dallas, TX 75219-4402 (214) 521-3461
Contact: Sally S. Mashburn, Pres.

Established in 1989 in TX.
Foundation type: Independent foundation.
Financial data (yr. ended 09/30/13): Assets, $23,573,964 (M); expenditures, $1,670,703; qualifying distributions, $1,119,619; giving activities include $1,030,518 for 17 grants (high: $510,000; low: $1,000).
Purpose and activities: Giving for higher education, medical education and research, health, community enrichment, and arts and culture.
Fields of interest: Arts; Education; Health care; Community/economic development.
Type of support: General/operating support; Continuing support; Annual campaigns; Capital campaigns; Building/renovation; Equipment; Endowments; Program development; Scholarship funds; Research; Matching/challenge support.
Limitations: Applications accepted. Giving primarily in the Dallas, TX, area. No support for political organizations. No grants to individuals.
Publications: Application guidelines.
Application information: Application form required.
Initial approach: Letter
Copies of proposal: 1
Deadline(s): None
Final notification: Via letter
Officers and Directors:* Jean K. Smith,* Chair.; Sally Smith Mashburn, Pres.; Marty S. Kelley; Scott R. Smith; Suzanne S. Welfelt; Robert H. West; Bill R. Womble.
Number of staff: 2 full-time professional; 1 full-time support.
EIN: 510137245
Selected grants: The following grants are a representative sample of this grantmaker's funding activity:
$300,000 to Parkland Foundation, Dallas, TX, 2011. For unrestricted grant.
$300,000 to Texas Health Presbyterian Foundation, Dallas, TX, 2011. For unrestricted grant.
$150,000 to AT&T Performing Arts Center, Dallas, TX, 2011. For unrestricted grant.
$55,000 to Christ the King Catholic Church, Dallas, TX, 2011. For unrestricted grant.
$25,000 to Crystal Charity Ball, Dallas, TX, 2011. For unrestricted grant.
$10,000 to Big Thought, Dallas, TX, 2011. For unrestricted grant.
$10,000 to Prevent Blindness Texas, Dallas, TX, 2011. For unrestricted grant.
$10,000 to United Way of Metropolitan Dallas, Dallas, TX, 2011. For unrestricted grant.

9185
The Smith Foundation ✧
(formerly The Lester and Sue Smith Foundation)
c/o Sharin A. Scott, Secy.
1001 Fannin St., Ste. 3850
Houston, TX 77002-6706

Established in 2002 in TX.
Donor: Lester H. Smith.
Foundation type: Independent foundation.
Financial data (yr. ended 12/31/12): Assets, $4,830,157 (M); gifts received, $11,259,425; expenditures, $7,559,999; qualifying distributions, $7,453,995; giving activities include $7,149,847 for 75 grants (high: $1,500,000; low: $98).
Purpose and activities: Giving primarily for education and medical research; funding also for the arts, social services, and Jewish temples.
Fields of interest: Museums; Arts; Higher education; Education; Hospitals (specialty); Health organizations, association; Medical research, institute; Cancer research; Breast cancer research; Human services; Jewish agencies & synagogues.
Limitations: Applications not accepted. Giving primarily in Houston, TX. No grants to individuals.
Application information: Contributes only to pre-selected organizations.
Board meeting date(s): Annually in May
Officers and Trustees:* Lester H. Smith,* Pres.; Trish Morille, Exec. V.P.; Sue A. Smith,* V.P.; Karla Neal, Secy.; Jill McDonald,* Treas.; M.S. Hendry; S.M. Smith.
EIN: 270040023

9186
Vivian L. Smith Foundation ✧
1900 W. Loop S., Ste. 1050
Houston, TX 77027-3207
Contact: Amy Meckel

Established in 1981 in TX.
Donor: Vivian L. Smith†.
Foundation type: Independent foundation.
Financial data (yr. ended 12/31/12): Assets, $80,790,296 (M); expenditures, $4,519,903; qualifying distributions, $3,971,247; giving activities include $3,918,000 for 111 grants (high: $200,000; low: $1,000).
Purpose and activities: Giving primarily for arts and cultural programs, education, medical research, and religious agencies and churches.
Fields of interest: Arts; Education; Medical research; Christian agencies & churches.

Type of support: General/operating support; Continuing support; Annual campaigns; Capital campaigns; Building/renovation; Equipment; Research.
Limitations: Applications accepted. Giving primarily to Harris County and Houston, TX. No grants to individuals.
Publications: Application guidelines; Annual report.
Application information: Application form not required.
Initial approach: Proposal
Copies of proposal: 1
Deadline(s): Feb. 15, May 15, Aug. 15, and Oct. 25
Board meeting date(s): Approximately Apr. 15, July 15, Oct. 15, and Nov. 15
Final notification: 3 weeks after meeting
Officers and Trustees:* Suzanne R. Benson,* Pres.; H. Devon Graham, Jr., V.P.; Cynthia Adkins; Sandra Smith Dompier; James A. Elkins III; Ransom Lummis; Kirby Cohn McCool; Amy M. Meckel; Richard H. Skinner.
Number of staff: None.
EIN: 760101380

9187
The William A. and Madeline Welder Smith Foundation ✧
1300 Post Oak Blvd.. Ste. 2000
Houston, TX 77056-8000

Established in 1992 in TX.
Donors: William A. Smith†; Ernestine Hooper Testamentary Trust.
Foundation type: Independent foundation.
Financial data (yr. ended 06/30/13): Assets, $18,256,596 (M); expenditures, $962,860; qualifying distributions, $774,050; giving activities include $774,050 for grants.
Purpose and activities: Giving primarily for higher and other education, medical research, including a cancer center, youth and social services, the arts, and federated giving programs.
Fields of interest: Performing arts; Arts; Education, early childhood education; Higher education; Libraries/library science; Education; Medical research, institute; Cancer research; Eye research; Human services; Youth, services; United Ways and Federated Giving Programs.
Type of support: General/operating support; Capital campaigns; Scholarship funds.
Limitations: Applications not accepted. Giving primarily in TX, with emphasis on Houston.
Application information: Contributes only to pre-selected organizations.
Trustees: Joe E. Coleman; Dee S. Osborne; Joseph W. Royce; Anne McCullough Shallenberger; H. Michael Tyson.
EIN: 766076267
Selected grants: The following grants are a representative sample of this grantmaker's funding activity:
$60,000 to Baylor University, Waco, TX, 2013. For Freestone County Scholarship.
$50,000 to University of Texas, Austin, TX, 2013. For Briscoe Center for American History.
$25,000 to American Cancer Society, Houston, TX, 2013. For Hope Lodge Houston.
$20,000 to Baylor College of Medicine, Houston, TX, 2013. For honoring.
$20,000 to Baylor University, Waco, TX, 2013. For Royce Scholarship.
$20,000 to Phi Delta Theta Educational Foundation, Oxford, OH, 2013. For FBO Students at Southwestern University.
$20,000 to Southwestern University, Georgetown, TX, 2013. For baseball program.
$12,000 to University of Texas System, Austin, TX, 2013. For Ashbel Smith Circle.
$10,000 to Baylor College of Medicine, Houston, TX, 2013. For Comprehensive Healthcare Clinic.
$10,000 to University of Texas, Austin, TX, 2013. For Dobie Paisano Fellowship Project.

9188
Nancy and John Snyder Foundation ✧
(formerly Nancy and John Foundation)
c/o Linda Gosdin
201 Main St.
Fort Worth, TX 76102-3108

Established in 1980.
Donor: John C. Snyder.
Foundation type: Independent foundation.
Financial data (yr. ended 12/31/12): Assets, $7,976,001 (M); expenditures, $604,559; qualifying distributions, $519,841; giving activities include $497,448 for 58 grants (high: $420,000; low: $100).
Purpose and activities: Giving primarily for community funds and Christian religious organizations.
Fields of interest: Human services; United Ways and Federated Giving Programs; Christian agencies & churches.
Type of support: General/operating support.
Limitations: Applications not accepted. Giving primarily in Fort Worth, TX.
Application information: Contributes primarily to pre-selected organizations.
Officers and Directors: John C. Snyder,* Pres.; Marcus M. Snyder,* V.P.; Linda Gosdin, Secy.-Treas.; Beverly B. Snyder; Dudley R. Snyder; Todd Snyder; Thomas L. Wilson.
EIN: 751737014

9189
The Sooch Foundation ✧
c/o Navdeep Sooch
600 W. 7th St.
Austin, TX 78701-2710 (512) 472-5755
FAX: (512) 472-5748; E-mail: cnewman@sooch.net; Main URL: http://www.soochfoundation.org

Established in 2003 in TX.
Donors: Janet Harman; Navdeep S. Sooch; Isabel Welland.
Foundation type: Independent foundation.
Financial data (yr. ended 12/31/12): Assets, $14,048,169 (M); gifts received, $10,000; expenditures, $875,555; qualifying distributions, $812,449; giving activities include $676,500 for 17 grants (high: $150,000; low: $1,000).
Purpose and activities: The foundation seeks to make a positive and permanent change in the lives of economically disadvantaged people in Austin, Texas. The foundation now focuses on programs that help adults and their families earn self-sustaining wages that were not previously on track to do so, as well as on programs that increase graduation rates from college and other post-secondary institutions for students from economically disadvantaged backgrounds.
Fields of interest: Education; Human services; Economically disadvantaged.
Limitations: Applications not accepted. Giving primarily in the Austin, TX area. No support for for-profit organizations, or for on-going fund drives or organizations not classified as public charities by the IRS. No grants to individuals, or for endowments, capital campaigns, gala, dinner or raffle tickets, operating expenses or deficits.
Publications: Annual report.
Application information: Unsolicited requests for funds not accepted.
Board meeting date(s): Quarterly
Officers and Trustees:* Navdeep S. Sooch, Pres. and Treas.; David R. Welland, V.P.; Isabel Welland,* Secy.; Mary Ellen Pietruszynski, Exec. Dir.; John McGovern.
Number of staff: 2 full-time professional; 1 part-time professional.
EIN: 200399480
Selected grants: The following grants are a representative sample of this grantmaker's funding activity:
$25,000 to Goodwill Industries of Central Texas, Austin, TX, 2012. For organization's purpose.

9190
Soref-Breslauer Texas Foundation ✧
7602 Coachwood Dr.
Houston, TX 77071-2303

Established in 2005 in TX.
Donor: Samuel and Helene Soref Foundation.
Foundation type: Independent foundation.
Financial data (yr. ended 12/31/13): Assets, $8,371,082 (M); expenditures, $662,029; qualifying distributions, $622,023; giving activities include $592,500 for 21 grants (high: $155,000; low: $5,000).
Purpose and activities: Giving primarily to Reform Jewish organizations.
Fields of interest: Health organizations, association; Jewish federated giving programs; Jewish agencies & synagogues.
Limitations: Applications not accepted. Giving primarily in Houston, TX, and New York, NY.
Application information: Contributes only to pre-selected organizations.
Officers: Stephen Breslauer, Pres. and Secy.; Kathy Breslauer, V.P.; David Breslauer, Treas.
EIN: 202226858
Selected grants: The following grants are a representative sample of this grantmaker's funding activity:
$160,000 to Jewish Federation of Greater Houston, Houston, TX, 2011.
$100,000 to World Union for Progressive Judaism, New York, NY, 2011.
$65,000 to Washington Institute for Near East Policy, Washington, DC, 2011.
$25,000 to Henry S. Jacobs Camp for Living Judaism, Utica, MS, 2011.
$25,000 to Men of Reform Judaism, New York, NY, 2011.
$7,500 to Muscular Dystrophy Association, Tucson, AZ, 2011.
$5,000 to Investigative Project on Terrorism Foundation, Washington, DC, 2011.
$5,000 to Jewish Family Service, Houston, TX, 2011.
$5,000 to Jewish Institute for National Security Affairs, Washington, DC, 2011.

9191
South Texas Outreach Foundation ✧
(formerly Auxiliaries to the Devotion of the Holy Infant of Good Health)
P.O. Box 818
Laredo, TX 78042-0818

Supporting organization of Instituto Cultural En Pro De La Ninez.
Donor: Joseph O. Neuhoff Charitable Trust.
Foundation type: Independent foundation.
Financial data (yr. ended 12/31/12): Assets, $39,046,404 (M); expenditures, $2,099,497; qualifying distributions, $1,953,657; giving activities include $1,895,400 for 33 grants (high: $630,000; low: $10,000).
Purpose and activities: Giving primarily to an organization for the assistance of underprivileged girls and destitute women; funding also for human services.
Fields of interest: Education; Women; Girls; Economically disadvantaged.
Limitations: Applications not accepted. Giving primarily in TX and Mexico. No grants to individuals.
Application information: Contributes only to pre-selected organizations.
Officers and Directors:* William J. Dickinson,* Pres.; Bertha G. Dickinson,* Secy.-Treas.; William J. Dickinson, Jr., C.P.A.; Paula B. Orr; Paul Phillips.
EIN: 746106704

9192
James and Elizabeth Sowell Foundation ✧
(formerly James E. Sowell Foundation)
1601 Elm St., Ste. 300
Dallas, TX 75201-7277

Established in 1997 in TX.
Donors: James E. Sowell; Elizabeth Sowell.
Foundation type: Independent foundation.
Financial data (yr. ended 12/31/13): Assets, $8,542,188 (M); expenditures, $677,376; qualifying distributions, $505,561; giving activities include $504,561 for 2 grants (high: $503,504; low: $1,057).
Fields of interest: Hospitals (general); Human services; Christian agencies & churches.
Limitations: Applications not accepted. Giving primarily in Dallas, TX. No grants to individuals.
Application information: Unsolicited requests for funds not accepted.
Officers: James E. Sowell, Pres.; Keith Martin, Secy.-Treas.
Directors: Larry James; Elizabeth Sowell.
EIN: 752641436

9193
Spangenberg Family Foundation to Benefit Childrens Education and Healthcare ✧ ☆
2515 McKinney Ave., Ste. 1000
Dallas, TX 75201

Donors: Bright Responce LLC; Clear with computers LLC; Manufacturing systems Technologies; Presentation specialists technologies; SFA Systems LLC; Audrey Spangenberg; Tech Dev.
Foundation type: Independent foundation.
Financial data (yr. ended 12/31/13): Assets, $2,377,324 (M); gifts received, $2,398,276; expenditures, $1,521,600; qualifying distributions, $1,511,571; giving activities include $1,511,571 for 14 grants (high: $1,000,000; low: $100).
Fields of interest: Education; Health care; Children.
Limitations: Applications not accepted. Giving primarily in New York, NY, OH, PA, TX and VA.
Application information: Unsolicited requests for funds not accepted.
Officer: Audrey Spangenberg, Pres.
EIN: 262931718

9194
The Sparrow Charitable Foundation ✧
211 N. Record St., Ste. 222
Dallas, TX 75202-3347

Established in 2003 in TX.
Donors: Marydel Harris; Raymond Harris.
Foundation type: Independent foundation.
Financial data (yr. ended 12/31/13): Assets, $8,392 (M); gifts received, $1,600,000; expenditures, $1,617,773; qualifying distributions, $1,617,032; giving activities include $1,616,300 for 38 grants (high: $500,000; low: $500).
Fields of interest: Health organizations, association; Human services; Christian agencies & churches; Protestant agencies & churches.
Limitations: Applications not accepted. Giving primarily in TX. No grants to individuals.
Application information: Contributes only to pre-selected organizations.
Directors: Elizabeth A. Harris; Marydel Harris; Raymond Harris; Stephen R. Harris.
EIN: 200488561

9195
Spec's Charitable Foundation ✧
(formerly Carroll & Carolynn Jackson Charitable Foundation)
2410 Smith St.
Houston, TX 77006-2316

Established in 1995 in TX.
Donors: Carolynn F. Jackson; Spec's Family Partners, Ltd.; Gabriel Holdings, Ltd.
Foundation type: Independent foundation.
Financial data (yr. ended 12/31/12): Assets, $2,078,555 (M); gifts received, $358,896; expenditures, $1,059,599; qualifying distributions, $880,000; giving activities include $880,000 for grants.
Fields of interest: Performing arts, orchestras; Higher education; Catholic agencies & churches.
Limitations: Applications not accepted. Giving primarily in TX, with emphasis on Houston. No grants to individuals.
Application information: Unsolicited requests for funds not accepted.
Officers: Karen Lynn Rydman, Pres.; Robert J. Heisler, V.P.; John A. Rydman, V.P.; Lisa R. Key, Secy.-Treas.
EIN: 760488033

9196
SS Foundation ✧ ☆
(formerly The Scheef Family Foundation)
7103 82nd St.
Lubbock, TX 79424-4703

Donors: Samuel R. Scheef; Marisa L. Scheef.
Foundation type: Independent foundation.
Financial data (yr. ended 09/30/13): Assets, $3,277,916 (M); expenditures, $527,676; qualifying distributions, $508,000; giving activities include $508,000 for 3 grants (high: $500,000; low: $2,000).
Fields of interest: Education; Human services.
Limitations: Applications not accepted. Giving primarily in Lubbock, TX; some giving also in Orlando, FL.
Application information: Contributes only to pre-selected organizations.
Officers: Samuel R. Scheef, Pres.; Carroll Leon, V.P.; David Scheef, Secy.
EIN: 263022597
Selected grants: The following grants are a representative sample of this grantmaker's funding activity:
$500,000 to High Point Village, Lubbock, TX, 2013. For building fund.
$6,000 to Womens Protective Services of Lubbock, Lubbock, TX, 2013. For general support.
$2,000 to Texas Tech University, Burkhart Center for Autism, Lubbock, TX, 2013. For general support.

9197
Star Foundation ✧
100 Waugh Dr., Ste. 400
Houston, TX 77007-5962

Established in TX.
Donor: Russell D. Gordy.
Foundation type: Independent foundation.
Financial data (yr. ended 12/31/13): Assets, $3,196,978 (M); expenditures, $1,015,553; qualifying distributions, $1,000,150; giving activities include $1,000,000 for 1 grant.
Purpose and activities: Giving primarily to a children's cancer center.
Fields of interest: Medical school/education; Children/youth, services.
Limitations: Applications not accepted. Giving primarily in Houston, TX. No grants to individuals.
Application information: Contributes only to pre-selected organizations.
Officers: Russell D. Gordy, Pres.; Glenda J. Gordy, V.P.; Shaun C. Gordy, V.P.
EIN: 200292721

9198
Nelda C. and H. J. Lutcher Stark Foundation ✧
P.O. Drawer 909
Orange, TX 77631-0909
Contact: Grant Dept.
Address for physical delivery: 601 W. Green Ave. Orange, TX 77630-5718; Main URL: http://www.starkfoundation.org/
E-Newsletter: http://www.starkfoundation.org/sign-up/

Incorporated in 1961 in TX.
Donors: H.J. Lutcher Stark†; Nelda C. Stark†.
Foundation type: Operating foundation.
Financial data (yr. ended 12/31/12): Assets, $564,419,643 (M); gifts received, $32,477; expenditures, $21,014,634; qualifying distributions, $17,020,580; giving activities include $2,851,945 for 16 grants (high: $1,905,000; low: $5,000), $49,500 for 21 grants to individuals (high: $6,500; low: $1,500), and $12,798,239 for foundation-administered programs.

Limitations: Applications not accepted. No grants to individuals (except local contest award winners), or for endowment funds or operating budgets.
Publications: Annual report.
Application information: Unsolicited requests for funds not accepted. The foundation makes infrequent grants, and they are at the sole discretion of the Board of Directors.
Board meeting date(s): Quarterly
Officers and Directors:* Deborah L. Hughes,* Chair.; R. Frederick Gregory, M.D.*, Vice-Chair.; Walter G. Riedel III,* C.E.O. and Pres.; Clyde V. McKee III,* V.P., C.F.O, and Treas.; Elizabeth C. Turley, V.P., C.C.O. and Gen. Counsel; James R. Dunaway,* Secy.; Roy S. Wingate,* Dir. Emeritus; Laurence R. David; John Cash Smith; Ruby J. Wimberley.
Number of staff: 13 full-time professional; 3 part-time professional; 45 full-time support; 37 part-time support.
EIN: 746047440

9199
Dorothy Richard Starling Foundation ✧
P.O. Box 66709
Houston, TX 77266-6709
Contact: Dunham F. Jewett, Tr.

Foundation established in 1969 in TX.
Donor: Frank M. Starling†.
Foundation type: Independent foundation.
Financial data (yr. ended 12/31/12): Assets, $33,401,028 (M); expenditures, $2,341,104; qualifying distributions, $1,874,059; giving activities include $1,772,500 for 21 grants (high: $301,500; low: $25,000).
Purpose and activities: Giving limited to classical violin discipline, teaching, and scholarships made through institutions.
Fields of interest: Performing arts, music.
Type of support: General/operating support; Endowments; Professorships; Fellowships; Scholarship funds.
Limitations: Applications accepted. Giving in the U.S., with emphasis on IN, NY, OH, TX, and WA. No grants to individuals.
Publications: Annual report.
Application information: Application form required.
Initial approach: Letter
Copies of proposal: 3
Deadline(s): None
Trustees: Dunham F. Jewett; Melinda M. Kacal.
Number of staff: 1 part-time professional.
EIN: 746121656

9200
Stedman West Foundation ✧
(formerly Neva and Wesley West Foundation)
P.O. Box 7
Houston, TX 77001-0007 (713) 520-0400
Contact: Stuart W. Stedman, Tr.

Trust established in 1956 in TX.
Donors: Wesley West†; Neva Watkins West†.
Foundation type: Independent foundation.
Financial data (yr. ended 12/31/12): Assets, $27,379,370 (M); expenditures, $1,582,771; qualifying distributions, $1,294,500; giving activities include $1,294,500 for 44 grants (high: $250,000; low: $1,000).
Purpose and activities: Giving primarily for the arts, education, the environment, health care, and medical research.
Fields of interest: Museums (art); Arts; Higher education; Education; Environment; Health care; Health organizations, association; Medical research, institute; Human services.
Type of support: General/operating support; Capital campaigns; Building/renovation; Professorships; Research.
Limitations: Applications accepted. Giving primarily in TX. No grants to individuals, or for scholarships or fellowships; no loans.
Application information: Application form required.
Initial approach: Letter or proposal
Deadline(s): Nov. 30
Trustees: Randolph L. Pullin; Betty Ann West Stedman; Stuart West Stedman.
EIN: 746039393

9201
Stemmons Foundation ✧
P.O. Box 143127
Irving, TX 75014-3127 (972) 650-9162
Contact: Mary Lee J. Virden, Secy.

Established in 1963 in TX.
Foundation type: Independent foundation.
Financial data (yr. ended 12/31/13): Assets, $30,276,654 (M); expenditures, $1,764,213; qualifying distributions, $1,480,445; giving activities include $1,480,445 for 57 grants (high: $202,500; low: $5,000).
Fields of interest: Arts; Education; Human services; Children/youth, services.
Type of support: Capital campaigns; Building/renovation; Equipment; Program development; Curriculum development; Technical assistance.
Limitations: Applications accepted. Giving primarily in Dallas, TX. No grants to individuals, or for scholarships; no loans.
Publications: Application guidelines.
Application information:
Initial approach: Letter
Copies of proposal: 1
Deadline(s): None
Board meeting date(s): May and Nov.
Officers: Allison S. Simon, Pres.; Jean H. Rose, V.P.; Heinz K. Simon, V.P.; Mary Lee J. Virden, Secy.; Kathryn Magruder, Treas.
Director: Karen J. Simon.
Number of staff: 2 full-time professional; 1 part-time support.
EIN: 756039966
Selected grants: The following grants are a representative sample of this grantmaker's funding activity:
$50,000 to Providence Christian School of Texas, Dallas, TX, 2012. For pledge (2/2).
$30,000 to Irving Symphony Orchestra, Irving, TX, 2012. For pledge (3/5).
$20,000 to SPCA of Texas, Dallas, TX, 2012. For E/O.
$10,050 to Heroes for Children, Richardson, TX, 2012. For Discretionary.
$10,000 to Trinity River Mission, Dallas, TX, 2012. For Disc.

9202
Sterling Family Foundation ✧ ☆
P.O. Box 1837
Bellaire, TX 77402-1837 (713) 659-6551
Contact: Daniel Dominguez, Tr.; Jay Epstein, Tr.

Established in 2003 in TX.
Donor: Lillie Sterling†.
Foundation type: Independent foundation.
Financial data (yr. ended 12/31/13): Assets, $7,316,362 (M); expenditures, $579,358; qualifying distributions, $421,500; giving activities include $421,500 for 20 grants (high: $195,000; low: $500).
Fields of interest: Education; Health organizations; Human services; Jewish federated giving programs; Christian agencies & churches.
Limitations: Applications accepted. Giving primarily in TX.
Application information: Application form required.
Initial approach: Letter
Deadline(s): None
Trustees: Daniel Dominguez; Jay A. Epstein.
EIN: 046995246

9203
Sterling-Turner Foundation ✧
(formerly Turner Charitable Foundation)
5850 San Felipe St., Ste. 125
Houston, TX 77057-3292 (713) 237-1117
Contact: Patricia Moser Stilley, Exec. Dir.
FAX: (713) 223-4638; Email: pstilley@stfdn.org; additional contact: Jeannie Arnold, Exec. Asst., email: Jeannie.arnold@stfdn.org; Main URL: http://sterlingturnerfoundation.org

Incorporated in 1960 in TX.
Donors: Isla Carroll Turner†; P.E. Turner†.
Foundation type: Independent foundation.
Financial data (yr. ended 12/31/12): Assets, $59,245,389 (M); expenditures, $2,948,250; qualifying distributions, $2,859,813; giving activities include $2,709,500 for 55 grants (high: $500,000; low: $2,000).
Purpose and activities: Giving for higher and secondary education, social services, youth, the elderly, fine and performing arts groups and other cultural programs, Catholic, Jewish, and Protestant church support and religious programs, hospitals, health services, AIDS research, hospices, programs for women and children, minorities, the homeless, the handicapped, urban and community development, civic and urban affairs, libraries, and conservation programs.
Fields of interest: Visual arts; Museums; Performing arts; Performing arts, theater; Historic preservation/historical societies; Arts; Education, association; Education, research; Education, fund raising/fund distribution; Elementary/secondary education; Child development, education; Secondary school/education; Higher education; Adult education—literacy, basic skills & GED; Libraries/library science; Education, reading; Education; Environment, natural resources; Hospitals (general); Medical care, rehabilitation; Health care; Substance abuse, services; Mental health/crisis services; Cancer; Heart & circulatory diseases; AIDS; Cancer research; Heart & circulatory research; AIDS research; Crime/violence prevention, domestic violence; Food services; Recreation; YM/YWCAs & YM/YWHAs; Children/youth, services; Child development, services; Family services; Residential/custodial care, hospices; Minorities/

immigrants, centers/services; Homeless, human services; Community development, business promotion; Community/economic development; Protestant agencies & churches; Catholic agencies & churches; Jewish agencies & synagogues; Religion; Children; Youth; Aging; Minorities; African Americans/Blacks; Hispanics/Latinos; Women; AIDS, people with; Homeless.
Type of support: General/operating support; Annual campaigns; Capital campaigns; Building/ renovation; Equipment; Land acquisition; Endowments; Debt reduction; Emergency funds; Program development; Conferences/seminars; Professorships; Publication; Seed money; Curriculum development; Fellowships; Scholarship funds; Research; Matching/challenge support.
Limitations: Applications accepted. Giving limited to Travis, Harris, Kerr, Fort Bend, and Tom Greene counties, TX. No grants to individuals.
Publications: Application guidelines; Financial statement.
Application information: Select application form on foundation web site depending on geographic county. In addition to emailing the application form, mail necessary documents to foundation. Application form and complete list of necessary documents available on foundation web site. Application form required.
Initial approach: On-line application
Copies of proposal: 1
Deadline(s): Mar. 1 at 5:00 PM; if Mar. 1 falls on Saturday or Sunday proposals will be accepted until the following Monday by noon
Board meeting date(s): First Tues. in Apr.
Officers and Trustees:* T.R. Reckling III,* Pres.; L. David Winston,* V.P.; Christiana R. McConn,* Secy.; Isla C. Reckling,* Treas.; Patricia Moser Stilley, Exec. Dir.; Carroll R. Goodman; Chaille W. Hawkins; Isla C. Jornayvaz; James S. Reckling; John B. Reckling; Stephen M. Reckling; T.R. "Cliff" Reckling IV; Thomas K. Reckling; E. Carroll Schuler; Bert F. Winston III; Blake W. Winston.
Number of staff: 2 full-time professional.
EIN: 741460482

9204
Sidney Stern Memorial Trust ✧
c/o Wells Fargo Bank, N.A.
P.O. Box 41629
Austin, TX 78704-9926
Application address: c/o Board of Advisors, P.O. Box 893, Pacific Palisades, CA 90272, tel.: (800) 352-3705

Trust established in 1974 in CA.
Donor: S. Sidney Stern†.
Foundation type: Independent foundation.
Financial data (yr. ended 08/31/13): Assets, $28,002,601 (M); expenditures, $1,970,780; qualifying distributions, $1,817,808; giving activities include $1,571,389 for 518+ grants (high: $87,465).
Purpose and activities: Giving primarily for higher education, social service agencies, including aid to the handicapped; youth and child welfare agencies; scientific and medical organizations, including health associations; and cultural programs.
Fields of interest: Arts; Higher education; Environment; Hospitals (general); Health care; Health organizations, association; Legal services; Human services; Children/youth, services; Civil/ human rights, disabled; Civil/human rights; Disabilities, people with; Asians/Pacific Islanders; African Americans/Blacks; Hispanics/Latinos; Native Americans/American Indians; Immigrants/ refugees.
Type of support: General/operating support; Annual campaigns; Building/renovation; Equipment; Land acquisition; Endowments; Emergency funds; Program development; Scholarship funds; Research; Matching/challenge support.
Limitations: Giving primarily in CA; all funds must be used within the U.S. No grants to individuals, or for conferences or redistribution; no loans.
Publications: Application guidelines.
Application information: Application form not required.
Initial approach: Proposal
Copies of proposal: 1
Deadline(s): None
Officer: Betty S. Hoffenberg, Chair.
Board of Advisors: Ira E. Bilson; David A. Hoffenberg; Marvin Hoffenberg; Peter H. Hoffenberg; Howard O. Wilson.
EIN: 956495222
Selected grants: The following grants are a representative sample of this grantmaker's funding activity:
$20,000 to Brady Center to Prevent Gun Violence, Washington, DC, 2011. For general charitable use.
$12,500 to California Science Center Foundation, Los Angeles, CA, 2011. For general charitable use.
$10,000 to Punahou School, Honolulu, HI, 2011. For general charitable use.
$10,000 to Saint Jude Memorial Foundation, Fullerton, CA, 2011. For general charitable use.
$7,000 to Boys Republic, Chino Hills, CA, 2011. For general charitable use.
$3,000 to DesertArc, Palm Desert, CA, 2011. For general charitable use.
$2,500 to Center for the Partially Sighted, Culver City, CA, 2011. For general charitable use.
$2,500 to Childrens Scholarship Fund, New York, NY, 2011. For general charitable use.
$2,500 to Southwest Chamber Music Society, Pasadena, CA, 2011. For general charitable use.
$2,500 to Western Center on Law and Poverty, Los Angeles, CA, 2011. For general charitable use.

9205
Perry & Ruby Stevens Charitable Foundation ✧
741 Water St., Ste. 216
Kerrville, TX 78028-5331
E-mail: Stevensfdn@hctc.net; Application address: c/o Laurie Milton, Exec. Dir., P.O. Box 291929, Kerrville, TX 78029-1929; tel.: (830) 896-0630; Main URL: http://www.stevensfdn.org

Established in 2006 in TX.
Donor: Ruby Stevens.
Foundation type: Independent foundation.
Financial data (yr. ended 12/31/12): Assets, $53,788,589 (M); gifts received, $75,000; expenditures, $1,513,468; qualifying distributions, $1,328,673; giving activities include $1,328,673 for 32 grants (high: $150,000; low: $2,500).
Purpose and activities: Giving primarily to provide assistance to qualified non-profit organizations that direct their activities toward: 1) the care and treatment of mentally or physically handicapped persons; 2) the care and treatment of abused or neglected women; 3) the promotion, development and support of volunteer firefighting programs and organizations, and related matters; 4) assistance to needy persons who are victims of some public natural disaster or similar event; 5) the protection and prevention of cruelty to animals and to provide for the welfare of animals in general; 6) the prevention, research and treatment of Parkinson's disease; 7) assistance to children and young adults who are financially disadvantaged, or who have suffered physical or mental abuse, or neglect; 8) resources to elderly persons who are unable to provide financial support for themselves; and 9) assistance to individual persons afflicted with disease or illness, regardless of their age or gender.
Fields of interest: Animal welfare; Crime/violence prevention, abuse prevention; Human services; Children/youth, services; Foundations (public); Aging; Disabilities, people with; Physically disabled; Mentally disabled; Women; Economically disadvantaged.
Limitations: Applications accepted. Giving primarily in the TX hill country.
Publications: Application guidelines.
Application information: Grant proposals are by invitation, upon review of letter of inquiry. Application form required.
Initial approach: Letter of inquiry
Deadline(s): See foundation web site for current deadlines
Board meeting date(s): See foundation web site for current board meeting dates
Final notification: 2 weeks
Officer: Laurie Milton, Exec. Dir.
Trustees: Leon Jeffcoat; Phillip Milton; Allan G. Paterson.
EIN: 204169959
Selected grants: The following grants are a representative sample of this grantmaker's funding activity:
$125,000 to BCFS Health and Human Services, San Antonio, TX, 2012. For Capital Campaign - Kerrville.
$20,000 to San Antonio Family Endeavors, San Antonio, TX, 2012. For Childcare Support.
$15,000 to Bandera County Committee on Aging, Bandera, TX, 2012. For Meals on Wheels Support.
$15,000 to Wildlife Rescue and Rehabilitation, Kendalia, TX, 2012. To purchase freezer.
$10,000 to Partners in Ministry, Kerrville, TX, 2012. For KIDS Program.
$5,000 to Laity Renewal Foundation, Kerrville, TX, 2012. For operating support for OE Camp.

9206
Stevens Family Charitable Trust ✧
123 W. Mills Ave., Ste. 600
El Paso, TX 79901-1577

Established in 2009 in TX.
Donors: Jeff Allan Stevens; Sharon A. Sayre.
Foundation type: Independent foundation.
Financial data (yr. ended 12/31/12): Assets, $13,170,885 (M); expenditures, $5,763,957; qualifying distributions, $5,755,000; giving activities include $5,755,000 for 10 grants (high: $4,400,000; low: $5,000).
Fields of interest: Higher education.
Limitations: Applications not accepted. Giving primarily in AZ, TX, and WA.
Application information: Contributes only to pre-selected organizations.
Trustees: Timothy Allan Demore; Kevin Michael Reis; William Wallace Sheely; Alexandra Marie Stevens; Colin Michael Stevens; Jeff Allan Stevens; Sharon Ann Stevens.
EIN: 266824259

Selected grants: The following grants are a representative sample of this grantmaker's funding activity:
$7,000,000 to University of Arizona Foundation, Tucson, AZ, 2011. For athletic department.
$4,000,000 to University of Arizona Foundation, Tucson, AZ, 2010.
$200,000 to Gonzaga University, Spokane, WA, 2010.
$200,000 to Gonzaga University, Spokane, WA, 2011. For athletic department.
$175,000 to University of Arizona Foundation, Tucson, AZ, 2011.
$50,000 to University of Arizona Foundation, Tucson, AZ, 2010.
$35,000 to United Way of El Paso County, El Paso, TX, 2011.
$25,000 to El Paso Zoological Society, El Paso, TX, 2011.
$25,000 to University of Arizona Foundation, Tucson, AZ, 2010.
$25,000 to University of Arizona Foundation, Tucson, AZ, 2011. For men's golf program.
$1,000 to University of Arizona Foundation, Tucson, AZ, 2010.

9207
Still Water Foundation ✧

c/o Ellen Ray
3939 Bee Caves, Ste. C-100
Austin, TX 78746-6429
FAX: (512) 327-1940;
E-mail: pomeara@padminc.com

Established in 1982 in NM.
Donor: Julia Matthews Wilkinson.
Foundation type: Independent foundation.
Financial data (yr. ended 12/31/12): Assets, $53,761,687 (M); gifts received, $36,085; expenditures, $3,915,957; qualifying distributions, $3,046,595; giving activities include $2,684,692 for 67 grants (high: $501,450; low: $2,500).
Purpose and activities: Giving primarily in the areas of education, the arts, the environment, spirituality, and community-based social services.
Fields of interest: Arts, multipurpose centers/programs; Higher education; Education; Environment; Health care; Infants/toddlers; Children/youth; Children; Youth; Disabilities, people with; Immigrants/refugees; Economically disadvantaged; Homeless.
Type of support: Program development; General/operating support; Annual campaigns; Capital campaigns; Building/renovation; Endowments; Seed money; Curriculum development; Scholarship funds; Matching/challenge support.
Limitations: Applications not accepted. Giving primarily in central TX. No grants to individuals.
Application information: The foundation has instituted a self-directed grantmaking policy, whereby only those organizations invited to submit proposals will be reviewed. Unsolicited requests for funds not accepted.
Board meeting date(s): Quarterly
Directors: James Flieller; Duncan E. Osborne; Julia Matthews Wilkinson.
Number of staff: 1 part-time professional.
EIN: 850307646
Selected grants: The following grants are a representative sample of this grantmaker's funding activity:
$1,000,000 to Saint Johns College, Annapolis, MD, 2011.
$218,693 to Childrens Learning Institute, Houston, TX, 2011.
$150,000 to Environmental Defense Fund, New York, NY, 2011.
$100,000 to Hill Country Conservancy, Austin, TX, 2011.
$100,000 to Lady Bird Johnson Wildflower Center, Austin, TX, 2011.
$100,000 to University of Texas, Austin, TX, 2011.
$75,000 to Khabele School, Austin, TX, 2011.
$50,000 to Austin Explore, Austin, TX, 2011.
$50,000 to McMurry University, Abilene, TX, 2011.
$25,000 to Care Communities, Austin, TX, 2011.

9208
Strake Foundation ✧

712 Main St., Ste. 3300
Houston, TX 77002-3215 (713) 400-1170
Contact: George W. Strake, Jr., Pres. and Treas.

Trust established in 1952 in TX; incorporated in 1983.
Donors: George W. Strake, Sr.‡; Susan K. Strake‡; George W. Strake, Jr.; Susan S. Dilworth‡; Georganna S. Parsley‡.
Foundation type: Independent foundation.
Financial data (yr. ended 12/31/12): Assets, $65,953,156 (M); expenditures, $3,769,709; qualifying distributions, $3,337,664; giving activities include $3,014,000 for 156 grants (high: $50,000; low: $1,000).
Purpose and activities: Giving primarily to secondary and higher educational institutions, and for cultural and social services, including programs for youth.
Fields of interest: Museums; Secondary school/education; Higher education; Zoos/zoological societies; Hospitals (general); Health care; Medical research, institute; Boy scouts; Human services; Children/youth, services; Catholic agencies & churches; Religion; Disabilities, people with; Minorities.
Type of support: General/operating support; Continuing support; Annual campaigns; Capital campaigns; Building/renovation; Equipment; Program development; Professorships; Scholarship funds; Research; Matching/challenge support.
Limitations: Applications accepted. Giving primarily in TX, especially Houston; no grants outside the U.S. No support for elementary schools or federally funded institutions of higher learning. No grants to individuals, or for deficit financing, consulting services or technical assistance; no loans.
Publications: Application guidelines; Annual report (including application guidelines); Informational brochure.
Application information: Application form required.
Initial approach: Completed application form
Copies of proposal: 1
Deadline(s): Apr. 1 or Oct. 1
Board meeting date(s): May and Nov.
Officers: George W. Strake, Jr., Pres. and Treas.; Diana D. Hoover, V.P.; Robert S. Parsley, Secy.; Paul L. Robison, Jr., Exec. Dir.
Directors: Lupe Fraga; Steve Herod; Linda W. Johnson; Sandra P. Moffet; Robert W. Painter; Gregory P. Strake.
Number of staff: 3 part-time professional.
EIN: 760041524

9209
Charles Edward Stuart Charitable Foundation ✧

c/o Bank of America, N.A.
P.O. Box 831041
Dallas, TX 75283-1041

Established in 1980; supporting organization of Seattle Children's Home, Salvation Army, Historical Society of Seattle, Seattle Symphony Orchestra, Inc., Fred Hutchinson Cancer Research Center, Ryther Child Center, Seattle Art Museum, Seattle Opera Association, American Heart Association of Washington, University of Washington School of Medicine, and the Children's Home Society of Washington.
Foundation type: Independent foundation.
Financial data (yr. ended 06/30/13): Assets, $62,269,733 (M); gifts received, $177,709; expenditures, $3,315,360; qualifying distributions, $2,988,627; giving activities include $2,850,004 for 11 grants (high: $895,821; low: $149,304).
Purpose and activities: Giving primarily for the arts, education, health, and human services.
Fields of interest: Museums (art); Performing arts, orchestras; Performing arts, opera; Historic preservation/historical societies; Arts; Higher education, university; Health organizations, association; Cancer research; Human services; Salvation Army; Children/youth, services.
Limitations: Applications not accepted. Giving primarily in WA.
Application information: Contributes only to pre-selected organizations. Unsolicited requests for funds not considered or acknowledged.
Trustees: Patrick W. Sullivan; Bank of America, N.A.
EIN: 911088288
Selected grants: The following grants are a representative sample of this grantmaker's funding activity:
$707,274 to Fred Hutchinson Cancer Research Center, Seattle, WA, 2011. For unrestricted contribution.

9210
Louis H. and Mary Patricia Stumberg Foundation ✧ ☆

227 W. Olmos Dr.
San Antonio, TX 78212 (210) 271-0448
Contact: Diana M. Stumberg, Tr.

Established in 1989 in TX.
Donors: Louis H. Stumberg; Mary Pat Stumberg; Eric B. Stumberg.
Foundation type: Independent foundation.
Financial data (yr. ended 12/31/13): Assets, $7,857,385 (M); gifts received, $100,000; expenditures, $535,658; qualifying distributions, $498,358; giving activities include $493,750 for 23 grants (high: $200,000; low: $250).
Purpose and activities: Giving primarily for health and human services and to religious organizations.
Fields of interest: Arts; Higher education; Education; Health care; Human services; United Ways and Federated Giving Programs; Christian agencies & churches.
Type of support: Annual campaigns; Capital campaigns; Equipment; Endowments; Emergency funds; Research.
Limitations: Applications accepted. Giving primarily in San Antonio, TX. No grants to individuals.
Publications: Annual report.

Application information: Application form required.
Initial approach: Letter
Deadline(s): Dec.
Trustees: Diana M. Stumberg; Eric B. Stumberg; Louis H. Stumberg, Jr.; Mary Pat Stumberg.
EIN: 746367261
Selected grants: The following grants are a representative sample of this grantmaker's funding activity:
$120,000 to First Presbyterian Church, San Antonio, TX, 2011.
$1,600 to Blessings in a Backpack, Louisville, KY, 2011.

9211
Roy & Christine Sturgis Charitable Trust ✧

c/o US Trust, Philanthropic Solutions
901 Main St., 19th Fl.
Dallas, TX 75202-3707 (214) 209-1965
Contact: David T. Ross, Sr. V.P.
E-mail: tx.philanthropic@ustrust.com; Main URL: http://www.bankofamerica.com/grantmaking

Established in 1981 in AR.
Donor: Christine Sturgis†.
Foundation type: Independent foundation.
Financial data (yr. ended 09/30/13): Assets, $43,386,583 (M); expenditures, $2,457,377; qualifying distributions, $2,041,845; giving activities include $1,858,000 for 61 grants (high: $200,000; low: $4,000).
Purpose and activities: The trust supports and promotes quality educational, cultural, human services, and health care programming for all people.
Fields of interest: Arts; Libraries/library science; Education; Hospitals (general); Health care; Health organizations, association; Medical research, institute; Food services; Human services; Homeless, human services; Engineering/technology; Science; Economically disadvantaged; Homeless.
Type of support: General/operating support; Capital campaigns; Building/renovation; Equipment; Endowments; Program development; Scholarship funds; Research; Matching/challenge support.
Limitations: Applications accepted. Giving primarily in AR and the Dallas, TX, area. No grants to individuals or for seminars; no loans.
Publications: Application guidelines; Program policy statement.
Application information: See trust web site for application form, guidelines and requirements, including specific grantmaking procedures for Texas applicants. Application form required.
Initial approach: Use application form on foundation web site
Deadline(s): Mar. 1
Board meeting date(s): Apr.
Final notification: Prior to June 30
Trustee Bank: Bank of America, N.A.
Number of staff: 1 part-time professional; 1 part-time support.
EIN: 756331832
Selected grants: The following grants are a representative sample of this grantmaker's funding activity:
$200,000 to Union Rescue Mission, Little Rock, AR, 2012. For capital campaign to construct a new men's facility.
$200,000 to University of Arkansas, Little Rock, AR, 2012. For the Endowed Professorship for the Nanotechnology and Educational Center.
$200,000 to University of Arkansas, Little Rock, AR, 2013. For Endowed Professorship for the Nanotechnology and Educational Center.
$154,000 to University of Arkansas Foundation, Fayetteville, AR, 2013. For Undergraduate and Graduate Student Support to Endow the Roy and Christine Sturgis International Honors Scholars Program.
$112,000 to Pulaski Technical College Foundation, North Little Rock, AR, 2012. For furnishings and educational technology for the new Fine Arts and Humanities facility.
$100,000 to Arkansas Childrens Hospital Foundation, Little Rock, AR, 2012. For the South Wing expansion; meet increasing demand for inpatient and outpatient space.
$100,000 to Arkansas Childrens Hospital Foundation, Little Rock, AR, 2013. To provide funding in support of the South Wing expansion to meet increasing demand for inpatient and outpatient space.
$100,000 to Arkansas Technical University, Russellville, AR, 2012. For construction of the Roy and Christine Sturgis Center.
$100,000 to Our House, Little Rock, AR, 2012. For the Education Programs Capital Campaign; expand and improve the facilities housing education programs for homeless children and adults.
$75,000 to Boy Scouts of America, Little Rock, AR, 2013. For Boy Scouts of America Science, Technology, Engineering, and Mathematics (STEM) Education Center.
$50,000 to Arkansas Repertory Theater Company, Little Rock, AR, 2012. To complete interior renovations on the theatre's historic building.
$50,000 to Positive Atmosphere Reaches Kids, Little Rock, AR, 2012. For the Summer Enrichment Program.
$45,000 to Fort Smith Childrens Emergency Shelter, Fort Smith, AR, 2013. For Emergency Electrical Generator.
$25,000 to Jubilee Park and Community Center Corporation, Dallas, TX, 2012. For the Jubilee Children's Education Initiative.
$25,000 to Methodist Family Health Foundation, Little Rock, AR, 2013. For New Playground for Methodist Behavioral Hospital in Maumelle, AR.
$20,000 to Open Arms, Dallas, TX, 2013. For Medically Managed Child Care Program.
$20,000 to Parkland Foundation, Dallas, TX, 2013. For Pediatric Burn Center and Playroom.
$15,000 to Communities in Schools Dallas Region, Dallas, TX, 2013. For CISDR Program in Dallas County.
$15,000 to CONTACT Crisis Line, Dallas, TX, 2013. For CONTACTPlus Program.
$15,000 to Friends of Wednesdays Child, Dallas, TX, 2012. For the Stitched In Clothing Program; provide new coats, shoes (Winter Hug and Warm Soles), and school or work outfits (Dress for Success) to children and youth in foster care.

9212
The Suder Foundation ✧

3701 E. Plano Pkwy.
Plano, TX 75074-1819
Contact: Diane Schorr, Exec. Dir.
FAX: (866) 363-7423;
E-mail: info@suderfoundation.org; E-mail for questions regarding research grants program: dschorr@suderfoundation.org; Main URL: http://www.suderfoundation.org/

Established in 2008 in TX.
Donor: Eric Suder.
Foundation type: Independent foundation.
Financial data (yr. ended 12/31/13): Assets, $2,559,440 (M); gifts received, $1,630,000; expenditures, $1,907,457; qualifying distributions, $1,914,455; giving activities include $1,542,172 for 8 grants (high: $348,374; low: $50,000).
Purpose and activities: The mission of the foundation is to dramatically improve the graduation rate of selected first-generation college-bound students by providing them financial, academic, emotional, and social assistance at selected state universities throughout the United States. The foundation defines "first-generation students" as those whose parents have no education beyond high school.
Fields of interest: Higher education; Scholarships/financial aid; Education, services.
Type of support: Scholarship funds; General/operating support.
Limitations: Applications not accepted. Giving on a national basis. No grants or scholarships to individuals directly.
Application information: University partners selected through competitive RFP process, announced in the first quarter of each year. Individual scholarships will be administered through selected partner universities as the program model is implemented on those campuses. The foundation does not fund individual scholarship requests.
Board meeting date(s): Annual meeting in Dec, special meetings as needed
Officers and Directors:* Eric Suder,* Pres.; Aaron Suder,* Secy.; Diane Schorr, Exec. Dir.; Andrea Stanaland; Deborah Suder.
Number of staff: 1 full-time professional; 1 part-time professional.
EIN: 263041654
Selected grants: The following grants are a representative sample of this grantmaker's funding activity:
$144,461 to Washington State University, Pullman, WA, 2012. For First Scholars - scholarships and Program operating funds.

9213
The Summerlee Foundation ✧

5556 Caruth Haven Ln.
Dallas, TX 75225-8146 (214) 363-9000
Contact: John W. Crain, Pres.
FAX: (214) 363-1941; E-mail: info@summerlee.org; Animal Protection Program address: c/o Melanie K. Anderson, Prog. Dir., 6660 Delmonico Dr., Ste. D429, Colorado Springs, CO 80919-1856, tel.: (800) 256-7515 or (719) 266-5460, fax: (719) 266-5459, e-mail: mal3@summerlee.org; Texas History Program contact: John W. Crain, Prog. Dir. at the foundation's Dallas, TX, address, tel., and fax, e-mail: jwcrain@summerlee.org; Main URL: http://www.summerlee.org/

Established in 1988 in TX.
Donor: Annie Lee Roberts†.
Foundation type: Independent foundation.
Financial data (yr. ended 06/30/13): Assets, $67,026,636 (M); gifts received, $427; expenditures, $3,049,026; qualifying distributions, $2,964,007; giving activities include $1,823,580 for 83 grants (high: $500,000; low: $750).

Purpose and activities: Giving limited to 1) the alleviation of pain and suffering and the prevention of cruelty to animals; and 2) for the study, promotion, preservation, and documentation of all facets of TX history.
Fields of interest: History/archaeology; Historic preservation/historical societies; Animal welfare; Animals/wildlife, preservation/protection.
International interests: Canada; Mexico.
Type of support: Capital campaigns; Building/renovation; Equipment; Land acquisition; Program development; Conferences/seminars; Professorships; Film/video/radio; Publication; Seed money; Curriculum development; Fellowships; Internship funds; Research; Technical assistance; Matching/challenge support.
Limitations: Applications accepted. Giving primarily in TX for history programs; National and international giving for animal welfare program. No support for religious purposes. No grants to individuals.
Publications: Application guidelines; Grants list.
Application information: See foundation web site for programs, and application guidelines including deadlines and procedures. Faxed, e-mailed or incomplete applications will not be accepted. Application form not required.
Initial approach: Telephone, letter, e-mail
Copies of proposal: 1
Deadline(s): Deadlines vary every year. See foundation web site.
Board meeting date(s): Quarterly
Final notification: 3 months
Officers and Directors:* John W. Crain,* Pres. and Prog. Dir., TX history; Melanie Anderson,* V.P. and Prog. Dir., Animal Protection; Hon. David D. Jackson,* V.P.; Hon. Nikki DeShazo,* Secy.; Martha Benson, Treas.; Michael H. Collins; Ron Tyler, Ph.D.
Number of staff: 2 full-time professional; 1 full-time support.
EIN: 752252355

9214
Hatton W. Sumners Foundation for the Study and Teaching of Self-Government, Inc. ✧
(formerly Hatton W. Sumners Foundation)
325 N. Saint Paul St., Ste. 3920
Dallas, TX 75201-3821 (214) 220-2128
Contact: Hugh C. Akin, Exec. Dir.
FAX: (214) 953-0737;
E-mail: info@hattonsumners.org; Additional e-mail: hugh@hattonsumners.org; Main URL: http://www.hattonsumners.org

Trust established in 1949 in TX, became a Texas nonprofit corporation in 1998.
Foundation type: Independent foundation.
Financial data (yr. ended 12/31/12): Assets, $59,236,128 (M); gifts received, $23,200; expenditures, $4,558,780; qualifying distributions, $2,920,121; giving activities include $2,400,400 for 51 grants (high: $299,000; low: $500).
Purpose and activities: Giving for youth organizations, higher education and others for the study and teaching of the science of self-government.
Fields of interest: Higher education; Law school/education; Teacher school/education; Big Brothers/Big Sisters; Youth, services; Social sciences, public policy; Political science; Government/public administration; Children; Youth; Adults; Young adults.
Type of support: General/operating support; Continuing support; Endowments; Program development; Conferences/seminars; Curriculum development; Fellowships; Internship funds; Scholarship funds; Research; Matching/challenge support.
Limitations: Applications accepted. Giving primarily in AR, KS, LA, MI, NE, NM, OK, and TX. No support for religious organizations. No grants to individuals directly.
Publications: Application guidelines; Grants list; Informational brochure (including application guidelines); Newsletter.
Application information: Summary Grant Application form required. One of the copies of the proposal must be unbound. Summary Grant Application form and related instructions available on foundation web site. Separate application guidelines for challenge grants. Scholarships are controlled by various universities administering the program. Applications sent via e-mail or fax are not accepted. Application form required.
Initial approach: Letter
Copies of proposal: 2
Deadline(s): Aug. 1
Board meeting date(s): Varies
Final notification: Early Nov.
Officers and Trustees:* David G. Drumm,* Chair.; Charles L. Moore,* Vice-Chair.; William C. Pannell,* Secy.; Jerry D. Reis,* Treas.; Hugh Clark Akin,* Exec. Dir.; Thomas Slater Walker,* Tr. Emeritus; Gordon R. Carpenter; William Dale Crane; Scott Higginbotham; David B. Long; William W. Meadows; Christy Thompson; Lon R. Williams, Jr.
Number of staff: 1 full-time professional; 2 full-time support.
EIN: 752734032

9215
Sunnyside Foundation, Inc. ✧
(formerly Sunnyside, Inc.)
8222 Douglas Ave., Ste. 815
Dallas, TX 75225-5900 (214) 692-5686
Contact: Jane McLane, Exec. Dir.
FAX: (214) 692-1968;
E-mail: info@sunnysidetexas.org; Toll free tel.: (888) 293-6918; Main URL: http://www.sunnysidetexas.org

Established in 1928 in TX.
Donors: I. Jalonick†; K. Jalonick†.
Foundation type: Independent foundation.
Financial data (yr. ended 12/31/13): Assets, $27,959,696 (M); gifts received, $3,084; expenditures, $1,124,016; qualifying distributions, $1,485,348; giving activities include $775,203 for grants to individuals, and $593,155 for 1 loan/program-related investment.
Purpose and activities: Giving exclusively to members of the Christian Science faith for education, summer camp, Christian Science nursing care and general assistance.
Fields of interest: Education; Youth development, religion; Protestant agencies & churches.
Type of support: Emergency funds; Grants to individuals; Scholarships—to individuals.
Limitations: Giving limited to residents of TX who regularly attend a Christian Science church or Sunday school and are members of a Branch church and/or the First Church of Christ, Scientist in Boston, MA.
Publications: Application guidelines; Informational brochure (including application guidelines); Program policy statement (including application guidelines).
Application information: Application form required.
Initial approach: Tel., fax or use electronic request form on foundation web site to request an application
Deadline(s): 1 week before board meeting
Board meeting date(s): Last Fri. of each month
Final notification: 2 to 3 days after board meeting
Officers: Angela Kennerly, Pres.; Nadine Givens, Treas.; Jane McLane, Exec. Dir.
Trustees: John Borin; Christie Haggard; Curt Ridgway.
Number of staff: 1 full-time professional; 1 part-time support.
EIN: 756037004

9216
Susman Family Foundation ✧
c/o Ellen Susman
2001 Kirby Dr., Ste. 603
Houston, TX 77019-6043

Established in 1998 in TX.
Donors: Stephen D. Susman; Ellen S. Susman.
Foundation type: Independent foundation.
Financial data (yr. ended 12/31/12): Assets, $10,559,603 (M); gifts received, $4,750,000; expenditures, $698,861; qualifying distributions, $655,215; giving activities include $651,080 for 51 grants (high: $200,000; low: $50).
Fields of interest: Museums (art); Arts; Higher education, university; Human services; Jewish agencies & synagogues.
Limitations: Applications not accepted. Giving primarily in NY and TX.
Application information: Contributes only to pre-selected organizations.
Officers: Ellen S. Susman, Pres.; Harry P. Susman, V.P. and Secy.; Stacy M. Kuhn, V.P. and Treas.; Stephen D. Susman, V.P.
EIN: 760569093
Selected grants: The following grants are a representative sample of this grantmaker's funding activity:
$100,000 to Texas Tribune, Austin, TX, 2010.
$100,000 to University of Texas at Dallas, Richardson, TX, 2010.
$10,000 to Alliance for Justice, Washington, DC, 2011.
$10,000 to New York City Opera, New York, NY, 2011.
$3,500 to Aspen Institute, Washington, DC, 2011.
$2,000 to Leukemia & Lymphoma Society, White Plains, NY, 2011.
$1,500 to American Leadership Forum, Stanford, CA, 2011.
$1,000 to Green Corps, Boston, MA, 2011.
$1,000 to Planned Parenthood Los Angeles, Los Angeles, CA, 2011.
$1,000 to University of Houston-Downtown, Houston, TX, 2010.

9217
SWBC Foundation ✧ ☆
9311 San Pedro Ave., Ste. 600
San Antonio, TX 78216-4459 (210) 321-7213
Contact: Lisa W. Wilson, Dir.

Established in 2003 in TX.

Donor: Southwest Business Corp.
Foundation type: Company-sponsored foundation.
Financial data (yr. ended 11/30/13): Assets, $15,806,812 (M); expenditures, $801,396; qualifying distributions, $664,886; giving activities include $625,660 for 27 grants (high: $150,000; low: $1,000).
Purpose and activities: The foundation supports organizations involved with opera, homelessness, and Catholicism.
Fields of interest: Education; Youth development; Human services.
Type of support: Capital campaigns.
Limitations: Applications accepted. Giving primarily in the San Antonio, TX, area.
Application information: Application form required.
Initial approach: Request application form
Deadline(s): None
Directors: Charles E. Amato; Gary L. Dudley; Lisa W. Wilson.
EIN: 200511684

9218
Edward F. Swinney Trust ✧
c/o Bank of America, N.A.
P.O. Box 831041
Dallas, TX 75283-1041
Application address: c/o Greater Kansas City Community Foundation, 1055 Broadway, Ste. 130, Kansas City, MO 64105; tel.: (816) 842-0944

Trust established in 1946 in MO; affiliated trust of the Greater Kansas City Community Foundation and its Affiliated Trusts.
Donor: Edward F. Swinney‡.
Foundation type: Independent foundation.
Financial data (yr. ended 12/31/13): Assets, $21,191,932 (M); expenditures, $1,101,701; qualifying distributions, $933,552; giving activities include $825,000 for 8 grants (high: $494,000; low: $75,000).
Purpose and activities: Giving to further and develop local charitable and educational purposes; grants for mental health, higher education, hospitals, rehabilitation, and other health and welfare and community action programs; support for consolidation and monitoring of present arts and humanities projects. Giving for demonstration and experimental projects, extension and improvement of human services, with preference in the voluntary sector, planning and cooperation among voluntary agencies and between public and private agencies, and for education and training in community service.
Fields of interest: Arts; Mental health/crisis services; Health organizations, association; Human services; Children/youth, services; Urban/community development; Community/economic development; Foundations (community).
Type of support: Continuing support; Equipment; Program development; Seed money; Technical assistance; Program evaluation; Matching/challenge support.
Limitations: Applications accepted. Giving limited to Kansas City, MO. No grants to individuals, business start-up, debt reduction or annual appeals.
Publications: Application guidelines; Annual report; Grants list; Newsletter.
Application information: Application guidelines available on Greater Kansas City Community Foundation's website: http://www.gckf.org. Application form required.
Initial approach: See website http://www.gckf.org
Copies of proposal: 1
Deadline(s): seee website http://www.gckf.org
Board meeting date(s): Quarterly
Trustee: Bank of America, N.A.
Number of staff: 13 full-time professional; 1 part-time professional; 8 full-time support; 1 part-time support.
EIN: 446009264
Selected grants: The following grants are a representative sample of this grantmaker's funding activity:
$275,000 to Greater Kansas City Community Foundation, Kansas City, MO, 2012. To support Kansas City Cares Fund.

9219
The J. T. and Margaret Talkington Foundation ✧
5010 University Ave., No. 433
Lubbock, TX 79413-4429 (806) 792-1014
Contact: Charlotte Park, Secy.-Treas.
E-mail: info@talkingtonfoundation.com; Main URL: http://www.talkingtonfoundation.com

Established in TX.
Donor: Margaret K. Talkington‡.
Foundation type: Operating foundation.
Financial data (yr. ended 03/31/14): Assets, $64,896,105 (M); gifts received, $378,788; expenditures, $32,118,157; qualifying distributions, $31,443,946; giving activities include $31,344,962 for 38 grants (high: $10,500,000; low: $4,200).
Purpose and activities: Giving primarily for (but not limited to) arts and culture, community-based education, youth services, and other areas of community improvement.
Fields of interest: Arts; Higher education; Education; Human services; Youth, services.
Type of support: General/operating support.
Limitations: Giving primarily in Hockley and Lubbock counties, TX. No grants to individuals.
Publications: Application guidelines.
Application information: See foundation web site for specific application guidelines. Application form required.
Initial approach: Summary Request Form which is available on foundation web site
Copies of proposal: 6
Officers and Directors:* Norton Baker,* C.E.O. and Pres.; Dr. Kitty S. Harris,* V.P.; Alan Henry,* V.P.; Myrna Verner,* V.P.; Charlotte Park,* Secy.-Treas.
EIN: 752733220
Selected grants: The following grants are a representative sample of this grantmaker's funding activity:
$11,500,000 to Texas Tech University, Lubbock, TX, 2013. For education and research.
$5,150,000 to Lubbock Christian University Foundation, Lubbock, TX, 2013. For general support.
$5,000,000 to Lubbock Independent School District, Lubbock, TX, 2013. For Margaret Talkington School for Young Women Leaders (SYWL) serving girls in grades 6-12.
$4,925,305 to South Plains Food Bank, Lubbock, TX, 2013. For construction of new facility.
$3,450,000 to Science Spectrum, Lubbock, TX, 2013. For science and technology exhibits.
$2,500,000 to Salvation Army of Lubbock, Lubbock, TX, 2013. For Red Shield Home Project, free emergency shelter.
$2,000,000 to South Plains College Foundation, Levelland, TX, 2013. For scholarships.
$1,150,000 to Science Spectrum, Lubbock, TX, 2012. For Museum for Science and Technology Exhibits.
$500,000 to Lubbock Independent School District, Lubbock, TX, 2012. For Margaret Talkington School for Young Women Leaders (SYWL) serving girls in grades 6-12.
$300,000 to Wayland Baptist University, Plainview, TX, 2013. For scholarships.
$250,000 to George W. Bush Foundation, Dallas, TX, 2012. To endow Presidential Archival Depository.
$100,000 to Ballet Lubbock, Lubbock, TX, 2013. For general support.
$100,000 to Lubbock Christian University, Lubbock, TX, 2012.
$100,000 to Lubbock, City of, Lubbock, TX, 2012. For construction of animal shelter.
$100,000 to Texas Tech Foundation, Lubbock, TX, 2012. To build new business building.
$50,000 to Breedlove Dehydrated Foods, Lubbock, TX, 2013. To help feed the hungry.
$25,000 to Texas Tech Foundation, Lubbock, TX, 2012.

9220
The Tapestry Foundation of Mary Carmel and Thomas P. Borders ✧
610 Guadalupe St.
Austin, TX 78701 (512) 347-8050
Contact: Mary Carmel Borders, Pres.
E-mail: info@tapestryfoundation.org; Main URL: http://www.tapestryfoundation.org/

Established in 1994 in MI.
Donors: Thomas P. Borders; Mary Carmel Borders.
Foundation type: Independent foundation.
Financial data (yr. ended 12/31/13): Assets, $5,335,522 (M); gifts received, $96; expenditures, $496,000; qualifying distributions, $471,554; giving activities include $471,500 for 24 grants (high: $111,000; low: $1,000).
Purpose and activities: The foundation primarily partners with innovative literacy groups.
Fields of interest: Adult education—literacy, basic skills & GED; Education, reading; Education; Family services.
Limitations: Applications accepted. Giving primarily in the Austin, TX, metropolitan area. No grants to individuals.
Application information: Application form required.
Initial approach: See Website
Deadline(s): Aug. 15
Officers: Mary Carmel Borders, Pres.; Joshua T. Borders, V.P.; Thomas P. Borders, Secy.-Treas.
Board Member: Samantha Borders Halloran.
EIN: 383196007

9221
Tartaglino-Richards Foundation ✧ ☆
16850 N. Dallas Pkwy., Ste. 100
Dallas, TX 75248-1919 (214) 526-5434
Contact: Nancy G. Tartaglino, Pres. and Dir.

Established in 2004 in TX.
Donors: Nancy T. Richards; Nancy G. Tartaglino; First Preston Management, Inc.
Foundation type: Independent foundation.

Financial data (yr. ended 09/30/13): Assets, $9,435,133 (M); gifts received, $2,000,000; expenditures, $852,701; qualifying distributions, $798,025; giving activities include $798,025 for 17 grants (high: $500,000; low: $500).
Purpose and activities: The focus of the foundation is to provide grants to worthy recipients in the areas that benefit women and their families, for housing, career building, safety, education or general overall well being of women and their families.
Fields of interest: Education; Human services; Women.
Limitations: Applications accepted. Giving primarily in TX, with emphasis on the Dallas area.
Application information: Application form required.
Initial approach: Letter (2 to 3 pages)
Deadline(s): Apr. 1 and Nov. 1
Board meeting date(s): May and Dec.
Officers and Directors:* Nancy G. Tartaglino,* Pres.; Lisa Barrentile,* Secy.; Jenny Caslelaw; David Richards; Michael S. Richards; Jerry Tartaglino.
EIN: 300256097
Selected grants: The following grants are a representative sample of this grantmaker's funding activity:
$25,000 to Cornerstone Baptist Church, Dallas, TX, 2013. For kitchen project.
$2,500 to Waller Creek Conservancy, Austin, TX, 2013. For Palm Park Pinic.

9222
Hope Pierce Tartt Scholarship Fund ✧
P.O. Box 1964
Marshall, TX 75671-1964
Contact: E.N. Smith, Jr., Chair.

Established in 1978 in TX.
Donor: Hope Pierce Tartt†.
Foundation type: Independent foundation.
Financial data (yr. ended 05/31/13): Assets, $16,767,282 (M); expenditures, $915,250; qualifying distributions, $836,000; giving activities include $792,500 for grants to individuals.
Purpose and activities: Giving to assist in providing education for east Texas students attending a tax exempt school in Texas or Centenary College of Louisiana. Scholarship awards shall be given only to students who are United States citizens and who have resided in Harrison, Gregg, Marion, Panola or Upshur Counties, in Texas for 24 months. All eligible Harrison County residents will be funded before allocations are made to eligible students from other counties. Residence is determined as of Sept. 1 of the school year.
Fields of interest: Higher education.
Type of support: Scholarship funds.
Limitations: Applications accepted. Giving primarily to residents of Harrison, Panola, Marion, Gregg, and Upshur counties, TX. No support for tax supported colleges or universities.
Publications: Application guidelines; Program policy statement.
Application information: Students must contact financial aid offices of participating schools for application. Foundation does not select individuals for grants; they are selected by the individual schools. Application form required.
Initial approach: Letter
Copies of proposal: 1
Deadline(s): Varies
Board meeting date(s): Feb. and as required
Final notification: Varies
Officers: E.N. Smith, Jr., Chair.; Robert L. Duvall, Secy.-Treas.
Directors: Rev. Rodger Garbs; Joel D. McMahon III.
Number of staff: 1 part-time support.
EIN: 756263272

9223
T. L. L. Temple Foundation
204 Champions Dr.
Lufkin, TX 75901-7321 (936) 634-3900
Contact: M.F. "Buddy" Zeagler, Exec. Dir.; Laura L. Squiers, Deputy Exec. Dir.
FAX: (936) 639-5199; E-mail: lsquiers@tlltf.com; E-mail for M.F. "Buddy" Zeagler: bzeagler@tlltf.com. E-mail for Laura L. Squiers: lsquiers@tlltf.com

Trust established in 1962 in TX.
Donors: Georgie T. Munz†; Katherine S. Temple†; Thomas Keeler†; Cora Keeler†.
Foundation type: Independent foundation.
Financial data (yr. ended 11/30/13): Assets, $457,855,595 (M); expenditures, $17,940,006; qualifying distributions, $15,950,905; giving activities include $12,541,657 for 68 grants, and $2,663,152 for 41 employee matching gifts.
Purpose and activities: Support for education, health, and community and social services; support also for civic affairs and cultural programs.
Fields of interest: Arts; Elementary school/education; Higher education; Adult/continuing education; Education; Animal welfare; Hospitals (general); Medical care, rehabilitation; Health care; Substance abuse, services; Mental health/crisis services; Human services; Residential/custodial care, hospices; Community/economic development; Government/public administration; Children; Youth; Economically disadvantaged.
Type of support: General/operating support; Capital campaigns; Building/renovation; Equipment; Emergency funds; Program development; Professorships; Scholarship funds; Research; Program-related investments/loans; Employee matching gifts; Matching/challenge support.
Limitations: Applications accepted. Giving primarily in counties in TX constituting the East Texas Pine Timber Belt. No support for private foundations. No grants to individuals, or for deficit financing.
Publications: Application guidelines; Program policy statement.
Application information: Application form required.
Initial approach: Letter
Copies of proposal: 1
Deadline(s): None
Board meeting date(s): As required
Final notification: 2 - 3 months
Officers and Trustees:* Arthur Temple III,* Chair.; M.F. "Buddy" Zeagler, Exec. Dir.; Laura L. Squiers, Deputy Exec. Dir.; Thomas P. Darmstadter; H.J. Shands III; Jack C. Sweeny; Charlotte Temple; W. Temple Webber III.
Number of staff: 2 full-time professional; 2 full-time support.
EIN: 756037406
Selected grants: The following grants are a representative sample of this grantmaker's funding activity:
$3,600,000 to Methodist Hospital Foundation, Houston, TX, 2012. To establish East Texas Heart and Vascular Initiative.
$2,425,370 to University School, Hunting Valley Campus, Hunting Valley, OH, 2013. For Keeler Grant Program and matching grant.
$2,252,625 to Texas State Aquarium Association, Corpus Christi, TX, 2013. For Keeler Grant Program Caribbean Wing.
$2,000,000 to Texas Childrens Hospital, Houston, TX, 2012. For endowment for Plastic Surgery Division.
$2,000,000 to Texas State Aquarium Association, Corpus Christi, TX, 2012. For Caribbean Wing.
$2,000,000 to University School, Hunting Valley, OH, 2012. For Keeler Grant Funds.
$1,502,000 to University of Texas M.D. Anderson Cancer Center, Houston, TX, 2013. For Center for Cancer Epigenetics matching grant.
$1,500,000 to Rice University, Houston, TX, 2012. For neuroplasticity research laboratory.
$1,000,000 to Diboll, City of, Diboll, TX, 2012. For Neches Pines Golf Course Irrigation Project.
$1,000,000 to Texas Childrens Hospital, Houston, TX, 2013. For endowment for plastic surgery division.
$850,000 to Texarkana Special Education Center, Texarkana, TX, 2012. To purchase land.
$833,333 to Saint Stephens Episcopal School, Austin, TX, 2013. For Student Center Dining Hall.
$800,000 to Saint Cyprians Episcopal School, Lufkin, TX, 2012. For construction expansion project.
$555,694 to University School, Hunting Valley, OH, 2012. For general support.
$500,000 to University of Texas Medical Branch, Galveston, TX, 2013. For Jennie Sealy Hospital Project.
$421,821 to T.L.L. Temple Memorial Library and Archives, Diboll, TX, 2012. For general support.
$365,000 to Humane Society, Gulf Coast, Corpus Christi, TX, 2013. For equipment and general support.
$185,118 to Salvation Army of Corpus Christi, Corpus Christi, TX, 2013. For Keeler Grant Program.
$100,000 to W. Oscar Neuhaus Memorial Foundation, Neuhaus Education Center, Bellaire, TX, 2013. For building modifications.
$75,000 to Angelina County and Cities Health District, Lufkin, TX, 2013. For Prescription Assistance Program.

9224
The Mike and Mary Terry Family Foundation ✧
(formerly The Mike Terry Family Foundation)
5950 Berkshire Ln., Ste. 400
Dallas, TX 75225-5832
Contact: Allison Salas, Assoc. Dir.
FAX: (214) 361-4835;
E-mail: info@TerryFamilyFoundation.org; Main URL: http://www.terryfamilyfoundation.org

Established in 2001 in TX.
Donors: Michael F. Terry; Mary D. Terry.
Foundation type: Independent foundation.
Financial data (yr. ended 12/31/13): Assets, $17,596,855 (M); gifts received, $36,935; expenditures, $2,185,162; qualifying distributions, $1,673,716; giving activities include $1,666,488 for 57 grants (high: $500,000; low: $500).
Purpose and activities: Giving primarily for children and youth services, particularly for programs that assist mentally or physically abused children, develop opportunities and provide education assistance for children and youth in need, and provide cultural education through the performing arts; funding also for initiatives addressing

homelessness and assistance for families facing poverty.
Fields of interest: Arts; Education; Human services; Children/youth, services; Catholic agencies & churches; Infants/toddlers; Children/youth; Children; Youth; Adults; Young adults; Physically disabled; Mentally disabled; Military/veterans; Substance abusers; Single parents; Crime/abuse victims; Economically disadvantaged; Homeless.
Type of support: Management development/ capacity building; General/operating support; Curriculum development; Annual campaigns; Building/renovation; Capital campaigns; Endowments; Matching/challenge support; Program development; Program evaluation; Scholarship funds.
Limitations: Applications not accepted. Giving limited to the North TX, area, with emphasis on Dallas. No grants to individuals.
Application information: Contributes only to pre-selected organizations. The grant submission process is currently reserved for organizations already in dialogue with the foundation; see web site for details.
Board meeting date(s): Mid-Apr. and mid-Oct.
Officers: Melissa T. Pridmore, Pres. and Exec. Dir.; Michael F. Terry, V.P. and Treas.; Mary D. Terry, Secy.
Number of staff: 1 full-time professional; 1 part-time professional.
EIN: 752902847
Selected grants: The following grants are a representative sample of this grantmaker's funding activity:
$26,000 to Reading Partners, Oakland, CA, 2012. For education.

9225
The Terry Foundation ✧
3104 Edloe St., Ste. 205
Houston, TX 77027-6022 (713) 552-0002
Contact: Beth Freeman, Dir., Scholar Relations
FAX: (713) 622-6352; Toll free tel: (800) 675-2414; E-mail: (for Beth Freeman) Beth.freeman@terryfoundation.org
Facebook: https://www.facebook.com/pages/The-Terry-Foundation/1391187554448130

Established in 1986 in TX.
Donors: Howard L. Terry; Nancy M. Terry.
Foundation type: Independent foundation.
Financial data (yr. ended 12/31/13): Assets, $282,412,848 (M); gifts received, $63,927,411; expenditures, $18,127,789; qualifying distributions, $16,705,233; giving activities include $14,462,900 for 11 grants (high: $3,843,150; low: $46,650).
Purpose and activities: The foundation's goal is to strengthen the state of Texas by identifying Texas high school graduates who have promise of future leadership distinction and assisting them in developing their future and the future of those around them. To achieve this goal, the foundation selects each year an outstanding group of Terry Scholars who are awarded collegiate scholarships for attendance at the University of Texas (Austin), Texas A&M University (College Station), the University of Houston (Main Campus), Texas State University-San Marcos, University of Texas at San Antonio, the University of Texas at Dallas, or the University of North Texas, or Texas Tech University.
Fields of interest: Higher education; Scholarships/ financial aid.
Type of support: Scholarship funds.
Limitations: Applications not accepted. Giving primarily in TX. No grants to individuals (directly).
Publications: Newsletter.
Application information: Contributes only to pre-selected organizations. Eligible students are nominated by the universities associated with the program.
Officers and Directors:* Rhett Campbell,* Chair. and C.E.O.; Edward T. Cotham,* Pres.; Robert L. Parker, V.P., Admin.; John W. Storms,* Treas.; Yvonne R. Moody,* Exec. Dir.; James Davis; Elizabeth R. Keeler; R. Carter Overton III; Jeff Stichler; Gayle Stinson; Brian G. Yarbrough.
EIN: 311551093
Selected grants: The following grants are a representative sample of this grantmaker's funding activity:
$3,843,150 to University of Texas, Austin, TX, 2013. For scholarships.
$3,192,000 to University of Texas, Austin, TX, 2012. For scholarships.
$3,021,550 to Texas A & M University, College Station, TX, 2013. For scholarships.
$2,451,750 to Texas A & M University, College Station, TX, 2012. For scholarships.
$1,388,700 to University of Texas Health Science Center, Dallas, TX, 2013. For scholarships.
$1,265,900 to Texas Tech University, Lubbock, TX, 2013. For scholarships.
$1,217,550 to University of North Texas, Denton, TX, 2013. For scholarships.
$1,171,900 to University of Texas at San Antonio, San Antonio, TX, 2013. For scholarships.
$1,151,100 to Texas State University, San Marcos, TX, 2013. For scholarships.
$1,035,550 to University of Houston-University Park, Houston, TX, 2013. For scholarships.
$933,000 to Texas State University, San Marcos, TX, 2012. For scholarships.
$876,000 to University of Texas at San Antonio, San Antonio, TX, 2012. For scholarships.
$838,000 to University of Houston-University Park, Houston, TX, 2012. For scholarships.
$834,500 to University of Texas at Dallas, Richardson, TX, 2012. For scholarships.
$665,750 to University of North Texas, Denton, TX, 2012. For scholarships.
$523,750 to Texas Tech University, Lubbock, TX, 2012. For scholarships.
$241,600 to Texas Woman's University, Denton, TX, 2013. For scholarships.
$119,000 to University of Texas Health Science Center, San Antonio, TX, 2012. For scholarships.
$79,250 to University of Texas Health Science Center, San Antonio, TX, 2013. For scholarships.
$8,250 to Texas A & M Health Science Center, College Station, TX, 2012. For scholarships.

9226
Texas Flying Legends Museum ✧
4203 Yoakum Blvd., Ste. 200
Houston, TX 77006-5455

Established in TX.
Donors: The Southport Trust; Black Rhino LP; W.E. Bosarge; Marie Bosarge; Bruce Eames; Todd Kramer.
Foundation type: Independent foundation.
Financial data (yr. ended 12/31/12): Assets, $24,459,260 (M); gifts received, $1,733,340; expenditures, $2,296,196; qualifying distributions, $750,985; giving activities include $750,985 for grants.
Purpose and activities: Giving primarily to organizations that support and educate the public about World War II aircraft.
Fields of interest: Museums (specialized); Military/ veterans.
Limitations: Applications not accepted. No grants to individuals.
Application information: Unsolicited requests for funds not accepted.
Officers and Directors:* W. E. Bosarge,* Chair.; Chris Griffith, Pres.; Marie T. Bosarge,* V.P.; Darla Tolefson, Secy.-Treas.
EIN: 273870495

9227
Texas Instruments Foundation ✧
P.O. Box 650311, M.S. 3998
Dallas, TX 75265-0199 (214) 480-6873
FAX: (214) 480-6820; E-mail: giving@ti.com; Additional tel.: (214) 480-3221; Main URL: http://www.ti.com/corp/docs/csr/communities.html

Trust established in 1951 in TX; incorporated in 1964.
Donor: Texas Instruments Inc.
Foundation type: Company-sponsored foundation.
Financial data (yr. ended 12/31/13): Assets, $47,187,359 (M); gifts received, $15,000,000; expenditures, $13,638,277; qualifying distributions, $13,350,424; giving activities include $10,904,622 for 59 grants (high: $2,113,525; low: $1,000), and $2,359,128 for employee matching gifts.
Purpose and activities: The foundation supports programs designed to promote arts and culture, K-12 education; and community investment.
Fields of interest: Museums; Performing arts; Performing arts, orchestras; Arts; Education, management/technical assistance; Elementary/ secondary education; Secondary school/education; Teacher school/education; Education; Health care; Disasters, preparedness/services; Youth, services; Homeless, human services; Human services; Business/industry; Community/economic development; United Ways and Federated Giving Programs; Mathematics; Engineering/technology; Science; Minorities; Girls.
Type of support: General/operating support; Continuing support; Annual campaigns; Capital campaigns; Building/renovation; Program development; Curriculum development; Scholarship funds; Research; Employee volunteer services; Employee matching gifts.
Limitations: Applications accepted. Giving primarily in areas of company operations in Dallas, TX. No support for private foundations, sectarian, denominational, or religious organizations, discriminatory organizations, political parties or candidates, veterans', fraternal, or labor organizations, hospitals, individuals schools, robotics teams, or sports teams. No grants to individuals, or for sponsorships, endowments, political activities, courtesy advertising, program books, yearbooks, entertainment events, scholarships, or conferences, sporting events, golf tournaments, or travel or tours; no product donations.
Publications: Application guidelines; Program policy statement.

Application information: The majority of TI grants are made by invitation or in conjunction with ongoing partnerships. Application form required.

Initial approach: Complete online eligibility quiz and application

Deadline(s): None

Board meeting date(s): Quarterly

Final notification: 3 weeks following board meetings

Officers and Directors:* Lewis H. McMahan, Chair.; Terri L. West,* Vice-Chair.; Bart Thomas,* Secy.; Kevin P. March,* Treas.; Andy Smith, Exec. Dir.; David K. Heacock; Rafael R. Lizardi; Venugopal B. Menon; Julie M. VanHaren; Darla H. Whitaker.
Number of staff: 1 full-time professional.
EIN: 756038519
Selected grants: The following grants are a representative sample of this grantmaker's funding activity:
$2,273,000 to Communities Foundation of Texas, Dallas, TX, 2012. For operating support.
$1,700,000 to Perot Museum of Nature and Science, Dallas, TX, 2012.
$1,138,692 to National Math and Science Initiative, Dallas, TX, 2012. For operating support and scholarships.
$350,000 to Uplift Education, Irving, TX, 2012. For operating support.
$161,860 to New Teacher Project, Cedar Park, TX, 2012. For operating support.
$143,160 to United Way of Grayson County, Sherman, TX, 2012. For operating support.
$73,500 to Dallas Education Foundation, Dallas, TX, 2012. For operating support of STEM.
$25,000 to Perot Museum of Nature and Science, Dallas, TX, 2012.

9228
Texas Pioneer Foundation ✧
3911 Moores Ln.
Texarkana, TX 75503-2193

Established in TX.
Donors: SASL; CTFSC.
Foundation type: Independent foundation.
Financial data (yr. ended 06/30/13): Assets, $50,566,418 (M); expenditures, $2,619,148; qualifying distributions, $2,432,960; giving activities include $1,973,392 for 80 grants (high: $115,740; low: $500), and $153,358 for 1 foundation-administered program.
Fields of interest: Higher education; Education.
Limitations: Applications not accepted. Giving primarily in TX. No grants to individuals.
Application information: Contributes only to pre-selected organizations.
Officers: Fred J. Markham, Pres.; Cliff Bandy, V.P.; Dick Cummins, V.P.; Margaret Lindsey, Secy.-Treas.
Director: Mary Borm, C.P.A.
EIN: 741966306
Selected grants: The following grants are a representative sample of this grantmaker's funding activity:
$118,100 to Skillpoint Alliance, Austin, TX, 2011.

9229
Thank Heaven Foundation ✧ ☆
3322 Shorecrest Dr., Ste. 235
Dallas, TX 75235-2045

Donors: The Florida Co.; Chatham Hill Foundation.
Foundation type: Independent foundation.
Financial data (yr. ended 12/31/13): Assets, $2,121,090 (M); gifts received, $329,000; expenditures, $585,114; qualifying distributions, $580,093; giving activities include $580,093 for 25 grants (high: $250,000; low: $1,000).
Fields of interest: Media/communications; Education; Medical research; Religion.
Limitations: Applications not accepted. Giving primarily in TX and VA.
Application information: Unsolicited requests for funds not accepted.
Officers and Directors:* Joe C. Thompson, Jr.,* Pres.; Dean A. Renkes, V.P.; Dorothy Key Thompson,* Secy.; Shannon Saalfield Thompson.
EIN: 261800335

9230
The Thirteen Foundation ✧
10235 Interstate 20
Eastland, TX 76448-5643

Donors: Farris Wilks; JoAnn Wilks.
Foundation type: Independent foundation.
Financial data (yr. ended 12/31/12): Assets, $97,579,811 (M); gifts received, $2,501,000; expenditures, $13,375,996; qualifying distributions, $13,170,445; giving activities include $12,841,324 for 47 grants (high: $2,242,857; low: $3,000).
Fields of interest: Christian agencies & churches.
Limitations: Applications not accepted. Giving primarily in TX.
Application information: Contributes only to pre-selected organizations.
Officer: Jonathan Francis, Exec. Dir.
Trustees: Farris C. Wilks; JoAnn Wilks.
EIN: 276977311

9231
Billie and Gillis Thomas Family Foundation ✧
(formerly The Thomas Foundation)
8333 Douglas Ave., Ste. 1414
Dallas, TX 75225-5821
Contact: Robyn T. Conlon, Pres.

Established in 1997 in TX.
Donors: H. Gillis Thomas; Billie D. Thomas†.
Foundation type: Independent foundation.
Financial data (yr. ended 12/31/13): Assets, $15,206,995 (M); gifts received, $2,297,929; expenditures, $685,330; qualifying distributions, $620,985; giving activities include $620,047 for 24 grants (high: $100,000; low: $3,605).
Fields of interest: Elementary/secondary education; Higher education; Human services; Protestant agencies & churches.
Type of support: Capital campaigns; Scholarships—to individuals.
Limitations: Applications not accepted. Giving primarily in Dallas, TX.
Application information: Unsolicited requests for funds not accepted.
Officers: Robyn T. Conlon, Pres.; Donald T. Conlon, V.P.; William K. Conlon, Secy.; Walter T. Shank, Treas.
EIN: 752721588
Selected grants: The following grants are a representative sample of this grantmaker's funding activity:
$30,000 to Dallas Academy, Dallas, TX, 2012. For capital campaign fund.

9232
The Thomas Foundation ✧
P.O. Box 797066
Dallas, TX 75379

Established in TX.
Foundation type: Independent foundation.
Financial data (yr. ended 12/31/13): Assets, $12,183,393 (M); expenditures, $683,732; qualifying distributions, $577,000; giving activities include $541,000 for 48 grants (high: $80,000; low: $2,000).
Fields of interest: Human services; Children/youth, services; Pregnancy centers; Christian agencies & churches.
Limitations: Applications not accepted. Giving primarily in TX.
Application information: Unsolicited requests for funds not accepted.
Officers and Directors:* Stanley Thomas,* Pres.; Deborah Thomas,* Secy.-Treas.; Michael Thomas.
EIN: 201831468
Selected grants: The following grants are a representative sample of this grantmaker's funding activity:
$50,300 to Dallas Pregnancy Resource Center, Dallas, TX, 2012. For Christian Crisis Pregnancy Center.
$50,000 to Harvesters Reaching the Nations, Plano, TX, 2012. For Sudan Orphanage and Heath Center.
$30,000 to Union Gospel Mission, Dallas, TX, 2012. For Help for Homeless Women and Kids.
$20,000 to Dallas LIFE Foundation, Dallas, TX, 2012. For Meeting Needs of the Homeless.
$15,000 to Prestonwood Pregnancy Center, Dallas, TX, 2012. For Pro-Life Pregnancy Help.
$10,000 to Christian Community Action, Lewisville, TX, 2012. For Help with Expenses for Poor.
$10,000 to Gospel for Asia, Carrollton, TX, 2012. To Provide Help for untouchable Kids.
$10,000 to Samaritan Inn, McKinney, TX, 2012. For services for homeless.
$10,000 to Wilkinson Center, Dallas, TX, 2012. For Emergency Aid with Essentials.
$5,000 to Leader Formation International, Dallas, TX, 2012. For Church Leadership Training.

9233
Jim and Angela Thompson Foundation ✧
(also known as The James and Angela Thompson Foundation)
6125 Luther Ln., No. 386
Dallas, TX 75225-6202
Contact: Angela M. Thompson, Pres.
Main URL: http://www.jatf.us

Established in 2006 in TX.
Donors: James R. Thompson; Clifford M. Weiner.
Foundation type: Independent foundation.
Financial data (yr. ended 12/31/12): Assets, $1,053,341 (M); gifts received, $1,540,000; expenditures, $730,811; qualifying distributions, $729,310; giving activities include $710,112 for 24 grants (high: $425,000; low: $100).
Purpose and activities: Giving primarily for children and family services, education, general aviation, free speech and animal services.

Fields of interest: Education; Animal welfare; Health organizations; Medical research; Children/youth, services; Family services; Space/aviation.
Limitations: Applications not accepted. Giving primarily in TX, with some emphasis on Dallas. No grants to individuals.
Application information: Contributes only to pre-selected organizations.
Officers: James R. Thompson, Chair.; Angela M. Thompson, Pres.; Andrew P. Lester, Secy.
Director: Kathleen E. Collisson.
EIN: 205856025

9234
Raul Tijerina, Jr. Foundation ✧
P.O. Box 6176
Kingwood, TX 77325-6176 (713) 951-5857
E-mail: info@RaulTijerinaJrFoundation.org; Contact for additional information and questions: Lynn Stanley, Private Foundation Svcs., Inc., tel.: (713) 960-6616; Main URL: http://www.raultijerinajrfoundation.org

Established in 2002 in TX.
Donors: Raul Tijerina, Jr.‡; Hortensia C. Tijerina.
Foundation type: Independent foundation.
Financial data (yr. ended 12/31/12): Assets, $10,992,156 (M); expenditures, $621,738; qualifying distributions, $554,542; giving activities include $545,395 for 32 grants (high: $66,750; low: $111).
Purpose and activities: Giving primarily for the benefit of the people and community of South Texas by supporting and encouraging organizations that promote and advance education and youth programs, health and human services, community development, and cultural, arts, and humanities programs.
Fields of interest: Arts; Education; Health care; Human services; Children/youth, services; Community/economic development.
Limitations: Applications accepted. Giving limited to Cameron, Hidalgo, Starr and Willacy counties, TX. No support for governmental agencies. No grants to individuals, or for research, or internal operations and capital campaigns of churches.
Publications: Application guidelines.
Application information: See foundation web site for specific application guidelines. Application form required.
Initial approach: Letter on inquiry (no more than 4 pages)
Deadline(s): Apr. 1 for letter of inquiry Aug. 1
Officers and Directors:* Hortensia C. Tijerina, Pres.; Dr. Carlos A. Lozano, M.D., V.P.; Boris A. Hidalgo, Secy.-Treas.; Mike A. Hernandez II; Cullen R. Looney.
EIN: 331076963

9235
Tingari-Silverton Foundation, Inc. ✧
(also known as Silverton Foundation)
1000 Rio Grande St.
Austin, TX 78701-2014 (512) 782-0005
Contact: Andrea Crow
FAX: (512) 597-8518;
E-mail: info@silvertonfoundation.org; Main URL: http://www.silvertonfoundation.org

Established in 2000 in TX.
Donors: William P. Wood; Pamela M. Ryan; Silverton Partners, LP.
Foundation type: Independent foundation.
Financial data (yr. ended 12/31/12): Assets, $11,727,985 (M); expenditures, $562,401; qualifying distributions, $505,732; giving activities include $461,000 for 5 grants (high: $225,000; low: $1,000).
Purpose and activities: Giving primarily for disadvantaged and underserved populations, specifically for programs that provide services related to health, education, social services, and economic development.
Fields of interest: Education; Human services; Economic development.
Limitations: Applications accepted. Giving in Australia, East Timor, and the U.S., with primary emphasis on central TX. No grants to individuals, or for endowments, capital campaigns, ongoing operating expenses, existing deficits or lobbying.
Publications: Application guidelines; Annual report (including application guidelines); IRS Form 990 or 990-PF printed copy available upon request.
Application information: Full proposals are by invitation only, upon review of 1-page summary. Application form not required.
Initial approach: 1-page summary via regular mail or e-mail (preferred)
Deadline(s): None
Officers: Pamela M. Ryan, Chair.; Karen Skelton, Pres.; Melissa D. Abel, Secy.
EIN: 742936881

9236
The Tobin Endowment ✧
P.O. Box 90869
San Antonio, TX 78209-9092 (210) 930-5160
Contact: J. Bruce Bugg, Jr., Chair.

Established in 1999 in TX.
Donors: J. Bruce Bugg, Jr.; Robert L.B. Tobin‡; Lloyd A. Denton; Ann D. Wells; Robert Batts Tobin Trust.
Foundation type: Independent foundation.
Financial data (yr. ended 12/31/13): Assets, $77,030,719 (M); expenditures, $2,552,145; qualifying distributions, $1,956,568; giving activities include $1,394,666 for 28 grants (high: $508,500; low: $1,570).
Purpose and activities: The Tobin Endowment supports and promotes the arts, together with other charitable, scientific, literacy and educational organizations.
Fields of interest: Arts, fund raising/fund distribution; Museums (art); Performing arts; Performing arts, opera; Arts; Higher education; Cancer research; Children, services; United Ways and Federated Giving Programs.
Type of support: Matching/challenge support; Research; General/operating support; Equipment; Endowments; Continuing support; Capital campaigns; Building/renovation.
Limitations: Applications accepted. Giving primarily in San Antonio, TX. No grants to individuals.
Application information: Application form required.
Initial approach: Letter
Copies of proposal: 1
Deadline(s): None
Officer and Trustee:* J. Bruce Bugg, Jr.,* Chair.
EIN: 746478848

9237
Tocker Foundation ✧
3814 Medical Pkwy.
Austin, TX 78756-4002 (512) 452-1044
Contact: Darryl Tocker, Exec. Dir.
FAX: (512) 452-7690; E-mail: grants@tocker.org; Main URL: http://www.tocker.org

Established in 1964 in TX.
Donors: Phillip Tocker‡; Mrs. Phillip Tocker‡.
Foundation type: Independent foundation.
Financial data (yr. ended 11/30/13): Assets, $32,630,887 (M); expenditures, $1,932,687; qualifying distributions, $1,510,524; giving activities include $1,350,218 for 153 grants (high: $90,000; low: $51).
Purpose and activities: Giving primarily for the support, encouragement of and assistance to, small, rural libraries in Texas, which serve populations of 12,000 or less.
Fields of interest: Libraries/library science.
Type of support: Management development/capacity building; Equipment; Program development; Conferences/seminars.
Limitations: Applications accepted. Giving primarily in TX. No grants to individuals, or for debt service, endowment funds, salaries, employee benefits, normal operating expenses, construction, electrical, flooring, phones or other items supported by the municipality, or e-books or membership fees to e-book providers.
Publications: Application guidelines; Informational brochure (including application guidelines).
Application information: Application form available on foundation web site. Application form required.
Initial approach: Applicants are encouraged to contact the foundation's Director of Grants Mgmt., Karin Gerstenhaber, to discuss their project and provide a preliminary grant review
Copies of proposal: 1
Deadline(s): Jan. 15 and June 1 for Library Grants (short extensions can be obtained by contacting the foundation via fax, letter, or e-mail); none for Library Automation Upgrade Program
Final notification: 45-60 days after the application deadline
Officers and Directors:* Robert Tocker,* Chair.; Darryl Tocker, Exec. Dir.; Beth Fox; Mel Kunze; Barbara Tocker; Terry Tocker.
Number of staff: 1 full-time professional; 1 full-time support.
EIN: 756037871
Selected grants: The following grants are a representative sample of this grantmaker's funding activity:
$26,038 to Lone Oak Area Public Library, Lone Oak, TX, 2011.
$25,000 to Texas Book Festival, Austin, TX, 2011. For annual support.
$25,000 to University of Texas Press, Austin, TX, 2011.
$19,785 to Eden Public Library, Eden, TX, 2011.
$10,000 to University of Texas-Pan American, Edinburg, TX, 2011.
$9,828 to Marlin Public Library, Marlin, TX, 2011.
$8,775 to Texas Library Association, Austin, TX, 2011.
$6,100 to Medina Community Library, Medina, TX, 2011.
$5,000 to Lindale Library, Lindale, TX, 2011.
$1,000 to Texas Book Festival, Austin, TX, 2011.

9238
Max and Minnie Tomerlin Voelcker Fund ✧

c/o Banks Smith
112 E. Pecan St., Ste. 3000
San Antonio, TX 78205-1516
Contact: Emily Harrison Lijenwall
FAX: (210) 224-7983;
E-mail: voelckerfund@scs-law.com; Email for Emily Harrison Lijenwall: elijenwall@scs-law.com; Main URL: http://www.voelckerfund.org

Foundation type: Independent foundation.
Financial data (yr. ended 06/30/13): Assets, $68,276,438 (M); expenditures, $3,917,679; qualifying distributions, $3,038,689; giving activities include $2,954,275 for 22 grants (high: $344,528; low: $5), and $58,844 for 1 foundation-administered program.
Purpose and activities: The foundation funds charitable organizations engaged in medical research with emphasis on awarding grants to be given to research to find cures for cancer, heart disease, arthritis, muscular dystrophy, retinitis, and/or emasculative degeneration of the retina.
Fields of interest: Cancer research; Eye research; Heart & circulatory research; Medical research.
Type of support: Seed money; Matching/challenge support.
Limitations: Applications accepted. Giving primarily in San Antonio and Bexar County, TX, area. No grants to individuals, or for administrative costs, debt reduction, or fund-raising efforts.
Publications: Application guidelines; Grants list.
Application information: Full grant proposals are by invitation only, after review of LOI. Application guidelines available on fund web site.
Initial approach: Letter of inquiry (no longer than 4 pages)
Deadline(s): None
Trustees: David P. Berndt; Banks M. Smith; Forrester M. Smith III.
EIN: 742985834
Selected grants: The following grants are a representative sample of this grantmaker's funding activity:
$200,000 to Henry M. Jackson Foundation for the Advancement of Military Medicine, Bethesda, MD, 2011.

9239
Topfer Family Foundation ✧
(formerly The Morton & Angela Topfer Family Foundation)

3600 N. Capital of TX Hwy., Bldg. B, No. 310
Austin, TX 78746-3314 (512) 329-0009
Contact: Erica Gustafson, Prog. Off., Austin
FAX: (512) 329-6462;
E-mail: info@topferfoundation.org; Toll free tel.: (866) 897-0298; application e-mail: application@topferfoundation.org; Main URL: http://www.topferfamilyfoundation.org

Established in 2000 in TX.
Donors: Angela Topfer‡; Morton Topfer.
Foundation type: Independent foundation.
Financial data (yr. ended 12/31/12): Assets, $42,845,219 (M); expenditures, $3,767,929; qualifying distributions, $3,500,778; giving activities include $3,246,651 for 245 grants (high: $250,000; low: $10).
Purpose and activities: The foundation is committed to helping people connect to the tools and resources needed to build self-sufficient and fulfilling lives.
Fields of interest: Education, drop-out prevention; Health care, infants; Pediatrics; Crime/violence prevention, child abuse; Employment, services; Employment, job counseling; Employment, training; Housing/shelter, aging; Youth development; Children/youth, services; Family services, parent education; Family services, adolescent parents; Economically disadvantaged.
Type of support: General/operating support; Continuing support; Capital campaigns; Building/renovation; Program development; Matching/challenge support.
Limitations: Applications accepted. Giving primarily in the greater metropolitan areas of Chicago, IL (particularly to organizations serving Cook and DuPage counties), and Austin, TX. No support for political campaigns or purposes, academic or scientific research. No grants to individuals, advertising, dinner, gala, or raffle tickets, school fundraisers or events; no loans.
Publications: Application guidelines.
Application information: The foundation has suspended accepting unsolicited proposals for the Chicago metropolitan area for the foreseeable future. If the applicant's supporting documents are too large to submit with the online application, please submit them as an e-mail attachment addressed to the application e-mail. Attachments that cannot be submitted electronically may be mailed. Applications available on foundation web site. Application form required.
Initial approach: Online grant application with required documents
Copies of proposal: 1
Deadline(s): None
Board meeting date(s): Mar., June, Sept., and Dec.
Officers and Directors:* Mort Topfer,* Chair. and Pres.; Alan Topfer,* V.P. and Treas.; Richard Topfer,* Secy.; Patricia Hayes, Ph.D.; Jacqueline Hynek; Steven L. Hynek; Bonnie Vozar.
Number of staff: 2 full-time professional; 1 part-time professional.
EIN: 742961304
Selected grants: The following grants are a representative sample of this grantmaker's funding activity:
$1,000,000 to University of Texas M.D. Anderson Cancer Center, Houston, TX, 2012. For the Neurodegeneration Consortium, payable over 5.00 years.
$100,000 to Positive Parenting DuPage, Villa Park, IL, 2012. To increase effective parenting by improving knowledge of child development and strengthening support services for families.
$75,000 to Community House, Hinsdale, IL, 2012. For after-school and summer programs for the Willowbrook Corner Neighborhood.
$60,000 to Communities in Schools, Central Texas, Austin, TX, 2012. For XY Zone male involvement program.
$60,000 to Greater Chicago Food Depository, Chicago, IL, 2012. For senior-friendly produce and shelf-stable items to low-income older adults.
$55,000 to Any Baby Can of Austin, Austin, TX, 2012. For the Nurse-Family Partnership Program, serving low-income, first time mothers.
$42,000 to Austin Child Guidance Center, Austin, TX, 2012. For children's mental health services.
$25,000 to DuPage Senior Citizen Council, Lombard, IL, 2012. For a home maintenance and minor repair program for seniors.
$25,000 to Robert Crown Center for Health Education, Hinsdale, IL, 2012. For a health education program for low-income students.
$18,000 to Assistance League of Austin, Austin, TX, 2012. For Operation School Bell which provides school clothing for children.

9240
The Trull Foundation

404 4th St.
Palacios, TX 77465-4812 (361) 972-5241
Contact: E. Gail Purvis, Exec. Dir.
FAX: (361) 972-1109;
E-mail: gpurvis@trullfoundation.org; Main URL: http://www.trullfoundation.org

Established in 1967 in TX. Originally established in 1948 as The B.W. Trull Foundation.
Donors: R.B. Trull‡; Florence M. Trull‡; Gladys T. Brooking; Jean T. Herlin‡; Laura Shiflett.
Foundation type: Independent foundation.
Financial data (yr. ended 12/31/13): Assets, $24,878,153 (M); gifts received, $180,000; expenditures, $2,590,658; qualifying distributions, $2,301,680; giving activities include $2,221,295 for 287 grants (high: $80,000; low: $200).
Purpose and activities: The foundation's grant focus areas include: concern for needs of the Palacios and Matagorda County, where the foundation has its roots; concern for children, channeling lives away from abuse, neglect, hunger, and poverty; concern for those persons and families devastated by the effects of substance abuse; concern for the coastal Texas environment, recognizing and including water issues, estuaries, birds, agriculture, and aquaculture.
Fields of interest: Museums; Elementary/secondary education; Child development, education; Elementary school/education; Secondary school/education; Higher education; Theological school/education; Adult education—literacy, basic skills & GED; Libraries/library science; Education; Environment; Substance abuse, services; Food services; Human services; Children/youth, services; Child development, services; Family services; Minorities/immigrants, centers/services; Homeless, human services; International relief; Community/economic development; Religion; Children/youth.
Type of support: Annual campaigns; Continuing support; Equipment; General/operating support; Management development/capacity building; Matching/challenge support; Program development; Publication; Scholarship funds; Seed money; Technical assistance.
Limitations: Applications accepted. Giving primarily in TX, with emphasis on the rural TX, south TX, and the Palacios and Matagorda County areas. No grants to individuals directly, or for capital building campaigns, endowment funds; no loans.
Publications: Application guidelines; Biennial report (including application guidelines); Grants list; IRS Form 990 or 990-PF printed copy available upon request.
Application information: Proposals submitted by fax or e-mail not considered. Telephone inquiries about proposals and grants will be answered Mon.-Fri., from 8:00am-12:00pm. Application guidelines and proposal fact sheet available on foundation web site. Please do not send 990s, audits, CDs, videos,

information concerning staff, Board of Dirs., plaques or certificates of appreciation. Application form required.
Initial approach: Download foundation's fact sheet from foundation web site
Copies of proposal: 1
Deadline(s): See foundation web site for application deadlines
Board meeting date(s): Usually twice a year; contributions committee 10 times per year and as required
Final notification: 1-2 months
Officers and Trustees:* R. Scott Trull,* Chair.; Cara P. Herlin,* Vice-Chair.; Craig A. Wallis, Secy.-Treas.; E. Gail Purvis, Exec. Dir.; Kristan Olfers, Advisory Tr.; Colleen Claybourn; Sarah H. Olfers.
Number of staff: 1 full-time professional; 1 full-time support.
EIN: 237423943
Selected grants: The following grants are a representative sample of this grantmaker's funding activity:
$60,000 to Palacios Community Medical Center, Palacios, TX, 2012. For Recruitment and Retention Of Doctor For Palacios.
$50,000 to Friends of Elder Citizens, Palacios, TX, 2012. For Nutrition Operations and Transportation.
$50,000 to Palacios Independent School District, Palacios, TX, 2012. For Marine Education Center.
$40,000 to Billy T. Cattan Recovery Outreach, Victoria, TX, 2012. For Alcohol and Drug Education and Outpatient Aftercare Program.
$30,000 to Palacios Independent School District, Palacios, TX, 2012. For Scholarships.
$25,000 to Rainbow Land Day Care Center of Palacios Texas, Palacios, TX, 2012. For Operations, Education and Building Loan.
$12,000 to Ministry of Challenge, Austin, TX, 2012. For Replacing Chapel Floor/Building Security.
$10,000 to Katy Prairie Conservancy, Houston, TX, 2012. For Operating Support.
$10,000 to University of Texas, Austin, TX, 2012. For Center for Students in Recovery Scholarships.
$5,100 to Palacios Independent School District, Palacios, TX, 2012. For AP Scholarship and Fee Assistance.
$5,000 to Childrens Advocacy Center of Hidalgo County, Edinburg, TX, 2012. For Sexual Assault Nurse Examiner/Physician.
$5,000 to Corpus Christi Metro Ministries, Corpus Christi, TX, 2012. For Rainbow House Shelter for Homeless Women and Children.

9241
Art and Eva Camunez Tucker Foundation ✧
P.O. Box 4029
San Angelo, TX 76902-4029
Application address: P.O. Box 391, San Angelo, TX 76902, tel.: (325) 655-4104

Established in 1993 in TX.
Donor: Eva Camunez Tucker.
Foundation type: Independent foundation.
Financial data (yr. ended 12/31/13): Assets, $13,135,044 (M); expenditures, $698,552; qualifying distributions, $590,202; giving activities include $590,202 for 27 grants (high: $101,661; low: $513).
Purpose and activities: Giving primarily for Hispanic heritage research and education, higher education, geriatric research, food services, youth services and for Roman Catholic churches.
Fields of interest: Arts, multipurpose centers/programs; Museums (art); Elementary/secondary education; Food distribution, meals on wheels; Residential/custodial care, hospices; Protestant agencies & churches; Catholic agencies & churches.
Type of support: Annual campaigns; Building/renovation; Emergency funds; Program development; Seed money; Scholarship funds.
Limitations: Applications accepted. Giving primarily in San Angelo, TX. No grants to individuals.
Application information: Application form required.
Initial approach: Proposal
Copies of proposal: 1
Deadline(s): Apr. 1 (for May grants), Oct. 1 (for Nov. grants)
Board meeting date(s): Dec.
Final notification: 1-2 months
Officers: Len Mertz, Pres.; Terry Mikeska, Secy.
Trustees: Linda Berry; Suzanne Campbell; Kyle Peavy; Charlie Powell.
Number of staff: None.
EIN: 752490509

9242
Courtney S. Turner Charitable Trust ✧
c/o Bank of America, N.A.
P.O. Box 831041
Dallas, TX 75283-1041
Application address: c/o Bank of America, N.A., Tony Twyman, P.O. Box 219119, Kansas City, MO, 64121-9119, tel.: (816) 292-4300

Established in 1986 in MO.
Donor: Courtney S. Turner.
Foundation type: Independent foundation.
Financial data (yr. ended 12/31/13): Assets, $29,590,045 (M); expenditures, $1,685,737; qualifying distributions, $1,559,065; giving activities include $1,397,896 for grants (high: $450,000; low: $1,265).
Purpose and activities: Giving primarily for higher education, the arts, and human services.
Fields of interest: Arts; Higher education; Education; Hospitals (general); Human services; YM/YWCAs & YM/YWHAs; Children/youth, services; Community/economic development.
Type of support: Capital campaigns; Program development; Seed money; Matching/challenge support.
Limitations: Applications accepted. Giving primarily in Atchison KS, and Kansas City, MO.
Application information:
Initial approach: Letter (not exceeding 3 pages)
Deadline(s): None
Trustees: John H. Mize, Jr.; Daniel C. Weary; Bank of America, N.A.
EIN: 436316904
Selected grants: The following grants are a representative sample of this grantmaker's funding activity:
$237,500 to Benedictine College, Atchison, KS, 2012. For Refurbishment of New Man Hall.
$50,000 to Boy Scouts of America, Heart of America Council, Kansas City, MO, 2012. To support 'shelter Our Troops' Campaign.
$50,000 to Kansas University Endowment Association, Lawrence, KS, 2012. To support NCI Designation for Ku Cancer Center.
$25,000 to Kansas City Public Library, Kansas City, MO, 2012. To support 'Meet the Past' Programming.
$25,000 to Metropolitan Community Colleges Foundation, Kansas City, MO, 2012. For Physical and Occupational Teaching Equipment.
$12,250 to YMCA of Greater Kansas City, Kansas City, MO, 2012. For Swim Lessons - 3rd Graders at Atchison YMCA.
$10,000 to Science Pioneers, Kansas City, MO, 2012. To support Website Upgrade.
$9,000 to Atchison County Historical Society, Atchison, KS, 2012. For Flood Damage Repairs.

9243
Isla Carroll Turner Friendship Trust ✧
5850 San Felipe St., Ste. 125
Houston, TX 77057-3292 (713) 237-1117
Contact: Patricia "Pat" Stilley, Exec. Dir.
FAX: (713) 223-4638; E-mail: pstilley@ictft.org; Additional e-mail: jarnold@ictft.org; Main URL: http://www.islacarrollturnerfriendshiptrust.org

Established in TX.
Foundation type: Independent foundation.
Financial data (yr. ended 12/31/13): Assets, $59,957,675 (M); expenditures, $2,492,708; qualifying distributions, $2,368,586; giving activities include $2,234,000 for 70 grants (high: $140,000; low: $5,000).
Purpose and activities: Giving to benefit the elderly in the state of Texas, or those born with Down syndrome, age 47 and over also living in TX.
Fields of interest: Down syndrome; Aging, centers/services; Aging.
Limitations: Giving limited to TX. No grants to.
Publications: Application guidelines.
Application information: Application form will only be accepted via e-mail; all supporting documents should be mailed and submitted at the same time as the application form. See foundation web site for application guidelines and form. Application form required.
Deadline(s): From Aug. 1-Jan. 31. If the 31st falls on a Saturday or a Sunday, the proposals will be accepted until noon on the following Monday.
Officers and Trustees:* Phillip W. Winston,* Chair.; Msgr. Frank H. Rossi,* 1st Vice-Chair.; Rosalind W. Newton,* Vice-Chair.; Inez O. Reymond,* Secy.-Treas.; Patricia "Pat" Stilley, Exec. Dir.; S. Anne Hardiman; James S. Reckling; Stephen M. Reckling.
EIN: 741460483
Selected grants: The following grants are a representative sample of this grantmaker's funding activity:
$50,000 to University of Houston-Downtown, Graduate School of Social Work, Houston, TX, 2011.
$40,000 to Interfaith Caring Ministries, League City, TX, 2011.

9244
TurningPoint Foundation ✧
c/o Morgan Stanley
6145 Luther Ln., Ste. 244
Dallas, TX 75225

Established in 2005 in TX.
Donors: Richard C. McKenzie, Jr.; Molly L. Byrne.
Foundation type: Independent foundation.
Financial data (yr. ended 12/31/13): Assets, $20,605,309 (M); expenditures, $1,123,948; qualifying distributions, $991,267; giving activities include $962,560 for 45 grants (high: $170,000; low: $1,000).

Fields of interest: Performing arts centers; Arts; Education; Health organizations; Women.
Type of support: General/operating support; Income development; Capital campaigns; Endowments; Program development; Scholarship funds; Research.
Limitations: Applications not accepted. Giving primarily in Greenwich, CT, New York, NY and Dallas, TX; some giving also in CA and PA. No grants to individuals.
Application information: Contributes only to pre-selected organizations.
Officers: Molly L. Byrne, Pres.; Kathleen Byrne, Secy.; Susan Byrne Montgomery, Treas.
Directors: Robert Byrne; Trevor Colhoun.
EIN: 203979782
Selected grants: The following grants are a representative sample of this grantmaker's funding activity:
$125,000 to Woodall Rogers Park Foundation, Dallas, TX, 2012. Toward the purchase of River Birch Trees in the Children's Park.
$118,000 to Dallas Museum of Art, Dallas, TX, 2012. For special event underwriting ($18,000) and general support ($100,000).
$85,000 to Dallas Theater Center, Dallas, TX, 2012. For Centerstage 2012 support ($25,000) and general operating support ($60,000).
$51,250 to Millbrook School, Millbrook, NY, 2012. To establish a new learning center.
$32,500 to Planned Parenthood Federation of America, New York, NY, 2012. Toward the mobile/cellular campaign ($25,000), special event underwriting ($2,500) and general support ($5,000).
$5,000 to Audubon Nature Institute, New Orleans, LA, 2012. Toward the Olmsted Renewed campaign.
$5,000 to Legacy Donor Foundation, Metairie, LA, 2012. Toward the educational needs for organ donor participation.
$5,000 to Suffield Academy, Suffield, CT, 2012. Toward financial aid and the endowment fund.

9245
The USAA Foundation, Inc. ✧
9800 Fredericksburg Rd., D-03-E
San Antonio, TX 78288-3500 (210) 498-1225
Contact: Barbara B. Gentry

Established in 2004 in TX as successor to the USAA Foundation, a Charitable Trust.
Donors: Barbara B. Gentry; The USAA Educational Foundation.
Foundation type: Company-sponsored foundation.
Financial data (yr. ended 06/30/13): Assets, $124,738,601 (M); expenditures, $12,151,015; qualifying distributions, $11,906,550; giving activities include $11,906,550 for grants.
Purpose and activities: The foundation supports organizations involved with arts and culture, education, health, human services, and economic development.
Fields of interest: Arts; Higher education; Education; Hospitals (general); Health care; Food banks; American Red Cross; Homeless, human services; Human services; Economic development; United Ways and Federated Giving Programs.
Type of support: Program development; General/operating support.
Limitations: Applications accepted. Giving primarily in Phoenix, AZ, Colorado Springs, CO, Tampa, FL, San Antonio, TX, and Norfolk, VA. No grants for capital campaigns (for colleges or universities) or for monuments or memorials.
Publications: Annual report (including application guidelines).
Application information: Application form not required.
Initial approach: Proposal
Copies of proposal: 1
Deadline(s): None
Officers and Directors:* Josue Robles, Jr., Chair.; Harriet E. Martin, Pres.; Steven Alan Bennett,* Exec. V.P. and Secy.; David K. Kimball, Sr. V.P. and Treas.; Kenneth W. Smith, Sr. V.P.; Patrick A. Wageman, V.P. and Tax Off.; Christine J. Warren, V.P.; Stuart B. Parker; Wendi E. Strong.
EIN: 202303140
Selected grants: The following grants are a representative sample of this grantmaker's funding activity:
$3,500,000 to United Way of San Antonio and Bexar County, San Antonio, TX, 2013.
$3,000,000 to CHRISTUS Santa Rosa Childrens Hospital Foundation, San Antonio, TX, 2013.
$1,000,000 to San Antonio Food Bank, San Antonio, TX, 2013.
$250,000 to Alamo Community College District Foundation, San Antonio, TX, 2013.
$100,000 to American Red Cross, San Antonio Area Chapter, San Antonio, TX, 2013.
$10,000 to Brooke Army Medical Center Women's Auxiliary, San Antonio, TX, 2013.
$5,000 to Foodbank of Southeastern Virginia, Norfolk, VA, 2013.
$5,000 to Helping Hands for Single Moms, Glendale, AZ, 2013.
$5,000 to United Way Suncoast, Tampa, FL, 2013.
$5,000 to University of Colorado Foundation, Colorado Springs, CO, 2013.

9246
Valero Energy Foundation ✧
(formerly Ultramar Diamond Shamrock Foundation)
1 Valero Way
P.O. Box 696000
San Antonio, TX 78269-6000 (210) 345-2000
Contact: Sylvia Rodriguez, Exec. Dir.
FAX: (210) 345-2103;
E-mail: valeroenergyfoundation@valero.com; E-mail address for Sylvia Rodriguez:
Sylvia.Rodriguez@valero.com; Main URL: http://www.valero.com/Community/Community_Giving/Pages/Home.aspx
RSS Feed: http://www.valero.com/NewsRoom/_layouts/NewsRSS.aspx?Category=Community%20News

Established in 1999 in TX.
Donors: Ultramar Diamond Shamrock Corp.; Valero Energy Corp.
Foundation type: Company-sponsored foundation.
Financial data (yr. ended 09/30/13): Assets, $24,069,133 (M); gifts received, $18,375,317; expenditures, $35,463,223; qualifying distributions, $35,375,371; giving activities include $26,073,777 for 1,069 grants (high: $3,938,457; low: $5).
Purpose and activities: The foundation supports zoos and food banks and organizations involved with arts and culture, education, health, muscular dystrophy, multiple sclerosis, recreation, human services, and military and veterans.
Fields of interest: Museums; Museums (art); Arts; Elementary/secondary education; Higher education; Libraries (public); Education; Zoos/zoological societies; Hospitals (general); Reproductive health; Health care, patient services; Health care; Muscular dystrophy; Multiple sclerosis; Food banks; Athletics/sports, amateur leagues; Recreation; Boys & girls clubs; Big Brothers/Big Sisters; Boy scouts; Girl scouts; American Red Cross; Salvation Army; YM/YWCAs & YM/YWHAs; Children/youth, services; Family services; Family services, domestic violence; Residential/custodial care; Developmentally disabled, centers & services; Homeless, human services; Human services; United Ways and Federated Giving Programs; Military/veterans' organizations.
Type of support: Continuing support; General/operating support; Capital campaigns; Building/renovation; Program development; Sponsorships.
Limitations: Applications accepted. Giving primarily in areas of company operations, with emphasis on TX. No grants to individuals.
Publications: Application guidelines.
Application information: Application form required.
Initial approach: Download application form and e-mail or mail to foundation
Deadline(s): None
Officers: William R. Kleese, Chair. and C.E.O.; Joseph W. Gorder, Pres.; Michael S. Ciskowski, Exec V.P. and C.F.O.; J. Stephen Gilbert, Sr. V.P. and Secy.; Jay D. Browning, Sr. V.P. and Genl. Counsel; Lawrence M. Schmeltekopf, Sr. V.P. and Cont.; Donna Marie Titzman, Sr. V.P. and Treas.; Stephanie A. Davis, V.P. and Tax Dir.; William D. Day, Jr., V.P.; Eric A. Fisher, V.P.; Mathew S. Maloy, V.P.; John L. Perry, V.P.; Sylvia C. Rodriguez, Exec. Dir.
EIN: 742904514
Selected grants: The following grants are a representative sample of this grantmaker's funding activity:
$2,849,822 to United Way of San Antonio and Bexar County, San Antonio, TX, 2012. For fund-raising activities.
$1,110,000 to San Antonio Food Bank, San Antonio, TX, 2012. For fund-raising activities.
$1,010,000 to San Antonio Childrens Museum, San Antonio, TX, 2012. For fund-raising activities.
$333,334 to Dress for Success San Antonio, San Antonio, TX, 2012. For fund-raising activities.
$200,000 to Lamar University Foundation, Beaumont, TX, 2012. For fund-raising activities.
$25,000 to Center for Family Relations, San Antonio Kids Exchange, San Antonio, TX, 2012. For fund-raising activities.
$10,000 to San Antonio Chamber Music Society, San Antonio, TX, 2012. For fund-raising activities.
$5,500 to United Way of Amarillo and Canyon, Amarillo, TX, 2012. For fund-raising activities.
$5,000 to South San Antonio Independent School District, San Antonio, TX, 2012. For fund-raising activities.
$3,500 to Food Bank of Contra Costa and Solano, Concord, CA, 2012. For fund-raising activities.

9247
Vanberg Family Foundation ✧
25 Highland Park Village, Ste. 100
P.O. Box 506
Dallas, TX 75205-2785 (214) 692-6868
Contact: Anne V. Waldie, Pres. and Dir.

Established in 1990 in TX.
Donors: Harold E. Vanberg, Sr.‡; Anne M. Vanberg; Harold Vanberg Charitable Lead Trust.
Foundation type: Independent foundation.

Financial data (yr. ended 12/31/13): Assets, $7,144,057 (M); expenditures, $3,980,288; qualifying distributions, $3,785,116; giving activities include $3,785,116 for 98 grants (high: $1,250,000; low: $40).
Purpose and activities: Giving primarily to Protestant schools, ministries, missions, and organizations, including a Christian camp for children and young teens.
Fields of interest: Performing arts; Education; Human services; Children/youth, services; Community/economic development; Protestant agencies & churches.
Type of support: General/operating support; Capital campaigns; Building/renovation; Land acquisition; Conferences/seminars; Matching/challenge support.
Limitations: Applications accepted. Giving primarily in Warrenton, MO and TX, with emphasis on Dallas; some funding nationally. No grants to individuals.
Application information: Application form required.
Initial approach: Letter
Deadline(s): None
Officers and Directors:* Anne Vanberg Waldie,* Pres.; Virginia Jackson,* Secy.; Phillip W. Cruz.
EIN: 752342463

9248
The Susan Vaughan Foundation, Inc. ✧
(formerly McAshan Foundation, Inc.)
c/o Jennifer Grosvenor, Legacy Trust Co., N.A.
600 Jefferson St., Ste. 300
Houston, TX 77002-7377 (713) 651-8980
Contact: Kevin Biekert
E-mail: jgrosvenor@legacytrust.com

Trust established in 1952 in TX; reorganized in 1991 under current name.
Donors: Susan C. McAshan; Susan Vaughan Clayton Trust No. 1.
Foundation type: Independent foundation.
Financial data (yr. ended 12/31/12): Assets, $22,941,991 (M); expenditures, $1,599,734; qualifying distributions, $1,304,625; giving activities include $1,211,350 for 41 grants (high: $150,000; low: $2,500).
Purpose and activities: Giving primarily for education, particularly to a library; funding also for the arts and human services.
Fields of interest: Museums (art); Arts; Elementary/secondary education; Higher education; Libraries/library science; Education; Environment, natural resources; Reproductive health, family planning; Human services.
Type of support: General/operating support; Annual campaigns; Capital campaigns; Building/renovation; Matching/challenge support.
Limitations: Giving primarily in Houston and Austin, TX.
Publications: Application guidelines.
Application information: Application form not required.
Initial approach: Letter
Copies of proposal: 1
Deadline(s): None
Board meeting date(s): Quarterly (Feb., May, Aug., and Nov.)
Final notification: Within 3 months
Trustees: Susan Clayton Garwood; Duncan E. Osborne; Elizabeth B. Osborne; George Peterkin; Legacy Trust Co., N.A.
EIN: 760285765

9249
Lamar Bruni Vergara Trust ✧
106 Del Ct.
Laredo, TX 78041-2276 (956) 712-9190
Contact: J.C. Martin III, Tr.

Established in 1990 in TX.
Donor: Lamar Bruni Vergara†.
Foundation type: Independent foundation.
Financial data (yr. ended 12/31/13): Assets, $80,985,864 (M); expenditures, $3,439,346; qualifying distributions, $2,624,766; giving activities include $2,624,766 for 29 grants (high: $1,050,000; low: $1,000).
Purpose and activities: Giving primarily for education; funding also for children, youth and social services.
Fields of interest: Higher education; Education; Human services; Children/youth, services; Christian agencies & churches.
Limitations: Applications accepted. Giving primarily in Laredo, TX. No grants to individuals.
Application information: Application form not required.
Initial approach: Proposal
Deadline(s): None
Trustees: J.C. Martin III; Pearl Assocs., LC.
EIN: 746374699

9250
VHA Foundation, Inc. ✧
(formerly The VHA Health Foundation, Inc.)
290 E. John Carpenter Freeway
Irving, TX 75062 (877) 847-1450
FAX: (972) 830-0332;
E-mail: vhahealthfoundation@vha.com; Main URL: https://www.vha.com/sustainability2011/community.htm
VHA Foundation Celebrating 10 Years Video: http://vhatv.vha.com/media/2008/vha/hf/hf-full.asx

Donors: VHA Inc.; VHA Gulf States; Blessing Hospital Foundation; Parrish Meducal Center; VHA Southeast; Aspirus Wausau Hospital; Carolina East Medical Center; Center Care Health; Cox Health; Doblin Group, Inc.; Fairmont Olympic Hotel; FMOL Health System; Grand View Hospital; Health East Care Bethesda Hospital; Karla Strange; Marion General Hospital; Maritan Memorial Hospital; Stormont-Vail Foundation; The Queen's Medical; University Hospital od Eastern Carolina; Yale New Haven Health.
Foundation type: Company-sponsored foundation.
Financial data (yr. ended 12/31/13): Assets, $672,928 (M); gifts received, $347,527; expenditures, $505,781; qualifying distributions, $504,514; giving activities include $482,102 for 8 grants (high: $192,482; low: $1,220).
Purpose and activities: The foundation supports programs designed to improve individual and community health. Special emphasis is directed toward programs designed to promote patient safety and provide disaster relief.
Fields of interest: Health care.
Type of support: General/operating support; Program development; Grants to individuals.
Limitations: Applications not accepted. Giving on a national basis.
Publications: Financial statement; Grants list.
Application information: Contributes only to pre-selected organizations.
Board meeting date(s): Feb. 19, Apr. 15, Oct. 16, and Dec. 11
Officers and Director: Curt Nonomaque, Chair.; Colleen M. Risk,* Secy.; Franco Dooley, Treas.
Number of staff: 1 full-time professional; 1 part-time professional.
EIN: 222710552
Selected grants: The following grants are a representative sample of this grantmaker's funding activity:
$264,000 to Trinity Health Foundation, Minot, ND, 2011.
$224,000 to Freeman Health System, Joplin, MO, 2011.
$117,000 to Access East, Greenville, NC, 2011.
$107,000 to MedCenter One Foundation, Bismarck, ND, 2011.
$100,000 to AmeriCares, Stamford, CT, 2011.
$45,000 to Pinnacle Health System, Harrisburg, PA, 2011.
$33,500 to Baptist Health System, Birmingham, AL, 2011.
$9,000 to Cayuga Medical Center at Ithaca, Ithaca, NY, 2011.
$7,000 to Access East, Greenville, NC, 2011.
$7,000 to Ephrata Community Hospital, Ephrata, PA, 2011.

9251
Waco Foundation ✧
1227 N. Valley Mills Dr., Ste. 235
Waco, TX 76710 (254) 754-3404
Contact: Ashley Allison, Exec. Dir.; Grantmaking: Nicole Wynter, Dir., Grants and Capacity Building
FAX: (254) 753-2887;
E-mail: info@wacofoundation.org; Additional tel.: (254) 752-9457; Grant inquiry e-mail: nwynter@wacofoundation.org; Main URL: http://www.wacofoundation.org
MAC College Money Program: https://www.facebook.com/wacomac
MAC College Money Program: https://twitter.com/wacomac

Established in 1958 in TX.
Foundation type: Community foundation.
Financial data (yr. ended 03/31/13): Assets, $67,828,605 (M); gifts received, $4,448,223; expenditures, $5,414,376; giving activities include $3,660,722 for 43 grants (high: $397,040), and $255,380 for 240 grants to individuals.
Purpose and activities: The foundation seeks to make a positive difference in the lives and future of the people in Waco and McLennan County through grantmaking, promotion of community philanthropy, and support of the nonprofit sector.
Fields of interest: Arts; Education; Environment; Animals/wildlife; Health care; Mental health/crisis services; Medical research, institute; Children/youth, services; Children, day care; Family services; Women, centers/services; Human services; Community/economic development; Infants/toddlers; Children; Youth; Disabilities, people with; Women; Economically disadvantaged; Homeless.
Type of support: Management development/capacity building; Capital campaigns; Building/renovation; Equipment; Program development; Seed money; Scholarship funds; Technical assistance; Matching/challenge support.
Limitations: Applications accepted. Giving limited to McLennan County, TX. No support for religious activities or for medical or scholarly research. No grants to individuals (except for scholarships), or for annual campaigns, continuing support, membership

fees, deficit financing, endowments, or student loans.
Publications: Application guidelines; Annual report; Financial statement; Grants list; Informational brochure; Newsletter.
Application information: Initial questions may be emailed or telephoned; visit foundation web site for application form and guidelines. Application form required.
Initial approach: Online submission
Deadline(s): Jan. 12, Apr. 1, June 1, Aug. 1, Sept. 12, and Nov. 1
Board meeting date(s): 4th Wed. of each month
Final notification: Mid-June and mid-Nov.
Officers and Trustees:* Jim Haller,* Chair.; David Dickson,* Vice-Chair.; Cara Chase,* Secy.-Treas.; Ashley Allison, Exec. Dir.; Sam Allison; Betty Bauer; Steve Cates; Kyle Deaver; Lisa Jaynes; Kris Kaiser Olson; Maggie Stinnett.
Number of staff: 10 full-time professional; 3 part-time professional; 6 part-time support.
EIN: 746054628
Selected grants: The following grants are a representative sample of this grantmaker's funding activity:
$74,663 to Waco Community Development Corporation, Waco, TX, 2012. For East Waco Community Development Plan.
$60,000 to Baylor University, Baylor Research and Innovation Collaborative, Waco, TX, 2012. For STEM Interactive Exhibits and Displays.
$60,000 to Carter BloodCare, Bedford, TX, 2012. For new facility.
$43,000 to Planned Parenthood of Central Texas, Waco, TX, 2012. For electronic health records implementation.
$37,000 to Arc of McLennan County, Waco, TX, 2012. For purchase of mini bus.
$36,736 to Kids and Company, Waco, TX, 2012. For energy efficiency improvements at facility.
$28,434 to YMCA of Central Texas, Waco, TX, 2012. For purchase of mini bus.
$25,000 to Scott and White Healthcare Foundation, Temple, TX, 2012. For Hillcrest Cancer Treatment Center.
$24,361 to Habitat for Humanity of Waco, Waco, TX, 2012. For information technology upgrade.
$23,547 to Central Texas Senior Ministry, Meals and Wheels, Waco, TX, 2012. For kitchen equipment and computer equipment.

9252
Crystelle Waggoner Charitable Trust ✧

c/o U.S. Trust, Bank of America, N.A.
500 W. 7th St., 15th Fl.
Fort Worth, TX 76102-4772 (817) 390-6028
Contact: Mark J. Smith, Philanthropic Rels. Mgr.
E-mail: tx.philanthropic@ustrust.com

Established in 1982 in TX.
Donor: Crystelle Waggoner†.
Foundation type: Independent foundation.
Financial data (yr. ended 06/30/13): Assets, $18,550,443 (M); expenditures, $3,345,194; qualifying distributions, $3,004,634; giving activities include $2,939,405 for 42 grants (high: $250,000; low: $1,000).
Purpose and activities: Giving to Texas charitable organizations in existence before Jan. 24, 1982, including health organizations, the arts, and children, youth and social services.
Fields of interest: Arts; Education; Botanical gardens; Health organizations, association; Human services; Children/youth, services; Catholic federated giving programs.
Type of support: General/operating support; Continuing support; Annual campaigns; Capital campaigns; Building/renovation; Equipment; Endowments; Emergency funds; Program development; Professorships; Publication; Seed money; Curriculum development; Scholarship funds; Research.
Limitations: Applications accepted. Giving limited to TX. No support for organizations not in existence before Jan. 24, 1982. No grants to individuals, or for consulting services, deficit financing, or conferences; no loans.
Publications: Annual report (including application guidelines).
Application information: Application form required.
Initial approach: Letter
Copies of proposal: 1
Deadline(s): Mar. 31 and Sept. 30
Trustee: Bank of America, N.A.
EIN: 751881219
Selected grants: The following grants are a representative sample of this grantmaker's funding activity:
$125,000 to Catholic Charities Diocese of Fort Worth, Fort Worth, TX, 2012. For Affordable Housing Apartment Project.
$125,000 to Meals-on-Wheels of Tarrant County, Fort Worth, TX, 2012. To construct new facility to house food production, volunteer training, client services and administrative office.
$100,000 to Fort Worth Zoological Association, Fort Worth, TX, 2012. For Museum of Living Art.
$100,000 to Junior League of Fort Worth, Fort Worth, TX, 2012. For capital campaign, Room to Work, Room to Grow, Room to Serve.
$100,000 to Perot Museum of Nature and Science, Dallas, TX, 2012. To build Perot Museum of Nature and Science.
$100,000 to Ronald McDonald House of Fort Worth, Fort Worth, TX, 2012. For capital campaign, Making More Rooms for Love.
$100,000 to Streams and Valleys, Fort Worth, TX, 2012. For matching grant for Texas Department of Transportation (TxDOT) work on 5 major improvements to the Trinity Trail (biking/cycling, running/walking trails) system in Fort Worth.
$50,000 to Fort Worth Art Association, Modern Art Museum of Fort Worth, Fort Worth, TX, 2012. For education programs.
$50,000 to Jewel Charity Ball, Fort Worth, TX, 2012. For A Simple Wish - Jewel Charity Signature Projects, The Cancer Center, Case Management and Uncompensated Care.
$50,000 to Texas Wesleyan University, Fort Worth, TX, 2012. For ASPIRED: A Scholarship to Persist In Realizing Educational Dreams.

9253
Todd Wagner Foundation ✧

3008 Taylor St.
Dallas, TX 75226-1910 (214) 413-2800
Contact: Leslie McMahon, Treas.
E-mail: info@toddwagnerfoundation.org; Main URL: http://www.toddwagnerfoundation.org

Established in 2000 in TX.
Donors: Todd R. Wagner; TRW Charitable Annuity Remainder Trust.
Foundation type: Independent foundation.
Financial data (yr. ended 12/31/12): Assets, $10,146,609 (M); gifts received, $1,138,800; expenditures, $2,553,408; qualifying distributions, $2,486,594; giving activities include $1,702,234 for 32 grants (high: $383,300; low: $500).
Purpose and activities: The foundation is dedicated to improving the lives of at-risk children and building strong communities through education, technology, healthcare and enrichment opportunities.
Fields of interest: Education; Recreation; Children/youth, services; Computer science.
Type of support: Program-related investments/loans.
Limitations: Giving primarily in CA , GA, and TX. No grants to individuals.
Application information:
Initial approach: Letter
Deadline(s): None
Officers and Directors:* Todd R. Wagner,* Chair. and C.E.O.; Kevin Parke, Pres.; Matthew J. Dolan, Secy.; Leslie W. McMahon,* Treas.; Robin Hutchison, Exec. Dir.
EIN: 912028112

9254
Wal-Dot Foundation ✧

7557 Rambler Rd., Ste. 268
Dallas, TX 75231-2390
Contact: Dolores K. Neustadt, Pres.
E-mail: dotneu412@aol.com

Established in 1993 in OK.
Donors: Walter Neustadt, Jr.; Dolores K. Neustadt.
Foundation type: Independent foundation.
Financial data (yr. ended 12/31/13): Assets, $4,988,735 (M); gifts received, $108,242; expenditures, $572,906; qualifying distributions, $523,461; giving activities include $517,650 for 35 grants (high: $103,000; low: $200).
Purpose and activities: Giving primarily for education and human services.
Fields of interest: Arts education; Museums; Elementary/secondary education; Higher education; Education; Human services; American Red Cross; Children/youth, services; Family services; Residential/custodial care, hospices.
Type of support: Continuing support; Annual campaigns; Capital campaigns; Emergency funds; Professorships; Scholarship funds; Research.
Limitations: Applications not accepted. Giving primarily in TX. No grants to individuals.
Application information: Contributes only to pre-selected organizations.
Board meeting date(s): Jan. and July
Officer and Director:* Dolores K. Neustadt,* Pres.
EIN: 731414803

9255
Richard Wallrath Educational Foundation ✧

P.O. Box 1249
Centerville, TX 75833-1249
Application addresses: c/o Texas FFA, 614 E. 12th St., Austin, TX 78701, tel.: (512) 480-8045; c/o Texas 4-H, 2473 TAMU, College Station, TX 77843-2473, tel.: (979) 845-1213

Established in 2005 in TX.
Donor: Richard Wallrath.
Foundation type: Independent foundation.
Financial data (yr. ended 12/31/12): Assets, $6,902,886 (M); expenditures, $1,026,102; qualifying distributions, $955,803; giving activities

include $952,875 for 73 grants (high: $391,875; low: $625).
Fields of interest: Higher education; Education.
Type of support: Scholarship funds.
Limitations: Applications accepted. Giving primarily in TX. No grants to individuals.
Application information: Consult Texas FFA and Texas 4-H for application guidelines. Application form required.
Officers: Robert Adam, Pres.; Richard Wallrath, V.P.; Patsy Murphy, Secy.; Pamela Dolenz, Treas.
EIN: 204091122

9256
Walsh Foundation ✧

500 W. 7th St., Ste. 1007
Fort Worth, TX 76102-4732 (817) 335-3741
Contact: G. Malcolm Louden, Pres.

Established in 1956 in TX.
Donors: Mary D. Walsh; F. Howard Walsh, Sr.
Foundation type: Independent foundation.
Financial data (yr. ended 12/31/13): Assets, $18,028,832 (M); gifts received, $1,007,564; expenditures, $4,683,153; qualifying distributions, $9,217,500; giving activities include $4,608,750 for 88 grants (high: $110,000; low: $750).
Purpose and activities: Giving limited to education, health the performing arts, and general welfare.
Fields of interest: Performing arts; Higher education; Health organizations, association; Human services.
Type of support: General/operating support; Continuing support.
Limitations: Applications accepted. Giving primarily in Fort Worth, TX. No grants to individuals.
Application information: Application form required.
Initial approach: Letter
Deadline(s): None
Officers: G. Malcolm Louden, Pres.; Gary Goble, Secy.-Treas.
EIN: 756021726

9257
Walter Christian Development Foundation ✧

1100 Louisiana St., Ste. 200
Houston, TX 77002-5215

Established in 2007 in TX.
Donor: Joseph Charles Walter III.
Foundation type: Independent foundation.
Financial data (yr. ended 12/31/13): Assets, $39,633,813 (M); gifts received, $5,000,000; expenditures, $4,043,251; qualifying distributions, $3,927,110; giving activities include $3,923,595 for 33 grants (high: $500,000; low: $95).
Fields of interest: Human services; Christian agencies & churches; Protestant agencies & churches.
Limitations: Applications not accepted. Giving primarily in TX.
Application information: Contributes only to pre-selected organizations.
Trustees: Steven D. Arnold; Joseph Charles Walter III; Paula L. Walter.
EIN: 208481719

9258
Mamie McFadden Ward Heritage Foundation ✧

c/o Capital One Bank, N.A.
P.O. Box 3928
Beaumont, TX 77704-3928 (409) 880-1415

Established in 1976 in TX.
Donor: Mamie McFaddin Ward†.
Foundation type: Independent foundation.
Financial data (yr. ended 12/31/12): Assets, $38,533,906 (M); expenditures, $2,069,237; qualifying distributions, $1,580,262; giving activities include $1,580,262 for 21 grants (high: $816,542; low: $4,800).
Purpose and activities: Support for the McFaddin-Ward House historical site and other cultural programs, education, and human services.
Fields of interest: Museums; Historic preservation/historical societies; Education; Human services; Children/youth, services; Family services; Protestant agencies & churches.
Type of support: Capital campaigns; Building/renovation; Equipment; Seed money.
Limitations: Giving limited to southeast TX. No grants to individuals.
Publications: Application guidelines.
Application information: Application form provided by Capital One, N.A. Application form required.
Initial approach: Letter requesting application form
Copies of proposal: 9
Deadline(s): Aug. 31
Final notification: Nov.
Trustees: Eugene H.B. McFaddin; Ida M. Pyle; Rosine M. Wilson; Capital One Bank, N.A.
EIN: 746260525

9259
The Ware Foundation ✧

c/o Amarillo National Bank- Tr.
P.O. Box 1
Amarillo, TX 79105-0001

Established in 1996 in TX.
Donors: B.T. Ware II; Richard C. Ware II; Mary S. Ware.
Foundation type: Independent foundation.
Financial data (yr. ended 12/31/12): Assets, $13,891,966 (M); gifts received, $1,300,000; expenditures, $1,233,301; qualifying distributions, $1,084,230; giving activities include $1,084,230 for 37+ grants (high: $500,000).
Purpose and activities: Giving primarily for education, human services, federated giving programs, and Christian and Protestant churches.
Fields of interest: Higher education; Scholarships/financial aid; Education; Health organizations, association; Human services; United Ways and Federated Giving Programs; Christian agencies & churches; Protestant agencies & churches.
Limitations: Applications not accepted. Giving primarily in Amarillo, TX. No grants to individuals.
Application information: Contributes only to pre-selected organizations.
Officers: B.T. Ware II, Pres.; Pat Ware, V.P.; Richard C. Ware II, V.P.; William J. Ware, Secy.-Treas.
EIN: 752662421

9260
Gil and Dody Weaver Foundation ✧

1845 Woodall Rodgers Freeway, Ste. 1275
Dallas, TX 75201-2299 (214) 999-9497
Contact: William R. Weaver M.D., Tr.

Established in 1980 in TX.
Donors: Galbraith McF. Weaver; Elizabeth Eudora Weaver.
Foundation type: Independent foundation.
Financial data (yr. ended 09/30/13): Assets, $15,339,021 (M); expenditures, $1,288,385; qualifying distributions, $726,564; giving activities include $712,405 for 87 grants (high: $125,000; low: $100).
Purpose and activities: Giving primarily for education, health organizations, and children, youth and social services.
Fields of interest: Education; Health organizations, association; Cancer; Recreation, camps; Human services; Children/youth, services.
Type of support: General/operating support; Continuing support; Annual campaigns; Scholarship funds.
Limitations: Giving primarily to LA, OK, and TX. No grants to individuals.
Publications: Application guidelines.
Application information: Application form not required.
Initial approach: Letter including organizational information
Copies of proposal: 1
Deadline(s): May 31
Final notification: Sept. 30
Trustee: William R. Weaver, M.D.
EIN: 751729449

9261
William M. Weaver Foundation ✧ ☆

2651 JBS Pkwy., Bldg 4, Ste. E
Odessa, TX 79762
Application address: c/o Elwood Freeman, P.O. Box 301, Lamesa, TX 79331, tel.: (806) 872-5457

Established in 2003 in TX.
Donor: William M. Weaver Charitable Trust.
Foundation type: Independent foundation.
Financial data (yr. ended 12/31/13): Assets, $13,697,891 (M); expenditures, $763,377; qualifying distributions, $577,617; giving activities include $577,617 for 11 grants (high: $195,000; low: $1,714).
Fields of interest: Community/economic development; Protestant agencies & churches.
Limitations: Applications accepted. Giving primarily in Dawson County, TX.
Application information: Application form required.
Initial approach: Proposal
Deadline(s): None
Trustee: First Financial Tr. Asset Management.
EIN: 300140386

9262
The Webber Family Foundation ✧

3112 Windsor Rd., Ste. A336
Austin, TX 78703-2350 (512) 495-9494
FAX: (512) 479-2656;
E-mail: questions@webberfoundation.org; Main URL: http://www.webberfoundation.org

Established in 1999 in TX.

Donors: Neil Webber; Noelie Alito.
Foundation type: Independent foundation.
Financial data (yr. ended 12/31/12): Assets, $17,540,344 (M); expenditures, $1,015,326; qualifying distributions, $903,320; giving activities include $788,928 for 31 grants (high: $80,000; low: $1,000).
Purpose and activities: The foundation offers grants to organizations that are aligned with its mission of helping lower-income youth perform at the highest levels of achievement in academics and the arts. Currently there are three areas of focus: 1) School readiness/early literacy, with a goal to increase the number of lower-income students who enter kindergarten as high-achievers (at or above grade-level norms). Grants will fund preschool programs that provide structured, school- or center-based education for children ages 3-5, with a focus on early literacy and parent engagement; 2) Out-of-school time programs for grades 6-12, an initiative to increase the number of lower-income students who: enter high school as high-achievers, are prepared for and enroll in selective colleges, and develop artistic skills and talents without regard to financial barriers. Grants will fund long-term, intensive programs that serve lower-income students in grades 6-12 who are exceeding grade-level norms. Specific interests include enrichment programs that help students fulfill their potential through academics and/or the arts. This initiative does not include development of leadership and/or social skills, mentoring (except in the context of academics or the arts), nor remedial programs to help struggling students achieve grade-level expectations. In the arts, grants will fund programs that allow students to study music, dance, visual arts, and/or theater in depth. Artistic skill development, not exposure, is the goal. Another interest is college preparation and guidance programs that encourage high-achieving, lower-income students to attend selective colleges; and 3) Charter schools, an initiative to expand the capacity of outstanding charter schools that serve predominantly lower-income students. Grants will fund schools serving grades 6-12 that produce exceptionally well-prepared graduates.
Fields of interest: Education; Youth, services.
Limitations: Applications accepted. Giving primarily Austin, TX. No support for religious organizations. No grants to individuals, or for capital campaigns, recurring expenses, endowments, or fundraisers.
Publications: Application guidelines; Grants list.
Application information: Application form required.
Initial approach: See Website
Copies of proposal: 4
Deadline(s): None
Officers: Neil Webber, Pres. and Treas.; Erica Webber, V.P.; Jessica S. D'Arcy, Secy. and Exec. Dir.
EIN: 742927126

9263
The WEDGE Foundation ✧
1415 Louisiana St., Ste. 3000
Houston, TX 77002-7351

Established in 2001 in TX.
Donors: WEDGE Group Incorporated; WEDGE Holdings, Inc.
Foundation type: Company-sponsored foundation.
Financial data (yr. ended 12/31/13): Assets, $107 (M); gifts received, $428,300; expenditures, $535,311; qualifying distributions, $535,000; giving activities include $535,000 for 4 grants (high: $300,000; low: $10,000).
Purpose and activities: The foundation supports organizations involved with cultural awareness, higher education, health, children and youth, public policy, and Christianity.
Fields of interest: Arts, cultural/ethnic awareness; Higher education; Health care, association; Health care, clinics/centers; Health care, patient services; Health care; American Red Cross; Children/youth, services; Public policy, research; Christian agencies & churches.
Type of support: General/operating support; Building/renovation; Endowments; Fellowships; Sponsorships.
Limitations: Applications not accepted. Giving primarily in Washington, DC, MA, MN, NJ, NY, and TX.
Application information: Contributes only to pre-selected organizations.
Officers: Fares I. Fares, Pres.; Richard J. Reese, V.P. and Secy.; Gregory J. Armstrong, V.P. and Treas.
EIN: 760533546

9264
David Weekley Family Foundation ✧
1111 N. Post Oak Rd.
Houston, TX 77055-7211
GiveSmart: http://www.givesmart.org/Stories/Donors/David-Weekley

Established in 1990 in TX.
Donors: David M. Weekley; Bonnie S. Weekley.
Foundation type: Independent foundation.
Financial data (yr. ended 12/31/12): Assets, $79,963,835 (M); gifts received, $5,497,092; expenditures, $8,225,693; qualifying distributions, $8,006,496; giving activities include $7,588,718 for 59 grants (high: $1,250,000; low: $100), and $350,174 for foundation-administered programs.
Purpose and activities: Giving primarily for cancer, youth services, and to Christian agencies and churches.
Fields of interest: Health organizations, association; Youth, services; Christian agencies & churches.
Type of support: General/operating support; Annual campaigns; Capital campaigns.
Limitations: Applications not accepted. Giving primarily in Houston, TX. No grants to individuals.
Application information: Contributes only to pre-selected organizations.
Officers: David M. Weekley, Pres.; Robin Weekley Bruce, V.P.; Bonnie S. Weekley, Secy.
EIN: 760324538

9265
Leroy and Merle Weir Trust ✧
c/o Frost National Bank
P.O. Box 2127
Austin, TX 78768-2127

Established in 2002 in TX.
Foundation type: Independent foundation.
Financial data (yr. ended 12/31/13): Assets, $14,817,148 (M); expenditures, $497,784; qualifying distributions, $456,594; giving activities include $420,500 for 6 grants (high: $160,200; low: $10,000).
Purpose and activities: Giving primarily for higher education; some funding also for a health organization and children services.
Fields of interest: Higher education; Health organizations, single organization support; Children/youth, services.
Limitations: Applications not accepted. Giving primarily in TX.
Application information: Contributes only to pre-selected organizations.
Trustee: Frost National Bank.
EIN: 742656448
Selected grants: The following grants are a representative sample of this grantmaker's funding activity:
$130,232 to Wayland Baptist University, Plainview, TX, 2012. To Fund Organization's Exempt Purpose.

9266
The Weiser Foundation ✧
16 Trinity Oaks Rd.
Westworth Village, TX 76114-4100

Established in 1994 in TX.
Donors: John M. Weiser; Terri L. Weiser.
Foundation type: Independent foundation.
Financial data (yr. ended 12/31/13): Assets, $3,679,071 (M); gifts received, $1,150; expenditures, $1,123,723; qualifying distributions, $1,123,106; giving activities include $1,122,490 for 11 grants (high: $300,000; low: $10,000).
Purpose and activities: Giving primarily for Christian education, medical services, and organizations.
Fields of interest: Theological school/education; Health care; Christian agencies & churches.
Limitations: Applications not accepted. Giving primarily in GA and TX; some support also in PA. No grants to individuals.
Application information: Unsolicited requests for funds not accepted.
Officers: John M. Weiser, Pres.; Elizabeth Maurice, Secy.; Terri L. Weiser, Treas.
Directors: Susan Floyd; Andrea Qualkinbush.
EIN: 752561493

9267
Welborn-Payne Endowment Trust ✧
c/o Prosperity Bank
1401 Ave. Apt. Q
Lubbock, TX 79401-3819

Established in 1998 in TX.
Donors: Ernestine Payne-Welborn; J. M. Welborn Trust.
Foundation type: Independent foundation.
Financial data (yr. ended 12/31/13): Assets, $30,609,019 (M); gifts received, $2,652; expenditures, $1,699,053; qualifying distributions, $1,107,713; giving activities include $1,106,735 for 11 grants (high: $250,000; low: $590).
Fields of interest: Education; Food banks; Human services; Family services; Christian agencies & churches.
Type of support: General/operating support.
Limitations: Applications not accepted. Giving primarily in Lubbock, TX. No grants to individuals.
Application information: Contributes only to pre-selected organizations.
Trustee: Prosperity Bank.
EIN: 756435671

Selected grants: The following grants are a representative sample of this grantmaker's funding activity:
$600,000 to First United Methodist Church, Lubbock, TX, 2011.
$100,000 to Salvation Army of Lubbock, Lubbock, TX, 2010.
$100,000 to Sears Methodist Retirement System, Abilene, TX, 2011.
$80,000 to Meals on Wheels, Lubbock, Lubbock, TX, 2011.
$80,000 to South Plains Food Bank, Lubbock, TX, 2011.
$50,000 to Lubbock Womens Club Historical Foundation, Lubbock, TX, 2010.
$25,000 to United Way, Lubbock Area, Lubbock, TX, 2011.
$15,000 to Texas Boys Ranch, Lubbock, TX, 2011.
$12,500 to Texas Tech University, Lubbock, TX, 2010.
$1,643 to First United Methodist Church, Lubbock, TX, 2011.

9268
The Robert A. Welch Foundation ✧
5555 San Felipe St., Ste. 1900
Houston, TX 77056-2730
Contact: Norbert Dittrich, Pres.
E-mail: info@welch1.org; Main URL: http://www.welch1.org

Established in 1954 in TX as a private foundation.
Donor: Robert A. Welch†.
Foundation type: Independent foundation.
Financial data (yr. ended 08/31/13): Assets, $630,013,043 (M); expenditures, $34,053,388; qualifying distributions, $29,193,444; giving activities include $26,595,362 for 338 grants (high: $754,995; low: $10,000), $989,988 for grants to individuals, and $303,237 for 1 foundation-administered program.
Purpose and activities: The general policy of the foundation is to support fundamental chemical research at colleges and universities within the state of Texas.
Fields of interest: Chemistry.
Type of support: Research.
Limitations: Applications accepted. Giving limited to TX.
Publications: Application guidelines; Annual report.
Application information: To be eligible for consideration, an applicant must be a full-time tenured or tenure-track faculty member from a university, college or other educational institution within the state of TX. See foundation's website for more information. Application form required.
Initial approach: Written application
Copies of proposal: 1
Deadline(s): Feb. 1 for regular research grant program and for Robert A. Welch Award in Chemistry
Board meeting date(s): As needed
Final notification: Approximately 2 months
Officers and Directors:* Wilhelmina E. Robertson,* Chair.; Charles W. Tate,* Vice-Chair.; Norbert Dittrich, Pres.; Carin Marcy Barth,* Secy.; Ernest H. Cockrell,* Treas.; Robert C. Robbins, M.D.
Number of staff: 8 full-time professional.
EIN: 760343128
Selected grants: The following grants are a representative sample of this grantmaker's funding activity:
$164,500 to Texas Interscholastic League Foundation, Austin, TX, 2012. For Undergraduate Scholarships.
$104,000 to University of Texas, Austin, TX, 2012. For Welch Summer Scholar Program.
$100,000 to Rice University, Houston, TX, 2012. For research, Chemical and Photophysical Properties on Complex Nanoparticles and Nanoparticle Complexes.
$100,000 to Rice University, Houston, TX, 2012. For research, Chemical Mechanisms of Ligand Binding to Heme Proteins.
$100,000 to University of Texas, Austin, TX, 2012. For research, A Mass-Spectrometry-Based Map of Human Protein Complexes.
$100,000 to University of Texas Southwestern Medical Center, Dallas, TX, 2012. For research, Analysis of the Functional Significance of Complex Protein/Protein Interactions.
$100,000 to University of Texas Southwestern Medical Center, Dallas, TX, 2012. For research, Atomic Structure and Mechanism of the g-Secretase Complex.
$100,000 to University of Texas Southwestern Medical Center, Dallas, TX, 2012. For research, Biochemical Mechanism of NF-kB Inhibition by Deubiquitination Enzymes.
$60,000 to Rice University, Houston, TX, 2012. For research, Probing Molecular Orientations of Liquid Crystals at the Surface of Plasmonic Nanoparticles with Particle Absorption and Scattering Spectroscopy.

9269
The West Endowment ✧
P.O. Box 491
Houston, TX 77001-0491

Established in 1995 in TX.
Donors: Martron Corp.; Margene W. Lloyd; W.R. Lloyd, Jr.
Foundation type: Independent foundation.
Financial data (yr. ended 12/31/13): Assets, $13,090,815 (M); expenditures, $725,207; qualifying distributions, $671,736; giving activities include $670,000 for 19 grants (high: $100,000; low: $5,000).
Purpose and activities: Giving primarily for education; funding also for eye research and human services.
Fields of interest: Education; Hospitals (general); Eye research; Human services; Foundations (private grantmaking).
Limitations: Applications accepted. Giving primarily in TX. No grants to individuals.
Application information: Application form required.
Initial approach: Letter
Deadline(s): None
Officers and Directors:* W.R. Lloyd, Jr.,* Chair.; William West Lloyd,* Pres.; Margene West Lloyd,* V.P.; Roger A. Soape,* V.P.; Ronald S. Webster,* Secy.; Barbara Keyes, Treas.
EIN: 760481204
Selected grants: The following grants are a representative sample of this grantmaker's funding activity:
$250,000 to University of Saint Thomas, Houston, TX, 2011.
$50,000 to Joy Development School, Houston, TX, 2011.
$50,000 to Saint John the Divine Episcopal Church, Houston, TX, 2011.
$50,000 to San Marcos Baptist Academy, San Marcos, TX, 2011.
$40,000 to Star of Hope Mission, Houston, TX, 2011.
$25,000 to Houston Society for the Prevention of Cruelty to Animals, Houston, TX, 2011.
$25,000 to Ronald McDonald House of Houston, Houston, TX, 2011.
$20,000 to Cypress Creek Fine Art Association, Spring, TX, 2011.
$15,000 to Rebuilding Together Houston, Houston, TX, 2011.
$15,000 to Trees for Houston, Houston, TX, 2011.

9270
West Foundation ✧
15950 N. Dallas Pkwy., Ste. 600
Dallas, TX 75248-6685

Established in 1973 in TX.
Donors: Gordon T. West†; Ellen B. West†; Gordon T. West, Jr.
Foundation type: Independent foundation.
Financial data (yr. ended 09/30/13): Assets, $17,714,185 (M); expenditures, $1,038,851; qualifying distributions, $839,864; giving activities include $631,800 for 16 grants (high: $155,300; low: $5,000), and $100,000 for 20 grants to individuals (high: $5,000; low: $5,000).
Purpose and activities: Support limited to education, through excellence in teaching awards to public school teachers and scholarships, and other educational programs on the public school and university levels.
Fields of interest: Education.
Type of support: Scholarship funds; Grants to individuals.
Limitations: Applications not accepted. Giving limited to the Wichita Falls, TX, area.
Application information: Unsolicited requests for funds not accepted.
Officers and Trustees:* Kim W. Dinsdale,* Pres.; Andrew L. West,* V.P.; Stuart B. West,* V.P.
Number of staff: 1 full-time professional; 2 part-time support.
EIN: 237332105
Selected grants: The following grants are a representative sample of this grantmaker's funding activity:
$10,000 to American Red Cross, Des Moines, IA, 2013. For Endowments/Scholarships.

9271
The Clarence Westbury Foundation ✧
(formerly The Scaler Westbury Foundation)
800 Gessner Rd., Ste. 1260
Houston, TX 77024-4273

Established in 1996 in TX.
Donors: Jacques C. Boissonnas; Jaguar Trust; Jasper Trust; Blue Bridge Wealth Mgmt.
Foundation type: Independent foundation.
Financial data (yr. ended 12/31/13): Assets, $5,603,154 (M); expenditures, $1,798,753; qualifying distributions, $1,733,497; giving activities include $1,733,497 for 9 grants (high: $1,317,454; low: $5,000).
Fields of interest: Museums; Health organizations, association; Human services.
International interests: France.

Limitations: Applications not accepted. Giving primarily in Paris, France; giving also in the U.S. with emphasis on TX. No grants to individuals.
Application information: Contributes only to pre-selected organizations.
Officers and Directors:* Jacques C. Boissonnas,* Pres.; Nicolas N. Boissonnas,* Sr. V.P.; Catherine B. Coste,* V.P.; Marvin A. Wurzer, Secy. and Co-Treas.; Glenn H. Johnson, Co-Treas.
EIN: 760507294
Selected grants: The following grants are a representative sample of this grantmaker's funding activity:
$488,556 to Fondation de France, Paris, France, 2011. For general support.
$35,000 to Periwinkle Foundation, Houston, TX, 2011. For general support.
$25,000 to Be An Angel Fund, Houston, TX, 2011. For general support.
$25,000 to Star of Hope Mission, Houston, TX, 2011. For general support.

9272
The Whalley Foundation ✧
5 Carsey Ln.
Houston, TX 77024-6548

Donors: Lawrence G. Whalley; Mary Whalley.
Foundation type: Independent foundation.
Financial data (yr. ended 12/31/13): Assets, $5,879,014 (M); expenditures, $1,214,645; qualifying distributions, $1,191,200; giving activities include $1,191,200 for 36 grants (high: $250,000; low: $500).
Fields of interest: Education; Health care; Human services; Children/youth, services; Catholic agencies & churches.
Limitations: Applications not accepted. Giving primarily in TX.
Application information: Unsolicited requests for funds not accepted.
Officers: Lawrence G. Whalley, Pres.; Elizabeth M. Taylor, V.P.; Mary Whalley, V.P.
EIN: 262291525
Selected grants: The following grants are a representative sample of this grantmaker's funding activity:
$5,500 to Child Advocates, Houston, TX, 2012. To fund programs.

9273
Whitacre Family Foundation ✧
745 E. Mulberry Ave., Ste. 475
San Antonio, TX 78212-3127

Established in 2003 in TX.
Donors: Edward E. Whitacre; Linda Lawrence Whitacre; Bushnell Securities.
Foundation type: Independent foundation.
Financial data (yr. ended 12/31/13): Assets, $37,790 (M); gifts received, $2,000,000; expenditures, $2,069,018; qualifying distributions, $2,062,207; giving activities include $2,062,207 for 1 grant.
Fields of interest: Higher education; Education; Health organizations; Human services; Children/youth, services; Foundations (public); Christian agencies & churches; Protestant agencies & churches.
Limitations: Applications not accepted. Giving primarily in TX. No grants to individuals.
Application information: Contributes only to pre-selected organizations.
Directors: Jennifer R. Hindert; Jessica L Thorne; Edward E. Whitacre, Jr.; Linda Lawrence Whitacre.
EIN: 200184488
Selected grants: The following grants are a representative sample of this grantmaker's funding activity:
$10,572,573 to Fidelity Charitable Gift Fund, Boston, MA, 2011.
$50,000 to Texas Tech University, Lubbock, TX, 2010.
$25,000 to United Way of San Antonio and Bexar County, San Antonio, TX, 2011.
$15,000 to Charity Ball Association of San Antonio, San Antonio, TX, 2011.
$15,000 to Teach for America, New York, NY, 2010.
$10,000 to Ducks Unlimited, Memphis, TN, 2010.
$10,000 to University of Texas at San Antonio, San Antonio, TX, 2010.
$5,000 to National Jewish Health, Denver, CO, 2010.
$1,000 to Texas Tech University, Lubbock, TX, 2010.

9274
Melovee White Trust ✧
1250 N.E. Loop 410, Ste. 315
San Antonio, TX 78209

Donor: Melovee White†.
Foundation type: Independent foundation.
Financial data (yr. ended 12/31/12): Assets, $3,019,239 (M); gifts received, $3,627,748; expenditures, $675,133; qualifying distributions, $664,497; giving activities include $640,000 for 7 grants (high: $125,000; low: $40,000).
Fields of interest: Human services; Christian agencies & churches; Protestant agencies & churches.
Limitations: Applications not accepted. Giving primarily in San Antonio, TX.
Application information: Unsolicited requests for funds not accepted.
Trustee: Alice Clare.
EIN: 453245404
Selected grants: The following grants are a representative sample of this grantmaker's funding activity:
$125,000 to Bible Study Fellowship, San Antonio, TX, 2012. For Development and Implementation of Study Curriculum, Materials and Leader Training.
$100,000 to Assistance League of San Antonio, San Antonio, TX, 2012. For Adopt-A-Resident, Operation School Bell, Togs for Tots.
$100,000 to San Antonio Metropolitan Ministry, San Antonio, TX, 2012. For Transitional Living and Learning Center for Homeless Families.
$100,000 to TEAMability, San Antonio, TX, 2012. For Project Open Door — Donation for Unfunded Children and Capital Campaign.

9275
Whitener Family Foundation ✧ ☆
901 S. 1st St.
Abilene, TX 79602-1502

Established in 1996 in TX.
Donors: C. Cleve Whitener III; Lauren Engineers & Constructors, Inc.; Mary Rebecca Whitener.
Foundation type: Independent foundation.
Financial data (yr. ended 12/31/13): Assets, $10,234,331 (M); gifts received, $1,000; expenditures, $563,265; qualifying distributions, $455,653; giving activities include $455,653 for 18 grants (high: $121,600; low: $2,158).
Fields of interest: Christian agencies & churches.
Limitations: Applications not accepted. Giving primarily in GA; some giving in TX. No grants to individuals.
Application information: Unsolicited requests for funds not accepted.
Directors: C. Cleve Whitener III; Mary Rebecca Whitener.
Trustee: Les Hammond.
EIN: 752681790
Selected grants: The following grants are a representative sample of this grantmaker's funding activity:
$16,000 to Connecting Caring Communities, Abilene, TX, 2011. For general operations.
$3,000 to Young Life, Abilene, TX, 2011. For general operations.
$2,500 to Pregnancy Resources of Abilene, Abilene, TX, 2011. For general operations.
$1,500 to Abilene Christian University, Abilene, TX, 2011. For general operations.
$1,000 to Harmony Family Services, Abilene, TX, 2011. For general operations.
$1,000 to Messianic Jewish Bible Institute, Euless, TX, 2011. For general operations.

9276
Whole Planet Foundation ✧
550 Bowie St.
Austin, TX 78703-4677 (512) 542-0144
FAX: (512) 482-7000;
E-mail: general_info@wholeplanetfoundation.org;
Main URL: http://www.wholeplanetfoundation.org
E-Newsletter: https://www.wholeplanetfoundation.org/newsletter/
Instagram: http://instagram.com/wholeplanet
Pinterest: http://pinterest.com/wholefoods/whole-planet-foundation/
Twitter: http://twitter.com/wholeplanet
Whole Planet Blog: http://www.wholeplanetfoundation.org/blog/

Established in 2005 in DE and TX.
Donors: Whole Foods Market Services, Inc.; Pepsico; Seventh Generation; ITO EN.
Foundation type: Company-sponsored foundation.
Financial data (yr. ended 12/31/13): Assets, $11,029,995 (M); gifts received, $12,758,429; expenditures, $10,891,837; qualifying distributions, $10,887,218; giving activities include $8,994,331 for 51 grants (high: $500,000; low: $1,300).
Purpose and activities: The foundation creates and supports economic partnerships with the poor in developing-world communities that supply Whole Foods stores with product. Special emphasis is directed toward microfinance institutions in Latin America, Africa and Asia who in turn develop and offer microenterprise loan programs, training and other financial services to the self-employed poor.
Fields of interest: International development; International economic development; Economic development; Community development, business promotion; Social entrepreneurship; Community development, small businesses; Microfinance/microlending; Economically disadvantaged.
International interests: Africa; Asia; Latin America.

Type of support: Employee volunteer services; General/operating support; Capital campaigns.
Limitations: Applications not accepted. Giving primarily in NY and in developing communities in Africa, Argentina, Asia, Bangladesh, Costa Rica, Ethiopia, Guatemala, Haiti, Honduras, India, Indonesia, Kenya, Latin America, Nepal, Nicaragua, Peru, and Thailand. No grants to individuals.
Publications: Annual report; Financial statement; Newsletter; IRS Form 990 or 990-PF printed copy available upon request.
Application information: Contributes only to pre-selected organizations.
Officers and Directors:* John P. Mackey,* Co-Chair.; Lee Valkenaar,* Co-Chair.; Philip Sansone,* Pres. and Exec. Dir.; Glenda F. Flanagan; A.C. Gallo; Roberta Lang; Will Paradise; Walter E. Robb IV; Joe Rogoff; Jeff Teter; Jeff Turnas.
Number of staff: 6 full-time professional.
EIN: 202376273

9277
Wichita Falls Area Community Foundation ✧
807 8th St., Ste. 750
Wichita Falls, TX 76301-3334 (940) 766-0829
Contact: Teresa Pontius-Caves, Pres.
FAX: (940) 766-2861; E-mail: wfacf@wfacf.org; Additional e-mail: tpontiuscaves@wfacf.org; Main URL: http://www.wfacf.org
Facebook: http://www.facebook.com/pages/Wichita-Falls-Area-Community-Foundation/140029332687297?sk=wall

Established in 1999 in TX.
Foundation type: Community foundation.
Financial data (yr. ended 12/31/12): Assets, $39,961,797 (M); gifts received, $3,997,720; expenditures, $5,209,458; giving activities include $4,457,217 for 86+ grants (high: $1,300,000), and $292,290 for 163 grants to individuals.
Purpose and activities: The foundation seeks to provide charitable means for area residents to leave a legacy for the future benefit of their communities, to build agency endowments, and to promote philanthropy.
Fields of interest: Historic preservation/historical societies; Arts; Higher education; Education; Environment; Substance abuse, treatment; Health organizations, association; Medical research, institute; Offenders/ex-offenders, services; Employment, training; Recreation, community; Children/youth, services; Human services; Community development, neighborhood development; United Ways and Federated Giving Programs; Science; Disabilities, people with; Offenders/ex-offenders; Substance abusers.
Type of support: General/operating support; Continuing support; Capital campaigns; Building/renovation; Equipment; Emergency funds; Program development; Curriculum development; Fellowships; Technical assistance; Employee matching gifts; Scholarships—to individuals; Matching/challenge support.
Limitations: Applications accepted. Giving primarily to TX, particularly the metropolitan Wichita Falls area. No support for private foundations. No grants to individuals (except for scholarships).
Publications: Annual report; Informational brochure; Newsletter; Occasional report.
Application information: Visit foundation web site for application checklist, summary form, and guidelines. Letter of intent is required before submitting a full grant application; applicants will be notified that they are encouraged to submit a full application or that their project is unlikely to be funded based on letter of intent. Application form required.
Initial approach: Submit Letter of intent
Copies of proposal: 8
Deadline(s): Jan. 25 and Aug. 25 for letters of intent; Feb. 25 and Sept. 25 for full grant application; Mar. 1 for scholarships
Board meeting date(s): Feb., May, Aug., and Dec.
Final notification: June and Dec.
Officers and Directors:* Charles B. Prothro,* Chair.; Julia Whitmire,* Vice-Chair.; Teresa Pontius-Caves, Pres.; Warren Ayres,* Secy.-Treas.; D. Phil Bolin,* Emeritus; Ray Clymer,* Emeritus; Robert T. Priddy,* Emeritus; Joe Sherrill,* Emeritus; Gary H. Shores,* Emeritus; Kay Yeager,* Emeritus; Randy Aaron; Mac Cannedy; Drew Carnes; Barry Donnell; Carol Gunn; John Hirschi; Sarah Johnson; Matt LeVasseur; Katherine McGregor; Harry Patterson; Sara Jane Snell; Brian Stahler; Frank Tate; Danny W. Taylor; Pat Thacker; Carol Wagner; Chuck White.
Number of staff: 1 full-time professional; 2 full-time support.
EIN: 752817894

9278
The Wildcat Foundation ✧ ☆
301 Commerce St., Ste. 3300
Fort Worth, TX 76102-4133

Established in TX.
Donor: David Bonderman.
Foundation type: Independent foundation.
Financial data (yr. ended 12/31/13): Assets, $258 (M); gifts received, $4,248,910; expenditures, $4,299,902; qualifying distributions, $4,134,467; giving activities include $4,131,834 for 13 grants (high: $1,000,000; low: $50,000).
Fields of interest: Animals/wildlife.
Limitations: Applications not accepted. Giving primarily in CA, Washington, DC, and NY. No grants to individuals.
Application information: Unsolicited requests for funds not accepted.
Director: David Bonderman.
EIN: 456518655

9279
Todd A. Williams Family Foundation ✧
5119 Seneca Dr.
Dallas, TX 75209-2221 (214) 725-9265
Contact: Deborah Williams

Established in 2003 in TX.
Donors: Todd A. Williams; Water Street Advisors, LLC.
Foundation type: Independent foundation.
Financial data (yr. ended 12/31/12): Assets, $5,598,206 (M); gifts received, $1,430,285; expenditures, $1,077,126; qualifying distributions, $704,235; giving activities include $704,235 for grants.
Fields of interest: Education; Human services.
Application information: Application form required.
Initial approach: Proposal
Deadline(s): None
Officers: Todd A. Williams, Pres. and Treas.; Abigail Williams, V.P. and Secy.; Sandra Jo Williams, V.P.
Director: Kirk Rimer.
EIN: 550825689

9280
Ralph Wilson Public Trust ✧
5006 Sunflower Ln.
Temple, TX 76502-4887

Established in 1974 in TX.
Donor: Ralph Wilson†.
Foundation type: Independent foundation.
Financial data (yr. ended 12/31/11): Assets, $3,932 (M); expenditures, $3,187,425; qualifying distributions, $3,170,188; giving activities include $3,170,188 for 6 grants (high: $2,693,164; low: $139).
Purpose and activities: Giving mainly for the Ralph Wilson Youth Club; support also for cultural programs and child welfare.
Fields of interest: Arts; Youth development; Philanthropy/voluntarism.
Type of support: General/operating support; Capital campaigns.
Limitations: Applications not accepted. Giving limited to Temple, TX. No grants to individuals.
Application information: Contributes only to pre-selected organizations.
Officers: Jeff Wilson, Pres.; Jim Wilson, V.P.; Janice Wilson, Secy.; Sharon Wilson, Treas.
Trustees: Thomas Baird; John Cunningham; George Hester; William Reeder; Bette Snyder; Phillip Snyder; Maria Wilson; Sunny Wilson; Terri Wilson; Dean Winkler.
Number of staff: None.
EIN: 237351606

9281
Winkler Family Foundation ✧
960 Live Oak Cir.
Austin, TX 78746-3522
Contact: Matthew M. Winkler, Pres.
E-mail: mwink5@sbcglobal.net

Established in 2002 in TX.
Donor: Matthew M. Winkler.
Foundation type: Independent foundation.
Financial data (yr. ended 12/31/12): Assets, $13,357,290 (M); expenditures, $1,015,992; qualifying distributions, $983,000; giving activities include $983,000 for 46 grants (high: $100,000; low: $1,000).
Fields of interest: Education; Environment, natural resources.
Type of support: General/operating support.
Limitations: Applications not accepted. Giving primarily in TX. No grants to individuals.
Application information: Unsolicited requests for funds not accepted.
Officers: Matthew M. Winkler, Pres.; Margaret O. Winkler, V.P.
Trustee: Karen F. Phillips.
EIN: 710867442

9282
Winn Family Foundation ✧
5500 Preston Rd., No. 250
Dallas, TX 75205

Established in TX.

Donors: Stephen T. Winn; Christopher S. Winn; Natalie W. Amoroso.
Foundation type: Independent foundation.
Financial data (yr. ended 12/31/13): Assets, $14,101,457 (M); gifts received, $6,581,000; expenditures, $842,286; qualifying distributions, $770,584; giving activities include $770,500 for 7 grants (high: $500,000; low: $5,000).
Purpose and activities: Giving primarily to a school for boys.
Fields of interest: Elementary/secondary education.
Limitations: Applications not accepted. Giving primarily in TX. No grants to individuals.
Application information: Contributes only to pre-selected organizations.
Officers and Directors:* Stephen T. Winn,* Pres. and Treas.; Christopher S. Winn,* V.P.; Heather M. Winn,* V.P.; Melinda G. Winn,* V.P.; Natalie W. Amoroso,* V.P.; Sabrina King, Secy.
EIN: 452606351

9283
David and Eula Wintermann Foundation ✧
P.O. Box 337
Eagle Lake, TX 77434-0337 (979) 234-5551
Contact: Jack Johnson, Pres.

Established in TX.
Donors: Eula G. Wintermann†; Wintermann Marital Trust.
Foundation type: Independent foundation.
Financial data (yr. ended 09/30/13): Assets, $14,408,601 (M); expenditures, $844,049; qualifying distributions, $751,564; giving activities include $561,920 for 12 grants (high: $100,000; low: $500), and $24,000 for 4 grants to individuals (high: $8,000; low: $4,000).
Purpose and activities: Giving primarily for community development, and educational scholarships to students entering the medical field.
Fields of interest: Higher education; Medical school/education; Community/economic development.
Type of support: Scholarships—to individuals; Student loans—to individuals.
Limitations: Applications accepted. Giving limited to TX, with emphasis on Eagle Lake.
Application information: Application form required.
Initial approach: Proposal
Deadline(s): Apr. 1
Officers: Jack Johnson, Pres.; Donald N. Bendy, V.P.; Steve K. Balas, Secy.
Director: Judith Johnson.
EIN: 760082100
Selected grants: The following grants are a representative sample of this grantmaker's funding activity:
$100,000 to Texas A & M Foundation, College Station, TX, 2013. For Continuation of Funding the Wintermann Foundation Rice Improvement and Cropping Systems Fund.
$50,000 to American Cancer Society, Houston, TX, 2013. For Fund Research in the Name of David and Eula Wintermann Foundation.
$50,000 to Baylor College of Medicine, Houston, TX, 2013. For Continuation of Funding of the David and Eula Wintermann Foundation Brass Scholar Research Award.
$10,000 to Colorado River Foundation, Austin, TX, 2013. To Help Promote and Support the Natural Science Education and Outdoor Recreation Programs,.

9284
Irene S. Wischer Education Foundation ✧
c/o Frost National Bank
P.O. Box 2950
San Antonio, TX 78299-2950
Application address: P.O. Box 6730, Princeton, NJ 08541, tel.: (609) 771-7878

Established in 2007 in TX.
Donor: Irene S. Wischer†.
Foundation type: Independent foundation.
Financial data (yr. ended 12/31/13): Assets, $14,006,810 (M); expenditures, $1,013,332; qualifying distributions, $905,980; giving activities include $854,771 for 49 grants (high: $92,950; low: $571).
Purpose and activities: Giving scholarships to legal residents of Texas (who have been residing in the state for 12 consecutive months prior to completing the application), who are persons of good character, and who demonstrate academic potential and ability, as well as a need for financial assistance. Preference will be given to Christians who attend church regularly, though this is not an eligibility requirement.
Fields of interest: Higher education; Scholarships/financial aid.
Limitations: Applications accepted. Giving primarily in TX. No grants to individuals directly (scholarships are paid directly to the school).
Application information: Application form required.
Initial approach: Letter
Deadline(s): Mar. 1
Trustee: Frost National Bank, N.A.
EIN: 207532216
Selected grants: The following grants are a representative sample of this grantmaker's funding activity:
$15,000 to Saint Marys University, Graduate School Director of Grad Financial Aid, San Antonio, TX, 2012. For educational scholarship.

9285
Watson W. Wise Foundation ✧
(formerly Watson W. Wise Foundation & Charitable Trust)
110 N. College, Ste. 205
Tyler, TX 75702-7240 (903) 531-9615

Established around 1967 in TX.
Donor: Watson W. Wise†.
Foundation type: Independent foundation.
Financial data (yr. ended 12/31/12): Assets, $12,178,892 (M); expenditures, $712,872; qualifying distributions, $530,500; giving activities include $530,500 for grants.
Fields of interest: Arts; Higher education; Education; Health care; Health organizations, association; Human services; Children/youth, services; United Ways and Federated Giving Programs; Christian agencies & churches.
Limitations: Applications accepted. Giving primarily in TX, with emphasis on Tyler. No grants to individuals.
Application information: Application form not required.
Initial approach: Proposal
Deadline(s): None
Officers: Will A. Knight, Pres.; Calvin Clyde, Jr., V.P.; Shirley J. Chadwick, Secy.
Trustees: Thomas Clyde; Scott Knight.
EIN: 756064539

9286
Cyvia and Melvyn Wolff Foundation ✧ ☆
c/o ML Wolff
P.O. Box 219169
Houston, TX 77218

Established in 1997 in TX.
Donors: Curtis Wolff; Cyvia G. Wolff; Melvyn L. Wolff.
Foundation type: Independent foundation.
Financial data (yr. ended 11/30/13): Assets, $3,330,400 (M); expenditures, $640,345; qualifying distributions, $589,156; giving activities include $583,805 for 48 grants (high: $250,000; low: $300).
Fields of interest: Museums (art); Performing arts, orchestras; Libraries/library science; Education; Health care, clinics/centers; Cancer; Human services; United Ways and Federated Giving Programs; Jewish agencies & synagogues.
Limitations: Applications not accepted. Giving primarily in Houston, TX. No grants to individuals.
Application information: Contributes only to pre-selected organizations.
Board meeting date(s): Nov. and Apr.
Officers: Melvyn L. Wolff, Pres. and Treas.; Cyvia G. Wolff, V.P. and Secy.
Trustee: Curtis Wolff.
EIN: 760556526

9287
Pauline Sterne Wolff Memorial Foundation ✧
Texan Bldg., 333 W. Loop N., Ste. 410
Houston, TX 77024-7767 (713) 960-6616
Contact: Lynn Stanley
Application address: c/o Private Foundation Svcs., Inc., 4265 San Felipe, Ste. 1100, Houston, TX 77027, tel.: (713) 960-6616

Incorporated in 1922 in TX.
Donor: Henry J.N. Taub.
Foundation type: Independent foundation.
Financial data (yr. ended 12/31/12): Assets, $25,190,222 (M); expenditures, $1,229,227; qualifying distributions, $1,208,002; giving activities include $1,181,250 for 6 grants (high: $690,000; low: $10,000).
Purpose and activities: Giving primarily for Jewish welfare organizations, especially a home for the elderly and a community center; support also for medical education and research, and hospitals.
Fields of interest: Hospitals (specialty); Medical research, institute; Jewish federated giving programs.
Limitations: Applications accepted. Giving limited to TX, with emphasis on Harris County. No grants to individuals.
Application information: Application form required.
Initial approach: Letter
Deadline(s): Nov. 1
Officers: Henry J.N. Taub II, Pres.; H. Ben Taub, V.P. and Secy.-Treas.; Jenard M. Gross, V.P.; Regina J. Rogers, V.P.; Marc J. Shapiro, V.P.
EIN: 741110698

9288
The Wolslager Foundation ✧
P.O. Box 1191
San Angelo, TX 76902-1191 (325) 653-0478
Contact: Shirley Rogers, Secy.-Treas.

Established in 1993 in TX.
Donors: J.W. Wolslager; Josephine S. Wolslager†.
Foundation type: Independent foundation.
Financial data (yr. ended 12/31/13): Assets, $617,335 (M); expenditures, $3,634,997; qualifying distributions, $3,206,500; giving activities include $3,206,500 for 54 grants (high: $420,000; low: $2,500).
Purpose and activities: The foundation was established to improve the quality of life for individuals within the areas where the Wolslager family owned and operated their Coca-Cola business through Dec. 31, 1998. This goal is being met by providing support for many educational opportunities, making grants for medical facilities and services, supporting child development programs, and providing services for our elderly citizens.
Fields of interest: Health care; Geriatrics; Food services, congregate meals; Youth development, centers/clubs; Boys & girls clubs; Infants/toddlers; Children/youth; Youth; Minorities; Economically disadvantaged; Homeless.
Type of support: General/operating support; Capital campaigns; Building/renovation; Equipment; Program development; Curriculum development; Scholarship funds; Matching/challenge support.
Limitations: Giving limited to Tom Green, Irion, Runnels, McCulloch, Mills, Schleicher, El Paso, Concho, Sterling, Brown, Coke, Crockett, Culberson, and Hudspeth counties, TX, Dona Ana and Sierra counties, NM, and Pima, Cochise, and Santa Cruz counties, AZ. No support for religious and political organizations or for historical restoration. No grants to individuals.
Publications: Annual report.
Application information: Proposals accepted by invitation only. Application form required.
Initial approach: Letter of intent
Copies of proposal: 5
Deadline(s): Feb. 1st for letter of intent; May 15th for proposal
Board meeting date(s): Dec. 1
Final notification: Two months
Officers and Trustees:* J.W. Wolslager, Jr.,* Pres.; Stephen J. Wolslager,* V.P.; Shirley M. Rogers, Secy.-Treas.; James A. Carter; J.W. Wolslager III.
Number of staff: 2 full-time professional.
EIN: 752493763

9289
Wood Family Charitable Foundation, Inc. ✧

(formerly Clay and Louise Wood Charitable Foundation, Inc.)
3501 Faudree
Odessa, TX 79765 (432) 617-1387
Contact: Clay Wood, Pres.

Established in 1999 in TX.
Donors: Clay Wood; Jack Wood; Donald E. Wood.
Foundation type: Independent foundation.
Financial data (yr. ended 06/30/13): Assets, $1,118,774 (M); gifts received, $1,750,000; expenditures, $1,800,669; qualifying distributions, $1,800,669; giving activities include $1,800,000 for 4 grants (high: $1,650,000; low: $50,000).
Fields of interest: Performing arts centers; Arts; Higher education; Human services; United Ways and Federated Giving Programs.
Type of support: General/operating support; Scholarship funds; Scholarships—to individuals.
Limitations: Applications accepted. Giving primarily in Odessa, TX.
Application information: Application form required.
Initial approach: Proposal
Deadline(s): None
Officers: Clay Wood, Pres.; Donald E. Wood, V.P.; Jack Wood, V.P.; Louise Wood, V.P.; Gregory Wood, Secy.-Treas.
EIN: 752806006
Selected grants: The following grants are a representative sample of this grantmaker's funding activity:
$1,650,000 to Odessa College, Odessa, TX, 2013. For Construct Math and Science Building.

9290
The Woodforest Charitable Foundation ✧

1330 Lake Robbins Dr., Ste. 100
The Woodlands, TX 77380-3267
E-mail: info@woodforestcharitablefoundation.org; Main URL: http://www.woodforestcharitablefoundation.org/
Grants List: http://www.woodforestcharitablefoundation.org/gifts.htm

Established in 2005 in TX.
Donors: Woodforest National Bank; Southern States Brokerage; Mike Rose; Guy Lewis; Robert Marling; Michael H. Richmond; George Sowers; Fred Greene.
Foundation type: Company-sponsored foundation.
Financial data (yr. ended 12/31/13): Assets, $29,632,150 (M); gifts received, $5,233,376; expenditures, $997,854; qualifying distributions, $825,159; giving activities include $813,659 for 145 grants (high: $175,000; low: $100).
Purpose and activities: The foundation supports food banks and organizations involved with health, human services, and community development. Special emphasis is directed toward programs designed to address social issues; and promote public service.
Fields of interest: Health care, clinics/centers; Health care, patient services; Health care; Food banks; Boys & girls clubs; Children/youth, services; Aging, centers/services; Women, centers/services; Homeless, human services; Human services; Community/economic development.
Type of support: General/operating support; Program development.
Limitations: Applications not accepted. Giving primarily in areas of company operations in AL, FL, GA, IL, IN, KY, LA, MD, MS, NC, NY, OH, PA, SC, VA, and WV, with emphasis on TX. No grants to individuals.
Publications: Grants list.
Application information: Contributes only to pre-selected organizations.
Officers: Robert E. Marling, Jr., Pres.; Kim Marling, V.P. and Exec. Dir.; Vicki Richmond, Secy.-Treas.
Director: David Gottlieb.
EIN: 202516951

9291
The L.C. and Mary Worley Memorial Foundation ✧ ☆

P.O. Box 5427
Longview, TX 75608-5427 (903) 297-5101
Contact: Thomas D. Worley, Pres.

Established in 2005 in TX.
Donors: Thomas D. Worley; Dana Worley.
Foundation type: Independent foundation.
Financial data (yr. ended 12/31/13): Assets, $9,868,718 (M); expenditures, $538,010; qualifying distributions, $537,250; giving activities include $537,250 for 16 grants (high: $257,500; low: $1,500).
Fields of interest: Education; Human services; Religion.
Limitations: Applications accepted. Giving primarily in TX.
Application information: Application form not required.
Initial approach: Proposal
Deadline(s): None
Officers: Thomas D. Worley, Pres.; Tim Watson, V.P.; Dana Worley, Secy.-Treas.
EIN: 203964693
Selected grants: The following grants are a representative sample of this grantmaker's funding activity:
$257,500 to Fellowship Bible Church, Longview, TX, 2013. For building budget.
$100,000 to Coaches Outreach, Dallas, TX, 2013. For general support.
$50,000 to Pine Cove, Tyler, TX, 2013. For ministry to the military, Heights day camp.
$27,500 to LeTourneau University, Longview, TX, 2013. For Wheels project.
$5,000 to Child Evangelism Fellowship, Longview, TX, 2013. For general fund.
$4,000 to North American Mission Board, SBC, Alpharetta, GA, 2013. For New England Missions.
$3,750 to First Baptist Church of Longview, Longview, TX, 2013. For missions and children's ministries.
$3,000 to First Baptist Church Homer, Homer, LA, 2013. For general support.
$3,000 to Hiway 80 Rescue Mission, Longview, TX, 2012. For Hope Haven Women's Shelter.
$2,500 to LeTourneau University, Longview, TX, 2012. For Wheels project.
$1,500 to Wycliffe Bible Translators, Orlando, FL, 2013. For missionaries.

9292
The Wortham Foundation ✧

2727 Allen Pkwy., Ste. 1570
Houston, TX 77019-2125 (713) 526-8849
Contact: Barbara J. Snyder, Grants Coord.
FAX: (713) 526-7222; E-mail: bsnyder@wortham.org

Trust established in 1958 in TX.
Donors: Gus S. Wortham†; Lyndall F. Wortham†.
Foundation type: Independent foundation.
Financial data (yr. ended 09/30/13): Assets, $229,131,565 (M); expenditures, $11,939,620; qualifying distributions, $10,836,194; giving activities include $10,565,000 for 67 grants (high: $2,050,000; low: $5,000), and $35,750 for foundation-administered programs.
Purpose and activities: Support primarily for the arts, including the performing arts and museums, and community improvement, including civic beautification projects that benefit the citizens of Houston and Harris County, TX.
Fields of interest: Museums; Performing arts; Historic preservation/historical societies; Arts; Environment, beautification programs.
Type of support: General/operating support; Continuing support; Annual campaigns; Capital campaigns; Endowments; Emergency funds; Seed money; Matching/challenge support.

Limitations: Applications accepted. Giving limited to Houston and Harris County, TX. Generally, no grants to colleges, universities, or hospitals. No grants to individuals.
Publications: Annual report; Informational brochure (including application guidelines).
Application information: Please do not send bound copies of proposal. Application form required.
Initial approach: Letter
Copies of proposal: 1
Deadline(s): Submit unbound proposal preferably by the 2nd week of Jan., Apr., July, or Oct.
Board meeting date(s): Mid-Feb., May, Aug., and Nov.
Final notification: 3 months
Officers and Trustees:* Brady F. Carruth,* Chair.; R.W. Wortham III,* Pres.; Fred C. Burns,* Secy-Treas.; William V.H. Clarke, Cont.
Number of staff: 2 full-time support.
EIN: 741334356
Selected grants: The following grants are a representative sample of this grantmaker's funding activity:
$3,000,000 to Buffalo Bayou Partnership, Houston, TX, 2012. For capital support.
$1,300,000 to Houston Symphony Society, Houston, TX, 2012. For general operating support.
$1,000,000 to Hermann Park Conservancy, Houston, TX, 2012. For capital support.
$800,000 to Houston Grand Opera, Houston, TX, 2012. For general operating support.
$500,000 to Houston Parks Board, Houston, TX, 2012. For capital support.
$400,000 to Houston Ballet, Houston, TX, 2012. For general operating support.
$200,000 to Menil Foundation, Houston, TX, 2012. For general operating support.
$60,000 to Trees for Houston, Houston, TX, 2012. For general operating support.
$50,000 to Houston Center for Contemporary Craft, Houston, TX, 2012. For general operating support.
$25,000 to Audubon Society, Houston, Houston, TX, 2012. For capital support.

9293
Lola Wright Foundation ✧
c/o U.S. Trust
515 Congress Ave., 10th Fl.
Austin, TX 78701-3504 (512) 397-2001
Contact: Amber Carden
E-mail: amber.carden@ustrust.com; Main URL: http://fdnweb.org/lolawright

Incorporated in 1954 in TX.
Donor: Johnie E. Wright†.
Foundation type: Independent foundation.
Financial data (yr. ended 12/31/13): Assets, $26,723,025 (M); expenditures, $1,511,469; qualifying distributions, $1,172,779; giving activities include $1,145,420 for 73 grants (high: $270,000; low: $2,500).
Purpose and activities: Giving to support arts and culture, children and youth, community development, education, health, religion, social and human services, and sports and recreation.
Fields of interest: Media/communications; Visual arts; Museums; Performing arts; Arts; Education, early childhood education; Child development, education; Higher education; Adult education—literacy, basic skills & GED; Education, reading; Education; Environment; Medical care, rehabilitation; Health care; Substance abuse, services; Health organizations, association; Heart & circulatory diseases; AIDS; Alcoholism; Legal services; Human services; Children/youth, services; Child development, services; Family services; Residential/custodial care, hospices; Aging, centers/services; Minorities/immigrants, centers/services; Homeless, human services; United Ways and Federated Giving Programs; Infants/toddlers; Children/youth; Adults; Aging; Disabilities, people with; Minorities; Economically disadvantaged; Homeless.
Type of support: Continuing support; Building/renovation; Equipment; Program development.
Limitations: Applications accepted. Giving limited to within a 50-mile radius of Austin, TX. No grants to individuals; generally no support for operating budgets.
Publications: Application guidelines; Program policy statement (including application guidelines).
Application information: Application guidelines and forms available on foundation web site. Application form required.
Initial approach: Use application format on foundation web site
Copies of proposal: 10
Deadline(s): Feb. 28 and Aug. 31
Board meeting date(s): May and Nov.
Final notification: Within 3-4 months
Officers and Directors:* Wilford Flowers,* Pres.; Paul Hilgers,* V.P.; Ron Oliveira,* Secy.; Adrian Rhae Fowler; Carole Keeton; Hon. Brady Mueller; Jay Stewart.
EIN: 746054717

9294
Yarborough Foundation ✧
200 N. Loraine St., Ste. 1400
Midland, TX 79701-4782

Established in 2001 in TX.
Donors: W.B. Yarborough; Yarborough KRI, Inc.
Foundation type: Independent foundation.
Financial data (yr. ended 12/31/13): Assets, $12,256,198 (M); gifts received, $1,413,261; expenditures, $586,695; qualifying distributions, $511,568; giving activities include $490,676 for 41 grants (high: $35,000; low: $5,000).
Fields of interest: Higher education, university; Education.
Type of support: Program development; Conferences/seminars; General/operating support.
Limitations: Applications not accepted. Giving primarily in West TX. No support for religious or political organizations. No grants to individuals.
Application information: Contributes only to pre-selected organizations.
Officers: Ann A. Jackson, Pres.; Linda B. Yarborough, V.P.; Susan K. Yarborough, Secy.; Scott Dodds, Treas.
Number of staff: None.
EIN: 752919532
Selected grants: The following grants are a representative sample of this grantmaker's funding activity:
$10,000 to Big Bend Education Corporation, Terlingua, TX, 2012. For capital equipment project.
$10,000 to Commemorative Air Force, Midland, TX, 2012. For educational event.
$10,000 to Midland College Foundation, Midland, TX, 2012. For health programs.
$10,000 to Midland Memorial Foundation, Midland, TX, 2012. For nursing education Program.

9295
George & Fay Young Foundation, Inc. ✧
14850 Montfort Dr., Ste. 269
Dallas, TX 75254-7077 (972) 404-4001, ext. 3
Contact: Christopher Shaw, Grants. Off.
FAX: (972) 385-8990;
E-mail: christophershaw@gfyfoundation.org; E-mail for general inquiries: info@gfyfoundation.org; Main URL: http://www.gfyfoundation.org

Established in 1993 in TX as successor to George & Fay Young Charitable Foundation.
Donors: George Young†; Fay Cameron Young†.
Foundation type: Independent foundation.
Financial data (yr. ended 11/30/13): Assets, $68,066,297 (M); gifts received, $858,555; expenditures, $3,009,866; qualifying distributions, $2,493,131; giving activities include $2,208,980 for 43 grants (high: $100,000; low: $5,000).
Purpose and activities: Giving primarily for: 1) Education: The foundation seeks to support unique programs and experiences that have proven impact. The primary focus of its educational efforts is directed towards early childhood 0-5 and primary and secondary education. 2) Individual, Family, & Community Intervention: The foundation supports programs working to break destructive cycles and promote positive change while fostering self-reliance for individuals and families in part through equipping them with skills and knowledge to create and sustain healthy and successful lives. 3) Animal Awareness: The foundation focuses on programs in which animal welfare is the core component, as well as programs that promote the importance of the relationship between humans and animals. 4) Health: The foundation's focus for support to health issues revolves around several specific areas, research and support for cancer, diabetes, and vision loss. The foundation also looks to support environmental efforts that promote healthy living environments for all.
Fields of interest: Education; Animal welfare; Health care; Diabetes; Eye research; Human services; Children/youth, services; Family services; Aging, centers/services; Religion.
Type of support: General/operating support; Continuing support; Annual campaigns; Capital campaigns; Building/renovation; Endowments; Program development; Curriculum development; Scholarship funds; Matching/challenge support.
Limitations: Giving primarily in the Dallas/Fort Worth, TX, Metroplex, and the surrounding areas. No support for political organizations or research requests. No grants to individuals, or for conferences, deficit funding, or start-ups less than 3 yrs. old.
Application information: Videos, CDs, or cassettes are not accepted.
Initial approach: E-mail or telephone
Deadline(s): Apr. 15 and Sept. 15
Board meeting date(s): Oct. and May
Officers and Directors:* Carol Y. Marvin,* Pres.; Christopher Shaw, Exec. V.P.; John C. Franklin,* V.P.; Richard L. Ripley,* Secy.; Michael E. Marvin,* Treas.; John T. Green.
Number of staff: 2 full-time support.
EIN: 752478225

9296
The Zachry Foundation ✧
P.O. Box 33240
San Antonio, TX 78265-3240 (210) 258-2663
FAX: (210) 258-2199;
E-mail: foundation@zachry.com; Main URL: http://www.zachryfoundation.org

Incorporated in 1960 in TX.
Donors: H.B. Zachry Co.; Zachry Construction Corp.; Capitol Aggregates.
Foundation type: Independent foundation.
Financial data (yr. ended 12/31/13): Assets, $10,638,309 (M); gifts received, $50,000; expenditures, $2,251,858; qualifying distributions, $2,098,513; giving activities include $2,057,150 for 18 grants (high: $1,000,000; low: $10,000).
Purpose and activities: The areas of primary interest include: education, arts and humanities, and health and social services throughout San Antonio, TX.
Fields of interest: Humanities; Arts; Elementary/secondary education; Higher education; Health care; Human services; Engineering/technology.
Type of support: Annual campaigns; Capital campaigns; Building/renovation; Equipment; Program development; Matching/challenge support.
Limitations: Giving limited to San Antonio, TX, except for higher education grants, which are made only in Texas. No grants to individuals, or for endowments.
Application information: The foundation is not currently accepting unsolicited requests for funds.
Board meeting date(s): Early summer
Officers and Trustees:* J.P. Zachry,* Pres.; H.B. Zachry, Jr.,* V.P.; Murray L. Johnston, Jr.,* Secy.; Charles Ebrom,* Treas.; Ellen Zachry Carrie; Cathy Obriotti Green; Anne Zachry Rochelle; David S. Zachry; John B. Zachry; Mollie Steves Zachry.
Number of staff: 1 full-time professional.
EIN: 741485544

9297
M. B. and Edna Zale Foundation ✧
(formerly The Zale Foundation)
6360 LBJ Freeway, Ste. 205
Dallas, TX 75240-6479 (214) 855-0627
Contact: Leonard R. Krasnow, Pres.
FAX: (972) 726-7252;
E-mail: mail@zalefoundation.org; Main URL: http://www.zalefoundation.org

Incorporated in 1951 in TX.
Donor: Members of the Zale family.
Foundation type: Independent foundation.
Financial data (yr. ended 12/31/13): Assets, $32,825,940 (M); gifts received, $145,672; expenditures, $1,879,376; qualifying distributions, $1,610,836; giving activities include $1,252,783 for 139 grants (high: $300,000; low: $100).
Purpose and activities: Giving primarily for purposes that honor the tradition of its founders through grants that stimulate change. To accomplish this mission, the foundation acts as a catalyst for collaboration and makes grants in communities where the directors live or have an interest. Primary areas of interest include programs that serve the poor and disenfranchised, especially those that strengthen families, develop children, address the senior population, train people in job skills, and provide health services.
Fields of interest: Education; Hospitals (general); Human services; Children/youth, services; Homeless, human services; Jewish agencies & synagogues; Economically disadvantaged; Homeless.
Type of support: General/operating support; Seed money; Technical assistance.
Limitations: Applications accepted. Giving primarily in the communities of Dallas (Dallas County), TX, Palm Beach County, FL, and New York, NY (including Long Island). No grants to individuals, or for annual campaigns, emergency funds, deficit financing, renovation projects, endowment funds, conferences, study, films, publications, land acquisition, matching gifts, or continuing support; no loans. No grants for periods of more than 3 to 5 years.
Publications: Application guidelines; Annual report; Grants list.
Application information: Application form not required.
Initial approach: 1-2-page letter and proposal
Copies of proposal: 1
Deadline(s): 2 months prior to board meeting; see web site for exact dates
Board meeting date(s): Semiannually
Final notification: 3 months
Officers and Trustees:* Sheryl Bogen, Chair.; David Zale,* Vice-Chair.; Leonard R. Krasnow, Pres.; George Tobolowsky, Secy.-Treas.; David Fields; Leo Fields; Dana Gerard; Gloria Landsberg; Janet Landsberg; Maurice Plough, Jr.; Michael F. Romaine; Karen Seltzer; Barry Zale; Claudia Zale; Donald Zale.
Number of staff: 1 full-time professional; 1 full-time support; 1 part-time support.
EIN: 756037429
Selected grants: The following grants are a representative sample of this grantmaker's funding activity:
$1,750 to New York City Center, New York, NY, 2012. For arts/cultural.
$500 to University of Kentucky Research Foundation, Lexington, KY, 2012. For health/medical.

9298
Roger L. and Laura D. Zeller Charitable Foundation ✧ ☆
5005 West Avenue, Ste. 100
San Antonio, TX 78213-2711 (210) 343-3322
Contact: Ronald J. Herrmann, Tr.

Established in 1991 in TX.
Donors: Laura D. Zeller‡; Roger L. Zeller; Zeller Living Trust; Michael D. Zeller Trust of 1995; Ronald J. Herrmann.
Foundation type: Independent foundation.
Financial data (yr. ended 12/31/13): Assets, $1,787,718 (M); gifts received, $2,013,116; expenditures, $781,052; qualifying distributions, $763,900; giving activities include $763,900 for 12 grants (high: $517,000; low: $100).
Purpose and activities: Giving is limited to the following areas: health care, zoo and animal welfare, promotion of education, and charities related to the sport of bowling.
Fields of interest: Museums (children's); Education; Animal welfare; Zoos/zoological societies; Health care; Cancer; Cancer research; Recreation; Human services; Christian agencies & churches.
Type of support: General/operating support; Capital campaigns; Endowments.
Limitations: Applications accepted. Giving limited to Bexar County, TX, with emphasis on San Antonio. No grants to individuals.
Application information: Application form required.
Initial approach: Letter
Copies of proposal: 1
Deadline(s): None
Trustees: David S. Herrmann; Karen H. Herrmann; Ronald J. Herrmann.
EIN: 742610755
Selected grants: The following grants are a representative sample of this grantmaker's funding activity:
$50,000 to Haven for Hope of Bexar County, San Antonio, TX, 2010.
$50,000 to Saint Marys Hall, San Antonio, TX, 2011.
$30,133 to San Antonio Zoological Society, San Antonio, TX, 2011.
$25,000 to San Antonio Childrens Museum, San Antonio, TX, 2011.
$19,175 to San Antonio Museum of Art, San Antonio, TX, 2011.
$18,000 to University of Texas Health Science Center, San Antonio, TX, 2010.
$7,700 to Texas Biomedical Research Institute, San Antonio, TX, 2011.
$1,000 to Center for Security Policy, Washington, DC, 2011.
$1,000 to University of Texas Health Science Center, San Antonio, TX, 2011.

9299
Zephyr Foundation ✧ ☆
4006 FM 1035
Wellington, TX 79095-4420 (806) 447-2422
Contact: Valerie White, Pres.

Established in 1996 in TX.
Donors: Dave Swalm; Beth Swalm.
Foundation type: Independent foundation.
Financial data (yr. ended 12/31/13): Assets, $15,358,852 (M); expenditures, $1,170,016; qualifying distributions, $1,103,591; giving activities include $1,103,591 for 8 grants (high: $950,000; low: $2,500).
Purpose and activities: Giving primarily for education and community development.
Fields of interest: Education; Recreation; Human services.
Type of support: General/operating support; Continuing support; Capital campaigns; Building/renovation; Equipment; Scholarship funds; Matching/challenge support.
Limitations: Applications accepted. Giving primarily in Wellington, TX.
Application information: Application form not required.
Initial approach: Proposal
Deadline(s): None
Officers: Valerie White, Pres.; Pat White, V.P. and Secy.; Charles W. Darter, Jr., V.P.
EIN: 752647195
Selected grants: The following grants are a representative sample of this grantmaker's funding activity:
$20,000 to Amarillo Area Foundation, Amarillo, TX, 2012. For Educational Grant for the Postsecondary Success Initiative.

9300
Zimmer Family Foundation ✧
6380 Rogerdale Rd.
Houston, TX 77072-1646
Application address: c/o Noemi Warren, 40650 Encyclopedia Cir., Fremont, CA 94538-2453, tel.: (800) 777-8580

Established in 1992 in TX.
Donors: George Zimmer; Donna Zimmer; Robert E. Zimmer; David Edwab.
Foundation type: Independent foundation.
Financial data (yr. ended 12/31/12): Assets, $1,084,916 (M); gifts received, $467,400; expenditures, $1,165,127; qualifying distributions, $1,108,946; giving activities include $1,108,946 for grants.
Purpose and activities: Giving primarily for education, Jewish agencies, hospitals, and Jewish federated giving programs. The foundation awards scholarships to students who currently are enrolled in the final term of high school or who currently are enrolled in a community college, college, university or graduate school. The applicant's parent must be an employee or a former employee of The Men's Wearhouse, Inc.
Fields of interest: Higher education; Education; Hospitals (general).
Type of support: General/operating support; Scholarships—to individuals.
Limitations: Applications accepted. Giving in the U.S., with some emphasis on CA and TX.
Application information: Application form required.
Initial approach: Letter
Deadline(s): Feb. 11
Officers: George Zimmer, Chair.; David Edwab, Vice-Chair.; Kirk Warren, V.P.; Michael Conlon, Secy.; Gary Ckodre, Treas.
EIN: 760370782

9301
The Robert L. and Barbara Zorich Family Foundation ✧
1100 Louisiana St., Ste. 4900
Houston, TX 77002-5217

Established in 2000 in TX.
Donors: Barbara L. Zorich; Robert L. Zorich.
Foundation type: Independent foundation.
Financial data (yr. ended 12/31/13): Assets, $25,417,644 (M); gifts received, $6,035,493; expenditures, $1,497,676; qualifying distributions, $1,415,068; giving activities include $1,415,068 for 59 grants (high: $200,000; low: $1,000).
Fields of interest: Education; Health organizations, association; Christian agencies & churches; Protestant agencies & churches.
Limitations: Applications not accepted. Giving in the U.S., primarily in Houston, TX. No grants to individuals.
Application information: Contributes only to pre-selected organizations.
Trustees: Brynley Zorich Todd; Barbara L. Zorich; Bret A. Zorich; Robert L. Zorich; Robert M. Zorich.
EIN: 760664404
Selected grants: The following grants are a representative sample of this grantmaker's funding activity:
$110,000 to Holy Spirit Episcopal Church, Houston, TX, 2012. For Unrestricted use by Holy Spirit Episcopal Church.
$100,000 to Marine Corps Scholarship Foundation, Alexandria, VA, 2012. For Unrestricted use by Marine Corps Scholarship Foundation.
$60,000 to Cystic Fibrosis Foundation, Houston, TX, 2012. For Unrestricted use by Cystic Fibrosis Foundation.
$50,000 to Memorial Hermann Foundation, Houston, TX, 2012. For Unrestricted use by Memorial Hermann Foundation.
$45,000 to Memorial Assistance Ministries, Houston, TX, 2012. For Unrestricted use by Memorial Assistance Ministries.
$35,000 to Workfaith Connection, Houston, TX, 2012. For Unrestricted use by WorkFaith Connection.
$25,000 to United Way of Greater Houston, Houston, TX, 2012. For Unrestricted use by United Way of Greater Houston.
$25,000 to Won Heart Foundation, Sugar Land, TX, 2012. For Unrestricted use by WON Heart Foundation.
$10,000 to Child Advocates, Houston, TX, 2012. For Unrestricted use by child advocates.
$10,000 to Sigma Chi Foundation, Evanston, IL, 2012. For Unrestricted use by Sigma Chi Foundation.

UTAH

9302
The ALSAM Foundation ✧
6190 S. Moffat Farm Ln.
Salt Lake City, UT 84121-1793
Contact: Ronny L. Cutshall, Pres.

Established in 1984.
Donor: L.S. Skaggs.
Foundation type: Independent foundation.
Financial data (yr. ended 12/31/12): Assets, $161,566,486 (M); expenditures, $12,275,077; qualifying distributions, $11,764,943; giving activities include $11,298,846 for 35 grants (high: $6,486,346; low: $20,000).
Purpose and activities: Giving primarily for education, medical research, human services, and Catholic agencies and charities.
Fields of interest: Scholarships/financial aid; Education; Animals/wildlife, preservation/protection; Medical research, institute; Food services; Housing/shelter; Human services; Homeless, human services; Catholic federated giving programs; Science, research; Catholic agencies & churches; Religion; General charitable giving; Minorities; Hispanics/Latinos; Native Americans/American Indians; Economically disadvantaged; Homeless.
Type of support: Building/renovation; Scholarship funds; Research; Program-related investments/loans.
Limitations: Applications not accepted. Giving primarily in the western states. No grants to individuals.
Application information: Contributes only to pre-selected organizations.
Board meeting date(s): Varies
Officers and Trustees:* Ronny L. Cutshall,* Pres.; Rev. Msgr. J. Terrence Fitzgerald, V.P.; Claudia Skaggs Luttrell,* Secy.; Susie Skaggs Balukoff; Arnold LaGuardia; Don L. Skaggs; Mark S. Skaggs; The Northern Trust Co.
Number of staff: 1 full-time professional.
EIN: 742364289
Selected grants: The following grants are a representative sample of this grantmaker's funding activity:
$6,486,346 to University of Utah, Division of Genetic Epidemiology, Salt Lake City, UT, 2012. For recruitment.
$835,178 to Southern Utah University, Cedar City, UT, 2012. For building construction, scholarships and research.
$595,000 to Ducks Unlimited, Vancouver, WA, 2012. For positions of Project Biologist and Project Engineer.
$550,000 to Idaho State University Foundation, Pocatello, ID, 2012. For laboratory equipment for College Pharmacy.
$475,208 to Mater Dei Catholic High School, Chula Vista, CA, 2012. For Juan Diego English Language School and Science Academy.
$300,000 to University of Colorado Foundation, Aurora, CO, 2012. For Skaggs Scholars Program.
$245,000 to Scripps Health Foundation, San Diego, CA, 2012. For fellowship in Melanoma Surgery.
$60,000 to English Language Center of Cache Valley, Logan, UT, 2012. For scholarships and general support.
$60,000 to Idaho Zoological Society, Friends of Zoo Boise, Boise, ID, 2012. For general support.
$23,918 to University of Utah, College of Pharmacy, Salt Lake City, UT, 2012. For research.

9303
Art Works for Kids of Utah ✧
299 S. Main St., Ste. 2200
Salt Lake City, UT 84111

Donors: Beverley Sorenson; Christine Harris; The Sorenson Legacy Foundation; Joseph Sorenson.
Foundation type: Independent foundation.
Financial data (yr. ended 05/31/13): Assets, $189,979 (M); gifts received, $332,676; expenditures, $870,979; qualifying distributions, $866,813; giving activities include $762,561 for 37 grants (high: $175,442; low: $500).
Fields of interest: Arts, multipurpose centers/programs; Arts education; Elementary/secondary education.
Limitations: Applications not accepted. Giving primarily in Salt Lake City, UT. No grants to individuals.
Application information: Contributes only to pre-selected organizations.
Directors: Joan Fenton; James Sorenson; Joseph Sorenson.
EIN: 205711103
Selected grants: The following grants are a representative sample of this grantmaker's funding activity:
$67,040 to University of Utah, Salt Lake City, UT, 2011.
$20,000 to Granite School District, Salt Lake City, UT, 2011.
$20,000 to Spy Hop Productions, Salt Lake City, UT, 2011.
$20,000 to Utah Chamber Artists, Sandy, UT, 2011.
$20,000 to Utah State University, Logan, UT, 2011.
$18,000 to Southern Utah University, Cedar City, UT, 2011.
$17,053 to Brigham Young University, Provo, UT, 2011.
$13,000 to Uintah School District, Vernal, UT, 2011.
$12,671 to Childrens Dance Theater, Salt Lake City, UT, 2011.
$10,400 to Ririe-Woodbury Dance Company, Salt Lake City, UT, 2011.

9304
The Ashton Family Foundation ✧
199 N. 290 W., No. 100
Lindon, UT 84042-1810 (801) 226-1266
Contact: Dave Harkness
FAX: (801) 443-2310; E-mail: dee@bessmark.com

Established in 1993 in UT.
Donor: Alan C. Ashton.
Foundation type: Independent foundation.
Financial data (yr. ended 12/31/13): Assets, $11,959,098 (M); expenditures, $1,136,796; qualifying distributions, $1,106,700; giving activities include $1,054,611 for 95 grants (high: $264,200; low: $800).
Purpose and activities: Support for religious institutions, as well as education, the arts and health.
Fields of interest: Arts; Education; Health organizations, association; Mormon agencies & churches.
Type of support: Program development; Equipment; General/operating support.
Limitations: Applications accepted. Giving primarily in UT.
Publications: Application guidelines.
Application information: Application form required.
Initial approach: Letter
Copies of proposal: 1
Deadline(s): 15th of month prior to meeting
Board meeting date(s): Quarterly
Final notification: Varies
Officer: Dave Harkness, Exec. Dir.
Trustees: Adam Ashton; Alan C. Ashton; Annalura Ashton; Brigham Ashton; Elizabeth Ashton; Erin Ashton; Karen Ashton; Melissa Ashton; Morgan Ashton; Samuel Ashton; Spencer Ashton; Stephanie Ashton; Stephen Ashton; Traci Ashton; Emily Ann Eddington; Paul Eddington; Allison Norton; Toby Norton; Eliza Smith; Michael Smith; Heath Westfall; Rebekah Westfall; Amy Jo Young; Chad Young.
Number of staff: 1 part-time support.
EIN: 870480108

9305
Ruth Eleanor Bamberger and John Ernest Bamberger Memorial Foundation ✧
136 S. Main St., Ste. 418
Salt Lake City, UT 84101-1690 (801) 364-2045
Contact: Eleanor Roser, Chair.
E-mail: bambergermemfdn@qwestoffice.net; Main URL: http://www.ruthandjohnbambergermemorialfdn.org

Incorporated in 1947 in UT.
Donors: Ernest Bamberger†; Eleanor F. Bamberger†.
Foundation type: Independent foundation.
Financial data (yr. ended 12/31/12): Assets, $20,566,629 (M); expenditures, $1,465,329; qualifying distributions, $1,339,736; giving activities include $1,260,112 for 89 grants (high: $202,000; low: $2,000).
Purpose and activities: Giving primarily for secondary education, especially undergraduate scholarships for student nurses, and for schools, hospitals and health agencies, youth and child welfare agencies and a natural history museum.
Fields of interest: Museums (natural history); Elementary/secondary education; Higher education; Medical school/education; Nursing care; Health care; Human services; Children/youth, services.
Type of support: General/operating support; Continuing support; Equipment; Scholarship funds; Scholarships—to individuals.
Limitations: Giving limited to UT. No grants to individuals, except for scholarships to local students (which are not paid directly to the individual), or for endowment or building funds, research, or matching gifts.
Application information: The foundation is not accepting requests from new organizations at this time. Application form not required.
Initial approach: Letter to Ellie Roser, Chair.
Copies of proposal: 6
Deadline(s): Application deadlines available on foundation web site; application deadlines vary from year to year.
Board meeting date(s): Biannually
Final notification: 2 months

Officer and Members:* Eleanor Roser,* Chair.; Julie Barrett; Clark P. Giles; Carol Olwell; Harris Simmons.
Number of staff: None.
EIN: 876116540

9306
The B. W. Bastian Foundation ✧
51 W. Center St., Ste. 755
Orem, UT 84057-4605

Established in 1997 in UT.
Donor: Bruce W. Bastian.
Foundation type: Independent foundation.
Financial data (yr. ended 12/31/13): Assets, $11,526,540 (M); expenditures, $916,046; qualifying distributions, $915,286; giving activities include $703,600 for grants.
Purpose and activities: Giving primarily for the arts and human services.
Fields of interest: Performing arts; Performing arts, ballet; Arts; AIDS; Human services; Foundations (private grantmaking); LGBTQ.
Limitations: Applications not accepted. Giving primarily in UT. No grants to individuals.
Application information: Contributes only to pre-selected organizations.
Trustees: Bruce W. Bastian; Brent Erklens; Rich Ith; Michael S. Marriott.
EIN: 841378232

9307
Brent and Bonnie Jean Beesley Foundation ✧
20 N. Main St., Ste. 308
St. George, UT 84770-5897

Established in 1996 in UT.
Donors: Bonnie Jean Beesley; Brent Beesley; Ryan Denney; Laura Denney; Doug Jolley; Mary Jolley; Heritage Holding Company; Heritage Holding Corp.
Foundation type: Independent foundation.
Financial data (yr. ended 12/31/13): Assets, $21,151,195 (M); gifts received, $2,492,351; expenditures, $1,699,257; qualifying distributions, $1,627,130; giving activities include $1,562,850 for 48 grants (high: $951,067; low: $500).
Fields of interest: Arts; Higher education; Education; Health organizations; Human services.
Limitations: Applications not accepted. Giving primarily in UT. No grants to individuals.
Application information: Unsolicited requests for funds not accepted.
Officer and Trustees:* Bonnie Jean Beesley,* Pres.; Daniel Beesley,* Admin.; Katherine Beesley,* Admin.; Brent Beesley; David B. Beesley; Sarah Beesley; Amy Broadbent; Mark Broadbent; Brian D. Chadaz; Laura Jean Denney; Ryan C. Denney; Glenn Goodrich; Doug T. Jolley; Mary Jolley; Troy Lewis; Verlan Terry.
EIN: 870568595

9308
Bertin Family Foundation ✧ ☆
723 Mont Clair Dr.
North Salt Lake, UT 84054-3382

Established in 1999 in UT.
Donors: Kim C. Bertin; Jennifer Bertin.
Foundation type: Independent foundation.
Financial data (yr. ended 12/31/13): Assets, $11,005,254 (M); expenditures, $569,595; qualifying distributions, $493,282; giving activities include $493,282 for 37 grants (high: $140,000; low: $300).
Fields of interest: Arts; Higher education; Human services; Christian agencies & churches; Mormon agencies & churches.
Limitations: Applications not accepted. Giving primarily in UT.
Application information: Unsolicited requests for funds not accepted.
Directors: Alex M. Bertin; James A. Bertin; Stephanie Bertin; Michelle Garff; Elizabeth B. Mumford.
Trustees: Kim C. Bertin; Jennifer Bertin.
EIN: 870638640

9309
R. Harold Burton Foundation ✧
P.O. Box 58477
Salt Lake City, UT 84158-0477 (801) 715-7140
Contact: Richard G. Horne, Exec. Dir.
FAX: (801) 364-6783; Address for hand delivery or FedEx.: 709 E. South Temple St., Salt Lake City, UT 84102

Established in 1987 in UT.
Donor: Robert Harold Burton‡.
Foundation type: Independent foundation.
Financial data (yr. ended 12/31/13): Assets, $23,792,955 (M); expenditures, $1,504,540; qualifying distributions, $1,458,025; giving activities include $1,186,980 for 77 grants (high: $548,500; low: $1,000).
Purpose and activities: Giving primarily for education, science, literacy, and health.
Fields of interest: Higher education; Education; Health care; Health organizations, association.
Type of support: Continuing support; Annual campaigns; Building/renovation; Equipment; Emergency funds; Program development; Fellowships; Scholarship funds; Research; Matching/challenge support.
Limitations: Applications accepted. Giving primarily in the greater Salt Lake metropolitan area in UT. No grants for overhead expenses, or endowments.
Publications: Application guidelines.
Application information:
Board meeting date(s): Apr. and Sept.
Final notification: After June 1 and Nov. 1
Officers and Board Members:* Judith Burton Moyle,* Chair.; Frederick A. Moreton,* Vice-Chair.; Richard G. Horne,* Exec. Dir.; Lucy Moreton Hawes; Rebecca Burton Moyle; O. Wood Moyle IV.
Trustee: Wells Fargo Bank Northwest, N.A.
Number of staff: 1 full-time professional; 1 part-time professional.
EIN: 742425567
Selected grants: The following grants are a representative sample of this grantmaker's funding activity:
$20,000 to University of Utah, Department of Genetics, Salt Lake City, UT, 2012.

9310
The Call Foundation ✧
4 Dartmoor Ln.
Salt Lake City, UT 84103-2279

Established in 2007 in UT.
Donor: Flying J Inc.
Foundation type: Independent foundation.
Financial data (yr. ended 12/31/13): Assets, $4,516,967 (M); gifts received, $2,400,000; expenditures, $1,126,023; qualifying distributions, $1,126,023; giving activities include $1,125,894 for 51 grants (high: $550,000; low: $10).
Fields of interest: Youth development; YM/YWCAs & YM/YWHAs; Children/youth, services.
Limitations: Applications not accepted. Giving primarily in Salt Lake City, UT. No grants to individuals.
Application information: Unsolicited requests for funds not accepted.
Officers and Trustees:* Crystal Call Maggelet,* Pres.; Charles E. Maggelet,* V.P.; Thad J. Call,* Treas.
EIN: 208389909
Selected grants: The following grants are a representative sample of this grantmaker's funding activity:
$55,000 to Weber State University, Ogden, UT, 2012. For High Quality Educational Programs to Students.
$50,000 to University of Utah, Salt Lake City, UT, 2012. For High Quality Educational Programs to Students in Utah.
$7,500 to AAA Fair Credit Foundation, Salt Lake City, UT, 2012. To Benefit Families to Save Money.
$5,000 to Box Elder Community Pantry, Brigham City, UT, 2012. For Serve Less Fortunate with Emergency Food Service.
$5,000 to Family Summit Foundation, Ogden, UT, 2012. To assist to Support Families Through the Grieving Process.
$5,000 to Prevent Child Abuse Utah, Ogden, UT, 2012. To Assist with the Costs of Offering Prevention Programs.
$5,000 to Utah AIDS Foundation, Salt Lake City, UT, 2012. To Aid in the Awareness and Prevention on the Aids Virus.
$5,000 to Your Community Connection, Ogden, UT, 2012. To Assist with Maintaining the Family Crisis Center.

9311
The Community Foundation of Utah ✧
423 W. 800 S., Ste. A101
Salt Lake City, UT 84101 (801) 559-3005
Contact: Fraser Nelson, Exec. Dir.
FAX: (866) 935-2353; E-mail: info@utahcf.org; Main URL: http://www.utahcf.org
Facebook: https://www.facebook.com/utahcf
Twitter: http://twitter.com/utahcf
YouTube: http://www.youtube.com/TheUtahCF

Established in 2007 in UT.
Foundation type: Community foundation.
Financial data (yr. ended 12/31/12): Assets, $10,267,618 (M); gifts received, $7,425,891; expenditures, $1,372,408; giving activities include $1,113,308 for 27 grants (high: $271,665).
Purpose and activities: The foundation's mission is to harness Utah's entrepreneurial spirit in service to the common good through smart philanthropy.
Fields of interest: Arts; Education; Environment; Health care; Human services; Religion.
Limitations: Applications accepted. Giving primarily in Utah.
Publications: Annual report; Financial statement.
Application information:
Initial approach: Contact foundation for grant information

Officers and Trustees:* Greg Warnock, Ph.D.*, Chair.; Mary Hall,* Vice-Chair.; Jeramy Lund,* Treas.; Fraser Nelson, Exec. Dir.; Brent Andrewsen; Trish Coughlin; Stephanie Harpst; Lewis Hower; Scott Huntsman; Kimberley Jones; Kym McClelland; Blake Modersitzki; Eric Shaw; Elizabeth Tashjian, Ph.D.; Brent Thomson; Devin Thorpe.
EIN: 743211770

9312
Lawrence T. and Janet T. Dee Foundation ✧
P.O. Box 58767
Salt Lake City, UT 84158-0767 (801) 355-5113

Established in 1971 in UT.
Donors: L.T. Dee†; Janet T. Dee†; Thomas D. Dee II†.
Foundation type: Independent foundation.
Financial data (yr. ended 12/31/13): Assets, $59,599,435 (M); expenditures, $3,080,530; qualifying distributions, $2,583,479; giving activities include $2,454,233 for 122 grants (high: $500,000; low: $1,000).
Purpose and activities: Support for healthcare services, education, cultural programs, including the fine and performing arts, and community and social service agencies.
Fields of interest: Visual arts; Performing arts; Arts; Child development, education; Higher education; Education; Hospitals (general); Medical care, rehabilitation; Health care; Medical research, institute; Human services; Children/youth, services; Child development, services; Family services.
Type of support: General/operating support; Annual campaigns; Building/renovation; Equipment; Endowments; Program development; Scholarship funds; Research; Matching/challenge support.
Limitations: Applications accepted. Giving primarily in Salt Lake City and Ogden, UT. No grants to individuals; no loans.
Publications: Application guidelines.
Application information: Application form not required.
Initial approach: Letter
Deadline(s): None, but suggest no later than Sept. 30
Trustee: Wells Fargo Bank, N.A.
Directors: David Dee; Matthew T. Dee; Thomas D. Dee.
EIN: 876150803

9313
Dialysis Research Foundation ✧
5575 S. 500 E.
Ogden, UT 84405-6907 (801) 479-0351

Established in 1984.
Foundation type: Independent foundation.
Financial data (yr. ended 12/31/12): Assets, $0 (M); gifts received, $500; expenditures, $1,002,587; qualifying distributions, $760,890; giving activities include $760,890 for 5 grants (high: $707,000; low: $8,364).
Purpose and activities: Giving limited to renal disease research and treatment, and for non-profit kidney disease foundations.
Fields of interest: Medical research, institute.
Type of support: Research.
Limitations: Giving primarily in UT.
Application information: The foundation no longer awards grants to individual patients.
Initial approach: Letter
Deadline(s): None
Officers and Board Members:* Fred Galvez,* Pres.; Mardee Hagen,* Secy. and Exec. Dir.; Todd Schenck,* Treas.; Adhish Agarwal; Allen Berrett; Neal Berube; Pam Corbridge; Kelvin Jackson; Lee L. Miles; Harry Senekjian, M.D.
EIN: 942819009
Selected grants: The following grants are a representative sample of this grantmaker's funding activity:
$707,000 to University of Utah, Salt Lake City, UT, 2012. For Rural Center Support.

9314
Jarvis and Constance Doctorow Family Foundation
1238 Lake St.
Salt Lake City, UT 84105-1222
Contact: Suzanne Larson, Exec. Dir.; Zoe Rodriguez, Asst. and Advisory Comm.
E-mail: doctorowfoundation@gmail.com; Main URL: http://www.doctorowfoundation.org

Established in 2005 in NY.
Donors: Jarvis Doctorow; Constance Doctorow†.
Foundation type: Independent foundation.
Financial data (yr. ended 12/31/12): Assets, $8,816,494 (M); expenditures, $710,722; qualifying distributions, $646,372; giving activities include $545,250 for 49 grants (high: $130,000; low: $500).
Purpose and activities: The foundation is committed to supporting non-profit organizations that provide mental health services and also those that are devoted to cultural activity in the performing, visual, and written arts. The foundation also supports educational activities related to the areas mentioned above. Preference in mental health applications will be given to organizations based in metropolitan New York, NY.
Fields of interest: Performing arts, theater; Performing arts, music; Arts; Education; Mental health/crisis services; Human services.
Limitations: Applications not accepted. Giving primarily in Hunter and New York, NY, and UT. No support for political or religious organizations. No grants to individuals, or for operating expenses.
Application information: Grants are by invitation only, and the foundation does not accept letters of inquiry or unsolicited applications.
Board meeting date(s): Quarterly
Officer: Suzanne Larson, Exec. Dir.; Francois Camoin.
Trustees: Jarvis Doctorow; Suzanne Larson.
EIN: 137415914
Selected grants: The following grants are a representative sample of this grantmaker's funding activity:
$130,000 to Catskill Mountain Foundation, Hunter, NY, 2012. To support Performing Arts Programming, 2-13 Performance Season, and General Operating Expenses.
$15,000 to Perspectives Ensemble, New York, NY, 2012. For Promoting Music Performance - Recording.
$13,500 to VSA Arts of Utah, Salt Lake City, UT, 2012. To support programming.
$13,500 to Weber State University, Ogden, UT, 2012. For Bonneville Chamber Music Festival.
$10,000 to Dance Theater of Harlem, New York, NY, 2012. To support Music Education.
$7,500 to Cancer Wellness House, Salt Lake City, UT, 2012. For Supporting Wellness Through Art.
$5,000 to Salt Lake Acting Company, Salt Lake City, UT, 2012. To support New Play Sounding Series.
$4,500 to Jewish Family Services, Salt Lake City, UT, 2012. For counseling program.

9315
Dr. Ezekiel R. and Edna Wattis Dumke Foundation ✧
P.O. Box 776
Kaysville, UT 84037-0776 (801) 497-9474
Contact: Denise R. Johnsen, Office Mgr.
E-mail: erd@fndtn.org

Incorporated in 1959 in UT.
Foundation type: Independent foundation.
Financial data (yr. ended 12/31/12): Assets, $14,717,184 (M); expenditures, $806,879; qualifying distributions, $611,532; giving activities include $600,000 for 8 grants (high: $250,000; low: $10,000).
Purpose and activities: Support for organizations involved with arts and culture, education, the environment, and health and human services.
Fields of interest: Arts; Higher education; Environment, natural resources; Hospitals (general); Health care; Children/youth, services.
Type of support: Equipment; Land acquisition; Technical assistance; Matching/challenge support.
Limitations: Giving limited to the western region of the U.S., with emphasis on MT, NM, UT, and WY. No support for religious or political organizations. No grants to individuals or for scholarships.
Publications: Application guidelines.
Application information: Full proposals are by invitation only. Application form required.
Initial approach: Telephone, e-mail, or letter requesting application form and deadline
Copies of proposal: 4
Deadline(s): Varies by year
Board meeting date(s): Approx. Apr. and Aug.
Final notification: Within 6 weeks after board meeting
Officers: Andrea Dumke Manship, Pres.; Nancy H. Schwanfelder, V.P.; Claire Dumke Ryberg, Secy.; Ezekiel R. Dumke, Jr., Treas.
EIN: 876199783

9316
The Katherine W. and Ezekiel R. Dumke, Jr. Foundation ✧
P.O. Box 776
Kaysville, UT 84037-0776 (801) 544-4626
E-mail: kwd@fndtn.org

Established in 1988 in UT.
Donors: Ezekiel R. Dumke, Jr.; Katherine W. Dumke.
Foundation type: Independent foundation.
Financial data (yr. ended 12/31/13): Assets, $20,042,485 (M); expenditures, $986,306; qualifying distributions, $797,404; giving activities include $769,150 for 16 grants (high: $175,000; low: $1,000).
Purpose and activities: Giving primarily for higher education and health organizations.
Fields of interest: Higher education; Health care; Health organizations.

Type of support: Equipment; Program development; Technical assistance; Matching/challenge support.
Limitations: Applications accepted. Giving limited to the intermountain area, with emphasis on UT. No grants to individuals, or for scholarships or general operating expenses.
Application information: Full proposals are by invitation only, upon review of Letter of Inquiry. Application form required.
Initial approach: Request Letter of Inquiry via Email or Proposal
Deadline(s): Feb. 15 (for Letter of Inquiry); and March 25 (for proposal, if invited)
Officers and Trustees:* Katherine E. Thornton,* Pres.; Andrea Dumke-Manship, 1st V.P.; Erin T. Linder, 2nd V.P.; E.R. Dumke IV,* Secy.-Treas.; Ezekiel R. Dumke, Jr.; Mitchell Dumke; Elise D. Miller; Emily R. Nelson; Claire D. Ryberg; April T. Schutjer; Scott S. Thornton.
EIN: 870461899

9317
Willard L. Eccles Charitable Foundation ✧
P.O. Box 58198
Salt Lake City, UT 84158-0198 (801) 582-4483
Contact: Stephen Eccles Denkers, Exec. Dir.
FAX: (801) 582-2955; E-mail: steve@wleccles.org; Main URL: http://www.wleccles.org

Established in 1981 in UT.
Foundation type: Independent foundation.
Financial data (yr. ended 03/31/13): Assets, $31,210,202 (M); expenditures, $1,833,552; qualifying distributions, $1,702,980; giving activities include $1,354,321 for 54 grants (high: $690,000; low: $900).
Purpose and activities: Grants primarily for education, the environment, social services, basic science, and healthcare for the underserved.
Fields of interest: Higher education; Education; Environment; Health care; Human services.
Type of support: General/operating support; Capital campaigns; Building/renovation; Equipment; Land acquisition; Fellowships; Scholarship funds; Research; Matching/challenge support.
Limitations: Giving primarily in UT, with emphasis on Salt Lake City. No grants to individuals.
Application information:
Initial approach: Use online application process on foundation web site
Deadline(s): Applications are accepted only in the 3-month window prior to the committee meeting Apr., May and June
Board meeting date(s): Quarterly
Officer and Committee Members:* Stephen E. Denkers,* Exec. Dir.; William E. Coit, M.D., Secy.; Susan Coit; Julie Denkers; Stephen G. Denkers; Susan E. Denkers; Ann C. Goss; Barbara Coit Yeager.
Trustee: Wells Fargo Bank Northwest, N.A.
Number of staff: 1 full-time support.
EIN: 942759395
Selected grants: The following grants are a representative sample of this grantmaker's funding activity:
$249,913 to University of Utah, Salt Lake City, UT, 2012.
$61,000 to University of Utah, Salt Lake City, UT, 2012.
$50,000 to Ogden School Foundation, Ogden, UT, 2012.
$25,000 to Road Home, Salt Lake City, UT, 2012.
$25,000 to Utah Food Bank, Salt Lake City, UT, 2012.
$16,000 to Humane Society, Oregon, Portland, OR, 2012.
$15,000 to Spy Hop Productions, Salt Lake City, UT, 2012.
$10,000 to University of Utah, Salt Lake City, UT, 2012.
$5,000 to San Miguel Educational Fund, Telluride, CO, 2012.
$4,000 to Humane Society of Central Oregon, Bend, OR, 2012.

9318
Eccles Family Foundation ✧
(formerly Spencer F. & Cleone P. Eccles Family Foundation)
P.O. Box 3028
Salt Lake City, UT 84110-3028

Established in 1993 in UT.
Donors: Spencer F. Eccles; Hope Eccles Behle†; Daisy Griffin Charitable Remainder Trust; Bill Golding Charitable Remainder Trust.
Foundation type: Independent foundation.
Financial data (yr. ended 06/30/13): Assets, $49,534,971 (M); expenditures, $1,528,071; qualifying distributions, $1,234,943; giving activities include $1,190,356 for 25 grants (high: $400,000; low: $1,000).
Fields of interest: Historic preservation/historical societies; Education; Human services; Foundations (private grantmaking).
Limitations: Applications not accepted. Giving primarily in Salt Lake City, UT. No grants to individuals.
Application information: Contributes only to pre-selected organizations.
Trustees: Spencer Eccles; Wells Fargo Bank, N.A.
EIN: 876227329
Selected grants: The following grants are a representative sample of this grantmaker's funding activity:
$2,500 to Ballet West, Salt Lake City, UT, 2011.

9319
George S. and Dolores Dore Eccles Foundation ✧
79 S. Main St., 14th Fl.
Salt Lake City, UT 84111-1929 (801) 246-5340
Contact: Lisa Eccles, Pres.
FAX: (801) 350-3510; E-mail: gseg@gseccles.org; Main URL: http://www.gsecclesfoundation.org

Incorporated in 1958 in UT; absorbed Lillian Ethel Dufton Charitable Trust in 1981.
Donor: George S. Eccles†.
Foundation type: Independent foundation.
Financial data (yr. ended 12/31/13): Assets, $665,894,217 (M); expenditures, $26,760,221; qualifying distributions, $21,838,855; giving activities include $19,753,046 for 368+ grants (high: $5,000,000).
Purpose and activities: The foundation is dedicated to serving the people of the state of Utah by carrying forth the philanthropic interests and goals of its founders. The foundation supports projects and programs that have the potential to make a significant difference in bettering Utah's communities and enriching the quality of life of its citizens, granting funds in the following areas: arts and culture, social services, education, health care, and preservation and conservation.
Fields of interest: Visual arts; Performing arts; Arts; Higher education; Environment; Hospitals (general); Health care; Medical research, institute; Human services; Children/youth, services; Economics.
Type of support: General/operating support; Annual campaigns; Capital campaigns; Building/renovation; Equipment; Program development; Professorships; Scholarship funds; Research; Program-related investments/loans; Matching/challenge support.
Limitations: Applications accepted. Giving primarily in the intermountain area, particularly UT. No support for private foundations or conduit organizations. No grants to individuals, or for endowment funds, contingencies, deficits, debt reduction, conferences, seminars, or medical research.
Application information: Application form required.
Initial approach: Letter of inquiry or complete the online grant application form request on foundation's web site
Copies of proposal: 3
Deadline(s): None
Board meeting date(s): Quarterly
Final notification: Following meeting
Officers and Directors:* Spencer F. Eccles,* Chair. and C.E.O.; Lisa Eccles,* Pres.; Robert M. Graham,* Secy.-Treas. and Gen. Counsel.
Number of staff: 1
EIN: 876118245
Selected grants: The following grants are a representative sample of this grantmaker's funding activity:
$2,691,000 to University of Utah, Office of the President, Salt Lake City, UT, 2012. For a year-end grant to be held in the Special Fund.
$2,000,000 to University of Utah, David Eccles School of Business, Salt Lake City, UT, 2012. For significant additional support for construction of the new building for the David Eccles School of Business.
$2,000,000 to Utah Symphony and Opera, Salt Lake City, UT, 2012. For Annual support and for capital campaign.
$500,000 to Intermountain Healthcare, Salt Lake City, UT, 2012. For Child First and Always capital campaign, specifically for construction of Outpatient Services Building to be located on leased golf course property.
$475,000 to Ballet West, Salt Lake City, UT, 2012. For live orchestra music performed by the Utah Chamber Orchestra for its 2012/13 season.
$250,000 to Saint Annes Center, Ogden, UT, 2012. For Capital Campaign for a new St. Anne's Center (including a homeless shelter, soup kitchen and donations warehouse) in Ogden, Utah, serving homeless/underprivileged individuals and families.
$24,440 to University of Utah, Development Office, Salt Lake City, UT, 2012. To be a Presenting Sponsor of the President's Dinner, held October 26, 2012.
$20,000 to Salt Lake Arts Council Foundation, Salt Lake City, UT, 2012. For two projects: Twilight Concert Series and Living Traditions Festival.
$20,000 to Sunshine Terrace Foundation, Logan, UT, 2012. For its Therapy Walk and Gardens, specifically to purchase and install three ADA therapy stations.
$15,000 to Utah Youth Mentor Project, Salt Lake City, UT, 2012. For its program that mentors youth who are aging out of eligibility for foster care,

specifically to help with their transition to adult living.

9320
Marriner S. Eccles Foundation ✧
79 S. Main St., 13th Fl.
Salt Lake City, UT 84111-1929
Contact: Catherine Caine Stirling, Exec. Dir.
E-mail: mseccles@xmission.com

Established in 1973 in Utah.
Donor: Marriner S. Eccles†.
Foundation type: Independent foundation.
Financial data (yr. ended 03/31/13): Assets, $29,460,275 (M); expenditures, $1,343,511; qualifying distributions, $1,053,819; giving activities include $978,000 for 117 grants (high: $55,000; low: $1,000).
Purpose and activities: Giving primarily for higher education; health, hospitals, and medical research; arts and culture, including the performing arts, fine arts, and museums; and family and social services, including programs for rehabilitation, the elderly, drug and alcohol abuse and prevention, youth, women, the disabled, and the homeless.
Fields of interest: Visual arts; Museums; Performing arts; Performing arts, dance; Performing arts, theater; Humanities; Arts; Higher education; Medical school/education; Environment; Hospitals (general); Reproductive health, family planning; Medical care, rehabilitation; Nursing care; Health care; Substance abuse, services; Mental health/crisis services; Health organizations, association; AIDS; Alcoholism; Biomedicine; Medical research, institute; Cancer research; Food services; Housing/shelter, development; Human services; Children/youth, services; Family services; Aging, centers/services; Women, centers/services; Homeless, human services; Infants/toddlers; Adults; Aging; Disabilities, people with; Physically disabled; Blind/visually impaired; Deaf/hearing impaired; Mentally disabled; Minorities; Hispanics/Latinos; Native Americans/American Indians; Indigenous peoples; Women; Substance abusers; AIDS, people with; Single parents; Crime/abuse victims; Terminal illness, people with; Immigrants/refugees; Economically disadvantaged; Homeless.
Type of support: General/operating support; Continuing support; Program development; Conferences/seminars; Film/video/radio; Fellowships; Scholarship funds; Research; Program evaluation; Matching/challenge support.
Limitations: Applications accepted. Giving limited to UT. No support for religious organizations, government agencies, or conduit organizations. No grants to individuals, or for capital campaigns, K-12 education, trips, tours or travel, or endowments.
Publications: Application guidelines.
Application information: Guidelines revised annually, e-mail for revised guidelines in Nov. Application form required.
Initial approach: Letter of inquiry via mail or e-mail
Copies of proposal: 2
Deadline(s): Early spring
Board meeting date(s): 1-2 meetings annually
Final notification: Fall
Officers and Committee Members:* Spencer F. Eccles, Chair.; Anne Watson, Exec. Dir.; C. Hope Eccles; James M. Steele; Elmer D. Tucker.
Trustee: Wells Fargo Bank, N.A.
Number of staff: 1 part-time professional.
EIN: 237185855

9321
EnergySolutions Foundation ✧
423 W. 300 S.
Salt Lake City, UT 84101 (801) 649-2286
Contact: Karen Watson
Application address: P.O. Box 510583, Salt Lake City, UT 84151, tel.: (801) 649-2286; Main URL: http://www.energysolutionsfoundation.org
Blog: http://feeds.feedburner.com/ESFoundBlog
Facebook: http://www.facebook.com/esfound
Flickr: http://www.flickr.com/photos/energysolutionsfoundation/
Twitter: http://twitter.com/esfound

Established in 2005 in UT.
Donors: Lindsay Goldberg Bessemer; Energy Solutions.
Foundation type: Independent foundation.
Financial data (yr. ended 12/31/12): Assets, $1,115,434 (M); expenditures, $748,875; qualifying distributions, $742,777; giving activities include $250,000 for 1+ grant, and $430,550 for 1 grant to an individual.
Purpose and activities: The foundation is dedicated to the promotion of math, science, and engineering education. The foundation offers a scholarship to 10th grade students in selected high schools in GA, ID, IL, NM, OH, SC, TN, UT and WA, as well as offers an energy education program.
Fields of interest: Scholarships/financial aid; Education.
Limitations: Giving primarily in GA, ID, IL, NM, OH, SC, TN, UT and WA. No support for organizations that in turn make grants to others.
Application information:
Initial approach: Completed application form
Deadline(s): Jan. 31st
Board meeting date(s): Quarterly
Officer: Pearl Wright, Exec. Dir.
Board Members: David Lockwood; Mark Walker; Russ Workman.
EIN: 371521992

9322
The GFC Foundation ✧
881 W. State Rd., No. 140-214
Pleasant Grove, UT 84062-2131

Established in 1994 in UT.
Donors: Katherine Swim; Lauralyn Swim; The ALS Foundation.
Foundation type: Independent foundation.
Financial data (yr. ended 06/30/13): Assets, $31,893,252 (M); expenditures, $2,273,690; qualifying distributions, $1,849,235; giving activities include $1,849,235 for 29 grants (high: $731,000; low: $305).
Fields of interest: Higher education; Education; Human services.
Limitations: Applications not accepted. Giving primarily in UT.
Application information: Contributes only to pre-selected organizations.
Trustees: Brent McKinley; Paul T. Mero; Lauralyn B. Swim; Stanford Swim.
EIN: 870529248
Selected grants: The following grants are a representative sample of this grantmaker's funding activity:
$20,000 to Brigham Young University, Provo, UT, 2013. For Aspen Grove Family Camp.

9323
Florence J. Gillmor Foundation ✧
(formerly Edward Lincoln and Bessie Boyce Gillmor Foundation)
201 S. Main Ste., Ste. 1800
Salt Lake City, UT 84111-2218

Established in 1997 in UT.
Donor: Florence J. Gillmor†.
Foundation type: Independent foundation.
Financial data (yr. ended 12/31/13): Assets, $20,696,955 (M); expenditures, $1,492,295; qualifying distributions, $1,220,318; giving activities include $1,050,000 for 25 grants (high: $200,000; low: $15,000).
Fields of interest: Arts; Human services; Residential/custodial care.
Type of support: General/operating support.
Limitations: Applications not accepted. Giving primarily in Salt Lake City, UT. No grants to individuals.
Application information: Contributes only to pre-selected organizations.
Officers and Directors: James B. Lee,* Pres.; Robert M. Graham,* V.P.; David R. Bird, Secy.-Treas. and Genl. Counsel; Raymond J. Etcheverry; Bruce L. Olson; Francis M. Wikstrom.
EIN: 870483666
Selected grants: The following grants are a representative sample of this grantmaker's funding activity:
$35,000 to Road Home, Salt Lake City, UT, 2010.
$25,000 to And Justice for All, Salt Lake City, UT, 2010.
$25,000 to Utah Food Bank, Salt Lake City, UT, 2010.
$20,000 to Audubon Society, National, New York, NY, 2010.
$20,000 to Childrens Center, 2010.
$20,000 to National Ability Center, Park City, UT, 2010.
$20,000 to Utah Symphony and Opera, Salt Lake City, UT, 2010.
$15,000 to American Indian Services, Provo, UT, 2011.
$10,000 to Boys and Girls Clubs of Greater Salt Lake, Salt Lake City, UT, 2010.
$10,000 to Humane Society of Utah, Murray, UT, 2010.
$10,000 to Nature Conservancy, Arlington, VA, 2011.
$10,000 to United Way, 2010.

9324
The Alan and Jeanne Hall Foundation ✧
5929 S. Fashion Pt. Dr., Ste. 300
Ogden, UT 84403-4684
E-mail: support@hallfoundation.com; Main URL: http://www.hallfoundation.com/
Grants List: http://www.hallfoundation.com/grants/

Established in 1999 in UT.
Donors: Alan E. Hall; Jeannie Hall; Betty Nowak; Henry Nowak; Hall Family Investments, LLC.
Foundation type: Independent foundation.
Financial data (yr. ended 12/31/12): Assets, $13,973,811 (M); gifts received, $1,666,410; expenditures, $1,035,465; qualifying distributions, $956,968; giving activities include $956,968 for 25 grants (high: $241,183; low: $700).

Fields of interest: Arts; Education; Human services; Children/youth, services; Mormon agencies & churches.
Limitations: Applications accepted. Giving primarily in Ogden and Salt Lake City, UT. No grants to individuals.
Application information: See foundation web site for complete application guidelines.
Initial approach: E-mail
Officer: Alan E. Hall, Pres.
Trustees: Curtis Funk; Megan Funk; Aaron Hall; Adam Hall; Annette Hall; Cami Hall; Christian Hall; Emily Hall; Eric Hall; Jeannie Hall; Kim Hall; Laura West; Matt West.
EIN: 870644251

9325
The Leon & Arline Harman Foundation ✧
5544 Green St.
Salt Lake City, UT 84123-5798 (801) 313-8000, ext. 8088
Contact: Sherry Prendergast
Main URL: http://harmans.biz/

Established in 2005 in UT.
Donors: Leon Harman; Arline Harman.
Foundation type: Independent foundation.
Financial data (yr. ended 12/31/13): Assets, $14,345,567 (M); gifts received, $5,010,533; expenditures, $863,492; qualifying distributions, $857,145; giving activities include $777,795 for grants to individuals.
Purpose and activities: Giving limited to employees of certain companies in the retail food distribution industry. Eligible employees will be U.S. citizens or have an alien registration card, and have been working for one of the companies on the foundation's approved list for at least 1-year by the time school starts. The approved list contains all companies in the Harman Management consulting or food distribution network. Eligible employees will also be a high school graduate with at least a 2.8 grade point average or have earned a GED certificate.
Fields of interest: Higher education.
Type of support: Scholarships—to individuals.
Limitations: Giving primarily in CA, UT and WA.
Publications: Application guidelines.
Application information: Employees of certain food companies in the retail food distribution industry may refer to foundation web site for specific guidelines and form. Applicants must have a combined annual income for themselves and their parents, if still a dependent of their parents, of less than $100,000 for those living in the San Francisco Bay area, and $75,000 for employees living in all other areas. Those applicants who are no longer a dependent of their parents should use their income along with their spouse's income (if applicable) to determine income eligibility. If there are extraordinary circumstances regarding these financial requirements they will be considered on a case by case basis. Application form required.
Officers: Barry Harman, Pres.; Dawn Cook, V.P.; Mark B. Harman, Secy.; Jacob Florence, Treas.
Trustee: Todd B. Harman.
EIN: 201738267

9326
The Richard K. and Shirley S. Hemingway Foundation ✧
P.O. Box 11026
Salt Lake City, UT 84147-0026 (801) 363-5227
Contact: Brianne Johnson, Admin.
FAX: (801) 863-6157;
E-mail: briannej@xmission.com; Main URL: http://www.HemingwayFoundation.org

Established in 1987 in UT.
Donors: Richard Keith Hemingway†; Shirley Stranquist Hemingway†.
Foundation type: Independent foundation.
Financial data (yr. ended 12/31/13): Assets, $20,295,151 (M); expenditures, $1,123,154; qualifying distributions, $921,828; giving activities include $791,697 for 88 grants (high: $59,000; low: $500).
Purpose and activities: Giving for: the development of the arts, educational and developmental programs fostering positive values and behaviors relating to children, youth and family issues, the preservation, protection and enhancement of the environment, and educational and developmental programs fostering the implementation of healthier lifestyles. The foundation gives preference to programs, which have a direct and substantial human benefit over funding of capital campaigns or ordinary operations and focuses their resources upon projects that serve communities in the states of ID and UT.
Fields of interest: Arts; Education; Environment; Children/youth, services; Family services; Government/public administration.
Type of support: General/operating support; Continuing support; Building/renovation; Equipment; Emergency funds; Program development; Conferences/seminars; Curriculum development; Research; Consulting services; In-kind gifts.
Limitations: Applications accepted. Giving limited to ID and UT. No support for religious organizations. No grants to individuals, or for general operating expenses or building funds.
Publications: Application guidelines.
Application information: Grant applications are by invitation only, upon review of Letter of Inquiry. See foundation web site for additional application information. Application form required.
Initial approach: Letter of Inquiry, no more than 2-pages, via U.S. mail or e-mail
Deadline(s): Feb. 1 (for Letter of Inquiry)
Board meeting date(s): Apr. and Oct.
Final notification: Feb. (for Letter of Inquiry)
Officers and Trustees:* Jane Hemingway Mason,* Chair., Investment; Henry S. Hemingway,* Pres.; Helen Hemingway Cardon,* Secy.; Ann Hemingway; Hallie Hemingway.
Number of staff: 1 full-time professional.
EIN: 876205846
Selected grants: The following grants are a representative sample of this grantmaker's funding activity:
$7,000 to Wood River Land Trust, Hailey, ID, 2012. For Unrestricted Use Distribution to Tax Exempt Org.

9327
The Huntsman Foundation ✧
(formerly The Jon and Karen Huntsman Foundation)
500 Huntsman Way
Salt Lake City, UT 84108-1235
Jon and Karen Huntsman's Giving Pledge Profile: http://glasspockets.org/philanthropy-in-focus/eye-on-the-giving-pledge/profiles/huntsman

Established in 1988 in UT.
Donors: Jon M. Huntsman; Ellis Ivory.
Foundation type: Independent foundation.
Financial data (yr. ended 12/31/12): Assets, $362,949,131 (M); expenditures, $6,950,509; qualifying distributions, $6,875,530; giving activities include $6,526,275 for 38 grants (high: $2,500,000; low: $200).
Fields of interest: Higher education; Business school/education; Community/economic development.
Type of support: Program-related investments/loans.
Limitations: Applications not accepted. Giving primarily in ID, PA and UT. No grants to individuals.
Application information: Contributes only to pre-selected organizations.
Officers and Trustees:* Jon M. Huntsman,* Pres.; J. Kimo Esplin, V.P. and Treas.; Christena Durham,* V.P.; Kathleen Huffman,* V.P.; David H. Huntsman,* V.P.; James H. Hunstman,* V.P.; Karen H. Huntsman,* V.P.; Paul C. Huntsman,* V.P.; Jennifer H. Parkin,* V.P.
EIN: 742521914
Selected grants: The following grants are a representative sample of this grantmaker's funding activity:
$2,500,000 to Utah State University, Jon M. Huntsman Business School, Logan, UT, 2010. For general support.
$2,500,000 to Utah State University, JMH Business School, Logan, UT, 2011. For general support.
$1,000,000 to Utah State University, JMH Business School, Logan, UT, 2011. For general support.
$600,000 to University of Pennsylvania, Wharton School of Business, Philadelphia, PA, 2010. For general support for Dr. Patrick T. Harker Professorship.
$500,000 to Snow College, Ephraim, UT, 2010. For general support for Karen H. Huntsman Library.
$400,000 to University of Pennsylvania, Wharton School of Business, Philadelphia, PA, 2011. For general support.
$311,918 to Utah State University, Logan, UT, 2011. For general support.
$300,000 to Brigham Young University, Provo, UT, 2010. For general support for Alumni and Visitors Center.
$253,918 to Utah State University, Logan, UT, 2010. For general support for Armenian Scholarship.
$250,000 to Snow College, Ephraim, UT, 2011. For general support.
$200,000 to Utah Symphony and Opera, Salt Lake City, UT, 2011. For general support.
$183,000 to Utah Valley University, Orem, UT, 2011. For general support.
$100,000 to Brigham Young University, Melvin J. Ballard Center for Economic Self-Reliance, Provo, UT, 2010. For general support.
$100,000 to Harvard University, Cambridge, MA, 2010. For general support for Nolan Archibald Scholarship.

$100,000 to Idaho State University Foundation, Pocatello, ID, 2010. For general support.
$100,000 to Sigma Chi Foundation, Evanston, IL, 2010. For general support.
$100,000 to This is the Place Foundation, Salt Lake City, UT, 2011. For general support.
$100,000 to University of Utah, Salt Lake City, UT, 2011. For general support.
$83,000 to Utah Valley University, Orem, UT, 2010. For general support.
$10,000 to National Society of the Sons of Utah Pioneers, Salt Lake City, UT, 2011. For general support.

9328
I Am A Leader Foundation ✧ ☆
180 N. University Ave., Ste. 410
Provo, UT 84601-5648 (801) 377-9515
Main URL: http://www.leader.org

Established in UT.
Donors: Panda Charitable Foundation; Franklincovey, Inc.
Foundation type: Independent foundation.
Financial data (yr. ended 12/31/13): Assets, $2,060,700 (M); gifts received, $4,223,656; expenditures, $5,352,142; qualifying distributions, $4,714,422; giving activities include $4,714,422 for 212 grants (high: $44,908; low: $475).
Purpose and activities: The foundation is dedicated to providing programs and services that build students' character and leadership in elementary schools around the world. The foundation offers grants to highly qualified public schools with principals, teachers, staff, district-level leadership, and parents who have a strong interest and commitment toward long-term implementation of the process.
Fields of interest: Elementary school/education.
Publications: Application guidelines.
Application information: Application form required.
Initial approach: Online application form on foundation web site
Deadline(s): None
Officers and Directors:* Ellis Boyd Craig, Chair. and C.E.O.; Brad Pelo,* Pres.; Dave Carlston, C.O.O.; Melody Pelo,* Secy. and Treas.; John R. Miller.
EIN: 454625508

9329
Kirk Humanitarian ✧
201 S. Main St., Ste. 1100
Salt Lake City, UT 84111-4904

Established in 2006 in UT.
Donors: Spencer Kirk; Krispen Family Holdings; Kirk 101 Trust.
Foundation type: Operating foundation.
Financial data (yr. ended 06/30/13): Assets, $937,180 (M); gifts received, $3,435,426; expenditures, $462,142; qualifying distributions, $462,139; giving activities include $434,455 for 3 grants (high: $214,455; low: $60,000).
Fields of interest: Human services.
Limitations: Applications not accepted. Giving primarily in OR.
Application information: Unsolicited requests for funds not accepted.
Officers and Directors:* Spencer Kirk,* Pres.; Kristen Kirk, Secy.-Treas.; Ronald Moffitt.
EIN: 203920671

9330
Frederick Q. Lawson Foundation ✧
P.O. Box 45385
Salt Lake City, UT 84145-0385

Established around 1991 in UT.
Donors: Emma Eccles Jones†; Frederick Q. Lawson.
Foundation type: Independent foundation.
Financial data (yr. ended 12/31/12): Assets, $12,998,046 (M); gifts received, $1,000; expenditures, $984,928; qualifying distributions, $828,000; giving activities include $828,000 for grants.
Purpose and activities: Giving primarily to an Episcopal cathedral; support also for the arts, particularly the performing arts, and higher education.
Fields of interest: Performing arts; Arts; Higher education; Protestant agencies & churches.
Type of support: General/operating support.
Limitations: Applications not accepted. Giving primarily in Salt Lake City, UT. No grants to individuals.
Application information: Contributes only to pre-selected organizations.
Trustees: Frederick Q. Lawson; Herbert C. Livsey.
EIN: 870481510

9331
Janet Q. Lawson Foundation ✧
P.O. Box 45385
Salt Lake City, UT 84145-0385

Established around 1991 in UT.
Donors: Emma Eccles Jones†; Janet Q. Lawson†.
Foundation type: Independent foundation.
Financial data (yr. ended 12/31/12): Assets, $18,944,291 (M); gifts received, $477; expenditures, $1,391,313; qualifying distributions, $1,160,573; giving activities include $1,151,000 for 28 grants (high: $432,000; low: $1,000).
Purpose and activities: Giving primarily for the performing arts, children and social services, as well as to a children's medical center foundation, and to a zoological organization.
Fields of interest: Performing arts; Zoos/zoological societies; Hospitals (specialty); Human services; Children/youth, services.
Limitations: Applications not accepted. Giving limited to UT, with emphasis on Salt Lake City. No grants to individuals.
Application information: Contributes only to pre-selected organizations.
Advisory Committee and Trustees:* Erik C. Erlingsson, M.D.*, Advisor; Frederick Q. Lawson,* Advisor; Peter Q. Lawson,* Advisor; Charles H. Livsey,* Advisor; Herbert C. Livsey,* Advisor; Ellen E. Rossi,* Advisor.
EIN: 870481508

9332
McCarthey Family Foundation ✧
610 E. South Temple, Ste. 200
Salt Lake City, UT 84102-1208 (801) 578-1246
Contact: Todd F. Brashear, Exec. Dir.

Established in AK.
Donor: Jane F. McCarthey Trust.
Foundation type: Independent foundation.
Financial data (yr. ended 12/31/12): Assets, $41,197,856 (M); expenditures, $2,692,390; qualifying distributions, $2,107,000; giving activities include $2,107,000 for grants.
Fields of interest: Elementary/secondary education; Higher education; Education; Environment; Medical research, institute; Human services.
Limitations: Giving primarily in Salt Lake City, Utah.
Application information:
Initial approach: Letter
Deadline(s): None
Officers: John P. O'Brien, Secy.-Treas.; Todd F. Brashear, Exec. Dir.
Directors: Maureen P. McCarthey; Philip G. McCarthey; Sarah J. McCarthey; Thomas K. McCarthey, Jr.
EIN: 208067695

9333
Meldrum Foundation ✧ ☆
1808 Mohawk Way
Salt Lake City, UT 84108-3363

Established in 2000 in UT.
Donor: Peter D. Meldrum.
Foundation type: Independent foundation.
Financial data (yr. ended 12/31/13): Assets, $8,907,955 (M); gifts received, $1,028,000; expenditures, $586,300; qualifying distributions, $461,188; giving activities include $455,080 for 11 grants (high: $200,000; low: $1,000).
Fields of interest: Performing arts, ballet; Performing arts, theater; Arts; Higher education; Catholic agencies & churches.
Limitations: Applications not accepted. Giving primarily in Salt Lake City, UT. No grants to individuals.
Application information: Unsolicited requests for funds not accepted.
Officers: Catherine R. Meldrum, Secy.-Treas.; Peter D. Meldrum, Exec. Dir.
Trustees: Annette Meldrum; Christopher S. Meldrum.
EIN: 870657244
Selected grants: The following grants are a representative sample of this grantmaker's funding activity:
$200,000 to Pioneer Theater Company, Salt Lake City, UT, 2010. For endowment.
$40,000 to Pioneer Theater Company, Salt Lake City, UT, 2010. For endowment.
$40,000 to University of Utah, Salt Lake City, UT, 2011. For endowment.
$2,500 to Ballet West, Salt Lake City, UT, 2011.
$1,000 to Holy Cross Ministries, Salt Lake City, UT, 2011. For fundraiser.
$1,000 to Westminster College, Salt Lake City, UT, 2011. For fundraiser.

9334
Larry H. Miller Education Foundation ✧
c/o Krista Pace
9350 S. 150 E., Ste. 1000
Sandy, UT 84070-2721 (801) 563-4100

Established in 1996 in UT.
Donors: Karen G. Miller; Lawrence Horne "Larry H." Miller†.
Foundation type: Operating foundation.
Financial data (yr. ended 12/31/13): Assets, $67,728 (M); gifts received, $1,636,705; expenditures, $1,551,224; qualifying distributions,

$1,551,224; giving activities include $1,546,982 for 307 grants to individuals (high: $20,061; low: $37).
Purpose and activities: Giving to provide employee-related scholarships to individuals for post high school education at accredited institutions. The scholarships are for the dependents of employees only.
Fields of interest: Higher education; Young adults.
Type of support: Employee-related scholarships; Scholarships—to individuals.
Limitations: Applications not accepted. Giving limited to residents of Murray, UT.
Application information: Unsolicited requests for funds not accepted. Scholarships are for employees' dependents only.
Officer: Karen G. Miller, Pres.; Stephen F. Miller, V.P.; Gregory S. Miller, Secy.
Trustees: Bryan J. Miller; Roger L. Miller.
EIN: 870560678

9335
Larry H. Miller & Gail Miller Family Foundation ✧
9350 S. 150 E., Ste. 1000
Sandy, UT 84070-2721

Established in 2007 in UT.
Donors: Lawrence H. Miller; Karen Gail Miller.
Foundation type: Operating foundation.
Financial data (yr. ended 12/31/11): Assets, $16,755,852 (M); expenditures, $905,360; qualifying distributions, $854,686; giving activities include $850,000 for 4 grants (high: $400,000; low: $100,000).
Fields of interest: Historical activities; Education; Hospitals (specialty).
Limitations: Applications not accepted. Giving primarily in Salt Lake City, UT. No grants to individuals.
Application information: Contributes only to pre-selected organizations.
Directors: Bryan J. Miller; Gregory S. Miller; Roger L. Miller; Stephen F. Miller; Karen R. Williams; Karen Gail Miller Wilson.
EIN: 510641922

9336
John R. Miller Foundation ✧
299 S. Main St.
Salt Lake City, UT 84111-1919

Donor: John R. Miller.
Foundation type: Independent foundation.
Financial data (yr. ended 12/31/11): Assets, $1,447,375 (M); expenditures, $755,233; qualifying distributions, $737,000; giving activities include $737,000 for 5 grants (high: $720,500; low: $1,500).
Fields of interest: Historical activities; Education; Children/youth, services; Philanthropy/voluntarism; Mormon agencies & churches.
Limitations: Applications not accepted. Giving primarily in UT.
Application information: Contributes only to pre-selected organizations.
Officers: John R. Miller, Pres.; Victoria C. Monroe, Secy.; Ryan Miller, Treas.
EIN: 311492934

9337
The Mark and Kathie Miller Foundation ✧
3113 Carrigan Canyon
Salt Lake City, UT 84109-1476

Foundation type: Independent foundation.
Financial data (yr. ended 12/31/13): Assets, $3,887,883 (M); expenditures, $1,038,363; qualifying distributions, $1,033,217; giving activities include $1,033,217 for 31 grants (high: $467,500; low: $250).
Fields of interest: Arts; Higher education; Education; Health care; Employment; United Ways and Federated Giving Programs.
Limitations: Applications not accepted. Giving primarily in Salt Lake City, UT.
Application information: Contributes only to pre-selected organizations.
Trustees: Deborah S. Bayle; Dale Hansen; Mark Miller.
EIN: 870676533
Selected grants: The following grants are a representative sample of this grantmaker's funding activity:
$96,000 to University of Utah, Salt Lake City, UT, 2012. For general cash donation.
$50,000 to University Hospital Foundation, Salt Lake City, UT, 2012. For general cash donation.
$24,000 to Guadalupe Schools, Salt Lake City, UT, 2012. For general cash donation.

9338
My Good Fund ✧
2223 S. Highland Dr., E6-133
Salt Lake City, UT 84106-4181

Established in 2009 in UT.
Donor: Palladium Foundation.
Foundation type: Independent foundation.
Financial data (yr. ended 12/31/12): Assets, $29,912,853 (M); expenditures, $9,428,101; qualifying distributions, $9,263,255; giving activities include $9,263,255 for 100 grants (high: $1,820,000; low: $500).
Fields of interest: Education; Environment; Animals/wildlife, preservation/protection; Human services.
Limitations: Applications not accepted. Giving primarily in UT.
Application information: Contributes only to pre-selected organizations.
Officer: Jennifer Speers, Pres.
EIN: 276281660
Selected grants: The following grants are a representative sample of this grantmaker's funding activity:
$1,820,000 to Nature Conservancy, Salt Lake City, UT, 2012. For general support.
$750,000 to Grand Canyon Trust, Flagstaff, AZ, 2012. For general support.
$550,000 to Tracy Aviary, Salt Lake City, UT, 2012. For general support.
$426,000 to Artspace, Salt Lake City, UT, 2012. For general support.
$333,000 to Ronald McDonald House Charities of the Intermountain Area, Salt Lake City, UT, 2012. For general support.
$250,000 to Volunteers of America, Salt Lake City, UT, 2012. For general support.
$125,000 to Living Planet Aquarium, Sandy, UT, 2012. For general support.
$46,000 to Cornell University, Laboratory of Orinthology, Ithaca, NY, 2012. For general support.
$31,000 to Utah Rivers Council, Salt Lake City, UT, 2012. For general support.
$25,000 to Western Folklife Center, Elko, NV, 2012. For general support.

9339
The Ray and Tye Noorda Foundation ✧
(formerly The Worth of a Soul Foundation)
333 S. 520 W.
Linden, UT 84042-1911

Established in 2000 in UT.
Donors: Dialogic Systems Corp.; Lewena Noorda.
Foundation type: Independent foundation.
Financial data (yr. ended 12/31/13): Assets, $85,471,916 (M); expenditures, $4,339,382; qualifying distributions, $3,648,534; giving activities include $3,627,500 for 33 grants (high: $500,000; low: $1,000).
Purpose and activities: Giving primarily for higher education, health, human services, and children and youth services, including children's hospitals.
Fields of interest: Higher education; Hospitals (specialty); Health care; Human services; Children/youth, services.
Limitations: Applications not accepted. Giving primarily in UT. No grants to individuals.
Application information: Contributes only to pre-selected organizations.
Trustee: Lewena "Tye" Noorda.
EIN: 870649164

9340
The Nu Skin Force for Good Foundation ✧
(formerly The Force for Good Foundation)
c/o Nu Skin Enterprises, Inc.
75 W. Center St.
Provo, UT 84601-4432 (801) 345-2187
Contact: Jordan Karpowitz
E-mail: forceforgood@nuskin.com; Additional contact: Kara Schneck, tel.: (801) 345-2116, e-mail: kschneck@nuskin.com; E-mail for Jordan Karpowitz: jkarpowi@nuskin.com; Main URL: http://www.forceforgood.org

Established in 1998 in UT.
Donors: Diamond Technology Partners Inc.; Nu Skin Enterprises, Inc.; Blake M. Roney.
Foundation type: Company-sponsored foundation.
Financial data (yr. ended 12/31/13): Assets, $2,735,015 (M); gifts received, $2,576,598; expenditures, $1,612,705; qualifying distributions, $1,608,819; giving activities include $1,608,819 for 17 grants (high: $541,932; low: $658).
Purpose and activities: The foundation supports programs designed to improve the lives of children by offering hope for a life free for disease, illiteracy, and poverty.
Fields of interest: Elementary/secondary education; Education, reading; Education; Health care; Heart & circulatory diseases; Skin disorders research; Medical research; Agriculture; Disasters, preparedness/services; Children, services; Human services; Economic development; Economically disadvantaged.
Type of support: General/operating support; Continuing support; Building/renovation; Equipment; Research.
Limitations: Applications not accepted. Giving primarily in CA, UT, China, Ethiopia, Kenya, Malawi, and Uganda; giving also to national and international

organizations. No support for fraternal organizations, religious organizations, or political lobbyists. No grants to individuals, or for administrative costs, capital campaigns, seed money, advertising, or travel.
Application information: Contributes only to pre-selected organizations.
Officers and Trustees:* Blake M. Roney,* Chair. and Pres.; Gary Garrett, V.P.; M. Truman Hunt,* V.P.; Sandra N. Tillotson,* V.P.; Steven J. Lund,* Secy.; B.G. Hunt, Cont.; Brooke Roney.
EIN: 870577244

9341
The Park City Foundation ☆
1790 Bonanza Dr., Ste. 250
Park City, UT 84060 (435) 214-7476
Contact: For grants: Katie Wright, Exec. Dir.
FAX: (435) 214-7489;
E-mail: katie@theparkcityfoundation.org; Application address: P.O. Box 681499, Park City, UT 84068; Grant application e-mail: katie@theparkcityfoundation.org; Main URL: http://www.theparkcityfoundation.org
Facebook: https://www.facebook.com/parkcitycommunityfoundation

Established in 2003 in UT.
Donor: Bradley A. Olch.
Foundation type: Community foundation.
Financial data (yr. ended 12/31/12): Assets, $3,429,475 (M); gifts received, $836,517; expenditures, $1,000,132; giving activities include $423,008 for grants, and $80,406 for grants to individuals.
Purpose and activities: The foundation works to connect private philanthropy with the greater Park City community by optimizing the impact of each charitable gift. As a community foundation, it seeks to offer strategies and services for donors, and support to strengthen local nonprofits for the betterment of the community.
Fields of interest: Arts; Education; Environment; Animals/wildlife; Health care; Recreation; Human services; Community/economic development; Foundations (community); Public affairs.
Limitations: Applications accepted. Giving primarily in the greater Park City region of Summit County, UT. No support for grants that further political or religious doctrine, or political campaigns. No grants to individuals (except for scholarships), or for debt reductions or retiring past operating deficits, fellowships, litigation, endowment funds, or graduate or post-graduate research; no loans.
Application information: Visit foundation web site for application guidelines; qualified nonprofit organizations will be asked to submit a full application based on proposal. Application form required.
Initial approach: Submit proposal (300-400 words or less) via e-mail
Deadline(s): Apr. 4
Officers and Directors:* Jack Mueller,* Chair.; Katie Wright, Exec. Dir.; John D. Cumming, Dir. Emeritus; Hon. Judith M. Billings; William H. Coleman; Christopher M. Conabee; J. Taylor Crandall; Mark J. Fischer; Diane Foster; Jody Gross; Thomas Grossman; Cathy Hill; Jolie Iacoabelli; Becky Kearns; Robert M. La Forgia; Elizabeth Lockette; Hank Louis; Jon Monk; Franklin L. Morton; Emily Scott Pottruck; Sydney Reed; Bob Richer; Mike Ruzek; Stephen R. Sloan; Stephen A. Tyler; Linda Warren.
EIN: 300171971

9342
Charles Maxfield & Gloria F. Parrish Foundation ✧
c/o Erika Parrish Bunnell
2195 Dallin St.
Salt Lake City, UT 84109-1116

Established in 1992 in UT.
Donors: Charles Maxfield Parrish†; Gloria F. Parrish.
Foundation type: Independent foundation.
Financial data (yr. ended 12/31/13): Assets, $10,589,110 (M); expenditures, $596,190; qualifying distributions, $510,309; giving activities include $470,500 for 49 grants (high: $150,000; low: $1,000).
Fields of interest: Historical activities.
Type of support: General/operating support.
Limitations: Applications not accepted. Giving primarily in Washington, DC; some giving in TN, UT and WY. No grants to individuals.
Application information: Unsolicited requests for funds not accepted.
Officers: Erika Marie Parrish, Pres.; Kristine Ann Parrish, V.P.; Charles Kurt Parrish, Secy.; Charles Bryan Parrish, Treas.
EIN: 870490763

9343
Dinesh and Kalpana Patel Foundation ✧ ☆
P.O. Box 58887
Salt Lake City, UT 84158-0887

Established in 1994 in UT.
Donors: Dinesh C. Patel; Kalpana Patel.
Foundation type: Independent foundation.
Financial data (yr. ended 12/31/13): Assets, $239,304 (M); gifts received, $434,265; expenditures, $448,984; qualifying distributions, $441,606; giving activities include $441,606 for 59 grants (high: $134,000; low: $20).
Fields of interest: Arts; Higher education, university; Education; Hinduism.
Type of support: Annual campaigns; Capital campaigns; Building/renovation; Conferences/seminars; Scholarship funds; Matching/challenge support.
Limitations: Applications not accepted. Giving primarily in MI and UT. No grants to individuals.
Application information: Contributes only to pre-selected organizations.
Trustees: Dinesh C. Patel; Kalpana D. Patel; Kiran C. Patel.
EIN: 870532423

9344
The Louis S. Peery Charitable Foundation ✧
(formerly The Louis Scowcroft Peery Charitable Foundation)
P.O. Box 45385
Salt Lake City, UT 84145-0385

Established in 1990 in UT; Reincorporated with new name, corporate structure and IRS identification number in 2005.
Donors: Louis S. Peery; Janet P. Peery; Jeffrey Scowcroft Peery Trust; Louis S. Peery Special Purpose Trust.
Foundation type: Independent foundation.
Financial data (yr. ended 12/31/12): Assets, $33,655,297 (M); gifts received, $19,038; expenditures, $2,873,271; qualifying distributions, $2,254,359; giving activities include $2,159,872 for 18 grants (high: $500,000; low: $5,000).
Fields of interest: Environment, land resources; Human services; YM/YWCAs & YM/YWHAs; Children/youth, services; Foundations (private grantmaking).
Limitations: Applications not accepted. Giving primarily in Ogden and Salt Lake City, UT.
Application information: Contributes only to pre-selected organizations.
Officer and Board Members:* Leslie Peery Howa,* Chair.; Charles H. Livsey; Herbert C. Livsey; Scott C. Ulbrich.
EIN: 810614105

9345
The Mark and Nancy Peterson Foundation ✧ ☆
539 Blackhawk Ln.
Alpine, UT 84004-1224

Donors: Mark Peterson; Nancy Peterson†.
Foundation type: Independent foundation.
Financial data (yr. ended 12/31/12): Assets, $3,475,716 (M); gifts received, $3,914; expenditures, $1,278,652; qualifying distributions, $1,246,445; giving activities include $1,237,377 for 11+ grants (high: $1,164,000).
Fields of interest: Education; Health care; Human services.
Type of support: Grants to individuals.
Limitations: Applications accepted. Giving primarily in UT.
Application information:
Initial approach: Letter of request
Officer: Jeffrey Peterson, Chair.
Directors: Brian Peterson; Jonathan Peterson.
EIN: 801005721

9346
John and Marcia Price Family Foundation ✧
230 E. South Temple
Salt Lake City, UT 84111-1205 (801) 478-8000
Contact: Martin G. Peterson, Exec. Dir.

Established in 1997 in UT.
Donors: John Price; Fairfax Realty Inc.; Artibus Foundation.
Foundation type: Independent foundation.
Financial data (yr. ended 12/31/13): Assets, $14,688,424 (M); gifts received, $5,822,213; expenditures, $1,360,440; qualifying distributions, $1,352,228; giving activities include $1,351,691 for 40 grants (high: $686,666; low: $100).
Purpose and activities: Giving primarily for the arts, education, and human services.
Fields of interest: Performing arts centers; Performing arts, orchestras; Arts; Higher education; Human services; Children/youth, services.
Limitations: Applications accepted. Giving primarily in Washington, DC, and Salt Lake City, UT.
Application information: Application form not required.

Initial approach: Proposal
Deadline(s): None
Officer: Martin G. Peterson, Exec. Dir.
Directors: Deirdra Price; John Steven Price; Marcia Price; Jennifer Price Wallin.
Trustee: John Price.
EIN: 841402027

9347
S. J. & Jessie E. Quinney Foundation ✧
P.O. Box 45385
Salt Lake City, UT 84145-0385
Contact: Herbert C. Livsey, Dir.

Established about 1982 in UT.
Donor: S.J. Quinney†.
Foundation type: Independent foundation.
Financial data (yr. ended 12/31/12): Assets, $43,809,176 (M); gifts received, $5,000; expenditures, $1,743,556; qualifying distributions, $1,191,921; giving activities include $1,137,500 for 24 grants (high: $530,000; low: $1,000).
Purpose and activities: Giving primarily for higher and other education; support also for social services and cultural programs, including the performing arts.
Fields of interest: Performing arts; Arts; Higher education; Education; Human services.
Type of support: General/operating support.
Limitations: Applications not accepted. Giving primarily in UT. No grants to individuals.
Application information: Contributes only to pre-selected organizations.
Directors: Frederick Q. Lawson; Peter Q. Lawson; Stephen B. Nebeker; Ellen E. Rossi.
Trustees: Clark P. Giles; Charles H. Livsey; Herbert C. Livsey; David E. Quinney; David E. Quinney III.
EIN: 870389312

9348
RLC Family Foundation ✧
8047 Farm Brook Way
Salt Lake City, UT 84093-6484

Established in UT.
Donors: Robert B. Campbell; Lisa W. Campbell.
Foundation type: Independent foundation.
Financial data (yr. ended 12/31/13): Assets, $843,743 (M); gifts received, $500; expenditures, $1,590,733; qualifying distributions, $1,590,000; giving activities include $1,590,000 for 6 grants (high: $1,250,000; low: $5,000).
Fields of interest: Higher education; Human services; Mormon agencies & churches.
Limitations: Applications not accepted. Giving primarily in Salt Lake City, UT. No grants to individuals.
Application information: Unsolicited requests for funds not accepted.
Officers and Directors:* Robert B. Campbell,* Pres.; Lisa W. Campbell,* Secy.-Treas.; Jonathan L. Campbell.
EIN: 262071653
Selected grants: The following grants are a representative sample of this grantmaker's funding activity:
$35,000 to LDS Business College, Salt Lake City, UT, 2012. For general cash donation.

9349
The Rose Foundation ✧
3507 N. University Ave., Ste. 100
Provo, UT 84604-4478

Established in 1996 in UT.
Donors: Nedra Roney McKell; NR Rhino Co., LC.
Foundation type: Operating foundation.
Financial data (yr. ended 12/31/11): Assets, $1,357,870 (M); expenditures, $1,082,389; qualifying distributions, $1,062,000; giving activities include $1,062,000 for 9 grants (high: $500,000; low: $500).
Fields of interest: Education; Mormon agencies & churches.
Limitations: Applications not accepted. Giving primarily in UT. No grants to individuals.
Application information: Contributes only to pre-selected organizations.
Trustees: Robert McKell; Nedra Roney McKell.
EIN: 870565388

9350
Semnani Family Foundation ✧
(formerly Semnani Foundation)
P.O. Box 11623
Salt Lake City, UT 84147-0623 (801) 321-7725
Contact: Khosrow B. Semnani, Dir.
E-mail: info@semnanifamilyfoundation.org; E-mail for foundation program inquiries: programs@semnanifamilyfoundation.org; Main URL: http://www.semnanifamilyfoundation.org

Established in 1991 in UT.
Donor: Khosrow B. Semnani.
Foundation type: Independent foundation.
Financial data (yr. ended 12/31/12): Assets, $58,272,444 (M); gifts received, $1,978,553; expenditures, $2,735,327; qualifying distributions, $2,430,674; giving activities include $2,428,280 for 55 grants (high: $1,500,000; low: $250).
Purpose and activities: Giving primarily for promoting health, education, and disaster relief for marginal communities in the United States and around the world. Given the importance of religion to the life of many immigrant communities and refugees, the foundation has worked closely with religious communities and leaders to promote interfaith dialogue, understanding and integration. It has helped immigrant and refugee communities build houses of worship, extend and expand social services, and fight prejudice. The foundation's program interests include: social issues, health, children, women, disaster relief, Iranian-American issues, religious tolerance and interfaith dialogue, and advancing health, education and welfare of the people of UT.
Fields of interest: Arts, cultural/ethnic awareness; Higher education; Education; Health care, clinics/centers; Health organizations, association; Medical research, institute; Human services; International relief; Foundations (private grantmaking); Foundations (public); Islam; Religion, interfaith issues.
Limitations: Giving primarily in UT, with emphasis on Salt Lake City; some funding also in PA. No grants to individuals.
Application information: Application form not required.
Initial approach: Letter
Deadline(s): None
Directors: Nolan Karras; Shirin Kia; Ghazelah Semnani; Khosrow Semnani; Taymour Semnani.
EIN: 742639794

9351
Simmons Family Foundation ✧
722 W. Shepherd Ln., No. 103
Farmington, UT 84025-3845 (801) 550-5026
Contact: Elizabeth W. Gerner, Exec. Dir.
E-mail: elizabeth@simmonsfoundation.org; Main URL: http://www.simmonsfoundation.org/
Grants List: http://www.simmonsfoundation.org/id18.html

Established in 1986 in UT.
Donors: Roy W. Simmons; Roy W. Simmons Charitable Lead Trust No. 1; Roy W. Simmons Charitable Lead Trust No. 2.
Foundation type: Independent foundation.
Financial data (yr. ended 11/30/13): Assets, $12,289,986 (M); gifts received, $2,500; expenditures, $454,377; qualifying distributions, $451,877; giving activities include $443,975 for 14 grants (high: $135,000; low: $5,000).
Purpose and activities: Giving primarily to support organizations and projects that benefit the residents of Utah through education, art, health and religion.
Fields of interest: Higher education; Human services; Children/youth, services.
Type of support: General/operating support; Emergency funds; Program development; Scholarship funds; Research; Matching/challenge support.
Limitations: Giving primarily in UT. No grants to individuals, or for capital campaigns, or endowments.
Publications: Application guidelines.
Application information: Formal applications are by invitation only, upon review of initial letter of intent. Application information available on foundation web site. Application form required.
Initial approach: 1-page letter of intent (on letterhead) via e-mail
Copies of proposal: 1
Deadline(s): Aug. 15
Board meeting date(s): Annually in the fall
Final notification: Nov.
Officer: Elizabeth W. Gerner, M.A., M.P.A., Exec. Dir.
Trustees: Elizabeth S. Hoke; David E. Simmons; Harris H. Simmons; L.E. Simmons; Matthew R. Simmons; Julia S. Watkins.
Number of staff: 1 full-time professional.
EIN: 133420599

9352
Tanner Charitable Trust ✧
1930 S. State St.
Salt Lake City, UT 84115-2311

Incorporated in 1965 in UT.
Donors: Obert C. Tanner; O.C. Tanner Co.; O.C. Tanner Recognition Company.
Foundation type: Independent foundation.
Financial data (yr. ended 12/31/13): Assets, $4,190,734 (M); gifts received, $3,410,952; expenditures, $2,054,363; qualifying distributions, $2,032,304; giving activities include $2,032,304 for 25 grants (high: $745,802; low: $500).
Fields of interest: Performing arts; Arts; Higher education; Human services.

Limitations: Applications not accepted. Giving primarily in Salt Lake City, UT. No grants to individuals.
Application information: Contributes only to pre-selected organizations.
Officer and Trustees:* Carolyn T. Irish,* Chair.; David A. Petersen.
EIN: 876125059

9353
Thrasher Research Fund ✧
68 S. Main St., Ste. 400
Salt Lake City, UT 84101-1523 (801) 240-4753
Contact: Aaron V. Pontsler, Research Mgr.
FAX: (801) 240-1625; E-mail for Aaron V. Pontsler: pontslerav@thrasherresearch.org; Main URL: http://www.thrasherresearch.org
Grants List: http://www.thrasherresearch.org/sites/www_thrasherresearch_org/Default.aspx?page=43

Established in 1977 in UT.
Donor: E.W. "Al" Thrasher†.
Foundation type: Independent foundation.
Financial data (yr. ended 12/31/10): Assets, $89,598,327 (M); expenditures, $6,772,567; qualifying distributions, $5,511,803; giving activities include $5,511,803 for grants.
Purpose and activities: The fund provides grants for pediatric medical research. Because significant solutions for many children's health problems remain undiscovered, the fund invites a broad array of applications. The Thrasher Research Fund seeks to foster an environment of creativity and discovery aimed at finding solutions to children's health problems and awards grants for research that offers substantial promise for meaningful advances in prevention and treatment of children's diseases, particularly research that offers broad-based applications.
Fields of interest: Medical research, institute; Pediatrics research; Infants/toddlers; Children/youth; Children.
Type of support: Research.
Limitations: Applications accepted. Giving on a national and international basis. No support for research using fetal tissue, other funding organizations, behavioral science research, or educational programs. No grants for general operations, construction or renovation of facilities, student aid, or scholarships; no loans.
Publications: Application guidelines; Biennial report (including application guidelines); Informational brochure (including application guidelines).
Application information: Guidelines are available on web site, and should be viewed before submitting any applications. Applicants whose concept papers are approved will receive an invitation to submit a full proposal as well as an electronic application kit. Application form required.
Initial approach: Concept paper
Copies of proposal: 1
Deadline(s): Revolving
Board meeting date(s): Quarterly
Final notification: Generally 6-8 weeks via e-mail
Officer and Advisory Committee:* R. Justin Brown, MPH, Pres.; Daniel K. Benjamin, M.D., MPH, Ph.D; Carl L. Bose, M.D.; Carrie L. Byington, M.D.; Parul Christian, Dr.PH, M.Sc.; Davidson H. Hamer, M.D.; Fernando P. Polack, M.D.; William A. Weiss, M.D, Ph.D; Yvonne W. Wu, M.D., MPH.
Number of staff: 4 full-time professional; 1 full-time support; 1 part-time support.
EIN: 876179851

9354
The Vivint Giveback Foundation ✧
(formerly The Apx Family Foundation)
5132 N. 300 W.
Provo, UT 84604-5817

Established in UT.
Donors: Apx Alarm Systems; Vivint; Casey Baugh; Cody Veilbell; Jason Brown; Jeffrey Mendez; Mark Toone; Trevor Fronk; Tyler Williams; Eric Mealey.
Foundation type: Independent foundation.
Financial data (yr. ended 12/31/12): Assets, $708,598 (M); gifts received, $1,715,100; expenditures, $1,080,566; qualifying distributions, $1,065,614; giving activities include $1,065,614 for grants.
Purpose and activities: Giving primarily for education, human services, and medical assistance to individuals.
Fields of interest: Education; Health care; Human services.
Limitations: Applications not accepted. Giving primarily in Provo, UT.
Application information: Unsolicited requests for funds not accepted.
Board Members: Tom Coleman; Joshua Houser; Holly Mero; Christy Miller.
EIN: 266627266

9355
The I.J. and Jeanne Wagner Charitable Foundation ✧
775 North Hiltop Rd.
Salt Lake City, UT 84103-3311

Established in 2005 in UT.
Foundation type: Independent foundation.
Financial data (yr. ended 06/30/13): Assets, $12,608,482 (M); expenditures, $599,043; qualifying distributions, $550,000; giving activities include $550,000 for grants.
Fields of interest: Higher education, university; Education; Food banks; Children/youth, services; Minorities.
Limitations: Applications not accepted. Giving primarily in UT.
Application information: Unsolicited requests for funds not accepted.
Trustees: James R. Holbrook; Meghan Z. Holbrook; Herald O. Johnson.
EIN: 202380497
Selected grants: The following grants are a representative sample of this grantmaker's funding activity:
$130,000 to Utah Food Bank, Salt Lake City, UT, 2013. For grant to replace the HVAC system and new boiler, resurfacing the Volunteer Sort Room floors and Truck Wraps.
$75,000 to University of Utah, Salt Lake City, UT, 2013. For Veterans Support Center remodeling of the CORC Room on the 4th floor of the University's Olpin Student Union.
$40,000 to Utah Food Bank, Salt Lake City, UT, 2013. For Purchase of Food and Supplies for the Food Bank's Programs.
$25,000 to Calvary Baptist Church, Salt Lake City, UT, 2013. For Food and Supplies for the Church's Sunday morning Program to feed the poor at Pioneer Park in Salt Lake City.
$25,000 to Salt Lake Community College, Salt Lake City, UT, 2013. To support Minority Student Scholarships as determined by the College.
$25,000 to Snow College Foundation, Ephraim, UT, 2013. For Needs-based Minority Scholarship Fund to be awarded to students as determined by the school.
$25,000 to University of Utah, Law School, Salt Lake City, UT, 2013. For scholarships for Minority Students as determined by the Law School.
$25,000 to Utah Museum of Natural History, Salt Lake City, UT, 2013. For the Museum's Youth Teaching Program.
$15,000 to Catholic Community Services of Utah, Salt Lake City, UT, 2013. For Cafeteria Tables for the St Vincent DePaul Dining Hall.

9356
C. Scott and Dorothy E. Watkins Charitable Foundation ✧
1935 E. Vine St., Ste. 260
Salt Lake City, UT 84121-6559

Established in 1992.
Donor: C. Scott Watkins†.
Foundation type: Operating foundation.
Financial data (yr. ended 12/31/13): Assets, $51,645,438 (M); expenditures, $2,203,010; qualifying distributions, $2,100,000; giving activities include $2,100,000 for 84 grants (high: $160,000; low: $1,000).
Purpose and activities: Giving primarily for higher education, medical research, and health care.
Fields of interest: Higher education; Nursing school/education; Hospitals (general); Health care; Health organizations, association; Food banks; Youth development; Human services; Children/youth, services.
Limitations: Applications not accepted. Giving primarily in UT. No grants to individuals.
Application information: Contributes only to pre-selected organizations.
Trustees: Jay Rasmussen; Carol Watkins; Gary Watkins.
EIN: 876218993
Selected grants: The following grants are a representative sample of this grantmaker's funding activity:
$160,000 to Utah Food Bank, Salt Lake City, UT, 2011.
$100,000 to LDS Perpetual Scholarship Fund, Salt Lake City, UT, 2010.
$80,000 to Road Home, Salt Lake City, UT, 2011.
$70,000 to Primary Childrens Medical Center, Salt Lake City, UT, 2011.
$64,000 to Huntsman Cancer Foundation, Salt Lake City, UT, 2011.
$48,000 to Utah Valley University, Orem, UT, 2011.
$45,000 to American Red Cross, Salt Lake City, UT, 2011.
$32,000 to American Heart Association, Salt Lake City, UT, 2011.
$19,000 to Saint Annes Center, Ogden, UT, 2011.
$16,000 to Wasatch Homeless Health Care, Salt Lake City, UT, 2011.
$15,000 to University of Utah, Salt Lake City, UT, 2011.

9357
Yamagata Foundation ✧
1250 E. 200 S., Ste. 2D
Lehi, UT 84043-1483 (801) 326-3500
Contact: John Nitta, Dir.

Established in 2004 in UT.
Donor: Gene H. Yamagata.
Foundation type: Independent foundation.
Financial data (yr. ended 12/31/12): Assets, $43,030 (M); gifts received, $415,042; expenditures, $577,081; qualifying distributions, $568,720; giving activities include $568,720 for grants.
Fields of interest: Higher education; Mormon agencies & churches.
Limitations: Applications accepted. Giving primarily in HI and UT.
Application information: Application form not required.
Deadline(s): None
Directors: Matt Hawkins; John Nitta; Rick Nitta; Scott Oelkers; David M. Senior.
EIN: 201078807

VERMONT

9358
Ben & Jerry's Foundation, Inc. ✧
30 Community Dr.
South Burlington, VT 05403-6828 (802) 846-1500
Contact: Lisa Pendolino, Managing Dir.
E-mail: info@benandjerrysfoundation.org; Main URL: http://www.benandjerrysfoundation.org
Grants List: http://www.benandjerrysfoundation.org/grantees.html
Philanthropy's Promise: http://www.ncrp.org/philanthropys-promise/who

Established in 1985 in NY.
Donors: Ben & Jerry's Homemade, Inc.; Ben & Jerry's Corp.; Bennett Cohen.
Foundation type: Company-sponsored foundation.
Financial data (yr. ended 12/31/13): Assets, $4,926,500 (M); gifts received, $2,584,505; expenditures, $2,878,154; qualifying distributions, $2,845,307; giving activities include $2,551,226 for 618 grants (high: $50,000; low: $6).
Purpose and activities: The foundation promotes progressive social change by supporting grassroots organizations that utilize community organizing strategies to advance social and environmental justice.
Fields of interest: Environment, natural resources; Environment; Agriculture, community food systems; Youth, services; Human services; Civil/human rights, immigrants; Civil rights, race/intergroup relations; Labor rights; Civil/human rights; Community/economic development; Public policy, research; Public affairs, citizen participation; Minorities; Economically disadvantaged.
Type of support: General/operating support; Management development/capacity building; Program development; Employee matching gifts.
Limitations: Applications accepted. Giving on a national basis, with emphasis on St. Albans, South Burlington, and Waterbury, VT. No support for schools, colleges or universities, state agencies, businesses or business associations, other foundations or regranting organizations, organizations and programs that are focused or based outside of the United States, or organizations with annual budgets over $500,000. No grants to individuals, or for scholarship programs, advocacy programs, discretionary or emergency funds, research projects, capital campaigns, religious programs, international or foreign-based programs, government sponsored programs, social service programs, or arts and media programs.
Publications: Application guidelines; Annual report; Grants list; IRS Form 990 or 990-PF printed copy available upon request; Program policy statement.
Application information: A full proposal may be requested at a later date for the Grassroots Organizing for Social Change Program. Additional information and a site visit may be requested for Vermont Capacity Building Grant Program. Support is limited to 1 contribution per organization during any given year. Application form required.
Initial approach: Complete online letter of interest for Grassroots Organizing for Social Change Program; complete online application for Vermont Capacity Building Grant Program, Vermont Economic Justice Grant Program, and Vermont Community Action Teams Grant Program
Deadline(s): Apr. 15 and Oct. 15 for Grassroots Organizing for Social Change Program; May 5 for Vermont Capacity Building Grant Program; Aug. 29 for Vermont Economic Justice Program; None for Vermont Community Action Teams
Board meeting date(s): Monthly
Final notification: Oct. for Vermont Capacity Building Grant Program
Officers and Trustees:* Jerry Greenfield,* Pres.; Elizabeth Bankowski,* Secy.; Jeffrey Furman,* Treas.; Anuradha Mittal.
Number of staff: 2 part-time professional; 1 full-time support.
EIN: 030300865
Selected grants: The following grants are a representative sample of this grantmaker's funding activity:
$75,000 to Watersheds United Vermont, Montpelier, VT, 2013. For grant made through Vermont River Conservancy.
$40,000 to Western Regional Advocacy Project, San Francisco, CA, 2013. For Homeless Bill of Rights Campaign.
$35,000 to Vermont Workers Center, Burlington, VT, 2013. For Movement Building: Put People First.
$25,000 to Iowa Citizens for Community Improvement, Des Moines, IA, 2013. For Iowa CCI's Latino Organizing Project.
$20,000 to Chattanooga Organized for Action, Chattanooga, TN, 2013. For Chattanooga Organized for Action General Support Funding. Grant made through Community Foundation of Greater Chattanooga.
$20,000 to DARE, Providence, RI, 2013. For general support.
$20,000 to Northwest Atlantic Marine Alliance, Gloucester, MA, 2013. For Who Fishes Matters Campaign.
$20,000 to United Students Against Sweatshops, Washington, DC, 2013. For grant made through Alliance for Global Justice.
$15,000 to Environmental Justice Coalition for Water, Oakland, CA, 2013. For general support.
$15,000 to Southsiders Organized for Unity and Liberation, Chicago, IL, 2013. For SOUL Community Organizing and Movement Building.

9359
Helen E. Daly Narthex Project CRUT ✧ ☆
P.O. Box 1280
Brattleboro, VT 05302-1280

Established in VT.
Donor: Helen Daly Irrevocable Trust.
Foundation type: Independent foundation.
Financial data (yr. ended 12/31/13): Assets, $2,030,293 (M); gifts received, $2,209,983; expenditures, $470,570; qualifying distributions, $458,380; giving activities include $453,200 for 3 grants (high: $343,200; low: $50,000).
Fields of interest: Religion.
Limitations: Applications not accepted. Giving primarily in Binghamton and Syracuse, NY; some funding also in Victoria, British Columbia, Canada.
Application information: Unsolicited requests for funds not accepted.
Trustee: Trust Company of Vermont.
EIN: 207037351

9360
The Evslin Family Foundation, Inc. ✧
c/o Mary Evslin
2398 Stowe Hollow Rd.
Stowe, VT 05672-4430
E-mail: mary@evslin.com

Established in 2000 in NJ.
Donors: Mary Evslin; Tom Evslin.
Foundation type: Independent foundation.
Financial data (yr. ended 12/31/12): Assets, $0 (M); gifts received, $2,030; expenditures, $722,987; qualifying distributions, $722,971; giving activities include $722,955 for 24 grants (high: $300,000; low: $200).
Fields of interest: Arts; Medical school/education; Education; Medical research; Disasters, preparedness/services; International economic development; Economic development; Economically disadvantaged.
International interests: Developing Countries.
Type of support: General/operating support; Emergency funds; Research; Technical assistance; Program-related investments/loans; Matching/challenge support.
Limitations: Applications not accepted. No support for religious or political organizations. No grants to individuals.
Publications: Grants list.
Application information: Contributes only to pre-selected organizations.
Board meeting date(s): Jan.
Officers: Mary A. Evslin, Pres.; Tom I. Evslin, V.P. and Secy.
Directors: Kelly Evans; Kate Morris.
Trustee: Evslin Jarah.
Number of staff: None.
EIN: 223778394
Selected grants: The following grants are a representative sample of this grantmaker's funding activity:
$51,249 to Vermont Community Foundation, Middlebury, VT, 2012. To establish Donor Advised Fund.

9361
General Education Fund, Inc. ✧
(doing business as The Curtis Fund)
c/o Merchants Trust Co.
P.O. Box 8490
Burlington, VT 05402-8490
Contact: Dan Stanyon
E-mail: jboutin@thecurtisfund.org; Main URL: http://www.thecurtisfund.org/
E-Newsletter: http://www.thecurtisfund.org/e-newsletter/
Facebook: http://www.facebook.com/pages/The-Curtis-Fund/176700985676729
Twitter: http://twitter.com/thecurtisfund
Application address: General Education Fund (GEF), Inc. Scholarship - NEW, VSAC Scholarship Programs, 10 E. Allen St., P.O. Box 2000, Winooski, VT, 05404-2601

Incorporated in 1918 in VT.
Donors: Emma Eliza Curtis†; Lorenzo E. Woodhouse†.
Foundation type: Independent foundation.
Financial data (yr. ended 07/30/13): Assets, $31,262,653 (M); gifts received, $1,901; expenditures, $1,715,252; qualifying distributions, $1,565,638; giving activities include $1,512,494

for grants to individuals, and $52,874 for foundation-administered programs.
Purpose and activities: Provides undergraduate scholarships to Vermont high school graduates, who are nominated by a Vermont Student Assistance Corporation (VSAC) outreach counselor, who will attend an accredited postsecondary school approved for federal Title IV funding, who are enrolled in an undergraduate associate's or bachelor's degree program, and who demonstrate financial need.
Fields of interest: Higher education.
Type of support: Scholarships—to individuals.
Limitations: Giving limited to VT residents. No grants for building or endowment funds, operating budgets, or special projects.
Publications: Newsletter.
Application information: The foundation does not accept direct applications from students. The Vermont Student Assistance Corporation (VSAC) determines, through its Outreach program, which students meet the criteria for assistance. See foundation web site for additional information.
Initial approach: Contact the Vermont Student Assistance Corporation (VSAC)
Trustees: Joseph Boutin; Mike Breen; J. Churchill Hindes, Ph.D.; Spencer Knapp; Amy Mellencamp.
EIN: 036009912

9362
The Gibney Family Foundation, Inc. ✧
1233 Shelburne Rd., Ste. 440
South Burlington, VT 05403-7780
Contact: Frank A. Gibney, C.E.O. and Pres.
E-mail: grants@tgff.org; Main URL: http://www.tgff.org
RSS Feed: http://tgff.org/?feed=rss2

Established in 1991 in FL.
Donor: Albert L. Gibney†.
Foundation type: Independent foundation.
Financial data (yr. ended 12/31/13): Assets, $26,201,759 (M); expenditures, $1,237,714; qualifying distributions, $1,110,730; giving activities include $842,198 for 60 grants (high: $54,000; low: $300).
Purpose and activities: Support primarily for organizations that benefit the blind and visually impaired, as well as for distance learning programs for people who are blind or visually impaired.
Fields of interest: Children/youth; Youth; Young adults; Disabilities, people with; Physically disabled; Blind/visually impaired; Native Americans/American Indians; Infants/toddlers, female; Young adults, female; Infants/toddlers, male; Young adults, male.
Type of support: General/operating support; Income development; Management development/capacity building; Capital campaigns; Equipment; Program development; Publication; Curriculum development; Scholarship funds; Technical assistance; Consulting services; Program-related investments/loans; Matching/challenge support.
Limitations: Applications not accepted. Giving primarily in areas where foundation sponsors reside: AZ, CA, CT, FL, ID, MA, ME, NH, upstate NY, OR, UT, VT, and WA. No support for research projects or religious or political organizations. No grants to individuals.
Application information: Unsolicited full proposals are not accepted. Proposals are solicited by foundation associates.
Board meeting date(s): Quarterly
Officers and Trustees:* Frank A. Gibney,* C.E.O., C.I.O., and Pres.; Tracy Wasden,* V.P. and Secy.; Robert Whittaker,* V.P. and Treas.; Brian DiFatta; Joan Gibney Whittaker; Sue Young.
Number of staff: 1 full-time professional; 3 part-time support.
EIN: 650286170

9363
Frank M. & Olive E. Gilman Foundation ✧
P.O. Box 979
White River Junction, VT 05001-0979 (802) 295-3358
Contact: Reginald H. Jones, Pres.

Established in 1991 in VT; funded in 1992.
Donors: Frank Gilman†; Olive Gilman†; Valley Land Corp.
Foundation type: Independent foundation.
Financial data (yr. ended 12/31/13): Assets, $39,528,722 (M); gifts received, $800,000; expenditures, $2,013,072; qualifying distributions, $1,810,136; giving activities include $1,800,000 for 2 grants (high: $1,170,000; low: $630,000).
Purpose and activities: Giving primarily for educational assistance in Orange and Windsor counties, VT.
Fields of interest: Education.
Limitations: Applications accepted. Giving limited to Grafton County, NH, and Orange and Windsor counties, VT. No grants to individuals.
Application information:
Initial approach: Letter
Deadline(s): None
Board meeting date(s): Varies
Officers: Reginald H. Jones, Pres.; Joseph Jones, V.P.; Elizabeth Jones, Secy.; Brenda Jones, Treas.
EIN: 030330527

9364
Isaiah 61 Foundation ✧
P.O. Box 5505
Burlington, VT 05402-5505

Established in 2000 in NY.
Donors: Andrew J. Schonbek; Charlotte Schonbek; Eileen Schonbek-Beer.
Foundation type: Independent foundation.
Financial data (yr. ended 12/31/13): Assets, $16,127,261 (M); gifts received, $100; expenditures, $938,451; qualifying distributions, $613,142; giving activities include $576,400 for 11 grants (high: $415,000; low: $500).
Fields of interest: Protestant agencies & churches.
Limitations: Applications not accepted. Giving primarily in IL. No grants to individuals.
Application information: Contributes only to pre-selected organizations.
Trustees: Matthew Beer; Stephanie Beer; Michael Beer; Alexandra Schonbek; Alice J. Schonbek; Amelia Schonbek; Andrew J. Schonbek; Eileen Schonbek-Beer.
EIN: 141827942

9365
Lintilhac Foundation ✧
886 N. Gate Rd.
Shelburne, VT 05482-7211 (802) 985-4106
Contact: Crea S. Lintilhac, Dir.
FAX: (802) 985-3725; E-mail: lint@together.net; Main URL: http://www.lintilhacfoundation.org
Grants List: http://www.lintilhacfoundation.org/biennialreport.html

Established in 1975.
Donors: Claire Malcolm Lintilhac†; Claire D. Lintilhac Annuity Trust I; Claire D. Lintilhac Annuity Trust II.
Foundation type: Independent foundation.
Financial data (yr. ended 12/31/13): Assets, $19,988,171 (M); gifts received, $329,466; expenditures, $1,226,900; qualifying distributions, $1,072,859; giving activities include $945,903 for 99 grants (high: $100,000; low: $300).
Purpose and activities: The foundation's central purpose is to support organizations that are making sustainable, positive change for Vermont's environment and its people and providing Vermonters the information and resources they need to control their environmental destinies and strong traditions of democratic engagement.
Fields of interest: Arts; Education; Environment; Health care; Community/economic development; Science, research.
Type of support: General/operating support; Continuing support; Capital campaigns; Land acquisition; Program development; Conferences/seminars; Professorships; Seed money; Fellowships; Scholarship funds; Research; Matching/challenge support.
Limitations: Applications accepted. Giving limited to VT. No support for religious organizations. No grants to individuals.
Publications: Biennial report; Biennial report (including application guidelines); Grants list.
Application information: Applicants must submit proposals using the online application system found on the foundation website. Hard copy proposals will not be accepted. Application guidelines available on foundation web site.
Initial approach: Proposal
Deadline(s): See foundation web site for current deadlines
Final notification: 1-3 months
Officers and Directors:* Louise S. Lintilhac,* Pres.; William S. Lintilhac,* V.P.; Philip M. Lintilhac,* Secy.-Treas.; Raeman P. Sopher, Dir. Emeritus; Crea S. Lintilhac; Paul S. Lintilhac.
Number of staff: 1 full-time support.
EIN: 510176851
Selected grants: The following grants are a representative sample of this grantmaker's funding activity:
$10,000 to University of Vermont, Department of Geology Maja Smith, Burlington, VT, 2012. For a display for the Bedrock Geologic Map.
$10,000 to University of Vermont, Department of Geology Maja Smith, Burlington, VT, 2012. For a display for the Bedrock Geologic Map.
$500 to Partners in Adventure, Shelburne, VT, 2012. For In continued support for camps and year-round Programs partnering young people with and without disabilities throughout northern Vermont.

9366
McKenzie Family Charitable Trust ✧
P.O. Box 285
Putney, VT 05346-0285
Contact: J. Michael McKenzie, Tr.
E-mail: torin.koester@gmail.com; Main URL: http://mckenziefamilycharitabletrust.org/

Established in 1993 in VT.
Donor: J. Michael McKenzie.
Foundation type: Independent foundation.
Financial data (yr. ended 12/31/13): Assets, $14,538,939 (M); expenditures, $625,271; qualifying distributions, $572,998; giving activities include $472,414 for 10 grants (high: $157,128; low: $5,000).
Purpose and activities: Giving to public education, with an emphasis on music.
Fields of interest: Arts education; Performing arts, music; Performing arts, education; Higher education; Children/youth, services; Science.
Type of support: General/operating support; Scholarship funds.
Limitations: Applications not accepted. Giving primarily in MA and VT. No grants to individuals.
Application information: Contributes only to pre-selected organizations.
Trustees: Torin S. Koester, Managing Tr.; J. Michael McKenzie.
EIN: 226596096
Selected grants: The following grants are a representative sample of this grantmaker's funding activity:
$38,000 to Vermont Jazz Center, Brattleboro, VT, 2011.
$25,000 to Epiphany School, Dorchester, MA, 2011.
$20,000 to Yellow Barn Music School and Festival, Putney, VT, 2011.
$10,750 to Boys and Girls Club of Brattleboro, Brattleboro, VT, 2011.
$1,000 to Brattleboro Music Center, Brattleboro, VT, 2011.

9367
The Mill Foundation, Ltd. ✧ ☆
80 Industrial Pkwy.
P.O. Box 4449
Burlington, VT 05406-4449

Established in 2004 in VT.
Donors: John B. Carpenter; Donna G. Carpenter.
Foundation type: Independent foundation.
Financial data (yr. ended 12/31/13): Assets, $1,181,161 (M); gifts received, $1,005,049; expenditures, $504,704; qualifying distributions, $504,453; giving activities include $504,400 for 44 grants (high: $125,000; low: $500).
Fields of interest: Arts; Education; Health organizations; Crime/violence prevention, child abuse; Human services; United Ways and Federated Giving Programs; Children.
Limitations: Applications not accepted. Giving primarily in VT.
Application information: Unsolicited requests for funds not accepted.
Officers: John B. Carpenter, Pres.; Donna G. Carpenter, V.P. and Secy.; Carolyn Wright, Treas.
EIN: 201957778

9368
National Life Group Charitable Foundation, Inc. ✧ ☆
1 National Life Dr.
Montpelier, VT 05604-3377
Main URL: https://secure.nlgcf.com/
Facebook: http://www.facebook.com/pages/National-Life-Group-Charitable-Foundation/152257977559?ref=ts
Grants List: http://www.nlgcf.com/what_we_do/we_helped.php

Established in 2007 in VT.
Donor: National Life Insurance Company.
Foundation type: Company-sponsored foundation.
Financial data (yr. ended 12/31/13): Assets, $223,649 (M); expenditures, $500,987; qualifying distributions, $492,025; giving activities include $492,025 for 113 grants (high: $50,000; low: $50).
Purpose and activities: The foundation supports organizations involved with arts and culture, the environment, health, housing, and human services.
Fields of interest: Arts; Health care; Community/economic development.
Limitations: Applications accepted. Giving primarily in areas of company operations in VT, with emphasis on central VT. No support for veterans', labor, religious, political, fraternal, or athletic organizations, organizations currently receiving Employee Action Grants, higher educational institutions (except for employee matching gifts), daycare facilities, or discriminatory organizations. No grants to individuals, or for endowments, debt reduction, or school trips.
Publications: Application guidelines.
Application information: Application form required.
Initial approach: Complete online eligibility quiz and application
Copies of proposal: 1
Deadline(s): Dec. 31 for grant requests under $5,000; Mar. 31 and Sept. 30 for grant requests over $5000
Officers and Directors:* Thomas H. MacLeay,* Chair.; Beth Rusnock, Pres. and C.E.O.; Thomas H. Bronwell, C.I.O.; Kerry Jung, Secy.; Robert E. Cotton, Treas.; Mehran Assadi; Christopher Graff; Beth Rusnock.
EIN: 204818866

9369
Antonio B. and Rita M. Pomerleau Foundation Inc. ✧
P.O. Box 6
Burlington, VT 05402-0006 (802) 863-8210
Contact: Antonio B. Pomerleau, Pres.

Established in 2006 in VT.
Donors: Antonio B. Pomerleau; Southland Enterprises Inc.; St Albans Shoping Center Inc.; Pomerleau Family LLC.; Rita M. Pomerleau; Merchants Bank.
Foundation type: Independent foundation.
Financial data (yr. ended 12/31/13): Assets, $0 (M); gifts received, $200,000; expenditures, $1,053,375; qualifying distributions, $928,418; giving activities include $923,418 for 35 grants (high: $576,865; low: $300).
Fields of interest: Education; Human services; YM/YWCAs & YM/YWHAs; Catholic agencies & churches.
Limitations: Applications accepted. Giving primarily in Vermont.
Application information: Application form required.
Initial approach: Proposal
Deadline(s): None
Officers: Antonio B. Pomerleau, Pres.; Patricia M. Pomerleau, V.P.; Ernest A. Pomerleau, Secy.
EIN: 030355842

9370
The Rowland Foundation Inc. ✧
P.O. Box 88
South Londonderry, VT 05155-0088 (802) 824-6400
Contact: Charles Scranton, Exec. Dir.
E-mail: info@therowlandfoundation.org; Main URL: http://www.therowlandfoundation.org/
diigo: https://groups.diigo.com/group/rowland_foundation
Facebook: https://www.facebook.com/Rowland.Foundation

Established in 2008 in VT.
Donors: Benjamin A. Rowland, Jr.; Wendy G. Rowland.
Foundation type: Independent foundation.
Financial data (yr. ended 06/30/13): Assets, $12,152,100 (M); gifts received, $1,020,000; expenditures, $723,406; qualifying distributions, $695,927; giving activities include $475,000 for 5 grants (high: $100,000; low: $75,000).
Purpose and activities: The foundation provides Vermont secondary school educators with a unique professional development and leadership opportunity, and the resources to positively affect the culture and climate of their respective schools.
Fields of interest: Elementary/secondary education; Teacher school/education; Education.
Type of support: Fellowships; Scholarships—to individuals.
Limitations: Applications accepted. Giving limited to VT.
Publications: Application guidelines.
Application information: Application information and form available on foundation web site. Application form required.
Initial approach: 1-page cover letter, plus proposal (3 pages maximum)
Copies of proposal: 4
Deadline(s): Dec. 31
Officers and Trustees:* Benjamin A. Rowland, Jr., Pres. and Treas.; Wendy G. Rowland, Secy.; Charles W. Scranton,* Exec. Dir.; Heidi Lynn; James C. Mooney; Daniel B. Rowland; John A. Shepard, Jr.
EIN: 262698626
Selected grants: The following grants are a representative sample of this grantmaker's funding activity:
$100,000 to Rutland High School, Rutland, VT, 2011.
$100,000 to Saint Johnsbury Academy, Saint Johnsbury, VT, 2011.
$100,000 to Thetford Academy, Thetford, VT, 2011.
$100,000 to Vergennes Union High School, Vergennes, VT, 2011.

9371
Sills Family Foundation ✧
P.O. Box 425
Richmond, VT 05477-8241

Established in 1993 in DE.
Donors: M. Sills‡; Peter Sills; Sills Charitable Trust; Sills Remainder Trust; Larry Sills.
Foundation type: Independent foundation.
Financial data (yr. ended 12/31/13): Assets, $42,040,945 (M); expenditures, $1,442,090; qualifying distributions, $1,168,250; giving activities include $1,168,250 for grants.
Fields of interest: Education; Human services; Children/youth, services; Women, centers/services; Foundations (public).

Limitations: Applications not accepted. Giving primarily in MA, NY, and VT.
Application information: Unsolicited requests for funds not accepted.
Officers: Arthur S. Sills, Pres.; Peter S. Sills, V.P.; Deborah Sills Iarussi, Secy.
Director: Larry Sills.
EIN: 521790278

9372
Stiller Family Foundation ✧ ☆
(formerly Inner Solutions Institute)
c/o Betsy Stanford
180 Battery St., Ste. 250
Burlington, VT 05407-2263

Classified as an operating foundation in 2002 in VT and DE. Reclassified as a independent foundation in 2003.
Donors: Robert P. Stiller; Green Mountain Coffee Roasters Foundation.
Foundation type: Independent foundation.
Financial data (yr. ended 12/31/12): Assets, $1,031,829 (M); expenditures, $742,876; qualifying distributions, $626,800; giving activities include $626,800 for grants.
Fields of interest: Education.
Limitations: Applications not accepted. Giving primarily in CA, MT and VT. No grants to individuals.
Application information: Contributes only to pre-selected organizations.
Officers and Directors:* Christine Stiller,* Pres.; Robert P. Stiller,* Secy.
EIN: 820542046

9373
Richard E. and Deborah L. Tarrant Foundation, Inc. ✧
(formerly Richard E. Tarrant Foundation, Inc.)
P.O. Box 521
Winooski, VT 05404-0521 (802) 857-0495
Contact: Lauren A. Curry, Exec. Dir.
FAX: (802) 857-0496;
E-mail: lcurry@tarrantfoundation.org; Additional e-mail: info@tarrantfoundation.org; Main URL: http://www.tarrantfoundation.org
Twitter: https://twitter.com/TarrantGiving

Established in 1997 in VT.
Donor: Richard E. Tarrant.
Foundation type: Independent foundation.
Financial data (yr. ended 12/31/12): Assets, $12,047,735 (M); expenditures, $1,455,464; qualifying distributions, $1,315,907; giving activities include $1,144,660 for 61 grants (high: $250,000; low: $250).
Purpose and activities: Giving to enrich the quality of life and communities throughout Vermont.
Fields of interest: Higher education; Human services; Community/economic development.
Type of support: General/operating support; Annual campaigns; Capital campaigns; Building/renovation; Equipment; Program development; Scholarship funds.
Limitations: Applications accepted. Giving limited to VT. No support for political organizations, or for research, lobbying activities, environmental, arts or medical health programs, schools, classrooms, or school-based clubs/activities. No grants to individuals, or for endowments, events or fundraisers, debt retirement, or multi-year grants.
Publications: Application guidelines.
Application information: Full applications are by invitation only, upon review of initial letter. Application form required.
Initial approach: Letter (no more than 2 pages) via e-mail (to Lauren A. Curry, Exec. Dir.) or U.S. Mail
Copies of proposal: 1
Deadline(s): Jan. 1, Apr. 1, July 1 or Oct. 1
Board meeting date(s): Quarterly
Officer: Lauren A. Curry, Exec. Dir.
Directors: Ronald L. Roberts; Deborah L. Tarrant; Richard E. Tarrant; Kevin S. Veller.
Number of staff: 1 part-time professional.
EIN: 030364509
Selected grants: The following grants are a representative sample of this grantmaker's funding activity:
$75,000 to University of Vermont, Burlington, VT, 2012. For Tarrant Institute for Innovative Education/Burlington and Wino Oski.
$15,000 to Central Vermont Home Health and Hospice, Barre, VT, 2012. For Telehealth Program.
$15,000 to King Street Center, Burlington, VT, 2012. For Teen Futures/General Operating.
$10,000 to Mercy Connections, Burlington, VT, 2012. For Getting Ahead in a Just Gettin' By World.
$7,500 to Northeast Kingdom Astronomy Foundation, Barnet, VT, 2012. For Technical and Program Support.
$2,500 to DREAM Program, Winooski, VT, 2012. For Summer Camp Programming and Supplies.
$2,000 to Fairfield Community Center Association, East Fairfield, VT, 2012. For equipment and upgrades.
$1,000 to Champlain Valley Exposition, Essex Junction, VT, 2012. For David Grimm Legacy Fund.
$500 to Champlain Valley Exposition, Essex Junction, VT, 2012. For David Grimm Recognition Event.

9374
Three Thirty Three Foundation Inc. ✧
112 S. Main St.
P.O. Box 220
Stowe, VT 05672-4649

Established in 2006 in VT.
Donors: Peter D. Dreissigacker; Bari Dreissigacker.
Foundation type: Independent foundation.
Financial data (yr. ended 10/31/13): Assets, $19,912,096 (M); gifts received, $3,908,842; expenditures, $599,048; qualifying distributions, $560,680; giving activities include $550,000 for 3 grants (high: $250,000; low: $100,000).
Fields of interest: Food banks; Human services; Children/youth, services; Family services; Foundations (community).
Limitations: Applications not accepted. Giving in VT, with emphasis on Burlington.
Application information: Contributes only to pre-selected organizations. Unsolicited requests for funds not accepted.
Officers and Directors:* Peter Dreissigacker,* Pres.; Bari Dreissigacker,* Secy.- Treas.; Marlo Dreissigacker Kohn; Scott Kohn.
EIN: 203794102
Selected grants: The following grants are a representative sample of this grantmaker's funding activity:
$90,000 to Laraway Youth and Family Services, Johnson, VT, 2011.
$50,330 to Spectrum Youth and Family Services, Burlington, VT, 2011.
$30,000 to Vermont Community Foundation, Middlebury, VT, 2011.

9375
Vermont Community Foundation ✧
3 Court St.
Middlebury, VT 05753 (802) 388-3355
Contact: For questions about grants: Jen Peterson, V.P., Program and Grants; For questions about accounting and finance: Debra Rooney, V.P., Finance and C.F.O.; For media inquiries or questions about publications: Felipe Rivera, V.P., Communications
FAX: (802) 388-3398; E-mail: info@vermontcf.org; Main URL: http://www.vermontcf.org
Facebook: http://www.facebook.com/vermontcf
LinkedIn: http://www.linkedin.com/company/the-vermont-community-foundation
Philanthropy's Promise: http://www.ncrp.org/philanthropys-promise/who
President's Blog: What's Stu-ing?: http://www.vermontcf.org/AboutUs/PresidentsBlogWhatsStu-ing.aspx
RSS Feed: http://www.vermontcf.org/DesktopModules/DNNArticle/DNNArticleRSS.aspx?portalid=0&moduleid=412&tabid=95&categoryid=2&cp=False&uid=1
Twitter: http://twitter.com/vermontcf
YouTube: http://www.youtube.com/user/vermontcf?feature=watch

Established in 1986 in VT.
Foundation type: Community foundation.
Financial data (yr. ended 12/31/12): Assets, $167,245,557 (M); gifts received, $16,537,381; expenditures, $16,608,412; giving activities include $12,603,915 for grants.
Purpose and activities: To build philanthropy in order to sustain healthy and vital Vermont communities.
Fields of interest: Humanities; Historic preservation/historical societies; Arts; Education, early childhood education; Child development, education; Elementary school/education; Secondary school/education; Higher education; Adult/continuing education; Libraries/library science; Education; Environment, natural resources; Environment; Reproductive health, family planning; Health care; Substance abuse, services; Mental health/crisis services; AIDS; Alcoholism; Health organizations; Food services; Housing/shelter; Children/youth, services; Youth, services; Child development, services; Family services; Minorities/immigrants, centers/services; Homeless, human services; Human services; Civil/human rights; Economic development; Community/economic development; Public affairs.
Type of support: Program-related investments/loans; Grants to individuals; Film/video/radio; Building/renovation; General/operating support; Income development; Management development/capacity building; Equipment; Emergency funds; Program development; Publication; Seed money; Curriculum development; Technical assistance; Consulting services; Program evaluation; Mission-related investments/loans.
Limitations: Applications accepted. Giving limited to VT. No support for religious purposes. No grants for capital campaigns, continuing support, debt reduction, or general endowments.

Publications: Application guidelines; Annual report; Financial statement; Grants list; Newsletter; Occasional report.
Application information: Visit foundation web site for application, additional guidelines per grant type, and specific deadlines. Application form required.
Initial approach: Online application only
Deadline(s): Varies
Board meeting date(s): 4 times annually
Final notification: Varies
Officers and Directors:* A. Jay Kenlan,* Chair.; Tim Volk,* Vice-Chair.; Stuart Comstock-Gay, C.E.O. and Pres.; Patrick H. Berry, V.P., Philanthropy; Jen Peterson, V.P., Progs. and Grants; Felipe Rivera, V.P., Comms.; Debbie Rooney, V.P., Finance and C.F.O.; James G. Wheeler, Jr.,* Secy.; Deb Brighton,* Treas.; Lisa Cashdan; Staige Davis; John Killacky; Peter Kinder; Michael Metz; Julie Peterson; Betsy Rathbun-Gunn; Margaret Seely.
Number of staff: 14 full-time professional; 4 part-time professional; 3 full-time support; 1 part-time support.
EIN: 222712160
Selected grants: The following grants are a representative sample of this grantmaker's funding activity:
$197,754 to Vermont Land Trust, Montpelier, VT, 2012. For the operation of the Vermont Land Trust's Conservation Stewardship Program, a program which monitors and enforces perpetual conservation easements on properties throughout Vermont.
$190,000 to TechFoundation, Cambridge, MA, 2012. For where it's needed most.
$150,000 to Highfields Institute, Hardwick, VT, 2012. For the work of Highfields Center for Composting in establishing statewide food scrap recycling through its Close the Loop! Vermont program.
$150,000 to Vermont Community Loan Fund, Montpelier, VT, 2012. To fund the Vermont Birth to Three (VB3) small grants program.
$135,000 to Southwest Vermont Supervisory Union, Bennington, VT, 2012. For VCPC (Vermont Community Preschool Collaborative) implementation grant for Bennington to serve at least 98 pre-K children.
$125,000 to Pro Publica, New York, NY, 2012. For general support.
$53,740 to Vermont Youth Conservation Corps, Richmond, VT, 2012. For Irene Recovery Work.
$5,000 to Connecticut River Watershed Council, Greenfield, MA, 2012. For completing a video and supporting material related to the floodplain of the Otter Creek (co-partner w/Connecticut River Watershed Council).
$2,600 to Middlebury College, Middlebury, VT, 2012. For Donation to support the Middlebury College Womens Golf Team.
$2,250 to Bryan Memorial Gallery Foundation, Jeffersonville, VT, 2012. For $1,000 for the Alden Bryan Memorial Award for Best in Show (with medal), $750 for second prize, and $500 for third prize - Land and Light Summer Show.

9376
The WaterWheel Foundation ✧ ☆

P.O. Box 4400
Burlington, VT 05406-4400
E-mail: ww@phish.com; Main URL: http://www.phish.com/waterwheel

Established in 1997 in VT.
Donors: Ben & Jerry's Homemade, Inc.; Phish Mail Order, Inc.; The Mimi Fishman Foundation; Don Law Corporation.
Foundation type: Independent foundation.
Financial data (yr. ended 12/31/13): Assets, $3,040,354 (M); gifts received, $979,510; expenditures, $460,568; qualifying distributions, $451,912; giving activities include $451,912 for 43 grants (high: $76,067; low: $750).
Fields of interest: Arts; Environment, legal rights; Environment, natural resources; Health organizations, volunteer services; Legal services, public interest law; Food banks; Human services; Foundations (community); Children; Women.
Type of support: General/operating support.
Limitations: Applications not accepted. Giving primarily in VT. No grants to individuals.
Application information: Contributes only to pre-selected organizations.
Officers: Ernest Anastasio III, Pres.; Jonathan Fishman, V.P.; Page McConnell, Secy.; Michael Gordon, Treas.
EIN: 133948773

VIRGIN ISLANDS

9377
Community Foundation of the Virgin Islands ✧
(also known as CFVI)
5600 Royal Dane Mall, Ste. 19
Charlotte Amalie, VI 00802-6410 (340) 774-6031
Contact: Dee Baecher-Brown, Pres.
FAX: (340) 774-3852; E-mail: general.info@cfvi.net; Mailing Address: P.O. Box 11790, Charlotte Amalie, VI 00801-4790; Additional e-mail: dbrown@cfvi.net; Main URL: http://www.cfvi.net/
Facebook: http://www.facebook.com/CFVirginIslands

Established in 1990 in the U.S. Virgin Islands.
Foundation type: Community foundation.
Financial data (yr. ended 12/31/12): Assets, $7,731,641 (M); gifts received, $1,943,004; expenditures, $1,970,259; giving activities include $1,036,917 for 15+ grants (high: $12,000), and $464,216 for 393 grants to individuals.
Purpose and activities: The Community Foundation of the Virgin Island (CFVI) was created to serve both donors and nonprofit organizations of the Virgin Islands that want to ensure the highest quality of life for both present and future generations. Its primary goal is to build a growing collection of permanent funds, the income from which will be used to enhance the educational, physical, social, cultural and environmental well-being of the islands' people.
Fields of interest: Education; Environment; Health care; Children/youth, services; Child development, services; Family services; Aging, centers/services; Community/economic development.
Type of support: Grants to individuals.
Limitations: Applications accepted. Giving limited to St. Croix, St. John, St. Thomas, and Water Island, VI.
Publications: Financial statement; Newsletter.
Application information: Visit the foundation web site for full application guidelines, specific deadlines, and requirements, including forms for the mini-grants program and scholarships. Application form required.
Initial approach: Submit application form
Deadline(s): Varies
Board meeting date(s): Monthly
Officers and Directors:* George H. T. Dudley,* Chair.; Alda Monsanto,* 1st Vice-Chair.; Victoria B. Sanders,* 2nd Vice-Chair.; Ricardo J. Charaf, Chair. Emeritus; Dee Baecher-Brown,* Pres.; Trudie J. Prior,* Secy.; William L. Graham, Treas.; Scott Barber; Filippo Cassinelli; Vivek A. Daswani; William L. Graham; Letty Hulsman; Lawrence Kupfer; Catherine L. Mills; Trudie J. Prior; Mark Robertson; Margaret Sprauve-Martin; Claire Starkey.
Number of staff: 1 part-time professional.
EIN: 660470703

9378
Prior Family Foundation ✧
P.O. Box 12030
St. Thomas, VI 00801-5030 (340) 775-1555
Contact: Gertrude J. Prior, Tr.

Established in 2006 in VI.
Donor: Cornelius B. Prior, Jr.
Foundation type: Independent foundation.
Financial data (yr. ended 12/31/12): Assets, $14,632,704 (M); expenditures, $819,662; qualifying distributions, $816,150; giving activities include $816,150 for 100 grants (high: $150,000; low: $200).
Fields of interest: Elementary/secondary education; Higher education; Theological school/education; Education; Foundations (community).
Limitations: Applications accepted. Giving primarily in St. Thomas, VI; some funding also in CT.
Application information: Application form required.
Initial approach: Letter
Deadline(s): None
Trustee: Gertrude J. Prior.
EIN: 206975076

VIRGINIA

9379
4G Foundation ✧
P.O. Box. 2543
Richmond, VA 23218-2543

Donor: The Gottwald Foundation.
Foundation type: Independent foundation.
Financial data (yr. ended 12/31/13): Assets, $18,423,241 (M); expenditures, $840,987; qualifying distributions, $821,888; giving activities include $814,985 for 24 grants (high: $350,000; low: $2,830).
Fields of interest: Education; Health care; Agriculture/food.
Limitations: Applications not accepted. Giving primarily in VA; with some giving in CA.
Application information: Unsolicited requests for funds not accepted.
Officers: Bruce C. Gottwald, Sr., Pres.; Thomas E. Golttwald, Secy.
EIN: 454432900

9380
ACT for Alexandria ✧
(also known as Alexandria Community Trust)
1421 Prince St., Ste. 220
Alexandria, VA 22314-2805 (703) 739-7778
Contact: John L. Porter, Pres. and C.E.O.
FAX: (703) 739-7787;
E-mail: info@ACTforAlexandria.org; Additional e-mail: john.porter@actforalexandria.org; Additional tel.: 703-299-8440; Main URL: http://www.actforalexandria.org/
Facebook: https://www.facebook.com/ACTforAlexandria
RSS Feed: http://www.actforalexandria.org/rss.xml
Twitter: https://twitter.com/ACTforAlex
YouTube: https://www.youtube.com/user/ACTionAlexandria

Foundation type: Community foundation.
Financial data (yr. ended 12/31/13): Assets, $9,339,005 (M); gifts received, $3,173,806; expenditures, $2,132,347; giving activities include $1,384,555 for 58+ grants (high: $262,104).
Purpose and activities: The Alexandria Community Trust provides strategic support for Alexandria nonprofits by connecting donors to effective programs and fostering excellence in nonprofit management through grants and other support.
Fields of interest: Nonprofit management; Philanthropy/voluntarism; Infants/toddlers; Children/youth; Youth; Adults, women; Single parents.
Type of support: Matching/challenge support; In-kind gifts; Conferences/seminars; Annual campaigns; Income development; Management development/capacity building; Scholarship funds.
Limitations: Applications accepted. Giving limited to Alexandria, VA. No support for religious or political organizations.
Publications: Application guidelines; Grants list; Informational brochure; Newsletter.
Application information: See foundation web site for information about its capacity building grant programs. Application form required.
Copies of proposal: 2
Deadline(s): Mid-Nov.
Board meeting date(s): 3rd Thurs. of Jan., Mar., May, July, Sept. and Nov.
Final notification: 3 weeks
Officers and Board Members:* Gene Steuerle,* Chair.; Lauren Stack,* Vice-Chair.; John L. Porter,* Pres. and C.E.O.; Debra Collins,* Secy.; Scott Harris,* Treas.; Heather Scott,* C.O.O. and C.D.O.; Mary Ann Best; Chatrane Birbal; Caren Camp; Lynnwood Campbell; Lyles Carr; Lisa Collis; Mimi Conger; Brooke Curran; Rob Dugger; Bill Euille; David Frantz; Magaly Galdo-Hirst; Val Hawkins; Trip Howell; Jane Knops; Rev. Pierce Klemmt; Christopher Lewis; David Markley; Lori Morris; Alice Paik; Neil Parent; Daniel Rogers; Jeannie Shaughnessy; David Speck; Sean Walsh.
ACT Advisory Council: Leslie Ariail; Bill Babcock; Kathy Barsness; Andrew Blair; Robert Calhoun; Cathy Carney-Peters; Allison Cryor DiNardo; David DeJesus; Allison Erdle; Kimberly Fiske; Mary Catherine Gibbs; Harry Hopper; Amy Liu; Phil Kangas; Brian Kennedy; Joyce Manchester; Lori Murphy; Scott Price; Emily Rothberg; Stephen Rideout; Phil Sunderland; Cathy Thompson; Jean Traub; Jonelle S. Wallmeyer; Rob Whittle.
Number of staff: 5 full-time professional.
EIN: 264322369

9381
The Agena Foundation Inc. ✧
111 Mann Dr.
Chesapeake, VA 23322-5213

Donors: Linda Founds; Martha N. Founds†.
Foundation type: Independent foundation.
Financial data (yr. ended 12/31/13): Assets, $11,905,190 (M); gifts received, $644,802; expenditures, $784,691; qualifying distributions, $682,355; giving activities include $682,355 for 11 grants (high: $101,855; low: $30,000).
Fields of interest: Higher education; Boys & girls clubs; Salvation Army.
Limitations: Applications not accepted. Giving primarily in VA.
Application information: Unsolicited requests for funds not accepted.
Officers: Linda Founds, Pres.; Judy G. McReynolds, V.P.; Christopher H. Russi, Treas.
EIN: 262882583

9382
The Alleghany Foundation ✧
214 W. Main St.
P.O. Box 1176
Covington, VA 24426-1554 (540) 962-0970
Contact: Mary Fant Donnan, Exec. Dir.; Melenie Riley, Admin. Secy.
FAX: (540) 962-1770; E-mail: allegfnd@aol.com; Main URL: http://www.alleghanyfoundation.org

Established in 1995 in VA; converted from the sale of Alleghany Regional Hospital Corporation to Columbia/HCA Healthcare Corp. The foundation awarded its first grants in Nov. 1996.
Foundation type: Independent foundation.
Financial data (yr. ended 12/31/12): Assets, $62,566,903 (M); expenditures, $4,741,975; qualifying distributions, $2,731,741; giving activities include $2,153,802 for 15 grants (high: $269,327; low: $45,895).
Purpose and activities: The foundation awards grants to organizations serving the Alleghany County, Covington, and Clifton Forge areas of VA, with an emphasis on new and different programs that improve the community's quality of life. The foundation awarded its first grants in Nov. 1996.
Fields of interest: Education; Health care; Nonprofit management; Community/economic development; Leadership development.
Type of support: Continuing support; Capital campaigns; Building/renovation; Equipment; Land acquisition; Program development; Publication; Curriculum development; Technical assistance; Consulting services; Matching/challenge support.
Limitations: Applications accepted. Giving primarily in Alleghany County, Covington, and Clifton Forge, VA. No support for debt reduction, endowment funds, ongoing general operating expenses, or existing deficits. No grants to individuals, or to religious organizations.
Publications: Application guidelines; Annual report; Grants list; Informational brochure (including application guidelines).
Application information: Application form required.
Initial approach: Letter per published guidelines
Copies of proposal: 13
Deadline(s): Mar. 1 and Sept. 1
Board meeting date(s): Quarterly
Final notification: June 1 and Dec. 1
Officers and Directors:* Charles W. Kahle,* Pres.; William J. Withrow,* Secy.-Treas.; Mary Fant Donnan,* Exec. Dir.; Harrison L. Fridley, Dir. Emeritus; Wallace C. Nunley, Dir. Emeritus; Patrick H. Winston, Dir. Emeritus; Dr. Michele Ballou; James R. Eller; Jack A. Hammond; George J. Kostel; Dr. Leo T. Mulcahy; Jr. George C. Snead; James D. Snyder; Lynda N. Thompson; Anne L. Wright.
Number of staff: 1 full-time professional; 1 full-time support; 1 part-time support.
EIN: 541027400
Selected grants: The following grants are a representative sample of this grantmaker's funding activity:
$547,188 to Joint School Systems Alleghany County Public Schools and Covington Public Schools, Covington, VA, 2011. For joint grant to fund school nurses and mental health initiative in both school systems.
$325,609 to Alleghany Highlands Free Clinic, Covington, VA, 2011. For physician assistant, pharmacy services and administrative services.
$240,096 to Jackson River Enterprises, Covington, VA, 2011. For equipment to streamline operations to optimize use of facility.
$240,000 to Alleghany County of Virginia, Covington, VA, 2011. For Jackson River Scenic Trail.
$157,500 to Dabney S. Lancaster Community College, Clifton Forge, VA, 2011. To enhance existing Emergency Medical Services training program by hiring Emergency Medical Services Coordinator/Lead Instructor.
$140,000 to YMCA, Alleghany Highlands, Covington, VA, 2011. For Virginia Preschool Initiative and Child Care.
$83,453 to Alleghany County of Virginia, Covington, VA, 2011. For In-Car Cameras for local law enforcement.
$75,000 to Clifton Forge Company, Clifton Forge, VA, 2011. For repairs for the Clifton Forge School of the Arts.
$56,382 to Alleghany Highlands Humane Society, Low Moor, VA, 2011. For full-time shelter manager position.

$34,162 to Alleghany Highlands Drug Task Force, Covington, VA, 2011. For equiment to be used to combat drug abuse.

9383
AMERIGROUP Foundation ✧
P.O. Box 62509
Virginia Beach, VA 23466-2509 (757) 490-6900
FAX: (757) 222-2360;
E-mail: wellpoint.foundation@wellpoint.com; Main URL: http://www.amerigroup.com/about-amerigroup/amerigroup-foundation

Donor: AMERIGROUP Corp.
Foundation type: Company-sponsored foundation.
Financial data (yr. ended 12/31/12): Assets, $1,647,802 (M); gifts received, $134,423; expenditures, $3,075,181; qualifying distributions, $3,075,181; giving activities include $2,837,610 for grants, $4,793 for grants to individuals, and $194,602 for employee matching gifts.
Purpose and activities: The foundation supports programs designed to foster access to healthcare; encourage safe and healthy children and families; and promote community improvement and healthy neighborhoods. Special emphasis is directed toward programs designed to serve the financially disadvantaged, seniors, and people with disabilities.
Fields of interest: Higher education; Health sciences school/education; Education; Health care, research; Reproductive health; Reproductive health, prenatal care; Public health; Health care, insurance; Health care; Food services; Nutrition; Recreation; YM/YWCAs & YM/YWHAs; Children/youth, services; Children, services; Family services; Aging, centers/services; Developmentally disabled, centers & services; Independent living, disability; Community/economic development; United Ways and Federated Giving Programs; Aging; Disabilities, people with; Economically disadvantaged.
Type of support: General/operating support; Continuing support; Building/renovation; Program development; Research; Sponsorships; Employee matching gifts.
Limitations: Applications accepted. Giving primarily in AZ,CA, CO, CT, FL, GA, IN, KS, KY, LA, MA, MD, ME, MO, NH, NJ, NM, NV, NY, OH, SC, TN, TX, WV, and WI with emphasis on VA. No support for private foundations, fraternal, social, athletic, labor, or veterans' organizations, political parties or candidates, for profit-entities including start-up businesses, or for organizations not of direct benefit to the entire community. No grants to individuals, or for tickets, tables, benefits, raffles, souvenir programs, fundraising dinners, golf outings, trips, tours, or similar events.
Publications: Application guidelines; Program policy statement.
Application information: Visit website for additional application information. Foundation grants will be administered by Wellpoint. Telephone calls are not encouraged during the application process. Application form required.
Initial approach: Complete online application
Deadline(s): Varies
Final notification: 4 to 6 months
Officers: John E. Littel, Pres.; Scott W. Anglin, V.P.; Richard C. Zoretic, V.P.
EIN: 542014061
Selected grants: The following grants are a representative sample of this grantmaker's funding activity:
$175,000 to Habitat for Humanity, South Hampton Roads, Norfolk, VA, 2011. For general use.
$125,000 to Centering Healthcare Institute, Boston, MA, 2010. For general use.
$125,000 to National Kidney Foundation, New York, NY, 2011. For general use.
$25,000 to Morningside College, Sioux City, IA, 2011. For general use.
$25,000 to Virginia Aquarium and Marine Science Center, Virginia Beach, VA, 2011. For general use.
$25,000 to Virginia Health Care Foundation, Richmond, VA, 2011. For general use.
$20,000 to National Hispanic Council on Aging, Washington, DC, 2011. For general use.
$5,000 to Eastern Virginia Medical School Foundation, Norfolk, VA, 2011. For general use.
$5,000 to Newlife Homes, Albuquerque, NM, 2011. For general use.
$3,500 to Arthritis Association of Louisiana, Baton Rouge, LA, 2011. For general use.
$2,500 to Mother Seton House, Virginia Beach, VA, 2011. For general use.

9384
Arlington Community Foundation ✧
818 N. Quincy St., Ste. 103
Arlington, VA 22203 (703) 243-4785
Contact: Wanda L. Pierce, Exec. Dir.
FAX: (703) 243-4796; E-mail: info@arlcf.org; Grant inquiry e-mail: grants@arlcf.org; Main URL: http://www.arlcf.org
E-Newsletter: http://arlcf.org/index.cfm/newsletter
Facebook: http://www.facebook.com/pages/Arlington-Community-Foundation/130015137014
LinkedIn: http://www.linkedin.com/companies/arlington-community-foundation
Twitter: http://twitter.com/Arlcf

Established in 1991 in VA.
Foundation type: Community foundation.
Financial data (yr. ended 06/30/13): Assets, $10,034,870 (M); gifts received, $2,039,042; expenditures, $1,763,460; giving activities include $1,016,804 for 52+ grants (high: $500,500), and $300,900 for 129 grants to individuals.
Purpose and activities: The foundation is an independent charitable organization that actively promotes, protects and improves the quality of life for those who live or work in Arlington. The foundation provides philanthropic leadership and raises capital for grants and scholarships to address community needs now and in the future.
Fields of interest: Performing arts; Humanities; Arts; Adult education—literacy, basic skills & GED; Education, reading; Education; Environment; Health care; Food services; Housing/shelter; Disasters, Hurricane Katrina; Safety/disasters; Children/youth, services; Aging, centers/services; Minorities/immigrants, centers/services; Human services; Community/economic development; Government/public administration; Aging; Minorities; Native Americans/American Indians; Women; Economically disadvantaged.
Type of support: Scholarships—to individuals; General/operating support; Continuing support; Management development/capacity building; Emergency funds; Program development; Seed money; Curriculum development; Scholarship funds; Technical assistance; Consulting services; Grants to individuals.
Limitations: Applications accepted. Giving limited to the Arlington, VA, area. No support for religious purposes. No grants to individuals (except for scholarships or specific awards by nomination), or for endowments, capital campaigns or for debts.
Publications: Application guidelines; Annual report; Financial statement; Grants list; Informational brochure; Multi-year report; Newsletter; Program policy statement.
Application information: Visit foundation web site for application forms and guidelines. Application form required.
Initial approach: Letter or telephone
Copies of proposal: 1
Deadline(s): Varies
Board meeting date(s): Feb., Apr., June, Aug., Oct., and Dec.
Final notification: 1 week
Officers and Trustees:* Julian Fore,* Pres.; Vicki Foster,* V.P.; Hon. Mary Margaret Whipple,* Secy.; David W. Briggs,* Treas.; Wanda L. Pierce, Exec. Dir.; Hon. William T. Newman, Jr., Pres. Emeritus; John Andelin; Hon. David A. Bell; Jeanne Broyhill; Patricia Connally; Bradford R. Coyle; Susan S. Duke; Ronald J. Gordon; Greg Hamilton; Dr. Leonard L. Hamlin, Sr.; Robert H. Hawthorne; Deborah T. Johnson; Sona Nga Johnston; Artemis McDonald; Andrew McGeorge; Peggy Richardson; Libby Ross; Janet Schmidt; Dr. Matthew D. Shank; John G. Shooshan; Avril Ussery Sisk; Nancy Snell; Brian J. Steffan; Jim Whittaker.
Number of staff: 1 full-time professional; 2 part-time professional.
EIN: 541602838

9385
Balsells Foundation ✧
c/o Sterling Foundation Mgmt., LLC
2325 Dulles Corner Blvd., Ste. 670
Herndon, VA 20171-4683 (703) 437-9720

Established in 2005 in VA.
Donors: Peter J. Balsells; Jeanine Naviaux.
Foundation type: Independent foundation.
Financial data (yr. ended 12/31/13): Assets, $3,548,850 (M); gifts received, $1,000,000; expenditures, $704,118; qualifying distributions, $680,194; giving activities include $671,162 for 10 grants (high: $226,344; low: $150).
Fields of interest: Higher education; Protestant agencies & churches.
Type of support: General/operating support.
Limitations: Applications accepted. Giving primarily in CA.
Application information: Application form not required.
Initial approach: Proposal
Deadline(s): None
Officers and Directors:* Peter J. Balsells,* Pres. and Secy.-Treas.; Lawrence Gustafson,* V.P.; Eileen DeLucia; Jeanine Naviaux; Denise Stillman.
EIN: 203647654
Selected grants: The following grants are a representative sample of this grantmaker's funding activity:
$171,450 to University of Colorado Foundation, Boulder, CO, 2011. For general support.
$82,650 to Palos Verdes Sunset Rotary Charities, Palos Verdes Peninsula, CA, 2011. For general support.
$40,000 to University of California, Oakland, CA, 2011. For general support.

9386
Bangs-Russell Foundation ✧
c/o The Trust Company of Virginia
4350 New Town Ave., Ste. 202
Williamsburg, VA 23188-2810

Established in 2004 in VA.
Donors: Archie E. Russell‡; Marion B. Russell.
Foundation type: Independent foundation.
Financial data (yr. ended 12/31/13): Assets, $5,566,428 (M); expenditures, $590,901; qualifying distributions, $539,520; giving activities include $539,520 for 21 grants (high: $75,000; low: $5,000).
Fields of interest: Higher education; Housing/shelter, development; Human services; American Red Cross; Salvation Army; Christian agencies & churches.
Type of support: General/operating support.
Limitations: Applications not accepted. Giving primarily in Washington, DC, FL, GA, MO, NC and VA. No grants to individuals.
Application information: Contributes only to pre-selected organizations.
Officers: Marion B. Russell, Pres.; Elizabeth R. Ogburn, Secy.
Directors: William F. Russell; Barbara R. Valenti.
EIN: 201840390
Selected grants: The following grants are a representative sample of this grantmaker's funding activity:
$5,520 to World Vision, Tacoma, WA, 2012. For 14 Sponsored Children.

9387
The Bansal Foundation ✧
1230 Clarkewood Ct.
Mc Lean, VA 22102-2399 (703) 748-0428
Contact: Sanjeev K. Bansal, Tr.

Established in 1998 in MA and VA.
Donor: Sanjeev K. Bansal.
Foundation type: Independent foundation.
Financial data (yr. ended 12/31/13): Assets, $11,659,190 (M); gifts received, $2,010,150; expenditures, $558,527; qualifying distributions, $498,250; giving activities include $498,250 for 7 grants (high: $350,000; low: $750).
Purpose and activities: Giving primarily to a charitable gift fund, and to a university's radio station.
Fields of interest: Media, radio; Human services; Foundations (public).
Limitations: Applications accepted. Giving primarily in MA; some giving also in Washington, DC. No grants to individuals.
Application information: Application form required.
Initial approach: Letter
Deadline(s): None
Trustee: Sanjeev K. Bansal.
EIN: 541933631

9388
The D. N. Batten Foundation ✧
(also known as The Batten-Rolph Foundation)
c/o Signature Financial Management, Inc.
101 W. Main St., Ste. 700
Norfolk, VA 23510-1624

Established in 1997 in VA.
Donors: Dorothy B. Rolph; Dorothy N. Batten.
Foundation type: Independent foundation.
Financial data (yr. ended 12/31/13): Assets, $22,070,926 (M); gifts received, $3,000,000; expenditures, $1,820,779; qualifying distributions, $1,537,900; giving activities include $1,537,900 for 24 grants (high: $500,000; low: $500).
Fields of interest: Higher education; Hospitals (general); Boys & girls clubs; Foundations (public).
Limitations: Applications not accepted. Giving in VA. No grants to individuals.
Application information: Contributes only to pre-selected organizations.
Officer: Dorothy N. Batten, Pres.
Director: Frank Batten, Jr.
EIN: 541864288

9389
The Batten Foundation ✧
P.O. Box 3310
Norfolk, VA 23514-3310

Established in 1988 in VA.
Donor: Frank Batten, Sr.‡.
Foundation type: Independent foundation.
Financial data (yr. ended 12/31/13): Assets, $33,829,160 (M); gifts received, $5,001,694; expenditures, $1,833,600; qualifying distributions, $1,405,000; giving activities include $1,405,000 for 1 grant.
Purpose and activities: Giving primarily for a public library.
Fields of interest: Libraries (public); Disasters, preparedness/services.
Limitations: Applications not accepted. Giving primarily in VA. No grants to individuals.
Application information: Contributes only to pre-selected organizations.
Officer: Jane Batten, Pres.
EIN: 541451569

9390
Aimee & Frank Batten, Jr. Foundation ✧
150 Granby St.
Norfolk, VA 23510-1604

Established in 1998 in VA.
Donor: Frank Batten, Jr.
Foundation type: Independent foundation.
Financial data (yr. ended 12/31/12): Assets, $48,916,988 (M); expenditures, $6,631,012; qualifying distributions, $6,303,150; giving activities include $6,303,150 for 56 grants (high: $2,500,000; low: $2,500).
Purpose and activities: Giving primarily for Christian causes, as well as for education, the arts, and human services.
Fields of interest: Arts; Education; Environment, natural resources; Human services; Foundations (private grantmaking); Christian agencies & churches.
Limitations: Applications not accepted. Giving primarily in VA. No grants to individuals.
Application information: Contributes only to pre-selected organizations.
Officer and Director:* Frank Batten, Jr.,* Pres. and Secy.-Treas.
EIN: 541879266

9391
Beazley Foundation, Inc. ✧
3720 Brighton St.
Portsmouth, VA 23707-1788 (757) 393-1605
Contact: Hon. Richard S. Bray, Pres. and C.E.O.
FAX: (757) 393-4708;
E-mail: info@beazleyfoundation.org; Main URL: http://www.beazleyfoundation.org/index.html

Incorporated in 1948 in VA.
Donors: Fred W. Beazley‡; Marie C. Beazley‡; Fred W. Beazley, Jr.‡.
Foundation type: Independent foundation.
Financial data (yr. ended 12/31/13): Assets, $53,603,429 (M); expenditures, $3,796,404; qualifying distributions, $3,419,416; giving activities include $2,367,297 for 69 grants (high: $201,000; low: $500), and $425,971 for 1 foundation-administered program.
Purpose and activities: Giving to further the causes of charity, education, and religion. Support also for higher, secondary and medical education, youth agencies, community development, the aged, and other general charities, including health organizations and hospitals, the homeless, religion, and recreation.
Fields of interest: Secondary school/education; Higher education; Medical school/education; Education; Hospitals (general); Health care; Health organizations, association; Recreation; Youth, services; Aging, centers/services; Homeless, human services; Community/economic development; Religion; Children/youth; Youth; Aging; Disabilities, people with; Physically disabled; Mentally disabled; Terminal illness, people with; Economically disadvantaged; Homeless.
Type of support: Curriculum development; Building/renovation; Capital campaigns; Equipment; General/operating support; Matching/challenge support; Program development; Scholarship funds.
Limitations: Giving primarily in the South Hampton Roads area, VA. No support for environmental, cultural, media, international or national programs. No grants to individuals.
Publications: Biennial report; Financial statement; Grants list; Program policy statement.
Application information: As a result of the prolonged and continuing recession and attendant depressed investment markets, the foundation has suspended consideration of grants, subject only to urgent needs as determined in the sole discretion of the foundation. Application updates, information and form available on foundation web site.
Initial approach: Letter, telephone or e-mail
Copies of proposal: 1
Deadline(s): Jan. 1, Mar. 1, June 1 and Oct. 1
Board meeting date(s): Feb., Apr., Aug. and Dec.
Final notification: Within 2 weeks
Officers and Trustees:* Hon. Richard S. Bray,* C.E.O. and Pres.; Diane Pomeroy Griffin,* V.P.; P. Ward Robinett, Jr.,* Secy.; John W. Failes; Lawrence Warren I'Anson III; W. Ashton Lewis; Whitney G. Saunders.
Number of staff: 3 full-time professional.
EIN: 540550100
Selected grants: The following grants are a representative sample of this grantmaker's funding activity:
$211,393 to Portsmouth Schools Foundation, Portsmouth, VA, 2012. For First College Program, Scholarships, Portsmouth Reads Adult Literacy Initiative, Bayquest and Riverquest Summer Camps.

$62,500 to Saint Marys Home for Disabled Children, Norfolk, VA, 2012. For Capital and Endowment Campaign.
$56,250 to Bluefield College, Bluefield, VA, 2012. For curriculum improvements.
$50,000 to Academy of Music, Norfolk, VA, 2012. For Parkview Elementary School Strings Program.
$45,000 to Regent University, Virginia Beach, VA, 2012. For Lawrence W L'Anson Scholarship Fund.
$40,000 to United Way of South Hampton Roads, Norfolk, VA, 2012. For Tocqueville Society, Impact Fund, Boys and Girls Club, Edmarc, Computer Literacy Lab at P B Young Elementary.
$40,000 to Virginia College Fund, Richmond, VA, 2012. For Beazley Scholarship Endowment.
$35,000 to College of William and Mary, Williamsburg, VA, 2012. For New Elder Care Law Clinic.
$25,000 to ACCESS College Foundation, Norfolk, VA, 2012. For Portsouth High School Program.
$5,000 to Philanthropy Roundtable, Washington, DC, 2012. For Membership Fees and Operating Expenses.

9392
St. Roberto Bellarmin Foundation ✧
258 E. High St.
Charlottesville, VA 22902-5178

Established in 1987 in VA.
Donor: Niklas Schrenck von Notzing.
Foundation type: Independent foundation.
Financial data (yr. ended 12/31/13): Assets, $1,225,358 (M); gifts received, $390,662; expenditures, $505,795; qualifying distributions, $505,795; giving activities include $498,500 for 7 grants (high: $350,000; low: $3,500).
Purpose and activities: Primarily supports Roman Catholic priests, chapels, seminaries, and monasteries that are committed to the traditional Catholic view.
Fields of interest: Catholic agencies & churches.
Limitations: Applications not accepted. Giving primarily in the U.S; funding also in Europe. No grants to individuals.
Application information: Unsolicited requests for funds not accepted.
Officer: Niklas Schrenck, Pres.
Director: James E. Skeen.
EIN: 541407053
Selected grants: The following grants are a representative sample of this grantmaker's funding activity:
$3,500 to Missionaries of the Sacred Heart, Clarksburg, OH, 2012. For Catholic Support.

9393
Birdsong Charitable Foundation ✧
P.O. Box 1400
Suffolk, VA 23439-1400

Established in 1991 in VA.
Donor: Birdsong Corp.
Foundation type: Company-sponsored foundation.
Financial data (yr. ended 12/31/13): Assets, $13,027,951 (M); gifts received, $3,500,000; expenditures, $1,193,420; qualifying distributions, $1,117,450; giving activities include $1,117,450 for 20 grants (high: $250,000; low: $200).
Purpose and activities: The foundation supports organizations involved with arts and culture, education, science, and religion.
Fields of interest: Arts; Education; Religion.
Type of support: General/operating support.
Limitations: Applications not accepted. Giving primarily in VA. No grants to individuals.
Application information: Contributes only to pre-selected organizations.
Board meeting date(s): Varies
Officers and Directors:* Stephen L. Huber,* Secy.; George Y. Birdsong,* Treas.; Thomas H. Birdsong.
EIN: 541607210
Selected grants: The following grants are a representative sample of this grantmaker's funding activity:
$300,000 to Randolph-Macon College, Ashland, VA, 2011.
$156,000 to Virginia Wesleyan College, Norfolk, VA, 2011.
$3,500 to Chesapeake Bay Foundation, Norfolk, VA, 2011.
$1,125 to National FFA Foundation, Indianapolis, IN, 2011.

9394
Blue Moon Fund, Inc. ✧
(formerly W. Alton Jones Foundation, Inc.)
222 W. South St.
Charlottesville, VA 22902-5041 (434) 295-5160
FAX: (434) 295-6894;
E-mail: info@bluemoonfund.org; Additional address: 2000 Florida Ave. NW, Ste. 100, Washington, DC 20009; Main URL: http://www.bluemoonfund.org
Grants Database: http://www.bluemoonfund.org/grantmaking/search/

Incorporated in 1944 in NY as W. Alton Jones Foundation.
Donor: W. Alton Jones‡.
Foundation type: Independent foundation.
Financial data (yr. ended 12/31/12): Assets, $158,546,880 (M); expenditures, $15,682,446; qualifying distributions, $13,007,784; giving activities include $9,984,260 for 112 grants, and $81,487 for foundation-administered programs.
Purpose and activities: The fund supports initiatives that work to build human and natural resilience to a changing and warming world. It uses natural, social, and financial capital to implement new models in high-diversity regions around the world.
Fields of interest: Environment, climate change/global warming; Environment, natural resources; Environment, energy; Economic development.
Type of support: General/operating support; Program development; Program-related investments/loans; Matching/challenge support; Mission-related investments/loans.
Limitations: Applications accepted. Giving in Asia, primarily in China, the Greater Mekong region, and the Himalayas, in North America primarily in the Chesapeake, Appalachian and Gulf Coast regions, and in the Tropical Americas, primarily in the Andes-Amazon, the Eastern Amazon, and the Mesoamerica regions. No grants for lobbying, advertising, dissertations, thesis and other academic work.
Application information: The fund is an initiative-based organization and generally does not take unsolicited proposals. Staff selects organizations to fund that have the skills to further the projects developed by the staff. Organizations may also submit letters of inquiry through the foundation's web site. LOI's are reviewed periodically by staff who may invite full proposals.
Initial approach: Eligibility quiz on foundation web site
Board meeting date(s): Typically, five times annually
Officers and Trustees:* Diane Edgerton Miller,* C.E.O. and Pres.; Adrian Forsyth, Ph.D., V.P., Progs.; Ji-Qiang Zhang, V.P., Progs.; Diane Schmidt, C.F.O.; Jasem Green, C.I.O.
EIN: 136034219
Selected grants: The following grants are a representative sample of this grantmaker's funding activity:
$310,500 to Amazon Conservation Association, Washington, DC, 2012. For scale up work in promoting biodiversity conservation, sustainable agriculture, ecotourism, and other economic opportunities as integrated regional system within the Manu Biosphere Reserve.
$250,000 to Center for Climate Strategies, Washington, DC, 2012. For provincial level climate action planning in China, and to further sub-national US-China collaboration on climate change.
$250,000 to Field Museum of Natural History, Chicago, IL, 2012. For the creation of new major protected area in the Amazon headwaters along the border of Peru and Colombia.
$240,000 to Instituto del Bien Comun, Lima, Peru, 2012. For the expansion of the conservation corridor in the Selva Central of Peru.
$217,000 to MarketUmbrella.org, New Orleans, LA, 2012. For the local food economy in 50 Gulf South communities by expanding technical support for these businesses as well as providing detailed analysis of the attributes of what makes a successful business where opportunities in the sector exist and the effect of these business on their local economies.
$156,500 to Chinese Academy of Sciences, Institute of Zoology, Beijing, China, 2012. For development and dissemination of effective biodiversity and ecosystem conservation management systems in China.
$150,000 to Lower 9th Ward Center for Sustainable Engagement and Development, New Orleans, LA, 2012. For CSED as a central organizing and communications hub for the lower 9th ward of New Orleans in light of the BP oil spill.
$118,500 to China Environmental Protection Foundation, Beijing, China, 2012. For effective and meaningful enforcement of China's wildlife conservation laws specifically targeting international poaching and illegal trade, through a public award that recognizes and highlights the work of outstanding individuals or groups.
$100,000 to Capital E LLC, Washington, DC, 2012. For energy efficiency investments through implementation of new mechanism in California's Carbon market.
$75,000 to Mountain Association for Community Economic Development, Berea, KY, 2012. For capacity building for the advancement of sustainable food and agricultural economies in central Appalachia.

9395
Leonard X. Bosack and Bette M. Kruger Charitable Foundation, Inc. ✧
8458 W. Main St.
Marshall, VA 20115-3231

Re-established in 2002 in MA.
Donors: Leonard Bosack; Sandy Lerner; The Leonard X. Bosack & Bette M. Kruger Foundation.
Foundation type: Independent foundation.
Financial data (yr. ended 12/31/12): Assets, $6,858,294 (M); expenditures, $1,937,144; qualifying distributions, $1,867,080; giving activities include $1,714,726 for 28 grants (high: $168,809; low: $500).
Purpose and activities: Funding specifically in support of scientific education and the promotion of animal welfare, with a special emphasis on the welfare of captive wildlife, humane alternatives in veterinary education, collaborative spay and neuter programs, and protection of wild carnivores; funding also for the preservation and study of works by 17th, 18th, and early 19th century women writers.
Fields of interest: Higher education; Libraries/library science; Animal welfare; Engineering/technology; Science.
Type of support: Building/renovation; Equipment; Emergency funds; Program development; Conferences/seminars; Research.
Limitations: Applications not accepted. Giving primarily in the U.S.; some giving in the UK. No grants to individuals, or for operating budgets.
Application information: Contributes only to pre-selected organizations.
Board meeting date(s): Varies
Officers and Directors:* Sandy Lerner,* Pres.; Leonard Bosack,* Secy.; Brook Middleton,* Treas.; Alicia Falsetto; Robert Liebscher.
Number of staff: 1 part-time professional.
EIN: 753089497
Selected grants: The following grants are a representative sample of this grantmaker's funding activity:
$168,809 to Stanford University, School of Engineering, Stanford, CA, 2012. For STARlab Program.
$59,926 to University of Washington Foundation, Tacoma, WA, 2012. For Conservation Biology, DNA Project.
$38,227 to University of Washington Foundation, Tacoma, WA, 2012. For Center for Conservation Biology Division.
$25,000 to WildEarth Guardians, Santa Fe, NM, 2012. For Carnivore Protection Stopping Trapping in New Mexico.
$9,600 to University of Montana, Missoula, MT, 2012. For Wildlife Research Unit, Wolf DNA Analysis Project.
$5,000 to Animal Legal Defense Fund, Cotati, CA, 2012. For Hoarding Projects in Rural Oregon.
$2,500 to Multnomah County Animal Services, Troutdale, OR, 2012. For Masters in Behavior Conference.

9396
I. J. and Hilda M. Breeden Foundation ✧
8817 Portner Ave.
Manassas, VA 20110-8817 (434) 295-5676
Contact: Sue Breeden Minor, Pres. and Dir.

Established in 1998 in VA.
Donor: Hilda M. Breeden†.
Foundation type: Operating foundation.
Financial data (yr. ended 12/31/13): Assets, $7,880,123 (M); expenditures, $1,420,596; qualifying distributions, $829,000; giving activities include $829,000 for 65 grants (high: $35,000; low: $1,000).
Purpose and activities: Giving primarily for community services in the Charlottesville and Manassas, VA, areas.
Fields of interest: Health care; Health organizations; Human services.
Type of support: General/operating support.
Limitations: Applications accepted. Giving limited to the Charlottesville and Manassas areas of VA. No grants to individuals.
Application information:
Initial approach: Letter
Copies of proposal: 1
Deadline(s): None
Board meeting date(s): Quarterly, in Mar., June, Sept., and Dec.
Officers and Directors:* Sue Breeden Minor,* Pres.; Sandra T. Cottrell,* V.P.; Andrew Breeden,* Secy.; Carol Payne; John M. Weber.
EIN: 541898663
Selected grants: The following grants are a representative sample of this grantmaker's funding activity:
$10,000 to American Red Cross, Charlottesville, VA, 2012. To support Charlottesville Area Community.
$10,000 to American Red Cross, Manassas, VA, 2012. To support Manassas Area Community.
$10,000 to Arthritis Foundation, Richmond, VA, 2012. To support Virginia Area Community Service.
$5,000 to Trinity Episcopal Church, Manassas, VA, 2012. To support Charlottesville Area Community Service.
$5,000 to Youth for Tomorrow, Bristow, VA, 2012. To support Manassas Area Community Service.

9397
The Robert G. Cabell III and Maude Morgan Cabell Foundation ✧
901 E. Cary St., Ste. 1402
Richmond, VA 23219-4037 (804) 780-2050
Contact: Jill A. McCormick, Exec. Dir.
FAX: (804) 780-2198;
E-mail: Cabell.foundation@gmail.com

Incorporated in 1957 in VA.
Donors: Robert G. Cabell III†; Maude Morgan Cabell†.
Foundation type: Independent foundation.
Financial data (yr. ended 12/31/13): Assets, $114,578,332 (M); expenditures, $5,951,192; qualifying distributions, $5,444,350; giving activities include $5,444,350 for 28 grants (high: $500,000; low: $23,000).
Purpose and activities: Grants primarily for higher education, health care, historic preservation, the arts and cultural projects, community development, and social welfare.
Fields of interest: Historic preservation/historical societies; Arts; Higher education; Human services; Community/economic development.
Type of support: Capital campaigns; Building/renovation; Equipment; Endowments; Matching/challenge support.
Limitations: Applications accepted. Giving limited to VA with emphasis on the Metro Richmond region. No support for special interest groups or for religious organizations for exclusive use of its membership. No grants to individuals, or for operating programs, or research projects.
Publications: Application guidelines; Informational brochure (including application guidelines).
Application information: Application form not required.
Initial approach: Telephone or letter
Copies of proposal: 1
Deadline(s): Mar. 1st and Sept. 1st.
Board meeting date(s): Mar., May, and Nov.
Final notification: Promptly following spring and fall board grant review meetings
Officers and Directors:* J. Read Branch, Jr.,* Pres.; Patteson Branch, Jr.,* V.P.; Charles L. Cabell,* Pres.; John Branch Cabell, Secy.; Elizabeth Cabell Jennings,* Treas.; Jill A. McCormack, Exec. Dir.; Patteson Branch III; Mary Z. Zeugner.
Number of staff: 1 part-time professional; 1 part-time support.
EIN: 546039157

9398
The Cameron Foundation ✧
228 S. Sycamore St.
Petersburg, VA 23803-4260 (804) 732-8900
Contact: J. Todd Graham, Pres.; Jill C. Coleman, V.P., Progs.
E-mail: tgraham@camfound.org; Additional e-mail address: Michele Hornby, Grants Mgr.: Mhornby@camfound.org; Main URL: http://www.camfound.org/

Established in 2003 in VA; converted from the sale of Southside Regional Medical Center.
Foundation type: Independent foundation.
Financial data (yr. ended 12/31/12): Assets, $118,605,041 (M); gifts received, $362,292; expenditures, $5,222,415; qualifying distributions, $6,072,990; giving activities include $2,531,697 for 74 grants (high: $364,924; low: $1,250), and $62,444 for 50 employee matching gifts.
Purpose and activities: The foundation is dedicated to providing resources that will improve both the health and quality of life for people living in the communities it serves.
Fields of interest: Historic preservation/historical societies; Arts; Education; Health care; Human services; Economic development; Community/economic development.
Type of support: General/operating support; Continuing support; Management development/capacity building; Capital campaigns; Building/renovation; Equipment; Land acquisition; Program development; Seed money; Curriculum development; Technical assistance; Consulting services; Program evaluation; Matching/challenge support.
Limitations: Applications accepted. Giving limited to VA, specifically to the cities of Petersburg, Colonial Heights and Hopewell; the counties of Dinwiddie, Prince George and Sussex; and the portion of the county of Chesterfield lying south of Route 10. No support for religious or political purposes, or for-profit organizations. No grants for endowments, medical research, academic or scientific research, the purchase of tickets to fundraising events or for advertising, solely for publishing, producing or distributing audio, visual or printed material, or attendance at conferences, seminars or meetings.
Publications: Application guidelines; Biennial report (including application guidelines); Financial statement; Grants list; Informational brochure (including application guidelines); Newsletter.
Application information: The letter of intent must be accompanied by a pre-screening checklist that will be provided by the foundation. The letter of intent and the pre-screened checklist should be

hand-delivered or mailed to the foundation; faxes are not accepted. One copy of the letter of intent and the pre-screening checklist must be submitted at least six weeks prior to the deadline for proposals for the next grant cycle. After the letter of intent has been reviewed by the foundation, the second step is submission of a full proposal if your organization is invited to do so by the foundation. Application form not required.

Initial approach: Letter of intent (no more than 3 double-spaced pages in 12 point or larger font)
Copies of proposal: 2
Deadline(s): Jan. 2, May 1, and Sept. 1
Board meeting date(s): Feb., June, and Oct. for grants; Apr., Aug., and Dec. for policy
Final notification: The foundation will provide a response to the letter of intent no later than four weeks prior to the deadline for submitting proposals.

Officers and Directors:* Larry C. Tucker,* Chair.; Pam Martin Comstock,* Vice-Chair.; J. Todd Graham,* Pres.; Jill C. Coleman, V.P., Progs.; Kevin A. Hill,* Secy.; Donald L. Haraway,* Treas.; J. Tolleison Morriss, VI; Anne C. Taylor; James L. Thacker, Jr.; Cleveland A. Wright.
Number of staff: 6 full-time professional; 3 full-time support; 1 part-time support.
EIN: 200097152

9399
Camp Foundation ✧
P.O. Box 813
Franklin, VA 23851-0813

Incorporated in 1942 in VA.
Donors: P.D. Camp†; and their families.
Foundation type: Independent foundation.
Financial data (yr. ended 12/31/13): Assets, $16,679,626 (M); expenditures, $883,431; qualifying distributions, $872,210; giving activities include $629,680 for grants, and $125,000 for grants to individuals (high: $6,500; low: $3,500).
Purpose and activities: Giving to provide or to aid in providing, in or near the town of Franklin, VA, parks, playgrounds, recreational facilities, libraries, hospitals, clinics, homes for the aged or needy, refuge for delinquent, dependent or neglected children, training schools, or other like institutions or activities. Grants also to select organizations statewide, with emphasis on youth agencies, safety programs, hospitals, mental illness, and nursing programs, higher and secondary education, including scholarships filed through high school principals, recreation, the environment, historic preservation, and cultural programs.
Fields of interest: Education; Health care; Human services; Children/youth, services.
Limitations: Applications accepted. Giving primarily in the city of Franklin, and Southampton and Isle of Wight counties, VA.
Publications: Application guidelines.
Application information: Application form required.
Initial approach: Completed application form
Copies of proposal: 7
Deadline(s): None
Officers and Directors:* John R. Marks,* Chair. and Pres.; Randy B. Drake,* V.P.; W.J. Parker, Secy.; S. Waite Rawls III,* Treas.; S.C. Adams; N.M. Brewbaker; John M. Camp III; C.F. Fox; B.K. Hedgepeth; D.T. Marks; V.S. Pittman II; R.H. Ray; S.R. Williams.
Number of staff: 2 full-time professional; 1 part-time support.
EIN: 546052488

9400
Capital One Foundation ✧
(formerly North Fork Foundation)
1680 Capital One Dr.
McLean, VA 22102-3407 (804) 284-2118
Contact: Mary Johnson Fain, Sr. Mgr., Opers.
E-mail: communityaffairs@capitalone.com; Main URL: http://www.capitalone.com/about/corporate-citizenship/partnerships/

Established in 1994 in NY.
Donors: GreenPoint Bank; Capital One.
Foundation type: Company-sponsored foundation.
Financial data (yr. ended 12/31/12): Assets, $46,759,574 (M); gifts received, $6,500,000; expenditures, $6,375,406; qualifying distributions, $6,124,000; giving activities include $6,010,000 for 130 grants (high: $345,000; low: $5,000).
Purpose and activities: The foundation supports programs designed to promote safe and affordable housing; financial literacy; workforce and economic development; social improvement; and early childhood education.
Fields of interest: Elementary/secondary education; Education, early childhood education; Education, services; Education, reading; Education; Employment, services; Employment, training; Housing/shelter, home owners; Housing/shelter; Youth development; Children, day care; Human services, financial counseling; Community development, small businesses; Community/economic development.
Type of support: General/operating support; Continuing support; Management development/capacity building; Program development; Employee matching gifts.
Limitations: Applications accepted. Giving primarily in Washington, DC, greater New Orleans, LA, MD, northern and central NJ, New York City and Long Island, NY, the greater Dallas and Houston, TX, areas, and Fairfax County, VA; giving also to national organizations. No support for political, labor, fraternal organizations, or civic clubs, religious organizations not of direct benefit of the entire community, or health-related organizations. No grants to individuals, or for fundraising or fellowships, advertising or marketing activities, sports, athletic events, or athletic programs, travel-related events including student trips or tours, development or production of books, films, videos, or television programs, or memorial campaigns.
Publications: Application guidelines; Corporate giving report.
Application information:
Initial approach: Complete online letter of inquiry form
Deadline(s): None
Officers and Directors:* John G. Finneran, Jr.,* Chair.; Richard A. Woods, Vice-Chair.; Carolyn S. Berkowitz,* Pres.; Amy D. Cook, Secy.; Andrew D. Labenne, Treas.; Guenet M. Beshah; Dorothy Broadman; Heather M. Cox; Kenneth Kido; Robert J. Magnano; Michael C. Slocum.
EIN: 113276603
Selected grants: The following grants are a representative sample of this grantmaker's funding activity:
$599,000 to Enterprise Community Partners, Columbia, MD, 2011.
$299,000 to Local Initiatives Support Corporation, New York, NY, 2011.
$299,000 to National Academy Foundation, New York, NY, 2011.
$299,000 to New Visions for Public Schools, New York, NY, 2011.
$167,750 to Scholarship America, Saint Peter, MN, 2011.
$74,000 to Cypress Hills Local Development Corporation, Brooklyn, NY, 2011.
$49,000 to Communities in Schools Houston, Houston, TX, 2011.
$34,000 to Long Island Housing Partnership, Hauppauge, NY, 2011.
$14,000 to Saint Nicks Alliance Corporation, Brooklyn, NY, 2011.
$9,000 to Northern Manhattan Improvement Corporation, New York, NY, 2011.

9401
The CarMax Foundation ✧
12800 Tuckahoe Creek Pkwy.
Richmond, VA 23238-1115
Contact: Leslie Parpart, Mgr., Community Rels. and CarMax Fdn.
FAX: (804) 935-4516;
E-mail: kmxfoundation@carmax.com; Main URL: http://www.carmaxcares.com
Twitter: http://twitter.com/CarMaxCares

Established in 2003 in VA.
Donors: CarMax Auto Superstores, Inc.; CarMax Business Services, LLC.
Foundation type: Company-sponsored foundation.
Financial data (yr. ended 02/28/13): Assets, $9,398,303 (M); gifts received, $4,000,000; expenditures, $3,676,154; qualifying distributions, $3,676,154; giving activities include $2,896,380 for 721 grants (high: $661,200), and $490,170 for 453 employee matching gifts.
Purpose and activities: The foundation supports programs designed to promote education; youth leadership; and wellness in communities where CarMax associates live and work.
Fields of interest: Arts education; Elementary/secondary education; Vocational education; Education, drop-out prevention; Education; Public health, obesity; Food services; Nutrition; Recreation, camps; Recreation, parks/playgrounds; Recreation; Youth development, adult & child programs; Youth development; Family services; Family services, domestic violence; Human services; Mathematics; Engineering/technology; Science; Leadership development; Children/youth; Economically disadvantaged.
Type of support: Continuing support; Program development; Employee volunteer services; Employee matching gifts.
Limitations: Applications accepted. Giving primarily in areas of company operations, with emphasis on the greater Richmond, VA, area; giving also to national organizations. No support for discriminatory organizations, organizations posing a conflict of interest with CarMax's mission, goals, programs, or products, fraternal, athletic, social, labor, or political organizations. No grants for debt reduction, political campaigns, or capital campaigns, endowments, event sponsorships, or scholarships; no vehicle donations.
Publications: Application guidelines; Annual report; IRS Form 990 or 990-PF printed copy available upon request.

Application information: Letters of inquiry should include a statement describing the project; and indicate the approximate date when an application will be submitted. Application form required.
Initial approach: For Richmond, VA only, letter of intent by Oct. 15; invitations for full proposals by Feb. 15.
Copies of proposal: 1
Deadline(s): Feb. 15 for Richmond Giving Program
Board meeting date(s): Mar., June, Sept., and Dec.
Final notification: Mar. 31 for Richmond Giving Program
Officers and Directors:* Lynn Mussatt,* Pres.; Ron Bevers, V.P.; Dan Bickett,* V.P.; Natalie Wyatt, Treas.; Alice Heinz; Bill McCrystal.
Number of staff: 2 full-time professional.
EIN: 383681796
Selected grants: The following grants are a representative sample of this grantmaker's funding activity:
$75,500 to KaBOOM, Washington, DC, 2013.
$75,000 to Enrichmond Foundation, Richmond, VA, 2013.
$25,000 to Community Foundation of North Texas, Fort Worth, TX, 2013.
$25,000 to Enrichmond Foundation, Richmond, VA, 2013.
$25,000 to Give Kids the World, Kissimmee, FL, 2013.
$25,000 to Life Support Development Ministry, Houston, TX, 2013.
$25,000 to Reach Out and Read Virginia, Richmond, VA, 2011.
$25,000 to Second Harvest Food Bank of Orange County, Irvine, CA, 2013.
$20,000 to Boys and Girls Clubs of Metro Atlanta, Atlanta, GA, 2013.
$20,000 to Sunshine Angels, Phoenix, AZ, 2013.
$20,000 to Texas Lions Camp for Crippled Children, Kerrville, TX, 2013.
$15,000 to Big Brothers Big Sisters of Tampa Bay, Tampa, FL, 2011.
$15,000 to Chicago Cares, Chicago, IL, 2011.
$15,000 to Kids in Distress, Wilton Manors, FL, 2011.
$10,000 to Cal Ripken, Sr. Foundation, Baltimore, MD, 2011.
$10,000 to Childrens Health Education Center, Milwaukee, WI, 2011.
$10,000 to DC Youth Orchestra Program, Washington, DC, 2011.
$10,000 to FeedMore, Richmond, VA, 2011.
$10,000 to Greater Richmond SCAN, Richmond, VA, 2011.

9402
Alexander Berkeley & Ruth S. Carrington, Jr. Charitable Trust ✧

c/o American National Bank
P.O. Box 191
Danville, VA 24543-0191 (434) 773-3320
Contact: Debra L. Carlson
Application address: 628 Main St., Danville, VA 24541

Established in 1985 in VA.
Donors: Alexander Berkeley Carrington†; Ruth Simpson Carrington†.
Foundation type: Independent foundation.
Financial data (yr. ended 02/28/13): Assets, $20,703,506 (M); expenditures, $1,196,638; qualifying distributions, $818,987; giving activities include $818,987 for grants.
Purpose and activities: Giving primarily to cultural and educational institutions in the Danville, VA area.
Fields of interest: Arts; Higher education; Education; Health organizations, association; Human services; Community/economic development.
Limitations: Applications accepted. Giving primarily in Danville, VA. No grants to individuals.
Application information: Application form required.
Initial approach: Proposal
Deadline(s): Jan. 15
Trustees: Kirk B. Echols; Robert K. Floyd; Edward F. Hodges, Jr.; American National Bank & Trust Co.
EIN: 546223108
Selected grants: The following grants are a representative sample of this grantmaker's funding activity:
$40,000 to Averett University, Danville, VA, 2013. For Funds needs for orchestra pit as part as Phase I renovations of Pritchett Auditorium on Averett's main campus.
$35,403 to Danville Life Saving and First Aid Crew, Danville, VA, 2013. For annual distribution.
$25,000 to Danville Community College, Danville, VA, 2013. To help offset the costs of childcare for student parents using the services of the Families First Children's Center at the child development center or at the Families First at the Danville Regional Medical Center (DRMC).
$16,500 to Danville Science Center, Danville, VA, 2013. To fund a portion of the fees for the traveling exhibit, Raise the Roof and other travel exhibits to the Danville Science Center for the 2013 Season.

9403
The Beirne Carter Foundation ✧

1802 Bayberry Ct., Ste. 401
Richmond, VA 23226-3773 (804) 521-0272
Contact: Peter C. Toms, Exec. Dir.
E-mail: bcarterfn@aol.com; Main URL: http://www.bcarterfdn.org

Established in 1986 in VA.
Donor: Beirne B. Carter†.
Foundation type: Independent foundation.
Financial data (yr. ended 12/31/12): Assets, $30,080,343 (M); expenditures, $1,899,085; qualifying distributions, $1,382,522; giving activities include $1,265,703 for 57 grants (high: $370,000; low: $150).
Purpose and activities: Giving primarily for education, human services, health, and to Episcopal churches and schools.
Fields of interest: Secondary school/education; Higher education; Education; Environment; Medical research, institute; Human services; Protestant agencies & churches.
Type of support: Capital campaigns; Building/renovation; Equipment; Matching/challenge support.
Limitations: Giving generally limited to VA. Generally, no support for public secondary schools and colleges and local municipalities, or to religious organizations. No grants to individuals; endowment funds, existing deficits or debt reduction.
Publications: Application guidelines; Informational brochure (including application guidelines).
Application information: Formal grant applications are by invitation only, after review of preliminary proposal. See foundation web site for complete proposal and application guidelines. Application form required.
Initial approach: Complete preliminary proposal form which can be downloaded from foundation web site
Copies of proposal: 4
Deadline(s): See foundation web site for current deadlines
Board meeting date(s): Apr. and Oct.
Final notification: Following board meeting
Officers: Mary Ross Carter Hutcheson, Pres.; Kenneth Laughon, V.P.; Talfourd H. Kemper, Esq., Secy.-Treas.
Number of staff: 2 part-time professional.
EIN: 541397827
Selected grants: The following grants are a representative sample of this grantmaker's funding activity:
$370,000 to North Cross School, Roanoke, VA, 2012. To renovate Carter Athletic Center.
$50,000 to North Cross School, Roanoke, VA, 2012. For Improvements to Carter Athletic Center.
$21,000 to Woodrow Wilson Presidential Library Foundation, Staunton, VA, 2012. To purchase and Install Handicap Lift and New Signage.
$20,000 to Amazement Square, Lynchburg, VA, 2012. To renovate gallery.
$18,970 to Friends of the Blue Ridge Parkway, Roanoke, VA, 2012. To support Future Stewards of the BRP Youth Program.
$1,000 to North Cross School, Roanoke, VA, 2012. For general purposes (Memorial).

9404
The Charles Fund, Inc. ✧

c/o Richmond and Fishburne
250 E. High St.
Charlottesville, VA 22902-5177 (434) 977-8590
Contact: Joseph W. Richmond, Jr., Pres.

Established in NY.
Donors: Edward C. Eisenhart; Sarah Eisenhart Trust; Edward Eisenhart Marital Trust.
Foundation type: Independent foundation.
Financial data (yr. ended 12/31/13): Assets, $10,660,387 (M); gifts received, $18,307; expenditures, $562,461; qualifying distributions, $482,707; giving activities include $435,000 for 60 grants (high: $75,000; low: $250).
Fields of interest: Museums (science/technology); Hospitals (general); Geriatrics; United Ways and Federated Giving Programs.
Type of support: General/operating support.
Limitations: Applications accepted. Giving primarily in Charlottesville, VA; with some giving in NY. No grants to individuals.
Application information: Application form required.
Initial approach: Contact foundation for application form
Deadline(s): None
Officers: Joseph W. Richmond, Jr., Pres.; Betsy Carver, V.P.; Deborah Maggs, V.P.; J. Walker Richmond III, Secy.-Treas.
Directors: Timothy Alexander; Gregory Carver; Anne M. Farnham.
EIN: 168064401
Selected grants: The following grants are a representative sample of this grantmaker's funding activity:
$100,000 to Lewis and Clark Exploratory Center, Charlottesville, VA, 2011.

$100,000 to Martha Jefferson Hospital Foundation, Charlottesville, VA, 2011.
$32,500 to Montpelier Foundation, Montpelier Station, VA, 2011.
$25,000 to Rochester Museum and Science Center, Rochester, NY, 2011.
$25,000 to Third Presbyterian Church, Rochester, NY, 2011.
$5,000 to Thomas Jefferson Foundation, Charlottesville, VA, 2011.
$1,000 to Charlottesville Free Clinic, Charlottesville, VA, 2011.
$1,000 to Charlottesville-Albemarle Rescue Squad, Charlottesville, VA, 2011.
$1,000 to Jamestown-Yorktown Foundation, Williamsburg, VA, 2011.
$1,000 to Virginia Museum of Fine Arts, Richmond, VA, 2011.

9405
Charlottesville Area Community Foundation ✧

(formerly Charlottesville-Albemarle Community Foundation)
114 4th St. S.E.
P.O. Box 1767
Charlottesville, VA 22902-1767 (434) 296-1024
Contact: Brennan Gould, Dir., Grants and Strategic Initiatives
FAX: (434) 296-2503; E-mail: cacf@cacfonline.org; Additional e-mail: bgould@cacfonline.org; Grant application e-mail: communityendowment@cacfonline.org; Main URL: http://www.cacfonline.org

Established in 1967 in VA.
Foundation type: Community foundation.
Financial data (yr. ended 12/31/12): Assets, $103,891,600 (M); gifts received, $7,068,463; expenditures, $8,751,857; giving activities include $6,861,487 for 203+ grants (high: $470,000; low: $100), and $400,096 for 102 grants to individuals.
Purpose and activities: The mission of the foundation is to improve the quality of life for those living and working in the city of Charlottesville, VA and the surrounding counties of Albemarle, Buckingham, Fluvanna, Greene, Louisa, Nelson, and Orange.
Fields of interest: Humanities; Arts; Education; Environment; Health care; Human services; Community/economic development.
Type of support: General/operating support; Seed money; Scholarship funds; Matching/challenge support.
Limitations: Applications accepted. Giving limited to the Charlottesville, VA, area, including the City of Charlottesville and the counties of Albemarle, Greene, Orange, Louisa, Fluvanna, Buckingham, and Nelson east of the Blue Ridge Mountains. No support for religious programs. No grants to individuals (except for scholarships), or for endowments, deficit reduction, fundraising events, or annual appeals of well-established organizations.
Publications: Application guidelines; Annual report; Newsletter.
Application information: Full proposals will be solicited from organizations under consideration for funding based in letter of inquiry (staff recommendations are submitted to the Community Endowment Grants Committee, which is comprised of members of the Foundation's Governing Board and other community members). Visit foundation web site for complete application guidelines. Application form required.
Initial approach: Contact foundation
Deadline(s): Community Endowment: Apr. 1 for letters of inquiry for grant requests of $10,000 to $100,000; Oct. 1 for letters of inquiry for grant requests of $10,000 or less
Board meeting date(s): Twice annually
Officers and Board of Governors:* Lawrence J. Martin,* Chair.; Louise M. Dudley,* Vice-Chair.; John R. Redick,* Pres.; Constance Waite, Sr. V.P., Finance and Admin.; Kathleen Bowman,* Secy.; Peter A. Agelasto; Julian M. Bivins, Jr.; O. Whitfield Broome, Jr.; Alan N. Culbertson; Joe H. Gieck; James L. Jessup, Jr.; Eric S. Johnson; Meghan Murray; Kelli E. Palmer; Susan K. Payne; Joseph W. "Rick" Richmond, Jr.; Joseph T. Samuels, Jr.; Leonard W. Sandridge, Jr.; Frederic W. Scott, Jr.; Elizabeth H. Woodard; Bruce Woodzell.
Number of staff: 2 full-time professional; 1 part-time professional; 2 full-time support.
EIN: 541506312

9406
Chase Foundation of Virginia ✧

300 Preston Ave., Ste. 500
Charlottesville, VA 22902-5096 (434) 293-9104
Contact: Derwood S. Chase, Jr., Pres. and Tr.

Established in 1995 in VA.
Donors: Derwood S. Chase, Jr.; Johanna B. Chase.
Foundation type: Independent foundation.
Financial data (yr. ended 12/31/13): Assets, $18,019,642 (M); gifts received, $1,600,000; expenditures, $755,046; qualifying distributions, $726,227; giving activities include $715,000 for 56 grants (high: $50,000; low: $500).
Fields of interest: Social sciences, research; Social sciences, public policy; Public affairs.
Type of support: General/operating support.
Limitations: Applications accepted. Giving in the U.S., with emphasis on Washington, DC, and VA; some funding also in Canada. No grants to individuals.
Application information: Application form not required.
Initial approach: Proposal
Deadline(s): None
Officers and Trustees:* Derwood S. Chase, Jr.,* Pres.; Stuart F. Chase, V.P. and Treas.; Johanna B. Chase,* Secy.; Alejandro A. Chafuen, Ph.D.; Cheryl O. Chase; John C. Goodman; Stephen Moore; Walter E. Williams.
EIN: 541770697

9407
The Dr. Francis P. Chiaramonte Private Foundation ✧

44 Canal Ctr. Plz., Ste. 325
Alexandria, VA 22314-1584

Established in 1998 in MD.
Donor: Francis P. Chiaramonte.
Foundation type: Independent foundation.
Financial data (yr. ended 12/31/13): Assets, $44,519,932 (M); expenditures, $2,546,184; qualifying distributions, $2,546,100; giving activities include $2,546,100 for 73 grants (high: $200,000; low: $1,500).
Fields of interest: Education; Hospitals (general); Health care; Human services; American Red Cross; Children/youth, services.
Limitations: Applications not accepted. Giving primarily in MD; some funding also in VA. No grants to individuals.
Application information: Contributes only to pre-selected organizations.
Trustees: Cathe Chiaramonte; Francis P. Chiaramonte III; Mark S. Chiaramonte; Michael J. Chiaramonte; Clarie Chiaramonte Wagner.
EIN: 522136769

9408
Claws Foundation ✧

c/o Sterling Foundation Mgmt., LLC
2325 Dulles Corner Blvd., Ste. 670
Herndon, VA 20171-4683 (703) 437-9720

Established in 2005 in VA.
Donors: Arthur Dantchik; Artay Inc.
Foundation type: Independent foundation.
Financial data (yr. ended 12/31/13): Assets, $6,264,253 (M); gifts received, $16,290,551; expenditures, $15,275,136; qualifying distributions, $15,275,000; giving activities include $15,275,000 for 21 grants (high: $4,050,000; low: $10,000).
Purpose and activities: Giving primarily to a children's hospital and for medical research; funding also for a public interest law firm.
Fields of interest: Hospitals (specialty); Medical research, institute; Biomedicine research; Legal services, public interest law; Children/youth, services.
Limitations: Giving primarily in PA; funding also in VA. No grants to individuals.
Application information: Application form not required.
Initial approach: Letter
Deadline(s): None
Directors: Arthur Dantchik; Alan P. Dye; Jeff Yass.
EIN: 201658710
Selected grants: The following grants are a representative sample of this grantmaker's funding activity:
$4,050,000 to Childrens Hospital of Philadelphia, Philadelphia, PA, 2013. For general support.
$4,050,000 to Childrens Hospital of Philadelphia Foundation, Philadelphia, PA, 2012. For general support.
$3,250,000 to Shalom Hartman Institute of North America, New York, NY, 2012. For general support.
$3,250,000 to Shalom Hartman Institute of North America, New York, NY, 2013. For general support.
$2,200,000 to Fidelity Charitable Gift Fund, Boston, MA, 2013. For general support.
$1,425,000 to Imagination Productions, Jerusalem U, New York, NY, 2013. For general support.
$1,200,000 to Kids Connect Charitable Fund, Herndon, VA, 2013. For general support.
$1,000,000 to Institute for Justice, Arlington, VA, 2012. For general support.
$1,000,000 to Institute for Justice, Arlington, VA, 2013. For general support.
$900,000 to Wistar Institute of Anatomy and Biology, Philadelphia, PA, 2012. For general support.
$650,000 to Kids Connect Charitable Fund, Herndon, VA, 2012. For general support.
$500,000 to Reason Foundation, Los Angeles, CA, 2013. For general support.

$250,000 to Fidelity, Freedom Truth and Justice Fund, Herndon, VA, 2012. For general support.
$150,000 to David Horowitz Freedom Center, Sherman Oaks, CA, 2013. For general support.
$100,000 to Atlas Economic Research Foundation, Washington, DC, 2012. For general support.
$100,000 to Cato Institute, Washington, DC, 2012. For general support.
$100,000 to Cato Institute, Washington, DC, 2013. For general support.
$65,000 to Students for Liberty, Washington, DC, 2012. For general support.
$65,000 to Students for Liberty, Washington, DC, 2013. For general support.
$50,000 to Competitive Enterprise Institute, Washington, DC, 2012. For general support.

9409
The Colburn Family Foundation ✧

c/o Sterling Foundation Mgmt., LLC
2325 Dulles Corner Blvd., Ste. 670
Herndon, VA 20171-4683

Established in 1998 in VA.
Donors: David Colburn; Kathleen Colburn.
Foundation type: Independent foundation.
Financial data (yr. ended 12/31/13): Assets, $5,454,028 (M); expenditures, $961,207; qualifying distributions, $615,812; giving activities include $570,050 for grants.
Purpose and activities: Giving primarily to Jewish agencies, temples, and schools.
Fields of interest: Elementary/secondary education; Jewish federated giving programs; Jewish agencies & synagogues.
Limitations: Applications not accepted. Giving primarily in DC, MD, NY, and VA. No grants to individuals.
Application information: Unsolicited requests for funds not accepted.
Officers: David Colburn, Pres. and Secy; Kathleen Colburn, V.P. and Treas.
EIN: 541923880
Selected grants: The following grants are a representative sample of this grantmaker's funding activity:
$11,250 to Yeshiva of Greater Washington, Silver Spring, MD, 2012. For Fostering Jewish Education.
$1,250 to Operation Embrace, Potomac, MD, 2012. For Israel and Zionism.
$900 to Congregation Supporters of Torah, Brooklyn, NY, 2012. For Fostering Jewish Culture.
$180 to Manna Food Center, Gaithersburg, MD, 2012. For assisting those in need.

9410
Community Foundation for Northern Virginia ✧

2940 Hunter Mill Rd., Ste. 201
Oakton, VA 22124 (703) 879-7640
FAX: (703) 879-7644; E-mail: info@cfnova.org; Grant inquiry e-mail: lesley.macdonald@cfnova.org; Main URL: http://www.cfnova.org/
Effective Philanthropy: http://www.cfnova.org/effective-philanthropy
E-Newsletter: http://www.cfnova.org/news-events/enewsletter
Facebook: http://www.facebook.com/pages/Northern-Virginia-Community-Foundation/75557741776
Google Plus: https://plus.google.com/+CfnovaOrg/videos
LinkedIn: https://www.linkedin.com/company/community-foundation-for-northern-virginia
YouTube: https://www.youtube.com/user/CFNOVA703

Incorporated in 1978 in VA.
Foundation type: Community foundation.
Financial data (yr. ended 06/30/13): Assets, $32,310,209 (M); gifts received, $6,300,945; expenditures, $3,946,633; giving activities include $2,243,098 for 91+ grants (high: $110,000), and $243,368 for 83 grants to individuals.
Purpose and activities: As the premier community foundation serving Arlington, Fairfax, Loudoun, and Prince William Counties as well as the City of Alexandria, the foundation works to nurture philanthropy and strengthen our community by encouraging community endowments, addressing the region's needs, and providing leadership and research on the region's most critical needs.
Fields of interest: Arts; Education; Health care; Mental health/crisis services; Youth development; Children/youth, services; Family services; Community development, neighborhood development; Community/economic development; Children/youth; Youth; Aging; Military/veterans; Economically disadvantaged; Homeless.
Type of support: General/operating support; Continuing support; Equipment; Endowments; Emergency funds; Program development; Scholarship funds; Employee-related scholarships; Scholarships—to individuals; In-kind gifts; Matching/challenge support.
Limitations: Applications accepted. Giving limited to northern VA. No grants for capital improvements or endowments.
Publications: Annual report; Financial statement; Grants list; Informational brochure; Informational brochure (including application guidelines); Newsletter; Occasional report.
Application information: Visit foundation web site for online application and guidelines. Application form required.
Initial approach: Complete online application
Copies of proposal: 1
Deadline(s): Dec. for Community Investment Grants; Varies for others
Board meeting date(s): Quarterly
Final notification: Feb. for Community Investment Grants; Varies for others
Officers and Directors:* Lynn Tadlock,* Chair.; Paul Leslie,* Vice-Chair.; Eileen M. Ellsworth, Pres.; Jen McCollum, V.P., Donor Svcs.; Kevin DeSanto,* Secy.; Dean Peterson; Cindy K. Andreotti; John Chapel; Julian Chin; Brandon Elledge; Steve Gladis, Ph.D.; Thomas Hume; Ken Huntsman; Cheryl Janey; Joan Kasprowicz; Louis C. Kiessling; Cathy Lange; Bernard Mustafa; Susan Nolan; Donald Strehle; Sylvia von Bostel; Marc Wishkoff; John Wolff.
Number of staff: 2 full-time professional; 3 part-time professional.
EIN: 510232459

9411
The Community Foundation of Harrisonburg and Rockingham County ✧

(formerly Harrisonburg Rockingham Community Foundation)
311 S. Main St.
Harrisonburg, VA 22801 (540) 432-3863
Contact: Revlan Hill, Dir., Devel. and Community Rels.; For grants: Krystal Diehl, Assoc. Dir.
FAX: (540) 438-9589;
E-mail: revlan@the-community-foundation.org; Grant inquiry e-mail: krystal@the-community-foundation.org; Mailing address: P.O. Box 1068 Harrisonburg, 22803-1068; Main URL: http://www.the-community-foundation.org

Established in 2003 in VA.
Foundation type: Community foundation.
Financial data (yr. ended 06/30/13): Assets, $20,025,400 (M); gifts received, $3,054,196; expenditures, $1,830,405; giving activities include $1,506,737 for 51+ grants (high: $120,000).
Purpose and activities: The foundation seeks to enrich the quality of life in the Harrisonburg and Rockingham County, VA, community by developing and managing permanent endowments to respond to changing community needs.
Fields of interest: Historic preservation/historical societies; Arts; Education; Environment; Health care; Human services; Community/economic development; Religion; Children; Aging.
Type of support: Scholarship funds; Matching/challenge support; General/operating support; Continuing support; Annual campaigns; Capital campaigns; Building/renovation; Endowments; Emergency funds; Scholarships—to individuals.
Limitations: Applications accepted. Giving limited to Harrisonburg, Rockingham County and Central Shenandoah Valley, VA.
Publications: Application guidelines; Annual report; Financial statement; Newsletter.
Application information: Visit foundation web site for application information. Application form not required.
Initial approach: Telephone
Deadline(s): Mar. 3 and Sept. 3
Board meeting date(s): 3rd Wed. of Feb., May, Aug., and Nov.
Officers and Directors:* Steve Gordon,* Chair.; Stephanne S. Byrd,* Vice-Chair.; Michael E. Fiore,* Pres.; Revlan Hill,* V.P., Devel. and Community Rels.; Kimberly Haines,* Secy.; Phil C. Stone,* Treas.; Mike Fiore, Exec. Dir.; Jeffrey Adams; Toni Bentel Bailey; Kathleen M. Graves; Betsy Hay; W. Michael Heatwole III; Dale Lam; Joseph Paxton; Amy Rush; Jennifer Shirkey; Brian Shull; Daniel Uribe; Mark Warner; Peter Yates.
Number of staff: 2 full-time professional; 2 part-time support.
EIN: 541920746

9412
The Community Foundation of the Central Blue Ridge ✧

(doing business as Staunton Augusta Waynesboro Community Foundation)
117 S. Lewis St.
P.O. Box 815
Staunton, VA 24402 (540) 231-2150
Contact: For grants: Susan Lendermon, Dir., Nonprofit Srvs.

FAX: (540) 242-3387;
E-mail: info@communityfoundationcbr.org; Grant inquiry e-mail: slendermon@communityfoundationcbr.org; Grant inquiry tel.: 540-213-2150; Main URL: http://www.communityfoundationcbr.org
Additional URL: http://www.communityfoundationCBR.org
Facebook: https://www.facebook.com/pages/Community-Foundation-of-the-Central-Blue-Ridge/249542215372
LinkedIn: http://www.linkedin.com/company/608279?goback=.fcs_*2_Community+Foundation+of+Central+Blue+Ridge_*2_*2_*2_*2_*2_*2_*2_*2_*2_*2_*2&trk=ncsrch_hits
Twitter: http://twitter.com/CommFdn_CBR

Established in 1992 in VA.
Donor: H.D. "Buz" Dawbarn†.
Foundation type: Community foundation.
Financial data (yr. ended 12/31/13): Assets, $15,622,334 (M); gifts received, $656,199; expenditures, $921,615; giving activities include $441,371 for 80 grants (high: $115,536), and $159,875 for 62 grants to individuals.
Purpose and activities: The foundation's mission is to enhance the quality of life by meeting needs and inspiring philanthropy in the community.
Fields of interest: Historic preservation/historical societies; Arts; Education; Environment; Animal welfare; Health care; Agriculture/food; Housing/shelter; Safety/disasters; Recreation; Youth, services; Family services; Human services; Community development, neighborhood development.
Type of support: General/operating support; Equipment; Endowments; Program development; Curriculum development; Scholarship funds; Consulting services; Program evaluation.
Limitations: Applications accepted. Giving limited to Augusta County, Highland County, Nelson County, Staunton, and Waynesboro, VA. No support for sectarian, fraternal, or religious organizations. No grants for general annual fund appeals, deficit reduction, capital campaigns or endowments, fundraising or celebration events or start-up funds.
Publications: Application guidelines; Annual report; Financial statement; Grants list; Informational brochure; Newsletter.
Application information: Visit foundation web site for application form and guidelines. Applications must be submitted electronically. Application form required.
Initial approach: E-mail application and attachments
Copies of proposal: 1
Deadline(s): Feb. 9 for Community Grants; varies for others
Board meeting date(s): 4th Tues. of each month
Final notification: Apr.
Officers and Directors:* Steve Elkins,* Chair.; Dinah Gottschalk,* Vice-Chair.; Dan Layman,* Pres. and C.E.O.; Carl Rosberg,* Secy. - Treas.; Lewis M. Coiner, Emeritus; Harold C. Cook, Emeritus; Ken Boward; Cary Dahl; Ronald Denney, Esq.; Perry Fridley; David T. Gauldin II; William Larry Harrell, M.D.; John R. Higgs; Becky Kelly; Jan Mangun; Deborah T. Metz; Art Schlappi; John W. Sills III; Butch Smiley; Travis Tysinger; Wilson F. Vellines, Jr.
Number of staff: 1 full-time professional; 3 part-time professional; 1 full-time support.
EIN: 541647385

9413
Community Foundation of the Dan River Region ✧

(formerly DPC Community Foundation)
541 Loyal St.
Danville, VA 24541 (434) 793-0884
Contact: Debra L. Dodson, Exec. Dir.; For grants: Blair Lumpkins, Prog. Off.
FAX: (434) 793-6489; E-mail: info@cfdrr.org; Additional e-mail: cfdrr@gamewood.net; Grant inquiry e-mail: blair@cfdrr.org; Main URL: http://www.cfdrr.org
Facebook: https://www.facebook.com/cfdrr
Twitter: https://twitter.com/cfdrr1
YouTube: http://www.youtube.com/channel/UCgCV0T5duONci5f8A5DS8gQ

Established in 1996 in VA.
Foundation type: Community foundation.
Financial data (yr. ended 06/30/13): Assets, $25,383,913 (M); gifts received, $1,020,343; expenditures, $2,309,102; giving activities include $724,385 for 87+ grants (high: $90,000), and $126,970 for 78 grants to individuals.
Purpose and activities: The foundation helps donors meet community needs through endowment funds.
Fields of interest: Arts; Education; Human services.
Type of support: Scholarship funds; Scholarships—to individuals.
Limitations: Applications accepted. Giving primarily in Caswell County, NC, and Danville and Pittsylvania County, VA, as well as southern VA and northern NC.
Publications: Application guidelines; Annual report; Financial statement; Grants list; Informational brochure; Newsletter.
Application information: Visit foundation web site for application guidelines. Organizations wishing to be added to the foundation's mailing list for grant applications should contact the foundation's office. Application forms for scholarships are sent to guidance offices of public high schools in early spring. Application form required.
Initial approach: Preliminary grant request letter
Copies of proposal: 10
Deadline(s): Aug. 4
Board meeting date(s): Quarterly
Final notification: Late Dec.
Officers and Directors:* F. Lawrence McFall,* Pres.; Peter K. Howard,* V.P.; Margaret Scott,* Secy.; William S. Woods,* Treas.; Debra L. Dodson, Exec. Dir.; Gerald Adcock; Lamar Barr; Scott Batson; Brenda Blair; P. Niles Daly, Jr.; Gail Gunn; Harry T. Kolendrianos; Donald Nodtvedt; T. Wayne Oakes; Rev. Ed Pope; Dora Pradhan; Paul W. Thompson, Jr.; Lewis Wall; Verla Wall; Stuart Watlington; Logan Young.
Number of staff: 3 full-time professional.
EIN: 541823141
Selected grants: The following grants are a representative sample of this grantmaker's funding activity:
$25,000 to Bachelors Hall Volunteer Fire Department, Danville, VA, 2012. To purchase two Lifepack 15 automated external debrillators for placement in emergency response vehicles.
$24,000 to Caswell County Parish, Yanceyville, NC, 2012. To implement and operate mobile food pantry.
$18,000 to Danville Science Center, Danville, VA, 2012. For traveling exhibits Wild Music and Robots +Us.
$13,000 to Institute for Advanced Learning and Research Foundation, Danville, VA, 2012. To develop STEM University providing hands on STEM education to 300 K-12 students.
$12,910 to University of Virginia, Charlottesville, VA, 2012. For scholarships.
$9,025 to Averett University, Danville, VA, 2012. For scholarships.
$8,000 to Pittsylvania County Community Action, Chatham, VA, 2012. For services to persons living with HIV/AIDS in our community.
$2,300 to YMCA of Danville, Danville, VA, 2012. To purchase furniture, supplies and equipment for YMCA Child Care Program.

9414
Community Foundation of the Rappahannock River Region, Inc. ✧

Mill Race N. II Bldg., 725 Jackson St., Ste. 114
P.O. Box 208
Fredericksburg, VA 22404-0208 (540) 373-9292
Contact: Teri McNally, Exec. Dir.
FAX: (540) 373-3050; E-mail: info@cfrrr.net; Additional e-mail: TeriMcNally@cfrrr.org; Main URL: http://www.cfrrr.org/
Facebook: https://www.facebook.com/CommunityFoundationRRR?fref=ts

Incorporated in 1997 in VA.
Foundation type: Community foundation.
Financial data (yr. ended 06/30/13): Assets, $14,418,898 (M); gifts received, $5,623,740; expenditures, $1,036,004; giving activities include $667,506 for 30+ grants (high: $73,216), and $100,783 for 45 grants to individuals.
Purpose and activities: The foundation's mission is to create, maintain, and administer a permanent collection of charitable funds to improve the quality of life in the Rappahannock River region of Virginia.
Fields of interest: Arts; Scholarships/financial aid; Youth development; Women, centers/services; Human services; Community development, neighborhood development.
Type of support: General/operating support; Equipment; Endowments; Program development; Publication; Curriculum development; Scholarship funds; Technical assistance; Program evaluation; Scholarships—to individuals.
Limitations: Applications accepted. Giving limited to the counties of Caroline, King George, Spotsylvania, Stafford, and the City of Fredericksburg, VA. No support for sectarian or religious programs or activities. No grants to individuals (except for scholarships), operational, maintenance, or ongoing program expenses, programs that duplicate existing services and/or programs, testimonial dinners, fundraising events or advertising, payment of loans interest, taxes or debt retirement.
Publications: Application guidelines; Annual report; Grants list; Informational brochure; Newsletter; Newsletter (including application guidelines); Occasional report; Program policy statement.
Application information: Visit foundation web site for form and guidelines.
Initial approach: Telephone
Copies of proposal: 2
Deadline(s): Mar. 2 for Scholarship
Board meeting date(s): 3rd Thurs. of every month
Officers and Governors:* Kelly G. Johnson,* Pres.; Bruce L. Davis,* Pres.-Elect.; Michael A. O'Malley,* Secy.; Catherine M. Wack,* Treas.; Teri McNally, Exec. Dir.; Harry D. Dickinson, Ph.D.; Dori Eglevsky; John F. Fick III; R. Leigh Frackelton, Jr., Esq.; Christian B. Franklin, Esq.; Margaret F. Hardy, Esq.;

Lucy Harman; Cynthia Corbett Hoffman, Esq.; V. Veronica Kelly, Ph.D.; Michael T. Kennison; Benjamin R. Maxwell; John F. McManus, Esq.; Erik J. Muller; Mary Jane O'Neill; Chris Repp; Jamie A. Scully; Nicky Seay; Janet S. Taczak; Benjamin Wafle.
Number of staff: 1 full-time professional; 2 part-time professional; 1 part-time support.
EIN: 541843987

9415
Community Foundation of Western Virginia ✧

(doing business as Foundation for Roanoke Valley)
611 S. Jefferson St., Ste. 8
Roanoke, VA 24011 (540) 985-0204
Contact: For grants and scholarships: Michelle Eberly, Prog. Off.
FAX: (540) 982-8175;
E-mail: programs@foundationforroanokevalley.org; Mailing address: P.O. Box 1159, Roanoke, VA 24006; Main URL: http://www.foundationforroanokevalley.org
Facebook: http://www.facebook.com/foundationforroanokevalley

Established in 1988 in VA; funded in 1990.
Foundation type: Community foundation.
Financial data (yr. ended 06/30/13): Assets, $55,399,145 (M); gifts received, $4,485,316; expenditures, $3,889,673; giving activities include $2,497,431 for 91+ grants (high: $80,000).
Purpose and activities: The foundation seeks to foster positive change on behalf of the community by: 1) enabling donors to carry out their charitable intent through prudently administered permanent endowment funds; 2) offering a comprehensive array of services to encourage, advance and educate concerning effective philanthropy; 3) making creative grants to meet continuing and emerging community needs and opportunities; and 4) providing leadership in identifying and assessing community issues and acting as a catalyst to initiate specific responses.
Fields of interest: Arts; Education; Health care; Health organizations, association; Children/youth, services; Family services; Human services.
Type of support: General/operating support; Equipment; Emergency funds; Program development; Seed money; Scholarship funds.
Limitations: Applications accepted. Giving primarily in the greater Roanoke Valley, VA, area, with emphasis on Roanoke, Botetourt, Craig, Franklin and Rockbridge counties, VA. No support for sectarian, religious, or fraternal organizations. No grants to individuals (except for scholarships), or for deficit reduction, capital campaigns or endowments, fundraising events, or celebration events.
Publications: Annual report; Financial statement; Informational brochure; Newsletter.
Application information: Visit foundation web site for online application and guidelines. LOIs will be reviewed to determine if the project meets current grantmaking priorities and guidelines. If the LOI is selected for further consideration, the foundation's staff will notify the organization of the application deadline and additional materials required. Application form required.
Initial approach: Create online account
Copies of proposal: 1
Deadline(s): Varies
Board meeting date(s): Quarterly

Officers and Governors:* Melinda T. Chitwood,* Chair.; Susan K. Still,* Vice-Chair.; A. Damon Williams,* Treas.; Alan E. Ronk, Exec. Dir.; Rita D. Bishop; Lucy R. Ellett; William D. Elliot; Russell H. Ellis; Robert P. Fralin; Maryellen Goodlatte; Jim McAden; Stephen A. Musselwhite; Debbbie Oelschlager; Kathryn Krisch Oelschlager; Randall R. Rhea, M.D.; Cynthia M. Shelor; Cleo Simms; Kenneth Tuck; Jim Wade.
Number of staff: 2 full-time professional; 1 part-time professional.
EIN: 541959458

9416
The Community Foundation Serving Richmond & Central Virginia ✧

(formerly Greater Richmond Community Foundation)
7501 Boulders View Dr., Ste. 110
Richmond, VA 23225-4047 (804) 330-7400
Contact: Darcy S. Oman, C.E.O.; For grants: Susan Hallett, V.P., Progs.; For grants: Elaine Summerfield, V.P., Progs.
FAX: (804) 330-5992; E-mail: info@tcfrichmond.org; Additional e-mail: doman@tcfrichmond.org; Grant application e-mails: shallett@tcfrichmond.org and esummerfield@tcfrichmond.org; Main URL: http://www.tcfrichmond.org
Facebook: http://www.facebook.com/tcfrichmond
Twitter: http://twitter.com/giverichmond
Scholarship e-mail: skeeley@tcfrichmond.org

Established in 1968 in VA.
Foundation type: Community foundation.
Financial data (yr. ended 12/31/12): Assets, $497,636,734 (M); gifts received, $31,809,626; expenditures, $36,662,325; giving activities include $32,429,867 for grants.
Purpose and activities: The foundation serves and inspires people to build philanthropy for the region and to engage in the local community. The foundation works closely with donors and community partners to fulfill this mission by: 1) promoting a regional perspective; 2) developing and sharing community knowledge; 3) collaborating towards common goals; 4) demonstrating inclusiveness and respect; and 5) achieving transparency, accountability and efficiency.
Fields of interest: Arts; Education; AIDS; Housing/shelter, development; Youth development; Children/youth, services; Community/economic development.
Type of support: General/operating support; Continuing support; Equipment; Emergency funds; Program development; Seed money; Technical assistance; Grants to individuals; Scholarships—to individuals; Matching/challenge support.
Limitations: Applications accepted. Giving limited to residents of metropolitan Richmond, the tri-cities area, including Hopewell, Colonial Heights, and Petersburg, and Chesterfield, Hanover, and Henrico counties, VA. No grants for annual campaigns, deficit financing, land acquisition, or building funds.
Publications: Application guidelines; Annual report; Biennial report.
Application information: Visit foundation web site for additional guidelines per grant type. The foundation will invite organizations to submit a full proposal based on their letter of intent. Faxed or e-mailed letters of intent are not accepted. Application form required.
Initial approach: Preliminary letter of intent (no more than 2 pages)
Copies of proposal: 2
Deadline(s): May 5 and Nov. 5 for letter of intent; Jan. 6 and July 7 for proposals
Board meeting date(s): Quarterly
Final notification: May 19 and Nov. 19 for full proposal invitation; 3rd week of Mar. and Sept. for grant decision

Officers and Board of Governors:* Farhad Aghdami,* Chair.; Thomas N. Chewning,* Vice-Chair.; Darcy S. Oman,* C.E.O. and Pres.; Susan Brown Davis, Sr. V.P., Community Leadership Initiatives; Karen Hand, Sr. V.P., Finance & Admin.; Robert Thalhimer, Sr. V.P., Philanthropic Svcs. and Donor Engagement; Molly Dean Bittner, V.P., Philanthropic Svcs.; Susan H. Hallett, V.P., Progs.; Michelle A. Nelson, V.P., Finance; Lisa Pratt O'Mara, V.P., Donor Engagement; Kimberly Russell, V.P., Comms.; Elaine Summerfield, V.P., Progs.; Lissy S. Bryan,* Secy.; Thomas G. Snead, Jr.,* Treas.; Maureen C. Ackerly; Karen Booth Adams; Austin Brockenbrough IV; Thomas D. Byer; Thomas S. Gayner; Iris E. Holliday; John A. Luke, Jr.; Dee Ann Remo; Dianne L. Reynolds-Cane, M.D.; Pamela J. Royal, M.D.; Stuart C. Siegel; Mark P. Sisisky; Robert C. Sledd III; T. Kirk Tattersall; Christopher H. Williams.
Number of staff: 10 full-time professional; 1 part-time professional; 4 full-time support.
EIN: 237009135

9417
Jack Kent Cooke Foundation ✧

44325 Woodridge Pkwy.
Lansdowne, VA 20176-5297 (703) 723-8000
Contact: Adrianne Lewis, Prog. Coord.
FAX: (703) 723-8030;
E-mail: jkc@jackkentcookefoundation.org; Main URL: http://www.jkcf.org/
Facebook: https://www.facebook.com/JackKentCookeFoundation
Knowledge Center: http://www.jkcf.org/news-knowledge
LinkedIn: http://www.linkedin.com/company/the-jack-kent-cooke-foundation
Twitter: https://twitter.com/TheJKCF
YouTube: http://www.youtube.com/channel/UCyRYrDx—cYqrvRPDb2_uEQ
Application address: Jack Kent Cooke Foundation, ACT, P.O. Box 4030, Iowa City, IA 52243

Established in 1997 in VA. The foundation became active in 2000.
Donor: Jack Kent Cooke‡.
Foundation type: Independent foundation.
Financial data (yr. ended 05/31/13): Assets, $677,726,607 (M); gifts received, $65,380; expenditures, $32,477,625; qualifying distributions, $30,038,428; giving activities include $7,933,778 for 68 grants (high: $500,000; low: $50), and $11,512,402 for 883 grants to individuals (high: $50,000; low: $243).
Purpose and activities: The purpose of the foundation is to help young people of exceptional promise reach their full potential through education.
Fields of interest: Higher education; Higher education, college (community/junior); Higher education, college; Higher education, university; Scholarships/financial aid; Education.
Type of support: General/operating support; Scholarship funds; Grants to individuals; Scholarships—to individuals; Student loans—to individuals.
Limitations: Applications accepted. Giving on a national basis. No graduate scholarships awarded

(except to students who have already been awarded undergraduate scholarships by the foundation).
Publications: Application guidelines; Financial statement; Grants list; Informational brochure.
Application information: Additional application guidelines are available on foundation's web site. Faxed applications not accepted. Application form required.
Deadline(s): Nov. for Undergraduate Transfer Scholarship program; Mar. for Young Scholars program
Officers and Directors:* Linda J. King,* Pres.; Emily Froimson, V.P., Prog(s).; Mark Birmingham, C.F.O., C.I.O., and Treas.; Wanda G. Wiser,* Secy.; Marianne Stanley, Cont.; Harold O. Levy, Exec. Dir.; John Kent Cooke, Sr.; Gregory R. Dillon; Stuart A. Haney; Mark Pollak; Howard B. Soloway.
Number of staff: 36 full-time professional; 2 full-time support; 1 part-time support.
EIN: 541896244
Selected grants: The following grants are a representative sample of this grantmaker's funding activity:
$500,000 to From the Top, Boston, MA, 2012. To expand advanced music education.
$500,000 to KIPP Foundation, New York, NY, 2012. For expansion of schools, scholarships and enrichment program.
$480,000 to National Math and Science Initiative, Dallas, TX, 2012. To increase availability of AP courses to low-income students.
$450,000 to University of North Carolina, Chapel Hill, NC, 2012. For College Access.
$416,000 to Edvance Foundation, Boston, MA, 2012. For Community College Transfer Program.
$250,000 to College of William and Mary, Center for Gifted Education, Williamsburg, VA, 2012. For Camp Launch, an initiative that will bring together rising 7th- and 8th-grade students from low-income communities in Richmond, Petersburg and surrounding areas for two-week courses in science, math and writing.
$250,000 to Merit School of Music, Chicago, IL, 2012. To create a Conservatory Feeder Program that will prepare low-income students for entry into its Alice S. Pfaelzer Tuition-free Conservatory. Merit will expand programming through private lessons, sectionals and the availability of quality instruments at community sites in South Side Chicago neighborhoods and increase aid for private lessons for on-site students.
$237,500 to Levine School of Music, Washington, DC, 2012. To expand its Honors Program with advanced training, recitals, discounted or free instrument rentals, and professional development activities for outstanding young musicians from disadvantaged families in Greater Washington, DC. Levine will also award scholarships to intermediate-level students to prepare them for successful auditions into the Honors Program.
$150,000 to Jemicy School, Owings Mills, MD, 2012. To support low-to-moderate income Twice Exceptional Students.
$100,000 to Art of Problem Solving Foundation, Alpine, CA, 2012. For the Summer Program in Mathematical Problem Solving (SPMPS), a three-week residential summer program for rising eighth graders in New York City.

9418
James P. and Rebecca T. Craig Foundation ✧
P.O. Box 170
Keswick, VA 22947-0170

Established in VA.
Donors: James P. Craig III; Rebecca T. Craig.
Foundation type: Independent foundation.
Financial data (yr. ended 01/13/14): Assets, $2,388,305 (M); gifts received, $2,108,429; expenditures, $507,582; qualifying distributions, $504,238; giving activities include $502,500 for 10 grants (high: $300,000; low: $1,000).
Fields of interest: Higher education; Education; Health care.
Limitations: Applications not accepted. Giving primarily in VA; some giving also in TN and TX.
Application information: Contributes only to pre-selected organizations.
Officers and Directors:* Rebecca T. Craig,* Pres.; James P. Craig,* Treas.
EIN: 311654104
Selected grants: The following grants are a representative sample of this grantmaker's funding activity:
$400,000 to Nature Conservancy, Arlington, VA, 2012. For general charitable purposes.
$50,000 to Nature Conservancy, Arlington, VA, 2012. For general charitable purposes.
$5,000 to Computers4Kids, Charlottesville, VA, 2012. For general charitable purposes.
$4,000 to Computers4Kids, Charlottesville, VA, 2012. For general charitable purposes.

9419
The Dalis Foundation ✧
7461 N. Shore Rd.
Norfolk, VA 23505-1770

Established in 1956.
Donor: M. Dan Dalis†.
Foundation type: Independent foundation.
Financial data (yr. ended 05/31/13): Assets, $16,112,273 (M); gifts received, $41,873; expenditures, $891,469; qualifying distributions, $690,143; giving activities include $690,143 for grants.
Fields of interest: Arts; Education; Human services; Foundations (public).
Limitations: Applications not accepted. Giving primarily in Norfolk, VA; funding also in Boston, MA. No grants to individuals.
Application information: Contributes only to pre-selected organizations.
Officer: Joan W. Dalis, Mgr.
EIN: 546046229
Selected grants: The following grants are a representative sample of this grantmaker's funding activity:
$11,000 to American Cancer Society, Atlanta, GA, 2011.
$10,000 to Alzheimers Association, Chicago, IL, 2011.

9420
Danville Foundation House ✧ ☆
512 Bridge St., No. 100
Danville, VA 24541-1406

Established in VA.
Foundation type: Independent foundation.
Financial data (yr. ended 12/31/13): Assets, $2,235,174 (M); expenditures, $1,384,000; qualifying distributions, $842,000; giving activities include $842,000 for 4 grants (high: $550,000; low: $25,000).
Fields of interest: Education; Human services.
Type of support: In-kind gifts.
Limitations: Applications not accepted. Giving limited to Danville, VA.
Application information: Contributes only to pre-selected organizations.
Officers and Directors: James A. Motely,* Chair. and Pres.; Charles H. Majors,* Vice-Chair. and V.P.; Aubrey Dodson,* Secy.-Treas.; B. R. Ashby, M.D.; Richard Barkhouser; Ben J. Davenport, Jr.; Betty Jo Foster.
EIN: 540595000

9421
Danville Regional Foundation ✧
512 Bridge St., Ste. 100
Danville, VA 24541-1406 (434) 799-2176
Contact: Karl Stauber, C.E.O. and Pres.
FAX: (434) 799-2162; E-mail: info@drfonline.org; Additional e-mail for letter of inquiry questions: kstauber@drfonline.org; Main URL: http://www.drfonline.org
Facebook: https://www.facebook.com/DanvilleRegionalFoundation
LinkedIn: http://www.linkedin.com/companies/danville-regional-foundation?trk=ppro_cprof&lnk=vw_cprofile
YouTube: http://www.youtube.com/user/DRFOnline

Established in 2005 in VA with proceeds from the sale of Danville Regional Medical Center.
Donor: Danville Regional Health System.
Foundation type: Independent foundation.
Financial data (yr. ended 12/31/12): Assets, $188,790,257 (M); expenditures, $12,010,028; qualifying distributions, $11,120,159; giving activities include $9,043,053 for 54 grants (high: $4,522,500; low: $4,760).
Purpose and activities: The foundation seeks to develop, promote, and support programs designed to improve the health, welfare, and education of residents of the primary service area of Danville Regional Medical Center. The main areas of focus are: 1) Economic Transformation to produce a rising standard of living; 2) Educational Attainment to ensure that educational success is the community norm; 3) Health and Wellness; 4) Community Engagement, to build deep civic support for community innovations.
Fields of interest: Education; Health care; Human services; Community/economic development.
Type of support: General/operating support; Management development/capacity building; Program development.
Limitations: Applications accepted. Giving limited to Caswell County, NC and Pittsylvania County and Danville, VA. No support for faith-based organizations for religious purposes, or for any organization to supplant funding that is the responsibility of the government. No grants to individuals, for dinners, fundraisers or for organizations lacking 501(c)(3).
Publications: Application guidelines; Annual report; Financial statement; Grants list; Multi-year report; Newsletter; Occasional report.

Application information: Application form not required.
Initial approach: Letter of inquiry (two pages max), may be submitted at any time
Copies of proposal: 1
Deadline(s): Invited full proposal applicants will be informed of a deadline
Board meeting date(s): Jan., March, May, July, Sept. and Nov.
Final notification: Reviews of full grant proposals will take three to four months from the time they are received
Officers and Directors:* E. Gregory Hairston,* Vice-Chair.; Charles H. Majors,* Chair.; Karl Stauber, C.E.O. and Pres.; Margie Wilkinson, Secy., Dir., Opers., and Sr. Prog. Off.; Aubrey D. Dodson, Treas.; B.R. Ashby, M.D.; Gretchen Clark; George Daniel; Ben J. Davenport; Carolyn B. Evans; Betty Jo Foster, Ed.D.; William Henderson, M.D.; Everlena B. Ross; Rachael Sanford; Wayne Wilson.
Number of staff: 6 full-time professional; 1 part-time professional; 3 full-time support.
EIN: 203319727
Selected grants: The following grants are a representative sample of this grantmaker's funding activity:
$2,670,000 to Virginia Early Childhood Foundation, Richmond, VA, 2011. For 0-5 educational capacity and programs.
$617,843 to Industrial Development Authority of the City of Danville, Danville, VA, 2011. To transform inner city.
$548,333 to Averett University, Danville, VA, 2011. To increase health care capacity.
$433,336 to Institute for Advanced Learning and Research Foundation, Danville, VA, 2011. To provide agricultural related job opportunities.
$350,000 to YMCA of Danville, Danville, VA, 2011. For new facility.
$300,000 to Free Clinic of Danville, Danville, VA, 2011. For capacity building.
$250,000 to Community Foundation of the Dan River Region, Danville, VA, 2011. To foster health and wellness.
$75,000 to Danville, City of, Danville, VA, 2011. For revitalization of Danville.
$42,272 to United Way of Caswell County, Yanceyville, NC, 2011. To expand human and health services.
$10,000 to ENH Community Development, Danville, VA, 2011. For nutrition and leadership initiative, reduce obesity.

9422
Dominion Foundation ✧
(formerly Consolidated Natural Gas Company Foundation)
1 James Center
701 E. Cary St., 17th Fl.
Richmond, VA 23219 (804) 771-3355
Contact: James C. Mesloh, Sr. Philanthropy Mgr.
Tel. for Dominion Educational Partnership: (800) 730-7217, e-mail: Educational_Grants@dom.com; Main URL: http://www.dom.com/about/community/charitable-giving-and-the-dominion-foundation.jsp
Dominion Higher Educational Partnership Recipients: http://www.dom.com/about/education/grants/recent-higher-educational-awards.jsp
Multimedia: http://www.dom.com/about/media-downloads.jsp

Established about 1985 in PA.
Donors: Consolidated Natural Gas Co.; Dominion Resources, Inc.; Peoples Natural Gas Co.; Dominion Energy, Inc.; Dominion Energy New England; Dominion Transmission.
Foundation type: Company-sponsored foundation.
Financial data (yr. ended 12/31/13): Assets, $7,472,588 (M); gifts received, $7,472,588; expenditures, $16,149,380; qualifying distributions, $14,976,442; giving activities include $13,337,972 for 1,416 grants (high: $250,000; low: $400), and $1,638,470 for employee matching gifts.
Purpose and activities: The foundation supports organizations involved with arts and culture, education, the environment, health, human services, community development, and civic affairs.
Fields of interest: Museums; Arts; Elementary/secondary education; Business school/education; Engineering school/education; Libraries (public); Education; Environment, natural resources; Environment, energy; Environmental education; Environment; Health care; Food services; Food banks; Recreation, parks/playgrounds; Homeless, human services; Human services; Civil/human rights, equal rights; Community development, neighborhood development; Economic development; Business/industry; Community/economic development; Science, formal/general education; Mathematics; Engineering/technology; Engineering; Economics; Public affairs.
Type of support: General/operating support; Continuing support; Annual campaigns; Capital campaigns; Building/renovation; Equipment; Program development; Conferences/seminars; Curriculum development; Employee matching gifts; In-kind gifts; Matching/challenge support.
Limitations: Applications accepted. Giving primarily in areas of company operations in CT, Christian, Sangamon and Will, IL, Lake County, IN, MA, MD, Beaufort, Bertie, Camden, Chowan, Currituck, Dare, Edgecombe, Gates, Halifax, Hertford, Hyde, Martin, Nash, Northampton, Pasquotank, Perquimans, Pitt, Tyrell, Warren, and Washington counties, and the cities of Roanoke Rapids and Weldon, NC, NY, Allen, Ashland, Ashtabula, Auglaize, Belmont, Carroll, Columbiana, Cuyahoga, Geauga, Guernsey, Hardin, Holmes, Knox, Lake, Mahoning, Medina, Mercer, Monroe, Muskingum, Noble, Paulding, Portage, Putman, Shelby, Stark, Summit, Trumbull, Tuscarawas, Van Wert, Washington, Wayne, and Wood, OH, Allegheny, Armstrong, Beaver, Blair, Bucks, Butler, Cambria, Cameron, Clarion, Clearfield, Clinton, Crawford, Elk, Fayette, Franklin, Greene, Indiana, Jefferson, Juniata, Lawrence, Mercer, McKean, Potter, Somerset, Tioga, Venango, Washington, and Westmoreland, PA, RI, VA, WI, and WV. No support for churches or other sectarian organizations, fraternal, political, advocacy, or labor organizations, or discriminatory organizations. No grants to individuals, or for religious programs, general operating support for individual United Way agencies, fundraising events, golf tournaments or other sporting events, benefit or courtesy advertising, travel or student trips or tours, or memorial campaigns; no university research projects or endowed chairs.
Publications: Application guidelines; Program policy statement.
Application information: Grants generally range from $1,000 to $15,000, however higher amounts may be awarded. A password to access an online application form will be sent following receipt of a passing eligibility quiz. Proposals should be no longer than 3 pages for Dominion Educational Partnership. Funding requests are reviewed and approved by regional committees. Multi-year funding is not automatic. Organizations receiving support are asked to provide a final report.
Initial approach: Complete online eligibility quiz; complete online application and proposal for Dominion Educational Partnership
Copies of proposal: 1
Deadline(s): None; May 1 for Dominion Educational Partnership
Board meeting date(s): Quarterly
Final notification: 2 to 6 months; July 16 for Dominion Educational Partnership
Officers and Directors:* Cynthia P. Balderson, Secy.; Katharine M. Bond, Exec. Dir.; Hunter A. Applewhite; Robert M. Blue; David A. Christian; Iris E. Holliday; Paul D. Koonce; Diane Leopold; Mark F. McGettrick; Carter M. Reid; Daniel A. Weekley.
Trustee: The Bank of New York Mellon.
Number of staff: 6 full-time professional; 3 full-time support.
EIN: 136077762
Selected grants: The following grants are a representative sample of this grantmaker's funding activity:
$500,000 to Virginia Museum of Fine Arts Foundation, Richmond, VA, 2012. For Top Ten Fund Campaign.
$250,000 to Trust for Public Land, Cleveland, OH, 2012. To protect Pressure House Point.
$200,000 to Richmond 2015, Richmond, VA, 2012. To sponsor 2015 UCI Road World Cycling Championships.
$200,000 to United Way of Greater Richmond and Petersburg, Richmond, VA, 2012. For annual support.
$100,000 to Saint Josephs Villa, Richmond, VA, 2012. For programs provided by Flagler Services.
$82,823 to Virginia Tech Foundation, Blacksburg, VA, 2012. For Matching Gifts.
$10,000 to Dallas Arboretum and Botanical Society, Dallas, TX, 2012. For Illumination Sponsorship of Charity Nights exhibit.
$5,000 to Community Partnership for Arts and Culture, Cleveland, OH, 2012. For Artists in Resonance - Culture/Art.
$5,000 to Urban League, Northern Virginia, Alexandria, VA, 2012. For Annual Scholarship Awards Winner - Community Development.
$3,100 to Governors School for Government and International Studies, Richmond, VA, 2012. For Matching Gifts.

9423
Dreyfus Foundation ✧
5555 Greenwich Rd., No. 600
Virginia Beach, VA 23462-6542

Established in 1997 in VA.
Donors: Mark Dreyfus; Alfred Dreyfus.
Foundation type: Independent foundation.
Financial data (yr. ended 12/31/13): Assets, $6,193,980 (M); gifts received, $487,795; expenditures, $470,751; qualifying distributions, $438,607; giving activities include $437,375 for 7 grants (high: $300,895; low: $10,239).
Purpose and activities: Giving for education and community organizations.
Fields of interest: Education; Community/economic development.
Limitations: Applications not accepted. Giving primarily in VA. No grants to individuals.

Application information: Contributes only to pre-selected organizations.
Officers and Directors:* Alfred Dreyfus,* Pres.; Mildred Dreyfus,* Secy.; Mark Dreyfus,* Treas.; Claudia Dreyfus Levi.
EIN: 541851411
Selected grants: The following grants are a representative sample of this grantmaker's funding activity:
$499,707 to Multiple Myeloma Research Foundation, Norwalk, CT, 2011.
$92,500 to United Jewish Federation of Tidewater, Virginia Beach, VA, 2011.
$15,315 to University of Pennsylvania, Philadelphia, PA, 2011.

9424
Andrew H. & Anne O. Easley Trust ✧
(also known as The Easley Foundation)
P.O. Box 798
Lynchburg, VA 24505-0798

Established in 1968 in VA.
Donor: Andrew H. Easley†.
Foundation type: Independent foundation.
Financial data (yr. ended 06/30/13): Assets, $8,727,852 (M); expenditures, $465,042; qualifying distributions, $421,682; giving activities include $421,682 for grants.
Purpose and activities: Giving primarily for the arts, education and human services.
Fields of interest: Arts; Education; Human services.
Limitations: Giving limited to the central VA, area, within a 30-mile radius of Lynchburg. No support for religious organizations. No grants to individuals, or for research, deficit financing, seed money, annual campaigns, or conferences and seminars; no loans.
Publications: Application guidelines.
Application information: Application form not required.
Initial approach: Proposal (not exceeding 2 pages)
Copies of proposal: 6
Deadline(s): Apr. 1 and Oct. 1
Board meeting date(s): June and Dec.
Trustee: Frank G. Davidson, III.
EIN: 546074720

9425
The Elmo Foundation ✧ ☆
711-A Graves St.
Charlottesville, VA 22902-5721

Foundation type: Operating foundation.
Financial data (yr. ended 12/31/13): Assets, $8,431,776 (M); expenditures, $444,887; qualifying distributions, $424,707; giving activities include $424,707 for 31 grants (high: $50,000; low: $1,000).
Fields of interest: Education; Health care; Human services.
Limitations: Applications not accepted. Giving primarily in CA and VA.
Application information: Contributes only to pre-selected organizations.
EIN: 260795189
Selected grants: The following grants are a representative sample of this grantmaker's funding activity:
$5,000 to Virginia Organizing, Charlottesville, VA, 2011.
$3,000 to Mary House, Washington, DC, 2011.
$2,500 to Partners in Health, Boston, MA, 2011.
$2,000 to Alliance for Justice, Washington, DC, 2011.
$2,000 to Building Goodness Foundation, Charlottesville, VA, 2011.
$1,000 to EarthReports, Upper Marlboro, MD, 2011.

9426
W. C. English Foundation ✧
c/o English Construction
P.O. Box P7000
Lynchburg, VA 24505-7000 (434) 845-0301
Contact: Beverley E. Dalton, Tr.

Established in 1954 in VA.
Donor: Members of the English family.
Foundation type: Independent foundation.
Financial data (yr. ended 05/31/13): Assets, $18,459,720 (M); expenditures, $992,538; qualifying distributions, $779,500; giving activities include $779,500 for grants.
Purpose and activities: Giving primarily for higher and other education, human services, and Baptist and Christian churches and organizations.
Fields of interest: Higher education; Education; Human services; Christian agencies & churches; Protestant agencies & churches.
Type of support: General/operating support; Program-related investments/loans.
Limitations: Giving primarily in SC and VA. No grants to individuals.
Application information:
Initial approach: Letter
Deadline(s): None
Trustees: Joan E. Allen; Beverley E. Dalton; Margaret E. Lester; Suzanne E. Morse.
EIN: 546061817

9427
Estes Foundation ✧
5607 Grove Ave.
Richmond, VA 23226-2101

Established in 1969 in VA.
Donor: C.E. Estes.
Foundation type: Independent foundation.
Financial data (yr. ended 12/31/13): Assets, $3,948,139 (M); expenditures, $647,995; qualifying distributions, $555,900; giving activities include $525,000 for 16 grants (high: $266,614; low: $500).
Purpose and activities: Giving primarily for higher and other education.
Fields of interest: Museums; Higher education; Education; Human services.
Type of support: General/operating support.
Limitations: Applications not accepted. No grants to individuals.
Application information: Contributes only to pre-selected organizations.
Officers: C.E. Estes, Pres. and Treas.; Barbara Dodson, Secy.
Director: Martha E. Grover.
EIN: 237045252

9428
Edward P. Evans Foundation ✧
P.O. Box 46
Rte. 602
Casanova, VA 20139-0046

Established in 1983 in VA.
Donor: Edward P. Evans†.
Foundation type: Independent foundation.
Financial data (yr. ended 11/30/13): Assets, $279,356,481 (M); gifts received, $53,985,551; expenditures, $12,497,934; qualifying distributions, $10,686,029; giving activities include $9,034,735 for 25 grants (high: $3,200,000; low: $800).
Fields of interest: Education; Health organizations, association; Cancer; Cancer, leukemia; Prostate cancer.
Type of support: General/operating support.
Limitations: Applications not accepted. Giving primarily in Santa Monica, CA, MD, and NY. No grants to individuals.
Application information: Contributes only to pre-selected organizations.
Officer and Trustees:* Catherine Moraetis,* Exec. Dir.; Robert Evans; William Farish, IV; Jefferson Tarr.
Number of staff: None.
EIN: 256232129

9429
Eugene V. Fife Family Foundation ✧
413 Seventh St., NE, Ste. 201
Charlottesville, VA 22902-4723

Established in 1982 in CA.
Donor: Eugene V. Fife.
Foundation type: Independent foundation.
Financial data (yr. ended 01/31/12): Assets, $118,125 (M); expenditures, $732,368; qualifying distributions, $728,200; giving activities include $723,840 for 20 grants (high: $500,000; low: $100).
Purpose and activities: Giving primarily for higher education; some funding also for the arts, human services and public affairs.
Fields of interest: Arts; Higher education; Human services; Foundations (private grantmaking); Public affairs.
Type of support: General/operating support; Endowments.
Limitations: Applications not accepted. Giving primarily in VA, with some emphasis on Charlottesville and Blacksburg. No grants to individuals; no loans.
Application information: Contributes only to pre-selected organizations.
Trustees: Jonathan L. Cohen; Amy S. Fife; David Fife; Edward A. Fife; Elizabeth J. Fife; Eugene V. Fife.
EIN: 133153715
Selected grants: The following grants are a representative sample of this grantmaker's funding activity:
$500,000 to Virginia Tech Foundation, Blacksburg, VA, 2012.
$125,000 to Miller Center of Public Affairs, Charlottesville, VA, 2012.
$30,000 to Ash Lawn Opera Festival Foundation, Charlottesville, VA, 2012.
$20,000 to Martha Jefferson Hospital Foundation, Charlottesville, VA, 2012.
$15,000 to West Virginia University, Morgantown, WV, 2012.

$7,500 to Berklee College of Music, Boston, MA, 2012.
$7,500 to West Virginia Wesleyan College, Buckhannon, WV, 2012.
$5,000 to Duke University, Durham, NC, 2012.
$5,000 to Thomas Jefferson Foundation, Charlottesville, VA, 2012.
$3,390 to Paramount Theater, Charlottesville, VA, 2012.

9430
The Jane and Arthur Flippo Foundation ✧ ☆

P.O. Box 38
Doswell, VA 23047-0038
Application address: Sylvia S. Acors, Secy.-Treas., 16415 Washington Hwy., Doswell, VA 23047

Established in 1988 in VA.
Donors: Arthur P. Flippo; Arthur P. Flippo Trust.
Foundation type: Independent foundation.
Financial data (yr. ended 12/31/13): Assets, $4,503,359 (M); gifts received, $8,234,640; expenditures, $6,873,438; qualifying distributions, $6,822,875; giving activities include $6,822,875 for 27 grants (high: $6,600,000; low: $750).
Fields of interest: Education; YM/YWCAs & YM/YWHAs; Protestant agencies & churches.
Type of support: General/operating support.
Limitations: Applications accepted. Giving primarily in VA. No grants to individuals.
Application information: Application form required.
Initial approach: Letter
Deadline(s): None
Officers: J. Franklin Jones, Pres.; Norman L. Long, V.P.; Sylvia S. Acors, Secy.-Treas.
EIN: 541479553
Selected grants: The following grants are a representative sample of this grantmaker's funding activity:
$1,000 to Hanover Academy, Ashland, VA, 2012. For outdoor classroom.

9431
The Lee and Juliet Folger Fund ✧

(formerly The Folger Fund)
c/o Anne L. Stone & Assocs., LLC
6862 Elm St., Ste. 740
McLean, VA 22101-3862 (703) 847-1350

Incorporated in 1955 in DC.
Donors: Eugenia B. Dulin†; Kathrine Dulin Folger†; Lee Merritt Folger.
Foundation type: Independent foundation.
Financial data (yr. ended 08/31/13): Assets, $49,145,704 (M); expenditures, $2,560,739; qualifying distributions, $2,475,251; giving activities include $2,393,450 for 89 grants (high: $600,000; low: $250).
Purpose and activities: Giving primarily for the arts and education; funding also for human services.
Fields of interest: Museums; Performing arts; Historic preservation/historical societies; Secondary school/education; Higher education; Education; Hospitals (general); Health organizations, association; Human services.
Type of support: General/operating support; Building/renovation; Endowments; Scholarship funds.
Limitations: Applications not accepted. Giving primarily in Washington, DC, MA and MD. No grants to individuals.
Publications: Annual report.
Application information: Contributes only to pre-selected organizations.
Officers: Lee Merritt Folger, Pres.; John D. Folger, V.P. and Secy.; Juliet C. Folger, V.P. and Treas.; Cecily C. Colburn, V.P.
EIN: 520794388
Selected grants: The following grants are a representative sample of this grantmaker's funding activity:
$600,000 to National Gallery of Art, Washington, DC, 2013. To purchase painting A Still Life with Wild Strawberries Wan Li Bowl.
$250,000 to National Geographic Society, Washington, DC, 2013. For Exploration Fund.
$150,000 to Saint Marks School, Southborough, MA, 2013. For program to landscape Sundial Quad.
$100,000 to Georgetown University Medical Center, Washington, DC, 2013. For cardiovascular disease prevention programs.
$50,000 to Harvard University, Fairbanks Center, Cambridge, MA, 2013. For China Map Project.
$50,000 to Smithsonian Institution, Washington, DC, 2013. For 25th Anniversary Gala.
$35,000 to Harvard University, Asia Center, Cambridge, MA, 2013. For China Program Support.
$25,000 to University of Arizona Foundation, Tucson, AZ, 2013. For University of Arizona Cancer Center in honor of Nancy and Craig Berge.
$15,000 to George Washington University, Interior Design Department, Washington, DC, 2013. For Classroom Renovation Project.
$12,000 to Corcoran Gallery of Art, Washington, DC, 2013. For Ball Program.

9432
Foster Foundation Inc. ✧ ☆

P.O. Box 14624
Richmond, VA 23221

Donors: Janet P. Lewis†; The Flagler Foundation.
Foundation type: Independent foundation.
Financial data (yr. ended 12/31/13): Assets, $6,063,488 (M); gifts received, $26,182; expenditures, $780,445; qualifying distributions, $750,209; giving activities include $741,500 for 22 grants (high: $293,000; low: $1,000).
Fields of interest: Arts; Education; Health organizations; Human services; United Ways and Federated Giving Programs; Protestant agencies & churches.
Limitations: Applications not accepted. No grants to individuals.
Application information: Unsolicited requests for funds not accepted.
Officers and Directors:* Louise L. Foster,* Pres. and Treas.; John N. Foster, Jr.,* V.P. and Secy.; Gilbert L. Gates.
EIN: 200295545

9433
Horace G. Fralin Charitable Trust ✧

P.O. Box 29600
Roanoke, VA 24018-0796 (540) 776-7444
Contact: W. Heywood Fralin, Tr.

Established in 1989 in VA.
Foundation type: Independent foundation.
Financial data (yr. ended 12/31/13): Assets, $48,232,277 (M); expenditures, $3,295,650; qualifying distributions, $2,150,056; giving activities include $2,150,056 for 5 grants (high: $1,550,000; low: $56).
Purpose and activities: The trust primarily provides grants to qualified charitable organizations in Roanoke Valley, VA for the purchase, construction, renovation or expansion of buildings, equipment and other capital assets of a long-term nature that help the organizations to further their goals.
Fields of interest: Museums (art); Arts; Education; Human services.
Type of support: Building/renovation; Equipment; Land acquisition.
Limitations: Applications accepted. Giving primarily in Roanoke, VA. No support for private foundations. No grants to individuals, or for multi-year commitments, sponsorships, scholarships or fund-raisers.
Application information: Application form not required.
Initial approach: Proposal
Deadline(s): None
Trustees: W. Heywood Fralin; William H. Fralin.
Number of staff: 1 part-time support.
EIN: 541509505

9434
Franklin Southampton Charities ✧

P.O. Box 276
Franklin, VA 23851-0276
Contact: G. Elliott Cobb, Jr., Dir.
E-mail: fsc@belden.com

Established in 2000 in VA.
Donors: Old Hospital Corp.; Southampton Memorial Hospital Endowment Fund.
Foundation type: Independent foundation.
Financial data (yr. ended 12/31/13): Assets, $34,280,398 (M); expenditures, $1,779,972; qualifying distributions, $1,579,200; giving activities include $1,503,353 for 62 grants (high: $100,000; low: $1,550).
Purpose and activities: Giving primarily to new or established nonprofit organizations located in the service area of the foundation, and to provide community leadership, including convening current service providers to collaborate on areas of need, and to encourage cooperation and reduce any duplication of service. Funding priorities include proposals which: 1) provide specific health and safety benefits to the youth and elderly populations of the community, 2) develop ready-to-learn educational skills for students children, 3) provide job training and promote economic development, and 4) promote community leadership, dialogue and cooperation. Additional emphasis is given to community projects that: 1) reach a broad segment of the community with emphasis on meeting diverse needs, 2) assists those whose needs are not being met by existing services, 3) encourages challenge grants or matching gifts to garner additional funding from other sources, 4) brings together groups to work in partnership on issues that affect multiple jurisdictions in the foundation's service area, 5) promotes cooperation among agencies and organizations to avoid duplicating existing services, 6) yields substantial benefits to the community for the costs involved, and 7) clearly defines objectives and methods of evaluating results.

Fields of interest: Education; Health organizations, association; Children/youth, services; Community/economic development.
Limitations: Applications accepted. Giving primarily in the city of Franklin, and Southampton County, VA. No support for religious purposes, national or international organizations or purposes, hospitals or similar healthcare facilities. No grants to individuals, or for ongoing annual operating support (though exceptions will be considered for start-up projects where other sources of long-term funding are clearly identified), endowments, debt reduction, sponsorships, scholarships, fellowships, travel, or for projects normally the responsibility of the government.
Publications: Application guidelines.
Application information: Full proposals are by invitation only, after initial review of letter of intent. Application form required.
Initial approach: Letter of intent
Copies of proposal: 1
Deadline(s): Apr. 1 (for July funding) and Aug. 31 (for Dec. funding)
Board meeting date(s): 2nd Tues. of every month, unless specified differently
Final notification: 2 months
Officers and Directors:* William A. Peak,* Chair.; E. Warren Beale, Jr.,* Vice-Chair.; G. Elliott Cobb, Jr., Esq.*, Secy.; W. Elliott Whitfield,* Treas.; Glenn P. Bidwell, Jr., M.D.; Nancy M. Brewbaker; Ernest Claud, Jr.; Anita T. Felts; William H. Howell III; Edna R. King; Asa B. Johnson; Hon. Westbrook J. Parker.
Number of staff: 1 part-time professional.
EIN: 311613116
Selected grants: The following grants are a representative sample of this grantmaker's funding activity:
$100,000 to Franklin-Southampton Economic Development, Franklin, VA, 2012. For economic development.
$5,000 to Western Tidewater Tennis Association, Franklin, VA, 2012. For education/recreation.

9435
Freddie Mac Foundation ✧
c/o Grants Mgr.
8250 Jones Branch Dr., M.S. A-40
McLean, VA 22102-3110 (703) 918-8888
FAX: (703) 918-8895; Main URL: http://www.freddiemacfoundation.org
Grants List: http://www.freddiemacfoundation.org/grants/docs/2014_q2_grants.pdf

Established in 1991 in VA.
Donor: Federal Home Loan Mortgage Corp.
Foundation type: Company-sponsored foundation.
Financial data (yr. ended 12/31/13): Assets, $40,168,435 (M); expenditures, $88,242,113; qualifying distributions, $49,648,525; giving activities include $42,556,471 for 183 grants (high: $11,543,362; low: $7,500), $2,266,335 for 1,461 employee matching gifts, and $3,001,453 for 3 foundation-administered programs.
Purpose and activities: The foundation supports programs designed to make home a place where vulnerable children and their families can thrive. Special emphasis is directed toward programs designed to create stable homes and families; find adoptive homes for foster children; and help youth improve their academic achievement and achieve career success.
Fields of interest: Education, early childhood education; Elementary school/education; Secondary school/education; Education, services; Education; Employment, training; Housing/shelter, temporary shelter; Housing/shelter, homeless; Housing/shelter; Youth development; Children/youth, services; Children, adoption; Children, foster care; Family services; Economically disadvantaged; Homeless.
Type of support: General/operating support; Continuing support; Management development/capacity building; Capital campaigns; Program development; Conferences/seminars; Publication; Research; Technical assistance; Consulting services; Employee volunteer services; Sponsorships; Employee matching gifts.
Limitations: Applications not accepted. Giving primarily in the metropolitan Washington, DC, area, with emphasis on the District of Columbia, Charles, Frederick, Howard, Montgomery, and Prince George's counties, MD, and Alexandria, Arlington County, Fairfax County, Falls Church, Leesburg, Loudoun County, Manassas Park, and Prince William County, VA; giving also to statewide organizations in MD and VA and national organizations. No support for discriminatory organizations. No grants to individuals, or for training in or promotion of religious doctrine, debt reduction, endowments, or lobbying or political activity.
Publications: Annual report; Grants list; Informational brochure.
Application information: The foundation is winding down its giving and plans to conclude its grantmaking in 2014.
Board meeting date(s): 1st Thurs. in Mar., June, Sept., and Dec.
Officers and Directors:* Ronald F. Poe,* Chair.; Ralph F. Boyd, Jr., C.E.O. and Pres.; Margaret Meiers, V.P. and Prog. Dir.; Alicia Myara, Secy.; Adel Antoun, Treas and C.F.O.; Wendell J. Chambliss, Exec. Dir.; Carolyn Byrd; Paul E. Mullings; Nicolas Retsinas; Dwight Robinson; Clarice Dibble Walker.
Number of staff: 11 full-time professional.
EIN: 541573760
Selected grants: The following grants are a representative sample of this grantmaker's funding activity:
$1,000,000 to National Alliance to End Homelessness, Washington, DC, 2012.
$500,000 to Community of Hope, Washington, DC, 2012.
$500,000 to National Center for Children and Families, Bethesda, MD, 2012.
$500,000 to Transitional Housing Corporation, Washington, DC, 2012.
$450,000 to Montgomery County Coalition for the Homeless, Rockville, MD, 2012.
$315,000 to DC Public Education Fund, Washington, DC, 2012.
$200,000 to Higher Achievement Program, Washington, DC, 2012.
$75,000 to Shelter House, Reston, VA, 2012.
$50,000 to Main Street Child Development Center, Fairfax, VA, 2012.
$45,000 to Capital Partners for Education, Washington, DC, 2012.

9436
Fredericksburg Savings Charitable Foundation ✧
1111 Sunken Rd.
Fredericksburg, VA 22401 (540) 371-9617
Contact: Samuel C. Harding, Jr., Dir.

Established in 1998 in DE and VA.
Donor: Virginia Capital Bancshares, Inc.
Foundation type: Company-sponsored foundation.
Financial data (yr. ended 12/31/13): Assets, $11,658,460 (M); expenditures, $636,522; qualifying distributions, $616,675; giving activities include $609,500 for 57 grants (high: $90,000; low: $500).
Purpose and activities: The foundation supports programs designed to expand home ownership opportunities; and contribute to the quality of life in communities where Fredericksburg Savings Bank operates.
Fields of interest: Hospitals (general); Health care, clinics/centers; Food banks; Housing/shelter; Boys & girls clubs; American Red Cross; Salvation Army; YM/YWCAs & YM/YWHAs; Children/youth, services; Homeless, human services; Human services; Community/economic development.
Type of support: General/operating support.
Limitations: Applications accepted. Giving primarily in areas of company operations in Caroline, King George, Orange, Spotsylvania, and Stafford counties, VA, and Fredericksburg, VA. No grants to individuals.
Application information: Application form required.
Initial approach: Contact foundation for application form
Deadline(s): Contact foundation for application form
Directors: O'Conner G. Ashby; Ernest N. Donahoe; Samuel C. Harding, Jr.; William B. Young.
EIN: 541913172
Selected grants: The following grants are a representative sample of this grantmaker's funding activity:
$65,000 to Fredericksburg Area Food Bank, Fredericksburg, VA, 2010.
$65,000 to Salvation Army, 2010.
$60,000 to Fredericksburg Area Regional Health Council, Fredericksburg, VA, 2010.
$20,000 to Boys and Girls Club of Frederick County, Frederick, MD, 2010.
$10,000 to Helpline Center, Sioux Falls, SD, 2010.
$10,000 to Partnership for Academic Excellence, Signal Mountain, TN, 2010.
$10,000 to Thurman Brisben Homeless Shelter, Fredericksburg, VA, 2010.
$2,500 to American Cancer Society, Atlanta, GA, 2011.
$2,500 to Special Olympics, Washington, DC, 2011.

9437
The Friends of the Graduate Institute Geneva Inc. ✧
c/o Allen Lynch
120 Vincennes Rd.
Charlottesville, VA 22911-8538

Donor: Shelby Cullom Davis & Co.
Foundation type: Independent foundation.
Financial data (yr. ended 12/31/13): Assets, $515,928 (M); gifts received, $4,254,700; expenditures, $4,289,807; qualifying distributions, $4,252,906; giving activities include $4,250,000 for 2 grants (high: $4,000,000; low: $250,000).
Fields of interest: Higher education.
Limitations: Applications not accepted. Giving primarily in Geneva, Switzerland.
Application information: Unsolicited requests for funds not accepted.

Officers and Directors:* Rita Hauser,* Pres.; Richard Thoman,* Secy.; Allen Lynch,* Co-Treas.; Paul Mathieu,* Co-Treas.
EIN: 272229822

9438
The Funger Foundation, Inc. ✧
1650 Tysons Blvd., Ste. 820
McLean, VA 22102-4856

Established in 1998 in MD.
Donors: Morton Funger; Norma Lee Funger; Yetta K. Cohen‡.
Foundation type: Independent foundation.
Financial data (yr. ended 12/31/13): Assets, $3,120,911 (M); gifts received, $525,000; expenditures, $678,275; qualifying distributions, $675,135; giving activities include $675,135 for 49 grants (high: $150,000; low: $100).
Purpose and activities: Giving primarily for the arts, education, health organizations and hospitals, social services and Jewish organizations.
Fields of interest: Museums (art); Performing arts centers; Arts; Higher education; Education; Hospitals (general); Health organizations; Human services; Jewish federated giving programs; Jewish agencies & synagogues.
Limitations: Applications not accepted. Giving primarily in the eastern U.S., with emphasis on Washington, DC and MD. No grants to individuals.
Application information: Unsolicited requests for funds not accepted.
Officers: Morton Funger, Pres.; Norma Lee Funger, Secy.-Treas.
Directors: C. Richard Beyda; Keith Parker Funger; William Scott Funger; Lydia Joy McClain; Melanie Nichols.
EIN: 541893307
Selected grants: The following grants are a representative sample of this grantmaker's funding activity:
$15,075 to Adas Israel Hebrew Congregation, Washington, DC, 2011.

9439
Gannett Foundation, Inc. ✧
7950 Jones Branch Dr.
McLean, VA 22107-0001 (703) 854-6000
Contact: Pat Lyle, Exec. Dir.
FAX: (703) 854-2167;
E-mail: foundation@gannett.com; Main URL: http://www.gannettfoundation.org
Media Grants: http://www.gannettfoundation.org/media.htm

Established in 1991 in VA.
Donor: Gannett Co., Inc.
Foundation type: Company-sponsored foundation.
Financial data (yr. ended 12/31/13): Assets, $5,158,147 (M); gifts received, $5,738,388; expenditures, $6,660,669; qualifying distributions, $6,471,608; giving activities include $4,968,900 for 295 grants (high: $4,055,000; low: $100), and $1,438,668 for 3,750 employee matching gifts.
Purpose and activities: The foundation supports organizations involved with arts and culture, media and journalism, education, conservation, health, youth development, human services, diversity, community development, minorities, women, and economically disadvantaged people.
Fields of interest: Arts, cultural/ethnic awareness; Media/communications; Media, print publishing; Arts; Journalism school/education; Education; Environment, natural resources; Health care; Disasters, preparedness/services; Youth development; Human services; Civil/human rights, equal rights; Civil liberties, first amendment; Community development, neighborhood development; Economic development; Community/economic development; Minorities; Women; Economically disadvantaged.
International interests: United Kingdom.
Type of support: Capital campaigns; Equipment; Program development; Conferences/seminars; Scholarship funds; Employee matching gifts.
Limitations: Applications accepted. Giving on a national and international basis in areas of company operations, with emphasis on AZ, Washington DC, FL, IN, MI, NY, OH, VA, and the United Kingdom. No support for private foundations, regional or national organizations not addressing local needs, elementary or secondary schools (except to provide special initiatives or programs not provided by regular school budgets), political action or legislative advocacy groups, hospitals, medical or research organizations, animal charities, fraternal groups, athletic teams, bands, veterans' organizations, or volunteer firefighters. No grants to individuals (except for employee-related scholarships), or for religious programs or initiatives, fund salaries, professional fees, day-to-day running or maintenance costs, endowments, general appeals, or multi-year pledge campaigns.
Publications: Application guidelines; Annual report; Informational brochure; IRS Form 990 or 990-PF printed copy available upon request; Program policy statement.
Application information: Grants range from $1,000 to $5,000; Newsquest grants range from 5,000 to 10,000. Proposals should be no longer than 5 pages. Telephone calls during the application process are not encouraged. Visit website to confirm application deadline for specific areas. Application form required.
Initial approach: Download application form and mail proposal and form to the company's nearest daily newspaper or broadcast station; download application form and mail proposal and form to foundation for organizations located in the Washington, DC metropolitan area
Copies of proposal: 1
Deadline(s): Feb. 28 and Aug. 29 for Community Action Grants; Mar. 1, July 15, and Nov. 1 for Media Grants; Autumn for Newsquest Grants
Board meeting date(s): 3 times per year from Feb. to Oct.
Final notification: 90 to 120 days; 60 to 90 days for Media Grants
Officers and Directors:* Gracia C. Martore,* Chair. and Pres.; Tom Cox, V.P.; Todd A. Mayman,* Secy.; Michael A. Hart, Treas.; Pat Lyle, Exec. Dir.
Number of staff: 1 full-time professional; 1 full-time support.
EIN: 541568843
Selected grants: The following grants are a representative sample of this grantmaker's funding activity:
$540,000 to Quartet Community Foundation, Bristol, England, 2012. For grants recommended by Newsquest Media Group.
$302,000 to Arizona Community Foundation, Phoenix, AZ, 2012. For community donations to holiday program, Season for Sharing. Donations are matched up to $400,000 and granted to local non-profit agencies.
$88,000 to Online News Association, Washington, DC, 2012. For sponsorship of Digital training camp ($50,000), Excellence in Journalism Awards ($23,000) to be presented at annual convention and $15,000 for sponsorship of Job Fair/Career/Day at convention.
$75,000 to Central Indiana Community Foundation, Indianapolis, IN, 2012. To match community donations to annual Season for Sharing Holiday Program campaign that benefits local non-profit agencies.
$72,500 to United Way for Southeastern Michigan, Detroit, MI, 2012. For general campaign support.
$25,000 to Des Moines Public Library Foundation, Des Moines, IA, 2012. To support capital campaign to update and expand branch libraries.
$5,000 to United Way, Fond du Lac Area, Fond du Lac, WI, 2012. For program support to help the community in three impact areas.
$4,000 to Urban Arts Academy, Minneapolis, MN, 2012. For a neighborhood free art program for youth in both Spanish and English.
$3,000 to District of Columbia College Success Foundation, Washington, DC, 2012. For general support.
$3,000 to Heritage University, Toppenish, WA, 2012. For general support.
$2,600 to Ozarks Area Community Action Corporation, Springfield, MO, 2012. For love and Logic curriculum and parent handbooks for classes for 150 parents and guardians.
$2,500 to Guiding Light Mission, Grand Rapids, MI, 2012. To support the housing of 110 men every night and serving 350 meals per day.

9440
The Genan Foundation ✧
P.O. Box 5386
Charlottesville, VA 22905-5386

Established in 1986 in VA.
Donors: Anne R. Worrell; T. Eugene Worrell; T. Eugene Worrell 1989 Charitable Lead Unitrust.
Foundation type: Independent foundation.
Financial data (yr. ended 12/31/13): Assets, $21,482,946 (M); gifts received, $1,814,529; expenditures, $822,693; qualifying distributions, $779,073; giving activities include $779,073 for 11 grants (high: $500,000; low: $5,000).
Purpose and activities: Giving primarily for historical preservation and education, particularly education for economically disadvantaged children.
Fields of interest: Historic preservation/historical societies; Education; Children/youth, services; Aging, centers/services; Foundations (private grantmaking); Economically disadvantaged.
Limitations: Applications not accepted. Giving primarily in Charlottesville, VA. No grants to individuals.
Application information: Contributes only to pre-selected organizations.
Officers and Director:* Anne R. Worrell,* Pres.; Andrew J. Dracopoli, V.P. and Treas.; Judith S. Coleman, Secy.
EIN: 541393561
Selected grants: The following grants are a representative sample of this grantmaker's funding activity:

$250,000 to Miller Center Foundation, Charlottesville, VA, 2012. For grant to support Programs for the study of the presidency.
$50,000 to Jefferson Area Board for Aging, Charlottesville, VA, 2012. To support indigent nursing home residents and rural community centers.
$50,000 to Thomas Jefferson Foundation, Charlottesville, VA, 2012. For grant toward editing letters of Thomas Jefferson.
$50,000 to Virginia Historical Society, Richmond, VA, 2012. For grant to redesign and rebuild The Story of Virginia exhibit at museum.
$25,000 to American Red Cross, Charlottesville, VA, 2012. For local disaster relief efforts.
$20,000 to Virginia Intermont College, Bristol, VA, 2012. For grant to fund physical improvements on campus.
$10,152 to Charlottesville City Schools, Charlottesville, VA, 2012. For Summer camps and tutoring support for low income children.
$10,000 to Blue Ridge Area Food Bank, Charlottesville, VA, 2012. For operating funds to provide food for the needy.
$5,000 to Shelter for Help in Emergency, Charlottesville, VA, 2012. To sponsor event for the support of abused women.

9441
Genworth Foundation ✧
c/o Community Rels. Dept.
6620 W. Broad St.
Richmond, VA 23230-1716
Contact: Heidi Crapol, Secy.
Main URL: http://www.genworth.com/foundation

Established in 2005 in VA.
Donor: Genworth Financial, Inc.
Foundation type: Company-sponsored foundation.
Financial data (yr. ended 12/31/12): Assets, $1,989,798 (M); expenditures, $3,151,329; qualifying distributions, $3,146,164; giving activities include $2,239,956 for 108 grants (high: $300,000; low: $297), and $900,404 for employee matching gifts.
Purpose and activities: The foundation supports organizations involved with K-12 education, health, hunger, housing, human services, and senior citizens.
Fields of interest: Elementary/secondary education; Education, services; Education; Health care; Alzheimer's disease; Food services; Food banks; Housing/shelter, development; Housing/shelter, aging; Housing/shelter, temporary shelter; Housing/shelter; Youth development, adult & child programs; Youth, services; Human services, financial counseling; Aging, centers/services; Human services; United Ways and Federated Giving Programs; Aging.
Type of support: Management development/capacity building; Program development; Employee volunteer services; Employee matching gifts.
Limitations: Applications accepted. Giving on a national and international basis in areas of company operations, with emphasis on Raleigh, NC, Lynchburg and Richmond, VA, Australia, Canada, and Europe. No support for political, labor, fraternal, or social organizations, civic clubs, religious organizations not of direct benefit to the entire community, pass-through or third party organizations; sports, athletic, recreational, or little leagues, or private corporate or family foundations. No grants to individuals, or for advertising, development, or production of books, films, videos, radio, or television programs, endowments, or memorials.
Publications: Application guidelines; Annual report.
Application information: Letters of intent are required for organizations that have not previously received funding from the Genworth Foundation or have not received funding within the prior calendar year. Grants range from $5,000 to $25,000. A full proposal may be requested at a later date. Application form required.
Initial approach: Complete online letter of intent
Copies of proposal: 1
Deadline(s): None
Board meeting date(s): Quarterly
Officers and Directors:* Leon E. Roday,* Chair.; Daniel P. Healy, Vice-Chair.; Heidi Crapol, Secy.; Megan Dorn, Treas.
EIN: 203370235
Selected grants: The following grants are a representative sample of this grantmaker's funding activity:
$110,000 to Habitat for Humanity International, Americus, GA, 2011.
$11,500 to Connecticut Food Bank, East Haven, CT, 2011.
$10,000 to Blue Ridge Area Food Bank, Verona, VA, 2011.
$10,000 to Junior Achievement of Chicago, Chicago, IL, 2011.
$5,000 to Rebuilding Together, Washington, DC, 2011.
$2,500 to Blue Ridge Area Food Bank, Verona, VA, 2011.

9442
The Richard and Leslie Gilliam Foundation ✧
650 Peter Jefferson Pkwy.,Ste.230
Charlottesville, VA 22911-8845

Established in 2005 in VA.
Donor: Richard Gilliam.
Foundation type: Independent foundation.
Financial data (yr. ended 12/31/12): Assets, $59,343,627 (M); expenditures, $13,354,984; qualifying distributions, $12,879,875; giving activities include $12,879,875 for 77 grants (high: $5,060,000; low: $25).
Fields of interest: Higher education; Education; Health care; Human services.
Limitations: Applications not accepted. Giving primarily in VA.
Application information: Contributes only to pre-selected organizations.
Officers and Directors:* Richard B. Gilliam,* Pres.; Leslie F. Gilliam,* Secy.; James L Van Dyke.
EIN: 203691921

9443
Sam & Marion Golden Helping Hand Foundation ✧
(formerly Virginia Scrap Iron & Metal Co. Charitable Foundation, Inc.)
P.O. Box 8278
Roanoke, VA 24014-0278 (540) 977-6205
Contact: Mary Ann Ward, Pres. and Dir.

Donors: Virginia Scrap Iron & Metal Co., Inc.; Industrial & Mill Suppliers, Inc.; Robin Wohlleban; Samuel Golden†.
Foundation type: Company-sponsored foundation.
Financial data (yr. ended 12/31/13): Assets, $25,042,025 (M); gifts received, $3,588,007; expenditures, $1,100,934; qualifying distributions, $1,003,616; giving activities include $1,000,000 for 36 grants (high: $237,500; low: $1,000).
Purpose and activities: The foundation supports food banks and organizations involved with arts and culture, education, health, recreation, human services, and Judaism.
Fields of interest: Arts; Health care; Religion.
Type of support: General/operating support; Program development.
Limitations: Applications accepted. Giving primarily in VA. No grants to individuals.
Application information: Application form required.
Initial approach: Letter
Deadline(s): None
Officer and Directors: Mary Ann Ward,* Pres.; John Lichenstein; David Tenzer.
EIN: 546050920
Selected grants: The following grants are a representative sample of this grantmaker's funding activity:
$1,500 to Virginia Western Community College Educational Foundation, Roanoke, VA, 2012. For Org. Charity (All).

9444
Dixon Hughes Goodman Foundation ✧ ☆
c/o James M. Haggard
701 Ctr. Dr., Ste. 700
Newport News, VA 23606-4295

Established in 1997 in VA.
Donors: Goodman & Company, L.L.P.; Dixon Hughes Goodman, LLP; Wallace Dunn; Joel Flax.
Foundation type: Company-sponsored foundation.
Financial data (yr. ended 06/30/13): Assets, $216,669 (M); gifts received, $837,702; expenditures, $849,791; qualifying distributions, $849,321; giving activities include $849,321 for 74 grants (high: $126,100; low: $50).
Purpose and activities: The foundation supports organizations involved with higher education.
Fields of interest: Education.
Type of support: General/operating support; Scholarship funds.
Limitations: Applications not accepted. Giving limited to VA. No grants to individuals.
Application information: Unsolicited requests for funds not accepted.
Officers: James M. Haggard, Chair.; Tricia Wilson, Pres.; L. Kent Satterfield, Secy.-Treas.
EIN: 541847474

9445
Philip L. Graham Fund ✧
c/o Graham Holdings Co.
1300 N. 17th St., Ste. 1700
Arlington, VA 22209-3811 (202) 334-6640
Contact: Eileen F. Daly, Pres.
FAX: (202) 334-4498;
E-mail: plgfund@washpost.com; Main URL: http://plgrahamfund.org/
Grants Database: http://plgrahamfund.org/vw_grants_awarded

Trust established in 1963 in DC.

Donors: Katharine Meyer Graham; Frederick S. Beebe‡; The Washington Post Co.; Newsweek, Inc.; Post-Newsweek Stations.
Foundation type: Independent foundation.
Financial data (yr. ended 12/31/13): Assets, $113,642,918 (M); expenditures, $4,707,504; qualifying distributions, $4,486,487; giving activities include $4,097,500 for grants.
Purpose and activities: Support for one-time infrastructure investments in health and human services, for children, youth, and families, pre-collegiate education, arts and humanities, and community needs. Grants for journalism, media and communications are extremely limited, and generally awarded only to those who have received media grants in the past.
Fields of interest: Arts; Education, early childhood education; Education; Housing/shelter; Human services; Youth, services; Community development, neighborhood development.
Type of support: Capital campaigns; Building/renovation; Equipment; Program development; Seed money; Matching/challenge support.
Limitations: Applications accepted. Giving primarily in the metropolitan Washington, DC, area. No support for national or international organizations, membership organizations, lobbying or political activities, or for religious purposes. No grants to individuals, or for medical services, research, annual campaigns, fundraising events, endowments, seminars, conferences, publications, tickets, films, travel expenses, courtesy advertising, advocacy, or litigation.
Publications: Application guidelines; Program policy statement.
Application information: Letters of inquiry must be submitted via the foundation's online system. Application form not required.
Initial approach: Review guidelines and qualifications prior to submitting a letter of inquiry
Copies of proposal: 3
Deadline(s): See foundation web site for current deadlines
Board meeting date(s): 120 days from application deadline
Final notification: 6 months
Officers and Trustees:* Eileen F. Daly,* Pres.; Theodore C. Lutz,* Secy.; Martin Cohen,* Treas.; Donald E. Graham; Pinkie D. Mayfield; Carol D. Melamed; Laura O'Shaughnessy.
Number of staff: 1 full-time professional; 1 full-time support.
EIN: 526051781

9446
Guilford Foundation ✧
9030 Stony Point Pkwy., Ste. 460
Richmond, VA 23225

Established in 1987 in VA.
Donors: Ann K. Kirby‡; Roger H.W. Kirby; Annette S. Kirby; Wade H.O. Kirby; James W. Kirby, Jr.
Foundation type: Independent foundation.
Financial data (yr. ended 12/31/12): Assets, $12,303,113 (M); expenditures, $722,413; qualifying distributions, $612,500; giving activities include $612,500 for grants.
Purpose and activities: Giving primarily for the arts, health care, education, and social services.
Fields of interest: Arts; Education; Health care; Diabetes research; Human services; Foundations (private grantmaking).
Limitations: Applications not accepted. No grants to individuals.
Application information: Contributes only to pre-selected organizations.
Officers and Directors:* Roger H.W. Kirby,* Pres.; Annette S. Kirby,* V.P.; James R. Landrigan,* Secy.; Frank C. Page,* Exec. Dir.; L. James Borges; Alexandra Louise Kirby; Linda T. Kirby; Wade H.O. Kirby.
EIN: 541423873

9447
Richard and Caroline T. Gwathmey Memorial Trust ✧
c/o U.S. Trust, Philanthropic Solutions
1111 E. Main St., VA2-300-12-92
Richmond, VA 23219-3531
Contact: Sarah Kay, V.P., U.S. Trust
FAX: (804) 788-2673;
E-mail: sarah.kay@ustrust.com; E-mail to discuss application process and for questions: va.grantmaking@ustrust.com. (Foundation name should be indicated in subject line); Main URL: http://www.bankofamerica.com/grantmaking

Established in 1981 in VA.
Donor: Elizabeth G. Jeffress‡.
Foundation type: Independent foundation.
Financial data (yr. ended 06/30/13): Assets, $14,084,461 (M); expenditures, $786,575; qualifying distributions, $693,695; giving activities include $616,450 for 36 grants (high: $39,000; low: $5,000).
Purpose and activities: Giving primarily to the arts, cultural institutions, and for education.
Fields of interest: Museums; Historic preservation/historical societies; Arts; Education; Human services.
Type of support: Capital campaigns; Building/renovation; Equipment; Program development; Matching/challenge support.
Limitations: Applications accepted. Giving limited to VA. No support for active churches. No grants to individuals or for operating expenses.
Publications: Application guidelines; Informational brochure (including application guidelines).
Application information: Application form not required.
Initial approach: Letter requesting guidelines
Copies of proposal: 1
Deadline(s): Mar. 1 and Sept. 1
Board meeting date(s): Nov. and May
Final notification: June 15 (for Mar. deadline), and Dec. 31 (for Sept. deadline)
Advisor: Sarah Kay.
Allocations Committee: Richard Hamprick, M.D.; Ernest R. Lail; Carolyn A. White, Esq.; Raphael Witorsch, Ph.D.; David L. Yarter.
Trustee: Bank of America, N.A.
Number of staff: 1 part-time professional; 1 part-time support.
EIN: 546191586
Selected grants: The following grants are a representative sample of this grantmaker's funding activity:
$30,000 to Jacobs Ladder, Urbanna, VA, 2011.
$30,000 to Thomas Jefferson Foundation, Charlottesville, VA, 2011.
$25,000 to Free Foundation for Rehabilitation Equipment and Endowment, Roanoke, VA, 2011.
$25,000 to Gateway Homes of Greater Richmond, Richmond, VA, 2011.
$25,000 to Healing Place, Richmond, VA, 2011.
$20,000 to Saint Andrews School, Richmond, VA, 2011.
$20,000 to YWCA of Richmond, Richmond, VA, 2011.
$15,000 to Child Health Investment Partnership, Roanoke, VA, 2011.
$15,000 to Confederate Memorial Literary Society, Richmond, VA, 2011.
$12,000 to William Byrd Community House, Richmond, VA, 2011.

9448
Hampton Roads Community Foundation ✧
(formerly The Norfolk Foundation)
101 W. Main St., Ste. 4500
Norfolk, VA 23510-1644 (757) 622-7951
FAX: (757) 622-1751; Main URL: http://www.hamptonroadscf.org/
Blog: http://hamptonroadscf.blogspot.com/
Facebook: https://www.facebook.com/hamptonroadscf
Twitter: https://twitter.com/HamptonRoadsCF
YouTube: https://www.youtube.com/user/HamptonRoadsCF

Established in 1950 in VA.
Foundation type: Community foundation.
Financial data (yr. ended 12/31/13): Assets, $294,805,530 (M); gifts received, $10,475,168; expenditures, $16,383,087; giving activities include $14,080,733 for grants.
Purpose and activities: The mission of the Hampton Roads Community Foundation is to inspire philanthropy and transform the quality of life in southeastern Virginia.
Fields of interest: Arts education; Arts; Education, early childhood education; Elementary school/education; Higher education; Education, drop-out prevention; Education; Environmental education; Medical care, community health systems; Health care, clinics/centers; Dental care; Health care; Mental health, treatment; Employment, services; Food services; Food banks; Housing/shelter, SROs; Housing/shelter, temporary shelter; Housing/shelter, homeless; Human services.
Type of support: Capital campaigns; Building/renovation; Program development; Scholarships—to individuals.
Limitations: Applications accepted. Giving in the South Hampton Roads area of VA: the cities of Norfolk, Portsmouth, Virginia Beach, Chesapeake, Suffolk and Isle of Wight County, and the Eastern Shore. No support for religious activities, scholarly research, national or international organizations or purposes, private primary or secondary schools, or hospitals or similar healthcare facilities. No grants to individuals (except for scholarships), or for fundraising events, ongoing operating support, endowments, existing obligations, debts, camper fees, fellowships or travel.
Publications: Annual report; Financial statement; Newsletter.
Application information: Visit foundation web site for application guidelines and cover sheets. Proposals may be delivered by mail or hand delivered. Application form required.
Initial approach: Applicants are strongly encouraged to speak to a program officer prior to submitting a request
Copies of proposal: 2
Deadline(s): Varies by program area
Final notification: Varies by program area

Officers and Directors:* John O. "Dubby" Wynne,* Chair.; R. Bruce Bradley,* Vice-Chair.; Deborah M. DiCroce, C.E.O. and Pres.; Leigh Evans Davis, V.P., Donor Engagement; Robin C. Foreman, V.P., Admin.; Sally Kirby Hartman, V.P., Comms.; Donna S. Morris, V.P., Strategic Initiatives; Linda M. Rice, V.P., Community Impact; Kay A. Stine, V.P., Devel.; Debra R. Steiger, V.P., Regional Outreach; Timothy McCarthy, C.F.O.; Jody M. Wagner,* Treas.; Jane P. Batten; Gilbert T. Bland; Macon F. Brock; Deborah M. DiCroce; Andrew S. Fine; Paul O. Hirschbiel, Jr.; Mary Louis LeHew; Harry T. Lester; John F. Malbon; Vincent J. Mastracco, Jr.; Charles W. "Wick" Moorman; Louis F. Ryan.
EIN: 542035996
Selected grants: The following grants are a representative sample of this grantmaker's funding activity:
$438,000 to Business Consortium for Arts Support, Norfolk, VA, 2013. For general/operating support.
$310,000 to Old Dominion University Educational Foundation, Norfolk, VA, 2013.
$300,000 to Virginia Opera, Norfolk, VA, 2013. For general/operating support.
$250,000 to Fellowship of Cholmeleians in America, Wilton, CT, 2013. For endowment funds.
$250,000 to YMCA of South Hampton Roads, Chesapeake, VA, 2013. For capital campaign.
$100,000 to Chesapeake Bay Foundation, Hampton Roads Office, Norfolk, VA, 2013. For capital campaign.
$15,000 to Norfolk Botanical Garden Society, Norfolk, VA, 2013. For general/operating support.
$12,950 to Chincoteague Island Arts Organization, Chincoteague, VA, 2013. For piano.
$12,500 to Old Dominion University Educational Foundation, Norfolk, VA, 2013. For capital campaign.
$7,000 to YMCA, Hampton Roads Armed Services, Virginia Beach, VA, 2013. For general/operating support.

9449
Harrison Foundation ✧
P.O. Box 70
Manakin-Sabot, VA 23103-0070

Established in VA.
Foundation type: Independent foundation.
Financial data (yr. ended 09/30/13): Assets, $51,469,205 (M); expenditures, $2,657,761; qualifying distributions, $2,444,062; giving activities include $2,444,062 for 48 grants (high: $822,000; low: $2,500).
Fields of interest: Education; Health organizations, association; Human services.
Limitations: Applications not accepted. Giving primarily in VA.
Application information: Contributes only to pre-selected organizations.
Directors: Anne H. Armstrong; David A. Harrison IV; Mary H. Keevil; Marjorie Webb.
EIN: 260353463

9450
The Harvest Foundation of the Piedmont ✧
1 Ellsworth St.
P.O. Box 5183
Martinsville, VA 24112-2845 (276) 632-3329
Contact: Allyson Rothrock, Pres.
FAX: (276) 632-1878;
E-mail: info@theharvestfoundation.org; Main URL: http://www.theharvestfoundation.org
Facebook: https://www.facebook.com/pages/Harvest-Foundation-Piedmont/137147119666676
Twitter: https://twitter.com/Harvest_MHC

Established in 2002 in VA; converted from the sale of Memorial Health System to Province Healthcare of Brentwood, TN.
Foundation type: Independent foundation.
Financial data (yr. ended 12/31/12): Assets, $197,359,569 (M); expenditures, $13,936,843; qualifying distributions, $12,540,567; giving activities include $11,227,042 for 34 grants (high: $4,394,230; low: $8,425), and $251,295 for 1 foundation-administered program.
Purpose and activities: The foundation researches and responsibly invests in programs and initiatives to address local challenges in health, education, and community vitality.
Fields of interest: Education; Health care; Community/economic development.
Limitations: Applications accepted. Giving limited to Martinsville and Henry County, VA. No support for institutions that discriminate on the basis of race, creed, gender, or sexual orientation; international programs; sectarian religious activities; political lobbying; profit-making enterprises; or direct replacement of discontinued government support. No grants to individuals, or for scholarships, fellowships, debt reduction, medical research, emergency funding or extreme time-sensitive requests, or endowment funds.
Publications: Application guidelines; Annual report.
Application information: Program staff invites selected applying organizations to submit full proposals. Program Staff performs due diligence on possible applicants. As appropriate, program staff will present full proposals to the Board of Directors for consideration. The Board of Directors will make all final decisions to approve or decline requests. (Grant seekers are strongly discouraged from lobbying Board Members.) If approved, the applying Organization will receive, sign, and return a copy of the Letter of Agreement to the foundation. No organization should make commitments or expenditures until the full proposal has been approved by the Board of Directors and the Letter of Agreement has been signed and executed. Application form required.
Initial approach: Online application form required. Applying organizations should first review the foundation's funding priorities and guidelines and then, if appropriate, complete and submit online Program Summary.
Deadline(s): There are no specific deadlines for document submission. Funding requests are reviewed by the foundation's Board of Directors two times per year. As a rule, the foundation does not accept emergency or out-of-cycle proposals.
Final notification: The foundation's staff commits to keeping applying organizations continually informed throughout the Grants Application Process.
Officers and Directors:* James McClain II,* Chair.; W. Christopher Beeler,* Vice-Chair.; Allyson Rothrock, Pres.; Martha W. Medley,* Secy.; Eugene C. Madonia, M.D.*, Treas.; Georgia Compton, Cont.; Paul R. Eason, M.D.; Virginia W. Hamlet; Cynthia Ingram, Ed.D.; Amy P. Lampe; James K. Muehleck, D.D.S.; E. Larry Ryder; David L. Stone, Jr.
Number of staff: 7 full-time professional.
EIN: 311496872
Selected grants: The following grants are a representative sample of this grantmaker's funding activity:
$8,000,000 to New College Foundation, Martinsville, VA, 2012. To assist with construction of advanced manufacturing educational building for New College Institute.
$4,894,230 to New College Foundation, Martinsville, VA, 2012. For New College Institute as part of state pledge matching grant. NCI is a state-funded educational entity that provides access to bachelor's degree completion programs, master's degrees, teacher endorsement programs, teacher recertification courses, and more through partnerships with colleges and universities.
$250,000 to Henry, County of, Collinsville, VA, 2012. For construction of a 40-slip marina on Philpott Lake.
$200,000 to Martinsville-Henry County Regional Alliance for Economic Prosperity, Martinsville, VA, 2012. For matching grant to support a feasibility study for building construction for New College Institute.
$87,500 to Martinsville-Henry County Regional Alliance for Economic Prosperity, Martinsville, VA, 2012. For the Phoenix Community Development Corporation community development efforts.
$78,450 to Boys and Girls Clubs of the Blue Ridge, Martinsville, VA, 2012. For a youth summer camp pilot program.
$71,613 to Piedmont Virginia Dental Health Foundation, Martinsville, VA, 2012. For infrastructure support to provide dental care to medically under-served residents in Martinsville, Henry County.
$50,000 to Martinsville-Henry County Regional Alliance for Economic Prosperity, Martinsville, VA, 2012. For the Phoenix Community Development Corporation pre-development efforts.
$25,000 to Future of the Piedmont Foundation, Chatham, VA, 2012. For the Southern Virginia Regional Alliance's regional economic development efforts.

9451
Herndon Foundation ✧
P.O. Box 955
Goochland, VA 23063-0955

Established in 1965 in VA.
Donor: Floyd D. Gottwald, Jr.
Foundation type: Independent foundation.
Financial data (yr. ended 12/31/13): Assets, $76,519,787 (M); expenditures, $3,327,661; qualifying distributions, $3,248,450; giving activities include $3,248,450 for 127 grants (high: $500,000; low: $250).
Purpose and activities: Giving primarily for the arts, as well as for health organizations, and human services.
Fields of interest: Arts; Higher education; Health organizations, association; Human services; Children/youth, services; Foundations (private grantmaking).
Type of support: General/operating support; Endowments; Scholarship funds.
Limitations: Applications not accepted. Giving primarily in the Richmond, VA, area. No grants to individuals.
Application information: Contributes only to pre-selected organizations.

Officer: James T. Gottwald, Mgr.
Trustee: William Gottwald.
EIN: 546060809

9452
David & Suzanne Hillman Family Foundation ✧
1950 Old Gallows Rd., Ste. 600
Vienna, VA 22182-3970

Established in 2005 in VA.
Donors: David Hillman; Suzanne Hillman; Woodbridge Forest Apartments LLC; Wildecroft Terrace LLC; 39 West Lexington LLC; Historic Oella Mill LLC; 501 St Paul Street LLC; Park Ritchie LLC; North Forest Associates LP; Merion Apartments LLC; The Marlboro-Classic LP; Laurelton LP; Laurel Park LLC; Landmark Ridge Associates LP; Hampshire West LLC; Hampshire Village LLC; Gallery Towers LP; Fountain Park Apartments LP; Adelphi Associates LP; Chestnut Ridge LLC; Cherry Arms LLC; Capital View LLC; Hanover Apartments LLC; The Atrium at Market Square LLC; Aquahart Manor LLC; Palisades of Towson LLC; Palisades of Towson LLC; Summit Crest LLC; Horizon House Apartments LP; Liberty-Reisterstown II LP; Bethesda Triangle LLC; Woodland Landing LP; Vienna Park LLC; University Gardens LLC; Twin Towers LLC; Triangle Towers LLC; Summit Hills LLC; Steward Manor LLC; Southview Apartments LLC; Silver Spring Towers Apartments LLC; Roland Ridge Apartments LP; Powder Mill Apartments LLC; Penn Southern LLC; Parliaments Apartments LLC; Seven Mile Lane LP; Oxon Hill Apartments LLC; Park Charles Apartments Assoc LLC; Nob Hill LLC; Miramont Villas LP; Middletowne LLC; Marlborough House LLC; Longview Apartments LLC; Lakeside North Apartments LLC; Liberty - Reisterstown I LP; Kings Gardens Apartments LLC; Kent Village LLC; Hidden Cove Apartments LLC; Isabella Park LLC; High View Ventures LP; SMC Limited Partnership; Gateway Gardens Associates LP; Fountain Club LLC; Deertree Apartments Associates LP; Charles Towers LLC; Cavalier Club LLC; Carriage Hill Associates LP; Hillzo LP; Bayvue LLC; Admiral Farragut LLC.
Foundation type: Independent foundation.
Financial data (yr. ended 12/31/13): Assets, $2,124,859 (M); gifts received, $944,075; expenditures, $956,987; qualifying distributions, $952,453; giving activities include $944,075 for 4 grants (high: $344,192; low: $183,896).
Fields of interest: Higher education.
Limitations: Applications not accepted. Giving primarily in MD. No grants to individuals.
Application information: Contributes only to pre-selected organizations.
Officers: Suzanne Hillman, Pres.; David Hillman, V.P.; Steven A. Michael, Secy.
Trustees: Richard G.R. Hillman; Cheryl Anne Hillman Romanick.
Director: Frank F. Glorioso.
EIN: 201970693
Selected grants: The following grants are a representative sample of this grantmaker's funding activity:
$254,184 to Prince Georges Community College Foundation, Largo, MD, 2011. For tuition assistance.

9453
Mason Hirst Foundation, Inc. ✧
P.O. Box 320307
Alexandria, VA 22320-4307

Established in 2006 in DE and VA.
Donor: Thomas M. Hirst.
Foundation type: Independent foundation.
Financial data (yr. ended 12/31/12): Assets, $8,746,591 (M); expenditures, $478,204; qualifying distributions, $475,000; giving activities include $475,000 for grants.
Fields of interest: Education; Health care; Catholic agencies & churches.
Limitations: Applications not accepted. No grants to individuals.
Application information: Contributes only to pre-selected organizations.
Directors: Jeremy M. Hirst; Jessica F. Hirst; Thomas M. Hirst.
EIN: 208050841

9454
Hobbs Foundation ✧ ☆
c/o Sterling Foundation Management, LLC
2325 Dulles Corner Blvd., Ste. 670
Herndon, VA 20171-4683 (703) 437-9720

Established in 2003 in VA.
Donor: Russ Hobbs.
Foundation type: Independent foundation.
Financial data (yr. ended 12/31/13): Assets, $7,968,210 (M); expenditures, $567,645; qualifying distributions, $567,137; giving activities include $450,000 for 45 grants (high: $10,000; low: $10,000).
Fields of interest: Museums (science/technology); Youth development; Human services; Salvation Army; Christian agencies & churches.
Limitations: Applications accepted. Giving primarily in FL. No grants to individuals.
Application information: Application form not required.
Initial approach: Proposal
Deadline(s): None
Officer and Directors:* Russ Hobbs,* Pres.; Alan Dye.
EIN: 522287607
Selected grants: The following grants are a representative sample of this grantmaker's funding activity:
$10,000 to Alpha House of Tampa, Tampa, FL, 2011. For general assistance.
$10,000 to Big Brothers Big Sisters of Tampa Bay, Tampa, FL, 2011. For general assistance.
$10,000 to Boys and Girls Clubs of Tampa Bay, Tampa, FL, 2011. For general assistance.
$10,000 to Brookwood Florida-Central, Saint Petersburg, FL, 2011. For general assistance.
$10,000 to Caring Children/Clothing Children, Stuart, FL, 2011. For general assistance.
$10,000 to Childrens Home, Tampa, FL, 2010. For general assistance.
$10,000 to Computer Mentors Group, Tampa, FL, 2011. For general assistance.
$10,000 to Florida Baptist Childrens Homes, Lakeland, FL, 2011. For general assistance.
$10,000 to Grace Place for Children and Families, Naples, FL, 2011. For general assistance.
$10,000 to Museum of Science and Industry, Tampa, FL, 2011.
$10,000 to Neat Stuff, Miami, FL, 2011. For general assistance.

9455
The Cecil and Irene Hylton Foundation, Inc. ✧
5593 Mapledale Plz.
Dale City, VA 22193-4527
Contact: Malcolm W. Cook, Treas.

Established in 1989 in VA.
Donors: Cecil D. Hylton†; The First Grandchildren's Charitable Trust; The Second Grandchildren's Charitable Trust; Irene V. Hylton Charitable Lead Trust; The Second Childrens Charitable Trust.
Foundation type: Independent foundation.
Financial data (yr. ended 12/31/12): Assets, $96,708,706 (M); gifts received, $42,800; expenditures, $5,092,103; qualifying distributions, $4,852,403; giving activities include $4,758,684 for 22 grants (high: $1,650,000; low: $1,500).
Purpose and activities: Giving primarily for hospitals, education, human services, and to a performing arts center and a boys and girls club.
Fields of interest: Performing arts centers; Education; Hospitals (general); Boys & girls clubs; Human services.
Type of support: General/operating support; Capital campaigns; Land acquisition.
Limitations: Giving primarily in Prince William County, VA; funding also in northern VA, and metropolitan Washington County; giving on a national basis for land conservation and ecology. No grants to individuals.
Application information:
Initial approach: Letter
Deadline(s): None
Officers and Directors:* Conrad C. Hylton,* Pres.; Malcolm W. Cook,* Treas.; Kendall B. Lewis, Treas.; Cecilia M. Hylton.
EIN: 521633658

9456
ICE Charitable Foundation ✧
10302 Eaton Pl., Ste. 500
Fairfax, VA 22030-2229 (703) 272-1211
Contact: Jeffrey Schoen, Pres.

Established in 2004 in VA.
Donors: Jeffrey Schoen; Innovative Computer Engineering, Inc.
Foundation type: Independent foundation.
Financial data (yr. ended 12/31/12): Assets, $810,412 (M); gifts received, $990,600; expenditures, $1,345,076; qualifying distributions, $1,339,000; giving activities include $1,339,000 for 9 grants (high: $300,000; low: $1,500).
Fields of interest: Christian agencies & churches.
Limitations: Applications accepted. Giving primarily in AZ, CA, and VA; some giving also in India.
Application information:
Initial approach: Proposal on the organization's letterhead
Deadline(s): None
Officer: Jeffrey Schoen, Pres.
EIN: 202044398
Selected grants: The following grants are a representative sample of this grantmaker's funding activity:
$62,500 to Oakseed Ministries International, Dunn Loring, VA, 2011.
$50,000 to Crisis Pregnancy Center, Tucson, AZ, 2011.

9457
Thomas F. and Kate Miller Jeffress Memorial Trust ✧
c/o US Trust, Philanthropic Solutions
1111 E. Main St., VA2-300-12-92
Richmond, VA 23219-3573
Contact: Sarah Kay, V.P.
E-mail: sarak.kay@ustrust.com; Tel. for information regarding the application process for Jeffress Trust Awards Program in Interdisciplinary Research: (617) 279-2240, ext. 709; Main URL: http://www.bankofamerica.com/grantmaking

Established in 1981 in VA.
Donor: Robert M. Jeffress†.
Foundation type: Independent foundation.
Financial data (yr. ended 06/30/13): Assets, $31,370,851 (M); expenditures, $1,084,268; qualifying distributions, $880,536; giving activities include $671,450 for 14 grants (high: $120,000; low: $10,000).
Purpose and activities: Giving primarily to VA colleges and universities for basic research in chemical, medical, and other scientific research.
Fields of interest: Biomedicine; Medical research, institute; Science; Physical/earth sciences; Chemistry.
Type of support: Research.
Limitations: Applications accepted. Giving limited to VA. No support for clinical research, maintenance for institutionally-owned equipment, or instrument computer time. No grants to individuals, or for fringe benefits, indirect costs, common supplies and services, secretarial services, academic stipends or salaries, or for travel.
Publications: Application guidelines; Informational brochure (including application guidelines).
Application information: Application guidelines and form available on foundation web site. Application form required.
Deadline(s): Jan. 15
Board meeting date(s): May and Nov.
Officer: Sarah Kay, Secy.
Trustee: Bank of America, N.A.
Advisor: Richard B. Brandt, Ph.D.
Allocations Committee: James K. Cluverius, Esq.; Dr. Richard Hamrich; Gregory B. Robertson; Dr. Rafael Witorsch; David L. Yarter.
Number of staff: 1 part-time professional; 1 part-time support.
EIN: 546094925
Selected grants: The following grants are a representative sample of this grantmaker's funding activity:
$25,000 to College of William and Mary Foundation, Williamsburg, VA, 2011. For research.
$25,000 to College of William and Mary Foundation, Williamsburg, VA, 2011. For research.
$25,000 to Eastern Virginia Medical School, Norfolk, VA, 2011. For research.
$25,000 to George Mason University Foundation, Fairfax, VA, 2011. For research.
$25,000 to Hampden-Sydney College, Hampden Sydney, VA, 2011. For research.
$25,000 to University of Virginia, Charlottesville, VA, 2011. For research.
$25,000 to Virginia Commonwealth University Foundation, Richmond, VA, 2011. For research.
$25,000 to Virginia Tech Foundation, Blacksburg, VA, 2011. For research.
$25,000 to Virginia Tech Foundation, Blacksburg, VA, 2011. For research.
$20,000 to University of Virginia, Charlottesville, VA, 2011. For research.

9458
Sheila C. Johnson Foundation, Inc. ✧
(formerly Geron P. Johnson Foundation, Inc.)
3074 Zulla Rd.
The Plains, VA 20198-1937

Established in 1991 in VA.
Donors: Robert Johnson; Sheila Johnson; Black Entertainment, Inc.
Foundation type: Independent foundation.
Financial data (yr. ended 12/31/13): Assets, $1,340,990 (M); expenditures, $557,664; qualifying distributions, $545,658; giving activities include $545,658 for grants.
Purpose and activities: Giving primarily to provide access to the arts for disadvantaged children in the U.S. and to work for the freedom of missing and exploited children worldwide. The foundation is committed to providing opportunities for children in the U.S.A. to express their innate creativity through the arts, specifically music, design and the visual arts. Priority is given to programs that create ongoing structures for children to have access to arts education and to initiatives that incorporate the arts as an essential element in basic educational curricula. The foundation is also committed to addressing the cause of missing and exploited children worldwide, and to working for their freedom and well being. Specific focus is on ending child pornography and sexual exploitation through supporting innovative programs and institutions that make a measurable difference in the lives of the children caught in the cycle of poverty and violence.
Fields of interest: Arts; Elementary/secondary education; Human services.
Limitations: Applications not accepted. Giving primarily in Washington, DC, NY and VA. No grants to individuals.
Application information: Unsolicited requests for funds not accepted.
Officer: Sheila C. Johnson, Pres.
Board Members: Brett Johnson; Paige Johnson.
EIN: 521755871
Selected grants: The following grants are a representative sample of this grantmaker's funding activity:
$100,000 to Sundance Institute, Park City, UT, 2012. For Feature Film Contribution.
$65,000 to Accordia Global Health Foundation, Washington, DC, 2012. For pledge obligation.
$12,500 to Tiger Woods Foundation, Irvine, CA, 2012. For sponsorship package.
$5,000 to National Building Museum, Washington, DC, 2012. For Quilt in the Capital 2012.

9459
Kanter Family Foundation ✧
8000 Towers Crescent Dr., Ste. 1300
Vienna, VA 22182-2700 (703) 448-7688
Contact: Joel S. Kanter, Pres.

Established in 1989 in IL.
Donors: Burton W. Kanter†; Joshua S. Kanter; Joel S. Kanter; St. John's J1 Descendants Trust; St. John's J2 Descendants Trust; St. John's J3 Descendants Trust.
Foundation type: Independent foundation.
Financial data (yr. ended 10/31/13): Assets, $11,761,783 (M); expenditures, $816,684; qualifying distributions, $602,963; giving activities include $602,963 for 60 grants (high: $75,000; low: $100).
Purpose and activities: Giving primarily for the arts, education, and Jewish organizations and temples.
Fields of interest: Arts; Education; Jewish federated giving programs; Jewish agencies & synagogues.
Type of support: Annual campaigns; Capital campaigns; Building/renovation; Endowments; Program development; Scholarship funds; Matching/challenge support.
Limitations: Applications accepted. Giving primarily in Washington, DC, Chicago, IL, and Salt Lake City, UT. No grants to individuals.
Publications: Annual report.
Application information:
Initial approach: Proposal
Copies of proposal: 1
Deadline(s): None
Officers and Directors:* Joel S. Kanter,* Pres. and Treas.; Joshua S. Kanter,* V.P. and Secy.; Catherine M. Kanter,* V.P.; Janis S. Kanter,* V.P.; Ricki Kanter,* V.P.; Thomas McCormick,* V.P.; Phillip J. Karmin.
Number of staff: 1 part-time professional.
EIN: 363682199

9460
Charles B. Keesee Educational Fund, Inc. ✧
P.O. Box 431
Martinsville, VA 24114-0431 (276) 632-2229
Contact: Mrs. Vernie W. Lewis, Secy.-Treas.
E-mail: information@cbkeesee.com; Additional e-mail: cbkeesee@earthlink.net; Main URL: http://www.cbkeesee.com

Established in 1941 in VA.
Donors: Patricia Pilcher; Floyd Smith Charitable Remainder Unitrust.
Foundation type: Independent foundation.
Financial data (yr. ended 01/31/14): Assets, $69,847,470 (M); gifts received, $2,750; expenditures, $4,185,131; qualifying distributions, $3,461,385; giving activities include $1,357,500 for 8 grants (high: $207,500; low: $50,000), and $1,919,990 for grants to individuals.
Purpose and activities: The fund's purpose is to provide funds through grants to students of its supported organizations. Applicant must be a resident of NC, SC or VA for a minimum of 12 months prior to entering school. Applicant must be preparing to enter the Baptist ministry or religious work in the Baptist denomination, and must be a member of a Baptist church, and enrolled in a Master's degree program.
Fields of interest: Higher education; Theological school/education; Education; Religion, formal/general education.
Limitations: Applications accepted. Giving limited to NC, SC and VA.
Publications: Application guidelines.
Application information: Application guidelines and form available on fund web site. Do not fax or e-mail application; submit via US mail. Application form required.
Initial approach: Download application from fund web site
Deadline(s): See fund web site for current deadlines
Officers and Trustees:* David D. Burhans,* Pres.; Douglas T. Ramsey,* V.P.; Vernie W. Lewis, Secy.-Treas.; Frank R. Campbell; Georgia Compton;

G. Paul Fletcher; John T. Fulcher; Martha W. Medley; Betty Lou Pigg.
EIN: 540490435

9461
The Kellar Family Foundation ✧
P.O. Box 3547
Manassas, VA 20108-0964

Established in 1997 in VA.
Donors: Arthur Kellar; Elizabeth Kellar‡; Kellar Family Charitable Lead Trust.
Foundation type: Independent foundation.
Financial data (yr. ended 02/28/13): Assets, $44,900,133 (M); gifts received, $1,980,507; expenditures, $2,524,916; qualifying distributions, $2,223,302; giving activities include $2,200,014 for 2 grants (high: $2,200,000; low: $4).
Purpose and activities: Giving primarily for the arts, animal welfare, human services, and health organizations.
Fields of interest: Arts; Higher education; Education; Animal welfare; Health care; Health organizations, association; Human services.
Limitations: Applications not accepted. Giving primarily in Cincinnati, OH. No grants to individuals.
Application information: Contributes only to pre-selected organizations.
Officers: Mary K. Kellar, Pres.; Judith C. Kellar Box, V.P.; Anne Ridgway, Secy.-Treas.
EIN: 522026425
Selected grants: The following grants are a representative sample of this grantmaker's funding activity:
$539,500 to New York University, New York, NY, 2012.
$416,667 to New York University, New York, NY, 2012.
$61,333 to New York University, New York, NY, 2012.
$50,000 to Land Is Life, Somerville, MA, 2012.
$30,000 to Center for the Arts, Manassas, VA, 2012.
$10,000 to Center for the Arts, Manassas, VA, 2012.
$10,000 to Fairfax United Methodist Church, Fairfax, VA, 2012.
$6,000 to Fairfax United Methodist Church, Fairfax, VA, 2012.
$4,000 to Fairfax United Methodist Church, Fairfax, VA, 2012.
$1,000 to Link Media, San Francisco, CA, 2012.

9462
Kirk Family Foundation ✧
2677 Roanoke Ave. S.W.
Roanoke, VA 24015-5403

Established in 2004 in VA.
Donors: John W. Kirk III Revocable Trust; John W. Kirk III.
Foundation type: Independent foundation.
Financial data (yr. ended 09/30/12): Assets, $12,871,106 (M); expenditures, $700,682; qualifying distributions, $662,389; giving activities include $662,389 for 6 grants (high: $531,389; low: $1,000).
Fields of interest: Higher education, college; Youth development, services; Protestant agencies & churches.
Limitations: Applications not accepted. Giving primarily in VA. No grants to individuals.
Application information: Unsolicited requests for funds not accepted.
Officers and Directors:* John W. Kirk III,* Pres.; C. Shireen Kirk,* Secy.-Treas.
EIN: 202062442

9463
Charles Koch Foundation ✧
(formerly Charles G. Koch Charitable Foundation)
1515 N. Courthouse Rd., Ste. 200
Arlington, VA 22201-2915 (703) 875-1770
Contact: Admin.
FAX: (703) 875-1766;
E-mail: email@charleskochFoundation.org; Main URL: http://www.cgkfoundation.org

Established in 1981 in KS.
Donors: Charles G. Koch; Fred C. Koch Foundation; Fred C. Koch Trusts for Charity.
Foundation type: Independent foundation.
Financial data (yr. ended 12/31/12): Assets, $276,881,787 (M); gifts received, $60,025,464; expenditures, $18,498,180; qualifying distributions, $17,610,096; giving activities include $14,920,448 for 258 grants (high: $5,455,000; low: $404).
Purpose and activities: The mission of the foundation is to advance social progress and well-being through the development, application, and dissemination of the "Science of Liberty". Funding for academic and public policy research directed at solving significant social problems through voluntary action and free enterprise. Support for projects that find market-based solutions to problematic social issues. For research, the foundation primarily funds institutions working with doctorate-level investigators in disciplines such as economics, history, philosophy, political science, and organizational behavior.
Fields of interest: Environment; Legal services; Economics; Public policy, research.
Type of support: General/operating support; Program development; Conferences/seminars; Seed money; Research; Program evaluation.
Limitations: Applications accepted. Giving primarily in the Washington, DC area, including VA; some giving nationwide. No support for lobbying activities or candidates for political office. No grants to individuals (except through summer fellows program), or for capital construction, debt reduction or general fundraising drives or events.
Publications: Application guidelines.
Application information: See foundation web site for application guidelines and procedures. Application form not required.
Initial approach: Online grant proposal
Copies of proposal: 1
Deadline(s): None
Final notification: 3 months
Officers and Directors:* Charles G. Koch,* Chair.; Richard Fink,* Pres.; Kevin L. Gentry, V.P.; Brian Menkes, Secy. and General Counsel; Vonda Holliman, Treas.; Charles Chase Koch; Elizabeth B. Koch; Elizabeth Robinson Koch.
EIN: 480918408
Selected grants: The following grants are a representative sample of this grantmaker's funding activity:
$5,455,000 to George Mason University Foundation, Fairfax, VA, 2012. For general support.
$2,947,500 to Institute for Humane Studies, Arlington, VA, 2012. For General Support.
$510,000 to American Enterprise Institute for Public Policy Research, Washington, DC, 2012. For General Support.
$297,341 to Florida State University, Tallahassee, FL, 2012. For General Support.
$274,500 to Troy University Foundation, Troy, AL, 2012. For General Support.
$250,000 to Jack Miller Center for Teaching Americas Founding Principles and History, Bala Cynwyd, PA, 2012. For General Support.
$177,500 to Liberty Source, Providence, UT, 2012. For General Support.
$20,000 to Michigan State University, Department of Economics, East Lansing, MI, 2012. For General Support.
$14,000 to Alabama Policy Institute, Birmingham, AL, 2012. For General Support.
$9,300 to Barton College, Wilson, NC, 2012. For General Support.

9464
The Robert P. and Arlene R. Kogod Family Foundation ✧
2345 Crystal Dr., 11th Fl.
Arlington, VA 22202-4801

Established in 1998 in VA.
Donors: Arlene R. Kogod; Robert P. Kogod; Charles E. Smith Mgmt., Inc.; Charles E. Smith Family Foundation.
Foundation type: Independent foundation.
Financial data (yr. ended 12/31/12): Assets, $28,190,748 (M); gifts received, $2,500,000; expenditures, $5,633,043; qualifying distributions, $5,545,138; giving activities include $5,541,638 for 192 grants (high: $500,000; low: $100).
Purpose and activities: Giving primarily for Jewish education, temples and organizations.
Fields of interest: Human services; Jewish agencies & synagogues.
Type of support: Scholarship funds.
Limitations: Applications not accepted. Giving primarily in DC, MD, ME, and NY. No grants to individuals.
Application information: Contributes only to pre-selected organizations.
Officers and Directors:* Robert P. Kogod,* Pres.; Menachem Gottlieb, V.P. and Treas.; Arlene R. Kogod,* Secy.
EIN: 541813660

9465
Lafayette River Foundation ✧
c/o Lewis Webb & Edith G. Grandy
207 Granby St., Ste. 303
Norfolk, VA 23510-1825

Established in 2004 in VA.
Donor: M.O. Hartley.
Foundation type: Independent foundation.
Financial data (yr. ended 12/31/12): Assets, $6,550,394 (M); expenditures, $885,831; qualifying distributions, $768,173; giving activities include $764,000 for 4 grants (high: $405,000; low: $9,000).
Fields of interest: Arts, fund raising/fund distribution; Performing arts; Performing arts, opera; Arts.

Limitations: Applications not accepted. Giving primarily in Norfolk, VA. No grants to individuals.
Application information: Contributes only to pre-selected organizations.
Trustees: Edith G. Grandy; M.O. Hartley; Lewis W. Webb III.
EIN: 020729969

9466
The Lucille and Bruce Lambert Charitable Foundation, Inc. ✧
2100 Powhatan St.
Falls Church, VA 22043-1940 (703) 583-2400
Contact: Cynthia Butler, Pres.

Established in 1999 in VA.
Donor: Bruce E. Lambert†.
Foundation type: Independent foundation.
Financial data (yr. ended 12/31/12): Assets, $19,816,663 (M); expenditures, $1,055,212; qualifying distributions, $564,000; giving activities include $500,000 for 9 grants (high: $150,000; low: $15,000).
Fields of interest: Higher education; Nursing school/education; Christian agencies & churches.
Type of support: Capital campaigns; Consulting services.
Limitations: Applications accepted. Giving primarily in Washington, DC, IN, MD, MO, and VA. No grants to individuals.
Application information:
Initial approach: Proposal
Deadline(s): None
Officer and Directors:* Cynthia Butler,* Pres.; Holly Brockman; Shirley Butler; Anthony D. Hulbert; Harold M. Lambert; Scott Lambert; George P. Levendis.
EIN: 541898273

9467
The Landmark Foundation ✧
(formerly Landmark Communications Foundation)
150 Granby St., 19th Fl.
Norfolk, VA 23510-1604
Contact: Tina Wright

Incorporated in 1953 in VA.
Donors: Landmark Communications, Inc.; The Virginian-Pilot; Greensboro News Co.; Times-World Corp.; KLAS-TV; WTVF-News Channel 5 Network; Capital Gazette Communications, Inc.; Landmark Media Enterprises.
Foundation type: Company-sponsored foundation.
Financial data (yr. ended 12/31/12): Assets, $73,507,999 (M); expenditures, $5,875,879; qualifying distributions, $5,429,888; giving activities include $5,404,467 for 100 grants (high: $2,850,000; low: $250).
Purpose and activities: The foundation supports organizations involved with secondary education, arts and culture, leadership development, and the environment.
Fields of interest: Museums; Arts; Higher education; Education; Environmental education; Environment; Food banks; Homeless, human services; United Ways and Federated Giving Programs; Leadership development; Economically disadvantaged.
Type of support: Annual campaigns; Building/renovation; Capital campaigns; Continuing support; Curriculum development; Emergency funds; Equipment; Matching/challenge support; Program development; Scholarship funds; Seed money; Technical assistance.
Limitations: Applications accepted. Giving primarily in areas of company operations in Greensboro, NC, Las Vegas, NV, Nashville, TN, and Norfolk and Roanoke, VA. No support for religious organizations not of direct benefit to the entire community, health-related organizations, or organizations whose primary purpose is economic development. No grants to individuals, or for debt reduction, special events, dinners, festivals, medical education or research, fundraising, political purposes, or historic preservation.
Publications: Application guidelines.
Application information: Letters of inquiry should be no longer than 1 page. Additional information may be requested at a later date. Application form not required.
Initial approach: Letter of inquiry to nearest company facility
Copies of proposal: 1
Deadline(s): None
Board meeting date(s): As required
Final notification: Within 3 months
Officers and Directors:* Frank Batten, Jr.,* Pres.; Richard F. Barry III,* V.P.; Teresa F. Blevins, Treas.; Jack Ross.
Number of staff: 1 part-time support.
EIN: 546038902

9468
Ruth and Hal Launders Charitable Trust ✧
c/o Jeffrey J. Fairfield, P.C.
459 Herndon Pkwy., No. 14
P.O. Box 546
Herndon, VA 20170-6222
E-mail: jeff@jjfpc.com; Main URL: http://www.rhlct.org

Established in 2007 in VA.
Donor: Ruth C. Launders Marital Trust.
Foundation type: Independent foundation.
Financial data (yr. ended 04/30/13): Assets, $28,226,123 (M); expenditures, $2,396,219; qualifying distributions, $1,711,684; giving activities include $1,618,187 for 56 grants (high: $861,187; low: $2,500).
Fields of interest: Elementary/secondary education; Higher education; Human services; Community/economic development; Homeless.
Limitations: Applications not accepted. Giving in the U.S., with emphasis on FL, NY and VA. No grants to individuals.
Application information: Contributes only to pre-selected organizations.
Trustees: Jeffrey J. Fairfield, Esq.; Rebecca Fehrs; L. Farnum Johnson, Jr.; Jerome L. Lonnes; Eugenie W. Maine; John H. Webb; Catherine P. Whelan.
EIN: 020703907
Selected grants: The following grants are a representative sample of this grantmaker's funding activity:
$200,000 to Saint Lawrence University, Canton, NY, 2011.
$20,000 to Homestretch, Falls Church, VA, 2011.
$20,000 to Project CURE, Centennial, CO, 2011.
$20,000 to Solar Electric Light Fund, Washington, DC, 2011.
$10,000 to Barksdale Theater, Richmond, VA, 2011.
$10,000 to Boca Helping Hands, Boca Raton, FL, 2011.
$10,000 to FeedMore, Richmond, VA, 2011.
$5,000 to BrightFocus Foundation, Clarksburg, MD, 2011.
$5,000 to Phoenix Houses of the Mid-Atlantic, Arlington, VA, 2011.
$5,000 to University of Richmond, Richmond, VA, 2011.

9469
The Lipman Foundation ✧
(formerly The Eric and Jeanette Lipman Foundation)
c/o The Trust Company of Virginia
9030 Stony Point Pkwy., Ste 300
Richmond, VA 23235-1936

Established in 1985 in VA.
Donors: Eric M. Lipman†; Jeanette S. Lipman; Aubrey Sage MacFarlane†.
Foundation type: Independent foundation.
Financial data (yr. ended 12/31/13): Assets, $918,580 (M); expenditures, $2,619,485; qualifying distributions, $2,586,680; giving activities include $2,586,680 for 35 grants (high: $584,428; low: $10,000).
Fields of interest: Higher education; Law school/education; Medical school/education; Cancer; Health organizations; Jewish agencies & synagogues.
Limitations: Applications not accepted. Giving primarily in Richmond, VA. No grants to individuals.
Application information: Contributes only to pre-selected organizations.
Officers: Jeanette S. Lipman, Pres.; W. Birch Douglass III, Esq., V.P.; L. Michael Gracik, Jr., C.P.A., Treas.
Director: David L. Thompson.
EIN: 541360375

9470
Davis Love, III Foundation ✧
c/o HRH CPA
808 Moorefield Park Dr.
Richmond, VA 23236
Twitter: http://twitter.com/love3d

Established in 2005 in GA.
Donors: Davis M. Love III; PGA Tour Inc.; Christian Brothers Automotive Corp.; Harold McGraw III; Hugh Nunnally; John Justice III; Jonathan S. Linen; Omega SA; Stephen Kerrigan; Swisher International Inc.; The Right Thing an ADP Company; The Starnlicht Family Foundation; Timothy Neher; Wyndham Championship; Massachusetts Life Insurance Co.; McGladrey LLP; O'Brien International; The Evander Lewis Family Foundation; H B Hospitality; Karish Family Foundation; Community Fdn. of Chattanochee; Taylor Smith; Robert Walker; Crown Sports Management; Samuel T. Reeves.
Foundation type: Independent foundation.
Financial data (yr. ended 12/31/13): Assets, $2,687,134 (M); gifts received, $853,320; expenditures, $6,896,293; qualifying distributions, $1,031,263; giving activities include $1,031,263 for 36 grants (high: $479,605; low: $100).
Purpose and activities: Giving for the well-being and progress of society by supporting both national and community-based programs that focus on children and their families.
Fields of interest: Education; Human services; Community/economic development; Protestant agencies & churches; Children/youth.

Limitations: Applications not accepted. Giving primarily in GA, ID, and NC.
Application information: Unsolicited requests for funds not accepted.
Directors: Davis M. Love III; Robin B. Love.
EIN: 202920597

9471
The Loyola Foundation, Inc. ✧
10335 Democracy Ln., No. 202
Fairfax, VA 22030-2527 (571) 435-9401
Contact: Albert G. McCarthy III; Christine M. Rice
FAX: (571) 435-9402;
E-mail: info@loyolafoundation.org; Main URL: http://www.loyolafoundation.org/

Incorporated in 1957 in DC.
Donor: Members of the Albert Gregory McCarthy, Jr. family.
Foundation type: Independent foundation.
Financial data (yr. ended 10/31/13): Assets, $40,777,011 (M); expenditures, $1,916,290; qualifying distributions, $1,533,392; giving activities include $1,204,695 for 201 grants (high: $50,000; low: $250), and $1,533,392 for foundation-administered programs.
Purpose and activities: Grants primarily for basic overseas Roman Catholic missionary work and other Catholic activities of special interest to the trustees. Primary interest in nonrecurring requests for capital improvements in the missionary area, which are self-sustaining after completion; special consideration given to requests where there are matching contributions from the missionary area, itself.
Fields of interest: Catholic agencies & churches.
International interests: Africa; Asia; Developing Countries; Latin America.
Type of support: Building/renovation; Equipment; Matching/challenge support.
Limitations: Applications accepted. Giving primarily in Third World developing nations. Grants made in the U.S. only to institutions or organizations of special interest to the trustees. No support for minor seminaries. No grants to individuals, or for annual budgets, endowment funds, research, continuing support, operating expenses, emergency funds, deficit financing, publications, conferences, scholarships, tuitions, fellowships, travel and meetings, or for used or reconditioned vehicles; no loans.
Publications: Application guidelines; Financial statement; Multi-year report.
Application information: All requests must be in English. Applicants should only proceed with the application form after they have received the foundation's confirmation that their initial submission of the grant request is eligible for consideration. Application form available on foundation web site. For requests for projects whose cost is in excess of $50,000, applications cannot be accepted until at least 75 percent of the total funds needed for the project have been secured from other sources. The foundation acknowledges receipt of proposals and grants interviews with applicants upon request. Application form required.
Initial approach: Letter
Copies of proposal: 1
Deadline(s): Mar. 31 and Sept. 30
Board meeting date(s): June and Dec.
Final notification: Jan. and July
Officers and Trustees:* Andrea M. Hattler-Bramson,* Pres.; John N. Malyska,* V.P.; Amy Hattler Page,* Treas.; A. Gregory McCarthy IV,* Secy. and Exec. Dir.; Daniel J. Altobello; Rev. William J. Byron, S.J.; Kathleen D.H. Carr; William J. Fiore; Denise M. Hattler; Hillary A. Hattler; Cardinal Theodore E. McCarrick; Diana Hattler McDonough; Raymond W. Merritt.
Number of staff: 2 full-time professional; 1 part-time professional.
EIN: 520781255

9472
Luck Companies Foundation, Inc. ✧
(formerly Luck Stone Foundation, Inc.)
P.O. Box 29682
Richmond, VA 23242-0682 (804) 784-6300
E-mail: Foundation@LuckCompanies.com; Main URL: http://luckcompanies.com/about/foundation

Established in 1966 in VA.
Donor: Luck Stone Corp.
Foundation type: Company-sponsored foundation.
Financial data (yr. ended 10/31/13): Assets, $15,656,008 (M); expenditures, $789,066; qualifying distributions, $624,848; giving activities include $562,389 for 48 grants (high: $83,334; low: $450), and $62,459 for 117 employee matching gifts.
Purpose and activities: The foundation supports programs designed to promote youth development and education; and environmental stewardship.
Fields of interest: Visual arts; Elementary/secondary education; Higher education; Education; Environment, natural resources; Environment; Youth development, citizenship; Youth development; YM/YWCAs & YM/YWHAs; Leadership development.
Type of support: General/operating support; Program development.
Limitations: Applications accepted. Giving primarily in VA. No support for religious organizations, for-profit organizations, or discriminatory organizations. No grants to individuals, or for national disease-related fundraising, event sponsorships, or political campaigns.
Publications: Application guidelines.
Application information: Application form required.
Initial approach: Letter
Copies of proposal: 1
Deadline(s): Quarterly, Feb. 1, Apr. 1, July 1, Oct. 1
Board meeting date(s): Feb., Apr., July, and Oct.
Officers and Directors: Charles S. Luck III,* Chair.; Charles S. Luck IV,* V.P.; Douglas D. R. Palmore, Secy.; Wanda S. Ortwine, Treas.
EIN: 546064982

9473
The Luminescence Foundation, Inc. ✧
2125 Hatchers Mill Rd.
Marshall, VA 20115

Established in 2000 in DE.
Donors: Zohar Ben-Dov; Lisa Ben-Dov; Tamar Ben-Dov; Ariella Ben-Dov.
Foundation type: Independent foundation.
Financial data (yr. ended 12/31/12): Assets, $8,427,588 (M); gifts received, $200,000; expenditures, $534,591; qualifying distributions, $515,030; giving activities include $515,030 for 111 grants (high: $100,000; low: $50).
Fields of interest: Arts; Education; Medical research; Human services; United Ways and Federated Giving Programs; LGBTQ.
Limitations: Applications not accepted. No grants to individuals.
Application information: Unsolicited requests for funds not accepted.
Officers and Directors:* Zohar Ben-Dov,* Pres.; Lisa Ben-Dov, V.P.; Samuel B. Gunter, Secy.-Treas.; Andrew Albstein; Ariella Ben-Dov; Tamar Ben-Dov; Seth Brufsky.
EIN: 541989253

9474
Greater Lynchburg Community Trust ✧
101 Paulette Circle, Ste. B
Lynchburg, VA 24504 (434) 845-6500
Contact: Stuart C. Fauber, C.E.O.
FAX: (434) 845-6530; E-mail: challglct@verizon.net; Additional e-mail: sfauberglct@verizon.net; Main URL: http://www.lynchburgtrust.org

Established as a community trust in 1972 in VA.
Foundation type: Community foundation.
Financial data (yr. ended 06/30/13): Assets, $32,607,665 (M); gifts received, $840,161; expenditures, $1,861,956; giving activities include $1,306,126 for 78+ grants (high: $283,600), and $38,806 for 40 grants to individuals.
Purpose and activities: The principal mission of the Community Trust is to enhance the quality of life in the communities served by establishment of permanent endowments for the cities of Lynchburg and Bedford and the counties of Amherst, Appomattox, Bedford and Campbell, with income distributed annually to charitable organizations within the community. Needs served are broad in scope including education, health, the arts, the humanities, and human services to children, youth, the needy, and the elderly.
Fields of interest: Humanities; Arts; Libraries/library science; Education; Health care; Food services; Youth development, services; Children/youth, services; Family services; Aging, centers/services; Women, centers/services; Homeless, human services; Human services; Nonprofit management; Community/economic development; Social sciences; Youth; Aging; Disabilities, people with; Women; Economically disadvantaged; Homeless.
Type of support: Capital campaigns; Building/renovation; Equipment; Emergency funds; Program development; Seed money; Scholarship funds; Technical assistance; Employee-related scholarships; Scholarships—to individuals; Matching/challenge support.
Limitations: Applications accepted. Giving limited to Lynchburg and Bedford City, and Amherst, Bedford, and Campbell counties, VA. No support for religious organizations for sectarian or religious purposes. No grants to individuals (except for designated scholarship funds), or for routine operating expenses or deficit financing.
Publications: Application guidelines; Annual report; Informational brochure; Newsletter; Program policy statement.
Application information: Visit foundation web site for grant application information sheet and guidelines. Application form required.
Initial approach: Submit grant information sheet and attachments
Copies of proposal: 10
Deadline(s): Mar. 15 and Sept. 15

Board meeting date(s): June, Sept., Dec., Feb., and Apr.
Final notification: June and Dec.
Officers and Directors:* Stuart C. Fauber,* C.E.O. and Pres.; John R. Alford, Jr.; Mary Jane Dolan; Robert Finch, Jr.; John M. Flippin; Ernie T. Guill, Jr.; David A. Herrick; Hylan T. Hubbard; Ellen P. Jamerson; Wallace G. McKenna, Jr.; Ellen Nygaard; Augustus A. Petticolas, Jr.; James R. Richards; Marc A. Schewel; Massie G. Ware, Jr.; Charles B. White; James W. Wright.
Trustee Banks: Bank of America, N.A.; BB&T; SunTrust Bank; Wachovia Bank, N.A.
Number of staff: 1 full-time professional; 1 part-time professional; 1 part-time support.
EIN: 546112680

9475
The Malek Family Charitable Trust ✧
1259 Crest Ln.
McLean, VA 22101-1837

Established in 1995 in VA.
Donor: Frederic V. Malek.
Foundation type: Independent foundation.
Financial data (yr. ended 12/31/13): Assets, $1,536,057 (M); gifts received, $25,028; expenditures, $846,042; qualifying distributions, $812,506; giving activities include $794,978 for 115 grants (high: $60,000; low: $40).
Fields of interest: Performing arts; Arts; Health organizations, association; Cancer; Cancer research; Human services; Children/youth, services.
Limitations: Applications not accepted. Giving primarily in Washington, DC; some funding in CO. No grants to individuals.
Application information: Contributes only to pre-selected organizations.
Trustees: Frederic V. Malek; Frederic W. Malek; Marlene Malek; Michelle Olson.
EIN: 546373070
Selected grants: The following grants are a representative sample of this grantmaker's funding activity:
$5,000 to Teach for America, New York, NY, 2011.
$1,000 to Aspen Institute, Washington, DC, 2011.
$1,000 to Epilepsy Foundation, Landover, MD, 2011.
$1,000 to National Jewish Health, Denver, CO, 2011.

9476
Manning Family Foundation ✧ ☆
c/o Paul Manning
200 Garrett St., Ste. O
Charlottesville, VA 22902-5693

Established in 2002 in VA.
Donors: PBM Products; Paul Manning.
Foundation type: Independent foundation.
Financial data (yr. ended 12/31/12): Assets, $13,235,711 (M); expenditures, $837,406; qualifying distributions, $803,499; giving activities include $803,499 for 8 grants (high: $333,334; low: $1,000).
Fields of interest: Higher education; Medical research, institute; Eye research; Recreation.
Limitations: Applications not accepted. Giving primarily in Charlottesville and Woodberry Forest, VA; some funding in Columbia, MD, and Triangle Park, NC. No grants to individuals.
Application information: Unsolicited requests for funds not accepted.
Directors: Diane L. Manning; Paul B. Manning.
EIN: 743054138

9477
Mars Foundation ✧
6885 Elm St.
McLean, VA 22101-3810

Incorporated in 1956 in IL.
Donor: Mars, Inc.
Foundation type: Company-sponsored foundation.
Financial data (yr. ended 12/31/13): Assets, $18,754,142 (M); gifts received, $2,000,000; expenditures, $863,336; qualifying distributions, $823,586; giving activities include $797,000 for 87 grants (high: $65,000; low: $2,000).
Purpose and activities: The foundation supports organizations involved with arts and culture, education, natural resources, animal welfare, health, and human services.
Fields of interest: Arts; Health care; Human services.
Type of support: Continuing support; Annual campaigns; Building/renovation; Equipment; Endowments; Research; Matching/challenge support.
Limitations: Applications not accepted. Giving primarily in Washington, DC, MD, and VA. No grants to individuals, or for scholarships, fundraising, or recognition dinners; no loans.
Application information: Unsolicited requests for funds not accepted.
Board meeting date(s): Oct.
Officers: Jacqueline B. Mars, Pres.; Forrest E. Mars, Jr., V.P.; John F. Mars, V.P.; Otis O. Otih, Secy.-Treas.
EIN: 546037592

9478
Massey Foundation ✧
5002 Monument Ave.
Massey Building
Richmond, VA 23230-3634 (804) 648-1611
Contact: William E. Massey, Jr., Pres.

Established in 1958 in VA.
Foundation type: Independent foundation.
Financial data (yr. ended 11/30/13): Assets, $59,062,895 (M); expenditures, $2,874,631; qualifying distributions, $2,530,395; giving activities include $2,495,000 for 61 grants (high: $100,000; low: $5,000).
Purpose and activities: Giving primarily for a cancer center, and higher and secondary education; some support for cultural programs, and social services.
Fields of interest: Arts; Secondary school/education; Higher education; Hospitals (general); Health care; Cancer; Human services.
Type of support: General/operating support; Annual campaigns.
Limitations: Applications accepted. Giving primarily in Richmond, VA. No grants to individuals.
Application information:
Initial approach: Letter
Deadline(s): None
Board meeting date(s): Annually
Final notification: Apr.
Officers and Directors:* William E. Massey, Jr.,* Pres.; E. Morgan Massey,* V.P. and Secy.; William Blair Massey, Jr.,* Treas.; Craig L. Massey; William Blair Massey.
Number of staff: None.
EIN: 546049049
Selected grants: The following grants are a representative sample of this grantmaker's funding activity:
$100,000 to Lewis Ginter Botanical Gardens, Richmond, VA, 2011.

9479
The Jack M. Matthews Foundation ✧ ☆
2347 Patton's Mill Ln.
Galax, VA 24333 (276) 744-7814
Contact: James G. Nuckolls, Tr.

Established in 2003.
Donor: Clare B. Matthews†.
Foundation type: Independent foundation.
Financial data (yr. ended 12/31/13): Assets, $8,181,252 (M); expenditures, $517,024; qualifying distributions, $500,385; giving activities include $493,775 for 10 grants (high: $400,000; low: $100).
Fields of interest: Environment, forests.
Limitations: Applications accepted. Giving primarily in VA.
Application information: Application form not required.
Initial approach: Proposal
Deadline(s): None
Trustees: James M. Baxley; John W. Bolen, Jr.; James G. Nuckolls.
EIN: 200189021

9480
J. T. - Minnie Maude Charitable Trust ✧
223 Riverview Dr., Ste. G
Danville, VA 24541-3435 (434) 797-3330
Contact: Fred K. Webb, Jr., Exec. Dir.
FAX: (434) 797-3343; Main URL: http://www.jtmm.org
RSS Feed: http://jtmm.org/?feed=rss2

Established in 2007 in VA.
Donor: James T. Emerson†.
Foundation type: Independent foundation.
Financial data (yr. ended 12/31/12): Assets, $48,934,020 (M); expenditures, $2,662,880; qualifying distributions, $1,812,858; giving activities include $993,592 for grants, and $819,266 for grants to individuals.
Purpose and activities: Scholarship awards to residents of the Danville/Pittsylvania, VA, area, and surrounding counties in NC.
Fields of interest: Elementary/secondary education; Higher education; Human services.
Type of support: Scholarships—to individuals.
Limitations: Applications accepted. Giving limited to the Danville/Pittsylvania, VA, area, and in Caswell and Rockingham counties, NC, including all towns and cities located therein.
Publications: Application guidelines.
Application information: At this time, due to the trust's own existing scholarship program, the trust is not funding grants which provide or establish scholarship programs. See foundation web site for additional application information.

Initial approach: Letter on corporate letterhead
Deadline(s): See foundation web site for current deadlines
Officers: Katherine Emerson, C.F.O.; Fred K. Webb, Jr., Exec. Dir.
Trustees: Earl K. Emerson, Jr.; John D. Lovelace; Sarah E. Lovelace; Harry Sakellaris; Lessie E. Webb.
EIN: 260771142

9481
MAXIMUS Foundation, Inc. ✧ ☆
1891 Metro Ctr. Dr.
Reston, VA 20190-5207 (800) 629-4687
Contact: John Boyer, Chair.
E-mail: maximuscharitablefoundation@maximus.com; Main URL: http://www.maximus.com/foundation
Facebook: https://www.facebook.com/MAXIMUS501c3
Google Plus: https://plus.google.com/111357399481224373881/posts
Grants List: https://www.maximusfoundation.org/our-grant-recipients/
MAXIMUS Foundation Blog: http://www.maximusfoundation.org/
Twitter: https://twitter.com/MAXIMUS501c3

Established in 2000 in VA.
Donor: MAXIMUS, Inc.
Foundation type: Company-sponsored foundation.
Financial data (yr. ended 09/30/13): Assets, $248,291 (M); gifts received, $665,818; expenditures, $683,244; qualifying distributions, $682,930; giving activities include $682,930 for 168 grants (high: $50,000; low: $250).
Purpose and activities: The foundation supports programs designed to promote growth and self-sufficiency through improved health, augmented child and family development, and community development. Special emphasis is directed toward programs designed to serve disadvantaged populations and underserved communities.
Fields of interest: Arts; Education, reading; Education; Health care, home services; Health care; AIDS; Crime/violence prevention, child abuse; Employment, services; Employment, training; Food services; Nutrition; Disasters, preparedness/services; Children/youth, services; Family services; Developmentally disabled, centers & services; Homeless, human services; Human services; Community/economic development; Youth; Economically disadvantaged.
Type of support: General/operating support; Program development.
Limitations: Applications accepted. Giving primarily in CA, Washington, DC, GA, IL, MA, NY, TN, TX, and VA. No support for political candidates. No grants to individuals, or for advertising, ticket events, or dinners, political causes, endowments, or capital campaigns.
Publications: Application guidelines; Annual report; Grants list; Informational brochure (including application guidelines).
Application information: Support is limited to 1 contribution per organization during any given year. Application form required.
Initial approach: Completed application form
Deadline(s): Jan. 31 and Aug. 31
Officers and Directors:* John F. Boyer,* Chair.; David R. Francis, Secy.; David Casey; Benjamin R. Coss; Mark Elvin; Christine Vaughn Graham; Awilda L. Martinez-Rodriguez; Melinda Metteauer; Paula Wales.
EIN: 541993677
Selected grants: The following grants are a representative sample of this grantmaker's funding activity:
$25,000 to Austin Recovery, Austin, TX, 2011. For general operating expenditure.
$5,000 to Monarch School Project, San Diego, CA, 2011. For general operating expenditure.
$3,280 to Hugh OBrian Youth Leadership, Westlake Village, CA, 2011. For general operating expenditure.
$3,034 to Project HOPE - The People-to-People Health Foundation, Millwood, VA, 2011. For general operating expenditure.
$2,500 to Breathe California of Los Angeles County, Los Angeles, CA, 2011. For general operating expenditure.
$2,500 to Chesapeake Service Systems, Chesapeake, VA, 2011. For general operating expenditure.
$2,500 to Child Advocates, Houston, TX, 2011. For general operating expenditure.
$2,500 to Friends of Housing Corporation, Milwaukee, WI, 2011. For general operating expenditure.
$2,500 to Volunteer Mid-South, Memphis, TN, 2011. For general operating expenditure.
$2,000 to RAW Art Works, Lynn, MA, 2011.

9482
The James W. and Frances Gibson McGlothlin Foundation ✧
1005 Glenway Ave.
Bristol, VA 24201-3473

Donor: The United Company Charitable Foundation.
Foundation type: Independent foundation.
Financial data (yr. ended 12/31/13): Assets, $23,818,151 (M); gifts received, $12,500; expenditures, $1,848,574; qualifying distributions, $1,693,444; giving activities include $1,661,285 for 26 grants (high: $500,000; low: $500).
Fields of interest: Arts; Education; Agriculture/food.
Limitations: Applications not accepted. Giving primarily in CA, CT, FL, KY, MD, MN, TN, and VA.
Application information: Contributes only to pre-selected organizations.
Officers and Directors:* James W. McGlothlin,* Chair. and Pres.; Frances G. McGlothlin,* V.P. and Secy.; Barbara Bjerke, Treas.
EIN: 263533035

9483
The McGlothlin Foundation ✧
1005 Glenway Ave.
Bristol, VA 24201-3473 (276) 645-5370
Contact: Thomas D. McGlothlin, Pres.

Established in 1998 in VA.
Donor: Woodrow W. McGlothlin†.
Foundation type: Independent foundation.
Financial data (yr. ended 12/31/13): Assets, $18,794,877 (M); expenditures, $1,042,432; qualifying distributions, $848,102; giving activities include $725,500 for 5 grants (high: $500,000; low: $5,000).
Purpose and activities: Giving to worthy causes in higher education, health care, and the arts.
Fields of interest: Arts; Higher education; Health care; Human services.
Type of support: Building/renovation; Equipment; Land acquisition; Program development.
Limitations: Applications accepted. Giving in the southeastern U.S., with special emphasis on eastern KY, southwest VA, and northeast TN.
Publications: Informational brochure.
Application information: Application form not required.
Initial approach: Letter (not exceeding 2 pages)
Copies of proposal: 3
Deadline(s): None
Board meeting date(s): June and Dec.
Final notification: Dec.
Officers: Thomas D. McGlothlin, Pres.; Michael D. McGlothlin, Secy.; James W. McGlothlin, Treas.
Number of staff: 1 part-time professional; 1 full-time support.
EIN: 541907305
Selected grants: The following grants are a representative sample of this grantmaker's funding activity:
$113,478 to Blue Ridge Public Television, Roanoke, VA, 2012. For McGlothlin Award for Teaching Excellence including documentary.

9484
The MeadWestvaco Foundation
501 South 5th St.
Richmond, VA 23219-0501 (804) 327-6402
Contact: Kathryn A. Strawn, V.P. and Exec. Dir.
FAX: (804) 444-1971;
E-mail: foundation@mwv.com; Additional contacts: Christine W. Hale, Sr. Mgr., tel.: (804) 444-2531; Jennifer C. Venable, Employee Progs. Mgr., tel.: (804) 444-5216; Main URL: http://www.mwvfoundation.org

Established in 2003 in DE.
Foundation type: Company-sponsored foundation.
Financial data (yr. ended 12/31/14): Assets, $26,739,020 (M); expenditures, $5,764,622; qualifying distributions, $5,502,351; giving activities include $5,502,351 for grants.
Purpose and activities: The foundation supports programs designed to promote sustainable communities; education; and environmental stewardship.
Fields of interest: Museums; Arts; Higher education; Education; Environment, natural resources; Environment, forests; Environment; Youth, services; Economic development; Community/economic development.
Type of support: Management development/capacity building; Capital campaigns; Annual campaigns; General/operating support; Program development; Employee volunteer services; Employee matching gifts.
Limitations: Applications accepted. Giving on a national basis in areas of company operations, with emphasis on Washington, DC, OH, MA, SC, and VA. No support for lobbying or political organizations, religious organizations not of direct benefit to the entire community, fraternal organizations, sports teams, or student teams. No grants to individuals, or for advertising, endowments, film, radio, television, or video productions, fundraising events, scholarships, academic fellowships, or research, sports events, or student trips or competitions.
Publications: Application guidelines; Program policy statement.

Application information: Application form not required.
Initial approach: Phone or letter
Copies of proposal: 1
Deadline(s): None
Board meeting date(s): Jan.
Officers and Directors:* Wendell L. Willkie II,* Chair.; Linda V. Schreiner, Vice-Chair.; Kathryn A. Strawn, V.P. and Exec. Dir.; Katherine P. Burgeson, Secy.; Robert E. Birkenholz, Treas.; Kevin G. Clark; Donna O. Cox; D. Lynette Crowder; Robert A. Feeser; Ned W. Massee.
Trustee: Mellon Trust of New England.
EIN: 061652243

9485
Memorial Foundation for Children ✧
P.O. Box 18488
Richmond, VA 23226-8488 (804) 221-1994
Contact: Michelle Thomson, Grants Chair.
E-mail: MFCRichmond@gmail.com; Main URL: http://fdnweb.org/mfc

Established about 1934 in VA.
Donors: Alexander S. George†; Elizabeth Strother Scott†.
Foundation type: Independent foundation.
Financial data (yr. ended 12/31/13): Assets, $16,522,432 (M); expenditures, $783,956; qualifying distributions, $726,983; giving activities include $726,983 for grants.
Purpose and activities: Aid to nonprofit groups for the care and education of Richmond, VA, area children 18 years of age and under.
Fields of interest: Arts; Child development, education; Education; Human services; Children/youth, services; Child development, services; Infants/toddlers; Children/youth; Children; Disabilities, people with; Blind/visually impaired; Deaf/hearing impaired; Crime/abuse victims; Economically disadvantaged.
Type of support: General/operating support; Equipment; Program development; Seed money; Curriculum development; Scholarship funds.
Limitations: Applications accepted. Giving limited to the Richmond, VA, area, including Chesterfield, Goochland, Hanover and Henrico counties. No support for the Hopewell and Petersburg county, VA, areas. No grants to individuals, or for capital or endowment funds, annual campaigns, emergency funds, deficit financing, matching gifts, publications, conferences, scholarships, or fellowships; no loans.
Publications: Informational brochure (including application guidelines).
Application information: Application form required.
Initial approach: Letter
Copies of proposal: 2
Deadline(s): May 31
Board meeting date(s): Mar., May, Oct., and Nov.
Officers: Wendy Schultz, Pres.; Prem Hall, V.P.; Jean Oakey, Treas.; Missy Chase, Recording Secy.; Sallie Thalhimer, Corresponding Secy.
Number of staff: 1 part-time support.
EIN: 540536103
Selected grants: The following grants are a representative sample of this grantmaker's funding activity:
$30,000 to Anna Julia Cooper Episcopal School, Richmond, VA, 2011.
$30,000 to Boys and Girls Clubs of Metropolitan Richmond, Richmond, VA, 2011.
$30,000 to YWCA of Richmond, Richmond, VA, 2011.
$25,000 to CrossOver Ministry, Richmond, VA, 2011.
$25,000 to Richmond Boys Choir, Richmond, VA, 2011.
$22,000 to Positive Vibe Foundation, Richmond, VA, 2011.
$10,000 to Better Housing Coalition, Richmond, VA, 2011.
$10,000 to Legal Aid Justice Center, Charlottesville, VA, 2011.
$10,000 to Richmond Peace Education Center, Richmond, VA, 2011.
$7,500 to Saint Johns Church Foundation, Richmond, VA, 2011.

9486
The McGue Millhiser Family Trust ✧
P.O. Box 1535
Richmond, VA 23218-1535 (804) 788-8732

Established in VA.
Donors: Thomas McNally Millhiser; Ross R. Millhiser†.
Foundation type: Independent foundation.
Financial data (yr. ended 12/31/13): Assets, $11,909,329 (M); expenditures, $711,018; qualifying distributions, $664,838; giving activities include $664,838 for 40 grants (high: $320,000; low: $500).
Purpose and activities: Giving primarily for the arts and education.
Fields of interest: Performing arts, dance; Arts; Higher education; Education; Health organizations; Human services.
Limitations: Applications accepted. Giving primarily in NY and NC; giving also in ME, PA, and VA.
Application information: Application form not required.
Initial approach: Proposal
Deadline(s): None
Trustees: Mary McGue Millhiser; Ross R. Millhiser, Jr.; Thomas McNally Millhiser; Timothy McGue Millhiser.
EIN: 306068869

9487
Mitsubishi Electric America Foundation ✧
1560 Wilson Blvd., Ste. 1150
Arlington, VA 22209-2463 (703) 276-8240
Contact: Kevin R. Webb, Exec. Dir.
FAX: (714) 220-4855;
E-mail: kevin.webb@meus.mea.com; Main URL: http://www.meaf.org/index.php
Facebook: http://www.facebook.com/MEAFoundation
Twitter: https://twitter.com/#!/MEAF
YouTube: http://www.youtube.com/user/meafoundation?feature=results_main

Established in 1991 in DC.
Donors: Mitsubishi Electric Corp.; Mitsubishi Electric Power Products, Inc.
Foundation type: Company-sponsored foundation.
Financial data (yr. ended 12/31/13): Assets, $21,566,713 (M); gifts received, $398,154; expenditures, $1,127,303; qualifying distributions, $979,907; giving activities include $720,954 for 218 grants (high: $58,000; low: $25).
Purpose and activities: The foundation supports programs designed to advance the independence, productivity, and community of young people with disabilities. Special emphasis is directed toward programs designed to promote inclusion.
Fields of interest: Education, equal rights; Education; Employment, services; Independent living, disability; Leadership development; Children; Youth; Disabilities, people with; Physically disabled.
Type of support: General/operating support; Program development; Seed money; Curriculum development; Employee volunteer services; Employee matching gifts.
Limitations: Applications accepted. Giving on a national basis, with emphasis on areas of company operations, with emphasis on CA, Washington, DC, GA, IL, KY, MA, MI, OH, PA, TN, and VA; giving also to national organizations. No support for religious organizations not of direct benefit to the entire community, intermediary organizations, fraternal, labor, political, or lobbying organizations, discriminatory organizations, or individual schools or school districts. No grants to individuals, or for endowments, capital campaigns, equipment or devices for individual users, fundraising events, controversial social or political issues, or local activities without national impact; no loans or product donations.
Publications: Application guidelines; Grants list; Informational brochure (including application guidelines); Multi-year report.
Application information: The foundation is in the process of revising its grant giving priorities and guidelines. Visit website for updated information. Telephone calls during the application process are not encouraged. Application form required.
Initial approach: Concept paper
Deadline(s): June 1 for concept paper; July 1 for full proposal
Board meeting date(s): Fall
Final notification: 1 month
Officers: Katsuya Takamiya,* Pres.; Chris Gerdes, V.P.; Helaine Lobman, Esq., Secy.; Ittetsu Mori, Treas.; Shuji Moriaski, Sr. V.P. and Genl. Mgr.
Directors: Bruce Brenzier; Mike DeLano; Jack Greaf; Perry Pappous; David Rebmann; Susan Renda; Richard C. Waters; Kevin R. Webb; Jeff Whitelaw; Kenichiro Yamanishi.
Number of staff: 2 full-time professional.
EIN: 521700855
Selected grants: The following grants are a representative sample of this grantmaker's funding activity:
$210,000 to University of California, Tarjan Center, Los Angeles, CA, 2012. For Include Students in Entrepreneurial Leadership Programs for youth with disabilities.
$165,000 to American Association of People with Disabilities, Washington, DC, 2012. For AAPD Summer Internship Program.
$150,000 to Girl Scouts of the U.S.A., Council of the Nation's Capital, Washington, DC, 2012. For Include All Girls Initiative to develop inclusion tools and identify best practices from other Councils, disseminating those tools and practices to Councils throughout the Unites States.
$60,000 to Partners for Youth with Disabilities, Boston, MA, 2012. To develop Mentoring for All project to help Big Brothers Big Sisters develop strategies to ensure youth with disabilities have mentoring opportunities and professional role models.
$55,470 to University of New Hampshire, Durham, NH, 2012. To create Autistic Campus Leadership Academy for autistic college students.
$35,000 to American Association of People with Disabilities, Washington, DC, 2012. To expand

Disability Mentoring Day into Piplines of Talent Project.
$25,000 to National Inclusion Project, Research Triangle Park, NC, 2012. For I am Norm: Redefining Normal, Promoting Inclusion national campaign.

9488
The MLG Foundation ✧
0 Court Sq.
Charlottesville, VA 22902-5144 (434) 244-3317
Contact: Emily Erwin
Main URL: http://www.mlgfound.org/

Foundation type: Independent foundation.
Financial data (yr. ended 12/31/12): Assets, $4,174,071 (M); gifts received, $710,000; expenditures, $775,988; qualifying distributions, $747,512; giving activities include $727,850 for 18 grants (high: $181,000; low: $750).
Purpose and activities: Giving primarily for hunger, health and nutrition, children and families, education, and the betterment of the Charlottesville, VA, community.
Fields of interest: Education; Nutrition; Family services; Children.
Limitations: Applications accepted. Giving primarily in Charlottesville, VA.
Publications: Application guidelines.
Application information: Application form required.
Initial approach: Online grant application form
Deadline(s): See foundation web site for current deadlines. Foundation will review grant applications 2 times per year
Trustees: Ellen A. Geismar; Michael S. Geismar.
EIN: 263934845
Selected grants: The following grants are a representative sample of this grantmaker's funding activity:
$25,000 to Martha Jefferson Hospital Foundation, Charlottesville, VA, 2012. For Nursery, General Hospital, Capital Campaign.
$10,100 to Robin Hood Foundation, New York, NY, 2012. For general operating support.
$10,000 to Madison House, Charlottesville, VA, 2012. For general operating support.

9489
The Claude Moore Charitable Foundation ✧
11350 Random Hills Rd., Ste. 520
Fairfax, VA 22030-7429 (703) 934-1147
Contact: K. Lynn Tadlock, Deputy Exec. Dir., Giving
FAX: (703) 273-0152;
E-mail: claudemoorefoundation@claudemoore.org;
Main URL: http://www.claudemoorefoundation.org

Established in 1987 in VA.
Donor: Claude Moore†.
Foundation type: Independent foundation.
Financial data (yr. ended 12/31/13): Assets, $135,921,889 (M); expenditures, $5,808,743; qualifying distributions, $4,470,683; giving activities include $1,966,866 for 73 grants (high: $500,000; low: $400).
Purpose and activities: The mission of the foundation is to enhance educational opportunities, including higher education, for young people in the Commonwealth of Virginia and elsewhere.
Fields of interest: Museums (specialized); Higher education; Medical school/education; Nursing school/education; Teacher school/education; Adult education—literacy, basic skills & GED; Education; Health care, formal/general education; Boy scouts.
Type of support: General/operating support; Continuing support; Program development; Conferences/seminars; Scholarship funds; Matching/challenge support.
Limitations: Applications not accepted. Giving primarily in VA. No grants to individuals.
Application information: Unsolicited requests for funds not accepted.
Board meeting date(s): Monthly
Officer: J. Hamilton Lambert, Exec. Dir.
Trustees: Peter A. Arntson; Gary W. Brown; Guy M. Gravett; Leigh B. Middleditch, Jr.
EIN: 521558571
Selected grants: The following grants are a representative sample of this grantmaker's funding activity:
$75,000 to Virginia Mentoring Partnership, Richmond, VA, 2012. For mentor support.
$53,000 to James Madison University, Harrisonburg, VA, 2012. For Precious Times Program.
$50,000 to Loudoun Cares, Leesburg, VA, 2012. For Claude Moore Community Builders.
$50,000 to Loudoun Literacy Council, Leesburg, VA, 2012. For the Family Literacy Program.
$45,000 to Miller Center Foundation, Charlottesville, VA, 2012. To underwrite program.
$40,000 to Shenandoah University, Winchester, VA, 2012. For Claude Moore Center for Literacy.
$38,000 to Loudoun Education Foundation, Ashburn, VA, 2012. For the High School Graduation Party Project.
$25,000 to LEAD Virginia, Richmond, VA, 2012. For Virginia Class 2012.
$25,000 to Loudoun Education Foundation, Ashburn, VA, 2012. For Future Leaders.
$1,250 to Boy Scouts of America, Bethesda, MD, 2012. For Loudoun - Good Scout Dinner.

9490
Marietta McNeill Morgan & Samuel Tate Morgan, Jr. Trust ✧
c/o US Trust, Philanthropic Solutions
1111 E. Main St. VA2-300-12-92
Richmond, VA 23219-3531 (804) 788-2673
E-mail: va.grantmaking@ustrust.com; Main URL: http://www.bankofamerica.com/grantmaking

Trust established in 1967 in VA.
Donors: Marietta McNeill Morgan†; Samuel T. Morgan, Jr.†.
Foundation type: Independent foundation.
Financial data (yr. ended 06/30/13): Assets, $20,325,052 (M); expenditures, $1,149,631; qualifying distributions, $973,075; giving activities include $850,150 for 35 grants (high: $45,000; low: $10,000).
Fields of interest: Museums; Historic preservation/historical societies; Arts; Higher education; Education; Health care; Food banks; Human services.
Type of support: Building/renovation; Equipment; Matching/challenge support.
Limitations: Applications accepted. Giving limited to VA. No support for private foundations or individual churches or congregations. No grants to individuals, or for scholarships, endowment funds, multi-year grants, production of videos, movies, radio or TV programs, or for any purposes except capital projects; no loans.
Publications: Informational brochure (including application guidelines).
Application information: The foundation only makes grants for specific capital expenditures. Guidelines available on foundation web site. Application form not required.
Initial approach: Letter preferred
Copies of proposal: 1
Deadline(s): May 1 and Nov. 1
Board meeting date(s): Feb. and June
Final notification: June 30 and Feb. 28
Advisor: Elizabeth Seaman.
Trustee: Bank of America, N.A.
EIN: 546069447
Selected grants: The following grants are a representative sample of this grantmaker's funding activity:
$50,000 to Science Museum of Virginia Foundation, Richmond, VA, 2012. For Improving Grounds exhibition.
$40,000 to Henricus Foundation, Chester, VA, 2012. For Recreation of 1611 Anglican Church.
$40,000 to Washington and Lee University, Lexington, VA, 2012. For renovations of Robinson Hall.
$35,000 to Byrd Theater Foundation, Richmond, VA, 2012. For installation of a new HVAC system.
$35,000 to Randolph-Macon College, Ashland, VA, 2012. For 2:1 Matching Grant for construction of a library addition.
$30,000 to Instructive Visiting Nurse Association Home Health Care, Richmond, VA, 2012. To renovate of rental space.
$25,000 to Elk Hill Farm, Goochland, VA, 2012. For 1:1 Matching Grant for renovation of the administration building.
$25,000 to Glass-Glen Burnie Museum, Museum of the Shenandoah Valley, Winchester, VA, 2012. For restoration of outdated systems.
$25,000 to Radford University Foundation, Radford, VA, 2012. For College of Business and Economics complex.
$25,000 to United Network for Organ Sharing, Richmond, VA, 2012. For heating, cooling, electrical upgrades.

9491
The Mousetrap Foundation ✧
c/o Sterling Foundation Mgmt., LLC
2325 Dulles Corner Blvd., Ste. 670
Herndon, VA 20171-4683 (703) 437-9720

Established in 2002 in VA.
Donor: Judith Randal Hines.
Foundation type: Independent foundation.
Financial data (yr. ended 12/31/13): Assets, $13,668,334 (M); expenditures, $702,479; qualifying distributions, $580,423; giving activities include $505,000 for 6 grants (high: $170,000; low: $50,000).
Fields of interest: Environment, natural resources; Health care, clinics/centers; Legal services; International development.
Limitations: Applications accepted. Giving primarily in D.C., VA and WV. No grants to individuals.
Application information: Application form not required.
Initial approach: Proposal
Deadline(s): None
Officer: Judith Randal Hines, Pres.
EIN: 522285383

9492
Mustard Seed Foundation, Inc.
7115 Leesburg Pike, Ste. 304
Falls Church, VA 22043-2301 (703) 524-5620
Contact: Brian Bakke, Regional Dir., North America
FAX: (703) 533-7340; E-mail: info@msfdn.org; Main URL: http://www.msfdn.org

Established in 1983 in SC.
Donors: Eileen Harvey Bakke; Dennis W. Bakke; Warren Harvey; and members of the Bakke and Harvey families.
Foundation type: Independent foundation.
Financial data (yr. ended 12/31/13): Assets, $2,381,755 (M); gifts received, $100; expenditures, $2,310,015; qualifying distributions, $1,629,736; giving activities include $1,307,736 for 304 grants (high: $30,000; low: $140), and $322,000 for 39 grants to individuals (high: $12,000; low: $4,000).
Purpose and activities: Giving to advance the Kingdom of God through granting and scholarships. The foundation provides grants to churches and Christian organizations worldwide engaged in ministries such as outreach, discipleship, and empowerment. It provides scholarships to Christians pursuing advanced education in non-western theological studies or under-represented fields.
Fields of interest: Theological school/education; Christian agencies & churches.
International interests: Africa; Asia; Europe; Latin America; Middle East; South America.
Type of support: Fellowships; Scholarship funds; Scholarships—to individuals; Matching/challenge support.
Limitations: Applications accepted. Giving on a national basis in Los Angeles, CA, Washington, DC, Miami, FL, Chicago, IL, New York City, and Houston, TX, and internationally in large urban centers. No support for parachurch organizations, only local churches can apply. No support for U.S. elementary or secondary education. No grants for general purposes, or for television or radio projects, or for buildings, land purchases, small towns or rural projects, administrative costs or for ongoing operations, projects without local church financial support, or scholarships to undergraduate programs, or multi-year grants.
Publications: Application guidelines; Annual report; IRS Form 990 or 990-PF printed copy available upon request.
Application information: Check foundation web site for more information. Please submit one copy of application for grants. Application form required.
Initial approach: Letter, e-mail or telephone. Online application for Harvey Fellows
Copies of proposal: 1
Deadline(s): Grants - revolving; Harvey Fellows - Nov. 1
Board meeting date(s): Every 7 or 8 weeks
Final notification: Up to 3 months from submission date
Officers and Directors:* Dennis W. Bakke, Co-Chair.; Eileen Harvey Bakke,* Co-Chair.; Eric Hornberger, Co-Exec. Dir.; Lonni Jackson, Co-Exec. Dir.; Elizabeth Bakke; Lowell Bakke; Margaret Bakke; Raymond J. Bakke; W. Brantley Harvey, Jr.; Cathy Harvey; Warren Harvey; Tucker Laffite; Jill Nauta; Daniel Thompson; Margaret Thompson.
Number of staff: 11 full-time professional.
EIN: 570748914

9493
The Arthur and Eileen Newman Family Foundation ✧ ☆
c/o Silvercrest
614 E. High St.
Charlottesville, VA 22902-5513

Established in 2005 in NY.
Donor: Arthur B. Newman.
Foundation type: Independent foundation.
Financial data (yr. ended 11/30/13): Assets, $4,910,128 (M); expenditures, $2,517,698; qualifying distributions, $2,488,948; giving activities include $2,488,900 for 26 grants (high: $1,000,000; low: $400).
Fields of interest: Arts; Health organizations, association; Health organizations; Human services; Women, centers/services; Foundations (private grantmaking); United Ways and Federated Giving Programs; Jewish federated giving programs; Jewish agencies & synagogues.
Limitations: Applications not accepted. Giving primarily in New York, NY.
Application information: Unsolicited requests for funds not accepted.
Trustees: Allison Duman; Sondra Neuschotz; David Newman; Eileen D. Newman.
EIN: 161743917

9494
The NewMarket Foundation ✧
330 S. 4th St.
Richmond, VA 23219-4350 (804) 788-5000
Contact: Bruce Hazelgrove, V.P.
Application address: P.O. Box 2189 Richmond, VA 23218; tel: (804) 788-5000

Established in VA.
Donor: NewMarket Corporation.
Foundation type: Company-sponsored foundation.
Financial data (yr. ended 12/31/13): Assets, $2,866,518 (M); gifts received, $1,943,000; expenditures, $1,414,911; qualifying distributions, $1,414,911; giving activities include $1,358,170 for 81 grants (high: $500,000; low: $60), and $54,231 for 42 employee matching gifts.
Fields of interest: Higher education; Education; Medical research, institute; Cancer research; Human services; Children/youth, services.
Limitations: Applications accepted. Giving primarily in Richmond, VA.
Application information: 3-part application form required for matching gifts. Application form required.
Initial approach: Proposal
Deadline(s): Sept.
Officers and Directors:* Thomas E. Gottwald,* Pres.; Bruce Hazelgrove III,* V.P.; M. Rudolph West, Secy.; Bruce C. Gottwald, Sr.
EIN: 271586209
Selected grants: The following grants are a representative sample of this grantmaker's funding activity:
$100,000 to Medical College of Virginia Foundation, Richmond, VA, 2011.
$100,000 to Venture Richmond, Richmond, VA, 2010.
$50,000 to J. Sargeant Reynolds Community College, Richmond, VA, 2010.
$25,000 to Chamber Foundation, Greater Richmond, Richmond, VA, 2011.
$25,000 to Chamber Foundation, Greater Richmond, Richmond, VA, 2010.
$25,000 to J. Sargeant Reynolds Community College, Richmond, VA, 2011.
$25,000 to State Fair of Virginia, Doswell, VA, 2010.
$25,000 to Virginia Military Institute, Lexington, VA, 2011.
$20,000 to William Byrd Community House, Richmond, VA, 2010.
$20,000 to World Pediatric Project, Richmond, VA, 2011.
$16,000 to Virginia Foundation for Independent Colleges, Richmond, VA, 2010.
$15,000 to American Red Cross, Richmond, VA, 2011.
$15,000 to Childrens Home Society of Virginia, Richmond, VA, 2011.
$15,000 to ChildSavers, Richmond, VA, 2010.
$15,000 to Richmonds Future, Richmond, VA, 2011.
$10,290 to Saint Andrews School, Richmond, VA, 2011.
$10,000 to American Red Cross, Richmond, VA, 2010.
$10,000 to Metropolitan Richmond Sports Backers, Richmond, VA, 2010.
$8,310 to Saint Andrews School, Richmond, VA, 2010.
$5,000 to Virginia Council on Economic Education, Richmond, VA, 2011.

9495
Nirman Foundation ✧ ☆
600 N. Pickett St.
Alexandria, VA 22304-2110

Established in 1994 in VA.
Donors: Chandrakant C. Shroff; Harivadan Kapadia; Manjula Kapadia.
Foundation type: Independent foundation.
Financial data (yr. ended 06/30/13): Assets, $803,485 (M); gifts received, $28,860; expenditures, $472,836; qualifying distributions, $461,250; giving activities include $461,250 for 14 grants (high: $263,500; low: $100).
Fields of interest: Education; Health care; Human services.
Limitations: Applications not accepted. Giving primarily in MD. No grants to individuals.
Application information: Contributes only to pre-selected organizations.
Officer: Chandrakant C. Shroff, Pres.
Directors: Papan Devani; William H. Gruen; Jayshree Mehta; Bhikhu Parekh; Shirish Udeshi.
EIN: 541740988

9496
Norfolk Southern Foundation ✧
P.O. Box 3040
Norfolk, VA 23514-3040 (757) 629-2881
Contact: Katheryn Fletcher, Exec. Dir.
E-mail: katie.fletcher@nscorp.com; Main URL: http://www.nscorp.com/nscportal/nscorp/Community/NS%20Foundation/

Established in 1983 in VA.
Donors: Norfolk Southern Corp.; The Cincinnati, New Orleans and Texas Pacific Railway Co.; Rail Investment Co.
Foundation type: Company-sponsored foundation.

Financial data (yr. ended 12/31/13): Assets, $3,847,972 (M); gifts received, $6,996,000; expenditures, $7,381,958; qualifying distributions, $6,948,479; giving activities include $5,293,067 for 473 grants (high: $234,000; low: $250), and $1,655,412 for 501 employee matching gifts.
Purpose and activities: The foundation supports programs designed to promote education with emphasis on the post-secondary level; community enrichment with emphasis on cultural and artistic organizations; and health and human services, including food banks, homeless programs, and independent free clinics.
Fields of interest: Museums; Performing arts; Arts; Education, early childhood education; Higher education; Education; Environment, natural resources; Environment; Health care, clinics/centers; Health care; Food banks; Homeless, human services; Human services; Business/industry; Community/economic development; United Ways and Federated Giving Programs; Mathematics; Engineering/technology; Science.
Type of support: General/operating support; Continuing support; Annual campaigns; Capital campaigns; Building/renovation; Equipment; Endowments; Program development; Scholarship funds; Sponsorships; Employee matching gifts; Employee-related scholarships; Matching/challenge support.
Limitations: Applications accepted. Giving primarily in areas of company operations, with emphasis on Atlanta, GA and Hampton Roads, Norfolk, and Roanoke, VA. No support for religious, fraternal, social, or military, veterans' organizations, political or lobbying organizations, public or private elementary or secondary schools, PTA groups or any public or private school affiliated club or organizations, sports or athletic organizations, community or private foundations or pass-through organizations, or disease-related organizations, non-teaching hospitals, Boys and Girls Scouts or similar organizations, animal organizations, national or international organizations, civic leagues, or referral or consulting agencies or organizations. No grants to individuals (except for employee-related scholarships), or for fundraising events, telethons, races, or benefits, sports or athletic activities, or mentoring programs; no-kind gifts of land, structures, equipment, or materials from Norfolk Southern.
Publications: Application guidelines; Annual report; Informational brochure; Program policy statement.
Application information: Pre-approval via phone or email from the executive director is recommended for sponsorship requests. Additional information may be requested at a later date. Application form not required.

Initial approach: Complete online application; email foundation for sponsorships
Copies of proposal: 1
Deadline(s): From July 15 to Sept. 30; none for sponsorships
Board meeting date(s): As needed
Final notification: Dec. 31

Officers: Charles W. Moorman IV,* Chair., C.E.O., and Pres.; Deborah H. Butler, V.P.; Mark D. Manion, V.P.; John P. Rathbone, V.P.; Donald W. Seale, V.P.; James A. Squires, V.P.; Denise Hutson, Secy.; Colin M. Barton, Treas.; Katheryn Fletcher, Exec. Dir.
Number of staff: 1 full-time professional.
EIN: 521328375
Selected grants: The following grants are a representative sample of this grantmaker's funding activity:
$225,000 to United Way of South Hampton Roads, Norfolk, VA, 2012. For campaign pledge.
$95,000 to Chrysler Museum of Art, Norfolk, VA, 2012.
$94,070 to National Merit Scholarship Corporation, Evanston, IL, 2012. For National Merit Scholarship and Norfolk Southern Special Scholarships for 2012.
$70,000 to Foodbank of Southeastern Virginia, Norfolk, VA, 2012. For purchase of truck.
$20,000 to Virginia Museum of Contemporary Art, Virginia Beach, VA, 2012. For Andy Warhol exhibition.
$15,000 to Georgia Tech Foundation, Atlanta, GA, 2012. For GT CAP Program contribution.
$14,320 to United Way of Eastern Kentucky, Prestonsburg, KY, 2012. For campaign pledge.
$10,000 to Central Pennsylvania Food Bank, Harrisburg, PA, 2012. For food purchase.

9497
Northern Virginia Health Foundation ✧
1940 Duke St., Ste. 200
Alexandria, VA 22314-3452 (703) 486-5691
Contact: Patricia N. Mathews, C.E.O.
FAX: (703) 486-5692;
E-mail: pmathews@novahealthfdn.org; Main URL: http://www.novahealthfdn.org

Established in 2006 in VA.
Foundation type: Independent foundation.
Financial data (yr. ended 12/31/13): Assets, $35,794,871 (M); expenditures, $1,856,279; qualifying distributions, $1,642,855; giving activities include $861,000 for 13 grants (high: $180,000; low: $6,000).
Purpose and activities: Giving to improve the health of residents of Northern Virginia, with emphasis on supporting efforts to improve the health and health care of low-income, uninsured or underinsured persons, and on supporting the provision of health education, prevention of disease and wellness programs.
Fields of interest: Public health school/education; Medical care, community health systems; Public health; Health care; Economically disadvantaged.
Type of support: Mission-related investments/loans; General/operating support; Management development/capacity building; Endowments; Technical assistance.
Limitations: Applications not accepted. Giving limited to northern VA. No support for political organizations, or for medical services or procedures excluded by Medicaid, but required by a community health center. No grants to individuals, or for capital campaigns, or lobbying.
Publications: Annual report; Grants list; IRS Form 990 or 990-PF printed copy available upon request.
Application information: Unsolicited requests for funds not accepted.

Board meeting date(s): 2nd Tues. of every other month, starting in Jan. of each year

Officers and Board Members:* Verdia Haywood,* Chair.; Jane Delgado, Ph.D., M.S.*, Vice-Chair.; Patricia N. Mathews, C.E.O. and Pres.; Jeff Schragg,* Treas.; Marsha Allgeier; Jeanne Franklin, Esq.; Lisa Kaplowitz, M.D., M.S.H.A.; David G. Speck, Ed.D.; Jane Woods.
Number of staff: 3 full-time professional.
EIN: 204062932
Selected grants: The following grants are a representative sample of this grantmaker's funding activity:
$32,500 to Consumer Health Foundation, Washington, DC, 2012. For the Northern Virginia Health Services Coalition and the Regional Primary Care.

9498
The Northrop Grumman Foundation ✧
(formerly Foundation of the Litton Industries)
2980 Fairview Park Dr.
Falls Church, VA 22042
Contact: Carlene Beste, Secy. and Mgr.
E-mail: ngfoundation@ngc.com.; E-mail for Carlene Beste: carleen.beste@ngc.com; Main URL: http://www.northropgrumman.com/CorporateResponsibility/CorporateCitizenship/Philanthropy/Pages/Foundation.aspx

Incorporated in 1954 in CA.
Donors: Litton Industries, Inc.; Northrop Grumman Corp.
Foundation type: Company-sponsored foundation.
Financial data (yr. ended 12/31/12): Assets, $29,021,558 (M); gifts received, $10,000,000; expenditures, $10,726,229; qualifying distributions, $10,598,527; giving activities include $9,809,518 for 91 grants (high: $1,750,000; low: $1,000), and $763,809 for 774 employee matching gifts.
Purpose and activities: The foundation supports programs designed to provide educational opportunities for youth and educators. Special emphasis is directed toward programs designed to promote science, technology, engineering and mathematics (STEM) for students and teachers.
Fields of interest: Elementary/secondary education; Higher education; Education, reading; Education; Mathematics; Engineering/technology; Science; Youth.
Type of support: Employee matching gifts; Program development; Scholarship funds.
Limitations: Giving on a national basis for STEM programming. No support for campus student organizations, fraternities, sororities, honor societies, religious schools or colleges with a primary focus on religious beliefs, athletic teams or athletic support organizations, or choirs, bands, or drill teams. No grants to individuals (except for employee-related scholarships), or for fundraising events, advertising or underwriting expenses, capital campaigns, endowments, or tuition.
Publications: Annual report; Newsletter.
Application information:

Board meeting date(s): Annually

Officers and Directors:* Sandra Evers-Manly,* Pres.; Carleen Beste, Secy. and Mgr.; Silva Thomas,* Treas.; Shelia Cheston; Frank Flores; Darryl M. Fraser; Denise Peppard.
EIN: 956095343

9499
Oak Hill Fund ✧
P.O. Box 1624
Charlottesville, VA 22902-1624
Contact: Jeff Adams, C.F.O
E-mail: info@oakhillfund.org; Main URL: http://www.oakhillfund.org

Established in 2002 in VA as part of the restructure of the W. Alton Jones Foundation (now known as Blue Moon Fund).
Donor: Blue Moon Fund, Inc.

Foundation type: Independent foundation.
Financial data (yr. ended 12/31/13): Assets, $110,445,372 (M); expenditures, $7,585,914; qualifying distributions, $5,518,746; giving activities include $3,598,240 for grants.
Purpose and activities: The mission of the fund is to promote the well-being of mankind through effective and inspiring grantmaking. The fund currently has three programs: 1) to focus on the promotion of the principles of sustainable development into the design of affordable construction, with a primary focus on residential housing; 2) women's reproductive health and rights, and 3) a local program that addresses quality of life issues within the greater Charlottesville community, including the areas of health and safety, grassroots environment.
Fields of interest: Environment, natural resources; Reproductive health; Housing/shelter, development; Safety, education; Community development, neighborhood development; Women.
Limitations: Applications accepted. Giving limited to the southeastern U.S., including AL, DE, FL, GA, KY, MD, MS, NC, TN, SC, VA, WV, and Washington, DC. The fund's local program is limited to the Thomas Jefferson Planning District, in the foothills of central VA's Blue Ridge Mountains; the district includes the city of Charlottesville and the counties of Albemarle, Greene, Louisa, Fluvanna, and Nelson. No support for organizations lacking 501(c)(3) status. No grants to individuals, or for capital campaigns, endowments, bricks and mortar projects, books, or films; no general operating support or support for research.
Publications: Application guidelines.
Application information: See fund web site for application guidelines and requirements. Application form not required.
Initial approach: Use Letter of Inquiry process on the fund's web site
Copies of proposal: 1
Deadline(s): None
Board meeting date(s): Monthly
Final notification: 30 days from receipt
Officers: William A. Edgerton, Pres.; Liza T. Edgerton, V.P.; Robert W. Hurst, Exec. Dir.; Jeff Adams, C.F.O.
Number of staff: 5 full-time professional; 6 part-time professional.
EIN: 311810011

9500
Obici Healthcare Foundation, Inc. ✧
(formerly Obici Foundation, Inc.)
106 W. Finney Ave.
Suffolk, VA 23434-5265 (757) 539-8810
Contact: Lisa Kelch, Grants Assoc.
FAX: (757) 539-8887; E-mail: lkelch@obicihcf.org; Main URL: http://www.obicihcf.org/
Grants List: http://www.obicihcf.org/recipients.asp

Established in VA; reincorporated in 2006 as a private foundation.
Donor: Sentara Healthcare.
Foundation type: Independent foundation.
Financial data (yr. ended 03/31/13): Assets, $105,585,269 (M); expenditures, $6,116,116; qualifying distributions, $5,102,164; giving activities include $4,136,138 for 132 grants (high: $250,000; low: $85).
Purpose and activities: Giving to improve the health status of people in the Suffolk, VA, and surrounding communities, by addressing the unmet needs of the medically indigent and uninsured, and by supporting programs that have the primary purpose of preventing and reducing illness and disease.
Fields of interest: Health care; Human services; Youth, services; Family services, domestic violence; Residential/custodial care; Economically disadvantaged.
Limitations: Giving primarily in the cities of Suffolk and Franklin, VA, as well as Boykins, Courtland, Dendron, Elberon, Isle of Wright County, Ivor, Newsoms, Sedley, Surry, Wakefield and Waverly, VA; and in Gates County, NC. No grants to individuals, including patient assistance funds, or for lobbying or political activities, biomedical, clinical or educational research, meetings and conferences, unless they are essential to a larger project, scholarships, endowments, annual fund drives, or direct funding for direct medical or social services that already are funded through existing third-party reimbursement sources.
Publications: Application guidelines; Annual report; Financial statement; Grants list; Newsletter.
Application information: Full proposals are by invitation only, upon consideration of concept paper. Application form required.
Initial approach: Follow concept paper guidelines on foundation web site
Deadline(s): See foundation web site for current deadlines
Officers and Directors:* George Y. Birdsong,* Chair.; J. Samuel Glasscock,* Vice-Chair.; Robert M. Hayes,* Secy.-Treas.; Michael Hammond, C.F.O.; Gina L. Pitrone, Exec. Dir.
EIN: 510249728
Selected grants: The following grants are a representative sample of this grantmaker's funding activity:
$400,001 to Genieve Shelter, Suffolk, VA, 2011.
$150,000 to Suffolk Partnership for a Healthy Community, Suffolk, VA, 2011.
$120,000 to Eastern Virginia Medical School Foundation, Norfolk, VA, 2011.
$120,000 to Suffolk Partnership for a Healthy Community, Suffolk, VA, 2011.
$76,206 to Western Tidewater Health District, Suffolk, VA, 2011.
$57,486 to FORKids, Norfolk, VA, 2011.
$37,500 to Suffolk Partnership for a Healthy Community, Suffolk, VA, 2011.
$37,500 to Virginia Legal Aid Society, Lynchburg, VA, 2011.
$33,365 to FORKids, Norfolk, VA, 2011.
$25,000 to YMCA, Suffolk Family, Suffolk, VA, 2011.

9501
The George and Carol Olmsted Foundation ✧
80 E. Jefferson St., Ste. 300B
Falls Church, VA 22046-3566
FAX: (703) 536-5020;
E-mail: scholars@olmstedfoundation.org; Toll-free tel.: (877) 656-7833; Main URL: http://www.olmstedfoundation.org

Incorporated in 1960 in VA.
Donor: George Olmsted†.
Foundation type: Independent foundation.
Financial data (yr. ended 12/31/13): Assets, $44,559,872 (M); expenditures, $2,192,791; qualifying distributions, $1,749,296; giving activities include $310,000 for 13 grants (high: $110,000; low: $500), and $519,440 for 91 grants to individuals (high: $21,286; low: $60).
Purpose and activities: The primary objective of the foundation is to support programs designed to contribute to the nation's security by providing potential leaders with a comprehensive education, knowledge and depth of understanding of the political, economic and military factors involved in international relations. To this end, the foundation funds the Olmsted Scholar Program, through which career officers are awarded grants for study in a foreign country. The foundation supports active duty regular line officers, service academy cadets, and ROTC cadets. The foundation does not support civilian personnel.
Fields of interest: Education; Military/veterans' organizations.
Type of support: General/operating support; Scholarships—to individuals.
Limitations: Giving on a national basis. No grants to individuals (except for Olmsted Scholars).
Publications: Annual report; Informational brochure; IRS Form 990 or 990-PF printed copy available upon request.
Application information: Qualified military officers apply through their respective Military Service. Applicants are encouraged to take the candidate qualifications survey, which is available on the foundation web site.
Initial approach: Grant requests should be sent to the foundation for forwarding to the Board of Directors. Requests for grants considered when initiated by a member of the Board of Directors
Board meeting date(s): Mar. and Nov.
Officers and Directors:* William "Doug" D. Crowder,* Chair.; Maj. Genl. Bruce K. Scott,* C.E.O. and Pres.; Col. David G. Estep,* Exec. V.P.; Capt. Joseph McManus, Secy.-Treas.; Genl. John P. Abizaid; Lt. Genl. Emerson "Emo" N. Gardner; Kathryn "Kathy" L. Gauthier; Brig. Genl. Silvanus "Taco" Gilbert; Dr. Christopher "Chris" B. Howard; Edward "Ed" L. Jeep; Jeffrey "Jeff" J. Kim; Deborah A. Loewer; James H. Raymer; Col. Robert "Bob" A. Stratton; Angela "Angie" W. Suplisson.
Number of staff: 3 full-time professional; 1 part-time professional; 1 full-time support.
EIN: 546049005
Selected grants: The following grants are a representative sample of this grantmaker's funding activity:
$6,000 to Norfolk State University, Norfolk, VA, 2012. For Overseas Travel Program.

9502
Elis Olsson Memorial Foundation ✧
P.O. Box 51
West Point, VA 23181-0151 (804) 843-9066

Established in 1966 in VA.
Donors: Inga Olsson Nylander†; Signe Maria Olsson†; Sturge G. Olsson Trust.
Foundation type: Independent foundation.
Financial data (yr. ended 12/31/13): Assets, $20,947,998 (M); gifts received, $19,360; expenditures, $1,216,406; qualifying distributions, $1,040,394; giving activities include $991,033 for 63 grants (high: $300,000; low: $500).
Purpose and activities: Giving primarily for the arts, education, health, and human services.
Fields of interest: Museums; Arts; Higher education; Medical school/education; Education;

Health organizations; Human services; Children/youth, services.
Type of support: Professorships; Fellowships.
Limitations: Applications accepted. Giving primarily in VA. No grants to individuals.
Application information: Application form required.
Initial approach: Letter
Deadline(s): None
Officers and Directors:* C. Elis Olsson, Chair. and Pres.; Shirley C. Olsson,* V.P.; Lisa Everett,* Secy.-Treas.; Thelma L. Downey, Exec. Dir.; Anne O. Loebs; Inga O. Rogers.
Number of staff: 1 part-time professional.
EIN: 546062436

9503
The William & Catherine Owens Foundation, Inc. ✧ ☆

c/o Dexter C. Rumsey, III
P.O. Box 745
Mathews, VA 23109-0745

Established in MD.
Donor: William F. Owens†.
Foundation type: Independent foundation.
Financial data (yr. ended 06/30/13): Assets, $5,765,443 (M); gifts received, $36,697; expenditures, $641,896; qualifying distributions, $547,065; giving activities include $515,600 for 26 grants (high: $400,000; low: $600).
Fields of interest: Arts; Education; Health organizations; Human services; Protestant agencies & churches.
Limitations: Applications not accepted. Giving primarily in VA, with emphasis on Mathews. No grants to individuals.
Application information: Contributes only to pre-selected organizations.
Officers: Dexter Rumsey III, Pres.; Rosalyn White, V.P.; David Muffleman, Secy.; Joann Harfest, Treas.
Board Members: Herbert M. Carter; Debra Hancock; Peggy Hudgins; Sture Sigfred.
EIN: 526036018
Selected grants: The following grants are a representative sample of this grantmaker's funding activity:
$20,500 to Mathews High School, Mathews, VA, 2011.
$14,500 to Mathews Department of Social Services, Mathews, VA, 2011.
$2,000 to Jacobs Ladder, Urbanna, VA, 2011.

9504
The Mary Morton Parsons Foundation ✧

901 E. Cary St., Ste. 1404
Richmond, VA 23219-4037 (804) 780-2183
Contact: Amy P. Nisenson, Exec. Dir.
FAX: (804) 915-2737;
E-mail: mmparsons.foundation@gmail.com; Main URL: http://www.mmparsonsfoundation.org

Established in 1988 in VA.
Donor: Mary Morton Parsons†.
Foundation type: Independent foundation.
Financial data (yr. ended 12/31/13): Assets, $111,458,533 (M); expenditures, $5,914,340; qualifying distributions, $5,344,000; giving activities include $5,344,000 for 50 grants (high: $500,000; low: $25,000).
Purpose and activities: Support primarily for museums and historical groups, institutions concerned with education, and social services or welfare.
Fields of interest: Museums; Historic preservation/historical societies; Arts; Education; Environment; Human services.
Type of support: Capital campaigns; Building/renovation; Equipment.
Limitations: Applications accepted. Giving primarily in VA, with an emphasis on Richmond. No grants to individuals, or for debt reduction, endowments, research, or general operating expenses.
Publications: Informational brochure (including application guidelines).
Application information: Proposals submitted without contacting the foundation's Executive Director before the grant deadlines will not receive priority consideration. Faxed or e-mail proposals are not accepted. Application form not required.
Initial approach: Letter; the foundation encourages telephone inquiries
Copies of proposal: 1
Deadline(s): Mar. 15 and Sept. 15
Board meeting date(s): May and Nov.
Officers and Directors:* Thurston R. Moore,* Pres.; Charles F. Witthoefft,* V.P. and Secy.; Mrs. Palmer P. Garson,* Treas.; Amy P. Nisenson, Exec. Dir.
Number of staff: 1 part-time professional.
EIN: 541530891

9505
The Pauley Family Foundation ✧

c/o The Community Foundation Inc.
7501 Boulders View Dr., Ste. 110
Richmond, VA 23225-4047

Established in 1993 in VA.
Donors: Stanley F. Pauley; Dorothy A. Pauley.
Foundation type: Independent foundation.
Financial data (yr. ended 12/31/13): Assets, $86,838,051 (M); expenditures, $3,315,881; qualifying distributions, $2,965,108; giving activities include $2,965,108 for 21 grants (high: $1,250,000; low: $2,500).
Purpose and activities: Giving primarily for education and the arts.
Fields of interest: Museums (art); Performing arts; Higher education; Health care; Foundations (private grantmaking).
Limitations: Applications not accepted. Giving primarily in Richmond, VA. No grants to individuals.
Application information: Contributes only to pre-selected organizations.
Officers: Stanley F. Pauley, Chair.; Dorothy A. Pauley, Pres. and Treas.; Lorna P. Jordan, Secy.
Directors: John Sherman, Jr.; Fred T. Tattersall; Jane G. Watkins.
EIN: 541685158

9506
Perry Foundation, Inc. ✧

P.O. Box 8260
Charlottesville, VA 22906-8260 (434) 977-5679
Contact: Gary C. McGee, Pres.

Incorporated in 1946 in VA.
Donors: Hunter Perry†; Lillian Perry Edwards†.
Foundation type: Independent foundation.
Financial data (yr. ended 12/31/13): Assets, $2,993,623 (M); expenditures, $1,530,669; qualifying distributions, $1,407,946; giving activities include $1,380,937 for 46 grants (high: $115,000; low: $2,297).
Fields of interest: Education; Health care; Human services; Children/youth, services; Community/economic development.
Type of support: Annual campaigns; Building/renovation; Equipment; Matching/challenge support.
Limitations: Giving primarily in VA, with emphasis on Albemarle County and Charlottesville. No grants to individuals, or for operating budgets.
Application information: Application form not required.
Initial approach: Letter
Copies of proposal: 8
Deadline(s): None
Board meeting date(s): Quarterly
Officers and Trustees:* Gary C. McGee,* Pres.; Susan Cabell-Mains,* V.P.; Suzanne S. Brooks,* Secy.; Edward D. Tayloe II,* Treas.; Roberta F. Brownfield; Philip L. Sparks; Wade Tremblay.
Number of staff: 1 part-time support.
EIN: 546036446
Selected grants: The following grants are a representative sample of this grantmaker's funding activity:
$50,000 to University of Virginia, School of Nursing, Charlottesville, VA, 2012. For purpose of donee.
$5,500 to Second Street Gallery, Charlottesville, VA, 2012. For purpose of donee.

9507
Patricia and Douglas Perry Foundation ✧

999 Waterside Dr., Ste. 2220
Norfolk, VA 23510-3306

Established in 1993 in VA.
Donors: J. Douglas Perry; Patricia W. Perry; The Perry 2002 Charitable Lead Annuity Trust.
Foundation type: Independent foundation.
Financial data (yr. ended 12/31/12): Assets, $26,287,277 (M); expenditures, $2,708,563; qualifying distributions, $2,549,100; giving activities include $2,549,100 for grants.
Purpose and activities: Giving primarily for education, and human services in the Hampton Roads, VA, area.
Fields of interest: Elementary/secondary education; Higher education; Human services; Foundations (private grantmaking); Protestant agencies & churches.
Type of support: Scholarships—to individuals.
Limitations: Applications not accepted. Giving limited to residents of Virginia Beach and Norfolk, VA.
Application information: Contributes only to pre-selected organizations.
Officers: Patricia W. Perry, Pres.; Brandon D. Perry, V.P.; J. Christopher Perry, V.P.; L. Paige Perry, V.P.; J. Douglas Perry, Treas.
EIN: 541691140

9508
Peterson Family Foundation, Inc. ✧

12500 Fair Lakes Cir., Ste. 400
Fairfax, VA 22033-3804 (703) 631-7541
Contact: Blanca Rosa Ramos

Established in 1998 in VA.

Donors: Lauren P. Fellows; Jon M. Peterson; Milton V. Peterson; Steven B. Peterson; William E. Peterson; York Investments LC.
Foundation type: Independent foundation.
Financial data (yr. ended 12/31/13): Assets, $1,440,771 (M); expenditures, $1,203,142; qualifying distributions, $1,254,328; giving activities include $700,476 for grants.
Purpose and activities: Giving primarily for education, health associations, human services, and religious purposes.
Fields of interest: Education; Health organizations, association; Human services; Residential/custodial care, hospices; United Ways and Federated Giving Programs; Religion.
Type of support: In-kind gifts.
Limitations: Applications accepted. Giving primarily in Prince George's County, MD, and in VA, with emphasis on Fairfax.
Application information: Application form required.
Initial approach: Proposal
Deadline(s): None
Officers: Lauren P. Fellows, Pres.; Jon M. Peterson, V.P.; Steven B. Peterson, Secy.; William E. Peterson, Treas.
Directors: Carolyn S. Peterson; Milton V. Peterson.
Number of staff: 1 full-time professional.
EIN: 541870812

9509
Piedmont Community Foundation ✧ ☆

101 N. Jay St.
Middleburg, VA 20117 (540) 687-5223
Contact: Amy Owens, Exec. Dir.
FAX: (888) 624-5455;
E-mail: aowen@piedmontcf.org; Mailing address: P.O. Box 402, Middleburg VA 20118; Main URL: http://www.piedmontcf.org/

Established in 1999 in VA.
Foundation type: Community foundation.
Financial data (yr. ended 12/31/13): Assets, $2,004,119 (M); gifts received, $1,180,305; expenditures, $775,001; giving activities include $601,713 for 12+ grants (high: $410,111).
Purpose and activities: The foundation's mission is to facilitate and act as a catalyst, conduit and steward for charitable giving in meeting the ever-changing needs of the community in northern Virginia, focusing on Loudoun and Fauquier Counties; functioning as a positive and creative force to join donors and community in a collective power dedicated to the growth of a permanent endowment as the most effective means to meet the needs of the community now and in the future.
Fields of interest: Arts; Education; Environment; Health care; Family services; Human services; Community/economic development; Children/youth; Economically disadvantaged.
Limitations: Applications accepted. Giving primarily in Loudoun and Fauquier Counties, Virginia.
Publications: Annual report; Financial statement; Informational brochure.
Application information: Visit foundation web site for application guidelines. Application form required.
Initial approach: Preliminary Application Letter
Deadline(s): Varies
Board meeting date(s): Varies
Officers and Directors:* J. Bradley Davis,* Pres.; Susan Webb,* Secy.; Sandra L. Atkins,* Treas.; Amy Owens, Exec. Dir.; Kate Armfield; Andrew R. Bishop, M.D.; John J. Donovan; Verna Flemming, Ph.D.; Jim Herbert, Jr.; Cassandra Kincaid; Kirsten Lanhorne; Tom Northrup; Schuyler Richardson; John M. Rust; Patricia Stout; Bernardus Wegdam.
Number of staff: 1 full-time professional; 1 part-time support.
EIN: 541950727
Selected grants: The following grants are a representative sample of this grantmaker's funding activity:
$35,000 to Loudoun Community Health Center, Leesburg, VA, 2012. To establish and fund pediatric dental.
$30,000 to Good Shepherd Alliance, Ashburn, VA, 2012. For renovations at emergency housing shelter, Hebron House.
$25,000 to Blue Ridge Area Food Bank, Verona, VA, 2012. For take-home backpack for low-income children.
$9,000 to Loudoun Cares, Leesburg, VA, 2012. To create capacity building programs and workshop training.
$5,000 to Loudoun Breast Health Network, Leesburg, VA, 2012. To provide cancer patients with transportation.
$4,000 to Loudoun Education Foundation, Ashburn, VA, 2012. For science progams ad science fairs.
$3,730 to Feed Loudoun, Leesburg, VA, 2012. For startup support.
$3,600 to Loudoun Therapeutic Riding Foundation, Leesburg, VA, 2012. To fund three equine facilitated therapy sessions for returning military and their families.
$2,000 to Good Shepherd Alliance, Ashburn, VA, 2012. For renovations at emergency housing shelter, Hebron House.
$1,000 to Fauquier Community Theater, Warrenton, VA, 2012. For summer youth showcase theater show.
$1,000 to Loudoun Free Clinic, Leesburg, VA, 2012. To help offset cost for low-income cancer patients.
$1,000 to Mosby Heritage Area Association, Middleburg, VA, 2012. For general support.

9510
Portsmouth General Hospital Foundation

c/o Tricia Irwin, Dir., Admin. and Grants
360 Crawford St.
Portsmouth, VA 23704-2812 (757) 391-0001
Contact: Alan E. Gollihue, C.E.O. and Pres.; Patricia Clifford Irwin, Dir., Admin. and Grants
FAX: (757) 391-0004;
E-mail: office@pghfoundation.org; Main URL: http://www.pghfoundation.org

Established in 1987 in VA as the Seller's Trust; converted through the sale of Portsmouth General Hospital, Inc. to Tidewater Health Care, Inc.; funded in 1988.
Foundation type: Independent foundation.
Financial data (yr. ended 06/30/14): Assets, $13,592,344 (M); expenditures, $939,597; qualifying distributions, $857,752; giving activities include $501,029 for 37 grants (high: $49,200; low: $250).
Purpose and activities: The foundation's mission is to improve the health, wellness, and quality of life of the Portsmouth community through insightful, effective, and coordinated philanthropic grant making and collaborations. The foundation's vision is to be a catalyst for maximizing outcomes through community assessment, collaborative development, and focused grantmaking.
Fields of interest: Reproductive health, family planning; Health care; Youth, pregnancy prevention; Children/youth; Children.
Type of support: Program development; Technical assistance.
Limitations: Giving limited to healthcare programs in Portsmouth, VA. No support for political activities. No grants to individuals, scholarships, building funds, elimination of deficits, travel, research and development, or capital campaigns.
Publications: Application guidelines; Grants list.
Application information: Unsolicited applications are not encouraged. Application guidelines available on foundation web site.
Initial approach: Telephone
Copies of proposal: 1
Deadline(s): Jan. 1 for Mar. meeting; July 1 for Sept. meeting
Board meeting date(s): 1st Wed. in Mar., June, Sept. and Dec.
Final notification: 1 week.
Officers and Directors:* Earnhart A. Spencer, Jr.,* Chair.; Susan H. Burton,* Vice-Chair.; Alan E. Gollihue, C.E.O. and Pres.; Frances L. Gray, R.N.*, Secy.; Jessica P. Mullen,* Treas.; J. Richard Auman, M.D.; Richard M. Bikowski, M.D.; Cheran D. Cordell; Shandre Harasty; John Schalk; Helen W. Taylor, Ed.D.; Richard E.H. Wentz.
Number of staff: 2 full-time professional.
EIN: 541463392
Selected grants: The following grants are a representative sample of this grantmaker's funding activity:
$48,039 to Chesapeake Health Investment Program, Chesapeake, VA, 2013. For Comprehensive Health Investment Project for Portmouth.
$44,500 to Foodbank of Southeastern Virginia, Norfolk, VA, 2013. For BackPack and School-Based Mobile Pantry.
$23,000 to Tidewater Youth Services Foundation, Portsmouth, VA, 2013. For Aggression Replacement Training for at-risk youth.
$18,000 to Multi-Cultural Performing Arts Consulting, Norfolk, VA, 2013. For Junior Mosiac Steel Drum Band for Portsmouth Youth.
$15,080 to Citizens Committee to Protect the Elderly, Virginia Beach, VA, 2013. For Humanitarian Volunteer Visitor Program.
$10,000 to Bon Secours Maryview Foundation, Portsmouth, VA, 2013. For diabetic testing supplies for clinic patients.
$10,000 to Westmoreland Children and Youth Association, Portsmouth, VA, 2013. For youth baseball, flag football, and cheerleading.

9511
Potomac Health Foundation ✧

2296 Opitz Blvd., Ste. 200
Woodbridge, VA 22191-3352 (703) 523-0630
Contact: Sheri Warren, Dir., Grant Progs.
FAX: (571) 542-9964;
E-mail: info@potomachealthfoundation.org; Main URL: http://potomachealthfoundation.org/
RSS Feed: http://feeds.feedburner.com/potomachealthfoundation.org/OGpU
Twitter: https://twitter.com/@phfound
YouTube: http://www.youtube.com/user/PHFound

Established in VA in Dec. 2009.
Foundation type: Independent foundation.
Financial data (yr. ended 10/31/13): Assets, $101,321,082 (M); expenditures, $4,869,776;

qualifying distributions, $4,428,924; giving activities include $4,046,570 for 49 grants (high: $266,058; low: $10,500).
Purpose and activities: Giving limited to community-based, population health projects.
Fields of interest: Health care.
Type of support: Scholarship funds; Program development; Matching/challenge support; General/operating support; Building/renovation.
Limitations: Applications accepted. Giving primarily in eastern Prince William County, VA, and the immediately adjacent communities in eastern Fairfax and Stafford counties, including Aquia, Dale City, Dumfries, Garrisonville, Lake Ridge, Lorton, Manassas, Montclair, Quantico, Southbridge, Triangle and Woodbridge, VA.
Publications: Application guidelines; Financial statement; Grants list.
Application information: Application form required.
Initial approach: Submit letter of intent online via foundation web site
Deadline(s): See foundation web site for current deadline
Officers and Directors:* Marion M. Wall,* Chair.; Carol S. Shapiro, M.D.*, Vice-Chair.; Michael D. Lubeley,* Secy.; R. Michael Sorensen,* Treas.; Stephen V. Batsche, Exec. Dir.; Howard L. Greenhouse; Donnie Hylton; Deborah Johnson; Kenneth Krakaur; Wayne Mallard; William M. Moss; Sarah Pitkin, Ph.D.
Number of staff: 2 full-time professional.
EIN: 521340920

9512
Proteus Foundation ✧
c/o Yount, Hyde & Barbour, P.C.
P.O. Box 2560
Winchester, VA 22604-1760 (540) 662-3417
Contact: Celia W. Rutt, Dir.

Established in 2000 in VI.
Donors: Celia W. Rutt; James P. Rutt; Kathleen L. Rutt.
Foundation type: Independent foundation.
Financial data (yr. ended 09/30/13): Assets, $8,956,769 (M); expenditures, $586,184; qualifying distributions, $485,000; giving activities include $485,000 for 16 grants (high: $110,000; low: $5,000).
Purpose and activities: Giving primarily for scientific research in areas of environmental science and complex adaptive systems, preservation of historically or scientifically important documents and artifacts, environmental protection, preservation and enhancement.
Fields of interest: Historical activities; Elementary/secondary education; Graduate/professional education; Environment; Hospitals (general); Neighborhood centers; Civil liberties, advocacy; Civil/human rights; Community/economic development; Social sciences, interdisciplinary studies.
Limitations: Applications accepted. Giving primarily in NM and VA. No grants to individuals.
Application information: Application form required.
Initial approach: Letter
Deadline(s): None
Directors: Celia W. Rutt; James P. Rutt; Kathleen L. Rutt.
EIN: 542013543
Selected grants: The following grants are a representative sample of this grantmaker's funding activity:
$75,000 to Santa Fe Institute, Santa Fe, NM, 2013. For Fund Interdisciplinary Scientific Research.
$25,000 to American Shakespeare Center, Staunton, VA, 2013. To support Theatres and Educational Programs.
$25,000 to Electronic Frontier Foundation, San Francisco, CA, 2013. To support Digital Freedom.
$25,000 to Institute for Justice, Arlington, VA, 2013. To support Legal Rights.
$10,000 to Historic Staunton Foundation, Staunton, VA, 2013. To support Historic Resources.

9513
The Mitchell P. Rales Family Foundation ✧
(formerly The Glenstone Foundation)
8404 Parham Ct.
Mc Lean, VA 22102-1533

Established in 1995 in VA.
Donors: Mitchell P. Rales; The Mnuchin Foundation.
Foundation type: Independent foundation.
Financial data (yr. ended 12/31/13): Assets, $2,465,541 (M); gifts received, $2,117,325; expenditures, $2,856,270; qualifying distributions, $2,797,535; giving activities include $2,789,045 for 25 grants (high: $2,000,000; low: $100).
Purpose and activities: Giving primarily for the arts and education; funding also for health organizations.
Fields of interest: Museums (art); Education; Health organizations, association; Human services; Children, services; Foundations (private grantmaking).
Limitations: Applications not accepted. Giving emphasis is on the greater metropolitan Washington, DC, area. No grants to individuals.
Application information: Contributes only to pre-selected organizations.
Officers and Director:* Mitchell P. Rales,* Chair.; Michael G. Ryan, Pres.; Joseph O. Bunting III, V.P.; Teresa L.C. Baldwin, Secy.-Treas.
EIN: 541739159

9514
The Ratcliffe Foundation ✧
P.O. Box 310
Tazewell, VA 24651-0310 (276) 979-4268
Contact: Scott Cole, Pres. and Dir.

Established in 1970.
Donor: A.M. Ratliff†.
Foundation type: Independent foundation.
Financial data (yr. ended 05/31/13): Assets, $27,780,264 (M); expenditures, $1,785,911; qualifying distributions, $1,294,466; giving activities include $1,294,466 for 2 grants (high: $1,293,942; low: $524).
Fields of interest: Museums (history); Higher education; Education; Hospitals (specialty); Health care.
Limitations: Applications accepted. Giving primarily in TN, and VA; some funding in SD.
Application information:
Initial approach: Letter
Deadline(s): May 1
Officers and Directors:* Scott Cole,* Pres.; William Rife, Secy.-Treas.; Dave Farmer; Fred Harman.
EIN: 237126937

9515
The Ratner Family Foundation ✧
1577 Spring Hill Rd., Ste. 500
Vienna, VA 22182-2223

Established in 1990 in VA.
Donors: Creative Hairdressers, Inc.; Dennis F. Ratner; Warren A. Ratner.
Foundation type: Company-sponsored foundation.
Financial data (yr. ended 12/31/13): Assets, $44,996 (M); gifts received, $400,000; expenditures, $428,770; qualifying distributions, $482,770; giving activities include $428,770 for 47 grants (high: $120,500; low: $100).
Purpose and activities: The foundation supports museums and camps and organizations involved with education, science, and Judaism.
Fields of interest: Museums; Education; Recreation, camps; Residential/custodial care, group home; Jewish federated giving programs; Science; Jewish agencies & synagogues.
Type of support: General/operating support; Program development.
Limitations: Applications not accepted. Giving primarily in CO, Washington, DC, and MD, with emphasis on Bethesda, and Rockville. No grants to individuals.
Application information: Contributes only to pre-selected organizations.
Officers: Dennis F. Ratner, Pres.; Warren A. Ratner, Secy.
EIN: 521099125

9516
Reckitt Benckiser Pharmaceuticals Patient Help Foundation ✧
10710 Midlothian Tpke., Ste. 430
Richmond, VA 23235-4759

Donor: Reckitt Benckiser Pharmaceuticals, Inc.
Foundation type: Company-sponsored foundation.
Financial data (yr. ended 12/31/12): Assets, $0; gifts received, $24,141,468; expenditures, $24,141,468; qualifying distributions, $24,141,468; giving activities include $22,288,109 for grants to individuals.
Purpose and activities: The foundation provides pharmaceuticals used for the treatment of opiate addiction to indigent, uninsured, and low-income individuals. The program is administered by a third party vendor.
Fields of interest: Pharmacy/prescriptions; Health care; Economically disadvantaged.
Type of support: Grants to individuals; Donated products.
Limitations: Applications not accepted.
Application information: Unsolicited requests for funds not accepted. The program is administered by a third party vendor.
Officers and Trustees:* Dr. Rolley Johnson,* Pres.; Vicky Seeger, Secy.; Martyn Gibson,* Treas.; Shaun Thaxter.
EIN: 800723342

9517
The Reinhart Foundation ✧
c/o The Community Foundation Inc.
7501 Boulders View Dr., Ste. 110
Richmond, VA 23225-4047

Established in 2000 in VA.

Donor: Myron H. Reinhart.
Foundation type: Independent foundation.
Financial data (yr. ended 12/31/13): Assets, $17,654,067 (M); expenditures, $877,014; qualifying distributions, $665,306; giving activities include $622,748 for 37 grants (high: $111,248; low: $1,000).
Fields of interest: Higher education; Crime/violence prevention, domestic violence; Boys & girls clubs; Children/youth, services; Foundations (private grantmaking); Foundations (community).
Limitations: Applications not accepted. Giving primarily in New York, NY and Richmond, VA. No grants to individuals.
Application information: Contributes only to pre-selected organizations.
Officers: Myron H. Reinhart, Pres.; Cynthia R. Richards, V.P. and Secy.; William L. Reinhart, V.P. and Treas.
Director: Christopher R. Richards.
EIN: 542001451
Selected grants: The following grants are a representative sample of this grantmaker's funding activity:
$50,000 to Bon Secours Richmond Health Care Foundation, Richmond, VA, 2012. For Guest House at St. Mary's Hospital.
$25,000 to East Carolina University Foundation, Greenville, NC, 2012. For Reinhart Scholarship ($15,000), School of Music Gala ($1,000), Other Scholarships ($9,000).
$22,117 to Barnard College, New York, NY, 2012. For Class of 1973 Donor Match Challenge ($12,117), the Endowment ($10,000).
$20,000 to Hudson Opera House, Hudson, NY, 2012. For General Charitable Purposes ($10,000) Restoration ($10,000).
$10,000 to New York Community Trust, New York, NY, 2012. For Critical Needs Fund for Hurricane Sandy Relief.
$10,000 to YWCA of Richmond, Richmond, VA, 2012. For the domestic program.
$8,000 to Regional Food Bank of Northeastern New York, Latham, NY, 2012. For Salvation Army Programs in Hudson, NY ($6,000) and Zion Community Food Pantry ($2,000).

9518
Reinsch Pierce Family Foundation, Inc. ✧
2040 Columbia Pike
Arlington, VA 22204-6236 (703) 920-3600
Contact: Lola C. Reinsch, Pres. and Dir.

Established in 2003 in VA.
Donors: Dolores G. Reinsch Charitable Lead Annuity Trust; Emergon G. & Dolores G. Reinsch Foundation; Dolores G. Reinsch Charitable Lead Annuity Trust 2; Dolores G. Reinsch 2009 Charitable Lead Annuity Trust.
Foundation type: Independent foundation.
Financial data (yr. ended 12/31/13): Assets, $12,926,319 (M); gifts received, $349,112; expenditures, $598,167; qualifying distributions, $527,284; giving activities include $527,284 for 112 grants (high: $150,000; low: $15).
Fields of interest: Performing arts; Education; Hospitals (general); Youth development, services; Foundations (community); Protestant agencies & churches.
Limitations: Applications accepted. Giving primarily in Arlington, VA; giving also in Washington, DC.
Application information: Application form required.
Initial approach: Letter
Deadline(s): None
Officer and Director:* Lola C. Reinsch,* Pres.
Trustees: Guy Gotts; Sidney G. Simmonds.
EIN: 562402165

9519
Richard S. Reynolds Foundation ✧
1403 Pemberton Rd., Ste. 102
Richmond, VA 23233-4474 (804) 740-7350
Contact: Victoria Pitrelli
FAX: (804) 740-7807; E-mail: VPRSRFDN@aol.com

Incorporated in 1955 in VA.
Donors: David P. Reynolds; Julia L. Reynolds†; David P. Reynolds Irrevocable Trust.
Foundation type: Independent foundation.
Financial data (yr. ended 06/30/13): Assets, $26,763,617 (M); expenditures, $1,531,549; qualifying distributions, $1,281,599; giving activities include $1,201,228 for grants.
Purpose and activities: Giving primarily for higher and secondary education, health, arts and culture, and human services.
Fields of interest: Museums; Performing arts; Historic preservation/historical societies; Secondary school/education; Higher education; Education; Health organizations, association; Boys & girls clubs; Human services; Foundations (private grantmaking); Protestant agencies & churches.
Type of support: Annual campaigns; Capital campaigns; Building/renovation; Endowments; Professorships; Scholarship funds; Research; Matching/challenge support.
Limitations: Applications accepted. Giving primarily in VA. No grants to individuals.
Application information: Application form not required.
Initial approach: Letter
Copies of proposal: 1
Deadline(s): Apr. 30 and Oct. 31
Board meeting date(s): Mid-May and Mid-Nov.
Final notification: 30 days after board meeting
Officers: Richard S. Reynolds III, Pres.; Mrs. Glenn R. Martin, V.P.; Dorothy R. Brotherton, Secy.; Randolph N. Reynolds, Treas.
Number of staff: 1 full-time professional.
EIN: 546037003
Selected grants: The following grants are a representative sample of this grantmaker's funding activity:
$200,000 to J. Sargeant Reynolds Community College Educational Foundation, Richmond, VA, 2011.
$200,000 to Medical College of Virginia Foundation, Richmond, VA, 2011.

9520
The Rice Family Foundation ✧
4378 Montreux Rd.
Warrenton, VA 20187-2859

Established in 2001 in VA.
Donors: Paul Rice; Gina Rice.
Foundation type: Independent foundation.
Financial data (yr. ended 12/31/12): Assets, $35,807 (M); expenditures, $916,833; qualifying distributions, $903,910; giving activities include $903,910 for 3 grants (high: $500,000; low: $53,910).
Fields of interest: Elementary/secondary education; Higher education; Education.
Limitations: Applications not accepted. Giving limited to VA. No grants to individuals.
Application information: Contributes only to pre-selected organizations.
Officers: Gina Rice, Pres. and Treas.; Paul Rice, V.P. and Secy.
EIN: 542055867
Selected grants: The following grants are a representative sample of this grantmaker's funding activity:
$450,000 to University of Virginia, Charlottesville, VA, 2011.

9521
Richmond Memorial Health Foundation ✧
1801 Bayberry Ct., Ste. 104
Richmond, VA 23226-3771 (804) 282-6282
FAX: (804) 282-6255;
E-mail: info@rmhfoundation.org; Main URL: http://www.rmhfoundation.org

Donors: Arthur Glasgow Trust; Partners Investing in Nursing's Future.
Foundation type: Independent foundation.
Financial data (yr. ended 06/30/13): Assets, $182,490,207 (M); gifts received, $32,691; expenditures, $4,186,541; qualifying distributions, $3,277,802; giving activities include $2,220,292 for 77 grants (high: $400,000; low: $150), and $551,182 for 3 foundation-administered programs.
Purpose and activities: Giving to improve health care and wellness in Richmond and central Virginia. Some giving will be for Bon Secours Memorial Regional Medical Center.
Fields of interest: Nursing school/education; Health care; Alzheimer's disease; Geriatrics; Pediatrics.
Limitations: Giving primarily in Richmond and central VA.
Publications: Application guidelines; Annual report; Financial statement.
Application information: Full applications are by invitation, upon review of concept proposal. See foundation web site for complete application guidelines. Application form required.
Initial approach: Concept proposal
Copies of proposal: 3
Deadline(s): For concept proposals: noon, the first Wed. in Jan. for Winter Grant Cycle; and noon, the first Wed. in July for Summer Grant Cycle
Officers and Trustees:* Michele A.W. McKinnon, Esq.*, Chair.; Dee Ann Remo,* Vice-Chair.; Jeffrey S. Cribbs, Sr., C.E.O. and Pres.; Sheryl L. Garland, Secy.; Harry A. Thurton, Jr.,* Treas.; Danny TK Avula, M.D., MPH; A. Dale Cannady; Reginald E. Gordan, Esq.; Richard L. Grier, Esq.; JR Hipple; John W. Martin; William R. Nelson, M.D., MPH; Joe Schilling; Robert L. Thalhimer; Deborah L. Ulmer, RN, Ph.D.
EIN: 510211020
Selected grants: The following grants are a representative sample of this grantmaker's funding activity:
$120,000 to ChildSavers, Richmond, VA, 2011.
$65,650 to Medical College of Virginia Foundation, Richmond, VA, 2011.
$65,000 to Childrens Health Involving Parents, Richmond, VA, 2011.
$55,000 to Communities in Schools of Richmond, Richmond, VA, 2011.
$35,000 to Better Housing Coalition, Richmond, VA, 2011.

$35,000 to Partnership for Nonprofit Excellence, Richmond, VA, 2011.
$29,070 to Daily Planet, Richmond, VA, 2011.
$20,000 to Rx Partnership, Richmond, VA, 2011.
$16,000 to United Way of Greater Richmond and Petersburg, Richmond, VA, 2011.
$15,000 to Legal Aid Justice Center, Charlottesville, VA, 2011.

9522
The Rimora Foundation ✧ ☆
1065 Wood Ln.
Charlottesville, VA 22901-5038

Donor: Richard L. Booth, Jr.
Foundation type: Independent foundation.
Financial data (yr. ended 12/31/13): Assets, $9,459,307 (M); gifts received, $500,000; expenditures, $444,676; qualifying distributions, $442,500; giving activities include $442,500 for 26 grants (high: $210,500; low: $1,000).
Fields of interest: Performing arts; Higher education; Education; Human services; Family services.
Limitations: Applications not accepted. Giving primarily in Charlottesville, VA.
Application information: Unsolicited requests for funds not accepted.
Director: Richard L. Booth, Jr.
EIN: 611579580

9523
Robins Foundation
10 S. 3rd St.
Richmond, VA 23219-3702 (804) 523-1144
Contact: Martha Loving, Office Mgr.
FAX: (804) 523-1150; E-mail for Martha Loving: martha.loving@robinsfdn.org; Main URL: http://www.robinsfdn.org
Grants List: http://www.robinsfdn.org/what-we-fund/

Established in 1957 in VA.
Donor: E. Claiborne Robins†.
Foundation type: Independent foundation.
Financial data (yr. ended 12/31/12): Assets, $139,242,814 (M); expenditures, $8,714,366; qualifying distributions, $6,932,586; giving activities include $5,875,785 for 130 grants, and $447,647 for 1 loan/program-related investment.
Purpose and activities: Gives to a broad range of causes in the Richmond, VA, area.
Fields of interest: Children/youth, services.
Type of support: General/operating support; Income development; Management development/capacity building; Capital campaigns; Building/renovation; Equipment; Land acquisition; Endowments; Program development; Consulting services; Program evaluation; Program-related investments/loans.
Limitations: Applications not accepted. Giving primarily in Richmond, VA; the foundation does not accept unsolicited proposals from organizations outside of the Richmond metropolitan area. No grants to individuals, or for annual funds or special events.
Publications: Grants list.
Application information: The foundation is not accepting unsolicited grant proposals at this time. See foundation web site for updated application information.
Officers and Directors:* Sheryl Robins Nolt,* Pres.; Robin R. Shield, V.P.; Kelly Chopus, Exec. Dir.; Reginald N. Jones,* Treas.; Lewis T. Booker; E. Bruce Heilman; Ann Carol Marchant; Robert E. Marchant; Betty Robins Porter; E. Claiborne Robins, Jr.; Gregory C. Robins; Juliet E. Shield-Taylor.
Number of staff: 5 full-time professional; 1 part-time professional; 1 full-time support.
EIN: 540784484

9524
The Anne Carter Robins and Walter R. Robins, Jr. Foundation ✧
P.O. Box 397
Richmond, VA 23218-0397

Established in 1994 in VA.
Donors: M. Bruce Robins; Ann Carter Robins†.
Foundation type: Independent foundation.
Financial data (yr. ended 12/31/13): Assets, $9,826,382 (M); expenditures, $580,594; qualifying distributions, $506,962; giving activities include $486,750 for 39 grants (high: $100,000; low: $1,000).
Fields of interest: Education; Animal welfare; Human services; Christian agencies & churches.
Limitations: Applications not accepted. Giving primarily in VA. No grants to individuals.
Application information: Unsolicited requests for funds not accepted.
Officers: John B. O'Grady, Pres.; Betty A. Armentrout, V.P.; M. Anne Greggs, Secy.; Rita M. Smith, Treas.
Directors: Karen O'Grady; Hillary Smith.
EIN: 546362175

9525
The Marion & Robert Rosenthal Family Foundation ✧
c/o Donald Bavely
1100 S. Glebe Rd.
Arlington, VA 22204-4309

Established in 1995 in VA.
Donors: Marion Rosenthal; Robert M. Rosenthal.
Foundation type: Independent foundation.
Financial data (yr. ended 12/31/12): Assets, $7,253,603 (M); gifts received, $3,926,069; expenditures, $1,634,711; qualifying distributions, $1,534,506; giving activities include $1,534,506 for 31 grants (high: $500,000; low: $300).
Purpose and activities: Giving primarily for health care and to Jewish agencies and temples; support also for education.
Fields of interest: Museums (art); Performing arts; Arts; Elementary/secondary education; Education; Hospitals (general); Health care; Jewish federated giving programs; Jewish agencies & synagogues; Women.
Type of support: General/operating support; Program development; Scholarship funds; Research.
Limitations: Applications not accepted. Giving primarily in the CA, Washington, DC , MD, and MA. No grants to individuals.
Application information: Contributes only to pre-selected organizations.
Officers and Directors:* Robert M. Rosenthal,* Pres.; Jane R. Cafritz,* V.P.; Marion Rosenthal,* V.P.; Nancy Rosenthal,* Secy.; Brooke R. Peterson,* Treas.
EIN: 541740285
Selected grants: The following grants are a representative sample of this grantmaker's funding activity:
$200,000 to Temple University, Philadelphia, PA, 2012. For final pledge payment.
$95,600 to Life With Cancer, Fairfax, VA, 2012. For Gala Contribution.
$6,480 to Nantucket Atheneum, Nantucket, MA, 2012. For annual contribution and dance festival.

9526
Sacharuna Foundation ✧
P.O. Box 130
The Plains, VA 20198-0130
Contact: Lori Udall, Prog. Dir.

Established in 1985 in NY.
Donor: Lavinia Currier.
Foundation type: Independent foundation.
Financial data (yr. ended 12/31/13): Assets, $10,327,580 (M); expenditures, $810,945; qualifying distributions, $750,650; giving activities include $661,190 for 25 grants (high: $75,000; low: $5,000).
Purpose and activities: Giving primarily for conservation, environmental, and wildlife organizations, and indigenous peoples' issues; some support for education, and historic and cultural preservation.
Fields of interest: Environment; Animals/wildlife, preservation/protection; Indigenous peoples.
Type of support: General/operating support.
Limitations: Applications not accepted. Giving primarily in the U.S., with emphasis on CO, Washington, DC, HI, NY, and VA; some funding also in British Columbia, Canada. No grants to individuals.
Application information: Contributes only to pre-selected organizations. Unsolicited requests for funds not accepted.
Trustee: Lavinia Currier.
Number of staff: 1 part-time professional.
EIN: 133264132
Selected grants: The following grants are a representative sample of this grantmaker's funding activity:
$10,000 to Wildlands Network, Titusville, FL, 2012. For general fund.

9527
Samberg Family Foundation ✧
2107 Wilson Blvd., Ste. 750
Arlington, VA 22201-3077 (703) 351-9405
Contact: Laura J. Samberg, Co-Dir.
Main URL: http://www.sambergfdn.org

Established in 1996.
Donors: Arthur Samberg; Rebecca Samberg.
Foundation type: Independent foundation.
Financial data (yr. ended 11/30/13): Assets, $78,474,037 (M); expenditures, $6,969,013; qualifying distributions, $6,638,517; giving activities include $6,299,590 for 29 grants (high: $1,000,000; low: $5,795).
Purpose and activities: Giving primarily for children, youth and families; education; health; and Jewish issues.

Fields of interest: Museums; Education; Health care; Youth development, services; Children/youth, services; Family services; Jewish federated giving programs.
International interests: Israel.
Type of support: General/operating support; Continuing support; Management development/capacity building; Program development; Seed money; Curriculum development; Research; Technical assistance; Program evaluation; Matching/challenge support.
Limitations: Applications not accepted. Giving primarily in NY. No grants to individuals.
Publications: Grants list.
Application information: Unsolicited requests for funds not accepted.
Officer: Gerald D. Levine, Pres.
Directors: Laura Samberg Faino; Sue Ellen Madden.
Trustees: Arthur Samberg; Rebecca Samberg.
Number of staff: 3 full-time professional.
EIN: 066439895

9528
Scheidel Foundation ✧

1220 N. Filmore St., Ste. 400
Arlington, VA 22201
Main URL: http://scheidelfoundation.org/

Established in 1999 in FL.
Donors: Herbert Scheidel†; Learning Technologies, Inc.
Foundation type: Independent foundation.
Financial data (yr. ended 12/31/13): Assets, $25,548,553 (M); expenditures, $1,216,351; qualifying distributions, $1,093,869; giving activities include $871,512 for 113 grants (high: $50,000; low: $180).
Fields of interest: Health care; Cancer; Human services; United Ways and Federated Giving Programs.
Limitations: Applications not accepted. Giving primarily in Jacksonville and Sarasota, FL, and Kauai, HI; giving also in Lebanon and Taiwan.
Application information: Unsolicited requests for funds not accepted.
Officer and Trustees:* Miki Scheidel,* Pres.; Ema Saad; Henry Scheidel; Miyuki Scheidel; Wes Scheufler.
Director: Shielah Lee.
Number of staff: 1 part-time support.
EIN: 597160883

9529
The William H., John G., and Emma Scott Foundation ✧

P.O. Box 190
Manakin Sabot, VA 23103-0190
Application address: c/o Susanne Crump, Pres. 7106 Glen Pkwy., Richmond, VA 23229; tel.: (804) 285-0154

Incorporated in 1956 in VA.
Donors: John G. Scott†; Emma Scott Taylor†.
Foundation type: Independent foundation.
Financial data (yr. ended 09/30/13): Assets, $12,251,718 (M); expenditures, $622,715; qualifying distributions, $528,000; giving activities include $528,000 for 22 grants (high: $50,000; low: $8,000).
Purpose and activities: Giving primarily to support programs which alleviate human suffering, and improve the health of those families, individuals, and children in need of aid and/or education. A portion of the grants may be applied to support the needs of church schools in the Episcopal Diocese of VA, and private elementary and secondary education. To a lesser degree, grants may be available in support of the arts and humanities.
Fields of interest: Museums; Education; Health organizations; Human services; Christian agencies & churches.
Type of support: Capital campaigns; Building/renovation; Equipment; Program development; Seed money; Program evaluation.
Limitations: Applications accepted. Giving primarily in the Richmond, VA, metropolitan area. No grants to individuals, or for endowment funds, operating budgets, research, national fund drives, or debt reduction.
Publications: Application guidelines; Informational brochure (including application guidelines).
Application information: Scholarship program has been discontinued. Application form not required.
Initial approach: Letter
Copies of proposal: 1
Deadline(s): None
Board meeting date(s): Sept.
Final notification: 1 year
Officers: Susanne B. Crump, Pres.; T. Justin Moore III, V.P.; C. Cotesworth Pinckney, Secy.-Treas.
Trustees: Charles M. Guthridge; Rev. Melissa Hollerith; Robert F. Norfleet, Jr.; E. Bryson Powell.
Number of staff: 1 part-time professional.
EIN: 540648772

9530
Sellier Family Foundation ✧

3 Clarks Branch Rd.
Great Falls, VA 22066-4157

Established in VA.
Donor: Victor F. Sellier.
Foundation type: Independent foundation.
Financial data (yr. ended 12/31/13): Assets, $9,421,479 (M); expenditures, $639,162; qualifying distributions, $620,000; giving activities include $620,000 for 9 grants (high: $250,000; low: $5,000).
Fields of interest: Elementary/secondary education; Health care; Christian agencies & churches.
Limitations: Applications not accepted. Giving primarily in AZ, DC, and VA.
Application information: Contributes only to pre-selected organizations.
Director: Victor F. Sellier.
EIN: 272765823
Selected grants: The following grants are a representative sample of this grantmaker's funding activity:
$10,000 to Youth for Tomorrow, Bristow, VA, 2012. For Country Fair.

9531
Shearwater Foundation Inc. ✧ ☆

7900 World Trade Ctr.
101 W. Main St.
Norfolk, VA 23510-1646

Established in 2006 in VA.
Donor: Conrad M. Hall.
Foundation type: Independent foundation.
Financial data (yr. ended 12/31/13): Assets, $6,646,353 (M); expenditures, $831,124; qualifying distributions, $829,500; giving activities include $829,500 for 29 grants (high: $290,000; low: $500).
Fields of interest: Historic preservation/historical societies; Higher education; Education; Environment; Human services; United Ways and Federated Giving Programs.
Limitations: Applications not accepted.
Application information: Contributes only to pre-selected organizations.
Directors: Burton M. Hall; Conrad M. Hall; Cosby M. Hall; Margaret M. Hall.
EIN: 208075507

9532
Charles E. Smith Family Foundation ✧

2345 Crystal Dr., 11th Fl.
Arlington, VA 22202-4801 (703) 769-1023

Established in 1963 in VA.
Donors: Charles E. Smith†; Robert H. Smith; Robert P. Kogod; Charles E. Smith Trust.
Foundation type: Independent foundation.
Financial data (yr. ended 02/28/13): Assets, $28,382,509 (M); expenditures, $5,606,125; qualifying distributions, $5,353,719; giving activities include $5,350,167 for 18 grants (high: $1,300,000; low: $10,000).
Purpose and activities: Support primarily for a Jewish welfare fund and other Jewish organizations.
Fields of interest: Human services; Jewish federated giving programs; Jewish agencies & synagogues.
Limitations: Applications not accepted. Giving primarily in the greater Washington, DC, area, MD, VA, NJ, and NY. No grants to individuals.
Application information: Contributes only to pre-selected organizations.
Officers: Robert P. Kogod, Pres.; David B. Smith, V.P.; Clarice R. Smith, Secy.; Arlene R. Kogod, Treas.
EIN: 311570183
Selected grants: The following grants are a representative sample of this grantmaker's funding activity:
$2,000,000 to Hebrew Home of Greater Washington, Rockville, MD, 2011.
$1,000,000 to Charles E. Smith Jewish Day School of Greater Washington, Rockville, MD, 2011.
$1,000,000 to Charles E. Smith Jewish Day School of Greater Washington, Rockville, MD, 2011.
$1,000,000 to Jewish Federation of Greater Washington, Rockville, MD, 2011.
$1,000,000 to Johns Hopkins Medical Institutions, Baltimore, MD, 2011.
$666,667 to George Washington University, Washington, DC, 2011.
$500,000 to John F. Kennedy Center for the Performing Arts, Washington, DC, 2011.
$300,000 to Charles E. Smith Jewish Day School of Greater Washington, Rockville, MD, 2011.
$211,000 to American Friends of the Hebrew University, New York, NY, 2011.
$150,000 to American Friends of the Hebrew University, New York, NY, 2011.

9533
Hunter Smith Family Foundation ✧
1 Boar's Head Pt., Ste. 150
Charlottesville, VA 22903-4656

Established in 2007 in VA.
Donor: Hunter J. Smith.
Foundation type: Independent foundation.
Financial data (yr. ended 12/31/13): Assets, $56,500 (M); gifts received, $677,000; expenditures, $682,689; qualifying distributions, $682,675; giving activities include $680,807 for 14 grants (high: $200,000; low: $1,000).
Fields of interest: Arts; Human services; Residential/custodial care, hospices.
Limitations: Applications not accepted. Giving primarily in Charlottesville, VA.
Application information: Contributes only to pre-selected organizations.
Officers: Hunter J. Smith, Pres.; Randolph H. Huffman, C.F.O. and Treas.; Stuart P. Smith, Secy.
EIN: 261607153

9534
Robert H. Smith Family Foundation ✧
2345 Crystal Dr.
Arlington, VA 22202-4801 (703) 769-1023

Established in 1987 in VA.
Donors: Robert H. Smith‡; Clarice R. Smith; CES Mgmt., Inc.; RCS II, LLC; Charles E. Smith Family Foundation.
Foundation type: Independent foundation.
Financial data (yr. ended 11/30/13): Assets, $46,810,285 (M); expenditures, $15,259,877; qualifying distributions, $14,985,285; giving activities include $14,882,158 for 55 grants (high: $5,753,482; low: $2,000).
Purpose and activities: Giving primarily for the arts and education.
Fields of interest: Museums; Performing arts, opera; Historic preservation/historical societies; Arts; Higher education; Education; Environment; Hospitals (general); Jewish agencies & synagogues.
Limitations: Applications not accepted. Giving primarily in Washington, DC. No grants to individuals.
Application information: Contributes only to pre-selected organizations.
Officer and Directors:* Michelle Smith,* Pres.; Clarice R. Smith,* Secy.; David B. Smith, Treas.
EIN: 521502273
Selected grants: The following grants are a representative sample of this grantmaker's funding activity:
$5,753,482 to University of Maryland College Park Foundation, College Park, MD, 2013.
$2,000,000 to Thomas Jefferson Foundation, Charlottesville, VA, 2013.
$1,251,094 to New-York Historical Society, New York, NY, 2013.
$1,000,000 to Mayo Foundation, Rochester, MN, 2013.
$701,667 to George Washington University, Washington, DC, 2013.
$510,000 to Shakespeare Theater, Washington, DC, 2013.
$400,000 to Smithsonian American Art Museum, Washington, DC, 2013.
$350,000 to Johns Hopkins University, Baltimore, MD, 2013.
$100,000 to Georgetown University, Washington, DC, 2013.
$100,000 to Mount Vernon Ladies Association, Mount Vernon, VA, 2013.

9535
The Smithfield-Luter Foundation, Inc. ✧
200 Commerce St.
Smithfield, VA 23430-1204 (757) 365-3000
Contact: Stewart Leeth, Deputy Dir.
Main URL: http://www.smithfieldluterfoundation.com/

Established in 2002 in VA and NC.
Donors: Joseph W. Luter III; Smithfield Foods, Inc.
Foundation type: Company-sponsored foundation.
Financial data (yr. ended 11/30/13): Assets, $3,482,856 (M); gifts received, $1,968,166; expenditures, $2,289,460; qualifying distributions, $2,287,046; giving activities include $2,286,696 for 14 grants (high: $1,500,000; low: $2,300).
Purpose and activities: The foundation supports organizations involved with education and provides scholarships to dependent children and grandchildren of full-time and retired employees of Smithfield and its family of companies to attend select universities.
Fields of interest: Higher education; Scholarships/financial aid; Education; Cancer research; Economically disadvantaged.
Type of support: General/operating support; Program development; Scholarship funds; Employee-related scholarships.
Limitations: Applications not accepted. Giving primarily in areas of company operations in CA, IA, NC, TN, and VA.
Application information: Contributes only to pre-selected organizations and through employee-related scholarships.
Officer and Trustees:* Dennis H. Treacy,* Exec. Dir.; Joseph W. Luter IV; Francis Luter.
EIN: 542062029

9536
Snead Family Foundation ✧
103 Lockgreen Pl.
Richmond, VA 23226-1744 (804) 354-3510
Contact: Thomas G. Snead, Jr., Dir.; Vickie Snead, Dir.

Established in 2004 in VA.
Donors: Thomas G. Snead, Jr.; Vickie M. Snead.
Foundation type: Independent foundation.
Financial data (yr. ended 12/31/13): Assets, $2,426,030 (M); expenditures, $777,619; qualifying distributions, $761,148; giving activities include $759,050 for 27 grants (high: $500,000; low: $100).
Purpose and activities: The foundation focuses on projects that improve health, human services, and education.
Fields of interest: Higher education; Business school/education; Health care; Medical research; Human services; Children/youth, services.
Limitations: Applications accepted. Giving primarily in Richmond, VA. No grants to individuals.
Application information: Application form required.
Initial approach: Letter
Deadline(s): None
Directors: Lauren R. Snead; Thomas G. Snead, Jr.; Vickie M. Snead; Christen S. Trivette.
EIN: 201037290
Selected grants: The following grants are a representative sample of this grantmaker's funding activity:
$500 to CrossOver Ministry, Richmond, VA, 2012. For free clinic.

9537
Hattie M. Strong Foundation ✧
6551 Loisdale Ct., Ste. 160
Springfield, VA 22150-1820 (703) 313-6791
FAX: (703) 313-6793;
E-mail: hmsf@hmstrongfoundation.org; Main URL: http://www.hmstrongfoundation.org/

Incorporated in 1928 in DC.
Donors: Hattie M. Strong‡; L. Corrin Strong‡.
Foundation type: Independent foundation.
Financial data (yr. ended 08/31/13): Assets, $32,458,699 (M); gifts received, $2,113; expenditures, $1,537,651; qualifying distributions, $1,382,242; giving activities include $825,000 for 64 grants (high: $25,000; low: $5,000), and $150,000 for 15 grants to individuals (high: $10,000; low: $10,000).
Purpose and activities: The foundation administers two distinct programs: 1) a scholarship program aimed at college students enrolled in teacher-training programs at selected partnering institutions in addition to collecting outstanding student loans from previous student loan program. 2) A grant program, with the foundation's current priority aiming to assist organizations that provide out-of-school time (OST) programming during the after-school hours, Saturdays, and summers. Preference is given to programs that support, reinforce, and enrich the core academic objectives of the DC Public Schools, as well as character development, community service, good citizenship, and appreciation of the performing and visual arts.
Fields of interest: Elementary/secondary education; Adult education—literacy, basic skills & GED; Education, reading; Education; Infants/toddlers; Children/youth; Children; Minorities.
Type of support: General/operating support; Program development; Curriculum development; Scholarship funds.
Limitations: Applications not accepted. Giving limited to the Washington, DC, area for grant program. No support for programs of national or international scope. No grants to individuals, or for building or endowment funds, research, fellowships, equipment, conferences, special events or benefits, or projects designed to educate the general public.
Application information: Unsolicited requests for funds not accepted.
Board meeting date(s): Fall, spring, and summer
Officers and Directors:* Henry L. Strong,* Chair. and Pres.; Sigrid S. Reynolds,* V.P.; Robin C. Tanner, Secy.-Treas. and Exec. Dir.; Judith B. Cyphers; John M. Lynham, Jr.; Richard S.T. Marsh; H. Gregory Platts; C. Lockwood Reynolds; Carol L. Schwartz; Bente Strong.
Number of staff: 2 full-time professional; 1 full-time support; 1 part-time support.
EIN: 530237223
Selected grants: The following grants are a representative sample of this grantmaker's funding activity:
$25,000 to Salem College, Winston-Salem, NC, 2013. For HMSF Archiving Project.
$15,000 to Capital Partners for Education, Washington, DC, 2013. For out-of-school-time-program.

$15,000 to Community Lodgings, Alexandria, VA, 2013. For out-of-school-time academic support.
$15,000 to National Building Museum, Washington, DC, 2013. For out-of-school-time-programs(2).
$15,000 to Washington Animal Rescue League, Washington, DC, 2013. For out-of-school-time-programs.
$10,000 to Howard University, Washington, DC, 2013. For District of Columbia.
$10,000 to Salem College, Winston-Salem, NC, 2013. For North Carolina.
$10,000 to Shenandoah University, Winchester, VA, 2013. For Virginia.
$10,000 to Towson University, Towson, MD, 2013. For Maryland.
$5,000 to Washington Architectural Foundation, Washington, DC, 2013. For Programs Serving DCPS Children.

9538
Suffolk Foundation ✧ ☆
106 W. Finney Ave.
Suffolk, VA 23434 (757) 923-9090
Contact: William N. Hill, Exec. Dir.
FAX: (757) 539-8560;
E-mail: bhill@suffolkfoundation.org; Main URL: http://www.suffolkfoundation.org/

Established in 2006 in VA.
Foundation type: Community foundation.
Financial data (yr. ended 12/31/13): Assets, $5,509,147 (M); gifts received, $2,286,172; expenditures, $1,533,794; giving activities include $1,462,225 for 13+ grants (high: $510,000), and $5,000 for grants to individuals.
Purpose and activities: The foundation is an organization of individuals committed to the following: engage in charitable grant making; take other actions for a broad range of charitable needs to benefit the people of the City of Suffolk, Virginia, and the surrounding areas; and facilitate and develop philanthropy.
Fields of interest: Humanities; Arts; Education; Environment; Animal welfare; Health care; Children/youth, services; Aging, centers/services; Human services; Children/youth; Aging.
Limitations: Applications accepted. Giving primarily in the City of Suffolk, Virginia, and the surrounding areas. No support for religious purposes, hospitals and similar health-care facilities. No grants to individuals, or for deficit financing, debt reduction, research, event underwriting, seminar/conference registration or travel, annual fund drive, or ongoing operating support.
Publications: Application guidelines.
Application information: Applications must be mailed or hand delivered; visit foundation web site for grant application procedure. Application form required.
Initial approach: Submit application
Copies of proposal: 2
Deadline(s): Oct. 15
Board of Directors: Harry L. Cross III,* Pres.; James E. Butler III,* V.P.; Sarah H. Walden,* Secy.; Ryan E. Harrell,* Treas.; Willian N. "Billy" Hill,* Exec. Dir.; Richard F. Barry III; Charles Birdsong; George Y. Birdsong; R. Scott Carr; George W. Cornell, M.D.; Michael T. Haas; Les Hall; Angus I. Hines, Jr.; Oliver Kermit Hobbs, Jr.; David Mitnick; John Monroe; Charles B. Pond III; Whitney G. Saunders; Wayne K. Sawyer; Arthur L. Singleton; Marilyn H. Stulb; Michael Wendel; Eddie White.
EIN: 205998525

9539
SunTrust Foundation ✧
(formerly SunTrust Mid-Atlantic Foundation)
c/o SunTrust Banks, Inc.
919 E. Main St.
Richmond, VA 23219-4625 (804) 782-7907
Contact: Brenda L. Skidmore, Pres.
Main URL: https://www.suntrust.com/AboutUs/CommunityCommitment/Philanthropy

Established in 1973 in VA.
Donors: Crestar Bank; SunTrust Bank.
Foundation type: Company-sponsored foundation.
Financial data (yr. ended 12/31/12): Assets, $275,812,926 (M); gifts received, $39,000,000; expenditures, $11,613,559; qualifying distributions, $11,218,164; giving activities include $10,962,442 for grants.
Purpose and activities: The foundation supports organizations involved with arts and culture, education, health, cancer, human services, community and economic development, voluntarism promotion, and civic affairs.
Fields of interest: Museums; Museums (art); Performing arts centers; Performing arts, music; Performing arts, orchestras; Historic preservation/historical societies; Arts; Elementary/secondary education; Higher education; Business school/education; Theological school/education; Education, reading; Education; Medical care, community health systems; Hospitals (general); Health care; Cancer; Disasters, preparedness/services; American Red Cross; Salvation Army; YM/YWCAs & YM/YWHAs; Children, services; Human services, financial counseling; Human services; Urban/community development; Community development, business promotion; Community development, men's clubs; Community/economic development; Voluntarism promotion; United Ways and Federated Giving Programs; Leadership development; Public affairs.
Type of support: General/operating support; Annual campaigns; Capital campaigns; Building/renovation; Equipment; Employee matching gifts.
Limitations: Applications accepted. Giving limited to areas of company operations, with emphasis on Washington, DC, FL, GA, MD, NC, TN, SC, and VA. No support for government-supported, political, religious, or national organizations. No grants to individuals, or for research, scholarships, or fellowships; no loans.
Application information: Application form not required.
Initial approach: Proposal
Copies of proposal: 1
Deadline(s): Sept. 1
Board meeting date(s): Semiannually, and as required
Officers and Directors:* Brenda L. Skidmore,* Pres.; Jane A. Markins, Secy.-Treas.; Mark A. Chancy; C.T. Hll; Thomas G. Kuntz; William H. Rogers, Jr.; James M. Wells III; Jenner Wood.
Trustee: SunTrust Bank.
Number of staff: 2 full-time professional.
EIN: 237336418
Selected grants: The following grants are a representative sample of this grantmaker's funding activity:
$400,000 to New World Symphony, Miami Beach, FL, 2012. For general support.
$219,736 to JK Group, Trustees for SunTrust Foundation Matching Gift Program, Plainsboro, NJ, 2012. For general support.
$175,000 to Henry W. Grady Health System Foundation, Atlanta, GA, 2012. For general support.
$103,125 to Scholarship America, Saint Peter, MN, 2012. For general support.
$60,000 to Operation Hope, Los Angeles, CA, 2012. For general support.
$35,000 to Catholic Charities, 2012. For general support.
$5,000 to Arts Partnership of Greater Spartanburg, Spartanburg, SC, 2012. For general support.
$5,000 to Community Foundation of Greater Chattanooga, Chattanooga, TN, 2012. For general support.
$5,000 to Polk State College Foundation, Winter Haven, FL, 2012. For general support.
$3,000 to Second Chance Society, Fort Lauderdale, FL, 2012. For general support.

9540
Taubman Foundation for the Arts ✧ ☆
2965 Colonnade Dr.
Roanoke, VA 24018-3557 (540) 777-4506
Contact: Nicholas F. Taubman, Pres.

Established in VA.
Donor: Nicholas F. Taubman.
Foundation type: Independent foundation.
Financial data (yr. ended 12/31/12): Assets, $38,873,043 (M); gifts received, $3,889,801; expenditures, $3,831,475; qualifying distributions, $3,815,075; giving activities include $3,815,075 for 34 grants (high: $1,816,000; low: $1,000).
Fields of interest: Performing arts, opera; Arts.
Limitations: Applications accepted. Giving primarily in NY and VA.
Application information: Application form required.
Initial approach: Letter
Deadline(s): None
Officers and Director:* Nicholas F. Taubman, Pres.; Eugenia L. Taubman,* V.P.
EIN: 273136632

9541
Three Swallows Foundation ✧
12608 Wyclow Dr.
Clifton, VA 20124-1616

Established in 1981 in VA.
Foundation type: Independent foundation.
Financial data (yr. ended 10/31/13): Assets, $1,595,192 (M); expenditures, $1,175,216; qualifying distributions, $944,566; giving activities include $719,111 for 177 grants (high: $146,000; low: $15).
Fields of interest: Education; Health organizations, association; Neuroscience research; Human services; International development; United Ways and Federated Giving Programs; Christian agencies & churches.
Type of support: Research.
Limitations: Applications not accepted. No grants to individuals; no program-related investments.
Application information: Contributes only to pre-selected organizations.
Officer: Paul N. Temple, Pres.
Directors: Dunbar Abell; Marc Abell; James H. Brown; Monique Brown; Thomas Brown; Steven Greenberg; Lise Temple Greenberg; G. Michael Moore; Diane E. Temple; Nancy Temple; Paulina Temple; Robin Temple; Thomas Temple.
EIN: 521234546

Selected grants: The following grants are a representative sample of this grantmaker's funding activity:
$268,500 to International Foundation, Washington, DC, 2011.
$40,000 to Endowment for the Neurosciences, North Bellmore, NY, 2011.
$15,000 to Campus Crusade for Christ International, Orlando, FL, 2010.

9542
The John D. Tickle Foundation ✧
P.O. Box 1689
Bristol, VA 24203-1689

Established in 1989 in TN.
Donor: John D. Tickle.
Foundation type: Independent foundation.
Financial data (yr. ended 12/31/13): Assets, $9,583,325 (M); expenditures, $513,862; qualifying distributions, $473,105; giving activities include $470,000 for 11 grants (high: $250,000; low: $2,000).
Fields of interest: Higher education; Higher education, university; Boy scouts; United Ways and Federated Giving Programs.
Type of support: General/operating support.
Limitations: Applications not accepted. Giving primarily in FL and TN. No grants to individuals.
Application information: Contributes only to pre-selected organizations.
Trustee: John D. Tickle.
EIN: 541507449
Selected grants: The following grants are a representative sample of this grantmaker's funding activity:
$100,000 to Boy Scouts of America, Sequoyah Council, Johnson City, TN, 2012. For endowment fund.
$20,000 to Virginia Intermont College, Bristol, VA, 2012. For general purposes of the charitable donee.

9543
The Titmus Foundation, Inc. ✧
3516 Whippernock Farm Rd.
Sutherland, VA 23885-8720 (804) 265-5834
Contact: Edward B. Titmus, Pres.; Edward H. Titmus III, Exec. V.P.
FAX: (804) 265-5203; E-mail: tfound@aol.com; Mailing address: P.O. Box 10, Sutherland, VA 23885-0010

Incorporated in 1945 in VA.
Donors: Edward Hutson Titmus, Sr.†; Edward Hutson Titmus, Jr.†; Edward B. Titmus; Edward H. Titmus III.
Foundation type: Independent foundation.
Financial data (yr. ended 01/31/14): Assets, $25,354,348 (M); expenditures, $1,205,490; qualifying distributions, $1,052,341; giving activities include $902,700 for 106 grants (high: $164,500; low: $80).
Purpose and activities: Emphasis on Baptist church support and religious organizations, higher education, health, cancer research, and child welfare. Also giving for the United Methodist Church and two cancer-research centers. The foundation makes grants to organizations outside its normal giving area whenever there is a disaster such as the Gulf Coast disaster in 2005. This has been done on several occasions.
Fields of interest: Arts; Education; Health care; Health organizations, association; Cancer; Medical research, institute; Cancer research; Crime/violence prevention, domestic violence; Human services; Children/youth, services; Christian agencies & churches; Protestant agencies & churches; Religion; General charitable giving.
Type of support: General/operating support; Annual campaigns; Capital campaigns; Building/renovation; Equipment; Land acquisition; Endowments; Emergency funds; Professorships; Scholarship funds; Research; Matching/challenge support.
Limitations: Applications accepted. Giving primarily in VA; some funding also to various parts of NC. No support for a political party, or a specific politician regardless of their stand on any issue, or political organizations having anything to do with lobbyists. No grants to individuals; non tax-exempt organizations or organizations without a physical address.
Publications: Application guidelines; Annual report (including application guidelines).
Application information: Please contact foundation for application guidelines. The guidelines can be submitted via e-mail. No applications should be submitted in Jan. and Feb. Please check application guidelines for acceptable formats. Applications submitted by e-mail not accepted. Application form required.
Initial approach: Request guidelines
Copies of proposal: 1
Deadline(s): None
Board meeting date(s): Aug.
Final notification: Within 1 month prior to annual meeting
Officers: Edward B. Titmus, Pres.; Edward H. Titmus III, Exec. V.P.; William D. Allen II, V.P.; Andrew J. White, V.P.; William A. Young, Jr., V.P.; Kimberly T. Przybyl, Secy.; John J. Muldowney, Treas.
Number of staff: 1 full-time professional; 1 part-time professional; 1 full-time support.
EIN: 546051332

9544
Trehan Foundation ✧
(formerly Trehan Family Foundation, Inc.)
1308 Ballantrae Farm Dr.
McLean, VA 22101-3028

Established in 2003 in VA.
Donor: Ranvir Trehan.
Foundation type: Independent foundation.
Financial data (yr. ended 12/31/13): Assets, $14,117,365 (M); expenditures, $770,508; qualifying distributions, $711,779; giving activities include $701,754 for 27 grants (high: $225,000; low: $250).
Purpose and activities: Giving primarily for international development, particularly an organization focused on global poverty, as well as a performing arts center and human services.
Fields of interest: Performing arts centers; Human services; Children, services; International development; Public policy, research; Children.
International interests: India.
Limitations: Applications not accepted. Giving primarily in Washington, DC. No grants to individuals.
Application information: Contributes only to pre-selected organizations.
Officer: Ranvir Trehan, Pres. and Secy.
EIN: 270073510

9545
Truland Foundation ✧
1900 Oracle Way, Ste. 700
Reston, VA 20190-4733 (703) 464-3000
Contact: Robert W. Truland, Pres.

Established in 1954 in VA.
Donor: Truland Systems Corp.
Foundation type: Company-sponsored foundation.
Financial data (yr. ended 03/31/13): Assets, $196,885 (M); gifts received, $546,186; expenditures, $298,486; qualifying distributions, $514,417; giving activities include $514,417 for 26 grants (high: $230,000; low: $250).
Purpose and activities: The foundation supports maritime museums and organizations involved with education, health, cystic fibrosis, cancer, heart disease, and Christianity.
Fields of interest: Museums (marine/maritime); Historic preservation/historical societies; Elementary/secondary education; Higher education; Education; Hospitals (general); Health care; Cystic fibrosis; Cancer; Heart & circulatory diseases; Christian agencies & churches.
Type of support: Capital campaigns; General/operating support.
Limitations: Applications accepted. Giving primarily in Washington, DC, MD, and VA; some giving in Bermuda. No grants to individuals.
Application information: Application form required.
Initial approach: Letter
Deadline(s): None
Officers and Directors:* Robert W. Truland,* Pres.; Ingrid A. Moini, Secy.; Mary W. Truland.
EIN: 546037172
Selected grants: The following grants are a representative sample of this grantmaker's funding activity:
$100,000 to George Washington University, Washington, DC, 2012.
$100,000 to Shady Grove Adventist Hospital, Rockville, MD, 2011. For general operating support.
$7,500 to American Heart Association, Dallas, TX, 2012.
$5,000 to Boy Scouts of America, Philadelphia, PA, 2012.
$1,500 to Challenged Athletes Foundation, San Diego, CA, 2012.
$1,000 to Second Chance Wildlife Center, Gaithersburg, MD, 2012.

9546
The United Company Charitable Foundation ✧
(formerly United Coal Company Charitable Foundation)
1005 Glenway Ave.
Bristol, VA 24201-3473 (276) 645-1458
Contact: Jane Arnold, Admin. Asst.
FAX: (276) 645-1420; E-mail: jarnold@unitedco.net; Main URL: http://www.uccharitable.com/
Scholarship address: Rose Hurley, Mountain Mission School, 1760 Edgewater Dr., Grundy VA 24614, tel.: (276) 791-1514, e-mail: rhurley@unitedco.net

Established in 1986 in VA.
Donors: United Coal Co., Inc.; Burton Fletcher; The Summit Fund, LLC.
Foundation type: Company-sponsored foundation.
Financial data (yr. ended 12/31/13): Assets, $45,752,234 (M); expenditures, $3,661,331; qualifying distributions, $2,850,593; giving

activities include $2,290,243 for 100 grants (high: $400,000; low: $101).
Purpose and activities: The foundation supports organizations involved with arts and culture, education, health, hunger, human services, and the economically disadvantaged.
Fields of interest: Museums (art); Arts; Higher education; Libraries (public); Education; Health care, clinics/centers; Health care; Food services; Food banks; Boys & girls clubs; Boy scouts; Salvation Army; YM/YWCAs & YM/YWHAs; Children/youth, services; Human services.
Type of support: General/operating support; Capital campaigns; Building/renovation; Program development; Scholarship funds; Sponsorships; Scholarships—to individuals.
Limitations: Applications accepted. Giving primarily in TN and VA. No grants to individuals (except for scholarships) or for political or related causes; no loans.
Application information: Application form not required.
Initial approach: Contact foundation for application information for grants; contact foundation for application form for scholarships
Deadline(s): July 1 and Dec. 1 for scholarships
Final notification: 3 to 4 weeks for scholarships
Officers and Directors:* James W. McGlothlin,* Chair.; Martha McGlothlin-Gayle,* Pres.; Nicholas D. Street,* Secy.; Lois A. Clarke,* Treas.; Frances G. McGlothlin; David A. Street; Fay H. Street.
EIN: 541390453

9547
United Engineering Foundation, Inc. ✧
P.O. Box 651143
Potomac Falls, VA 20165-0070

Foundation type: Independent foundation.
Financial data (yr. ended 12/31/12): Assets, $17,318,306 (M); expenditures, $989,312; qualifying distributions, $771,735; giving activities include $678,816 for 10 grants (high: $148,000; low: $7,722).
Purpose and activities: The foundation seeks to support engineering and education by, among other means, making grants.
Fields of interest: Engineering school/education; Engineering/technology; Engineering.
Limitations: Applications not accepted. Giving primarily in the U.S., with emphasis on New York, NY.
Application information: Unsolicited requests for funds not accepted.
Officers: Dennis R. Martenson, Pres.; Michael E. Karmis, V.P.; Sam Y. Zamrik, Treas.; David L. Belden, Exec. Dir.
Trustees: Moshe Kam; Thomas G. Loughlin; Patrick J. Natale; E. James Prendergast; David O. Rosenthal; Ian Sadler; June C. Wispelwey.
EIN: 136162675

9548
Universal Leaf Foundation ✧
P.O. Box 25099
Richmond, VA 23260-5099 (804) 359-9311
Contact: H. Michael Ligon, V.P. and Dir.
Main URL: http://www.universalcorp.com/foundation/

Established in 1975 in VA.
Donor: Universal Leaf Tobacco Co., Inc.
Foundation type: Company-sponsored foundation.
Financial data (yr. ended 06/30/14): Assets, $17,223,454 (M); expenditures, $1,079,447; qualifying distributions, $1,063,700; giving activities include $1,063,700 for 309 grants (high: $275,000; low: $25).
Purpose and activities: The foundation supports organizations involved with arts and culture, education, conservation, health, cancer, hunger, human services, and community development.
Fields of interest: Performing arts; Historic preservation/historical societies; Arts; Higher education; Education; Environment, natural resources; Hospitals (general); Health care; Cancer; Food services; American Red Cross; YM/YWCAs & YM/YWHAs; Children/youth, services; Residential/custodial care; Aging, centers/services; Human services; Community/economic development; United Ways and Federated Giving Programs.
Type of support: General/operating support; Annual campaigns; Capital campaigns; Program development; Scholarship funds.
Limitations: Applications accepted. Giving primarily in Richmond, VA. No grants to individuals.
Application information: Application form not required.
Initial approach: Letter
Deadline(s): None
Officers and Directors:* George C. Freeman III,* Pres.; H. Michael Ligon,* V.P.; Catherine H. Claiborne,* Secy.; J. S. Rowe,* Treas.; David C. Moore; H. B. Smith.
Number of staff: 1 full-time professional; 1 part-time support.
EIN: 510162337
Selected grants: The following grants are a representative sample of this grantmaker's funding activity:
$100,000 to VCU Massey Cancer Center, Richmond, VA, 2011.
$25,000 to CenterStage Foundation, Richmond, VA, 2011.
$25,000 to United Way of Greater Richmond and Petersburg, Richmond, VA, 2011.
$25,000 to Virginia Foundation for Independent Colleges, Richmond, VA, 2011.
$22,937 to United Way of Greater Richmond and Petersburg, Richmond, VA, 2011.
$10,000 to Nature Conservancy, Charlottesville, VA, 2011.
$10,000 to YMCA, Lancaster Family, Lancaster, PA, 2011.
$5,000 to Better Housing Coalition, Richmond, VA, 2011.
$4,500 to Childrens Hospital, Richmond, VA, 2011.
$2,000 to Hampden-Sydney College, Development Office, Hampden Sydney, VA, 2011.

9549
The Volgenau Charitable Foundation ✧ ☆
c/o Maryanna Kieffer, Exec. Dir.
8300 Greensboro Dr., Ste. 1025
McLean, VA 22102-3621
Main URL: http://www.volgenaufoundation.org

Donors: Sara Lane Volgenau; Ernst Volgenau.
Foundation type: Independent foundation.
Financial data (yr. ended 12/31/13): Assets, $2,918,130 (M); gifts received, $3,388,660; expenditures, $608,265; qualifying distributions, $560,597; giving activities include $488,400 for 26 grants (high: $40,000; low: $5,000).
Fields of interest: Performing arts, music; Arts; Education; Environment; Human services.
Limitations: Applications not accepted.
Publications: IRS Form 990 or 990-PF printed copy available upon request.
Application information: Unsolicited requests for funds not accepted.
Officers: Ernst Volgenau, Ph.D., Pres.; Sara L. Volgenau, Secy.-Treas.; Maryanna L. Kieffer, Exec. Dir.
Directors: Lisa Volgenau; Lauren Volgenau Knapp; Jennifer Volgenau Wiley.
EIN: 451067224

9550
Elbert H., Evelyn J. and Karen H. Waldron Charitable Foundation, Inc. ✧
290 Boners Run Rd.
Shawsville, VA 24162

Established in 1982 in VA.
Donors: Elbert H. Waldron†; Evelyn J. Waldron; The E.H. Waldron Trust.
Foundation type: Independent foundation.
Financial data (yr. ended 12/31/13): Assets, $8,890,788 (M); expenditures, $459,981; qualifying distributions, $427,525; giving activities include $424,700 for 41 grants (high: $100,000; low: $750).
Purpose and activities: Giving primarily for community and public affairs, and service organizations.
Fields of interest: Higher education; Veterinary medicine; Community/economic development; Public affairs.
Limitations: Applications not accepted. Giving limited to VA. No grants to individuals.
Publications: Annual report.
Application information: Contributes only to pre-selected organizations.
Officers: Karen H. Waldron, Pres. and Treas.; Shawn A. Ricci, V.P. and Secy.
EIN: 521289232
Selected grants: The following grants are a representative sample of this grantmaker's funding activity:
$2,500 to Western Virginia Land Trust, Roanoke, VA, 2012. For Financial Support to Assist the Org. in Its Goals.

9551
Wardle Family Foundation ✧
3044 Beaumont Farm Rd.
Charlottesville, VA 22901-8705
Contact: William G. Wardle, Chair.

Established in 1987 in PA.
Donors: Robert V. Wardle†; Corinne G. Wardle†.
Foundation type: Independent foundation.
Financial data (yr. ended 12/31/13): Assets, $13,665,245 (M); expenditures, $739,426; qualifying distributions, $594,331; giving activities include $497,000 for 26 grants (high: $125,000; low: $500).
Purpose and activities: Giving primarily for children and youth services, and for human services.
Fields of interest: Human services; YM/YWCAs & YM/YWHAs; Children/youth, services.

Limitations: Applications not accepted. Giving primarily in Beaufort County, SC. Some giving in other communities where trustees reside. No grants to individuals.
Application information: Contributes only to pre-selected organizations.
Officers and Trustees:* William G. Wardle,* Chair. and Secy.; Megan W. Neary; Douglas G. Wardle; Robert B. Wardle.
EIN: 256290322
Selected grants: The following grants are a representative sample of this grantmaker's funding activity:
$115,000 to United Way of the Lowcountry, Beaufort, SC, 2012. For general support, Saint Helena Island Youth Project and abuse prevention.
$20,000 to YMCA of Beaufort County, Port Royal, SC, 2012. For camp and summer outreach programs in Jasper County and Sheldon and Port Royal.
$15,000 to Boys and Girls Clubs of the Lowcountry, Beaufort, SC, 2012. For Sheldon Boys and Girls Clubs.
$10,000 to Hope Haven of the Lowcountry, Beaufort, SC, 2012. For mental health treatment services for abused children.

9552
Washington Forrest Foundation ✧
2407 Columbia Pike, Ste. 200
Arlington, VA 22204-4470 (703) 920-3688
Contact: Deborah G. Lucckese, Pres.
FAX: (703) 920-0130; E-mail: washforr@aol.com

Incorporated in 1968 in VA.
Donors: Benjamin M. Smith†; Charlotte Smith Gravett†; Virginia N. Smith†.
Foundation type: Independent foundation.
Financial data (yr. ended 06/30/13): Assets, $16,462,513 (M); expenditures, $1,010,201; qualifying distributions, $881,340; giving activities include $798,945 for 118 grants (high: $25,000; low: $250).
Purpose and activities: Emphasis on youth programs; support also for the arts, education, health, community welfare and human services.
Fields of interest: Arts; Education; Health organizations, association; Human services; Children/youth, services; Religion.
Type of support: General/operating support; Continuing support; Annual campaigns; Capital campaigns; Building/renovation; Equipment; Endowments; Emergency funds; Program development; Seed money; Scholarship funds; Matching/challenge support.
Limitations: Applications accepted. Giving primarily in northern VA, with emphasis on South Arlington. The foundation defines northern VA as the counties of Arlington, Fairfax and Prince William, and the cities of Alexandria, Fairfax and Falls Church. Generally, no support for national programs, or foreign programs. No grants to individuals, or for fellowships or multi-year pledges.
Publications: Grants list; Program policy statement.
Application information: The foundation uses the WG Common Grant Application. Application form required.
Initial approach: Letter or telephone
Copies of proposal: 1
Deadline(s): Aug. 1, Nov. 1, Feb. 1, and May 1
Board meeting date(s): Mar., June, Sept., and Dec.
Final notification: 2 weeks after Board meeting
Officers and Directors:* Benjamin C. Gravett,* Pres.; Leslie Ariail,* V.P.; David D. Peete, Jr.,* Secy.; Allison Erdle,* Exec. Dir.; Rachel Mrad,* Treas.; Deborah G. Lucckese; Benjamin M. Smith, Jr.
Number of staff: 1 part-time professional.
EIN: 237002944

9553
The Watkins Family Charitable Foundation ✧
110 Wylderose Dr.
Midlothian, VA 23113-6842

Established in 1997 in VA.
Donors: Hays T. Watkins; H. Thomas Watkins III.
Foundation type: Independent foundation.
Financial data (yr. ended 12/31/13): Assets, $4,838,786 (M); expenditures, $1,185,537; qualifying distributions, $1,146,761; giving activities include $1,146,761 for 19 grants (high: $923,920; low: $500).
Fields of interest: Museums; Performing arts, music; Performing arts, orchestras; Higher education; Higher education, college; United Ways and Federated Giving Programs; Christian agencies & churches.
Limitations: Applications not accepted. Giving primarily in CT, Washington, DC, IL, and VA. No grants to individuals.
Application information: Contributes only to pre-selected organizations.
Trustees: Philip A. Huss; Betty J. Watkins; H. Thomas Watkins III; Hays T. Watkins; Wendy R. Watkins.
EIN: 541873256
Selected grants: The following grants are a representative sample of this grantmaker's funding activity:
$10,000 to University of Chicago, School of Business, Chicago, IL, 2012. For All contributions are Unrestricted unless otherwise noted.
$1,000 to Lake Forest Open Lands Association, Lake Forest, IL, 2012. For All contributions are Unrestricted unless otherwise noted.

9554
Weissberg Foundation ✧
1901 N. Moore St., Ste. 803
Arlington, VA 22209-1706
Contact: Marvin F. Weissberg, Pres.

Established in 1988 in DE.
Donors: Marvin F. Weissberg; Weissberg Corp.
Foundation type: Independent foundation.
Financial data (yr. ended 12/31/13): Assets, $8,474,069 (M); gifts received, $790,404; expenditures, $1,664,795; qualifying distributions, $1,638,710; giving activities include $1,313,423 for 66 grants (high: $325,000; low: $500).
Purpose and activities: The foundation works to strengthen social justice, combat poverty, improve health and enrich the arts in the Washington, DC, metropolitan area. The foundation is interested in programs that target underserved segments of society, as well as outreach that crosses and bridges ethnic and cultural communities. Interest also lies within artistic endeavors located in and genuinely involved with underserved communities, and in young organizations committed to new approaches to old problems. The foundation encourages proposals focused on community-centered initiatives and innovative approaches to effect socio-economic change.
Fields of interest: Performing arts; Arts; Health care; Women.
Type of support: General/operating support; Continuing support; Management development/ capacity building; Equipment; Program development; Publication; Seed money; Curriculum development; Fellowships; Scholarship funds; Technical assistance; Consulting services; Program evaluation; Program-related investments/loans; Matching/challenge support.
Limitations: Applications not accepted. Giving limited to the metropolitan Washington, DC, area (except for very limited circumstances). No support for programs that promote religious doctrine, or programs that receive Federal faith-based funding. No grants to individuals, or for special events or capital campaigns.
Publications: Grants list.
Application information: Unsolicited requests for funds not accepted.
Board meeting date(s): Spring and fall
Officers and Directors:* Marvin F. Weissberg,* Pres.; Nina V. Weissberg,* V.P.; Wallace K. Babington, Secy.; Barbara T. Napolitano,* Treas.; Ilene C. Trachtenberg,* Exec. Dir.; Martin Heyert; Courtney Morris; Weslie M. Weissberg.
Number of staff: 2 full-time professional.
EIN: 541475954
Selected grants: The following grants are a representative sample of this grantmaker's funding activity:
$400,000 to Global Fund for Women, San Francisco, CA, 2012. To create and support the Weissberg Fund for Women's Leadership.
$155,517 to Beloit College, Beloit, WI, 2012. For the Weissberg Program in Human Rights.
$100,000 to New York University, New York, NY, 2012. For the Weissberg Forum for Discourse in the Public Square, and construction of the NYU-DC Center.
$80,000 to Root Capital, Cambridge, MA, 2012. To fund the delivery of FASTrack services to gender inclusive businesses in the Andes.
$22,000 to 826DC, Washington, DC, 2012. For General operating support and to purchase a refurbished bookbinder for storytelling and bookmaking field trips.
$20,000 to DC Public Education Fund, Washington, DC, 2012. For the DCPS school improvement Catalyst Project.
$1,000 to Centenary College of Louisiana, Shreveport, LA, 2012. To carry out the mission of OUTreach on the Centenary College Campus.

9555
WestWind Foundation ✧
204 E. High St.
Charlottesville, VA 22902-5177 (434) 977-5762 x 24
FAX: (434) 977-3176;
E-mail: info@westwindfoundation.org; Main URL: http://www.westwindfoundation.org

Established in 1987 in DC.
Donors: Edward M. Miller; WWF, Ltd.
Foundation type: Independent foundation.
Financial data (yr. ended 12/31/12): Assets, $45,928,289 (M); expenditures, $3,989,059; qualifying distributions, $3,790,573; giving

activities include $3,790,573 for 125 grants (high: $356,000; low: $500).
Purpose and activities: The foundation is dedicated to protecting the integrity of natural ecosystems and the health of human communities through its grantmaking programs. WestWind tends to provide more general support grants, but the foundation will also provide grants for project or program specific requests.
Fields of interest: Education; Environment, land resources; Environment, forests; Environment; Reproductive health, family planning; Youth development; Human services; Youth; Young adults.
International interests: Caribbean; Latin America.
Type of support: General/operating support; Continuing support; Land acquisition; Program development; Conferences/seminars; Matching/challenge support.
Limitations: Giving on a national level, with emphasis on the Southeast, for environment program. Giving is primarily targeted toward benefiting Latin America and the Caribbean for Reproductive Health and Rights program, although domestic support is available. No support for religious organizations. No grants to individuals, or for capital campaigns, endowments or brick and mortar projects.
Publications: Application guidelines; Grants list.
Application information: Current application guidelines and deadlines available on foundation web site.
Board meeting date(s): May, Sept., and Nov.
Trustees: Janet H. Miller; Edward M. Miller.
Number of staff: 1 full-time support.
EIN: 526358830

9556
W.W. Whitlock Foundation ✧ ☆
P.O. Box 130
Mineral, VA 23117-0130 (540) 894-5451
Contact: John D. Whitlock, Pres.; Jane W. Sisk, V.P.

Established around 1980.
Donors: John D. Whitlock; Jane W. Sisk.
Foundation type: Independent foundation.
Financial data (yr. ended 12/31/13): Assets, $3,678,647 (M); expenditures, $674,552; qualifying distributions, $644,528; giving activities include $644,528 for 87 grants (high: $200,000; low: $25).
Fields of interest: Education; Human services; United Ways and Federated Giving Programs; Protestant agencies & churches; Religion.
Limitations: Applications accepted. Giving primarily in VA. No grants to individuals.
Application information:
Initial approach: Letter
Deadline(s): None
Officers: John D. Whitlock, Pres.; Jane W. Sisk, V.P.; Alison Tyler, Secy.
EIN: 521532383
Selected grants: The following grants are a representative sample of this grantmaker's funding activity:
$10,000 to CenterStage Foundation, Richmond, VA, 2011.
$10,000 to Saint Catherines School Foundation, Richmond, VA, 2011.
$8,750 to Family Foundation, Richmond, VA, 2011.
$5,625 to Family Foundation, Richmond, VA, 2011.
$5,625 to Family Foundation, Richmond, VA, 2011.
$5,625 to Family Foundation, Richmond, VA, 2011.
$5,000 to Mission to the World, Lawrenceville, GA, 2011.
$5,000 to Saint Catherines School, Richmond, VA, 2011.
$5,000 to Saint Christophers School Foundation, Richmond, VA, 2011.
$2,500 to Collegiate School, Richmond, VA, 2011.

9557
The William Gerald Willett Charitable Foundation ✧ ☆
2809 Whirlaway Cir.
Oak Hill, VA 20171-2031

Established in 2007 in VA.
Donors: William G. Willett; Lynne Willett.
Foundation type: Independent foundation.
Financial data (yr. ended 12/31/13): Assets, $5,704,496 (M); gifts received, $399,704; expenditures, $694,378; qualifying distributions, $687,776; giving activities include $683,675 for 12 grants (high: $220,000; low: $75).
Purpose and activities: Giving primarily for higher education; some funding also for Christian and Catholic church support.
Fields of interest: Higher education; Christian agencies & churches; Catholic agencies & churches.
Limitations: Applications not accepted. Giving primarily in KY, TN and VA. No grants to individuals.
Application information: Unsolicited requests for funds not accepted.
Officer: William G. Willett, Pres.
EIN: 260890463

9558
Williamsburg Community Health Foundation ✧
4801 Courthouse St., Ste. 200
Williamsburg, VA 23188-2678 (757) 345-0912
Contact: Jeanne Zeidler, C.E.O. and Pres.
FAX: (757) 345-0913;
E-mail: info@williamsburghealthfoundation.org;
Main URL: http://www.wchf.com

Established in 1996 in VA; converted from the partnership between the Williamsburg Community Hospital and Sentara Health System.
Foundation type: Independent foundation.
Financial data (yr. ended 12/31/12): Assets, $117,781,000 (M); expenditures, $5,627,000; qualifying distributions, $5,300,000; giving activities include $4,531,000 for 61 grants (high: $554,000; low: $500), and $124,000 for 5 foundation-administered programs.
Purpose and activities: Giving to improve the health of people living in Williamsburg, VA, and surrounding counties by strengthening access to quality health services and promoting responsible health practices. At present, the foundation is continuing to focus on challenges to the healthcare safety net, including challenges posed by the economic downturn and the resulting rise in citizens who are medically underserved. Grant consideration is also given to programs that strengthen health care for all citizens in the greater Williamsburg area by emphasizing wellness, offering preventive care, providing health-oriented educational programs and/or increase access to high-quality, cost-effective healthcare.
Fields of interest: Medical care, community health systems; Health care; Substance abuse, services; Infants/toddlers; Children/youth; Youth; Adults; Aging; Disabilities, people with; Substance abusers; Economically disadvantaged.
Type of support: Research; General/operating support; Continuing support; Management development/capacity building; Program development; Program evaluation.
Limitations: Applications accepted. Giving primarily to organizations and programs serving the cities of Williamsburg and Poquoson and the counties of James City, York, and Gloucester, VA. No support for organizations limiting services to an exclusive membership or to political organizations. No grants to individuals or for lobbying activities, annual appeals and fundraisers, real estate acquisition, or restoration of funds cut by government or other organizations; no multi-year grants.
Publications: Application guidelines; Annual report; Grants list; Program policy statement.
Application information: For application guidelines see foundation web site. Application form required.
Initial approach: Online letter of intent
Copies of proposal: 1
Deadline(s): First and Second annual grant cycles
Board meeting date(s): Quarterly
Final notification: Approximately 4 months
Officers and Trustees:* Douglas Myers,* Chair.; Jeffrey O. Smith,* Vice-Chair.; Jeanne Zeidler, Secy.; James R. Golden,* Treas.; Stephen R. Adkins; Catherine Allport; David C. Anderson; David E. Bush; Hon. Cressondra B. Conyers; Randall Foskey; F. Brian Hiestand; Dr. Joyce M. Jarrett; Laura J. Loda; Virginia L. McLaughlin; Stephen Montgomery; Richard H. Rizk; Lois F. Rossiter; Richard Schreiber; Richard G. Smith; Marshall N. Warner; Jonathan V. Weiss; Clarence A. Wilson; Kimberly Zeuli.
Number of staff: 6 full-time professional; 2 full-time support.
EIN: 541822359
Selected grants: The following grants are a representative sample of this grantmaker's funding activity:
$554,000 to Williamsburg-James City County Public Schools, Williamsburg, VA, 2012. For School Health Initiative Program (SHIP).
$515,816 to Olivet Medical Ministry, Yorktown, VA, 2012. For Chronic Care Collaborative.
$446,198 to Virginia Health Care Foundation, Richmond, VA, 2012. For Greater Williamsburg Medication Assistance Program (GWMAP).
$426,533 to Olde Towne Medical Center, Williamsburg, VA, 2012. For core program support.
$332,363 to Colonial Behavioral Health, 2012. For Children's Behavioral Health Initiative (CBHI).
$295,000 to Gloucester-Mathews Free Clinic, Hayes, VA, 2012. For Chronic Care Collaborative.
$245,000 to Olde Towne Medical Center, Williamsburg, VA, 2012. For Chronic Care Collaborative.
$128,000 to Peninsula Agency on Aging, Newport News, VA, 2012. For Senior Health Assistance Resource Project (SHARP).
$115,000 to New Horizons Family Counseling, VA, 2012. For Children's Emotional and Behavioral Health: Empowering At-Risk Families.
$100,000 to Historic Triangle Senior Center Association, Williamsburg, VA, 2012. For RIDES.

9559
Greater Williamsburg Community Trust ✧
(also known as Williamsburg Community Foundation)
424 Scotland St.
Williamsburg, VA 23185 (757) 259-1660
Contact: Nancy Cote Sullivan, Exec. Dir.
FAX: (757) 259-1227;
E-mail: office@williamsburgcommunityfoundation.org; Mailing Address: P.O. Box 2821, Williamsburg, VA 23187; Additional e-mail: ncsullivan@williamsburgcommunityfoundation.org; Main URL: http://www.williamsburgcommunityfoundation.org/
Facebook: http://www.facebook.com/WilliamsburgCommunityFoundation
LinkedIn: http://www.linkedin.com/company/williamsburg-community-foundation?trk=top_nav_home

Established in 1999 in VA.
Foundation type: Community foundation.
Financial data (yr. ended 01/31/14): Assets, $4,869,536 (M); gifts received, $623,508; expenditures, $779,603; giving activities include $442,947 for 15+ grants (high: $28,500), and $152,550 for 115 grants to individuals.
Purpose and activities: The foundation connects people who care with causes that matter in the local community. The foundation pursues this mission by: 1) helping donors respond to emerging and changing community needs; 2) building a permanent, flexible endowment; 3) providing effective stewardship of charitable funds; and 4) serving as a resource, catalyst and coordinator for charitable activities.
Fields of interest: Historic preservation/historical societies; Arts; Education; Health care; Human services; Community/economic development.
Limitations: Applications accepted. Giving primarily in Williamsburg, VA.
Publications: Annual report; Newsletter.
Application information: Visit foundation web site for application form and guidelines per grant type. Application form required.
Initial approach: Contact foundation
Board meeting date(s): Sept. and Dec.
Officers and Trustees:* Michael D. Maddocks,* Chair.; Margaret Beck Pritchard,* Vice-Chair.; Kendall S. Kerby,* Secy.; Robert G. Topping,* Treas.; Nancy Sullivan, Exec. Dir.; James N. Allburn; Betsy C. Anderson; Carol S. Beers; Joseph R. Burkart; John R. Curtis, Jr.; Margaret M. Driscoll; Paul Gerhardt; Susanna B. Hickman; Kathy Hornsby; Karen Jamison; Mark Monroe; Bill Morrison; Randy W. Myers; Joe Poole, III; William L. Roberts, Jr.; Roger E. Schultz, M.D.; Craig Stambaugh; Alfred L. Woods.
EIN: 541927558

9560
Wise Foundation ✧
P.O. Box 557
Marshall, VA 20116-0557

Established in 1999 in VA.
Donors: Mary L.F. Wiley†; The Flagler Foundation.
Foundation type: Independent foundation.
Financial data (yr. ended 12/31/13): Assets, $20,813,805 (M); gifts received, $26,182; expenditures, $836,541; qualifying distributions, $770,254; giving activities include $758,000 for 73 grants (high: $82,000; low: $500).
Purpose and activities: Giving to local community projects.
Fields of interest: Elementary/secondary education; Higher education; Education; Animal welfare; Disasters, fire prevention/control; Human services.
Limitations: Applications not accepted. Giving primarily in VA. No grants to individuals.
Application information: Contributes only to pre-selected organizations.
Officers and Directors:* Lewis B. Pollard,* Pres. and Secy.-Treas.; Lewis S. Wiley,* V.P.
EIN: 541942771

9561
The Bob Wiser Charitable Foundation Trust ✧
11032 Brent Town Rd.
Catlett, VA 20119-2404

Established in 1994 in VA.
Donor: Bob Wiser.
Foundation type: Independent foundation.
Financial data (yr. ended 06/30/13): Assets, $4,289,452 (M); expenditures, $480,758; qualifying distributions, $442,000; giving activities include $442,000 for grants.
Fields of interest: Youth, services; Residential/custodial care.
Limitations: Applications not accepted. Giving primarily in VA; with emphasis on Bristow. No grants to individuals.
Application information: Contributes only to pre-selected organizations.
Trustees: Irving L. Greenspon; Rhonda J. MacDonald; Nancy B. Padgett.
EIN: 546372531
Selected grants: The following grants are a representative sample of this grantmaker's funding activity:
$426,000 to Youth for Tomorrow, Bristow, VA, 2013. For Furtherance of Charitable Purposes.

9562
Wrinkle in Time Foundation, Inc. ✧
P.O. Box 306
The Plains, VA 20198-0306

Established in 1980 in NY.
Donor: Andrea B. Currier.
Foundation type: Independent foundation.
Financial data (yr. ended 12/31/13): Assets, $9,033,795 (M); expenditures, $646,631; qualifying distributions, $578,853; giving activities include $578,500 for 10 grants (high: $176,000; low: $2,500).
Purpose and activities: Giving primarily for improving the rural and urban environment; including wildlife and wilderness preservation; as well as to gather, preserve and disseminate information about the environment, make productive contributions to either the rural or urban surroundings; restore and maintain historic buildings, sites and antiquities; or encourage, promote and popularize art or design which enhances the rural or urban environment.
Fields of interest: Education; Environment, natural resources; Environment; Animals/wildlife, preservation/protection; Rural development.
Type of support: General/operating support; Capital campaigns; Program development; Seed money.
Limitations: Applications not accepted. Giving primarily in VA. No grants to individuals; no loans.
Application information: Contributes only to pre-selected organizations.
Board meeting date(s): Jan., Apr., July, and Oct.
Officers and Director:* Andrea B. Currier,* Chair.; Earl H. Douple, Jr., Secy.-Treas.
Number of staff: None.
EIN: 222351518
Selected grants: The following grants are a representative sample of this grantmaker's funding activity:
$440,000 to Bull Run Mountains Conservancy, Broad Run, VA, 2012. For operating support and capital campaign.

9563
Wythe-Bland Foundation ✧
(formerly Wythe-Bland Community Foundation)
180 W. Main St., Ste. 4
Wytheville, VA 24382-2330 (276) 228-8001
Contact: Travis Jackson, C.O.O. and Exec. Dir.
FAX: (276) 228-9001;
E-mail: tjackson@wbfoundation.org; Main URL: http://www.wbcfoundation.org
Scholarship address: c/o Wytheville Community College, 1000 E. Main St., Wytheville, CA 24382

Established in 1991 in VA.
Foundation type: Independent foundation.
Financial data (yr. ended 09/30/13): Assets, $50,997,525 (M); expenditures, $3,075,124; qualifying distributions, $2,941,241; giving activities include $2,191,131 for 26 grants (high: $607,206; low: $218), and $545,335 for grants to individuals.
Purpose and activities: Giving primarily to improve the health, education and welfare of the citizens of the Wythe and Bland communities, with an emphasis on health care needs. Interests include, but are not limited to: 1) projects that directly serve persons unable to afford basic healthcare; 2) projects that serve the general public through the provision of health education; and 3) projects that promote or improve the health and education of the citizens in Wythe and Bland counties.
Fields of interest: Health care; Community/economic development.
Type of support: Program development; Scholarships—to individuals.
Limitations: Giving limited to Wythe and Bland counties, VA. No support for religious organizations for religious purposes, or organizations outside of the foundation's service area. No grants to individuals (except for scholarships), endowments or other discretionary funding pools, dinners, fund-raisers, other ticketed special events, lobbying, or debt reduction.
Publications: Application guidelines; Annual report; Financial statement; Grants list; Newsletter.
Application information: Follow specific instructions on Grant Guidelines on foundation web site. Letters of general endorsement for the applicant's project are not accepted. However, letters from partnering agencies are acceptable. Each grant application should be bound with document clips. Do not use paper clips, rubber bands, three-ring binders or commercial binding services. Applications arriving past the deadline date will be returned to the applicant. Scholarship applications and information may be provided by a high school counselor. See foundation web site for scholarship brochure.

Initial approach: Submit application with cover page which can be downloaded from foundation web site
Copies of proposal: 14
Deadline(s): Feb. 1 and Aug. 1 for Grants
Board meeting date(s): Quarterly
Final notification: Apr. and Oct. for Grants

Officers: Stephen D. Bear, Chair. and C.E.O.; Mary S. Boenke, Vice-Chair.; Timothy D. Havens, Secy.; Stephen A. Moore, Treas.; Travis Jackson, C.O.O. and Exec. Dir.

Directors: Timothy A. Bess; G. Jack Bryant; Debbie D. Clark, D.P.T.; Joseph W. Freeman; Kathy H. Havens; Alan Hawthorne, Ph.D.; Lee H. Johnson; Betty K. Munsey; Michael W. Spraker, D.D.S.

Number of staff: 1 part-time professional.

EIN: 541609065

Selected grants: The following grants are a representative sample of this grantmaker's funding activity:

$10,000 to Rx Partnership, Richmond, VA, 2013. For technical and audit assistance for free clinic.

WASHINGTON

9564
25-40 Foundation ✧
P.O. Box 29566
Bellingham, WA 98228-1566

Established in WA.
Donor: Paul B. Carlson.
Foundation type: Independent foundation.
Financial data (yr. ended 12/31/13): Assets, $10,523,612 (M); expenditures, $698,770; qualifying distributions, $563,422; giving activities include $559,020 for 15 grants (high: $75,000; low: $15,000).
Fields of interest: International affairs; Foundations (community).
Limitations: Applications not accepted. Giving primarily in WA.
Application information: Unsolicited requests for funds not accepted.
Officers: Thomas O. Carlson, Pres.; Elizabeth R. Larcom, Secy.; Mary R. Carlson, Treas.
Directors: Roger W. Carlson; Anne L. Feiertag.
EIN: 205734304
Selected grants: The following grants are a representative sample of this grantmaker's funding activity:
$60,000 to World Vision, Federal Way, WA, 2012. For Uganda Water/Sanitation.

9565
444S Foundation ✧
(also known as 444 Sierra Foundation)
P.O. Box 1128
Bellevue, WA 98009-1128
Contact: Peggy Ford, Fdn. Admin.
E-mail: 444s@kamutlake.net

Established in 1998 in WA.
Donor: G. James Roush.
Foundation type: Independent foundation.
Financial data (yr. ended 12/31/13): Assets, $41,831,686 (M); expenditures, $2,363,127; qualifying distributions, $2,019,136; giving activities include $1,710,000 for 33 grants (high: $165,000; low: $5,000).
Purpose and activities: Giving to support environmental, wild lands and wildlife protection efforts. This includes northern wild lands and forests.
Fields of interest: Environment, natural resources; Animals/wildlife, preservation/protection.
International interests: Canada.
Type of support: General/operating support; Program development; Matching/challenge support.
Limitations: Applications not accepted. Giving primarily for the benefit of the Pacific Northwest, including western Canada, AK, and the Arctic. No grants to individuals or for media projects.
Application information: Contributes only to pre-selected organizations. Foundation will solicit proposals. Unsolicited requests for funds not accepted.
Board meeting date(s): Varies
Officer: Fred Munson, Exec. Dir.
Trustees: Amy Gulick; Del Langbauer; G. James Roush; William Morgan Roush; James Sheldon; Cynthia Wayburn; Corrie Yackulic.
Number of staff: 1 full-time professional; 1 part-time support.
EIN: 916468421

9566
Moss Adams Foundation ✧
999 Third Ave., Ste. 300
Seattle, WA 98104-4019
E-mail: christopher.myers@mossadams.com

Established in 1994 in WA.
Donors: Moss Adams LLP; Robert Bunting; Roger Peterson; Arthur Miles; Chris Schmidt; Rick Anderson; Joe Karas; Tony Maki; Russ Wilson.
Foundation type: Company-sponsored foundation.
Financial data (yr. ended 12/31/12): Assets, $402,564 (M); gifts received, $54,399; expenditures, $450,889; qualifying distributions, $450,889; giving activities include $450,864 for 45 grants (high: $81,220; low: $400).
Purpose and activities: Giving to support accounting programs at institutions of higher learning located in the western states.
Fields of interest: Education; Youth development; Human services.
Type of support: General/operating support.
Limitations: Applications not accepted. Giving primarily in the Western U.S. No grants to individuals.
Application information: Contributes only to pre-selected organizations.
Officer: Russ Wilson, Chair. and Pres.
Directors: David Allen; Gregg Amend; Corinne Baughman; Amy Runge; Trace Skopil.
EIN: 911496816

9567
The Paul G. Allen Family Foundation ✧
505 5th Ave. S., Ste. 900
Seattle, WA 98104-3821 (206) 342-2030
Contact: Lisa Arnold, Grants Mgr.
FAX: (206) 342-3030;
E-mail: info@pgafamilyfoundation.org; Additional contact inf. for Lisa Arnold, e-mail: lisaa@pgafamilyfoundation.org, fax: (206) 342-3085; Main URL: http://www.pgafamilyfoundation.org
Grants Database: http://www.pgafamilyfoundation.org/Grants/Grantee-List
Multimedia: http://www.pgafamilyfoundation.org/News
Paul G. Allen's Giving Pledge Profile: http://glasspockets.org/philanthropy-in-focus/eye-on-the-giving-pledge/profiles/allen

Established in 2005 in WA. In 2004, The Paul G. Allen Charitable Foundation, along with The Allen Foundation for the Arts, The Paul G. Allen Foundation for Medical Research, The Paul G. Allen Forest Protection Foundation, The Allen Foundation for Music, and The Paul G. Allen Virtual Education Foundation, were consolidated into a new foundation, The Paul G. Allen Family Foundation.
Donors: Paul G. Allen; The Paul G. Allen Foundation for Medical Research; The Paul G. Allen Virtual Education Foundation; The Allen Foundation for Music.
Foundation type: Independent foundation.
Financial data (yr. ended 12/31/12): Assets, $286,858,712 (M); expenditures, $19,444,808; qualifying distributions, $18,578,965; giving activities include $18,570,900 for 237 grants (high: $3,000,000; low: $539).
Purpose and activities: The mission of the foundation is to transform lives and strengthen communities by fostering innovation, creating knowledge, and promoting social programs. The foundation advances its mission through focusing on the following key areas: arts and culture, asset building, basic needs, libraries, innovations in science and technology and youth education.
Fields of interest: Museums; Performing arts; Arts; Libraries (public); Education; Human services; Youth, services; Science; Children/youth; Native Americans/American Indians; Economically disadvantaged.
Type of support: Income development; Management development/capacity building; Capital campaigns; Building/renovation; Emergency funds; Program development; Research; Technical assistance; Program evaluation; Matching/challenge support.
Limitations: Giving primarily in the Pacific Northwest, including AK, ID, MT, OR and WA. No support for sectarian or religious organizations whose principle activity is for the benefit of their own members or adherents, or for organizations whose policies or practices discriminate on the basis of ethnic, origin, gender, race, religion, or sexual orientation. No grants to individuals or for general operating support, annual appeals, federated campaigns, general fund drives, scholarships, special events or sponsorships, or for projects not aligned with the foundation's specified program areas; no loans.
Publications: Application guidelines; Grants list; Multi-year report; Occasional report.
Application information: Unsolicited letters of inquiry and proposals are not accepted. Full proposals are by invitation. Although foundation's process is by invitation, applicants are encouraged to contact the staff through the foundation's web site if their projects are aligned with the foundation's programs.
Copies of proposal: 1
Board meeting date(s): Spring and fall
Final notification: 7 months
Officers and Directors:* Paul G. Allen,* Chair.; Jo Lynn Allen,* Pres.; Susan Drake, V.P.; Allen D. Israel, Secy.
Number of staff: 8 full-time professional.
EIN: 943082532
Selected grants: The following grants are a representative sample of this grantmaker's funding activity:
$3,000,000 to University of Washington Foundation, Seattle, WA, 2012. For the Kenneth S. and Faye G. Allen Library Endowment.
$2,000,000 to Lakeside School, Seattle, WA, 2012. For capital campaign to build athletics center.
$600,000 to Seattle Public School District, Seattle, WA, 2012. For capacity building project focused on development and implementation of Diplomas Now Tool. Diplomas Now operates in middle and high schools and is a public-private partnership between three major national nonprofits, local school districts and our funders.
$340,000 to Book-It Repertory Theater, Seattle, WA, 2012. For the Faye G. Allen Book-It Roadshow.
$200,000 to Artspace, Seattle, WA, 2012. For capital campaign for construction of Mount Baker Station Lofts.
$190,000 to Library Foundation, Portland, OR, 2012. For capacity building project for new models of Reader Advisory services.

$150,000 to Home Forward, Portland, OR, 2012. To develop a financial education curriculum for affordable housing residents in Multnomah County.
$150,000 to Washington Community Alliance for Self Help, Seattle, WA, 2012. For asset building program for low-income entrepreneurs.
$116,000 to Online Computer Library Center, Seattle, WA, 2012. To support capacity building of public libraries for community engagement.
$100,000 to Innovative Changes, Portland, OR, 2012. To enhance loan program and financial education curriculum.
$100,000 to Seattle Tilth Association, Seattle, WA, 2012. To expand microenterprise program for low-income farmers.
$50,000 to Association for the Advancement of Contemporary Dance, Trey McIntyre Project, Boise, ID, 2012. For capacity building toward mplementation of earned income project.
$28,063 to Special Olympics Washington, Seattle, WA, 2012. For youth activities through Spirit of 12 program.
$25,000 to Hockaday Museum of Art, Kalispell, MT, 2012. For capacity building project for audience research and marketing.
$20,000 to Boise Contemporary Theater, Boise, ID, 2012. For production of A Nighttime Survival Guide.
$10,000 to Bunnell Street Arts Center, Homer, AK, 2012. For Visual Art Exhibition program.

9568
Allen Institute for Artificial Intelligence ✧ ☆
c/o Vulcan Inc.
505 5th Ave. S., Ste. 900
Seattle, WA 98104-3821

Donor: Paul G. Allen.
Foundation type: Independent foundation.
Financial data (yr. ended 12/31/12): Assets, $6,420 (M); gifts received, $950,000; expenditures, $953,658; qualifying distributions, $953,658; giving activities include $949,636 for 1 grant.
Purpose and activities: Giving primarily to a free non-profit knowledge database in Germany.
Fields of interest: Media/communications.
Limitations: Applications not accepted. Giving primarily in Berlin, Germany.
Application information: Unsolicited requests for funds not accepted.
Officers and Director:* Paul G. Allen, Chair.; Jo Lynn Allen,* Pres.; Susan Drake, V.P.; Mark Greaves, V.P.
EIN: 275430153

9569
Almi Foundation, Inc. ✧
(formerly The M.A.C.H. Foundation)
601 Union St., Ste. 3300
Seattle, WA 98101-4024

Established in 1989 in DE and CA; named Rafael Foundation; first name change in 1999 to The Mach Foundation; second name changed in 2007 to Almi Foundation, Inc.
Donor: Yolande L. Jurzykowski.
Foundation type: Independent foundation.
Financial data (yr. ended 12/31/12): Assets, $14,348,620 (M); expenditures, $3,780,215; qualifying distributions, $3,600,361; giving activities include $3,600,361 for 4 grants (high: $1,858,686; low: $25,000).
Fields of interest: Philanthropy/voluntarism; Buddhism.
Limitations: Applications not accepted. Giving primarily in CA; some giving also in AZ. No grants to individuals.
Application information: Contributes only to pre-selected organizations.
Officers: Yolande L. Jurzykowski, Pres.; Robyn Doecke, Secy.
EIN: 680203129

9570
Ames Family Foundation ✧ ☆
c/o Gary Ames
10566 N.E. Country Club Rd.
Bainbridge Island, WA 98110

Established in 2000 in WA.
Donors: A. Gary Ames; Barbara J. Ames.
Foundation type: Independent foundation.
Financial data (yr. ended 12/31/13): Assets, $462,971 (M); expenditures, $451,714; qualifying distributions, $448,000; giving activities include $423,000 for 9 grants (high: $250,000; low: $1,000).
Fields of interest: Arts; Higher education; Education; Human services.
Limitations: Applications not accepted. Giving primarily in NM, OR, and WA. No grants to individuals.
Application information: Contributes only to pre-selected organizations.
Trustees: A. Gary Ames; Barbara J. Ames; Eric C. Ames; Megan E. Barjesteh.
EIN: 916511506

9571
The Anders Foundation ✧ ☆
P.O. Box 184
Deer Harbor, WA 98243-0184
Contact: William A. Anders

Established in 1993 in WA.
Donors: William A. Anders; Valerie E. Anders; Tom Hanks.
Foundation type: Independent foundation.
Financial data (yr. ended 12/31/13): Assets, $4,224,445 (M); gifts received, $25; expenditures, $3,228,632; qualifying distributions, $3,171,650; giving activities include $3,171,650 for 24 grants (high: $2,210,000; low: $1,000).
Purpose and activities: Giving primarily for environmental educational programs.
Fields of interest: Museums (specialized); Arts; Education; Recreation; Foundations (community).
Type of support: General/operating support.
Limitations: Applications not accepted. Giving primarily in CA and WA. No grants to individuals.
Application information: Unsolicited requests for funds not accepted.
Directors: Valerie E. Anders; William A. Anders.
EIN: 911612850

9572
Anderson Foundation ✧
537 10th Ave. W.
Kirkland, WA 98033-4839

Established in 1952 in WA.
Donors: Charles M. Anderson†; Dorothy I. Anderson; William Anderson; Barbara A. Lawrence.
Foundation type: Independent foundation.
Financial data (yr. ended 06/30/13): Assets, $26,707,593 (M); expenditures, $1,856,800; qualifying distributions, $1,800,000; giving activities include $1,800,000 for 37 grants (high: $400,000; low: $2,500).
Purpose and activities: Giving primarily for education, social services, medical research, hospitals, including a children's hospital, as well as for other children and youth services.
Fields of interest: Higher education; Education; Hospitals (general); Hospitals (specialty); Medical research, institute; Human services; Children/youth, services.
Type of support: Building/renovation; Equipment; Professorships; Scholarship funds; Research.
Limitations: Applications not accepted. Giving primarily in WA, with emphasis on Seattle. No grants to individuals, or for endowment funds or matching gifts; no loans.
Application information: Contributes only to pre-selected organizations.
Board meeting date(s): Annually
Officers: Katharine L. Murray, Pres.; Charlie Anderson, V.P.; David Murray, Secy.
Number of staff: 2 part-time support.
EIN: 916031724
Selected grants: The following grants are a representative sample of this grantmaker's funding activity:
$200,000 to Salk Institute for Biological Studies, La Jolla, CA, 2011.
$200,000 to Whitman College, Walla Walla, WA, 2011.
$112,500 to Overlake Hospital Foundation, Bellevue, WA, 2011.
$100,000 to Independent Colleges of Washington, Seattle, WA, 2011.
$56,500 to Ryther Child Center, Seattle, WA, 2011.
$50,000 to Childhaven, Seattle, WA, 2011.
$50,000 to Santa Rosa Memorial Hospital Foundation, Santa Rosa, CA, 2011.
$25,000 to College Success Foundation, Issaquah, WA, 2011.
$10,000 to Northwest Kidney Centers Foundation, Seattle, WA, 2011.
$10,000 to Rise N Shine, Seattle, WA, 2011.

9573
Anduin Foundation ✧
601 Union St., Ste. 4600
Seattle, WA 98101-4050

Donors: John W. Zevenbergen, Jr.; Nancy A. Zevenbergen, Jr.
Foundation type: Independent foundation.
Financial data (yr. ended 12/31/13): Assets, $2,476,156 (M); gifts received, $168,035; expenditures, $677,006; qualifying distributions, $655,000; giving activities include $655,000 for 12 grants (high: $255,000; low: $5,000).
Fields of interest: Higher education, university; Cancer research; Children, adoption; Christian agencies & churches.
Limitations: Applications not accepted. Giving primarily in WA.
Application information: Unsolicited requests for funds not accepted.

Officers and Directors:* John W. Zevenbergen, Jr.,* Pres.; Nancy A. Zevenbergen, Jr.,* V.P.
EIN: 263904200
Selected grants: The following grants are a representative sample of this grantmaker's funding activity:
$50,000 to University of Washington Foundation, Seattle, WA, 2012. For education and athletics.
$20,000 to Street Youth Ministries, Seattle, WA, 2012. For Minister to Homeless Youth.
$10,000 to Boys and Girls Clubs of King County, Seattle, WA, 2012. For mentoring program.
$10,000 to YMCA of Greater Seattle, Seattle, WA, 2012. For youth summer camp.
$5,000 to Everett Gospel Mission, Everett, WA, 2012. For Minister to Homeless.

9574
Apex Foundation ✧
P.O. Box 245
Bellevue, WA 98009-0245 (425) 460-2500
Contact: Craig W. Stewart, Pres.

Established in 1999 in WA.
Donors: Bruce R. McCaw; The McCaw Foundation.
Foundation type: Independent foundation.
Financial data (yr. ended 12/31/12): Assets, $118,975,972 (M); expenditures, $2,342,143; qualifying distributions, $1,968,409; giving activities include $1,033,446 for 119 grants (high: $100,000; low: $36), and $31,280 for 52 employee matching gifts.
Purpose and activities: Giving to support programs that help children and families reach their highest potential.
Fields of interest: Performing arts; Education; Medical research, institute.
Type of support: Employee matching gifts.
Limitations: Applications not accepted. Giving primarily in Seattle, WA. No grants to individuals.
Application information: Contributes only to pre-selected organizations.
Board meeting date(s): As needed
Officers and Directors:* Craig W. Stewart,* Pres.; Bruce R. McCaw,* V.P.; Jolene M. McCaw, V.P.; David Brady, Secy.-Treas.
Number of staff: 1 part-time professional; 1 part-time support.
EIN: 911950397
Selected grants: The following grants are a representative sample of this grantmaker's funding activity:
$24,401 to University of Washington, School of Music, Seattle, WA, 2012. For general operating support.
$8,745 to Philanthropy Northwest, Seattle, WA, 2012. For Membership/Subscription.
$1,000 to Museum of Flight, Seattle, WA, 2012. For Greatest Need/Unrestricted.
$860 to National Automobile Museum, Reno, NV, 2012. For Membership/Subscription.

9575
Aven Foundation ✧
c/o John W. Stanton
P.O. Box 53508
Bellevue, WA 98015-3508 (425) 586-8011

Established in 1999 in WA.
Donors: John W. Stanton; Theresa E. Gillespie.
Foundation type: Independent foundation.
Financial data (yr. ended 12/31/12): Assets, $49,708,912 (M); expenditures, $2,824,824; qualifying distributions, $2,710,425; giving activities include $2,710,425 for grants.
Purpose and activities: Giving primarily for education, children, youth and social services, and federated giving programs.
Fields of interest: Elementary/secondary education; Higher education; Human services; Children/youth, services; United Ways and Federated Giving Programs.
Type of support: General/operating support.
Limitations: Applications accepted. Giving primarily in Seattle and Bellevue, WA. No grants to individuals.
Application information: Application form not required.
Deadline(s): None
Trustees: Theresa E. Gillespie; John W. Stanton.
EIN: 912009458

9576
The Avista Foundation ✧
1411 E. Mission Ave.
Spokane, WA 99202 (509) 495-8156
Contact: Patrick Lynch, Chair. and Pres.
E-mail: contributions@avistacorp.com; Application address: MSC-68, P.O. Box 3727, Spokane, WA 99202-3732; Main URL: http://www.avistafoundation.org

Established in 2002 in WA.
Donors: Avista Corp.; Avista Capital, Inc.
Foundation type: Company-sponsored foundation.
Financial data (yr. ended 12/31/13): Assets, $3,642,355 (M); expenditures, $521,010; qualifying distributions, $510,452; giving activities include $510,452 for 204 grants (high: $97,000; low: $25).
Purpose and activities: The foundation supports organizations involved with education, energy conservation, community economic development, science, senior citizens, and economically disadvantaged people.
Fields of interest: Elementary/secondary education; Higher education; Education; Environment, energy; Human services; Community/economic development; Physical/earth sciences; Mathematics; Engineering/technology; Science; Utilities; Aging; Economically disadvantaged.
Type of support: General/operating support; Capital campaigns; Equipment; Program development; Seed money; Scholarship funds; Employee matching gifts.
Limitations: Applications accepted. Giving primarily in areas of company operations in northern ID, Sanders County, MT, southern OR, and eastern WA. No support for religious, veterans', or fraternal organizations, discriminatory organizations, or national health organizations (or their local affiliates) or research/disease advocacy organizations. No grants to individuals, or for teams or extra-curricular school events, fundraising events, trips or tours, the development or production of books, films, videos, or television campaigns, or memorial campaigns.
Publications: Application guidelines; Informational brochure (including application guidelines); IRS Form 990 or 990-PF printed copy available upon request.
Application information: Application form required.
Initial approach: Complete online application form or download application form and mail to foundation
Copies of proposal: 1
Deadline(s): Apr. 30 and Oct. 3, but organization can submit at any time
Board meeting date(s): Feb., May, Aug., and Nov.
Officers and Directors:* Patrick Lynch,* Chair. and Pres.; Robert Beitz,* V.P.; Kevin Christie,* Secy.; Christy Burmeister-Smith,* Treas.; Kristine Meyer, Exec. Dir.; David J. Meyer; Dennis Vermillion; Steve Vincent.
EIN: 753003371
Selected grants: The following grants are a representative sample of this grantmaker's funding activity:
$20,000 to Lewis-Clark State College Foundation, Lewiston, ID, 2012. For Harns Field renovation.
$15,000 to Washington State University Foundation, Pullman, WA, 2012. For Power Engineering Program.
$5,000 to Family Promise, Summit, NJ, 2012. For start of Palouse area homeless shelter network.
$3,000 to Humanities Washington, Seattle, WA, 2012. For Literacy Program Training in Eastern WA.
$3,000 to Medical Teams International, Tigard, OR, 2012. For Douglas County mobile dental clinic.
$2,500 to Eastern Washington University Foundation, Cheney, WA, 2012. For Business Planning Program.
$2,500 to YMCA of the Inland Northwest, Spokane, WA, 2012. For youth legislative project.
$1,000 to Hearts with A Mission, Medford, OR, 2012. For general support for youth shelter facility.
$400 to Washington Gorge Action Programs, Bingen, WA, 2012. For general support for Food Bank.

9577
B&E Gilman Family Foundation ✧
(formerly Gilman Private Family Foundation)
c/o Foundation Management Group
1000 2nd Ave., Ste. 3400
Seattle, WA 98104-1022

Established in 2002 in WA.
Donors: Bert E. Gilman†; Eileen Gilman; Gilman Charitable Lead Trust; Bob Gilman Charitable Remainder Unitrust.
Foundation type: Independent foundation.
Financial data (yr. ended 12/31/13): Assets, $95,941 (M); gifts received, $15,154; expenditures, $515,621; qualifying distributions, $511,739; giving activities include $484,750 for 57 grants (high: $100,000; low: $500).
Purpose and activities: Giving primarily for health, education, and human services.
Fields of interest: Cancer research; Human services; Christian agencies & churches; Jewish agencies & synagogues.
Limitations: Applications not accepted. Giving primarily in NY and Seattle, WA.
Application information: Contributes only to pre-selected organizations.
Officers and Directors:* Eileen Gilman,* Pres. and Treas.; Daniel M. Asher, Secy.; Michael L. Cohen; Charles J. Pratt.
EIN: 030474038

9578
Bainbridge Community Foundation ✧
(formerly Bainbridge Island Community Endowment)
221 Winslow Way W., No. 305
Bainbridge Island, WA 98110-4918 (206) 842-0433
Contact: Jim Hopper, Exec. Dir.; For grants: Debbie Kuffel, Funds and Grants Admin.
E-mail: info@bainbridgecf.org; Additional address: 149 Finch Place SW, Suite 4, Bainbridge Island, WA 98110; Additional e-mail: jhopper@bainbridgecommunityfoundation.org; Grant inquiry e-mail: grants@bainbridgecf.org; Grant inquiry tel.: 206-842-0814; Main URL: http://www.bainbridgecommunityfoundation.org
Facebook: http://www.facebook.com/pages/Bainbridge-Community-Foundation/214785191915998
Twitter: http://twitter.com/investinbcf

Established in 2001 in WA.
Donors: Sada Ross Fund; Harold Hurlen Fund; H. Clay and Sherry Roberts Fund; Barry Peters; Channice Peters; The Mathurin Fund; The Emile Fund; Class of 1961 Fund.
Foundation type: Community foundation.
Financial data (yr. ended 12/31/13): Assets, $8,861,800 (M); gifts received, $1,821,165; expenditures, $2,172,752; giving activities include $1,893,013 for 20+ grants (high: $1,363,838), and $12,000 for 4 grants to individuals.
Purpose and activities: The foundation seeks to encourage philanthropy and build a stronger community on Bainbridge Island, Washington.
Fields of interest: Arts; Education; Environment; Animals/wildlife; Health care; Housing/shelter; Youth development; Human services; Science; Engineering/technology; Social sciences, public policy; Social sciences.
Type of support: General/operating support; Income development; Capital campaigns; Building/renovation; Equipment; Scholarship funds.
Limitations: Applications accepted. Giving limited to the Bainbridge Island, WA, area. No support for religious organizations (unless for secular purposes). No grants to individuals, or for fundraising events, debt reduction, items purchased or activities completed prior to grant decision; no multi-year grants.
Publications: Application guidelines; Annual report; Informational brochure; Occasional report.
Application information: Visit foundation web site online grant application and additional guidelines. Application form required.
Initial approach: Complete online application
Deadline(s): Mar. 10
Board meeting date(s): Six times annually
Final notification: June
Officer and Trustees:* Jim Hopper, Exec. Dir.; Lynn Agnew; Len Beil; Paul Carroll; Eric Cederwall; Jola Greiner; Cynthia Hall; Judy Karr; Mary Kerr; Omie Kerr; Shel Klasky; Carl Middleton; Wendy O'Connor; Chris Snow; Barbara Swartling; Elaine VonRosenstiel; Drew Wolff.
Number of staff: 2 part-time professional.
EIN: 912155208

9579
Thomas E. and Linda O. Baker Family Foundation ✧ ☆
14122 S.W. 220th St.
Vashon, WA 98070-6318
E-mail: info@bakerfamilyfoundation.org

Established in 1999 in NJ.
Donor: Thomas E. Baker.
Foundation type: Independent foundation.
Financial data (yr. ended 12/31/13): Assets, $896,754 (M); expenditures, $1,020,754; qualifying distributions, $1,000,744; giving activities include $896,095 for 4 grants (high: $838,595; low: $2,500), and $19,850 for grants to individuals.
Purpose and activities: Scholarships awarded for undergraduate education to individuals with financial need.
Fields of interest: Higher education.
Type of support: General/operating support; Scholarships—to individuals.
Limitations: Applications not accepted.
Application information: The foundation will no longer be accepting any new applications.
Trustees: Linda O. Baker; Thomas E. Baker.
Number of staff: 1 full-time professional.
EIN: 256611063

9580
The Bamford Foundation ✧
(formerly The Globe Foundation)
P.O. Box 2274
Tacoma, WA 98401-2274 (253) 620-4743
Contact: Holly Bamford Hunt
E-mail: info@bamfordfoundation.org; Main URL: http://bamfordfoundation.org/

Established in 1990 in WA.
Donors: Calvin D. Bamford, Jr.; JoAnne W. Bamford.
Foundation type: Independent foundation.
Financial data (yr. ended 11/30/13): Assets, $6,107,723 (M); gifts received, $1,660,000; expenditures, $703,201; qualifying distributions, $688,296; giving activities include $655,680 for 50 grants (high: $101,500; low: $1,000).
Purpose and activities: Giving primarily to improve the quality of life of individuals and to strengthen their communities, primarily in Tacoma, Washington and the South Puget Sound area of the Pacific Northwest.
Fields of interest: Museums; Higher education; Education; Human services; YM/YWCAs & YM/YWHAs; United Ways and Federated Giving Programs; Protestant agencies & churches.
Limitations: Giving primarily in Tacoma, WA, and the South Puget Sound area of the Pacific Northwest. No grants to individuals, or for basic research, sponsorships, or conferences.
Publications: Grants list.
Application information: Letters of Inquiry and full requests are by invitation only, upon consideration of initial e-mail.
Initial approach: E-mail inquiry to Holly Bamford Hunt asking for consideration of an invitation to submit a letter
Board meeting date(s): Quarterly
Officers and Directors:* Calvin D. Bamford, Jr., Pres. and Treas.; Joanne W. Bamford,* V.P.; Holly Bamford Hunt,* Secy.; Drew Bamford; Heather Bamford.
EIN: 911504193

Selected grants: The following grants are a representative sample of this grantmaker's funding activity:
$35,000 to Foss Waterway Seaport, Tacoma, WA, 2011. For program support.
$30,000 to Boys and Girls Clubs of South Puget Sound, Tacoma, WA, 2011.
$30,000 to University of Washington, Seattle, WA, 2011.
$25,000 to United Way of Pierce County, Tacoma, WA, 2011.
$22,000 to Annie Wright School, Tacoma, WA, 2011.
$16,667 to Franciscan Foundation, Tacoma, WA, 2011.
$15,000 to A Step Ahead in Pierce County, Tacoma, WA, 2011.
$5,000 to At the Crossroads, San Francisco, CA, 2011.
$3,000 to Community Alliance for Learning, Albany, CA, 2011.
$2,000 to D.A.S.H. Center for the Arts, Tacoma, WA, 2011. For general support.

9581
Barton Family Foundation ✧ ☆
c/o Peterson Sullivan, LLP
601 Union St., No. 2300
Seattle, WA 98101

Donors: Richard N. Barton; Sarah M. Barton.
Foundation type: Independent foundation.
Financial data (yr. ended 12/31/12): Assets, $3,667,137 (M); gifts received, $620; expenditures, $557,280; qualifying distributions, $518,770; giving activities include $518,770 for grants.
Purpose and activities: The foundation focuses on the problem of generational poverty in the United States.
Fields of interest: Arts; Education; Environment; Human services; Children/youth, services; Youth.
Limitations: Applications not accepted.
Application information: Unsolicited requests for funds not accepted.
Board meeting date(s): Quarterly
Trustees: Richard N. Barton; Sarah M. Barton.
EIN: 916563332

9582
Bates Family Foundation ✧
P.O. Box 6861
Tacoma, WA 98417-0383
FAX: (253) 752-4601;
E-mail: rwbates52@comcast.net; Main URL: http://www.batesfamilyfoundation.org

Established in 1999 in IL.
Donors: Rex J. Bates; Reva Bates†.
Foundation type: Independent foundation.
Financial data (yr. ended 12/31/13): Assets, $14,799,283 (M); expenditures, $1,140,593; qualifying distributions, $993,027; giving activities include $924,000 for 26 grants (high: $333,500; low: $2,500).
Fields of interest: Arts; Higher education; Education; Youth development.
Type of support: Annual campaigns; Capital campaigns; Building/renovation; Scholarship funds.
Limitations: Applications not accepted. Giving primarily in IL and WA; some giving also in

Washington, DC. No support for political organizations. No grants to individuals.
Application information: Contributes only to pre-selected organizations.
Board meeting date(s): June and Dec.
Trustees: Rex J. Bates; Rex W. Bates; Patricia Ann Mattingley.
EIN: 367294980
Selected grants: The following grants are a representative sample of this grantmaker's funding activity:
$222,000 to Annie Wright School, Tacoma, WA, 2012. For Payment for Educational Programs of the School.
$64,000 to Children's Museum of Tacoma, Tacoma, WA, 2012. For Payment for the Benefit of the Children's Museum of Tacoma.
$60,000 to University of Chicago, Chicago, IL, 2012. For Payment for the Benefit of the University of Chicago.
$40,000 to Whitman College, Walla Walla, WA, 2012. For Payment for Award Endowments for Students.
$20,000 to Seattle Pacific University, Seattle, WA, 2012. For Payment to Benefit Seattle Pacific University.
$15,000 to University of Washington, Tacoma, WA, 2012. For Payment to Benefit the School of Business.
$10,000 to Greenhill School, Addison, TX, 2012. For Payment to Benefit Greenhill School.

9583
Larry Benaroya Family Foundation ✧
3600 136th Pl. S.E., Ste. 250
Bellevue, WA 98006-1417 (425) 440-6700
Contact: Larry R. Benaroya, Pres.

Established in 2006 in WA.
Donors: Larry R. Benaroya; Jack A. Benaroya; Rebecca B. Benaroya.
Foundation type: Independent foundation.
Financial data (yr. ended 12/31/13): Assets, $11,993,233 (M); gifts received, $4,426,043; expenditures, $619,365; qualifying distributions, $606,006; giving activities include $605,993 for 39 grants (high: $274,294; low: $500).
Fields of interest: Higher education; Diabetes research; Human services; Jewish federated giving programs.
Limitations: Applications accepted. Giving primarily in WA.
Application information:
Initial approach: Letter
Deadline(s): None
Officers: Larry R. Benaroya, Pres.; Sherry-Lee Benaroya, Secy.-Treas.
Directors: Brooke E. Benaroya; Michael J. Benaroya.
EIN: 203890382

9584
The Berwick Degel Family Foundation ✧ ☆
c/o James A. Degel
P.O. Box 20099
Seattle, WA 98102-1099

Established in 2000 in WA.
Donors: Jeanne E. Berwick; James A. Degel.
Foundation type: Independent foundation.
Financial data (yr. ended 12/31/13): Assets, $2,030,335 (M); gifts received, $1,472,744; expenditures, $573,900; qualifying distributions, $570,666; giving activities include $570,666 for 22 grants (high: $125,000; low: $1,000).
Fields of interest: Education; Health organizations; Religion.
Limitations: Applications not accepted. Giving primarily in Seattle, WA. No grants to individuals.
Application information: Unsolicited requests for funds not accepted.
Directors: Jeanne E. Berwick; James A. Degel.
EIN: 912083120

9585
Bezos Family Foundation ✧
7683 S.E. 27th St., No. 224
Mercer Island, WA 98040-2804

Established in 2000 in WA.
Donors: Miguel A. Bezos; Jacklyn G. Bezos; Jeffrey P. Bezos.
Foundation type: Independent foundation.
Financial data (yr. ended 12/31/13): Assets, $24,851,414 (M); expenditures, $20,977,690; qualifying distributions, $20,926,855; giving activities include $17,117,267 for 145 grants (high: $2,654,269; low: $250).
Fields of interest: Higher education; Education; Children/youth, services; International exchange; Children/youth.
Limitations: Applications not accepted. Giving in the U.S., with emphasis on NY and WA. No grants to individuals.
Application information: Contributes only to pre-selected organizations.
Directors: Jacklyn G. Bezos; Jeffrey P. Bezos; Lisa Bezos; Mackenzie T. Bezos; Mark S. Bezos; Miguel A. Bezos; Christina Bezos Poore; Stephen S. Poore.
EIN: 912073258
Selected grants: The following grants are a representative sample of this grantmaker's funding activity:
$2,357,021 to African Leadership Foundation, San Francisco, CA, 2011. For Challenge Grant for Capital Campaign.
$1,495,142 to New Schools Fund, NewSchools Venture Fund, Oakland, CA, 2011. For Project School of One.
$780,696 to University of Washington, Seattle, WA, 2011. For I-LABS - Challenge Grant.
$727,938 to Harvard University, Cambridge, MA, 2011. For program support.
$390,348 to Architecture for Humanity, San Francisco, CA, 2011. For Students Rebuild Haiti Challenge Grant.
$139,994 to African Leadership Foundation, San Francisco, CA, 2011. For Challenge Grant for Capital Campaign.
$77,134 to Aspen Institute, Aspen, CO, 2011. For Bezos Scholars Program.
$27,113 to University of Washington, Seattle, WA, 2011. For I-LABS - Challenge Grant.
$25,000 to YM-YWHA, 92nd Street, New York, NY, 2011. For Poetry Center Schools Project.
$20,000 to Uncommon Schools, New York, NY, 2011. For general operating support.

9586
Sheri & Les Biller Family Foundation ✧
601 Union St., Ste. 3030
Seattle, WA 98101-2348 (206) 687-7909
E-mail: inquiries@billerfamilyfoundation.org; Main URL: http://www.billerfamilyfoundation.org
Facebook: http://www.facebook.com/pages/The-Sheri-and-Les-Biller-Family-Foundation/122644051043
Twitter: http://twitter.com/BillerFamFdtn
YouTube: http://www.youtube.com/user/billerfamfoundation

Established in 2001 in CA.
Donors: Les Biller; Sheri Biller.
Foundation type: Independent foundation.
Financial data (yr. ended 12/31/13): Assets, $9,284,081 (M); gifts received, $864,600; expenditures, $1,853,704; qualifying distributions, $1,746,360; giving activities include $1,208,427 for 91 grants (high: $350,000; low: $100).
Purpose and activities: Giving to enhance the quality of life in the community through support of: 1) women's organizations which relieve suffering, defend rights, and improve living conditions of women in areas of abuse, health, vocational, legal assistance and family planning; 2) higher education for children of immigrants, in which the foundation funds, through a third party organization candidate selection process, the higher education expenses of children of immigrants, immigrant (resident) children, and naturalized citizen children; 3) disadvantaged youth programs which focus on education, mentoring, developing leadership skills, encouraging community services and building self-esteem; and 4) theater arts programs in general education, the opera, theatrical arts, and in particular, youth performing arts that serve the needs of disadvantaged youth.
Fields of interest: Performing arts, theater; Arts; Higher education; Education; Medical research, institute; Cancer research; Human services; Children/youth; Women; Immigrants/refugees; Economically disadvantaged.
Limitations: Applications not accepted. Giving primarily in Los Angeles, CA, and WA. No support for projects outside the stated areas of interest, pilot or seed programs unless the Founding Trustee is actively involved, or for organizations determined to be unhealthy or financially unstable. No grants to individuals, or for requests less than $1,000, or for more than directed by the Trust document.
Application information: Unsolicited requests for funds not accepted.
Officer: Colleen Oliver, Exec. Dir.
Directors: Howard Behar; Yvonne Bell; Alexander Cappello; Lindsey C. Kozberg; John R. Ohanesian.
Trustees: Les Biller; Sheri Biller.
EIN: 841608504
Selected grants: The following grants are a representative sample of this grantmaker's funding activity:
$50,000 to Jewish Vocational Service, Los Angeles, CA, 2012. For BankWork$TM.
$15,000 to Museum of Flight, Seattle, WA, 2012. For WomenFly! Program.
$7,500 to Miami Country Day School, Miami, FL, 2012. For STEM Curriculum.
$5,000 to Concern Foundation, Los Angeles, CA, 2012. For Block Party 2012.
$5,000 to Jewish Vocational Service, Los Angeles, CA, 2012. For Strictly Business Lunch.

$2,500 to Antioch University Los Angeles, Culver City, CA, 2012. For Colors LGBTQ Youth Counseling Center.
$1,000 to New Teacher Center, Santa Cruz, CA, 2012. For Los Angeles Expansion.
$1,000 to Northwestern University, Evanston, IL, 2012. For The Terri Dial Scholarship.

9587
Blakemore Foundation ✧

1201 3rd Ave., Ste. 4900
Seattle, WA 98101-3095 (206) 359-8778
Contact: For all inquiries: Cathy Scheibner, Exec. Asst.
FAX: (206) 359-9778;
E-mail: blakemorefoundation@gmail.com; Additional e-mail: blakemore@perkinscoie.com; Main URL: http://www.blakemorefoundation.org
Facebook: http://www.facebook.com/pages/Blakemore-Foundation/79550692938
Grants List: http://www.blakemorefoundation.org/Recent%20Grants/Recent%20Grants.htm

Established in 1990 in WA.
Donors: Thomas L. Blakemore†; Frances L. Blakemore†; Eugene H. Lee; Freeman Foundation; Tokyo Club; Worldbridge LLC.
Foundation type: Independent foundation.
Financial data (yr. ended 12/31/13): Assets, $9,392,401 (M); gifts received, $400,000; expenditures, $1,085,513; qualifying distributions, $994,046; giving activities include $90,656 for 5 grants (high: $40,656; low: $5,000), and $784,105 for 27 grants to individuals (high: $67,007; low: $10,000).
Purpose and activities: Grants to individuals pursuing academic, business, or professional careers involving East or Southeast Asia for advanced study of East or Southeast Asian languages in Asia. Grants to museums, universities and other educational or art-related institutions in the United States for exhibitions and internships to broaden and deepen the understanding of Asian art in the United States.
Fields of interest: Museums; Language (foreign); Arts; Higher education.
Type of support: Fellowships; Scholarships—to individuals.
Publications: Application guidelines; Annual report; Grants list; Informational brochure; IRS Form 990 or 990-PF printed copy available upon request.
Application information: Application form, instructions, and grant guidelines for Language Grants to individuals are available on foundation web site. Asian Art Grant applications are by invitation only. See foundation web site for further information.
Initial approach: See foundation web site for forms and eligibility requirements
Copies of proposal: 1
Deadline(s): Postmarked by Dec. 30 for language grants (or Dec. 31 if the 30th falls on a postal holiday)
Board meeting date(s): Biannually, usually June and Dec.
Final notification: Late Mar. or early Apr. for Language Grants
Officer and Board Members:* Mimi Gardner Gates,* Chair.; Eugene H. Lee, Trustee; Griffith Way, Trustee Emeritus; Paul Atkins; Lorri Hagman; Christopher R. Helm; Heng-Pin Kiang; Joseph Massey; Haicheng Wang; Ted Woolsey.
EIN: 911505735

Selected grants: The following grants are a representative sample of this grantmaker's funding activity:
$35,282 to Seattle Art Museum, Seattle, WA, 2012. For Museum internships for University of Washington art history graduate students during 2012/2013 academic year.

9588
Blue Mountain Community Foundation ✧

(formerly Blue Mountain Area Foundation)
22 E. Poplar St., Ste. 206
P.O. Box 603
Walla Walla, WA 99362 (509) 529-4371
Contact: Kari Isaacson, Exec. Dir.
FAX: (509) 529-5284;
E-mail: bmcf@bluemountainfoundation.org; Main URL: http://www.bluemountainfoundation.org
Blog: http://www.bluemountainfoundation.org/?feed
Facebook: http://www.facebook.com/pages/Blue-Mountain-Community-Foundation/298194080507
LinkedIn: http://www.linkedin.com/company/1498208
RSS Feed: http://www.bluemountainfoundation.org/feed/
YouTube: http://www.youtube.com/user/BMCFoundation

Incorporated in 1984 in WA.
Foundation type: Community foundation.
Financial data (yr. ended 06/30/13): Assets, $34,182,386 (M); gifts received, $2,023,327; expenditures, $2,263,906; giving activities include $1,334,521 for 63+ grants (high: $63,934), and $410,233 for 76 grants to individuals.
Purpose and activities: The foundation promotes effective philanthropy by fostering private charitable giving, providing management of funds, and financially supporting students and charitable organizations to improve the quality of life in the community.
Fields of interest: Visual arts; Performing arts; Humanities; Historic preservation/historical societies; Arts; Higher education; Adult education—literacy, basic skills & GED; Education; Environment; Animal welfare; Reproductive health, family planning; Health care; Children/youth, services; Child development, services; Family services; Residential/custodial care, hospices; Aging, centers/services; Homeless, human services; Human services; Community development, neighborhood development; Economic development.
Type of support: General/operating support; Continuing support; Management development/capacity building; Equipment; Endowments; Program development; Curriculum development; Fellowships; Internship funds; Technical assistance; Scholarships—to individuals.
Limitations: Applications accepted. Giving limited to Umatilla County, OR, and Columbia, Garfield, and Walla Walla counties, WA. No support for sectarian religious programs. No grants for seed money, multi-year grants, operating expenses, annual fund drives, field trips, or travel to or in support of conferences.
Publications: Application guidelines; Annual report; Grants list; Informational brochure; Newsletter.
Application information: Visit foundation web site for application form and guidelines. Grants are only made to 501(c)(3) organizations in the Foundation's service area. Application form required.
Initial approach: Submit application summary and attachments
Copies of proposal: 10
Deadline(s): July 1 for grants; Mar. 1 for scholarships
Board meeting date(s): Quarterly
Final notification: Oct. for grants; June 1 for scholarships
Officers and Trustees:* Craig Sievertsen,* Pres.; Norm Passmore,* V.P.; Leslie Brown,* Secy.; Shannon Bergevin,* Treas.; Kari Isaacson, Exec. Dir.; Tony Billingsley; Sandi Blackaby; Sherilee Coffey; Kevin Michelson; Keith Olson; Laure Quaresma; Dan Reid; Anne-Marie Zell Schwerin; Anne Walsh.
Number of staff: 3 full-time professional; 1 part-time support.
EIN: 911250104

9589
John Spencer Bradley Collection Foundation ✧

155 108th Ave. N.E., Ste. 320
Bellevue, WA 98004

Established in 2006 in WA.
Foundation type: Independent foundation.
Financial data (yr. ended 12/31/13): Assets, $10,199,380 (M); expenditures, $655,711; qualifying distributions, $570,814; giving activities include $550,000 for 19 grants (high: $100,000; low: $5,000).
Fields of interest: Education; Human services.
Limitations: Applications not accepted. Giving primarily in WA.
Application information: Unsolicited requests for funds not accepted.
Officers and Directors:* Carl L. Bradley,* Pres. and Treas.; Donald W. Stetson,* V.P.; William J. Cruzen,* Secy.
EIN: 205813078

9590
The Brainerd Foundation ✧

1601 2nd Ave., Ste. 610
Seattle, WA 98101-1541 (206) 448-0676
Contact: Ann Krumboltz, Exec. Dir.
FAX: (206) 448-7222; E-mail: info@brainerd.org;
Main URL: http://www.brainerd.org
Grants Database: http://www.brainerd.org/grantee_profile.php

Established in 1995 in WA.
Donor: Paul Brainerd.
Foundation type: Independent foundation.
Financial data (yr. ended 12/31/12): Assets, $26,187,673 (M); expenditures, $3,907,815; qualifying distributions, $3,463,252; giving activities include $2,581,024 for 140 grants (high: $125,000; low: $20).
Purpose and activities: The foundation is a small family foundation which provides innovative grantmaking to Northwest communities and nonprofits to build a lasting conservation ethic at the local, state, and federal level. In addition to funding, it provides expertise to its nonprofit partners and collaborates with other foundations to find new methods of advocacy, policy implementation, and capacity building.

Fields of interest: Environment, natural resources.
Type of support: General/operating support; Continuing support; Income development; Management development/capacity building; Emergency funds; Program development; Conferences/seminars; Seed money; Technical assistance; Matching/challenge support.
Limitations: Applications accepted. Giving in AK, ID, MT, OR, WA, British Columbia, and the Yukon Territory. No support for for-profit organizations, or for candidates or lobbying. No grants to individuals, or for school education campaigns, direct land purchases or easements, endowments, capital campaigns, debt reduction, theoretical research, fellowships, or books and videos that are not components of a broader strategy.
Publications: Application guidelines; Financial statement; Grants list; Program policy statement; Program policy statement (including application guidelines).
Application information: Unsolicited proposals not accepted, except for opportunity grants. Publications available on foundation web site only. Please see web site for complete application instructions. Application form required.
Initial approach: Letter of inquiry
Copies of proposal: 1
Deadline(s): None
Board meeting date(s): Mar., June, and Nov.
Final notification: Usually less than 1 month
Officers and Directors:* Paul Brainerd,* Pres. and Treas.; Sherry Brainerd,* V.P. and Secy.; Ann Krumboltz, V.P. and Exec. Dir., Comms. and Capacity Building.
Number of staff: 2 full-time professional; 1 part-time professional; 1 full-time support; 2 part-time support.
EIN: 911675591

9591
The Bullitt Foundation ✧
1501 E Madison St., Ste. 600
Seattle, WA 98122-4465 (206) 343-0807
Contact: Denis Hayes, Pres.
FAX: (206) 343-0822; E-mail: info@bullitt.org; Main URL: http://www.bullitt.org
Grants Database: http://www.bullitt.org/grant-history
RSS Feed: http://www.bullitt.org/resources/resources/RSS

Incorporated in 1952 in WA.
Donors: Dorothy S. Bullitt‡; Members of the Bullitt family.
Foundation type: Independent foundation.
Financial data (yr. ended 12/31/13): Assets, $110,707,712 (M); gifts received, $129,000; expenditures, $7,885,919; qualifying distributions, $10,482,600; giving activities include $5,087,500 for 122 grants (high: $125,000; low: $5,000), $115,000 for 3 grants to individuals (high: $100,000; low: $7,500), $164,118 for 97 employee matching gifts, $269,658 for 3 foundation-administered programs and $149,670 for 1 loan/program-related investment.
Purpose and activities: Support primarily to safeguard the natural environment by promoting responsible human activities and sustainable communities in the Pacific Northwest.
Fields of interest: Environment, pollution control; Environment, water pollution; Environment, radiation control; Environment, toxics; Environment, climate change/global warming; Environment, water resources; Environment, land resources; Environment, energy; Employment, public policy; Agriculture/food, public policy; Public affairs, citizen participation; Transportation; Leadership development.
Type of support: Continuing support; Emergency funds; Employee matching gifts; Fellowships; General/operating support; Management development/capacity building; Matching/challenge support; Program development; Program-related investments/loans; Technical assistance.
Limitations: Applications accepted. Giving in the Pacific Northwest including AK, OR, WA, and British Columbia; giving also in ID and MT. No support for political organizations. No grants to individuals (except for fellowships), or for capital campaigns, equipment, building construction, or land acquisition.
Publications: Application guidelines; Grants list.
Application information: Once invited, the full application is available on the foundation web site. Full applications are by invitation only. Please follow the online inquiry process even if you have applied for or received a Bullitt Foundation grant in the past. Application form required.
Initial approach: Inquiry form to determine eligibility found on foundation web site. (Full applications are only accepted upon invitation, following letter of inquiry)
Copies of proposal: 1
Deadline(s): May 1 and Nov. 1 for full applications
Board meeting date(s): Apr. and Oct.
Final notification: 5 months by letter for full applications
Officers and Trustees:* Doug Raff,* Chair.; Harriet Bullitt,* Vice-Chair.; Denis Hayes,* C.E.O. and Pres.; Howard Frumkin,* Secy.; Salley Anderson,* C.F.O. and Treas.; Michael Allen; Rod Brown; Maud Daudon; Erim Gomez; Frank Greer; Martha Kongsgaard; Michael Parham; William D. Ruckelshaus.
Number of staff: 6 full-time professional.
EIN: 916027795
Selected grants: The following grants are a representative sample of this grantmaker's funding activity:
$130,000 to Climate Solutions, Seattle, WA, 2012. To continue coordinating the Power Past Coal campaign and to lead the charge for climate and clean energy policies in Washington and Oregon.
$130,000 to Washington Environmental Council, Seattle, WA, 2012. For 2012 Project Support Grant. For continuing program support that will focus on three areas: voter education, climate and clean energy, and clean water and green infrastructure.
$115,000 to Cascadia Region Green Building Council, Seattle, WA, 2012. For Advancing the Living Building Challenge in the Cascadia Bioregion and Beyond.
$110,000 to Futurewise, Seattle, WA, 2012. For The Livable Communities Initiative. For Futurewise's land use and transportation programs designed to promote planning practices and policies that reduce sprawl, green house gas emissions, and vehicles' miles traveled by building sustainable, affordable, and highly desirable urban centers.
$100,000 to Forterra, Seattle, WA, 2012. For Great Communities Initiative which seeks to build vibrant, compact, and connected cities and towns in order to draw pressure away from working farms and forests.
$100,000 to Washington State University, Pullman, WA, 2012. For 2012 Bullitt Environmental Fellowship.
$95,000 to Sightline Institute, Seattle, WA, 2012. For General Operating Support. For ongoing program support of Sightline's original research, interpretation and presentation of data through the aid of creative communications vehicles to drive progressive policy solutions.
$90,000 to Oregon Environmental Council, Portland, OR, 2012. For advocacy for progressive climate protection policies and regulations that reduce or eliminate toxics in consumer and commercial products.
$90,000 to Renewable Northwest Project, Portland, OR, 2012. For continuing operating support to focus on activities that ensure the growth of solar, wind and geothermal development in the region.
$35,000 to Georgia Strait Alliance, Nanaimo, Canada, 2012. For Safeguarding the greater Georgia Basin's ecosystem health: a strong and focused approach. For general support.

9592
Bushnell Family Foundation ✧ ☆
4638 95th Ave., N.E.
Bellevue, WA 98004-1301 (206) 646-9368
Contact: Julayne W. Bushnell, Tr.

Established in 2004 in WA.
Donors: Sherman Ward Bushnell III; Julayne Winn Bushnell.
Foundation type: Independent foundation.
Financial data (yr. ended 12/31/13): Assets, $3,491,922 (M); gifts received, $228,429; expenditures, $513,585; qualifying distributions, $503,408; giving activities include $500,998 for 9 grants (high: $350,000; low: $500).
Fields of interest: Human services; Youth, services; Protestant agencies & churches.
Limitations: Applications accepted. Giving primarily in WA.
Application information: Application form required.
Initial approach: Letter
Deadline(s): None
Trustees: Julayne Winn Bushnell; Sherman Ward Bushnell III.
EIN: 206383042

9593
Cameron Foundation ✧
c/o Gerry B. Cameron
5421 S.E. Scenic Ln., No. 300
Vancouver, WA 98661-0509

Established in 1997 in WA.
Donors: Gerry B. Cameron; Marilyn C. Cameron.
Foundation type: Independent foundation.
Financial data (yr. ended 12/31/12): Assets, $9,606,913 (M); gifts received, $436,658; expenditures, $580,198; qualifying distributions, $497,600; giving activities include $497,600 for grants.
Purpose and activities: Giving primarily for higher education and human services.
Fields of interest: Higher education; Food banks; Human services; Children/youth, services.
Type of support: General/operating support; Annual campaigns; Capital campaigns; Building/renovation; Professorships; Scholarship funds.

Limitations: Applications not accepted. Giving primarily in OR, with some emphasis on Eugene and Portland.
Application information: Unsolicited requests for funds not accepted.
Board meeting date(s): As necessary
Trustees: Paul E. Cameron; Susan Cameron McDonald.
Officers and Directors:* Gerry B. Cameron,* Pres.; Marilyn C. Cameron,* V.P. and Secy.
Number of staff: None.
EIN: 916437877

9594
Campion Foundation ✧
1904 3rd Ave., Ste. 405
Seattle, WA 98101-1150 (206) 686-5310
Contact: Melanie Matthews, Dir., Capacity Bldg. and Opers.
FAX: (206) 260-0106;
E-mail: info@campionfoundation.org; Main URL: http://www.campionfoundation.org

Established in 2005 in WA.
Donors: Thomas D. Campion; Sonya Campion.
Foundation type: Independent foundation.
Financial data (yr. ended 12/31/13): Assets, $309,895,520 (M); gifts received, $9,471,000; expenditures, $6,136,105; qualifying distributions, $6,043,932; giving activities include $4,970,708 for 58 grants (high: $1,537,250; low: $1,000).
Purpose and activities: The foundation focuses on three program areas: Protecting Wilderness, Ending Homelessness, and Strengthening Nonprofits.
Fields of interest: Environment; Housing/shelter; Community/economic development; Homeless.
Type of support: Matching/challenge support; General/operating support; Management development/capacity building; Program development; Program evaluation.
Limitations: Applications not accepted. Giving primarily in WA, ID, MT, AK and Western Canada (British Columbia, the North Western Territories and the Yukon) for wilderness protection. No support for salmon protection programs, or for water quality programs, environmental education programs or for energy, transportation or air-quality programs. No grants to individuals, or for land acquisition, capital construction projects.
Application information: Unsolicited requests for funds not accepted. Proposals accepted by invitation only.
Trustees: Sonya Campion; Thomas D. Campion.
Number of staff: 4 full-time professional.
EIN: 203421717
Selected grants: The following grants are a representative sample of this grantmaker's funding activity:
$1,530,000 to Alaska Wilderness League, Washington, DC, 2012.
$275,000 to Washington Low Income Housing Alliance, Seattle, WA, 2012.
$250,000 to Forest Ethics, San Francisco, CA, 2012.
$200,000 to Pew Charitable Trusts, Philadelphia, PA, 2012.
$150,000 to Building Changes, Seattle, WA, 2012.
$100,000 to Catholic Community Services of Western Washington, Seattle, WA, 2012.
$55,000 to Social Venture Partners, Seattle, WA, 2012.
$50,000 to Western Environmental Law Center, Eugene, OR, 2012.
$31,981 to Seattle-King County Coalition for the Homeless, Seattle, WA, 2012.
$25,000 to Tacoma-Pierce County Affordable Housing Consortium, Tacoma, WA, 2012.

9595
Casey Family Programs
2001 8th Ave., Ste. 2700
Seattle, WA 98121-2641 (206) 282-7300
Contact: Antoinette Malveaux
FAX: (206) 282-3555; New York Field Office address: 165 Broadway, 1 Liberty Plz., New York, N.Y., 10006, tel.: (212) 863-4860, Managing Dir., Zeinab Chahine; Main URL: http://www.casey.org
Google Plus: https://plus.google.com/+CaseyOrg/posts
Twitter: https://twitter.com/CaseyPrograms
YouTube: http://www.youtube.com/CaseyFamilyPrograms

Established in 1966. Classified as a private operating foundation in 1972.
Foundation type: Operating foundation.
Financial data (yr. ended 12/31/12): Assets, $2,061,764,408 (M); gifts received, $2,328,759; expenditures, $124,132,155; qualifying distributions, $111,763,619; giving activities include $3,528,325 for 104 grants (high: $1,690,000; low: $50), and $110,074,262 for foundation-administered programs.
Purpose and activities: The foundation serves children, youth, and families. Its primary focus is on children who cannot live safely within their own home.
Fields of interest: Substance abuse, services; Mental health/crisis services; Children, foster care.
Type of support: General/operating support; Continuing support; Program development; Scholarship funds; Research; Technical assistance; Program evaluation.
Limitations: Applications not accepted. Giving primarily in the U.S., with emphasis on Washington, DC, and WA. No grants to individuals.
Publications: Informational brochure.
Application information: Unsolicited requests for funds will not be accepted.
Officers and Trustees:* Robert A. "Bob" Watt,* Chair.; Joan B. Poliak,* Vice-Chair.; William C. Bell, C.E.O. and Pres.; Dave Danielson,* Exec. V.P., Admin. and C.F.O.; Marva Hammons,* Exec. V.P., Child and Family Svcs.; Alexandra McKay,* Exec.V.P. and Chief Prog. Counsel; Laura Sagen, Exec. V.P., Comms. and Human Resources; David Sanders, Exec. V.P., Systems Improvement; Joseph A. Boateng, C.I.O.; America Bracho,* Secy.; Sharon L. McDaniel,* Treas.; Shelia Evans-Tranum; Norm B. Rice.
Number of staff: 273 full-time professional; 6 part-time professional; 71 full-time support; 29 part-time support.
EIN: 910793881

9596
Marguerite Casey Foundation ✧
(formerly Casey Family Grants Program)
1425 4th Ave., Ste. 900
Seattle, WA 98101-2222 (206) 691-3134
Contact: Kathleen Baca, Dir., Comms.
FAX: (206) 286-2725; E-mail: info@caseygrants.org; TTY: (206) 273-7395; Main URL: http://www.caseygrants.org/
Equal Voice America's Family Story: http://www.equalvoiceforfamilies.org/#
Equal Voice for America's Families Blog: http://equalvoiceforamericafamilies.blogspot.com/
Equal Voice for America's Family: http://www.facebook.com/EqualVoiceNews
Equal Voice News: http://twitter.com/equalvoicenews
Flickr: http://www.flickr.com/photos/caseygrants/
Grants Database: http://www.caseygrants.org/pages/equalvoice/equalvoice_ourgrantees.asp
Knowledge Center: http://caseygrants.org/resources/
Marguerite Casey Foundation's Philanthropy Promise: http://www.ncrp.org/philanthropys-promise/who
President's Blog: http://caseygrants.org/category/blog/
YouTube: http://www.youtube.com/user/caseygrants

Established in 2001 in WA.
Donor: Casey Family Programs.
Foundation type: Independent foundation.
Financial data (yr. ended 12/31/13): Assets, $698,175,241 (M); expenditures, $33,013,687; qualifying distributions, $29,297,958; giving activities include $23,650,657 for 315 grants (high: $750,000; low: $200), and $926,431 for foundation-administered programs.
Purpose and activities: The foundation makes grants that encourage low-income families to strengthen their voices and mobilize their communities in order to build a more just and equitable society for all. Its grantmaking is informed and guided by the following goals and objectives: engage low-income parents in efforts to improve conditions for their families, connect grantee organizations within and across regions and disciplines for movement-building, and enhance the capacity and effectiveness of cornerstone organizations in low-income communities. The grantmaking is focused on three areas: education, advocacy and activism.
Fields of interest: Youth development; Children/youth, services; Family services; Economic development; Community/economic development; Disabilities, people with.
Type of support: General/operating support; Income development; Management development/capacity building; Program development; Research; Technical assistance; Program evaluation; Employee matching gifts.
Limitations: Applications not accepted. Giving primarily in four regions of the U.S.: CA; the Southwest, including the U.S./Mexico border; the Deep South; the Midwest, beginning in Chicago, IL; and WA state. No support for religious purposes. No grants to individuals, or for capital campaigns, endowments, fundraising drives, litigation, or film and video production.
Publications: Annual report; Financial statement; Grants list; Informational brochure; Program policy statement.
Application information: The foundation does not accept unsolicited proposals or letters of intent.
Board meeting date(s): Quarterly
Officers and Directors:* Freeman A. Hrabowski III,* Chair.; Patricia Schroeder,* Vice-Chair.; Luz Vega-Marquis, C.E.O. and Pres.; Douglas X. Patino,*

Secy.; Joyce Lee, C.F.O.; David Villa,* Treas.; Melody Barnes; Angela Diaz, M.D.; William H. Foege.
Number of staff: 7 full-time professional; 8 full-time support; 1 part-time support.
EIN: 912062197
Selected grants: The following grants are a representative sample of this grantmaker's funding activity:
$750,000 to PICO National Network, Oakland, CA, 2012. For general support.
$750,000 to PICO National Network, Oakland, CA, 2013. For general support.
$750,000 to Social Justice Fund Northwest, Seattle, WA, 2012. For general support.
$550,000 to Florida New Majority Education Fund, Miami, FL, 2012. To shift the public debate in Florida toward a more expansive and equitable culture of democracy, in alignment with the Equal Voice framework for movement building.
$500,000 to PolicyLink, Oakland, CA, 2013. For general support.
$400,545 to Asian Americans Advancing Justice - Los Angeles, Los Angeles, CA, 2013. For testing and assessing approaches to recruiting, engaging and retaining members for Equal Voice national family-led membership organization.
$360,000 to Chicago Coalition for the Homeless, Chicago, IL, 2012. For general support.
$300,000 to Public Interest Projects, New York, NY, 2012. For general support for State Capacity and Innovation Fund.
$232,500 to Federation of Community Controlled Centers of Alabama for Child Care, Montgomery, AL, 2013. For general support.
$225,000 to Consejo de Federaciones Mexicanas en Norteamerica, Los Angeles, CA, 2013. For general support.
$225,000 to Southern Rural Black Womens Initiative, Jackson, MS, 2013. For developing community leadership among low-income young and adult women in rural communities and engaging them in advocacy of equitable health care, education and job training policies, using the Equal Voice framework for movement building. Grant made through Children's Defense Fund.
$150,000 to Marin County Grassroots Leadership Network, San Rafael, CA, 2012. For general support.
$150,000 to Southwest Organizing Project, Chicago, IL, 2013. For general support.
$120,000 to Promise Arizona, Phoenix, AZ, 2012. For engagement of community leaders in advocacy for improved education and immigration policies, using the Equal Voice framework for movement building.
$112,500 to Black Alliance for Just Immigration, Oakland, CA, 2012. For general support.
$106,000 to Metropolitan Tenants Organization, Chicago, IL, 2013. For testing and assessing approaches to recruiting, engaging and retaining members for Equal Voice national family-led membership organization.
$100,000 to Casa Familiar, San Ysidro, CA, 2012. For general support.
$100,000 to Disciples Center for Public Witness, Washington, DC, 2013. For general support.
$25,000 to Resource Generation, Boston, MA, 2012. For general operating support.
$10,000 to Hope Community Center, Apopka, FL, 2013. For general support.

9597
Channel Foundation ✧

603 Stewart St., Ste. 415
Seattle, WA 98101-1247
E-mail: info@channelfoundation.org; Main URL: http://www.channelfoundation.org

Established in 1998 in WA.
Donor: Elaine M. Nonneman.
Foundation type: Independent foundation.
Financial data (yr. ended 12/31/13): Assets, $7,633,716 (M); gifts received, $359,110; expenditures, $931,865; qualifying distributions, $882,281; giving activities include $747,000 for 33 grants (high: $25,000; low: $3,000).
Purpose and activities: The foundation promotes leadership in women's human rights around the globe by supporting organizations engaged in combating gender inequality. Through grantmaking, advocacy, and collaboration with an international network of women's rights organizations and funders, the foundation seeks to create opportunities in order to ensure that women's rights are respected, protected, and fulfilled.
Fields of interest: Higher education; Housing/shelter, services; Women, centers/services; International affairs, equal rights; International human rights; Civil/human rights, women; Women.
Type of support: General/operating support; Scholarship funds; Scholarships—to individuals.
Limitations: Applications not accepted. Giving on a worldwide basis, with some emphasis on global organizations in CA, Washington, DC, and MA. No grants to individuals (except for the Women's Leadership Scholarship Program), or for service delivery projects, capital campaigns or electoral campaigns.
Application information: Unsolicited requests for funds not accepted.
Officer: Katrin Wilde, Exec. Dir.
Trustee: Elaine M. Nonneman.
EIN: 916478055

9598
Ben B. Cheney Foundation

3110 Ruston Way, Ste. A
Tacoma, WA 98402-5308 (253) 572-2442
Contact: Bradbury F. Cheney, Exec. Dir.; Application Questions: Kenneth Ristine, Sr. Prog. Off.
E-mail: info@benbcheneyfoundation.org; Main URL: http://www.benbcheneyfoundation.org

Incorporated in 1955 in WA.
Donors: Ben B. Cheney†; Marian Cheney Olrogg†.
Foundation type: Independent foundation.
Financial data (yr. ended 12/31/13): Assets, $77,304,422 (M); expenditures, $4,044,462; qualifying distributions, $3,368,266; giving activities include $2,744,480 for 91 grants (high: $900,000; low: $500), and $18,164 for 28 employee matching gifts.
Purpose and activities: The foundation makes grants to improve the quality of life in communities where Mr. Cheney's lumber company was active. Within those communities the foundation prefers to fund projects that develop new and innovative approaches to community problems, facilitate the improvement of services or programs, and invest in equipment or facilities that will have a long-lasting impact on community needs. The foundation organizes its grantmaking into eight categories: 1) Charity: Programs providing for basic needs such as food, shelter, and clothing; 2) Civic: Programs improving the quality of life in a community as a whole such as museums and recreation facilities; 3) Culture: Programs encompassing the arts; 4) Education: Programs supporting capital projects and scholarships, primarily for fourteen pre-selected colleges and universities in the Pacific Northwest; 5) Elderly: Programs serving the social, health, recreational, and other needs of older people; 6) Health: Programs related to providing health care; 7) Social Services: Programs serving people with physical or mental disabilities or other special needs; and 8) Youth: Programs helping young people to gain the skills needed to become responsible and productive adults.
Fields of interest: Museums; Arts; Higher education; Education; Hospitals (general); Health care; Health organizations, association; Human services; Youth, services; Aging, centers/services.
Type of support: Building/renovation; Capital campaigns; Emergency funds; Equipment; General/operating support; Program development; Scholarship funds; Seed money.
Limitations: Applications accepted. Giving limited to portions of Tacoma-Pierce County, and southwest WA; southwest OR, particularly the Medford area; and Del Norte, Humboldt, Lassen, Shasta, Siskiyou, Trinity, and the northern portion of Plumas counties, CA. No support for religious organizations for sectarian purposes. No grants to individuals or to school-related tours, general operating budgets, basic research, endowment funds, conferences or seminars, the production of books, videos or films; no loans.
Publications: Application guidelines; Annual report; Grants list.
Application information: The foundation does not open unsolicited e-mail attachments. Initial contact should be a 2- to 3-page proposal letter via regular mail. Based upon this letter the foundation will pursue projects that are likely to meet with the board's approval. Application deadline and final notification provided with application. Proposal letters submitted via e-mail will not be reviewed. Application information available on foundation web site. Application form not required.
Initial approach: Initial contact is a 2- to 3-page proposal letter. Proposal letters must be submitted via U.S. mail. E-mail attachments will not be reviewed. Formal applications are provided when a project has been slated for review by the Board of Directors.
Copies of proposal: 1
Deadline(s): None (for proposal letter)
Board meeting date(s): Spring (Mar. or Apr.), June, Sept. and Dec.
Final notification: Proposal letters are reviewed and a response made generally within 6 to 9 months
Officers and Directors:* Bradbury F. Cheney,* Pres. and Exec. Dir.; Piper Cheney,* V.P.; Carolyn J. Cheney, Secy.-Treas.; Matt Beckingham; Allan L. Undem.
Number of staff: 2 full-time professional; 1 full-time support.
EIN: 916053760

9599
Sunlin and Priscilla Chou Foundation ✧

7815 N.E. 192nd Way
Battle Ground, WA 98604-9597

Established in 2005 in WA.

Donors: Sunlin Chou; Priscilla Chou; IEEE Foundation.
Foundation type: Independent foundation.
Financial data (yr. ended 09/30/13): Assets, $11,181,820 (M); gifts received, $983,000; expenditures, $535,788; qualifying distributions, $500,000; giving activities include $500,000 for 6 grants (high: $125,000; low: $40,000).
Fields of interest: Higher education, university; Engineering school/education.
Limitations: Applications not accepted. Giving primarily in CA and MA. No grants to individuals.
Application information: Contributes only to pre-selected organizations.
Officers: Sunlin Chou, Pres.; Priscilla Chou, Secy.
Directors: Sunwen Chou; Emily Wong.
EIN: 203709951
Selected grants: The following grants are a representative sample of this grantmaker's funding activity:
$100,000 to Stanford University, Stanford, CA, 2011.
$75,000 to Massachusetts Institute of Technology, Cambridge, MA, 2011.
$75,000 to Oregon Health and Science University Foundation, Portland, OR, 2011.
$10,000 to Mathematical Sciences Research Institute, Berkeley, CA, 2011.

9600
College Spark Washington ✧
190 Queen Anne Ave. N., Ste. 260
Seattle, WA 98109-4926 (206) 461-7248
Contact: Rachel Clements, Prog. Off.
FAX: (206) 461-7208;
E-mail: info@collegespark.org; Tel. for Rachel Clements, Prog. Off.: (206) 461-5480; e-mail for Rachel Clements, Prog. Off: rachel@collegespark.org; Main URL: http://www.collegespark.org/
Facebook: https://www.facebook.com/CollegeSparkWashington
Twitter: https://twitter.com/CollegeSparkWA

Foundation type: Independent foundation.
Financial data (yr. ended 09/30/13): Assets, $127,276,302 (M); expenditures, $5,223,005; qualifying distributions, $4,803,508; giving activities include $3,822,526 for 44 grants (high: $522,685; low: $100).
Purpose and activities: Giving to organizations with a staffed and physical presence in Washington State that can demonstrate successful experience in reaching and serving low-income students. Students are considered low-income if they are eligible for Pell Grants or Washington State Need Grants, or from families eligible for one of the following public assistance programs: Food Stamps, Free and Reduced Price Lunch, or Temporary Assistance to Needy Families. The foundation is especially interested in projects that allow it to learn more about strategies identified as promising practices for improving Community Grants Program outcome indicators.
Fields of interest: Education.
Limitations: Applications accepted. Giving primarily in WA.
Application information: Application guidelines and form available on foundation web site. Application form required.
Initial approach: Letter of interest
Copies of proposal: 2
Deadline(s): See foundation website for application deadline
Officers and Trustees:* Steven C. Pumphrey,* Chair.; Deborah J. Wilds, Ph.D.*, Vice-Chair. and Treas.; John Rose,* Secy.; Christine A. McCabe, Exec. Dir.; Chio Flores, Ph.D.; Bob Gilb; Trevor L.T. Greene; Jean Hernandez, Ed.D.; Jesus Hernandez; Kris Lambright, CPA; Faith Li Pettis; Chris Reykdal; Barbara Richardson, Ph.D.; Ed Taylor, Ph.D.; Bernie Thomas.
EIN: 911215725
Selected grants: The following grants are a representative sample of this grantmaker's funding activity:
$665,300 to Achieving the Dream, Silver Spring, MD, 2012. For Achieving the Dream - Phase II.
$571,870 to Office of Superintendent of Public Instruction, Olympia, WA, 2012. For CRI AVID and Rigor District Grants yr. 3-6.
$544,635 to Office of Superintendent of Public Instruction, Olympia, WA, 2012. For CRI NAV and Rigor District Grants yr. 3-6.
$400,000 to Washington Student Achievement Council, Olympia, WA, 2012. For theWashBoard.org Phase III.
$225,000 to Office of Superintendent of Public Instruction, Olympia, WA, 2012. For CRI Admin yr. 3-6.
$170,000 to State Board for Community and Technical Colleges, Olympia, WA, 2012. For Achieving the Dream - Phase II.
$150,000 to AVID Center, San Diego, CA, 2012. For CRI Initiative YR 3-6 implementation.
$150,000 to Community Center for Education Results, Seattle, WA, 2012. For College Bound Seniors Support Services.
$150,000 to Green River Community College Foundation, Auburn, WA, 2012. For Trustee Discretionary Grant.
$75,000 to Bellingham Technical College Foundation, Bellingham, WA, 2012. For Achieving the Dream - Phase II.

9601
Colson Family Foundation ✧
9310 N.E. Vancouver Mall Dr., Ste. 200
Vancouver, WA 98662-8210 (360) 213-1550

Established in 2003 in OR.
Donors: Hugh Colson; Hugh Colson Living Trust; Hugh L. Colson Charitable Lead Annuity Trust.
Foundation type: Independent foundation.
Financial data (yr. ended 12/31/13): Assets, $26,179,111 (M); gifts received, $4,368,747; expenditures, $8,143,795; qualifying distributions, $8,059,887; giving activities include $8,057,500 for 46 grants (high: $1,000,000; low: $2,500).
Purpose and activities: Giving primarily to Seventh-day Adventist churches, organizations, and schools.
Fields of interest: Education; Human services; Protestant agencies & churches.
International interests: Africa.
Limitations: Applications not accepted. Giving primarily in OR and WA. No grants to individuals.
Application information: Contributes only to pre-selected organizations.
Officers: Barton G. Colson, Pres.; Norman L. Brenden, V.P.; Bradley A. Colson, V.P.; Patrick Kennedy, V.P.; Bruce D. Thorn, Secy.; Susan Haider, Treas.
Director: Bonnie Colson.
EIN: 931326316
Selected grants: The following grants are a representative sample of this grantmaker's funding activity:
$500,000 to General Conference of Seventh-Day Adventists, Silver Spring, MD, 2012. For Promise Keepers.
$350,000 to Andrews University, Berrien Springs, MI, 2012. For tuition.
$350,000 to General Conference of Seventh-Day Adventists, Silver Spring, MD, 2012. For Faith and Science Council.
$250,000 to Houchin Community Blood Bank, Bakersfield, CA, 2012. Toward new Platelet Wing in Seven.
$250,000 to U.S. Dream Academy, Columbia, MD, 2012. For general support.
$200,000 to Project PATCH, Vancouver, WA, 2012. For general support.
$200,000 to Share Him, Charlotte, NC, 2012.
$100,000 to Holbrook Adventist Indian School, Holbrook, AZ, 2012. For Worthy Student Fund.
$50,000 to Jubilee Womens Center, Seattle, WA, 2012. For matching grant for fall fundraiser.
$50,000 to Water First International, Seattle, WA, 2012. For matching grant for fall fundraiser.

9602
Columbia Basin Foundation ✧
234 1st Ave. N.W. , Ste. B
Ephrata, WA 98823-1603 (509) 754-4596
Contact: Donn Cook, Exec. Dir.
FAX: (509) 754-4194;
E-mail: info@columbiabasinfoundation.org; Additional e-mail: dcook@columbiabasinfoundation.org; Main URL: http://www.columbiabasinfoundation.org
Facebook: http://www.facebook.com/pages/Columbia-Basin-Foundation/197704690815

Established in WA in 1996.
Foundation type: Community foundation.
Financial data (yr. ended 12/31/13): Assets, $7,383,805 (M); gifts received, $189,764; expenditures, $610,202; giving activities include $341,942 for 16+ grants (high: $25,000), and $111,400 for 65 grants to individuals.
Purpose and activities: The foundation seeks to improve the quality of life and shape the future of the Columbia Basin through philanthropy.
Fields of interest: Arts; Education; Environment; Health care; Human services; Community/economic development.
Type of support: General/operating support; Continuing support; Capital campaigns; Building/renovation; Equipment; Scholarship funds; Employee-related scholarships; Scholarships—to individuals; Matching/challenge support.
Limitations: Applications accepted. Giving primarily in Columbia Basin, WA. No support for religious organizations for religious purposes. No grants to individuals (except for scholarships), or for endowments, debt retirement, fundraising events, advertising, or conferences.
Publications: Application guidelines; Annual report; Informational brochure; Newsletter.
Application information: Visit foundation web site for application form and guidelines. Application form required.
Initial approach: Submit application form and attachments
Copies of proposal: 1

Deadline(s): Mar. 31
Board meeting date(s): 2nd Mon. of every other month
Final notification: 2 months

Officers and Directors:* Wendy Mickelsen,* Pres.; Corinne Isaak,* V.P.; Dave Ponozzo,* Secy.; Jean Frazier,* Treas.; Donn Cook, Exec. Dir.; Huc Dilling; Wade Jordan; Dave Lemon; Tom Moncrief; Judy O'Brien; Tom Overcast; Joe Rogers.
Number of staff: 1 full-time professional.
EIN: 911733104

9603
Community Foundation for Southwest Washington ✧

(formerly Clark County Community Foundation)
610 Esther St., Ste. 201
Vancouver, WA 98660 (360) 694-2550
Contact: For grant applications: Anne Digenis, Sr. Philanthropic Advisor
FAX: (360) 737-6335; E-mail: director@cfsww.org; Grant application e-mail: anne@cfsww.org; Main URL: http://www.cfsww.org
Blog: https://www.cfsww.org/blog/
E-Newsletter: https://www.cfsww.org/newsletter-signup/
Facebook: http://www.facebook.com/pages/Community-Foundation-for-SW-Washington/76911354075
Flickr: http://www.flickr.com/photos/44519114@N04/sets/
Twitter: http://twitter.com/CFSWW
YouTube: http://www.youtube.com/user/CFSWW

Incorporated in 1984 in WA.
Foundation type: Community foundation.
Financial data (yr. ended 12/31/13): Assets, $80,166,552 (M); gifts received, $18,563,156; expenditures, $8,149,698; giving activities include $6,873,259 for grants.
Purpose and activities: The foundation seeks to enrich the quality of life in southwestern WA, by supporting the needs of the local region and sustaining existing organizations through grants made in the areas of health and human services, education, conservation, and the arts.
Fields of interest: Humanities; Arts; Education; Environment; Health care; Disasters, Hurricane Katrina; Children, services; Human services; Community/economic development.
Limitations: Applications accepted. Giving primarily in southwest WA, serving Clark, Cowlitz, and Skamania counties. No support for sectarian or religious programs, private schools, specific research or medical projects, or re-granting purposes. No grants to individuals (except for scholarships), or for endowment funds, capital campaigns, debt reduction, or travel expenses for individuals or groups such as bands, sports teams, or classes.
Publications: Annual report; Informational brochure; Newsletter.
Application information: Visit foundation web site for application form and guidelines per grant type. Application form required.
Initial approach: Submit Grant Inquiry form
Copies of proposal: 8
Deadline(s): Jan. 15 for Grant Inquiry form and Mar. 3 for complete applications for the Community Giving Fund; varies for others
Board meeting date(s): Quarterly
Final notification: Early Feb. for inquiry form notification and mid-spring for grant determination for the Community Giving Fund

Officers and Directors:* Kaycee Wiita,* Chair.; Brett Bryant,* Vice-Chair.; Jennifer Rhoads, Pres.; Mary Pringle, V.P. and C.F.O.; Dr. Jim Youde,* Secy.; Steve Hansen,* Treas.; Pam Cabanatuan, Cont.; Albert Angelo III; Jody Campbell; Mark Dodson; Marty Forsmann; Scott Keeney; Vaughn Lein; Mark Matthias; David Nierenberg; Terry Prill; Dr. David Ruiz; Scott South; Richard Wollenberg; Dr. Candace Young.
Number of staff: 4 full-time professional; 3 full-time support.
EIN: 911246778

9604
Community Foundation of North Central Washington ✧

(formerly Greater Wenatchee Community Foundation)
9 South Wenatchee Ave.
Wenatchee, WA 98807 (509) 663-7716
Contact: Beth A. Stipe, Exec. Dir.; For grants: Denise Sorom, Dir., Community Philanthropy
FAX: (888) 317-8314; E-mail: info@cfncw.org; Additional e-mails: beth@cfncw.org; Grant inquiry e-mail: denise@cfncw.org; Main URL: http://www.cfncw.org
Facebook: https://www.facebook.com/cfncw
Twitter: http://twitter.com/cfncw
YouTube: http://www.youtube.com/cfncw
Scholarship application e-mail: scholarships@cfncw.org

Incorporated in 1986 in WA.
Foundation type: Community foundation.
Financial data (yr. ended 06/30/13): Assets, $48,156,037 (M); gifts received, $3,921,516; expenditures, $3,886,063; giving activities include $2,702,911 for 46+ grants (high: $267,550), and $360,597 for 244 grants to individuals.
Purpose and activities: The foundation makes a difference by serving as a bridge between donors and the broader community. Primary areas of interest include the arts, education, the environment, and the disadvantaged, with emphasis on child welfare and the elderly.
Fields of interest: Media/communications; Visual arts; Museums; Performing arts; Performing arts, theater; Performing arts, music; Humanities; History/archaeology; Historic preservation/historical societies; Arts; Education, early childhood education; Child development, education; Elementary school/education; Higher education; Adult/continuing education; Adult education—literacy, basic skills & GED; Libraries/library science; Education, reading; Education; Environment, natural resources; Environment; Animal welfare; Animals/wildlife, preservation/protection; Hospitals (general); Reproductive health, family planning; Medical care, rehabilitation; Health care; Substance abuse, services; Mental health/crisis services; AIDS; Alcoholism; Food services; Housing/shelter, development; Safety/disasters; Recreation; Children/youth, services; Child development, services; Family services; Residential/custodial care, hospices; Aging, centers/services; Women, centers/services; Minorities/immigrants, centers/services; Homeless, human services; Human services; Community development, neighborhood development; Community/economic development; Voluntarism promotion; Children/youth; Aging; Disabilities, people with; Minorities; Women; Economically disadvantaged; Homeless.
Type of support: General/operating support; Management development/capacity building; Building/renovation; Equipment; Land acquisition; Endowments; Program development; Seed money; Technical assistance; Scholarships—to individuals; Matching/challenge support.
Limitations: Applications accepted. Giving limited to north central WA: Chelan, Douglas, and Okanogan counties. No support for religious sectarian purposes. No grants to individuals (except for scholarships), or for debt retirement or budget deficits, tuition, annual campaigns, fundraising campaigns or events, or purchases or activities that occur prior to grant decisions.
Publications: Application guidelines; Annual report; Grants list; Informational brochure; Informational brochure (including application guidelines); Newsletter; Occasional report.
Application information: Visit foundation web site for application information and guidelines. Application form not required.
Initial approach: Telephone or letter
Copies of proposal: 1
Deadline(s): Varies
Board meeting date(s): 6 times annually
Final notification: Within 90 days

Officers and Trustees:* Katie Kavanaugh Pauly,* Chair.; Ken Marson,* Vice-Chair.; Gil Sparks,* Secy.-Treas.; Beth A. Stipe, Exec. Dir.; Judy A. Cleveland, Cont.; Diane Carson; Bart Clennon; Lisa Day; Claudia DeRobles; Emira Forner; Jane Gilbertsen; Deborah Hartl; Craig Homchick; Ken Jackson; Mary Lou Johnson; Hank Manriquez; Danielle Marchant; Steve Robinson; Peter Rutherford, M.D.; Eliot Scull; Ron Skagen; Mark Spurgeon; Mike Stancil; Mike Steele; Kris Taylor; Nevio Tontini; Peter Valaas; Darci Waterman; David Weber, M.D.; Anne White.
Number of staff: 1 full-time professional; 1 part-time professional; 2 full-time support.
EIN: 911349486

9605
The Community Foundation of South Puget Sound ✧

(formerly Greater Thurston County Community Foundation)
212 Union Ave. S.E., Ste. 102
Olympia, WA 98501-1302 (360) 705-3340
Contact: Norma Schuiteman, Exec. Dir.
FAX: (360) 705-2656;
E-mail: legacy@thecommunityfoundation.com; Main URL: http://www.thecommunityfoundation.com
Facebook: https://www.facebook.com/thecommunityfoundationsouthsound

Established in 1989 in WA.
Foundation type: Community foundation.
Financial data (yr. ended 12/31/13): Assets, $16,813,810 (M); gifts received, $529,210; expenditures, $1,487,919; giving activities include $791,777 for 109+ grants (high: $92,031; low: $300).
Purpose and activities: The mission of the foundation is to encourage the growth and responsible distribution of charitable resources to build stronger communities.

Fields of interest: Arts; Education; Environment; Health care; Human services; Community/economic development.
Type of support: General/operating support; Emergency funds; Program development; Scholarship funds; Consulting services; In-kind gifts; Matching/challenge support.
Limitations: Applications accepted. Giving limited to Lewis, Mason and Thurston counties, WA. No support for religious organizations for religious purposes. No grants to individuals (except from scholarship funds), or for annual campaigns, debt reduction, capital campaigns, endowment funds, direct mail, special events, or for multiple year commitments.
Publications: Application guidelines; Annual report; Grants list; Informational brochure.
Application information: Visit foundation web site for application form and guidelines. Application form required.
Initial approach: Submit application form and attachments
Copies of proposal: 5
Deadline(s): Sept. 19
Board meeting date(s): Every 4th Thurs.
Officers and Directors:* Lori Drummond,* Chair.; Bob Buhl,* Vice-Chair.; Stefani Parsons,* Secy.; Sue Vickerman,* Treas.; Norma Schuiteman, Exec. Dir.; Patti Case; Marty Juergens; Joe Lynch; Jim Morrell; Stacie-Dee Motoyama; Thomas L. Purce, Ed.D.; Greg Rhodes; Rebecca Staebler; Melanie Stewart; Brian Vance; Mary Williams; Robert Wubbena; Rodney Youckton.
Number of staff: 2 full-time professional; 1 part-time professional.
EIN: 943121390

9606
Corvias Foundation ✧
(formerly Our Family for Families First, Inc.)
210 5th Ave. S., Ste. 202
Edmonds, WA 98020-3625 (401) 228-2836
Contact: Maria Montalvo, Exec. Dir.
FAX: (401) 336-2505;
E-mail: info@CorviasFoundation.org; E-mail for Maria Montalvo: Maria.Montalvo@CorviasFoundation.org; Main URL: http://www.corviasfoundation.org
Grants List: http://corviasfoundation.org/?id=charitable-giving

Established in 2006 in RI.
Donors: John C. Picerne; Brian Beauregard; USI Insurance; Armstrong; Severn Plumbing; Armstrong Wood Products; Armstrong World; Associated Materials; Bank of America; Barclays; Brian Beauregard; Brickman Group; Ch2M Hill; Builders First Choice; Cigna; Goebel; HD Supply; HB Communications; J. McDonald; Konica Minolta; L Stanley Shaw; John G P I Cerne; KCS Landscaping; Kimley-Horn; Master Brand; Michael Steiner; MOEN; Sherwin Williams; Picerne Real Estate Group; Real Page; Seagull Lighting; Tony Freedman; USI Insurance; Westrope; Winslow Tech Group; Yardi.
Foundation type: Independent foundation.
Financial data (yr. ended 12/31/13): Assets, $85,723 (M); gifts received, $863,644; expenditures, $860,842; qualifying distributions, $632,733; giving activities include $533,619 for 221 grants (high: $11,100; low: $20), and $99,114 for 25 grants to individuals (high: $5,000; low: $231).
Purpose and activities: Giving to support Army families in the pursuit of higher education, establishing a tradition of community service, and encouraging professional career paths through education, internships, and mentoring programs. Scholarships to high school seniors between the ages of 16 and 19 at the time of application, who have a minimum 3.0 G.P.A., who plan to attend a 4-year college or university as an undergraduate student, and who is a child of an active-duty Service Member stations at one of the following U.S. Military instillations: Aberdeen Proving Ground, MD; Edwards Air Force Base, CA; Eglin Air Force Base, FL; Eielson Air Force Base, AK; Fort Bragg, NC; Fort Meade, MD; Fort Polk, LA; Fort Riley, KS; Fort Rucker, AL; Fort Sill, OK; Hurlburt Field, FL; McConnell Air Force Base, KS; and Seymour Johnson Air Force Base, NC. Educational grants also to spouses of active-duty service members stationed at the same military instillations, who plan to attend a community, technical, or 4-year college as an undergraduate or graduate student.
Fields of interest: Education; Heart & circulatory diseases; Community/economic development.
Type of support: General/operating support; Scholarships—to individuals.
Limitations: Applications accepted. Giving limited to a child or a spouse of an active-duty Army Soldier stationed at one of the following U.S. Army installations: Aberdeen Proving Ground, MD; Edwards Air Force Base, CA; Eglin Air Force Base, FL; Eielson Air Force Base, AK; Fort Bragg, NC; Fort Meade, MD; Fort Polk, LA; Fort Riley, KS; Fort Rucker, AL; Fort Sill, OK; Hurlburt Field, FL; McConnell Air Force Base, KS; and Seymour Johnson Air Force Base, NC.
Publications: Application guidelines.
Application information: Complete application guidelines available on foundation web site.
Initial approach: See foundation web site
Officers and Directors:* John G. Picerne,* Pres.; Maria Montalvo,* Secy.; Claude Levesque,* Treas.; Janet G. Colantuono; Lynn Fossum.
EIN: 204848228
Selected grants: The following grants are a representative sample of this grantmaker's funding activity:
$10,000 to Baker University, School of Nur, Baldwin City, KS, 2012. For educational scholarship.
$5,716 to University of Kansas, Lawrence, KS, 2012. For educational scholarship.
$3,938 to University of Kansas, Lawrence, KS, 2012. For educational scholarship.
$2,000 to Fayetteville Urban Ministry, Fayetteville, NC, 2012. For general operating support.

9607
Harriet Cheney Cowles Foundation ✧
999 W. Riverside Ave., Ste. 605
Spokane, WA 99201-1006

Incorporated in 1944 in WA.
Donors: Spokane Chronicle Co.; Cowles Publishing Co.; Inland Empire Paper Co.
Foundation type: Independent foundation.
Financial data (yr. ended 12/31/12): Assets, $11,566,327 (M); expenditures, $692,810; qualifying distributions, $595,000; giving activities include $595,000 for 8 grants (high: $235,000; low: $10,000).
Fields of interest: Higher education; Human services; Salvation Army; Residential/custodial care, hospices; Foundations (private grantmaking).
Type of support: Capital campaigns; Endowments.
Limitations: Applications not accepted. Giving primarily in Spokane, WA. No grants to individuals.
Application information: Contributes only to pre-selected organizations.
Officers and Trustee:* E.A. Cowles, Pres.; W.S. Cowles,* V.P.; S.R. Rector, Secy.
EIN: 910689268

9608
Crystal Springs Foundation ✧
c/o Filament, LLC
701 Pike St., Ste. 2225
Seattle, WA 98101-2370

Established in 1999 in WA.
Donors: Michael R. Murray; Joyce B. Murray.
Foundation type: Independent foundation.
Financial data (yr. ended 12/31/12): Assets, $44,173,530 (M); expenditures, $1,953,892; qualifying distributions, $2,427,074; giving activities include $1,159,600 for 32 grants (high: $125,000; low: $100), $8,454 for 1 foundation-administered program and $910,000 for 6 loans/program-related investments (high: $250,000; low: $60,000).
Purpose and activities: Giving primarily for international economic development, education, as well as for social services.
Fields of interest: Higher education; Health organizations, association; Human services; Children/youth, services; International economic development; Foundations (private grantmaking).
Limitations: Applications not accepted. Giving primarily in UT, with emphasis on Salt Lake City, and Seattle, WA. No grants to individuals.
Application information: Contributes only to pre-selected organizations.
Officers and Directors:* Michael R. Murray,* Pres. and Treas.; Joyce B. Murray,* V.P. and Secy.
Number of staff: 1 full-time support.
EIN: 912008832

9609
The F. Danz Foundation ✧
600 106th Ave N.E., Ste. 200
Bellevue, WA 98004-5043

Established in 1998 in WA.
Donor: Frederic A. Danz‡.
Foundation type: Independent foundation.
Financial data (yr. ended 12/31/13): Assets, $99,468 (M); gifts received, $650,000; expenditures, $670,645; qualifying distributions, $670,625; giving activities include $670,600 for 22 grants (high: $250,000; low: $2,500).
Fields of interest: Higher education; Hospitals (general); Nursing home/convalescent facility; Family services; Jewish agencies & synagogues.
Type of support: Program development; Endowments; Capital campaigns.
Limitations: Applications not accepted. Giving primarily in Bellevue and Seattle, WA. No grants to individuals.
Application information: Contributes only to pre-selected organizations.
Trustee: Alison Danz.
EIN: 916477156
Selected grants: The following grants are a representative sample of this grantmaker's funding activity:

$40,000 to Overlake Hospital Foundation, Bellevue, WA, 2012. For Unrestricted use by donee.

9610
The Dimmer Family Foundation ✧
1019 Pacific Ave., Ste. 916
Tacoma, WA 98402-4492 (253) 572-4607
Contact: Diane C. Dimmer, Exec. Dir.
FAX: (253) 572-4647;
E-mail: info@dimmerfoundation.org; Main URL: http://www.dimmerfoundation.org
Facebook: https://www.facebook.com/DimmerFamilyFoundation?skip_nax_wizard=true#

Established in 1994 in WA.
Donor: John C. Dimmer.
Foundation type: Independent foundation.
Financial data (yr. ended 12/31/12): Assets, $14,244,087 (M); expenditures, $970,180; qualifying distributions, $610,894; giving activities include $521,480 for 125 grants (high: $57,750; low: $100).
Purpose and activities: Giving primarily for the arts, education, and for health care and human services.
Fields of interest: Museums; Museums (children's); Arts; Higher education; Education; Animal welfare; Hospitals (general); Health care; Medical research, institute; Youth development, centers/clubs; Human services.
Type of support: General/operating support; Continuing support; Annual campaigns; Capital campaigns; Building/renovation; Equipment; Endowments; Program development; Scholarship funds; Research; Matching/challenge support.
Limitations: Applications accepted. Giving primarily in Tacoma, WA.
Publications: Grants list; Informational brochure.
Application information: Application form required.
Initial approach: Proposal
Deadline(s): None
Board meeting date(s): 4-6 weeks after each deadline
Officers: John C. Dimmer, Pres.; Carolyn Dimmer, V.P.; Marilyn Dimmer, V.P.; Diane C. Dimmer, Secy. and Exec. Dir.; John B. Dimmer, Treas.
Number of staff: 1 part-time professional.
EIN: 911622059
Selected grants: The following grants are a representative sample of this grantmaker's funding activity:
$212,000 to Harold E. LeMay Museum, Tacoma, WA, 2011.
$50,000 to Washington State Historical Society, Tacoma, WA, 2011.
$32,451 to Annie Wright School, Tacoma, WA, 2011. For general support.
$12,500 to University of Washington Foundation, Seattle, WA, 2011. For general support.
$10,000 to Pierce County Library Foundation, Tacoma, WA, 2011. For general support.
$8,950 to Tacoma Art Museum, Tacoma, WA, 2011. For general support.
$7,500 to Museum of Glass, Tacoma, WA, 2011. For general support.
$5,000 to InvestED, Seattle, WA, 2011. For general support.
$5,000 to Northwest Sinfonietta, Tacoma, WA, 2011. For general support.
$5,000 to R. Merle Palmer Minority Scholarship Foundation, Tacoma, WA, 2011. For general support.
$3,500 to Tacoma Musical Playhouse, Tacoma, WA, 2010. For general support.

9611
Discuren Charitable Foundation ✧
1201 3rd Ave., Ste. 4900
Seattle, WA 98101-3099 (206) 359-8574
Contact: F. Jean Watson, Secy.-Treas.

Established in 2004 in WA.
Donor: Blue Heron Trust.
Foundation type: Independent foundation.
Financial data (yr. ended 12/31/13): Assets, $15,789,122 (M); expenditures, $1,782,222; qualifying distributions, $1,657,400; giving activities include $1,502,158 for 39 grants (high: $78,000; low: $13,000).
Purpose and activities: Giving to organizations that address the needs of literacy, basic education, drop-out prevention, and provide teaching and learning environments for children.
Fields of interest: Elementary/secondary education; Higher education; Education, drop-out prevention; Education; YM/YWCAs & YM/YWHAs; Children/youth, services; Family services.
Limitations: Applications accepted. Giving limited to WA.
Application information: Application form required.
Initial approach: Contact foundation for application form
Deadline(s): Quarterly and must be submitted 2 weeks prior to meetings
Officers: Colonel F. Betz, Pres.; Robert S. Mucklestone, V.P.; F. Jean Watson, Secy.-Treas.
Directors: Martha Ashenfelter; Greg Coy; Polly M. Olsen.
EIN: 202046554

9612
The Edgebrook Foundation ✧
c/o Jon Tullis
801 2nd Ave., Ste. 1600
Seattle, WA 98104-1521

Established in 1985 in WA.
Donors: Charlotte L. Taylor; Charlotte Taylor Trust.
Foundation type: Independent foundation.
Financial data (yr. ended 12/31/12): Assets, $3,429,466 (M); gifts received, $1,453,507; expenditures, $632,395; qualifying distributions, $622,000; giving activities include $622,000 for 1 grant.
Fields of interest: Foundations (public).
Limitations: Applications not accepted. Giving primarily in New York, NY. No grants to individuals.
Application information: Unsolicited requests for funds not accepted.
Officers: Jon Tullis, Pres.; Mary Jo Bowman, Secy.; Thomas Burnham, Treas.
EIN: 911307405

9613
Eggnog Latte Foundation ✧
(doing business as Renee and Jeff Harbers Family Foundation)
P.O. Box 298
Medina, WA 98039-0298
Main URL: http://www.harbersfoundation.org/

Established in WA.
Donor: Renee W. Harbers.
Foundation type: Operating foundation.
Financial data (yr. ended 11/30/12): Assets, $5,390,362 (M); gifts received, $1,602,228; expenditures, $1,412,381; qualifying distributions, $1,410,692; giving activities include $1,139,338 for 11 grants (high: $500,000; low: $491), and $703,773 for 4 foundation-administered programs.
Purpose and activities: The foundation brings human and environmental issues into focus by setting the aperture for inspiring and motivating visual narratives. Working with some of the world's leading photographers and visual storytellers, it creates exceptional visual narratives that represent the diverse initiatives of cutting edge non-profits and NGOs around the world, focusing on global conservation issues and humanitarian need.
Fields of interest: Arts; Environment; Health care; Human services.
Limitations: Applications not accepted.
Application information: Unsolicited requests for funds not accepted.
Officers: Renee W. Harbers, C.E.O.; Gretchen Huizinga, Exec. Dir.
Trustees: Geoff Cowper; Mark Kroese.
EIN: 261616837

9614
Ellison Foundation ✧
(formerly Tom and Sue Ellison Foundation)
400 112th Ave. N.E., Ste. 230
Bellevue, WA 98004-5545
Contact: Bob Hurlbut

Established in 2002 in WA.
Donors: Thomas A. Ellison; Maureen Sue Ellison; Legacy Family Investments.
Foundation type: Independent foundation.
Financial data (yr. ended 12/31/12): Assets, $47,544,337 (M); gifts received, $37,921,546; expenditures, $684,465; qualifying distributions, $601,159; giving activities include $582,979 for 45 grants (high: $150,000; low: $500).
Fields of interest: Education; United Ways and Federated Giving Programs.
Limitations: Giving primarily in WA.
Application information:
Initial approach: Letter
Deadline(s): None
Officers: Thomas A. Ellison, Pres.; Maureen Sue Ellison, V.P.
Director: Robert Hurlbut.
EIN: 916557865

9615
Empire Health Foundation ✧
P.O. Box 244
Spokane, WA 99210-0244 (509) 315-1323
E-mail: brian@empirehealthfoundation.org; Main URL: http://www.empirehealthfoundation.org
Blog: http://www.empirehealthfoundation.org/blog
E-Newsletter: http://www.empirehealthfoundation.org/mailing-list
Grants List: http://www.empirehealthfoundation.org/grants-awarded
RSS Feed: http://empirehealthfoundation.org/news/rss.xml
Twitter: http://twitter.com/empirehealth

Established in 2008 in WA.
Donors: Empire Health Services; Boone Foundation; Woodrow Foundation; Grant Makers in Health.
Foundation type: Independent foundation.
Financial data (yr. ended 12/31/12): Assets, $64,983,909 (M); gifts received, $177,515;

expenditures, $3,057,765; qualifying distributions, $8,018,223; giving activities include $1,331,614 for 90 grants (high: $150,579; low: $100), and $7,973,223 for foundation-administered programs.
Purpose and activities: The foundation works to improve the health of communities in eastern Washington. The foundation seeks to design and implement a strategic vision for impact, and establish itself as a catalyst and convener in the region.
Fields of interest: Arts; Education; Agriculture/food.
Limitations: Applications accepted. Giving primarily in Ferry, Stevens, Pend Oreille, Lincoln, Spokane, Adams and Whitman counties, WA. No grants to individuals.
Application information: Application form required.
Initial approach: E-mail
Officers and Trustees:* Garman Lutz,* Chair.; Sue Lanai W. Madsen,* Vice-Chair.; Antony Chiang, Pres.; Kristen West, V.P., Grant Progs.; Anne C. Cowles,* Secy.; Dave Luhn, C.F.O.; Matthew Layton,* Treas.; Lisa Brown; Craig Dias; Deb Harper; Todd Koyama; Teressa Martinez; Michael Nowling; Theresa Sanders; Mary C. Selecky; Sam Selinger, M.D.; Gary Stokes.
EIN: 263375286
Selected grants: The following grants are a representative sample of this grantmaker's funding activity:
$150,579 to Washington State University, Pullman, WA, 2012. To Assist Organization to Promote Good Health in Their Community.

9616
The Greater Everett Community Foundation ✧

2823 Rockefeller Ave.
P.O. Box 5549
Everett, WA 98201-3524 (425) 212-4056
Contact: Maddy Metzger-Utt, Pres. and C.E.O.; Karri Matau
FAX: (425) 212-4059;
E-mail: maddy@greatereverettcf.org; Mailing address: P.O. Box 5549, Everett, WA 98206-5549; Additional e-mail: info@greatereverettcf.org; Grant inquiry tel. 425-212-4056; Main URL: http://www.greatereverettcf.org

Established in 2001 in WA.
Foundation type: Community foundation.
Financial data (yr. ended 12/31/12): Assets, $10,525,375 (M); gifts received, $714,245; expenditures, $866,736; giving activities include $414,719 for 23+ grants (high: $25,840), and $28,200 for 16 grants to individuals.
Purpose and activities: The foundation works in partnership with donors to strengthen communities in greater Everett and Snohomish County, WA, by building permanent charitable funds, connecting donors to the causes they care about, making effective grants, and providing leadership to address community issues.
Fields of interest: Arts; Education; Environment; Health care; Youth development, adult & child programs; Developmentally disabled, centers & services; Human services; Children; Youth; Mentally disabled.
Type of support: General/operating support; Annual campaigns; Equipment; Endowments; Program development; Scholarship funds; Employee matching gifts; Scholarships—to individuals.
Limitations: Applications accepted. Giving primarily in Snohomish County, WA.
Publications: Application guidelines; Annual report.
Application information: Visit foundation web site for application forms and guidelines per grant type. Application form required.
Initial approach: Submit application form
Copies of proposal: 1
Deadline(s): Apr. 30 for Spring Grants and Oct. 31 for Fall Grants
Board meeting date(s): 4th Wed. of every other month
Final notification: 60 days
Officers and Directors:* Melinda Grout,* Chair.; Bill Neumeister,* Vice-Chair.; Maddy Metzger-Utt,* Pres. and C.E.O.; Karri Matau,* V.P., Grantmaking and Partnerships; Elena Pullen-Venema,* V.P., Devel.; Martha Dankers,* Secy.; Scott Murphy,* Treas.; Judy Baker; Patty DeGroodt; Sarah Duncan; Bonnie Eckley; Carlton Gipson; Mary Hale; Kelly Johnson; John Middleton; Ross Rettenmier.
Number of staff: 1 full-time professional; 2 part-time professional.
EIN: 943188703

9617
Evertrust Foundation ✧

(formerly Everett Mutual Savings Bank Foundation)
P.O. Box 1245
Everett, WA 98206-1245 (425) 339-1286
Contact: Mary B. Sievers, Exec. Dir.
Main URL: http://www.evertrustfoundation.com/

Established in 1993.
Donor: Everett Mutual Savings Bank.
Foundation type: Company-sponsored foundation.
Financial data (yr. ended 12/31/13): Assets, $10,466,176 (M); expenditures, $628,741; qualifying distributions, $498,656; giving activities include $456,036 for 40 grants (high: $40,000; low: $300).
Purpose and activities: The foundation supports programs designed to improve family services through food, shelter, clothing, healthcare, and educational initiatives that promote self-sufficiency.
Fields of interest: Higher education; Education; Health care; Employment, services; Food services; Food banks; Housing/shelter; Boys & girls clubs; Salvation Army; YM/YWCAs & YM/YWHAs; Youth, services; Family services; Human services; United Ways and Federated Giving Programs.
Type of support: General/operating support; Continuing support; Capital campaigns; Building/renovation; Equipment; Program development; Scholarship funds; Sponsorships; Matching/challenge support.
Limitations: Applications accepted. Giving limited to Snohomish County, WA. No support for lobbying organizations. No grants to individuals, or for endowments, land acquisition, conferences or seminars, trips or tours, media productions, or religious activities that serve specific religious groups or denominations and are not of direct benefit to the entire community.
Publications: Application guidelines.
Application information: A full proposal may be requested at a later date. Multi-year funding is not automatic. Organizations receiving support are asked to provide a final report. Application form not required.
Initial approach: Letter of inquiry
Deadline(s): 1 month before board meeting
Board meeting date(s): Feb., May, Aug. and Nov.
Final notification: Following board meeting
Officers and Directors:* Margaret Bavasi,* Pres.; Tom Collins,* V.P.; Mary B. Sievers,* Secy. and Exec. Dir.; Robert W. Baeur, Treas.; Kathy Atwood; Thomas J. Gaffney; Larry Hanson; Mike Kight; Nancy Kniest; George Newland; Ross Rettenmier; Bill Rucker; Harry Stuchell.
EIN: 911510567
Selected grants: The following grants are a representative sample of this grantmaker's funding activity:
$35,000 to Providence General Foundation, Everett, WA, 2011.
$28,000 to Housing Hope, Everett, WA, 2011.
$25,000 to Senior Services of Snohomish County, Everett, WA, 2011.
$22,000 to Providence General Foundation, Everett, WA, 2011.
$18,000 to Christmas House, Everett, WA, 2011.
$16,000 to Everett Public Schools Foundation, Everett, WA, 2011.
$12,000 to Everett Community College Foundation, Everett, WA, 2011.
$5,500 to Friends of Youth, Kirkland, WA, 2011.
$5,000 to Everett Gospel Mission, Everett, WA, 2011.
$4,500 to YMCA of Snohomish County, Everett, WA, 2011.

9618
The Martin Fabert Foundation ✧

c/o Foundation Management Group, LLC
1000 2nd Ave., 34th Fl.
Seattle, WA 98104-1094

Established in 2001 in IL.
Donors: Martin Foundation; Elizabeth Martin.
Foundation type: Independent foundation.
Financial data (yr. ended 06/30/13): Assets, $13,678,246 (M); expenditures, $663,977; qualifying distributions, $544,500; giving activities include $544,500 for grants.
Purpose and activities: Giving primarily for environmental conservation and human services.
Fields of interest: Environment, natural resources; Environment, water resources; Environment; Health organizations; Human services.
Limitations: Applications not accepted. Giving primarily in WA; some funding also in CA. No grants to individuals.
Application information: Unsolicited requests for funds not accepted.
Officers and Directors:* Elizabeth Martin,* Pres. and Treas.; Kenneth Fabert,* V.P.; Daniel Asher, Secy.; Geraldine Martin.
EIN: 364437950
Selected grants: The following grants are a representative sample of this grantmaker's funding activity:
$53,500 to Fred Hutchinson Cancer Research Center, Seattle, WA, 2013. To Uganda-Burkitt Lymphoma Program and Ida Islas Summer Internship Program.
$50,000 to Bainbridge Island Land Trust, Bainbridge Island, WA, 2013. For Hilltop Acquisition Project.
$50,000 to PATH, Seattle, WA, 2013. To Hepatitis B Vaccine Vietnam Project.
$35,000 to NatureBridge, Seattle, WA, 2013. For Staffing of the Science and Stewardship Position at the Olympic Campus.
$25,000 to Student Conservation Association, Seattle, WA, 2013. For the Elwha River Ecosystem Restoration Project.

9619
First Financial Northwest Foundation ✧
c/o Joann E. Lee
201 Wells Ave. S.
Renton, WA 98057-2131

Established in 2007 in WA.
Donor: First Financial Northwest, Inc.
Foundation type: Company-sponsored foundation.
Financial data (yr. ended 12/31/13): Assets, $14,536,461 (M); expenditures, $690,531; qualifying distributions, $661,861; giving activities include $650,000 for 10 grants (high: $500,000; low: $5,000).
Purpose and activities: The foundation supports community foundations and organizations involved with human services.
Fields of interest: Human services; Community/economic development.
Type of support: General/operating support.
Limitations: Applications not accepted. Giving primarily in Renton, WA. No grants for individuals.
Application information: Contributes only to pre-selected organizations.
Officers: Charles J. Delaurenti II, Chair.; Gary F. Faull, Secy.; JoAnn E. Lee, Treas.; Gary F. Kohlwes, Exec. Dir.
Trustee: Harry A. Blencoe.
EIN: 261421623

9620
Forest Foundation ✧
1250 Pacific Ave., Ste. 870
Tacoma, WA 98402-4334 (253) 627-1634
Contact: Bickley Barich, Office Admin.
FAX: (253) 627-6249;
E-mail: grants@grantmakerconsultants.com

Incorporated in 1962 in WA.
Donors: C. Davis Weyerhaeuser†; William T. Weyerhaeuser.
Foundation type: Independent foundation.
Financial data (yr. ended 10/31/13): Assets, $31,619,976 (M); expenditures, $1,799,369; qualifying distributions, $1,539,478; giving activities include $1,312,250 for 74 grants (high: $100,000; low: $1,000).
Fields of interest: Environment; Youth development; Economic development; Community/economic development.
Type of support: Program development; Equipment; General/operating support; Matching/challenge support.
Limitations: Applications accepted. Giving primarily in southwestern WA, with emphasis on Pierce County. Grants given for capital projects only in Clallum, Cowlitz, Clark, Grays Harbor, Jefferson, Kitsap, Lewis, Mason, Pacific, Skamania, Thurston and Wahkiakum counties. No support for religious organizations to promulgate religion. No grants to individuals, or for building or renovation projects.
Publications: Application guidelines.
Application information: Full proposals by invitation only. Application form required.
Initial approach: E-mail request for guidelines and instructions
Copies of proposal: 2
Deadline(s): Check guidelines for specific dates
Board meeting date(s): 6 times a year
Final notification: 60 to 90 days
Officers and Directors:* Gail T. Weyerhaeuser,* Pres. and Treas.; Annette B. Weyerhaeuser,* V.P.; Nicholas C. Spika, Secy.; Brian F. Boyd, Exec. Dir.; William T. Weyerhaeuser.
Number of staff: None.
EIN: 916020514
Selected grants: The following grants are a representative sample of this grantmaker's funding activity:
$430,000 to Greater Tacoma Community Foundation, Tacoma, WA, 2011.
$80,000 to Tacoma Art Museum, Tacoma, WA, 2011. For operating budget.
$50,000 to Boys and Girls Clubs of South Puget Sound, Tacoma, WA, 2011. For operating budget.
$50,000 to Charles Wright Academy, Tacoma, WA, 2011. For operating budget.
$35,000 to Catholic Community Services, Tacoma, WA, 2011. For operating budget.
$30,000 to Forterra, Seattle, WA, 2011. For operating budget.
$30,000 to Washington Womens Employment and Education, Tacoma, WA, 2011. For operating budget.
$20,000 to Exodus Housing, Sumner, WA, 2011. For operating budget.
$20,000 to Northwest Leadership Foundation, Tacoma, WA, 2011. For operating budget.
$20,000 to Pierce County Center for Dispute Resolution, Tacoma, WA, 2011. For operating budget.

9621
The Foster Foundation ✧
13 Central Way
Kirkland, WA 98033-6105 (206) 726-1815
Contact: Jill Goodsell, Exec. Dir.
E-mail: info@thefosterfoundation.org; Seattle, WA contacts: tel.: (206) 726-1815, fax: (206) 903-0628; Main URL: http://www.thefosterfoundation.org

Established in 1984 in WA.
Donors: Evelyn W. Foster†; Albert O. Foster†; Michael Foster†.
Foundation type: Independent foundation.
Financial data (yr. ended 12/31/12): Assets, $65,348,366 (M); expenditures, $6,313,875; qualifying distributions, $5,697,148; giving activities include $5,568,118 for 42 grants (high: $4,875,000; low: $50).
Purpose and activities: Giving to enhance the quality of life in the Pacific Northwest and in AK, through support of qualified needs in the areas of arts and culture, medical research, treatment and care, education, and human welfare.
Fields of interest: Performing arts; Arts; Higher education; Education; Health care; Health organizations, association; AIDS; Pediatrics; Medical research; Human services; YM/YWCAs & YM/YWHAs; Children/youth, services; Homeless, human services; United Ways and Federated Giving Programs.
Type of support: Building/renovation; Equipment; Program development; Seed money; Scholarship funds; Research; Matching/challenge support.
Limitations: Giving primarily in the Pacific Northwest, with emphasis on Seattle, WA. No support for sectarian or religious organizations whose activities benefit only their members. No grants to individuals directly, or for fundraising, endowment funds, scholarships, or unrestricted operating funds; no loans.
Publications: Application guidelines.
Application information: Application form required.
Initial approach: Submit grant form via foundation web site
Deadline(s): Aug. 31
Board meeting date(s): Dec.
Final notification: 3 months
Officers: Michael G. Foster, Jr.,* Chair.; Karen Okamura Rowe, Exec. Dir.; Todd Patrick; J. Bradford Smith.
EIN: 911265474
Selected grants: The following grants are a representative sample of this grantmaker's funding activity:
$4,875,000 to University of Washington, Seattle, WA, 2011.
$308,641 to Seattle Foundation, Seattle, WA, 2011.
$305,984 to Overlake School, Redmond, WA, 2011.
$18,750 to Youth Eastside Services, Bellevue, WA, 2011. For challenge grant.

9622
Foundation for the Future ✧
16150 N.E. 85th St., Ste. 119
Redmond, WA 98052-3542

Established in 1996 in WA as a private operating foundation.
Donor: Walter P. Kistler.
Foundation type: Independent foundation.
Financial data (yr. ended 12/31/12): Assets, $7,673,106 (M); expenditures, $3,693,619; qualifying distributions, $3,443,074; giving activities include $1,377,908 for 13 grants (high: $1,000,000; low: $5,000), $7,500 for 1 grant to an individual, and $98,643 for foundation-administered programs.
Purpose and activities: The mission of the foundation is to increase and diffuse knowledge concerning the long-term future of humanity. It conducts a broad range of programs and activities to promote an understanding of the factors in the social, genetic, biological, medical, psychological, physiological, cultural, technological, and ecological fields that may have an impact on human life.
Fields of interest: Education.
Type of support: Continuing support; Program development; Seed money; Research.
Limitations: Applications not accepted. Giving primarily in VA; funding also in India and Peru.
Application information: Unsolicited requests for funds not accepted.
Board meeting date(s): Quarterly
Officers and Trustees:* Walter Kistler,* Pres.; Sesh Velamoor,* Exec. Dir.; Donna Hines; Sylvia Thompson; Milton Woods.
Number of staff: 5 full-time professional; 1 part-time professional; 1 full-time support; 1 part-time support.
EIN: 911732102
Selected grants: The following grants are a representative sample of this grantmaker's funding activity:
$50,000 to University of Washington, Department of Anesthesiology, Seattle, WA, 2012. For research grant.

9623
Foundation of Caring Fund ✧
P.O. Box 2255
Wenatchee, WA 98807-2255

Established in 1989 in WA.
Donors: Carl W. Campbell; Betty F. Campbell; Cimco Enterprises, Inc.
Foundation type: Independent foundation.
Financial data (yr. ended 12/31/13): Assets, $19,029,435 (M); expenditures, $981,456; qualifying distributions, $816,500; giving activities include $816,500 for 13 grants (high: $313,500; low: $1,500).
Fields of interest: Secondary school/education; Medical school/education; Education; Human services; Human services; Christian agencies & churches.
Limitations: Applications not accepted. Giving primarily in Wenatchee, WA. No grants to individuals.
Application information: Contributes only to pre-selected organizations.
Officer: Thomas H. Dye, Pres.
EIN: 911461620

9624
The Gottfried & Mary Fuchs Foundation ✧

2825 Colby Ave., Ste. A
Everett, WA 98201-3554
Application address: c/o Gayleene Berry, 1011 Pacific Ave., Tacoma, WA 98402, tel.: (206) 591-2548

Trust established in 1960 in WA.
Donors: Gottfried Fuchs†; Mary Fuchs†; Gottfried Fuchs Trust.
Foundation type: Independent foundation.
Financial data (yr. ended 12/31/13): Assets, $27,537,339 (M); expenditures, $1,426,394; qualifying distributions, $1,235,618; giving activities include $1,170,450 for 76 grants (high: $113,664; low: $1,000).
Purpose and activities: Support for charitable, educational, or cultural activities in Pierce County, WA, not normally financed by tax funds. Prefers funding services projects rather than operating budgets.
Fields of interest: Arts; Higher education; Education; Human services.
Type of support: General/operating support; Continuing support; Annual campaigns; Capital campaigns; Building/renovation; Equipment; Emergency funds; Program development; Research; Technical assistance; Consulting services; Matching/challenge support.
Limitations: Applications accepted. Giving limited to Pierce County, WA. No grants to individuals.
Publications: Application guidelines.
Application information: Application form required.
Initial approach: Contact foundation for application form
Copies of proposal: 6
Deadline(s): None
Trustee: Union Bank, N.A.
Number of staff: 1 part-time professional.
EIN: 916022284
Selected grants: The following grants are a representative sample of this grantmaker's funding activity:
$7,500 to Special Olympics Washington, Seattle, WA, 2011.

9625
Bill & Melinda Gates Foundation

(formerly William H. Gates Foundation)
P.O. Box 23350
Seattle, WA 98102-0650 (206) 709-3100
Contact: Inquiry Admin.
E-mail: info@gatesfoundation.org; For grant inquiries: (206) 709-3140. East Coast Office address: P.O. Box 6176, Benjamin Franklin Station, Washington, DC 20044, tel.: (202) 662-8130; Main URL: http://www.gatesfoundation.org
Bill and Melinda Gates and Warren Buffett's Giving Pledge Profile: http://glasspockets.org/philanthropy-in-focus/eye-on-the-giving-pledge/profiles/gates
E-Newsletter: http://www.gatesfoundation.org/Pages/subscribe-email-rss.aspx
Facebook: http://www.facebook.com/billmelindagatesfoundation?v=info
Flickr: http://www.flickr.com/photos/gatesfoundation/
GiveSmart: http://www.givesmart.org/Stories/Donors/Melinda-Gates
Grand Challenges in Global Health: http://www.grandchallenges.org/Pages/Default.aspx
Grantee Perception Report: http://www.gatesfoundation.org/How-We-Work/Resources/Grantee-Perception-Report-Summary-2013
Grants Database: http://www.gatesfoundation.org/How-We-Work/Quick-Links/Grants-Database
Impatient Optimists: http://www.impatientoptimists.org/
Knowledge Center: http://www.gatesfoundation.org/learning/Pages/overview.aspx
Pinterest: http://pinterest.com/gatesfoundation/
Twitter: http://www.twitter.com/gatesfoundation
YouTube: http://www.youtube.com/GatesFoundation

Established in 1994 in WA as the William H. Gates Foundation.
Donors: William H. "Bill" Gates III; Melinda French Gates; Warren E. Buffett.
Foundation type: Independent foundation.
Financial data (yr. ended 12/31/13): Assets, $41,310,207,525 (M); gifts received, $4,115,412,226; expenditures, $4,136,540,821; qualifying distributions, $4,135,713,108; giving activities include $3,320,725,374 for grants, $340,691,253 for 4 foundation-administered programs and $45,731,170 for 13 loans/program-related investments (high: $16,380,000; low: $897,558).
Purpose and activities: Guided by the belief that every life has equal value, the Bill & Melinda Gates Foundation works to help all people lead healthy, productive lives. In developing countries, it focuses on improving people's health and giving them the chance to lift themselves out of hunger and extreme poverty. In the United States, it seeks to ensure that all people-especially those with the fewest resources-have access to the opportunities they need to succeed in school and life. Grantmaking areas are: 1) Global Development: to help the world's poorest people lift themselves out of hunger and poverty; 2) Global Health: to harness advances in science and technology to save lives in developing countries; and 3) U.S. Division: to improve U.S. high school and postsecondary education and support vulnerable children and families in Washington State.
Fields of interest: Education, public education; Elementary/secondary education; Middle schools/education; Elementary school/education; Secondary school/education; Higher education, college (community/junior); Libraries/library science; Education; Health care, infants; Reproductive health, family planning; Public health; Public health, clean water supply; Public health, sanitation; Health care; AIDS; Parasitic diseases research; Immunology research; Agriculture; Nutrition; Safety/disasters; Human services; International development; Economic development; Community/economic development; Philanthropy/voluntarism, alliance/advocacy; Financial services; Infants/toddlers; Children/youth; Children; Youth; Adults; Young adults; Women; Infants/toddlers, female; Girls; Adults, women; Young adults, female; Men; Infants/toddlers, male; Boys; Adults, men; Young adults, male; AIDS, people with; Economically disadvantaged; Homeless.
International interests: Africa; Asia; Developing Countries; Europe.
Type of support: General/operating support; Continuing support; Annual campaigns; Program development; Publication; Scholarship funds; Research; Technical assistance; Program-related investments/loans; Employee matching gifts.
Limitations: Applications accepted. Giving on a national and international basis. No support for projects addressing health problems in developed countries, nor for projects that exclusively serve religious purposes. No direct donations or grants to individuals, and no funding for building or capital campaigns, or for political campaigns and legislative lobbying efforts.
Publications: Application guidelines; Annual report; Financial statement; Grants list; Informational brochure; Newsletter; Occasional report; Program policy statement.
Application information: In general, the foundation directly invites proposals by directly contacting organizations. Review funding guidelines and eligibility overview on foundation's web site before initial contact with foundation. No mail-in applications are accepted. Application form required.
Initial approach: Online letter of inquiry not exceeding 4 pages only accepted for Global Health; submit formal funding proposal upon invitation from foundation
Deadline(s): Generally none
Officers and Trustees:* Melinda French Gates,* Co-Chair.; William H. "Bill" Gates III,* Co-Chair.; William H. Gates, Sr., Co-Chair.; Susan Desmond-Hellmann, M.D., M.P.H., C.E.O.; Leigh Morgan, C.O.O.; Christopher Elias, Pres., Global Devel.; Allan C. Golston, Pres., U.S. Prog.; Trevor Mundel, Pres., Global Health Prog.; Mark Suzman, Pres., Global Policy & Advocacy; Connie Collingsworth, Secy. and Genl. Counsel; Jim Bromley, C.F.O.; Dale Christian, C.I.O.; Miguel Vega-Pestana, Chief Comms. Off.; Susan Byrnes, Interim Chief Comms. Off.; Kurt Fischer, Chief HR Off.; Warren E. Buffett.
Global Health Scientific Advisory Committe: John Bell, Chair.; Alan Bernstein, Ph.D., FRSC; M.K. Bhan, M.D.; Zulfiqar A. Butta, Ph.D.; Tumani Corrah, M.D., Ph.D.; Yvonne Greenstreet, M.D., M.B.A.; H. Robert Horvitz, Ph.D.; Salim S. Abdool Karim, Ph.D.; Shabir A. Madhi, Ph.D.; Francine Ntoumi, Ph.D.; Harold Varmus, M.D.; Timothy Wright, M.D.; Elias A. Zerhouni, M.D.

U.S. Program Advisory Board: Ann Fudge, Chair.; Christopher Edley; Edward Glaeser; Jim Nussle; Margaret Spellings.
Number of staff: 1211
EIN: 562618866
Selected grants: The following grants are a representative sample of this grantmaker's funding activity:
$350,000,000 to Rotary Foundation of Rotary International, Evanston, IL, 2013. For global polio eradication activities through PolioPlus program, payable over 12.50 years.
$194,000,000 to World Health Organization, Geneva, Switzerland, 2013. To complete the eradication and containment of all wild, vaccine-related and Sabin polioviruses, such that no child ever again suffers paralytic poliomyelitis, payable over 2.75 years.
$39,817,533 to International Food Policy Research Institute, Washington, DC, 2013. To improve nutrition and public health by breeding and disseminating staple food crops that are rich in vitamins and minerals, payable over 5.25 years.
$29,979,906 to FHI Solutions LLC, Durham, NC, 2013. To develop and evaluate models for delivering integrated breastfeeding and complementary feeding interventions at scale in Bangladesh, Ethiopia, Vietnam and disseminate lessons for global adoption, payable over 9.00 years.
$25,562,737 to Heifer Project International, Little Rock, AR, 2013. To enable smallholder dairy farmers in Africa to increase their dairy productivity and income through the dairy hub approach, and achieve replication of the approach through private sector and government investment, payable over 5.00 years.
$13,763,544 to Acuitus, Inc., Sunnyvale, CA, 2013. Toward early-stage research and development for digital algebra instruction, payable over 2.00 years.
$866,045 to Sambodhi Research and Communications, New Delhi, India, 2013. To conduct impact assessment of intensified urban tuberculosis (TB) control intervention in Mumbai and Patna to ensure early and accurate diagnosis of tuberculosis (TB), payable over 2.75 years.
$850,000 to California Institute of Technology, Pasadena, CA, 2013. To transform the non-urban toilet into a sustainable, fossil-fuel-free self-contained treatment system for improved sanitation and hygiene with the goal of improving overall health and water quality, payable over 1.75 years.
$571,262 to World Food Programme, Rome, Italy, 2013. To improve market opportunities for smallholder farmers through the expansion of food purchasing mechanisms, payable over 7.50 years.
$240,000 to National Center on Education and the Economy, Washington, DC, 2013. To research professional learning for teachers in high-achieving nations.

9626
The Elizabeth George Foundation ✧
P.O. Box 1429
Langley, WA 98260-1429
Contact: Susan Elizabeth George, Dir.
E-mail: georgeassistant@yahoo.com; Main URL: http://www.elizabethgeorgeonline.com/foundation.htm

Established in 1998 in CA.
Donor: Susan Elizabeth George.
Foundation type: Independent foundation.
Financial data (yr. ended 10/31/13): Assets, $788,846 (M); gifts received, $502,935; expenditures, $519,050; qualifying distributions, $518,425; giving activities include $255,950 for 14 grants (high: $60,000; low: $3,500), and $262,475 for 24 grants to individuals (high: $22,575; low: $1,000).
Purpose and activities: The foundation makes artistic grants to unpublished fiction writers, poets, emerging playwrights, and organizations benefiting disadvantaged youth.
Fields of interest: Performing arts, theater (playwriting); Literature; Education; Youth, services.
Type of support: Continuing support; Program development; Conferences/seminars; Publication; Fellowships; Internship funds; Scholarship funds; Research; Grants to individuals; Scholarships—to individuals; Matching/challenge support; Student loans—to individuals.
Limitations: Applications accepted. No support for religious and political organizations.
Publications: Informational brochure.
Application information: Individual applicant's CV, 5 letters of recommendation from professionals in the field, and a writing sample. There is a $25 non-refundable application fee. Application form not required.
Initial approach: Letter of inquiry
Copies of proposal: 1
Deadline(s): July 1 for inquiry; Nov. 1 for application and references
Board meeting date(s): Annually in Dec.
Final notification: 6 weeks
Officers: Sheila Hillinger, Exec. Secy.; Christopher Eyre, Treas.
Director: Susan Elizabeth George.
Number of staff: 1 part-time professional.
EIN: 330829947

9627
Thomas V. Giddens, Jr. Charitable Foundation ✧
600 N. 36th Ave., Ste. 326
Seattle, WA 98103-8699

Established in 2002 in WA.
Donor: Thomas V. Giddens, Jr.
Foundation type: Independent foundation.
Financial data (yr. ended 05/31/13): Assets, $12,832,655 (M); expenditures, $1,350,105; qualifying distributions, $1,284,119; giving activities include $844,000 for 29 grants (high: $132,500; low: $6,500).
Fields of interest: Children, services; Family services; Homeless.
Limitations: Applications not accepted. Giving primarily in Seattle, WA.
Application information: Contributes only to pre-selected organizations.
Officers and Directors:* Richard Watkins,* Pres.; Mark Kotnour,* V.P.; Paul V. Cavanaugh,* Secy.
EIN: 412047741

9628
David and Patricia Giuliani Family Foundation ✧ ☆
1960 82nd Ave. S.E.
Mercer Island, WA 98040-2216 (206) 465-6852
Contact: David Giuliani, Treas.

Established in WA.
Donors: David Giuliani; Patricia Giuliani.
Foundation type: Independent foundation.
Financial data (yr. ended 12/31/12): Assets, $13,738,855 (M); gifts received, $5,998; expenditures, $853,419; qualifying distributions, $810,376; giving activities include $805,500 for 33 grants (high: $327,000; low: $1,000).
Fields of interest: Cancer research; Human services.
Application information: Application form required.
Initial approach: Proposal
Deadline(s): None
Officers: Patricia Roven Giuliani, Pres.; Nicole Roven Giuliani, V.P.; Daniel Roven Giuliani, Secy.; David Giuliani, Treas.
EIN: 453943382

9629
Glaser Foundation, Inc. ✧
P.O. Box 6548
Bellevue, WA 98008-0548
E-mail: info@paulglaserfoundation.org; Main URL: http://www.paulglaserfoundation.org

Incorporated in 1952 in WA.
Donor: Paul F. Glaser†.
Foundation type: Independent foundation.
Financial data (yr. ended 11/30/13): Assets, $14,441,600 (M); expenditures, $772,271; qualifying distributions, $698,460; giving activities include $649,000 for 91 grants (high: $50,000; low: $1,000).
Purpose and activities: Giving primarily to direct-line services for children and the elderly, particularly within areas concerning: health-related issues, education/vocational training, services for children with disabilities, and services for children from disadvantaged backgrounds.
Fields of interest: Vocational education; Medical care, rehabilitation; Health care; Health organizations, association; Employment; Human services; Children/youth, services; Family services; Aging, centers/services; Aging; Disabilities, people with; Economically disadvantaged.
Type of support: Program development; Seed money; Matching/challenge support.
Limitations: Giving limited to within King County, WA, and immediately adjoining areas. No grants to individuals, or for endowment funds, scholarships, fellowships, publications, or conferences; no loans.
Publications: Application guidelines.
Application information: Review process may take up to 9 months for invited applications. Application form required.
Initial approach: Take eligibility quiz on foundation web site
Copies of proposal: 2
Deadline(s): None, but refer to foundation web site for current cut off dates for each funding category
Board meeting date(s): Jan., Mar., May, July, Sept., and Nov.
Final notification: Usually in Nov.
Officers: R.N. Brandenburg, Pres.; R. William Carlstrom, V.P.; Walt Smith, Secy.; Matt Carlson, Treas.
Board Members: Krista Grinstein; R. Thomas Olson; Janet L. Politeo.
Number of staff: 1 part-time professional.
EIN: 916028694
Selected grants: The following grants are a representative sample of this grantmaker's funding activity:

$15,000 to Country Doctor Community Health Centers, Seattle, WA, 2011.
$15,000 to Food Lifeline, Shoreline, WA, 2011. For operating support.
$15,000 to Multiple Sclerosis Society, National, Seattle, WA, 2011.
$15,000 to Village Project, Seattle, WA, 2011.
$15,000 to YMCA of Greater Seattle, Seattle, WA, 2011.
$10,000 to Building Changes, Seattle, WA, 2011.
$10,000 to Camp Korey, Carnation, WA, 2011.
$7,500 to Seattle Education Access, Seattle, WA, 2011.
$5,000 to Bellevue Civic Theater, Bellevue, WA, 2011.
$5,000 to Bridgeways, Everett, WA, 2011.

9630
Glaser Progress Foundation ✧
(formerly The Glaser Foundation)
1601 2nd Ave., Ste. 1080
Seattle, WA 98101-3526
Contact: Melessa Rogers, Operations Mgr.
FAX: (206) 728-1123;
E-mail: grants@glaserprogress.org; E-mail for application questions: melessa@glaserprogress.org; Main URL: http://www.glaserprogress.org

Established in 1993 in WA.
Donor: Robert D. Glaser.
Foundation type: Independent foundation.
Financial data (yr. ended 12/31/13): Assets, $7,564,161 (M); gifts received, $423,579; expenditures, $1,514,932; qualifying distributions, $1,501,266; giving activities include $1,014,469 for 9 grants (high: $749,664; low: $5,000).
Purpose and activities: The foundation focuses on four program areas: 1) Measuring Progress: build a more equitable and sustainable world by improving our understanding and measurement of human progress, 2) Animal Advocacy: make animal treatment a crucial consideration in business, policy and personal decision-making, 3) Independent Media: strengthen democracy by making independent voices heard (the foundation has also launched a Progress Education Project which will influence all grant awards in this area), and 4) Global HIV/AIDS: to identify and implement programs that provide support for and fulfillment of the goals of the Global Fund to Fight AIDS, tuberculosis, and malaria.
Fields of interest: Media/communications; Animal welfare; International economic development.
Type of support: General/operating support; Program development; Conferences/seminars; Technical assistance.
Limitations: Applications accepted. Giving on a national basis. No support for political organizations. No grants to individuals.
Publications: Application guidelines; Grants list; IRS Form 990 or 990-PF printed copy available upon request.
Application information: Unsolicited grant proposals for the Global HIV/AIDS program are not accepted. Please do not include supporting materials (videos, CDs, newsletters, reports, books) at the early stage of the application process. Application form not required.
Initial approach: Letter via U.S. Mail, e-mail, or fax (choose only one option)
Copies of proposal: 1
Deadline(s): None
Board meeting date(s): Approx. 6 months after receipt of application letter to staff and board review
Final notification: Approx. 6 months
Officer: Martin Collier, Exec. Dir.
Trustee: Robert D. Glaser.
Number of staff: 3 full-time professional.
EIN: 911626010

9631
Grays Harbor Community Foundation ✧
707 J St.
P.O. Box 615
Hoquiam, WA 98550-3624 (360) 532-1600
Contact: Jim Daly, Exec. Dir.; For grants: Cassie Lentz, Prog. Off.
FAX: (360) 532-8111; E-mail: info@gh-cf.org; Additional e-mail: cassie@gh-cf.org; Main URL: http://www.gh-cf.org
Facebook: http://www.facebook.com/GraysHarborCommunityFoundation

Established in 1994 in WA.
Foundation type: Community foundation.
Financial data (yr. ended 12/31/12): Assets, $37,380,788 (M); gifts received, $4,061,246; expenditures, $1,746,455; giving activities include $1,010,514 for 31+ grants (high: $164,750), and $379,034 for 237 grants to individuals.
Purpose and activities: The foundation aims to improve the quality of life in communities throughout Grays Harbor County by: 1) promoting philanthropy at all levels of giving; 2) seeking permanent endowment funds and other contributions from a diverse and ever-widening group of donors; 3) helping donors achieve their charitable and financial goals by offering services that make charitable giving easy, effective and satisfying; 4) providing responsible and effective financial management; 5) distributing earnings from investments according to community needs and donor intent; and 6) championing good works in every community served. Grantmaking priorities include arts and culture, education, health, human services, and community development.
Fields of interest: Historic preservation/historical societies; Arts; Adult education—literacy, basic skills & GED; Student services/organizations; Education; Health care; Mental health/crisis services; Agriculture/food; Homeless, human services; Human services; Community/economic development; Children/youth.
Type of support: General/operating support; Income development; Management development/capacity building; Capital campaigns; Building/renovation; Equipment; Land acquisition; Emergency funds; Program development; Conferences/seminars; Seed money; Curriculum development; Scholarships—to individuals; In-kind gifts; Matching/challenge support.
Limitations: Applications accepted. Giving primarily to residents of Grays Harbor County, WA, area. No support for religious organizations for religious purposes. No grants to individuals (except for scholarships), or for endowments, debt retirement, fundraising events, advertising, or attending conferences.
Publications: Application guidelines; Annual report; Grants list; Informational brochure; Informational brochure (including application guidelines); Newsletter.
Application information: Visit foundation web site for grant application cover sheet and guidelines. The foundation welcomes phone calls and letters of inquiry at all times. Application form required.
Initial approach: Submit application cover sheet and attachments
Copies of proposal: 7
Deadline(s): Jan. 1, Apr. 1, July 1, and Oct. 1
Board meeting date(s): 3rd Thurs. of alternating months
Final notification: Quarterly
Officers and Directors:* Tom Quigg,* Chair.; Jon Parker,* Vice-Chair.; Dr. David Westby,* Secy.; Bob Preble,* Treas.; Jim Daly, Exec. Dir.; Dr. Donald J. Arima; Barbara Bennett-Parsons; Tom Brennan; David Burnett; Ron Caufman; George Donovan; Martin Kay; Todd Lindley; Dennis Long; John Mertz; Wes Peterson; Stan Pinnick; Randy Rust; Bill Stewart; Mike Stoney; Rich Vroman; John Warring; Maryann Welch.
Number of staff: 2 full-time professional; 1 full-time support.
EIN: 911607005

9632
Joshua Green Foundation ✧
1425 4th Ave., Ste. 420
P.O. Box 21829
Seattle, WA 98101-2218 (206) 622-0420
Contact: Sandra Spurlock, Secy.
FAX: (206) 467-1176;
E-mail: sandras@joshuagreencorp.com; Main URL: http://www.joshuagreencorp.com/
Grants List: http://new.joshuagreencorp.com/foundation/

Established in 1956 in WA.
Donors: Joshua Green†; Mrs. Joshua Green†; Charles P. Burnett III; Joshua Green III; Jennifer Carter; Frances Davidson; Laura Gowen; Herbert Gowen; William C. Gowen; Louisa Gowen; Shirley Burnett; William Burnett; Vivian Burnett; William Burnett, Jr.; Shannon Hoffer; Laura Brisbane; Louisa Malatos; Sarah Burnett; Leslie Hawkins; Jean Tannehill; David Burnett; Leah Holser; Paige Dunn; William Burnett; Vivian Burnett; William Burnett, Jr.; Jean Tannehill; Rocky Tannehill; Robert Burnett; Joshua Green Corporation; H. Gowen II; Reagam Dunn.
Foundation type: Independent foundation.
Financial data (yr. ended 12/31/12): Assets, $41,985,032 (M); gifts received, $832,850; expenditures, $1,644,707; qualifying distributions, $1,479,126; giving activities include $1,477,800 for 157 grants (high: $150,000; low: $50).
Fields of interest: Arts; Elementary/secondary education; Higher education; Health care; Human services; Family services; Christian agencies & churches.
Type of support: Capital campaigns; Building/renovation; Land acquisition; Emergency funds.
Limitations: Applications accepted. Giving primarily in the King County, WA, area. No grants to individuals, or for scholarships or fellowships; no loans.
Publications: Application guidelines.
Application information: See foundation web site for complete application guidelines. Application form required.
Initial approach: Letter or E-mail
Copies of proposal: 1
Deadline(s): None
Officers: Joshua Green III, Pres.; Charles P. Burnett III, V.P.; Stanley P. McCammon, V.P.; Sandra Spurlock, Secy.

Trustees: Jennifer Carter; Louisa Malatos; Charles E. Riley.
EIN: 916050748

9633
Greenstein Family Foundation ✧ ☆
c/o Wellspring Group
10885 N.E. 4th St., Ste. 320
Bellevue, WA 98004-5525

Foundation type: Independent foundation.
Financial data (yr. ended 10/31/13): Assets, $4,064,786 (M); expenditures, $663,297; qualifying distributions, $556,188; giving activities include $553,029 for 21 grants (high: $121,800; low: $180).
Fields of interest: Arts; Health organizations; Human services.
Limitations: Applications not accepted.
Application information: Unsolicited requests for funds not accepted.
Officers: Judith E. Greenstein, Pres.; Jeffrey I. Greenstein, V.P. and Secy.-Treas.
EIN: 274334621

9634
Hagan Foundation ✧ ☆
(formerly Cornelius and Lydiellen Hagan Foundation)
15326 N. Edencrest Ct.
Spokane, WA 99208-9738 (509) 443-1933

Classified as a private operating foundation in WA in 1997.
Donor: Cornelius E. Hagan, M.D.
Foundation type: Independent foundation.
Financial data (yr. ended 12/31/13): Assets, $8,818,074 (M); expenditures, $498,730; qualifying distributions, $441,918; giving activities include $441,918 for 14 grants (high: $93,549; low: $4,000).
Fields of interest: Education; Agriculture/food.
Type of support: General/operating support.
Limitations: Applications accepted. Giving primarily in the Spokane, WA, area. No grants to individuals.
Application information: At present, no application for a grant in an amount greater than $5,000 will be considered. Application form required.
Initial approach: Letter
Deadline(s): Sept. 1
Board meeting date(s): Feb.
Officer: Roger Bragdon, Chair.
Board Members: Robert Blume; Kathie Burch, M.D.; Ross Wood.
EIN: 911762315
Selected grants: The following grants are a representative sample of this grantmaker's funding activity:
$230,000 to Spokane Community College, Spokane, WA, 2012. For contribution to Hagan Center for the Humanities.

9635
Albert Haller Foundation ✧
P.O. Box 2739
Sequim, WA 98382-2739

Established in 1992 in WA.
Donor: Albert G. Haller†.
Foundation type: Independent foundation.
Financial data (yr. ended 12/31/12): Assets, $10,087,409 (M); expenditures, $537,911; qualifying distributions, $497,727; giving activities include $411,958 for 63 grants (high: $68,958; low: $600), and $78,000 for 20 grants to individuals (high: $4,000; low: $2,000).
Purpose and activities: Funding primarily to projects that provide food, housing, clothing, medical care and other programs that may enhance and enrich the lives of the poor and needy of Clallam County, WA. Special attention is given to distributing food to those in need, and clothing and other necessities to children who lack the essentials to progress in school.
Fields of interest: Education; Health care; Food services; Recreation; Human services; Community/economic development; United Ways and Federated Giving Programs.
Type of support: General/operating support; Scholarships—to individuals.
Limitations: Applications accepted. Giving limited to Clallam County, WA.
Publications: Informational brochure (including application guidelines).
Application information: Application form required.
Initial approach: Scholarships: Contact Superintendents of public high schools, Grants: Contact United way for application form
Copies of proposal: 1
Deadline(s): Scholarships: Jan., Grants: June
Board meeting date(s): At least 4 times per year
Officers: Gary Smith, Pres.; Richard Schneider, V.P.; David Blake, Secy.-Treas.
Directors: Jane Pryne; Patrick Kelly Shea.
EIN: 911556810

9636
Lenore Hanauer Foundation ✧
c/o King & Oliason PLLC
925 4th Ave., Ste. 2288
Seattle, WA 98104-1145

Established in 2007 in DE.
Donor: Lenore Hanauer.
Foundation type: Independent foundation.
Financial data (yr. ended 12/31/13): Assets, $14,417,640 (M); expenditures, $1,445,749; qualifying distributions, $1,352,462; giving activities include $1,350,000 for 34 grants (high: $200,000; low: $1,000).
Fields of interest: Human services.
Limitations: Applications not accepted. Giving primarily in WA. No grants to individuals.
Application information: Contributes only to pre-selected organizations.
Officers and Director:* Lenore Hanauer,* Pres.; Kristi Mandt, Secy.
EIN: 260378733
Selected grants: The following grants are a representative sample of this grantmaker's funding activity:
$1,000,000 to Seattle Foundation, Seattle, WA, 2012. For Fund Public Charities That Help Support the Foundation's Mission.
$10,000 to Progressive Animal Welfare Society, Lynnwood, WA, 2012. For animal services.

9637
The Nick and Leslie Hanauer Foundation ✧
The Highlands
179 N.W. Cascade Dr.
Shoreline, WA 98177-8000

Established in 2007 in WA.
Donors: Nick Hanauer; Leslie Hanauer; Gerald Hanauer†.
Foundation type: Independent foundation.
Financial data (yr. ended 12/31/12): Assets, $8,386,581 (M); expenditures, $786,213; qualifying distributions, $722,545; giving activities include $722,545 for grants.
Fields of interest: Performing arts, opera; Environment.
Limitations: Applications not accepted. Giving primarily in Seattle, WA. No grants to individuals.
Application information: Contributes only to pre-selected organizations.
Directors: Leslie Hanauer; Nick Hanauer.
EIN: 261593306

9638
Handsel Foundation ✧
c/o Laird Norton Tyee Trust Co.
801 2 Ave., Ste. 1600
Seattle, WA 98104 (206) 464-5100

Established in 1990 in CA.
Donors: Theodore R. Johnson, Sr.†; T.R. Johnson, Jr.; Johnson Charitable Lead Trust; Diane Johnson Trust.
Foundation type: Independent foundation.
Financial data (yr. ended 12/31/13): Assets, $2,493,301 (M); gifts received, $46,049; expenditures, $1,507,421; qualifying distributions, $1,490,169; giving activities include $1,472,003 for 44 grants (high: $728,000; low: $2,000).
Purpose and activities: Giving primarily for animal welfare, principally spay/neuter programs.
Fields of interest: Animal welfare.
Type of support: Research; Consulting services; General/operating support; Continuing support; Management development/capacity building; Equipment; Program development; Seed money; Program evaluation.
Limitations: Applications accepted. Giving primarily in CA, OR and WA. No support for religious or political organizations. No grants to individuals, or for scholarships.
Publications: Application guidelines; Grants list.
Application information: Application form not required.
Initial approach: Proposal
Copies of proposal: 1
Deadline(s): None
Board meeting date(s): Quarterly
Officers: Diane N. Johnson, Pres.; Theodore R. Johnson, Jr., Secy.-Treas.
Director: Hilary Austen May.
Number of staff: None.
EIN: 943112006

9639
Hanson Family Foundation ✧ ☆
P.O. Box 4246
Bellevue, WA 98009-4246

Foundation type: Independent foundation.

Financial data (yr. ended 12/31/12): Assets, $3,152,025 (M); gifts received, $3,480,288; expenditures, $428,949; qualifying distributions, $420,000; giving activities include $420,000 for grants.
Fields of interest: Museums (specialized).
Limitations: Applications not accepted.
Application information: Unsolicited requests for funds not accepted.
Officers: James R. Ladd, Pres. and Treas.; Sharon S. Ladd, Secy.
Trustees: Christopher B. Smith; Randolph C.H. Smith; Mark G. Hanson.
EIN: 204562272

9640
Harder Foundation ✧
401 Broadway, Ste. 303
Tacoma, WA 98402-3904 (253) 593-2121
Contact: Mary G. Martin, Off. Mgr.
FAX: (253) 593-2122;
E-mail: info@theharderfoundation.org; Main URL: http://www.theharderfoundation.org
Grants List: http://theharderfoundation.org/2013-grantees/

Incorporated in 1955 in MI.
Donor: Delmar S. Harder†.
Foundation type: Independent foundation.
Financial data (yr. ended 12/31/13): Assets, $35,865,197 (M); gifts received, $1,800; expenditures, $1,853,306; qualifying distributions, $1,671,963; giving activities include $1,260,000 for 41 grants (high: $85,000; low: $1,500).
Purpose and activities: The foundation is dedicated to the preservation of an American quality of life that includes clean air and drinking water, unpolluted lakes and rivers, and healthy forests, parks, and wildland. It has a special concern for the protection of wildlife populations and the habitats on which they depend. Projects funded by the foundation typically involve efforts to achieve long-term protection of specific public forests and wildlands, rivers, near shore marine ecosystems, and estuaries.
Fields of interest: Environment, natural resources; Environment.
Type of support: General/operating support; Continuing support; Annual campaigns; Endowments; Seed money; Matching/challenge support.
Limitations: Applications not accepted. Giving limited to AK (South Central and Southeast), ID (Central ID and the High Divide), OR (Southwest and Coast), WA (Pacific Coast, Olympic Peninsula, Columbia River Estuary and Northeast Washington), and MT and WY (Greater Yellowstone Ecosystem, including the High Divide); limited support each year to groups in FL. No support for agriculture, toxics, transportation, or urban environment issues, land acquisition or land trust projects, local land management or restoration efforts, organizations that are currently operating with an IRS designation as a 509(a)(3) supporting organization, or for-profit organizations. No grants to individuals, or for deficit financing, building funds, equipment, renovation projects, scholarships, fellowships, research, publications, conferences, book, film, or video productions, or environmental education; no loans.
Publications: Annual report; Grants list.
Application information: Unsolicited requests for funds not accepted; proposals accepted by invitation only.
Board meeting date(s): Feb.
Officers and Trustees:* Del Langbauer,* Pres.; John Driggers, V.P.; Robert Langbauer,* Treas.; Kay Treakle, Exec. Dir.
Number of staff: 3 full-time professional; 1 full-time support; 1 part-time support.
EIN: 386048242
Selected grants: The following grants are a representative sample of this grantmaker's funding activity:
$87,000 to Alaska Conservation Foundation, Anchorage, AK, 2011. For general support.
$70,000 to Northern Rockies Conservation Cooperative, Jackson, WY, 2011.
$65,000 to Wilderness Society, Denver, CO, 2011.
$60,000 to Surfrider Foundation, San Clemente, CA, 2011.
$50,000 to Geos Institute, Ashland, OR, 2011.
$45,000 to Wildlands Center for Preventing Roads, Missoula, MT, 2011. For general support.
$30,000 to Earthjustice, San Francisco, CA, 2011. For general support.
$30,000 to Pew Charitable Trusts, Philadelphia, PA, 2011.
$25,000 to Save Our Wild Salmon Coalition, Seattle, WA, 2011. For general support.
$25,000 to Wild Salmon Center, Portland, OR, 2011.

9641
Harnish Foundation ✧
17035 W. Valley Hwy.
Tukwila, WA 98188-5519

Established in 2005 in WA.
Donors: John J. Harnish; Harnish Group, Inc.; Katherine A. Harnish.
Foundation type: Company-sponsored foundation.
Financial data (yr. ended 12/31/13): Assets, $20,588,699 (M); gifts received, $3,000; expenditures, $1,697,338; qualifying distributions, $1,679,342; giving activities include $1,679,342 for 14 grants (high: $500,000; low: $25,000).
Purpose and activities: The foundation supports camps and organizations involved with secondary education, health, substance abuse treatment, children, and residential care.
Fields of interest: Health care; Recreation; Human services.
Type of support: General/operating support.
Limitations: Applications not accepted. Giving primarily in MN and WA. No grants to individuals.
Application information: Contributes only to pre-selected organizations.
Officers and Directors:* John J. Harnish,* Pres. and Treas.; Jennifer C. Harnish,* V.P. and Secy.; Richard C. Bellin, V.P.; Katherine A. Harnish,* V.P.; John W. Harnish; Troy Hickey.
EIN: 383730146
Selected grants: The following grants are a representative sample of this grantmaker's funding activity:
$50,000 to Eastside Academy, Bellevue, WA, 2011.
$50,000 to Treehouse, Seattle, WA, 2011.
$25,000 to Church of Mary Magdalene, Seattle, WA, 2011.
$25,000 to Eagle Mount Billings, Billings, MT, 2011.
$5,000 to Eagle Mount Bozeman, Bozeman, MT, 2011.

9642
Harvest Foundation ✧
P.O. Box 75554
Seattle, WA 98175-0554
Contact: Marjorie Ringness, Secy.-Treas.
FAX: (206) 299-9850; E-mail: info@harvestf.org; Main URL: http://www.harvestf.org

Established in 2000 in WA.
Donors: Edward Ringness; Marjorie Ringness.
Foundation type: Independent foundation.
Financial data (yr. ended 12/31/12): Assets, $9,868,263 (M); expenditures, $520,075; qualifying distributions, $435,982; giving activities include $430,000 for 43 grants (high: $10,000; low: $10,000).
Purpose and activities: The foundation was created to provide funding primarily in the areas of social services and education. It is specifically interested in organizations that promote economic self-sufficiency through education and training of youth or families with children; it also supports organizations that serve the elderly by providing services to help senior citizens live independently. Grants for education are made in 2 areas: 1) teacher training in technology and curriculum development; and 2) supporting arts programs.
Fields of interest: Arts education; Human services; Engineering/technology; Aging; Minorities.
Type of support: Building/renovation; Capital campaigns; Conferences/seminars; Continuing support; Curriculum development; General/operating support.
Limitations: Giving primarily in AK, ID, MT, OR, and WA. No grants to individuals.
Publications: Application guidelines; Annual report; Annual report (including application guidelines); Grants list.
Application information: Unsolicited applications are not accepted but letters of inquiry are accepted up to 2 weeks prior to application deadline. Application information available on foundation web site.
Initial approach: 1-page letter or e-mail
Copies of proposal: 1
Deadline(s): Apr. 15 and Oct. 15
Board meeting date(s): Varies
Final notification: May 31 and Nov. 30
Officers and Directors:* Edward Ringness,* Pres.; Marjorie Ringness,* Secy.-Treas.
EIN: 912065635
Selected grants: The following grants are a representative sample of this grantmaker's funding activity:
$10,000 to Arts Central, Bend, OR, 2012. For Artists in Schools.
$10,000 to Bainbridge Island Arts and Humanities Council, Bainbridge Island, WA, 2012. For Arts in Education.
$10,000 to FareStart, Seattle, WA, 2012. For general operating support.
$10,000 to Greater Maple Valley Community Center, Maple Valley, WA, 2012. For Maple Valley Senior Program.
$10,000 to Hopelink, Redmond, WA, 2012. For financial literacy and employment programs.
$10,000 to Phinney Neighborhood Association, Seattle, WA, 2012. For Greenwood Senior Center ESML programming.
$10,000 to Powerful Schools, Seattle, WA, 2012. For Integrated Arts Programming.
$10,000 to Seattle Jobs Initiative, Seattle, WA, 2012. For general operating support.

$10,000 to Technically Learning, Seattle, WA, 2012. For general operating support.
$10,000 to Whatcom Literacy Council, Bellingham, WA, 2012. For general operating support.

9643
Richard P. Haugland Foundation ✧
(formerly Haugland Foundation)
2103 Harrison Ave. N.W., PMB 2602
Olympia, WA 98502-2636

Established in 1996.
Donors: Alexander D. Haugland; Hans Morsbach; Richard P. Haugland; Rosaria P. Haugland.
Foundation type: Independent foundation.
Financial data (yr. ended 09/30/13): Assets, $174,949,301 (M); expenditures, $7,972,349; qualifying distributions, $6,994,000; giving activities include $6,994,000 for 7 grants (high: $6,000,000; low: $2,000).
Purpose and activities: Giving primarily for the arts, education, and human services.
Fields of interest: Arts; Education; Human services; Children/youth, services.
Type of support: General/operating support.
Limitations: Applications not accepted. Giving primarily in Bellingham, WA; some giving also in MN, OR, and in Thailand. No support for religious organizations. No grants to individuals.
Application information: Contributes only to pre-selected organizations.
Officers: Richard P. Haugland, Pres.; Rosaria P. Haugland, V.P.; Alexander D. Haugland, Secy.-Treas.
Board Member: Francesco Caruso.
EIN: 931220478
Selected grants: The following grants are a representative sample of this grantmaker's funding activity:
$3,295,000 to Starfish Country Home School Foundation, Chingmai, Thailand, 2011. For educational programs.
$1,705,700 to ADM Capital Foundation, Hong Kong, China, 2011. For alleviation of poverty and education of children..
$500,000 to Medica Foundation, Minneapolis, MN, 2011. For medical relief.
$200,000 to Hamline University, Saint Paul, MN, 2011. For educational programs.
$50,000 to Eugene Ballet Company, Eugene, OR, 2011. For MOWGLI ballet Production.

9644
The Honzel Family Foundation ✧
1000 Town Center, No. 180
Tacoma, WA 98422-1194

Established in 1996 in OR.
Donors: Andrew J. Honzel; Education Empowerment Fund.
Foundation type: Independent foundation.
Financial data (yr. ended 12/31/13): Assets, $28,230,781 (M); expenditures, $1,362,135; qualifying distributions, $1,112,450; giving activities include $1,112,450 for 40 grants (high: $75,000; low: $1,000).
Purpose and activities: Giving primarily for education, human services, health, and Roman Catholic agencies and churches.
Fields of interest: Education; Health organizations; Human services; Catholic federated giving programs; Catholic agencies & churches.
Limitations: Applications not accepted. Giving primarily in OR. No grants to individuals.
Application information: Contributes only to pre-selected organizations.
Trustees: Andrew J. Honzel; Karen Musica.
EIN: 931223928

9645
Horizons Foundation ✧
4020 E. Madison St., Ste. 322
Seattle, WA 98112-3150 (206) 323-8061

Established in 1990 in WA as partial successor to the McAshan Foundation, Inc.
Donor: The McAshan Foundation, Inc.
Foundation type: Independent foundation.
Financial data (yr. ended 12/31/12): Assets, $21,040,492 (M); expenditures, $1,164,168; qualifying distributions, $1,116,923; giving activities include $1,045,700 for 132 grants (high: $30,000; low: $1,000).
Purpose and activities: Giving primarily to address the social and environmental problems of the Pacific Northwest. Emphasis is on the prevention of problems through educational projects and citizen education programs aimed at improving the quality of the environment; some support also for the arts.
Fields of interest: Arts; Environment, natural resources; Environment; Reproductive health, family planning; Crime/violence prevention, domestic violence; Human services; Youth, pregnancy prevention; Family services, domestic violence; Family services, adolescent parents; Family services, counseling; Human services, emergency aid; Women, centers/services; Crime/abuse victims.
Type of support: General/operating support; Capital campaigns; Land acquisition; Emergency funds; Program development.
Limitations: Applications accepted. Giving primarily in WA. No support for religious or political organizations. No grants to individuals, or for scholarships, debt retirement, operating deficits, endowment funds; no loans.
Publications: Application guidelines; Program policy statement.
Application information: Full proposal required if foundation accepts synopsis. Application form required.
Initial approach: 2-page synopsis
Copies of proposal: 4
Deadline(s): None
Board meeting date(s): Monthly
Final notification: Within 4-8 weeks for synopsis; within 10 days for full proposal
Officers and Directors:* Lucy J. Hadac,* Pres.; Jerald Forster,* V.P.; Stephen Hadac,* Secy.
Number of staff: 1 full-time professional.
EIN: 911493424
Selected grants: The following grants are a representative sample of this grantmaker's funding activity:
$12,500 to Environmental Science Center, Burien, WA, 2012. For environ education.
$12,000 to Wild Fish Conservancy, Duvall, WA, 2012. For water quality.
$10,000 to Skagit Land Trust, Mount Vernon, WA, 2012. For Habitat Preservation.
$10,000 to Transportation Choices Coalition, Seattle, WA, 2012. For environmental educ.
$5,000 to Chief Seattle Club, Seattle, WA, 2012. For sexual assault.
$5,000 to Jefferson Land Trust, Port Townsend, WA, 2012. To preserve environment.
$4,000 to Hope in Christ Ministries, Bremerton, WA, 2012. For at-risk youth.

9646
Richard W. Hotes Foundation ✧
5808 N.E. Lake Washington Blvd., Rm. 215
Kirkland, WA 98033-7336 (425) 889-1205
Contact: Carolyn Bishop, Secy.

Established in 2003 in WA.
Donor: Richard W. Hotes.
Foundation type: Operating foundation.
Financial data (yr. ended 12/31/11): Assets, $13,844,934 (M); gifts received, $10,000,000; expenditures, $5,245,499; qualifying distributions, $5,277,151; giving activities include $1,603,000 for 4 grants (high: $1,348,318; low: $59,925), and $3,574,131 for foundation-administered programs.
Purpose and activities: Giving primarily to reduce or eliminate homelessness and poverty.
Fields of interest: Housing/shelter, homeless; Safety/disasters; Economically disadvantaged.
Type of support: General/operating support.
Limitations: Giving on a national basis.
Application information:
Initial approach: Letter
Deadline(s): None
Officers: Richard W. Hotes, Chair.; Carolyn Bishop, Secy.; Elisabeth Hotes, Treas.
EIN: 010760054

9647
Howard Charitable Foundation ✧
4616 25th Ave. NE, PMB 617
Seattle, WA 98105-4183 (760) 730-7342
Contact: Richard D. Newell, Secy.-Treas.

Established in 1999 in WA.
Donor: Robert S. Howard.
Foundation type: Independent foundation.
Financial data (yr. ended 12/31/13): Assets, $15,232,160 (M); expenditures, $3,687,164; qualifying distributions, $3,134,890; giving activities include $2,992,300 for 30 grants (high: $1,000,000; low: $2,000).
Purpose and activities: Giving primarily to health care, educational, and domestic humanitarian charities.
Fields of interest: Education; Health care; Human services.
Limitations: Applications accepted. Giving primarily in San Diego, CA and Washington, DC. No grants to individuals.
Application information: Application form required.
Initial approach: Letter requesting application form
Deadline(s): None
Officer: Richard D. Newell, Secy.-Treas.
EIN: 911952040

9648
The John C. & Karyl Kay Hughes Foundation ✧
2323 Eastlake Ave. E.
Seattle, WA 98102-3305

Established in 1984 in WA.
Donor: Karyl Kay Hughes.

Foundation type: Independent foundation.
Financial data (yr. ended 11/30/13): Assets, $28,114,489 (M); expenditures, $2,514,286; qualifying distributions, $2,462,423; giving activities include $2,460,000 for 32 grants (high: $460,000; low: $3,000).
Purpose and activities: Giving primarily for human services, and to Christian agencies; funding also for a Baptist church, Christian Scientist churches, and the United Way.
Fields of interest: Arts; Education; Animals/wildlife, preservation/protection; Health care; Cancer research; Human services; United Ways and Federated Giving Programs; Christian agencies & churches; Protestant agencies & churches.
Limitations: Applications not accepted. Giving primarily in Seattle, WA. No grants to individuals.
Application information: Contributes only to pre-selected organizations.
Trustee: Christopher R. Hughes.
EIN: 911286019
Selected grants: The following grants are a representative sample of this grantmaker's funding activity:
$100,000 to Union Gospel Mission, Aberdeen, WA, 2011.

9649
The Hussey Foundation ✧
5219 N.E. Laurelcrest Ln.
Seattle, WA 98105

Established in 1999 in WA.
Donor: Jeffrey S. Hussey.
Foundation type: Independent foundation.
Financial data (yr. ended 12/31/13): Assets, $11,408,280 (M); expenditures, $726,838; qualifying distributions, $677,692; giving activities include $677,692 for grants.
Fields of interest: Higher education, university; Human services; Foundations (community); Christian agencies & churches.
Limitations: Applications not accepted. Giving primarily in CA and Seattle, WA. No grants to individuals.
Application information: Contributes only to pre-selected organizations.
Director: Jeffrey S. Hussey.
EIN: 912013522

9650
Inland Northwest Community Foundation ✧
(formerly Foundation Northwest)
421 West Riverside Ave., Ste. 606
Spokane, WA 99201-0405 (509) 624-2606
Contact: Mark Hurtubise, C.E.O.
E-mail: admin@inwcf.org; Additional tel.: (888) 267-5606; Additional e-mail: mhurtubise@inwcf.org; Main URL: http://www.inwcf.org
LinkedIn: http://www.linkedin.com/companies/inland-northwest-community-foundation

Incorporated in 1974 in WA.
Foundation type: Community foundation.
Financial data (yr. ended 06/30/13): Assets, $75,854,003 (M); gifts received, $3,830,183; expenditures, $4,852,853; giving activities include $3,001,953 for grants.
Purpose and activities: The foundation seeks to foster vibrant and sustainable communities in the Inland Northwest. Primary areas of interest include the arts, humanities, education, community development, and human services.
Fields of interest: Humanities; Historic preservation/historical societies; Arts; Education; Environment; Animals/wildlife; Health care; Youth, services; Aging, centers/services; Human services; Community development, neighborhood development; Economic development; Community/economic development; Aging.
Type of support: General/operating support; Management development/capacity building; Capital campaigns; Building/renovation; Equipment; Program development; Seed money; Technical assistance; Program evaluation.
Limitations: Applications accepted. Giving limited to the Inland Northwest: Benewah, Bonner, Boundary, Clearwater, Idaho, Kootenai, Latah, Lewis, Nez Perce, and Shoshone counties, ID, and Adams, Asotin, Columbia, Ferry, Garfield, Lincoln, Pend Oreille, Spokane, Stevens, and Whitman counties, WA. No support for sectarian religious purposes, chambers of commerce, or programs addressing specific disease or health conditions. No grants to individuals (except for scholarship awards), or for deficit financing, debt reduction, conferences (including travel), endowments, publications and film production, private or parochial education, academic or scientific research, one-time fundraising events or campaigns, or replacement of government funding.
Publications: Application guidelines; Annual report; Financial statement; Newsletter.
Application information: Visit foundation Web site for grant program guidelines per grant type and online application. Application form required.
Initial approach: Complete online grant application
Copies of proposal: 1
Deadline(s): Varies
Board meeting date(s): Sept. through June
Final notification: 3 to 6 months
Officers and Directors:* Dale N. Schuman,* Chair.; Bob Bishopp,* Vice-Chair.; Mark Hurtubise,* C.E.O. and Pres.; Shelley L. Bennett,* Secy.; Tony Braga, Cont.; Janice H. Baldwin; Michael Bibin; William O. Bouten; K. Duane Brelsford; Scott K. Jones; Patricia McRae; Charles R. Nipp; William A. Simer; Betsy Wilkerson; Carol Wilson.
Number of staff: 5 full-time professional; 2 full-time support; 1 part-time support.
EIN: 910941053
Selected grants: The following grants are a representative sample of this grantmaker's funding activity:
$105,000 to Scholarship America, Saint Peter, MN, 2011. For Scholarship Awards, payable over 2.00 years.
$60,000 to Spokane First Foursquare Church, Spokane, WA, 2011. For general support, payable over 2.00 years.
$30,000 to Saint Vincent de Paul Society, Coeur d Alene, ID, 2011. For St. Vincent de Paul H.E.L.P. Center, payable over 2.00 years.
$30,000 to YWCA of Spokane, Spokane, WA, 2011. For Women's Opportunity Center, payable over 2.00 years.
$20,000 to Mobius Science Center, Spokane, WA, 2011. For capital campaign, payable over 2.00 years.
$20,000 to Palouse Community Center, Palouse, WA, 2011. For Renewable Energy Demonstration Project, payable over 2.00 years.
$6,625 to Southside Christian Church, Spokane, WA, 2011. For general operating support, payable over 2.00 years.
$5,000 to Spokane Symphony, Spokane, WA, 2011. For Spokane Symphony Arts in Education, payable over 2.00 years.
$3,500 to NATIVE Project, Spokane, WA, 2011. For Breast health education and screening, payable over 2.00 years.
$2,000 to Gonzaga Preparatory School, Spokane, WA, 2011. For general operating support, payable over 2.00 years.

9651
Intermec Foundation ✧
(formerly The UNOVA Foundation)
6001 36th Ave. W.
Everett, WA 98203-1264
Main URL: http://www.seattlefoundation.org/intermec/Pages/IntermecFoundation.aspx

Established in 1993 in CA.
Foundation type: Independent foundation.
Financial data (yr. ended 06/30/13): Assets, $16,454,423 (M); expenditures, $1,106,606; qualifying distributions, $1,040,692; giving activities include $989,998 for 212 grants (high: $72,760; low: $500).
Purpose and activities: The foundation focuses on educational, food banks, art and cultural programs, health and wellness organizations and on occasion, community relief causes.
Fields of interest: Arts; Education; Health care; Food banks.
Type of support: Equipment; Employee volunteer services; Employee matching gifts; Employee-related scholarships.
Limitations: Applications not accepted. Giving primarily in IA, OH, and WA.
Application information: Unsolicited requests for funds not accepted. Employees of Intermec apply for foundation grants on behalf of nonprofit organizations. See foundation web site for specific eligibility requirements.
Officers: Sue Taylor, Pres.; Frank McCallick, V.P. and Treas.; Scott Anderson, V.P.; Paula A. Bauert, V.P.; Nancy Gallup, V.P.; Ronald Kubera, V.P.; Constance Chapman, Secy.
Directors: Robert Driessnack; Douglas Stubsten.
EIN: 954453230
Selected grants: The following grants are a representative sample of this grantmaker's funding activity:
$61,862 to National Merit Scholarship Corporation, Evanston, IL, 2011.
$40,000 to Foundation 2, Cedar Rapids, IA, 2011.
$10,000 to Big Brothers and Big Sisters of Cedar Rapids and East Central Iowa, Cedar Rapids, IA, 2011.
$2,000 to Snohomish Education Foundation, Snohomish, WA, 2011.

9652
Invested ✧
(formerly Saul & Dayee G. Haas Foundation)
911 8th Ave. N.
Seattle, WA 98109-2777 (206) 352-1199
Contact: Deborah Cushing

Main URL: http://www.invested.org
Facebook: https://www.facebook.com/InvestEdWash
Twitter: http://twitter.com/investedWash

Incorporated in 1972 in WA.
Donors: Saul Haas†; Dayee G. Haas†; Rowayne Maguire; Thomas Maguire; Lake Washington Schools Foundation; Thompson Family Foundation; Microsoft Corporation Matching Gifts Program; Schwab Charitable Trust; Paul Lauzier Foundation; D.A. Davidson & Co.; Dimmer Family Foundation; United Way of King County; Lee Miller; Dan Barritt; Realnetworks Foundation; Daffodil Valley Kiwanis Club; Moran Education Foundation; Muckleshoot Indian Tribe; RSVP Advisory Council; The Seattle Foundation; Salesforce; Bill & Melinda Gates Foundation; Community Foundation of North Central WA; Betty Fletcher; Robert Fletcher; Grays Harbor Community Foundation; Murdock Charitable Trust; Renaissance Charitable Foundation, Inc.; The Neeb Family Foundation; Tulalip Tribes Charitable Fund; Robert Munoz; Pamela Hughes.
Foundation type: Independent foundation.
Financial data (yr. ended 06/30/13): Assets, $8,680,892 (M); gifts received, $954,096; expenditures, $841,896; qualifying distributions, $808,381; giving activities include $450,813 for 657 grants (high: $5,615; low: $197).
Purpose and activities: Emphasis on a school-administered fund to aid at-risk and low-income secondary school students in WA in completing their education. Also sponsors a local university lecture series on broadcasting.
Fields of interest: Secondary school/education; Education; Human services; Minorities; Economically disadvantaged.
Type of support: Emergency funds; Matching/challenge support.
Limitations: Applications accepted. Giving limited to WA. No support for religious organizations, or political organizations. No grants to individuals, or for equipment, land acquisition, renovation projects, or endowment funds.
Application information: Application form required.
Copies of proposal: 1
Officers: Lisa Schaures, Pres.; Paul Ishii, V.P.; Dan Barritt, Secy.; Thomas E. Gleason, Treas.; Julie Davis, Exec. Dir.
Directors: Emory Bundy; Paul Condrat; Michael Dunn; Nancy Fike; Tom Horton; Pamela J. Hughes; Jim Ivers; Tanya Lamb; Martin J. Neeb; Roger D. Percy; Tom Rath; Alan Sugiyama; Debbie Williams.
Number of staff: 1 full-time professional; 2 part-time professional; 1 part-time support.
EIN: 237189670
Selected grants: The following grants are a representative sample of this grantmaker's funding activity:
$7,715 to Mount Vernon High School, Mount Vernon, WA, 2011.
$3,030 to Mount Vernon High School, Mount Vernon, WA, 2011.
$2,880 to Chief Sealth High School, Seattle, WA, 2011.
$1,753 to Nathan Hale High School, Seattle, WA, 2011.
$1,605 to Odea High School, Seattle, WA, 2011.
$1,440 to Chief Sealth High School, Seattle, WA, 2011.
$1,415 to Oak Harbor Middle School, Oak Harbor, WA, 2011.
$1,135 to West Seattle High School, Seattle, WA, 2011.
$1,125 to Eastlake High School, Sammamish, WA, 2011.

9653
Islands Fund ✧
c/o John Munn
6523 California Ave., S.W., Ste. 137
Seattle, WA 98136-1833 (206) 283-4790
Contact: Sarah R. Werner, Dir.

Established in 1995.
Donor: Sarah R. Werner.
Foundation type: Independent foundation.
Financial data (yr. ended 12/31/13): Assets, $170,642,983 (M); gifts received, $24,999,971; expenditures, $9,724,958; qualifying distributions, $9,220,621; giving activities include $9,200,000 for 68 grants (high: $2,000,000; low: $10,000).
Purpose and activities: Giving primarily for conservation and the environment.
Fields of interest: Education; Environment, natural resources; Children/youth, services.
Limitations: Applications not accepted. Giving primarily in OH, VA, WA, WV and Canada; some giving also in Costa Rica. No grants to individuals.
Application information: Contributes only to pre-selected organizations.
Directors: James Flaggert; E. Leeds Gulick; George G. Gulick; Rick S. Werner; Sarah R. Werner.
EIN: 911663838
Selected grants: The following grants are a representative sample of this grantmaker's funding activity:
$900,000 to Aloha Foundation, Fairlee, VT, 2012.
$625,000 to Future Generations, Franklin, WV, 2012.
$500,000 to Yellowstone to Yukon Conservation Initiative, U.S. Office, Bozeman, MT, 2012.
$300,000 to Seattle Academy of Arts and Sciences, Seattle, WA, 2012.
$250,000 to Overlake School, Redmond, WA, 2012.
$200,000 to Big Brothers Big Sisters of Central Oregon, Bend, OR, 2012.
$150,000 to Trail Blazer Camps, New York, NY, 2012.
$100,000 to Thacher School, Ojai, CA, 2012.
$50,000 to Boys and Girls Club of Bellevue, Bellevue, WA, 2012.
$50,000 to Conservation Northwest, Seattle, WA, 2012.

9654
The Jain Foundation, Inc. ✧
9725 3rd Ave. N.E., Ste. 204
Seattle, WA 98115 (425) 882-1492
Contact: Sarah Shira, Prog. Mgr.
E-mail: sshira@jain-foundation.org; Main URL: http://www.jain-foundation.org
Facebook: http://www.facebook.com/JainFoundation

Established in 2005 in NY.
Foundation type: Independent foundation.
Financial data (yr. ended 12/31/12): Assets, $21,674,038 (M); gifts received, $15,213,818; expenditures, $2,544,440; qualifying distributions, $2,506,241; giving activities include $1,250,579 for 23 grants (high: $233,334; low: $3,150), and $737,578 for foundation-administered programs.
Purpose and activities: Giving primarily to cure muscular dystrophies caused by dysferlin protein deficiency, which includes the clinical presentations Limb-girdle muscular dystrophy type 2B (LGMD2B) and Miyoshi muscular dystrophy 1 (MMD1). The foundation's focused strategy includes funding and actively monitoring the progress of scientific research projects in key pathways towards a cure, providing financial and logistical support to promising drug candidates to accelerate them to clinical trials, funding clinical trials and studies, encouraging collaboration among scientists, and educating LGMD2B/Miyoshi patients about their disease and helping them with their diagnosis (e.g.: funding dysferlin protein and gene mutational analysis).
Fields of interest: Muscular dystrophy research.
Type of support: Research.
Limitations: Giving primarily in MA; giving also in France, the Netherlands, and the U.K.
Publications: Application guidelines.
Application information: See foundation web site for detailed proposal guidelines and application cover page. Application form not required.
Initial approach: The foundation encourages 1-2 page pre-proposals (via e-mail to Prog. Mgr.) to gauge its interest level
Deadline(s): None
Final notification: Typically within 4-6 weeks
Officer: Dr. Plavi Mittal, C.E.O. and Pres.
Directors: Ajay Jain; Ajit Jain; Akshay Jain; Indrima Jain.
EIN: 200284800
Selected grants: The following grants are a representative sample of this grantmaker's funding activity:
$23,333 to Immune Disease Institute, Boston, MA, 2012. For scientific research grant.
$3,500 to University of Pennsylvania, Philadelphia, PA, 2012. For conference sponsor.

9655
The Herbert B. Jones Foundation ✧
c/o Key Private Bank
601 108th Ave. N.E., Ste. 260
Bellevue, WA 98004-8606 (206) 285-1729
Main URL: http://www.hbjfoundation.com
Grants Database: http://www.hbjfoundation.com/grant_history.html

Established in 1989 in WA.
Donor: Herbert B. Jones.
Foundation type: Independent foundation.
Financial data (yr. ended 08/31/13): Assets, $11,350,911 (M); expenditures, $558,566; qualifying distributions, $545,746; giving activities include $485,510 for 22 grants (high: $80,000; low: $5,000).
Purpose and activities: The foundation promotes small-business and entrepreneurism through programs managed by post-secondary educational institutions.
Fields of interest: Higher education; Business school/education; Education.
Type of support: Program development; Conferences/seminars; Seed money; Curriculum development.
Limitations: Applications accepted. Giving limited to WA. No grants to individuals, or for equipment, capital projects, gifts, endowments or food costs.
Publications: Application guidelines.

Application information: Refer to foundation web site for complete guideline information. Application form required.
Initial approach: Proposal (2 pages maximum, with a minimum font size of 11)
Copies of proposal: 6
Deadline(s): First Mon. in Apr.
Board meeting date(s): May
Final notification: Within 8 weeks
Trustees: Michael R. Bauer; Tom Crha; Bill Erwert; Tammy Miller; Terry Smith; Janet Woods.
Number of staff: None.
EIN: 943124801

9656
JRS Biodiversity Foundation ☆
P.O. Box 15178
Seattle, WA 98115-0178 (206) 454-7915
Contact: Don S. Doering, Exec. Dir.
E-mail: info@jrsbiodiversity.org; Main URL: http://jrsbiodiversity.org/
Blog: http://jrsbiodiversity.org/category/jrs-blog/
CEP Study: http://jrsbiodiversity.org/news/
Facebook: https://www.facebook.com/JRSBDF
Grants List: http://jrsbiodiversity.org/grant/
LinkedIn: http://www.linkedin.com/company/jrs-biodiversity-foundation
Twitter: https://twitter.com/JRSBiodiversity

The J.R.S. Biodiversity Foundation was created in January 2004 when the nonprofit scientific abstracting company, BIOSIS was sold to Thomson Scientific, now Thomson Reuters. The proceeds from that sale funded the foundation's endowment and created a new private foundation to carry on the tradition of making biological knowledge accessible and useful.
Foundation type: Independent foundation.
Financial data (yr. ended 12/31/13): Assets, $45,261,572 (M); expenditures, $2,255,597; qualifying distributions, $1,811,230; giving activities include $1,313,190 for 29 grants (high: $138,286; low: $3,960).
Purpose and activities: The foundation's mission is to enhance the knowledge of biodiversity for the benefit of life on earth. It focuses on supporting biodiversity informatics that is used to preserve and to sustainably manage biodiversity, especially in those developing economies where it is most threatened. Through the projects it funds, the foundation works to make biodiversity information more widely available to researchers, local communities, conservation practitioners, policy makers and the public.
Fields of interest: Environment, forests; Environment; Biology/life sciences.
International interests: Africa; Latin America.
Type of support: Research; Program development; Management development/capacity building; Conferences/seminars.
Application information: See foundation web site for current application information.
Officer and Trustees:* Don S. Doering,* Exec. Dir.; Richard Kiome Bagine; Sarah Feresu; Allyson Fish; Robert Guralnick; Lucy W. Irungu; Leonard Krishtalka; Ellen Martz; Daniel Masiga; Aaron McNevin; Benjamin Rader; Jon Paul Rodriguez; Ruth K. Temple.
EIN: 231352035

9657
The Kaphan Foundation ✧
c/o King & Oliason, P.S.
514 2nd Ave. W.
Seattle, WA 98119-3928

Established in 2003 in WA.
Donor: Sheldon J. Kaphan.
Foundation type: Independent foundation.
Financial data (yr. ended 12/31/12): Assets, $42,968,093 (M); gifts received, $5,153,195; expenditures, $1,610,130; qualifying distributions, $1,624,050; giving activities include $1,525,000 for 20 grants, $2,328 for 1 foundation-administered program and $90,704 for 1 loan/program-related investment.
Fields of interest: Arts; Medical research; Human services; Children/youth, services; International development; Civil/human rights; Foundations (private grantmaking).
Limitations: Applications not accepted. Giving in the U.S., with some emphasis in AZ, CA, Washington DC, MA, MO, NY and WA. No grants to individuals.
Application information: Contributes only to pre-selected organizations.
Officers: Sheldon J. Kaphan, Pres., V.P., and Treas.; Matthew B. McCutchen, Secy.
EIN: 651211107

9658
The Forest C. & Ruth V. Kelsey Foundation ✧
P.O. Box 404
Montesano, WA 98563-0404 (360) 249-6878
Contact: Charles Caldwell, Pres.
E-mail: kelsey@reachone.com

Established in 1999 in WA.
Donors: Forest Kelsey†; Ruth Kelsey; Eda Esses†.
Foundation type: Independent foundation.
Financial data (yr. ended 12/31/13): Assets, $12,241,064 (M); expenditures, $645,780; qualifying distributions, $493,750; giving activities include $141,884 for grants, and $351,866 for grants to individuals.
Purpose and activities: Scholarships awarded to residents of Grays Harbor County, WA, or businesses within the county or businesses that serve county residents.
Fields of interest: Education; Human services.
Type of support: Scholarships—to individuals.
Limitations: Applications accepted. Giving limited to residents and organizations of Grays Harbor County, WA.
Publications: Application guidelines.
Application information: Application form required.
Initial approach: Request application guidelines for grants, or application form for scholarships
Deadline(s): June 1 and Nov. 1 (for grants); refer to application form for current scholarship deadline
Officers: Charles Caldwell, Pres.; Larry James Hliboki, V.P.; Linda Caldwell, Secy.; Joann Hliboki, Treas.
Trustees: Loni Crass; Teresa Frafjord.
EIN: 912013369
Selected grants: The following grants are a representative sample of this grantmaker's funding activity:
$7,200 to Grays Harbor Community Hospital, Aberdeen, WA, 2012. To Promote Education and Other Programs for the Youth in Grays Harbor.

9659
Kitsap Community Foundation ✧ ☆
9657 Levin Rd. NW, Ste. L08
P.O. Box 3670
Silverdale, WA 98383 (360) 698-3622
Contact: Kol Medina, Exec. Dir.
FAX: (360) 698-6043;
E-mail: kcf@kitsapfoundation.org; Main URL: http://www.kitsapfoundation.org
E-Newsletter: http://www.kitsapfoundation.org/join-our-email-list.aspx
Facebook: https://www.facebook.com/KitsapCommunityFoundation
LinkedIn: http://www.linkedin.com/company/kitsap-community-foundation?trk=hb_tab_compy_id_3223269
Twitter: https://twitter.com/kitfoundation
YouTube: https://www.youtube.com/channel/UCgONiE71Oyy3Cs_VSDiepbA

Incorporated in 1993 in WA.
Foundation type: Community foundation.
Financial data (yr. ended 09/30/13): Assets, $4,441,752 (M); gifts received, $2,196,402; expenditures, $935,675; giving activities include $764,993 for 4+ grants (high: $380,000), and $7,748 for 8 grants to individuals.
Purpose and activities: The foundation seeks to improve the quality of life in Kitsap County through endowment-funded grants.
Fields of interest: Arts; Education; Environment; Animal welfare; Health care; Safety/disasters; Recreation; Youth development, adult & child programs; Youth, services; Human services; Community development, neighborhood development; Economic development; Community/economic development; Children/youth; Children; Youth.
Type of support: General/operating support; Continuing support; Management development/capacity building; Building/renovation; Equipment; Land acquisition; Emergency funds; Program development; Publication; Curriculum development; Research; Technical assistance; Program evaluation; In-kind gifts.
Limitations: Applications accepted. Giving limited to Kitsap County, WA and surrounding area. No support for religious organizations for sacramental or theological purposes. No grants for individuals (except for scholarships), or for annual campaign appeals, endowments, deficit reduction, or publications (except those that grow out of research and experiments underwritten by the foundation).
Publications: Annual report; Biennial report; Financial statement; Grants list; Informational brochure; Newsletter.
Application information: Visit foundation web site for online application and guidelines. Application form required.
Initial approach: Create online account
Deadline(s): Jan. 26
Board meeting date(s): Monthly
Final notification: Approx. 3 months
Officers and Directors:* Harriette Bryant,* Chair.; Joan Davis,* Vice-Chair.; R. A. Montgomery,* Secy.; Dave Schureman,* Treas.; Kol Medina, Exec. Dir.; Tina Marie Bright; Steve Green; Joan Hanten; Judy Henry; Beverly Kincaid; Frank Leach; Patty Lent; Stephen Oliver, Jr.; Alice Tawresy; Walt Washington.
Number of staff: 1 part-time professional.
EIN: 943205217

9660
KMR Group Foundation ✧ ☆
9604 N.E. 126th Ave., Ste. 2330
Vancouver, WA 98682-2312 (360) 737-7700
Contact: Martin S. Rifkin, Pres.

Established in 2006 in WA.
Donors: Martin S. Rikfin; Kathryn E. Jones.
Foundation type: Independent foundation.
Financial data (yr. ended 12/31/13): Assets, $15,472,991 (M); gifts received, $1,500,956; expenditures, $823,961; qualifying distributions, $815,302; giving activities include $700,029 for 44 grants (high: $368,512; low: $18).
Purpose and activities: Scholarship awards to students out of high school for at least one year who demonstrate financial need.
Fields of interest: Higher education; Homeless.
Type of support: Scholarships—to individuals.
Limitations: Applications not accepted. Giving primarily in NY and WA.
Application information: Unsolicited requests for funds not accepted.
Officers: Martin S. Rifkin, Pres.; Kathryn E. Jones, Secy.
EIN: 320185357

9661
Kongsgaard-Goldman Foundation ✧
1932 1st Ave., Ste. 602
Seattle, WA 98101-2447 (206) 448-1874
Contact: Kathleen Arthur
FAX: (206) 448-1973;
E-mail: kgf@kongsgaard-goldman.org; Main URL: http://www.kongsgaard-goldman.org

Established in 1988 in WA.
Donors: Peter Goldman; Martha Kongsgaard; Ross Goldman.
Foundation type: Independent foundation.
Financial data (yr. ended 12/31/12): Assets, $94,745 (M); gifts received, $584,788; expenditures, $499,464; qualifying distributions, $495,010; giving activities include $448,500 for 47 grants (high: $50,000; low: $1,000).
Purpose and activities: Giving primarily for Puget Sound restoration and protection, including public policy, citizen involvement, education, restoration, sustainable land use and environmental justice. Grants in this area are awarded for both general operating expenses and special projects. Funding also for forest protection in WA and OR, including conservation, policy, sustainable land use; and for climate change initiatives aimed at addressing climate change challenges in Washington State.
Fields of interest: Education; Environment, land resources; Environment.
International interests: Canada.
Type of support: General/operating support; Continuing support; Annual campaigns; Equipment; Land acquisition; Emergency funds; Program development; Conferences/seminars; Seed money; Technical assistance; Matching/challenge support.
Limitations: Applications accepted. Giving limited to AK, ID, MT, OR, and WA, with emphasis on Seattle; giving also in British Columbia, Canada. No support for institutions of higher learning, medical institutions, or for wildlife rehabilitation programs. No grants to individuals, or for scholarships, fellowships, medical research or general animal welfare; no direct services in the human services sector, or for land acquisition.
Publications: Grants list.
Application information: Unsolicited applications are not accepted, only letters of inquiry are accepted. Application form required.
Initial approach: Letter of Inquiry
Deadline(s): None
Board meeting date(s): Contributions made in Feb. and Aug.
Officers: Martha Kongsgaard, Pres.; Peter Goldman, V.P. and Secy.-Treas.
Number of staff: 1 full-time professional.
EIN: 943088217

9662
Wayne D. & Joan E. Kuni Foundation ✧ ☆
1053 Officers Row
Vancouver, WA 98661 (360) 694-2550
E-mail: lynne_siegel@kunifoundation.org; Main URL: http://www.kunifoundation.org
Grants List: http://www.kunifoundation.org/grant_awards.htm

Established in 2005 in WA.
Donors: Wayne D. Kuni†; Joan E. Kuni; Wayne D. Kuni Trust; Andersen Construction Co.
Foundation type: Independent foundation.
Financial data (yr. ended 12/31/12): Assets, $30,850,913 (M); gifts received, $4,431,400; expenditures, $3,689,053; qualifying distributions, $2,657,965; giving activities include $2,657,965 for grants.
Purpose and activities: Giving for medical research, especially for the diagnosis and treatment of cancer, and to support and enhance the lives of mentally disabled adults.
Fields of interest: Medical research, institute; Cancer research; Mentally disabled.
Limitations: Applications accepted. Giving primarily in WA. No grants to individuals.
Application information: Application form required.
Initial approach: See website for application form
Deadline(s): See website for deadline
Officer: Lynne F. Siegel, Exec. Dir.
Trustee: Washington Trust Bank.
EIN: 616316804

9663
Jean K. Lafromboise Foundation ✧
c/o Deyonne Tegman
10510 N.E. Northup Way, Ste. 250
Kirkland, WA 98033-7948

Established in 1988 in WA.
Donor: Jean K. Lafromboise†.
Foundation type: Independent foundation.
Financial data (yr. ended 12/31/12): Assets, $9,739,415 (M); expenditures, $582,836; qualifying distributions, $465,000; giving activities include $465,000 for grants.
Purpose and activities: Giving to West Seattle High School, Roosevelt High School and Enumclaw High School in WA, for their scholarship programs. Giving also for rowing activities, and scholarships for the United States Marines; some funding for the arts, and children and youth services.
Fields of interest: Arts; Higher education; Children/youth, services.
Type of support: Scholarship funds.
Limitations: Applications accepted. Giving primarily in Seattle, WA. No grants to individuals.
Application information: Application form required.
Initial approach: Letter
Deadline(s): Mar. 31
Officers: Frank Coyle, Pres.; Deyonne Tegman, V.P. and Secy.; Leo Sheehan, Treas.
EIN: 911416209

9664
Laird Norton Family Foundation ✧
(formerly Laird Norton Foundation)
801 2nd Ave., 13th Fl.
Seattle, WA 98104-1576 (206) 501-4510
Contact: Katie Briggs, Managing Dir.
FAX: (206) 501-4511;
E-mail: lnffinfo@lairdnorton.org; Main URL: http://www.lairdnorton.org
Arts in Education Grants: http://www.lairdnorton.org/arts-in-education.html
Climate Change Grants: http://www.lairdnorton.org/climate-change.html
Global Fundamentals Grants: http://www.lairdnorton.org/global-fundamentals.html
Sixth Sense Grants: http://www.lairdnorton.org/sixth-sense.html
Watershed Stewardship Grants: http://www.lairdnorton.org/watershed-stewardship.html

Incorporated in 1940 in Winona, MN, as the Briarcombe Fund.
Donors: Laird Norton Co. LLC; MDCCP; Mary Lee Clapp Irrevocable Trust; Matthew G. Norton Co.; Lanoga Corp.
Foundation type: Company-sponsored foundation.
Financial data (yr. ended 12/31/13): Assets, $38,337,612 (M); gifts received, $98,193; expenditures, $1,812,991; qualifying distributions, $1,622,255; giving activities include $1,312,252 for 92 grants (high: $145,000; low: $110).
Purpose and activities: The foundation supports programs that honor, support, and reflect the philanthropic values of the Laird Norton family. Special emphasis is directed toward programs designed to promote arts in education; climate change; global fundamentals; and watershed stewardship.
Fields of interest: Arts education; Environment, water resources; Public health, clean water supply; Public health, sanitation.
Type of support: Research; Program-related investments/loans; General/operating support; Management development/capacity building; Program development.
Limitations: Applications not accepted. Giving primarily in the Pacific Northwest; giving also to U.S.-based organizations with international projects in Africa, Asia, and Central America. No support for religious organizations, for-profit organizations, or unincorporated associations or groups. No grants to individuals, or for scholarships, endowments, capital campaigns, publications, documentary films, or television productions.
Application information: The foundation does not accept unsolicited applications for grants. Phone calls, e-mails, and mailed applications that have not been requested will not be accepted. Due to the high volume of inquiries, the foundation will only respond if work is well-aligned with their priorities. The foundation utilizes family advisory committees for its grantmaking and each committee has a slightly different invitation-only process for accepting applications.
Officer: Bruce Reed, Pres.

Number of staff: 1 full-time professional; 1 part-time professional.
EIN: 916339917

9665
The Firoz and Najma Lalji Foundation ✧
10655 N.E. 4th St., Ste. 700
Bellevue, WA 98004

Established in 2007 in SD.
Donors: Firoz Lalji; Najma Lalji.
Foundation type: Independent foundation.
Financial data (yr. ended 11/30/13): Assets, $5,858,567 (M); gifts received, $898,500; expenditures, $943,369; qualifying distributions, $846,306; giving activities include $802,970 for 11 grants (high: $573,300; low: $100).
Fields of interest: Arts; Human services.
Limitations: Applications not accepted.
Application information: Unsolicited requests for funds not accepted.
Trustee: Firoz Lalji.
EIN: 208817765
Selected grants: The following grants are a representative sample of this grantmaker's funding activity:
$26,000 to Seattle Art Museum, Seattle, WA, 2011.

9666
The Laurel Foundation ✧
911 N. 145th St.
Seattle, WA 98133-6522
Contact: Julia Calhoun, Pres. and Secy.

Established in 1995 in WA.
Donors: Julia Larson Calhoun; Chris Larson.
Foundation type: Independent foundation.
Financial data (yr. ended 12/31/13): Assets, $724,492 (M); gifts received, $350,000; expenditures, $1,586,774; qualifying distributions, $1,584,376; giving activities include $1,582,050 for 27 grants (high: $600,000; low: $100).
Purpose and activities: Giving primarily for neglected and abused children in the Pacific Northwest region; funding also for social services.
Fields of interest: Youth development; Human services; Family services.
Type of support: General/operating support; Continuing support; Capital campaigns; Program development.
Limitations: Applications not accepted. Giving primarily in King County, WA. No grants to individuals.
Application information: Contributes only to pre-selected organizations.
Officer: Julia Larson Calhoun, Pres. and Secy.
EIN: 911689238
Selected grants: The following grants are a representative sample of this grantmaker's funding activity:
$400,100 to Treehouse, Seattle, WA, 2011.
$35,000 to Youth in Focus, Seattle, WA, 2011.
$25,000 to Mockingbird Society, Seattle, WA, 2011.
$20,000 to Washington Womens Foundation, Seattle, WA, 2011.
$10,000 to Rainier Scholars, Seattle, WA, 2011.
$1,000 to Alliance for Education, Seattle, WA, 2011.

9667
Paul Lauzier Charitable Foundation ✧
P.O. Box 1230
117 Basin St. N.W.
Ephrata, WA 98823-1230 (509) 754-3209
Contact: Michael Rex Tabler, Tr.
FAX: (509) 754-8481; E-mail: ck.lauzuer@nwi.net; Main URL: http://www.lauzier.org/charitable-foundation

Established in 1997 in WA.
Donor: Paul Lauzier‡.
Foundation type: Independent foundation.
Financial data (yr. ended 12/31/12): Assets, $8,380 (M); gifts received, $452,558; expenditures, $454,599; qualifying distributions, $450,600; giving activities include $450,600 for 18 grants (high: $130,000; low: $100).
Purpose and activities: Giving primarily for higher and other education, as well as for health care, and children, youth and social services.
Fields of interest: Higher education; Education; Health care; Health organizations; Agriculture; Human services; Children/youth, services; Community development, neighborhood development; Catholic agencies & churches.
Type of support: Capital campaigns; Equipment.
Limitations: Giving primarily in rural communities located in central and eastern WA, with emphasis on Grant County. No support for political campaigns. No grants to individuals, or for salaries, debt retirement, or tuition assistance.
Publications: Application guidelines.
Application information: Complete application guidelines available on foundation web site. Application form not required.
Initial approach: Proposal (not exceeding 5 pages)
Deadline(s): See foundation web site for current deadline
Trustee: Michael Rex Tabler.
EIN: 911701539

9668
Paul Lauzier Scholarship Foundation ✧ ☆
117 Basin St. N.W.
P.O. Box 1230
Ephrata, WA 98823-1623 (509) 754-3209
E-mail: ck.lauzier@nwi.net; Main URL: http://www.lauzier.org/scholarship-foundation
Hand delivered address: 117 Basin St. N.W., Ephrata, WA

Established in 1997.
Donor: Paul Lauzier‡.
Foundation type: Independent foundation.
Financial data (yr. ended 12/31/12): Assets, $3,058 (M); gifts received, $425,000; expenditures, $442,216; qualifying distributions, $438,200; giving activities include $438,200 for 195 grants to individuals (high: $5,000; low: $1,000).
Purpose and activities: Scholarships to graduates of Grant County, WA, high schools who attend a college or vocational school (full time) within the State of Washington. Students pursuing graduate degrees are also eligible for scholarship awards. Applicants must reside in Grant County for a minimum of 2 years prior to high school graduation.
Fields of interest: Higher education.
Type of support: Scholarships—to individuals.
Limitations: Applications accepted. Giving limited to residents of Grant County, WA. No grants for salaries, debt retirement, or tuitions assistance.
Publications: Application guidelines.
Application information: Application forms available on foundation web site. There are two different application forms: one for graduating seniors, and another for students who are out of high school. Applicants should make sure they complete the appropriate form. All applications must be typed. Handwritten applications, as well as faxed or e-mailed applications will not be considered. Applicants should not use folders, binders, covers, or double-sided copies, or staple any material. Application form required.
Deadline(s): See application form for current deadlines
Trustee: Michael Rex Tabler.
EIN: 911701545

9669
The Gunnar and Ruth Lie Foundation ✧
3248 Hunts Point Rd.
Bellevue, WA 98004-1126

Established in 2000 in WA.
Donors: Gunnar Lie; Ruth Lie.
Foundation type: Independent foundation.
Financial data (yr. ended 12/31/13): Assets, $14,108,059 (M); gifts received, $1,926,988; expenditures, $562,864; qualifying distributions, $501,782; giving activities include $500,100 for 12 grants (high: $156,500; low: $1,500).
Purpose and activities: Giving primarily to Christian organizations.
Fields of interest: Human services; Children/youth, services; Christian agencies & churches.
Limitations: Applications not accepted. Giving primarily in WA. No grants to individuals.
Application information: Contributes only to pre-selected organizations.
Directors: Elizabeth Lie; Gunnar Lie; Ruth Lie; Kirsten Miller.
EIN: 912090480
Selected grants: The following grants are a representative sample of this grantmaker's funding activity:
$50,000 to Jubilee REACH Center, Bellevue, WA, 2011.
$45,000 to Medical Teams International, Redmond, WA, 2010.
$30,000 to Kidzana Ministries, Mukilteo, WA, 2010.
$25,000 to City Church, Kirkland, WA, 2011.
$25,000 to Everett Gospel Mission, Everett, WA, 2011.
$7,000 to Care Net Pregnancy and Family Services of Puget Sound, Tacoma, WA, 2011.
$1,000 to Multiple Sclerosis Society, National, Seattle, WA, 2011.

9670
The Lochland Foundation ✧
P.O. Box 327
Medina, WA 98039 (425) 548-3482
Contact: Katherine Binder, Secy.-Treas.
Application address: 90 Cascade Key, Bellevue, WA 98006, tel.: (425) 548-3482

Established in 2002 in WA.
Donors: Phyllis Lindsey; Exotic Metals Forming Co., LLC; Mark Lindsey; Katherine A. Binder.
Foundation type: Company-sponsored foundation.

Financial data (yr. ended 12/31/13): Assets, $12,873,501 (M); gifts received, $4,000,000; expenditures, $652,093; qualifying distributions, $645,240; giving activities include $640,500 for 14 grants (high: $150,000; low: $500).
Purpose and activities: The foundation supports flight museums and organizations involved with education, animal welfare, and Christianity and awards college scholarships to high school students in the Seattle area.
Fields of interest: Arts; Education; Religion.
Type of support: General/operating support; Scholarship funds; Scholarships—to individuals.
Limitations: Applications accepted. Giving primarily in WA.
Application information: Application form required.
Initial approach: Proposal
Deadline(s): None
Officers: Phyllis Lindsey, Pres.; Mark Lindsey, V.P.; Katherine A. Binder, Secy.-Treas.
EIN: 510420961
Selected grants: The following grants are a representative sample of this grantmaker's funding activity:
$100,000 to League of Education Voters Foundation, Seattle, WA, 2011. For general fund.
$100,000 to Montana State University, Bozeman, MT, 2011. For scholarships.
$55,000 to First Presbyterian Church of Bellevue, Bellevue, WA, 2011. For general fund.
$27,500 to CRISTA Ministries, Seattle, WA, 2011.
$22,000 to Museum of Flight Foundation, Seattle, WA, 2011. For general fund.
$2,500 to Center for New Creation, Seattle, WA, 2011. For general fund.
$2,000 to K C T S Television, Seattle, WA, 2011. For general fund.

9671
Byron W. and Alice L. Lockwood Foundation ✧

P.O. Box 4
Mercer Island, WA 98040-0004
Contact: Lee Kraft, Exec. Dir.
E-mail: Lockwoodfdn@earthlink.net

Established in 1968 in WA.
Foundation type: Independent foundation.
Financial data (yr. ended 12/31/12): Assets, $19,893,821 (M); gifts received, $249,476; expenditures, $1,181,729; qualifying distributions, $945,958; giving activities include $718,500 for 51 grants (high: $50,000; low: $2,000).
Purpose and activities: Giving primarily for education, health care, and human services in King County, WA.
Fields of interest: Higher education; Education; Health care; Housing/shelter; Human services.
Type of support: General/operating support; Continuing support; Equipment; Emergency funds; Professorships; Scholarship funds; Research.
Limitations: Applications accepted. Giving limited to King County, WA. No support for religious organizations. No grants to individuals.
Application information: Application form required.
Initial approach: Letter
Copies of proposal: 1
Deadline(s): Oct. 1
Board meeting date(s): Nov.
Officers and Trustees:* Paul R. Cressman, Sr.,* Pres.; Lee Kraft,* Exec. Dir.; Kyle T. Cressman; Paul R. Cressman, Jr.
Number of staff: 1 part-time professional.
EIN: 910833426

9672
Loeb Charitable Foundation ✧ ☆

c/o Foundation Management Group, LLC
1000 2nd Ave., Fl. 34
Seattle, WA 98104-1022

Established in WA.
Donor: Francine Loeb.
Foundation type: Independent foundation.
Financial data (yr. ended 11/30/13): Assets, $14,630,849 (M); expenditures, $1,261,079; qualifying distributions, $1,197,409; giving activities include $1,176,575 for 53 grants (high: $265,000; low: $500).
Fields of interest: Arts; Education; Jewish federated giving programs; Jewish agencies & synagogues.
Limitations: Applications not accepted. Giving primarily in Seattle, WA.
Application information: Unsolicited requests for funds not accepted.
Officers and Directors:* Francine R. Loeb,* Pres.; Donald K. Loeb,* V.P.; Daniel M. Asher, Secy.; Stephen B. Loeb,* Treas.; Richard Loeb.
EIN: 271318376
Selected grants: The following grants are a representative sample of this grantmaker's funding activity:
$240,000 to Jewish Federation of Greater Seattle, Seattle, WA, 2011.
$100,000 to URJ Camp Kalsman, Bellevue, WA, 2011.
$55,000 to Jewish Family Service, Seattle, WA, 2011.
$40,000 to Pomona College, Claremont, CA, 2011.
$36,000 to City Year Seattle/King County, Seattle, WA, 2011.
$35,000 to Seattle Childrens Hospital Foundation, Seattle, WA, 2011.
$33,500 to Museum of Glass, Tacoma, WA, 2011.
$30,000 to Temple De Hirsch Sinai, Seattle, WA, 2011.
$30,000 to United Way of King County, Seattle, WA, 2011.
$10,000 to Northwestern University, Evanston, IL, 2011.
$1,000 to Market Foundation, Seattle, WA, 2010.

9673
The Lucky Seven Foundation ✧

3414 N.E. 55th St.
Seattle, WA 98105-2310
Contact: Susan Stoller, Pres.
Main URL: https://online.foundationsource.com/public/home/luckyseven

Established in 1996 in WA.
Donors: Frances A. Backus†; Manson Backus†.
Foundation type: Independent foundation.
Financial data (yr. ended 12/31/12): Assets, $27,677,114 (M); expenditures, $1,524,505; qualifying distributions, $1,378,629; giving activities include $1,316,152 for 270 grants (high: $164,000; low: $100).
Purpose and activities: Giving primarily for social services, the arts, the environment, and education.
Fields of interest: Higher education; Education; Human services; Children/youth, services; Family services.
Type of support: General/operating support; Annual campaigns; Capital campaigns; Building/renovation; Equipment; Debt reduction; Program development; Seed money; Curriculum development; Scholarship funds; Program evaluation; Program-related investments/loans; Matching/challenge support.
Limitations: Applications accepted. Giving primarily in Puget Sound Basin, WA. No grants to individuals.
Application information: Maximum grants are $5,000, unless otherwise informed. Application form required.
Initial approach: Use application form on foundation web site
Deadline(s): Feb. 28 and Sept. 30
Board meeting date(s): Feb., June, and Sept.
Officers: Susan B. Stoller, Pres.; Valerie Backus, V.P.; Robert Fikso, Secy.; John T. Backus, Treas.
Directors: Carol S. Backus; Valerie F. Backus; Willard Steckel; Philip Stoller.
EIN: 911722000
Selected grants: The following grants are a representative sample of this grantmaker's funding activity:
$52,000 to Seattle Central Community College Foundation, Seattle, WA, 2012. For Seattle Vocational Institute.
$25,000 to Youthcare, Seattle, WA, 2012. For YouthCare's GED Program.
$15,000 to Kent Youth and Family Services, Kent, WA, 2012. For The Head Start and Early Child Education and Assistance Program.
$12,500 to Center for Wooden Boats, Seattle, WA, 2012. To assist Young Adults Who Struggle With Conventional Education.
$10,000 to Interfaith Community Health Center, Bellingham, WA, 2012. For The Caring Campaign.
$10,000 to Low Income Housing Institute, Seattle, WA, 2012. For Urban Rest Stop (URS) Project.
$7,500 to Peace Community Center, Tacoma, WA, 2012. For Hilltop Scholars Program.
$5,000 to Shared Housing Services, Tacoma, WA, 2012. For Shared Housing Services HomeShare Program.
$5,000 to Virginia Mason Medical Center, Seattle, WA, 2012. For Bailey-Boushay House (BBH) Kitchen Renovation Project.
$5,000 to Wing-It Productions, Seattle, WA, 2012. For youth education outreach Program.

9674
Luke 12:48 Foundation ✧

c/o Heather Tuininga, Exec. Dir.
333 108th Ave. N.E., Ste. 2010
Bellevue, WA 98004-5777 (425) 974-3755
E-mail: heather@luke1248.org; Main URL: http://www.luke1248.org
Grants List: http://luke1248.org/grant-making/grantees/

Established in 2007 in WA.
Donors: Michael Johnston; Marybeth Johnston.
Foundation type: Independent foundation.
Financial data (yr. ended 12/31/13): Assets, $321,321 (M); gifts received, $150,000; expenditures, $681,677; qualifying distributions, $673,272; giving activities include $460,244 for 30 grants (high: $100,000; low: $50), and $1,209 for foundation-administered programs.
Purpose and activities: The vision of the foundation is to serve as witness to the realness of Jesus and His relentless, transforming love by supporting organizations that: 1) make fishers of men, 2)

transform communities, 3) promote justice, and 4) care for the least of these.
Fields of interest: Human services; Children/youth, services; Community/economic development; Christian agencies & churches.
International interests: Uganda.
Limitations: Applications not accepted. Giving primarily in the Pacific Northwest and Uganda, Africa.
Publications: Grants list.
Application information: Contributes only to pre-selected organizations.
Board meeting date(s): Quarterly
Officers: Marybeth Johnston, Pres. and Treas.; J. Michael Johnston, V.P. and Secy.; Heather Tuininga, Exec. Dir.
Number of staff: 1 full-time professional.
EIN: 261110518
Selected grants: The following grants are a representative sample of this grantmaker's funding activity:
$2,000 to Moyer Foundation, Seattle, WA, 2012. For a table at their annual fundraising luncheon.
$1,000 to Swedish Medical Center Foundation, Seattle, WA, 2012. For their work.
$600 to Smile Train, New York, NY, 2012. For cleft lip surgery for needy children.
$200 to IslandWood, Bainbridge Island, WA, 2012. For the team in the AlderDash.
$150 to Leukemia & Lymphoma Society, Seattle, WA, 2012. For Big Climb 2012 fundraiser.
$150 to Panhandle Alliance for Education, Sandpoint, ID, 2012. For the ChaFE 150 Cycle Hard for Education ride.
$100 to Reign Ministries, Minneapolis, MN, 2012. For Royal Servants.

9675
Keith & Mary Kay McCaw Family Foundation ✧
201 Terry Ave. N., Ste. A
Seattle, WA 98109-5208

Established in 1995 in WA.
Donors: Keith McCaw; Mary Kay McCaw.
Foundation type: Independent foundation.
Financial data (yr. ended 12/31/13): Assets, $28,960,734 (M); expenditures, $1,607,051; qualifying distributions, $1,483,522; giving activities include $1,480,100 for 73 grants (high: $200,000; low: $100).
Fields of interest: Performing arts; United Ways and Federated Giving Programs.
Limitations: Applications not accepted. Giving primarily in Seattle, WA. No grants to individuals.
Application information: Contributes only to pre-selected organizations.
Board meeting date(s): 1st Tues. in Nov.
Officers: Mary Kay McCaw, Pres.; Debra Tawney Stroh, V.P.; Joseph D. Weinstein, Secy.
EIN: 911920617

9676
The Craig and Susan McCaw Foundation ✧
P.O. Box 2908
Kirkland, WA 98083-2908 (425) 828-8000

Established in 1998 in WA.
Donor: Craig O. McCaw.
Foundation type: Independent foundation.
Financial data (yr. ended 12/31/12): Assets, $36,590,205 (M); gifts received, $7,852,325; expenditures, $3,769,775; qualifying distributions, $3,663,626; giving activities include $3,657,050 for 22 grants (high: $2,000,000; low: $500).
Fields of interest: Higher education; Human services.
Limitations: Applications accepted. Giving primarily in CA and WA. No grants to individuals.
Application information:
Initial approach: Letter or telephone
Deadline(s): None
Officers and Directors:* Craig O. McCaw,* Pres.; Susan R. McCaw,* V.P.; Amit Mehta, V.P.; Teresa Mason, Secy.; Cindy Hegge, Treas.; Ben Wolf.
EIN: 911943269
Selected grants: The following grants are a representative sample of this grantmaker's funding activity:
$6,000,000 to Stanford University, Stanford, CA, 2011.
$1,750,000 to Horatio Alger Association of Distinguished Americans, Alexandria, VA, 2011.
$600,000 to Grameen Foundation USA, Washington, DC, 2011.
$250,000 to Nuru International, Palo Alto, CA, 2011.
$50,000 to Team Read, Seattle, WA, 2011.
$35,000 to Pacific Council on International Policy, Los Angeles, CA, 2011.
$25,000 to Pacific Lutheran University, Tacoma, WA, 2011.
$10,500 to CollegeSpring, San Francisco, CA, 2011.
$10,000 to Laguna Blanca School, Santa Barbara, CA, 2011.
$10,000 to Scholarship Foundation of Santa Barbara, Santa Barbara, CA, 2011.

9677
The Tod and Maxine McClaskey Family Foundation ✧
P.O. Box 61963
Vancouver, WA 98666-1963

Established in WA.
Donor: Tod K. McClaskey.
Foundation type: Independent foundation.
Financial data (yr. ended 12/31/13): Assets, $8,823,852 (M); expenditures, $545,574; qualifying distributions, $486,020; giving activities include $466,000 for 7 grants (high: $200,000; low: $25,000).
Fields of interest: Higher education, university.
Limitations: Applications not accepted. Giving primarily in WA.
Application information: Contributes only to pre-selected organizations.
Officers: Larry Ogg, Pres. and V.P.; Lynette Angelo, Secy.-Treas.
Directors: Collin Hagstrom; Jillian McClaskey Hagstrom; Kathleen McClaskey; Rod McClaskey; Robert Schaefer.
EIN: 912010845

9678
D. V. & Ida McEachern Charitable Trust ✧
(formerly Ida J. McEachern Charitable Trust)
c/o McEachern Trust, Union Bank, Personal Trust
P.O. Box 3123
Seattle, WA 98114-3123 (206) 781-3472
Contact: Therese Ogle, Grants Consultant
E-mail: OgleFounds@aol.com; Physical address: 1201 3rd Ave., Ste. 900, Seattle, WA 98101; Main URL: http://fdnweb.org/mceachern
Grants List: http://fdnweb.org/mceachern/grants/year/2013/

Trust established in 1966 in WA.
Donors: Ida J. McEachern‡; D.V. McEachern‡.
Foundation type: Independent foundation.
Financial data (yr. ended 08/31/14): Assets, $19,460,476 (M); expenditures, $999,734; qualifying distributions, $829,490; giving activities include $796,309 for 78 grants (high: $60,000; low: $300).
Purpose and activities: Giving exclusively for capital funding of youth agencies serving children under the age of 18, where the purpose is to give a better start in life, both physically and mentally, to all children. The trust prefers organizations in existence at least five years and whose operational funding comes generally from a non-tax-based source.
Fields of interest: Performing arts; Education; Health organizations, association; Recreation; Human services; Children/youth, services.
Type of support: Capital campaigns; Building/renovation; Equipment.
Limitations: Giving limited to the Puget Sound area of WA, particularly King, Pierce, and Snohomish counties. Generally no support for organizations established less than five years (absent indications of community leadership and reputation, offering unique enrichment programs for children), or for religious institutions. No grants to individuals, or for endowment funds, scholarships, fellowships, operating budgets, continuing support, annual campaigns, seed money, deficit financing, publications, conferences, research programs, or matching gifts; no loans.
Publications: Application guidelines; Grants list.
Application information: See foundation web site for full application guidelines. Application form not required.
Initial approach: Proposal (narrative not to exceed 4 pages)
Copies of proposal: 1
Deadline(s): Mar. 8, Sept. 8, and Dec. 8
Board meeting date(s): Usually in May and Oct.
Trustee: Union Bank, N.A.
EIN: 916063710

9679
Jack and Shirley McIntyre Charitable Foundation ✧
18609 15th Ave. N.W.
Shoreline, WA 98177-3307

Established in 2000 in WA.
Donors: Maurice J. McIntyre; Shirley A. McIntyre‡.
Foundation type: Independent foundation.
Financial data (yr. ended 06/30/13): Assets, $11,854,020 (M); gifts received, $12,431; expenditures, $620,308; qualifying distributions, $533,062; giving activities include $533,062 for grants.

Fields of interest: Performing arts; Performing arts centers; Boys & girls clubs.
Limitations: Applications not accepted. Giving primarily in WA. No grants to individuals.
Application information: Contributes only to pre-selected organizations.
Officers: Brian James McIntyre, Pres. and V.P.; Sarah Ann McIntyre-Hess, Secy.-Treas.
Directors: John Stuart McIntyre; Mary Irene McIntyre-Lee.
EIN: 912073172
Selected grants: The following grants are a representative sample of this grantmaker's funding activity:
$125,000 to Skagit Valley Hospital Foundation, Mount Vernon, WA, 2011.
$5,000 to Aeolian Art and Music Institution, Greenwood Village, CO, 2011.

9680
McKinstry Company Charitable Foundation ✧

c/o William Teplicky
P.O. Box 24567
Seattle, WA 98124-0567
Main URL: http://www.mckinstry.com/about/giving

Established in 1998 in WA.
Donors: McKinstry Co.; Dean Allen; Earl Davie; Anita Davie; George Allen; Vicki Allen.
Foundation type: Company-sponsored foundation.
Financial data (yr. ended 09/30/13): Assets, $33,220 (M); gifts received, $613,500; expenditures, $606,391; qualifying distributions, $606,391; giving activities include $601,350 for 261 grants (high: $101,250; low: $100).
Purpose and activities: The foundation supports arts museums and organizations involved with education, global health, medical research, human services, international development, and microfinance.
Fields of interest: Museums (art); Higher education; Education; Hospitals (general); Health care, clinics/centers; Health care; Diabetes research; Biomedicine research; Medical research; Boys & girls clubs; Boy scouts; YM/YWCAs & YM/YWHAs; Children/youth, services; Developmentally disabled, centers & services; Human services; International development; Microfinance/microlending; Economically disadvantaged.
Type of support: General/operating support; Annual campaigns; Program development; Scholarship funds.
Limitations: Applications not accepted. Giving primarily in Seattle, WA. No grants to individuals.
Application information: Contributes only to pre-selected organizations.
Trustees: Dean C. Allen; Vicki Allen; J. William Teplicky, Jr.
EIN: 911942024

9681
The Robert B. McMillen Foundation ✧

P.O. Box 176
Cle Elum, WA 98922-0176 (425) 313-5711
E-mail: Cassandra@mcmillenfoundation.org; Main URL: http://www.mcmillenfoundation.org

Established in 2004 in WA.
Donor: Robert B. McMillen†.
Foundation type: Independent foundation.
Financial data (yr. ended 12/31/13): Assets, $9,681,067 (M); expenditures, $781,960; qualifying distributions, $658,090; giving activities include $490,016 for 16 grants (high: $251,423; low: $500), and $15,402 for 1 grant to an individual.
Purpose and activities: The foundation is dedicated to providing funding for medical research in the areas of lipid, organ transplant and cardiology; supporting education at the university and college level in states of AK and WA, and providing funding for social service organizations. Fifty percent of the foundation's funding is earmarked for medical research. The foundation also makes scholarships to students who intend to seek a degree or certification at an accredited institution of higher learning within AK and/or WA, in the area of Visual Arts.
Fields of interest: Arts, formal/general education; Visual arts; Medical school/education; Health organizations, research; Heart & circulatory diseases; Human services.
Type of support: Scholarship funds; Scholarships—to individuals.
Limitations: Applications accepted. Giving primarily in WA; some funding also in AK. No support for religious, political, or fraternal organizations. No grants for multi-year grants (with the exception of scholarships).
Application information: Unsolicited proposals not accepted. Application form required.
Initial approach: Submit Letter of Introduction form on foundation web site
Officers: Mike McMillen, Chair.; Cassandra Town, Pres.; Christi Clark, V.P.; David Larson, Secy.; Dawn Naye, Treas.
Director: Mark Barrett.
EIN: 200011616
Selected grants: The following grants are a representative sample of this grantmaker's funding activity:
$40,000 to Elements of Education Partners, Tacoma, WA, 2012. For adjunct artist Program.
$30,500 to University of Puget Sound, Tacoma, WA, 2012. For Visiting Artist Program.
$20,000 to Seattle Pacific University, Seattle, WA, 2012. For New Media Program Equip and Visiting Artist Series.
$13,600 to Gallery One, Ellensburg, WA, 2012. For Ceramic Facilities Enhancement.
$9,000 to Teens in Public Service, Seattle, WA, 2012. For 4 Art - Related Teen Internships.
$6,200 to Walla Walla University, College Place, WA, 2012. For pottery equipment and artist workshop.

9682
Medina Foundation ✧

c/o Jennifer Teunon, Exec. Dir.
801 2nd Ave., Ste. 1300
Seattle, WA 98104-1517 (206) 652-8783
Contact: Aana Lauckhart, Prog. Off.; Jessica Case, Prog. Off.
FAX: (206) 652-8791;
E-mail: info@medinafoundation.org; Main URL: http://www.medinafoundation.org
Grants Database: http://www.medinafoundation.org/index.php?p=Our_Grantees&s=4

Incorporated in 1947 in WA.
Foundation type: Independent foundation.
Financial data (yr. ended 12/31/13): Assets, $97,136,470 (M); expenditures, $4,782,142; qualifying distributions, $4,427,704; giving activities include $3,861,935 for 152 grants (high: $175,000; low: $3,100), and $19,230 for foundation-administered programs.
Purpose and activities: The Medina Foundation is a family foundation that works to foster positive change in the Greater Puget Sound region of Washington State. In honoring the vision of its founder, Norton Clapp, the foundation aspires to improve lives by funding human service organizations that provide direct support to Puget Sound residents. Areas of interest include: housing and homelessness, youth development, hunger, education, family support, and economic development.
Fields of interest: Education; Food services; Housing/shelter; Children/youth, services; Family services; Homeless, human services; Economic development.
Type of support: General/operating support; Management development/capacity building; Building/renovation; Program development; Program evaluation; Matching/challenge support.
Limitations: Applications accepted. Giving limited to the greater Puget Sound, WA, area, including the counties of Clallam, Grays Harbor, Island, Jefferson, King, Kitsap, Mason, Pacific, Pierce, San Juan, Skagit, Snohomish, Thurston, and Whatcom.
Publications: Application guidelines; Grants list.
Application information: The foundation will provide a grant application online if the Letter of Inquiry is accepted. If your organization received funding from the foundation within the last year, please wait at least twelve months from receipt of last grant before submitting another letter of inquiry. Application form required.
Initial approach: Online letter of inquiry on foundation web site
Deadline(s): None
Board meeting date(s): Monthly
Final notification: 30 to 60 days
Officers and Trustees:* Piper Henry-Keller,* Pres.; Gail Gant,* V.P.; Jill Gardner,* Secy.; Jean Gardner,* Treas.; Jennifer Teunon, Exec. Dir.; Edelveis Clapp; James N. Clapp II; Margaret Clapp; Matthew N. Clapp, Jr.; Tamsin O. Clapp; Steve Gant; Patricia Henry; William Henry; Marion Clapp Rawlinson; Elizabeth Williams.
EIN: 910745225
Selected grants: The following grants are a representative sample of this grantmaker's funding activity:
$200,000 to Express Advantage, Seattle, WA, 2012. For general operating support.
$175,000 to Express Advantage, Seattle, WA, 2013. For general operating support.
$100,000 to Saint Thomas Episcopal Church, Medina, WA, 2013. For capital campaign for new community center.
$75,000 to Building Changes, Seattle, WA, 2012. For $50,000 general operating grant and $25,000 for innovations campaign fund.
$75,000 to Plymouth Housing Group, Seattle, WA, 2013. For general operating.
$63,000 to Communities in Schools of Washington State, Federal Way, WA, 2013. For general operating.
$55,000 to Mercy Housing Northwest, Seattle, WA, 2013. For general operating.
$50,000 to Food Lifeline, Shoreline, WA, 2012. For general operating support.
$50,000 to Northwest Harvest, Seattle, WA, 2013. For general operating.
$50,000 to Powerful Schools, Seattle, WA, 2012. For general operating support.

$40,000 to Boys and Girls Clubs of South Puget Sound, Tacoma, WA, 2012. For general operating support.
$30,000 to Garden-Raised Bounty, Olympia, WA, 2013. For general operating.
$25,000 to Alternatives to Hunger, Bellingham, WA, 2012. For general operating support.
$25,000 to Catholic Community Services of Western Washington, Seattle, WA, 2013. For Benedict House, innovative program that provides emergency shelter and transitional housing with supportive services for single homeless men and homeless men with children. This unique program incorporates two elements of the Continuum of care model emergency housing and transitional housing.
$25,000 to Chief Seattle Club, Seattle, WA, 2012. For general operating support.
$25,000 to City Year Seattle/King County, Seattle, WA, 2012. For general operating support.
$25,000 to Noel House, Seattle, WA, 2013. For general operating.
$25,000 to Street Youth Ministries, Seattle, WA, 2012. For general operating support.
$20,000 to First Place, Seattle, WA, 2013. For general operating.
$15,000 to Listen and Talk, Seattle, WA, 2012. For general operating support.

9683
Gary E. Milgard Family Foundation ✧

(formerly Gary & Carol Milgard Family Foundation)
1701 Commerce St.
Tacoma, WA 98402-3207 (253) 274-0121
Contact: Christine Zemanek, C.E.O.
FAX: (253) 274-0478; Christine Zemanek, C.E.O., e-mail: chris@milgardfamily.com, tel.(253) 572-9330; Main URL: http://www.garymilgardfamilyfoundation.org

Established in 2000 in WA.
Foundation type: Independent foundation.
Financial data (yr. ended 12/31/12): Assets, $256,231,051 (M); expenditures, $13,883,996; qualifying distributions, $12,680,782; giving activities include $11,722,969 for 113 grants (high: $1,000,000; low: $20).
Purpose and activities: The goal of the foundation is to support the work of a wide variety of organizations that serve our community. The foundation believes this is a way for the family to give back and continue to educate their descendants in the value of community service.
Fields of interest: Education; Health care; Human services; Children/youth, services.
Type of support: Matching/challenge support; Scholarship funds; Program development; Equipment; Endowments; Capital campaigns; Building/renovation; Annual campaigns; General/operating support.
Limitations: Applications accepted. Giving primarily in Pierce County and the greater Puget Sound, WA, area. No support for political organizations or religious organizations where funds would be used to further a religious purpose. No grants for deficit reduction.
Publications: Grants list.
Application information: For applicants who do not have internet access, contact foundation. Application form required.
Initial approach: Online application
Copies of proposal: 1
Deadline(s): 4:00pm on the last business day of each month
Board meeting date(s): Jan., Apr., July, and Oct.
Final notification: 60 days
Officers: Christine Zemanek, C.E.O. and Pres.; Jim Sheehan, Exec. Dir.
Directors: Cari Milgard-DeGoede; Lori Milgard-Rivera; Mark Milgard.
EIN: 912074073
Selected grants: The following grants are a representative sample of this grantmaker's funding activity:
$1,000,000 to Boys and Girls Clubs of South Puget Sound, Tacoma, WA, 2012.
$1,000,000 to Charles Wright Academy, Tacoma, WA, 2012.
$945,286 to Boys and Girls Club, Variety, Los Angeles, CA, 2012. For swimming pool construction.
$500,000 to American Lake Veterans Golf Course, Friends of, Lakewood, WA, 2012. For construction costs for New Veterans Golf Course.
$500,000 to Franciscan Foundation, Tacoma, WA, 2012.
$405,752 to Pasados Safe Haven, Sultan, WA, 2012. For Rehab Barn.
$200,000 to Community Health Care, Tacoma, WA, 2012. For building the Hilltop Regional Health Center.
$174,949 to Northwest Resource Associates, Seattle, WA, 2012. For the Milgard Adoption Project.
$50,000 to Caring for Kids, Fircrest, WA, 2012. For Holiday and Ready to Learn Fairs, Clothing Bank.
$48,000 to Communities in Schools of Tacoma, Tacoma, WA, 2012. For Ready Set Read Program.

9684
Pendleton and Elisabeth Carey Miller Charitable Foundation ✧

P.O. Box 77377
Seattle, WA 98177-0377

Established in 1995 in WA.
Donor: Elisabeth Miller†.
Foundation type: Independent foundation.
Financial data (yr. ended 12/31/13): Assets, $16,479,612 (M); expenditures, $986,668; qualifying distributions, $846,821; giving activities include $783,120 for 22 grants (high: $263,848; low: $5,000).
Purpose and activities: Giving primarily for education, museums, botanical gardens, horticulture organizations, and other garden clubs.
Fields of interest: Museums; Museums (art); Higher education; Higher education, university; Botanical gardens.
Type of support: Continuing support; Equipment; Endowments; Program development; Conferences/seminars; Publication; Seed money; Internship funds; Research; Technical assistance; Program evaluation; Program-related investments/loans; Matching/challenge support.
Limitations: Applications not accepted. Giving primarily in WA.
Application information: Unsolicited requests for funds not accepted.
Board meeting date(s): May and Nov.
Officers: Winlock W. Miller,* Pres.; Geoffrey Revelle, V.P.; Frank D. Minton,* Secy.-Treas.; Richard Brown, Exec. Dir.
Trustees: Thomas Bayley; Elisabeth A. Bottler; W. Howarth Meadowcroft; Carey K. Miller; Malcolm Moore.
Number of staff: 2 part-time professional.
EIN: 911671814
Selected grants: The following grants are a representative sample of this grantmaker's funding activity:
$2,500 to University of Washington, Law School, Seattle, WA, 2012. To Assist Org. in Carrying Out Charitable Purpose.
$2,500 to Yale University, New Haven, CT, 2012. To Assist Org. in Carrying Out Charitable Purpose.

9685
Hazel Miller Foundation ✧ ☆

1000 2nd. Ave., 34th Fl.
Seattle, WA 98104-1022 (206) 667-0300
FAX: (206) 682-1874;
E-mail: info@hazelmillerfoundation.org; Main URL: http://hazelmillerfoundation.org

Established in WA.
Donor: Hazel Miller Trust.
Foundation type: Independent foundation.
Financial data (yr. ended 12/31/12): Assets, $12,603,512 (M); gifts received, $454,267; expenditures, $557,875; qualifying distributions, $487,970; giving activities include $465,470 for 27 grants (high: $97,200; low: $2,500).
Fields of interest: Arts, cultural/ethnic awareness; Education; Housing/shelter; Recreation, parks/playgrounds; Children/youth, services; Community development, civic centers; Religion.
Limitations: Applications accepted. Giving primarily in Edmonds and South Snohomish County, WA.
Application information: See foundation web site for guidelines and application form. Application form required.
Initial approach: Letter
Deadline(s): Jan. 31, Apr. 4, July 11, and Oct. 10
Officers and Trustees:* Renee Mcrae,* Chair.; Leigh Bennett,* Vice-Chair.; Patrick Shields,* Secy.; Jack Loos,* Treas.; Maria Montalvo; Diana White; Dick Ellis.
EIN: 271173049
Selected grants: The following grants are a representative sample of this grantmaker's funding activity:
$62,150 to Edmonds School District, Lynnwood, WA, 2012. For Academic Coaching and After-School Tutoring and Medowdale HS German Program.
$25,000 to Edmonds Senior Center, Edmonds, WA, 2012. For Senior Center Van Replacement.
$10,000 to Lynnwood Food Bank, Lynnwood, WA, 2012. For Food and Food Programs.
$5,000 to Christmas House, Everett, WA, 2012. For Purchase of Holiday Gifts for Children in Need.
$5,000 to Edmonds Daybreakers Foundation, Edmonds, WA, 2012. To the Edmonds Jazz Connection.
$4,946 to Humanities Washington, Seattle, WA, 2012. For Hazel Miller Humanities Lecture Series at Edmonds Library.

9686
The Miller Foundation ✧ ☆

P.O. Box 12680
Seattle, WA 98111-4680

Established in WA.
Donor: Steven H. Miller.
Foundation type: Independent foundation.
Financial data (yr. ended 10/31/13): Assets, $1,096,438 (M); expenditures, $606,960;

qualifying distributions, $600,303; giving activities include $600,000 for 1 grant.
Fields of interest: Human services.
Limitations: Applications not accepted. Giving primarily in MA. No grants to individuals.
Application information: Contributes only to pre-selected organizations.
Directors: Irvin H. Karl; Steven H. Miller.
EIN: 942538647

9687
Moccasin Lake Foundation ✧
1405 42nd Ave. E.
Seattle, WA 98112-3807 (206) 329-8899
Contact: Lisa P. Anderson
E-mail: mlfoundation@moccasinlake.org; Main URL: http://www.moccasinlake.org

Established in 1991 in WA.
Donors: James C. Pigott; Gaye T. Pigott; Maureen Pigott; Paul Pigott; Mark Kranwinkle; Sara Kranwinkle; Lisa Anderson; Michael Anderson; Julie Gould; Frederick Beau Gould; James C. Pigott 2005 Charitable Lead Annuity Trust; James C. Pigott 2005 Charitable Lead Unitrust; James C. Piggott 2012 Charitable Lead Annuity Trust.
Foundation type: Independent foundation.
Financial data (yr. ended 12/31/13): Assets, $3,397,181 (M); gifts received, $6,448,001; expenditures, $6,494,727; qualifying distributions, $6,494,243; giving activities include $6,493,858 for grants.
Purpose and activities: The foundation is a private not-for-profit organization founded in 1991 as a long-term philanthropic program. The foundation has been established with broad charitable purposes so that its grant making policies may always reflect the diverse interests of the Moccasin Lake Foundation and its individual board members. Currently the Moccasin Lake Foundation has developed a special focus on the Methow Valley in the State of Washington.
Fields of interest: Arts; Education; Environment, natural resources; Animals/wildlife, preservation/protection; Hospitals (general); Reproductive health, family planning; Cancer; Multiple sclerosis; Human services; Religion.
Limitations: Applications accepted. Giving primarily in WA, with a special focus on the Methow Valley. No grants to individuals.
Application information: Application guidelines and concept paper available on foundation web site. Submission of full proposals is by request only, after concept paper has been reviewed. Proof of tax exemption status will only be asked for if a full proposal is requested.
Initial approach: Concept paper (no more than 3 pages)
Deadline(s): None
Board meeting date(s): Quarterly
Final notification: 6 months
Officers and Directors:* Lisa Anderson,* Pres.; Maureen "Dina" Pigott,* V.P.; Mark Kranwinkle,* Secy.; James C. Pigott,* Treas.; Michael Anderson; Frederick Beau Gould*; Julie Gould; Gaye T. Pigott; Paul Pigott.
EIN: 911545081

9688
The Moraine Foundation ✧
c/o Susan W. Pohl
14419 Greenwood Ave. N.
P.O. Box 334
Seattle, WA 98133-6865
Main URL: http://www.morainefoundation.org/

Established in WA.
Donor: Susan W. Pohl.
Foundation type: Independent foundation.
Financial data (yr. ended 12/31/13): Assets, $6,606,940 (M); gifts received, $393,881; expenditures, $434,822; qualifying distributions, $430,348; giving activities include $425,000 for 4 grants (high: $250,000; low: $25,000).
Purpose and activities: Giving primarily for higher education, as well as for social services, and children services, including a children's hospital.
Fields of interest: Arts; Education; Human services.
Limitations: Applications not accepted. Giving primarily in Seattle, WA; funding also in Carlisle, PA. No grants to individuals.
Application information: Contributes only to pre-selected organizations.
Officers: Susan W. Pohl, Pres.; John C. Pohl, V.P. and Secy.-Treas.
EIN: 204195024

9689
M. J. Murdock Charitable Trust
703 Broadway, Ste. 710
Vancouver, WA 98660-3308 (360) 694-8415
Contact: Dana Miller, Sr. Prog. Dir.
FAX: (360) 694-1819; Mailing address: P.O. Box 1618, Vancouver, WA 98668; Main URL: http://www.murdock-trust.org
Grants Database: http://www.murdock-trust.org/grants/grants-awarded.php

Trust established in 1975 in WA.
Donor: Melvin Jack Murdock†.
Foundation type: Independent foundation.
Financial data (yr. ended 12/31/13): Assets, $1,048,190,889 (M); expenditures, $58,738,536; qualifying distributions, $39,379,086; giving activities include $33,944,270 for grants, $585,320 for 4 foundation-administered programs and $370,696 for 1 loan/program-related investment.
Purpose and activities: The M. J. Murdock Charitable Trust seeks to enrich the quality of life in the Pacific Northwest by providing grants and enrichment programs to non-profit organizations that seek to strengthen the region's educational, spiritual, and cultural base in creative and sustainable ways.
Fields of interest: Museums; Arts; Higher education; Education; Health care, rural areas; Human services; Family services; Science, research; Physical/earth sciences; Science; Children/youth; Youth; Adults; Aging; Young adults; Disabilities, people with; Economically disadvantaged.
Type of support: Management development/capacity building; Building/renovation; Equipment; Land acquisition; Program development; Research; Technical assistance; Program-related investments/loans; Employee matching gifts; Matching/challenge support.
Limitations: Applications accepted. Giving primarily in the Pacific Northwest (AK, ID, MT, OR, and WA). No support for government programs; projects common to many organizations without distinguishing merit; sectarian or religious organizations whose principal activities are for the benefit of their own members; no organizations which in policy or practice unfairly discriminate against race, ethnic origin, sex, creed, or religion. No grants to individuals, or for deficit financing, debt retirement, political activities, generally no grants for annual campaigns, general support, continuing support, endowments, or emergency funds.
Publications: Application guidelines; Annual report (including application guidelines); Grants list.
Application information: Application form required.
Initial approach: Letter of inquiry (no longer than 2 pages)
Copies of proposal: 1
Deadline(s): None
Board meeting date(s): Feb., May, Aug., and Nov.
Final notification: 6 to 9 months
Officers and Trustees:* Steven G. W. Moore, C.E.O and Exec. Dir.; Julie D. Cieloha, C.F.O.; James R. Martin, C.I.O.; John W. Castles; Jeffrey T. Grubb; Lynwood W. Swanson, Ph.D.
Number of staff: 21 full-time professional; 1 part-time professional.
EIN: 237456468
Selected grants: The following grants are a representative sample of this grantmaker's funding activity:
$600,000 to Saint Martins University, Lacey, WA, 2012. For Engineering Building Construction - To enhance undergraduate and master's-level education.
$400,000 to Northwest Indian College, Bellingham, WA, 2012. For Campus Technology Improvements - For enhanced, culturally based education.
$250,000 to Youth Villages, Memphis, TN, 2012. For Capital Upgrades - To expand family-based care for children with behavioral disorders.
$200,000 to Anchorage Neighborhood Health Center, Anchorage, AK, 2012. For New Facility - To expand services for low-income populations.
$200,000 to Gritman Medical Center, Moscow, ID, 2012. For New MRI Equipment - To serve rural residents.
$177,000 to Washington Nonprofits, Olympia, WA, 2012. For New Staff - To support education programs.
$160,000 to Hacienda Community Development Corporation, Portland, OR, 2012. For New Staff - For the Latino food vendor incubator project.
$120,000 to Foundation for Research on Economics and the Environment, Bozeman, MT, 2012. For Economics and Environmental Seminars - For religious leaders.
$68,000 to Mount Baker Theater Center, Bellingham, WA, 2012. For New Equipment - To increase efficiencies and enhance audience experience.

9690
Names Family Foundation ✧
1019 Regents Blvd., Ste. 201
Fircrest, WA 98466-6037 (253) 566-7000
Contact: Erin Shagren, Treas.
Main URL: http://www.namesfoundation.org/

Established in 1997 in WA.
Donors: T. Scott Names; Evelyn Names; Sidney W. Names Charitasble Remainder Trust.
Foundation type: Independent foundation.
Financial data (yr. ended 12/31/13): Assets, $8,079,004 (M); expenditures, $573,596;

qualifying distributions, $523,295; giving activities include $498,650 for 16 grants (high: $250,000; low: $200).
Purpose and activities: Giving primarily to exempt organizations providing research, education, or services in the fields of health, physical education, or sports activities.
Fields of interest: Health organizations; Safety/disasters; Athletics/sports, school programs; Boys & girls clubs; YM/YWCAs & YM/YWHAs.
Type of support: General/operating support; Building/renovation.
Limitations: Applications accepted. Giving primarily in Tacoma, WA. No grants to individuals.
Application information: Application form required.
Initial approach: Proposal
Deadline(s): Sept. 30
Officers: Thomas S. Names, Pres.; Evelyn Names, V.P.; Paula Larkin, Secy.; Erin Shagren, Treas.
Trustees: Kim Hegardt; Diane Names; Richard Names.
EIN: 943250195
Selected grants: The following grants are a representative sample of this grantmaker's funding activity:
$200,000 to University of Puget Sound, Tacoma, WA, 2012. To help fund improvements to sport facilities and to fund athletic endowment.
$25,000 to Leukemia & Lymphoma Society, Seattle, WA, 2012. To help fund medical research.
$10,000 to Children's Museum of Tacoma, Tacoma, WA, 2012. For the museum's Construction Capital Campaign.
$10,000 to Pacific Lutheran University, Tacoma, WA, 2012. To help fund sports Programs and equipment.
$10,000 to Special Olympics Washington, Seattle, WA, 2012. To help fund charitable activities.
$5,000 to Zee Speed, Tacoma, WA, 2012. For education for at risk youth in Pierce County.

9691
Nesholm Family Foundation ✧
120 Lakeside Ave., Ste. 340
Seattle, WA 98122-6548 (206) 324-3339
FAX: (206) 568-6946;
E-mail: grants@nesholmfamilyfoundation.org; E-mail address for Laurel Nesholm, Exec. Dir.: lnesholm@nesholmfoundation.org; Main URL: http://www.nesholmfamilyfoundation.org

Established in 1987 in WA.
Donor: Elmer J. Nesholm‡.
Foundation type: Independent foundation.
Financial data (yr. ended 12/31/13): Assets, $44,175,365 (M); expenditures, $2,377,553; qualifying distributions, $2,228,198; giving activities include $2,033,961 for 51 grants (high: $500,000; low: $500).
Purpose and activities: Giving primarily for the performing arts, health and human services, and education.
Fields of interest: Performing arts; Education; Health care; Health organizations, association; Human services.
Type of support: Matching/challenge support; Equipment; Building/renovation; Capital campaigns; Program development.
Limitations: Applications accepted. Giving limited to King County, WA, with emphasis on Seattle. No support for conduit organizations, i.e., tax-exempt organizations that pass funds on to organizations not tax-exempt in their own right, organizations that carry on propaganda or attempt to influence legislation or elections, institutions that in policy or practice unfairly discriminate against race, ethnic origin, sex, or creed, or for activities of sectarian or religious organizations that principally benefit their own members or adherents. No grants for ongoing normal operations or operating deficits, debt retirement or endowment funds, general fund drives, annual appeals, federated campaigns, scholarships and fellowships, or the benefit of specific individuals or for basic science research; no loans.
Publications: Application guidelines; Annual report; Grants list; Program policy statement.
Application information: Application guidelines available on foundation web site. Application form required.
Initial approach: E-mail
Copies of proposal: 7
Deadline(s): See foundation web site or telephone foundation for current deadline
Board meeting date(s): 4-6 times yearly
Final notification: Within 3 months of the board meeting
Officers and Trustees:* John F. Nesholm,* Pres.; Joseph M. Gaffney,* V.P. and Secy.; Edgar K. Marcuse, M.D., M.P.H.*, Treas.; Laurel Nesholm, Exec. Dir.; Carol Lewis; Erika J. Nesholm; Kirsten Nesholm.
Agent: Bank of America, N.A.
Number of staff: 1 full-time professional.
EIN: 943055422
Selected grants: The following grants are a representative sample of this grantmaker's funding activity:
$400,000 to Seattle Opera, Seattle, WA, 2012. For Production of Attila and Artistic Fund.
$400,000 to Seattle Opera, Seattle, WA, 2012. For Artistic Excellence (6th of 8 Installments).
$210,000 to Alliance for Education, Seattle, WA, 2012. For Kids in the Middle Initiative.
$100,000 to Sound Mental Health, Seattle, WA, 2012. To support of the MSSP.
$50,000 to Sound Mental Health, Seattle, WA, 2012. For Middle School Support Project 2012-12 (3rd $ Final Installment).
$45,300 to Seattle Opera, Seattle, WA, 2012. For Trustee Discretionary Grant.
$45,000 to Seattle Opera, Seattle, WA, 2012. For Artistic Campaign TTEE Discretionary Grants.
$40,000 to Pacific Northwest Ballet, Seattle, WA, 2012. To support of Apollo and Carmina Burana.
$7,500 to Alliance for Education, Seattle, WA, 2012. For PPPE Contribution - First Installment of $15,000 Commitment.
$5,000 to Seattle University, Seattle, WA, 2012. For Mental Health Court Law Clinic.

9692
Neukom Family Foundation ✧
925 4th Ave. Ste. 2900
Seattle, WA 98104-1158

Established in 1998 in WA.
Donor: William H. Neukom.
Foundation type: Independent foundation.
Financial data (yr. ended 03/31/13): Assets, $64,744,833 (M); gifts received, $12,850,000; expenditures, $2,933,298; qualifying distributions, $2,002,967; giving activities include $2,002,967 for 7 grants (high: $500,000; low: $200,000).
Fields of interest: Higher education; Environment; United Ways and Federated Giving Programs.
Limitations: Applications not accepted. Giving primarily in CA and WA. No grants to individuals.
Application information: Contributes only to pre-selected organizations.
Directors: Gillian Neukom; John McMakin Neukom; Josselyn Neukom; Samantha Neukom; William H. Neukom.
EIN: 911737888
Selected grants: The following grants are a representative sample of this grantmaker's funding activity:
$1,250,000 to World Justice Project, Washington, DC, 2012. For general support.
$500,000 to Planned Parenthood of Metropolitan Washington, DC, Washington, DC, 2013. For general support.
$500,000 to University of Puget Sound, Tacoma, WA, 2013. For general support.
$400,000 to DonorsChoose.org, New York, NY, 2013. For general support.
$200,000 to Childrens Rights, New York, NY, 2013. For general support.
$200,000 to Doctors Without Borders USA, New York, NY, 2013. For general support.
$200,000 to Plymouth Housing Group, Seattle, WA, 2013. For general support.
$23,627 to Stanford University, Stanford, CA, 2012. For general support.

9693
The Norcliffe Foundation ✧
(formerly The Norcliffe Fund)
999 3rd Ave., Ste. 1006
Seattle, WA 98104-4001 (206) 682-4820
Contact: Dana Pigott, Pres.
FAX: (206) 682-4821;
E-mail: arline@thenorcliffefoundation.com; Main URL: http://www.thenorcliffefoundation.com/

Incorporated in 1952 in WA.
Donors: Theiline M. McCone‡; Mary Ellen Hughes; Mary Pigott; Lee W. Rolfe; Theiline P. Scheumann; Ann Pigott Wyckoff; Christy Wyckoff.
Foundation type: Independent foundation.
Financial data (yr. ended 11/30/13): Assets, $395,113,987 (M); gifts received, $23,475; expenditures, $12,524,689; qualifying distributions, $12,334,612; giving activities include $12,161,460 for 219 grants (high: $1,500,000; low: $500).
Purpose and activities: Giving for the arts and cultural activities, Roman Catholic church support and religious associations, hospitals, early childhood, higher and secondary education, and historic preservation; support also for medical research and health associations, hospices, the environment and conservation, and social services, including programs for the disabled, the homeless, child welfare, youth agencies, wildlife organizations, and the aged.
Fields of interest: Visual arts; Visual arts, architecture; Performing arts; Performing arts, theater; Performing arts, music; Historic preservation/historical societies; Arts; Education, association; Education, fund raising/fund distribution; Elementary/secondary education; Vocational education; Higher education; Adult education—literacy, basic skills & GED; Libraries/library science; Education, reading; Education; Environment, natural resources; Environment; Animals/wildlife, preservation/protection; Hospitals (general); Dental care; Health care; Substance abuse, services; Mental health/crisis

services; Health organizations, association; Cancer; AIDS; Alcoholism; Biomedicine; Medical research, institute; Cancer research; AIDS research; Legal services; Employment; Food services; Nutrition; Housing/shelter, development; Recreation; Human services; Children/youth, services; Child development, services; Family services; Residential/custodial care, hospices; Community/ economic development; Voluntarism promotion; United Ways and Federated Giving Programs; Mathematics; Computer science; Christian agencies & churches; Infants/toddlers; Children/ youth; Children; Youth; Adults; Aging; Young adults; Disabilities, people with; Physically disabled; Blind/ visually impaired; Deaf/hearing impaired; Mentally disabled; Minorities; Asians/Pacific Islanders; African Americans/Blacks; Hispanics/Latinos; Native Americans/American Indians; Indigenous peoples; Women; Infants/toddlers, female; Girls; Adults, women; Young adults, female; Men; Infants/ toddlers, male; Boys; Adults, men; Young adults, male; Substance abusers; AIDS, people with; Single parents; Crime/abuse victims; Terminal illness, people with; Immigrants/refugees; Economically disadvantaged; Homeless.

Type of support: General/operating support; Annual campaigns; Capital campaigns; Building/ renovation; Equipment; Land acquisition; Endowments; Program development; Professorships; Curriculum development; Fellowships; Scholarship funds; Research; Matching/challenge support.

Limitations: Applications accepted. Giving in the Puget Sound region of WA, with emphasis in and around Seattle. No grants to individuals, or for deficit financing, matching gifts, or scholarships; no loans.

Publications: Application guidelines; Program policy statement.

Application information: May use letter proposal or Common Grant application form, which is available on the foundation web site. Only 1 request per year from date of funding or denial, except 2 years from final payment of $50,000 grants. Requests by USPS, UPS or FED EX; no electronic submissions; do not require signature. Application form not required.

Initial approach: Telephone or submission based on guidelines
Copies of proposal: 1
Deadline(s): None
Board meeting date(s): As required
Final notification: 3 to 6 months

Officers and Trustees:* Dana Pigott,* Pres.; Nora Kenway,* V.P.; Arline Hefferline, Secy.; Charles M. Pigott, Treas.; Lisa Anderson; James C. Hughes; James C. Pigott; Mary Pigott; Susan W. Pohl; Theiline P. Scheumann; Ann Pigott Wyckoff.

Number of staff: 1 full-time professional.

EIN: 916029352

Selected grants: The following grants are a representative sample of this grantmaker's funding activity:

$6,885,905 to Seattle Childrens Hospital Foundation, Seattle, WA, 2012. To construct Children's Emergency Department.

$1,385,330 to Seattle Art Museum, Seattle, WA, 2012. For Sam's Fund for Special Exhibition - Phase II, five years from 2012 thru 2016, payable over 5.00 years.

$868,881 to Seattle Preparatory School, Seattle, WA, 2012. To demolish Adelphia Hall and renovate and expand Peyton Hall.

$631,119 to Seattle Preparatory School, Seattle, WA, 2012. To demolish Adelphia Hall and renovate and expand Peyton Hall.

$614,670 to Seattle Art Museum, Seattle, WA, 2012. For Sam's Fund for Special Exhibition - Phase II, five years from 2012 thru 2016, payable over 5.00 years.

$614,095 to Seattle Childrens Hospital Foundation, Seattle, WA, 2012. To construct Children's Emergency Department.

$500,000 to Overlake Hospital Foundation, Bellevue, WA, 2012. To build New Heart and Vascular Center - Phase I.

$25,000 to Planned Parenthood of the Great Northwest, Seattle, WA, 2012. For Phone System Replacement Project at 7 King County health centers.

$25,000 to Washington Early Learning Fund, Seattle, WA, 2012. For Home Visiting Services account.

$15,000 to Seattle Youth Symphony Orchestras, Seattle, WA, 2012. For final concert of the 2011/2012 Season.

9694
Oki Foundation ✧

(formerly The Oki Charitable Foundation)
1416 112th Ave. N.E.
Bellevue, WA 98004-3710

Established in 1988 in WA.

Donors: Laurie D. Oki; Scott B. Oki; Nanny & Webster.

Foundation type: Independent foundation.

Financial data (yr. ended 12/31/12): Assets, $33,988 (M); gifts received, $483,140; expenditures, $591,221; qualifying distributions, $572,390; giving activities include $572,390 for grants.

Purpose and activities: Giving primarily for children's health and welfare issues in King County, WA; funding also for higher education and human services.

Fields of interest: Arts; Higher education; Education; Hospitals (specialty); Human services; YM/YWCAs & YM/YWHAs; Children, services.

Type of support: Continuing support; Annual campaigns; Capital campaigns.

Limitations: Applications not accepted. Giving primarily in Bellevue and Seattle, WA. No grants to individuals.

Application information: Unsolicited requests for funds not accepted.

Officers: Laurie D. Oki, Pres. and Treas.; Scott B. Oki, V.P. and Secy.

EIN: 911394156

9695
OneFamily Foundation ✧ ☆

(formerly Wood Family Foundation)
6723 Sycamore Ave. N.W.
Seattle, WA 98117-4849 (206) 781-3472
Contact: Therese Ogle
E-mail: OgleFounds@aol.com; Main URL: http://fdnweb.org/onefamily
Grants List: http://fdnweb.org/onefamily/grants/year/2014/

Established in 1997 in WA.

Donors: Bill Morgan; Sara Morgan; Brenda K. Wood.

Foundation type: Independent foundation.

Financial data (yr. ended 12/31/13): Assets, $11,707,113 (M); gifts received, $183; expenditures, $713,540; qualifying distributions, $635,478; giving activities include $590,250 for 59 grants (high: $150,000; low: $750), and $33,183 for 3 foundation-administered programs.

Purpose and activities: The goals of the foundation are to provide resources to enhance the lives of women living in poverty and at-risk youth, to support services for abused women, and to aid efforts to end violence and sexual assault against women and children.

Fields of interest: Education; Health care; Human services; Children/youth, services; Family services, domestic violence; Women, centers/services; Christian agencies & churches; Economically disadvantaged.

Type of support: General/operating support.

Limitations: Applications accepted. Giving limited to King and Snohomish counties, WA, and the Olympic Peninsula. No support for schools, summer camps, low-income housing or shelter programs (unless they are specifically focused on serving women), or groups that have been declined three times. No grants to individuals, or for capital grants, scholarships, research, multi-year grants, athletic events, video or film projects, website development, or book publications.

Publications: Application guidelines; Grants list.

Application information: After receiving three grants, a group must wait two years before re-applying. Incomplete applications will be forwarded to the next funding cycle pending receipt of any missing materials.

Initial approach: Proposal (not exceeding 3 pages)
Copies of proposal: 2
Deadline(s): 2nd Fri. in Mar. and Aug.
Final notification: 1st Mon. in May and Oct.

Officers: Brenda K. Wood, Pres.; Donald R. Wood III, V.P.; Brandon C. Wood, Secy.-Treas.

EIN: 911722889

9696
Opportunities for Education Foundation ✧

155 N.E. 100th St., Ste. 404
Seattle, WA 98125-8010

Established in 2000 in WA.

Donors: Christopher Larson; Julia Calhoun.

Foundation type: Independent foundation.

Financial data (yr. ended 12/31/13): Assets, $632,398 (M); gifts received, $1,152,000; expenditures, $1,153,147; qualifying distributions, $1,151,227; giving activities include $1,149,307 for 1 grant.

Fields of interest: Education.

Limitations: Applications not accepted. Giving primarily in Seattle, WA. No grants to individuals.

Application information: Contributes only to pre-selected organizations.

Officer: Chris Larson, Pres. and Secy.

EIN: 912091348

Selected grants: The following grants are a representative sample of this grantmaker's funding activity:

$382,589 to New School Foundation, Seattle, WA, 2011.

$300,236 to League of Education Voters Foundation, Seattle, WA, 2011.

9697
Orcas Island Community Foundation ✧
141 Prune Alley, Ste. 201
P.O. Box 1496
Eastsound, WA 98245
Contact: Hilary Canty, Exec. Dir.; For grants: Coleen O'Brien, Grants Comm. Chair.
E-mail: info@oicf.us; Fax: same as phone number, call to ask that fax machine be plugged in; Grant inquiry e-mail: ckobrien44@gmail.com, tel: 360-376-4808; Main URL: http://www.oicf.us/ Facebook: http://www.facebook.com/pages/Orcas-Island-Community-Foundation/146762648713458

Established in 1995 in WA.
Foundation type: Community foundation.
Financial data (yr. ended 12/31/13): Assets, $6,780,596 (M); gifts received, $1,949,151; expenditures, $1,103,446; giving activities include $879,550 for 21+ grants (high: $250,000).
Purpose and activities: The foundation aims to foster philanthropy to enhance and preserve the quality of life on Orcas Island.
Fields of interest: Community/economic development.
Type of support: General/operating support; Program development.
Limitations: Applications accepted. Giving primarily on Orcas Island. No support for religious organizations for religious purposes. No grants for general fund drives, endowments, or fundraising expenses, or to conduit organizations.
Publications: Application guidelines.
Application information: Visit foundation web site for application form and guidelines. The foundation's Committee Chair. will pre-review draft applications; drafts must be e-mailed to by Mar. 1. Application form required.
Initial approach: E-mail or hand deliver application and attachments
Copies of proposal: 1
Deadline(s): Mar. 15
Final notification: Early May
Board of Trustees:* Steve Jung,* Pres.; Coleen O'Brien,* Secy. and Chair., Grants Comm.; Jim Keyes,* Treas.; Hilary Canty,* Exec. Dir.; Craig Anderson; Helen Bee; Diane Berreth; Sally Buchanan; Bruce Coffey; Jim Connell; Margie Doyle; Martha Farish; Joan Pedrick; Steve Spence; Dimitri Stankevich.
EIN: 911680527

9698
PACCAR Foundation ✧
c/o PACCAR Inc
P.O. Box 1518
Bellevue, WA 98009-1518
Contact: Ken Hastings
E-mail: ken.hastings@paccar.com; Main URL: http://www.paccar.com/company/foundation.asp

Incorporated in 1951 in WA.
Donor: PACCAR Inc.
Foundation type: Company-sponsored foundation.
Financial data (yr. ended 12/31/13): Assets, $2,275,060 (M); gifts received, $6,000,000; expenditures, $5,556,965; qualifying distributions, $5,507,145; giving activities include $5,507,145 for 82+ grants (high: $2,700,000).
Purpose and activities: The foundation supports hospitals and organizations involved with arts and culture, higher education, and economic education.
Fields of interest: Arts, cultural/ethnic awareness; Museums; Arts; Secondary school/education; Higher education; Business school/education; Education, reading; Hospitals (general); Health care, clinics/centers; Health care; Human services; United Ways and Federated Giving Programs; Science.
Type of support: Continuing support; Annual campaigns; Capital campaigns; Building/renovation; Scholarship funds; Employee matching gifts.
Limitations: Applications accepted. Giving primarily in areas of company operations, with emphasis on King County, WA. No support for churches for the purpose of religious activity. No grants to individuals, or for scholarships or fellowships, program development, general operating support, fundraising events, sponsorships, dinners, or event tickets, or advertising space for charitable causes in yearbooks, programs, or publications.
Publications: Application guidelines.
Application information: Support is limited to 1 contribution per organization during any given year. Multi-year funding is not automatic. Telephone solicitations are not encouraged. Application form not required.
Initial approach: Complete online application
Copies of proposal: 1
Deadline(s): None
Board meeting date(s): Semi-annual; dates vary
Final notification: Within 6 months
Officers and Directors:* Mark C. Pigott,* Pres.; Ken Hastings, V.P. and Genl. Mgr.; Ronald E. Armstrong, V.P.; Dan D. Sobic, V.P.; David C. Anderson, Secy.; Robin E. Easton, Treas.
Number of staff: None.
EIN: 916030638

9699
PAH Foundation ✧
500 108th Ave. N.E., Ste. 1750
Bellevue, WA 98004-5576
Contact: Peter A. Horvitz, Pres.

Established in 1998 in WA as a follow-up to the Harry R. Horvitz Family Foundation.
Donor: Lois U. Horvitz Foundation.
Foundation type: Independent foundation.
Financial data (yr. ended 12/31/13): Assets, $97,392 (M); gifts received, $483,500; expenditures, $690,609; qualifying distributions, $680,338; giving activities include $668,623 for 26 grants (high: $100,000; low: $1,000).
Purpose and activities: Giving primarily for the arts, particularly to an art museum, and a ballet company; funding also for education, human services, and health associations. Scholarships awarded to high school seniors who either are presently attending a high school in Lake, Lorain, Richland, and Tuscarawas counties in OH, or Renssealaer County, NY, or any direct descendants (including adopted children, but not step children), of a person who by Aug. 1, 1987, had been a full-time employee of either The Mansfield News Journal, The Lorain Journal, The Luke County News Herald, The Dover/New Philadelphia Times Reporter, The Troy Times Record, or The Multi-Channel TV Cable Co., for at least two years.
Fields of interest: Museums (art); Performing arts, ballet; Arts; Higher education; Education; Hospitals (general); Health organizations, association; Human services; United Ways and Federated Giving Programs; Jewish federated giving programs.
Type of support: Scholarships—to individuals.
Limitations: Applications not accepted. Giving on a national basis with an emphasis on communities where foundation members reside. No grants to individuals (except for scholarships), operating budgets, recurring expenses for direct services or administrative costs, annual appeals, debt reduction, campaigns, religion, publications, seminars or workshops, travel, or governmental services.
Application information: Unsolicited requests for funds not accepted.
Officers and Trustee:* Peter A. Horvitz,* Pres.; Margaret A. O'Meara, V.P.; Peter A. Kuhn, Secy. and Exec. Dir.
EIN: 911866138
Selected grants: The following grants are a representative sample of this grantmaker's funding activity:
$50,000 to Syracuse University, SI Newhouse School Building Campaign, Syracuse, NY, 2012. For the school and its Programs.
$15,000 to Jewish Federation of Greater Seattle, Seattle, WA, 2012. For the organization and its Programs.
$12,125 to HRH Scholarship Fund, Cleveland, OH, 2012. For grant for scholar - ships to qualifying persons.

9700
Charles Pankow Foundation ✧
P.O. Box 820631
Vancouver, WA 98682-0014 (360) 326-3767
Contact: Mark Perniconi P.E., Exec. Dir.
E-mail: info@pankowfoundation.org; E-mail for Mark Perniconi, P.E., Exec. Dir.: mperniconi@pankowfoundation.org; Main URL: http://www.pankowfoundation.org

Established in 2002 in CA.
Donors: Charles J. Pankow†; Pankow Family Trust of 1976; Foundation of Integrated Services.
Foundation type: Independent foundation.
Financial data (yr. ended 12/31/12): Assets, $26,232,274 (M); expenditures, $1,423,449; qualifying distributions, $1,304,521; giving activities include $925,000 for 38 grants (high: $169,000; low: $1,000).
Purpose and activities: The foundation exists to advance innovations in building design and construction through research, so as to provide the public with buildings of improved quality, efficiency, and value.
Fields of interest: Housing/shelter, research; Engineering.
Type of support: Research.
Limitations: Giving primarily in CA. No grants to individuals.
Publications: Application guidelines; Annual report.
Application information: See foundation web site for Research Need Statement guidelines.
Initial approach: Submit a Research Need Statement (not more than 2 pages)
Deadline(s): None, for Research Need Statement
Officers and Directors:* Richard M. Kunnath, P.E.*, Pres.; Timothy P. Murphy, Esq.*, Secy. and C.F.O.; Mark J. Perniconi, P.E., Exec. Dir.; Ron Klemencic, P.E.
Number of staff: 1 part-time professional.
EIN: 710919052

Selected grants: The following grants are a representative sample of this grantmaker's funding activity:
$169,000 to Georgia Tech Research Corporation, Atlanta, GA, 2012. For Research Grant Precast Concrete National BIM Standard Project.
$100,000 to Northeastern University, Boston, MA, 2012. For CPF Research Grant. Thermal Break Strategies for Cladding Systems in Building Structures.
$75,000 to Lehigh University, Bethlehem, PA, 2012. For CPF Research Grant. Unbonded Post-Tensioned Cast-in-Place Walls for Seismic Resistance.
$70,000 to Pennsylvania State University, State College, PA, 2012. For CPF Research Project: Owner's Guide to Building Information Modeling.
$30,000 to University of Michigan, Ann Arbor, MI, 2012. For Effect of Shear Stud Layout on the Seismic Behavior of Slab-column Connections.
$20,000 to University of Cincinnati, Cincinnati, OH, 2012. For Continuous Stirrups for Shear and Torsion Reinforcement in Beams.
$20,000 to University of Notre Dame, Notre Dame, IN, 2012. For Hybrid Precast Walls For Seismic Regions project.
$10,000 to Colorado State University, Fort Collins, CO, 2012. For education grant: enhancing design-build learning and curriculum.
$10,000 to University of Florida, Gainesville, FL, 2012. For CPF Education Grant: Enhancing Design-Build Learning and Curriculum.
$2,500 to Pasadena Educational Foundation, Pasadena, CA, 2012. For Designation for the Engineering and Environmental Science Collage and Career Pathway at John Muir High School.

9701
Peach Foundation ✧
1601 2nd Ave., Ste. 615
Seattle, WA 98101-1539

Established in 2001 in WA.
Donor: Priscilla B. Collins.
Foundation type: Independent foundation.
Financial data (yr. ended 12/31/13): Assets, $11,203,984 (M); expenditures, $682,383; qualifying distributions, $590,609; giving activities include $585,350 for 46 grants (high: $50,000; low: $150).
Fields of interest: Museums (history); Performing arts, music; Environment, formal/general education; Environment.
Limitations: Applications not accepted. Giving primarily in Seattle, WA. No grants to individuals.
Application information: Contributes only to pre-selected organizations.
Officers: Jean Gardner, Pres.; Pat Baillargeon, V.P.; Shelley Rolfe, Secy.; Gail Ransom, Treas.
EIN: 912094325
Selected grants: The following grants are a representative sample of this grantmaker's funding activity:
$50,000 to Preserve Our Islands, Vashon Island, WA, 2010.
$41,000 to Town Hall Los Angeles, Los Angeles, CA, 2010.
$30,000 to Seattle Opera, Seattle, WA, 2010.
$25,500 to Wing Luke Asian Museum, Seattle, WA, 2010.
$23,000 to Seattle University, College of Science and Engineering, Seattle, WA, 2010.
$20,000 to Climate Solutions, Olympia, WA, 2011.
$17,500 to Washington Wildlife and Recreation Coalition, Seattle, WA, 2010.
$17,000 to Pike Market Child Care and Preschool, Seattle, WA, 2010.

9702
PEMCO Foundation, Inc. ✧
325 Eastlake Ave. E.
Seattle, WA 98109-5407
Contact: Stan W. McNaughton, Pres. and Treas.

Established in 1965 in WA.
Donors: Gladys McLaughlin†; PEMCO Corp.; Washington School Employees Credit Union; Evergreen Bank, N.A.; Evergreen Bancorp, Inc.; Teachers Foundation; PEMCO Technology Services, Inc.; School Employees Credit Union of Washington; PEMCO Mutual Insurance Co.; PCCS, Inc.
Foundation type: Company-sponsored foundation.
Financial data (yr. ended 06/30/13): Assets, $2,127,892 (M); gifts received, $166,980; expenditures, $636,613; qualifying distributions, $636,613; giving activities include $634,670 for 345 grants (high: $94,100; low: $25).
Purpose and activities: The foundation supports organizations involved with television, education, crime and violence prevention, youth development, human services, and business and awards college scholarships to high school students located in Washington.
Fields of interest: Media, television; Secondary school/education; Higher education; Education; Crime/violence prevention; Boys & girls clubs; Camp Fire; Youth development, business; Youth development; American Red Cross; Children, services; Human services; Business/industry; United Ways and Federated Giving Programs.
Type of support: General/operating support; Program development; Scholarship funds; Scholarships—to individuals.
Limitations: Applications accepted. Giving primarily in WA, with emphasis on Seattle; giving limited to WA for scholarships.
Application information: Application form not required.
Initial approach: Letter
Deadline(s): None
Final notification: 2 months for scholarships
Officers and Trustees:* Stan W. McNaughton,* Pres. and Treas.; Sandra M. Kurack,* V.P.; Denice M. Town, Secy.; Gayle C. Grass; Brian R. McNaughton; Astrid I. Thompson.
EIN: 916072723
Selected grants: The following grants are a representative sample of this grantmaker's funding activity:
$55,000 to Independent Colleges of Washington, Seattle, WA, 2011.
$25,091 to United Way of King County, Seattle, WA, 2011.
$25,000 to Boys and Girls Clubs of King County, Seattle, WA, 2011.
$20,000 to Discovery Institute, Seattle, WA, 2011.
$10,000 to American Red Cross, Spokane, WA, 2011.
$10,000 to Association of Washington School Principals, Olympia, WA, 2011.
$10,000 to Camp Fire USA, Everett, WA, 2011.
$6,339 to United Way of Snohomish County, Everett, WA, 2011.
$5,500 to Northwest Burn Foundation, Seattle, WA, 2011.
$3,000 to Pacific Northwest Ballet, Seattle, WA, 2011.

9703
James B. Pendleton Charitable Trust ✧
601 108th Ave. N.E., Ste. 1900
Bellevue, WA 98004-4376
Contact: Dayle E. Iverson, Tr.

Established in 1992 in CA.
Donor: James B. Pendleton†.
Foundation type: Independent foundation.
Financial data (yr. ended 12/31/13): Assets, $28,405,587 (M); expenditures, $1,629,647; qualifying distributions, $1,140,603; giving activities include $985,512 for 6 grants (high: $255,000; low: $77,131).
Purpose and activities: Giving solely for basic research on causes, cures, and prevention of AIDS/HIV.
Fields of interest: AIDS research.
Type of support: Equipment; Research.
Limitations: Giving primarily for established research in the western U.S. No grants to individuals.
Application information: Application form not required.
Initial approach: Letter
Copies of proposal: 2
Deadline(s): None
Final notification: Upon review of proposal
Officers and Trustees:* Dayle E. Iverson,* C.E.O.; David E. Ellison,* Dir., Investments.
Number of staff: 2 full-time professional.
EIN: 956944277

9704
Plum Creek Foundation ✧
999 3rd Ave., Ste. 4300
Seattle, WA 98104-4096 (206) 467-3664
Contact: Holly Nicholes
FAX: (206) 467-3795;
E-mail: foundation@plumcreek.com; Contact for Montana Great Classroom Awards: Renee Erickson, tel.: (406) 892-6227, e-mail: renee.erickson@plumcreek.com; Contact for organizations in FL: Rose Fagler, Community Rels. Mgr., tel.: 352-333-3733, e-mail: rose.fagler@plumcreek.com; Main URL: http://www.plumcreek.com/CommunityInvolvement/tabid/69/Default.aspx

Established in 1993 in WA.
Donors: Plum Creek Timber Co., L.P.; Plum Creek Timber Co., Inc.
Foundation type: Company-sponsored foundation.
Financial data (yr. ended 12/31/13): Assets, $6,142 (M); gifts received, $1,786,000; expenditures, $1,847,676; qualifying distributions, $1,847,641; giving activities include $1,847,641 for 5 grants (high: $100,000; low: $5,000).
Purpose and activities: The foundation supports organizations involved with arts and culture, education, the environment, health, youth development, human services, community development, and civic affairs. Special emphasis is directed toward programs designed to improve the quality of life and provide services that would not otherwise be available to residents in areas of company operations.

Fields of interest: Museums; Performing arts; Arts; Elementary/secondary education; Higher education; Libraries (public); Education; Environmental education; Environment; Hospitals (general); Health care; Food banks; Disasters, fire prevention/control; Girl scouts; Youth development; American Red Cross; Children/youth, services; Human services; Community/economic development; Public affairs.
Type of support: Grants to individuals; Employee-related scholarships; Building/renovation; Equipment; Program development; Employee volunteer services; Employee matching gifts.
Limitations: Applications accepted. Giving primarily in areas of company operations in AL, AR, FL, GA, LA, ME, MI, MS, MT, NH, OK, OR, SC, TX, VT, WA, WI, and WV. No support for religious organizations not of direct benefit to the entire community, veterans' or fraternal organizations, national health organizations, Chambers of Commerce or taxpayer associations, or political organizations or candidates. No grants to individuals (except for the Plum Creek Scholarship Program and Montana Great Classroom awards), or for salaries, stipends, or other forms of compensation, endowments, fundraising events, tickets, dinners, or telethons, corporate memberships, general operating support for United Way agencies, or political campaigns; no loans or land donations.
Publications: Application guidelines; Annual report; Grants list; Program policy statement.
Application information: Applications for Montana Great Classroom Awards must be approved by the school's principal or district administrator. Faxed or e-mailed applications are not accepted. Support is limited to 1 contribution per organization during any given year. Organizations located in Florida must contact the Community Relations Manager for funding information. Application form required.
Initial approach: Download application form and mail to foundation
Copies of proposal: 1
Deadline(s): Postmarked by Jan. 31, Apr. 30, July 31, and Oct. 31; June 1 and Dec. 1 for Montana Great Classroom Awards
Board meeting date(s): Mar., June, Sept., and Dec.
Final notification: 2 weeks following board meeting; Feb. and Aug. for Montana Great Classroom Awards
Officers and Trustees:* James A. Kraft,* Chair.; Robert J. Jirsa,* Pres.; Kirsten D. Smith, V.P.; Julie Stewart, Secy.; Elizabeth J. Duxbury, Treas.; Jacey Barnaby; Charlie Becker; Christie Bennett; Charlie Cornish; Bill Dempsey; Mark A. Doty; Ben Dow; Rose Fagler; Greg Galpin; Steve Hanley; Rebecca Hendrix; Rob Hicks; Jenny Krueger; Dan Lemke; Luke Muzzy; Bill O'Brion; Todd Powell; Tricia Quinn; Tom Ray; Charlie Reece; Thomas M. Reed; Jim Rundorff; Mark Sherman; Jerry Sorensen; Richard Stitch; Jack Thomas; Arnulfo Zendejas.
EIN: 911621028

9705
Puget Sound Energy Foundation ✧
10885 N.E. 4th St., Ste. 1200
Bellevue, WA 98004-5591
Contact: Sandra M. Carson, Exec. Dir.
E-mail: psefoundation@pse.com; Main URL: http://www.psefoundation.org/
Grants List: http://www.psefoundation.org/grantHistory.shtml

Established in 2006 in WA.
Donor: Puget Energy.
Foundation type: Company-sponsored foundation.
Financial data (yr. ended 12/31/13): Assets, $23,452,973 (M); expenditures, $1,031,912; qualifying distributions, $992,132; giving activities include $884,978 for 340 grants (high: $50,000; low: $13).
Purpose and activities: The foundation supports programs designed to promote public safety and emergency preparedness. Special emphasis is directed toward programs designed to respond to the needs of vulnerable communities; encourage energy conservation and environmental stewardship; and promote workforce development at universities and community and technical colleges.
Fields of interest: Education; Environment, natural resources; Environment, energy; Environment; Employment, services; Disasters, preparedness/services; Safety/disasters; Human services.
Type of support: Capital campaigns; Program development; Scholarship funds; Employee volunteer services; Employee matching gifts.
Limitations: Applications accepted. Giving primarily in areas where Puget Sound Energy provides services or has operations: Chelan, Columbia, Cowlitz, Douglas, Island, Jefferson, King, Kitsap, Kittitas, Klickitat, Lewis, Pierce, Snohomish, Skagit, Thurston, and Whatcom counties, WA. No support for individual K-12 schools, youth groups, clubs, teams, choirs, or bands, political or discriminatory organizations, or religious organizations of any kind, unless the program is open to the public such as a food bank, for tuition or membership dues made to service clubs, social or fraternal organizations. No grants to individuals, or for general operating expenses, fundraising events, or endowments.
Publications: Application guidelines; Grants list.
Application information: Organizations that receive funding will be eligible to apply for another grant one year later. Application form required.
Initial approach: Complete online eligibility quiz and application
Copies of proposal: 1
Deadline(s): Apr. 1 and Oct. 1
Officers and Directors.: Andy Wappler,* Chair. and Pres.; Marla D. Mellies, V.P.; Paul Wiegand, Secy.; Donald E. Gaines, Treas.; Sandra M. Carson, Exec. Dir.; Daniel A. Doyle.
EIN: 204863534
Selected grants: The following grants are a representative sample of this grantmaker's funding activity:
$20,000 to Washington Explorer Search and Rescue, Silverdale, WA, 2012. For Mobile Logistics Support Unit (MLSU) Project.
$15,000 to University of Washington Foundation, Tacoma, WA, 2012. For PSE and the UW Medicine Regional Burn Center at Harborview: Partnering for Burn Prevention and Safety Project.
$10,000 to Food Lifeline, Shoreline, WA, 2012. For Safety and Emergency Relief Program Project.
$10,000 to Lake Washington Institute of Technology, Kirkland, WA, 2012. For Facilitating Emergency Response Readiness Project.
$10,000 to World Vision, Federal Way, WA, 2012. For World Vision Disaster Preparedness and Response Program for Western Washington Project.
$9,000 to Catholic Community Services of Western Washington, Seattle, WA, 2012. For Upgrade Facility First Aid/Disaster Preparedness Project.
$5,000 to Point Defiance Zoological Society, Tacoma, WA, 2012. For Fire Doors for the South Pacific Aquarium at Pdza Project.
$5,000 to Washington Poison Center, Seattle, WA, 2012. For Poison Prevention Education Project.
$5,000 to Whidbey Island Hospital Foundation, Coupeville, WA, 2012. For Emergency Preparedness Through Fire Alarm Upgrade for Hospital Project.
$2,000 to Vashon Youth and Family Services, Vashon, WA, 2012. For Viva Project.

9706
PWH Educational Foundation Inc. ✧ ☆
5720 59th Ave. N.E.
Seattle, WA 98105-2028 (206) 525-6369
Contact: Robert Leong, Pres.

Donor: PWH Trust.
Foundation type: Independent foundation.
Financial data (yr. ended 12/31/13): Assets, $0 (M); gifts received, $600,000; expenditures, $549,429; qualifying distributions, $541,360; giving activities include $541,360 for 9 grants (high: $500,000; low: $360).
Fields of interest: Education; Human services.
Type of support: Scholarship funds.
Application information: Application form required.
Initial approach: Letter
Deadline(s): None
Officers: Robert Leong, Pres.; Fr. Thomas R. Von Behran, Secy.-Treas.
Director: Tom Gehrig.
EIN: 880327058

9707
Quixote Foundation, Inc.
5405 Leary Ave. N.W., Ste. 2
Seattle, WA 98107-4079
Contact: June Wilson, Operations Dir.
FAX: (206) 784-5516;
E-mail: june@quixotefoundation.org; Main URL: http://www.quixotefoundation.org/
Facebook: http://www.facebook.com/pages/Quixote-Foundation/264215195547
Quixote Foundation's Philanthropy Promise: http://www.ncrp.org/philanthropys-promise/who
Twitter: http://www.twitter.com/quixotetilts

Established in 1998 in WI.
Donor: Arthur S. Hanisch‡.
Foundation type: Independent foundation.
Financial data (yr. ended 12/31/12): Assets, $13,656,338 (M); expenditures, $2,084,784; qualifying distributions, $1,839,713; giving activities include $1,108,500 for 21 grants (high: $265,500; low: $500).
Purpose and activities: Giving to advance progressive causes through the action, education and policy work of dynamic nonprofit groups. Current interests of the foundation are: 1) protecting reproductive rights; 2) developing effective message strategies to safeguard the world's natural environment; 3) reforming media coverage and promoting public awareness of economic inequality; and 4) restoring U.S. democracy by making sure every vote is counted as cast.
Fields of interest: Environment; Civil liberties, reproductive rights; Civil/human rights; Minorities; Women; Young adults, female; Economically disadvantaged.

Type of support: General/operating support; Continuing support; Income development; Management development/capacity building; Equipment; Land acquisition; Emergency funds; Program development; Conferences/seminars; Professorships; Publication; Seed money; Curriculum development; Fellowships; Research; Technical assistance; Consulting services; Program evaluation; In-kind gifts; Matching/challenge support.
Limitations: Applications not accepted. Giving in the U.S. No support for partisan efforts, in general or religious organizations. No grants to individuals, or for endowments, in general, and bricks and mortar campaigns.
Publications: Grants list; Multi-year report; Newsletter; IRS Form 990 or 990-PF printed copy available upon request.
Application information: Unsolicited applications are not accepted. Proposals are by invitation only. In order to best leverage resources, the foundation is planning to spend its entire endowment base by 2017.
Board meeting date(s): Winter, spring, summer, and fall (dates determined yearly)
Officers and Directors:* Erik M. Hanisch, Chair. and Pres.; Lenore M. Hanisch,* Co-Exec. Dir.; June Wilson,* Co-Exec. Dir.
Number of staff: 2 full-time professional; 1 full-time support.
EIN: 391916960
Selected grants: The following grants are a representative sample of this grantmaker's funding activity:
$187,500 to Proteus Fund, Amherst, MA, 2012. For Media Democracy Fund.
$100,000 to Tides Center, San Francisco, CA, 2012. For Center for Social Inclusion and Epip.
$50,000 to Third Sector New England, Boston, MA, 2012. For resource generation.
$10,000 to PCC Farmland Trust, Seattle, WA, 2012. For Project: Capacity Building.

9708
Raikes Foundation ✧
2157 N. Northlake Way, Ste. 220
Seattle, WA 98103-9184 (206) 484-8855
Contact: Erin Kahn, Dir.
E-mail: info@raikesfoundation.org; E-mail for Erin Kahn: erin@raikesfoundation.org; Main URL: http://www.raikesfoundation.org

Established in 2002 in WA.
Donors: Jeffrey S. Raikes; Patricia M. Raikes.
Foundation type: Independent foundation.
Financial data (yr. ended 12/31/12): Assets, $122,079,628 (M); gifts received, $1,055,498; expenditures, $8,037,109; qualifying distributions, $7,599,833; giving activities include $6,002,370 for 137 grants (high: $1,000,000; low: $150).
Purpose and activities: Giving to empower young people to transform their lives.
Fields of interest: Higher education; Education; Youth development; Human services; Children/youth, services; Children/youth; Children; Youth; Minorities; Economically disadvantaged; Homeless.
Type of support: Continuing support; General/operating support; Matching/challenge support; Program development; Program evaluation.
Limitations: Giving on a national basis for the Student Agency Initiative; giving in WA for Youth and Program Quality Initiative; and giving in King County, WA for the Youth and Young Adult Homelessness Initiative. No support for religious organizations, or for organizations in the midst of a leadership transition. No grants to individuals, or for debt reduction.
Publications: Grants list.
Application information: Grants for the foundation's Student Agency Initiative and Youth and Young Adult Homelessness Initiative are by invitation only. Please see foundation web site for application policies and guidelines. Grants for the Youth Program Quality Initiative are facilitated by School's Out Washington and application deadlines are posted on their web site.
Copies of proposal: 1
Trustees: J.J. Leary, Jr.; Jeffrey S. Raikes; Patricia M. Raikes.
Director: Erin Kahn.
Number of staff: 5 full-time professional; 2 full-time support.
EIN: 912173492
Selected grants: The following grants are a representative sample of this grantmaker's funding activity:
$750,000 to United Way of King County, Seattle, WA, 2012. For regional efforts to prevent Youth and Young Adult Homelessness.
$691,953 to University of Texas, Department of Psychology, Austin, TX, 2013. For research to study how certain educational practice can enhance how middle school students construe the purpose and relevance of learning.
$570,000 to Carnegie Foundation for the Advancement of Teaching, Stanford, CA, 2013. For the planning and pilot of a national networked improvement community to design, refine and implement mindsets and learning strategies interventions at different transition points in the learning spectrum.
$500,000 to University of Nebraska Foundation, Lincoln Office, Lincoln, NE, 2013. For Raikes School of Computer Science and Management.
$307,968 to School's Out Washington, Seattle, WA, 2013. For leadership of the Youth Program Quality Initiative in Washington state.
$250,000 to University of Chicago, Chicago, IL, 2013. For Consortium on Chicago School Research to build teacher capacity to support students in becoming effective learners.
$178,689 to Harvard College Fund, Cambridge, MA, 2013. For analysis of Tripod Survey Data to understand practices that build student agency.
$170,000 to Greater Tacoma Community Foundation, Tacoma, WA, 2013. For management of the Youth Program Quality Initiative in Pierce County.
$25,000 to Forum for Youth Investment, David P. Weikart Center for Youth Program Quality, Washington, DC, 2012. For research to analyze out-of-school time program quality benchmarks.
$20,000 to Boys and Girls Clubs of King County, Seattle, WA, 2013. For scale up use of the Youth Program Quality Initiative across all programs.

9709
James D. and Sherry Raisbeck Foundation Trust ✧
7536 Seward Park Ave. S.
Seattle, WA 98118-4247
Main URL: http://www.raisbeck.com/about/raisbeckfoundation

Established in 1999 in WA.
Donors: James D. Raisbeck; Sherry L. Raisbeck.
Foundation type: Company-sponsored foundation.
Financial data (yr. ended 12/31/12): Assets, $27,283,556 (M); expenditures, $1,626,177; qualifying distributions, $1,535,028; giving activities include $1,527,988 for 12 grants (high: $1,459,750; low: $778).
Fields of interest: Arts; Human services; United Ways and Federated Giving Programs.
Limitations: Applications not accepted. Giving primarily in Seattle, WA. No grants to individuals.
Application information: Contributes only to pre-selected organizations.
Trustees: James D. Raisbeck; Sherry L. Raisbeck.
EIN: 916478077

9710
Raven Trust Fund ✧
999 3rd Ave., Ste. 3400
Seattle, WA 98104-1053

Established in 1997 in WA.
Donors: John Standford Endowment; Tom A. Alberg.
Foundation type: Independent foundation.
Financial data (yr. ended 12/31/13): Assets, $25,951,443 (M); expenditures, $1,304,876; qualifying distributions, $1,168,322; giving activities include $1,124,987 for 75 grants (high: $690,000; low: $17).
Purpose and activities: Giving for the arts, education, and environmental conservation.
Fields of interest: Arts; Higher education; Education; Environment; Health organizations, association; Human services; Children/youth, services.
Limitations: Applications not accepted. Giving primarily in Seattle, WA. No grants to individuals.
Application information: Contributes only to pre-selected organizations.
Officers and Trustee:* Tom A. Alberg, Pres. and Treas.; Judith Beck,* V.P. and Secy.
EIN: 911816037

9711
Raynier Institute & Foundation ✧
1425 Broadway, No. 10
Seattle, WA 98122-3854 (206) 384-6736
Contact: Jeff Hauser, Exec. Dir.
FAX: (206) 342-9593; E-mail: jhauser@raynier.org; Main URL: http://www.raynier.org

Established in 1994 in WA.
Donor: James Widener Ray†.
Foundation type: Independent foundation.
Financial data (yr. ended 12/31/12): Assets, $81,668,856 (M); expenditures, $3,391,364; qualifying distributions, $2,958,500; giving activities include $2,958,500 for grants.
Purpose and activities: The foundation's mission is to fund causes of a charitable nature that will carry out projects and programs of high merit for the betterment of humanity, particularly in the areas of animal welfare, arts and culture, education, the environment, health care and human services.
Fields of interest: Arts; Environment, natural resources; Environment; Animals/wildlife, preservation/protection; Health care; Human services.
Limitations: Applications not accepted. Giving primarily in PA and WA. No grants to individuals.
Publications: Grants list; IRS Form 990 or 990-PF printed copy available upon request.

Application information: Contributes only to pre-selected organizations.
Officers and Directors:* Michael Valucci,* Pres.; Bradford Trenary,* V.P.; Robert Warth,* Secy.; Edward D. Gardner,* Treas.; Jeff Hauser, Mgr.
EIN: 911644205
Selected grants: The following grants are a representative sample of this grantmaker's funding activity:
$25,000 to Handmaids of the Sacred Heart of Jesus, Haverford, PA, 2011.
$25,000 to Urban League of Philadelphia, Philadelphia, PA, 2011.

9712
RealNetworks Foundation ✧
2601 Elliot Ave.
Seattle, WA 98121-1399 (866) 604-5477
E-mail: realgrants@easymatch.com; Main URL: http://www.realnetworks.com/realnetworks-foundation/
Grants List: http://www.realnetworks.com/realnetworks-foundation/2011-grant-recipients.aspx
The RealNetworks Blog: http://www.realnetworks.com/blog/?tag=realnetworks-foundation

Established in 2000 in WA.
Donor: RealNetworks, Inc.
Foundation type: Company-sponsored foundation.
Financial data (yr. ended 12/31/13): Assets, $16,603,301 (M); expenditures, $1,511,719; qualifying distributions, $1,398,474; giving activities include $1,209,590 for 124 grants (high: $32,504; low: $1,000).
Purpose and activities: The foundation supports programs designed to enhance the quality of life in areas of company operations; and enable alternative voices or foster the right of free speech throughout the world.
Fields of interest: Arts; Education; Environment, climate change/global warming; Environment; Employment, services; Employment, training; Employment; Human services; Civil liberties, first amendment; Civil/human rights; Community/economic development; Public affairs; Economically disadvantaged.
Type of support: Continuing support; Program development; Employee volunteer services; Employee matching gifts.
Limitations: Applications accepted. Giving primarily in areas of company operations for Community Enhancement Grants, with emphasis on San Francisco, CA (Bay Area), New York, NY, Reston, VA (Metro D.C.), and Seattle, WA (Puget Sound Region). No support for religious or membership-based organizations unless the program is open to the public without regard to affiliation; discriminatory organizations, organizations designated under Section 509 of the U.S. Internal Revenue Service code, K-12 schools, youth groups, clubs, teams, choirs, bands, or PTSA. No grants to individuals, or for capital campaigns, general operating funds, endowments, or event or conference sponsorships.
Publications: Application guidelines; Grants list.
Application information: Application form required.
Initial approach: Complete online eligibility quiz and application
Deadline(s): May 1 and Oct. 1
Officers: Robert Glaser, Pres. and Treas.; Sid Ferrales, V.P.; Michael Paraham, Secy.
EIN: 912033075

9713
The REI Foundation ✧
P.O. Box 1938
Sumner, WA 98390-0800
Main URL: http://www.rei.com/stewardship/report/community/rei-foundation.html

Established in 1993 in WA.
Donor: Recreational Equipment Inc.
Foundation type: Company-sponsored foundation.
Financial data (yr. ended 12/31/13): Assets, $11,222,730 (M); gifts received, $2,585; expenditures, $526,647; qualifying distributions, $475,243; giving activities include $462,500 for 4 grants (high: $167,500; low: $50,000).
Purpose and activities: The foundation supports programs designed to ensure that tomorrow's outdoor enthusiasts and conservation stewards reflect the diversity of America.
Fields of interest: Environment, natural resources; Environment, land resources; Recreation; American Red Cross; YM/YWCAs & YM/YWHAs; Youth, services.
Type of support: General/operating support.
Limitations: Applications not accepted. Giving primarily in CA.
Application information: Contributes only to pre-selected organizations.
Officers and Directors:* Michael Collins, Pres.; Kevin Hagen,* V.P.; David Jayo, V.P.; Catherine Walker, Secy.; Rick Palmer, Treas.; Marc Berejka; Anne Farrell; Sally Jewell; Jerry Stritzke; Laura Swapp.
EIN: 911577992

9714
Satya and Rao Remala Foundation ✧
c/o Smith Sunday Berman Britton
11808 Northup Way, Ste. 240
Bellevue, WA 98005-1936

Established in 1998 in WA.
Donors: Rao V. Remala; Satya K. Remala.
Foundation type: Independent foundation.
Financial data (yr. ended 12/31/13): Assets, $11,692,021 (M); gifts received, $339,100; expenditures, $546,011; qualifying distributions, $448,716; giving activities include $439,834 for 65 grants (high: $201,000; low: $65).
Fields of interest: Elementary/secondary education; Higher education; Human services; United Ways and Federated Giving Programs; Philanthropy/voluntarism; Hinduism.
Type of support: General/operating support.
Limitations: Applications not accepted. Giving primarily in WA. No grants to individuals.
Application information: Contributes only to pre-selected organizations.
Trustees: Rao V. Remala; Satya K. Remala.
EIN: 916477106
Selected grants: The following grants are a representative sample of this grantmaker's funding activity:
$300,000 to Carnegie Mellon University, Pittsburgh, PA, 2012. For Sciences Research and Education.
$26,560 to United Way of King County, Seattle, WA, 2012. To Enhance the Ability for People to Support Each Other.
$25,830 to Fred Hutchinson Cancer Research Center, Seattle, WA, 2012. For Research, Prevention, Detection and of Cancer.
$15,000 to Pratham USA, Houston, TX, 2012. To Under Privileged Children.
$10,710 to Powerful Schools, Seattle, WA, 2012. For Literacy, Arts, After-School and Leadership.
$5,000 to Literacy Bridge, Seattle, WA, 2012. To Connect Poor, Rural Communities with the Vital Knowledge They Need to Improve Their Lives.
$2,300 to University of Washington Foundation, Seattle, WA, 2012. For Computer Science Scholarships and Engineering.
$500 to Rainier Scholars, Seattle, WA, 2012. For Opportunities for Education Success.
$250 to Alliance for Education, Seattle, WA, 2012. To Ensure Every Child in Seattle Public Schools Is Prepared for Success.
$250 to Hope Heart Institute, Bellevue, WA, 2012. For Research, Diagnosis and Treatment of Heart Disease.

9715
Renton Community Foundation ✧
1101 Bronson Way N.
P.O. Box 820
Renton, WA 98057 (425) 282-5199
Contact: Lynn Bohart, Exec. Dir.
FAX: (425) 282-5889;
E-mail: lbohart@rentonfoundation.org; Main URL: http://www.rentonfoundation.org
E-Newsletter: http://www.rentonfoundation.org/e-connections-newsletter.html
YouTube: http://www.youtube.com/user/rentonfoundation?feature=watch

Established in 1999 in WA.
Foundation type: Community foundation.
Financial data (yr. ended 12/31/13): Assets, $7,503,186 (M); gifts received, $805,069; expenditures, $699,803; giving activities include $543,979 for 4+* grants (high: $216,067).
Purpose and activities: The foundation manages a group of individual charitable funds for a broad array of community services such as the arts, health care, pet care, education, emergency services and more.
Fields of interest: Arts education; Museums; Performing arts; Historic preservation/historical societies; Arts; Education, early childhood education; Child development, education; Adult/continuing education; Adult education—literacy, basic skills & GED; Education, continuing education; Education; Environment; Animals/wildlife; Health care; Mental health, counseling/support groups; Crime/violence prevention, domestic violence; Crime/violence prevention, child abuse; Food banks; Housing/shelter; Disasters, fire prevention/control; Safety/disasters; Recreation; Youth development; Neighborhood centers; Children, services; Residential/custodial care, hospices; Aging, centers/services; Homeless, human services; Human services; Community/economic development.
Type of support: Equipment; Building/renovation; General/operating support; Continuing support; Endowments; Program development; Scholarship funds.
Limitations: Applications accepted. Giving primarily in greater Renton, WA, area.
Publications: Annual report; Grants list; Newsletter.
Application information: Visit foundation web site for application forms and guidelines. Application form required.
Initial approach: Telephone
Copies of proposal: 2
Deadline(s): Varies
Officers and Directors:* Rich Wagner,* Pres.; Gene Sens,* V.P.; Marlene Winter,* Secy.; Vicki Faull,*

Treas.; Lynn Bohart, Exec. Dir.; Karyn Beckley; Kim Browne; Robert Cugini; Mark Gropper; Steve Hanson; J. Michael Hardy, D.D.S.; Dave Kroeger; Jim Medzegian; Marilyn Milne; Valerie O'Halloran; Vicky Persson; Jim Poff; Brian Quint; Bob Raphael; Dr. Merri Rieger; Judi Schafer; Lynn Wallace.
Number of staff: 1 full-time professional.
EIN: 237069988

9716
Rice Family Foundation ✧
c/o Carol R. Bowditch
620 N.E. Vineyard Ln., No. B304
Bainbridge Island, WA 98110-2431

Established in 1986 in IL.
Donor: Arthur L. Rice, Jr.†.
Foundation type: Independent foundation.
Financial data (yr. ended 11/30/13): Assets, $10,057,605 (M); expenditures, $467,672; qualifying distributions, $460,267; giving activities include $460,000 for 56 grants (high: $47,000; low: $1,000).
Fields of interest: Arts, alliance/advocacy; Humanities; Arts; Higher education; Education; Environment, natural resources; Health care; Health organizations, association; United Ways and Federated Giving Programs; Protestant agencies & churches.
Limitations: Applications not accepted. Giving primarily in, but not limited to IL, MN, and WI. No grants to individuals.
Application information: Contributes only to pre-selected organizations.
Directors: Carol R. Bowditch; James A. Bowditch; Emily R. Douglass; John P. Douglass; Arthur Rice; Lynn D. Rice.
Number of staff: None.
EIN: 363529826

9717
M. Valeria Richardson Irrevocable Trust ✧
c/o Wells Fargo Bank, N.A.
P.O. Box 21927
Seattle, WA 98111-3927
Application addresses: University of Wyoming, 1000 E. University Ave., Laramie, WY 82071, tel.: (307) 766-1121; Casper College, 125 College Dr., Casper, WY 82601, tel.: (307) 268-2713

Established in WY.
Foundation type: Independent foundation.
Financial data (yr. ended 06/30/13): Assets, $26,327,148 (M); expenditures, $1,235,407; qualifying distributions, $1,135,561; giving activities include $1,052,370 for 2 grants (high: $679,512; low: $372,858).
Fields of interest: Higher education.
Limitations: Applications accepted. Giving primarily in Casper and Laramie, WY.
Application information: Application form required.
Initial approach: Letter
Deadline(s): None
Trustee: Wells Fargo Private Client Services.
EIN: 836003603

9718
Riverstyx Foundation ✧
c/o VWC
10510 Northrup Way, Ste. 300
Kirkland, WA 98033-7928
Main URL: http://www.riverstyxfoundation.org

Established in 2000 in WA.
Donors: James L. Swift; Lauren Swift; Marilyn S. Tennity; MSST Foundation.
Foundation type: Independent foundation.
Financial data (yr. ended 12/31/12): Assets, $30,137,711 (M); gifts received, $750,468; expenditures, $1,999,218; qualifying distributions, $1,736,054; giving activities include $1,703,481 for grants (high: $200,000; low: $2,000).
Fields of interest: Arts; Education; Foundations (community).
Limitations: Applications not accepted. Giving primarily in WA. No grants to individuals.
Application information: Contributes only to pre-selected organizations.
Officers: James L. Swift, Pres.; T. Cody Swift, V.P.; Steven Brinn, Secy.; Don R. Carlin, Treas.
EIN: 943373712
Selected grants: The following grants are a representative sample of this grantmaker's funding activity:
$5,000 to Ohio Campus Compact, Granville, OH, 2012. For Public Charity Donation.

9719
Roma Charitable Foundation ✧
1711 W. Nickerson St., Ste. A
Seattle, WA 98119

Established in 1991 in WA.
Donor: Ray O'Leary†.
Foundation type: Independent foundation.
Financial data (yr. ended 11/30/13): Assets, $22,605,779 (M); expenditures, $1,464,934; qualifying distributions, $1,109,704; giving activities include $1,100,000 for 23 grants (high: $150,000; low: $5,000).
Fields of interest: Health organizations; Human services; Children/youth, services; Family services; Blind/visually impaired.
Limitations: Applications not accepted. Giving primarily in OR and WA. No grants to individuals.
Application information: Unsolicited requests for funds not accepted.
Officers: Robert Berry, Pres.; Lawrence Podnar, V.P.; Carmen Angiuli, Secy.-Treas.
EIN: 943142398

9720
Roots and Wings ✧ ☆
816 35th Ave.
Seattle, WA 98122-5234

Established in 2006 in WA.
Donors: Michael T. Galgon; Gretl Dupre Galgon.
Foundation type: Independent foundation.
Financial data (yr. ended 12/31/12): Assets, $14,761,736 (M); gifts received, $37,531; expenditures, $907,830; qualifying distributions, $747,000; giving activities include $747,000 for grants.
Fields of interest: Education; Philanthropy/ voluntarism, management/technical assistance; Public affairs, finance; Financial services.
Limitations: Applications not accepted. Giving primarily in OH and WA. No grants to individuals.
Application information: Unsolicited requests for funds not accepted.
Directors: Gretl Dupre Galgon; Michael T. Galgon.
EIN: 203885457

9721
The Robert P. Rotella Foundation ✧
800 Bellevue Way N.E., Ste. 200
Bellevue, WA 98004-4229

Established in 2002 in IL.
Donors: Robert P. Rotella; Rosemarie C. Rotella; Christopher Aquino.
Foundation type: Independent foundation.
Financial data (yr. ended 12/31/13): Assets, $9,425,640 (M); expenditures, $539,220; qualifying distributions, $493,417; giving activities include $464,917 for 50 grants (high: $50,000; low: $100).
Fields of interest: Environment; Animal welfare; Animals/wildlife, preservation/protection; Human services; Children, services; Public affairs, research; Public policy, research.
Limitations: Applications not accepted. Giving in the U.S., with emphasis on CA and Washington, DC.
Application information: Unsolicited requests for funds not accepted.
Trustees: Robert P. Rotella; Rosemarie C. Rotella.
EIN: 616295351

9722
The Russell Family Foundation ✧
P.O. Box 2567
Gig Harbor, WA 98335-4567 (253) 858-5050
Contact: Linsey Sauer, Grants Mgr.
FAX: (253) 851-0460; E-mail: info@trff.org; Toll Free tel.: (888) 252-4331; Main URL: http://trff.org

Established in 1994 in WA.
Donors: George F. Russell, Jr.; Jane T. Russell†.
Foundation type: Independent foundation.
Financial data (yr. ended 12/31/12): Assets, $135,271,084 (M); expenditures, $5,575,808; giving activities include $4,842,535 for 163 grants (high: $1,000,000; low: $20), $97,200 for 10 grants to individuals, and $19,133 for 46 employee matching gifts.
Purpose and activities: The foundation invests in resources and relationships in grassroots leaders, environmental sustainability and global peace.
Fields of interest: Environment.
Type of support: Mission-related investments/ loans; General/operating support; Program development; Fellowships; Program-related investments/loans; Employee matching gifts; Grants to individuals.
Limitations: Applications accepted. Giving primarily in the Puget Sound region of WA. No support for lobbying, city or county government programs, work on water quantity or water rights, watershed planning, or corporate development of new products or services, energy-related programs or for land use planning. No grants for capital construction or purchases of land.
Publications: Application guidelines; Financial statement; Newsletter.
Application information: Full proposals are accepted by invitation only. Application form required.

Initial approach: Online letter of inquiry
Copies of proposal: 1
Deadline(s): See foundation web site for current deadlines
Board meeting date(s): Quarterly; grants awarded in May and Nov/Dec.
Final notification: Following board meeting

Officers and Directors:* Richard Woo, C.E.O.; Phyllis Gill,* Pres.; Dion Rurik,* Secy.; Tim Cavanaugh, Treas.; Sarah Cavanaugh; Hubert Locke; Eric Russell; Jileen Russell; Richard Russell; Zac Russell; Yvonne Sanchez.
Number of staff: 5 full-time professional; 1 part-time professional.
EIN: 911663336
Selected grants: The following grants are a representative sample of this grantmaker's funding activity:
$1,000,000 to National Bureau of Asian Research, Seattle, WA, 2011. For general operating support.
$1,000,000 to National Bureau of Asian Research, Seattle, WA, 2012. For General Operating Support.
$400,000 to Boys and Girls Clubs of South Puget Sound, Tacoma, WA, 2011. For Gig Harbor HOPE Center.
$300,000 to Franciscan Foundation, Tacoma, WA, 2011. For St. Anthony Hospital Capital Campaign for the Jane Thompson Russell Cancer Care Center.
$246,202 to Vanguard Charitable Endowment Program, Boston, MA, 2011. For MG Fund.
$246,202 to Vanguard Charitable Endowment Program, Boston, MA, 2011. For MG Fund.
$200,000 to Mary Bridge Childrens Foundation, Tacoma, WA, 2012. For Emergency Services Campaign.
$150,000 to Forterra, Seattle, WA, 2011. For Cascade Agenda Campaign.
$150,000 to Mary Bridge Childrens Foundation, Tacoma, WA, 2011. For Emergency Services Campaign.
$150,000 to Multicare Health Foundation, Tacoma, WA, 2011. For Emergency Services Campaign.
$150,000 to Washington State University Foundation, Pullman, WA, 2012. For Field Evaluations of Low Impact Development Techniques for Cleaning Polluted Run-off.
$117,900 to North Carolina State Engineering Foundation, Raleigh, NC, 2012. For Research Advancing the Field of Nuclear Waste Transmutation and Fuel Cycle Technologies.
$50,000 to Pacific Lutheran University, Tacoma, WA, 2012. For Loren and MaryAnn Anderson Wang Center Student-Faculty Research Fund.
$50,000 to Pacific Lutheran University, Tacoma, WA, 2012. For Loren and MaryAnn Anderson Wang Center Student-Faculty Research Fund.
$50,000 to United Way of Pierce County, Tacoma, WA, 2012. For The Rescue Mission.
$40,000 to CERES, Boston, MA, 2011. For Financing Sustainable Water Systems.
$30,000 to IslandWood, Bainbridge Island, WA, 2012. For Homewaters.
$10,000 to University of Washington Foundation, Seattle, WA, 2012. For Harborview Fund for the Greatest Need.
$5,000 to National Center for Family Philanthropy, Washington, DC, 2011. For general operating support.
$5,000 to Tacoma Community House, Tacoma, WA, 2012. For Read2Me support for 2011 and 2012.

9723
Safeco Insurance Fund ✧
1001 4th Ave., Safeco Plaza, Ste. 1800
Seattle, WA 98154-1117 (206) 473-5745
Contact: Paul Hollie, Fdn. Dir.
E-mail: Safeco.Foundation@libertymutual.com; Main URL: http://www.safeco.com/about-safeco/community/foundation

Established in 2006 in WA.
Donors: Safeco Corp.; Safeco Insurance Co.
Foundation type: Company-sponsored foundation.
Financial data (yr. ended 12/31/12): Assets, $56,927,367 (M); expenditures, $3,260,417; qualifying distributions, $3,100,025; giving activities include $3,100,000 for 682 grants (high: $200,000; low: $3).
Purpose and activities: The foundation supports nonprofit organizations involved with arts and culture, hunger, human services, youth, the disabled, economically disadvantaged people, and the homeless. Special emphasis is directed toward programs designed to promote education and health and safety.
Fields of interest: Performing arts; Arts; Elementary school/education; Vocational education; Libraries (public); Education, services; Education, reading; Education; Health care, clinics/centers; Health care; Food services; Safety/disasters; YM/YWCAs & YM/YWHAs; Family services; Developmentally disabled, centers & services; Homeless, human services; Human services; United Ways and Federated Giving Programs; Youth; Disabilities, people with; Economically disadvantaged; Homeless.
Type of support: Curriculum development; General/operating support; Continuing support; Capital campaigns; Program development; Employee matching gifts.
Limitations: Applications accepted. Giving primarily in areas of company operations OR and WA. No support for grantmaking agencies, fraternal, social, labor, or political organizations. No grants to individuals, or for sectarian activities, trips, tours, or transportation, deficit spending or debt liquidation, conferences, forums, or special events.
Publications: Application guidelines; Grants list; Program policy statement.
Application information: Visit website for Education Initiative and Basic Services Initiative Request for Proposals (RFP) announcement. Support is limited to 1 contribution per organization during any given year. Application form required.
Initial approach: Complete online application
Deadline(s): None
Final notification: 10 weeks

Officers and Directors:* David H. Long,* Chair.; Michael H. Hughes,* Pres.; Dexter K. Legg, V.P. and Secy.; Dennis J. Langwell,* V.P., C.F.O., and Treas.; A. Alexander Fontanes,* V.P. and C.I.O.; Christopher C. Mansfield,* V.P. and Genl. Counsel; Melissa M. MacDonnell, V.P.; Gary J. Ostrow, V.P.; Mathew D. Nickerson.
EIN: 204894146

9724
Sahsen Foundation ✧
1420 5th Ave., No. 4100
Seattle, WA 98101-2375
Main URL: http://www.sahsen.org/

Donors: Christine White; Bryan White.
Foundation type: Independent foundation.
Financial data (yr. ended 12/31/13): Assets, $17,662,298 (M); gifts received, $2,751,678; expenditures, $869,588; qualifying distributions, $855,470; giving activities include $850,000 for 1 grant.
Fields of interest: Community/economic development.
Type of support: General/operating support.
Limitations: Applications not accepted. Giving primarily in MA.
Application information: Unsolicited requests for funds not accepted.
Officers and Directors:* Christine White,* Pres.; Bryan White,* Secy.-Treas.
EIN: 271420373

9725
Samis Foundation ✧
208 James St., Ste. C
Seattle, WA 98104-2220 (206) 622-3363
Contact: Eddie I. Hasson, Co-Chair.
FAX: (206) 622-4918; E-mail: samis@samis.com; Main URL: http://www.samis.com/foundation/index.html

Established in 1979.
Donor: Samuel Israel.
Foundation type: Independent foundation.
Financial data (yr. ended 12/31/13): Assets, $128,389,743 (M); expenditures, $10,564,395; qualifying distributions, $4,647,135; giving activities include $4,206,127 for 18+ grants (high: $824,090).
Purpose and activities: Giving primarily for Jewish day schools, Jewish overnight camps and Israel experiences for students in WA, with a focus on grades K-12.
Fields of interest: Education; Jewish agencies & synagogues; Religion.
International interests: Israel.
Type of support: General/operating support; Continuing support; Building/renovation; Emergency funds; Program development; Publication; Seed money; Scholarship funds; Research; Technical assistance; Exchange programs; Matching/challenge support.
Limitations: Applications not accepted. Giving primarily in WA and Israel. No grants to individuals.
Publications: Grants list.
Application information: Contributes only to pre-selected organizations.
Board meeting date(s): Quarterly

Officers and Directors:* Eddie I. Hasson,* Co-Chair. and Pres.; Albert S. Maimon,* Co-Chair. and V.P.; Irwin L. Treiger,* Secy.; Rob Toren, Exec. Dir.; Morris Piha, Tr. Emeritus; Victor D. Alhadeff; Eli J. Almo; David Azose; Dana Behar; Jerome O. Cohen; David A. Ellenhorm; Barry D. Ernstoff; Eli Genauer; Connie Kanter; Lucy Pruzan; Ernest Sherman; Alex Sytman; Rabbi David Twersky.
Number of staff: 2 full-time professional; 1 part-time professional; 1 full-time support.
EIN: 911641746

9726

San Juan Island Community Foundation ✧
P.O. Box 1352
Friday Harbor, WA 98250-1352 (360) 378-1001
E-mail: info@sjicf.org; Additional e-mail: grants@sjicf.org; Main URL: http://www.sjicf.org
Grants List: http://sjicf.org/category/news/recent-grants/
RSS Feed: http://www.sjicf.org/feed/
Scholarship e-mail: scholarships@sjicf.org

Established in 1994 in WA.
Donors: Barry A. Ackerley; David Bayley.
Foundation type: Community foundation.
Financial data (yr. ended 12/31/12): Assets, $8,387,321 (M); gifts received, $3,390,473; expenditures, $3,055,492; giving activities include $2,712,315 for 11+ grants (high: $2,543,694), and $130,993 for 28 grants to individuals.
Purpose and activities: The mission of the foundation is to enhance the quality of life on San Juan Island, WA, by encouraging philanthropy, growing an endowment for purposeful grants to community charitable organizations, and building partnerships that effectively connect donors with island nonprofit organizations.
Fields of interest: Arts; Education; Environment; Animals/wildlife; Health care; Children/youth, services; Human services; Community/economic development.
Type of support: Capital campaigns; Building/renovation; Scholarship funds; In-kind gifts; Matching/challenge support.
Limitations: Applications accepted. Giving limited to San Juan Island, WA. No support for religious organizations for religious purposes. No grants for operating expenses, or endowments.
Publications: Application guidelines; Annual report; Grants list; Informational brochure; Informational brochure (including application guidelines); Newsletter.
Application information: Visit foundation web site for application Cover Sheet and guidelines. Application form required.
Initial approach: Letter or telephone
Copies of proposal: 1
Deadline(s): Apr. 28, July 22, Oct. 27
Board meeting date(s): Quarterly, varies
Final notification: 6 weeks
Officers and Directors:* Charles Anderson,* Chair.; Lauren Levinson,* Vice-Chair.; Barbara Cable,* Secy.; Barbara Von Gehr,* Treas.; Susan Matthews, Exec. Dir.; Jim Barnhart; Scott Boden; Tom Cable; Maude Cumming; Jan Cyre; Peg Gerlock; Pamela Gross; Rebecca Pohlad.
Number of staff: 1 full-time professional.
EIN: 911648730

9727

Herman & Faye Sarkowsky Charitable Foundation ✧
(formerly Sarkowsky Family Charitable Foundation)
1201 3rd Ave., Ste. 5450
Seattle, WA 98101-3018

Established in 1991 in WA.
Donors: Herman Sarkowsky; Faye Sarkowsky.
Foundation type: Independent foundation.
Financial data (yr. ended 12/31/12): Assets, $1,007,859 (M); gifts received, $8,763; expenditures, $661,681; qualifying distributions, $655,307; giving activities include $654,907 for 45 grants (high: $200,000; low: $50).
Purpose and activities: Giving primarily for the arts and Jewish organizations.
Fields of interest: Museums (art); Performing arts; Arts; United Ways and Federated Giving Programs; Jewish federated giving programs; Jewish agencies & synagogues.
Limitations: Applications not accepted. Giving primarily in WA. No grants to individuals.
Application information: Contributes only to pre-selected organizations.
Officers: Faye Sarkowsky, Pres.; Herman Sarkowsky, V.P. and Treas.; Cathy Sarkowsky, V.P.; Steve Sarkowsky, V.P.; Louis Treiger, Secy.
EIN: 911479527
Selected grants: The following grants are a representative sample of this grantmaker's funding activity:
$200,000 to United Way of King County, Seattle, WA, 2010. For general support.
$200,000 to University of Washington Foundation, Seattle, WA, 2011. For general support.
$85,500 to Seattle Art Museum, Seattle, WA, 2011. For general support.
$58,000 to Jewish Federation of Greater Seattle, Seattle, WA, 2011. For general support.
$45,000 to Union for Reform Judaism, New York, NY, 2011. For general support.
$43,430 to Palm Springs Art Museum, Palm Springs, CA, 2011. For general support.
$27,850 to Temple De Hirsch Sinai, Seattle, WA, 2010. For general support.
$25,600 to Seattle Symphony Orchestra, Seattle, WA, 2011. For general support.
$15,000 to Seattle Opera, Seattle, WA, 2011. For general support.
$10,150 to Cancer Lifeline of King County, Seattle, WA, 2010. For general support.
$10,000 to FareStart, Seattle, WA, 2010. For general support.
$5,530 to Friends of the Cultural Center, Palm Desert, CA, 2011. For general support.
$3,000 to Washington State Holocaust Education Resource Center, Seattle, WA, 2011. For general support.
$1,900 to Oregon Health and Science University Foundation, Portland, OR, 2011. For general support.

9728

Satterberg Foundation ✧ ☆
825 Securities Bldg.
1904 3rd Ave.
Seattle, WA 98101-1126 (206) 441-3045
Contact: Peter F. Helsell, Treas.
FAX: (206) 374-9336; E-mail: info@satterberg.org; Main URL: http://www.satterberg.org
Grants List: http://www.satterberg.org/open_grants/current_grantees
Grants List: http://www.satterberg.org/capacity_building_grants/past_grantees

Established in 1990 in WA.
Donors: Virginia S. Helsell†; Judy P. Swenson; William A. Helsell†.
Foundation type: Independent foundation.
Financial data (yr. ended 12/31/13): Assets, $106,171,361 (M); gifts received, $100,668,180; expenditures, $2,592,247; qualifying distributions, $2,567,663; giving activities include $2,370,099 for 38 grants (high: $1,003,890; low: $1,750).
Purpose and activities: The mission of the foundation is to maintain and enjoy the interconnection of its family and to provide funds to non-profit organizations that enrich and support its communities.
Fields of interest: Education; Health care; Housing/shelter, development; Youth development, centers/clubs; Human services; Children/youth, services; Family services.
Type of support: Income development; Management development/capacity building.
Limitations: Applications accepted. Giving primarily in CA and WA. No support for evangelical groups. No grants to individuals.
Application information: Application guidelines for capacity-building only, may be obtained by writing to the foundation or from the web site. Application form required.
Initial approach: Letter or e-mail
Copies of proposal: 1
Deadline(s): Available on request
Board meeting date(s): Quarterly
Final notification: Quarterly
Officers and Directors:* Ben Lazarus,* Pres.; Katherine Lazarus, Secy.; Peter F. Helsell,* Treas.; Mary Pigott,* Exec. Dir.; Frank P. Helsell; J. David Lazarus; Mashanda Lazarus; Judy Pigott; Michael J. Pigott; Amy Shamah.
Trustee: Bank of America, N.A.
EIN: 911501066
Selected grants: The following grants are a representative sample of this grantmaker's funding activity:
$20,000 to Legal Voice, Seattle, WA, 2012. For Open Grant - Advancing Justice for Women.
$15,000 to Stonewall Youth, Olympia, WA, 2012. For Open Grant - General Operating Support.
$10,000 to Investigatewest, Seattle, WA, 2012. For Open Grant - Aging Out of Foster Care Series.
$7,500 to American Friends Service Committee, Seattle, WA, 2012. For Open Grant - Capacity Building.
$5,000 to Coyote Foundation, Port Hadlock, WA, 2012. For Invitational Grant - Operating Support.
$5,000 to Express Advantage, Seattle, WA, 2012. For Invitational Grant.
$5,000 to Puget Sound SAGE, Seattle, WA, 2012. For Open Grant - Puget Sound Transit Equity Project.
$5,000 to San Diego River Park Foundation, San Diego, CA, 2012. For Capacity Building Award - Consultant/Planning.
$4,500 to Seattle JazzED, Seattle, WA, 2012. For capacity building award.
$4,000 to WestSide Baby, Seattle, WA, 2012. For Invitational Grant -Community Collect/Distribute.

9729

Scan Design By Inge & Jens Bruun Foundation ✧
c/o Mary DeLorme, Grants and Opers. Mgr.
1001 4th Ave., Ste. 4400
Seattle, WA 98154-1192
E-mail: Mary.DeLorme@scandesignfoundation.org; Additional U.S. e-mail: admin.us@scandesignfoundation.org; Danish contact: Torben Storm Nielsen, Grants and Opers. Mgr., Kuhlausvej 3, 9200 Aalborg, e-mails: tsn@stormnielsen.eu, and admin.dk@scandesignfoundation.org; Main URL: http://www.scandesignfoundation.org

Established in 2003 in WA.
Donor: Jens C. Bruun†.

Foundation type: Independent foundation.
Financial data (yr. ended 12/31/13): Assets, $42,344,104 (M); expenditures, $2,480,945; qualifying distributions, $1,607,177; giving activities include $1,300,966 for 21 grants (high: $200,000; low: $500).
Purpose and activities: Giving primarily to promote Danish-American relations; giving also for medical research, particularly pain research, as well as for education; including the funding of student exchange programs between U.S. and Danish Universities, as well as programs which send U.S. students and professors to Denmark to engage in a specialized study curriculum at a Danish University.
Fields of interest: Higher education; Medical research; International affairs, goodwill promotion; International affairs.
Limitations: Applications not accepted. Giving primarily in Seattle, WA, and Madison, WI. No grants to individuals.
Publications: Grants list.
Application information: Contributes only to pre-selected organizations.
Officers and Directors:* Mark T. Schleck,* Pres.; Robert Thompson,* Secy.-Treas.; Rob Harris; Tage Kristensen.
EIN: 680537904
Selected grants: The following grants are a representative sample of this grantmaker's funding activity:
$179,000 to University of Wisconsin Foundation, Madison, WI, 2012. For 2013-2014 fellowship program.
$165,503 to University of Washington Foundation, Seattle, WA, 2012. For 2013 Travel Study/Master Studio.
$155,000 to International Association for the Study of Pain, Seattle, WA, 2012. To support 3 Programs.
$66,000 to University of Washington Foundation, Seattle, WA, 2012. For 2014 Ma Intern Program.
$54,820 to University of Washington Foundation, Seattle, WA, 2012. For 2013 Gehl Intern Program.
$33,000 to University of Washington Foundation, Seattle, WA, 2012. For 2013 Master of Architecture Intern Program.
$32,000 to University of Wisconsin Foundation, Madison, WI, 2012. For 2012-2013 Danish Scholars Fund.
$24,000 to University of Wisconsin Foundation, Madison, WI, 2012. For Danish Scholars Fund.
$17,250 to University of Wisconsin Foundation, Madison, WI, 2012. For 2013 Summer Scholarships.
$15,900 to University of Oregon Foundation, Eugene, OR, 2012. For Sustainable Bicycle Transportation 2012 Trip.

9730
Schultz Family Foundation ✧
4209 21st Ave. W., Ste. 401
Seattle, WA 98199-1254 (206) 623-9395
Contact: Loren D. Hostek CPA, Tr.

Established in 1996 in WA.
Donors: Howard D. Schultz; Sheri K. Schultz.
Foundation type: Independent foundation.
Financial data (yr. ended 06/30/13): Assets, $52,117,140 (M); gifts received, $10,650,000; expenditures, $3,758,098; qualifying distributions, $3,748,098; giving activities include $3,716,335 for 46 grants (high: $3,039,978; low: $1,000).
Fields of interest: Education; Health organizations, association; Human services; Children/youth, services; United Ways and Federated Giving Programs; Jewish federated giving programs.
Limitations: Giving primarily in Seattle, WA. No grants to individuals.
Application information:
Initial approach: Letter
Deadline(s): None
Trustees: Loren D. Hostek; Sheri Kersch-Schultz; Mathew McCutchen; Howard D. Schultz.
EIN: 911746414

9731
The Seattle Foundation ✧
1200 5th Ave., Ste. 1300
Seattle, WA 98101-3151 (206) 622-2294
Contact: Ceil Erickson, Dir., Community Progs.
FAX: (206) 622-7673;
E-mail: info@seattlefoundation.org; Grant application e-mail: grantmaking@seattlefoundation.org; Main URL: http://www.seattlefoundation.org
Facebook: http://www.facebook.com/TheSeattleFoundation
Giving Center: http://www.seattlefoundation.org/givingcenter/Pages/default.aspx
Grants List: http://www.seattlefoundation.org/nonprofits/grantmaking/Pages/RecentGrants.aspx
Twitter: http://twitter.com/TheSeattleFdn/

Incorporated in 1946 in WA.
Foundation type: Community foundation.
Financial data (yr. ended 12/31/13): Assets, $802,875,771 (M); gifts received, $78,235,412; expenditures, $76,154,902; giving activities include $65,653,979 for grants.
Purpose and activities: The foundation seeks to foster powerful and rewarding philanthropy to make King County a stronger, more vibrant community for all.
Fields of interest: Media, film/video; Media, radio; Visual arts; Performing arts, dance; Performing arts, music; Humanities; Literature; Historic preservation/historical societies; Arts; Education, early childhood education; Adult/continuing education; Education, ESL programs; Libraries (public); Education, reading; Education; Environment, public education; Environment, air pollution; Environment, water pollution; Environment; Animals/wildlife; Health care; Mental health/crisis services; Health organizations, association; Medical research; Agriculture/food; Housing/shelter; Recreation, parks/playgrounds; Recreation; Youth development; Children/youth, services; Homeless, human services; Human services; Economic development; Community development, small businesses; Community/economic development; Public affairs.
Type of support: General/operating support; Capital campaigns; Building/renovation; Equipment; Mission-related investments/loans.
Limitations: Applications accepted. Giving limited to King County, WA. No support for religious purposes. No grants for endowment funds, debt reduction, fundraising events, fundraising feasibility projects, conferences or seminars, film or video production, publications, first year organizations, or operating expenses for public or private elementary and secondary schools, colleges, and universities.
Publications: Annual report; Financial statement; Grants list; Informational brochure; Newsletter; Program policy statement.
Application information: Seattle Foundation will no longer offer a traditional annual grantmaking program. Grants will be provided via targeted, multi-year community leadership initiatives, and programs that connect donors to King County nonprofit organizations. Visit foundation web site for more information. Application form required.
Initial approach: Telephone or e-mail
Deadline(s): Varies
Board meeting date(s): Mar., June, Sept., and Dec.
Officers and Trustees:* Ann Watson,* Chair.; Fraser Black,* Vice-Chair.; Tony Mestres,* C.E.O. and Pres.; Jared Watson, Sr. V.P.; Jane Repensek, Sr. V.P., Finance and Opers.; Michael Brown, V.P., Community Progs.; Jennifer Martin, V.P., Organizational Excellence; Fidelma McGinn, V.P., Philanthropic Svcs.; Mary Grace Roske, V.P., Mktg. and Comms.; Jeanette Lodwig,* Secy.; Pete Shimer,* Treas.; Kareen Holmquist, Cont.; Libby Armintrout; David Bley; Nathaniel T. "Buster" Brown; Martha Choe; Carolyn Corvi; Jean Enersen; Bob Flowers; Marcia Fujimoto; Joe Gaffney; Mark Gibson; Steve Hill; John Hotta; Linda Park, Ph.D.; Chris Rivera; Scott Shapiro; John Stanton; Kevin Washington; Jan Whitsitt; Tay Yoshitani; Grace T. Yuan.
Number of staff: 17 full-time professional; 1 part-time professional; 8 full-time support; 1 part-time support.
EIN: 916013536
Selected grants: The following grants are a representative sample of this grantmaker's funding activity:
$3,346,013 to Schwab Charitable Fund, San Francisco, CA, 2014. For the Judith T. Drake Donor Advised Fund.
$750,000 to Eastside Preparatory School, Kirkland, WA, 2014. For the capital campaign for the new Upper School building.
$400,000 to Hopelink, Redmond, WA, 2014. For the capital campaign.
$375,000 to Seattle Art Museum, Seattle, WA, 2014. For the Special Exhibition Fund.
$2,302 to Sightline Institute, Seattle, WA, 2014. For Stretch: $2,302.05.
$2,000 to Chorus America, Washington, DC, 2014. For general support.
$1,800 to Samuel and Althea Stroum Jewish Community Center, Mercer Island, WA, 2014. For general support.

9732
Sequoia Foundation ✧
1250 Pacific Ave., Ste. 870
Tacoma, WA 98402-4334
Contact: Amy Rose; Bickley Barich, Office Admin.
FAX: (253) 627-6249;
E-mail: grants@grantmakerconsultants.com; Main URL: http://www.sequoiafound.org/

Established in 1982 in WA.
Donors: W. John Driscoll; C. Davis Weyerhaeuser‡; F.T. Weyerhaeuser; William T. Weyerhaeuser.
Foundation type: Independent foundation.
Financial data (yr. ended 10/31/13): Assets, $32,738,979 (M); gifts received, $2,053,621; expenditures, $6,334,271; qualifying distributions, $6,072,437; giving activities include $5,665,526 for 116 grants (high: $1,000,000; low: $1,500), and $30,000 for 1 loan/program-related investment.
Purpose and activities: The foundation is committed to strengthening and enriching the quality of life in Tacoma and Pierce County, WA, and

to enhancing environmental and economic outcomes in the Pacific Northwest.
Limitations: Applications not accepted. Giving primarily in Pierce County, WA.
Application information: The foundation solicits proposals at its sole discretion. Unsolicited proposals are not considered.
Officers and Directors:* William T. Weyerhaeuser,* Pres. and Treas.; Gail T. Weyerhaeuser,* V.P.; Nicholas C. Spika, Secy.; Brian F. Boyd, Exec. Dir.; Benjamin D. Weyerhaeuser; W. Drew Weywrhaeuser.
Number of staff: None.
EIN: 911178052
Selected grants: The following grants are a representative sample of this grantmaker's funding activity:
$910,000 to Harold E. LeMay Museum, Tacoma, WA, 2011. For capital support.
$800,000 to Harold E. LeMay Museum, Tacoma, WA, 2011. For operating support.
$750,000 to University of Puget Sound, Tacoma, WA, 2011. For capital support.
$428,333 to Seattle Opera, Seattle, WA, 2011. For operating support.
$260,000 to College Success Foundation, Issaquah, WA, 2011. For operating support.
$190,000 to Tacoma Art Museum, Tacoma, WA, 2011. For operating support.
$150,000 to Stanford University, Stanford, CA, 2011. For capital support.
$90,000 to University of Puget Sound, Tacoma, WA, 2011. For operating support.
$50,000 to Beethoven, Seattle, WA, 2011. For operating support.
$20,000 to Charles Wright Academy, Tacoma, WA, 2011. For operating support.

9733
Sherwood Trust ✧
P.O. Box 1855
Walla Walla, WA 99362-0035 (509) 529-3362
Contact: George M. Edwards, Pres.

Established in 1991 in WA.
Foundation type: Independent foundation.
Financial data (yr. ended 12/31/13): Assets, $33,133,366 (M); expenditures, $1,767,542; qualifying distributions, $1,424,563; giving activities include $1,373,075 for 34 grants (high: $235,000; low: $665).
Purpose and activities: The foundation's purpose is to serve the Walla Walla Valley as a catalyst to build the community's capacity and will to achieve in appreciation of its originators, Donald and Virginia Sherwood.
Fields of interest: Performing arts; Higher education, college; Education, services; Human services; Community/economic development; Economically disadvantaged.
Type of support: Matching/challenge support; Management development/capacity building; Capital campaigns; Building/renovation; Land acquisition; Endowments; Technical assistance.
Limitations: Applications accepted. Giving limited to the Walla Walla, WA, area. No support for religious or political organizations. No grants to individuals.
Publications: Application guidelines; Program policy statement.
Application information: Application form not required.
Initial approach: Telephone or letter
Copies of proposal: 2
Deadline(s): Mar. 1
Board meeting date(s): Monthly
Final notification: 1-2 months from receipt for final approval or rejection
Officers and Directors:* Larry Mulkerin,* Chair.; George M. Edwards,* Pres.; Peggy Sanderson,* V.P.; Jean Adams; Allan Gillespie; Robert Zagelow.
Number of staff: 1 full-time support; 1 part-time support.
EIN: 916337526
Selected grants: The following grants are a representative sample of this grantmaker's funding activity:
$31,545 to Philanthropy Northwest, Seattle, WA, 2012. For Bronze Sponsor for 2012.
$2,500 to Boy Scouts of America, Blue Mount Council, Kennewick, WA, 2012. For operating award.

9734
The Jon and Mary Shirley Foundation ✧
c/o Groff Murphy Trachtenberg & Everhard
300 E. Pine St.
Seattle, WA 98122-2029

Established in 1992 in WA.
Donors: Jon A. Shirley; E. Mary L. Shirley.
Foundation type: Independent foundation.
Financial data (yr. ended 09/30/13): Assets, $38,573,681 (M); expenditures, $2,132,693; qualifying distributions, $1,849,701; giving activities include $1,847,650 for 51 grants (high: $500,000; low: $100).
Purpose and activities: Giving primarily for the arts, with emphasis on support for art museums.
Fields of interest: Museums; Museums (art); Arts; Higher education; Education; Health organizations; Human services; United Ways and Federated Giving Programs.
Type of support: General/operating support; Annual campaigns.
Limitations: Applications not accepted. Giving primarily in WA. No grants to individuals.
Application information: Contributes only to pre-selected organizations.
Directors: E. Mary L. Shirley; Jon A. Shirley.
EIN: 943163120

9735
Charles and Lisa Simonyi Fund for Arts and Sciences ✧
(formerly Charles Simonyi Fund for Arts and Sciences)
P.O. Box 85900
Seattle, WA 98145-1900 (206) 522-7000
Contact: Susan Hutchison, Exec. Dir.
E-mail: susan@simonyifund.org; Main URL: http://www.simonyifund.org/

Established in 2003 in WA.
Donor: Charles Simonyi.
Foundation type: Independent foundation.
Financial data (yr. ended 12/31/12): Assets, $3,564,830 (M); gifts received, $5,391,200; expenditures, $7,035,853; qualifying distributions, $6,941,064; giving activities include $6,341,179 for 30 grants (high: $2,050,000; low: $214).
Purpose and activities: The foundation distributes funds to worthy organizations that demonstrate excellence in the arts, sciences and education.
Fields of interest: Arts; Education; Science, public education; Science.
Limitations: Applications not accepted. Giving primarily in Seattle, WA. No grants to individuals.
Application information: Contributes only to pre-selected organizations.
Officer: Susan Hutchison, Exec. Dir.
Director: Charles Simonyi; Lisa Simonyi.
EIN: 550846712
Selected grants: The following grants are a representative sample of this grantmaker's funding activity:
$2,050,000 to Institute for Advanced Study, Princeton, NJ, 2012. For general operating support.
$1,100,000 to Seattle Art Museum, Seattle, WA, 2012. For general operating support.
$1,010,000 to Woodland Park Zoological Society, Woodland Park Zoo, Seattle, WA, 2012. For general operating support.
$525,000 to Museum of Flight, Seattle, WA, 2012. For general operating support.
$500,000 to Russian Arts Foundation, Montpelier, VT, 2012. For general operating support.
$500,000 to Saint Thomas School, Medina, WA, 2012. For general operating support.
$300,000 to Metropolitan Opera, New York, NY, 2012. For general operating support.
$80,000 to King Baudouin Foundation United States, New York, NY, 2012. For general operating support.
$54,465 to Hungarian-American Coalition, Washington, DC, 2012. For general operating support.
$52,500 to Woodrow Wilson International Center for Scholars, Washington, DC, 2012. For general operating support.

9736
The Sloan Foundation ✧
1301 5th Ave., Ste. 3000
Seattle, WA 98101-2641

Established in 1997 in WA.
Donor: Stuart M. Sloan.
Foundation type: Independent foundation.
Financial data (yr. ended 12/31/12): Assets, $13,615,002 (M); gifts received, $4,034,610; expenditures, $637,978; qualifying distributions, $635,365; giving activities include $632,750 for 13 grants (high: $450,000; low: $250).
Purpose and activities: Giving primarily for education.
Fields of interest: Education; Jewish federated giving programs.
Type of support: General/operating support.
Limitations: Applications not accepted. Giving primarily in CA and WA. No grants to individuals.
Application information: Contributes only to pre-selected organizations.
Officers: Stuart M. Sloan, Pres.; Margaret E. Weiland, Secy.
EIN: 911799087

9737
Orin Smith Family Foundation ✧
4963 N.E. 85th St.
Seattle, WA 98115-3913

Established in 2004 in WA.
Donor: Orin C. Smith.
Foundation type: Independent foundation.
Financial data (yr. ended 12/31/13): Assets, $21,047,060 (M); gifts received, $2,299,565;

expenditures, $1,157,983; qualifying distributions, $1,033,462; giving activities include $1,031,000 for 11 grants (high: $250,000; low: $4,000).
Fields of interest: Higher education; Environment; United Ways and Federated Giving Programs.
Limitations: Applications not accepted. Giving primarily in VA and WA.
Application information: Contributes only to pre-selected organizations.
Directors: Kevin Smith; Orin C. Smith.
EIN: 200477535
Selected grants: The following grants are a representative sample of this grantmaker's funding activity:
$50,000 to United Way of King County, Seattle, WA, 2012. For Seattle Foundation - Mother House Fund.

9738
Frank and Emily Smith Foundation ✧
(formerly Endesha Group)
4020 E. Madison St., Ste. 321
Seattle, WA 98112-3150

Donors: Gary Smith; Steve Radcliffe.
Foundation type: Independent foundation.
Financial data (yr. ended 11/30/13): Assets, $38,675,477 (M); gifts received, $4,000; expenditures, $2,526,283; qualifying distributions, $1,789,345; giving activities include $1,656,807 for 26 grants (high: $611,550; low: $1,000).
Fields of interest: Education; Human services; Children/youth, services; Family services; Christian agencies & churches.
Limitations: Applications not accepted. Giving in the U.S., with emphasis on OR. No grants to individuals.
Application information: Contributes only to pre-selected organizations.
Officers: Gary Smith, Pres.; Kyle Smith, V.P.; Susan Elder, Co-Exec. Dir.; Jason Johnson, Co-Exec. Dir.
EIN: 931329668

9739
Frost & Margaret Snyder Foundation ✧
c/o KeyBank, N.A., Trust Division
P.O. Box 11500, M.S. WA 31-01-0210
Tacoma, WA 98411-5052

Trust established in 1957 in WA.
Donors: Frost Snyder†; Margaret Snyder†.
Foundation type: Independent foundation.
Financial data (yr. ended 12/31/13): Assets, $13,037,651 (M); expenditures, $703,120; qualifying distributions, $650,113; giving activities include $631,350 for 11 grants (high: $169,350; low: $12,000).
Purpose and activities: Giving primarily for the promotion and advancement of the Roman Catholic church; funding also for education, including Roman Catholic education.
Fields of interest: Secondary school/education; Higher education; Education; Human services; Catholic agencies & churches.
Limitations: Applications accepted. Giving primarily in WA, particularly to religious facilities or activities within the Archdiocese of Seattle, with primary emphasis given to those in Pierce County, or which directly serve it. No grants to individuals, or for ongoing operating costs, lobbying, or for the production of books, films or videos; no loans.
Application information:
Initial approach: Letter
Deadline(s): June 1
Trustee: Andrea S. Gernon; Robert Mallon; Mary Smith; KeyBank, N.A.
EIN: 916030549
Selected grants: The following grants are a representative sample of this grantmaker's funding activity:
$105,000 to Fulcrum Foundation, Seattle, WA, 2011.
$30,000 to Saint Martins University, Lacey, WA, 2011. For scholarship.
$20,000 to Gonzaga University, Spokane, WA, 2011. For scholarship.
$1,000 to Holy Rosary School, Tacoma, WA, 2011. For scholarships.

9740
The Gordon D. Sondland and Katherine J. Durant Foundation ✧
(formerly Gordon D. Sondland Foundation)
1531 7th Ave., 20th Fl.
Seattle, WA 98101-1703
Main URL: http://www.sondlanddurant.org/

Established in 1991 in WA.
Donors: Gordon D. Sondland; Katherine Durant.
Foundation type: Independent foundation.
Financial data (yr. ended 12/31/13): Assets, $2,977 (M); gifts received, $380,250; expenditures, $455,874; qualifying distributions, $436,036; giving activities include $432,502 for 22 grants (high: $150,000; low: $500).
Fields of interest: Museums (art); Education; Health care, support services; YM/YWCAs & YM/YWHAs; Foundations (community); Jewish agencies & synagogues; Religion; Women.
Limitations: Applications not accepted. Giving primarily in OR, with emphasis on Portland. No grants to individuals.
Application information: Contributes only to pre-selected organizations.
Officer: Gordon D. Sondland, Pres.
EIN: 911534721

9741
Spark Charitable Foundation ✧ ☆
c/o Nahwatzel, LLC
P.O. Box 21866
Seattle, WA 98111-3866

Established in 2008 in WA.
Donors: Furman C. Moseley; Susan R. Moseley.
Foundation type: Independent foundation.
Financial data (yr. ended 05/31/13): Assets, $1,604,858 (M); gifts received, $309,438; expenditures, $527,448; qualifying distributions, $515,000; giving activities include $515,000 for grants.
Purpose and activities: Giving primarily for the arts, and to Episcopal churches; funding also for higher education and human services.
Fields of interest: Arts; Higher education; Human services; Science; Protestant agencies & churches.
Type of support: Capital campaigns.
Limitations: Applications not accepted. Giving primarily in WA.
Application information: Unsolicited requests for funds not accepted.
Officers: Susan R. Moseley, Pres. and Treas.; Furman C. Moseley, V.P. and Secy.
EIN: 262667609
Selected grants: The following grants are a representative sample of this grantmaker's funding activity:
$350,000 to Pacific Science Center, Seattle, WA, 2013. For the 50 for 50th Future Ready Capital Campaign.
$15,000 to Smithsonian Institution, Washington, DC, 2013. To support of the Board Annual Giving Fund.
$10,000 to Seattle University, Seattle, WA, 2013. For Financial Support to the Seattle University Fund.

9742
The Starbucks Foundation ✧
c/o Starbucks Corp.
2401 Utah Ave. S.
Seattle, WA 98134-1436
E-mail: foundationgrants@starbucks.com; Main URL: http://www.starbucks.com/responsibility/community
Youth Leadership Grant Recipients: http://globalassets.starbucks.com/assets/a3e82bc037324a238bebd95184e25a18.pdf

Established in 1997 in WA.
Donors: Starbucks Corp.; Starbucks Coffee Co.; Pepsico; Schultz Family Foundation.
Foundation type: Company-sponsored foundation.
Financial data (yr. ended 09/30/13): Assets, $17,999,827 (M); gifts received, $14,606,154; expenditures, $7,969,506; qualifying distributions, $7,959,567; giving activities include $7,930,752 for 1,649 grants (high: $550,000; low: $11).
Purpose and activities: The foundation supports programs designed to support young people creating change in local communities; water projects through the Ethos Water Fund; and social investments in countries where Starbuck buys coffee, tea, and cocoa.
Fields of interest: Education; Environment, water resources; Public health, clean water supply; Public health, sanitation; Health care; Agriculture; Nutrition; Disasters, preparedness/services; Youth development; International economic development; Social entrepreneurship; Microfinance/microlending; Community/economic development; Children/youth.
International interests: Africa; Asia; Canada; China; Europe; Latin America; Middle East; United Kingdom.
Type of support: Seed money; General/operating support; Continuing support; Emergency funds; Program development; Employee volunteer services; Employee matching gifts.
Limitations: Applications not accepted. Giving on a national and international basis in areas of company operations and in countries where the company buys coffee, tea, and cocoa. No support for private foundations, political, labor, or fraternal organizations, religious organizations not of direct benefit to the entire community, hospitals or medical research institutions, universities or academic research institutions, individual schools or parent teacher associations, or sporting teams. No grants to individuals, or for neighborhood clean-ups or tree plantings, wildlife conservation projects, capital campaigns, capital expenditures or land acquisition, school bands or orchestras or non-literacy art programs, fundraising events, one-time events or programs, event sponsorships,

trips or travel, league sports programs, scholarships or fellowships, expeditions, political campaigns, the production of marketing material promoting Starbucks, the production of products to sell in Starbucks stores, endowments, conferences or symposia, contests, festivals, or parades, advertising, tickets to events, or supply drives.
Publications: Grants list.
Application information: Youth Leadership Grants are by invitation only. Unsolicited requests are currently not accepted for the Ethos Water Fund and Social Investments in Coffee, Tea, & Cocoa Communities.
Officers and Directors:* Blair Taylor, Pres.; Lucy Helm,* Secy.; Jill Walker, Treas.; Rodney Hines, Exec. Dir.; Cliff Burrows; John Culver; Matt Ryan; Vivek Varma.
Number of staff: 3 part-time professional; 1 part-time support.
EIN: 911795425
Selected grants: The following grants are a representative sample of this grantmaker's funding activity:
$350,000 to Urban League of Los Angeles, Los Angeles, CA, 2011.
$25,000 to City Year San Jose/Silicon Valley, San Jose, CA, 2011.
$25,000 to City Year Seattle/King County, Seattle, WA, 2011.
$10,000 to Jumpstart for Young Children, Boston, MA, 2011.

9743
Bruce and Mary Stevenson Foundation, Inc. ✧ ☆

(formerly Mary Hoyt Stevenson Foundation, Inc.)
2507 2nd Ave. N.
Seattle, WA 98109-1806

Established in 1986 in OR.
Donors: Mary H. Stevenson†; Leslie Stevenson Campbell.
Foundation type: Independent foundation.
Financial data (yr. ended 09/30/13): Assets, $10,502,403 (M); gifts received, $25; expenditures, $549,389; qualifying distributions, $459,379; giving activities include $459,379 for 32 grants (high: $160,000; low: $100).
Fields of interest: Museums (art); Museums (natural history); Arts; Medical school/education.
Limitations: Applications not accepted. Giving primarily in OR and WA. No grants to individuals.
Application information: Contributes only to pre-selected organizations.
Officer: Laura Stevenson Cheney, Pres.
Directors: Leslie Stevenson Campbell; Anne Stevenson.
Number of staff: None.
EIN: 943028591
Selected grants: The following grants are a representative sample of this grantmaker's funding activity:
$61,025 to Maryhill Museum of Art, Goldendale, WA, 2011. For general operations.
$40,000 to Billings Middle School, Seattle, WA, 2011. For general operations.
$35,000 to Portland Art Museum, Portland, OR, 2011. For general operations.
$15,000 to Thomas A. Edison High School, Portland, OR, 2011. For general operations.
$2,500 to Oregon Public Broadcasting, Portland, OR, 2011. For general operations.
$1,000 to Childrens Cancer Association, Portland, OR, 2011. For general operations.

9744
The Stewardship Foundation ✧

P.O. Box 1278
Tacoma, WA 98401-1278
Contact: Cary Paine, Exec. Dir.
E-mail: info@stewardshipfdn.org; Main URL: http://www.stewardshipfdn.org

Trust established in 1962 in WA.
Donor: C. Davis Weyerhaeuser Irrevocable Trust.
Foundation type: Independent foundation.
Financial data (yr. ended 12/31/12): Assets, $124,121,620 (M); expenditures, $6,518,971; qualifying distributions, $5,857,118; giving activities include $5,050,826 for 169 grants (high: $82,684; low: $250).
Purpose and activities: The foundation provides resources to Christ centered organizations which have their primary goal to bring people into a relationship with God through faith in Jesus Christ. The foundation will consider making grants to organizations that promote: 1) Leadership: Preparation and training of servant leaders for the church and marketplace; favors mentoring and discipleship of indigenous leadership in the least evangelized world. 2) Poverty: community development (i.e. health, agriculture, water, education); economic development primarily in the developing world. 3) Reconciliation and Justice: advocacy and intervention on behalf of people suffering injustice, oppression and persecution; protection for refugees and displaced people around the world, and efforts which seek to end the conditions that create displacement; promotion of reconciliation and healing among current and historic enemies; and advocacy and promotion of religious liberty. 4) Relational Evangelism and Discipleship: building relationships and friendships with people for the purpose of introducing them to Jesus Christ. 5) Children at Risk: outreach and support of vulnerable children, protecting then from abuse and unfair treatment; solutions and best practices which enable children to develop into the people God created them to be.
Fields of interest: Public health, clean water supply; Youth development, services; Youth development, religion; Youth, services; International economic development; International peace/security; Community/economic development; Leadership development; Christian agencies & churches.
Type of support: General/operating support; Continuing support; Program development; Matching/challenge support.
Limitations: Giving internationally, nationally and in Tacoma and King, Snohomish counties. No support for churches (except for religious support to Christian parachurch organizations and Christian-Evangelical purposes). No grants to individuals, or for seed money, endowment funds, deficit financing, research, videos, media time or program production.
Publications: Application guidelines.
Application information: Application limited to once a year. Applicants should not submit full proposals unless requested to do so by the foundation or have received a grant payment from the foundation within the past three years. Application form not required.
Initial approach: Letter of inquiry (1-2 pages)
Deadline(s): None for letter of inquiry
Board meeting date(s): Mar., June, Sept., and Dec.
Final notification: 30 days for letter of inquiry
Officers and Directors:* William T. Weyerhaeuser,* Chair.; Gail T. Weyerhaeuser,* Vice-Chair. and Treas.; Nicholas C. Spika, Secy.; Cary A. Paine, Exec. Dir.; Kerry L. Dearborn; Chi-Dooh "Skip" Li; William P. Robinson; Todd D. Silver.
Number of staff: 1 full-time professional.
EIN: 916020515
Selected grants: The following grants are a representative sample of this grantmaker's funding activity:
$500,000 to Young Life, Colorado Springs, CO, 2012. For Malibu Club Nootka dorm renovation.
$225,000 to Rural Development Institute, Landesa, Seattle, WA, 2012. For Karnataka, India microplot distribution and land access advocacy.
$200,000 to Food for the Hungry, Phoenix, AZ, 2012. For HIV-Free Generation - Northern Uganda.
$138,552 to Free Wheelchair Mission, Irvine, CA, 2012. For extensive field study.
$125,000 to Young Life, Colorado Springs, CO, 2012. For Capernaum ministries.
$82,684 to Kids Hope USA, Zeeland, MI, 2012. For affiliate fee gap for 28 new church/school partnerships.
$75,000 to Alpha USA, Bannockburn, IL, 2012. For general operations.
$36,250 to Peace and Hope International, Minneapolis, MN, 2012. For Free to Thrive.
$30,000 to Helping Hand House, Puyallup, WA, 2012. For general operations.
$25,000 to International Fellowship of Evangelical Students USA, Platteville, WI, 2012. For recognition of IFES' faithful years of service throughout the world - encouragement grant.

9745
Estate of Joseph L. Stubblefield ✧

P.O. Box 1757
Walla Walla, WA 99362-2809 (509) 527-3500
Contact: James K. Hayner, Tr.

Established in 1902 in WA.
Donors: Joseph L. Stubblefield†; Murr Family Foundation; Blue Mountain Arts Alliance.
Foundation type: Independent foundation.
Financial data (yr. ended 12/31/12): Assets, $7,967,316 (M); expenditures, $612,014; qualifying distributions, $525,354; giving activities include $474,134 for 55 grants (high: $50,000; low: $100).
Purpose and activities: Giving only to schools and organizations in the Walla Walla, WA, area.
Fields of interest: Education; Human services; Children/youth, services; Economically disadvantaged.
Type of support: General/operating support; Grants to individuals.
Limitations: Applications accepted. Giving limited to Walla Walla, WA.
Application information: Application form not required.
Initial approach: Proposal
Deadline(s): None
Trustee: James K. Hayner.
EIN: 916031350

9746
Sunbridge Foundation ✧
(formerly Allchin Foundation)
c/o Wellspring
10885 N.E. 4th St., Ste. 320
Bellevue, WA 98004-5525

Established in 2002 in WA.
Donors: James E. Allchin; Catherine M. Allchin; Steven Balmer; Watermark Estate Mgmt. Svcs.
Foundation type: Independent foundation.
Financial data (yr. ended 12/31/13): Assets, $22,537,809 (M); expenditures, $1,186,228; qualifying distributions, $1,055,947; giving activities include $1,048,270 for 18 grants (high: $330,561; low: $5,000).
Fields of interest: Arts; Higher education; Environment, natural resources; Hospitals (specialty); Prostate cancer research; Human services; Children.
Limitations: Applications not accepted. Giving primarily in WA; some funding also in GA and VA. No grants to individuals.
Application information: Contributes only to pre-selected organizations.
Trustees: Catherine M. Allchin; James E. Allchin; Judy Courshon.
EIN: 912080918

9747
Suskin Foundation ✧
11665 Holmes Point Dr. N.E.
Kirkland, WA 98033-7012

Established in 1999 in WA.
Donor: Margie Suskin.
Foundation type: Independent foundation.
Financial data (yr. ended 12/31/13): Assets, $12,884,690 (M); expenditures, $603,805; qualifying distributions, $600,000; giving activities include $600,000 for 23 grants (high: $75,000; low: $10,000).
Fields of interest: Animal welfare; Hospitals (general); Cancer; Children/youth, services; Human services.
Type of support: General/operating support.
Limitations: Applications not accepted. Giving primarily in WA. No grants to individuals.
Application information: Unsolicited requests for funds not accepted.
Trustees: Stacy Suskin Rottinghaus; Margie Suskin; Steven C. Suskin.
EIN: 912015382

9748
The Swigert-Warren Foundation ✧
2129 G St.
Washougal, WA 98671-1642

Established in 1994 in WA and OR.
Donors: Nani S. Warren; Hank Swigert.
Foundation type: Independent foundation.
Financial data (yr. ended 12/31/13): Assets, $13,997,517 (M); gifts received, $987,449; expenditures, $930,438; qualifying distributions, $775,643; giving activities include $775,643 for 127 grants (high: $150,000; low: $50).
Purpose and activities: Giving primarily for the arts, particularly museums, education, environmental preservation, health organizations, and human services.
Fields of interest: Museums; Arts; Higher education; Education; Environment, natural resources; Health organizations, association; Human services; Catholic agencies & churches.
Limitations: Applications not accepted. Giving primarily in OR; some giving also in CA and WA. No grants to individuals.
Application information: Contributes only to pre-selected organizations.
Officer: Penny Guest, Treas.
Directors: Jack B. Schwartz; Elizabeth Warren; Nani S. Warren.
EIN: 931083078

9749
T.E.W. Foundation ✧
1000 2nd Ave., 34th Fl.
Seattle, WA 98104-1022

Established in 1997 in WA.
Donor: T. Evans Wyckoff†.
Foundation type: Independent foundation.
Financial data (yr. ended 12/31/12): Assets, $8,498,877 (M); expenditures, $550,573; qualifying distributions, $459,000; giving activities include $459,000 for grants.
Purpose and activities: Giving primarily for education.
Fields of interest: Museums (art); Elementary/secondary education; Secondary school/education; Higher education, university; Environment, natural resources; Human services; Catholic agencies & churches.
Limitations: Applications not accepted. Giving primarily in WA. No grants to individuals.
Application information: Contributes only to pre-selected organizations.
Officers and Directors: Sheila Wyckoff-Dickey,* Pres.; Susan Wyckoff Pohl,* V.P.; Daniel Asher, Secy.; Paul L. Wyckoff,* Treas.; Theiline Wyckoff Cramer; Alison Wyckoff Milliman; Ann P. Wyckoff; Martha Wyckoff.
EIN: 911817398

9750
The Greater Tacoma Community Foundation ✧
950 Pacific Ave., Ste. 1100
P.O. Box 1995
Tacoma, WA 98402-4423 (253) 383-5622
Contact: For grants: Carol Park, Grants Admin.
FAX: (253) 272-8099; E-mail: info@gtcf.org; Grant application e-mail: cpark@gtcf.org; Main
URL: http://www.gtcf.org
Blog: https://www.gtcf.org/blog/
E-Newsletter: http://www.gtcf.org/newsletters
Facebook: http://www.facebook.com/?sk=ff#!/pages/The-Greater-Tacoma-Community-Foundation/236157808732
Fund for Women and Girls: http://twitter.com/fundwomengirls
Twitter: http://twitter.com/GreaterTacoma

Incorporated in 1977 in WA.
Foundation type: Community foundation.
Financial data (yr. ended 06/30/13): Assets, $92,152,393 (M); gifts received, $8,205,614; expenditures, $6,887,335; giving activities include $2,881,070 for grants, and $275,842 for grants to individuals.
Purpose and activities: The foundation fosters generosity by connecting people who care with causes that matter, forever enriching the community.
Fields of interest: Arts education; Museums; Performing arts; Performing arts, theater; Humanities; Historic preservation/historical societies; Arts; Child development, education; Higher education; Adult/continuing education; Libraries/library science; Education; Environment, natural resources; Environment; Animal welfare; Hospitals (general); Health care; Substance abuse, services; Mental health/crisis services; Health organizations, association; AIDS; AIDS research; Food services; Housing/shelter, development; Recreation; Youth development, services; Children/youth, services; Child development, services; Family services; Residential/custodial care, hospices; Aging, centers/services; Homeless, human services; Human services; Community/economic development; Voluntarism promotion; Government/public administration; Leadership development; Children/youth; Aging; Disabilities, people with; Women; Girls; Economically disadvantaged; Homeless.
Type of support: General/operating support; Continuing support; Management development/capacity building; Equipment; Land acquisition; Emergency funds; Program development; Seed money; Technical assistance; Consulting services; Program evaluation; Program-related investments/loans; Scholarships—to individuals; Matching/challenge support.
Limitations: Applications accepted. Giving limited to Pierce County, WA. No support for religious organizations for sacramental/theological purposes. No grants to individuals (except for scholarships), or for annual campaigns, fellowships, seminars, meetings or travel, fundraising events or fundraising feasibility projects, endowments or debt reduction, or publications, unless specified by donor.
Publications: Application guidelines; Annual report; Financial statement; Informational brochure; Informational brochure (including application guidelines); Newsletter.
Application information: Visit foundation web site for application forms and guidelines per grant type. A letter of intent is required prior to submitting a full grant request. Faxed or e-mailed applications are not accepted. Application form required.
Initial approach: Letter of intent (1 page)
Deadline(s): Jan. 15 and July 15 for letter of intent for Vibrant Community grants; varies for others
Board meeting date(s): 6 times yearly
Final notification: Within 10 days for letter of intent determination and June and Dec. for grant determination for Vibrant Community grants; varies for others
Officers and Directors:* T. Gary Connett,* Chair.; Ed Grogan, Vice-Chair.; Rose Lincoln Hamilton,* C.E.O. and Pres.; Katherine Severson,* Secy.; Sheri Tonn,* Treas.; Gary Brooks; Maro Imirizian; Laurie Jinkins; John Korsmo; Scott Limoli; Lamont Loo; Joe Mayer; Carla Pelster; Patricia Talton; Cindy Thompson; Dwight Williams.
Number of staff: 9 full-time professional; 1 full-time support.
EIN: 911007459
Selected grants: The following grants are a representative sample of this grantmaker's funding activity:

$34,422 to South Sound Outreach Services, Tacoma, WA, 2012. For heating assistance for Pierce County senior citizens.
$22,500 to Birth to Three Development Center, Federal Way, WA, 2012. For Early Intervention Services for Infants/Toddlers, Birth to Three which provides special education and medically prescribed therapy programs for Pierce County babies and toddlers with developmental disorders in order to give them every possible chance to overcome their challenges and maximize their potential in life.
$22,500 to D.A.S.H. Center for the Arts, Tacoma, WA, 2012. For The Performing Arts Excellence Project (PAEP), DASH's premier arts education program, offering quality performing arts classes to a population of at-risk, inner-city kids from low-income households who are interested in pursuing the arts.
$22,500 to Guadalupe Land Trust, Tacoma, WA, 2012. For Guadalupe Land Trust, supporting community building in the Hilltop through the maintenance and support of two community gardens, one devoted to food security and cultural continuity for immigrants, the other a learning garden and a resource for all.
$22,500 to YMCA of Pierce and Kitsap Counties, Tacoma, WA, 2012. For YMCA Camp Seymour Outdoor Environmental Education (OEE) program, designed to increase the knowledge of ecological concepts and positive behaviors for youth participants, with funding towards scholarships to support 100 low-income youth in the OEE program.
$15,000 to Building Changes, Seattle, WA, 2012. For general operating grant to support efforts to improve housing and employment services for homeless adults and children in Pierce County.
$6,000 to Earth Economics, Tacoma, WA, 2012. For Spatially Specific Valuation for the Puyallup Watershed to inform public agency decision-making and potentially improve over $200 million of investment in emergency preparedness, flood damage avoidance, restoration and economic development in Pierce County.
$5,000 to Bethel School District No. 403, Spanaway, WA, 2012. For The Bethel School District to implement Ready! for Kindergarten to educate childcare providers and parents on how to prepare children for entry into kindergarten; classes will be offered to parents and childcare providers of children ages 2-5 years.
$5,000 to Centrum Foundation, Port Townsend, WA, 2012. For Young Artists Project, Artist faculty guide grades 5-12 students through week-long experiences in the arts while in residence at Fort Worden State Park, creating cultural community and discovering/strengthening individuals talents.
$5,000 to Tacoma Community House, Tacoma, WA, 2012. For Read2Me Literacy Program Expansion.

9751
The Atsuhiko and Ina Goodwin Tateuchi Foundation ✧
(also known as Tatuechi Foundation)
c/o Foundation Mgmt. Group, LLC
1000 2nd Ave., 34th Fl.
Seattle, WA 98104-1022
E-mail: info@tateuchi.org; Main URL: http://www.tateuchi.org
Grants List: http://www.tateuchi.org/grants.html

Established in 2000 in Japan and then in 2006 in WA.
Donors: Atsuhiko Tateuchi; Ina Tateuchi.
Foundation type: Independent foundation.
Financial data (yr. ended 12/31/13): Assets, $12,369,026 (M); expenditures, $1,030,918; qualifying distributions, $1,000,731; giving activities include $958,850 for 24 grants (high: $320,000; low: $600).
Purpose and activities: The foundation's mission seeks to promote and improve international understanding, knowledge, and the quality of relations between Japan and the United States.
Fields of interest: Arts, cultural/ethnic awareness; Museums (ethnic/folk arts); Higher education, university; Botanical gardens; Foundations (community).
Type of support: General/operating support; Capital campaigns; Seed money; Matching/challenge support.
Limitations: Applications accepted. Giving primarily in CA and WA; some giving also in Japan.
Publications: Application guidelines.
Application information: Application guidelines available on foundation web site.
Initial approach: 1-2 page concise letter or e-mail of inquiry
Deadline(s): None
Final notification: Within 30 days of the conclusion of the grant review process
Officers: Ina Tateuchi, Pres., V.P., and Treas.; Laura Hurdelbrink, Secy.
EIN: 912090773

9752
The Thompson Foundation ✧ ☆
100 Kin Ct.
Steilacoom, WA 98388-1416 (253) 620-6468

Established in WA.
Donor: Cynthia A. Thompson.
Foundation type: Independent foundation.
Financial data (yr. ended 12/31/12): Assets, $296,481 (M); expenditures, $3,932,948; qualifying distributions, $3,913,317; giving activities include $3,900,000 for 2 grants (high: $3,800,000; low: $100,000).
Purpose and activities: Giving primarily for hunger relief, affordable housing, and family services. The foundation will consider grants in areas outside of these interests where extraordinary need or merit arise.
Fields of interest: Agriculture/food; Housing/shelter; Family services; Foundations (community).
Application information: Application form required.
Initial approach: U.S. mail or e-mail
Deadline(s): 30 days
Officers: Cynthia A . Thompson, Pres.; Christine F. Buckley, V.P.
Director: Alan D. MacPherson.
EIN: 270536028

9753
Mark & Susan Torrance Foundation ✧
(formerly Mark Torrance Foundation)
712 N. 34th St., Ste. 200
Seattle, WA 98103-2419

Established in 2000 WA.
Donors: Mark Torrance; Susan Torrance.
Foundation type: Independent foundation.
Financial data (yr. ended 12/31/13): Assets, $12,094,845 (M); expenditures, $624,452; qualifying distributions, $531,703; giving activities include $521,735 for 21 grants (high: $263,500; low: $250).
Fields of interest: Education; Environment; Human services.
Limitations: Applications not accepted. Giving primarily in Seattle, WA; some giving also in Vancouver, Canada. No grants to individuals.
Application information: Contributes only to pre-selected organizations.
Officers and Directors:* Mark Torrance,* Pres.; Chris Birkeland; Michael Mathieu; Dana Bass Solomon.
EIN: 911939909
Selected grants: The following grants are a representative sample of this grantmaker's funding activity:
$50,000 to United Republic Education Fund, Florence, MA, 2012. For Program support - Social Services.
$48,340 to Agros International, Seattle, WA, 2012. For Program support Social Services.
$10,000 to Seattle Art Museum, Seattle, WA, 2012. For Program support - Education Services.

9754
Lawrence True & Linda Brown Foundation ✧
1108 Willard Ave. W.
Seattle, WA 98119-3458
Contact: Linda Brown, Secy.

Established in 1997 in VA.
Donors: Lawrence True; Linda Brown.
Foundation type: Independent foundation.
Financial data (yr. ended 12/31/13): Assets, $15,095,375 (M); gifts received, $80; expenditures, $645,151; qualifying distributions, $628,560; giving activities include $626,050 for 14 grants (high: $125,000; low: $500).
Fields of interest: Arts; Education; Human services.
Type of support: Program development; Curriculum development; Research.
Limitations: Applications accepted. Giving primarily in CO and Seattle, WA.
Application information: Application form not required.
Initial approach: Proposal
Deadline(s): None
Officers: Lawrence True, Pres.; Linda Brown, Secy.
EIN: 911817055
Selected grants: The following grants are a representative sample of this grantmaker's funding activity:
$125,000 to University of Washington Foundation, Seattle, WA, 2012. To further charitable purposes.

9755
Alice C. Tyler Perpetual Trust ✧ ☆
c/o Anders Brown
2431 Warren Ave. N.
Seattle, WA 98109

Established in 1994 in CA.
Donors: Alice C. Tyler†; Alice C. Tyler Charitable Trust.
Foundation type: Independent foundation.
Financial data (yr. ended 12/31/13): Assets, $10,668,081 (M); expenditures, $692,599; qualifying distributions, $590,636; giving activities include $500,551 for 10 grants (high: $100,000; low: $25,000).

Purpose and activities: Giving primarily for education, environmental research, and children's services.
Fields of interest: Higher education, college; Education; Environment, research; Zoos/zoological societies; Human services; Children, services.
Limitations: Applications not accepted. Giving primarily in CA and OR; giving also in Chile. No grants to individuals.
Application information: Contributes only to pre-selected organizations.
Officer and Trustees: Paul J. Livadary,* Mgr.; John Hoag; Nancy Sharp; Martha Appello; Paul H. Barber; Allyn E. Brown, Esq.; Anders M. Brown; Courtney L. Brown.
EIN: 956967787

9756
Vista Hermosa ✧
1111 Fishhook Park Rd.
Prescott, WA 99348-9618 (509) 749-2217
Contact: Suzanne Broetje, Exec. Dir.
FAX: (509) 749-2354;
E-mail: SuzanneB@firstfruits.com; Main URL: http://www.firstfruits.com/vista-hermosa-foundation.html
Scholarship contact: Theresa Morton, Prog. Mgr., tel.: (509) 460-0350

Established in 1990 in WA.
Donors: Cheryl Broetje; Ralph Broetje; Broetje Orchards.
Foundation type: Independent foundation.
Financial data (yr. ended 12/31/12): Assets, $30,099,082 (M); gifts received, $6,203,718; expenditures, $3,648,640; qualifying distributions, $3,350,685; giving activities include $1,612,895 for 24+ grants (high: $280,000), $70,010 for 28 grants to individuals, and $1,544,737 for 4 foundation-administered programs.
Purpose and activities: The foundation was established for the purpose of using proceeds from Broetje Orchards to serve children and underserved communities, both at home and around the world. The foundation also provides FirstFruits Scholarships for children of Broetje Orchards' employees, and graduates of Jubilee Christian Academy.
Fields of interest: Education; Agriculture/food; Housing/shelter, development; Youth development, services; International relief; Community/economic development; Children/youth; Hispanics/Latinos; Women; Girls; Economically disadvantaged.
International interests: El Salvador; Guatemala; Haiti; India; Kenya; Mexico; Uganda.
Type of support: Income development; Program development; Employee-related scholarships; Matching/challenge support.
Limitations: Giving primarily in WA; giving also in Mexico, Central America, Haiti, Dominican Republic, El Salvador, Guatemala, India, Kenya and Uganda. No support for universities or university-led programs. No grants to individuals (except for scholarships), or endowments, professorships; no student loans, or loans to individuals.
Application information: Unsolicited proposals not accepted. Only letters of inquiry if an applicant feels their organization meets the foundation's criteria. See foundation web site for information.
Initial approach: 2-page letter of inquiry, via e-mail to Exec. Dir.
Board meeting date(s): Monthly
Officers: Cheryl Broetje, Pres.; Ralph Broetje, V.P.; Theresa Morton, Secy.; Sandra Gamble, Treas.; Suzanne Broetje, Exec. Dir.
Number of staff: 1 full-time professional.
EIN: 911491438

9757
Washington Research Foundation ✧
2815 Eastlake Ave. E., Ste. 300
Seattle, WA 98102-3086
Contact: Amy McCormick, Office Mgr.
FAX: (206) 336-5615;
E-mail: amccormi@wrfseattle.org; Main URL: http://www.wrfseattle.org

Established in 1981 in WA.
Foundation type: Independent foundation.
Financial data (yr. ended 06/30/13): Assets, $276,893,961 (M); expenditures, $76,099,649; qualifying distributions, $6,081,810; giving activities include $5,452,718 for 35 grants (high: $1,250,000; low: $250), and $569,162 for foundation-administered programs.
Purpose and activities: The foundation's mission is to capture and enhance the value of intellectual property, arising from Washington State research institutions, to support research and scholarship.
Fields of interest: Higher education; Science, research.
Type of support: Seed money; Research; Program-related investments/loans.
Limitations: Applications not accepted. Giving limited to research institutions in Seattle, WA. No grants to individuals.
Publications: Annual report; Informational brochure.
Application information: Contributes only to pre-selected organizations.
Board meeting date(s): Jan., Apr., July, and Oct.
Officers and Directors:* C. Kent Carlson,* Chair.; Thomas J. Cable,* Vice-Chair.; Ronald S. Howell,* C.E.O. and Pres.; Jeff Eby, C.F.O.; Emer Dooley, Ph.D.; Barry Forman, D. Phil.; David Galas, Ph.D.; Sally Narodick; Brooks Simpson; George I. Thomas, M.D.; James R. Uhlir.
Number of staff: 8 full-time professional; 3 full-time support.
EIN: 911160492
Selected grants: The following grants are a representative sample of this grantmaker's funding activity:
$500,000 to University of Washington, Seattle, WA, 2013. For Genome Sequencers.
$500,000 to University of Washington, Seattle, WA, 2013. For Fischer-Wrf Endowed Chair in Biochemistry.
$400,000 to University of Washington, Seattle, WA, 2013. For Microfabrication Lab.
$250,000 to University of Washington, Seattle, WA, 2013. For Coulter Translational Research Partnership.
$200,000 to University of Washington, Seattle, WA, 2013. For Ben Hall Endowment.
$62,500 to University of Washington, Seattle, WA, 2013. For Commercialization Gap Fund.
$55,000 to Washington State University, Pullman, WA, 2013. For Research Project Norton.
$53,778 to University of Washington, Seattle, WA, 2013. For Research Project Cardiovascular Disease.
$50,000 to University of Washington, Seattle, WA, 2013. For Undergraduate Research Fellowships Awarded By UW College of Arts and Sciences.
$50,000 to University of Washington, Seattle, WA, 2013. For Recruitment and Retention Program Chiu.

9758
Wendt Family Charitable Foundation ✧
c/o Henry Wendt, III
560 Warbass Way
Friday Harbor, WA 98250-8043

Established in 2009 in WA.
Donors: Henry Wendt III; Holly P. Wendt; Wendt Family Revocable Trust.
Foundation type: Independent foundation.
Financial data (yr. ended 12/31/13): Assets, $2,705,294 (M); gifts received, $2,415,817; expenditures, $3,418,239; qualifying distributions, $3,390,500; giving activities include $3,390,500 for 12 grants (high: $1,000,000; low: $5,500).
Fields of interest: Higher education; Education; Environment.
Limitations: Applications not accepted. Giving primarily in CA, DC, NJ, VA and WA. No grants to individuals.
Application information: Contributes only to pre-selected organizations.
Officers: Henry Wendt III, Pres.; Holly P. Wendt, V.P.; Laura Mitchell, Secy.; Henry Wendt IV, Treas.
EIN: 270472921

9759
Whatcom Community Foundation ✧
119 Grand Ave., Ste. A
Bellingham, WA 98225-4400 (360) 671-6463
Contact: Mauri Ingram, C.E.O. and Pres.
FAX: (360) 671-6437; E-mail: wcf@whatcomcf.org; Main URL: http://www.whatcomcf.org
Facebook: https://www.facebook.com/WhatcomCommunityFoundation
YouTube: http://www.youtube.com/user/whatcomcf

Established in 1996 in WA.
Foundation type: Community foundation.
Financial data (yr. ended 06/30/13): Assets, $19,358,887 (M); gifts received, $5,514,355; expenditures, $4,356,842; giving activities include $3,565,959 for 40+ grants (high: $2,500,999), and $95,125 for 88 grants to individuals.
Purpose and activities: Mission - To enhance philanthropy to strengthen Whatcom County by linking people who care with causes that matter. Vision - A community working together, giving generously and moving forward. Core Values - Operate with integrity, include new people and new ideas, encourage collaboration, creative solutions and action.
Fields of interest: Arts; Education; Environment; Mental health/crisis services; Children/youth, services; Family services; Foundations (community).
Type of support: General/operating support; Management development/capacity building; Program development; Scholarship funds; Technical assistance; Consulting services; In-kind gifts.
Limitations: Applications accepted. Giving primarily in Whatcom County, WA. No support for religious activities or for-profit organizations. No grants to individuals (except for post-secondary education scholarships), or for capital requests (bricks and mortar), endowment funds, debt retirement, memberships, courtesy advertising, tickets for benefits, or fundraising events.
Publications: Application guidelines; Annual report; Financial statement; Grants list; Informational brochure; Newsletter.

Application information: Visit foundation web site for complete grant round information. Application to be submitted online. Application form required.

Initial approach: One stage grant round process in January
Copies of proposal: 1
Deadline(s): Jan. 27
Board meeting date(s): 4th Wed. of each month
Final notification: Late Apr.

Officers and Directors:* Bob Trunek,* Chair.; Sati Mookherjee,* Vice-Chair.; Mauri Ingram,* C.E.O. and Pres.; Kevin DeYoung,* Secy.-Treas.; Jennifer Hine; Brenda-Lee Karasik; Cheryl Macpherson; Fred Miller; Joyce Pedlow; Chuck Robinson; Steve Swan.
Number of staff: 1 full-time professional; 3 part-time professional; 1 full-time support; 4 part-time support.
EIN: 911726410
Selected grants: The following grants are a representative sample of this grantmaker's funding activity:
$632,200 to Alternatives to Hunger, Bellingham Food Bank, Bellingham, WA, 2011. For Agricultural Program Partnership by pushing the food bank in an exciting and bold direction. The goal is to be different from many food banks by working towards offering all families enough nutrient rich food to meet all of the recommended guidelines issued by the USDA. To meet this goal, they will need to increase their local produce production four-fold. With strategic and intentional efforts, the goal can be met in the next 5-10 years., payable over 5.00 years.
$40,000 to Puget Sound Restoration Fund, Bainbridge Island, WA, 2012. To increase shellfish harvest and clean water and broaden their base of support throughout Whatcom County by implementing a multi-faceted outreach and education approach.
$39,862 to Cloud Mountain Farm Center, Everson, WA, 2011. For program development and support.
$32,500 to Ferndale, City of, Ferndale, WA, 2011. For New Ferndale Library Project design support.
$10,000 to Brigid Collins House, Bellingham, WA, 2012. For improving classroom behavior and academic achievement for children with Adverse Childhood Experiences (ACE'S).
$10,000 to ReUse Works, Bellingham, WA, 2012. For Jobs From Waste program.
$9,924 to Arc of Whatcom County, Bellingham, WA, 2012. For Single Entry Access to Services (SEAS) for Children and Youth with Special Health Care Needs (CYSHCN).
$4,920 to Max Higbee Community Recreation Center, Bellingham, WA, 2012. For Farm to School program: nutrition support.

9760
Wheeler Foundation ✧

900 Washington St., Ste. 900
Vancouver, WA 98660-3455

Established in 1965 in OR.
Donors: Coleman H. Wheeler†; Coleman H. Wheeler, Jr.†; Cornelia T. Wheeler†.
Foundation type: Independent foundation.
Financial data (yr. ended 12/31/13): Assets, $16,510,904 (M); expenditures, $910,021; qualifying distributions, $852,466; giving activities include $792,151 for 96 grants (high: $40,000; low: $1,000).
Purpose and activities: Giving primarily to cultural institutions.
Fields of interest: Arts; Higher education; Health care; Medical research, institute; Children/youth, services.
Type of support: General/operating support.
Limitations: Applications accepted. Giving primarily in OR. No grants to individuals.
Application information: Application form not required.

Initial approach: Letter
Copies of proposal: 1
Deadline(s): None
Board meeting date(s): Mar., June, Sept., and Dec.

Directors: Charles B. Wheeler; John C. Wheeler; Thomas K. Wheeler.
EIN: 930553801
Selected grants: The following grants are a representative sample of this grantmaker's funding activity:
$5,000 to University of Chicago, Booth Business School, Chicago, IL, 2012.

9761
Wiancko Charitable Foundation Inc. ✧

2312 1st Ave. N.
Seattle, WA 98109

Established in 1989 in WY.
Donors: Thomas H. Wiancko†; Sibyl S. Wiancko†.
Foundation type: Independent foundation.
Financial data (yr. ended 12/31/13): Assets, $37,455,873 (M); expenditures, $2,169,947; qualifying distributions, $1,773,835; giving activities include $1,773,500 for 78 grants (high: $100,000; low: $5,000).
Purpose and activities: Giving primarily for environmental and wildlife conservation.
Fields of interest: Environment, natural resources; Environment; Animals/wildlife, preservation/protection; Reproductive health, family planning.
Type of support: Matching/challenge support; Program development; Continuing support; Capital campaigns.
Limitations: Applications not accepted. Giving in the U.S., with some emphasis on Washington, DC, OR, and WA. No grants to individuals.
Application information: Contributes only to pre-selected organizations.
Officers: R. Dennis Wiancko, Pres.; Anna K. Wiancko-Chasman, V.P.; Emily Boniface, Secy.; Bradley Parker, Treas.
Trustees: Chris Boniface; Paul Chasman; David Parker; Judith W. Parker; Cynthia Wiancko.
EIN: 830291490

9762
The Wilburforce Foundation ✧

2034 NW 56th St., Ste. 300
Seattle, WA 98107-3127
Contact: Timothy Greyhavens, Secy. and Exec. Dir.
FAX: (206) 632-2326;
E-mail: grants@wilburforce.org; Additional address (Montana office): P.O. Box 296, Bozeman, MT 59771-0296, tel.: (406) 586-9796, fax: (406) 586-3076, e-mail: jennifer@wilburforce.org; Additional tel.: (800) 201-0148 (Seattle office), (800) 317-8180 (Montana office); Main URL: http://www.wilburforce.org
Grants Database: http://www.wilburforce.org/grant-history

Established in 1990 in WA.
Donors: James Letwin; Rosanna W. Letwin.
Foundation type: Independent foundation.
Financial data (yr. ended 12/31/13): Assets, $42,980,023 (M); gifts received, $43,352,000; expenditures, $13,685,069; qualifying distributions, $13,410,374; giving activities include $11,091,430 for grants, and $20,000 for grants to individuals.
Purpose and activities: The foundation is dedicated to protecting nature's richness and diversity through funding programs that help to preserve our remaining wild places. The foundation focuses on increasing the amount of protected critical wildlife habitat, assuring the quality and extent of key connective land between core habitat areas, lessening immediate threats to critical wildlife habitat, improving management programs that preserve the ecological integrity of existing or proposed protected areas, increasing knowledge of wildlife populations and/or improving managements plans that ensure the viability of local species in a region and building the capacity of organizations working to protect priority areas.
Fields of interest: Environment, natural resources; Environment.
International interests: Canada.
Type of support: General/operating support; Continuing support; Management development/capacity building; Capital campaigns; Equipment; Program development; Seed money; Research; Technical assistance; Consulting services; Program evaluation; Matching/challenge support.
Limitations: Applications accepted. Giving primarily in the western U.S. and western Canada, particularly AK, AZ, MT, NM, OR, UT, WA, British Columbia, and the Yellowstone to Yukon region of U.S.-Canada. No support for schools or universities, governmental agencies, agricultural issues, air quality or other clean air programs, energy-related programs; environmental education, environmental justice programs, habitat restoration, marine or other water-only programs, pollution prevention on other pollution-related projects, salmon recovery programs, sustainable development or other economically based programs, sprawl or other growth management programs, transportation-related programs, wildlife rehabilitation programs or youth education programs. No grants to individuals (except for Leadership Awards), or for fellowships or scholarships, endowment funds, operating budgets, deficit financing or indirect costs, annual meetings, conferences or symposia, or land acquisition and/or stewardship; no loans.
Publications: Application guidelines; Grants list.
Application information: Applicants who are interested in submitting a grant proposal must contact the appropriate staff member prior to developing a proposal. Please do not submit a full proposal without first contacting a program officer. When contacting a program officer regarding the possibility of a grant, be sure to specify the dollar level of your request. Grant Application Form will be sent to an organization only after it has received approval to submit a full proposal. Application form required.

Initial approach: Telephone
Copies of proposal: 1
Deadline(s): See web site for details
Board meeting date(s): Feb., Mar., July and Nov.
Final notification: Grants of more than $25,000: Quarterly; Six to eight weeks for grants of $25,000 or less

Officers and Directors:* Rosanna W. Letwin,* Pres.; Timothy Greyhavens, Secy. and Exec. Dir.; Stephanie Nichols-Young,* Treas.
Number of staff: 11 full-time professional.
EIN: 943137894
Selected grants: The following grants are a representative sample of this grantmaker's funding activity:
$1,250,000 to Rockefeller Philanthropy Advisors, Philanthropic Collaborative, New York, NY, 2011. For Training Resources for the Environmental Community.
$350,000 to League of Conservation Voters Education Fund, Washington, DC, 2011. For Western Voter Education Programs.
$300,000 to Yukon Conservation Society, Whitehorse, Canada, 2011. For Campaign for the Yukon's Peel Watershed.
$215,000 to Canadian Parks and Wilderness Society, Ottawa, Canada, 2011. For Protecting Habitat and Corridors in Northern Y2Y.
$200,000 to Endangered Species Coalition, Washington, DC, 2011. For Polling, Messaging and General Support.
$185,000 to Western Environmental Law Center, Eugene, OR, 2011. For Protecting Western Midlands and Species.
$100,000 to Defenders of Wildlife, Washington, DC, 2011. To protect the Mexican Gray Wolf in the Southwest Crescent.
$100,000 to National Wildlife Refuge Association, Washington, DC, 2011. For Seizing the Moment for Desert Tortoise and Sage-Grouse.
$40,000 to New Mexico Wildlife Federation, Albuquerque, NM, 2011. For Southwest New Mexico Building Capacity for Pro-Wildlife.
$25,000 to Sierra Club Foundation, San Francisco, CA, 2011. For Resilient Habitats Arctic Ecoregion Campaign.

9763
Wockner Foundation ✧
c/o HKP & Co., P.S.
601 Union St., Ste. 2700
Seattle, WA 98101-2329

Established in 2006 in WA.
Donor: Irene Wockner‡.
Foundation type: Independent foundation.
Financial data (yr. ended 06/30/13): Assets, $5,386,171 (M); expenditures, $615,611; qualifying distributions, $579,000; giving activities include $579,000 for grants.
Fields of interest: Education; Human services; Children/youth, services; Residential/custodial care, hospices.
Limitations: Applications not accepted. Giving primarily in WA. No grants to individuals.
Application information: Contributes only to pre-selected organizations.
Officer: Michael R. Bauer, Secy.-Treas.
Trustees: Frances A. Wockner; William E. Wockner.
EIN: 421624231
Selected grants: The following grants are a representative sample of this grantmaker's funding activity:
$35,000 to Childhaven, Seattle, WA, 2013. To Fund the Therapeutic Child Care Program.
$25,000 to Arc of Snohomish County, Everett, WA, 2013. To Fund Programs That Provide Assistance to Individuals with Developmental Disabilities.
$20,000 to Housing Hope, Everett, WA, 2013. For Activities of Housing Hope.
$12,500 to Lake Washington Schools Foundation, Redmond, WA, 2013. To Fund Educational Services to Children.
$10,000 to Seattle Education Access, Seattle, WA, 2013. To Buy Books for Low Income Families.

9764
The Wren Foundation ✧ ☆
1846 W. Beaver Lake Dr. S.E.
Sammamish, WA 98075-3704
Contact: Marvin F. Wren

Established in 1999 in IL.
Donor: Marvin F. Wren.
Foundation type: Independent foundation.
Financial data (yr. ended 12/31/13): Assets, $128,049 (M); gifts received, $500,598; expenditures, $489,996; qualifying distributions, $489,996; giving activities include $488,891 for 6 grants (high: $246,044; low: $3,200).
Fields of interest: Education; Religion.
Limitations: Applications not accepted. No grants to individuals.
Application information: Contributes only to pre-selected organizations.
Officers and Directors:* Marvin F. Wren,* Pres. and Treas.; Monica Lee Magnan,* Secy.; Paige Richardson; Michele M. Wren.
EIN: 364335176

9765
Bagley and Virginia Wright Foundation ✧
(formerly The Bagley Wright Family Fund)
407 Dexter Ave. N.
Seattle, WA 98109-4704
Contact: Jan Day

Established in 2001 in WA.
Donor: Bill True.
Foundation type: Independent foundation.
Financial data (yr. ended 12/31/12): Assets, $15,746,949 (M); expenditures, $9,095,210; qualifying distributions, $8,970,329; giving activities include $8,824,000 for 16 grants (high: $4,059,000; low: $2,000).
Purpose and activities: Giving primarily for arts and culture.
Fields of interest: Museums (art); Performing arts centers; Performing arts, theater; Arts.
Type of support: Capital campaigns.
Limitations: Applications not accepted. Giving primarily in Seattle, WA. No grants to individuals.
Application information: Contributes only to pre-selected organizations.
Trustees: Robin Wright Moll; Charles B. Wright III; Merrill Wright; Prentice "Bing" Wright; Virginia B. Wright.
EIN: 916526097

9766
Julie Ann Wrigley Foundation, Inc. ✧
c/o Peterson Sullivan LLP
601 Union St., Ste. 2300
Seattle, WA 98101-2345

Established in 2001 in WI.
Donor: Julie A. Wrigley.
Foundation type: Independent foundation.
Financial data (yr. ended 12/31/12): Assets, $59,355 (M); gifts received, $1,300,000; expenditures, $1,271,937; qualifying distributions, $1,270,698; giving activities include $1,269,430 for 19 grants (high: $922,093; low: $500).
Fields of interest: Higher education; Animal welfare; Health care; Human services.
Limitations: Applications not accepted. Giving primarily in AZ and Washington, DC; funding also in CA and ID. No grants to individuals.
Application information: Contributes only to pre-selected organizations.
Officers: Julie Ann Wrigley, Pres.; Peter Teutsch, V.P.; Brian D. Collins, Secy.-Treas.
EIN: 030395312

9767
Yakima Valley Community Foundation
111 S. University Pkwy., Ste. 103
Yakima, WA 98901-1471 (509) 457-7616
FAX: (509) 457-7625;
E-mail: info@yakimavalleycf.org; Grant application e-mail: grants@yvcf.org; Main URL: http://www.yvcf.com/

Established in 2004 in WA.
Foundation type: Community foundation.
Financial data (yr. ended 12/31/13): Assets, $61,899,511 (M); gifts received, $2,051,768; expenditures, $3,575,905; giving activities include $2,038,320 for 54+ grants (high: $649,811).
Purpose and activities: The foundation seeks to improve the cultural, economic, social, health and educational quality of life for residents of Yakima County, WA, with special attention to unmet needs, and to help donors achieve their philanthropic goals.
Fields of interest: Arts, folk arts; Media/communications; Visual arts; Performing arts; Literature; Arts; Elementary/secondary education; Education, early childhood education; Vocational education; Higher education; Adult/continuing education; Libraries/library science; Education, services; Education; Environment, natural resources; Environment; Health care; Mental health/crisis services; Housing/shelter; Youth development; Family services, parent education; Human services; Economic development; Community/economic development; Philanthropy/voluntarism; Aging.
Type of support: Equipment.
Limitations: Applications accepted. Giving primarily in Yakima County, WA. No support for academic or scientific research, individual school classrooms and individual schools, colleges and universities, or religious organizations for religious purposes. No grants to individuals, or for operating support, capital expenditures (real estate/bricks and mortar), debt retirement or reduction, conferences, workshops, or symposia, travel, endowments, publications, video, or film, special fundraising events, or annual campaign appeals.
Publications: Annual report; Financial statement.
Application information: Visit foundation web site for application format and guidelines. Based on the letters of intent, applicants selected for further consideration will be asked to provide additional information and materials about the project and submitting organization. Faxed and e-mailed applications are not accepted. Application form not required.
Initial approach: Submit Letter of Intent (limited to 3 pages)
Copies of proposal: 5
Deadline(s): June 1 for Letter of Intent

Officers and Directors:* Dave Edler,* Chair.; Minerva Morales,* Vice-Chair.; Linda G. Moore,* Pres. and C.E.O.; Mary Rita Rohde,* Secy.; Ann Hittle,* Treas.; David Abeyta; Crystal Bass; Michele Besso; Gina Gamboa; Ricardo Garcia; Hank Heffernan; Leah Holbrook; Ester Huey; Paul Larson; Elizabeth McGree; Jessie Randhawa.
EIN: 200697012
Selected grants: The following grants are a representative sample of this grantmaker's funding activity:
$649,811 to Yakima Rotary Trust, Yakima, WA, 2013. For Davis Fund Grant.
$641,699 to Yakima Rotary Trust, Yakima, WA, 2012. For scholarship disbursement.
$250,000 to Goldman Sachs Philanthropy Fund, Jersey City, NJ, 2012.
$109,750 to Heritage University, Toppenish, WA, 2012. For One Voice in Higher Education.
$68,000 to Nature Conservancy, Arlington, VA, 2013.
$37,500 to Association of Washington State Hispanic Chambers of Commerce, Seattle, WA, 2013.
$35,000 to Saint Joseph Marquette Catholic School, Yakima, WA, 2013.
$30,000 to Hospice Friends, Ellensburg, WA, 2012.
$30,000 to Hospice Friends, Ellensburg, WA, 2013. For Schaake grant.
$25,000 to United Way of Central Washington, YC Life, Yakima, WA, 2012.
$25,000 to Yakima Valley Memorial Hospital Charitable Foundation, Yakima, WA, 2012. For Children's Village Expansion.
$25,000 to Yakima Valley Memorial Hospital Charitable Foundation, Yakima, WA, 2013. For Sundquist Grant for Children's Village Expansion.
$24,000 to Yakima Rotary Trust, Yakima, WA, 2012.
$20,000 to Saint Joseph Marquette Catholic School, Yakima, WA, 2012.
$20,000 to Yakima Valley Hearing and Speech Center, Yakima, WA, 2012.
$11,000 to YWCA of Yakima, Yakima, WA, 2013. For Responsive Grants Docket.
$10,000 to Cowiche Canyon Conservancy, Yakima, WA, 2013.
$10,000 to Yakima Valley Hearing and Speech Center, Yakima, WA, 2013. For Responsive Grants Docket.
$7,485 to Entrust, Colorado Springs, CO, 2013. For Responsive Grants Docket.
$7,000 to American Red Cross, 2012. For relief - Taylor Bridge Fire 2012.

9768
Zumiez Foundation ✧

4001 204th St. S.W.
Lynnwood, WA 98036-6864 (425) 551-1500
Contact: Thomas Campion, Pres. and Dir.
Application address: 6300 Merrill Creek Pkwy., Ste. B, Everett, WA 98203; Main URL: http://www.zumiez.com/foundation

Established in 2005 in WA.
Donors: Rick Brooks; Ann Trapp; Deanna Hudson; Rick Brooks; Zumiez Inc.; The Campion Foundation; Andrew Traynham.
Foundation type: Operating foundation.
Financial data (yr. ended 12/31/12): Assets, $833,035 (M); gifts received, $1,202,136; expenditures, $888,206; qualifying distributions, $888,206; giving activities include $730,463 for grants.
Fields of interest: Education; Human services; Children/youth, services; Family services; Christian agencies & churches.
Limitations: Applications accepted. Giving primarily in WA.
Application information: Application form required.
Initial approach: Letter
Deadline(s): None
Officers and Directors:* Thomas Campion,* Pres.; Ann Trapp, Secy.; Andrew Traynham, Treas.; Will Eaton; Ben Hughes; Keith Lowinske; Todd Morgan; Jason Rose; Deeann Roundy.
EIN: 203313651

WEST VIRGINIA

9769
Beckley Area Foundation, Inc. ✧
129 Main St., Ste. 203
Beckley, WV 25801-4615 (304) 253-3806
Contact: Susan S. Landis, Exec. Dir.
FAX: (304) 253-7304; E-mail: info@bafwv.org; Main URL: http://www.bafwv.org/

Established in 1985 in WV.
Foundation type: Community foundation.
Financial data (yr. ended 03/31/13): Assets, $31,560,282 (M); gifts received, $1,609,941; expenditures, $974,282; giving activities include $668,387 for 178 grants (high: $31,385), and $4,456 for grants to individuals.
Purpose and activities: The foundation focuses its grantmaking on the arts, health and human services, public recreation, education, and civic beautification in specific geographic areas of southern West Virginia.
Fields of interest: Arts; Education; Environment, beautification programs; Health organizations, association; Recreation; Human services; Community development, neighborhood development.
Type of support: Capital campaigns; Building/renovation; Equipment; Program development; Conferences/seminars; Seed money; Scholarship funds; Technical assistance; Consulting services; Matching/challenge support.
Limitations: Applications accepted. Giving limited to the Beckley and Raleigh County, WV, area for Discretionary grant program; designated funds support a number of counties in WV. No support for sectarian religious programs. No grants for ongoing maintenance and operating expenses, annual campaigns, debt reduction, or endowments.
Publications: Application guidelines; Annual report; Financial statement; Grants list; Informational brochure; Informational brochure (including application guidelines); Newsletter; Occasional report; Program policy statement (including application guidelines).
Application information: Visit foundation web site for application form and guidelines. Faxed or e-mailed applications are not accepted. Application form required.
Initial approach: Mail grant request form and proposal
Copies of proposal: 1
Deadline(s): Dec. 16 for grants; Sept. 30 for "Student's First" mini-grants
Board meeting date(s): Mar., Apr., June, Sept., and Dec.
Final notification: Mar. for grants; Oct. 31 for "Student's First" mini-grants
Officers and Directors:* William H. File,* Pres.; Michael Cavendish,* V.P.; Rachel Abrams Hopkins,* Secy.; Jon Calfee,* Treas.; Dena Cushman,* C.F.O.; Susan S. Landis, Exec. Dir.; Bill Baker; Hazel Burroughs; Dawn Dayton; Dan Doman; Dr. Brett Eckley; Deborah Songer Gray; Bill O'Brien; Susan Pietrantozzi; Linda Polly; Yvonne D. Seay; William L. Turner.
Number of staff: 3 full-time professional.
EIN: 311125328

9770
Ethel N. Bowen Foundation ✧ ☆
c/o First Century Bank, N.A.
500 Federal St.
Bluefield, WV 24701-3010 (304) 325-8181

Established about 1968 in WV.
Donor: Ethel N. Bowen†.
Foundation type: Independent foundation.
Financial data (yr. ended 12/31/13): Assets, $10,027,059 (M); expenditures, $529,682; giving activities include $142,210 for 39 grants (high: $25,000; low: $150), and $281,940 for 510 grants to individuals (high: $1,000; low: $250).
Purpose and activities: Giving primarily for scholarships to further the education of students in southern WV and southwestern VA; support also for higher, secondary, and other education, and a municipality.
Fields of interest: Secondary school/education; Higher education; Education; Government/public administration.
Type of support: General/operating support; Scholarship funds; Scholarships—to individuals.
Limitations: Giving limited to residents of southwestern VA and southern WV.
Application information: Students required to submit transcript. Application form not required.
Initial approach: Letter
Copies of proposal: 1
Deadline(s): Prior to beginning of academic year for scholarships.
Board meeting date(s): Monthly
Officers and Directors:* Frank W. Wilkinson,* Pres.; R.W. Wilkinson,* Secy.; B.K. Satterfield,* Treas.; Henry Bowen.
Investment Agent: First Century Bank, N.A.
EIN: 237010740

9771
Brickstreet Foundation, Inc. ✧ ☆
400 Quarrier St.
Charleston, WV 25301-2010 (304) 941-1000
Contact: Lucy Allara

Established in WV.
Donor: Brickstreet Mutual Insurance Company.
Foundation type: Independent foundation.
Financial data (yr. ended 12/31/13): Assets, $31,463,016 (M); expenditures, $3,827,729; qualifying distributions, $3,816,704; giving activities include $3,811,416 for 40 grants (high: $1,500,000; low: $250).
Fields of interest: Education; Environment; Youth development.
Application information: Application form required.
Initial approach: Proposal
Deadline(s): None
Officers: Gregory A. Burton, Pres.; Thomas J. Obrokta, Jr., Secy.; J. Christopher Howat, Treas.
EIN: 800772825

9772
James B. Chambers Memorial ✧ ☆
P.O. Box 3047
Wheeling, WV 26003-0207 (304) 243-9373
Contact: Emily Schramm-Fisher
Main URL: http://jbchambersfoundation.org/

Established in 1924 in WV.
Foundation type: Independent foundation.
Financial data (yr. ended 12/31/13): Assets, $11,204,509 (M); expenditures, $594,164; qualifying distributions, $471,611; giving activities include $424,704 for 15 grants (high: $150,000; low: $2,500).
Purpose and activities: Giving limited to funding for indigent children in Ohio County, WV.
Fields of interest: Education; Recreation; Human services; Children/youth, services; Community/economic development; Foundations (community); Children; Economically disadvantaged.
Type of support: Capital campaigns; Building/renovation; Equipment; Program development; Seed money; Technical assistance; Matching/challenge support.
Limitations: Applications accepted. Giving limited to Ohio County, WV. No support for political organizations, or for non-501(c)3 organizations. No grants to individuals, or for salaries.
Application information: Application form required.
Initial approach: Proposal
Deadline(s): None
Board meeting date(s): Bimonthly
Officers: Thomas L. Thomas, Pres.; James E. Altmeyer, V.P.; Edward G. Sloane, Jr., Secy.-Treas.
Directors: Thomas L. Gompers; Brian E. Joseph; Arthur M. Recht; C. Jack Savage.
Number of staff: 1 part-time professional.
EIN: 550360517
Selected grants: The following grants are a representative sample of this grantmaker's funding activity:
$1,730 to Ohio County Schools, Wheeling, WV, 2012. For Youth and Government Seminars.

9773
Community Foundation for the Ohio Valley, Inc. ✧
(also known as CFOV)
1310 Market St., Ste. 1
Wheeling, WV 26003-0085 (304) 242-3144
Contact: Susie Nelson, Exec. Dir.; For grants: Renee George, Grants Admin.
FAX: (304) 234-4753; E-mail: info@cfov.org; Mailing address: P.O. 670, Wheeling, WV 26003-0085; Additional e-mail: director@cfov.org; Grant inquiry e-mail: renee@cfov.org; Main URL: http://www.cfov.org

Established in 1972 in WV.
Foundation type: Community foundation.
Financial data (yr. ended 06/30/13): Assets, $29,203,518 (M); gifts received, $1,636,018; expenditures, $1,817,475; giving activities include $1,411,975 for 60+ grants (high: $230,915).
Purpose and activities: To increase a permanent endowment that can respond to the current and future needs of the Upper Ohio Valley. The foundation accomplish this mission via several ways: 1) works with donors and their financial advisors to provide a flexible, efficient and lasting way for them to benefit their community; 2) is a faithful steward and prudent manager of philanthropic assets; 3) initiates responses that focus on the needs within the community; 4) makes grants that will have a significant impact upon the recipients.
Fields of interest: Historic preservation/historical societies; Arts; Education; Health care; Human services; Economic development; Community/economic development; Children/youth; Youth; Women; Girls; Economically disadvantaged.

Type of support: Building/renovation; Conferences/seminars; Consulting services; Equipment; Matching/challenge support; Program development; Scholarship funds; Seed money; Technical assistance.
Limitations: Applications accepted. Giving in the Upper Ohio Valley area: Brooke, Jefferson, Marshall, Ohio, Tyler and Wetzel counties, WV, and Belmont, Guernsey and Monroe counties, OH. No support for sectarian religious purposes. No grants to individuals (except for scholarships), or for endowment campaigns, or general operating or maintenance expenses for established organizations; no loans.
Publications: Application guidelines; Annual report; Annual report (including application guidelines); Grants list; Informational brochure; Newsletter; Program policy statement.
Application information: Visit foundation web site for required pre-application form and guidelines. Application form required.
Initial approach: Telephone or letter
Copies of proposal: 1
Deadline(s): Pre-application due Apr. 15; full application due May 31
Board meeting date(s): Jan., Apr., July, and Oct.
Final notification: Determination in early May to submit full application. Final determination in July.
Officers and Directors:* Sue Seibert Farnsworth,* Pres.; Bob Robinson,* V.P.; David B. Dalzell, Jr.,* Secy.; Edward Gompers,* Treas.; Susie Nelson, Exec. Dir.; Joseph W. Boutaugh, Emeritus; Mark C. Ferrell; Beri Fox; Joseph Glaub; Jay Goodman; Christine Hargrave; Carlos Jimenez, M.D.; Dr. H. Lawrence Jones; Charles J. Kaiser, Jr.; Mark A. McKeen; Tulane Mensore; William O. Nutting; Elsie Reyes; Fredrick Dean Rohrig; James G. Squibb, Jr.; Joan Corson Stamp; Will Turani; William J. Yaeger, Jr.
Trustee Banks: Huntington Bank; Monteverde Group; Premier Bank and Trust; Security National Trust Co.; United Bank; WesBanco Trust & Investment Services, Inc.
Number of staff: 1 full-time professional; 1 full-time support; 1 part-time support.
EIN: 310908698
Selected grants: The following grants are a representative sample of this grantmaker's funding activity:
$6,050 to West Liberty University Foundation, West Liberty, WV, 2012. For series of interactive workshops for parents to gain expertise in raising healthy children and adolescents.
$5,220 to Martins Ferry Public Library, Martins Ferry, OH, 2012. For computer for the public.
$5,000 to Faith in Action Caregivers, Wheeling, WV, 2012. For seminar for caregivers of Alzheimer's patients.
$5,000 to Helping Heroes, Moundsville, WV, 2012. To end homelessness among veterans and their families throughout Northern Panhandle.
$5,000 to YMCA of Wheeling, Wheeling, WV, 2012. For pool and exercise equipment for handicapped children and adults.
$5,000 to Youth Services System, Wheeling, WV, 2012. For transitional housing for young adults aging out of foster care system.
$4,903 to Oglebay Institute, Wheeling, WV, 2012. To connect art, history and science through Raku at Cameron High School, Wheeling Middle School and Franklin Primary School.
$4,500 to Strand Theater of Shreveport Corporation, Shreveport, LA, 2012. For Missoula Children's Theater Camp.
$4,000 to Ohio State University, Belmont County Extension, Columbus, OH, 2012. For course for high school freshman and sophomore girls from Belmont County Schools to celebrate women 's health and wellness.
$4,000 to Saint Clairsville Elementary Playground Committee, 2012. For outdoor classroom.
$2,500 to Ohio County Family Resource Network, Wheeling, WV, 2012. For respite care services and parenting support for parents of children with mild to moderate disabilities.
$1,200 to House of the Carpenter, Wheeling, WV, 2012. To teach music classes for children ages 8-12.
$950 to Artslink, Inc., New Martinsville, WV, 2012. For Vaudeville performance in Wetzel County.

9774
The Daywood Foundation, Inc. ✧

707 Virginia St. E., Ste. 1600
Charleston, WV 25301-2723
Application address: c/o William W. Booker, 1500 Chase Tower, Charleston, WV 25301, tel.: (304) 345-8900

Incorporated in 1958 in WV.
Donor: Ruth Woods Dayton†.
Foundation type: Independent foundation.
Financial data (yr. ended 12/31/13): Assets, $19,511,356 (M); expenditures, $1,170,683; qualifying distributions, $1,077,087; giving activities include $1,069,600 for 64 grants (high: $200,000; low: $1,500).
Purpose and activities: Giving primarily for community service organizations focusing on the arts, and health and human services.
Fields of interest: Museums; Arts; Higher education; Education; Human services; American Red Cross; Children/youth, services; Family services; Community/economic development.
Type of support: Debt reduction; Continuing support; General/operating support; Annual campaigns; Capital campaigns; Building/renovation; Equipment; Emergency funds; Seed money; Matching/challenge support.
Limitations: Applications accepted. Giving limited to Barbour, Greenbrier and Kanawha counties, WV. No grants to individuals, or for endowment funds, research, individual scholarships, or fellowships; no loans.
Application information: Application form required.
Initial approach: Letter
Copies of proposal: 1
Deadline(s): Sept. 15
Officers: L. Newton Thomas, Jr., Pres.; Richard E. Ford, V.P.; William W. Booker, Secy.-Treas.
Directors: William Satterfield; Charles Stansbury.
Number of staff: 1 part-time support.
EIN: 556018107

9775
Eastern West Virginia Community Foundation ✧

229 E. Martin St., Ste. 4
Martinsburg, WV 25401-4307 (304) 264-0353
Contact: Michael Whalton, Exec. Dir.
FAX: (888) 507-8375; E-mail: info@ewvcf.org; Main URL: http://www.ewvcf.org
Facebook: http://www.facebook.com/pages/Eastern-West-Virginia-Community-Foundation/130566868758

Established in 1995 in WV.
Foundation type: Community foundation.
Financial data (yr. ended 12/31/13): Assets, $17,969,329 (M); gifts received, $622,053; expenditures, $779,803; giving activities include $441,875 for 22+ grants (high: $132,000), and $67,050 for 58 grants to individuals.
Purpose and activities: The foundation seeks to build and sustain endowment growth in the West Virginia's Eastern panhandle to benefit charitable programs and activities.
Fields of interest: Arts education; Performing arts, theater; Arts; Education; Environment; Health care; Substance abuse, services; Recreation; Children/youth, services; Family services; Community development, neighborhood development; Economic development; Infants/toddlers; Children/youth; Children; Youth; Disabilities, people with; Homeless.
Type of support: General/operating support; Continuing support; Management development/capacity building; Annual campaigns; Capital campaigns; Building/renovation; Equipment; Land acquisition; Endowments; Program development; Seed money; Curriculum development; Internship funds; Scholarships—to individuals; Matching/challenge support.
Limitations: Applications accepted. Giving primarily in Berkeley, Hardy, Hampshire, Jefferson, and Morgan counties, WV.
Publications: Application guidelines; Annual report; Financial statement; Grants list; Informational brochure; Newsletter.
Application information: Visit foundation web site for application cover forms and guidelines. Application form required.
Initial approach: Telephone or submit application cover form and proposal
Copies of proposal: 11
Deadline(s): Varies
Board meeting date(s): Varies
Final notification: Varies
Officers and Directors:* Scott Roach,* Pres.; Darlene Truman,* V.P.; Chip Hensell,* Secy.; Lisa Welch,* Treas.; Michael Whalton, Exec. Dir.; Alan Brill; Diane Dailey; Joan Ergin; George Karos; Jim Keel; Judi McIntyre; Neil McLaughlin; Diane Melby; Charlotte Norris; Chris Palmer; Ruth Pritchard; B. Lee Snyder; Terry Walker; Bill White; Jan Wilkins.
Number of staff: 3 full-time professional.
EIN: 550742377

9776
The Jeanne G. and Lawson W. Hamilton, Jr. Family Foundation, Inc. ✧

P.O. Box 175
Hansford, WV 25103-0000 (304) 595-1077
Contact: Charles L. Jarrell, Tr.
FAX: (304) 595-1104; Application address: P.O. Box 175, Hansford, WV 25103, tel.: (304) 595-1077

Established in 2004 in WV.
Donors: Lawson W. Hamilton, Jr.; Jeanne G. Hamilton; Lawson W. Hamilton III.
Foundation type: Independent foundation.
Financial data (yr. ended 12/31/12): Assets, $9,981,102 (M); expenditures, $518,817;

qualifying distributions, $461,900; giving activities include $461,900 for grants.
Fields of interest: Arts; Higher education, university; Animal welfare; Human services; Christian agencies & churches.
Type of support: General/operating support; Building/renovation; Equipment; Research.
Limitations: Applications accepted. Giving primarily in WV. No support for political organizations. No grants to individuals.
Application information: Application form required.
Initial approach: Required application form
Deadline(s): None
Board meeting date(s): June and Dec.
Officers and Trustees:* Jeanne G. Hamilton,* Pres.; Barbara Hamilton Ford,* Secy.; Lawson W. Hamilton III,* Treas.; Meredith M. German; Charles L. Jarrell; Courtney M. O'Neil.
EIN: 201885473

9777
Chris Hess Foundation ✧
117 Edgington Ln.
Wheeling, WV 26003-1534
Contact: Joseph N. Gompers, Tr.
FAX: (304) 242-3854; E-mail: joe@gomperscpa.com

Established in 2003 in WV.
Donor: Andrew Christopher Henry Hess.
Foundation type: Independent foundation.
Financial data (yr. ended 12/31/13): Assets, $10,622,823 (M); expenditures, $598,987; qualifying distributions, $502,330; giving activities include $476,200 for 17 grants (high: $227,000; low: $2,500).
Fields of interest: Higher education; Education; American Red Cross; Salvation Army; YM/YWCAs & YM/YWHAs; United Ways and Federated Giving Programs; Christian agencies & churches.
Limitations: Applications accepted. Giving primarily in WV.
Application information: Application form not required.
Initial approach: Letter
Deadline(s): None
Trustees: William V. Busick; John E. Gompers; Joseph N. Gompers; Security National Trust Co.
EIN: 016225742

9778
Hollowell Foundation, Inc. ✧ ☆
(formerly Hollowell-Ford Foundation, Inc.)
103 E. Washington St.
Lewisburg, WV 24901-1427 (304) 645-3313
Contact: Allen Carson, Pres.
Application address: 117 N. Court St., Lewisburg, WV 24901

Established in 1975 in WV.
Donors: Margaret F. Hollowell†; John R. Dawkins†; Otto Hollowell Unitrust.
Foundation type: Independent foundation.
Financial data (yr. ended 06/30/13): Assets, $7,804,064 (M); expenditures, $595,711; qualifying distributions, $438,255; giving activities include $426,300 for 50 grants (high: $45,000; low: $500).
Purpose and activities: Giving primarily for community improvement and renovation projects.
Fields of interest: Arts; Higher education; Human services; Community/economic development.
Type of support: Capital campaigns; General/operating support; Building/renovation; Matching/challenge support.
Limitations: Applications accepted. Giving limited to Greenbrier County, WV. No grants to individuals.
Application information: Application form required.
Initial approach: Letter
Copies of proposal: 1
Deadline(s): Apr. 1
Board meeting date(s): Jan., Apr., June, and Sept.
Final notification: June 30
Officers: Allen Carson, Pres.; Thomas G. McMillan, V.P.; Marshall Musser, Secy.; H. Richard Marshall, Treas.
Number of staff: 1 part-time professional.
EIN: 510183517

9779
The H. P. and Anne S. Hunnicutt Foundation, Inc. ✧
P.O. Box 309
Princeton, WV 24740-0309 (304) 425-9259
Contact: William Stafford II, Secy.

Established in 1987 in WV.
Donors: H.P. Hunnicutt; Anne S. Hunnicutt†.
Foundation type: Independent foundation.
Financial data (yr. ended 06/30/13): Assets, $19,173,748 (M); expenditures, $893,543; qualifying distributions, $753,371; giving activities include $718,119 for 26 grants (high: $129,263; low: $107).
Fields of interest: Education, administration/regulation; Secondary school/education; Libraries (public); Education; Human services; Salvation Army; Protestant agencies & churches.
Limitations: Applications accepted. Giving limited to southern WV.
Application information: Application form required.
Initial approach: Letter
Deadline(s): None
Officers: William P. Stafford, Pres.; James H. Sarver, V.P.; William Stafford II, Secy.; James H. Sarver II, Treas.
Agent: First Community Bank, Inc.
EIN: 550670462

9780
The Greater Kanawha Valley Foundation ✧
1600 Huntington Sq.
900 Lee St. E.
Charleston, WV 25301-1741 (304) 346-3620
Contact: Rebecca Ceperley, C.E.O.; For grants: Stephanie Hyre, Prog. Off.
FAX: (304) 346-3640; E-mail: tgkvf@tgkvf.org; Additional address: P.O. Box 3041, Charleston, WV 25331; Additional tel.: (800) 467-5909; Grant application E-mail: shyre@tgkvf.org; Main URL: http://www.tgkvf.org
Facebook: http://www.facebook.com/pages/The-Greater-Kanawha-Valley-Foundation/105286039510527?ref=sgm
Scholarship e-mail: shoover@tgkvf.org

Established in 1962 in WV.
Foundation type: Community foundation.
Financial data (yr. ended 12/31/12): Assets, $192,410,440 (M); gifts received, $61,470,336; expenditures, $7,700,708; giving activities include $5,966,002 for grants, and $473,100 for grants to individuals.
Purpose and activities: The mission of the foundation is to improve the quality of life and promote philanthropy.
Fields of interest: Museums; Performing arts; Performing arts, dance; Humanities; Historic preservation/historical societies; Arts; Education, early childhood education; Elementary school/education; Higher education; Libraries/library science; Education; Environment, natural resources; Environment; Dental care; Nursing care; Health care; Substance abuse, services; Housing/shelter, development; Recreation; Children/youth, services; Family services; Residential/custodial care, hospices; Women, centers/services; Homeless, human services; Human services; Economic development; Community/economic development; Social sciences; Disabilities, people with; Women; Homeless.
Type of support: Continuing support; Capital campaigns; Building/renovation; Equipment; Emergency funds; Program development; Publication; Seed money; Scholarship funds; Research; Technical assistance; Program evaluation; Scholarships—to individuals; Matching/challenge support.
Limitations: Applications accepted. Giving limited to the greater Kanawha Valley, WV, area, except scholarships which are limited to residents of WV. No support for religious activities of religious organizations. No grants to individuals (except for designated scholarship funds), or for general operating budgets for established organizations, annual campaigns, membership drives, travel, uniforms, ongoing support for the same project, staff costs, consultants, consultant fees, conferences, workshop speakers, student aid or fellowships, or endowments; no loans.
Publications: Application guidelines; Annual report (including application guidelines); Financial statement; Grants list; Informational brochure; Occasional report.
Application information: The foundation offers free grant information sessions; visit foundation web site for more information and online grant application. Application form required.
Initial approach: Submit online application and attachments
Deadline(s): Feb. 1 for Education, Arts, & Culture, May 2 for Health and Human Svcs., and Aug. 1 for Recreation & Land Use; Jan. 15 for scholarships
Board meeting date(s): Quarterly, usually in Mar., June, Sept., and Dec.
Final notification: Immediately after Board action
Officers and Trustees:* Nelle Chilton,* Chair.; Melvin Jones,* Vice-Chair.; Rebecca Ceperley, C.E.O. and Pres.; Patricia Majic, C.F.O.; Susan L. Basile; Dayton Carpenter; Monika Hussell; Dr. Jamal Khan; Charles Loeb, Jr.; Todd Mount; Ron L. Potesta; Susan Shumate; Troy Stallard; Phillip Tissue.
Advisory Committee: Paul Arbogast; G. Thomas Battle; Frederick H. Belden, Jr.; Charles L. Capito, Jr.; Elsie P. Carter; William D. Chambers; T. Randolph Cox; Elizabeth E. Chilton; Stephen Crislip; William M. Davis; Deborah A. Faber; Rebecca B. Goldman; Charles R. McElwee; Thomas N. McJunkin; Harry S. Moore; Rick Morgan; William E. Mullett, Ph.D.; Sandra Murphy; David Rollins; Barbara Rose; Virginia Rugeley; Mark H. Schaul; Dolly Sherwood; K. Richard C. Sinclair; Olivia R. Singleton; Louis B. Southworth; L. Newton Thomas, Jr.; Adeline J. Voorhees.

Trustee Banks: City National Bank of Charleston; BB&T; The Huntington National Bank; JPMorgan Chase Bank, N.A.; United Bank; WesBanco Bank, Inc.
Number of staff: 8 full-time professional; 2 part-time support.
EIN: 556024430

9781
George A. Laughlin Trust ✧
1 Bank Plz.
Wheeling, WV 26003-3543 (304) 234-9400
Contact: Lea Ridenhour
E-mail: ridenhour@wesbanco.com

Established in 1936 in WV.
Foundation type: Independent foundation.
Financial data (yr. ended 12/31/13): Assets, $16,767,390 (M); expenditures, $858,397; qualifying distributions, $749,813; giving activities include $742,290 for 103 grants to individuals (high: $94,665; low: $789).
Purpose and activities: The trust awards non-interest-bearing home loans to local area low-income individuals.
Fields of interest: Housing/shelter; Economically disadvantaged.
Type of support: Student loans—to individuals.
Limitations: Applications accepted. Giving limited to Ohio County, WV, residents.
Application information: Application form required.
Initial approach: Proposal
Deadline(s): Apr. 1 to Apr. 30
Trustee: WesBanco Bank, N.A.
EIN: 556016889

9782
Maier Foundation, Inc. ✧
(formerly Sarah & Pauline Maier Foundation)
P.O. Box 6190
Charleston, WV 25362-0190
Contact: Brad M. Rowe, Pres.
Main URL: http://www.maierfoundation.org
Grants List: http://www.maierfoundation.org/granthistory.php

Established in 1958 in WV.
Donors: William J. Maier, Jr.†; Pauline Maier†; General Corporation.
Foundation type: Independent foundation.
Financial data (yr. ended 10/31/13): Assets, $27,212,043 (M); expenditures, $1,677,486; qualifying distributions, $1,162,126; giving activities include $1,161,000 for 23 grants (high: $250,000; low: $1,000).
Purpose and activities: Giving for higher education in West Virginia and other educationally-related pursuits in Kanawha County, West Virginia.
Fields of interest: Higher education; Education.
Type of support: General/operating support; Annual campaigns; Capital campaigns; Building/renovation; Equipment; Endowments; Program development; Professorships; Scholarship funds; Matching/challenge support.
Limitations: Applications accepted. Giving limited to WV. No support for religious or political organizations, or primary or secondary educational institutions. No grants to individuals.
Publications: Application guidelines; Program policy statement.
Application information: Application form required.
Initial approach: Letter
Copies of proposal: 11
Deadline(s): Oct. 1
Board meeting date(s): 1st Fri. in Dec.
Final notification: Dec. 31
Officers and Board Members:* Edward H. Maier,* Chair.; Bradley M. Rowe,* Pres.; Sandra D. Thomas,* Secy.; Sara M. Rowe,* Treas.; John T. Copenhaver; Charles I. Jones, Jr.; J. Holmes Morrison; Thomas W. Rowe; J. Randy Valentine.
Number of staff: None.
EIN: 556023833

9783
The Martha Gaines and Russell Wehrle Memorial Foundation ✧ ☆
c/o Adventure WV Resort
P.O. Box 78
Lansing, WV 25862

Established in WV.
Foundation type: Independent foundation.
Financial data (yr. ended 12/31/13): Assets, $12,684,892 (M); expenditures, $683,646; qualifying distributions, $620,250; giving activities include $616,000 for 47 grants (high: $60,000; low: $1,000).
Fields of interest: Education; Health care; Youth development.
Limitations: Applications not accepted.
Application information: Unsolicited requests for funds not accepted.
Trustees: Thomas A. Heywood; Katherine Wehrle Kend; Martha Chilton Mueller; E. Gaines Wehrle; Michael H. Wehrle.
EIN: 266428986

9784
Bernard McDonough Foundation, Inc. ✧
311 4th St.
Parkersburg, WV 26101-5315 (304) 424-6280
FAX: (304) 424-6281; Main URL: http://www.mcdonoughfoundation.org/

Incorporated in 1961 in WV.
Donor: Bernard P. McDonough†.
Foundation type: Independent foundation.
Financial data (yr. ended 12/31/13): Assets, $37,412,845 (M); expenditures, $1,924,643; qualifying distributions, $1,722,358; giving activities include $1,393,206 for 115 grants (high: $90,000; low: $100).
Purpose and activities: Giving primarily for 1) Health and Medical (support of hospitals, clinics and other health related charities); 2) Social Welfare (those organizations whose primary function is to serve the general welfare requirements of people whose circumstances in life require that they receive financial or social aid to improve their quality of life); and 3) Civic and Community Enterprises (organizations and municipalities whose projects need financial support to enhance the economic growth and general welfare of the community).
Fields of interest: Health care; Human services; Community/economic development.
Type of support: General/operating support; Annual campaigns; Capital campaigns; Building/renovation; Equipment; Emergency funds; Program development; Employee matching gifts; Matching/challenge support.
Limitations: Applications accepted. Giving primarily in Washington County, OH, and WV; applicants whose services extend to the residents of the primary geographical area, but whose location may be just outside the primary geographical area are accepted. No support for religious or political organizations, or for public or private school clubs, extra-curricular organizations, or facilities used primarily for athletics or athletic events. No grants to individuals, or for sports, travel or start-up operations.
Publications: Application guidelines.
Application information: Application form not required.
Initial approach: Letter
Copies of proposal: 1
Deadline(s): None
Board meeting date(s): Feb., May, Aug. and Oct.
Final notification: 2 to 4 weeks
Officers and Directors:* Robert W. Stephens, Ed.D.*, Pres.; Mary Riccobene,* V.P.; Katrina A. Valentine, Secy.; Francis C. McCusker,* Treas.; Robert S. Boone; Dale A. Knight.
Number of staff: 2 full-time professional.
EIN: 556023693

9785
Hazel Ruby McQuain Charitable Trust ✧
(formerly H. L. Robinson Charitable Trust)
P.O. Box 683
Morgantown, WV 26507-0683 (304) 599-4037

Established in 1989 in WV.
Donors: Hazel Ruby McQuain†; Hazel Ruby McQuain Trust.
Foundation type: Independent foundation.
Financial data (yr. ended 12/31/13): Assets, $166,373,038 (M); expenditures, $7,389,996; qualifying distributions, $7,289,996; giving activities include $6,304,513 for 40 grants (high: $4,000,000; low: $100).
Fields of interest: Higher education, university; Hospitals (general); Human services; Children/youth, services; Community/economic development.
Limitations: Applications not accepted. Giving primarily in Morgantown, WV. No grants to individuals.
Application information: Contributes only to pre-selected organizations.
Trustees: Charles D. Dunbar; George R. Farmer, Jr.; Stephen B. Farmer; Robert A. Toepfer.
EIN: 346899181
Selected grants: The following grants are a representative sample of this grantmaker's funding activity:
$3,000,000 to West Virginia University Foundation, College of Law, Morgantown, WV, 2012. For renovations.
$2,222,500 to Boy Scouts of America, Mountaineer Area Council, Morgantown, WV, 2012. For general support and Welcome Center.
$1,050,000 to Monongalia County Board of Education, Morgantown, WV, 2012. For Sports Complex.
$259,389 to West Virginia University Foundation, Morgantown, WV, 2012. For WVU basketball facility.
$25,000 to Mountain Heart Foundation, Star City, WV, 2012. For general support.
$15,000 to West Virginia University Foundation, Morgantown, WV, 2012. For Rogers House.

$11,000 to Board of Park and Recreation Commissioners, Morgantown, WV, 2012. For general support.

9786
Meagel Charitable Trust ✧
c/o United Bank, Inc.
514 Market St.
Parkersburg, WV 26101

Established in WV.
Foundation type: Independent foundation.
Financial data (yr. ended 12/31/13): Assets, $22,399,623 (M); expenditures, $1,122,333; qualifying distributions, $1,035,365; giving activities include $974,244 for 16 grants (high: $97,425; low: $48,712).
Fields of interest: Higher education; Human services; Children/youth, services.
Limitations: Applications not accepted. Giving primarily in WV.
Application information: Contributes only to pre-selected organizations.
Trustee: United Bank, Inc.
EIN: 556138839
Selected grants: The following grants are a representative sample of this grantmaker's funding activity:
$46,452 to American Heart Association, Columbus, OH, 2012. For Research in West Virginia.
$46,452 to House of the Carpenter, Wheeling, WV, 2012. For Care for Homeless and Those in Need Charitable.

9787
Myles Family Foundation ✧
P.O. Box 1274
Elkins, WV 26241-1274

Established in 2000 in WV.
Donor: Virginia R. Myles‡.
Foundation type: Independent foundation.
Financial data (yr. ended 12/31/13): Assets, $13,196,036 (M); expenditures, $1,436,963; qualifying distributions, $1,337,300; giving activities include $1,337,300 for 11 grants (high: $1,184,800; low: $5,000).
Fields of interest: Higher education, college; Higher education, university; Education; Human services.
Limitations: Applications not accepted. Giving primarily in Elkins, WV. No grants to individuals.
Application information: Contributes only to pre-selected organizations.
Trustees: R. Faye Channell; June B. Myles.
EIN: 556126320

9788
The Nutting Foundation ✧ ☆
1500 Main St.
Wheeling, WV 26003-2826

Established in WV.
Donors: Robert M. Nutting; William O. Nutting.
Foundation type: Independent foundation.
Financial data (yr. ended 12/31/13): Assets, $10,610,732 (M); expenditures, $481,390; qualifying distributions, $465,125; giving activities include $465,100 for 23 grants (high: $120,000; low: $100).
Fields of interest: Higher education; Education.
Limitations: Applications not accepted. Giving primarily in MA and WV. No grants to individuals.
Application information: Contributes only to pre-selected organizations.
Officers: Robert M. Nutting, Pres.; William O. Nutting, Secy.
EIN: 311683582
Selected grants: The following grants are a representative sample of this grantmaker's funding activity:
$49,000 to Wheeling Country Day School, Wheeling, WV, 2012. For Designated 22,500 for the Capital Campaign Building Fund; 24,000 to a school matching campaign; and 2,500 to the Annual Giving Fund 2012-2013.
$25,000 to University of Mary Washington, Fredericksburg, VA, 2012. To establish and fund a named scholarship endowment.
$10,000 to Harvard College Fund, Cambridge, MA, 2012. For general operating use of recipient organization.
$10,000 to West Liberty University Foundation, West Liberty, WV, 2012. For Designated for the 2012-2013 Annual Fund to support the Arts and Ideas Program.
$5,000 to Texas Heart Institute, Houston, TX, 2012. For Research and/or Greatest Need.

9789
Parkersburg Area Community Foundation ✧
(also known as Our Community's Foundation)
1620 Park Ave.
P.O. Box 1762
Parkersburg, WV 26102-1762 (304) 428-4438
Contact: Judy Sjostedt, Exec. Dir.; Marian Clowes, Prog. and Devel. Off.
FAX: (304) 428-1200; E-mail: info@pacfwv.com; Additional tel.: (866) 428-4438; Additional e-mail: marian.clowes@pacfwv.com; Ripley field office tel.: (304) 372-8588; Main URL: http://www.pacfwv.com
Facebook: https://www.facebook.com/pages/Our-Communitys-Foundation/94685606425
YouTube: http://www.youtube.com/user/PACFWV?feature=creators_cornier-http%253A%2F%2Fs.ytimg.com%2Fyt%2Fimg%2Fcreators_corner%2FYouTube%2Fyoutube_32x32.png

Established in 1963 in WV.
Donors: Albert Wolfe; The Keystone Foundation.
Foundation type: Community foundation.
Financial data (yr. ended 06/30/11): Assets, $28,536,938 (M); gifts received, $2,272,062; expenditures, $2,245,062; giving activities include $1,505,215 for grants, and $293,055 for grants to individuals.
Purpose and activities: The foundation serves the people of region by providing leadership and inspiring people to build permanent resources for the betterment of their communities through the foundation.
Fields of interest: Museums; Historic preservation/historical societies; Arts; Child development, education; Higher education; Adult education—literacy, basic skills & GED; Libraries/library science; Education, reading; Education; Animal welfare; Health care; Mental health/crisis services; Recreation; Children/youth, services; Child development, services; Family services; Human services; Economic development; Community/economic development.
Type of support: Management development/capacity building; Capital campaigns; Building/renovation; Equipment; Emergency funds; Program development; Seed money; Scholarship funds; Scholarships—to individuals; Matching/challenge support.
Limitations: Applications accepted. Giving limited to the Mid-Ohio Valley communities of Calhoun, Doddridge, Gilmer, Jackson, Mason, Pleasants, Ritchie, Roane, Wirt, and Wood counties, WV, and Washington County, OH. No support for sectarian religious purposes. Generally no grants for annual campaigns, endowments, sectarian religious purposes, retiring existing obligations, debts or liabilities, student travel or student participation in meetings, seminars or study exchange programs.
Publications: Application guidelines; Annual report; Informational brochure; Newsletter.
Application information: Visit the foundation's web site to access information about grantmaking programs, guidelines, and the online application form. May also e-mail, telephone, or send letter for guidelines. Application form required.
Initial approach: Review the Quick Eligibility Quiz
Deadline(s): Feb. 15 and Sept. 15; emergency and mini-grants may be considered at other times
Board meeting date(s): 3rd Fri. in Jan., Mar., May, July, Sept., and Nov.
Final notification: May and Nov.
Officers and Governors:* Ann Beck,* Chair.; Marie Caltrider,* Vice-Chair.; Dr. Usha Vasan,* Secy.; Curtis Miller,* Treas.; Judy Sjostedt,* Exec. Dir.; James Bennett; Cynthia Brown; Gwen Bush; Becky Deem; Randy Dick; Beau Ellison; Michael L. Fleak; Rob Fouss; Linda Gerrard; Larry Hancock; Greg Herrick; Paul Hicks; Bob Kent; Dr. Mansoor Matcheswalla; John Ralsten; Missi Scraberry; Donna Smith; Jim Strader; John Tebay; Tom Whaling; Daniel B. Wharton.
Number of staff: 2 full-time professional; 2 part-time professional; 1 full-time support.
EIN: 556027764

9790
The Preservati Family Charitable Trust Foundation ✧
c/o Arnold D. Lively, C.P.A.
1460 E. Main St.
Princeton, WV 24740-3068

Established in 2008 in WV.
Donors: Richard G. Preservati; N. Karen Preservati.
Foundation type: Independent foundation.
Financial data (yr. ended 12/31/13): Assets, $18,320,673 (M); gifts received, $2,538,507; expenditures, $560,025; qualifying distributions, $551,000; giving activities include $551,000 for 5 grants (high: $355,000; low: $7,500).
Fields of interest: Secondary school/education; Higher education; Athletics/sports, school programs.
Limitations: Applications not accepted. Giving primarily in Williamson and Morgantown, WV.
Application information: Contributes only to pre-selected organizations.
Trustees: Arnold D. Lively, C.P.A.; N. Karen Preservati; Richard G. Preservati.
EIN: 266679325

9791
Board of Trustees of the Prichard School ✧
c/o City National Bank Trust Wealth Mgmt.
1900 3rd Ave.
Huntington, WV 25703-1107
Application address: c/o Edward W. Morrison, 415 W. Whitaker Blvd., Huntington, WV 25701, tel.: (304) 523-3484

Established in 1923 in WV.
Foundation type: Independent foundation.
Financial data (yr. ended 12/31/13): Assets, $16,311,192 (M); expenditures, $2,013,584; qualifying distributions, $1,980,717; giving activities include $1,976,900 for 33 grants (high: $250,000; low: $3,500).
Purpose and activities: Giving primarily for education, the arts, health, and youth services.
Fields of interest: Arts; Elementary/secondary education; Higher education; Boys clubs; Big Brothers/Big Sisters; Children/youth, services; Residential/custodial care, hospices.
Type of support: General/operating support; Scholarship funds.
Limitations: Applications accepted. Giving primarily in VA and WV. No grants to individuals.
Application information: Application form not required.
Initial approach: Proposal
Deadline(s): None
Officers: Edward W. Morrison, Jr.,* Pres.; Marc W. Wild,* V.P.; Don O'Dell, Secy.-Treas.
Directors: Sharon Frazier; Steve Hatten; Elizabeth B. Jenkins; John F. Speer.
EIN: 550435910
Selected grants: The following grants are a representative sample of this grantmaker's funding activity:
$90,000 to Hospice of Huntington, Huntington, WV, 2012. For Charitable activities of Project Noah's Ark.
$25,000 to Marshall University Foundation, Huntington, WV, 2012. For Educational scholarships at Marshall University.
$15,000 to Huntington Museum of Art, Huntington, WV, 2012. For Educational and charitable activities of the recipient institution.

9792
The Ross Foundation Inc. ✧
200 Star Ave., Ste. 212
Parkersburg, WV 26101-5459 (304) 865-7294
E-mail: apply@therossfoundation.org; Main URL: http://www.therossfoundation.org

Established in 2006 in WV.
Donors: Ross Tailwind; Samuel B. Ross II; Samuel B. Ross III.
Foundation type: Independent foundation.
Financial data (yr. ended 12/31/13): Assets, $17,828,336 (M); expenditures, $780,980; qualifying distributions, $720,988; giving activities include $577,540 for 37 grants (high: $100,000; low: $1,000).
Purpose and activities: Giving primarily for education, arts and culture, programs for people with disabilities, animals, temporary assistance and community initiatives.
Fields of interest: Education; Animals/wildlife; Human services; Community/economic development; Disabilities, people with.
Limitations: Applications accepted. Giving primarily in WV, with emphasis on the five counties of Doddridge, Jackson, Pleasants, Ritchie, and Wood. No grants to individuals.
Publications: Grants list.
Application information: A staff member of the foundation will be available to provide guidance to nonprofits on what each section of the online application requires and why. A conference call with a staff member will be available to all applicants for 1-hour on the second Monday of the first month of the grant period if enough nonprofits wish to be part of it. If not enough nonprofits wish to be part of the conference call, then one on one contact with the few nonprofits asking about that process will be available. Application form required.
Initial approach: See foundation web site for application form
Deadline(s): Application should be submitted during the first month of a given grant cycle
Officers: Samuel B. Ross II, Chair.; Samuel B. Ross III, Exec. Dir.
Board Members: Melissa Ross; Spencer B. Ross; Susan S. Ross.
EIN: 204652067

9793
The Albert Schenk III & Kathleen H. Schenk Charitable Trust No. 1 ✧
(also known as Schenk Charitable Trust)
1031 National Rd.
Wheeling, WV 26003-5700 (304) 243-5440
Contact: Frank A. Jackson

Established in 1998 in WV.
Donors: Kathleen H. Schenk Charitable Lead Unitrust; Schenk Charitable Remainder Annuity Trust.
Foundation type: Independent foundation.
Financial data (yr. ended 12/31/13): Assets, $8,513,182 (M); gifts received, $620,310; expenditures, $1,123,378; qualifying distributions, $936,325; giving activities include $936,325 for 46 grants (high: $160,000; low: $3,000).
Purpose and activities: Giving to promote philanthropic causes in and around Wheeling, West Virginia.
Fields of interest: Arts; Higher education; Education; Health care; Mental health, treatment; Human services; Children/youth, services; Religion; Disabilities, people with; Economically disadvantaged.
Type of support: Capital campaigns; Building/renovation; Equipment; Program development; Seed money; Scholarship funds.
Limitations: Applications accepted. Giving limited to the Wheeling, WV area, including Ohio and Marshall counties, WV. No grants to individuals or for endowments, operating expenses or general overhead.
Application information: Application form required.
Initial approach: Letter or telephone
Copies of proposal: 16
Deadline(s): None
Final notification: Generally within 90 days
Officer: Chase DeFelice, Chair.
Trustees: Brian Bonacci; Frank Bonacci; Louise S. Coulling; Alex DeFelice; Mary Hamilton; Natalie Hamilton; William Hogan, Jr.; Sean Hughes; Kristine Luciano, Jr.; Karen Silgar; Shelly Sligar; Holly Hughes Welp; Brooke Wetmore; Sara Casey Yanko.
EIN: 550764535
Selected grants: The following grants are a representative sample of this grantmaker's funding activity:
$5,000 to Minority Aviation Education Association, Wheeling, WV, 2012. For program assis.

9794
Hugh I. Shott, Jr. Foundation Inc. ✧
c/o First Century Bank Trust Dept.
500 Federal St.
P.O. Box 1559
Bluefield, WV 24701-3010 (304) 324-3222

Established in 1985 in WV.
Donor: Hugh I. Shott, Jr.‡.
Foundation type: Independent foundation.
Financial data (yr. ended 12/31/13): Assets, $38,056,086 (M); expenditures, $1,930,404; qualifying distributions, $1,584,074; giving activities include $1,523,970 for 23 grants (high: $355,050; low: $326).
Purpose and activities: Giving primarily for education, human services and community development.
Fields of interest: Higher education; Education; Human services; Community/economic development.
Type of support: Annual campaigns; Capital campaigns; Building/renovation.
Limitations: Applications accepted. Giving limited to southwestern VA and southern WV. No grants to individuals.
Application information: Application form required.
Initial approach: Completed application form
Deadline(s): None
Officers: R.W. Wilkinson, Pres.; John H. Shott, V.P.; Frank W. Wilkinson, Secy.; B.K. Satterfield, Treas.
Directors: James H. Shott III; Michael R. Shott; W. Chandler Swope.
Number of staff: 1 part-time professional.
EIN: 550650833

9795
The James H. and Alice Teubert Charitable Trust ✧
P.O. Box 2131
Huntington, WV 25722 (304) 525-6337
Contact: Jimelle Bowen, Exec. Dir.
E-mail: teubert@accessmountain.net

Established in 1987 in WV.
Donor: WV Culture and Arts Grant.
Foundation type: Independent foundation.
Financial data (yr. ended 09/30/13): Assets, $21,890,540 (M); expenditures, $1,145,546; qualifying distributions, $1,033,908; giving activities include $944,764 for 9 grants (high: $699,464; low: $100).
Purpose and activities: Support for organizations which provide aid to the blind in Cabell and Wayne Counties in West Virginia.
Fields of interest: Eye diseases; Disabilities, people with.
Limitations: Applications accepted. Giving primarily in Cabell and Wayne counties, WV. No grants to individuals.
Publications: Application guidelines; Informational brochure.
Application information: Application form required.
Initial approach: Request application form
Copies of proposal: 8

Deadline(s): Mar. 1 for Apr. awards and Oct. 1 for Nov. awards
Board meeting date(s): Apr. and Nov.
Trustees: Dina Blom; Betty Bruce; David H. Lunsford; Michael Nuce; Aaron Preece; Sue Richardson; Dr. Matthew A. Rohrbach.
Officers: Grant McGuire, Chair.; Jimelle Bowen, Exec. Dir.
Number of staff: 1 part-time professional.
EIN: 556101813

9796
Tucker Community Foundation ✧
100 Education Ln.
P.O. Box 491
Parsons, WV 26287 (304) 478-2930
Contact: Robert A. Burns, Exec. Dir.
FAX: (304) 478-9966; E-mail: tcf1@frontiernet.net; Main URL: http://www.tuckerfoundation.net
Facebook: https://www.facebook.com/tucker.commfound?

Established in 1988 in WV.
Foundation type: Community foundation.
Financial data (yr. ended 12/31/13): Assets, $20,950,937 (M); gifts received, $435,723; expenditures, $1,478,038; giving activities include $1,007,021 for 15+ grants (high: $610,820), and $58,500 for 43 grants to individuals.
Purpose and activities: The foundation seeks to build a permanent pool of endowed funds to serve the broad charitable needs of the community, to manage these funds responsibly, and to use them efficiently in responding to the community's changing needs and opportunities. Scholarships for local community services, including playgrounds, art and cultural programs, and for fire and medical services.
Fields of interest: Visual arts; Performing arts; Libraries/library science; Education; Health care; Recreation.
Type of support: General/operating support; Continuing support; Endowments; Program development; Seed money; Curriculum development; Scholarship funds; Technical assistance; Employee-related scholarships; Scholarships—to individuals.
Limitations: Applications accepted. Giving limited to Barbour, Grant, Pocahontas, Preston, Randolph, and Tucker counties, WV, and Garrett County, MD. No support for annual fund campaigns, deficit financing or debt retirement, fraternal organizations, religious organizations for sectarian purposes, scientific research, or political organizations or campaigns. No grants to individuals, except for selected scholarships.
Publications: Annual report; Grants list; Newsletter.
Application information: Visit foundation web site for application guidelines per grant size. Application form required.
Initial approach: Letter or telephone
Deadline(s): 3rd Fri. in Sept. for grant requests over $500; grant requests under $500 accepted anytime
Board meeting date(s): Jan., May, July, and Oct.
Final notification: May and Oct.
Officers and Directors:* David Cooper,* Pres.; Jim Cooper, III*, V.P.; David Moran,* Secy.; Marvin Parsons,* Treas.; Robert A. Burns, Exec. Dir.; Shannon Anderson; Amy Barb; Diane Beall; Dan Bucher; Beth Clevenger; Rachelle Davis; Cheryl DeBerry; Mark Doak; Nancy K. Dotson; Sam Goughnour; Lyndsey Nestor; Milan Nypl; Donna Patrick; Jessica Scowcroft; Kelly Stadleman.
Number of staff: 1 full-time professional.
EIN: 550687098

9797
H.B. Wehrle Foundation ✧ ☆
c/o Henry B. Wehrle, Jr.
835 Hillcrest Dr. E.
Charleston, WV 25311-1627

Established in WV.
Foundation type: Independent foundation.
Financial data (yr. ended 12/31/12): Assets, $8,255,950 (M); expenditures, $516,187; qualifying distributions, $438,945; giving activities include $429,500 for 31 grants (high: $75,000; low: $1,000).
Fields of interest: Higher education; Libraries/library science; Education; Health organizations; Children/youth, services; Community/economic development.
Limitations: Applications not accepted. Giving primarily in WV.
Application information: Unsolicited requests for funds not accepted.
Trustees: F. Thomas Graff, Jr.; Thomas Newton; Elizabeth Marie Wehrle; H. Bernard Wehrle III; Henry B. Wehrle, Jr.; Stephen D. Wehrle; Lynne Wehrle-Zande.
EIN: 266449761

9798
Arthur and Joan Weisberg Family Foundation, Inc. ✧ ☆
2010 2nd Ave.
P.O. Box 5346
Huntington, WV 25703-1108

Established in 1995 in WV.
Donors: Arthur Weisberg; Joan Weisberg; Arthur & Joan Weisberg Charitable Lead Trust.
Foundation type: Independent foundation.
Financial data (yr. ended 08/31/13): Assets, $1,663,397 (M); gifts received, $722,500; expenditures, $676,280; qualifying distributions, $676,226; giving activities include $676,226 for 35 grants (high: $402,000; low: $100).
Fields of interest: Education; Science; Jewish agencies & synagogues; Blind/visually impaired.
Type of support: General/operating support.
Limitations: Applications not accepted. Giving primarily in Washington, DC, New York, NY, TX and Huntington, WV. No grants to individuals.
Application information: Unsolicited requests for funds not accepted.
Officers: Joan Weisberg, Chair. and Pres.; Martha Weisberg Barvin, Vice-Chair. and V.P.; Pamela Weisberg, Secy.; Charles Weisberg, Treas.
EIN: 550746517
Selected grants: The following grants are a representative sample of this grantmaker's funding activity:
$75,000 to American Israel Education Foundation, Washington, DC, 2011.
$54,000 to Friends of the Israel Defense Forces, New York, NY, 2011.
$20,000 to American Society for Technion-Israel Institute of Technology, New York, NY, 2011.
$14,750 to Birthright Israel Foundation, New York, NY, 2011.
$10,000 to Huntington Museum of Art, Huntington, WV, 2011.
$10,000 to Jerusalem Foundation, New York, NY, 2011.
$5,000 to Central Fund of Israel, New York, NY, 2011.
$3,000 to Jewish Federation of Greater Houston, Houston, TX, 2011.
$1,000 to Emery/Weiner Center for Jewish Education, Houston, TX, 2011.
$1,000 to Marshall University Foundation, Huntington, WV, 2011.

9799
Your Community Foundation, Inc. ✧
(formerly Greater Morgantown Community Trust, Inc.)
111 High St.
P. O. Box 409
Morgantown, WV 26505 (304) 296-3433
Contact: Beth Fuller, Pres.
E-mail: beth@ycfwv.org; Main URL: http://www.ycfwv.org/
Facebook: https://www.facebook.com/pages/Your-Community-Foundation-YCF/154019484631226?ref=ts&fref=ts
Twitter: https://twitter.com/YCF_Morgantown?refsrc=email
YouTube: http://www.youtube.com/channel/UCZdLI7tlFwpKJsOhsPoYq1A?feature=watch

Established in 2001 in WV.
Foundation type: Community foundation.
Financial data (yr. ended 12/31/12): Assets, $9,023,414 (M); gifts received, $1,772,178; expenditures, $899,105; giving activities include $583,479 for 9+ grants (high: $50,000), and $81,194 for 58 grants to individuals (high: $4,684; low: $500).
Purpose and activities: The foundation enables people with philanthropic interests to easily and effectively support the issues they care about, immediately, or through their will.
Fields of interest: Arts; Education; Health care; Recreation; Youth, services; Family services; Human services.
Type of support: Emergency funds; Program development; Equipment; Endowments; Seed money; Scholarship funds; Matching/challenge support.
Limitations: Applications accepted. Giving primarily in North Central, WV. No grants for operational expenses, ongoing programs, existing obligations, debts or liabilities, conferences, seminars, annual campaigns, endowments, travel, or work training.
Publications: Annual report; Informational brochure.
Application information: Visit foundation web site for application form and guidelines. Faxed and e-mailed applications are also accepted. Application form required.
Initial approach: Mail application form and attachments
Deadline(s): Mar. 31
Board meeting date(s): Quarterly
Final notification: June 1
Officers and Directors:* Gerry Schmidt,* Chair.; Barbara Alexander McKinney,* Vice-Chair.; Beth Fuller,* Pres.; Billy Atkins,* Secy.; Mike DeProspero,* Treas.; Billy L. Coffindaffer; Judy Collett; Steve Decker; Robert Greer; James Griffin; Ranjit Majumder; M.L. Quinn; Scott Rotuck; Ginna Royce; Ian Rudick; Tara Stevens.

Number of staff: 1 full-time professional; 2 part-time professional.
EIN: 275249383

WISCONSIN

9800
1923 Fund ✧
c/o U.S. Bank, N.A.
P.O. Box 2043
Milwaukee, WI 53201-9668

Established in 1994 in IL.
Donors: David A. Cofrin; Mary Ann Cofrin; David A. Cofrin Irrevocable Trust.
Foundation type: Independent foundation.
Financial data (yr. ended 12/31/13): Assets, $56,101,716 (M); expenditures, $2,531,352; qualifying distributions, $2,194,307; giving activities include $2,088,000 for 17 grants (high: $993,000; low: $8,000).
Purpose and activities: Giving primarily for higher education.
Fields of interest: Higher education; Environment, land resources; Foundations (community).
Limitations: Applications not accepted. Giving primarily in FL, NY and WI. No grants to individuals.
Application information: Contributes only to pre-selected organizations.
Officer: Cindy Follick, Secy.
Trustee: U.S. Bank, N.A.
Advisors: David H. Cofrin; Mary Ann Harn Cofrin; Steven P. Dhein; Sam Goforth; Robert Howe; Joe Neidenbach; Ed Poppell; Ellen Weidner.
EIN: 367070455
Selected grants: The following grants are a representative sample of this grantmaker's funding activity:
$250,000 to University of Wisconsin Foundation, Green Bay, WI, 2012. For Weidner Center Strategic.
$75,000 to University of Wisconsin Foundation, Green Bay, WI, 2012. For Cofrin Center.
$15,000 to University of Wisconsin Foundation, Green Bay, WI, 2012. For Bio Diversity STRI Course.
$15,000 to University of Wisconsin Foundation, Green Bay, WI, 2012. For Theater Department.
$10,000 to University of Wisconsin Foundation, Green Bay, WI, 2012. For Stri Panama Course.
$8,000 to University of Wisconsin Foundation, Green Bay, WI, 2012. For Cofrin Assistantships.

9801
Acuity Charitable Foundation Inc. ✧
2800 S. Taylor Dr.
P.O. Box 58
Sheboygan, WI 53082-0058 (920) 458-9131
Contact: Lynn Yunger

Established in 2003 in WI.
Donor: Acuity, a Mutual Insurance Co.
Foundation type: Company-sponsored foundation.
Financial data (yr. ended 12/31/13): Assets, $7,474,500 (M); gifts received, $1,999,996; expenditures, $1,092,519; qualifying distributions, $1,066,948; giving activities include $1,062,365 for 33 grants (high: $127,495; low: $500).
Purpose and activities: The foundation supports hospices and community foundations and organizations involved with arts and culture, education, cancer, abuse prevention, food distribution, and youth development.
Fields of interest: Media/communications; Performing arts, theater; Arts; Elementary/secondary education; Education; Cancer; Crime/violence prevention, abuse prevention; Food distribution, meals on wheels; Youth development, business; Salvation Army; Residential/custodial care, hospices; Foundations (community); United Ways and Federated Giving Programs.
Type of support: Continuing support; General/operating support; Program development; Sponsorships.
Limitations: Applications accepted. Giving primarily in Sheboygan, WI.
Application information: Application form required.
Initial approach: Letter
Deadline(s): None
Officers and Directors:* Benjamin M. Salzmann,* Pres. and C.E.O.; Richard A. Waldhart,* V.P.; Sheri L. Murphy,* Secy.; Wendy R. Schuler,* Treas.; Laura J. Conklin; Edward L. Felchner; Thomas C. Gast; Adam R. Norlander; Shane A. Paltzer.
EIN: 200354193
Selected grants: The following grants are a representative sample of this grantmaker's funding activity:
$50,000 to Milwaukee Area Technical College, Milwaukee, WI, 2012. For the sole benefit of the MPTV Fund.
$7,500 to Mead Public Library Foundation, Sheboygan, WI, 2012. For Cool Picks Program Sponsorship.

9802
Alexander Charitable Foundation, Inc. ✧
P.O. Box 9
Port Edwards, WI 54469-0009
Contact: John A. Casey, Pres.

Incorporated in 1955 in WI.
Donor: John E. Alexander‡.
Foundation type: Independent foundation.
Financial data (yr. ended 12/31/13): Assets, $19,335,417 (M); gifts received, $250; expenditures, $863,428; qualifying distributions, $666,888; giving activities include $588,000 for 51 grants (high: $152,000; low: $500), and $69,384 for foundation-administered programs.
Purpose and activities: Emphasis on community centers, Protestant church support, and hospitals.
Fields of interest: Hospitals (general); Human services; Family services; Community/economic development; Protestant agencies & churches; Religion.
Type of support: Capital campaigns; Continuing support.
Limitations: Applications not accepted. Giving primarily in WI. No grants to individuals.
Publications: Annual report; Financial statement.
Application information: Contributes only to pre-selected organizations.
Board meeting date(s): Semiannually
Officers and Directors:* John A. Casey,* Pres.; J. Marshall Buehler, V.P.; Leslie V. Arendt, V.P.; Charles R. Lester,* V.P.; Karen Thiel, Secy.-Treas.; Lauren Arendt; Tracy McCormick; Tim Wright.
Number of staff: 1 part-time professional.
EIN: 396045140
Selected grants: The following grants are a representative sample of this grantmaker's funding activity:
$152,000 to YMCA, 2012.
$37,000 to United Methodist Church, New London, WI, 2012.
$35,000 to American Folklore Theater, Fish Creek, WI, 2012.
$26,000 to Riverview Hospital Association, Wisconsin Rapids, WI, 2012.
$10,000 to Family Center, Wisconsin Rapids, WI, 2012.
$10,000 to Marshfield Clinic Research Foundation, Marshfield, WI, 2012.
$5,000 to Lyric Opera House, Baltimore, MD, 2012.

9803
Judd S. Alexander Foundation, Inc. ✧
500 1st St., Ste. 10
P.O. Box 2137
Wausau, WI 54402-2137 (715) 845-4556
Contact: Gary W. Freels, Pres.
FAX: (715) 843-9018;
E-mail: office@alexanderprop.org; Main URL: http://www.juddsalexanderfoundation.org

Incorporated in 1973 in WI.
Donor: Anne M. Alexander‡.
Foundation type: Independent foundation.
Financial data (yr. ended 06/30/14): Assets, $50,803,182 (M); expenditures, $2,159,600; qualifying distributions, $2,592,132; giving activities include $1,268,392 for 52 grants (high: $150,000; low: $600), and $940,000 for 2 loans/program-related investments (high: $750,000; low: $190,000).
Purpose and activities: Giving for the direct benefit of residents of Marathon County, WI; primary areas of interest include community development, social services, youth, educational programs, economic development, arts and human services.
Fields of interest: Arts; Education, early childhood education; Elementary school/education; Higher education; Adult/continuing education; Education; Health care; Crime/law enforcement; Recreation; Human services; Children/youth, services; Economic development; Community/economic development.
Type of support: Program development; Capital campaigns; Building/renovation; Equipment; Land acquisition; Emergency funds; Seed money; Technical assistance; Program-related investments/loans; Matching/challenge support.
Limitations: Applications accepted. Giving limited to Marathon County, WI, or to organizations directly benefiting the residents of Marathon County. No support for religion, or for medical research, international programs or organizations, or for organizations or projects whose mission is to prevent, eradicate and/or alleviate the effects of a specific disease, requests from hospitals (unless they are for community wide capital campaigns with a slated goal and beginning and ending dates), or charities operated by service clubs. No grants to individuals, or for endowment funds, fellowships, fundraising campaigns, research, publications, film, videos, television programs, travel, conferences, the writing or publication of books, private businesses, or annual operating support.
Publications: Application guidelines.
Application information: Application information is available on foundation web site. Fax or e-mail proposals are not accepted. Proposals should not be bound or placed in protective covers or other presentation formats. Application form not required.
Initial approach: Letter, proposal, or telephone
Copies of proposal: 5
Deadline(s): None
Board meeting date(s): Monthly
Final notification: 60 days

Officers and Directors:* Gary W. Freels,* Pres.; Lon E. Roberts,* Secy.-Treas.; Dwight E. Davis,* V.P.; John Dudley.
EIN: 237323721

9804
Alliant Energy Foundation, Inc. ✧
(formerly Wisconsin Power and Light Foundation, Inc.)
4902 N. Biltmore Ln., Ste. 1000
Madison, WI 53718-2148 (608) 458-4483
Contact: Julie Bauer, Exec. Dir.
FAX: (608) 458-4820;
E-mail: foundation@alliantenergy.com; Additional tel.: (866) 769-3779; contact for Community Service Scholarships: Dawn Lehtinen, Prog. Mgr., tel.: (507) 931-0482, e-mail: dlehtinen@scholarshipamerica.org; Main URL: http://www.alliantenergy.com/CommunityInvolvement/index.htm
Community Service Scholarship Recipients: http://www.alliantenergy.com/CommunityInvolvement/CharitableFoundation/Programs/ssLINK/026251
Facebook: http://www.facebook.com/AlliantEnergyFoundation
Grants List: http://www.alliantenergy.com/wcm/groups/wcm_internet/@int/documents/document/mdaw/mdi2/~edisp/026251.pdf

Established in 1984 in WI.
Donors: Wisconsin Power and Light Co.; Alliant Energy Corp.; Interstate Power and Light Co.
Foundation type: Company-sponsored foundation.
Financial data (yr. ended 12/31/12): Assets, $12,563,716 (M); gifts received, $1,000,000; expenditures, $3,949,204; qualifying distributions, $3,885,399; giving activities include $2,543,140 for 682+ grants (high: $100,000), and $1,023,918 for 3,550 employee matching gifts.
Purpose and activities: The foundation supports organizations involved with arts and culture, education, the environment, health, employment, housing, safety, human services, community development, civic affairs, and minorities.
Fields of interest: Humanities; Arts; Higher education; Libraries (public); Education; Environment, natural resources; Environmental education; Environment; Health care; Crime/law enforcement, police agencies; Employment, training; Employment; Housing/shelter; Disasters, preparedness/services; Disasters, fire prevention/control; Safety/disasters; Boys & girls clubs; Youth development, business; YM/YWCAs & YM/YWHAs; Human services; Civil/human rights, equal rights; Economic development; Community/economic development; United Ways and Federated Giving Programs; Leadership development; Public affairs; Minorities.
Type of support: Continuing support; Annual campaigns; Building/renovation; Equipment; Emergency funds; Program development; Conferences/seminars; Seed money; Scholarship funds; Research; Employee volunteer services; Employee matching gifts; Employee-related scholarships; Scholarships—to individuals; Matching/challenge support.
Limitations: Applications accepted. Giving limited to areas of company operations in IA, MN, and WI. No support for athletes or teams, fraternal or social clubs, third party funding groups, religious organizations not of direct benefit to the entire community, or discriminatory organizations. No grants to individuals (except for scholarships), or for advertising, door prizes, raffle tickets, dinner tables, golf outings or sponsorships of organized sports teams or activities, sporting events or tournaments, endowments, registration fees or participation fees, books, magazines or professional journal articles, political activities, salaries, facilities costs or general operating expenses, capital campaigns, or "bricks and mortar" projects.
Publications: Application guidelines; Annual report (including application guidelines); Grants list; Informational brochure (including application guidelines); Program policy statement.
Application information: Additional information may be requested at a later date. Support is limited to 1 contribution per organization during any given year. Organizations receiving support are asked to provide a final report. Application form required.
Initial approach: Complete online eligibility quiz and application for Community Grants and Community Service Scholarships; download application form and mail to foundation for Hometown Challenge Grant
Copies of proposal: 1
Deadline(s): Jan. 15, May 15, and Sept. 15 for Community Grants; Feb. 15 for Community Service Scholarships; none for Hometown Challenge Grant
Board meeting date(s): Quarterly
Final notification: Apr. 1, Aug. 1, and Dec. 1 for Community Grants; 15 days for Hometown Challenge Grant
Officers and Directors:* Thomas L. Aller,* Pres.; Patricia L. Kampling,* V.P.; Julie Bauer, Secy. and Exec. Dir.; Colleen Thomas, Treas.; Robert J. Bartlett; John O. Larsen.
Number of staff: 3 full-time professional; 3 part-time professional.
EIN: 391444065

9805
Anon Charitable Trust ✧
c/o U.S. Bank, N.A.
P.O. Box 2043
Milwaukee, WI 53201-9668
Application address: U.S. Bank, N.A., P.O. Box 3194, MK-WI-TWPT, Milwaukee, WI 53201-3194, tel.: (414) 765-6038

Established in 1993 in WI.
Donor: Clarice Soref Turer.
Foundation type: Independent foundation.
Financial data (yr. ended 12/31/13): Assets, $20,873,508 (M); gifts received, $3,163,516; expenditures, $1,398,052; qualifying distributions, $1,243,133; giving activities include $1,142,040 for 91 grants (high: $110,000; low: $1,000).
Fields of interest: Arts; Boys & girls clubs; Human services; United Ways and Federated Giving Programs; Jewish federated giving programs.
Limitations: Applications accepted. Giving primarily in Milwaukee, WI. No grants to individuals.
Application information: Application form required.
Initial approach: Letter
Deadline(s): None
Trustees: Herbert L. Bilsky; Wayne R. Lueders; Harris J. Turer.
EIN: 391771579

9806
The Victor and Christine Anthony Foundation, Inc. ✧
P.O. Box 385
Waupaca, WI 54981-1958
Application address: c/o Victor Anthony, Christine Anthony, 134 Shadow Lake Dr., Waupaca, WI 54981; tel.: (715) 258-2587

Established in 2007 in WI.
Foundation type: Independent foundation.
Financial data (yr. ended 12/31/13): Assets, $19,463,669 (M); expenditures, $1,155,673; qualifying distributions, $1,019,346; giving activities include $1,012,255 for 56 grants (high: $200,000; low: $500).
Fields of interest: Food services; Safety/disasters; Human services; American Red Cross; Salvation Army; Family services.
Limitations: Applications accepted. Giving primarily in IL and WI.
Application information:
Initial approach: Letter
Deadline(s): None
Officers: Victor W. Anthony, Jr., Pres. and Treas.; Christine A. Anthony, V.P. and Secy.
Directors: Carol C. Anthony; Katherine A. Anthony; Karen A. Gabler.
EIN: 260851891

9807
Antioch Foundation ✧
230 Front St. N.
La Crosse, WI 54601-3219 (608) 782-1148
Contact: Darwin Isaacson

Established in 1998 in WI.
Donors: Jill Swanson; Scott Zietlow; Donald Zietlow; Lavonne Zietlow; Dan Kunz; Vicki Kunz; St. Johns Lutheran Church; Jill Zietlow.
Foundation type: Independent foundation.
Financial data (yr. ended 12/31/13): Assets, $11,689,990 (M); gifts received, $60,821; expenditures, $1,170,396; qualifying distributions, $1,030,744; giving activities include $1,023,769 for 53 grants (high: $110,069; low: $500).
Purpose and activities: Giving primarily to Lutheran churches, organizations, and schools; funding also for medicine through grants for facilities, research, and training, and for humanitarian causes.
Fields of interest: Education; Health organizations; Human services; Protestant agencies & churches.
Type of support: General/operating support; Building/renovation; Matching/challenge support.
Limitations: Applications accepted. Giving primarily in the LaCrosse, WI and Rochester, MN, areas. No grants to individuals.
Application information: Application form not required.
Initial approach: Proposal
Deadline(s): None
Trustees: Dan Vicky Kunz; Scott Jill Zietlow; Steve Amy Zietlow; Trust Point Inc.
EIN: 363779525
Selected grants: The following grants are a representative sample of this grantmaker's funding activity:
$53,500 to Wisconsin Evangelical Lutheran Synod, Milwaukee, WI, 2012. For Christian Aid and Relief, Wash Program.

$40,000 to Bethany Lutheran College, Mankato, MN, 2012. To establish a Media Production Company.
$10,000 to Arizona Lutheran Academy, Phoenix, AZ, 2012. To establish International Student Coordinator.
$10,000 to Lighthouse Youth Center, Milwaukee, WI, 2012. For Expansion of Education Programs.
$10,000 to Wisconsin Lutheran Seminary, Mequon, WI, 2012. For Pastoral Studies Institute Program.
$7,000 to Evangelical Lutheran Synod, Mankato, MN, 2012. For Summer Educational Programs.
$3,000 to Luther High School, Onalaska, WI, 2012. For fundraiser expenses.

9808
The Argosy Foundation ✧
(formerly The Abele Family Charitable Trust)
555 E. Wells St., Ste. 1650
Milwaukee, WI 53202-3819
Contact: Jeneye Abele, C.E.O.
E-mail address for inquiries in Spanish: ayuda@argosyfnd.org; Main URL: http://www.argosyfnd.org/
E-Newsletter: http://www.argosyfnd.org/enews/

Established in 1997 in MA. Over the next few years, the Abele family plans to more than double the foundation's endowment, which would make it one of the larger foundations in the nation with assets eventually approaching $2 billion.
Donor: John E. Abele.
Foundation type: Independent foundation.
Financial data (yr. ended 12/31/13): Assets, $14,589,134 (M); expenditures, $5,282,362; qualifying distributions, $5,372,357; giving activities include $4,716,406 for 72 grants (high: $666,667; low: $3,000), and $125,000 for 1 loan/program-related investment.
Purpose and activities: The mission of the foundation is to support people and programs that make our society a better place to live. The foundation seeks to employ creative and entrepreneurial approaches that help people to help themselves, and become self-sustaining whenever possible. The intention is to solve systemic problems, build teams and communities, create replicable solutions, and inspire others to contribute in their own ways.
Fields of interest: Arts; Education; Environment; Health care; Human services; International affairs; Public affairs.
Type of support: Annual campaigns; Emergency funds; Program development; Conferences/seminars; Scholarship funds; Research; Matching/challenge support.
Limitations: Applications not accepted. Giving primarily to CO, MA, VT and WI. No grants to individuals.
Publications: Annual report.
Application information: Unsolicited requests for funds not accepted.
Officers and Trustees:* John E. Abele,* Chair.; Jeneye Abele,* C.E.O. and Pres.; Mary Abele.
EIN: 046752868

9809
Ted & Grace Bachhuber Foundation, Inc. ✧
14 Tower Dr.
P.O. Box 228
Mayville, WI 53050-1746
Contact: JoAnn Bachhuber, Pres. and Treas.

Established in 1982.
Donors: Theodore J. Bachhuber†; Mayville Engineering Co., Inc.
Foundation type: Independent foundation.
Financial data (yr. ended 12/31/13): Assets, $40,320,645 (M); expenditures, $1,928,162; qualifying distributions, $1,834,182; giving activities include $1,733,206 for 19 grants (high: $551,511; low: $2,000).
Purpose and activities: Supports a scholarship program administered by the Mayville Public School System to provide financial aid to graduates who plan to pursue an engineering, business, or technology degree. Support also for local projects that offer opportunities for an enriched life to a substantial number of people, or provide members of the community with skills, knowledge and assistance to accomplish positive social goals.
Fields of interest: Historic preservation/historical societies; Engineering school/education; Scholarships/financial aid; Human services; Science; Christian agencies & churches.
Type of support: Equipment; General/operating support; Building/renovation; Scholarship funds.
Limitations: Applications accepted. Giving limited to the Mayville, WI, area. No grants to individuals.
Application information: Application form not required.
Initial approach: Letter
Copies of proposal: 1
Deadline(s): None
Board meeting date(s): 4 times annually
Final notification: 30 days
Officers and Directors:* JoAnn Bachhuber,* Pres. and Treas.; Leo R. Fisher,* V.P.; Dan Edgarton,* Secy.; Carl N. Bachhuber; Glen Helmbrecht; George Olson; William Steinbach.
Number of staff: 1 part-time professional.
EIN: 391415821
Selected grants: The following grants are a representative sample of this grantmaker's funding activity:
$321,435 to Mayville Public Schools, Mayville, WI, 2012. For Scholarships, Music Department Costumes and Trailer, Football Field Repair, Weight Lifting Equipment.
$20,000 to Mayville Public Library, Mayville, WI, 2012. For materials.
$15,000 to Mayville Historical Society, Mayville, WI, 2012. For maintenance.

9810
Bader Philanthropies ✧
(formerly Helen Bader Foundation, Inc.)
233 N. Water St., 4th Fl.
Milwaukee, WI 53202-5729 (414) 224-6464
Contact: Daniel J. Bader, Pres.
FAX: (414) 224-1441; Main URL: http://bader.org/
Facebook: https://www.facebook.com/pages/Bader-Philanthropies/214502355248175
Grants List: http://www.hbf.org/awarded-grants
LinkedIn: https://www.linkedin.com/company/helen-bader-foundation-inc-
Vimeo: http://vimeo.com/user4326975

Established in 1991 in WI.
Donors: Daniel Bader Charitable Trust; David Bader Charitable Trust.
Foundation type: Independent foundation.
Financial data (yr. ended 08/31/13): Assets, $16,554,789 (M); gifts received, $20,611,800; expenditures, $13,080,315; qualifying distributions, $15,144,109; giving activities include $11,143,520 for 234 grants (high: $2,575,000; low: $500), $33,911 for 2 foundation-administered programs and $2,098,927 for 5 loans/program-related investments.
Purpose and activities: The Helen Bader Foundation, Inc. strives to be a philanthropic leader in improving the quality of life of the diverse communities in which it works. The foundation makes grants, convenes partners, and shares knowledge to affect emerging issues in key areas: Alzheimer's and Aging, Workforce Development, and Community Partnerships for Youth.
Fields of interest: Alzheimer's disease; Employment; Youth development; Human services; Children/youth, services; Community/economic development.
International interests: Israel.
Type of support: Building/renovation; Capital campaigns; Conferences/seminars; General/operating support; Program development; Program-related investments/loans; Technical assistance.
Limitations: Applications accepted. Giving primarily in the greater Milwaukee, WI, area for education and economic development; giving locally and nationally for Alzheimer's disease and dementia; giving in Israel for early childhood development. PRI emphasis is Milwaukee. No grants to individuals, including individual scholarships.
Publications: Application guidelines; Annual report (including application guidelines); Grants list.
Application information: The grants process has now moved online. After receipt of the preliminary application form, the foundation will send an e-mail regarding the status of the application. If a full proposal is requested, an on-site visit will also be required. Full proposals may not be submitted via fax or E-mail. Application form required.
Initial approach: Preliminary application form
Copies of proposal: 1
Deadline(s): Check website for upcoming dates
Board meeting date(s): Spring and Fall
Final notification: Within 2 weeks
Officers and Directors:* Jere D. McGaffey,* Chair. and Treas.; Daniel J. Bader,* C.E.O. and Pres.; Maria Lopez Vento, V.P., Prog(s) and Partnerships; David M. Bader,* V.P.; Lisa G. Hiller, V.P., Admin.; Deirdre H. Britt,* Secy.; Linda C. Bader; Michelle Berrong; Margaret Foster; Frances Klitsner Wolff.
Number of staff: 10 full-time professional; 2 part-time professional; 3 full-time support; 1 part-time support.
EIN: 391710914
Selected grants: The following grants are a representative sample of this grantmaker's funding activity:
$1,500,000 to Jewish Federation, Milwaukee, Milwaukee, WI, 2012. For Helen Bader Day School Scholarship Fund for Jewish Education, payable over 3.00 years.
$607,200 to Chaim Sheba Medical Center, Tel Hashomer, Israel, 2012. For The Israel Registry for Alzheimer's Prevention-Building the Infrastructure, payable over 2.00 years.

$231,250 to Wisconsin Regional Training Partnership, Milwaukee, WI, 2012. For Acquisition And Remodeling of New Training Facility.
$200,000 to Jewish Home and Care Center, Milwaukee, WI, 2012. For Helen Bader Center Renovation - 1410 Building, payable over 2.00 years.
$150,000 to UEC/MVP Project, Milwaukee, WI, 2012. For Menomonee Valley - From the Ground Up, payable over 2.00 years.
$100,000 to Risen Savior Evangelical Lutheran Church, Milwaukee, WI, 2012. For Capital Campaign for Youth/Community Center.
$25,000 to Alzheimer's Disease International, London, England, 2012. For Alzheimer University for Emerging Associations.
$25,000 to YWCA of Greater Milwaukee, Milwaukee, WI, 2012. For FoodShare Employment and Training Match (FSET Match) Program.
$20,000 to Silver Spring Neighborhood Center, Milwaukee, WI, 2012. For Community Learning Centers Support.
$15,000 to Foster Youth Independence Center of Milwaukee, Milwaukee, WI, 2012. For Life Skills Case Management and Housing for Foster Care Youth, payable over 2.00 years.

9811
Baird Foundation, Inc. ✧

(formerly Robert W. Baird and Company Foundation, Inc.)
777 E. Wisconsin Ave.
Milwaukee, WI 53202-5302 (414) 298-1722
Contact: Audrey Warner
E-mail: awarner@rwbaird.com; Additional contact: Margaret Welch, Fdn. Assoc., mmwelch@rwbaird.com, tel.: (414) 298-6197; Main URL: http://www.rwbaird.com/about-baird/culture/baird-foundation.aspx

Established in 1967 in WI.
Donor: Robert W. Baird and Co.
Foundation type: Company-sponsored foundation.
Financial data (yr. ended 12/31/12): Assets, $28,940,737 (M); gifts received, $13,521,249; expenditures, $2,632,066; qualifying distributions, $2,604,861; giving activities include $2,604,861 for 1,832 grants (high: $75,000; low: $5).
Purpose and activities: The foundation supports programs designed to promote education; health and human services; the arts; and diversity and organizations with which Baird associates are actively engaged in order to maximize the impact on those organizations and communities.
Fields of interest: Museums (art); Performing arts; Performing arts, ballet; Performing arts, opera; Arts; Secondary school/education; Higher education; Education; Hospitals (general); Health care; Mental health, grief/bereavement counseling; Cystic fibrosis; Boys & girls clubs; Boy scouts; American Red Cross; YM/YWCAs & YM/YWHAs; Children/youth, services; Human services; Civil/human rights, equal rights; Community/economic development; United Ways and Federated Giving Programs.
Type of support: General/operating support; Annual campaigns; Capital campaigns; Program development; Employee volunteer services; Employee matching gifts.
Limitations: Applications not accepted. Giving on a national basis, with emphasis on WI; giving also to national and international organizations. No grants to individuals.
Publications: Annual report.
Application information: Contributes only to pre-selected organizations.
Officers: James D. Bell, Jr.,* Chair.; Paul E. Purcell, Pres.; Leslie H. Dixon, V.P.; Peter S. Kies, V.P.; C.H. Randolph Lyon, V.P.; Mary Ellen Stanek, V.P.; Glen F. Hackmann, Secy.; Dominick P. Zarcone, Treas.
EIN: 396107937
Selected grants: The following grants are a representative sample of this grantmaker's funding activity:
$75,000 to United Way of Greater Milwaukee, Milwaukee, WI, 2011.
$50,000 to United Performing Arts Fund, Milwaukee, WI, 2011.
$30,000 to University of Chicago, Chicago, IL, 2011.
$20,000 to Saint Jude Childrens Research Hospital, Memphis, TN, 2011.
$20,000 to Vera Bradley Foundation for Breast Cancer, Fort Wayne, IN, 2011.
$10,000 to Big Brothers Big Sisters of Metropolitan Milwaukee, Milwaukee, WI, 2011.
$10,000 to CityTeam Ministries, Chester, PA, 2011.
$3,500 to Levitt Pavilion, Friends of the, Westport, CT, 2011.
$2,500 to City on a Hill Charter School, Roxbury, MA, 2011.
$2,000 to Cream City Foundation, Milwaukee, WI, 2011.

9812
Pat and Jay Baker Foundation, Inc. ✧

c/o Peter M. Sommerhauser
780 N. Water St.
Milwaukee, WI 53202-3512

Established in 1993 in WI.
Donors: Jay H. Baker; Jay Baker Living Trust.
Foundation type: Independent foundation.
Financial data (yr. ended 12/31/12): Assets, $23,839,777 (M); gifts received, $19,042,000; expenditures, $4,781,500; qualifying distributions, $4,780,500; giving activities include $4,771,000 for 15 grants (high: $3,000,000; low: $1,000).
Purpose and activities: Giving primarily for the performing arts, education and health care.
Fields of interest: Museums; Performing arts; Arts; Business school/education; Health care; Human services.
Limitations: Applications not accepted. Giving primarily in NY and Naples, FL; some giving also in PA. No grants to individuals.
Application information: Contributes only to pre-selected organizations.
Officers and Directors:* Jay H. Baker,* Pres. and Treas.; Pat Good Baker,* V.P. and Secy.; Peter M. Sommerhauser.
EIN: 391776268

9813
Theodore W. Batterman Family Foundation, Inc. ✧

P.O. Box 1783
Madison, WI 53701-1783 (608) 233-2083
Contact: Ann J. Flynn, Exec. V.P.
E-mail: foundation.management@charter.net

Established in 1990 in WI.
Donors: Theodore W. Batterman; Spacesaver Corp.
Foundation type: Independent foundation.
Financial data (yr. ended 12/31/13): Assets, $56,886,006 (M); gifts received, $625,000; expenditures, $5,228,890; qualifying distributions, $4,402,150; giving activities include $4,225,358 for 66 grants (high: $675,000; low: $3,800).
Purpose and activities: Giving primarily for Christian faith advancement, education and organizations located in Rock/Jefferson Counties in Wisconsin.
Fields of interest: Education; Christian agencies & churches.
Limitations: Applications not accepted. Giving primarily in the communities of Rock and Jefferson Counties in WI. No grants to individuals, or for endowments.
Application information: Contributes only to pre-selected organizations.
Officers and Directors:* Theodore W. Batterman,* Pres. and Treas.; Christopher T. Batterman, V.P. and Secy.; Ann J. Flynn, Exec. V.P.; Linda C. Batterman Johnson; Andrew R. Lauritzen; Laura G. Batterman Wilkins.
EIN: 391688812

9814
Beloit Foundation, Inc. ✧

2870 Riverside Dr.
Beloit, WI 53511-1506 (608) 368-1300
Contact: Gary G. Grabowski, Treas., Exec. Dir., and Dir.

Incorporated in 1959 in WI.
Donors: Elbert H. Neese, Sr.†; Walter K. Neese 1960 Trust.
Foundation type: Independent foundation.
Financial data (yr. ended 12/31/13): Assets, $9,316,146 (M); expenditures, $725,306; qualifying distributions, $555,821; giving activities include $510,877 for 23 grants (high: $100,000; low: $1,775).
Purpose and activities: Giving only to local community organizations for special projects and new program development; support also for education; family and social services, including children and youth services; building funds and community development.
Fields of interest: Arts; Higher education; Health care; Human services; Children/youth, services; Family services; Community development, neighborhood development; Children/youth; Children; Youth; Minorities; Economically disadvantaged.
Type of support: Emergency funds; Capital campaigns; Building/renovation; Equipment; Program development; Seed money; Matching/challenge support.
Limitations: Applications accepted. Giving limited to the local Stateline area, including South Beloit, Rockton, Roscoe, IL and Beloit, WI. No support for religious or political organizations. No grants to individuals, or for scientific research, national capital campaigns, international/foreign affairs or endowments.
Application information: Application form required.
Initial approach: Letter requesting application form
Copies of proposal: 10
Deadline(s): None
Board meeting date(s): May and Sept.
Officers and Directors:* Alonzo A. Neese, Jr.,* Pres.; Kim M. Kotthaus, Secy.; Gary G. Grabowski,* Treas. and Exec. Dir.; Diane M. Hendricks; Laura N. Malik; Harry C. Moore, Jr.; Gordon C. Neese; Walter K. Neese; Jane Petit-Moore.

Number of staff: 1 part-time professional; 1 part-time support.
EIN: 396068763

9815
Bemis Company Foundation ✧
One Neenah Ctr., 4th Fl.
P.O. Box 669
Neenah, WI 54957-0669 (920) 527-5300
Contact: Kim Wetzel, Fdn. Consultant
E-mail: kwetzel@bemis.com; Application contact and address: Kim Wetzel, Fdn. Consultant, tel.: (920) 734-2707, e-mail: kwetzel@bemis.com; Main URL: http://www.bemis.com/citizenship/

Trust established in 1959 in MO.
Donor: Bemis Co., Inc.
Foundation type: Company-sponsored foundation.
Financial data (yr. ended 12/31/12): Assets, $62,971 (M); gifts received, $3,410,000; expenditures, $3,370,726; qualifying distributions, $3,370,726; giving activities include $3,304,829 for 1,397 grants (high: $700,000; low: $25).
Purpose and activities: The foundation supports programs designed to encourage through basic needs and emergency assistance; empower through basic education and health and fitness; and elevate through higher education and arts and culture.
Fields of interest: Performing arts, dance; Performing arts, theater; Historic preservation/historical societies; Arts; Higher education; Education; Environment, natural resources; Animal welfare; Public health, physical fitness; Health care; Food services; Food banks; Athletics/sports, school programs; Recreation, fairs/festivals; Recreation; Youth development; Salvation Army; Youth, services; Human services; United Ways and Federated Giving Programs; Mathematics; Engineering/technology; Science; Public affairs.
Type of support: General/operating support; Continuing support; Annual campaigns; Capital campaigns; Building/renovation; Program development; Employee matching gifts; Employee-related scholarships.
Limitations: Applications accepted. Giving limited to areas of company operations in Crossett and Russellville, AR, Centerville, Clinton, and Des Moines, IA, Batavia and Bellwood, IL, Columbus and Terre Haute, IN, Shelbyville, KY, West Monroe, LA, Mankato and Minneapolis, MN, Joplin, MO, Edgewood, NY, Akron, Fremont, and Stow, OH, Pauls Valley, OK, Lebanon, Philadelphia, Scranton, and West Hazleton, PA, Shelbyville, TN, and Appleton, Boscobel, Lancaster, Menasha, Neenah, New London, and Oshkosh, WI. No support for religious, lobbying, or political organizations, hospitals, or other foundations. No grants to individuals (except for employee-related scholarships), or for endowments, research, educational capital campaigns, or trips or tours; no loans.
Publications: Application guidelines.
Application information: Grants are limited to 3 years in length. Telephone calls during the application process are not encouraged. Application form required.
Initial approach: Complete online eligibility quiz and application for Small Grants; letter of inquiry for Community Support Grants Program
Copies of proposal: 1
Deadline(s): None for Small Grants; Dec. 12 for Basic Needs Emergency Assistance, Mar. 18 for Basic Education Health & Wellness, and June 17 for Higher Edcuation and Arts & Culture
Board meeting date(s): Mar. 15, June 15, Sept. 15, and Dec. 15
Final notification: 4 weeks for Small Grants
Trustees: Timothy S. Fliss, Jr.; Jerry Krempa; Scott B. Ullem.
Number of staff: 2 part-time professional.
EIN: 416038616
Selected grants: The following grants are a representative sample of this grantmaker's funding activity:
$593,952 to Scholarship America, Saint Peter, MN, 2011.
$500,000 to Fox Cities Performing Arts Center, Appleton, WI, 2011.
$250,000 to University of Wisconsin Foundation, Madison, WI, 2011.
$105,000 to University of Wisconsin Foundation, Oshkosh, WI, 2011.
$100,000 to COTS, Appleton, WI, 2011.
$35,000 to Fox Valley Warming Shelter, Appleton, WI, 2011.
$24,928 to United Way of the Wabash Valley, Terre Haute, IN, 2011.
$6,996 to United Way of Lebanon County, Lebanon, PA, 2011.
$2,000 to Dallas Theological Seminary, Dallas, TX, 2011.
$1,000 to Fox Valley Symphony, Appleton, WI, 2011.

9816
Charles E. Benidt Foundation, Inc. ✧
P.O. Box 86
Elm Grove, WI 53122-0086
Contact: Maureen E. Crowley, Prog. Dir.; Beatrice A. Benidt, Pres.
E-mail: Benidtfoundation@mac.com; Additional e-mail: benidtfoundation@mac.com; Main URL: http://charlesebenidtfoundation.org/

Established in 2003 in WI.
Donor: Charles E. Benidt†.
Foundation type: Independent foundation.
Financial data (yr. ended 12/31/13): Assets, $67,331,998 (M); expenditures, $3,581,522; qualifying distributions, $3,160,576; giving activities include $2,843,908 for 25 grants (high: $650,000; low: $500).
Purpose and activities: Giving primarily for education for disadvantaged people, Lutheran missionaries via LCMS, Lutheran pastor training, shelters for abused women and children, medical research, the Mayo Clinic (for heart and cancer), and social services.
Fields of interest: Education; Human services; Children/youth; Youth; Physically disabled; Minorities; Adults, women; Economically disadvantaged.
Type of support: Research; General/operating support; Capital campaigns; Scholarship funds.
Limitations: Applications not accepted. Giving primarily in southeastern WI, and Scottsdale and Phoenix, AZ. No support for arts/cultural endeavors, museums, or the Red Cross. No grants to individuals, or for recreation or entertainment.
Application information: The foundation is currently not accepting unsolicited applications.
Board meeting date(s): Quarterly
Officers: Beatrice A. Benidt, Pres. and Treas.; James Mohr, V.P.; Maureen Crowley, Secy. and Prog. Dir.
Directors: Nancy Bonniwell; Lee Mevis; Mark W. Miller; Reuben W. Peterson, Jr.
Number of staff: 2 full-time professional.
EIN: 364522803
Selected grants: The following grants are a representative sample of this grantmaker's funding activity:
$261,914 to Journey House, Milwaukee, WI, 2012. For Capital Campaign; Auction Appeal; Citizenship Program; General Support.
$98,000 to Froedtert Hospital Foundation, Milwaukee, WI, 2012. For Chaplaincy and General Support.
$500 to Donors Forum of Wisconsin, Milwaukee, WI, 2012. For Discretionary Funds Program Support.
$500 to Marquette University, Milwaukee, WI, 2012. For Discretionary Funds - Feed My Starving Children.

9817
Berbeewalsh Foundation, Inc. ✧ ☆
c/o Fred G. Broihahn, C.P.A.
P.O. Box 620676
Middleton, WI 53562-0676

Established in 2006 in WI.
Donors: James G. Berbee; Karen A. Berbee; Karen A. Walsh.
Foundation type: Independent foundation.
Financial data (yr. ended 12/31/13): Assets, $3,407,381 (M); expenditures, $716,605; qualifying distributions, $706,800; giving activities include $706,800 for 16 grants (high: $200,000; low: $5,000).
Fields of interest: Performing arts, opera; Education, fund raising/fund distribution; Human services.
Limitations: Applications not accepted. Giving primarily in Madison, WI. No grants to individuals.
Application information: Contributes only to pre-selected organizations.
Officers and Directors:* James G. Berbee,* Pres. and Treas.; Karen A. Walsh,* V.P.; Paul S. Peercy; Paul S. Shain.
EIN: 205892278
Selected grants: The following grants are a representative sample of this grantmaker's funding activity:
$100,000 to Access Community Health Centers, Madison, WI, 2012. For Improving Health Improving Lives Campaign.
$15,000 to Dane County Friends of Ferals, Madison, WI, 2012. For veterinarian support.
$10,000 to Dane County Friends of Ferals, Madison, WI, 2012. For Daily Care and Medical Treatment for Feral Cats.
$10,000 to Gary Comer Youth Center, Chicago, IL, 2012. For youth programs.
$5,000 to Morgridge Institute for Research, Madison, WI, 2012. For Morgridge Institute Board of Trustees Postdoctoral Fellowship.

9818
Bleser Family Foundation, Inc. ✧
P.O. Box 328
Shawano, WI 54166-0328

Established in 1986 in WI.
Donor: Clarence P. Bleser†.
Foundation type: Independent foundation.

Financial data (yr. ended 12/31/13): Assets, $37,002,281 (M); expenditures, $2,038,604; qualifying distributions, $1,805,000; giving activities include $1,805,000 for 41 grants (high: $250,000; low: $1,000).
Purpose and activities: Giving primarily for education, health organizations and hospitals, including a children's hospital, and social services.
Fields of interest: Higher education; Education; Hospitals (general); Hospitals (specialty); Health organizations, association; Medical research, institute; Human services; Christian agencies & churches; Catholic agencies & churches.
Limitations: Applications not accepted. Giving primarily in WI. No grants to individuals.
Application information: Contributes only to pre-selected organizations.
Officers and Directors:* Mary B. Hayes,* Pres.; James E. Bleser,* V.P.; Christa Schoenhofen, Secy.-Treas.
EIN: 391585269

9819
The Lynde and Harry Bradley Foundation, Inc. ✧

1241 N. Franklin Pl.
Milwaukee, WI 53202-2901 (414) 291-9915
Contact: Daniel P. Schmidt, V.P., Progs.
FAX: (414) 291-9991; Main URL: http://www.bradleyfdn.org
Twitter: https://twitter.com/bradleyfdn

Incorporated in 1942 in WI as the Allen-Bradley Foundation, Inc.; adopted present name in 1985.
Donors: Harry L. Bradley†; Caroline D. Bradley†; Margaret B. Bradley†; Margaret Loock Trust; Allen-Bradley Co.; Michael Keiser; Mrs. Michael Keiser.
Foundation type: Independent foundation.
Financial data (yr. ended 12/31/13): Assets, $922,303,709 (M); gifts received, $203,931,525; expenditures, $46,231,639; qualifying distributions, $40,153,715; giving activities include $34,178,862 for 546 grants (high: $3,000,000; low: $52), and $178,885 for 2 foundation-administered programs.
Purpose and activities: Support for projects that cultivate a renewed, healthier, and more vigorous sense of citizenship, at home and abroad. Projects will reflect the assumption that free men and women are genuinely self-governing, personally responsible citizens, able to run their daily affairs without the intrusive therapies of the bureaucratic, social service state. Consequently, they will seek to reinvigorate and revive the authority of the traditional institutions of civil society - families, schools, churches, neighborhoods, and entrepreneurial enterprises - that cultivate and provide room for the exercise of citizenship, individual responsibility, and strong moral character. Projects reflecting this view of citizenship and civil society may be demonstrations with national significance; public policy research in economics, politics, culture, or foreign affairs; or media and public education undertakings. Local support is directed toward cultural programs, education, social services, medical and health programs, and public policy research.
Fields of interest: Humanities; History/archaeology; Arts; Education, research; Higher education; Education; Youth development, citizenship; International affairs, foreign policy; International affairs; Economics; Political science; Public policy, research; Public affairs, citizen participation; Public affairs.
Type of support: General/operating support; Continuing support; Annual campaigns; Building/renovation; Equipment; Program development; Conferences/seminars; Professorships; Publication; Curriculum development; Fellowships; Internship funds; Scholarship funds; Research; Program-related investments/loans; Matching/challenge support.
Limitations: Applications accepted. Giving primarily in Milwaukee, WI; giving also on a national and international basis. No support for strictly denominational projects. No grants to individuals (except for Bradley Prizes), or for endowment funds.
Publications: Application guidelines; Annual report; Grants list; Occasional report (including application guidelines).
Application information: If the foundation determines the project to be within the current program interests as determined by its Board of Directors, the applicant will be invited to submit a formal proposal. Application form not required.
Initial approach: Letter of inquiry
Copies of proposal: 1
Deadline(s): Feb. 1, May 1, Aug. 1 and Nov. 1
Board meeting date(s): Feb., May or June, Aug., and Nov.
Final notification: 3 to 5 months
Officers and Directors:* Dennis J. Kuester,* Chair.; David V. Uihlein, Jr.,* Vice-Chair.; Michael W. Grebe,* C.E.O. and Pres.; Cynthia K. Friauf, V.P., Finance and Treas.; Terri L. Farmer, V.P., Admin.; R. Michael Lempke, V.P., Investments; Robert E. Norton II, V.P., Donor Relations; Daniel P. Schmidt, V.P., Progs.; Cleta Mitchell, Secy.; Mandy L. Hess, Cont.; Terry Considine; Patrick J. English; Richard W. Graber; Robert P. George; Diane M. Hendricks; James Arthur Pope; Thomas L. Smallwood; Shelby Steele; George F. Will.
Number of staff: 9 full-time professional; 8 full-time support; 3 part-time support.
EIN: 396037928
Selected grants: The following grants are a representative sample of this grantmaker's funding activity:
$3,000,000 to Charter Fund, Broomfield, CO, 2012. For program activities.
$1,000,000 to Encounter for Culture and Education, New York, NY, 2012. For Encounter Books.
$335,000 to National Strategy Information Center, Washington, DC, 2012. For general operations.
$325,000 to Milwaukee Symphony Orchestra, Milwaukee, WI, 2012. For general operations.
$40,000 to Institute for Foreign Policy Analysis, Cambridge, MA, 2012. For a research project on intelligence.
$35,000 to Hudson Institute, Washington, DC, 2012. For research and writing activities.
$35,000 to Johns Hopkins University, Baltimore, MD, 2012. For a senior fellowship.
$25,000 to Duke University, Department of Political Science, Durham, NC, 2012. For the Bradley Graduate and Post-Graduate Fellowship Program.
$25,000 to Ohio State University, Department of History, Columbus, OH, 2012. For the Bradley Graduate and Post-Graduate Fellowship Program for the furtherance of military history.

9820
Bradshaw-Knight Foundation, Inc. ✧

(formerly Cavaliere Foundation, Inc.)
1906 Monroe St.
Madison, WI 53711-2027
Contact: James A. Knight, Pres.
E-mail: bkfd@mac.com; Main URL: http://www.bkfnd.org

Established in 1999 in WI.
Donor: James A. Knight, Sr.†.
Foundation type: Independent foundation.
Financial data (yr. ended 12/31/13): Assets, $5,769,954 (M); gifts received, $200,000; expenditures, $757,715; qualifying distributions, $683,862; giving activities include $486,906 for 14 grants (high: $282,000; low: $1,000).
Purpose and activities: The foundation serves to promote the preservation and conservation of the ecological health of the United States.
Fields of interest: Environment, ethics; Environment, natural resources; Environment.
Type of support: General/operating support; Equipment; Program development; Conferences/seminars; Film/video/radio; Seed money; Curriculum development; Research.
Limitations: Giving primarily in the Upper Midwest Region of IL, IA, MN, and WI, and the West Slope of CO, especially the North Fork of the Gunnison River Valley. No grants to individuals.
Publications: Grants list; Program policy statement.
Application information: The proposal process is initiated only by the foundation. However, an informal discussion about a project or initiative may be initiated by submitting via email a short (not to exceed 200 words) letter of interest. The foundation is presently not accepting any new grant proposals. See foundation web site for current information and updates.
Board meeting date(s): Oct. 15
Officers and Directors:* James Alton Knight, Jr.,* Pres.; Renee Miller Knight,* Exec. Dir.; Xia Lynton Magnus.
Number of staff: 1 part-time professional.
EIN: 391960035

9821
Brady Corporation Foundation Inc. ✧ ☆

6555 W. Good Hope Rd.
Milwaukee, WI 53223-4634
E-mail: foundation@bradycorp.com; Main URL: http://www.foundation.bradycorp.org

Established in 2005 in WI.
Donor: Brady Corporation.
Foundation type: Company-sponsored foundation.
Financial data (yr. ended 07/31/13): Assets, $4,782,703 (M); gifts received, $750,000; expenditures, $1,782,558; qualifying distributions, $1,776,923; giving activities include $1,772,488 for 39 grants (high: $287,500; low: $250).
Purpose and activities: The foundation supports programs designed to promote formative development; skills development; and leadership development. Special emphasis is directed toward programs focusing on education.
Fields of interest: Education; Youth development; Human services.
Limitations: Applications accepted. Giving primarily in areas of company operations in WI.
Publications: Application guidelines.
Application information: Application form required.
Initial approach: E-mail

Deadline(s): Feb. 15
Board meeting date(s): June
Officers: Thomas J. Felmer, Pres.; Kathryn Campbell,* V.P. and Treas.; Loius Bolognini,* Secy.
Directors: Bentley Curran; Elizabeth Pungello.
EIN: 203304824
Selected grants: The following grants are a representative sample of this grantmaker's funding activity:
$30,000 to Milwaukee Art Museum, Milwaukee, WI, 2011.
$10,000 to United Way of Greater Milwaukee, Milwaukee, WI, 2011.
$5,000 to Lawrence University, Appleton, WI, 2011.

9822
Briggs & Stratton Corporation Foundation, Inc. ✧
12301 W. Wirth St.
Wauwatosa, WI 53222 (414) 259-5333
Contact: Robert F. Heath, Secy. and Treas.; Jodi A. Chaudoir
Application address: P.O. Box 702, Milwaukee, WI 53201

Incorporated in 1953 in WI.
Donor: Briggs & Stratton Corp.
Foundation type: Company-sponsored foundation.
Financial data (yr. ended 11/30/13): Assets, $14,092,205 (M); gifts received, $300,000; expenditures, $586,960; qualifying distributions, $586,950; giving activities include $550,600 for 85 grants (high: $100,000; low: $250), and $35,500 for grants to individuals.
Purpose and activities: The foundation supports organizations involved with arts and culture and education.
Fields of interest: Performing arts; Arts; Secondary school/education; Higher education; Education; Hospitals (general); Health care; Boys & girls clubs; YM/YWCAs & YM/YWHAs; Human services; United Ways and Federated Giving Programs.
Type of support: General/operating support; Annual campaigns; Capital campaigns; Building/renovation; Program development; Employee-related scholarships.
Limitations: Applications accepted. Giving primarily in areas of company operations in Auburn, AL, Statesboro, GA, Murray, KY, Poplar Bluff, MO, and Milwaukee, WI. No support for religious organizations. No grants to individuals (except for employee-related scholarships).
Application information: Application form not required.
Initial approach: Letter
Copies of proposal: 1
Deadline(s): None
Board meeting date(s): June and Nov.
Officers and Directors:* F.P. Stratton, Jr.,* Pres.; J.S. Shiely,* V.P.; R.F. Heath, Secy. and Treas.; M.D. Hamilton; T.J. Teske.
EIN: 396040377
Selected grants: The following grants are a representative sample of this grantmaker's funding activity:
$205,000 to United Way of Greater Milwaukee, Milwaukee, WI, 2011.
$110,000 to United Performing Arts Fund, Milwaukee, WI, 2011.
$50,000 to Childrens Hospital of Wisconsin, Milwaukee, WI, 2011. For operating support.
$35,000 to National FFA Foundation, Indianapolis, IN, 2011. For program support.
$25,000 to Enactus, Springfield, MO, 2011. For operating support.
$25,000 to Milwaukee School of Engineering, Milwaukee, WI, 2011. For operating support.
$25,000 to Taliesin Preservation Commission, Spring Green, WI, 2011. For program support.
$10,000 to Boys and Girls Clubs of Greater Milwaukee, Milwaukee, WI, 2011. For operating support.
$10,000 to Next Act Theater, Milwaukee, WI, 2011. For operating support.
$5,000 to UWM Foundation, Milwaukee, WI, 2011. For program support.

9823
The Brookby Foundation ✧ ☆
(formerly The Blodgett Foundation and Ferris Greeney Family Foundation)
10936 N. Port Washington Rd., #181
Mequon, WI 53092 (262) 478-0629
Contact: Nicole Lightwine, Prog. Off.

Established in 1994 in MI.
Donor: Edith I. Blodgett†.
Foundation type: Independent foundation.
Financial data (yr. ended 12/31/13): Assets, $37,825,155 (M); gifts received, $25,845,463; expenditures, $1,022,076; qualifying distributions, $1,005,471; giving activities include $936,822 for 113 grants (high: $260,000; low: $100).
Purpose and activities: The Brookby Foundation seeks to promote community well-being by supporting endeavors that advance artistic and scientific literacy, with a special interest in those that protect or improve the environment.
Fields of interest: Performing arts, music; Performing arts, orchestras; Environment, water resources; Environmental education; Human services, emergency aid.
Limitations: Applications accepted. Giving primarily in Edith Blodgett Legacy Fund gives primarily in Grand Rapids and western MI. No support for religious groups. No grants to individuals, or to support lobbying.
Publications: Application guidelines.
Application information: Application form required.
Initial approach: Letter of Interest through email or regular mail
Copies of proposal: 1
Deadline(s): Letter of Interest deadlines: May 15 and Sept. 15 for Brookby Foundation review; Feb. 15 for Edith Blodgett Legacy Fund review
Board meeting date(s): Aug. and Dec. for Brookby Foundation review; Apr. for Edith Blodgett Legacy Fund review
Final notification: Within 1 month
Officers: Wendy Greeney, Pres. and Secy.; Paul Greeney, V.P. and Treas.
Number of staff: 1 part-time professional.
EIN: 383202330
Selected grants: The following grants are a representative sample of this grantmaker's funding activity:
$57,500 to Grand Rapids Symphony, Grand Rapids, MI, 2012. To underwrite chair.
$15,000 to Grand Rapids Art Museum, Grand Rapids, MI, 2012. For Sunday Classical Series.
$10,000 to Hospice of Michigan, Detroit, MI, 2012. For Second Career Nursing.
$7,000 to Blue Lake Fine Arts Camp, Twin Lake, MI, 2012. For Grand Rapids Symphony Concert.

9824
The Brookhill Foundation ✧
N14W23755 Stone Ridge Dr., No. 250
Waukesha, WI 53188-1147

Established in 2006 in WI.
Donor: Marica K. Peterson.
Foundation type: Independent foundation.
Financial data (yr. ended 12/31/12): Assets, $26,198,026 (M); expenditures, $2,157,235; qualifying distributions, $2,080,020; giving activities include $1,392,000 for 15 grants (high: $250,000; low: $1,000).
Fields of interest: Higher education; Education; Boys & girls clubs; Human services; Mathematics.
Limitations: Applications not accepted. Giving primarily in WI. No grants to individuals.
Application information: Contributes only to pre-selected organizations.
Officer: Kathryn Stumpf, Exec. Dir.
Trustee: Marica K. Peterson.
EIN: 205818635

9825
Frank G. & Frieda K. Brotz Family Foundation, Inc. ✧
(formerly Frank G. Brotz Family Foundation, Inc.)
3518 Lakeshore Rd.
Sheboygan, WI 53083-2903 (920) 458-2121

Incorporated in 1953 in WI.
Donor: Plastics Engineering Co., Inc.
Foundation type: Independent foundation.
Financial data (yr. ended 09/30/13): Assets, $23,249,514 (M); expenditures, $1,969,663; qualifying distributions, $1,909,680; giving activities include $1,909,680 for 81 grants (high: $300,000; low: $500).
Purpose and activities: Giving primarily for education, hospitals, and human services.
Fields of interest: Higher education; Education; Hospitals (general); Human services; Foundations (private grantmaking).
Type of support: Building/renovation.
Limitations: Applications accepted. Giving primarily in WI. No grants to individuals.
Application information:
Initial approach: Letter
Deadline(s): None
Board meeting date(s): Periodically
Officers: Stuart W. Brotz, Pres.; Jesse R. Brotz, Secy.
Trustees: Adam T. Brotz; Roland M. Neumann.
EIN: 396060552
Selected grants: The following grants are a representative sample of this grantmaker's funding activity:
$25,000 to Concordia University Wisconsin, Mequon, WI, 2011.

9826
The Edwin E. and Janet L. Bryant Foundation, Inc. ✧
(formerly BGB Foundation)
3039 Shadyside Dr.
P.O. Box 600
Stoughton, WI 53589-0600 (608) 873-4378
Main URL: http://edwinandjanetbryantfoundation.org/

Established in 1993 in WI.

Donor: Janet L. Bryant‡.
Foundation type: Independent foundation.
Financial data (yr. ended 12/31/13): Assets, $67,005,798 (M); gifts received, $195,107; expenditures, $2,627,446; qualifying distributions, $2,755,429; giving activities include $1,578,901 for 52 grants (high: $226,000; low: $3,600), and $547,882 for 1 loan/program-related investment.
Fields of interest: Education; Hospitals (general); Human services; Aging, centers/services; Community/economic development.
Limitations: Applications accepted. Giving primarily in the Stoughton, WI, area; Dane County requests may be considered if not duplicative. No support for national or statewide WI causes. No grants to individuals.
Application information: Application form required.
Initial approach: Request application form
Deadline(s): None
Officers and Directors:* Rockne G. Flowers,* Pres.; David W. Bjerke,* V.P.; June C. Bunting, Secy. and Exec. Dir.; Jerry A. Gryttenholm,* Treas.; Patrick Lyons; Paul G. Selbo.
EIN: 391746858
Selected grants: The following grants are a representative sample of this grantmaker's funding activity:
$20,000 to Aldo Leopold Nature Center, Monona, WI, 2011.
$2,000 to Exponent Philanthropy, Washington, DC, 2011. For program support.

9827
William J. & Gertrude R. Casper Foundation ✧
c/o U.S. Bank, N.A.
P.O. Box 3194
Milwaukee, WI 53201-3194 (715) 723-6618
Contact: M. Berry
Application address: c/o The Edward Rutledge Charity, Kim King, 404 N. Bridge St., Chippewa Falls, WI 54729, tel.: (715) 723-6618

Established in 1988 in WI.
Donors: William J. Casper‡; Gertrude R. Casper‡.
Foundation type: Independent foundation.
Financial data (yr. ended 05/31/13): Assets, $18,482,374 (M); expenditures, $922,288; qualifying distributions, $802,918; giving activities include $554,450 for 44 grants (high: $75,000; low: $200), and $204,450 for 180 grants to individuals (high: $2,000; low: $400).
Purpose and activities: Scholarships awards to students who are residents of the Chippewa Falls; grants to organizations that improve the quality of life for residents of the Chippewa Falls, WI, area.
Fields of interest: Higher education; Human services; Children/youth, services.
Type of support: General/operating support; Scholarships—to individuals.
Limitations: Giving limited to residents of the Chippewa Falls, WI, area.
Application information: Application form required.
Initial approach: Letter requesting an application for scholarship; Proposals for community based organizations for grants
Deadline(s): None
Trustee: U.S. Bank, N.A.
EIN: 396484669
Selected grants: The following grants are a representative sample of this grantmaker's funding activity:
$25,000 to Chippewa Valley Cultural Association, Chippewa Falls, WI, 2011.
$25,000 to United Way of Chippewa County, Chippewa Falls, WI, 2011.
$17,500 to YMCA, Chippewa Valley Family, Chippewa Falls, WI, 2011.
$15,000 to Boy Scouts of America, Chippewa Valley Council, Eau Claire, WI, 2011.
$15,000 to Chippewa Area Catholic Schools, Chippewa Falls, WI, 2011.
$12,000 to Chippewa Youth Hockey Association, Chippewa Falls, WI, 2011.
$6,500 to Chippewa Valley Cultural Association, Chippewa Falls, WI, 2011.
$5,000 to Chippewa Area Catholic Schools, Chippewa Falls, WI, 2011.
$5,000 to YMCA, Chippewa Valley Family, Chippewa Falls, WI, 2011.
$2,500 to Make-A-Wish Foundation of Wisconsin, Butler, WI, 2011.

9828
Caxambas Foundation Inc. ✧ ☆
5320 N. Lake Dr.
Milwaukee, WI 53217-5372

Established in 1995 in WI.
Donors: George S. Parker II; George S. Parker Living Trust II; George S. Parker Charitable lead Trust II.
Foundation type: Independent foundation.
Financial data (yr. ended 12/31/12): Assets, $25,380,248 (M); gifts received, $273,097; expenditures, $750,530; qualifying distributions, $571,000; giving activities include $571,000 for grants.
Fields of interest: Museums (art); Historic preservation/historical societies; Arts; Higher education, university; Education.
Limitations: Applications not accepted. Giving primarily in NC and WI. No grants to individuals.
Application information: Contributes only to pre-selected organizations.
Officers and Directors:* Martha E. Parker,* Pres. and Treas.; Patricia Parker Schultz,* V.P.; J. Gardner Govan,* Secy.; Andrew R. Lauritzen.
EIN: 391826516

9829
Charter Manufacturing Company Foundation Inc. ✧
411 E. Wisconsin Ave., Ste. 2350
Milwaukee, WI 53202-4426

Established in 1984 in WI.
Donor: Charter Manufacturing Co., Inc.
Foundation type: Company-sponsored foundation.
Financial data (yr. ended 12/31/13): Assets, $5,719,479 (M); expenditures, $1,119,557; qualifying distributions, $1,119,250; giving activities include $1,119,250 for 43 grants (high: $200,000; low: $500).
Purpose and activities: The foundation supports organizations involved with performing arts, higher, medical, and engineering education, conservation, health, housing development, and youth development.
Fields of interest: Performing arts; Arts; Higher education; Medical school/education; Engineering school/education; Education; Environment, natural resources; Hospitals (general); Health care; Housing/shelter, development; Youth development, business; United Ways and Federated Giving Programs.
Type of support: General/operating support; Annual campaigns; Capital campaigns.
Limitations: Applications not accepted. Giving primarily in Milwaukee, WI. No grants to individuals.
Application information: Contributes only to pre-selected organizations.
Officers and Directors:* Linda T. Mellowes,* Pres.; John A. Mellowes,* V.P. and Treas.; Patrick J. Goebel,* Secy.; Charles A. Mellowes; John W. Mellowes; Kathleen J. Mellowes; R. Jan Pirozzolo-Millowes.
EIN: 391486363

9830
Emory T. Clark Family Foundation ✧
c/o US Bank, N.A.
P.O. Box 7900
Madison, WI 53707-7900 (414) 765-5118
Contact: Linda J. Hansen, Exec. Dir.
Application address: 125 N. Executive Dr., Ste. 363, Brookfield, WI 53005

Established in 1982 in WI.
Donor: Emory T. Clark‡.
Foundation type: Independent foundation.
Financial data (yr. ended 03/31/13): Assets, $9,199,072 (M); expenditures, $593,185; qualifying distributions, $536,480; giving activities include $536,480 for grants.
Purpose and activities: Giving primarily for the arts, education, health, and human services.
Fields of interest: Arts; Higher education; Adult/continuing education; Education; Hospitals (general); Health organizations; Human services; Children/youth, services.
Type of support: Capital campaigns; Building/renovation; Equipment; Scholarship funds; Research.
Limitations: Applications accepted. Giving primarily in WI.
Publications: Application guidelines; Informational brochure.
Application information: Application form required.
Initial approach: Proposal
Copies of proposal: 1
Deadline(s): None
Board meeting date(s): Nov.
Final notification: Dec. 1
Officer: Linda J. Hansen, Exec. Dir.
Trustees: Patrick Goebel; Helen Ruth La Badie; Marjorie J. Takton; US Bank, N.A.
EIN: 391410324
Selected grants: The following grants are a representative sample of this grantmaker's funding activity:
$30,000 to AIDS Resource Center of Wisconsin, Milwaukee, WI, 2011. To support operations.
$25,000 to Froedtert Hospital Foundation, Milwaukee, WI, 2011. To support operations.
$20,000 to Humane Society, Elmbrook, Brookfield, WI, 2011. To support operations.
$15,000 to Goodwill Industries of Southeastern Wisconsin, Milwaukee, WI, 2011.
$15,000 to Hunger Task Force, Milwaukee, WI, 2011.
$15,000 to Milwaukee Rescue Mission, Milwaukee, WI, 2011.
$15,000 to Neighborhood House of Milwaukee, Milwaukee, WI, 2011. To support operations.
$15,000 to Viterbo University, La Crosse, WI, 2011. To support operations.

$15,000 to Wisconsin Lutheran College, Milwaukee, WI, 2011.
$10,000 to Ronald McDonald House Charities of Eastern Wisconsin, Wauwatosa, WI, 2011.

9831
Cleary-Kumm Foundation, Inc. ✧
(formerly Cleary Foundation)
310 Sky Harbour Dr.
La Crosse, WI 54603-1343
Contact: Gail K. Cleary, Pres.

Established in 1982 in WI; merged with the Kumm Foundation in 2000.
Donors: Gail K. Cleary; Russell G. Cleary†; Lillian H. Kumm†.
Foundation type: Independent foundation.
Financial data (yr. ended 11/30/13): Assets, $14,183,660 (M); expenditures, $643,609; qualifying distributions, $586,347; giving activities include $548,407 for 81 grants (high: $101,500; low: $50).
Purpose and activities: The foundation is organized exclusively for charitable, educational, scientific, and religious purposes. It is further dedicated to supporting community activities and programs primarily within the greater La Crosse, Wisconsin, area.
Fields of interest: Arts; Higher education; Human services; Children/youth, services; United Ways and Federated Giving Programs.
Type of support: Annual campaigns; Capital campaigns; Endowments; Scholarship funds.
Limitations: Applications accepted. Giving primarily in the greater La Crosse, WI, area. No grants to individuals.
Publications: Annual report.
Application information: Application form not required.
Initial approach: Letter
Copies of proposal: 1
Deadline(s): None
Board meeting date(s): May, July, Sept., and Oct.
Final notification: Normally 1 month or less
Officer and Directors:* Gail K. Cleary,* Pres.; Kristine H. Cleary; Sandra G. Cleary.
Number of staff: 1 part-time professional; 2 part-time support.
EIN: 391426785

9832
Community Foundation for the Fox Valley Region, Inc. ✧
4455 W. Lawrence St.
P.O. Box 563
Appleton, WI 54912-0563 (920) 830-1290
Contact: Curt S. Detjen, C.E.O.; Martha Hemwall, V.P., Community & Donor Engagement; For grants: Heidi Dusek, Mgr., Community Engagement
FAX: (920) 830-1293; E-mail: info@cffoxvalley.org; Grant application e-mail: hdusek@cffoxvalley.org; Main URL: http://www.cffoxvalley.org
Facebook: https://www.facebook.com/cffvr
Flickr: http://www.flickr.com/photos/cffoxvalley
Grants List: http://www.cffoxvalley.org/page.aspx?pid=385
LinkedIn: http://www.linkedin.com/companies/community-foundation-for-the-fox-valley-region
Pinterest: http://www.pinterest.com/cffoxvalley/
Twitter: http://twitter.com/CFFoxValley
YouTube: http://www.youtube.com/user/CFFVR

Organized in 1986 in Appleton, WI.
Foundation type: Community foundation.
Financial data (yr. ended 06/30/14): Assets, $290,085,841 (M); gifts received, $31,291,232; expenditures, $18,148,159; giving activities include $15,853,187 for grants.
Purpose and activities: The foundation exists to enhance the quality of life for all citizens of the Fox Valley region by using funds entrusted to the foundation's stewardship to address community problems and opportunities.
Fields of interest: Arts; Education; Environment; Health care; Human services; Community/economic development; Children/youth; Aging; Disabilities, people with; Women; Economically disadvantaged.
Type of support: Technical assistance; Program evaluation; General/operating support; Curriculum development; Management development/capacity building; Equipment; Emergency funds; Program development; Conferences/seminars; Consulting services; Scholarships—to individuals.
Limitations: Applications accepted. Giving limited to Calumet, Outagamie, Shawano, Waupaca and northern Winnebago counties, WI. No support for sectarian or religious purposes, or medical projects. No grants for annual fund drives, deficit financing, endowment funds, travel expenses, capital construction, ongoing operating expenses, or research.
Publications: Application guidelines; Annual report; Financial statement; Grants list; Newsletter.
Application information: Potential grant applicants are strongly encouraged to attend Navigating Your Community Foundation and Writing a Compelling Grant Request workshops to learn how the foundation works and how to apply for grants from funds within the foundation that have competitive grant application processes. Visit foundation web site for application form and guidelines per grant type. Application form required.
Initial approach: Telephone
Copies of proposal: 1
Deadline(s): Varies
Board meeting date(s): Mar., June, Sept. and Dec.
Final notification: Approx. 2 months
Officers and Directors:* Jeff Werner,* Chair.; Curt S. Detjen,* C.E.O. and Pres.; Bob Ellis, V.P., Devel. and Donor Svcs.; Martha Hemwall, V.P., Community & Donor Engagement; Terri Towle, V.P., Finance and Admin.; Tammy Williams, V.P., Mktg. and Devel.; Rosie Sprangers, Cont.; Ben Adams; Omar Atassi; Keith Depies; Jim Eagon; Tim Higgins; John Hogerty; Steve Hooyman; Mike Lokensgard; Barbara A. Merry; Paul Mueller; Jack Rhodes; Rick Schinke; Kathi Seifert; Kathryn Sieman; Markalan Smith; Jon Stellmacher; Raquel Strayer; Cathie Tierney; Dave Vander Zanden; Alan Zierler.
Number of staff: 11 full-time professional; 2 part-time professional; 4 full-time support; 1 part-time support.
EIN: 391548450
Selected grants: The following grants are a representative sample of this grantmaker's funding activity:
$1,000,000 to University of Wisconsin Foundation, Madison, WI, 2013.
$419,359 to Greater Green Bay Community Foundation, Green Bay, WI, 2013.
$100,000 to Childrens Hospital of Wisconsin-Fox Valley, Neenah, WI, 2013.
$76,052 to Lutheran Social Services of Wisconsin and Upper Michigan, Northeast Regional Office, Appleton, WI, 2013.
$75,000 to Fox Cities Performing Arts Center, Appleton, WI, 2013.
$32,000 to Appleton Alliance Church, Appleton, WI, 2013.
$2,842 to Appleton Medical Center Foundation, Appleton, WI, 2013.
$2,500 to Salvation Army of Appleton, Appleton, WI, 2013.
$2,500 to United Way Fox Cities, Menasha, WI, 2013.
$2,000 to University of North Dakota, Student Account Services, Grand Forks, ND, 2013. For scholarship.

9833
Community Foundation of Central Wisconsin, Inc. ✧
(formerly Community Foundation of Portage County, Inc.)
1501 Clark St.
P.O. Box 968
Stevens Point, WI 54481-0968 (715) 342-4454
Contact: Terry Rothmann, Exec. Dir.
FAX: (715) 342-5560; E-mail: foundation@cfcwi.org; Additional E-mail: terryr@cfpcwi.org; Main URL: http://www.cfcwi.org/
Blog: http://cfcwi.blogspot.com/
Facebook: https://www.facebook.com/cfcwi
Grants List: http://www.cfcwi.org/receive/grant-award-listing.html

Established in 1982 in WI.
Foundation type: Community foundation.
Financial data (yr. ended 06/30/13): Assets, $15,029,986 (M); gifts received, $1,930,102; expenditures, $1,152,545; giving activities include $811,970 for 16+ grants (high: $34,500), and $142,970 for 160 grants to individuals.
Purpose and activities: The foundation seeks to help make the Portage County community a better place to grow, work, play, and retire by helping people, enhancing education, enriching arts and culture, contributing to wellness, and improving the environment through financial management of gifts and grants from individuals and organizations.
Fields of interest: Arts; Education; Environment; Health care; Human services; Women; Economically disadvantaged.
Type of support: General/operating support; Continuing support; Building/renovation; Equipment; Land acquisition; Program development; Conferences/seminars; Seed money; Curriculum development; Scholarship funds; Research; Matching/challenge support.
Limitations: Applications accepted. Giving limited to Portage and Waushara County, WI. No support for sectarian causes. No grants to individuals (except for scholarships), or for annual fund drives, capital campaigns, debt retirement, endowment funds, or operation losses.
Publications: Application guidelines; Annual report; Grants list; Informational brochure.
Application information: Visit foundation web site for application form and guidelines. Application form required.
Initial approach: Telephone or e-mail
Copies of proposal: 10
Deadline(s): Aug. 15
Board meeting date(s): Monthly
Final notification: Oct.
Officers and Directors:* Rob Manzke,* Pres.; Bev Laska,* Pres.-Elect; Jim Canales,* V.P.; Carie

Winn,* Secy.; Jim Robinson,* Treas.; Terry Rothman, Exec. Dir.; Trish Baker; Soua Cheng; Michele Dufresne; Michael Faeth; Rick Flugaur; Vicki Jenks; Jerry King; Jim Koziol; Katy Olson; Craig Reinking; Linda Steffen; Dave Williams; Carie Winn; Jennifer Young.
Number of staff: 1 part-time professional; 1 part-time support.
EIN: 390827885

9834
Community Foundation of North Central Wisconsin, Inc. ✧

(formerly Wausau Area Community Foundation, Inc.)
500 1st St., Ste. 2600
Wausau, WI 54403 (715) 845-9555
Contact: Jean C. Tehan, Exec. Dir.; For grants: Sue E. Nelson, Prog. Mgr.
FAX: (715) 845-5423; E-mail: info@cfoncw.org; Additional tel.: (888) 845-9223; Community Arts application e-mail: sue@cfoncw.org; Main URL: http://www.cfoncw.org
Facebook: http://www.facebook.com/pages/Community-Foundation-of-North-Central-Wisconsin/411517308312
LinkedIn: http://www.linkedin.com/company/3138631?trk=tyah

Incorporated in 1987 in WI.
Foundation type: Community foundation.
Financial data (yr. ended 12/31/13): Assets, $43,671,784 (M); gifts received, $3,063,404; expenditures, $1,919,787; giving activities include $1,306,944 for 67+ grants (high: $65,440; low: $28), and $190,573 for 160 grants to individuals.
Purpose and activities: The foundation is a nonprofit community corporation, created by and for the people of north central Wisconsin. The foundation devotes special emphasis to programs enriching life in five distinct areas: education, the arts, health, social services, and the conservation and preservation of resources, including historical and cultural.
Fields of interest: Historic preservation/historical societies; Arts; Education; Environment, natural resources; Health care; Health organizations, association; Housing/shelter, development; Human services; Community/economic development.
Type of support: Capital campaigns; Building/renovation; Equipment; Program development; Curriculum development.
Limitations: Applications accepted. Giving limited to the greater Wausau, WI, area, including Marathon County. No support for sectarian causes. No grants to individuals (except for designated scholarships), or for annual campaigns, operating expenses or losses, endowments, or debt retirement.
Publications: Application guidelines; Annual report; Informational brochure (including application guidelines); Newsletter.
Application information: Visit foundation web site for application forms and additional guidelines per grant type. Application form required.
Initial approach: Letter or telephone
Copies of proposal: 11
Deadline(s): First working day of Mar., June, Sept., and Dec. for Community Enhancement Grants
Board meeting date(s): Monthly
Officers and Directors:* Jennifer Sweeney,* Pres.; Jamie C. Schaefer,* V.P.; Susan L. Tiedemann,* Secy.; Fred T. Lundin,* Treas.; Jean C. Tehan, Exec. Dir.; Dennis M. DeLoye; Steven M. Immel; Polly James; Hugh E. Jones; Jim Kemmerling; Cari Logemann; Mary Nell Reif; Phil Valitchka; Randy P. Verhasselt; Manee Vongphakdy.
Number of staff: 3 full-time professional; 1 part-time professional.
EIN: 391577472

9835
Community Foundation of Southern Wisconsin, Inc. ✧

(formerly United Community Foundation, Inc.)
26 S. Jackson St.
Janesville, WI 53548-3838 (608) 758-0883
Contact: Ann Heiden, Exec. Dir.; For grants: Lindsey Hulstrom, Grants and Scholarships Mgr.
FAX: (608) 758-8551; E-mail: info@cfsw.org; Additional tel.: (800) 995-CFSW; Grant inquiry e-mail: lindsey@cfsw.org; Additional e-mail: ann@cfsw.org; Main URL: http://www.cfsw.org
Facebook: http://www.facebook.com/pages/Community-Foundation-of-Southern-Wisconsin-Inc/105619273962
Twitter: https://twitter.com/cfsw2014

Established in 1991 in Wisconsin.
Foundation type: Community foundation.
Financial data (yr. ended 06/30/13): Assets, $35,220,164 (M); gifts received, $4,445,221; expenditures, $3,112,179; giving activities include $1,604,930 for 46 grants (high: $84,498), and $532,263 for 385 grants to individuals.
Purpose and activities: The foundation primarily supports the arts, the environment, education, health, human services, and historic preservation in Crawford, Grant, Green, Iowa, Lafayette, Rock, Sauk, Vernon and Walworth counties, WI.
Fields of interest: Historic preservation/historical societies; Arts; Education; Environment; Health care; Safety/disasters; Recreation; Human services; Asians/Pacific Islanders; African Americans/Blacks; Hispanics/Latinos; Native Americans/American Indians; Women; Girls; Single parents.
Type of support: General/operating support; Management development/capacity building; Capital campaigns; Building/renovation; Equipment; Endowments; Emergency funds; Program development; Conferences/seminars; Seed money; Curriculum development; Internship funds; Scholarship funds; Technical assistance; Program evaluation; Scholarships—to individuals; In-kind gifts; Matching/challenge support.
Limitations: Applications accepted. Giving limited to Crawford, Grant, Green, Iowa, Lafayette, Rock, Sauk, Vernon and Walworth counties, WI. No grants to individuals (except for scholarships), or for endowments.
Publications: Application guidelines; Annual report; Financial statement; Informational brochure (including application guidelines); Newsletter.
Application information: Visit foundation web site for application guidelines per grant type. Application form required.
Initial approach: Letter of inquiry or telephone
Copies of proposal: 2
Deadline(s): Varies
Board meeting date(s): Quarterly
Final notification: Varies
Officers and Directors:* Steve Sheiffer,* Pres.; Ronald Spielman,* V.P.; Dick Jaeger,* Secy.; Steve Olsen,* Treas.; Tina Lorenz, C.F.O.; Sue S. Conley, Exec. Dir.; Larry Barton; Roberta Bernet; Laura Carney; Jim Finley; Carol Hatch; Cheryl Mader; William McDaniel; Joseph Nemeth; Dawn Ripkey; Cindy Tang.
Number of staff: 1 full-time professional; 5 part-time professional; 3 part-time support.
EIN: 391711388
Selected grants: The following grants are a representative sample of this grantmaker's funding activity:
$27,974 to ECHO, Janesville, WI, 2012. For food pantry.
$25,100 to YMCA, Northern Rock County Family, Janesville, WI, 2012. For general support.
$10,000 to ShelterBox USA, Lakewood Ranch, FL, 2012. For Japan Earthquake Relief.
$7,866 to YMCA, Green County Family, Monroe, WI, 2012. For general support.
$7,650 to Adams School Breakfast Club, Janesville, WI, 2012. For general support for food purchases.
$7,638 to Monroe Arts Center, Monroe, WI, 2012. For general support and youth programs.
$5,128 to Darlington Community Schools, Darlington, WI, 2012. For fieldtrips and computer equipment.
$1,975 to Grant Regional Health Center, Lancaster, WI, 2012. For AED's.
$1,800 to Platteville Community Arboretum, Platteville, WI, 2012. For butterfly field guides and equipment.
$870 to Rainbow Childcare, Monroe, WI, 2012. For tuition assistance.

9836
Cornerstone Foundation of Northeastern Wisconsin Inc. ✧

111 N. Washington St., Ste. 450
Green Bay, WI 54301-4208 (920) 490-8290
Contact: Sheri R. Prosser, V.P. & Secy.

Incorporated in 1953 in WI.
Foundation type: Independent foundation.
Financial data (yr. ended 12/31/13): Assets, $27,538,603 (M); expenditures, $1,851,887; qualifying distributions, $1,560,124; giving activities include $1,404,845 for 81 grants (high: $100,000; low: $250).
Purpose and activities: Emphasis on education, cultural programs, and social service and youth agencies; support also for healthcare facilities.
Fields of interest: Education, association; Adult education—literacy, basic skills & GED; Health care; Human services; Youth, services; Children/youth; Disabilities, people with; Blind/visually impaired; Mentally disabled; Substance abusers; AIDS, people with; Crime/abuse victims; Economically disadvantaged; Homeless.
Type of support: General/operating support; Continuing support; Annual campaigns; Capital campaigns; Building/renovation; Equipment; Endowments; Debt reduction; Emergency funds; Program development; Matching/challenge support.
Limitations: Applications accepted. Giving primarily in Brown County, WI. No support for religious or political organizations. No grants to individuals.
Publications: Application guidelines.
Application information: Application form required.
Initial approach: Telephone
Copies of proposal: 12
Deadline(s): None
Board meeting date(s): Feb. and Oct.
Officers and Directors:* Paul J. Schierl,* C.E.O.; Sheri R. Prosser, V.P. and Secy.; James J. Schoshinski,* V.P. and Treas.; Tim Day,* V.P.; John

W. Hickey,* V.P.; Mark J. McMullen,* V.P.; Thomas L. Olson,* V.P.; Carol A. Schierl,* V.P.; Michael J. Schierl,* V.P.; Mary G. Schaupp; Susan P. Watts.
Number of staff: 1 full-time professional; 1 part-time support.
EIN: 362761910
Selected grants: The following grants are a representative sample of this grantmaker's funding activity:
$50,000 to Rawhide, New London, WI, 2012. For Taste of the Town Auction Sponsor.
$40,000 to American Foundation of Counseling Services, Green Bay, WI, 2012. For Ethics in Business Awards Sponsor.
$10,000 to AIDS Resource Center of Wisconsin, Milwaukee, WI, 2012. For Green Bay Dental Clinic.
$5,000 to Prevent Blindness Wisconsin, Green Bay, WI, 2012. For pre-school vision screening Program.
$2,500 to ASPIRO, Green Bay, WI, 2012. For Jewels, Jeans and Tropical Breeze Sponsor.
$2,000 to ASPIRO, Green Bay, WI, 2012. For Clancy Caper Golf Classic Sponsor.
$1,500 to Boy Scouts of America, Bay Lakes Council, Appleton, WI, 2012. For Green Bay Outing for Scouting Golf Sponsor.
$1,000 to Green Bay Botanical Garden, Green Bay, WI, 2012. For Garden of Lights.
$800 to American Red Cross, Green Bay, WI, 2012. For Dancing with the Stars Sponsor.

9837
Culver's V.I.P. Foundation, Inc. ✧
1240 Water St.
Prairie du Sac, WI 53578-1091
Main URL: http://www.culvers.com/

Established in 2001 in WI.
Donors: Culver Franchising System Inc.; PepsiCo, Inc.; Leola Culver; Craig Culver; Baker Tilly Virchow Krause LLP; Classic Mix Partners; Ecolab; Fieldale Farms Corp.; Kerry; Pepsi; W.W. Johnson Meat; Valley Meats; Ventura Foods; Vienna Beef; Gordon Food Service; Masterson; Golden Country Foods.
Foundation type: Company-sponsored foundation.
Financial data (yr. ended 10/31/13): Assets, $2,126,749 (M); gifts received, $517,712; expenditures, $552,174; qualifying distributions, $501,443; giving activities include $225,440 for 61 grants (high: $25,000; low: $250), and $270,000 for 250 grants to individuals (high: $2,000; low: $500).
Purpose and activities: The foundation awards college scholarships to children of employees of Culver Franchising System and awards grants to various local organizations.
Fields of interest: Higher education; General charitable giving.
Type of support: Employee-related scholarships.
Limitations: Applications not accepted.
Application information: Contributes only through employee-related scholarships and to pre-selected organizations.
Officers and Directors:* Craig C. Culver,* Pres. and Treas.; Leola Culver,* V.P. and Secy.; Joseph Koss.
EIN: 392042139

9838
CUNA Mutual Group Foundation, Inc. ✧
(formerly CUNA Mutual Insurance Group Charitable Foundation, Inc.)
5910 Mineral Point Rd.
Madison, WI 53705-4456 (800) 356-2644
Contact: Steven A. Goldberg, Exec. Dir.
FAX: (608) 236-7755;
E-mail: Foundation@cunamutual.com; E-mail for Steven A. Goldberg: steven.goldberg@cunamutual.com; Additional address: P.O. Box 391, Madison, WI 53701; Main URL: http://www.cunamutual.com/portal/server.pt/community/community_involvement/728
Facebook: http://www.facebook.com/CUNA.Mutual.Foundation

Incorporated in 1967 in WI.
Donor: CUNA Mutual Insurance Society.
Foundation type: Company-sponsored foundation.
Financial data (yr. ended 12/31/13): Assets, $178,144 (M); gifts received, $859,801; expenditures, $741,072; qualifying distributions, $741,022; giving activities include $741,022 for 178 grants (high: $76,000; low: $125).
Purpose and activities: The foundation supports organizations involved with arts and culture, education, health, mental health, human services, and community development. Special emphasis is directed toward programs designed to serve at-risk youth.
Fields of interest: Museums (art); Arts; Secondary school/education; Charter schools; Higher education; Libraries (public); Education; Health care, clinics/centers; Health care; Mental health/crisis services; Boys & girls clubs; Big Brothers/Big Sisters; YM/YWCAs & YM/YWHAs; Family services; Family services, domestic violence; Human services; Community/economic development; United Ways and Federated Giving Programs; Youth.
Type of support: General/operating support; Continuing support; Capital campaigns; Building/renovation; Program development; Scholarship funds; Employee volunteer services; Employee matching gifts.
Limitations: Applications accepted. Giving primarily in areas of company operations in Waverly, IA, Fort Worth, TX, and Madison, WI. No support for political parties or candidates, professional associations, religious organizations, or labor unions. No grants to individuals, or for political campaigns, tickets or items for fundraising events, or endowments.
Publications: Application guidelines.
Application information: Organizations receiving support are asked to submit a final report. Application form not required.
Initial approach: E-mail letter of inquiry
Deadline(s): None
Officers and Directors: Faye A. Patzer, Pres.; James H. Metz, V.P.; Steven A. Goldberg, Secy.-Treas. and Exec. Dir.; Gerald W. Pavelich; James M. Power; Steven R. Suleski.
EIN: 396105418

9839
DeAtley Family Foundation Inc. ✧
1440 S. County Rd. JG
Mount Horeb, WI 53572-2992

Established in 1997 in WI.
Donor: William B. DeAtley.
Foundation type: Independent foundation.
Financial data (yr. ended 12/31/13): Assets, $10,262,517 (M); gifts received, $50; expenditures, $691,131; qualifying distributions, $673,344; giving activities include $673,344 for grants (high: $254,344; low: $5,000).
Purpose and activities: Giving primarily for human services, particularly housing development; funding also for children and youth services, and health organizations.
Fields of interest: Health organizations, association; Housing/shelter, development; Human services; Children/youth, services; Foundations (community).
Limitations: Applications not accepted. Giving primarily in WI. No grants to individuals.
Application information: Unsolicited requests for funds not accepted.
Officers: William B. DeAtley, Chair. and Treas.; Janine B. DeAtley, Secy.
Trustees: Brantner M. DeAtley; Leesa D. Schlimgen.
EIN: 061496358
Selected grants: The following grants are a representative sample of this grantmaker's funding activity:
$20,000 to Habitat for Humanity International, Americus, GA, 2011. For general use.
$20,000 to Smile Train, New York, NY, 2011. For general use.
$19,000 to American Cancer Society, Atlanta, GA, 2011. For general use.

9840
Eugene J. Eder Charitable Foundation, Inc. ✧
788 N. Jefferson St., Ste. 200
Milwaukee, WI 53202-3710

Established in 1997 in WI.
Donor: Eugene J. Eder.
Foundation type: Independent foundation.
Financial data (yr. ended 12/31/12): Assets, $11,056,435 (M); gifts received, $3,000,000; expenditures, $2,920,847; qualifying distributions, $2,758,096; giving activities include $2,758,096 for grants.
Fields of interest: Arts; Education; Human services; Children/youth, services; Jewish agencies & synagogues.
Type of support: General/operating support.
Limitations: Applications not accepted. No grants to individuals.
Application information: Unsolicited requests for funds not accepted.
Officers and Directors:* Allan J. Carneol,* Pres.; Craig H. Zetley,* V.P.; Jacob Herber.
EIN: 391870043

9841
Ralph Evinrude Foundation, Inc. ✧
411 E. Wisconsin Ave., Ste. 2350
Milwaukee, WI 53202-4426

Incorporated in 1959 in WI.
Donor: Ralph Evinrude‡.
Foundation type: Independent foundation.
Financial data (yr. ended 07/31/13): Assets, $17,453,129 (M); expenditures, $937,630; qualifying distributions, $755,612; giving activities include $693,333 for 66 grants (high: $50,000; low: $1,000).

Purpose and activities: Giving primarily for education, health, and social services, including programs for the homeless, hunger, the handicapped, youth and child welfare, and family services.
Fields of interest: Museums (marine/maritime); Education; Health care; Mental health/crisis services; Health organizations, association; Employment; Food services; Human services; Children/youth, services; Family services; Homeless, human services; Disabilities, people with.
Type of support: General/operating support; Continuing support; Annual campaigns; Capital campaigns; Building/renovation; Equipment.
Limitations: Applications not accepted. Giving primarily in Milwaukee, WI. No grants to individuals; no loans.
Application information: Contributes only to pre-selected organizations.
Officers and Directors:* Paul J. Tilleman,* Pres.; John W. Daniels, Jr.,* V.P. and Secy.; Ann M. Murphy,* Treas.
EIN: 396040256
Selected grants: The following grants are a representative sample of this grantmaker's funding activity:
$125,000 to Maritime and Yachting Museum, Jensen Beach, FL, 2011.
$5,000 to AIDS Resource Center Ohio, Columbus, OH, 2011.

9842
Weber Family Foundation, Inc. ✧ ☆
230 Front St. N.
La Crosse, WI 54601-3219

Established in WI.
Donor: Donald Weber.
Foundation type: Independent foundation.
Financial data (yr. ended 12/31/13): Assets, $667,688 (M); expenditures, $830,242; qualifying distributions, $820,760; giving activities include $820,000 for 6 grants (high: $400,000; low: $10,000).
Fields of interest: Arts; Higher education; Education; Human services.
Limitations: Applications not accepted. Giving primarily in La Crosse, WI.
Application information: Unsolicited requests for funds not accepted.
Officers: Elizabeth F. Weber,* Pres.; Tom Walch, V.P.; Darwin Isaacson, Secy.-Treas.
EIN: 611644894

9843
Fond du Lac Area Foundation ✧
384 N. Main St., Ste. 4
Fond du Lac, WI 54935-2310 (920) 921-2215
Contact: Sandi Roehrig, Exec. Dir.
FAX: (920) 921-1036;
E-mail: info@fdlareafoundation.com; Main URL: http://www.fdlareafoundation.com
Facebook: https://www.facebook.com/pages/Fond-du-Lac-Area-Foundation/160412896964

Established as a trust in 1975 in WI.
Foundation type: Community foundation.
Financial data (yr. ended 12/31/13): Assets, $28,827,270 (M); gifts received, $1,025,785; expenditures, $1,369,951; giving activities include $897,370 for 26+ grants (high: $50,000).
Purpose and activities: The foundation's purpose is to accept, manage, and distribute charitable contributions that will fulfill the needs and enhance the present and future quality of life within the Fond du Lac, WI, community.
Fields of interest: Arts; Education; Environment; Health care; Youth, services; Human services; Community/economic development.
Type of support: Program development; Seed money; Scholarship funds.
Limitations: Applications accepted. Giving limited to Fond du Lac, WI and the surrounding area. No support for religious organizations for religious purposes. No grants to individuals (except for scholarships), or for ongoing operating expenses or building funds, capital campaigns, endowments, debt reduction, scholarly research, fund drives, or for travel.
Publications: Application guidelines; Annual report (including application guidelines); Financial statement; Grants list; Informational brochure (including application guidelines); Newsletter.
Application information: Visit foundation Web site for application guidelines; contact the foundation to receive an application form. Application form required.
Initial approach: Telephone or letter
Copies of proposal: 1
Deadline(s): Jan. 15 and July 31
Board meeting date(s): Quarterly
Final notification: June 30 and Dec. 4
Officers and Directors:* Tom Herre,* Chair.; Steve Peterson,* Vice-Chair.; Patricia A. Miller,* Secy.; Stephen L. Franke,* Treas.; Sandi Roehrig, Exec. Dir.; Steven Cramer; Steven J. Dilling; Carol Hyland; Steven G. Millin; Paul Rosenfeldt; Mimi M. Sager; Jack E. Twohig; Scott Wittchow; Karen A. Wuest.
Number of staff: 3 full-time professional.
EIN: 510181570

9844
John & Alice Forester Charitable Trust ✧
P.O. Box 65
Wausau, WI 54402-0065 (715) 845-9201
Contact: San W. Orr, Jr., Tr.

Established in 1992 in WI.
Donor: John E. Forester.
Foundation type: Independent foundation.
Financial data (yr. ended 06/30/13): Assets, $14,464,233 (M); expenditures, $783,853; qualifying distributions, $677,400; giving activities include $677,400 for grants.
Fields of interest: Museums (art).
Limitations: Applications accepted. Giving primarily in Wausau, WI. No grants to individuals.
Application information: Application form not required.
Initial approach: Proposal
Deadline(s): None
Trustees: John E. Forester; San W. Orr, Jr.; Leigh H. Tuckey.
EIN: 391741441
Selected grants: The following grants are a representative sample of this grantmaker's funding activity:
$500,000 to Leigh Yawkey Woodson Art Museum, Wausau, WI, 2012.
$176,650 to Leigh Yawkey Woodson Art Museum, Wausau, WI, 2012.

9845
Fort Atkinson Community Foundation ✧
244 N. Main St.
Fort Atkinson, WI 53538-1829 (920) 563-3210
Contact: For grants: Sue Hartwick, Prog. Admin.
E-mail: facf@fortfoundation.org; Additional tel.: (920) 222-1191; Main URL: http://fortfoundation.org/

Established in 1973 in WI.
Foundation type: Community foundation.
Financial data (yr. ended 06/30/13): Assets, $21,583,830 (M); gifts received, $468,237; expenditures, $696,119; giving activities include $356,861 for 9 grants, and $200,419 for grants to individuals.
Purpose and activities: The mission of the foundation is to receive donations for educational, cultural, charitable, or benevolent purposes and use them to benefit residents and enhance the quality of life in the Fort Atkinson area.
Fields of interest: Arts; Education; Environment, beautification programs; Recreation; Human services; Community/economic development.
Type of support: General/operating support; Scholarships—to individuals.
Limitations: Applications accepted. Giving limited to the Fort Atkinson, WI, area. No support for sectarian or religious purposes. No grants to individuals (except through award or pre-established scholarship fund), or for endowment funds, debt retirement, wages or salary, or operating expenses (in response to annual fund drives or to eliminate previously incurred deficits).
Publications: Annual report.
Application information: Visit foundation web site for application guidelines. Application form required.
Initial approach: Contact foundation for application form
Deadline(s): Mar. 15, June 15, Sept. 15, and Dec. 15 for grants; varies for scholarships
Board meeting date(s): Jan., Apr., July, and Oct.
Final notification: Following board meetings
Officers and Directors:* W. Phil Niemeyer,* Chair.; Dean Brown,* Vice-Chair.; James J. Vance,* Secy. and Legal Counsel; Mary Behling; Beth McLaughlin; Christopher Rogers; Kristin Wallace.
Trustee: Rod Ellenbecker; Ann Herdendorf; Premier Bank, N.A.
EIN: 396220899

9846
Fotsch Family Foundation ✧ ☆
20985 Carrington Dr.
Brookfield, WI 53045-1823

Donor: Geraldine D. Fotsch.
Foundation type: Independent foundation.
Financial data (yr. ended 12/31/13): Assets, $25,417,553 (L); gifts received, $14,509,441; expenditures, $587,334; qualifying distributions, $586,000; giving activities include $586,000 for 33 grants (high: $75,000; low: $1,000).
Fields of interest: Education; Human services; Christian agencies & churches.
Limitations: Applications not accepted. Giving primarily in WI.
Application information: Unsolicited requests for funds not accepted.
Officers: Geraldine D. Fotsch, Pres.; Thomas A. Fotsch, V.P. and Secy.-Treas.
EIN: 462601906

9847
John J. Frautschi Family Foundation, Inc. ✧
303 Lakewood Blvd.
Madison, WI 53704-5917

Established in 1986 in WI.
Donors: John J. Frautschi; members of the Frautschi family.
Foundation type: Independent foundation.
Financial data (yr. ended 12/31/13): Assets, $4,640,521 (M); expenditures, $463,417; qualifying distributions, $436,297; giving activities include $423,000 for 77 grants (high: $175,000; low: $1,000).
Purpose and activities: Giving primarily for education, the arts, health associations, human services, and to a Presbyterian church.
Fields of interest: Museums; Performing arts; Arts; Elementary/secondary education; Higher education; Education; Environment, natural resources; Health organizations, association; Cancer research; Human services; United Ways and Federated Giving Programs; Protestant agencies & churches.
Type of support: General/operating support.
Limitations: Applications not accepted. Giving primarily in Madison, WI. No grants to individuals.
Application information: Contributes only to pre-selected organizations. Unsolicited requests for funds not considered.
Board meeting date(s): Annually
Officers and Directors:* John J. Frautschi,* Pres.; Elizabeth J. Frautschi,* V.P.; Christopher J. Frautschi,* Co-Secy.-Co-Treas.; Peter W. Frautschi,* Co-Secy.-Co-Treas.
EIN: 391561017

9848
W. Jerome Frautschi Foundation ✧
(formerly Overture Foundation)
6120 University Ave.
Middleton, WI 53562-3461 (608) 294-9000
Contact: Sandy Derer, Admin.

Established in 1996.
Donors: W. Jerome Frautschi; W. Jerome Frautschi Charitable Lead Unitrust.
Foundation type: Independent foundation.
Financial data (yr. ended 12/31/12): Assets, $19,588,953 (M); gifts received, $2,013,968; expenditures, $1,625,908; qualifying distributions, $842,515; giving activities include $842,515 for grants.
Purpose and activities: Giving primarily to arts and cultural programs, and education.
Fields of interest: Arts, single organization support; Arts; Education.
Limitations: Applications accepted. Giving primarily in Madison, and Dane County, WI.
Application information: Specific guidelines will be sent with the application form. Application form required.
Initial approach: Letter
Deadline(s): None
Officer and Directors:* Walter Jerome Frautschi,* Chair.; George E. Austin; Grant J. Frautschi; Lance A. Frautschi.
Number of staff: 1 full-time professional; 1 full-time support.
EIN: 391855130

Selected grants: The following grants are a representative sample of this grantmaker's funding activity:
$500,000 to Madison Public Library Foundation, Madison, WI, 2012. For downtown library construction.
$250,000 to Wisconsin Alumni Association, Madison, WI, 2012. To develop Alumni Park.
$25,000 to Fountain Valley School of Colorado, Colorado Springs, CO, 2012. To support childhood education.
$25,000 to Madison Community Foundation, Madison, WI, 2012. To support long-term philanthropy in Madison.
$25,000 to University of Wisconsin Foundation, Madison, WI, 2012. For fine arts.
$15,000 to Madison Symphony Orchestra, Madison, WI, 2012. For Gassman Opportunity Fund.

9849
Fund for Wisconsin Scholars, Inc. ✧
(formerly Fund for Wisconsin Scholarship, Inc.)
P.O. Box 5506
Madison, WI 53705-0506 (608) 238-2400
Contact: Mary Gulbrandsen, Exec. Dir.
FAX: (608) 238-0044;
E-mail: mgulbrandsen@ffws.org; Main URL: http://www.ffws.org
GiveSmart: http://www.givesmart.org/Stories/Donors/Tashia-and-John-Morgridge
Tashia and John Morgridge's Giving Pledge Profile: http://glasspockets.org/philanthropy-in-focus/eye-on-the-giving-pledge/profiles/morgridge

Established in 2007 in WI.
Donors: John P. Morgridge; Tashia Morgridge; Ted Kellner; Mary Kellner.
Foundation type: Independent foundation.
Financial data (yr. ended 06/30/13): Assets, $159,913,107 (M); gifts received, $21,145,000; expenditures, $9,784,723; qualifying distributions, $8,195,192; giving activities include $7,861,579 for 2 grants (high: $7,038,353; low: $823,226), and $25,000 for 50 grants to individuals.
Purpose and activities: The fund provides need-based grants to support the access to and completion of college, to graduates of Wisconsin public high schools who are attending Wisconsin public colleges. The Fund for Wisconsin Scholars will help reduce the financial barriers to college and lighten the debt that many Wisconsin students incur during their college years by providing need-based grants.
Fields of interest: Higher education.
Type of support: Scholarships—to individuals.
Limitations: Applications not accepted. Giving limited to WI.
Publications: Annual report.
Application information: Unsolicited requests for funds not accepted. Students do not apply to the fund for grants. Recipients are randomly selected from a group of eligible students. Refer to the fund's web site for eligibility guidelines.
Officers and Directors:* John P. Morgridge,* Chair. and Pres.; David Ward,* V.P.; Ted Kellner,* Treas.; Mary W. Gulbrandsen,* Exec. Dir.; John Daniels, Jr.; Tashia F. Morgridge.
EIN: 261412296
Selected grants: The following grants are a representative sample of this grantmaker's funding activity:
$7,038,353 to University of Wisconsin System, Madison, WI, 2013. For stipends and need-based grants.
$823,226 to Wisconsin Technical College System, Madison, WI, 2013. For stipends and need-based grants.

9850
Dudley and Constance Godfrey Foundation Inc. ✧ ☆
P.O. Box 510260
Milwaukee, WI 53203-0054

Established in 1986 in WI.
Donors: Dudley J. Godfrey, Jr.; Constance P. Godfrey; D. Godfrey Jr. Charitable Lead Trust.
Foundation type: Independent foundation.
Financial data (yr. ended 12/31/13): Assets, $138,654 (M); gifts received, $393,400; expenditures, $652,439; qualifying distributions, $652,439; giving activities include $650,300 for 3 grants (high: $650,000; low: $100).
Fields of interest: Education.
Limitations: Applications not accepted. Giving primarily in WI. No grants to individuals.
Application information: Contributes only to pre-selected organizations.
Officers and Directors:* Constance P. Godfrey,* Pres. and Treas.; J. Gardner Govan,* V.P. and Secy.; Sue E. Christensen.
EIN: 391562846

9851
Raymond and Marie Goldbach Foundation, Inc. ✧
(formerly Goldbach Charitable Foundation, Inc.)
304 East St.
Marathon, WI 54448-9643

Established in 1997 in WI.
Donors: Marie S. Goldbach Life Trust; Marathon Cheese Corp.; Packaging Tape, Inc.; Marie S. Goldbach.
Foundation type: Independent foundation.
Financial data (yr. ended 12/31/13): Assets, $25,804,189 (M); gifts received, $250,000; expenditures, $881,658; qualifying distributions, $731,132; giving activities include $717,632 for 50 grants (high: $250,000; low: $40), and $13,500 for 13 grants to individuals (high: $1,500; low: $500).
Purpose and activities: Giving primarily for education, human services, and to a swim team association. Scholarships also to residents of Wisconsin for higher education.
Fields of interest: Elementary/secondary education; Education; Athletics/sports, water sports; Human services; Foundations (community); Catholic agencies & churches.
Type of support: General/operating support; Building/renovation; Scholarships—to individuals.
Limitations: Applications not accepted. Giving primarily in WI.
Application information: Unsolicited requests for funds not accepted.
Officers: John L. Skoug, Pres. and Treas.; Marie S. Goldbach, V.P.
Director: Rev. Joseph G. Diermeier.
EIN: 391877824

9852
Irwin A. and Robert D. Goodman Foundation, Inc. ✧
(formerly Goodman's, Inc.)
P.O. Box 44966
Madison, WI 53744-4966

Established in 1961 in WI.
Donors: Irwin A. Goodman; Robert D. Goodman.
Foundation type: Independent foundation.
Financial data (yr. ended 08/31/13): Assets, $49,491,899 (M); expenditures, $2,416,073; qualifying distributions, $2,113,248; giving activities include $1,946,121 for 25 grants (high: $360,000; low: $2,000).
Fields of interest: Libraries (public); Human services; United Ways and Federated Giving Programs; Jewish federated giving programs; Jewish agencies & synagogues.
Limitations: Applications not accepted. Giving primarily in Madison, WI. No grants to individuals.
Application information: Contributes only to pre-selected organizations.
Officers: Howard A. Sweet, Pres.; E.G. Schramka, V.P. and Exec. Dir.; Steve Morrison, Secy.-Treas.
Director: Robert Pricer.
EIN: 396056619
Selected grants: The following grants are a representative sample of this grantmaker's funding activity:
$360,000 to University of Wisconsin Foundation, Madison, WI, 2013. For Indoor Training Center.
$347,564 to United Way of Dane County, Madison, WI, 2013. For General Operations and Wi-Fi.
$236,849 to Jewish Federation of Madison, Madison, WI, 2013. For General Operations, Goodman Campus and Strategic Plan.
$50,000 to Community GroundWorks, Madison, WI, 2013. For Youth Grow Local Farm.
$50,000 to Madison Parks Foundation, Madison, WI, 2013. For Pool Scholarship.
$35,000 to Madison Public Library Foundation, Madison, WI, 2013. For Capital Campaign Central Library.
$32,000 to East Madison Community Center, Madison, WI, 2013. For Fit for the Future Program.
$25,000 to Madison Metropolitan School District, Madison, WI, 2013. For Springharbor Middle School Sustainable Greenhouse.

9853
Gertrude S. Gordon Foundation ✧
c/o Trust Point Inc.
230 Front St. N.
La Crosse, WI 54601-3219

Established in WI.
Foundation type: Independent foundation.
Financial data (yr. ended 12/31/13): Assets, $10,656,810 (M); expenditures, $526,745; qualifying distributions, $435,171; giving activities include $431,171 for 10 grants (high: $112,657; low: $21,486).
Fields of interest: Boys & girls clubs; Human services; Foundations (private grantmaking); Foundations (community); Protestant agencies & churches.
Limitations: Applications not accepted. Giving primarily in La Crosse, WI. No grants to individuals.
Application information: Contributes only to pre-selected organizations.
Trustee: Trust Point.
EIN: 316672080

9854
Greater Green Bay Community Foundation, Inc. ✧
310 W. Walnut St., Ste. 350
Green Bay, WI 54303-2734 (920) 432-0800
Contact: David Z. Pamperin, C.E.O.; For grants: Martha Ahrendt, V.P., Progs.
FAX: (920) 432-5577; E-mail: ggbcf@ggbcf.org; Grant inquiry e-mail: martha@ggbcf.org; Grant inquiry tel.: 920-432-0800; Main URL: http://www.ggbcf.org
Twitter: http://twitter.com/ggbcfoundation
Scholarship inquiry e-mail: jennifernelson@ggbcf.org

Established in 1991 in WI.
Foundation type: Community foundation.
Financial data (yr. ended 06/30/14): Assets, $91,355,837 (M); gifts received, $8,218,615; expenditures, $4,778,673; giving activities include $4,197,891 for grants.
Purpose and activities: The foundation seeks to inspire and encourage charitable giving in northeastern Wisconsin by connecting caring people with solutions that strengthen the local community: 1) serving donors by providing a flexible and responsive vehicle for their charitable interests; 2) using resources wisely and efficiently through sensitive and creative grants addressing the emerging and changing needs of the community in the areas of the arts, education, health and human services, the youth and elderly, and resource conservation and preservation; 3) demonstrating community leadership by acting as a catalyst in identifying community needs and opportunities and sharing information with other foundations, corporations and organizations, both private and non-profit, to shape effective responses to those needs; and 4) acting as a responsible solicitor and prudent manager of philanthropic assets created by charitable gifts and bequests.
Fields of interest: Arts, cultural/ethnic awareness; Historic preservation/historical societies; Arts; Education; Environment; Health care; Alzheimer's disease; Diabetes; Youth development; Residential/custodial care, hospices; Human services; Community development, neighborhood development; Community/economic development; Infants/toddlers; Children/youth; Children; Adults; Aging; Young adults; Disabilities, people with; Physically disabled; Blind/visually impaired; Mentally disabled; Minorities; African Americans/Blacks; Hispanics/Latinos; Native Americans/American Indians; Military/veterans; Substance abusers; AIDS, people with; Single parents; Crime/abuse victims; Terminal illness, people with; Economically disadvantaged; Homeless.
Type of support: Continuing support; Management development/capacity building; Equipment; Computer technology; Emergency funds; Program development; Seed money; Curriculum development; Scholarship funds; Technical assistance; Program evaluation; Scholarships—to individuals; Matching/challenge support.
Limitations: Applications accepted. Giving limited to Brown, Door, Kewaunee, and Oconto counties, WI. No support for religious programs for religious purposes. No grants to individuals (except scholarships), or for annual or capital campaigns, endowments, capital improvement requests, fundraising activities or events, or debt retirement.
Publications: Application guidelines; Annual report; Financial statement; Informational brochure; Occasional report.
Application information: Visit foundation web site for grant application forms and guidelines per grant type. Faxed applications are not accepted. Application form required.
Initial approach: Contact foundation
Copies of proposal: 1
Deadline(s): Apr. 1 and Oct. 1 for Funds for Greater Green Bay grants; varies for others
Board meeting date(s): Mar., June, Sept., and Dec.
Final notification: Within 5 weeks of application deadline for Funds for Greater Green Bay grants
Officers and Board Members:* Tim Weyenberg,* Chair.; Mark McMullen,* Vice-Chair.; David Z. Pamperin,* C.E.O. and Pres.; Martha Ahrendt, Ph.D.*, V.P., Progs.; Christine Woleske,* Secy.; Mike Simmer,* Treas.; Jonathan J. Kubick, C.F.O.; Terry Fulwiler; Mark Kaspar; Charles Lieb; Gary Lofquist; Gail McNutt; Betsy Mitchell; Sue Olmsted; Therese Pandl; Mark Skogen; Adrian Ulatowski; and 7 additional board members.
Number of staff: 3 full-time professional; 3 part-time professional; 2 part-time support.
EIN: 391699966

9855
Green Bay Packers Foundation ✧
1265 Lombardi Ave.
Green Bay, WI 54307-0628 (920) 569-7323
Contact: Bobbi Jo Eisenreich, Secy.
Application address: P.O. Box 10628, Green Bay, WI 54307-0628 tel.: (920) 569-7323
Grants List: http://www.packers.com/community/packers-foundation/complete-listing.html

Established in 1986 in WI.
Donors: Youth Football Fund, Inc.; Green Bay Packers.
Foundation type: Company-sponsored foundation.
Financial data (yr. ended 03/31/14): Assets, $19,258,917 (M); gifts received, $6,461,201; expenditures, $1,228,696; qualifying distributions, $1,125,700; giving activities include $1,125,700 for 230 grants (high: $203,000; low: $1,000).
Purpose and activities: The foundation supports programs designed to benefit education, health, human services, civic affairs, and youth-related initiatives.
Fields of interest: Secondary school/education; Education; Hospitals (general); Health care; YM/YWCAs & YM/YWHAs; Human services; Foundations (community); Public affairs; Youth.
Type of support: General/operating support; Continuing support; Equipment; Program development; Scholarships—to individuals.
Limitations: Applications accepted. Giving primarily in WI, with emphasis in Brown County and Green Bay. No support for political organizations.
Publications: Application guidelines; Grants list.
Application information: Application form required.
Initial approach: Compete online application
Deadline(s): July 1
Directors: Tom Arndt; Rick Chernick; Valarie Daniels-Carter; Ricardo Diaz; Terrence R. Fulwiler; Gerald L. Ganoni; Johnnie Gray; George F. Hartmann; Edward N. Martin; Mark J. McMullen; Thomas L Olson; Mark Skogen; John P. Zakowski.
Officers: Charles R. Lieb,* Chair.; Bobbi Jo Eisenreich,* Secy.
EIN: 391577137

Selected grants: The following grants are a representative sample of this grantmaker's funding activity:
$52,000 to Saint Vincent Hospital, Green Bay, WI, 2011.
$7,500 to Scholarships Inc., Green Bay, WI, 2011.
$5,000 to Court Appointed Special Advocates of Brown County, Green Bay, WI, 2011.
$5,000 to Family Services of Northeast Wisconsin, Green Bay, WI, 2011.
$5,000 to Growing Power, Milwaukee, WI, 2011.
$4,000 to Einstein Project, Green Bay, WI, 2011.
$3,500 to Big Brothers Big Sisters of Northeastern Wisconsin, Green Bay, WI, 2011.
$2,500 to Milwaukee Kickers Soccer Club, Milwaukee, WI, 2011.
$2,000 to COTS, Appleton, WI, 2011.
$2,000 to Trinity Lutheran Church, Eau Claire, WI, 2011.

9856
B.A. and Esther Greenheck Foundation ✧ ☆
500 1st St., Ste. 2200
Wausau, WI 54403-4871
Main URL: http://www.providingopportunities.org/

Established in WI.
Donors: Esther M. Greenheck Survivor's Trust; Bernard A. Greenheck Marital Trust.
Foundation type: Independent foundation.
Financial data (yr. ended 12/31/13): Assets, $53,394,934 (M); gifts received, $500,000; expenditures, $2,680,644; qualifying distributions, $2,147,664; giving activities include $1,833,404 for 73 grants (high: $425,000; low: $545).
Fields of interest: Education; Health care; Human services; Foundations (community); United Ways and Federated Giving Programs.
Limitations: Applications not accepted. Giving primarily in WI. No grants to individuals.
Application information: Unsolicited requests for funds not accepted.
Officer and Trustees:* Brian Gumness,* Exec. Dir.; Mark J. Bradley; Barb Brown; Pamela A. Coenen; Donald L. Grade; Sandra L. Gumness; Eben Jackson; Jon A. Jackson; Dave Johnson; Jean C. Tehan; Bob Weirauch.
EIN: 391937735
Selected grants: The following grants are a representative sample of this grantmaker's funding activity:
$128,086 to Community Foundation of North Central Wisconsin, Wausau, WI, 2012. For Charitable Grant to the Wausau Curling Club to Build a New Facility.
$64,082 to Aspirus Health Foundation, Wausau, WI, 2012. For Charitable Contribution for NICU Transporters.
$50,000 to Aspirus Health Foundation, Wausau, WI, 2012. For Charitable Grant for NICU.
$30,000 to Community Foundation of North Central Wisconsin, Wausau, WI, 2012. For Community Arts Grant.
$25,000 to Community Foundation of North Central Wisconsin, Wausau, WI, 2012. For Charitable Grant for 25 for 25 Year Anniversary Grant.
$25,000 to Wausau Area Hmong Mutual Association, Wausau, WI, 2012. For Charitable Grant to Provide Training and Support for Individuals Seeking New Or Better.
$15,000 to Community Foundation of North Central Wisconsin, Wausau, WI, 2012. For Gannett Foundation Stock the Shelves - Matching Grant.
$12,000 to Wausau Area Hmong Mutual Association, Wausau, WI, 2012. For Charitable Grant for Emergency Food Project.
$10,000 to United Way of Marathon County, Wausau, WI, 2012. For Charitable Grant for Workplace Volunteer Council Fill a Backpack Fill a Need Program.
$9,000 to United Way of Marathon County, Wausau, WI, 2012. For Charitable Grant for Hunger Coalition.

9857
The James E. Griffiss Charitable Trust ✧ ☆
c/o U.S. Bank, N.A.
P.O. Box 2043
Milwaukee, WI 53201-9668

Established in 2003 in IL.
Donor: James E. Griffiss Trust.
Foundation type: Independent foundation.
Financial data (yr. ended 06/30/13): Assets, $0 (M); expenditures, $539,051; qualifying distributions, $530,911; giving activities include $528,566 for 3 grants (high: $252,833; low: $22,900).
Fields of interest: Religion.
Type of support: General/operating support.
Limitations: Applications not accepted. Giving primarily in IL and New York, NY. No grants to individuals.
Application information: Unsolicited requests for funds not accepted.
Trustee: U.S. Bank, N.A.
EIN: 396782574

9858
Sally Mead Hands Foundation ✧
404 S. Blount St., Ste. 101
Madison, WI 53703-1416

Donor: Sally M. Hands Trust.
Foundation type: Independent foundation.
Financial data (yr. ended 12/31/13): Assets, $29,577,983 (M); expenditures, $1,538,548; qualifying distributions, $1,287,000; giving activities include $1,287,000 for 37 grants (high: $95,000; low: $2,000).
Fields of interest: Performing arts; Education; Environment; Human services.
Limitations: Applications not accepted. Giving primarily in IL, MI, and WI.
Application information: Unsolicited requests for funds not accepted.
Officers: John L. Hands, Jr., Pres.; Louise H. Murphy, Secy.; Helen M. Hands, Treas.
Director: Collier M. Hands.
EIN: 320263007

9859
Harley-Davidson Foundation, Inc. ✧
3700 W. Juneau Ave.
P.O. Box 653
Milwaukee, WI 53208-2818 (414) 343-4001
Contact: Mary Ann Martiny, Secy. and Mgr.
E-mail: foundationapplications@Harley-Davidson.com; Main URL: http://www.harley-davidson.com/en_US/Content/Pages/Company/Sustainability/Foundation/foundation.html?locale=en_US&bmLocale=en_US
Grants List: http://www.harley-davidson.com/en_US/Media/downloads/Foundation/Grant-Recipients-2013.pdf

Established in 1994 in WI.
Donors: Harley-Davidson, Inc.; Karl Eberle; John Mink.
Foundation type: Company-sponsored foundation.
Financial data (yr. ended 12/31/12): Assets, $23,180,070 (M); gifts received, $2,000,135; expenditures, $2,637,159; qualifying distributions, $2,501,385; giving activities include $2,501,385 for 268 grants (high: $283,499; low: $30).
Purpose and activities: The foundation supports programs designed to meet basic needs of the community; improve the lives of Harley-Davidson stakeholders; and encourage social responsibility. Special emphasis is directed toward education programs within the public school systems located in areas of Harley-Davidson operations.
Fields of interest: Arts education; Arts; Elementary/secondary education; Education; Environment, natural resources; Botanical/horticulture/landscape services; Environmental education; Environment; Public health; Health care; Mental health/crisis services; Food services; Youth development; Human services; Community development, neighborhood development; Community/economic development; United Ways and Federated Giving Programs; Military/veterans' organizations.
Type of support: Capital campaigns; Program development; Conferences/seminars; Curriculum development; Scholarship funds; Employee volunteer services; Employee matching gifts.
Limitations: Applications accepted. Giving primarily in areas of company operations in Mohave County and Yucca, AZ, Chicago, IL, Kansas City, MO, Valley View, OH; York, PA, Plano, TX, and Milwaukee, Menomonee Falls, Tomahawk, and Wauwatosa, WI; giving also to national organizations. No support for political candidates, athletic teams, or religious organizations not of direct benefit to the entire community. No grants to individuals, or for political causes, general operating, or endowment funds.
Publications: Application guidelines; Corporate giving report; Grants list; IRS Form 990 or 990-PF printed copy available upon request.
Application information: National organizations or organizations requesting conference or capital campaign support must e-mail a letter of intent to the foundation. Application form required.
Initial approach: Complete online eligibility quiz and application
Copies of proposal: 1
Deadline(s): Mar. 7, July 11, Oct. 10, and Dec. 12
Officers and Directors:* Tonit M. Calaway,* Pres.; John A. Olin,* V.P. and C.F.O.; J. Darrell Thomas, V.P. and Treas.; Mary Anne Martiny, Secy.; John P. Baker; Joanne M. Bischmann; Matthew S. Levatich; Patrick Smith.
EIN: 391769946

9860
Ann E. & Joseph F. Heil, Jr. Charitable Trust ✧
c/o BMO Harris Bank N.A.
P.O. Box 2980
Milwaukee, WI 53201-2977

Established in 1999 in WI.

Donors: Marjorie Heil†; Ann E. Heil Marital Trust; Ann E. Heil Admin Trust.
Foundation type: Independent foundation.
Financial data (yr. ended 12/31/13): Assets, $6,274,662 (M); expenditures, $723,899; qualifying distributions, $692,765; giving activities include $690,800 for 23 grants (high: $300,000; low: $700).
Fields of interest: Visual arts; Performing arts; Performing arts, ballet; Environment, natural resources; Botanical gardens; Health care; Boys & girls clubs; Human services; United Ways and Federated Giving Programs.
Limitations: Applications not accepted. Giving primarily in Milwaukee, WI; some giving in AZ and ID. No grants to individuals.
Application information: Unsolicited requests for funds not accepted.
Trustee: Katherine A. Heil.
EIN: 396713764
Selected grants: The following grants are a representative sample of this grantmaker's funding activity:
$35,000 to Association for the Advancement of Contemporary Dance, Boise, ID, 2011.
$5,000 to Discovery World, Milwaukee, WI, 2011. For general support.
$5,000 to Milwaukee Film, Milwaukee, WI, 2011. For general support.
$5,000 to Planned Parenthood of Wisconsin, Milwaukee, WI, 2011. For general support.
$4,000 to Milwaukee Art Museum, Milwaukee, WI, 2011.
$3,500 to United Performing Arts Fund, Milwaukee, WI, 2011.
$2,500 to Penfield Childrens Center, Milwaukee, WI, 2011. For general support.
$2,000 to Radio for Milwaukee, Milwaukee, WI, 2011. For general support.
$1,500 to Childrens Hospital and Health System Foundation, Milwaukee, WI, 2011.
$1,500 to Danceworks, Milwaukee, WI, 2011. For general support.

9861
Evan and Marion Helfaer Foundation ✧

P.O. Box 147
Elm Grove, WI 53122-0147 (262) 784-9778
Contact: Thomas L. Smallwood, Admin.

Established in 1971 in WI.
Donor: Evan P. Helfaer†.
Foundation type: Independent foundation.
Financial data (yr. ended 07/31/13): Assets, $22,237,410 (M); expenditures, $1,181,435; qualifying distributions, $838,922; giving activities include $838,922 for grants.
Purpose and activities: Giving primarily for the arts, education, health organizations and medical research, children, youth, and social services, and community development, including a baseball campaign.
Fields of interest: Arts; Higher education; Health organizations, association; Medical research, institute; Athletics/sports, baseball; Human services; Children/youth, services; Community/economic development; United Ways and Federated Giving Programs; Blind/visually impaired.
Type of support: Building/renovation; Professorships; Curriculum development; Research.
Limitations: Giving limited to WI. No grants to individuals.
Application information: Application form not required.
Initial approach: Letter
Deadline(s): None
Board meeting date(s): Periodically
Final notification: Within 90 days after end of fiscal year
Trustees: William T. Gaus; Thomas L. Smallwood; M&I Bank.
Number of staff: 1
EIN: 396238856
Selected grants: The following grants are a representative sample of this grantmaker's funding activity:
$200,000 to Medical College of Wisconsin, Milwaukee, WI, 2013. For 2nd and 3rd Installment - Transplant Center for Adult Heart Transplant Campaign.
$25,000 to City Year Milwaukee, Milwaukee, WI, 2013. For AmeriCorps Service Program in Milwaukee School.
$15,000 to Milwaukee Symphony Orchestra, Milwaukee, WI, 2013. For Continued Programming and Operating Support.
$10,000 to Family House, Milwaukee, WI, 2013. For Construction and Renovation Campaign.
$5,000 to Marquette University, Law School, Milwaukee, WI, 2013. For operations and Programming.
$5,000 to Medical College of Wisconsin, Milwaukee, WI, 2013. For Warren P Knowles Award Dinner - did not attend.
$2,500 to Milwaukee Center for Independence, Milwaukee, WI, 2013. For Reagan High School Student Scholarship Program.
$2,000 to Milwaukee Repertory Theater, Milwaukee, WI, 2013. For artistic intern program.
$1,500 to Urban Day School, Milwaukee, WI, 2013. For Summer School Program.
$1,000 to Sojourner Family Peace Center, Milwaukee, WI, 2013. For emergency shelter program.

9862
The Herma Family Foundation ✧

c/o Peter M. Sommerhauser
780 N. Water St.
Milwaukee, WI 53202-3512

Established in 1993 in WI.
Donors: John F. Herma; Susan M. Herma.
Foundation type: Independent foundation.
Financial data (yr. ended 12/31/13): Assets, $7,028,810 (M); expenditures, $624,350; qualifying distributions, $614,350; giving activities include $609,000 for 7 grants (high: $500,000; low: $500).
Purpose and activities: Giving primarily to a children's hospital, as well as for higher education.
Fields of interest: Higher education; Hospitals (specialty); Human services; Children, services.
Limitations: Applications not accepted. Giving primarily in WI; some funding also in NJ. No grants to individuals.
Application information: Contributes only to pre-selected organizations.
Officers and Directors:* John F. Herma,* Pres. and Treas.; Susan M. Herma,* V.P. and Secy.; Peter M. Sommerhauser.
EIN: 391776108

9863
The Richard & Ethel Herzfeld Foundation, Inc. ✧

219 N. Milwaukee St., 7th Fl.
Milwaukee, WI 53202-5818
Contact: Laura Gembolis, Prog. Dir.
FAX: (414) 727-1136;
E-mail: lgembolis@herzfeldfoundation.org; Main URL: http://www.herzfeldfoundation.org

Established around 1973 in WI.
Donors: Ethel D. Herzfeld†; Richard P. Herzfeld†.
Foundation type: Independent foundation.
Financial data (yr. ended 12/31/12): Assets, $73,739,206 (M); expenditures, $3,880,083; qualifying distributions, $3,588,266; giving activities include $3,004,195 for 76 grants (high: $250,000; low: $5,000).
Purpose and activities: Giving primarily to arts organizations and for education; on a limited and by-invitation only basis, the foundation will consider grant requests for civic improvement projects that enhance the vitality, attractiveness, and quality of life of the greater Milwaukee, WI, area.
Fields of interest: Arts education; Arts; Education, early childhood education; Education; Community/economic development.
Type of support: General/operating support; Capital campaigns; Building/renovation; Program development; Research; Matching/challenge support.
Limitations: Applications accepted. Giving limited to WI, with emphasis on the greater Milwaukee area. No support for political, labor, religious or business organizations. No grants to individuals, fundraising, deficit reduction or repayment of loans.
Publications: Application guidelines; Annual report; Grants list.
Application information: Full proposals are by invitation only, after review of preliminary application form. Grants are only awarded for 1 year, continuation subject to review. Application form required.
Initial approach: Use online preliminary application form on foundation web site
Copies of proposal: 1
Deadline(s): Feb. 1, May 1, and Aug. 1
Board meeting date(s): Spring, summer, and fall
Final notification: Approximately 3 months
Officers and Directors:* F. William Haberman, Pres.; Carmen Haberman,* V.P., Arts and Culture; Edward Hinshaw,* V.P.; Richard L. Weiss,* Treas.; Fred Haberman; Sarah Haberman; Gordon Miller.
Number of staff: 3 full-time professional.
EIN: 237230686

9864
Jerome J. and Dorothy H. Holz Family Foundation ✧

10400 W. Innovation Dr., Ste. 110
Milwaukee, WI 53226-4840 (414) 774-1031
Contact: Don Tushaus, Fdn. Admin.
FAX: (414) 774-3570; Main URL: http://www.holzfamilyfoundation.com

Reorganized and renamed in 2002 in WI.
Donors: Jerome J. Holz; Dorothy H. Holz†; Jerome and Dorothy Holz Family Foundation.
Foundation type: Independent foundation.
Financial data (yr. ended 08/31/13): Assets, $11,544,011 (M); gifts received, $250,000; expenditures, $620,324; qualifying distributions,

$543,014; giving activities include $500,500 for 28 grants (high: $75,000; low: $1,000).
Purpose and activities: Giving primarily for education, including special education of handicapped individuals; student services, scholarships and student financial aid; health, specifically patient counseling; senior continuing care communities; zoos; and community events for the general public.
Fields of interest: Higher education; Engineering school/education; Zoos/zoological societies; Children/youth, services; Community/economic development.
Type of support: General/operating support; Continuing support; Capital campaigns; Building/renovation; Equipment; Scholarship funds.
Limitations: Applications accepted. Giving primarily in Hales Corners, WI and the surrounding area. No support for religious purposes or political organizations. No grants to individuals, or for fundraisers, deficit financing or loans.
Publications: Application guidelines.
Application information: Application form required.
Initial approach: Online, letter or telephone requesting application
Copies of proposal: 7
Deadline(s): May 1st
Board meeting date(s): June
Final notification: 3 months
Officers and Trustees:* Jerome J. Holz,* Pres.; J.J. Weis,* Exec. V.P.; Barbara Holz Weis,* V.P.; Judith Holz Stathas,* Secy.; Donald H. Tushaus, Treas.; Traci Weis.
EIN: 367368506
Selected grants: The following grants are a representative sample of this grantmaker's funding activity:
$50,000 to Milwaukee Symphony Orchestra, Milwaukee, WI, 2012.
$45,000 to Zoological Society of Milwaukee County, Milwaukee, WI, 2012. For student programs.
$25,000 to Boerner Botanical Gardens, Friends of the, Hales Corners, WI, 2011.
$15,000 to Boerner Botanical Gardens, Friends of the, Hales Corners, WI, 2012.
$15,000 to Milwaukee Public Museum, Milwaukee, WI, 2011.
$10,000 to Big Brothers Big Sisters of Metropolitan Milwaukee, Milwaukee, WI, 2012.
$10,000 to Center for Veterans Issues, Milwaukee, WI, 2011.
$10,000 to Habitat for Humanity, Milwaukee, Milwaukee, WI, 2012.
$10,000 to Rawhide, New London, WI, 2012.
$10,000 to Zoological Society of Milwaukee County, Milwaukee, WI, 2012. For Platypus Society.
$5,000 to Badger Association of the Blind and Visually Impaired, Milwaukee, WI, 2011.
$5,000 to Feeding America Eastern Wisconsin, Milwaukee, WI, 2011.
$5,000 to Feeding America Eastern Wisconsin, Milwaukee, WI, 2012.
$5,000 to Milwaukee Public Museum, Milwaukee, WI, 2012.
$5,000 to Vision Forward Association, Milwaukee, WI, 2012.
$5,000 to Wisconsin Academy for Graduate Service Dogs, Madison, WI, 2012.
$2,500 to Big Brothers Big Sisters of Metropolitan Milwaukee, Milwaukee, WI, 2011.

9865
The Eric D. & Steven D. Hovde Foundation ✧

122 W. Washington Ave., Ste. 350
Madison, WI 53703-2758 (608) 255-5175, ext. 35
Contact: Jeffrey Boyd, Exec. Dir.
E-mail: jboyd@hovdefoundation.org; Main URL: http://www.hovdefoundation.org
Facebook: https://www.facebook.com/hovdefoundation

Established in 1998 in IL.
Donors: Eric D. Hovde; Steven D. Hovde; Curt Sidden; Jennifer Sidden; Hovde Financial, Inc.; Banco Popular North America; Hovde Capital I, LLC; The Lili Claire Foundation, Inc.; Ellis Management Svcs., Inc.
Foundation type: Independent foundation.
Financial data (yr. ended 12/31/13): Assets, $11,825,516 (M); gifts received, $585,957; expenditures, $1,095,319; qualifying distributions, $976,201; giving activities include $774,857 for 19 grants.
Purpose and activities: Giving to find a cure for Multiple Sclerosis (MS), and to help people in crisis situations, especially homeless children.
Fields of interest: Medical research, institute; Multiple sclerosis research; Human services; International development; Christian agencies & churches.
Limitations: Applications not accepted. Giving in the U.S., with emphasis on Washington, DC, and NY. No grants to individuals.
Application information: Contributes only to pre-selected organizations.
Officers: Jeffrey Cashdin, C.F.O.; Jeffrey Boyd, Exec. Dir.
Trustees: Eric D. Hovde; Steven D. Hovde; Richard J. Perry, Jr.
EIN: 522107093

9866
Iddings Benevolent Trust ✧

(also known as Iddings Foundation)
c/o JPMorgan Chase Bank, N.A.
P.O. Box 3038
Milwaukee, WI 53201-3038
Application address: c/o Becky Coughlin, Kettering Twr., Ste. 1620, Dayton, OH 45423; tel.: (937) 224-1773

Established in 1973 in OH.
Donors: Roscoe C. Iddings‡; Andrew S. Iddings‡.
Foundation type: Independent foundation.
Financial data (yr. ended 12/31/13): Assets, $14,671,078 (M); expenditures, $590,550; qualifying distributions, $564,061; giving activities include $502,612 for 35 grants (high: $279,132; low: $1,000).
Purpose and activities: Grants for improvement of the greater Dayton, Ohio, area, through capital and small grants; and through innovative projects which benefit at-risk youth and change the system—for example: education, health, justice, and economics.
Fields of interest: Arts; Education; Reproductive health, family planning; Human services; Children/youth, services.
Type of support: Capital campaigns; Building/renovation; Equipment; Land acquisition; Program development; Seed money; Matching/challenge support.
Limitations: Applications accepted. Giving limited to OH, with emphasis on the Dayton metropolitan area. No grants to individuals, or for endowment funds or deficit financing; no loans.
Publications: Informational brochure (including application guidelines).
Application information: Application form required.
Initial approach: Letter (synopsis form, 3-page narrative) or telephone
Copies of proposal: 7
Deadline(s): Mar. 1, June 1, Sept. 1 and Nov. 1
Board meeting date(s): Mar., June, Sept., and Dec.
Final notification: 10 days after committee meeting
Officer: Ken Trent, Trust Off., JP Morgan Chase Bank, N.A.
Trustee: JPMorgan Chase Bank, N.A.
Number of staff: 1 part-time professional.
EIN: 316135058

9867
Incourage Community Foundation, Inc. ✧

(formerly Community Foundation of Greater South Wood County, Inc.)
478 E. Grand Ave.
Wisconsin Rapids, WI 54494 (715) 423-3863
Contact: Kelly Ryan, C.E.O.; For grants: Dawn Vruwink, V.P., Community Resources
FAX: (715) 423-3019;
E-mail: hello@incouragecf.org; Grant request E-mail: dvruwink@incouragecf.org; Main URL: http://www.incouragecf.org
Blog: http://kellyincourage.blogspot.com
Facebook: https://www.facebook.com/incouragecf
LinkedIn: http://www.linkedin.com/company/incourage-community-foundation?trk=tyah
RSS Feed: http://incouragecf.org/feed/
Twitter: https://twitter.com/incouragecf
YouTube: http://www.youtube.com/incouragecf

Established in 1993 in WI.
Foundation type: Community foundation.
Financial data (yr. ended 12/31/13): Assets, $34,601,113 (M); gifts received, $908,742; expenditures, $3,069,105; giving activities include $665,661 for grants.
Purpose and activities: The foundation is a not-for-profit community foundation incorporated under the laws of the State of Wisconsin in 1993. Its primary mission is to promote strategic philanthropy, build social capital, and leverage community resources for the common good. The foundation's vision is a resilient, thriving community that embraces and supports all people. It receives and maintains funds to be utilized for philanthropic activities that meet the requirements of the foundation's governing documents.
Fields of interest: Museums (art); Performing arts; Performing arts, theater; Historic preservation/historical societies; Arts; Elementary/secondary education; Higher education; Education; Hospitals (general); Health care; Health organizations; Disasters, preparedness/services; Boys & girls clubs; Youth development; Children/youth, services; Family services; Aging, centers/services; Human services; Community/economic development.
Type of support: Management development/capacity building; Building/renovation; Equipment; Emergency funds; Program development; Seed money; Scholarship funds; Research; Technical assistance; Program-related investments/loans;

Scholarships—to individuals; Matching/challenge support.
Limitations: Applications accepted. Giving limited to south Wood County, WI, and the Town of Rome. No support for religious organizations for sectarian purposes. No grants to individuals (except for scholarships), or for debt retirement, deficit financing, fundraising activities, endowment funds, operating expenses for United Way agencies, routine operating needs, annual fundraising, capital fund drives, or for umbrella funding.
Publications: Application guidelines; Financial statement; Informational brochure; Newsletter.
Application information: Visit foundation web site for application form and guidelines. Application form required.
Initial approach: Telephone, e-mail, or letter of inquiry
Copies of proposal: 1
Deadline(s): None
Board meeting date(s): At least quarterly
Final notification: 4 to 6 weeks
Officers and Directors:* Helen Jungwirth,* Chair.; Carl Wartman,* Vice-Chair.; Kelly Ryan,* C.E.O. and Pres.; Dawn Vruwink,* V.P., Community Resources; Mary Wirtz,* V.P., Donor Svcs.; Dawn Neuman,* C.F.O. and C.O.O.; Kirk Willard,* Secy.; Dale Bikowski; Paul Liebherr; Kristie Rauter.
Number of staff: 11 full-time professional; 2 part-time professional; 3 full-time support; 4 part-time support.
EIN: 391772651
Selected grants: The following grants are a representative sample of this grantmaker's funding activity:
$138,193 to Wisconsin Rapids Public Schools, Wisconsin Rapids, WI, 2011. For general and program related support.
$78,536 to Boys and Girls Club of the Wisconsin Rapid Area, Wisconsin Rapids, WI, 2011. For general and capacity building support.
$37,187 to Family Center, Wisconsin Rapids, WI, 2011. For general and program related support.
$36,128 to Opportunity Development Centers, Wisconsin Rapids, WI, 2011.
$34,714 to South Wood Emergency Pantry Shelf, Wisconsin Rapids, WI, 2011. For general support.
$28,487 to Mid-State Technical College, Wisconsin Rapids, WI, 2011. For program related support.
$26,286 to Wisconsin Rapids Area Senior Center Association, Wisconsin Rapids, WI, 2011. For general support.
$13,700 to Arts Council of South Wood County, Wisconsin Rapids, WI, 2011. For general and program related support.
$10,500 to North Central Community Action Program, Wisconsin Rapids, WI, 2011. For program related support.
$9,920 to CAP Services, Stevens Point, WI, 2011. For program related support.

9868
Integrity Trust ✧

1218 McCann Dr.
Altoona, WI 54720-2561

Established in WI.
Foundation type: Independent foundation.
Financial data (yr. ended 12/31/12): Assets, $5,326 (M); gifts received, $1,520,000; expenditures, $1,516,478; qualifying distributions, $1,515,600; giving activities include $1,515,600 for 2 grants (high: $1,500,000; low: $15,600).
Fields of interest: Elementary/secondary education; Christian agencies & churches.
Limitations: Applications not accepted. Giving primarily in Eau Claire, WI; some giving also in Yankton, SD.
Application information: Contributes only to pre-selected organizations.
Trustees: Beverly Childs; James Embke; Margaret Larsen.
EIN: 456288684

9869
Jeffris Family Foundation, Ltd. ✧

P.O. Box 1160
Janesville, WI 53547-1160 (608) 757-1039
Contact: Thomas M. Jeffris, Pres.
FAX: (608) 757-2352;
E-mail: info@jeffrisfoundation.org; Main URL: http://www.jeffrisfoundation.org/

Established in 1977 in WI.
Donor: Thomas M. Jeffris.
Foundation type: Independent foundation.
Financial data (yr. ended 12/31/12): Assets, $23,838,926 (M); gifts received, $100; expenditures, $2,277,655; qualifying distributions, $2,059,427; giving activities include $1,814,463 for 20 grants (high: $350,000; low: $1,000).
Purpose and activities: Giving primarily to: 1) support the preservation of history and culture and the unique sense of place in small towns and cities; 2) develop significant historic sites in eight Midwestern states; 3) assure sustainability and quality restoration through good research and planning; and 4) inspire and motivate community leaders and local families to support historic preservation in their towns.
Fields of interest: Historic preservation/historical societies.
Type of support: Building/renovation; Matching/challenge support.
Limitations: Giving primarily in IA, IL, IN, MI, MN, MO, OH, and WI. No grants to individuals, or for endowments, maintenance projects, acquisition, debt, operating budgets, or compensation.
Publications: Application guidelines; Informational brochure.
Application information:
Initial approach: Use preliminary request form on foundation web site
Copies of proposal: 4
Board meeting date(s): Fall
Officers and Directors:* Thomas M. Jeffris,* Pres.; Roman Vetter; Royce Yeater.
EIN: 391281879
Selected grants: The following grants are a representative sample of this grantmaker's funding activity:
$350,000 to Albion Community Foundation, Albion, MI, 2012. For Charitable - Bohm Theatre.
$150,000 to Illinois Conservation Foundation, Springfield, IL, 2012. For Charitable - Black Hawk Statue.
$150,000 to Springfield Art Association of Edwards Place, Springfield, IL, 2012. For Charitable - Edwards Place.
$150,000 to Whiting-Robertsdale Community Improvement Corporation, Whiting, IN, 2012. For Charitable - Whiting Community Center.
$65,788 to National Trust for Historic Preservation, Washington, DC, 2012. For Charitable - Circuit Rider.
$1,000 to American Heart Association, Chicago, IL, 2012. For charitable.
$1,000 to Rock County Historical Society, Janesville, WI, 2012. For Charitable - Tallman Arts Festival.
$1,000 to Rock County Historical Society, Janesville, WI, 2012. For charitable.
$1,000 to Wisconsin Historical Foundation, Madison, WI, 2012. For Charitable - Web Initiative.

9870
Johnson Controls Foundation, Inc. ✧

(formerly Johnson Controls Foundation)
5757 N. Green Bay Ave.
P.O. Box 591
Milwaukee, WI 53201-0591 (414) 524-2296
Contact: Mary J. Dowell, Dir., Global Community Rels.
E-mail: mary.j.dowell@jci.com; Main URL: http://www.johnsoncontrols.com/publish/us/en/about/our_community_focus/johnson_controls_foundation.html

Trust established in 1952 in WI.
Donor: Johnson Controls, Inc.
Foundation type: Company-sponsored foundation.
Financial data (yr. ended 12/31/12): Assets, $21,312,041 (M); gifts received, $7,000,000; expenditures, $8,103,647; qualifying distributions, $8,042,549; giving activities include $8,041,049 for 1,059 grants (high: $689,894; low: $50).
Purpose and activities: The foundation supports organizations involved with arts and culture, education, health, human services, and community development.
Fields of interest: Media, television; Media, radio; Visual arts; Museums; Performing arts; Literature; Arts; Higher education; Adult/continuing education; Libraries (public); Scholarships/financial aid; Education; Hospitals (general); Health care; Youth, services; Human services, financial counseling; Human services; Urban/community development; Community/economic development; United Ways and Federated Giving Programs; Economically disadvantaged.
Type of support: General/operating support; Continuing support; Annual campaigns; Capital campaigns; Building/renovation; Emergency funds; Program development; Seed money; Scholarship funds; Employee matching gifts; Employee-related scholarships.
Limitations: Applications accepted. Giving primarily in areas of company operations in Milwaukee, WI. No support for political or lobbying organizations, public or private pre-schools, elementary or secondary schools, sectarian institutions or organizations not of direct benefit to the entire community, foreign-based institutions, fraternal or veterans' organizations, or private foundations. No grants to individuals (except for employee-related scholarships), or for testimonial dinners, fundraising events, tickets to benefits, shows, advertising, travel or tours, seminars or conferences, book or magazine publication, media productions, specific medical or scientific research projects, or endowments; no equipment, product, or labor donations.
Publications: Application guidelines; Program policy statement.
Application information: Proposals are preferred in concise letter form. Telephone calls and personal visits are not encouraged. Multi-year funding is not automatic. Additional information may be requested at a later date. Requests to finance office equipment

and computer systems receive low priority. Application form not required.
Initial approach: Proposal
Copies of proposal: 1
Deadline(s): None
Board meeting date(s): Usually Mar. and Sept.
Final notification: Up to 120 days
Officers and Directors:* Charles A. Harvey,* Pres.; Susan F. Davis,* Secy.; Stephen A. Roell,* Treas.; Alex Molinaroli.
Trustee: U.S. Bank, N.A.
Number of staff: 1 full-time professional.
EIN: 203510307

9871
C. Paul Johnson Family Charitable Foundation ✧
10000 Innovation Dr., No. 250
Milwaukee, WI 53226-4837

Established in 1988 in IL.
Donor: C. Paul Johnson.
Foundation type: Independent foundation.
Financial data (yr. ended 12/31/12): Assets, $107,753 (M); gifts received, $383,077; expenditures, $442,138; qualifying distributions, $427,747; giving activities include $427,747 for grants.
Fields of interest: Higher education; Education; Environment, natural resources; Human services; Science.
International interests: Africa; Israel.
Type of support: Endowments; Capital campaigns; General/operating support; Scholarship funds; Research.
Limitations: Applications not accepted. Giving in the U.S., with emphasis on CA. No grants to individuals.
Application information: Contributes only to pre-selected organizations.
Trustees: Deborah De La Reguera; Adrienne Johnson; C. Paul Johnson; Debra Johnson; Julianne Johnson; Vince Mancuso; Rebecca Milne.
EIN: 366891454

9872
Johnson Family Foundation ✧
555 Main St., Ste. 500
Racine, WI 53403-4616

Established in 1995 in WI.
Foundation type: Independent foundation.
Financial data (yr. ended 12/31/13): Assets, $13,919,660 (M); expenditures, $999,316; qualifying distributions, $974,151; giving activities include $969,000 for 43 grants (high: $601,000; low: $500).
Purpose and activities: Giving primarily for education; support also for recreation, conservation of natural resources, and to fire departments.
Fields of interest: Higher education; Education; Environment, natural resources; Disasters, fire prevention/control; Recreation, country clubs; Recreation; Youth, services; Christian agencies & churches.
Limitations: Applications not accepted. Giving primarily in WI. No grants to individuals.
Application information: Unsolicited requests for funds not accepted.
Officer: Winifred J. Marquart, Pres.
Trustees: H. Fisk Johnson; Imogene P. Johnson; Helen P. Johnson-Leipold; S. Curtis Johnson.
EIN: 367092273

9873
Lester & Frances Johnson Foundation, Inc. ✧
c/o Robert Anderson
701 Deming Way, Ste. 100
Madison, WI 53717-2916

Established in 2000 in WI.
Donors: Frances M. Johnson; Lester O. Johnson.
Foundation type: Independent foundation.
Financial data (yr. ended 12/31/13): Assets, $8,517,479 (M); expenditures, $925,274; qualifying distributions, $650,438; giving activities include $643,200 for 40 grants (high: $105,000; low: $200).
Purpose and activities: Giving primarily to Lutheran churches and other Christian organizations; funding also for social services.
Fields of interest: Museums (specialized); Health organizations, association; Food banks; Human services; Children/youth, services; Foundations (private grantmaking); Christian agencies & churches; Protestant agencies & churches.
Limitations: Applications not accepted. Giving primarily in WI, with emphasis on Madison; giving also in IA, IL, and some funding in MA.
Application information: Unsolicited requests for funds not accepted.
Officers: Graham L. Johnson, Pres.; Robert W. Anderson, V.P.; Aubrey R. Fowler, Secy.; Laurie A. Anderson, Treas.
Directors: Michael R. Anderson; Randall J. Anderson; Michael R. Heald; Courtney Johnson; Erik S. Johnson; Kyle P. Johnson; Megan C. Westrum.
EIN: 391988285
Selected grants: The following grants are a representative sample of this grantmaker's funding activity:
$15,000 to Middleton Outreach Ministry, Middleton, WI, 2012. For Food Pantry and General Operations.

9874
SC Johnson Giving, Inc. ✧
(formerly SC Johnson Fund, Inc.)
1525 Howe St.
Racine, WI 53403-2237
E-mail: USCommu@scj.com; Main URL: http://www.scjohnson.com/en/commitment/focus-on/creating/giving-back.aspx

Incorporated in 1959 in WI.
Donors: S.C. Johnson & Son, Inc.; JohnsonDiversey, Inc.
Foundation type: Company-sponsored foundation.
Financial data (yr. ended 06/28/13): Assets, $12,694,284 (M); gifts received, $8,353,831; expenditures, $3,120,447; qualifying distributions, $3,076,928; giving activities include $3,049,510 for 105 grants (high: $886,693; low: $25).
Purpose and activities: The foundation supports organizations involved with arts and culture, education, the environment, health, social services, and community development.
Fields of interest: Museums; Performing arts; Humanities; Historic preservation/historical societies; Arts; Elementary/secondary education; Higher education; Education; Environment, pollution control; Environment, natural resources; Environment, energy; Environment, beautification programs; Environment; Animal welfare; Employment, training; Athletics/sports, amateur leagues; Youth, services; Family services, domestic violence; Homeless, human services; Human services; Community/economic development; United Ways and Federated Giving Programs; Economically disadvantaged.
Type of support: General/operating support; Management development/capacity building; Annual campaigns; Capital campaigns; Building/renovation; Equipment; Endowments; Program development; Seed money; Scholarship funds; Sponsorships; Employee matching gifts; Employee-related scholarships.
Limitations: Applications accepted. Giving primarily in areas of company operations in Racine, WI. No support for political, religious, social, athletic, veterans', labor, or fraternal organizations, United Way-supported organizations, or national health organizations. No grants to individuals (except for scholarships) or for staff or administrative payrolls.
Publications: Application guidelines; Corporate giving report.
Application information: Support is limited to 1 contribution per organization during any given year. Additional information may be requested at a later date. Organizations receiving grants of more than $5,000 are expected to submit an outcome report at the end of the project or program year. Application form not required.
Initial approach: Complete online application
Copies of proposal: 1
Deadline(s): None
Board meeting date(s): Feb., June, and Oct.
Final notification: 90 to 120 days
Officers and Trustees:* H. Fisk Johnson III,* Chair. and C.E.O.; Kelly M. Semrau, Vice-Chair. and Pres.; Gregory L. Anderegg, V.P. and Secy.; Steven M. Carter, V.P. and Treas.
Number of staff: 2 full-time professional; 2 part-time professional; 2 part-time support.
EIN: 396052089
Selected grants: The following grants are a representative sample of this grantmaker's funding activity:
$2,900,000 to Johnson Foundation, Racine, WI, 2012. For unrestricted support.
$887,993 to Racine Charter One, Racine, WI, 2012. For season support and toward principa and interest pay.
$813,238 to United Way of Racine County, Racine, WI, 2012. For Campaign Match.
$437,660 to Scholarship America, Saint Peter, MN, 2012. For management fee.
$370,350 to Scholarship America, Saint Peter, MN, 2012. For Sons and Daughters Scholarship Awards.
$49,000 to Human Capital Development, Racine, WI, 2012. For operating support.
$31,514 to Prairie School, Racine, WI, 2012. For unrestricted support.
$28,939 to Saint Catherines High School, Racine, WI, 2012. For unrestricted support.
$16,766 to University of Wisconsin Foundation, Madison, WI, 2012. For unrestricted support.
$15,000 to Racine Literacy Council, Racine, WI, 2012. For general operating support.

9875
Jordan Family Foundation, Inc. ✧
(formerly William P. and Dorian S. Jordan Foundation, Inc.)
c/o G & K Wisconsin Services LLC
780 N. Water St.
Milwaukee, WI 53202-3590

Established in 2007 in WI.
Donors: William Paul Jordan; Dorian S. Jordan.
Foundation type: Independent foundation.
Financial data (yr. ended 06/30/13): Assets, $19,169,045 (M); gifts received, $1,476,633; expenditures, $901,285; qualifying distributions, $800,000; giving activities include $800,000 for grants.
Fields of interest: Human services; American Red Cross.
Limitations: Applications not accepted. Giving in the U.S., with emphasis on Washington, DC, and IL. No grants to individuals.
Application information: Contributes only to pre-selected organizations.
Officers: William Paul Jordan, Pres.; Dorian S. Jordan, V.P. and Secy.-Treas.
Director: Julia K. Jordan.
EIN: 205940739
Selected grants: The following grants are a representative sample of this grantmaker's funding activity:
$50,000 to University of Wisconsin Foundation, Madison, WI, 2011.

9876
Joy Global Foundation, Inc. ✧ ☆
(formerly Harnischfeger Industries Foundation)
135 S. 84th St., Ste. 300
Milwaukee, WI 53214
Contact: Sandy McKenzie
Application address: 100 E. Wisconsin St., Ste. 2780 Milwaukee, WI 53202

Established in 1989 in WI.
Donors: Harnischfeger Industries, Inc.; Joy Global Inc.
Foundation type: Company-sponsored foundation.
Financial data (yr. ended 10/25/13): Assets, $10,342,791 (M); expenditures, $606,102; qualifying distributions, $554,850; giving activities include $554,850 for 32 grants (high: $90,000; low: $5,000).
Purpose and activities: The foundation supports organizations involved with arts and culture, education, health, medical research, and community development.
Fields of interest: Arts; Youth development; Human services.
Limitations: Applications accepted. Giving primarily in areas of company operations in WI. No support for religious organizations or institutions primarily supported by taxes or public lands. No grants to individuals.
Publications: Application guidelines.
Application information: Application form not required.
Initial approach: Letter
Copies of proposal: 1
Deadline(s): Within a period of 90 days following receipt
Board meeting date(s): 2nd Mon. in Dec.
Officers: Michael W. Sutherlin, Pres.; James M. Sullivan, V.P.; Sean D. Major, Secy.; Kenneth J. Stark, Treas.
Directors: Randal W. Baker; Edward L. Doheny II.
EIN: 391659070
Selected grants: The following grants are a representative sample of this grantmaker's funding activity:
$90,000 to Junior Achievement of Wisconsin, Milwaukee, WI, 2011.
$60,000 to Milwaukee Symphony Orchestra, Milwaukee, WI, 2011.
$25,000 to Betty Brinn Childrens Museum, Milwaukee, WI, 2011.
$25,000 to Boys and Girls Clubs of Greater Milwaukee, Milwaukee, WI, 2011.
$25,000 to Urban Ecology Center, Milwaukee, WI, 2011.
$20,000 to Childrens Hospital of Pittsburgh Foundation, Pittsburgh, PA, 2011.
$20,000 to Woodlands Foundation, Wexford, PA, 2011.
$14,500 to United Way of Greater Milwaukee, Milwaukee, WI, 2011. For annual campaign.
$14,500 to United Way of Greater Milwaukee, Milwaukee, WI, 2011. For annual campaign.
$10,000 to Lebanon, City of, Lebanon, KY, 2011.

9877
Kelben Foundation, Inc. ✧
100 E. Wisconsin Ave., St., 2200
Milwaukee, WI 53202-3620 (414) 226-4545
Application address: c/o Mary Kellner, 5112 W. Highland, Mequon, WI 53092; tel.: (414) 226-4545

Established in 1983 in WI.
Donors: Ted D. Kellner; Jack W. Kellner; Jack F. Kellner†; Fiduciary Management, Inc.; Mary Kellner.
Foundation type: Independent foundation.
Financial data (yr. ended 12/31/13): Assets, $22,642,121 (M); gifts received, $300,000; expenditures, $1,285,069; qualifying distributions, $1,187,528; giving activities include $872,369 for 44 grants (high: $400,000; low: $500), and $155,056 for 137 grants to individuals (high: $3,000; low: $500).
Purpose and activities: Giving primarily for higher education, including scholarships to graduating seniors from the Milwaukee Public School System in WI, who rank in the top 50 percent of their class, intend to pursue a four-year college degree, and demonstrate a need for financial assistance. Funding also for health and human services.
Fields of interest: Higher education; Education; Hospitals (general); Health care; Human services.
Type of support: General/operating support; Continuing support; Annual campaigns; Capital campaigns; Building/renovation; Debt reduction; Emergency funds; Program development; Seed money; Curriculum development; Scholarship funds; Scholarships—to individuals.
Limitations: Applications accepted. Giving limited to WI. No support for political organizations.
Application information: Scholarship application forms are available at school guidance office, or may be downloaded upon a request to the foundation via e-mail to Mary Kellner. Application form required.
Initial approach: Letter (for grant applications); use application form for scholarship requests
Copies of proposal: 1
Officers and Directors:* Mary T. Kellner,* Pres. and Treas.; Ted D. Kellner,* V.P. and Secy.; Jack T. Kellner; Karen Kellner; W. David Knox; Laura Kellner Lueck; Kristin Kellner Schultz.
Number of staff: 1 part-time professional.
EIN: 391494625

9878
J. J. Keller Foundation, Inc. ✧
(formerly Keller Foundation, Inc.)
3003 Breezewood Ln.
P.O. Box 368
Neenah, WI 54957-0368 (920) 720-7872
Contact: Mary Harp-Jirschele, Exec. Dir.
FAX: (920) 727-7503;
E-mail: mharp-jirschele@jjkeller.com; Main URL: http://www.jjkellerfoundation.org
Grants List: http://www.jjkellerfoundation.org/grants/grant-recipients/

Established in 1990 in WI.
Donors: J.J. Keller & Associates, Inc.; John J. and Ethel D. Keller†.
Foundation type: Independent foundation.
Financial data (yr. ended 12/31/13): Assets, $79,823,458 (M); expenditures, $3,905,117; qualifying distributions, $3,573,857; giving activities include $3,573,857 for 154 grants (high: $490,665; low: $50).
Purpose and activities: The foundation supports programs designed to positively impact lives in the greater Fox Valley community, including the homeless, disadvantaged, elderly, children, and youth. Special emphasis is directed toward initiatives designed to promote physical and mental health and healing; human services; education programs; preventative programs; and critical community needs.
Fields of interest: Health care; Mental health/crisis services; Aging, centers/services; Homeless, human services; Human services; Aging; Mentally disabled; Economically disadvantaged.
Type of support: Employee matching gifts; General/operating support; Matching/challenge support; Program development.
Limitations: Applications accepted. Giving primarily in Fox Valley, WI. No support for political organizations or for youth, adult sports programs, or schools. No grants to individuals, or for raffle tickets or door prizes, endowments, or capital campaigns.
Publications: Application guidelines; Annual report; Grants list.
Application information: Additional information may be requested at a later date. A site visit may be requested. Organizations receiving support are asked to submit a final report. Application form required.
Initial approach: Complete eligibility quiz on foundation web site
Copies of proposal: 1
Deadline(s): None; small requests reviewed monthly; large requests reviewed in Mar., June, Sept., and Dec.
Board meeting date(s): Quarterly
Final notification: 30 days for grants of $15,000 or less; 120 days for grants larger than $15,000
Officers and Directors:* Robert L. Keller,* Pres.; James J. Keller,* V.P. and Treas.; Marne Keller-Krikava, Secy.; Mary Harp-Jirschele, Exec. Dir.; Brian Keller.
Number of staff: 1 full-time professional.
EIN: 391683437
Selected grants: The following grants are a representative sample of this grantmaker's funding activity:
$800,000 to Basic Needs Giving Partnership, Green Bay, WI, 2012.
$140,000 to Habitat for Humanity, Greater Fox Cities Area, Menasha, WI, 2012.

$65,000 to Emergency Shelter of the Fox Valley, Appleton, WI, 2012.
$65,000 to Rebuilding Together Fox Valley, Appleton, WI, 2012.
$50,000 to Fox Cities Community Health Center, Menasha, WI, 2012.
$45,000 to Boys and Girls Club of Oshkosh, Oshkosh, WI, 2012.
$42,571 to Housing Partnership of the Fox Cities, Appleton, WI, 2012.
$25,000 to Big Brothers Big Sisters of the Fox Valley Region, Appleton, WI, 2012.

9879
The Kellogg Family Foundation, Inc. ✧
c/o Godfrey & Kahn
780 N. Water St.
Milwaukee, WI 53202-3512

Established in 1993 in WI.
Donor: William S. Kellogg.
Foundation type: Independent foundation.
Financial data (yr. ended 12/31/13): Assets, $30,169,408 (M); gifts received, $699; expenditures, $4,529,442; qualifying distributions, $3,690,380; giving activities include $2,655,000 for 12 grants (high: $1,115,000; low: $10,000).
Fields of interest: Health organizations, association; Diabetes research; Recreation, camps; Human services; Children/youth, services; United Ways and Federated Giving Programs; Protestant agencies & churches; Blind/visually impaired; Deaf/hearing impaired.
Type of support: Program-related investments/loans.
Limitations: Applications not accepted. Giving primarily in Milwaukee, WI. No grants to individuals.
Application information: Contributes only to pre-selected organizations.
Officers and Directors:* William S. Kellogg,* Pres. and Treas.; Madelaine Kellogg,* V.P. and Secy.; Peter M. Sommerhauser.
EIN: 391775567
Selected grants: The following grants are a representative sample of this grantmaker's funding activity:
$1,000,000 to Evangelical Lutheran Church in America, Greater Milwaukee Synod, Outreach for Hope, Milwaukee, WI, 2011. For general operating support.
$500,000 to Juvenile Diabetes Research Foundation International, New York, NY, 2011. For general operating support.
$100,000 to Childrens Hospital of Wisconsin, Milwaukee, WI, 2011. For general operating support.
$30,000 to American Red Cross National Headquarters, Washington, DC, 2011. For general operating support.
$25,000 to United Way of Greater Milwaukee, Milwaukee, WI, 2011. For general operating support.
$10,000 to Center for Deaf-Blind Persons, Milwaukee, WI, 2010.
$10,000 to Center for Deaf-Blind Persons, Milwaukee, WI, 2011. For general operating support.
$10,000 to Goodwill Industries of Southeastern Wisconsin, Milwaukee, WI, 2010.
$10,000 to Goodwill Industries of Southeastern Wisconsin, Milwaukee, WI, 2011. For general operating support.
$10,000 to Lutherdale Bible Camp, Elkhorn, WI, 2010.
$10,000 to Penfield Childrens Center, Milwaukee, WI, 2010.
$10,000 to Penfield Childrens Center, Milwaukee, WI, 2011. For general operating support.

9880
The Kern Family Foundation, Inc. ✧
W305 S4239 Brookhill Rd.
Waukesha, WI 53189-9126 (262) 968-6838
E-mail: info@kffdn.org; Main URL: http://www.kffdn.org/

Established in 1998 in WI.
Donors: Robert D. Kern; Patricia E. Kern.
Foundation type: Independent foundation.
Financial data (yr. ended 12/31/12): Assets, $627,060,713 (M); gifts received, $200; expenditures, $32,062,515; qualifying distributions, $32,020,538; giving activities include $27,197,469 for 236 grants (high: $3,000,000; low: $190), $338,434 for 2 foundation-administered programs and $1,000,000 for 1 loan/program-related investment.
Purpose and activities: The foundation's purpose is to seek to enhance and encourage religious values, family and community competitive educational structures, and moral and ethical values in society. The foundation supports the promotion of religious values in religious ministry and promotes the study and enhancement of competitive educational structures in the U.S.
Fields of interest: Education; Youth development; Protestant agencies & churches.
Type of support: Program development; Scholarship funds.
Limitations: Applications not accepted. Giving primarily in the Midwest. No support for individual public or private K-12 schools. No grants to individuals, or for endowments, indirect costs as part of the grant request, debt reduction, or annual fund drives for sustaining support.
Application information: Unsolicited proposals are not accepted.
Board meeting date(s): Jan., Apr., July, and Oct.
Officers and Directors:* Marcia Peterson,* Chair.; James Rahn,* Pres.; Daniel Kelly, V.P.; Robert D. Kern,* V.P.; Richard A. Van Deuren, Secy.; Michael Senske, C.F.O. and Treas.; Rick Graber; Deborah Kern; Patricia E. Kern; William (Chip) H. Mellor; Dawn Tabat; Hermann Viets.
Number of staff: 4 full-time professional; 1 full-time support.
EIN: 391923558
Selected grants: The following grants are a representative sample of this grantmaker's funding activity:
$2,500,000 to Charter Fund, Charter School Growth Fund, Broomfield, CO, 2012. For General Operating Purposes.
$2,500,000 to Charter Fund, Charter School Growth Fund, Broomfield, CO, 2012. For General Operating Purposes.
$1,445,000 to Acton Institute for the Study of Religion and Liberty, Grand Rapids, MI, 2012. For General Operating Purposes.
$1,000,000 to Project Lead the Way, Indianapolis, IN, 2012. For Pre-Engineering Program.
$999,750 to American Enterprise Institute for Public Policy Research, Washington, DC, 2012. For General Operating Purposes.
$500,000 to Project Lead the Way, Indianapolis, IN, 2012. For Pre-Engineering Program.
$287,864 to Ifo Institute for Economic Research, Munich, Germany, 2012. For General Operating Purposes.
$91,100 to Bethel College, Mishawaka, IN, 2012. For Theological Education Initiative.
$52,500 to Americans for Prosperity Foundation, Arlington, VA, 2012. For General Operating Purposes.
$20,000 to Winona Area Public Schools, Winona, MN, 2012. For Pre-Engineering Program.

9881
Kikkoman Foods Foundation, Inc. ✧
P.O. Box 69
Walworth, WI 53184-0069 (262) 275-6181
Contact: Robert V. Conover, Dir.

Established in 1993 in WI.
Donor: Kikkoman Foods, Inc.
Foundation type: Company-sponsored foundation.
Financial data (yr. ended 12/31/13): Assets, $11,443,995 (M); expenditures, $448,558; qualifying distributions, $429,082; giving activities include $429,072 for 67 grants (high: $100,000; low: $300).
Purpose and activities: The foundation supports organizations involved with arts and culture, education, human services, and international exchange and economics.
Fields of interest: Arts; Education; Human services.
Type of support: General/operating support; Annual campaigns; Scholarship funds; Sponsorships.
Limitations: Applications accepted. Giving primarily in WI. No support for private organizations, political organizations, religious or sectarian organizations, or discriminatory organizations. No grants to individuals, or for raffle tickets or product purchases, non-food-related scientific or development research, travel or lodging, or promotional events.
Publications: Application guidelines.
Application information: Application form required.
Initial approach: Request application form
Deadline(s): None
Board meeting date(s): Monthly
Directors: Gilles Bousquet; Robert V. Conover; James S. Haney; Noriaki Horikiri; Karl N. Keane; Makoto Kurose; Daniel P. Miller; Osamu Mogi; Yuzaburo Mogi; William E. Nelson; Milton E. Neshek; Kenichi Saito; Kazuo Shimizu; Robert R. Spitzer, Ph.D.; Ryohei Tsuji, Ph.D.
EIN: 391763633
Selected grants: The following grants are a representative sample of this grantmaker's funding activity:
$20,000 to University of Wisconsin Foundation, Madison, WI, 2012. For Financial Support-President's Fund.
$20,000 to University of Wisconsin Foundation, Madison, WI, 2012. For Financial Support - President's Fund.
$15,000 to University of Wisconsin Foundation, Madison, WI, 2012. For Financial Support - Chancellor's Fund.
$10,000 to Gateway Technical College Foundation, Kenosha, WI, 2012. For Financial Support for Scholarships.
$9,000 to Folsom High School, Folsom, CA, 2012. For 3 Scholarship at $3,000.00.

$6,200 to Milwaukee School of Engineering, Milwaukee, WI, 2012. For Financial Support - Regents' Golf Outing.
$2,500 to Milwaukee Public Museum, Milwaukee, WI, 2012. For Financial Support - Annual Campaign.
$2,500 to Wisconsin Historical Society, Madison, WI, 2012. For Financial Support - Business Partners Program.
$2,000 to Milwaukee Public Museum, Milwaukee, WI, 2012. For Financial Support - 26th Anniversary Gala Event.
$1,000 to Friends of Wisconsin Public Television, Madison, WI, 2012. For Financial Support for Directors Circle.

9882
F. Albert Klein Trust ✧
P.O. Box 2043
Milwaukee, WI 53201-9668

Donor: Charles and Florence Phelps Trust.
Foundation type: Independent foundation.
Financial data (yr. ended 06/30/13): Assets, $12,779,513 (M); gifts received, $54,227; expenditures, $879,936; qualifying distributions, $751,142; giving activities include $751,142 for grants.
Fields of interest: Health care.
Limitations: Applications not accepted. Giving primarily in West Burlington, IA.
Application information: Unsolicited requests for funds not accepted.
Trustee: U.S. Bank, N.A.
EIN: 420859994

9883
Herbert H. Kohl Charities, Inc. ✧
825 N. Jefferson St., Ste. 350
Milwaukee, WI 53202-3731

Established in 1977 in WI.
Donors: Herbert H. Kohl; Mary Kohl.
Foundation type: Independent foundation.
Financial data (yr. ended 06/30/13): Assets, $6,802,635 (M); expenditures, $542,306; qualifying distributions, $526,411; giving activities include $526,411 for grants.
Purpose and activities: Giving primarily for higher and other education, health associations, children, youth and social services, arts and culture, federated giving programs, and community development; some funding also for Christian organizations and churches, and Jewish organizations.
Fields of interest: Arts; Elementary/secondary education; Higher education; Education; Health organizations, association; Medical research, institute; Boys & girls clubs; Human services; Children/youth, services; Community/economic development; United Ways and Federated Giving Programs; Jewish federated giving programs; Protestant agencies & churches; Catholic agencies & churches; Jewish agencies & synagogues.
Limitations: Applications not accepted. Giving primarily in WI, with strong emphasis on Milwaukee. No grants to individuals.
Application information: Contributes only to pre-selected organizations.
Officers and Directors:* Herbert H. Kohl,* Pres.; Allen D. Kohl,* V.P.; Sidney A. Kohl,* Secy.; Dolores K. Kohl,* Treas.
EIN: 391300476
Selected grants: The following grants are a representative sample of this grantmaker's funding activity:
$20,000 to Boys and Girls Clubs of Greater Milwaukee, Milwaukee, WI, 2011.
$2,000 to Girl Scouts of the U.S.A., Milwaukee, WI, 2011.
$1,000 to Friends of Wisconsin Public Television, Madison, WI, 2011.

9884
Kohler Foundation, Inc. ✧
725 Woodlake Rd., Ste. X
Kohler, WI 53044-1354 (920) 458-1972
Contact: Terri Yoho, Exec. Dir.
FAX: (920) 458-4280;
E-mail: terri.yoho@kohler.com; Main URL: http://www.kohlerfoundation.org
Facebook: https://www.facebook.com/kohlerfoundation
Twitter: https://twitter.com/KohlerFdn

Incorporated in 1940 in WI.
Donors: Herbert V. Kohler†; Marie C. Kohler†; Evangeline Kohler†; Lillie B. Kohler†; O.A. Kroos†.
Foundation type: Independent foundation.
Financial data (yr. ended 12/31/12): Assets, $201,620,916 (M); expenditures, $8,845,567; qualifying distributions, $8,757,756; giving activities include $501,105 for 60 grants (high: $100,000; low: $400), $356,771 for 98 grants to individuals (high: $15,000; low: $1,250), $6,068,992 for 21 in-kind gifts, and $1,301,981 for 2 foundation-administered programs.
Purpose and activities: Supports education and the arts in WI. Annual program funds provide scholarships for students graduating from Sheboygan County high schools. All scholarship recipients are chosen by their schools. The Distinguished Guest Series, a performing arts series, is presented as a cultural benefit to the community.
Fields of interest: Visual arts; Performing arts; Arts; Higher education; Education.
Type of support: Program development; Seed money; Scholarships—to individuals.
Limitations: Applications accepted. Giving limited to WI, primarily in Sheboygan County. No support for health care or medical programs. No grants to individuals (except for scholarships in Sheboygan County), or for operating budgets, capital campaigns, or annual fundraising drives; no loans.
Application information: See foundation web site for additional application information.
Initial approach: Online application form
Copies of proposal: 1
Deadline(s): Mar. 15th and Sept. 15th
Board meeting date(s): June, Dec. and as required
Final notification: 1 week after contributions meetings
Officers and Directors:* Natalie A. Black,* Pres.; Jeffrey P. Cheney,* V.P. and Treas.; Paul H. Ten Pas,* Secy.; Terri Yoho, Exec. Dir.
Number of staff: 5 full-time professional; 1 part-time support.
EIN: 390810536

9885
John M. Kohler Foundation Inc. ✧ ☆
c/o US Bank, N.A.
P.O. Box 2043
Milwaukee, WI 53201-9668
Application address: US Bank N.A., 605 N. 8th St., Sheboygan, WI 53081, Tel.: (920) 459-6942

Established in 2003 in WI.
Donor: W.M. Collins Kohler.
Foundation type: Independent foundation.
Financial data (yr. ended 12/31/13): Assets, $104,381 (M); gifts received, $457,713; expenditures, $613,381; qualifying distributions, $611,451; giving activities include $609,414 for 15 grants (high: $85,000; low: $2,000).
Fields of interest: Arts, multipurpose centers/programs; Higher education; Environment, water resources; Human services; International affairs.
Limitations: Applications accepted. Giving primarily in WI, with some giving in GA.
Application information: Application form not required.
Initial approach: Proposal
Deadline(s): None
Directors: Julilly W. Kohler; Robert T. Melzer; Cindy Miller.
EIN: 200497413

9886
Krause Family Foundation, Inc. ✧
(formerly Charles A. Krause Foundation)
5225 N. Ironwood Rd., Ste. 109
Glendale, WI 53217-4909

Incorporated in 1952 in WI.
Foundation type: Independent foundation.
Financial data (yr. ended 12/31/13): Assets, $6,102,865 (M); expenditures, $553,919; qualifying distributions, $494,902; giving activities include $483,000 for 57 grants (high: $200,000; low: $1,000), and $11,125 for 5 employee matching gifts.
Fields of interest: Museums; Arts; Secondary school/education; Higher education; Education; Environment, natural resources.
Type of support: General/operating support; Continuing support; Annual campaigns; Capital campaigns; Building/renovation; Endowments.
Limitations: Applications not accepted. Giving limited to southeastern WI. No support for religious or political organizations. No grants to individuals, or for medical research.
Application information: Unsolisited requests for funds not accepted.
Officers: Carol Krause Wythes, Pres.; Charles A. Krause, Secy.-Treas.
EIN: 396044820

9887
The George Kress Foundation, Inc. ✧
c/o Associated Trust Co.
P.O. Box 12800
Green Bay, WI 54307-2800
Application address: John Kress c/o Green Bay Packing Co., P.O. Box 19017, Green Bay, WI 54307-9017

Incorporated in 1953 in WI.
Donor: Green Bay Packaging, Inc.
Foundation type: Independent foundation.

Financial data (yr. ended 12/31/13): Assets, $16,051,453 (M); gifts received, $3,000,000; expenditures, $2,801,149; qualifying distributions, $2,728,185; giving activities include $2,728,185 for 178 grants (high: $1,000,000; low: $75).
Purpose and activities: Giving primarily to federated giving programs, libraries, Christian agencies and churches, and higher education; funding also for arts and culture, historical preservation, hospitals, health associations, recreation, particularly local sporting events, children and youth services, social and family services, community development, and the United Way.
Fields of interest: Historic preservation/historical societies; Arts; Higher education; Libraries (public); Education; Hospitals (general); Health organizations, association; Recreation; Boys & girls clubs; Human services; YM/YWCAs & YM/YWHAs; Children/youth, services; Family services; Community/economic development; United Ways and Federated Giving Programs; Christian agencies & churches.
Type of support: Continuing support; Annual campaigns; Capital campaigns; Building/renovation; Program development; Professorships; Scholarship funds; Research.
Limitations: Applications accepted. Giving primarily in Green Bay and Madison, WI.
Application information: Application form not required.
Initial approach: Letter
Copies of proposal: 1
Deadline(s): None
Officer: John F. Kress, Pres.
Trustees: Ingred Kress; James F. Kress; William F. Kress; Marilyn Swanson; Terry Swanson.
Number of staff: 1 full-time professional; 1 part-time support.
EIN: 396050768
Selected grants: The following grants are a representative sample of this grantmaker's funding activity:
$200 to Boy Scouts of America, Bay Lakes Council, Appleton, WI, 2012. For program support.

9888
The John E. Kuenzl Foundation Inc. ✧
c/o Cliftolarsonallen LLP
P.O. Box 2886
Oshkosh, WI 54903-2886 (920) 231-5890
Contact: Gerald J. Stadtmueller, Dir.

Established in 2000 in WI.
Donors: Sheboygan Beverage, Inc.; Gambrinus Enterprises; John E. Kuenzl†.
Foundation type: Company-sponsored foundation.
Financial data (yr. ended 12/31/12): Assets, $21,362,444 (M); expenditures, $1,159,083; qualifying distributions, $1,079,172; giving activities include $1,071,400 for 45 grants (high: $175,000; low: $1,000).
Purpose and activities: The foundation supports museums, fire departments, and community foundations and organizations involved with performing arts, hunger, housing development, and human services.
Fields of interest: Agriculture/food; Human services; Community/economic development.
Type of support: General/operating support.
Limitations: Applications accepted. Giving primarily in WI. No grants to individuals.
Application information: Application form required.
Initial approach: Letter
Deadline(s): Dec. 1
Directors: Norma Kuenzl; Gerald Stadtmueller; James J. Williamson.
EIN: 391998578

9889
La Crosse Community Foundation ✧
401 Main St., Ste. 205
La Crosse, WI 54601-4019 (608) 782-3223
Contact: Sheila Garrity, Exec. Dir.
FAX: (608) 782-3222;
E-mail: lacrosscommfoundation@centurytel.net;
Main URL: http://www.laxcommfoundation.com
E-Newsletter: http://visitor.constantcontact.com/manage/optin/ea?v=0011QHrsLot1-fGgHBL9f8nDtZNlU9IU3pFQc49_C5NhtUsUdxyXr_IyY1QuOLXRS0qychke9acyjLwfe-17tK0lg%3D%3D
Facebook: http://www.facebook.com/pages/La-Crosse-Community-Foundation/148545897282

Established in 1930 in WI.
Foundation type: Community foundation.
Financial data (yr. ended 12/31/13): Assets, $61,821,319 (M); gifts received, $2,277,161; expenditures, $4,764,834; giving activities include $3,699,448 for 60+ grants (high: $537,126), and $214,877 for 180 grants to individuals.
Purpose and activities: The purpose of the foundation is to enrich the quality of life in the greater La Crosse area by: 1) attracting charitable gifts promoting community philanthropy; 2) serving as a steward for entrusted funds and using these precious resources wisely and efficiently; 3) supporting programs and activities of economic, educational, social and cultural nonprofit organizations; 4) providing leadership by serving as a convenor/catalyst in identifying problems and opportunities and shaping effective responses to them; and 5) being a community resource and providing services to donors, nonprofit agencies and the community-at-large.
Fields of interest: Arts; Higher education; Education; Health care; Recreation; Children/youth, services; Family services; Human services; Government/public administration; Children/youth; Youth; Adults; Aging; Young adults; Disabilities, people with; Physically disabled; Blind/visually impaired; Deaf/hearing impaired; Minorities; Asians/Pacific Islanders; African Americans/Blacks; Women; Substance abusers; Single parents; Immigrants/refugees; Economically disadvantaged; Homeless; LGBTQ.
Type of support: General/operating support; Continuing support; Capital campaigns; Equipment; Program development; Seed money; Curriculum development; Scholarship funds; Scholarships—to individuals; Matching/challenge support.
Limitations: Applications accepted. Giving primarily in La Crosse County, WI, and surrounding area. No support for sectarian or religious purposes. No grants to individuals (except for scholarships), or for operating expenses of well-established organizations, deficit financing, endowment funds, travel, land acquisition, consulting services, or technical assistance; no loans.
Publications: Annual report (including application guidelines).
Application information: Visit foundation web site for application information; contact foundation for initial application form and guidelines. Application form required.
Initial approach: Telephone
Deadline(s): Submit proposal by the 15th of Jan., Apr., July, and Oct.
Board meeting date(s): Feb., May, Aug., and Nov.
Final notification: Within 1 month of committee meetings
Officers and Directors:* Sue Christopherson,* Chair.; Sandy Brekke,* Vice-Chair.; Barb Erickson,* Secy.; Sheila Garrity, Exec. Dir.; T.J. Brooks; Larry Kirch; Julie S. Nordeen; Todd Poss; Tom Sleik; Brent Smith; Randy Smith; Gina Yang.
Trustee: North Central Trust Co.
Number of staff: 1 full-time professional; 2 part-time professional; 1 part-time support.
EIN: 396037996

9890
Ladish Company Foundation ✧
13500 Watertown Plank Rd., Ste. 108
Elm Grove, WI 53122-2200

Established in 1952 in WI.
Donor: Ladish Co., Inc.
Foundation type: Company-sponsored foundation.
Financial data (yr. ended 11/30/13): Assets, $33,214,152 (L); expenditures, $1,597,320; qualifying distributions, $1,577,000; giving activities include $1,577,000 for 106 grants (high: $200,000; low: $1,000).
Purpose and activities: The foundation supports zoological societies and organizations involved with arts and culture, education, health, multiple sclerosis, diabetes, hunger, human services, and the visually impaired.
Fields of interest: Museums; Performing arts; Arts; Elementary/secondary education; Secondary school/education; Higher education; Libraries (public); Education; Zoos/zoological societies; Hospitals (general); Health care, clinics/centers; Health care, patient services; Multiple sclerosis; Diabetes; Food services; Food banks; YM/YWCAs & YM/YWHAs; Children/youth, services; Human services; United Ways and Federated Giving Programs; Blind/visually impaired.
Type of support: General/operating support; Annual campaigns; Capital campaigns; Program development; Scholarship funds; Research.
Limitations: Applications not accepted. Giving primarily in WI. No grants to individuals.
Application information: Contributes only to pre-selected organizations.
Board meeting date(s): Oct.
Trustees: Wayne E. Larsen; Gary J. Vroman; Ronald O. Wiese.
EIN: 396040489
Selected grants: The following grants are a representative sample of this grantmaker's funding activity:
$65,000 to Milwaukee School of Engineering, Milwaukee, WI, 2013. For classroom.
$30,000 to Midwest Athletes Against Childhood Cancer, Milwaukee, WI, 2013. For Research for Childhood Cancer.
$30,000 to Vision Forward Association, Milwaukee, WI, 2013. For Rehabilitation of Visually Impaired.
$12,000 to Milwaukee Rescue Mission, Milwaukee, WI, 2013. For Care and Support of Needy.
$7,000 to Goodwill Industries of Southeastern Wisconsin, Milwaukee, WI, 2013. For day services program.
$7,000 to Marquette University, Milwaukee, WI, 2013. For Scholarships - Business Administration.

$6,000 to Aurora Visiting Nurse Association of Wisconsin, Milwaukee, WI, 2013. For Pediatric Impact Fund.
$4,000 to Elmbrook School District, Brookfield, WI, 2013. For Nature Center.

9891
Herman W. Ladish Family Foundation, Inc. ✧
13255 W. Bluemound Rd., Ste. 201A
Brookfield, WI 53005-6245 (262) 780-9640
Contact: William J. Ladish, Pres.

Incorporated in 1956 in WI.
Donor: Herman W. Ladish†.
Foundation type: Independent foundation.
Financial data (yr. ended 06/30/13): Assets, $10,393,854 (M); gifts received, $10,354; expenditures, $674,128; qualifying distributions, $557,000; giving activities include $557,000 for grants.
Purpose and activities: Giving primarily for education, Roman Catholic churches, and hospitals; some funding also for the arts.
Fields of interest: Arts; Higher education; Hospitals (general); Catholic agencies & churches.
Limitations: Applications accepted. Giving primarily in WI, with strong emphasis on Milwaukee; some funding in Chicago, IL. No grants to individuals.
Application information: Application form not required.
Initial approach: Proposal
Deadline(s): None
Board meeting date(s): 2 times per year
Officers and Directors:* William J. Ladish,* Pres.; Robert T. Stollenwerk,* Secy.-Treas.; Margaret L. Exner; Mary L. Selander.
EIN: 396063602
Selected grants: The following grants are a representative sample of this grantmaker's funding activity:
$200,000 to Marquette University, Milwaukee, WI, 2011.
$80,000 to Froedtert Memorial Lutheran Hospital, Milwaukee, WI, 2011.
$75,000 to Rush University Medical Center, Chicago, IL, 2011.
$50,000 to Lyric Opera of Chicago, Chicago, IL, 2011.
$50,000 to Marquette University, Milwaukee, WI, 2011.
$25,000 to Medical College of Wisconsin, Milwaukee, WI, 2011.
$20,000 to Marquette University, Milwaukee, WI, 2011.
$15,000 to Chicago Historical Society, Chicago, IL, 2011.
$15,000 to Medical College of Wisconsin, Milwaukee, WI, 2011.
$10,000 to Hunger Task Force, Milwaukee, WI, 2011.

9892
The Lakeview Foundation, Inc. ✧
P.O. Box 253
Thiensville, WI 53092-2053
Contact: William H. Foshag, Dir.

Established in 1996 in WI.
Foundation type: Independent foundation.
Financial data (yr. ended 07/31/13): Assets, $10,291,163 (M); expenditures, $749,296; qualifying distributions, $635,000; giving activities include $635,000 for grants.
Purpose and activities: Giving primarily for programs benefiting youth in the inner city of Milwaukee, WI.
Fields of interest: Education; Boys & girls clubs; Children/youth; Children; Youth; Girls; Boys.
Type of support: Capital campaigns; Building/renovation; Equipment; Program development; Curriculum development.
Limitations: Giving primarily in the inner city of Milwaukee, WI. No grants to individuals.
Publications: IRS Form 990 or 990-PF printed copy available upon request.
Application information: Unsolicited requests for funds are generally not accepted. Application form required.
Deadline(s): Mar. 31
Board meeting date(s): Quarterly
Final notification: 90-120 days
Officers and Directors:* Charles J. Osborne, Pres.; John H. Woodin,* V.P.; Ruth H. McGuire,* Secy.; Robert R. Magliocco,* Treas.; Fred J. Bartkowski; Robert H. Brogan; Kelly Denk; William H. Foshag; Ron Perri; E. Thomas Sheahan; Vernon H. Swanson.
EIN: 391857646

9893
Loehrke Family Charitable Foundation ✧
N29 W27510 Peninsula Dr.
Pewaukee, WI 53072-4328

Established in 2003 in WI.
Donors: Kent Loehrke; Wynne Loehrke.
Foundation type: Independent foundation.
Financial data (yr. ended 12/31/13): Assets, $596,676 (M); gifts received, $100,000; expenditures, $751,868; qualifying distributions, $738,737; giving activities include $738,737 for 27 grants (high: $500,000; low: $250).
Fields of interest: Higher education; Medical research; Human services; YM/YWCAs & YM/YWHAs; Christian agencies & churches.
Type of support: General/operating support.
Limitations: Applications not accepted. Giving primarily in WI. No grants to individuals.
Application information: Unsolicited requests for funds not accepted.
Trustees: Kent Loehrke; Wynne Loehrke.
EIN: 396779459
Selected grants: The following grants are a representative sample of this grantmaker's funding activity:
$13,750 to Young Life, Lake Country, Hartland, WI, 2011.
$5,000 to VSA Arts of Wisconsin, Madison, WI, 2011.
$5,000 to Womens Center, Waukesha, WI, 2011.
$2,000 to Camp Heartland, Milwaukee, WI, 2011.
$1,500 to Pewaukee Food Pantry, Pewaukee, WI, 2011.
$1,000 to CaringBridge, Eagan, MN, 2011.
$1,000 to Positively Pewaukee, Pewaukee, WI, 2011.
$1,000 to Teen Challenge International Wisconsin, Milwaukee, WI, 2011.

9894
The Lubar Family Foundation, Inc. ✧
700 N. Water St., Ste. 1200
Milwaukee, WI 53202-4259

Established in 1968 in WI.
Donors: Marianne S. Lubar; Kristine Lubar MacDonald; David J. Lubar; Susan Lubar Solvang; John P. Lubar; Sheldon B. Lubar; Joan P. Lubar; members of the Lubar Family.
Foundation type: Independent foundation.
Financial data (yr. ended 12/31/13): Assets, $51,535,820 (M); gifts received, $5,908,798; expenditures, $856,608; qualifying distributions, $693,643; giving activities include $693,643 for 75 grants (high: $200,000; low: $50).
Fields of interest: Museums; Performing arts; Arts; Higher education; Health care; Human services; Family services; Jewish federated giving programs; Jewish agencies & synagogues.
Type of support: Capital campaigns; Endowments.
Limitations: Applications not accepted. Giving primarily in Milwaukee, WI.
Application information: Unsolicited requests for funds not accepted.
Officers: Sheldon B. Lubar, Chair.; Marianne S. Lubar, Pres.; David M. Bauer, Treas.
Director: David J. Lubar.
EIN: 391098690

9895
Lunda Charitable Fund, Inc. ✧ ☆
N7142 Waters Edge Rd.
Black River Falls, WI 54615-5829
Contact: Carl Holmquist, Secy.-Treas.

Established in WI.
Foundation type: Independent foundation.
Financial data (yr. ended 12/31/13): Assets, $40,437,530 (M); expenditures, $2,350,436; qualifying distributions, $2,204,222; giving activities include $2,204,222 for 41 grants (high: $2,000,000; low: $500).
Fields of interest: Education; Youth development; Neighborhood centers; Community/economic development.
Limitations: Applications accepted. Giving primarily in Black River Falls, WI.
Application information: Application form required.
Initial approach: Letter
Deadline(s): July 31st
Officers: Larry Lunda, Pres.; Marlee Slifka, V.P.; Carl Holmquist, Secy.-Treas.
Trustees: Mary Van Gordon; William Waughtal.
EIN: 460836946

9896
Lunda Charitable Trust ✧
620 Gebhardt Rd.
Black River Falls, WI 54615-0669
Contact: Carl Holmquist, Tr.

Established in 1988 in WI.
Donors: Milton Lunda†; Marlee Slifka.
Foundation type: Independent foundation.
Financial data (yr. ended 12/31/12): Assets, $0 (M); gifts received, $4,000; expenditures, $2,318,433; qualifying distributions, $2,042,363; giving activities include $2,006,363 for 53 grants (high: $900,000; low: $350).

Purpose and activities: Giving primarily for community services. Funding priority will be given to perpetuating existing Lunda family endeavors (Lunda Theater, Lunda Park, and Lunda Center).
Fields of interest: Arts; Education; Health care; Recreation.
Type of support: Capital campaigns; Building/renovation; Equipment; Land acquisition; Seed money; Scholarship funds; Matching/challenge support.
Limitations: Applications accepted. Giving primarily in Jackson County, WI. No support for political or religious organizations. No grants to individuals.
Publications: Financial statement.
Application information: Application form required.
Initial approach: Letter
Copies of proposal: 1
Deadline(s): Applications accepted July 1 through July 31
Board meeting date(s): Varies
Final notification: 3 months
Trustees: Carl Holmquist; Larry Lunda; Lydia Lunda; Marlee Slifka; Mary van Gorden; Bill Waughtal.
Number of staff: 2 part-time professional; 1 part-time support.
EIN: 396491037
Selected grants: The following grants are a representative sample of this grantmaker's funding activity:
$5,000 to University of Wisconsin, Eau Claire, WI, 2011.

9897
Madison Community Foundation ✧
2 Science Ct.
P.O. Box 5010
Madison, WI 53705-0010 (608) 232-1763
Contact: For grants: Tom M. Linfield, V.P., Grantmaking
FAX: (608) 232-1772;
E-mail: frontdesk@madisoncommunityfoundation.org; Toll free tel.: (888) 400-7643; Grant inquiry/application e-mail: tlinfield@madisoncommunityfoundation.org; Main URL: http://www.madisoncommunityfoundation.org
E-Newsletter: http://www.madisoncommunityfoundation.org/Page.aspx?pid=373
Facebook: https://www.facebook.com/madisoncommunityfoundation
Grants List: http://www.madisoncommunityfoundation.org/Page.aspx?pid=269
Twitter: http://twitter.com/MSNCF

Established in 1942 in WI.
Foundation type: Community foundation.
Financial data (yr. ended 12/31/12): Assets, $139,017,505 (M); gifts received, $7,632,241; expenditures, $11,138,848; giving activities include $9,642,156 for grants.
Purpose and activities: The mission of the foundation is to encourage, facilitate and manage long-term philanthropy.
Fields of interest: Arts; Education; Environment; Food services; Housing/shelter; Human services; Community/economic development; Children; Youth; Aging.
Type of support: Management development/capacity building; Building/renovation; Equipment; Land acquisition; Program development; Seed money; Technical assistance; Matching/challenge support.
Limitations: Applications accepted. Giving limited to Dane County, WI. No support for religious organizations for religious purposes, health care services, including mental health, or substance abuse treatment. No grants to individuals, or for annual campaigns, endowment funds, debt retirement, short-term events (such as conferences, festivals, celebrations and fund raising functions), or scholarships; no capital grants to support ongoing maintenance.
Publications: Annual report; Annual report (including application guidelines); Financial statement; Newsletter.
Application information: A full grant proposal will be invited based on the foundation's determination of the organization's Letter of Inquiry. Application form required.
Initial approach: Submit Letter of Inquiry
Copies of proposal: 1
Deadline(s): Jan. 15 and July 15 for letter of inquiry; Mar. 1 and Sept. 3 for full grant proposals
Board meeting date(s): 6 times a year
Final notification: May 1 and Nov. 1
Officers and Board of Governors:* Jac B. Garner,* Chair.; Blaine Renfert,* Vice-Chair.; Bob Sorge,* Pres.; Ann E. Casey, V.P., Finance and Planned Giving; Tom M. Linfield, V.P., Grantmaking and Community Initiatives; Amy T. Overby, V.P., Donor Rels.; Diane Ballweg; Jim Bradley; Steve Brown; Joan A. Burke; Frank D. Bryne, M.D.; Jim Cavanaugh; Craig Christianson; Bill DeAtley; Beth Donley; Roberta Gassman; Enid Veronica Glenn; Peter Lundberg; Ismael Ozanne; Jeff Pertl; Dave Stark; Martha A. Taylor.
Number of staff: 4 full-time professional; 2 part-time professional; 3 full-time support; 1 part-time support.
EIN: 396038248
Selected grants: The following grants are a representative sample of this grantmaker's funding activity:
$350,000 to Madison Metropolitan School District, Madison, WI, 2012. For Digging In: Outdoor Garden-Based Learning.
$330,000 to Kennedy Heights Neighborhood Association, Madison, WI, 2012. For Creating Opportunity in Math, Engineering, Technology and Science (COMETS).
$300,000 to Clean Lakes Alliance, Madison, WI, 2012. For Capacity Building for Phosphorous Reduction.
$200,000 to Access Community Health Centers, Madison, WI, 2012. For South Clinic Capital Campaign.
$75,000 to Fitchburg Optimists Club, Madison, WI, 2012. For Splash Pad.
$70,000 to YMCA of Dane County, Madison, WI, 2012. For Sun Prairie Community Schools Program.
$60,000 to Madison Metropolitan School District, Madison, WI, 2012. For Piano Keyboard Labs.
$33,000 to Madison Ballet, Madison, WI, 2012. For Dracula.
$30,000 to University of Wisconsin, Wisconsin Institutes for Discovery, Madison, WI, 2012. For Sparks of Discovery.
$27,000 to Verona Area School District, Verona, WI, 2012. For Whalen Pond Neighborhood Ecology Education Initiative.

9898
Madison Gas and Electric Foundation, Inc. ✧
P.O. Box 1231
Madison, WI 53701-1231 (608) 252-7279
Contact: Bonnie Juul

Established in 1966 in WI.
Donors: Madison Gas and Electric Co.; MGE Energy, Inc.
Foundation type: Company-sponsored foundation.
Financial data (yr. ended 12/31/13): Assets, $20,427,967 (M); gifts received, $2,500,000; expenditures, $921,566; qualifying distributions, $825,638; giving activities include $825,638 for 133 grants (high: $160,000; low: $200).
Purpose and activities: The foundation supports organizations involved arts and culture, education, health, heart disease, rowing, human services, and civic affairs.
Fields of interest: Arts; Education; Human services.
Limitations: Applications accepted. Giving primarily in areas of company operations WI.
Application information: Application form required.
Initial approach: Proposal
Copies of proposal: 1
Deadline(s): None
Officers: Gary J. Wolter, Pres.; Kristine A. Euclide, V.P.; Lynn K. Hobbie, V.P.; Scott A. Neitzel, V.P.; Jeff. C. Newman, Secy.-Treas.
EIN: 396098118
Selected grants: The following grants are a representative sample of this grantmaker's funding activity:
$25,000 to Congress for the New Urbanism, Chicago, IL, 2011. For program support.
$3,000 to American Heart Association, Dallas, TX, 2011. For program support.
$2,000 to NAACP, Baltimore, MD, 2011. For program support.
$1,500 to National Alliance on Mental Illness, Arlington, VA, 2011. For program support.

9899
ManpowerGroup Foundation, Inc. ✧
(formerly Manpower Foundation, Inc.)
10 Manpower
Milwaukee, WI 53212-4030
Main URL: http://www.manpower.us/en/About-Us/Social-Responsibility.htmresponsibility/philanthropy/default.jsp

Established in 1953 in WI.
Donor: Manpower Inc.
Foundation type: Company-sponsored foundation.
Financial data (yr. ended 12/31/13): Assets, $528,770 (M); gifts received, $542,000; expenditures, $565,734; qualifying distributions, $565,734; giving activities include $553,650 for 31 grants (high: $210,000; low: $650), and $12,000 for 3 grants to individuals (high: $4,000; low: $4,000).
Purpose and activities: The foundation supports programs designed to promote youth development and bridges to employment.
Fields of interest: Education; Employment, training; Employment; Youth development; United Ways and Federated Giving Programs.
Type of support: General/operating support; Scholarship funds; Employee-related scholarships.
Limitations: Applications accepted. Giving primarily in areas of company operations in Milwaukee, WI.

Application information: Contributes only to pre-selected organizations and through employee-related scholarships. Application form not required.
Officers and Directors:* Jeffrey A. Joerres,* Pres.; Julie Krey, V.P.; Michael J. Van Handel,* Secy.-Treas.
EIN: 396052810
Selected grants: The following grants are a representative sample of this grantmaker's funding activity:
$15,000 to Boys and Girls Clubs of Greater Milwaukee, Milwaukee, WI, 2010.
$5,000 to United Negro College Fund, Fairfax, VA, 2011.

9900
Marcus Corporation Foundation, Inc. ✧
100 E. Wisconsin Ave., Ste. 1900
Milwaukee, WI 53202-4125
Contact: Stephen H. Marcus, Pres., Treas. and Dir.

Established in 1961 in WI.
Donor: The Marcus Corp.
Foundation type: Company-sponsored foundation.
Financial data (yr. ended 12/31/13): Assets, $3,004,159 (M); gifts received, $450,547; expenditures, $771,418; qualifying distributions, $762,848; giving activities include $729,848 for 126 grants (high: $117,000; low: $100).
Purpose and activities: The foundation supports organizations involved with arts and culture, education, cancer, heart disease, human services, and community development.
Fields of interest: Arts; Education; Human services.
Type of support: General/operating support; Program development.
Limitations: Applications accepted. Giving limited to Milwaukee, WI. No grants to individuals.
Application information: Application form required.
Initial approach: Letter
Deadline(s): None
Officers and Directors:* Stephen H. Marcus,* Pres. and Treas.; Thomas F. Kissinger,* Secy.; Gregory S. Marcus.
EIN: 396046268
Selected grants: The following grants are a representative sample of this grantmaker's funding activity:
$106,400 to Medical College of Wisconsin, Milwaukee, WI, 2011.

9901
Faye McBeath Foundation ✧
101 W. Pleasant St., Ste. 210
Milwaukee, WI 53212-3963
Contact: Scott E. Gelzer, Exec. Dir.
FAX: (414) 272-6235;
E-mail: info@fayemcbeath.org; Main URL: http://www.fayemcbeath.org

Trust established in 1964 in WI.
Donor: Faye McBeath†.
Foundation type: Independent foundation.
Financial data (yr. ended 12/31/13): Assets, $1,471,279 (M); gifts received, $315; expenditures, $1,189,242; qualifying distributions, $1,142,373; giving activities include $966,130 for 65 grants (high: $65,000; low: $500).
Purpose and activities: Giving to benefit the people of Wisconsin by providing homes and care for elderly persons, promoting education in medical science and public health, providing medical, nursing, and hospital care for the sick and disabled, promoting the welfare of children, and promoting research in civics and government, directed towards improvement in the efficiency of local government.
Fields of interest: Education, early childhood education; Elementary school/education; Secondary school/education; Medical school/education; Dental care; Nursing care; Health care; Substance abuse, services; Mental health/crisis services; Health organizations, association; AIDS; Alcoholism; Biomedicine; Nutrition; Youth development, citizenship; Human services; Children/youth, services; Child development, services; Family services; Residential/custodial care, hospices; Aging, centers/services; Public policy, research; Government/public administration; Public affairs, citizen participation; Aging.
Type of support: General/operating support; Continuing support; Program development; Seed money; Technical assistance; Matching/challenge support.
Limitations: Applications not accepted. Giving limited to WI, with emphasis on the greater Milwaukee area, including Milwaukee, Ozaukee, Waukesha and Washington counties. No grants to individuals, or for annual campaigns, capital projects, scholarships, fellowships, or specific medical or scientific research projects; grants rarely for emergency funds; no loans.
Publications: Annual report; Grants list; Informational brochure; Program policy statement.
Application information: Unsolicited requests for funds not accepted.
Board meeting date(s): Feb., May, Sept., Dec.
Officers and Trustees:* P. Michael Mahoney,* Chair.; Mary T. Kellner,* Vice-Chair.; Gregory Wesley,* Secy.; Scott E. Gelzer, Exec. Dir.; Sara E. Aster; Steven J. Smith.
Number of staff: 1 part-time professional; 1 part-time support.
EIN: 396074450
Selected grants: The following grants are a representative sample of this grantmaker's funding activity:
$65,000 to Greater Milwaukee Foundation, Milwaukee, WI, 2012. For Nonprofit Management Fund of Milwaukee, Ozaukee and Washington Co's.
$50,000 to Metropolitan Milwaukee Association of Commerce, Milwaukee, WI, 2012. For Teach for America - Milwaukee.
$40,000 to Grand Avenue Club, Milwaukee, WI, 2012. For Education Collaborative with MATC.
$40,000 to Urban Day School, Milwaukee, WI, 2012. For summer school.
$35,000 to Milwaukee Public Library Foundation, Milwaukee, WI, 2012. For Summer Reading Outreach Program.
$30,000 to Seeds of Health, Milwaukee, WI, 2012. For Summer School, Grades 1 - 8.
$25,000 to Aurora Sinai Medical Center, Milwaukee, WI, 2012. For Bread of Healing Partnership.
$23,200 to Marquette University, Milwaukee, WI, 2012. For Community Impact Journalism Project.
$23,000 to YMCA of Metropolitan Milwaukee, Milwaukee, WI, 2012. For Young Leaders Academy Accelerated Reading and Math Program.
$5,000 to Greater Milwaukee Foundation, Milwaukee, WI, 2012. For Camps for Kids.

9902
Mead Witter Foundation, Inc. ✧
(formerly Consolidated Papers Foundation, Inc.)
P.O. Box 39
Wisconsin Rapids, WI 54495-0039 (715) 424-3004
Contact: Cynthia Henke, Pres. and Treas.

Incorporated in 1951 in WI.
Donors: George W. Mead; Consolidated Papers, Inc.; and members of the George W. Mead family.
Foundation type: Independent foundation.
Financial data (yr. ended 12/31/13): Assets, $60,209,090 (M); expenditures, $3,223,998; qualifying distributions, $3,109,368; giving activities include $2,790,053 for 120 grants (high: $1,000,000; low: $100).
Purpose and activities: Giving primarily for higher education and for local community causes, and youth and social service agencies in communities where Mead Witter Inc. conducts operations; higher education grants generally limited to those in WI; support also for the fine and performing arts and other cultural programs.
Fields of interest: Performing arts; Performing arts, theater; Historic preservation/historical societies; Arts; Higher education; Libraries (public); Education; Health care; Human services; Youth, services.
Type of support: General/operating support; Continuing support; Annual campaigns; Capital campaigns; Building/renovation; Equipment; Endowments; Emergency funds; Professorships; Seed money; Scholarship funds; Employee matching gifts.
Limitations: Applications accepted. Giving primarily in Rapon and Madison, WI, usually near areas of company operations; funding also in MA. No grants to individuals, or for deficit financing, research, or conferences; no loans.
Publications: Informational brochure (including application guidelines).
Application information: Full proposal is by invitation only. Application form not required.
Initial approach: 1-page letter of inquiry
Copies of proposal: 1
Deadline(s): None
Board meeting date(s): June and Dec.
Final notification: Following June and Dec. meetings
Officers: George W. Mead, Chair.; Susan A. Feith, Vice-Chair. and Secy.; Cynthia Henke, Pres. and Treas.
Directors: Helen B. Ambuel; Robert B. McKay.
Number of staff: 1 part-time professional; 1 full-time support.
EIN: 396040071
Selected grants: The following grants are a representative sample of this grantmaker's funding activity:
$15,000 to Living Water International, Stafford, TX, 2012. For Underwrite.

9903
Menasha Corporation Foundation ✧
P.O. Box 367
Neenah, WI 54957-0367 (920) 751-2036
Contact: Kevin Schuh, Treas.
Main URL: http://www.menasha.com/Foundation

Established in 1953 in WI.
Donor: Menasha Corp.
Foundation type: Company-sponsored foundation.

Financial data (yr. ended 12/31/13): Assets, $2,369,799 (M); gifts received, $1,493,000; expenditures, $917,596; qualifying distributions, $905,537; giving activities include $802,047 for 464 grants (high: $56,250; low: $50), $66,000 for 44 grants to individuals (high: $1,500; low: $1,500), and $37,490 for 84 employee matching gifts.
Purpose and activities: The foundation supports programs designed to promote safe and healthy citizens; an educated society; community betterment; and environmental sustainability.
Fields of interest: Arts; Higher education; Education; Health care.
Type of support: General/operating support; Employee volunteer services; Employee matching gifts; Scholarships—to individuals.
Limitations: Applications accepted. Giving primarily in areas of company operations in Neenah, WI. No grants to individuals (except for employee-related scholarships).
Application information: Application form not required.
Initial approach: Proposal
Copies of proposal: 1
Deadline(s): None
Board meeting date(s): Mar., June, Sept. and Dec.
Officers and Directors:* Jim Kotek, Chair.; Mike Waite,* Pres.; Tom Rettler,* V.P.; Angie Burns, Secy.; Kevin Schuh, Treas.; Andy Gansner; Pierce Smith; Bill Ash.
EIN: 396047384
Selected grants: The following grants are a representative sample of this grantmaker's funding activity:
$3,600 to Gleaners Community Food Bank, Detroit, MI, 2011.
$2,000 to American Cancer Society, Atlanta, GA, 2011.
$2,000 to City of Hope, Duarte, CA, 2011.
$1,666 to American Cancer Society, Atlanta, GA, 2011.
$1,500 to City of Hope, Duarte, CA, 2011.
$1,500 to Cystic Fibrosis Foundation, Bethesda, MD, 2011.
$1,500 to University of Michigan, Ann Arbor, MI, 2011. For scholarships.
$1,500 to University of Michigan, Ann Arbor, MI, 2011. For scholarships.
$1,500 to University of Michigan, Ann Arbor, MI, 2011. For scholarships.
$1,500 to University of Wisconsin, Madison, WI, 2011. For scholarships.

9904
John and Engrid Meng Inc. ✧
301 N. Broadway No. 202
De Pere, WI 54115-2856

Established in 1982 in WI.
Donors: Engrid Meng; John C. Meng; Angela M. Chetcuti; Jere Dhein.
Foundation type: Independent foundation.
Financial data (yr. ended 12/31/12): Assets, $9,290,932 (M); gifts received, $986,082; expenditures, $695,741; qualifying distributions, $447,621; giving activities include $447,621 for grants.
Purpose and activities: Giving primarily for education, health and human services.
Fields of interest: Nursing school/education; Education; Health organizations, association; Human services; Salvation Army; Residential/custodial care, hospices.
Limitations: Applications not accepted. Giving limited to northeastern WI, with emphasis on Green Bay and Brown County. No grants to individuals.
Application information: Unsolicited requests for funds not accepted.
Officers: John C. Meng, Pres.; Engrid H. Meng, V.P.; Gerald C. Condon, Jr., Secy.; Angela M. Chetcuti, Treas.
Number of staff: 1 part-time professional.
EIN: 391432568

9905
Mercy Works Foundation, Inc. ✧
5733 Grande Market Dr., Ste. H
Appleton, WI 54913-8472
Contact: Jody Lueck, Exec. Dir.

Established in 2002 in WI; as a successor to the Mercy Works Foundation, 1996.
Donors: Brian Follett; Mark Follett; Sally Follett; Joe Malone; Paula Malone; Mercy Works Foundation.
Foundation type: Independent foundation.
Financial data (yr. ended 12/31/13): Assets, $33,803,357 (M); expenditures, $2,826,484; qualifying distributions, $2,581,551; giving activities include $2,288,441 for 96 grants (high: $175,000; low: $2,000).
Fields of interest: Human services; Catholic agencies & churches.
Limitations: Applications not accepted. No grants to individuals.
Application information: Contributes only to pre-selected organizations.
Board meeting date(s): Three times per year
Officers and Directors:* Joseph Malone,* Chair.; Sally E. Follett, Vice-Chair.; Scott Follett, Secy.; David Krause, Treas.; Jody Lueck, Exec. Dir.; Bob Follett; Brian Follett; Mark C. Follett.
Number of staff: 1 full-time professional; 2 full-time support.
EIN: 431954871

9906
Dale R. & Ruth L. Michels Family Foundation ✧
P.O. Box 414
Brownsville, WI 53006-0414

Established in 1999 in WI.
Donors: Ruth L. Michels; Patrick D. Michels; Michels Corp.
Foundation type: Independent foundation.
Financial data (yr. ended 12/31/13): Assets, $7,157,919 (M); gifts received, $5,001,000; expenditures, $2,663,654; qualifying distributions, $2,623,537; giving activities include $2,596,050 for 58 grants (high: $1,000,000; low: $500).
Purpose and activities: Giving primarily for education, children, youth and social services, Roman Catholic churches, a hospital foundation, and to YMCAs.
Fields of interest: Higher education; Education; Hospitals (general); Human services; YM/YWCAs & YM/YWHAs; Children/youth, services; Catholic agencies & churches.
Limitations: Applications not accepted. Giving primarily in WI.
Application information: Contributes only to pre-selected organizations.
Trustees: Kevin P. Michels; Patrick D. Michels; Ruth L. Michels; Steven R. Michels; Timothy J. Michels.
EIN: 391949453

9907
Greater Milwaukee Foundation ✧
(formerly Milwaukee Foundation)
101 W. Pleasant St., Ste. 210
Milwaukee, WI 53212 (414) 272-5805
FAX: (414) 272-6235;
E-mail: info@greatermilwaukeefoundation.org; Main URL: http://www.greatermilwaukeefoundation.org
Facebook: http://www.facebook.com/GreaterMilwaukeeFoundation
Twitter: http://twitter.com/grmkefdn

Established in 1915 in WI by declaration of trust.
Foundation type: Community foundation.
Financial data (yr. ended 12/31/12): Assets, $612,115,000 (M); gifts received, $28,421,000; expenditures, $36,659,000; giving activities include $30,050,000 for 3,414 grants.
Purpose and activities: Present funds include many discretionary funds and some funds designated by the donors to benefit specific institutions or for special purposes, including educational institutions, arts and cultural programs, community development, social services, and health care; support also for conservation and historic preservation.
Fields of interest: Visual arts; Performing arts; Performing arts, dance; Historic preservation/historical societies; Arts; Education, early childhood education; Child development, education; Elementary school/education; Secondary school/education; Higher education; Adult/continuing education; Education; Environment, natural resources; Environment; Animal welfare; Reproductive health, family planning; Health care; Substance abuse, services; Mental health/crisis services; Health organizations, association; Parkinson's disease; AIDS; Nerve, muscle & bone research; Multiple sclerosis research; Diabetes research; Lupus research; Medical research; Crime/violence prevention, youth; Legal services; Employment, training; Employment; Food services; Nutrition; Housing/shelter, development; Recreation; Youth development; Children/youth, services; Child development, services; Family services; Aging, centers/services; Women, centers/services; Homeless, human services; Human services; Civil rights, race/intergroup relations; Urban/community development; Community/economic development; Public policy, research; Government/public administration; Children/youth; Youth; Adults; Aging; Young adults; Disabilities, people with; Minorities; Girls; Military/veterans; Offenders/ex-offenders; AIDS, people with; Economically disadvantaged; Homeless; LGBTQ.
Type of support: Continuing support; Management development/capacity building; Capital campaigns; Building/renovation; Equipment; Land acquisition; Emergency funds; Program development; Seed money; Fellowships; Scholarship funds; Research; Technical assistance; Program evaluation; Scholarships—to individuals; Matching/challenge support.
Limitations: Applications accepted. Giving primarily in Milwaukee, Ozaukee, Washington, and Waukesha counties, WI. No support for 501(c)(4)s or 501(c)(6)s. No support for the general use of churches or for sectarian religious purposes, except from donor advised and designated funds. No grants to

individuals (except for established awards), or for ongoing operating expenses, debt reduction, or agency endowments.
Publications: Application guidelines; Annual report; Financial statement; Grants list; Informational brochure; Newsletter; Program policy statement.
Application information: Visit foundation web site for online letter of inquiry and application guidelines. The foundation's staff will invite selected applicants to submit full proposals based on letter of inquiry. Application form required.
Initial approach: Set up and complete an organizational profile on Philanthropy Online
Copies of proposal: 1
Deadline(s): Quarterly
Board meeting date(s): Mar., June, Sept., Dec., and as needed
Final notification: 1 week after board meetings
Officers and Directors:* Thomas L. Spero,* Chair.; David J. Lubar,* Vice-Chair.; Ellen M. Gilligan,* C.E.O. and Pres.; Kathryn Dunn, V.P., Community Investment; Timothy Larson, V.P., Philanthropic Svcs.; Susan M. Smith, V.P., Mktg. and Comms.; Marcus White, V.P., Civic Engagement; Patti Dew,* C.F.O., V.P., Finance and Admin., Secy., and Treas.; Wendy Ponting, Cont.; Wendy Reed Bosworth; Peter W. Bruce; Ness Flores; Janine P. Geske; Cecelia Gore; Jacqueline Herd-Barber; Paul J. Jones; Judy Jorgenson; David J. Kundert; Gregory S. Marcus; Cory L. Nettles.
Number of staff: 22 full-time professional; 4 part-time professional; 9 full-time support; 1 part-time support.
EIN: 396036407

9908
MMG Foundation, Inc. ✧
702 Eisenhower Dr., Ste. B
Kimberly, WI 54136-2152

Established around 1994 in WI.
Donors: Cynthia F. Moeller Stiehl; Cynvestors, LP; Cynvestors Limited Partnership.
Foundation type: Independent foundation.
Financial data (yr. ended 12/31/13): Assets, $4,535,518 (M); gifts received, $623,693; expenditures, $828,880; qualifying distributions, $750,325; giving activities include $750,325 for 53 grants (high: $285,000; low: $100).
Fields of interest: Performing arts, music; Arts; Higher education; Education; Human services; YM/YWCAs & YM/YWHAs; Children/youth, services.
Limitations: Applications not accepted. Giving primarily in WI. No grants to individuals.
Application information: Contributes only to pre-selected organizations.
Officers: Cynthia F. Moeller Stiehl, Pres.; William D. Calkins, Secy.; Daniel J. Peterich, Treas.
EIN: 396571237

9909
Mortenson Family Foundation ✧
P.O. Box 486
Belleville, WI 53508

Established in 1997 in WI.
Donor: Loren D. Mortenson.
Foundation type: Independent foundation.
Financial data (yr. ended 12/31/12): Assets, $0 (M); expenditures, $448,984; qualifying distributions, $442,330; giving activities include $442,330 for grants.
Fields of interest: Children/youth, services; United Ways and Federated Giving Programs; Christian agencies & churches.
Limitations: Applications not accepted. No grants to individuals.
Application information: Unsolicited requests for funds not accepted.
Trustees: Ryan Henderson; Joelle Mortenson Hunter; Barbara J. Mortenson; Jay P. Mortenson; Loren D. Mortenson.
EIN: 396659441
Selected grants: The following grants are a representative sample of this grantmaker's funding activity:
$2,000 to Leukemia & Lymphoma Society, White Plains, NY, 2011. For general operating expenses.
$1,500 to United Way Worldwide, Alexandria, VA, 2011. For general operating expenses.
$1,000 to Fellowship of Christian Athletes, Kansas City, MO, 2011. For general operating expenses.

9910
Mound Properties Inc. ✧ ☆
1525 Howe St.
Racine, WI 53403-2237 (262) 260-2503

Established in WI.
Foundation type: Independent foundation.
Financial data (yr. ended 08/31/13): Assets, $1,798,484 (M); expenditures, $498,493; qualifying distributions, $498,493; giving activities include $498,493 for 10 grants (high: $261,236; low: $609).
Fields of interest: Youth development; Human services; Philanthropy/voluntarism.
Limitations: Applications accepted. Giving primarily in Racine, WI.
Application information: Application form required.
Initial approach: Proposal
Deadline(s): None
Officers and Directors:* Matthew L. Wagner,* Pres.; Julie Branick,* V.P.; William Harold Van Lopik, V.P.; Thomas S. Simpson,* Secy.; James B. Hennessy, Treas.
EIN: 043610852

9911
Neese Family Foundation, Inc. ✧ ☆
2870 Riverside Dr.
Beloit, WI 53511-1506 (608) 368-1200

Incorporated in 1986 in IL.
Donors: Margaret L. Neese 1957 Trust; Robert H. Neese Trust of 1954.
Foundation type: Independent foundation.
Financial data (yr. ended 06/30/13): Assets, $2,663,181 (M); gifts received, $3,131; expenditures, $500,979; qualifying distributions, $493,868; giving activities include $487,858 for 5 grants (high: $417,858; low: $2,000).
Fields of interest: Higher education; Libraries (public); Hospitals (general); Human services; YM/YWCAs & YM/YWHAs; United Ways and Federated Giving Programs.
Type of support: Endowments; Annual campaigns; General/operating support; Capital campaigns; Building/renovation; Scholarship funds.
Limitations: Applications accepted. Giving primarily in WI. No grants to individuals.
Application information: Application form not required.
Initial approach: Letter
Deadline(s): None
Board meeting date(s): Varies
Officers: Margaret L.N. Brooks, Pres.; Robert H. Neese, V.P.; Gary G. Grabowski, Secy.-Treas.
Director: Wendy L. Neese.
EIN: 363473918
Selected grants: The following grants are a representative sample of this grantmaker's funding activity:
$200,000 to Beloit College, Beloit, WI, 2011.
$25,000 to Beloit Public Library, Beloit, WI, 2011. For capital campaign.

9912
The Nelson Family Foundation, Inc. ✧
P.O. Box 365
Prescott, WI 54021-0365

Established in 1996 in WI.
Donors: Carol J. Nelson; Grant E. Nelson.
Foundation type: Independent foundation.
Financial data (yr. ended 12/31/12): Assets, $47,547,108 (M); expenditures, $4,658,273; qualifying distributions, $4,286,669; giving activities include $4,286,669 for 17 grants (high: $2,286,669; low: $5,000).
Purpose and activities: Giving primarily for education, human services and Christian organizations.
Fields of interest: Higher education; Education; Human services; Children/youth, services; Christian agencies & churches.
Limitations: Applications not accepted. Giving primarily in MN; some funding nationally, particularly in CA. No grants to individuals.
Application information: Contributes only to pre-selected organizations.
Officers: Grant E. Nelson, Pres.; Carol J. Nelson, Exec. V.P.; Sarah Curtis, V.P. and Secy.; Rodney G. Nelson, V.P. and Treas.
Directors: Curtis D. Curtis; Maybeth Nelson.
EIN: 391868979

9913
Nicholas Family Foundation Trust ✧
10309 N. River Rd.
Mequon, WI 53092-4561 (262) 242-3040
Contact: Lynn S. Nicholas, Tr.

Established in 1993 in WI.
Donors: Albert Nicholas; Wisconsin Sports Development Corporation.
Foundation type: Independent foundation.
Financial data (yr. ended 12/31/13): Assets, $49,898,860 (M); expenditures, $2,116,023; qualifying distributions, $1,987,186; giving activities include $1,959,619 for 57 grants (high: $200,000; low: $2,500).
Purpose and activities: Giving primarily for children and social services, giving also for a children's hospital.
Fields of interest: Performing arts, theater; Historic preservation/historical societies; Arts; Education; Hospitals (specialty); Health organizations, association; Youth development, centers/clubs; Human services; Children/youth, services; United Ways and Federated Giving Programs; Blind/visually impaired.

Limitations: Applications accepted. Giving primarily in WI, with emphasis on Milwaukee. No grants to individuals.
Application information: Application form required.
Initial approach: Typewritten letter
Deadline(s): None
Trustees: Susan N. Fasciano; Albert O. Nicholas; David O. Nicholas; Lynn S. Nicholas; Nancy J. Nicholas.
EIN: 396589261

9914
Northwestern Mutual Foundation, Inc. ✧
(formerly Northwestern Mutual Foundation)
720 E. Wisconsin Ave.
Milwaukee, WI 53202-4703 (414) 665-2200
Contact: John Kordsmeier, Pres.
FAX: (414) 665-2199;
E-mail: foundationonline@northwesternmutual.com;
Main URL: http://www.nmfn.com/tn/aboutus—fd_intro
Northwestern Mutual Philanthropic Videos: http://www.northwesternmutual.com/learning-center/videos/philanthropy.aspx
YouTube: http://www.youtube.com/playlist?list=PL1B4660ADEB4813C7

Established in 1992 in WI.
Donors: The Northwestern Mutual Life Insurance Co.; Lydell Inc.
Foundation type: Company-sponsored foundation.
Financial data (yr. ended 06/30/13): Assets, $104,959,041 (M); gifts received, $13,299,518; expenditures, $17,825,441; qualifying distributions, $17,567,915; giving activities include $16,490,064 for grants.
Purpose and activities: The foundation supports organizations involved with arts and culture, education, health, childhood cancer, disaster relief, human services, and community economic development.
Fields of interest: Arts education; Museums; Performing arts; Arts; Elementary/secondary education; Education, early childhood education; Higher education; Education, reading; Education; Health care; Cancer; Disasters, preparedness/services; Boys & girls clubs; Youth development, adult & child programs; American Red Cross; Family services; Human services; Community development, neighborhood development; Economic development, visitors/convention bureau/tourism promotion; Community/economic development; United Ways and Federated Giving Programs; Economically disadvantaged.
Type of support: General/operating support; Continuing support; Annual campaigns; Capital campaigns; Building/renovation; Emergency funds; Program development; Curriculum development; Scholarship funds; Research; Employee volunteer services; Sponsorships; Employee matching gifts; Matching/challenge support.
Limitations: Applications accepted. Giving primarily in Milwaukee, WI; giving also to national organizations. No support for organizations with an operating budget under $300,000, groups or organizations that re-grant to other organizations or individuals, school teams, bands, or choirs, or labor, religious, or fraternal groups. No grants to individuals, or for debt reduction, capital, or endowment campaigns unless approved by the foundation in advance; conferences, conventions, golf outings, school trips, concerts, or performances, athletic events, equipment, uniforms, travel or any in-kind support of special events, or lobbying activities.
Publications: Application guidelines; Corporate giving report.
Application information: Applications are accepted up to 30 days in advance of deadlines. There are no open national deadlines for Northwestern Mutual's Childhood Cancer Program. Support is limited to 1 contribution per organization during any given year.
Initial approach: Complete online application
Deadline(s): 60 days prior to need for table or event sponsorships; Sept. 15 for Higher Education; Oct. 15 for Early Childhood Education and Literacy; Mar. 15 for Arts Education and Mentoring; Feb. 15 for Building Neighborhood Capacity
Board meeting date(s): Bimonthly
Final notification: 90 days
Officers and Directors:* John E. Schlifske,* C.E.O.; John Kordsmeier,* Pres.; Scott J. Morns, Secy.; Karen A. Molloy, Treas.; Kimberley Goode; Jean M. Maier; Gregory C. Oberland; Gary A. Poliner.
Number of staff: 3 full-time professional; 1 full-time support.
EIN: 391728908
Selected grants: The following grants are a representative sample of this grantmaker's funding activity:
$1,615,000 to United Way of Greater Milwaukee, Milwaukee, WI, 2013.
$785,336 to United Performing Arts Fund, Milwaukee, WI, 2013.
$265,000 to Alexs Lemonade Stand Foundation, Wynnewood, PA, 2013.
$255,225 to Scholarship America, Saint Peter, MN, 2013.
$220,000 to City Year Milwaukee, Milwaukee, WI, 2013.
$200,000 to Starlight Childrens Foundation, Los Angeles, CA, 2013.
$13,500 to Admirals Power Play Foundation, Milwaukee, WI, 2013.
$10,000 to Defenders of Children, Phoenix, AZ, 2013.
$10,000 to I Have A Dream Foundation, McLean, VA, 2013.
$6,000 to First Stage Childrens Theater, Milwaukee, WI, 2013.

9915
Ocular Physiology Research and Education Foundation, Inc. ✧ ☆
3006 Harvard Dr.
Madison, WI 53705-2107

Established in 1989 in WI.
Donors: Pfizer (Pharmacia) Corp.; Inspire Pharmaceuticals; MEMX; Alcon Foundation; Frey Research; NU Lens, Ltd.; QLT, Inc.; Santen, Inc.; Edward W. Smith Jr. Foundation.
Foundation type: Independent foundation.
Financial data (yr. ended 06/30/13): Assets, $490,129 (M); gifts received, $5,000; expenditures, $447,913; qualifying distributions, $441,636; giving activities include $440,000 for 1 grant.
Purpose and activities: Giving primarily for eye research, particularly ocular physiology.
Fields of interest: Eye research.
Type of support: General/operating support.
Limitations: Applications not accepted. No grants to individuals.
Application information: Unsolicited requests for funds not accepted.
Officers and Directors:* Paul L. Kaufman, M.D.*, Pres.; Howard S. Goldman,* V.P.; Margaret G. Kaufman, Secy.-Treas.; Katherine B. Foehl.
EIN: 391661745

9916
Oshkosh Area Community Foundation ✧
(formerly Oshkosh Foundation)
230 Ohio St., Ste. 100
Oshkosh, WI 54902 (920) 426-3993
Contact: Diane Abraham, C.E.O.; For grants: Amy Putzer, Dir., Progs.
FAX: (920) 426-6997;
E-mail: info@oshkoshareaf.org; Additional e-mail: diane@oshkoshareacf.org; Grant inquiry e-mail: amy@oshkoshareacf.org; Main URL: http://www.oshkoshareacf.org
E-Newsletter: http://www.oshkoshareacf.org/signup.cfm
Facebook: http://www.facebook.com/OshkoshFoundation
Flickr: http://www.flickr.com/photos/oshkoshareacf
Twitter: http://twitter.com/OACF
YouTube: http://www.youtube.com/user/oshfdn

Established in 1928 in WI by declaration of trust.
Foundation type: Community foundation.
Financial data (yr. ended 06/30/13): Assets, $87,475,004 (M); gifts received, $5,358,462; expenditures, $4,707,217; giving activities include $4,057,085 for grants.
Purpose and activities: The foundation seeks to address community needs by providing leadership through grantmaking and fund development.
Fields of interest: Arts; Higher education; Education; Recreation; Children/youth, services; Community/economic development; Children/youth; Youth; Aging; Women; Girls.
Type of support: Management development/capacity building; General/operating support; Continuing support; Capital campaigns; Building/renovation; Equipment; Endowments; Emergency funds; Program development; Conferences/seminars; Seed money; Scholarship funds; Program-related investments/loans; Scholarships—to individuals; Matching/challenge support.
Limitations: Applications accepted. Giving limited to Green Lake, Waushara, and Winnebago, counties, WI. No grants to individuals (except for scholarships), or for deficit financing, research, or publications; no loans.
Publications: Application guidelines; Annual report; Financial statement; Informational brochure; Newsletter.
Application information: Visit foundation web site for application forms, guidelines, and specific deadlines. Applications not accepted unless service area requirements and funding guidelines are met. Application form required.
Initial approach: Submit application form and attachments
Copies of proposal: 1
Deadline(s): Varies
Board meeting date(s): 8 times a year
Final notification: 12 weeks
Officers and Board of Governors:* Beth Wyman,* Pres.; Mark Lasky,* V.P.; Diane Abraham,* Pres. and C.E.O.; Jason Hirschberg,* Secy.; Cathy Luther,* Treas.; Nancy Albright, Dir. Emeritus; John Bermingham, Dir. Emeritus; Larry Bittner, Dir.

Emeritus; Mike Castle, Dir. Emeritus; Marcy Coglianese, Dir. Emeritus; Bob Hergert, Dir. Emeritus; Tom Harenburg, Dir. Emeritus; Ginna Nelson, Dir. Emeritus; Jack Schloesser, Dir. Emeritus; Pat Seubert, Dir. Emeritus; Sam Sundet, Dir. Emeritus; Jack Sullivan, Dir. Emeritus; Bill Wyman, Dir. Emeritus; Gary Yakes, Dir. Emeritus; Dave Elbing; Peter Lang; Jim Malczewski; Sylvia McDonald; Kate Pfaendtner; Peter Prickett; Bruce Rounds; Steve Sorenson; Carol Sullivan; Jeff Trembly.
Trustees: Advisory Small Cap Value; Artisan International Value; Associated Banc-Corp; BMO Harris Bank; Capital Counsel; Colchester Global Bond; Forester Offshore; Gryphon International Growth; JPMorgan Chase Bank, N.A.; McClain Select Value; PIMCO; Post Traditional High Yield Fund; Reinhart Partners; TIFF ARP III; UBP/Smith Barney; Vanguard.
Number of staff: 5 full-time professional; 1 part-time professional; 1 full-time support; 1 part-time support.
EIN: 392034571
Selected grants: The following grants are a representative sample of this grantmaker's funding activity:
$33,900 to Fox Valley Technical College Foundation, Appleton, WI, 2012. For Riverside (Alternative Education) Program for Career Kickstart.
$30,000 to CAP Services, Stevens Point, WI, 2012. For skills enhancement program.
$25,000 to Tri-County Community Dental Clinic, Appleton, WI, 2012. For Dental Bus.
$5,230 to Christine Ann Domestic Abuse Services, Neenah, WI, 2012. For crisis advocacy services.
$5,000 to Jazz Corner Society, Menasha, WI, 2012. For Fox Jazz Festival.
$4,000 to Fox River Industries, Berlin, WI, 2012. For Green Lake Thrift Store.
$3,500 to Clarity Care, Oshkosh, WI, 2012. For Help at Home Program.
$1,200 to Oshkosh Family Inc, Oshkosh, WI, 2012. For Meals on Wheels.
$750 to Green Lake Association, Green Lake, WI, 2012. For Green Team Outings.

9917
Oshkosh Corporation Foundation, Inc. ✧ ☆
(formerly Oshkosh Truck Foundation, Inc.)
P.O. Box 2566
Oshkosh, WI 54903-2566 (920) 233-9622
Contact: Kerry Dereszynski

Incorporated in 1960 in WI.
Donors: Oshkosh Corp.; Oshkosh Truck Corp.
Foundation type: Company-sponsored foundation.
Financial data (yr. ended 09/30/13): Assets, $2,362,739 (M); gifts received, $1,000,000; expenditures, $690,467; qualifying distributions, $685,330; giving activities include $681,700 for 33 grants (high: $117,500; low: $500).
Purpose and activities: The foundation supports community foundations and firefighters and organizations involved with education, health, hunger, housing development, youth development, and human services. Special emphasis is directed toward programs designed to address basic needs and cultural development.
Fields of interest: Arts; Housing/shelter, development; Big Brothers/Big Sisters; Youth development; Salvation Army; YM/YWCAs & YM/YWHAs; Community/economic development; Foundations (community); United Ways and Federated Giving Programs.
Type of support: General/operating support; Continuing support; Annual campaigns; Program development.
Limitations: Applications accepted. Giving primarily in areas of company operations in Oshkosh and the Winnebago County, WI, area. No grants for start-up needs, debt reduction, land acquisition, special projects, research, publications, conferences, or endowments; no loans; no matching gifts.
Application information: Application form required.
Initial approach: Letter
Copies of proposal: 1
Deadline(s): None
Officers and Trustees:* Charles L. Szews,* Pres.; David M. Sagehorn,* V.P. and Treas.; Bryan J. Blankfield,* V.P.; Wilson R. Jones,* V.P.; Michael K. Rohrkaste,* V.P.; Jana C. Heft, Secy.
EIN: 396062129

9918
Peck Foundation Milwaukee Ltd. ✧
(formerly Miriam & Bernard Peck Foundation, Ltd.)
P.O. Box 441
Milwaukee, WI 53201-0441 (414) 273-7325
Contact: Karen Katz, Co-Pres.

Established in 1985 in WI.
Donors: Jodi Peck; Miriam Peck; Bernard Peck; Karen Peck Katz.
Foundation type: Independent foundation.
Financial data (yr. ended 12/31/12): Assets, $12,820,394 (M); expenditures, $677,080; qualifying distributions, $534,150; giving activities include $534,150 for grants.
Purpose and activities: Giving for education, including a medical school, health, human services, and Jewish organizations.
Fields of interest: Arts; Medical school/education; Education; Health organizations, association; Recreation, parks/playgrounds; Human services; Jewish federated giving programs; Jewish agencies & synagogues.
Type of support: General/operating support; Annual campaigns; Capital campaigns.
Limitations: Applications accepted. Giving primarily in Milwaukee, WI; some giving also in FL. No grants for political organizations.
Application information: Application form not required.
Initial approach: Proposal
Deadline(s): None
Board meeting date(s): Sept.
Officers: Karen Katz, Co-Pres.; Jodi Peck, Co-Pres.; Bernard Peck, V.P.; Miriam Peck, V.P.; William L. Komisar, Secy.-Treas.
Director: Harvey Alligood.
EIN: 391519687

9919
Jane Bradley Pettit Foundation
(formerly Jane and Lloyd Pettit Foundation, Inc.)
1200 N. Mayfair Rd., Ste. 430
Wauwatosa, WI 53226-3282 (414) 982-2880
Contact: Kara A. Nehring, Dir., Admin.
FAX: (414) 982-2889;
E-mail: knehring@staffordlaw.com; Tel. for Kara Nehring, Dir., Admin.: (414) 982-2875; Main URL: http://www.jbpf.org

Incorporated in 1986 in WI.
Donor: Jane Bradley Pettit†.
Foundation type: Independent foundation.
Financial data (yr. ended 12/31/14): Assets, $20,278,000 (M); expenditures, $2,986,279; qualifying distributions, $2,475,000; giving activities include $2,475,000 for 92 grants (high: $300,000; low: $5,000).
Purpose and activities: The foundation will provide funds to initiate and sustain projects in the Greater Milwaukee, WI, community. The foundation will focus on programs and projects that serve low-income and disadvantaged individuals, women, children and the elderly. The foundation will support charitable organizations that address these concerns through arts and culture, community and social development, education and health.
Fields of interest: Arts; Secondary school/education; Higher education; Education; Hospitals (general); Health care; Health organizations, association; Human services; Children/youth, services; Children, services; Aging, centers/services; Women, centers/services; Community/economic development; Children/youth; Adults; Disabilities, people with; Economically disadvantaged; Homeless.
Type of support: General/operating support; Annual campaigns; Capital campaigns; Building/renovation; Program development; Research.
Limitations: Applications accepted. Giving primarily in the greater Milwaukee, WI, area. No grants to individuals.
Publications: Application guidelines.
Application information: The foundation will not consider requests for additional support for the period in which an organization currently has a grant in effect. Requests for capital projects will only be considered in the Jan. 15 grant cycle.
Initial approach: Use online application system on foundation web site
Copies of proposal: 1
Deadline(s): Jan. 15, May 15, and Sept. 15
Board meeting date(s): Quarterly
Final notification: May, Sept., and Dec.
Officers and Directors:* Francis R. Croak,* Pres.; Margaret T. Lund,* V.P.; JoAnn C. Youngman,* Secy.-Treas.
EIN: 391574123
Selected grants: The following grants are a representative sample of this grantmaker's funding activity:
$105,000 to M P T V Friends, Milwaukee, WI, 2013. For operating support.
$100,000 to United Way of Greater Milwaukee, Milwaukee, WI, 2013.
$10,000 to House of Peace, Milwaukee, WI, 2013. For operating support.
$10,000 to Toys for Tots, Milwaukee, WI, 2013. For operating support.

9920
Melitta S. Pick Charitable Trust ✧
c/o George A. Dionisopoulos
777 E. Wisconsin Ave.
Milwaukee, WI 53202-5306 (414) 297-5750

Established in 1972 in WI.
Donor: Melitta S. Pick†.
Foundation type: Independent foundation.
Financial data (yr. ended 01/31/13): Assets, $21,361,100 (M); gifts received, $1,211,255; expenditures, $1,917,659; qualifying distributions,

$1,742,439; giving activities include $1,699,000 for 45 grants (high: $600,000; low: $1,000).
Purpose and activities: Giving primarily for the arts and human services.
Fields of interest: Museums; Performing arts; Performing arts, orchestras; Arts; Human services; Youth, services.
Type of support: General/operating support; Annual campaigns; Capital campaigns; Building/renovation; Endowments; Emergency funds.
Limitations: Giving primarily in Milwaukee, WI. No grants to individuals.
Application information: Application form not required.
Initial approach: Letter
Deadline(s): None
Board meeting date(s): Usually quarterly
Trustees: George A. Dionisopoulos; Richard S. Gallagher; Joan M. Pick.
EIN: 237243490
Selected grants: The following grants are a representative sample of this grantmaker's funding activity:
$300,000 to West Bend Community Foundation, Milwaukee, WI, 2012.
$200,000 to West Bend Community Foundation, Milwaukee, WI, 2012.
$50,000 to Juvenile Diabetes Research Foundation International, New York, NY, 2012.

9921
Pollybill Foundation, Inc. ✧
111 E. Kilbourn Ave., 19th Fl.
Milwaukee, WI 53202-6622

Incorporated in 1960 in WI.
Donors: William D. Van Dyke; Polly H. Van Dyke.
Foundation type: Independent foundation.
Financial data (yr. ended 12/31/12): Assets, $1,279,982 (M); gifts received, $2,500,000; expenditures, $3,543,363; qualifying distributions, $3,518,275; giving activities include $3,515,500 for 41 grants (high: $1,650,000; low: $1,000).
Purpose and activities: Giving primarily for arts and culture, particularly for the symphony; funding also for education, and children, youth, and social services.
Fields of interest: Museums; Performing arts, orchestras; Education; Human services; Children/youth, services; Foundations (private grantmaking).
Limitations: Applications not accepted. Giving primarily in Milwaukee, WI. No grants to individuals.
Application information: Contributes only to pre-selected organizations.
Officers and Directors:* Polly H. Van Dyke,* Pres. and Treas.; William D. Van Dyke III,* V.P. and Secy.; Ellen Van Dyke Holtgers; Helen Deborah Van Dyke King; Joseph E. Tierney III; Kathryn Van Dyke.
EIN: 396078550

9922
Gene & Ruth Posner Foundation, Inc. ✧ ☆
c/o Michael Best & Friedrich LLP
330 E. Kilbourn Ave., No. 1170
Milwaukee, WI 53202-3146
Contact: Joshua Gimbel, Dir.

Established in 1963 in WI.
Donors: Gene Posner†; Ruth Posner†.
Foundation type: Independent foundation.
Financial data (yr. ended 12/31/13): Assets, $9,223,100 (M); expenditures, $620,488; qualifying distributions, $476,683; giving activities include $476,683 for 81 grants (high: $55,000; low: $100).
Purpose and activities: Grants limited to educational, civic, medical and religious fields.
Fields of interest: Arts; Education; Health care; Health organizations, association; Jewish federated giving programs; Jewish agencies & synagogues.
Limitations: Applications not accepted. Giving primarily in Milwaukee, WI, or in communities where family members reside. No grants to individuals.
Application information: Contributes only to pre-selected organizations.
Board meeting date(s): June/July
Directors: Joshua L. Gimbel; David Posner; Frederic G. Posner; Barbara P. Ward.
Number of staff: None.
EIN: 396050150

9923
Henry Predolin Foundation, Inc. ✧
P.O. Box 2719
Madison, WI 53701-2719

Established in 1999 in WI.
Donors: Henry Predolin; Henry Predolin Revocable Trust.
Foundation type: Independent foundation.
Financial data (yr. ended 12/31/13): Assets, $61,365,467 (M); expenditures, $3,365,509; qualifying distributions, $2,790,416; giving activities include $2,500,000 for 3 grants (high: $925,000; low: $750,000).
Fields of interest: Higher education; Hospitals (specialty); United Ways and Federated Giving Programs.
Limitations: Applications not accepted. Giving primarily in MN and WI. No grants to individuals.
Application information: Contributes only to pre-selected organizations.
Officers: Robert Chritton, Pres. and Treas.; Anthony Medyn, V.P. and Secy.
Directors: David Erickson; Yolanda Medyn; Jack Robson.
EIN: 391931309

9924
Racine Community Foundation, Inc. ✧
(formerly Racine County Area Foundation, Inc.)
1135 Warwick Way, Ste. 200
Racine, WI 53406 (262) 632-8474
Contact: Liz Powell, Exec. Dir.; For grants: Tracy Middlebrook, Prog. Off.
FAX: (262) 632-3739;
E-mail: info@racinecommunityfoundation.org; Grant inquiry e-mail: tracy.middlebrook@racinecommunityfoundation.org; Main URL: http://www.racinecommunityfoundation.org
Facebook: https://www.facebook.com/RacineCommunityFoundation
LinkedIn: http://www.linkedin.com/company/racine-community-foundation?trk=hb_tab_compy_id_1224926

Incorporated in 1975 in WI.
Foundation type: Community foundation.
Financial data (yr. ended 12/31/13): Assets, $51,762,452 (M); gifts received, $3,265,424; expenditures, $3,079,518; giving activities include $2,598,756 for 87+ grants (high: $402,000).
Purpose and activities: The mission of the foundation is to encourage and provide opportunities for charitable giving, to manage and distribute the funds in a responsible manner, and to enhance the quality of life for the people of Racine County, WI.
Fields of interest: Arts; Education; Environment; Health care; Human services; Community/economic development; Youth; Aging; Disabilities, people with; Mentally disabled; Economically disadvantaged.
Type of support: Equipment; Endowments; Program development; Conferences/seminars; Seed money; Scholarships—to individuals; Matching/challenge support.
Limitations: Applications accepted. Giving limited to Racine County, WI. No support for church or missionary groups unless for entire community benefit, grantmaking foundations, or social, athletic, veterans', labor, or fraternal organizations. No grants to individuals (except for donor directed scholarships), or for capital expenditures, including building funds, endowment funds, research, travel, or publications.
Publications: Application guidelines; Annual report; Financial statement; Informational brochure; Newsletter.
Application information: Visit foundation web site for application guidelines. Application form required.
Initial approach: Telephone
Copies of proposal: 16
Deadline(s): Jan. 15, Apr. 15, July 15, and Oct. 15
Board meeting date(s): Mar., June, Sept., and Dec.
Final notification: 8-10 weeks
Officers and Directors:* Steen Sanderhoff,* Pres.; Sheila R. Bugalecki,* V.P., Grants; Roger Dower,* V.P., Mktg.; Jose Martinez,* V.P., Donor Rels.; Russell C. Weyers,* V.P., Investments; Tracy Short,* Secy.; Ted Hart,* Treas.; Chris Greco, Cont.; Jill Heller, Co-Exec. Dir.; Liz Powell, Co-Exec. Dir.; Bryan D. Albrecht; David C. Easley; R. David Foster; Danice C. Griffin; April Johnson-Howell; Brian Lauer; David Novick; Eric Olesen; Robert F. Siegert, M.D.; James Small; Michael P. Staeck; GeorgAnn Stinson; Ernest C. Styberg, Jr.
Number of staff: 2 full-time professional; 2 part-time professional.
EIN: 510188377

9925
Raibrook Foundation ✧
30 N. 18th Ave., Unit 4
Sturgeon Bay, WI 54235-3207 (920) 746-2995
FAX: (920) 746-2996; Application e-mail: julie@raibrookfoundation.com; Main URL: http://www.raibrookfoundation.com

Established in 1990 in WI.
Donor: George R. Brooks†.
Foundation type: Independent foundation.
Financial data (yr. ended 12/31/12): Assets, $27,069,836 (M); gifts received, $2,521; expenditures, $2,907,624; qualifying distributions, $2,164,251; giving activities include $1,629,826 for 67 grants (high: $221,788; low: $282).
Purpose and activities: The foundation is dedicated to providing support to local nonprofit organizations which strive to improve the communities it serves and to assist projects that reflect the philosophy of its founder. The foundation funds projects which

address community needs in the areas of education, history and recreation.
Fields of interest: Museums; Historic preservation/historical societies; Elementary/secondary education; Education; Human services; YM/YWCAs & YM/YWHAs; Family services; Community/economic development.
Limitations: Applications accepted. Giving limited to Door County, WI, with emphasis on Nasewaupee, Sevastopol and Sturgeon Bay. No support for businesses, for-profit organizations, or projects of organizations whose policies or practices discriminate on the basis of ethnic origin, gender, race, religion or sexual orientation. No grants to individuals, or for general operating support for ongoing activities, debt retirement, endowment funds, annual appeals, general fund drives, special events, or sponsorships; no loans.
Publications: Application guidelines.
Application information: Application form available on foundation web site. Proposals sent by mail or fax are not accepted. Late applications will be considered, but not until the following month. Application form required.
Deadline(s): 1st of each month
Final notification: Applications are reviewed monthly
Officer and Board Members:* Julie LaLuzerne,* Grant Prog. Mgr.; Mike Madden; Karl May; Roger Wood; Cap Wulf.
EIN: 391683091

9926
Agustin A. Ramirez, Jr. Family Foundation ✧
411 E. Wisconsin Ave., Ste. 2040
Milwaukee, WI 53202-4497

Established in 1995 in WI.
Donors: Agustin A. Ramirez, Jr.; HUSCO International, Inc.
Foundation type: Independent foundation.
Financial data (yr. ended 12/31/12): Assets, $1,152,498 (M); gifts received, $1,450,000; expenditures, $451,996; qualifying distributions, $451,339; giving activities include $288,000 for 7 grants (high: $100,000; low: $3,000), and $160,250 for 175 grants to individuals (high: $2,500; low: $500).
Fields of interest: Higher education.
Type of support: Scholarships—to individuals.
Limitations: Applications accepted. Giving primarily to residents of WI.
Application information: Application form required.
Initial approach: Request application form
Deadline(s): Apr.
Trustees: Agustin A. Ramirez, Jr.; Rebecca Page Ramirez; Eric J. Van Vugt.
EIN: 396626017

9927
Rath Foundation, Inc. ✧
P.O. Box 80
Janesville, WI 53547-0080
Application address: c/o James D. Dodson, Pres., P.O. Box 1990, Janesville, WI 53547, tel.: (608) 754-9090

Established in 1989 in WI.
Donor: V. Duane Rath.
Foundation type: Independent foundation.
Financial data (yr. ended 12/31/12): Assets, $23,558,168 (M); expenditures, $4,373,661; qualifying distributions, $4,202,593; giving activities include $4,157,690 for 13 grants (high: $710,026; low: $84,447).
Fields of interest: Higher education; Higher education, university; Medical school/education; Education; Foundations (community).
Limitations: Applications accepted. Giving primarily in WI. No grants to individuals.
Application information: Application form not required.
Initial approach: Letter
Deadline(s): None
Officers: James D. Dodson, Pres.; Robert Dodson, V.P.; James R. Sanger, V.P.; Kate M. Fleming, Secy.
EIN: 391657654

9928
RDK Foundation ✧
c/o US Bank, N.A.
P.O. Box 7900
Madison, WI 53707-7900

Established in 1984 in WI.
Donor: Ruth DeYoung Kohler.
Foundation type: Independent foundation.
Financial data (yr. ended 06/30/13): Assets, $15,040,091 (M); gifts received, $1,500,000; expenditures, $734,060; qualifying distributions, $624,000; giving activities include $624,000 for grants.
Purpose and activities: Support primarily to an arts center, as well as for education and human services.
Fields of interest: Arts, multipurpose centers/programs; Higher education; Education; Human services.
Limitations: Applications not accepted. No grants to individuals.
Application information: Unsolicited requests for funds not accepted.
Trustees: Ruth DeYoung Kohler; U.S. Bank, N.A.
EIN: 391524311
Selected grants: The following grants are a representative sample of this grantmaker's funding activity:
$160,000 to Kohler Arts Center, Sheboygan, WI, 2011. For general purpose.
$80,000 to YMCA of Sheboygan County, Sheboygan, WI, 2011. For general purpose.
$25,000 to Aldo Leopold Foundation, Baraboo, WI, 2011. For general purpose.
$19,200 to Beloit College, Beloit, WI, 2011. For general purpose.
$15,000 to Edgewood College, Madison, WI, 2011. For general purpose.
$15,000 to Friends of Fred Smith, Phillips, WI, 2011. For general purpose.

9929
Reiman Foundation, Inc. ✧
(formerly Reiman Charitable Foundation, Inc.)
115 S. 84th St., Ste. 221
Milwaukee, WI 53214-1474 (414) 456-0600
Contact: Michael J. Hipp, Secy.
FAX: (414) 456-0606;
E-mail: reimanfoundation@hexagoninc.com; Main URL: http://www.reimanfoundation.org

Established in 1986 in WI.
Donors: Roy J. Reiman; Roberta M. Reiman; Scott J. Reiman; Joni R. Winston; Cynthia A. Lambert; Julia M. Ellis; Terrin S. Riemer.
Foundation type: Independent foundation.
Financial data (yr. ended 12/31/12): Assets, $121,589,825 (M); gifts received, $6,000,000; expenditures, $14,147,671; qualifying distributions, $11,839,852; giving activities include $11,839,852 for 168 grants (high: $1,000,000; low: $100).
Purpose and activities: Giving primarily for education, health care, and children's initiatives.
Fields of interest: Education; Health care; Children, services; Children.
Limitations: Applications accepted. Giving primarily in WI; giving also in CO, GA, IA, MO, and NY. No grants to individuals.
Publications: Application guidelines.
Application information: The foundation will acknowledge receipt of application. See foundation web site for further details. Application form not required.
Initial approach: Letter
Deadline(s): None
Officers and Directors:* Scott J. Reiman,* Pres.; Brian F. Fleischmann,* V.P.; Roberta M. Reiman,* V.P.; Roy J. Reiman,* V.P.; Michael J. Hipp,* Secy.; Julia M. Ellis; Troy G. Hildebrandt.
EIN: 391570264

9930
D.B. and Marjorie A. Reinhart Family Foundation ✧
(formerly D. B. Reinhart Family Foundation)
P.O. Box 2228
La Crosse, WI 54602-2228

Established in 1987 in WI.
Donors: Marjorie A. Reinhart†; D.B. Reinhart Enterprises; Reinhart Institutional Foods; Marjorie A. Reinhart Revocable Trust.
Foundation type: Independent foundation.
Financial data (yr. ended 08/31/13): Assets, $8,283,163 (M); expenditures, $9,843,081; qualifying distributions, $9,821,669; giving activities include $9,821,669 for 5 grants (high: $3,951,583; low: $300,000).
Purpose and activities: Giving primarily for education, children, youth and social services, and Roman Catholic agencies and churches.
Fields of interest: Higher education; Human services; Children/youth, services; Catholic agencies & churches.
Limitations: Applications not accepted. Giving primarily in La Crosse, WI. No grants to individuals.
Application information: Contributes only to pre-selected organizations.
Trustees: Gerald E. Connolly; Patti Harrison; Nancy Hengel.
EIN: 391564353
Selected grants: The following grants are a representative sample of this grantmaker's funding activity:
$300,000 to University of Wisconsin Foundation, La Crosse, WI, 2011.

9931
The Oscar Rennebohm Foundation, Inc. ✧
P.O. Box 5187
Madison, WI 53705-0187 (608) 274-1916
Contact: Steven F. Skolaski, Pres. and Dir.

Incorporated in 1949 in WI.
Donors: Oscar Rennebohm†; Leona Sondregger.
Foundation type: Independent foundation.
Financial data (yr. ended 12/31/13): Assets, $55,619,470 (M); expenditures, $2,950,561; qualifying distributions, $2,665,964; giving activities include $2,483,000 for 8 grants (high: $1,520,000; low: $13,000).
Fields of interest: Higher education; Education; Human services.
Type of support: Building/renovation; Equipment; Research.
Limitations: Applications accepted. Giving limited to the Madison, WI area.
Application information:
Initial approach: 1-page letter
Deadline(s): None
Officers and Directors: Steven F. Skolaski,* Pres.; Patrick E. Coyle,* V.P.; Curtis F. Hastings,* Secy.; Mary W. Gulbrandsen,* Vice-Secy.; Gary L. Schaefer,* Treas.
EIN: 396039252
Selected grants: The following grants are a representative sample of this grantmaker's funding activity:
$100,000 to Saint Marys Hospital Foundation, Madison, WI, 2011.

9932
Rexnord Foundation Inc. ✧
c/o Tax Dept.
P.O. Box 2191
Milwaukee, WI 53201-2191

Incorporated in 1953 in WI.
Donors: Rexnord Industries LLC; Praveen Jeyarajah.
Foundation type: Company-sponsored foundation.
Financial data (yr. ended 10/31/13): Assets, $4,227,031 (M); gifts received, $256,000; expenditures, $529,932; qualifying distributions, $517,886; giving activities include $517,886 for 351 grants (high: $100,000; low: $50).
Purpose and activities: The foundation supports organizations involved with arts and culture, education, multiple sclerosis, medical research, and human services.
Fields of interest: Museums (art); Arts; Elementary/secondary education; Higher education; Education; Multiple sclerosis; Medical research; Food services; Children/youth, services; Human services; United Ways and Federated Giving Programs.
Type of support: Building/renovation; Program development; Employee matching gifts; Employee-related scholarships.
Limitations: Applications accepted. Giving primarily in areas of company operations, with some emphasis on Milwaukee, WI. No support for religious organizations. No grants to individuals (except for employee-related scholarships), or for endowments.
Publications: Application guidelines.
Application information: Application form required.
Initial approach: Proposal
Copies of proposal: 1
Deadline(s): May
Board meeting date(s): 2 or 3 times per year
Officers and Directors:* C. R. Roy,* Pres.; Patricia Whaley,* V.P.; Linda Groth,* Secy.; Mark Peterson,* Treas.; T.A. Adams; R. M. MacQueen; R.R. Wallis; W. E. Schauer.
EIN: 396042029

9933
Michael T. Riordan Family Foundation ✧
c/o Michael T. Riordan
W3563 Meredith Ln.
Green Lake, WI 54941-9650

Established in 2001 in WI.
Donor: Michael T. Riordan.
Foundation type: Independent foundation.
Financial data (yr. ended 12/31/13): Assets, $10,412,903 (M); expenditures, $520,208; qualifying distributions, $452,441; giving activities include $450,000 for 44 grants (high: $40,000; low: $80).
Fields of interest: Education; Health organizations, association; Boys & girls clubs; Human services; Children/youth, services; Foundations (private grantmaking); Catholic agencies & churches.
Limitations: Applications not accepted. Giving primarily in Green Bay, WI. No grants to individuals.
Application information: Contributes only to pre-selected organizations.
Trustee: Michael T. Riordan.
EIN: 306000348
Selected grants: The following grants are a representative sample of this grantmaker's funding activity:
$50,000 to Childrens Hospital Los Angeles, Los Angeles, CA, 2011. To further program services.
$20,000 to CooperRiis, Mill Spring, NC, 2011. To further program services.
$20,000 to People Assisting the Homeless, Los Angeles, CA, 2011. To further program services.
$15,000 to Freedom House Ministries, Green Bay, WI, 2011. To further program services.
$15,000 to N.E.W. Community Clinic, Green Bay, WI, 2011. To further program services.
$10,000 to Books for Africa, Saint Paul, MN, 2011. To further program services.
$10,000 to Boys and Girls Club of Green Bay, Green Bay, WI, 2011. To further program services.
$10,000 to Just Detention International, Los Angeles, CA, 2011. To further program services.
$10,000 to Special Operations Warrior Foundation, Tampa, FL, 2011. To further program services.
$10,000 to United Way of Brown County, Green Bay, WI, 2011. To further program services.

9934
Rockwell Automation Charitable Corp. ✧
c/o Marie Olmsted
1201 S. 2nd St
Milwaukee, WI 53204-2410
Contact: Marie Olmsted
E-mail: RACharitable_Corp@ra.rockwell.com; E-mail for Milwaukee, WI: Marie Olmsted, meolmsted@ra.rockwell.com, 414-382-3382; e-mail for Cleveland, OH: Marcia Hendershot, mjhendershot@ra.rockwell.com.; Main URL: http://www.rockwellautomation.com/rockwellautomation/about-us/community/overview.page?

Established in 2003 in WI.
Donors: Rockwell International Corporation Trust; Rockwell Automation.
Foundation type: Company-sponsored foundation.
Financial data (yr. ended 09/30/13): Assets, $7,651,720 (M); gifts received, $7,000,000; expenditures, $5,706,247; qualifying distributions, $5,705,613; giving activities include $5,283,508 for 48 grants (high: $1,000,000; low: $3,200), and $360,008 for employee matching gifts.
Purpose and activities: The foundation supports programs designed to address education and workforce development; health and human services; arts and culture; and civic and disaster relief. Special emphasis is directed toward programs designed to promote K-12 science, technology, engineering, and math education.
Fields of interest: Performing arts; Performing arts, orchestras; Arts; Elementary/secondary education; Education; Disasters, preparedness/services; Boys & girls clubs; Human services; United Ways and Federated Giving Programs; Mathematics; Engineering/technology; Science; Public affairs; Women; Economically disadvantaged.
Type of support: Employee matching gifts; General/operating support; Program development; Scholarship funds.
Limitations: Applications accepted. Giving in areas of company operations, with emphasis on Greater Cleveland, OH and Milwaukee, WI. No support for religious organizations for religious purposes, or fraternal or social organizations. No grants to individuals, or for unsolicited capital campaigns, or unsolicited multi-year pledges.
Publications: Application guidelines.
Application information: Application form required.
Initial approach: Complete online application for organizations located in the U.S.; e-mail application contact for organizations located in Cleveland, OH and Milwaukee, WI
Deadline(s): Oct. 15 and Apr. 15
Board meeting date(s): Semi-annually
Final notification: 3 to 6 months
Officers and Directors:* Keith D. Nosbusch,* Chair.; Doug M. Hagerman, V.P. and Treas.; Theodore D. Crandall, V.P.; Susan J. Schmitt, V.P.; Eileen M. Walter, Secy.
Trustee: BMO Harris Bank, N.A.
EIN: 481307009
Selected grants: The following grants are a representative sample of this grantmaker's funding activity:
$500,000 to UWM Foundation, Milwaukee, WI, 2013. For Headquarter.
$20,000 to Milwaukee Repertory Theater, Milwaukee, WI, 2013. For Headquarters.

9935
Thomas J. Rolfs Foundation ✧
P.O. Box 70
Nashotah, WI 53058-0070
Contact: Theodore R. Rolfs, Secy.-Treas.

Established in 1959 in WI.
Donors: Amity Leather Products Co.; Mary K. Rolfs Charitable Lead Annuity Trust; Paul J. Tilleman; Sarah A. Duffy.
Foundation type: Independent foundation.
Financial data (yr. ended 12/31/13): Assets, $23,787,333 (M); expenditures, $1,251,160; qualifying distributions, $1,147,566; giving activities include $1,081,500 for 31 grants (high: $250,000; low: $1,000).
Fields of interest: Higher education; Education; Environment; Health care; Human services; Christian agencies & churches.
Limitations: Applications accepted. Giving primarily in WI, some emphasis on Milwaukee and West Bend.
Application information: Application form required.
Initial approach: Letter
Deadline(s): None

Officers: Claire L. Rolfs, Pres.; Thomas J. Rolfs, Jr., V.P.; Theodore R. Rolfs, Secy.-Treas.
Director: Janet M. Storr.
EIN: 396043350
Selected grants: The following grants are a representative sample of this grantmaker's funding activity:
$100,000 to Notre Dame University, Philippines, 2011. For general support.
$6,000 to Friends of Abused Families of Washington County, West Bend, WI, 2011. For general support.

9936
Roundy's Foundation, Inc. ✧
P.O. Box 473
Milwaukee, WI 53201-0473
Main URL: http://www.roundys.com/Home.gsn

Established in 2003 in WI.
Donors: Roundy's, Inc.; Roundy's Supermarkets, Inc.
Foundation type: Company-sponsored foundation.
Financial data (yr. ended 12/31/13): Assets, $1,156,278 (M); gifts received, $160,808; expenditures, $1,321,161; qualifying distributions, $1,321,161; giving activities include $1,003,114 for 163 grants (high: $4,000; low: $500).
Purpose and activities: The foundation supports programs designed to address literacy, hunger relief, and families in crisis.
Fields of interest: Education; Agriculture/food; Religion.
Type of support: General/operating support; Annual campaigns; Capital campaigns; Program development; Donated products; In-kind gifts.
Limitations: Applications accepted. Giving primarily in areas of company operations in IL, MN, and WI. No support for religious organizations not of direct benefit to the entire community, educational institutions for regular programs, foundations, or athletic teams. No grants to individuals, or for capital campaigns or sporting events.
Publications: Application guidelines; Annual report (including application guidelines); Program policy statement.
Application information: Application form required.
Initial approach: See Website for application form
Deadline(s): None
Directors: Flamont T. Butler; Darren W. Karst; Robert A. Mariano; Jessie W. Terry; Sarah Jane Voichcik.
EIN: 200299349
Selected grants: The following grants are a representative sample of this grantmaker's funding activity:
$20,000 to Urban League, Milwaukee, Milwaukee, WI, 2011.
$15,500 to Milwaukee Womens Center, Milwaukee, WI, 2011.
$8,000 to Boys and Girls Clubs of Greater Milwaukee, Milwaukee, WI, 2011.
$5,000 to Hope House of Milwaukee, Milwaukee, WI, 2011.
$5,000 to Junior League of Minneapolis, Minneapolis, MN, 2011.
$5,000 to Saint Vincent de Paul Society of Milwaukee, Milwaukee, WI, 2011.
$4,918 to Hope House of Milwaukee, Milwaukee, WI, 2011.
$4,500 to AIDS Resource Center of Wisconsin, Milwaukee, WI, 2011.
$2,478 to AIDS Resource Center of Wisconsin, Milwaukee, WI, 2011.

9937
Pleasant T. Rowland Foundation, Inc. ✧
3415 Gateway Rd., Ste. 200
Brookfield, WI 53045-5111
Contact: Grants Mgr.
Application address: 6120 University Ave., Middletown, WI 53562, tel.: (608) 729-2811

Established in 1997 in WI.
Donor: Pleasant T. Rowland.
Foundation type: Independent foundation.
Financial data (yr. ended 12/31/12): Assets, $52,822,527 (M); expenditures, $4,952,694; qualifying distributions, $3,934,960; giving activities include $3,934,960 for 88 grants (high: $1,600,000; low: $100).
Purpose and activities: Giving primarily for arts, education and historic preservation.
Fields of interest: Historic preservation/historical societies; Arts; Education.
Type of support: Program development; Matching/challenge support.
Limitations: Applications accepted. Giving primarily in WI, with emphasis on Dane County. No support for religious or political organizations. No grants to individuals.
Publications: Application guidelines.
Application information: Application form required.
Initial approach: Telephone
Copies of proposal: 1
Deadline(s): June 30 and Nov. 30
Board meeting date(s): Apr., July, Oct., and Dec.
Final notification: 4 - 6 weeks
Officers and Directors: Pleasant T. Rowland, Pres.; Rhona E. Vogel, Secy.; Barbara Thiele Carr; Walter Jerome Frautschi; Valerie Tripp; Catharine B. Waller.
Number of staff: 1 full-time professional.
EIN: 391868295
Selected grants: The following grants are a representative sample of this grantmaker's funding activity:
$1,600,000 to Saint Benedict Center, Madison, WI, 2012. For land conservation of Sumner Property.
$1,506,350 to Rowland Reading Foundation, Middleton, WI, 2012. For phonics-based reading program for K-2 elementary students.
$122,328 to Madison Community Foundation, Madison, WI, 2012. For Great Performance Fund for Theater, created specifically to endow a competitive grant to support professional theater in Madison's Overture Center for the Arts.
$65,000 to Madison Symphony Orchestra, Madison, WI, 2012. For two concerts, one withGarrick Ohlsson and one with Saint Thomas Choir of Men and Boys.
$50,000 to Madison Opera, Madison, WI, 2012. For operating support.
$35,000 to Madison Museum of Contemporary Art, Madison, WI, 2012. For operating support.
$27,000 to Madison Symphony Orchestra, Madison, WI, 2012. For summer organ concert series.
$25,000 to Chazen Museum of Art, Madison, WI, 2012. For operating support.
$19,514 to Wells College, Aurora, NY, 2012. For 50th reunion 1962 Class Gift.
$12,500 to Voices from the American Land, Taos, NM, 2012. For general support.

9938
Runzheimer Foundation, Inc. ✧
1 Runzheimer Pkwy.
Waterford, WI 53185-3599

Established in NY.
Donor: Runzheimer Internatioanl Ltd.
Foundation type: Independent foundation.
Financial data (yr. ended 06/30/13): Assets, $4,071 (M); gifts received, $972,742; expenditures, $970,647; qualifying distributions, $960,571; giving activities include $960,571 for grants.
Fields of interest: Secondary school/education; Education; Human services.
Limitations: Applications not accepted. Giving primarily in WI.
Application information: Unsolicited requests for funds not accepted.
Officers: Gregory Harper, Pres.; Jackie Strelow, Secy.; Dawn Kirby, Treas.
EIN: 272914749
Selected grants: The following grants are a representative sample of this grantmaker's funding activity:
$500 to Boy Scouts of America, Potawatomi Area Council, Waukesha, WI, 2013. For general support.

9939
Edward and Hannah M. Rutledge Charities, Inc. ✧
(formerly Edward Rutledge Charity)
P.O. Box 758
Chippewa Falls, WI 54729-0738

Incorporated in 1911 in WI.
Donor: Edward Rutledge†.
Foundation type: Independent foundation.
Financial data (yr. ended 05/31/13): Assets, $23,185,304 (M); gifts received, $1,231; expenditures, $1,114,950; qualifying distributions, $1,033,869; giving activities include $669,645 for 72 grants (high: $60,000; low: $100), $200,950 for 169 grants to individuals (high: $3,000; low: $400), and $657 for loans to individuals.
Purpose and activities: Giving to furnish relief and charity for the worthy poor and to aid charitable associations or institutions; also administers college scholarship program.
Fields of interest: Education; Human services; Youth, services; Aging, centers/services; Economically disadvantaged.
Type of support: General/operating support; Program development.
Limitations: Giving limited to Chippewa County, WI. No grants for endowment funds.
Application information: Application form required for scholarships and other grants to individuals.
Initial approach: Letter
Copies of proposal: 1
Deadline(s): Scholarship applications must be submitted by June 1; no deadline for other grants
Board meeting date(s): Twice a month
Final notification: 2 months for scholarships
Officers and Directors:* Gerald J. Naiberg,* Pres.; David Hancock,* V.P.; Thomas Leinenkugel,* Secy.-Treas.; Kimberly J. King, Exec. Mgr.
Number of staff: 1 full-time professional; 1 part-time support.
EIN: 390806178

Selected grants: The following grants are a representative sample of this grantmaker's funding activity:
$43,917 to Starting Points, Chippewa Falls, WI, 2012.
$30,000 to Chippewa Falls Area Senior Center, Chippewa Falls, WI, 2012.
$26,500 to Family Support Center, Chippewa Falls, WI, 2012. For parenting program.
$25,000 to United Way of Chippewa County, Chippewa Falls, WI, 2012.
$15,500 to Chippewa Valley Health Clinic, Eau Claire, WI, 2012.
$15,000 to Family Literacy Program, 2012.
$9,000 to Salvation Army, WI, 2012.
$4,000 to Chippewa Area Food Pantry, Chippewa Falls, WI, 2012.
$3,000 to Chippewa County Department of Public Health, Chippewa Falls, WI, 2012. For charity outreach program.
$1,000 to Chippewa County Association for Home and Community Education, Chippewa Falls, WI, 2012. For First Book Project.

9940
Ryan Memorial Foundation ✧
10936 N. Port Washington Rd., Ste. 305
Mequon, WI 53092-5031

Established in 1996 in PA.
Donor: Independent foundation.

Foundation type: Independent foundation.
Financial data (yr. ended 12/31/13): Assets, $29,411,065 (M); expenditures, $1,494,085; qualifying distributions, $1,489,519; giving activities include $1,486,649 for 55 grants (high: $179,440; low: $100).
Purpose and activities: Giving primarily for education, including Roman Catholic high schools; funding also for social services, and other Roman Catholic agencies.
Fields of interest: Arts; Secondary school/education; Higher education; Human services; Children/youth, services; Foundations (private grantmaking); United Ways and Federated Giving Programs; Catholic federated giving programs; Catholic agencies & churches.
Limitations: Applications not accepted. Giving primarily in PA, with emphasis on Pittsburgh. No grants to individuals.
Application information: Contributes only to pre-selected organizations.
Trustees: Julia Ryan Parker; Daniel H. Ryan; John T. Ryan III; Michael Denis Ryan; William F. Ryan; Irene R. Shaw.
EIN: 251781266

9941
Sadoff Family Foundation ✧
c/o Gary Sadoff, Badger Liquor Co.
850 S. Morris St.
Fond du Lac, WI 54935-5649

Established in 1999 in WI.
Donor: Badger Liquor Co.
Foundation type: Independent foundation.
Financial data (yr. ended 12/31/13): Assets, $2,239,004 (M); gifts received, $2,000,000; expenditures, $607,391; qualifying distributions, $607,300; giving activities include $607,300 for 25 grants (high: $350,000; low: $500).
Fields of interest: Arts; Health care; Human services.
Limitations: Applications not accepted. Giving primarily in Fond du Lac, WI. No grants to individuals.
Application information: Contributes only to pre-selected organizations.
Trustees: Arthur Callistein; Amy Sadoff; Gary Sadoff; Victoria Sadoff.
EIN: 396713550

9942
Schneider National Foundation, Inc. ✧
P.O. Box 2545
301 S. Packerland Dr.
Green Bay, WI 54306-2545 (920) 592-2000
Contact: Mary Gronnert
E-mail: foundation@schneider.com; Additional tel.: (800) 558-6767 ext. 592-3904; Main URL: http://www.schneider.com/About_Schneider/Schneider_Foundation/index.htm

Established in 1983.
Donor: Schneider National, Inc.
Foundation type: Company-sponsored foundation.
Financial data (yr. ended 12/31/13): Assets, $71,158 (M); gifts received, $915,000; expenditures, $897,748; qualifying distributions, $897,748; giving activities include $897,748 for grants.
Purpose and activities: The foundation supports organizations involved with arts and culture, children, education, and health and human services.
Fields of interest: Arts; Higher education; Education, reading; Education; Public health, physical fitness; Health care; Housing/shelter, development; Disasters, preparedness/services; Boys & girls clubs; Youth development; Salvation Army; Children/youth, services; Family services; Developmentally disabled, centers & services; Human services; Community/economic development; United Ways and Federated Giving Programs.
Type of support: General/operating support; Continuing support; Capital campaigns; Equipment; Emergency funds; Program development; Scholarship funds; Employee volunteer services; Use of facilities; Donated equipment; In-kind gifts.
Limitations: Applications accepted. Giving primarily in areas of company operations, with emphasis on Green Bay, WI; giving also in Canada, China, Mexico, and the Netherlands. No support for religious organizations. No grants to individuals or for political campaigns.
Publications: Application guidelines.
Application information: Application form required.
Initial approach: Complete online application form
Deadline(s): None
Officers: Steve Matheys, Pres.; LuEllen Oskey, Secy.-Treas.
EIN: 391457870
Selected grants: The following grants are a representative sample of this grantmaker's funding activity:
$2,000 to Ann and Robert H. Lurie Children's Hospital of Chicago Foundation, Chicago, IL, 2011. For general support.
$2,000 to Freedom House, Washington, DC, 2011. For general support.
$2,000 to North Texas Food Bank, Dallas, TX, 2011. For general support.
$1,000 to Freedom House, Washington, DC, 2011. For general support.

9943
Sensient Technologies Foundation, Inc. ✧
777 E. Wisconsin Ave.
Milwaukee, WI 53202-5304

Incorporated in 1958 in WI.
Donors: Sensient Technologies Corp.; Universal Foods Corp.
Foundation type: Company-sponsored foundation.
Financial data (yr. ended 12/31/13): Assets, $13,165,372 (M); expenditures, $694,402; qualifying distributions, $685,489; giving activities include $685,489 for 109 grants (high: $50,000; low: $25).
Purpose and activities: The foundation supports organizations involved with arts and culture, education, health, mental health, medical research, hunger, nutrition, human services, community development, minorities, and homeless people.
Fields of interest: Arts; Human services; Religion.
Limitations: Applications not accepted. Giving primarily in Indianapolis, IN, St. Louis, MO, and Milwaukee, WI. No support for sectarian, religious, fraternal, or partisan political organizations. No grants to individuals.
Application information: Unsolicited requests for funds not accepted.
Officers: Kenneth P. Manning, Pres.; Richard F. Hobbs, V.P.; Paul Manning, V.P.; Stephen J. Rolfs, V.P.; Douglas L. Arnold, Secy.-Treas.
EIN: 396044488

9944
Sentry Insurance Foundation, Inc. ✧
(formerly Sentry Foundation, Inc.)
1800 N. Point Dr.
Stevens Point, WI 54481-1283 (715) 346-6000
Main URL: https://www.sentry.com/sentry-insurance-foundation.aspx

Incorporated in 1963 in WI.
Donor: Sentry Insurance.
Foundation type: Company-sponsored foundation.
Financial data (yr. ended 12/31/13): Assets, $9,112,510 (M); gifts received, $1,573,971; expenditures, $2,895,472; giving activities include $1,421,500 for 73 grants (high: $822,087; low: $500), and $456,190 for 211 employee matching gifts.
Purpose and activities: The foundation supports organizations involved with fine arts and community services. Special emphasis is directed toward educational initiatives.
Fields of interest: Visual arts; Performing arts; Arts; Higher education; Education, reading; Education; Boys & girls clubs; YM/YWCAs & YM/YWHAs; Children, services; Community/economic development; United Ways and Federated Giving Programs.
Type of support: Employee-related scholarships; General/operating support; Continuing support; Scholarship funds; Sponsorships; Employee matching gifts.
Limitations: Applications accepted. Giving primarily in areas of company operations in WI. No support for religious organizations.
Application information: Application form required.
Initial approach: Letter
Copies of proposal: 1
Deadline(s): None
Officers and Directors:* James J. Weishan, Chair. and Pres.; Peter G. McPartland,* V.P.; Kenneth J.

Erier, Secy.; Carol P. Sanders, Treas.; Michael J. Williams.
EIN: 391037370
Selected grants: The following grants are a representative sample of this grantmaker's funding activity:
$20,000 to Lawrence University, Appleton, WI, 2011.
$20,000 to Milwaukee School of Engineering, Milwaukee, WI, 2011.
$20,000 to University of Wisconsin, Eau Claire, WI, 2011.
$20,000 to University of Wisconsin, Milwaukee, WI, 2011.
$20,000 to University of Wisconsin, Oshkosh, WI, 2011.
$20,000 to University of Wisconsin, River Falls, WI, 2011.
$20,000 to University of Wisconsin, Stevens Point, WI, 2011.
$20,000 to University of Wisconsin-Green Bay, Green Bay, WI, 2011.
$20,000 to University of Wisconsin-Superior, Superior, WI, 2011.
$20,000 to University of Wisconsin-Whitewater, Whitewater, WI, 2011.

9945
Herman and Gwen Shapiro Foundation ✧
c/o David W. Reinecke, Foley & Lardner LLP
P.O. Box 1497
Madison, WI 53701-1497 (608) 258-4224

Established in 1996 in WI by the late Herman and Gwen Shapiro.
Donors: Gwendolyn H. Shapiro†; Gwen Shapiro Revocable Trust.
Foundation type: Independent foundation.
Financial data (yr. ended 07/31/13): Assets, $11,710,945 (M); expenditures, $771,886; qualifying distributions, $710,537; giving activities include $677,000 for 2 grants (high: $652,000; low: $25,000).
Purpose and activities: Giving primarily for scholarships for the study of medicine and nursing at the University of Wisconsin.
Fields of interest: Medical school/education; Nursing school/education.
Type of support: Scholarship funds.
Limitations: Applications not accepted. Giving limited to Madison, WI.
Application information: Unsolicited requests for funds not accepted.
Board meeting date(s): Quarterly
Officer and Trustees:* David W. Reinecke,* Secy.; Dean Robert N. Golden, M.D.; Henry W. Ipsen; Dean Katharyn A. May, DNSc., RN; John W. Thompson; David G. Walsh; John B. Walsh.
EIN: 391941051

9946
Siebert Lutheran Foundation, Inc. ✧
300 N. Corporate Dr., Ste. 200
Brookfield, WI 53045-5862 (262) 754-9160
Contact: Ronald D. Jones, Pres.
FAX: (262) 754-9162;
E-mail: contactus@siebertfoundation.org; Main URL: http://www.siebertfoundation.org

Incorporated in 1952 in WI.
Donors: A.F. Siebert†; Reginald L. Siebert†.
Foundation type: Independent foundation.
Financial data (yr. ended 12/31/13): Assets, $96,400,186 (M); expenditures, $4,997,289; qualifying distributions, $4,238,960; giving activities include $3,891,187 for 87 grants (high: $257,000; low: $1,200).
Purpose and activities: The Siebert Lutheran Foundation, using its resources, stewardship and relationships, enables the Lutheran community to be more collaborative, creative, and effective in sharing the Word of God, educating and instilling Christian values in youth, and serving people in need. The foundation's areas of interest include sharing the Gospel through Lutheran Churches and Organizations, Breaking the Poverty Cycle through Faith-Based Education, and Supporting Bible-Based Human Services. Special grants are made to seminary students who are members of Lutheran churches in Wisconsin.
Fields of interest: Elementary/secondary education; Education, early childhood education; Child development, education; Secondary school/education; Higher education; Education; Youth development, religion; Human services; Child development, services; Protestant federated giving programs; Protestant agencies & churches; Religion; Minorities; Economically disadvantaged.
Type of support: Program development; Seed money; Consulting services; Matching/challenge support.
Limitations: Applications accepted. Giving primarily in WI. No support for one hundred percent of a project. No grants to individuals directly, or for endowment funds, trusts, scholarships or fellowships; no loans.
Publications: Application guidelines; Annual report.
Application information: On-line grant application required. Grantees are required to sign Grant Agreement Form. Grantees are required to submit a final report after project completion. Application form not required.
Initial approach: Letter of Inquiry part of on-line grant application.
Deadline(s): Feb. 1, Aug. 1, and Nov. 1
Board meeting date(s): Jan., Apr., July, and Oct.
Final notification: 1 week after board meeting
Officers and Directors:* Knute Jacobson,* Chair.; Brenda Skelton,* Vice-Chair.; Ronald D. Jones, Pres.; Kurt Bechtold,* Secy.; Kurtiss R. Krueger,* Treas.; David W. Romoser; John Sellars; Julie Van Cleave; John Zimdars.
Number of staff: 1 full-time professional; 2 full-time support.
EIN: 396050046
Selected grants: The following grants are a representative sample of this grantmaker's funding activity:
$400,000 to Saint Marcus Lutheran Church, Milwaukee, WI, 2011. For construction of new school.
$350,000 to Time of Grace Ministry, Milwaukee, WI, 2011. To increase broadcasting area.
$200,000 to Wisconsin Lutheran College, Milwaukee, WI, 2011. For continuing support for Pathway to College.
$150,000 to Evangelical Lutheran Church in America, Northwest Synod of Wisconsin, Chetek, WI, 2011. For Bishop's Initiative Phase III.
$125,000 to Feeding America Eastern Wisconsin, Milwaukee, WI, 2011. For Lutheran food pantries.
$50,000 to Evangelical Lutheran Church in America, Greater Milwaukee Synod, Milwaukee, WI, 2011. For continuing support of six-synod educational taskforce.
$25,000 to Hunger Task Force, Milwaukee, WI, 2011. For food for Lutheran food pantries.
$9,660 to Council on Foundations, Arlington, VA, 2011.
$7,000 to Kettle Moraine Lutheran High School, Jackson, WI, 2011. For tuition assistance.
$4,000 to Our Saviors Lutheran Church, Milwaukee, WI, 2011. For summer youth program.

9947
A.O. Smith Foundation, Inc. ✧
c/o Tax Dept.
P.O. Box 245008
Milwaukee, WI 53224-9508
Contact: Mark A. Petrarca, Secy. and Dir.
Main URL: http://www.aosmith.com/About/Detail.aspx?id=132&ekmensel=c580fa7b_8_0_132_6

Incorporated in 1955 in WI.
Donor: A.O. Smith Corp.
Foundation type: Company-sponsored foundation.
Financial data (yr. ended 12/31/13): Assets, $5,513,781 (M); gifts received, $1,500,000; expenditures, $1,454,027; qualifying distributions, $1,452,315; giving activities include $1,452,315 for 178 grants (high: $175,000; low: $200).
Purpose and activities: The foundation supports programs designed to strengthen higher education throughout the country; promote the civic, cultural, and social welfare of communities; and advance medical research and improve local health services.
Fields of interest: Arts; Higher education; Hospitals (general); Health care; Medical research; Human services; Community/economic development; United Ways and Federated Giving Programs; Public affairs.
Type of support: Annual campaigns; Building/renovation; Capital campaigns; Continuing support; Employee matching gifts; Employee volunteer services; General/operating support; Program development; Scholarship funds; Sponsorships.
Limitations: Applications accepted. Giving primarily in areas of company operations in KY, NC, SC, TN, TX, WA, and WI. No support for political or lobbying organizations. No grants to individuals.
Publications: Application guidelines; Annual report (including application guidelines).
Application information: Application form required.
Initial approach: Letter
Copies of proposal: 1
Deadline(s): None
Board meeting date(s): June and Dec.
Officers and Directors:* Bruce M. Smith,* Pres.; Mark A. Petrarca,* Secy.; John J. Kita, Treas.; Paul W. Jones; Edward J. O'Connor; Roger S. Smith.
Number of staff: 1 part-time support.
EIN: 396076924
Selected grants: The following grants are a representative sample of this grantmaker's funding activity:
$50,000 to Empower Me Day Camp, Lebanon, TN, 2012. To support continuing Programs.
$50,000 to Greater Milwaukee Foundation, Milwaukee, WI, 2012. To support job training Programs.
$40,000 to Cheatham County Chamber Foundation, Ashland City, TN, 2012. To support of workforce development.
$33,500 to United Performing Arts Fund, Milwaukee, WI, 2012. To support Performing Arts Center activities.

$20,000 to University of Wisconsin, Business School, Milwaukee, WI, 2012. To support of international business initiatives.
$18,000 to Milwaukee Symphony Orchestra, Milwaukee, WI, 2012. To support Milwaukee Symphony activities.
$17,500 to Discovery World, Milwaukee, WI, 2012. To support of Discovery World at Pier Wisconsin.
$10,000 to Milwaukee Public Museum, Milwaukee, WI, 2012. To support scientific and educational Programs.
$5,000 to Medical College of Wisconsin, Milwaukee, WI, 2012. For Contribute to Healthcare 2012 campaign.
$5,000 to Next Door Foundation, Milwaukee, WI, 2012. To support of Programs and services.

9948
Daniel M. Soref Charitable Trust ✧
c/o Audrey J. Strnad
P.O. Box 170504
Milwaukee, WI 53217-8041

Established in 2002 in WI.
Donor: Soref Operating Trust.
Foundation type: Independent foundation.
Financial data (yr. ended 06/30/13): Assets, $61,486,127 (M); expenditures, $3,264,333; qualifying distributions, $2,953,820; giving activities include $2,953,820 for grants.
Fields of interest: Museums; Arts; Education; Health care; Boys & girls clubs; Human services; Children/youth, services; Family services; Foundations (private grantmaking); Jewish federated giving programs; Jewish agencies & synagogues.
Limitations: Applications not accepted. Giving primarily in Milwaukee, WI. No grants to individuals.
Application information: Contributes only to pre-selected organizations.
Trustee: Audrey Strnad.
EIN: 396758434
Selected grants: The following grants are a representative sample of this grantmaker's funding activity:
$200,000 to Congregation Emanu-El Bne Jeshurun, River Hills, WI, 2011.
$200,000 to Jewish Federation, Milwaukee, Milwaukee, WI, 2011.
$115,798 to Technion-Israel Institute of Technology, Haifa, Israel, 2011.
$110,400 to Childrens Hospital and Health System Foundation, Milwaukee, WI, 2011.
$100,000 to Boys and Girls Clubs of Greater Milwaukee, Milwaukee, WI, 2011.

9949
Nancy Woodson Spire Foundation, Inc. ✧
602 First American Ctr.
Wausau, WI 54403 (715) 845-9201
Contact: San W. Orr, Jr., Pres.
Application address: c/o Wilmington Trust Co., 1100 N. Market St., Wilmington, DE 19801-1289; tel.: (302) 651-8159

Established in WI.
Foundation type: Independent foundation.
Financial data (yr. ended 06/30/13): Assets, $29,604,387 (M); expenditures, $1,426,556; qualifying distributions, $1,257,505; giving activities include $1,207,500 for 5 grants (high: $450,000; low: $1,000).
Fields of interest: Museums (art); Historic preservation/historical societies; YM/YWCAs & YM/YWHAs.
Limitations: Giving primarily in Wausau, WI; some funding also in Washington, DC, and VA.
Application information: Application form not required.
Initial approach: Letter
Deadline(s): None
Officers and Directors:* San W. Orr, Jr.,* Pres.; John P. Garniewski, Jr., V.P.; Thomas J. Howatt; Charles M. Rombach.
EIN: 391367383
Selected grants: The following grants are a representative sample of this grantmaker's funding activity:
$450,000 to National Trust for Historic Preservation, Washington, DC, 2013. For Building Maintenance at Shadows-On-The Teche.
$450,000 to National Trust for Historic Preservation, Washington, DC, 2013. For Restoration of James Madison's Home.

9950
St. Croix Valley Foundation ✧
516 2nd St., Ste. 214
Hudson, WI 54016 (715) 386-9490
Contact: Jane Hetland Stevenson, Pres.; For grants: Angie Pilgrim, Grants and Progs. Off.
FAX: (715) 386-1250;
E-mail: info@scvfoundation.org; Additional E-mail: jstevenson@scvcfoundation.org; Grant inquiry E-mail: apilgrim@scvfoundation.org; Main URL: http://www.scvfoundation.org/
YouTube: http://www.youtube.com/user/TheSCVF?feature=watch

Established in 1995 in WI and MN.
Foundation type: Community foundation.
Financial data (yr. ended 06/30/13): Assets, $31,623,123 (M); gifts received, $1,479,352; expenditures, $2,343,680; giving activities include $1,652,485 for 44+ grants (high: $253,208).
Purpose and activities: The foundation's mission is to advance the quality of life in the St. Croix Valley of WI and MN.
Fields of interest: Arts; Education; Environment; Health care; Human services; Community/economic development; Children; Youth; Adults.
Type of support: Technical assistance; Seed money; Scholarships—to individuals; Scholarship funds; Program evaluation; Matching/challenge support; Management development/capacity building; General/operating support; Endowments; Consulting services; Conferences/seminars.
Limitations: Applications accepted. Giving primarily in Chisago and Washington counties, MN and Pierce, Polk and St. Croix counties, WI.
Publications: Application guidelines; Annual report; Financial statement; Informational brochure.
Application information: Visit foundation web site for application forms and additional guidelines per grant type. Application form required.
Initial approach: Letter
Copies of proposal: 8
Deadline(s): Varies
Board meeting date(s): 2nd Tues. of each month
Final notification: Within 2 months of submission
Officers and Directors:* Marty Harding,* Chair.; Todd Gillingham,* Vice-Chair.; Jane Hetland Stevenson,* Pres.; Jennifer Anderson; Chuck Arneson; Ann Brookman; Suzann Brown; Jill Burchill; Dwight Cummins; Sue Gerlach; Andy Kass; Andy Kubiak; Katrina Larsen; Jim Lutiger; David Palmer; Lisa Rinde; Rod Rommel; Steve Schroeder; Linda Skoglund; Gretchen Stein; Jeanne Walz; David Wettergren; Steven Wilcox.
Number of staff: 3 full-time professional; 1 full-time support; 1 part-time support.
EIN: 411817315
Selected grants: The following grants are a representative sample of this grantmaker's funding activity:
$253,208 to Saint Croix Therapy Inc, Hudson, WI, 2012.
$85,560 to Stillwater, City of, Stillwater, MN, 2012.
$65,998 to Croixdale, Bayport, MN, 2012.
$60,000 to Retreat, The, East Hampton, NY, 2012.
$30,000 to Pepin County Department of Human Services, Durand, WI, 2012.
$30,000 to Trinity Lutheran Church, Eau Claire, WI, 2012.
$25,000 to National Parkinson Foundation Minnesota, Golden Valley, MN, 2012.
$24,828 to Joshua Charitable Foundation, Golden, CO, 2012.
$20,000 to Presbyterian Homes Foundation, Roseville, MN, 2012.
$20,000 to Saint Paul Lutheran Church, Hillsboro, WI, 2012.

9951
Stackner Family Foundation, Inc. ✧
c/o Paul J. Tilleman
411 E. Wisconsin Ave., Ste. 2350
Milwaukee, WI 53202-4426
E-mail: Stackner@msn.com; Application address: c/o John A. Treiber, Pres. and Dir., Stackner Family Foundation, Inc., P.O. Box 597, Hartland, WI 53029, tel.: (262) 646-7040; Main URL: http://www.stackner.com/

Incorporated in 1966 in WI.
Donors: John S. Stackner†; Irene M. Stackner†.
Foundation type: Independent foundation.
Financial data (yr. ended 08/31/13): Assets, $13,803,006 (M); expenditures, $852,850; qualifying distributions, $770,788; giving activities include $565,800 for 76 grants (high: $40,000; low: $500).
Purpose and activities: Support for social service and youth agencies, including family services, the homeless, hunger programs, child welfare, employment, and minorities, health agencies, including those serving the mentally ill and the handicapped, and drug and alcohol abuse programs.
Fields of interest: Health care; Substance abuse, services; Mental health/crisis services; Employment; Food services; Human services; Children/youth, services; Family services; Minorities/immigrants, centers/services; Homeless, human services; Community/economic development; Disabilities, people with; Minorities.
Type of support: General/operating support; Capital campaigns; Building/renovation; Program development.
Limitations: Applications accepted. Giving limited to Milwaukee and Waukesha counties, WI. No grants to individuals; or for deficit financing or fellowships; no loans; no scholarships.
Application information: Application form required.
Initial approach: Letter
Copies of proposal: 1

Deadline(s): Prior to quarterly meeting in Jan., Apr., July and Oct.
Board meeting date(s): Jan., Apr., July, and Oct.
Final notification: Within 3 weeks after board meetings
Officers and Directors:* John A. Treiber,* Pres.; Phillip J. Treiber,* V.P.; David L. MacGregor,* Secy.; Paul J. Tilleman,* Treas.
Number of staff: 1 full-time support.
EIN: 396097597
Selected grants: The following grants are a representative sample of this grantmaker's funding activity:
$10,000 to Marquette University, Milwaukee, WI, 2013. For Peers Program.
$1,500 to Oakwood Church, Hartland, WI, 2013. For Touched Twice Services.

9952
Bert L. and Patricia S. Steigleder Charitable Trust ✧
c/o US Bank, N.A.
P.O. Box 2043
Milwaukee, WI 53201-9668 (414) 277-5000

Established in 1991 in WI.
Donor: Bert L. Steigleder‡.
Foundation type: Independent foundation.
Financial data (yr. ended 06/30/13): Assets, $8,943,641 (M); expenditures, $552,209; qualifying distributions, $443,000; giving activities include $443,000 for grants.
Fields of interest: Museums; Performing arts; Arts; Higher education; Education; Health organizations; Human services.
Type of support: General/operating support; Building/renovation.
Limitations: Applications accepted. Giving primarily in the Milwaukee, WI, area. No grants to individuals.
Application information: Application form required.
Initial approach: Letter
Deadline(s): None
Trustees: Paul J. Tilleman; U.S. Bank, N.A.
EIN: 396541246
Selected grants: The following grants are a representative sample of this grantmaker's funding activity:
$30,000 to Milwaukee Art Museum, Milwaukee, WI, 2013. To support of 125th.
$25,000 to Alverno College, Milwaukee, WI, 2013. To support of the Promise.
$20,000 to Medical College of Wisconsin, Milwaukee, WI, 2013. To support of Women's Health.
$20,000 to Milwaukee Youth Symphony Orchestra, Milwaukee, WI, 2013. For Addition to Fran's.
$17,500 to United Performing Arts Fund, Milwaukee, WI, 2013. For annual gift 2013 campaign.
$10,000 to Medical College of Wisconsin, Milwaukee, WI, 2013. To support of the Cancer.
$10,000 to United Way of Greater Milwaukee, Milwaukee, WI, 2013. To support of 2012 Campaign.
$7,500 to Milwaukee Film, Milwaukee, WI, 2013. To support of Milwaukee 2012.
$7,500 to Milwaukee Film, Milwaukee, WI, 2013. To support of Milwaukee 2013.
$5,000 to Discovery World, Milwaukee, WI, 2013. To support of Thirst for The.

9953
K. C. Stock Foundation, Inc. ✧
111 N. Washington St., Ste. 450
Green Bay, WI 54301-4208 (920) 490-8290

Established in 1990 in WI.
Donors: Kenneth C. Stock; Georgia L. Stock.
Foundation type: Independent foundation.
Financial data (yr. ended 12/31/12): Assets, $12,334,137 (M); expenditures, $732,492; qualifying distributions, $631,578; giving activities include $625,030 for 87 grants (high: $50,000; low: $250).
Purpose and activities: Giving primarily for hospitals, athletics and recreation, human services, and federated giving programs. Also giving must benefit the residents of Brown and Oconto Counties, WI.
Fields of interest: Arts, alliance/advocacy; Hospitals (general); Athletics/sports, professional leagues; Boys & girls clubs; Youth development; YM/YWCAs & YM/YWHAs; Children/youth; Aging; Disabilities, people with; Physically disabled; Blind/visually impaired; Mentally disabled; AIDS, people with; Terminal illness, people with; Homeless.
Type of support: General/operating support; Continuing support; Annual campaigns; Capital campaigns; Building/renovation; Equipment; Land acquisition; Endowments; Program development; Curriculum development; Scholarship funds; Technical assistance; Employee-related scholarships.
Limitations: Applications accepted. Giving primarily in Brown and Oconto Counties, WI. No support for religious or political organizations.
Application information: Application form required.
Initial approach: Letter
Copies of proposal: 1
Deadline(s): None
Officers: Kenneth C. Stock, Pres.; Georgia L. Stock, V.P.; Steven Stock, Secy.-Treas.
Number of staff: 1 part-time support.
EIN: 391688221

9954
The Stone Foundation, Inc. ✧
130 S. Main St.
Fond du Lac, WI 54935-4210
Application address: c/o Eric Stone or James Chatterton, P.O. Box 988, Fond du Lac, WI 54936-0988; tel.: (920) 921-7700

Established in WI.
Donors: Peter E. Stone; NEB Corp.; American Bank.
Foundation type: Independent foundation.
Financial data (yr. ended 12/31/13): Assets, $42,101,211 (M); gifts received, $360,000; expenditures, $1,992,759; qualifying distributions, $1,867,036; giving activities include $1,857,060 for 81 grants (high: $500,000; low: $250).
Purpose and activities: Giving primarily for human services.
Fields of interest: Substance abuse, treatment; Human services; Children/youth, services; Community/economic development; Foundations (community).
Limitations: Applications accepted. Giving primarily in Fond du Lac, WI. No grants to individuals.
Application information: Application form required.
Initial approach: Proposal
Deadline(s): None
Officers and Directors:* Peter E. Stone,* Pres. and Treas.; James R. Chatterton,* V.P.; Eric P. Stone,* V.P.; S. Adam Stone,* V.P.; Barbara S. Stone,* Secy.; Michael L. Burch.
EIN: 391597843

9955
Jack DeLoss Taylor Charitable Trust ✧ ☆
701 Deming Way, Ste. 100
Madison, WI 53717-2916 (608) 827-6400
Contact: Christopher Bugg, Tr.

Established in 1989 in WI.
Foundation type: Independent foundation.
Financial data (yr. ended 06/30/13): Assets, $6,668,368 (M); expenditures, $1,424,407; qualifying distributions, $1,394,017; giving activities include $1,369,000 for 54 grants (high: $900,000; low: $1,000).
Purpose and activities: Giving primarily to organizations which provide financial assistance to needy people throughout the world, with preference given to children of underdeveloped countries whose needs are the most fundamental, such as food and medical care.
Fields of interest: Health care; Youth development; Human services.
International interests: Developing Countries.
Type of support: Building/renovation; Equipment; Emergency funds; Program development; Matching/challenge support.
Limitations: Applications accepted. Giving in the U.S., and in underdeveloped and developing countries. No grants to individuals.
Application information: Application form required.
Initial approach: Letter
Copies of proposal: 1
Deadline(s): Jan. 31
Board meeting date(s): Early May
Final notification: June 30
Trustees: Christopher Bugg; Catherine H. Taylor; Philip Taylor.
EIN: 396510710
Selected grants: The following grants are a representative sample of this grantmaker's funding activity:
$102,000 to United Way of Dane County, Madison, WI, 2011.

9956
Thrivent Financial for Lutherans Foundation ✧
(formerly Lutheran Brotherhood Foundation)
4321 N. Ballard Rd.
Appleton, WI 54919-0001 (800) 236-3736
FAX: (920) 628-5448;
E-mail: foundation@thrivent.com; E-mail for Corporate Communities: CommunityGrants@thrivent.com; Main URL: https://www.thrivent.com/foundations/tflfoundation/index.html

Established in 1982 in MN.
Donors: Lutheran Brotherhood; Lutheran Brotherhood Research Corp.; Aid Association for Lutherans; Thrivent Financial for Lutherans.
Foundation type: Company-sponsored foundation.
Financial data (yr. ended 12/31/12): Assets, $89,287,105 (M); gifts received, $11,024,190; expenditures, $15,103,732; qualifying distributions, $15,019,648; giving activities include $15,000,062 for 8,281 grants (high: $1,125,000; low: $3).

Purpose and activities: The foundation supports organizations involved with education, health, employment, housing, youth developing, human services, volunteerism, the Lutheran community, and economically disadvantaged people.
Fields of interest: Elementary/secondary education; Education, early childhood education; Education; Health care; Employment, services; Employment; Housing/shelter, homeless; Housing/shelter, home owners; Housing/shelter; Youth development, business; Youth development; Family services, parent education; Human services, financial counseling; Homeless, human services; Human services; Religion, management/technical assistance; Religion, fund raising/fund distribution; Protestant agencies & churches; Economically disadvantaged.
Type of support: General/operating support; Management development/capacity building; Program development; Conferences/seminars; Seed money; Curriculum development; Research; Employee volunteer services; Employee matching gifts; Matching/challenge support.
Limitations: Applications accepted. Giving on a national basis to Lutheran communities for the Lutheran Grant Program; giving limited to the Twin Cities, MN, including Minneapolis and St. Paul, and the Fox Cities, WI for Corporate Communities Grants. No support for national or international organizations or churches or church organizations for expenses normally regarded as church responsibility for Corporate Communities Grants. No grants to individuals, or for political activities or causes, debt reduction, capital costs involving the purchase of major equipment including technological equipment such as computers or associated software, furnishings, vehicles, facility construction or renovation, consultation services (except for feasibility studies), or publications; no grants for services duplicated by other organizations, religious causes, or endowments for Corporate Communities Grants; no loans or investments for Corporate Communities Grants.
Publications: Application guidelines; Informational brochure (including application guidelines).
Application information: Funding preference is given to Challenge Grant requests. Grants range from $5,000 to $100,000. Organizations receiving support are asked to submit a final report. Application form required.
Initial approach: Download application form and e-mail to foundation for Lutheran Grant Program requests under $25,000; e-mail concept proposal for Lutheran Grant Program requests over $25,000; download application form and e-mail for Corporate Communities
Copies of proposal: 1
Deadline(s): None for Lutheran Grant Program; Feb. 1, May 1, Aug. 1, and Nov. 1 for Corporate Communities
Board meeting date(s): Monthly
Final notification: 8 weeks for Lutheran Grant Program requests under $25,000; 4 weeks for Lutheran Grant Program requests over $25,000
Officers and Trustees:* Teresa J. Rasmussen, Chair. and Pres.; Richard Kleven, V.P.; David Hayman, Secy.; Randall L. Boushek,* Treas.; Anne Sample; Terry Timm; Marie A. Uhrich.
EIN: 411449680
Selected grants: The following grants are a representative sample of this grantmaker's funding activity:
$1,425,000 to Evangelical Lutheran Church in America, Chicago, IL, 2012. For Churchwide-Foundation.
$100,000 to Emergency Shelter of the Fox Valley, Appleton, WI, 2012. For Foundation Community Grant.
$100,000 to LEAVEN, Menasha, WI, 2012. For Foundation Community Grant.
$57,251 to Lutheran Church-Missouri Synod, Saint Louis, MO, 2012. For Disaster relief.
$50,000 to Achieve Minneapolis, Minneapolis, MN, 2012. For Foundation Community Grant.
$25,000 to Alliance Housing, Minneapolis, MN, 2012. For Special Projects Fund.
$15,000 to Child Care Aware of Minnesota, Saint Paul, MN, 2012. For Foundation Community Grant.
$15,000 to Minnesota Literacy Council, Saint Paul, MN, 2012. For Foundation Community Grant.
$10,000 to Mount of Olives Evangelical Lutheran Church, Phoenix, AZ, 2012. For Lutheran Community Special Projects.

9957
U.S. Venture/Schmidt Family Foundation, Inc. ✧

(formerly U.S. Oil/Schmidt Family Foundation, Inc.)
425 Better Way
Appleton, WI 54915-6192
Contact: Cathy Mutschler, Dir. of Giving
E-mail for Cathy Mutschler: cmutschler@usventure.com; tel. for Cathy Mutschler: (920) 243-5798; Main URL: http://www.usventure.com/Community/Pages/Foundation.aspx

Established in 1984 in WI.
Donors: Raymond Schmidt; Arthur J. Schmidt; William Schmidt; Thomas A. Schmidt; U.S. Oil Co., Inc.; U.S. Venture, Inc.
Foundation type: Independent foundation.
Financial data (yr. ended 12/31/13): Assets, $6,695,470 (M); gifts received, $1,679,266; expenditures, $844,309; qualifying distributions, $808,487; giving activities include $808,487 for grants.
Purpose and activities: Giving primarily for education, international relief, health, human services, community development, arts and culture, and environmental stewardship.
Fields of interest: Arts; Education; Environment, natural resources; Health organizations, association; Human services; Community/economic development.
Type of support: General/operating support; Continuing support; Annual campaigns; Building/renovation; Equipment; Land acquisition; Emergency funds; Publication; Seed money; Employee matching gifts; Matching/challenge support.
Limitations: Giving primarily in WI. No support for government-sponsored programs (where 50 percent or more of an organization's budget is obtained from government contracts or initiatives). No grants to individuals, or for conferences.
Publications: Application guidelines.
Application information: The foundation may request additional information if the applying organization's work coincides with the foundation's goals. Contact information must also be e-mailed along with letter of intent. Complete application guidelines available on foundation web site.
Initial approach: E-mail or call Dir. of Giving
Deadline(s): See foundation web site
Officers: Jackie Sharkey, Pres.; Emily Schmidt, V.P.; Allison Schmidt, Secy.; Andrew Schmidt, Treas.
Number of staff: 1 part-time professional; 2 part-time support.
EIN: 391540933
Selected grants: The following grants are a representative sample of this grantmaker's funding activity:
$2,500 to Fox Valley Literacy Coalition, Appleton, WI, 2012. For education and scholarships.

9958
David and Julia Uihlein Charitable Foundation, Inc. ✧

322 E. Michigan St., Ste. 302
Milwaukee, WI 53202-5005

Established in 1995 in WI.
Donor: David V. Uihlein, Jr.
Foundation type: Independent foundation.
Financial data (yr. ended 12/31/13): Assets, $17,212 (M); gifts received, $4,407,645; expenditures, $4,406,644; qualifying distributions, $4,401,315; giving activities include $4,326,500 for 68 grants (high: $1,100,000; low: $250).
Fields of interest: Performing arts; Arts; Higher education; Education; Human services; United Ways and Federated Giving Programs.
Limitations: Applications not accepted. Giving primarily in WI, with some emphasis on Milwaukee; funding also in Washington, DC. No grants to individuals.
Application information: Contributes only to pre-selected organizations.
Officers and Directors:* David V. Uihlein, Jr.,* Pres. and Treas.; Julia A. Uihlein,* V.P. and Secy.
EIN: 391822364

9959
David V. Uihlein Foundation ✧

(formerly David Uihlein Racing Museum Foundation)
322 E. Michigan St., Ste. 302
Milwaukee, WI 53202-4104

Established in WI. Classified as a private operating foundation in 1977.
Donor: David V. Uihlein.
Foundation type: Operating foundation.
Financial data (yr. ended 12/31/13): Assets, $9,778,289 (M); expenditures, $470,234; qualifying distributions, $426,320; giving activities include $425,000 for 30 grants (high: $50,000; low: $5,000).
Fields of interest: Education; Environment; Health organizations; Human services.
Type of support: General/operating support.
Limitations: Applications not accepted. Giving in the U.S., with emphasis in WI. No grants to individuals.
Application information: Contributes only to pre-selected organizations.
Trustees: Kathryn M. Kuehn; Philip G. Kuehn, Jr.; Margery H. Uihlein.
EIN: 391284018
Selected grants: The following grants are a representative sample of this grantmaker's funding activity:
$50,000 to Hill School, Pottstown, PA, 2011.
$50,000 to Ozaukee Washington Land Trust, West Bend, WI, 2011.
$40,000 to Mayo Clinic, Rochester, MN, 2011.

$25,000 to Arthritis Foundation, Washington, DC, 2011.
$15,000 to Ducks Unlimited, Memphis, TN, 2011.
$15,000 to Medical College of Wisconsin, Milwaukee, WI, 2011.
$15,000 to Nature Conservancy, Arlington, VA, 2011.
$10,000 to Memorial Sloan-Kettering Cancer Center, New York, NY, 2011.
$10,000 to University of Wisconsin, Madison, WI, 2011.
$5,000 to Multiple Sclerosis Society, National, Hartland, WI, 2011.

9960
Vine and Branches Foundation, Inc.

c/o The Legacy Group, Inc.
P.O. Box 2430
Brookfield, WI 53008-2430 (262) 754-2799
Contact: Patricia Woehrer, Philanthropic Advisor
FAX: (262) 754-4486;
E-mail: info@vineandbranchesfoundation.org; Main URL: http://www.vineandbranchesfoundation.org

Established in 1995 in WI.
Foundation type: Independent foundation.
Financial data (yr. ended 12/31/13): Assets, $23,956,111 (M); expenditures, $2,835,031; qualifying distributions, $2,435,211; giving activities include $2,081,500 for 45 grants (high: $360,000; low: $2,500).
Purpose and activities: Built upon the Scripture verse John 15:5, the mission of the foundation is "to promote Christianity and the building of God's Kingdom through partnerships with organizations that have the same beliefs and overt expression of Christian faith through their programs." Funding is targeted primarily to organizations whose primary focus is the spiritual development of Christian pastors, healthy marriages, or evangelism and discipleship of youth.
Fields of interest: Youth development, religion; Religion, formal/general education; Christian agencies & churches.
Type of support: General/operating support; Continuing support; Management development/capacity building; Technical assistance; Matching/challenge support.
Limitations: Giving limited to southeastern WI and southwestern FL. No grants awarded for work outside of the United States. No support for non-Christian organizations. No grants to individuals; no loans.
Publications: Application guidelines; Informational brochure (including application guidelines).
Application information: Unsolicited letter of inquiry with preliminary eligibility form is accepted. Application is by invitation. E-mailed applications are accepted and preferred. Proposals will be invited; unsolicited proposals are not accepted. It is the Board of Directors' philosophy that the foundation's work is in response to a calling to glorify the Lord and not themselves. Therefore, all gifts are to remain anonymous, and the foundation's name may not be used without permission. Application form required.
Initial approach: Preliminary eligibility form with letter of inquiry
Copies of proposal: 1
Deadline(s): Call foundation for deadlines
Board meeting date(s): Spring, summer and fall
Final notification: One week following board meeting
Officer: Patricia Woehrer, Philanthropic Advisor.
EIN: 391827808

9961
The Wagner Foundation, Ltd. ✧

(formerly R. H. Wagner Foundation, Ltd.)
P.O. Box 307
Lyons, WI 53148-0307

Established in 1981 in WI.
Donors: Richard H. Wagner; Roberta L. Wagner; Ken Essman; Marcy Essman; Bob O'Neil; Julie O'Neil; S. Heekin; Molly Carl; Roger Ringelman; Burlington Rotary Club; Robert W. Baird Foundation; The Word at Work Foundation; Rotary Club of Elmbrook; Kikkoman Foods Foundation.
Foundation type: Independent foundation.
Financial data (yr. ended 06/30/13): Assets, $13,460,955 (M); gifts received, $293,000; expenditures, $549,680; qualifying distributions, $545,032; giving activities include $476,522 for 23 grants (high: $85,000; low: $1,500).
Purpose and activities: Giving primarily for humanitarian aid in Central America and Africa; support also for education, including Roman Catholic schools, and human services.
Fields of interest: Education; Human services; Children/youth, services; International relief; Catholic agencies & churches.
International interests: Belize; Bermuda; Bolivia; Central America; Philippines.
Type of support: Equipment; Scholarship funds; Grants to individuals.
Limitations: Applications not accepted. Giving in the U.S. and in Africa, Central America and South America.
Application information: Unsolicited requests for funds not accepted.
Officers: Richard H. Wagner, Pres.; Roberta L. Wagner, V.P.
Directors: Melissa Doyle; Paul B. Edwards, CPA; Abbey Essman; Adam Essman; Ken Essman; Marcy Essman; Emily LaBadie; Bob O'Neill; Julie O'Neill; Meghan O'Neill; Molly O'Neill; Marci Rueter.
EIN: 391311452

9962
The Todd & Karen Wanek Family Foundation, Ltd. ✧

1 Ashley Way
Arcadia, WI 54612-1218
Contact: Karen A. Wanek, Dir.

Established in WI.
Donors: Todd R. Wanek; Karen A. Wanek; Ronald Wanek; Joyce Wanek.
Foundation type: Independent foundation.
Financial data (yr. ended 12/31/13): Assets, $5,636,174 (M); expenditures, $2,888,719; qualifying distributions, $2,858,845; giving activities include $2,858,845 for 2 grants (high: $1,858,845; low: $1,000,000).
Fields of interest: Health care.
Limitations: Applications accepted. Giving primarily in Rochester, MN.
Application information: The foundation will accept only 1 request from each organization per year. Application form required.
Initial approach: Letter not exceeding 1 typewritten page with 1-inch margins on all sides, and with a type no smaller than 10 point
Deadline(s): None
Final notification: Approximately 12 weeks from receipt of application
Directors: Cameron R. Wanek; Karen A. Wanek; Todd R. Wanek.
EIN: 273309697

9963
The Ronald & Joyce Wanek Foundation, Ltd. ✧

1 Ashley Way
Arcadia, WI 54612-1218 (608) 323-6222
Contact: Nell Bryson

Established in WI in 1998.
Donors: Ronald G. Wanek; Joyce A. Wanek.
Foundation type: Independent foundation.
Financial data (yr. ended 12/31/13): Assets, $40,213,922 (M); gifts received, $8,061,615; expenditures, $12,691,900; qualifying distributions, $12,582,169; giving activities include $12,582,169 for 14 grants (high: $10,000,000; low: $500).
Fields of interest: Health care; Heart & circulatory research; Protestant agencies & churches; Catholic agencies & churches.
Limitations: Applications accepted. Giving primarily in MN and WI. No grants to individuals.
Application information: Letter must not exceed one typewritten page, margins must be one inch on all sides and the type must not be smaller than 10 points.
Initial approach: Letter
Deadline(s): None
Final notification: Approximately 12 weeks
Officer and Directors:* Ronald G. Wanek,* Pres.; Shari S. Wagner; Joyce A. Wanek; Todd R. Wanek; Katie S. Wanek-Forsythe.
EIN: 391948292
Selected grants: The following grants are a representative sample of this grantmaker's funding activity:
$2,173,927 to Mayo Clinic, Rochester, MN, 2012. For Program for hypoplastic left heart syndrome-clinical practice/natural history, genetics.

9964
The Wanek-Vogel Foundation, Ltd. ✧

c/o Ashley Furniture Industries, Inc.
1 Ashley Way
Arcadia, WI 54612-1218 (608) 323-6249
Contact: Paulette Rippley

Established in WI.
Donor: Ashley Furniture Industries.
Foundation type: Company-sponsored foundation.
Financial data (yr. ended 12/31/12): Assets, $34,559,816 (M); gifts received, $20,000,000; expenditures, $3,002,306; qualifying distributions, $2,973,564; giving activities include $2,973,564 for 44 grants (high: $2,173,927; low: $100).
Purpose and activities: The foundation supports arts councils and organizations involved with secondary education, health, human services, and community development.
Fields of interest: Arts councils; Secondary school/education; Health care, clinics/centers; Health care; Residential/custodial care, hospices; Human services; Community development, business promotion; Community/economic development.
Type of support: General/operating support.

Limitations: Applications accepted. Giving primarily in WI. No grants to individuals.
Application information: The letter of inquiry should have a margin of 1 inch on all sides and type not smaller than 10 point. Support is limited to 1 contribution per organization during any given year. Application form not required.
Initial approach: Letter of inquiry
Deadline(s): None
Final notification: 12 weeks
Directors: Benjamin Charles Vogel; Charles H.E. Vogel; Ronald G. Wanek; Todd R. Wanek.
EIN: 391948289
Selected grants: The following grants are a representative sample of this grantmaker's funding activity:
$2,114,171 to Mayo Clinic, Rochester, MN, 2011. For general support.

9965
Waukesha County Community Foundation ✧
2727 N. Grandview Blvd., Ste. 122
Waukesha, WI 53188-6100 (262) 513-1861
Contact: Kathryn Leverenz, Pres.
E-mail: wccf@waukeshafoundation.org; Main URL: http://www.waukeshafoundation.org

Established in 1999 in WI.
Foundation type: Community foundation.
Financial data (yr. ended 12/31/13): Assets, $33,179,563 (M); gifts received, $1,545,810; expenditures, $1,864,082; giving activities include $1,454,896 for 64+ grants (high: $155,000).
Purpose and activities: The foundation is a pool of permanent endowment and project funds created primarily by and for the people of Waukesha County to provide grant support to charitable organizations.
Fields of interest: Historic preservation/historical societies; Arts; Education; Environment; Health care; Human services; Community/economic development.
Type of support: General/operating support; Continuing support; Annual campaigns; Equipment; Program development; Curriculum development; Technical assistance.
Limitations: Applications accepted. Giving primarily in Waukesha County, WI. No support for religious organizations. No grants for capital campaigns.
Publications: Application guidelines; Annual report (including application guidelines); Financial statement; Grants list; Informational brochure; Newsletter.
Application information: Visit foundation web site for application guidelines. Following receipt of letter of intent, the foundation's Board will determine if a full proposal is of interest. Application form not required.
Initial approach: Letter of intent (no longer than 2 pages)
Copies of proposal: 5
Deadline(s): Aug. 1 for letter of intent; Oct. 1 for full proposal
Board meeting date(s): Oct.
Final notification: Nov.-Dec.
Officers and Directors:* Jeffrey D. Wiesner,* Chair.; Kathryn Leverenz,* Pres.; John P. Macy,* V.P. and Chair.-Elect; Kenneth P. Riesch,* V.P.; Kathleen A. Gray,* Secy.; Michael R. Duckett,* Treas.; Susan C. Bellehumeur; Andrea B. Bryant; Gerald E. Couri; Daniel J. D'Angelo, D.D.S.; Brian Dorow; Anne Foster; Karin M. Gale; Steven L. Johnson; Brian D. Kaminski; Karin I. Kultgen, M.D.; Richard C. Larson; Kathy A. Ledvina; Rhody J. Megal; Charles B. Palmer; James P. Riley; Rexford W. Titus III; James R. Walden, Jr.; Stewart M. Wangard; Stephen J. Ziegler.
Number of staff: 1 full-time professional; 2 part-time support.
EIN: 391969122

9966
The Todd Wehr Foundation, Inc. ✧
9212 Wilson Blvd.
Wauwatosa, WI 53226-1729

Incorporated in 1953 in WI.
Donor: C. Frederic Wehr†.
Foundation type: Independent foundation.
Financial data (yr. ended 12/31/13): Assets, $11,062,775 (M); expenditures, $707,013; qualifying distributions, $631,834; giving activities include $580,000 for 10 grants (high: $150,000; low: $10,000).
Purpose and activities: Giving primarily for education and human services.
Fields of interest: Elementary/secondary education; Human services; Children/youth, services.
Limitations: Giving primarily in Milwaukee, WI. No grants to individuals.
Officers and Directors:* Allan E. Iding,* Pres.; James A. Feddersen,* V.P. and Co-Secy.; Richard J. Harland,* V.P. and Co-Secy.
Number of staff: 1 full-time professional.
EIN: 396043962
Selected grants: The following grants are a representative sample of this grantmaker's funding activity:
$50,000 to Eastbrook Academy, Milwaukee, WI, 2011. For general support.
$50,000 to Notre Dame Middle School, Milwaukee, WI, 2011. For general support.
$10,000 to Journey House, Milwaukee, WI, 2011. For general support.
$10,000 to Marquette University, Milwaukee, WI, 2011. For general support.

9967
Ruth St. John & John Dunham West Foundation, Inc. ✧
(also known as West Foundation, Inc.)
915 Memorial Dr.
Manitowoc, WI 54220-2240
Contact: Thomas J. Bare, Chair., C.E.O. and Pres.
FAX: (920) 684-7381;
E-mail: info@westfoundation.us; Main URL: http://www.westfoundation.us

Established in 1957.
Donors: Ruth St. John West†; John Dunham West†.
Foundation type: Independent foundation.
Financial data (yr. ended 12/31/13): Assets, $63,379,920 (M); gifts received, $1,500,000; expenditures, $4,491,693; qualifying distributions, $3,871,384; giving activities include $3,202,412 for 73 grants (high: $1,500,000; low: $100), and $366,941 for 1 foundation-administered program.
Purpose and activities: Giving primarily for civic affairs and humanitarian causes; some support for the arts and higher education; also maintains and operates a public garden.
Fields of interest: Arts; Higher education; Botanical gardens; Human services; Public affairs; Infants/toddlers; Children/youth; Children; Youth; Adults; Aging; Young adults; Disabilities, people with; Physically disabled; Blind/visually impaired; Deaf/hearing impaired; Mentally disabled; Minorities; Asians/Pacific Islanders; African Americans/Blacks; Hispanics/Latinos; Women; Infants/toddlers, female; Girls; Adults, women; Young adults, female; Men; Infants/toddlers, male; Boys; Adults, men; Young adults, male; Substance abusers; Single parents; Crime/abuse victims; Terminal illness, people with; Economically disadvantaged; Homeless.
Type of support: Annual campaigns; Building/renovation; Equipment; Land acquisition; Endowments; Debt reduction; Program development; Scholarship funds; Matching/challenge support.
Limitations: Applications accepted. Giving primarily in Manitowoc County, WI. No support for religious, political, veterans', social or fraternal, or undergraduate organizations, or parochial, public or private schools. No grants to individuals.
Publications: Application guidelines; Annual report (including application guidelines); Financial statement; IRS Form 990 or 990-PF printed copy available upon request.
Application information: Application guidelines and form available on foundation web site. Application form required.
Initial approach: Proposal
Copies of proposal: 6
Deadline(s): 1 week prior to monthly meeting
Board meeting date(s): Monthly (3rd week)
Final notification: 1 month from receipt
Officers and Directors:* Thomas J. Bare,* Chair, C.E.O. and Pres.; Phyllis Schippers,* V.P.; Gail Fox,* Secy.; Bernadine Zimmer,* Treas.; John Jagemann.
Number of staff: 1 full-time professional; 1 part-time professional.
EIN: 396056375
Selected grants: The following grants are a representative sample of this grantmaker's funding activity:
$500,000 to Domestic Violence Center, Manitowoc, WI, 2011. For building addition.
$100,000 to Bookworm Gardens, Sheboygan, WI, 2011. For Secret Garden Project.
$100,000 to Lakeland College, Sheboygan, WI, 2011. For classroom technology.
$25,000 to Salvation Army, Manitowoc, WI, 2011. For child care program.
$20,000 to Aurora Health Foundation, Two Rivers, WI, 2011. For emergent transportation program.
$20,000 to United Way Manitowoc County, Manitowoc, WI, 2011. For building improvements.

9968
Windhover Foundation, Inc. ✧
N61 W23044 Harry's Way
Sussex, WI 53089-9807
E-mail: contact@windhoverfoundation.org; Main URL: https://www.windhoverfoundation.org/

Established in 1983.
Donors: Quad/Graphics, Inc.; Harry V. Quadracci 1998 Trust.
Foundation type: Company-sponsored foundation.
Financial data (yr. ended 12/31/12): Assets, $82,336,076 (M); gifts received, $3,239,638; expenditures, $3,526,150; qualifying distributions, $3,230,885; giving activities include $2,922,885 for 114 grants (high: $485,925; low: $10), and

$308,000 for 188 grants to individuals (high: $2,500; low: $1,000).
Purpose and activities: The foundation supports parks and playgrounds and organizations involved with arts and culture, education, health, hunger, sports, and human services. Special emphasis is directed toward projects designed to meet unfilled social needs.
Fields of interest: Museums (art); Arts; Elementary/secondary education; Higher education; Libraries (public); Education; Hospitals (general); Reproductive health, family planning; Health care; Food services; Food banks; Recreation, parks/playgrounds; American Red Cross; Children/youth, services; Residential/custodial care, hospices; Women, centers/services; Human services; United Ways and Federated Giving Programs; Christian agencies & churches.
Type of support: General/operating support; Continuing support; Annual campaigns; Employee matching gifts; Employee-related scholarships.
Limitations: Applications accepted. Giving primarily in areas of company operations in Milwaukee, WI. No support for religious organizations or teams or leagues. No grants to individuals (except for employee-related scholarships), or for sponsorships, fundraising events, competitions, or contests.
Publications: Application guidelines.
Application information: Application form not required.
Initial approach: Complete online application
Copies of proposal: 1
Deadline(s): None
Officers and Directors: Elizabeth E. Quadracci, Pres.; Elizabeth Quadracci Harned, V.P.; John C. Fowler, Secy.-Treas.; Kathryn Q. Flores; J. Joel Quadracci.
EIN: 391482470

9969
Wisconsin Energy Corporation Foundation, Inc. ✧

(formerly Wisconsin Electric System Foundation, Inc.)
231 W. Michigan St., Rm. P409A
Milwaukee, WI 53203-0001 (414) 221-2107
Contact: Patricia L. McNew, Fdn. Admin.
FAX: (414) 221-2412;
E-mail: wec.foundation@we-energies.com; E-mail for Patricia L. McNew: patti.mcnew@we-energies.com;
Main URL: http://www.wec-foundation.com/
Wisconsin Energy Foundation Blog: http://wisconsinenergyfoundation.blogspot.com/

Incorporated in 1982 in WI.
Donors: State of Wisconsin Dept. of Adm.; Wisconsin Energy Corp.
Foundation type: Company-sponsored foundation.
Financial data (yr. ended 12/31/13): Assets, $38,487,767 (M); gifts received, $6,600,000; expenditures, $7,613,977; qualifying distributions, $7,718,422; giving activities include $7,296,952 for 187 grants (high: $500,000; low: $25), and $254,328 for loans/program-related investments.
Purpose and activities: The foundation supports organizations involved with arts and culture, economic health, education, and the environment.
Fields of interest: Museums; Performing arts; Arts; Higher education; Libraries (public); Education; Environment, natural resources; Environmental education; Environment; Employment, services; Goodwill Industries; Employment; Disasters, preparedness/services; Boys & girls clubs; YM/YWCAs & YM/YWHAs; Children, services; Human services; Economic development; Business/industry; Community/economic development; United Ways and Federated Giving Programs.
Type of support: General/operating support; Capital campaigns; Equipment; Endowments; Program development; Scholarship funds; Sponsorships; Employee matching gifts; In-kind gifts.
Limitations: Applications accepted. Giving limited to areas of company operations in the Upper Peninsula, MI, area and WI. No support for political action or legislative advocacy organizations or veterans' or fraternal organizations. No grants to individuals, or for trips, tours, pageants, team or extra-curricular school events, or student exchange programs, programs whose primary purpose is the promotion of religious doctrine or tenets, or programs whose purpose is solely athletic in nature; no renewable energy projects.
Publications: Application guidelines; Program policy statement.
Application information: Additional information may be requested at a later date. Requests by telephone are not accepted. A site visit may be requested. Application form required.
Initial approach: Complete online application form
Deadline(s): Jan. 31, Apr. 30, July 31, and Oct. 31
Board meeting date(s): Quarterly
Final notification: 90 days
Officers and Directors:* Gale E. Klappa,* Pres.; Susan H. Martin,* V.P.; Keith H. Ecke, Secy.; J. Patrick Keyes,* Treas.; Kevin Fletcher; Allen L. Leverett; Thelma Sias.
EIN: 391433726
Selected grants: The following grants are a representative sample of this grantmaker's funding activity:
$1,666,600 to Marquette University, Milwaukee, WI, 2012. For State of Wisconsin 'Study of Engineering Grant'.
$500,000 to United Performing Arts Fund, Milwaukee, WI, 2012.
$250,000 to Marquette University, Milwaukee, WI, 2012. For Discovery Learning Complex and Urban Scholars Fund.
$250,000 to Partners Advancing Values in Education, Milwaukee, WI, 2012. For Messmer Catholic Schools.
$233,610 to United Way of Greater Milwaukee, Milwaukee, WI, 2012. For United Way campaign.
$6,350 to United Way of Dickinson County, Iron Mountain, MI, 2012. For 2012 United Way Contribution.
$5,000 to Milwaukee Repertory Theater, Milwaukee, WI, 2012. For 2013 Gala Sponsorship.
$4,150 to UWM Foundation, Milwaukee, WI, 2012. For Education 1St Quarter 2012.
$1,000 to Invent Now, North Canton, OH, 2012. For Camp Invention Programs in Wisconsin (Northern Portion).
$1,000 to Invent Now, North Canton, OH, 2012. For Camp Invention Programs in Wisconsin (Western Portion).

9970
Wisconsin Public Service Foundation ✧

(formerly WPS Foundation, Inc.)
700 N. Adams St.
P.O. Box 19001
Green Bay, WI 54307-9001
Main URL: http://www.wisconsinpublicservice.com/company/foundation.aspx
2010 Beneficiaries of Wisconsin Public Service Foundation: http://www.wisconsinpublicservice.com/company/involvement.aspx

Incorporated in 1964 in WI.
Donor: Wisconsin Public Service Corp.
Foundation type: Company-sponsored foundation.
Financial data (yr. ended 12/31/13): Assets, $24,795,714 (M); expenditures, $1,201,733; qualifying distributions, $1,192,733; giving activities include $1,181,321 for 862 grants (high: $33,000).
Purpose and activities: The foundation supports programs designed to promote arts and culture; education; the environment; human services and health; community and neighborhood; and awards college scholarships.
Fields of interest: Arts, cultural/ethnic awareness; Museums; Performing arts; Arts; Vocational education; Higher education; Business school/education; Engineering school/education; Adult/continuing education; Education; Environment, natural resources; Environment, energy; Environment, forests; Environment; Animals/wildlife; Hospitals (general); Health care; Mental health/crisis services; Employment; Agriculture; Youth development, adult & child programs; Aging, centers/services; Developmentally disabled, centers & services; Human services; Community/economic development; Minorities; Women.
Type of support: General/operating support; Continuing support; Annual campaigns; Capital campaigns; Building/renovation; Equipment; Program development; Scholarship funds; Research; Employee volunteer services; Employee matching gifts; Employee-related scholarships; Scholarships—to individuals.
Limitations: Applications accepted. Giving generally limited to areas of company operations in upper MI and northeastern WI. No support for churches and other religious organizations, political organizations, discriminatory organizations, or public or private K-12 schools. No grants to individuals (except for scholarships), or for natural gas or electric service, moving of poles, or utility construction.
Publications: Application guidelines; Grants list; Informational brochure.
Application information: Application form required.
Initial approach: Letter
Copies of proposal: 1
Deadline(s): None
Board meeting date(s): May and as required
Officers: Lawrence T. Bogard, Pres.; Charles A. Schrock, V.P.; Jodi J. Caro, Secy.; John R. Wilde, Treas.
EIN: 396075016
Selected grants: The following grants are a representative sample of this grantmaker's funding activity:
$46,500 to University of Wisconsin, Madison, WI, 2011. For scholarship.
$2,000 to University of Wisconsin, La Crosse, WI, 2011. For scholarship.

9971
Joseph and Vera Zilber Charitable Foundation, Inc. ✧ ☆
710 N. Plankinton Ave., Ste. 1200
Milwaukee, WI 53203-2418

Established in 2008 in WI.
Donor: Vera Zilber Marital Trust.
Foundation type: Independent foundation.
Financial data (yr. ended 06/30/13): Assets, $47,868,854 (M); gifts received, $48,934,898; expenditures, $1,500,104; qualifying distributions, $1,499,082; giving activities include $1,492,372 for 15 grants (high: $1,285,714; low: $500).
Fields of interest: Education; Human services; Community/economic development.
Limitations: Applications not accepted. Giving primarily in Milwaukee, WI.
Application information: Unsolicited requests for funds not accepted.
Officers and Directors:* Marcy Jackson,* Pres.; James F. Janz,* V.P.; Stephan J. Chevalier,* Secy.-Treas.; Melissa S. A. Jackson; Shane M. Jackson; Michael P. Mervis; John K. Tsui; Marilyn Zilber.
EIN: 392076346

9972
Joseph J. and Vera Zilber Family Foundation ✧
710 N. Plankinton Ave., Ste. 1200
Milwaukee, WI 53203-2404 (414) 274-2447
E-mail: info@zilberfamilyfoundation.org; Main URL: http://www.zilberfamilyfoundation.org

Established in 1962 in WI.
Donors: Joseph J. Zilber†; Vera J. Zilber; Zilber, Ltd.
Foundation type: Independent foundation.
Financial data (yr. ended 06/30/13): Assets, $24,806,020 (M); gifts received, $23,500; expenditures, $5,249,765; qualifying distributions, $5,070,092; giving activities include $4,370,697 for 87 grants (high: $1,000,000; low: $32).
Purpose and activities: Giving primarily for human services and neighborhood development.
Fields of interest: Museums (specialized); Higher education; Environment; Health organizations, association; Boys & girls clubs; Human services; Community development, neighborhood development; Jewish federated giving programs.
Type of support: Program evaluation; Program development; Matching/challenge support; Management development/capacity building; General/operating support; Employee matching gifts; Capital campaigns.
Limitations: Giving primarily in WI, with emphasis on Milwaukee. No support for political or religious organizations. No grants to individuals, or for endowments, annual appeals, conferences, workshops, fundraising events, scholarships, fellowships, research, loans, travel, athletic events, or film or media projects.
Publications: Application guidelines.
Application information: Full proposals are by invitation only, after review of initial letter of inquiry. Videos, CDs, press clippings or books are not accepted (unless they are requested).
Initial approach: Letter of inquiry (preferably sent via e-mail)
Final notification: Within 30 days
Officers and Directors:* Marcy Zilber Jackson,* Pres.; James F. Janz,* V.P.; Stephan J. Chevalier,* Secy.-Treas.; Susan Lloyd, Ph.D., Exec. Dir.; Melissa S.A. Jackson; Shane M. Jackson; Michael P. Mervis; John K. Tsui; Marilyn Zilber.
Number of staff: 4 full-time professional.
EIN: 396077241
Selected grants: The following grants are a representative sample of this grantmaker's funding activity:
$1,000,000 to Marquette University, Milwaukee, WI, 2011.
$400,000 to Boys and Girls Clubs of Greater Milwaukee, Milwaukee, WI, 2011.
$300,000 to Discovery World, Milwaukee, WI, 2011.
$300,000 to Discovery World, Milwaukee, WI, 2011.
$250,000 to Local Initiatives Support Corporation, New York, NY, 2011.
$250,000 to Local Initiatives Support Corporation, New York, NY, 2011.
$150,000 to United Neighborhood Centers of Milwaukee, Milwaukee, WI, 2011.
$150,000 to United Way of Greater Milwaukee, Milwaukee, WI, 2011.
$125,000 to Walnut Way Conservation Corporation, Milwaukee, WI, 2011.
$100,000 to United Community Center, Milwaukee, WI, 2011.
$100,000 to United Community Center, Milwaukee, WI, 2011.
$50,000 to Milwaukee Community Service Corps, Milwaukee, WI, 2011.
$7,500 to New Life Community Development, Milwaukee, WI, 2011.

WYOMING

9973
The Andrew Allen Charitable Foundation ✧
c/o Thomas N. Long
P.O. Box 87
Cheyenne, WY 82003-0087

Established in 1998 in WY.
Donor: Andrew Allen‡.
Foundation type: Independent foundation.
Financial data (yr. ended 10/31/13): Assets, $22,042,349 (M); expenditures, $1,487,901; qualifying distributions, $1,016,066; giving activities include $1,016,066 for grants.
Purpose and activities: Giving primarily for education, health organizations and hospitals, including a children's hospital, as well as for children, youth, and social services.
Fields of interest: Elementary/secondary education; Higher education; Education; Hospitals (general); Hospitals (specialty); Health organizations, association; Human services; Children/youth, services; Foundations (private grantmaking).
Limitations: Applications not accepted. Giving in the U.S., primarily in PA, Nashville, TN, and WY. No grants to individuals.
Application information: Contributes only to pre-selected organizations.
Trustees: Carol Kirshner; Thomas N. Long; William Ver Brugge.
EIN: 237862257

9974
Christian Mission Concerns of Tennessee, Inc. ✧
3125 Tucker Ranch Rd.
Wilson, WY 83014-9703 (307) 733-8112
Contact: Paul P. Piper, Jr.

Established in TN.
Donors: Mary Piper; Paul P. Piper.
Foundation type: Independent foundation.
Financial data (yr. ended 12/31/12): Assets, $17,366,588 (M); expenditures, $1,084,256; qualifying distributions, $910,031; giving activities include $816,500 for 7 grants (high: $400,000; low: $500).
Purpose and activities: Giving primarily to Christian programs and projects. In addition, the grantmaker runs a childcare center that provides daytime child care and education in a Christian environment. As part of their education, children are taught Bible stories on a weekly basis.
Fields of interest: Performing arts, music (choral); Education, early childhood education; Theological school/education; Children, day care; Christian agencies & churches; Protestant agencies & churches.
Limitations: Giving primarily in Washington, FL, GA, TX, and WY.
Application information:
Initial approach: Concept letter (not exceeding 3 pages)
Deadline(s): None
Officers: Paul Piper, Pres.; Ronald K. Piper, V.P.
Director: Lynn Piper.
EIN: 582021971

9975
Community Foundation of Jackson Hole ✧
255 E. Simpson St.
P.O. Box 574
Jackson, WY 83001-0574 (307) 739-1026
Contact: Katharine Conover, Pres.; For grants: Pam Sather, Finance and Opers. Off.
FAX: (307) 734-2841;
E-mail: info@cfjacksonhole.org; Grant application e-mail: psather@cfjacksonhole.org; Main URL: http://www.cfjacksonhole.org
Facebook: http://www.facebook.com/pages/Community-Foundation-of-Jackson-Hole/52967406299
Application address for scholarships: c/o Julie Stayner, Guidance Counselor, Jackson Hole High School, P.O. Box 568, Jackson, WY, 83001, tel.: (307) 732-3710, e-mail: jstayner@tcsd.org

Established in 1989 in WY as a component fund of Wyoming Community Foundation; in 1995 became a separate entity.
Foundation type: Community foundation.
Financial data (yr. ended 12/31/13): Assets, $47,829,171 (M); gifts received, $21,244,122; expenditures, $16,477,173; giving activities include $14,597,580 for 239+ grants (high: $517,552; low: $50), and $103,433 for 53 grants to individuals.
Purpose and activities: The foundation seeks to enhance philanthropy and strengthen the sense of community in the Jackson Hole, WY, area, by providing a permanent source of funding and other support for nonprofit organizations and scholarship recipients.
Fields of interest: Arts; Education; Environment; Animals/wildlife; Recreation; Human services; Public affairs.
Type of support: Employee matching gifts; Building/renovation; Capital campaigns; Conferences/seminars; Consulting services; Continuing support; Curriculum development; Emergency funds; Endowments; Equipment; General/operating support; In-kind gifts; Management development/capacity building; Matching/challenge support; Program development; Program-related investments/loans; Publication; Research; Scholarship funds; Scholarships—to individuals; Seed money; Technical assistance.
Limitations: Applications accepted. Giving limited to Teton County, WY through discretionary funds; no geographic limitations through donor-advised funds. No support for religious programs. No grants for debt retirement, tickets for benefits, or telephone solicitations.
Publications: Application guidelines; Annual report; Financial statement; Grants list; Informational brochure.
Application information: Visit foundation web site for application, guidelines, and specific deadlines. Application form required.
Initial approach: Complete online application
Deadline(s): May and Oct. for Competitive grants; varies for others
Board meeting date(s): 6 times annually
Final notification: 31 days
Officers and Directors:* Karen Terra,* Chair.; Pete Lawton,* Vice-Chair.; Bill Weiss,* Vice-Chair.; Katharine Conover, Pres.; Karen Coleman, V.P., Finance and Opers.; Dick Collister,* Secy.; Jim Auge,* Treas.; David Carlin; Scott Gibson; Bill Hoglund; Mercedes Huff; Cathy Kehr; Bob Kopp; Grant Larson; Brad Mead; Tom Muller; Erika Pearsall; Veronica Silberberg; Margo Snowdon; Karla Tessler.
Number of staff: 6 full-time professional; 1 full-time support.
EIN: 830308856
Selected grants: The following grants are a representative sample of this grantmaker's funding activity:
$31,000 to Good Samaritan Mission, Jackson Hole, WY, 2012. For Homeless Shelter Operations and Repairs.
$30,000 to Jackson Hole Community Counseling Center, Jackson, WY, 2012. For access to services.
$30,000 to Teton Youth and Family Services, Jackson, WY, 2012. For Infrastructure Upgrade Project.
$25,000 to Teton Literacy Program, Jackson, WY, 2012. For literacy services.
$17,000 to Senior Center of Jackson Hole, Jackson, WY, 2012. For Friday Feast.
$16,500 to Saint Johns Medical Center Foundation, Jackson, WY, 2012. For Pre-Natal Entry Program for low-income women.
$15,000 to Rendezvous Lands Conservancy, Jackson, Wy, 2012. For Community Park Design.
$10,000 to Community Visual Art Association of Jackson Hole, Jackson, WY, 2012. For Community Outreach.
$10,000 to PAWS of Jackson Hole, Jackson, WY, 2012. For Animal Shelter Kennel Upgrade.
$4,500 to Snake River Fund, Jackson, WY, 2012. For RiverAmbassador.

9976
Cumming Foundation ✧
P.O. Box 4902
Jackson, WY 83001-4902 (801) 524-1786
Contact: Ian M. Cumming, Pres. and Tr.

Established in 1986 in UT.
Donor: Ian M. Cumming.
Foundation type: Independent foundation.
Financial data (yr. ended 12/31/13): Assets, $36,446,434 (M); gifts received, $17,943,756; expenditures, $2,319,968; qualifying distributions, $2,263,653; giving activities include $2,247,334 for 43 grants (high: $500,000; low: $1,000).
Fields of interest: Arts; Higher education; Health care; Eye diseases; Foundations (private grantmaking).
Limitations: Applications not accepted. Giving in the U.S., with emphasis on NY and UT. No grants to individuals.
Application information: Contributes only to pre-selected organizations. Unsolicited requests for funds not considered.
Board meeting date(s): Varies
Officers and Trustees:* Ian M. Cumming,* Pres.; Annette P. Cumming,* V.P. and Exec. Dir.; Cathy Handley, Secy.-Treas.; David E. Cumming; John Darnaby Cumming; Stephen D. Swindle.
Number of staff: 1 part-time professional; 1 full-time support.
EIN: 870440091

9977
The John P. Ellbogen Foundation ✧
P.O. Box 1735
Casper, WY 82602-1735 (307) 234-3360
Contact: Mary E. Garland, Pres.

Established in 2003 in WY.
Donor: John P. Ellbogen‡.
Foundation type: Independent foundation.
Financial data (yr. ended 12/31/13): Assets, $37,820,482 (M); expenditures, $2,287,520; qualifying distributions, $1,671,577; giving activities include $1,423,379 for 39 grants (high: $388,600; low: $500).
Purpose and activities: Giving to create or cause change through the support of science, education, and charity.
Fields of interest: Higher education; Education; Children/youth, services; Foundations (community).
Type of support: General/operating support; Annual campaigns; Capital campaigns; Endowments; Program development; Conferences/seminars; Fellowships; Scholarship funds; Research; Program evaluation.
Limitations: Applications accepted. Giving primarily in WY.
Publications: Application guidelines.
Application information: Application form required.
Initial approach: Letter
Copies of proposal: 1
Deadline(s): None
Board meeting date(s): May and Oct.
Final notification: May and Oct.
Officers: Martin H. Ellbogen, Chair.; Mary E. Garland, Pres.; Rae Lynn Job, V.P.; Theresa A. Ellbogen, Secy.; Steve Ott, Treas.
Directors: Thomas M. Ellbogen; Spencer Garland; Marilyn Dymond Wagner.
Number of staff: 1 full-time professional.
EIN: 830355691

9978
The Lynn and Foster Friess Family Foundation ✧
(formerly Life Enrichment Foundation)
P.O. Box 9790
Jackson, WY 83002-9790 (307) 739-9699
Contact: Foster Friess, Pres. and V.P.

Established around 1981 in DE.
Donor: Foster S. Friess.
Foundation type: Independent foundation.
Financial data (yr. ended 04/30/13): Assets, $85,867,413 (M); expenditures, $5,893,446; qualifying distributions, $5,032,974; giving activities include $4,810,000 for 3 grants (high: $4,800,000; low: $5,000).
Purpose and activities: Giving primarily to faith-based entrepreneurial inner-city programs, especially one-on-one mentoring.
Fields of interest: Education; Safety/disasters; Youth development; Christian agencies & churches.
Type of support: General/operating support; Program-related investments/loans; Matching/challenge support.
Limitations: Applications accepted. Giving primarily in Alpharetta, GA.
Publications: Occasional report.
Application information:
Initial approach: Letter
Deadline(s): None
Officers: Foster S. Friess, Pres. and V.P.; Lynnette E. Friess, Secy.-Treas.
EIN: 510260302
Selected grants: The following grants are a representative sample of this grantmaker's funding activity:
$4,800,000 to National Christian Foundation, Alpharetta, GA, 2013. For general operating support.
$5,000 to Buffalo Bill Memorial Association, Cody, WY, 2013. For general support.
$5,000 to Council for National Policy, Washington, DC, 2013. For general support.

9979
Vernon S. & Rowena W. Griffith Foundation ✧
2 N. Main St., Ste. 401
Sheridan, WY 82801-6324
Contact: Roman Skatula, Treas.

Established in 1971 in WI.
Foundation type: Independent foundation.
Financial data (yr. ended 12/31/13): Assets, $16,736,962 (M); expenditures, $652,401; qualifying distributions, $538,471; giving activities include $510,056 for 8 grants (high: $200,000; low: $5,000).
Fields of interest: Higher education; Hospitals (general); Human services; Protestant agencies & churches.
Type of support: General/operating support.
Limitations: Applications accepted. Giving limited to WY. No grants to individuals.
Application information: Application form required.
Initial approach: Letter
Deadline(s): None
Officers: Arthur Felker, Pres.; Roman Skatula, Treas.
EIN: 237135835

9980
Marieluise Hessel Foundation ✧
65 W. Avalanche Canyon Dr.
Jackson, WY 83001-9009

Established in 1996 in WY.
Donor: Marieluise Hessel.
Foundation type: Operating foundation.
Financial data (yr. ended 12/31/12): Assets, $18,130,366 (M); gifts received, $543,936; expenditures, $995,701; qualifying distributions, $1,577,845; giving activities include $955,705 for 1 grant.
Purpose and activities: The principle activity of the foundation is to circulate works of art on a continuing basis to educational institutions, public museums, and similar non-profit institutions, for 1) public exhibition and display, 2) use by teachers, scholars and others for the study of art and culture, and 3) training of museum and museum-related professionals in curatorial skills.
Fields of interest: Arts education; Art history; Arts.
Limitations: Applications not accepted. Giving primarily in Annandale-on-Hudson, NY. No grants to individuals.
Application information: Contributes only to pre-selected organizations.
Board meeting date(s): Annually, based upon tax return extension
Officers and Directors:* Marieluise Hessel,* Pres. and Treas.; Gretchen Elkins, Secy.; Christina Lockwood.
EIN: 830318485

9981
The Robert S. and Grayce B. Kerr Foundation, Inc. ✧
c/o William G. Kerr
P.O. Box 1750
Wilson, WY 83014-1750

Chartered in 1986 in OK.
Donors: Grayce B. Kerr Flynn‡; William G. Kerr.
Foundation type: Independent foundation.
Financial data (yr. ended 12/31/13): Assets, $38,031,969 (M); expenditures, $1,976,882; qualifying distributions, $1,843,737; giving activities include $1,593,055 for 34 grants (high: $900,500; low: $750).
Purpose and activities: Giving limited to organizations that benefit the specified fields of interest and geographic affiliations of the foundation.
Fields of interest: Arts education; Museums (specialized); Environment, natural resources; Animals/wildlife, preservation/protection; Human services.
Type of support: General/operating support; Building/renovation; Equipment; Emergency funds; Program-related investments/loans; Matching/challenge support.
Limitations: Applications not accepted. Giving primarily in OK and WY. No grants to individuals, or for endowments, annual campaigns, memberships, or medical or scientific research.
Application information: Unsolicited proposals not considered.
Board meeting date(s): June and Dec.
Officers and Trustees:* William G. Kerr,* Chair.; Jo Arthur G. Kerr,* Vice-Chair.; Kavar Kerr,* Pres.; Mara Kerr,* Secy.-Treas.
Number of staff: 1 part-time professional.
EIN: 731256123

9982
Liana Foundation, Inc. ✧
c/o John W. Jackson
P.O. Box 10815
Jackson, WY 83002-0815

Established in 2001 in NJ. Classified as a private operating foundation in 2002.
Donor: John W. Jackson.
Foundation type: Operating foundation.
Financial data (yr. ended 12/31/13): Assets, $62,920,417 (M); gifts received, $9,250,167; expenditures, $3,809,736; qualifying distributions, $3,510,608; giving activities include $3,510,608 for 26 grants (high: $3,350,000; low: $500).
Fields of interest: Arts; Higher education; Environment, natural resources; Health care; Human services.
Limitations: Applications not accepted. Giving primarily in CT; some giving also in NJ and NY.
Application information: Unsolicited requests for funds are not considered.
Officers and Trustees:* John W. Jackson,* Chair.; Susan G. Jackson, Pres.; Alexandra Jackson; Donald M. Jackson; Jennifer Jackson; Kimberly Jackson.
EIN: 223846401
Selected grants: The following grants are a representative sample of this grantmaker's funding activity:
$9,300,000 to Yale University, New Haven, CT, 2012. For general support.

$50,000 to Community Foundation of Jackson Hole, Jackson, WY, 2012. For general support.
$25,000 to Vermont Studio Center, Johnson, VT, 2012. For general support.
$10,000 to Colegio Mexico-Americano Association, Roselle, IL, 2012. For general support.
$10,000 to Poets and Writers, New York, NY, 2012. For general support.

9983
The LOR Foundation, Inc. ✧
c/o Amy E. Wyss
P.O. Box 11810
Jackson, WY 83002-1810 (307) 733-2332
FAX: (307) 733-7142;
E-mail: info@lorfoundation.org; Main URL: http://www.lorfoundation.org/

Established in 2007 in PA.
Donor: Amy E. Wyss.
Foundation type: Independent foundation.
Financial data (yr. ended 12/31/12): Assets, $362,769,160 (M); gifts received, $145,000,000; expenditures, $9,284,136; qualifying distributions, $6,710,135; giving activities include $6,147,920 for 27 grants (high: $2,000,000; low: $5,000).
Fields of interest: Libraries/library science; Environment; Recreation; Neighborhood centers.
Limitations: Applications not accepted. Giving primarily in CO and WY. No grants to individuals.
Application information: Contributes only to pre-selected organizations.
Officer and Director:* Amy E. Wyss,* Pres.; Hal Hutchinson, Exec. Dir.
EIN: 205682977
Selected grants: The following grants are a representative sample of this grantmaker's funding activity:
$1,601,281 to Jackson Hole Land Trust, Jackson, WY, 2011.
$328,650 to Sonoran Institute, Tucson, AZ, 2011.
$250,000 to Wyoming Outdoor Council, Lander, WY, 2011.
$214,071 to Community Foundation of Jackson Hole, Jackson, WY, 2011.
$75,000 to Friends of Pathways, Jackson, WY, 2011.
$65,000 to Teton County Education Foundation, Jackson, WY, 2011.
$30,000 to Pinhead Institute, Telluride, CO, 2011.

9984
The Martin Family Foundation ✧
c/o Larry G. Bean
P.O. Box 50190
Casper, WY 82605-0190 (406) 656-8435
Contact: Cindy Martin Beers, Exec. Dir.
FAX: (406) 656-8436;
E-mail: cindy@martinfamilyfoundation.com; Main URL: http://www.martinfamilyfoundation.com

Established in 2001 in WY.
Donors: John W. Martin; Larry G. Bean; Robin Smith; Cynthia Beers.
Foundation type: Independent foundation.
Financial data (yr. ended 12/31/12): Assets, $26,271,708 (M); gifts received, $4,016,286; expenditures, $1,930,525; qualifying distributions, $1,861,581; giving activities include $1,823,300 for 60 grants (high: $150,000; low: $4,000).
Purpose and activities: The foundation believes that strong communities are a reflection of strong families. It is dedicated to supporting programs that build family values and create assets for communities. It tends to concentrate its resources within areas that impact children, religion, education, and health and human services.
Fields of interest: Higher education; Human services; Children/youth, services; Christian agencies & churches.
Type of support: General/operating support; Capital campaigns; Building/renovation; Program development; Seed money; Scholarship funds; Matching/challenge support.
Limitations: Giving primarily in CO, MT and WY. No support for political or lobbying organizations, or for arts and cultural organizations. No grants to individuals, or for endowments.
Publications: Application guidelines.
Application information:
Initial approach: Letter of inquiry to be submitted electronically, via foundation web site
Deadline(s): Varies; see foundation web site
Board meeting date(s): Varies; generally in Feb. or Mar., May or June, and Nov. or Dec.
Final notification: Generally, within 2-3 months
Officers and Directors:* John W. Martin,* Pres.; Brian J. Martin,* Secy.; Larry G. Bean,* Treas.; Cynthia L. Martin Beers,* Exec. Dir.; Mari Ann Martin.
Number of staff: 1 full-time professional.
EIN: 830335099
Selected grants: The following grants are a representative sample of this grantmaker's funding activity:
$25,000 to Central Wyoming Rescue Mission, Casper, WY, 2012. For operating matching grant.
$25,000 to Mile High Ministries, Denver, CO, 2012. For program support grant.
$5,000 to Regis University, Denver, CO, 2012. For scholarship grant.

9985
The Henry A. McKinnell Foundation ✧ ☆
P.O. Box 524
Jackson, WY 83001-0524
Application address: Robert J. Miller, Esq. c/o Day Pitney LLP, 1 Canterbury Green, Stamford, CT 06901, tel.: (203) 977-7300

Donor: Henry A. McKinnell.
Foundation type: Independent foundation.
Financial data (yr. ended 12/31/13): Assets, $15,943,467 (M); gifts received, $3,141,317; expenditures, $930,263; qualifying distributions, $873,822; giving activities include $873,822 for 6 grants (high: $850,000; low: $100).
Fields of interest: Health care; Diseases (rare) research.
Limitations: Applications accepted. Giving primarily in Washington, DC.
Application information: Application form not required.
Initial approach: Proposal
Deadline(s): None
Trustee: Henry A. McKinnell.
EIN: 271279165
Selected grants: The following grants are a representative sample of this grantmaker's funding activity:
$13,568 to Vanguard Charitable Endowment Program, Boston, MA, 2012. For programs and activities.
$5,000 to Stanford University, Graduate School of Business, Stanford, CA, 2012. For programs and activities.

9986
The McMurry Foundation ✧
P.O. Box 2016
Casper, WY 82602-2016
Contact: Trudi McMurry, Fdn. Dir.
FAX: (307) 234-4631; E-mail: trudi@mcmurry.net; Additional e-mail: Jaci Schoup, Asst. Dir., Jschoup@mcmurry.net; Main URL: http://www.mcmurryfoundation.org/

Established in 1998 in WY.
Donors: Neil A. McMurry; Susie McMurry.
Foundation type: Independent foundation.
Financial data (yr. ended 12/31/13): Assets, $53,299,122 (M); gifts received, $1,000,000; expenditures, $5,498,106; qualifying distributions, $4,767,936; giving activities include $4,498,739 for 108 grants (high: $1,200,000; low: $55).
Purpose and activities: The foundation places special emphasis on the areas of education, religion, children and advocacy for children, health and human services, the arts and humanities, and a favorable business environment. In carrying out its work, the foundation is guided by the values of excellence and compassion. The foundation invests in innovative ventures as well as established community programs that have the potential to make a lasting difference. It provides seed money to start new programs as well as general funds to expand or improve services offered by established agencies. The foundation also helps organizations within its community become more self-sufficient and efficient through strategic planning, increasing management capacity and board development, in order to better serve community needs.
Fields of interest: Humanities; Arts; Education; Human services; Children/youth, services; Religion; Infants/toddlers; Children/youth; Children; Adults; Aging; Disabilities, people with.
Type of support: Scholarship funds; General/operating support; Continuing support; Capital campaigns; Building/renovation; Equipment; Endowments; Emergency funds; Program development; Seed money; Technical assistance.
Limitations: Applications accepted. Giving primarily in WY, with special emphasis on Natrona County. No grants to individuals.
Publications: Application guidelines.
Application information: See web site for application guidelines. Application form required.
Initial approach: Online letter of inquiry
Copies of proposal: 1
Deadline(s): See web site for current deadlines
Board meeting date(s): Quarterly
Final notification: Within 2 months
Officers and Directors:* Mick McMurry,* Pres.; Susie McMurry,* Secy.; George Bryce,* Treas.
Number of staff: 1 full-time professional; 2 part-time professional.
EIN: 830323982
Selected grants: The following grants are a representative sample of this grantmaker's funding activity:
$1,000,000 to University of Wyoming Foundation, Laramie, WY, 2012. For McMurry Foundation College of Business Dean's Excellence Fund.
$412,626 to Saint Anthony Tri-Parish Catholic School, Casper, WY, 2012. For matching grant to Joy Fund.

$300,000 to Mercer Family Resource Center, Casper, WY, 2012. For Prevention With Purpose capital campaign.
$200,000 to Wyoming Medical Center Foundation, Casper, WY, 2012. For Get ER Done, Emergency Department renovation campaign.
$166,666 to Literacy Leadership, Davenport, IA, 2012. For We Read Project.
$150,000 to Kelly Walsh High School, Casper, WY, 2012. For East Casper Community Activity Complex.
$125,000 to University of Wyoming Foundation, Laramie, WY, 2012. For McMurry Graduate Assistantship for Western Thunder Marching Band.
$71,000 to YMCA, Casper Family, Casper, WY, 2012. For Strong Kids Campaign.
$15,000 to Make-A-Wish Foundation of Wyoming, Casper, Wy, 2012. For operating support.
$12,346 to Troopers Drum and Bugle Corps, Casper, WY, 2012. For general operating support.

9987
The Niner Foundation, Inc. ✧
P.O. Box 6754
Jackson, WY 83002-6754 (203) 536-1022
Contact: Richard T. Niner, Chair. and Pres.

Established in 1996 in CT.
Donor: Richard T. Niner.
Foundation type: Independent foundation.
Financial data (yr. ended 12/31/13): Assets, $12,372,000 (M); expenditures, $470,116; qualifying distributions, $470,116; giving activities include $462,238 for 21 grants (high: $100,000; low: $2,000).
Fields of interest: Higher education; Education; Botanical gardens; Human services; Catholic agencies & churches.
Limitations: Applications accepted. Giving primarily in CT, NJ, NY, VA and WY. No grants to individuals.
Application information: Application form required.
Initial approach: Proposal
Deadline(s): None
Officers and Directors:* Richard T. Niner,* Chair. and Pres.; Pamela S. Niner,* V.P.; Kathryn S. Niner,* Secy.; Andrew S. Niner,* Treas.
EIN: 061468635

9988
B. F. & Rose H. Perkins Foundation ✧
45 E. Loucks St., Ste. 110
Sheridan, WY 82801-6329 (307) 674-8871
FAX: (307) 674-8803;
E-mail: bfperkin@fiberpipe.net; Main URL: http://www.perkinsfoundation.org/

Established in 1933 in WY.
Donor: Benjamin F. Perkins†.
Foundation type: Independent foundation.
Financial data (yr. ended 12/31/12): Assets, $9,428,191 (M); expenditures, $829,199; qualifying distributions, $1,014,578; giving activities include $590,500 for 5 grants (high: $550,000; low: $3,500), $79,843 for 67 grants to individuals, $238,540 for 50 loans to individuals, and $32,263 for foundation-administered programs.
Purpose and activities: Medical and educational assistance to individuals under the age of 21; recipients of educational loans must be graduates of a Sheridan County, Wyoming, high school.
Fields of interest: Higher education; Youth, services; Economically disadvantaged.
Type of support: General/operating support; Grants to individuals; Student loans—to individuals.
Limitations: Applications accepted. Giving limited to residents of Sheridan County, WY.
Publications: Application guidelines; Informational brochure.
Application information: Minimum 1 year residency in Sheridan County, WY. Application form required.
Initial approach: Letter
Copies of proposal: 1
Deadline(s): June 1 for fall registration; 1st of each month for other educational grants and for medical grants
Board meeting date(s): Third Tues. or second to last Tues. of each month
Officers and Trustees:* Victor Garber,* Chair.; Paddy Bard,* Vice-Chair.; Stephen D. Carroll,* Treas.; George P. Fletcher; Michael Pilch.
Number of staff: 1 full-time professional; 5 full-time support; 2 part-time support.
EIN: 830138740

9989
Homer A. & Mildred S. Scott Foundation ✧
P.O. Box 2007
Sheridan, WY 82801-2007 (307) 672-1448
Contact: Jenny Craft, Exec. Dir.
FAX: (307) 672-1443; E-mail: jenny.craft@fib.com; Foundation office telephone: (307) 672-1440; Main URL: http://www.scottfoundation.org
Grants List: http://www.scottfoundation.org/grant-recipients/

Established in 1982 in WY.
Donors: Homer A. Scott†; Mildred S. Scott†.
Foundation type: Independent foundation.
Financial data (yr. ended 02/28/14): Assets, $27,616,227 (M); expenditures, $1,228,922; qualifying distributions, $1,120,378; giving activities include $969,335 for 274 grants (high: $125,000; low: $25).
Purpose and activities: The trustees will look favorably upon grant requests that are designed to intervene in and prevent the problems of young people; build public awareness of early childhood and youth issues particularly in Sheridan County, WY; and promote coordination and communication among programs and agencies serving young people and the larger community. The trustees also encourage grants that support community development and improvement.
Fields of interest: Humanities; Arts; Education; Health care; Human services; Children/youth, services; Community/economic development; Infants/toddlers; Children/youth; Children.
Type of support: General/operating support; Continuing support; Management development/capacity building; Program development; Curriculum development; Scholarship funds; Employee matching gifts; Matching/challenge support.
Limitations: Applications accepted. Giving within a 35-mile radius of Sheridan, WY, and in specific areas of MT. No grants to individuals.
Publications: Application guidelines; Grants list; Program policy statement.
Application information: Application form required.
Initial approach: Telephone or e-mail for guidelines
Copies of proposal: 1
Deadline(s): Varies, contact office for dates
Board meeting date(s): Quarterly
Final notification: 1 week after board meeting
Officer and Trustees:* Jenny Craft, Exec. Dir.; Jay M. McGinnis; Tom S. Heyneman; Mark Kinner; Lynette Scott; Michelle Sullivan; Sandra Scott Suzor; Arin Waddell.
Number of staff: 1 full-time professional.
EIN: 742250381

9990
The Seeley Foundation ✧
P.O. Box 513
Wilson, WY 83014-0513
Contact: Ellen Fales Roberts, V.P.

Incorporated in 1945 in MI.
Donors: Halsted H. Seeley†; Laurel H. Seeley†.
Foundation type: Independent foundation.
Financial data (yr. ended 12/31/13): Assets, $14,853,526 (M); expenditures, $694,288; qualifying distributions, $632,292; giving activities include $631,000 for 31 grants (high: $80,000; low: $1,300).
Purpose and activities: Giving primarily for performing arts and arts centers, protection of the environment, conservation, health and human services.
Fields of interest: Arts; Environment; Recreation; Human services.
Type of support: General/operating support; Continuing support; Annual campaigns; Capital campaigns; Equipment; Endowments; Seed money; Research.
Limitations: Applications not accepted. Giving primarily in CA, CT, KS, MO, VA and WY. No grants to individuals.
Application information: The foundation engages in objective grantmaking. Unsolicited requests or proposals are not considered or acknowledged.
Board meeting date(s): Oct.
Officers and Trustees:* Judith S. Renshaw,* Co-Pres. and Treas.; Miles P. Seeley,* Co-Pres.; Ellen Fales Roberts,* V.P. and Secy.; Dana M. Seeley.
Number of staff: None.
EIN: 366049991
Selected grants: The following grants are a representative sample of this grantmaker's funding activity:
$75,000 to Kansas City Ballet Association, Kansas City, MO, 2012.
$75,000 to Nature Conservancy, Virginia Office, Charlottesville, VA, 2012.
$30,000 to San Elijo Lagoon Conservancy, Encinitas, CA, 2012.
$20,000 to Planned Parenthood Federation of America, New York, NY, 2012.
$15,000 to Kansas City Symphony, Kansas City, MO, 2012.
$15,000 to Planned Parenthood of the Rocky Mountains, Denver, CO, 2012.
$10,000 to Lyric Opera of Kansas City, Kansas City, MO, 2012.

9991
Seven Pillars Foundation ✧
P.O. Box 2091
Sheridan, WY 82801-2091 (307) 675-5098
Contact: Hannah Barnes, Secy.

Foundation type: Independent foundation.
Financial data (yr. ended 12/31/12): Assets, $1,749,094 (M); gifts received, $1,419,496; expenditures, $2,257,725; qualifying distributions, $2,247,105; giving activities include $2,223,105 for 16 grants (high: $1,000,000).
Purpose and activities: Giving primarily to Christian organizations to spread the word of Jesus Christ.
Fields of interest: Christian agencies & churches.
Limitations: Giving in the U.S., with emphasis on WY.
Application information:
Initial approach: Proposal
Deadline(s): None
Final notification: Within 6 weeks
Officers: Casey H. Osborn, Pres.; Susan J. Osborn, V.P. and Treas.; Hannah Barnes, Secy.
EIN: 263174574

9992
George B. Storer Foundation, Inc. ✧
P.O. Box 8159
Jackson, WY 83002-8159 (307) 733-0800
Contact: Kathleen Belk, Exec. Dir.
E-mail: Kathleen@storerfoundation.org; Additional tel. and fax: (307) 733-0805

Incorporated in 1955 in FL.
Foundation type: Independent foundation.
Financial data (yr. ended 12/31/13): Assets, $75,103,947 (M); expenditures, $4,410,768; qualifying distributions, $3,604,123; giving activities include $2,965,000 for 41 grants (high: $242,000; low: $2,000).
Purpose and activities: Giving primarily for educational, environmental and medical purposes.
Fields of interest: Arts; Higher education; Environment, natural resources; Hospitals (general); Human services; Children/youth, services; Disabilities, people with.
Type of support: General/operating support; Building/renovation; Endowments; Research; Matching/challenge support.
Limitations: Applications not accepted. Giving primarily in WY, OH, and the Intermountain West. No grants for scholarships or fellowships; no multi-year pledges or endowments; no loans.
Publications: Grants list.
Application information: Unsolicited requests for funds not accepted.
Board meeting date(s): Dec.
Officers: Elizabeth Storer, Pres.; Suzie Hultman, C.O.O.
Trustees: Linda Anderson; John Flicker; Doug Givens; Luther Propst; Leslie Smith Self; Dede Storer; Peter Storer, Jr.
EIN: 596136392

9993
Elbridge & Evelyn Stuart Foundation ✧
c/o Pendleton Fiduciary Management, Inc.
P.O. Box 1905
Jackson, WY 83001-1905 (310) 551-7618
Contact: Bny Mellon
*Application address:*1 Wall St., New York,NY 10286 (310) 551-7618

Trust established in 1961 in CA.
Foundation type: Independent foundation.
Financial data (yr. ended 12/31/12): Assets, $7,520,683 (M); expenditures, $596,317; qualifying distributions, $425,000; giving activities include $425,000 for grants.
Purpose and activities: Giving primarily for higher and other education.
Fields of interest: Secondary school/education; Higher education; Youth, services; Christian agencies & churches.
Limitations: Applications accepted. Giving primarily in CA; funding also in WY. No grants to individuals.
Application information: Application form required.
Initial approach: Letter
Deadline(s): None
Trustees: Evelyn Nelson Attaway; Clarke A. Nelson.
EIN: 956014019

9994
Pike and Susan Sullivan Foundation ✧ ☆
P.O. Box 4158
Jackson, WY 83001-4158
Contact: George R. Harris, Exec. Dir. and Treas.
E-mail: grogersh@gmail.com; Application address: P.O. Box 864, Wilson, WY 83014-0864, tel.: (703) 627-0698

Established in WY.
Donor: Pike Sullivan.
Foundation type: Independent foundation.
Financial data (yr. ended 12/31/13): Assets, $4,038,356 (M); expenditures, $1,104,295; qualifying distributions, $1,103,735; giving activities include $1,100,000 for 3 grants (high: $1,050,000; low: $25,000).
Fields of interest: Education.
Limitations: Applications accepted. Giving primarily in Aurora, NY; some funding also in AZ and Washington, DC.
Application information: Application form required.
Initial approach: Letter
Deadline(s): Dec. 31
Officers: Pike Sullivan, Pres. and Secy.; Susan Sullivan, V.P.; George R. Harris, Treas. and Exec. Dir.
EIN: 461127429

9995
The True Foundation ✧
P.O. Box. 2360
Casper, WY 82602-2360 (307) 237-9301

Established in 1958 in WY.
Donors: True Oil LLC; H. A. True, Jr.†; Jean D. True†; H.A. True III.
Foundation type: Company-sponsored foundation.
Financial data (yr. ended 11/30/13): Assets, $1,532,492 (M); expenditures, $538,768; qualifying distributions, $530,175; giving activities include $530,175 for 84 grants (high: $115,300; low: $100).
Purpose and activities: The foundation supports organizations involved with arts and culture, education, health, substance abuse services, legal aid, agriculture, and human services.
Fields of interest: Education; Human services; Community/economic development.
Type of support: General/operating support; Program development; Scholarship funds; Employee-related scholarships.
Limitations: Applications accepted. Giving primarily in WY and the Rocky Mountain area.
Application information: Application form required.
Initial approach: Completed application form
Deadline(s): None
Trustee: H. A. True III.
EIN: 836004596

9996
The Tyrrell Foundation, Inc. ✧ ☆
6800 Ellen Creek Rd., No. 667
Teton Village, WY 83025-0667

Established in 1996 in CT.
Donors: Jonathan T. Dawson; James Thorburn; Deborah Pratt Dawson; Dawson Family Partners, Lp.
Foundation type: Independent foundation.
Financial data (yr. ended 12/31/13): Assets, $17,398,109 (M); expenditures, $692,522; qualifying distributions, $623,846; giving activities include $623,846 for 17 grants (high: $250,000; low: $5,000).
Fields of interest: Elementary school/education; Education; Environment, forests; Human services.
Limitations: Applications not accepted. Giving primarily in CA, CT, MT, NH, and WY. No grants to individuals.
Application information: Contributes only to pre-selected organizations.
Officers and Directors:* Jonathan T. Dawson,* Pres. and Treas.; Judith A. Mack,* V.P. and Secy.; Alexandra Dawson; Christopher Dawson; Deborah Pratt Dawson.
Number of staff: 1 part-time professional.
EIN: 061469527

9997
Joe and Arlene Watt Foundation Inc. ✧
P.O. Box 6085
Sheridan, WY 82801-6085 (307) 672-1498

Established in WY.
Foundation type: Independent foundation.
Financial data (yr. ended 12/31/13): Assets, $24,079,785 (M); expenditures, $1,189,382; qualifying distributions, $1,060,772; giving activities include $1,055,500 for 15 grants (high: $200,000; low: $2,500).
Purpose and activities: Giving primarily to a hospital, as well as for higher education, human services, and to a YMCA.
Fields of interest: Higher education; Hospitals (general); Human services; YM/YWCAs & YM/YWHAs.
Limitations: Applications accepted. Giving primarily in Sheridan, WY.
Publications: Annual report.
Application information: Application form required.
Initial approach: Letter
Deadline(s): None
Officers: Jack E. Pelissier, Pres.; John M. Pradere, V.P.; Robert Eberhart, Secy.-Treas.
Directors: Ky Dixon; Richard Hammer, Jr.; Debra Wendtland.
EIN: 830330482

9998
Whitney Benefits, Inc. ✧
P.O. Box 5085
Sheridan, WY 82801-1385 (307) 674-7303
Contact: Patrick Henderson, Exec. Dir.
FAX: (307) 674-4335;
E-mail: assistant@whitneybenefits.org; Physical

address: 145 N. Connor St., Ste. 1, Sheridan, WY 82801; Main URL: http://www.whitneybenefits.org

Incorporated in 1927 in WY.
Donors: Edward A. Whitney‡; Scott Foundation; Sheridan County YMCA.
Foundation type: Independent foundation.
Financial data (yr. ended 06/30/13): Assets, $127,739,290 (M); expenditures, $7,152,788; qualifying distributions, $8,474,350; giving activities include $6,181,888 for 7 grants (high: $5,716,739; low: $2,207), and $1,872,505 for loans/program-related investments.
Purpose and activities: Giving primarily for the township of Sheridan, WY. The foundation also provides interest-free student loans to men and women with modest financial assistance, so they may pursue undergraduate academic and vocational studies. Applicants should either be graduates of high schools in Sheridan and Johnson counties, WY, GED recipients from Sheridan County, WY, or individuals who have had at least seven years of continuous residency in Sheridan or Johnson County immediately prior to applying for a loan.
Fields of interest: Higher education; Community/economic development.
Type of support: General/operating support; Program-related investments/loans; Student loans—to individuals.
Limitations: Applications accepted. Giving limited to Sheridan County, WY.
Publications: Annual report.
Application information: Applications accepted for loan program only. Application form required.
Initial approach: Request loan application
Board meeting date(s): Monthly
Officers and Directors:* Tom Kinnison,* Pres.; Roy Garber,* V.P.; Tom Belus,* Secy.; Stephen Holst,* Treas.; Patrick Henderson, Exec. Dir.; Maureen Humphrys; Kim Love; Everett McGlothlin; Lori McMullen; Lynie Phipps; Tom Pilch; Robert Prusak; Peter Schoonmaker; Sam Scott.
Number of staff: 1 full-time professional; 1 full-time support.
EIN: 830168511
Selected grants: The following grants are a representative sample of this grantmaker's funding activity:
$114,738 to Sheridan College, Sheridan, WY, 2013. For Property Donation for Sheridan College.

9999
Wyoming Community Foundation ✧
1472 N. 5th St., Ste. 201
Laramie, WY 82072 (307) 721-8300
Contact: For grants: Samin Dadelahi, C.O.O.
FAX: (307) 721-8333; E-mail: wcf@wycf.org; Additional tel.: (866) 708-7878; Grant inquiry e-mail: samin@wycf.org; Main URL: http://www.wycf.org
Facebook: https://www.facebook.com/pages/Wyoming-Community-Foundation/138109556202547
RSS Feed: http://www.wycf.org/feed
YouTube: http://www.youtube.com/wyomingcf

Incorporated in 1989 in WY.
Foundation type: Community foundation.
Financial data (yr. ended 12/31/13): Assets, $108,424,458 (M); gifts received, $7,788,481; expenditures, $5,965,214; giving activities include $2,636,591 for 100 grants, and $111,470 for 88 grants to individuals.
Purpose and activities: The foundation seeks to foster the community and enhance the quality of life for Wyoming residents through asset building, grantmaking and increased civic engagement, participation and leadership. Current statewide areas of need from the foundation's unrestricted funds are children and youth and civic projects.
Fields of interest: Arts; Education; Environment, natural resources; Health care; Health organizations, association; Children/youth, services; Human services; Community development, public/private ventures; Rural development; Community/economic development; Voluntarism promotion.
Type of support: General/operating support; Continuing support; Management development/capacity building; Program development; Conferences/seminars; Seed money; Technical assistance; Program evaluation; Scholarships—to individuals; Matching/challenge support.
Limitations: Applications accepted. Giving primarily in WY. No grants to individuals (except for scholarships), or generally for block grants, capital campaigns, annual campaigns, or debt retirement.
Publications: Application guidelines; Annual report; Grants list; Informational brochure (including application guidelines); Newsletter; Program policy statement.
Application information: Visit foundation web site for online account access, application forms and guidelines. Application form required.
Initial approach: Create online account
Copies of proposal: 11
Deadline(s): June 15 and Dec. 15
Board meeting date(s): Quarterly
Final notification: Sept. 15 and Mar. 15
Officers and Directors:* Diane Harrop,* Chair.; Ryan Lance,* Vice-Chair.; Craig R. Showalter,* C.E.O. and Pres.; Samin Dadelahi, C.O.O.; Misty Gehle, C.F.O.; Connie Brezik,* Secy.; Jim Gersack,* Treas.; Billie Addleman; John Andrikopoulos; Robert B. Betts, Jr.; Kathryn Boswell; Carolyn Bing; Affie Ellis; Alison Ochs Gee; Greg Irwin; Arne Jorgensen; Cathy MacPherson; Douglas McLaughlin; Anna Moscicki; Lollie Benz Plank; Jim Rice; Kent Richins; Scott Sissman; Kathy Tomassi; Sandra Wallop.
Number of staff: 7 full-time professional; 2 full-time support; 1 part-time support.
EIN: 830287513

10000
Zimmerman Family Foundation ✧
400 E. 1st St., Ste. 201
Casper, WY 82601-2560 (307) 473-8975
FAX: (307 235-5350; Main URL: http://www.zfamilyfoundation.com

Established in 1998 in WY.
Donors: Gail D. Zimmerman; Anne D. Zimmerman.
Foundation type: Independent foundation.
Financial data (yr. ended 12/31/12): Assets, $1,878,326 (M); gifts received, $348,670; expenditures, $769,269; qualifying distributions, $756,434; giving activities include $749,671 for 43 grants (high: $225,000; low: $100).
Fields of interest: Education; Medical research, institute; Boys & girls clubs; Human services; Foundations (public); Christian agencies & churches.
Type of support: General/operating support; Continuing support; Annual campaigns; Capital campaigns; Research.
Limitations: Giving primarily in WY. No grants to individuals.
Application information:
Initial approach: Use application process on foundation web site
Board meeting date(s): Dec.
Officer and Directors:* Gail D. Zimmerman,* Pres.; Greg Carroll; Cory Stirling; Renee D. Stirling; Collin Zimmerman; Eva M. Zimmerman; Lily Zimmerman; Michael D. Zimmerman; Mitchel D. Zimmerman; Rhonda S. Zimmerman.
EIN: 830322568

APPENDIX A

The following foundations appeared in the previous edition of *The Foundation Directory* but are not included in this edition for the reasons stated.

Achilles Memorial Fund, Edith & F. M., The
New York, NY
Specified beneficiaries.

Ahlers Charitable Trust, Clifford F.
San Francisco, CA
Specified beneficiary.

Alexander & Baldwin Foundation
Honolulu, HI
The foundation terminated.

Anna Fund, Inc., The
Lauderdale By The Sea, FL
The foundation terminated on Dec. 7, 2011.

Anthony Foundation, Barbara Cox, The
Atlanta, GA
The foundation merged with the Trailsend Foundation on Dec. 7, 2012.

Belo Corporation Foundation, A. H.
See Belo Foundation, The

Belo Foundation, The
(Formerly Belo Corporation Foundation, A. H.)
Dallas, TX
The foundation terminated.

Berry Campbell Trust For Columbia Theological Seminary, Laura
Orlando, FL
Specified beneficiary.

Better and Better Foundation
(Formerly Green Mountain Coffee Roasters Foundation)
Burlington, VT
The foundation terminated June 28, 2013 and transferred its assets to the Stiller Family Foundation.

Blue Knight Foundation, The
(Formerly Griffin Foundation, Kenneth and Anne, The)
Chicago, IL
The foundation terminated in 2013.

Bolden Foundation, Herman & Emmie
Birmingham, AL
The foundation terminated in 2013.

Brennan Trust, Robert E.
Pittsburgh, PA
Specified beneficiaries.

Buck Family Foundation
Jacksonville, FL
Current information not available.

Carlton Foundation, Albert E. and Ethel I.
(Formerly Carlton Trust, The)
Winston-Salem, NC
Specified beneficiaries.

Carlton Trust, The
See Carlton Foundation, Albert E. and Ethel I.

Cash Foundation, Inc., Raymond M., The
Smyrna, GA
The foundation terminated in Sept. 2013.

Chanan Foundation, Inc.
Denver, CO
Specified beneficiary.

Charles Charitable Trust Two, Roy R.
Richmond, VA
The trust terminated in 2010.

City of Hope Self Insurance Trust
See City of Hope-Workers Comp

City of Hope-Workers Comp
(Formerly City of Hope Self Insurance Trust)
San Francisco, CA
Specified beneficiary.

Clapp Foundation, M. Roger and Anne Melby, The
Arlington, MA
The foundation terminated in 2013.

Clisby Charitable Trust, The
See Flagler Foundation, The

CNA Foundation
(Formerly CNA Insurance Companies Foundation)
Chicago, IL
The foundation has terminated.

CNA Insurance Companies Foundation
See CNA Foundation

Cooper Industries Foundation
Houston, TX
The foundation terminated.

Crapo Charitable Foundation, Henry H.
New Bedford, MA
The foundation terminated in 2010.

Culver Theatre Foundation
See DeVito/Perlman Family Foundation, The

Davis Foundation, Irene E. and George A., The
Springfield, MA
Duplicate foundation record.

DeVito/Perlman Family Foundation, The
(Formerly Culver Theatre Foundation)
Los Angeles, CA
Current information not available.

Dillon, Jr. Foundation, Roderick H.
Columbus, OH
The foundation terminated in 2011.

Douglass Foundation, Terry D. and Rosann B., The
Knoxville, TN
The foundation terminated in 2011.

Draper Foundation
Winsted, CT
The foundation terminated and transferred its assets to the Community Foundation of Northwest Connecticut, Inc. in 2014.

Dunn Foundation Inc., Elizabeth Ordway
Miami, FL
The foundation is in the process of terminating.

EJF Foundation
Bismarck, ND
The foundation terminated in 2013.

Elkins for Hahnemann, George
Pittsburgh, PA
Specified beneficiary.

Empower Baltimore Management Corporation
Baltimore, MD
The foundation terminated in 2013.

Farmhouse Foundation, The
Rockland, DE
The foundation terminated in 2011.

First Data Foundation
Greenwood Village, CO
The foundation terminated in 2013.

Flagler Foundation, The
(Formerly Clisby Charitable Trust, The)
Richmond, VA
The foundation terminated in 2012.

Fluor Foundation, Marjorie L. and J. Simon
Golden, CO
Current information not available.

Fotsch Foundation, The
Brookfield, WI
The foundation terminated in 2014.

Fund for Children of the Americas, The
Montvale, NJ
Current information not available.

Gelman Trust, Jacques and Natasha
New York, NY
The foundation terminated in 2013, and transferred all of its assets to the Jacques & Natasha Gelman Foundation, Inc.

Goizueta Foundation, The
Atlanta, GA
The foundation terminated and transferred its assets to The Goizueta Foundation Inc.

Great Bay Foundation
(Formerly Great Bay Foundation for Social Entrepreneurship)
Portland, ME
The foundation terminated in 2013.

Great Bay Foundation for Social Entrepreneurship
See Great Bay Foundation

Green Mountain Coffee Roasters Foundation
See Better and Better Foundation

Griffin Charitable Trust, Helen
Providence, RI
Specified beneficiaries.

Griffin Foundation, Kenneth and Anne, The
See Blue Knight Foundation, The

Grousbeck Family Foundation
Stanford, CA
The foundation terminated in 2012.

Gurvetch Foundation
Dallas, TX
The foundation terminated in 2013, and distributed its assets to the Gurvetch Vision Assistance Fund, to be managed by the Dallas Jewish Community Foundation.

H. P. Farrington-Hpf Foundation Rsdy
Providence, RI
Specified beneficiaries.

Haas Foundation, Chuck & Ellen, The
Cupertino, CA
The foundation terminated in 2013.

Hale Family Foundation
Overland Park, KS
The foundation terminated in 2013.

Hall Foundation, Inc.
Meridian, MS
The foundation terminated in 2011.

Hambro Family Foundation
Perrysburg, OH
The foundation terminated in 2010.

Henfield Foundation, The
See McCrindle Foundation, Joseph F.

HJW Foundation
(Formerly Wyss Foundation, Hansjoerg)
Washington, DC
The HJW Foundation merged with The Wyss Foundation on 12/31/2013.

HKH Foundation
New York, NY
The foundation terminated in 2013.

Isaacs Brothers Foundation, The
Del Mar, CA
The foundation terminated in 2011.

John and Hasmik Foundation
Beverly Hills, CA
The foundation terminated in 2013.

Katz Foundation, Inc., Marilyn & Stanley
Palm Beach, FL
Current information not available.

Kaufman Dance Foundation, Glorya
Los Angeles, CA
Pursuant to a reorganization, the foundation transferred its assets to the Glorya Kaufman Dance Foundation, EIN: 806167949.

Keller Foundation, George M. and Adelaide M., The
Denver, CO
The foundation terminated in 2010.

Kennedy Family Foundation, Louis and Clara, The
Beverly Hills, CA
The foundation terminated in 2013.

Kennedy Funding Invitational Corporation, The
New City, NY
Current information not available.

Ketterlinus Trust f/b/o University of Pennsylvania Hospital, E.
Pittsburgh, PA
Specified beneficiary.

Kitchen Window Foundation, The
Winstom-Salem, NC
The foundation terminated in 2013.

Knabusch Charitable Trust No. 1, Edward M. and Henrietta M.
Monroe, MI
The foundation terminated in 2014.

Lambe Charitable Foundation, Claude R.
Wichita, KS
The foundation terminated in 2013, and transferred its assets to the Fidelity Investments Charitable Gift Fund.

Leach II Foundation, Charles Henry
Pittsburgh, PA
The foundation terminated in 2013.

Lee Foundation, Rowena, The
(Formerly Teagle Foundation, The)
New York, NY
The foundation merged with The Teagle Foundation.

Leeoma Charitable Trust
Boulder, CO
The foundation terminated in 2011.

Lewis Jr. Charitable Foundation, Carol Sutton & William M., The
New York, NY
The foundation terminated in 2011.

Lockhard H.E.R.C., J. M. Ally
Pittsburgh, PA
Specified beneficiary.

M.E. Foundation, The
Lampeter, PA
The foundation terminated on Dec. 31, 2012.

Martin Foundation Inc., Gloria
Miami, FL
Current information not available.

Matthew Six Ten Foundation, Inc.
Wheaton, IL
Current information not available.

McCrindle Foundation, Joseph F.
(Formerly Henfield Foundation, The)
New York, NY
The foundation terminated in 2013.

McKesson Foundation
Cleveland, OH
Specified beneficiary.

Meadowlark Foundation
Denver, CO
The foundation terminated in 2011.

Miller Trust, Darius
Providence, RI
Specified beneficiary.

Mitnick Fund, Louis
See Mitnick Trust, Louis

Mitnick Trust, Louis
(Formerly Mitnick Fund, Louis)
Providence, RI
Specified beneficiaries.

Muse Foundation, The
Cleveland, OH
The foundation terminated in 2013.

O'Hara Trust, J.B.
Dallas, TX
Specified beneficiary.

O'Malley Foundation, Inc., The
Amawalk, NY
The foundation terminated in 2013.

Occupational Physicians Scholarship Fund
Elk Grove Village, IL
The foundation terminated in 2011.

Original Sorenson Legacy Foundation
(Formerly Sorenson Legacy Foundation, The)
Salt Lake City, UT
The foundation terminated on Dec. 28, 2012 and distributed its assets to Sorenson Legacy Foundation and Sorenson Impact Foundation.

Pfeiffer Family Foundation
Newark, DE
The foundation terminated in 2010.

Promise Foundation, Matt's
See Promise Foundation, The

Promise Foundation, The
(Also known as Promise Foundation, Matt's)
Brooklyn, NY
Status changed to public charity.

Rhoads Foundation, Ross R. & Sara G.
Charlotte, NC
Specified beneficiary.

Rhodebeck Charitable Trust
New York, NY
The foundation is in the process of terminating and is transferring all of its assets to Community Funds, Inc.

Rinpoche International Charitable Foundation, Kangyur
Santa Fe, NM
Specified beneficiary.

Riverside Foundation Charitable Trust, The
Lampeter, PA
The foundation terminated in 2013.

Rose Family Foundation, The
(Formerly Rose Foundation, Karen & Gary)
New York, NY
The foundation terminated in 2014.

Rose Foundation, Karen & Gary
See Rose Family Foundation, The

Ruffin Foundation, Peter B. and Adeline W.
New York, NY
Duplicate foundation record.

Rumsey Foundation, Mary A. H.
New York, NY
The foundation terminated in 2013.

Rylander Memorial Library Trust
Milwaukee, WI
The trust terminated in 2012 and transferred its assets to Friends of The Rylander Memorial Library.

Sacerdote Foundation, Peter M., The
New York, NY
Current information not available.

Saint Joseph Hospital Trust
Dallas, TX
Current information not available.

Scheinfeld Foundation, Larry and Jane, The
New York, NY
Current information not available.

Sclavos Family Foundation
Palo Alto, CA
The foundation terminated in 2010.

Seacor Foundation
Ft. Lauderdale, FL
The foundation has terminated in 2012.

Seed Capital Development Fund, Ltd.
New York, NY
The fund terminated on Dec. 23, 2013.

Serrato Foundation, Jose Carlos and Margaret Francis
Atlanta, GA
Current information not available.

Sharp Foundation
See Sharp Foundation, Peter Jay, The

Sharp Foundation, Peter Jay, The
(Formerly Sharp Foundation)
New York, NY
The foundation terminated on October 29, 2014.

Shea Family Foundation
Philadelphia, PA
The foundation terminated in 2013.

Simon Family Foundation, Herbert, The
Indianapolis, IN
The foundation terminated on Oct. 31, 2013.

Sisler Foundation, Joe & Charlyne
Clovis, NM
Current information not available.

Sledd Foundation Charitable
Pittsburgh, PA
Specified beneficiaries.

Smithville Charitable Fund
Ellettsville, IN
The foundation terminated in 2013, and transferred its assets to a newly formed corporation, Smithfield Charitable Foundation.

Sorenson Legacy Foundation, The
See Original Sorenson Legacy Foundation

Soroka Charitable Trust, William
La Jolla, CA
The trust terminated in 2013.

Soros Charitable Foundation
New York, NY
The foundation terminated on July 18, 2012.

Spirit Services, Inc.
Seven Hills, OH
The foundation terminated in 2011.

Square D Foundation
Palatine, IL
The foundation terminated in April, 2014.

Stabler Foundation, Donald B., The
Harrisburg, PA
The foundation terminated in 2013.

Stip Charitable Remainder Unitrust, Milo
Sioux Falls, SD
Specified beneficiaries.

Suubi Project, The
Mansfield, TX
Status changed to public charity.

Sweetfeet Foundation, Inc.
Roseland, NJ
Specified beneficiary.

Taishoff Family Foundation Inc., The
Naples, FL
Duplicate record.

Teagle Foundation, The
See Lee Foundation, Rowena, The

Thornton Trust Venable Memorial Fund
Orlando, FL
Specified beneficiaries.

Tibstra Charitable Foundation, Thomas & Gertrude
Pennington, NJ
Current information not available.

University of Rochester Rivas Clinic UA HWR
Providence, RI
Specified beneficiary.

W. I. H. Pitts Memorial Fund
Orlando, FL
Specified beneficiaries.

Wallach Foundation, Miriam G. and Ira D.
Purchase, NY
The foundation terminated in 2013.

Watanabe Charitable Trust, Terry K.
San Jose, CA
Current information not available.

Woods Foundation, Abbey
Frankfort, IL
The foundation terminated in 2011.

Wunderman Family Foundation, Severin, The
Las Vegas, NV
The foundation merged with The Severin Wunderman Family Foundation, a Nevada nonprofit public benefit corporation.

Wyss Foundation, Hansjoerg
See HJW Foundation

APPENDIX B

The following organizations are classified as private non-operating foundations under the IRS tax code. On the basis of statements from the organizations or an analysis of their most recent fiscal statements, it appears that these foundations contribute only to a few specified beneficiaries or to the support of a single organization or institution. Therefore, they are not included in this volume. Without further information, grantseekers are advised NOT to apply to these foundations for grant support. EIN refers to the Employer Indentification Number assigned to the foundation by the IRS.

STATE	EIN
Alabama	
Beeson Charitable Remainder, Lucille S., Mobile	726278911
Beeson Charitable Trust, Dwight M., Birmingham	636150745
Forchheimer Memorial Foundation, Louis & Josie, Mobile	636161119
Roberts Charitable Trust, Belle G., Mobile	726214520
Roberts Charitable Trust, E. A., Mobile	636215720
Arizona	
Salter Family Foundation Inc, Peter and Nancy, Paradise Valley	201828772
Shaw Foundation., Mary Elizabeth Dee, Phoenix	876116370
California	
1140 Foundation, The, Saratoga	770456449
Ahlers Charitable Trust, Clifford F., San Francisco	956187060
Anderson Living Trust, Clarence E., The, Valencia	957121299
Bowles Memorial Fund, Ethel Wilson & Robert, Pasadena	956481575
Braun Trust, Carl F., Los Angeles	956016828
Carr Foundation, William George, Calistoga	202927907
City of Hope-Workers Comp, San Francisco	953935626
Colburn Music Fund, Los Angeles	954804766
Friends of Wonderland, Los Angeles	954296007
Fund for Humanity United, Los Gatos	262583590
Hammer United World College Trust, Armand, The, Los Angeles	954031114
Hartwell Charitable Trust, Constance, Santa Monica	686251551
Kelly Family Foundation, Matthew, San Mateo	261151512
Lynch Trust, Frank, San Francisco	956010453
McMahan Foundation, Catherine L. & Robert O., Carmel	946061273
Powell Foundation, Charles Lee, The, La Jolla	237064397
Scandinavian Consortium for Organizational Research, Stanford	770392307
Simon Foundation, Norton, The, Pasadena	956035908
Swall Foundation, San Francisco	946169932
Wyman Charitable Foundation f/b/o Southern California Chapter, Arthritis Foundation, Jane, Los Angeles	261842108
Colorado	
Berry Foundation, Walter V. and Idun Y., Estes Park	330284355
Chanan Foundation, Inc., Denver	300211587
Davis 1993 Charitable Trust, Sam & Freda, The, Englewood	846261346
Delaware	
Bishop Trust for SPCA Manatee County, Edward E., Wilmington	237366312
Cantwell's Bridge Foundation, Greenville	510385661
Coughlin Foundation, Inc., Bert T., The, Wilmington	611446700
Foster Fund, Jane M.G., The, Newark	137037154
Lesieur Foundation, Henri and Flore, Newark	510378395

STATE	EIN
Florida	
Ackland Trust, William H., Jacksonville	526029941
Bacardi Foundation, Fort Lauderdale	650342998
Berry Campbell Trust For Columbia Theological Seminary, Laura, Orlando	586320346
Campbell Trust, Laura, Orlando	586320345
Clark Foundation, Virginia W., Jacksonville	597256496
Culbreath Trust f/b/o First Baptist Church of Tampa, Jacksonville	596131254
Donor Irrevocable Trust, Orlando	526027109
Genius Foundation, Elizabeth Morse, Winter Park	136115217
Gies Charitable Foundation Trust, Father Norman Joseph, Jacksonville	597012346
Hall Charitable Foundation, D. Ray and Sibyl, Williston	597190426
Holdcroft Trust, Samuel W., Jacksonville	546030447
Jenkins III Trust, Hershel, Jacksonville	586346914
Krauss, Miller, Lutz Charitable Trust Foundation, Inc., Tampa	201727663
Thornton Trust Venable Memorial Fund, Orlando	586174419
Titus Foundation, Ray E. & Staseli B., The, West Palm Beach	592828498
Townsend Irrevocable Trust, Martha G., Orlando	522006240
VA Museum of Fine Arts Trust, Jacksonville	546030663
W. I. H. Pitts Charitable Trust, Orlando	586374907
W. I. H. Pitts Memorial Fund, Orlando	586374908
Williams for VCU, A.D., Jacksonville	546030516
Georgia	
Glass Family Foundation, James W., Duluth	586292832
Idaho	
Opportunity Foundation, Inc., The, Coeur D' Alene	263928645
Illinois	
Allen Charitable Trust, Harry J., Chicago	656386878
American Friends of Ophel Bas Zion Inc., Chicago	363566181
Bohmfalk Charitable Trust, Chicago	133501941
Coon Foundation, Owen L., Chicago	366066907
JJY Family Foundation, La Grange	266156331
Johnston Wright Memorial Trust, Dr. Marius E. and Margaret, Chicago	626200642
Knaphurst Family Trust, Frank A., Chicago	616357627
Knaphurst Trust f/b/o St Paul UCC, Frances H., Chicago	616357839
Knaphurst Trust f/b/o St. Paul Health Care Center, Frances H., Chicago	616357841
Mandel, Jr. Foundation, Edna and Fred L., Chicago	311734957
Potter Trust, Valerie Blair, Chicago	581309898
Pro Archia Foundation, The, Chicago	366784984
Progressive Education Foundation, Inc., Chicago	300259919
Ross Fund, Earl and Erna, The, Chicago	136317580
Salwil Foundation, Chicago	363377945
Schulte Trust, Helen D., Chicago	366459927
Souers Charitable Trust, Chicago	436079817

STATE	EIN
Tyson Fund, Chicago	356009973
White Memorial Trust, Kelton E. & Alma M., Chicago	436236634
Young Charity Trust, Chicago	366897850
Indiana	
Basso Foundation, Virginia Kells, The, Indianapolis	050601767
Goodrich Charitable Trust, John B., Muncie	356214045
Goodrich Trust FBO Hanover College, Percy E., Evansville	356020284
Louisiana	
McFarland Trust, D. A., New Orleans	582003466
Maryland	
Michael Trust, Catherine Iola, Baltimore	206988404
Pollin Foundation, Inc., Linda and Kenneth, Chevy Chase	521510398
Smith School of Business Foundation Inc., Robert H., The, College Park	237332043
Massachusetts	
Adams Trust, Seth, Boston	237125976
Aequa Foundation, Boston	716225066
Ashton Trust, Elisha V., Boston	046016303
Eaton Memorial Fund, Georgiana Goddard, Boston	046112820
Leach Memorial Home, Ellen M., Sterling	010485292
Ragon Institute Foundation, Phillip and Susan, Cambridge	263919459
Roxbury Home for Aged Women, West Roxbury	042104858
Spector Foundation, Boston	271536343
Students House Incorportated, Boston	042105949
Michigan	
Lee Charitable Foundation, Charles O., Jr. & Louise K., Bloomfield Hills	206559686
Minnie Ballenger Trust 1302 f/b/o Womens Hosp, Flint	386041158
Tiffany Charitable Trust, Wilda C., Traverse City	306092098
Valade Endowment for the Arts, Gretchen C., The, St. Clair Shores	043843795
Minnesota	
Barnes Memorial Fund, Edna C., Minneapolis	431960285
Dunwoody Trust, Kate L., St. Paul	416014903
Hotchkiss Foundation, W. R., St. Paul	416038562
Minnesota American Legion and Auxiliary Research Foundation, St. Paul	510172292
Whiteside Charitable Trust, Muriel, St. Paul	416370669
Missouri	
Bohan Foundation, Ruth H., Kansas City	436269867
Frank A. Ruf Trust, St. Louis	436018953
Frank And Mattie Thompson Trust, St. Louis	436019079
Humane Society Of Missouri Trust, St. Louis	436018587
Jordan Trust, Mary R., St. Louis	436019552
Parrish Charitable Trust, Elizabeth, St. Louis	436673904
Reilly Trust, Richard G., Clayton	026169187
Montana	
Haynes Foundation, Helena	816013577
Nebraska	
Cabela Family Foundation, Sidney	470833542
Nevada	
Bing Fund Corporation, Reno	942476169
New Hampshire	
Rowell Intervivos Trust, Annie L., Concord	026110470

STATE	EIN
New Jersey	
B'Seter Foundation, Inc., Matan, Roseland	223692921
Fernholz Foundation, Lebanon	900403980
Highstead Fund, Inc., The, Red Bank	205823379
NSN Foundation, Inc., Roseland	223769097
Quercus Fund, Inc., The, Red Bank	134156738
Sweetfeet Foundation, Inc., Roseland	223271692
New Mexico	
Rinpoche International Charitable Foundation, Kangyur, Santa Fe	272545756
New York	
136 Fund, New York	261595284
Achilles Memorial Fund, Edith & F. M., The, New York	137102170
American Friends of Binyan-Av Foundation, Inc., Brooklyn	113472950
American Friends of Sfath Emeth Yeshiva, Brooklyn	113613483
Avi Chai House, Inc., New York	271601574
Bamberger Foundation, Eileen W., New York	137053837
Bayer Family Fund, Inc., The, New York	134085263
Blenheim Foundation, The, New York	133258422
Borrego Foundation, Inc., Larchmont	133980920
Brown University Charitable Trust, New York	137070437
Brunner Foundation, Inc., Robert, The, New York	136067212
Dunning Trust, Eleanor M., Long Island City	137442896
Friends of San Andres Inc, New York	651180666
Goldberg Family Foundation, Inc., A. & D., New York	202560710
Good News Foundation Trust, New Hartford	166413692
HLMH, Inc., New York	134072644
JG Family Foundation, The, New York	133748049
JLRJ, Inc., New York	134077806
LMCL, Inc., New York	134077883
Lockhart Trust, John Marshall, New York	136042350
Lurje Memorial Foundation, S. & J., New York	136176033
MRHM, Inc., New York	134077880
Murphy Charitable Fund, George E. & Annette Cross, New York	136887044
Netanya Foundation, Inc., The, New York	521594262
New HAFTR Fund, The, Lawrence	266148234
Phipps Family Foundation, John S., New York	136861582
Ryan Foundation, Inc., Nina M., The, Cold Spring	136111038
Steinhardt Family Foundation, New York	137067570
Stibbe Charitable Trust, Katherine S., Long Island City	226715670
Wehle, Sr. Foundation, Inc., John L., Rochester	223041829
Whitehead Trust f/b/o The National Spiritual Assembly of the Baha'is Trust, O.Z., New York	137202416
Williams Care-Salvation Army, Thomas Lyle, New York	366673112
North Carolina	
Carlton Foundation, Albert E. and Ethel I., Winston-Salem	846331869
Deaver Fund, Delema G., The, Charlotte	237745467
Elkins Fund, Lewis, Charlotte	236214962
Harrison Jr. Abington Hospital Trust, W.W., Charlotte	236417240
Hitchner Trust f/b/o Memorial Hospital of Salem, J.E., Charlotte	232751711
Hunt Trust, Elise P., Winston Salem	946245970
Kenan, Jr. Fund, William R., The, Chapel Hill	570757568
Kenan, Jr. Fund for Engineering, Technology and Science, William R., The, Chapel Hill	561761145
Kenan, Jr. Fund for Ethics, William R., The, Chapel Hill	561919423
Kenan, Jr. Fund for the Arts, William R., Chapel Hill	581976597
Miller Trust, Anna Shawde, Charlotte	236221403
Rhoads Foundation, Ross R. & Sara G., Charlotte	236271698
Ohio	
Bicknell Memorial Fund, Brooklyn	341312815
Boles Endowment Fund Trust, Ewing T., Cleveland	316470522
Clark Family Charitable Foundation, Morrow	311680960
Domhoff Trust, Jessie P., Cincinnati	316019888
Hanger Charitable Trust, W. A., Cleveland	616114573
Hayward Trust, Kendall, Brooklyn	346500653
Mason Memorial Fund Sch A, M. L., Cleveland	256020713
McKesson Foundation, Cleveland	346518820
Mill Creek Park Foundation, Columbus	341490268
Mitchell Foundation, William & Mary, Cleveland	356536740

STATE	EIN
Moser Charitable Trust, William E., Cleveland	346511386
Phi Delta Kappa Education Foundation, Columbus	316077706
Price Foundation, Harley C. & Mary Hoover, Brooklyn	346510993
Women's Philanthropic Union, Cleveland Heights	340782268

Oklahoma

Grimes Foundation, Otha H., Tulsa	731293858

Oregon

English Charitable Trust, Michael M., Portland	237088795

Pennsylvania

Ally Herc 2, Lockhart J.M., Pittsburgh	256018607
Bloss & Christine T. Bloss Trust, George S., Philadelphia	946278318
Brennan Trust, Robert E., Pittsburgh	616063803
Dunlap Jr. Foundation, Edward B., Canonsburg	256361678
Edwin M. Fdn Gtn Acad U Agmt, Lavino, Pittsburgh	236578511
Elkins for Hahnemann, George, Pittsburgh	236205943
Farley Family Foundation, James N. and Nancy J., Philadelphia	363938355
Father Flanagan's Boys Home Trust No. 3, Pittsburgh	900102166
Gahagen Charitable Foundation, Zella J., Pittsburgh	256219884
Guthrie Foundation, Emily B., Pittsburgh	236632667
Hall, II Charitable Trust, Edwin, Philadelphia	237892195
Hopkins Trust, Mary Kellogg, Philadelphia	946052489
Hyacinth Foundation, The, Philadelphia	516183634
Ketterlinus Trust f/b/o University of Pennsylvania Hospital, E., Pittsburgh	256838700
Lavino Foundation, Edwin M., Pittsburgh	232032639
Lilly for Christ Church, Eli, Pittsburgh	356324982
Lockhard H.E.R.C., J. M. Ally, Pittsburgh	256018593
McDivitt Perpetual Charitable Trust, William A & Grace S, Pittsburgh	256782006
McKelvy Memorial Fund, B. T. & E. G. Morrison, Pittsburgh	256220228
Mercy Hospital-Weiss Trust, Pittsburgh	251534319
Morton Charitable Trust I, Marian Grace, Philadelphia	516589610
Shuff Foundation, The, Philadelphia	526955775
Smurr Charitable Trust, Rosemary Hancock, Philadelphia	956670586
Stanton Trust, May Bonfils, Philadelphia	846027976
Sullivan Foundation, Frances W., Philadelphia	232657930
Ulmer Trust, Edward M., Philadelphia	236516167
Van Dusen Trust, Mary W., Pittsburgh	236293111
Yee Foundation, S. K., Pittsburgh	133202047

Rhode Island

Abbe Fund Trust, Providence	066030466
Borden Trust f/b/o Fall River Jewish Home for the Aged, F., Providence	597269666
Bracchi-Parenti Trust Fund Inc., The, North Kingstown	760798627
Burr Trust, Willie O., Providence	066027512
Burt Trust, Elizabeth M., Providence	066052373
Champlin Trust, Robert H., Providence	056011297
Davis Trust, M. G., Providence	136138067
Elliot Charitable Trust, John S. & Sarah C., Providence	046282546
Griffin Charitable Trust, Helen, Providence	367169702
H. P. Farrington-Hpf Foundation Rsdy, Providence	136172804
Hawthorne Charities Trust, Marguerite C., Providence	136963498
Hellmann Foundation, Sibilla, Providence	066024715
Hellmann Trust f/b/o American Cancer Society, et al., Rhoda M., Providence	066263343
Hellmann Trust f/b/o Sibella Hellmann Fund, Rhoda M., Providence	066263709
Higgins Charity, Eugene, Providence	136073358
Lange Fund, Adolph Frederick, Providence	367092202
Luce Charitable Foundation, Stephen C., Providence	237105691
Marlin Trust f/b/o Ynhh, Mahlon H., Providence	066020978
Mee Charitable Trust, Timothy J., Providence	056077239
Nuckols For A Belding Fund, Providence	237425259
Paine Foundation, Martin S., Providence	136074009
Pearsall for Cornell University, Samuel, Providence	136203949

STATE	EIN
Shaw Fund, Miriam, Providence	046497465
Swebilius Trust, C. G., Providence	066021035
University of Rochester Rivas Clinic UA HWR, Providence	166022850
Welsh Charitable Trust, Stanley G., The, Providence	137095254

South Dakota

Charitable Trust, Parsen E.M., Sioux Falls	263503674
Stip Charitable Remainder Unitrust, Milo, Sioux Falls	276423243
Via-Bradley College of Engineering, South Dakota, Sioux Falls	522283401

Tennessee

MBA Wilson Trust, Nashville	207496568
Point of Impact Global Missions Inc., Memphis	274217698

Texas

Baker Foundation Trust, James A. & Laura L., Dallas	527237499
Columbus Community Hospital Foundation, Columbus	742464333
Davis Endowment Fund, John Blodgett, Dallas	766183615
Davis Trust, Ella A., Dallas	916361944
Dow Foundation, Matilda & Jack, Dallas	916268970
Glassell Family Foundation Inc., The, Houston	760295076
Gordon and Julia Gordon Gray Memorial Trust, Charles and Susan, San Antonio	746410729
Harris Trust, Charles H., Dallas	756009016
Hull Charitable Trust, Elizabeth A., Dallas	436345246
LGR Foundation, Austin	742955428
Lohman Foundation, Carolyn S. and Tommie E., The, Houston	752571005
Longenbaugh Foundation, Gillson, Houston	760001952
Lux Trust, Dr. Konrad & Clara, Austin	746338117
Marek Family Foundation, Houston	746108373
Miles Production Co. Trust, Ellison, The, Fort Worth	206189386
Miller Community Fund, Rudolph C., Beaumont	741983753
Newell Charitable Trust, W. P. & Dell Andrews, Abilene	756059309
O'Hara Trust, J.B., Dallas	756224893
Olshan Foundation, Immanuel & Helen B., Houston	741997923
Peeler Charitable Trust, R. G. and Claudine Pope, Amarillo	756599973
Pogue Foundation, The, Dallas	752894071
Read 1985 Charitable Trust, Norman H., Amarillo	752622754
Rose Trust, W. Morgan & Lou Claire, The, New Braunfels	746471295
Sowell Charitable Trust, Thomas & Lillian, Dallas	597247352
Stevens-Dallas Foundation, A.L., Dallas	756006795
Trimble Fund, George W., Dallas	916026531
Wells Foundation, A.Z., Dallas	916026580
Wilson Charitable Trust, Victor, Dallas	446006696

Virginia

Grant Charitable Trust, E. Stuart James, Danville	546315085
Schoolfield Memorial Fund, Robert Addison, Danville	510250919

Washington

Egtvedt Charitable Trust, Clairmont L. and Evelyn S., The, Seattle	916062228

Wisconsin

Amherst College Foundation Trust, Milwaukee	516522862
Delfing Charitable Trust, Sister Irmgard, Milwaukee	396781271
Gordon Stuart Trust, S.J. & Margaret, Milwaukee	756265346
Raynor Charitable Trust, Father John P., Milwaukee	396781273
Rieth Foundation, Lee & Mary Jane, The, Milwaukee	351979838
Shinnick Trust, William M., Milwaukee	316024875
Surgical Science Foundation for Research & Development, Madison	930846339
Tabat Family Foundation Inc., New Berlin	010852699

INDEX TO DONORS, OFFICERS, TRUSTEES

09 PGC Charitable Lead Annuity Trust, 8506

10-Year Charitable Trust, 3385
12-Year Charitable Trust, 3385
120 Broadway Partners, 6269
122 Maryland Corp., 1948
1220 Broadway, LLC, 6851
125 North Industrial Boulevard LLC, 6008
1301 N. Troy, LLC, 2077
1345 Cleaning Service Co. II LP, 5982
136 East 55th Street, Inc., 6768
144 West Corp., 6768
15-Year Charitable Trust, 3385
17 West Orange Realty Corp., 932
1820 Security Corp., 4108
1834 Realty Inc., 3972
1889 Bancorp, Inc., 4458
1955 TWH Trust, 5174
1988 Kettering Tower Trust, 7521
1994 Elizabeth Turner Campbell Trust, 8539
1996 Mary Shea Trust, 1156
1998 Katina Charitable Trust No. 2, The, 6223
1998 Katina Charitable Trust, The, 6223
1998 MJ Trust, The, 6223
1999 Bistricer Family Trust, 6407
1st Source Bank, 3251, 3270
1st Source Bank Charitable Trust, 3251
1st Source Capital, 3251
1st Source Corp., 3251

2000 LTT Asset Corp., 6680
2001 Frederick DeMatteis Revocable Trust, 5873
2002 Charitable Lead Annuity Trust, The, 2092
2003 Dynamic Irrevocable Trust, 5135
2004 Falcon Fund C.L.T., The, 5966
2008 Hecht Trust, 1114
2032 Trust, 6607
211 E. 70th St. L.P., 6767
215 E. 68th St. L.P., 6767
271 Johns Island Dr., 2183
295 Central Park W., Inc., 6768
299 Cleaning Service Co. II LP, 5982

3 A Holdings, LLC, 385
3-D Corp., 3322
345 Park Avenue L.P., 6767
3510 LLC, 3816
39 West Lexington LLC, 9452
3M Center Building, 3201
3M Co., 4597

40 E. 52nd L.P., 6767
41 Madison L.P., 6767
415 Madison, Inc., 6768
4510-4526 Realty Corp., 6409

5-Year Charitable Trust, 3385
501 St Paul Street LLC, 9452
5800 Building, LLC, 5040

6000 Fulton, LLC, 5040
605 Cleaning Service Co. II LP, 5982
63rd Street Equities, 7106

78/79 York Assocs., LLC, 7012

8020 Foundation, 9149
8101 Sepulveda LLC, 323
845 3rd L.P., 6767

9th Avenue Equities, 7106

A & E Trust, 6707
A to Z Mud Co., Inc., 9118
A&E Realty, 6409
A'Court, Divonne Holmes, 5967
A-W Contractors, 3212
A.F. and A.M Grand Lodge of Colorado, 1389
A.F. Holding Co., 7513
Aalfs, Joann "Joan" E., 7236
Aamodt, Patsy, 81
Aamoth, Gordon M., 4753
Aaron, Jerry, 3555
Aaron, Jonathan, 4390, 4526
Aaron, Mary, 4390
Aaron, Patrice, 4471
Aaron, Randy, 9277
Aaron, Sharon Weil, 262
Aaronson, Estee, 564
Aaronson, Joel, 1308
AARP, 476
Aase, Craig, 1940
ABA Realty, 5399
Abarbanel, Jeffrey, 3856
Abate, Ernest N., 1860
Abate, Joseph A., 4003
Abbamont, Thomas J., 8280
Abbe, Jay, 420
Abbett, Kim, 3369
Abbott Laboratories, 2649, 2650, 3833
Abbott, Alan, 9083
Abbott, Caroline H., 7821
Abbott, Clara, 2648
Abbott, David T., 7478
Abbott, Ethel S., 5020
Abbott, Gerald, 8383
Abbott, Gordon L., 3955
Abbott, Herschel L., Jr., 3612, 3628
Abbott, James W., 1907
Abbott, John J., 6024
Abboud, A. Robert, 3099
Abbs, David J., 4532
Abbs, Jim, 3359
Abdalla, Zein, 6627
Abdul-Latif, Saad, 6627
Abdulrazzak, Rula, 3589
Abedon, Todd, 8472

Abel Partners, 5178
Abel, Alice V., 5021
Abel, David, 7878
Abel, Elizabeth N., 5021
Abel, Gregory E., 3465
Abel, I.B., Inc., 8127
Abel, James P., 5021, 5023, 5072
Abel, John C., 5021
Abel, Mary C., 5021
Abel, Melissa D., 9235
Abel-Smith, Mary Mills, 1754
Abele, Jeneye, 9808
Abele, John, 3957
Abele, John E., 9808
Abele, Mary, 9808
Abeles, Barbara, 5544
Abeles, Joseph C., 5544
Abeles, Sophia, 5544
Abeles, Vicki Haberkorn, 5133
Abell Co., A.S., 3712
Abell Foundation, Nelson, 8870
Abell, Anthony F., 3713
Abell, Betsy G., 8870
Abell, Christopher S., Jr., 3713
Abell, Christopher S., Sr., 3713
Abell, Cindy Work, 3713
Abell, Dunbar, 9541
Abell, G. Hughes, 8870
Abell, George T., 8650
Abell, Gladys H., 8650
Abell, Gregory T., 3713
Abell, Kevin O'C., 3713
Abell, Luke, 3713
Abell, Marc, 9541
Abell, Patricia O'Callaghan, 3713
Abell, Teresa T., 2556
Abell, W. Shepherdson, 3712
Abell, William S., 3713
Abelman, Judy, 272
Abels, Bruce, 2123
Abels, Kathy Simon, 1171
Abelson, John, 221
Abendshein, Nancy, 8731
Aberly, Naomi D., 8975
Aberman, Stanley, 6216
Abernathy, Chad, 2817
Abernathy, Gail, 4936
Abernathy, James H., 2288
Abernathy, Maggie E., 4837
Abernathy, Robyn, 9034
Abernathy, Tom, 2433
Abernethy, Bruce, 6947
Abernethy, John S., 3289
Abernethy, Todd, 2037
Abessinio, Mary F., 7904
Abessinio, Peter G., 7904
Abessinio, Rocco A., 7904
Abessinio, Vincent T., 7904
Abeyta, David, 9767
Abitante, Pete, 3245
Abizaid, John P., Genl., 9501
Able, Jeannie Looper, 8990
Ableidinger, Esther, 4370
Ables, Steve, Hon., 8742
Ablon, Ben, 8828
Abney, David P., 2566

Abney, John S., 8454
Abney, Kim, 3283
Abney, Susie M., 8454
Aboodi, Oded, 6881, 7047
Abosch, John P., 3802
Aboussie, Marilyn, 9147
Abplanalp, Dean, 3330
Abraham, Andy, 165
Abraham, Anthony R., 1962
Abraham, Chuck, 7597
Abraham, Diane, 9916
Abraham, Estanne, 6277
Abraham, Jane, 3890
Abraham, Nancy, 5545
Abraham, Norma Jean, 1962
Abraham, Patricia J., 7857
Abraham, Stephen H., 3890
Abraham, Thomas G., 1962
Abrahams, Helene, 3512
Abrahamson, B. Elka, Rabbi, 7713
Abrahamson, Eric John, 8524
Abram, Ben, 3132
Abrams Foundation, Inc., 4298
Abrams, Amy, 3914
Abrams, David C., 3914
Abrams, Donald, 175
Abrams, Elliott, 6981
Abrams, Howard J., 670
Abrams, James, 3019
Abrams, James D., 3019, 3029
Abrams, Jeffrey, 217
Abrams, Jeffrey I., 1199
Abrams, Karen, 3966
Abrams, Keith R., 7931
Abrams, Marilynn R., 8046
Abrams, Melinda, 5800
Abrams, Orin, 239
Abrams, Wendy, 3019
Abramson Revocable Trust, Albert, The, 1877, 3715
Abramson, Albert, 1877, 3715
Abramson, Anne E., 1877
Abramson, Gary, 3715
Abramson, Gary M., 3715
Abramson, Jeffrey, 3715
Abramson, Leonard, 1963
Abramson, Madlyn, 1963
Abramson, Ronald, 3715
Abramson, Ronald D., 1877, 3715
Abregu, Martin, 5994
Abroms, Martin R., 5
Abrons, Adam, 5546
Abrons, Alix, 5546
Abrons, Anne S., 5546
Abrons, Eleanor, 5546
Abrons, Henry, 5546
Abrons, John, 5546
Abrons, Leslie, 5546
Abrons, Louis, 5546
Abrons, Peter, 5546
Abrons, Richard, 5546
Abshire, David M., 1926
Abshire, Jennifer, 2548
ABT Electronics, Inc., 2651
Abt, Michael, 2651
Abt, Richard L., 2651

Abt, Robert J., 2651
Abt, William P., 2651
Abundis, Susan, 549
Academy for Education Development, 2631
Acadia Insurance Company, 1741
Acamovic, Millie, 4729
Accenture, LLP, 4785
Access Community Health Network, 2761
Acclaim Entertainment, 7012
ACCO, 3201
ACCO Brands Corporation, 3201
Acco Engineered Systems, 5482
ACE American Insurance Co., 7905
Ace Beverage Co., 243
Ace Endowment Fund, 2259
Ace Pipe Cleaning, Inc., 2735
Acee, William, 6876
Aceves, Ann N., 1649
Achelis, Elisabeth, 5549
Achenbaum, Barb, 1650
Achepohl, E., 3025, 3057, 3107
Achepohl, Eric F., 3026
Achor, Robert L., 2264
Achuthan, Lakshman, 5196, 5328
Acker, Susan, 6722
Ackerley, Barry A., 9726
Ackerly, Maureen C., 9416
Ackerman, Barbara Berkman, 3945
Ackerman, Christina, 8655
Ackerman, David B., 8651
Ackerman, Edward M., 8651
Ackerman, Edward W., 8651
Ackerman, James F., 3252
Ackerman, Joanne Leedom, 1881
Ackerman, John F., 3252
Ackerman, Lee, 287
Ackerman, Loraine S., 287
Ackerman, Peter, 1881
Ackerman, Sybil, 7864
Ackerman, Wilhelmina, 8651
Ackley, Carlyle, 3578
Ackley, Lilly, 1549
Acklie, Duane W., 5022
Acklie, Irene, 5022
Acklie, Phyllis A., 5022
Ackman, Karen, 6629
Ackman, Lawrence D., 6629
Ackman, William, 6629
Acmaro Securities Corp., The, 2579
Acone, Tony, 1399
Acors, Sylvia S., 9430
ACP Holdings Inc., 5691
ACP Luxury Corp., 5691
ACP MacDouglas Corp., 5691
Acquavella Charitable Lead Trust, Edythe C., 5550
Acquavella, Donna Jo, 5550
Acquavella, William R., 5550
Acri, Mark, 500
ACT-UP, 6133
Action Energy, Inc., 9053
Action Fund of Lehman Brothers Holdings, The, 6538
Activision Publishing, Inc., 369
Acuff, A. Marshall, Jr., 4510
Acuity, a Mutual Insurance Co., 9801
Acumen Solutions, 1892
Acuna, Teresa, 3182
Adair, Maria F., 8633
Adair, Marla, 8585
Adam Corp., 5359
Adam, Diane, 1116
Adam, Patricia, 8522
Adam, Robert, 9255
Adam, Todd V., 8958
Adame, Gabe, 8775
Adams LLP, Moss, 9566
Adams Trust, Jean Pape, 7725
Adams, Aileen, 1307
Adams, Alan B., 8525
Adams, Alice E., 7132
Adams, Allan B., 1431
Adams, Andrew, 8526
Adams, Anthony A., 8526
Adams, Beatrice D., 3916
Adams, Ben, 9832
Adams, Billie Wright, 2933
Adams, Boe, 2575
Adams, Bruce H., 5727
Adams, Bryan G., 5727
Adams, Burt A., 3664
Adams, Carl, 8525
Adams, Carl E., 8525
Adams, Carol, 2742, 6722
Adams, Caroline J., 3917
Adams, Charles E., 3917
Adams, Charles F., 3916
Adams, Christina M., 4420
Adams, Craig S., 8819
Adams, Cynthia, 8776
Adams, Daniel Nelson, Jr., 5727
Adams, David Welborn, 8496
Adams, Deborah, 1478
Adams, Donnalyn Frey, 3717
Adams, Dorothy, 8526
Adams, Fred, 8525
Adams, Frederick M., Jr., 4371
Adams, Gabrielle, 8834
Adams, Greg, 7585
Adams, Holmes S., 4833
Adams, J. Dann, 2455
Adams, J.A., 3626
Adams, James E., 7400
Adams, James F., 8710
Adams, Jean, 4714, 9733
Adams, Jeff, 9499
Adams, Jeffrey, 9411
Adams, Jennie Mae, 8525
Adams, Jerry, 197
Adams, Joanna, 2540
Adams, Jodi S., 3664
Adams, John, 1394, 8653
Adams, John L., 8652
Adams, John R., 8652
Adams, Joseph, 396
Adams, Karen Booth, 9416
Adams, Kate, 5243
Adams, Kendall Wishnick, 2646
Adams, Kristen Barney, 2682
Adams, Larry S., 8222
Adams, Lee, 1002
Adams, Lynne G. Butler, 2729
Adams, Mary Lou, 9171
Adams, Maurean B., 7182
Adams, Nathan, 3366
Adams, Nell, 3626
Adams, Patricia, 8653
Adams, Peter W., 7499
Adams, Richard, 3717
Adams, Richard L., Jr., 3717
Adams, Richard N., 7569
Adams, Robert M., 5391
Adams, S.C., 9399
Adams, Scott R., 8468
Adams, Susan, 1136
Adams, Suzanne L., 8652
Adams, T.A., 9932
Adams, Timothy M., 7552
Adams, W. Andrew, 8525, 8526
Adams, Wayne, 3279
Adams, William James "will.i.am", Jr., 720
Adamson, Cheryl, 8507
Adamson, Judy, 3261
Adamson, Pete, III, 7810
Adamson, Rebecca, 5652
Adamson, Roger, 8863
Adamson, Stephanie, 95
Adamson, Terrence B., 6398
Adaya Family Trust, 225
Adaya, Ahmad, 225
Adaya, Amina, 225
Adaya, Salim, 225
Adaya, Tehmina, 225
Adcock, Gerald, 9413
Adcock, Louis N., Jr., 2269
Addams, Cynthia G., 7836
Addams, R. David, 1600
Addeo, Patricia, 7630
Adderley, Terence E., 4371
Addington, Susan, 3529
Addington, Whitney Wood, 3172
Addison, Garrick, 9033
Addison, Jerry, 8809
Addison, Loveanne, 2525
Addison, R. Elaine, 7313
Addleman, Billie, 9999
Adelman, Ethel, 5554
Adelman, Philip, 5554
Adelphi Associates LP, 9452
Adelson, Andrew, 5555
Adelson, Ellen G., 7726, 7755
Adelson, Ellen Jane, 7755
Adelson, James, 7807
Adelson, Miriam, Dr., 3918, 3919, 5099
Adelson, Nancy, 5555
Adelson, Sheldon G., 3918, 3919, 5099
Adelson, Warren, 6187
Adelstein, Stan, 1548
ADEO, LLC, 4951
Ader, Richard M., 2046
Adidas, 3303
Adjmi Dwek Foundation, 5557
Adjmi, Eric, 5557
Adjmi, Harry, 5558
Adjmi, Jack, 5557
Adjmi, Mark, 5557
Adjmi, Rachel, 5557
Adjmi, Ronald, 5557
Adkerson, Richard C., 112
Adkins, Cynthia, 9186
Adkins, Lisa, 3560
Adkins, Stephen R., 9558
Adkinson, Jeri, 2351
Adkisson, Hermoine Corlew, 57
Adler, Beth Ann Griffin, 2138
Adler, Betsy Buchalter, 582
Adler, Constance, 3699
Adler, Eric, 1893
Adler, Irving, 1533
Adler, Leo, 7822
Adler, Les K., Dr., 1322
Adler, Marc, 167
Adler, Maria, 6861
Adler, Michael, 4311
Adler, Robert, 4005
Adler, Robert S., 4327
Adleta, Charles Derek, 8985
Admiral Farragut LLC, 9452
Adobe, 991
Adobe Systems Incorporated, 1734
ADP Rental Co., 2444
Adrean, Lee, 2455
Adrian & James, Inc., 6216
Aduddell, Larry D., 8768
Advance Publications, Inc., 6550
Advanced Financial Services, Inc., 2185
Advanced Systems Inc, 8834
Advest, Inc., 8026
Advisory Small Cap Value, 9916
Advisory Trust Co. of Delaware, 1752, 8284
Adwan, Teresa B., 7793
Adzema, Gregg, 2443
AEGON Transamerica Foundation, 3449
AEGON USA, Inc., 3409
Aerospace Service and Controls, 1233
Aerotek, Inc., 3719
AES Corp., 1950
Aetna, 6904, 7638
Aetna Freight Lines, Inc., The, 3789
Aetna Health Inc., 1531
Aetna Inc., 1531
Aetna Life Insurance Company, 1531
Affiliated Managers Group, Inc., 3924
AFIKIM, 6229
Afikim, 6972
Afram-Gyening, Francis, 7639
Afsar, Kamran, 8136
Afshar Hospital, 1301
Aft, David, 2436
After School Matters, 2761
Agami, Amy H., 2484
AGAO, LLC, 4951
Agarwal, Adhish, 9313
Agarwal, Aditya, 6795
Agarwal, Avadhesh, 219
Agarwal, Ravin, 6795
Agarwal, Sunil, 571
Agassi, Nili, 6795
Agata, Tetsuo, 7002
Agather, Elaine, 5528
Agather, Jean, 5014
Agather, Ruth K., 8951
Agather, V. Neils, 8737
Agdern, Lisa, 1692
Agee, John H., 383
Agee, Steve, Dr., 7781
Agelasto, Peter A., 9405
Agger, David, 997
Aghamirzadeh, Reza, 8374
Aghdaei, Amie, 7894
Aghdami, Farhad, 9416
Agilent Technologies, Inc., 220
AGL Foundation, 2400
AGL Resources Inc., 2400
Agness, Kent E., 3372
Agnew, A. Vincent, 3226
Agnew, Alex, 4829
Agnew, Lynn, 9578
Agnone, Charlotte, Dr., 7416
Agnoni, Michael D., 7704
Agostini, Nanci, 3123
Agouron Institution, 1558
Agrawal, Sudhir K., 8549
Agre, Peter, 3833
Agresta, Maurice, 3745
Agri Beef Co., 2640
Agri-Mark Cabot, 3245
Agualia Foundation, 4628
Agualimpia, Juan, 9032
Aguiar, Ellen, 2175
Aguiar, Guma, 2175
Aguiar, Lauren, 6868

Aguiar, Luis, 2175
Aguilar, Don, 1166
Aguilar, Francisco, 141
Aguillard, Susan M., Dr., 8530
Agus, Saul, 7124
Agus, Saul G., 5562, 5789, 5855, 5952, 5977, 6036, 6207, 6524, 6576, 6622, 7028, 7110
Agus, Saul G., Dr., 5655
Ahaba Ve Ahva Congregation, 5768
Ahearn, Dan, 9104
Ahearn, Jennifer P., 9104
Ahern, Celeste W., 7811
Ahern, John Patrick, 5162
Ahern, Kate, 1891
Aherne, Damon, 8084, 8346
Ahi Ezer Congregation, 5768, 6054
Ahlstrom, Theresa, 5349
Ahmad, N. Nina, 8221
Ahmadi, Hoshang, 5566
Ahmanson, Caroline L., 832
Ahmanson, Howard F., 222
Ahmanson, Howard F., Jr., 222
Ahmanson, Robert H., 222
Ahmanson, William Hayden, 222
Ahmanson, William Howard, 222
Ahmed, Mohamed, 8011
Ahmed, Mohammed Raheemuddin, 224
Ahn, Sun Ho, 8383
Ahold Financial Services, LLC, 4297
Ahrendt, Martha, 9854
Ahrens, Barbara, 1423
Ahrens, Chad W., 3410
Ahrens, Claude W., 3410
Ahuja, Elias, 1785
Ahyakak, Eddie, 81
Aicher Trust, Paul J., The, 3677
Aicher, Paul J., 3677
Aicher, Peter, 3677
Aid Association for Lutherans, 9956
Aidekman, Gary O., 5296
Aidikoff, Uhl & Bakhtiari, 1035
Aidlin, Joseph W., 1090
Aidner, Sandye, 5205
Aids Institute, Inc., The, 2259
AIDS Walk San Diego, Inc., 229
Aidsani, Maureen, 2877
AIDSERVE Indiana, 3317
Aiello, Dorian, 1154
Aiello, Leslie C., 7075
Aiello-Fantus, Judith, 2826
AIG, 6904
Aiken, Jeffrey P., 8356
Aiken, Tim, 7272
Aiken-O'Neil, Patricia, 2035
Aikenhead, David S., 663
Aikenhead, Kathleen Hannon, 651
Aikman, Sheryl, 7182
Ainhorn, Chanie, 5905
Ainhorn, Jakob, 5905
Ainslie, Lee S., III, 9005
Ainsman, Meryl, 7980
Ainsworth, Anne-Marie, 8308
Air Conditioning Control Systems, Inc, 503
Air Products and Chemicals, Inc., 7907
AirTouch Communications, Inc., 1519
Aitken, Frances A., 7939
Aizenberg, Salo, 6865
Ajalat, Charles R., 995
Ajalat, Marilee N., 995
Ajax Metal Processing, Inc., 4367
Ajello, James A., 2603
AK Steel Corp., 7366
AK Villiage Initiatives, 85
Akel, Ferris G., 5863
Akel, Ron, 6286
Akerman, Yehuda, 6229
Akers, Christopher T., 8025
Akers, Sharon, 3888
Akey, Lin, 5019
Akiba, Shinichiro, 6997
Akin, Hank, 8960
Akin, Hugh Clark, 9214
Akin, Jeff, 1856
Akin, Matt, 23
Akin, Steven P., 3678
Akina, Charman J., 2600
Akins, Martin P., 4888
Akins, Nicholas K., 7368
Akman, Larry, 3785
Akman, Nonie, 3785
Akre, Elizabeth I., 4984
Aksel, Marsha R., 7306
Akselrad, Ira, 6236
Aksoy, Haluk, 1223
Al Shamir, Rofaidah, 109
Al-Alusi, Hesham, 224
Ala Moana Property Developer, LLC, 2077
Alabama Power Co., 1
Alagia, Claire, 3569
Alamo Resources, 9049
Alan, Robert, 6451
Alandt, Lynn F., 4331
Alandt, Lynn Ford, 4426
Alandt, Paul D., 4331
Albanese, Virginia, 7367
Albemarle Corp., 3609
Alberding, Ellen S., 2946
Alberg, Tom A., 9710
Albernaz, Marcus, Dr., 7217
Albers, Anni, 1532
Albers, John, 4731
Albers, Josef, 1532
Albert Charitable Trust, Beatrice, 5567
Albert, Leo, 1964
Alberts, Bruce, 938, 3833, 7164
Alberts, Bruce D., 1315
Alberts, Ka, 5009
Albertson, J.A., 2626
Albertson, Kathryn, 2626
Albery Society, W.H., 5927
Albin, David R., 9053
Albin, Douglas M., 3518
Albinder, Barbara Zucker, 7127
Albracht, Cory, 9144
Albrecht, Anne O'C., 4850
Albrecht, Barry D., 4850
Albrecht, Bryan D., 9924
Albrecht, Douglas A., 4850
Albrecht, F. Steven, 7367
Albrecht, Ralph W., Sr., 2585
Albrecht, Seta, 6530
Albrecht, Sophie E., 7420
Albrecht, Steven, 5165
Albrecht, Wendy, 8986
Albright, Adam, 2672, 8489
Albright, Holly, 3295
Albright, Jay, 3360
Albright, Joanna, 5791
Albright, Joseph P., 8489
Albright, Mika, 2672
Albright, Nancy, 9916
Albright, Rachel, 2672
Albright, Shari, 9149
Albright, Tenley, 5684
Albro, Les, 3261
Albstein, Andrew, 9473
Alcantar, Joe, Jr., 8825
Alcatel-Lucent, 5190
Alchu, Kay F., 5137
Alcoa Corp., 7908
Alcoa Inc., 7908
Alcon Foundation, 9915
Alcon Laboratories, Inc., 8655
Alcus, Mary Pat, 1893
Alden, A.F. Drew, 1562, 1714
Alden, Bernie, 6285
Alden, George I., 3921
Alden, Lizzie King, 2960
Alderfer, Todd, 8234
Alderman, Heather Higgins, 2933
Alderman, James F., 2110
Alderson, Patti, 7417
Aldieri, David J., 1634
Aldrich, Hope, 3852
Aldrich, John R., 5966
Aldridge LLP, McKenna Long, 7638
Aldridge, Alexandra A., 8195
Aldridge, Elizabeth, 7231
Aldridge, Elizabeth A., 7780
Aldridge, Fred C., Jr., 8195
Aleppo, Ezio, 1974
Aleppo, Georgia, 1974
Aleppo, Joseph A., 1974
Alerus Financial, 7351
Alessi, Helen Dorado, 197
Aleut Corp., The, 80
Aleutian Pribilof Islands Restitution Trust, 80
Alevizon, Sarah, 239
Alex, Sarah Armstrong, 1888
Alexander Building Co., 3178
Alexander Charitable Trust, The, 5691
Alexander Foundation, Inc., 1965
Alexander, Allan L., 381
Alexander, Amanda, 4820
Alexander, Andrew M., 8656
Alexander, Anne M., 9803
Alexander, Arthur, 6867
Alexander, Bret, 9115
Alexander, Bruce K., 1431
Alexander, Cory, 4785
Alexander, Cynthia K., 8686
Alexander, Denis R., 8313
Alexander, Duncan, 2767
Alexander, Duncan M., 3178
Alexander, Elaine B., 2406
Alexander, Elisabeth H., 7621
Alexander, Emily H., 3178
Alexander, Gregory, 5569
Alexander, Helen C., 8962
Alexander, Henrietta K., 8962
Alexander, James L., 2861, 3039
Alexander, James N., 3172
Alexander, James R., 5568
Alexander, Jane, 4820
Alexander, Jay B., 8040
Alexander, Joan, 8656
Alexander, John, 3178
Alexander, John D., Jr., 8962
Alexander, John E., 9802
Alexander, John S., 7620
Alexander, John W., 6568
Alexander, Jon, 8819
Alexander, Joseph, 7910
Alexander, Kathleen H., 4908
Alexander, Kevin B., 8656
Alexander, Larry, 2105
Alexander, Leslie L., 1965
Alexander, Lynn, 4373
Alexander, Margo N., 5568
Alexander, Mark C., 5232
Alexander, Martha J., 3178
Alexander, Michael C., 7829
Alexander, Milroy A., 1487
Alexander, Nanci, 2249
Alexander, Nichol C., 5568
Alexander, Pamela, 1368
Alexander, Quentin, 7621
Alexander, Rex, 648
Alexander, Robert C., 5568
Alexander, Scott, 2166
Alexander, Stanford, 8656
Alexander, Susan, 8363
Alexander, Tedd, III, 3726
Alexander, Thomas S., 3178
Alexander, Timothy, 9404
Alexander, W. Robert, 1431
Alexander, Walter, 3178
Alexander, Wynn, 4830
Alexander-Stewart Lumber Co., 3178
Alexandra Trust, 3054
Alexion Pharmaceuticals, Inc., 1533
Alexis, Ceaneh, 3336
Alfa Mutual Fire Insurance Co., 2
Alfa Mutual Insurance Co., 2
Alfiero, Charles C., 5570
Alfiero, James J., 5570
Alfiero, Salvatore H., 5570
Alfiero, Victor S., 5570
Alfond Charitable Lead Annuity Trust, Theodore B., 3915
Alfond, Barbara, 3915
Alfond, Dorothy, 3678
Alfond, Harold, 3678
Alfond, Joan, 3679
Alfond, Justin, 3679
Alfond, Kenden, 3679
Alfond, Peter, 3678
Alfond, Reis, 3679
Alfond, Theodore B., 3678, 3915
Alfond, William, 3678, 3679
Alfonso-McGoldrick, Rosa, 6546
Alford, Barbara, 77
Alford, Bobby R., 8658
Alford, Bobby, Dr., 8804
Alford, Brian, 7782
Alford, Ericka, 7051
Alford, John R., Jr., 9474
Alford, Katie, 8774
Alford, Laura James, 742
Alford, Lisa, 6153
Alford, Sandra E., 8679
Alford, Susan Hager, 3597
Alger, Robert E., 293
Algranati, Mike, 5486
Alhadeff, Victor D., 9725
Alhers, David, 4666
Ali, Bashir, 2763
Ali, Farad, 7328
Ali, Fred J., 1307
Aliah Home Care Inc., 5890
Alice Manufacturing Co., Inc., 8486
Alicea, Jaime, 6049
Alico, Bill, 2559
Alioto, Alison J., 8307
Alisiswanto, Candra, 7362
Alito, Noelie, 9262
Alix Living Trust, Jay, 4333
Alix, Jay, 4333
Alix, Maryanne, 4333
Aljoe, Hugh, 8809
Alkek, Albert B., 8658
Alkek, Margaret M., 8657, 8658

Altman, Steve R., 233
Altmeyer, James E., 9772
Altmire, Jason, 2101
Altobello, Daniel J., 9471
Altom, Joey, 8495
Alton, Gregg H., 586
Altpeter, Franz, 4777
Altschul, Arthur G., 6604
Altschul, Charles, 6604
Altschul, Frank, 6604
Altschul, Helen G., 6604
Altschul, Jeanette Cohen, 5582
Altschul, Louis, 5582
Altschul, Stephen F., 6604
Altschul-Miller, Emily, 6604
Altshuler, Ruth Sharp, 9167
Altvater, Donna S., 3814
Aluminum Co. of America, 7908
Alumni Association Foundation, 973
Alvarado, David, 332
Alvarado, Gilbert, 1163
Alvarado, Rudy, 7742
Alvarez, Abigail C., 5584
Alvarez, Antonio C., 5584
Alvarez, Carlos, 8924
Alvarez, Carlos E., 8924
Alvarez, Frank, 5490
Alvarez, Frank D., 3345
Alvarez, Jose, 3289
Alvarez, Jose B., 2946
Alvarez, Kim, 5405
Alvarez, Maria G., 8924
Alvarez, Robert K., 8594
Alverio, Marilyn, 1567
Alverno Health Care Corp., 3297
Alvord, Adrienne, 3709
Alwang, Walter G., 1643
Alzheimer's Association, 328
Amado, Ellen, 235
Amado, Maurice, 235
Amado, Richard, 235
Amado, Ted, 235
Amaral, John E., 700
Amato, Charles E., 9217
Amaturo, Douglas Q., 1966
Amaturo, Joseph C., 1966
Amaturo, Lawrence V., 1966
Amaturo, Winifred J., 1966
Amaturo, Winifred L., 1966
AMB Charitable Lead Trust, 6410
Amber Trust, 2161
Ambery, Richard M., 2467
Ambler, Bruce, 3714
Ambler, John O., 8706
Ambler, Read, 744
Ambler, Sarah H.C., 4174
Amblin Entertainment, Inc., 1348
Amboian, Andrew L., 3191
Amboian, Ann L., 3191
Amboian, John P., Jr., 3191
Ambrose, Lee, 1520
Ambrosio, Denise, 589
Ambuel, Helen B., 9902
Ambutas, Vytas, 5153
Amdisys, Inc., 3622
Amend, Gregg, 9566
Ameren Corp., 4851
AMEREX (USA), Inc., 6033
America Online, Inc., 6982
American and Efird Mills, Inc., 7192
American Antiquarian Society, 5707
American Bank, 9954
American Book Wholesale, 7214
American Bottling Company, The, 1771
American Century Co., Inc., 4852
American Contractors Insurance Group, 9016
American Dairy Assoc & Dairy Council, 3245
American Dairy Association Mideast, 3245
American Electric Power Service Corp., 7368
American Express, 5587
American Express Co., 5588
American Express Foundation, 6532
American Family Life Assurance Co. of Columbus, 2399
American Fidelity Assurance Co., 7728
American Financial Holdings, Inc., 1537
American Friends for Charities, 5707
American Friends Of Heritage, Inc., 6229
American Gas Assn., 1140
American Healthways, 2604, 4618
American Honda Motor Co., Inc., 237
American Hospital Supply Corp., 2690
American Industries, Inc., 7851
American Institute of Foreign Studies, 5746
American International Group, Inc., 5563, 5564
American Land Management Corp., 4208
American Legacy Foundation, 2627
American Legal Foundation, 1952
American Legend Homes, 8756
American Livestock Insurance Co., 3178
American Manufacturers Mutual Insurance Co., 2955
American Manufacturing Corp., 7927
American Motorists Insurance Co., 2955
American Mutual Life Insurance Co., 3411
American National Bank, 4757
American National Bank & Trust Co., 1495, 9402
American Ocean Campaign, 396
American Oil & Gas Reporter, 9049
American Proteins, 2407
American Retail Group, Inc., 6654
American Retail Properties, Inc., 6654
American Savings Bank, 3710
American Snuff Co., 8528
American Society for the Prevention of Cruelty to Animals, 674
American Technion Society, 3824
American Tinnitus Association, 2300
American Trading and Production Corp., 3735, 3873, 3894
American Trim, 7376
American United Life Insurance Co., 3364
Americans for Oxford, 5707
AmeriCorps, 3143
AMERIGROUP Corp., 9383
Ameris Bank, 8465
Ameristar East Chicago, 3306
Ameritas Life Insurance Corp., 5023
AmerUs Group Co., 3411
Ames, A. Gary, 9570
Ames, Aubin Z., 5441
Ames, B. Charles, 7371
Ames, B. Charles, Mrs., 7371
Ames, Barbara J., 9570
Ames, Brooks A., 3987
Ames, Carmen H., 7234
Ames, Cynthia, 7371
Ames, Eric C., 9570
Ames, George J., 6481
Ames, Harold, 8969
Ames, Joyce G., 7371
Ames, Kathleen L.F., 6137
Ames, Kathryn, 3720
Ames, Marshall, 2210
Ames, Richard S., 7371
Ametek, Inc., 7913
Amey, Kenneth, 8199
Amgen Inc., 238, 3833
Amica Mutual Insurance Co., 8356
Amin, Dhruvika Patel, 5733
Amine, Jim, 5826
Amiss, Jason, 6898
Amity Leather Products Co., 9935
Amlick, Joyce, 500
Amlung, Stephanie R., 7634
Amman, Daniel, 4442
Ammar, Pamela, 3555
Ammer, Katrina, 1518
Ammon, Carol A., 5593
Ammon, Generosa, 5594
Ammon, R. Theodore, 5594
Amoco Corp., 81, 8718
Amoco Production Co., 8718
Amonette, Tracy L., 1453
Amoroso Construction, 293
Amoroso, Natalie W., 9282
Amory, Daniel, 4112
Amory, Jenny, 3962
Amory, Robert, 4112
Amos Charitable Lead Annuity Trust, William L., 1967
Amos Charitable Lead Trust, Olivia D., 2505
Amos IRA, Olivia D., 1967
Amos Trust, Jean, 2401
Amos Trust, Paul, 2401
Amos Trust, Paul S. and Jean R., 2401
Amos, Courtney, 2402
Amos, Courtney G., 2402
Amos, Daniel P., 2401
Amos, Kathleen V., 2399
Amos, Olivia D., 1967, 2505
Amos, Paul S., II, 2402
Amos, William L, Jr., 1967
Amos, William L., III, 1967
AMP Inc., 6966
AMPCO-Pittsburgh Foundation, 8030
Amr, Hady, 5714
Amr, Thea, 5714
Amrani, E. Nora Harwit, 660
AmSouth Bancorporation, 61
AmSouth Bank, 61
Amstad, Mary, 7857
Amsterdam, Adam, 5214
Amsterdam, Jack, 5595
Amundson, Dana, 1817
Amundson, Diane, 4806
Amzak Capital Management, 2180
Amzak Corp., 2179
Analytic Risk Management, 4183
Anast-May, Linda, 3297
Anastasi, Giacchino "Jack", 5398
Anastasio, Curtis V., 9065
Anastasio, Ernest, III, 9376
Anchia, Rafael M., 8912
Anchorage Times Publishing Co., 82
Andel, Marie, 421
Andelin, John, 9384
Anderegg, Gregory L., 9874
Anderi, Richard C., 5071
Anders, Betty, 3444
Anders, Jay, 4512
Anders, Thomas, 7382
Anders, Tim, 2423
Anders, Valerie E., 9571
Anders, William A., 9571
Andersen Construction Co., 9662
Andersen Corp., 4601
Andersen, Anne Heller, 676
Andersen, Carole, 549
Andersen, Christine E., 4603
Andersen, Eric C., 7928
Andersen, Frank N., 4339
Andersen, Fred C., 4602, 4677
Andersen, Gracia B., 1968
Andersen, Hugh J., 4603
Andersen, Jane K., 4603
Andersen, John A., 2720
Andersen, Katherine B., 4603, 4677
Andersen, Mark, 1528
Andersen, Sarah J., 4603
Anderson Aluminum Corp., 5482
Anderson Capital Advisors, L.P., Kayne, 240
Anderson Fam. Foundation, Harold & Kayrita, The, 6864
Anderson Foundation, Elizabeth Mendenhall, 7373
Anderson Foundation, Rose-Marie and Jack R., 3756
Anderson Media, 5
Anderson Merchandisers, 5
Anderson, Alan C., 4758
Anderson, Alice Childs, 1558
Anderson, Amy, 4417, 8808
Anderson, Annie Wallingford, 7373
Anderson, Barbara, 4657
Anderson, Barbara W., 3227
Anderson, Beth B., 5
Anderson, Betsy C., 9559
Anderson, Beville, 2076
Anderson, Bradford L., 548
Anderson, Bradley S., 2153
Anderson, Bruce, 4636
Anderson, Butch, 5108
Anderson, Calvin, 8634
Anderson, Carl C., III, 8663
Anderson, Carl C., Sr., 8663
Anderson, Carl E., Esq., 8351
Anderson, Chana, 877
Anderson, Charles, 9726
Anderson, Charles C., 5
Anderson, Charles C., Jr., 5
Anderson, Charles M., 9572
Anderson, Charlie, 9572
Anderson, Charlotte Jones, 8943
Anderson, Christina S.T., 2767
Anderson, Christopher, 6795
Anderson, Claudia, 5138
Anderson, Corey S., 197
Anderson, Craig, 9697
Anderson, Curtis B., 3575
Anderson, Daniel, 5134
Anderson, Darcy Glen, 9093
Anderson, David, 8522
Anderson, David C., 9558, 9698
Anderson, David G., 8582
Anderson, David J., 7080
Anderson, Dennis, 4667
Anderson, Dial H., 8814
Anderson, Dick, 2644
Anderson, Don, 2645
Anderson, Dorothy, 6571
Anderson, Dorothy I., 9572
Anderson, Douglas K., 1690
Anderson, Dwight, 788

Anderson, Edward T., 5600
Anderson, Edwin A., 4667
Anderson, Edwin J.S., 5355
Anderson, Erik K., 242
Anderson, Ethel D., 2433
Anderson, Frederic, 1563
Anderson, Gary, 5046
Anderson, Gerard M., 4371, 4498
Anderson, Grant A., 690
Anderson, Greg, 1393
Anderson, Harold J., Inc., 9049
Anderson, Holly, 806
Anderson, Jack R., 8665
Anderson, Jacob V., 90
Anderson, James C., 7462
Anderson, Jan G., 8768
Anderson, Jay, 5973
Anderson, Jeff, 7876
Anderson, Jeffrey, 806
Anderson, Jeffrey W., 7372
Anderson, Jennifer, 9950
Anderson, Jennifer A., 4644
Anderson, Jim, 714
Anderson, Johanna Edens, 7148
Anderson, John, 1395
Anderson, John A., Jr., 6997
Anderson, John E., 243
Anderson, John E., Jr., 243
Anderson, John T., 2946
Anderson, John W., 3255
Anderson, Jonathan S., 4758
Anderson, Joseph B., Jr., 3358
Anderson, Joseph P., 90
Anderson, Judith, 109
Anderson, Judy, 882
Anderson, Julie, 86
Anderson, Kari L., 626
Anderson, Katherine, 2621
Anderson, Keith, 4667
Anderson, Keith T., 5597, 8750
Anderson, Kelly Lawrence, 4001
Anderson, Ken, 4104
Anderson, Kenneth J., 724
Anderson, Kerry, 1264
Anderson, Kyle, 5075
Anderson, Lafe, 5046
Anderson, Lars D., 4001
Anderson, Laurie A., 9873
Anderson, Lawrence, 6286
Anderson, Lee, 3503
Anderson, Linda, 2676, 9992
Anderson, Lisa, 9687, 9693
Anderson, Lyn, 1805
Anderson, M.D., 8664
Anderson, Marie Jo, 8663
Anderson, Marion, 243
Anderson, Mark, 3199
Anderson, Mark D., 2977
Anderson, Matt, 1394
Anderson, Matthew C., 7372
Anderson, Melanie, 9213
Anderson, Melissa M., 8092
Anderson, Melissa Neubauer, 8196
Anderson, Michael, 1557, 9687
Anderson, Michael J., 7372, 7374
Anderson, Michael K., 2468, 2554
Anderson, Michael R., 9873
Anderson, Michael W., 293
Anderson, Mike, 7686
Anderson, Monica, 4383
Anderson, Monica Rose, 90
Anderson, Neil R., 8665
Anderson, Nicole, 8675
Anderson, Patricia A., 2404
Anderson, Peg, 3481
Anderson, Peggy A., 5597
Anderson, Peyton Tooke, Jr., 2403
Anderson, Priscilla M., 3240
Anderson, Rachel, 6571
Anderson, Randall J., 9873
Anderson, Ray C., 2404
Anderson, Richard E., 471
Anderson, Richard H., 7191
Anderson, Richard M., 7372
Anderson, Richard P., 7372
Anderson, Rick, 9566
Anderson, Rob, 5062
Anderson, Robert, 1479, 4777
Anderson, Robert G., 6206
Anderson, Robert Mailer, 1736
Anderson, Robert W., 9873
Anderson, Roger, 882
Anderson, Ronald R., 7994
Anderson, Ronene E., 1779
Anderson, Rose-Marie, 8665
Anderson, Ross E., 3227
Anderson, S. Eric, 722
Anderson, Salley, 9591
Anderson, Scott, 9651
Anderson, Scott P., 4738
Anderson, Shannon, 9796
Anderson, Sheldon G., 3918
Anderson, Sherry, 4496
Anderson, Stefan S., 3264
Anderson, Steve, 1127, 6795
Anderson, Steven L., 5143
Anderson, Susan A., 85
Anderson, T. Curtis, 167
Anderson, Tammy, 1073, 1348
Anderson, Thomas I., 2818
Anderson, Thomas M., 7605
Anderson, Tom, 4730
Anderson, Warrenn, 4800
Anderson, William, 9572
Anderson, William S., 243
Andersons, Inc., The, 7374
Andover Publishing Co., 4243
Andrae-Pianta, Gail, 9118
Andras, David S., 8666
Andras, Louis J., 8666
Andras, Oscar S., 8666
Andreadis, Alexander, 396
Andreae, Carol, 6864
Andreas, D.O., 4605
Andreas, David, 4604
Andreas, Lowell W., 4604
Andreas, Michael, 4605
Andreas, Michael D., 4605
Andreas, Terry, 4605
Andreoli, Andrew, 749
Andreoli, Anthony, 749
Andreoli, James A., 749
Andreoli, James M., 749
Andreotti, Cindy K., 9410
Andreotti, Lamberto, 5711
Andresakis, Robert, 8742
Andresakis, Robert S., 8741
Andresakis, Summer, 8742
Andrew Corp., 2662
Andrew, Anne, 1512
Andrew, Edith G., 2661
Andrew, Edward J., 2661, 2662
Andrew, Edward J., Jr., 2661
Andrew, Laurel J., 2661, 2662
Andrew, Richard G., 2661, 2662
Andrew, Robert, 3269
Andrew, William V., 2661
Andrew, William V., Dr., 92
Andrews, Alison E., 4310
Andrews, Ann Skilling, 4542
Andrews, Brad F., 2315
Andrews, Charles J., 4560
Andrews, Christopher, 8668
Andrews, Christopher C., 4560
Andrews, Daryl, 3396
Andrews, Delphine J., 4560
Andrews, Edward, Jr., 2431
Andrews, Geoffrey C., 3932, 4310
Andrews, Judith E., 8668
Andrews, Kenneth, 4542
Andrews, Margaretta, 3990
Andrews, Mary Linda, 8060, 8061
Andrews, Michael, 8179
Andrews, Michael C., 4310
Andrews, Nancy, 7164
Andrews, Nathan, 1572
Andrews, Oakley, 7499
Andrews, Paul E., 8668
Andrews, Paul R., 1578
Andrews, Raymond S., Jr., 1589
Andrews, Robert, 6150
Andrews, Robin, 2675
Andrews, Steven, 4542
Andrews, Sumner R., III, 4310
Andrews, Sumner R., Jr., 4310
Andrews, Tracey, 4560
Andrews-Graham, Emelie, 8668
Andrewsen, Brent, 9311
Andrikopoulos, John, 9999
Andringa, Dale J., 3486
Andringa, Mary Vermeer, 3486, 4470
Andrus Memorial, John E., Inc., 5662
Andrus, Colby L., Jr., 5662
Andrus, Elizabeth H., 5662, 6947
Andrus, John E., 6947
Angel Charitable Remainder Annuity Trust, 5600
Angel, Marc D., 5620
Angela Clark Living Trust, 8048
Angelakis, Christine B., 7914
Angelakis, Michael J., 7914
Angeles, Fatima, 368
Angeli, Enrico, 8217
Angelica, Robert E., 5483
Angelides, Michael, 3159
Angelilli, Larry, 9032
Angell Family Trust, 244
Angell Trust, Dorothy, 244
Angell, Charles T., 2663
Angell, Christopher, 6193
Angell, Christopher C., 4253, 5240, 6304
Angell, James S ., 2663
Angell, Janice K., 4703
Angell, Michael T., 2663
Angelle, Frank E., 8757
Angelo, Albert, III, 9603
Angelo, Lynette, 9677
Angelos, Georgia K., 3721
Angelos, John Peter, 3721
Angelos, Louis P., 3721
Angelos, Peter G., 3721
Angerholzer, Maxmillian, III, 1926
Angiuli, Carmen, 9719
Angle, Steve, 4334
Angle, Tamimi, 7671
Anglea, Tom, 2369
Anglin, Anthony, Jr, 8637
Anglin, Dale Robinson, 5232, 5391
Anglin, Kimberly, 8637
Anglin, Scott W., 9383
Anglo Platinum, 7272
Angoff, Walter, 4046
Angood, Arthur W., 4503
Anguilla, Melissa Alpert, 7139
Angus, Charles D., 3256
Anheuser-Busch Cos., Inc., 4853
Anixter Trust, Lester J., 2664
Anixter, Steven, 2664
Anlyan, William G., 7195
Ann's House of Nuts, 3793
Anna, Gary, 2698
Annamanthodo, Guy, 524
Annegers, Clarice, 1578
Annenberg, Wallis, 245
Annenberg, Walter H., Hon., 245
Annestad Family, 4606
Annette, Kathleen, 4617
Annexstad, Albert T., 4606
Annexstad, Catherine C., 4606
Annexstad, Kaci, 4606
Annexstad, Shane, 4606
Annexstad, Tom, 4606
Annibale, Roberto, 5780
Annis, Elmira F., 3256
Annis, John, 2038
Annis, Michael R., 8706
Annis, Robert B., 3256
Anquillare, Ceasae, 6904
Anreus, Alejandro, 6489
Ansara, Karen, 4039
Ansari, Husam, 2665
Ansari, Mohsin, 2665
Ansari-Berna, Farnaz, 7412
Ansbacher, Henry, 4102
Ansbacher-Hunt, Theodore, 4102
Anschel, Daniel, 2666
Anschel, Trude, 2666
Anschuetz, Sara, 3036
Anschutz Corp., The, 1365
Anschutz, Fred B., 1364
Anschutz, Nancy P., 1365
Anschutz, Philip F., 1365
Anschutz-Rodgers, Sue, 1364
Ansin, Edmund N., 1969
Ansin, Ronald M., 4194
Ansley, Nancy, 1983
Anstine, Mary K., 1431
Antekeian, Sedda, 258
Antes, Shirley M., 3514
Anthem Health Plans of New Hampshire, Inc., 3257
Anthem Insurance Cos., Inc., 3257
Anthem, Inc., 3257, 3317
Anthony Charitable Lead Annuity Trust, 3408
Anthony Vineyards, 4606
Anthony, Alison, 7814
Anthony, Beverly S., 3408
Anthony, Carmelo K., 246
Anthony, Carol C., 9806
Anthony, Christine A., 9806
Anthony, Donald, 4636
Anthony, E. Jean, 3851
Anthony, J. Danford, 1547
Anthony, James R., 3408
Anthony, James T., 3408
Anthony, Joseph M., 3851
Anthony, Katherine A., 9806
Anthony, Mary, 1530
Anthony, Nancy B., 7781
Anthony, Nancy S., 4303
Anthony, Rebecca R., 1015
Anthony, Sarah D., 1547
Anthony, Shellie, 3408
Anthony, Tucker, 5927

Anthony, Victor W., Jr., 9806
Antion, Kathleen, 397
Antiquarian Book Foundation, 5707
Antle, Mike, 654
Antle, Tonya, 414
Antman, Karen, 4325
Anton, A., 7537
Anton, Raymond, Jr., 3714
Antonacci, Vance, 8135
Antonatos, Julia, 2800
Antongiovanni, A.J., 780
Antonia Investments, Ltd., 4934
Antonino, Bernie, 7597
Antopol, Marcia, 526
Antoun, Adel, 9435
AO/ASIF Foundation, 7915
AOL Time Warner Inc., 6982
Aon Corp., 2667
Aon Risk Services Co., 3750
Aospine International, 7916
Aoun, Adrian, 6795
Aoyama-Martin, Jane, 6148
Apallas, Yeoryios, 523
Apatow Family, The, 247
Apatow, Judd, 247
APB Real Estate Trust, 6409
Apel, Daniel, 7931
Apex Oil Co., Inc., 4854
Apex Settlement, 1035
Apgar, John N., IV, 3258
Apgar, Karl W., 3258
Apgar, Martha B., 3258
Apicella, Salvatore C., 7640
Apodaca, Patrick, 5532
Apoliona, S. Haunani, 2588
Apolisky, Harold I., 8574
Apollo Group, Inc., 172
Aponick, Charie K., 8152
Appaloosa Management, L.P., 5193
Appel, Daniel, 3375, 3397
Appel, Daniel C., 3301
Appel, Helen, 5603
Appel, Robert, 5603
Appel, Wendy, 4259
Appelget, Kristin, 5412
Appell, Josephine S., 8310
Appell, Louis J., Jr., 8310
Appello, Martha, 9755
Appelson, Marilyn, 3226
Appenteng, Kofi, 5994
Apple, Ed, 7742
Apple, Jim B., 8477
Apple, Timothy, 7972
Applebaum Charitable Lead Trust, Eugene, 4341
Applebaum, Alan T., 1970
Applebaum, Eugene, 4341
Applebaum, Joseph, 1970
Applebaum, Leila, 1970
Applebaum, Lisa S., 4341
Applebaum, Marcia, 4341
Applebaum, Pamela A., 4341
Applebaum, Stanley A., 6568
Appleby, Lois W., 2166
Appleby, Scott B., 2668
Applegate, Marc, 3279
Appleman Charitable Trust, 5604
Appleman, Nathan, 5604
Appleton, Edith Marie, 2669
Appleton, James, 672
Appleton, Thomas R., 4175
Applewhite, Hunter A., 9422
Applied Card Systems, Inc., 7904
Applied Materials, Inc., 249
Appold, Patricia J., 7686
Apregan, Craig, 1028
April, Steven, 1646
Apx Alarm Systems, 9354
Aqua Funding LLC, 5228
Aqua Pennsylvania, Inc., 7917
Aqua-Africa, 9118
Aquahart Manor LLC, 9452
Aquino, Christopher, 9721
Aquino, David, 109
Arader, Walter G., 8250
Aragon, Andrea, 1406
Arai, Alan, 730
Arai, Tomie, 6489
Arakas, Peter, 1627
Arakelian, George H., 7006
Arambula, Miguel, 4230
Aramburu, Justo Mendez, 8353
Aramony, Diane, 6518
Aran, Peter P., 7809
Aranda, Olivia O., 265
Aranow, Judith, 5546
Aranow, Rita, 5546
Aratani, George T., 250
Aratani, Linda Y., 250
Aratani, Sakaye I., 250
Araujo, Jeremy, 1671
Arbeit & Co., 4614
Arbeit Investment, 4614
Arbella, Inc., 3926
Arbesfeld, Ann, 5605
Arbesfeld, Benjamin, 5605
Arbesfeld, Hyman, 5605
Arbogast, Paul, 9780
Arbolino, Maija, 6593
Arbough, Daniel K., 3586
Arbury, Julie Carol, 4407
Arbus, Loreen, 251
Arbut, Ed, 4448
Arcay, Arnaldo, 8708
Arce, Jorge, 5876
ArcelorMittal USA, Inc., 2670
Archabal, Nina M., 4600
Archbold, Armar A., 4710
Archdiocese of New York, 6924
Archdiocese of St. Louis, 4991
Archer Western Contractors, 3212
Archer, Arlene, 7557
Archer, Cynthia A., 8308
Archer, David, 3373
Archer, Galen, 1407
Archer, Keith, 3373
Archer, Rick, 7401
Archer, Robert A., 252
Archibald, Simon, 5315
Archie Trust, Roxie, 5124
Archuleta, Katherine, 4102
Arctic Slope Regional Corp., 81
Ardali, Azade, 6693
Arden, Peter, 8432
Ardiff, Ralph, 4009
Ardinger and Sons, H.T., 5047
Ardisana, Lizabeth, 4510, 4543
Area, Mary Lou, 620
Arecchi, Gloria P., 8914
Arellano, Daniel, 109
Arellano, Michelle, 1005
Arellano, Stephen, 4372
Arena Energy, LLC, 8670
Arena, Salvatore, 6748
Arenare, Scott A., 7048
Arencibia, Lizbeth Dunn, 2071
Arend, Chas, 4701
Arendt, David, 3475
Arendt, Lauren, 9802
Arendt, Leslie V., 9802
Arentz, Richard, 1055
Arenz, Antoinette Kienow, 7901
Aresty, Catherine, 5610
Aresty, James, 5609
Aresty, Jerome, 5609
Aresty, Joseph, 5610
Aresty, Lorraine, 5609
Aresty, Steven, 5610
Arevim Philanthropic Group, 6229
Argidius Foundation, 6654
Argiro, Vincent, 6795
Argo Associates, LLP, 2405
Arguelles, John, 5422
Arguello, Alfredo, 1591
Argyris, George T., 537
Argyros Charitable Trusts, The, 254
Argyros, George L., 254
Argyros, Julie A., 254
Ariail, Leslie, 9380, 9552
Arias, Ron R., 929
Ariel Corporation, 7377
Ariel Funding, LLC, 2050
Ariel Holdings, LLC, 2050
Arima, Donald J., Dr., 9631
Arison Family Foundation USA Inc., Ted, The, 1971
Arison, Cassie, 1972
Arison, David, 1972
Arison, Jason, 1972
Arison, Madeleine, 1971
Arison, Marilyn, 1972
Arison, Micky, 1971
Aristeguieta, Francisco, 5780
Arisumi, Alan H., 2598
Arizona Dental Insurance Services, Inc., 106
Arizona Public Service Co., 91
Arjomandi, Fay, 1519
Arkansas Aluminum Alloys, Inc., 206
Arkansas Baptist Foundation, 3249
Arkansas Blue Cross and Blue Shield, 181
Arkwright, Jill Ann, 6905
Arkwright, Richard T., 6905
Arlen, Alice, 8489
Arlington Assocs., 6
Arlington Capital Advisors, 6
Arloma Corp., 1097
Arman, Kambiz, 722
Armann, Claudia, 900
Armantrout, Natalie, 3543
Armbrister, Denise McGregor, 8333
Armbrust, Joseph W., Jr., 2677
Armel, Helen, 6403
Armendariz, Jim, 3532
Armenian Missionary Association of America, 1036
Armenti, Val, 461
Armentrout, Betty A., 9524
Armentrout, William E., 8671
Armfield, Adair P., 7137
Armfield, Edward M., Sr., 7137
Armfield, Kate, 9509
Armfield, W.J., 7137
Armiger, Earl, 3759
Armintrout, Libby, 9731
Armistead, Leonard H., III, 8607
Armitage, Robert A., 3340
Armon, Navila, 5675
Armour, Laurance H., III, 8878
Armour, Lolita S., 8358
Armour, Monica, 4379
Armour, Vernon, 3172
Armoury, Bernard, 5437
Armstrong, 9606
Armstrong Communications, Inc., 8276
Armstrong Family Foundation, 5613
Armstrong Telephone Co. of Maryland, 8276
Armstrong Telephone Co. of West Virginia, 8276
Armstrong Utilities, Inc., 8276
Armstrong Ventures, 1366
Armstrong Wood Products, 9606
Armstrong World, 9606
Armstrong World Industries, Inc., 7922
Armstrong, Alan S., 7814
Armstrong, Allen L., 4810
Armstrong, Amy, 8472
Armstrong, Andrew J., Jr., 5395
Armstrong, Andrew M., 130
Armstrong, Anne H., 9449
Armstrong, Anthony J., Dr., 7686
Armstrong, C. Michael, 5613
Armstrong, Carol, 1512
Armstrong, Dick, 3320
Armstrong, Doug, 9109
Armstrong, Eleanor S., 4328, 4329
Armstrong, Elisabeth, 1366
Armstrong, George W., Sr., 4810
Armstrong, Gregory J., 9263
Armstrong, Harvey, 463
Armstrong, J. Samuel, IV, 5745
Armstrong, Jack G., 7996
Armstrong, James D., 130
Armstrong, James H., Jr., 2514
Armstrong, Jeannette, 1230
Armstrong, Jeffrey R., 1439
Armstrong, Jo-Ann, 130
Armstrong, Linda, 3291
Armstrong, Lucille, 5612
Armstrong, Meta, 5044
Armstrong, Mike, 1512
Armstrong, Page, 7678
Armstrong, Patrick D., 6573
Armstrong, R. Stephen, 4738
Armstrong, Richard, 8039
Armstrong, Robert E., 6398
Armstrong, Ronald E., 9698
Armstrong, Sallie B., 5108
Armstrong, Sarah Anne, 5613
Armstrong, Thomas K., 4810
Armstrong, Thomas K., Jr., 4810
Armstrong, Victor, 7294
Armstrong, Waymon, 2015
Armstrong, William, 1366
Armstrong-Gustafson, Peg, 3420
Arnaboldi, Nicole, 5826
Arnall, Dawn, 256
Arnall, Roland, 256
Arnaud, Randall T., 2170
Arndt, Celestine Favrot, 8842
Arndt, Tom, 9855
Arnell, Nathan E., 5846
Arneson, Chuck, 9950
Arneson, Jerry, 4800
Arney, Susan Scheidt, 8625
Arnhart, James R., 8545
Arnhold, Clarisse, 5614
Arnhold, Henry H., 952, 5614
Arnhold, John, 1781
Arnhold, John P., 952, 5614
Arnhold, Michele, 5614
Arnholt, Cynthia Haslam, 8580
Arnn, Larry P., 5560
Arno, Andrew, 7021

Atkinson, Mildred M., 265
Atkinson, Patricia D., 5195
Atkinson, Paul D., 5195
Atkinson, Richard C., 264, 801
Atkinson, Rita L., 264
Atkinson, Steven R., 5195
Atkinson, Susan R., 265
Atkinson, Terry, 1053
Atlan Management Corp., 5622
Atlanta Fixture & Sales Co., 3245
Atlanta/Sosnoff Capital Corp., 2607
Atlantic Foundation, The, 2287
Atlantic Media, 1892
Atlantic Philanthropies, 4238
Atlantic Realty Co., 2441
Atlantic Richfield Co., 8718
Atlantic Trust Co., 4116
Atlantic Trust Co., N.A., 1735, 1794, 4048
Atlas Carpet Mills, Inc., 706
Atlas Lighting Products Inc., 7237
Atlas Realty Co., 568
Atlas, Lezlie, 266
Atlas, Richard S., 266
Atlas, Sol G., 5650
Atnip, Janice Pierce, 1408
Atol, Genevieve, 267
Atran, Frank Z., 5197
Atrium at Market Square LLC, The, 9452
ATT, 7638
Attaway, Evelyn Nelson, 9993
Attaway, John, 2275
Attfield, Gillian, 2795, 5995
Attias, Daniel R., 268
Attias, Diana, 268
Attias, Elaine, 268
Attias, Jane, 268
Atticus Capital LLC, 6685
Attiyeh, Robert, 410
Attman, Jeffrey, 3722
Attman, Leonard J., 3722
Attman, Phyllis L., 3722
Attridge, R. Byron, 2569
Atwater, Benjamin, 8135
Atwater, Edward S., IV, 5485
Atwater, H. Brewster, Jr., 4747
Atwater, Martha Clark, 4747
Atwater, William E., III, 2598
Atwood, Elaine, 82
Atwood, Jonathan, 5484
Atwood, Kathy, 9617
Atwood, Robert B., 82
Atzeff, Anne, 3016
Au, Carlton K.C., 2593
Aubin, Nicole, 174
Auble, Mark A., 7704
Aubuchon, William E., IV, 4194
Auburn, Hubert C., 7632
Auchenpaugh, Faye, 4730
Auchincloss Foundation, Lily, 5623
Auchincloss, Andrew, 6217
Auchincloss, Lily, 5623
Aucker, Kendra, 7972
Auda Advisor Associates, 6951
Audet, Anne-Marie J., 5800
Auen, Ronald M., 269, 309
Auer Irrevocable Trust, Ione Breeden, 3260
Auerbach, Andrew, 6225
Auerbach, Arnold, 6225
Auerbach, John M., 3774
Auerbach, Justine, 6225
Auerbach, Nina, 6225
Aufdem-Brinke, Daniel N., 5422
Aufdem-Brinke, Jason, 5422
Aufdem-Brinke, Jason M., 5422
Auge, Jim, 9975
Augello, Terri, 782
Augello-Cook, Alicia, 782
Augur, Harrison H., 1430
August, Bruce A., 1646
August, Roberta Lee, 1565, 1721
Augusta National Inc., 2514
Auguste, Macdonald, 2281
Auguste, Rhonda, 5501
Augustin, Reinhard, 6247
Augustine, Avery, 3361
Augustine, Erika F., 6099
Augustine, Julie, 3475
Augustine, Rose L., 5625
Ault, James F., 3346
Ault, Marilyn C., 8734
Ault, Wendy L., 3700
Auman, Christine M., 7988
Auman, J. Richard, 9510
Aumann, James, 7702
Aupperle, Tammy, 8083
Auritt, Joycellen, 4248
Aurora Capital Assocs., LLC, 5755
Aurora Chamber of Conference, 1411
Ausherman, Justin E., 3723
Ausherman, Kari A., 3723
Ausherman, Lisa S., 3723
Ausherman, Marvin E., 3723
Aust, Bruce E., 3857
Austen, Christopher M., 2191
Austgen, Dave, 3337
Austin Ethiopian Women Assn., 8649
Austin, Clemont R., 8026
Austin, Donald G., III, 7380
Austin, Donald G., Jr., 7380
Austin, Edward H., Jr., 8885, 8886
Austin, George E., 9848
Austin, James W., 7380
Austin, Jeffrey A., 3474
Austin, John C., 7380
Austin, Juan, 1312, 7273
Austin, Kenneth, 7043
Austin, Lawrence B., III, 8544
Austin, Liz, 6564
Austin, Mary K., 759
Austin, Paul, 7380
Austin, Qiana L., 7202
Austin, Samuel H., 7380
Austin, Sidley, 2677
Austin, Sidley, LLP, 2677
Austin, Stewart G., Jr., 7380
Austin, Stewart G., Sr., 7380
Austin, Susan G., 75
Austin, Thomas G., 7380
Austin, Tracy L., 6490
Australian Center for International Ag Research, 1791
Ausubel, Jesse H., 1926
Auto Mark Inc., 4650
Autobahn Imports, Inc., 9151
Automatic Data Processing Corp., 4254
Automotive Management Services, Inc., 2243
AutoNation, 2243
Autrey, Larry, 8776
Autry Foundation, 1268
Autry, Gene, 270
Autry, Jacqueline, 270
Autumn Ventures, 3912
Autzen, Thomas J., 7823
Avalon Trust, 234
Avansino, Kristen A., 5159
Avansino, Raymond C., Jr., 5159
Avant! Corp., 271
Avant, Steve, 8462
Avanzino, Richard, 486
Avedisian, James R., 265
Avedon, Marcia, 5314
Aventis Pharmaceuticals Inc., 5437
Avera, Mark, 2036
Averitt, George R., 3297
Averitte, Judy T., 7266
Avery Dennison Corp., 272
Avery Foundation, R. Stanton, The, 273, 289
Avery, Caroline, 9128
Avery, Caroline D., 487
Avery, Christian O., 7192
Avery, Halina, 487
Avery, John S., Sr., 8873
Avery, Judith, 289, 487
Avery, Karen, 3269
Avery, Sally M., 5627
Avex 2009 Charitable Lead Annuity Trust, 453
Aviad, Janet, 5717
Avian, Bob, 2034
Aviation Fuel Terminals, Inc., 7161
Aviles, Jesus, 3421
Avis, Anne R., 274
Avis, Charles D., 274
Avis, Emily R., 274
Avis, Greg, 727
Avis, Gregory M., 274
Avista Capital, Inc., 9576
Avista Corp., 9576
Aviv, Linda Wasserman, 4576
Aviva Life and Annuity Co., 3411
Avner, Eric, 7480
Avner, Marcia, 1882
Avondale Mills, 20
Avula, Danny TK, 9521
AVX Corp., 8457
Awaya, Alvin, 3908
Awoniyi, Bea, 2174
AXA Financial, Inc., 5629
AXA Foundation Charitable Gift Fund, 7012
Axel, Blair, 6309
Axel, Richard, 3833
Axelrod, Elizabeth, 493
Axelrod, Margaret G., 6258
Axelson, Frances R., 8825
Axt, Gysbert, 374
Axton, Lisa, 3639
Axton, Mike, 4829
Ayad, Yamila M., 1108
Aycock, James M., 18
Aycox, Leslie, 2541
Aycox, Roderick, 2541
Aydelotte, Nanci, 1878
Ayer, Laura, 6802
Ayer, Louise D., 1539
Ayer, Ramani, 1539
Ayers, Carol, 4834
Ayers, James W., 8532
Ayers, Janet, 8532
Ayers, John S., 7184
Ayers, Jon, 8532
Ayers, Kristy, 8532
Ayers, Mark, 7563
Ayers, Nancy Sharon, 8532
Ayling, Alice S., 3932
Ayo, Brenda B., 3674
Ayres, Margaret, 9170
Ayres, Nancy, 3361
Ayres, Nuri Delacruz, 2042
Ayres, Patricia Shield, 9170
Ayres, Robert Atlee, 9170
Ayres, Robert M., Jr., 9170
Ayres, Robert Moss, Jr., 9170
Ayres, Susan, 4452
Ayres, Warren, 9277
Azad McIver Trust, 5124
Azar, Joe, 4821
Azark, Daniel, 2875
Azeez, Anne, 1975
Azeez, Kathleen, 1975
Azeez, Michael, 1975
Azeez, Michael B., 2310
Aziz, Nikhil, 6571
Azose, David, 9725
Azrael, Hilary, 6157
Azrak, Adam, 5630
Azrak, Elliot, 5630
Azrak, Elliott, 5630
Azrak, Marvin, 5630
Azrak, Victor, 5630
Azuara, Katherine, 2690

B & H Foto and Electronics, 6998
B&B Lease Co., 4656
B.E. Investments LLC, 3730
B.F.Goodrich Co., The, 7213
B.O.A.T. Fund, 1565
Baader, Marilyn J., 6153
Baalman-DeBoer, Annie, 3505
Baas, Janet Heldt, 3363
Baba, Gwendolyn, 324
Babbio, Lawrence T., Jr., 7043
Babbit, Edward J., 7710
Babcock, Ann Kelsey, 565
Babcock, Betsy, 7138
Babcock, Bill, 9380
Babcock, Bruce M., 7138
Babcock, Charles H., 7138
Babcock, Charles H., Jr., 7138
Babcock, Gwendolyn Garland, 565
Babcock, John Carlile, 565
Babcock, John E., 4679
Babcock, John J., 4679
Babcock, Mary Reynolds, 7138, 7298
Babcock, Sarah Garland, 565
Babcock, Susan Hinman, 565
Babcock, Tim, 3403
Babcock, William, Dr., 8468
Babcok, Judith, 6187
Baber, Wilbur H., Jr., 8806
Babicka, Jerry, 1578, 1839
Babicka, Jonathan, 1578
Babicka, Lynn P., 1578, 1779, 1839
Babicka, Missy, 1578
Babineau, Timothy J, 8383
Babington, Wallace K., 9554
Babiran, Ali, 5566
Babitt, J. Lawry, 7412
Babock, B. A., 8833
Babson, James A., 3933
Babson, Katherine L., 3933
Babson, Katherine L., Jr., 4209, 4286
Babson, Paul T., 3933
Babylon, Caroline, 3757
Bacak, Sandra, 8658
Bacardi, 2351
Bacardi, Joaquin, 2351
Bacardi, Sonia, 2351
Baccaglio, Martin, 1160
Bach, Nathan, 2763
Bach, Norma J., 2118

Bach, Timothy J., 2118
Bachard, Deborah K., 1719
Bachard, Robert, 1719
Bachhuber, Carl N., 9809
Bachhuber, JoAnn, 9809
Bachhuber, Theodore J., 9809
Bachman, Dale S., 2597
Bachman, Greg, 3523
Bachman, Gregory A., 8945
Bachman, James B., 7587
Bachman, John Q., 5050
Bachman, Shannon, 3929
Bachmann, B., 5632
Bachmann, Bruce R., 3084
Bachmann, Louis, 5632
Bachrach, Linda, 1391
Back Home Again Foundation, 3317
Back, George, 7766
Backer, Beth Lebovitz, 8597
Backus, Carol S., 9673
Backus, Frances A., 9673
Backus, John T., 9673
Backus, Lisa, Dr., 434
Backus, Manson, 9673
Backus, Valerie, 9673
Backus, Valerie F., 9673
Bacon, Andrew, 1370
Bacon, Herbert, 1370
Bacon, John O., 7439, 7444
Bacon, Laura May, 1370
Bacon, Louis M., 5661, 6500
Bacon, Matthew L., 3569
Bacon, Stephen, 1370
Bacot, S. Ashley, 2294
Baczewski, Kimberlee K., 4549
Bade, Mark J., 8400
Baden, Helen T., 8479
Baden, Jan Schwartz, 5210
Baden, Robert D., 6722
Bader Charitable Trust, Daniel, 9810
Bader Charitable Trust, David, 9810
Bader, Daniel J., 9810
Bader, David M., 9810
Bader, Linda C., 9810
Bader, Paul, 6549
Badgeley, Rose, 5633
Badger Liquor Co., 9941
Badgett, Bentley F., II, 3558
Badgett, Claude R., 3558
Badgett, J. Rodgers, Sr., 3558
Badiner, India Hunt, 8100
Baecher-Brown, Dee, 9377
Baechle, John L., 7448
Baeder, Charles, 6564
Baehren, Jim, 7400
Baenziger, Tom, 371, 1078
Baer, Helen K., 4856
Baer, Jr. Trust, Sidney R., 4857
Baer, Timothy R., 4776
Baeur, Robert W., 9617
Bafundo, Donna, 8475
Bafunno, Norm, 3402
Bagaason, Linda, 1345
Bagget, Art, Jr., 1002
Baggett, Art, 1002
Baggette, John, 22
Bagian, James P., 471
Bagine, Richard Kiome, 9656
Bagley, Diane M., 2633
Bagley, James W., 277
Bagley, Jean A., 277
Bagley, Mark C., 277
Bagley, Nancy R., 1880, 7298
Bagley, Nicole, 1880, 2546
Bagley, Teri, 277
Bagley, Thomas F., III, 4194
Bagwell, Chantal, 2407
Bagwell, Thomas N., 2407
Baharestani, Martin, 6963
Bahena, Jorge, 2151
Bahl, Lalit, 6310
Bahl, Roy W., 4146
Bahl, William, 7717
Bahnik, Claude, 5634
Bahnik, Lore, 5634
Bahnik, Roger L., 5634
Bahr, Adam, 3481
Bahr, Bahr, 3532
Baier, Jon, 3418
Baig, Mirza, 224
Baig, Patricia, 224
Bailes, Lamar, 8478
Bailey, Andrew C., 3934, 4207
Bailey, Ann Haslam, 8581
Bailey, Beverly W., 1976
Bailey, Bobbie, 1977
Bailey, Charles D., Jr., 2260
Bailey, Cornelia, 7381
Bailey, Cynthia A. Haslam, 8581
Bailey, Dan, 7703
Bailey, Darlyne, 8303
Bailey, Dianne Chipps, 7214
Bailey, Emily F., 8458
Bailey, Hoyt Q., 7194
Bailey, Jackie, 4820
Bailey, James N., 4323
Bailey, Joe M., 8658
Bailey, John, 180, 1581, 8351
Bailey, John Warrington, 7703
Bailey, Josh, 3543
Bailey, Judith, 416
Bailey, L'Tanya, 7231
Bailey, Lauren L., 3866
Bailey, Leon, 1562
Bailey, Michael C., 295
Bailey, Nancy, 1962
Bailey, Patricia, 180
Bailey, Patricia B., 3926
Bailey, Rich, 5063
Bailey, Robert, 1566
Bailey, Robert S., 8001
Bailey, Ron K., 1976
Bailey, Ronald, Bishop, 6542
Bailey, Ronnie Kyle, 1976
Bailey, Ryan Kent, 1976
Bailey, Sam, 7703
Bailey, Shelley, 7860
Bailey, Stephanie, 755
Bailey, Steven J., 7640
Bailey, Tammy, 4446
Bailey, Toni Bentel, 9411
Bailitz, Ron, 3190
Baillargeon, Pat, 9701
Bailon, Katherine, 5598
Bain, Karen, 6548
Bain, Kevin, 3402
Bainum, Barbara, 3756
Bainum, Bruce, 3756
Bainum, Jane, 3756
Bainum, Roberta, 3756
Bainum, Stewart, Jr., 3794
Bainum, Stewart, Sr., 3756
Baio, Betsy, 6876
Bair Ranch Foundation, 5004
Bair, Preston, 7421
Bair, Shannon, 8896
Baird and Co., Robert W., 9811
Baird Foundation, Robert W., 9961
Baird, Alison L., 1848
Baird, Brent D., 5635
Baird, Brian D., 5635
Baird, Bridget B., 5635
Baird, Bruce C., 5635
Baird, Cameron, 5636
Baird, D. Ann, 7569
Baird, Dee, 3439
Baird, Flora M., 5636
Baird, Frank B., Jr., 5636
Baird, Karen, 9059
Baird, Kyle, 9059
Baird, Laura Trammell, 8853
Baird, Mark, 3391
Baird, Pat, 3449
Baird, Patrick, 3449
Baird, Rob, 4947
Baird, Robert, 7474, 9059
Baird, Sandy, 9059
Baird, Thomas, 9280
Baird, William C., 5636
Baird, Zoe, 6431
Baither, Thomas A., 4431
Baity, Gail, 5804
Bajan, Janet, 6778
Bajek, Gerard B., 7258
Bakal, Max Bessie, 6
Bakar, Anne, 278
Bakar, Barbara Bass, 278
Bakar, Gerson, 278
Bakely, Claudia, 3524
Baker and Daniels, LLP, 3317
Baker Associates LLC, R., 8834
Baker Commodities, Inc., 749
Baker Corporation, Michael, 7925
Baker Hughes Inc., 8679
Baker Lewis, David, 4543
Baker Living Trust, Jay, 9812
Baker Tilly Virchow Krause LLP, 9837
Baker, Barbara W., 8568
Baker, Beverly, 53
Baker, Bill, 9769
Baker, Brian, 3348
Baker, Carolyn, 7926
Baker, Cindy, 4334
Baker, Curtis, 8789
Baker, David S., 2537
Baker, Debra Ann, 3302
Baker, Dexter F., 7926
Baker, Diana, 2040
Baker, Donald E., 1985
Baker, Dorothy H., 7926
Baker, Douglas M., Jr., 4651
Baker, Elinor Patterson, 1540
Baker, Elizabeth Stephans, 8256
Baker, Ellen L., 5808
Baker, Frank, 7921
Baker, Gerson, 278
Baker, Gordon B., Jr., 8461
Baker, Howard H., Jr., 1907
Baker, Jack, 1566
Baker, James A., III, 774, 3818
Baker, James B., 8634
Baker, Jason, 138
Baker, Jay H., 9812
Baker, Jeffrey B., 4738
Baker, John P., 9859
Baker, John W., Jr., 8636
Baker, Joseph R., 1581
Baker, Judith, 1962
Baker, Judy, 9616
Baker, Julia C., 3724, 3836
Baker, Kate, 7604
Baker, Larry F., 7586
Baker, Leesa, 7569
Baker, Linda O., 9579
Baker, Marjorie Montgomery Ward, 3216
Baker, Martha, 2031
Baker, Maxine, 1939
Baker, Michael, 7421
Baker, Nancy, 7271
Baker, Nichole D., 365
Baker, Norman D., Jr., 8410
Baker, Norton, 9219
Baker, Pat Good, 9812
Baker, Patricia, 1567
Baker, Paula, 4334
Baker, Pauline, 1935
Baker, Randal W., 9876
Baker, Richard W., 2328
Baker, Robert C., 5638
Baker, Theodore W., 7475
Baker, Thomas, 8637
Baker, Thomas E., 9579
Baker, Tracy A., 4443
Baker, Trish, 9833
Baker, W.K., 2375
Baker, Walter S., Jr., 8681
Baker, William, 8765
Baker, William A., Jr., 2430
Baker-Doyle, Kira, 8175
Bakers Food, 4529
Bakhshi, Nandita, 3710
Baking Co., Roskam, 4529
Bakke, Dennis W., 9492
Bakke, Eileen Harvey, 9492
Bakke, Elizabeth, 9492
Bakke, Lowell, 9492
Bakke, Margaret, 9492
Bakke, Raymond J., 9492
Bakkedahl, Robyn, 5006
Bakken, Bradley E., 4608
Bakken, Constance L., 4608
Bakken, Eric A., 4750
Bakken, Jeffrey, 4608
Bakker Family Fund of Coastal Community Foundation, 8492
Balachandran, Madhu, 238
Balart, Dena R., 3662
Balas, David, 4334
Balas, Steve K., 9283
Balazs, Endre A., 5199
Balbier, Jennifer, 6408
Baldasare, Joseph B., 7428
Baldauf, Hans, 517
Baldauf, Marian, 517
Balderson, Cynthia P., 9422
Baldini, Tom, 4495
Baldino, Eugene W., 6945
Baldree, Gary H., Sr., 7141
Baldwin, Alexander R., 5639
Baldwin, Alfred W., 3934
Baldwin, Barbara, 5640
Baldwin, Dan, 414
Baldwin, David M., 5640
Baldwin, Edward, 2617
Baldwin, George, 7285
Baldwin, George M., 1978
Baldwin, H. Furlong, 3857
Baldwin, Harold L., 5073
Baldwin, Janice H., 9650
Baldwin, Jeffrey V., 1474
Baldwin, Julie G., 2435
Baldwin, Kitt, 2594
Baldwin, Kittredge A., Dr., 2593
Baldwin, Michael, 4065
Baldwin, Michael C., 2587
Baldwin, Nancy E., 121

Baldwin, Phillip N., 197
Baldwin, Priscilla V., 2587
Baldwin, Robert M.B., 5243
Baldwin, Susan, 4343
Baldwin, Teresa L.C., 9513
Baldwin, Winifred B., 1541
Bales, Carol, 3518
Bales, Hazel, 3261
Bales, John F., III, 8169
Bales, Mayuli, 4679
Bales, Walter T., 3261
Balestrieri, Thomas, 7957
Balfour, L.G., 3935
Balhoff, William E., 3613
Balian, Eileen, 248
Balk, Mark D., 4162
Balka, Don, 3348
Ball Corp., 1371
Ball Investments LP, 2679
Ball, Andrew L., 7927
Ball, Ann Marie, 4562
Ball, Anna C., 2679
Ball, Anne F., 4422
Ball, Braden, Jr., 2074
Ball, Charles F., 3263
Ball, Chris, 2414
Ball, Christi, 5063
Ball, Deborah Lowenberg, 3171
Ball, Dwight R., 6467
Ball, Edmund B., 3262
Ball, Edmund F., 3262, 3263
Ball, Emmylou, 3417
Ball, Frank C., 3262
Ball, Frank E., 3263
Ball, G. Carl, 2679
Ball, George A., 3262, 3264
Ball, Lucius L., 3262
Ball, Lucy, 1632
Ball, Lynne, 4097
Ball, Nancy Elitharp, 140
Ball, Robert B., 3263
Ball, Russell C., III, 7927
Ball, Susannah P., 2679
Ball, Virginia B., 3262, 3263
Ball, William A., 3262
Ball-Miller, Rebecca, 3298
Ball-Rokeach, Sandra, 900
Ballantine, Richard, 1395
Ballard, A.L., 645
Ballard, Andy, 1109
Ballard, Christopher, 4477
Ballard, Edwin Lee, 8680
Ballard, Rachel Maria, 8680
Ballas, Craig, 7565
Ballenger, Kelley F., 7750
Ballenger, Robin F., 7750
Balliet, Karen Prager, 6944
Ballingall, Keith R., 5175
Ballinger, Leslie Ann, 7892
Ballou, Ben, 3291
Ballou, E. Spencer Pardoe, 4206
Ballou, Michele, Dr., 9382
Balloun, Julie W. Lanier, 2499
Ballton, Carl A., 1271
Ballweg, Diane, 9897
Bally Gaming, 964
Balmat, Mary Adams, 7133
Balmer, Steven, 9746
Balsam, Cheryl, 2766
Balsells, Peter J., 9385
Balsley, Jacob, III, 7294
Balson, Anissa Boudjakdji, 6155, 6156
Balthazar, Herman, 6007
Baltimore Gas and Electric Co., 3868
Baltimore, David, 3833
Baltycki, Mary, 6783
Balukoff, Susie Skaggs, 9302
Bam, Foster, 1588
Bam, Patricia S., 1588
Bamattre, William, 1013
Bamberger, Eleanor F., 9305
Bamberger, Ernest, 9305
BAMCO, Inc., 5646
Bame, Tracy L., 112
Bamesberger, Karen, 5045
Bamford, Calvin D., Jr., 9580
Bamford, Drew, 9580
Bamford, Gregory L., 149
Bamford, Heather, 9580
Bamford, JoAnne W., 9580
Ban, George, Dr., 6336
Banaka, Jerry, 3532
Banco Popular Foundation, Inc., 3085
Banco Popular North America, 3085, 9865
Bancorpsouth Bank, 4812
BancorpSouth, Inc., 4812
Bancroft, Charles, 5711
Bancroft, James R., 1200
Bancroft, John, 5055
Bancroft, Paul M., 1200
BancWest Corp., 2598
Bandy, Cliff, 9228
Bandzak, Melvin L., 8118
Bane, Marylou, 2990
Bane, Richard C., 4030
Banerjee, Rini, 6477
Banet, Gary, 3288
Banfi Products Corp., 5641
Bang, Dolores, 5039
Bangor Savings Bank, 3680
Banis, Richard P., 5139
Banister, Michael, 4430
Bank of America, 1728, 7638, 8365, 8366, 8385, 8394, 8399, 8408, 8414, 8419, 8451, 9606
Bank of America Corp., 7139
Bank of America Merrill Lynch, 1669
Bank of America Private Client Group, 196
Bank of America, N.A., 839, 1562, 1565, 1575, 1580, 1609, 1639, 1666, 1699, 1703, 1925, 1979, 2009, 2052, 2163, 2171, 2201, 2262, 2269, 2389, 2652, 2696, 2725, 2746, 2861, 2905, 2937, 2963, 2972, 3073, 3087, 3157, 3187, 3216, 3233, 3237, 3917, 3935, 3971, 3986, 4043, 4122, 4170, 4215, 4217, 4299, 4757, 4851, 4912, 4963, 4966, 4978, 4979, 5430, 5676, 5719, 5743, 5748, 5760, 5866, 6544, 6754, 6833, 7012, 7139, 7282, 7318, 7329, 7340, 8101, 8354, 8358, 8360, 8361, 8362, 8364, 8367, 8369, 8372, 8373, 8375, 8376, 8377, 8378, 8382, 8389, 8395, 8396, 8398, 8400, 8401, 8405, 8407, 8408, 8411, 8412, 8413, 8415, 8417, 8418, 8420, 8424, 8425, 8426, 8427, 8430, 8431, 8436, 8439, 8440, 8441, 8442, 8443, 8445, 8447, 8450, 8452, 8453, 8481, 8667, 8697, 8735, 8747, 8748, 8783, 8786, 8791, 8795, 8796, 8909, 8925, 8945, 8970, 8971, 8980, 8988, 8991, 8995, 9013, 9015, 9043, 9056, 9084, 9085, 9094, 9129, 9139, 9148, 9160, 9179, 9209, 9211, 9218, 9242, 9252, 9447, 9457, 9474, 9490, 9691, 9728
Bank of Hawaii, 2586, 2588, 2600, 2605, 2612, 2621, 2624
Bank of Herrin, N.A., The, 2894
Bank of Highland Park Financial Corp., 2833
Bank of Kentucky, Inc., The, 3601
Bank of New York Mellon Corp. Foundation, 7945
Bank of New York Mellon, N.A., 8057, 8248
Bank of New York Mellon, N.A., The, 7908
Bank of New York Mellon, The, 9422
Bank of New York, The, 7945
Bank of Oklahoma, N.A., 7804
Bank of Stockton, 430
Bank of Texas, N.A., 9007
Bank of the West, 413, 629, 866, 7351
Bank of Tokyo, Mitsubishi Trust Co., The, 5724
Bank of Tokyo, Mitsubishi UFJ Trust Co., The, 5724
Bank One Investment Corp., 6244
Bank One, Texas, N.A., 9148
Bank, Katie Firth, 5913
Bank, Premier, 7673
Bank, Raymond L., 3726
BankBoston, N.A. Fund, 1565
Banker, Alex, 841
Bankers Trust Co., 3445, 5876
Banknorth Group, Inc., 3710
Bankowski, Elizabeth, 9358
Bankowski, Elizabeth A., 5220
Banks, Dennis, 3280
Banks, Elizabeth, 8672
Banks, Kate Ferrell, 4920
Banks, Keith T., 7139
Banks, Leslie Waterman, 3446
Banks, Particia, 8492
Banks, Richard, 5807
Banks, Ronald, 8492
BankTrust, 29
Banner, Matthew R. "Pete", III, 1440
Bannick, Matthew, 984
Bannigan, Patrick, 1469
Bannish, Robert G., 4161, 4209, 4240, 4260
Bannister, Michael E., 4371
Bannon, David, 4056
Bansal, Sanjeev K., 9387
Banta, Charles W., 6299
Banta, Tom, 7396
Bantivoglio, Thomas N., 8252
Banuelos, Alma, 1201
Bany, David C., 7863
Bany, Sarah A., 7863
Baptist Bible College West, 2279
Baptist Community Ministries, 3612
Baptiste, K., 6073
Bara, Roy, 8660
Barabino, John, 1421
Baradaran, Sharon, 962
Baraka Realty, 5768
Barakett, Brett, 5642
Barakett, Michele, 5643
Barakett, Timothy, 5643
Barakett, Timothy R., 6685
Barazzone, Esther L., 7935
Barb, Amy, 9796
Barbar, Martin S., 6918
Barbara B. Gentry, 9245
Barbara Oil Co., 2716
Barbara Wheatland Recobable Trust, 4160
Barbarino, Robert J., 5398
Barbato, Virginia, 7594
Barbato, Virginia N., 7595
Barber, Charles M., 8152
Barber, Charles P., 8289
Barber, Gerald, 4339
Barber, Jim, 7321
Barber, Joseph H., 8289
Barber, Kathryn L., 3680
Barber, Lionel, 5747
Barber, Paul H., 9755
Barber, Roger L., 5080
Barber, Sandy, 8601
Barber, Scott, 9377
Barberi, Alison, 4452
Barbieri, Barbara, 3403
Barbo, A. Dennis, 4184
Barbour, Bernice, 1980
Barbour, F.E., Mrs., 5611
Barbour, Larry D., 7295
Barbour, Margaret Sewall, 3708
Barbour, Patricia A., 5171
Barbour, Tom, 8936
Barclay, Donald, 5885
Barclay, Gilian R., 1531
Barclays, 9606
Barcroft, Adam, 7512
Barcus, Marian, 4617
Bard, C.R., Inc., 5202
Bard, Holly Hewitt, 5596
Bard, Karen, 5511
Bard, Paddy, 9988
Bardack, Phillip M., 620, 1248
Bardakjian, Kevork, 2982
Bardel, William, 6115
Bardige, Arran, 6418
Bardige, Betty S., 6418
Bardige, Kori, 6418
Bare, John, 2413
Bare, Thomas J., 9967
Barefield, Lun Ye Crim, 2826
Barefoot, Samuel V., 5920
Barer, Meri I., 5203
Barer, Sol J., 5203
Barfield, Mary F., 8567
Barfield, Melissa G., 8471
Barg, Stanley, 7980
Barger, Colleen, 5045
Barger, John, 9001
Barhoum, Ann Francis, 4893
Barhrambeygui, Sherry, 1043
Baribeau, Cara, 3569
Baring, B.A., Jr., 8867
Barjesteh, Megan E., 9570
Bark, Dennis L., 4413
Barkalow, C. Thomas, 5374
Barkan, Jeffrey, 8403
Barkan, Mel P., 6068
Barker, Amy N., 8803
Barker, Calvin E., 7144
Barker, Chelsea, 3521
Barker, Clyde F., 8170
Barker, Coeta, 282
Barker, David S., 3321
Barker, Dick, 3851
Barker, Donald R., 282
Barker, Gregory D., 3936
Barker, Gregory J., 1
Barker, James M., 3936

Barker, James R., 3936
Barker, Jeff, 2431
Barker, Jonathan, 3560
Barker, Judy Liff, 8550
Barker, Kathryn, 3936
Barker, Larry W., 9151
Barker, Margaret R., 3936
Barker, Mary L., 166
Barker, Peter K., 756, 774
Barker, Robert R., 3936
Barker, Robert W. "Bob", 469
Barker, W.B., 3936
Barker, William S., 3936
Barkheimer, Marlene, 7704
Barkhouser, Richard, 9420
Barkin, Kyla, 6001
Barkley, Kirsten Hansen, 2889
Barks, Herbert, 8576
Barksdale, David, 3656
Barksdale, James L., 4837
Barksdale, Kathleen M., 2540
Barksdale, Sally M., 4837
Barkus, Paul R., 7266
Barletta, Robert J., 6663, 6895
Barlette, Sheldon W., Jr., 7401
Barley, Harold W., 2390
Barley, Inc., 4183
Barlin, Wayne, 2048
Barlin, Wayne A., 2047
Barlow, David S., 368, 1225
Barlow, Ed, 1512
Barlow, Toby, 4463
Barmann, Allison, 4621
Barmeier, Bill, 493
Barmonde, Charles, 7659
Barnaby, Jacey, 9704
Barnard Trust, George D., 3929
Barnard, D. Douglas, Jr., 2434
Barnard, Judith A., 2766
Barnard, June D., 2806
Barnard, Katherine, 918
Barnard, Ray F., 8851
Barnea, Ronny, 6929
Barner, Julie A., 7352
Barnes & Sons, M. Nelson, Inc., 3889
Barnes Group Inc., 1542
Barnes, Bill, 3285, 3514
Barnes, Brett W., 3178
Barnes, Bruce, 1346
Barnes, Bryant G., 8484
Barnes, Chaplin Bradford, 6717
Barnes, Chris, 3178
Barnes, Edwin L., 8484
Barnes, Hannah, 9991
Barnes, Jack P., 1671
Barnes, Janet, 2204
Barnes, John M., Jr., 8484
Barnes, Kenneth W., 3178
Barnes, Ladson A., Jr., 8484
Barnes, Mark, 6105
Barnes, Martina G., 2429
Barnes, Melody, 9596
Barnes, Ron, 4830
Barnes, Ronald R., 971
Barnes, Thomas O., 1542
Barnes, William C., 846
Barnet, Geoff, 1797
Barnet, Howard, Jr., 1797
Barnet, Jane, 1797
Barnet, Peter, 1797
Barnet, Saretta, 1797
Barnet, Will, 5585
Barnet, William, III, 7195
Barnett Trust No. 1, Marjorie C., 2680
Barnett, Albert E., 722
Barnett, Barney, 2123
Barnett, Bert E., 8549
Barnett, Carol, 2275
Barnett, Crawford F., Jr., 2580
Barnett, Harvey J., 3110
Barnett, Hoyt, 2275
Barnett, James Joseph, 5645
Barnett, Janet, 3280
Barnett, Kathleen M., 3108
Barnett, Ken, 22
Barnett, Kerry, 7829
Barnett, Laurey J., 5645
Barnett, Lawrence R., 5645
Barnett, Lawrence R., Jr., 5645
Barnett, Marjorie C., 2680
Barnett, Robert B., 1927
Barnette, Joseph D., Jr., 3331
Barney, Carl B., 5141
Barney, James, Dr., 7558
Barney, John, 3291
Barney, Lynne C., 2682
Barney, Stephen M., Jr., 2682
Barney, Stephen M., Sr., 2682
Barnhardt, Martha, 3502
Barnhart, Cynthia, 6872
Barnhart, Douglas E., 283
Barnhart, Jim, 9726
Barnhart, Nancy J., 283
Barnhill, Robert E., Jr., 7273
Barnholt, Edward W., 1006
Barnum, Laura Melilo, 3608
Baroco, J. H., III, 1981
Baroco, James H., Sr., 1981
Baroco, Julie M., 1981
Baroco, Ronald Anthony, 1981
Baroco, Vicki Ann, 1981
Baron, Charles B., 4973
Baron, David R., 5646
Baron, Frederick M., 8682
Baron, Jason, 1916
Baron, John F., 6504
Baron, Jules M., 6068
Baron, Laura, 5357
Baron, Lisa A. Blue, 8682
Baron, Michael R., 5646
Baron, Nancy C., 2136
Baron, Richard K., 6068
Baron, Rick, 4343
Baron, Ronald, 5646
Barone, Anna M., 7091
Barone, Samuel, 7413
Baronofsky, Debroah, 7425
Barr, Christopher Michael, 8683
Barr, Donald M., 8361
Barr, Frank Theodore, 8683
Barr, Garland H., III, 3560
Barr, Harry C., 4211
Barr, Jason, 3201
Barr, L. Graham, Jr., 1968
Barr, Lamar, 9413
Barr, Lisa, 2986
Barr, Lynn E., 293
Barr, Melza M., 8683
Barr, Terence David, 8683
Barra, Frank N., 5339
Barra, Lori, 227
Barraclough, Thor, 2034
Barrak, Marion L., 1613
Barranda, Michael, 3276, 3281
Barrat, Sherry S., 2032
Barreiro, Terri D., 4628
Barren, Veronica Teresa, 4178
Barrentile, Lisa, 9221
Barrera, Janie, 9148
Barrera, Joel, 4173
Barrera, Mari Brennan, 4037
Barrera, Mario, 9149
Barret, Paul, 1646
Barrett, Ann Dobson, 1015
Barrett, Barbara, 96, 6333
Barrett, Clint, 4461
Barrett, Craig, 96
Barrett, David J., 6155, 6156
Barrett, David O., 3310
Barrett, Diana, 5987
Barrett, Elizabeth, 6634
Barrett, Frank, 8061
Barrett, J. Andrew, 7283
Barrett, Jacqueline, 3310
Barrett, James, 7445
Barrett, John, 4461
Barrett, John B., 4194
Barrett, John F., 7443
Barrett, John Finn, 7710
Barrett, John P., 3760
Barrett, Julie, 9305
Barrett, Kerry, 4940
Barrett, Mark, 9681
Barrett, Paul, 3201
Barrette, Cynthia, 5163
Barrette, David R., 5163
Barrette, Julie A., 5163
Barrette, Kaitlyn S., 5163
Barrette, Raymond, 5163
Barrick, Lise M., 8040
Barrick, William R., 2698
Barriere, Micheal T. (Mike), 7908
Barriocanal, Nelson, 5865
Barrios, Domingo, 9135
Barrist, Michael, 7929
Barrist, Natalie, 7929
Barritt, Dan, 9652
Barron, Cate, 8046
Barron, Charles, 3097
Barron, Charles J., 3093
Barron, Patricia C., 157
Barrow, Christopher T., 4185
Barrow, James P., 8684
Barrow, Jean S., 8684
Barrows, Dana R., 3992
Barrs, W. Craig, 2468
Barrueta, Fernando, 1893
Barrus, Avis B., 8360
Barrus, Clifford B., Jr., 8360
Barry, Esto K., 5307
Barry, John M., 7144
Barry, John P., 5819
Barry, Julie, 4920
Barry, Michael J., 4107
Barry, Pat, 3476
Barry, Richard Allen, 284
Barry, Richard F., III, 9467, 9538
Barry, Roy, 3700
Barry, Susan A., 3569
Barsalou, Judy, 1903
Barsam, Joyce, 5479
Barshad, Janice, 5476
Barshefsky, Charlene, Amb., 3818
Barsky, Neil S., 5851
Barsness, Kathy, 9380
Barsness, W.E., 4710
Barsophy, Jan, 3369
Barsotti, John S., 7986
Barsumian, Bruce R., 8626
Bartek, Brad, 5517
Bartell, Laurence A., 7709
Bartelmo, Thomas, 2187
Bartels, Elizabeth, 4565
Bartels, Larry M., 6782
Bartenbach, Jennifer K., 3272
Barth, Andrew C., 7749
Barth, Andrew F., 1320
Barth, Anthony S., 458
Barth, Carin Marcy, 9268
Barth, Kevin G., 4871
Barth, Robert, 285
Barth, Suzanne, 285
Barth, Theodore H., 5648
Barthebaug, Richard, 7421
Barthebaug, Richard, Mrs., 7421
Bartholomae, Richard, 5856
Bartholomay, Virginia, 3181
Bartholomew, Lesley M., 3480
Bartholomew, Thomas J., 4327
Bartichek, Constance E., 5304
Bartichek, John J., 5304
Bartkowski, Fred J., 9892
Bartle, Barbara, 5063
Bartlett, David, 7474
Bartlett, Dewey, 7807
Bartlett, Edward E., 7732
Bartlett, Harrison I., III, 7732
Bartlett, Jack A., 2789
Bartlett, Kathie, 5108
Bartlett, Kerry A., 2166
Bartlett, Robert J., 9804
Bartley, Anne, 1882, 6723
Bartley, Bruce, 198
Bartman, Cecile C., 286
Bartman, David, 286
Bartman, John, 286
Bartman, N., 286
Barto, JJ, 182
Bartolotta, Joseph, 4152
Barton, Andrew P., Jr., 2166
Barton, Annette D., 3613, 3618
Barton, Benjamin P., 8015
Barton, Colin M., 9496
Barton, Dick K., 8015
Barton, Harris, 936
Barton, Larry, 9835
Barton, Richard N., 9581
Barton, Sarah M., 9581
Barton, Thomas, Dr., 8265
Barton, Wilson, Jr., 8594
Barton-Navitsky, Elizabeth, 6057
Bartos & Altman, CLT, 5513
Bartos Charitable Trust, Celeste & Adam, The, 6613
Bartos, Adam, 6613
Bartos, John N., 4549
Bartow, Beverly, 4417
Bartow, Cliff, 4417
Bartow, Earl Clifford, 4417
Bartram, Ann Cox, 4874
Bartram, John C., 7558
Bartram, Thomas L., 1584
Bartwink, Theodore S., 6134
Baruch, Fran, 1771
Baruch, Jordan J., 7140
Baruch, Lawrence K., 7140
Baruch, Rhoda W., 7140
Barvin, Martha Weisberg, 9798
Barwick, Ed, 566
Barwick, Kent L., 5786
Barzun, Brooke Brown, 3557, 3559, 3562, 3595
Bas Properties, LLC, 5262
Basan, Patricia, 3008
Basch, Jack, 5649
Basch, Miriam, 5649

Bascom, Roxanne, 5055
Basden, Mildred, 6439
Base, Elizabeth, 7793
Basey, Pamela Kenney, 1401
BASF Corp., 7383
Basgal, Ophelia B., 1109
Basgoz, Nesli, 6163
Bash, Edward, 7924
Basham, Arthur A., 1279
Basham, Robert D., 1982
Bashinsky, Joann, 7
Bashinsky, Joann F., 7
Bashinsky, Sloan Y., Sr., 7
Bashor, Beth, 1394
Basier, Frank, 4026
Basile, Louis A., 1105
Basile, Susan L., 9780
Baskes, Daniel L., 2684
Baskes, Jeremy A., 2684
Baskes, Julie Z., 2683, 2684
Baskes, Roger S., 2683, 2684
Baskin Family Charitable Lead Trust, 2685
Baskin, Avshalom, 6229
Baskin, Dorsey, 2877
Baskin, Hadassah, 2685
Baskin, Joan, 8874
Baskin, Richard, 1224
Baskin, Samuel J., 2685
Baskin, Sheldon L., 2685
Basnight, Gina, 7303
Basralian, Joseph L., 5408
Bass Irrevocable Trust, Thomas Ebert, 4192
Bass Trust, William, 2686
Bass, Alice W., 8689
Bass, Angela, 1014
Bass, Anne T., 8687
Bass, Crystal, 9767
Bass, Doris L., 8690
Bass, Edward P., 8686, 9130
Bass, Gary D., 1882
Bass, Harry W., Jr., 8690
Bass, Harry W., Sr., 8689
Bass, Harry W., Sr., Mrs., 8689
Bass, James C., 8383
Bass, James E., 8773
Bass, John T., 1398
Bass, Kirk A., 7883
Bass, Lee M., 8685, 8686, 8688, 9130
Bass, Letty, 1385
Bass, M.M., 8867
Bass, Morton, 5650
Bass, Nancy Lee, 8685
Bass, Perry R., 8685, 8686
Bass, Perry R., Inc., 8686
Bass, Ramona S., 8688
Bass, Richard D., 8689
Bass, Robert, 4636
Bass, Robert M., 8687
Bass, Sandra Atlas, 5650
Bass, Sid R., 9130
Bass, William, 8558
Bassett, Betty, 7363
Bassett, Ronald D., 9099
Bassler, Bonnie L., 6872
Basslian, Shlomo, 6358
Basso, Rob, 5826
Bast, William, 5745
Bastean, Todd A., 4865
Bastian, Bruce W., 9306
Bastian, Clark, 3555
Bastian, Edward H., 7191
Baston, Bryan, 2400
Basye, Matthew J., 3480
Bat Hanadiv Foundation, 5651
Bat Hanadiv Foundation No. 2, 5651
Batchelder, Herbert W., 3954
Batchelder, Jeffrey, 1463
Batcheler, Colleen, 5029
Batcheler, Colleen R., 5030
Batchelor Enterprises, 1983
Batchelor, George E., 1983
Batchelor, Jon, 1983
Batchelor, Michael L., 8026
Batchelor-Robjohns, Anne O., 1983
Bate, David S., 6813
Bateman, Isabell, 8538
Bateman, Kenneth, 5521
Bateman, Maureen, 4242
Bateman, Stephanie, 3569
Bates, Devin, 9147
Bates, Hudson K., 7272
Bates, Janet Fleishhacker, 534
Bates, Jeanne, 4905
Bates, Jon, 2766
Bates, Leon, 8236
Bates, Liz, 9146
Bates, Mark, 3291
Bates, Reva, 9582
Bates, Rex J., 9582
Bates, Rex W., 9582
Bates, Robert D., 5074
Bates, Timothy L., 7305
Bates, Tom, 24
Bates, William B., 3241
Bates, William B., Jr., 3241
Bath, Margaret, 4473
Bath, Paquita, 1263
Bathco (The Navy Yard), 6651
Batlle, Ann K., 1878
Batman, Missy, 2764
Baton, Bob, 588
Bator, Francis, Hon., 3692
Batrus, Veronique Casimir-Lambert, 5300
Batsche, Stephen V., 9511
Batson, Scott, 9413
Batt, Shirley, 3398
Battaglia, Joseph P., 634
Battaglia, Richard, 634
Batten, Dorothy N., 9388
Batten, Frank, Jr., 9388, 9390, 9467
Batten, Frank, Sr., 9389
Batten, Jane, 9389
Batten, Jane P., 9448
Batten, Kimberly, 1776
Battenburg, James, 2768
Batterman, Christopher T., 9813
Batterman, Theodore W., 9813
Battey, Jane, 1166
Battin, Molly, 6982
Battistoni, Rick, 9122
Battle, G. Thomas, 9780
Battle, LaVeeda, 7138
Battle, William Patrick, 2514
Batts, Deborah A., Hon., 6148
Battye, Kenneth S., 3727
Battye, Susan A., 3727
Batusic, Dave, 3291
Bau-Madsen, Kai, 8062
Bauchman, Robert W., 6406
Baudot-Queguiner, Elise, 6211
Bauer USA Foundation, 5194
Bauer, Betty, 9251
Bauer, Brad, 1543
Bauer, C. Douglas, 8691
Bauer, Carol, 1543
Bauer, Charles T., 8691, 8692
Bauer, D., 909
Bauer, David M., 9894
Bauer, Doug, 5786
Bauer, Evalyn M., 287, 2687
Bauer, Frank, 3104
Bauer, Gary W., 3402
Bauer, George P., 1543
Bauer, Jocelyn, 1543
Bauer, John R., 8914
Bauer, Joyce, 3104
Bauer, Julie, 9804
Bauer, Kathryn M., 1379
Bauer, Kristen, 8314
Bauer, Laurie, 4601
Bauer, M.R., 287
Bauer, Mary F.L., 4932
Bauer, Michael R., 9655, 9763
Bauer, Michelle M., 2638
Bauer, Modestus R., 2687
Bauer, Richard J., 2948
Bauer, Ruth J., 8691
Bauer, Theodore Wingate, 8692
Bauerly, Rick, 4679
Bauernfeind, George G., 3582
Bauert, Paula A., 9651
Baugh Charitable Lead Trust, Barbara, 8693
Baugh, Barbara N., 8693
Baugh, Casey, 9354
Baugh, Eula Mae, 8693
Baugh, John, 991
Baugh, John F., 8693
Baugh, Scott R., 1031
Baughman Farms Co., John W., The, 3493
Baughman, Corinne, 9566
Baughman, John, 7445
Baughman, Megan, 3298
Baughman, Robert W., 3493
Baughman, Willard, 7421
Bauknight, John E., 8501
Baum, Alexio R., 4444
Baum, Alvin H., 2689
Baum, Charles, 3890
Baum, Dale, 4335
Baum, E. Richard, 5929
Baum, Marc, 3857
Baum, Michael, 5854
Baum, Steven C., 543, 7017
Baum, Timothy L., 5854
Baum-Baicker, Cindy, 8267
Bauman, Amy, 1882, 4343
Bauman, Catherine, 2288
Bauman, Elizabeth H., 1984
Bauman, Jeffrey, 1884
Bauman, Jessica, 1882
Bauman, John, 1984
Bauman, Joseph, 7934
Bauman, Lionel R., 1882
Bauman, Marvin J., 4481
Bauman, Mary Ann, 7781
Bauman, Patricia, 1882, 1984
Bauman, Robert, 1984
Bauman, William H., 7824
Baumbach, Martha, 4748
Baumberger, Charles, Jr., 8694
Baumer, Charles B., Esq., 258
Baumert, Steve, 5074
Baumgaertner, Michael, 7915
Baumgardner, Christine, 4370
Baumgardner, Earl C., 63
Baumgart, Melissa, 5801
Baumgartner, Jeff, 8598
Baumgartner, Ron, 3336
Baumgartner, Tracy J., 7989
Baumrind, Martin, 5718
Baun, Caprice W., 4581
Bausch, David K., 7974
Bauta, Christian, 1659
Bauta, Gretchen A., 1659
Bauta, Humberto P., 1659
Bauta, Nicholas, 1659
Bauta, Pilar, 1659, 9064
Bavasi, Margaret, 9617
Bavendick, Frank, 7353
Bavly, Beverly G., 2113
Bawek, Kerri, 4685
Baxley, James M., 9479
Baxter Allegiance Foundation, The, 7398
Baxter International Inc., 2690
Baxter Sr. Trust of 2000, George W., 7142
Baxter, Anita, 1565
Baxter, Blair, 8695
Baxter, Delia B., 288
Baxter, Eliza Wright, 3687
Baxter, G. Steven, Sr., 7142
Baxter, George W., Sr., 7142
Baxter, John, 4830
Baxter, Kate Davis, 3687
Baxter, Murphy, 8695
Baxter, Murphy H., 8695
Baxter, Richard, 175
Baxter-Simons, Laura, 1131
Bay Area Primary Care, 2259
Bay Street Corp., 4832
Bay, Charles Ulrick, 5652
Bay, Frederick, 5652
Bay, Mogens, 5033
Bay, Mogens C., 5057
Bayer Corp., 7932
Bayer Healthcare Pharmaceuticals Inc., 5194, 7931
Bayle, Deborah S., 9337
Bayless, Betsey, 92
Bayless, Ginny, 1401
Bayless, Glenda, 419
Bayley, David, 9726
Bayley, Thomas, 9684
Baylor, Tim, 4714
Bayne, Betsy, 5019
Bayrd Trust, Blanche Simpson, 3938
Bayrd, Blanche S., 3938
Bayrd, Frank A., 3938
BayTree Fund, 487
Bayvue LLC, 9452
BB&T, 7340, 7347, 9474, 9780
BB&T Corp., 7143, 7144
BBDO, 7012
BBH Trust, The, 662
BBVA Compass Bank, 8880, 9149
BCL, LLC, 7348
BCSB Securities Corp Inc., 3960
BD & A, 977
BDG Foundation, 5875
BEA Assocs., Inc., 6199
Beach Ball Foundation, The, 8465
Beach Terrace Care Center, 6287, 6288, 6763
Beach, Dana, 5733
Beach, Darlene E., 3693
Beach, Kim, 7483
Beach, Larry, 167
Beach, Marianna, 3494
Beach, Marilyn, 8683
Beach, Ross, 3494
Beach, Stewart, 2811

Beachlawn Mortgage Co., 4367
Beacon Baptist Church, 9059
Beaird, Carolyn W., 3614
Beaird, Charles T., Dr., 3614
Beaird, John B., 3614
Beaird, Susan, 3614
Beal, Barry, Jr., 8696
Beal, Bruce A., 3940
Beal, Bruce A., Jr., 5656
Beal, Carlton, 8696
Beal, Carlton, Jr., 8696
Beal, George P., 4084
Beal, Kathryn, 5656
Beal, Keleen H., 8696
Beal, Kelly S., 8696
Beal, Mitty, 7324
Beal, Richard M., 560
Beal, Robert L., 3940
Beal, Spencer E., 8696
Beal, Stuart, 8696
Beal, Whitney, 5802
Beale, E. Warren, Jr., 9434
Beall, Diane, 9796
Beall, Dorothy M., 2327
Beall, Kenneth S., Jr., 2385
Beals, III Residuary Trust, David, 8697
Beam, Robert M., 4445
Beaman, Kelley S., 8534
Beaman, Lee A., 8534
Beaman, Phillip, 3288
Beaman, Sally M., 8534
Beamer, William E., 1012
Beamer, William E., Esq., 1134
Beamon, Tina Clark, 1549
Beams, Mary E., 7038
Bean, A.H., 10
Bean, Atherton, 4607
Bean, Becky, 2550
Bean, Bruce W., 4607
Bean, Elizabeth N., 5164
Bean, Glen, 4607
Bean, Larry G., 9984
Bean, Mary F., 4607
Bean, Norwin S., 5164
Bean, R.E., 8867
Bean, Ralph J., Jr., 7935
Bean, Robert R., 2602
Bean, Roy H., 7379
Bean, Winifred W., 4607
Beane, Agnes R., 7170
Bear, Diane, 3481
Bear, Geraldine, 5927
Bear, Stephen D., 9563
Beard Payne Family Foundation, 2514
Beard Trust, Robert F., 4345
Beard, Allison Lamar, 3647
Beard, Anson, 2032
Beard, Anson H., 2362, 5966
Beard, Anson McCook, Jr., 2362
Beard, Bradley, 8853
Beard, Bruce F., 670
Beard, Debra, 2362
Beard, James M., 2362
Beard, James McCook, 5966
Beard, Jean J., 5966
Beard, John, 4345
Beard, Laurie F., 4447
Beard, Michael, 4345
Beard, Robert F., 4345
Beard, Veronica M., 2362
Beard, Veronica S., 2362
Bearden, Steven W., 4574
Beardsley, George, 6571
Bearfield, Maribeth N., 4086
Bearman, Arlene, 3728
Bearman, Mark, 3728
Bearman, Sheldon, 3728
Beary Properties Inc., 2735
Beaser, Lawrence J., 8221
Beasley, Charles E., 3612
Beasley, Laura, 7273
Beasley, Mary Evans, 8698
Beasley, Robert R., 8698
Beasley, Teresa Metcalf, 7406
Beasley, Theodore P., 8698
Beason, Amos "Ted", 2438
Beaton, Susanne, 4152
Beaton, Tim, 7351
Beattie, Arthur P., 2554
Beattie, Brian, 1232
Beattie, Katherine L., 1636
Beattie, Michael G., 1636
Beattie, Patricia, 1879
Beattie, Richard, 5747
Beattie, Richard I., 6306
Beattie, Scott, 417
Beattie, William G., 1636
Beatty, Benjamin M., 7619
Beatty, Eunice, 3560
Beatty, Helen D. Groome, 7933
Beatty, John, 3284
Beatty, Mary, 7619
Beatty, Scott, 3851
Beaty, Jeff, 3265
Beaty, John T., Jr., 5775
Beaty, John Terry, 1893
Beauchamp, Gary K., Dr., 7027
Beaud, Marie-Claude, 6002
Beaulieu, Jo-Ann, 3929
Beaulieu, Rita H., 8450
Beaumont Investments, Ltd., 1369
Beauregard, Brian, 9606
Beaver Street Fisheries, Inc., 1986
Beaver, Thomas, 4421
Beavers, Ben, 9116
Beavers, Inc., The, 293
Beavers, John P., 7576
Beazley, E., 777
Beazley, Elizabeth, 777
Beazley, Fred W., 9391
Beazley, Fred W., Jr., 9391
Beazley, Marie C., 9391
Bebee, Leslie A., 5041
Bebee, Meredith Miller, 9027
Beccalli-Falco, Nani, 1591
Beccaria, Louis J., 8223
Becerra, M. Isabel, 368
Bechard, Kristin, 4921
Bechdol, Matthew A., 3295
Becher, Richard, 1050
Bechet, Ronald, 6489
Bechinski, Linda, 3297
Becht, Colleen, 5801
Bechtel Corp., 295
Bechtel Group, Inc., 295
Bechtel Power Corp., 295
Bechtel Systems of Infrastructure, Inc., 295
Bechtel, Brendan P., 976
Bechtel, Chuck, 7474
Bechtel, Cynthia, 4173
Bechtel, Darren H., 976
Bechtel, Elizabeth H., 294, 823, 976
Bechtel, Elizabeth Hogan, 296
Bechtel, Gary Hogan, 537
Bechtel, Jacquie L., 537
Bechtel, Katherine E., 976
Bechtel, Riley P., 295, 976
Bechtel, S.D., Jr., 296
Bechtel, Stephen D, Jr., 976
Bechtel, Stephen D., Jr., 294, 537, 823
Bechtel, Stephen D., Jr., Mrs., 537
Bechtel, Susan P., 976
Bechtle, Joachim, 5657
Bechtle, Nancy, 1128, 5657
Bechtle, Scott C., 1682
Bechtle, Tom, 1565
Bechtol, Dan M., 8560
Bechtold, John, 4995
Bechtold, Kurt, 9946
Beck Educational Foundation, AGT Lewis H., 2463
Beck, Ann, 9789
Beck, Dave, 5067
Beck, John C., 6448
Beck, Judith, 7023, 7024, 9710
Beck, Lauren, 5484
Beck, Lynne, 1512
Beck, Mark, 6157
Beck, Maureen Bazinet, 4714
Beck, Melissa, 1578
Beck, Norman E., 3264
Beck, Phyllis W., Hon., 8107
Beck, Robin, 5527
Beck, Scott, 1377
Beck, Scott A., 1377
Beck, Sue, 3481
Beck, Ted, 1469
Beck, Teri, 5067
Beck, Thomas, 1377
Beck, Thomas C., 4322
Beck, Wayne, 3313
Beck-Friedrich, Anke, 6221
Beck-Racek, Audrey, 5062
Becker, Bruce, 5119
Becker, Carol R., Dr., 3761
Becker, Charles E., Jr., 6826
Becker, Charlie, 9704
Becker, Douglas L., 1867
Becker, Howard C., 7599
Becker, Jeanne, 7838, 7890
Becker, Jeffery T., 7038
Becker, Jeffrey M., 8560
Becker, Jennifer, 3477
Becker, Jim, 1069
Becker, Katrina H., 5644
Becker, Kim, 5108
Becker, Marilyn, 8182
Becker, Patrick E., Sr., 7834
Becker, Paul A., 2166
Becker, Pauline S., 1987
Becker, Richard C., 3140
Becker, Scott, 8613
Becker, Shawn, 1886
Becker, Steve, 633
Becker, Steven R., 2347
Becker, Suzanne Sheehan, 8041
Becker, Ulrich, 4234
Beckett Air, Inc., 7470
Beckett Corp., R.W., The, 7470
Beckett Family, 7470
Beckett, Carolyn J., 7470
Beckett, Catherine E., 7470
Beckett, Joel D., 7470
Beckett, John D., 7470
Beckett, Jonathan M., 7470
Beckett, Riley, 5129
Beckingham, Matt, 9598
Beckler, Mathew, 172
Beckley, David, Dr., 4822
Beckley, Karyn, 9715
Beckman Coulter, Inc., 433
Beckman, Arnold O., 297
Beckman, David, 1038
Beckman, Jill, 3522
Beckman, Joel, 7036
Beckman, Mabel M., 297
Beckner, Jay, 6477
Beckort, Paul, 3314
Beckos, Barbara J., 1725
Beckos, Dean J., 1725
Beckos-Wood, Georgia, 1725
Beckwith, David, 603
Beckwith, G. Nicholas, III, 7935
Beckworth, Laura H., 8911
Bed Bath & Beyond, Inc., 5250
Bedard, Daniel L., 1566
Bedard, Kipp A., 2637
Bedard, Paul, 5194
Bedel, Elaine, 3272
Bedford Family LLC, 6687
Bedke, Michael A., 1469
Bednar, Marie, 8077
Bednarz, Billy, 3713
Bedolfe, Herbert M., 878
Bedrosian, John C., 766
Bedrosian, Judith D., 766
Bedsole, Ann Smith, 66
Bedsole, J.L., 11
Bedsole, Travis M., Jr., 11
Bedward, Royce, 2921
Bee, Helen, 9697
Beebe, Frederick S., 9445
Beebe, Steve, 7742
Beech, Allen A., Jr., 2409
Beech, Greta, 2409
Beech, Jeff, 2409
Beech, Randy, 2409
Beeghly, Bruce R., 7415
Beehler, David W., 4754
Beekman, William B., 3923
Beeler, W. Christopher, 9450
Beeman, Tom, 3346
Beemer, Michael G., 2660
Beene, Dennis, 8734
Beene, Geoffrey, 5658
Beene, Steve, 4821
Beener, Michelle, 7990
Beer Institute, 3714
Beer, Matthew, 9364
Beer, Michael, 9364
Beer, Robert A., 1545, 1584
Beer, Ron, 7742
Beer, Stephanie, 9364
Beere, Polly, 6174
Beerman, Molly, 8228
Beers, Carol S., 9559
Beers, Carol Stratton, 8304
Beers, Cynthia, 9984
Beers, Cynthia L. Martin, 9984
Beesley, Bonnie Jean, 9307
Beesley, Brent, 9307
Beesley, Daniel, 9307
Beesley, David B., 9307
Beesley, Katherine, 9307
Beesley, Sarah, 9307
Befesa Zinc SLU, 7349
Begalla, Martha E., 8560
Begoun, Sherwin, 3150
Behan, Mark L., 6057
Behar, Dana, 9725
Behar, Howard, 9586
Behle, Hope Eccles, 665, 9318
Behling, Mary, 9845
Behm, Susan J., 7688
Behn, Marlene, 3423

Behn, Richard J., 1628
Behnke, Eric, 7459
Behnke, Karen, 3280
Behr, Gregg, 8064
Behrens, Gregg D., 3059
Behrens, Thomas J., 3172
Beidler, Francis, III, 2692
Beidler, Greg, 3303
Beigie, David, 3174
Beijing Industrial Development Co. Ltd., 6651
Beil, Len, 9578
Beiler, Anne, 8669
Beiler, Jonas Z., 8669
Beilock, Richard, 1723
Beim, N.C., 4609
Beim, Raymond N., 4609
Beimfohr, Edward G., 5954
Beinecke, Benjamin B., 6663
Beinecke, Candace K., 7043
Beinecke, Frances G., 6663
Beinecke, Frederick W., 6308, 6663, 6895
Beinecke, Jacob S., 6663
Beinecke, John B., 6663, 6895
Beinecke, William S., 6663, 6895
Beinhaker, Gary, 5296
Beirow, Paula, 5046
Beiser, Bernard J., 1138
Beisker, Michelle, 3417
Beisler, Ralph, 6721
Beitz, Robert, 9576
Bekavac, Nancy, 1133
Bekenstein Charitable Fund, Josh and Anita, 4298
Beker, Harvey, 5659, 7083, 8109
Beker, Jayne, 5659
Bel Brands USA Inc., 2761
Belair, Paul, 7367
Beland, Michael D., 8383
Belanger, Keith M., 6406
Belcher, Anne, 3317
Belcher, Philip, 7182
Belcher, S.E., Jr., 2410
Beldecos, J. Nicholas, 8017
Belden, Catherine, 7811
Belden, David L., 9547
Belden, Frederick H., Jr., 9780
Belden, Ted, 179
Belding, Annie K., 6003
Belding, Milo M., 6003
Belew, David L., 7481
Belfer Two Corp., 5660
Belfer, Laurence D., 5660
Belfer, Renee E., 5660
Belfer, Robert A., 5660
Belfry Holdings, Inc., 4841
Belgrade Town Pump, Inc., 5016
Belin, James Bruce, Jr., 8699
Belin, Mary Ann, 8699
Beling, Janna, 328
Beling, Kristen, 328
Belinkie, Jason, 1885
Belisle, Barbara J., 67
Belive, 6042
Belk Department Stores, The, 7148
Belk Enterprises, 7148
Belk, Claudia W., 7146
Belk, Danny E., 8455
Belk, H.W. McKay, 7147
Belk, Inc., 7148
Belk, John M., 7146
Belk, John R., 7147, 7148
Belk, Judy, 368, 6947
Belk, Katherine M., 7147
Belk, Matthews, 7148
Belk, Thomas M., Jr., 7147, 7148
Belk-Simpson Co., 7224
Belknap, Charles R., 7771
Bell Atlantic Corp., 5489
Bell Family Foundation, 2514
Bell Revocable Trust, Helen W., 1990
Bell Trust, John Willie, 3203
Bell, Andy, 7671
Bell, Ann, 430
Bell, Ben H., Jr., 1389
Bell, Bobby, 9133
Bell, Bradley P., 300
Bell, Caitlin M., 7139
Bell, Daniel M., 1991
Bell, Daniel M., Jr., 1991
Bell, David A., Hon., 9384
Bell, Diane Fisher, 1585
Bell, Eileen, 1774
Bell, Evan R., 6595
Bell, Frank M., Jr., 7254
Bell, G. Russell, 433
Bell, Garrett, 1774
Bell, Gloria, 8505
Bell, Hugh H., 2656
Bell, James D., Jr., 9811
Bell, James R., 4107
Bell, Jane A., 3966
Bell, Jeff, 4332
Bell, Joan, 1400
Bell, John, 9625
Bell, John, Dr., 7793
Bell, John, Jr., 7181
Bell, Judith M., 1406
Bell, Katharine, 8700
Bell, Kathleen Conway, 7419
Bell, Kenneth D., 5969
Bell, Larry, 8696
Bell, Laura, 4485
Bell, Lauralee K., 300
Bell, Lee Phillip, 300
Bell, Mary Lynn, 1228
Bell, Megan, 7088
Bell, Millicent, 3941
Bell, Monty, 8462
Bell, Patricia B., 1991
Bell, R. Terry, 9135
Bell, R.S., 8700
Bell, Ranlet S., 7251, 7252, 7254
Bell, Robert T., 5495
Bell, Rodney H., 1991
Bell, Samuel P., 756
Bell, Sharon J., 7807
Bell, Shirley, 7321
Bell, Steve, 6
Bell, Terri, 4829
Bell, Tom, 3514
Bell, Vance D., 2436
Bell, Walter W., 2383, 2985, 3035, 3044
Bell, William C., 4869, 9595
Bell, William J., 300
Bell, William James, 300
Bell, Yvonne, 9586
Bell-McKoy, Diane, 3726
Bell-Rose, Stephanie, 1940, 2191
Bell-Stevens, Robin, 5612
Bellamah, Dale J., 861
Bellamy, Brian, 1723
Bellamy, Chris, 7412
Bellamy, William D., 1384
Bellanca, Rose B., Dr., 4340
Bellatti, Barbara W., 9135
Bellehumeur, Susan C., 9965
Belles, Lawrence L., 2745
Bellet, Edward, 8298
Bellet, Laura, 8298
Bellet, Sally, 8298
Bellet, Wayne, 8914
Bellett, John, 8914
Bellett, Nancy, 8914
Bellin, Richard C., 9641
Bellinger, Geraldine G., 6038
Bellizzi, John, 1211
Bellmann, Charles H., 2434
Bellmore, Chris J., 2874
Bello, Richard, 5685, 6107
Bellotti, Frances X., 3926
Bellotti, Mario, 853
Belly, Armando, 6891
Belmonte, Kathleen J., 2308
Belron World Conference Foundation, 7638
Belshaw-Jones, Sharon, 548
Belsky, Nancy Kaplan, 6250
Belsky, Scott Kaplan, 6250
Belsky, Shenyu, 841
Belton, John, 3649
Belton, Marc, 4661
Beltran-del Olmo, Magdalena, 368
Beltz, Susan W., 8226
Beluga, Inc., 5557
Belus, Tom, 9998
Belway Electrical, 5482
Belyea, Desa C., 549
Belz, Jack A., 8530
Belz, Ronald, 8530
Belzberg, Wendy, 6898
Bemis Co., Inc., 9815
Ben & Jerry's Corp., 9358
Ben & Jerry's Homemade, Inc., 9358, 9376
Ben-Aviv, Matan, 2189
Ben-Aviv, Zipora, 2189
Ben-Dov, Ariella, 9473
Ben-Dov, Lisa, 9473
Ben-Dov, Tamar, 9473
Ben-Dov, Zohar, 9473
Benaroya, Brooke E., 9583
Benaroya, Jack A., 9583
Benaroya, Larry R., 9583
Benaroya, Michael J., 9583
Benaroya, Rebecca B., 9583
Benaroya, Sherry-Lee, 9583
Benasich, April, 5782
Benasich, Kristin, 5782
Benassi, Peter, 6609
Benben, Nancy, 1609
Benbough Foundation, Legler, The, 1040
Benbough, Legler, 303
Bench Online, LLC, The, 3517
Bender 2002 Trust, Stanley S., The, 1885
Bender, Barbara A., 1885
Bender, David S., 1885
Bender, George A., 1285
Bender, Howard M., 1885
Bender, Jack I., 1885
Bender, Kurt, 4562
Bender, Matthew, IV, 5803
Bender, Nanette, 1885
Bender, Richard A., 498
Bender, Sondra, 1885
Bender, Stanley S., 1885
Bendheim, Joanne, 6395
Bendheim, John M., Jr., 6395
Bendheim, John M., Sr., 6395
Bendheim, Kim, 6395
Bendy, Donald N., 9283
Bene, Robert Del, 6203
Benecke, Lars, 7932
Benedict, Davis, 5662
Benedict, James, 279
Benedict, Peter B., II, 6947
Benedum, Michael Late, 7935
Benedum, Paul G., Jr., 7935
Benedum, Sarah N., 7935
Beneficial Corp., 1759
Beneficial Mutual Bancorp, Inc., 7936
Beneficial New Jersey, 1759
Benenson, Bruce W., 5663
Benenson, Charles B., 5663
Benenson, Frederick C., 5663
Benenson, Gladys S., 5664, 5665
Benenson, Lawrence B., 5663
Beneski, Kristin M., 8701
Beneski, Laurie M., 8701
Beneski, Ted W., 8701
Beneson, Clement C., 7695
Beneson, James, III, 7695
Beneson, James, Jr., 7695
Benet, Celine, 5473
Benet, Jay S., 4783
Bengard Charitable Lead Trust, 733
Bengard Foundation, 733
Bengard, Kim C., 733
Bengard, Thomas P., 733
Bengard, Tyler T., 733
Bengier, Brooke N., 304
Bengier, Cynthia S., 304
Bengier, Gary F., 304
Benglis, Lynda, 6085
Benham, Robert, 1142
Benhase, Dan, 7417
Benidt, Beatrice A., 9816
Benidt, Charles E., 9816
Benike, John, 4755
Benjamin, Adelaide Wisdom, 3663
Benjamin, Alvin, 306
Benjamin, Clarence, 1120
Benjamin, Daniel K., 9353
Benjamin, Edward W., 3663
Benjamin, Elizabeth, 5204
Benjamin, John F., 3110
Benjamin, Martin A., 2228
Benjamin, Medea Susan, 306
Benjamin, Rose, 306
Benka, Carla, 3962
Benkert, Jerome A., Jr., 3394
Bennack, Frank A., Jr., 6155, 6156
Benner, Kim, 5067
Bennet, Jacquelyn, 1958
Bennett, Andy, 4791
Bennett, Beverly Edmundson, 2518
Bennett, C. Eugene, 1739
Bennett, Carol, 7414
Bennett, Christie, 9704
Bennett, David, 5210
Bennett, David J., 3281
Bennett, David W., 530
Bennett, Diana, 5101
Bennett, Diana L., 5101
Bennett, Elizabeth A., 4385
Bennett, Germaine, 7705
Bennett, Gloria K., 23
Bennett, J. Mac, 7594, 8468
Bennett, James, 9789
Bennett, James A., 8289
Bennett, Jay L., 4791
Bennett, Jim, 3990
Bennett, Joel I., 1992

Bittner, Larry, 9916
Bittner, Molly Dean, 9416
Bittner, R. Richard, 3412, 3413
Bitto, George G., 7907
Bitzan, Mimi, 4631
Bivins, Jeffrey, 2264
Bivins, Julian M., Jr., 9405
Bixby, R. Philip, 4961
Bixby, Walter E., III, 4961
Bixby, Walter Edwin, Sr., 4961
Bixler, Susie, 3330
Bizoza, Brian, 5865
Bizzell, Thomas M., 2307
Bjella, Brian, 7353
Bjerg, Jorge L. Fernandez, 8352
Bjerg, Jose E. Fernandez, 8352
Bjerke, Barbara, 9482
Bjerke, David W., 9826
Bjorklund, Alexandra O., 4705
Blacher, Paula, 5530
Black Entertainment, Inc., 9458
Black Lance, Charles, 4679
Black, Brent J., 7688
Black, Brian A., 3555
Black, Carl O., 6
Black, Chris, 3570
Black, Dameron, III, 2522
Black, Debbie, 8529, 8635
Black, Debra R., 5681
Black, Fraser, 9731
Black, Frederick, 197
Black, Gary, Jr., 3712
Black, Gary, Sr., 3712
Black, Harry C., 3712
Black, Jack, 317
Black, James, 8899
Black, James Bell, 7273
Black, James I., III, 6056
Black, Janice R., 8046
Black, John, 500
Black, John E., 1503
Black, John F., Jr., 7178
Black, Joyce, 317
Black, Karen E., 2452
Black, Leon D., 5681
Black, Linda C., 3968
Black, Linda Cabot, 3952
Black, Louis E., 5892
Black, Lynne, 4447
Black, Marilyn S., 6
Black, Natalie A., 9884
Black, Paula Cooper, 1528
Black, Peter M., 6406
Black, Robert, III, 3872
Black, Sherry Salway, 1916, 2174
Black, Sophie C., 3968
Black, Stanley, 317, 1234
Black, Stephen Michael, 3376
Black, Tasha Hussain, 7374
Black, Thomas F., III, 8410
Black, Vincent, 7102
Black, William D., 7989
Blackaby, Sandi, 9588
Blackbaud, Inc., 8492
Blackburn, John, III, 7990
Blackburn, Joseph D., 25
Blackburn, Sharon L., 53
Blackford, Elizabeth, 3579
Blackford, Robert N., Esq., 2225
Blackhurst, Jan Jones, 5106
Blackketter, Jim, 1565
Blackman, Linda, 2436
Blackman, Martin, 6869
Blackman, Murray I., 8115
Blackmar, Alfred O., 2399
Blackstone, Michael, 8277
Blackstone, Richard, 3659
Blackwell, Carolyn A., 2762
Blackwell, Cathy J., 7184
Blackwell, Daisy S., 4832
Blackwell, Fred, 1109
Blackwell, William, 1389
Blackwood, C. Michael, 8092
Blackwood, Richard, 7934
Blackwood, Sandra, 41
Blades, A.T., 3734
Blades, Mary H., 3734
Blahnik, Richard J., 3213
Blaikie, David L., 2174
Blaine, Anthony L., 4786
Blair & Co., William, L.L.C., 2699
Blair Trust, Dorothy, 2700
Blair, Andrew, 9380
Blair, Bertha Brossman, 7954
Blair, Brenda, 9413
Blair, Dean, 7671
Blair, Diane J., 8073
Blair, Donald W., 7875
Blair, Dorothy, 2700
Blair, Edward, 1063
Blair, Edward McCormick, Jr., 3100
Blair, Gregg, 3757
Blair, James, 975
Blair, James B., 207
Blair, Jeffrey D., 8878
Blair, Jill, 1322
Blair, John N., 6999, 7000
Blair, Joseph, 101
Blair, Kathleen D., 8538
Blair, Larry S., 8054
Blair, Michael, 1679
Blair, Wesley K., 3980
Blake, Ashley, 8873
Blake, Beverly, 2435
Blake, Christopher R., 1
Blake, David, 9635
Blake, Dwight C., 8380
Blake, James, 5378
Blake, Jonathan D., 8380
Blake, Kathryn T., 7766
Blake, Kent W., 3586
Blake, Michael, 643
Blake, Patricia, 6249
Blake, Patrick, 903
Blake, Ruth E. Mengle, 8174
Blake, Susan, 3625
Blake, Veronica, 1039
Blakely, Carolyn, 179, 181
Blakely, John, 2412
Blakely, Matt, 3043
Blakely, Patricia, 8175
Blakely, Sara, 2412
Blakemore, Frances L., 9587
Blakemore, Thomas L., 9587
Blakeslee, Bill, 3758
Blakeslee, Edie, 8472
Blakeway, Nigel, 3063
Blakley, Kari, 7742
Blalock, Becky, 2432
Blalock, Robert G., 1745, 1829
Blanc, Gene, 3033
Blanchard, Anna Neal, 7322
Blanchard, Arthur F., 7944
Blanchard, Ashley Snowdon, 1915
Blanchard, Bill, 2826
Blanchard, Brenda, 6569
Blanchard, Lisa G., 4522
Blanchard, Lynda P., 2514
Blanchard, Mark, 3656
Blanchard, Olivia C., 2505
Blanchard, Peter P., III, 8049
Blanchard, Peter P., Jr., 7943
Blanchard, Thomas M., Jr., 2434, 2514
Blanchard, William R., 2505, 2556
Blanchett, Lauren A., 83
Blanco, Sally G., 7211
Bland, C. Wayne, Dr., 7805
Bland, Cara, 7786
Bland, Gilbert T., 9448
Bland, Joe B., 9066
Blandin Foundation, 4667, 4730
Blandin, Charles K., 4617
Blanding, Beatrice W., 7054
Blaney, Charlotte E., 2122
Blank, Andrew S., 1997
Blank, Arthur M., 2413
Blank, Jerome, 1997
Blank, Kathleen, 1997
Blank, Kenny, 2413
Blank, Mark, 2102
Blank, Martin, Jr., 585
Blank, Matthew S., 5682
Blank, Michael, 2413
Blank, Nancy, 2413
Blank, Nancy L., 5682
Blank, Robert S., 5682
Blank, Samuel A., 5682
Blankemeyer, Carolyn, 8536
Blankemeyer, James C., 8536
Blankenhorn, P.J., 3971
Blankenship, David, 3409
Blankenship, Elizabeth Warren, 7809
Blankenship, Marian, 7878
Blankenship, Mark H., 736
Blankenship, Patricia Buehler, 8364
Blankfield, Bryan J., 9917
Blanton, Anna Hopwood, 8096
Blanton, Ben W., 3274, 3275
Blanton, Eddy S., 9162
Blanton, Jack S., Jr., 9162
Blanton, Jack S., Mrs., 9162
Blanton, Jack S., Sr., 9162
Blanton, Jean, 3277
Blanton, Larry, Hon., 3365
Blanton, Thomas K., 2243
Blanz, Dennis, 2357
Blase, William A., Jr., 8675
Blaser, Chip, 3509
Blasetto, James W., 1738
Blasi, John, 5309
Blasi, John R., 5253
Blatnick, Gary, 714
Blattmachr, Jonathan, 1947
Blatz, Kathleen, 4753
Blau, Avrohom, 6450
Blau, Cecile A., 3362
Blau, Helen M., 504
Blau, Judah, 6450
Blau, Lawrence, 6185
Blau, Marilyn, 6450
Blau, Olivia, 6185
Blaustein, Jacob, 3735
Blaustein, Jeanne P., 3736
Blaustein, Mary Jane, 3736
Blaustein, Morton K., 3736
Blaustein, Robert S., 6879
Blaustein, Susan B., 3736
Blavatnik, Emily, 1677
Blavatnik, Leonard, 1677
Blaylock, Lou Ann, 9132
Blazczynski, Keane, 4452
Blazek, Jody, 8662
Blazek-White, Doris D., 1895
Blazer, Cedric W., 2730
Blazer, Mark, 2730
Bleakman, Bruce, 5530
Bleday, Maureen H., 4328
Bleiberg, Rob, 1520
Bleier, Chaya, 5654
Bleier, Edward, 5845
Bleil, Barbara R., 8901
Blencoe, Harry A., 9619
Blend, John, 4417
Bleser, Clarence P., 9818
Bleser, James E., 9818
Blessing Hospital Foundation, 9250
Blessing, Linda J., 111
Blessing, Mary Ann, 8596
Blessing, Vicki, 5750
Blevins, Jeff, 8669
Blevins, Kerrie, 4622
Blevins, Teresa F., 9467
Blew, C.J., 4636
Blew, Denise M., 8136
Blew, Jim, 5390
Bley, David, 9731
Bley, Geoff, 9149
Bleyer, Stephen A., 8242
Blickensderfer, Sharon L., 4922
Blickle, John, 7401
Blinkenberg, Linda J., 845, 918, 1323, 1349
Blinkilde, Peter, Dr., 4452
Bliss, Aden, 320
Bliss, Dors S., 5927
Bliss, James W., 7702
Bliss, Rosalynn, 4412
Blissard, Lani, 2099
Blitt, C., 262
Blitt, Chela, 262
Bliumis-Dunn, Sarah W., 5738
Blizzard, Mel, 3757
Blobel, Guenter, 6247
Bloch, Alan, 311
Bloch, Henry W., 4902
Bloch, Mary, 4950
Bloch, Nancy Berman, 311
Block Charitable Lead Annuity Trust, George P., 2701
Block Revocable Trust, Adele G., 5683
Block, Adele G., 5683
Block, Alexandra Skestos, 7501
Block, Andrew K., 3110
Block, Ellen, 8404
Block, Ellen H., 1998
Block, George P., 2701
Block, George P., Jr., 2701
Block, Greg, 3549
Block, Herbert L., 1888
Block, Jennifer Berylson, 4277
Block, Jill, 4298
Block, John D., 5620
Block, Jonathan, 4277
Block, Judith S., 2831
Block, June E., 2701
Block, Laurie A., 1998
Block, Leonard, 5683
Block, Michael H., 1998
Block, Thomas, 5683
Blocker, Chad, 6564
Blodgett, Ed, 1053
Blodgett, Edith I., 9823
Blodgett, Louisa K., 1770
Bloem, James H., 3582
Blohm, Donald E., 4481
Blohm, Jon, 7405

Blokker, Joanne W., 918
Blom, David P., 7411
Blom, Dina, 9795
Blondet, Virgil, Jr., 1609
Bloodgood, Jack, 3896
Bloodworth, Carolyn A., 4376
Bloom, Aimee Simon, 6859
Bloom, Amy, 1568
Bloom, Barry L., 5844, 6984, 6986, 6987, 6988, 6989, 6990
Bloom, Brad, Rabbi, 8475
Bloom, Bradley M., 7486
Bloom, Edward D., 6722
Bloom, Ellen, 5747
Bloom, Ronnie L., Ms., 8303
Bloom, Sandy, 5473
Bloom, Shari K., 6903
Bloomberg, 6904, 7012
Bloomberg, Emma, 5684
Bloomberg, Georgina, 5684
Bloomberg, Michael R., 5684
Bloomfield Trust fbo Westley Graves, Rie, 319
Bloomfield, Bill, 318
Bloomfield, Doug, 7596
Bloomfield, Margaret, 318
Bloomfield, Randall D., 6024
Bloomfield, Rie, 319
Bloomfield, Sam, 319
Bloomfield, William E., Jr., 318
Bloomington Acura, 4698
Bloss, Leigh V., 8825
Blossom, C. Bingham, 7387
Blossom, C. Perry, 7387
Blossom, David B., 7387
Blossom, Elizabeth B., 7387
Blossom, Jonathan B., 7387
Blossom, Laurel, 7387
Blossom, Robin Dunn, 7387
Blount, Rebecca, 7217
Blount, Reginald, Rev., 2900
Bludworth, Curt, 7894
Blue & Co., Ronald, LLC, 2087
Blue Bridge Wealth Management, 9155
Blue Bridge Wealth Mgmt., 9271
Blue Chip Casino, Inc., 3354
Blue Cross and Blue Shield of Alabama, Inc., 18
Blue Cross and Blue Shield of Florida, Inc., 2101
Blue Cross and Blue Shield of Georgia, Inc., 2482
Blue Cross and Blue Shield of Iowa, 3490
Blue Cross and Blue Shield of Kansas, Inc., 3497
Blue Cross and Blue Shield of Massachusetts, Inc., 3953
Blue Cross and Blue Shield of Minnesota, 4618
Blue Cross and Blue Shield of Mississippi, 4815
Blue Cross and Blue Shield of North Carolina, Inc., 7153
Blue Cross and Blue Shield of South Carolina, 8460
Blue Cross and Blue Shield of South Dakota, 3490
Blue Cross and Blue Shield of Tennessee, 8634
Blue Cross Blue Shield of Louisiana, 3615
Blue Cross of Idaho Health Service, Inc., 2627, 2637
Blue Heron Trust, 9611
Blue Moon Fund, Inc., 9499
Blue Mountain Arts Alliance, 9745
Blue Ridge Capital LLC, 5685
Blue Ridge Wealth Mgmt., 8793
Blue School, 5557
Blue, Robert M., 9422
Blue, Ronald W., 8601
Blue, Suzanne, 4749
Bluechoice Health Plan of SC, Inc., 8460
Bluemle, Lewis W., 7995
Bluhm, Andrew G., 2704
Bluhm, Leslie, 2746
Bluhm, Leslie N., 2704
Bluhm, Mark, 2742
Bluhm, Neil G., 2704
Bluhm-Wolf, Meredith A., 2704
Blum Foundation, 6301
Blum Foundation, Edith C., 5686
Blum Revocable Trust, Adi, 1999
Blum Trust, 3110
Blum, Carolyn P., M.D., 3737
Blum, Eva T., 8230
Blum, Felicia H., 5786
Blum, Harry, 2706, 2964
Blum, Howard Z., 8560
Blum, Irving, 3737
Blum, James A., 3268
Blum, Jeffrey D., M.D., 3737
Blum, John R.H., 5912
Blum, John S., 966
Blum, Jonathan, 3608
Blum, Kenneth, 966
Blum, Lawrence A., M.D., 3737
Blum, Lynn Waterman, 3446
Blum, Marcia, 5054
Blum, Nathan, 2705
Blum, Ray, 1397
Blum, Richard C., 321
Blume, Jene F., 322
Blume, John A., 322
Blume, Marshall E., 8170
Blume, Robert, 9634
Blume, Ruth C., 322
Blumenfeld, Jay, 5296
Blumenfrucht, Jonah, 5498
Blumenstein, Carol, 4351
Blumenstein, Harold, 4351
Blumenstein, Penny B., 4351, 4371
Blumenstein, Randall S., 4351
Blumenstein, Richard, 4351
Blumenstein, Richard C., 4351
Blumenstein, Robi, 5228
Blumenthal, Alan, 7154
Blumenthal, Cynthia M., 6422
Blumenthal, David, 5800, 6414
Blumenthal, Herman, 7154
Blumenthal, I.D., 7154
Blumenthal, Margo, 3420
Blumenthal, Philip, 7154
Blumenthal, Samuel, 7154
Blumer, Herman, 6802
Bluth, Lawrence N., 4519
Blutt, Margo K., 5687
Blutt, Mitchell J., 5687, 5800
Bly, Rachel, 3475
Bly, Yvonne Marie, 7968, 8266
Blystone, John, 7563
Blythe, Joanna Vinson, 55
BMC West, 1394
BMO Harris Bank, 9916
BMO Harris Bank, N.A., 2674, 2705, 2746, 2823, 2843, 2879, 3003, 3112, 9934
BMS/Sanofi Pharmaceuticals Partnership, 5712
BNSF Railway, 8706
BNY Capital Corp., 7945
BNY Mellon, 2056, 4239
BNY Mellon, N.A., 1540, 2393, 6043, 6544, 6878, 7409, 7906, 7930, 7933, 7943, 7944, 7983, 7993, 8008, 8009, 8019, 8024, 8026, 8045, 8046, 8050, 8051, 8074, 8075, 8086, 8136, 8140, 8145, 8146, 8166, 8167, 8177, 8191, 8201, 8204, 8207, 8228, 8243, 8246, 8247, 8270, 8286, 8318, 8339, 8340, 8342, 8347, 8348
BNY Mellon, N.A., The, 5834
Boales, Keith, 7378
Boar's Head Provisions Co., Inc., 5678
Boardman, Braye C., 2434
Boardman, C.P., III, 2434
Boardman, Clayton P., III, 2514
Boardman, Cynthia R., 7637
Boardman, Shirley, 3269
Boas, Andrew M., 1813
Boas, Carol A., 1813
Boas, Carol L., 1813
Boas, Hans, 8718
Boas, Rick, 1813
Boas, Suzanne E., 2432
Boas-Levins, Marjorie, 1813
Boateng, Joseph A., 9595
Boatman, Dennis L., 3439
Boatright, Randy J., 8719
Boazman, Dianne C., 3612
Bob's Discount Furniture of Mass., LLC, 1548
Bob's Discount Furniture, Inc., 1548
Bob's Discount Furniture, LLC, 1548
Bobb, Jay, 4256
Bobby, Theodore N., 8083
Bobilya, David A., 3304
Bobst, Elmer H., 5690
Bobst, Mamdouha, 5690
Bobst, Mamdouha S., 5690
Bobzien, David, 7848
Bocanegra, Juanita, 4374
Boccalatte, John L., 1644
Bocchino, Andrew J., 5360
Boccio, Frank M., 6548
Bochenek, Christine A., 7480
Bochnowski, Benjamin, 3337
Bock, Sarah, 1401
Bocko, Miranda Fuller, 5172
Bocko, R., 777
Bocko, Robert J., 777
Bodden, Mark L., 6769
Bodden, Walter P., Jr., 4366
Boden, Scott, 9726
Bodenheimer, Henry, 3637
Bodenhofer, Eric, 4234
Bodenmiller, Jim, 3282
Bodenweber, Holly J., 2164
Bodfish, Paul, Sr., 81
Bodhi, Ven Bhikkhu, 5507
Bodine, George, 5116
Bodine, Jean G., 8169
Bodini, Daniele D., 5691
Bodman, George M., 5692
Bodman, Louise C., 5692
Bodman, Ralph L., 4540
Bodner, David, 5693
Bodner, Moishe, 5693
Bodner, Naomi, 5693
Bodstrom, Stefan, 1743
Bodstrom, Vicki, 1743
Boecher, John C., 2676
Boeckman, Duncan E., 8707
Boeckman, Elizabeth Mayer, 8707
Boeckman, Robert, 7816
Boeckmann, Herbert F., II, 323
Boeckmann, Jane, 323
Boeckmann, Jane F., 323
Boedecker, George, 1373
Boedecker, George, Jr, 1373
Boegel, Risa, 4643
Boehm, Esther, 3738
Boehm, Hershel, 3738
Boehm, Howard M., 3738
Boehm, Ken, 7416
Boehne, Richard A., 7659
Boehner, Leonard B., 5721, 8449
Boehringer Ingelheim Pharmaceuticals, Inc., 1549
Boehringer Ingelheim USA Corp., 1549
Boeing Co., The, 1411
Boenke, Mary S., 9563
Boer, Carrie L., 4378
Boersma, Philip, 3238
Boes, Gary, 4968
Boesch, Donald, 3897
Boeschenstein, Harold, 7400
Boesel, Stephen W., 3865
Boesen, James M., 2796
Boesen, Theodore J., Jr., 3490
Boettcher, C.K., 1374
Boettcher, C.K., Mrs., 1374
Boettcher, Charles, 1374
Boettcher, Charles, II, Mrs., 1374
Boettcher, Fannie, 1374
Boettcher, Irene, 1394
Boettcher, Mae B., 1374
Boettcher, Richard, 1394
Boettiger, John R., 4238
Boeving, Betty Ann, 6440
Bogard, Lawrence T., 9970
Bogart, Jane Olds, 728
Bogart, Stacy L., 4746
Bogen, Andrew E., 1307
Bogen, Roberta, 5694
Bogen, Sheryl, 9297
Bogen, Stanley, 5694
Bogert, Jeremiah M., 5323, 5385
Bogert, Jeremiah M., Jr., 5385
Boghetich, Jilene K., 7787
Boghetich, Tony, 7787
Boghosian, Varujan, 5585
Bogigian, Bob, 3313
Bogle, Charlotte, 2435
Bogle, Peter C., 3991
Bogo, Alexis G., 8576
Bogue, Lauren, 3909
Boh, Robert S., 3656
Bohart Trust, Barbara, 1839
Bohart Trust, James, 1839
Bohart, Holly, 1578
Bohart, James, Jr., 1578
Bohart, Lynn, 9715
Bohbrink, Marshall P., 2881
Bohling, Jeffrey W., 3450
Bohnen, Michael, 3918, 4080, 8131
Bohnett, David C., 324
Bohnn, Anne S., 8662
Bohnsack, Jim, 7731
Bohon, Sergio, 419
Boice, Anesta P., 2040
Boies, Stephen, 3144
Boise, April Miller, 7639
Boisi, Geoffrey T., 5695, 5747

BP Amoco Corp., 8718
BP Corp., 4745
BP Corp. North America Inc., 8718
BP Products North America, Inc., 8718
Braaksma, Christopher, 2489
Brabander, Cynthia, 7442
Brabeck, Jim, 1110
Braberg, Lennart C., 4214
Braca, Greg, 3710
Bracale, Scott, 7589
Bracco, Holly, 8613
Brach, Abraham, 5700
Brach, Ann, 1520
Brach, Helen, 2712
Brach, Samuel, 5700
Brach, Zigmond, 5699
Brach, Zivia, 5700
Brachfeld, Joseph, 5959, 6145
Bracho, America, 9595
Bracht, Berend, 4354
Brack, Bob, 4056
Bracken, Alexander E., 1391
Bracken, Frank A., 3264
Bracken, Richard M., 8582
Bracken, S. Terry, 8890
Bracken, Thomas C., 3264
Bracken, William M., 3262
Brackenridge, George W., 8719
Brackett, Mark, 6285
Brackett, Mike, 4395
Brackney, Keith, 3373
Bradbury, Louis, 5740
Braddock, Clarence H., III, 4107
Braddock, Richard S., 5701
Braddock, Susan, 5701
Braddock, Susan S., 5701
Bradford Exchange, Ltd., 2990
Bradford, David T., 2810, 2852
Bradford, Elaine, 5403
Bradford, Elsa, 1643
Bradford, Mark, 3278
Bradford, Nancy, 78
Bradford, Robert, 3423
Bradford, Sharon H., 1349
Bradham, J. Elizabeth, 8472
Bradigan, Sandy, 7921
Bradler, Harry, 5942
Bradley Trust, Mark S., 2001
Bradley, Betsy, 2924
Bradley, Bill, 5110
Bradley, Bobby, 22
Bradley, Carl L., 9589
Bradley, Caroline D., 9819
Bradley, David, 8273
Bradley, David A., 2924
Bradley, David G., 1892
Bradley, Denise, 8314
Bradley, Dona, 8874, 9123
Bradley, Erroll, 4814
Bradley, Frank, 3967
Bradley, Gini, 1511
Bradley, Harry L., 9819
Bradley, Jeff, 8475
Bradley, Jerry, 8873
Bradley, Jim, 9897
Bradley, John F., 1214
Bradley, John J., 3996
Bradley, Joseph S., 5110
Bradley, Julie, 4311
Bradley, Katherine B., 1892
Bradley, Katherine Brittain, 1892
Bradley, Margaret B., 9819
Bradley, Mark J., 9856
Bradley, Marshall, Jr., 3569
Bradley, Mary Lyons, 5805
Bradley, R. Bruce, 9448
Bradley, Randy, 8789
Bradley, Robert, 854, 855
Bradley, Spencer, 1892
Bradley, Stu, 4495
Bradley, Todd, 3469
Bradley, W.C., 2414
Bradshaw, James, 9004
Brady Corporation, 9821
Brady, Benjamin F., 2415
Brady, David, 9574
Brady, Jack, 8789
Brady, Larry, 2253
Brady, Louise F., 7162
Brady, Park, 2331
Brady, Richard R., 7444
Brady, Sharon M., 2934
Brady, Veronica, 2142
Brady, W. Thomas, 2648
Brady, William P., 8195
Braendle, Deborah M., 2327
Braestrup, Angel, 1933
Braestrup, Angelica, 6564
Braeutigam, Rita, 8914
Brafman, Lenard, 5955
Braga, Damian, 5437
Braga, Larry D., 2642
Braga, Tony, 9650
Bragdon, Roger, 9634
Bragg, Caprice, 7594
Brailofsky, Elimelech, 5242
Brain, David L., 2416
Brain, Frances H., 2416
Brain, Nancy R., 2416
Brainerd, Mary K., 4715, 4757
Brainerd, Paul, 9590
Brainerd, Sherry, 9590
Braka, Benjamin, 5702
Braka, David, 5702
Braka, Ivor, 5702
Braly, Angela F., 3257
Bramante, Christina, 3966
Bramble, Forrest F., Jr., 3850
Bramblett, George W., Jr., 8909
Brame, Scott, 3626
Bramel, Kelly, 7417
Bramel, Randy, 530
Bramel, Susan, 530
Bramsen, Elizabeth C., 2888
Bramson, James B., 8092
Bramson, Robert S., 8052
Branch Banking and Trust Co., 7143
Branch, Anita, 8720
Branch, C.B., 8720
Branch, George, 3602
Branch, J. Read, Jr., 9397
Branch, Patteson, III, 9397
Branch, Patteson, Jr., 9397
Branch, Ted, 5750
Branches 1999 Charitable Lead Annuity Trust, 8512
Branches Charitable Annuity Trust, 8512
Brand, Dean, 5062
Brand, Elizabeth D., 7187
Brand, Jacques, 5876
Brand, Jennifer, 9158
Brand, Jesse, 3321
Brand, Nancy, 9158
Brand, R. Alfred, III, 7187
Brand, Steve A., 4637
Brand, Wendy, 5750
Branden, Cris V., 2165
Branden, Gary R., 7866
Brandenborg, John, 4619
Brandenborg, Laurie Douglass, 4619
Brandenburg, Julius, 1979
Brandenburg, R.N., 9629
Brandes Family Foundation, 336
Brandes Investment Partners, 7367
Brandes, Linda, 336
Brandman, Etta, 6020, 6134, 6632, 6640
Brandman, Saul, 337
Brandner, Bruce, 8522
Brandon, Anthony D., 3285
Brandon, Dave, 2764
Brandrup, Douglas W., 1541
Brandt, Donald E., 91
Brandt, Donald K., 2628
Brandt, E.N., 4444
Brandt, Eric K., 349
Brandt, John H., 2628
Brandt, Lee, 7816
Brandt, Richard B., 9457
Brandt, Robert S., 8603
Brandwein, Steve, 4723
Brandywine Recyclers, Inc., 8012
Brane, Marcela, 1888
Branham, C. Michael, 8472
Branham, Michael W., 3190
Branic, Nicholas A., 3723
Branick, Julie, 9910
Brannen, Tyler, 5175
Bransfield, John R., Jr., 6543
Branson, Cheryl, 338
Branson, Ken, 338
Branson, Tracy, 992
Branstrom, John T., 7178
Brant, Robert, 7511
Brantley, Dee Dee, 1109
Brantley, Rena, 672
Brantley, Thomas M., 7139
Brantley, Vicki, 3570
Brantner, Laine, 7351
Branton, Dan, 4823
Brants, Harry, 9159
Brantz, David, 1391
Brasel, Susan S., 4986
Brashear, Todd F., 9332
Brasier, Anne, 8952
Brass, Arthur J., 8721
Brass, Catherine M., 8721
Brass, Joyce, 8721
Brass, Stacie, 3423
Braswell Marital Trust, James R., The, 7158
Braswell, James R., 7158
Braswell, Katie E., 7481
Bratcher, Joe W., III, 8986
Bratcher, Joe W., Jr., 8986
Brater, D. Craig, 3375, 3397
Bratton Family Partners, 8722
Bratton, Douglas K., 8722
Bratton, Teresa, 3166
Bratton, William, 5806
Braud, Walter, 2787
Brauer, Camilla, 4860
Brauer, Stephen F., 4860
Braufman, Jill E., 5704
Braught, Barbara M., 7772
Brault, Michael, 1634
Brauman, John I., 5912
Braun, Barbara, 6539
Braun, Greg, 2632
Braun, Henry A., 6905
Braun, Hugo E., Jr., 4585
Braun, Mary C., 1800
Braun, Richard W., 4991
Braun, Robert, Jr., 5065
Braun-Glazer, Julia, 3433
Braun-Glazer, Lisa, 3433
Brauner, Berish, 5953
Brauner, Chana, 6288
Brauner, David A., 6068
Braunstein, Barbara, 5874
Braunstein, Barry, 5654
Braunstein, Israel, 5654
Braunstein, Jacqueline, 5654
Braunstein, Meryl L. Mandell, 1635
Braunstein, Michael, 5874
Bravmann, Carol, 5705
Bravmann, Lotte, 5705
Bravmann, Ludwig, 5705
Bravo Natural Resources, 9053
Braxton, Peter, 3100
Bray, Clarence, 9073
Bray, Marge, 4732
Bray, Richard S., Hon., 9391
Bray, Ronald E., 2033
Bray, Skye Lemoine, 3662
Bray, Theresa, 4334
Bray, Thomas J., 4413
Brayton, Deborah, 7000
Brayton, Lori G., 1568
Brazas, Elizabeth, 7182
Brazda, Scott, 3668
Breakwater RES Ltd NA, 7349
Breall, Joseph M., 691
Breall, William S., 691
Brean, JoEllen, 517
Brearton, Robert D., 7728
Breault, Diane, 3929
Breaux, Ernest P., 3623
Brecht, Christy, 5766
Brecount, Margaret W., 7395
Brede, Helen, 2305
Brede, J. Daniel, 2305
Bredin, Gay, 3590
Breeden, Andrew, 9396
Breeden, Hilda M., 9396
Breen, Marion I., 4861
Breen, Mike, 9361
Breen, Richard, 3820
Breen, Yellow Light, 3680
Bregar, Hymen, 2706
Bregenzer, Jill, 6643
Bregstein, Henry, 2951
Breheny, Kevin, 2764
Brehm, Lyle, 5473
Breidinger, Dave R., 7989
Breier, Robert G., 2223
Brekke, Sandy, 9889
Brelsford, Jonathan, 8228
Brelsford, K. Duane, 9650
Bremekamp, Theodore H., III, 1845
Bremer Bank, N.A., 7351
Bremer Foundation, The, 4730
Bremer, Otto, 4620
Bremer, Paul C., 2286
Bremer, Richard, 3657
Bren, Donald L., 339
Bren, Gerald C., 4672
Brenden, John, 5130
Brenden, Norman L., 9601
Brendle, Heather, 2839
Brendle, Jimmy, 2839
Breneman, Gary L., 4873
Brenengen, Robert, 3884
Brennan, Anita M., 5706
Brennan, B. Lawrence, 328
Brennan, Carrie, 101

Brennan, James C., 8170
Brennan, Janice, 5256
Brennan, John D., 282
Brennan, John O., 5706
Brennan, John V., 5706
Brennan, Mary B., 6130
Brennan, Michael, 3393, 7848
Brennan, Murray, 3774
Brennan, Nora, 5315
Brennan, Paul F., 5706, 7927
Brennan, Tom, 9631
Brenneis, James A., 861
Brenneman, Jean, 3417
Brenner, Bill, 5808
Brenner, David A., 3714
Brenner, Mervyn L., 340
Brenner, Nancy, 7180
Brenner, Nanette, 5290
Brenner, Williard C., 2766
Brenninkmeyer, Anthony, 5837
Brennock, Erin, 1232
Brent, Timothy, 4359
Brenzier, Bruce, 9487
Breon, Willard S., 7421
Bresch, Heather, 8192
Bresette, Matthew J., 3974
Bresky, Helen A., 3958
Bresky, Patricia A., 3958
Bresky, Steven J., 3958
Breslau, Warren, 677
Breslauer, Alan D., 1199
Breslauer, Benjamin F., 1199
Breslauer, David, 9190
Breslauer, Elizabeth H., 341
Breslauer, Gerald, 1073, 1348
Breslauer, Irma G., 1199
Breslauer, James M., 341
Breslauer, Kathy, 9190
Breslauer, Michele, 1199
Breslauer, Stephen, 9190
Breslaw, Betty, 2736
Bresler, Shirley B., 7014
Breslin, Andrew, 3600
Breslin, Ben, 3600
Breslin, Danielle, 7153
Breslin, Hugh J., III, 3791
Breslin, Maureen, 6453
Breslin, Tim, 8217
Breslow, Warren, 889
Bresnahan, Ann, 3706
Bresnahan, Ann W., 3218
Bresnahan, David H., 3706
Bresnahan, Elizabeth W., 3706
Bresnahan, Richard, 3706
Bresnahan, Richard A., 3706
Bresnahan, Richard M., 3706
Bressi, Samuel J., 8135
Bressler, Alan S., 3959
Bressler, Daryl, 3959
Bressler, Karen S., 3959
Bressler, Lorraine D., 3959
Bressler-Starn, Nancy, 3959
Bretherton, Jeff, 5013
Brett, Elaine, 1520
Brett, Emily P. Shoemaker, 1378
Brett, Matthew S., 1378
Brett, Stephen M., 1378
Brett, Thomas R., 7770
Bretzlaff, Hilda E., 4355
Breuer, J. Andrew, 5757
Breuil, James F., 8804
Breunig, Roland E., 6832
Brevorka, Peter J., 6771
Brewbaker, N.M., 9399
Brewbaker, Nancy M., 9434
Brewer, Helen, 3201
Brewer, Jackson, 3578
Brewer, Mark, 2015
Brewer, Michael F., 1890, 2946
Brewer, Robby, 3898
Brewer, Robert D., 2713
Brewer, Robert N., 2713
Brewer, Sebert, Jr., 8535
Brewer, Wendy, 2774
Brewer, William A., III, 8705
Brewer, William H., 2774
Brewers Association of Canada, 3714
Brewington, Mary Ellen, 8560
Brewster, Allison, 8435
Brewster, Frederick, 8435
Brewster, Priscilla, 8435
Breyfogle, Nancy, 4691
Brezik, Connie, 9999
Breznay, Deborah B., 6846
Brice, Deborah L., 5708
Brice, Elizabeth, 3851
Brice, Todd D., 8259
Bricker, John F., 3616
Bricker, Nina B., 3616
Brickley-Raab, Marie, 8242
Brickman Group, 9606
Brickman, John M., 6361
Brickman, Patrice, 3739
Brickman, Sally, 7949
Brickman, Scott, 3739
Brickman, Scott W., 7949
Brickman, Steven G., 7949
Brickman, Theodore, 7949
Brickner, Laura, 7682
Brickner, Lynne M. O., 3358
Brickner, Rebecca Scripps, 7659
Brickstreet Mutual Insurance Company, 9771
Bridenbaugh, Julie, 8536
Bridge, Morgan, 1520
Bridgegate Sales, 6409
Bridgeland, James R., Jr., 7660
Bridgeland, Larry, 2766
Bridgens, Pepper Woodard, 7899
Bridges, Bill, 8474
Bridges, Dorothy J., 1469
Bridges, Doug, 2433
Bridges, Kenneth, 7776
Bridges, R. Darlene, 8725
Bridges, William A., 8481
Bridgestone Americas Holding, Inc., 8537
Bridgestone Americas, Inc., 8537
Bridgestone/Firestone, Inc., 8537
Bridson, John T., 3553
Bridwell, J.S., 8726
Bridwell, Ralph S., 8726
Bridwell, Tucker S., 9076
Bridy, William A., 7316
Brielle, Jonathan, 917
Brienza, Mary L., 6573
Briganti, Stephen A., 5900
Briger, Paul, 1760
Briges, James W., 8725
Briggs & Stratton Corp., 9822
Briggs Residuary Trust, Thomas W., 8538
Briggs, Andrew, 3253
Briggs, David W., 9384
Briggs, Eleanor, 4669
Briggs, Jessica, 7934
Briggs, Kathleen, 229
Briggs, Margaret, 7950
Briggs, Robert, 7598
Briggs, Robert G., 4752
Briggs, Stephen Michael, 8944
Briggs, Susan, 7179
Briggs, Susan S., 536
Brigham, L.G., 630
Brigham, Phillip, 3596
Bright Angel Foundation, 4298
Bright Realty, LLC, 8756
Bright Responce LLC, 9193
Bright, Ashley S., 3631
Bright, Becky, 8773
Bright, Calvin E., 361
Bright, Cameron, 4123
Bright, Christopher R., 8756
Bright, Clay V.N., 8756
Bright, James R., 7685
Bright, Tina Marie, 9659
Brighter Sky Foundation, 9149
Brighton, Cynthia Z., 1731
Brighton, Deb, 9375
Brighton, W. Curtis, 3327
Brighton-Best Socket Screw Manufacturing, Inc., 5417
Brightpoint North America, LP, 4817
Brightwater Fund, The, 5967
Brightwater Trust, The, 1552
Briglia, Beth Harper, 7979
Brignola, Paul J., 6148
Brill, Alan, 9775
Brill, Betsy, 2770, 2981
Brill, David, 7618
Brill, Debra, 1288
Brill, Edward W., 7506
Brill, Elyse Arnow, 5615
Brill, Jonathan, 1747
Brill, Lisa, 2511
Brill, Lisa F., 1747
Brill, Marcia A., 7506
Brill, Matt, 1747
Brill, Peter, 5530
Brill, Robert J., 9142
Brill, Ronald M., 1747
Brill, Steve, 7618
Brilliant, Larry, 1175
Briman, Steve, 3552
Brin, Michael, 343
Brin, Sergey, 343, 615
Brinberg, Simeon, 6732
Brind, Ira, 7995
Brinda, Sean E., 8047
Brinkerhoff, Allan, 2656
Brinkerhoff, Elizabeth, 3929
Brinkley, Amy Woods, 7139
Brinkley, Diane C., 4009
Brinkley, Donald K., 7141
Brinkley, William M., 7178
Brinkman, Amanda K., 4644
Brinkman, Mary, 8536
Brinkman, Sue E., 7828
Brinks, Dawn, 4402
Brinks, Kurt, 4402
Brinley, Charles, 3038
Brinley, Margot, 3038
Brinn, Steven, 9718
Brinshore Development, LLC, 2839
Brinson, Bob, 7321
Brinson, Gary P., 2715
Brinson, Suzann A., 2715
Brint, David, 2839
Brint, Elizabeth, 2839
Brinton, William D., 2031
Briones, Lesley, 8672
Brisbane, Laura, 9632
Briscoe, Dave, 8527
Briscoe, Robert B., 4814
Brisker, Arthur B., 3768
Brisker, Hazel, 3768
Briskey, Lauren, 8603
Briskin, Bernard, 344
Briskin, Judy, 344
Brisson, Katie G., 4371
Bristol County Savings Bank, 3960
Bristol Door and Lumber Co., Inc., 2019
Bristol Motor Speedway, 7214
Bristol-Myers Squibb Co., 5711, 5712
Bristol-Myers Squibb Pharmaceutical Research Institute, The, 3833
Briston, Peter M., 8477
British Embassy, 6904
Britt, Deirdre H., 9810
Britt, Kenneth, 2432
Britt, Wayman P., 4447
Brittain, Randy W., 2818
Brittingham, Ella, 345
Brittingham, Scott, 345
Brittingham, Steve, 3435
Britton, Brigham, 7951
Britton, Charles S., II, 7951
Britton, Donald W., 7038
Britton, Gertrude H., 7951
Britton, John, 6829
Britton, Lynda R., 7951
Britton, Terence B., 7951
Britton, Timothy C., 7951
Broach, James, 3833
Broach, Theresa, 1563
Broad Trust, Shepard, 2002
Broad, Edythe L., 346, 347
Broad, Eli, 346, 347
Broad, Morris N., 2002
Broad, Ruth K., 2002
Broad, Shepard, 2002
Broadbent, Amy, 9307
Broadbent, Camille W., 4581
Broadbent, Mark, 9307
Broadbent, Robert R., 7584
Broadcom Corp., 349
Broadfoot, Holli Leigh, 9019
Broadfoot, John W., 9019
Broadfoot, John, Jr., 9019
Broadhurst, Anna, 6721
Broadman, Dorothy, 9400
Broadridge Financial Solutions, Inc., 5214
Broadway Cares, 3317
Broadway National Bank, 8769, 8782, 9148
Broadway National Bank, N.A., 8984
Broadway Video, Inc., 6482
Brocade, 1153
Broccoli Administrative Trust, Dana, 350
Broccoli, Albert R., 350
Broccoli, Christina, 350
Broccoli, Dana, 350
Brochier, Karen, 1232
Brock, Brennin, 8727
Brock, Charles M., 2648
Brock, David, 1882
Brock, Diana, 8727
Brock, Harry B., Jr., 13
Brock, Jane H., 13
Brock, John R., 1380
Brock, M.H., 8941, 9133
Brock, Macon F., 9448
Brock, Nancy E., 6406
Brock, Nathaniel, 8062
Brock, Paul K., Jr., 8535

Brock, Stanley M., 13
Brock, Todd, 8727
Brock, Todd O., 8727
Brock-Wilson, Jane, 4097
Brockenbrough, Austin, IV, 9416
Brockett, Rebee, 9001
Brockman, Henry, 7702
Brockman, Holly, 9466
Brockman, Murray, Dr., 8505
Brockway, Jerome R., 7379
Brod, William C., 5757
Broder, Sherry, 3684
Broder, William, 352
Broderick, Michael, 2602
Broderick, Rosemary, 8275
Brodersen, Ellen H., 1288
Brodeur, Susan W., 2388
Brodhead, Richard, 6470, 6719
Brodie, Brenda B., 1768
Brodie, Bryson B., 1768
Brodie, Cameron K., 1768
Brodie, E.H., 1768
Brodie, H. Keith H., 1768
Brodie, Kent, 3235
Brodie, L.S., 1768
Brodie, Tyler H., 1768
Brodke, Darrel, 7916
Brodsky, Barbara, 8140
Brodsky, Daniel, 5713
Brodsky, Debra G., 7952
Brodsky, Ellen G., 7952
Brodsky, Estrellita, 5713
Brodsky, Herb, 1395
Brodsky, Jeff, 6507
Brodsky, Julian A., 7952, 7989
Brodsky, Katherine, 5714
Brodsky, Laura G., 7952
Brodsky, Lois G., 7952
Brodsky, Nathan, 5714
Brodsky, Shirley, 5714
Brodsky, William H., 5018
Brody Living Trust, Frances L., 6333
Brody, Christopher, 6333
Brody, Christopher W., 6333
Brody, Jeffrey M., 8383
Brody, Ken, 6748
Brody, Kenneth D., 6782
Brody, Mike, 2826
Brody, Paul, 5967
Brody, Samantha, 5967
Brody, Sheldon, 6675
Brody, William R., 774
Broek, Doreen, 1220
Broer, Victoria Urban, 3489
Broetje Orchards, 9756
Broetje, Cheryl, 9756
Broetje, Ralph, 9756
Broetje, Suzanne, 9756
Brogan, James, 3781
Brogan, Robert H., 9892
Brogdon, William A., 2486
Brogna, Christopher, 6782
Broidy, Steven D., 1307
Broin, Kenneth, 4787
Brokas, Erich, 1891
Brokaw, Lea Carpenter, 1785
Brokehuizen, Elsa D. Prince, 4525
Broker, William K., 2546
Bromley, Jim, 9625
Bronfman Living Trust, Jeffrey, 5515
Bronfman Trust II, Charles, The, 662
Bronfman Trust, Ann L., The, 5716
Bronfman Trust, Edgar Miles, 5717
Bronfman, Adam, 2003
Bronfman, Adam R., 5715
Bronfman, Andrea M., 5717
Bronfman, Ann L., 2003, 5716
Bronfman, Charles R., 5717
Bronfman, Clarissa, 5716
Bronfman, Edgar M., Sr., 5715
Bronfman, Edgar Miles, Jr., 2003
Bronfman, Edgar, Jr., 5716
Bronfman, Jeffrey, 5515
Bronfman, Matthew, 2003
Bronk, Helen, 5927
Bronner, David, 479
Bronner, Jim, 1528
Bronner, Michael, 479
Bronner, Ralph, 479
Bronner, Trudy, 479
Bronson, Barbara J., 7702
Bronstein, Jean G., 6228
Bronstein, Julie, 509
Bronstein, Richard J., 1571
Bronwell, Thomas H., 9368
Bronxwood Home for the Aged Inc., 6229
Brooke Point High School, 9118
Brooke, Deborah, 3929
Brooke, Dell S., 69
Brooke, Margaret W., 14
Brooke, William W., Jr., 14
Brooke, William W., Sr., 14
Brooker, T. Kimball, 2716
Brookfield Partners Foundation, 7098
Brookhart, J.D., 8940
Brooking, Gladys T., 9240
Brookins, Gary, 6876
Brooklace, Inc., 3201
Brooklawn Gardens Inc., 5444
Brooklyn Queens Nursing Home, 5668
Brookman, Ann, 9950
Brookman, Blyth, 4772
Brookout, Ann H., 8709
Brookout, John F., III, 8709
Brooks Bank Fund, 1565
Brooks Pierce McLendon Humphrey & Leonard, 7162
Brooks, Amy, 352
Brooks, Balbi A., 2611
Brooks, Blake, 4448
Brooks, Cali, 5556
Brooks, Chloe, 352
Brooks, Christopher, 5995, 7834
Brooks, Clarence S., 351
Brooks, Conley, 4702
Brooks, Conley, Jr., 4702
Brooks, Cooper, 352
Brooks, Denise M., 4373
Brooks, Edward, 4702
Brooks, Edwin, 1650
Brooks, Gary, 9750
Brooks, George R., 9925
Brooks, Heidi, 8374
Brooks, Hilda, 5927
Brooks, J. Michael, 7605
Brooks, James E., 3963
Brooks, James L., 352
Brooks, Jim, 633
Brooks, John H., 1565
Brooks, Joseph, 352
Brooks, Kelli J., 5349
Brooks, Larry J., 2717
Brooks, Louise, 1650
Brooks, Margaret L.N., 9911
Brooks, Mark A., 222
Brooks, Markell, 4801
Brooks, Markell C., 4702
Brooks, Marva J., 8475
Brooks, Mary Anne, 7184
Brooks, Mary C., 3963
Brooks, Rick, 9768
Brooks, Robert A., 111
Brooks, Roger, 3452
Brooks, Roger K., 3420
Brooks, Stephen B., 4702
Brooks, Susan, 9146
Brooks, Suzanne S., 9506
Brooks, T.J., 9889
Brookshire, Michelle, 8819
Brookshire, William A., 8728
Brookshire-Garrison, Lori, 8728
Broome, O. Whitfield, Jr., 9405
Broome, Paul, 4996
Brorsen, Jennifer L., 5872
Brosco, Gian, Esq., 5134
Brosnan, Betsy K., 2812
Brosnan, Tim, 8649
Brossart, Darcie, 9089
Brost, Gary, 5801
Brostrom, Nathan, 490
Brotchi, Jacques Baron, 6007
Brotherhood Mutual Insurance Co., 3268
Brothers Lumber, Schilling, 3347
Brothers, Gary, 2587
Brotherton, Dorothy R., 9519
Brotherton, Emily, 5216
Brotherton, Fred J., 5216
Brotherton, Wayne A., 5216
Brotherton, William, 98
Brotherton, William P., 5216
Brotz, Adam T., 9825
Brotz, Jesse R., 9825
Brotz, Stuart W., 9825
Broughel, Sara Hunt, 4123
Brougher Trust, W. Dale, 5217
Brougher, Bill, 7671
Brougher, Nancy, 5217
Brougher, W. Dale, 5217
Broughton Petroleum Inc., 8761
Broughton, Carl L., 7557
Broughton, G.C., 8729
Broughton, Jean, 8729
Broun, Elizabeth, 6398
Broussard IRR Trust, Rebecca C., 7389
Broussard No. 2 LP, 7389
Broussard Pledged Trust, Jerome T., 7389
Broussard, Jerome T., 7389
Brouwer Family L.P., 1220
Brouwer, Chris, 1220
Brouwer, Garrett, 1220
Brouwer, Jack, 1220
Brouwer, Jacob, 1220
Brouwer, Jane, 1220
Brouwer, Jeanette, 1220
Brouwer, Matthew P., 9057
Brouwer, Richard, 1220
Browdy, Candace A., 3143
Browdy, Michelle, 6203
Browe, Matthew, 6898
Brower, Robert D., 4378
Brown & Root, Inc., 8884
Brown 2012 Charitable Lead Annuity Trust, Christina Lee, 3562
Brown Advisory, 3718
Brown Advisory LLC, 3740
Brown Advisory Securities, 3740
Brown Brothers Harriman, 1855
Brown Brothers Harriman Trust Co., 6544
Brown Brothers Harriman Trust Co., N.A., 1801, 5742
Brown Charitable lead & Annuity Trust, Harold, The, 4085
Brown Charitable Lead Annuity Trust, H.L., Jr., 8732
Brown Charitable Lead Trust, Robert J., 4507
Brown Charitable Rem Unitrust, 6069
Brown Family Agape Foundation, 4417
Brown Group Inc., Charitable Trust, Inc., 2004
Brown Library, John Carter, 5707
Brown Shoe Co., Inc., 2004
Brown, Adrian, 3398
Brown, Albertine M., 4507
Brown, Alice Cary, 3565
Brown, Alice Pratt, 8731
Brown, Allyn E., 9755
Brown, Alma, 2763
Brown, Alvin I., 3741
Brown, Anders M., 9755
Brown, Andrew, 2931
Brown, Ann, 414
Brown, Anne S., 8662
Brown, Anthony J., 8273
Brown, Anthony S., 6719
Brown, Anthony, Dr., 7730
Brown, Ariana M., 4704
Brown, Barb, 9856
Brown, Barbara, 2931, 3741, 7503
Brown, Barbara L., 101
Brown, Barrett C., 1717
Brown, Barrie, Mrs., 6672
Brown, Bates, 9005
Brown, Bernard H., Jr., 6567
Brown, Bob, 8971
Brown, Brooke Johnson, 1382
Brown, Bruce M., 8289
Brown, Bynum R., 7319
Brown, C.L., III, 9054
Brown, Calvin, 2817
Brown, Carlyle, 4681
Brown, Carol Anne Smullin, 1190
Brown, Carol L., 2746
Brown, Carol R., 8084
Brown, Carolyn M., 7737
Brown, Carolyn Thompson, 4420
Brown, Cary, 3564
Brown, Cedric, 764
Brown, Charles S., 2648
Brown, Charles S., Mrs., 2648
Brown, Charlotte, 179
Brown, Chester "Trip", 7174
Brown, Christian T., 3656
Brown, Christie, 2432
Brown, Christina Lee, 3557, 3559, 3562, 3595
Brown, Christopher, 5514
Brown, Chuck, 7002
Brown, Constance W., 7390
Brown, Courtney L., 9755
Brown, Craig J., 7428
Brown, Crichton W., 3631
Brown, Cuyler, 3061
Brown, Cynthia, 9789
Brown, D. Randolph, Jr., 7780
Brown, Dana, 4862
Brown, Daniel, 1108
Brown, David, 1399
Brown, David A., 689, 3345
Brown, Dawn, 3280
Brown, Dean, 9845
Brown, Dennis C., 2035

Brown, Diane L., 5802
Brown, Diane Solomon, Dr., 3754
Brown, Donald D., 3833
Brown, Donald E., 8182
Brown, Donna, 3741
Brown, Dorothy Dorsett, 3617
Brown, Dorothy S., 4488
Brown, Douglass J., 2827
Brown, Drew M., 111
Brown, Ed, 3418
Brown, Elizabeth, 420, 1901
Brown, Elizabeth Byron, 3232
Brown, Elizabeth M., 8531
Brown, Emery N., 7164
Brown, Forrest C., 2204
Brown, Frances A., 2430
Brown, Francis A., 2500
Brown, Frank D., 2528
Brown, Frank D., Dr., 2438
Brown, Frederick O., 4507
Brown, Gabrial, 4704
Brown, Gail Feiger, 2931
Brown, Gary W., 9489
Brown, George R., 8731
Brown, George W., 1288
Brown, Georges Pezon, 3232
Brown, Gregory B., 1845
Brown, H. Bonnie, 3683
Brown, Hank, 1399
Brown, Harmon, 1512
Brown, Henry, 2931
Brown, Herman, 8731
Brown, Hillary, 6804
Brown, Himan, 5720, 6672
Brown, Holly, 59
Brown, Howard S., 3766
Brown, Hubert L., III, 8732
Brown, Hugh M., 2174
Brown, Ira A., 6406
Brown, Isaac, 4704
Brown, J. Graham, 3563
Brown, Jake F., II, 3974
Brown, James H., 9541
Brown, James Keith, 7050
Brown, James O., Jr., Rev., 1786
Brown, James W., III, 7390
Brown, James W., Jr., 63, 7390
Brown, Jameson, 4085
Brown, Jane, 3779
Brown, Jason, 9354
Brown, Jeffrey N., 3321
Brown, Jeffrey R., 2931
Brown, Joanne, 1512
Brown, Joanne D., 5819
Brown, Joe W., 3617
Brown, John E., III, 213
Brown, John Seely, 2989
Brown, John W., 4356
Brown, Judy L., 4521
Brown, Karen, 689, 1581
Brown, Kathleen, 7629
Brown, Kathryn C., 8540
Brown, Keith A., 7578
Brown, Kevin Smullin, 1190
Brown, Kiyoko O., 5893
Brown, Kris Nolan, 5044
Brown, Kristen, Mayor, 3321
Brown, L.P., III, 1379
Brown, LaRay, 6549
Brown, Leslie, 9588
Brown, Linda, 1951, 9754
Brown, Linda W., 3833
Brown, Lisa, 9615
Brown, Loren, 421
Brown, Louise Ingalls, 7503
Brown, Malcolm M., 3232
Brown, Margaret Monroe, 935
Brown, Margarett Root, 8731
Brown, Mark J., 62
Brown, Marla, 624
Brown, Marshall, 3042
Brown, Martin S., 3564, 8531
Brown, Martin S., Jr., 8612
Brown, Martin S., Sr., 8531, 8612
Brown, Mary B., 97
Brown, Mary Rose, 9065
Brown, Maura, 4085
Brown, Meghan Binger, 4709
Brown, Melina, 6672
Brown, Meredith A., 1190
Brown, Michael, 9731
Brown, Michael C., Jr., 7189
Brown, Michael J., 4920
Brown, Michael L., 3205
Brown, Michael S., 3833, 5589
Brown, Minette, 3672
Brown, Molly, 5115
Brown, Monique, 9541
Brown, Montgomery B., 4413
Brown, Nancy Juckett, 6791
Brown, Nancy L., 6339
Brown, Nathaniel T. "Buster", 9731
Brown, Neil, 2332
Brown, Neil A., 7454
Brown, Owen, 2931
Brown, Owsley, II, 3562
Brown, Owsley, III, 3557, 3559, 3562, 3564, 3595
Brown, Patricia, 3741
Brown, Patricia J., 7453
Brown, Paul, 4194
Brown, Peggy S., 3741
Brown, Peter, 4897
Brown, Peter D., 4488
Brown, Peter F., 1941
Brown, Peter P., 4270
Brown, Peter R., 4047, 4132
Brown, R. Justin, 9353
Brown, Rachel, 157, 1941
Brown, Randal L., 3257
Brown, Raymond, 4830
Brown, Raymond L., 8827
Brown, Richard, 6368, 8548, 9684
Brown, Rita O., 19
Brown, Robert, 7992
Brown, Robert C., 7199
Brown, Robert D., Jr., 964
Brown, Robert J., 4507
Brown, Robert L., 2432
Brown, Robert M., 4507
Brown, Robert M., Jr., 4507
Brown, Robert W., 3656, 8752
Brown, Rod, 9591
Brown, Roddey, 7329
Brown, Roger O., 2931
Brown, Rosemary K., 4356
Brown, Russell, 3530
Brown, Sara S., 3557, 3559, 3562, 3564, 8531
Brown, Sara Shallenberger, 3565
Brown, Scott, 3418
Brown, Sharon Shiroma, 2598
Brown, Sheri, 2034
Brown, Shona, 615
Brown, Solange Stephanie Pezon, 3232
Brown, Solange, Dr., 3232
Brown, Stephen J., 6791
Brown, Steve, 9897
Brown, Steven, 6087
Brown, Stuart, 3754
Brown, Stuart R., 3565
Brown, Susan, 5807, 7780
Brown, Susie, 7558
Brown, Suzann, 9950
Brown, T.J., 8730
Brown, Tad, 2569
Brown, Tamara M., 4704
Brown, Tara, 689
Brown, Taylor, 4343
Brown, Thomas, 9541
Brown, Thomas H., 8887
Brown, Thomas P., 5486
Brown, Timothy H., 2800
Brown, Timothy S., 6791
Brown, Tom, 2765, 8819
Brown, Victoria, 5696
Brown, W.L. Lyon, Jr., 3565
Brown, W.L. Lyons, 3564
Brown, W.L. Lyons, III, 3565
Brown, W.L. Lyons, Mrs., 3562, 3565
Brown, Walter J., 2569
Brown, Walter R., 5893
Brown, Willard W., Jr., 7503
Brown, William, 7421
Brown, William C., 7737
Brown, William G., 3232
Brown, William Gardner, 3232
Brown, William M., 2149
Brown, William W., 8463, 8464, 8465
Brown-Dean, Kalilah, 1562
Brown-Graham, Anita, 7298
Brown-Schirato, Kimbo, 1368
Brown-Stevenson, Tina, 1567, 4785
Brownback, Mary, 3552
Browne, Caroline Cooley, 7838
Browne, Caroline Muir, 2472
Browne, Charles, 633
Browne, Christopher Howard, 6748
Browne, David, 7838
Browne, David M., 4417
Browne, Kim, 9715
Browne, Robert S., 7179
Browne, Tim, 8505
Brownell, Frank R., III, 3414
Brownell, Megan, 92
Brownell, Nancy Rossi, 5808
Brownell, Patricia, 7584
Brownells, Inc., 3414
Brownfield, Roberta F., 9506
Browning, Barbara K., 7738
Browning, Bruce W., 5104
Browning, Christopher, 5104
Browning, Dorothy W., 7624
Browning, Jay D., 9246
Browning, John, 5104
Browning, Jr. Charitable Lead Unitrust, L.L., 7624
Browning, Matt S., 7738
Browning, Nicholas V., 7664
Browning, Nick, 7367
Browning, Robert P., 8227
Browning, Val A., 5104
Brownlee, Susan H., 8039, 8064
Brownlie, E.C., 2074
Brownstone Residuary Trust, Ethel, 5722
Brownstone, Clyde R., 5722
Brownstone, Diane, 5722
Brownstone, Jennifer, 5722
Brownstone, Spencer, 5722
Broyhill Furniture Industries, Inc., 7160
Broyhill, B. Claire, 7160
Broyhill, Caron J., 7160
Broyhill, James E., 7160
Broyhill, Jeanne, 9384
Broyhill, M. Hunt, 7160
Broyhill, Paul H., 7160
Broyles, Mike, 3320
Brozowski, Catherine, 994
Brozowski, Marion S., 5218
BRRH Foundation, 2300
Brubaker, Jeffrey R., 407
Brubaker, Sara, 4448
Bruce Company of Wisconsin, Inc., The, 7698
Bruce, Ailsa Mellon, 6470
Bruce, Betty, 9795
Bruce, Carole W., 7162
Bruce, David B., 2302
Bruce, Holly McGrath, 4098
Bruce, James McDuffie, III, 7240
Bruce, John L., Jr., 8461
Bruce, Julia Harrison, 2894
Bruce, Mamie J., 7240
Bruce, Peter W., 9907
Bruce, Robin Weekley, 9264
Bruckner, Sandra, 753
Bruder-Stiftung, 5614
Brudin, Carole S., 3718
Brudnaya, Rufina, 4251
Brudzinski, Tina, 1392
Brueggemann, W. George, 3374
Bruening, Eva L., 7391
Bruening, Joseph M., 7391
Brueshaber, Sandy, 7417
Bruett, William H., 5220
Bruffey, Mike, 4830
Brufsky, Seth, 9473
Bruga, Richard D., 595
Bruggeman, Kelly, 5009
Bruininks, Robert, 4709, 4760
Brumbaugh, Sherri Garner, 7453
Brumfield, Bruce A., 8504
Brumi, Stephen T., 1866
Brumley, George W., Jr., 2584
Brumley, Jean S., 2584
Brumley-Robitaille, Nancy J., 2584
Brummell, Tara, 3759
Brummett, Paul E., II, 3676
Brummond, J.C., 293
Bruncati Charitable Lead Remainder Trust, 1035
Brunckhorst 2002 Trust, Lilian Edith, 5723
Brunckhorst 2010 Trust, Barbara, 5723
Brunckhorst, Barbara, 5723
Brunckhorst, Frank, III, 5723
Bruner, 5482
Bruner, James D., 152
Bruner, John, 3419
Bruner, Paula, 3293
Bruney, Catherine Hughes, 8899
Bruni, Jerome V., 1380
Bruni, Michael, 2769
Bruni, Pamela S., 1380
Brunick, Holly, 8521
Bruning, Charles, III, 2717
Bruning, Edwin C., 2717
Bruning, Herbert F., 2717
Bruning, Kathleen, 2717
Bruning, Paul J., 2717
Bruning, Tracy, 2717
Brunner, Alice, 2850
Brunner, Fred J., 2718
Brunner, Fred M., 2718
Brunner, James E., 4376

Brunner, Janell S., 4863
Brunner, John G., 4863
Brunner, L. Keith, 7645
Bruno & Carol Ann Rumore Trust, Vincent A., 17
Bruno Trust, Vincent Bruno & Carol Ann, 16
Bruno, Carmela June, 6498
Bruno, Lauretta J., 6532
Bruno, Mary Ann, 16
Bruno, Paul, 16
Bruno, Tommy, 7367
Bruno, Vincent John, 16
Bruno, Vincent Joseph, 16
Brunoehler Scholarship Fund, Carl J., 2390
Bruns, Andy, 3761
Bruns, Daniel, 4928
Bruns, Kathleen, 4928
Bruns, Michael J., 8530
Brunson, Philip, 1572
Brunst, Robert, 828
Brush, Ed, 2436
Brush, Gerald F., Jr., 786
Bruski, Kate, 4370
Brutto, Daniel J., 2566
Bruun, Jens C., 9729
Brvenik, Richard, 1664
Bryan Rev. Trust, Alan P., 8465
Bryan, Ann, 8474
Bryan, C. Russell, 7150
Bryan, Douglas D., 5885
Bryan, Jerry, 7415
Bryan, John D., 2424
Bryan, Joseph M., 7162
Bryan, Joseph M., Jr., 7135
Bryan, Larry, 8549
Bryan, Lissy S., 9416
Bryan, Martha, 2424
Bryan, Peggy, 2031
Bryan, R.A., III, 7161
Bryan, R.A., Jr., 7161
Bryan, Richard C., Jr., 5832
Bryan, Ruby M., 7161
Bryan, Sophie, 5885, 5921
Bryan, Stephen C., 7161
Bryan, Thomas J., 7934
Bryan, William H., 7319
Bryan, William J., 8916
Bryans, Martha B., 8284
Bryant, Andrea B., 9965
Bryant, Andy, 5446
Bryant, Brett, 9603
Bryant, David J., 2951
Bryant, Dawn, 8313
Bryant, Diane, 2416
Bryant, Doris B., 7324
Bryant, Douglas, 9128
Bryant, Ellen, 8834
Bryant, Ernest A., III, 611
Bryant, Forrest, 563
Bryant, G. Jack, 9563
Bryant, Gigi, 8676
Bryant, Harriette, 9659
Bryant, Helen, 3288
Bryant, Ivan O. "Buddy", Jr., 4828
Bryant, J. Stephenson, 7171
Bryant, Janet L., 9826
Bryant, John Landrum, Jr., 1882
Bryant, Kate, 4772
Bryant, Kathryn H., 2416
Bryant, Magalen O., 6582
Bryant, Maurita J., 7942
Bryant, Michael D., 2416
Bryant, N.W., 7809
Bryant, Nancy, 2353
Bryant, Pedro A., 3569
Bryant, R. Jeep, 7946
Bryant, Rachelle, 5055
Bryant, Robert, 1064
Bryant, Ruth D., 6584
Bryant, Sallie, 59
Bryant, Sharon W., 8468
Bryant, William, 2000
Bryce, George, 9986
Bryce-Laporte, Rene, 197
Bryd, Leverett S., 4174
Bryn Mawr Trust Co., 8031
Bryn Mawr Trust Company, 8046
Bryne, Frank D., 9897
Bryner, Jeff, 3291
Bryson, John E., 774
Bryson, Louis Henry, 365
Bryson, N. Catherine, 7163
Bryson, Nancy F., 7163
Bryson, Vaughn D., 7163
Bryson, William D., 7163
Brzezinski, Zbigniew, Hon., 1679
BSG Revocable Trust, 6039
BSI Constructors, Inc., 4969
BSI Redevelopment Corp., 4969
Bsumek-Hannon, Erika, 372
BT Capital Corp., 5876
BTIG, LLC, 1850
Bubarth, Robin, 7991
Bubb, Hillary, 4347
Bucaro, Thomas, 2655
Buccaneer L.P., 2124
Bucco, Diana, 7956
Buchanan, Carol Phipps, 2030
Buchanan, D.W., Jr., 2720
Buchanan, D.W., Sr., 2720
Buchanan, David, 8492
Buchanan, Julia, 3243
Buchanan, Kenneth H., 2720
Buchanan, Kevin, 2803
Buchanan, Leslie, 2073
Buchanan, Margaux, 2720
Buchanan, Patricia, 7878
Buchanan, Paul D., 2030
Buchanan, Sally, 9697
Buchbinder, Bradley, 2721
Buchbinder, Gilda, 2721
Buchbinder, Henry, 2721
Buchbinder, Leslie, 2721
Buchele, Ken, 3514
Bucher, Dan, 9796
Bucher, Trent, 3403
Buchheit, Karen Niemic, 5750
Buchheit, Paul, 353
Buchholz, Donna, 5114
Buchholz, Karen Dougherty, 7936
Buchignani, J. Richard, 8556
Buchler, Judith, 5272
Buchman, Diana, 5976
Buchman, Lorne M., 1159
Bucholtz, Gary A., 2342
Bucholz, Frederick S., 5087, 5088
Bucholz, Kurt S., 5087, 5088
Buck, 1997 Trust No. 1, Alexander K., Jr., 3691
Buck, 1997 Trust No. 2, Alexander K., Jr., 3691
Buck, Alexander K., Jr., 3691
Buck, Alexander K., Sr., 3691
Buck, Anne E., 3691
Buck, Carol Franc, 5105
Buck, Christine K., 2680
Buck, Christopher, 5725
Buck, Elia, 7131
Buck, Elinor, 7131
Buck, J. Marlon, Jr., 7131
Buck, James Wallace, Jr., 8735
Buck, James, III, 7131
Buck, Jason, 722
Buck, Michael, 5725
Buck, N. Harrison, 3691
Buck, Nancy B., 3691
Buck, Peter, 5725
Buck, Sara L., 3691
Buck, William, 5725
Buckalew, Steve, 2881
Buckbee, Kevin, 2650
Buckbinder, Gregg, 7083, 8109
Buckey, Marilyn Myers, 7367
Buckhantz, Diana, 354
Buckhouse, Coleman Floyd, M.D., 8461
Buckhout, Craig, 5757
Buckingham, Cynthia B., 7194
Buckingham, Lisa M., 3344
Buckingham, Matt, 3475
Buckius, Richard, 3375
Buckley, Andre, 4532
Buckley, Christine F., 9752
Buckley, Constance, 8224
Buckley, Jean C., 3189
Buckley, Marie L., 3480
Buckley, Michael, 5162
Buckley, Mortimer, 8327
Buckley, Peter, 426
Buckley, R. Michael, Jr., 8041
Buckley, Roe, 8819
Buckley, Stephen, 2332
Buckley, Thomas D., 5026
Buckley, William, 4111
Buckley, William F., 7572
Buckmaster, James, 436
Buckmaster, Raleigh D., 3461
Buckner, Elizabeth, 6241
Buckner, Helen W., 7058
Buckner, Laura, 8696, 8852
Buckner, Linda, 8810
Buckner, Linda S., 8955, 8978
Buckner, Liz, 7058
Buckner, Walker, 7058
Buckner, Walker G., Jr., 4302
Buckner, William, 7780
Buckridge, Steeve, 4412
Bucksbaum Family Foundation, Matthew & Carolyn, 2846
Bucksbaum Family Foundation, Matthew and Carolyn, The, 2723
Bucksbaum, Ann, 2846
Bucksbaum, Carolyn, 2724
Bucksbaum, Jacolyn, 2723, 2724
Bucksbaum, John, 2723, 2724
Bucksbaum, Matthew, 2724
Bucksbaum, Melva, 3137, 6069
Bucksbaum, Tom, 2846
Buda, James B., 2738
Budd, Hollis S., 5969
Buddin, Glenn D., Jr., 8478
Buder Special Trust No. 1, Leo R., 2725
Buder Special Trust No. 2, Leo R., 2725
Buder Special Trust No. 3, Leo R., 2725
Buder, Kathryn M., 4864
Buder, Marshall O., 4864
Buder, Theodore A., 4864
Budganowitz, Sheila, 1487
Budge, Jennifer W., 1197
Budge, Joseph H., 1197
Budge, Willa Kathleen, 1197
Budge, William W., 1197
Budig, David H., 7392
Budig, Mark E., 7392
Budig, Otto M., Jr., 7392
Budig, Sandra F., 7392
Budinger, Donald V., 158
Budinger, Jean-Paul, 8907
Budinger, William D., 158
Buehler, A.C., 8364
Buehler, Albert C., 8364
Buehler, Emil, 5219
Buehler, J. Marshall, 9802
Buehler, Kevin J., 8655
Buehler, Knute, Dr., 7845
Buel, Steve F., 125
Buell, Bruce T., 1405
Buell, Stephanie, 5062
Buell, Temple Hoyne, 1381
Buenger, Ann M., 7393
Buenger, Clement L., 7393
Buerger, Theodore V., 7078
Buerstatte, Jon V., 282
Buescher, Rebecca, 103
Buettner, Jeff, 5075
Buffalo News, Inc., 58
Bufferd, Allan S., 5329
Buffett Foundation, Susan A., 5027
Buffett, Devon G., 2726
Buffett, Doris B., 7324
Buffett, Doris E., 7341
Buffett, Howard, 5081
Buffett, Howard G., 2726
Buffett, Howard W., 2726
Buffett, Jennifer, 6570
Buffett, Katherine, 4106
Buffett, Pamela, 2727
Buffett, Peter, 6570
Buffett, Peter A., 5028
Buffett, Sarah, 2727
Buffett, Susan, 5027
Buffett, Susan A., 5028, 5081
Buffett, Susan T., 2726, 5028
Buffett, Thomas M., 4106
Buffett, Warren E., 2726, 5028, 5081, 6570, 6630, 9625
Buffett, Wendy O., 4106
Buffett, William N., 4106
Buffett-Kennedy, Noah E., 4106
Buffin Foundation, The, 5737, 6209
Buffkin, Buron, 2824
Buffoni, Brad, 3449
Buford, Calvin D., 7404
Buford, Linda C., 8736
Buford, Robert P., 8736
Bugalecki, Sheila R., 9924
Bugg, Christopher, 9955
Bugg, J. Bruce, Jr., 9236
Bugge, Mark, 4568
Bugge, Mark J., 4566
Bugher, Frederick McLean, 5727
Buhl, Bob, 9605
Buhl, Henry M., 5254
Buhl, Henry, Jr., 7956
Buhl, Miriam, 6804
Buhl, Thomas C., 4371
Buhler, John, 1511
Buhler, Shelly, 3524, 3552
Buhlke, Brian, 5067
Buhlman, Karla, 270
Buhrmann, David L., 5525
Bui, Andy, 5161
Bui, Andy T., 393
Buice, Charles, 6980
Buice, Charles U., 6915

Buice, Paula, 2559
Buice, William T., III, 6915
Buick, Kevin, 2792
Buie, Frederick V., 3420
Builders First Choice, 9606
Building Owners & Mgrs. of O.C., 1268
Buitrago, Kerrie, 6650
Bukowsky, Isaac Mordecai, 6229
Bukrinsky, Marian, 244
Bukstein, Katherine, 340
Bukstein, Roy, 280
Buku, Michele, 4485
Bula, Barbara, 4100
Bulan, Eileen, 7444
Buley, Paula Marie, 5182
Bulfin, John J., 2120
Bulkeley, Harry, 2853
Bull, Elizabeth W., 8773
Bull, Lauren, 5805
Bull, Marcia, Dr., 1584
Bullard Foundation, George Newton, 8642
Bullard, Frank J., III, 8507
Bullard, Ginger, 208
Bullard, Peter, 3991
Bullen, Lawrence, 4577
Bullen, Mary, 7488
Bullens, Sally, 7421
Buller, Mary, 5039
Bullerman, Jay, 3423
Bulletin Co., 8169
Bullington, Roger, 5044
Bullion Ltd., 6519
Bullitt, Anne M., 5728
Bullitt, Dorothy S., 9591
Bullitt, Harriet, 9591
Bullitt, Judy, 3962
Bullitt, William, 8221
Bulloch, T. Robert, 2035
Bullock, Bruce, 5146
Bullock, Frances, 7180
Bullock, Maree G., 2922
Bullock, Mary Brown, 3982, 6398
Bullock, Michelle, 1014
Bumgardner, Brad C., 3366
Bumgarner, Joyce, 7241
Bump, Kirsten, 1496
Bumpus, R. Leroy, 7413
Bunch, Charles E., 8235
Bunch, Herb, 3320
Bunch, Patricia D., 3508
Buncher Co., The, 7957
Buncher Rail Car Service Co., 7957
Buncher Trust, Jack G., 7957
Buncher, Bernita, 7957
Buncher, Jack G., 7957
Bundy, Emory, 9652
Bunegar, James, 3247
Bunge North America, Inc., 4865
Bunges, Barbara Bush, 6903
Bunje, Bob, 914
Bunker Hill Insurance Co., 4222
Bunkley, Phyllis B., 8497
Bunn, Arthur H., 2762
Bunn, Karan, 7321
Bunn, Lesley W., 5493
Bunnell, Terry, 3570
Bunnen, Lucinda W., 6396
Bunnen, Melissa, 6565
Bunnen, Robert L., 6396
Bunnen, Robert L., Jr., 6396
Bunnen, Robert L., Sr., Dr., 6396
Bunning, Bonnie B., 5165
Bunning, David G., 2728
Bunning, Denise A., 2728
Bunshoft, Barry, 914
Bunsness, Julie, 1493
Bunting 2012 Charitable Trust, Mary Catherine, 3743
Bunting Charitable Trust, Dorothy W., 3742
Bunting, Barbara E., 5473
Bunting, Christopher L., 3742, 3743
Bunting, Dorothy W., 3742
Bunting, George L., Jr., 3712, 3742, 6105
Bunting, George L., Sr., 3742
Bunting, Jeffrey G., 3742
Bunting, Joseph O., III, 9513
Bunting, Josiah, III, 6115
Bunting, June C., 9826
Bunting, Marc G., 3742
Bunting, Mary Catherine, 3742, 3743
Bunting, Mary Ellen, 3742
Bunting, Robert, 9566
Buntz, M.A., 7809
Bunzl, Frances B., 2417
Bunzl, Walter Y., 2417
Buonadonna, Joseph, 6451
Buono, Stella, 5598
Bupp, Timothy J., Esq., 8351
Buquet, James J., III, 3656
Burak, H. Paul, 6581
Burak, Mark A., 2588
Burbage, Todd E., 3760
Burbank, John H., III, 1016
Burch, Angie, 8778
Burch, Catherine C., 5729
Burch, Dale J., 5729
Burch, Frank, 3781
Burch, Kathie, 9634
Burch, Kevin, 3314
Burch, Michael L., 9954
Burch, R.D., 5111
Burch, Robert L., 5729
Burch, Robert L., III, 5729
Burcham, David W., 651
Burchett, Cindy, 7790
Burchfield, Albert H., III, 7966
Burchill, Jill, 9950
Burchinal, Margaret R., 6093
Burckel, David, 4829
Burd, Karen, 1394
Burda, Jeffrey P., 1211
Burden, Childs Frick, 8049
Burden, Dixon Frick, 8049
Burden, Frances D., 8049
Burden, Henry S., 8049
Burden, I. Townsend, III, 8049
Burden, Susan L., 7014
Burdett, Barbara J., 3865
Burdett, Jack L., 9026
Burdette, H. Speer, III, 2418, 2419
Burdick, Martha, 5927
Buresh, Ernie, 3439
Buretta, Sheri D., 84
Burford, Sam P., Jr., 8653
Burge, Christopher, 6271
Burger, Edward A., 5523
Burger, Wendy, 7425
Burgeson, John C., 3428
Burgeson, Katherine P., 9484
Burgess, Bill, 7742
Burgess, Charlotte G., 1060
Burgess, Denise, 1401
Burgess, Ken, Sr., 8774
Burgess, Malcom S., Jr., 2435
Burgess, Melanie A., 2243
Burgess, Michael J., 6567
Burgess, Ruth, 1039
Burgess, Sarah, 4059
Burgess, Shari L., 4482
Burgett, William, 7563
Burggraf, Steve, 4667
Burghart, Susan Smith, 1506, 7797
Burgin, Walter, 5995
Burgos, Raquel, 1255
Burgoyne, Anne Marie, 481
Burgoyne, Bonnie, 6603
Burhans, David D., 9460
Burhans, Stanley, 2944
Burish, Pamela, 3289
Burk, Amy, 4448
Burk, Frank W., 8694
Burk, Larry, 3502
Burkart, Joseph R., 9559
Burke 2002 Health and Educational Trust, James J., 5731
Burke Charitable Lead AnnuityTrust 00, Charles R., 7958
Burke Charitable Lead AnnuityTrust 02, Charles R., 7958
Burke Charitable Lead AnnuityTrust 03, Charles R., 7958
Burke Charitable Lead AnnuityTrust 99, Charles R., 7958
Burke Charitable Lead Unitrust 03, Charles R., 7958
Burke Charitable Lead Unitrust 08, Charles R., 7958
Burke Charitable Lead Unitrust 98, Charles R., 7958
Burke Charitable Trust, Charles R., 7958
Burke, Austin J., 8333
Burke, Bill, 2437
Burke, Brian, 5731
Burke, Brian T., 2706
Burke, Bruce, 141
Burke, Catherine L., 4232, 4258, 4269
Burke, Charles R., 7958, 7959
Burke, Charles R., Jr., 7958, 7959, 8064
Burke, Deborah M., 4784
Burke, Donald M., 2590
Burke, F. William, 1925
Burke, Gerald P., 2590
Burke, Gretchen H., 5730
Burke, James D., 4894
Burke, James J., III, 5731
Burke, James J., Jr., 5731
Burke, James M., 5579
Burke, James W., 2388
Burke, Jeanne J., 5731
Burke, Jennifer J., 5731
Burke, Joan A., 9897
Burke, John, 4282
Burke, Jonica, 7657
Burke, Joseph J., 5394
Burke, Jr. 2002 Charitable Lead Annuity Trust, James J., 5731
Burke, Kevin, 6872
Burke, Linda Beerbower, 8043
Burke, Marilyn, 2590
Burke, Marilyn C., 2590
Burke, Mary L., 2884
Burke, Michael, 5027, 5718
Burke, Pamela, 3781
Burke, Patricia G., 7958, 7959
Burke, Patricia Grable, 8064
Burke, Philip L., 6722
Burke, Philippa C., 5731
Burke, Richard W., 7536
Burke, Richard W., Jr., 2884
Burke, Richard W., Sr., 2884
Burke, Rick, 7597
Burke, Robert M., 2590
Burke, Sandra, 4806
Burke, Sheila, 329
Burke, Sheila P., 5800
Burke, Sheryl A., 1531
Burke, Spencer, 2995
Burke, Stephen B., 5730
Burke, Steven E., 7958, 7959, 8064
Burke, Timothy, 3269
Burke, Vincent C., III, 3751
Burke, Walter, 3788
Burke, Walter F., III, 3788
Burke, Yvonne B., 809
Burket, Joan, 8495
Burkett, Charles G., 8565
Burkey, Brett L., 1344
Burkey, Eric, 7939
Burkey, J. Brad, 1344
Burkey, James, 1344
Burkey, Jared P., 1344
Burkey, Jenna M., 1344
Burkey, Ken, 500
Burkey, Noelle Claeyssens, 1344
Burkhardt, Cheryl L., 7620
Burkhart, Mindy, 3502
Burkhart, W. R., 7683
Burkholder, Charles N., 8002
Burkholder, Eugene N., 8002
Burkholder, J Michael, 8002
Burkholder, Kenneth N., 8002
Burkholder, Leon Ray, 8002
Burkholder, Reagan, 5473
Burkle, Ronald W., 355, 1273
Burks, Kay, 4344
Burks, Lawrence, 4549
Burks, Lewis G., Jr., 67
Burks, William P., 5411
Burleigh Point, Ltd., 1388
Burleigh, Anne O'Herron, 1660
Burleigh, Annie, 1581
Burleigh, Catherine Anne Husted, 7395
Burleigh, David W., 7395
Burleigh, William R., 7395
Burleson, Judy, 8935
Burlingame, Kristi, 519
Burlingham, Frank, 657
Burlington Northern Santa Fe Corp., 8706
Burlington Rotary Club, 9961
Burma, Jacob, 6783
Burman, J. Dale, 3436
Burmeister, Neil J., 6547
Burmeister-Smith, Christy, 9576
Burn, Harry, III, 2237
Burn, Jean, 2237
Burnap, Candida D., 2791
Burnes, Richard M., Jr., 3774
Burnett, Charles P., III, 9632
Burnett, Charles, III, 4821, 9064
Burnett, David, 9631, 9632
Burnett, G. Bruce, 8734
Burnett, H.E. "Gene", 8614
Burnett, Ipek S., 1006
Burnett, James F., 1780
Burnett, Jason K., 1006
Burnett, John M., 3321
Burnett, Nancy Packard, 1006
Burnett, Robert, 9632
Burnett, Sarah, 9632
Burnett, Shirley, 9632
Burnett, Timothy Brooks, 7268

Burnett, Vivian, 9632
Burnett, William, 9632
Burnett, William, Jr., 9632
Burnette, Berleen B., 7141
Burney, Janet E., 7639
Burnham Way, 357
Burnham, Alice B., 7497
Burnham, Jon M., 7940
Burnham, Malin, 357
Burnham, Melissa M., 8878
Burnham, Patricia R., 8615
Burnham, Philip C., 8289
Burnham, Roberta, 357
Burnham, Robin, 7894
Burnham, Thomas, 9612
Burnley, Cynthia, 8560
Burno, Katherine, 2896
Burno, Philip M., 2896
Burns & McDonnell, Inc., 4866
Burns Charitable Lead Trust, Rosalie, 5732
Burns, Allyson, 1891
Burns, Angie, 9903
Burns, Ann, 4714
Burns, Barbara, 1650
Burns, Daniel J., 6406
Burns, Donald A., 2006
Burns, Fred C., 9292
Burns, Fritz B., 359
Burns, Geraldine H., 7639
Burns, Greg, 3390, 8603
Burns, Hilda, 3283
Burns, Jacob, 5732
Burns, James, 3390
Burns, John, 1650
Burns, Karon M., 4854
Burns, Laurie, 2051
Burns, Lucy, 3271
Burns, Maribeth, 7704
Burns, Marvin G., 494
Burns, Nicholas, 6723
Burns, Patricia, 987
Burns, R. Nicholas, 1926
Burns, Ray, 5226
Burns, Richard R., Jr., 3938
Burns, Robert A., 9796
Burns, Shannon, 3302
Burns, Stephanie A., 4549
Burns, Steven, 6674
Burns, Susan T., 358
Burns, Tim, 3419
Burns, Tori A., 358
Burns, Truman, 1002
Burns, Ursula, 1728
Burns, Wes, 1037
Burpee, Noreen S., 1855
Burr, Henry, 5894
Burr, Jeffrey L., 5119
Burr, Robert B., Jr., 2166, 8172
Burrage, Darrell, 309
Burrage, Roberta, 7742
Burrell, George, 8818
Burrill, W. Gregory, 4101
Burris, John E., 7164
Burroughs Wellcome Co., 7164
Burroughs Wellcome Fund, The, 3833
Burroughs, Christine, 1160
Burroughs, Ethan, 8459
Burroughs, Hazel, 9769
Burroughs, Keith, 8560
Burrows, Cliff, 9742
Burrows, Marcia, 7796
Burrows, Sunny H., 7225
Burrus, John E., 8028
Bursch, Fred, 4631
Burson, John H., 7572
Burston, James L., 7294
Burt's Bees, Inc., 3686
Burt, Allen, 8819
Burt, Ashley, 1392
Burt, Brady T., 7610
Burt, Gregory, 3434
Burt, John F., 4062
Burt, Karla, 167
Burt, Laurie, 4062
Burt, S. Jeffrey, 4062
Burt, Stephen M., 2812
Burt, Susan G., 3458
Burt, Susan Glazer, 3434
Burt, Susan J., 3434
Burt, Suzie Glazer, 3420
Burton Industries, Wm. T., Inc., 3619
Burton, Alan, 3683
Burton, Ann, 4349
Burton, Bob, 7671
Burton, Davis S., 25
Burton, Freddie G., Jr., Hon., 4424
Burton, Gregory A., 9771
Burton, Ian, 3244
Burton, Julie, 1948
Burton, Katrina, 3759
Burton, Leonard, 4869
Burton, Lynda, 3844
Burton, Marion, 198
Burton, Matthew D., 2489
Burton, Michael A., 7484
Burton, Robert Harold, 9309
Burton, Susan H., 9510
Burton, Todd, 1634
Burton, William K., 7574
Burton, William T., 3619
Burwasser, Peter, 8236
Burwell, Keith, 7686
Burwitz, Jacqueline E., 2824
Bury, David, 5652
Busam, Ray, 2763
Busby, Bret R., 7305
Busby, Gail, 1411
Buscaglia, Frank, 5438
Busch Entertainment Corp., 2294, 2315
Busch, August A., III, 4867
Busch, Dean E., 4673
Busch, Howard W., 8289
Busch, Lawrence S., 8172, 8173
Busch, Paul B., 4627
Busch, Virginia M., 2315, 4867
Buse, John B., 1738
Busey Trust Co., 3133, 3198
Bush, Ann H., 3519
Bush, Archibald Granville, 4621
Bush, Barbara, 5446, 8944
Bush, Carol, 1480
Bush, David E., 9558
Bush, Edyth Bassler, 2008, 4621
Bush, Gene, 8703
Bush, Greg, 8001
Bush, Gwen, 9789
Bush, J. Frederick, 4159
Bush, James R., 8234
Bush, Jeb, 5684
Bush, Lori, 4374
Bush, William, 5208
Bush, William L., 4443
Bushinger, Lynn, 4679
Bushnell Securities, 9273
Bushnell, Julayne Winn, 9592
Bushnell, Sherman Ward, III, 9592
Busick, Brett, 3365
Busick, William V., 9777
Busmire, Bruce, 8661
Busot, Aldo C., 2223
Buss, David, 6751
Buss, William D., II, 7564
Busse, Keith E., 3389
Bussel, Ann B., 2002
Bussel, Daniel J., 2002
Bussel, Deborah, 2002
Bussel, John M., 2002
Bussell, Patrice Irene, 610
Busselle, Chris, 615
Bussing, Wilfred C., III, 3312
Busskohl, Doyle, 6898
Bustamante, Carlos J., 7164
Bustamante, Thomas, 5533
Buster, Walter L., Ed.D., 366
Bustillo, Rafael, 9
Butcher, James R., 3782
Butcher, Jason, 5006
Butcher, Jeanne D., 3782
Butcher, John, 5927
Butcher, Joseph F., 8152
Buthman, Mark A., 8957
Butler Capital Corp., 5733
Butler Charitable Lead Trust, Gladys A., 2729
Butler Charity Lead Annuity Trust, Sarah T., 2414
Butler Foundation, J.E. and Z.B., 1889
Butler Trust, Clara W., 5165
Butler Trust, Thomas, 5165
Butler Trust, WM P., 7396
Butler, Aimee Mott, 4622
Butler, Alice L., 3415
Butler, Andrew J., 3415
Butler, Ashley Novak, 3587
Butler, Ayanna, 3644
Butler, Barbara, 5165
Butler, Brigid M., 4622
Butler, Bryce, 3266
Butler, Carol W., 36
Butler, Catherine C., 4622
Butler, Cathy, 2763
Butler, Christa, 7396
Butler, Clara W., 5165
Butler, Cynthia, 9466
Butler, David, 95, 7272
Butler, Deborah H., 9496
Butler, Debra, 3415
Butler, Donald L., 5766
Butler, Edna Loewy, 6389
Butler, Eugene W., 3058
Butler, Flamont T., 9936
Butler, Francis J., 7560
Butler, Fred, 5734
Butler, Frederick K., 8429
Butler, Gilbert, 5733, 5734
Butler, Gregory B., 1567, 1656
Butler, Henry King, 8545
Butler, Ildiko, 5734
Butler, Jack E., 5735
Butler, James E., III, 9538
Butler, Joel, 7217
Butler, John D., 8446
Butler, John E., 3415
Butler, John K., 4622
Butler, John M., 4376
Butler, Kevin, 7396
Butler, Kevin J., 4484
Butler, Kirby, 2439
Butler, Larry, 975
Butler, Letitia K., 5316
Butler, Linda, 7295
Butler, Maria R., 4754
Butler, Marjorie W., 5165
Butler, Marty, 7396
Butler, Mary Sue, 7396
Butler, Nancy O., 4484
Butler, Nicole, 5390
Butler, Patricia M., 4622
Butler, Patrick, 4622
Butler, Patrick, Jr., 4622
Butler, Paul S., 4622
Butler, Peter M., 4622
Butler, Rex, 2626
Butler, Rhett W., 2729
Butler, Roberta H., 8393
Butler, Ron, 92
Butler, Sandra K., 4622
Butler, Shirley, 9466
Butler, Steve, 2414
Butler, Susan Storz, 5086
Butler, Thomas, 426
Butler, William P., 7396
Butler, Zella B., 5735
Butt Grocery Co., H.E., 8738, 9149
Butt, Barbara Dan, 8738
Butt, Howard E., Jr., 8738
Butt, Howard E., Sr., 8738
Butt, Patricia, 3284
Butt, Tariq H., 3172
Butta, Zulfiqar A., 9625
Buttenwieser, Catherine F., 5736
Buttenwieser, Lawrence B., 6750
Buttenwieser, Paul A., 5736
Butterfield Trust Bermuda Ltd, 5779
Butterfield, Frank, 2519
Butterfield, John, 4467
Butterfield, Steve, 5072
Butterworth, Gary, 1406
Butterworth, Sharon, 9083
Buttinger, Muriel M., 6551
Buttram, Susan, 3521
Buttress, Christine, 7373
Buttress, Christine A., Esq., 7600
Buttrey, Donald W., 3383
Buttrey, Karen Lake, 3383
Buttrick, Marguerite D. R., 8197
Butts, David, 3027
Butynes, Michelle, 6980
Butz, Edgar, 6569
Butz, Greg L., 8136
Butz, Lee A., 7974
Butzel, Laura, 6477
Buuck, David A., 4623
Buuck, Gail P., 4623
Buuck, John R., 4623
Buuck, Robert E., 4623
Buurma Charitable Foundation, Deborah S., The, 6783
Buurma, Rachel, 6783
Buyck, Mark, Jr., 8461
Buzaglo, Meir, 5628
Buzzard, Vanessa, 8660
Buzzard, Vanessa G., 9086
Buzzelli, Robert A., 7659
Byala, Brian, 8192
Byant, R. Jeep, 7945
Byars, G. Rice, 8549
Bybee, Charles L., 8739
Bybee, Faith P., 8739
Bye, Larry, 4723
Byer, Allan G., 360
Byer, Marian, 360
Byer, Thomas D., 9416
Byerlein, Anne, 3608
Byerly, Patricia A., 7378

Byerly, Stacy S., 8631
Byers, Alison M., 8172, 8173
Byers, Karen, 6431
Byers, Marie G., 8644
Byers, Patricia Burch, 5430
Byers, W. Russell G., Jr., 8173
Byington, Carrie L., 9353
Bylancik, Robert, 6802
Bynum, Bill, 4827
Byorick, Joe, 8135
Byram, Jennifer, 959
Byrd, Ames, 4174
Byrd, Beth, 4817
Byrd, Beth C., 4817
Byrd, Carolyn, 9435
Byrd, D. Harold, Jr., 8909
Byrd, Daryl G., 3656
Byrd, Edward R., 1003
Byrd, Harry F., 4174
Byrd, Jesse H., Jr., 7184
Byrd, Marianne, 3087
Byrd, Mark, 2435
Byrd, Richard E., III, 4174
Byrd, Stephanne S., 9411
Byrd, Susan, 818
Byrne, Brendan, 5749
Byrne, Brendan Thomas, 5270
Byrne, Bruce, 5501
Byrne, Dorothy, 5166
Byrne, Dorothy M., 5166
Byrne, Emily, 1562
Byrne, Gary, 415
Byrne, Gary D., 5068
Byrne, James R., 6951
Byrne, John J., 5166
Byrne, Kathleen, 9244
Byrne, Mary Elizabeth Scripps, 3600
Byrne, Mary Jo, 4496
Byrne, Molly L., 9244
Byrne, Moyra, 8840
Byrne, Rebecca, 24
Byrne, Rebecca C., 6951
Byrne, Robert, 9244
Byrne, Susan, 4772
Byrnes, Brian, 5533
Byrnes, John H., 7000
Byrnes, Mary Elizabeth, 3964
Byrnes, Mollie, 4039
Byrnes, Mollie T., 6999
Byrnes, Mollie Tower, 7000
Byrnes, Randall W., 3964
Byrnes, Susan, 9625
Byrnes, William H., Jr., 5339
Byrnes, William L., 3964
Byrns, Priscilla Upton, 4565
Byron, William J., Rev., 9471
Byrum Land and Timber Inc. Porter Byrum, 7166
Byrum, D. Michael, 1996
Byrum, Porter B., 7166
Byzewski, Sandra, 4791

C & E Enterprises, 7315
C Black Hills Trust, 2379
C&A Industries, Inc., 5058
C&M Arts LP, 6493
Caban-Owen, Catalina, 1630
Cabanatuan, Pam, 9603
Cabatu, Elena, 2604
Cabe, Charles L., Jr., 182
Cabe, Charles Lee "Sandy", 182
Cabe, Horace C., 182
Cabe, Robert D., 181
Cabe, Thomas H., 182
Cabela, James W., 5037
Cabell, Charles L., 9397
Cabell, John Branch, 9397
Cabell, Maude Morgan, 9397
Cabell, Robert G., III, 9397
Cabell-Mains, Susan, 9506
Cable, Andrew M., 4248
Cable, Barbara, 9726
Cable, Thomas J., 9757
Cable, Tom, 9726
Cabot 1986 Conduit Trust, Thomas D., 3968
Cabot 1994 Charitable Lead Unitrust, Thomas D., 3968
Cabot 1996 Charitable Lead Unitrust, Virginia W., 3968
Cabot Corp., 3966
Cabot Oil & Gas Corp., 9049
Cabot Revocable Trust, Virginia W., 3968
Cabot, Alexis, 3968
Cabot, Amiel, 3968
Cabot, Bradford W., 3968
Cabot, Elizabeth C., 3968
Cabot, F. Colin, 5181
Cabot, Godfrey L., 3967
Cabot, James W., 3968
Cabot, John G.L., 3967
Cabot, Thomas D., Jr., 3968
Cabrera, Phillip R., 2812
Cabrera, Raymond, 2803
Cacciamani, John D., 8239
Cacciatore, Mark, 5223
Caceres, Melanie G., 2129
Cachine, Michael N., Sr., 3014
Cacossa, Brenda, 5383
Cadawallader, Glenda M., 6343
Caddie Homes, Inc., 3770
Caddock, John B., 7828
Caddock, Richard E., Jr., 7828
Cade, Brian, 4625
Cade, Joe, 4625
Cade, Joseph, 4625
Cade, Martha, 1784
Cade, Mary, 1784
Cade, Molly F., 4625
Cadence Design Systems, Inc., 1153
Cades, Charlotte M., 2591
Cades, J. Russell, 2591
Cades, Milton, 2591
Cadiente, Katherine, 1818
Cadieux, Chester, 7807
Cadoux, Bob, 5662
Cady, John, 6462
Caesars Entertainment Operating Company, Inc., 5106
Cafaro Charitable Lead Trust, Alyce, 7397
Cafaro Charitable Lead Trust, William M., 7397
Cafaro, Anthony M., 7397
Cafaro, Flora M., 7397
Cafaro, Phyllis C., 7397
Cafferty, Lisa, 8444
Caffrey, John J., 6339
Caforio, Giovanni, 5711
Cafritz, Anthony W., 1890
Cafritz, Calvin, 1890
Cafritz, Elliot S., 1890
Cafritz, Gwendolyn D., 1890
Cafritz, Jane Lipton, 1890
Cafritz, Jane R., 9525
Cafritz, Morris, 1890
Cafuir, Jeff, 1153
Cagan, Danielle, 421
Caggiano, Franklin B., 8488
Cagigas, Gloria, 7415
Cagle, Ronald E., 7776
Cahalan, Joseph M., 1728
Cahalin, Helen J., 2085
Cahill, Michael, 8260
Cahill, Michele, 5747
Cahill, Robert V., 397
Cahill, William, 744
Cahillane, Mary J., 3171
Cahn, Judy, 2142
Cahoon, Frank K., 8874
Cahshill, Robert M., 5317
Caiaze, Robert M., 1634
Cailloux 1997 Charitable Remainder Unitrust, Kathleen C., 8741
Cailloux, Floyd A., 8742
Cailloux, Kathleen C., 8741, 8742
Cailloux, Kenneth F., 8741, 8742
Cailloux, Sandra, 8742
Cain Foundation, Gordon A. and Mary, The, 8744
Cain Foundation, Gordon and Mary, The, 7268
Cain, David H., 8883
Cain, Edmund J., 692
Cain, Effie Marie, 8743
Cain, Jeffrey J., 1097
Cain, Jennifer, 8883
Cain, John C., 8743
Cain, Jonathan, 1249
Cain, Kevin M., 7295
Cain, R. Wofford, 8743
Caine, Marie Eccles, 7167
Cajthaml, Mary J., 2397
Cajun Constructors, Inc., 3640
Calabrese, Alex, 1171
Calabrese, Denis, 8672
Calabrese, Thomas, 6543
Calabresi, Guido, 4630
Calabrise, Richard A., 5887
Calabro, Tina, 8043
Calamos, John P., Jr., 2731
Calamos, John P., Sr., 2731
Calaway, Tonit M., 9859
Calciano, Marilyn, 418
Caldeira, Ernesto, 8739
Calder Foundation, Louis, 7893
Calder, Donald Grant, 6583
Calder, Louis, 1554
Calder, Peter D., 1554
Calderon, Dee-Ann, 9148
Calderon-Rosado, Vanessa, 4061
Calderone, Philip D., 5641
Calderwood Trust, Stanford, 3969
Calderwood, Stanford M., 3969
Caldwell, Alan L., 7296
Caldwell, Bob, 5063
Caldwell, Charles, 9658
Caldwell, Charles F., 9105
Caldwell, Christa, 6109
Caldwell, Christopher, 324
Caldwell, Desiree, 5170, 5178
Caldwell, Elizabeth W., 8642
Caldwell, James D., 9141
Caldwell, Jennifer, 363
Caldwell, Kevin, 714
Caldwell, Kim, 272
Caldwell, Linda, 9658
Caldwell, Samuel D., 8284
Caldwell, Stacy, 1263
Caldwell-Johnson, Teree, 3420
Caldwell-Johnson, Terry, 3466
Cale, Charles G., 364
Cale, Elizabeth J., 364
Cale, Jessie R., 364
Cale, Walter G., 364
Cale, Whitney R., 364
Calfee, Jon, 9769
Calhoon, Ann, 4842
Calhoun, Annetta, 1337
Calhoun, Essie L., 6099
Calhoun, F. David, 8690
Calhoun, Gwen, 92
Calhoun, Julia, 9696
Calhoun, Julia Larson, 9666
Calhoun, Ken, 3514
Calhoun, Kevin J., 2209, 2344
Calhoun, Marianne K., 2908
Calhoun, Michael, 8690
Calhoun, Phillip L., 8036
Calhoun, Robert, 9380
Cali, Philip S., 2933
California Baptist Foundation, 98
California Endowment, The, 223
California Italian-American Cultural Institute, Inc., 430
California Physicians' Service Agency Inc., 320
California Superstores, 783
California Wellness Foundation, The, 667
Caliguri, Katie, 4984
Calinski, Rick, 3369
Calista, Joanne, 4327
Calk, Sherri L., 7528
Calkins, William D., 9908
Call, Bradley C., 1270
Call, Thad J., 9310
Callahan, Charles Kent, 7771
Callahan, Christopher M., 3301
Callahan, Daniel M., 6339
Callahan, David M., 7991
Callahan, Eugene J., 8615
Callahan, Kathy, 5070
Callahan, Kevin, 467
Callahan, Meredith C., 3865
Callahan, Michael A., 41
Callahan, Patricia F., 2674
Callahan, Richard, 5805
Callan, John C., Jr., 2516
Callarman, Denise, 3185
Callas, Darcy, 3033
Callaway Foundation, Inc., 2009, 2418
Callaway Institute, Inc., 2419
Callaway Mills, 2419
Callaway, Amy Roach, 9132
Callaway, Cynthia H., 7178
Callaway, Fuller E., Sr., 2418
Callaway, J.L., Jr., 8746
Callen, C.J., 1322
Callen, Gloria Gaines, 3948
Caller, Bret, 7511
Calleton, Theodore, 1029
Callicott, Bradley L., 8461
Callier, James A., 3669
Callihan, William, 2777
Callin, Sabrina, 1037
Callins, Aldrich, 59
Callison, Kay Nichols, 4949
Callison, Mark, 4949
Callistein, Arthur, 2772, 9941
Callistein, Fern, 2772
Calloway, Pamela, 490
Calloway, W. Harold, 3402
Calmat Co., 73
Calone Law Group, 417

Caplan, Perry, 7962
Caplan, Sloan, 7962
Caplis, Jennifer, 4496
Caplow, Dorothy D., 5573
Caplow, Mildred R., 6752
Caplow, Theodore, 5573
Caplow, Theodore, Jr., 5921
Capobianco, Anthony J., 5803
Capodilupo, Larry, 3974
Caporale, Jay, 4039
Capote, Truman, 376
Capozzoli, Danielle, 5486
Capp, Carol, 5012
Cappelletti, Matthew, Jr., 8234
Cappello, Alexander, 9586
Capper, Donald R., 3575
Capps, Randy, 3578
Cappuccino, Andrew, 975
Cappuccino, Helen, 975
Capranica, Ruth M., 3825
Capranica, Steven F., 3825
Caprio, Frank, 22
Caprio, Tony, 7398
Capron, Jeffery P., 3795
Caputo, Joseph A., 8272
Caputo, Lisa, 4783
Cara, Frank, 6205
Caraballo, Alicia, 1562
Caranci, Kerry, 1154
Carano, Donald L., 5139
Caravello, Lorene, 3170
Caraway, Ray, 1393
Carbert, Jennifer, 4746
Carbone, Michael, 3710
Carbone, Peter, 4316
Carboneau, David K., 7881
Carbonel, Paloma, 870
Carbonneau, Daniel P., 4097
Card, Catherine E., 627
Cardamone, Steven J., 5278
Cardenas, Jose A., 152
Cardenas, Renato E., 8733
Cardenas, Susan, 2041
Cardillo, Mark J., 5912
Cardillo, Sara A., 6406
Cardin, Sanford, 7752, 7791
Cardin, Sanford "Sandy" R., 7794
Cardinal Health, Inc., 7398
Cardinal Solutions Group, 7638
Cardinale, Ruth, 4986
Cardini, Filippo, 7001
Cardon, Carol M., 5662
Cardon, Helen Hemingway, 9326
Cardona, Evette M., 3084
Cardone Foundation, Michael, 7964
Cardone Industries, 7964
Cardone, Jacqueline, 7964
Cardone, Michael, III, 7964
Cardone, Michael, Jr., 7964
Cardone, Ryan D., 7964
Cardoso, Carlos M., 8120
Cardwell Family Limited Partnership, 9114
Cardwell, Bickerton W., Jr., 2420
Cardwell, Brandon, 1581
Cardwell, R. Craig, 7294
Cardwell, Sonja, 3649
Care Now, 9098
CareFusion 303, Inc., 377
Carell 2002 Trust, Ann & Monroe, 8540
Carell Jr. Testmentary Q-Tip Trust, Monroe, 8540
Carell, Ann Scott, 8540
Carell, Jr. 1995 Trust, Monroe, 8540
Carell, Monroe, Jr., 8540
Cares- Sacramento, 378
Carey, Al, 6627
Carey, Amie, 2792
Carey, Brian, 1563
Carey, Charles P., 2756
Carey, Chase, 1650
Carey, Dan, 7360
Carey, Elizabeth, 7876
Carey, Elizabeth P., 5745
Carey, Emily N., 5745
Carey, Francis J., 5745
Carey, Francis J., III, 5745
Carey, Henry H., 2546
Carey, J. Meade, 5745
Carey, Jennifer L., 4649
Carey, Laura G., 5745
Carey, Linda, 3593
Carey, Lisa, 7153
Carey, Philip N., 2546
Carey, Rea, 1904
Carey, Wendy, 1650
Carey, William P., 5745
Carey, William P., II, 5745
Cargile, Samuel D., 3345
Cargill Charitable Trust, 4628
Cargill Meat Solutions Corp., 3510
Cargill, Inc., 4628
Cargill, Margaret A., 4627
Cargill, Shelley, 707
Carignan, Robert E., 3249
Caris Revocable Trust, Shirley C., The, 99
Caris, Shirley C., 99
Carl, Charles W., Jr., 6802
Carl, Molly, 9961
Carlan, Sarah W., 1805
Carleton, David H., 3358
Carleton, Gigi, 1029
Carleton, Julia, 5237
Carlex, 7638
Carlin, David, 9975
Carlin, Don R., 9718
Carlin, Marti, 9099
Carlin, Stephanie Klingzell, 3540
Carling Technologies, Inc., 2326
Carlingswitch, Inc., 2326
Carlisle, Lorenzo T., 7509
Carlite, 7638
Carlos, Chris M., 2422
Carlotti, C.M., 6526
Carls, William, 4358
Carlson 2000 BCG Charitable Annuity Trust, Arleen M., 4629
Carlson 2000 MCN Charitable Annuity Trust, Arleen M., 4629
Carlson Companies, Inc., 4629
Carlson, Alison, 1906
Carlson, Anne S., 4969
Carlson, Arleen M., 4629, 4726
Carlson, Bruce, 4421
Carlson, Bruce M., 4420
Carlson, C. Kent, 9757
Carlson, Cathy, 6037
Carlson, Cheryl C., 8450
Carlson, Christopher A., 7599
Carlson, Clint D., 5597, 8750
Carlson, Colette, 4631
Carlson, Curtis L., 4629
Carlson, David, 1222
Carlson, Deborah, 4210
Carlson, Dennis, 4636
Carlson, Don, 4717
Carlson, Gary L., 3443
Carlson, Herbert E., 7421
Carlson, Herbert E., Jr., 8450
Carlson, Jeff, 1411
Carlson, Jennie P., 4784
Carlson, John, 8777
Carlson, Leslie, 8908
Carlson, Martha, 8521
Carlson, Mary R., 9564
Carlson, Matt, 9629
Carlson, Nancy, 8750
Carlson, Nancy Packer, 8750
Carlson, Paul B., 9564
Carlson, Rebecca, 430
Carlson, Roger W., 9564
Carlson, Scott A., 5777, 6201
Carlson, Thomas O., 9564
Carlson, W.W., 2074
Carlston, Dave, 9328
Carlstrom, R. William, 9629
Carlton Investments, LP, 2265
Carlton, Andrea Waitt, 8541
Carlton, David, 2437
Carlton, Jerry, 774
Carlton, Jerry W., 456, 457
Carlton, John M., Jr., 2437
Carlton, Lisa, 2142
Carlucci, Leonard, 5398
Carlyss, Ann Schein, 3884
CarMax Auto Superstores, Inc., 9401
CarMax Business Services, LLC, 9401
Carmel, Judy, 2899
Carmen Family Charitable Foundation, 4057
Carmichael, Daniel P., 3342
Carmichael, Danny R., 2011
Carmichael, David R., 2011
Carmichael, E. Cecilia, 2011
Carmody, Christine M., 1656
Carmody, Thomas G., 3657
Carmody, Timothy J., 3419
Carmola, Jack, 7213
Carmon, Greg, 8521
Carmouche, David, 3615
Carnahan, Katharine J., 7965
Carnaroli, Craig R., 7995
Carnation Co., 9056
Carne, Will, Sr., 4375
Carnegie Corporation of New York, 1934
Carnegie, Andrew, 5747, 7966
Carneol, Allan J., 9840
Carneros, A., 1327
Carneros, A.J., 1327
Carnes, Clifford, 3285
Carnes, Drew, 9277
Carnes, Martha, 8916
Carnevale, Anthony, 6087
Carnevale-Henderson, Marisa, 2390
Carney, Dan, 3510
Carney, Gayla, 3510
Carney, Jane, 727
Carney, Laura, 9835
Carney, Lillian, 3975
Carney, Patrick, 3975
Carney-Peters, Cathy, 9380
Carnielli, Sandra, 6447
Carnival Cruise Lines, Inc., 1972
Carnrick, Mary E., 7173
Caro, Elias, 2047
Caro, Jodi J., 9970
Caro, Robert A., 6116
Carob Trust, 5744
Carol M. Jacobsohn Trust, 3819
Carola, Christopher, 5398
Carolan - Faga, Kimberly, 5225
Carolan, Richard C., 5225
Carolan, Richard V., 5225
Carolan, Tina, 5225
Carolan-Faga, Kimberly M., 5225
Carolina Casualty Insurance Company, 1741
Carolina East Medical Center, 9250
Carolina Finance, 7225
Carolina First Foundation, 3710
Carome, Kevin M., 5564
Caron, Daniel, 1566
Carpenter, Alfred S.V., 7831
Carpenter, Alison, 4485
Carpenter, Andy, 4814
Carpenter, Carroll M., 1785
Carpenter, Catherine E., 7661
Carpenter, Dan, 2824
Carpenter, David R., 1270, 7728
Carpenter, Dayton, 9780
Carpenter, Donna G., 9367
Carpenter, E. Rhodes, 7967
Carpenter, Edmund, 1542
Carpenter, Gayle, 8736
Carpenter, Gordon R., 9214
Carpenter, Helen Bundy, 7831
Carpenter, James O., 8997
Carpenter, John B., 9367
Carpenter, Karen H., 4207
Carpenter, Leona B., 7967
Carpenter, Lynn, 4424
Carpenter, Matt, 1406
Carpenter, Michael, 6951
Carpenter, Michael, Mrs., 6951
Carpenter, Robert, 4523
Carpenter, Thomas S., 3926
Carpenter-Brokaw, Lea, 2121
Carr 2001 Charitable Remainder Unitrust, Robert O., The, 5278
Carr Administrative Trust, Wilma, 83
Carr Holdings LLC, 5278
Carr, Ann K., 2957
Carr, Barbara Thiele, 9937
Carr, Betty, 2629
Carr, Elliott, 3973, 3974
Carr, Gregory C., 2629, 2631
Carr, Gregory M., 83
Carr, Jacqueline, 83
Carr, Jill A., 5278
Carr, Jim, 2210
Carr, Joseph S., 2876
Carr, Julie B., 7949
Carr, Justine M., 5925
Carr, Kathleen D.H., 9471
Carr, L.J., 83
Carr, Lyles, 9380
Carr, N., 4404
Carr, Nathan K., 83
Carr, R. Scott, 9538
Carr, Rebecca, 195, 5182
Carr, Richard C., 2957
Carr, Robert Venn, 1565
Carr, Robert W., 8060
Carr, Steve, 2632
Carragan, Craig, 1566
Carraher, Ruth A., 1503
Carras, Barbara D., 4408
Carreau, Robert A., 6802
Carreras, Lisa S., 2980
Carriage Hill Associates LP, 9452
Carrick, Cindri, 2647
Carrick, Elizabeth, 3171
Carrick, John, 5216
Carrico, Jim, 5159
Carrico, John D., 5316

Carrie, Ellen Zachry, 9296
Carrier, Patrick, 9149
Carrig, John A., 9044
Carrigan, Laura Cabot, 3967, 3968
Carrigg, James A., 5863
Carrignan, Catherine L., 3249
Carrillo, A. David, 2154
Carrington, Alexander Berkeley, 9402
Carrington, Clay, 3361
Carrington, Ruth Simpson, 9402
Carrington, Susan C., 2509
Carrino, Frank, 7711
Carrion, Richard L., 3085
Carrocci, Noreen, 3555
Carroll, Caitlin Bell, 1027
Carroll, Charles, 1020
Carroll, Constance M., 1108
Carroll, Cynthia, 400
Carroll, Daniel B., 8158
Carroll, Elizabeth, 3222
Carroll, Greg, 10000
Carroll, Heather, 1405
Carroll, Howard W., Hon., 3110
Carroll, James, III, 1027
Carroll, Jane C., 5410
Carroll, Kevin, 2881
Carroll, Kristin, 7315
Carroll, Lelia, 1382
Carroll, Michael, 7702
Carroll, Paul, 9578
Carroll, Sean B., 3818
Carroll, Stephen D., 9988
Carroll, Timothy G., 2896
Carroll, William J., 5059
Carros and Robert Carros Foundation, Jean Keller, The, 1675
Carros Foundation, Jean Keller & Robert, The, 2361
Carros Revocable Trust, Jean, 2012
Carros, Jean, 2012
Carrus, Gerald, 2734
Carrus, Janet, 2734
Carruth, Allen H., 8751
Carruth, Anne S., 23
Carruth, Brady F., 8751, 9292
Carruth, Ethel G., 8751
Carruth, Laura T., 1266
Carruthers, Sara P., 7481
Carruthers, Wendy, 3957
Carsey, John J., 380
Carsey, John Peterson, 380
Carsey, Marcia L., 380
Carsey, Rebecca P., 380
Carson Trust, John W., The, 381
Carson, Allen, 9778
Carson, Anne Ber, 1740
Carson, Benjamin S., Sr., 3726
Carson, Betty, 8351
Carson, Cecily M., 5748
Carson, David E.A., 1589
Carson, Deborah O., 9076
Carson, Diane, 9604
Carson, Don, 3530
Carson, Drew T., 183
Carson, Edward S., 5748
Carson, Emmett D., 1166
Carson, Gale Jones, 8549
Carson, James F., 183
Carson, Judith M., 5748
Carson, Mary, 183
Carson, Mary L., 7810
Carson, Patsy Q., 8560
Carson, Robert L., 4125
Carson, Russell L., 5748, 8206
Carson, Sandra M., 9705
Carson, Thomas J., 7810
Carson, Tom J., 183
Carstarphen, Catharine Pharr, 7309
Carstarphen, William P., 7179
Carstens, Godfrey H., Jr., 6703
Carstens, Inc., 2701
Carswell, Bruce, 1626
Carswell, Gale Fisher, 2621
Cartagena, Luis, 7639
Cartee, Joseph B., 8, 9
Carter Enterprises, LLC, 5962
Carter Foundation Production Co., 8752
Carter, Adrianna, 7274
Carter, Alexandra, 5551
Carter, Amon G., 8752, 8753
Carter, Anne Strong, 2617
Carter, Beirne B., 9403
Carter, Chris, 3354
Carter, Don, 5047
Carter, Elizabeth W., 2575
Carter, Elsie P., 9780
Carter, Ernie, 7303
Carter, Evelyn, 5757
Carter, George P., 1671
Carter, Herbert M., 9503
Carter, James A., 9288
Carter, Jennifer, 9632
Carter, Jimmy Dick, 4823
Carter, Jimmy, Hon., 7019
Carter, John B., Jr., 2462
Carter, John S., Jr., 8368
Carter, K., 7470
Carter, Karen S., 4834
Carter, Kathleen, 2525
Carter, Ken, 3651
Carter, Kirsten, 3517
Carter, Kristen A., 8493
Carter, Larry, 5134
Carter, Lary, 402
Carter, Lee A., 7443
Carter, Leigh H., 7509
Carter, Letitia M., 8368
Carter, Liane S., 6312
Carter, Linda, 5047
Carter, Linda B., 2034
Carter, M., 7470
Carter, Maureen, 500
Carter, Michael, 3317, 8603
Carter, Mollie H., 3524
Carter, N.B., 8752
Carter, Nick, 3575
Carter, Norman M., Jr., 8322
Carter, Prudence L., 6093
Carter, Richard J., Jr., 5551
Carter, Robert, 9000
Carter, Robert S., Jr., 1647
Carter, Ron, 7202
Carter, S. Theresa, 7601
Carter, Steven M., 9874
Carter, Susan, 4795
Carter, Susan M., 2468, 2554
Carter, Timothy L., 4743
Carter, Travis J., 8705
Carter-Robertson, Kira, 4357
Carter-Thomas, Karen, 500
Cartier Charitable Foundation, 782
Cartier, Barbara, 294, 296
Cartinella, Sherrie, 5157
Carto, David D., 7630
Cartwright, David W., 270
Cartwright, Herbert L., 8650
Cartwright, Herbert L., III, 8647
Cartwright, Maggie, 7992
Carty, Dave, 2435
Carusi, Bruce, 5116, 5675
Carusi, Bruce J., 5675
Carusi, Sue, 5116
Carusi, Susan Altamore, 5675
Caruso, Christina J., 382
Caruso, Francesco, 9643
Caruso, Gloria G., 382
Caruso, Henry J., 382
Caruso, Marc A., 382
Caruso, Mike, 7859
Caruso, Rick J., 382
Caruso, Tina P., 382
Caruth, W.W., III, 8909
Caruth, W.W., Sr., Mrs., 8909
Caruthers, Carol R., 4802
Carvel 1991 Trust, Agnes, The, 5749
Carvel Unitrust Remainderman, Thomas, 5749
Carvel, Agnes, 5749
Carvel, Thomas, 5749
Carver, Betsy, 9404
Carver, Gregory, 9404
Carver, John A., 3416
Carver, Martin G., 3416
Carver, Roy J., Jr., 3416
Carver, Roy J., Sr., 3416
Carvin, Lorrie Hulston, 4911
Casabona, Joseph E., 1404
Casagrande, Genevieve, 4928
Casalou, Allan, 533
Casamento, Laura, 5805
Casarotto, David, 2656
Casavant, Arthur F., 1671
Cascade Lounge Corp., 5016
Cascade Natural Gas Corp., 7354
Cascapara, Judy, 9056
Cascella, Michael, 2944
Cascepara, Judy, 965
Cascone, Brian J., 2013
Cascone, Elizabeth B., 2013
Cascone, Michael J., 2013
Cascone, Michael, Jr., 2013
Cascone, Steven D., 2013
Casdin, Susan S. Block, 1998
Case, Barb, 4342
Case, Daniel H., 383
Case, Gregory C., 2667
Case, Jean N., 1891
Case, Mary Lou, 4585
Case, Patti, 9605
Case, Peter G., 3670
Case, Stacey B., 383
Case, Stephen M., 1891
Casell, Karl, 3417
Casellas, Gilbert F., 5415
Caselli, Richard J., 111
Casey Family Grants Program, 4869
Casey Family Programs, 3898, 9596
Casey Foundation, Annie E., The, 4869
Casey Trust, Iris, 5927
Casey, A. Michael, 331, 580
Casey, Ann E., 9897
Casey, Annie E., 3745
Casey, Betty Brown, 3746
Casey, Carol, 1302
Casey, David, 9481
Casey, J. Robert, 4082, 4141
Casey, James E. "Jim", 3745
Casey, Jean K., 301, 580
Casey, Jeffrey A., 8821
Casey, John A., 9802
Casey, Kevin M., 7989
Casey, Lyman H., 331
Casey, Marian M., 9105
Casey, Michael, 8914
Casey, Michael J., 423, 918, 1349
Casey, Paul C., 4003
Casey, Phillip, 2040
Casey, R. Dennis, 5750
Casey, R.R., III, 8867
Casey, Sarah O'Herron, 1660
Casey, Terrence W., 8152
Cash, Ashley B., 8754
Cash, Clay Collin, 8754
Cash, Harvey Berryman, 8778
Cash, Michelle, 5411
Cash, Roy Don, 8754
Cash, Sondra Kay, 8754
Cash, Terry L., 8501
Cashaw, Allan, 7990
Cashdan, Lisa, 9375
Cashdin, Jeffrey, 9865
Cashin, Arthur D., Jr., 6573
Cashin, Steve, 4614
Cashion Living Trust, Howard, 3257
Cashman, Carol, 8817
Cashman, Chistopher, 8106
Cashman, Stephanie, 1393
Cashman, Timothy, 5126
Cashmore, Judith A., 5261
Casias, Ed, 1511
Casimir-Lambert, Charles, 5300
Casimir-Lambert, Pierre, 5300
Casini, Marlene A., 7431
Caslelaw, Jenny, 9221
Cason, Dallas G., 973, 1120
Cason, Edgar F., 3620
Cason, Flora C., 3620
Cason, Stacy, 3620
Cason, William H., II, 8468
Caspall, Ken, 4943
Casparino, Michael J., 1671
Casper, David R., 3105
Casper, Gerhard, 3186
Casper, Gertrude R., 9827
Casper, William J., 9827
Caspersen, Finn M.W., Jr., 1759
Cass Productions, 396
Cass, Florence, 6352
Cass, Richard W., 3726
Cassady, Lori, 4670
Cassar, George V., Jr., 4554
Cassel, Christine K., 6105
Cassel, Rita Allen, 5191
Casselman, Beth, 3279
Casselman, Elizabeth A., 3275
Cassels Charitable Lead AnnuityTrust I, Rosalie O., 8467
Cassels Charitable Lead AnnuityTrust II, Rosalie O., 8467
Cassels, Charlotte, 8467
Cassels, Charlotte R., 8467
Cassels, Merryman, 7179
Cassels, William Tobin, III, 8467
Cassels, William Tobin, Jr., 8467
Cassens, Raphaelle, 5161
Cassese, John, 8383
Cassett, Louis N., 7969
Cassidy, Tom, 3346
Cassin, B.J., 853
Cassinelli, Deborah, 2346
Cassinelli, Filippo, 9377
Cassity, Colleen, 991
Cassling, Mike, 5074
Cassuto, Isadore, 5567
Castagna, Robert J., 3957
Casteel, Beth, 7991

Casteel, Chip, 4888
Casteel, Lauren Y., 1401
Castel, P. Kevin, Hon., 6148
Castellini, Robert H., 7399
Castellini, Susan F., 7399
Castellon, Margarita T., 2034
Castiel, Matilde, 4327
Castillo, Dan, 5518
Castillo, Ernesto, 5096
Castillo, Gloria, 2831
Castillo, Herb, 420
Castillo, Katherine, 4454
Castle Equity Group, LLC, 6166
Castle Foundation, 6668
Castle Hills Development Corp., 8756
Castle, Alfred L., 2594
Castle, Harold K.L., 2593
Castle, Harold K.L., Mrs., 2593
Castle, Mary, 2594
Castle, Mike, 9916
Castle, Samuel N., 2594
Castleman, Marilyn, 5927
Castleman, Peter M., 5107
Castleman, Sloane C., 5107
Castles, John W., 9689
Castor, Betty, 2040
Castor, Bruce L., 8336
Castori, Pamela, 1708
Castro, Abel, 8994
Castro, Ida, 8275
Castro, Martin R., 2746
Castro, Michael J., 458
Castro, Ricardo A., 6004, 6593
Castro-Matukewicz, Cristina, 5074
Castruccio, Louis M., 825
Casty, Ronald G., 3976
Caswell, Alexander L., 3950
Caswell, Jonathan, 3950
Caswell, Philip, 3950
Caswell, Ward Slocum, 3950
Catalano, Joe, 7272
Catalina Assocs., 672
Catalina Island Conservancy, 1132
Catania, Angelo, 5394
Catanzaro, Michael J., 1631
Cate, Ruth L., 8459
Catell, Robert B., 5718, 6527
Catellus Land & Development Corporation and Subsidiaries, 1485
Caterpillar Inc., 2738, 4254
Cates, Alan, 8597
Cates, Andy, 8610
Cates, David C., 3335
Cates, G. Staley, 8616
Cates, Irene Jones, 5396
Cates, M.L., Sr., 8456
Cates, Rodney, 8994
Cates, Sheryl, 8994
Cates, Staley, 8610
Cates, Steve, 9251
Cates, Vicki, 5091
Cathay Bank, 385
Cathcart-Rake, Ruth, 3540
Cathers, Debra L., 319
Catherwood, Susan W., 8220
Cathey, Aaron, 5529
Cathey, Catharine Mellon, 8172, 8173
Cathy, Donald M., 2577
Cathy, S. Truett, 2577
Catlin, John "Jack", 2746
Catlin, Robin, 3755
Cato, Hal, 8640
Cato, Jessica, 1383
Cattarulla, Elliot R., 6449, 9051
Catto, Elizabeth Pettus, 1383
Catto, Henry, 1383
Catto, William Halsell, 1383
Cattran, Cynthia L., 4340
Catz, Safra A., 991
Caudill, Jeffrey, 5751
Caudill, Sarah, 5751
Caudill, Susan S., 5751
Caudill, W. Lowry, 5751
Caudill, Walter Lowry, 5751
Caufield, Frank J., 386
Caufield, Frank R., 386
Caufield, Kirsten N., 386
Caufman, Ron, 9631
Caughlin, Thomas F., 2889
Caughman, Rita Bragg, 8468
Cauldwell, Charles M., 1819
Caulfield, E. Michael, 5232
Caulfield, Gary, 2602
Caulfield, Gary L., 2598
Caulfield, James H., 5232
Caulton-Harris, Helen, 3953
Causby, Cindy, 7181
Causey, C. Chad, 4827
Cauthen, Irvin L., 8478
Cavaco, Isabella, 5312
Cavagna, Joseph F., 3844
Cavalcanti, Glynda, 3
Cavalier Club LLC, 9452
Cavallaro, Alfred, 5737, 6209
Cavallaro, Liz, 5757
Cavallaro, Peter I., 6826
Cavalletto Charitable Lead Annuity Trust, Dale H., 387
Cavalletto Charitable Lead Annuity Trust, George A., 387
Cavalletto Charitable Lead Unitrust, George A., 387
Cavalletto Family Trust, George and Dale, 387
Cavalletto Non Exempt Marital Trust, George A., 387
Cavalletto, Daniel R., 387
Cavan, Sarah P., 3308
Cavanagh, Geri J., 110
Cavanagh, Harry J., Jr., 110
Cavanagh, Michael, 110
Cavanah, Cindy, 4996
Cavanaugh, Jim, 9897
Cavanaugh, Kathleen M., 4420
Cavanaugh, March A., 5627
Cavanaugh, Nancy R., 5995
Cavanaugh, Paul V., 9627
Cavanaugh, Philip G., 5627
Cavanaugh, Sarah, 9722
Cavanaugh, Sean A., 5627
Cavanaugh, Tim, 9722
Cave, Lori, 5067
Cavender, Richard, 4872
Cavendish, Michael, 9769
Caveney, Ken, 1153
Caviness, Terry, 8660
CAW 1966 Trust, 4634
CAW 1968 Trust, 4634
CAW 1969 Trust C, 4634
CAW 1972 Trust, 4634
CAW Charitable Unitrust, 4634
Cawley, Wesley G., 8280
Cawood, Benjamin, 2423
Cawood, Frank, 2423
Cawood, Gayle, 2423
Cawood, Joseph, 2423
Cawood, Mimi, 2423
Cawsl Enterprises, Inc., 8119
Cawthon, Catherine A., 4451
Cay, Christopher, 2548
Caye, C.G. "Pete", Jr., 2434
Caye, Charles G., Jr., 2514
Cayhesse, 9024
Cayne, Richard, 5903, 6357
Cayre Irrevocable Grantor Trust, Grace, 5753
Cayre Irrevocable Grantor Trust, Jack K., 5753
Cayre Irrevocable Grantor Trust, Michelle, 5753
Cayre Irrevocable Grantor Trust, Nathan, 5753
Cayre Irrevocable Grantor Trust, Rachel, 5753
Cayre, Daniel, 5752
Cayre, Frieda, 5755
Cayre, Grace, 5752
Cayre, Grace K., 5753
Cayre, Grace S., 5755
Cayre, Jack, 5752
Cayre, Jack K., 5753
Cayre, Joseph, 5752
Cayre, Kenneth, 5752, 5753
Cayre, Lillian, 5753
Cayre, Michael, 5752, 5754
Cayre, Michelle, 5753
Cayre, Nathan, 5753
Cayre, Raquel, 5753
Cayre, Shirley, 5754
Cayre, Stanley, 5752, 5755
Cayre, Steven, 5752
Cayre, Trina, 5752
Cayton, Andrea Goldrich, 607
Cayton, Barry, 607
Caywood, Calvin, 7672
CB&T, 21
CC Myers, Inc., 293
CD Associates, 3773
CDC of Health and Human Services Dept., 6024
Cearley, Michael, 3554
Cecere, Andrew, 4784
Cecere, Joe, 8097
Cecere, Rebecca, 8097
Cech, Thomas, 3833
Cecil, Alec, 6226
Cecil, Art, 3851
Cecil, Donald, 6226
Cecil, Jane, 6226
Cecil, John F.A.V., 7195
Cecil, Larry G., 7640
Cecil, Leslie, 6226
Cedar Brook 2005 L.P., 5468
Cedar Brook 3 Corporate Center L.P., 5468
Cedar Brook 5 Corporate Center L.P., 5468
Cedar Funding Trust, 4017
Cedar Rapids Bank & Trust, 3449
Ceddia, Anthony F., 8272
Cederwall, Eric, 9578
Cedillo-Perez, Liz, 8795
Cejas, Pablo, 2238
Celebron-Brown, Alli, 7202
Celedinas, Ray S., 2032
Celerina Holdings, 1897
Celeste, Richard, 1418
Celico, Kristi P., 3276
Celio, Elizabeth, 2986
Celio, Elizabeth Lumpkin, 2986
Cella, Richard A., 4194
Celli, Ellen Unterberg, 5604
Cellino, A.M., 6526
Cellular South, Inc., 4817
Celorio, Alicia, 2065
Celorio, Justino, 2065
CEMEX Corp., 8757
Cenex Harvest States Cooperatives, 4636
CENEX, Inc., 4636
Centene Management Company, LLC, 4870
Centennial Foundation, 6891
Centennial State Banking Assn., 8741
Centeno-Gomez, Diana, 7639
Center Care Health, 9250
Center for Aids Research Education and Services - Sacramento, 378
Center, Hugh Stuart, 388
Center, Steve, 237
Centerior Energy Corp., 7455
Centerplate, 4196
CentiMark Corp., 7970
Central Financial Svcs., Inc., 2245
Central Indiana Community Foundation, 3317
Central Maine Power Co., 3693
Central Mills, Inc., 5768
Central Mouldings Corp., 7638
Central National-Gottesman, Inc., 5756
Central Pacific Bank, 2595, 2607
Central Shares Corp., 8599
Central Trust & Investment Co., 4964
Central Trust Bank, 4968
Central-Med Distribution Inc., 2091
Centre Island Properties, 9024
Centrella, Roy R., 5149
Centunan Management, Corp., 5702
Century 21, Inc., 5758
Ceperley, Rebecca, 9780
Ceran, Jennifer, 493
Cerciello, Amy, 5826
Cerf, Elizabeth Weintz, 6132
Cernera, Anthony J., 6349, 6705
Cerow, Michael S., 2033
Cerrone, Pamela, 6658
Cerruti, Dominique, 6573
Certain, Jackie, 3280
Ceryanec, Joseph H., 3463
CES Mgmt., Inc., 9534
Cessna Aircraft Co., The, 2272
Cessna Foundation, Inc., 8446
Cessna, Jodi, 7971
Cestare, Thomas D., 7936
Cestello, Louis R., 3725, 3726
Cestone, Maria A., 7976
Cestone, Maria A., II, 7975
Cestone, Michele J., 7975, 7976
Cestone, Ralph M., 7976
CFA Properties, Inc., 2577
Ch Robinson Company, 4779
CH2M Hill, 1384
Ch2M Hill, 9606
CH2M Hill Companies, Ltd., 1384
Chabraja, Eleanor, 2016
Chabraja, Nicholas, 2016
Chace, Helen Clay, 8049
Chace, Richard, 5171
Chada Foundation, 5937
Chadaz, Brian D., 9307
Chaddick, Elaine M., 2740
Chaddick, Harry F., 2740
Chadick, Gary R., 3477
Chadwick, Dorothy J., 5760
Chadwick, Douglas, 5783
Chadwick, John W., 5394

Chadwick, Laura Farish, 8838
Chadwick, Patricia W., 8356
Chadwick, Shirley J., 9285
Chafetz Group LLC, 3979
Chafetz, Howard, 3979
Chafetz, Irwin, 3979
Chafetz, Laurence, 3979
Chafetz, Roberta, 3979
Chaffee, Fred, 101
Chaffee, Paul, 4532
Chaffin, Donald J., 7798
Chaffin, Jim, 2123
Chaffin, Lawrence, Jr., 1284
Chafuen, Alejandro A., 9406
Chahine, Toufic, 8981
Chaho, Joseph B., 1613
Chaho, Michael B., 1613
Chaifetz, Malcolm, 5361
Chaikin, Wendy Blank, 5682
Chaimov, John, 3417
Chain, John T., Jr., Genl., 2955
Chait, Gerald, 8055
Chakko, M., 1258
Chalkley, Michael, 7272
Challenge Foundation, Inc., 7893
Challenge Me Now, 6042
Chamberlain Group, Inc., The, 2809
Chamberlain, Charles C., 6754
Chamberlain, David, 517
Chamberlain, David K., 6406
Chamberlain, Karin, 517
Chamberlain, Kathryn C., 6754
Chamberlain, Thomas, 7992
Chamberlin, Nat, 4171
Chamberlin, Stephen W., 389
Chamberlin, Susan C., 389
Chambers, Anne Cox, 2425, 2445
Chambers, Caroline E., 4368
Chambers, Carolyn Silva, 7832
Chambers, Constance E., 390
Chambers, Elizabeth, 7832
Chambers, Evelyn H., 1385
Chambers, Florence, 3621
Chambers, James Cox, 2425
Chambers, John T., 390
Chambers, Karla S., 7845
Chambers, M. Susan, 210
Chambers, Merle C., 1385
Chambers, Michael, 7630
Chambers, Raymond G., 5377
Chambers, Ronald J., 7771
Chambers, Scott D., 7832
Chambers, Silva L., 7832
Chambers, T. Edgar, 5275
Chambers, William D., 9780
Chamblee, Roland, Jr., 3289
Chambliss, Wendell J., 9435
Chamerlin, Katie, 4171
Champ, Kathryn L., 1980
Champ, Regis G., 7924
Champagne, Rene R., 3273
Champagne, Teresa I., 3273
Champer, Jeanne M., 4941
Champlin, George S., 8370
Chan, Allen, 6719, 7230
Chan, Amy H. Caplow, 6752
Chan, Annie M.H., 512
Chan, Ben, 4432
Chan, Cam, 849
Chan, Chi-Chao, 841
Chan, Deborah, 6400
Chan, Gerald, 4183
Chan, Ida Lopez, 414
Chan, Kenyon, 841
Chan, Michele, 391
Chan, Paul, 5360
Chan, Paul H., 1374
Chan, Ronnie, 4183
Chan, Stephen, 3956
Chan, Ted, 1108
Chancy, Mark A., 9539
Chandlee, Chad, 3421
Chandler, Bert, 157
Chandler, C.L., Jr., 2426
Chandler, Carol, 549
Chandler, Charles Q., IV, 3522
Chandler, Christine, 5518
Chandler, Edward K., 3172
Chandler, Ellen B., 1552
Chandler, Joy, 8120
Chandler, Jr. Charitable Remainder Trust, C.L., 2426
Chandler, Kay, 1108
Chandler, Linda, 3379
Chandler, Mark, 2426
Chandler, Mary, 3292
Chandler, Ralph B., 38
Chandler, Richard B., Jr., 2433
Chandler, Stephen M., 1280
Chandler, Walker, 2426
Chandley, Brian M., 4327
Chandra, Suresh, 7180
Chaney, Carla, 9000
Chaney, Hulet, 8634
Chang, Andrew I.T., 2604
Chang, Claire, 4715
Chang, Debbie, 2390
Chang, Hemmie, 4061
Chang, Jae Min, 809
Chang, Kevin, 8383
Chang, Sofia, 6982
Chang-Muy, Fernando, 8175, 8333
Channell, R. Faye, 9787
Channer, Barron, 2238
Channing, Susan Stockard, 2105, 2106
Chao Family Trust, 394
Chao, Albert, 2741
Chao, Amy, 394
Chao, Anne S., 8917
Chao, James, 2741
Chao, Jessica, 6003
Chao, Ping, 394
Chao, Ryan, 3745
Chao, Wei-Fong Chu, 2741
Chaolley, 7446
Chaolley Limited Partnership, 7460
Chapel, John, 9410
Chapelard, Frederic, 5190
Chapin, Charles M., III, 5490
Chapin, Michelle, 2015
Chapin, Samuel C., 7218, 7290
Chapin, Terry D., 1251
Chapin, William H., 8535
Chapla, Robert, 4369
Chaplin, Arlene, 2017
Chaplin, Chuck, 6451
Chaplin, Harvey R., 2017, 2347
Chaplin, Karen, 2017
Chaplin, Monica, 2017
Chaplin, Paul, 2017
Chaplin, Paul B., 2017, 2347
Chaplin, Wayne, 2017
Chaplin, Wayne E., 2347
Chapman & Associates, 395
Chapman High School, 8485
Chapman Nebraska Land, Mark A., 8761
Chapman Royalty, Mark A., 8761
Chapman, Annette, 4343
Chapman, Benson J., 8162
Chapman, Brian, 4152
Chapman, Carl L., 3394
Chapman, Christopher, 2232
Chapman, Colleen, 5138
Chapman, Constance, 9651
Chapman, Daniel H., 9019
Chapman, Don, 7846
Chapman, Drupgyu Anthony, 7010
Chapman, Elizabeth W., 3399
Chapman, Gerald S., 395
Chapman, Gregory S., 395
Chapman, H.A., 7739
Chapman, Howard L., 3399
Chapman, Jefferson, 8560
Chapman, Jens R., 7916
Chapman, John S., 2874
Chapman, Mark A., 8761
Chapman, Mary K., 7739, 7740
Chapman, Norman H., 8485
Chapman, Patricia Tynan, 654
Chapman, Peter R., 7096
Chapman, Philip, 5967
Chapman, Robert, 2514
Chapman, Robert H., 8485
Chapman, Roxanne B., 864
Chapman, Stephen, 3399
Chapman, Susan, 5967, 7096
Chapoton, John E., 1890
Chappel, Donald R., 7814
Chappell, Inajo Davis, 7406
Chaprnka, Karen A., 4467
Charach, Jeffrey, 4490
Charach, Manuel, 4490
Charach, Natalie, 4490
Charaf, Ricardo J., 9377
Charboneau, Donna, 4360
Charboneau, Kenneth, 4360
Charboneau, Kent, 4360
Charboneau, Michael, 4360
Charbonnet, J. Storey, 3644
Charbonnet, J. Story, 3648
Charbonnet, John D., 3631
Charbonnet, Michael D., 3631
Chardan Capital, 1850
Charitable Lead Annuity Trust 1, 4767
Charitable Lead Annuity Trust 2, 4767
Charitable Lead Annuity Trust A, 5973
Charitable Lead Annuity Trust B, 5973
Charitable Lead Annuity Trust C, 5973
Charitable Lead Annuity Trust D, 5973
Charitable Lead Annuity Trust E, 5973
Charitable Lead Annuity Trust under H. Gershman Survivors Trust, 575
Charitable Lead Trust, The, 4487
Charitable Lead Unitrust under Harold Gershman Survivors Trust, 575
Charitable Remainder Trust, Rieker, 2648
Charitable Remainder Unitrust U/W/O John Tyler, 8322
Charitable Trust dated 4/28/83, 6051
Charitable Trust No. 2, 4559
Charitable Trust, Roger O. Brown, 2931
Charitable Trusts 16, P. Guth, 7612
Charities Aid Foundation, 426
Charity Buzz, 1850, 1943
Charity Folks, Inc., Inc., 6573
Charles Apartments Assoc LLC, Park, 9452
Charles D. McCrary Family, The, 1
Charles Schwab Bank, 1841
Charles Schwab Bank, N.A., 1841
Charles Towers LLC, 9452
Charles, Amanda, 7698
Charles, Joseph, 6049
Charles, Kris, 4475
Charles, Marion Oates, 5917
Charles, Thomas, 8040
Charles, Willis, 3362
Charlotte Hornets, The, 8627
Charlson, Lynn L., 4633
Charlton, E.P., II, 8372
Charlton, Kenneth E., 685
Charlton, Robert W., 4522
Charlton, Stacey, 8372
Charney, Jack G., 364
Charreton, Didier, 8679
Charter Manufacturing Co., Inc., 9829
Charter One Bank, 8374
Charters, Amy G., 3456
Chartock, Lewis, 4973
Chartrand, Gary R., 2018
Chartrand, Jeffrey, 2018
Chartrand, Meredith, 2018
Chartrand, Nancy J., 2018
Charwat, Eleanor, 5808
Chase Charitable Lead Annuity Trust, W. Rowell, 1753
Chase Enterprises Holdings LLC, 1556
Chase Enterprises Inc., David T., 1556
Chase Manhattan Bank, The, 6244
Chase Oil Co., 5517
Chase, Alison Mason, 1753
Chase, Anthony, 8917
Chase, Barbara K., 1753
Chase, Beverly F., 5579
Chase, Cara, 9251
Chase, Chad, 9151
Chase, Cheryl A., 1555
Chase, Cheryl Anne, 1555
Chase, Cheryl O., 9406
Chase, Colton Hoover, 7491
Chase, Dave, 1753
Chase, David T., 1555, 1556
Chase, Dawn K., 1753
Chase, Deb, 5517
Chase, Derwood S., Jr., 9406
Chase, Diann, 9151
Chase, Edith, 1566
Chase, Johanna B., 9406
Chase, John M., Jr., 4401
Chase, John S., 9151
Chase, Karla, 5517
Chase, Lavinia B., 4263
Chase, Lee J., III, 8530
Chase, Lee Molen, 1753
Chase, Mack C., 5517
Chase, Marilyn Y., 5517
Chase, Missy, 9485
Chase, Rhoda L., 1556
Chase, Richard, 5517
Chase, Robert, 5517
Chase, Rodney, 525
Chase, Sandy L., 525
Chase, Stuart F., 9406
Chase, Susan L., 8043
Chase, W. Rowell, 1753
Chase, William J., 4027
Chasin, Charlie, 6507
Chasin, Laura, 7009
Chasman, Paul, 9761
Chastain, James G., 4838
Chastain, Linda, 3398
Chastain, Merritt B., Jr., 3657
Chatam, Inc., 5185
Chatham Hill Foundation, 9229

Chatham Investment Partners, LLC, 2821
Chatham Ventures, Inc., 6244
Chatham, Lucy Hanes, 7268
Chatlos, Janet, 2019
Chatlos, William F., 2019
Chatlos, William J., 2019
Chatlos, William J., III, 2019
Chatman, Michael, 4872
Chattem, Inc., 8576
Chatterjee Charitable Foundation, 6951
Chatterjee, Purnendu, 5765
Chatterjee, Siddarth, 6211
Chatterton, James R., 9954
Chattooga Partners Fund, 2514
Chatzinoff, Howard, 7062
Chau, Micheline, 367, 855
Chau, Wayne, 6997
Chau, Windon, 9089
Chaudoin, Don, 3402
Chavez, Cile, 1374
Chavez, Joann, 4410
Chavez, John F., 809
Chavez, Monte, 1153
Chavez, Oscar, 420
CHAW 2012 Charitable Trust, 4634
Chazan, Cindy, 7713
Chazanoff, Lucille, 6568
Chazen & Graf Repetti & Co., Jerome, LLP, 5767
Chazen Museum of Art, 5707
Chazen, Jerome, 5767, 5976
Chazen, Simona, 5767
Cheatham, Elizabeth, 7209
Chebbani, Ahmad, 4371
Checchia, Anthony P., 8236
Cheek, Georgia L., 1449
Cheek, Yvonne, 4617
Cheers, Pennie Gonseth, 3481
Cheetham, Philippa, 6904
Cheever, Charles A., 4025
Cheever, Daniel S., 4157
Chehebar Family Foundation, Joseph, 5768
Chehebar, Abraham Y., 5769
Chehebar, Albert, 5768
Chehebar, Gabriel Y., 5769
Chehebar, Jack, 5768
Chehebar, Joseph, 5768, 5769
Cheiftain, 3454
Cheil Communications America, Inc., 782
Chelan Fresh Marketing, 3245
Chell, Jeffrey W., 7214
Chemaly, John P., 4152
Chemers, Martin M., 418
Chemical Investments, Inc., 6244
Chemung Canal Trust Co., 6578
Chemung Canal Trust Company, 5679
Chen, Albert, 841
Chen, Alex, 1011
Chen, Alice Huan-mei, 4016
Chen, Chi Yueh, 6166
Chen, Ida K., 8035
Chen, Iris, 6368
Chen, Karen S., Ph.D., 6898
Chen, Kent, 5507
Chen, Lincoln C., 3982
Chen, Stanley, 1346
Chen, Timothy, 514
Chen, Vivian, 7425
Chen, Wan-Ju, 5507
Chen, Wen Chi, 514
Chen, Winston H., 1011
Chen, Y.C., 6959
Chen, Yueh Chuen, 6960
Chen-Courtin, Dorothy, 4152
Chenault, Kenneth I., 5588, 5684
Cheney Trust, Elizabeth F., 2745
Cheney, Amy L., 7404
Cheney, Ben B., 9598
Cheney, Bradbury F., 9598
Cheney, Carolyn J., 9598
Cheney, Daniel L., 5237
Cheney, Eleanora L., 5237
Cheney, James A., 2488
Cheney, Jeffrey P., 9884
Cheney, Kathleen S., 2099
Cheney, Laura Stevenson, 9743
Cheney, Piper, 9598
Cheng, Andrew, 586
Cheng, Eva, 6144
Cheng, Linda Y.H., 1033
Cheng, Soua, 9833
Chenoweth, Chris, 548
Cherbec Advancement Foundation, 4802
Chernesky, Richard J., 7560
Cherng, Andrew, 1010
Chernick, Richard, 744
Chernick, Rick, 9855
Chernin, David, 5770
Chernin, John, 5770
Chernin, Margaret, 5770
Chernin, Megan, 5770
Chernin, Peter, 5770
Chernoff, Julie, 2826
Cherokee 2000 Investments, LLC, 7810
Cherp, Macon, 2495
Cherrier, Steve, 7153
Cherry Arms LLC, 9452
Cherry, Elyse, 3939
Cherry, James R., Jr., 6734
Cherry, Kimberley C., 8565
Chertavian, Kate, 4246
Cherundolo, John C., Hon., 5116
Chesapeake Energy Corp., 9001
Chesapeake Operating Co., 9001
Chesebrough, Donna, 966
Chesebrough, Robert N., III, 966
Chesed Congregation of America, 6336
Chesed Global Foundation, 5759
Cheslack, Brian G., 8794
Chesney, James D., 9122
Chesnoff, Adam, 1101, 1340
Chestang, Nicole M., 6087
Chester Square Partners LP, 1571
Chester, Jack, 2020
Chester-Tomiyasu, Judith, 2619
Chestnut Ridge LLC, 9452
Cheston, Shelia, 9498
Chetcuti, Angela M., 9904
Cheu, Leslie A., 7006
Cheung, Sharon, 491
Cheung, Virginia, 1893
Chevalier, Stephan J., 9971, 9972
Chevan, David, 5612
Cheves, Bettye A., 2505
Cheves, Cecil M., 2438, 2505
Chevron Corp., 4254
Chevron Corporation, 1935
Chevron U.S.A., Inc., 81
Chew, Barbara, 5750
Chew, Ching-Meng, 4651
Chewning, Thomas N., 9416
Chi, Vivian, 7829
Chi, YoungSuk "YS", 4036
Chia, Candice, 2021
Chia, Douglas K., 2021
Chia, Frances T.C., 2021
Chia, Katherine, 2021
Chia, Kitty S.H., 2021
Chia, Pei-Yuan, 2021
Chialdikas, Mike, 2921
Chiang, Anne, 1346
Chiang, Antony, 9615
Chiang, Bessie, 5774
Chiang, Gloria K., 453
Chiang, Helen, 5774
Chiang, Michael, 5774
Chiar, Paul, 1346
Chiaramonte, Cathe, 9407
Chiaramonte, Cheryle, 7379
Chiaramonte, Francis P., 9407
Chiaramonte, Francis P., III, 9407
Chiaramonte, Mark S., 9407
Chiaramonte, Michael J., 9407
Chiarito, Susan, Dr., 4848
Chicago Blackhawks Alumni Association, 2823
Chicago Board of Trade Foundation, 2823
Chicago Community Trust, The, 2747, 2761, 3013
Chicago Mercantile Exchange Trust, 2756
Chicago Mercantile Exchange, Inc., 2755
Chicago Tourism Fund, 3200
Chick-fil-A, Inc., 2577
Chidester, Colleen, 3758
Chief Oil & Gas, LLC, 9118
Chien, Shu, 298
Chiesa, Melanie, 1211
Chigier, Benjamin, 4039
Child Abuse Prevention Council, 417
Child, J. Timothy, 579
Child, Rex, 5007
Childears, Linda, 1399
Childers, Alfred G., 5751
Childree, Mike, 57
Children's Hunger Alliance, 3245
Children's Investment Fund, LP, The, 1557
Children's Investment Fund, Ltd., The, 1557
Children's Scholarship Fund, 7608
Childress, Dean, 8789
Childs Trust, Brian, 8665
Childs, Beverly, 9868
Childs, Bridget, 417
Childs, Bronwen A., 1558
Childs, James E., Dr., 1558
Childs, John D., 1558
Childs, John W., 1558
Childs, Richard S., Jr., Dr., 1558
Childs, Sam, 1563
Childs, Starling W., 1558
Chiles, Beth, 8591
Chiles, Douglas C., 8693
Chiles, Earle A., 7833
Chiles, Earle M., 7833
Chiles, Margaret C., 7380
Chiles, Virginia H., 7833
Chilman, Bill, 4512
Chilton, Elizabeth E., 9780
Chilton, Greg, 414
Chilton, Nelle, 9780
Chilton, Nelle Ratrie, 7144
Chilton, Philip N., 4856
Chin, Christy Remy, 481
Chin, Gwin Joh, 8306
Chin, James V., 4754
Chin, Julian, 9410
Chin, Linda, 3971
Chin, Wally, 2602
Chinea, Manuel, 3085
Ching, Catherine H.Q., 2596
Ching, Deborah, 385
Ching, Gerry, Mrs., 2612
Ching, Glenn, 2595
Chinn, Susan, 7588
Chinn, Timothy R., 1312
Chiota, John P., Hon., 1581
Chipotle Mexican Grill, Inc., 1388
Chirco, Melissa, 4345
Chirico, Emanuel, 6637
Chisholm Charitable Trust, Margaret A., 4818
Chisholm, A.F., 4818
Chisholm, E.G., 8373
Chisholm, M.A., 8373
Chisnell, Michael, 7382
Chisser, Jean, 3075
Chisser, Robert, 3075
Chisser, Robert Jean, 3075
Chitjian, Janice, 1028
Chitwood, Dewayne E., 8875
Chitwood, Melinda T., 9415
Chiu, Jennifer, 5569
Chiu, Kevin Y.T., 7415
Chiu, M.S., 711
Chiuchiarelli, Cheryl, 4394
Chivan, 1791
Chlapaty, Joseph A., 7411
Chmelnicki, Cila, 6664
Chmelnicki, Samuel, 6664
Cho, Ken, 9156
Choate, Ed, 184
Choate, Jill, 2236
CHOBANI, 3245
Chodor, Lawrence, 6918
Chodroff, Charles H., 8351
Choe, Martha, 9731
Chofnas, Eric S., 2415
Choi, Audrey, 6507
Choice Hotels International Services Corp., 3748
Chomiak, Sarah, 2803
Chong, Arthur, 349
Choo, Shinjoo, 8333
Choppin, Purnell W., 6333
Chopra, Deepak, M.D., 216
Chopra, Sandeep, 216
Chopus, Kelly, 9523
Chosky, Philip, 7980
Chosy, James L., 4784
Chou, Priscilla, 9599
Chou, Sunlin, 9599
Chou, Sunwen, 9599
Choucair, Bechara, 3110
Chouinard, Malinda P., 1017
Chouinard, Yvon, 1017
Chow, Edward, 841
Chow, Myra, 1109
Chow, Ronald G., 722
Chow, Winston K.H., 2598
Choy, Michael K.K., 67
Choy, Venus, 2615
Chrisman, Lance, 3257
Chrisman, Sarah L., 1124
Chrisoffersen, Terri, 3417
Christ Church, 9118
Christ, Chris T., 4350
Christ, Donald, 892
Christ, Henry J., 8351
Christen, Muffy, 8522
Christensen, Allen D., 399

Christensen, Barbara, 5039
Christensen, C. Diane, 399
Christensen, Carmen M., 399
Christensen, Clay, 7793
Christensen, Dale, 8522
Christensen, Douglas A., 7352
Christensen, Gary, 4761
Christensen, Gillian R., 5995
Christensen, Henry, III, 6174, 6473, 6853
Christensen, Maren, 6531
Christensen, Rhys, 1393
Christensen, Scott, 8521
Christensen, Stefanie K., 5094
Christensen, Sue E., 9850
Christenson, James E., 4470
Christenson, Nancy K., 7354
Christian Alliance for Humanitarian Aid, 8927
Christian Art Gifts, Inc., 4417
Christian Brothers Automotive Corp., 9470
Christian Business Network, 2087
Christian Foundation of the Triangle, The, 7873
Christian Health Ministries Foundation, 3612
Christian, Blake, 846
Christian, Carolyn McKnight, 4630
Christian, Cheryl, 2482
Christian, Dale, 9625
Christian, David A., 9422
Christian, Frank P., 9139
Christian, Harley, 149
Christian, John, 108
Christian, Lou, 7742
Christian, Paige, 5804
Christian, Parul, 9353
Christian, Ronald C., 7404
Christian, Ronald E., 3394
Christian, William R., 1350
Christianson, Craig, 9897
Christianson, David, 8512
Christianson, David O., 8512
Christianson, Julia, 8512
Christianson, Megan, 4667
Christianson, Tessa, 8512
Christianson, Theresa L., 4635
Christianson, Todd J., 8512
Christianson, Trudy, 8512
Christianson, Trudy A., 8512
Christianson, Warren G., 4635
Christie, Elizabeth W., 5483
Christie, Ellen, 4061
Christie, Kevin, 9576
Christman Irrevocable Trust, Anne, 7403
Christman, Chip, 7488
Christman, Jolley Bruce, 7240
Christman, Marc, 3100
Christmas Charitable Remainder Trust, R.L., 4123
Christophel, Randy, 3298
Christopher, Brent E., 8773
Christopher, Gail C., 4474
Christopher, Jay, 2748
Christopher, Jay W., 2748
Christopher, John, 1499
Christopher, Julie, 2748
Christopher, Mark M., 4120
Christopherson, Elizabeth G., 5191
Christopherson, Sue, 9889
Christu, Eric, 2096
Christy, Dana, 2585
Christy, Debbi, 3373
Christy, Jennifer, 7557
Chritton, Robert, 9923
Chroman, Susan E., 3491
Chromiak Testamentary Trust, Emerick, 5299
Chromiak, Mary V., 5299
Chronis, Amy, 1572
Chrysler Corp., 4366
Chrysler Financial Svcs., 783
Chrysler Group LLC, 4366
Chrysler, Harold Zeigler, 4529
Chrystyn-Opperman, Julie, 988
Chrzan, Janet C., 8341
CHS Inc., 4636
Chu, Benjamin K., 5800
Chu, Christina, 849
Chu, Hsieh-ho, 711
Chuang, Juichang, 5507
Chubb & Son, 293
Chubb, Hendon, 5229, 5490
Chubb, Percy, III, 5490
Chubb, Sally, 5490
Chueng, Ven T., 5507
Chugach Alaska Corp., 84
Chugach Alaska Regional Corp., 84
Chumley, Brenda, 4920
Chun Tiu, Celia Yuk, 7425
Chun, Michael J., 2588, 2604
Chun, Miyoung, 771
Chun, Tammi, 2602
Chung, Ray Jui Chuang, 5507
Church & Dwight Co. Inc., 4254
Church, John R., 4661
Church, Phillip E., 7178
Church, Steve A., 3334
Churchill, Clinton R., 2588
Churchill, Daniel, 2941
Churchill, Hugo, 7942
Churchill, Suzanne Smith, 2605
Churchman, Caroline A., 7955
Churchman, J. Alexander, 7955
Churchman, Lee Stirling, 7955
Churchman, Leidy McIlvaine, 7955
Churchman, W. Morgan, 7955
Chwat, Anne, 6206
Chwojnicki, Lauren, 4372
Ciafardini, Anthony, 7563
Ciampa, Dominick, 6543
Cianbro Companies, The, 3683
Cianbro Corp., 3683
Cianciotto, Melanie, 2235
CIBC Trust Co. (Bahamas) Ltd., 3095
CIBC Trust Co., Ltd., 3094
Cicatiello, Anthony, 5441
Cicchetti, Carl R., 1537
Ciccone, Madonna, 1058
Ciccone, Melanie, 1058
Cicconi, James W., 8675
Cicero, Richard J., 1878
Cicerone, Ralph J., 5747
Cicigoi, Robert, 7446
Ciciora, Susan, 3520
Cider Barrell, Inc., 3768
Cieloha, Julie D., 9689
Cieri, Mauro A., 7316
Cifrulak, Stephen, 4404
Ciga, LLP, 1468
Cigarroa, Francisco, 5994
Cigarroa, Graciela, 8676
Cigna, 9606
CIGNA Corp., 7981
Cimbalik, Marian L., 4549
Cimco Enterprises, Inc., 9623
Ciminelli, Annlouise, 5778
Ciminelli, Frank L., II, 5778
Ciminelli, Louis C., 5778
Ciminelli, Louis P., 5778
Ciminelli, Matthew, 5778
Ciminelli, Nina, 5778
Cimini, Ronald, 8040
Cimino, Anthony "Skip", 5411
Cimino, Audrey S., 3757
Cimmino, Susan L., 5381
Cincinnati Foundation, Greater, The, 3293
Cincinnati, New Orleans and Texas Pacific Railway Co., The, 9496
Cindrich, Robert J., 7966
Cinerama Inc., 1004
Cinergy Foundation, 7196
Cintani, Bill, 5063
Cintani, William, 5072
Ciocca, Arthur, 401
Ciocca, Carlyse, 401
Ciociola, Christina M., 1562
Cioffi, Meghan Walsh, 5436
Cioffi, Robert F., 5436
Ciokajlo, Gregory, 2774
Ciolfi, Deborah, 5663
Ciongoli, Adam G., 3344
Cipares, Tom, 3297
Cipollone, Tony, 3689
Cipperley, Cheri A., 3464
Ciprich, Paula M., 6526
Cirame, Graceann B., 4041
Ciresi, Ann C., 4637
Ciresi, Michael V., 4637
CIRI, Inc., 85
Cirone, Frank J., 8223
Cischke, Susan M., 4430
Cisco, 6532
Cisco Systems, Inc., 402
Ciskowski, Michael S., 9246
Cisneors, Gilbert R., 403
Cisneros, Gilbert, 403
Cisneros, Jacki, 403
Cisneros, Jacki Marie Wells, 403
Cisneros, Suzanne Ortega, 5533
Cistulli, Peter, 1063
Citation Homes Central, 977
CITC, 85
CITGO Petroleum Corporation, 8708
Citibank, N.A., 4457, 5780, 6487, 6626, 6924, 7004
Citicorp, 5780
Citicorp Trust, N.A., 47
Citigroup, 6544
Citigroup Global Impact Funding Trust, Inc., 6044
Citigroup Inc., 5780
Citigroup UK, 6904
Citigroup Venture Capital Ltd., 5780
Citizens Bank, 4051, 4414
Citizens Bank Mid-Atlantic Charitable Foundation, The, 8374
Citizens Bank of Rhode Island, 8374
Citizens Bank of Southern Pennslyvania, 8046
Citizens Business Bank, 657
Citizens Charitable Foundation, 8374
Citizens Energy Corp., 3985
Citizens of Southern Oklahoma, 7798
Citizens Savings Bank, 8374
Citizens Trust Co., 8374
Citrin, Jeffrey, 1559
Citrin, Rona Hollander, 1559
Citrix, 1153
Citrone, Neil, 2755
City Front Chicago, LLC, 2077
City National Bank of Charleston, 9780
City of Bainbridge, 2186
City of Chicago Charitable Giving Program, 2823
City of New York, The, 8586
City Spire Mgmt. Holidings, Inc., 2722
Citysights LLC, 6434
Citywide Banks, 1493
Civgin, Don, 2657
Civic Parkway Assocs., 3452
Cizik, Jane Morin, 8764
Cizik, Paula J., 8764
Cizik, Robert, 8764
CJS Partnership, 6803
CKGH Law, PC, 118
Ckodre, Gary, 9300
Clabaugh, Gavin T., 4510
Cladis, Nick R., 2105
Claeyssens Charitable Trust, 1344
Claeyssens, Ailene B., 1344
Claeyssens, Pierre P., 1344
Claflin, Janis A., 4420
Claiborne Inc., Liz, 5976
Claiborne, Catherine H., 9548
Clain, Michael J., 6068
Claire Foundation, Lili, Inc., The, 9865
Claire Sudler 2003 Trust, 5472
Clamer Trust, Guilliam, 7177
Clancey, Jerry, 7446
Clancy, Alexandra, 1900
Clancy, George P., Jr., 1925
Clancy, Maureen E., 6543
Clancy, Michael, 8336
Clancy, Thomas, 1900
Claneil Enterprises, Inc., 7982
Clannin, Robert J., 3745
Clanon, Paul, 1002
Clapham 1997 Rev. Trust, Mary, 2750
Clapham Trust No. 1, Mary D., 2750
Clapham, Clarence, 7533
Clapp Irrevocable Trust, Mary Lee, 9664
Clapp, Charles E., III, 4017
Clapp, Edelveis, 9682
Clapp, George H., 7983
Clapp, James N., II, 9682
Clapp, Margaret, 9682
Clapp, Matthew N., Jr., 9682
Clapp, Rebecca Greenleaf, 6901
Clapp, S. Daniel, 4971
Clapp, Tamsin O., 9682
Clapp, Wade, 7214
Clapper, Kellie, 3174
Clapttrap Trust, 5181
Clare, Alice, 9274
Clare, Christopher E., 5230
Clare, David R., 5230
Clarian Health, 7214
Clark Endowment, The, 3750
Clark Enterprises, Inc., 3750
Clark Family Foundation, 542
Clark, A. James, 3750
Clark, Agenia, 8532
Clark, Allen O., 8480
Clark, Amy Plant Statter, 8441
Clark, Andrew M., Dr., 6374
Clark, Angela, 8048
Clark, Angelica K., 1013
Clark, Benic M., III, 8599
Clark, Bill, 8558
Clark, Bobby, 1421
Clark, Brian, 4345
Clark, Brittney, 7834
Clark, Bruce E., 6903

Clark, C. Nathan, 2790
Clark, Carol, 7979
Clark, Celeste A., 4474
Clark, Charles, 3939
Clark, Christi, 9681
Clark, Collette, 367
Clark, Dan, 5013, 5062
Clark, Dave, 936
Clark, David, 4109
Clark, David W., 7552
Clark, Debbie D., 9563
Clark, Deborah D., 3242
Clark, Donald C., Sr., 2751
Clark, Edna McConnell, 5784
Clark, Elizabeth, 6692
Clark, Elizabeth G., 3751
Clark, Emily, 8072
Clark, Emory T., 9830
Clark, Etta, 8561
Clark, Florence B., 7787
Clark, Frank, 2827
Clark, Frank M., 2746
Clark, G. Thomas, 6077
Clark, Garret, 4345
Clark, Gary, 2039
Clark, Grace, 4822
Clark, Gretchen, 9421
Clark, H. Lawrence, 5784
Clark, Harris Whitlock, 3776
Clark, Hays, 3776
Clark, Hays Lawrence, 3776
Clark, J. H. Cullum, 8832
Clark, J.H. Cullum, 9013, 9112
Clark, James, 3503
Clark, James H., 2022
Clark, James K., 2022
Clark, James M., 6824
Clark, James M., Jr., 6824
Clark, James M., Mrs., 6824
Clark, James McConnell, 5784
Clark, James McConnell, Jr., 5784
Clark, James R., 4345
Clark, James, Jr., 6692
Clark, Jane B., 6499
Clark, Jane F., 5975
Clark, Jane Forbes, 5786
Clark, Jean W., 2751
Clark, Jessie Wilcox, 1643
Clark, John, 3986
Clark, John R., 5007
Clark, Jon, 332
Clark, Jonathan, 7445
Clark, Joseph P., II, 8351
Clark, Katherine, 4109
Clark, Kathleen, 6692
Clark, Kathy, 1268, 9091
Clark, Kelly Lynn, 8048
Clark, Kevin, 5185
Clark, Kevin G., 9484
Clark, Kim, 3991, 4109
Clark, Kristen, 8083
Clark, Larry W., 4828
Clark, Lawrence S., 1186
Clark, Len, 3400
Clark, Linda A., 1397
Clark, Lisa Marie, 8048
Clark, Lucille, 3503
Clark, Malcolm N., 7294
Clark, Marcella S., 7669
Clark, Margaret Barker, 3936
Clark, Margot, 3337
Clark, Marie, 5919
Clark, Mark, 3303
Clark, Mark T., 7455
Clark, Marshall, 8549
Clark, Marvin, 3398
Clark, Mary Chichester duPont, 1754
Clark, Mary H., 7834
Clark, Mary W., 8979
Clark, Maurie D., 7834
Clark, Midori, 1504
Clark, Nita, 8795
Clark, Nita C., 9112
Clark, Paul, 8660, 9109
Clark, Peggy, 199
Clark, Randy, 1211
Clark, Rhea P., 6692
Clark, Richard J., 7532, 7584
Clark, Richard M., 7834
Clark, Richard, Jr., 8048
Clark, Robert Sterling, 5785
Clark, Roger E., 1408
Clark, Rosamond, 3776
Clark, Sarah, 3579
Clark, Sonja, 5486
Clark, Stanley L., 2379
Clark, Stephen, 4109
Clark, Stephen W., 579
Clark, Susan, 4345
Clark, Susan Reed, 255
Clark, Thomas, 3578
Clark, Thomas R., 2751
Clark, Tim, 3313
Clark, Tim L., 5074
Clark, Tina S., 3612
Clark, Tracy A., 7834
Clark, Trent, 2632
Clark, W. Van Alan, 5784
Clark, W. Van Alan, Jr., 4109
Clark, Wendy, 2070
Clark, William, 4109
Clark, William C., III, 3861
Clark, William G., 6099
Clark-Johnson, Sue, 92
Clarkdale Estates, Inc., 6768
Clarke, Adam, 5067
Clarke, Amy, 2442
Clarke, Athalie R., 1182
Clarke, Bonnie A., 3861
Clarke, Carol, 5208
Clarke, Charles F., Jr., 3172
Clarke, Glenn, 6491
Clarke, Heather, 7345
Clarke, Jesse, 3861
Clarke, Kathleen M., 3016
Clarke, Lois A., 9546
Clarke, Sally, 5927
Clarke, Steven W., 3861
Clarke, Stuart A., 3897
Clarke, Theodore J., 1397
Clarke, William, 7182
Clarke, William C., III, 3861
Clarke, William C., III, Mrs., 3861
Clarke, William V.H., 8751, 9292
Clarkson Family Foundation, The, 6148
Clarkson, Andrew M., 8587
Clarkson, Bayard D., 6148
Clarkson, Carole G., 8587
Clarkson, John, 2235
Clarkson, William M., 8587
Clarkson, William, IV, 2449
Clarkton Estates, Inc., 6768
Claro, Cesar J., 6703
Clasquin, Lorraine, 8961
Class Act Arts, 3898
Class of 1961 Fund, 9578
Classen, Peter K., 8230
Classic Mix Partners, 9837
Classical Theatre of Harlem, 5967
Classon, Bruce, 4762
Claster, Mark, 1813
Claster, Susan, 1813
Claster, Susan B., 1813
Claton, Larry, 7971
Clatpag Trust, 5181
Clatscatt Trust, 5181
Clattaur Trust, 5181
Clattecam Trust, 5181
Clattesad Trust, 5181
Claud, Ernest, Jr., 9434
Claudepierre, Dale, 4448
Claugus, Melissa, 2461
Claugus, Thomas, 2461
Claugus, Thomas, II, 2461
Claus, Thomas H., 4378
Clauser, Ruth A., 8308
Clausing, W. Kirk, 7778
Clausman, Linette, 24
Clauson, Peter C., 5635
Clauss, Ben, 8474
Clay, Aaron, 1520
Clay, David, 3410
Clay, James, 7711
Clay, Jonathan C., 5410
Clay, Phillip L., 4479
Clay, Richard H.C., 3592
Clayborne, Michael K., 4822
Claybourn, Colleen, 9240
Claybourn, Joshua, 3394
Clayes III Living Trust, Joseph A.W., 404
Clayes, Trulette M., 404
Clayman, Bradford, 7984
Clayman, Deborah, 7984
Clayman, Roberta, 7984
Claypool, Jim, 414
Clayton Trust No. 1, Susan Vaughan, 9248
Clayton, B. Joe, 8547
Clayton, Elizabeth, 8498
Clayton, James L., 8547
Clayton, Janice K., 8547
Clayton, Kay, 8547
Clayton, Kevin T., 8547
Clayton, Lawrence, 6374
Clayton, Susan V., 8765
Clayton, Valerie, 8035
Clayton, William L., 8765
Clear Channel Communication Foundation, 9008
Clear with computers LLC, 9193
Clearing Corporation Trust Fund, 2752
Clearwater Equity Group, Inc., 4598
Cleary, Claudia, 8072
Cleary, Donald, 5601
Cleary, Gail K., 9831
Cleary, Kristine H., 9831
Cleary, Mary Ann, 959
Cleary, Patrick, 714
Cleary, Russell G., 9831
Cleary, Sandra G., 9831
Cleary, Teresa A., 2640
Cleaveland, Cliff, 8548
Cleaver, Dianne, 4937
Clegg, Cynthia H., 1644
Clegg, Jackie M., 1940
Cleland, Bruce, 3860
Cleland, Isobel, 3860
Clem, Toni, 3569
Clemens, Ethel M., 7835
Clemens, Rex, 7835
Clement, Dale, 8524
Clement, Dolly Plaster, 4957
Clement, Don K., 7353
Clement, J.C., Jr., 8971
Clement, Sally D., 4790
Clemente, C. L., 6633
Clemente, James F., 8275
Clements Foundation, B. Gill, 8766
Clements Foundation, Bill, 8766
Clements Foundation, Gigi, 8766
Clements, Carolyn, 3365
Clements, Maurice, 2644
Clements, Michael, 7321
Clements, Patricia L., 8767
Clements, Peter J., 4602
Clements, Rita, 9067
Clements, Robert, 7766
Clements, William P., Jr., 8766
Clemins, Archie, 4107
Clemons, Erin, 7417
Clemons, G. Scott, 157
Clemons, Sheila, 8634
Clendening, John, 1127
Clennon, Bart, 9604
Cless, Bryan C., 2753
Cless, Gerhard, 2753
Cless, Martin, 2753
Cless, Ruth I., 2753
Cless, Stephen G., 2753
Cleveland Electric Illuminating Co., The, 7455
Cleveland, Alfred, 7264
Cleveland, Barbara, 2561
Cleveland, Judy A., 9604
Cleveland, Levi, 88
Cleveland, Odell, Rev., 7180
Cleveland, Rose Ann, 1890
Cleveland-Cliffs Inc., 7407
Clevenger, Beth, 9796
Clevenger, Jerry, 3336
Click Charitable Lead Annuity Trust, 100
Click, Carrie W., 100
Click, Christian J., 100
Click, James H., 100
Click, James H., Jr., 100
Click, Vicki M., 100
Clif Bar & Co., 405
Cliff, Ursula, 6088, 6192
Cliff, Walter C., 6088, 6192
Clifford, Charles H., Jr., 819
Clifford, John P., Jr., 4783
Clifford, Linda M., 7602
Clifford, Michele, 1016
Clifford, Nancy L., 3337
Clifford, Robert C., 4738
Cliffs Natural Resources, 7407
CliffStar Corp., 2335
Clift, Edward, 2766
Climie, Judy, 3360
Cline, Adam K., 7252
Cline, Brenda K., 7252
Cline, Bud, 4448
Cline, Christopher, 2024
Cline, Junior, 4947
Cline, Mike, 3280
Cling, Michael D., 885
Clinkscale, M. Darnetta, 4966
Clinton Investment Co., 8458
Clinton, Bruce E., 2754
Clinton, Chelsea V., 5787
Clinton, Edward X., 2747
Clinton, Hillary Rodham, 5787
Clinton, Martha O., 2754
Clinton, William Jefferson, 5787
Clise, Al, 5119
Clive, Winifred Johnson, 406

Clodfelter, Daniel G., 7298
Cloonan, Brian, 5415
Clooney, Michael, 1753
Clore, Dale Ann, 7706
Clorox Co., The, 407
Close Charitable Lead Trust No. 2, Patricia, 8506
Close, Anne Springs, 8504
Close, Chuck, 5526
Close, Derick S., 8504, 8506
Close, Elliott S., 8504
Close, Frances A., 8504
Close, Francie, 8506
Close, H.W., 8504
Close, Katherine A., 8504
Close, Leroy S., 8506
Close, M. Scott, 8504
Closius, Sharon R., 1714
Cloud, Amanda, 9175
Cloud, Henry, 530
Cloud, John M., 7645
Cloud, Julia B., 8693
Cloud, Sanford, 1567
Cloud, Sanford, Jr., 1589
Cloud, Victoria, 530
Cloud, William J., 7771
Clough, Charles I., Jr., 4329
Clough, William P., III, 5676
Clouse, David, 1409
Clouse, Elizabeth L., 1409
Clouse, Elizabeth Lynn, 1409
Clouse, Matthew, 1409
Clouse, McKenzie, 1409
Clouse, Michael, 1409
Clouse, Robert, 4438
Cloutier, Clive, 3623
Clover Capital Mgmt., 7367
Clow, Reggie, 4679
Clowes, Alexander W., Dr., 3275
Clowes, Allen W., 3274, 3275
Clowes, Douglas S., 3275
Clowes, Edith W., 3275
Clowes, George H.A., 3275
Clowes, George H.A., Jr., 3275
Clowes, Jonathan J., 3275
Clowes, Margaret, 3275
Clubb, Sandy Hatfield, 3420
Cluck, Bruce W., 2829
Cluck, Frank D., Jr., 2829
Clulow Revocable Trust, Margaretta M., 8423
Clune, Dotty, 4412
Clunie, Heather, 3314
Cluster, Darryl W., 790
Clutts, James, 9108
Clutts, Jim, 9108
Cluverius, James K., 9457
Clyde, Calvin, Jr., 9285
Clyde, Thomas, 9285
Clyde, Wilfred W., 293
Clymer, Ray, 9277
Clyne, Richard A., 5117
CM Miesel Charitable Lead Annuity Trust, 2118
CME Group Inc., 3234
CMM Children Charitable Lead Annuity Trust, 2118
CMRCC, Inc., 6244
CNA Property Co., 1151
CNL Financial Group, Inc., 2025
Co RMS MGMT Company 50 Public Squar, 1847
Coach, Inc., 5790
Coale, Thomas G., 3759
Coate, Carol, 7569
Coates Trust, Vincent J., 408
Coates, C. Grant, 9026
Coates, Elizabeth Huth, 8769
Coates, J. Trevor, 408
Coates, Norman, 408
Coates, Philip, 5622
Coates, Stella, 408
Coates, Thomas K., 3760
Coats, Dell, 959
Coats, Lonnell, 5249
Coatsworth, John H., 6983
Coatue Charitable LLC, 5791
Coatue Management, LLC, 6319
Cobb, Barbara R., 8078
Cobb, Bradley, 2027
Cobb, Brent, 3417
Cobb, Charles E., Jr., 2026
Cobb, Christian M., 2026
Cobb, Darryl, 1387
Cobb, G. Elliott, Jr., 9434
Cobb, Henry N., 5585
Cobb, Kevin W., 4442
Cobb, Kolleen O., 2026
Cobb, Luisa S., 2026
Cobb, Patrick, 3449
Cobb, Patty, 59
Cobb, Rhoda W., 2027
Cobb, Sara B., 3331, 3342
Cobb, Steve, 365
Cobb, Sue M., 2026
Cobb, Susan, 4412
Cobb, Tobin T., 2026
Cobb, Tyrus R., 2427
Coberley, Charlotte, 4485
Coble, Christopher L., 3342
Coble, Paul Y., 7171
Coblentz, Lisa Y., 3758
Cobler, Larry, 4362
Coblitz, Richard, 7580
Coblitz, Rick, 7379
Coburn, Pip, 1469
Coca Cocal Bottling, 2294
Coca Cola Bottling Company NY, 1771
Coca-Cola Co., The, 2428, 8669
Cochran, Becky, 3253
Cochran, Eli, 8397
Cochran, Jan, 4194
Cochran, John R., III, 7985
Cochran, Patricia A., 7985
Cochrane, Charles G., 1063
Cochrane, Eugene W., Jr., 7195
Cochrane, Katharine C., 26
Cochrane, Nick, 3419
Cockayne Fund, 8612
Cockayne Fund, Inc., The, 3561
Cockerell, Martha, 4996
Cockerham, Chris, 3278
Cockerham, Sally, 3626
Cockrell, David A., 8770
Cockrell, Dula, 8770
Cockrell, Ernest D., II, 8770
Cockrell, Ernest H., 8770, 9268
Cockrell, Ernest, Jr., 8770
Cockrell, Ernie D., II, 8916
Cockrell, Janet S., 8770
Cockrell, Virginia H., 8770
Cockren, Robert W., 5430
Cockrum, Brigid Anne, 8986
Cocks, David, 5806
Cocotis, Paul A., 293
Coddington, Ricci, 617
Code, Adam, 2757
Code, Andrew W., 2757
Code, David, 2757
Code, Kevin, 2757
Code, Susan K., 2757
Codell, J. Hagan, 3598
Codey, John, 6160
Codrington, George W., 7409
Cody, Jean M., 4895
Cody, Nympha H., 6869
Cody, Tom, 598
Coe, Holly, 8873
Coelho, Rosemarie, 4173
Coen, Beverly J., 7596
Coen, Bill, 4943
Coen, Steve, 3524
Coenen, Pamela A., 9856
Cofer, Debs, 8775
Cofer, Susan Seydel, 2581
Coffey, Bruce, 9697
Coffey, Deeda M., 7187
Coffey, Greg, 2817
Coffey, Jeff, 7183
Coffey, Larry R., 3568
Coffey, Shelby, III, 1907
Coffey, Sherilee, 9588
Coffin, Alice S., 1558
Coffindaffer, Billy L., 9799
Coffman, Chad, 3314
Coffman, Cindy, 5039
Coffman, Elizabeth, 7691
Coffman, Faye, 2817
Coffman, Greg, 7421
Coffman, Joe, 8999
Coffman, Joyce, 2853
Coffman, Marcia, 2850
Coffman, Rick, 2644
Cofrin Irrevocable Trust, David A., 9800
Cofrin, David A., 9800
Cofrin, David H., 1735, 9800
Cofrin, Edith Dee, 1735
Cofrin, Gladys G., 1735
Cofrin, Mary Ann, 9800
Cofrin, Mary Ann H., 1735
Cofrin, Mary Ann Harn, 9800
Cofrin, Mary Ann P., 1735
Cofrin, Paige W., 1735
Cogan, Gregory, 3988
Cogan, John F., Jr., 3988
Cogan, Jonathan, 3988
Cogan, Michele M., 5185
Cogan, Peter G., 3988
Cogen, Mark A., 6944
Cogen, Ruth P., 6944
Coggin, Gerald, 8525
Coggin, Joan, Dr., 8527
Coggin, Joanne, 8525
Coggins, Christa, 5533
Coggins, Colleen M., 8421
Coghlan, Alicia, 5712
Coglianese, Marcy, 9916
Cognetti, Richard, 6285
Cognis Corp., 7383
Cogswell, Leander A., 5167
Cogswell, Susan, 4448
Cogswell, Wilton W., III, 1489
Cohan, Lucy, 6579
Cohasset Ltd., 9005
Cohen Family Foundation, Inc., The, 3303
Cohen Foundation, John S., The, 2028
Cohen Foundation, Sam L., 3684
Cohen Revocable Trust, Sonya, 6228
Cohen Trust, Ben, 3752
Cohen, Alexandra M., 1560
Cohen, Barton J., 4897
Cohen, Barton P., 3500
Cohen, Ben, 3752
Cohen, Bennett, 9358
Cohen, Betsy Z., 7919
Cohen, Betty S., 6828
Cohen, Charles C., 8282
Cohen, D. Gideon, 5233
Cohen, Daniel G., 7919
Cohen, David, 540, 923
Cohen, David L., 7989
Cohen, David M., 7984
Cohen, Debra L., 3831
Cohen, Diana, 2826
Cohen, Edward E., 7919
Cohen, Edward H., 6918
Cohen, Edward L., 3831
Cohen, Eileen, 1835
Cohen, Eileen Phillips, 1840
Cohen, Eileen R., 6527
Cohen, Eleanor, 2050
Cohen, Elizabeth Ann, 2028
Cohen, Emanuel, 3754
Cohen, Eric, 6981
Cohen, Haskell, 5792
Cohen, Holly B., 8131
Cohen, Howard, 564
Cohen, Israel, 3754
Cohen, J., 777
Cohen, Janet L., 5184
Cohen, Jenny, 2028
Cohen, Jeremy, 35, 5717
Cohen, Jerome O., 9725
Cohen, Jerrold, 178
Cohen, Jerry, 670
Cohen, Jill R., 5184
Cohen, Joanne, 2031
Cohen, John, 6825
Cohen, Jonathan L., 5626, 6898, 9429
Cohen, Jonathan Z., 7919
Cohen, Julie, 7742
Cohen, Julie W., 7820
Cohen, K. P., 8833
Cohen, Kenneth P., 6967
Cohen, Lauren A., 4351
Cohen, Leah, 35
Cohen, Linda, 5805
Cohen, Lisa, 5612
Cohen, Louis M., 2022
Cohen, Marcy E., 3753
Cohen, Mark, 3753
Cohen, Mark L., 3753
Cohen, Martin, 9445
Cohen, Martin D., 4173
Cohen, Mary, 3499, 3500
Cohen, Maryjo, 1835
Cohen, Maryjo R., 1840
Cohen, Melvin S., 3753
Cohen, Menachem, 2050
Cohen, Michael L., 9577
Cohen, Mitch, 4026
Cohen, N.M., 3754
Cohen, Naomi, 3754
Cohen, Neil, 3753
Cohen, Neil D., 3753
Cohen, Nina L., 8312
Cohen, Oscar, 5612
Cohen, Perry L., 5184
Cohen, Philippa, 5717
Cohen, Rachel, 1972
Cohen, Rachel F., 5184
Cohen, Rhoda R., 4046
Cohen, Richard, 6380
Cohen, Richard B., 5184
Cohen, Richard J., 8239

Cohen, Richard S., 2028
Cohen, Russell A., 4046
Cohen, Ryna G., 3753
Cohen, Sam L., 3684
Cohen, Shear-Yashuv, Chief Rabbi, 5980
Cohen, Sheldon, 1896
Cohen, Stephanie S., 799
Cohen, Stephen A., 7984
Cohen, Stephen J., 564
Cohen, Steven, 4039
Cohen, Steven A., 1487, 1560
Cohen, Thea E., 3753
Cohen, Theresa, 3753
Cohen, Wendy H., 2128
Cohen, Yetta K., 9438
Cohen, Yomtob, 5792
Cohen, Zelda G., 3752
Cohl, Claudia, 3122
Cohn Foundation, Betsy and Alan, The, 6228
Cohn Living Trust, David A. & Devon W., 1822
Cohn, Alan D., 5793, 6228
Cohn, Allan L., 3375
Cohn, Betsy, 5793
Cohn, David, 1040
Cohn, David A., 1822
Cohn, Devon Wiel, 1822
Cohn, Donald, 1040
Cohn, Hillel, Rabbi, 419
Cohn, Lisa Reckler, 1487
Cohn, Mark, 4409
Cohn, Shelly, 92
Cohn, Susan L., 2975
Cohn, Ted J., 1363
Cohne, Martin, 4325
Cohon, Jared L., 5747, 7946, 8084
Cohron, Kristi E., 2452
Cohrs Trust, Oscar, 7405
Cohrs, Oscar, 7405
Cohrs, Torben, 5106
Coiner, Lewis M., 9412
Coit, Donna M., 409
Coit, R. Ken, 409
Coit, Susan, 9317
Coit, William E., 9317
Coker, Charles W., 8473
Coker, Charles W., Jr., 8473
Coker, Frances M., 8872
Coker, Richard G., Jr., 2380
Coker, Tom, 5531
Coker, William M., 8459
Colagiuri, Patricia, 6302
Colaianne, Melonie B., 4497
Colangelo, Carol, 7451
Colantoni, Alfred, 2270
Colantuono, Janet G., 9606
Colavincenzo, Norman J., 897
Colbert Family Fund of Coastal Community Foundation, 8492
Colbert, Celia A., 1929
Colbert, Tom, 5807
Colbourne, Larry C., 7266
Colburn Trust, Elizabeth W., 2852
Colburn Trust, Richard, 410
Colburn, Betsy P., 2852
Colburn, Cecily C., 9431
Colburn, David, 410, 9409
Colburn, Kathleen, 9409
Colburn, Keith W., 2852
Colburn, Richard D., 410
Colburn, Richard W., 410, 3047
Colburn, Robin Tennant, 3047
Colby, Benjamin M., 2668
Colby, David C., 5329
Colby, F. Jordan, 2668
Colchester Global Bond, 9916
Cold Heading Co., 4367
Cold, Kathleen Holbrook, 2117
Cole Productions, Kenneth, Inc., 5231
Cole Trust, Helen C., 7410
Cole, Amy Skoczlas, 4739
Cole, Andrea, 4424
Cole, Carolyn J., 6604
Cole, Christopher A., 6108
Cole, David E., 4395
Cole, Douglas G., 6898
Cole, Gretchen, 7380
Cole, Helen C., 7410
Cole, Ilene S., 2758
Cole, Jeffrey, 4386
Cole, Jerome J., 2758
Cole, Jody, 9068
Cole, John, 5927
Cole, Joseph L., 1267
Cole, Keith, 3271
Cole, Kenneth D., 5231, 5795
Cole, Kimberly A., 8493
Cole, Maria Cuomo, 5795
Cole, Mary T., 4574
Cole, Olive B., 3276
Cole, Quincy, 2389
Cole, Ralph A., 4549
Cole, Richard R., 3276
Cole, Robert J., 4828
Cole, Ronnie, 9179
Cole, Sarah R., 7380
Cole, Scott, 9514
Cole, Susan P., 7014
Colella, Louis, 7542
Colella, Thomas C., 5116
Colello, Joan, 6643
Coleman Living Trust, Ruth S., 139
Coleman, Amy B., 4479
Coleman, Audrey, 2038
Coleman, Barbara B., 5377
Coleman, Barbara Bell, 5441
Coleman, Beverly, 8035
Coleman, Charles P., III, 5796
Coleman, Claudia, 849
Coleman, Dave, 4342
Coleman, Denis P., 2233
Coleman, Denis P., Jr., 2276
Coleman, Dorothy W., 2759
Coleman, Faith P., 3501
Coleman, Gregory J., 561
Coleman, H. Richard, 3501, 3535
Coleman, Henry A., Dr., 5270
Coleman, J. Reed, 2955
Coleman, J. Wilbur, 5275
Coleman, J.D. Stetson, 2759
Coleman, Jack, 5275
Coleman, James E., 561
Coleman, Jeff, 1211
Coleman, Jill C., 9398
Coleman, Joe E., 9011, 9187
Coleman, Judith S., 9440
Coleman, Julie, 91
Coleman, Karen, 9975
Coleman, Kent, 8545
Coleman, Leah Doyle, 5848
Coleman, Leonard S., 5441
Coleman, Louise, 2933
Coleman, Marjorie Thalheimer, 3894
Coleman, Mary Sue, 771
Coleman, Michael, 1907
Coleman, Morton, Dr., 8228
Coleman, Nancy, 8504
Coleman, Neill, 6724
Coleman, Sally C., 8400
Coleman, Stacey, 5601
Coleman, Stephanie A., 5796
Coleman, Thomas, 1633
Coleman, Tom, 9354
Coleman, Tony, 2040
Coleman, William H., 9341
Colen, Gerald R., 2029
Colen, Ina A., 2029
Colen, Kenneth D., 2029
Colen, Leslee R., 2029
Colen, Robert, 2029
Colen, Sidney, 2029
Coles, Gloria, 4511
Colestrip Casino, Inc., 5016
Coletta, Carol, 2191
Coletti, Brynne F., 7447
Coletti, Robert E., 7447
Coley, Amy, 4800
Coley, Brigitte J., 669
Coley, Warren, 669
Colglazier, Boyd, 7405
Colglazier, DeAnna, 992
Colhoun, Alexander H.P., 3755
Colhoun, Howard P., 3755
Colhoun, Trevor, 9244
Colin Charitable Lead Trust, Cynthia G., 6048
Colin, Barbara F., 5797
Colin, Cynthia Green, 6101
Colin, Fred, 5797
Colin, Samuel F., 5797
Colin, Stephen, 5797
Colinear, Janine, 8092
Colket, Bryan D., 7987
Colket, Tristram C., Jr., 7987
Collat, Charles A., 49
Collat, Charles A., Jr., 49
Collato, Richard, 1053
Collato, Richard A., 1108
Collens, Lew, 3091
Collesano, Marguerite, 6913
Colleton, Elizabeth, 6531
Colleton, Elizabeth A., 7989
Collett, J. Rountree, Jr., 7178
Collett, Judy, 9799
Collett, Sterling R., III, 7178
Colley, Jennifer, 1423
Collier, Chris, 535
Collier, Christina C., 9128
Collier, D. Brian, 7202
Collier, Isabel, 2240
Collier, Judge Robert A., Jr., 7299
Collier, M. H., 2738
Collier, Mark, 3379
Collier, Mark, Dr., 7509
Collier, Martin, 9630
Collier, Miles C., 2240, 2284
Collier, Parker J., 2240
Collier, Thomas A., 3714
Collier, William H., Jr., 777
Collin, William, 7983
Collings, Kanisa, 7102
Collingsworth, Connie, 9625
Collins Building Services, 7012
Collins Electrical Company Inc., 5482
Collins Foundation, Carr P., 9167
Collins, Andre, 1939
Collins, Atwood, III, 1710, 6406
Collins, Brian D., 9766
Collins, Calvert K., 8771
Collins, Carol L., 412
Collins, Carr P., 8771
Collins, Debra, 9380
Collins, Derrick C., 4451
Collins, Donald A., 8017
Collins, Douglas, 5885, 5921
Collins, Douglas W., 3364
Collins, Erin Lynn, 5776
Collins, Frances, 5885, 5921
Collins, G. Fulton, III, 7741
Collins, J. Christopher, 4327
Collins, James A., 412
Collins, James E., 3921
Collins, James M., 8772
Collins, Jamie, 4016
Collins, John P., Jr., 1189
Collins, Joseph, 5798
Collins, Judy, 6024
Collins, Julia D., 5799
Collins, Kelly L., 412
Collins, Kristine E., 4958
Collins, Lauren, 1710
Collins, Lisa N., 3402
Collins, Maribeth W., 7836
Collins, Mark M., Jr., 5885, 5921
Collins, Mark R., 594
Collins, Martin, 2429
Collins, Michael, 8772, 9713
Collins, Michael H., 9213
Collins, Michael J., 8772
Collins, Michelle, 2749
Collins, Michelle L., 3172
Collins, Patrick F., 663
Collins, Paul J., 5799
Collins, Petere, 9125
Collins, Phillip N., 3058
Collins, Phyllis D., 5921
Collins, Phyllis Dillon, 5885
Collins, Priscilla B., 9701
Collins, Rachel, 2429
Collins, Richard H., 8771
Collins, Roger, 186
Collins, Ronald, 5799
Collins, Roy T., 4958
Collins, Ruth M., 1183, 1189
Collins, Sara, 5800
Collins, Scott, 2142
Collins, Stacey L., 3758
Collins, Susanne, 2429
Collins, Suzanne M., 7741
Collins, Thomas, 1020
Collins, Thomas R., 4966
Collins, Tom, 9617
Collins, Truman W., 7837
Collins, Truman W., Jr., 7836, 7837
Collins, Walter R., Jr., 7448
Collins, William L., 4616
Collis, Lisa, 9380
Collisson, Kathleen E., 9233
Collister, Dick, 9975
Collopy, Francis W., 122
Colman, Stephen, 6175
Colombel, Andrea, 6213
Colombel, Andrea Soros, 6005
Colombel, Eric, 6005, 6213, 7003, 7010
Colombo, Elsie T., 413
Colon, Fabina, 5807
Colon, Nelson I., Dr., 8353
Colonial Company, 45
Colonial Oil Industries, Inc., 2430
Colony Cabinets, Inc., 118
Colony Club Apartments LLc, 3505
Colorado Rockies Baseball Club Foundation, 1850
Colosi, Michael F., 5231

Colson Charitable Lead Annuity Trust, Hugh L., 9601
Colson Living Trust, Hugh, 9601
Colson Trust, 3092, 3093, 9088
Colson, Barton G., 9601
Colson, Bonnie, 9601
Colson, Bradley A., 9601
Colson, Hugh, 9601
Colson, Philip L., 4840
Colt, Inc., The, 5170
Columbia Cleaning, 5982
Columbia Energy Group, 7591
Columbia Gas of Ohio, Inc., 7591
Columbia Gas System, Inc., The, 7591
Columbia Management Co., 7876
Columbia University, 5707
Columbia/HCA Healthcare Corp., 8582
Columbus Bank & Trust Co., 2556
Columbus Foundation and Affiliated Organizations, The, 7605
Columbus Life Insurance Co., 7710
Columbus, Christie, 8808
Colvin, Gill, 208
Colvin, Jawanza, Rev., 7509
Colwell, C. Perry, 7328
Colwell, Rita, Dr., 4036
Colwell, Stephen, 1131
Colwell, William S., 1562
Colyear, Richard, 784
Colyer, Robert, 2288
Comai, Barbara L., 4503
Comber, Neil, 7404
Combs, Jennifer Malloy, 6946
Combs, Katherine, 2827
Combs, Sara Walter, 3598
Combs-Dulaney, Rebecca, 4831
Comcast CICG, LP, 7989
Comcast QVC, Inc., 7989
Comeford, Michael, 6159
Comenos, T. Phillip, 4070
Comer Foundation, The, 2761
Comer, Frances, 2760
Comer, G.L., 8643
Comer, Gary C., 2760, 2761
Comer, Guy, 2760, 2761
Comer, Jane S., 69
Comer, John D., 2403
Comer, Mark, 497
Comer, Neil, 3376
Comer, Randall, 7671
Comer, Richard J., Jr., 20
Comer, Stephanie, 2760, 2761
Comer, Theresa, 7052
Comer-Avondale Mills, Inc., 20
Comerica, 8136
Comerica Bank, 4368, 4369, 4497, 4533, 4577, 4587
Comerica Bank and Trust, N.A., 7306
Comerica Inc., 4368
Comes, Dean, 5006
Comes, Sonny, 5006
Comfort Mattress, Inc., 4569
Commemorative Derby Promotions, 946
Commerce Bancorp, Inc., 3710
Commerce Bancshares, 4871
Commerce Bank, N.A., 4926, 4946, 4950, 4966, 4980, 4983
Commerce Trust Co., 4899
Commercial Brick Corp., 7767
Commercial Realty, 5399
Commercial Security Mortgage Credit, Inc., 5251
Commers, Christen, 3287
CommonSense Partners, 7876
Commonwealth Hotels, LLC, 7396
Communication Technology Services, LLC, 4193
Communities Foundation of Texas, 8736
Community Fdn. of Chattanochee, 9470
Community Foundation of Johnson County, 7359
Community Foundation of North Central WA, 9652
Community Foundation, The, 2629
Community Hospitals of Indiana, 3317
Community National Bank & Trust, 8818
Community TV Corp., 4139
Commuri, Chandrasekhar, 780
Companion Healthcare Corp., 8460
Compass Bank, 8, 9, 21, 8795
Compton Family Trust, 1153
Compton, Clyde D., 3255
Compton, Elizabeth K., 6113
Compton, Georgia, 9450, 9460
Compton, Janice A., 8551
Compton, Kelly H., 8913
Compton, Robert, 1107
Compton, Robert A., 8551
Compton, Vanessa, 422
Compton, W. Danforth, 422
Compton, Walter K., 185
Compton, Wilson M., 5339
Comstock, Pam Martin, 9398
Comstock, Richard, 4357
Comstock, Robert F., 3866
Comstock, Ross, 4474
Comstock-Gay, Stuart, 9375
Conabee, Christopher M., 9341
ConAgra Foods, Inc., 5029, 5030, 7012
ConAgra, Inc., 5029, 5030
Conant, Carolyn E., 2327
Conant, John A., 2477
Conant, Miriam H., 2477
Conard, Edward J., 5809
Conard, Edward W., 5809
Conarroe, Joel, 6116
Concelman, Scott, 2087
Concelman, Tara, 2087
Concepcion, Lisa, 7945
Concert Association of Southeast Tex, 8899
Conda, Joseph, 3164
Conde Nast Publications, 782
Conde Nast Publications, Inc., The, 6550
Condict, Kevin, Dr., 3391
Condioti, Steve, 855
Condit, Edward M., Jr., 8452
Condliffe, David C., 6148
Condon, Freeman J., 4108
Condon, Gerald C., Jr., 9904
Condon, Larry E., 6477
Condon, Thomas J., 375
Condos, Barbara S., 9139
Condrat, Paul, 9652
Cone Charitable Lead Annuity Trust 2, Edward T., 5810
Cone Charitable Lead Annuity Trust 3, Edward T., 5810
Cone Charitable Lead Annuity Trust 4, Edward T., 5810
Cone Charitable Lead Annuity Trust 6, Edward T., 5810
Cone Charitable Lead Trust, Edward T., 5810
Cone, Ashley E., 7174
Cone, Ceasar, II, 7174
Cone, Ceasar, III, 7174
Cone, David, 2437
Cone, Dawn M., 8042
Cone, Edward, 8277
Cone, Edward F., 7326
Cone, Edward H., 8042
Cone, Kristen G., 7174
Cone, Lawrence M., 7174
Cone, Martha A., 7174
Cone, Robert L., 8042
Cone, Walter "Butch", 7174
Conely, Chris W., 569
Conexant, 297
Conference of European Rabbis, 6336
Confranceso, Elaine R., 1531
Cong Ahavas Tzedokah Vchese, 5937
Congdon, Earl, 7231
Congeni, Jeff, 7491
Conger, Mimi, 9380
Congregation Tifereth Uziel, 5699
Congregation Z.Y.C., 5557
Congregation Zichron Mayer Zvi, 5699
Congressional Quarterly, 2332
Conklin, Carl L., 8475
Conklin, Fred W., 1857
Conklin, Hugh, 4361
Conklin, Laura J., 9801
Conklin, Michael, 4739
Conklin, Patricia Berry, 312
Conlee, Cecil D., 2499
Conlee, G. Virginia, 2762
Conlee, Richard, 2008
Conley, Joan C., 3857
Conley, Kathy, 195
Conley, Michael, 8610
Conley, Renea, 3630
Conley, Sue S., 9835
Conley, Terence P., 5506
Conlin, Jan, 4714
Conlin, Jan M., 4754
Conlin, Kelly, 7659
Conlin, Kevin P., 5305
Conlin, Patrick J., Jr., 4362
Conlon, Donald T., 9231
Conlon, James J., 3680
Conlon, Michael, 9300
Conlon, Robyn T., 9231
Conlon, Tim, 3421
Conlon, William K., 9231
Conn, Andrew D., 7418
Conn, Edith F., 2042
Conn, Fred K., 2042
Conn, James P., 7277
Conn, Joan D., 7418
Conn, Nicolette, 7418
Conn, Olivia D., 7418
Conn, Raymond A., 7418
Conn, Robert W., Dr., 771
Connally, Christopher, 6454
Connally, Patricia, 9384
Connaught Music Inc., 6704
Connaughton, James L., 3868
Connaughton, Suzanne, 1478
Connecticut Light and Power Co., The, 1656
Connell, Christopher, 424
Connell, Denise, 3284
Connell, George, 7955
Connell, Hope Holding, 7233, 7319
Connell, James V., 7509
Connell, Jim, 9697
Connell, Michael J., 424
Connell, Mike, 2768
Connell, Tim, 4768
Connell, W. David, 92
Connelly, Christine C., 7995
Connelly, Daniele M., 7995
Connelly, Diedre P., 7274
Connelly, Gerard, 2632
Connelly, John F., 7995
Connelly, Josephine C., 7995
Connelly, Patricia D., 4108
Connelly, Serena Simmons, 9174
Connelly, Stephan T., 7995
Connelly, Thomas S., 7995
Conner, Ernest Gerald, 3619
Conner, Lauren E., 3263
Conners, John-Paul, 2087
Connett, T. Gary, 9750
Connolly, Arthur G., III, 1800
Connolly, Arthur G., Jr., 1800
Connolly, Christopher, Dr., 1800
Connolly, Cynthia Sprague, 951, 1027, 1207
Connolly, Darleen, 3285
Connolly, Elizabeth Atwater, 4747
Connolly, Gerald E., 9930
Connolly, J. Joe, 1027
Connolly, Michael W., 6978
Connolly, Paul M., 4030
Connolly, Robert M., 8158
Connolly, Ronald C., 425
Connolly, Ronald G., 425
Connolly, Ruth E., 3311
Connolly, Thomas A., 425
Connolly, Timothy, 3201
Connolly, William M., 7169
Connolly-Keesler, Eileen, 2035
Connor & Assoc. Ltd., William E., Ltd., 5109
Connor, Barbara, Dr., 5575
Connor, Christopher M., 7661
Connor, Merlene, 1035
Connor, Michael, 1035
Connor, Robert, 5987
Connor, Robert P., 3936
Connor, W. Robert, 7274
Connor, William E., 5109
Connor, William E., II, 5109
Connor, Yvonne, 7934
Connors, Colleen, 4618
Connors, Gregory, 2043
Connors, John P., Jr., 6568
Connors, Julia B., 2043
Connors, Michael M., 2043
Connors, Patrick E., 2043
Connors, Timothy J., 5171
Connors, William, 7989
Conomikes, John G., 6155, 6156
Conover, Catherine M., 1878
Conover, Charles W., 3255
Conover, Jane, 8351
Conover, John C., III, 2270
Conover, Katharine, 9975
Conover, Robert V., 9881
Conrad Hilton Foundation, 3644
Conrad, Cecilia, 2989
Conrad, Deborah S., 7853
Conrad, Frank P., 4091
Conrad, Heather L., 8295
Conrad, Mary B., 6193
Conrad, Olivia, 5068
Conrad, Pete, 3365
Conrad, Tipton S., 6935
Conrad, William C., 8295
Conradi, Charles R., 407
Conrado, Susan L., 6945
Conron, William, 6854
Conroy, Caroline, 966

Copp, B. Allyn, 1667, 9082
Copp, Betsey A., 1667
Copp, Eugenie C.T., 1667
Copp, Joseph A., 1667
Copp, Lucy A., 1667
Copp, Mary Wagley, 9082
Coppedge, Ronald S., 7771
Coppinger, Virginia L., 4942
Copple, E. Don, 2633, 2634
Copple, Terry, 2633
Copple, Terry C., 2634
Coppler, Mark, 3290
Coppola, Michael P., 1063
Copses, Peter, 429
Coqui Development Co., 1904
Corallo, Christopher, 5806
Corbally, Richard V., 6453
Corbet, Kathleen, 1650
Corbet, Thomas R., 4958
Corbett Charitable Lead Trust, 1327
Corbett, Adelaide T., 3222
Corbett, Annette W., 1327
Corbett, Cornelia Gerry, 2045, 8838
Corbett, George, 1327
Corbett, J. Richard, 7170
Corbett, Jeannette M., 2276
Corbett, Joyce George, 7205
Corbett, Richard A., 2045
Corbett, Richard E., 7575
Corbin, Andrew C., 3497
Corbin, Brian R., 7415
Corbin, David C., 7420
Corbin, Hunter W., 5281, 5310
Corbin, Karl, 7835
Corbin, Ronald L., 8550
Corbin, S. Wells, 6802
Corboy, Philip H., 2773
Corbridge, Pam, 9313
Corby, Thomas B., 1056
Corcoran, Alison, 4282
Corcoran, Debbie, 3910
Corcoran, Edward, 901
Corcoran, Gail, 3347
Corcoran, Gerald F., 2752
Corcoran, James, 6159
Corcoran, Jane R., 3760
Corcoran, Jerry, 3347
Corcoran, John M., 3995
Corcoran, John M., Jr., 3995
Corcoran, Thomas M., 3995
Corcoran, Timothy J., 7587
Corcoran, William W., 3986
Cord, E.L., 5110
Cordani, David M., 7981
Cordano, Michael D., 1316
Cordeiro, Paula A., 727
Cordell, Cheran D., 9510
Corder, Tyler, 5119
Cordero, Paul M., 5398
Cordish, David S., 3764
Cordish, Jonathan A., 3764
Cordon, Frank, 789
Cordova, Robert, 2990
Corelogic Real Estate Solutions, 8834
CoreStates Financial Corp, 8333
Coretz, Kim, 7744
Coretz, Robert, 7744
Corey Delta Constructors, 293
Corey, Elizabeth, 3047
Corey, Emilie, 5816
Corey, Kathryn, 21
Corey, Michael, 5816
Corey, William G., 866
Cori, Thomas, Dr., 2995
Corigliano, John, 5814
Corkins, David, 1756
Corl, James M., 4403
Corl, Kelli R., 4403
Corl, Mary W., 4403
Corl, Mary Welch, 4403
Corl, Robert W., III, 4403
Corl, Robert W., Jr., 4403
Corleto, Richard, 1360
Corlett, John R., 7639
Corlett, Roger, 7379
Corlew, Kathy, 8591
Corley, Ginger A., 8958
Corley, Joan, 6705
Corliss Estates, Inc., 6768
Corman, Steven D., 7164
Cormican, Joanne, 1016
Corn, Betty, 2414
Corn, Elizabeth T., 2411, 2414
Corn, Lovick P., 2411
Corneille, Barbara Berry, 312
Cornelio, Charles C., 3344
Cornelius, Jeffrey, 8236
Cornell Marital Trust, Alverin, 2774
Cornell Trust, Peter C., 6584
Cornell, Alex, 3765
Cornell, Ann, 3765
Cornell, Ann D., 1955
Cornell, Brian, 6627
Cornell, George L., Jr., 3765
Cornell, George W., 9538
Cornell, Heather M., 5802
Cornell, Holly, 3765
Cornell, Joseph, 2046
Cornell, Lee, 5744
Cornell, Michael, 2839
Cornell, N. Thomas, 7484
Cornell, Robert, 7924
Cornell, Roger, 1108
Cornerstone Auto, 4650
Cornerstone Bank, N.A., 5052
Cornerstone CSO, 5395
Cornerstone Trust, 530, 7846
Cornett, Donald J., 2435
Cornett, Kathleen, 7876
Cornett, Kathy, 8660
Cornett, Robert, 4829
Cornille, Mary, 3988
Corning Inc., 5818
Corning, Dwight B., 7369
Corning, Henry H., 1208
Corning, Ursula, 7030
Cornish, Charlie, 9704
Cornish, John M., 3969, 4066
Cornsweet, David, 637
Cornu, Thomas W., 3980
Cornwall, John W., 5270
Cornwell, Dominique, 2775
Cornwell, Joan, 4792
Cornwell, Ron, 4792
Cornwell, W.D., Jr., 7320
Coronas, Jose, 6722
Corpening Memorial Trust, Maxwell M., 7183
Corpening, M.M., Mrs., 7183
Corporacion Agga Sa De Cv Mexico, 8834
Corporex Companies, LLC, 7396
Corporex Cos., Inc., 7396
Corrado, Lorene A., 5843
Corrah, Tumani, 9625
Correll, Ada F., 2440
Correll, Ada L., 2440
Correll, Alston D., 2440
Correll, Alston D., III, 2440
Corrente, Judith-Ann, 6498, 6748
Corrigan, Daniel, 140
Corrigan, David R., 8795
Corrigan, E. Gerald, 5762
Corrigan, Elizabeth A., 5762
Corrigan, Jennifer, 3231
Corrigan, John, 6518
Corrigan, Karen B., 5762
Corrigan, Patrick J., 5074
Corrigan, Stephen M., 140
Corrigan, William S., 1435
Corsello, Dan, 1283
Corson, Mary, 5697
Cortes, Emilie, 422
Cortese, Arline S., 5462
Cortese, Shannon, 5462
Cortessi, Claire, 2839
Cortessi, Richard, 2839
Cortina, Raniero, Jr., 7012
Cortopassi, Dean A., 430
Cortopassi, Joan A., 430
Cortopassi, Tom, 430
Cortright, Michelle, 4361
Corty, Andrew P., 2332
Corvi, Carolyn, 9731
Corvin, Adele K., 1226
Corvin, Dana A., 1226
Corvin, Stuart, 1226
Corwin/Moretrench, Arthur, 6205
Corzine Foundation, Jon and Joanne, The, 5819
Corzine, Jennifer, 1401
Corzine, Joanne D., 5819
Cosby, Lula, 7671
Cosentino, Crystal, 5575
Cosentino, Julia S., 4272
Cosentino, Julia Satti, 4004
Cosenza, Tony, 3356
Cosgrove, Edward M., 8355
Cosgrove, Michael J., 1591
Cosgrove, Peter, 5979
Cosner, Chris, 3330
Cosper, Judith McBean Hunt, 893
Coss, Benjamin R., 9481
Costa, Anisa Kamadoli, 6978
Costa, Myrna, 1288
Costa, Robin Grindstaff, 4834
Costantino, Jo-Ann, 6549
Costanza, Dennis, 700
Costas, Elizabeth, 5834
Coste, Catherine B., 9155, 9271
Costello, Ann M., 6077
Costello, Brian F., 6109
Costello, Janet S., 2762
Costello, Jeffrey, 3289
Costello, Marcy, 4768
Costello, Tom, 2765
Coster, Kevin, 2134
Costigan, Edward J., III, Jr., 8400
Costin, Roann, 4323
Cota, Stephanie, 886
Cote, Leann, 4212
Cote-Ackah, Carra, 6947
Cotese, Casey, 1432
Cotham, Edward T., 9225
Coto CLAT-Whittier Trust Company, Melanie, 431
Coto, Chloe, 431
Coto, Melanie, 431
Cotre, Stephen P., 4108
Cotsen Library - Princeton, 5707
Cotsen, Lloyd, 432
Cotsen, Lloyd E., 222, 432
Cotsen, Margit, 432
Cotter, Anna Marie, 5572
Cotter, Christopher B., 100
Cotter, Colleen M., 7639
Cotter, John, 7698
Cottingham & Butler Insurance, 3415
Cottingham, Patty, 7659
Cottingham, Robin, 7715
Cottingham, Sarah Toole, 154
Cotton, Anne, 1650
Cotton, Gertrude, 8378
Cotton, Kate H., 59
Cotton, Leonard, 1650
Cotton, Robert E., 9368
Cottrell, Frederick Gardner, 157
Cottrell, Sandra T., 9396
Coty, Eva, 1565
Couch, Annette M., 8163
Couch, Genevieve R., 191
Couch, Geoff, 936
Couch, Kenneth R., 8499
Couch, Richard W., 5182
Couchman, John G., 4672
Coudert, Cynthia, 5820
Coudert, Frederic R., III, 5820
Coudert, Margaret M., 5820
Coudert, Sandra, 5820
Coughlan, Gary P., 2648
Coughlan, John, 6995
Coughlin, Anne S., 3626
Coughlin, Catherine, 8675
Coughlin, Edward John, 7507
Coughlin, F.H., 3626
Coughlin, Francis, 1686
Coughlin, Jeg Anthony, 7507
Coughlin, Michael, 7876
Coughlin, Michael Allen, 7507
Coughlin, Phillip Troy, 7507
Coughlin, Trish, 9311
Coughlin, William H., 4920
Coukos, Stephen J., 3972
Coulling, Louise S., 9793
Coulon, Robbin M., 92
Coulson, Frank L., Jr., 8000
Coulson, Sarah Miller, 8000
Coulter 2006 Management Trust, 6898
Coulter Charitable Remainder Unitrust, Wallace H., 2047
Coulter Irrevocable Trust, Wallace H., 2048
Coulter Trust, Wallace H., 2047
Coulter, Chuck, 3422
Coulter, Joan M., 3661
Coulter, Patricia A., 8221
Coulter, Wallace H., 2048
Coulton, Claudia J., 7639
Countryman, Merle, 905
Counts, Andy, 7414
Couper, William, 1925
Couri, Gerald E., 9965
Cournoyer, Nicholas N., 1608
Cournoyer, Sabina G., 1608
Courrier, Dinah, 3762
Courshon, Judy, 9746
Courtenay, C.T., 8605, 8630
Courtice, Lisa Schweitzer, 7411
Courtnage, Kathleen A., 5058
Courtnage, Larry J., 5058
Courtney, Charlene W., 1725
Courtney, Dorothy, 437
Courtney, Q. Peter, III, 8732
Courtois, Patricia, 2038
Courts, Clay L., 2441
Courts, Malon C., 2441

Courts, Malon W., 2420, 2441
Courts, Richard W., 2441
Courts, Richard W., II, 2441, 2463
Courts, Richard W., IV, 2441
Courts, T. Brad, 2463
Courts, T. Bradbury, 2441
Courts, Virginia Campbell, 2420, 2441
Courtside Charitable Foundation, The, 6881
Courville, Donna L., 1103
Coury, Robert J., 8192
Coury, Thomas, 4270
Cousins Charitable Lead Annuity Trust, 2442
Cousins Life Insurance Trust, Thomas G., 2442
Cousins Real Estate Corp., 2443
Cousins, Ann D., 2442
Cousins, Grady, 2442
Cousins, Joselyn, 5134
Cousins, Thomas G., 2442
Coustar, Pascal, 1004
Coutinho, Candace, 9145
Coutts, Jeffrey D., 3344
Couvillon, Susan, 3610
Couzens, Henry Porter, 1364
Couzens, John Manning, Jr., 1364
Couzens, Melinda Rodgers, 1364
Covello, Alfred V., Hon., 1647
Covenant Church of Pittsburgh, 9118
Coventry, Kim, 2805
Cover, Allen Michael, 8926
Cover, Angela Marie, 8926
Cover, Ann Marie, 8926
Cover, Jonathan Mark, 8926
Cover, Mark Allen, 8926
Cover, William Randall, 8926
Covey, Joy D., 291
Covington, Alec C., 4727
Covington, Betsy W., 2438
Covington, Dennis, 920
Covington, Faison, 7264
Covington, George M., 2876
Covington, Joe S., 4831
Covington, Marguerite, 2327
Covington, Ned, 7231
Covington, Richard L., 8903
Cowal, Sally Grooms, 6983
Cowan Irrevocable Trust, Marylouise, 7803
Cowan Trust, 5518
Cowan Trust, Marylouise, 7803
Cowan, Allison, 5028
Cowan, Barbara, 7738
Cowan, Barbara Browning, 7738
Cowan, Fred, 1075
Cowan, Geoffrey, 5028
Cowan, George A., 5518
Cowan, Helen Dunham, 5518
Cowan, Jolyon Ellis, 2028
Cowan, Kathy W., 8549
Cowan, Lisa, 7738
Cowan, Marylouise Tandy, 7803
Cowan, Sherry Lynn, 99
Cowan, William, 7738
Cowan, William B., 7738
Cowan-Eksten, Nancy, 3291
Coward, E. Walter, Jr., 399
Cowboys Wives Association, 8943
Cowden, Louetta M., 8783
Cowden, W.H., Jr., 9095
Cowdin, Christi L., 4593
Cowell, Janet, 7295
Cowell, John F., 7313
Cowell, Michelle P., 7313
Cowell, Phyllis S., 7313
Cowell, Robert, 4495
Cowell, S.H., 434
Cowen, Anne K., 7378
Cowen, Jeanine M., 4313
Cowenhoven, Anna, 7139
Cowikee Mills, 20
Cowin, Daniel, 5822
Cowin, Joyce B., 5822
Cowles Publishing Co., 9607
Cowles, Anne C., 9615
Cowles, Charles, 5234
Cowles, E.A., 9607
Cowles, Gardner, 5234
Cowles, Gardner, III, 5234
Cowles, James C., 5780
Cowles, Jan S., 5234
Cowles, W.S., 9607
Cownie Charitable Trust, 3452
Cownie, Jim, 3420
Cowper, Geoff, 9613
Cowperthwait, Jonathan E., 2590
Cox Charitable Lead Trust, 3953
Cox Enterprises, Inc., 2445, 2560
Cox Health, 9250
Cox, Angela, 79
Cox, Berry R., 8784
Cox, C. Lee, 1055
Cox, Cathy, 2427
Cox, Christopher, 4451
Cox, Cooper, 6604
Cox, Cynthia, 3396
Cox, David C., 4639
Cox, Donna O., 9484
Cox, Ferber & Associates, LLC, 3906
Cox, G. Bridger, 7798
Cox, Gary, 9146
Cox, Harold D., 4016
Cox, Heather M., 9400
Cox, Heidi, 4874
Cox, Howard E., 2023
Cox, Howard E., Jr., 2023
Cox, James M., Jr., 2560
Cox, Jeanne, 6090
Cox, Jeanne T., 8773, 8784
Cox, Jeff, 2123, 5075, 7540
Cox, Jim, 7416
Cox, John G.T., 8784
Cox, John L., 8785
Cox, Judith, 6133
Cox, Justin B., 8784
Cox, Kathryn, 8224
Cox, Kelly, 8785
Cox, Marilyn, 7756
Cox, Mark A., 7520
Cox, Martha, 4874
Cox, Martha B., 7826
Cox, Martha W., 4874
Cox, Maurine T., 8785
Cox, Molly, 4795
Cox, Nancy, 2027
Cox, Natalie, 8025
Cox, Norma, 4795
Cox, Patricia, 1127
Cox, Patricia Nixon, 5690
Cox, Paul A., 7796
Cox, Ralph C., Jr., 3637
Cox, Sarah, 883
Cox, Steve, 7401
Cox, Steven, 7367
Cox, Steven E., 7605
Cox, T. Randolph, 9780
Cox, Thomas J., 1389
Cox, Tom, 9439
Cox, Vicki B., 4639
Cox, William C., Jr., 4874
Coxhead, Peter C., 8197
Coy, Greg, 9611
Coy, Oona, 1716
Coy, Robert E., 1288
Coy, Sara McAdoo, 2503
Coye, Molly J., 1531
Coyer, Steve, 1518
Coyle, Bonnie S., 8136
Coyle, Bradford R., 9384
Coyle, Frank, 9663
Coyle, Jim, 2525
Coyle, Katherine G., 7725
Coyle, Kathie, 7742
Coyle, Patrick E., 9931
Coyle, Sue, 1714
Coyne, Ava, 1151
Coyne, Beth A., 8195
Coyne, Eric P., 435
Coyne, Jean A., 435
Coyne, Karen Bedrosian, 766
Coyne, Kevin, 5116
Coyne, Marshall B., 1896
Coyne, Martha R., 435
Coyne, Patrick P., 7928
Coyne, Patrick S., 435
Cozzo, Joseph J., 6153
CPS Energy, 9149
Cptc, LLC, 5624
CPTC, LLC, 5709
CPX Commercial Development, LLC, 7396
CPX Development & Construction Management, LLC, 7396
Crabb, Wendy B., 2592
Crabill, John, Esq., 1826
Cracchiolo, Andrea, III, 165
Cracchiolo, Constance M., 4382
Cracchiolo, Daniel, 165
Cracchiolo, Grace E., 4382
Cracchiolo, Peter J., 4382
Cracchiolo, Peter T., 4382
Cracknell, Neil, 633
Craddock, Jan, 5158
Craddock, Margaret, 8538
Craft, Brenda, 2092, 2123
Craft, Daniel, 7174
Craft, Jenny, 9989
Craft, Joseph E., 6401
Craft, Joseph, III, 7807
Craft, Kathleen S., 7745
Crafts, Patricia Callan, 5273
Crafts, Putnam L., Jr., 5273
Cragon, Harvey, 9108
Crahan, Michele McGarry, 7261
Craig, Arlene R., 718
Craig, C.A., II, 8553
Craig, Chris, 4872
Craig, Debbie F., 7870
Craig, Debora Kuchka, 3749
Craig, Deborah Ann, 8553
Craig, Ellis Boyd, 9328
Craig, James P., 9418
Craig, James P., III, 9418
Craig, Jane Alice, 2418
Craig, Jane Alice Hudson, 2419
Craig, Jerome H., 1170
Craig, Jonathan W., Jr., 7294
Craig, Mary Ellen, 5587, 5588
Craig, Nancy Jo, 3618
Craig, Pamela J., 5869
Craig, Rebecca M., 3575
Craig, Rebecca T., 9418
Craig, Richard K., 7179
Craig, Teresa, 3317
Craig, Tracy A., 4327
Craigen, Megan, 8421
Craighead, Jennifer, 8135
Craighead, Martin, 8679
Craighead, Sophie Engelhard, 5954
Craigle, Mary, 5013
Craigslist, Inc., 436
Crain Resources, 8787
Crain, Alan R., Jr., 8679
Crain, Ann Lacy, 8787
Crain, Ann Lacy, II, 8787
Crain, B. Walter, III, 8787
Crain, Beatrice G., 2778
Crain, James T., Jr., 3571
Crain, Joan K., 2034
Crain, John W., 9213
Crain, Lucy, 1202
Crain, Rogers L., 8787
Crais, Pamela J., 5869
Cram, Catherine Neilson, 4725
Cramer, Ann W., 2432
Cramer, Craig, 1932
Cramer, Daphna, 5824
Cramer, Douglas, 5824
Cramer, Gerald B., 5824
Cramer, Harold, 8153
Cramer, Lauren B., 5824
Cramer, Marc, 7850
Cramer, Meta S., Rev., 7640
Cramer, Steven, 9843
Cramer, Theiline Wyckoff, 9749
Cramer, Thomas, 5824
Crampton, Stuart B., 157
Cranch, Laurence E., 3923
Crandall, Fonda, 3384
Crandall, J. Taylor, 8687, 9341
Crandall, Mark, 3710
Crandall, Nancy L., 4369
Crandall, Theodore D., 9934
Crandall, William W., Jr., 265
Crane, C. Joseph, 417
Crane, Carlotta, 7653
Crane, Charles, 3766
Crane, Christopher M., 2827
Crane, Ellen, 4585
Crane, Ellen E., 4508
Crane, Frank, III, 7653
Crane, G. Price, 3637
Crane, Helen, 417
Crane, James R., 8788
Crane, Kathleen, 598
Crane, Peter R., 2800
Crane, Stephen, 744
Crane, W. Carey, III, 6582
Crane, William Dale, 9214
Crane, William S., 5211
Crank, Celia Whitfield, 8853
Cransberg, Alan, 7908
Crapol, Heidi, 9441
Crapple, George E., 5659, 7083, 8109
Crary, Evans, Jr., 2202
Crary, Horace I., Jr., 5549, 5692
Crary, Miner, 4299
Crary, Oliver N., 878
Crasby, David, 4709
Crass, Loni, 9658
Crat, Albert Harris, 3820
Crat, Ruth, 3820
Craven, David, 8781
Craven, David L., 1806
Craven, Elizabeth B., 7334

Craven, Julie H., 4676
Craven, Mari Hatzenbuehler, 2740
Craven, Tracy M., 8781
Cravens, Douglas M., 4809
Craver, Dave, 1632
Craver, David, 1632
Craver, Vicki, 1581
Cravero-Kristoffersson, Kathleen, 7276
Crawford, Alva Jean, 7404
Crawford, Amy, 3447
Crawford, Carl, 4732
Crawford, Denise V., 1469
Crawford, Donna W., 3249
Crawford, Edward, III, 3624
Crawford, George, III, 8591
Crawford, Helen H., 1615
Crawford, Joe, 8774
Crawford, John, 7173
Crawford, Kathleen F., 405
Crawford, Kevin, 1053
Crawford, Lucy, 3592
Crawford, Mimi A., 7620
Crawford, Peggy, 3700
Crawford, Robert W., Jr., 3358
Crawford, Shawn, 7731
Crawford, William C., 5409
Crawford, William H.W., IV, 1682
Crawley Petroleum Corp., 7746
Crawley, James B., 7746
Crawley, Mary W., 7746
Crawley, Sara B., 7746
Crawshaw, Christopher D., 4743
Cray, Cloud L., 4876
Cray, Thomas M., 4876
Crayola, LLC, 4906
CRB Foundations, The, 5717
CRB Prize, 5717
Creamer & Son, J. Fletcher, Inc., 5236
Creamer, Dale A., 5236
Creamer, J. Fletcher, 5236
Creamer, J. Fletcher, Jr., 5236
Crean, Andrew, 439
Crean, Donna S., 439
Crean, John C., 439
Creason, Karen K., 7858
Creason, Kennard, 4446
Creative Artists Agency, 6356
Creative Artists Agency, LLC, 362
Creative Banner Assemblies, 4777
Creative Hairdressers, Inc., 9515
Credit Agricole Asset Management, 6898
Credit Bureau of Nashville, Inc., 8546
Credit Bureau of San Janquin County Charitable Foundation, 417
Credit Suisse First Boston Corp., 5826
Credit Suisse First Boston LLC, 5826, 7012
Credit Suisse USA, 5826
Creech, Carter, 9005
Creek, Phillip G., 7550
Creekmore, James H., 4817
Creekmore, John, 4822, 4828
Creekmore, Meredith, 4817
Creekmore, Wade, 4817
Creel Foundation, The, 2447
Crego, Mary, 3174
Creighton Charitable Lead Unitrust, 4187
Creighton, Albert M., III, 4187
Creighton, Albert M., Jr., 4187
Creighton, Hilary H., 4187
Creighton, John, 1391
Creighton, Peter H., 4187
Crenshaw, Carol Y., 2746
Crenshaw, E. Brown, Jr., 8497
Creo, Claudia, 8322
Cresci, Andrew A., 568
Crespino, Ryan, 3656
Crespo, Robert, 6542
Cress, Robert G., 196
Cressey, Bryan C., 2779
Cressey, Christina I., 2779
Cressman, Barry, Rev., 8001
Cressman, Kyle T., 9671
Cressman, Paul R., Jr., 9671
Cressman, Paul R., Sr., 9671
Cressman, Warren, 6658
Crestar Bank, 2345, 9539
Creswell, Al, 8595
Cretin, Shan, Ph.D., 366
Creveling, Kevin, 3481
Crews, Edna, 8472
Crews, Gary, 4562
Crews, Mark S., 1
Crews, Sidney, 4817
CRF Charitable Lead Trust, 5981
Crha, Tom, 9655
Cribb, T. Kenneth, Jr., 8266
Cribbs, Elizabeth R., 6538
Cribbs, Jeffrey S., Sr., 9521
Crichlow, Rhoda, 5393
Crider, Kathleen Vatterott, 2371
Crim, Gloice Y., 2575
Crimmins, Timothy, 4009
Crimmins, Timothy P., Jr., 1671
Crion Trust, Marion O., 2769
Cripe, Rob, 3298
Cripps-Downey, Lisa, 4347
Criscuoli, Phyllis M., 5892
Criser, Marshall M., 2286
Crislip, Stephen, 9780
Crisman, C. Benjamin, Jr., 6868
Crisp, Don W., 8795, 9140
Crisp, Peter O., 5828
Crispen, Deanna, 3271
Crispo, Arthur, 6651
Criss, C.C., 4640
Criss, Mabel L., 4640
Cristiano, Robert, 279
Cristo, Alex, 7756
Criswell, Pamela, 1817
Criswell, W.A., 8789
Critchfield, Jack, 7012
Critchfield, Paul N., 152
Crites, Jana, 3366
Critser, Charlotte, 3596
Critser, Gary, 3596
Crittenden, Casey, 709
Crittenden, Paul, 709
Critz, Dale C., Jr., 2548
Croak, Francis R., 9919
Croce, Darren, 8787
Crockard, Francis H., Jr., 20
Crocker, Bruce I., 8093
Crocker, Charles, 440
Crocker, Mark, 8474
Crocker, Mary A., 440
Crocker, Matt, 3532
Crocker, Ruth, 1563
Crockett, Barbara, 7156
Crockett, Daryl, 3393
Crockett, Donnie, 3365
Crockett, John R., III, 3577
Crocodile Bay Lodge, 742
Croft, David L., 4602
Croft, Edward, 2432
Croft, Mary, 5234
Croft, Thomas D., 7404
Croggon, Charles C., 1572
Croisant, Kim, 3193
Croll, David D., 4000
Croll, Victoria B., 4000
Cromley, Janet, 7749
Cromley, Marian, 7749
Crompton, Cathy, 7671
Crompton, John L., 3358
Cromwell Irrevocable Trust, George, The, 3767
Cromwell Music Inc., 6704
Cromwell, Barbara T., 3767
Cromwell, P. McEvoy, 3766
Cron, Maurice, 7567
Cronan, Joan C., 8560
Cronan, John J., 8383
Crone, Julie Cole, 2758
Crone, Marvin R., 2758
Cronenwett, Linda, 6414
Cronin, Charles F., 4086
Cronin, Dennis, 279
Cronin, Elizabeth, 4383
Cronin, Greg, 4830
Cronin, Janet B., 8522
Cronin, Jennifer C., 6451
Cronin, Karen E., 2660
Cronin, Mary Virginia, 4383
Cronin, Michele, 2718
Cronin, Thomas C., 3083
Cronin, Tom, 1650
Cronquist, Kent, 7355
Cronson, Mary, 6839
Cronson, Paul, 6839
Crook, Caryl, 8790
Crook, Deb, 1511
Crook, Eleanor, 8790
Crook, Eleanor Butt, 8790
Crook, Elizabeth, 8790
Crook, Mary Elizabeth, 8790
Crook, Molly, 5038
Crook, William H., 8790
Crook, William H., Jr., 8790
Crooke, Paulette M., 7078
Cropper, Spencer S., 7702
Cropper, Stephen W., 6052
Crosbie, Barbara, 4005
Crosby, Andrew, 4630
Crosby, Brewster, 4630
Crosby, Claire, 4630
Crosby, Heather, 8371
Crosby, Heather D., 3877
Crosby, Jack, 1518
Crosby, Lesley, 4630
Crosby, Lindsey, 2491
Crosby, Meg, 8549
Crosby, Mike, 4630
Crosby, Ron J., 7798
Crosby, Sara, 8521
Crosby, Teri, 4630
Crosby-Newman, Dale, 4630
Crosier, Louis, 4056
Cross Living Trust, C. Walker, 5007
Cross, Amanda B., 5829
Cross, Barbara, 1154
Cross, Beverly, 6151
Cross, C. Walker, 5007
Cross, Christine E., 793
Cross, Cynthia Page, 6504
Cross, David L., 8351
Cross, Harry L., III, 9538
Cross, Iris M., 8718
Cross, John W., III, 6504
Cross, John W., IV, 6504
Cross, Karen, 5348
Cross, Mary, 5829
Cross, Ronald, 2514
Cross, Theodore L., 5829
Cross, William, 3768
Crosse, Leslie, 5874
Crosse, Richard L., 5471
Crossed, Andrew I., 5830
Crossed, Carol N., 5830
Crossed, David, 5830
Crossed, Katherine, 5830
Crossed, Nicholas, 5830
Crossed, Richard C., 5830
Crossett, Jennifer A., 1383
Crossett, Susan M., 6527
Crosson, David, 8199
Crosswell, C. Mark, 2449
Crosswell, Nancy L., 2449
Crosswhite, R. Joe, 6406
Croston Estates, Inc., 6768
Crothers, Thomas, 4343
Crotty, Cindy P., 7523
Crotty, Sharolyn K., 4002
Crotty, Thomas J., 4002
Crotty, Tom, 4056
Crouch, John Clayton, 4846
Crouch, Robert F., 428
Crouch, Stanley, 5612
Croul, John Bradford, 441
Croul, John V., 441
Croul, Spencer Behr, 441
Crow, Barry, 2642
Crow, Cindy, 2642
Crow, Dan, 3552
Crow, Emerald, 2642
Crow, J. Greg, 8695
Crow, Robert, 973, 1120
Crowder, D. Lynette, 9484
Crowder, Megan, 7806
Crowder, Sheff, 2042
Crowder, William "Doug" D., 9501
Crowe, Adrienne, 366
Crowe, John T., 8260
Crowe, Maria, 3340
Crowell Benevolence and Education Trust, Henry P., 1398
Crowell Trust, Henry P. and Susan C., 1398
Crowell, Frederick P., 303
Crowell, Henry P., 1398
Crowell, John, 1100
Crowell, Richard L., Jr., 3643
Crowl, Rick, 3447
Crowley, George, 2436
Crowley, John, 5046
Crowley, Martin, 1329
Crowley, Maureen, 9816
Crowley, Michael, 977
Crowley, Patrick, 2732
Crowley, Peter, 5412
Crowley, Robert, 7993
Crown Acquisitions Inc., 5768
Crown Equipment Corp., 7436
Crown Group Ltd., 7507
Crown Kings Highway LLC, 6054
Crown Point Community Foundation, 3347
Crown Sports Management, 9470
Crown, A. Steven, 2781
Crown, James S., 2781
Crown, Lester, 2781
Crown, Rebecca, 2781
Crown, Susan, 1368, 2780, 2781
Crown, William, 2781

Crownover, Tyler, 5059
Crozer, Taliaferro F., 2459
Crozier, Daniel G., Jr., 8163
Crozier, James Brooks, 8163
Crozier, Jennifer, 6203
Crozier, Nancy R., 8163
Cruikshank, Robert J., 8848
Crum & Forster Holdings Corporation, 9178
Crum, Gary T., 8758
Crum, Sylvie P., 8758
Crumb, Lucille, 1015
Crumly, Kevin W., 2762
Crumm, Michelle, 4340
Crummer, M. Philip, 4640
Crump, Ed, Jr., 3626
Crump, Linda, 5031
Crump, Susanne B., 9529
Crumpacker, Mark, 1388
Cruse Trust, Lee H., 4877
Crutcher, Walter T., 3581
Crutchfield, Brian C., 7273
Crutchfield, James N., 2191
Crute, Phifer, 7137
Cruver, Mark, 2423
Cruver, Natalie, 2423
Cruz, Aida Torres, 8353
Cruz, Carl J., 3991
Cruz, Edward, 6703
Cruz, Frank H., 727
Cruz, Phillip W., 9247
Cruz, Roxanne, 1069
Cruzen, William J., 9589
Cryan, Kim, 7686
Cryer, Arthur W., 5636
Cryer, Marnie Fitzmaurice, 1721
Crysdale, James, 3249
Crystal Glass, 7638
Crystal, Norman S., 5113
Crystal, Steven B., 5113
CSAA Insurance Exchange, 421
CSFB, 6904
CT Health Foundation, 3953
CTB, Inc., 2565
CTFSC, 9228
Cu, Patricia A., 4003
Cubit, Andrew, 3469
Cuccaro, Randy, 5805
Cuddy, Gerard P., 7936
Cuddy, John, Fr., 2502
Cudiamat, Celia, 419
Cudlie Accessories, LLC, 6949
Cuellar, Mariano-Florentino, 686
Cuevas, Jim, 419
Cuff, Courtney, 1421
Cugini, Robert, 9715
Culang, Malka, 7129
Culbertson, Alan N., 9405
Culbertson, Judy Broadfoot, 9019
Culbertson, Richard W., Jr., 5463
Culbertson, William, 7451
Culbertson, William J., 7694
Cullen, Albert F., Jr., 4325
Cullen, Ann P., 1832
Cullen, Carolyn Colket, 7987
Cullen, Hugh Roy, 8792
Cullen, Lillie, 8792
Cullen, Matthew P., 4371, 4463
Cullen, Roy Henry, 8792
Cullerot, Marc, 5175
Cullinan, George, 4830
Culliton, Adam B., 8073
Culliton-Metzger, Carol, 8073
Cullman, Dorothy F., 5831
Cullman, Edgar M., Jr., 5831
Cullman, Lewis B., 5831
Culman, Anne LaFarge, 3712
Culp, Frosty, 7231
Culp, Stephen A., 8599
Culp, Susan, 7231
Culpeper, Daphne Seybolt, 1568
Culpepper, Bruce, 9168
Culpepper, Jerry, 9179
Culver Franchising System Inc., 9837
Culver, Craig, 9837
Culver, Craig C., 9837
Culver, Jan, 7715
Culver, John, 9742
Culver, Leola, 9837
Culverhouse, Joy McCann, 2232
Cumberland Security Bank, 3591
Cumberland Trust, 8570
Cumberland Trust & Investment, 8636
Cumberland Trust & Investment Co., 8573
Cumings, Susan Hurd, 8101
Cumming, Annette P., 9976
Cumming, David E., 9976
Cumming, Ian M., 9976
Cumming, John D., 9341
Cumming, John Darnaby, 9976
Cumming, Maude, 9726
Cumming, R. Malcolm, 4412
Cummings 1987 Revocable Trust, Barbara, 4186
Cummings Properties Foundation, 4003
Cummings Realty Trust, W.S., 4003
Cummings Trust UAD 1, Anthony Fisher, 4384
Cummings Trust, Ruth, 5020
Cummings, Adam N., 5833
Cummings, Alexander B., 2428
Cummings, Anthony F., 4384
Cummings, Caroline B., 4384
Cummings, Don, 3330
Cummings, Edwin L., 5834
Cummings, Eliza A., 3178
Cummings, Frances L., 5834
Cummings, Hannah, 5833
Cummings, James H., 5832
Cummings, James K., 5833
Cummings, Jason, 5833
Cummings, Jim, 9147
Cummings, Jon, 5191
Cummings, Joyce M., 4003, 4199
Cummings, Julie Fisher, 4384, 4423
Cummings, Keith L., 4384
Cummings, Kevin, 5317
Cummings, Kurt P., 8457
Cummings, Molly, 6158
Cummings, Nathan, 5833
Cummings, Ornelia, Dr., 4822
Cummings, Patricia A., 4003, 4199
Cummings, Peter D., 4384
Cummings, Rick, 5833
Cummings, Roberta Friedman, 5833
Cummings, Ruth, 5833
Cummings, Sonia Simon, 5833
Cummings, Susan Hurd, 3073
Cummings, William S., 4003, 4199
Cummins Engine Co., Inc., 3292
Cummins Farm, Jay H., 3666
Cummins Inc., 3292
Cummins, Betty S., 3666
Cummins, Bruce, 7630
Cummins, Dick, 9228
Cummins, Dwight, 9950
Cummins, F. James, 4372
Cummins, Joan, 4641
Cummins, Joan M., 4641
Cummins, Robert, 4641
Cummins, Susan, 1092
Cummiskey, Thomas M., 7610
Cumper, Yan, 2031
CUNA Mutual Insurance Society, 9838
Cundiff, Ben, 8550
Cuneo, John F., 2783
Cunin, Marilyn A., 7391
Cunniff, June, 67
Cunningham, Charlotte, 5885
Cunningham, Daniel B., 7702
Cunningham, Daniel P., 6260
Cunningham, Deborah Sue, 4391
Cunningham, Dennis D., 685
Cunningham, Edward V.K., Jr., 6572
Cunningham, Elaine, 7103
Cunningham, Gary, 4729
Cunningham, Helen, 8035
Cunningham, Jane W., 7605
Cunningham, Jim, 1016
Cunningham, John, 9280
Cunningham, John B.E., 7342
Cunningham, Kurt, 7280
Cunningham, Larry, 3360
Cunningham, Laura Moore, 2630
Cunningham, Nancy B., 651
Cunningham, Pam, 7280
Cunningham, Paul, 1774
Cunningham, Phil, 7474
Cunningham, Raymond C., Jr., 4391
Cunningham, Sarah, 7366
Cunningham, Suzanne, 8175
Cunningham, William, 9070
Cunningham, William J., Jr., 6913
Cuno, James, 579
Cuomo, Margaret I., 6549
Cupps, Wendy, 1037
Curb, Linda, 8554
Curb, Mike, 8554
Curci Trust, John, 443
Curci, John, 443
Curci, John L., Jr., 697
Curci, John V., 7695
Curci, Kay, 444
Curci, Robert, 443
Curci, Shurl, 444
Curcio, Pat, 1051
Curdumi, Abelardo S., 1581
Curiel, Terese Coudreaut, 2191
Curl, Eschol, 7540
Curl, Paul T., 9101
Curley, John J., 6144
Curley, Robert M., 3946
Curley, Walter J.P., Hon., 5549, 5692
Curmark, 1850
Curnes, Thomas J., 1381
Curns, Jeannine, 7682
Curphey, John M., 7512
Curran Trust, Catherine G., 6624
Curran, Bentley, 9821
Curran, Brooke, 9380
Curran, Carol Cockrell, 8770
Curran, Catherine G., 6624
Curran, Constance A., 5835
Curran, David, 5275
Curran, Edward L., 7152
Curran, Elaine, 1160
Curran, John P., 5835
Curran, Karen Mitchell, 2034
Curran, Meredith, 5835
Curran, Michael, 7185
Curran, Peter, 3538, 6624
Curran, Richard B., 8770
Curran, Sean, 5835
Curran, William E., 3708
Currault, Douglas N., II, 112
Currey, Melisa, 8550
Currey, Richard, 3289
Currie, Greg, 7223
Currie, Jo H., 841
Currie, Rebecca, 7324
Currier, Andrea B., 9562
Currier, Lavinia, 9526
Currier, Michael, 4191
Currin, Katherine N., 8599
Currin, William, 7496
Curry, Elizabeth R., 5310, 5836
Curry, Lauren A., 9373
Curry, Ravenel B., 5836
Curry, Ravenel B., III, 5836, 7195
Curry, Richard, 2712
Curry, Yvonne, 1227
Curt, Timothy J., 7048
Curtin, Jack, 4061
Curtin, Michael, 779
Curtin, Susan, 779
Curtis, Alfred B., Jr., 6703
Curtis, Barbara H., 7186
Curtis, Boyd Willett, 1523
Curtis, Curtis D., 9912
Curtis, Diane, 5644
Curtis, Donald W., 7186
Curtis, Eileen A., 4344
Curtis, Elizabeth H., 265
Curtis, Emma Eliza, 9361
Curtis, Jennie, 4065
Curtis, John R., Jr., 9559
Curtis, Krysten, 411
Curtis, Louise Willett, 1523
Curtis, Pamela A., 2066
Curtis, Pat, 4562
Curtis, Patricia A., 1219
Curtis, Sarah, 9912
Curves International, Inc., 8898
Cusak, Michael, 7474
Cusenbary, Laura, 1528
Cusenza, Geraldine, 445
Cusenza, John, 445
Cushing, Brenda J., 3411
Cushing, H. Eric, 4162
Cushing, Raymond L., 7412
Cushing, Robert T., 6802
Cushman, Anne Adams, 3972
Cushman, Dena, 9769
Cushnie, Douglas J., 7520
Cushnie, Karen W., 7520
Custard, Linda P., 8912
Custer, Greg E., 845, 1323
Custom Nutrition Services, LLC, 175
Custom Shops, The, 5361
Customer 1 One, Inc., 8571
Cuthbert, Brant, 1463
Cutler Assocs., Inc., 4005
Cutler, Douglas, 4005
Cutler, Eliot R., 3695
Cutler, Elizabeth J., 4005
Cutler, Joan H., 4006
Cutler, Kimberly, 5804
Cutler, Laura Katz, 2177
Cutler, Linda Beech, 1103
Cutler, Melanie Stewart, 3695
Cutler, Melvin S., 4005
Cutler, Paul I., 2251
Cutler, Robert, 4006
Cutler, Scott, 6573
Cutler, Stephen, 6224

Cutler, Theodore H., 4006
Cutler, Tracy, 8135
Cutlip, Kimberly E., 7657
Cutright, James M., 7378
Cutshall, Ronny L., 9302
Cutter, Nancy L., 5171
Cutter, W. Bowman, III, 6782
Cutting, Carol T., 1266
Cuzzort, Pamela K., 8638
CVS Corp., 8379
CVS Pharmacy, Inc., 8379
Cwierzyk, Theresa A., 5838
Cwikiel, J. Wilfred, 4522
Cynvestors Limited Partnership, 9908
Cynvestors, LP, 9908
Cypen, Stephen H., 2396
Cyphers, Judith B., 9537
Cypress Foundation, Inc., 2514
Cypress Living Trust, The, 909
Cyr, Pamela M., 7936
Cyre, Jan, 9726
Cytryn, Aron, 6664
Czaplicki, Daniel A., 8020
Czapski, Max, 6972
Czarnecki, Mark J., 6406
Czarsty, Craig W., 7343

D'Adamo, DeeDee, 1002
D'Adamo, Gene, 3372
D'Addario, James, 5841
D'Addario, Janet, 5841
D'Addario, Robert, 5841
D'Agostino, Max, 5843
D'Agostino, Sharon, 5327
D'Amato & Lynch, 6904
D'Amato, Catherine, 3956
D'Amato, F. Marino, 1643
D'Amelio, Frank, 6633
D'Amico, Kimberly, 5887
D'Amore, Robert R., 1671
D'Angelo, Daniel J., 9965
D'Angelo, Margaret A., 5238
D'Angelo, Peter P., 5238, 5348
D'Anniballe, Nick, 6203
d'Ansembourg, Marianne, 536
D'Antignac, Louisa Glenn, 2471
D'Arcangelo, Inez E., 6971
D'Arcy, Jessica S., 9262
D'Arcy, Stephen R., 4463
D'Atri, E. Lang, 7673
d'Autremont, Gene, 7866
D'Elia, Lorraine, 568
D'Hemery, Elizabeth Budge, 1197
D'Olier, H. Mitchell, 2593
D'Souza, Bernadette, 3644
Da Silva, Terezinha, 2631
Daab, Justin, 3038
Daaleman, Henry J., 5388
Daaleman, Mark, 5388
Dab, John M., 8613
Dabah, Ezra, 5840
Dabah, Kim, 5557
Dabah, Renee, 5840
Dabah, Solomon, 5557
Dabdoub, Tony, 101
Daboul, Peter J., 3992
Dachs Charitable Foundation, Harvey and Shelli, The, 5768
Dachs, Alan B., 294
Dachs, Alan M., 296, 446, 823
Dachs, Lauren B., 294, 296, 446, 823
DaCosta, Igor, 7050
Dacus, Shannon, 8819
Dada, Nargis, 225
Dadd, Robert, 5404
Daddario, Nicholas, 4284
Dadelahi, Samin, 9999
Dadisman, Carrol, 2037
Dadisman, Mildred, 2037
Dado, Craig, 1053
Dadourian, Dadour, 7018
Dadourian, Melanie, 7018
Dadourian, Stephen, 7018
Daetz, Alta, 4369
Daffey, Michael, 5661
Daffin, Zack O., 2434
Daffodil Valley Kiwanis Club, 9652
Dagenais, Scott E., 6406
Daggett, Christopher J., 5243, 5441
Daggett, Sharon Lord, 8992
Dagostino, Sharon Kathryn, 5326
Dahan Homes, Inc., 3770
Dahan, Elisabeth, 8794
Dahan, Haron, 3770
Dahan, Rene, 8794
Dahl, Amy, 4780
Dahl, Carol, 7865
Dahl, Cary, 9412
Dahl, David A., 1349
Dahl, Doris, 7767
Dahl, Felicity, 4178
Dahl, Felicity Ann, 4178
Dahl, Jean M., 3902
Dahl, Kathy, 2037
Dahl, Leslie, 1632
Dahl, Lucy, 4178
Dahl, Marilyn, 3469
Dahl, Ophelia M., 4178
Dahl, Richard J., 2592
Dahl, Tessa, 4178
Dahl, Theo M.R., 4178
Dahl, W.T., 3425
Daignault, Sarah, 8380
Dailey, Diane, 9775
Dailey, George, Jr., 5414
Dailey, Julia, 5598
Dailey, Trent, 3280
DaimlerChrysler Corp., 4366
Dain Rauscher Inc., 4748
Dairy Council of Arizona, 3245
Dairy Farmers of Florida, 3245
Dairy Management, 3245
Dairy Max, 3245
Dajani, Lorraine H., 2288
Dajani, Virginia, 5585
Dake, Gary C., 5803
Dakin, John, 1518
Dal Pra, Marilee L., 152
Dalba, Jeanne Trulaske, 4995
Dalbec, Keith, 7181
Dalbey, Joan, 7088
Dalbey, T., 7088
Dalby, Linda S., 4160
Dale, Angela Henkels, 8089
Dale, Berteline Baier, 6247
Dale, Brett M., 2812
Dale, Douglas, 1263
Dale, Harvey, 5622
Dalen, James, 175
Dales, Joanna Donnelly, 4472
Dalessandro, Frances C., 4007
Dalessandro, John J., 4007
Daley, Ann, 1433
Daley, Charles J., Jr., 3828
Daley, William M., 2746
Dalio, Barbara, 1569
Dalio, Devon, 1569
Dalio, Matthew, 1569
Dalio, Raymond T., 1569
Dalis, Joan W., 9419
Dalis, M. Dan, 9419
Dall'Olmo, Gail, 4448
Dallas Cowboys Football Club, Ltd., 8943
Dallas Cowboys Merchandising, 8943
Dallas Jewish Community Foundation, 7791
Dallas, H. James, 4712
Dallepezze, Georgia D., 2049
Dallepezze, Joanne M., 2049
Dallepezze, John R., 2049
Dallepezze, Peter A., 2049
Dalquist, Donja, 918
Dalrymple, S.D. Sackler, 6779
Dalton Charitable Lead Trust, 8448
Dalton, Ann V., 2073
Dalton, Beverley E., 9426
Dalton, Daniel J., 5471
Dalton, Donna, 4721
Dalton, Dorothy U., 4385
Dalton, Mark, 1512
Dalton, Mark F., 6056
Dalton, Robert, 986
Dalton, Sharon C., 1531
Daly Charitable Foundation, Carole & Robert, The, 8586
Daly Irrevocable Trust, Helen, 9359
Daly, Aileen H., 2662
Daly, Andrew, 1518
Daly, Beth A., 2234
Daly, Bettina M., 5207
Daly, Carole, 447
Daly, Charles U., 2946
Daly, Dan, 2864
Daly, Eileen F., 9445
Daly, James J., 2234, 5719
Daly, Jim, 9631
Daly, Mary W.C., 8429
Daly, Megan Lewis, 2212
Daly, Michael P., 3946
Daly, P. Niles, Jr., 9413
Daly, Paul E., 2380
Daly, Robert, 447
Daly, Robert A., 447
Daly, Robert C., 7002
Daly, William, 6528
Dalzell, David B., Jr., 9773
Daman, Tim, 4357
Damasco, Jude, 1336
Damato, Charles A., 6068
Dambach, Michael, 8363
Dambacher, Gary, 1198
Dameron, Beth, 8495
Damery, Sean, 1423
Damicone, Jim, 4026
Damie, Robert, 3879
Damm, Carla, 3504
Damon, Brenden A., 3504
Damon, Catherine B., 4211
Damon, Donald H., 3504
Damon, Doneen Keemer, 1765
Damon, Karen L., 3504
Damon, Kathleen J., 3504
Damonti, John L., 5711, 5712
Dan, Hideo, 5249
Dana Corporation, 4386
Dana Holding Corporation, 4386
Dana, Alan G., 4008
Dana, Charles A., 5845, 6144
Dana, Charles A., III, 5845
Dana, Eleanor Naylor, 5845
Dana, Herman, 4008
Dana, Myer R., 4008
Danaher, Kevin, 306
Dance Consultants Unlimited Inc., 7425
Dance, Jed, 8560
Danchak, Peter J., 8152
Dane, Arabella S., 8049
Dane, Edward M., 4122
Danelian, Richard, 1036
Daney, Lee E., 8289
Danford, Gladys B., 448
Danher Corp., 7424
Danial, Robert, 2050
Danial, Terrence, 2050
Danic, Jennifer, 3390
Daniel Industries, Inc., 4885
Daniel International Corp., 8476
Daniel, Charles E., 8476
Daniel, Charles W., 27
Daniel, Christopher J., 8848
Daniel, D. Ronald, 5684
Daniel, Desmon, 4532
Daniel, George, 9421
Daniel, Jamal, 8981
Daniel, James L., Jr., 8848
Daniel, Libby Stanfield, 7184
Daniel, Lyndra P., 27
Daniel, Nicole C., 3609
Daniel, Rania, 8981
Daniel, Suzanne T., 8225
Daniel, Thomas F., 1189
Daniel, Veronica, 5218
Daniel, William, 7353
Daniel-Brima, Doris, 1211
Daniell, Barbara E., 1570
Daniell, Robert F., 1570
Daniels, Aaron, 6475
Daniels, Angel Roberson, 244
Daniels, Bill, 1399
Daniels, Bruce, 7416
Daniels, Cathy Hunter, 5100
Daniels, Dianne J., 5652
Daniels, Eleanor G., 8380
Daniels, Fred H., 8380
Daniels, Fred H., II, 8380
Daniels, James C., 5802
Daniels, Jere F., 2112
Daniels, Jere F., Jr., 2112
Daniels, John W., Jr., 9841
Daniels, John, Jr., 9849
Daniels, Lee, 888
Daniels, Lillian I., 1819
Daniels, Nicholas, 1962
Daniels, Raymond L., 3556
Daniels, Ronald J., 3726, 3803
Daniels, Sandra Segerstrom, 1135, 1136
Daniels, Terry, 888
Daniels-Carter, Valarie, 9855
Danielson, Barbara D., 2791
Danielson, Barbara S., 2791
Danielson, Danny, 3320
Danielson, Dave, 9595
Danielson, Donald C., 3397
Danielson, Patty, 3320
Danielson, Richard E., Jr., 2791
Danlely-Woolfolk, Eliza, 320
Danis, Joseph, 5422
Daniski, Joe, 4666
Dankenbrink, Kristine A., 7989
Danker, Richard, 1982
Danker-Basham Foundation, 7012
Dankers, Martha, 9616
Dankers, Paul, 6492

Davis, Gale L., 6774
Davis, Gale Lansing, 4669
Davis, Gary, 1571
Davis, Gary A., 7771
Davis, Gary B., 1274
Davis, Gary Bo, 4722
Davis, Gary S., 1571
Davis, George, 2514
Davis, Greg, 3303
Davis, H. Coleman, III, 104
Davis, H. Scott, Jr., 3581
Davis, Henry, 8109
Davis, Henry A., 5034
Davis, Henry C., 104
Davis, Hilda J., 8005
Davis, Holbrook R., 2056
Davis, Howard C., 4751
Davis, J. Bradley, 3015, 9509
Davis, J. Homer, Rev., 9034
Davis, J.H. Dow, 2056
Davis, J.R., 3099
Davis, J.R., III, 3099
Davis, Jack, 92
Davis, James, 9225
Davis, James C., 3719, 3771, 3872
Davis, James M., 5794
Davis, James P., 106
Davis, James S., 4189
Davis, Jana, 8582
Davis, Jana J., 8550
Davis, Jay M., 2444
Davis, Jeannine M., 104
Davis, Jeff, 2765
Davis, Jill A., 5809
Davis, Joan, 9659
Davis, Joe C., 8555
Davis, Joel, 1373
Davis, Joel F.C., 4642
Davis, Joel P., 2056
Davis, John H., 3772, 4011
Davis, John L., 4642, 4802
Davis, John Martin, 8959
Davis, John R., 4391
Davis, Jonathan P., 2056
Davis, Judith M., 8460, 8468
Davis, Judy, 4806
Davis, Julie, 9652
Davis, Karen, 3398
Davis, Kassie, 2756
Davis, Kathryn W., 1761, 3887
Davis, Kathy, 3272, 3345
Davis, Kelly, 2514
Davis, Ken W., Jr., 8799
Davis, Kimberly J., 3771
Davis, Kris, 1762
Davis, Kyle, 9059
Davis, Lancing, 6774
Davis, Lansing, 1761
Davis, Lant, 3396
Davis, Lawrence M., 8383
Davis, Leigh Evans, 9448
Davis, Leroy, 2075
Davis, Linwood, 7228
Davis, Lois E., 8798, 8800
Davis, Loren, 7846
Davis, Lucy, 1400
Davis, M., 4404
Davis, M. Margrite, 4391
Davis, Margaret, 5014
Davis, Mark, 3366
Davis, Marna, 5853
Davis, Martin C., 8918, 8953
Davis, Marty, 7417
Davis, Mary, 3370
Davis, Mary W., 6876
Davis, Mary Yates, 5537
Davis, Matt, 4448
Davis, Maynard K., 2056
Davis, Melissa M., 4802
Davis, Michael, 1177
Davis, Michael L., 4661
Davis, Michael M., 3915
Davis, Milton Austin, 2055
Davis, Milton C., 19
Davis, Murphy, 9109
Davis, Nancy E., 1530
Davis, Norm, 15
Davis, Patricia, 1959, 4772
Davis, Patricia J., 90
Davis, Paul, 9034
Davis, Paul E., 4827
Davis, Paula, 5807
Davis, Peyton, 5537
Davis, Peyton Yates, 5538
Davis, Phillip A., 796
Davis, Preston, 8005
Davis, Rachelle, 9796
Davis, Randall, 4383
Davis, Randy, Dr., 4496
Davis, Ray C., 1762
Davis, Rebecca, 7336
Davis, Richard, 3099
Davis, Richard A., 7749
Davis, Richard K., 4784
Davis, Rita M., 4010
Davis, Robert G., 7771
Davis, Robert J., 4010
Davis, Robert M., 2690, 7771
Davis, Robert P., 1900
Davis, Robin A., 7659
Davis, Roger J., 7972
Davis, Ron, 1518
Davis, Sadie, 3685
Davis, Samuel S., 4642
Davis, Sandra, 796
Davis, Shelby M.C., 1761, 6774
Davis, Shelley A., 3079
Davis, Shirley Cameron, 8747
Davis, Sonya Meyers, 4945
Davis, Staige, 9375
Davis, Stephanie A., 9246
Davis, Stephen A., 4011
Davis, Steve, 2439
Davis, Steven, 1750
Davis, Steven C., 7781
Davis, Steven D., 1140
Davis, Susan, 8043
Davis, Susan Brown, 9416
Davis, Susan F., 9870
Davis, T. Wayne, 2054
Davis, T.C., 8799
Davis, Tammy, 1035
Davis, Terry C., Dr., 3624
Davis, Tine W., 2054
Davis, Tony, 1750
Davis, Ulla, 645
Davis, Velma, 2786
Davis, Virginia, 3330
Davis, Vivian, 7846
Davis, W.R., 8696
Davis, Walt, 8809
Davis, William, 3771, 8004
Davis, William M., 9780
Davis, Wilma H., 4103
Davis, Winifred S., 2477
Davis-Kusek, Jane, 4011
Davish, Patrick, 5381
Davison & McCarthy, PC, 8151
Davison, David, 1537
Davison, Henry P., II, 6217
Davison, J. Scott, 3364
Davison, James, 3649
Davison, Jane I., 7503
Davison, Katusha, 6088
Davison, Kristina P., 4213
Davison, Maxine B., 5854
Davison, Michael E., 7806
Davison, Richard, 3752, 3773
Davison, Richard H., 4299
Davison, Rosalee C., 3752, 3773
Davison, William M., IV, 8236
Davlin, Jim, 4442
Davoren, Peter J., 5482
Dawbarn, H.D. "Buz", 9412
Dawkins, Clint, 2288
Dawkins, John R., 9778
Dawley, Gary C., 4349
Dawley, John T., 4009
Dawley, Michael C., 2752
Dawn, Donald D., 3838
Dawson Development Co., LLC, 3715
Dawson Family Partners, Lp, 9996
Dawson, Alexandra, 9996
Dawson, Christopher, 9996
Dawson, Deborah Pratt, 9996
Dawson, E. Douglas, 1129
Dawson, Jonathan T., 9996
Dawson, Judith M., 2586
Dawson, Kelly, 6841
Dawson, Mackenzie, 1578
Dawson, Melanie A., 7826
Dawson, Peter, 5412
Dawson, Peter A., 295
Dawson, Tom, 7351
Day Cos., Inc., 8556
Day Foundation, W.K., 1219
Day Interim Trust, Margaret, 1764
Day, Ann B., 7967
Day, Barbara Arnold, 4833
Day, Bryan W., 105
Day, C. Burke, 2448
Day, C. Parke, 2448
Day, C. Peyton, 2448
Day, Carolyn, 3571
Day, Cecil B., 2448
Day, Clarence C., 8556
Day, Clinton M., 2448
Day, Dana L., 4802
Day, Diana L., 1140
Day, Donald, 4715
Day, Donald R., 4757
Day, Doris D., 2787
Day, Dorothy W., 457
Day, Elizabeth S., 951
Day, Elizabeth Sprague, 1207
Day, Elizabeth Y., 3758
Day, Frank R., 4833
Day, Frederick K.W., 4804
Day, H. Corbin, 21, 43, 5310
Day, Helen D., 95
Day, Howard M., 457
Day, Howard M., Jr., 457
Day, James C., 7780, 8801
Day, James C., Jr., 8801
Day, Janet L., 7074
Day, Joan Cralle, 3571
Day, Joseph, 456
Day, Kathie, 2448
Day, Kellyann, 1562
Day, Lincoln W., 4804
Day, Lisa, 9604
Day, Lynn Weyerhaeuser, 4804
Day, Marian P., 5526
Day, Martha Bonsal, 5441
Day, Matt, Sr., 774
Day, Michael, 421
Day, Mike, 3761
Day, Nancy Sayles, 1763
Day, Paul B., Jr., 7967
Day, Robert A., 456, 457, 774, 1219
Day, Robert A., Jr., 456, 457
Day, Sandra R., 105
Day, Sherm, 2427
Day, Stan, 4802
Day, Stanley R., 4804
Day, Stanley R., Jr., 4802, 4804
Day, Steven, 3314
Day, Susan, 3571
Day, Tammis, 457
Day, Tammis A., 457
Day, Teresa K., 8801
Day, Theodore J., 457
Day, Tim, 9836
Day, Timothy T., 105
Day, Timothy T., Jr., 105
Day, Victor B., 2787
Day, Vivian W., 4802, 4804
Day, Willametta K., 457
Day, William D., Jr., 9246
Dayak, Allyson Griswold, 1787
Dayal, Shirish, 1239
Daylight Motors, 9124
Dayries, John, 5012
Dayton Hudson Corp., 4776
Dayton Power and Light Co., The, 7429
Dayton, Ann C., 4773
Dayton, Christine, 3825
Dayton, Dawn, 9769
Dayton, Edward N., 4643
Dayton, James G., 4773
Dayton, Joan L., 4773
Dayton, John, 2487, 8912
Dayton, Mae F., 4773
Dayton, Mary L., 4790
Dayton, Mary Lee, 4790
Dayton, Megan M., 4773
Dayton, Robert J., 4773
Dayton, Ruth Woods, 9774
Dayton, Scott N., 4773
Dayton, Sherry Ann, 4643
Dayton, Tobin J., 4773
Dayton, Wallace C., 4790
Dayton, Wimberly Charlotte, 2487
Daytona International Speedway, 2294
DDF 2005 Charitable Remainder Annuity Trust, 370
DDFY2K Family Trust, 532
de Alonso, Marcela Perez, 687
de Barona, Maryann Santos, 3282
de Beaumont, Pierre, 3774
de Castro, Audie, 1108
De Cordova, Michael, 6572
De Cordova, Noel, Jr., 6572
De Ganahl, Frank A., 4012
de Geus, Aart, 1232
de Gunzburg, Charles, 5744
De Gunzburg, Jean, 2999
De Gunzburg, Terry, 2999
de Kay, Helen M., 2788
de la Fuente, Aura, 2947
de la Garza, Luis, 9148
de la Pena, Alfredo, 8199
De La Reguera, Deborah, 9871
de la Renta, Anne E., 5954
De La Vega, Ralph, 8675
De Laski Family Foundation, The, 7898

De Laski Grubb, Kathleen, 7898
De Laski, Donald, 7898
de Leon, Jana L., 8189
de Limur, Genevieve Bothin, 331
De Llano, Matias, 8802
De Luca, Victor, 6571
De Luxembourg, Robert, 5885
De Meester, Paul Baron, 6007
de Moaraes, Antonuio Carlos Viela, 8260
De Narp, Frederic, 7093
De Nicola, Anthony J., 5239
De Nicola, Christie, 5239
De Nicola, Christie B., 5239
De Orchis, Douglas F., 8383
De Palchi, Alfredo, 8057
de Peyster, Electra Ducommun, 485
de Pineres, Cristina Gutierrez, 6042
De Ramel, Guillaume, 8381
de Ramel, Regis A., 1864
De Rivera, Ana Luisa Diez, 6319
de Rothchild, Robert, 6229
de Rothschild, Ariane, 5857
de Rothschild, Benjamin, 5857
de Rothschild, Edmond, 5857
de Rothschild, Nadine, 5857
De Silva, Duminda, 7807
de Simone, Ashley, 5593
De Sousa, Joseph, 6528
de Vegh, Diana, 5653
de Vegh, Pierre J., 5653
De Vegh, Pierre J., 6180
de Venoge, Marc, 5662, 6947
De Vivo, Darryl C., 6898
de Vries, Shlomit, 1972
de Watteville, Irene, 6901
de Weerdt, Tom, 2944
Deadrick, Chris, 4667
Deal, Jane, 2867
Deal-Koestner, Janet J., 4564
Dealey, Mandy, 8840
Dean Foods Corporation, 8803
Dean Management Corp., 8803
Dean Revocable Trust, Jimmy, 2789
Dean's Foods, 3245
Dean, Anthony M., 2702
Dean, Caroline W., 5858
Dean, Danny, 3303
Dean, Danny R., 3274
Dean, Donna, 2789, 6724
Dean, Doug, 3593
Dean, Howard, 2516
Dean, Jeff, 704
Dean, Jill D., 3508
Dean, Jim, 2315
Dean, Jimmy, 2789
Dean, John, 2595
Dean, John W., 3249, 3639
Dean, Lori, 3249
Dean, Thompson, III, 5858
Dean, Tracey L., 9007
Dean, Trina R., 358
Dean, Victoria S., 1132
Dean, Victoria Seaver, 1133
Dearborn, Kerry L., 9744
Deardorff, Kevin, 3336
Dearman, Raymond, 4811
Dearstyne, Elizabeth T., 5510
Dearstyne, Katharine B., 5510
Dearstyne, William D., 5510
DeAscentis, Michael J., Jr., 7589
DeAtley, Bill, 9897
DeAtley, Brantner M., 9839
DeAtley, Janine B., 9839
DeAtley, William B., 9839
Deaton, Chad C., 8679
Deaton, P. Paul, 7178
Deatrick, Deborah, 3699
Deaver Foundation, Delema, 7190
Deaver, Carolyn J., 1890
Deaver, Kyle, 9251
DeBakey, Lois, 8804
DeBakey, Marsha L., 29
DeBakey, Michael E., 8804
Debare, Mary A., 7021
DeBauge, Jeff, 3514
Debbane, Raymond, 5859
DeBenedictis, Nicholas, 7917
Debernardi, Michael, 5398
DeBerry, Cheryl, 9796
DeBerry, Stephen, 764
Deberry, Trish, 9149
Debevoise, Dickinson R., Hon., 5270
DeBlasio, John, 2132
DeBlasio, Pasquale, 2132
Debnaun, Betty, 5396
DeBoer, Alexander, 3505
DeBoer, Christopher, 3505
DeBoer, Jack P., 3505
DeBoer, Marilyn S., 3505
DeBoer, Penny K., 3505
DeBoer, Skyler S., 3505
Debow, Adelaide M., 9044
Debrowski, Tom, 886
DeBruicker, Tim, 3278
DeBruyn, Nicolette, 2726
Debs Revocable Trust, Richard A., 5860
Debs, Barbara K., 5860
Debs, Elizabeth A., 5860
Debs, Nicholas A., 5860
Debs, Richard A., 5860
DeBuse, Chip, 5063
deButts, Kappy Kellett, 2584
deButts, Richard, 7306
deBuys, William, 5783
Dec, Katherine, 8256
DeCabooter, Art, 152
DeCamp, Cameron, 1394
DeCamp, Douglas A., 4393
Decamp, James, 4393
Decamp, Kenneth, 4393
Decamp, Margaret, 4393
Decamp, Matthew, 4393
Decamp, Timothy L., 2578
DeCardy, Chris, 1006
DeCarolis, D.L., 6526
Decesaris, Elizabeth, 3775
Decesaris, Geaton A., Jr., 3775
Decesaris, JoAnn, 3775
Decesaris, Josephine A., 3775
Decesaris, Kristen, 3775
Dechman, David A., 5862
DeChristina, Stephanie, 5546
Deckard, Jenniffer D., 7406, 7446
Decker, Bettina L., 6075
Decker, G. Clifford, 5863
Decker, Midge, 3324
Decker, Philip G., 8152
Decker, Shirley Martin, 4512
Decker, Steve, 9799
Decker, Vicki, 4806
Deckert, Myrna, 9083
DeClercq, Margaret, 8531
DeClue, John, 4715
DeClue, John M., 4757
DeCoizart Charitable Trust, 6904
Decola, Timothy G., 5359
DeCoudreaux, Alecia A., 686
DeCuir, Laurie G., 3612
Decurion Corp., The, 1004
Deddens, Dave, 3293
Dedecker, Clotilde Perez-Bode, 5801
Dedic, Nancy, 3207
Dedman, Bob, Jr., 9067
Dedoes, Shirley, 4402
DeDomenico, Lois, 490
Dedrick, Imojean, 3365
Dee, David, 9312
Dee, Janet T., 9312
Dee, L.T., 9312
Dee, Matthew T., 9312
Dee, Shelly H., 8913
Dee, Thomas D., 9312
Dee, Thomas D., II, 9312
Deeb, Matt, 8533
Deegan, Jennifer E., 4522
Deegan-Day, Joseph, 774
Deegan-Day, Thomas Joseph, 457
Deely, Brendan J., 3200
Deem, Becky, 9789
Deen, R.B., Jr., 4844
Deen, Robert B., Jr., 4831
Deep South Industrial Services, 2735
Deep South Solutions, Inc, 2735
Deer Creek Foundation, 4894
Deere & Co., 2790
Deere, Cynthia A. P., 9168
Deerfield Management Company, 5865
Deering, Anne Lawrence, 3883
Deering, Anthony W., 3877, 8371
Deering, Kathryn R., 8371
Deering, Maron, 8371
Deering, Spencer, 8371
Deertree Apartments Associates LP, 9452
Dees, Joyce, 184
Dees, Maarton, 986
Dees, Meg Kluttz, 7202
Deese, Carol, 2654
Deetjen, Jose M., 679
Deetjen, Leonor, 679
Deevy, Brian, 1399
Defalco, Diane D., 4237
DeFelice, Alex, 9793
DeFelice, Chase, 9793
Defenbaugh, Raymond E., 3072
Deffenbaugh, Sr. Irrevocable Trust, Ronald, 3506
Deffenbaugh, Sr. Mgmt. Trust, Ronald, 3506
DeFinnis, John E., Dr., 7972
DeFlavia, Laura, 8234
DeFoor, Byron, 8527
DeFord, Nicky, 1511
deForest, Lydia Collins, 5866
DeFrancesco, Anne, 3926
DeFrantz, Anita L., 809
deFreitas, JoAnne, 6628
DeFreitas, Rosalie, 4013
DeFreitas, V. Eugene, 4013
Degarmo, Jacqueline, 7491
Degel, James A., 9584
DeGeorge, Florence A., 5867
DeGeorge, Lawrence J., 5867
Degheri, Bert, 8207
Degioia, John J., 5747
Degnan, Stephen, 4948
DeGraaf, John, 5226
DeGraan, Edward F., 8356
DeGraw, Ronald J., 4383
DeGroodt, Patty, 9616
DeHaan Family Foundation, Christel, 3317
Dehaan, C.H., Dr., 8527
DeHaan, Christel, 3294
Dehaan, Derek, 3486
DeHaan, Jon Holden, 2057
DeHaan, Keith A., 3294
DeHaan, Kirsten A., 3294
DeHaan, Thomas H., 2057
DeHaan, Timothy E., 3294
Dehart, Michael G., 3668
DeHaven, Char, 3469
Dehmlow, Jonathan, 7557
Dehner, Helen, 4723
Dehner, Richard J., 3480
DeHoyos, Rick, 9147
Deighan, Jean M., 3698
Deikel, Beverly, 4615
Deily, Linnet F., 8917
Deininger, Peter, 4359
Deison, Dave, 8776
Deitchman, Martin J., 5455, 5464
Deitsch, Gloria S., 6828
Deiwert, Ed, 3330
Dejana, Peter, 5868
DeJesus, David, 9380
Dejoria Family Trust, John Paul, 1793
Dejoria, Eloise, 1793
DeJoria, John Paul, 1793
Dejoy, Louis, 7345
DeKarver, Martin, 894
Dekelboum Charitable Remainder Trust, Elsie, 3777
Dekelboum Revocable Trust, Marvin, 3777
Dekelboum, Elsie, 3777
Dekelboum, Marvin, 3777
Dekker, Hans, 5232, 5310
Dekko, Chester E., 3296
Dekko, Erica D., 3296
Dekko, Tad, 3296
Deknatel, Elizabeth, 4296
Deknatel, Gabriel, 4296
Deknatel, Maria, 4296
DeKruif, Robert M., 222
DeKuyper, Mary H., 3883
Del Cristo, Maria A., 5412
Del Frisco's New York, 7012
Del Giudice, Gina, 6695
Del Pepin, Claude, 9102
del Rio, Carlos H., 8353
Del Tredici, David, 5814
Delabretonne, Paula P., 3659
Delafield, George, 357
Delahaya, Steve, 9149
DeLan, Lisa, 578
Deland, Emme L., 6304
Deland, Emme Levin, 3923
DeLaney, Beth, 7630
Delaney, Brenda, 3272
Delaney, J. Michael, 3604
Delaney, Marie A., 2713
Delaney, Matthew, 5869
Delaney, Peter B., 7782
Delaney, Philip A., Jr., 2038
Delaney, Q., 262
Delaney, Quinn, 223
Delaney, Rich, 6627
Delaney, Rick, 3324
Delaney, Robert V., 5869
Delaney, Tammy, 1528
Delaney, Wayne E., 9179
Delano, Earl, 4334
DeLano, Mike, 9487

Delany, Beatrice P., 2793
Delany, Brendan, 7995
Delany, Sean, 5834
Delaplaine, Bettie, 3778
Delaplaine, Edward S., 3778
Delaplaine, Edward S., II, 3778
Delaplaine, Elizabeth B., 3778
Delaplaine, George B., III, 3778
Delaplaine, George B., Jr., 3778
Delaplaine, James W., 3778
Delaplaine, John F., 3778
Delaplaine, John P., 3778
DeLaski, David, 1899
DeLaski, Donald, 1899
DeLaski, Kathleen, 1899
deLaski, Kathleen, 7898
DeLaski, Kenneth, 1899
DeLaski, Kenneth E., 1899
deLaski, Kenneth E., 7898
DeLaski, Nancy L., 1899
Delaurenti, Charles J., II, 9619
DeLauro, Deborah G., 8071
Delaware Management Co., 8195
Delawder, C. Daniel, 7610
DeLawder, Dan, 7610
Delbanco, Andrew, 6967
Delcap, Inc., 7320
Delcor, Inc., 7320
Delee, Debra, 1932
Deleery, Seth, 8901
DeLeon, Dan C., 366
Delevati, Hank, 848
Delgado, Deivid, 67
Delgado, Jane, 9497
Delgado, Lisa, 1139
Delgado, Louis, 7588
Delgado, Sonia, 5411
Delgato, Ximena A., 7139
DeLise, Laura, 2151
Delka, Ryane, 3526
Dell'Amico, Len, 914
Dell, Alexander, 8805
Dell, Michael, 8805
Dell, Susan, 8805
Della Bella, Michael, 1725
Dellacca, David, 3313
Dellaquila, Frank, 2822
Delmas, Gladys V.K., 5871
Delmas, Jean Paul, 5871
Delo, Anne, 1566
DeLoach, Frank, Jr., 2431
Deloach, H.E., Jr., 8500
DeLoach, Harris, 8462
DeLoach, Harris E., Jr., 7195, 8505
DeLoach, Tia, 2512
DeLoache, William R., Jr., 8555
Deloitte & Touche LLP, 1572
Deloitte & Touche USA LLP, 1572
Deloitte Haskins & Sells, 1572
Deloitte LLP, 1572
Delong, Dennis, 2060
Delong, Donald A., 4358
DeLong, Gary, 846
Delorenzo, Lou, 7201
Delorey, Gail, 414
Delori, Rosamond, 5186
DeLoye, Dennis M., 9834
Delp, Lawrence F., 4256
Delp, Robert A., 3873
Delphi Automotive Systems Corp., 4394
Delphi Corp., 4394
Delponte, Karen, 4144
Delta Air Lines, Inc., 7191
Delta Dental Insurance Company, 458
Delta Dental of California, 458
Delta Dental of Delaware Inc., 458
Delta Dental of New York Inc., 458
Delta Dental of Pennsylvania, 458
Delta Dental of the District of Columbia, 458
Delta Dental of West Virginia Inc., 458
Delta Dental Plan of Arkansas, Inc., 184
Delta Dental Plan of Kansas, Inc., 3507
Delta Dental Plan of Massachusetts, 4016
Delta Power Equipment Co., 3639
DeLuca, Anthony F., 9173
DeLuca, Elizabeth, 1573
DeLuca, Francis, 1584
DeLuca, Frederick A., 1573
DeLuca, Gwen, 5612
DeLuca, Jonathan, 1573
DeLucia, Eileen, 9385
DeLucia, Michael S., 5179
DeLuise, Veronica, 5398
Deluxe Corp., 4644
Demak, Richard, 1199
Demakis, Gregory C., 4070
Demakis, John N., 4070
Demakis, Paul C., 4070
Demakis, Thomas C., 4070
Demakis, Thomas L., 4070
DeMana, Jacqueline M., 1316
DeMarco, Michelle, 7607
DeMars, Dan R., 3331
Demars, Phyllis A., 4382
DeMartini, James G.B., III, 1175
Demartini, James G.B., III, 1176
Demartini, Richard M., 5872
Demas, Lorraine B., 66
Demas, Olivia, 7367
Demashkieh, Rasha, 4373
Dematic, 3201
DeMatteis, Frederick, 5873
DeMatteis, Nancy, 5873
DeMatteis, Richard F., 5873
DeMatteis, Scott L., 5873
Demchak, William S., 8230
Dement, Steve, 8819
Demere, Robert H., Jr., 2430
Demery, Monique B., 2715
Demery, Thomas R., 2715
Demetree, Betty A., 2058
Demetree, Christopher C., 2058
Demetree, Elisa A., 2058
Demetree, Jack C., 2058
Demetree, Jack C., Jr., 2058
Demetree, Mark C., 2058
Demetree-Doherty, Leslie A., 2058
Deming, Richard, 3420
Deming, Wendy, 2142
Demirjian, Betsy Pappas, 4204
Demma, Francine, 3347
DeMoor, Barbara, 4389
Demopoulos, Harry, 5918
Demopoulos, Harry B., 5917
DeMore, Dillon, 1518
Demore, Timothy Allan, 9206
Demoss, April Williams, 2575
DeMoss, Arthur S., 2059
DeMoss, Charlotte, 2059
DeMoss, Elizabeth J., 2059
Demoss, Georgia A., 2575
Demoss, James, 8776
DeMoss, Nancy S., 2059
DeMoss, Robert G., 2059
DeMoss, Todd, 3480
Demoulas Super Markets, Inc., 4014
Demoulas, Arthur T., 4014, 4015
Demoulas, Irene, 4015
Demoulas, Telemachus A., 4015
Dempsey, Austin M., 2767
Dempsey, Bill, 5833, 9704
Dempsey, Mary A., 2773
Dempsey, Michael J., 119
Dempsey, Patrick, 637
Dempsey, Ray C., 8718
Dempze, Nancy E., 3961
Demsey, John D., 6408
Demsky, Howard, 2315
Demtrak, Carolyn, 5802
DeMuth, Deb, 1390
Demyan, Kirk C., 8046
Den Herder, Sue, 4374
DeNale, Carol A., 8379
Denault, Leo P., 3630
Denberg, Dawn, 2971
Denbo, Samuel, 4136
Dender, Washington C., 5564
Denekas, Craig N., 3696
Denham, Robert E., 727, 6782
Denigan, Susan, 4948
Denious, Robert W., 8236
Denisof, Antoinette, 8057
Denius, F. Wofford, 8743
Denius, Franklin W., 8743
Denk, Kelly, 9892
Denker, Jill, 5062
Denkers, Julie, 9317
Denkers, Stephen E., 9317
Denkers, Stephen G., 9317
Denkers, Susan E., 9317
Denlea, Leo E., Jr., 825
Denlinger, Janet L., 5199
Denmark, David, 8601
Denmark, Ethel, 8475
Dennert, Richard B., 2723, 2846
Dennert, Rick B., 2724
Dennery, Linda, 5270
Dennett, Andrea S., 6938
Denney, Corwin D., 460
Denney, Emily, 1738
Denney, K. Duane, 460
Denney, Laura, 9307
Denney, Laura Jean, 9307
Denney, Ronald, 9412
Denney, Ryan, 9307
Denney, Ryan C., 9307
Dennin, Mike, 157
Denning, Bradford C., 8593
Denning, Richard B., 4158, 4162
Denning, Roberta B., 1687
Denning, Steven A., 1468, 1687
Dennis & Phyllis Washington, 5018
Dennis, Andre, 8107
Dennis, Edward A., 1063
Dennis, Jane, 4830
Dennis, Kathryn H., 2435
Dennis, Kimberly O., 1097, 1946, 4413
Dennis, Mark V., 6806
Dennis, Rita, 9060
Dennis, Robin, 7570
Dennis, Russ, 2766
Dennison, Heather, 3356
Dennison, Phillip, 7415
Denniston, Brackett B., II, 1591
Denny Elwell Companies, 3452
Denny's, Inc., 2087
Denny, Benjamin L., 3649
Denny, Charles M., Jr., 4792
Denny, James M., 3128
Denomme, Thomas, 4594
Denoon, Ashby, 7909
Denoon, Clarence E., Jr., 7909
Denoon, David B.H., 7909
Denova, James V., 7935
Densch Charitable Trust, Wayne M., 2294
Densco Corp., 5773
Denslow, Faith, 7444
DENSO International America, Inc., 4395
Dent, Rebecca H., 7475
Dental Services of Massachusetts Inc., 4016
Denton, A. Louis, 7928
Denton, Amy, 4359
Denton, David M., 8379
Denton, Gus B., 8634
Denton, James, 2565
Denton, James N., III, 8643
Denton, Lloyd A., 9236
Denver, Michael, 7563
Denworth, Joanne R., 8041
DePalma, Patrick, 3417
DePaoli, Edward M., 5438
Depaoli, James J., 3347
DePaolo, Valerie A., 1634
Department of Education, 927
Department of Family Support Services, 2761
DePetro, Wyndsor, 1710
DePierro, John, 6568
Depies, Keith, 9832
DePillis, Mark S., 8336
DePizzo, Jason, 117
Depolo, Gary L., 312
Deposit Guaranty National Bank, 4843
Deppe, Michael John, 8914
DePrez, John, Jr., 3265
DeProspero, Mike, 9799
Dept. of Energy, Energy Biosciences Research Division, 3833
DePuy Mitek, Inc., 5327
DePuy, Warner, 1675
Deraad, Dale, 4693
deRaad, Mark P., 884
Deramus, William N., IV, 3508
Derflinger, Casey, 8511
Derfner, Harold, 5874
Derfner, Helen, 5874
Derham, Kyle, 8635
Derham, Matthew, 8635
Derkacz, Mike, 8314
DeRobles, Claudia, 9604
DeRodes, William J., 7704
Derose, Dan, 1504
Derouen, D. Troy, 8888
DeRoy, Helen L., 4396
Derrer, Suzanne, 4238
Derrick, James V., Jr., 8958
Derrickson, Sophie M., 1754
Derrico, Patricia, 5486
Derry Publishing Co., 4243
Derry, Chris, 2644
Derwingson, Harriet, 420
Desai, Bharat, 2067
Desai, Pia, 2067
Desai, Rohit M., 5718
Desai, Saahill, 2067
DeSanto, Kevin, 9410
Desenberg, Karen, 9074
Desert Valley Medical Group, 461
Deshaies, Michael, 8179
DeShazior, Samuel, 7367
DeShazo, Nikki, Hon., 9213
Deshe, Ann, 2062, 7435

Deshe, Ari, 2062
Deshe, Daniel, 2062
Deshe, Dara, 2062
Deshe, David, 2062
Deshe, Elie, 2062
Deshong, J.K., 295
Desich, Richard, 1766
DeSilva, Peter, 4957
Desisto, Courtney, 2185
DeSisto, Rena M., 7139
DesJardins, Linda Eich, 4679
Desler, Michael D., 1280
Desloges, Lynda, 420
Desmond-Hellmann, Susan, 3818, 9625
DeSole, Gloria, 5803
Despeaux, Kim, 3630
Despina, Eleanore, 262
Desroches, Pascal, 6982
Dessler, Reuven D., 5905
Dessouky, Hilary, 1017
DeStefano, Rocky, 2039
Destination Concepts, 1158
Destler, William, Dr., 6077
Detar, D. Scott, 8234
Dethlefs-Trettin, Angela, 3420
Detjen, Curt S., 9832
Detkin, Michelle, 1767
Detkin, Peter, 1767
Detloff, Jocelyn, 4412
Detre, Antony, 5967
Detroit Edison Co., The, 4410
Detroit Salt Company, 4419
Dettmer, Dale, Esq., 2033
Deuble, Andrew H., 7433
Deuble, Maxwell F., 7433
Deuble, Stephen G., 7433
Deuble, Walter J., 7433
Deur, Jan, 4369
Deutsch, Alvin, 917
Deutsch, Anna, 5875
Deutsch, Carl, 462
Deutsch, David, 3779, 6644
Deutsch, Eugene H., 3308
Deutsch, Jack, 5875, 7107
Deutsch, Lawrence E., 1074
Deutsch, Lisa, 932
Deutsch, Moishe, 7107
Deutsch, Robert W., 3779
Deutsch, Roberta, 462
Deutsche Bank AG, 121, 1268, 6700
Deutsche Bank Americas, 6544
Deutsche Bank Americas Holding Corp., 5876
Deutsche Bank Trust Co., 5552, 6297
Deutsche Bank Trust Co., N.A., 5867, 5972, 6142, 6560, 6932
Deutscher, David, 5413
Dev, Vipul R., 780
Devaney, Martin, 7103
Devani, Papan, 9495
Devanney, Timothy J., 1690
Devegh, Diana, 4198
Development Mgmt., Inc., 1471
Development Services Trust, 1485
Devens, Susan, 5612
DeVeny, Flavia, 4380
Dever, Douglas J., 9149
Devereaux Trust, Adelyn, 4397
Devereaux, Leslie C., 4397
Devereaux, Richard C., Mrs., 4397
Devereaux, Zilph P., 4846
DeVeydt, Wayne S., 3257
Devilbiss, Greg, 7474
deVillers, Rebecca, 7605
Devine, Donald, 9005
Devine, Tammy, 8499
DeVinney, Bonnie, 6099
DeVitt, Christine, 8759
Devitt, Terry, 4616
Devlin, Dee, 9040
Devlin, Eric, 9040
Devlin, Erin C., 5877
Devlin, Katharine B., 5877
Devlin, Matthew B., 5877
Devlin, Michael, 5877
Devlin, Robert M., 5877
Devlin, Robert S., 5281
Devlin, Timothy, 2305
DeVoe, Sally A., 3346
DeVoge, Jarol A., 8332
Devoll, Jennifer, 424
Devoll, Jennifer F., 1024
DeVoll, Jennifer Fleming, 1015
Devon, Marge, 5520
Devore, Helen S., 1949
Devorris, Nancy, 7971
DeVos Foundation, Richard and Helen, The, 4398
DeVos, Betsy, 4418
DeVos, Daniel, 4398
DeVos, Daniel G., 4398
DeVos, Dick, 4418
DeVos, Douglas, 4399
Devos, Douglas L., 4572
DeVos, Elisabeth, 4418, 4525
DeVos, Helen J., 4400, 4559
DeVos, Maria, 4399
DeVos, Pamella, 4398
DeVos, Richard, 4400
DeVos, Richard M., 4400
DeVos, Richard M., Jr., 4418
Devriendt, Beverly, 4580
DeVries, Laura, 2943
DEW Building, 2794
DEW Texas Building, 2794
Dew, Carol, 2426
Dew, Patti, 9907
Dewald, Eric, 7972
Dewan, Erica, 5878
Dewan, Feroz, 5878
Dewan, Joe, 4357
Dewar, James A., 5879
Dewar, Jessie Smith, 5879
Dewar, Patrick M., 3837
Dewar, Robert, 5783
Dewey, Ed, 2104
Dewey, Henry B., 8405
Dewey, Lisa, 3781
Dewine, Frances, 7434
DeWine, Jean L., 7434
Dewine, John, 7434
DeWine, Karen, 7434
DeWine, R. Michael, 7434
DeWine, Richard L., 7434
Dewire, Norman, Rev. Dr., 7431
DeWitt Ltd. Partners, Gary & Joyce, 4402
DeWitt Trust, Donald L., 4402
DeWitt Trust, Merle J., 4402
Dewitt, Barbara A., 8158
DeWitt, Brian, 4402
DeWitt, Donald, 4402
DeWitt, Donald L., 4402
DeWitt, Gary D., 4402
DeWitt, J. Denton, 3236
DeWitt, Jerene L., 4402
DeWitt, Joyce, 4402
DeWitt, Keith, 4402
DeWitt, Kelly, 4402
DeWitt, Kristin, 4402
DeWitt, Lisa, 4402
DeWitt, Marvin G., 4402
DeWitt, Mary, 4402
DeWitt, Mary E., 4402
DeWitt, Merle, 4402
DeWitt, Minnie, 4402
DeWitt, Sheri, 4402
DeWitt, William, Jr., 4402
Dewk, Joey, 5557
DeWoody, Beth Rudin, 6767, 6768, 6769
DeWoody, James Carlton, III, 6767
DeWoody, Kyle Hardin, 6767
DeWyngaert, Richard, 2986
DeWyngaert, Susan, 2986
Dexter Jennison Assocs., 6061
Dexter, Ed, 5067
Dexter, J. Robert, 7743
Dexter, Mike, 3291
Dey, Kimberly W., 2602
DeYoung, Janet, 4374
DeYoung, Kevin, 9759
DeYounker, Alex J., 4544
Deyst, Katherine A., 4037
Deziel Charitable Lead Trust, George H., 4645
Deziel Trust, George H., 4645
Deziel, Annette, 4645
DFF Article III Trust, 532
Dhanraj, Vidia, 3759
Dharma Holdings, Ltd., 2395
Dhawan-Gray, Neetu, 3844
Dhein, Jere, 9904
Dhein, Steven P., 9800
Dhillon, Janet, 9089
Dhimitri, Sandy, 5807
Dhont Irrevocable Trust, Eveline, 464
Dhont, Andre G., 464
DHR Holdings, 1943
Di Rita, Lawrence, 1943
Diab, Steve, 1776
Diablo Contractors, Inc., 293
Diakov, Leanne, 3578
Dial, Karen J., 483
Dial, Kenneth P., 483
Dial, Natalie J., 483
Dial, Terry R., 483
Dialogic Systems Corp., 9339
Dialynas, Chris, 1037
Dialynas, Chris P., 465
Dialynas, S.P., 465
Dialynas, Sheri Horne, 465
Diamente, Christine, 5190
Diamond Investments Corp., 8285
Diamond Ridge Development, LLC, 385
Diamond Technology Partners Inc., 9340
Diamond, Alice B., 6912
Diamond, Chris, 1528
Diamond, Irene, 5882
Diamond, Irvin F., 5515
Diamond, Ivan, 3714
Diamond, Jennifer, 5881
Diamond, Jon, 7435
Diamond, Marylin G., 6041
Diamond, Michael L., 7326
Diamond, Nancy, 3435
Diamond, Nell, 5881
Diamond, Robert E., III, 5881
Diamond, Robert E., Jr., 5881
Diamond, Robin, 471
Diamond, Sandra F., 2269
Diamond, Susan, 7435
Diana, Andrew J., 7932
Dias, Craig, 9615
Diaz, Angela, 9596
Diaz, Antonio M., 8733
Diaz, Billie, 299
Diaz, Cameron, 299
Diaz, David, 8708
Diaz, Fred, 4366
Diaz, Kerry A., 2276
Diaz, Manny, 5684
Diaz, Manuel, 2238
Diaz, Patricia J., 5774
Diaz, Ricardo, 9855
Diaz, Rita, 1015
Diaz, Susan, 1520
Diaz-Infante, Alred, 414
DiBattista, Raymond, 7990
Dibble, Robert, 5876
Dibble, Terrence D., 1284
DiBenedetto, Dennis, 8432
Dibner Fund, Inc., The, 4018, 7920
Dibner, Aurora C., 3681
Dibner, Avalon B., 3681
Dibner, Bern L., 3681
Dibner, Brent, 4018
Dibner, Daniel, 3681
Dibner, Mark, 7920
Dibner, Rachel, 4018
Dibner, Rachel Zax, 7920
Diboll, Collins C., 3628
Diboll, Donald W., 3628
DiCarlo, Dana M., 3780
DiCesare, Thor D., 7970
Dichner, David, 505
Dick, Cheryl J., 3318
Dick, David, 3521
Dick, David, Dr., 3335
Dick, Frank, 4485
Dick, Helen E., 3318
Dick, Henry, 4830
Dick, Melvin A., 2347
Dick, Randy, 9789
Dick, Rollin M., 3318
Dick, Stacy S., 6693
Dick, Sylvia, 2561
Dicke, Eileen W., 7436
Dicke, James, 7436
Dicke, James F., II, 2253, 7436
Dicke, James F., III, 7436
Dicke, James, Sr., 7436
Dickenson, Harriet Ford, 2795
Dickenson, J.T., 8947
Dickerson, Amina J., 2849, 3242
Dickerson, Annie, 6862
Dickerson, Brad, 8328
Dickerson, Dan, 7569
Dickerson, Lynn, 1211
Dickey, Eileen D., 1759
Dickey, Jeb, 1399
Dickie, Rita, 3650
Dickinson, Bertha G., 9191
Dickinson, Elizabeth M., 466
Dickinson, Harry D., 9414
Dickinson, Kristopher, 466
Dickinson, Martin C., 466
Dickinson, William J., 9191
Dickinson, William J., Jr., 9191
Dickman, J. Jerry, 7739, 7740
Dickman, Norbert J., 9106
Dickson, Alex D., Bishop, 8458
Dickson, Carolyn B., 9067
Dickson, Cary, 886
Dickson, David, 9251
Dickson, James, 1879, 7588
Dickson, R. Stuart, 3714, 7192

Dickson, Raymond, 8806
Dickson, Rebecca, 5108
Dickson, Robert T., 9106
Dickson, Rush S., III, 7192
Dickson, Thomas W., 7192
DiCola, Lee, 7597
Dicovitsky, Gary, 5316
DiCroce, Anthony J., 5394
DiCroce, Deborah M., 9448
Dicus, John B., 3498, 3552
Dicus, John C., 3498
Didlake, Ralph, 4816
DiDomenico, Gregory, 2769
DiDomenico, Rebecca, 422
Didriksen, Neil, 3779
Diebold, Caitlin, 1574
Diebold, Dorothy, 8469
Diebold, Dudley, 1574
Diebold, Honoria, 1574
Diebold, Inc., 7437
Diede, Shelley, 1373
Diederich, John, 2767
Diederich, John H., 7979
Diederich, John J., 3255
Diegel, Sandy, 8524
Diehl, Betty, 860
Diehl, Harrison L., 8272
Diehl, Ryan, 3521
Diekemper Trust, H., 4928
Diener, Michelle S., 8807
Diener, Robert B., 8807, 8987
Dienhart, Mark, 4760
Dienstag, Jules, 4325
Dienstfrey, Ted, 278
Dierberg, Ellen, 4879
Dierberg, James F., 4879
Dierberg, James F., II, 4879
Dierberg, Mary W., 4879
Dierberg, Michael J., 4879
Dieringer Trust, Victoria Evelyn, 7839
Dieringer, Eugene, 7839
Diermeier, Jeffrey J., 2063
Diermeier, Joseph G., Rev., 9851
Diermeier, Julia M., 2063
Diermeier, Julie M., 2063
Diers, Melissa, 5039
Dietel, Kimberly R., 4047
Dietel, William, 4999
Dieter, Sue, 4800
Dieterich, Barbara, 7597
Dieterich, Kevin, 5586, 6334
Dietrich Charitable Lead Annuity Trust, William B., 8010
Dietrich Trust No. 1, William B., 8010
Dietrich, Sheila Kemper, 4923
Dietrich, William B., 8010
Dietz, Carolyn Emmerson, 1164
Dietz, Debra, 6854
Dietz, Kerry, 3992
Dietz, Margaret H., 663
Dietz, Philip E.L., Jr., 3897
Dietz, Ryan, 395
Dietz, Tim, 3379
Dietz, William L., 4598
Dietze, David, 5473
Dietzel, Lois Fisher, 1585
DiFabio, Lou, 5804
DiFatta, Brian, 9362
Digate, Gail, 1392
Digennaro, A., 1614
Digges, Charles W., IV, 4984
Diggs, Alisa, 106
Diggs, Cokie, 3555
Digiusto, Alessandra, 5876
Dijkgraaf, Robbert, 5191
Diker, Charles, 5883
Diker, Valerie, 5883
Dilatush, L., 92
Dilday, N. Jack, 8343
DiLeonardi, Robert N., 3206
Dilgard, Charles K., 7702
Dill, Heather Templeton, 8313
Dill, Janet, 75
Dill, Louise F., 2034
Dill, Stanley, 3757
Dillaplain, Paul, 7474
Dillard, Gray, 181
Dillbeck, Michael, 1018
Dillbeck, Susan, 1018
Diller, Barry, 5884
Diller, Edward D., 7528
Dillin, Carol, 7881
Dilling, Huc, 9602
Dilling, Steven J., 9843
Dillion, Eileen M., 6070
Dillon Casino, Inc., 5016
Dillon, C. Douglas, 5885
Dillon, Clarence, 5885, 5921
Dillon, David B., 7531
Dillon, Donald F., 5035
Dillon, Eileen M., 3855
Dillon, Gregory R., 9417
Dillon, Jessica, 3475
Dillon, John, 3851
Dillon, Judith, 500
Dillon, Kenneth A., 4540
Dillon, Margo, 2796
Dillon, Mike, 1734
Dillon, Pat, 4461
Dillon, Patrick, 2796
Dillon, Paul W., 3521
Dillon, Peter W., 2796
Dillon, Susan S., 5885
Dillon, Tim, 1714
Dilly, Arthur, 9171
DiLorenzo, Paul, 8303
DiLucia, Tony, 1368
Dilworth, Susan S., 9208
Dimaiti, Carl, 4195
Dimanna, Sara E., 1404
DiMare Management, Inc., 2064
DiMare, Anthony, 2064
DiMare, Paul J., 2064
Dimasi, Brian M., 7638
DiMenna, Diana, 5886
DiMenna, Joseph A., 5886
Dimicco, Daniel R., 7275
Dimichele, Tony, 886
Dimick, Jan, 7854
DiMino, Anthony, 5887
DiMino, Frank, 5887
DiMino, Ronald, 5887
DiMino-Lara, Mary Kay, 5887
Dimitriou, K.E., 3209
Dimling, Marilyn, 6903
Dimling, Sarah, 7497
Dimmer Family Foundation, 9652
Dimmer, Carolyn, 9610
Dimmer, Diane C., 9610
Dimmer, John B., 9610
Dimmer, John C., 9610
Dimmer, Marilyn, 9610
Dimon, James, 2797
Dimon, Judith K., 2797
Dimon, Theodore, 2797
Dimond, Paul R., 4371
Dimond, Robert B., 4727
DiMuccio, Robert A., 8356
Dinan, Curtis L., 7783
Dinan, James G., 5888
Dinan, William A., 5888
DiNardo, Allison Cryor, 9380
Dine-Jergens, Peter H., 7510
Dineen, John K., 4210
Dinerman, Laura Z., 2583
Dines, Tyson, III, 1400
Dingee, Alexander L.M., 3970
Dingeldein, Michael P., 7481
Dingell, Deborah I., 4371
Dingwell, Park T., 517
Dinkel, John F., Jr., 5164
Dinndorf, Elizabeth A., 8468
Dinos, Jack, 2431
DiNovi, Anthony, 5185
Dinovi, Anthony J., 4019
Dinovi, Deanna L., 4019
Dinsdale, Kim W., 9270
Dinsmoor, Dorothy, 5912
Dinsmore, Nancy L., 5237
Dinsmore, Richard D., 5237
Dintersmith, Ted R., 4020
Diocese of Orlando, 2294
Dion, Ernest E., 5179
Dionisopoulos, George A., 9920
Dionne, Joan, 1650
Dionne, Joseph, 1650
DiPanfilo, Melissa, 4217
DiPietro, Eleanor Monroe, 973
DiPietro, Rudy, 3690
Dippold, David J., 7688
Dippold, Jim, 7567
Diq Deep, 9118
DiQuollo, Robert J., 5384
Dir Trading Inc., 2091
Dircks, Robert E., 5241
Dircks, Robert J., 5241
Dircks, Thomas C., 5241
Dircks, William C., 5241
Director, David, 1644
DiRisio, Derek M., 5416
Dirkes, George R., 1200
Dirks, Carolyn, 618
Dirks, Martin, 618
Dirks, Michael W., 9177
Dirks, Troy, 3554
Dirksen, Carri, 3285
DiRocco, John J., Jr., 8308
Disbrow, Marilyn, 1263
Disher, Linda, 3303
Dishman, Tammy, 3498
DiSilvestro, Anthony P., 5223
Dismuke, Bill, 8776
Disney Co., Walt, The, 467
Disney Worldwide Services, Inc., 7012
Disney, Abigail, 6864
Disney, Abigail E., 5848
Disney, Lillian B., 468
DiSomma, Mary, 2798
DiSomma, William, 2798
Dispatch Printing Co., The, 7719
Dissinger, Debra E., 8218
Dissinger, Ronald L., 4473
Distelhorst, Neil B., 7576
Ditchley Trust, Jessie Ball DuPont, 2074
Ditenhafer, Stephanie R., 4261
Ditrolio, Jospeh F., 7989
Ditsler, Jacqueline, 8739
Ditsler, Steve, 8739
Dittman Incentive Marketing, 7012
Dittman, David, 5019
Dittman, John, 5063
Dittman, Ralph E., 8920
Dittmann, Harry G., 8288
Dittmer, Ellen, 3373
Dittrich, Amy Rogers, 4243
Dittrich, Norbert, 9268
Dittrich, T. Tyler, 4243
Ditullo, Mike, 7103
Ditz, Nancy J., 1119
Ditzler, Hugh W., III, 517
Ditzler, Hugh W., Jr., 517
Ditzler, Kate, 517
Ditzler, Nancy M., 517
Divelbiss, Jason, 3761
Divelbiss, Terry L., 7413
Dively, Joseph, 2986
Diversified Technology, Inc., 4824
Divine, Robert, 8602
Divita, Chuck, 2101
Divola, Julie, 1283
Dix, Charles, II, 7673
Dix, Gary W., 2223
Dix, Stuart, 6910
Dixie Denning Supply Co., 7225
Dixit, Vishva, 571
Dixon Hughes Goodman, 9444
Dixon, Corliss, 5055
Dixon, David, 8012
Dixon, Edith R., 8336
Dixon, Elizabeth Irene Brown, 2456
Dixon, Francis J., 8012
Dixon, Frank, 8012
Dixon, George W., 8336
Dixon, Hillary A., 6136
Dixon, Joan M., 2765
Dixon, Ky, 9997
Dixon, Laura, 9149
Dixon, Leslie H., 9811
Dixon, Martha B., 30
Dixon, Michael J., 2276
Dixon, Rebecca Keegan, 7751
Dixon, Roger M., 8808, 8809
Dixon, Sally J., 8351
Dixon, Solon, 30
Dixon, Stewart S., 3172
Dixon, Thomas, 8012
Dixon, Thomas F., 6136
Dixon, William B., 3872
Dizov, Leticia J., 8927
Djerejian, Edward P., Amb., 5747
DKB Foundation, 6492
DKS Foundation, 3517
DL Trust, 2081, 2161
DLA Piper U.S.A. LLP, 3781
Doak, Mark, 9796
Doan, Ruth Alden, 4407
Dobberpuhl, Holly S., 8557
Dobberpuhl, Joel E., 8557
Dobbins, Allen L., 672
Dobbins, Fred, 2308
Dobbins, Patricia K., 2327
Dobbins, Sandra J., 4496
Dobbs, Carolyn M., 5535
Dobbs, Katy, 4282
Dobbs, R. Howard, Jr., 2449
Dobbs, S. B., 8851
Doberneck, Megan, 1519
Doberstein, Stephen C., 1758
Dobias, Mark, 4334
Dobkin Family Foundation, 6864
Dobkin, Barbara, 5891
Dobkin, David, 7848
Dobkin, Eric S., 5891
Dobkin, Rachel L., 5891
Doblin Group, Inc., 9250
Doblin, Lynne J., 4277

Dobos, David, 667
Dobras, Amy, 7676
Dobras, Darryl, 101
Dobras, Dawn, 7676
Dobras, Mary Ann, 7676
Dobriansky, Paula J., Dr., 1679
Dobrof, Rose, 6546
Dobrusin, Charles E., 2901, 3091
Dobson, Andrea M., 197
Dobson, Charles C., 4630
Dobson, Christopher M., 4630
Dobson, Douglas R., 8295
Dobson, Everett R., 7747
Dobson, Megan, 4630
Dobson, Michael, 4630
Dobson, Robbin L., 7747
Dobson, Stephen T., 7747
Doby, Cris, 4511
Docherty, Susan E., 4442
Docken, Paula, 4727
Dockery, J. Lee, Dr., 2235
Dockery, Michael L., 2235
Dockery, William J., 6159
Dockman, William, 3807
Doctorow, Constance, 9314
Doctorow, Jarvis, 9314
Doctors Co., The, 471
Doctors Hospital, 7605
Dodd, Jeanne D., 4405
Doddridge, Kevin, 4821
Dodds, Hamish, 2147
Dodds, Jeanne, 9108
Dodds, Scott, 9294
Dodero, Corinne L., 7438
Dodero, Lorraine, 5267
Dodero, Lorraine C., 7438
Dodero, William, 5267, 7438
Dodge Jones Foundation, 8978
Dodge, Bayard, 5892
Dodge, Cleveland H., 5892
Dodge, Cleveland H., Jr., 5892
Dodge, Geraldine R., 5243
Dodge, Kathryn, 79
Dodge, Lore Moran, 2032
Dodge, Margret L., 5061
Dodge, Stewart P., 1489
Dodson, Aubrey, 9420
Dodson, Aubrey D., 9421
Dodson, Barbara, 9427
Dodson, Betty Jo, 2030
Dodson, David, 1940, 7138
Dodson, Debra L., 9413
Dodson, James D., 9927
Dodson, Mark, 9603
Dodson, Melissa, 4094
Dodson, Robert, 9927
Dodson, Stephanie, 4298
Dodson, Thomas L., 7189
Dodsworth, Sherie, 849
Doe Run Res USA, 7349
Doe Trust 2004, Shirley B., 4022
Doe, Barbara, 4022
Doe, Charles F., Jr., 4022
Doe, Dana G., 4022
Doe, William, 4022
Doecke, Robyn, 9569
Doellefeld-Clancy, Kathy, 4963
Doenng, Mark, 9053
Doerger, Jerry, 7414
Doerhoff, Claudia, 1243
Doerhoff, Neil, 1243
Doering, Don S., 9656
Doering, Shannon, 5021
Doerr, Ann Howland, 305
Doerr, L. John, 305
Doerr, L. John, III, 305
Doetsch, George, Jr., 3759
Doft, Ellen B., 2494
Doggett, William B., 7442
Doheny, Edward L., II, 9876
Doheny, Edward L., Mrs., 473
Doherty, Brian, 1632
Doherty, Brigid, 5832
Doherty, Diana Loukedis, 8047
Doherty, Dianne Fuller, 3992
Doherty, Edmund J., 3926
Doherty, Henry L., Mrs., 5893
Doherty, Janice L., 3548
Doherty, Kathryn, 4243
Doherty, Kevin, 2989
Doherty, Tom, 4958
Dohn, Constance, 1393
Doin, Jean Marie, 5187
Dolan Children's Foundation, 5896
Dolan, Charles F., 5895, 5896
Dolan, Deborah A., 1802
Dolan, Helen, 5895
Dolan, Helen A., 5896
Dolan, John D., 7379
Dolan, Kevin, 2650
Dolan, Mark V., 3693
Dolan, Mary Jane, 9474
Dolan, Matthew J., 9253
Dolan, Meg, 3201
Dolan, Paul J., 7406
Dolan, Paul R., 5785
Dolan, Ronald J., 7599
Dolan, Terrance, 4784
Dolan, Terrance R., 4714
Dolan, Thomas, 5895, 5896
Dolan, Traci M., 3272
Dolby, Dagmar, 474
Dolby, Ray M., 474
Dole Food Company, 3245
Dole, Elizabeth H., 1900
Dole, Senator Elizabeth H., 1900
Dolenz, Pamela, 9255
Dolfinger, Henry, 8013
Doll, Becky, 3335
Doll, Gemma, Sr., 4763
Doll, Paul W., Jr., 7258
Doll, Thomas J., 5471
Dollar Bank, FSB, 8014
Dollar General Corp., 8558, 8639
Dollar Land Syndicate, 932
Dollar, Joann F., 2448
Dollens, Ronald W., 3375
Dollinger, Marci, 836
Dollison, Mary L., 3286
Dolliver, Barbara, 517
Dolliver, Peter, 517
Doman, Dan, 9769
Domani Trust, The, 7476
Dombrose, Fred, 8579
Domeck, Brian, 7623
Domingues, Robert A., 912
Dominguez, Carlos, 402
Dominguez, Daniel, 9202
Dominguez, Jorge I., Prof., 7707
Dominguez-Arms, Amy, 727
Dominiak, Mary, 2900
Dominick, Kirk, 7217
Dominion Energy New England, 9422
Dominion Energy, Inc., 9422
Dominion Resources, Inc., 9422
Dominion Transmission, 9422
Domino's Pizza, 3245
Dominquez, Joseph, 2827
Domke, Doreeta J., 898
Dompier, Sandra Smith, 9183, 9186
Don, Stephanie, 2207
Donaghue, Ethel F., 1575
Donaghy, James W., 2329
Donahey, Robert W., 7602
Donaho, Jackie, 1202
Donahoe, Ernest N., 9436
Donahue, David W., 4023
Donahue, David, Jr., 4207
Donahue, J. Christopher, 8033
Donahue, James C., 8015
Donahue, Joanie, 7088
Donahue, Joe, 4152
Donahue, John F., 8015, 8033
Donahue, Kim, 2717
Donahue, Mary B., 7564
Donahue, Nancy L., 4023
Donahue, Rhodora J., 8015
Donahue, Richard K., 4023
Donahue, Richard K., Jr., 4023
Donahue, Richard K., Sr., 4152
Donahue, Thomas R., 8033
Donahue, William J., 8015
Donahue-Wallach, Kathleen M., 8015
Donald, Arnold, 5001
Donald, Arnold W., 3656
Donald, Brenda, 4869
Donald, Dan, 3625
Donaldson Co., Inc., 4646
Donaldson, Carla, 430
Donaldson, Charlotte D'Arcy, 4150
Donaldson, David A., 73
Donaldson, Matthew S., Jr., 8170
Donaldson, Oliver S., 2066
Donaldson, Phil, 4601
Donaldson, Robert P., 5523
Donati, John, 1100
Donavan, James J., 6406
Donchian, Richard D., 1576
Donegan, Linda Livingston, 8383
Donelly, Norbert, 2142
Donelson, LeRayne, 8660
Donerkiel, Linda Leuthold, Dr., 4695
Dong, Glenn, 4380
Donghia, Angelo, 5897
Doniger, Beatrice B., 5735
Doniger, Bruce, 5735
Donisi, Philip A., 9020
Donkersloot, Norman, 4432
Donlevie, John C., 8037
Donley, Beth, 9897
Donley, Michele, 3061
Donley, Richard S., 8015
Donnan, Mary Fant, 9382
Donnell, Barry, 9277
Donnell, Terry O', 8446
Donnelley & Sons Co., R.R., 2801
Donnelley Family Trust, Laura, 612
Donnelley, Barbara C., 2802
Donnelley, Ceara, 2800
Donnelley, David E., 2802
Donnelley, Dorothy Ranney, 2800
Donnelley, Elliott, 2802
Donnelley, Gaylord, 2800
Donnelley, James R., 2802, 3358
Donnelley, Laura, 612, 2800
Donnelley, Miranda S., 2802
Donnelley, Nina H., 2802
Donnelley, Robert G., 2802
Donnelley, Shawn M., 2746, 2800
Donnelley, Thomas E., II, 2802
Donnelley, Vivian, 2800
Donnelly, Edward J., III, 8228
Donnelly, Ellen, 8025
Donnelly, Harriet L., 2156
Donnelly, Joseph C., Jr., 4211
Donnelly, Mike, 2580
Donnelly, Robert W., Sr., 2156
Donnelly, Robert, Jr., 2156
Donnelly, Thomas J., 7989
Donner, Alexander B., 5899
Donner, Amy K. Dore', 3629
Donner, David A., 5898
Donner, David W., 5899
Donner, Deborah, 5899
Donner, Joseph W., III, 5899
Donner, Joseph W., Jr., 5899
Donner, Shulamith, 5898
Donner, Timothy E., 5899
Donner, William H., 5899, 8107
Donnici, Peter J., 690
Donoghue, Jeff, 3180
Donohoe, Carol, 2994
Donohoe, Robin R., 481
Donohue, Bernadine Murphy, 956
Donohue, Fay, 4016
Donohue, John F., 3926
Donoso, Larry A., 41
Donovan, Adam, 975
Donovan, Carol A., 4003
Donovan, David A., 2849
Donovan, George, 9631
Donovan, John J., 9509
Donovan, Kevin, 7412
Donovan, Les, 3539
Donovan, Linda Ramsey, 5900
Donovan, Michael D.S., 5900
Donovan, Thomas J., 5164
Donovan, Tina, 6340
Donovan, William, 8325
Donworth, Mary E., 2380
Dooley Charitable Lead Unity Trust Foundation, Mary Kathryn, 1402
Dooley, Emer, 9757
Dooley, Franco, 9250
Doolin, Charles W., 1402
Doolin, David, 418
Doolin, Earl L., 1402
Doolin, Kaleta, 1402
Doolin, Willadean, 1402
Dooling, John E., Jr., 4934
Doolittle, Harry, 5901
Doolittle, Misook, 5901
Doore, Daniel P., 1279
Doppstadt, Eric, 5994
Dorado, Raymond, 6375, 7945
Doran, Brian, 3085
Doran, Brian F., 3085
Doran, Evelyn H., 4024
Doran, Kenneth M., 583
Doran, Robert W., 4024
Doran-Khewhok, Carol, 5919
Dorchester, C. Ronald, 8716
Dorcy, Daryl, 2650
Dordell, Timothy P., 4780
Dordelman, William E., 7989
Dore', Deborah K., 3629
Dore', William J., Jr., 3629
Dore', William J., Sr., 3629
Dore, William J., Sr., 3629
Dorer, Benno, 407
Dorf, Alexandra, 3962
Dorf, Roger, 1392
Dorhauer, Robert, 4864
Dorhout, Peter K., 157
Doring, H. William, 7957
Doring, Matthew P., 4039

Doris, Peter E., 2933
Dorko, Carol, 2034
Dorman, Bill, 2123
Dorman, Wes, 8777
Dormitory Dept. of New York State, 6044
Dorn, Andrew W., 7078
Dorn, Estelle M., 7439
Dorn, Holbrook, 8731
Dorn, Jeffrey, 4347
Dorn, Megan, 9441
Dorn, Nancy, 1591
Dornbusch, Linda L., 4364
Dornbusch, Raymond P., 4364
Dornette, Helen G., 7440
Dornsife, David H., 672
Doroshow, Carol, 5527
Dorot Foundation, 543
Dorothy Stotsenberg Trust, 1221
Dorow, Brian, 9965
Dorr, George A., III, 5180
Dorrance, Bennett, 107
Dorrance, Bennett, Jr., 107
Dorrance, Charles A., 1529
Dorrance, Gunda S., 1529
Dorrance, Jacqueline, 297
Dorrance, Jacquelynn W., 107
Dorrance, John T., III, 1529
Dorrance, John T., IV, 1529
Dorrego, Christa, 952
Dorris, James F., 4816
Dorris, Thomas B., 2692
Dorsa, Caroline, 5416
Dorsett Family Foundation, 9059
Dorsett, Betty, 7302
Dorsett, David, 9059
Dorsett, Stuart B., 7273
Dorsey & Whitney Trust Co. LLC, 8519
Dorsey & Whitney Trust Co., LLC, 8513
Dorsey, Ellen, 1956
Dorsey, Gayle S., 3607
Dorsey, Heather A., 4807
Dorsey, J. Kevin, 2933
Dorsey, Jacqueline, 4715
Dorsey, Jacqueline A., 4757
Dorsey, Jill, 2817
Dorsey, Lynn L., 1754
Dorsey, Patrick B., 6978
Dorsey, Susan Ford, 1112
Dorsin, Leslie, 631
Dorsman, Peter, 2524
Dortch, Blanche, 7631
Dortch, Sebastian, 2332
Dorwart, Fred, 7807
Doscher, Drew, 7012
Doss, James, 8812
Doss, Jim, 8812
Doss, John, 8812
Doss, M.S., 8813
Doss, Meek Lane, 8813
Dossa, Alfred, 1194
Dossman, Curley M., Jr., 2469
Doswell, Florence A., 8814
Dot Foods, Inc., 3189
Doti, David, 3396
Doti, James L., 1171
Dotson, George S., 7748
Dotson, Greg, 4503
Dotson, Nancy K., 9796
Dotson, Phyllis N., 7748
Dotterweich, Maria Miceli, 4577
Doty, Barbara E., 5902
Doty, Beth, 7727
Doty, Christopher S., 5902
Doty, Dan, 3530
Doty, George E., 5902
Doty, Mark A., 9704
Doty, Michelle M., 5800
Doty, Rick, 1391
Doty, Steve, 5216
Doty, Virginia M., 5902
Doty, William W., 5902
Doucette, Kathleen, 1630
Doud, Jacqueline Powers, 825
Douenias, Steven, 6011
Dougherty, Bill, 1162
Dougherty, Gregory, 475
Dougherty, Matthew W., 2903
Dougherty, Merry, 4849
Dougherty, Nancy, 475
Dougherty, Neil, 220
Douglas, Anne, 476
Douglas, Brianna, 8462
Douglas, Charles, 2264
Douglas, Charles H., 2677
Douglas, David W., 1955
Douglas, Dianne, 886
Douglas, Jean, 1955, 3765
Douglas, Kirk, 476
Douglas, Laura M., 3586
Douglas, Laurinda Lowenstein, 7232
Douglas, Margaret C., 8661
Douglas, Mark, 7688
Douglas, Patricia L., 2040
Douglas, Peter, 476
Douglas, Ron, 3360
Douglas, Rosann B., 8619
Douglas, Terry D., 8619
Douglas, Tim, 3475
Douglas, W. Leslie, 3765
Douglas-Bailey, Hyacinth, 1547
Douglass Foundation, Terry and Rosann, 530
Douglass, Emily R., 9716
Douglass, John P., 9716
Douglass, Lee, 181
Douglass, Susan, 7471
Douglass, W. Birch, III, 9469
Doup, Diane, 3321
Doupe, Allison J., 4708
Douple, Earl H., Jr., 9562
Douthat, Neil T., 4974
Douthat, Paul N., 4974
Douzinas, Nancy R., 6681
Douzinas, Nancy Rauch, 6681
Douzinas, Ruth F., 6681
Dove Givings Foundation, 5904
Dove, Carol L., 7587
Dove, Chris, 7201
Dove, Eddie, 1321
Dove, G. Mack, 31
Dove, Nancy R., 31
Dove, Reid B., 31
Dovid, Khal Binyomin, 5668
Dovydenas, Elizabeth D., 4790
Dow 2005 Charitable Annuity Trust, 4406
Dow 2011 Trust, Christina Seix, 5244
Dow Automotive, 7638
Dow Charitable Unitrust, Vada B., 4408
Dow Chemical Co., The, 4404
Dow Corninci Toray Co., Ltd., 4405
Dow Corning Corp., 4405
Dow Jones & Company, Inc., 5906
Dow, Alden, 4408
Dow, Barbara C., 4406
Dow, Ben, 9704
Dow, Christina Seix, 5244
Dow, Grace A., 4407
Dow, Herbert H., 4406
Dow, Melanie, 1781
Dow, Melvin, 8656
Dow, Michael Lloyd, 4407, 4408
Dow, Pamela G., 4406
Dow, Peggy, 646
Dow, Peggy Ann, 1168
Dow, Robert S., 5244
Dow, Steven, 7734, 7807
Dow, Vada, 4408
Dow, Willard H., II, 4406
Dowd, Anthony J., 7035
Dowd, Brian, 7905
Dowd, John, 8152
Dowd, Michael G., 5594
Dowda, Tanya, 4691
Dowdy, Jacqueline, 4907
Dower, Roger, 9924
Dowley, Jennifer, 3948
Dowling Trust, William C., Jr., 5907
Dowling, J. Robert, 3926
Dowling, Patrick, 365
Down, Anne, 853
Down, David, 1053
Down, Gerald C., 517
Down, Jerry, 853
Downer, Amy C., 1581
Downer, E.M., III, 1069
Downer, Edwin E., 4844
Downes, Krystin B., 2160
Downes, Laurence M., 5389
Downey, Geraldine A., 7145
Downey, James E., 477
Downey, John A., 7030
Downey, Keith M., 477
Downey, Maria, 82
Downey, Matthew J., 3991
Downey, Paul C., 3991
Downey, Thelma L., 9502
Downey, Timothy, 167
Downham, Doreen, 1690
Downie, Jocelyn, 5662, 6947
Downing, Barry L., 3510
Downing, Diane, 7391
Downing, Frances V.S., 6933
Downing, John O., 6933
Downing, Paula M., 3510
Downing, Terri, 8787
Downs, Betsy Warburton, 8331
Downs, Charlie, 500
Downs, Dawn, 4796
Downs, Harry S., Dr., 2427
Downs, Mike D., 8331
Downton, Christine V., 5622
Dox, Lillian, 3707
Doyal, Stephen D., 4906
Doyel, Patrick J., 5802
Doyle, Alice P., 1713
Doyle, Allen, 1713
Doyle, Cynthia T., 6999
Doyle, Cynthia Tower, 7000
Doyle, Daniel A., 9705
Doyle, Doug, 5115
Doyle, Erin, 2804
Doyle, F. Patrick, 5115
Doyle, Frank, 6408
Doyle, Gertrude R., 5115
Doyle, James E., 760
Doyle, James L., Jr., 5398
Doyle, John C., 2829
Doyle, Jonathan, 5839
Doyle, Kathy A., 2804
Doyle, Kay, 4152
Doyle, Margie, 9697
Doyle, Mary Nabers, 56
Doyle, Melissa, 9961
Doyle, Nancy, 5115
Doyle, Noreen, 5925
Doyle, Patrick, 3245
Doyle, Richard P., 5717
Doyle, Robert M., 7000
Doyle, T. Lawrence, 3231
Doyle, Thomas F., 8328
Doyle, Tina, 3846
Doyle, Valentine, 1713
Doyle, William J., 2804
Doyle, William M., Jr., 2770, 3491
Doyon Ltd. and Affiliates, 86
DPC Midstream, 7196
DPR Construction, Inc., 478
DPS Foundation, 1487
Drabing, Darin B., 263
Drackett, Roger, 7717
Dracopoli, Andrew J., 9440
Drahzal, Kaye M., 3462
Drain, Scott, 4477
Drake Trust, Susan, 1773
Drake, Barbara, 5108
Drake, Daniel, 4246
Drake, Erin, 917
Drake, Jamie, 6544
Drake, Jay D., 4194
Drake, Michael V., 5800
Drake, Michael V., M.D., 367
Drake, Randy B., 9399
Drake, Richard J., 2948
Drake, Rodney, 6038
Drake, Shelley C., 6406
Drake, Skip, 4667
Drake, Susan, 9567, 9568
Drane, Frank N., 9054
Dranow, Alan, 186
Draper Corp., 4101
Draper, Dana, 6115
Draper, Jeanne N., 4573
Draper, Melissa, 480
Draper, N. C., 1770
Draper, Phyllis, 480
Draper, Polly, 480
Draper, Rebecca, 480
Draper, Stephen E., 2578
Draper, Tim C., 480
Draper, Tom, 4467
Draper, William, 480
Draper, William H., III, 481
Drasheff, Linda M., 5378
Draughn, John, 8507
Drawdy, Larry, 4814
Drawe, Carol L., 8758
Dray, James R., 6808
Drazen, Michael D., 4780
Drebin, Allan R., 2745
Dregne, Eric, 3421
Dreicer, Elizabeth, 229
Dreilbelbis, M.D., 3459
Dreiling, Leo J., 3511
Dreisbach, James, 1397
Dreiseszun Grantor Trust, Richard J., 3512
Dreiseszun, Irene, 3512
Dreiseszun, Richard, 3512
Dreiseszun, Sherman, 3512
Dreiss, Meredith Mitchell, 9029
Dreissigacker, Bari, 9374
Dreissigacker, Peter, 9374
Dreissigacker, Peter D., 9374
Dreitzer, Albert J., 5910
Dreitzer, Mildred H., 5910

Drennan, A. Don, 3635
Drennan, Rudith A., 3635
Drennen, Mark C., 3613
Drenth, Kenneth, Dr., 4375
Dresdale, Richard C., 7012
Dresher, James T., Jr., 3782
Dresher, James T., Sr., 3782
Dresher, Jeffrey M., 3782
Dresher, Joshua, 3782
Dresher, Patricia K., 3782
Dresher, Virginia M., 3782
Dresner, Bruce M., 3788
Dresner, Joseph, 4409
Dresner, Lori, 4409
Dress, Norman, 862
Dresser, Joyce, 5611
Dresser, Mary, 4550
Drew, Angelika, 2175
Drew, Dennis M., 700
Drew, Ellen, 482
Drew, Ellen Todd, 482
Drew, Elton F., 4034
Drew, Everitt, 2037
Drew, Gail McMichael, 7265
Drew, John, 482
Drew, John L., 482
Drew, Justin Corey, 2175
Drew, Lisa, 7496
Drew, Sandra S., 1757
Drew, William F., Jr., 8507
Drexler, Millard S., 5911
Drexler, Peggy F., 5911
Dreyer, David, 2072
Dreyfus, Alfred, 9423
Dreyfus, Alice L., 2784
Dreyfus, Andrew, 3953
Dreyfus, Bradley, 1004
Dreyfus, Camille, 5912
Dreyfus, Carolyn S., 2784
Dreyfus, Louis, 5913
Dreyfus, Mark, 9423
Dreyfus, Max, 1901
Dreyfus, Mildred, 9423
Dreyfus, Victoria, 1901
Dreyfuss, Norma, 5590
Drezner, Julie Kenny, 414
Driehaus, Elizabeth, 2805
Driehaus, Richard H., 2805
Driemeyer Trust, Derick L., 4967
Driemeyer, Derick L., 4967
Driemeyer, Sally M., 4967
Driesen, Katherine, 1212
Driessnack, Robert, 9651
Driggers, John, 9640
Driker, Eugene, 4588
Drinane, Juliana, 5324
Drinkwater, Clover, 5804
Driscoll Revocable Trust, W. John, 4648
Driscoll, Dawn-Marie, 2327
Driscoll, Elizabeth S., 4648
Driscoll John B., 4648, 4802
Driscoll, Margaret L., 4648
Driscoll, Margaret M., 9559
Driscoll, Timothy, 5171
Driscoll, W. John, 9732
Driscoll, William L., 4648
Driskill, Lucienne, 2806
Driskill, Walter S., 2806
Driver, Cyrus, 1609
Drizin, Channy, 5914
Drizin, Mendel, 5914
DRL Enterprises, 2978
Drobot, Joseph, 2808
Drobot, Judy, 2808
Drollinger, H. James, 483
Drollinger, Howard B., 483
Drop in the Bucket, 9118
Droppa, Jane W.I., 1618
Drossner, Audrey B., 3727
Drossos, Eugenia, 3570
Drost, Charles Mitchell, 3619
Drost, William T., 3619
Drown, Joseph W., 484
Drowota, Frank F., III, 8568
Drozd, Taras, 2907
Druckenmiller, Fiona, 5684, 5915
Druckenmiller, Stanley F., 2514, 5915
Drug Plastics & Glass Co., Inc., 7941
Drug Plastics & Glass Inc Profit Sharing Plan, 7941
drugstore.com, inc., 175
Druley, Cynthia, 418
Drumm, David G., 9214
Drumm, Susan Rodgers, 1364
Drummond, Abbie, 74
Drummond, Jere, 4353
Drummond, Kenneth J., 6236
Drummond, Lori, 9605
Drumwright, Elenita M., 1819
Drumwright, Elizabeth R.M., 1819
Drushel, William H., Jr., 8792
Druss, Ellen, 9165
DRW Holdings LLC., 2807
Dryer, Ellen, 2808
Drymiller, Michael K., 3424
DS Associates, 6949
DSD Realty, Inc., 3449
DTE Energy Ventures, Inc., 4410
du Pont, E. Bradford, Jr., 1872
du Pont, Edward B., 1806, 1872
du Pont, Eleuthere I., II, 1806
du Pont, Henry B., IV, 1824
du Pont, M. Lynn, Dr., 1806
du Pont, Pierre S., 1806, 1872
du Pont, Pierre S., IV, 1806
Duan, Yong Ping, 507
Duane, Paul, 8468
Dubas, Kathy, 5067
Dubbert, Paige Laurie, 4933
Dube, Eric, 8061
Dubel, Gregory J., 8383
Dubester, Ilana, 7298
Dubia, Chris, 254
Dubiago, Nicholas, 1584
Dubick, Marc, 1924
Dubiel, Douglas, 2379
Dubiel, Mandy, 4332
Dubin and Swieca Capital Management Inc., 6955
Dubin, Eva Andersson, 5916
Dubin, Glenn R., 5916
Dubin, Hinda, 3766
Dubin, James M., 1971, 6714
Dubina, Beth, 78
Dubois, Dick, 3290
DuBois, Philip, 4246
DuBose Family Charitable Annuity Trust, 2450
DuBose, Beverly M., III, Mr., 2450
DuBose, Eileen Erickson, 2450
DuBose, Elizabeth Egleston, 2450
DuBose, Frances W., 2450
DuBose, Ginger, 7780
Dubose, Sam, 7780
Dubose, Vivian N., 7780
Dubovsky, Betsy, 6912
DuBow, Helen A., 2068
DuBow, Lawrence J., 2068
DuBow, Linda J., 2068
DuBow, Michael, 2031
DuBow, Michael I., 2068
Dubow, Susan, 2068
DuBow, Susan E., 2068
Dubrow, David Lewis, 1861
Dubrow, Eli B., 489
Ducayet, Wally, 1511
Ducceschi, Laura J., 8275
Ducci Electrical Contractors, 5482
Duch, Mike, 8523
Ducharme, Alexandria W., 3846
Duchossois Group, Inc., The, 2809
Duchossois Industries, Inc., 2809
Duchossois Technology Partners, LLC, 2809
Duchossois, Craig J., 2809
Duchossois, Kimberly T., 2809
Duchossois, Richard L., 2809
Duckett, Michael R., 9965
Duckmann, Stephanie, 3262
Duckwall, Frank E., 2069
Duckworth, Connie K., 6248
Duckworth, Thomas J., 6248
Ducommun, Robert E., 485
Duda & Sons Inc., A., 2070
Duda, Ferdinand S., 2070
Duda, Fritz L., 8815
Duda, Fritz L., Jr., 8815
Duda, Fritz L., Mrs., 8815
Duda, James F., 8815
Duda, Mary L., 8815
Duden, Mary G., 7995
Dudenhoeffer, John, 3277
Dudley, Ahrian Tyler, 67
Dudley, Bruce K., 3588
Dudley, C.R., Jr., 67
Dudley, Calmeze H., Dr., 4424
Dudley, Chad, 8775
Dudley, Gary C., 8958
Dudley, Gary L., 9217
Dudley, George H. T., 9377
Dudley, John, 9803
Dudley, Louise M., 9405
Dudley, Stewart R., 67
Dudley, William N., Jr., 295
Dudnick, Andrew L., 504
Duehay, Frank, 3971
Duemling, Louisa C., 1821
Duermmeier, Christopher, 1706
Duerr, Patrick, 4487
Duesenberg, Phyllis B., 4880
Duesenberg, Richard W., 3311, 4880
Duff, Andrew S., 4743
Duff, Barbara, 1504
Duff, Christopher Bruce, 1405
Duff, James C., 1907
Duff, Mary, 5353
Duff, Patrick, 6050
Duff, Patrick D., 5353
Duff, Sean, 1405
Duff, Susan, 3598
Duffalo, Michael, 6960
Duffell, Carol, 9166
Duffell, David K., 8422
Duffey, Diana C., 6784
Duffey, Harry J., III, 6784
Duffey, Lois S., 6784
Duffield, Cheryl D., 486
Duffield, David A., 486
Duffield, Michael D., 486
Duffield, Richard, 169
Duffield, Sally, 4859
Duffy, Angela, 3775
Duffy, Arthur X., 8448
Duffy, Bernard J., III, 4942
Duffy, Catherine, 633
Duffy, Elizabeth A., 5243
Duffy, Michael P., 417
Duffy, Nancy, 4359
Duffy, Nuala, 3759
Duffy, Sarah A., 9935
Duffy, Terrance A., 2755, 2756
Dufour, Edith Libby, 3648
Dufresne, Michele, 9833
Dugan, Ann M., 5950
Dugan, Mariellen, 5389
Dugas, Laura Jo, 8559
Dugas, Laura Jo Turner, 8639
Dugas, Lynn King, 8559
Dugas, Pam, 8559
Dugas, Stephen H., 8559
Dugas, Wayne F., Jr., 8559
Dugas, Wayne F., Sr., 8559
Dugdale, Bill, 1765
Dugdale, J.W., Jr., 2785
Duggan, Agnes B., 3563
Duggan, John, 1563
Duggan, John K., Jr., 7924
Duggan, Patricia Miller, 7924
Duggan, Teresa O'Shaugnessy, 4734
Dugger, Edward, III, 3939
Dugger, Rob, 9380
Duhl, Joanne, 6659
Duhme, Carol M., 4963
Duhme, David W., 4963
Duhme, Jeremy, 4963
Duhon, Jonathan, 4829
Duisterhof, Miki, 1565
Duke Charitable Foundation, Doris, 5918, 5919, 8423
Duke Energy, 7394
Duke Energy Business Services, 7196
Duke Energy Corp., 7196
Duke Energy Field Services, LP, 7196
Duke Energy Foundation, 7183
Duke Power Co., 7183, 7196
Duke, Doris, 5917, 5918, 8423
Duke, James Buchanan, 7195
Duke, Jennifer Johnson, 2287
Duke, Lisa Walker, 4724
Duke, Michael T., 210
Duke, Susan S., 9384
Dukes, Carl Elias Bailey, 8471
Dukes, David D., 55
Dukes, David R., 1171
Dukes, Floyd M., 2482
Dukes, Harold T., Sr., 8471
Dukes, Jane, 55
Dukes, Joan M., 6006
Dulaney, Betty Jo, 4821
Dulaney, Daryl, 5454
Dulaney, Deborah, 7428
Dulaney, Robert W., 3592
Dulaney, Tommy E., 4844
Dulany, Peggy, 6725
Dulin, Eugenia B., 9431
Dulin, R. Kenneth, 330
Dumais, Richard J., 1893
Dumais, Val, 1634
Duman, Allison, 9493
Duman, Louis J., 1376
Dumaresq, Carolyn C., 8046
Dumas, David, 8537
Dumas, Michael R., 8916
Dumke, Carol Browning, 5104
Dumke, E.R., IV, 9316
Dumke, Edmund, 5104

Dumke, Ezekiel R., Jr., 9315, 9316
Dumke, Katherine W., 9316
Dumke, Mitchell, 9316
Dumke-Manship, Andrea, 9316
DuMouchel, William H., 3926
Dunagan, Robert, 2669
Dunavant, Linda J., 8889
Dunaway, James R., 9198
Dunbar, Bruce C., 5245
Dunbar, C. Wendell, 4557
Dunbar, Charles D., 9785
Dunbar, Ida D., 5245
Dunbar, Jessica, 5008
Dunbar, Joe, 3283
Dunbar, Mary, 4347
Dunbar, Mary L., 4523
Dunbar, William, 1931
Duncan, Barry, 8595
Duncan, Christina, 2986
Duncan, Cynthia "Mil", 5182
Duncan, Dale, 3407
Duncan, Deborah L., 294, 296, 446
Duncan, Debra Kay, 809, 956
Duncan, George L., 4152
Duncan, Georgetta, 9024
Duncan, Greg, 1934
Duncan, Haskell A., 5920
Duncan, Joe, 7569
Duncan, Mark D., 2637
Duncan, Mona, 1233
Duncan, Monique N., 4674
Duncan, Phillip, 4674
Duncan, R. Foster, 3631
Duncan, Ryan, 1233
Duncan, Sarah, 3013, 9616
Duncan, W.W., 3851
Duncan, William G., Jr., 3577
Dunckel, Jeanette M., 1358
Dundon, Tom, 5395
Dunford, Denise, 6153
Dunford, Leslie A., 7406
Dunford, Lissa, 2597
Dunham Trust, John C., 2811
Dunham, Lynn, Dr., 6038
Dunham, Robert H., 7296
Dunham, Scott, 966
Dunigan Trust, Mitchell, 3322
Dunigan, Derek, 3322
Dunigan, E. Bryan, 3212
Dunigan, Larry, 3322
Dunigan, Sharon, 3322
Dunkelmann, Dianne, 7394
Dunkin Brands Inc., 4026
Dunkin, Craig, 3346
Dunklau, Rupert, 5036
Dunklau, Ruth, 5036
Dunkle, Terry K., 7990
Dunkleman, Dorene, 3076
Dunklin, Robert, 4332
Dunlaevy, J. Williar, 3946, 3947, 3948
Dunlap, Bonni, 8296
Dunlap, Edward B., Jr., 7970
Dunlap, Lorena Gore, 2871
Dunlap, Michael S., 5072
Dunlap, Nancy, 43
Dunlap, Timothy M., 7970
Dunlap, William C., 9141
Dunlap, William H., 5164
Dunlavy, Teri, 3313
Dunleavy, Kathy, 8459
Dunleavy, Nancy Alba, 8199
Dunlop, Tim, 2792
Dunmire, Cyril C., Jr., 8294
Dunn Construction, J.E., 4882
Dunn Trust, William A., 2072
Dunn, Betty L., 2071
Dunn, Charles A., 2223
Dunn, David H., 4549
Dunn, Debra L., 1175
Dunn, Geoffrey P., 8026
Dunn, Greg, 3417
Dunn, Gregory W., 8622
Dunn, John, 77
Dunn, John M., 3402
Dunn, John S., Jr., 8816
Dunn, John S., Sr., 8816
Dunn, Kathryn, 9907
Dunn, Kevin A., 4882
Dunn, Kristen Thun, 8350
Dunn, Loretta S., 2071
Dunn, Louise, III, 4027
Dunn, Lowell, II, 2071
Dunn, Marcia, 6882
Dunn, Margaret, 4027
Dunn, Mark, 3517
Dunn, Martin, 4027
Dunn, Michael, 9652
Dunn, Paige, 9632
Dunn, Patricia B., 1634
Dunn, Patricia M., 1362
Dunn, Peter, 4027
Dunn, Peter A., 5757
Dunn, Randy J., Dr., 7723
Dunn, Raymond J., III, 4027
Dunn, Raymond J., IV, 4027
Dunn, Reagam, 9632
Dunn, Rebecca Water, 2072
Dunn, Robert P., 4882
Dunn, Sarah, 5790
Dunn, Stephen D., 4882
Dunn, Steven D., 4882
Dunn, Susan, 3909
Dunn, Terrence P., 4882, 4949
Dunn, Terry, 4882
Dunn, Wallace, 9444
Dunn, William A., 2072
Dunn, William H., Jr., 4882
Dunn, William H., Sr., 4882
Dunnan, Bruce B., 1541
Dunnan, D. Stuart, Rev., 1541
Dunnan, D. Suart, Rev., 3761
Dunnan, Diana B., 1541
Dunnan, Douglas M., 1541
Dunnan, John M., 1541
Dunne, James, 5839
Dunne, James, III, 5839
Dunne, Rick, 1714
Dunne, Tiffany, 8, 9
Dunnell, John R., 4309
Dunner, Aba M., 6336
Dunner, Shulamith, 5898
Dunning, Richard, 4438
Dunnington, Patricia, 6901
Dunstan, Kristin, 2432
Dunwoody, Mac, 2647
Dupkin, Carol N., 3783
Dupkin, Manuel, II, 3783
Duplessis, Ernest L., 3034
duPont Trust, Margaret F., 1814
duPont, A. Felix, Jr., 1754
duPont, A.I., 5235
duPont, Christopher T., 1754
duPont, Henry B., 1757
duPont, Henry B., IV, 1824
duPont, Irenee, 1758
duPont, Irenee, Jr., 1758
duPont, Jessie Ball, 2074, 2075
duPont, Lammot J., 1814
duPont, Lydia Chichester, 1754
duPont, Miren Dea, 1814
DuPont, Ruth S., 3950
duPont, Willis H., 1814
Dupree, Thomas H., Jr., 583
Dupree, Tracey, 5262
Duprey, Margaret H., 8078, 8444
Dupuy, Damian, 8383
Dur, Christeen Bernard, 1632
Dura Medical Inc., 9098
Duran, Joe, 1211
Durand, Bonnie, 5801
Durand, Carolyn Thrune, 4549
Durant, Katherine, 9740
Durante, Katherine B., 5394
Duray, Mary Lucille, 455
Durazo, Felix, 106
Durbin, Rebecca, 3253
Durchslag, Danielle, 5833
Durchslag, Ruth Mayer, 3006
Durell, Anne B., 7441
Durell, David, 3319
Durell, David A., 7441
Durell, George Edward, 7441
Durgin, James K., 3427
Durgin, Pauline C., 3427
Durham Charitable Lead Annuity Trust no. 2, Charles W., 8817
Durham Charitable Lead Annuity Trust, Charles, 5038
Durham Charitable Lead Annuity Trust, Charles W., 8817
Durham Resources, 5038
Durham Revocable Trust, Charles W., 5038
Durham Trust, Charles W., 5025
Durham Trust, Charles W., II, 5025
Durham, Andrew D., 9169
Durham, Barbara, 8817
Durham, Christena, 9327
Durham, Cynthia Lambert, 8136
Durham, David R., 9169
Durham, Debra A., 5038
Durham, Jane A., 2405
Durham, Jolene, 3359
Durham, Sindy Shelton, 9169
Durham, Steven H., 8817
Durham, Terri, 369
Durham, Wendy H., 9169
Durie, John, 9175
Durkan, James, 3162
Durkee, Brewster J., 2076
Durkee, Kendall G., 2076
Durkee, Thomas V., 2015
Durkin, Bryan T., 2755
Durkin, Debra D., 1744
Durkin, Timothy, 8223
Duron, Rosalie, 7881
Durr, Julie J., 3430
Durr, R.C., 3572
Durrence, Tamera "Tami", 7411
Durrett, William E., 7728
Durst, Helena, 5922
Durst, Leslie B., 5922
Dury, David F., 2813
Dutcher, Judi, 4611
Dutra Group, The, 293
Dutra, Craig J., 3991
Dutra, Robert, 7103
Dutton, Andrea, 419
Dutton, Ian, 89
Dutton, Julia, 8041
Dutton, Uriel E., 8664
Dutton, William, 2839, 7575
Duty Free Americas, Inc., 2091
Duval Spirits, Inc., 3672
Duvall, Robert L., 9222
Duvick, David F., 4651
Duxbury, Elizabeth J., 9704
Dvorak, Elizabeth, 2008, 7502
Dvorak, Kevin J., 7357
Dvoryak, George, 8351
Dwan, Mary McGahey, 4596
Dweck, Frances, 1902
Dweck, Frances R., 1902
Dweck, Ralph S., 1902
Dwek, Joseph, 5559
Dwek, Terry, 5559
Dworkis, Sam, 5601
Dworman, Alvin, 1842
Dworsky, Alan J., 4225
Dworsky, David, 5894
Dwoskin, Albert James, 1772
Dwoskin, Lisa Claire, 1772
Dwyer, Dan, 1565
Dwyer, Dean P., 428
Dwyer, Mary M., 3140
Dwyer, Mike, 4646
Dwyer, Robert G., Esq., 8026
Dwyer, Timothy J., 4686
Dybala, Richard L., 2662
Dybul, Mark, 1557
Dye, Alan, 9454
Dye, Alan P., 9408
Dye, Guilford, 416
Dye, James, 1194
Dye, Jerry, 1276
Dye, John, 1521
Dye, Kappy, 1194
Dye, Susan M., 3129
Dye, Thomas H., 9623
Dyer, Barbara, 1916
Dyer, Bob, 8819
Dyer, Gary, 2627
Dyer, James, 4383
Dyer, Julie, 824
Dyer, Kay, 7749
Dyer, Laura, 8774
Dyer, Rick, 4386
Dyer, Sara R., 7628
Dyess, Kirby, 7876
Dyke, Elaine Van, 5175
Dykhuizen, Constance, 1793
Dykstra, Craig R., 3342
Dykstra, Thomas, 2981
Dynamet Inc., 8256
Dynes, Robert, 1108
Dyott, Ingrid S., 6538
Dyson, Charles H., 5923
Dyson, Christopher, 5923
Dyson, Margaret M., 5923
Dyson, Molly, 5923
Dyson, Robert R., 5923
Dyson, Roger, 3324
Dzau, Ruth, 7328
Dziedziak, Bryan J., 5125
Dziedzic, John, 8355

E & M Charities, 3468
E.ON U.S. LLC, 3586
Eads, Jacqueline L., 2356
Eady, John Thomas, 8818
Eagan, Gail, 3926
Eagan, Gayle L., 5801
Eagan, Margot T., 5721
Eagan, Mark, 5803
Eagle-Tribune Publishing Co., 4243

Eagleton, Barbara, 5001
Eagon, Jim, 9832
Eakes, Brian, 3759
Eakes, Martin, 5994
Eakins, Ray, 3284
Eames, Bruce, 9226
Ear, Sophal, 5833
Earhart, Anne G., 878
Earhart, Harry Boyd, 4413
Earl, Anthony S., 2946
Earl, James A., 3812
Earl, Margaret H., 3812
Earl, Orrin K., 1015
Earl, Sylvia, 3812
Earl, Tiffany, 3417
Earle, Anne Gordon, 8095
Earle, O. Perry, III, 7325
Earle, Sharon Reynolds, Dr., 8468
Earls, Christopher B., 1787
Earls, David, 1787
Earls, Jeffrey W., 1787
Earls, John G., 1787
Earls, Michael G., 1787
Earls, Samantha Rudin, 6768
Early, Gerald, Dr., 5001
Early, Tom, 9147
Early, Tracey B., 5278
Early, W. B., 7856
Earnest, Jennifer R., 2158
Earnhart, V.J., 8730
Easi, Inc., 5249
Easley, Andrew H., 9424
Easley, David C., 9924
Eason, Elizabeth, 2378
Eason, Paul R., 9450
Eason-Watkins, Barbara, 3297
East Chicago Development Foundation, Inc., 3242
East Lane LLC, 2090
East Main Assoc., 8526
East Rock Village, Inc., 5444
East West Bank, 491
East, Sarita Kenedy, 5925
Eastdil Realty, Inc., LLC, 6160
Easter, Arlene, 5095
Easter, Colette R., 8568
Easter, Lowell, 7180
Easterling, Iris, 4829
Eastern American Energy Corp., 1404
Eastern Bank, 4013, 4030
Eastern Bank, N.A., 4309
Eastern Excavation, 5482
Eastham, Cathy, 9091
Eastman Chemical Co., 8561
Eastman, John, 1532
Eastman-Cook, Ursula, 1212
Easton Revocable Trust, Ruth, 4652
Easton, Gregory J., 492
Easton, James L., 492, 809
Easton, Kenneth E., 7776
Easton, Ray A., 4450
Easton, Robin E., 9698
Eastwood, Clint, 936
Eaton Corp., 7442
Eaton Estate Trust, Hubert, 263
Eaton Foundation, 4209
Eaton, Alice, 6395
Eaton, Christina N., 8380
Eaton, Cornelia, 1015
Eaton, George F., II, 3680
Eaton, Joseph, 8893
Eaton, Kanyere, 6864
Eaton, Roger, 3608
Eaton, Ruth, 8893
Eaton, Ruth Ann, 4683
Eaton, Will, 9768
Eay III Foundation, George E., 8766
eBay Inc., 493
Ebb, Fred, 5928
Ebel, William E., 5511
Eber, Ahron, 6229
Eberhard, Marie, 7590
Eberhardt, John E., Jr., 7971
Eberhart, Andrew, 8085
Eberhart, Cornelia Ober, 4703
Eberhart, James P., 3063
Eberhart, Mike, 4522
Eberhart, Ralph, 1943
Eberhart, Robert, 9997
Eberhart, Samuel, 4703
Eberle, John G., 5757
Eberle, Karl, 9859
Eberly, Kathy, 5361
Ebershoff, David A., 1319
Eberstadt, Vera, 5929
Eberstadt, Walter, 5929
Eberstein, Lanny, 1097
Ebert, Catherine G., 2079
Ebert, Cecile G., 2079
Ebert, Lyda G., 2079
Ebert, Michael G., 4443
Ebert, Michael L., 2079
Ebert, Robert O., 2079
Eberts, Randall W., 4564
Ebey, John G., 697
Eble, John N., 3328
Eblen, Gary, 7181
Eblen, Jennie, 7182
Ebrahimi, Farhad A., 3984
Ebrhamimi, Alireza, 5566
Ebright, Mitchell, 749
Ebrom, Charles, 9296
Eby, George, 8820
Eby, Jeff, 9757
Eby, Patsy Ann, 8820
Eccles, C. Hope, 9320
Eccles, George S., 9319
Eccles, Katie A., 1262
Eccles, Lisa, 9319
Eccles, Marriner S., 9320
Eccles, Spencer, 9318
Eccles, Spencer F., 127, 1262, 9318, 9319, 9320
Eccles, Tom, 6133
Echaveste, Maria, 367
Echevarria, Anita, 3289
Echolds, Leslie, 633
Echolds, Mike, 633
Echols, Kirk B., 9402
Eck, Dale F., 3996
Eck, Jack, 1518
Eckardt, Robert E., 7406
Ecke, Keith H., 9969
Eckel, John R., Jr., 8821
Eckel, Joyce A., 2122
Eckel, Paul F., 2122
Eckelkamp, L.B., Jr., 4966
Eckerle, Annette, 4908
Eckerle, Mary, 3280
Eckerson, John, 5246
Eckert, Alfred C., III, 7893
Eckert, James, 5642
Eckert, Karen, 3049
Eckert, Kathryn Bishop, 4337
Eckert, Marilee, 877
Eckert, Robert A., 664
Eckert, Ross, 5801
Eckhart Corp., 216
Eckhart, Walter, 685
Eckholdt, Eric, 5826
Eckley, Bonnie, 9616
Eckley, Brett, Dr., 9769
Eckloff, Ron, 5055
Ecklun, Nancy, 5075
Eckstein, J. Norman, 7428
Eckstein, Kathryn A., 3573
Eckstein, Moses, 5817
Eckstein, Ray A., 3573
Eckstein, Teresa R., 3573
Eckstrom, Elizabeth, 7837
Eco Duct, Inc., 503
Ecolab, 9837
Ecolab Inc., 4254, 4651
Econome, Kathryn C., 1262
Economic Studies Inc., 3820
Economou, James S., 774
Economy Freight, Inc., 6123
Edberg, Sharron, 2794
Eddie, Gloria, 753
Eddie, Gloria Jeneal, 753
Eddington, Emily Ann, 9304
Eddington, Paul, 9304
Eddleman, Bill D., 40
Eddy, Arthur D., 4414
Eddy, John, 6506
Eddy, Krista, 1402
Eddy, Robert, Jr., 3623
Eddy, Susan, 4806
Edelheit, Aaron, 7791
Edelman Trust, William, 5930
Edelman, Alex, 5931
Edelman, Catherine, 6556
Edelman, Cindy, 2031
Edelman, Cornelia S., 5932
Edelman, Cynthia G., 2080
Edelman, Daniel M., 2080
Edelman, David P., 5231
Edelman, Dewey, 5930
Edelman, Edmund, 410
Edelman, Jeffrey, 5931
Edelman, Richard, 3245
Edelman, Richard J., 6556
Edelman, Stanley, 6556
Edelman, Susan, 5931
Edelman, Susan Datz, 2031
Edelman, Thomas J., 5932
Edelsberg, Charles "Chip", 302
Edelstein Administrative Trust, H., 494
Edelstein Charitable Remainder Unitrust No. 2, Harold, 494
Edelstein, David, 4652
Edelstein, Florence, 5933
Edelstein, Geoff, 1263
Edelstein, Michael, 5933
Edelstein, Mildred, 5247
Edelstein, Sidney M., 5247
Eden Hall Farm, 8021
Edens, Anette, 9072
Edens, Steve, 4985
Edenshaw, Cheryl, 88
Eder Trust, Yvette, 1577
Eder, Arthur, 1577
Eder, Eugene J., 9840
Eder, Jill P., 1577
Eder, Jo Ann, 5008
Eder, Mark D., 5008
Edgar County Bank & Trust Co., 2969
Edgar, Robert V., 1819, 6544
Edgarton, Dan, 9809
Edge, John H., 77
Edge, Robert G., 2506
Edgerley Family Foundation, The, 4298
Edgerley, Paul, 4031
Edgerley, Sandra, 3956, 4031
Edgerton, Bradford W., 495
Edgerton, Larry, 9091
Edgerton, Liza T., 9499
Edgerton, Louise D., 495
Edgerton, William A., 9499
Edgington Oil Co., 4854
Edgman-Levitan, Susan, 4107
Edhi, Abdul S., 5934
Edhi, Bilquis, 5934
Edhi, Qutub, 5934
EDI-Special Projects Program, 6044
Edible Arrangements Franchise Group, Inc., 1582
Edible Brands, 1582
Edin, Kathryn, 6782
Edison, Bernard, 4883
Edison, Charles, 5248
Edison, Harry, 4883
Edison, Hope R., 3913, 4884
Edison, Julian, 4883
Edison, Julian I., 4884
Edison, Peter, 4883
Edison, Robert, 2587
Edler, Dave, 9767
Edley, Christopher, 9625
Edlis, Stefan, 2815
Edlow, Brian Lewis, 5935
Edlow, Donald, 5935
Edlow, Donald William, 5935
Edlow, Elizabeth Fielding, 5935
Edlow, Kenneth Lewis, 5935
Edlow, Mary, 5935
Edmiston, Robert Gray, 7568
Edmond, Lisette S., 5376
Edmonds Charitable Remainder Trust, Mary Virginia, 7665
Edmonds, Clarence, 8607
Edmonds, David B., 61
Edmonds, Franklin, 6283
Edmonds, Maria N., 2269
Edmonds, Matthew E., 3259
Edmonds, Pamela S., 7665
Edmonds, Sharon, 3259
Edmund A Cyrol Trust, 3340
Edmunds, J.B., Jr., 2576
Edmunds, Matthew J., 6685
Edmundson, Chad, 3303
EDS Foundation, 687
Education & Research Foundation of Florida, Inc., 2078
Education Empowerment Fund, 9644
Education for Youth Society, 1596, 6399
Educational Health Alliance LLC, 1947
Educational Support Foundation, 5951
Edwab, David, 9300
Edwards Trust Co., A.G., 4966
Edwards Trust, Joan C., 1773
Edwards, Adam B., 8161
Edwards, Alice, 1565
Edwards, Andrew W., 786
Edwards, Anita Winsor, 5899
Edwards, Ann, 8914
Edwards, Berryman W., 8475
Edwards, Bob, 1774
Edwards, Bruce, 744
Edwards, Bruce M., 6467
Edwards, Bryant, 8823
Edwards, Carl T., 8454
Edwards, Carol, 5611
Edwards, Christopher, 3955
Edwards, Chuck, 7181
Edwards, Claude D., 25

Edwards, David, 3656
Edwards, David F., 3628
Edwards, David L., 5529
Edwards, David M., 5529
Edwards, David N., 272
Edwards, Dawn N., 1542
Edwards, Dianne, 420
Edwards, Dorothy B., 8823
Edwards, Duncan, 6904
Edwards, Eddie, 5169
Edwards, Erik, 343
Edwards, George M., 9733
Edwards, Gregory, 7560
Edwards, Gregory J., 6038
Edwards, Ishmell, Dr., 4821
Edwards, J.N., 5008
Edwards, James B., 6115
Edwards, James M., 5529
Edwards, Jane, 1774
Edwards, Jeanette, 8160
Edwards, Jeffrey S., 4380
Edwards, Joel, 7188
Edwards, John, 2378
Edwards, John H., 8161
Edwards, John M., 5529
Edwards, Kee, 7570
Edwards, Kerry-Anne, 6546
Edwards, Laura Deboisfeuillet, 1841
Edwards, Lillian Perry, 9506
Edwards, Linda Pfleger, 1032
Edwards, Lisa, 1139
Edwards, Malcolm, 8497
Edwards, Marc, 1032
Edwards, Marion Wm., 1565
Edwards, Mark, 2378
Edwards, Mark B., 7142, 7208
Edwards, Martie, 1520
Edwards, Megan, 123
Edwards, Meredith, 5586
Edwards, Michael M., 8161, 8359
Edwards, Mona G., 7180
Edwards, Monica, 3656
Edwards, Morris, 3320
Edwards, Paul B., 9961
Edwards, Ray, 4653
Edwards, Rock S., 115
Edwards, Ronald, 7835
Edwards, Sharon, 9135
Edwards, Shirley, 8994
Edwards, Terry, 3494
Edwards, Thomas J., 3558
Edwards, Thomas J., Jr., 5506
Edwards, Trevor, 7875
Edwards, William E., 5008
Edwardson, Catharine O., 2816
Edwardson, John A., 2816
EFC Bancorp, Inc., 2818
Eff, Dianne, 5422
Effron, Blair, 5938
Effron, Cheryl Cohen, 5938, 6693
Effron, Drew, 5938
Efird, Claire, 7224
Efird, Tim, 7179
Efromyson Fund, 3317
Efron, Jeanette Oshman, 9074
Efroymson Fund, Gustave Aaron, 1932
Efroymson, Clarence W., 1932
Efroymson, Robert A., 1932
Efrusy, Molly, 529
Egan Family Charitable Trust, 2082
Egan, Christopher F., 4032
Egan, J. Murray, 8319
Egan, J.B., III, 2082
Egan, Jennifer Catherine, 914
Egan, John R., 4032
Egan, Marsha, 3990
Egan, Maureen E., 4032
Egan, Michael J., 4032
Egan, Mike F., 8757
Egan, Rita, 3064
Egan, William P., 4025
Egbert, Marcia, 7564
Egedy, Laura, 1392
Eggeman, Gail, 2040
Eggerlirg, Kristin, 4730
Egglin, Thomas, 8383
Eggum, Mari Oyanagi, 4616
Eglevsky, Dori, 9414
Egner, David O., 4463
Egolf, Monte, 3359
Egyhazi, Andrew, 865
EH Family LP, 5904
EH Limited Partnership, 5904
EHK Securities LP, 1919
Ehlerman, P. Michael, 7939
Ehlers, Michael, 4708
Ehmcke, Lance D., 3480
Ehrenberg, Randy, 5807
Ehrenberg-Chesler, Laura, 9148
Ehrenkranz, Anne B., 5941
Ehrenkranz, Joel, 6334, 6337
Ehrenkranz, Joel S., 5941, 7076
Ehrgood, Kristin, 1904
Ehrlich, Anne, 6551
Ehrlich, Delia Fleishhacker, 534
Ehrlich, Jack, 2664
Ehrlich, Jodi, 534
Ehrlich, John, Jr., 534
Ehrlich, Neal M., 3205
Ehrlich, Ned, 1939
Ehrlich, Philip S., Jr., 1358
El DuPont DE Nemours Co., 7214
Eichenbaum, Inez, 497
Eichenbaum, J.K., 497
Eichenberger, Steve, 3319
Eichenthal, Gail, 410
Eichler, David F., 8272
Eicholtz, Sonya L., 5217
Eickman, Liz, 7766
Eickmann, Margaret, 7895
Eidemueller, John, Jr., 8114
Eidman, Diane Bennett, 1911
Eidson, Dennis, 4544
Eielson, Rodney S., 1568
Eifert, Donald A., 7287
Eigen, Steven, 5756
Eighme, Martha, 8775
Eilers, Patrick C., 3140
Eilert, Norman, 1244
Eilian, Charlene, 2666
Eilian, Jonathan, 2666
Einaudi, Luigi R., 1945
Einaudi, Roberta, 1945
Einhorn, Cheryl, 5942
Einhorn, David, 5942
Einhorn, Emily, 828
Einhorn, Jane, 1103
Einhorn, Peggi, 5329
Einhorn, Shelley, 5943
Einhorn, Steven G., 5943
Einstandig, Jo, 3396
Einstein, Albert E., 2084
Einstein, Birdie W., 2084
Eischens, Curt, 4636
Eisele, C. R., 5090
Eisen, Lisa B., 7794
Eisen, Stacey, 2921
Eisen, William, 4196
Eisenbeis, Christina H., 4959
Eisenberg, George M., 2819
Eisenberg, Jack, 8825
Eisenberg, Leah, 6745
Eisenberg, Lewis M., 7011
Eisenberg, Maxine, 5250
Eisenberg, Miriam, 5944
Eisenberg, Ronald, 5250
Eisenberg, Sharon, 8615
Eisenberg, Sharon D., 8615
Eisenberg, Solomon, 5944
Eisenberg, Todd, 8409
Eisenberg, Warren, 5250
Eisenberg-Keefer, Joyce, 498
Eisenbud, David, 6861
Eisenbud, Karen, 2207
Eisenhardt, Elizabeth H., 642
Eisenhardt, Elizabeth Haas, 643
Eisenhart Marital Trust, Edward, 9404
Eisenhart Trust, Sarah, 9404
Eisenhart, Edward C., 9404
Eisenhart, Margaret, 1934
Eisenhut, Steve, 3324
Eisenreich, Avery, 5251
Eisenreich, Bobbi Jo, 9855
Eisenreich, Joel, 5251
Eisenreich, Toby, 5251
Eisenson, Michael, 3956
Eisenstadt, Thomas, 670
Eiserle, Timothy, 3968
Eisiminger, Terri L., 3521
Eisner, Anders D., 499
Eisner, Breck, 499
Eisner, Eric D., 499
Eisner, Jane B., 499
Eisner, Michael, 5804
Eisner, Michael B., 499
Eisner, Michael D., 499
Eitel, Ken, 3373
Eitel, Maria S., 7875
Eiting, Jack R., 7840
Eiting, John R., 7840
Eiting, Katherine A., 7847
Eiting, Marie E., 7840
Eizikowitz, Jack, 5761
Ekern, Nancy A., 4900
Ekland, David, 3449
Eklund, Wes, 4369
EL 2002 Trust, 6334, 6337
El-Erian, Mohamed, 1037
El-Hibri, Fuad, 1903
El-Hibri, Ibrahim Y., 1903
El-Hibri, Karim, 1903
El-Hibri, Nancy, 1903
El-Sayed, Farouk, 5690
Elahi, Maryam, 1563
Elam, Deborah A., 1591
Elam, Ed, 8545
Elam, James H., 2357
Elam, Jennifer, 7264
Elbaum, Abigail Black, 5781
Elbaz, Elyssa, 502
Elbaz, Gilad, 502
Elbel, Christine, 534
Elbing, Dave, 9916
Elbogen, Aaron, 5548, 5945
Elbogen, Chaya, 5548, 5945
Elcan, Patricia Frist, 8568
Elcock, Walter B., 7139
Elden, A.D., 1697
Elden, Vera, 1697
Elder, Edward, 3576
Elder, James C., Dr., 2438
Elder, R. J., 4366
Elder, Susan, 9738
Elderfield, John, 5864
Elderkin, David, 7979
Eldora Speedway, Inc., 7214
Eldred, Don, 8718
Eldred, Marshall P., Jr., 7940
Eldridge, Hunt, III, 2720
Eldridge, Huntington, Jr., 2720
Eldridge, Joseph, 517
Eldridge, Mary Elizabeth, 179, 199
Eldrige, Joseph, The Rev., 1880
Electro Rent Corp., 624
Electronic Arts Inc, 6159
Electronic Institutes Foundation, 7980
Electronic Institutes, Inc., 7980
Elefante, Michael B., 3965
Elementary Teachers' Foundation of Ontario, The, 1791
Eletz, Bonnie, 6332
Eleventh Generation, LP, 7999
Elfers, Deborah B., 4033
Elfers, William, 4033
Elfers, William R., 4033
Elg, Annette, 2643
Elgart, Alice, 6071
Elgin Financial Savings Bank, 2818
Elgin Riverboat Resort, 2875
Elgo, Justice Nina, 1589
Eli Scholarship Fund, 7280
Elias, Alma, 8022
Elias, Christine, 4715
Elias, Christopher, 9625
Elias, Gabriel, 8022
Elicker, John, 5712
Eliel, Ruth L., 410
Elim, Raga S., 7407
Eliopoulos, Edward, 7367
Eliot, Theodore L., Jr., 420
Elishis, Brenda, 5946
Elishis, David, 5946
Elishis, Isser, 5946
Elison, Manoucher, 2619
Elizabeth Clements, Catherine, 8766
Elizabeth II Trust-Bermuda, The, 675
Elizabeth Ruan Trust, 3478
Elkay Holdings, LP, 5332
Elkes Trust, 5947
Elkes, Daniel A., 5947
Elkes, David A., 5947
Elkes, Steven A., 5947
Elkes, Terrence A., 5947
Elkhorn Auto Services LLC, 7214
Elkin, James, 6569
Elkind, Howard A., 3195
Elkins Family Charitable Lead Annuity Trust, 8826
Elkins Fund, Lewis, 8175
Elkins, Barry, 708
Elkins, Dina K., 6254
Elkins, Dina Karmazin, 5331
Elkins, Eric M., 8468
Elkins, Gretchen, 9980
Elkins, James A., III, 9186
Elkins, Steve, 9412
Elkins, Virginia A., 8826
Ellafrits, Dick, 4452
Ellard, Dan, 3424
Ellard, James V., 4108
Ellbogen, John P., 9977
Ellbogen, Martin H., 9977
Ellbogen, Theresa A., 9977
Ellbogen, Thomas M., 9977
Elledge, Brandon, 9410
Ellenbecker, Rod, 9845

Ellenberg, Michael, 6982
Ellenberger, John, 4691
Ellenburg, Alex, 8495
Ellender, Philip, 2469
Ellenhorm, David A., 9725
Ellens, Eileen, 4525
Eller, James R., 9382
Eller, Martha W., 7251, 7252
Ellett, Lucy R., 9415
Elliman, Ann R., 6606
Elliman, Christopher (Kim), 5733
Elliman, Christopher J., 5243, 6606, 8396
Elliman, Donald M., Jr., 1418
Elliman, Edward H., 6606
Elliman, Leatrice D., 1872
Ellingson, Rachel, 4770
Ellinor, Dan, 7807
Ellins, Brad, 1464
Elliot Street Investments, Ltd., 5083
Elliot, Aaron L., 4865
Elliot, Donald H., 6527
Elliot, Kathy K., 6619
Elliot, William D., 9415
Elliott Trust, Patricia Adams, 3036
Elliott, Al, 9146
Elliott, Andrew C., Jr., 9120
Elliott, Anita C., 8558
Elliott, Beth, 4344
Elliott, Bill, 3169
Elliott, C. Bill, 654
Elliott, Cheryl W., 4340
Elliott, Donald H., 5718
Elliott, Edward, 3027
Elliott, Edward A., 3195
Elliott, J. Nelson, 3513
Elliott, Janice, 4170
Elliott, Janice C., 4445
Elliott, John A., 3513
Elliott, John R., 9120
Elliott, Laura, 3369
Elliott, Leslie Pincus, 1836
Elliott, Maggie, 3422
Elliott, Marla, 288
Elliott, Rita, 3398
Elliott, Roger D., 3513
Elliott, Steven G., 7946
Elliott, Susan, 4056
Ellis Charitable Trust, 4305
Ellis Management Svcs., Inc., 9865
Ellis Real Estate Holdings, LLC, 503
Ellis, Affie, 9999
Ellis, Billie S., 2452
Ellis, Bob, 9832
Ellis, C. Lee, 2
Ellis, Carlene M., 411
Ellis, Charles D., 1579, 5329
Ellis, Charles E., 8023
Ellis, Claire, 416
Ellis, Constance, 3923
Ellis, David, III, 7404
Ellis, Dick, 9685
Ellis, Douglas, 5111
Ellis, Florida S., 2821
Ellis, Florida Smith, 2821
Ellis, Gail G., 2820
Ellis, Gary L., 4712
Ellis, Gregory S., 503
Ellis, J. Todd, 8542, 8581
Ellis, James E., 2452
Ellis, James W., Jr., 2452
Ellis, Jim, 2452
Ellis, John B., 2441, 2462
Ellis, Jon S., 503
Ellis, Joyce M., 9101
Ellis, Julia M., 9929
Ellis, Kathleen T., 5389
Ellis, Kathy, 4816
Ellis, Keith, 2533
Ellis, Kendrick G., 503
Ellis, Kenneth M., 503
Ellis, Melissa, 3283
Ellis, Patricia, 6903
Ellis, Peter S., 4101
Ellis, Phil, 4448
Ellis, Raymond, 1012
Ellis, Richard N., 3688
Ellis, Russell H., 9415
Ellis, Samuel H., 2928
Ellis, Stanley J., 503
Ellis, Steven G., 4101
Ellis, Susan G., 7212
Ellis, Theresa M., 4039
Ellis, W.D., Jr., 2821
Ellis, Wilbert, 3649
Ellison Family Foundation, The, 7162
Ellison Medical Foundation, 3833
Ellison, Beau, 9789
Ellison, Dan, 4800
Ellison, David E., 9703
Ellison, Eben H., 4034
Ellison, Elizabeth Frame, 7768
Ellison, Frances D., 8555
Ellison, Lawrence J., 504
Ellison, Maureen Sue, 9614
Ellison, Melanie Craft, 504
Ellison, Thomas A., 9614
Ellison, William P., 4034
Ells, Steve, 1388
Ellspermann, Carrie, 3402
Ellsworth, Eileen M., 9410
Ellsworth, Frances, 2632
Ellsworth, J. Bradley, 3394
Ellsworth, Laura E., 8161
Ellsworth, Linda, 5146
Ellsworth, Peter, 1040
Ellsworth, Peter K., 303
Ellsworth, Ruth H., 4035
Ellsworth, Tim, 9118
Ellwein, Charles E., 434
Ellwood, D.C., 8827
Ellwood, Irene L., 8827
Elm 2006 Charitable Trust, 608
Elmer, Corey, 7351
Elmezzi Chariable Unitrust, Jeanne, 5948
Elmezzi Charitable Remainder Annuity Trust, Thomas and Jeanne, The, 5948
Elmezzi Revocable Trust, Thomas, The, 5948
Elmezzi, Jeanne, 5948
Elmezzi, Thomas, 5948
Elmore, Dale, 3676
Elmore, George T., 2032
Elmore, John, 3509, 4784
Elmore, John M., 3676
Elmore, Wayne, 3623
Elms, Tracy, 8839
Eloff, Theuns, 6532
Elorza, Jorge O., 8429
Elrod, Donald S., 3015
Elrod, Maxine, 3015
Elrod, Scott M., 3015
Elsaesser, Jean, 2632
Elsbach, Janet Reich, 6666
Elsberg, Mickey, 3851
Elsberry, Terence L., Rev., 5385
Elsbury, William M., 3129
Elservier, Inc., 4036
Elsey, Linda C., 9041
Elsom, Kristi, 8852
Elston, Elizabeth B., 6663
Elston, Frances Beinecke, 6895
Elston, Mary B., 6663
Elterman, Roy D., M.D., 9087
Elton, Aaron B., 7867
Elton, Kay F.S., 7867
Elton, Michael D., 7867
Elvin, Mark, 9481
Elwell, Dennis, 3452
Elwood, Mark S., 3321
Ely, B. Danforth, 1530
Ely, William L., 5850
Ely-Jacobs Trust, Sylvia, 3731
Elzerman, Alan W., 8502
Embke, James, 9868
Embrace Home Loans Inc., 2185
Embretson, Kim, 4800
Embrey, Bobbie, 8828
Embrey, Gayle, 6864, 8828
Embrey, James L., Jr., 8828
Embrey, Lauren, 6864, 8828
Embry, Robert C., Jr., 3712
Emeny, Caroline Bush, 8312
Emeny, Mary T., 8312
Emerald Asset Advisors, Inc., 2131
Emerick, Bernadette, 2082
Emerine, Richard J., II, 93
Emerson Electric Co., 2822, 4885
Emerson Ventures, 4885
Emerson, Alice F., 5784
Emerson, Christopher S., 5950
Emerson, Don, 7705
Emerson, Earl K., Jr., 9480
Emerson, Frances B., 2790
Emerson, Fred L., 5950
Emerson, Gail, 4795
Emerson, Harry, 8506
Emerson, Harry B., 8504
Emerson, Heather A., 5950
Emerson, J. Steven, 505
Emerson, James T., 9480
Emerson, Katherine, 9480
Emerson, Mary, 7691
Emerson, Monica, 692
Emerson, Peter J., 5950
Emerson, Ralph W., Jr., 6406
Emerson, Rita, 505
Emerson, Thomas C., 6876
Emerson, Tish, 4102
Emerson, W. Gary, 5950
Emery, Glenn, 8156
Emery, Jean, 3278
Emery, John M., 3776
Emery, Kitty Moon, 8550
Emery, Mary Muhlenberg, 7443
Emery, Patrick, 420
Emes Foundation, 6756
EMG Madonna Educational Foundation, 6951
Emig, Carol, 8303
Emig, Don, 973, 1120
Emile Fund, The, 9578
Emmer, Phil, 2036
Emmerson, George, 1164
Emmerson, M.D., 1164
Emmett, Dan, 508
Emmett, Kathleen B., 2032
Emmons, Barbara Brooks, 7421
Emmons, Rebecca F., 2166
Emmons, Robert J., 945
Emory, John B., 3697
Empire Blue Cross/Blue Shield, 6549
Empire Health Services, 9615
Empire Iron Mining Partnership, 7407
Empire State Development Corp., 6044
Employers Mutual Casualty Co., 3428
Empress Nickel Refinery, Ltd., 7272
Emrick, John, 7870, 7883
Emslie, Robert, 1584
Emunah Trust, The, 5951
ENB Charitable Trust, 3195
Encana Cares USA Foundation, 2483
Encana Oil & Gas (USA), Inc., 1407
Ench, Alberta, 5248
Endagered Species Chocolate, 3317
Endeavor Agency, LLC, The, 782
Enders, Anthony T., 6136
Enders, Blair Pillsbury, 3182
Enders, Robert, 1149
Endicott, Eve, 4302
Endo Laboratories, Inc., 1797
Endowment Foundation of UJA Federation of Bergen County & North Hudson, 5477
Endres, Michael, 7563
Energen Corporation, 32
Energen Resource Corp., 32
Energizer Holdings, Inc., 2824
Energy Corp. of America, 1404
Energy Solutions, 9321
Enersen, Jean, 9731
Enfield, Lisa, 5533
Eng, Loren, 6898
Eng, Loren A., 6898
Engdahl, Brian E., 4654
Engdahl, David R., 4654
Engdahl, Herbert A., 5086
Engdahl, Marion E., 4654
Engel, Alan Z., 39
Engel, Glenn, 9005
Engel, Ileana Ovalle, 1108
Engel, Suzanne B., 5281, 5485
Engel, William V., 5281, 5310, 5485
Engelberg, Alfred, 2086
Engelberg, Burt, 3075
Engelhard Hanovia, Inc., 5954
Engelhard, Charlene B., 5954
Engelhard, Charles, 5954
Engelhard, Jane, 5954
Engelhardt, Erin, 4886
Engelhardt, Irl, 4886
Engelhardt, John R., 674
Engelhardt, Sue, 4886
Engelhorn, Philipp, 5779
Engelmeyer, Michael, 9032
Engelstad Trust, Ralph and Betty, 5117
Engelstad, Betty, 5117
Engelstad, Ralph, 5117
Engeman, John, 5976
Engemann, Michele, 506
Engemann, Roger, 506
Engen, Anne E., 1712
Engen, D. Travis, 1712
Engen, Leigh E., 1712
Engh, Rolf, 4786
Engh-Grady, Linda, 5019
England, Catherine S., 3785
England, David C., 1634
England, Diana, 3785
England, John, Hon., 25
England, Lois H., 3785
England, Richard, 3785
England, Rick, 3785
Englander Capital Corp., 5955

Englander, Israel A., 5955
Englar, John, 7180
Engle, William, III, 3598
Englebardt, Jane S., 1998
Engleman, Ephraim P., 645
Engler Charitable Remainder, 5472
Engler, John, 3745
Engler, Mike, 8660
Engler, Paul F., 8830
Englert, Kent L., 1000
Engles, Gregg L., 8803
Englin, Kaye, 3423
English, Carl L., 7368
English, Florence Cruft, 2453
English, Mary Tower, 3299
English, Pam, 200
English, Patrick J., 9819
English, Philip D., 3883
English, Robert, 7808
English, Stephen R., 218
English, Tom, 2039
English, Warren, 4550
Engmyr, Jennifer, 945
Engstrom, Alan K., 1838
Engstrom, Alyson T., 1838
Engstrom, Randall Robert, 1838
Engstrom, Randall Robert, Jr., 1838
Engstrom, Timothy, 3209
Enloe, William C., 5518
Ennevor, Bridget Larson, 8516
Ennis, Bruce, 5014
Ennis, Dolores, 4511
Ennis, Erin, 2037
Eno, Kathy E., 3439
Enoch, Leslie B., II, 8546
Enoch, Margaret, 1775
Enock, Adam, 5242
Enote, Jim, 6571
Enrico, Aaron J., 8831
Enrico, Roger A., 8831
Enrico, Rosemary, 8831
Enright, Michael, 825
Enright, Michael A., 397
Enright, Victoria Nimick, 8198
Enright, William G., 3342
Enriquez, Mary Schneider, 3967
Enroth, Charlly, 1937
Enroth, Mary P., 1937
Enroth, Susan Le Mieux, 1937
Ens, James A., 4536
Ensign, Deborah, 6879
Ensign, Katherine Dalbey, 7088
Ensing, William, 2900
Ensworth, Antoinette L., 1580
Entegris, Inc., 4791
Entel, Robert, 2269
Enteman, John H.F., 6068
Entergy Corp., 3630
Enterprise Holdings, Inc., 4887
Enterprise Rent-A-Car Co., 4887
Entertainment Industry Foundation, 720
Entinger, Richard, 7874
Entmann, Mark L., 9020
Entwisle, Robert M., 8158
Entwistle Company, The, 3996
Enzerra, David J., 7546
EOG Resources, Inc., 6973
Ephraim, David M., 3082
Ephraim, Donald M., 3082
Ephraim, Eliot S., 3082
Ephrata National Bank, 7954
Ephrata National Bank, The, 8091
Epilepsy Foundation, 2300
Episcopal Church, 4432
Epker, Arthur G., III, 4038
Epley, Marcell, 846
Eppel, Mark, 2732
Eppenheimer, William, 3556
Epperly, Ted, 4107
Epperson, David, 9163
Epping Investments, LLC, 880
Eppinger, Frederick H., 4086
Eppley, Marion, 5957
Epstein Charitable Remainder Trust, 2825
Epstein Investment Trust, James, 2773
Epstein Residuary Trust, 2825
Epstein, A. Cary Brown, 3565
Epstein, Andrew, 1836
Epstein, Dan J., 2825
Epstein, Daniel J., 509
Epstein, Danielle, 5595
Epstein, Dasha, 5595
Epstein, Diana Ely, 3786
Epstein, Eileen M.L., 3698
Epstein, Eric, 1836
Epstein, Ian, 3177
Epstein, Jay A., 9202
Epstein, Jeffrey, 5681
Epstein, Jeffrey R., 3177
Epstein, Michael, 3731
Epstein, Michael David, 3786
Epstein, Nicholas, 3177
Epstein, Paul, 6386
Epstein, Phyllis, 509
Epstein, Robert, 8649
Epstein, Roger, 2615
Epstein, Samantha, 3177, 3786
Epstein, Sidney, 3084
Epstein, Stuart A., 3177
Epstein, Thomas, 5958
Epstein, Thomas W., 320
Epstein, William, 8072
Epstein, William A., 5958
EQD Holdings Co., LLC, 8025
Equalizer Industries, 7638
Equifax Inc., 2455
Equipart Assocs., 5959
Equitable Cos. Inc., The, 5629
Equitable Life Assurance Society of the U.S., The, 5629
Equitable Production Co., 8025
Equitable Trust Co., 8628
Equizi, Mark C., 7640
Eramet, 7272
Erario, Vincent, 2478
Erb, Barbara M., 4415
Erb, Debbie D., 4415
Erb, Eric, 7557
Erb, Fred A., 4415
Erb, John M., 4371, 4415
Erbacher, John N., 6802
Erbaugh, J. Martin, 7578
Erber, Kathy, 4522
Erdahl, Rebecca L., 4630
Erdel, Laura White, 4900
Erdle, Allison, 9380, 9552
Erdman, Christian P., 5105
Erdman, Daryl, 4667
Erdman, Joseph, 2046
Ergin, Joan, 9775
Ergon Asphalt & Emulsions, Inc., 4824
Ergon Exploration, Inc., 4824
Ergon Nonwovens, Inc., 4824
Ergon Refining, Inc., 4824
Ergon, Inc., 4824
Ergon-West Virginia, Inc., 4824
Erhard, Gerald A., 7635
Erickson, Alan J., 5068
Erickson, Andrew M., 8356
Erickson, Barb, 9889
Erickson, Chris, 5075
Erickson, Cynthia L., 3573
Erickson, David, 9923
Erickson, Gary E., 1287
Erickson, Gary J., 405
Erickson, Greg, 8635
Erickson, Hubbard H., 2660
Erickson, Hubbard H., Jr., 2660
Erickson, Jeff, 8522
Erickson, Jennifer Weyrauch, 3042
Erickson, Joan C., 2660
Erickson, John, 2660
Erickson, John H., 2660
Erickson, Kate, 4785
Erickson, Lisa, 4612
Erickson, Liz, 5411
Erickson, Marilyn, 4792
Erickson, Nancy, 2853
Erickson, Peter C., 4661
Erickson, Peter E., 2660
Erickson, Peter H., 2660
Erickson, Robert M., 7505
Erickson, Rolin, 5018
Erickson, Theresa, 4829
Erickson, Zachary, 2660
Ericson, Brent, 2881
Ericson, Lois G., 838
Ericson, Steven L., 838
Erier, Kenneth J., 9944
Erikson, Cindy, 8374
Erikson, Susanne W., 7709
Erion, Douglas J., 1408
Erion, Helen, 1408
Erion, Justin, 1408
Erion, Ken, 1408
Erion, Travis, 1408
ERJ Living Trust, 755
ErkenBrack, Stephen, 1381
Erklens, Brent, 9306
Erlbaum Family 2005 Trust, 8027
Erlbaum Family Limited Partnership, 8027
Erlbaum Investments LP, 8027
Erlbaum, Daniel A., 8027
Erlbaum, Gary E., 8027
Erlbaum, Jon L., 8027
Erlbaum, Marc N., 8027
Erlbaum, Vicki O., 8027
Erlin, Beatrice, 5461
Erlingsson, Erik C., 9331
Ermitage Selz Fund, 6830
Ermler, Julie, 4463
Ernest, Robert, 5424
Ernsberger, Marylyn, 3390
Ernst & Young, 8649
Ernst & Young, LLP, 7012
Ernst, Bob, 3761
Ernst, Dorothy A., 2897
Ernst, John, 5556
Ernst, Katherine R., 5200, 5424
Ernst, Paul, 2897
Ernst, Robert J., 5200
Ernst, Robin, 8001
Ernstoff, Barry D., 9725
Eronfroind, Meir, 6229
Erskine, Frances, 4311
Erskine, Gary, 3346
Erstad, Shannon E.H., 2632
Ertel, Barbara, 8229
Ervin, Charles, 7682
Ervin, Dean Wilson, 5826
Ervin, Elisabeth C., 7178
Ervin, Glenda Lehman, 7704
Ervin, John W., Jr., 7178
Ervin, Le N., 7178
Ervin, Mark A., 3286
Ervin, Thomas M., 8509
Ervin, Valerie, 396
Erwert, Bill, 9655
Erwin, Anna, 7170
Erwin, Harry C., III, 207
Erwin, Kevin L., 2327
Erwin, Peter, 6579
Esbenshade, Richard, 521
Esbenshade, Richard D., 954
Escalente, Daniel, 1401
Escamilla Poneck & Cruz LLP, 9149
Escamilla, James, 4472
Escava, Hyman, 5768
Escobar, F. Patrick, 809
Escondido Ready Mix Concrete, Inc., 1220
Esham, Debra, 7657
Eshelman, Fred, 1776
Eskenazi, Lois, 3300
Eskenazi, Sandra, 3300
Eskenazi, Sidney, 3300
Eskenazi, Sidney Lois, 3300
Eskew, Michael L., 3745
Eskind, Jane, 8563
Eskind, Richard, 8563
Eskind, Richard J., 8550
Eskind, William H., 8563
Eskridge, Carl, 5096
ESL Federal Credit Union, 5960
Esman, Theresa, 2088
Esmiol, Morris A., Jr., 1489
Espaillat, Benigno, 4039
Espe, Marchell, 84
Espel, Thomas K., 7358
Espineli, Christopher, 669
Espinosa, Gustavo, 2769
Espinosa, John, 1548
Espinosa, Sara, 6340
Esplin, J. Kimo, 9327
Esposito, Anthony G., 7599
Esposito, Caolionn Leonetti, 832
Esposito, Cara Leonetti, 832
Esposito, Liliana M., 8803
Esposito, Louis E., 8118
Esposto, James E., 804
Espy, George E., 8026
Espy, Jay, 3708
Esque, Shelly M., 7853
Esquenazi, Edmundo, 6042
Esquenazi-Shaio, Carolina, 6042
Esquivel, David, 8603
Esquivel, Eric, 8475
Esrey, William, 1518
Esry, William C., 4996
ESSA Bancorp, Inc., 8028
Esser, Eloise, 5157
Esser, Julia Keough, 1436
Esser, Richard B., 1436
Esses, Eda, 9658
Essex Music Inc., 6704
Essig Family Trust, 5927
Essig, Rod, 8550
Essig, Stuart, 5315
Essman, Abbey, 9961
Essman, Adam, 9961
Essman, Ken, 9961
Essman, Marcy, 9961
EST Assocs. LP, 6600
Estep, David G., Col., 9501

Estepp, Larry R., 8560
Esterle, John, 574, 1322
Esterline, Bruce H., 9019
Esterson, Robin, 7001
Estes, C.E., 9427
Estes, Deborah Ann, 1203
Estes, Deonna F., 4343
Estes, Joel, 2853
Estes, Scott, 3314
Estes, Scott A., 7686
Estess, Sandra, 8909
Esteva, Marc, 4067
Estey Charitable Income Trust, 4128
Estey, Dede, 890
Estopinal, Betty M., 3617
Estrada, Ric, 2703
Estrada, Ricardo (Ric), 3242
Estrada, Richard, 3612
Estrin, Mary Lloyd, 1419
Estrin, Robert L., 1419
Estrin, Zoe, 1419
Etchell, Lawrence, 2868
Etcheverry, Raymond J., 9323
Etchison, Dirk, 1201
Etheridge, Frank S., III, 2438, 2528
Etheridge, Lynn, 4334
Etherington, Charles, 4852
Etnier, Oliver L., 1778
Ettelson, John R., 2699
Etter, Dione, 4146
Ettinger, Barbara P., 1578, 1779
Ettinger, Christian, 1779
Ettinger, Christian P., 1578
Ettinger, Elsie, 1578
Ettinger, Heidi, 1779
Ettinger, Heidi P., 1578, 1779
Ettinger, John R., 6160
Ettinger, Mark I., 6835
Ettinger, Matthew P., 1578
Ettinger, Richard P., 1578
Ettinger, Richard P., Jr., 1578
Ettinger, Virgil P., 1578
Ettinger, Wendy P., 1779
Ettinger, Wendy W.P., 1578
Etzel, Tim, 3552
Etzwiler, David D., 5454
Euclide, Kristine A., 9898
Eude, Elisabeth, 5190
Euille, Bill, 9380
Eule, Daniel R., 6004, 6890, 6891
Eurich, Juliet, 3796
Eurich, Juliet A., 3726, 3894
European-American Economic Corp., 6636
Eustace, Robert A., 511
Evander Lewis Family Foundation, The, 9470
Evangelical Free Church of Mankato, 3517
Evangelista, Peter Thomas, 8383
Evangelisti, Joseph, 8530
Evans Foundation, Charles, The, 7008
Evans, Angie M., 3569
Evans, Anthony, 5750
Evans, Arthur, 4170
Evans, Barbara R., 7232
Evans, Bonnie L. Pfeifer, 5254
Evans, Brian R., 2120
Evans, Bridgitt, 1512
Evans, Bridgitt B., 4040
Evans, Bruce R., 4040
Evans, Carolyn B., 9421
Evans, Caswell A., 3172
Evans, Caswell A., Jr., 4016
Evans, Catherine, 7417
Evans, Catherine Kobrinsky, 414
Evans, Charles, 5254, 7008
Evans, Charles, Jr., 5254
Evans, Cynthia Sherwood, 5243
Evans, Doug, 3517
Evans, Edward P., 9428
Evans, Eli, 2780
Evans, Ernest L., 7303
Evans, Hugh M., III, 3865
Evans, Jack, 3485
Evans, Jack B., 3439
Evans, Jay, 3243
Evans, Jeff, 8475
Evans, John, 1211, 5505
Evans, John C., 6398
Evans, John H., 5505
Evans, John T., 5907
Evans, Karen, 1184
Evans, Kathryn, 8223
Evans, Kelli, 556
Evans, Kelly, 9360
Evans, Kim, 179
Evans, Kimberly H., 8959
Evans, Linda J., 2548
Evans, Linda P., 9019
Evans, Lucia Brown, 6606
Evans, Malik, 6722
Evans, Marie, 5907
Evans, Megan A., 3523
Evans, Mike, 378
Evans, Nick, 2514
Evans, Randall E., 9036
Evans, Robert, 9428
Evans, Roy Gene, 8778
Evans, Scott, 6093
Evans, Sheldon, 3948
Evans, Skip, 3514
Evans, Stephen, 7030
Evans, Stephen J., 3606
Evans, Stephen O., 92
Evans, Steven, 9079
Evans, Thomas, 3974
Evans, Thomas H., 3814
Evans, V. Lynn, 8538
Evans, William, 2487
Evans-Tranum, Shelia, 9595
Evarts, Helen C., 7030
Eveillard, Elizabeth, 6308
Eveillard, Elizabeth M., 5963
Eveillard, Jean-Marie R., 5963
Eveillard, Pauline M., 5963
Eveillard, Suzanne M., 5963
Evening Post Industries, 8492
Evening Post Publishing Co., 8492
Evensen, Andrew, 1792
Evensen, Daniel C., 1792
Evensen, Danielle M., 1792
Evensen, Deborah D., 1792
Evensen, Jessica, 1792
Evensen, Joan C., 1792
Evensen, Randolph E., 1792
Evensen, Walter S., 1792
Evenson, Jeffrey W., 5818
Event Brite, 1388
Everest, Christine Gaylord, 7753, 7760
Everest, Tricia, 7760
Everett Mutual Savings Bank, 9617
Everett, Carolyn, 5964
Everett, Chandler, 7499
Everett, David F., 5964
Everett, Edith B., 5964
Everett, Henry, 5964
Everett, Jim, 4107
Everett, Junetta, 3524
Everett, Katie, 4159
Everett, Lisa, 9502
Everett, Mary, 7217
Everett, Nora, 3476
Evergreen Bancorp, Inc., 9702
Evergreen Bank, N.A., 9702
Evergreen Enterprises, 4417
Everhart, Jennifer, 4451
Everhart, Thomas E., 771
Everhart, Thomas E., Dr., 774
Evers, Mark, 3442
Evers-Manly, Sandra, 9498
Eversole, Dan, 4512
Eversoll, Bob, 5067
Everton, Marsha M., 8351
Evertt, Nora, 3420
Eves, David L., 4808
Evinrude, Ralph, 9841
Evnin, Anthony B., 6333
Evslin, Mary, 9360
Evslin, Mary A., 9360
Evslin, Tom, 9360
Evslin, Tom I., 9360
Ewald, Neal, 714
Ewbank, Mary, 3293
Ewbank, Thomas P., 3331
Ewen, Elaine S., 650
Ewend, Peter, 4585
Eweson, Dorothy D., 5573
Ewig, Thelma, 1600
Ewing, Anne, 7324
Ewing, Charles, Sr., 8610
Ewing, Frank M., 3787
Ewing, J.D., 7991
Ewing, Judy, 3787
Ewing, Kelly MacMahon, 1810
Ewing, Lakweshia, 8548
Ewing, Lorraine, 3313
Ewing, Lucinda B., 1055
Ewing, Robyn, 7807
Ewing, Robyn L., 7814
Ewing, Stephen E., 4543
Excell Mktg., LLC, 3479
Exclusively Misook, Inc., 5901
Exco Resources, Inc., 9049
Execution LLC Charitable Foundation, 1689
Executive Focus International, 2382
Executive Planning, Inc., 3183
Exelon Corporation, 2827
Exner, Margaret L., 9891
Exop Investors LLC, 5978
Exotic Metals Forming Co., 9670
Expedia, Inc., 4311
Express Scripts, Inc., 4888
Extra Sportswear, Inc., 5488, 6950
Exxaro Resources Ltd SA, 7349
Exxon Corp., 8833
Exxon Mobil Corp., 4254, 8833
Eychaner, Fred, 2658
Eychner, Thomas D., 973, 1120
Eydt, Bob, 1581
Eye, Ear, Nose and Throat Hospital, 3631
Eyer, Robert J., 7990
Eyer, Thomas E., 7887
Eyman, Amy, 7445
Eyre, Christopher, 9626
Eyre, Joe, 849
Eyskens, Mark, 6007
Ezell, F. Miles, Jr., 8564
Ezell, F. Miles, Sr., 8564
Ezell, John W., 8564
Ezell, Mark, 8557, 8640
Ezell, Miles, Jr., 8643
Ezell, Roy C., 8564
Ezerski, Ronald E., 4738
Fabens, Andrew L., III, 7564, 7668
Faber, Deborah A., 9780
Faber, Doug, 1035
Faber, Marilyn, 1035
Fabert, Kenneth, 9618
Fabian, Patricia, 2767
Fabiano, James, II, 4532
Fabish, Sarah J.H., 1562
Fabri-Kal Corp., 4416
Fabrizio, Joanne F., 7904
Facchine, Thomas J., 6573
Facini, Deborah L., 8133
Factor, David, 513
Factor, Dean, 513
Factor, Jennifer, 513
Factory Mutual Insurance Co., 8393
Fader, Elizabeth, 5918
Fadim, Melissa Sage, 4531
Faerber, George O., 7605
Faessel, Steve, 239
Faeth, Michael, 9833
Fagan, Helene Irwin, 728
Fagan, Lisa Lainer, 812
Fagan, Patrick, 2123
Fagen, Leslie G., 6300
Fagler, Rose, 9704
Fagot, Tom, 5062
Fahey, Peter M., 6070
Fahey, Richard, 1175
Fahl, Greg, 3407
Fahrenkopf, Frank J., Jr., 5159
Faigen, Amanda, 2089
Faigen, Andrew, 2089
Faigen, George, 2089
Faigen, Greta, 2089
Failes, John W., 9391
Failla, Frank J., Jr., 5425, 5496
Failor, Andrea S., 3468
Fain Charitable Lead Trust, Jonathan D., 8388
Fain, Jonathan D., 8388
Fain, Martha, 8835
Fain, Norman M., 8388
Fain, Rosalie B., 8388
Faino, Laura Samberg, 9527
Fainor, Scott V., 8122
Fair, David R., 8267
Fair, F. Doyle, 3518
Fairbanks Charitable Lead Unitrust, 5255
Fairbanks, Betsy, 556
Fairbanks, David, 5062
Fairbanks, Jonathan B., 3301, 5255
Fairbanks, Marsha, 5055
Fairbanks, Richard M., 3301
Fairbanks, Richard M., III, 5255
Fairbanks, Shannon A., 5255
Fairbanks, Woods A., 5255
Fairchild, May, 3788
Fairchild, Sherman, 3788
Faircloth Trust, Nancy B., 7136
Faircloth, Anne B., 7136, 7322
Faircloth, Karen E., 8307
Faircloth, Nancy B., 7136, 7322
Fairfax Realty Inc., 9346
Fairfield National Bank, 7610
Fairfield, Jeffrey J., 9468
Fairholme Capital Mgmt. LLC, 2090

Fairman, Frank E., 4743
Fairman, Ronald M., 8170
Fairmont Olympic Hotel, 9250
Fairmount Minerals, Ltd., 7446
Fairrington, Kathryn, 980
Fairview Nursing Care Center, Inc., 6287
Fairview Nursing Center Inc., 6288
Fairview Partners, 7422
Faith, David M., 5080
Faith, Marshall E., 5080
Fakes, Roger, Jr., 8594
Falahee, William P., 6252
Falatok, Andrew J., 8501
Falbaum, Rand, 3624
Falbaum, Rand H., 3249
Falck, David P., 91
Falcon, Kandace Creel, 4617
Falcone, Mark G., 1376
Falcone, Nicholas, 8031
Falconer, Barbara E., 8307
Falconer, Keith D., 8307
Falder, Mike, 3280
Falgoust, Dean T., 112
Falic, Fima, 2091
Falic, Jerome, 2091
Falic, Leon, 2091
Falic, Nily, 2091
Falic, Simon, 2091
Falk Trust, Marian Citron, 8389
Falk, Jack, 1983
Falk, Stephen, 7398
Falk, Thomas J., 8957
Fall, William, 7686
Fallas, Moses Michael, 5558
Fallen Angel Corp., 3912
Falletta, Nancy E., 2122
Fallin, Richard, 1920
Fallon Co., LLC, The, 4041
Fallon, Bill, 6451
Fallon, Elizabeth J., 4041
Fallon, James P., 188
Fallon, Michael J., 4041
Fallon, Susan G., 4041
Falls, Amy, 5994, 6727
Falls, Robert, 1334
Falsetto, Alicia, 9395
Falsgraf, William W., 5269
Falter, Robert R., 6686
Falvey, Mary R., 5506
Falvo, Maria A., 1537
Family Celebration, 396
Family Christian LLC, 4417
Family Christian Stores, Inc., 4417
Family Doctors of Broward, 2168
Family Video Inc., 2920
Famsea Corp., 6853
Fancelli 2002 Charitable Lead Annuity Trust, Julia J., 2092
Fancelli 2006 Charitable Lead, Julia J., 2092
Fancelli, Julia J., 2092
Fanch, Robert C., 1505
Fandrei, Philip F., 4650
Fangman, John, 4660
Fanning, Leigh, 7217
Fanning, Robert R., Jr., 4039
Fanslau, Eleanor, 7571
Fansler Living Trust, 516
Fansler, D. Paul, 516
Fansler, Davis, 1512
Fansler, Marlene, 516
Fant Energy, 8837
Fant Properties, 8837
Fant, Alta Fay, 8837
Fant, George C., 1449
Fant, Jana, 8837
Fant, Richard E., 8837
Fantaci, Anna, 5675
Fantaci, James, 5675
Farabee, Holly C., 7796
Farah, Jean Claude, 1521
Farah, Lucky, 8011
Farah, Roger, 6651
Farash, Lynn, 5969
Farber, Ellen, 8032
Farber, Ellen B., 8032
Farber, Gloria, 5970
Farber, Hilliard, 5970
Farber, Howard, 230
Farber, Jack, 8032
Farber, Jake J., 230
Farber, Janet, 5079
Farber, Jeff, 1241
Farber, Jeffrey A., 801
Farber, Jennifer, 5970
Farber, Melissa, 5970
Farber, Rudolph E., 4889
Farber, Vivian, 8032
Farber, William A., 5359
Fares, Fares I., 9263
Farese, Conor, 518
Farese, Nancy R., 518
Farese, Robert, 518
Farese, Robert V., Jr., 518
Fargo, Doug, 5044
Faria, Brigham, 8208
Farias, Brandt G., 2598
Farid, Kamran, 1582
Farid, Tariq, 1582
Farina, Steven, 1960
Farina, Terrance, 1488
Farish, Libbie Rice, 8838
Farish, Maia, 8423
Farish, Martha, 9697
Farish, William, 9428
Farish, William Stamps, 8838
Farkas, Carol, 6449
Farkas, Janos, 6447
Farkovits, Esther, 6580
Farkovits, Josh, 6580
Farkovitz, Esther, 6580
Farley, Becky G., 4844
Farley, James S., 828
Farley, Katherine G., 6470, 6896
Farley, Suzie T., 8028
Farley, Thomas, 6573
Farm Service Co., 312
Farman-Farma, Amir, 536
Farmer, Carrie W., 4634
Farmer, Dave, 9514
Farmer, George R., Jr., 9785
Farmer, Joyce E., 7447
Farmer, Mary J., 7447
Farmer, Mychelle Y., 3726
Farmer, Richard T., 2253, 7447
Farmer, Scott D., 7447
Farmer, Sonja Kelly, 4042
Farmer, Stephen B., 9785
Farmer, Terri L., 9819
Farmers & Mechanics Bank, 2967
Farmers Branch, 5361
Farmers State Bank, 1441
Farmers State Bank, The, 1477
Farmers Trust Co., 7403, 7489, 7525
Farmers Trust Company, 7629
Farmers Trust of Carlisle, 8046
Farmers Union Central Exchange, Inc., 4636
Farnet, Samuel S., Jr., 3611
Farnet, Stewart, 3611
Farney, Sharon Cook, 1278
Farnham, Anne M., 9404
Farnham, Glorianne Demoulas, 4015
Farnham, Katharine G., 2463
Farnsworth, Anne E., 6844
Farnsworth, Charles H., 4043
Farnsworth, D.E., 9162
Farnsworth, David L., 6844
Farnsworth, Sue Seibert, 9773
Farnum, Amanda, 3841
Farnum, Jonathan K., 8370
Farquhar, David, 7873
Farquhar, Marjorie, 5510
Farr, David, 2822
Farr, Kevin, 886
Farr, Olivia H., 4172
Farrand-Borgerson, Arlene, 5746
Farrar, Arch, 2559
Farrar, Elizabeth Shepard, 1819
Farrar, Susan J., 418
Farrell, Ann Brown, 6260
Farrell, Anne, 9713
Farrell, Betty L., 422
Farrell, Cathy, 988
Farrell, Jane, 8511
Farrell, Kathy, 5072
Farrell, Martha, 4874
Farrell, Mary C., 6052
Farrell, Michael J., 519
Farrell, Paul A., 519
Farrell, Peter C., 519, 1063
Farrell, Robert Michael, 8878
Farrell, Robert S., 6703
Farrell, Susan M., 7269
Farren, Mary, 6854
Farrington, Alberta B., 110
Farrington, Duane, 3174
Farrow, Jackson, 179
Farrow, Stephen R., 3814
Farver, Adam, 3456
Farver, Benjamin, 3456
Farver, Charles, 3456, 3473
Farver, Charles Jacob, 3456
Farver, Joan, 3473
Farver, Joan Kuyper, 3456
Farver, Melissa, 3456
Farwell Trust, Ava W., 2747
Fasciano, Susan N., 9913
Fascitelli, Elizabeth Cogan, 5971
Fascitelli, Michael D., 5971
Fashano, Raymond, 6841
Fashion Retailers, 5813
Fasken Special Trust, David, 9106
Fasken, Andrew A., 8839
Fasken, Barbara, 9106
Fasken, F. Andrew, 9120
Fasken, Paula, 8839
Fasken, Steve, 8839
Faskin, Dede E., 9120
Faskin, Helen T., 9120
Fasman, Kenneth H., Ph.D., 3919
Fasold, Sandra J., 959
Fass, Alison, 3817
Fast, Stephanie, 8649
Fata, Patricia, 645
Fath, Creekmore, 8840
Fath, Linda C., 7404
Fatovic, Robert D., 2302
Fatzinger, Walter R., Jr., 1925
Fauber, Robert, 6499
Fauber, Stuart C., 9474
Faucett Family Trust, 520
Faucett, Benjamin, 520
Faucett, Carol Ann, 520
Faucett, Robert, 520
Faucett, Russell B., 520
Faucett, Sam, 25
Faucett, Sam P., 2410
Faucett, Scott, 520
Fauci, Anthony S., 5917, 5918
Faulconer, Vernon E., 8841
Fauliso, Anne Marie, 1613
Faulk, Bennie, 2500
Faulkner, Edmund, 5218
Faulkner, Karen, 4263
Faulkner, Larry, 9067
Faull, Gary F., 9619
Faull, Vicki, 9715
Fauntleroy, Elizabeth M., 8486
Fauquher, Ronald K., 3264
Faust, Mary Lou, 5863
Faust, Winifred D., 1541
Fauth, Kristen, 8523
Fauth, Wade, 4617
Favero, Joan, 1154
Favorite, Donna, 7569
Favre, Trent, 4830
Favrot, Laurence, 8842
Favrot, Leo M., 8842
Favrot, Romelia, 8842
Fawcett, Linda, 418
Fawley, Dan A., 7296
Fawn, Janis, 2142
Fawzy, A. Christopher, 3243
Fay, Cornelius Ryan, III, 3758
Fay, Paul, III, 7277
Fay-Bustillos, Theresa, 399
Fayard, Gary P., 2428
Fayed, Ali, 1534
Fayock, Daniel, 8235
Fazendeiro, Anne, 4079
FBE Limited, 5402
FBE Limited LLC, 6027
FCR Guardian Trust, 6409
Fead, Bob, 917
Feagans, Timothy L., 8260
Feagin, Moses, 4839
Fealy, Jim, 7231
Fearnside, Philip M., 3993
Fearon, Charles, 8175
Fearons, George, 5972
Feather, Jeffrey P., 8122
Feather-Francis, Carol, 3493
Featherman, Sandra, 3698, 8035
February Charitable Trust, The, 4305
Fechter, John F., 4958
Fecser, Frank, 7721
Feddersen, James A., 9966
Fedele, John E., 4291
Fedeli, Davida, 1521
Feder, Abigail Jones, 6148
Feder, Franklin L. (Frank), 7908
Federal Home Loan Mortgage Corp., 9435
Federated Department Stores, Inc., 7552
Federated Foundation, 4606
Federated Investors, Inc., 8033
Federated Mutual Insurance, 4606
Federico, Alyssa R., 7202
Federico, Barbara, 2986
FedEx, 975
Fedorovich, Rick, 7367
Fedrick, Ronald M., 293
Fedun, Darlene, 6044
Feed the Children, 8927, 9004

Feehan, Loretta, 4102
Feeley, Michael S., 473
Feeney, Charles F., 5622
Feeney, James E., 7994
Feeney, Thomas J., 1113
Feeney, Thomas M., 7638
Feenstra, Patrick W., 2645
Feeser, Robert A., 9484
Fehlings, Michael G., 7916
Fehr, Gloria J., 7363
Fehrenbaker, Allison D., 6638
Fehrenbaker, Lawrence G., 6638
Fehrs, Rebecca, 9468
Fehsenfeld, Ashlee, 3302
Fehsenfeld, Frank, 3302
Fehsenfeld, Fred, 3302
Fehsenfeld, Judee, 3302
Fehsenfeld, Mac, 3302
Fehsenfeld, Robin, 3302
Fei, Barbara, 7053
Feiberg, Ann Merriam, 1566
Feibleman, Susan Root, 2293
Feibus, Arthur J., 6918
Feibus, Nancy Rozen, 6918
Feiertag, Anne L., 9564
Feigenbaum, Armand V., 4044
Feigenbaum, Donald S., 4044
Feigenbaum, Harvey, 3375
Feil Marital Trust, Gertrude, 5973
Feil, Carole, 5973
Feil, Gertrude, 5973
Feil, Jeffrey, 5973
Feil, Louis, 5973
Feinberg, Ann Merriam, 1616
Feinberg, Betsy, 1879
Feinberg, Helen H., 2162
Feinberg, Janice, 2830
Feinberg, Joseph, 2830
Feinberg, Mike, 1014
Feinberg, Mitchell, 2968
Feinberg, Reuben, 2778, 2830
Feinberg, Rhonda, 2830
Feinberg, Ross, 744
Feinblatt Revocable Trust, Lois B., 3737
Feinblatt, Lois B., 3737
Feinblatt, Lois Blum, 3737
Feinblum, Julieus, 1548
Feiner, Vicki, 5546
Feingold, Chad, 3536
Feinman, Frances, 1289
Feinman, Steven C., 7121
Feinstein, Alan Shawn, 8390, 8391
Feinstein, Amy, 5974
Feinstein, Ari, 8390, 8391
Feinstein, Leila, 8391
Feinstein, Leonard, 5974
Feinstein, Martin, 6918
Feinstein, Michael, 917
Feinstein, Richard, 8391
Feinstein, Susan, 5974
Feit, Norman, 5814
Feith, Susan A., 9902
Feitler, Robert, 1697
Fejes, Frank S., 6194
Fekete, Frank L., 5283
Fel Pro Mecklenburger Foundation, 3052
Fel-Pro Inc., 3052
Felburn, Phil, 3789
Felchner, Edward L., 9801
Feld, Alan R., 5628
Feld, Ann, 4346
Feldberg Family Foundation, 5468
Feldkemp, I.M., 8527
Feldman Charitable Lead Trust, Jacob, 8034
Feldman Charitable Lead Trust, Sara, 8034
Feldman Charitable Lead Trust, Wendy F., 8388
Feldman Foundation, The, 8034, 8843
Feldman Marital Trust, Jacob, 8034
Feldman, Alison Korman, 8132
Feldman, Arthur, 6865
Feldman, Beth, 6360
Feldman, Daniel E., 8843
Feldman, Donald, 7363
Feldman, Jill, 8072
Feldman, Joseph, 5558
Feldman, Moses, 8034
Feldman, Oscar, 4390
Feldman, Paula, 3925
Feldman, Richard E., 6848
Feldman, Robert L., 8843
Feldman, Ronald, 8072
Feldman, Ross, 5807
Feldman, Susan, 8034
Feldman, Wendy B., 8388
Feldman, Wendy F., 8388
Feldmann, Suzanne Mead, 8868
Feldstein, Martin, Dr., 1679
Felgoise, Judith Abramson, 1963
Felix, June, 6904
Felker, Arthur, 9979
Felker, Patti, 1089
Fella, Leon, 6808
Fella, Robert H., 6808
Feller, Robert, 968
Feller, Robert D., 990
Fellner, Susan, 2227
Fellowes, 3201
Fellows, Glenn, 5511
Fellows, Lauren P., 9508
Fellows, Ryan, 4523
Fellows, William H., 7579
Felmer, Thomas J., 9821
Fels, Gerald, 4045
Fels, Marilyn, 4045
Fels, Marilyn T., 4045
Fels, Samantha, 2210
Fels, Samuel S., 8035
Felsinger, Donald E., 1140
Feltes, Anita, 3511
Feltes, Tom, 5062
Feltl, Mary Jo, 4769
Felton, John, Dr., 3369
Felts, Anita T., 9434
Felts, Thomas J., Hon., 3304
Femino, Dominic, 521
Femino, James J., 521
Femino, Sue, 521
Fender, Laura, 5071
Feng, Michael, 6049
Fenig, Mickey, 1099
Fenley, Gigi, 1053
Fenlon, Katherine F., 6567
Fenn, Forrest, 1943
Fennelly, Christine, 4242
Fenner, David T., 7576
Fenniman, Andrew, 3698
Fenoglio, John, 8695
Fenstemacher, Keith, 5805
Fenster, Fred, 1121
Fenster, Suzanne, 4379
Fenstermaker, Ginny, 3403
Fenter, Thomas C., 4815
Fenton, Joan, 9303
Fenty, Brent, 7848
Fenway Partners, 7012
Feoli, Ludovico, 3656, 3675
Feoli, Stephanie Stone, 3675
Feragen, Jody H., 4676
Ferar, Barkat, 7645
Ferber, Robert, 623
Ferdinand, Jo Ann, 7053
Ferdinand, Rachel, 7053
Ferdowsi, Farzin, 8550
Ferenbach, Carl, 4097
Ferenbach, Judy, 4097
Ferens, Joseph F., Esq., 7991
Ferentz, JoAnne, 7972
Feresu, Sarah, 9656
Ferguson Irrevocable Trust, Mildred F., 7450
Ferguson, Becky, 8874, 9123
Ferguson, Daniel C., 2093
Ferguson, Emily, 3471
Ferguson, Ernest E., 7182
Ferguson, Frances Daly, 579
Ferguson, Gary, 80
Ferguson, Gerene Dianne Chase, 5517
Ferguson, Jerry L., 3355
Ferguson, Jerry L., Mrs., 3355
Ferguson, Joan, 4821
Ferguson, John D., 8550
Ferguson, John W., Jr., 8819
Ferguson, Jon, 2768
Ferguson, Julie, 2525
Ferguson, Randall, 4937, 4996
Ferguson, Rhonda S., 7455
Ferguson, Robert B., 1775
Ferguson, Robert E., 4442
Ferguson, Sanford B., 8017
Ferguson, Sarah, 8774
Ferguson, Stanley, 2922
Ferguson, Stanley L., 3200
Ferguson, Stephen L., 3375
Ferguson, Thomas C., Amb., 3669
Ferland, Tina, 4357
Fernalld Trust, Kylee McVaney, 1516
Fernandez, Eduardo, 7659
Fernandez, Eric J., 2818
Fernandez, Frank, 2413, 4618
Fernandez, Gustavo, 4473
Fernandez, Henry L., 3272
Fernandez, James N., 6978
Fernandez, Jose, 5598
Fernandez, Joseph A., 2238
Fernandez, Judith, 5327
Fernandez, Mary M., 7369
Fernandez, Nancy, 5598
Fernandez, Robert C., 8053
Fernandez, Robert I., 8959
Fernos, Maria D., 8353
Ferolie Family Foundation, 7015
Ferrales, Sid, 9712
Ferranti, Anthony L., 6635
Ferrantino, Janette, 4419
Ferrara, Albert E., Jr., 7366
Ferrara, Louiza, 6636
Ferraresi, Daniel J., 1983
Ferrari, George P., Jr., 5807
Ferraro, James L., 2094
Ferraro, James L., Jr., 2094
Ferraro, Kris, 4617
Ferraro, Luella S., 2094
Ferree, Robert B., IV, 8296
Ferreira, Marilyn, 415
Ferrell, Mark C., 9773
Ferrell, Paget, 7678
Ferrer, Barbara, 3953, 4474
Ferrero, Thomas V., 7673
Ferriby, Robin D., 4371
Ferrigno, Carmen, 8260
Ferrigno, Steve, 3751
Ferrill, Sharon A., 5526
Ferring, Alison N., 4891
Ferring, John H., IV, 4891
Ferris, Carolyn Zecca, 1231
Ferris, David R., 6722
Ferro, Kevin, 6223
Ferro, Michael W., Jr., 2746
Ferry, Ashley Belcher, 2410
Ferry, Carolyn P., 7451
Ferry, Michael J., 3946
Fertel Charitable Lead Unitrust, Ruth U., 3633
Fertel, Randy, 3633
Fessenden, Daniel J., 5950
Fessler, Erin D., 8026
Festivale Maritime, Inc., 1972
Festus Bahamas Trust, 9111
Fetcher, Jay, 1528
Fetes, Daniel, 2787
Fett, David, 638
Fetterman, Annabelle L., 7273
Fettig, Matt, 1108
Fetting, Mark R., 3726
Fetz, Courtney Gaines, 2466
Fetzer Memorial Trust, John E., 4420
Fetzer Revocable Trust, John E., 4421
Fetzer, Bruce, 4421
Fetzer, Bruce F., 4420
Fetzer, John E., 4420
Fetzer, Thomas H., Jr., 7171
Feuer, Michael, 1934
Feulner, Edwin J., Jr., 8266, 8494
Feulner, Edwin, Jr., 5560
Feuss, Bert, 1166
Feussner, John R., 8502
Fey, Grace, 3956, 4239
Fey, Robert, 419
Fiala, Robert A., 7681
Fialkoff, Jay, 6590
Fialkowski, Geraldine, 3743
Fica, Michelle, 1566
Ficalora, Joseph R., 6543, 6703
Ficaro, M. Lauren, 589
Ficaro, Ron, 589
Fick, John F., III, 9414
Fick, Larry, 4943
Fick, Ronald L., 1988
Fidel, Arthur C., 8188
Fidelity Capital, 4193
Fidelity Charitable Gift Fund, 7873, 8391
Fidelity Charitable Gift Trust, 8865
Fidelity Exploration & Production Co., 7354
Fidelity Investments, 4193
Fidelity National Information Services, Inc., 2097
Fidelity Products Co., 4656
Fidelity Ventures Ltd., 5170
Fiducuary Trust Co. Int'l., 4965
Fidlar, Stacie, 2787
Fidler, Josh E., 3726
Fidler, Steve, 3298
Fiduciary Management, Inc., 9877
Fiduciary Trust Co., 4157, 4312
Fiduciary Trust Co. International, 6544
Fiduciary Trust Intl. of California, 5794
Fiedler, David, 5960
Field Private Trust, Frances K., The, 523
Field, Arthur Norman, 5419
Field, Claire-Marie, 1615
Field, Cynthia A., 7799

Field, Eris M., 522
Field, James M., 2790
Field, John V., 5463
Field, Joseph M., 8037
Field, Lawrence N., 522
Field, Lisa S., 522
Field, Margaret W., 1566
Field, Marie H., 8037
Field, Marshall, IV, 2831
Field, Marshall, V, 2831, 3111
Field, Robyn L., 522
Fieldale Farms Corp., 9837
Fielder, Ann C., 8959
Fielder, Mary C., 4940
Fielding, Daniel, 5571
Fielding, Donna M., 5571
Fielding, Ronald H., 5571
Fields, Carmen, 6527
Fields, Charles, 6151
Fields, Curtland E., 5483
Fields, David, 9297
Fields, Gregory F., 1754
Fields, Howard, 1319
Fields, James P., Jr., 8488
Fields, John M., Jr., 5398
Fields, Kenneth H., 6294
Fields, Laura Kemper, 4926, 4927, 4950
Fields, Leo, 9297
Fields, Linda, 4473, 4475
Fields, Michael D., 4980
Fields, Polly, 4252
Fields, Sylvia V., 8021
Fieler, Ana Cecilia, 5776
Fieler, Sean, 5776
Fienberg, Linda, 1884
Fiery, Douglas A., 3761
Fiewell, Shirley, 515
Fife, Amy S., 9429
Fife, Andrew, 6232
Fife, Barbara J., 6232
Fife, David, 9429
Fife, Edward A., 9429
Fife, Elizabeth J., 9429
Fife, Eugene V., 9429
Fife, Howard, 6232
Fife, Richard, 6232
Fife, Stephen, 6232
Fifth & Pacific Companies, Inc., 5976
Fifth Third Bank, 2269, 4369, 7399, 7404, 7428, 7440, 7452, 7470, 7504, 7547, 7548, 7638, 7646, 7651
Fifth Third Bank, N.A., 7389
Fifth Third Bank, The, 7534
Figel, Reid, 1913
Figliola, Dan, 1363
Figliuzzi, David, 7981
Figueredo, Jorge L., 903
Figueroa, Bruce, 8374
Figueroa, Rhonda M., 5389
Fike, Jared, 3762
Fike, Nancy, 9652
Fikes, Amy L., 8844
Fikes, Brendan J., 8844
Fikes, Catherine W., 8844
Fikes, Lee, 8844
Fikes, Leland, 8844
Fikso, Robert, 9673
Filderman, Jon, 5379
File, William H., 9769
Filene, Lincoln, 4047
Fili-Krushel, Patricia, 6531
Filice, Kay, 415
Filler, Ronald, 2752
Fillman, Gordon B., 5098
Fillmore, Bill, 2033
Filo, Angela, 1354
Filo, David, 1354
Filosa, Tracy Abedon, 4039
Finan, C., 777
Financial Partners, 3317
Financial Trust Services, 8046
Finch, Aaron, 5936
Finch, Christopher, 5936
Finch, Christopher E., 5936
Finch, Edward Ridley, Jr., 6905
Finch, Greg, 1511
Finch, James A., III, 4954
Finch, Robbin, 1774
Finch, Robert, Jr., 9474
Finch, Ronald, 5936
Finch, Thomas Austin, Jr., 4048
Finch-Nguyen, Sandra, 5936
Finchem, Tim, 1518
Findlay Cadillac, 5119
Findlay Management Group, 5119
Findlay Shack Properties LLC, 5119
Findlay, Clifford J., 5119
Findlay, David, 3298
Findlay, Jack, 4448
Findlay, Marjorie M., 7982, 8264
Findlay, Sharyn, 5162
Findley, Barry B., 205
Findley, Brian, 205
Findley, Kevin C., 780
Fine Irrevocable Trust of 1998, Milton, The, 8039
Fine Irrevocable Trust of 2000, Milton, The, 8039
Fine, Andrew S., 9448
Fine, Art, 298
Fine, David, 8039
Fine, Martin, 2095
Fine, Milton, 8039
Fine, Paul, 3638
Fine, Roger S., 5329
Fine, Ruth, 3186
Fine, Sheila, 8039
Fine, Shelia, 8282
Finear, David R., 1003
Fineberg 2007 Charitable Trust, Joseph, 525
Fineberg, Harvey, 938
Fineberg, Harvey V., 686, 3982, 6414
Finegan, Cole, 1401
Finegan, James W., Jr., 8029
Finegan, William F., 3631
Finer, Michael, 8391
Finerman, R., 926
Finerman, Ralph, 927
Fineshriber, Ruth Moskin, 526
Finfer, Susan, 8676
Finger Interests, Marvy A., Ltd., 8845
Finger Trust, Linda K., 8664
Finger, Edward, 8845
Finger, Elaine W., 8845
Finger, Marvy A., 8845
Finger, Suzette, 7139
Fingerhut, Ronald, 4615
Finigan, Barbara, 8403
Finish Line, Inc., The, 3303
Fink, Betsy, 1583
Fink, Courtney, 7050
Fink, Eva, 6972
Fink, Jesse, 1583
Fink, Joseph, 6972
Fink, Patricia, 699
Fink, Richard, 3529, 9463
Fink, Steve, 1076
Finke, Jeff, 3360
Finke, Ron, 4996
Finkelstein Partners, Ltd., 9020
Finkelstein, David, 6839
Finkelstein, Hubert S., 9020
Finkelstein, Richard, 5247
Finklestein, Michael, 1585
Finlay, Curtis, 33
Finlay, D.F.K., 6951
Finlay, Duncan, Dr., 2038
Finlay, Francis, 6904
Finlay, John David, Jr., 50
Finlay, Louis E. "Ed", 9069
Finlay, Marcie, 5807
Finlay, Richard D., 33
Finlay, Sally, 33
Finlayson, John L., 8310
Finley Charitable Remainder Unitrust, R., 527
Finley, A.E., 7199
Finley, Earle, 7199
Finley, Ernest L., 527
Finley, Jim, 9835
Finley, John H., IV, 4218
Finley, Michael, 2563
Finley, Patrick T., 7578
Finley, Renee, 2101
Finley, Ruth W., 527
Finn, Patrick, 402
Finn, Thomas L., 7405
Finnegan, Mary M., 2832
Finnegan, Mike, 8521
Finnegan, Paul J., 2832
Finnegan, Wilfred A., 5579
Finneran Thru Exop Investors LP, William B., 5978
Finneran, John G., Jr., 9400
Finneran, William B., 5978
Finnigan, Becky, 4731
Finser, Mark, 8330, 9102
Finstad, Keith, 4631
Finucane, Anne M., 7139
Fiore, Michael E., 9411
Fiore, Mike, 9411
Fiore, William J., 9471
Fiorella, Peter J., Jr., 6913
Fioretti, Robert W., 3100
Fiorile, Michael J., 7719
Fiorile, Michael R., 7411
Fiorito, Daniel, 905
FIP Corp., 1585
Fireman's Annuity and Benefit Fund of Chicago, 2823
Fireman, Paul, 4049
Fireman, Phyllis, 4049
Fireman, Simon C., 2096
Firemens Association of Chicago, 2823
Firestein, Michael, 513
Firestone Tire and Rubber Co., The, 8537
Firestone, John D., 5260
Firestone, Lisa F., 5260
Firestone, Lucy D., 5260
Firestone, Marc S., 3034
Firestone, Mary C., 5260
Firestone, Nicholas, 5260
Firestone, Sarah Catherine, 5260
Firm, Woodruff Law, 7425
Firman, Pamela H., 7454
Firman, Royal, III, 7454
Firman, Stephanie, 7454
First Allmerica Financial Life Insurance Co., 4086
First American Bank, 2834
First American National Bank, 4843
First and Main, LLC, 1471
First Bank of Highland Park, 2833
First Bank System, Inc., 4784
First Banks, Inc., 4879
First Century Bank, N.A., 9770
First Citizens Bancorporation of South Carolina, Inc., 8477
First Citizens Bancorporation, Inc., 8477
First Citizens Bank, 7299, 7340
First Commonwealth Bank Trust, 8174
First Community Bank, Inc., 9779
First County Bank, 1584
First Data Corp., 1521
First Eagle Investment Management LLC, 1781
First Financial Bank, 7481
First Financial Northwest, Inc., 9619
First Financial Tr. Asset Management, 9261
First Fruits, 3245
First Grandchildren's Charitable Trust, The, 9455
First Hawaiian Bank, 2598
First Horizon National Corp., 8565
First International LLC, 5274
First Interstate Bank, 5009
First Interstate Bank of Commerce, 5009
First Mid-Illinois Bank & Trust, 3165
First National Bancshares, Inc., 4458
First National Bank, 1408, 2991
First National Bank & Trust of Waynesboro, 8046
First National Bank of Greencastle, 8046
First National Bank of Litchfield, 1565
First National Bank of Litchfield Fund, 1565
First National Bank South Dakota, 8515
First Niagara Bank, 1594, 5979
First Niagara Financial Group, Inc., 5979
First Preston Management, Inc., 9221
First Republic Bank, 8387
First Security Federal Savings Bank, 2907
First Tennessee Bank, 8577
First Tennessee Bank, N.A., 8583, 8588
First Tennessee National Corp., 8565
First Union Corp., 8333
First Union National Bank, 2395, 7302
First Virginia Bank, 7143
First-Knox National Bank, The, 7413
Firstenberg, David J., 8466
FirstEnergy Corp., 7455
FirstGiving, 7638
FirstMerit Bank, 7388
FirstMerit Bank, N.A., 7367, 7406, 7456, 7673
Firstrust Bank, 8070
Firth, Edmee de M., 5913
Firth, James, 2827
Firth, Nicholas L.D., 5913
Firth, Thomas T., 1925
Firuta, Paul, 8328
Fisackerly, Haley R., 3630
Fisch, Amy C., 544
Fisch, Ben, 8846
Fisch, Maytee R., 8846
Fisch, Sandra, 8846
Fisch, Stephanie, 8846
Fischbach, Gerald, 6898
Fischbach, Gerald D., 6861

Fischbach, Nancy, 1644
Fischel, Harry, 5980
Fischer, A., 1837
Fischer, Aaron, 4878
Fischer, Addison M., 426
Fischer, Avery, 6651
Fischer, B.D., 1151
Fischer, Billie A., 1350
Fischer, Chaim, 5981
Fischer, Chari, 4375
Fischer, Charles K., 8847
Fischer, Charles K., Jr., 8847
Fischer, Darrin, 3030
Fischer, David G., 8847
Fischer, David T., 4371
Fischer, Diane, 5197
Fischer, Elaine M., 3574
Fischer, Elizabeth S., 1038
Fischer, F. Conrad, 3240
Fischer, F.K., 1151
Fischer, Gordon R., 3420
Fischer, Henry K., 3574
Fischer, Jaki, 1350
Fischer, Jan, 2826
Fischer, Jennifer Atler, 1487
Fischer, Jill A., 8847
Fischer, Kurt, 9625
Fischer, Lauri D., 349
Fischer, M. Peter, 4878, 4894
Fischer, Malinda Berry, 7742
Fischer, Mark D., 6637
Fischer, Mark J., 9341
Fischer, Martha, 4894
Fischer, Martha C., 4878
Fischer, Matthew A., 4878
Fischer, Matthew G., 4894
Fischer, Michael P., 4878, 4894
Fischer, Patrick N., 8847
Fischer, Seth, 1648
Fischer, Teresa M., 4878
Fischer, Tom, 3438
Fischil, Meir, 6580
Fischmann, George, 531
Fischmann, Roberto, 8128
Fischvogt, Amber, 3321
Fisette, Sara B., 3417
Fish and Mirtha G. Fish Trust, Ray C., 8848
Fish, Allyson, 9656
Fish, Atsuko Toko, 4051
Fish, Edward Takezo, 4051
Fish, Emily, 4051
Fish, Kim Nedelman, 7671
Fish, Lawrence K., 4051
Fish, Leah Okajima Toko, 4051
Fish, Mirtha G., 8848
Fish, Raymond Clinton, 8848
Fish, Sarah, 7151
Fish, Tracy Gardner, 1102
Fishback, Harmes C., 1410
Fishbein, Michael, 7963
Fishburne, Lynne, 1249
Fishel, David, 5221
Fisheman, Joshua, 7119
Fisher 120 Wall, 5982
Fisher 92nd St., 5982
Fisher Brothers, 5982
Fisher Capital Assets, 5982
Fisher Charitable Remainder Trust, 4052
Fisher Charitable Trust, 7281
Fisher Charitable Trust, Zachary & Elizabeth, 5982
Fisher Foundation, Don and Doris, 1387
Fisher Fund, Doris and Donald, 5390
Fisher Park Lane Co., 5982
Fisher Scientific, 5185
Fisher Trust, Stanley D., 1585
Fisher, A. Tony, 8459
Fisher, Andrew S., 6339
Fisher, Arnold, 5982
Fisher, Beth, 7411
Fisher, Brian, 2033
Fisher, C.P., 1586
Fisher, Catherine M., 848
Fisher, Cheryl, 3314
Fisher, David H., 5089
Fisher, David J., 3428
Fisher, Donald G., 370
Fisher, Doris, 532
Fisher, Doris F., 370, 563
Fisher, Eileen, 5983
Fisher, Elizabeth M., 4247
Fisher, Elizabeth S., 1038
Fisher, Eric A., 9246
Fisher, Erica, 3512
Fisher, Frances H., 3368
Fisher, George A., 448
Fisher, Grace Pond, 8231
Fisher, Hinda N., 1585
Fisher, Irwin E., 8550
Fisher, J. William, 3790
Fisher, James A., 3262
Fisher, Janice B., 3262
Fisher, Jeff, 1043
Fisher, John, 363, 1387
Fisher, John J., 370
Fisher, John W., 3262
Fisher, Joseph, 1959
Fisher, Joseph E., 8150
Fisher, Joseph M., 1958
Fisher, Jud, 3262, 3286
Fisher, Julia G., 8150
Fisher, Katherine F., 448
Fisher, Kenneth, 5982
Fisher, Laura S., 8021
Fisher, Leo R., 9809
Fisher, Lynn, 8971
Fisher, Marjorie M., 4423
Fisher, Marjorie S., 4384, 4423
Fisher, Mary D., 4423
Fisher, Matt, 3484
Fisher, Matthew, 4052
Fisher, Max M., 4423
Fisher, Michael, 5598, 7511
Fisher, Michael J., Jr., 3263
Fisher, Nancy, 7538
Fisher, Paul, 7202
Fisher, Peggy, 3420
Fisher, Phillip W., 4371
Fisher, Phillip William, 4423
Fisher, Richard, 6713
Fisher, Robert J., 1038
Fisher, Robert P., 5349
Fisher, Ronald, 4052
Fisher, Shelly Lotman, 8150
Fisher, Smaul A., 8150
Fisher, William S., 7169
Fisher, Winston C., 5982
Fishkin, James, 1586
Fishkin, Shelley, 1586
Fishman Foundation, Mimi, The, 9376
Fishman, Alan H., 5718
Fishman, Bob, 2524
Fishman, C.J., 2038
Fishman, Jill, 8044
Fishman, Jonathan, 9376
Fishman, Joseph, 6511
Fishman, Mark, 3833, 8044
Fishman, Marty, 670
Fishman, Matt, 3953
Fishman, Nancy, 2875
Fishman, Pamela, 5496
Fishman, Richard G., 3609
Fishoff, Abraham, 5984
Fishoff, Avi, 5984
Fishoff, Benjamin, 5984
Fishoff, Donald, 5984
Fishoff, Marilyn, 5984
Fisk, Barbara M., 3
Fisk, Jed A., 3476
Fisk, Kelly, 3
Fisk, William C., 3146
Fiske Trust, L.S., 4211
Fiske, Abigail, 3222
Fiske, Elaine, 3222
Fiske, Kimberly, 9380
Fisker, Linda R., 91
Fisler, Christine M., 4107
Fister, Christopher L., 7399, 7404
Fister, Nancy, 7417
Fitch, Lydia J., 8045
Fitch, Orville, 5169
Fitch, Ruth Ellen, 4157
Fiterman, Linda, 4656
Fiterman, Michael, 4656
Fites, Donald V., 2098
Fites, Sylvia D., 2098
Fitgerald, Thomas J., 7279
Fithian, Jerry, 3534
Fitt, Lawton W., 5985
Fitton, James K., 7481
Fitzgerald, Anne, 7343
Fitzgerald, Bernard, 7208
Fitzgerald, Betty, 2457
Fitzgerald, Cantor, 5116
Fitzgerald, Davis, 2457
Fitzgerald, Dennis M., 7026
Fitzgerald, Dennis W., 3015
Fitzgerald, Donna M., 5821
Fitzgerald, Gail M., 3758
Fitzgerald, Gloria, 120
Fitzgerald, J. Terrence, Rev. Msgr., 9302
Fitzgerald, Jennifer Perkins, 5599
Fitzgerald, Judy, 3280
Fitzgerald, Katharine, 5806
Fitzgerald, L. Michael, 5805
Fitzgerald, Margaret Boles, 6398
Fitzgerald, Maria Vatterott, 2371
Fitzgerald, Michele C., 7026
Fitzgerald, Paul, Dr., 184
Fitzgerald, Stephen B., 7139
Fitzgerald, Timothy D., 8040
Fitzgerald-Schultz, Shannon, 3410
Fitzgibbon, Herbert S., 6198
FitzGibbon, Thomas P., Jr., 2702
Fitzgibbons, James M., 4211
Fitzgibbons, S. Dorothy Anne, 6024
Fitzmorris, Ann, 3611
Fitzmorris, Scott, 1956
Fitzpatrick, Barry C., 466
Fitzpatrick, Brian, 3226, 3648
Fitzpatrick, Frank, 3578
Fitzpatrick, Jack, 568
Fitzpatrick, Margaret M., 7981
Fitzpatrick, Michael J., 5394
Fitzpatrick, Sue, 4370
Fitzpatrick, Susan M., 4941
Fitzpatrick, Tim, 1033
Fitzpatrick, Will, 984
Fitzpatrick-Donahue, Anne, 6159
Fitzsimmons, Hugh A., Jr., 8885
FitzSimmons, John S., 5923
Fitzsimmons, John T., 5863
Fitzsimmons, Kelly, 5784
Fitzsimons, Hugh A., Jr., 8886
FitzSimons, Michael J., 4522
Five Seasons Country Clubs, LLC, 7396
Five Way Partners, LLP, 1628
Fiverson, Marjorie Gershwind, 6046
Fjarli, Bruce, 7842
Fjarli, Clint, 7843
Fjarli, Joann, 7842, 7843
Fjarli, Lola, 7843
Fjarli, Merlin, 7842, 7843
FJC, 5717
Flack, David, 9109
Flack, Eleanor E., 34
Flack, J. Hunter, 34
Flack, Kathi, 8152
Flagg, Scott, 4152
Flaggert, James, 9653
Flagler Foundation, The, 9432, 9560
Flaherty, Dana S., 3599
Flaherty, Jay C., 4510
Flaherty, Jonathan P., 5986
Flaherty, Pamela, 5986
Flaherty, Pamela P., 5986
Flaherty, Peter A., 5986
Flaherty, Victoria, 1242
Flake, Floyd, Rev. Dr., 6024
Flam, Jack, 5864
Flament, Doug, 5006
Flamme, Larry, 5039
Flanagan, Glenda F., 9276
Flanagan, Jason, 9143
Flanagan, Kathleen, 5534
Flanagan, Laura, 255
Flanagan, Leo M., Jr., 2818
Flanagan, Patricia J., 8429
Flanagan, Sheila B., 1690
Flanagan, Shelly, 3201
Flanagan, Shiela B., 1651
Flanders, Bryon, 973
Flanders, Byron, 1120
Flanery, Steven, 8524
Flanigan, Megan F., 6667
Flanigan, Peter M., 6667
Flanigan, Robert W., 6667
Flanigan, Timothy P., 6667
Flannery, Richard J., 8195
Flannigan, Suzanne, 8518
Flather, Newell, 4207
Flatley, Charlotte E., 4053
Flatley, Daniel T., 4053
Flatley, John J., 4053
Flatley, Thomas J., 4053
Flatt, Stephen F., Dr., 8550
Flatto, Olivia Tournay, 6629
Flaville, Victoria K., 7995
Flaws, James B., 5818
Flax, Joel, 9444
Flax, Steven I., 6406
Fleak, Michael L., 9789
Fleck, Laurie, 2439
Flederbach, Linda, 8234
Fleece, Joseph W., III, 2269
Fleeman, Stewart, 325
Fleer Trading Cards, 7012
Fleet, 9053
FleetBoston Financial Corp., 7012
FleetBoston Financial Foundation, 7139
Fleetguard, Inc., 3292
Fleischer, Bruce M., 4358
Fleischer, Henry, 4358
Fleischer, Liz, 8776
Fleischman, Albert, 5664, 5665

Fontana, Philip, 3052
Fontanes, A. Alexander, 4145, 9723
Fonteyne, Paul, 1549
Food Lion LLC, 7201
Food Marketing Institute Foundation, 3245
Foodmaker, Inc., 736
Fooks, Thomas H., V, 1780
Foose, Randy, 5169
Foote Trust Co. 1, S.M., 4458
Foote, David R., 4458
Foote, Frederick C., 4458
Foote, Kenneth J., 4458
Foote, Lynne, 4458
Foote, Marnie, 4458
Foote, Shirley A., 4458
Foote, Steven M., 4458
Foote, Susan L., 4458
Foote, Theresa M., 4458
Foote-Hudson, Marilyn E., 7274
Forasiere, Barbara, 2326
Forbes Foundation, 7012
Forbes, Elisabeth Eisner, 1108
Forbes, George, 6393
Forbes, J. Michael, 1404
Forbes, Janice L., 1039
Forbes, Moira, 5821
Forbes, Orcilla Zuniga, 7870
Forbes, Stephanie, 1069
Forbs, Claudia, 6659
Force, Hudson La, III, 3807
Forchheimer, Leo, 5992
Ford Foundation, The, 1421, 3242
Ford Meter Box Co., Inc., The, 3305
Ford Motor Co., 4430, 6904, 7638
Ford Motor Credit Co., 4430
Ford, Ada, 7459
Ford, Adelaide, 4560
Ford, Alex, 7365
Ford, Alfred B., 4430
Ford, Allen H., 7365
Ford, Allyn C., 7845
Ford, Ann, 3019
Ford, Barbara Hamilton, 9776
Ford, Benson, 4426
Ford, Benson, Jr., 4426
Ford, Charles, 7365
Ford, Clara, 4055
Ford, Cynthia N., 4429, 4498
Ford, Daniel H., 3305
Ford, David B., 5993, 6248
Ford, David B., Jr., 5993
Ford, David Kingsley, 7365
Ford, David Knight, 7365
Ford, David, Jr., 7365
Ford, Edsel, 5994
Ford, Edsel B., II, 4429
Ford, Edward E., 5995
Ford, Eleanor C., 4425
Ford, Eleanor Clay, 4427
Ford, Elizabeth Brooks, 7365
Ford, Gerald J., 8854
Ford, Hallie E., 7845
Ford, Hamlet, 8473
Ford, Henry, 5994
Ford, Henry, II, 4429
Ford, Henry, III, 4429
Ford, James M., 5993
Ford, James W., 4522
Ford, Jenice C. Mitchell, 4371
Ford, Jeremy B., 8854
Ford, Joe T., 2514
Ford, Jon, 3396
Ford, Joseph F., 4055
Ford, Kenneth W., 7845
Ford, Lawrence Charles, 400
Ford, Lawrence Charles, Jr., 400
Ford, Linda, 3363
Ford, Lisa V., 4425
Ford, Lise, 7365
Ford, Lucille G., 7378
Ford, Mark S., 3305
Ford, Martha F., 4422, 4427, 4428
Ford, Martha Firestone, 4428
Ford, Nancy, 7742
Ford, Ned, 7365
Ford, Pat, 3175
Ford, Richard, 4516
Ford, Richard E., 9774
Ford, Sandra, 202
Ford, Thomas, 4009
Ford, Thomas W., 1112
Ford, Virginia M., 5993
Ford, William Clay, 4427, 4428
Ford, William Clay, Jr., 4425
Ford, William E., 6976
Fordham Foundation, Thomas B., 7608
Fordham Renaissance Management, 1555
Fordham Renaissance Mgmt., 1556
Fordham, Kiki, 7016
Fordney Foundation, 7425
Fordyce, James W., 6333
Fordyce, Marshall, 6333
Fore, Julian, 9384
Foreman Trust, 3110
Foreman, Chris, 3163
Foreman, Christine, 8874
Foreman, Christopher, 3163
Foreman, Jeff, 3163
Foreman, Peter B., 3163
Foreman, Robin C., 9448
Foreman, Stephen A., 6406
Foreman, Virginia, 3163
Forest Lawn Co., 263
Forest Trust, The, 7276
Forestar, 9049
Forester Offshore, 9916
Forester, Burton, 350
Forester, John E., 9844
Foresther, Charlotte, 8001
Forgason, Caroline A., 8962
Forger, Alexander D., 6698
Forgit, Cathy, 4730
Forhan, Drew, 7496
Forlenza, Karen, 4298
Forlenza, Robert, 4298
Forman, Barry, 9757
Forman, Christopher S., 1004
Forman, Michael R., 1004
Forman, Scott A., 912
Formanek, Peter R., 8566
Forminard, Elizabeth R., 5326
Forner, Emira, 9604
Forney, Ann W., 61
Fornof, Pete, 2817
Fornstrom, Ryan, 2639
Forrest, Myra Gehert, 8234
Forrest, Robert, 852
Forrestel, Margaret, 5327
Forrester, Judy, 4996
Forrester, Robert H., 1652
Forrester, Traci L., 7407
Forrester, W. Thomas, 7623
Forsch, Randall T., 4362
Forshay, Wendy, 6940
Forsmann, Marty, 9603
Forst, Edward C., 5997
Forst, Susan R., 5997
Forster, Elizabeth D., 1905
Forster, Jerald, 9645
Forster, Peter C., 1905
Forsyte, Carol, 3042
Forsyth, Adrian, 9394
Forsyth, J. & M., 4003
Forsyth, John D., 3490
Forsyth, William H., Jr., 7014
Forsythe, Garry V., 8546
Forsythe, Greg, 3291
Forsythe, Ralph, 2
Fort Irrevocable Trust No. 1, Mildred, 2460
Fort Worth Star-Telegram, 8753
Fort, James C., 8473
Fort, John C., 4966
Fort, Mildred Miller, 2460
Fortang, Chaim, Rabbi, 5761
Forte, Cheryl, 4061
Forte, Linda D., 4368
Fortenberry, David, 4829
Fortier, Anne-Marie, 1521
Fortier, Chris, 5804
Fortin Foundation of Florida, 2105
Fortin, Mary Alice, 2105, 2106
Fortine Irrevocable Trust, Mary Alice, 2105
Fortino, Barbara, 1504
Fortino, Dominick, 5948
Fortino, Phil, 415
Fortis Benefits Insurance Co., 5621
Fortis Insurance Co., 5621
Fortis, Inc., 5621
Fortson, Benjamin J., 8737
Fortune Metal Group Inc. of Rhode Island, 5263
Fortune Plastic Mental Inc., 5263
Fortus, Charles A., 4055
Fosburgh, Whit, 6564
Foshag, William H., 9892
Foshay, William W., III, 8241
Foshee, Douglas L., 8917
Fosheim, Jon, 297
Foskey, Randall, 9558
Fosse, Eric, 8834
Fossett, J. Stephen, 2838
Fossett, Peggy V., 2838
Fossum, Lynn, 9606
Fosta-Tek Optics, 2245
Foster Admin. Trust, Gladyce, 539
Foster Trust, Robert C., 4431
Foster, Albert O., 9621
Foster, Anne, 9965
Foster, Betty Jo, 9420, 9421
Foster, Bob, 846
Foster, Chesley, 4675
Foster, Chuck, 3896
Foster, Clay, 4822
Foster, Constance B., 8129
Foster, Diana K., 7696
Foster, Diane, 9341
Foster, Edward L., 4838
Foster, Evelyn W., 9621
Foster, Fred L., 8478
Foster, Geoff, 529
Foster, Gregory A., 539
Foster, John N., Jr., 9432
Foster, Kate, 4431
Foster, Katherine C., 2411
Foster, Lawrence T., 7696
Foster, Lee B., II, 8228
Foster, Leonard, 7597
Foster, Loleta Wood, Dr., 7184
Foster, Louis, 539
Foster, Louise L., 9432
Foster, Margaret, 9810
Foster, Marie B., 2584
Foster, Mark, 4937
Foster, Marshall L., 1449
Foster, Michael, 9621
Foster, Michael G., Jr., 9621
Foster, Patricia A., 2792
Foster, Paul, 1521
Foster, Phyllis L., 4431
Foster, R. Brad, 2584
Foster, R. David, 9924
Foster, R. Scott, 539
Foster, Richard N., 774
Foster, Rob, 4872
Foster, Rock A., 4948
Foster, Stephen A., 6604
Foster, Steve, 5750, 7421
Foster, Susan H., 8549
Foster, Tim, 1488
Foster, Timothy, 7678
Foster, Tracy McFerrin, 4905
Foster, Trevor, 7678
Foster, Vicki, 9384
Foster, William, 3695, 4110, 7678
Foster, William L., 539
Foszcz, Cooper, 2851
Foszcz, Joshua, 2851
Foszcz, Russell, 2851
Foszcz, Sara, 2851
Foszcz, Sara Smock, 3235
Foti, Vincent, 5879
Fotsch, Geraldine D., 9846
Fotsch, Thomas A., 9846
Fouberg, Rod, 8523
Foudree, Chuck, 4996
Fouladi, A. Holly, 2152
Foulger, Bryant F., 3792
Foulger, Clayton F., 3792
Foulger, Mary, 3792
Foulger, Sidney W., 3792
Foulkrod, Patricia G., 8059
Foundation Energy Company, Inc., 9049
Foundation for the Mid South, 4838
Foundation Health Plan of Sacramento, 1163
Foundation of Integrated Services, 9700
Founds, Linda, 9381
Founds, Martha N., 9381
Foung, Alejandro, 605
Foung, Jessica Goldman, 605
Fountain Club LLC, 9452
Fountain Industries, 4774
Fountain Park Apartments LP, 9452
Fountain, Edmund M., Jr., 8857
Fountain, Nancy Frees, 8857
Fountain, W. Frank, 4371, 4463
Four Ark Charitable Lead Trust, 6536
Four J's Ranch, 8492
Four Winds Casino Resort, 4523
Fournier, Alan P., 5264
Fournier, Jennifer L., 5264
Fournier, Lucinda Day, 774
Fournier, Lucinda M., 457
Fournier, Susan, 9089
Fourteen Four Group, The, 530
Fouss, Rob, 9789
Foutz, James R., 7991
Fowke, Benjamin G.S., III, 4808
Fowle, Stephen A., 1765
Fowler, Adrian Rhae, 9293
Fowler, Amber, 1249
Fowler, Amy Goldman, 6064

Fowler, Aubrey R., 9873
Fowler, Bill, 1399
Fowler, Cary, 6064
Fowler, Charles D., 7446, 7460
Fowler, Charlotte, 7460
Fowler, Charlotte A., 7460
Fowler, Elizabeth P., 7005
Fowler, Ellen B., 8560
Fowler, John C., 9968
Fowler, Lynn, 8743
Fowler, Pearl Gunn, 3795
Fowler, Peggy Y., 7881
Fowler, Rob, 2525
Fowler, Robert D., 2433
Fowler, Stephanie J., 7884
Fowler, Tom, 4565
Fowler, W. Beal, 8136
Fowler, Wyche, Jr., 2569, 6850
Fowler-Spellman, Chann, 7460
Fowlkes, Annabelle B., 8732
Fowlkes, Rita Kay, 183
Fox Channel Services LLC, 7214
Fox Mounsey, Anne E., 1412
Fox, Anne E. Mounsey, 1452
Fox, Ashton L., 7184
Fox, Becca Selvidge, 1412, 1452
Fox, Beri, 9773
Fox, Beth, 9237
Fox, C.F., 9399
Fox, Carol Parry, 92
Fox, Cheri, 4892
Fox, Christy B., 4894
Fox, David, 569
Fox, Debbie, 7539
Fox, Dennis, 3033
Fox, Dennis J., 7663
Fox, Elizabeth Q., 7461
Fox, Eric R., 5199
Fox, Eugene, 5473
Fox, Gail, 9967
Fox, Gregory, 4892
Fox, Jeffrey, 187, 4892
Fox, Jerry D., 3332
Fox, John F., Jr., 1412
Fox, John M., 1412
Fox, John M., Jr., 1412
Fox, John Macgregor, Jr., 1452
Fox, Judy, 5278
Fox, Katherine L., 2922
Fox, Kelley P., 1412, 1452
Fox, Lewis M., 9101
Fox, Maggie, 1424
Fox, Marcella F., 1412
Fox, Marilyn, 4892
Fox, Mary L., 2922
Fox, Marye Anne, 5912
Fox, Richard T., 8560
Fox, Robert K., 7461
Fox, Robert L., 7461
Fox, S., 926
Fox, Sam, 4892
Fox, Sondra, 9059
Fox, Steven, 4892
Fox, Susan M., 927
Fox, William C., 2824
Fox-Claman, Pamela, 4892
Foxley, Zoe L., 1419
Foy, Douglas J., 3262, 3263, 3264
Foyer, Julie Kemper, 4926
Fracassa, P. D., 7683
Frackelton, R. Leigh, Jr., 9414
Fracyon, Noelle M., 1845
Fradd, R. Brandon, 6904
Fraenkel, Barnet H., 8128, 8320
Frafjord, Teresa, 9658
Fraga, Lupe, 9208
Fraim, Martha B., 7386
Fraim, William L., 7386
Fralick, Desiree, 7973
Fralick, William, 7671
Fralin, Robert P., 9415
Fralin, W. Heywood, 9433
Fralin, William H., 9433
Fram, Debra, 1561
Frame House Press, 9058
Framptom, Joseph H., 3570
Frampton, George, 8396
Frampton, Harry, III, 1518
France Stone Co., The, 7462
France, Annita, 3796
France, George A., 7462
France, Jacob, 3796
Frances, Eric, 6044
Frances, William H., Jr., 7259
Franceschelli, Anthony D., 5950
Franceschini, Donald D., 1866
Francis, Alexandra, 6788
Francis, Bob, 3281
Francis, Carl, 7979
Francis, David, 4937
Francis, David R., 9481
Francis, David V., 4893
Francis, H.D., 2055
Francis, Helen Lovely, 2775
Francis, J. Scott, 4893
Francis, Jonathan, 9230
Francis, Laurel, 1796
Francis, Lee, 3172
Francis, Mary B., 4893
Francis, Michael D., 5296
Francis, Parker B., 4893
Francis, Parker B., III, 4893
Francis, Paul, 6549, 6936
Francis, Robert D., 471
Francis, Roger, 1198
Francis, Steve, 7490
Francisco, Ellen, 1076
Franciscovich, Linda, 1602
Franck, C. Duffy, Jr., 8614
Franckhauser, Margaret, 5169
Franco, Alan, 3644
Franco, Camilo, 8495
Franco, Diane, 3638
Franco, Juan, 5063
Franco, Robert S., 2288
Franco, Sara Z., 2583
Francois, Yvette, 1715
Franconia Foundation, 5937
Francqui, Frederic Count, 6007
Francy, Patricia L., 6121
Frandsen, Olaf, 3540
Frangiosa, Joseph D., 7995
Frank Consolidated Enterprises, 2840
Frank Family Trust, H.R., 1052
Frank, Barry, 6008
Frank, Brian, 656
Frank, Brian H., 2536
Frank, Diana D., 1052
Frank, Elizabeth T., 5391
Frank, Faith, 5629
Frank, George W., 6681
Frank, Harold R., 1052
Frank, Herbert, 6008
Frank, Irvin E., 7752
Frank, James A., 1052
Frank, James S., 2840
Frank, Jay L., 8550
Frank, Jessica, 1052
Frank, Joseph, 6008
Frank, Karen, 2840
Frank, Mariel, 8236
Frank, Mary, 9118
Frank, Michael J., 4945
Frank, Noemi, 6008
Frank, Paul M., 6598
Frank, Roxanne H., 3125
Frank, Seth E., 6402
Frank, Sidney E., 544
Frank, Stanley J. "Jack", Jr., 7426
Franke, Barbara E., 2841
Franke, C. William, 4675
Franke, Katherine, 2841
Franke, Richard J., 2841
Franke, Stephen L., 9843
Franke, Thomas F., 4496
Franke-Molner, Jane, 2841
Frankel 2007 Investment Trust, Keith, 5265
Frankel Family LP, 2842
Frankel Living Trust, Matthew, 2842
Frankel, Bernard, 2842
Frankel, Bruce, 4435, 4436
Frankel, David Henry, 1992
Frankel, Edward, 5265
Frankel, Edward M., 7486
Frankel, Gerald, 2843
Frankel, Gustav, 2843
Frankel, Jean, 4435, 4436, 4437
Frankel, Judith, 4433, 4437
Frankel, Julius N., 2843
Frankel, Keith, 5265
Frankel, Marya, 2842
Frankel, Matthew, 2842
Frankel, Maxine, 4434
Frankel, Miriam, 2842
Frankel, Peter, 2842
Frankel, Robert, 7059
Frankel, Samuel, 4435, 4437
Frankel, Sandor, 6160
Frankel, Stanley, 4433, 4435, 4437
Frankel, Stuart, 3031, 4434, 4435
Frankenberg, Regina Bauer, 6009
Frankfort, Lew, 5790
Frankfort, Lewis, 6010
Frankfort, Roberta, 6010
Frankino, Connie M., 5266
Frankino, Samuel J., 5266, 7438
Franklin Holding Corp., 921
Franklin, Alice, 6565
Franklin, Barbara, 8775
Franklin, Carla, 6546
Franklin, Carmela Vircillo, 6308
Franklin, Charlotte A., 8856
Franklin, Christian B., Esq., 9414
Franklin, Christopher E., 5745
Franklin, David, 2609
Franklin, Douglas, Hon., 7415
Franklin, Fred W., 7296
Franklin, Gene, 6025
Franklin, Hassell H., 4822
Franklin, Jeanne, 9497
Franklin, Jeff, 4839
Franklin, Jennifer, 6106
Franklin, Jennifer L., 6582
Franklin, John, 2462
Franklin, John C., 9295
Franklin, Julie, 2107
Franklin, Kathy, 5313
Franklin, Larry, 1187
Franklin, Larry D., 8856
Franklin, Lisa, 5313
Franklin, Martin E., 2107
Franklin, Mary O., 2462
Franklin, Max, 5313
Franklin, Perry J., 3613
Franklin, Ronald, 8788
Franklin, Sterling C., 1187
Franklin, Wei-Ching K., 1187
Franklincovey, Inc., 9328
Franks Foundation, Alta, The, 3249
Franks Foundation, John, The, 3249
Franks, Alta V., 3634
Franks, Dawn, 8819
Franks, Gary, 4828
Franks, John, 3634
Franks, Lawrence M., 5648
Franks, Peter J., 4310
Frantz, Barbara, 4370
Frantz, David, 9380
Frantzis, Lisa, 4178
Franz, J. Denise, 4916
Frapwell, Dottie, 3278
Fraser, Alex, 2238
Fraser, Darryl M., 9498
Fraser, E. W., 1591
Fraser, Hugh P., 8549
Fraser, Ian H., 7030
Fraser, Maureen, 1703
Fraser, Stu, 1512
Fraser, Wayne "Skipp", 2040
Frasier, Eleanor, 4996
Frasz, Nicole, 793
Fraternal Order of Angeles Charity Foundation, 2351
Fraternal Order of Police, 2823
Fratila, Barbara, 8775
Fratzke, Katherine E., 4623
Frauenthal, Harold, 4369
Frautschi Charitable Lead Unitrust, W. Jerome, 9848
Frautschi, Christopher J., 9847
Frautschi, Elizabeth J., 9847
Frautschi, Grant J., 9848
Frautschi, John J., 9847
Frautschi, Lance A., 9848
Frautschi, Peter W., 9847
Frautschi, W. Jerome, 9848
Frautschi, Walter Jerome, 9848, 9937
Fraydun Foundation Inc., 6775
Frazee, Alexena, 8350
Frazer, David R., 111
Frazier, D. Mell, 3464
Frazier, Daveed, 975
Frazier, Deborah J., 5412
Frazier, Evan, 8228
Frazier, Evan S., 8092
Frazier, H. Matthew, 5341
Frazier, J. Walter, 3635
Frazier, James Walter, Jr., 3635
Frazier, Janet, 4061
Frazier, Jean, 9602
Frazier, Mell Meredith, 3463
Frazier, Mikal, 3635
Frazier, Robert, 246
Frazier, Sharon, 9791
Frazier, W. Edwin, III, 2281
Frechette, Patricia, 2844
Frechette, Peter, 1518
Frechette, Peter L., 2844
Freckman, Joanie C., 1068
Fredel, Timothy C., 1255
Frederick Trust, C. Lydia, 2747
Frederick, Brian R., 7412
Frederick, Charles, 7182
Frederick, Karen, 4152
Frederick, Ron, 8036

Frierson, Chip, 2525
Fries, Amber L., 1413
Fries, Michael T., 1413
Friese, Julius F., 1700
Friesen, Monty, 1409
Friesen, Patricia, 1409
Friesen, Robert, 101
Friess, Foster S., 9978
Friess, Lynnette E., 9978
Friess, Polly Jackson, 6677
Friess, Robert M., 249
Frieze Family Foundation, 4298
Frigon, Sussanah Weis, 8026
Frimmer, Paul, 231, 1094
Friou, Roger P., 4833
Frisbie, Margaret, 3278
Frisch, Adam, 1986
Frisch, Benjamin, 1986
Frisch, Hans, 1986
Frisch, Mark, 1986
Frishman, Kay B., 3987
Friskics-Warren, Mary K. "Kaki", The Rev., 8603
Frist, Bill, Dr., 3990
Frist, Dorothy Cate, 8567
Frist, Patricia C., 8568
Frist, Robert A., 8567
Frist, Thomas F., III, 8568
Frist, Thomas F., Jr., 8567, 8568
Frist, Thomas F., Jr., Dr., 8550
Frist, Thomas F., Sr., Dr., 8567
Frist, William H., 760, 5329, 8567
Frist, William R., 8568
Fritch, Barbara A., 8569
Fritch, Herbert A., 8569
Fritel, Steve, 4636
Fritsch, Janice, 1440
Fritz, Kathy May, 5132
Fritz, Mark, 8873
Fritz, Martin A., 8025
Fritz, Nancy, 3699
Fritze, Steve, 4757
Fritze, Steven, 4715
Fritzinger, John, 5556
Frizzell, Kerri, 5528
Frock, Scott, 4016
Frodel, John, 7915
Froderman, Carl, 3307
Froderman, Chris, 3307
Froderman, Harvey, 3307
Froderman, Harvey, Mrs., 3307
Froehlich, Lisa R., 5040
Froehlich, Monte L., 5040
Froelich, Georgia A., 7487
Froelich, Lisa R., 5040
Froelich, Mark, 8221
Froelich, William G., 6025
Frohlich, Susan, 1109
Frohring, Maxine A., 5269
Frohring, Paul R., 5269
Frohring, Paula, 5269
Froimson, Emily, 9417
Fromm Charitable Lead Annuity Trust, Alfred and Hanna, 553
Fromm, Alfred, 553
Fromm, Barbara, 553
Fromm, Daniel, 4937
Fromm, David George, 553
Fromm, Hanna, 553
Fromm, Ronald A., 2004
Fromme, Michelle Simon, 1172
Frommer, Jacob, 5282
Frommer, Sara M., 5282
Fron, M., 777
Fronk, Trevor, 9354
Frontczak, Joan, 3148
Frontier Capital Mgmt., 7367
Frontiere Revocable Trust, Georgia, 1751
Frontiere, Georgia, 1751
Frontline Technologies, 8277
Froom, Alexander, 3756
Fross, Roger R., 2946
Frost Bank, 8977, 9118, 9149
Frost National Bank, 9113, 9127, 9148, 9165, 9265
Frost National Bank, N.A., 9284
Frost, Camilla Chandler, 392
Frost, Carolyn Barry, 2667
Frost, Joan M., 5885, 5921
Frost, Karin A., 2599
Frost, Louis B., 8360
Frost, Michael, 4550
Frost, Mike, 3481
Frost, Robert D., 6379
Frost, Virginia C., 5519
Frozen Ropes of Morris County NJ, LLC, 1850
Fruchthandler Bros. Enterprises, 6027
Fruchthandler, Abraham, 6027
Fruchthandler, Abraham H., 6027
Fruchthandler, Baruch Dov, 6027
Fruchthandler, Joseph, 6027
Fruchthandler, Ruth, 6027
Fruchthandler, Solomon, 6027
Fruchthandler, Zachary, 6027
Frueauff, Anna Kay, 188
Frueauff, Charles A., 188
Frueauff, David A., 188
Frueauff, Sue M., 188
Fruehauf, Harvey C., Jr., 5159
Fruhman, Rhea Fay, 8858
Frulla, William E., 8530
Frumkin, Howard, 9591
Frunzi, Susan C., 5847, 6004, 6243
Frus, Fred L., 7698
Fruth, Jean, 554
Fruth, John, 554
Fry, Cynthia D., 555
Fry, L. Edward, 7620
Fry, Lloyd A., 2849
Fry, Lloyd A., III, 2849
Fry, Rita A., 2831
Fry, Roxanne, 1393
Fry, Stephen T., 555
Fry, Susan, 106
Fry, Terry, 3539
Frye, Bret, Dr., 7557
Frye, Carol, 7160
Frye, Henry E., 7273
Frye, Irene, 3113
Frye, Shirley, 7162
Frye, Shirley T., 7274
Frye, Stephen F., 3340
Frye, Tom, 8591
Fryer, Tom, 3532
Fryman, Paul, 3578
FSAR Fee Associates, 5982
Fu, Tony, 711
Fuccillo, Ralph, 4016
Fuchs Trust, Gottfried, 9624
Fuchs, Bernard, 6028
Fuchs, Diane J., 1897
Fuchs, Elaine, 3833
Fuchs, Gottfried, 9624
Fuchs, Mary, 9624
Fuchs, Morris, 6028
Fuchs, Rachel, 6028
Fudge, Ann, 9625
Fudge, Ann M., 6724
Fuemmeler, Carl D., 4900
Fuentes, Eric, 5806
Fuermann, Amy E., 444
Fuerst, David, 8846
Fuerst, Jan F., 8846
Fuerst, Mandy, 8846
Fuerst, Martee F., 8846
Fuette, Valerie J., 387
Fugett, Anthony S., 6365
Fuhrman, Susan H., 1934
Fuji, Yoshihide, 6997
Fujimoto, Lisa C., 393
Fujimoto, Marcia, 9731
Fujioka, Robert T., 2598
Fujisawa USA Charitable Trust Fund, 2675
Fujita, Hiroyuki, 7406
Fulcher, John T., 9460
Fuld, Florentine M., 6029
Fuld, Leonhard Felix, 6029
Fulenwider, C. Michael, 7178
Fulk Farms, Inc., 2850
Fulk, Robert W., 2850
Fulk, Wilma B., 2850
Fulker, William J., 7688
Fulkerson, Julie, 714
Fullenkamp, David, 3370
Fuller Co., H.B., 4659
Fuller Fund, Anna, 1558
Fuller Marital Trust, Constance, 4324
Fuller, Albert D., 1916
Fuller, Alvan T., Sr., 5172
Fuller, Arlan F., Jr., 4003
Fuller, Beth, 9799
Fuller, Charles, 4947
Fuller, Constance B., 4324
Fuller, George Freeman, 4063
Fuller, Howard, 1014
Fuller, Jack, 2989
Fuller, Janice L., 4063
Fuller, Joyce I., 4063
Fuller, Kathryn S., 1950, 5329
Fuller, Kenneth G., 1989
Fuller, Laurie, 7742
Fuller, Lincoln E., 4063
Fuller, Mark W., 4063
Fuller, Mike, 8495
Fuller, Moira H., 4324
Fuller, Peter, 5172
Fuller, Peter D., Jr., 5172
Fuller, Phillip, 7188
Fuller, Randolph J., 4324
Fuller, Robert G., Jr., 4324
Fuller, Sybil H., 4063
Fullerton, Alma H., 8479
Fullerton, Baxter, 1415
Fullerton, Jessica, 1415
Fullerton, John B., 1415
Fullerton, Robert, 4714
Fullinwider Trust, Carol, 8967
Fullinwider, Carol, 8967
Fullmer, Peggy, 7972
Fullwood, Doris, 7178
Fulmer, Terry, 6414
Fulmer, Terry T., 5786
Fulp, J.R., Jr., 8454
Fulp, John R., III, 8454
Fulstone, Suellen, 5132
Fulton Bank, N.A., 8099
Fulton Financial Advisors, N.A., 8046
Fulton, Annette, 1394
Fulton, Chris, 4667, 6868
Fulton, Douglas S., 113
Fulton, Ira A., 113
Fulton, Mark, 3761
Fulton, Mary Lou, 113
Fulton, Rita E., 59
Fulwiler, Terrence R., 9855
Fulwiler, Terry, 9854
Fumagalli, John, 2238
Fumagalli, John D., 2035
Fumagalli, Robert J., 9107
Funck, Robert, 2648
Fund, Steve, 4282
Fundacao Ciocle AE Tecnologia, 2631
Fundacion Flamboyan, 1904
Funds for Life Foundation, The, 6756
Fung, Bill, 4183
Fung, Deborah, 4049
Fung, William, 711
Funger, Keith Parker, 9438
Funger, Morton, 9438
Funger, Norma Lee, 9438
Funger, William Scott, 9438
Funk, Arthur P., Jr., 1634
Funk, Curtis, 9324
Funk, John, 9108
Funk, Megan, 9324
Funk, Wayne E., 3295
Funke, Mark W., 7781
Funkhauser, Peggy, 432
Funkhouser, Michael, 4467
Fuqua Family Charitable Lead Unitrust, J.B., 2464
Fuqua, Dorothy C., 2464
Fuqua, Duvall S., 2464, 2535
Fuqua, J. Rex, 2464, 2535
Fuqua, J.B., 2464
Fuqua, Jeffry B., 1968
Furcron, Sharon, 7412
Furer, Elise, 1852
Furey, Roger P., 2951
Furgason, Robert, Dr., 8768
Furia, Helen M., 2131
Furihata, Keiichi, 6491
Furlong, Kevin, 4409
Furlong, R. Michael, 2759
Furlotti, Alex, 1416
Furlotti, Allison, 1416
Furlotti, Michael, 1416
Furlotti, Nancy, 1416
Furlotti, Patrick, 1416
Furman, Jeffrey, 9358
Furman, Majorie, 1650
Furman, Matt, 4612
Furmansky, Stewart, 8128
Furnas Trust, Leto M., 2889
Furnas, Leto M., 2889
Furnas, W.C., 2889
Furness, Bruce, 7351
Furniture Auctions of America, 1548
Furniture Brands International, Inc., 4914
Furr, Lisa, 972
Furst, Ken, 3421
Furtivo, Andrea, 483
Fusco, Jack A., 3800
Fusco, Kristin A., 3800
Fuse-Hall, Rosalind, 7180
Fuson, Brad, 3307
Fuson, Kendra, 3193
Fuson, Mark, 3307
Fuss, Daniel J., 4064
Fuss, Kevin, 2792
Fuss, Rosemary B., 4064
Fussel, Stephen R., 2649

Fussell, Stephen R., 2648
Fusting, Jim, 633
Futo, Kyle Monfort, 1465
FW Townhouse, LLC, 5040
Fyler, Carlton D., 1565
Fyler, Jenny R., 1565
Fyrberg, Katy, 3987

G P I Cerne, John, 9606
G&G, Ltd., 9049
G-5 Trading Inc., 2091
G. Byers, W. Russell, Jr., 8172
G.P.G. Foundation, 578
G.S. Revocable Living Trust, 7690
Gaalswyk, Kathy, 4618, 4679
Gabbard, Kevin, 3284
Gabehart, Alan D., 3657
Gabel, Caroline D., 3882
Gabel, Peter, 5527
Gabelli Group Capital Partners, Inc., 5120
Gabelli, Marc J., 5120
Gabelli, Mario J., 5120, 5159
Gabelli, Matthew R., 5120
Gabelli, Michael, 5120
Gaber, Steve, 5533
Gaberino, John A., Jr., 7809
Gabier, Russell L., 4445
Gabino, Mary A., 8353
Gable, Christopher M., 3759
Gabler, Karen A., 9806
Gabow, Patricia A., 5329
Gabran, Niclas, 7001
Gabriel Holdings, Ltd., 9195
Gabriel, Chris, 3639
Gabriele, Stephanie K. Skestos, 7501
Gabriele, Stephanie Skestos, 7501
Gabus, Charles, 3429
Gabus, Gene, 3429
Gabus, Jan, 3429
Gaby Investments, L.P., 2465
Gaby, Barbara Van Andel, 2465
Gaby, Richard, 2465
Gacinski, John A., 6735
Gadbois, Richard, III, 587
Gaddes, Richard, 7031
Gaddis, Larry R., 1478
Gaddy, Sandra Herring, 7229
Gadomski, Robert E., 8136
Gadsden, William F., 5191
Gadson, George, 2243
Gadus, Mary Beth, 3397
Gaeng, J. Brian, 3723
Gaerte, Stephen C., 3397
Gaffen, Harvey, 3225
Gaffney, Joe, 9731
Gaffney, Joseph M., 9691
Gaffney, Rob, 1518
Gaffney, Robert, 3955
Gaffney, Steve, 3549
Gaffney, Thomas J., 9617
Gagan, Claire, 3308
Gagan, James L., 3308
Gagan, Pamela M., 3308
Gage, Barbara Carlson, 4629
Gage, Geoffrey Carlson, 4629
Gage, Howell N., 4848
Gage, Rick Carlson, 4629
Gage, Scott Carlson, 4629
Gagen, Tim, 1511
Gager, James, 6408
Gagliardi, Joan, 3003
Gagne, J. Leo, 1564
Gagne-Holmes, Sara, 3699
Gagnon, Brian, 5271
Gagnon, Christine L., 2085
Gagnon, David, 8001
Gagnon, James E., 5109
Gagnon, Lois E., 5271
Gagnon, Neil J., 5271
Gaguine Foundation, 248
Gaguine, Alexander, 248
Gaguine, Benito, 248
Gaguine, Cynthia, 87
Gaguine, John, 87, 248
Gahagan, Alexis D., 1754
Gahagan, Katharine, 1754
Gail, Leonard A., 3175
Gain, Judith K., 272
Gain, Judy, 1015
Gaines, Courtney Knight, 2466
Gaines, Donald E., 9705
Gaines, Ezekiel B., III, 2466
Gaines, Katina, 8549
Gaines, Laura L., 8148
Gaines, Louisa M., 3581
Gaines, William B., 2466
Gainey, Daniel H., 4771
Gains, Nancy, 287
Gainsley, Gloria, 2607
Gainsley, Gloria J., 2607
Gainsley, Stephen E., 2607
Gaisman, Henry J., 6031
Gaither, Gloria, 3346
Gaither, James C., 938
Gaither, Linda, 8994
Galanes, Gloria, Dr., 4872
Galang, Astra Anderson, 1013
Galas, David, 9757
Galasso, August J., 6032
Galasso, Emil J., 6032
Galasso, Martin A., 6032
Galbraith, Anna Mae, 8223
Galbraith, James R., 692
Galbraith, Steve, 9005
Galbreath, David K., Jr., 7620
Galcom International USA, 7846
Galdo-Hirst, Magaly, 9380
Gale, Catherine A., 6153
Gale, Edwin, 8859
Gale, Fournier J., III, 61
Gale, Karin M., 9965
Gale, Nancy N., 1866
Gale, Rebecca S., 8859
Gale, Tom, 9019
Galen Charitable Remainder Trust No. 1, Louis and Helen, 558
Galen, Helene V., 558
Galen, Louis J., 558
Galeti, Mary, 8312
Galey, Glenn, 4811
Galgon, Gretl Dupre, 9720
Galgon, Michael T., 9720
Galia, Gary C., 4416
Galik, Jeffrey, 5711
Gall, Blake, 7973
Gallagher & Co., Arthur J., 2855
Gallagher Marital Trust, Robert E., 2854
Gallagher, Dan, 3826
Gallagher, Ellen M., 4660
Gallagher, Gerald P., 4660
Gallagher, Gerald R., 4660
Gallagher, Hollie, 7631
Gallagher, J. Patrick, Jr., 2855
Gallagher, James, 5403
Gallagher, James P., 7995
Gallagher, Joan D., 8860
Gallagher, John, 4503
Gallagher, John J., Jr., 8094
Gallagher, John Peter, 7232
Gallagher, K.C., 1401
Gallagher, Laura A., 6805
Gallagher, Lindsay R., 3826
Gallagher, Margaret W., 7232
Gallagher, Matthew D., 3803
Gallagher, Michael D., 8860
Gallagher, Michael L., 5057
Gallagher, Michael T., 8860
Gallagher, Patricia A., 2918
Gallagher, Patrick S., 6610
Gallagher, Paul J., 3971
Gallagher, Richard S., 9920
Gallagher, Robert E., 2854
Gallagher, Robert E., Jr., 2854, 2855
Gallagher, Sean, 8860
Gallagher, Thomas, 3245
Gallagher, Thomas G., 7950
Gallagher, Tim, 1287
Gallagher, William J., Esq., 7979
Galland, Michael S., 7715
Gallatin, Ron, 5824
Gallatin, Thomas, 6997
Gallery Towers LP, 9452
Gallery, Robert E., 7139
Galliher, Michael B., 3286
Gallivan, Karen Park, 4666
Gallo Survivor's Trust, Aileen, 561
Gallo Trust, Ernest, 560
Gallo Winery, E. & J., 559, 560, 561
Gallo, A.C., 9276
Gallo, Aileen, 561
Gallo, Andrew, 9059
Gallo, Carol, 6202
Gallo, Christopher D., 559, 560
Gallo, Ernest, 560
Gallo, Ernest J., 560
Gallo, John, 997
Gallo, John R., 561
Gallo, Joseph E., 560
Gallo, Joseph Y., 7719
Gallo, Julio R., 561
Gallo, Linnea, 1733
Gallo, Mary C., 559
Gallo, Mary I., 560
Gallo, Molly, 3040
Gallo, Robert J., 561
Gallo, Ronald V., 1116
Gallo, Theresa M., 559
Gallogly, Jim, 2142
Galloway Trust, Sarah B., 2112
Galloway, Debbie, 8647
Galloway, Gale L., 8804
Galloway, Harvey L., 8460
Galloway, Peter, 3003
Galloway, Roderick S., 2467
Galloway, Winslow H., 7169
Galloway-Tabb, Pamela Y., 1907
Galluci-Davis, Sheila, 5471
Gallup, Nancy, 9651
Galluzzo, Jay A., 7051
Gallwas, Gerald E., 297
Galowitz, Tracy, 4782
Galper, David, 4080
Galpin, Greg, 9704
Galtney, Rob, 8916
Galvan, Bobby, Judge, 8768
Galvez, Fred, 9313
Galvin, Christopher, 2858
Galvin, Christopher B., 2856, 2857
Galvin, Cynthia, 2856
Galvin, Helen M., 2858
Galvin, Mary G., 2857
Galvin, Michael, 2858
Galvin, Michael P., 2857
Galvin, Robert E., 4217
Galvin, Robert W., 2857
Galvin, Walter, 2822
Galyen, Jeff, 3320
Gamb, James, 1020
Gamba, John, 2327
Gambaiani, Tony, 3321
Gambet, Daniel G., 8122
Gambet, Daniel G., Fr., 8320
Gambill, Sandra E., 1999
Gamble, Cedric, 3306
Gamble, George F., 562
Gamble, George T., 562
Gamble, James N., 276
Gamble, Jim, 562
Gamble, Joan L., 562
Gamble, Launce E., 562
Gamble, Launce L., 562
Gamble, Laura L., 3726
Gamble, Mark D., 562
Gamble, Mary S., 562
Gamble, Sandra, 9756
Gamble-Booth, Gwyneth, 7881
Gamboa, Gina, 9767
Gambrell, Sarah Belk, 7273
Gambrinus Co., The, 9149
Gambrinus Enterprises, 9888
GAMCO Investors, 1811
Gamco Investors, Inc., 5963
Gamm, Gary, 3555
Gamoran, Adam, 6093
Gamper, Christopher E., 5008
Gamper, David E., 5008
Gamper, Gisela, 5008
Gamper, Harriet E., 5008
Gamper, Yogeeta, 5008
Gampp, Michael, 7657
Ganatra, Rajesh T., 1783
Ganatra, Sarlaben T., 1783
Ganatra, Sharlaben T., 1783
Ganatra, Tansukh V., 1783
Gandelot, Elizabeth Mower, 2808
Gandelot, Jon B., 2808
Gandia, Naomi, 1850
Gandy, Greg, 1478
Gang, Laura, 4271
Ganger, Aviva, 6033
Ganger, Ira, 6033
Ganger, Joe, 6033
Ganger, Shoshana, 6033
Gangolli, Julian S., 228
Gann, Herbert M., 2113
Gann, Joseph, 2113
Gann, Rae, 2113
Gannett Co., Inc., 9439
Gannett, John D., 4101
Gannett, Richard B., 4101
Gannett, William B., 4101
Gannicott, Robert, 7093
Gannon, Maureen, 5532
Gannon, Patty, 4056
Gannon, Paul, 3956
Gannon, Tony, 8649
Gannon, William S., 5483
Gano, Charles H., 4522
Ganon, Shawn, 6644
Ganoni, Gerald L., 9855
Ganot Corp., 2189
Gans, Richard, Esq., 2038
Gansbourg, Hensha, 7677
Gansheimer, Jan, 7490

Gansner, Andy, 9903
Gant, Gail, 9682
Gant, Jason, 8541
Gant, Steve, 9682
Gantz, Norman J., 2886
Ganz, Carole, 3968
Ganz, Mark, 7829
Ganzi, Patricia M., 6034
Ganzi, Victor, 6034
Ganzi, Victor F., 6034
Gap, Inc., The, 563
Gappa, Jennifer, 3360
Gara, James, 5623
Garacochea, Stephanie L., 774
Garanzini, Michael J., 2783
Garatoni, Judith A., 3309
Garatoni, Lawrence A., 3309
Garaud, Jean-Jacques, 1083
Garb, Andrew, 1086
Garb, Andrew S., 1234
Garb, Melvin, 564
Garb, Sheila, 1086
Garbarino, John R., 5394
Garbe, Thomas F., 8230
Garber, Chris, 3290
Garber, Dan, 3521
Garber, Karlene Beal, 8696
Garber, Matt, 7971
Garber, Phyllis B., 3674
Garber, Roy, 9998
Garber, Victor, 9988
Garberding, Scott R., 4366
Garbs, Rodger, Rev., 9222
Garcetti, Eric, 1093
Garcetti, Gil, 664, 1093
Garcetti, Sukey, 1093
Garcia, Angelo, 855
Garcia, Anne, 1487
Garcia, Art A., 2302
Garcia, Bo, 4357
Garcia, Brigitte, 921
Garcia, David, 5398
Garcia, Eugene E., 6003
Garcia, Francisco, 1399
Garcia, Greg, 9118, 9149
Garcia, Jane, 366
Garcia, Joseph C., Jr., 685
Garcia, Juan Carlos, 6042
Garcia, Juan M., 722
Garcia, Juliet V., 5994
Garcia, Juliet Villarreal, 1940
Garcia, Kristina, 2792
Garcia, Lillian D., 2363
Garcia, Linda, 1287
Garcia, Marcela, 9083
Garcia, Margaret, 9149
Garcia, Pedro, 7833
Garcia, Peter, 490
Garcia, Ricardo, 9767
Garcia, Richard, 1391
Garcia, Rosario, 9118
Garcia, Rosie, 109
Garcia, Sonja, 2042
Garcia-Lathrop, Angie, 7139
Garcia-Tunon, Carlos, 6361
Gard, Christine Mary, 1203
Garden City Charitable Trust, 2336
Gardens of Mount Carmel, 2317
Gardenswartz, Ian D., 1526
Gardiner, Catherine Grimm, 627
Gardiner, Nancy B., 4084
Gardiner, Robert, 4172
Garding, Ed, 5009
Gardner 1992 Charitable Trust, 7466
Gardner Family 2000 Charitable Trust, 7466
Gardner Trust, A. Somers, 5927
Gardner Trust, Ed, 3576
Gardner, Ashley G., 7104
Gardner, Cindy, 6531
Gardner, David J., 5041
Gardner, David W., 1491
Gardner, Denise, 2746
Gardner, Denise E., 7320
Gardner, Dozier, 4303
Gardner, Dozier L., 3977
Gardner, Edward D., 9711
Gardner, Emerson "Emo" N., Lt. Genl., 9501
Gardner, Emma, 1515
Gardner, Frederick C., 4532
Gardner, Gregory A., 6567
Gardner, J. Alston, 1515
Gardner, James J., 7466
Gardner, Jean, 9682, 9701
Gardner, Jeanne M., 5041
Gardner, Jill, 9682
Gardner, Joan A., 7466
Gardner, John B., 185
Gardner, Kirk N., 5041
Gardner, Lewis B., 8025
Gardner, M. Dozier, 3977
Gardner, Margaret B., 3977
Gardner, Mary, 1491
Gardner, Pamela J., 8674
Gardner, Patricia, 4349
Gardner, Patricia F., 7466
Gardner, Peter J., 2042
Gardner, Roger L., 6242
Gardner, Sarah, 6903
Gardner, Scott, 5801
Gardner, Spencer J., 7466
Gardner, Timothy J., 1738
Gardner, Warren, 1643
Gardner-Goodno, Joan, 4683
Garelick Farms, 3245
Garen, Wendy, 1013
Garey, Patrick, 6802
Garff, Michelle, 9308
Garfield Trust, 5889
Garfield Trust, Sherrie S., 2115
Garfield, Brian, 4065
Garfield, Eugene, 8052
Garfield, Gary A., 8550
Garfield, Joshua, 8052
Garfield, Michael, 8372
Garfield, Seth, 3991
Garfield, Sherrie S., 2115
Garfinkel, Barry H., 6868
Garfinkel, Steven, 3919
Garfinkle, Paul, 6174
Gargaro, Eugene A., Jr., 4491, 4492, 4497
Gargiulo, Andrea, 3926
Gargiulo, Evanne S., 6785
Gargiulo, Sidney H., 8620
Garibaldi, Marie L., 5283
Garich, Russell, 2650
Garigan, Jane, 159
Garigan, Tim, 159
Garino, Peter, 5372
Garland Trust, John Jewett, 565
Garland, Hillary Duque, 565
Garland, Janet E., 6491
Garland, Mary E., 9977
Garland, Sheryl L., 9521
Garland, Spencer, 9977
Garland, William M., II, 565
Garlanda, Victoria, 6886
Garlasco, Marc E., 5821
Garlington, Jennie Turner, 2563
Garlington, Sarah Jean Turner, 4561
Garlotte, Helen W., 3311
Garmisa, William J., 3066
Garmon-Brown, Ophelia, 7148
Garner USA LP, 5482
Garner, Jac B., 9897
Garner, Leslie H., Jr., Dr., 3417
Garner, Lynne, 1575
Garner, Richard, 153
Garniewski, John P., Jr., 9949
Garnsey, Cecily Coors, 1396
Garnsey, John, 1518
Garofalo, Becky Cahill, 1765
Garofalo, John, 7367
Garofalow, Leigh, 5715
Garr Tool Co., 4486
Garr, Louis J., Jr., 4934
Garrard, Gardiner W., 2492
Garrard, Lenora, 2492
Garraux, James D., 8325
Garrett, Bryan, 7757
Garrett, David, 8328
Garrett, Douglas R., 4815
Garrett, Ezra, 1033
Garrett, Gary, 9340
Garrett, Jill, 986
Garrett, Judith H., 7757
Garrett, Mark, 1734
Garrett, Robert, 3712, 5892
Garrett, S., 777
Garrett, Sophia, 9078
Garrett, Stephen P., 7728
Garrison, Arnold, 4066
Garrison, James, 4194
Garrison, John, 8468
Garrison, Sandra L., 8918
Garrison, Timothy P., 4066
Garrity, Sheila, 9889
Garrott, Thomas M., 2116
Garrou, Linda, Sen., 7340
Garschina, Kenneth, 6035
Garsoian, Nina, 2982
Garson, Palmer P., Mrs., 9504
Gart, Margie, 1518
Garten, Jeffrey E., 1531
Garten, Morris L., 3780
Gartenberg, Deborah Sands, 5435
Garth, Bryant G., 3035
Garth, Mark, 1672
Gartland, Michael G., 6453
Gartlir, Bernard D., 6704
Gartner, Paul, 7052
Garton, Caitlin, 7088
Garton, Deirdre Wilson, 7088
Garton, Elenore, 7088
Garton, Josie, 7088
Garvey Charitable Trust No. 1, Willard W., 3516
Garvey Charitable Trust No. 2, Willard W., 3516
Garvey Homes, 8756
Garvey Revocable Trust, Jean K., 3516
Garvey Revocable Trust, Willard W., 3516
Garvey, Inc., 3516
Garvey, James W., 3516
Garvey, Jean K., 3516
Garvey, Jennifer, 2631
Garvey, Willard W., 3516
Garvin, Charles, Dr., 7558
Garvin, Eric, 5750
Garwood, Susan Clayton, 9248
Garwood, William L., Jr., 8765
Gary, Bob, 1518
Gary, Leah S., 7602
Gary, Nancy, 1480, 1481
Gary, Rob, 1480, 1481
Gary, Samuel, 1480, 1481
Gary-Williams Company, The, 1481
Garza, Alejandra, 3100
Garza, Danette, 3337
Garza, David, 8733
Garza, Nora, 1394
Gasch, Alice True, 1951
Gasch, Daniel, 157
Gasch, Wendy, 1879
Gasiorowski, Kevin M., 4108
Gaskill, Joseph, 8267
Gasner, Stuart, 517
Gaspar, Clay, 9060
Gaspard, Dinah, 3236
Gaspard, James L., 3236
Gasser, Peter A., 566
Gasser, Vernice H., 566
Gassert, Timothy B., 3956
Gassman, Robert S., 6121
Gassman, Roberta, 9897
Gast, Thomas C., 9801
Gaston, Jerry, 3539
Gaston, Marilyn K., 2812
Gaston, Patrick, 1521
Gasty, Ronald G., 3976
Gatchel, Cathy, 3290
Gately, Bill, 3534
Gately, James, 8216
Gates Foundation, Bill & Melinda, 1387, 5390, 9652
Gates Young Trust, 7347
Gates, Brad J., 2468
Gates, Charles C., 1418
Gates, Charles C., Sr., 1418
Gates, Gerald, 4327
Gates, Gerald M., 4327
Gates, Gilbert L., 9432
Gates, Hazel, 1418
Gates, Jerry, 3348
Gates, John, 1418
Gates, John S., Jr., 2859
Gates, June S., 1418
Gates, K&L, 4324
Gates, Melinda French, 9625
Gates, Mimi Gardner, 3186, 9587
Gates, Moore, Jr., 5191
Gates, Theaster, 2873
Gates, Valerie, 1418
Gates, William H. "Bill", III, 9625
Gates, William H., Sr., 9625
Gateway Gardens Associates LP, 9452
Gathers, Tom, 2051
Gathof, W. Lawrence, 3608
Gatins, Martin, 2522
Gatins, Phillip, 2522
Gattas, James J., 8530
Gattis, Grace Gaines, 2466
Gattis, James Thomas, 2466
Gatton, C.M., 8571
Gaucher, Harry S., 1690
Gaudard, Cheryl, 4512
Gaudette, Gerald "Lee", III, 4327
Gaudiani, Claire L., 6398
Gaudio, Julius, 5737
Gaughan, John D., 5042
Gaughan, Michael J., 5042
Gauldin, David T., II, 9412
Gaulding, Pamela Seegers, 9164

Gault, Stanley C., 7578
Gaunce, Patricia, 3556
Gaunch, C. Edward, 7144
Gauntlett, Barbara, 5240
Gauntlett, Suwanna, 5240
Gauron, Paul R., 4189
Gaus, William T., 9861
Gausas, Roberta, 6495
Gause, Dick, 3287
Gaustad, Blaine, 4802
Gauthier, Kathryn "Kathy" L., 9501
Gautier, Agnes, 6158
Gautreau, David, 8223
Gautreaux, William C., 4920
Gauwitz, Mary, 2950
Gavaldon, Miguel, 877
Gavel, Frank J., Jr., 8469
Gavel, Stephen L., 8469
Gavin Irrevocable Trust, Zita C., 2860
Gavin, Austin F., 473
Gavin, Carol, 3185
Gavin, James J., 4212
Gavin, James J., Jr., 2860
Gavin, James L., 2860
Gavin, Martin "Marty", 1567
Gavin, Steven J., 2860
Gavin, William, 2860
Gavin, Zita C., 2860
Gawande, Atul, 4253
Gawryk, Terry, 2907
Gawthrop, Samuel M., 8069
Gay Mechanical Contractors of Orlando, W.W., Inc., 2117
Gay, Brigida C., 5845
Gay, Eloise D., 2117
Gay, Kevin, 4502
Gay, W.W., 2117
Gayden, Cynthia N., 8861
Gayden, William K., 8861
Gayden, William, Mrs., 8861
Gayeski, Leonard J., 4554
Gayheart, Jack, 7474
Gayle, Gibson, Jr., 8664
Gayle, Helene D., 6724
Gayle, Jacob A., 4712
Gaylord, Charles Reid, 1060
Gaylord, Edith Kinney, 7749, 7760
Gaylord, Edward L., 7753
Gaylord, Thelma F., 7753
Gayman, Benjamin F., 5174
Gayner, Thomas S., 9416
Gaynor, George N., 3058
Gaynor, Richard, 3397
Gaynor, Vere W., 7600
Gazeley, Dave, 7825
Gazzillo, Lori, 3946, 3947
GB 30 Year Charitable Trust, 2931
Gbur, Carol, 5909
Gcsym Realty LLC, 5890
Gdovin, David, 6374
Gdowski, Tom, 5044
GE, 3303
Geare, Lori, 125
Gearen, John J., 3140
Gearing, Dan, 7991
Gearity, Peggy, 3948
Geary, Bruce G., 6037
Geary, G. Stanton, 1530
Geary, James, 545
Geary, James E., 3698
Geballe 1996 Trust B, G.T., 1688
Geballe, Adam, 510
Geballe, Adam P., 510
Geballe, Alison F., 510
Geballe, Benjamin D., 1688
Geballe, Dan, 1223
Geballe, Daniel W., 1688
Geballe, Frances K., 510
Geballe, Gordon T., 510, 1688
Geballe, Joshua G., 1688
Geballe, Shelley, 4170
Geballe, Shelley D., 1688
Geballe, Theodore H., 510
Gebbie, Marion B., 6038
Gebedou, Massie, 109
Gebo, John R., 3199
Geddes, David, 5108
Geddes, John F., 4583
Gedeller, Anthony, 3244
Gee, Alison Ochs, 9999
Gee, Susan Crothers, 2997
Gee, William A., IV, 2997
Geekie, Mathew W., 4898
Geelan, John W., 4743
Geelhoed, Judy, 9149
Geenen, Dave, 2787
Geer, Maria, 1989
Geer, Sandy, 3418
Geesey, Jennifer, 8351
Geeslin, Douglas R., 7356
Gefen, Nan, 847
Geffen, David, 567, 769, 1213
Gehin-Scott, Gilbert A., 5427
Gehl, Danis, 5801
Gehl, Stephanie, 254
Gehle, Misty, 9999
Gehner, Timothy C., 7422
Gehrig, Cynthia A., 4681
Gehrig, Tom, 9706
Gehring, Kurt, 8734
Geier, Philip O., 1761
Geil, Gus, 7671
Geis Construction, Inc., 7467
Geis, Alfred, 7467
Geis, Gregory, 7467
Geis, Katherine, 7467
Geisen, Larry, 3291
Geisenberger, Steve, 8135
Geiser, Jodi, 7394
Geismar, Ellen A., 9488
Geismar, Michael S., 9488
Geisse, John F., 7468
Geisse, Lawrence J., 7468
Geisse, Mary A., 7468
Geisse, Timothy F., 7468
Geissler, Larry, 7558
Geist Trust, Bradley L., 2600
Geist, Carol Berg, 5676
Gelb, Bruce S., 6039
Gelb, Jay, 5591
Gelb, John T., 6039
Gelb, Lawrence M., 6039
Gelb, Lawrence N., 6039
Gelb, Myrl, 5591
Gelb, Phyllis N., 6039
Gelb, Richard L., 6039
Gelbard, Georgette, 5547
Gelbart, Moe, 905
Gelbaugh, Bruce, 4526
Gelber, Marilyn G., 5718
Gelbman Charitable Trust, 7469
Gelbman Trust, Frank, 7469
Gelbman Trust, Pearl, 7469
Gelbwachs, Shulamis, 5590
Gelbwaks, Marian, 3885
Geletka, Elizabeth D., 5510
Gelfand, Todd, 782
Gelfen, Irene, 351
Gelinas, Ashleigh, 4194
Gelke, Heidi, 328
Gell, Carl L., 1925
Geller, Alan, 4173
Geller, Andrew, 9153
Geller, Maryana, 6981
Geller, Thomas, 7012
Gellerstedt, Larry L., III, 2443, 2573
Gellert, Carl, 568
Gellert, Catherine A., 6040
Gellert, Celia Berta, 568
Gellert, David B. Spohn, 6040
Gellert, G., 5351
Gellert, Gertrude E., 568
Gellert, Mary C., 6040
Gellert, Michael E., 6040
Gellert, Robert J., 6931
Gelley, Heidi, 6811
Gellis, Louis, 5984
Gelman 2001 Trust, Susan R., 3854
Gelman Charitable Lead Trust, Susan R., 3854
Gelman, Emmaia, 6894
Gelman, Felice, 6894
Gelman, Michael C., 3854
Gelman, Susan, 604
Gelman, Susan R., 3854
Gelman, Yoram, 6894
GelmanTrust, Jacques & Natasha, 6041
Geltzeiler, Michael S., 6573
Gelzer, Scott E., 9901
Gemmill, Helen, 1391
Gemuend, Markus, 571
Gemunder, Joel F., 2119
Gen, Stephen, 1233
Gename, David L., 2713
Genauer, Eli, 9725
GenCorp Foundation Inc., 569, 7601
Genecov, A.S., 8862
Genecov, Hilda J., 8862
Genentech, 1558
Genentech, Inc., 570, 571
General Atlantic Corp., 5622
General Atlantic Service Corp., 1468, 1681
General Board of Global Ministries, 4432
General Corporation, 9782
General Elec Co., 4254
General Electric Co., 1591
General Electric Foundation, 6802
General Electric, Inc., 2382
General Land Abstract Co. Inc., 5435
General Mills, 3245, 4775
General Mills, Inc., 4661, 4727
General Motors Corp., 4442
General Motors Foundation, Inc., 4394
General Trading USA, Inc., 2317
General Trust Co., 2724
Genereux, Mark, 3447
Genesee Valley Group Health Assoc., 6153
Genesis Apparel, Inc., 4680
Genesis Concepts & Consultants LLC, 9149
Genesis Endowment, 6042
Genetti, August F., Jr., 8152
Gengler, Charles J., 5640
Genius, Richard M., Jr., 3039
Genn, Jonathan, 3809
Genrich, Brian, 2758
Genser, Josh, 1069
Gensler Jr. Charitable Lead Annuity Trust, M. Arthur, 572
Gensler, Drucilla C., 572
Gensler, M. Arthur, Jr., 572
Genter, Anne, 8329
Genter, Beth H., 2309
Genter, Edward F., Jr., 5718
Gentis, Laura, 3403
Gentry, John R., 340
Gentry, Kevin L., 9463
Gentry, N. Brian, 3420
Gentry, Nolden, 3466
Gentsch, Richard A., 1765
Gentzel, Tammy, 7973
Gentzler, Roland G., 4676
Genuardi, Anthony D., 8053
Genuardi, Charles A., 8053
Genuardi, David T., 8053
Genuardi, Dominic S., Jr., 8053
Genuardi, Francis L., 8053
Genuardi, Gasper A., 8053
Genuardi, James V., 8053
Genuardi, Laurence P., 8053
Genuardi, Michael A., 8053
Genuardi, Tom, Jr., 8053
Genuine Parts Co., 2530
Genworth Financial, Inc., 9441
Genzy, Robin, 8495
Genzyme Corp., 4067, 5437
Genzyme Corporation, 6898
GEO Group Foundation Inc., The, 9149
Geoghan, Stephanie, 4575
Geoghegan, John A., 8201
Geopedior Assocs., LP, 8116
Georgantas, Aristides, 5191
Georgantas, Aristides W., 8220
Georgas, John L., 2843
George, A.P., 8863
George, Alexander S., 9485
George, Anton Hulman, 3327
George, Armond R., 6286
George, Boyd, 7205
George, Emil, 4044
George, G. Lee, 7205
George, Harry, III, 3758
George, James Conway, 189
George, Jeffrey Pilgram, 4662
George, Jonathan R., 4662
George, Karin, 3992
George, Kimberly D., 7205
George, L. Scott, 2284
George, Mamie E., 8863
George, Mari Hulman, 3327
George, Mary, 2035
George, Meredith M., 1592
George, Pamela, 8911
George, Patrick R., 5854
George, Penny Pilgram, 4662
George, Robert P., 9819
George, Russell, 1374
George, Susan Elizabeth, 9626
George, Terrence R., 2593
George, Terry, 2604
George, Trudy, 3517
George, W. Whitney, 1592
George, William W., 4662
Georgescu, Andrew, 1593
Georgescu, Barbara, 1593
Georgescu, Peter, 1593
Georgetown University, 5707
Georgia Financial, LLC, 7609
Georgia Gas Co., 2400
Georgia Power Co., 2468
Georgia-Pacific Corp., 2469
Geosor Corp., 6890
Gephart, Robert, 1846
Geppel, Gregory Thomas, 5506

Geppert, Bill, 1108
Geppert, William K., 1108
Geppi, John T., 8560
Gerace, Frank E., 4444
Gerace, John, 4104
Geraci-Carver, Anita, 2039
Geraghty, Elisabeth, 2745
Geranium, Inc., 4183
Gerard, Anne, 7474
Gerard, Dana, 9297
Gerard, Greg, Dr., 8527
Gerard, Jamie K., 1652
Gerard, Sheridah, 1260
Gerardot, Jane, 3281
Gerber, Ann Rogers, 5519
Gerber, Cindy, 8054
Gerber, Cindy Akers, 8054
Gerber, David, 2817
Gerber, Geoff, 7164
Gerber, Jennifer Braddock, 5701
Gerber, Murray, 8054
Gerber, Murry S., 8054
Gerber, Roger M., 6598
Gerber, Terry, 3251
Gerberding, Julie L., 384
Gerbode, Frank A., 573
Gerbode, Sharon, 573
Gerdes, Chris, 9487
Gerdes, Stephanie, 3369
Gerdin, Ann S., 3430
Gerdin, Michael J., 3430
Gerdin, Russell A., 3430
Gere, Richard, 1076
Geren, Charles Lupton, 8730
Geren, Pete, 8686, 9130
Geren, Preston M., III, 8688
Gerene Furguson, 5517
Gergely, Michael, 4421
Gerhardt, Paul, 9559
Gerig, Stacey, 9091
Gering, William, 3757
Gerkin, Linda, 3365
Gerlach, David P., 7471
Gerlach, John B., 7471
Gerlach, John B., Jr., 7471
Gerlach, John J., 7471
Gerlach, Pauline, 7471
Gerlach, Sue, 9950
Gerline, Greg, 3265
Gerlock, Peg, 9726
Germ-Cramer, Kimberly, 5824
German, Deborah C., 2008
German, Meredith M., 9776
German, Robert D., 8105
German, Todd, 2041
Germanacos, Anne H., 574
Germano, C. Dean, 366
Germeraad, Katherine S., 2762
Gerner, Elizabeth W., 9351
Gernert, Joseph, 7551
Gernert, Margaret, 7551
Gernon, Andrea S., 9739
Gerrard, Linda, 9789
Gerry - Martha Farish Gerry Declaration of Trust, Matha F., 4114
Gerry Foundation, 5806
Gerry, Adam, 6044
Gerry, Alan, 6044
Gerry, Annelise, 6044
Gerry, Elbridge T., III, 6136
Gerry, Elbridge T., Jr., 6136
Gerry, James E., 7915
Gerry, Peggy N., 6043
Gerry, Robyn, 6044
Gerry, Roger G., 6043
Gerry, Sandra, 6044
Gersack, Jim, 9999
Gersch, Nicole V., 4368
Gerschel, Marianne, 5949, 6902
Gerschel, Patrick A., 6045
Gersh, Judah, 5019
Gershenhorn, Alan, 2566
Gershman Family Survivors/ Administrative Trust, Harold, 575
Gershman, Catherine, 575
Gershman, Mortimer, 5253
Gershman, Ronald A., 575
Gershon Fund, Ben-Ephraim, 1932
Gershwind, Erik, 6046, 6219
Gerson, Barbara N., 6047
Gerson, David, 6336
Gerson, Frederick E., 6047
Gerson, James, 6047
Gerson, Jennifer, 6022
Gerson, Kara O., 6047
Gerson, Ralph, 4390
Gerson, Simon F., 6047
Gerspacher, Bill, 2427
Gerstacker, Carl A., 4444
Gerstacker, Eda U., 4444
Gerstacker, Lisa J., 4444, 4517
Gerstein, Gary, 6874
Gerstle, Allan, 1512
Gerstner, Elizabeth R., 2121
Gerstner, Jr. Trust, Louis V., 2121
Gerstner, Louis V., III, 2121
Gerstner, Louis V., Jr., 2121
Gerstung, Sandra L., 8082
Gerten, Richard, Pastor, 4496
Gertmenian, Dennis, 365
Gerton, Jordan, 157
Gertz, H. F., 4481
Gertz, Jami, 1066
Gervais, Noelle, 1161
Gery, Carolyn, 3282
Geschke, Charles M., 576
Geschke, John M., 576
Geschke, Nancy A., 576
Geschke, Peter C., 576
Gesell, Heidi, 4616
Geske, Janine, 8518
Geske, Janine P., 9907
Geslot-Bonnefoy, Emilie, 3966
Gesseck, Richard H., 1616
Gessner, Nancy, 7673
Gethers-Clark, Michelle, 7180
Getman, Frank, 5879
Getman, Michael F., 5879
Gettle Inc., 8127
Gettle, Inc., 8127
Gettler, Benjamin, 7634
Gettler, Deliaan A., 7634
Getty, Aileen, 577
Getty, Gordon P., 578
Getty, J. Paul, 579
Getty, Kathy, 3762
Getty, William P., 7935
Getz, Bert A., 92, 115
Getz, Bert A., Jr., 115
Getz, Dennis A., 8299, 8300
Getz, George F., 115
Getz, George F., Jr., 115
Getz, Jenifer, 6571
Getz-Schmidt, Lynn, 115
Getzinger, Karl, 7640
Geuting, Patricia, Sr., 1845
Gewirz, Bernard S., 1909
Gewirz, Jonathan K., 1909
Gewirz, Michael K., 1909
Gewirz, Sarah M., 1909
Gewirz, Steven B., 1909
Geyer, Bev, 4791
Geyer, Paul R., 5229
Geyer, Stan, 4791
Geyer-Sylvia, Zelda, 2627
Geygan, Michael, 7702
GFM, LLC, 382
Ghannoum, Annie, 9176
Gheens, C. Edwin, 3577
Ghelardi, Ellen Baker, 7926
Gheno, Kenneth, 1871
Ghermezian, Syd, 5274
GHF, Inc., 8046
Ghidinelli, Dan, 1154
Ghidotti, Marian, 7206
Ghidotti, William, 7206
Ghigiarelli, Christy A., 8263
Ghriskey, H. Williamson, Jr., 6439
GHTP LLC, 7690
Ghubril, Saleem H., 7956
Ghuman, Minaski, 3369
GI Research Institute, 2300
Giachino, Phillip J., 7747
Giacoletto Living Trust, 3431
Giacomin, Jon, 7398
Giambi, Jason, 7012
Giambrone, Vicki S., 7608
Giammarino, Frank M., 3391
Giampaoli, Diane, 421
Gianelli, Mike, 1211
Gianforte, Greg, 5010
Gianforte, Richard, 5010
Gianforte, Susan, 5010
Giannini, A.P., 581
Giannone, R. John, 8223
Giarusso, Deb, 3423
Gibb, Joshua D., 2853
Gibb, Margaret K., 1657
Gibble, Mary, 3313
Gibbons, Adam, 89
Gibbons, David, 5253
Gibbons, John A., 6598
Gibbons, John J., Hon., 5270
Gibbons, Lile R., 89, 6144
Gibbons, Lucia, 8333
Gibbons, Mary Jo, 4667
Gibbons, Miles J., Jr., 7073
Gibbs Die Casting Corp., 3334
Gibbs International, Inc., 8480
Gibbs, Ellen Berland, 6003
Gibbs, George, 473
Gibbs, Jacqueline C., 3569
Gibbs, James R., 1189
Gibbs, Jason, 3481
Gibbs, Jimmy I., 8480
Gibbs, Judith W., 8773
Gibbs, Katie, 416
Gibbs, Lisa K., 1796
Gibbs, Marsha H., 8480
Gibbs, Mary Catherine, 9380
Gibbs, Patricia Hellman, 677
Gibbs, Richard D., 677
Gibbs, Rose Delores, 8502
Gibbs, Sara C., 7402
Gibbs, Sharon, 8474
Giberson, Robert C., 8939
Gibertson, Holden, 4781
Gibis, Margot, 6349, 6705
Giblin, John, 8634
Gibney, Albert L., 9362
Gibney, Frank A., 9362
Gibney, Tommie Ann, 5229
Gibson Trust, The, 2678
Gibson, Addison H., 8056
Gibson, Ami Jo, 2646
Gibson, Charles, 760
Gibson, Dana, 5276
Gibson, Deb, 7567
Gibson, Donald, 6068
Gibson, Dunn & Crutcher LLP, 583
Gibson, Frank B., Jr., 7273
Gibson, George C., 1431
Gibson, Guy R., 1039
Gibson, Harry, 3509
Gibson, J.W., 8549
Gibson, James G., 5277
Gibson, Jayne, 3348
Gibson, Jennifer L., 5766
Gibson, Jill R., 5277
Gibson, Jodi, 4473
Gibson, John W., 7783
Gibson, Lisa, 7421
Gibson, Mark, 9731
Gibson, Martyn, 9516
Gibson, Mary R., 8866
Gibson, Michael, 2585
Gibson, Nancy Q., 6670
Gibson, Peter, 5276
Gibson, Rose Jacobs, 1166
Gibson, Scott, 9975
Gibson, Stanley G., Jr., 2085
Giddens, Thomas V., Jr., 9627
Gidley, Marta D., 3305
Gidwitz, Betsy R., 2862
Gidwitz, Joseph L., 2862
Gidwitz, Ronald J., 2862
Gieck, Joe H., 9405
Gielen, L.J., 3623
Gierach, Denice A., 2812
Giering, Edmund J., IV, 3613
Gies, Beth G., 2863
Gies, Larry W., 2863
Gies, Larry W., Jr., 2863
Giesel, William G., Jr., 6584
Giesen, Greta, 2924
Gietzen, Kenneth, 4362
Giffin, John D., 777
Gifford Foundation, The, 977
Gifford, Jeffrey R., 7333
Gifford, John F., 584
Gifford, John K., 5808
Gifford, John, Mrs., 973
Gifford, L. Andrew, 460
Gifford, Nancy K., 6269
Gifford, Rhodine, 584
Gifford, Rosamond, 6049
Giga, Aziz S., 8235
Giglio, Lawrence R., 4898
Gil, Holly Cresho, 8383
Gil-Wal Corp., 4071
Gilb, Bob, 9600
Gilberg, Josh, 3334
Gilbert 1982 Trust, A & R, 585
Gilbert, Cal, 973, 1120
Gilbert, Dick, 5103
Gilbert, Douglas E., 8056
Gilbert, Faith N., 3634
Gilbert, J. Stephen, 9246
Gilbert, James, M.D., 22
Gilbert, Jane, 6502
Gilbert, Jeffrey Z., 6502
Gilbert, Julanna V., 1376
Gilbert, Katherine, 3631
Gilbert, Louisa, 6502
Gilbert, Marion M., 6502
Gilbert, Roger, 6502

Glass, Nancy J., 7210
Glass, Robert I., 4072
Glass, Ruth A., 190
Glass, Sandra A., 4072
Glass, Scott L., 4072
Glasscock, J. Samuel, 9500
Glasscock, Melbern G., 8867
Glasscock, Susanne M., 8867
Glasser, Emily, 2784
Glasser, James J., 2784
Glasser, Louise R., 2784
Glassman, Beth Ourisman, 1879
Glassman, Elizabeth, 3186
Glassman, Jeffrey, 1296
Glassman, Jeffrey L., 1150
Glassman, Jennifer, 7001
Glassman, Robert A., 4030
Glatfelter Charitable Lead Trust, Anne M., 8059
Glatfelter, Elizabeth, 8059
Glatt, Jordan, 5473
Glaub, Joseph, 9773
Glaxo Wellcome Americas Inc., 7274
GlaxoSmithKline, 3833
GlaxoSmithKline Holdings (Americas) Inc., 7274
GlaxoSmithKline LLC F.K.A. SmithKline, 8060
Glazer, Anna, 3433
Glazer, Avie, 2124
Glazer, Bryan, 2124
Glazer, Edward, 2124
Glazer, Jeffrey W., 3433, 3458
Glazer, Joel, 2124
Glazer, Kevin, 2124
Glazer, Lowell R., 3802
Glazer, Madelyn L., 3434
Glazer, Michael F., 3772
Glazer, Shari Arison, 1972
Glazman, Jon, 7180
Gleaser, Mitch, 2036
Gleason, James S., 592
Gleason, Janis F., 592
Gleason, Nancy, 6038
Gleason, Ron, 8841
Gleason, Thomas E., 9652
Gleason, Todd R., 4739
Gleason, Tracy R., 592
Gleason, William Eric Christopher, 105
Gleba, Michael W., 7968, 8266
Gleberman, Carson, 6683
Gleberman, Joseph H., 6683
Gleeson, Patrick, 959
Gleim, Sandy, 3393
Gleis, Josephine D., 593
Glen, John Fitten, 2470
Glen, Molly K.D., 5115
Glen, Nancy J., 8046
Glendi Publications, Inc., 8116
Glenmede Trust Co., The, 8220, 8330
Glenmede Trust Company, The, 7705
Glenn Irrevocable Trust, Wilbur, 2471
Glenn, Alston, 2125, 2470
Glenn, Anne, 2470, 7329
Glenn, Bernadette, 1320
Glenn, Donna, 8572
Glenn, Enid Veronica, 9897
Glenn, Gordon H., 3877
Glenn, J. Kirk, Jr., 7211
Glenn, Jack, 2125, 2470
Glenn, James K., 7211
Glenn, James K., Jr., 7211
Glenn, L., 7809
Glenn, Lewis, 2125, 2470
Glenn, Louise R., 2471
Glenn, Paul F., 594
Glenn, Robert, 2125, 2470
Glenn, Steve G., 7048
Glenn, T. Michael, 8572
Glenn, Thomas K., II, 2471
Glenn, Tom, 8548
Glenn, W. Raoul, Jr., 8508
Glenn, Wadley R., III, 8508
Glenn, William D., 1226
Glenn, Willie, 7306
Glenner, Lisa, 2866
Glenner, Sidney, 2866
Glenville Capital Partners, L.P., 8238
Gleser, C'Ardiss Gardner, 3003
Gless, Michael M., 777
Glew, William B., 1879
Glick, Alvin L., 4336
Glick, Barry J., 4336
Glick, Carlton L., 4336
Glick, Eugene B., 3310
Glick, Jerrold L., 1487
Glick, Marianne, 3272, 3310
Glick, Marilyn K., 3310
Glick, Nancy, 3110
Glick, Randal L., 4336
Glickenhaus, James, 6058
Glickenhaus, Sarah, 6058
Glickenhaus, Seth M., 6058
Glickman, Albert B., 3688
Glickman, David G., 9164
Glickman, David P., 3688
Glickman, Judith L., 3688
Glide, Katrina D., 595
Gliedman, Kenneth, 6642
Glinn, Jim, 1110
Global Aid Network, 2087
Global Initiative Partners, 6532
Global Leadership Foundation, 6765
Global Rental Co., 4
Global Securities, Inc., 3996
Globe Oil and Refining Companies, 4734
Globetti, Steven, 74
Globis, Roxanne L., 5412
Glore, Gregory, 4893
Glorioso, Frank F., 9452
Glosser, Daniel, 7990
Glosser, William L., Esq., 7990
Glover Park Group LLC, 1892
Glover, Daniel K., 1
Glover, Ethel M., 1594
Glover, Gordon, 4282
Glover, Marion B., 2462
Glowiak, Brian G., 4366
Gloyd, Steve, 3376
Gluck, Carol, 7707
Gluck, Frederick W., 1116
Gluck, Maxwell H., 596
Gluck, Suzanne, 6693
Gluckman, Fred, 1101, 1340
Glynn, Christopher, 2763
GMO City of London, 7876
GMT Interim Trust, 4995
Gnandt, Ken, 5044
Gobet, Catherina LaLanne, 4291
Gobioff, Ahron, 5242
Goble, Gary, 9256
Goble, Gary F., 8850
Gochnauer, Richard, 3201
Godbold Foundation, 2332
Godbout, Beth, 5052
Godchaux, Justin A., 2548
Goddard Systems, Inc., 7927
Goddard Trust, Adele H., 2223
Goddard, Bill, 7743
Goddard, Deborah M., 1129
Goddard, Jim, 1153
Goddard, Robert C., 2530
Goddard, Thomas, 8423
Goddard, William R., Jr., 7780
Godeke, Steven, 6571
Godet, Eric, 2036
Godfather Charitable Trust, 8662
Godfrey Jr. Charitable Lead Trust, D., 9850
Godfrey, Constance P., 9850
Godfrey, David L., 1839
Godfrey, Dudley J., Jr., 9850
Godfrey, Flavel McMichael, 7265
Godfrey, Gene, 2482
Godfrey, Ginger, 7569
Godley, Betty, 5749
Godlove, Ernest, 7742
Godsey, R. Kirby, 2403
Godsil, Raymond D. (Tad), III, 4738
Godstein, Gilbert, 1450
Godward, William W., 527
Godwin, Laurna C., 4966
Godwin, Rhonda, 7781
Goebel, 9606
Goebel, Patrick, 9830
Goebel, Patrick J., 9829
Goedde, Bill, 3277
Goeddel, David V., 3833
Goedecke, Nancy Collat, 49
Goedhart, LaWonna, 8669
Goeke, Clayton, 5093
Goel, Manju, 2127
Goel, Mukesh, 2127
Goergen, B.J., 9118
Goergen, Pamela M., 1595
Goergen, Robert B., 1595
Goergen, Robert B., Jr., 1595
Goergen, Todd A., 1595
Goergen, Todd A., Jr., 1595
Goerges, Karlo, 4631
Goeringer, Louis F., 8152
Goertzen, Becky, 5045
Goertzen, Jack E., Hon., 650
Goertzen, Ron, 3542
Goettler, Ralph H., 7911
Goetz, Barbara, 2517
Goff, James H., 3680
Goff, Jonathan K., 1845
Goff, Laura, 877
Goff, Marcia, 7444
Goff, Phyllis, 4709
Goff, Phyllis Rawls, 4703
Goff, Robert W., Jr., 9010
Goff, Stacey, 1750
Goforth, Sam, 9800
Gogel, Blair L., 5061
Goggans, Tommie J., III, 23
Goggins, John J., 6499
Gogian, John, 598
Gogian, John J., Jr., 598
Gogian, Rosalia, 598
Gogolak, John, 92
Goings, Everett V., 6059
Goings, Susan Porcaro, 6059
Goings, Wesley, 4817
Goins, Charlynn, 6544
Goins, Jim, 1069
GOJO Industries, Inc., 7542
Gokaslan, Ziya, 7915
Gold Glass Group, 7638
Gold Mine Gin, Inc., 3666
Gold Mine Plantation, 3666
Gold, Barbara, 1368, 5984
Gold, Carolyn, 4908
Gold, Dave, 601
Gold, David, 601
Gold, David B., 600
Gold, Elaine, 600
Gold, Emily, 600
Gold, Howard, 601
Gold, Ilene C., 599
Gold, Israel, 6060
Gold, Jeff, 601
Gold, Joel, 5668
Gold, Judith, 5477
Gold, Katherine, 1487
Gold, Mendel, 6060
Gold, Michael A., 2604
Gold, Paula, 4222
Gold, Richard, 5541, 6976
Gold, Richard L., 8383
Gold, Sherry, 601
Gold, Stanley P., 599
Gold, Steven A., 600
Gold, Yehudis, 5672
Gold-Bubier, Diane, 600
Gold-Lurie, Barbara, 600
Goldbach Life Trust, Marie S., 9851
Goldbach, Marie S., 9851
Goldbaum, Elizabeth, 5875
Goldberg Family Trust, 637
Goldberg, Alan E., 6823
Goldberg, Alan J., 2131
Goldberg, Avram J., 3913
Goldberg, Bradley L., 6061
Goldberg, Carol R., 3913
Goldberg, David S., 6372
Goldberg, Jay B., 6631
Goldberg, Jeffrey, 6693
Goldberg, Jerold, 6918
Goldberg, Jerome, 3684
Goldberg, Michael, 5279, 6632
Goldberg, Miriam P., 6823
Goldberg, Mitchell B., 2687
Goldberg, Paul, 2830
Goldberg, Robert M., 6372
Goldberg, Robin, 6372
Goldberg, Rosalie A., 5732
Goldberg, Roy A., 4057
Goldberg, Steve, 420
Goldberg, Steven A., 9838
Goldberg, Steven E., 8472
Goldberg, Sunny, 6061
Goldberg, Veronica, 5279
Goldberg, Wendy, 1893
Goldberg, William, 5578
Goldberg, Yitzchok, 5817
Goldbrenner, Isaac, 5959, 6145
Goldbum, Bonnie, 3644
Goldcorp, 7349
Golden Country Foods, 9837
Golden Leaf Foundation, 7153
Golden State Foods, 3201
Golden State Foods Corp., 633
Golden, Adolph, 7421
Golden, Alanna, 3170
Golden, Andrew K., 5411
Golden, Charles E., 3342
Golden, David, 8561
Golden, Irene L., 4073
Golden, James R., 9558
Golden, Jamie, 4073
Golden, Joanne, 4512
Golden, Jonathan K., 1727
Golden, Juliet Asher, 2537
Golden, Olivia, 6093

Golden, Pamela P., 5280
Golden, Paula, 349
Golden, Robert N., Dean, 9945
Golden, Sam, 8878
Golden, Samuel, 9443
Golden, Sibyl L., 5280
Golden, Sibyl R., 5280
Golden, Web, 3509
Golden, William T., 5280
Golden-Icahn, Gail, 6204
Goldenberg, Agnes, 7120
Goldenberg, Chaim, 7120
Goldenberg, Daniel, 369
Goldenberg, Edward M., 1866
Goldenberg, Elizabeth K., 4874
Goldenberg, Fredericka Anne, 3197
Goldenberg, Leon, 7120
Goldenberg, Scott, 4308
Goldenburg, Blanche, 6967
Goldenson Arbus Foundation, 251
Goldenthal, Hanan, 6000
Goldenvoice, LLC, 396
Goldfarb Trust, Alvin, 4895
Goldfarb, Allan, 9083
Goldfarb, Alvin, 4895
Goldfarb, Robert, 4895
Goldfarb, Robert B., 1609
Goldfarb, Robert D., 5746, 6869
Goldfarb, Stanley, 8170
Goldgrabe, Curt, 2639
Goldhirsh Foundation, 603, 1891
Goldhirsh, Benjamin A., 602
Goldhirsh, Claire Denise Hoffman, 602
Goldhrish-Yellin, Elizabeth A., 603
Goldin, Claudia Brett, 1378
Goldin, Marc S., 439
Goldin, Philipe, 6640
Golding Charitable Remainder Trust, Bill, 9318
Golding, Daniel M., 8383
Goldirsh Foundation, 602
Goldman 1997 Charitable Lead Annuity Trust, Richard, 3854
Goldman Administrative Trust, Richard N., 1910
Goldman Charitable Trust, Sol, The, 6064
Goldman Children Trust, 6066
Goldman Fund, Richard and Rhoda, 3854
Goldman Grandchildren Trust, 6066
Goldman Sachs, 1936, 6517, 7012
Goldman Sachs & Co., 783, 2707, 5762, 6021, 6108, 6257, 6369, 6440, 6478, 6898
Goldman Sachs Group, Inc., 6070
Goldman Sachs Philanthropy Fund, 6044
Goldman, Aaron D., 605
Goldman, Alice R., 1910
Goldman, Allan H., 6065
Goldman, Amy, 6067
Goldman, Amy P., 6067
Goldman, Amy R., 4614, 4664
Goldman, Angela, 5079
Goldman, Beverly T., 8858
Goldman, Daniel S., 1910
Goldman, Dorian, 6066
Goldman, Dorothy Tapper, 6116
Goldman, Douglas E., 604, 606
Goldman, Guido, 5744
Goldman, Herman, 6068
Goldman, Howard S., 9915
Goldman, Jane H., 6065
Goldman, Janis, 317
Goldman, Jason E., 606
Goldman, Joe, 8858
Goldman, Joel, 2301
Goldman, John D., 604, 605, 642
Goldman, Katja, 6066
Goldman, Kenneth A., 344
Goldman, Laurie Ann, 2412
Goldman, Lisa M., 606
Goldman, Lloyd, 6066
Goldman, Marcia L., 605
Goldman, Matthew E., 606
Goldman, Michael, 8858
Goldman, Patricia, 5735
Goldman, Peter, 9661
Goldman, Philip, 4763
Goldman, Rebecca B., 9780
Goldman, Rhoda H., 604
Goldman, Richard N., 604, 1910
Goldman, Rob, 3759
Goldman, Robert, 362, 2236
Goldman, Robert I., 6069
Goldman, Robert P., 4073
Goldman, Roger A., 1538, 5364, 7076
Goldman, Ronald, 8858
Goldman, Ross, 9661
Goldman, Sachs & Co., 6070, 6914
Goldman, Sol, 6064, 6065
Goldman, William A., 7641
Goldman, William S., 642, 1910
Goldner, Brian, 8403
Goldner, David, 3856
Goldner, David A., 3780
Goldrich & Kest Industries, 607
Goldrich Trust, 607
Goldrich, Doretta, 607
Goldrich, Jona, 607
Goldrich, Melinda, 607
Goldrick, James M., 6306
Goldring Corp., N., 3638
Goldring, Gary F., 1596
Goldring, Gregory, 1596
Goldring, Jeffrey, 3638, 3672
Goldring, Rebecca, 1596
Goldring, William, 3638, 3672
Goldsberry, Yvonne, 5169
Goldsbury Charitable Trust, 8868
Goldsbury, Angela Aboltin, 8868
Goldsbury, Christopher, Jr., 8868
Goldschmidt IRA at Baird, 2867
Goldschmidt IRA at Morgan Stanley, 2867
Goldschmidt Trust, Karla, The, 2867
Goldschmidt Trust, Walter, 2867
Goldschmidt, David M., 255
Goldschmidt, James, 2867
Goldschmidt, Karla, 2867
Goldschmidt, Susan, 2867
Goldschmidt, Walter, 2867
Goldseker, Ana, 3803
Goldseker, Deby, 3803
Goldseker, Morris, 3803
Goldseker, Sharna, 3803, 5717
Goldseker, Sheldon, 3726, 3803
Goldseker, Simon, 3803
Goldsmith Charitable Trust, Barbara Lubin, 6071
Goldsmith Foundation, Horace W., 5763
Goldsmith, Adam, 3804
Goldsmith, Barbara Lubin, 6071
Goldsmith, Beth, 964, 3804
Goldsmith, Bram, 497, 608
Goldsmith, Bram, Mrs., 608
Goldsmith, Bruce L., 608
Goldsmith, Donald A., 6064, 6067
Goldsmith, Elaine, 608
Goldsmith, H. Josh, 3804
Goldsmith, Harriet, 8474
Goldsmith, Harry, 8530
Goldsmith, Horace W., 6072, 7033
Goldsmith, Jere W., 5409
Goldsmith, Karen, 608
Goldsmith, Marcia, 6228
Goldsmith, Margaret Anne, 22
Goldsmith, Russell, 608
Goldsmith, Stephen, 1953
Goldstein, Abraham, 6073
Goldstein, Alan J., 2253
Goldstein, Alfred R., 2128
Goldstein, Ann L., 2128
Goldstein, Arlene, 6074
Goldstein, Arnold, 6074
Goldstein, Barbara, 5082
Goldstein, Bruce, 6637
Goldstein, Burton, 8573
Goldstein, Cynthia, 2128
Goldstein, Danielle, 6743
Goldstein, Darin, 6743
Goldstein, Dorothy L., 6075
Goldstein, Eliot, 7175
Goldstein, Elliott, 8573
Goldstein, Eugene S., 8387
Goldstein, George S., 722
Goldstein, Jan, 5629
Goldstein, Jeffrey, 1422
Goldstein, Jerome, 6075
Goldstein, Jerome R., 6075
Goldstein, Joseph, 6333
Goldstein, Joseph L., 3818, 3833
Goldstein, Julie Ann, 1422
Goldstein, Kari Wolff, 4590
Goldstein, Larry M., 8387
Goldstein, Leon, 2227
Goldstein, Leslie, 6076
Goldstein, Leslie Karen, 1422
Goldstein, Marvin, 6869
Goldstein, Merle F., 8387
Goldstein, Michael L., 6068
Goldstein, Michelle Gitlin, 8058
Goldstein, Mildred, 6073
Goldstein, Peter S., 6651
Goldstein, Richard, 2128
Goldstein, Richard C., 1422
Goldstein, Robert, 4061
Goldstein, Roslyn, 6076
Goldstein, Seth M., 5980
Goldstein, Shephard, 4016
Goldstein, Stanley P., 8387
Goldstein, Steven, 1581
Goldstein, Steven R., 2128
Goldstein, Susan B., 6743
Goldstein, Sylvia, 5814
Goldstein, Virginia J., 6216
Goldston Family Trust, June E., 3249
Goldstone, Elizabeth, 1597
Goldstone, Steven F., 1597
Goldwyn, Anthony, 609
Goldwyn, Catherine, 609
Goldwyn, Frances H., 609
Goldwyn, Francis, 609
Goldwyn, John, 609
Goldwyn, Samuel, 609
Goldwyn, Samuel, Jr., 609
Goldy, Marjorie L., 3697
Goldy, Susan, 6542
Golieb, Abner J., 6258
Golieb, John A., 6258
Golis, Pete, 420
Golisano, B. Thomas, 6077
Golkin, David L., 6078
Golkin, Donna, 6078
Golkin, Dorie C., 6078
Golkin, Gregory W., 6078
Golkin, Perry, 6078
Golla, Clare, 3061
Golliher, Darrin, 3502
Gollihue, Alan E., 9510
Gollin, James D., 5514
Gollin, Suzanne D., 5514
Goloff, Carol, 2320
Golson, William T., 1411
Golston, Allan C., 1387, 9625
Golttwald, Thomas E., 9379
Golub Corp., 6658
Golub Trust, Neil M., 6079
Golub, Estelle, 6079
Golub, Jane, 6079, 6658
Golub, Mona, 6079
Golub, Neil M., 6079, 6658
Golub, William, 6079
Golwitzer, Christopher L., 3241
Golwitzer, David L., 3241
Gombos Revocable Family Trust, The, 610
Gombos, Corlene, 610
Gombos, John Michael, 610
Gombos, Julia Lynn, 610
Gombos, Michael N., 610
Gomby, Deanna, 675
Gomer, Adelaide P., 6615
Gomez, Elizabeth M., 368
Gomez, Erim, 9591
Gomez, Iris, 4103
Gomez, Jorge, 7398
Gomez, Leo, 9149
Gomez, Lorenzo, III, 8648
Gomez, Manuel, 992
Gomez, Ralph, 8768
Gomez, Victor, 4532
Gompers, Edward, 9773
Gompers, John E., 9777
Gompers, Joseph N., 9777
Gompers, Thomas L., 9772
Goncalves, Armando F., 1671
Goncz, Edward J., 8017
Gong, Bing, 262
Gonnason, Jeff, 85
Gonnella, Carol H., 5007
Gonring, Jennifer, 5248
Gonsalves, Steve, 700
Gonsoulin, Al A., 8869
Gonsoulin, Gene J., 8869
Gonzales, Alberto R., Hon., 8550
Gonzales, Judith, 4872
Gonzales, Nancy, 6093
Gonzales, Nick, 1491
Gonzalez, Alexander, 1469
Gonzalez, Ana, 9003
Gonzalez, Fernando, 415
Gonzalez, Jerry, 2546, 7138
Gonzalez, Jorge, 2331
Gonzalez, Jose D., 8550
Gonzalez, M. Lorena, 4729
Gonzalez, Maria, 4438
Gonzalez, Martha, 2670
Gonzalez, Paola, 407
Gonzalez, Paul M., 6032
Gonzalez, Robert, 9003
Gonzalez, Robert J., Jr., 9003
Gonzalez, Shirley, 9003
Gonzalez-Mares, Elba, 959
Gooch, J.A., 8730
Gooch, James, 8643

Gottovi, Dan, 7189
Gotts, Guy, 9518
Gottschalk, Dinah, 9412
Gottschalk, Evan, 3360
Gottwald Foundation, The, 9379
Gottwald, Bruce C., Sr., 9379, 9494
Gottwald, Floyd D., Jr., 9451
Gottwald, James T., 9451
Gottwald, Thomas E., 9494
Gottwald, William, 9451
Gottwals, Bill, 5005
Goudie, Mary, 1903
Gougeon, Thomas A., 1418
Gough, Richard, 3287
Gough, Tom, 5804
Goughnour, Sam, 9796
Gougis, Chet, 3186
Gould Corporation, Stephen, 975
Gould, Anthony, 6086
Gould, Florence J., 6088
Gould, Frederick Beau, 9687
Gould, Fredric H., 6089
Gould, George D., Hon., 3692
Gould, Helaine, 6089
Gould, James G., 6099
Gould, Jane Mack, 7019
Gould, Jason, 1224
Gould, Jeffrey, 6089
Gould, Jeffrey A., 6089
Gould, John W., 8175
Gould, Joseph B., 618
Gould, Julie, 3939, 9687
Gould, Karen, 5482
Gould, Lois, 6086
Gould, Matthew, 6089
Gould, Matthew J., 6089
Gould, Robert R., 6643
Gould, Russ, 366
Gould, Russell S., 411
Goundar, Nalraj, 278
Gourevitch, Marc, 6549
Gouw, Julia, 491
Govan, J. Gardner, 9828, 9850
Gover, R. Clements, 8152
Government Employees Insurance Co., 3801
Gow, Robert, 4523
Goward, Abigail, 7139
Gowdy, Michelle, 3474
Gowen, H., II, 9632
Gowen, Herbert, 9632
Gowen, James E., II, 4021
Gowen, Laura, 9632
Gowen, Louisa, 9632
Gowen, William C., 9632
Goyins, Yvonne, 5501
GPU Service, Inc., 7455
Grabe, David, 2315
Grabel, Jeffrey N., 6387
Graber, Kenneth W., 3904
Graber, Richard W., 9819
Graber, Rick, 9880
Graber, Samuel W., 9007
Grabinski, Tim, 3465
Grable, Minnie K., 8064
Grabois, Neil R., 6228
Grabowski, Debra S., 5171
Grabowski, Gary G., 9814, 9911
Grace & Co., W.R., 3807
Grace Baptist Church, 7280, 9059
Grace Charitable Lea Ann Trust, Ann K., 116
Grace Community Baptist Church, 9059
Grace III, LLC, 8264
Grace, Barb, 116
Grace, Charles B., III, 7014
Grace, Ellen D., 4790
Grace, Howard T., 116
Grace, J. Peter, 6792
Grace, John M., 3553
Grace, Margaret F., 5925, 6792
Grace, Matt, 116
Grace, Mike, 415
Grace, Patrick P., 5925, 6792
Grace, Paula M., 7825
Grace, W. R., 3807
Graceton Estates, Inc., 6768
Gracey, William M., 8634
Gracik, L. Michael, Jr., 9469
Graco Inc., 4666
Graddick-Wier, Miriam M., 5379
Grade, Donald L., 9856
Gradowski, Ann O'Neil, 3859
Grady, Christina, 7823
Grady, Graham C., 2849
Grady, Jo Anne, 5068
Grady, Kenneth A., 4593
Grady, Lesley, 2432
Grady, Shane, 3762
Grady, Sheri, 1182
Grady, Susanna F., 2040
Grady, Thomas M., 7169
Grady-White Boats, Inc., 7315
Graebner, Nancy, 4362
Graf, Don, 8759
Graf, Robert T., 7546
Grafa, Trey, 9091
Graff, Christopher, 9368
Graff, F. Thomas, Jr., 9797
Graff, Jacob, 941
Graff, Kathleen, 8275
Graff, Pnina, 941
Grafman, Laura R., 152
Graham Architectural Products Corp., 8065
Graham Capital Corp., 8065
Graham Engineering Corp., 8065
Graham Foundation, 8465
Graham Marital Trust, Allen J., 8481
Graham Packaging Co., L.P., 8065
Graham Packaging Holdings Co., 8065
Graham, Allen J., 8481
Graham, Baxter, 5473
Graham, Charles, 6077
Graham, Christine Vaughn, 9481
Graham, Christopher F., 2516
Graham, Daryl A., 1765
Graham, David R., 1868
Graham, Donald C., 8065
Graham, Donald E., 9445
Graham, Elizabeth, 3934
Graham, Ernest R., 2873
Graham, Garth, 1531
Graham, H. Devon, Jr., 9183, 9186
Graham, Ingrid A., 8065
Graham, J. Todd, 9398
Graham, James, 1391
Graham, John J., 3612
Graham, Julie, 6604
Graham, Katharine Meyer, 9445
Graham, Kathryn G., 6604
Graham, Katie, 5114
Graham, Kerry, 8550
Graham, Kristiane C., 6582
Graham, Kristin, 8065
Graham, Laurel A., 1868
Graham, Laurel A.W., 1868
Graham, Leo, 1154
Graham, Mark, 7807
Graham, Mary, 2989
Graham, Peter M., 6701
Graham, Robert C., Jr., 6346, 6604
Graham, Robert H., 1868
Graham, Robert M., 1262, 9319, 9323
Graham, Spencer R., 1868
Graham, Ted, 7558
Graham, Terry, 7742
Graham, Terry, Ed.D., 23
Graham, William L., 9377
Graig Carr Foundation, 2631
Grain Processing Corp., 3450
Grainger, David W., 2874
Grainger, Hally W., 2874
Grainger, Joseph C., 654
Grainger, William W., 2874
Gralton, Dan, 1771
Gram, W. Dunbar, 3821
Grams, Blake, 4780
Gramshammer, Pepi, 1483
Gramshammer, Sheika, 1483, 1518
Granahan, Laura, 4282
Grand Circle Corp., 4076
Grand Circle Travel, 4076
Grand Circle Trust, 4076
Grand Sand, 7446
Grand Valley State University, 5707
Grand Victoria Casino, 2875
Grand View Hospital, 9250
Grand, Cindy, 619
Grand, David, 8383
Grand, Debra L., 3021
Grand, Marcia, 619
Grand, Rena, 619
Grand, Richard, 619
Grandchamps Charitable Remainder Trust, G., 4123
Grande, Arlene, 3310
Grande, Michelle, 1743
Grande, Thomas J., 3310
Grandell Rehabilitation, 6287, 6288
Grandinetti, Francis, 8295
Grandon, Carleen, 3439
Grandsand LLC, 7460
Grandy, Edith G., 9465
Granfors, Donna, 1591
Granger Associates, Inc., 4449, 4450
Granger Construction Co., 4449
Granger Electric Co., 4450
Granger Energy, 4450
Granger Energy of Decatur, LLC, 4450
Granger Energy of Honeybrook, LLC, 4450
Granger Holdings II LLC., 4450
Granger Holdings, LLC, 4450
Granger Meadows, LLC, 4450
Granger, Alison, 1609
Granger, Alton L., 4449
Granger, Donna, 4449
Granger, Gordon, 8472
Granger, Janice, 4449
Granger, Jerry P., 4449
Granger, Keith L., 4450
Granger, L. Keith, 18
Granger, Lynne, 4449
Granger, Ronald K., 4449
Granger, Todd J., 4450
Granillo, Paul, 419
Granite Assocs., LP, 6044
Granite Construction Co., 293
Granlund, Cheryl, 4701
Granoff, Martin J., 6091
Granoff, Michael, 6091
Granoff, Perry, 6091
Grant Makers in Health, 9615
Grant Thornton LLP, 2877
Grant, Celia, 3987
Grant, Chad, 8994
Grant, Charisse L., 2238
Grant, Cy, 7303
Grant, Dick, 9099
Grant, Emily, 6092
Grant, Eugene M., 6092
Grant, Evalyn N., 1929
Grant, Frederic, 7565
Grant, Frederic J., III, 7635
Grant, Hugh A., 1385
Grant, John, 8729
Grant, John R., 4365
Grant, Katharine R., 2546
Grant, Kimberly, 277
Grant, Leslie E., 4016
Grant, Madeleine B., 6514
Grant, Marilee, 3957
Grant, Michael, 2546
Grant, Patty, 3290
Grant, Richard A., Jr., 956
Grant, Robert N., 2659
Grant, Stanley J. "Bud", 6024
Grant, Terry E., 6092
Grant, Warren, 1076, 1791
Grant, William, 3762
Grant, William T., 6093
Grantham Foundation, 6607
Grantham, Isable, 4077
Grantham, Jeremy, 4077
Grantham, Oliver, 4077
Grantham, R. Jeremy, 4077
Grantham, Rupert, 4077
Grantland Avenue, LLC, 1301
Granville Homes, Inc., 1301
Granville, William "Billy", III, 9135
Graphics Atlanta Inc, 1771
Graser, Janice, 2245
Graser, Nancy M., 4654
Grass Charitable Lead Annuity Trust, 8067
Grass, Alex, 8066
Grass, Alexander, 8067
Grass, Edgar, 5437
Grass, Gayle C., 9702
Grass, Jody, 8068
Grass, Lois Lehrman, 8068
Grass, Roger L., 8067
Grassey, Ernest J., 4135
Grassgreen, Randi, 1391
Grassham, Jennifer, 5528
Grassi and Co., 6205
Grassi, Anthony P., 5733
Grassi, Eleuthera S., 8315
Grassilli, Robert J., 568
Grassmann, Edward J., 5281, 5485
Grasso, Richard, 6904
Grata, Mel, 7994
Gratopp, William C., 4373
Gratry, Barbara Bolton, 7614
Grattan, Pamela, 1100
Grauer, Laura, 6095
Grauer, Laura M., 6095
Grauer, Peter T., 6095
Graunke, James, 1020
Graunke, Terence, 3015
Graustein, Archibald R., 1600
Graustein, Hallie H., 1600
Graustein, Jean, 1600
Graustein, Lisa, 1600
Graustein, William C., 1600

Greenfield, Joan, 8072
Greenfield, Michael, 8072
Greenfield, Van David, 6748
Greenfield, William, 8072
Greengrass, Jeff, 975
Greenhaven Assocs., 7039
Greenhaw, Elaine, 8797
Greenheck Marital Trust, Bernard A., 9856
Greenheck Survivor's Trust, Esther M., 9856
Greenhill, LeShane, 8603
Greenho, Jim, 8472
Greenholtz, Tom, 8548
Greenhouse, Howard L., 9511
Greenhouse, Scott, 2803
Greenhouse, Timothy, 7285
Greenleaf, Michael H., 5196, 5328
Greenlee, Amanda Link, 4825
Greenlight Capital, 6042
Greeno, Janet, 2331
Greenough, Donald M., 4108
GreenPoint Bank, 9400
Greensboro News Co., 9467
Greenspon, Irving L., 9561
Greenstein, Jeffrey I., 9633
Greenstein, Judith E., 9633
Greenston, Jessica, 2631
Greenstreet, Yvonne, 9625
Greenup, Marion, 6861
Greenville Symphony Assoc., 8465
Greenwald, Benjamin, 3766
Greenwald, Sheryl, 1994
Greenwall, Anna A., 6105
Greenwall, Frank K., 6105
Greenway-Leibowitz, Tara, 6348
Greenwell, Melissa, 3303
Greenwood Gardens, Inc., 5444
Greenwood, Donald F., 4866
Greenwood, Maryscott, 2516
Greenwood, Scott, 2225
Greer, Bruce, 2039
Greer, Dallas M., 8616
Greer, Donna, 8927
Greer, Frank, 9591
Greer, Gayle, 1399
Greer, George C., 8021
Greer, Jack, 7405
Greer, Joel, 3484
Greer, Lucie C., 4802
Greer, Robert, 9799
Greevy, Charles F., III, 8229
Grefenstette, C.G., 8093
Greffin, Judith P., 2657
Greger, Ray, 886
Gregg, Bill, 4709
Gregg, Brian W., 1541
Gregg, Gene E., 661
Gregg, Ingrid A., 4413
Gregg, Jason, 2287
Gregg, Kirk P., 5818
Gregg, Simon, 2287
Gregg, Vicky B., 8634
Gregg, Virginia C., 5803
Greggs, M. Anne, 9524
Gregoire, Chris, 3837
Gregoire, Karn, 3484
Gregoria, Ric, 2260
Gregorian, Lisa, 6982
Gregorian, Vartan, 5747
Gregory, Charles E., Jr., 5567
Gregory, Dennis, 4631
Gregory, James, 8596
Gregory, Joan P., 8596
Gregory, John M., 8596
Gregory, Joseph M., 6538
Gregory, Joseph R., 8608
Gregory, Kitsy, 1497
Gregory, Lucinda, 8608
Gregory, Lucinda J., 8608
Gregory, Mary, 301, 1226
Gregory, R. Frederick, 9198
Gregory, Robert E., Jr., 8501
Gregory, Robert W., Jr., 1389
Gregory, Theophilus, 1406
Gregory, Todd, 4532
Gregurich, Doug, 3363
Greifeld, Robert, 3857
Greig, Jerome "Jerry", 3615
Greig, Jim, 3313
Greiman, Soo, 3437
Grein, Thomas W., 3341, 3397
Greiner, Amy, 3403
Greiner, Jessica, 85
Greiner, John T., Jr., 7749
Greiner, Jola, 9578
Greiner, Julie, 7552
Greiner, K. Don, 7754
Greiner, Shellie, 7754
Greisbaum, Kathy, 80
Greissing, Edward, 6024
Gremel, Meredith, 4544
Gremer, John, 3209, 3210
Grenier, Benjamin, 6636
Grenrock, Gwyn L., 228
Gresham, Tom, 4821
Greshik, Joan, 4806
Gressette, L. Marion, III, 8468
Greswold, Kate M., 1259
Greve, John H., 3451
Greve, Mary P., 6106
Grewell, Jan, 2742
Grey, Bonnie, 1213
Grey, Elizabeth Pardoe, 4206
Greyhavens, Timothy, 9762
Greystone Funding Corp., 2545
Grice, Cheryl, 3532
Gridish, Eli, 6277
Gridish, Rebecca, 6277
Griego, Linda, 1006
Griego, Linda M., 1013
Grien, James, 2511
Grier, Richard L., 9521
Grier, Rosey, 927
Gries, Sally, 7406
Griesbaum, Kathy, 80
Griesbeck, George M., 8549
Griesbeck, William G., 8556
Griesgraber, Stephen, 5625
Griesmer, Jim, 1399
Griff, Christine, 6627
Griffen, John, 6718
Griffin Charitable Remainder Trust, Daisy, 9318
Griffin, Amy M., 5685, 6107
Griffin, Beatrice C., 1425
Griffin, Carl R., III, 3711
Griffin, Charles William, 2514
Griffin, Chester B., 2133
Griffin, Danice C., 9924
Griffin, Diane Pomeroy, 9391
Griffin, Edward R., 2299
Griffin, James, 9799
Griffin, Jan, 2263
Griffin, Janet, 3490
Griffin, John, 5685
Griffin, John A., 5685, 6107
Griffin, John F., 2138
Griffin, Judith, 8001
Griffin, Karen, 79
Griffin, Lynn E., 2514
Griffin, Martin P., 2138
Griffin, Nancy M., 2138
Griffin, Pat, 1425
Griffin, Sean P., 2138
Griffin, Sharon, 1644
Griffin, Sidney G., Jr., 1166
Griffin, William M., 6174
Griffin-Cole, Barbara, 6108
Griffinger, Theodore, 331
Griffiss Trust, James E., 9857
Griffith, Benjamin W., III, 2473
Griffith, Chris, 9226
Griffith, Chuck, 5067
Griffith, Dolores, 8217
Griffith, H. Ronald, 4467
Griffith, J. Brian, 4943
Griffith, J. Larry, 3416
Griffith, James W., Jr., 3456
Griffith, John D., 4776
Griffith, Larry, 3356
Griffith, Lawrence S.C., 6947
Griffith, Mary, 3456
Griffith, R. Riggs, 7973
Griffith, Teresa M., 2473
Griffiths, Anthony F., 9178
Griffiths, Kathleen, 4362
Griffiths, Paul "Stoney", III, 8296
Grigg, Charles R., 4901
Grigg, Kaatri, 4901
Grigg, Margaret B., 4901
Griggs, Denise M., 7578
Griggs, Mary L., 4669
Griglun, Thomas, 1643
Grignon, David, 3328
Grigor, Carol Colburn, 410
Grigsby, L. Lane, 3640
Grigsby, Peter, 3365
Grigsby, Todd William, 3640
Grill, Brian, 5379, 5380
Grill, Josh, 1161
Grill, Steve, 3335
Grillo, Christopher, 6044
Grimaldi, Joseph, 4039
Grimaldi, Megan, 4234
Grimes, Anne W., 8737
Grimes, David, 5194
Grimes, Donald T., 4593
Grimes, George, 3164
Grimes, Kelly, 7973
Grimes, Kirk, 8851
Grimes, Mike, 3303
Grimes, Patti, 3797
Grimm, Brandon A., 626
Grimm, Bryan, 627
Grimm, Kimberly C., 2019
Grimm, Klaus, 5108
Grimm, M. Sandlin, 1996
Grimm, Melissa, 627
Grimm, Sarah K., 3515
Grimm, Stephen K., 1657
Grimm, Valerie, 1563
Grimm-Marshall, Barbara, 627
Grimmway Enterprises, Inc., 626, 627
Grimshaw, Eric, 7783
Grimsley, Diane, 7324, 7341
Grimsley, John G., 1978
Grimsrud, Courtney, 4772
Grimwood, Paul, 965, 9056
Gringlas, Marcy, 8278
Grinney, Jay, 21
Grinold, Leilani, 628
Grinold, Richard, 628
Grinspoon, Harold, 4080
Grinspoon, Winnie Sandler, 4080
Grinstein, Krista, 9629
Grippardi, Paul, 1180
Grisanti, Eugene P., 6497, 7027
Griscom, Karin A., 4191
Grisham, Elizabeth Renee, 4841
Grisham, John R., 4841
Grisham, John R., Jr., 4841
Grisier, Jim, 1520
Grismer, Pat, 3608
Grissom, Steve L., 2986
Griswell, J. Barry, 3420
Griswold Industries, 838
Griswold Industries, Inc., 794
Griswold, Benjamin H., IV, 5745
Griswold, D. Ross, Jr., 1787
Griswold, John C., 1787
Griswold, Katherine, 6706
Griswold, Mark, 1787
Griswold, Rhonda, 2591
Grizzard, Claude H., Sr., 2474
Grizzard, Elizabeth H., 2474
Groark, Eunice S., 1671
Grobman, Linda, 8336
Groccia, Christine Herrforth, 3156
Grocers Supply Co., Inc., The, 8982
Grocholski, Gregory, 4344
Grode, George F., 8129
Groenendyke, Cheryl F., 4458
Groff, Peter, 1014
Groff, Wayne, 8135
Grogan, Cande, 101
Grogan, Ed, 9750
Grogan, Paul S., 3956
Grogan, Sheila, 4815
Grohman, Martin J., 5676
Grohne, David, 2880
Grohne, Jeffrey, 2880
Grohne, Margaret, 2880
Grolier Club, 5707
Groll, Matthew A., 7911
Gromek, Joseph R., 7051
Gronauer, Helen Scheidt, 8625
Gronewaldt, Alice Busch, 2139
Gronquist, Addison, 7841
Groody, Laird Grant, 2035
Groom, Michael P., 887
Groome, Katherine S., 5885
Groomes, David, 2211
Groover, Gregory, Rev. Dr., 3956
Gropper, Mark, 9715
Grosfeld, James, 4453
Grosfeld, Nancy, 4453
Grosh, Gregory, 2927
Gross Family Foundation, Phillip and Elizabeth, 4298
Gross Trust, Virginia Fay, 8789
Gross, Amy, 3796
Gross, Bill, 1037
Gross, Chaim, 6111
Gross, Charles H., 4485
Gross, Cornelia B., 8159
Gross, Courtlandt D., 485
Gross, Daniel, 6111
Gross, Daniel L., 367
Gross, Dov, 6111
Gross, Elizabeth Cochary, 4081
Gross, Esther, 6111
Gross, Faigie, 6111
Gross, Gaila, 7794
Gross, Gregory S., 3110
Gross, James L., Jr., 7702

Gross, Jeffrey, 6110
Gross, Jenard M., 9287
Gross, Jennifer, 6110
Gross, Jerome, 7080
Gross, Jody, 9341
Gross, Malcolm J., 8320
Gross, Meryl, 5984
Gross, Michael, 6112, 6758
Gross, Nicholas, 6110
Gross, Norman, 6372
Gross, Pamela, 9726
Gross, Patrick W., 1916
Gross, Phill, 4298
Gross, Phillip T., 4081
Gross, Pinchus, 6111
Gross, Pincus, 6111
Gross, Richard F., Dr., 4218
Gross, Stella B., 629
Gross, Stephan, 5296
Gross, Steve, 1263
Gross, Steven, 6087
Gross, Sue, 6110
Gross, Vicki, 6112
Gross, William, 6110
Gross, William H., 1037
Grossinger, Ken, 1897
Grossman, Adam D., 7791
Grossman, Alan R., 6732
Grossman, Aryn, 1603
Grossman, Daniel, 1088
Grossman, David, 6858
Grossman, Dena, 1517
Grossman, Ed, 2123
Grossman, Elizabeth Rice, 2602
Grossman, Gina, 2646
Grossman, Jay, 3893
Grossman, Jeffrey, 5247
Grossman, Jennifer, 6564
Grossman, Lewis, 6096
Grossman, Lynn, 5948
Grossman, Matthew, 1603
Grossman, Nathan M., 3048
Grossman, Pamela, 1934, 3171
Grossman, Paul, 424
Grossman, Robert, 6918
Grossman, Sanford J., 1601
Grossman, Steven, 1602
Grossman, Thomas, 4757, 9341
Grossman, Tom, 4715
Groswold, Jerry, 1423
Grote, Matthew, 3061
Grotemeyer, Kathy, 1511
Groth, Linda, 9932
Grotjohn, Mo, 7777
Grotzinger, John, Ph.D., 221
Group Health Assn., Inc., 1894
Grousbeck Family Foundation, 5201, 5222
Grousbeck, Brie Cameron, 5201
Grousbeck, Peter Walker, 5201
Grout Trust, Elizabeth Q., 630
Grout, Melinda, 9616
Grove, Andrew, 9149
Grove, Andrew S., 631
Grove, Eva K., 631
Grove, Jane, 3287
Grove, Karen, 631
Grover, Jeff, 1211
Grover, Katherine, 6864
Grover, Martha E., 9427
Groves, Bradford, 7630
Groves, Greggory, 4907
Groves, Helen K., 8962
Groves, Ray J., 1397
Growald, Adam, 6725
Growald, Danny, 6725
Growald, Paul, 6725
Growmark, Inc., 2881
Groza, Jani, 7711
Grt. Grand Charitable Remainder Unitrust, 6232
Grubb, Gordon, 7322
Grubb, James S., 5871
Grubb, Jeffrey T., 9689
Grubb, Kristen, 4731
Grubb, Kristin, 4614
Grube, Stanley, 419
Gruber, Deborah, 214
Gruber, Jon D., 632
Gruber, Linda W., 632
Gruber, Vivian, 4736
Grubman, Eric P., 6113
Gruebele, Martin, 157
Gruel, John, 4467
Gruen, Daniel F., 659
Gruen, Julia, 6133
Gruen, Margaret A., 659
Gruen, William H., 9495
Gruenberg, Jennifer, 6441
Gruenberg, Jon, 6441
Gruenberg, Leonard, 6441
Gruenberg, Wendy, 6441
Gruennert, Ruth M., 9108
Grulke, Kara, 4370
Grum, Clifford J., 8876
Grum, Dona Janelle, 8876
Grum, Mary K., 8876
Grumbach, Antonia M., 7079
Grundfest, Jack D., 206
Grundy, Laurence S., 2140
Grundy, Terrill S., 2140
Gruodis, Victor, 6264
Grupo Aliades Sa De Cv Mexico, 8834
Grupo Outhelping Sc Mexico, 8834
Gruppo, David, 5724
Gruss Charitable and Educational Foundation, O. and R., 6114
Gruss Settlor Trust, Joseph S., 2141
Gruss Trust, Joseph S., 2141
Gruss, Audrey B., 2141
Gruss, Brenda, 6114
Gruss, Emanuel, 6114
Gruss, Leslie, 6114
Gruss, Martin D., 2141, 2284
Gruss, Riane, 6114
Gryphon International Growth, 9916
Gryttenholm, Jerry A., 9826
Grzewinski, Philip M., 4194
Gschwendtner, Sara, 2732
GST Charitable Lead Trust, 5632
GTI Services, Inc., 7846
Guajardo, Maria, 1401
Guan, Yibing, 6230
Guaranty Trust Co. of Missouri, The, 4966
Guardian Exploration, LLC, 8090
Guardian Industries Corp., 4454, 7713
Guardian Protection Services, Inc., 8276
Guarini, Frank J., 5283
Guarnieri, Philip, 5806
Guastaferro, John, 239
Guazza, Keith, 106
Guberman, Tina, 5939
Gudas, Elysia M., 5802
Gudas, Viki, 4523
Gudelsky, John, 3809
Gudelsky, Medda, 3809
Gudim, Melissa Collins, 412
Guedj, Kate, 3956
Guel, Roy, 9059
Guelfi, Hillary Hedinger, 7851
Guelli, Rebecca Bree, 5887
Guenther & Sons Inc., C.H., 9149
Guenther, Fred, 4575
Guenther, Jack, 8877, 9018
Guenther, Jack E., Jr., 8877
Guenther, Pearl H., 634
Guenther, Valerie Urschel, 8877
Guerin, Dana, 1150
Guerin, Lisa, 1150
Guerin, Michael, 1150
Guerin, Paul, 1150
Guerin, Vera, 1150
Guerin, Wilfred L., 3657
Guernsey, Helen, 3437
Guernsey, Max E., 3437
Guerra, Fernando, Dr., 9144
Guerra, Frank A., 9150
Guerra, Guiomar Garcia, 1904
Guerra, Lucas H., 4103
Guerrero, Ana, 7588
Guerrero, Andre, 197
Guerrero, Anthony R., Jr., 2598
Guerrero, George, 1406
Guerry, John P., 8576
Guerry, Zan, 8576
Guess ?, Inc., 635
Guess, Francis, 8550
Guess, Mark, 7474
Guessoum, Nidhal, 8313
Guest, Penny, 9748
Guest, Sandra M., 4837
Guevara, Julia, 4412
Guevara, Zac, 366
Guffey, Alan, 1255
Guffey, Cynthia King, 1255
Gugenheim, Ada Mary, 3172
Guggenheim, Harry Frank, 6115
Guggenheim, Simon, 6116
Guggenheim, Simon, Mrs., 6116
Guggenhime, Andrew, 819
Guggenhime, Richard J., 819
Guggino, Kathleen P., 861
Guglielmo, D. Anthony, 1651
Guiabo, Paul L., 7132
Guiabo, Renee C., 7132
GuideOne Life Insurance Co., 3438
Guido, Jeannine, 346
Guido, Patrick, 7332
Guidry, Carolyn, 5121
Guidry, David, 3612
Guidry, Eric, 3623
Guidry, Mark, 5121
Guidry, Theodore, II, 9148
Guidugli, John J., 7481
Guihan, J. Lawrence, 4098
Guilarte, E. Andres, 2282
Guilarte, Olga, 2282
Guilbault, Keith, 736
Guilbault, Rose, 421
Guilbert, Mike, 8511
Guild, Alice F., 2592
Guill, Ernie T., Jr., 9474
Guillies, Wendy, 4921
Guimaraes, Enderson, 6627
Guinan, Thomas G., 5398
Guine, Joyce Davis, 1035
Guinn, Jo H., 8482
Guinn, Linda A., 417
Guinn, Max, 2790
Guirlinger, Richard B., 7328
Gulbrandsen, Mary W., 9849, 9931
Gulf Coast Asphalt Company, 8721
Gulfstream Park, 1942
Gulick, Amy, 9565
Gulick, Barbara, 3011
Gulick, E. Leeds, 9653
Gulick, George G., 9653
Gulick, Robert S., 4028
Gulla, John C., 5995
Gullen, David J., 111
Gulley, Joan L., 8230
Gulley, Philip G., 8296
Gulmi, James S., 8550
Guloien, David E., 6467
Gulton, Edith, 5284
Gulton, Leslie K., 5284
Gumbiner, Alis, 636
Gumbiner, Burke, 636
Gumbiner, Josephine S., 636
Gumbiner, Lee, 636
Gumirov, Maya, 2714
Gumm, Vicki, 794
Gummer, Donald, 5458
Gummer, M.S., 5458
Gummey, Charles F., Jr., 1814
Gumness, Brian, 9856
Gumness, Sandra L., 9856
Gump, Patricia, 536
Gumpert Trust, William, 637
Gund Charitable Lead Trust 3, Gordon and Llura Liggett, 7475
Gund Charitable Lead Trust 5, Gordon and Llura Liggett, 7475
Gund Charitable Lead Trust 6, Gordon and Llura Liggett, 7475
Gund Charitable Lead Trust 7, Gordon and Llura Liggett, 7475
Gund Charitable Lead Trust 8, Gordon and Llura Liggett, 7475
Gund Foundation, Gordon & Llura, 8109
Gund Trust, Gordon and Llura Liggett, 7475
Gund, Agnes, 7476
Gund, Ann L., 7478
Gund, Catherine, 7476, 7478
Gund, G. Zachary, 7475
Gund, Geoffrey, 7477, 7478
Gund, George, 7478
Gund, George, IV, 7478
Gund, Gordon, 5285
Gund, Grant, 7475
Gund, Llura, 5285
Gund, Llura A., 5285
Gund, Louise, 7472, 7720
Gund, Zachary, 7478
Gunden, June, 8090
Gundlach, Andrew, 6013, 6268
Gundlach, Roger, 7444
Gundlach, Susan Jones, 3645
Gundling, Henry, 566
Gunkel, Alan, 3403
Gunn, Carol, 9277
Gunn, Curtis, Jr., 8806
Gunn, Daniel, 3517
Gunn, Gail, 9413
Gunnar, Rolf, 2673
Gunnin, John M., 587
Gunsteens, Anne, 3841
Gunstone, Lauren, 5115
Gunstream, Susie, 1473
Gunter Cemetery Trust, Dorothy H., 8483
Gunter, Brenda, 9146
Gunter, Samuel B., 9473
Gunterberg, Robert J., 8073
Gunzberg, Joan, 2826

Hager, Lee, 2347
Hager, Lindsay, 4438
Hager, Louis Busch, Jr., 2139
Hager, Marjorie, 3597
Hager, Moshe, 644
Hager, Tanis, 9120
Hagerman, Doug M., 9934
Hagerman, Lisa H., 6155, 6156
Hagerty, Megan H., 6152
Hagey, Hank, 709
Hagey, Harry R., 709
Hagey, Shirley, 709
Haggai, Thomas S., 1427
Haggard, Charlie, 9115
Haggard, Christie, 9215
Haggard, James M., 9444
Haggerty, Beatrice M., 8881
Haggerty, Fred, 6285
Haggerty, Gretchen R., 8325
Haggerty, Matthew E., Esq., 8275
Haggerty, Michael G., 8881
Haggerty, Patrick E., 8881
Haggerty-Bearden, C. Gwen, 4574
Haggett, Robert M., 4170
Haggin, Margaret Voorhies, 8075
Haggins, Jason, 3132
Haglund, Deborah D., 2796
Hagman, Lorri, 9587
Hagman, Paul, 7705
Hagny, Dennis, 8523
Hagopian, Joanne, 677, 678
Hagstrom, Collin, 9677
Hagstrom, Jillian McClaskey, 9677
Hague, John, 1037
Hague, Valerie, 3359
Hahm, Jeannette, 1161
Hahn Waianae Land, LLC, 2144
Hahn, Barry, 5288
Hahn, Bevra H., 6401
Hahn, David J., 2144
Hahn, Elliot, 5288
Hahn, Gregory F., 3272
Hahn, Hai Joung, 2144
Hahn, Hai Joung Yoon, 2144
Hahn, Herbert H., Jr., 8974
Hahn, Lillian, 5288
Hahn, Marsha, 6369
Hahn, Paul, 2144
Hahn, Robert, 1605
Hahn, Sang Hoon, 2144
Hahsler, Kristina, 8883
Haider, Ali, 5934
Haider, Susan, 9601
Haidet, Jeffrey K., 2516
Haile Jr. Foundation, Carol Ann and Ralph V., 7394
Haile Trust, Ralph V., 7480
Haile, Ralph V., 7480
Haines & Haines, Inc., 5289
Haines, Bruce S., 8267
Haines, David, Dr., 3335
Haines, Holly, 5289
Haines, Kimberly, 9411
Haines, Lana, 2792
Haines, Robert H., 6124
Haines, William S., 5289
Haines, William S., Jr., 5289
Hair, Lanny, 167
Haire, Susan L., 7178
Hairston, E. Gregory, 9421
Haisley, Jimmie Anne, Dr., 6374
Haje, Helen, 6129
Haje, Katie, 6129
Haje, Michael, 6129
Haje, Peter R., 6129
Hajek, Douglas J., 8521
Hajek, Josef, 2363
Hajim, Edmund A., 2253
Hajra, Neel, 4340
Hajtman, L. Michael, 8905
Hakuta, Kenji, 1934
Halbert Trust, Jo Ann Walling, 8882
Halbert Trust, JoAnn Walling, 8749
Halbert, David D., 8749
Halbert, Jo Ann Walling, 8882
Halbert, Jon S., 8882
Halbert, Kathryn Ann, 8749
Halbert, Kristen S., 8749
Halbert, Linda M., 8882
Halbert, Lindsay M., 8882
Halbert, Margaret, 2534
Halbert, Michael D., 8749
Halbert, Patrick, 8749
Halbreich, Kathy, 5917, 5918
Halbreicht, Nancy, 8889
Halbritter, Barry, 7971
Halby, Peter C., 1419
Halby, Will, 1419
Haldeman, Barbara C., 8076
Haldeman, Catherine J., 8076
Haldeman, Charles, 8076
Haldeman, Charles Edgar, Jr., 8076
Haldeman, Charlotte E., 8076
Haldeman, Matthew A., 8076
Hale Makua, 2604
Hale, Chris, 2777
Hale, Elwyn C., 645
Hale, Gabrielle, 8739
Hale, Joanne D., 270
Hale, Joe, 3990
Hale, Jr. 2010 Trust, Robert T., 4190
Hale, Judith, 4190
Hale, Karen R., 4190
Hale, M. Eugenie, 645
Hale, Mary, 9616
Hale, Robert T., Jr., 4190
Hale, Robert, Sr., 4190
Hale, T. Douglas, 8138
Halepeska, Robert, 8941
Hales, Wendy, 254
Halevy, Drew, 6681
Halevy, Renee Hasten, 3315
Haley, Ben P., 3649
Haley, Carl T., 8550
Haley, Joanie, 9017
Haley, Kathleen Powers, 4083
Haley, Lynn C., 7219
Haley, Lynne M., Dr., 4496
Haley, Michael W., 7219
Haley, Narley L., 7548
Haley, Steven, 4083
Halfhide, Jon, 1154
Halfon, Ellen E., 7532
Halfon, Jay R., 6615
Halick, John V., 8730
Halkyard, Jonathan, 5136
Hall Capital, 7762
Hall Charitable Lead Annuity Trust, Craig and Kathryn, 8883
Hall Family Investments, LLC, 9324
Hall Financial Group, 8883
Hall, Aaron, 9324
Hall, Adah F., 4084
Hall, Adam, 9324
Hall, Alan E., 9324
Hall, Andrew J., 2145
Hall, Annette, 9324
Hall, Anthony W., Jr., 8917
Hall, Arthur E., 5118
Hall, Barbara, 7887
Hall, Beverly, 2540, 6025
Hall, Blair Penske, 4519
Hall, Brijetta Lynn, 8883
Hall, Brijetta Waller, 8883
Hall, Brooks, Jr., 7762
Hall, Burton M., 9531
Hall, Cami, 9324
Hall, Carla, 3245
Hall, Carol, 3369
Hall, Charles W., 8664
Hall, Christian, 9324
Hall, Christine C., 2145
Hall, Christoper E., 3926
Hall, Conrad M., 9531
Hall, Cosby M., 9531
Hall, Craig, 8883
Hall, Cynthia, 9578
Hall, Dan, 8789
Hall, David, 2489
Hall, David E., 4906
Hall, Diane, 7850
Hall, Donald J., 4905
Hall, Donald J., Jr., 4906
Hall, Donald R., 2085
Hall, E.A., 4905
Hall, Emily, 9324
Hall, Emma, 2145
Hall, Eric, 9324
Hall, F. Marie, 8852
Hall, Florence Marie, 8852
Hall, Fred Jones, 7762
Hall, Gary, 490
Hall, Gordon, 7272
Hall, H. Andrew McMicking, 904
Hall, James R., 7632
Hall, Jamie, 1019
Hall, Jeannie, 9324
Hall, Jim, 3319
Hall, Joan, 1019
Hall, Joanne, 5118
Hall, Jodi, 1019
Hall, John, 1019, 3249, 3317
Hall, John, Jr., 1019
Hall, Jonathan C., 8167
Hall, Joseph C.M., 904
Hall, Joy, 1385
Hall, Joyce C., 4905
Hall, Joyce Wetzel, 4035
Hall, Karla D., 4410
Hall, Kate Warren, 7841
Hall, Kathryn, 1256
Hall, Kathryn A., 6470
Hall, Kathryn Walt, 8883
Hall, Kent A, 3451
Hall, Kevin, 1387
Hall, Kim, 9324
Hall, Kirke T., 3222
Hall, Kirkland, 7762
Hall, Les, 9538
Hall, Leslie Kelly, 4107
Hall, Lewis L., 2625
Hall, Lilisa, 7877
Hall, Lisa, 8917
Hall, Lou, 7742
Hall, Lyle G., 8295
Hall, Lyle G., Jr., 8295
Hall, Lyle G., Sr., 8295
Hall, Margaret M., 9531
Hall, Marie Fondren, 8853
Hall, Marjorie-Padula, 3249
Hall, Mark, 2145
Hall, Marvin B., 2604
Hall, Mary, 8561, 9311
Hall, Matthew A., 578
Hall, Megan, 8295
Hall, Nancy, 7816
Hall, Neil, 8230
Hall, Pat, 3451
Hall, Prem, 9485
Hall, R.B., 4905
Hall, Roderick C.M., 904
Hall, Serena Davis, 2056
Hall, Tom, 5108
Hall, Tripp, 7742
Hall, Trudie, 3556
Hall, Whitney, 420
Hall, William, 5622
Hall, William A., 4902, 4905
Halle, Bruce T., 170
Halle, Bruce T., Jr., 118
Halle, Bruce T., Sr., 118
Halle, Diane M., 118, 170
Halle, Michael, 169
Halle, Nikki, 118
Halle-Lyle, Susan, 118
Hallenbeck, Alfred M., 6808
Haller, Albert G., 9635
Haller, Heinz, 4404
Haller, Henry E., Jr., 2146
Haller, Jim, 9251
Haller, Karen, 5149
Haller, Linda L. Boyce, 2146
Hallett, Susan H., 9416
Hallgren, Carl R., 8272
Halliburton Co., 8884
Halliday, Susan, 739
Halligan, John R., 2886
Halligan, Mike, 5018
Halligan, Patrick, 6090
Halligan, Robert, 5424
Hallinan, Cornelia, 7559
Hallinan, Cornelia I., 7559
Hallinan, Kathy, 6249
Hallinan, Tess Ireland, 7559
Hallman, Elisabeth, 368
Hallman, Timothy H., 8497
Hallman, William P., Jr., 8685
Hallmark Cards, Inc., 4905, 4906
Hallock, David P., 4063
Hallock, Meloni M., 365
Hallock, Robert B., 157
Halloran, Beth, 4714
Halloran, John W., 5829
Halloran, Kathleen L., 2933
Halloran, Owen, 6285
Halloran, Samantha Borders, 9220
Hallow, Barbara, 7152
Hallow, Barbara B., 7152
Hallow, Joseph, 7152
Hallquist, Carol, 4906
Halm, Jeffrey, 7684
Halme, Morgan, 9080
Halme, Paul, 9080
Halper, Robert, 6539
Halperin, Alan, 2999
Halperin, Mark, 646
Halperin, Maurine S., 1168
Halperin, Philip W., 646, 1168
Halperin, Robert, 646
Halperin, Ruth, 646
Halpern, Arie, 5290
Halpern, Christina Lewis, 6365
Halpern, Eva, 5290
Halpern, Mark, 3672
Halpern, Philip M., 1811
Halpern, Steven, 5910

Halpern, Susan U., 6863
Halpert, Lois, 3817
Halprin, Matt, 984
Halsell, Ewing, 8885
Halsell, Ewing, Mrs., 8885
Halsell, Oliver L., 647
Halsey, Karen, 7570
Halstead, Cathy, 544
Halstead, George, 2279
Halstead, Peter, 544
Halterman, Darlene F., 8272
Halton, Dale F., 1426
Halverson, Gary B., 7407
Halverstadt, Douglas, 2942
Halverstadt, Loren Thomas, Jr., 2942
Halvorsen, Bradley W., 111
Halvorsen, Diane K., 1606
Halvorsen, O. Andreas, 1717
Halvorsen, Ole Andreas, 1606
Halvorson, Newman T., Jr., 1931
Ham, Bill, 4452
Hamadi, Ramsey, 7180
Hamann, Jennifer, 5074
Hamatie, John, 2087
Hambleton, L.B., 630
Hambly, Nancy, 4304
Hambrick, James L., 7546
Hambrick, Thomas G., Jr., 8695
Hamburg, David, 5747
Hamburg, Margaret A., 1941
Hamel, Dana A., 2887
Hamel, Richard P., 3932
Hamel, Rodolphe, 3144
Hamer, Davidson H., 9353
Hamer, Donald W., 8077
Hamer, Mickey, 633
Hamerschlag, James, 6905
Hamerton-Kelly, Robert, 1249
Hamil, Greg, 2551
Hamil, Jeanne S., 2551
Hamil, Michael, 2551
Hamill, Claud B., 8887
Hamill, Corwith, 2888
Hamill, Deirdre, 6115
Hamill, Frances, 5703
Hamill, Janice, 2590
Hamill, Joan B., 2888
Hamill, Jonathan C., 2888
Hamill, Laura, 238
Hamill, Marie G., 8887
Hamill, Patrick, 1411
Hamill, Stephen, 2590
Hamilton, B.A., 3570
Hamilton, Barbara, 7567
Hamilton, Betsey, 4822
Hamilton, Bud, 5533
Hamilton, Carey, 5074
Hamilton, Dorrance H., 8078, 8444
Hamilton, Elizabeth, 3392
Hamilton, Emory A., 8962
Hamilton, Florence C., 8370
Hamilton, George, 1949
Hamilton, Greg, 9384
Hamilton, Jeanne G., 9776
Hamilton, Josh, 138
Hamilton, Lawson W., III, 9776
Hamilton, Lawson W., Jr., 9776
Hamilton, Lisa, 4869, 4954
Hamilton, Lisa M., 3745
Hamilton, M. Hayne, 8638
Hamilton, M.D., 9822
Hamilton, Mary, 9793
Hamilton, Nancy, 5396
Hamilton, Natalie, 9793
Hamilton, Nathaniel P., 8078
Hamilton, Neil, 6064
Hamilton, Peter, 877
Hamilton, Peter B., 2955
Hamilton, Robert E., 2936
Hamilton, Rose Lincoln, 9750
Hamilton, S. Matthews V., Jr., 8078
Hamilton, Scott, 1479
Hamilton, Thomas J., 1851
Hamit, Pat, 3502
Hamlainen, Pasi, 1037
Hamlet, Virginia W., 9450
Hamlin, Leonard L., Sr., Dr., 9384
Hamm, Charles J., 1607
Hamm, Duke, 3320
Hamm, Edward H., 4673
Hamm, Edward H., Jr., 4673
Hamm, Irene F., 1607
Hamm, Liza H., 1607
Hamm, William, Jr., 4673
Hammack, John A., 9019
Hamman, Beverly O., 5112
Hamman, George, 8888
Hamman, Henry R., 8888
Hamman, Mabel Lene, 3312
Hamman, Mary Josephine, 8888
Hamman, Russell R., 8888
Hamman, Stephen R., 5112
Hammel, Kenneth W., 8088
Hammel, Linda Sue, 8088
Hammer, Armand, 648
Hammer, Kouhaila G., 4371
Hammer, Laurel A., 5349
Hammer, Lesley Schwartz, 162
Hammer, Michael A., 648
Hammer, Richard, Jr., 9997
Hammer, Stacy, 7462
Hammer, Viktor A., 648
Hammergren, John H., 903
Hammerness, V., 581
Hammerslag, David, 126
Hammersley, Frederick H., 5520
Hammersmith, Suann D., 4485
Hammett, Willie A., 7006
Hammock, Kelli M., 185
Hammon, Craig, 8644
Hammond and Associates, 1116
Hammond, Frank M., 7946
Hammond, Howell A., 7182
Hammond, Jack A., 9382
Hammond, Les, 9275
Hammond, Michael, 9500
Hammond, Philip W., 3778
Hammond, Ray, Rev., 4329
Hammonds, Evelynn M., 5608
Hammons, Brian, 4872
Hammons, Marva, 4102, 9595
Hammons, Ryan C., 3372
Hamner, Emily H., 3660
Hamner, Lucille Donlon, 3660
Hamner, Michael G., 3660
Hamner, Millie, 1511
Hamon, Nancy B., 8889
Hamoui, Omar, 4330
Hamp, Sheila Ford, 4430
Hamp, Steven K., 4371, 4479
Hampl, Patricia, 4681
Hamprick, Richard, 9447
Hampshire Village LLC, 9452
Hampshire West LLC, 9452
Hampson, Craig, 975
Hampton, Floris Jean, 3502
Hampton, Maria G., 3569
Hampton, Mark, 6841
Hampton, Wade, 2765
Hamrich, Richard, Dr., 9457
Hamrick, A. Wardlaw, 8479
Hamrick, Charles F., II, 8479
Hamrick, Harvey B., Jr., 7194
Hamrick, Leslie Hille, 7759
Hamrick, Lyman W., 8479
Hamrick, Mike, 1974
Hamrick, Sallie, 3910
Hamrick, W. Carlisle, 8479
Hamrock, Joseph, 7591
Hamzy, Anita, 1634
Han, Amy, 3337
Han, Fang, 6861
Hanaghan, Dennis, 7700
Hanan, Benjamin, 2142
Hanas, Susan D., 2070
Hanauer, Diane, 1650
Hanauer, Gerald, 9637
Hanauer, Lenore, 9636
Hanauer, Leslie, 9637
Hanauer, Lisa E., 7428
Hanauer, Nick, 9637
Hanavan, Claire F., 1615
Hanaway, Andrea, 8223
Hanback, Scott, 3282
Hancher, Bill, 3324
Hancock, Allan G., 7971
Hancock, Chrystal, 9059
Hancock, David, 9939
Hancock, Debra, 9503
Hancock, James, 9059
Hancock, John W., 5057
Hancock, Jonathan, 3281
Hancock, Larry, 9789
Hancock, Lisa D., 6070
Hancock, Paul, 1139
Hancock, W.J., 1060
Hand, Donna S., 2528
Hand, Karen, 9416
Hand, Kerry W., 2438
Hand, Lauren Colleen, 1810
Handel, Nancy H., 1166
Handelman, Donald E., 6446
Handelman, Irving, 6802
Handelman, James H., 6446
Handelman, Richard, 6446
Handelman, Sara, 6802
Handelman, William R., 6446
Handelsman, Phyllis, 2968
Hander, Linda B., 5473
Handke, David P., Jr., 7564
Handleman, Lynn, 649
Handleman, Scott, 649
Handler, Lawrence, 4526
Handler, Peter, 2983
Handley, Cathy, 9976
Handley, Leon H., Esq., 2225
Handran, George B., 4857
Hands Trust, Sally M., 9858
Hands, Collier M., 9858
Hands, Helen M., 9858
Hands, John L., Jr., 9858
Handwerger, Samuel, 3798
Handy, Ned, 8429
Handy, Philip, 143
Hanenberger, Melissa B., 1768
Hanenburg, Edward, 4446
Hanes, F. Borden, Jr., 7221
Hanes, Norman, 3649
Haney, James S., 9881
Haney, Jamie, 3341
Haney, Michael P., 2310
Haney, Stuart A., 9417
Haney, William, 6873
Hanflik, Nancy J., 4372
Hanford, Deirdre, 1232
Hang, MaryKao L., 4757
Hang, May Kao, 4715
Hangsleben, Melissa, 92
Hanifan, Jack R., 5147
Hanisch, Arthur S., 9707
Hanisch, Erik M., 9707
Hanisch, Lenore M., 9707
Hanisee, Robert, 298
Hanisko, Mike, 4344
Hank, Allen B., 2673, 2828
Hank, Bernard J., Jr., 3134
Hank, John C., 2828
Hank, Joyce M., 3134
Hank, Sheri, 4684
Hank, Viola, 3134
Hank, Viola D., 2828
Hank, William J., 2673
Hankamer, Doris K., 8890
Hankamer, Earl Curtis, III, 8890
Hankamer, Earl Curtis, Jr., 8890
Hankel, Richard, 5098
Hankin, Michael D., 3726
Hankin, Rockell N., 771
Hankins Living Trust, Mari Alyce, 5521
Hankins, Mari Alyce, 5521
Hankovszky, Zoltan, 6636
Hanks, Tom, 9571
Hanle, Dorothy, 5261
Hanle, Dorothy B., 5261
Hanley, Daniel, 3776
Hanley, Jack, 2476
Hanley, Janet, 3061
Hanley, John W., Jr., 2476
Hanley, John W., Sr., 2476
Hanley, Kristen, 2476
Hanley, Linda H., 2476
Hanley, Mary Jane, 2476
Hanley, Mary Reel, 2476
Hanley, Michael J., 2476
Hanley, Michael J., Jr., 2476
Hanley, Michael J., Sr., 2476
Hanley, Mimi, 2476
Hanley, Sondra, 2476
Hanley, Steve, 9704
Hanley, William Lee, Jr., 5323
Hanlon, Charles G., 2109
Hanlon, Diane E., 2109
Hanlon, Kevin, 8391
Hanlon, Timothy G., 1312
Hanlon, Tom, 8333
Hanlon, Victoria, 1053
Hanlon-Stolte, Mardy, 7416
Hann, Daniel P., 3355
Hanna, Ashraf, 571
Hanna, Bill, 3510
Hanna, Jack, 2315
Hanna, Janice, 3510
Hanna, John O., 7993
Hanna, Linda, 2040
Hanna, Rod, 1528
Hanna, Troy M., 8501
Hanna, William, 739
Hannaford Bros. Co., 3690
Hannah, Bill, 194
Hannah, Carol, 713
Hannah, John R., 9144, 9166
Hannah, Kenneth, 9089
Hannah, Mary, 7425
Hannan, Kathy A.H., 5349
Hannan, Rich, 4448
Hannasch, Brian, 3321

Hanneman, Judy, 849
Hanni, Carrie, 3319
Hannig, Frank L., 448
Hannigan, Charlie, 5598, 6451
Hannigan, Michael R., 1478
Hannon, James A., 651
Hannon, Jane, 2669
Hannon, John, 3369
Hannon, William H., 650
Hannon, William Herbert, 651
Hanover Apartments LLC, 9452
Hanover Insurance Co., The, 4086
Hanrahan, Dan, 4750
Hanrahan, Jim, 4056
Hanrahan, Katherine, 8303
Hanratty, Janet L., 3714
Hans, Judith, 214
Hans, N. Theodore, 2927
Hans, R.J., 3209
Hans, Rick, 3210
Hansberry, James, 2766
Hanschen, Richard, 8671
Hansen Foundation, Mark and Anne, 5160
Hansen Trust, Dane G., 3518
Hansen, Anne, 1913
Hansen, Betty, 3481
Hansen, Beverly, 5075
Hansen, Bill, 4683
Hansen, Chip, Jr., 4361
Hansen, Chris, 3475
Hansen, Dale, 9337
Hansen, Dane G., 3518
Hansen, Darlene, 1077
Hansen, David, 1263
Hansen, Donna L., 6130
Hansen, Edwina, 5291
Hansen, Elisabeth, 1913
Hansen, G.W., 1077
Hansen, Gail A., 5372
Hansen, Gretchen, 8079
Hansen, Harold C., 5173
Hansen, Inc., 8079
Hansen, James, 2889
Hansen, Jennifer, 5291
Hansen, Joan, 7857
Hansen, Joanne B., 2889
Hansen, Jody, 6903
Hansen, John, 652
Hansen, John Barrett, 652
Hansen, John J., 6130
Hansen, K.N., Jr., 1077
Hansen, K.N., Sr., 1077
Hansen, Katie, 652
Hansen, Linda J., 9830
Hansen, Lisa, 2889
Hansen, Lisa D., 971
Hansen, Mark, 1893, 1913
Hansen, Mark W., 6130
Hansen, Maxine, 270
Hansen, Michele, 591
Hansen, Nancy Huston, 8103
Hansen, Nancy K., 8079
Hansen, Patricia A., 3440
Hansen, Paul E., 6130
Hansen, Randy, 4446
Hansen, Richard W., 2889
Hansen, Robert, 1477
Hansen, Robert H., 3440
Hansen, Robert U., 1441
Hansen, Roger B., 5291
Hansen, Roger M., 3440
Hansen, Sally, 1368
Hansen, Scott, 1287, 2889
Hansen, Steve, 9603
Hansen, Teri A., 2142
Hansen, Thomas L., 3440
Hansen, Thomas P., Hon., 629
Hansen, Todd, 5039
Hansen, Walter, 1077
Hansen, William Gregg, 8079
Hansen, Willis M., 3440
Hansen-Strom, Amy L., 6130
Hansford, Brendon, 1961
Hansmann, Ralph E., 5280
Hanson Aggregates West, Inc., 4578
Hanson Family Trust, 653
Hanson, Abigail, 5292
Hanson, Alden Lee, 4407
Hanson, Alexander D., 5292
Hanson, Bill, 3288
Hanson, Brian, 3444
Hanson, Burton M., 8853
Hanson, Calvin J., 1288
Hanson, Daniel, 856
Hanson, Eliza F., 5292
Hanson, Erik A., 6389
Hanson, Heidi Ann, 856
Hanson, John V., 3441
Hanson, Kari M., 4650
Hanson, Kirk O., 1175
Hanson, Larry, 9617
Hanson, Laura F., 5292
Hanson, Lee, 4679
Hanson, Mark D., 4650
Hanson, Mark G., 9639
Hanson, Matt R., 7359
Hanson, Michael E., Jr., 8853
Hanson, Paul D., 3441
Hanson, Peggy, 4716
Hanson, Phillip J., 4996
Hanson, R. Reid, 2403
Hanson, Stephanie K., 5899
Hanson, Steve, 9715
Hanson, Todd, 992
Hanson, Victor Davis, 6115
Hanson, Virginia, 9019
Hanson, William C., 4483
Hanten, Joan, 9659
Hanton, Jackie, 4373
Hapgood, Barbara, 1578
Hapgood, Elaine P., 1578, 1779, 1839
Hapgood, Matthew, 1578
Hapke, Andrew, 739
Hapke, Claire, 739
Hapke, Norman, 739
Hapke, Norman F., Jr., 739
Hapke, Valerie Jacobs, 739
Happer, William, 1926
Happy Valley School, 2958
Hara, Julie, 4668
Hara, Julie S., 4702
Haraksin, Tracy, 1035
Harary, Gloria, 6131
Harary, Joseph, 6131
Harary, Ralph J., 6131
Harasty, Shandre, 9510
Haraway, Donald L., 9398
Harbaugh, R.H., 7784, 7817
Harbaugh, Russell H., Jr., 7785
Harbers, Renee W., 9613
Harbert, Kathryn D., 21
Harbert, Raymond, 53
Harbison, Jean, 7742
Harbor Associates, 2194
Harbour, Nancy, 82
Harckham, Janet, 676
Hard Candy LLC, 2091
Hard Rock Cafe International (USA) Inc., 2147
Hardacre, David, 432
Hardaway, Cathy Ann, 8275
Hardcastle, Jeff, 4362
Hardee, Jerry, 2478
Hardegree, William B., Jr., 2528
Harden, Ercia E., 654
Harden, Eugene E., 654
Harden, Lynn, 7829
Harden, Wanda D., 4372
Hardenbergh Charitable Annuity Trust, I., 4672
Hardenbergh, Gabrielle, 4672
Hardenbergh, Ianthe B., 4672
Harder, Adam, 3403
Harder, Delmar S., 9640
Harder, Scott E., 2891
Hardester, Gregory R., 1059
Hardesty, Donna J., 7756
Hardesty, F. Roger, 7756
Hardesty, Jane G., 2477
Hardesty, Les, 3245
Hardesty, Michelle, 7756
Hardgrove, Ian F., 4597
Hardie, Chris, 3400
Hardie, David, 5138
Hardie, Donald, 2487
Hardie, Thornton, III, 9125
Hardiek, Shannon, 3281
Hardiman, Dennis, 2185
Hardiman, Lisa, 2185
Hardiman, S. Anne, 9243
Hardin Trust, Helen E., 8577
Hardin Trust, Nicole A., 5616
Hardin's Bakeries Corp., 4831
Hardin, Claudia J., 801
Hardin, Janie, 3319
Hardin, Katharine Harrison, 7273
Hardin, P. Russell, 2571, 2579
Hardin, Philip Bernard, 4831
Harding Service, LLC, 5377
Harding, Cheryl, 3466
Harding, David R., 2732
Harding, Marty, 9950
Harding, Matthew K., 5359
Harding, Samuel C., Jr., 9436
Harding, William Giles, 1565
Hardke, David, 189
Hardman, E. Davisson, 444
Hardt, Carrie, 2897
Hardt, Edwin E., 2897
Hardt, Joshua, 2897
Hardt, Karl W., 2897
Hardwick, Kelly, 8856
Hardwick, Mark K., 3286
Hardy, Alexander, 570
Hardy, Ann S. Donnelley, 2802
Hardy, Cary, 5473
Hardy, George, 2040
Hardy, H. Michael, 7360
Hardy, J. Michael, 9715
Hardy, John C., 4846
Hardy, Leslie M., 5379
Hardy, Leslie Warrington Bailey, 7703
Hardy, Margaret F., Esq., 9414
Hardy, Ralph W., Jr., 3843
Hardy, S. Michael, 2431
Hardy, Tammy, 8332
Hardy, Tom, 1178, 3288
Hardy, W. Marvin, IV, 2390
Hare, Bonnie, 3285
Hare, Christina M., 17
Hare, Jeffrey R., 6499
Harelson, Julie, 344
Harenburg, Tom, 9916
Harfest, Joann, 9503
Harford, Luke, 3714
Hargrave, Christine, 9773
Hargrave, Jennifer D., 8738
Hargreaves, David D.R., 8403
Hargrove, Lafeye, 2434
Haring, Allen, 6133
Haring, Keith, 6133
Haring, Kristen, 6133
Harison, Julie M., 2447
Harison, Phil S., Jr., 2447
Harker, Martin, 3280
Harkleroad, Joe, 7474
Harkness, Dave, 9304
Harkness, Edward S., 5800
Harkness, Edward S., Mrs., 5800
Harkness, Rebekah, 6134
Harkness, Stephen V., Mrs., 5800
Harkness, William Hale, 6134
Harla, JoAnne, 5315
Harlan, Aurzella S., 4969
Harlan, Leigh M., 6978
Harlan, Stephen D., 1925
Harland, John H., 2477
Harland, Richard J., 9966
Harle, Kimberly, 9149
Harlem, Richard A., 7054
Harley, Jill A., 2755
Harley-Davidson, Inc., 9859
Harlos, Mike, 3279
Harlow, Lynne, 5623
Harlow, Thomas R., 7972
Harman Administrative Trust, Sidney, 656
Harman, Arline, 9325
Harman, Barbara, 656
Harman, Barry, 9325
Harman, Dan, 656
Harman, Fred, 9514
Harman, Frederic, 655
Harman, Jane, 656
Harman, Janet, 9189
Harman, Janet E., 8949
Harman, Leon, 9325
Harman, Lucy, 9414
Harman, Lynn, 656
Harman, Mark B., 9325
Harman, Stephanie Curtis, 655
Harman, Tim, 3348
Harman, Todd B., 9325
Harmelink, Kevin, 4447
Harmon Charitable Fund Unitrust, Margaret W., 4803
Harmon, Carol, 7411
Harmon, Chris, 3277
Harmon, Christopher, 8749
Harmon, Debra A., 4376
Harmon, John C., 8204, 8228
Harmon, John Campbell, 8256
Harmon, Laura, 19
Harmon, Lawrence A., 2572
Harmon, Margaret Weyerhaeuser, 4803
Harmon, T. Craig, 2789
Harmon, Tom, 3321
Harmon, William, 9126
Harmon-Ramsey, Lola, 4438
Harms, Ted E., 1365
Harmsworth, Esmond, 4087
Harnden, Thomas, 7382
Harned, Elizabeth Quadracci, 9968
Harnett, Craig C., 6528
Harnett, Gordon, 7448

Harter, Ruth, 3076
Hartford Courant Co., The, 1589
Hartford Trust, Huntington, 5551
Hartford, George L., 6144
Hartford, Harold, 2359
Hartford, Harold L., 2359
Hartford, John A., 6144
Hartford, Scott, 7481
Hartgering, Bill, 744
Harthorn, Sophie, 3132
Hartigan, Pat, 6760
Hartin, Christy, 8994
Hartin, Susan F., 8839
Hartke, Selma, 2897
Hartl, Deborah, 9604
Hartl, Michael J., 1690
Hartl, Roger A., 7916
Hartley, Fred L., Jr., 659
Hartley, Indya, 6157
Hartley, Jane, 6807
Hartley, Linda, 2040
Hartley, M.O., 9465
Hartley, Margaret A., 659
Hartley, Michael, 2236
Hartley, Patricia, 3519
Hartley, Therese C., 659
Hartley, Thomas D., 4945
Hartley, W.C., 3519
Hartloff, Paul W., 1267
Hartman Charitable Lead Annuity Trust, John W., 1610
Hartman Family Foundation, Shamai & Richu, 5959
Hartman Family Trust, 2898
Hartman, Alexander, 6145
Hartman, Bill, 8351
Hartman, David, 5473
Hartman, Debra F., 2898
Hartman, Esther Kelly B., 1610
Hartman, Gary, 1392
Hartman, Gordon, 8893
Hartman, Gordon V., 8893
Hartman, Israel, 5959, 6145
Hartman, Janet Bauer, 8692
Hartman, John W., 1610
Hartman, Judith K., 7688
Hartman, Larry, 8294
Hartman, Larry A., 6458
Hartman, Lynn Pike, 8223
Hartman, Margaret M., 8893
Hartman, Marla, 549
Hartman, Renee, 3366
Hartman, Robert, 2898, 3518
Hartman, Sally Kirby, 9448
Hartman, Sid, 877
Hartman, Sima, 6145
Hartman, Teri, 2482
Hartman, Todd, 4612
Hartman-Horvitz, Erica, 7493
Hartmann, George F., 9855
Hartnell, Melissa, 7857
Hartner, John, 2803
Hartness, Robert G., 8482
Hartness, Thomas P., 8482
Hartness, Thomas S., 8482
Hartnett, Shane, 1295
Hartquist Trust, Mildred, 7246
Harts, Jon, 3291
Hartshorn, Sue, 5808
Hartsock, Linda Dickerson, 5757
Hartstein, Gail, 3777
Hartwell, Lucy B., 4767
Hartwell, Mary Lynn, 2632
Hartwig, Ron, 579
Harty, Barbara A., 3178
Harty, Barbara K., 2495
Hartz, Rayna, 85
Harvard College Charitable Lead Trusts, 4033
Harvard Partners, 5402
Harvest Foundation, 4791
Harvey Enterprises, 7225
Harvey's, 7225
Harvey, Ann, 6551
Harvey, Bruce, 3759
Harvey, C. Felix, 7225
Harvey, Cannon Y., 1365
Harvey, Cathy, 9492
Harvey, Charles A., 9870
Harvey, Constance, 6551
Harvey, Dave, 975
Harvey, Ellen D., 8288
Harvey, Hal, 6551
Harvey, Herbert J., Jr., 3611
Harvey, Hugh E., Jr., 1428
Harvey, J. Dale, 746, 1320
Harvey, Joan, 6551
Harvey, Margaret B., 7225
Harvey, Marion W., 3611
Harvey, Michelle M., 1428
Harvey, Robin L., 3990
Harvey, Rose, 5243
Harvey, Stephanie F., 746
Harvey, Susan, 823
Harvey, W. Brantley, Jr., 9492
Harvey, Warren, 9492
Harvill, Alan D., 2040
Harward, Donald W., 6235
Harward, Todd, 8474
Harwell, Aubrey B., Jr., Mr., 8550
Harwell, Jeffery, Jr., 8828
Harwell, Joseph W., 8539
Harwit Administrative Trust, Manya, 660
Harwit Trust, Manya, 660
Harwit, Manya, 660
Harwit, Steven, 660
Harwood, Alice G., 1417
Harwood, R. R., 4898
Hasbro, Inc., 8403, 8404
Hasburg, Charles, 1643
Hasek, Jane, 3421
Haseltine, William A., 6146
Hashemi, Pari, 8035
Hashim, Edward J., 1028
Hashimoto, Takeshi, 6961
Haskel, Antoinette, 810
Haskins, Greg, Dr., 5039
Haslam, Anne S., 1244
Haslam, Cristen G., 8542
Haslam, James A., II, 8581
Haslam, James A., III, 8580, 8581
Haslam, Natalie L., 8581
Haslam, Susan B., 8580
Haslam, William E., 8542, 8581
Haslanger, Kathryn, 5800
Haslinger, Benjamin G., 7482
Haslinger, Douglas S., 7482
Haslinger, Jennifer S., 7482
Haslinger, Kimberly M., 7482
Haslinger, Melissa A., 7482
Haslinger, Myriam Eve, 7482
Haslinger, Sandra L., 7482
Hasnedl, Jerry, 4636
Hass, Jennifer C., 642
Hassan, James, 455
Hassani, Hassan, 5566
Hassell, Gerald L., 7945
Hasselman, Michael W., 3295
Hassenfeld Charitable Lead Trust, Stephen, 8404
Hassenfeld Revocable Trust, Sylvia K., 8404
Hassenfeld, Alan G., 8404
Hassenfeld, Sylvia, 8404
Hassenfeld, Sylvia K., 8404
Hassman, Jeff, 3423
Hasson, Eddie I., 9725
Hasson, James, Jr., 2152
Hasten, Andrea, 2783
Hasten, Anna Ruth, 3315, 3316
Hasten, Bernard, 3315
Hasten, Edward, 3316
Hasten, Hart N., 3315
Hasten, Joshua, 3315
Hasten, Judith, 3316
Hasten, Mark, 3316
Hasten, Michael, 3316
Hasten, Simona, 3315
Hastings, Charles, 5046
Hastings, Curtis F., 9931
Hastings, David R., III, 3702
Hastings, G. Richard, 3530
Hastings, Jennings, 1765
Hastings, Joseph V., 6419, 6420
Hastings, Ken, 9698
Hastings, Peter G., 3702
Haston, Roger, 1363
Hatao, Katsumi, 5724
Hatch, Augustus, 5850
Hatch, Carol, 9835
Hatch, Dave, 569
Hatch, Eliza, 4171
Hatch, George, 4172, 4253
Hatch, Henry, 4171
Hatch, Ian, 4171
Hatch, Mary Alice Marriott, 3840, 3842
Hatch, Robert A., 127
Hatch, Serena M., 4253
Hatch, Terry F., 2933
Hatch, Whitney, 4171, 4172, 4253
Hatcher, Claud A., 2528
Hatcher, Robert F., Jr., 2435
Hatcher, Sally B., 2460
Hatcher, Susan, 7431
Hatcher, Wiley, 8997
Hatfield, Carol, 2432
Hatfield, Gary A., 5160
Hatfield, John S., 91
Hathaway, Harry L., 717
Hathaway, Phillips, 3850
Hatridge, Helen, 4996
Hattem, Gary S., 5876
Hatten, Steve, 9791
Hattensty, Jean, 7798
Hattery, Max, 3360
Hattler, Denise M., 9471
Hattler, Hillary A., 9471
Hattler-Bramson, Andrea M., 9471
Hattman, David W., 3926
Hatton, Esther Marie, 7483
Hatton, Katherine, 5329
Hatton, Kenneth, 7483
Hatton, Nikki C., 1190
Hatton, Vincent P., 5818
Hattum, David, 1037
Haub, Rita, 3398
Hauber, Charles G., 1461, 1462
Hauck Marital Trust, John M., 4908
Hauck, Danielle G., 6034
Hauck, David P., 4908
Hauck, Deborah, 4908
Hauck, Edward C., 8259
Hauck, Ellen, 4908
Hauck, John C., 4908
Hauck, John M., 4908
Hauck, Jonathan M., 6034
Hauck, Steven J., 4908
Hauck, William, 320
Hauenstein, Glen W., 7191
Hauge, Rachel H., 860
Haugen, David, 1166
Haugen, Richard, 2550
Haugen, Rick, 530
Haughy, Carey, 1198
Haugland, Alexander D., 7849, 9643
Haugland, Richard P., 9643
Haugland, Rosaria P., 7849, 9643
Haun, C. K., 2632
Hauptfuhrer, W. Barnes, 7202
Hauptman, Andrew, 662, 5717
Hauptman, Ellen, 5717
Hauptman, Ellen Bronfman, 662
Hauptman, Jeff, 4340
Hausback, Paul, 281
Hauser, Gustave M., 6147
Hauser, Jeff, 9711
Hauser, Jessica R.R., 2416
Hauser, Pierre, II, 5848
Hauser, Rita, 9437
Hauser, Rita E., 6147
Hausler, Lisa M., 565
Hausman, Richard, 593
Hauswirth, Lisa Guggenhime, 819
Havard, Donald P., 1918
Havard, Harris W., 1918
Havard, Joyce, 1918
Havard, Stephanie, 1918
Haveman, Robert, 4525
Havens Living Trust, Westen, 7226
Havens, Charles Gerard, 6148
Havens, Kathy H., 9563
Havens, Philip V., 5995
Havens, Timothy D., 9563
Haver, Don, 1392
Haverlick, Brett, 7382
Haviland Plastic Products Co., 7642
Havner, Debi, 186
Hawaii Community Services Council, 2604
Hawaii Institute for Integrative Healthcare Research, 2604
Hawaii State Center for Nursing, 2604
Hawaiian Electric Industries, Inc., 2603
Hawes, Kevin, 417
Hawes, Lucy Moreton, 9309
Hawes-Saunders, Ronita, 7608
Hawk, Arlene F., 7376
Hawk, Bryan, 7376
Hawk, David, 8275
Hawk, Marc C., 7413
Hawk, Timothy, 7376
Hawker, Mary Stake, 4878
Hawkins Trust, Kathryn Ackley, 5123
Hawkins, Amy, 8706
Hawkins, Bruce E., 7413
Hawkins, Chaille, 8777
Hawkins, Chaille W., 9203
Hawkins, Christopher R., 5719
Hawkins, Diana M., 8895
Hawkins, Frances L., R.N., 3612
Hawkins, Jack, Dr., 27
Hawkins, Jay L., 2637
Hawkins, Jim, 7730
Hawkins, John C., 1765
Hawkins, John F., 6947
Hawkins, Katherine D., 8620

Hawkins, Laura B., 8895
Hawkins, Lawton, 2428
Hawkins, Leslie, 9632
Hawkins, Mason, 1387
Hawkins, Matt, 9357
Hawkins, O. Mason, 8616, 8620
Hawkins, Prince A., 5123
Hawkins, Robert Z., 5123
Hawkins, Russell B., 8895
Hawkins, Stan, 2644
Hawkins, Sue, 3398
Hawkins, Val, 9380
Hawkins, Wendy Ramage, 7853
Hawkins, William, 2428
Hawkins, Winsome, 2540
Hawks, Heather L., 5047
Hawks, Howard, 5047
Hawks, Howard L., 5047
Hawks, Neal H., 5047
Hawks, Rhonda, 5047
Hawks, Rhonda A., 5047
Hawks, Tom, 5047
Hawks, Troy T., 5047
Hawksworth, Keith J., 6621
Hawley, Anne, 5917, 5918, 5919
Hawley, James M., 1429
Hawley, Jon, 4448
Hawley, Laura, 2123
Hawley, MacDonald, 1429
Hawley, Nancy H., 7296
Hawley, Neil, 3554
Hawley, Philip M., 664
Hawley, Raymond, 88
Hawn, Ben, 4742
Hawn, Bruce Sams, 9145
Hawn, Caitlyn J., 9145
Hawn, Gates Helms, 5786
Hawn, Joe V., Jr., 8896
Hawn, Joe, Officer, 3335
Hawn, Mary C., 8896
Hawn, Mildred, 8896
Hawn, Nancy E., 9145
Hawn, Sarah, 8896
Hawn, Susan G., 9145
Hawn, W.R., 8896
Hawrys, Jessica, 6001
Hawthorn Bank, 4939
Hawthorne, Alan, 9563
Hawthorne, G. Trippe, 3618
Hawthorne, Robert A., 3618
Hawthorne, Robert H., 9384
Haxall, Bolling W., Jr., 5892
Haxton, Danielle A., 4236
Hay, Andrew MacKenzie, 6904
Hay, Betsy, 9411
Hay, Carol S., 5766
Hay, Jay, 3503
Hay, Kay, 3503
Hay, Laura J., 5349
Hayashi, Jaruki, 6490
Hayden Charitable Lead Trust I, Virginia, 663
Hayden Charitable Lead Trust II, Virginia, 663
Hayden, Carl, 5804
Hayden, Charles, 6150
Hayden, David S., 663
Hayden, John W., 7659
Hayden, Laureen, 9115
Hayden, Lindsay, 6149
Hayden, Marcia M., 663
Hayden, Richard M., 6149, 7126
Hayden, Stanley D., 663
Hayden, Susan, 6149
Hayden, Susan F., 6149
Hayden, Tim, 3277
Hayden, William B., 2874
Hayden, William R., 663
Hayden, William R., II, 663
Hayden, William R., Mrs., 663
Hayden, William T., 7087
Haydon, Richard L., 5116
Hayes Trust, Mariam C., 7227
Hayes, Brad, 3373
Hayes, Brian, 3283
Hayes, Daniel K., 3457
Hayes, Denis, 9591
Hayes, Diane K., 1291
Hayes, Elaine Bryant, 7184
Hayes, Geralyn F., 4865
Hayes, J. Stoddard, Jr., Esq., 7979
Hayes, James C., 4792
Hayes, James D., 4677
Hayes, Jerry, 5556
Hayes, Jimmy W., 2560
Hayes, John, 9148
Hayes, John A., 1371
Hayes, Katherine D.R., 4677
Hayes, Laurence J., 8073
Hayes, Mary B., 9818
Hayes, Patricia, 9239
Hayes, Preston, 2451
Hayes, Ralph W., 1755
Hayes, Rob, 3466
Hayes, Robert C., 7169
Hayes, Robert M., 9500
Hayes, Scott M., 2638
Hayes, Shaun, 5001
Hayes, Stephen, 3821
Hayes, Steve, 98
Hayes, Sutton Mora, 8549
Hayes, Synnova B., 5652
Hayes, Thomas F., 5389
Hayford, Michael D., 2097
Haygood, Paul, III, 3637
Hayman, David, 9956
Hayner, James K., 9745
Haynes, David, 8560
Haynes, Dora Fellows, Mrs., 664
Haynes, Dorothy "Honey Bun", 2602
Haynes, John Randolph, 664
Haynes, Larry N., 8545
Haynes, Lawrence E., 7994
Haynes, Lukas, 6477
Haynes, Wycliffe E., 8477
Haynie, Gilmore S., Jr., 3332
Hayon, Beverly, 921
Hays, George W.S., 7640
Hays, Lucille, 3222
Hays, Mary Ann, 7510
Hays, Michael B., 7510
Hays, Thomas C., 7510
Hayse, Dana G. Seeley, 7450
Hayton, Allan, 86
Hayward, Archie B., Jr., 2327
Hayward, Bill, 665
Hayward, Elizabeth Steiner, 6587
Hayward, Erik K., 3696
Hayward, Homer M., 665
Hayward, Hope, 665
Hayward, John T., 2150
Hayward, Marilyn, 1821
Hayward, Marilyn Rushworth, 1765
Hayward, Nancy Eccles, 665
Hayward, Wendy, 665
Hayward, Wendy A., 665
Hayward, Winifred M., 2150
Haywood, Jennifer, 4342
Haywood, Verdia, 1893, 9497
Hayworth Foundation, The, 7228
Hayworth, Charles E., Jr., 7228
Hayworth, Christine, 8560
Hayworth, David R., 7228
Hazan Trust, Morris A., 2899
Hazan, Morris A., 2899
Hazan, Morris A., Jr., 2899
Hazard, Elizabeth, 4020
Hazard, Elizabeth S., 4020
Hazard, Stephen, 5168
Hazard, Susan J., 820
Hazel, John T., 1925
Hazel, Peter K., 4194
Hazelgrove, Bruce, III, 9494
Hazelip, Harold, 8643
Hazen, Cassandra, 2514
Hazen, Edward Warriner, 6151
Hazen, Elizabeth, 157
Hazen, Helen Russell, 6151
Hazen, Lucy Abigail, 6151
Hazen, Paul M., 2514
Hazleton, Richard, 4549
Hazlitt, Chris, 1391
Hazzard, Shirley, 5585
HB Communications, 9606
HBI Financial Inc., 254
HBS Associates, 6131
HC Miasteczko E, 7349
HCA Inc., 8582
HCA—The Healthcare Co., 8582
HCM Energy Holdings, LLC, 2924
HD Supply, 9606
HDSA, 5228
Heacock, David K., 9227
Head, Beverly P., III, 43
Head, Carol A., 8081
Head, James W., 490
Head, Marion Daniel, 27
Head, Martha, 1518
Head, Randy, 3271
Headley, Mark, 7731
Heafy, Andria, 7815
Heafy, Paul G., 7815
Heald, Catherine M., 8600
Heald, Catherine Maclellan, Mrs., 8601
Heald, Michael R., 9873
Healey, Bridget Cathleen, 2233
Healey, Dennis, 282
Healey, James P., 4328, 4329
Healey, Kim A., 1651
Healey, Margaret S., 6152
Healey, Otis M., 1320
Healey, Sean M., 3924
Healey, Terrance T., 8383
Healey, Thomas J., 5243, 6152
Healey, Thomas Jeremiah, 6152
Health and Hospital Corp., 3317
Health Care Service Corp, 9149
Health Care Services Corp., 2933
Health East Care Bethesda Hospital, 9250
Health Management Resources Corp., 4292
Health Options, Inc., 2101
Health Plan Hawaii Foundation, 2604
Healthcare CEO Summit, 1268
Healy Family Foundation, M.A., Inc., 5522
Healy, Ann Marie, 8041
Healy, Bridget M., 7038
Healy, Cameron, 7850
Healy, Daniel P., 9441
Healy, Ed, 3555
Healy, Edmund, 5522
Healy, Gary M., 2101
Healy, John, 7184
Healy, Justin, 3555
Healy, Kathleen, 7850
Healy, Martha, 5516
Healy, Martha Ann, 5522
Healy, Richard, 4198
Healy, Thomas B., 7006
Healy, Tim, 7850
Heaney, Beth, 7825
Heaney, John J., 1450
Heard, Patsy, 3392
Heard, Whitney Brigman, 7265
Hearin, Robert M., Jr., 4832
Hearin, Robert M., Sr., 4832
Hearin, William J., 38
Hearne, Nancy S., 6695
Hearst Corp., 6904
Hearst, Austin, 6154
Hearst, David Whitmire, Jr., 669
Hearst, George R., III, 6155, 6156
Hearst, Margaret C., 1111
Hearst, William R., III, 1111, 6155, 6156
Hearst, William Randolph, 6155, 6156
Heartland Trust Co., 7351
Heasley, Karen, 8291
Heasley, Lucas, 8291
Heasley-Treadwell, Christina, 8291
Heath, Cynthia, 2822
Heath, Jill Wells, 7295
Heath, Jim, 3576
Heath, Josie, 1391
Heath, Karen, 4342
Heath, R.F., 9822
Heath, Ralph, 8776
Heath, Ruth, 7225
Heath, Sheila, 7445
Heathwood, Desmond, 4104
Heatley, Alvin T., 8462
Heatley, Craig, 2514
Heatley, Craig L., 2514
Heaton, Beth, 7731
Heaton, Gary, 2768
Heaton, Mary Alice J., 4584
Heatwole, W. Michael, III, 9411
Heavin, Diane, 8898
Heavin, Gary, 8898
Heavin, Gary H., 8898
Heavin, Karen Nelson, 3373
HEB, 9149
Heberle, Donald J., 7946
Hebert, Ann, 3650
Hebert, Effie Mae, 8899
Hebert, John, 5171
Hebert, Raymond J., 3623
Hebert, Wilton P., 8899
Hecht Family, LLC, The, 1114
Hecht, Alexander, 8082
Hecht, Amara, 1114
Hecht, James Christopher, 1114
Hecht, James Grey, 1114
Hecht, Jennifer, 1114
Hecht, Margaret, 1114
Hecht, Marya, 1114
Hecht, Michael, 6393, 6608, 6753, 6871
Hecht, Nicoya, 1114
Hecht, Sean, 1114
Hecht, Selma H., 8082
Heck, Gary, 3279
Heckard, Tom, 3271
Heckel, Gary, 4026

Hecker, Bruce G., 4909
Hecker, Harvard K., 4909
Hecker, Patricia G., 4909
Hecker, Stinson Morrison, LLP, 9160
Heckes, H.C., 4786
Heckman, Lois B., 8028
Heckscher, August, 6157
Heckscher, Martin A., 8236
Hecla Mining, 7349
Hedberg, Joel, 4659
Hedgepeth, B.K., 9399
Hedges, Charles F., Jr., 9106
Hedges, John, 3061
Hedinger, Blake H., 7851
Hedinger, Howard H., 7851
Hedlund, Bob, 5662
Hedman, Mary Jan, 3289
Hedrick, Deborah, 8171
Hedrick, Judy, 3398
Heeden, John L., 7319
Heekin, S., 9961
Heenan, David A., 2588
Heenan, Earl H., III, 4413
Heenan, Timothy S., 1676
Heerey, Bernard A., 2901
Heerwagen, John R., 4056
Heeschen, Paul, 508
Heeschen, Paul C., 992
Hefferline, Arline, 9693
Heffernan Insurance Brokers, 673
Heffernan, E. Mary, 6561
Heffernan, F. Michael, 673
Heffernan, Hank, 9767
Heffernan, James B., 7387
Hefferon, Timothy W., 4380
Heffner, Jane E., 5958
Hefni, Ibrahim, 4306
Hefni, Wensley, 4306
Heft, Crystal, 1035
Heft, Jana C., 9917
Hegardt, Kim, 9690
Hegarty, Matt, 4009
Hegarty, Michael, 6116
Hegarty, Neal R., 4510
Hegge, Cindy, 9676
Hegi, Frederick B., Jr., 8773
Hegi, Frederick, Jr., 3201
Heginbotham, Stanley J., 6888
Heher, Garrett M., 5196, 5328
Hehir, Sara A., 2519
Heide, Elizabeth C., 4091
Heide, Elizabeth H., 4091
Heide, Ulf B., 4091
Heidecorn, David, 5556
Heiden, Cara, 3420
Heidenreich, Astrid, 1611
Heidenreich, Fritz, 1611
Heidenreich, Per, 1611
Heider, Charles F., 5048
Heider, Mark J., 5048
Heider, Mary C., 5048
Heider, Scott C., 5048
Heidmann, Julia L.W., 4803
Heidrick, Clarke, 9171
Heidt, Julia & Robert, 7659
Heidt, Julia Scripps, 7659
Heien, Janet, 418
Heigentz, Missak, 2982
Height, Dorothy, 4343
Heigl, Katherine, 674
Heigl, Katherine M., 674
Heigl, Margaret L., 674
Heigl, Nancy E., 674
Heil Admin Trust, Ann E., 9860
Heil Marital Trust, Ann E., 9860
Heil, Eugene D., 2638
Heil, Jeffrey, 5917
Heil, Josephine, 2670
Heil, Katherine A., 9860
Heil, Marjorie, 9860
Heilbrunn Trust, Harriet, 6541
Heilbrunn Trust, Robert, 6541
Heilbrunn, Harriet, 6541
Heilburnn, Harriet, 6496
Heileman, Paula L., 8741
Heilemann, Blackie, 8742
Heilemann, Paula, 8742
Heilig, William W., 8289
Heilman, E. Bruce, 9523
Heim, Dirk, 545
Heim, Mark, 1136
Heiman, David, 1160
Heiman, Gary, 7486, 7511
Heiman, Kim, 7486
Heiman/Fidelity Foundation, 1558
Heimann, John G., 9051
Heimbold, Charles A., Jr., 1612
Heimbold, Eric C., 1612
Heimbold, Joanna M., 1612
Heimbold, Leif C., 1612
Heimbold, Monika A., 1612
Heimbold, Peter, 1612
Heimburger, Meredith, 9029
Heimes, Terry J., 5072
Heimlich, Philip, 5683
Heine, Deborah, 6898
Heine, Lucilee, 2648
Heineman, Dannie N., 6158
Heineman-Schur, Joan, 6158
Heinen, Roger, 2041
Heinmiller, John C., 4770
Heinrich, Amy, 3038
Heinrich, Greg, 5119
Heinrich, Michael, 3422
Heinrich, Rob, 3038
Heinrich, Virginia, 2110
Heinrichs, Haven S., 9140
Heinsheimer, Alfred M., 6546
Heinsheimer, Louis A., 6546
Heintz, Stephen, 6725
Heintz, Stephen B., 6723
Heinz Co., H.J., 8083
Heinz III Charitable and Family Trust, H. John, 8085
Heinz III Charitable Trust, Teresa and H. John, 8085
Heinz, Alice, 9401
Heinz, Andre, 8085
Heinz, Andre T., 8084
Heinz, Christopher, 8084
Heinz, Drue, 8084, 8086
Heinz, H. John, 8084
Heinz, Howard, 8084
Heinz, Sasha, 8084
Heinz, Teresa F., 8084, 8085
Heinz, Vira I., 8084
Heinze, Dyke, 4512
Heisen, Joann Heffernan, 5329
Heisey, Glenn P., 8046
Heisey, John L., 7970
Heising, Caitlin, 6860
Heising, Mark, 6860
Heising, Mark W., 675
Heiskell, Marian S., 6942
Heisler, Lawrence R. "Larry", 2438
Heisler, Robert J., 9195
Heisley, Agnes M., 2902
Heisley, Michael, 8610
Heisley, Michael E., Jr., 2902
Heisley, Michael E., Sr., 2902
Heisser, Amy, 4369
Heit, Philip, 7589
Heiting, Manfred, 1076
Heitman, Ann D., 4092
Heitzman, Joanna Hill, 7569
Hejna, JoAnn, 4965
Hekemian, Robert S., Jr., 5398
Helco Holding, Inc., 8610
Held, Julie B., 7392
Held, Michael, 9172
Heldman, Paul W., 7531
Helen, Suzanne L., 2220
Helfaer, Evan P., 9861
Helfen Wir, 9118
Helfet, David, 1959
Helfgott, Michael, 1630
Helfman, Helen, 5288
Helge, Kathleen, 4861
Helgeson, Terry, 4395
Helies, Brenda, 6302
Heligman, Sol, 6092
Helis Oil & Gas Co., LLC, 9049
Helisek, Cynthia, 4578
Hellauer, Marianne Schmitt, 3889
Heller Residuary Trust for Alyce, 2904
Heller, Alfred, 676
Heller, Benjamin, 1947
Heller, Clarence E., 676
Heller, David B., 2903
Heller, Diane B., 2903
Heller, Ellen M., 3726, 3908
Heller, Fanny, 1947
Heller, Fanya, 1947
Heller, Francie, 6451
Heller, Helen, 6662
Heller, Jacqueline, 1947
Heller, Jill, 9924
Heller, Jordan, 6799
Heller, Katherine, 676
Heller, Lawrence, 381
Heller, Lee E., 2903
Heller, Lesley, 2176
Heller, Richard K., 7932
Heller, Ruth, 676
Heller, Sara, 6763
Heller, Walter E., 2904
Hellerman, Brett D., 1558
Hellman, Chris, 678
Hellman, Daryl A., 4030
Hellman, F. Warren, 677, 678, 1223
Hellman, Frances, 677, 678
Hellman, Judith, 677
Hellman, Marco, 677
Hellman, Mick, 678, 1088
Hellman, Patricia C., 677, 678
Hellman, Sabrina, 677
Hellmuth, Andrew P., 5187
Hellmuth, John S., 5187
Hellmuth, Mary Ann, 5187
Hellmuth, Robert L., 5187
Hellwig, Chad L., 4666
Hellwig, John, 248
Helm, Christopher R., 9587
Helm, John, 1178
Helm, John C., 7858
Helm, Lucy, 9742
Helm, Ralph W., 2818
Helman, Daisy, 4298
Helman, Frank G., 3711
Helman, William, 4298
Helmbrecht, Glen, 9809
Helmerich, Dow Zachary, 7758
Helmerich, Hans, 7807
Helmerich, Hans C., 7758
Helmerich, Jonathan D., 7758
Helmerich, Matthew G., 7758
Helmerich, W.H., 7758
Helmerich, Walter H., III, 7758
Helmerich, Walter H., IV, 7758
Helmholz, Richard, 3226
Helmick, Neal, 3532
Helmken, John C., II, 2548
Helmly, Robert L., 8484
Helms Family Foundation, 98
Helms, Besse Hauss, 7484
Helms, Christopher A., 7591
Helms, Michael, 340
Helms, Michael L., 524
Helms, W.B., 7484
Helms, William, 9
Helmsbriscoe, 2351
Helmsley Enterprises, Inc., 6160
Helmsley, Leona M., 6160
Helmstadter, Marsha, 4159
Helmuth, Paul J., 7663
Helpenstell, Amy, 3442
Helpenstell, Bonnie, 3442, 7889
Helpenstell, Emily, 7889
Helpenstell, Eric, 3442, 7889
Helpenstell, Esta R., 3442
Helpenstell, Franz, 3442
Helpenstell, Lily, 7889
Helppie Trust, Richard D., 4456
Helppie, Leslie S., 4456
Helppie, Richard, 4456
Helppie, Richard D., Jr., 4456
HELPS, 888
Helps, Robert Eugene, 5814
Helsell, Frank P., 9728
Helsell, Peter F., 9728
Helsell, Virginia S., 9728
Helsell, William A., 9728
Helseth, Nancy L., 7837
Helstrom, Carl, 5323, 5385
Helstrom, Carl O., 5340, 8494
Helton, Christy B., 2483
Helton, Darrell, 9024
Helton, Rodney, 2483
Helton, Todd L., 2483
Heman, Jane S., 5012
Hemenway, Robert E., 4905
Hemenway, Russell, 1948
Heminger, Pam, 7490
Hemingway, Ann, 9326
Hemingway, Hallie, 9326
Hemingway, Henry S., 9326
Hemingway, Richard Keith, 9326
Hemingway, Shirley Stranquist, 9326
Hemlock Semiconductor Corp., 4405
Hemmelstein, Julius, 2735
Hemmelstein, Marcie, 2735
Hemmen, Pam, 4738
Hemmer, J. Michael, 5090
Hemmings, Collette, 7875
Hemphill, Ross F., 1679
Hempstead, David M., 4331, 4371, 4425, 4426, 4427, 4428, 4429, 4537, 4589
Hemsley, Barbara K., 4638
Hemsley, Matthew S., 4638, 4743
Hemsley, Stephen J., 4638
Hemus, Simon, 5784
Hemwall, Martha, 9832
Henceroth, Alan, 1511
Hench Family Living Trust A, 679
Hench Family Living Trust B, 679

Hench, John C., 679
Hench, Lowry, 679
Hendel, Myron, 6161
Hendel, Ruth, 6161
Hendel, Stephen, 6161
Henderson, Al, 3475
Henderson, Allen Douglas, 2152
Henderson, Anne W., 4802
Henderson, Barbara K., 2152
Henderson, Benson G., 1917
Henderson, Bruce K. M., 8172
Henderson, Bruce King Mellon, 8173
Henderson, Charles R., Jr., 7139
Henderson, Diann C., 150
Henderson, Dink, 2036
Henderson, Erin E., 1845
Henderson, Frederick, 6872
Henderson, Helen Lee, 1917
Henderson, Helen Ruth, 1917
Henderson, Holly, 8900
Henderson, James D., II, 5172
Henderson, Jan, 3391
Henderson, Loise J., 8901
Henderson, Louise, 8900
Henderson, Lucia, 2152
Henderson, Mary F., 1456
Henderson, Monty, 2565
Henderson, Patrick, 9998
Henderson, Pete, 2826
Henderson, Phillip, 6947
Henderson, Rhoe B., 6038
Henderson, Robert, 3744
Henderson, Ryan, 9909
Henderson, Scott M., 7531
Henderson, Simon W., III, 8900
Henderson, Terry A., 2435
Henderson, Todd, 3744
Henderson, Troy, 3744
Henderson, Vincent, 3289
Henderson, Virginia L., 8900
Henderson, William, M.D., 9421
Hendler, Lee M., 3849
Hendley, Albert H., 7635
Hendrick Gordon Leasing, 7214
Hendrick Motorsports, 7214
Hendrick, Cal, 9091
Hendrick, Rick, 7214
Hendrick, Wlliam A., 4585
Hendricks, D. Eugene, 7160
Hendricks, Diane M., 9814, 9819
Hendricks, John S., 3813, 5747
Hendricks, Maureen D., 3813
Hendrickson, G.E., 4786
Hendrickson, John T., 4521
Hendrickson, Kathryn B., 7624
Hendrickson, Shyla, 742
Hendrickson, Stephen J., 4093
Hendrickson, Virginia, 2905
Hendrickx, Laurent, 4454
Hendrigan, Aimee, 4170
Hendriksen, Dick, 5039
Hendrix, Adelia R., 63
Hendrix, Harville, 6864
Hendrix, Lynn P., 1437
Hendrix, Rebecca, 9704
Hendry, M.S., 9185
Henebry, Brian, 1566
Heneghan, Eileen, 5903, 5904
Heneghan, Kevin, 5904
Heneghan, Kevin J., 5903, 5904
Hengel, Nancy, 9930
Henke, Cynthia, 9902
Henkel, Joe, 8768
Henkels & McCoy, Inc., 8089
Henkels, Barbara B., 8089
Henkels, Christopher B., 8089
Henkels, Paul M., Jr., 8089
Henkhaus, John, 8521
Henkle, Dan, 563
Henle, David L., 6162
Henle, Joan C., 6162
Henley Group, Inc., The, 1219
Henley Manufacturing, Inc., 1219
Henley, Dolores, 680
Henley, Doy B., 680
Henley, Jeffrey O., 734
Henley, Judy P., 734
Henline, Carson S., 7314
Henna Two LLC, 6811
Henneman, Jack, 5315
Hennessee, David, 9148
Hennessey, Marilyn, 3113
Hennessy, Anne Griffith, 2482
Hennessy, James B., 9910
Hennessy, John, 938
Hennessy, Michael W., 2759
Hennessy, Sean P., 7661
Henney, Jane E., 3982, 5800
Hennig, Ruth G., 4172
Hennigan, Kathryn, 835
Hennigan, Nancy, 172
Hennigton, Keith, 9005
Henning, Heidi E., 3818
Henning, Rich, 5486
Henning, Thomas E., 5072
Henninger, Don, 106
Hennings, Ed W., 681
Hennington, Keith, 9005
Hennip, Bob, 4334
Hennon, Marilyn, 4332
Henricks, Vern, 3532
Henricksen, Bob, 9175
Henrickson, Ronald J., 334
Henriques, George, 4738
Henrotin Hospital, 3217
Henry Charitable Trust, David, The, 7924
Henry, Alan, 9219
Henry, Bobby, 8726
Henry, C. Wolcott, III, 1933, 2906
Henry, Charles, Jr., 8223
Henry, Daniel T., 5588
Henry, Edward P., 5917, 5918, 5919
Henry, Frances Turner, 3615
Henry, Frederick B., 6002
Henry, H. Alexander, 1933, 2906
Henry, Jake, 7807
Henry, James A., 330
Henry, Jeanette, 7444
Henry, John W., 2154
Henry, Judy, 9659
Henry, Kim, 7793
Henry, Leland W., 7386
Henry, Mary, 6766
Henry, Megan, 6808
Henry, Merton G., 3701
Henry, Patricia, 9682
Henry, Russ, 2437
Henry, Scott, 8152
Henry, Susan Hough, 2162
Henry, William, 9682
Henry-Keller, Piper, 9682
Hensel, Russel R., 8199
Hensell, Chip, 9775
Hensely, Darrel, 4996
Hensleigh, Inez M., 3021
Hensley, Jamie, 7474
Hensley, Russell J., 8579
Henson Sales Group, 3201
Henson, Kenneth M., Jr., 2438
Henson, Richard A., 3814
Hensyn, Inc., 5444
Hentgen, Steve, 3290
Hentz, Kathryn Iacocca, 4104
Hepburn, Michael, 5327
Hepburn, Valerie, Dr., 2427
Hepler, Cindy, 3355
Hepting, Robert, 4996
Heptner, Joyce, 3723
Hequembourg, Mark, 3570
Herbein, Kathleen D., 7939
Herber, Jacob, 9840
Herberger Enterprises, Inc., 119
Herberger Revocable Trust, G.R., 119
Herberger, Billie Jo, 119
Herberger, G.R., 92, 119
Herberger, G.R., Mrs., 119
Herberger, Gary K., 119
Herberger, Jeanne L., 119
Herberger, Judd R., 119
Herbert, Allen, 3649
Herbert, Ann D., 8478
Herbert, Benjamin, 6121
Herbert, Dale M., 61
Herbert, Gavin S., 228
Herbert, Gavin, Jr., 593
Herbert, Jim, Jr., 9509
Herbert, Michael, 3507
Herbert, Penny, 378
Herbert, Peter A., 6121
Herbert, Robert M., 6813
Herbst, Ann Colin, 6048
Herbst, David A., 651
Herbst, George H., 2390
Herbst, Herman H., 682
Herbst, Linda Vitti, 1484
Herbst, Maurice H., 682
Herczeg, Andrea, 4806
Herd 2005 Charitable Trust, J.H., 8760
Herd, Bob L., 8902
Herd, Dan, 8676, 8760
Herd, H. Tevis, 8760
Herd, Harriet D., 8760
Herd, J. Harvey, 8760
Herd, Jay, 8964
Herd, Michael, 8902
Herd, Patty, 9091
Herd, Tevis, 8650, 8839
Herd-Barber, Jacqueline, 9907
Herda, Sarah, 2873
Herdendorf, Ann, 9845
Herdesty, Peggy, 3417
Herding, George T., 8527
Herdman, Bruce W., 8041
Herdman, Roger C., 6024
Heredia, Anthony, 4621
Herendeen, Burniece, 5927
Herff Jones, Inc., 172
Hergert, Bob, 9916
Hergert, John P., 3100
Heritage Group, The, 3302
Heritage Holding Company, 9307
Heritage Holding Corp., 9307
Heritage Partners, 5091
Heritage Trust Co., 7795
Herlands, Joyce C., 6929
Herlands, Tiffany, 6929
Herliczek, Thaddeus, 8383
Herlihy, Edward D., 2514, 7040
Herlin, Cara P., 9240
Herlin, Jean T., 9240
Herma, John F., 9862
Herma, Susan M., 9862
Herman Furniture Co., 4504
Herman Miller Inc., 4470
Herman, Agnes, 5543
Herman, Gary J., 1090
Herman, Howard, 7044
Herman, Mike, 1518
Herman, Ronald D., 3428
Herman, Russ, 3651
Herman, Theodore L., 6518
Herman, Tom, 672
Hermance, Frank S., 7913
Hermann Charitable Remainder Trust 2000, Francoise, 4094
Hermann, Francoise, 4094
Hermann, Grover M., 2908
Hermann, Natalie, 5927
Hermann, William M., 4371
Hermanson, John, 3484
Hermes, Brian, 8789
Hermocillo, Jose, 1163
Hermundslie, Carol, 120
Hermundslie, Gerold D., 120
Hern, Paula, 8936
Hern, Paula A., 8936
Hernandez, Alex, 1387
Hernandez, Antonia, 320, 365
Hernandez, Carlos, 5243
Hernandez, Carlos M., 5414, 8851
Hernandez, David, 8923
Hernandez, Diego E., VADM., 3669
Hernandez, Enrique, Jr., 664
Hernandez, Fred, 9146
Hernandez, Jean, 9600
Hernandez, Jesus, 9149, 9600
Hernandez, Mario, Dr., 2042
Hernandez, Mike A., II, 9234
Hernandez, Philip N., 1391
Hernandez, Robert, 7905
Hernandez, Robert M., 7966
Hernandez, Roman, 7876
Hernandez, Sandra R., 320, 367
Hernandez, Victor Rivera, 8353
Hernreich, Robert, 1518
Hero, Peter, 1175
Herod, Steve, 9208
Herold, H. Robert, II, 5405
Herold, Matthew G., Jr., 5405
Heron, Winell I., 8879
Herr Foods, Inc., 8090
Herr, Edwin, 8090
Herr, Eric, 5182
Herr, Gene, 8090
Herr, James M., 8090
Herr, James S., 8090
Herr, Jeffrey M., 2909
Herr, Julie, 2909
Herr, Lawrence W., 2155
Herr, Miriam, 8090
Herr, Nancy R., 2155
Herr, Toby, 2909
Herre, Tom, 9843
Herreid, Warren, II, 4685
Herrell, John E., 265
Herrera-Mata, Lydia, 549
Herrero, Judy Sly, 1211
Herres, Rebecca Gilbreth, 8492
Herrick Corp., 672
Herrick, David A., 9474
Herrick, Greg, 9789
Herrick, Hazel M., 4459
Herrick, Jason, 8660
Herrick, Kent B., 4459
Herrick, Ray W., 4459
Herrick, Scott, 3373

Herrick, Todd W., 4459
Herrick-Pacific Corp., 672
Herrick-Pacific Corporation, 1050
Herrigel, Rodger K., 5317
Herring, Albert Lee, 7229
Herring, Carol P., 5411
Herring, J. Andrew, 4714
Herring, Kay, 3481
Herring, Leonard G., 7229
Herring, Paula, 9019
Herring, Rozelia S., 7229
Herrington, Christian, 3164
Herrington, Marilyn A., 6191
Herrington, Terri, 8585
Herrington, Terri L., 8633
Herrinstein, James R., 6165
Herrling, Sheila, 1891
Herrmann, Bryan, 1020
Herrmann, David S., 9298
Herrmann, Karen H., 9298
Herrmann, Lois M., 5648
Herrmann, Ronald J., 9298
Herrnstein, James R., 6165
Herrnstein, Robeson M., 6165
Herro, David, 2910
Herron, John, 3630
Herron, Mark, 5114
Herron, Mary, 1012
Herrshner, Ronald L., Esq., 8351
Hersch, Dennis, 7712
Hersch, Dennis S., 7713
Hersch, Julie K., 8903
Hersch, Kenneth A., 8903
Herschede, Allison, 7718
Herschede, Holly, 7718
Herscher, Uri D., 6869
Hersey, Eleanor M., 4009
Hersh, Ahron, 6166
Hersh, Dena, 6580
Hersh, Dorothy B., 2156
Hersh, Julie K., 8903
Hersh, Kenneth, 8773
Hersh, Kenneth A., 8903, 9053
Hersh, Toby, 6166
Hershaft, Arthur N., 6167
Hershaft, Carol H., 6167
Hershaft, Janet, 6167
Hershberg, Elliot M., 5334
Hershey Trust Co., 8046
Hershey, Barry J., 4095
Hershey, Connie, 4095
Hershey, Jeffrey, 8904
Hershey, John R., III, 3761
Hershey, Loren W., 7487
Hershey, Olive, 8904
Hershey, Terese T., 8904
Hershman, Hannah, 6168
Hershman, Ronnie A., 6168
Herskovits, David, 914
Herskovitz, Amy, 6629
Herskowitz, Barry, 5533
Herst, Patricia U., 5411
Hertel, Amy Locklear, 4864
Hertel, Kristen, 3136
Herterich, Karyn Kennedy, 2182
Herterich, Morgan, 2182
Hertfelder, Eric, 8423
Hertog, Roger, 2157, 6981
Hertog, Susan, 2157
Hertz Family Foundation Inc., 2484
Hertz, Arthur, 2392
Hertz, Debra, 1675
Hertz, Doug, 2511
Hertz, Douglas, 2484
Hertz, Isaac, 683
Hertz, Jennings, 2484
Hertz, Judah, 683
Hertz, Lila, 2484
Hertz, Michael, 2484
Hertz, Sarah, 683
Hertz, William, 683
Hertzke, Lawrence, 1394
Herwaldt, Jo Ann, 684
Herwaldt, Louis, 684
Herzan, Alexandra, 7023, 7024
Herzan, Alexandra A., 5623
Herzan, Paul K., 5623
Herzberg, Pam, 3418
Herzfeld, Ethel D., 9863
Herzfeld, Richard P., 9863
Herzka, Judy, 6773
Herzka, Ralph, 5718, 6773
Herzog, Aaron, 5272
Herzog, Arie, 6111
Herzog, Davic, 5272
Herzog, Eleanor W., 4139
Herzog, Eli, 5272
Herzog, Gary, 5272
Herzog, Herman, 5272
Herzog, James, 4139
Herzog, James J., 4368
Herzog, Joseph, 5272
Herzog, Kim, 4633
Herzog, Michael, 5272
Herzog, Michael B., 5272
Herzog, Mordechai, 5272
Herzog, Morris, 5272
Herzog, Nathan, 5272
Herzog, Noah, 4139
Herzog, Phillip, 5272
Herzog, Robert, 5272
Herzog, William, 1248
Herzstein, Albert H., 8905
Herzstein, Ethel Avis, 8905
Heseltine, Peter, 433
Heslop, James G., 8, 9
Hess, Andrew Christopher Henry, 9777
Hess, Anne H., 1882
Hess, Diana, 3171
Hess, Donald E., 39
Hess, James H., 7378
Hess, Jerry, 2628
Hess, John B., 5298
Hess, Joseph A., 3511
Hess, Leon, 5298
Hess, Lisa Kabaker, 1192
Hess, Lydia M., 3588
Hess, Maggie, 7702
Hess, Mandy L., 9819
Hess, Marlene, 5298, 6785
Hess, Nancy, 3543
Hess, Ray, 7971
Hess, Ronne, 39
Hess, Ronne M., 21
Hessburg, Sally, 2039
Hesse, Chad, 7437
Hesse, Eric, 4666
Hesse, Thomas G., 3119
Hessel, David, 8695
Hessel, Marieluise, 9980
Hession, Cathleen Collins, 412
Hesske, Connie, 7597
Hessler, David J., 7513
Hessler, Deborah J., 2008
Hessler, Kevin, 3758
Hessler, Stephanie, 6748
Hessley, Bernard J., 7993
Hestand Trust, Magalou W., 8996
Hester, C. Herman, 4828
Hester, Evette, 19
Hester, George, 9280
Hester, James, 6115
Hester, Roy, 1548
Hester, Suzanne F., 5863
Hestings, Marilu, 8829
Heth, Tim, 3443
Hetherington, Karen, 5526
Hetterscheidt, Robert M., 7551
Hettinger, Albert J., Jr., 6170
Hettinger, Betty, 6170
Hettinger, Corinna, 6170
Hettinger, John, 6170
Hettinger, William R., 6170
Hetz, Douglas J., 2484
Heubusch, John, 1900
Heule, Paulus C., 4381
Heule, Rosemary L., 4381
Heun, Robert, 5683
Heuschele, Richard, 4585
Hewes, Bobby, 77
Hewett, Charles E., 3680
Hewit, Randi, 5804
Hewitt Family Trust, 685
Hewitt Trust No. 1, George E., 685
Hewitt Trust No. 2, George E., 685
Hewitt Trust No. 4, George E., 685
Hewitt Trust No. 5, George E., 685
Hewitt Trust No. 6, George E., 685
Hewitt Trust, George E., 685
Hewitt, Chet P., 1163
Hewitt, George E., 685
Hewitt, James, 4495
Hewitt, Robert J., 9066
Hewitt, Robert J., Jr., 9066
Hewitt, William D., 1389
Hewlett Foundation, 1081
Hewlett Packard, 3245
Hewlett Trust, William R., 536
Hewlett, Ben, 536
Hewlett, David, 536
Hewlett, Flora Lamson, 686
Hewlett, Justin, 9001
Hewlett, Walter B., 686, 1007
Hewlett, William R., 686
Hewlett-Packard Co., 687
Hewsenian, Rosalind M., 6160
Hexberg Charitable Trust, The, 688
Hexberg, Deborah L., 688
Hexberg, Eric, 688
Hexberg, Gregory, 688
Hexberg, Jane, 688
Hexberg, Jill, 688
Hey, David R., 3228
Heydinger, Richard B., Dr., 4616
Heydlauff, Amy, 4362
Heydon, Henrietta M., 4509
Heydon, Peter N., 4509
Heyer, Andrew R., 6171
Heyer, Mindy B., 6171
Heyert, Martin, 9554
Heyman, Anne, 6172
Heyman, Barbara G., 7755
Heyman, Harriet, 438
Heyman, Mimi, 5296
Heyman, Stephen, 6546
Heyman-Layne, Carolyn, 82
Heymann, Andrew W., 6902
Heymann, Gerard E., 6902
Heymann, Jerry, 3642
Heymann, Jimmy, 3642
Heymann, Jimmy, Mrs., 3642
Heymann, Jonas John, 3642
Heymann, Leon, 3642
Heymann, Leon, Mrs., 3642
Heymann, Marjorie, 3642
Heymann, Peter E., 4802
Heyneman, Charles, 5009
Heyneman, Tom S., 9989
Heynen, Cynthia, 2829
Heyward, C. Carroll, 8468
Heyward, Elisabeth C., 3698
Heywood, Thomas A., 7935, 9783
HGJ Licensing LLC, 7214
HHD, LLC, 5168
HI 120 Properties Inc., 1004
Hiam, Alexander W., 4322
Hiam, Robert P., 2604
Hiatt, Amy R., 3912
Hiatt, Arnold S., 3912
Hiatt, Frances L., 4128
Hiatt, Howard, 4253
Hiatt, Jacob, 4128
Hiatt, Jane, 4820
Hiatt, Matthew T., 3912
Hibbard, John, 120
Hibbard, John D., Jr., 4412
Hibben, Seabury J., 3146
Hibbing Taconite Co., 7407
Hibbs, Scott, 8774
Hibler, Joe Anna, 7742
Hibshman Trust for Ephrata, The, 8091
Hickerson, Jillian L., 3950
Hickey Trust, Frank, 121
Hickey, Brian E., 6406
Hickey, Francis G., Jr., 121
Hickey, James A., 2562
Hickey, John, 4061
Hickey, John W., 9836
Hickey, Troy, 9641
Hickie, Lisa J., 171
Hickman, David S., 4485
Hickman, Don, 4679
Hickman, Franklin J., 7721
Hickman, Keith, 8873
Hickman, Paula H., 3624
Hickman, Roger, 3208
Hickman, Sally D., 4460
Hickman, Stephen L., 4460
Hickman, Susanna B., 9559
Hickman, Tommy L., 7340
Hickman, Tracy L., 4460
Hickman-Boyse, Stephanie L., 4460
Hickok, Jeffrey, 8397
Hickox, Charles V., Mrs., 5644
Hickox, Frances B., 5644
Hickox, James A.B., 5644
Hicks, Caitlyn, 3162
Hicks, Henry B., 8550
Hicks, John E., Jr., 3162
Hicks, Michael E., 7601
Hicks, Patrick H., 912
Hicks, Paul, 9789
Hicks, Rob, 9704
Hicks, Ruell L., Jr., 8507
Hicks, Stephen, 1116
Hicks, Valerie Bradley, 7721
Hidalgo, Boris A., 9234
Hidden Cove Apartments LLC, 9452
Hidlay, William "Skip", 3555
Hieber, Carl O., 8229
Hield, James, 4799
Hieronimus, Jill M., 3848
Hieronymus, Mark, 24
Hiersteiner, Joseph L., 4990
Hiestand, F. Brian, 9558
Hietbrink, Larry, 2342

Hirsch, I. Jerome, 136
Hirsch, Jason T., 6175
Hirsch, Jeffrey M., 6175
Hirsch, Laurence, 8910
Hirsch, Rochelle C., 6175
Hirsch, Sanford, 6085
Hirsch, Susan, 677, 678, 8910
Hirsch, Wayne, 5005
Hirsch, Wendy, 2811
Hirschberg, Jason, 9916
Hirschbiel, Paul O., Jr., 9448
Hirschfeld, Benjamin G., 5049
Hirschfeld, Daniel J., 5049
Hirschfeld, David J., 5049
Hirschfeld, Matthew, 89
Hirschfeld, Michael A., 7443
Hirschfeld, Monya A., 5049
Hirschfield, Ira S., 643
Hirschhorn, Barbara B., 3735, 3816
Hirschhorn, Daniel B., 3816
Hirschhorn, David, 3816
Hirschhorn, George, 1836
Hirschhorn, Michael J., 3735, 3816
Hirschi, John, 9277
Hirschl, Irma T., 2912
Hirschman, Esther, 3900
Hirschman, Orin Z., 3900
Hirschmann, James W., 1315
Hirschy, Matthew G., 3268
Hirsh, Barry, 1224
Hirsh, Bobbe, 2968
Hirsh, Jill Takiff, 2833
Hirshberg, Mimi, 4888
Hirsig, Alan R., 8221
Hirst, Jeremy M., 9453
Hirst, Jessica F., 9453
Hirst, Thomas M., 9453
Hirt, Dana Westreich, 1317
Hirth Family Foundation, 607
Hirth, Ana, 607
Hirth, Emanuel, 607
Hirthler, Michael, 8152
His Way Homes, 4849
Hiscock, Dana W., 5728
Historic Oella Mill LLC, 9452
Hitachi, Ltd., 1916
Hitch, Henry H., 5191
Hitchcock Trust, Eleanor H., 1430
Hitchcock, Martha H., 5050
Hitchcock, Nelson, 3294
Hitchcock, Todd, 3365
Hitchings, Roy, Jr., 3699
Hite, Ruth Joyce, 8992
Hitt, Lisa, 2437
Hittinger, J. Brian, 3337
Hittle, Ann, 9767
Hittman, Suzanne, 7425
Hittner, Barry G., 8356
Hitz, David, 694
Hitz, Ken, 694
Hitz, Yen, 694
Hixson, Christina M., 5128
Hjelle, Angella J., 4613
Hlavaty, Todd E., Dr., 5068
Hlavka, Elizabeth D., 4648
Hliboki, Joann, 9658
Hliboki, Larry James, 9658
Hll, C.T., 9539
HLM & JM Charitable Lead Trust, 3107
HLM and JM 2006 Charitable Lead Trust, 3057
HMO Minnesota, 4618
Hnasko, Thomas M., 5530
HNI Corp., 3443
Ho, C.K., 695
Ho, Christopher K., 695
Ho, Hing Kay, 695
Ho, Hing-Lan, Dr., 1342
Ho, Kay, 695
Ho, Linda, 5608
Ho, Peter, 2602, 2612
Ho, Peter S., 2588, 2617
Ho, Vanessa K., 695
Ho, Wayne, 6546
Ho, Y.C., 5774
Hoag, George Grant, 697
Hoag, George Grant, II, 697
Hoag, George Grant, III, 697
Hoag, Grace E., 697
Hoag, Jay, 696
Hoag, Jay C., 696
Hoag, John, 9755
Hoag, Michaela, 696
Hoag, Sheila R., 7506
Hoagland, Karl K., Jr., 3036
Hoagland, Sarah, 3036
Hoar, Brad, 1565
Hoard, Steve, 8660
Hobart, Edwin T., 3955
Hobart, Wendy C., 3521
Hobbie, Lynn K., 9898
Hobbs, Ben B., 3391
Hobbs, Christine, 4451
Hobbs, Joyce C., 2914
Hobbs, Larry A., 2327
Hobbs, Oliver Kermit, Jr., 9538
Hobbs, Richard F., 9943
Hobbs, Rowland P., 529
Hobbs, Russ, 9454
Hobbs, Truman M., 2914
Hobbs, Truman M., Jr., 1933, 2914
Hobby 1985 Grantor Trust, Oveta Culp, 8911
Hobby Family Foundation, 1383
Hobby, Diana P., 8911
Hobby, Paul W., 8911
Hobby, W.P., 8911
Hoberman, Gerald, 5051
Hobick, Joy, 4996
Hoblitzelle, Esther T., 8912
Hoblitzelle, Karl St. John, 8912
Hobson, Elana M., 736
Hobson, Mellody, 855
Hobson, William H., 4901
Hoch, Harry, 5044
Hochberg, Andrew S., 2915
Hochberg, Jacqueline Harris, 6138, 6139
Hochberg, Joseph, 2915
Hochberg, Larry J., 2915
Hochberg, William I., 4227
Hochfelder, Peter, 6177
Hochfelder, Stacy, 6177
Hochschuler, Joshua Henri, 6243
Hochstein, Bernard, 6178
Hochstein, Michael, 6178
Hochstein, Miriam, 6178
Hochstein, Richard, 6178
Hochstein, Stephen, 6178
Hochwalt, J.R., 7700
Hochwender, J. Michael, 7578
Hock, Doug, 1407
Hockaday, Irvine O., Jr., 4905
Hocker, Kimberly A., 8094
Hocker, Kirsten, 8094
Hocker, Marcia, 8094
Hocker, Marcia A., 8094
Hocker, Richard A., 8094
Hocker, Sam L., 8979
Hockert, Lorance, 6899
Hockfield, Susan, 5747
Hodder, Melville T., 3971
Hodesh, Jake, 7480
Hodge, Clark, 2036
Hodge, Edwin, Jr., 8095
Hodge, Gail, 3062
Hodge, Janet A., 2812
Hodges, Ashley, 7335
Hodges, Brett E., 1349
Hodges, Brian M., 1349
Hodges, Carol, 78
Hodges, David G., 8468
Hodges, Don, 8789
Hodges, Edward F., Jr., 9402
Hodges, John K., 8001
Hodges, Lillia, 2327
Hodges, Priscilla, 1563
Hodges, Richard, 1007
Hodges, Roxanna, 698
Hodges, Trudy Strewler, 1478
Hodges, William J., 92
Hodges-Lawton Charities, 8438
Hodgkins, William E., 3659
Hodgman, John F., 3962
Hodgson, David C., 5541
Hodgson, Fiona K., 1581
Hodgson, Laurie B., 5541
Hodnik, Alan R., 4716
Hodsdon, Ann, 5171
Hodsdon, Louise, 7026
Hodshire, Jeremiah, 4461
Hoe, Edward, 3948
Hoebelheinrich, Jill Bailey, 8774
Hoechst Marion Roussel, Inc., 5437
Hoeck, James T., 3974
Hoefer, Bob, 3421
Hoeffel, Ellen, 3990
Hoefinghoff, Richard, 7405
Hoefle, Daniel C., 5171
Hoehl Family Trust, Robert H., 2160
Hoehl, Cynthia K., 2160
Hoehl, John M., 2160
Hoehl, Robert F., 2160
Hoehn Trust, Dorothy S., 2916
Hoehn, Catheryn Emily, 2916
Hoehn, Dorothy, 2916
Hoehn-Saric, Chris, 1697
Hoehn-Saric, R. Christopher, 1867
Hoehne, Helen, 701
Hoel, George O., 4602
Hoelscher, Larry, 8670
Hoeme, Kelly, 3543
Hoenlein, Malcolm, 6336
Hoensheid, Gary, 4448
Hoerle, Ann S., 4524
Hoerle, Robert F., 6180
Hoerle, Sheila A., 6180
Hoeschler, Linda L., 4729
Hofer, Steven C., 8696
Hoff Family Trust, Robert A. & Ann W., 7364
Hoff, Ann W., 7364
Hoff, Diana, 7884
Hoff, Robert A., 7364
Hoff, Robert A., Mrs., 7364
Hoff, Susan S., 4612
Hoffberger, Douglas, 3817
Hoffberger, Judith R., 3873
Hoffberger, LeRoy E., 3817
Hoffenberg, Betty S., 9204
Hoffenberg, David A., 9204
Hoffenberg, Marvin, 9204
Hoffenberg, Peter H., 9204
Hoffenberg, Steven, 1397
Hoffer, Shannon, 9632
Hoffer, Taffy, 2875
Hoffman, Abraham, 7020
Hoffman, Alan, 1842
Hoffman, Alfred, Jr., 3682
Hoffman, Arthur S., 6349, 6705
Hoffman, Blake, 8522
Hoffman, Carol, 2513
Hoffman, Chad, 7416
Hoffman, Charlotte C., 2377
Hoffman, Cynthia Corbett, Esq., 9414
Hoffman, David A., 1117
Hoffman, David L., 3758
Hoffman, Dina, 418
Hoffman, Eileen, 8280
Hoffman, Elaine S., 699
Hoffman, Elisabeth, 3682
Hoffman, Frances, 5408
Hoffman, George M., 7551
Hoffman, H. Leslie, 699
Hoffman, James, 7523
Hoffman, James A., 7686
Hoffman, Jane, 6181
Hoffman, Jane Steiner, 6549
Hoffman, Jascha S., 1117
Hoffman, Jean Marie, Sr., 7405
Hoffman, Joyce, 3476
Hoffman, Judy, 3049
Hoffman, Karen A., 222
Hoffman, Leonard R., 9169
Hoffman, Marion O., 6182
Hoffman, Maximilian, 6182
Hoffman, Michael, 1548, 6181
Hoffman, Michael J., 4780
Hoffman, Michael S., 1117
Hoffman, Nancy E., Esq., 5803
Hoffman, Peggy, 7020
Hoffman, Shay Shelton, 9169
Hoffman, Steven M., 8046
Hoffman, Therese H., 3143
Hoffman, Thomas F., 8332
Hoffman, Tyler P., 3222
Hoffman-Zehner, Jacquelyn M., 7118
Hoffmann, Marty, 7350
Hoffmann, Richard, 3428
Hoffmann-La Roche Inc., 1083
Hoffner, Darin R., 8325
Hoffritz, Helen, 2917
Hofman, Thomas D., 4450
Hofmann 1987 Revocable Trust, The, 700
Hofmann Co., The, 700
Hofmann Foundation, 977
Hofmann, Ken, 977
Hofmann, Kenneth H., 700
Hofmann, Martha J., 700
Hofmann, Martha Jean, 700
Hofmann, Renate, 2918
Hofmann-Morgan, Lisa A., 700
Hofstedter Foundation, David, 5242
Hogan, Camille, 3423
Hogan, Cheryl, 6057
Hogan, David O., 7749, 7753, 7760
Hogan, Gerald F., 2040
Hogan, John, 5214
Hogan, Mary, 5396
Hogan, Paul T., 6584
Hogan, Randall J., 4739
Hogan, William, Jr., 9793
Hogarty, Daniel J., Jr., 7006
Hogel, Carol C., 2810
Hogel, Catherine C., 2810

Hogel, Elisabeth, 2810
Hogen, Charles "Robin", 5329
Hogerty, John, 9832
Hogle, Francis, 3798
Hoglund, Bill, 9975
Hoglund, Forrest E., 8913
Hoglund, Sally R., 8913
Hogue, Cyrus D., Jr., 7189
Hoguet, Karen M., 7552
Hohenberg, Paul M., 5803
Hohenlohe, Christian C., 5674
Hohlman, Cristina, 5865
Hohn, David C., 6343
Hoi, Samuel, 727
Hokanson, Neil C., 1053
Hoke, Elizabeth S., 9351
Hoke, Jim, 4869
Hoke, Michael N., 50
Hoke, Steve, 1077
Holbert, Ronald, 1584
Holbrook, Alice Hager, 2139
Holbrook, James R., 9355
Holbrook, Kevin, 1512
Holbrook, Leah, 9767
Holbrook, Meghan Z., 9355
Holbrook, Richard E., 4030
Holbrook, Sherry, 972
Holbrook, Tiffany, 7271
Holcomb, Allen K., 2225
Holcomb, Douglas Clay, 5531
Holcomb, Gary, 6286
Holcombe, Marie, 5749
Holcombe, P. G., 2738
Holcombe, Paul A., Jr., 7274
Holcombe, Robert, Jr., 8504
Holden Trust, The, 7139
Holden, Brent, 1037
Holden, Henry R., 3974
Holder Construction Co., 2485
Holder, J.R., 7795
Holder, Lofton, 6087
Holder-Price, Sue, 3282
Holderness, Haywood, 7322
Holding Charitable Lead Annuity Trust, Ella and Frank, 7233
Holding, Ella, 7233
Holding, Frank B., 7233, 7234, 7319, 8477
Holding, Frank B., Jr., 7233
Holding, Maggie B., 7234
Holding, Olivia B., 7233, 7234
Holding, Robert, 7234
Holding, Wendy, 6571
Holdren, Charles A., 7378
Holdren, Thomas, 7585
Hole, Richard D., 5757
Holekamp, Kerry L., 4910
Holekamp, William F., 4910
Holeman, Laura P., 8755
Holiday Home Health Care Corp. of Evansville, 3322
Holiday Retirement Village, 3322
Holiday, Sherry, 3390
Hollan, Larry, 3365
Holland, Augusta Brown, 3557, 3559, 3562, 3595
Holland, Bernice, 8981
Holland, Bruce B., 4966
Holland, Charles M., 2617
Holland, Darrell, 1426
Holland, Dixie, 8734
Holland, Ed, 4839
Holland, Hudson, III, 3990
Holland, Marilyn M., 5051
Holland, Mary A., 5051
Holland, Nancy L., 7592
Holland, Richard D., 5051
Holland, Robert, Jr., 157
Holland, Stacy, 8333
Hollander, John, 5585
Hollander, Sidney, 2966
Hollander, Stuart, 6968
Hollar, Jennifer, 3336
Holleman, Matthew L., III, 4832
Hollenback 1998 Trust, Edwin, 2601
Hollenback, Edwin, 2601
Hollenbeck, David W., 2205
Hollenbeck, Douglas, 2205
Hollenbeck, Drew, 2205
Holler, William E., 462
Holleran, Carolyn R., 8112
Holleran, Mary F., 6722
Holleran, Patrick B., 8112
Holleran, T. Jerome, 8112
Hollerith, Melissa, Rev., 9529
Holley, Jeffrey D., 3364
Holliday, Iris E., 9416, 9422
Holliday, Linda, 4679
Holliday, Susan, 6706
Holliman, Vonda, 3528, 9463
Hollinger, Christopher L., 7316
Hollingsworth, Audrey, 2556
Hollingsworth, Bobby J., 3249
Hollingsworth, Lee Ann, 3249
Hollingsworth, Sophie Hunt, 8100
Hollingsworth, Susan Hunt, 8100
Hollins, Karen, 825
Hollis, Clayton, 2123
Hollis, Scott Burnham, 4821
Hollister, Don, 7474
Hollister, Lee, 1110
Hollman, Don B., 3295
Holloman-Price Fdn., 7060
Hollomon, Thaddeus, 8914
Holloway, Alan, 1194
Holloway, Janet M., 4945
Holloway, Jon, 8496
Holloway, Wes, 6658
Hollowell Unitrust, Otto, 9778
Hollowell, Harry H., 7587
Hollowell, Margaret F., 9778
Holly Beach Public Library, 6898
Hollywood Foreign Press Association, 701
Holm, Herbert W., 2008
Holman 1993 Charitable Remainder Unitrust, 5301
Holman, John W., III, 5310
Holman, John W., Jr., 3936, 5310
Holman, Robert, 5138
Holman, Robin R., 7854
Holman, Tom, 4792
Holman, Wayne J., III, 5301
Holmberg, Dennis M., 5528
Holmberg, John, 1407
Holmberg, Ruth S., 6942
Holmes, Alexandra Skestos, 7501
Holmes, Amy, 894
Holmes, Andrea L., 4411
Holmes, Barbara, 1139
Holmes, Bill, 101
Holmes, Bonnie, 5302
Holmes, Bonnie L., 5302
Holmes, Brendan A., 404
Holmes, Christine, 4573
Holmes, Christine M., 4411, 4573
Holmes, Daisy, 7945
Holmes, Edward A., 5316
Holmes, Fred, 1139
Holmes, Garry R., 4056
Holmes, Gary S., 4675
Holmes, Gordon, 7001
Holmes, Hal, Jr., Dr., 8507
Holmes, Howard S., 4411, 4530
Holmes, Howard S., II, 4530
Holmes, Jack, 9108
Holmes, Kathryn W., 4411, 4530
Holmes, Lisette, 2035
Holmes, Lisette E., 5808
Holmes, Louise, 7557
Holmes, Mary B., 4411
Holmes, Mary L., 4675
Holmes, Mary M., 7184
Holmes, Mitch, 4872
Holmes, Nancy, 7915
Holmes, Nancy H., 7916
Holmes, Patricia, 5059
Holmes, Rebecca L., 9086
Holmes, Robert C., 5490
Holmes, Robert W., Jr., 4239
Holmes, Robert, Jr., 21
Holmes, Sheila, 257
Holmes, Stephen, 5302
Holmes, Stephen P., 5302, 5506
Holmes, William, 4234
Holmlund, Mark, 1053
Holmquist, Carl, 9895, 9896
Holmquist, Kareen, 9731
Holms Trust, Christine, 4573
Holoch, Kristie, 5052, 5098
Holoman, Smallwood, 4532
Holoubek, Phil, 3560
Holser, Leah, 9632
Holst, Stephen, 9998
Holstein, David A., 5757
Holstein, Michelle, 847
Holston, Martin J., 687
Holt, Allan M., 1914
Holt, Allison J., 8942
Holt, David, 1142
Holt, David H., 1914
Holt, Larry G., 8866
Holt, Shelley L., 1914
Holt, Shelly L., 1914
Holt, Susan, 7336
Holt, Timothy J., 7907
Holt, Winston, 9005
Holt, Winston, IV, 9005
Holte, Doug, 992
Holtel, Joseph A., 7605
Holtgers, Ellen Van Dyke, 9921
Holthouse, Colleen, 8915
Holthouse, Colleen M., 8915
Holthouse, Lisa, 8915
Holthouse, Michael H., 8915
Holthus, C.G., 5052, 5098
Holthus, Kendell, 5052
Holthus, Kristie, 5052
Holthus, Marcy, 5052
Holthus, Tom, 5052
Holthus, Virginia, 5052
Holtmeier, Jeffrey, 7483
Holton, A. Linwood, Jr., 1925
Holton, Raymond B., 8136
Holton, Thomas A., 7608
Holtz, Mana, 2035
Holtzer, Jane, 5773
Holtzmann, Howard M., 6184
Holtzmann, Jacob L., 6184
Holtzmann, Lillian, 6184
Holwerda, Donald J., 8602
Holz Family Foundation, Jerome and Dorothy, 9864
Holz, Dorothy H., 9864
Holz, Jerome J., 9864
Holzapfel, Alice A., 5253
Holzer, Alan, 6544
Holzer, Bambi, 722
Holzgrafe, Candace, 7834
Holzgrafe, Jon, 7834
Hom, Tom, 273
Hom, Winston, 1103
Homan, Andrew, 9005
Homan, Benjamin, Jr., 2919
Hombach, Robert J., 2690
Homchick, Craig, 9604
Home Savings and Loan Co., 7489
Home State Bank, 1442
Home, Gale, 8397
Homecall Hospice, 4785
Homeless Youth Project, 870
Homes, Richmond, 1411
Homestead Co., 3588
Homewood Corp., 7641
Hommer, Katheryn M., 7235
Homonoff, Burt, 1548
Homra, Susan F., 3573
Homsher, Pamela A., 7621
HON Industries Inc., 3443
Honda of America, 7490
Hondru, K., 3149
Honeycutt, A.C., Jr., 7182
Honeycutt, J. Brian, 8480
Honeycutt, Terri W., 7195
Honickman, Harold, 5303
Honickman, Jeffrey, 5303
Honickman, Lynne, 5303
Honig, Marvin, 5567
Honings, Mark, 2754
Honzel, Andrew J., 9644
Hood, Bruce, 6951
Hood, Charles H., 2281
Hood, Donald C., 6115
Hood, Haven J., 7448
Hood, James W., 4843
Hood, Jane Renner, 5031
Hood, John, 5602, 6718
Hood, John, Dr., 6719
Hood, Mary Elizabeth, 5732
Hood, Philip, 1394
Hood, Rachelle, 2087
Hood, Robert, 6205
Hood, Robert C., 890
Hood, Teresa Rebozo, 2282
Hoogendoorn, Case, 3061
Hoogland, Charles E., 2920
Hoogland, Charles R., 2920
Hoogland, Kathleen, 2920
Hoogland, Keith A., 2920
Hook, Jonathan, 157
Hook, Jonathan D., 3908
Hooker, Brian, 5262
Hooker, Paul, 8472
Hooks, Larry B., 2446, 2481
Hoolihan, James, 4617
Hooper Testamentary Trust, Ernestine, 9187
Hooper, Collins W., 8617
Hooper, Henry O., 1472
Hooper, Jeanne R., 1472
Hooper, Mary Bolton, 7614
Hoops, Alan, 1268
Hoops, Teri, 1268
Hooser, John D., 8919
Hooser, Karen R., 7628

Hooton, Dwight, 3376
Hooton, Paula, 8848
Hoover Foundation, The, 7491
Hoover, Anne, 3323
Hoover, Bob, 2632
Hoover, Charles H., 7492
Hoover, Cynthia K., 3323
Hoover, David C., 3323
Hoover, David H., 3249
Hoover, Deborah D., 7578
Hoover, Diana D., 9208
Hoover, Elizabeth Lacey, 7491
Hoover, James E., 3323
Hoover, Jewell D., 7202
Hoover, John, 5717
Hoover, Katherine C., 3323
Hoover, Lawrence R., 7492
Hoover, Mildred M., 3323
Hoover, Rebecca, 7214
Hoover, Rose, 8030
Hoover, Timothy R., 7492
Hooyman, Steve, 9832
Hoozer, Daniel Van, 633
Hope Christian Community Foundation, 8610
Hope Trust, Dolores, 702
Hope, Betsy, 7481
Hope, Camille, 2435
Hope, Dolores, 702
Hope, Lester T. "Bob", 702
Hope, Linda, 702
Hope, Miranda, 702
Hope, William Kelly, 702
Hope, Zachary, 702
Hopeman, Henry W., 5176
Hopeman, Lynn G., 5176
Hopey, Christopher, 4195
Hopfenberg, David H., 4151, 4169, 4281
Hopkin, Nancy, 761
Hopkins Medicine, John, 2300
Hopkins, Ann, 2437
Hopkins, Bruce, 582
Hopkins, C. Timothy, 2632
Hopkins, Charles, 3030
Hopkins, Donald J., 1385
Hopkins, Donald R., 2989
Hopkins, Jason, 7731
Hopkins, John P., 1390
Hopkins, Marvin, 6196
Hopkins, Rachel Abrams, 9769
Hopkins, Robert D., 3909
Hopkins, Ronnie, 2525
Hopkins, Rusty, 2525
Hopkins, Thomas E., 7661
Hopkins, Vince, 7405
Hopkins, Virginia, 7234
Hopkinson, Sealy H., 3850
Hoppe Charitable Remainder Annuity Trust, W.J., 703
Hoppe Sunset Living Trust, 703
Hoppe, Lea Ann, 703
Hoppe, William James, 703
Hoppe-Sunset Trust, William, Dr., 703
Hopper, Berenice, 1418
Hopper, Cameron F., 1657
Hopper, Harry, 9380
Hopper, Heidi, 704
Hopper, J. Steven, 659
Hopper, Jim, 9578
Hopper, Robert, 1418
Hoppes, Zac, 3534
Hoppman, Elsa M., 8111
Hoppmann, Robert D., 2158
Hopson, Courtney Cohn, 9183
Hopwood, Andrew P., 8718
Hopwood, John M., 8096
Hopwood, Mary S., 8096
Hopwood, William T., 8096
Horak, H. Lynn, 3420
Horan, David C., 6343
Horan, Patrick, 4343
Horan, Robert, 6261
Horan, Terry, 4354
Hord, Jeffrey, 4359
Hord, Juanita A., 2662
Hord, Robert E., Jr., 2662
Hord, Thomas E., III, 8545
Horejsi, Inc., 3520
Horejsi, John, 3520
Horejsi, Stewart, 3520
Horii, Akinori, 7019
Horikiri, Noriaki, 9881
Horiszny, Laurene H., 4353
Horizon Equity Group, LLC, 6166
Horizon Healthcare Services, Inc., 5305
Horizon House Apartments LP, 9452
Hormel Foods Corp., 4676
Hormel, James C., 1180
Horn, Alan F., 705
Horn, Cindy, 705
Horn, Craig W., 4585
Horn, Cynthia, 705
Horn, Daniel L., 7387
Horn, David C., 7366
Horn, Jeff, 2742
Horn, Mildred V., 3581
Horn, Rebecca, 6285
Horn, Robyn, 213
Horn, Thomas E., 1091
Hornady, Ellen, 5044
Hornbach, Mike, 3293
Hornbaker, Denise K., 119
Hornberger, Eric, 9492
Hornberger, Lauren, 7607
Hornblower, Jonathan M., 8768
Horne, Eleanor, 5411
Horne, Richard G., 9309
Horne, Steve, 3282
Horner, Constance J., 5415
Horner, Donald G., 2598
Horner, Duncan, 1518
Horner, Gary C., Esq., 7990
Horner, Pamela J., 5537
Horner, Robert W., III, 7587
Horness, Lois A., 685
Hornig, Steven A., 4647, 4700
Horning, Chuck, 1512
Horning, Sandra, 570
Hornsby, Kathy, 9559
Horntvedt, Jody, 4730
Horonzy, Joseph G., 4555, 4556
Horowitch, David, 6205
Horowitz Charitable Lead Trust, Gedale B., 6186
Horowitz March 31, 1994 Charitable Lead Annuity Trust, Gedale B. & Barbara S., 6186
Horowitz, Alison, 6628
Horowitz, Barbara S., 6186
Horowitz, Gedale B., 6186
Horowitz, Margaret, 6187
Horowitz, Naftali, 6836
Horowitz, Robert H., 6447
Horowitz, Ruth, 6186
Horowitz, Seth, 6186
Horr, Susan B., 6567
Horrigan, D. Gregory, 1670
Horrigan, Judith Anne, 1670
Horsager, Naomi, 4627
Horst, Mary Lynn, 5068
Horton Fund, Alan & Beverley, 7659
Horton, Alan M., 2035
Horton, Alice Kirby, 5339
Horton, Barbara, 4795
Horton, Charles E., 7178
Horton, James A., 1312
Horton, Kathi, 4372
Horton, Martha, 8543
Horton, Neil, 3532
Horton, Tom, 9652
Horvitz Foundation, Lois U., 7573, 8238, 9699
Horvitz, David W., 2081, 2161
Horvitz, Francie, 2161
Horvitz, H. Robert, 9625
Horvitz, Jane R., 7573, 7637
Horvitz, Marcy R., 7493
Horvitz, Michael I., 7573
Horvitz, Michael J., 7529, 7573
Horvitz, Peter A., 9699
Horvitz, Richard A., 7493
Horwich, Ada, 706
Horwich, Ada R., 706
Horwich, James, 706
Horwich, Tracey, 3201
Horwitz, Robert, 6188
Horwood, Richard M., 2862
Hoshaw, Betsy, 3283
Hosking, John H., 4350
Hoskins, Anne. E., 5416
Hoskins, Richard J., 3100
Hospice of San Joaquin, 417
Hospira, Inc., 2921
Hospital Corp. of America, 8568
Hoss, Shelley, 992
Hosser, Ottilie Wagner, 8406
Host, Jerry, 4833
Host, W. James, 3593
Hostek, Loren D., 9730
Hostetler, Baker, 7638
Hostetter, Amos B., Jr., 3937
Hostetter, Barbara W., 3937
Hostetter, Mark D., 6126
Hotaling, Bruce, 8175
Hotchkis, John F., 745
Hotchkis, Preston B., 745
Hotchkiss, Craig, 3449
Hotel Americana, 6988
Hotes, Elisabeth, 9646
Hotes, Richard W., 6595, 9646
Hotta, John, 9731
Hotta, Keiichi, 5724
Hotzler, Heidi, 6544
Hou, Grace B., 2769, 3242
Hou, Ryan C., 3321
Houck, Gayle L., 6584
Houck, Jonathan, 1392
Hough, Bonnie, 4462
Hough, David R., 4462
Hough, Hazel C., 2162
Hough, Richard T., 4462
Hough, Shirley, 545
Hough, W. Robb, 2162
Hough, William, 4462
Hough, William R., 2162
Houghton, James R., 5818
Houkom, Betty, 2327
Houle, Irene, 1389
Houlihan, Cathy, 1805
Houlihan, Robert W., 3480
Houlik, Steve, 3555
Houlsby, John R., 2922
Houpt, Kathy, 3205
Houren, Jay C., 8691
Hourihan, Edward, Jr., 5969
House of Lloyd, Inc., 3530
House, David, 707
House, Helen Fasken, 8839
House, Jim, 9048
House, Joyce, 707
House, Patricia, 686
House, Robert, 707
Houseal, John, 3061
Household Bank, 1953
Householder, Joseph A., 1140
Houser, John D., 2435
Houser, Joshua, 9354
Houston McLane Co., Inc., 8674
Houston, Alice, 3563
Houston, David J., 8715
Houston, Gary, 8618
Houston, J. Wayne, 73
Houston, Jamie, 4820
Houston, Jamie G., III, 4833
Houston, Janet L., 7624
Houston-Philpot, Kimberly R., 4405
Houswort, Alton, 2409
Hovde Capital I, LLC, 9865
Hovde Financial, Inc., 9865
Hovde, Eric D., 9865
Hovde, Steven D., 9865
Hoverter, Julia, 8097
Hoverter, Lawrence, 8097
Hovey, Kathy, 3470
Hovington, Penelope, 7102
Hovland, Ann M., 1376
Hovnanian Enterprises, Inc., 3775
Hovnanian, Anna, 5306
Hovnanian, Ara K., 5307
Hovnanian, Armen, 5306
Hovnanian, Edele, 5306
Hovnanian, Hirair, 5306
Hovnanian, Kevork S., 5307
Hovnanian, Leela, 5306
Hovnanian, Sirwart K., 5307
Hovnanian-Baghdassarian, Tanya, 5306
How, Melissa, 5028
Howa, Leslie Peery, 9344
Howab Trust, 3996
Howald, D. Aaron, 4405
Howard Trust, Jack R., 7659
Howard, Alton, 7199
Howard, Andrea M., 4212
Howard, Barbara, 2433
Howard, Burgie, 2826
Howard, Chandler J., 1630
Howard, Christopher "Chris" B., Dr., 9501
Howard, Dana W., 7313
Howard, Danette, 3345
Howard, Daryll T., 9060
Howard, David M., 3195
Howard, Denise, 3278
Howard, Derrick, 9149
Howard, Don, 727
Howard, Fred, 6016
Howard, G. Jean, 6099
Howard, Harrison, 3887
Howard, James, 7742
Howard, Jessica, 8495
Howard, John L., 2874
Howard, Josh, 7657
Howard, Kelly D., 7835
Howard, Kim, 7607
Howard, Marven E., 667

Howard, Peter K., 9413
Howard, Randy, 4872
Howard, Robert, 7672
Howard, Robert S., 5086, 9647
Howard, Roscoe, 1288
Howard, Sam, 4502
Howard, Steven R., 5864
Howard, Sunny Rice, 6189
Howard, Teresa F., 8847
Howard, Tim, 1480, 1481
Howard, Wayne, 3851
Howard, Wayne L., 7835
Howard, Zoe, 3336
Howard-Malm, Laurie, 5158
Howard-Potter, Jack, 7659
Howat, J. Christopher, 9771
Howatt, Thomas J., 9949
Howd, Kathryn Boeckman, 8707
Howe, Debara, 3337
Howe, J. Patrick, 4594
Howe, James E., 5248
Howe, Kay, 4185
Howe, Maureen L., 2636
Howe, Robert, 9800
Howe, Robert G., 4185
Howe, Ruth, 5927
Howe, Theresa B., 4864
Howell, Alfred H., Jr., 5892
Howell, Brad, 3283
Howell, Douglas K., 2855
Howell, Gary M., 9134
Howell, George B., III, 2040, 2308
Howell, George S., 3556
Howell, James S., 7329
Howell, Jeffrey F., 5518
Howell, Jim, 4361
Howell, Joe, Dr., 7766
Howell, Katie S., 8476
Howell, Laverne, 8918
Howell, Louise L., 1449
Howell, Michael, 3324
Howell, Pam, 7678
Howell, Philip B., 5519
Howell, R. Rodney, 2223
Howell, Ronald S., 9757
Howell, Trip, 9380
Howell, William H., III, 9434
Howell, Winston, 2037
Howenstine, Brian, 3290
Hower, Bob, 3971
Hower, Lewis, 9311
Howerton, J. William, 3567
Howerton, W. Clay, 3567
Howes, Deborah S., 5848
Howett, Ciannat M., 2449
Howey, Gregory B., 1537
Howie, Barbara L., 1431
Howitt, Robert, 6150
Howland Trust, Melita S. & Weston, 4017
Howland, Jacob, 7752
Howland, John M., 8981
Howland, Melita S., 4017
Howland, Weston, III, 4017
Howland, Weston, Jr., 4017
Howley, Lauralee V., 7494
Howley, W. Nicholas, 7494
Howley, W. Nicholas, Mrs., 7494
Howlin, Diane, 4362
Howrey, Matt, 3319
Hoxie, Jaqueline Jones, 8113
Hoy, Ariane, 5208
Hoyer, David, 9117
Hoyos, Jose, 109
Hoyt, Alex Crawford, 8098
Hoyt, May Emma, 8098
Hozey, G. Harold, 5463
HP Hood, 3245
Hrabowski, Freeman A., III, 3796, 6872, 9596
Hrabowski, Jacqueline C., 3712, 3865
HRB Management, Inc., 4902
HRM SLM Realty Trust, 6409
Hrncir, Eleanor, 2070
Hroblak, Gerald J., 3784
Hryhorczuk, Linda L., Dr., 4424
HS Management, LP, 1106
HSBC Bank USA, N.A., 5633, 6029, 6544, 6904
HSBC Bank, USA, 6330
HSBC Card Retail Services, 1953
HSC Health Care Foundation, 3898
Hsieh, Fang Zhi Liu, 710
Hsieh, Ming, 710
HSM Management Services, Inc., 4989
HSP Gaming L.P., 8217
Hsu, Alice Wan-Tsen, 711
Hsu, Claire, 6002
Hsu, F. Richard, 6959
Hsu, K.W., 6959
Hsu, Ming Chen, 6959
Hsu, Steve G.K., 711
Hsu, T.C., 6911
HTC Global Services Inc., 4480
HTOOB, Inc., 2000
Htun, MaDoe, 8216
Hu, Fred Z., 3982
Huang, Alice, 9109
Huang, Alice S., 6724
Huang, Ching, 810
Huang, Jen-Hsun, 712
Huang, Lori L., 712
Huang, Mikiko, Dr., 434
Huang, Phyllis, 1011
Huang, Shauna, 7908
Huang, Shu, 446, 537, 823, 976
Hubbard Broadcasting, Inc., 4678
Hubbard Charitable Lead Trust, Claire M., 5053, 5054
Hubbard, Al, 1518
Hubbard, Allan, 3345
Hubbard, Anne A., 2795
Hubbard, Anne M., 5053, 5054
Hubbard, C. Mark, 3402
Hubbard, Claire M., 5053, 5054
Hubbard, Colleen, 5053
Hubbard, David J., 2795, 5995
Hubbard, Galbreath, 7983
Hubbard, Hylan T., 9474
Hubbard, Jean, 1015
Hubbard, Joan Dale, 5523
Hubbard, Julie, 3171
Hubbard, Karen H., 4678
Hubbard, Kenneth E., 18
Hubbard, M.C., 1178
Hubbard, Peggy, 5533
Hubbard, R.D., 5523
Hubbard, Robert W., 4678
Hubbard, Robin, 1421
Hubbard, Stanley E., 4678
Hubbard, Stanley S., 4678
Hubbard, Theodore F., Jr., 5053, 5054
Hubbard, Thomas J., 2795
Hubbell Inc., 1614
Hubbell, Charlotte, 3445
Hubbell, Fred S., 3420
Hubbell, Frederick S., 3445
Hubble, Butch, 7481
Hubbs, Donald H., 692
Huber, David R., 5305
Huber, Jennifer, 2880
Huber, Joseph F., 8138
Huber, Linda S., 6499
Huber, Michael C., 7378
Huber, Patricia, 3291
Huber, Paul L., 8001
Huber, Robert A., 790
Huber, Sandy, 4446
Huber, Stephen L., 9393
Huber, Timothy J., 8012
Huber, Willam F., 8262
Huberfeld, 5761
Huberfeld Family Foundation, 5693
Huberfeld, Alexander, 6190
Huberfeld, Murray, 6190
Huberfeld, Rachel, 6190
Huberfeld-Bodner Family Foundation, 6190
Huberfield, Alexander, 6190
Huberfield, Ariela, 6190
Huberfield, Jacob, 6190
Huberfield, Rachel, 6190
Hubert Foundation, 7495
Hubert, A. Franklin, 7640
Hubert, Ed, 7495
Hubert, Joann, 7495
Hubert, Richard N., 2163
Hubscher, Chuck, 4512
Huck, Karma, 3543
Huck, Paul E., 7907
Huckabee, Chris, 8776
Huckabee, Donna, 198
Huckaby, Hank, 2427
Huckenberg, Mark, 1487
Hudak, Robert, 7282
Hudbay Minerals, 7349
Huddleston, Bob, 5055
Huddleston, William Henry, III, 8545
Hudetz, Frank C., 2812
Hudgens, D. Scott, Jr., 2486
Hudgens, Dallas S., III, 2486
Hudgins, Jeffrey, 2325
Hudgins, Peggy, 9503
Hudler, Carol, 8550
Hudner, Philip, 524
Hudner, Philip, Jr., 454
Hudner, Steve, 415
Hudnut, Thomas, 611
Hudson Charitable Fund, 6483
Hudson Co., J.L., The, 4463
Hudson River Bank & Trust Co., 6191
Hudson, Charles D., Jr., 2418, 2419
Hudson, Craig, 7417
Hudson, David T., 4808
Hudson, Deanna, 9768
Hudson, Edward R., Jr., 8737
Hudson, Gilbert, 4463
Hudson, Harris W., 2164, 2165
Hudson, Howard, Mrs., 2514
Hudson, J. Clifford, 5994
Hudson, J.D., 8763
Hudson, Jerry, 7990
Hudson, Jerry E., 7836
Hudson, John O., III, 1
Hudson, Johnny K., 189
Hudson, Joseph L., IV, 4463
Hudson, Joseph L., Jr., 4463
Hudson, Kellie Dawn, 2242
Hudson, Leslie, 7781
Hudson, M.R., 8919
Hudson, Mike, 1395
Hudson, Murdock, 8919
Hudson, Pam, 22
Hudson, Rose, 3613
Hudson, Sonny, 8981
Hudson, Steven W., 2034, 2164
Hudson, W. Howard, Dr., 2514
Hudspeth, Larry, 841
Hueber, Stuart R., 8803
Huebner, Constance, 4157
Huesman, Terri Donlin, 7605
Huey, Bruce E., 2747
Huey, Ester, 9767
Huey, Jeanne W., 1125
Huff, Florida, 2580
Huff, Florida Ellis, 2821
Huff, Gisele, 715
Huff, Mercedes, 9975
Huff, Olson, 7321
Huffaker, Hugh D., Jr., 8544
Huffenus, Daniel S., 2951
Huffington, Michael, 5606, 8920
Huffington, Phyllis Gough, 8920
Huffington, Roy M., 8920
Huffington, Terry L., 8920
Huffman, Ann Bryan, 7161
Huffman, Charmel, 1127
Huffman, Gary T., 7599
Huffman, Kathleen, 9327
HUffman, Kelle B., 7178
Huffman, Lloyd, 9054
Huffman, Mark A., 8229
Huffman, Meredith, 8053
Huffman, Randolph H., 9533
Hufford, Jamie, 110
Huggins, Anita, 4061
Huggins, John, 4839
Hughes Family Non-Exe Trust, R. Dale, 8099
Hughes Medical Institute, Howard, 1558
Hughes, Alan F., 8275
Hughes, Alana, 7794
Hughes, Baker, 9118
Hughes, Ben, 9768
Hughes, Bill M., 5026
Hughes, Brennan, 1432
Hughes, Brian, 548, 3438
Hughes, Bruce W., 8468
Hughes, Carolyn R., 3304
Hughes, Charles, 7303
Hughes, Chris, 2191
Hughes, Christopher R., 9648
Hughes, David R., 7991
Hughes, Deborah L., 9198
Hughes, Elizabeth L., 4232, 4258, 4269
Hughes, Frances M., 8099
Hughes, Fred Lee, 8774
Hughes, Geoffrey C., 6192
Hughes, Hattie Hyman, 548
Hughes, Holly, 6340
Hughes, Howard R., 3818
Hughes, James C., 9693
Hughes, James S., 3991
Hughes, Jancie, 1423
Hughes, John E., 2759
Hughes, Karyl Kay, 9648
Hughes, Katherine Nouri, 927
Hughes, Ken, 7231
Hughes, Kevin D., 8099
Hughes, Leona, 1979
Hughes, Mark, 3777
Hughes, Mark F., Jr., 5798
Hughes, Mary Ellen, 9693
Hughes, Michael, 2728
Hughes, Michael H., 9723
Hughes, Michelle, 8315

Hughes, Nita, 8001
Hughes, Pamela, 9652
Hughes, Pamela J., 9652
Hughes, Patricia, 1083
Hughes, Patricia G., 8099
Hughes, R. Dale, 8099
Hughes, Renee Cardwell, 8239
Hughes, Robert J., 6613
Hughes, Sandra, 7335
Hughes, Sean, 9793
Hughes, Shelby, 1344
Hughes, Shirley, 4618
Hughes, Teresa F., 2605
Hughes, Vester T., Jr., 8773
Hughey, James F., Jr., 27
Hughey, Richard M., Jr., 4445
Hugin, Kathleen M., 5308
Hugin, Robert J., 5308
Hugo Neu Corp., 6537
Hugon, Jacques, 3923
Huguenard, John E., 444
Huhtala, David, 4194
Huiskamp, Heidi, 3442
Huisking, Charles L., III, 1615
Huisking, Frank R., 1615
Huisking, Paul, 1615
Huisking, Richard V., 1615
Huisking, William W., 1615
Huizenga Charitable Lead Annuity Trust, Jean, 2164
Huizenga Foundation, Elizabeth I., 4365
Huizenga Restated Living Trust, Jean, 2164
Huizenga, Elizabeth I., 4338
Huizenga, H. Wayne, 2165
Huizenga, H. Wayne, Jr., 2165
Huizenga, Heidi A., 2924
Huizenga, J.C., 4365
Huizenga, Jay, 8521
Huizenga, John C., 4365
Huizenga, Martha Jean, 2165
Huizenga, P.J., 2924
Huizenga, Peter H., 2924
Huizenga, Tim, 2924
Huizinga, Gretchen, 9613
Hulbert, Anthony D., 9466
Hulbert, Maureen P., 7054
Hulbert, William H., 7054
Huleatt, Steven J., 1567
Hulewicz, Mike, 4373
Hulings, Albert D., 4677
Hulings, Mary Andersen, 4677
Hull Fund, Jim & Karen, 2514
Hull, Alan, 4816
Hull, Blair, 2925
Hull, Courtney, 2925
Hull, Herbert R., 7852
Hull, James, 395
Hull, James M., 2434
Hull, Jeffrey, 2925
Hull, John E., 6470
Hull, Joseph L., III, 7730
Hull, Kenneth, 3317
Hull, Kristin, 2925
Hull, Lisa, 3418
Hull, M. Blair, Jr., 2925
Hull, Megan, 2925
Hull, Nancy, 7852
Hull, R. Joseph, 1027
Hull, Ralph, 9069
Hull, Teri, 4591
Hullet, Diane, 4408
Hullet, Diane Dow, 4407
Hulme, Christine, 7569
Hulme, Christine J., 7620
Hulsman, Letty, 9377
Hulst, Titia, 6936
Hulston, John K., 4911
Hulston, John L., 4911
Hulston, John Patrick, 4911
Hulston, Joseph Fred, 4911
Hulston, Lucia C., 4911
Hult, Keith C., 912
Hultman, Suzie, 9992
Hulvey, Michael, 3205
Human Genome Sciences NY Inc., 6231
Human Svcs. Corp., 4152
Humana Inc., 3582
Humann, Phil, 2142
Humble, Jeanie, 1368
Humble, Jerry, 7676
Humble, Ryan, 7676
Humble, Susan, 5009
Hume, Caroline H., 715
Hume, Gene, 1276
Hume, George H., 715
Hume, Jaquelin H., 715
Hume, Thomas, 9410
Hume, William J., 715
Humes, Cori, 1564
Humes, Jim, 3419
Humes, Kerry, Dr., 3033
Humiston, Mary E., 249
Huml, Jeffrey P., 2673
Hummel, Alethia, 2792
Hummel, Bobbie J., 7439
Hummel, Carolyn, 4438
Hummel, Chad, 5309
Hummel, David R., 5309
Hummel, Jane, 5309
Hummel, Rolf E., 2257
Hummel, Todd, 5309
Hummel, Waltrude E., 2257
Hummer, Philip Wayne, 2831
Hummer-Tuttle, Maria, 774
Hummer-Tuttle, Maria D., 579
Humphrey, George M., 7497
Humphrey, Jeffrey, 1373
Humphrey, Louise, 2037
Humphrey, Pamela S., 7497
Humphrey, Sytske, 3962
Humphrey, Tom, 4495
Humphreys Revocable Trust, Ethelmae, 4875
Humphreys, Christian D., 2516
Humphreys, David, 4875
Humphreys, David C., 4875, 4913
Humphreys, Debra G., 4875, 4913
Humphreys, Ethelmae, 4875
Humphreys, Ethelmae C., 4875, 4913
Humphreys, Ethelmae Craig, 4913
Humphreys, Gail, 5108
Humphreys, Geraldine Davis, 8921
Humphreys, J.P., 4913
Humphreys, Lance, 2853
Humphreys, Lewis H., 4912
Humphreys, Ruth Boettcher, 1374
Humphries, Cary, 4791
Humphries, Paul, 535
Humphries, William, 579
Humphrys, Maureen, 9998
Hundley, Charles, 2765
Hundley, David, 9125
Hundley, James D., M.D., 7170
Hung, Wen-Hsiung, 1936
Hungarian-American Enterprise Fund, 3692
Hungerpiller, James R., 2548
Hungtington Homes, 8756
Hunker, Ann Marie, 7550
Hunker, Fred D., 18
Hunnicutt, Anne S., 9779
Hunnicutt, H.P., 9779
Hunsaker, Craig, 975
Hunsaker, H. Scott, 8890
Hunstman, James H., 9327
Hunt Electric Supply, 7237
Hunt Family Foundation, Swanee, 6864
Hunt, A. James, 8100
Hunt, Alexandra K., 8100
Hunt, Andrew McQ., 8100
Hunt, Avery S., 8100
Hunt, B.G., 9340
Hunt, Brenda L., 4343
Hunt, Christopher, 1365, 3010
Hunt, Christopher M., 8100
Hunt, Daniel K., 8100
Hunt, Dave, 1650
Hunt, Dennis, 179
Hunt, Douglas, 2690
Hunt, Edward M., 8100
Hunt, Elizabeth H., 8100
Hunt, Evan McMasters, 8100
Hunt, Gayle G., 8922
Hunt, Heather, 8923
Hunt, Helen Lakelly, 6864
Hunt, Holly Bamford, 9580
Hunt, Hunter L., 9047
Hunt, Ian C., 3010
Hunt, James W., Jr., 3953
Hunt, Joan, 3348
Hunt, John B., 8100
Hunt, Joshua W., 8922
Hunt, Justin, 8100
Hunt, Kathlee S., 8599
Hunt, Lila C., 8100
Hunt, M. Truman, 9340
Hunt, Marion M., 8100
Hunt, Nancy Ann, 8923, 9047
Hunt, Natasha, 893, 966
Hunt, Oliver, 8100
Hunt, Penny, 4753
Hunt, R. Samuel, III, 7237
Hunt, R. Samuel, IV, 7237
Hunt, Ray L., 8923, 9047
Hunt, Richard E., 7569
Hunt, Richard L., 1097
Hunt, Richard M., 8100
Hunt, Roy, 563
Hunt, Roy A., 8100
Hunt, Roy A., III, 8100
Hunt, S.S. Sackler, 6779
Hunt, Samuel P., 5177
Hunt, Sarah Anschutz, 1364, 1365
Hunt, Scott E., 4864
Hunt, Stephanie E., 8795
Hunt, Swanee, Hon., 4102
Hunt, Torrence M., Jr., 8100
Hunt, Torrence W.B., 8100
Hunt, Tyler B., 8100
Hunt, Victoria S., 7237
Hunt, William E., 8100, 8228
Hunt, Woody L., 8922
Hunte, Danista, 3726
Hunter Charitable Lead Annuity Trust, Maxine M., 2926
Hunter Douglas, Inc., 6196
Hunter's Glen/Ford, Ltd., 8854
Hunter, A.V., 1431
Hunter, Allan B., 6197
Hunter, Andre, 6197
Hunter, Britton, 7801
Hunter, Bruce, 6408
Hunter, Carol Bright, 8756
Hunter, Catrelia, 7305
Hunter, Christine F., 3790
Hunter, Dett P., 7524
Hunter, Edwin F., III, 3625
Hunter, Edwin Ford, III, 3617
Hunter, Edwin K., 3617
Hunter, George Thomas, 8535
Hunter, Jack, 3276
Hunter, Jeff, 239
Hunter, Joanne, 318
Hunter, Joanne B., 318
Hunter, Joelle Mortenson, 9909
Hunter, Joseph C., 7227
Hunter, Kelly, 6197
Hunter, Maxine, 2926
Hunter, Sue Stone, 7801
Hunter, Susan L., 7605
Hunter, Tammy Y., 5349
Hunter, Thomas B., III, 2926
Hunter, Thomas B., IV, 2926
Hunter, Timothy M., 8026
Hunter, Willard M., 2926
Hunter, William T., 3790
Hunter, William T., Jr., 3790
Hunter-Ishikawa, Zen, 1903
Huntin, Bradford D., 5416
Hunting, John R., 4412
Hunting, Mary Anne, 4547
Huntington Bank, 9773
Huntington National Bank, 7458, 7469
Huntington National Bank, N.A., 7450
Huntington National Bank, The, 4369, 7404, 7406, 7492, 7673, 7676, 9780
Huntington, Al, 3285
Huntington, Archer M., 5585
Huntington, John, 7499
Huntington, Robert H., Dr., 7682
Huntley, Allan, 4039
Huntley, Lynn, 2432
Huntley, Mary Lynn, 2075
Huntsman, David H., 9327
Huntsman, Jon M., 9327
Huntsman, Karen H., 9327
Huntsman, Ken, 9410
Huntsman, Paul C., 9327
Huntsman, Scott, 9311
Hunzeker, Pam, 5063
Huot, Larry, 5180
Huot, Lauren, 2108
Hupe, Walt, 2764
Hupfer, Virginia M., 3349
Hurand, Gary, 4520
Hurd Char. Lead Annuity Trust, Priscilla Payne, 8101
Hurd, Jeffrey J., 5563
Hurd, Jennifer Jacoby, 2780
Hurd, Joseph D., Jr., 7971
Hurd, Priscilla Payne, 3073
Hurdelbrink, Laura, 9751
Hurdle, Lanier, 4834
Hurdus, Syde, 6198
Huret, Robert A., 2588
Hurford, John B., 6199
Hurlburt, Bradley, 2032
Hurlbut, Robert, 9614
Hurlbut, Robert S., Jr., 3971
Hurlbut, Sally D., 4211
Hurlen Fund, Harold, 9578
Hurley, Cheryl, 6308
Hurley, James L., 3598
Hurley, John M., 2120

Hurley, Mark, 335
Hurley, Phil, 2644
Hurley, Willard L., 40
Hurst, Alexander B., 6200
Hurst, Amanda K., 6200
Hurst, Anthony P., 4464
Hurst, Dean W., 166
Hurst, Elizabeth S., 4464
Hurst, Peter F., 4464
Hurst, Robert J., 5811, 6200
Hurst, Robert W., 9499
Hurst, Soledad, 1368
Hurst, Soledad D., 6200
Hurst-Hyde, Kristen, 166
Hurston, Karl A., 4666
Hurt, Kathleen C., 1320
Hurt, Laura, 3321
Hurt, Sarah S., 1320
Hurt, William H., 1320
Hurtt, Nancy J., 716
Hurtt, Robert S., Jr., 716
Hurtubise, Mark, 9650
Hurvis, Christina, 2930
Hurvis, J. Thomas, 2930, 3214
Hurvis, Julie A., 2930
Hurvis-Younkin, Sara, 2930
Hurwich, Cecelia, 255
Hurwitz, Barbara, 6287
Hurwitz, Kenneth D., 5652
Hurwitz, Roger T., 4950
Huschke, Kathryn Wise, 4516
HUSCO International, Inc., 9926
Huseby, Sven, 1578
Huskey, Leon, 3360
Huskins, Sandra L., 679
Husky, Richard, 1233
Husmann, Joyce, 3287
Huss, David, 8618
Huss, Philip A., 9553
Hussa, Benjamin M., 7907
Hussain, Brian, 8472
Hussell, Monika, 9780
Hussey, Bernice H., 8538
Hussey, Herbert E., 2327
Hussey, Jeffrey S., 9649
Hussman, John P., 3815
Hussman, Tom, 8825
Huston, Charles L., III, 8102, 8103
Huston, Charles L., IV, 8103
Huston, Charles L., Jr., 8103
Huston, Joy, 7991
Huston, Mike, 5009
Huston, Morrison C., Jr., 8303
Huston, Ruth, 8103
Huston, Scott G., 8103
Huston, Stewart, 8102
Hutaff, Lucile, 7184
Hutcherson, John, 8777
Hutcheson, Dorothea W., 213
Hutcheson, Karen, 213
Hutcheson, Mary E., 213
Hutcheson, Mary Ellen, 2008
Hutcheson, Mary Ross Carter, 9403
Hutcheson, Richard, 213
Hutcheson, Ryan, 7214
Hutcheson, Susanne Lilly, 4696
Hutcheson, Tad, 2432
Hutcheson, William L., 213
Hutchings, Gillian, 6532
Hutchings, Jack, 3216
Hutchins Family Foundation, Inc., 5777
Hutchins Generation Skipping Transfer Exempt Trust, Waldo, 6202
Hutchins Jr. Non Exempt Trust, Waldo, 6202
Hutchins, Bruce, 1
Hutchins, Deborah D., 6201
Hutchins, Dorothy, 3543
Hutchins, Elizabeth E., 6202
Hutchins, Glenn H., 5777, 6201
Hutchins, Jeffrey D., 4227
Hutchins, Mary J., 6202
Hutchins, Priscilla, 1
Hutchins, Robert, 1520
Hutchins, Waldo H., Jr., 6202
Hutchinson, Doug, 1393
Hutchinson, Elaine S., 6361
Hutchinson, Eric, 179
Hutchinson, Hal, 9983
Hutchinson, Howard G., 1738
Hutchinson, Les, 4461
Hutchinson, Marc C., 2274
Hutchinson, Raymond J., 4443
Hutchinson, Robert E., 7302
Hutchinson, Sarah H., 7223
Hutchinson, Susan E., 8768
Hutchison, Jeffrey, 7605
Hutchison, Laura, 1888
Hutchison, Robin, 9253
Hutchison, Susan, 9735
Hutchisson, Rachel, 8472
Huter, Michael E., 2635
Hutsenpiller, Bob, 7417
Hutson, Chris, 3570
Hutson, Denise, 9496
Hutson, Robert E., 8865
Hutson, Tracy A., 1315
Hutta, Jane, 6873
Huttenlocher, Daniel, 2989
Huttle, Frank, III, 5400
Huttler, Stephen B., 3797
Hutto, Clare P., 717
Hutto, Eileen C., 717
Hutto, Scott W., 8507
Hutton, Ann, 7979
Hutton, Billy J., Jr., 7488
Hutton, Edward A., 7500
Hutton, Edward L., 7500
Hutton, G. Thompson, 5658
Hutton, Kathryn Jane, 7500
Hutton, Mara, 5658
Hutton, Thomas C., 7500
Huurman, Susan D., 277
Hux, Glenn H., 7567
Hux, Vernon E., 3325
Huyck, E.B., 630
Huynen, Diana, 2273
Hwang Donor Advised Fund at Fuller, 6090
Hwang, Becky, 6090
Hwang, C. Gemma, 719
Hwang, K. Phillip, 719
Hwang, Sung Kook, 6090
Hwee, Koh Boon, 686
HWL Incestements, 2214
Hyams, Godfrey M., 4103
Hyams, Sarah A., 4103
Hybl, Kyle, 1406
Hybl, William, 1518
Hybl, William J., 1406
Hyche, J. Tod, 8474
Hyde Park, 246
Hyde Park Nursing Home, Inc., 6287
Hyde, Allen B., 8584
Hyde, Barbara, 8610
Hyde, Barbara R., 8584
Hyde, David G., 1141
Hyde, Fran, 8575
Hyde, J. R., III, 8610
Hyde, J.R., III, 8584
Hyde, J.R., Sr., 8584
Hyde, Lillia Babbitt, 5310
Hyde, Margaret, 8584
Hyde, Truman, 8537
Hyland, Carol, 9843
Hyland, M. Elise, 8025
Hylton Charitable Lead Trust, Irene V., 9455
Hylton, Cecil D., 9455
Hylton, Cecilia M., 9455
Hylton, Conrad C., 9455
Hylton, Donnie, 9511
Hyman, Alan L., 548
Hyman, Charles D. "Chuck", 2031
Hyman, Daniel R., 4354
Hyman, Debra B., 7940
Hyman, Erik, 1076
Hyman, Howard L., 548
Hyman, Steven E., 5845
Hyman, Steven, Dr., 6693
Hyndman, Thomas M., Jr., 8236
Hynek, Jacqueline, 9239
Hynek, Steven L., 9239
Hynes, Mary Ann, 3141
Hynnek, Julia L., 4677
Hyundai Village of Danvers, 4196
Hyzer, Nancy, 2766

I'Anson, Lawrence Warren, III, 9391
Iacoabelli, Jolie, 9341
Iacocca, Lido A. "Lee", 4104
Iacomini, Maryanne, 1115
Iacovone, Albert F., 7635
Iacullo, Robert J., 5486
Iancu, Manssa, 2778
Iannaccone, Sophia, 3240
Iannelli, Ralph, 1116
Iarussi, Deborah Sills, 9371
IAT Syndicate, Inc., 6270
Ibach, Teresa, 5055
Ibarguen, Alberto, 2191
Ibarra, Ricardo, 886
Iberia Bank, 66
IBM, 7307, 9149
IBS, Inc., 4099
Ibsen, Marlene M., 4783
Icahn, Carl C., 6204
ICAP Securities USA LLC, 7214
Ice, Carl R., 8706
Ickler, Nancy, 3259, 3289
ID Diary Council United Dairymen of ID, 3245
Iddings, Andrew S., 9866
Iddings, Roscoe C., 9866
Idels, Michele, 1788
Idema, Beatrice A., 4465
Idema, William, 1403
Idema, William W., 4465
Iding, Allan E., 9966
IDT Corp., 5311
IEEE Foundation, 9599
Ieuter, Cal, 4502
IFG Corp., 5557
Iger, Robert A., 467
Igler, Sarah, 8302
Igler, Thomas, 8302
Ignat, Brian, 7594
Ignite the Spirit, 2823
Igoe, Brian, 1051
IJO, 7214
ILC Holdings, Inc., 6325
Iler, Barbara Welles, 4218
Iler, Donald Carey, 3154
Iler, N. Carey, Jr., 3154
Iler, Robert Gordon, Jr., 3154
Ilitch, Denise, 4543
Illescas, Beatriz, 2461
Illick, Virginia B., 7624
Illinois Consolidated Telephone Co., 2986
Illinois State Board of Education, 2761
Illinois Tool Works Inc., 2934
ILTS, 4183
Imani Bros., 6833
Imbasciani, Michelle, 3085
Imbesi, Anthony M., 8214
Imbesi, Charles L., 8214
Imbesi, Giovanna C., 8214
Imbesi, John C., 8214
Imbesi, Patricia H., 8214
Imbesi, Paul H., 8214
Imboden, Connie E., 3725
Imburgia, Anthony, 3326
Imburgia, Anthony Jessica, 3326
Imburgia, Jessica, 3326
IMG, 7012
Imhof, Mike, 1518
Imhoff, Quincey, 542
Imhoff, Quincey T., 426
Imirizian, Maro, 9750
Imlay, Cindy, 2487
Imlay, John P. "Scott", III, 2487
Imlay, John P., Jr., 2487
Imlay, Mary Ellen, 2487
Imler, Fred, Sr., 7971
Immekus, Jason, 3302
Immekus, Sarah, 3302
Immel, Steven M., 9834
Immerwahr, John, Dr., 7075
Imondi, Deborah, 8446
Imorde, Scott, 8605
IMPACT, 417
Impala Asset Management LLC, 1705
Impemba, Dominick, 6724
Imperial Promenade Assocs., LLC, 261
Imrie, Kent, 959
Inabnett, Carrick R., 3666
Inbar, Tomer, 5733
Inc., Sewer System Evaluations, 2735
Incandela, Mary Kay, 7370
Incerti, Carlo, 4067
Inch, Steve, 5115
Inch, Tara, 5115
Inco, Ltd., 7272
Ind Minera Mexico, 7349
Indenbaum, Michael A., 4459
Independence Bank, 3583
Independence Blue Cross, 8106
Independence Communications, Inc., 8169
Independence Community Bank Corp., 5718
Independent Publications, Inc., 8169
Indiana Diary and Nutrition Council, 3245
Indiana Energy, Inc., 3394
Indiana Gas and Chemical Corp., 3327
Indiana Mills & Manufacturing, Inc., 3408
Indiana State Dept. of Health, 3317
Indiana Thrift for AIDS, 3317
Indianapolis Foundation, The, 3317
Indigo, 9049
Industrial & Mill Suppliers, Inc., 9443

Industrial Bank of Japan Trust Co., The, 6492
Industrial Bank of Japan, Ltd., The, 6492
Industrial Manufacturing Co., 7695
Industrial Tools Inc., 243
Indy Pride, 3317
Indyke, Dottie, 5533
Infield, Jack, 7973
Infinity Contact, 3449
Infosoft Group, Inc., 1943
Ing, Kendra, 721
Ing, Michele W., 721
Ing, Nita, 721
Ing, Tasha, 721
Ingall, Seth M., 3801
Ingalls, David S., 7503
Ingalls, David S., Jr., 7503
Ingalls, George, 8312
Ingalls, Louise H., 7503
Ingalls, Timothy, 8312
Ingber, Adam F., 6628
Ingber, Lori, 5203
Ingerman, Brad, 8108
Ingerman, Laurie, 8108
Ingerman, Steven L., 6187
Ingersoll, J. David, 7631
Ingersoll-Rand Co., 5314
Ingham, Ray, 3279
Ingledue, Jim, 3390
Inglee, Gale D., 2796
Inglee, Mark, 2796
Inglis, Timothy M., 7986
Inglish, David Winston, 4557
Inglish, Douglas, 4557
Ingold, Kelly, 2650
Ingraham, Patricia, 6286
Ingraham, Sandy, 7742
Ingraham, Timothy A., 4160
Ingram, Ben W., 59
Ingram, Cynthia, 9450
Ingram, Eddie, Dr., 8505
Ingram, Joe, 8925
Ingram, Lee Ann, 8532
Ingram, Mauri, 9759
Ingram, Michael, 2041
Ingram, Milliard, 7743
Ingram, Robert A., 7274
Ingram, Robert L., Jr., 2410
Ingrassia, Francis J., 6208
Ingstad, D. Scott, 3416
Ingwall, Teresa M., 7139
Ingwer, Craig, 5196
Inland Empire Paper Co., 9607
Inland Management Corp., 4208
Inman Mills, 8485
Inman, Bill, 4375
Inman, Douglas L., 3370
Inmart Group, 172
Innovative Computer Engineering, Inc., 9456
Insel, Michael S., 5940, 6302
Inserra, Robert, 5327
Insignares, Valerie L., 2051
Inskeep, Harriett J., 3332
Inskeep, Julie, 3332
Inskeep, Richard G., 3332
Inskeep, Thomas R., 3332
Inskip, Gregory A., 1780
Inspire Pharmaceuticals, 9915
Installer Edge, 7638
Institute for Research on Unlimited Love, 4420
Institute for Student Achievement, 6357
Institution Food House, Inc., 7205
Institution for Savings, 4108
Insulation Tech, 503
Int'l Merchandising Corp., 7214
Integra LifeSciences Corp., 5315
Intel Capital Corp., 7853
Intel Corp., 4254, 4314, 7853
Intel Foundation, 7307
Interactive Communications Intl Inc., 1771
Interchange Bank, 3710
Intercon Overseas, Inc., 1972
Intercontinental Terminals Co. LCC, 6491
Interdyn BMI, 4779
Interlake Corp., The, 2865
Interlink I Charitable Trust, 6773
Interlink III Charitable Trust, 6773
Interlink VI Charitable Trust, 6773
Intermedics, Inc., 2151
Intermountain Gas Co., 7354
International Air Leases, Inc., 1983
International Bank of Commerce, 8802
International Bible College, 7280
International Business Machines Corp., 6203
International Cobalt, 7272
International Flavors & Fragrances, Inc., 6206
International Mental Health Research Organization, 2296
International Ministries ABC, 4432
International Ore and Fertilizer Corp., 6705
International Paper, 3201
International Paper Co., 8585
International Risk Management, 9016
International Zinc Association, 7349
Interocean Industries, Inc., 5984
Interpacific Holdings, Inc., 5622
Interstate Power and Light Co., 9804
Interstate Realty, 5399
Interviewing Services of America, 7012
Intrepid Production Corp., 1444
INTRUST Bank, N.A., 3510, 3522, 7725
Intuit Inc., 723
Inui, Thomas S., 3982
Investigative Project on Terrorism Foundation, The, 341
Investment Capital Tech, LLC, 5135
Investors Savings Bank, 5317
Investors Trust, 5739
Invue Security Products, Inc., 7643
Inzlicht, David, 6212
Inzlicht, Michael, 5649, 6212
Inzlicht, Pearl, 6212
Ioka Fund, 2914
Ion Bank, N.A., 1616
Iovine, Peter, 157
Iovino Charitable Lead Annuity Trust, The, 6205
Iovino, Mary, 6205
Iovino, Thomas, 6205
Iowa Farm Bureau Federation, 3245
Iowa Periodicals, Inc., 3479
Iowa State Bank, 3487
Iowa West Racing Assn., 3447
Iozzia, Rachel, 1464
IPAD, 2631
Ipsen, Henry W., 9945
Irace, Gregory, 5437
Irani Charitable Trust, Ray, 724
Irani, Ray R., 724
Irby, Abby C., 2411
Irby, Charles L., 4843
Ireland, Ellen S., 7428
Ireland, George R., 7559
Ireland, Gregg Alden, 7239
Ireland, James D., 7559
Ireland, James D., III, 7559
Ireland, James D., IV, 7559
Ireland, Katherine R., 7559
Ireland, Lori, 7239
Irgang, Tory, 6038
Irgens-Moller, Kirsten, 306
Irick, Beverly G., 8713
Iridian Asset Mgmt., 7876
Irig, Christy, 4839
Irish, Ann K., 4413, 4522
Irish, Carolyn T., 9352
Irish, Cynthia Johanson, 854
Irish, Roberta P., 444
Irish, Thomas G., 444
Irmas, Audrey, 726
Irmas, Audrey M., 725
Irmas, Matthew, 726
Irmas, Robert, 726
Irmas, Robert J., 725
Irmas, Sydney M., 725
Irmscher, Thomas A., 3352
Ironside, Alfred, 5994
Irungu, Lucy W., 9656
Irvin, Nike, 365
Irvine, James, 727
Irvine, Tom, 2746
Irwin Charitable Remainder Annuity Trust, Richard D., 2936
Irwin Trust No. 1, Richard D., 2936
Irwin, Anna M., 1618, 6148
Irwin, Fannie M., 728
Irwin, Gail H., 7971
Irwin, Genevieve T., 1618
Irwin, Greg, 9999
Irwin, Jeanet H., 1618
Irwin, John, 7058
Irwin, John N., II, Mrs., 7058
Irwin, John N., III, 1618, 5549, 5692, 7079
Irwin, Kevin W., Rev. Msgr., 1882
Irwin, Philip D., 866
Irwin, Robert J.A., 5636, 5832
Irwin, Terry, 9024
Irwin, William B., 5636
Irwine, James E., 8648
Isaac Stauffer Clinic, 3631
Isaac, Kristine E., 4789
Isaacs, Bryan, 826
Isaacs, Elwood M. "Ike", 7771
Isaacson, Darwin, 9842
Isaacson, Irving, 3689
Isaacson, Kari, 9588
Isaacson, Walter, 5684
Isaak, Corinne, 9602
Isabella Edificaciones Sa De Cv Mex, 8834
Isabella Park LLC, 9452
Isbell, Jim, 3314
Isberg, Margaret, 1037
Isbin, Sharon, 5625
Isdaner, Scott Rosen, 7323
Isdell, E. Neville, 5990
Isdell, E. Niville, 5318
Isdell, Pamela Anne, 5318
Isermann, Betty, 5319
Isermann, Carol, 5319
Isermann, Howard, 5319
Isetti, Duane, 417
Isherwood, Elizabeth, 3991
Ishigaki, Cynthia E., 1312
Ishii, Paul, 9652
Ishii, Yasuo, 2675
Ishimaru, Todd, 8001
Ishiyama, George S., 730
Ishiyama, Nelson, 730
Ishiyama, Patsy, 730
Isinger, William R., 1030
Iskrant, John D., 8005, 8343
Island Co., Daniel, 8492
Island Insurance Co., Ltd., 2606
Island Insurance Foundation, 2607
Isler, William H., 8064
Isles, Philip H., 6347
Isley, Dawn, 8324
Isley, Geof, 8324
Isom, Gerald A., 8189
Isom, Janis, 2181
Isom, Lucille E., 8189
Isom, Nancy, 8938
Isono, Denis K., 2595
Ispahani, Mahnaz, 6613
Israel Enterprises, A.C., Inc., 6216
Israel Trust, Marcia, 731
Israel, Adrian C., 6216
Israel, Allen D., 9567
Israel, Marcia, 731
Israel, Samuel, 9725
Israel, Thomas C., 6216
Israel, William B., 6
Isroff, Richard, 7570
Issa, Darrell E., 732
Issa, Katharine S., 732
Isselbacher, Kurt J., 4057
Itasca Medical Center Foundation, 4667
Itell, John P., 3761
Ith, Rich, 9306
ITO EN, 9276
Ito, Joi, 2191, 2989
Ito, Katsuhiro, 6490
Iton, Anthony B., 366
ITT Educational Services Inc., 3273
ITT Rayonier Inc., 2281
ITT Sheraton Corp., 4284
Ittigson, Mary, 4372
Ittleson, Blanche F., 6217
Ittleson, H. Anthony, 5550, 6217
Ittleson, H. Philip, 6217
Ittleson, Henry, 6217
Ittleson, Henry, Jr., 6217
Ittleson, Lee F., 6217
Ittleson, Nancy S., 6217
Ittleson, Stephanie, 6217
Iuliano, Susan, 4299
Ivanchenko, Andrew, Dr., 2714
Ivens, Barbara J., 4443
Ivers, Jim, 9652
Ivers, Mary, 4557
Iverson, Brent, 157
Iverson, Dayle E., 9703
Ives, Charles, 5585
Ives, Deborah M., 1307
Ives, Karen, 4304
Ives, Lynn C., 7313
Ives, Mary, 4667
Ivey, Claudia, 8922
Ivey, Tammy C., 7269
Ivory, Ellis, 9327
Ivy Trust, Ben F., 123
Ivy, Ben F., 123
Ivy, Catherine, 123
Ivy, Catherine E., 123
Ivy, Octavious, 4822
Iwasawa, Hideki, 6943
Iwata, John C., 6203

Iwelumo, Kenneth C., 7316
Izaks, Lauren, 3024
Izlar, Charles E., 2503
Izumda, Ryugo, 6490
Izzo, Scott D., 8173

J & J Partnership, 3103
J&B Group, Inc., 4670
J&D Family Foundation, 735, 1070
J-C Press, 4606
J-M Manufacturing Co., Inc., 752
J-Track LLC, 6205
J.B. Land Co., Inc., 8699
J.S.B. Foundation, 3245
Jablon, Paul, 244
Jablonski, Christine, 2390
Jacangelo, Nicholas, 5640, 6571
Jacangelo, Nick, 6571
Jaccar, Michael G., 8723
Jack in the Box Inc., 736
Jack, Jeffrey L., 3524
Jackel, Margareta, 6182
Jackman, Jonathan, 965
Jacknewitz, Dennis J., 4966
Jackson Family Charitable Trust, Ann, The, 737
Jackson, Alexandra, 9982
Jackson, Ann A., 9294
Jackson, Ann G., 737
Jackson, Bacardi L., 2034
Jackson, Bill, 1211
Jackson, Blake A., 3329
Jackson, Bruce, 7630
Jackson, Cade Brennan, 8496
Jackson, Carmelle, 8516
Jackson, Carolynn F., 9195
Jackson, Catherine T., 8550
Jackson, Charles, 141
Jackson, Charles A., 737
Jackson, Dauphen, 9035
Jackson, David, 8742
Jackson, David D., Hon., 9213
Jackson, Deborah C., 4030
Jackson, Don, 9045
Jackson, Donald M., 9982
Jackson, Douglas J., 61
Jackson, Eben, 9856
Jackson, Edgar B., 7639
Jackson, Edward R., 74
Jackson, Emily Tow, 1708
Jackson, Ethan I., 3329
Jackson, Eugene W., 8047
Jackson, Gayle P.W., 157
Jackson, Gene, 7413
Jackson, Geoffrey W., 8047
Jackson, Glaphrey, 2490
Jackson, Horace B., 2490
Jackson, James H., 737
Jackson, Janet A., 7179
Jackson, Jennifer, 9982
Jackson, Jimmy S., 7283
Jackson, John, 9054
Jackson, John Henry, 4825
Jackson, John J., 7302
Jackson, John W., 1396, 9982
Jackson, Jon A., 9856
Jackson, Joyce A., 3329
Jackson, Katie, 420
Jackson, Kelvin, 9313
Jackson, Ken, 9604
Jackson, Kenneth T., 6398
Jackson, Kimberly, 9982
Jackson, Kory, 3521
Jackson, Kyle E., 3329
Jackson, Lisa, 3510
Jackson, Lloyd G., II, 7935
Jackson, Lonni, 9492
Jackson, Lori A., 1949
Jackson, Marcy, 9971
Jackson, Marcy Zilber, 9972
Jackson, Margaret, 820
Jackson, Maria C., 7855
Jackson, Marie-Louise, 8047
Jackson, Marilyn, 2009
Jackson, Mark, 5906
Jackson, Mark E., 2764
Jackson, Mary Beth, 3329
Jackson, Melissa S. A., 9971
Jackson, Melissa S.A., 9972
Jackson, Monty J., 9077
Jackson, Nancy L., 2799
Jackson, Oscar B., Jr., 7781
Jackson, Palmer G., 737
Jackson, Palmer G., Jr., 737
Jackson, Paul, 3510
Jackson, Peter F., 4616
Jackson, Polly C., 8497
Jackson, Robert, Hon., 4827
Jackson, Ronald, 3570
Jackson, Shane M., 9971, 9972
Jackson, Shelley S., 7761
Jackson, Shelly S., 7761
Jackson, Sonya Y., 3199
Jackson, Stephen E., 7761
Jackson, Stephon A., 3726
Jackson, Steven M., 8384
Jackson, Susan G., 9982
Jackson, Tammy, 4432
Jackson, Thomas H., 5969
Jackson, Travis, 9563
Jackson, Victoria, 638
Jackson, Virginia, 9247
Jackson, Wessley E., 3329
Jackson, William L., 737
Jackson, William R., Jr., 8110
Jacksonville Jaguars, Ltd., 2167
Jacob Associates, 293
Jacob, Beth M., 4776
Jacob, Dean L., 7558
Jacob, Ravi, 7853
Jacobi, Judy, 3297
Jacobius, Bina H., 644
Jacobowitz, Gerald N., 5806
Jacobs Engineering Group Inc., 738
Jacobs, Alexandria M., 9100
Jacobs, Alice, 5801
Jacobs, Barbara, 2894
Jacobs, Barbara M., 7430
Jacobs, Brenda, 3011
Jacobs, Christopher, 2390
Jacobs, Christopher A., 332
Jacobs, Craig, 7103
Jacobs, David H., 7430
Jacobs, David H., Jr., 7430
Jacobs, Debra M., 2260
Jacobs, Evelyn, 1154
Jacobs, Fred, 4342
Jacobs, Irwin, 1040
Jacobs, Joseph J., 739
Jacobs, Libby, 3466
Jacobs, Lisbeth, 6228
Jacobs, Luke T., 6584
Jacobs, Margaret E., 739
Jacobs, Marvin L., 3669
Jacobs, Milbrey R., 1780
Jacobs, Paul E., 740, 1048
Jacobs, Roy, 5247
Jacobs, Russell C., III, 2548
Jacobs, Stacy R., 740
Jacobs, Steven, 5757
Jacobs, Sylvia Ely, 3731
Jacobs, Todd, 4438
Jacobs, Violet J., 739
Jacobs, Violet Jabara, 739
Jacobs, Wesley, 4448
Jacobs, Yvonne, 1518
Jacobsen, Brian, 7001
Jacobsen, Diane E., 4915
Jacobsohn, Carol M., 3819
Jacobsohn, Howard G., 3819
Jacobson Family Foundation, 4298
Jacobson, Jerome, 3820
Jacobson, Joanna, 4110, 4298
Jacobson, Jonathon, 4110
Jacobson, Joyce, 1738
Jacobson, Kathy Howard, 6219
Jacobson, Knute, 9946
Jacobson, Lana, 4446
Jacobson, Malcolm B., 7969
Jacobson, Melinda, 2686
Jacobson, Mitchell, 6219
Jacobson, Richard O., 3448
Jacobstein, Richard E., 8560
Jacobus, Catherine H., 5674
Jacoby, Jennie Hutton, 7500
Jacoby, Lenore, 1289
Jacoff, Natalie, 6220
Jacoff, Rachel Mildred, 6220
Jacoff, Richard, 6220
Jacques Moret, Inc., 6131
Jade, Hathaway F., 7982
Jaeb, Lorena, 1989
Jaeb, Robert, 1989
Jaeb, Sandra D., 1989
Jaeb, Stephen, 1989
Jaeb, Stephen L., 1989
Jaeger, Dick, 9835
Jaffe Family Limited Partnership, The, 5320
Jaffe, David R., 5320
Jaffe, Elise P., 5320
Jaffe, Ellen S., 4267
Jaffe, Elliot, 5320
Jaffe, Elliot S., 5320
Jaffe, Howard, 586
Jaffe, Ira J., 4415, 4498
Jaffe, Jon, 741
Jaffe, Karen, 741
Jaffe, Kenneth, 5296
Jaffe, Mary H., 686
Jaffe, Richard E., 5320
Jaffe, Rona F., 6222
Jaffe, Roslyn, 5320
Jaffe, Seth, 1223
Jaffe, Suzanne D., 157
Jaffe, Wendy, 4994
Jaffee, Brian, 7511
Jaffee, Elliot, 4784
Jaffee, Randy, 1548
Jaffenagler, Alissa, 5393
Jaffer, Fauzia, 2168
Jaffer, Mohsin, 2168
Jafferjee, Husein, 6958
Jagemann, John, 9967
Jaguar Trust, 9271
Jagunos, Bern, 4432
Jaharis, Kathryn, 6223
Jaharis, Mary, 6223
Jaharis, Michael, 6223
Jaharis, Michael, Jr., 6223
Jaharis, Steven, 6223
Jahn, Carolyn L., 2938
Jahn, Charles L., 2938
Jahn, Reinhardt E., 2938
Jahr, Gina, 8521
Jain, Ajay, 9654
Jain, Ajit, 9654
Jain, Akshay, 9654
Jain, Anshu, 3585
Jain, Asha, 3585
Jain, Indrima, 9654
Jain, Kanika Virmani, 8933
Jain, Kirti, 3585
Jain, Suman, 6765
Jain, Vinay K., 8933
Jakelski, Richard, 6621
Jakobsen, Kasper, 2944
Jakovic, Joseph M., 7957
Jalkut, Thomas P., 3941, 4186, 4241, 4272
Jalonick, I., 9215
Jalonick, K., 9215
Jalonick, Mary, 8908
Jalonick, Mary M., 8795
Jama, Mustafa, 8011
Jama, Mustafa A., 8011
Jamail, David G., 8928
Jamail, Joseph D., 8929
Jamail, Joseph D., III, 8929
Jamail, Lillie H., 8929
Jamail, Randall Hage, 8929
Jamail, Robert Lee, 8929
Jamail, Sharon, 8928
Jamerson, Ellen P., 9474
James, Amabel B., 5322
James, Barbara L., 4472
James, Benjamin, 8149
James, Bradley, 742
James, Bradley G., 742
James, Christopher M., 742
James, Court, 2169
James, Don, 43
James, Donald M., 73
James, Ellen, 744
James, Hamilton E., 5322
James, Holly M., 4941
James, Hunt, 2169
James, J. Hatcher, III, 4810
James, Jacob, 1108, 1295
James, Juanita, 1674
James, Juanita T., 1581
James, Larry, 9192
James, Lynda, 9106
James, Mary S., 2169
James, Neil, 2769
James, Nora, 5108
James, Paul A., 826
James, Paula, 4842
James, Phyllis, 2875
James, Polly, 9834
James, Ralph M., 1789
James, Rick, 3377
James, Rick L., 3357
James, Robert, 1789
James, Roger, 5321
James, Ron, 4783
James, Thomas A., 2169
James, Thomas M., 1489, 3002
James, Vicki, 3377
James, Virginia, 5299
James, William D., 4918
James, William R., 4843
James-Brown, Christine, 6093
Jameson, Bill, 8863
Jameson, Ida M., 743

Jamieson, Beth Kiyoko, 5270
Jamil, Dhiaa M., 7196
Jamison, Alan, 3469
Jamison, Greg, 936
Jamison, Karen, 9559
Jamison, Nelle Woods, 5096
Jamrog, Amy, 3992
Janatka, Lucille, 1616
Janc, Christopher M., 2812
Jancik, Liza Lanier, 2499
Jandernoa Trust, Susan M., 4513
Jandernoa, Carl, 4513
Jandernoa, Michael J., 4513
Jandernoa, Susan M., 4513
Jandl, George P., 4922
Janelle, Debra, 8862
Janer, Thomas, 7769
Janes, Leah, 3313
Janeway, Elizabeth Bixby, 745
Janey, Cheryl, 9410
Jang, G. David, 3957
Janke, Chris, 2766
Jankiewicz, Dennis, 3759
Jannarone, Gary, 5216
Jannotta, Edgar D., 2699
Janoch, T., 7537
Janoch, Thomas J., 7545
Janoush, Lucy, 4821
Jansen, Dan, 1512
Jansen, Doug, Dr., 3359
Jansen, Elizabeth, 1039
Jansen, Heather, 7405
Jansen, Marlis Corning, 1208
Jansen, Paul, 2780
Jansky, Dennis, 7367
Jansma, Rosy, 3335
Janson, Robert, 4337
Janssen Pharmaceutica Inc., 5327
Janssen, Angela K., 3430
Janssen, Daniel Baron, 6007
Jantz, Sue Ann, 3542
Janus Capital Corp., 1432
Janus Capital Management LLC, 1432
Januzelli, Eric, 4452
Janz, James F., 9971, 9972
Janzen, Pete, 4691
Janzow, Greg, 3400
Japale, Ltd., 9024
Jarah, Evslin, 9360
Jaramillo, Mary Lou, 4893
Jarc Endowment fund, 2300
Jardine, Robert A. "Drew", Jr., 3612
Jarecki, Andrew R., 5967
Jarecki, Donna M. C., 1552
Jarecki, Eugene D., 5967
Jarecki, Gloria, 1552
Jarecki, Henry G., 5967
Jarecki, John, 5967
Jarecki, Lianna, 5967
Jarecki, Maxson D., 5967
Jarecki, Nancy, 1552
Jarecki, Nicholas M., 5967
Jarecki, Thomas A., 5967
Jark, Heidi, 7505
Jarnot, Chris, 1518
Jarrell, Charles L., 9776
Jarrell, Scarlet S. Johnson, 5224
Jarrett, Joyce M., Dr., 9558
Jarry, Timothy M., 4327
Jarvis, Julietta, 8931
Jarvis, Sonia, 6151
Jasek, John, 9060
Jasinski, John, 2933
Jaskowiak, Joe, 3369
Jaskowiak, Scott E., 4931
Jasper Trust, 9271
Jasper, Thomas F., 4778
Jath Oil Co., 7772
Jauert, Douglas, 7484
Jaunich, Robert, II, 3358
Javaid, Manzhar, 160
Javedan, Li-Su Huang, 2327
Javitch, Jennifer, 5084
Javitch, Mark, 5084
Javitch, Rachel, 5084
Javits, Carla, 4170
Javne Fund, 6336
Jaxtimer, Joanne, 7945
Jay, Ann F., 4335
Jay, Brian, 8383
Jay, Ramsey, Jr., 396
Jay, Vicky, 8874, 9123
Jayaraman, Mahesh, 8383
Jaynes, Lisa, 9251
Jayo, David, 9713
Jazwinski, Robert C., 7994
JBC Investment Co., 7746
JCBF, 530
JCS Chelyabinsk ZP E, 7349
JD 2006 Charitable Lead Trust, 2797
Jealous, Benjamin Todd, 1088
Jeandron, Raymond J., Jr., 3669
Jeannero, Jane M., 4443
Jeans, Michael D., 8356
Jeary, Michael, 5403
Jeavons, Thomas, 2075
Jed Trust, The, 4116
Jedlicka, Cecilie H., 1611
Jedrezejek, David, 563
Jeep, Edward "Ed" L., 9501
Jeffcoat, Leon, 9205
Jeffcoat, Otis Allen, III, 8507
Jeffe, Elizabeth R., 1617
Jeffe, Robert A., 1617
Jeffers, Sharon M., 3344
Jefferson State Bank, 9148
Jefferson, Ted, 6542
Jefferson, Thomas, 7351
Jefferson-Pilot Financial, 7162
Jefford, Charles, 5328
Jeffords, David G., III, 2502
Jeffress, Elizabeth G., 9447
Jeffress, Robert M., 9457
Jeffries, Dawn Harris, 2763
Jeffries, M. Hill, Jr., 2581
Jeffries, William, 7208
Jeffris, Thomas M., 9869
Jeffs, James A., 1323
Jeffs, Jim, 845
Jeg's Automotive, Inc., 7507
Jeker, Julius C., 2634
Jeld-Wen Co. of Arizona, 7856
Jeld-Wen Fiber Products, Inc. of Iowa, 7856
Jeld-Wen Holding, Inc., 7856
Jeld-Wen, Inc., 7856
Jelks, Bobby, 3624
Jelks, Bobby E., 3634
Jenkin, Thomas M., 5106
Jenkins, Anne H., 7508
Jenkins, Barbara, 1394, 2390
Jenkins, Beth Boney, 7273
Jenkins, Carlton, Dr., 4532
Jenkins, Carolyn S., 1471
Jenkins, Cathy, 2036
Jenkins, Christopher S., 1471
Jenkins, Danielle, 1743
Jenkins, David D., 1471
Jenkins, Decosta E., 8550
Jenkins, Dorothy, 2741
Jenkins, Elizabeth B., 9791
Jenkins, Evan H., 3575
Jenkins, Forrest N., 8530
Jenkins, Franklin Clay, 7302
Jenkins, George W., 2275
Jenkins, Jeanne Stratton, 8304
Jenkins, Jennifer, 24
Jenkins, John O., 523
Jenkins, Johnetta, 747
Jenkins, Katha, 1511
Jenkins, Kevin, 8228
Jenkins, Margaret, 2087
Jenkins, Mary Marks, 7742
Jenkins, Matthew, 747
Jenkins, Meredith, 5747
Jenkins, N. H., 8833
Jenkins, N.E., 909
Jenkins, Patricia C., 7189
Jenkins, Rick, 1394, 3298
Jenkins, Roberta, 747
Jenkins, Roger W., 185
Jenkins, Rosemary Ordonez, 6368
Jenkins, Scott M., 7995
Jenkins, Stephen H., 7508
Jenkins, Susan, 7182
Jenkins, Thomas K., Hon., 7558
Jenkins, Timothy J., 7508
Jenkins, Tom H., 7508
Jenkins, Tony, 2015
Jenkins, Tyrie Lee, 2602
Jenkins, Victoria, 2171
Jenkins, Wayne, Esq., 7431
Jenkins-Scott, Jackie, 3956
Jenks, John R., 727
Jenks, R. Murray, 2186
Jenks, Vicki, 9833
Jennings, A.K., 748
Jennings, C.M., 748
Jennings, Cassandra, 1103
Jennings, Cledith, 748
Jennings, Dee, 1116
Jennings, Elizabeth Cabell, 9397
Jennings, J. Webb, 8770
Jennings, Joel, 4680
Jennings, John M., 4874
Jennings, Keith S., 4165
Jennings, Kevin, 5608
Jennings, Lisa, 3287
Jennings, Louise, 19
Jennings, Martha Holden, 7509
Jennings, Martin, 4617
Jennings, Mary Lee, 4680
Jennings, T.L., 748
Jennings, Tamozelle, 748
Jennings, Toni, 2390
Jenoure, Terry, 3992
Jensen, Alison W., 7336
Jensen, Ann, 9035
Jensen, David C., 8472
Jensen, Janet Jarie, 8677
Jensen, Joan, 2931
Jensen, Jon, 6615
Jensen, Julie, 8762
Jensen, Larry, 3245
Jensen, Melissa Smith, 7665
Jensen, Pamela Simon, 1170
Jensen, Philip H., 1876
Jensen, R.J., 8932
Jensen, Todd, 1039
Jensen, Tom, 4671
Jensen, Traci, 4659
Jensen, Wayland, 4613
Jensen, Wilbur, 3798
Jenson, Dena C., 1287
Jenson, Lawrence, 8538
Jenson, Michael, 5019
Jenson, Randy, 4721
Jephson, Lucretia Davis, 2939
Jeppesen, Dave, 2627
Jepson, Hans G., 5616
Jepson, Larry, 5032
Jerde, Roxanne, 2038
Jeremiah Project, 9118
Jeresaty, Robert M., 1613
Jergens, Andrew M., Rev., 7510
Jergens, Andrew N., 7510
Jergens, Linda Busken, 7510
Jermoluk, Thomas A., 2022
Jernagan, Luke, 5827
Jernigan, Lisa R., 42
Jernigan, Melissa Bunnen, 6396
Jernigan, Thomas E., 42
Jernstedt Trust, Dorothy, 1050
Jernstedt, Derek, 672, 1050
Jernstedt, Dorothy, 672, 1050
Jernstedt, Jaci, 1050
Jernstedt, Jennifer, 1050
Jerome, Frank, 749
Jerome, Richard, 749
Jersey Central Power & Light Co., 7455
Jerusalem Capital LLC, 5905
Jeschke, Thomas, 3466
Jessee, Chandra, 6209
Jessell, Thomas M., 4708, 7080
Jesselson, Michael, 5992
Jessen, Gwen, 2826
Jessup, Dan, 1497
Jessup, Debbie, 1364
Jessup, James L., Jr., 9405
Jessup, Jim, 3393
Jester, Chad A., 7587
Jet Lag Productions LLC, 6600
Jeter, David, 4996
Jeter, Dennis, 3481
Jeter, Derek, 7012
Jeter, Derek S., 7012
Jeter, Dorothy, 7012
Jeter, James M., 2437
Jeter, Mark L., 4778
Jeter, S. Charles, Dr., 7012
Jeter, Sharlee, 7012
Jethrow, K. L., 7546
Jetmore, David, 3400
Jetson, Raymond A., Rev., 3613
Jett, Richard W., Jr., 8819
Jetter, Dean, 3370
Jetton, Ann Marie, 5398
Jewell, Beth, 8062
Jewell, Bob, 5807
Jewell, Sally, 9713
Jewett, Betsy, 4682
Jewett, Brenda C., 4682
Jewett, Dunham F., 8806, 9199
Jewett, George F., III, 4682
Jewett, George F., Jr., 4682
Jewett, Jack B., 111
Jewett, Jill F., 8845
Jewett, Lucille M., 4682
Jewish Agency for Israel, 6336
Jewish Community Fdn. of CO, 1825
Jewish Community Fdn. of San Diego, 1040
Jewish Community Federation, 7713
Jewish Federation of South Palm Beach County, 7713
Jewish Funders Network, 7791

Johnson, Mark L., 8752, 8753
Johnson, Marla, 181
Johnson, Mary Lou, 9604
Johnson, Matthew, 8721
Johnson, Matthew E., 7445
Johnson, Melinda, 7742
Johnson, Michael D., 1704
Johnson, Michael, Dr., 3253
Johnson, Michael, Sr., 7807
Johnson, Michella L., 4700
Johnson, Mike, 4617
Johnson, Mindy, 8647
Johnson, Nadine, 2900
Johnson, Nan H., 8938
Johnson, Nancy, 7357
Johnson, Nancy Bellows, 8768
Johnson, Neil E., 3784
Johnson, Norman, 4354
Johnson, Oliver M., II, 3749
Johnson, Orville, 4782
Johnson, Paige, 9458
Johnson, Patricia C., 7858
Johnson, Paul, 888, 4663
Johnson, Paul C., 4369, 4663
Johnson, Paula A., 8334
Johnson, Pete, 4821
Johnson, Peter, 221
Johnson, Peter James, Jr., 6238
Johnson, Peter James, Sr., 6238
Johnson, Phil, 3971
Johnson, Philip H., 6406
Johnson, Preston L.C., 365
Johnson, R. Mark, 8588
Johnson, R. Milton, 8582
Johnson, Rafer, 809
Johnson, Reba, 8590
Johnson, Rhett, 4667
Johnson, Rob, 402
Johnson, Robbin S., 4628
Johnson, Robert, 437, 3337, 9458
Johnson, Robert C., 3538
Johnson, Robert K., 328
Johnson, Robert L., 5490
Johnson, Robert W., IV, 6240
Johnson, Robert Wood, 5329
Johnson, Robert Wood, IV, 6547
Johnson, Rolley, Dr., 9516
Johnson, Ronald M., 3598
Johnson, Ronald P., 7135
Johnson, Rosalind G., 4663
Johnson, Rosemarie Marshall, 229
Johnson, Rosemarie Torres, 3971
Johnson, Rupert H., Jr., 754
Johnson, Russell, 4663, 8199
Johnson, Ruth, 8937
Johnson, S. Curtis, 9872
Johnson, Samuel Lamont, 753
Johnson, Samuel S., 7858
Johnson, Samuel, Jr., 1166
Johnson, Sandee, 3075
Johnson, Sarah, 2541, 9277
Johnson, Scott, 3419
Johnson, Sean, 570
Johnson, Seth, 3682
Johnson, Shanna, 4370
Johnson, Sharyn, 2868
Johnson, Sheila, 9458
Johnson, Sheila B., 8752
Johnson, Sheila C., 9458
Johnson, Shielia, 174
Johnson, Si, 4472
Johnson, Stacy, 8548
Johnson, Stanley D., 8497
Johnson, Steger, 406
Johnson, Stephen, 7204
Johnson, Stephen P., 4230
Johnson, Steven L., 9965
Johnson, Susan P., 8491
Johnson, Susanna P., 8491
Johnson, Susannah, 709
Johnson, Suzanne M. Nora, 6237
Johnson, Suzanne Nora, 6431
Johnson, T.R., Jr., 9638
Johnson, Ted, 1222
Johnson, Theodore R., 2174
Johnson, Theodore R., Jr., 9638
Johnson, Theodore R., Sr., 9638
Johnson, Thomas P., 406
Johnson, Thomas P., Jr., 6239
Johnson, Thomas Phillips, Jr., 6239
Johnson, Thomas Phillips, Sr., 6239
Johnson, Thomas S., 2766
Johnson, Timothy E., 7422
Johnson, Timothy, Dr., 7590
Johnson, Tina, 2275
Johnson, Tom, 2403, 3021
Johnson, Tony, 4370
Johnson, Veronica, 6238
Johnson, Veronica F., 6238
Johnson, Vivian M., 2174
Johnson, Wallace "Buster", 7180
Johnson, Walter S., 753
Johnson, Warren T., 1390
Johnson, Weldon, 184
Johnson, Wendy, 1790
Johnson, Wendy S., 7138
Johnson, Whitney H., 8580
Johnson, Willard, 8937
Johnson, Willard T.C., 6240
Johnson, William, 4438
Johnson, William A., 1007
Johnson, William G., 7342
Johnson, William T., 8939
Johnson, Willis, 8590
Johnson, Winifred M., 1790
Johnson, Zach, 3449
Johnson-Brebner, Angel, 8472
Johnson-Drenth, Susan E., 7351
Johnson-Helm, Elizabeth K., 7858
Johnson-Howell, April, 9924
Johnson-Leipold, Helen P., 9872
JohnsonDiversey, Inc., 9874
Johnston, A. Carl, 8814
Johnston, Anne E., 4469
Johnston, Beverly, 4217
Johnston, Carolyn, Dr., 3760
Johnston, Cathy, 5556
Johnston, David S., 4539
Johnston, Emily, 3757
Johnston, Fred, 7421
Johnston, G. David, 77
Johnston, Gillian, 8638
Johnston, Hugh F., 6627
Johnston, J. Michael, 9674
Johnston, J.C., III, 7704
Johnston, James, 184
Johnston, James "Jim", 7202
Johnston, James M., 3821
Johnston, Lavinia, 8638
Johnston, Linda A., 3946
Johnston, Mary E., 3594
Johnston, Mary Kaye, 4539
Johnston, Marybeth, 9674
Johnston, Megan M., 4469
Johnston, Michael, 9674
Johnston, Michael B., 4469
Johnston, Michael J., 6813
Johnston, Murray L., Jr., 9296
Johnston, Nancy K., 7620
Johnston, Neil C., 52
Johnston, Oscar, 7973
Johnston, Peter E., 7605
Johnston, Philip W., 3953
Johnston, Renee, 4532
Johnston, Robert L., 2514
Johnston, Robert T., 8638
Johnston, Ronnie, 2533
Johnston, Rose M., 8487
Johnston, Rosemary, 68
Johnston, S.K., Jr, 8638
Johnston, Sona Nga, 9384
Johnston, Vivian G., III, 48
Johnston, Vivian G., V, 48
Johnston, William, 4469
Johnston, William D., 4469
Johnston, William E., 5526
Johnston-Cusak, Gloria, 529
Johnstone, Ann, 7781
Johnstone, Gail, 2274
Johnstone, Janet Jyll, 1177
Joiner, Clint, 8618
Joiner, Katherine, 331
Joines, Connie V., 3259
Joines, Michael, 3259
Joines, Michael A., 3259
Jokiel, Judith Ann, 2118
Jolie, Angelina, 1791
Jolley, Doug, 9307
Jolley, Doug T., 9307
Jolley, James E., 7240
Jolley, James F., 7459
Jolley, Mary, 9307
Jolley, R.A., Jr., 7240
Jolliffe, Judy K., 4385
Jolliffe, Mancy, 4630
Jollon, Katherine, 6070
Jolly, Cynthia, 7321
Jolly, Eric J., 4621
Jolly, Ken, 1939
Jolly, Linda E., 5818
Joly, Hubert, 4612
Jonaitis, Simone, 4412
Jonas, A.G., 7241
Jonas, A.G., Sr., 7241
Jonas, Bly, 7241
Jonassen, Hans B., 3612
Jonathan Manufacture Corp., 5729
Joncas, Steven, 4152
Jones Apparel Group, Inc., 6651
Jones Charitable Lead Trust, Seby B., 7242
Jones Educational and Cultural Fund, Carol E., 9149
Jones Family Fund, 6
Jones Foundation, Dodge, 5525, 8955
Jones Foundation, W. Alton, 495
Jones Living Trust, 755
Jones Trust Co., Edward, 4999
Jones Trust, Joseph E., 1918
Jones Trust, Marjorie B., 1918
Jones Trust, Walter S. and Evan C., 3523
Jones, Amelia, 5104
Jones, Ann M., 8654
Jones, Anthea, 1996
Jones, B. Bryan, III, 4825
Jones, B. Bryan, IV, 4825
Jones, Ben, 8901
Jones, Bernie, 3757
Jones, Bill, III, 2431
Jones, Bob, Dr., 8265
Jones, Bobby, 8839
Jones, Brenda, 9363
Jones, Carrie, 1202
Jones, Charles E., 7455
Jones, Charles H., 2491
Jones, Charles I., Jr., 9782
Jones, Charles J., 2491
Jones, Cheryl, 3287
Jones, Christina B., 7242
Jones, Cliff, 4996
Jones, Corinna, 7008
Jones, Cynthia, 1384
Jones, D. Paul, Jr., 8942
Jones, Daisy Marquis, 6242
Jones, Dan B., 8658
Jones, David, 2426, 4346, 5805
Jones, David A., 3566, 3582
Jones, David A., Jr., 3582
Jones, David L., 4522
Jones, David P., 8560
Jones, David R., 690, 6804
Jones, Debra B., 737
Jones, Denise, 8113
Jones, Denise R., 5766
Jones, Dennis M., 4916
Jones, Dennis M., Jr., 4916
Jones, Derek, 3348
Jones, Dewitt, 3939
Jones, Donald, 229
Jones, Donald F., 157
Jones, Donna B., 8351
Jones, Douglas L., 1487
Jones, Dwight C., 2491
Jones, E. Richard, 755
Jones, Ed, 7770
Jones, Eddie E., Jr., 2075
Jones, Elaine F., 3645
Jones, Eleanor Miniger, 7572
Jones, Elizabeth, 2462, 9363
Jones, Emily N., 4105
Jones, Emma Eccles, 127, 9330, 9331
Jones, Erin, 2038
Jones, Eugenie P., 3645
Jones, Ewa, 3047
Jones, Fletcher, 756
Jones, Fred, 7762
Jones, Fred, Jr., 8610
Jones, George M., III, 7572
Jones, George M., Jr., 7572
Jones, Geraldine M., 8332
Jones, Gussie, 7474
Jones, H. Lawrence, Dr., 9773
Jones, Hannah, 7875
Jones, Helayne B., 1487
Jones, Helen DeVitt, 8944
Jones, Helen Jeane, 5142
Jones, Herbert B., 9655
Jones, Hugh E., 9834
Jones, Irene, 973
Jones, J. Franklin, 9430
Jones, J. Patrick, 3575
Jones, J.K., 9000
Jones, Jack, 3279
Jones, Jack L., 3393
Jones, James, 369
Jones, James H., 2759
Jones, James R., 7242
Jones, Jana, 2332
Jones, Jerral W., 8943
Jones, Jerral W., Jr., 8943
Jones, Jerry D., 3015
Jones, Jerry G., 3425, 5533
Jones, Jesse H., 8917
Jones, Jesse H., II, 8917
Jones, Jesse H., Mrs., 8917
Jones, Jill, 3337

Jones, Joann G., 2516
Jones, John, 3280
Jones, John Marvin, 1918
Jones, John P., III, 8113
Jones, John Stephen, 8943
Jones, Johnny C., 7795
Jones, Jon Rex, 8654
Jones, Joseph, 9363
Jones, Joseph M., 3645
Jones, Judith, 1531
Jones, Judith A., 4916
Jones, Judith Ann Browning, 5104
Jones, Julie LaValle "Valle", 3569
Jones, Karen, 9126
Jones, Karen S., 7359
Jones, Katherine J., 259
Jones, Kathleen E., 1671
Jones, Kathryn E., 9660
Jones, Kenneth M., II, 3745
Jones, Kim, 1932
Jones, Kim B., 2439
Jones, Kim Harris, 3034
Jones, Kimberley, 9311
Jones, Kyle J., 7466
Jones, L. Bevel, III, Bishop, 2529
Jones, Landon Y., 5191
Jones, Leigh H., 7219
Jones, Linda, 4535, 7241
Jones, Lisa L., 8626
Jones, Lorrie, 2953
Jones, Lucy H., 7184
Jones, Lucy R., 4802
Jones, Marcelle, 8113
Jones, Marcia, 3289
Jones, Margaret M., 7466
Jones, Marilyn, 755
Jones, Marion, 1962
Jones, Marjorie B., 1918
Jones, Mary D.T., 7195
Jones, Mary Eddy, 7762
Jones, Mary K. W., 2790
Jones, Mary Kay, 5077
Jones, Mary S., 5074
Jones, Mary Shaddock, 3625
Jones, Mary T., 7150
Jones, Maureen, 3244
Jones, Melvin, 9780
Jones, Meredith H., 3698
Jones, Michael, 3807
Jones, Michael D., 5038
Jones, Michael J., 4108
Jones, Nancy, 2380
Jones, Nancy E., 8776
Jones, Orville, III, 5096
Jones, Pamela S., 2614
Jones, Patricia A., 8103
Jones, Paul, 1663
Jones, Paul J., 9907
Jones, Paul T., II, 1711
Jones, Paul Tudor, 6547
Jones, Paul Tudor, II, 6056
Jones, Paul W., 9947
Jones, Phillip G., 30
Jones, Reginald, 3175
Jones, Reginald H., 9363
Jones, Reginald N., 9523
Jones, Rhonda, 3407
Jones, Rich, 2142
Jones, Rick, 959
Jones, Robert, 5146
Jones, Robert "Bob", 24
Jones, Robert J., 4621
Jones, Robert L., 7242, 7273
Jones, Robert S., 8129
Jones, Robin, 3923
Jones, Rockwell, 7431
Jones, Ron, 8775
Jones, Ronald D., 9946
Jones, Ross M., 4105
Jones, Rudy, 3423
Jones, Ruth Leggett, 8810
Jones, Scott K., 9650
Jones, Seby B., 7242
Jones, Seby B., Jr., 7242
Jones, Seby Russell, 7242
Jones, Shelley, 25
Jones, Sherrie, 4448
Jones, Soni, 3320
Jones, Stephanie, 3369
Jones, Stephen C., 6597
Jones, Terrell, 7973
Jones, Thomas H., 8626
Jones, Thomas K., 3547
Jones, Timothy J., 4420
Jones, Tommy, 2426
Jones, Tony, 6191
Jones, Tracy, 584
Jones, Trevor O., 7668
Jones, Ves, 2491
Jones, Vicki L., 7202
Jones, Victoria, 407
Jones, W. Alton, 9394
Jones, Wallace C., 1644
Jones, Wellington D., III, 3251
Jones, William M., 8152
Jones, William S., 8545
Jones, Wilson, 198
Jones, Wilson R., 9917
Jones-Kelley, Helen E., 7428
Jones-Weber, Karla, 3420
Jonson, Hollt L., 658
Jonson, Karl, 477
Jonsson Cancer Center Foundation, 1132
Jonsson Foundation, The, 192
Jonsson, Christina A., 192
Jonsson, Philip R., 192
Jonsson, Steven W., 192
Jonsson, Suzanne E., 192
Joos, Ann, 2004
Jope, Robert, 3955
Jordache Enterprises, Inc., 6522
Jordache Ltd., 6522
Jordan Charitable Lead Annuity Trust, Helen S., 2492
Jordan Charitable Lead Annuity Trust, Randolph Swift, 2492
Jordan Companies, The, 2945
Jordan II Revocable Trust, John W., 2945
Jordan Industries, Inc., 2945
Jordan, Arthur, 3331
Jordan, Barbara M., 7982, 8038
Jordan, Blake, 4098
Jordan, Brooke, 5827
Jordan, D. Raines, 2438
Jordan, Darlene L., 4113
Jordan, Dorian S., 9875
Jordan, Ettie A., 4917
Jordan, Gerald R., Jr., 4113
Jordan, Ginny, 5827
Jordan, Helen S., 2492
Jordan, I. King, 2174
Jordan, J. Craig, 8235
Jordan, Janet C., 2034
Jordan, Jeff, 9118
Jordan, Jennifer L., 2945
Jordan, Jerry A., 7243
Jordan, Jim, 7825
Jordan, John R., Jr., 7273
Jordan, John W., II, 2945
Jordan, John W., III, 2945
Jordan, Joseph, 7905
Jordan, Julia K., 9875
Jordan, Kathryn H., 7514
Jordan, Linda, 386
Jordan, Lorna P., 9505
Jordan, Maria, 4511
Jordan, Mary Ranken, 4917
Jordan, Michael, 8545
Jordan, Nicole, 5827
Jordan, Phil, 1019
Jordan, Raymond, 238
Jordan, Rhonda, 3245
Jordan, Robert, 4438
Jordan, Rodney W., 4729
Jordan, Shirley H., 8114
Jordan, Taylor, 5827
Jordan, Trudie Evon Smith, 7243
Jordan, Vernon E., Jr., 5587
Jordan, Virginia W., 5827
Jordan, Wade, 9602
Jordan, Wayne, 223
Jordan, Wayne E., 5920
Jordan, William, 9051
Jordan, William Chester, 6967
Jordan, William Paul, 9875
Jordan, William R., III, 2356
Jordan-Simpson, Emma, 5718
Jordheim, Neil, 7351
Jorgensen, Arne, 9999
Jorgensen, Ted, 5511
Jorgenson, Erik, 3170
Jorgenson, G. Robert, 8259
Jorgenson, Joel, Dr., 7351
Jorgenson, Judy, 9907
Jorgenson, Megan, 3170
Jornayvaz, Isla C., 9203
Jornayvaz, Louisa Craft, 1444
Jornayvaz, Robert, 1444
Jorndt, L. Daniel, 3209
Jortner, Joshua, 5589
Joseloff Foundation Trust, Morris, 1622
Joseloff, Lillian L., 1622
Joseloff, Morris, 1622
Joseph, Amy F., 7447
Joseph, Brian E., 9772
Joseph, Charles S., 2101
Joseph, Donita, 846
Joseph, Dvora, 302
Joseph, Elise E., 8826
Joseph, Erica N., 3760
Joseph, George R., 7447
Joseph, Jack, 7565
Joseph, James A., 6164
Joseph, Jeanne, 2717
Joseph, Jim "Shimon ben Yosef", 302
Joseph, Joshua, 302
Joseph, Mary Terrell, 3613
Joseph, Patricia, 3726
Joseph, Penny, 5396
Joseph, William, 6535
Josephson, John, 6383
Josey, Clint, 8808
Josey, Clint W., Jr., 8808
Josey, Clinton W., Jr., 8809
Josey, Lenior M., 8842
Joskow, Paul L., 6872
Joslin, David C., 4443
Joslyn Corp., 7424
Jostens, Inc., 4684
Joul, Steven R., 4631
Journal-Gazette Co., 3332
Journay, Rex, 3370
Jouryan, Carole, 598
Joy Global Inc., 9876
Joy, Judith N., 3026
Joy, Margaret P., 8021
Joyal, Renee Graphia, 3671
Joyce, Colleen T., 1631
Joyce, Cynthia, 6898
Joyce, Stephen, 3748
Joyce, Steve, 7137
Joyce, William, 5801, 8152
Joyce, William L., 5832
Joyner, Pamela, 367
JPMorgan, 2741
JPMorgan Chase, 6042
JPMorgan Chase Bank, 3249
JPMorgan Chase Bank, N.A., 1554, , 1594, 1826, 2647, 2656, 2671, 2719, 2746, 2750, 2766, 2776, 2777, 2782, 2786, 2788, 2793, 2795, 2887, 2912, 2917, 2918, 2919, 2923, 2929, 2935, 2939, 2952, 2956, 2979, 2982, 2988, 3018, 3020, 3039, 3045, 3055, 3056, 3065, 3070, 3086, 3102, 3106, 3121, 3132, 3139, 3144, 3161, 3188, 3194, 3203, 3211, 3213, 3218, 3219, 3222, 3230, 3236, 3250, 3613, 3624, 4565, 5517, 5856, 5995, 6009, 6128, 6244, 6397, 6544, 6904, 6915, 7012, 7058, 7088, 7248, 7367, 7404, 7406, 7428, 7521, 7522, 8387, 8393, 8711, 9131, 9148, 9780, 9866, 9916
JPMorgan Chase, N.A., 5861
JPMorgan Services, Inc., 2911
Jreisat, Wijdan, 7404
JRF Charitable Lead Unitrust, 2535
JRF Charitable Lead Unitrust 99, 2535
JRO Charitable Lead Annuity Trust, 7394
JSB Trusts, 332
JSP Investments, LP, 2265
JSwartz Charitable Lead Trust, 6953
JSY Foundation Inc., 5228
Juarez, Ashley Smith, 2018
Juarez, Rumaldo Z., 8768
Juba, George, 7934
Jubb, David, 588
Jubel, Donald A., 4919
Jubilee Group, 761
Jubitz Investments, LP, 7859
Jubitz, Katherine H., 7859
Jubitz, M. Albin, Jr., 7859
Jubitz, Raymond G., 7859
Jubitz, Sarah C., 7859
Juchter, Elia, 5927
Juckett, J. Walter, 6791
Juckett, Rhoda, 2027
Judd, Alison, 5659
Judd, Robert, 420
Judd, Sonali, 2259
Judd, Virginia K., 3582
Judd, Wendell W., 9077
Judge, James J., 1656
Judge, William, 7382
Judice, Kevin, 5532
Judkins, Lafayette, 7294
Judlau Contracting, Inc., 6205
Judson, K. Leonard, 594
Judson, Mary Humann, 2573
Judson, Sara, 3625
Judson, Stephanie, 8522
Judy, Rhonda F., 4458

Juedicshe Gemeinde Hamburg, 6336
Jueptner, Peter, 6408
Juergens, Marty, 9605
Juhlke, David P., 4676
Julian, David W., 7202
Julian, Joseph, 7640
Julian, Paul C., 903
Juliano, Robert J., 7936
Julius, David, 4708
Julson, Althea, 5927
Junck, Mary E., 3457
Jundi-Samman, Randa, Dr., 4373
Juneau, Polly, 1393
Jung, Chris, 8523
Jung, Kerry, 9368
Jung, Steve, 9697
Jungwirth, Helen, 9867
Juniata Valley Bank, 8046
Junior League, 4792
Junker, Christopher A., Esq., 8001
Jurcic, James T., 8014
Jurcyk, John J., Jr., 3556
Jurecky, Marylee Warwick, 8825
Jurgensen, Jerry, 7411
Juris, Hervey A., 5533
Jurkonis, Mary, 5138
Jurzykowski, M. Christine, 9102
Jurzykowski, Yolande L., 9569
Just Marketing, Inc., 7214
Just Rite Acoustics, Inc., 7214
Juster, Anne Conway, 7509
Justesen, Joan, 7351
Justice, John, III, 9470
Justice, Rita F., 2030
Justice-Moore, Kathleen, 938
Justice-Moore, Kathleen E., 937
Justin, Jane C., 8947
Justin, Mary C., 8947
Justis, Cleveland, 877
Juzang, Angie, 4830
Jwell, Mary Louise Brown, 2456
JWH Testamentary Trust, 8749

K Black Hills Trust, 2379
K N Energy, Inc., 1439
K'Burg, Bill, 973, 1120
K'Hal Adath Jeshrun, 6972
Kaanon, Marian, 1211
Kabbes, David G., 4865
Kabelin, Jerry, 3393
Kabler, Elizabeth R., 8254
Kacal, Melinda M., 9199
Kacer, Jim, 3690
Kachavos, Peter, 5167
Kachiu, Linda, 420
Kackley, James R., 4470
Kaczmarz, Kenneth, 2823
Kadar, Avraham, 6523
Kadar, Einat, 6523
Kadar, Maya, 6523
Kadar, Nadav, 6523
Kade, Fritz, Jr., 6247
Kade, Max, 6247
Kaden, Lewis B., 6431
Kadesh Investments Ltd., 4183
Kadifa, Sally Rathmann, 3867
Kadinger, Suzanne, 3286
Kadoya, Tetsuo, 6997
Kaemmer, Arthur W., 4677
Kaemmer, Frederick C., 4677
Kaemmer, Julia L., 4677
Kaemmer, Martha H., 4677
Kafer, David, 1423
Kaganoff, Moshe, 5311
Kahana, Yoram, 701
Kahil, Mark E., 6581
Kahle, Brewster L., 759
Kahle, Charles W., 9382
Kahler, Jeffrey, 1409
Kahlert, Greg W., 3822
Kahlert, Roberta, 3822
Kahlert, William E., 3822
Kahn, Alan R., 6228
Kahn, Bruce, 3709
Kahn, Charles, 8072
Kahn, David B., 2493
Kahn, David D., 4471
Kahn, Elliot, 2077
Kahn, Erica, 2077
Kahn, Erin, 9708
Kahn, Howard, 611
Kahn, Irving, 6228
Kahn, Jennifer M., 2493
Kahn, Joseph, 4116
Kahn, Julius "Sandy", III, 973
Kahn, Karen M., 255
Kahn, Michael A., 7245
Kahn, Richard D., 3936
Kahn, Rosa Taub, 8804
Kahn, Sonny, 2077
Kahn, Stephen B., 255
Kahn, Suzanne, 2077
Kahn, Todd, 5790
Kahn, Virginia, 4238
Kahn, William, 5803
Kahne, Daniel, 7080
Kahng, Choonja, 8948
Kahng, Stephen, 8948
Kaichen, Lisa M., 3637
Kail, Karl, IV, 7992
Kaiman, Jay, 2511
Kain, Herbert, 1279
Kain, Robert L., 4405
Kairouz, Habib, 6231
Kaiser, Bess F., 760
Kaiser, Charles J., Jr., 9773
Kaiser, David, 6725, 7567
Kaiser, Heather G., 116
Kaiser, Henry J., 760
Kaiser, Henry J., Jr., 760
Kaiser, Herman, 7763
Kaiser, Kate, 116
Kaiser, Katie B., 760
Kaiser, Kay Lynn, 3365
Kaiser, Miranda, 6725
Kaiser, Miranda M., 6723
Kaish, Harvey, 5712
Kaissar, Tal S., 5563
Kajiwara, Gary, 2604
Kalama, Corbett A.K., 2593, 2598
Kalan, Jeremiah L., 1064
Kalangis, Suzanne Barker, 5535
Kalathur, Rajesh, 2790
Kalb, Marianne Bernstein, 1887
Kalb, Robert, 1887
Kalberer, Jean C., 7515
Kalberer, Lori, 7515
Kalberer, Walter E., 7515
Kaldis, Catherine Daniel, 8848
Kalian, Lucy K., 5307
Kalikow, N. Richard, 6159
Kalimanis, Joan C., 309
Kalimanis, Thomas, 309
Kalinich, John, 176
Kalish, Ursula, 6016
Kalisman, Gayle T., 4553
Kalisman, Gayle Taubman, 4552
Kalispell Lounge Corp., 5016
Kallaus, Kurt J., 4986
Kalleward, Howard, 4385
Kalleward, Howard D., 4445
Kallgren, Charles, 533
Kallman, Linda, 2036
Kallstrom, Bob, 7579
Kalman, Catherine, 4468
Kalmanovitz, Lydia, 762
Kalnins, Vicki, 2760, 2761
Kaloski, John F., 7366
Kalson, David J., 8282
Kalvert, Seth, 4311
Kam, Moshe, 9547
Kamal, Alex, 5865
Kamal, Terence, 5865
Kamen, Dean, 5168
Kamen, Steven R., 5296
Kamensky, Marvin, 2747
Kameron 2006 Charitable Remainder Trust, 1151
Kameron Trust, Pete, 1151
Kamerschen, Robert W., 2455
Kami, Nancy S., 606
Kaminski, Brian D., 9965
Kampfer, Merlin W., 111
Kampling, Patricia L., 9804
Kampmann, Abigail G., 8877
Kamps, Dick, 4369
Kanaan, Margaret Mary, 8043
Kanaly, Andrew, 8801
Kanas, Elaine, 6249
Kanas, John A., 6249
Kanas, Mary, 1405
Kanashiro, Kozo, 5471
Kandel, Eric R., 504
Kandel, Gene, 2283
Kandel, Richard, 7063
Kandelman, Allan, 2978
Kane, Ann Marie, 1115
Kane, Anne Sangiacomo, 1115
Kane, Brian, 3421
Kane, Charles F., Jr., 2720
Kane, Charles J., 3569
Kane, Cindy, 2149
Kane, David Paul, 1234
Kane, Edward W., 4318
Kane, Eileen, 5921
Kane, Eileen B., 5573
Kane, Elizabeth, 2989
Kane, Eric, 6360
Kane, Jacqueline P., 407
Kane, Jami S., 312
Kane, John B., 7769
Kane, John C., 2648
Kane, John F., 7769
Kane, Maureen, 1643
Kane, Micah A., 2602
Kane, Michael, 7990
Kane, Michael G., 6722
Kane, Patrick J., 8025
Kane, Robert, 5979
Kane, Robin Berlin, 7385
Kane, Russell, 6360
Kane, Susan, 1020, 6360
Kane, Tina, 4667
Kane, William, 6943
Kanel, Keith, 8039
Kanemaru, Maile, 2604
Kanfer, Joseph, 7542
Kanfer, Pamela, 7542
Kang, Jemo, 5363
Kang, Monica, 5363
Kang, Roger, 5363
Kang, Walter, 5363
Kangas, Paul, 4308
Kangas, Phil, 9380
Kanin, Paul R., Jr., 891
Kanis, Herman, 4338
Kanis, Michael J., 4338
Kanis, Suzanne, 4338
Kanjo, Kathryn, 9079
Kanner, Raymond, 5562, 5655, 5789, 5855, 5952, 5977, 6036, 6207, 6524, 6576, 6622, 7028, 7110, 7124
Kanofsky, Gordon, 964
Kanofsky, Gordon R., 964
Kanofsky, Marcia, 964
Kantardjieff, Stefan A., 1186
Kanter, Burton W., 9459
Kanter, Catherine M., 9459
Kanter, Connie, 9725
Kanter, Janis S., 9459
Kanter, Joel S., 9459
Kanter, Joshua S., 9459
Kanter, Ricki, 9459
Kanter, Robert, 7511
Kantor, Kim Ciccarelli, 2035
Kao, Jennifer, 3525
Kao, Kenneth, 3525
Kao, Min-Hwan, 3525
Kao, Yu-Fan C., 3525
Kaohi, Aletha, 2621
Kapadia, Harivadan, 9495
Kapadia, Manjula, 9495
Kaper, Marilyn, 3291
Kaphan, Sheldon J., 9657
Kapiolani Properties Corp., 2615
Kapla, Liz, 4502
Kaplan 1999 Revocable Trust, Hilda, 8409
Kaplan Charitable Lead Unitrust, Rita J. and Stanley H., The, 6250
Kaplan Trust, Rita J. and Stanley H., The, 6250
Kaplan, Alan, 2949
Kaplan, Amy, 2948
Kaplan, Anne, 2947
Kaplan, Arlene, 763
Kaplan, Ashley Dorrance, 107
Kaplan, Barbara S., 7516
Kaplan, Beth Karmin, 2289
Kaplan, Burton B., 2947
Kaplan, Carol K., 2949
Kaplan, Carolyn J., 3905
Kaplan, Charles, 2947
Kaplan, Curt, 2947
Kaplan, Dafna Recanati, 2175
Kaplan, David, 763, 2947
Kaplan, Diane, 79
Kaplan, Diane S., 89
Kaplan, Edward, 2949
Kaplan, Edward H., 1919
Kaplan, Gabe, 1681
Kaplan, Gizelle, 7109
Kaplan, Harold, 2948
Kaplan, Helene L., 5280
Kaplan, Herbert, 8355
Kaplan, Hilda, 8409
Kaplan, Irene R., 1919
Kaplan, Irving, 6828
Kaplan, Jean, 2947
Kaplan, Jeffrey, 5193
Kaplan, Jerome A., 1919
Kaplan, Joan P., 2948
Kaplan, Karen Stone, 3179
Kaplan, Marjorie C., 3996

Kaplan, Mark E., 4722
Kaplan, Martin, 2949
Kaplan, Martin S., 4069
Kaplan, Martine, 1919
Kaplan, Mary E., 6252
Kaplan, Meredith, 763
Kaplan, Michael, 2947, 7109
Kaplan, Michael D., 1368
Kaplan, Morris, 2947
Kaplan, Myron, 6862
Kaplan, Neil, 763
Kaplan, Neil S., 3777
Kaplan, Renee, 1175
Kaplan, Richard D., 6252
Kaplan, Richard M., 7516
Kaplan, Rita J., 6250
Kaplan, Robert, 2947
Kaplan, Robert S., 481, 5994, 6251
Kaplan, Saul, 5740
Kaplan, Sheila, 2948
Kaplan, Stanley H., 6250
Kaplan, Steven J., 7516
Kaplan, Susan A., 6546
Kaplan, Susan Beth, 6250
Kaplan, Thomas, 2175
Kaplan, Wilson R., 5330
Kaplan, Yitzcak, 7109
Kaplen, Alexander, 5330
Kaplen, Lawrence, 5330
Kaplen, Margaret R., 5330
Kaplen, Wilson R., 5330
Kaplowitz, Lisa, 9497
Kaplus, Laura Herzog, 8101
Kapnick, Jim, 4485
Kapnick, Kathleen, 2035
Kapnick, Kathleen G., 6253
Kapnick, Richard B., 6253
Kapnick, Scott B., 6253
Kapoor, Editha Sue, 2950
Kapoor, John N., 2950
Kapoor, Nina, 1002
Kapor, Mitchell, 764
Kapp, Bonnie Adams, 8472
Kapp, Constance Elizabeth Mellon, 8173
Kapp, Steven H., 9005
Kappa Graphics, LP, 8116
Kappa Media Group, Inc., 8116
Kappas, Attallah, Dr., 6688
Kappner, Augusta Souza, 7043
Kaprielian, Rachel, 3953
Kapusta, Susan M., 8325
Kapustiak, Wendall A., 2752
Karabim-Ahern, Rebecca, 1564
Karabots, Athena, 8116
Karabots, Nicholas G., 8116
Karageorglou, Anna, 8495
Karakul, Kurt, 7681
Karam, Christopher, 3289
Karam, Laura, 8825
Karangelen, Michael, 7001
Karaoglan, Alain, 7038
Karas, Joe, 9566
Karasick, Mark, 5508
Karasik, Brenda-Lee, 9759
Karasiuk, Brent P., 4933
Karatsu, Jeanne, 929
Karatz, Bruce E., 765
Karatz, Elizabeth D., 765
Karatz, Matthew D., 765
Karatz, Theodore S., 765
Karbowiak, Christine, 8537
Kare-Sue Energy, 9049
Karet, Laura, 8055
Karet, Laura M., 8282
Karfunkel Family Foundation, 5772, 6179
Karfunkel, Ann, 5772
Karfunkel, Barry, 6179
Karfunkel, George, 5772
Karfunkel, Leah, 6179
Karfunkel, Michael, 5772, 6179
Karfunkel, Rene, 5772
Karfunkel, Robert, 6179
Karges, James M., 4790
Karibjanian, Nancy, 1765
Karickhoff, Brenda C., 6982
Karim, Quarraisha Abdool, 6408
Karim, Salim S. Abdool, 9625
Karish Family Foundation, 9470
Karl Hoblitzelle Trust, 8912
Karl, Irvin H., 9686
Karl, Kenneth, 2253, 8087
Karl, Stephanie, 8087
Karlawish, Jason H., 6105
Karle, Patricia J., 4789
Karle, Peter S., 4789
Karmanos, Peter, Jr., 7563
Karmazin Charitable Lead Annuity Trust, Sharon, 5331
Karmazin Trust, 6254
Karmazin Trust II, 6254
Karmazin Trust, Sharon, 5331
Karmazin, Bruce, 2986
Karmazin, Craig, 5331
Karmazin, Melvin, 6254
Karmazin, Sharon, 5331
Karmin, Beth Kaplan, 2947
Karmin, Phillip J., 9459
Karmis, Michael E., 9547
Karnemaat, Kent, 4438
Karnes, Frances, Dr., 4829
Karnes, Mark, 199
Karnig, Al, Dr., 419
Karoff, H. Peter, 4753
Karoff, Peter, 4664, 8387
Karol, Kathryn D., 2738
Karon, Sarah, 4795
Karos, George, 9775
Karow, Andrew, 1512
Karp, Jill E., 4117
Karp, Roberta, 5976
Karp, Stephen R., 4117
Karpa, Stephen, 950
Karr, Bernard L., 7617
Karr, Carol J., 4447
Karr, Judy, 9578
Karr, Robert A., 6183
Karr, Susanne, 6183
Karr, Tim, 8040, 9151
Karras, Nolan, 9350
Karrasch, Craig, 5122
Karre, Paul J., 8585, 8633
Karsch, Sol, 6665
Karsh, Bruce A., 767
Karsh, Martha L., 767
Karson, Jack, 2095
Karst, Darren W., 9936
Karsten Manufacturing Corp., 163
Kartiganer, Joseph, 7529
Kartiganer, Larry, 946
Kartsotis, Bill, 6619
Kartsotis, Sofia, 6619
Karwic, Michael B., 7979
Kasabach, Chris, 7058
Kasdorf, Gail B., 4507
Kasevich, Ray, 6884
Kash, Gary, 2749
Kasha, Alon, 5535
Kason Industries, Inc., 2494
Kaspar, Mark, 9854
Kasper, Keith, 8041
Kasperski, Mike, 5750
Kasperzak, Mike, 849
Kasprowicz, Joan, 9410
Kass, Andy, 9950
Kass, Roger E., 8449
Kassap, Harry, 3729
Kassap, Sigmund, 3729
Kassel, Ruth, 5806
Kassel, Terry, 6862
Kassewitz, Darcie Glazer, 2124
Kast, Steve, 4779
Kastanis, Laure W., 1323
Kasten, Rebecca, 7214
Kasten, Stan, 809
Kastenholz, James P., 3175
Kastler, Lesa, 8474
Kastner, Richard, 4659
Kasuga-Laliberte, Theresa A., 1556
Kaswick, Jennifer, 596
Kaswick, Jon A., 596
Kaswick, Julie, 596
Kaszovitz, Robert, 6111
Katch, Barbara, 8144
Katch, Robert J., 1287
Katcher, Dorothy, 2176
Katcher, Gerald, 2176
Katcher, Jane, 2176
Kates, Dana, 670
Kathman, Daniel, 6038
Katris, Darcy, 6598
Katten Muchin Rosenman LLP, 2951
Katten Muchin Zavis, 2951
Katten Muchin Zavis Rosenman, 2951
Katterjohn, Eugene, Jr., 3570
Katz Charitable Income Trust, 3848
Katz Charitable Income Trust II, 3848
Katz Family Foundation, Maurice N., The, 4057
Katz, Abraham J., 2494
Katz, Ada, 6256
Katz, Alex, 6256
Katz, Alexander S., 2494
Katz, Benjamin A., 8117
Katz, Brooke D., 8117
Katz, Daniel, 2177
Katz, Daniel R., 6341
Katz, David, 529, 2494
Katz, David M., 529, 6255
Katz, Drew, 5332
Katz, Eleanor, 3848
Katz, Eleanor M., 2177
Katz, Elise, 8117
Katz, Elise R., 8117
Katz, Elizabeth Berylson, 4277
Katz, Esther, 2494, 6972
Katz, Ezra, 2210
Katz, Frank L., 8117
Katz, Gerald M., 3802
Katz, Herbert D., 2177
Katz, Iris J., 6255
Katz, Jane L., 6257
Katz, Joan, 6911, 8776
Katz, Karen, 9918
Katz, Karen Peck, 9918
Katz, Laurence M., Dean, 3766
Katz, Lawrence F., 6782
Katz, Lewis, 5332
Katz, Madelyn, 768
Katz, Michael D., 2115, 5333
Katz, Molly, Dr., 7404
Katz, Monique C., 5333
Katz, Mordecai D., 5333
Katz, Ofir, 8391
Katz, Peter A., 2494
Katz, Philip J., 8117
Katz, Phillipe, 6972
Katz, Phyllis, 2494
Katz, Randy, 768
Katz, Richard, 4585
Katz, Robert, 1518, 4277
Katz, Robert J., 6070, 6257
Katz, Robert L., 5314
Katz, Ronald, 768
Katz, Sally, 2177
Katz, Saul B., 6255
Katz, Thomas O., 2177, 3996
Katz, Todd, 768
Katz, Vincent, 6256
Katz, Vivien Bittencourt, 6256
Katz, Walter, 2177
Katzenbach, Shirley S., 6448
Katzenberg Family Trust, 769
Katzenberg, Jeffrey, 769
Katzenberg, Marilyn, 769
Katzenberg, Susan B., 3803
Katzenberger, Helen Katherine, 6258
Katzenberger, Walter B., 6258
Katzman, Chaim, 2178
Katzman, Julie T., 2989
Katzman, Ronald M., 8097
Katzovicz, Roy, 6629
Kaufer, Stephen, 4311
Kauffman, Adelaide, 5334
Kauffman, Ewing M., 4921
Kauffman, Fritz, 5334
Kauffman, Julia Irene, 4921, 4922
Kauffman, Muriel McBrien, 4922
Kaufman Charitable Lead Trust, Henry, 6259
Kaufman, Arlene G., 1912
Kaufman, Craig S., 6259
Kaufman, Dan, 2433
Kaufman, Daniel S., 6259
Kaufman, David, 7581
Kaufman, Elaine, 6259
Kaufman, Glenn D., 6259
Kaufman, Glorya, 770
Kaufman, Henry, 6259
Kaufman, Herbert M., 92
Kaufman, Hershel, 6123
Kaufman, Ilene, 1548
Kaufman, Isabelle, 6123
Kaufman, Margaret G., 9915
Kaufman, Marvin A., 6788
Kaufman, Micha, 5761
Kaufman, Miriam, 6123
Kaufman, Paul L., 9915
Kaufman, Paula, 4036
Kaufman, Robert, 1548, 3151
Kaufman, Robert M., 6039
Kaufman, Yidle, 6123
Kaufmann, Al, 4512
Kaufmann, Charles B., III, 1854
Kaufmann, E.K., 8799
Kaufmann, Marion Esser, 1436
Kaufthal, Ilan, 5206
Kaufthal, Judith E., 5705
Kaul, Hugh, 43
Kaung, Joseph, 4432
Kaung, Thomas TS, 7631
Kauppila, Mary H. Myers, 4133
Kaus, Jodi, 3532
Kauth, Laurie Bentson, 4611
Kautz, Daniel B., 6260
Kautz, James C., 6260, 7128

Kautz, Leslie B., 6260
Kavadas, Kathryn B., 1437
Kavanagh, T. James, 8118
Kavanagh, Thomas E., 8118
Kavanau, Earl W., 1151
Kavanau, Flavia J., 1151
Kavanaugh, Gerald, 3846
Kavanaugh, Gerry, 3991
Kavanaugh, James P., 5002
Kavanaugh, Robert, 417
Kavich, Daphne, 783
Kavli, Fred, 771
Kawaguchi, Yoriko, Hon., 7019
Kawaichi, Ken, 490
Kawamura, Takashi, 1916
Kawanabe, Kenzo, 1374, 1401
Kawano, Nolan N., 2606
Kawasaki Steel Investments, Inc., 7366
Kawashima, Yoshiyuki, 6491
Kay, Colleen W., 4404
Kay, David R., 6068
Kay, Eleanor, 772
Kay, Elim, 772
Kay, Ethan, 772
Kay, F. Stevon, 8478
Kay, Herma Hill, 1088
Kay, Jami, 3530
Kay, Jean S., 1216
Kay, John, 378
Kay, Lay K., Dr., 776
Kay, Linda, 3441
Kay, Lucy, 1511
Kay, Martin, 9631
Kay, Richard, 6672
Kay, Richard L., 5720
Kay, Robert B., 5554
Kay, Sarah, 9447, 9457
Kay, Steeve, 772
Kay, Terry, 1216
Kayden, Suzanne, 6261
Kaye, Alan, 886
Kaye, Bonnie, 6016
Kaye, Charles R., 6262, 7048
Kaye, Danny, 1920
Kaye, Dena, 1920
Kaye, Elizabeth R., 8671
Kaye, Judith S., Hon., 6868
Kaye, Sheryl, 6262
Kaye, Sheryl J., 6262
Kaye, Sylvia Fine, 1920
Kaylie, Gloria W., 6263
Kaylie, Harvey, 6263
Kaylie, Roberta, 6263
Kaylor, Leigh A., 8574
Kayne, Jerry D., 773
Kayne, Maggie, 773
Kayne, Richard, 240
Kayne, Richard A., 773
Kayne, Suzanne L., 773
Kayser, David, 4636
Kayser, Kraig H., 6832
Kazee, Thomas A., 3402
Kazhe, Christina, Esq., 366
Kazickas, John A., 6264
Kazickas, Joseph M., 6264
Kazickas, Joseph P., 6264
Kazickas, Jurate, 5581, 6264
Kazickas, Michael, 6264
Kazickas, Michael V., 6264
Kazma, Gerald, 2179, 2180
Kazma, Leigh-Anne, 2179, 2180
Kazma, Margaret, 2179, 2180
Kazma, Michael, 2179, 2180
Kazmaier, John, 7971
Kazmer Tile & Stone, Inc., 5482
Kazmierczak, George, 3354
Kazmierczak, Scott, 3075
Kazzinc AP, 7349
KCH Group, 1850
KCM-SA, 7349
KCS Landscaping, 9606
KEA Motor Car Corp., 5304
Keady, George C., III, 3992
Kean Residuary Trust, Stewart B., 1530
Kean, Beatrice Joyce, 2946
Kean, Janet H., 7246
Kean, Melissa C., 8950
Kean, Nora K., 8950
Kean, Steven J., 8950
Kean, Stewart B., 1530
Kean, Teresa Anne, 7246
Kean, Thomas H., 5298, 5747
Kean, Thomas H., Hon., 5191
Kean, Thomas J., Jr., 7246
Kean-Teed, Anne Marie, 7246
Keane, Fay, 4361
Keane, Gregory H., 4621
Keane, Heather K.L., 4119
Keane, Jack, 1679
Keane, John, 4118
Keane, John F., Sr., 4118
Keane, John J., 7596
Keane, Karl N., 9881
Keane, Marilyn, 4118
Keane, Marilyn T., 4118
Keane, Robert S., 4119
Kearney, Catherine O'Malley, 7715
Kearney, Chris, 7202
Kearney, Daniel P., 2946
Kearney, Eric H., 7510
Kearney, John P., 8275
Kearney, Ken, 5808
Kearney, Robert, 1393
Kearns, Becky, 9341
Kearny, Conor, 4282
Kears, David J., 320
Keaschall-Kiser, Konnie, 167
Keasling, Karen, 7597
Keast, Margaret, 2323
Keathley, Duane, 780
Keating, Brian, 275
Keating, Dwight M., 7935
Keating, Michael, 3956
Keating, Michael K., 7393
Keating, Nancy N., 7393
Keating, Pollyanna, 1043
Keating, Richard, 3049
Keating, Sarah Beth Price, 275
Keating, William J., 7393, 7419
Keck, Howard B., Jr., 774
Keck, Katherine Cone, 907
Keck, Stephen M., 774
Keck, Theodore J., 774
Keck, W.M., III, 774
Keck, William M., 774
Keck, William M., II, 775
Keck, William M., Jr., 775
Keddy, Jim, 366
Kee, Dorothy Davis, 2056
Kee, Dorothy Given, 2056
Keefe, Anita L., 1619
Keefe, Carol A., 1619
Keefe, Harry V., III, 1619
Keefe, Harry V., Jr., 1619
Keefe, Pamela B., 7497
Keefe, Stephen T., 7497
Keegan, George Q., 5248
Keegan, John P., 5248
Keegan, Michael T., 6406
Keegan, Peter W., 6388
Keel, Jim, 9775
Keeler, Cora, 9223
Keeler, Dennis C., 3687
Keeler, Elizabeth R., 9225
Keeler, Robert T., 7517
Keeler, Thomas, 9223
Keeley, Dawn, 7357
Keeley, Fred, 418
Keeling, J. Wayne, 7294
Keeling, James W., 2730
Keely-Dinger, Kristen, 8533
Keen, Gordon L., Jr., 7955, 8159
Keenan, Candice Cline, 2024
Keenan, Daniel J., Jr., 7509
Keenan, Frances Murray, 3712
Keenan, Francis, 7998
Keenan, J. Patrick, 5068
Keenan, James, 3289
Keenan, James F., 3338
Keenan, Julie, 5473
Keenan, Julie Ann Marriott, 3842
Keenan, Katherine G., 8861
Keenan, Mary Jean, 6903
Keene, Kim, 3277
Keene, Margaret, 1133
Keene, Steven, 5511
Keener, Tara, 7202
Keeney, Anne Herold, 5405
Keeney, Elizabeth Marler, 7184
Keeney, Matthew Mayro, 5405
Keeney, Scott, 9603
Keep, Paul, 4447
Keesal, Samuel A., Jr., 777
Keesal, Young & Logan, P.C., 777
Keesee, Christian K., 7766
Keeshin, Joyce J., 7510
Keet, Bonnie Falkenstine, 6266
Keet, Ernest E., 6266
Keet, Nancy, 5556
Keet, Nancy R., 6266
Keeton, Carole, 9293
Keeton, Fred, 5106
Keever, Graham, 7182
Keever, William, 1519
Keevil, Mary H., 9449
Keeyes, Sarah A., 8980
Keffer, E. Brooks, Jr., 8273
Keffer, William W., 8273
Keffler, James, 2357
Kehr, Cathy, 9975
Keidan, Amanda, 6267
Keidan, David B., 6267
Keidan, Georgia, 6267
Keidan, Jonathan, 6267
Keilitz, Dave, 4512
Keilman, Frank, 3347
Keilman, Tom, 3337
Keilty, Nancy B., 3262, 3263
Keim, Melody, 8135
Keinath 1969 Trust, Pauline Macmillan, 4807
Keinath Family 1974 Trust, David S., 4807
Keinath, David S., 4807
Keinath, Pauline M., 4647
Keinath, Pauline Macmillan, 4807
Keinath, Steven W., 4807
Keinath, Warren C., 4807
Keinath, Warren G., Jr., 4647
Keiser, Michael, 9819
Keiser, Michael, Mrs., 9819
Keiser, Tom, 563
Keister, Rudy, 7414
Keith, Colleen Perry, 8459
Keith, Daniel, 7012
Keith, Garnett L., 3818
Keith, Gavin R., 478
Keith, Graeme M., Jr., 7247
Keith, India E., 7247
Keith, Jayne, 6967
Keith, Sheri, 2648
Keithley, Joseph P., 7518
Keithley, Nancy F., 7518
Kekst, David, 1212
Kela, Ajay, Dr., 1294
Kelderhouse, Robert, 3201
Kelderhouse, Robert J., 3201
Keleher, John, 8336
Keliipio, Kau'i, 442, 1299
Kell, Gwen, 5416
Kellar Family Charitable Lead Trust, 9461
Kellar, Arthur, 9461
Kellar, Elizabeth, 9461
Kellar, Lorrence, 7394
Kellar, Mary K., 9461
Kellar, Rick, 7579
Kelleher, David, 3317
Kelleher, David N., 8951
Kelleher, Denis, 6912
Kelleher, Harry B., Jr., 3648
Kelleher, Herbert D., 8951
Kelleher, J. Michael, 6032, 8951
Kelleher, Joan N., 8951
Kelleher, Steve, 7382
Kellen Foundation, A.M. & S.M., 6013
Kellen, Anna-Maria, 6268
Kellen, Michael, 6268
Kellen, Stephen M., 6268
Keller & Associates, J.J., Inc., 9878
Keller Group Investment, The, 5514
Keller, Allison M., 457, 774
Keller, Brian, 9878
Keller, Casey, 3244
Keller, Charles C., 8332
Keller, Charles, Jr., 3646
Keller, Christina, 4447
Keller, Fred P., 4474
Keller, James J., 9878
Keller, John J. and Ethel D., 9878
Keller, Joseph P., 7524
Keller, Robert A., 1166
Keller, Robert G., 6527
Keller, Robert L., 9878
Keller, Roberta, 7882
Keller, Rosa F., 3646
Keller, Sarah M., 883
Keller, Sean, 2873
Keller, Stephen F., 883
Keller, Sue, 4370
Keller, Susan K., 3980
Keller, Thomas A., III, 4652
Keller-Krikava, Marne, 9878
Kellerman, John, II, 3379
Kellerman, Kelli, 358
Kellerman, Norman, 2886
Kelley Grandchildren Trust, M.H., 4686
Kelley, Brian S., 3987
Kelley, Bruce G., 3428
Kelley, Craig C., 778
Kelley, Daniel T., 7587
Kelley, David E., 470
Kelley, Deberah B., 420
Kelley, Doug, 8896
Kelley, E. Dennis, Jr., 3960
Kelley, Ed, 7749

Kenney, Susan F., 3980
Kenney, Suzanne, 4061
Kennickell, Al, Jr., 2548
Kennifer, Rick, 414
Kennis, Bob, 876
Kennison, Michael T., 9414
Kenny, Heather, 6903
Kenny, Maugha, 7075
Kent Nutrition Group, Inc., 3450
Kent Precision Foods Group, 3450
Kent Village LLC, 9452
Kent, Bob, 9789
Kent, Fred, Jr., 2074
Kent, Gage A., 3450
Kent, Harold, 7846
Kent, JoAnn, 7846
Kent, Scott, 2264
Kentz, Frederick C., III, 1083
Kenway, Nora, 9693
Kenworth of Birmingham, 62
Kenworthy, Charles, 391
Kenworthy, Harriet, 4511
Kenyon, Dione D., 8370
Kenyon, James, III, 5019
Kenyon, Rebecca, 106
Kenyon, Robert W., 8370
Keogh, John, 7905
Keohane, Nannerl O., 5917, 5918
Keon, Margaret L., 2986
Keough, Bill, 7973
Keough, Donald R., 2496
Keough, Marilyn M., 2496
Kepco, Inc., 6313
Kepler, Dave E., 4404
Keppler, Jim, 4583
Keppner, Judy L., 1682
Kerby, Kendall S., 9559
Keri Tours Inc., 5313
Kerker, Michael A., 917
Kerlin, William H., Jr., 8065
Kerly, Diane M., 8077
Kerman, Michael G., 2530
Kern, Anita, 2530
Kern, Deborah, 9880
Kern, Diana, 5108
Kern, Herbert A., 2958
Kern, Jerome, 1438
Kern, John C., 2958
Kern, Judith A., 4632
Kern, Mary, 1438
Kern, Michael, 5101
Kern, Patricia E., 9880
Kern, Robert D., 9880
Kernan, Joseph E., 4484
Kerns, Pete, 1198
Kerouac, Ann, 1233
Kerouac, Michael, 1233
Kerpel, Martin D., 2901
Kerr, Berta, 5210
Kerr, Breene M., 3823
Kerr, Catherine O., 5892
Kerr, Charissa, 3692
Kerr, Cody T., 7764
Kerr, Jo Arthur G., 9981
Kerr, Kavar, 9981
Kerr, Lou C., 7764
Kerr, Mara, 9981
Kerr, Mary, 9578
Kerr, Michael, 6545
Kerr, Michael T., 1320
Kerr, Omie, 9578
Kerr, Sheryl V., 3823
Kerr, Steven. S., 7764
Kerr, W. David, 7991
Kerr, William G., 9981
Kerrey, Bob, 6993
Kerrigan, Daniela Megan, 155
Kerrigan, Joseph, 5035
Kerrigan, Patrick J., 5035
Kerrigan, Stephen, 9470
Kerry, 9837
Kersch-Schultz, Sheri, 9730
Kerschen, John, 4452
Kersey, Jenn, 3366
Kershnaum, Susan, 7969
Kerstein, David A., 3641
Kersten, Priscilla, 3173
Kersten, Samuel, Jr., 3173
Kersten, Steven, 3173
Kersten, Steven A., 3173
Kertzner, Daniel, 8429
Kervandjian, Heddy, 7973
Kesler, Charles R., 8167
Keslter, Kathleen F., 5975
Kessel, Annette, 3808
Kessinger, Tom G., 3982
Kessler, Carl E., 8954
Kessler, Carla Kay, 8954
Kessler, Cheryl, 1086
Kessler, David R., 8954
Kessler, Gary, 237
Kessler, Irvin R., 4657
Kessler, Jack J., 8198
Kessler, Jim, 3514
Kessler, Jonathan, 3762
Kessler, Kenneth R., 8954
Kessler, Matthew, 8298
Kessler, Mort, 1086
Kessler, Richard, 5663
Kessler, Robert, 490
Kessner, Katherine, 7290
Kest 2009 Charitable Lead Trust No 2, 757
KEST 2009 Charitable Trust, 889
Kest, Matthew, 757
Kest, Michael, 757
Kest, Sol, 757, 889
Kest, Susanne, 757
Kestenbaum, Gertrude, 781
Kestenbaum, Joseph, 8121
Kestenbaum, Louis, 781
Kestenbaum, Sharon Tobin, 8121
Kester, Doris, 1504
Kester, Gene, 7231
Kestner, R. Steven, 7623
Ketcham, Susan, 686
Ketchum Charitable Lead Annuity Trust, 7765
Ketchum, Brian C., 7765
Ketchum, John W., 2251
Ketchum, Kent H., 7765
Ketchum, Kevin B., 7765
Ketchum, Lewis Craig, 7765
Ketchum, Stuart M., 1285
Kettenbach, Frances Demoulas, 4015
Ketter, Pamela J., 3553
Ketterer, Sarah H., 745
Kettering, Charles F., 7522
Kettering, Charles F., III, 7520
Kettering, E.W., 7520
Kettering, Glen L., 7591
Kettering, Jean S., 7520
Kettering, Lisa S., 7520
Kettering, Susan S., 7520, 7522
Kettering, Virginia W., 7520, 7521
Kettle, J. Michael, 2292
Keul, Jim, 4768
Keusch, Suzanne H., 6228
Keuther, Isabelle, 5927
Keve, Paula, 5906
Key, David G., 8816
Key, Donald, 9104
Key, Lisa R., 9195
Key, Lonnie, 3
Key, Robert, 3
KeyBank, 6802
KeyBank N.A., 7391, 7404, 7406, 7428, 7432, 7442, 7477, 7523, 7541, 7664, 7673, 7676, 7714, 7715, 7720, 8537
KeyBank, N.A., 7449, 7459, 7472, 7491, 7512, 7633, 7658, 7666, 7687, 7697, 9739
KeyCorp, 7523
Keyes, Barbara, 9269
Keyes, J. Patrick, 9969
Keyes, Jim, 9697
Keynan, Alex, 5589
Keys, Charlene H., 8468
Keys, Scott, 240
Keysor, Rhonda, 3163
KeySpan Corp., 6527
Keyston, David, 5560
Keystone Foods Corp., 8150
Keystone Foundation, The, 9789
Keystone Nazareth Bank & Trust Co., 8122
Keystone, LP, 8687
Keywell, Bradley, 2971
Keywell, Kim, 2971
Kezer, C. Henry, 3938
KF Elmhurst Holding LLC, 5890
Kfoury, Nancy, 1893
KG Investments, 3454
Khachaturian, Henry, 783
Khachaturian, Natasha, 783
Khachaturian, Rita M., 783
Khaghan, Mojdeh, 2050
Khalaf, Michel, 6479
Khalil, Hanan, 8383
Khan, Ahmad S., 160
Khan, Ahmad Saeed, 160
Khan, Ann Margaret, 1795
Khan, Anthony Rafiq, 1795
Khan, Gordon, 6196
Khan, Jamal, Dr., 9780
Khan, Julius "Sandy", III, 1120
Khan, Mehmood, 6627
Khan, Samina, 1795
Khan, Shahid Rafiq, 1795
Khan, Shanna Noelle, 1795
Khan, Zakia, 1795
Khan, Zia, 6724
Khanuk, L., 3025, 3057
Khanuk, T., 3057
Khatib, Georgianna, 6278
Khatib, Reza, 6278
Kheder, Susan, 4362
Khinduka, Shanti K., 4864
Khor, Jacqueline, 411
Khosla, Neeru, 236
Khosla, Vinod, 236
Khosrowshahi, Dara, 4311
Khouri, Naif A., 4410
Khoyi, Reza, 8391
Kia, Shirin, 9350
Kiang, Heng-Pin, 9587
Kiani, Joe E., 884
Kiani, Sarah, 884
Kibbe, Sharon, 3310
Kichler, Pascale, 2997
Kick, Frank J., 5738
Kicklighter, Kurt, 739
Kicklighter, Kurt L., 2516
Kidd, Alan, 1040
Kidd, Christen L., 6235
Kidd, Julie J., 6235
Kidder, Dorothy R., 5760
Kidder, Robert C., 7411
Kiddoo, Michael, 3205
Kido, Kenneth, 9400
Kidwell, Carla, 3277
Kidwell, Scott, 9091
Kieckhefer, John I., 129
Kieckhefer, John W., 129
Kieckhefer, R., 92
Kiefer, Kathleen S., 3257
Kiefer, Kathryn L., 4966
Kiefer, Markell, 4702
Kieffer, Maryanna L., 9549
Kieling, Nancy W., 5411
Kiely, Richard G., 1418
Kieman, Christine K., 8119
Kienstra, Christina L., 4928
Kienstra, Faith, 4928
Kienstra, Theodore A., Jr., 4928
Kienstra, Theodore A., Sr., 4928
Kierlin, Lara, 4674
Kierlin, Robert A., 4674
Kiernan, Eaddo H., 6279
Kiernan, Ellen, 7341
Kiernan, Peter D., 6279
Kies, Mabel B., 1657
Kies, Peter S., 9811
Kies, W.S., 1657
Kies, William S., III, 1657
Kieschnick, Michael, 255
Kiesel, Bill, 3330
Kiessling, Louis C., 9410
Kieu, Quynh, 667
Kiewit & Sons Co., Peter, 5056
Kiewit Construction Group Inc., 5056
Kiewit Diversified Group Inc., 5056
Kiewit Sons', Peter, Inc., 5056
Kiewit, Peter, 5057
Kiewlich, Stephanie J., 406
Kiffin, Irvin A,, 2243
Kiger, Daniel, Rev., 7558
Kiger, Stephanie, 5533
Kight, Bennett L., 2417
Kight, Mike, 9617
Kight, Peter, 2558
Kight, Peter J., 2558
Kight, Teresa, 2558
Kight, Teresa J., 2558
Kiguchi, Stafford J., 2588
Kihi Foundation, 1151
Kihn, Cecily, 1878
Kikkoman Foods Foundation, 9961
Kikkoman Foods, Inc., 9881
Kilbane, Kathleen C., 2013
Kilborn, Vincent F., 71
Kilburn Law Firm, PLLC, The, 9049
Kildebeck, Margaretta, 1336
Kiley, Michael, 3544
Kiley, Thomas R., 3926
Kilgore, Don, 5068
Kilgore, Jack C., 2431
Kilgore, James B., 844
Kilgore, Keith, 7401
Kilgore, Leonard L., III, 3618
Kilgore, Ronald N., 4385, 4445, 4518
Kilkowski, James M., 653
Killackey, Maureen, 5786
Killacky, John, 9375
Killebrew, Manuel, 4821

Killen, John V., 4256
Killian, George, Jr., 3201
Killiher, Daniel, 3759
Killin, Jennifer Clarkson, 8587
Killin, Tripp, 8587
Killinger, Elizabeth, 9126
Killingsworth, Mary, 1958
Killingsworth, Tom, 2632
Killion, Rick, 3447
Killoran, Michelle, 7359
Kilmer, Craig, 7971
Kilmer, Joe, 3346
Kilpatrick, Marjorie K., 6275
Kilpin, Tim, 886
Kilroy, John B., 784
Kilroy, Lora Jean, 8956
Kilroy, Mari Angela, 8956
Kilroy, Nelly Llanos, 784
Kilroy, William S., 8956
Kilroy, William S., Jr., 8956
Kilts, James M., 6280
Kilts, James M., Jr., 6280
Kilts, Sandra M., 6280
Kilts, Sarah, 6280
Kim, Agnes C., 8123
Kim, Andy, 3760
Kim, Byung, 437
Kim, Hyeok, 4729
Kim, James J., 8123
Kim, Jeffrey "Jeff" J., 9501
Kim, John Y., 6548
Kim, Kyle W., 7520
Kim, Leezie, 92
Kim, M. Molly, 4274
Kim, Michael B., 6452
Kim, Mickey, 3321
Kim, Mimi Okkyung, 6452
Kim, Peter S., 6872
Kim, Randy, 692
Kim, Robert, 8655
Kim, Steve Y., 785
Kim, Steven, 4026
Kim, Susan Y., 8123
Kimball, Anne C., 786
Kimball, David K., 9245
Kimball, Dena, 2413
Kimball, Gretchen B., 786
Kimball, H. Earle, 8410
Kimball, Jeffrey L., 786
Kimball, Jennifer, 5533
Kimball, Josh, 2413
Kimball, Kristi, 1128
Kimball, Robert, 917
Kimball, Roger, 8266
Kimball, Sara H., 786
Kimball, Sherry E., 356
Kimball, Stephen C., 786
Kimball, William R., 786
Kimber, Nancy, Dr., 929
Kimberly Clark Corp., 4254
Kimberly, Dean, 4612
Kimberly-Clark, 1771
Kimberly-Clark Corp., 8957
Kimble, Doris, 7526
Kimble, Floyd E., 7526
Kimble, Greg, 7526
Kimbrell Agency Investment, W. Duke, 7249
Kimbrough, Julius E., Jr., 3644
Kime, Jack E., 8085
Kimelman, Martin, 1842
Kimley-Horn, 9606
Kimmel, Adam P., 6281
Kimmel, Gregory A., 3023
Kimmel, Margaret Mary, 8043
Kimmel, Martin S., 5812, 6281
Kimmel, Sidney, 8124
Kimmel, Steve, 3324
Kimmelman Charitable Remainder Annuity Trust, David, 2184
Kimmelman, Carol, 6282
Kimmelman, David, 2184
Kimmelman, Douglas W., 6282
Kimmelman, Milton A., 7032
Kimmelman, Peter, 5882
Kimmet, Gary J., 592
Kimmins, Barbara, 8637
Kimoto, Paul, 690
Kimpel, Stephen, 7563
Kimpton, Graham Lawrence, 914
Kimpton, Isabelle, 914
Kimpton, Laura, 914
Kimpton, William D., 914
Kimsey, Frank C., Dr., 8583
Kimsey, James V., 1921
Kimsey, Mark J., 1921
Kimsey, Michael P., 1921
Kimsey, Raymond C., 1921
Kincaid, Beverly, 9659
Kincaid, Cassandra, 9509
Kincaid, Nick, 7348
Kincaid, Stephen, 4995
Kind, Christina, 7023, 7024, 8125
Kind, Ken, 8125
Kind, Kenneth A., 7023, 7024
Kind, Patricia, 7023, 7024, 8125
Kind-Rubin, Valerie, 7023, 7024, 8125
Kindel, Maureen, 809
Kinder Morgan, Inc., 1439
Kinder, Anne Lamkin, 1392
Kinder, David D., 8958
Kinder, Garry, 8789
Kinder, Nancy G., 8958
Kinder, Peter, 9375
Kinder, Richard D., 8958
Kindfuller, Andrew, 7023, 7024, 8125
Kindle, Carolyn, 4887, 4987
Kindle, Jo Ann, 4987
Kindle, Jo Ann Taylor, 4887
Kindred, John J., III, 6128
King Provision Corp., 2337
King Street Capital Advisors, 6283
King Street Capital Mgmt. LP, 6283
King Trust, Charlene, The, 5126
King, Abby D., 8180
King, Barbara P., 7171
King, Bruce, 362
King, Bruce E., 362
King, Carl B., 8959
King, Charles A., 4122
King, Christopher J., 1894
King, Chuck, 3403
King, Craig, 5108
King, Cynthia M., 8126
King, David, 7321, 7731
King, David C., 8454
King, Del, 3298
King, Dorothy E., 8959
King, Dorothy J., 1255
King, Dottie, 1255
King, Edna R., 9434
King, Elizabeth, 5561
King, Emily, 2960
King, Emily H., 2960
King, Florence E., 8959
King, Gayle, 3067
King, Heather A., 3947
King, Helen Deborah Van Dyke, 9921
King, J. Dudley, Jr., 8475
King, Jackie, 8775
King, James, 416
King, James P., 6953
King, Jeanne Anne, 7816
King, Jeffery L., 8126
King, Jena Fassett, 787
King, Jennifer C., 1255
King, Jerry, 9833
King, Jill, 3400
King, John P., Jr., 1031
King, Judith S., 4293
King, Kathy A., 8752
King, Kenneth Kendal, 1440
King, Kimberly Davis, 1053
King, Kimberly J., 9939
King, Lance, 1421
King, Levi, 3298
King, Linda J., 9417
King, Louise Straus, 1702
King, Margaret, 6215
King, Marie, 6406
King, Mary E., 1880
King, Mary Jane, 4958
King, Maxwell, 8228
King, Michael, 787
King, Michael J., 568
King, Nancy, 3289
King, Patricia, 4297
King, Peter J., 4687
King, Regina, 5422
King, Robert E., 1255, 2960
King, Robert E., Jr., 2960
King, Roberta F., 4447
King, Russell S., 4687
King, Sabrina, 9282
King, Sandy, 4800
King, Sibyl Fine, 8039
King, Spencer, 7731
King, Stephen E., 3694
King, Steven, Sr., 8175
King, Susan Basil, 4792
King, Tabitha, 3694
King, Thomas, 1702
King, Thomas A., 3331
King, Tom, 7321
King, Victor E.D., 5968
King, W. Winburne, III, 1679
King, Wayne, 2039
King-O'Neal, Renate, 920
Kingdon Charitable Lead Annuity Trust II, M., 6284
Kingdon Charitable Lead Annuity Trust III, M., 6284
Kingdon Charitable Lead Annuity Trust, M., 6284
Kingdon, Anla Cheng, 6284
Kingdon, Mark, 6284
Kingery, Brett, 3169
Kingma, Theo, 701
Kingma, Todd W., 4521
Kings Gardens Apartments LLC, 9452
Kings Point Industries, Inc., 6118
Kingsbury, Brigitte L., 3704
Kingsbury, Sherilyn, 3014
Kingsland, Richard M., 1280
Kingsley, Charles, 1532
Kingsley, Mitchell, 3542
Kingsley, Tony, 8363
Kingston, John, III, 3924
Kingston, Sarah C., 7380
Kingston, Wm., 3317
Kingzett, Robert, 7856
Kiniry, Sue, 7990
Kinko's Corporation, 994
Kinlaw, M. Carlyle, Jr., 7340
Kinman, Sheila, 3420
Kinnaird, Helen W., 2691
Kinnebrew, Jack M., 8773
Kinner, Mark, 9989
Kinney Drugs, Inc., 6285
Kinney Trust, Mary, 6285
Kinney, Daniel, 3947
Kinney, Martha Hodsdon, 7026
Kinniard, Helen, 2691
Kinnison, Tom, 9998
Kinray, Inc., 7008
Kinsel, Rick A., 7031
Kinser, Sara, 179
Kinsey, Hugh, 2327
Kinsey, Mike, 3336
Kinship Trust Co., 1946
Kinsley Construction, Inc., 8127
Kinsley, Anne W., 8127
Kinsley, Christopher A., 8127
Kinsley, Robert A., 8127
Kinsley, Timothy, 8351
Kinsley, Timothy J., 8127
Kinsman, Elizabeth T., 7860
Kinsman, John W., 7860
Kinsman, Katherine, 8511
Kinsman, Keith, 7860
Kinsman, Paige, 7860
Kinter, Michael E., 4496
Kintz, James P., 2276
Kintzel, Lee A., 9136
Kintzel, Roger S., 9136
Kinzel, Judith, 7444
Kinzer, Raymond E., 8849
Kiplinger, Austin H., 1922
Kiplinger, Knight A., 1922
Kiplinger, Willard M., 1922
Kipp, Robert A., 4905
Kipper, Richard E., 328
Kirazian, Boghos, 9176
Kirban, Elise, 2524
Kirbo, Bruce W., 2186
Kirbo, Bruce W., Jr., 2437
Kirbo, Charles H., Jr., 2186
Kirby 2010 Trust, Allan, 5340
Kirby Foundation, 1796
Kirby, Alexandra Louise, 9446
Kirby, Allan P., Jr., 5340
Kirby, Allan P., Sr., 5339
Kirby, Ann K., 9446
Kirby, Annette S., 9446
Kirby, Coray S., 5340
Kirby, Dawn, 9938
Kirby, F.M., 5339
Kirby, F.M., II, 5339
Kirby, James W., Jr., 9446
Kirby, Jefferson W., 5339
Kirby, Kristin E., 1796
Kirby, Linda T., 9446
Kirby, Milan S., 5340
Kirby, Robert G., 1796
Kirby, Robin S., 1796
Kirby, Roger H.W., 9446
Kirby, S. Dillard, 5339
Kirby, Scott D., 1796
Kirby, Sharon Jean, 3154
Kirby, Slater B., 5340
Kirby, Wade H.O., 9446
Kirby, Walker D., 5339
Kirch, Larry, 9889
Kirchen, Evan, 7112
Kirchen, Helen S., 7112
Kirchen, Robert V., 7112

Kircher, Christopher P., 5029, 5030
Kircher, Kathleen, 2035
Kirchheimer Trust, 3110
Kirchner, Fred, 8591
Kirgan, Mary Anne, 3862
Kirgan, Robert S., 3862
Kirgan, Tiffany, 8819
Kirihara, Wayne H., 2595
Kirk 101 Trust, 9329
Kirk Humanitarian, 888
Kirk III Revocable Trust, John W., 9462
Kirk, Andrew M., 3527
Kirk, Anna Drew, 7265
Kirk, C. Shireen, 9462
Kirk, Clay Kenan, 3602
Kirk, David, 3527
Kirk, Frank, 3527
Kirk, Frank H., 3527
Kirk, Garrett, Jr., 7292
Kirk, James C., 3527
Kirk, James Philip, Sr., 3527
Kirk, John W., III, 9462
Kirk, Kenneth C., 8025
Kirk, Kristen, 9329
Kirk, Kristin, 3527
Kirk, Larry, 4822
Kirk, Michael, 3527
Kirk, Michael C., 3527
Kirk, Natalie, 3527
Kirk, Rose Stuckey, 5489
Kirk, Spencer, 9329
Kirkbride, Cheryl M., 7704
Kirkham, Ryan P., 2629
Kirkland 2004 Charitable Trust, 8592
Kirkland 2005 Charitable Trust, 8592
Kirkland 2007 Charitable Trust, 8592
Kirkland Foundation, Robert E. & Jenny D., 8618
Kirkland, Bedford F., 8592
Kirkland, Christopher, 8592
Kirkland, Gregg, 3159
Kirkland, Jenny D., 8592
Kirkland, Michele A., 4357
Kirkland, Robert, 8592
Kirkland, Robert E., 8618
Kirkland, William G., 6193
Kirkpatrick Oil Co., 7766
Kirkpatrick, C. Kris, 3613
Kirkpatrick, Christina M., 539
Kirkpatrick, Eleanor B., 7766
Kirkpatrick, Elizabeth, 2883
Kirkpatrick, Elizabeth Stanton, 3950
Kirkpatrick, Frederick S., 4510
Kirkpatrick, Isabel, 2327
Kirkpatrick, Joan E., 7766
Kirkpatrick, John E., 7766
Kirkpatrick, Jon, 3539
Kirkpatrick, Mary Alice, 8001
Kirkpatrick, Shaun A., 103, 111
Kirkpatrick, Taylor, 2883
Kirkpatrick, Timothy L., 18
Kirksey, Jack B., 7178
Kirkwood Realty, 8990
Kirkwood, Amanda H., 580
Kirkwood, Brooks, 301
Kirkwood, John H., 301, 580
Kirkwood, Robert C., 301
Kirsch, John, 7481
Kirsch, Peter, 1939
Kirsch, Susan, 8043
Kirsch, Tom, 3347
Kirschenbaum, Larry, 653
Kirschenbaum, Malcolm R., 1907
Kirshner, Carol, 9973
Kirtley, John, 5685
Kirwin, Kelly, 4667
Kirwood, Jeffrey C., 1451
Kiser, Anthony C.M., 6106
Kiser, Ben, 5072
Kiser, John W., III, 6106
Kiser, Sandy, 5530
Kiser, Stephanie Norris, 7182
Kish, Jason, 3303
Kish, Joan, 5341
Kish, John C., 5341
Kishbaugh, James, 7972
Kishel, Judith, 4616
Kishner, Judith Z., 7820
Kishner, Judy, 7818
Kislak, J.I., Inc., 2187
Kislak, Jay I., 2187
Kislak, Jean, 2187
Kislak, Philip Thomas, 2187
Kiss Products, 1771
Kissam, L., 3609
Kissam, Luke, 3609
Kissel, Richard O., II, 3388
Kissel, Wendy, 7570
Kissick, John H., 791
Kissick, John R., 791
Kissick, Mary K., 791
Kissick, Mary Kathleen, 791
Kissinger, Cathy, 4438
Kissinger, Henry A., 6610
Kissinger, Thomas F., 9900
Kistenbroker, David H., 2951
Kistler, Daniel G., 3021
Kistler, Walter, 9622
Kistler, Walter P., 9622
Kita, John J., 9947
Kitaoka, Shin'ichi, Dr., 7019
Kitch, Patti, 3348
Kitchel, William L., III, 1872
Kitchelle Custom Homes, 638
Kitchen, J. Edward, 7162
Kitchens, Dean J., 583
Kitchens, John, 2491
Kitchings, Chester W., Jr., 1621
Kitchings, Chester W., Sr., 1621
Kitchings, Margaret Howe, 1621
Kittredge, Francine S., 6538
Kittredge, Lisa R., 4124
Kittredge, Michael J., 4124
Kittredge, Robert P., 4416
Kitz, Hilary, 7742
Kitzmiller, Edna B., 1441
Kivell, Rochelle, 6761
Kizziah, Barbara H. Malott, 2996
Kjolhaug, Aaron, 4684
Kjos, Andrew B., 7352
Kjos, David, 4796
KLA-Tencor Corporation, 792
Klabzuba, Doris, 8960
Klabzuba, John, 8960
Klabzuba, Melinda, 8960
Klabzuba, Robert, 8960
Klaff, Avril R., 2961
Klaff, Hersch M., 2961
Klag, Michael J., 1006
Klagsbrun, Micheline, 1897
Klagsburn, Micheline, 1897
Klahr, Suzanne Mckechnie, 6868
Klapholz, Henry, 4325
Klappa, Gale E., 9969
Klarman Family Foundation, 4298
Klarman, Beth S., 4126
Klarman, Seth A., 4126
Klarr, Louise S., 3190
Klarr, S. Gunnar, 3190
KLAS-TV, 9467
Klasen, Frazierita D., 7928, 8303
Klasky, Shel, 9578
Klatskin Associates LLC, 5768
Klatskin Assocs., 5557
Klatskin, Charles, 5342, 5448
Klatskin, Deborah, 5342
Klatskin, Lynne, 5342
Klatskin, Samuel, 5342
Klatsky, Arthur L., 3714
Klatzky, Howard T., 4649
Klauer, William R., Jr., 3421
Klauke, Joseph, 3034
Klaus, Christopher, 2497
Klaus, Christopher W., 2497
Klaus, Fred M., 7270
Klaus, Howard, 5558
Klaus, Jack, 3426
Klaus, Melynne, 3294
Klauser, Kenneth, 5249
Klavan, Ruchel Friedman, 450
Klavans, Nancy G., 4069
Kleberg, Caesar, 8963
Kleberg, Chris, 8963
Kleberg, Helen C., 8962
Kleberg, Robert J., Jr., 8962
Kleberg, Stephen J., 8963
Klecha, Roy W., Jr., 4373
Kleckza, Kevin O., 944
Klee, Conrad C., 6286
Klee, Virginia, 6286
Kleese, William R., 9246
Kleger, Lisa, 761
Klein Charitable Foundation, Sam W., 3386
Klein Irrevocable Trust, Sara Dina, 6288
Klein, Abraham, 6287, 6288, 6763
Klein, Barry, 1648
Klein, Bradford, 1571
Klein, Calvin, 6289
Klein, Casey, 2077
Klein, Chaim, 5890
Klein, Charles A., 6632
Klein, Christine Erion, 1408
Klein, Christopher E., 2466
Klein, Conrad Lee, 713
Klein, Daniel J., 3824
Klein, David L., 1797
Klein, Elaine S., 1648
Klein, Elisabeth, 793
Klein, Freada Kapor, 764
Klein, Gabrielle, 3470
Klein, Gershon, 5890
Klein, Harriet J., 3824
Klein, Ira, 1151
Klein, Irene M., 6018
Klein, James L., 793
Klein, Jeffrey F., 3824
Klein, Kara, 2121
Klein, Kelly, 6289
Klein, Kenneth, 793
Klein, Laura Colin, 6048
Klein, Linda S., 1690
Klein, Lloyd E., 793
Klein, Mark, 6112
Klein, Michael, 321
Klein, Michael F., 3824, 4783
Klein, Miriam, 1797, 5890
Klein, Mordechai, 6287
Klein, Peter J., 6018
Klein, Philip E., 3824
Klein, Sarah Dinah, 6287, 6288
Klein, Steven M., 6568
Klein, Tibor, 5890
Klein, Vickie, 5075
Kleine, Mark, 2853
Kleiner, Eugene M., 2635
Kleiner, Michael, 2635
Kleinert, Ashlee Hunt, 8923
Kleinert, Chris, 8773
Kleinert, Christopher W., 9047
Kleinfeld, Dru, 5476
Kleinfeld, Sanders, 5476
Kleinheinz, John B., 8964
Kleinheinz, Marsha, 8964
Kleinman, Beth, 6290
Kleinman, Joseph S., 6290
Kleinman, Martin, 6290
Kleinpeter, Ben, 3618
Kleinsmith, Vickey, 5065
Kleist, Mark, 4446
Klemencic, Ron, 9700
Klemesrud, Mellony, 3481
Klemm, Connie, 5068
Klemmt, Pierce, Rev., 9380
Klenck, Marilyn, 3402
Kleper, Ann-Louise, 3110
Klepfer, Robert O., Jr., 7326
Klepper, Heidi, 1394
Kleptz, Melissa A., 7688
Klettner, Robert C., 2112
Klevansky, Vyacheslav, 1074
Kleven, Cynthia F., 4597
Kleven, Richard, 9956
Kline, Audrey D., 3569
Kline, Bessie H., 8129
Kline, Carolyn, 3348
Kline, Charles, 8128
Kline, Daniel L., 2702
Kline, Darrell, 7795
Kline, Figa Cohen, 8128
Kline, Josiah W., 8129
Kline, Keith, 7417
Kline, Terrance A., 7947
Kline, William J., Jr., 7936
Kline, William M., III, 8332
Kling, Allen, 794
Kling, Barclay, 7088
Kling, Breck, 7088
Kling, Chris, 7088
Kling, Daryl, 794
Kling, Donalyn G., 794
Kling, Josh, 7088
Kling, Kenneth, 794
Kling, Paul Fritz, 3505
Kling, Scott, 4515
Klingenstein 1999 Trust, John, 6294
Klingenstein Charitable Lead Trust, Andrew, 6291
Klingenstein, Andrew, 6291
Klingenstein, Andrew D., 5343, 6125, 6292
Klingenstein, Andrew Davis, 3685
Klingenstein, Esther A., 6292
Klingenstein, Frederick A., 6293
Klingenstein, John, 3685, 5343, 5793, 6125, 6291, 6292, 6294
Klingenstein, Joseph, 6292
Klingenstein, Julie, 3685, 6291, 6292
Klingenstein, Patricia, 6291, 6294
Klingenstein, Patricia D., 6292
Klingenstein, Patricia Davis, 3685
Klingenstein, Paul, 2989
Klingenstein, Thomas D., 5343, 6125, 6291, 6292
Klingenstein, Thomas Davis, 3685
Klingerman, Daniel A., 8040

Klingsporn, Gary, Rev. Dr., 3990
Klink, Edwin H., 3392
Klink, Edwin Howard, 3392
Klink, Kathleen, 7481
Klink, Sheila K., 3392
Klinke, Ray, 7876
Klocko, Dan, 2632
Klooster, Henry, 4369
Kloosterboer, Jay, 2803
Klopp, Marjorie K.C., 6299
Klopping, George, 973, 1120
Klorfine, Leonard, 2188
Klorfine, Norma E., 2188
Klotman, Paul, 8658
Klotnia, Diane, 2900
Klotzman, Jeff, 8994
Kloza, Brian T., 6918
Kluber, William, 4316
Klug, Jonathan P., 8675
Kluge, Mary Kay, 2812
Kluger, Joseph E., 8152
Klugman, Rob, 1487
Klurman 1994 Trust, Debbie, The, 2189
Klurman, Samuel A., 2189
Klurman, Sisel, 2189
Klusmann, Scott G., 7901
Klute, Dean, 5045
Kluttz, Margaret H., 7305
Klyce, Ellen Cooper, 8549
KMP Charitable Lead Trust I, 6639
KMP Charitable Lead Trust III, 6692
KMP Charitable Lead Trust V, 6639
KMP Charitable Trust II, 6510
KMP Charitable Trust VI, 6510
KMP Charitable Trust VII, 6692
KMP Trust I, 6639
KMP Trust V, 6639
KMP Trust, II, 6510
Knabusch Marital Trust, Edward M., 4476
Knabusch, Charles T., Jr., 4476
Knabusch, E. M., 4481
Knabush-Taylor, June E., 4481
Knall, David W., 3375
Knapik, Michelle, 1710
Knapp Realty Co., 3452
Knapp, Albert, 6295
Knapp, Charles, 6295
Knapp, Danielle, 6215, 6296
Knapp, David, 6215
Knapp, David E., 6296
Knapp, David L., 3402
Knapp, Emily, 6295
Knapp, Jane, 2114, 6296
Knapp, John, 416
Knapp, Joseph Palmer, 3825
Knapp, Judy, 1394
Knapp, Lauren Volgenau, 9549
Knapp, Michele, 6215
Knapp, Priscilla, 2114, 6215, 6296
Knapp, Priscilla S., 6296
Knapp, Russell S., 6295
Knapp, Spencer, 9361
Knapp, Steve, 2871
Knapp, William, 2114
Knapp, William C., 3452
Knapp, William C., II, 3452
Knapp, William L., 6296
Knappenberger, Mindy, 7921
Knauer, Louise Whall, 4872
Knauer, William J., 2288
Knauss, Donald R., 407
Kneale, Mike, 5044
Knecht, Alexander, 3180
Knecht, Randy, 4636
Knecht, Timothy, 4372
Knedlik, Ron, 7205
Knee, Joan, 797
Knee, Kevin, 797
Kneeley, Anita M., 5394
Kneeshaw, Warren, 1048
Knell, Theresa N., 3850
Kneppler, Robert, Jr., 8779
Knez, Andrew, 4277
Knez, Brian J., 4127
Knez, Debra S., 4277
Knez, Debra Smith, 4127
Knez, Jessica, 4277
Knickman, James R., 6549
Kniest, Nancy, 9617
Knife & Son, L., Inc., 4271
Knife River Corp., 7354
Knight Charitable Remainder Trust, 7527
Knight Inc., 1439
Knight Trust, James A., 4477
Knight, Andrew, 6898
Knight, Athelia, 1888
Knight, Bill, 8812
Knight, Bobbie J., 1
Knight, Dale A., 9784
Knight, Floyd C., 7527
Knight, Georgianne, 500
Knight, James A., Sr., 9820
Knight, James Alton, Jr., 9820
Knight, James L., 2191
Knight, Jeremiah, 22
Knight, Jessie, Jr., 1040, 1140
Knight, John S., 2191
Knight, Lynn, 3851
Knight, Melanie Ann, 7194
Knight, Nancy, 8812
Knight, Patricia Nesbitt, 3051
Knight, Penelope P., 7861
Knight, Philip H., 7861
Knight, Renee Miller, 9820
Knight, Richard, 4742
Knight, Robert M., Jr., 5090
Knight, Rory, 8313
Knight, Scott, 9285
Knight, Thomas E., Jr., 8726
Knight, Tommy, 10
Knight, Travis A., 7861
Knight, Virginia, 7527
Knight, W.H., Jr., 3174
Knight, Warren, 744
Knight, Will A., 9285
Knight-Drain, Carol, 4477
Knighton, Maurine D., 5833
Knights, Darcy, 3423
Knipe, Cortland J., 6297
Knipfing, Janet, 758
Knipfing, Kevin, 758
Knipfing, Leslie, 758
Knisley, Rex, 8209
Knispel, Lester, 1224
Knobel, Dale, 3788
Knobel, Jeffrey A., 1371
Knobel, Mark, 5122, 5155
Knobel, Sara, 5807
Knoble, William T., 5850
Knobloch, Carl W., Jr., 8965
Knobloch, Carla, 8731, 8965
Knobloch, Emily, 8965
Knobloch, Emily C., 8965
Knobloch, Emily J., 8965
Knobloch, Kevin F., 3613
Knobloch, Mark D., 3858
Knock, Jan, 3481
Knocker LLC, Inch, 5590
Knoepfle, Clarence, 7824
Knoepfler, Charles A., 3480
Knoll International Holdings, Inc., 1151
Knoll, Allan F., 7358
Knoll, Jeffrey, 7579
Knoll, Tom, 7367, 7427
Knoop Unitrust, Rose, 8411
Knopman, Debra S., 6398
Knopp, Paul J., 5349
Knopp, Theresa G., 8478
Knops, Jane, 9380
Knorr, Johnny, 5517
Knott, David M., 6298
Knott, Erin, 3826
Knott, Frances, 961
Knott, Henry J., Sr., 3826
Knott, Marion I., 3826
Knott, Martin G., Jr., 3826
Knott, Martin G., Sr., 3826
Knott, Owen M., 3826
Knott, Ron, Fr., 3563
Knott, Teresa A., 3826
Knous, Kristi, 3420
Knowles, C. Harry, 5344, 5345
Knowles, Cindy J., 7836
Knowles, Janet H., 5344, 5345
Knowles, Joe, 4039
Knowles, Marie, 1133
Knowles, Merry L., 7787
Knowles, Rachel Hunt, 8100
Knowles, Steve, 2675
Knowles, Wade, 5248
Knowlton, Austin E., 7528
Knowlton, Glenn, 8260
Knowlton, Leslie, 1572
Knowlton, Timothy S., 4473
Knox Charitable Lead Annuity Trust, George Ann, The, 2498
Knox Charitable Lead Annuity Trust, Pat, The, 2498
Knox Enterprises, 1620
Knox, Boone A., 2498
Knox, Charles, 2514
Knox, James H., 5210
Knox, Jefferson, 2514
Knox, Jefferson B.A., 2498
Knox, John T., 8934
Knox, John T., Jr., 8934
Knox, Julia P.R., 2498
Knox, Linda S., 8934
Knox, Ltd., 2498
Knox, Norman L., 149
Knox, Northrup R., Jr., 6299
Knox, Ruth A., 2435
Knox, Seymour H., 6299
Knox, Seymour H., IV, 6299
Knox, W. David, 9877
Knox, Wallace W., 292
Knox, Wendell J., 4030
Knudsen, Derek T., 606
Knudsen, Jamie, 7698
Knudsen, Leon, 8438
Knudsen, Richard, 5031
Knudson, Jeanette L., 7669
Knudson, Laura, 3019
Knupp, C.O., 3209
Knusten, Harry L., 3468
Knutsen, Charlene, 3468
Knutson, Craig, 7742
Knutson, Lisa A., 7659
Knutzen, Sally, 4795
Ko, Chung, 6090
Ko, J.J., 5724
Ko, Jensen, 6090
Kobara, John E., 365
Kobayashi, Naomi H., 375
Kobel, Cynthia, 3035
Kober, Jane, 7694
Koblentz, Jeff, 1004
Koblik, Steven, Dr., 432
Kobori, Michael, 1223
Kobus, Thomas A., 8014
Kobusch, Margaret W., 4881
Koby, Eugene A., 7444
Koch Companies, 9149
Koch Enterprises, Inc., 3334
Koch Foundation, Fred C., 9463
Koch Industries, 3510
Koch Industries, Inc., 3529
Koch Sons, George, Inc., 3334
Koch Sons, George, LLC, 3334
Koch Trusts for Charity, Fred C., 3528, 9463
Koch, Brad, 1263
Koch, Carl E., 2192
Koch, Charles Chase, 9463
Koch, Charles G., 3529, 9463
Koch, Chris, 8630
Koch, Curtis J., 7650
Koch, David H., 3528, 3529
Koch, David M., 3334
Koch, Donald G., 7444
Koch, Elizabeth, 3510
Koch, Elizabeth B., 3529, 9463
Koch, Elizabeth Robinson, 9463
Koch, Fred C., 3529
Koch, Janet C., 7650
Koch, Kevin J., 8746
Koch, Kevin R., 3334
Koch, Kimberly, 428
Koch, Mary R., 3529
Koch, Nancy J., 938
Koch, Paul, 3424
Koch, Paula, 2192
Koch, Paulette, 2032
Koch, Robert J., 7932
Koch, Robert L., II, 3334
Koch, William C., Jr., Hon., 8550
Koch-Schumaker, Robyn, 7671
Kochevar, Deborah T., 4003
Kochman, Ronald S., 6034
Kodosky, Gail T., 8966
Kodosky, Jeffrey L., 8966
Koe, Susan K., 301
Koehler, Adrian L., 8780
Koehn, John Mark, 3542
Koehn, Linda, 3453
Koehn, Thomas, 3453
Koehn, William, 3542
Koelle, Lisa P., 8370
Koelliker, Susan L., 8383
Koeneman, Jim, 4893
Koenig, Aaron, 7414
Koenig, Jennifer, 7180
Koenig, Joseph G., 5002
Koentopf, Marin, 4684
Koepplinger, Suzanne, 4714
Koerber, Cyndy, 5039
Koester, Torin S., 9366
Kogod, Arlene R., 9464, 9532
Kogod, Robert P., 9464, 9532
Koguan, Leo, 5346
Kohelet Yeshiva High School, 8131
Kohl Charitable Trust No. AK2, Max, 799
Kohl, Allen D., 799, 9883
Kohl, Anne, 6352

Kohl, Atlee, 8967
Kohl, Barbara, 8967
Kohl, Benedict M., 5232
Kohl, Caroline, 8967
Kohl, Clayton, 8967
Kohl, David J., 799
Kohl, Dolores K., 9883
Kohl, Herbert H., 9883
Kohl, Jerry, 1798
Kohl, Karyn, 1798
Kohl, Marian, 8967
Kohl, Mary, 9883
Kohl, Matthew, 1798
Kohl, Michelle, 5067
Kohl, Nicole F., 8967
Kohl, Ronald W., Dr., 5766
Kohl, Sidney A., 9883
Kohl, Terri Marilyn, 1798
Kohlberg Foundation, The, 6300
Kohlberg, Jerome, 6300
Kohler, Evangeline, 9884
Kohler, Herbert V., 9884
Kohler, Julilly W., 9885
Kohler, Leslie, 5383
Kohler, Lillie B., 9884
Kohler, Marie C., 9884
Kohler, R. Hagan, 2285
Kohler, Ruth DeYoung, 9928
Kohler, W.M. Collins, 9885
Kohlheim, Paul, 8472
Kohlwes, Gary F., 9619
Kohn Family Trust, 6301
Kohn, Al, 917
Kohn, Bernard L., Jr., 1622
Kohn, Bill, 1154
Kohn, Herb, 6301
Kohn, Joan J., 1622
Kohn, Marlo Dreissigacker, 9374
Kohn, Richard M., 7159
Kohn, Sara, 6301
Kohn, Scott, 9374
Kohnen, Christine S., 7679
Kohout, David W., 871
Kohout, Heather Catto, 1383
Kohout, Martha L., 871
Kohout, Thomas J., 871
Kohrs, Bob, Jr., 3534
Koirtyohann, Barbara, 4996
Kojima, Akira, 7019
Kojima, Beth, 6898
Kojima, Chris, 6898
Koken, M. Diane, 7587
Kokino LLC, 1662
Kokot, Nadyne, 3306
Kolano, Edward, 8084
Kolatch, Jonathan L., 5347
Kolatch, Mindy S., 5347
Kolb, Kathy, 3281
Kolb, Sandra Kiely, 7639
Kolehmainen, Sophia M, 3978
Kolenda, Helena, 841
Kolendrianos, Harry T., 9413
Kolhmeir, J. Bleich, 5927
Kolisaus Associated, 6229
Kolisch, H. Vira, 1871
Kolitz, Robert, 8968
Kolitz, Sandora, 8968
Kollel, Freehold, 5817
Kollman, Robert, 8994
Kolluri, Mini, 3962
Kolodgy, Kathleen, 3113
Kolschowsky, Gerald A., 2962
Kolschowsky, Karen A., 2962
Kolschowsky, Michael J., 2962
Kolschowsky, Timothy J., 2962
Kolt, Robert, 4357
Koltnow, Jennifer, 8610
Koly, David M., 7536
Koman, Amy M., 4929
Koman, William J., 4929
Komansky, Daniel S., 6858
Komisar, William L., 9918
Komitee, Eric R., 1717
Komp, George, III, 4811
Kompkoff, Gabriel, 84
Kompo Family Company, LLC, 2296
Kompothecras, Gary, Dr., 2296
Kompsi, Keith, 516
Konar, Howard, 5969
Konen, Mark E., 3344
Kong, Albert, 1265
Kong, Diana, 1227
Kongsgaard, Martha, 9591, 9661
Konig, Michael, 5258
Konigsberg, Julie E., 7553
Konkel, Harry W., 7423
Konkel, James Donnell, 7423
Konkel, Susan, 7423
Konkel, Susan Donnell, 7423
Konkle, Bernie, Jr., 4332
Konneker, James R., 7184
Konner, Joan, 6813
Kono, Taro, Hon., 7019
Kontz, Peggy, 5494
Koo, Grace J., 5826
Kookyer, Willem, 6748
Koonce, Beverly, 8412
Koonce, Charlene C., 8412
Koonce, Joel, 315
Koonce, K. Terry, 8412
Koonce, Kelly M., 8412
Koonce, Kenneth T., 8412
Koonce, Kimberly, 8412
Koonce, Paul D., 9422
Koontz, Dean R., 800
Koontz, Gerda A., 800
Koop, Deb, 4402
Koop, Dick, 8941
Koop, J.P., 4402
Koopman, Martin, 5039
Koos, John, 6489
Koos, Ronald L., 7883
Kooyker, Willem, 6498
Kooyumjian, Thomas A., 4930
Kooyumjian, Tony, 4930
Kopczick, E.M., 5235
Kopelman, Eli, 6672
Kopf, R.C., 6302
Kopf, Robert Y., Jr., 8209
Koplan, Jeffrey, 2511
Koplan, Jeffrey P., 3982, 5329
Kopp, Barbara, 4688
Kopp, Bob, 9975
Kopp, Kristin, 4688
Kopp, LeRoy, 4688
Koppel, Lynette P., 48
Kopper, Carolyn S., 1495
Kopsa, Lawrence R., 5098
Kora, Vidya, 3393
Koraleski, John J., 5090
Koran, Ida, 4689
Kordsmeier, John, 9914
Korea Zinc Co Ltd, 7349
Korell, Brad, 5031
Korenvaes, Amy B., 8969
Korenvaes, Harlan B., 8969
Koret, Joseph, 801
Koret, Stephanie, 801
Koret, Susan, 801
Korf, Gene R., 5319, 5357
Korf, Larry, 4679
Korf, Mordechai, 2193
Korf, Mordechai Y., 2193, 2197
Korf, Nechama A., 2193
Korf, Scott, 5357
Korff, Phyllis, 6228
Kormag Construction Co., 803
Korman, Berton E., 6303
Korman, Hyman, Inc., 6303
Korman, Jane, 8132, 8960
Korman, Josh, 8960
Korman, Leonard, 8132
Korman, Leonard I., 6303
Korman, Steven H., 6303
Kornfeld, Emily Davie, 6304
Kornfeld, Sandy, 6540
Kornfeld, Stuart A., 2995
Korniczky, Anna T., 6136, 6137
Kornland Building Co., 802
Kornwasser Life Insurance, Mila, 644, 1099
Kornwasser, Jacob, 803
Kornwasser, Joseph, 802
Kornwasser, Mark, 802
Kornwasser, Mila, 803
Kornwasser, Sonia, 802
Korolkiewicz, Linda, 1563
Korologos, Ann McLaughlin, 5845
Kors, Michael, 1833
Korsmo, John, 9750
Korstad, Heidi, 4617
Korstange, Jason E., 4778
Kortan, Ron, 5039
Korte, Hope, 3390
Korth, Colleen, 4478
Korth, James, 4478
Korth, James E., 4478
Korth, Paul, 4478
Korth, Robin, 4478
Korth, Thomas, 4478
Korth, Valerie, 4478
Kortun, Vasif, 6002
Kosanovic, Gerry, 7825
Kosanovich, John, Dr., 4532
Kosasa, Lisa C., 2607
Kosasa, Minnie, 2607
Kosasa, Paul, 2602
Kosasa, Paul J., 2607
Kosasa, Sidney S., 2607
Kosasa, Susan M., 2607
Kosasa, Thomas S., 2607
Kosh, Mitchell, 6651
Koshland, Daniel E., Jr., 804
Koshland, Douglas, 3712
Koshland, Douglas E., 804, 3833
Koshland, Ellen, 804
Koshland, James M., 804
Koshland, Marian E., 804
Koshland, Phlyssa, 804
Koshland, Yvonne, 804
Kosinski, John, 6037
Koskovich, Jerome, 4690
Koskovich, Marlyce, 4690
Koslovski, James, 5218
Koslow, Harry, 5813
Koslow, Jonathan L., 5673
Kosmes, Kara, 4316
Kosowsky, Harold, 5070
Koss, Joseph, 9837
Kossak, Evelyn K., 1623
Kossak, Jeffrey, 1623
Kossak, Jeffrey M., 1623
Kossak, Steven M., 1623
Kossman, Charles R., 471
Kostanecki, Sheila K., 6770
Kostel, George J., 9382
Koster, Barbara G., 5415
Koster, Preston, 2121
Koster, Stephen P., 4092
Kostich, Robert, 369
Kostolansky, David J., 7415
Kotak, Nitin, 3818
Kotalac, Marsha, 3990
Kotcamp, Kathy, 3563
Kotek, Jim, 9903
Kothari, Yogi, Dr., 5750
Kotick, Nina, 214
Kotick, Robert, 214, 369
Kotik, Charlotta, 6085
Kotin, Daniel M., 2773
Kotnour, Mark, 9627
Kott Grandchildren Charitable Trust, 2963
Kott Trust, Josephine, 2963
Kott Trust, Russell, 2963
Kott, Michael Steven, 2963
Kotthaus, Kim M., 9814
Kottmeier, Suanne, 7882
Kountze, Elizabeth Mallory, 5050
Kountze, Mary L., 5050
Kountze, Neely, 5050
Kountze, Tower, 5050
Kouri, Ann K., 8835
Kourkousis, Athas, 4070
Kouroyen, Angela, 5162
Koury, Frederick S., 4739
Koury, Michelle A., Dr., 5806
Kouvas, Patrice, 7415
Kovac, James J., 2818
Kovacevich, Kathy, 736
Kovach, Kenneth, 7375
Kovach, Richard A., 7375
Kovalcheck, Joseph P., Jr., 7497
Kovaleski, James, 8223
Kovar, Victoria, 5031
Kovarik, Emily, 5013
Kovler, Benjamin, 2964
Kovler, Everett, 2706, 2964
Kovler, H. Jonathan, 2706
Kovler, Jonathan, 2964
Kovler, Peter, 2706, 2964
Kovner, Bruce S., 5348
Kovner, Suzanne F., 5348
Kovtun, Jay, 1040
Kovtun, Lael, 1040
Kovvali, Lakshmi, 3249
Kovvali, Venkata R., 3249
Kowach, John W., 8209
Kowalchuk, E. J., 8851
Kowalik, Raymond J., 4866
Kowalski, Michael J., 6978
Kowles, Carolyn Ford, 4560
Koyama, Todd, 9615
Koyenova, Lyudmila, 5553, 6536
Kozberg, Joanne Corday, 365, 579
Kozberg, Lindsey C., 9586
Koziel, Jeffrey, 1771
Koziol, Jim, 9833
Kozitza, William, 4777
Kozlak, Jodeen A., 4776
Kozlov, Herbert, 6016
Kozmetsky, Cynthia H., 9128
Kozmetsky, Daniel A., 9128
Kozmetsky, George, 9128
Kozmetsky, Gregory A., 9128
Kozmetsky, Ronya, 9128

Kozuskp, Donald, 7477
KPH Trust, 2892
KPK Holdings, 2050
KPMG, 975, 1268
KPMG LLP, 5349
Krabbe, Joseph, 7373
Krabbe, Melissa, 7404
Krabbe, Susan F., 1147
Kracium, Mike, 3403
Krafchuk, Markell B., 4801
Kraft Foods Global, Inc., 3034, 7214
Kraft Foods, Inc., 3245
Kraft Group, LLC, 4128
Kraft Total, 6547
Kraft, Cynthia, 3514
Kraft, Daniel A., 4128, 4193
Kraft, David H., 4193
Kraft, James A., 9704
Kraft, Jonathan A., 4128, 4193
Kraft, Joshua M., 4128, 4193
Kraft, Lee, 9671
Kraft, Myra, 4128
Kraft, Robert K., 4128, 4193
Kraiem, Elizabeth Leiman, 6228
Krajacic, Frederick M., 6406
Krakaur, Kenneth, 9511
Kral, Barbara H., 5051
Krall, Ron, 1528
Kralwasser, David, 1632
Kraly, Ellen Percy, 5757
Kram Construction, 802
Kramer Revocable Living Trust, Rose Blank, 1997
Kramer Trust, Victor, 7250
Kramer, Benjamin, 7529
Kramer, Catherine, 2195
Kramer, Charlotte R., 7529
Kramer, Diana, 790
Kramer, Elizabeth, 7529
Kramer, Gerry, 4373
Kramer, Henry E., 2742
Kramer, John, 5019
Kramer, John M., 478
Kramer, Karl F., 790
Kramer, Kathleen McGrath, 790
Kramer, Katie S., 1374
Kramer, Keith, 3421
Kramer, Larry, 686
Kramer, Manuel, 2971
Kramer, Mark R., 7529
Kramer, Mary L., 4543
Kramer, Michael, 790, 9089
Kramer, P.S., 4931
Kramer, Rachel Slosburg, 5083
Kramer, Sandra, 3033
Kramer, Susan, 2971
Kramer, Toby, 7529
Kramer, Todd, 9226
Krames, Crysta, 849
Kramzer, Joyce A., 2101
Krane, Hilary, 7875
Kranenburg, 3259
Kranich, Michael, Sr., 7971
Krantz, Richard A., 6047
Kranwinkle, Mark, 9687
Kranwinkle, Sara, 9687
Krapf, Julia G. Morton, 6425
Krapp, Elizabeth, 8135
Krarup, Irene, 6679
Krasner, Lee, 6650
Krasner, Martin P., 5771
Krasno, Richard M., 7248
Krasnow, Leonard R., 9297
Krasny, Janet, 2749
Krasny, Michael P., 2749
Krass, Lisa, 2214
Kratchman, Eden M., 7905
Kratus, Eugene A., 7473
Kratz Foundation, 298
Kratz, Richard P., 298
Kratzer, Raymond, 2896
Kraus, Avishai, 5980
Kraus, Jill G., 6305
Kraus, John P., 7372
Kraus, Kevin, 2409
Kraus, Lawrence, 2648
Kraus, Lawrence E., 6216
Kraus, Peter S., 6305
Kraus, Sandy, 5075
Krause Gentle Corporation, 3454
Krause, Alan M., 7530
Krause, Andrew J., 1990
Krause, Bobby, 2174
Krause, Charles A., 9886
Krause, David, 9905
Krause, Douglas, 491
Krause, Harold, 7530
Krause, Kyle, 3420
Krause, L. Gay, 805
Krause, L. William, 805
Krause, Lori, 3543
Krause, Richard A., 2174, 2286
Krause, Robin, 7079
Krause, Sandra S., 7323
Krause, Stephen, 3033
Krause, William A., 3454
Krausman, Steven, 5258
Krauss Co., Ltd., 3642
Krauss, Erica, 1061
Kraut, Gary A., 1581
Kravis, Bessie R., 6307
Kravis, George R., II, 6307
Kravis, Henry R., 6306, 6307
Kravis, Kimberly R., 6307
Kravis, Raymond Field, 6307
Kravis, Robert S., 6307
Krawitt, A.L., 5235
Kraybill, Dave, 8234
Kreamer, Janice, 4921
Kreamer, Janice C., 5784
Krebs, Susan D., 8351
Kreckle, Kathryn A., 4474
Kredel, Richard, 1210
Kreeger, Keith, 5922
Kreeger, Wendy Durst, 5922
Kreger, Shirley, 3437
Krehbiel, Anne, 7702
Kreher, Rick, 4996
Kreid, Christopher, 3036
Kreider, Matthew S., 4986
Kreiling, Scott, 7829
Kreiner, Charles F., Jr., 5832
Kreisler, Amy Rollins, 2542, 2543
Kreitzer, Joan, 7488
Krell, Joanne K., 4474
Krelstein, Vanessa Elias, 7969
Kremer, Ken, 7567
Kremer, Selman, 7751
Kremin, Patricia, 4591
Kremin, Patricia A., 4591
Krempa, Jerry, 9815
Krems, David Z., 1361
Krems, Nathan S., 1361
Krendl, Kathy, 7605
Krenek, Lois, 8761
Krenicky, Kenneth, 8223
Krenn, Jim, 861
Krenowicz, Mary A., 7858
Krenzel, Sharla, 3554
Kresa, Joyce, 5350
Kresa, Kent, 774, 5350
Kresa-Reahl, Kiren, 5350
Kresek, Bob, 849
Kresge, Cynthia L., 4479
Kresge, Sebastian S., 4479
Kresha, Sharon R., 5074
Kresnak, Diane M., 4371
Kresnak, Jack, 4424
Kress, Amy C., 7647
Kress, Claude W., 6308
Kress, Elizabeth A., 2099
Kress, Ingred, 9887
Kress, James F., 9887
Kress, John F., 9887
Kress, Rush H., 6308
Kress, Samuel H., 6308
Kress, William F., 9887
Kresse, Robert J., 7074
Kretschmer, R. David, 3257
Kretsinger, Mary, 3514
Kreuchauf, Katherine, 7453
Kreul, Juliana, 2033
Kreul, Sandra, 2151
Kreuter, Randy, 7575
Kreutzberg, Robin Hintze, 98
Kreutzer, Bob, 3554
Kreuzmann, Susan S., 2346
Krey, Bradley R., 6084
Krey, Julie, 9899
Krey, Mary Gorter, 6084
Kreyling 2001 Trust, Marcia, 2965
Kreymerofkreymer Investments, Karol, 3249
Kriak, John M., 7990
Krich, Rachel, 5527
Kridel, Nancy, 5296
Kridler, Douglas F., 7411
Krieble, Daniel C., 4129
Krieble, Frederick B., 4129
Krieble, Helen E., 4129
Krieble, Nancy B., 4129
Krieble, Robert H., 4129
Krieble, Robert K., 4129
Krieg, Iris J., 3079
Krieg, Katie, 2414
Krieger, John B., 5549, 5692
Krieger, Kristie Macosko, 1348
Krieger, Teresa R., 4358
Krieger-Burke, Teresa, 4358
Kriendler Unitrust, Maxwell C.C., 6309
Kriendler, H. Peter, 6309
Kriendler, John, 6309
Kriesel, Jack, 2281
Krigstein, Alan, 8106
Krikorian, John, 4173
Krikovich, Peter, 3186
Krimendahl, H. Frederick, II, 6132, 6428
Krinzman, Melissa, 2238
Kripal, D. Francis, 5026
Kripp, Betty, 7942
Krishan Tarsadia Trust, 1239
Krishnamurti, Vasili, 6159
Krishtalka, Leonard, 9656
Krisko, Diane, 6634
Krispen Family Holdings, 9329
Kriss, Thomas, Dr., 3514
Kristensen, Tage, 9729
Kristofcak, Alexander, 5865
Kristol, William, 6981
Krivacs, James, 7012
Krivacs, Victoria, 7012
Kroeger, Dave, 9715
Kroeger, Eileen, 1979
Kroeger, Paul, 3271
Kroell, Scott, 2482
Kroes, Rich, 5556
Kroese, Mark, 9613
Kroger Co., The, 7531
Kroger, Kevin, 2807
Krogh, Chris, 784
Krognes, Steve, 570
Kroh Marital Trust, Lois L., 1442
Kroh, Loren H., 8351
Krohn, Mark, 7367
Krohn, Rebecca, 3480
Krohn, S. D., 4597
Kroll, Kathleen J., Hon., 2032
Kromer, Megan, 9073
Kromm, Michael, 750
Kron, Judy, 1394
Kron, Robert, 1394
Krone, Bruce A., 7426
Krone, Dorothy G., 7426
Kronebusch, Jennifer, 8541
Kroner, Daryl, 806
Kroner, Jennifer, 806
Kroner, Jennifer G., 806
Kroner, Jennifer J., 806
Kroner, Kenneth, 806
Kroner, Kenneth F., 806
Kronick, Susan D., 2191
Kronkosky, Albert, Jr., 8970
Kronkosky, Bessie Mae, 8970
Kronstadt, Allen R., 3732
Kronstadt, Sunya Perlmutter, 3732
Kroonenberg, Sherri, 1127
Kroos, O.A., 9884
Krop, Pamela S., 4770
Kropf, Susan J., 5790
Kroske, Doug, 8474
Krosman, Susan M., 1531
Kroszner, Randall, 2873
Krotona Institute of Theosophy, 2958
Krouse Family Foundation, Inc., 2344
Krouse, Hillary, 2196
Krouse, Rodger, 2196
Krouse, Rodger R., 2196, 2209, 2344
Krudy, Courtney, 3330
Krueger, Blake W., 4593
Krueger, Dale W., 7862
Krueger, Faith A., 5232
Krueger, Jenny, 9704
Krueger, Kurtiss R., 9946
Krueger, Robert C., 5416
Krueger, Steve, 4996
Krueger, Tiphani, 1432
Krug, Daniel W., 7275
Kruger, Greg, 4636
Kruger, Jim, 5072
Krugh, Bradley, 3687
Krugh, Charlotte, 3687
Kruidenier, Elizabeth, 3455
Kruidenier, Lisa, 3455
Krukowski, Jan, 7092
Krulewitch, Deborah, 6334
Krulewitch, Peter, 5808
Krull, Dana, 3336
Krull, Dana L., Mr., 3335
Krumboltz, Ann, 9590
Krumland, Carole A., 6921
Krumm, Tim, 3422
Kruntorad, Virginia Blossom, 7387
Krupp, Douglas, 4131
Krupp, George, 4130
Krupp, Judith, 4131
Krupp, Lizbeth, 4130

Krupskas, Joan, 6334, 6337
Kruse, Anthony H., 1373
Kruse, Rebecca, 3421
Kruse, Shelly, 2881
Krush, Phyllis J., 3314
Krzys, Robert, 1567
KSTP, Inc., 4678
Kuan, Kah-Jin Jeffrey, 4432
Kubera, Ronald, 9651
Kubert, Arthur J., 4333
Kubiak, Andy, 9950
Kubick, Jonathan J., 9854
Kubisch, Anne, 7845
Kubota, Tetsuya, 7272
Kubzansky, Mike, 984
Kucera, Matthew, 2033
Kuck Trust, Paul, 2283
Kuck, Duane, 2283
Kuck, Tim, 2283
Kuck, Timothy, 2283
Kudisizaden, Albert, 1233
Kuechle, Scott, 7213
Kuechler, Henry N., III, 3616
Kuehn, Kathryn M., 9959
Kuehn, Kurt P., 2566
Kuehn, Philip G., Jr., 9959
Kuehner, Carolyn, 5045
Kuehnlein, Tim, 4370
Kuelbs, John, 8776
Kuennen, Christa, 3490
Kuenstner, Paul, 5170
Kuenzl, John E., 9888
Kuenzl, Norma, 9888
Kuenzli, Gwen, 7453
Kuerbis, Paul, 5345
Kuester, Dennis J., 9819
Kuester, Steven G., 3312
Kuffner, Helene, 5929
Kuflik, Karen, 6311
Kuflik, Mitchell, 6177, 6311
Kuhl, David S., 5314
Kuhlik, Bruce N., 1929
Kuhlke, Dessey L., 2514
Kuhlman, Randy, 3419
Kuhn, Anna Lefer, 1880
Kuhn, J. A., 7224
Kuhn, Lori, 7577
Kuhn, Mark, 7156, 7328
Kuhn, Peter A., 7573, 9699
Kuhn, Pricilla, 108
Kuhn, Richard W., 2812
Kuhn, Stacy M., 9216
Kuhn, Steve, 4742
Kuhne, Jack, 7312
Kuhne, John A., 7224
Kuhne, Lucy, 7312
Kuhne, Lucy S., 7224
Kuhne, William D.S., 7224
Kuhns, Carole, 7444
Kuijpers, Roelfien, 5876
Kuioka, Alton T., 2588
Kuipers, Laura, 118
Kuipers, Richard, 118
Kukuchka, Ronald G., 8227
Kukui Gardens Corporation, 2596
Kulak, Sharon J., 2733
Kulas, E.J., 7532
Kulas, Fynette H., 7532
Kulas, Julian E., 2907
Kulbersh, David, 8468
Kulis, Leslie J., 7922
Kulkarni, Bhushan, 4340
Kulkarni, Nirupama "Nima", 3569
Kullman, Mary Caola, 4931
Kullman, Mary Ellen, 253
Kulnis, Pamela, 3085
Kultgen, Karin I., 9965
Kulynych, Petro, 7251, 7252
Kum & Go LC, 3454
Kumar, Bandana, 5620
Kumar, Daryn, 1211
Kumm, Lillian H., 9831
Kummer, Gordon H., 4468
Kummer, Linda, 4468
Kummer, Robert W., Jr., 756
Kump, Robert D., 3693
Kunberger, George A., 738
Kundert, David J., 9907
Kuni Trust, Wayne D., 9662
Kuni, Joan E., 9662
Kuni, Wayne D., 9662
Kunkel, John C., II, 8133
Kunkel, Molly, 7973
Kunkel, Paul A., 8133
Kunkler, William C., III, 2780
Kunnath, Richard M., 9700
Kunselman, Scott, 4366
Kuntz, John F., 5414
Kuntz, Lee A., 1534
Kuntz, Thomas G., 9539
Kuntzleman, Charles, 4464
Kunz, Carol, 8397
Kunz, Dan, 9807
Kunz, Dan Vicky, 9807
Kunz, Vicki, 9807
Kunze, Cliff, 3366
Kunze, Mel, 9237
Kunzman, Kenneth F., 5208
Kuohwa Garment & Enamel Industry Co., Inc., 6651
Kupfer, Lawrence, 9377
Kupferberg, Barbara, 3064
Kupferberg, Jesse, 6313
Kupferberg, Jesse M., 6312
Kupferberg, Martin, 6313
Kupferberg, Martin R., 6312
Kupferberg, Max, 6313
Kupferberg, Saul, 6313
Kuprion-Thomas, Sandra R., 8771
Kurack, Sandra M., 9702
Kurcias, Stephen S., 5907
Kurek, Jane, 5414
Kurland, Gerald, 744
Kurmas, Steven E., 4410
Kuronen, Amy, 4649
Kurose, Makoto, 9881
Kursman, Scott, 3817
Kurstjens, Sef, 2675
Kurtenbach, Al, 8522
Kurth, Ernest L., 8971
Kurth, Sandra G., 8971
Kurtz Foundation Inc., 5228
Kurtz, Caroline Lupfer, 7543
Kurtz, Daniel L., 6052, 6899
Kurtz, Daniel L., Esq., 5582
Kurtz, Nancy, 3929
Kurtz, Willis O., 7543
Kurz, Ellen, 6314
Kurz, Herbert, 6314
Kurz, Leonard, 6314
Kurzman, Jayne M., 5799, 6199
Kurzrok Foundation, The, 7394
Kusakawa, Katsuyuki, 7002
Kusch, Jenifer, 4373
Kushel, Gloria Joan, 6315
Kushel, John Richard, 6315
Kushel, Stephen, 6315
Kushelevsky, Shlomo, 6229
Kushiner, Sharon, 2785
Kushlan, Kritsin, 5269
Kushlan, Paula Frohring, 5269
Kushlan, Philip, 5269
Kushner, Andrew, 2032
Kushner, Charles, 5351, 5768
Kushner, Jared, 5351
Kushner, Josh, 5351
Kushner, Seryl, 5351
Kusmer, James, 7623
Kustanbauter, Kay, 7973
Kustel, Karen, 5609
Kuszaj, Elizabeth, 1563
Kutak Rock LLP, 6451
Kutler, Jon B., 2608
Kutler, Sara L., 2608
Kutliroff, Susan, 5447
Kutmah, Kheder, 3589
Kuykendall, John, Rev. Dr., 5208
Kuyper, E. Lucille Gaass, 3456
Kuyper, Jacqueline, 3456
Kuyper, Jill, 3456
Kuyper, Peter C., 3456
Kuyper, Peter H., 3456
Kuzio, Keith S., 8040
Kuzma, Lisa, 8173
Kvamme, Damon, 807
Kvamme, E. Floyd, 807
Kvamme, Jean, 807
Kvamme, Todd, 807
Kwai, Mitsuhiko, 6491
Kwan, Kathy A., 511
Kwiat-Hess, Kathy, 2766
Kwok, Pui Lan, 4432
KWWH Trust, 2892
KXAS-TV, 8753
Kydd, Michelle, 362
Kyle, Louis B., 2648
Kyriss, Karl, 7917
Kyte, Lawrence, 7590

L'Oreal Paris Division, 1771
L'Oreal USA, 6651
L-3 Link Communications, 6374
L-K Marketing, 9024
La Badie, Helen Ruth, 9830
La Dow, Anne M., 7659
La Fetra, Anthony W., 808
La Fetra, Michael W., 808
La Fetra, Suzanne, 808
La Forgia, Robert M., 9341
La Mesa Property Inc., 685
LA Outside Counsel, 3651
La Riche, Jeffrey, 5269
La Russo, Eileen, 1075
La Vea, James Annenberg, 8134
La-Z-Boy Chair Co., 4481
La-Z-Boy Inc., 4481
Laak, Philip, 8721
LaBadie, Emily, 9961
Labanz, Leeanne S., 2340
Labaree, Aaron, 6604
Labaree, Frances, 6604
LaBate, Anne, 5411
Labate, James B., 2034
LaBelle, John D., Jr., 1690
Labenne, Andrew D., 9400
Laber, Bassie, 2197
Laber, Ricky, 4451
Laber, Uri, 2197
Laborde, Alden, 3610
Laborde, James, 3610
Laborde, John, 3610
Laborde, Lucien P., Jr., 3618
Laborde, Stephanie, 3610
Laborey, Annette, 6593
Labouisse, Eve C., 6844
LaBounty, Gordon, 3015
LaBrie, Lawrence, 3700
Labriola, Michael A., 8230
Labrum, Joseph T., Jr., 8020
Labuda, Cindy A., 5481
Labuda, David S., 5481
LaCamera, Paul A., 3956
LaCava Gift Annuity, 9108
Lacayo, Henry L. "Hank", 1287
Lacaze, Catherine, 7093
Lachenmyer, L. M., 8833
Lachman, Joan, 6318
Lachman, Julie, 6318
Lachman, Lawrence, 6318
Lachman, Leon, 6318
Lachowicz, Cheryl, 5116, 5675
Lachowicz, Ted, 5675
Lachowicz, Theodore, 5116
Laciak, Geoff, 3369
LacKamp, Robin R., 3497
Lackner, David, 5354
Lackner, Thomas, 8363
Laclede Gas Co., 4931
LaCorte, Melissa M., 7463
Lacouture, Dick, 1423
LaCroix, Caitlin E., 1748
LaCroix, Christopher, 1748
LaCroix, Kathleen, 1748
Lacy Charitable Lead Annuity Trust, Linwood A., The, 2198
Lacy Holdings Ltd., 8787
Lacy, Adam M., 2198
Lacy, Benjamin H., 3987
Lacy, Christopher L., 2198
Lacy, Constance C., 2198
Lacy, F. Dwight, 8738
Lacy, Karlene, 1432
Lacy, Linwood A., Jr., 2198
Lacy, Lois D., 4962
Lacy, Mark, 1363
Lacy, Stephen M., 3420, 3463
Lacy, Terri, 7707, 8916
Ladak, Firoz, 5857
Ladd, David J., 4047, 4132
Ladd, Gene, 3360
Ladd, J. Scott, 4047
Ladd, James R., 9639
Ladd, John D., 4047
Ladd, Jr. Charitable Trust, George E., 4132
Ladd, Kate Macy, 6414
Ladd, Lincoln F., 4132
Ladd, Robert M., 4132
Ladd, Samuel A., III, 1671
Ladd, Sharon S., 9639
Ladd, William L., 4047
Laderer, Theresa M., 7934
Laderman, Ezra, 5585
Ladin, Felicia, 8314
Lading, Phil, 2817
Ladish Co., Inc., 9890
Ladish, Herman W., 9891
Ladish, William J., 9891
Ladner, Ann Marie, 4932
Ladner, Frank S., 4932
Ladner, John, 577
Ladner, Julia M., 4932
Ladner, Margaret M., 4932
Ladner, Thomas M., 4932
Ladner, William P., 4932

Levi, Richard H., 2976, 8082
Levi, Robert H., 8082
Levi, Ryan M., 2976
Levi, Ryda H., 8082
Levi, Stanley A., 3844
Levian Corp., 6358
Levian, Edmond, 6358
Levian, Lawrence, 6358
Levian, Moossa, 6358
Levian, Pary, 6358
Levin Foundation, 1018
Levin, Adam, 5359
Levin, Alan A., 3272
Levin, Allen, 7539
Levin, Barbara, 7539
Levin, Becky Ruhmann, 4255
Levin, Daniel E., 2977
Levin, Donald R., 2978
Levin, Fay Hartog, 2977
Levin, Frenda, 7884
Levin, Irving J., 7884
Levin, Janice H., 5359
Levin, Jeffrey S., 6443
Levin, John A., 5708
Levin, Karen, 7539
Levin, Louis, 7539
Levin, Marc, 4386
Levin, Marc V., 1644
Levin, Mark J., 4255
Levin, Meir, 6229
Levin, Murray, 2088
Levin, Philip J., 5359
Levin, Richard C., 686
Levin, Richard C., Dr., 1558
Levin, Ryan, 7539
Levin, Shira, 6870
Levin, Steven, 2088
Levin, Suzie, 623
Levine Investments Limited Partnership, 133
Levine, Adam, 2749
Levine, Arnold J., 504
Levine, Arthur E., 829
Levine, Chuck, 1393
Levine, David, 836
Levine, Elliot H., 6054, 6948
Levine, Emily Ruth Hess, 39
Levine, Gerald D., 9527
Levine, Heidi, 3781
Levine, Hirschell E., 6073, 6825
Levine, Howard, 836, 7202, 7255
Levine, Irene, 836
Levine, James, 6360
Levine, Jay, 836, 6360
Levine, Jay David, 133
Levine, Jay N., 1629
Levine, Jen, 3095
Levine, Jerome L., 6559
Levine, Joel A., 660
Levine, Jonathan, 3001
Levine, Jonathan L., 133
Levine, Laurence W., 6360
Levine, Lee A., 5360
Levine, Leon, 7255
Levine, Michael, 6360
Levine, Michael J., 6543
Levine, Mildred, 6359
Levine, Mitch, 6205
Levine, Richard, 5906, 6359
Levine, Richard E., 3872
Levine, S. Robert, 4142
Levine, Sandra P., 7255
Levine, Scott M., 8383
Levine, Tammy, 1629
Levine, Todd, 6359
LeVine, Victoria M., 7928
Levine, William, 6359
Levine, William S., 133
Levins, Rich, 8217
Levinson, Carl A., 5527
Levinson, Charlotte, 5527
Levinson, David, 1581
Levinson, Ed, 5527
Levinson, Ellen, 5598
Levinson, Gordon, 5527
Levinson, John, 5598
Levinson, Julian, 5527
Levinson, Lauren, 9726
Levinson, Max, 5527
Levis Trust, Adolph, 8140
Levis, William, 5416
Levis, William E., 7400
Levit, Leah S., 8982
Levit, Max S., 8982
Levit, Milton H., 8982
Levit, Rochelle, 8982
Levitetz, Jeffery A., 2211
Levitetz, Tyler, 2211
Levitetz, Zachary, 2211
Levithan, Allen, 5228, 5421
Levithan, Beth, 5296
Leviton, Susan, 3890
Levitt and Sons, Inc., 6361
Levitt, Abraham, 6361
Levitt, Alfred, 6361
Levitt, Alvin T., 302
Levitt, AnneMarie, 5361
Levitt, Jeanne, 3832
Levitt, Madelyn, 3433
Levitt, Madelyn M., 3458
Levitt, Mark, 3832
Levitt, Matthew L., 4738
Levitt, Michael J., 5360
Levitt, Mortimer, 5361
Levitt, Patricia, 5360
Levitt, Randall, 3832
Levitt, Richard S., 3832
Levitt, William, 6361
Levitt-Hirsch, Elizabeth, 5361
Levkovich, Natalie, 8041
Levoff, Janet, 5623
Levoff, Jeffery, 2807
Levovitz, Marilyn, 4143
Levy, Alan, 2034
Levy, Austin T., 4144
Levy, Brooke, 3512
Levy, Carol, 4487, 8795
Levy, Daniel, 6723
Levy, David B., 6767, 6768
Levy, Edward C., Co., 4487
Levy, Edward C., Jr., 4487
Levy, Ellen, 4487
Levy, Ellen White, 1819
Levy, Gregg H., 5562, 5655, 5789, 5855, 5952, 5977, 6036, 6207, 6524, 6576, 6622, 7028, 7110, 7124
Levy, Harold J., 6228
Levy, Harold O., 9417
Levy, Jill S., 6443
Levy, Joseph W., 6443
Levy, Karen, 6362
Levy, Kenneth, 7893
Levy, Larry, 5362
Levy, Leon, 6363, 6364, 6525
Levy, Linda Dresner, 4487
Levy, Meyer, 4173
Levy, Paul, 6362
Levy, Peter, 6260
Levy, Reynold, 6693
Levy, Richard D., 1312
Levy, Robert, 3060
Levy, S. Jay, 6363
Levy, Sarah K., 6379
Levy, Saul D., 5984
Levy, Sid, 7318
Levy-Pounds, Nekima, Esq., 4714
Lew, Kim Y., 5747
Lewandowski, Rick J., 1821
Lewin, Dan'l, 1166
Lewin, Dora, 3971
Lewin, John, 6768, 6769
Lewin, Stephen, 6768, 6769
Lewis and Early, 8756
Lewis Broadcasting Corp., 2503
Lewis Charitable Annuity Trust, Henrietta J., 2985
Lewis Family Trust, 1035
Lewis Motor Co., J.C., 2503
Lewis Revocable Trust, George T., 7257
Lewis, A. Bart, 4488
Lewis, A. Daniel, 4606
Lewis, Adam, 1368
Lewis, Alan E., 4076
Lewis, Andy, 1511
Lewis, Anne, 8228
Lewis, Arnet, 7256
Lewis, Beverly J., 837
Lewis, Bonita, 4606
Lewis, Bonnie, 4606
Lewis, Bradford H., 1447
Lewis, Carol, 9691
Lewis, Carol A., 1447
Lewis, Charles A., 2980
Lewis, Christina S.N., 6365
Lewis, Christopher, 9380
Lewis, Claudette R., 8228
Lewis, Cornelius A., 3671
Lewis, Craig, 3850
Lewis, Craig C., 1211
Lewis, D. Scott, 2503
Lewis, Dale, 6350
Lewis, Dan, 4606
Lewis, Daniel E., 3393
Lewis, Daniel R., 2126
Lewis, David, 5262
Lewis, David Baker, 4371
Lewis, Denise J., 4498
Lewis, Diana, 2212, 4827
Lewis, Diana D., 4689
Lewis, Donna, 3757
Lewis, Dorothy V., 2502
Lewis, Earl, 6470
Lewis, Edward D., 2212
Lewis, Eileen J., 192
Lewis, Elizabeth, 4408
Lewis, Emily S., 4174
Lewis, Emma, 1532
Lewis, George, 4174
Lewis, George R., 2955
Lewis, George T., 7257
Lewis, Greta Roemer, 3289
Lewis, Guy, 9290
Lewis, Harriet R., 4076
Lewis, Heather, 7481
Lewis, Henrietta G., 6109
Lewis, J. Christian, 2503
Lewis, J.C., III, 2503
Lewis, J.C., Jr., 2503
Lewis, James E., 7257
Lewis, Jan, 4820
Lewis, Janet P., 9432
Lewis, Janet R., 134
Lewis, Jennifer L., 8957
Lewis, Jeremiah T., 4108
Lewis, Joanna M., 7928
Lewis, Joanne McNeil, 6464
Lewis, John, 289, 3851
Lewis, John C., Jr., 2503
Lewis, John D., 4371
Lewis, John T., 1398
Lewis, Julius, 2659, 3115
Lewis, Karen J., 5223
Lewis, Kendall B., 9455
Lewis, Laura B., 7610
Lewis, Leon E., Jr., 4826
Lewis, Lillian, 5362
Lewis, Lisa S., 4174, 4216
Lewis, Loida N., 6365
Lewis, Lori, 3261
Lewis, Lynn, 4174
Lewis, M. Patricia, 2212
Lewis, M. Todd, 3373
Lewis, Marc, 5393, 8790
Lewis, Marley B., 2126
Lewis, Matt, 9146
Lewis, Michael, 744, 7496
Lewis, Michael J., 7915
Lewis, Michaela, 5055
Lewis, Mildred, 7256
Lewis, Nancy, 3552, 8908
Lewis, Nancy V., 2503
Lewis, Nathan, 1020
Lewis, Pamela J., 718
Lewis, Patsy A., 4327
Lewis, Peter C., 2980
Lewis, Philip D., 2212
Lewis, Philip E., 6470
Lewis, Rachel, 4357
Lewis, Reginald F., 6365
Lewis, Richard H., 1447
Lewis, Robert, 8736
Lewis, Roderick W., 2637
Lewis, S. Wistar, 2503
Lewis, Sarah Elizabeth, 7050
Lewis, Sheila, 9014
Lewis, Sherry L., 7719
Lewis, Shirley Long, 137
Lewis, Stan, 229
Lewis, Stephen, 1210
Lewis, Stephen R., Jr., 4753, 4792
Lewis, Susan, 4488
Lewis, Thomas Edward, 2450
Lewis, Thomas W., 134
Lewis, Thomas W., Jr., 134
Lewis, Timothy P., 2212
Lewis, Tom, 5170
Lewis, Troy, 9307
Lewis, Vernie W., 9460
Lewis, W. Ashton, 9391
Lewis, Walter G., Rev., 1882
Lewis, Walter N., 2503
Lewis, Wendy, 5529
Lewis, William, 7992
Lewis-Raymond, Jane R., 7285
Lewis-Sheets, Leslie, 3288
Lewnes, Ann, 1734
Lexington 55th St., 6768
Lexvold, Thomas, 2796
Leyba, Yvonne, 249
Leyden, Timothy M., 1316
Leyden-Dunbar, Eleanor, 1889
Leydorf, Fred L., 743
Leyhe, Denise, 8374
Lezak, Brigid S. Flanigan, 6667
LG&E Energy Corp., 3586

Link, William M., Jr., 4825
Linker, Susan B., 1721
Links, Inc., The, 2294
Linn Charitable Remainder Unitrust, Ruby W., 4149
Linn Foundation, Ruby Winslow & Lavon Parker, 4149
Linn, Dawn M., 8040
Linn, Milman H., III, 7565
Linn, Rebecca, 5396
Linn, Ruby W., 4149
Linn, Timothy H., 7565
Linnartz, John H., 5424
Linnartz, Victoria, 5200
Linnehan, Janet Bodnar, 1922
Linnell, Jon, 4730
Linnen, Mary Lou, 3393
Linnert, Terrence G., 7213
Linsky, Michele A., 8122
Linsley, Sarah, 2831
Lintecum, Laura H., 3519
Lintilhac Annuity Trust I, Claire D., 9365
Lintilhac Annuity Trust II, Claire D., 9365
Lintilhac, Claire Malcolm, 9365
Lintilhac, Crea S., 9365
Lintilhac, Louise S., 9365
Lintilhac, Paul S., 9365
Lintilhac, Philip M., 9365
Lintilhac, William S., 9365
Linton, Donald C., 3768
Linton, Jeffrey, 433
Linton, Rebecca, 3768
Linton, Tina, 7382
Lintott, James W., 7019
Lintzenich, James C., 3345
Lintzenich, Madonna, 1990
Linville NTC Charitable Lead Unity Trust, 6376
Linville Trust, 6376
Linville, Clarence, 6376
Linville, Don, 3554
Linville, James Coker, 6376
Linville, John Evans, 6376
Linville, Susanne Gay, 6376
Linz, Brigitte Loewy, 6389
Linz, Peter Erwin, 6389
Liparidis, George S., 1140
Lipford, Rocque E., 4539
Liphardt, Constance M., 2118
Lipman, Benjamin H., 5364
Lipman, Beverly S., 5364
Lipman, Eric M., 9469
Lipman, Howard W., 5364
Lipman, Jean, 5364
Lipman, Jeanette S., 9469
Lipman, Peter W., 5364
Lipman, Robert S., 8550
Lipman, Timothy E., 5364
Lipnick, Jonathan, 6390
Lipoff, Norman H., 2020, 2301
Lipp, Jeffrey D., 6377
Lipp, Robert I., 6377
Lipp, Wendy A., 6377
Lippard, Cathy, 7781
Lipper, Evelyn, 5939
Lippman, Al, 3623
Lippman, Alexandra, 843
Lippman, James M., 843
Lippman, Jerome, 7542
Lippman, Linda, 843
Lippman, Matthew, 843
Lippman, Michael, 6852
Lipschultz, S. Brian, 4620
Lipschutz, Lester, 8131
Lipshutz, Patty, 6855
Lipsitz Administrative Trust, Helen V., 8144
Lipsitz, Helen, 8144
Lipsitz, Herman, 8144
Lipsky, Burton G., 6427
Lipstein, Sanford, 8292
Lipton, Evelyn Segal, 6232
Lipton, Holly, 6896
Lipton, Louis, 6349
Lipton, Martin, 7040
Liquidity Solutions Inc., 5221
Lirakis, Christopher, 2066
Lirakis, Stephen, 2066
Lirakis, Susan, 2066
Lisa, James P., Jr., 8293
Lisagor, Terri E., 1287
Lischick, Karen E., 1937
Lischick, Peter, 1937
Lisher, Mary K., 3342
Lisi, Ann T., 4327
Lisi, Joan, 6571
Lisker, Marc, 8805
Liss, Cathy, 7091
Liss, Tom, 3291
Lissau, W.R., 7809
List, Bobye G., 6304
Lister, Alan, 7756
Listi, Frank, 633
Liston, David J., 382
Liszewski, Robert J., 2398
Litan, Robert E., 1679
Litchfield, Melanie, 8527
Litchfield, Ruth, 3490
Litman, David S., 8807, 8987
Litman, Malia A., 8987
Litman, Mark, 670
Litow, Stan, 2121
Litow, Stanley S., 6203
Litowitz, Arthur, 2218
Litowitz, Budd, 2218
Litowitz, Donna, 2218
Litowitz, Robert, 2218
Litowitz, Susan, 2218
Littauer, Lucius N., 6379
Littel, John E., 9383
Litterman, Robert, 5329, 6872
Little Memorial Trust Fund, Edward H., 8543
Little, Amaris, Dr., 3758
Little, Barbara, 3835, 8953
Little, Barbara J., 3835
Little, Cam W., 7825
Little, Dan, 7793
Little, Fletcher, 7878
Little, Gregory, 1980
Little, Jacqueline, 1980
Little, James, 3835
Little, James M., 3835
Little, Jennifer, 2027
Little, Judith, 1980
Little, Lew, 9171
Little, Lew, Jr., 8676
Little, Louisa, 6065
Little, Nicole C., 3835
Little, Noeleen, 3984
Little, Royal, 8145
Little, Teresa, 6802
Littlefair, Andrew, 9099
Littlefield, Allison J.D., 844
Littlefield, Christopher J., 3411
Littlefield, Edmund W., 844
Littlefield, Edmund W., Jr., 844
Littlefield, James A., Dr., 8459
Littlefield, Nick, 3953
Littlefield, Scott R., 844
LittleJohn, Angus C., 2504
LittleJohn, Angus C., Jr., 2504
Littlejohn, Leslie A., 3135
Littlejohn, Paul D., 3135
Littlejohns, Linda, 5315
Littles, Douglas M., 24
Littleton, Torrey B., 8795
Littmann, Jeffrey C., 4588
Litton Industries, Inc., 9498
Litton, Arthur C., II, 4458
Litwin Foundation, 6545
Litwin, Gordon N., 6804
Litwin, Laura Baskes, 2684
Litwin, Leonard, 6380, 6545
Liu, Amy, 9380
Liu, Anna Luk, 841
Liu, Arthur, 6382
Liu, Erica Sze-Hua, 6381
Liu, Ernest S., 6381
Liu, Hanmin, 4474
Liu, Joan S., 6381
Liu, Peter, 399
Liu, Wyna, 6382
Liu, Xin, 507
Liu, Yvonne, 6382
Livadary, Paul J., 9755
Lively, Arnold D., 9790
Livengood, Julia S., 6841
Liverett, Deborah, 3059
Liveris, Andrew N., 4407
Liveris, Paula A., 4444
Livesay, Jeff, 2765
Livezey, Barbara, 3366
Living Water Foundation, 7846
Livingston, Claudia M., 2499
Livingston, Lanien, 86
Livingston, Lisa K., 8455
Livingston, Martha, 6911
Livingston, Paul H.,Jr., 7266
Livingston, Randy, 1002
Livorna Investments, 293
Livsey, Charles H., 9331, 9344, 9347
Livsey, Herbert C., 9330, 9331, 9344, 9347
Lizardi, Rafael R., 9227
Lizza, Sandra R., 5473
LJS Revocable Trust, 7791, 7794
LKC Foundation, 6600
Llambelis, Lillian, 6546
LLC, Stuhrling Palace, 5981
Llewellyn, Carol, 263
Llewellyn, David, 2075
Llewellyn, John, 263
Llewellyn, Rich, 324
Lloyd Barnas, Patty, 4357
Lloyd Charitable Trust, Harry, 7846
Lloyd, Bill, 3269
Lloyd, Bordman, 5823
Lloyd, Demi, 3530
Lloyd, Edward, 5270
Lloyd, Frances K., 517
Lloyd, Harry J., 3530
Lloyd, Jeanette, 3530
Lloyd, Karen, 1980, 5400
Lloyd, Marcia, 1527
Lloyd, Margene W., 9269
Lloyd, Margene West, 9269
Lloyd, Pamela, 517
Lloyd, Ralph, 7846
Lloyd, Randy, 3278
Lloyd, Sophia, 3061
Lloyd, Susan, 9972
Lloyd, Susan L., 2205
Lloyd, Teresa, 7846
Lloyd, Thomas T., 4332
Lloyd, W. James, 517
Lloyd, W.R., Jr., 9269
Lloyd, Warren, 1527
Lloyd, William West, 9269
LLYR Charitable Annuity Trust, 5599
Lo Monaco, Paulette, Sr., 6121
Lo, Angie, 5691
Lo, Bernard, 6105
Lo, Pei-Loh, 2021
Loadcraft Industries, Ltd., 9118
Loba, Suntara, 5527
Lobach, David, 8136
Lobach, Jeffrey, 8351
Lobato, Kathryn, 714
Lobatz, Michael, Dr., 1053
Lobdell, James, 7881
Lobeck, Jr. Trust, William E., 7768
Lobeck, Kathy Taylor, 7768
Lobeck, William E., Jr., 7768
Lobel, Steven E., 5803
Lobert, Sandra, 7394
Lobin, Marshall G., 2676
Lobitz, Roseanne McCathy, 6454
Lobman, Helaine, 9487
Lobo, Donald Ajit, 398
Local Loan Co., 3166
Locane, Jennifer, 7139
Lochen, Richard, Jr., 7992
Lock, Pam, 3277
Lock, Sheri, 1423
Locke, Hubert, 9722
Locke, Jean, 4755
Locke, Kathleen, 2764
Locke-Paddon, William F., 329
Locker, David S., 5980
Lockett, Helen B., 1015
Lockette, Elizabeth, 9341
Lockheed Martin, 9149
Lockheed Martin Corp., 3837
Lockport Savings Bank, 5979
Locks, Gene, 8147
Locks, Sueyun, 8147
Locks, Sueyun Pyo, 8041
Lockshin, Michael D., 6401
Lockwood, Cheryl, 5046
Lockwood, Christina, 9980
Lockwood, Dan, 4373
Lockwood, David, 9321
Lockwood, Dorothy P., 7327
Lockwood, Glenn C., 5389
Lockwood, John, 2609
Lockwood, Susan, 1112
Lockwood, Theodore, 6115
Locniskar, Dana M., 4371
LoCurto, Matthew, 6070
Loda, Laura J., 9558
Loden, Elliot, 2618
Loder, David E., 8013, 8142
Lodwig, Jeanette, 9731
Lodygowski, Karen, 2714
Loeb, Ann R., 7014
Loeb, Arthur L., 6384
Loeb, Charles, Jr., 9780
Loeb, Daniel S., 6383
Loeb, Donald K., 9672
Loeb, Francine, 9672
Loeb, Francine R., 9672
Loeb, John L., Jr., 6385
Loeb, Justus H., 7544
Loeb, Margaret M., 6383
Loeb, Marjorie, 623

Loudermilk, Joey M., 2438, 2507
Loudermilk, Justin M., 2507
Loudermilk, Ramona L., 2507
Loughlin, Caroline K., 3646
Loughlin, Peter, 5171
Loughlin, Thomas G., 9547
Loughlin, Thomas K., 3646
Loughnane, Maureen, 3231
Loughran, John, 1925
Loughrey, F. Joseph, 3345
Loughridge, Mark, 6203
Loughry, Ed C., Jr., 8545
Louie, Gilman, 6431
Louie, May, 841
Louie, Sinclair, 841
Louis Charitable Trust, Henrietta J., 2984, 2985
Louis Charitable Trust, Michael W., 2985
Louis Foundation, John J., 2985
Louis Trust, Henrietta J, 2985
Louis Trust, Michael W., 2985
Louis, A. Andrew R., 9174
Louis, Hank, 9341
Louis, Herbert J., 2984
Louis, John J., Jr., 2985
Louis, Josephine P., 2985
Louis, Jr. Charitable Annuity Trust, John J., 2985
Louis, Jr. Trust, John J., 2985
Louis, Michael W., 2984
Louisville Timber Co., 3588
Lounsbery Foundation Trust, Richard, Inc., 1926
Lounsbery, Richard, 1926
Lount, Suzanne, 2035
Lourenco, Ana, 8383
Lourenco, Margaret, 1223
Lourenco, Vera, 5725
Lourie, Kylee, 1516
Lourie, Robert, 1807
Lovaas, Helen, 597
Lovaas, Leeland M., 597
Lovallo, Michael A., 3094
Lovato, Walther, 1016
Love Family Charitable Lead Trust, 2508
Love Trust, Audrey B., 7258
Love, Davis M., III, 9470
Love, Dennis M., 2508
Love, Gay M., 2508
Love, Heather, 3529
Love, Jeff, 3282
Love, John, 1440
Love, Kim, 9998
Love, Paula, 7774
Love, Robin B., 9470
Love, Vincent B., 6049
Lovejoy, Mary F., 8429
Lovejoy, Stuart, 1650
Lovejoy, Susan, 1650
Lovelace, Charles E., Jr., 7268
Lovelace, James B., 375, 751
Lovelace, Jeffrey K., 751
Lovelace, John D., 9480
Lovelace, Jon B., 751
Lovelace, Lillian P., 751
Lovelace, Robert W., 751
Lovelace, Sarah E., 9480
Loveless, Barbara, 342
Lovell, Lura M., 175
Lovett, Anne R., 4151
Lovett, Daniel Clay, 2138
Lovett, Richard, 362
Lovett, Tiffany W., 4455, 4466, 4510
Loving Co., T.A., 7161
Loving, Rush, 2074
Lovvorn, Andrew, 2439
Low, Roger M., 1079
Lowder, Catherine, 45, 2509
Lowder, Charlotte, 2509
Lowder, Heather Anne, 2509
Lowder, James K., 45, 2509
Lowder, Jarman F., 2509
Lowder, Joshua K., 45
Lowder, Margaret B., 45
Lowder, Thomas H., 2509
Lowdermilk, James E., 7178
Lowe Charitable Trust, Erma, 8993
Lowe's Food Stores, Inc., 7205
Lowe, David, 4666
Lowe, Elizabeth, 1013
Lowe, Erma, 8993
Lowe, Jane K., 46
Lowe, Ken, 7659
Lowe, Mary Ralph, 8993
Lowe, Megan, 2393
Lowe, Richard, 2393
Lowe, Sandra Lois, 2393
Lowe, Terry D., 239
Lowe, Tom, 8601
Lowell Museum Corp., 4152
Lowell, James H., II, 3916
Lowell, John, 4153
Lowell, Monica E., 4327
Lowell, Sara M., 878
Lowell, William A., 3969, 4033, 4149, 4153, 4201
Lowenfels, Fred M., 6907
Lowenstein Holding Company Inc., 1633
Lowenstein, Carol, 1633
Lowenstein, John, 2915
Lowenstein, Leon, 6395
Lowenstein, Michael, 6320
Lowenstein, Michael B., 1633
Lowenstein, Richard, 6320
Lowenstein, Steven S., 2749
Lower, Jackie, 3396
Lower, James Paul, 774
Lowery, Darlene, 7444
Lowery, Dee, 7367
Lowery, Dolores J., 7455
Lowery-Born, Beryl, 3497
Lowes, 7214
Lowet, Henry A., 6379
Lowi, Irwin, 913
Lowinske, Keith, 9768
Lowitz, Barry, 850
Lowitz, Joseph, 850
Lowitz, Linda, 850
Lowitz, Robert, 672
Lowndes III Trust, 4154
Lowndes, Henrietta M., 4154
Lowndes, William, III, 4154
Lowney, Jeremiah J., Jr., 1703
Lowney, Meghan, 1732
Lowrance, Jim, 3484
Lowry, Glenn D., 6470
Lowry, Karin, 3193
Lowry, Michael, 6903
Lowry, Robert L., 3372
Lowry, Scott T., 5202
Lowther, David, 7835
Lowther, Fred, 7835
Lowther, Steven, 7835
Lowther/Wells Fargo Advisors, Stan, LLC, 7835
Lox, William, 898
Loy, Alma Lee, 2166
Loyalty Development Co., Ltd., 2596
Loyce, James E., Jr., 921
Loyd, L. Karen, 1441
Loyd, Robert, 1441
Loynd, Michael R., 4914
Loynd, Richard B., 4914
Loyrette, Henri, 3186
Lozano, Carlos A., M.D., Dr., 9234
Lozano, Jose, 6868
Lozano, Monica, 1307, 6724
Lozeau, Donnalee, 5182
Lozick, Catherine, 7545
Lozick, Catherine L., 7545
Lozick, E.A., 7537
Lozick, Edward A., 7545
Lozier, Allan, 5065
Lozier, Dianne, 5065
Lozier, Dianne S., 5065
Lozier, Sandy, 5065
Lozier, Susan, 5065
LPL Finanacial, 8026
LRFA LLC, 1310
LRO 10-Year Charitable Lead Annuity Trust, The, 6597
LRO 15-Year Charitable Lead Annuity Trust, The, 6597
LSC Design Inc., 8127
LSUS, 3657
Lubar, David J., 9894, 9907
Lubar, Joan P., 9894
Lubar, John P., 9894
Lubar, Marianne S., 9894
Lubar, Sheldon B., 9894
Lubash, Barbara N., 367
Lubbers, Arend, 4447
Lubberstedt, Wes, 5062
Lubchenco, Jane, 1006
Lubcher, Frederick, 6387, 6403, 6785
Luber, Charles B., 4934
Luberski, Timothy E., 852
Lubetkin, Andrew, 9074
Lubin, Joseph I., 2128, 6071
Lubin, Kate E., 4155
Lubin, Nancy K., 4155
Lubin, Richard K., 4155
Lubin, Simon, 4155
Lubken, Robert, 5089
Lubleley, Michael D., 9511
Lubrizol Corp., The, 7546
Lucas, Ann Violet, 1206
Lucas, Arthur M., 2431
Lucas, Benjamin F., II, 3850
Lucas, Charles C., III, 7195
Lucas, Christopher B., 853
Lucas, Donald A., 853
Lucas, Donald L., 853
Lucas, Donald Lee, 1808
Lucas, Donna, 411
Lucas, George W., Jr., 854, 855
Lucas, John T., 3837
Lucas, John W., 853
Lucas, Larry, 1261
Lucas, Nancy, 1261
Lucas, Peter, 4646
Lucas, Sally Steadman, 1808
Lucas, Stuart E., 1225
Lucas, William L., 319
Lucasfilm Foundation, 854
Lucasfilm Ltd., 854, 855
Lucchese, John J., 3857
Lucckese, Deborah G., 9552
Luce, Clare Boothe, 6398
Luce, H. Christopher, 6398
Luce, Henry R., 6398
Luce, Michael D., 21
Luce, Priscilla M., 8071
Lucent Technologies Inc., 5190
Lucero, Priscilla, 1381, 1504
Lucht, Jennifer, Dr., 3335
Luciano, Kristine, Jr., 9793
Lucien, Kent, 2588
Luck Stone Corp., 9472
Luck, Charles S., III, 9472
Luck, Charles S., IV, 9472
Luck, Ted, 3758
Luckey, Tom, 4375
Luckow Corp., Robert W., The, 6399
Luckow, Audrey J., 6399
Luckow, Michael P., 6399
Luckow, Robert, 6399
Luckow, Robert W., 6399
Luckow, Stephanie A., 6399
Lucy, William P., 1671
Ludaway, Natalie, 1893
Ludcke, Eleanor R., 4157
Ludcke, Gipp L., 4157
Luddy, Robert L., 7259
Ludington, Thomas L., 4444
Ludlam, Charles Stewart, 1572
Ludwick, Arthur J., 856
Ludwick, Eileen, 856
Ludwick, Erik Arthur, 856
Ludwick, Sarah Lynne, 856
Ludwig, Bob, 22
Ludwig, Carol, 1927
Ludwig, Eugene A., 1927
Ludwig, James J., 3553
Ludwig, Robert A., 6153
Ludwig, S. Peter, 7031
Luebke, Catherine, 4646
Lueck, Jody, 9905
Lueck, Laura Kellner, 9877
Lueck, Martin R., 4754
Luedeke, J. Barton, 5391
Luedeking, Otto, 7405
Lueders, Wayne R., 9805
Luehs, Beverly, 5229
Luers, William H., 7009
Luetke, Mark D., 7686
Luetkemeyer, John A., Jr., 3872
Lufrano, Robert, 2101
Luftglass, Richard E., 6990
Luger, Ellen Goldberg, 4661
Lugo, Rene Pinto, 8353
Luh, Bing, 5398
Luhman, Dave, 3282
Luhn, Dave, 9615
Lui Trust, Francis C., 6400
Lui, Francis C., 6400
Lui, Lawrence, 6400
Lui, Livia S. Wan, 6400
Lui, Livia Wan, 6400
Lui, Yvonne, 6400
Luisa, Jennifer F., 4086
Lujan, Lisa, 8819
Lukaacs, Joan, 3249
Lukacs, George, 3249
Lukas, Alan, 3682
Luke, Cathy, 2602
Luke, John A., Jr., 9416
Lukens, Wanda C., 7688
Lukianov, Alex, 975
Lukianov, Kathy, 975
Lukowski, Stanley J., 4030
Lumarda, Joseph M., 368
Lumbermens Mutual Casualty Co., 2955
Lumbert, Elizabeth, 4502
Lumia, Melanie M., 8152
Lummis, Fred R., 3818

Lummis, Ransom, 9186
Lumpkin, Benjamin I., 2986
Lumpkin, Besse Adamson, 2986
Lumpkin, Brent, 3625
Lumpkin, John R., 5329
Lumpkin, Mary G., 2986
Lumpkin, Richard Adamson, 2986
Lumpkin, Richard Anthony, 2986
Luna, Paul J., 92
Lund, Alison, 106
Lund, Arthur K., 388, 629
Lund, Bradford D., 857
Lund, Cynthia D., 1111
Lund, Jay, 4601
Lund, Jeramy, 9311
Lund, John T., 1682
Lund, Margaret T., 9919
Lund, Michelle A., 857
Lund, Sharon D., 857
Lund, Steven J., 9340
Lund-Jurgensen, Kirsten, 6633
Lunda, Larry, 9895, 9896
Lunda, Lydia, 9896
Lunda, Milton, 9896
Lunday, Lisa J., 406
Lundberg, Dana, 5766
Lundberg, Jan, 3340
Lundberg, Peter, 9897
Lundebrek, Jan, 4768
Lundeen, Dean, 2792
Lunder, Alan, 3697
Lunder, Marc, 3697
Lunder, Paula, 3697
Lunder, Peter, 3186, 3678, 3697
Lunder, Steven, 3697
Lundevall, Jessica Kaplan, 2947
Lundevall, Kaja, 2947
Lundevall, Tellef, 2947
Lundgren, Jessica Anne, 1693
Lundgren, Tracey Kay, 1693
Lundin, Craig, 1263
Lundin, Fred T., 9834
Lundin, Gloria, 2766
Lundquist, Ingrid, 7629
Lundqvist, Bertil, 6911
Lundy, Peter L. L., 3446
Lungren, Daniel E., 756
Lungren, Lisa, 822
Luning, Christopher, 7917
Lunn, Scott, 109
Lunney, J. Robert, 6339
Lunsford, David H., 9795
Lunsford, Holt, 8723
Lunsford, Margaret, 7483
Lunsford, Michael O., 3286
Lunsford, Walter, 7483
Lunt, Thomas D., 7074
Luntz, Gregory W., 7673
Lupberger, Ed, 4827
Lupfer, Jonathan B., 7543
Lupfer, Sarah H., 7543
Lupin, Arnold M., 3652
Lupin, E. Ralph, 3652
Lupin, Jay, 3652
Lupin, Lisa R., 3652
Lupin, Louis J., 3652
Lupin, Michael, 3652
Lupin, Samuel, 3652
Lupin, Timothy, 3652
Luplow, Trish, 4532
Lupo, Elizabeth Canning, 2733
Lupton, C.A., 8730
Lupton, David, 9147
Lupton, T. Cartter, 8599
Lurcy, Georges, 6402
Luria, Alayna, 7836
Luria, Don, 101
Lurie Revocable Trust, Connie L., 858
Lurie Revocable Trust, Robert A., 858
Lurie Trust, Robert H. & Ann, 2987
Lurie, Alison, 5585
Lurie, Andrew, 2987
Lurie, Ann, 2987
Lurie, Ari A., 641
Lurie, Benjamin, 2987
Lurie, Bob A., 858
Lurie, Brian L., Rabbi, 553
Lurie, Caroline, 553
Lurie, Cary, 5108
Lurie, Cathy J., 4162
Lurie, Connie L., 858
Lurie, Daniel, 742, 1223
Lurie, Daniel L., 641
Lurie, Elizabeth, 2987
Lurie, Helen, 6403
Lurie, Jeffrey R., 4158, 4162
Lurie, Robert, 2987
Lurie, Robert A., 858
Lusardi, Henry, 4094
Luscomb, Brian, 736
Luse, Susan M., 3375
Lusk, Barbara, 7180
Lusk, Charles M., III, 8816
Luskey, Randolph K., 5760
Luskin, Meyer, 613
Lust, Angela, 8660
Lust, Corby L., 144
Lustberg, Lawrence S., 5270
Lustenberg, Anna, 5412
Lusthoff, Craig, 2963
Lute, Jane, 4102
Luter, Francis, 9535
Luter, Joseph W., III, 9535
Luter, Joseph W., IV, 9535
Luterman, William, 8137
Lutes, Dennis L., 8671
Lutgring, Michael D., 3622
Luth, Marcy, 5044
Luther Family Ford, 4698
Luther King Capital Management, 1116
Luther Nissan Kia, 4698
Luther Trust, Frances R., 7548
Luther, Cathy, 9916
Luther, Charles David, 4698
Luther, Jon, 4196
Luther, Jon L., 4026
Luther, Rudy Dan, 4698
Luther, Toby, 7845
Lutheran Brotherhood, 9956
Lutheran Brotherhood Research Corp., 9956
Lutiger, Jim, 9950
Lutnick, Howard, 7012
Lutron Electronics Co., Inc., 8151
Luttrell, Claudia Skaggs, 9302
Lutz & Co., PC, 5095
Lutz, Calvin C., 4520
Lutz, Debra, 4344
Lutz, Gail, 5095
Lutz, Garman, 9615
Lutz, Nancy, 5095
Lutz, Robert S., 7424
Lutz, Sarah, 4156
Lutz, Theodore C., 9445
Luwa, Edwin, 810
Lux, Michael, 1880
Luxembourg, Robert, 5921
Luzzatto, Ernesto V., 7035
Luzzi, Richard D., 8334
LVM Limited Partnership, 4989
LWG Family Partners, 6337
Lydell Inc., 9914
Lyden, Shawn, 7496
Lyford, Shelley M., 1314
Lygren, Rolf, 676
Lykins, Elizabeth Welch, 4547
Lyle, Bobby B., 8773
Lyle, Jo, 3532
Lyle, Pat, 9439
Lyle, Susan Halle, 118
Lyles, Thomas W., Jr., 8781
Lyman, Charles, 4734
Lyman, Elizabeth, 5724
Lyman, Mary Alice, 6903
Lyman, Princeton, 1935
Lyman, Rachel, 8995
Lyman, Zeldy, 3990
Lynagh, John J., 5662
Lynch Trust Co., Merrill, 5386
Lynch, Allen, 9437
Lynch, Amy, 3417
Lynch, Annette, 7340
Lynch, Carolyn, 4159
Lynch, Carolyn A., 4159
Lynch, Charles R., 6404
Lynch, Colleen, 5791
Lynch, Con, 7852
Lynch, Debbie, 8098
Lynch, Denise, 8314
Lynch, Dennis, 7260
Lynch, Donald D., 7260
Lynch, Jennifer, 7231
Lynch, Joe, 9605
Lynch, Kevin J., 5398
Lynch, Laural, 584
Lynch, Linda, 2817
Lynch, M. Judith, 8060
Lynch, Maria M., 7136
Lynch, Maureen A., 7428
Lynch, Patrick, 9576
Lynch, Paul E., 4068
Lynch, Paul M., 8509
Lynch, Peter S., 4159
Lynch, Richard, 648
Lynch, Robert L.K., 8952
Lynch, Robert W., 2936
Lynch, Ronald P., 6404
Lynch, Russell E., Jr., 32
Lynch, Scott D., 2232
Lynch, Susan E., 6404
Lynch, Thomas, 1210
Lynch, William, 6661
Lynch, William O.J., 7189
Lyneis, Mary M., 4391, 4582
Lynham, John M., Jr., 9537
Lynn, Byran L., 780
Lynn, Cassie, 8532
Lynn, Christine E., 2221
Lynn, E.M., 2221
Lynn, E.M., Mrs., 2221
Lynn, Edward R., 3490
Lynn, Elizabeth R., 8449
Lynn, Heidi, 9370
Lynn, Joann, 8532
Lynn, Karen, 3411
Lynn, Linda, 8862
Lynn, Maureen, 7446
Lynne, Janine, 7218
Lynton Asset LP, 6405
Lynton, Carol, 6405
Lynton, Lili, 6405
Lynton, Marion, 6405
Lynton, Michael, 6405
Lyon, C.H. Randolph, 9811
Lyon, E.H., 7769
Lyon, Marina Munoz, 4745
Lyon, Melody, 7769
Lyon, Wilford C., Jr., 2130
Lyons, Barbara, 4795
Lyons, Becky, 3293
Lyons, Bente S., 2222
Lyons, Bill, 4937
Lyons, Charlie, 3972
Lyons, Daniel M., 2222
Lyons, Dianne M., 3485
Lyons, John, 5171
Lyons, Leo M., 6242
Lyons, Louis, 2732
Lyons, Mark A., 9012
Lyons, Mary A., 859
Lyons, Patrick, 9826
Lyons, Patti, 2609
Lyons, Phillip N., 859
Lyons, Richard T., 8996
Lyons, Robert, Jr., 1651
Lyons, Sammie, 8996
Lyons, Sammie W., 8996
Lyons, Terrence M., 3341
Lyons, Thomas F., 3991
Lyons, Tim, 4562
Lyons, Timothy L., 7805
Lyons, Volina V., 8479
Lyons-Gardner, Melissa, 9012
Lyons-Spier, Michelle, 9012
Lysinger, Todd, 4375
Lysne, Lee, 5060
Lytel, Bertha Russ, 860
Lytle, Julie W., 423, 918, 1139
Lytvinenko, Linda, 7341
Lyu-Volckhausen, Grace, 6979
Lyu-Volckhausen, Sharon, 6979

M & T Invesment Group, 8307
M & T Trust Co., 7073
M&I Bank, 9861
M&R Management, 6545
M&T Bank, 6359, 6406, 7007, 8046
M&T Bank, N.A., 3862
M&T Trust Co., 3903, 6486, 6966
M.B. Insurance, Inc., 644
M.D. Orthopaedics Inc., 3471
M.D.C. Holdings, Inc., 1450
M/I Homes, Inc., 7550
M/I Schottenstein Homes, Inc., 7550
Ma'a, Stacie, 573
Maahs, Frederick J., 7989
Maar, William P., 3369
Maas, George E., 4699
Maas, J. David, 3345
Maas, Patricia A., 4699
Mabe, Emily A., 3374
Mabee, J.E., 7770
Mabee, Joe, Sr., 7770
Mabee, Joseph Guy, Jr., 7770
Mabee, L.E., 7770
Mabie Trust, Inez, 863
Mabie, Inez, 863
Mabie, J. Clinton, 101
Mabie, James W., 3079
Mabie, William J., 863
Mabry, Michelle, 4829
Mabry, Rhett N., 7195
Mabry, Tim, 7876
MacAffer, John A., 5803
MacAleer, R. James, 8249

MacAllister, Jim, 1392
MacArthur Foundation, Catherine T., 3090
MacArthur Foundation, John D., 3090
MacArthur Foundation, John D. and Catherine T., 2805
MacArthur, Catherine T., 2989
MacArthur, Deborah A., 5312
MacArthur, J. Roderick, 2990
MacArthur, John D., 2989, 3113
MacArthur, John R., 2990
MacArthur, Solange D., 2990
MacArthur, Thomas C., 5312
Macaskill, Bridget, 1781
Macaulay, Kim, 272
Macauley, Victoria J., 8307
MacBride, Teri, 8040
MacCallum, Ian, 5300
Macchia, John, 4540
MacClarence, Margaret P., 6639
MacCloud Investment Company, LLC, 58
MacCormick, A. Malcolm, 7104
MacCowatt, Thomas H., 5310
MacCutcheon, James, 3756
MacDermott, Kristin Bishop, 8636
Macdonald, Agnes, 6802
MacDonald, Ann, 5482
Macdonald, Anne F., 1166
MacDonald, Beth, 3283
MacDonald, Bruce, 3884
MacDonald, Corey Fuller, 5172
MacDonald, John, 4372
MacDonald, John A., 4905
MacDonald, Kristine Lubar, 9894
Macdonald, Maybelle Clark, 7866
MacDonald, Rhonda J., 9561
MacDonald, Scott, 3700
Macdonnell, Melissa M., 4145
MacDonnell, Melissa M., 9723
MacDougall, Peter, 1116
MacEwen, Bruce, 2454
Macfarland, Christina M., 2032
Macfarlane, Alex, 865
MacFarlane, Aubrey Sage, 9469
MacFarlane, J. Thomas, 4416
Macfarlane, Jessica, 865
Macfarlane, Katherine, 865
Macfarlane, Nicole, 865
Macfarlane, Roger I., 865
Macfarlane, Ruth B., 865
Macfarlane, Taryn, 865
MacFarlene, John, 4800
MacFie, Valerie, 6878
Macgill, Frank S., 2548
MacGillivray, James B., 3723
MacGillivray, Stephen, 8444
MacGlashan, Catherine D., 6784
MacGovern, Rob, 1765
MacGregor, David L., 9951
MacGuire, Betty, 8825
Mach, John R., Jr., 6144
Machamer, Susan, 2000
Macht, Amy, 3766
Machtinger, Sidney, 1306
Machtinger, Sidney J., 1309
Machtley, H. Ronald K., 8429
Machtley, Ronald K., 8356
MacIlwinen, Frances G., 8481
MacIntosh, John, 7723
Macioce, Frank, 5473
Mack Oil Co., 7772
Mack, Charlotte S., 1088
Mack, Christy K., 6411
Mack, David, 5366, 6412
Mack, Debra, 80
Mack, Dianne, 6148
Mack, Earle I., 6412
Mack, John E., IV, 5808
Mack, John J., 5684, 5917, 6411
Mack, John W., 1307
Mack, Judith A., 9996
Mack, Phyllis, 5367
Mack, Richard, 5367, 6412, 7621
Mack, Richard L., 4722
Mack, Roszell, III, 6087
Mack, Ruth, 6412
Mack, Stephen, 5367
Mack, Thomas, 80
Mack, William, 5367
Mackall, Corinne, 7640
Mackall, John, 1291, 5139
Mackall, John R., 1267, 5125
Mackarey, Paula, 8275
MacKay Manufacturing, 975
Mackay, Calder M., 907
Mackay, Leo S., 3837
MacKay, Malcolm, 5718
Mackay, Richard N., 907
Mackay, Robert B., 6043
MacKay, Robert B., 6905
Mackay, William, 588
Macke, Fred, 3253
Mackenzie Trust, 1809
MacKenzie, Charles E., 7993
Mackenzie, Doug, 936
Mackenzie, Douglas, 1809
MacKenzie, Douglas, 5395
MacKenzie, George, 5404
Mackenzie, Gloria, 2224
Mackenzie, Gloria C., 2224
MacKenzie, Kenneth Collins, 5232
Mackenzie, Melinda A., 2224
MacKenzie, Robert K., 8356
Mackenzie, Shawn, 1809
MacKenzie, Sophia, 866
Mackenzie, Wendy, 8084
MacKenzie, Wendy, 8085
Mackessey, Richard, 5253
Mackey, Bruce B., 4489
Mackey, Frank, 8908
Mackey, John P., 9276
Mackey, Robert B., 4489
Mackey, Stanley D., 4489
Mackey, Wendy, 7955
Mackey, William K., 3998, 4320
Mackey, William T., 3998
Mackey, Winnie Crane, 3998
MacKinnon, Kathleen, 5115
Mackler, Alexander, 7910
Mackler, Harvey, 7910
Macklin Family Charitable Trust, Gordon S., 3838
Macklin Family Charitable Trust, Marilyn C., 3838
Macklin, Gordon, 3838
Macklin, Marilyn, 3838
Macklin, Thomas, 3455
Macklin, Tony, 8100
Mackston, Jack, Hon., 6858
MacLachlan, Don, 8550
MacLaury, Bruce, 1916
MacLean, Brian, 4783
MacLeay, Thomas H., 9368
Maclellan, Christopher, 8601
MacLellan, Christopher H., 8600
MacLellan, Daniel O., 8600
MacLellan, Hugh O., Jr., 8544, 8600
Maclellan, Hugh O., Jr., 8601
Maclellan, Kathrina H., 8602
Maclellan, R.L., Mrs., 8601
MacLellan, Robert H., 8544
Maclellan, Robert H., 8601, 8602
Maclellan, Robert J., 8601
MacLeod, Marcia, 7807
Macleod, R. Malcolm, 2174
MacLeod, Richard, 98
Maclure, Mac, 3779
MacMahon, Sarah, 1810
MacMahon, Thomas P., 1810
MacMaster, Donald F., Jr., 5745
MacMaster, Frances W., 5745
MacMaster, John, 4370
MacMichael, H. Ross, 1024
MacMilan, Marsha, 4628
MacMillan 1989 Trust, W., 4799
MacMillan, A.S. Pat, 8601
MacMillan, Albert, 8602
MacMillan, Alissa C., 6413
MacMillan, Courtney D., 1320
MacMillan, Duncan, 6413
MacMillan, Elizabeth S., 4799
MacMillan, Jr. 2003 Charitable Annuity Trust, W., 4799
MacMillan, Jr. 2005 Charitable Annuity Trust, W., 4799
MacMillan, Jr. Charitable Annuity Trust, W., 4799
MacMillan, Jr. Family '74 Trust, W., 4799
MacMillan, Kevin, 6413
MacMillan, Nancy, 6413
MacMillan, Terrence A., 1320
MacMillan, W. Duncan, 4700
MacMillan, Whitney, 4799
MacMillan, Whitney, Jr., 4799
MacMillian, Jamie, 2626
Macmillian, Nivin S., 4700
MacMurray, Katherine, 867
MacNamara, J. Terry, 5070
MacNaughton, Angus A., 868
MacNaughton, Cathy Clement, 868
Macomber, George, 3980
Macomber, Tom, 1288
Macon, Randy, 7742
MacPhail, Carol S., 8043
MacPhee, Barbara C., 3637
MacPhee, Trey, 1113
MacPherson Lead Trust, Joe, 869
MacPherson, Alan D., 9752
MacPherson, Anne L., 869
MacPherson, Cathy, 9999
Macpherson, Cheryl, 9759
MacPherson, James, 869
MacPherson, Jeffrey, 869
MacPherson, Rob, 3272
MacQueen, R. M., 9932
Macropoulous, George J., 4070
Macy, John P., 9965
Madaj, Kim, 4395
Maddalena, Joe, 1149
Madden, Frank, 5316
Madden, Jill Bacon, 7496
Madden, Mark, 638
Madden, Mike, 9925
Madden, Robert V., 787
Madden, Sheryl, 4479
Madden, Sue Ellen, 9527
Madden, Susan C., 8269
Madden, Ted, 4710
Madden, Todd, 4722
Maddocks, Michael D., 9559
Maddox Trust, Margaret, 4834
Maddox, Antoinette, 2432
Maddox, Benjamin W., 5528
Maddox, Catherine M., 5528
Maddox, Dan, 4834
Maddox, Dan W., 8603
Maddox, Don, 5528
Maddox, Elton, 2565
Maddox, Fleetwood, 2533
Maddox, J.F, 5528
Maddox, James M., 5528
Maddox, Jay, 2730
Maddox, Jennifer, 23
Maddox, John L., 5528
Maddox, Laura, 2821
Maddox, Mabel S., 5528
Maddox, Margaret, 8603
Maddox, Margaret H., 4834
Maddox, Patricia, 2390
Maddox, R. Scott, 7305
Maddox, Sue, 5528
Maddox, Susan, 5528
Maddox, Thomas M., 5528
Maddox, Tommye, 8603
Madel, Christopher W., 4754
Madelain, Michel F., 6499
Mader, Cheryl, 9835
Mader, Kathryn E., 3531
Mader-Schaefer, Melissa D., 3531
Madhaven, Ashok, 5223
Madhi, Shabir A., 9625
Madigan, Holly W., 2992
Madigan, John W., 2992
Madigan, Lawrence, 9087
Madipalli, Srin, 6898
Madison Gas and Electric Co., 9898
Madison GMT, 2863
Madison Tyler LLC, 2755
Madison York ALP, 5890
Madison, Lorinda Beth, 8997
Madison, Paula Williams, 3234
Madonia, Eugene C., 9450
Madonia, Peter, 6724
Madover, Arielle Tepper, 5359
Madrazo, Jesus, 4945
Madsen Medical, Inc., 975
Madsen, Bruce, 5095
Madsen, Freda, 9023
Madsen, Matthew J., 4966
Madsen, Sue Lanai W., 9615
Maertens, Mary, 4768
Maes, Dennis, Hon., 1406
Maes, Donna, 1504
Maes, Patricia, 4274
Maestas, Steve, 5511
Maffei, Gregory B., 1448, 1451
Maffei, Maria, 3939
Maffitt, James S., 3823
Magaram, Philip S., 484
Magasinn, Vicki, 497
Magasinn, Vicki Fisher, 900
Magavern, James L., 6153
Magdiel, John L., 2625
Magee, Allison, 1358
Magee, Ian, 6164
Magee, James, 8825
Magee, Karen, 6982
Magee, Marc Porter, 6087
Magee, Marybeth B., 5706
Magen Israel Society, 5768
Mager, Reeva S., 6228
Magerman, David, 8131
Magerman, David M., 8131
Magers, Michael, 8828
Maggelet, Charles E., 9310
Maggelet, Crystal Call, 9310

Maggio-Calkins, Erin, 2766
Maggos, Mark, 3049
Maggs, Deborah, 9404
Maggs, Tom, 3990
Magid, Lawrence, 5423
Magill, Paul K., 2649
Magill, Sherry P., 2075
Magill, Warren, 1355
Maginn, John, 5070
Maglio, Madeline, 1743
Maglio, Michael S., 5232
Maglio, William, 1743
Magliocco, Robert R., 9892
Maglione, Louis A., 7420
Magnan, Monica Lee, 9764
Magnano, Robert J., 9400
Magno, Anthony M., 667
Magnolia Liquor Co., Inc., 3638, 3672
Magnolia Marine Transport Co., 4824
Magnone, Jennifer, 6300
Magnus Asset Management Trust, The, 2993
Magnus, Alexander B., Jr., 2993
Magnus, Victoria, 2993
Magnus, Xia Lynton, 9820
Magnuson, Regina, 4645
Magnuson, Warren, 4613
Mago, Marianne Cracchiolo, 165
Magowan, Mark, 6157
Magowan, Mark E., 5409
Magrath, Charles, 6205
Magri, Patrick, 5381
Magruder Trust, Chesley G., 2225
Magruder, Elaine, 8650
Magruder, G.Brock, Sr., 2225
Magruder, Kathryn, 9201
Magruder, Teresa, 4971
Maguire, Colleen, 5403
Maguire, Daniel, 2812
Maguire, Frances, 6416
Maguire, Frances M., 6416
Maguire, James G., 4329
Maguire, James J., 6416
MaGuire, James, Jr., 6415
MaGuire, Jamie, Jr., 6415
MaGuire, Lisa, 6415
Maguire, Lynne M., 3321
Maguire, Pamela Mitchell, 9029
Maguire, Rowayne, 9652
Maguire, Thomas, 9652
Maguire, Tobey, 1681
Maguire, Walter, 1935
Mah, Adeline Yen, 515
Mah, Robert, 515
Mah, Robert A., 515
Mahaffey, Elizabeth, 4838
Mahaffey, H. William, 1491
Mahaffey, Mike, 3475
Mahan, John, 4334
Mahana, Elliott, 5557
Mahana, Joy, 5557
Maharal Institute, 6229
Mahelis, Jane R., 5420
Maher, Basil, 5295
Maher, Christian, 8001
Maher, M. Brian, 5368
Maher, Miriam Duffy, 5295
Maher, Sandra, 5368
Maher, Shawn, 6755
Maher, Yvonne, 8228
Mahler, Sayeda, 8803
Mahler, Sue, 7431
Mahlmann, Chad, 8699
Mahlmann, Laurie, 8699
Mahmood, Tariq, 5934
Mahmud, Hamid, 160
Mahnken, Sally, 3336
Mahon, Grace M., 8040
Mahon, Nancy, 6408
Mahon, Regina, 6974
Mahone, Rodney K., 2438
Mahoney, Alice, 1650
Mahoney, Elaine, 484
Mahoney, Hildegarde E., 5845
Mahoney, Jackie, 5803
Mahoney, Joe, 4763
Mahoney, Judy, 4614, 4763
Mahoney, Kathleen M., 4727
Mahoney, P. Michael, 9901
Mahoney, William, 1650
Mahony, Anne, 4614
Mahony, Susan, 3340
Mahowald, Douglas A., 7354
Mahowald, Maryanne, 4631
Mai, Anne, 6417
Mai, Chiara, 6417
Mai, James, 6417
Mai, John, 752
Mai, Rebecca, 6417
Mai, Timothy, 6417
Mai, Vincent A., 6417
Mai-Weis, Frieda, 3540
Maico, Daniel, 2257
Maier, Bob, 9108
Maier, David, 2838
Maier, Edward H., 9782
Maier, Jean M., 9914
Maier, Julie, 1387
Maier, Marcel, 2120
Maier, Pauline, 9782
Maier, Peter K., 553
Maier, William J., Jr., 9782
Maiers, Randy D., 4373
Maiers, Sarah, 3422
Mailman Foundation, Inc., The, 6418
Mailman, Abraham L., 6418
Mailman, Joseph L., 6419
Mailman, Joseph S., 6419
Mailman, Joshua, 6420
Mailman, Joshua L., 6419
Mailman, Phyllis, 6419, 6420
Maiman, Kenneth, 5193
Maimon, Albert S., 9725
Maimone, Joseph A., 7893
Maine Dairy Promotion Board, 3245
Maine, Donald, 4389
Maine, Eugenie W., 9468
Mainiero, Martha B., 8383
Maino, Patricia McGee, 7774
Maiocco, Stephen D., 4261
Mais, Stephen M., 1614
Maisano, Ilyssa, 5203
Maislin, Stephen D., 8916
Maitland, Kate, 6688
Maitra, Sidhartha, 5765
Maiurro, Peter, 1406
Maize and Blue Charitable Trust, 6139
Majer, Sol, 1099
Majic, Patricia, 9780
Major League Baseball, 1850
Major, Bill, 7819, 7820
Major, Donata Russell, 2432
Major, Gabriella, 6818
Major, John, 1053
Major, Martin, 6423
Major, Paul, 1512
Major, Sandra, Rep., 7992
Major, Sean D., 9876
Majors, Charles H., 9420, 9421
Majumder, Ranjit, 9799
Makagon, Kira, 639
Make-Up Art Cosmetics Inc., 6408
Maki, Phil, 4347
Maki, Tony, 9566
Maki, William D., 4617
Makihara, Jun, 6421
Making Good LLC, 1793
Makley, Michael, 7672
Mako Foundation, 3125
Makovsky, Evan, 1487
Makray, Elise, 2994
Makray, Paul, Jr., 2994
Makray, Paul, Sr., 2994
Maksoudian, Kevork, Dr., 2982
Makupson, Amyre, 4543
Malafarina, Gregory J., 7631
Malarik, Diane O., 7493
Malaska, Theodore P., 7887
Malatos, Louisa, 9632
Malbon, John F., 9448
Malbur Realty Trust, 6409
Malburg, Angela, 4580
Malburg, Donald, 4580
Malcolm, Brett, 1402
Malcolm, Carrie Rossip, 5196, 5328
Malcolm, Daniel, 5284
Malcolm, Jan K., 4618, 4621
Malcolm, John, 5284
Malcolm, Marian G., 5284
Malcolm, Waynewright, 2210
Malcom, Shirley M., 8084
Malcom, Susan, 235
Malczewski, Jim, 9916
Maldonado, Jeff, 6852
Maldonado, Maria, 6852
Maldonado, Melissa Lopez, 6852
Maldonado, Roger Juan, 6544
Malebra, James J., 4285
Malek, Frederic V., 9475
Malek, Frederic W., 9475
Malek, Marlene, 9475
Malench, Joseph, 2817
Maletta, Matthew J, 228
Maletta, Sammie L., 3347
Maley, Ryan, 2811
Malfavon, Marco, 5190
Malfitano, Jayne, 2348
Malgieri, Patricia, 6077
Malhotra, Devinder, 4631
Malhotra, Vinnie, 6982
Malicki, Beth, 3449
Malik, Andrew James, 3238
Malik, Daniel James, 3238
Malik, Laura N., 9814
Malik, Nancy W., 3238
Malik, Natalie Jane, 3238
Malin, Kathleen, 8429
Maling, Elise A., 2778
Maling, Michael S., 2778
Malinger, Kathleen M., 3170
Malinger, Kevin, 3170
Malinger, Lynette, 3170
Malino, Sarah, 4990
Malkin, Anthony E., 6711
Malkin, Barry, 3131
Malkin, David, 5843
Malkin, Isabel W., 6422
Malkin, Jessica A., 5843
Malkin, Jodi, 3131
Malkin, Judd, 3131
Malkin, Karen, 3131
Malkin, Peter L., 6422
Malkin, Rachelle B., 6711
Malkin, Scott D., 6422
Malkin, Stephen S., 3131
Mallah, Barry, 6424
Mallah, Darryl, 6423, 6424
Mallah, Diane, 6423
Mallah, Joel, 6423, 6424
Mallah, Sheldon, 6424
Mallah, Yvette, 6423, 6424
Mallard Oil Co., 7225
Mallard, John E., 3491
Mallard, Wayne, 9511
Mallery, John L., 6467
Mallery, Richard, 105
Malley, Bonnie J., 1609
Mallin, Lisa, 1407
Mallinckrodt, Edward, Jr., 2995
Mallison, Andrew, 4849
Mallison, Vickie, 8839
Mallon, Robert, 9739
Mallory, Charles, 1675
Mallory, Jean L., 5129
Mallory, Linda, 8543
Mallott, Anthony, 89
Malloy, Edwin A., 6946
Malloy, Susan R., 6946
Malloy, Timon J., 6946
Malone Custom Builders, Shelly, 8756
Malone, Beverly, 760
Malone, David J., 8228
Malone, Debi, 2084
Malone, E. Phillips, 3607
Malone, Eron, 1805
Malone, Evan D., 1453
Malone, Frank M., Jr., 2462
Malone, Herbert J., Jr., 52
Malone, Joe, 9905
Malone, John C., 1453
Malone, Joseph, 9905
Malone, Leslie A., 1453
Malone, Michael W., 4746
Malone, Paula, 9905
Malone, Richard G., 342
Malone, Rob, 7367
Malone, Robert, 7383
Malone, Ronald Hayes, 863
Maloney, Carey, 6408
Maloney, E. Mayer, 3278
Maloney, Estelle Cameron, 8747
Maloney, Evan Coyne, 1097
Maloney, James V., 4959
Maloney, Leslie, 7480
Maloney, Robert K., 1284
Maloney, Thomas, 2853
Maloney, Timothy, 7480
Malool, Roy M., 5180
Malool, Susannah M., 5180
Malott, Robert Deane, 2996
Malott, Robert H., 2996
Malouf, Thomas H., 1962
Maloy, Mathew S., 9246
Maloy, Michael, 2431
Malpass, Barbara, 4361
Malson, Micheline, 7322
Maltz, Daniel, 7553
Maltz, David, 7553
Maltz, Milton S., 7553
Maltz, Tamar, 7553
Malveaux, Floyd J., 1929
Malvin, Adrienne Helis, 3641
Maly, Nancy, 3475
Malyska, John N., 9471
Malzone, Janet, 2877
Mamula, Milosh, 8001

Manafort Brothers, Inc., 5482
Manahan, Ron, 3336
Manahan, Vincent D., III, 5317
Manatt, Laura, 3475
Manavian, John, 1004
Mancasola, John A., 898
Mancebo, Stephen, 4691
Mancheski, Fred, 1811
Mancheski, Judith, 1811
Manchester, Joyce, 9380
Mancini, Pierluigi, 2482
Mancini, Stephen, 532
Mancuso, Henry, Fr., 3629
Mancuso, Vince, 9871
Mancuso, Vincent J., 6153
Mandanch, David D., 1450
Mandarin Theaters Corp., 2615
Mandel, Alan, 2327
Mandel, Amy C., 7555
Mandel, Barbara A., 7555
Mandel, Florence, 7554
Mandel, Jack N., 7556
Mandel, Joseph C., 7554, 7556
Mandel, Lilyan, 7556
Mandel, Morton L., 7554, 7555, 7556
Mandel, Stacy L., 7555
Mandel, Stephen F., Jr., 1632, 1732
Mandel, Susan Z., 1732
Mandel, Thomas A., 7555
Mandelbaum, Barry, 5428
Mandelbaum, Moshe, 6630
Mandelbaum, Olexa Celine, 6069
Mandelbaum, Stacey, 6057
Mandelblatt, Eric, 6898
Mandelko, Patty, 5062
Mandell, Andrew J., 1635
Mandell, Bruce A., 1635
Mandell, Gerald, 8153
Mandell, Ida S., 8153
Mandell, Joyce D., 1635
Mandell, Judith, 8153
Mandell, Mark N., 1635
Mandell, Morton, 8153
Mandell, Paula, 6406
Mandell, Ronald, 8153
Mandell, Samuel P., 8153
Mandell, Sarah Coade, 676
Mandell, Seymour, 8153
Mandella, Teresa, 417
Mander, Walter S., 2998
Manderino, Louis, 5398
Mandeville, Caroline, 7995
Mandeville, Josephine C., 7995
Mandeville, Nicole F., 1907
Mandle, Roger, 8423
Mandt, Kristi, 9636
Mandujano, Gabriel, 8035
Manduzzi, Lee, 4354
Manegold, Robert H., 6006
Manegold, Sally S., 6006
Maneikis, Charles J., Jr., 3980
Maneka, Yosef, 757
Maness, Tinsley, 8495
Manetta, Alberto, 992
Manfredonia, Linda R., 1755
Mangan, Lawrence T., 8041
Mangan, Stephen A., 4732
Mangelsdorf, Paul C., 157
Manger, Constance G., 3761
Mangers, Dennis, 1103
Mangin, Caroline M., 5283
Mangin, Peter G., 5283
Mangold, Robert, 6085
Mangravite, Paula, 2187
Mangun, Jan, 9412
Mangurian, Harry T., Jr., 2226
Mangurian, Pierce, 1527
Manhart, Marcia Y., 7725
Manhattan Nursing Home Realty Inc., 6288
Manheimer, Virginia, 5299
Maniatis, William, 496
Manigault, Pierre, 8492
Manilla, Robert J., 4479
Manilow, Barbara Goodman, 2781
Manilow, Barry, 917
Manion, Mark D., 9496
Manion, Mel, 6837
Maniscalco, Benedict, 2151
Manitoba Foundation, The, 5717
Manjarres, Rodrigo, 2900
Mankoff, Douglas F., 8998
Mankoff, Jeffrey W., 8998
Mankoff, Joy S., 8998
Mankoff, Ronald M., 8998
Manley, James A., III, 2435
Manley, Jeff, 2435
Manley, Marie, 4523
Manley, Sandy, 709
Manly, Marc E., 7196
Mann Foundation of Minnesota, Tedd & Roberts, The, 8513
Mann Foundation, Ted and Roberta, 5130
Mann, Alison, 5252
Mann, Anastasia, 5252
Mann, Bob, 3475
Mann, Carolyn, 3373
Mann, Cathy, 8884
Mann, Curtis J., 4397
Mann, Dan, 8468
Mann, Dave, 3290
Mann, David, 2736
Mann, Elizabeth N., 3301
Mann, Esther, 2736
Mann, Jacqueline, 5252
Mann, James, 4887
Mann, James E., 5252
Mann, Jane, 2679
Mann, Jennifer L., 8136
Mann, John, 3210
Mann, Leslie, 247
Mann, Louisa, 30
Mann, Neil, 3719
Mann, Peter, 2775
Mann, Rachel Kronstadt, 3732
Mann, Sandra, 5175
Mann, Ted, 1169
Mann, Victoria, 2775
Mann, W. Randall, 2288
Manners, J. Christopher, 7639
Manning, Bob, 1406
Manning, Camille, 6631
Manning, Carol M., 7513
Manning, Chuck, 4370
Manning, Cory, 8468
Manning, Darryl, 408
Manning, Diane L., 9476
Manning, James, 5496
Manning, Jeanne, 2431
Manning, Jerome, 5775
Manning, Jerome A., 5708, 6384, 6632, 6660
Manning, Kathy, 7180
Manning, Kenneth P., 9943
Manning, Lee, 3996
Manning, Marilyn, 849
Manning, Michael, 7575
Manning, Nancy, 849
Manning, O. Raymond, Jr., 7184
Manning, Paul, 3283, 9476, 9943
Manning, Paul B., 9476
Mannion Family Foundation, 4298
Mannion, Gwyn, 6049
Mannion, Martin, 4298
Mannion, Martin J., 4161
Mannion, Martin J., Mrs., 4161
Mannion, Tristin, 4298
Mannion, Tristin L., 4161
Manns, Jon, 3625
Manocherian, Greg, 1976
Manofksy, JoAnne, 8635
Manoogian, Alex, 4491, 4492, 4493
Manoogian, Jane C., 4492
Manoogian, Marie, 4491, 4492, 4493
Manoogian, Richard A., 4491, 4492, 4497
Manpower Inc., 9899
Manriquez, Hank, 9604
Mansell, Charles Y., 8098
Mansfield, Christopher C., 4145, 9723
Mansfield, Todd, 7202
Manship, Andrea Dumke, 9315
Manske, Susan E., 2989
Manson, Kay, 4211
Mansour, Jeff, 8529
Mansour, Rita N.A., 7686
Mansueto, Joseph D., 3000
Mansur, Bernadette, 6528
Mansur, Cathy, 2764
Mansur, Susan C., 3938
Mansuri, Dinaz, 2947
Manternach, Amy, 3421
Manton, Edwin, Sir, 6425, 6904
Manton, Lady, 6425
Mantooth, Carrie, 5006
Mantooth, Stan, 1287
Mantzuranis, Catherine C., 7741
Manu, James, 4987
Manufacturers and Traders Trust Co., 6406
Manufacturing systems Technologies, 9193
Manzke, Rob, 9833
Manzo, Susan, 6848
Manzulli, Michael F., 6703
Maounis, Nicholas, 1663
Mapes Charitable Trust, 5066
Mapes, Timothy W., 7191
Mapother, William R., 3569
Mapp Trust, Mary E.F., 47
Mapp, Karen L., 4103
Mapp, Louis, 47
Mapp, Louis E., 47
Mapp, Mary Elizabeth Faulkner, 47
Mapplethorpe, Robert, 6427
Mar, Larry, 515
Maraghy, Patrick B., 4012
Maralo, Inc., 8993
Marano, Jean F., 5866
Maranto, Joe, 3759
Marasco, Chris, 3759
Marathon Cheese Corp., 9851
Marathon Corp., 42
Marc-Aurele, Drew, 4108
Marcacci, Donna, 2763
Marcario, Rose, 1017
Marceau, Layne, 1031
Marcello, Beth, 7942
Marcello, Joe, 3955
March 23, 2006 Trust, The, 1794
March, Karen, 5315
March, Kevin P., 9227
Marchand, Victoria, 8952
Marchant, Ann Carol, 9523
Marchant, Danielle, 9604
Marchant, Robert E., 9523
Marchetti, Leon, 8171
Marciano, Georges, 6630
Marciano, Kenneth L., 1241
Marciano, Maurice, 635, 873
Marciano, Paul, 635, 874
Marciano, Shelley, 2102
Marciniak, Rob, 4334
Marcks, Eula D., 4401
Marcks, Oliver Dewey, 4401
Marcled Foundation, The, 932
Marcon, Fred R., 5369
Marcon, L. Charles, 8136, 8320
Marcon, Natalie, 5369
Marcu, Mihai, 7942
Marcus Corp., The, 9900
Marcus Group, Neiman, 2412
Marcus Pointe Baptist Church, 7214
Marcus, Bernard, 2511
Marcus, Carol P., 5296
Marcus, Ellen F., 6428
Marcus, Emilie, Dr., 4036
Marcus, Frederick R., 2511
Marcus, George, 876
Marcus, Gregory S., 9900, 9907
Marcus, James, 6174
Marcus, James S., 5740, 6428
Marcus, Judith, 876
Marcus, Julie, 3962
Marcus, Stephen H., 9900
Marcus, Urla, Dr., 8511
Marcuse, Edgar K., 9691
Marder, Ruth R., 3873
Mardigian, Arman, 4494
Mardigian, Edward S., 4494
Mardigian, Grant, 4494
Mardigian, Helen, 4494
Mardigian, Janet M., 4494
Mardigian, Matthew, 4494
Mardigian, Robert D., 4494
Mardikian, Sasha, 383
Maren Royalty Trust, 2227
Maren, David K., 2227
Maren, Emily, 2227
Maren, James, 2227
Maren, Peter, 2036, 2227
Mares, Donald J., 1390
Maresca, Robert, 3954
Marfin, Debra, 9081
Margaret Energy, Inc., 4834
Margerum, Sonya, 3282
Margiotta, Charles, 2281
Margo, Cynthia, 4667
Margolis Trust, Lisa, The, 1812
Margolis Trust, Robert, The, 1812
Margolis, Barry H., 8916
Margolis, E. David, 7997
Margolis, James, 8136
Margolis, Lisa, 1812
Margolis, Nancy, 4340
Margolis, Robert J., 1812
Margolius, Edwin A., 5936
Margolius, Philip, 1912
Margulies, Ari, 5637
Margulies, Aryeh, 5637
Margulies, David, 5637
Margulies, Esther, 5637
Margulies, Goldy, 5637
Margulies, Harry, 5637
Margulies, Solomon, 5637

Mariani, Cristina N., 5641
Mariani, Harry F., 5641
Mariani, James W., 5641
Mariani, John, 5641
Mariano, Robert A., 9936
Mariel, Serafin U., 6542
Marien, Marcia, 1563
Marignoli, Kapi 'Olani K., 2592
Marin, Carol, 5146
Marin, Lynda, 556
Marinakos, Plato A., 8106
Marine Environmental Testing, 8492
Mariner, Marion H.M., 8428
Mariners Care, 1850
Marinkovich, Tom, 1399
Marino, Anthony, 5724
Marino, John, 7681
Marino, Lynda, 781
Marino, Robert A., 5305
Marino, Thomas M., 8616
Marinovich, Mackenzi, 4606
Marinovich, Morgan, 4606
Marinovich, Patti, 4606
Marinovich, Robert F., 7783
Mario, Christopher B., 5370
Mario, Ernest, 5370
Mario, Ernest, Dr., 5370
Mario, Gregory G., 5370
Mario, Jeremy K., 5370
Mario, Mildred M., 5370
Mario, Mildred Martha, 5370
Marion County Health Department, 3317
Marion General Hospital, 9250
Marion Merrell Dow Inc., 5437
Marion, Anne W., 8737
Marion, John L., 8737
Maris, Mahlon, 181
Maris, Mahlon, Dr., 179
Marisco, James, 1455
Marital Trust, 6541
Marital Trust f/b/o Dorothy, A. M. Roberts, 6717
Maritan Memorial Hospital, 9250
Mark, Florine, 4371
Mark, Jim, 7876
Mark, Melvyn I., 682
Mark, Morris, 6430
Mark, Sarah E., 8071
Mark, Susan, 6430
Mark, Thomas M., 2223
Markel, Kate Levin, 4498
Markel, Larry G., 7769
Markel, Steven A., 2253
Markel, Tom, 8841
Markell, Peter K., 4030
Market Connect Group, Inc., 6676
Market Vectors Gold Miners, 4254
Marketing Response Solutions, 8834
Marketplace One Foundation, 7873
MarketSpan Corp., 6527
Markham, Fred J., 9228
Markham, Leah, 6492
Markham, Marianna, 8944
Markham, Nancy Louise Brown, 2456
Markins, Jane A., 9539
Markkula, Armas C., Jr., 879
Markkula, Linda K., 879
Markle, John, 6431
Markle, Mary, 6431
Markley, Allan, Dr., 4996
Markley, Autumn Y., 4896
Markley, David, 9380
Markley, Larry, 7704
Markman, Joanne W., 8226
Markovich, C.B., 630
Markow, John C., 1533
Markowitz, Rachelle, 6870
Markowitz, Teresa, 3745
Marks, Alan, 493
Marks, Brian J., 2434
Marks, Carole, 880
Marks, Carolyn, 6432
Marks, Cynthia, 6442
Marks, D.T., 9399
Marks, David, 2948
Marks, Edwin S., 6432
Marks, George E., 8199
Marks, Howard, 6160
Marks, James L., 8472
Marks, James S., 5329
Marks, John R., 2421, 9399
Marks, Jr. Trust, Charles E., 3001
Marks, Judy, 5454
Marks, Melanie L., 2548
Marks, Michael, 535, 880
Marks, Nancy, 9109
Marks, Nancy A., 6432
Marks, Nancy L., 4158, 4162
Marks, Nancy Lurie, 4162
Marks, Paul, 5589
Marks, Paul Camp, 7168
Marks, Sam, 5876
Marks, Sr. Trust, Charles E., 3001
Markson, Leona E., 1929
Markward, David, Dr., 3033
Markwort, Melissa A., 4919
Marlboro-Classic LP, The, 9452
Marlborough House LLC, 9452
Marley Trust, Kemper, 140
Marley, Ethel, 140
Marley, Jane W., 7192
Marling, Kim, 9290
Marling, Robert, 9290
Marling, Robert E., Jr., 9290
Marlon, Anthony, 6433
Marlon, Brad, 6433
Marlon, Renee, 6433
Marlon, Robert, 6433
Marlow, James R., 7670
Marlow, Linda K., 7670
Marmalade, Inc., 9005
Marmer, Lynn, 7531
Marmion, William H., 929
Marmor, Andrea, 881
Marmor, David J., 881
Marmor, Jane B., 881
Marmor, Judd, 881
Marmor, Katherine, 881
Marmor, Max, 6308
Marmor, Michael F., 881
Marmurstein, Jacob, 6434
Marmurstein, Renee, 6434
Marmurstein, Rita, 6434
Marmurstein, Yacov, 6434
Marmurstein, Zev, 6434
Maroney, C. Roderick, 1806
Maroney, Eleanor S., 1758
Marotta, Justin, 7630
Marousis, Dean J., 2819
Marousis, James K., 2819
Marpat Foundation, 1931
Marple, Anthony, 3699
Marquardt, Dorwin, 7351
Marquart, Kuulei M., 5077
Marquart, Rex, 5077
Marquart, Winifred J., 9872
Marquette Bancshares, Inc., 4745
Marquez, Bernadette, 1454
Marquez, Michael A., 2238
Marquez, Timothy, 1454
Marquez, Wendy Thompson, 1893
Marquez-Hudson, Christine, 1374
Marquis Jet, 7012
Marquis, Bryan, 8828
Marr, Ann, 5002
Marr, Brian, 4334
Marr, Rob, 3407
Marran, Elizabeth, 2183
Marran, Ethel, 2183
Marran, Ethel K., 2183
Marran, Laura, 2183
Marrero, Anitza Cox, 8353
Marriott Charitable Annuity Trust, J. Willard, 3841
Marriott Lifetime Trust, Alice S., 3843
Marriott, Alice S., 3841
Marriott, J. Willard, 3841
Marriott, J. Willard, Jr., 3841
Marriott, Jr. Foundation, J. Willard, 3843
Marriott, Julie Ann, 3840
Marriott, Karen Christine, 3840, 3842
Marriott, Michael S., 9306
Marriott, Nancy P., 3843
Marriott, Nancy Peery, 3842
Marriott, Richard E., 3841, 3842, 3843
Marriott, Stephen, 3841
Marron, Donald B., 6435
Marrus, Andrew, 6436
Marrus, David, 6436
Marrus, Judith, 6436
Marrus, Lauren, 6436
Marrus, Michael, 6436
Mars Charitable Lead Trust, Virginia C., 6437
Mars, Forrest E., Jr., 9477
Mars, Inc., 9477
Mars, Jacqueline B., 9477
Mars, John F., 9477
Mars, Joshua, 4829
Mars, Lisa, 6681
Mars, Marijke E., 6437
Mars, Valerie A., 6437
Mars, Victoria B., 6437
Mars-Wright, Pamela D., 6437
Marsal 2010 Clat Co., Bryan P., The, 6438
Marsal, Bryan, 6438
Marsal, Kathleen, 6438
Marsal-Wallin, Dawn M., 5584
Marsala, Vincent, 3657
Marsalis, Wynton, 5612
Marsch, Susan, 7557
Marsden, Gary, 4631
Marsden, K. Gerald, Dr., 4375
Marsella, Al, 867
Marsh & McLennan, J & H, 3750
Marsh Foundation, Inc., 8999
Marsh, Alana, 8799
Marsh, Barnaby, 8313
Marsh, Catherine H., 663
Marsh, Charlene, 8999
Marsh, Charlene C., 8999
Marsh, Charles A., 8999
Marsh, Charles Edward, 1940
Marsh, Estelle Fariss, 8999
Marsh, George, Jr., 4061
Marsh, Gordon, 6085
Marsh, Holly, 1578
Marsh, Jack, 1907
Marsh, Jacob, 70, 1578
Marsh, Kelly, 3193
Marsh, Lucy Thompson, 70
Marsh, Mel, 7671
Marsh, Richard H., 7664
Marsh, Richard S.T., 9537
Marsh, Tom F., 8999
Marsh, W. Rodger, Jr., 3541
Marshall Estates, Inc., 6768
Marshall, April W., 3588
Marshall, Colin S., 1770
Marshall, David, 7181
Marshall, Douglas B., III, 9000
Marshall, Douglas B., Jr., 9000
Marshall, Dwight W., Jr., 3760
Marshall, E. Pierce, Jr., 3653
Marshall, Edward W., III, 8284
Marshall, Elaine T., 3653
Marshall, Elizabeth "Libby", 2032
Marshall, Ellen, 1525
Marshall, H. Richard, 9778
Marshall, Jeffrey A., 8155
Marshall, Joe, 2632
Marshall, John, 917, 8729
Marshall, Katherine, 8518
Marshall, Louise F., 141
Marshall, Lydia M., 7587
Marshall, Lydia Micheaux, 1940
Marshall, Maggie T., 3588
Marshall, Phillip H., Jr., 3588
Marshall, Phillip H., Sr., 3588
Marshall, Preston L., 3653
Marshall, Regina, 4173
Marshall, Robert Wood, Jr., 3588
Marshall, Schuyler B., IV, 9140
Marshall, Shauna I., 1088
Marshall, Stephanie Pace, 2849, 3185
Marshall, Sue Ellen, 3588
Marshall, Theresa, 8155
Marshall, Thomas, 8155
Marshall, Thomas C., 484
Marshall, Thurgood, Jr., 5994
Marshall, Tom, 3475
Marshall, William H., 3274, 3275
Marshall-Blake, Lorina L., 8106
Marshall-King, Karen, 5927
Marshalls of MA, Inc., 4308
Marshon, Karen, 6720
Marsicano, Michael, 7202
Marsico, Cydney, 1455
Marsico, Peter, 1455
Marsico, Tom, 1455
Marsiglia, Nancy M., 3656
Marsini, Nicholas, 1755
Marskbury, Logan, 3560
Marson, Ken, 9604
Marston, Roseline H., 8221
Marston, Wes, 2036
Marszalek Bekmyrza, Diana E., 1985
Marszalek, Diana E., 6698
Martahus, Craig R., 7409
Martel, Lysane, 7908
Martell, Arianna Packard, 1007
Martell, C. Michael, 3685
Martell, Sally, 3685
Martell, Sally Klingenstein, 6292
Martella, Michael P., 2038
Marten, David K., 3349
Marten, James W., 3349
Marten, Virginia A., 3349
Martens, Holley Fowler, 7460
Martens, Troy, 3419
Martenson, Dennis R., 9547
Marter, Barbara J., 8614
Marth, Edward C., 8410
Marti, George W., 9001
Marti, Jo C., 9001

Massry, Esther, 6444
Massry, Morris, 6444, 7006
Massry, Norman, 6444
Mast, Allen, 2529
Mast, Kent, 2455
Master Brand, 9606
Master, Carol, 6777
Master, Carol, Dr., 6776
Master, Daniel, 6912
Masters, Mark, 7630
Masters, Michael, 2555
Masters, Seth, 7075
Masters, Suzanne, 2555
Masterson, 9837
Masterson, Jeffrey, 5893
Mastracco, Vincent J., Jr., 9448
Mastro, Randy M., 583
Mastronardi, Charles A., 1815
Mastronardi, Margaret, 1815
Mastronardi, Nicholas D., 1815
Mastronardi, Val, 1815
Masucci, William, 5887
Masuda, Mel, 1350
Masumoto, David Mas, 727
Matarazzo, James M., 7087
Matau, Karri, 9616
Matcheswalla, Mansoor, Dr., 9789
Matchett, Terri E., 3262
Mateo, Laura D., 816
Mateyo, George, 7639
Mathas, Theodore A., 6548
Matheny, Edward T., Jr., 4902
Mather, Elizabeth Ring, 7559
Mather, Henry T., 4431
Mathern, Tim, 4621
Mathers, G. Harold, 6446
Mathers, Leila Y., 6446
Mathers, William L., 3903
Matheson, Alline, 5644
Matheson, Bonnie B., 4407
Matheson, Marjorie A., 5596
Mathew, Joseph, 3321
Mathews, Bert, 8550
Mathews, Koshy, Rev. Dr., 8223
Mathews, Margaret, 6909
Mathews, Mark, 6997
Mathews, Patricia N., 9497
Mathews, Rebecca H., 8103
Mathews, Ruth, 8350
Mathews, Steven C., 1384
Mathewson, Charles N., 5131
Mathewson, Curtis N., 5131
Mathewson, Paulina G., 5131
Mathewson, Robert A., 5131
Mathey, Dean, 5220
Matheys, Steve, 9942
Mathias, Alison, 5976
Mathias, Leonard G., 3904
Mathiasen, Jerry, 3447
Mathiason, Garry G., 912
Mathieson, Peter F., 7956
Mathieu, Michael, 9753
Mathieu, Paul, 9437
Mathile Family Foundation, 7608
Mathile, Clayton L., 7608
Mathile, Clayton Lee, 7560
Mathile, MaryAnn, 7560
Mathile, Timothy, 7560
Mathios, Alan, 5807
Mathis, Betty K., 9175
Mathis, David B., 2955
Mathis, James E., Jr., 2525
Mathis, William N., 8731
Mathur, Anshul, 8718
Mathurin Fund, The, 9578
Matias-Melendez, Dinorah, 6604
Matisse Revocable Trust, Maria-Gaetana, The, 6447
Matisse, Maria-Gaetana, 6447
Matlack, Anne H., 8267
Matlack, Rex, 3540
Matos, Kica, 1562, 1600
Matos, Maria, 8333
Matousek, Mary Therese, 7631
Matricaria, Andrew S., 142
Matricaria, Lee M., 142
Matricaria, Lucille E., 142
Matricaria, Ronald, 142
Matricaria, Ronald A., Jr., 142
Matson, Patti, 5028
Matson, Sandy, 2533
Matsui Nursery, Inc., 885
Matsui, Connie L., 1108
Matsui, Toshikiyo Andy, 885
Matsui, Yasuko, 885
Matsukado, Ann, 2593
Matsumoto, Colbert M., 2606
Matsumoto, Iris Y., 2598
Matsumoto, Marilynn, 2609
Matsuo, Masayuki, 281
Matsuoka, Martha, 6571
Matt, Susan G., 5805
Matta, Anne Grousbeck, 5222
Mattel, Inc., 886
Matteliano, Cara, 5801
Mattern, L. Jeffrey, 8046
Mattes, Martin, 3418
Matteson, C. John, 6242
Matthew, Amy, 533
Matthew, Steve, 7592, 7704
Matthews, Ann C., 454
Matthews, Anne H., 2528
Matthews, Annie Nagel, 2639
Matthews, Beverly, 3320
Matthews, Clare B., 9479
Matthews, Debra, 4779
Matthews, Dee, 7340
Matthews, Dewayne, 3345
Matthews, Douglas L., 1816
Matthews, Edward E., 1816, 6911
Matthews, Edwin S., Jr., 6086
Matthews, Emily L., 4357
Matthews, Gene, 7179
Matthews, Gregory E., 1816
Matthews, John A., Jr., 8810, 8955, 8978
Matthews, Joseph B., 5525
Matthews, Julia Jones, 5525, 8810, 8978
Matthews, Kade L., 8810, 8955, 8978
Matthews, Kalyn, 7196
Matthews, Lindsay M., 2976
Matthews, Lois, 1015
Matthews, Marie L., 1816
Matthews, N. Ross, 411
Matthews, Robert, 8374
Matthews, Robert E., 2489
Matthews, Russell E., 1816
Matthews, Susan, 9726
Matthias, Mark, 9603
Matthies, Katharine, 1639
Matthiesen, Carrie N., 9048
Mattice, W. Scott, 8614
Mattingley, Patricia Ann, 9582
Mattingly, Joseph, 8721
Mattocks, Robert L., II, 7141
Mattone, Joseph M., 6024
Mattoon, Peter M., 8336
Matus, Kristi A., 1531
Matuslnec, Karen A., 3012
Matwiczyk, Peter, 2032
Matwijkow, Deborah Margaret, 90
Matz, Dorothy A., 8962
Matzke, Gerald E., 5037
Matzl, Rosemary, 2934
Maude, Cathy, 3036
Maue, R. A., 5235
Mauer, Kent, 4540
Mauff, Erich, 5876
Maughan, Deryck C., Sir, 6904
Maughan, Janet, 1906
Maultsby, Vance K., Jr., 9006
Mauna Kea Villages, LLC, 2144
Maunz, Bettina, 8655
Maupin, Bill, 9054
Maupin, Ernest J., 6598
Maupin, John E., Jr., Dr., 8550
Mauran, Frank, 8392
Mauran, Hope Ives, 8428
Mauran, Louise S., 8428
Maurania Corp., 8428
Maurer, Carol M., 5283
Maurer, Frederick, 7382
Maurer, Gilbert C., 6155, 6156
Maurer, K.C., 7014, 7050
Maurice, Elizabeth, 9266
Mauritz, William W., 3015
Mauro Motors, 1577
Mauro, Albert P., Jr., 4906
Maus, Blair Collins, 3010
Maust, Carolyn, 6296
Mauze, Abby Rockefeller, 6723
Mavec, Ellen Stirn, 7668
Maverick Capital Charities, Ltd., 9005
Mavrakis, Carol Seidler, 3479
Mavrogordato, Helen S., 8475
Mavrovtis, Leo, 5625
Maxey, Charles, 1287
Maxey, Ken, 1069
Maxfield, A. Melissa, 7989
Maxfield, Melinda C., 887
Maxfield, Robert R., 887
Maxfield, W. Dale, Sr., 8546
Maxfield, William D., 8546
MAXIMUS, Inc., 9481
Maxson, Justin, 7138
Maxson, Robert C., 253
Maxwell, Annie, 1176
Maxwell, Benjamin R., 9414
Maxwell, Carol B., 73
Maxwell, Joan Hunt, 8100
Maxwell, Laird, 2644
Maxwell, Neil H., 7629
Maxwell, Robert W., 8768
Maxwell, T. Nyle, 8873
Maxwell, William L., 7173
May Charitable Lead Unitrust, Daniel, 2230
May Charitable Lead Unitrust, Jeanette, 2230
May Department Stores Foundation, The, 7552
May Trust, Ben, 48
May, Alysia, 5132
May, Angie, 3321
May, Barbara V., 2370
May, Betty R., 4825
May, Brian S., 2230
May, Bruce, 7382
May, Cindy S., 4825
May, Cordelia S., 7986
May, Daniel, 2230
May, Dianne L., 2230
May, Dixie, 5132
May, Dorothy Duffy, 5132
May, Ernest N., Jr., 1758
May, Florence, 3313
May, Hilary Austen, 9638
May, Isabel, 2137
May, J. Thomas, 181
May, Joan, 1512
May, Karl, 9925
May, Katharyn A., Dean, 9945
May, Linda J., 2033
May, Linda K., 9175
May, Lou Adele, 8681, 8768
May, Martha, 3477
May, Mike, 7731
May, Nancy, 9048, 9073
May, Nancy F., 8694
May, Patti, 9146
May, Peter, 1518, 2137
May, Samuel D., 2137
May, Thomas J., 1656
May, Wilbur, 5132
May, William B., 6109
May, William H., 297
Maybee, Terri R., 4906
Maybelline, 1771
Mayberry, Doug, 2041
Mayberry, Richard, 2486
Mayborn Charitable Lead Annuity Trust, Anyse Sue, 9006
Mayborn, Anyse Sue, 9006
Maybruck, Zev, 5984
Mayer Charitable Trust, Helen, 8439
Mayer Electric Supply Co., Inc., 49
Mayer, Allan C., Jr., 3005
Mayer, Anthony R., 1433, 1457
Mayer, Beatrice C., 3006, 3124
Mayer, Beatrice Cummings, 5833
Mayer, Becky, 6042
Mayer, Charles B., 3616, 3637
Mayer, Christine Amer, 7465
Mayer, Coni, 3253
Mayer, Delisa A., 1457
Mayer, Eugene, 7416
Mayer, Frederick M., 1433
Mayer, Frederick R., 1433
Mayer, Gregory C., 3110
Mayer, Harold F., 3005
Mayer, Jan Perry, 1433
Mayer, Jeffrey, 5876
Mayer, Jimmy, 6042
Mayer, Joe, 9750
Mayer, Louis B., 6449
Mayer, Mark, 3758
Mayer, Michael, 1046
Mayer, Oscar H., 3005
Mayer, Richard A., 3005
Mayer, Richard H., 7990
Mayer, Robert B., 3006
Mayer, Robert N., 3006, 3124
Mayer, Scott T., 3005
Mayer, Solomon, 5905
Mayer, Susie, 6042
Mayer, William E., 3005
Mayers, Daniel K., 1893
Mayers, Dezarie, 6633
Mayerson Charitable Annuity Lead Trust, Manuel D., 7561
Mayerson Charitable Lead Trust, 2002 Arlene and Neal, The, 7561
Mayerson, Arlene B., 7561
Mayerson, Donna, 7561
Mayerson, Frederic H., 7561

Mayerson, Manuel D., 7561
Mayerson, Matthew, 991
Mayerson, Neal H., 7561
Mayerson, Rhoda, 7561
Mayes, Jeff, 4344
Mayes, Kent, 8949
Mayes, Michele C., 2657
Mayfair Medical Mgmt., 2168
Mayfield, Deanna, 9146
Mayfield, Jim, 416
Mayfield, Mabel, Hon., 4347
Mayfield, Michael G., 1116
Mayfield, Pinkie D., 9445
Mayhall, Michael, 7776
Mayhew, George, 6527
Maykrantz, Lawrence, 3888
Mayman, Todd A., 9439
Maynard, Ann, 3626
Maynard, Easter, 7328
Maynard, Edwin P., 4211
Maynard, Kay, 7231
Maynard, Kristi L., 2598
Maynard, Olivia P., 4510
Mayo Clinic, 2300
Mayo, Elizabeth B., 8475
Mayo, Rachel, 418
Mayo-Smith, William, 8383
Mayor, Oliver Dewey, 9007
Mayr, George Henry, 7261
Mays Family 2000 Charitable Lead Annuity Trust, 9008
Mays, L. Lowry, 9008
Mays, Mark, 9008
Mays, Mark P., 9008
Mays, Peggy P., 9008
Mays, Randall, 9008
Mays, Randall T., 9008
Maytag, Fred, II, 3460
Maytag, Frederick L., III, 3460
Maytag, Kenneth P., 3460
Mayton, Catherine H., 201
Mayton, Michael R., 201
Mayville Engineering Co., Inc., 9809
Mayworm, Daniel E., 3140
Maza, Bruce A., 3566
Mazadoorian, Harry N., 1537
Mazany, Terry, 2746
Mazar, Anne, 4164
Mazar, Brian, 4164
Mazar, Jose Luis, 671
Mazarakis, Helen, 5232
Mazmanian, Daniel A., 664
Mazry, Ginny Solari, 418
Mazur, John M., 8021
Mazurkiewicz, Gerard, 5801
Mazurkiewicz, Joe, Jr., 2327
Mazza Trust, Louise T., 3007
Mazza, David, 890
Mazza, Ral, 6720
Mazzarantani, George, 2114
Mazzerella, Kathleen M., 4898
Mazzie, A. Vincent, 2948
Mazzola, James, 377
Mazzolla, Mary, 5120
Mazzoula, Sandra, 417
Mazzullo, Theresa, 5969
MB 2006 Lead Trust, 6407
MB Financial Bank, N.A., 3008
MBI Development Co., Inc, 8108
MBI Equities Corp., 8108
MBIA Insurance Corp., 6451
McAdam, Lowell C., 5489
McAdam, Robert S., 2051
McAdam, Sally Welker, 4963
McAden, Jim, 9415
McAfee Corp., 4314
McAfee, Carolyn T., 2515
McAfee, James T., III, 2515
McAfee, James T., Jr., 2515
McAfee, Jim, 8777
Mcafee, Mary E., 5360
McAfee, Robert E., 3708
McAlexander, Dan, 2529
McAlister, David, 6621
McAlister, Elizabeth, 8617
McAlister, Fern Smith, 891
McAlister, Harold, 891
McAlister, James P., 891
McAlister, Mari, 891
McAlister, Michael H., 891
McAlister, Michelle, 891
McAllister, Brendan, 4742
McAllister, Bryan, 2436
McAllister, Dale, 3418
McAllister, Dorothy N., 3351
McAllister, Lee, 7335
McAllister, Lonnie J., 7184
McAllister, Michael, 744
McAllister, Sandy, 3851
McAnaney, Brian T., 6770
McAnaney, Edward G., 6770
McAnaney, Kevin G., 6770
McAndrews, Tom, 3418
McAniff, Peter, 1015
McAninch, Janeen, 7834, 7866
Mcannally, Robert S., 32
McAra, Heidi, 4372
McArdle, James, Jr., 1584
McArthur, Gary L., 2149
McArthur, Harry, 4811
McArtor, Kevin, 2792
McAshan Foundation, Inc., The, 3836, 9645
McAshan, Susan C., 9248
McAuliffe, Hawley Hilton, 692
McAuliffe, Kevin P., 694
McAvoy, Brian V., 2035
McBean, Alletta Morris, 892
McBean, Edith, 8423
McBean, Judith, 893
McBeath, Faye, 9901
McBournie, Ann, 1493
McBournie, Ann E., 1493
McBrayer, Katie, 4849
McBrian, Bruce A., 7446
McBride Charitable Lead Annuity Trust, Rita, 7562
McBride, Arthur B., Jr., 7562
McBride, B. Gary, 7462
McBride, Beverly J., 7686
McBride, Brian A., 7562
McBride, Cindy, 7310
McBride, Gerald, 8094
McBride, Jack, 8459
McBride, John, 3400
McBride, John P., 1367
McBride, John P., Jr., 1367
McBride, Katharine S., 3878
McBride, Katherine, 3222
McBride, Katherine H., 1367
McBride, Laurie M., 1367
McBride, Maureen, 7562
McBride, Michael, 1488
McBride, Mike, 2632
McBride, Peter, 1367
McBride, Peter M., 1367
McBride, Rebecca, 2765
McBride, Rita, 7562
McBrier, Lynn M., 8026
McBrine, John A., 4186
McBroom, Amanda, 917
McBryde, Nowlin, 9095
McCabe, Ann, 4655
McCabe, Ann L., 4655
McCabe, Beth, 6222
McCabe, Christine A., 9600
McCabe, Daniel J., 7429
McCabe, David J., 1587
McCabe, James B., 2577
McCabe, John F., IV, 1737
McCabe, Kathleen, 6507
McCabe, Laura, 8852
McCabe, Lindsay, 4655
McCabe, Lindsay E., 4655
McCabe, Nancy White, 6300
McCabe-Thompson, Elsie Crum, 3358
McCafferty, John, 9005
McCaffrey, Stephen W., 6527
McCahill, Elizabeth, 2231
McCahill, James, 2231
McCahill, James J., 2231
McCahill, Tara, 2231
McCahill, Tara F., 2231
McCain, Joseph J., Jr., 7800
McCalister, Michael, 3828
McCall, Donald J., 7178
McCall, Gail, 8797
McCall, Jennifer, 3418
McCall, R. Keith, 7258
McCallick, Frank, 9651
McCallie, Thomas H., III, 8602, 8644
McCallister, Michael B., 3582
McCallum, Jim, 1103
McCally, Albert Ward, III, 2832
McCalpin, William F., 6164
McCamey, Megan, 2516
McCammon, Stanley P., 9632
McCance, Elizabeth, 4165
McCance, Henry F., 4165
McCann Foundation, 5808
McCann, Fergus, 4050
McCann, James J., 6453
McCann, Jonathan, 7702
McCann, Kimberly S., 3575
McCann, Nancy W., 7532, 7584
McCann, Robert, 4007
McCann, Sue Ellen, 1322
McCann, Thomas D., 2035
McCanna, Katherine, 4558
McCanna, Michael, 84
McCarrick, Theodore E., Cardinal, 9471
McCarrick, Theodore, Cardinal, 4664
McCarroll, Andrew R., 8616, 8620
McCarroll, Elizabeth M., 6499
McCarroll, Steve, 77
McCarron, Suzanne M., 8833
McCartan, Michael, 4373
McCartan, Patrick F., 7532
McCarten, Kathleen M., 8383
McCarter, Fred, 3293
McCarter, John W., Jr., 3358
McCarthey Trust, Jane F., 9332
McCarthey, Maureen P., 9332
McCarthey, Philip G., 9332
McCarthey, Sarah J., 9332
McCarthey, Thomas K., Jr., 9332
McCarthy Charitable Lead Annuity Trust, Kathleen L., 795
McCarthy Group, Inc., 5047
McCarthy, A. Gregory, IV, 9471
McCarthy, Alexander, 3968
McCarthy, Amelia, 1896
McCarthy, Ann M., 6584
McCarthy, Brian A., 6455
McCarthy, Bridget, 6454
McCarthy, Christine M., 467
McCarthy, Cullen H., 3388
McCarthy, Dan, 6612, 7022
McCarthy, Darby A., 3388
McCarthy, David M., 3948
McCarthy, Deborah Berg, 5626
McCarthy, Denis, 6454
McCarthy, Edward, III, 2076
McCarthy, Edward, Jr., 2076, 2388
McCarthy, Edwin J., 4705, 8435
McCarthy, Eugenie Ross, 4963
McCarthy, George, 4146
McCarthy, Giovanna, 6456
McCarthy, Helen C., 3968
McCarthy, James T., 895
McCarthy, James W., 5415
McCarthy, Jane D., 895
McCarthy, John, 825, 2826, 8332
McCarthy, John T., 1566
McCarthy, Juliana Allen, 4963
McCarthy, Julie, 2076
McCarthy, Kathleen L., 795, 825
McCarthy, Kevin, 1504
McCarthy, Kristin L., 895
McCarthy, Laura, 6454
McCarthy, Louise Roblee, 4963
McCarthy, Lucy, 6454
McCarthy, Lucy A., 6454
McCarthy, Margaret M., 1531
McCarthy, Michael D., 5626
McCarthy, Michael J., 3909
McCarthy, Michael R., 5037
McCarthy, Pamela, 6454
McCarthy, Patrick, 3726, 3745, 4869, 8833
McCarthy, Patrick C., 6456
McCarthy, Patrick M., 896
McCarthy, Peter F., 6454
McCarthy, Peter H., 6454
McCarthy, Rachel K., 895
McCarthy, Robert H., 6454
McCarthy, Robert P., 6454
McCarthy, Roblee, Jr., 4963
McCarthy, Sarah S. P., 5405
McCarthy, Susan B., 8435
McCarthy, Terri, 4579
McCarthy, Thomas A., 7981
McCarthy, Thomas O., 4705
McCarthy, Timothy, 9448
McCarthy, Vincent, 4061
McCarthy, Winifred, 6454
McCartney, Charles, 2703
McCartney, Madeleine, 2703
McCartor, Alice P., 7871
McCarty, Dan, 3539
McCarty, Marilu H., 2462
McCarty, Morgan, 4829
McCarty, Steve, 1110
McCarty, Tom, 5055
McCarvel, Cynthia, 3553
McCarvel, Tom, 5017
McCary Foundation, Tom and Mary, 4792
McCaskey, Raymond F., 3009
McCasland, T.H., Jr., 7772
McCasland, Tom, III, 7742
McCasland, Tom, Jr., 7742
McCaslin, Teresa E., 6015
McCaul, Elizabeth, 6208
McCaul, Linda Mays, 9008
McCaul, Mack E., Jr., 8549

McCauley, Ann, 4308
McCauley, Tamme Simon, 3386
McCauley-Burrows, Mary, 7878
Mccausland, Alexander, 7262
McCausland, Bonnie, 8159
McCausland, Peter, 8159
McCausland, Thomas N., 5454
McCausland, Tim, 5806
McCaw Foundation, The, 9574
McCaw, Bruce R., 9574
McCaw, Craig O., 897, 9676
McCaw, Jolene M., 9574
McCaw, Keith, 9675
McCaw, Mary Kay, 9675
McCaw, Susan R., 9676
McCaw, Wendy P., 897
McCaw, William J., 3351
McClafferty, Charles C., 4540
McClain Select Value, 9916
McClain, Dewey, 1939
McClain, James, II, 9450
McClain, Jerry, 7540
McClain, Joseph S., 3714
McClain, Lydia Joy, 9438
McClamroch, Michael T., 8560
McClanahan, Jan, 9133
McClanahan, Marjorie, 92
McClaren, Robert S., 8674
McClaskey, Kathleen, 9677
McClaskey, Rod, 9677
McClaskey, Tod K., 9677
McClatchey, Donna C., 7186
McClave, Christin C., 7964
McClean, Mary Gaylord, 7753
McClear, Kevin R., 2752
McCleary, Linda W., 3850
McCleary, Monique M., 7866
McCleery, Tania L.J., 6115
McClellan, James G., 9081
McClellan, Robert, 3049
McClelland, Frances, 108
McClelland, Kym, 9311
McClelland, Scott, 3283
McClelland, Stephanie, 6457
McClelland, Stephanie P., 6457
McClelland, W. Carter, 6457
McClenahan, Patrick, 809
McClendon Revocable Trust, Katie Rose, 4964
McCleod, James E., 4888
McClimon, Timothy J., 5587, 5588
McClintock, Emily N., 7595
McClintock, Greg, 2768
McClintock, T.K., 7594
McClintock, Virginia, 9081
McClister, Chase, 7921
McCloskey, Karen, 101
McCloskey, Shaun, 7490
McCloud Investments, 58
McCloud, William Bernard, 2431
McCluiston, Deborah, 1390
McClung, James F., Jr., 973, 1120
McClung, Lori, 7639
McClure Oil Company, Inc., 9049
McClure, Don, 1407
McClure, Donald, 2253
McClure, Gayle, 5046
McClure, Peggy, 8543
McClure, Teri Plummer, 2566, 3745
McCluskey, Cameron, 5521
McClymont, Jim, 5068
McClymont, Mary E., 1940
McColgin, Alice, 3319
McColl, Hugh L., Jr., 2514
McCollam, Jan-Gee, 1589
McCollum, Jen, 9410
McCollum, Steven, 2369
McComas, Murray K., 7993
McComb, Donovan, 5009
McComb, William, 5976
McCombs Family Charitable Lead Trust, 9009
McCombs, Lynda G., 9009
McComsey, Robert, 7425
McComsey, Robert R., 7425
McConaghy, Tara Roth, 602
McCone, Theiline M., 9693
McConn, Christiana R., 9203
McConn, Margaret E., 9135
McConnell, Alicia, 1478
McConnell, Allen, 1394
McConnell, Beverly Anne, 7955
McConnell, Britt, 1020
McConnell, C. Douglas, 3195
McConnell, Carl R., 898
McConnell, Charlotte, 5157
McConnell, Jane, 1391
McConnell, John D., Dr., 7340
McConnell, John H., 7563
McConnell, John P., 7563
McConnell, Kathryn, 7181
McConnell, Leah F., 898
McConnell, LeeAnn, 4550
McConnell, Marion, 3686
McConnell, Matthew, 1445
McConnell, Michelle, 2827
McConnell, Page, 9376
McConnell, September, 3407
McConnell, Stacey Willits, Esq., 7979
McConnell, Warren L., 7771
McConnell, William, 7540, 7610
McCool, Kirby Cohn, 9186
McCorkle, Patricia, 6338
McCormack, Duncan, III, 1200
McCormack, Elizabeth J., 5622, 7009
McCormack, Elizabeth P.W., 157
McCormack, Jill A., 9397
McCormack, Jill B., 2708
McCormack, Judith B., 2708
McCormack, Kristen J., 4263, 6150
McCormack, Mike, 8705
McCormack, Wayne P., 1566
McCormack, William, 4768, 5316
McCormick Trust, Anne, 6458
McCormick Trust, Brooks, 3010
McCormick Trust, Charles Deering, 3010
McCormick Trust, Margaret, 6458
McCormick Trust, Roger, 3010
McCormick Trust, Vance C., 6458
McCormick, Ben, 3614
McCormick, Brooks, 3010
McCormick, Charles, 2792
McCormick, Courtney M., 5416
McCormick, James G., 2752
McCormick, Jennifer, 3614
McCormick, Kathleen, 278
McCormick, Margaret O., 6458
McCormick, Robin, 3296
McCormick, Robin Y., 4822
McCormick, Steve, 3245
McCormick, Susan R., 7934
McCormick, Thomas, 9459
McCormick, Thomas P., 5644
McCormick, Tracy, 9802
McCortney, John J., 3229
McCosker, Pamela, 331
McCotter, Kevin, 3615
McCourt, MaryFrances, 3278
McCovern, Robert B., 5379
McCown, J. Ross, 5021
McCown, Pete, Dr., 3298
McCown, Teresa, 7488
McCoy, Alan H., 7366
McCoy, Cathy, 3552
McCoy, Chris, 4349
McCoy, Dena Woodard, 7899
McCoy, Dru, 3280
McCoy, Floyd, 8109
McCoy, Jacqueline R., 3999
McCoy, James, 2525
McCoy, James N., 9010
McCoy, Joanne R., 3758
McCoy, Louise Boney, 7232
McCoy, Mark, 9010
McCoy, Richard T., 1286
McCoy, Stephen, 6285
McCoy, Terri, 3319
McCoy, Vicki D., 9010
McCracken, Carol, 2105
McCracken, Merrick, 8655
McCrady, Christopher R., 7966
McCrady, Priscilla J., 7966
McCrae, Angela H., 8504
McCrary, Guy, 9091
McCrary, James, 21
McCrary, Margaret, 1615
McCrary, Mary L., 8855
McCraven, Paul, 5979
McCraven, Paul A., 1651
McCray, Mark, 1037
McCray, Robert B., 229
McCrea, Colin, 5622
McCready, Mathilda Staunton Craig, 8296
McCready, Travis, 3956
McCreary, Robert G., III, 7499
McCrimlisk, George H., 621
McCrimlisk, Kathleen, 621
McCrory, J. Lyndall, 7773
McCrory, Ken, 3295
McCrory, Kenneth, 7942
McCrury, Phillip W., 8776
McCrystal, Bill, 9401
McCuan, Suzanna, 4407
McCubbin, Donald J., 786
McCubbin, Rebecca, 7766
McCue, Howard M., III, 2745, 2849
McCulley, Paul, 1037
McCulloch, Deb, 7640
McCulloch, Dorothy, 8416
McCulloch, Dorothy R., 8416
McCulloch, Norman Estes, Jr., 8416
McCulloch, Rob, III, 7640
McCulloch, Robert, 9046
McCulloch, Scorr, 1771
McCullough, Barbara C., 899
McCullough, Brian J., 899
McCullough, Frank H., III, 1404
McCullough, Hubert L., Jr., 8545
McCullough, James T., 9011
McCullough, Lawrence I., 899
McCullough, Lisa, 186
McCullough, Mike, 4342
McCullough, P. Mike, 9019
McCullough, Ralph H., 9011
McCullough, Robert F., Jr., 899
McCullough, Robert F., Sr., 899
McCullough, Ruth J., 9011
McCullough, Stacey A., 8416
McCully, A.C., 188
McCully, Michael, 5327
McCune, Barron P., Jr., 8332
McCune, Charles L., 8161
McCune, David F., 900
McCune, Florence M., 3533
McCune, James, 8332
McCune, John R., IV, 8160
McCune, Marshall L., 5529
McCune, Perrine Dixon, 5529
McCune, Sara Miller, 900
McCune, Stephanie, 1394
McCune-Elmore, Louisa, 7766
McCurdy, Jeffrey, 2038
McCurdy, Matilda G., 8417
McCusker, Francis C., 9784
McCutchen, Brunson S., 8162
McCutchen, Charles W., 8162
McCutchen, Margaret W., 8162
McCutchen, Mathew, 9730
McCutchen, Matthew B., 9657
McCutchen, Woodrow C., 5784
McCutcheon, Hilary H., 3010
McDade, Robert E., 4841
McDaniel, John P., 1925
McDaniel, Lola, 9012
McDaniel, Mark, 4451
McDaniel, Marvin, 4808
McDaniel, Meta, 7290
McDaniel, Meta L., 7218
McDaniel, Ronald, 3011
McDaniel, Ronald L., 3011
McDaniel, Sharon L., 9595
McDaniel, Tom J., 7728
McDaniel, William, 9835
McDaniel-Lowe, Sharon L., 4869
McDaniels, Duval Meade, 8680
McDavid, Stephan L., 4846
McDavitt, Linda, 9073
McDede, David P., 1083
McDemmond, Marie V., 3345
McDermott, Allison S., 6148
McDermott, Edward H., 1109
McDermott, Eugene, 8832, 9013
McDermott, Eugene, Mrs., 8832, 9013
McDermott, Peter, 1557
McDermott, Richard G., Jr., 2166
McDevitt, Caryl, 5183
McDevitt, Jerry S., 1642
McDevitt, John, 2566
McDevitt, Robert J., 5183
McDonald Charities, Ronald, 341
McDonald's Corporation, 3012
McDonald's Twin Cities Co-Op, 3245
McDonald, Alisa, 7196
McDonald, Artemis, 9384
McDonald, Barbara Anderson, 8665
McDonald, Barry, 3576
McDonald, Bill, 1394
McDonald, Bob, 5162
McDonald, Brian, 3826
McDonald, Charles Pat, 8901
McDonald, Craig, 4502
McDonald, Debbie S., 2643
McDonald, Denis H., 3648
McDonald, Eric, 8994
McDonald, Frederick L., 4340
McDonald, Hugh, 3666
McDonald, J., 9606
McDonald, J.M., Sr., 144
McDonald, James, 2478
McDonald, James M., Sr., 1817
McDonald, James P., 7945, 7946
McDonald, Jennifer, 19
McDonald, Jill, 9185
McDonald, Joe, Jr., 2523
McDonald, Judy, 1012

McDonald, Kevin, 1511
McDonald, Kristen, 4543
McDonald, Meghan, 3826
McDonald, Micheal J., 7932
McDonald, Pat, 8863
McDonald, Peter D., 3199
McDonald, Richard A., 901
McDonald, Sharon, 8875
McDonald, Susan, 7180, 7332
McDonald, Susan Cameron, 9593
McDonald, Susan Montgomery, 7585
McDonald, Sylvia, 9916
McDonald, Thomas M., 1773
McDonald, Todd, 144
McDonald, Walter J., 7837
McDonald, William E., 7256
McDonnall, Jeffrey M., 4941
McDonnell Charitable Trust A, James S., 4166
McDonnell Charitable Trust B, James S., 4166
McDonnell Foundation, James S., 4918
McDonnell Trust, Thomas A., 4940
McDonnell, Alicia S., 4918, 4941
McDonnell, James S., III, 4166, 4918, 4941
McDonnell, Jean, 4937, 4940
McDonnell, Jeffrey M., 4918
McDonnell, John, 702
McDonnell, John F., 1458, 4166, 4918, 4941
McDonnell, Katherine H., 4166
McDonnell, Matthew J., 1458
McDonnell, Patricia L., 1458
McDonnell, Thomas A., 4940
McDonough, Bernard P., 9784
McDonough, Bill, 4830
McDonough, C. Jean, 4167
McDonough, Diana Hattler, 9471
McDonough, Diane, 5807
McDonough, Jim, 8529
McDonough, Joanne, 5473
McDonough, Kathleen, 1765
McDonough, Kevin M., Rev., 4729
McDonough, Kevin, Fr., 4614
McDonough, Kimberly, 4928
McDonough, Lindsay Y., 8529
McDonough, Mark E., 1929, 5379
McDonough, Myles, 4167
McDougal Family Foundation, 2761
McDougal, Alfred L., 3013
McDougal, Jan, 3013
McDougal, Stephen, 3013
McDougal, Thomas, 3013
McDougall, Duane, 7876
McDougall, Ruth Camp, 5742
McDowell, Boyd, III, 3146
McDowell, Catherine P., 5182
McDowell, Jay H., 5880
McDowell, Mary M., 1321
McDowell, Mike, 1040
McDowell, Phil, 1178
McDowell, Richard E., 8200
McDowell, Tom, 8521
McEachern, D.V., 9678
McEachern, Ida J., 9678
McElhinney, Christie, 1390
McElory, Andrew M., 7379
McElrath, Karen K., 4633
McElroy, Evan, 1005
McElroy, Mark, 5137
McElroy, R.J., 3461
McElwain, Floyd H., 8098
McElwee, Charles R., 9780
Mcelwee, Joseph M., Jr., 8470
McEnery, James, Fr., 2656
McEnroe, Ericka Varga, 1232
McEvily, Paul, 5209
McEvoy, David, 95
McEvoy, George H., 4168
McEvoy, Mildred H., 4168
McEvoy, Patrick, 8778
McEwen, Beatrice G., 1563
McFadden Trust, 2459
McFadden, Bruce, 945
McFadden, Chris A., 3085
McFadden, Jeanmarie, 6507
McFadden, Jim, 3336
McFadden, Mary, 4292
McFadden, Michael, 7945
McFadden, Roger, 4172
McFaddin, Eugene H.B., 9258
McFaden, Frank T., 7424
McFadyen, Barbara Nicholson, 6558, 8064
McFall, F. Lawrence, 9413
McFarland Trust, C.E., 3612
McFarland Trust, D.A., 3612
McFarland, Barry, 5062
McFarland, Charlie, 7691
McFarland, Dolly, 2742
McFarland, Duncan, 7982
McFarland, Duncan M., 3961
McFarland, Elizabeth M., 3961
McFarland, Ellen B., 3961
McFarland, John, 208
McFarland, John A., 3807
McFarland, Richard D., 4709
McFarlane, Brian, 986
McFarlane, R. Cathleen Cox, 2233
McFate, Robert W., 8222
McFawn, Lois Sisler, 7664
McFeely, Nancy K., 8163
McFerran, Billie Love, 9054
McGaffey, Jere D., 9810
McGarry, Kris, 5117
McGarvey, Matthew, 3466
McGaughey, Frank, 2519
McGawn, Mike, 1388
McGee and Sons, Thomas, 4942
McGee, B. Lee, 1867
McGee, Chris, 3552
McGee, David, 4942
McGee, Dean A., 7774
McGee, Flo, 8996
McGee, Frank, 4942
McGee, Frank, Mrs., 4942
McGee, Gary C., 9506
McGee, John R., 4942
McGee, Joseph J., 4942
McGee, Joseph J., Jr., 4942
McGee, Joseph J., Mrs., 4942
McGee, Josh B., 8672
McGee, Julie, 4942
McGee, Louis B., 4942
McGee, Molly, 4942
McGee, Nancy, 8462
McGee, Shirley, 7181
McGee, Simon, 4942
McGee, Simon P., 4942
McGee, Suzanne P., 9092
McGee, Thomas R., Jr., 4942
McGee, Vincent, 6864
McGehee, Hobson C., III, 4825
McGehee, Hobson C., Jr., 4825
McGehee, Holly, 8543
McGeogh, Ed, 1890
McGeorge, Andrew, 9384
McGettrick, Mark F., 9422
McGhee, C. Andrew, 8014
McGhee, Terry, 7445
McGill University, 5707
McGill, Charmaine D., 8743
McGill, Jason, 5608
McGill, Joe K., 8813
McGill, Larry, 633
McGill, Peter R., 3826
McGill, Thomas, 4353
McGinley, John C., 8164
McGinley, John R., Jr., 8164
McGinley, Rita M., 8164
McGinn, Deborah E., 6093
McGinn, Fidelma, 9731
McGinn, Suzanne, 1668
McGinnes, Larry D., 2243
McGinness, James J., 8599
McGinness, Janet M., 6573
McGinnis, Jay M., 9989
McGinnis, Jim, 4831
McGinnis, John, 3851
McGinnis, John W., 8461
McGinnis, Susan Stratton, 8304
McGivern, Arthur J., 3040
McGladrey LLP, 9470
McGlinn, Barbara T., 7988
McGlinn, John F., 7988
McGlinn, John F., II, 7988
McGlinn, Kristin E., 7988
McGlinn, Terrence J., Sr., 7988
McGlothlin, Everett, 9998
McGlothlin, Frances G., 9482, 9546
McGlothlin, James W., 9482, 9483, 9546
McGlothlin, Michael D., 9483
McGlothlin, Thomas D., 9483
McGlothlin, Woodrow W., 9483
McGlothlin-Gayle, Martha, 9546
McGlynn, Burton J., 4706
McGlynn, Daniel J., 4706
McGlynn, Michael J., 4706
McGlynn, Patricia J., 4706
McGlynn, Thomas P., 4706
McGoldrick, John T., Jr., 2502
McGoldrick, Richard J., 3680
McGonagle, Dextra Baldwin, 6460
McGonigle, Cathy, 111
McGonigle, John W., 8033
McGourthy, Nadia T., 4327
McGovern, Jean, 6451
McGovern, John, 9189
McGovern, John P., 9014
McGovern, Kathrine G., 9014
McGovern, Katie, 2806
McGovern, Lynn A., 1166
McGovern, Margaret, 860
McGovern, Renee, 2265
McGovern, Robert B., 5381
McGovern, Rondi, 7358
Mcgowan Charitable Fund, William G., 5114
McGowan, Archie, 5171
McGowan, Brenda, 2089
McGowan, David M., 2812
McGowan, Gertrude, 3014
McGowan, Gertrude C., 8152
McGowan, Leo, 3014
McGowan, Mark S., 2101
McGowan, Stephen, 414
McGowan, Sue Gin, 3014
McGowan, Tim, 3014
McGowan, William G., 3014
McGowan, William P., 3014
McGowan-Swartz, MaryPat, 3014
McGrail, Joseph A., Jr., 4285
McGrail, Lauren, 6326
McGrann, Sharon, 4591
McGrath, Christina, 1406
McGrath, Christopher R., 4098
McGrath, Cori T., 206
McGrath, David J., III, 4098
McGrath, David J., Jr., 4098
McGrath, JoAnn, 4098
McGrath, Kathleen, 217
McGrath, Kevin B., Jr., Hon., 6339
McGrath, Marian H., 3258
McGrath, Mary Ann, 6774
McGrath, Nancy, 4780
McGrath, Raymond J., Hon., 6024
McGrath, Roz, 1287
McGrath, Scott J., 4098
McGrath, Sean P., 4098
McGrath, Susan B., 7949
McGraw Charitable Lead Annuity Trust, Donald C., 6461
McGraw Charitable Trust, D., 6461
McGraw Foundation, Donald C., Inc., 6462
McGraw Hill Companies, 6904
McGraw, A. William, 7579
McGraw, David W., 6461
McGraw, Donald C., 6461
McGraw, Donald C., III, 6461
McGraw, Harold W., III, 1640
McGraw, Harold W., Jr., 1640
McGraw, Harold, III, 9470
McGraw, John L., 6462
McGraw, John L., Jr., 6462
McGraw, Lee, Ms., 6462
McGraw, Lora, 5422
McGraw, Max, 3015
McGraw, Michael, 7660
McGraw, Regina, 3231
McGraw, Richard F., 3015
McGraw, Robert L.W., 6461
McGraw, Robert P., 1640
McGraw, Suzanne, 1640
McGraw-Edison Co., 3015
McGree, Elizabeth, 9767
McGregor, Katherine, 9277
McGregor, Katherine W., 4498
McGregor, Nanci, 7341
McGregor, Scott, 349
McGregor, Tracy W., 4498
McGrew, George, 3506
McGrew, Mike, 3509
McGrory, Mary, 6760
McGrory, Patrick W., III, 1845
McGruder, Mary Helen, 2525
McGuigan, Chris Ann, 4369
McGuiness, Luke, 2673
McGuinn, Ann M., 7966
McGuinness, J. Luke, 2828
McGuire, Allen, 9157
McGuire, Christopher M., 309
McGuire, Frank, 30
McGuire, Grant, 9795
McGuire, James C., 1703
McGuire, Michael, 2877, 4359
McGuire, Nadine M., 4707
McGuire, Patricia, 1890, 1893
McGuire, Peggy, 8830
McGuire, Raymond J., 5780, 6174
McGuire, Robert A., Jr., 7916
McGuire, Ruth H., 9892
McGuire, Tina, 7182
McGuire, Tom, 7295

McGuire, Tricia L.M., 4500
McGuire, Vanessa J.B., 2931
McGuire, William W., Dr., 4707
McGuirt, Milford W., 5349
McHale, Brandee, 5780
McHale, David R., 1656
McHale, James E., 4474
McHale, Patrick J., 4666
McHarque, Jay, 2142
McHenry, Pat, 4462
McHenry, Richard J., 1926
McHenry, Stacy, 3263
McHugh, Alaistair C.H., 904
McHugh, Alice L., 1800
McHugh, Consuelo Hall, 904
McHugh, Frank, 1818
McHugh, Frank A., Jr., 1800
McHugh, Marie L., 1800
McHugh, Paul, 7631
McHugh, Theresa, 1818
McIlhenny Charitable Lead Unitrust, G.W., 3654
McIlhenny, John S., 2777
McIlhenny, Paul C.P., 3654
McIlvaine, Andrew M., 8332
McInaney, Nancy Clair Laird, 2449
McInerney, Christina, 6104
McInerney, Stephen, 5540
McInerny, Elizabeth DeCamp, 5861
McInerny, Ella, 2612
McInerny, James D., 2612
McInerny, Judith, 5804
McInerny, William H., 2612
McIninch, Douglas A., 5177
McInnes, Brian D., 4617
McInnes, Roderick R., 7164
McInnis, James J., 4195
McInnis, Marybeth, 4195
McIntee, David, 5423
McIntire, John, 7565
McIntosh, Bruce A., 970
McIntosh, Colin H., 1928
McIntosh, David, 3016
McIntosh, Frederick J., 970
McIntosh, Hunter H., 1928
McIntosh, James C., 2593, 2594
McIntosh, Jessa, 7088
McIntosh, Joan H., 1928
McIntosh, John V., 7208
McIntosh, Jon, 970
McIntosh, Josephine H., 1928
McIntosh, Karen, 1928
McIntosh, Katie, 970
McIntosh, Marie Joy, 1928
McIntosh, Michael, 3016
McIntosh, Michael A., 1928
McIntosh, Michael A., Jr., 1928
McIntosh, Nettie M., 7178
McIntosh, Peter, 1928
McIntosh, Thomas J., 970
McIntosh, William A., 3016
McIntosh, Winsome D., 1928
McIntyre Financial Svcs., 9016
Mcintyre, Allen H., 8477
McIntyre, Brian James, 9679
McIntyre, Daniel, 8363
McIntyre, Dee Ann, 3462
McIntyre, J. Scott, Jr., 3462
McIntyre, James B., 3283
McIntyre, John Stuart, 9679
McIntyre, Judi, 9775
McIntyre, Maurice J., 9679
McIntyre, Mildred, 3462
McIntyre, Shirley A., 9679
McIntyre, Shirley C., 9016
McIntyre, Susan, 6015
McIntyre, William S., 9016
McIntyre-Hess, Sarah Ann, 9679
McIntyre-Lee, Mary Irene, 9679
McJunkin Red Man Corp., 7765
McJunkin, Donald R., 1817
McJunkin, Thomas N., 9780
McKaig, A. Stuart, III, 7173
McKaig, Tom, 3360
McKay, Alan L., 319
McKay, Alexandra, 9595
McKay, Charles, 3285
McKay, Christine, 1104
McKay, Elaine, 902, 1104
McKay, Janet, 6778
McKay, Jeanne, 1267
McKay, John, 1104
McKay, John P., 902
McKay, Marcella, 4838
McKay, Matthew G., 3613
McKay, Monika, 3656
McKay, Rich, 6451
McKay, Robert, 902
McKay, Robert B., 9902
McKay, Robert L., 1104
McKay, Robert L., Jr., 1104
McKay, Robert L., Sr., 902
McKay, Sarah, 2123
McKay, Verlon L., 319
McKean, Linda B., 5209
McKean, Quincy A.S., III, 5209
McKee Foods Corp., 8527
McKee, Clyde V., III, 9198
McKee, E. Marie, 5818
McKee, James G., 6853
McKee, Jay, 5726
McKee, Joan H., 3264
McKee, John, 4814
McKee, John S., Jr., 8825
McKee, Rose A., 7935
McKeehan, David, 4194
McKeehan, Steve, 6
McKeen, Mark A., 9773
McKeen, Mary Alice, 87
McKeever, Lester, Jr., 3099
McKelfresh, Greg, 3333
McKell, Nedra Roney, 9349
McKell, Robert, 9349
McKellar, Archie C., 6970
McKellar, Marie T., 6970
McKelvy, Nancy H., 2906
McKenna, Anna, 8217
McKenna, Charles B., 2812
McKenna, Cheryl, 7412
McKenna, Deborah J., 8288
McKenna, Katherine M., 8166
McKenna, Laura K, 7023
McKenna, Laura K., 7024
McKenna, Laura Kind, 8125
McKenna, Long and Aldridge, LLP, 2516
McKenna, Mark, 1076
McKenna, Martha B., 3971
McKenna, Philip M., 8167
McKenna, Wallace G., Jr., 9474
McKennarich, Zan, 8167
Mckenzie 2008, 1035
Mckenzie, Barbara, 1035
McKenzie, Charles "Lad", 6721
McKenzie, D. Ray, Jr., 2418, 2419
McKenzie, J. Michael, 9366
McKenzie, Lance, 5108
McKenzie, Mickey, 1035
McKenzie, Richard C., Jr., 9244
McKeone, Tod, 5062
McKeown, Deb, 4342
McKeown, Ellen, 9054
McKeown, Jean M., 5801
McKeown, Scott, 4342
McKernan, Cynthia S., 9181
McKernan, R. Jack, Jr., 8040
McKervey, Michael, 3354
McKesson Corp., 903
McKesson HBOC, Inc., 903
McKibben, Andrew, 5200
McKibben, Diana, 5200
McKiernan, Holiday Hart, 3345
McKillop, Janet Feldstein, 579
McKim, Jim, 4609
McKinley, Brent, 9322
McKinley, Dick, 1520
McKinley, Mark, 7376
McKinnell, Henry A., 9985
McKinney, Barbara Alexander, 9799
McKinney, Catherine A., 8168
McKinney, David, 7058
McKinney, David E., 3219
McKinney, Tom, 3391
McKinnon, Michele A.W., 9521
McKinnon, Paul, 5780
McKinstry Co., 9680
McKinzie, Addie, 77
McKissack, Cheryl Mayberry, 2800
McKissack, Eric T., 2873, 2875
McKissic, James, 8548
McKissick, Ellison Smyth, III, 8486
McKleroy, John P., Jr., 7
McKnight Foundation, The, 4708, 4730
McKnight Stock Fund, William D., 2514
McKnight, Evelyn Franks, 2235
McKnight, H. James, 7925
McKnight, Marquette M., 2438
McKnight, Mason H., III, 2434
McKnight, Maude L., 4709
McKnight, Steven L., 3833
McKnight, William L., 4709
McKown, Charles H., Jr., Dr., 1773
McLain, Adam, 7001
McLain, Beverley, 2040
McLain, Kathleen G., 3760
McLain, Tim, 7585
McLanahan, Astride, 7971
McLanahan, Barbara H., 4681
McLanahan, Martha, 6368
McLanahan, Sara S., 6782
McLane, Cooper, 1578
McLane, Drayton, Jr., 8674
McLane, Jane, 9215
McLane, Linda Harper, 4169
McLane, P. Andrews, 4169
McLaren, James, 5985
McLaren, James I., 5985
McLaughlin, Beth, 9845
McLaughlin, David, 9087
McLaughlin, Deborah A., 3991
McLaughlin, Donald A., 3205
McLaughlin, Donald E., 5394
McLaughlin, Douglas, 9999
McLaughlin, Francis M., 8385
McLaughlin, Gladys, 9702
McLaughlin, Jill, 3424
McLaughlin, Jill A., 2148
McLaughlin, Joseph J., 7936
McLaughlin, Kathleen, 210
McLaughlin, Maureen, 2329
McLaughlin, Neil, 9775
McLaughlin, Ottavia, 5439
McLaughlin, Sheila Ortega, 5533
McLaughlin, Stephen M., 2148
McLaughlin, Steve, 3356
McLaughlin, Virginia L., 9558
McLaughlin, William B., III, 8236
McLaughlin, William P., 4482
Mclaurin, Charles S., III, 8477
McLean Bible Church, 9059
McLean Contributionship, The, 7977
McLean, E.D., Jr., 4835
McLean, E.D., Mrs., 4835
McLean, Elizabeth P., 8169
McLean, Elizabeth R., 8169
McLean, Julie, 3788
McLean, Justina, 4835
McLean, Justina W., 4835
McLean, Kerry, 723
McLean, Lisa, 8169
McLean, Marcia, 7009
McLean, Margaret B., 1384
McLean, Mary, 4921
McLean, Robert, 8169
McLean, Sandra, 8169
McLean, Sandra L., 8169
McLean, Susan Johnson, 6193
McLean, Susannah, 8169
McLean, Thomas R., 7264
McLean, Wendy, 8169
McLean, William L., III, 8169
McLean, William L., IV, 8169
McLean, William L., Jr., 8169
Mclellan, Richard, 4722
McLendon, William E., 2433
McLennan, Matt, 1781
McLeod, Christopher K., 1641
McLeod, Elaine M., 1641
McLeod, George E., 179
McLeod, James A. W., 7078
McLeod, Martha, 5175
McLeod, Phillip, 777
McLeod, Scott, 1641
McLeod, Tommy D., 91
McLester, Scott G., 5506
McLintock, Nick, 7594
McLoraine, Helen M., 1479
McLoud, David, 3910
McLoughlin, Hugh, 6040
McMahan, Lewis H., 9227
McMahon, Ashley R., 58
McMahon, Betty T., 58
McMahon, Bill, 6507
McMahon, Caroline D., 8013
McMahon, Carrie C., 58
McMahon, David A., 58
McMahon, Deb, 3281
McMahon, Eugene D., 7776
McMahon, Joel D., III, 9222
McMahon, Joel W., 58
McMahon, John, 51
McMahon, John J., III, 58
McMahon, John J., Jr., 58, 2475
McMahon, John, Jr., 43
McMahon, Kevin G., 8759
McMahon, Leslie W., 9253
McMahon, Linda E., 1642
McMahon, Louise D., 7776
McMahon, Mary M., 8013
McMahon, Rob, 6127, 6820
McMahon, Vincent K., 1642
McManemin, Megan, 1512
McMannis, Sandra, 2041
McManus, Deborah H.M., 6463
McManus, James T., II, 32
McManus, Jason D., 6463
McManus, John F., Esq., 9414

McManus, Joseph, Capt., 9501
McManus, Phil, 248
McManus, Sophie, 6463
McManus, Sydney, 2199
McManus, Timothy K., 6183
McManus, Victoria, 3990
McMath, Kent, 7496
McMichael, Dalton L., Jr., 7265
McMichael, Dalton L., Sr., 7265
McMichael, R. Daniel, 7968
McMichael, Warren, 2512
McMicking, Brent, 904
McMicking, Henry C., 904
McMicking, Joseph R., 904
McMickle, Marvin A., Rev., 6722
McMillan Living Trust, Genevieve, 4291
McMillan Trust, D.W., 50
McMillan, Bev, 5511
McMillan, Daniel W., 50
McMillan, David J., 4716
McMillan, Fiona, 3010
McMillan, Genevieve, 4291
McMillan, James, 279
McMillan, John, 3132
McMillan, L. Richards, II, 112
McMillan, Thomas G., 9778
McMillan, Whit, 8502
McMillen, Carol, 905
McMillen, Dale W., 3352
McMillen, Dale W., III, 3352
McMillen, John F., 3352
McMillen, Karl, Jr., 905
McMillen, Mike, 9681
McMillen, Robert B., 9681
McMillen, Shannon, 905
McMillian, Amanda M., 8661
McMillian, Annie, 4829
McMillian, Hellen W., 3
McMillian, Lonnie M., 3
McMillian, Lonnie S., 3
McMillin, Kelly, 414
McMillion, Donald C., 7266
McMinn, Anne, 906
McMinn, Anne W., 906
McMinn, Charles, 906
McMinn, Charles J., 906
McMinn, Kimbela, 7181
McMorris, Clare T., 5721
McMorrow, Melissa S., 4186
McMullan, Holt, 4829
McMullen, Catherine, 5378
McMullen, Jacqueline, 5378
McMullen, John J., Jr., 5378
McMullen, John J., Sr., 5378
McMullen, Karen, 5414
McMullen, Lori, 9998
McMullen, Mark, 9854
McMullen, Mark J., 9836, 9855
McMullen, Peter, 5378
McMullin, Jeffrey C., 177
McMullin, Kimball R., 4966
McMurchie, Jack, 7854
McMurdy Fund, Robert & Janet, 2747
McMurray, McCain, 5662
McMurray, Michael, 7607
McMurray-Russ, Martha, 7178
McMurrey, Charles D., 8887
McMurry, Mick, 9986
McMurry, Neil A., 9986
McMurry, Susie, 9986
McMurtrie, Sandra, 4605
McMurtry Charitable Lead Trust of 2003, Ann Kathryn, 2236
McMurtry, Ann, 2236
McMurtry, Ann K., 2236
McMurtry, Burton, 2236
McMurtry, Burton J., 2236
McMurtry, Cathryn, 2236
McMurtry, John, 2236
McNab, Connie M., 9009
McNabb, F. William, III, 8327
McNabb, Larry, 581
McNair, Alfred, 4814
McNair, Daniel Calhoun, 9017
McNair, James, 1537
McNair, Janice, 9017
McNair, Janice S., 9017
McNair, Kyle, 3908
McNair, Leon, 7698
McNair, Robert C., 9017
McNair, Robert Cary, Jr., 9017
McNairy, Francine, 8135
McNairy, John, 7225
McNairy, John O., 7298
McNairy, Leigh, 7225
McNairy, Leigh H., 7225
McNally, Danny, 7282
McNally, Fritter, 8819
McNally, Jan, 8560
McNally, Jeffrey W., 4339
McNally, Michael, 1627
McNally, Teri, 9414
McNamara, Gerald, 6243
McNamara, Jennifer, 6343
McNamara, Julia M., Dr., 1651
McNamara, Pat, 3700
McNamara, Paula, 8421
McNamara, Robert, 7992
McNamee, Alexandra, 4304
McNamee, Brian M., 238
McNamer, Bruce, 6244
McNaught, Bruce, 98
McNaughton, Brian R., 9702
McNaughton, Christopher J., 121
McNaughton, Stan W., 9702
McNay, Colin, 4192
McNay, Joseph C., 4192
McNeal, A. Scott, 8041
McNeal, Cynthia, 5158
McNeal, James A., 7624
McNeely, Ash, 1112
McNeely, Bob, 1108
McNeely, Donald G., 4701
McNeely, Greg, 4710
McNeely, Gregory, 4701
McNeely, Irene E., 4710
McNeely, Kevin, 4701, 4710
McNeely, Nicholas, 4710
McNeely, Nora, 4701
McNeely, Valerie, 3776
McNeer, J. Frederick, 7809
McNeil, Collin F., 7928, 8240
McNeil, Henry S., 7982
McNeil, Jane, 8141
McNeil, Jennifer, 7982
McNeil, Jennifer C., 8293
McNeil, Jr. 2000 Trust, Robert L., 6464
McNeil, Judson, 4780
McNeil, Kae, 8523
McNeil, Robert D., 7982, 8293
McNeil, Robert L., III, 7928, 8141
McNeil, Robert L., Jr., 1870, 7928, 8141
McNeil, Stanley, 8418
McNeil-Miller, Karen, 7297
McNeill, Dan K., 7184
McNeill, Paul, 4820
McNevin, Aaron, 9656
Mcnew, Robert, 3164
McNicholas, Anthony J., III, 2276
McNiff, Audrey A., 6144
McNight, Paul, 2822
McNinch, Charles, Dr., 4452
McNish, Mary Ellen, 8284
McNulty, Anne Welsh, 6465
McNulty, Donna, 1888
McNulty, John P., 6465
McNulty, Rich, 6285
McNutt, Amy Shelton, 9018
McNutt, Gail, 9854
McNutt, Tom, 8863
McParland, Nathaniel P., 3113
McParland, Peter G., 9944
McPhee, Constance Curran, 6624
McPhee, Penelope "Penny", 2413
McPheeters, Paul, 3938
McPheron, Philip, 5807
McPherson, Ellen, 2383
McPherson, Heidi, 1110
McPherson, Michael, 4016
McPherson, Michael S., 3171
McPherson, Sally, 7287
McPhillips, Frank L., 29
McPhillips, Paul R., 6057
McQuade, Eugene M., 8408
McQuade, Peggy, 8408
McQuade, Peggy J., 8408
McQuain Trust, Hazel Ruby, 9785
McQuain, Hazel Ruby, 9785
McQueen, Jereld E., 9020
McQueen, Robert D., 7104
McQueen, Scott, 3419
McQueeney, Chris, 3313
McQuinn, JoAnn, 3391
McRae Charitable Lead Annuity Trust, Richard D., 4836
McRae, Lawrence D., 5818
McRae, Patricia, 9650
Mcrae, Renee, 9685
McRae, Richard D., Jr., 4836, 4843
McRae, Richard D., Sr., 4836
McRae, Stephanie, 123
McRae, Vaughan W., 4836
McRae, Willard, 1630
McRee, Laurie H., 4832
McRee, Mike, 4820
McReynolds, J. Scott, 7404
McReynolds, Judy G., 9381
McRobbie, Laurie Burns, 3278
McShane, Joseph, 5684
McShane, Kelly Sweeney, 7602
McShepard, Randell, 7478
McSherry, Allison, 3336
McSherry, William, 6080
McShine, Kynaston, 6002
McStay, Ellen, 9040
McStay, John, 8773, 9040
McStay, John D., Mrs., 9040
McStay, Judge, 9040
McSwain, Lawrence, 7180
McSwiggan, Daniel J., 7059
McSwiney, F. Graham, 5165
McTeer, Victor, 4827
McTier, Charles H., 2571, 2579
McTier, John, 2437
McUsic, Molly, 1958
McVaney Family Foundation, 1497
McVaney Trust, Kevin Edward, 1516
McVaney, Carole, 1516
McVaney, Charles, 1516
McVaney, Colleen K., 1446
McVaney, Kevin E., 1446, 1516
McVay, Donna, 3366
McVay, Lucy C., 27
McVay, M.D., 4711
McVay, Marcelle, 4711
McVay, Mary, 4711
McVay, Sara, 4711
McVay, Scott, 5345
McVay, T. Todd, 4711
McVety, Meghan, 7979
McVey, Patricia, 1984
McVie, Alexander S., 3353
McVie, Douglas S., 3353
McVie, Sue Anne, 3353
McWain, Teresa L., 7368
McWane, C. Phillip, 51
McWane, Inc., 51
McWhorter, Carol, 8759
McWhorter, Robert, 2559
McWilliams, Alison, 3754
McWilliams, Anne G., 581
McWilliams, Terrence, 1406
MDCCP, 9664
MDSC, 4774
MDU Construction Services Grp., 7354
MDU Resources Group, Inc., 7354
Mead 2008 Charitable Lead Annuity Trust, Jaylee, The, 3845
Mead Johnson Nutrition Company, 2944
Mead, B. Kathlyn, 229, 366
Mead, B. Kathryn, 1108
Mead, Betsy, 3845
Mead, Brad, 9975
Mead, Diana, 3845
Mead, E. Scott, 6466
Mead, Elise G., 907
Mead, Elizabeth, 3845
Mead, George W., 9902
Mead, Gilbert D., 3845
Mead, Giles W., 907
Mead, Jane W., 907
Mead, Jaylee M., 3845
Mead, Marilyn, 3845
Mead, Marilyn K., 3845
Mead, Parry W., 907
Mead, Stanton, 3845
Mead, Suling C., 6466
Mead-Siohan, Diana, 3845
Meade, Caroline O., 1001
Meade, Gary J., 1001
Meade, Thomas, 1001
Meader Irrevocable Trust, Mary, 4564
Meader Revocable Trust, Edwin, 4564
Meader, Edwin, 4564
Meador, David E., 4463
Meadowcroft, W. Howarth, 9684
Meadows, Algur Hurtle, 9019
Meadows, Amy, 8919
Meadows, Curtis W., Jr., 9019
Meadows, Karen L., 9019
Meadows, Robert A., 9019
Meadows, Stanley, 8610
Meadows, Virginia, 9019
Meadows, William W., 9214
Meadows, Willis L., 3673
Meadows-Efram, Corinne, 442, 1299
Meads, M., 3492
Meage, Choy, 2615
Meagher, Ann Chambers, 5808
Meagher, Kathryn, 1020
Meagher, Laura, 7332
Meagher, Mark J., 2516
Meaher, Augustine, III, 55
Meaher, Joseph L., 55
Meaher, Margaret, 55

Meale, Al, 7972
Mealey, Carol-Ann, 6847
Mealey, Eric, 9354
Mealing, Don, 888
Meaney, Lisa Collins, 3010
Meanning and Napier, 5850
Means, Barbara, 991
Means, Rick L., 4971
Meara, Michael, 418
Meares, Tracey L., 2946
Mearns, Daniel J., 5404
Mears, Joy, 8053
Measamer, Marty, 7217
Measey, William Maul, 8170
Measho, Yema, 7825
Meat, W.W. Johnson, 9837
Meates, Helen, 6898
Meates, Helen, Esq., 6898
Meats, Valley, 9837
Mebane, G. Allen, IV, 7266
Mebane, John G., Jr., 7150
Mebane, Marianne Cheek, 7266
Mebane, W. Carter, III, 7170
Mebane, William, 7266
Mecane, Joseph, 6573
Mechanic, Morris A., 3846
Mechenbier, Jeff, 5532
Meck, Terrence, 6609
Meckel, Amy M., 9183, 9186
Medford Multicare Center, 6288
Medford, William L., 8826
Medgyesy, Erma, 3884
Medical Bridges, Inc., 8927
Medich, William C., 8472
Medichem Trust, The, 6779
Medina Properties, Inc., 2168
Medina, Cesar, 3085
Medina, Kol, 9659
Medina, Monica, 3317
Medina, Terry, 418
Medina, Vicente, 2038
Medina, Vincente, 2038
Medinge, Kelly C., 3826
Medley, Joellen, 2649
Medley, Martha W., 9450, 9460
Medleycott, Alice E., 8171
Medleycott, Mary E., 8171
Medlin, George L., 6518
Medline Industries, Inc., 3019
Medlock Trust, Mary L., 2747
Medlock, Jodie, 666
Medow, Rivkah Beth, 1051
Medsker, Malinda, 3396
Medtronic Foundation, 4792
Medtronic, Inc., 2151, 4712
Medure, Pat, 4703
Medusa Corp., 8757
Meduski, Richard P., 1690
Medyn, Anthony, 9923
Medyn, Yolanda, 9923
Medzegian, Jim, 9715
Medzie, Margaret, 7367
Mee, Margaret, 6467
Meece, Robert S., 7931
Meehan, Avice A., 3818
Meehan, Deborah, 4618
Meehan, Emily Souvaine, 6468
Meehan, Peter J., 7328
Meehan, Terence S., 6468
Meek, Brian, 1154
Meek, Tom J., 3618
Meeker, David, 5437
Meeker, David P., 4067
Meeker, Robert D.C., Jr., 6448
Meekins, Lois, 208
Meeks, Elizabeth C., 2505
Meeks, Elizabeth Cheves, 2505
Meeks, Elsie, 4729
Meeks, Eugene, 6153
Meeks, Randall A., 2170
Meeks, Ryan L., 2505
Meeks, Steve, 2687
Meeks, Terri, 1869
Meena, Hu, 4817
Meena, V. Hugo, Jr., 4817
Meenan, Julie, 636
Meenan, Robert, 3953
Meer, Stephen, 3141
Meers, Elizabeth B., 7387
Meersman, Terrence R., 4627
Meese, Richard, 959
Meeske, Larry, 3033
Meetre, Steve, 5506
Meewes, Kenneth, 2096
Megal, Rhody J., 9965
Megrue, Lizanne G., 1581
Meh Holding Company, Ltd, 8893
Mehallis, Stephen G., 2226
Mehan, Marian, 2995, 4952, 4959
Mehan, Marian V., 4997
Mehiel, Michael, 5572
Mehnert, D., 2149
Mehra, Karen Petersen, 6469
Mehra, Sanjeev, 6469
Mehrberg, Randall E., 5416
Mehta, Amit, 9676
Mehta, Dharmesh, 9021
Mehta, Jainesh, 9021
Mehta, Jay, 9021
Mehta, Jayshree, 9495
Mehta, Nisha B., 9021
Mehta, Rahul, 9021
Mehta, Rahul B., 9021
Meier, Aileen, 3407
Meier, Anne R., 5200
Meier, Bill, 1394
Meier, Charles R., 5424
Meier, Steve, 1030
Meier, Walter C., 5200
Meiers, Margaret, 9435
Meijer, Douglas F., 4499
Meijer, Frederik G.H., 4499
Meijer, Hendrik G., 4499
Meijer, Inc., 4499
Meijer, Lena, 4499
Meijer, Mark D., 4499
Meikle, Bruce E., 375
Meili, Laurie, 1421
Meiling, Dean, 1037, 5138
Meinders, Herman, 7777
Meinders, LaDonna, 7777
Meinders, Robert, 7777
Meinerding, James, 3287
Meiners, Diane, 3409
Meinkiewicz, Richard E., 1755
Meinziger, Rodger, 4839
Meis, Robert F., 3480
Meisels Family Trust, Arthur and Miriam, The, 5543
Meisels, Agnes, 5543
Meisels, Arthur, 5543, 6212
Meisels, Chayem, 5962
Meisels, Joseph, 5905
Meisels, Martin, 5543
Meisels, Miriam, 5543
Meisels, Pearl, 5543
Meisels, Shaindy, 5962
Meisels, Shifra, 5543
Meisinger Trust, 1035
Meisner, Mary Jo, 3956
Meissner, Rose, 3289
Mekhjian, Hagop, 7641
Mekras, George D., 2223
Mekrut, William A., 8393
Melamed, Carol D., 9445
Melamed, Leo, 2756
Melancon, Paul D., 736
Melarkey, Michael, 5124
Melarkey, Michael J., 5103, 5126
Melass, Vicki, 8775
Melbert, J. Michael, 8002
Melbert, R. Barry, 3333
Melbourne, Barbara J., 3424
Melby, Diane, 9775
Melcher, C. LeRoy, 8662
Melcher, James, 5782
Melcher, Marc C., 8662
Melcher, Pierre S., 8662
Melcher, Thomas, 1755
Melchior-Kopp, Janet, 5074
Melchner, Susan, 6918
Meldrum, Annette, 9333
Meldrum, Catherine R., 9333
Meldrum, Christopher S., 9333
Meldrum, Peter D., 9333
Mele, Charles A., 5425, 5496
Mele, Victoria, 8423
Melendez de Santa Ana, Thelma, 579
Melendez, Ada, 5317
Melendez, Carla, 5530
Melendez, Jessica, 8197
Melendez, Yvette, 1609
Melero, Megan, 488
Melfi, Pauline P., 5433
Melgary, Bruce, 8137, 8138
Melgary, L. Bruce, 7912
Melhorn, John, 3545
Melhorn, Julie E., 3545
Melikhov, Anthony, 2714
Melikhov, Anthony S., 2714
Melillo, Samuel T., 5394
Melinson, James, 744
Melisz, Rose, 5979
Melitschka, Bernice, 7640
Melkus Partners, Ltd., 8609
Melkus, Barbara L., 8609
Melkus, Kenneth J., 8609
Melkus, Lauren E., 8609
Mellam, Laural D., 910
Mellencamp, Amy, 9361
Meller, Pat, 8221
Mellies, Marla D., 9705
Mellin, Dorothy, 2805
Mellish, Tom, 3356
Mellman, Ira, 3833
Mello, Glenn, 4152
Mello, Lorraine, 3929
Mellon Bank, 7946
Mellon Bank, N.A., 8307
Mellon Financial Corp., 7946
Mellon Trust of New England, 9484
Mellon, Armour N., 8172, 8173
Mellon, Constance B., 8172
Mellon, Constance Elizabeth, 8172
Mellon, Paul, 6470
Mellon, Richard A., 8172, 8173
Mellon, Richard K., 8173
Mellon, Richard P., 8172, 8173
Mellon, Seward Prosser, 8172, 8173
Mellon, Thomas J., Jr., Hon., 645
Mellor, C. Michael, 1731
Mellor, William (Chip) H., 9880
Mellowes, Charles A., 9829
Mellowes, John A., 9829
Mellowes, John W., 9829
Mellowes, Kathleen J., 9829
Mellowes, Linda T., 9829
Melly, Alice P., 6471
Melly, Alice Pack, 6471
Melly, David Randolph, 6471
Melly, L. Thomas, 6471
Melly, Laura A., 6471
Melly, Lee Scott, 6471
Melly, Thomas L., 6471
Melman, Martha, 3022
Melman, R.J., 3022
Melman, Richard, 3022
Melmed, Matthew, 5483
Melnicke, Breindy, 6664
Melnicke, Michael, 6664
Melo Enterprises, Inc., 246
Melohn, Alfons, 6472
Melohn, Leon, 6472
Melohn, Martha, 6472
Melone, Andrew H., 2715
Melone, Tally S., 2715
Melott, Debra, 7762
Melrose, Kendra L., 4713
Melrose, Kendrick B., 4713
Melrose, Robert A., 4713
Melrose, Velia E., 4713
Melson, Bobby, 8774
Melton, Campbell, 4821
Melton, Chris, 3596
Melton, Jennifer, 3240
Melton, Judy, 3320
Melton, Karen, 8797
Meltzer, Allan H., 8266
Meltzer, Cori Flam, 2034
Meltzer, Roger, 3781
Melville Corp., 8379
Melville, Dorothy, 4170
Melville, Ruth, 4170
Melville, Stephen, 4170
Melvin, E.S., 7162
Melvin, Heather, 755
Melvin, Robin, 5695
Melvin, Ron, 7329
Melzer, Robert, 4141
Melzer, Robert T., 9885
MEMC Electronic Materials, Inc., 4985
MEMX, 9915
Menapace, Herman N., 7474
Menard 1979 Family Trust, 911
Menard, Barbara, 911
Menard, Bernard, 911
Menard, Didier, 1384
Menard, Edward F., 5995
Menard, Joan, 3991
Menard, Marcel, 911
Menard, Mary, 911
Menard, Raymond N., 4144
Menard, William L., 5995
Menasha Corp., 9903
Mencotti, Melissa, 8001
Mendell, Lorne M., 964
Mendelsund, Judy, 6053
Mendenhall, Diane, 5063
Mendenhall, Judy, 7231
Mendenhall, Matt, 3424
Mendez, Bobby, 7180
Mendez, David Louis, 8917
Mendez, Jeffrey, 9354
Mendez-Morgan, Lily, 4103
Mendicina, Dan, 3540
Mendillo, Jane, 3956

Mendlein, Susan, 7505
Mendlovics, Esther, 5543
Mendolowitz, David, 6998
Mendoza, Adela, 8474
Mendoza, Natalie Camacho, 4729
Mendoza, Susana, 2823
Menefee, Albert L., III, 3087
Menefee, Tandy, 208
Menefee, Valere, 3087
Meneilly, Kimberly, 7400
Menendez, Paul Ackerman, 8651
Meng, Engrid, 9904
Meng, Engrid H., 9904
Meng, John C., 9904
Mengebier, David G., 4376
Mengel, Andrea L., 8107
Menges, Glenda, 878
Menges, Kenneth, Jr., J., 7833
Mengle, Glenn A., 8174
Menin Charitable Foundation Inc., Bruce and Julie, 2077
Menkes, Brian, 9463
Menlo, Sam, 913
Menlo, Vera, 913
Mennicke, Michelle, 4738
Mennonite Foundation, 8090
Menon, Venugopal B., 9227
Menoudakos, Chryssanthy L., 6574
Menoudakos, John K., 6574
Menschel Foundation, The, 5764
Menschel, David F., 6473, 7033
Menschel, Joyce F., 6473
Menschel, Lauren E., 6473, 7033
Menschel, Richard B., 7033
Menschel, Richard L., 5763, 5764
Menschel, Robert B., 5763, 6473, 7033
Menschel, Ronay, 5764, 7033
Menschel, Ronay A., 5763
Menshy, Bruce, 3281
Mensore, Tulane, 9773
Menton-Nightlinger, Deborah, 6561
Mentzer, Teresa, 5108
Menzer, Cynthia, 7540
Menzer, James, 7742
Menzies, Gretchen, 7982
Meoli, Anthony J., 3782
Meoli, Michael, 3782
Meoli, Virginia, 3782
Merage, David, 1459, 1460
Merage, Elisabeth, 915
Merage, Katherine, 915, 916, 1459, 1460
Merage, Laura, 1460
Merage, Paul, 915, 916
Merali, Karim, 9022
Merali, Mehdi, 9022
Merali, Pandju, 9022
Mercedes, 8756
Mercer, C. K., 1837
Mercer, Dianne, 1671
Mercer, Elizabeth M., 917
Mercer, Ian, 3295
Mercer, Rebekah, 6474
Mercer, Robert, 6474
Merchan, Dario, 8708
Merchant's National Properties, Inc., 932
Merchant, Jane, 3280
Merchant, Kathryn E., 7404
Merchant, Thomas C., 3828
Merchants Bank, 9369
Merchants Distributors, Inc., 7205
Merchants National Properties, Inc., 1638
Mercier, Michele Bahnik, 5634
Mercik, Kuczarski & Bolduc LLC, 1610
Merck & Co. Inc., 4254
Merck & Co., Inc., 1558, 5379, 5380, 5381
Merck Company Foundation, The, 1929
Merck Foundation, 5380
Merck Research Laboratories, 3833
Merck Sharp & Dohme Corp., 5381
Merck, Elliott, 4171
Merck, Josephine, 1716
Merck, Serena S., 4172
Merck, Wil, 4171
Merco Ventures II, 920
Mercola Foundation, 3046
Mercola, Joseph M., 3046
Mercola.com Natural Health Resource, 3046
Merculief, Boris, 80
Mercury Foundation of New York, 6715
Mercy Works Foundation, 9905
Mercy, Andrew Seth, 6475
Mercy, Eugene, III, 6475
Mercy, Eugene, Jr., 6475, 6493
Meredith Corp., 3463
Meredith Publishing Co., 3464
Meredith, Donald W., 8209
Meredith, E.T., IV, 3464
Meredith, Harry W., 9023
Meredith, Katherine, 3464
Meredith, Katherine C., 3464
Meredith, Kim, 854
Meredith, Lynn M., 9025
Meredith, Thomas J., 9025
Mericle, Kim E., 8176
Mericle, Robert K., 8176
Meridor, Sallai, 6981
Merillat, Lynette S., 5382
Merillat, Orville D., 4500
Merillat, Richard D., 4500, 5382
Merillat, Ruth A., 4500
Merin, Kenneth D., 6150
Meringoff, Stephen J., 6476
Merion Apartments LLC, 9452
Merisotis, Jamie P., 3345
Meriwether, Karen, 5804
Merkatz, Ruth, 5194
Merkin, Lauren K., 5628
Merkin, Richard, 919
Merksamer, Linda, 1103
Merlin, Jean, 617
Mermans, Andy, 7267
Mermans, Bryan K., 7267
Mermans, Cornelis A.M., 7267
Mermans, Jennifer E., 7267
Mermans, Johanna K., 7267
Mermans, Nicole A., 7267
Mermans, Robin B., 7267
Merns, Marcy Syms, 5475
Mero, Holly, 9354
Mero, Paul T., 9322
Merrell, Linda S., 6567
Merriam, Jeffrey, 1151
Merrice, Bruce, 357
Merrick, Anne M., 3796
Merrick, Frank, 7742, 8919
Merrick, Randolph V., 4846
Merrick, Robert, 7742
Merrick, Robert G., III, 3796
Merrick, Robert G., Jr., 3796
Merrick, Robert G., Sr., 3796
Merrick, Robert W., 3633
Merrick, Will, 7742
Merrifield, Ginny, 1314
Merrihew, Linda, 7882
Merrild, Sonja, 4667
Merrill Charitable Lead Trust, 3847
Merrill Charitable Lead Trust, Philip, 3847
Merrill Charitable Lead Unitrust, Dorothy Scott, 8811
Merrill Lynch, 5371
Merrill Lynch & Co., Inc., 7139, 7316
Merrill Lynch Pierce Fenner & Smith, 7428
Merrill Lynch Trust Co., 2269, 4966, 5356, 6544, 7540, 8026, 8136, 9148
Merrill Lynch Trust Company, 5321
Merrill Lynch, Pierce, Fenner & Smith Inc., 6573
Merrill, Amy, 5409
Merrill, Anna, 8511
Merrill, Anthony C., 7868
Merrill, Blythe T., 6584
Merrill, Charles, 7868
Merrill, Danielle, 8811
Merrill, Dorothy Scott, 8811
Merrill, Douglas, 3847
Merrill, Eleanor, 3847
Merrill, Frank G., 8811
Merrill, Harriette M., 8428
Merrill, Holly S., 8811
Merrill, Joan B., 2589
Merrill, Kay, 7868
Merrill, Lenore, 7868
Merrill, Mark B., 2589
Merrill, Nancy, 3847
Merrill, Philip, 3847
Merrill, Scott B., 2589
Merrill, Steven L., 920
Merrill, Tracy Louis, 2985
Merriman, Elaine A., 1930
Merriman, Joe Jack, 1930
Merriman, Kellie C., 626
Merriman, Linda, 7343
Merriman, M. Heminway, II, 7343
Merriman, Michael A., 1930
Merrin, Seth, 6172
Merritt, Edward A., 4644
Merritt, Raymond W., 9471
Merrow, Katherine B., 5182
Merry, Barbara A., 9832
Mersel, Kenneth, 6698
Mershon, Tracey, 4996
Merson, Harry, 7781
Mertens, Joan, 7151
Merton, Juliana L. Johnson, 5224
Mertz, John, 9631
Mertz, Joyce, 6477
Mertz, Len, 9241
Merves, Audrey, 8250
Merves, Stanley, 8250, 8297
Merves-Robbins, Jennifer, 8250
Mervis, Michael P., 9971, 9972
Merz, Lynn, 641
Merz, Steven P., 2482
Merzbacher, Celia I., 7307
Mesdag, Lisa Ann, 6478
Mesdag, T. Willem, 6478
Meserve, Lauren, 7075
Meserve, Richard A., 771
Meservey, Patricia Maguire, 4039
Meshbane, Alice, 3310
Meshri, Sanjay D., 7807
Mesite, I. Margaret, 1643
Mesite, Rose, 1643
Mesivta Torah Institute, 6811
Mesker, David, 4894
Mesler, Jennifer, 4501, 4514
Mesmer, Patti, 8523
Mesrobian, Peter, 8964
Messaro, Maureen, 7671
Messenger, Harold L., 6448
Messer, Joe, 3290
Messer, William B., 3132
Messick, Rod, 8135
Messinger, Alida, 6864
Messinger, Ruth, 6228
Messmer, Steven F., 8260
Messner, Elaine, 5383
Messner, Harold, 5383
Messner, Jenny K., 8503
Messner, Laura, 5383
Messner, Michael G., 8503
Mestdagh, Kristine B., 4352
Mestemacher, Carol, 2817
Meston, Susan, 4369
Mestres, Tony, 9731
Meszoly, Robin, 1888
Metal Technologies, Inc., 3357
Metavante Technologies, Inc., 2097
Metcalf Charitable Trust No. 1, Dorothy A., 8178
Metcalf Charitable Trust No. 2, Dorothy A., 8178
Metcalf Charitable Trust No. 3, Dorothy A., 8178
Metcalf Charitable Trust No. 4, Dorothy A., 8178
Metcalf Charitable Trust No. 5, Dorothy A., 8178
Metcalf Charitable Trust, Dorothy A., 8178
Metcalf, Dorothy A., 8178
Metcalf, James S., 3200
Metcalf, Paula, 5063
Metcalf, Pauline C., 8392
Metcalf, Robert A., 8178
Metcalf, Tim, 894
Metropolitan Baptist Church, 9059
Metropolitan Edison Co., 7455
Metropolitan Environmental Services, 2735
Metropolitan Life Insurance Co., 6479
Metropolitan Museum of Art, 5707
Metteauer, Melinda, 9481
Metz, Dara, 6834
Metz, Deborah T., 9412
Metz, Don, 8670
Metz, Douglas, 7512
Metz, James H., 9838
Metz, Michael, 9375
Metzger, Geneive Brown, 6904
Metzger, Michael J., 2742
Metzger, Moshe, 5598
Metzger, Richard, 8073
Metzger-Utt, Maddy, 9616
Meurer, Mark, 8994
Meurer, Zeena M., 6553
Mevis, Lee, 9816
Mewbourne, Curtis, 1037
Mexico Vendor Casa Deb, 8834
Meybohm, E.G., 2434
Meyer Foundation, Paul E. & Helen S., 5158
Meyer Trust, Dorothy, 668
Meyer Trust, Lillian H., 922
Meyer Wellman, Laura L., 7202
Meyer, A.C., Jr., 3023
Meyer, Adolph H., 4337
Meyer, Agnes E., 1931

Meyer, Alex A., 3439
Meyer, Alice Jane, 9024
Meyer, Alice K., 9127
Meyer, Alvin Reynold, 212
Meyer, Amy, 5158
Meyer, Anthony, 6480
Meyer, Averil Payson, 7080
Meyer, Barbara J., 7080
Meyer, Barry, 922
Meyer, Carla E., 4261
Meyer, Dan, 4679
Meyer, Daniel, 2893, 3125
Meyer, Daniel, M.D., 8216
Meyer, David, 3260
Meyer, David J., 9576
Meyer, Dominique, 6636
Meyer, Edward H., 6480
Meyer, Erie H., 52
Meyer, Eugene, 1931, 5301
Meyer, Eva Chiles, 7833
Meyer, Fred G., 7870
Meyer, Gary, 3284
Meyer, Ginger, 4337
Meyer, Harriet, 2893
Meyer, Ida M., 4337
Meyer, Jack R., 3956
Meyer, Jane, 9024
Meyer, Jane K., 7564
Meyer, Janis, 3514
Meyer, Jennifer, 8468
Meyer, Jenny Love, 7781
Meyer, John E., 53
Meyer, Joyce, 692
Meyer, Karen H., 3023
Meyer, Kristin, 4284
Meyer, Kristine, 9576
Meyer, Linda L., 7813
Meyer, Maggie, 1043
Meyer, Margaret, 6480
Meyer, Michael G., 4739
Meyer, Michelle, 4631
Meyer, Nancy, 2893, 3125
Meyer, Nicole, 5351
Meyer, Noa, 6070
Meyer, Pat, 3473
Meyer, Patricia, 9073
Meyer, Paul J., Sr., 9024
Meyer, Phil, 3390
Meyer, Robert D., 7813
Meyer, Robert R., 53
Meyer, Roslyn M., 6488
Meyer, Sandra, 6480
Meyer, Steven J., 7094
Meyer, Thomas, 3125
Meyer, Vincent, 6481
Meyer, Wendy, 922
Meyer, William, 7405
Meyer, William A., 2276
Meyercord, Champ, 24
Meyerhoefer, Trent M., 7442
Meyerhoff Charitable Income Trust, 3848
Meyerhoff Charitable Income Trust II, 3848
Meyerhoff Memorial Trusts, Rebecca, 3848
Meyerhoff Philanthropic Fund, Rebecca, The, 3848
Meyerhoff, Harvey M., 3849
Meyerhoff, Joseph, 3848
Meyerhoff, Joseph, II, 3848
Meyerhoff, Joseph, Mrs., 3848
Meyerholtz, Rod, 3265
Meyerkopf, Rick, 3690
Meyers Charitable Trust, Joanne, 2834
Meyers, Beverly, 3856
Meyers, Donald Leigh, 6399
Meyers, Dori, 3300
Meyers, Eric, 8818
Meyers, Evan, 3524
Meyers, Gail, 6157
Meyers, Geoffrey G., 7686
Meyers, Howard, 8216
Meyers, Jeremy, 500
Meyers, Jim, 586
Meyers, Judith C., 1602
Meyers, Kathryn, 6157
Meyers, Ken, 2921, 4121
Meyers, Lori L., 3267
Meyers, Mara "Mitch", 4966
Meyers, Mary, 8994
Meyers, Susan, 8811
Meyersiek, Axel, 7001
Meyerson Foundation, David and Minnie, The, 7791
Meyerson, Marvin, 3113
Meyrowitz, Carol, 4308
Meystre, Douglas Q., 3921
Mezey, Naomi, 1894
Mezuman Associates LLC, 3378
MF Global, 2755
MFA Inc., 4943
MFA Oil Co., 4943
MGE Energy, 9898
MGM Grand Las Vegas, 783
MGough, Dennis R., 7279
Mgrublian, Margaret, 1015
MH Equipment, 7638
MH Equipment Co., 2913
MH Logistics, 2913
MHC Investment Co., 3465
Miami Corp., 2791
Miars, Billye, 9108
Micallef, Joseph S., 4634, 4724
Miccio, Maeve, 1166
Michaan, Allen, 2239
Michaan, Joseph, 2239
Michaan, Suzanne, 2239
Michael Alan Group, The, 1771
Michael Supera Trust Dated 11/1/2008, 3183
Michael Supera Trust Dated 3/31/20008, 3183
Michael Supera Trust Dated 3/31/2005, 3183
Michael Supera Trust Dated 9/1/2006, 3183
Michael, Ellen A., 59
Michael, Gary, 2626
Michael, James C., 6226
Michael, Marcie, 3782
Michael, Steven A., 9452
Michael, Ted, 2166
Michael, Todd, 5291
Michaelis, Mary Frances, 7772
Michaels, Alice, 6482
Michaels, Howard, 7539
Michaels, Jack, 3443
Michaels, John, 1566
Michaels, Lorne, 6482
Michalak, Steven R., 7268
Michalski, Peter, 79
Michan, Jane, 570
Michaud, James R., 7407
Michaud, Rachel, 4357
Michel, Betsy S., 5243, 5325
Michel, Clifford F., 5325
Michel, Gary, 905
Michel, Jason L., 5325
Michel, Katherine B., 5325
Michel, Sally J., 3712
Micheli, Michael, 7585
Michelin North America, Inc., 118
Michels Corp., 9906
Michels, Kevin P., 9906
Michels, Patrick D., 9906
Michels, Ruth L., 9906
Michels, Steven R., 9906
Michels, Susan, 4683
Michels, Timothy J., 9906
Michelson, Ellen A., 260
Michelson, Gary Karlin, 540, 923
Michelson, Jere G., 3696
Michelson, Kevin, 9588
Michelson, Michael W., 260
Michener, James A., 7998
Michener, Meredith, 4048
Michigan, Alan, 6068
Mickaco 2003 CRT, 2647
Mickel, Charles, 8476
Mickelsen, Wendy, 9602
Mickens, Helen Pratt, 4357
Mickey, Amy, 7502
Mickey, Joan, 7502
Mickey, R. Bruce, 7502
Micklash, Ken, 4562
Miclat, Joseph F., 7412
Microelectonics Advanced Research Corp., 7307
Microfibres, Inc., 8416
Micron Semiconductor Products, Inc., 2637
Micron Technology, Inc., 2637
Microsoft Corp., 9112
Microsoft Corporation Matching Gifts Program, 9652
Mid Atlantic Arts Foundation, 3083
Mid-Atlantic Dairy Association, 3245
Mid-Coast Trust, 8715
Mid-South Telecommunications Company, 8716
Mid-South Telecommunications Trust, 8716
Midamerican Energy Holdings Co. LTTP, 3465
Middaugh, Amy, 3348
Middendorf, Alice C., 3850
Middendorf, Frank J., 8420
Middendorf, J. William, Jr., 3850
Middendorf, Patricia A., 8420
Middleditch, Leigh B., Jr., 9489
Middlegate Securities, Ltd., 5768, 5769
Middleton, Barbara, 3314
Middleton, Brian, 98
Middleton, Brook, 9395
Middleton, Carl, 9578
Middleton, Carole, 924
Middleton, Diana, 4107
Middleton, Ellen R., 4803
Middleton, Evelyn, 8455
Middleton, Fred A., 924
Middleton, G. Scott, 8455
Middleton, John, 9616
Middleton, Payne, 7080
Middleton, Ralph "Sonny", 71
Middleton, Sarah, 1037
Middleton, Scott, 9054
Middletowne LLC, 9452
Midkiff, Robin S., 2586, 2598
Midland Tech LLC, 6205
Midler, Bette, 8586, 8611
Midnite Express, 975
Midway Baptist Church, 9059
Midway Kids Village LLC, 2568
Midwest Dairy Council, 3245
Midwest Maintenance and Construction, 7214
Midwest Oilseeds Inc., 3482
Midwest Trust Co., 3499, 3500, 3531
Mierlo, Chris van, 1003
Miers, Gina, 25
Miers, Harriet, 8789
Miers, Meghan Trulaske, 4995
Mieziner, Orla, 7511
Mifflin, Robert B., 8545
Migdon, Andrew, 6768
Migeon, Claude J., 3923
Mignone, John, 3324
Mikell, JoAnn, 8779
Mikeska, Terry, 9241
Mikita, Stephen, Esq., 6898
Mikles, Donalyn, 794
Mikolay, Yurianna, 2253
Mikuen, Scott T., 2149
Milagro de Ladera, L.P., 4133
Milam, Karen, 3279
Milanese, Wendy A., 5223
Milano Charitable Lead Trust, Sidonia, 5384
Milano, Bernard J., 5349
Milano, Robert J., 5384
Milas, Lawrence W., 6877
Milbank, Albert G., 1819
Milbank, Jeremiah, 5323
Milbank, Jeremiah, III, 5323, 5385
Milbank, Katharine S., 5323
Milbank, Michelle, 1819
Milbank, Samuel L., 1819
Milbank, Thomas L., 1819
Milbourn, George B., 7509
Milbury, Cassandra M., 8172
Milbury, E. Van R., 8266
Milby, Charles D., Jr., 8888
Milby, Mary J., 8888
Milch, Randal S., 5489
Milder, Daniel C., 3747
Milder, Donald B., 3747
Milder, Terri L., 3747
Mildren, Matt, 9118
Mildren, Nikki, 9118
Mildren, William, Sr., 7557
Mildren, William, Sr., Mrs., 7557
Milek, Shelley, 4806
Miles EM Trust, Ellison, The, 9026
Miles Production Co. Trust, Ellison, The, 9026
Miles Production, Co., Inc., 9026
Miles, Amy E., 8622
Miles, Arthur, 9566
Miles, David P., 4902
Miles, Edward, 1045
Miles, Ellison, 9026
Miles, Gene, 3360
Miles, Jenny, 3379
Miles, Kenneth, 731
Miles, Lee L., 9313
Miles, Loree, 3420
Miles, Michael, 9083
Miles, Paityn, 4372
Miles, Phoebe C., 1784
Miles, William T. "Skip", 4828
Miles-LaGrange, Vicki, 7781
Miles-Polka, Becky, 3466
Miletich, Joseph P., 238
Miley, Gwendolyn, 5327
Milford, J. Robert, 3567

Milgard, Mark, 9683
Milgard-DeGoede, Cari, 9683
Milgard-Rivera, Lori, 9683
Milgram, Anne, 8672
Milgram, Debra, 4223
Milgram, Debra Michelle, 4223
Milgram, Eitan, 4223
Milias, Elizabeth A., 925
Milias, Katherine M., 925
Milias, Margot A., 925
Milias, Mary Ann, 1358
Milias, Mitchell C., 925
Milias, Mitchell J., 925
Miligan, Stephen D., 1316
Milikowsky, Nathan, 4176
Milke, Kristen Olewine, 8068
Milken, D., 926
Milken, Ferne, 927
Milken, Gregory A., 927
Milken, J., 926
Milken, L., 926
Milken, Lori A., 927
Milken, Lowell, 927
Milken, Michael, 927
Milken, R., 926
Milken, S., 926
Milken, Sandra, 927
Milken-Noah, Joni, 927
Mill Park Foundation, Inc., 2284
Millan, Jackie, 1581
Millar, Kenneth, 1267
Millar, Margaret, 1267
Millard, Bethany, 6484
Millard, Katrina Gilbert, 6502
Millard, Robert B., 6484
Millbank, J.M., III, 6115
Millendorf, Howard, 5311
Millenium Pharmaceuticals, 6231
Miller and Smith, Inc., 3886
Miller Charitable Fund LLLP, 2241
Miller Charitable Trust, Jack, 3026
Miller Clock Co., Howard, 4504
Miller Family Charitable Foundation, Audrey and Jack, 3026
Miller Foundation, John D. and Doreen, 5908
Miller Foundation, Joseph F., 3317
Miller Irrev. Trust, Thomas W., 8182
Miller Trust, Hazel, 9685
Miller Trust, Louis H., 7778
Miller, Adam, 3253, 6531
Miller, Adam L., 7989
Miller, Adrienne E., 2079
Miller, Alan B., 8180
Miller, Alice, 7974
Miller, Allen L., 4503
Miller, Alon, 928
Miller, Amos, 8097
Miller, Ann T., 484
Miller, Anna, 4468
Miller, Anne H., 7220
Miller, Arlene Michaels, 3206
Miller, Arthur, 935
Miller, Barbara H., 3100
Miller, Ben R., Jr., 3671
Miller, Betty, 9108
Miller, Bradley S., 4420
Miller, Bryan, 8905
Miller, Bryan J., 9334, 9335
Miller, C. Thomas, 3570
Miller, Carey K., 9684
Miller, Carl E., III, 21
Miller, Carolyn Lacy, 9027
Miller, Catherine, 7421
Miller, Catherine B., 3946
Miller, Chris, 9128
Miller, Christian, 331
Miller, Christopher, 5501
Miller, Christopher D., 468
Miller, Christy, 9354
Miller, Cindy, 9885
Miller, Clara, 5785, 6164
Miller, Constance Marks, 6432
Miller, Curtis, 9789
Miller, Cynthia, 8492
Miller, D., 3107
Miller, D. Byrd, III, 8459
Miller, Dan, 973, 1120
Miller, Dana K., 6722
Miller, Dane A., 3355
Miller, Dane A., Mrs., 3355
Miller, Daniel, 4468
Miller, Daniel P., 9881
Miller, Darryl, 3291
Miller, David, 7231
Miller, David B., 9027
Miller, David J., 1401, 8492
Miller, David T., 7428
Miller, Deanna, 8873
Miller, Diane, 6380
Miller, Diane Edgerton, 9394
Miller, Don, 5524
Miller, Doreen D., 5908
Miller, Doris, 86, 4811
Miller, Duncan L., 8549
Miller, Edith D., 8336
Miller, Edward E., Jr., 8545
Miller, Edward J., 4371
Miller, Edward M., 9555
Miller, Elinor, 3684
Miller, Elisabeth, 9684
Miller, Elise D., 9316
Miller, Elizabeth, 5888
Miller, Elizabeth R., 5888
Miller, Emily, 3554
Miller, Emily Altschul, 6346
Miller, Eric, 8181
Miller, Erin J., Esq., 8351
Miller, Eugene A., 4371, 4498
Miller, F. Robert, 935
Miller, Fitzgerald, 6546
Miller, Frances Cameron, 8747
Miller, Frank R., 2767
Miller, Fred, 9759
Miller, Gail Jackson, 7417
Miller, Georgette, 3280
Miller, Gerard, 8629
Miller, Gilbert, 2414
Miller, Gilbert B., 2411
Miller, Glen, 3024, 3093, 3097
Miller, Goldie Wolfe, 3026
Miller, Gordon, 9863
Miller, Gregory S., 9334, 9335
Miller, H. Fred, 3297
Miller, H. L., 3025
Miller, Harold E., 8299
Miller, Harvey L., 3025
Miller, Harvey R., 7062
Miller, Harvey S.S., 7918
Miller, Harvey Shipley, 5627
Miller, Helen, 3436
Miller, Herman, 4177
Miller, Holly D., 1570
Miller, Howard J., 4504
Miller, J., 3025
Miller, Jack, 3026, 8179
Miller, Jack H., 4504
Miller, James F., 7871
Miller, James H., 8181
Miller, James J., 137
Miller, James O., 7650
Miller, James R., 7583
Miller, Jane E., 5057
Miller, Janet, 3713
Miller, Janet H., 9555
Miller, Jean, 7874
Miller, Jeff, 4026
Miller, Jeffrey, 2241
Miller, Jennifer, 7808
Miller, Jerry D., 8830
Miller, Jill S., 8180
Miller, Jim, 4467
Miller, Joann Schoenbaum, 2313
Miller, Joel, 2350
Miller, John, 4102, 5745
Miller, John A., 8478
Miller, John E., 7378
Miller, John J., 3258
Miller, John R., 8097, 9328, 9336
Miller, John, Dr., 1564
Miller, Jon, 2634
Miller, Joseph, Jr., 2648
Miller, Joseph, Jr., Mrs., 2648
Miller, Judy M., 692
Miller, Julia A., 5483
Miller, Karen, 4872
Miller, Karen G., 9334
Miller, Karen Gail, 9335
Miller, Karen Halverstadt, 2942
Miller, Kate, 1589
Miller, Kate W., 7621
Miller, Katharine P., 4518
Miller, Katherine H., 3206
Miller, Kathy M., 780
Miller, Kenneth, 98
Miller, Kirsten, 9669
Miller, Kristie, 169
Miller, Kyle David, 9027
Miller, Larry, 4448
Miller, Laura, 3279, 8682
Miller, Laura M., 8768
Miller, Lawrence, 3201
Miller, Lawrence H., 9335
Miller, Lawrence Horne "Larry H.", 9334
Miller, Lawrence J., 2032, 8134
Miller, Lee, 3781, 9652
Miller, Lee I., 3781
Miller, Leonard, 2241
Miller, Leslie A., 8183
Miller, Linda, 5062
Miller, Lori, 5019
Miller, Louise B., 4503
Miller, Lucy, 1713
Miller, Luther L., 7621
Miller, Lyle, 3666
Miller, Marc D., 8180
Miller, Maria, 7571
Miller, Mark, 4372, 9337
Miller, Mark F., 6155, 6156
Miller, Mark McCormick, 169
Miller, Mark W., 9816
Miller, Marlene, 911
Miller, Marlin, Jr., 8181
Miller, Martha Barnes, 6260
Miller, Mary Grace, 1153
Miller, Mary Kathleen, 24
Miller, Mary Louise, 3355
Miller, Maurice Lim, 366
Miller, Michael, 1738
Miller, Michael E., 7456
Miller, Michael H., 3411
Miller, Michael S., 8327
Miller, Myron, 4177
Miller, Nancy, 4374
Miller, Nathan R., 2864
Miller, P. Jon, 3313
Miller, Pam, 3480
Miller, Patricia A., 9843
Miller, Paul S., 8490
Miller, Paula, 6652
Miller, Philip D., 4504
Miller, Phillip S., 7872
Miller, Polly C., 2411
Miller, Quincy, 8374
Miller, R., 3025
Miller, R.N. "Bo", 4404
Miller, Randolph L., 7881
Miller, Regina, 8181
Miller, Richard G., 3535
Miller, Robert B., 4503
Miller, Robert C., 2215, 6199
Miller, Robert J., 1626, 1653
Miller, Robin, 2734
Miller, Roger L., 9334, 9335
Miller, Ron, 2763
Miller, Ronald C., 5712
Miller, Ronald W., Sr., 468
Miller, Rory L., 7814
Miller, Rosa Copeland, 8043
Miller, Rosana, 928
Miller, Ruth, 7412
Miller, Ryan, 9336
Miller, S., 3025, 3107
Miller, Sally Cheney, 9019
Miller, Samuel H., 7571
Miller, Sandy, 3313
Miller, Sarah C., 7814
Miller, Sarah K., 9128
Miller, Shakirah, 5501
Miller, Shar, 3337
Miller, Sharon, 2275
Miller, Sheila M., 9028
Miller, Sherman, 2565
Miller, Sherri, 5045
Miller, Sherry Thompson, 5534
Miller, Stephen, 3520
Miller, Stephen F., 9334, 9335
Miller, Steve, 3398
Miller, Steven H., 9686
Miller, Steven L., 9028
Miller, Steven L., Jr., 9028
Miller, Stuart, 2241
Miller, Stuart A., 2210
Miller, Sue, 3298, 7876
Miller, Sue M., 3447
Miller, Susan, 2241
Miller, Susan L., 3224
Miller, Suzan A., 7853
Miller, T. W., Jr., 8182
Miller, Tammy, 9655
Miller, Theodore N., 2677
Miller, Tim, 3447
Miller, Valerie, 2070
Miller, Vance, 2639
Miller, Walter E.D., 468
Miller, Warren, 2089
Miller, Warren Pullman, 3100
Miller, Wendy, 3024
Miller, William I., 3292, 7043
Miller, William R., 6904
Miller, William S., 6446
Miller, William T., 8887
Miller, Winlock W., 9684
Miller, Wynne, 9108
Miller-Rosenstein, Gladys, 5417
Milleson, Julie, 3534

Millet, Mark, 3389
Millhiser, Mary McGue, 9486
Millhiser, Ross R., 9486
Millhiser, Ross R., Jr., 9486
Millhiser, Thomas McNally, 9486
Millhiser, Timothy McGue, 9486
Millhouse, Barbara B., 7138
Millians, Philip, 2529
Milligan, Cynthia H., 4474
Milligan, Gretchen, 1116
Milligan, Gretchen Hartnack, 411
Milligan, James H., 7787
Milligan, Kenneth E., 7378
Milligan, Lois Darlene, 7787
Milligan, Mardie, 7414
Milligan, Matthew C., 5038
Milligan, Michael J., 7787
Milligan, Sharon, 7564
Milliken and Co., 6487
Milliken, Gerrish H., 1851, 6487
Milliken, Gerrish H., Sr., 1851
Milliken, Justine V., 1851
Milliken, Nancy, 1851
Milliken, Roger, 1851
Milliken, Ron, 3700
Milliken, Sarah C., 634
Milliken, W.D., 634
Millikin, Anu, 5183
Millikin, James, 3027
Milliman, Alison Wyckoff, 9749
Millin, Steven G., 9843
Milling, David A., 6153
Milling, R. King, 3656
Million, Ellicott, 1052
Millis, Craig, 9108
Millis, Craig, Mrs., 9108
Millis-Hedgecock, Molly, 7231
Millisor, Rob, 1511
Millman, Ann, 3033
Millman, Jode, 5923
Millman, Robert, 912
Mills, Alice duPont, 1754
Mills, Andrew J., 3019, 3029
Mills, Bryan A., 3301, 3397
Mills, Catherine L., 9377
Mills, Charles, 3028
Mills, Cheryl, 2725
Mills, Helen Crow, 67
Mills, Isobel P., 2463
Mills, James, 3028
Mills, James W., 2598
Mills, Jim T., 9175
Mills, John B., 8814
Mills, John W., 8502
Mills, Jonathan M., 3029
Mills, Karen, 1002
Mills, Kendall, 4408
Mills, Lloyd, 4408
Mills, Lois, 3029
Mills, Michael R., 73
Mills, Robert A., 2130
Mills, Robert K., 8599
Mills, Ruth B., 3287
Mills, S. Peter, III, 3698
Mills, Shannon, 5175
Mills, W. Richard, 1032
Mills, Wallace V., 1090
Mills, William J., 5780
Mills, William P., III, 3668
Millsap, Deborah, 7845
Millspaugh, Gordon A., Jr., 5490
Millsport, 7012
Millstein, Ira M., 7062
Millstone, Colleen, 4944
Millstone, Goldie G., 4944
Millstone, I.E., 4944
Millstone, Robert D., 4944
Milman, Roberta, 1894
Milne, Marilyn, 9715
Milne, Rebecca, 9871
Milowski, Nicholas, 6160
Milros Co., Inc., 928
Milstein Descendant's Trust, Vivian L., 5670
Milstein Family Foundation, 7113
Milstein Foundation, 5228
Milstein, Adam, 930
Milstein, Adam Gila, 930
Milstein, Andrew, 5198
Milstein, Carol, 5198
Milstein, Cheryl, 6647
Milstein, Constance, 5781
Milstein, Constance J., 6952
Milstein, Edward, 1681, 6488
Milstein, Gila, 930
Milstein, Guilat, 930
Milstein, Howard, 6488
Milstein, Irma, 6488, 7113
Milstein, Joanna, 5781
Milstein, Lyron, 930
Milstein, Merav, 930
Milstein, Monroe, 5198
Milstein, Natalie, 930
Milstein, Paul, 6488, 7113
Milstein, Philip L., 6647, 6952
Milstein, Ronald, 7180
Milstein, Seymour, 5781, 6952
Milstein, Tuvia, 930
Milstein, Vivian, 5670, 5781, 6647, 6952
Milster, Richard, 4344
Milston, Martin J., 6688
Miltenberger, Gina, 7570
Milton, Catherine H., 529
Milton, Janis, 266
Milton, Laurie, 9205
Milton, Phillip, 9205
Milward, John, 3560
Milwaukee Golf Development Corp., 2783
Milway, Katie Smith, 4286
Milzcik, Gregory F., 1542
Mims, Marcus, 5511
Mims, Rhoda, 7038
Mina, William, 9176
Minar, Clyde, 1120
Minar, Clyde D., 973
Minard, Marcia, 3360
Minardi, Emanuele, 5398
Minarovic, Jane C., 8670
Minars, Michael, 6680
Mincey, Susan, 8787
Mindich, Eric M., 6470
Mine Safety Appliances Co., 8184
Mineck, Suzanne, 3466
Minehan, Cathy E., 5762
Minella, Lynn C., 7907
Minelli, Michael A., 7631
Mineman, Julie Owens, 3068
Miner Anderson 2009 Charitable Lead Annuity Trust, 1736
Miner Fleet Management Group, 8834
Miner, Josh, 4288
Miner, Joshua L., IV, 4289
Miner, Justine, 280
Miner, Luke, 280
Miner, Mary M., 280
Miner, Michael, 3030
Miner, Michael J., 3030
Miner, Mike, 1110
Miner, Nicola, 280, 1736
Miner, Nina, 6856
Miner, Sharon, 8660
Miner-Swartz, Robin, 4357
Minger, Terry, 1481
Mingst, Caryll S., 951
Mingst, Caryll Sprague, 1207
Miniotas, Kristen, 3827
Mink, Deane, 2478
Mink, John, 9859
Minneapolis Foundation, 4795
Minnesota Life Insurance Co., 4761
Minnesota Mining and Manufacturing Co., 4597
Minnesota Twins, 1850
Minnich, Margaret W., 368
Minolta, Konica, 9606
Minor, Daniel J., 7563
Minor, Oraetta, 237
Minor, Sue Breeden, 9396
Minow, Martha, 2780, 2989, 6868
Minter, Brenda, 4343
Minter-Jordan, Myechia, Dr., 3956
Mintmire, Donald F., 1848
Mintmire, Patricia R., 1848
Minton, Frank, 4809
Minton, Frank D., 9684
Minton, Janis, 773
Minton, John, 8819
Minton, Kim, 3330
Mintz, Joshua J., 2989
Minutolo, James, 7363
Minzberg, Samuel, 2999
Mir, Gasper, III, 8916
Mirabello, Francis "Frank", 8221
Mirabello, Francis J., 8078
Mirabito, John, 5802
Miracle, Andrew Martin, 7265
Miramont Villas LP, 9452
Miranda, Adam, 5827
Miranda, Cameron, 5827
Miranda, Jinny, 2616
Miree, Kathryn, 21
Mirgliotta, James, 7467
Mirman, Rita, 3031
Mirmiran, Fred, 3853
Miro, Jeffrey H., 4552, 4553
Mirowski Family Ventures, 4179
Mirowski, Anna, 4179
Mirowski, Ginat W., 4179
Mirrer, Louise, 6228
Mirsepassi, Nadder, 1039
Mirsky, Burton M., 5845
Mirvis, Theodore N., 5334
Mirza, Candace R., 3032
Mirza, Jerome, 3032
Miscikowski, Cynthia Ann, 1075
Mishan, Ahrin, 6174
Mishler, Kent, 3369
Misiak, David G., 4738
Misinec, Joseph A., Jr., 7379
Miskell, Eileen C., 3974
Miskell, Marian S., 7992
Mission Society of Mandeville, 2860
Mississippi Board of Nursing, 4838
Mississippi Development Authority, 4838
Mississippi Power Co., 4839
Mississippi Power Education Fdn., 4839
Mississippi State Dept. of Health, 4838
Missoula Casino, Inc., 5016
Mistry, Dinyar B., 1033
Miszklevitz, Katherine B., 3166
Mitchell, A.S., 55
Mitchell, A.S., Mrs., 55
Mitchell, Abraham A., 54
Mitchell, Amy E., 9100
Mitchell, Anna, 931
Mitchell, Betsy, 9854
Mitchell, Brian Gregory, 9029
Mitchell, C.B., 6779
Mitchell, Cara, 2525
Mitchell, Carleton Grant, 9029
Mitchell, Cleta, 9819
Mitchell, Cynthia W., 8829, 9029
Mitchell, Donna, 9058
Mitchell, Edward D., 931
Mitchell, Edward T., 2490
Mitchell, Garfield, 9064
Mitchell, George K., 181
Mitchell, George P., 8829, 9029
Mitchell, George Scott, 9029
Mitchell, Hayden, 4829
Mitchell, Heather L., 8973
Mitchell, James, 2645
Mitchell, James G., 444
Mitchell, James, Dr., 7138
Mitchell, Janet, 1650
Mitchell, Jason H., 931
Mitchell, Jean, 3471
Mitchell, Joan, 6489
Mitchell, John, 3471
Mitchell, John Kirk, 9029
Mitchell, John P., Rev. Dr., 5483
Mitchell, Jonathan E., 931
Mitchell, Joseph, 7416
Mitchell, Joseph C., 5871, 6232, 6788
Mitchell, Julia, 9014
Mitchell, Julie, 8660
Mitchell, Laura, 151, 9758
Mitchell, Laurie C., 226
Mitchell, Lee Roy, 9030
Mitchell, Lisa, 254
Mitchell, Lois, 994
Mitchell, Mack C., Jr., 3714
Mitchell, Manny, 4844
Mitchell, Marcus W.H., Jr., 7178
Mitchell, Margaret, 4717
Mitchell, Mark, 1650
Mitchell, Mark Douglas, 9029
Mitchell, Mary S., 7860
Mitchell, Michael Kent, 9029
Mitchell, Mike, 3356
Mitchell, N. Malone, III, 9100
Mitchell, Noah M., 9100
Mitchell, Pat, 3360
Mitchell, Richard A., 7605
Mitchell, Sarah Scott, 9029
Mitchell, Susan A., 2516
Mitchell, Sydney L., 2636
Mitchell, Tandy, 9030
Mitchell, Thomas N., 5622
Mitchell, Tyrone, 6489
Mitchell, W. Harold, 7178
Mitchell, Wildey H., 4717
Mitchell, William, 6011
Mitchell-Miller, Rochelle, 1394
Mitchener, Frank, 4821, 4823
Mithoefer, Heather M., 7517
Mithoefer, Peter P., 7517
Mithoff Family Foundation, 8721
Mithoff, Michael, 8721
Mithun Enterprises, Inc., 4718
Mithun Trust, Doris, 4718
Mithun, Doris B., 4718
Mithun, John C., 4718

Montgomery, Harold, 8773
Montgomery, John D., 3521
Montgomery, Joseph S., 7575
Montgomery, Judy, 3265
Montgomery, Kenneth F., 4509
Montgomery, L.J., 2518
Montgomery, L.J., III, 2518
Montgomery, Mary, 2518
Montgomery, Pam, 1392
Montgomery, Paul, 8561
Montgomery, R. A., 9659
Montgomery, Rebecca, 4839
Montgomery, Scott, 7575
Montgomery, Stephanie Stenger, 4872
Montgomery, Stephen, 9558
Montgomery, Susan Byrne, 9244
Montgomery, Virginia, 7612
Montgomery, Walter S., 8487
Montgomery, Walter S., Jr., 8456, 8487
Montgomery-Tabron, La June, 4474
Monti-Catania, Diane, 3948
Montoya, Eric, 1411
Montoya, Melanie, 1512
Montoya, Ronald E., 1487
Montrone, Angelo, 5185
Montrone, Jerome, 5185
Montrone, Paul M., 5185
Montrone, Sandra G., 5185
MONY Group, Inc., The, 5629
Moody's Corp., 6451
Moody's Investors Service, Inc., 6499
Moody, Amy, 2959
Moody, Jacquelin A., 4574
Moody, Jon, 6
Moody, Kevin, 3623
Moody, Libbie Shearn, 9033
Moody, Marcy M., 2078
Moody, Robert L., 9063
Moody, Robert L., Sr., 9033
Moody, Ross R., 9033
Moody, Tania, 8994
Moody, William Lewis, Jr., 9033
Moody, Yvonne R., 9225
Moody-Dahlberg, Frances A., 9033
Moog, Donna L., 4994
Moog, Dorothy, 4994
Moog, James R., 4994
Moog, Mary, 4994
Moog, Thomas H., 4994
Mook, Saundra, 8001
Mookherjee, Sati, 9759
Moon, Lawrence E., 4511
Moon, William, 5784
Mooney, Abigail S., 1417
Mooney, Dee K., 2637
Mooney, F. Steven, 1417
Mooney, Gregory, 2761
Mooney, James, 4181
Mooney, James C., 9370
Mooney, James F., III, 4181
Mooney, Kay D., 1531
Mooney, Lisa, 4181
Mooney, Margaret E., 146
Mooney, Maureen, 5359
Mooney, Michael E., 4047
Moor, M. Eugene, Jr., 18
Moor, Walter, 6514
Moore Capital Mgmt., LLC, 6500
Moore, Aaron, 5138
Moore, Albert W., 592
Moore, Alice, 5807
Moore, Anita J., 7428
Moore, Ann S., 7043
Moore, Anne, 6544
Moore, Ardon E., 8686
Moore, Barry, 8739
Moore, Betty I., 937, 938
Moore, Bielle, 1069
Moore, Blanche Davis, 9034
Moore, Bob, 3121
Moore, Brian J., 7597
Moore, Bruce, Jr., 8582
Moore, C.R., 1060
Moore, Carolyn, 3884
Moore, Cathy, 7295
Moore, Charles L., 9214
Moore, Cheryl, 3818
Moore, Christopher, 4109
Moore, Christopher S., 6368
Moore, Cindy, 3761
Moore, Claude, 9489
Moore, Connie, 4984
Moore, Danielle, 2106
Moore, Danielle H., 5644
Moore, Danielle Hickox, 2105
Moore, Darla D., 8488, 9119
Moore, David, 1719, 6138, 6139
Moore, David C., 9548
Moore, David E., Sr., 6501
Moore, David W., 1645
Moore, Dawn, 3130
Moore, Deborah L., 1644
Moore, Diana, 2208
Moore, Doreen, 2630
Moore, Evelyn, 8775
Moore, G. Michael, 9541
Moore, George W., 8444
Moore, Gerald H., 7402
Moore, Gordon, 3298
Moore, Gordon E., 937, 938
Moore, Grace Danley, 8186
Moore, Hannah, 4109
Moore, Harry C., Jr., 9814
Moore, Harry S., 9780
Moore, Heather D., 3851
Moore, Hugh, 8548
Moore, Jack, 8878, 8901
Moore, Jacqueline B., 8693
Moore, James, 9035
Moore, James L., 4843
Moore, Jaqueline A., 1719
Moore, Jennifer, 8668
Moore, Jerry, 7402
Moore, John, 2039, 3370
Moore, John H., 4413
Moore, John R., 8217
Moore, Johnny B., 8615
Moore, Judith H., 4445
Moore, Judith Livingston, 6505
Moore, Katherine C., 6501
Moore, Kathy, 8649
Moore, Kenneth G., 937, 938
Moore, Kevin S., 5786, 5975
Moore, Kristen L., 937, 938
Moore, Kristi, 6503
Moore, LaRae Dixon, 2438
Moore, Lauren, 493
Moore, Lee Wayne, 9035
Moore, Leslie, 8649
Moore, Leslie R., 4391
Moore, Lin, 25
Moore, Linda G., 9767
Moore, Mackey, 4821
Moore, Madison M., 4971
Moore, Malcolm, 9684
Moore, Malcolm A., 1475
Moore, Margaret S. Barker, 3936
Moore, Marilyn, 2357
Moore, Mark, 8742
Moore, Mary J.P., 1645
Moore, Melanie, 8949
Moore, Meredith C., 5411
Moore, Michael, 4109, 4660
Moore, Nancy Powell, 9105
Moore, Nicholas, 1685
Moore, Nicholas J., 1645
Moore, Noel, 8790
Moore, Noel C., 8790
Moore, Oliver, 4109
Moore, Patricia, 7402
Moore, Patricia P., 7402
Moore, Patrick C., 4827
Moore, Patrick K., 8015
Moore, Randy, 3424
Moore, Randy W., 7270
Moore, Richard, 5533, 8790
Moore, Richard W., 5718, 6501
Moore, Rick R., 9079
Moore, Robert, 6503
Moore, Samuel, 4109
Moore, Sara Giles, 2519, 2520
Moore, Sarah Kaplan, 2947
Moore, Scott, 4612
Moore, Shabri, 3758
Moore, Stacie, 9053
Moore, Starr, 2520
Moore, Stephen, 5301, 9406
Moore, Stephen A., 9563
Moore, Stephen C., 2276
Moore, Stephen F., 8550
Moore, Stephen O., 4831
Moore, Steven E., 937, 938
Moore, Steven G. W., 9689
Moore, Sue, 7540
Moore, T. Justin, III, 9529
Moore, Taylor Frost, 5519
Moore, Theresa Jean Harris, 3580
Moore, Thomas, 3417, 8971
Moore, Thomas A., 6505
Moore, Thurston R., 9504
Moore, Tom, 9035
Moore, Toni, 7608
Moore, Tonya, 4838
Moore, Tracy, 8554
Moore, Virginia L., 2742
Moore, Virginia Reid, 1060
Moore, W.R., 1060
Moore, Wendy, 2587
Moore, Wes, 3726
Moore, William, 4109
Moore, William Martin, 3578
Moore, Yvonne L., 5848
Moorehead, Emery, 1939
Moorehead, Jim, 416
Moores, Harry C., 7576
Moorman, Bette D., 4642, 4802
Moorman, Carol E., 3015
Moorman, Charles W. "Wick", 9448
Moorman, Charles W., IV, 9496
Moors, Dean, 5046
Moose Mountain Trust, 3704
Moose, Sandra O., 6872
Moosey, Robert, 8881
Moot, Amey D., 7078
Moot, Richard E., 7078
Moot, Welles V., 7078
Mooty, Bruce W., 4720
Mooty, Charles W., 4720
Mooty, David N., 4720
Mooty, Jane N., 4719
Mooty, John W., 4720
Mora, Carolyn, 9083
Moraco, Suzie, 2123
Moraetis, Catherine, 9428
Morales, Amsi Y., 4152
Morales, Carlos, 8994
Morales, Estela, Sr., 645
Morales, Hugo, 1088
Morales, Jerry, 9091
Morales, Manuel A., Dr., 8353
Morales, Martha E., 749
Morales, Minerva, 9767
Moran & Associates, Jim, Inc., 2243
Moran Education Foundation, 9652
Moran, Amanda Ann, 4563
Moran, Asha Morgan, 7577
Moran, Barbara F., 5243
Moran, Carole O., 2242
Moran, David, 9796
Moran, David, Dr., 3762
Moran, Elizabeth, 2242
Moran, George P., 3994
Moran, James, 7971
Moran, James M., 2243
Moran, Janet, 3337
Moran, Janice M., 2243
Moran, Jean, 3424
Moran, John A., 2242
Moran, John R., 122
Moran, Katherine Lynn, 4563
Moran, Lynn, 4563
Moran, Madison Dianne, 4563
Moran, Marty, 7577
Moran, Melvin, 7742
Moran, Tami Grigsby, 3640
Moran, W.T., Mrs., 9036
Morascyzk, Edward C., 8332
Moraski, Gayle, 1565
Moravitz, Edward, 8055
Morby, Carolyn R., 4443
Morby, Jacqueline C., 2244
Morby, Jeffrey, 2244
Morby, Jeffrey L., 2244
Morcos, Alexander, 5540
Morcos, Amanda, 5540
Morcos, Michael J., 2811
Mordecai, Janet, 1820
Mordell, Jayne S., 312
More, Pat, 3288
Moreau, McKenna, 5791
Morehead, Arthur E., IV, 7195
Morehead, John Motley, III, 7268
Morehouse, C. Schuyler, 5461
Morehouse, Ellen S., 5461
Morehouse, K. Frank, 7354
Moreland Management Co., 2161
Moreland, Mary, 2648
Moreland, Steven, 4446
Morella, Constance A., Hon., 1890
Morelli, Juliana C., 3249
Morelli, Michele A., 4505
Morelli, Rita, 4505
Morello, Maurizio J., 6497, 7027
Morency, Jeanne L., 7864
Morency, Michael, 7864
Moreno, Albert F., 1088
Moreno, Arturo, 147
Moreno, Bernie, 7406
Moreno, Carlos R., Hon., 365
Moreno, Carole, 147
Moreno, Julie, 2037
Moreno, Paula, 5994
Moret, Pamela, 4621
Moreton, Frederick A., 9309
Moretti, Wayne, 2740
Morey, Krista, 4508

Morey, Lon, 4508, 4512
Morey, Norval, 4508
Morey, Sandra, 1002
Morf, Darrel A., 3439
Morgan Charitable Lead Annuity Trust, Frank, 3536
Morgan Charitable Lead Unitrust, Frank, 3536
Morgan Co. of Laurel Hill, Inc., The, 7269
Morgan Construction Co., 4182
Morgan Farms, Inc., 7269
Morgan Foundation, Pete, 1497
Morgan Library & Museum, 5707
Morgan Mills, Inc., 7269
Morgan Stanley, 6507
Morgan Stanley & Co. Inc., 6507
Morgan Stanley Dean Witter & Co., 6507
Morgan Stanley Group Inc., 6507
Morgan Stanley Private Bank, N.A., 6717
Morgan Stanley Smith Barney, 8136
Morgan Stanley Trust, N.A., 6597
Morgan Stanley, Dean Witter, Discover & Co., 6507
Morgan Trust, Frank, 3536
Morgan Trust, Russell Guy and Ruth Louise, 667
Morgan, Amanda K., 3536
Morgan, Amanda Parrish, 1830
Morgan, Anne, 7742
Morgan, Anne H., Dr., 7766
Morgan, Anne Hodges, 9079
Morgan, Axson B., 1379
Morgan, Barrett, 4182
Morgan, Bennett J., 4746
Morgan, Bill, 9695
Morgan, Brian J., 3536
Morgan, Burton D., 7578, 7579
Morgan, Catherine A., 9038
Morgan, Charles O., 2019
Morgan, Chip, 4823
Morgan, Christine R., 9038
Morgan, Darcia B., 1379
Morgan, Dorothy, 1563
Morgan, Edwin, 7269
Morgan, Edwin E., 4840
Morgan, Elise, 7269
Morgan, Elizabeth E., 7269
Morgan, Erin M., 2726
Morgan, Frank, 3536
Morgan, G. Bryan, 1379
Morgan, G. Dan, 5103
Morgan, G.E., 4840
Morgan, Gail M., 4182
Morgan, Glen W., 9037
Morgan, Hilarie L., 8187
Morgan, J. Grey, 7319
Morgan, James, 939, 5388
Morgan, James C., 939, 940
Morgan, James L., Jr., 7269
Morgan, Jeff, 940
Morgan, Judy B., 2055
Morgan, Karen, 383
Morgan, Karen M., 4840
Morgan, Karla, 7577
Morgan, Kathy, 2533
Morgan, Lee M., 7577
Morgan, Leigh, 9625
Morgan, Lillian L., 7305
Morgan, Lisa, 337
Morgan, Lisa M., 2032
Morgan, Margaret Clark, 7579
Morgan, Marietta McNeill, 9490
Morgan, Marilyn J., 3536
Morgan, Mark A., 3536
Morgan, Michael B., 3536
Morgan, Michael C., 9038
Morgan, Mitchell L., 8187
Morgan, Octavia E., 1379
Morgan, Patricia A., 1544
Morgan, Paul F., 2586
Morgan, Philip R., 4182
Morgan, Rebecca, 939
Morgan, Rebecca Q., 939, 940
Morgan, Rick, 9780
Morgan, Rob, 8474
Morgan, Robert, 1699
Morgan, Robert B., 7702
Morgan, Ronnie, 8649
Morgan, Ruby C., 4840
Morgan, Samuel L., 6148
Morgan, Samuel T., Jr., 9490
Morgan, Sara, 9695
Morgan, Sara S., 9038
Morgan, Sarah H., 8535
Morgan, Stephen, 3201
Morgan, Suzanne, 7579
Morgan, Tedd, 4806
Morgan, Thomas S., 3536
Morgan, Todd, 9768
Morgan, Todd D., 3536
Morgan, Tom, 2478
Morgan, Tony, 8819
Morgan, Trudy, 8522
Morgan, Victoria A., 7577
Morgan, Vinessa, 2088
Morgan, William P., 1379
Morgan, William V., 9038
Morganti Tedas Casias A Joint Venture, 9149
Morgens West Charitable Lead Annuity Trust, 2521
Morgens, E.H., 2521
Morgens, Edwin H., 7084
Morgens, Howard J., 7084
Morgens, James H., 2521
Morgens, Lauren, 7084
Morgens, Linda M., 7084
Morgens, S.F., 2521
Morgenstern, Dan, 5612
Morgenthaler, Gary, 1310
Morgenthau, Robert P., 6003
Morgridge, Bob, 3075
Morgridge, Carrie, 1466
Morgridge, John D., 1259, 1466
Morgridge, John P., 402, 1259, 1466, 9849
Morgridge, Rhonda, 3075
Morgridge, Robert, 2927
Morgridge, Tashia, 1466, 9849
Morgridge, Tashia F., 1259, 9849
Morhman, Gregory, Fr., 4992
Mori, Ittetsu, 9487
Mori, Renzo, 5895, 5896
Mori, Sandy Ouye, 921
Morial, Sybil H., 3615
Morian, S. Reed, 9039
Moriarty, Brunilda, 5310
Moriaski, Shuji, 9487
Moriearty, Perry, 4709
Morikis, John G., 7661
Morille, Trish, 9185
Morimoto, Gary S., 2600
Morimoto, Tokiwa, 6961
Morin, Barbara, 2355
Morin, Francois, 5857
Morino Trust, Mario M., 1772
Morishita, Ken, 1236
Morison, Nathaniel A., 742
Morita, Josina, 3242
Moritz, Michael, 438
Moriuchi, N. Chiyo, 8267
Moriyama, Lisa, 3257
Mork, John F., 1404
Mork, Julie M., 1404
Mork, Kyle M., 1404
Morley, Catherine W., 4803
Morning Star Family Limited Partnership, The, 9040
Morning, John, 4510, 5483
Morns, Scott J., 9914
Moro, Isabelle, 8808
Moroney, Barbara B., 8689
Moroney, James M. "Jim", III, 8795
Moroney, Michael J., 7623
Morong, Caroline W., 3218
Morouse, James, 1116
Moroz, John, 5976
Morradian, Anne, 5398
Morreale, Justin P., 4329
Morrell, Elner, 1566
Morrell, Jim, 9605
Morrell, Michael W., 5489
Morrill, Christopher C., 1589
Morrill, Richard L., 6967
Morris Communications Company, LLC, 2514
Morris Cos. Inc., Philip, 6403
Morris Family, Albert, 7640
Morris, Adrienne, 6909
Morris, Anne, 415
Morris, Anthony, Esq., 7979
Morris, Ben T., 9152
Morris, Bette M., 3537
Morris, Carol, 7202
Morris, Charles M., 8188
Morris, Christopher, 613
Morris, Courtney, 9554
Morris, Darren, 1103
Morris, David, 3398
Morris, Dolores, 6912
Morris, Donna, 1734
Morris, Donna S., 9448
Morris, Donna T., 4549
Morris, Earl W., 7874
Morris, Eleanor W., 7999
Morris, Gabriella, 8333
Morris, Gabriella E., 3745
Morris, I. Wistar, III, 7999
Morris, Jack B., 9041
Morris, James, 4003
Morris, James F., 3760
Morris, James T., 1003
Morris, Jason A., 4003
Morris, Jason Z., 4003
Morris, Joseph W., 7793
Morris, Jr. Trust, Mark L., 3537
Morris, Julie Lancaster, 9019
Morris, June C. Heineman, 6158
Morris, Kate, 9360
Morris, Katherine B., 7148
Morris, Katherine Belk, 7146, 7147
Morris, Katie, 6859
Morris, Kenneth R., 942
Morris, Linda A., 942
Morris, Linda C., 9041
Morris, Lori, 9380
Morris, Louise Fisk, 3146
Morris, Lydia P., 7999
Morris, Margaret T., 148
Morris, Maria R., 6479
Morris, Marilyn, 4003
Morris, Marilyn C., 4199
Morris, Marilyn Cummings, 4003
Morris, Mark L., Jr., 3537
Morris, Martha, 7999
Morris, Martha H., 7999
Morris, Melissa H., 7999
Morris, Michael, 2511
Morris, Michael G., 7368
Morris, Paul, 8874, 9123
Morris, Paul T., 4834
Morris, Robert W., 8474
Morris, Ronald D., Jr., 2567
Morris, Rosemary, 3064
Morris, Sally J., 4338
Morris, Stewart, Jr., 9069
Morris, Stewart, Sr., 9069
Morris, Stuart L., 2219
Morris, Susan, 6508
Morris, Tammy, 5044
Morris, Thomas Q., 5719, 5786
Morris, Virginia H., 4678
Morris, William, 6508
Morris, William E., 2639
Morris, William S., III, 2434
Morris, William T., 1646
Morris-Singer, Andrew, 1859
Morrisey, Anne, 8221
Morrison Trust, Eunice B., 4184
Morrison Trust, John C., 4184
Morrison, Adeline S., 3038
Morrison, Ann, 3037
Morrison, Bill, 9559
Morrison, C. Maxine, 9108
Morrison, Edward W., Jr., 9791
Morrison, Ellen, 3037
Morrison, Emily Cade, 1784
Morrison, Eunice B., 4184
Morrison, G. Lowe, 2069
Morrison, Grace A., 3552
Morrison, Gregg S., 349
Morrison, Harold M., 3038
Morrison, Helen, 3038
Morrison, Holmes, 7144
Morrison, Ian, 367
Morrison, J. Holmes, 9782
Morrison, Jack R., 8941
Morrison, James K., 860
Morrison, Jerri L., 5209
Morrison, John M., 2245
Morrison, John M., Jr., 2245
Morrison, Julia M., 4402
Morrison, Julie, 2245
Morrison, Kate, 3037
Morrison, Kate B., 3037
Morrison, Lois, 3038
Morrison, Lois L., 3038
Morrison, M. Holly, 7972
Morrison, Mary S., 2245
Morrison, N. Jane, 2850
Morrison, Nina, 1889
Morrison, Patricia, 8993
Morrison, Ralph R., 2529
Morrison, Rebecca, 1889
Morrison, Richard J., 1656
Morrison, Robert, 6864
Morrison, Robert L., 1784
Morrison, Robert S., 2166, 7580
Morrison, Robert, III, 4848
Morrison, Sarah, 3037
Morrison, Scott C., 1371
Morrison, Steve, 9852
Morrison, Susan, 6864
Morrison, Susan M., 2245
Morrison, Thomas A., Dr., 3278
Morrison, Velma V., 2638

Morrison, William B., 3037
Morrison, William L., 3037
Morrisroe, Sylvia, 3306
Morriss, Cynthia, 9087
Morriss, J. Tolleison, 9398
Morrissette, Vaughan, 75
Morrissey, Allison, 1395
Morrissey, Colleen Shea, 1156
Morrissey, Joan S., 2812
Morrissey, Michael, 5134
Morrissey, Robert F., 2001
Morrissey, Robert J., 2001, 4295
Morrissey, Wendy Stark, 1213
Morrow, Alice Mills, 7825
Morrow, Cynthia B., 6049
Morrow, Lori, 9042
Morrow, Luke, 9042
Morrow, Peter C., 1872
Morrow, Polly O'Brien, 1674
Morrow, Sherry, 5032, 5055
Morrow, Teresa, 4714
Morrow-Clouse, Jenna, 1409
Morsani, Carol D., 2246
Morsani, Frank L., 2246
Morsbach, Hans, 9643
Morse, Carole E., 7881
Morse, Christine M., 4627
Morse, David L., 5818
Morse, Douglas A., 6509
Morse, Enid W., 6509
Morse, Herbert E., 3956
Morse, James T., 8380
Morse, Lester S., Jr., 6509
Morse, Mary, 5805
Morse, Nancy, 5075
Morse, Peter C., 5323
Morse, Sarah D., 8380
Morse, Saul J., 2762
Morse, Susan, 7865
Morse, Suzanne E., 9426
Mortellaro, Janine, 7540
Morten, Elisabeth, 1581
Mortensen, Alice, 1647
Mortensen, Sharon, 4502
Mortensen, Trice, 1647
Mortensen, William, 1647
Mortenson Co., M.A., 4721
Mortenson, Alice D., 4721
Mortenson, Barbara J., 9909
Mortenson, Christopher D., 4721
Mortenson, David C., 4714, 4721
Mortenson, Jay P., 9909
Mortenson, Loren D., 9909
Mortenson, Mark A., 4721
Mortenson, Mathias H., 4721
Mortenson, Mauritz A., Jr., 4721
Mortimer, David H., 6137
Mortimer, Thomas, 4316
Morton 2013 Charitable Lead Annuity Trust, Helen K., 944
Morton, Brian T., 944
Morton, Diana H., 6425
Morton, Dorothea L., 3254
Morton, Franklin L., 9341
Morton, Helen K., 944
Morton, James T., 8497
Morton, Karla, 8813
Morton, Margaret H., 4209
Morton, Marti, 2571
Morton, Mildred D., 3701
Morton, Paul F., 944
Morton, Peter, 943
Morton, S. Sidney, 973
Morton, Sally, 944
Morton, Theresa, 9756
Morton, Thomas A., 944
Morvant, Camille A., III, 3650
Mosaic Company, The, 4722
Mosakowski, Jane Rossetti, 5387
Mosakowski, William S., 5387
Mosbacher Jr. Charitable Annuity Trust, Emil, The, 1119
Mosbacher, Emil, Jr., 1119
Mosbacher, Jack Ryan, 1119
Mosbacher, R. Bruce, 1119
Moscicki, Anna, 9999
Moscrop, Tony, 8374
Moseley Trust, Edward S., 4185
Moseley, Anne, 3141
Moseley, Donna, 2576
Moseley, Furman C., 9741
Moseley, Jene M., 9012
Moseley, Joe L., 4971
Moseley, Susan R., 9741
Moser, Bobby, 4474
Moser, Monica M., 4467
Moser, Robert W., 8470
Moses & Yetta Charitable Trust, 5654
Moses Trust, Henry L., 6511
Moses Trust, Lucy G., 6511
Moses, Ansley, 8548
Moses, Cissy, 9125
Moses, Donald, 5980
Moses, Henry L., 6511
Moses, Leann O., 3656
Moses, Lucy G., 6511
Moses, Monte, 1487
Moshell, Marie, 2414
Mosher Charitable Lead Annuity Trust, George A., 3041
Mosher Charitable Lead Annuity Trust, Julie A., 3041
Mosher Charitable Trust, 3041
Mosher, George, 3041
Mosher, Julie, 3041
Mosher, Margaret C., 945
Mosher, Paul, 1012
Mosher, Samuel B., 945
Mosher, Scott, 434
Moshier, Dusty, 3540
Moshiri, Alireza, 1935
Mosich, A.N., 650
Mosier, Lynn, 5143
Mosiman, Louis E., 3497
Moskin, Jeffrey M., 526
Moskovits, Judy, 802
Moskowitz, Bruce, 6138, 6139
Moskowitz, Cherna, 2247
Moskowitz, Herman, 1995
Mosley, Charles, 8541
Mosley, Daniel L., 3219, 5929, 6561, 6610, 6643, 6859, 7058
Mosley, Edward S., 4185
Mosley, I. Sigmund, Jr., 2487
Mosley, Linda, 8548
Mosley, Paul, 1182
Mosley, Ralph W., 8550
Moss Trust for Euluos Moss, Jack, 2648
Moss, Andree K., 3656
Moss, Ann Holbrook, 946
Moss, Anne Palmer, 5806
Moss, Charlotte, 6017
Moss, Charlotte A., 6017
Moss, Christine, 7921
Moss, Florence M., 9043
Moss, Harry S., 9043
Moss, Harvey, 8906
Moss, I. Barney, 6303
Moss, Jerome S., 946
Moss, Lynda Bourque, 4729
Moss, Robert, 1947
Moss, Sara, 6408
Moss, William M., 9511
Mossett, Janal, 4373
Mossier, Kevin J., 4723
Mostov, Charles, 558
Mostue, Emily C., 7831
Mosty, John, 9095
Moszkowski, Neal, 7001
Motamed, Margaret, 1202
Motely, James A., 9420
Motes Curt, Sarah Mosely, 3203
Motes, Holly, 2632
Motherwell, Renate, 5864
Motherwell, Robert, 5864
Motiva, 9168
Motley, Joel W., 6105
Motley, John, 2817
Motley, Mark, 3159
Motley, Sandra D., 5190
Motorists Mutual Insurance Co., 7581
Motorola Solutions Foundation, 3042
Motorola Solutions, Inc., 3043
Motorola, Inc., 3043
Motorsports Authentics, 7214
Motorsports Charities, 7214
Motorsports Marketing, 7214
Motoshita, Toshihide, 5724
Motoyama, Stacie-Dee, 9605
Motsenbocker, Anne B., 8795
Mott Trust, C.S. Harding, 8080
Mott, C.S. Harding, 4455
Mott, C.S. Harding, II, 4455
Mott, Charles Stewart, 4510
Mott, Kerry K., 774
Mott, Kevin, 2826
Mott, Maryanne, 442, 1299, 4510, 4511
Mott, Milo I., 8080
Mott, Ruth R., 4511
Mott, Willard, 4407
Motta, Elliott, 3201
Mottier, Bradley D., 2325
Mottola, Maria, 6546
Mouch, Virginia, 4448
Mouden, Sip B., 4827
Moulds, Donald, 5800
Moules, Todd, 5979
Moulton, Amy, 3282
Moulton, Benjamin W., 4107
Moulton, Mari Beth C., 3911
Mounsey, Anne, 1412
Mounsey, Anne E. Fox, 1452
Mounsey, Pete, 1452
Mounsey, Peter, 1412
Mount Sinai Medical Center, 7631
Mount, Todd, 9780
Mountain, Janet, 8805
Mountain, Paul, 86
Mountaineer Gas Co., 1404
Mountaire Corp., 191
Mountcastle, Katharine B., 7138, 7298
Mountcastle, Katherine R., 7138
Mountcastle, Kenneth F., III, 7138
Mountcastle, Laura L., 7138
Mountcastle, Mary, 7138, 7298
Mountjoy, Michael B., 3577
Mourand, Don, 4495
Mourier Construction, John, Inc., 949
Mourier Land Investment Corporation, 949
Mourier, John, III, 949
Mourier, Laura, 949
Moutinho, Maria, 2101
Movassaghi, Kam, 3623
Movshon, Anthony, 4708
Movson, Jonathan S., 8383
Mow, Melvin W.Y., 2598
Mowery, William, 3449
Mowry, Barbara, 4921
Moye, Mike, 2483
Moyer, Ariel C., 3774
Moyer, Charles I., 3518
Moyer, D. Scott, 7585
Moyer, Glenn E., 8350
Moyer, Scott, 6327
Moyer, Sherill T., 8294
Moyers, Bill D., 6813
Moyers, Richard L., 1931
Moylan, John P., 4442
Moyle, Judith Burton, 9309
Moyle, O. Wood, IV, 9309
Moyle, O.W., III, 328
Moyle, Rebecca Burton, 9309
Moynihan, David J., 5757
Moynihan, Elizabeth B., 6364
Moynihan, Kevin, 1650
Moynihan, Timothy J., 1690
Mozilo, Angelo R., 6512
Mozilo, Phyllis G., 6512
Mr. White LLC, 7008
Mrad, Rachel, 9552
Mrkonich, Marko J., 912
Mrozek, Ernest J., 2812
MS Associates, LLC, 5937
MS Management Company LLC, 3207
Ms. Foundation for Women, 6864
MSG Charitable Trust, 562
MSS Trust Assocs., 5951
MSST Foundation, 1230, 9718
MST 2000 Charitable Lead Annuity Trust, 1230
MST 2000 Charitable Lead Trust, 1782
MTD Products, Inc., 7513
MTGLQ Investors, L.P., 6070
MTS Assocs. LLC, 6798
Mucha, Christian, 4064
Muchemore, Agnes B., 5070
Muchmore, Iris E., 3439
Muckleshoot Indian Tribe, 9652
Mucklestone, Robert S., 9611
Mudd, Becky, 3423
Mudd, Gregory B., 4933
Mudd, Jane W., 8478
Mudge, Rob, 8511
Mudge, Steve, 2817
Mudumby, Narasimhachary, 4480
Muegge, Linda, 3313
Mueggenborg, Debbie, 7731
Muehlbauer, Brad J., 3334
Muehlbauer, Glen J., 3334
Muehlbauer, James, 3402
Muehlbauer, James H., 3334
Muehleck, James K., 9450
Muehlhauser, Regina L., 727
Mueller, Adam T., 7466
Mueller, Aimee, 5598
Mueller, Bill, 5063
Mueller, Brady, Hon., 9293
Mueller, Charles G., 2812
Mueller, Dan, 598
Mueller, Diane, 1392
Mueller, Douglas, 5598
Mueller, Eric G., 7466
Mueller, Jack, 9341
Mueller, Jonathan J., 7466

Mueller, Joyce Ann, 2252
Mueller, Judith, 429
Mueller, Kathleen C., 2043
Mueller, Laura K., 7466
Mueller, Linda, 4361
Mueller, Linda G., 7466
Mueller, Martha Chilton, 9783
Mueller, Nancy Sue, 6302
Mueller, Paul, 9832
Mueller, Stacey, 5013
Mueller, Thomas J., 7466
Mueller, Todd W., 4738
Muessle, John C., 93
Muffleman, David, 9503
Mufson, Kathleen Ryan, 1674
Muglia, Dean, 118
Muhammad, Fayrene, 2766
Muhl, Shauna Sullivan, 2445, 2560
Muir, Bonnie, 98
Muir, Cameron K., 4582
Muir, Douglas Gordon, III, 2472
Muir, Gordon J., 4582
Muir, Martha M., 4582
Muirhead, Nancy L., 6723
Mukkamala, Bobby, 4372
Mulcahey, Michael, 4636
Mulcahy, Betty Jane, 7479
Mulcahy, Forrest, 2182
Mulcahy, Katie M., 3068
Mulcahy, Leo T., Dr., 9382
Mulder, Karen, 4514
Mulder, Kimberly, 4501, 4514
Mulder, Larry, 4514
Mulder, Michael, 4501, 4514
Mulder, P. Haans, 4374
Mulders, William, 4344
Muldowney, John J., 9543
Mule, Edward A., 6513
Mulero-Betances, Marlene, 3336
Mulford, Clarence E., 3702
Mulford, Donald, 6514
Mulford, Edith, 6514
Mulford, Nancy P., 9092
Mulford, Vincent S., 6514
Mulford, Vincent S., Jr., 6514
Mulheren, Alexander, 6224
Mulheren, John, 6224
Mulheren, John, Jr., 6224
Mulheren, Nancy B., 6224
Mulholland, Ann, 4715
Mulholland, Donna A., 2276
Mulholland, Soapy, 1002
Mulitz, Laura Bryna Gudelsky, 1912
Mulitz, Shelley G., 1912
Mulka, John S., 7972
Mulkerin, Larry, 9733
Mullainathan, Sendhil, 2989
Mullan, Ellen H., 3712
Mullan, Mary Jo, 6340
Mullan, Mike, 2296
Mullan, Thomas F., III, 3872
Mullane, Donald A., 581
Mullane, William, 7705
Mullaney, Deborah, 6802
Mullaney, John J., 7594
Mullen Pension & Benefits Group, 9149
Mullen, Anthony P., 6654
Mullen, Donald R., 6515
Mullen, Donald R., Jr., 6515
Mullen, J. T., 7668
Mullen, Jessica P., 9510
Mullen, Joan A., 8190
Mullen, John J., 8190
Mullen, Mark William, 3409
Mullen, Michael, 8083
Mullen, Mike, 5684
Mullen, Patrick A., 4716
Mullen, Scott M., 9025
Mullenbrock, Craig M., 7620
Mullendore, Stuart L., 3761
Muller, Dolores, 953
Muller, Erik J., 9414
Muller, Frank, 953
Muller, Hans, 2252
Muller, Harry, 6122
Muller, Henry H., 947, 948
Muller, Hyman, 6122
Muller, Jillian, 5846
Muller, John, 953
Muller, Joyce, 2252
Muller, Leonard J., 3228
Muller, Marisa, 2252
Muller, Melissa, 953
Muller, Peter, 5846
Muller, Shiela, 953
Muller, Tom, 9975
Mullett, William E., 9780
Mullholland, Ann, 4757
Mulligan, Cathie, 7570
Mulligan, Donal Leo, 4661
Mulligan, Ed, 7421
Mulligan, Frederic, 4005
Mulligan, Janet L., 5793
Mulligan, John J., 4776
Mulligan, Larry, Hon., 7570
Mulligan, Nancy, 6082
Mulligan, Terence P., 959
Mullikin, Anu, 5182
Mullikin, Phil, 3757
Mullin, Dave, 4482
Mullin, Dennis, 3532
Mullin, Scott, 3710
Mullineaux, J., 420
Mulliner, Raymond L., 1180
Mullings, Paul E., 9435
Mullinix, Marvin B., 7141
Mullins, R. Robert, 9036
Mullins, Rick, 2030
Mullins, Shelley Dru, 7780
Mullins, Terrell, 8941
Mullins, Timothy P., 667
Mullis, Harold H., 3598
Mulloy, Martin J., 4430
Mulot, Regis, 4282
Mulpas, Joe, 7429
Multivest, 4453
Mulva, James J., 9044
Mulva, Miriam B., 9044
Mulvoy, James E., 4483
Mulvoy, Maree R., 4483
Mumford, Elizabeth B., 9308
Munana, Clare, 2703, 3186
Munana, Clare M., 2703
Munchak, Janet, 2559
Muncherian, Lori, 1247
Munchin, Allan, 2953
Munday, Heidi B., 3108
Munday, Reuben A., 4498
Mundel, Trevor, 9625
Munden, Karla, 7180
Mundinger, Richard, 101
Mundy, Gardner, 1558
Munford, Jennifer Sullican, 7171
Munford, Lara, 8602
Munford, R. Donavon, Jr., 7171
Munger, Charles, 218
Munger, Charles T., 954
Munger, Kathleen (Kathy) Dies, 9162
Munger, Melinda Sick, 1467
Munger, Molly, 218
Munger, Nancy B., 954
Munger, Reuban S., 1467
Munger, Wendy, 1015
Muni, Craig, 5726
Munitz, Barry, Dr., 432
Muniz, Andre, 8352
Munn, Monte, 2644
Munn, Rico, 1401
Munoz, Cecilia, 5622
Munoz, Robert, 9652
Munro, Alexandra, 6748
Munro, Christopher R., 7866
Munro, Clark C., Jr., 7866
Munro, Clark C., Sr., 7866
Munro, Don, 4827
Munro, J. Richard, 2035
Munro, Julie Simon, 6859
Munro, Maurie M., 7866
Munro, Pamela Harrington, 657
Munro, Warner R., 7866
Munroe, Alexandra, Dr., 7019
Munroe, Ginny, 3348
Muns, Betty Bell, 8700
Muns, James N., 8700
Muns, John B., 8700
Munsen, Kenneth N., 5744
Munsey, Betty K., 9563
Munsinger, Gary M., 95, 103
Munson, Ed, 239
Munson, Eddie R., 4543
Munson, Fran, 2092
Munson, Fred, 9565
Munson, Jon, 164
Munson, Josh, 3359
Munson, Linda J., 5254
Munson, Nina, 172
Muntz, Martin, 8862
Muntz, Maurine Genecov, 8862
Munz, Georgie T., 9223
Munzer, Anne Bourne, 955
Munzer, Daniel W., 955
Munzer, Daphne A., 955
Munzer, Rudolph J., 955
Munzig, Judith, 243
Murabito, John M., 7981
Muraco, Julie, 5785
Muraki, David, 1002
Murano, Katsuyoski, 1236
Murase, Satoru, 7019
Murata, Tetsuo, 250
Murch, Creighton B., 7582
Murch, Maynard H., 7582
Murch, Maynard H., V, 7582
Murch, Robert B., 7582
Murchie, Michael S., 6406
Murchison, John R., II, 7189
Murchison, Lucille G., 9046
Murchison, Virginia L., 9045
Murdoch, Anne, 2826
Murdoch, Melissa Baron, 2136
Murdoch, Stephen, 2136
Murdoch, Stephen I., 2136
Murdock Charitable Trust, 9652
Murdock, Melissa Baron, 9064
Murdock, Melvin Jack, 9689
Murdough, Jody P., 7583
Murdough, Joy P., 7583
Murdough, Marshall C., 7583
Murdough, Peter R., 7583
Murdough, Thomas G., 7583
Murdough, Thomas G., Jr., 7583
Murff, Ron, 8935
Murfree, Matt B., III, 8545
Murguia, Ramon, 3556, 4474
Murnane, Richard, 3171
Murnane, Tim, 4731
Murnen, Amy D., Dr., 7413
Murphey, Kris, 5527
Murphy Oil Corp., 185
Murphy, Ann M., 9841
Murphy, Bill, 5807
Murphy, Brian, 8383
Murphy, Brian J., 1652
Murphy, Bruce D., 7523, 7564
Murphy, Carmen C., 3270
Murphy, Carol, 1488
Murphy, Charles H., Jr., 193
Murphy, Christopher J., III, 3251, 3270
Murphy, Cornelius, Dr., 5575
Murphy, Daniel, 6634
Murphy, Darrell, 7539
Murphy, Diana M., 2431
Murphy, Edie, 6462
Murphy, Eileen, 1805
Murphy, Eugene W., Jr., 1999
Murphy, Frank, 7540
Murphy, Glenn, 563
Murphy, Harold L., 7270
Murphy, Henry L., Jr., 3951, 4030
Murphy, Jacques, 2936
Murphy, James E., 8432
Murphy, Jeremiah T., Msgr., 956
Murphy, John, 633, 1650
Murphy, John P., 7584
Murphy, Judith, 1194
Murphy, Kathleen, 5169
Murphy, Kevin K., 7939
Murphy, Lori, 9380
Murphy, Louise H., 9858
Murphy, Lucy, 3027
Murphy, Margaret, 5561
Murphy, Mark, 4628, 4731
Murphy, Marsha, 2035
Murphy, Mary F., 6109
Murphy, Mary G., 1630
Murphy, Mary Holt Woodson, 7342
Murphy, Maura E., 4307
Murphy, Michael, 720, 5482
Murphy, Mike, 208
Murphy, Pam, 7874
Murphy, Patrick T., 6573
Murphy, Patsy, 9255
Murphy, Patty, 4714
Murphy, Paul B., Jr., 8917
Murphy, Philip D., 6517
Murphy, Phillip D., 6898
Murphy, R. Madison, 193
Murphy, Robbie, 2590
Murphy, Sandra, 9780
Murphy, Scott, 9616
Murphy, Sheri L., 9801
Murphy, Susan, 1630, 5807
Murphy, Suzann Baricevic, 7857
Murphy, Suzanne M., 6148
Murphy, Tammy S., 6517
Murphy, Thomas, 3624
Murphy, Thomas J., 5808, 6406
Murphy, Thomas S., Jr., 788
Murphy, Thomas W., 7779
Murphy, Timothy P., 8383, 9700
Murphy, Virginia, 3249
Murphy, William J., 6578
Murphy, William K., Esq., 8136
Murphy-Erby, S. Yvette, 197
Murr Family Foundation, 9745
Murray Family Annuity, 8421

Murray Hill Properties, 5752
Murray Irrevocable Trust, Grace Healy, 3855
Murray, Barbara B., 5396
Murray, Catherine Underwood, 8853
Murray, Cecil L., Rev., 396
Murray, Christopher D., 8421
Murray, Corlis, 2648
Murray, David, 9572
Murray, Dorothy, 8825
Murray, Douglas R., 7569
Murray, Douglas S., 1320
Murray, Elizabeth, 1320
Murray, Elizabeth E., 8396
Murray, Eulene H., 2523
Murray, Eve-Lynne G., 1320
Murray, Grace H., 3855
Murray, Grey B., 2514
Murray, Helen J., 3304
Murray, Ian, 7417
Murray, J.B., 2032
Murray, Jack, 8914
Murray, James D., 6077
Murray, James H., Jr., 2398
Murray, James R., 1320
Murray, Jason B., 7630
Murray, Jennifer, 1116
Murray, Jerome S., 3855
Murray, Jim, 321
Murray, Joan D., 1955
Murray, John, 1109
Murray, Josephine L., 4198
Murray, Joyce B., 9608
Murray, Kantahyanee, 3844
Murray, Karen, 7604
Murray, Katharine L., 9572
Murray, Leo K., 3855
Murray, Linda, 1160
Murray, Linda T., 7026
Murray, Mary Jo, 8521
Murray, Meghan, 9405
Murray, Michael J., 8313
Murray, Michael R., 9608
Murray, Mike, 1368
Murray, Nancy, 4291
Murray, Palmer N., 326
Murray, Pamela, 8396
Murray, Patrick J., Jr., 3960
Murray, Richard K., 1929
Murray, Robert, 640
Murray, Stanton, 3855
Murray, Terrence, 8421
Murray, Terrence J., 8421
Murray, Troy Y., 3936
Murray, Verne, 2550
Murrell, Marilyn, 7742
Murrill, Paul W., 3618
Murrin, Ryan, 1388
Murthy, Krishna, 1393
Murthy, N.R. Narayana, 5994
Musayev, Yuri, 6685
Muscarolas, Miriam, 1307
Muscheid, Kendis, 106
Muse, Tyron, 5802
Museum of Contemporary Art, The, 558
Musgrave, Jeannette, 4947
Musgrave, Ken P., 8774
Musgrave, Mark, 5906
Musgrave, Travis, 3560
Mushett Estate, The, 5388
Mushett, Charles, 5388
Music Festival for Mental Health, 2296
Music in Motion Family Fun Center, 8471
Music Mastermind Inc., 6852
Music Today LLC, 7214
Musica, Karen, 9644
Musicaro, John R., Jr., 1723
Musictoday, LLC, 362
Musk, Elon, 957
Musk, Kimbal, 957
Muskavitch, Charles, 958
Muskavitch, Gail, 958
Musolino, Stefano, Jr., 5296
Muss, Sandra, 2248
Muss, Stephen, 2248
Mussato, Cheryl, 3523
Mussatt, Lynn, 9401
Musselman, Elaine G., 3561
Musselman, Jamie P., 8320
Musselman, W. Austin, Jr., 3561
Musselwhite, Stephen A., 9415
Musser, Clifton R., 1419
Musser, Laura J., 4724
Musser, Marcie, 1368
Musser, Marcie J., 1419
Musser, Margaret K., 1419
Musser, Marshall, 9778
Musser, Robert W., 1419
Mussman, Gaylord, 5039
Mustafa, Bernard, 9410
Mustico, Michael, 5804
Mutch, Ruth O'Donnell, 9067
Mutenba, Mateous, 2631
Muth, Maria G., 7369
Muth, Maria M., 7369
Muth, Robert C., 8347
Muther, Catherine S., 1254
Muther, Jane Elfers, 4033
Mutual of America Life Insurance Co., 6518
Mutual of Omaha Insurance Co., 5071
Muyskens, Chris, 4402
Muyskens, Kathy, 4402
Muzzy, Jim, 1037
Muzzy, Luke, 9704
MVP Health Plan, Inc., 6099
Mwanza, Angela K., 5917, 5918
Myara, Alicia, 9435
Myer, Diane Lenfest, 7912
Myerberg, Neal P., 5240
Myers Charitable Lead, Israel, 3856
Myers, Beverly, 3856
Myers, Carol P., 4515
Myers, Daniel M., 5950
Myers, Daria, 175
Myers, David G., 4515
Myers, Dick, 3320
Myers, Donna, 3061
Myers, Douglas, 9558
Myers, Eliza H., 6173
Myers, Israel, 3856
Myers, James J., 2415
Myers, John Peterson, 234
Myers, Jonathan P., 3856
Myers, Larry, 1002
Myers, Louise, 4614
Myers, Mark, 2100
Myers, Mary Lynn, 2035
Myers, Max, 7782
Myers, Michele, 3788
Myers, Nellie, 3366
Myers, Peter, 3968
Myers, Randy W., 9559
Myers, Robert C., 6903
Myers, Roger M., 569
Myers, Ronald, 5927
Myers, S.L., 2375
Myers, Samford T., 24
Myers, Steve, 8522
Myers, Sue, 3757
Myers, Susan H., 2476
Myers, Susan Hanley, 2476
Myers, Sylvan, 2392
Myers, Tim D., 7908
Myers, Vincent, 5209
Mygrant Glass Co., 7638
Myhers, Richard, 1840
Mylan Laboratories Inc., 8192
Mylan Pharmaceuticals, 8192
Mylander, George L., 7444
Myles, June B., 9787
Myles, Paula, 419
Myles, Virginia R., 9787
Myott, Shirley, 1725
Myra, John E., 7355
Myre, Jane Carson, 3567
Myres, Brian, 4631
Myrick, H. Gordon, 4830
Myrie, Sharon, 5728
Myrin, Karin, 8330
Myrin, Mabel Pew, 8220
Mytelka, Andrew, 8952

N-1 Trust, 9088
N-1 Trust, The, 9111
Nabers, Drayton, Jr., 56
Nabers, Fairfax Smathers, 56
Nabers, Hugh Comers, Jr., 20
Nabhloz Mechanical & Electrical, Inc., 194
Nabholz Construction Corp., 194
Nabholz Propoerties Inc., 194
Nabholz, Charles, 194
Nabholz, Inc., 194
Nabholz, Robert D., 194
Nabisco Brands, Inc., 7296
Nabors, James D., 63
Nabron International, Inc., 4183
Nachman, Gail, 3898
Nachtigal, Anita, 8522
Nachtwey, Peter H., 3828
Nacken, L.J.G., 7272
Nada, Sherif A., 7000
Nadal, Michael A., 2432
Nadal, Nicole, 6383
Nadgwick, Rebecca J., 5033
Nadler, Beverly, 6521
Nadler, David, 6521
Nadler, Julie, 6521
Nadler, Louise M., 8428
Nadler, Paul S., 6521
Nadler, Saul, 6521
Nadosy, Perer A., 5918
Nadosy, Peter A., 5845, 5917, 5919, 5994
Nadwondny, Austin, 2038
Nadzikewycz, Paul, 2907
Naeve, Brian, 2626
Nagao, Osamu, 6491
Nagel Beverage Co., Inc., 2639
Nagel, Barbara, 5577
Nagel, David, 3851
Nagel, Mildred E., 2639
Nagel, Ralph J., 1468
Nagel, Rob D., 7043
Nager, Anita, 234
Nager, Charles, 517
Nager, Elizabeth, 7287
Nager, Eric, 24
Nager, Karen, 517
Nager, Karen D., 517
Nagle, Geoffrey, 3644
Nagle, Patricia Herold, 5405
Nagler, Tracy S., 6666
Nagy, Louis, Jr., 85
Nahigian, Patricia, 3166
Naiberg, Gerald J., 9939
Naiff, Kenneth L., 121
Naify, Carlin, 1103
Najafi, F. Francis, 153
Najam, Edward, Jr., 3278
Najarian, Sossie K., 5307
Najim, Harvey E., 9048
Najork, Susan, 5806
Nakajima, Nobu, 3321
Nakajima, Yukiko, 701
Nakamura, Joyce, 1401
Nakash Holding LLC, 6522
Nakash, Avi, 6522
Nakash, Joseph, 6522
Nakash, Ralph, 6522
Nakata, Theresa, 1108
Nakatomi, Debra, 368
Nally, Joseph, 473
Nalty, Elizabeth S., 3656, 3665
Nalty, Jill K., 3665
Nalty, Morgan S., 3631
Naman, Elisabeth C., 6026
Namath, Donna, 2690
Names Charitasble Remainder Trust, Sidney W., 9690
Names, Diane, 9690
Names, Evelyn, 9690
Names, Richard, 9690
Names, T. Scott, 9690
Names, Thomas S., 9690
Namingha, Michael, 5533
Nan Tie, Gary, 4681
NAN, Inc., 2616
Nance, Frederick R., 7406
Nance, Jennifer, 1960
Nance, Jessie, 7780, 7798
Nance, William, 7296
Nanci's Animal Rights Foundation, Inc., 469
Nanikian, Aida Kantzabedian, 9176
Nanny & Webster, 9694
Nanz, Barry, 3293
Naon, Inc., 6576, 6622
Napier, Buddy, 8774
Napier, Jeff, 9050
Napier, Margaret, 8766
Napier, Margaret Gill Clements, 8767, 9050
Naples, Allen J., 6406
Napoli, Douglas D., 2511
Napoli, Paul, 1602
Napolitano, Barbara T., 9554
Naquin, Sarah, 3658
Naragon, Frederic E., 7640
Narayen, Shantanu, 1734
Narcisse, Sonja, 8083
Narisetti, Raju, 5906
Narita, Yoko, 701
Narodick, Sally, 9757
Narron, James W., 7273
Narum, Larry M., 2818
Narwhal Capital Management, 2489
Nasby, James M.C., 6734
Nasdaq Stock Market, Inc., The, 3857
Naseer-Ghiasuddin, Saira, 4108
Nasella, Henry, 2087
Nash Finch Co., 4727
Nash, Beth, 6062
Nash, David, 4386

Nash, Helen, 6525
Nash, Jack, 6525
Nash, Joshua, 6062, 6525
Nash, Martin, 2182
Nash, Marvin, 4369
Nash, Sandra P., 8197
Nasher Mgmt. Trust Estate, Raymond D., 9051
Nasher, Andrea, 9051
Nasher, Raymond D., 9051
Nason Foundation, Alex G., 1650
Nason Foundation, The, 7549
Nasr, Bassam, Dr., 4373
Nasr, Vali, 6723
Nass, Connie K., 3402
Nass, Marcia Thayer, 1903
Natale, Patrick J., 9547
Natalicio, Diana, 6724
Nathan, Pat, 7328
Nathan, Sandra, 877
Nathan, Scott A., 4188
Nathan, Walter R., 3110
Nathanson, Jeff, 3710
Nathanson, Jeffrey, 3684
Nathanson, Ruth Leventhal, 8297
Nathoo, Raffiq, 6544
Nathu, Vinesh, 1121
Nation, Fred, 3396
National AIDS Fund, 229
National Amusements, Inc., 4233
National Bank & Trust Co., 8026
National Bank of Commerce, 21
National Bank of Indianapolis, The, 3317
National Beer Wholesalers Association, 3714
National Christian Foundation, 8536
National Christian Foundation, The, 4417
National City Bank, 3317, 4369, 7367, 7406, 7428, 7540, 7960, 8026, 8160, 8161, 8228
National Council of Negro Women, 2294
National Dairy Council, 3245
National Distributing Co., Inc., 2444, 2544
National Football League Alumni, Inc., 7638
National Football League Players Association, The, 1939
National Football League, The, 1939
National Fuel Gas Company, 6526
National Gallery of Art, 5707
National Health Services, 1791
National Hockey League, 6528
National Indemnity Co., 6097
National Industrial Maintenance - MI, 2735
National Industrial Maintenance Services, 2735
National Land Partners, LLC, 4208
National Life Insurance Company, 9368
National Machinery Co., 7586
National Machinery LLC, 7586
National Mah Jongg League, Inc., 6529
National Park Service, 898
National Philanthropy Trust, 6044
National Plant Services, Inc., 2735
National Power Rodding, 2735
National Presto Industries, Inc., 1840
National Society Of Hebrew Day Schools, 6229
National Society of Hebrew Day Schools, 6277
National Speaking of Women's Health, 7394
National Sporting Library, 5707
National Water Main Cleaning Co., 2735
Nationwide Corp., 7587
Nationwide Life Insurance Co. of America, 7587
Nationwide Mutual Insurance Co., 7587
Natoli, Joseph T., 2392
Natorp, Kenneth, 7702
Nature's Bounty Inc., 1771
Nature's Therapy, Inc., 7012
Nauck, Fritz, 7202
Naugatuck Savings Bank, 1616
Naughton, Amy B., 3922
Nault, Henry, 6603
Naumes, Sue, 7876
Nauta, Jill, 9492
Nautilus Insurance Company, 1741
Nava, Carolyn, 972
Navarrette, Steve, 5039
Navarro, Guy, 698
Navarro, Michael, 2364
Naviaux, Jeanine, 9385
Navikas, David B., 8235
Navota, Katherine, 2767
Nayak, Deepak, 6310
Naye, Dawn, 9681
Naylor, Alonzo, 3762
Naylor, Bartlett, 3762
Naylor, Diane G., 8194
Naylor, Irvin S., 8194
Naylor, James, 4725
Naylor, Leah R., 8194
Naylor, Robert, 7328
Naylor, S. Chester, II, 8194
Naylor, Sarah R., 8194
Nazar, Jose Luis, 671
Nazarian, Artemis, 6530
Nazarian, David, 962
Nazarian, Deann, 1247
Nazarian, Levon, 6530
Nazarian, Nazar, 6530
Nazarian, Shulamit, 962
Nazarian, Soraya J., 962
Nazarian, Younes, 962
Nazel Family Trust, 5937
NBC Studio, 674
NBC Universal, Inc., 6531
NCL America, Inc., 7008
NCR Corp., 2524
Neal, Alesha, 3379
Neal, Brenda D., 6314
Neal, David L., 7298
Neal, Homer A., 1926
Neal, Karla, 9185
Neal, Richard, 744
Neal, Robert F., 4830
Neal, Shannon, 3170
Neal, Shelly, 7358
Neal, Stephen C., 686
Neal, Stephen L., 7298
Neal, Susan Falck, 3320
Neal, Vivian, 7367
Neal, Warner, 2460
Neale, Gary, 1528
Nearburg, Charles E., 9055
Nearburg, Dana E., 9055
Neary, Megan W., 9551
Neaves, Hope C., 8370
NEB Corp., 9954
Nebbe, Douglas E., 3436
NEBCO, Inc., 5021
Nebeker, Stephen B., 9347
Nebenzahl, Adina, 3900
Nebenzahl, Samuel, 3900
Nechay, Kim, 1672
Nedley, R.E., 2074
Neeb Family Foundation, The, 9652
Neeb, Martin J., 9652
Needham, Eddie, 2390
Needler, Michael S., 7453
Neel, Hibbett, 4820
Neeley, Alison, 963
Neeley, Lucille, 963
Neeley, Lucille A., 963
Neeley, Ronald, 963
Neely, Greg, 3288
Neely, H. Edward, 3575
Neely, Mary M., 4335, 4517
Neely, Suzanne, 4825
Neely, Walter, 4816
Nees, Kenneth L., 6581
Nees, Lowell, 7569
Neese 1957 Trust, Margaret L., 9911
Neese 1960 Trust, Walter K., 9814
Neese Trust of 1954, Robert H., 9911
Neese, Alonzo A., Jr., 9814
Neese, Elbert H., Sr., 9814
Neese, Gordon C., 9814
Neese, Robert H., 9911
Neese, Walter K., 9814
Neese, Wendy L., 9911
Neeson, Heather Gael, 2815
Neff, Daniel A., 7040
Neff, James R., 2764
Neff, Jodi, 2971
Neff, Kathy, 2550
Neff, Kathy A., 2550
Neff, Paul A., 2550
Neff, Peter Gibbons, 2385
Neff, Ralph, 3369
Neff, Richard B., 5279
Nefsky, Robert, 5031
Negal, Merideth, 2039
Negley, Nancy Brown, 8731
Negrin, Richard, 8221
Negron, Eduardo J., 3085
Neher, Timothy, 9470
Neher, Timothy H., 5395
Neher, Timothy P., 2514
Nehrt, Sue, 3284
Neibart, Marilyn, 5396
Neibauer, Shelly, 1423
Neidenbach, Joe, 9800
Neidich, Brooke Garber, 6534
Neidich, Daniel M., 6534
Neidlinger, Darlene, 4496
Neidorff, Michael F., 4870
Neier, Aryeh, 6004
Neil Tillotson Trust, 2559
Neilan Trust, Florence, 589
Neill, Lauren M., 4245
Neilsen, Craig H., 964
Neilsen, Ray H., 964
Neilson, George W., 4725
Neilson, Judith R., 4021
Neilson, Sara A., 5073
Neiman, Janet, 6535
Neiman, LeRoy, 6535
Neinstein, Jack, 731
Neisel, Bridgette, 7673
Neisser, Edward, 3048
Neisser, Judith E., 3048
Neisser, Katherine M., 3048
Neiswander, D. Kirk, 7564
Neitzel, Scott A., 9898
Nejes, Peter F., 5336
Nekritz, Edward S., 1485
Nellis, Mike, 8676
Nelms, Charlie, 4510
Nelnet, Inc., 5072
Nelson Publishers, Thomas, 4417
Nelson, Andrew, 7191
Nelson, Anita, 5194
Nelson, Ann, 4306
Nelson, Anna Spangler, 2191, 7320
Nelson, Anne, 141
Nelson, Arvid R., 1679
Nelson, Aune, 3049
Nelson, Bill D., 7359
Nelson, C. David, 4629, 4726
Nelson, Carol J., 9912
Nelson, Catherine, 3015
Nelson, Cathy, 1077
Nelson, Celeste J., 4086
Nelson, Charles F., 3338
Nelson, Charley, 4684
Nelson, Chris, 5390
Nelson, Christopher, 532
Nelson, Christopher E., 3420
Nelson, Clarke A., 9993
Nelson, David, 4800
Nelson, David R., Jr., 39
Nelson, Deborah, 7295
Nelson, Diana L., 4629, 4726
Nelson, Doug, 5108
Nelson, Edward, Jr., 9070
Nelson, Emily R., 9316
Nelson, Erica, 88
Nelson, Ethel, 4613
Nelson, Faye Anderson, 4410
Nelson, Fraser, 9311
Nelson, Gary, 598, 3437
Nelson, Gary D., 2482
Nelson, Ginna, 9916
Nelson, Glen D., 4629, 4726
Nelson, Grace, 8195
Nelson, Grant E., 9912
Nelson, Greg, 416
Nelson, Gregory P., 2082
Nelson, Helen P., 7998
Nelson, Holly J., 3948
Nelson, Jane, 1935
Nelson, Jane S., 8422
Nelson, Janice, 4768
Nelson, John C., 8873
Nelson, John P., 3447
Nelson, Jon, 7825
Nelson, Jonathan M., 8422
Nelson, Julie, 4625
Nelson, Kathy J., Rev. Dr., 5261
Nelson, Kerry, 4448
Nelson, Kimberly A., 4661
Nelson, L. Steven, 7153
Nelson, Larry R., 2059
Nelson, Leonard M., 5744
Nelson, Lori L., 2610
Nelson, Lynel Rae, 4751
Nelson, Marilyn C., 4629, 4726
Nelson, Marilyn Carlson, 4629
Nelson, Mark, 4872
Nelson, Mary, 3467
Nelson, Mary A., 3467
Nelson, Mary Goodwillie, 4547, 4579
Nelson, Maybeth, 9912
Nelson, Melody S., 3760
Nelson, Merlin E., 6492
Nelson, Michael S., 7763, 7779
Nelson, Michael Stewart, 7779
Nelson, Michelle A., 9416
Nelson, Mitchell, 6995

Nelson, Nancy, 4618
Nelson, P. Erik, 7998
Nelson, Pamela B., 7763, 7779
Nelson, Pamela Blair, 7779
Nelson, Pat, 1989
Nelson, R.W., 3467
Nelson, Randolph M., 7763, 7779
Nelson, Randolph Miles, 7779
Nelson, Richard, 1989
Nelson, Richard A., 6297
Nelson, Rodney G., 9912
Nelson, Ruth Kaiser, 7779
Nelson, Steve, 7421
Nelson, Susan K., 3749
Nelson, Susie, 9773
Nelson, Theron, 2644
Nelson, Thomas M., Rev., 3974
Nelson, Timothy B., 7763, 7779
Nelson, Tom, 2514
Nelson, Travis, 7001
Nelson, Vince, 1077
Nelson, W. Linton, ADM., 8195
Nelson, Ward, 8548
Nelson, Wendy M., 4621, 4629, 4726
Nelson, William E., 9881
Nelson, William J., 4636
Nelson, William R., 9521
Nemanic, Marc, 972
Nemec, Fred J., 8768
Nemeth, Joseph, 9835
Nemetz, William J., 2534
Nemovicher, Sivan, 5191
Nemy, Corinne, 8306
Nemy, Enid, 8306
Nepales, Ruben V., 701
Neptune, Elizabeth, 3698
Neptune, Vivian, 8353
Nerangis, James T., 5897
Neri, Janis L., 1634
Nerman, Susan Seidler, 3479
Nerz, Donald, 5194
NES Group, Inc., 7625
Nesbary, Dale K., 4369
Nesbeda, Hannah, 4109
Nesbeda, Peter, 4109
Nesbit, Jacqueline L., 8549
Nesbit, Robert, 2482
Nesbitt, Anne B., 8642
Nesbitt, Greg, 714
Nesbitt, John, 8001
Nesbitt, Theresa, 2902
Nesbitt, William A., 9019, 9122
Neschis, Janet C., 6041
Neshat, Shirin, 7050
Neshe, Dana, 4173
Neshek, Milton E., 9881
Nesholm, Elmer J., 9691
Nesholm, Erika J., 9691
Nesholm, John F., 9691
Nesholm, Kirsten, 9691
Nesholm, Laurel, 9691
Nesle, Heather Nesle, 6548
Ness, Ian, 6408
Ness, Mary K., 4591
Ness, Mary Kay, 4591
Ness, Nikki Herreid, 4685
Nessen, Peter, 3956
Nesser, Noel, 9070
Nessier, Stephen, 1335
Nestle Dreyer's Grand Ice Cream Company, 965
Nestle Purina PetCare Co., 4948
Nestle USA, Inc., 965, 9056
Nestor, John G., 7668
Nestor, Karen R., 7499
Nestor, Lyndsey, 9796
Neth, Robert H., Jr., 5216
Netherton, Jane, 846
NetJets Aviation, Inc., 7012
Netsolace, Inc., 1582
Nett, Roy W., 3362
Nettles, Cory L., 9907
Nettles, Thomas A., IV, 25
Nettleton, Marimon, 9177
Network for Good, 8675
Neu, John L., 6537
Neu, Robert T., 6537
Neu, Wendy K., 6537
Neubach, Paul, 8808
Neubauer, Jane M., 7509
Neubauer, Joseph, 8196
Neubauer, Lawrence, 8196
Neuberger, James A., 1649
Neuberger, Marie S., 1649
Neuberger, Roy R., 1649
Neuberger, Roy S., 1649
Neuenschwander, Jack L., 7620
Neufeld, Jordan J., 7357
Neufeld, Katherine, 9005
Neugent, Gerard D., 3452
Neuharth, Jan, 1907
Neuhauser, Stuart, 7107
Neuhoff Charitable Trust, Joseph O., 9191
Neuhoff, Joseph Boyd, 8778
Neuhoff, Patricia, 8585, 8633
Neuhoff, Pauline S., 8766
Neukom, Gillian, 9692
Neukom, John McMakin, 9692
Neukom, Josselyn, 9692
Neukom, Samantha, 9692
Neukom, William H., 9692
Neuman, Dawn, 9867
Neuman, Gerald, 6540
Neuman, Judith, 1470
Neuman, Linda, 3424
Neuman, Neal, 6540
Neuman, Suzanne, 1470
Neuman, Vera, 6540
Neuman, Werner, 1470
Neuman, William, 1470
Neumann, David P., 8383
Neumann, Roland M., 9825
Neumann, Roxann S., 8958
Neumann, Susan M., 1676
Neumeister, Bill, 9616
Neuro Rays Imaging, 1850
Neurogena, 5327
Neuschotz, Sondra, 9493
Neustadt, Dolores K., 9254
Neustadt, Walter, Jr., 9254
Neustein, Chana, 6836
Neustein, Robin Chemers, 6367
Neuwirth, Felice, 6539
Neuwirth, Marvin R., 6539
Nevels, Reggie, 3280
Neverthirst, 9118
Neviaser Marital Trust B, Charles, 7271
Neviaser Trust, Charles, 7271
Neviaser, C.M., 7271
Neviaser, Michael, 7271
Neville, Richard, 744
Nevin, Crocker, 5496
Nevin, Janice E., 1765
Nevin-Folino, Nancy, 4443
Nevlin, Linda K., 3036
Nevrivy, Michael, 5046
New Albany Company, The, 7713
New Alliance Bank, 1562
New Balance Athletic Shoe, Inc., 4189
New Bidnis Inc., 6852
New Breed Corporate Services, Inc., 7162
New Castle Corp., 6872
New Century Mgmt. Svcs. LLC, 6301
New Convnant Foundation, 8766
New Covenant Foundation, The, 9163
New Discovery, Inc., 700
New England Dairy and Food Council, 3245
New England Patriots LP, 4193
New Horizon Enterprises, Inc., 3150
New Life Church, 9143
New Mighty US Trust, 1936
New Millennium Trust, The, 2394
New Orleans Redevelopment Authority, 6661
New Process Steel, 8837
New Springville Jewish Center, 5553
New Times Group Holdings Ltd., 6651
New York Community Bancorp., Inc., 6703
New York Life Insurance Co., 6548, 6756
New York Mercantile Exchange, 7012
New York Mercantile Exchange, Inc., 2755, 6547
New York State Dept. of Economic Development, 6044
New York State Electric and Gas, 3693
New York State Extended Day Grant, 6406
New York State Urban Development Corp., 6044
New York Stock Exchange LLC, 6573
NewAlliance Bancshares, Inc., 1651
Newberry Library, 5707
Newberry, S. Lloyd, Jr., 2431
Newberry, Tom, 4678
Newbold, N. Carter, 8602
Newborg, Barbara, 7151
Newby, Jerry A., 2
Newby, L. Kristin, 1738
Newcom, Jennings J., 135
Newcombe, Artie, IV, 7179
Newcombe, Charlotte W., 5391
Newcombe, Douglas, 4344
Newell, Cara Z., 4922
Newell, Cheryl, 4772
Newell, Marjory A., 2611
Newell, Richard D., 9647
NewellRubbermaid, 3201
Newfield Exploration Co., 9060
Newgen Family Trust, Elma L., The, 2636
Newgen, Elma Lightfoot, 2636
Newhall Land and Farming Co., The, 966
Newhall, Anthony, 966
Newhall, David, 966
Newhall, George A., 966
Newhall, John B., 4241
Newhall, Leila G., 966
Newhall, Roger, 966
Newhouse, Donald E., 6550
Newhouse, Joseph P., 1531
Newhouse, Mitzi E., 6550
Newhouse, Samuel I., Jr., 6550
Newhouse, Samuel I., Sr., 6550
Newkirk, Jonathan, 487
Newkirk, Michael A., 487
Newland, George, 9617
Newland, Robert, 2015
Newlon, Shaun, 2690
Newman Trust, R. & C., 967
Newman's Own, 1652
Newman, Andrew E., 4883
Newman, Anita, 2250
Newman, Ann, 2439
Newman, Ann J., 9061
Newman, Annalee, 6554
Newman, Arthur B., 9493
Newman, Bobbi, 1019
Newman, Christine H., 967
Newman, David, 9493
Newman, Dixie, 5425, 5496
Newman, Eddie, 746, 1015
Newman, Eileen D., 9493
Newman, Elizabeth V., 6553
Newman, Eric P., 4883
Newman, Evelyn E., 4884
Newman, Florence B., 9061
Newman, Frank, 6552
Newman, Frank N., 6552
Newman, Harold, 7352
Newman, Howard, 6553
Newman, Howard H., 6553
Newman, J. Bonnie, 3345
Newman, Jeff, 1497
Newman, Jeff. C., 9898
Newman, Joan M., 4973
Newman, Joanne Woodward, 1652
Newman, John, 8639
Newman, John E., Jr., 9061
Newman, John H., 7963
Newman, Leslie, 7511
Newman, Lizabeth, 6552
Newman, Martha G., 3680
Newman, Maryam R., 6553
Newman, Melvin David, 2250
Newman, Michael, 4783
Newman, Paul, 7474
Newman, Paul L., 1652
Newman, Peter G., 5802, 6406
Newman, Richard A., 1849
Newman, Richard G., 967
Newman, Robert H., Jr., 6406
Newman, W.R., III, 4843
Newman, William, 2250
Newman, William T., Jr., Hon., 9384
Newmark, Craig Alexander, 436
Newmark, Michael, 4995
NewMarket Corporation, 9494
Newquist, Dana E., 282
Newsham, Siriporn, 2616
Newsom, William A., 578
Newsome, Lenora, 208
Newsome, Michael, 8351
Newsome, P. David, Jr., 7735
Newswanger, Greg, 8324
Newswanger, Gregory, 8324
Newswanger, Janet, 8324
Newswanger, Janet Weaver, 8324
Newswanger, Kendall, 8324
Newswanger, Larry, 8324
Newswanger, Larry W., 8324
Newswanger, Randall, 8324
Newsweb Corp., 2658
Newsweek, 6748
Newsweek, Inc., 9445
Newton, Alex, 1777
Newton, Amy, 1222
Newton, Coco, 1777
Newton, David I., 1567
Newton, Denise, 8797
Newton, Don, 3348
Newton, E. Anthony, 2385
Newton, Jane, 7474

Nolan, Joseph R., Jr., 1656
Nolan, Mathew J., 4405
Nolan, Maureen, 3469
Nolan, Mike, 3713
Nolan, Peter G., 3116
Nolan, Robin G., 3116
Nolan, Susan, 9410
Noland, John "Jay", Jr., 3613
Noland, John B., 3618
Noland, Mariam C., 4371
Nolen, Eliot Chace, 6097
Nolen, James S., 23
Nolen, Wilson, 6097
Noll, Dennis E., 9148
Noll, Gregg, 1786
Noll, Pamela D., 5766
Noll, Patricia R., 970
Nolletti, David, 7210
Nolletti, Lara, 7210
Nolt, Edwin B., 8002
Nolt, Sheryl Robins, 9523
Nolte, Anothy M., 9168
Noltenius, Jeanette, 1894
Nomina, Jan J., 7208
Noneman, Joan Carol, 1203
Nong, Kristin D., 1386
Nonneman, Anita C., 7593
Nonneman, Elaine M., 9597
Nonneman, Frederick E., 7593
Nonneman, Lois, 7593
Nonneman, Lois E., 7593
Nonomaque, Curt, 9250
Nook, Teresa, 3418
Noon, George P., 6333
Noon, George P., Dr., 8804
Noon, Nicholas, 4191
Noon, Prudence J., 966
Noonan Trust, Walter J., 8424
Noonan, Jay, 969
Noonan, Mary Antonia, 1981
Noonan, Michael, 4631
Noone, Laura Palmer, 3345
Noorda, Lewena, 9339
Noorda, Lewena "Tye", 9339
Noordhoek, Jeff, 5072
Noordzij, Amy Doe, 4022
Noort, Hans E. Vanden, 2281
Nootens, Raymond, 2673
Nooyi, Indra K., 6627
Noranda, 7272
Norcia, Jerry, 4410, 4543
Norcross, Arthur D., 6564
Norcross, Arthur D., Jr., 6564
Nord, Cindy, 7594
Nord, Eric T., 7595
Nord, Jane B., 7595
Nord, Richard E., 7595
Nord, Shannon, 7594, 8468
Nord, Walter G., 7594
Nord, Walter G., Mrs., 7594
Nordeen, Julie S., 9889
Nordeman, Anne, 5834
Norden, William, 6375
Nordenberg, Mark A., 7946
Nordick, Brett A., 7356
Nordick, Ralph, 7846
Nordick, Ralph B., 7356
Nordlinger, Jay S., 3258
Nordlund, Judi, 5098
Nordson Corp., 7594, 7596
Nordt, John C., III, 2223
Noren, Ronald B., 1581
Norfleet, Robert F., Jr., 9529
Norfolk Southern Corp., 9496
Norgard, Susanne, 416
Norgart, Randall E., 7883
Norgren, Anneka, 6633
Norgren, Harriet S., 4799
Norich, Sam, 5197
Noriega, Arthur, IV, 2151
Norland, Cynthia J., 7354
Norlander, Adam R., 9801
Norman Crat, Brooks, 7151
Norman Foundation, The, 6173
Norman Fund, Aaron E., Inc., The, 6566
Norman, Aaron E., 6565
Norman, Abigail, 6566
Norman, Alex, 636
Norman, Andrew E., 6566
Norman, Anne, 1879
Norman, Cynthia D., 5068
Norman, Eleanor, 1563
Norman, Greg, Dr., 3283
Norman, Harold, 3407
Norman, Kenneth G., 7294
Norman, Margaret, 6565, 6566
Norman, Marilyn, 4402
Norman, Paul, 4475
Norman, Sarah, 6566
Norman, Thomas, 4402
Normandie Foundation, Inc., 6565
Normile, Robert, 886
Norosz, Kris, 79, 89
Norquist, S. Griffin, Jr., 4833
Norrington, Margaret, 1015
Norrington, Ralph, 1015
Norris, Bradley K., 971
Norris, Charlotte, 9775
Norris, Cindie, 3303
Norris, David E., 3708
Norris, Dellora A., 3058
Norris, Eileen L., 971
Norris, Harlyne J., 971
Norris, J. Carl, 9023
Norris, Jeff, 1805
Norris, Jon L., 1690
Norris, Kenneth T., 971
Norris, Lester J., 3058
Norris, Pamela, 3058
Norris, Robert A., 3058
Norris, Robert Windsor, 3948
Norris, Stefan, 1805
Norris, William, 7276
Norris-McCluney, Corena, 7340
North American Foundation for University of Manchester, 5707
North Central Trust Co., 9889
North Forest Associates LP, 9452
North Fork Investment Co., 1527
North Metro Church, 9059
North Park Baptist Church, 9059
North Side Bank & Trust Co., 7404
North Star Fund, Inc., The, 6341
North Star Ventures, 4614, 4731
North, Aaron, 4921
North, Elizabeth Hendricks, 3813
North, Jim, 4375
North, Katie, 5098
Northbrook Properties, Inc., 410
Northcutt, Gordon L., 8819
Northeast Nuclear Energy Co., 1656
Northeast Utilities, 1656
Northen, John, 7306
Northen, Mary Moody, 9063
Northern Life Insurance Co., 7038
Northern Manhattan Nursing, 6288
Northern Ohio Golf Charities, Inc., 7597
Northern Trust, 3050
Northern Trust Bank, 2260
Northern Trust Bank of Florida, N.A., 2075, 2269
Northern Trust Bank, N.A., 2301, 3156
Northern Trust Co. of Delaware, The, 4176
Northern Trust Co., The, 2668, 2681, 2700, 2822, 2848, 2958, 3041, 3059, 3215, 3220, 3221, 4885, 4954, 9302
Northern Trust Company, 2027, 3117
Northern Trust Company, The, 1398, 2746, 2965
Northern Trust, N.A., 3051, 3127
Northridge, Mark, 5167
Northrop Grumman Corp., 9498
Northrop, Amanda, 4285
Northrop, Mike, 3303
Northrop, Wilhelm E., 6136
Northrup, Thomas P., 8332
Northrup, Tom, 9509
Northshore Mining Co., 7407
Northwest Arkansas Community Foundation, 200
Northwest Christian Community Foundation, 7873
Northwest Savings Bank, 7993
Northwest Savings Bank, N.A., 7965
Northwestern Mutual Life Insurance Co., The, 9914
Norton Co., 8260
Norton Co., Matthew G., 9664
Norton, Alice, 3036
Norton, Allison, 9304
Norton, Brad, 7676
Norton, Brenda, 7676
Norton, Brent, 7676
Norton, Burke F., 4311
Norton, C. Diane, 3468
Norton, Chris, 662
Norton, Elizabeth B., 1887
Norton, George W., Mrs., 3592
Norton, H. Wilbert, Jr., 1907
Norton, James M., 7172
Norton, Jane, 7676
Norton, John A., 7172
Norton, Lenore Trilby, 7172
Norton, Michael, 2005
Norton, Michael A., 7172
Norton, Paul S., 7172
Norton, Peter, 729
Norton, Pierce H., II, 7783
Norton, Richard, 6289
Norton, Richard M., 2876
Norton, Robert, 1887
Norton, Robert E., II, 9819
Norton, Thomas K., 3468
Norton, Toby, 9304
Norvell, Barbara C., 7178
Norwalk Police Union Show Fund, 6528
Norwest Corp., 1312
Norwest Ltd., 1312
Norwick, Greg, 1423
Norwin Estates, Inc., 6768
Norwood, Ballard G., 7310
Nosbusch, Keith D., 9934
Nosbusch, Thomas D., 7354
Nosek, Julie, 3417
Nosier, Peter, 478
Nosler, Victoria Davis, 1761
Nostitz, Drewry H., Mrs., 7221
Nostro, Louis, 2329, 2387
Nota, Chris, 1002
Notis, Tzippy Friedman, 450
Noto, Richard, 8383
Notopoulos, Philip J., 3980
Notter, John L., 692
Nottingham, Ben G., 7199
Nottingham, Charles, III, 7199
Novack, Deborah S., 7888
Novack, Kenneth M., 7888
Novak Foundation, David and Wendy, 2514
Novak, David C., 3587, 3608
Novak, Susan B., 3587
Novak, Wendy L., 3587
Novartis Consumer Health, 1771
Novartis Corp., 3833
Novartis Inc., 6569
Novartis Pharmaceuticals Corp., 5393
Novelly, Paul A., 4854
Novelly, Paul A., II, 4854
Novick, Azriel, 5628
Novick, David, 9924
Novo Foundation, 5027
NoVo Foundation, 7875
Novo Foundation, The, 6864
Novotny, Yetta Deitch, 8202
Now Trust, 1098
Nowak, Betty, 9324
Nowak, Carole M., 7454
Nowak, Henry, 9324
Nowak, Mark A., 4114
Nowers Fund, Lola E., 2390
Nowicki, Douglas R., 8163
Nowlin, Kelly D., 6947
Nowlin, Newman R., 23
Nowling, Michael, 9615
Noyce Residual Trust, Robert N., 974
Noyce, Elizabeth B., 3696
Noyce, Pendred, 974
Noyce, Pendred E., 3696
Noyes, Charles F., 6571
Noyes, Dan, 3361
Noyes, Elizabeth H., 3361
Noyes, Henry S., 3361
Noyes, Marguerite Lilly, 3361
Noyes, Nicholas H., 3361
Noyes, Nicholas S., 3361
NR Rhino Co., LC, 9349
NS Associates, Inc., 3150
NSPB Corp., 3322
Ntoumi, Francine, 9625
NU Lens, Ltd., 9915
Nu Skin Enterprises, Inc., 9340
Nuce, Michael, 9795
Nuckolls, James G., 9479
Nucor Corp., 7275
Nudo, Alan, 2765
Nuernberg, Amy, 1520
Nuernberger, David, 3424
Null, Audrey C., 7640
Null, John, 8863
Nulsen, Carol, 4609
Nulsen, David, 4609
Numann, Patricia J., 6153
Numanville, Brian, 4727
Nunes, Mary Louise, 3991
Nunes, Paul, 1563
Nunez, Craig W., 8884
Nunley, Wallace C., 9382
Nunn, Dana MacLaurin, 1255
Nunn, Larry E., 3374
Nunn, Mary Ann, 3374
Nunn, Sam, 5684
Nunnally, Hugh, 9470
Nuorala, Kelsey L., 4522
Nurmi, Elaine Abell, 3713

O'Neill, Meghan, 9961
O'Neill, Michael, 1893
O'Neill, Molly, 9961
O'Neill, Peter J., 6153
O'Neill, Peter M., 6723
O'Neill, Rita R., 7354
O'Neill, Sher M., 4686
O'Neill, Timothy J., 6591
O'Neill, Wendy Harrison, 3982
O'Neill, William D., 1690
O'Neill, William J., Jr., 7602
O'Quinn, John M., 9072
O'Reilly, James F., 7424
O'Reilly, Maureen, 6595
O'Reilly, Michael, 884
O'Reilly, Patrick J., 419
O'Reilly, William, 6595
O'Rourke, Colleen, 4733
O'Rourke, Eileen M., 3712
O'Rourke, James, 1537
O'Rourke, James Joc, 4722
O'Rourke, L.D., 860
O'Rourke, Patrick, 4733
O'Rourke, Sean, 4733
O'Rourke, Timothy, 4733
O'Rourke, William J., 7908
O'Shaughnessey, W. John, 2435
O'Shaughnessy, Betty L., 1345
O'Shaughnessy, Chevonne E., 4734
O'Shaughnessy, Daniel J., 4734
O'Shaughnessy, Eileen A., 4734
O'Shaughnessy, Fran, 7474
O'Shaughnessy, I.A., 4734
O'Shaughnessy, John F., 4734
O'Shaughnessy, John F., Jr., 4734
O'Shaughnessy, Karen J., 4734
O'Shaughnessy, Laura, 9445
O'Shaughnessy, Susan, 1345
O'Shaughnessy, Terence P., 4734
O'Shea, Erin, 3818
O'Shea, Erin K., 7080
O'Shea, John M., 5248
O'Shea, Michele K., 6599
O'Shea, Mort, 5473
O'Shea, Peggy, 2269, 5805
O'Shea, Robert J., 6599
O'Sullivan, Anne S., 6601
O'Sullivan, Marie T., 6601
O'Sullivan, Patrick, 181, 1166
O'Sullivan, Sean M., 6601
O'Toole, Beverly L., 6070
O'Toole, Dennis A., 3484
O'Toole, Terence M., 6602
O'Toole, Theresa, 8207
O'Toole, Thomas, 3484
O'Tuel, Muriel Ward, 8507
OA3, LLC, 355
Oak Assocs., 7367
Oak Hill Capital Management LLC, 1771
Oak Hills Church, 7846
Oak Tree Trust, 2770
Oak Trust, The, 7276
Oakes, T. Wayne, 9413
Oakey, Jean, 9485
Oakley Family Trust, 978
Oakley, Eloy Ortiz, 411
Oakley, James E., III, 8580
Oaks, Nancy, 571
Oakwood Homes, Inc., 5444
Oakwood Homes, LLC, 1411
Oare, Carol F., 4484
Oare, Ernest M., 4484
Oasis Center, 8532
Oasis Petroleum North America, LLC, 9049
Oates, James F., 3115
Oates, Joyce Carol, 6116
Oates, Marvin Buzz L., 980
Oates, Michael, 2097
Oates, Phillip D., 980
Oates, William A., 6082
Oates, William A., Jr., 3961
Obata, Gyo, 4894
Obata, Kiku, 5001
Obenauer, Christie, 7357
Ober, Agnes E., 4703
Ober, David G., 2032
Ober, Gayle M., 4662, 4703
Ober, Richard, 5182
Ober, Richard B., 4703
Ober, Theodore E., 4216, 4270
Ober, Timothy M., 4703
Oberbroeckling, Katie, 3417
Oberfeld, Neil, 1487
Oberfest, Bruce, 5852, 6481
Obergfell, Brian, 6159
Oberhelman, Douglas, 2864
Oberkotter, Joyce, 5183
Oberkotter, Mildred L., 8203
Oberkotter, Paul, 8203
Oberland, Gregory C., 9914
Oberlander, Eileen, 5917
Oberlander, Michael, 2004
Oberlin College, 5707
Oberlin, Wendy, 3295
Oberman, Alicia Schuyler, 3026
Oberman, Michael S., 5562, 5655, 5789, 5855, 5952, 5977, 6036, 6207, 6524, 6576, 6622, 7028, 7110, 7124
Obermann, Stuart, 22
Obermeyer, Walter, 1418
Oberndorf, Susan C., 981
Oberndorf, William E., 981
Oberrender, Robert, 4785
Oberste, Rachel, 180
Obrist, John H., 8025
Obrock, John A., 8129
Obrokta, Thomas J., Jr., 9771
Obrow, Norman C., 484
Obstfeld, Leah, 5905
Ocanas, J. Reymundo, 8, 9
Ocean Federal Savings Bank, 5394
Ocean Financial Corp., 5394
OceanFirst Bank, 5394
OceanFirst Financial Corp., 5394
Oceanside Care Center, 6287, 6288
Oceanside Care Center Inc., Inc., 6763
Och, Daniel S., 6575
Och, Jane C., 6575
Ochs, Gail J., 530
Ochs, Marilyn, 7287
Ochs, Peter M., 530
Ochsner, Lena, 1394
Ochylski, Daniel, 3470
Ochylski, Edward, 3470
Ochylski, Edward, Mrs., 3470
Ockerbloom, Richard, 4003
Ocmulgee Fields, Inc., 2491
Octave West LLC, 2236
Oda, Jim, 7569
Odahowski, David A., 2008
Oddleifson, Eric, 4077
Oddo, Nancy E., 1901
Odell, Helen Pfeiffer, 7277
Odell, Mary, 1270
Odell, Robert Stewart, 7277
Odesco Industrial Services, 2735
Odgers, Richard, 1283
Odille, Shelley Taylor, 7415
Odinet, Christopher L., 3618
Odle, Samuel L., 3331
Odne, Kathleen L., 833
Odom, Charles L., 7327
Odom, Dan, 7231
Odom, DeWayne, 237
Odom, James, 2378
Odom, P.B., III, 7781
Oechsle, Christa, 7278
Oechsle, Walter, 7278
Oehrli, Diana, 4082
Oeken, Ashley Basile, 7639
Oelkers, Scott, 9357
Oelschlager, Debbbie, 9415
Oelschlager, James, 7598
Oelschlager, Jim, 7598
Oelschlager, Kathryn Krisch, 9415
Oelschlager, Vanita, 7598
Oertel, Anna J., 7444
Oesterle, Stephen N., 4712
Oestreicher, Julius, 6956
Oestreicher, Michael, 7511
Oetinger, Judith F., 3262
Oettinger, M.D., 3209
Ofat, Theodore M., 7605
Offen, Samuel, 5773
Offer Family Trust, Robert and Daryl, The, 1791
Offer, Robert, 1791
Office Depot, 8834
Offield Charitable Lead Unitrust, 3062
Offield Charitable Lead Unitrust, James, 3062
Offield Charitable Lead Unitrust, Paxon, 3062
Offield, Chase, 3062
Offield, Dorothy Wrigley, 3062
Offield, James S., 3062
Offield, Meighan, 3062
Offield, Paxson H., 3062
Offit, Louise, 1186
Offutt, Karen, 7358
Offutt, Ronald D., 7358
Ofstedal, Donald S., 4723
Oftedal, Gunnhild, 986
Ogawa, Diane Harrison, 5511, 5532
Ogaz, Brian, 943
Ogburn, Elizabeth R., 9386
Ogden, Henry M., 5473
Ogden, Margaret, 5575
Ogden, Margaret H., 6579
Ogden, Mark J., 912
Ogden, Mary Allison, 3567
Ogden, Megan, 3201
Ogden, Ralph E., 6579
Ogden, Roger, 7659
Ogden, Steve, 1392
Ogg, Larry, 9677
Ogie, Elizabeth, 2414
Ogie, Elizabeth C., 2411, 2529
Ogie, Wilds, 2414
Ogilvie, Andrew, 7445
Ogilvie, Dian, 7002
Ogle Trust, Helene Salade, 7831
Ogle, Laura Kerr, 7764
Ogle, Paul W., 3362
Oglesby, John, 2821
Oglesby, Sharon, 3422
Oglethorpe, Ray, 2166
Ogorzaly, Mary, 5954
Ogorzaly, Tamara A., 1494
Ogren, Jennifer, 7038
Ogstrup-Pedersen, Anne-Margrete, 6679
Oh Huber, Marie, 220
Oh, Juli, Esq., 6898
Oh, Julie, 6898
Ohanesian, John R., 9586
Ohanian, Zapur, 9176
Ohga, Midori, 6581
Ohio Co., The, 7719
Ohio Edison Co., 7455
Ohio National Financial Svcs., 7599
Ohio National Life Insurance Co., The, 7599
Ohio Northwestern University, 3209
Ohio State University, 5707
Ohio Valley Bancorp, 3596
Ohiohealth Parent, 7563
Ohm, Paul R., 4503
Ohnell, Ernst, 1661
Ohnell, Ernst, III, 1661
Ohnell, Patricia, 1661
Ohnmacht, Susan, 9145
Ohrstrom, Christopher, 6582
Ohrstrom, Clarke, 6582
Ohrstrom, Elias Buchanan, 4407
Ohrstrom, George F., 6582
Ohrstrom, George L., Jr., 6583
Ohrstrom, Mark J., 6582
Ohrstrom, Wright R.S., 6583
Oifer, David, 5479
Oiness, S. A., 5090
Oishei Consolidated Trust No. 1, 6584
Oishei Consolidated Trust No. 2, 6584
Oishei, John R., 6584
Oishi, Corrine, 7876
Ojakli, Ziad S., 4430
Ojala, Liwanag, 4617
Oka, Megumi, 6421
Okada, Kiyoshi, 6961
Okamoto, Kenneth T., 2596
Okenica, Kathleen, 6451
Okeson, Ken, 7639
Oki, Laurie D., 9694
Oki, Scott B., 9694
Oklahoma Gas and Electric Co., 7782
Oko, Scott A., 2055
Okonak, James R., 8163
Okonjo-Iweala, Ngozi, Dr., 6724
Okonow, Dale, 6205
Okoroafor, Michael, 8083
Okoye, Chinwe Mary, 101
Okrzynski, Maren, 3201
Okum, Nan, 1020
Okuma America Corporation, 4779
Okun, Andrew M., 5431
Okun, Laurie R., 5431
Olafsson, Olaf, 6982
Olam Chesed Yiboneh, 6998
Olander, Chris, 5323, 5385
Olayan America Corp., 6585
Olayan, Hutham S., 6585
Olch, Bradley A., 9341
Old American Insurance Co., 4942
Old Guard Insurance Company, 7711
Old Hospital Corp., 9434
Old National Bancorp, 3363
Old National Bank, 3363
Old National Trust Co., 3327
Olderog, Karen, 3443
Oldershaw, Peter W., 4213
Oldfather, Alan, 5032
Oldfather, William, 5032
Oldford, Will G., Jr., 4373
Oldford, William G., Jr., 4373

Orr, Susan Packard, 1006, 1007
Orr, Tilda R., 1857
Orrock, Nan Grogan, Hon., 2546
Orscheln Co., 4951
Orscheln, Donald W., 4951
Orscheln, Robert J., 4951
Orscheln, William L., 4951
Orsi, Bernard, 762
Orsi, Jennifer, 2332
Orsi, Mark, 762
Orsinger, Genevieve McDavitt, 9073
Orsino, Jeannette M., 3926
Orswell, Lois, 8359
Orszag, Peter R., 5329
Ortberg, Robert K., 3477
Ortega, Jose A., 1828
Ortega, Theresa, 5017
Ortega, Xavier, 106
Ortenberg, Arthur, 5783
Ortenberg, Elisabeth Claiborne, 5783
Ortenzio, Angela D., 8205
Ortenzio, John M., 8206
Ortenzio, Martin J., 8206
Ortenzio, Robert A., 8205, 8206
Ortenzio, Rocco A., 8206
Orth, Sarah, 1020
Ortho Biotech Inc., 5327
Ortho Womens Health & Urology, 5327
Ortho-McNeil Pharmaceutical, Inc., 5327
Orthopaedic Research & Education
Foundation, 7916
Orthwein, Laura R., 6597
Orthwein, William R., 6597
Ortiz, Barbara, 2029
Ortiz, Carlos R., 6099
Ortiz, Diane, 415
Ortiz, Edward, 6275
Ortiz, Jorge, 2900
Ortiz, Roger G., Dr., 8825
Ortt, Brianne, 2019
Ortwine, Wanda S., 9472
Orvis, Mae Zenke, 6598
Orvis, Wayne, 3209
Ory, Andrew D., 4200
Ory, Leslie K., 3599
Ory, Linda G. Hammett, 4200
Ory, Linda Hammett, 4200
Orzechowski, Barbara F., 3480
Osagie, Emmanuel, 7991
Osako, John, 3417
Osberg, Sally, 991, 1175, 1176
Osborn, Casey H., 9991
Osborn, Edward B., 8426
Osborn, James, 517
Osborn, Joann, 3515
Osborn, Melissa Coors, 1396
Osborn, Nancy, 517
Osborn, Robin, 5800
Osborn, Stanley, 4689
Osborn, Susan J., 9991
Osborn, William A., 3059
Osborne Building Corp., 8614
Osborne Enterprises, Inc., 8614
Osborne, Alfred E., Jr., 1484
Osborne, Charles J., 9892
Osborne, Dee S., 9011, 9187
Osborne, Duncan E., 5515, 9207, 9248
Osborne, Elizabeth B., 9248
Osborne, James B., Sr., 2480
Osborne, James C., 433
Osborne, John C., 5046
Osborne, John M., 5506
Osborne, Karen, 7557
Osborne, Kathy Polk, 4524
Osborne, R. Brady, Jr., 2265
Oschin Trust, Samuel, 996
Oschin, Daniel, 996
Oschin, Lynda, 996
Oschin, Michael, 996
Osco-Bingeman, Gigi, 1329
Oseland, Lucille, 3412, 3413
Osgood, Hamilton, 4123
Osgood, Kimberly, 6451
Oshei, Jean R., 6584
Oshei, R. John, 6584
Osheowitz, Michael W., 6087
Osher, Barbro, 997, 998
Osher, Bernard, 997, 998
Osheyack, Daniel J., 6982
Oshima, Alan, 2603
Oshkosh Corp., 9917
Oshkosh Truck Corp., 9917
Oshlo, Rick, 1511
Oshman's Sporting Goods, Inc., 9074
Oshman, Marilyn, 9074
Oshsner, Robert, 1394
Oskey, LuEllen, 9942
Oski, Jessica A., 7549
Oskouian, Anoosheh M., 992
Osman, Christopher B., 2713
Osmer, Patrick S., 157
Osmon, Dave, 3277
Osmun, Doreen E., 7509
Osprey Investment Partners, 7367
Ossen Revocable Trust, Jeffrey P., 1664
Ossen, Eileen M., 1664
Ossmann, Olaf, 6336
Ostahowski, Mark, 4335
Ostby, H. Signe, 1278
Osteen, Carolyn, 3275
Osteen, H.M., Jr., 2434
Oster Finance, 5399
Oster Properties LLP, 5399
Oster Realty, 5399
Oster, Ann, 5399
Oster, Avi, 5399
Oster, Dan, 5399
Oster, Miriam, 5399
Ostergard, Holly Acklie, 5022
Osterink, Beverly, 4393
Ostler, John, 1201
Ostrich, Rabbi David, 7973
Ostrie, Seth, 5598
Ostrovsky, Rose, 6600
Ostrovsky, Vivian S., 6600
Ostrow, Gary J., 4145, 9723
Ostrow, John B., 2099
Ostrowski, Elaine, 7180
Oswald, Charles W., 4735
Oswald, David C., 4735
Oswald, Ellen Smart, 1697
Oswald, Julie, 4735
Oswald, Kathleen, 4735
Oswald, Sara, 4735
Oswald, Thomas, 4735
Oswald, William, 1697
Oswalt, Connie, 10
Oswalt, Roy, 8674
Otaguro, Curt T., 2598
Otero, Maria, 1940, 4479
Otih, Otis O., 9477
Otis, Clarence, Jr., 2051
Otis, Lee Liberman, 5301
Otsuka American Pharmaceutical, Inc.,
5712
Ott, Alan W., 4444, 4517
Ott, David A., 9072
Ott, Joseph L., 8616
Ott, Luther, 4820
Ott, Steve, 9977
Ottauquechee Health Foundation, 3953
Ottaway Jr. Trust, James, 5806
Ottaway, Alexandra H., 6603
Ottaway, Audra, 6603
Ottaway, Christopher H., 6603
Ottaway, David, 6603
Ottaway, Eric B., 6603
Ottaway, James H., Jr., 5806, 6603
Ottaway, James W., 6603
Ottaway, Marina S., 6603
Ottaway, Mary, 6603
Ottaway, Robin, 6603
Ottaway, Ruth B., 6603
Ottaway-Velder, Katrin, 6603
Otte, Jane, 4211
Ottens, John, 1472
Ottens, Sophie, 1472
Otter Creek, LLC, 8761
Otter Products, 1473
OtterBox Products, 1473
Otterlei, John, 6164
Ottinger, Betty Ann, 1525
Ottinger, Jim, 8314
Ottinger, Ronald, 974
Ottison, Susan, 3990
Ottley, Marian W., 2580, 7343
Ottmar, Steve, 7357
Otto, Chris, 1393
Otto, Douglas, 176
Otto, Martin H., 8879
Ottosen, Barbara, 150
Ottosen, Barbara J., 150
Ottosen, Donald R., 150
Ouchi, William G., 692
Ouellett, Neal, 5171
Oustalet, Richard C., 3676
Outcalt, David B., 7606
Outcalt, Jane Q., 7606
Outcalt, Jon H., 7509, 7606
Outcalt, Jon H., Jr., 7606
Outcalt, Kenneth W., 7606
Outerstuff, Ltd., 5498
Outhwaite Revocable Trust, 1994 June
G., The, 1000
Outlaw, Karen, 6564
Ouyalady Corporation, 7109
OVB Charitable Trust, 7144
Ovel, John A., 4980
Overby, Amy T., 9897
Overby, Joe, 3607
Overcast, Tom, 9602
Overdeck, John A., 6605
Overdeck, Laura B., 6605
Overdeer, Bill, 3407
Overholser, Geneva, 5191
Overlock, William J. "Mike", 6333
Overly Trust, Edith H., 4201
Overly, Edith H., 4201
Overmyer, Michael, 3348
Overseas Adventure Travel, 4076
Overstreet, Jane, 3530
Overstreet, Jane, Dr., 1398
Overstrom, Gunnar, 9005
Overton, R. Carter, III, 9225
Overton, Suellen, 3447
Oviatt, Kim A., 1141
Owen, Alberta M., 9075
Owen, B.B., 9077
Owen, Bethany M., 4649
Owen, Bill, 7798
Owen, Brad, 3552
Owen, Charles, 6285
Owen, Gwen P., 8538
Owen, Jay L., 1937
Owen, Louis, 9075
Owen, Louis P., 9075
Owen, Louis W., 9075
Owen, Mack, 8994
Owen, Marie G., 9075
Owen, Mary M., 4588
Owen, Mary N., 7172
Owen, Mike, 7188
Owen, Norman, 973, 1120
Owen, Richard, 4636
Owen, Richard A., 3249
Owen, Sarah, 2327
Owens Corning, 7607
Owens, Amy, 9509
Owens, Anna E., 4377
Owens, Brig, 1939
Owens, Christopher, 7188
Owens, Donna, 7000
Owens, Edward P., 4202
Owens, Elizabeth H., 8892
Owens, Jay, 496
Owens, Jennifer, 5757
Owens, Jim, 4659
Owens, Katie, 2819
Owens, Kenneth R., 2528
Owens, Linda B., 4202
Owens, Mary M., 3068
Owens, Michael, 3068
Owens, Nancy C., 3643
Owens, Paul D., Jr., 33
Owens, Robert T., 2299
Owens, Sharon, 3068
Owens, Thomas M., 3068
Owens, Thomas M., Jr., 3068
Owens, William F., 9503
Owens-Illinois Inc., 7400
Owings Family Foundation, 8495
Ownbey, Ron, 184
Owsley, Alvin M., 9078
Owsley, Alvin M., Jr., 9078
Owsley, David T., 9078
Owsley, Kathleen, 4354
Owsley, Lucy B., 9078
Oxford League, Inc., The, 5185
Oxley, Debby M., 7784
Oxley, John C., 7784, 7785
Oxley, John T., 7785
Oxley, Kevin, 4467
Oxley, Scott A., 3680
Oxman, David C., 1600
Oxman, Elena G., 8441
Oxman, Lee W., 8441
Oxman, Phyllis, 6645
Oxman, Phyllis S., 8441
Oxman, Stephen A., 5747
Oxnard, Thomas Thornton, 1001
Oxon Hill Apartments LLC, 9452
Oyens, Felix, 5707
Oyler, Gregory, 3751
Oyler, Tennyson S., 1003
Oyloe, Susan, 3910
Ozanne, Ismael, 9897
Ozbirn, Bob, 1198
Ozer, Esra, 7908
Ozimek, Michael, 6802
Ozmun, Beverly L., 5112

P'Pool, William C., 2944
P.N.C. Bank, N.A., 3725
Pabalan, Steven S., 2223
Pabst, Tim, 4694

PACCAR Inc, 9698
PACCAR, Inc., 6904
Pace 2005 Charitable Lead Annuity Trust, 9079
Pace, Alicia M., 5909
Pace, Ben, 5909
Pace, James C., Jr., 8485
Pace, Linda M., 9079
Pace, Meghan E., 5909
Pace, Nolan D., Jr., 7142
Pace, Peter, 6205
Pace, Samantha, 8993
Pace, Thomas W., 2699
Pace-McVeigh, Kerry A., 5909
Pacelli, Kathy, 8779
Pacesetter Corp., The, 5079
Pacesetter Systems, Inc., 2151
Pacheco, Emilio J., 3311
Pacheco, Fernando, 147
Pachorek, Joseph James, 866
Pacific BMW, 385
Pacific Capital Group, 1333
Pacific Century Trust, 2604
Pacific Coast Construction Co., 568
Pacific Gas and Electric Co., 1002
Pacific Gas and Electric Company, 1033
Pacific Hospital Assn., 7878
Pacific Life Insurance Co., 1003
Pacific Mutual Holding Co., 1003
Pacific Technical Resources, 7214
Pacific Tube Co., 8119
Pacific Vascular Research Foundation, 476
Pacific West Management, 644, 930
Pacifica Real Estate Services, 888
Pacificare Health Systems Foundation, 4785
PacifiCorp, 7877
PacificSource Health Plans, 7878
Pacilio, Robert C., 3081
Pack, Carol, 3249
Pack, Gary, 8582
Pack, James, 2433
Pack, Sam, 3249
Pack, Zachary J., 5745
Packaging Tape, Inc., 9851
Packard Foundation, David and Lucile, The, 1007
Packard, David, 1006
Packard, David W., 1007
Packard, George R., 7019
Packard, Julie, 4609
Packard, Julie E., 1006
Packard, Lucile, 1006
Packard, Pamela M., 1007
Packard, Woodley, 1007
Packer Family Foundation, The, 7012
Packer, Barbara, 6810
Packer, Barbara Bell, 8700
Packer, Barry D., 8700
Packer, Jessica, 5859
Packman, Jeffrey N., 4147
Packman, Karen Linde, 4147
Pacoe, Clara L., 7991
Padar, Ed, 8916
Paddack, Susan, 7742
Paddock, James W., 3538
Paden, Ralph S., 8544
Padgett, Jodi O., 92
Padgett, Melissa Rodgers, 1364
Padgett, Nancy B., 9561
Padha, Adi, 1572
Padmanabhan, Mukund, 6310
Padmanabhan, Ram, 2667
Padon, Linda, 1935
Paducah Bank and Trust Co., 3567
Padway Survivor's Trust, 1008
Padway, Beatrix Finston, 1008
Padzik, Magdalena, 3990
Paen, Mariana S., 5376
Paez, Pablo E., 2120
Pagan, Roberto, 8353
Pagano, Jeffrey J., 681
Pagano, John, 5398
Page, Amy Hattler, 9471
Page, Anthony, 8703
Page, Arthur B., 4007, 4084
Page, Blakely C., 7524
Page, Clarence, 1888
Page, Easter, 7678
Page, Evan C., 4209
Page, Frank C., 9446
Page, G. Ruffner, Jr., 21
Page, Gloria, 1009
Page, John, 633
Page, Kenneth R., 6931, 7014
Page, Lawrence, 615, 1009
Page, Lincoln, 5650
Page, Lucinda Southworth, 1009
Page, Patrick, 5808
Page, Ron, 8779
Pagel, Jack, 4736
Pagel, Jack W., 4736
Paget, Stephen A., 6401
Paglia, Catherine James, 1789
Pagliaro, Joseph A., Jr., 1714
Pagliaro, Susan R., 7422
Pagliuca, Stephen G., 4115
Pahl, Janet, 5138
Paige, Detra G., 977
Paige, Gini, 7597
Paight, Audrey S., 1657
Paik, Alice, 9380
Pail, Norbert J., 8167
Pain, George H., 7279
Paine Foundation, Martin S., 7014
Paine, Anne Marie, 5902
Paine, Cary, 3505
Paine, Cary A., 9744
Paine, Louis B., 8921
Paine, Peter, 5556
Paine, Robert H., 4819
Paine, Susan W., 4211
Paine, W.K., 4819
Painter, Dean E., Jr., 7273
Painter, Melissa, 7231
Painter, Robert W., 9208
Painter, Tom, 888
Painter, William S., 4816
Paiva, Lee, 870
Pakis, Frederick M., 92
Pakistan League of USA, 5934
Pakula, Lawrence, 3808
Pakula, Sheila S., 3808
Palacios, Carlos, 418
Palacios, Mario, 3306
Palakodeti, Ratna, M.D., 7428
Palamara, Nancy, 8164
Palandjian, Tracy, 6947
Palank, Angelica, 2256
Palank-Sharlet, Angelica, 2256
Palash, Carl, 6500
Palazzolo, Lori, 1485
Palen, Cody, 3543
Palenchar, David J., 1406
Palermo, Marlee, 5101
Palestroni, Alfiero, 5400
Palestroni, Lucia, 5400
Paley, William C., 6610
Paley, William S., 6610
Palfrey, John, 2191
Paliotta, Mike, 5826
Palisades of Towson LLC, 9452
Palisades Safety & Insurance Assoc., 4222
Palisano, Donald J., 471
Palkhiwala, Akash, 1048
Palladino, Charles F., 8234
Palladium Foundation, 9338
Paller, Alan T., 3839
Paller, Channing, 3839
Paller, Marsha, 3839
Palley, Marilyn, 7425
Pallotta, James, 4298
Pallotta, Kimberly, 4298
Palm, Gregory K., 6611
Palm, Jennifer, 6611
Palm, Katherine, 6611
Palm, Susan Rose, 6611
Palma, Robert A., 7605
Palmateer, Dean, 3075
Palmer, Adam H., 2040
Palmer, Alphonse, 1584
Palmer, Anthony J., 8957
Palmer, Bruce A., 8136
Palmer, Charles B., 9965
Palmer, Chris, 9775
Palmer, Cynthia S., 3758
Palmer, David, 9950
Palmer, Denise, 3206
Palmer, E. Christopher, 4178
Palmer, Greg, 992
Palmer, Howell, 5530
Palmer, Ian Campbell, 3950
Palmer, Johnnye K., 8454
Palmer, Joseph Beveridge, 3950
Palmer, Justice Richard N., 1589
Palmer, Kelli E., 9405
Palmer, Lesley, 6492
Palmer, Mary, 1937
Palmer, Nancy J., 1817
Palmer, Rebekah T., 8562
Palmer, Rick, 9713
Palmer, Rogers, 1937
Palmer, Roy, 4808
Palmer, Scott Michael, 1817
Palmer, Sheryl Rogers, 9138
Palmer, Spiro, 1393
Palmer, Virginia, 1666
Palmisano, Gaier N., 2514
Palmisano, Samuel J., 2514, 5684, 6203
Palmore, Douglas D. R., 9472
Palmore, Roderick A., 4661
Palms, John, 8396
Palms, John M., 2827
Palo Alto Town & Country Village, Inc., 1325
Palo, John, 7580
Paloheimo Trust, Leonora Curtin, 9080
Paloheimo, George, 9080
Paloheimo, George, Jr., 9080
Paloheimo, Martti, 9080
Paltzer, Shane A., 9801
Palumbo, A.J., 8209
Palumbo, Antonio J., 8209
Palumbo, Joseph, 8209
Palumbo, P.J., 8209
Paluszek, Stephen J., 6801
Paluzzi, Mary Bess, 25
Pam, Leslie, 3078
Pambianchi, Christine M., 5818
Pamperin, David Z., 9854
Pampusch, Anita, 4600
Panaggio, Peter, 4294
Panaritis, Andrea, 4238
Panas, Gary, 927
Panatopoulos, Brady, 2626
Panazzi, Donna M., 7986
Pancoast, James R., 7428
Pancoast, Terrence R., 7895, 7896
Panda Charitable Foundation, 9328
Panda Management Co., Inc., 1010
Panda Restaurant Group, Inc., 1010
Pandl, Therese, 9854
Pandolfi, Francis P., 3358
Panduren, Leanne, 4372
Panepinto, Robert, 2015
Panico, Greg, 5327
Panigel, Michael, 5454
Pankow Family Trust of 1976, 9700
Pankow, Charles J., 9700
Pannell, William C., 9214
Panos, Ernie, 3985
Pansing, Thomas R., 5051
Pansing, Thomas R., Jr., 5074
Pantaleo, Peter, 3781, 7963
Pantalone, Brenda M., 7279
Panzer, Marcy C., 7936
Panzirer, David, 6160
Panzirer, Walter, 6160
Papa, Anthony T., 4826
Papa, Barzella, 2036
Papa, Christine A., 5324
Papa, John A., 5326
Papa, Joseph, 5324
Papa, Joseph C., 4521
Papasan, Katie, 186
Pape, Jean W., 6408
Pape, Kathy, 8046
Paperin, Stewart J., 6593
Paperno, Arnold, 1684
Papini, Melissa J., 6538
Papp, Rosellen C., 111
Pappajohn, John, 3472
Pappajohn, Mary, 3472
Pappas, Arthur M., 4205
Pappas, John, 4204
Pappas, Martha R., 4205
Pappas, Sarah, 2316
Pappas, Stephen, 1879
Pappas, Thomas Anthony, 4204
Pappas, Thomas C., 4204
Pappas, Tommy, 3214
Pappous, Perry, 9487
Paquette, Ellen, 7993
Paquette, Heather, 3690
Paquette, Jennifer, 1390
Paradis, Daisy, 5653
Paradis, J.A., 3563
Paradis, Shelley, 5290
Paradise Beverages Inc., 243
Paradise, Will, 9276
Paragigm Agency, 674
Paraham, Michael, 9712
Paramount Ford, LLC, 7348
Paramount Motor Sales, LLC, 7348
Paraount Kia of Asheville, 7348
Parastie, Toni L., 2622
Pardee, Elsa U., 4517
Pardes, Herbert, 6431
Pardini, Jim, 516
Pardo, Clifford, 5416
Pardoe Trust, Helen P., 4206
Pardoe, Charles E., 4206
Pardoe, Charles H., II, 4206

Pardoe, Edward D., III, The Rev., 7014
Pardoe, James A., 4496
Pardoe, Prescott Bruce, 4206
Pardoe, Samuel P., 4206
Paredes, Lina, 1567
Parekh, Bhikhu, 9495
Parent, Burdette R., 1745
Parent, Neil, 9380
Parentebeard, LLC, 8311
Parham, Michael, 9591
Parilli, Orestes, 8708
Paris, Alex E., 8332
Paris, Steven, Dr., 5175
Pariseau, Edward P., 3960
Pariser, Alan D., 2258
Pariser, Benjamin S., 2258
Pariser, Paul S., 2258
Parish Irrevocable Trust, Suzanne U.D., 4518
Parish, Ivy, 4724
Parish, P. William, 4518
Parish, Preston L., 4518
Parish, Suzanne U.D., 4518
Parisi, Christopher, 7922
Parisi, Joseph, 1279
Park Casino, Inc., 5016
Park Circle Motor Co., 3829
Park Clipper Leasing Associates, 5982
Park Corp., 7609
Park Corporation, 114
Park Foundation, Inc., 7005
Park National Bank, The, 7540, 7610
Park National Corp., 7610
Park Roads Shopping Centerporter By, 7166
Park Terrace Care Center, 6287, 6288, 6763
Park Water Co., 1319
Park, Alice, 8960
Park, C.S., 1166
Park, Chan, 1894
Park, Chang K., 6614
Park, Charlotte, 9219
Park, Dale, Jr., 2954, 8364
Park, Dan K., 7609
Park, Hyun, 1033
Park, James C., 4349
Park, John J., 5745
Park, Jon, 7711
Park, Judith, 8960
Park, Kelly C., 114, 7609
Park, Linda, 9731
Park, Michelle M., 114
Park, Patrick M., 7609
Park, Piper A., 7609
Park, Raymond P., 7609
Park, Roy H., 6615
Park, Roy H., III, 7005
Park, Roy Hampton, Jr., 7005
Park, Yeonjung, 4372
Parke, Jennifer Hudson, 4463
Parke, Jim A., 6616
Parke, Kevin, 9253
Parke, Shirley, 6616
Parker Charitable lead Trust, George S., II, 9828
Parker Foundation, Theodore Edson, The, 4152
Parker High School Alumni Association, 8465
Parker Living Trust, George S., II, 9828
Parker Trust, 2459
Parker Trust, Ruth F., 7464
Parker, Adelaide, 6802
Parker, Alan M., 7276
Parker, Arthur, 4079
Parker, Arthur H., 4263
Parker, Beverly J., 1745
Parker, Bonnie, 2123
Parker, Bradley, 9761
Parker, Byron A., 9051
Parker, David, 4061, 9761
Parker, DeAnne, 1154
Parker, Desiree, 4671
Parker, Diane W., 2572
Parker, Donald R., 7212
Parker, Edward, 7852
Parker, Faith K., 5401
Parker, Franklin E., IV, 5490
Parker, George S., II, 9828
Parker, Gerald T., 1012
Parker, Glenn P., 5401
Parker, Grant, 5783
Parker, Gray S., 3616
Parker, Harold, Jr., 395
Parker, Inez Grant, 1012
Parker, Jane Ellen, 7425
Parker, Jennifer J., 5801
Parker, Jette, 7276
Parker, John B., 7972
Parker, John F., 5490
Parker, John S., 41
Parker, John, Jr., 4100
Parker, Jon, 9631
Parker, Josh, 6087
Parker, Judith W., 9761
Parker, Julia Ryan, 9940
Parker, Kate, 1185
Parker, Kathy S., 7406
Parker, Kay, 9069
Parker, Kevin J., 6722
Parker, Kristian, 7276
Parker, Leroy, 3774
Parker, Maclyn T., 3276
Parker, Margaret H., 5490
Parker, Martha E., 9828
Parker, Mary E., 1745, 1829
Parker, Mary Kay, 3616
Parker, Mary Webber, 4463
Parker, Michael, 2933
Parker, Nancy F., 2463
Parker, Pam, 25
Parker, Patrick, 5560
Parker, Penny, 2642
Parker, R. Latanae, Jr., 2223
Parker, Renee, 8524
Parker, Richard, 3348
Parker, Richard C., 2420
Parker, Richard Carlyle, 2463
Parker, Richard K., 1397
Parker, Rob, 3336
Parker, Robert L., 9225
Parker, Robert S., 7321
Parker, Ruth F., 7444, 7464
Parker, Scott, 9095
Parker, Sean, 720
Parker, Stephen T., 2572
Parker, Steven, 3863
Parker, Stuart B., 9245
Parker, Susan, 718
Parker, Terry, 2435
Parker, Theodore Edson, 4207
Parker, Thomas C., 718
Parker, Thomas W., 2572
Parker, Timothy, 4446
Parker, Virginia, 7295
Parker, W.J., 9399
Parker, Westbrook J., Hon., 9434
Parker, William A., III, 2463
Parker, William A., Jr., 2441, 2463
Parker-Hannifin Corp., 7611
Parkerson, Alice B., 3656
Parkhurst, Hillary A., 7807
Parkhurst, Patricia D., 6784
Parkin, Jennifer H., 9327
Parkin, John F., 2939
Parkinson, Catherine, 2633
Parkinson, Geoffrey M., 1576, 1654, 1655, 8005
Parkinson, Geoffrey M., Jr., 1576
Parkinson, Marianne, 7711
Parkinson, Molly O., 7014
Parkinson, Tracy, Dr., 8505
Parks, Don L., 8647
Parks, Edward M., 4556
Parks, Floyd L., 4445, 4564
Parks, Fred, 9081
Parks, James R., 990
Parks, Jenny, 5530
Parks, Martin "Skip", 6721
Parks, Sallie, 2269
Parks, Shannon, 7908
Parkview Realty Co., 6617
Parlange, Brandon, 3618
Parlato, Frank, 341
Parliaments Apartments LLC, 9452
Parman, Brad, 9148
Parmelee, Brian, 744
Parmer, Barbara J., 8212
Parmer, Carolyn N., 3069
Parmer, Carolyn Noonan, 3069
Parmer, George A., 8212
Parmer, James W., 3069
Parmer, John F., 3069
Parmer, Raymond C., 3069
Parners Investing in Nursing's Future, 5305
Parnes, Emanuel, 5402
Parnes, Herschel, 5402
Paroo, Iqbal, 984
Parr, Martha Sue, 3070
Parra, Ivan Kohar, 7138
Parravano, Carlo, 5380
Parravano, Paul, 3971
Parravano, Teresa Haggerty, 8881
Parris, Lori, 972
Parrish Medical Center, 9250
Parrish, Alfredo, 3420
Parrish, Bill, 8649
Parrish, Carol, 5735
Parrish, Charles Bryan, 9342
Parrish, Charles Kurt, 9342
Parrish, Charles Maxfield, 9342
Parrish, Clay, 1830
Parrish, Cynthia V., 7481
Parrish, Diane S., 1830
Parrish, Edna, 3460
Parrish, Erika Marie, 9342
Parrish, Gloria F., 9342
Parrish, Kristine Ann, 9342
Parrish, Lee H., 7481
Parrish, Margaret, 8649
Parrish, Melissa T., 8488
Parrish, Robert J., 3367
Parrish, Steven C., 1830
Parrish, Tom, 8624
Parrish, Will, 2439
Parrott, James M., Jr., 7273
Parrott, Rex, 7558
Parrott, Vann K., 2437
Parrotte, Dianne, 1158
Parry, David C., 2934
Parry, Frances, 7678
Parry, Gwyn P., 697
Parry, Virginia, 7588
Parry-Okeden, Blair, 2560
Parsky, Gerald, 339
Parsley, Georganna S., 9208
Parsley, Robert S., 9208
Parsons Brinckehroff Group, Inc., 6621
Parsons Brinckerhoff Construction Svcs., 6621
Parsons Brinckerhoff Quade & Douglas, Inc., 6621
Parsons Brinckerhoff, Inc., 6621
Parsons Trust, P.D. and Tracy, 8957
Parsons, Anna, 2630
Parsons, David W., 77
Parsons, Gregory A., 6618
Parsons, James D., 2715
Parsons, Kathryn M., 4705
Parsons, Laura, 6382
Parsons, Laura A., 6618
Parsons, Leslie J., 6618
Parsons, Marianne, 2092
Parsons, Marvin, 9796
Parsons, Mary Morton, 9504
Parsons, Morgan, 7412
Parsons, Myers B., 8545
Parsons, Ralph M., 1013
Parsons, Rebecca L., 6618
Parsons, Renee Labelle, 151
Parsons, Richard D., 6618, 6724
Parsons, Rick, 186
Parsons, Robert, 151
Parsons, Robert W., Jr., 5310
Parsons, Roger, 6619
Parsons, Roger B., 5310
Parsons, Stefani, 9605
Parsons, Stephen C., 3801
Parsons, Stu, 7540
Parsons, Susan E., 3334
Parsons, William, Jr., 2739, 3222
Partee, Stan, 3121
Partee, Sue Garrett, 3121
Parthe, Mary, 3091
Partin, Ron, 7181
Partners Healthcare System, 4003
Partners Investing in Nursing's Future, 9521
Partnership for a Drug-Free America, 7012
Partridge, Barbara Leigh, 1110
Partridge, Charles Kent, Sr., 356
Partridge, Charles W., Jr., 356
Partridge, H. Roy, Jr., 3708
Partridge, Herbert Scott, 356
Partridge, Kathryn B., 356
Partridge, Lamar J., 8634
Parvis, Douglas S., 5745
Parvizian, Alan, 1548
Parzen, Ted, 1043
Parzych, Cheryl A., 8043
Pascavage, Michael H., 4003
Paschal, Justin, 720
Pasco, Jayne, 459
Pascoe, Virgilio Perez, 2525
Pascucci, Christopher S., 6826
Pascucci, Michael C., 6826
Pascucci, Ralph P., 6826
Pasculano, Lynne, 1668
Pasculano, Mark, 1668
Pasculano, Richard, 1668
Pasewaldt, Dieter C., 5231
Pashcow, Joel, 7008
Pashcow, Joel M., 5254

Pasi, Geralyn, 4571
Pasko, Anne W., 3947
Paskoski, Joe, 2276
Pasky, Cynthia J., 4371
Pasquale, Caren Demoulas, 4015
Pasqualoni, Sheri C., 1537
Pasquerella, Mark, 5351
Pasquerilla, Leah M., 8213
Pasquerilla, Mark E., 7990, 8213
Pasquerilla, Sylvia T., 8213
Pasquinelli Homebuilding, LP, 3071
Pasquinelli, Anthony R., 3071
Pasquinelli, Bruno A., 3071
Pass-Durham, Deborah S., 2031
Passaro, Tim, 4347
Passen, Richard B., 5451
Passios, Tom, 1716
Passmore, Norm, 9588
Passov, Richard, 6633
Pastega Trust, 7879
Pastega, Dennis, 7879
Pastega, Gary, 7879
Pastega, Kenneth, 7879
Pastega, Mario, 7879
Pastorello, Thomas J., 1630
Pastrick, Courtney Clark, 1879, 3750
Patagonia, Inc., 1017
Patch, Earl, 4737
Pate, Helen, 3821
Pate, Jackie, 2439
Patek, Christopher, 1744
Patek, Rose B., 1744
Patel, Atul, 229
Patel, B.U., 1239
Patel, Dinesh C., 9343
Patel, Jigs, 6904
Patel, Kalpana, 9343
Patel, Kalpana D., 9343
Patel, Kiran C., 2259, 9343
Patel, M.D., Ravi, Inc., 1018
Patel, Naina, 1018
Patel, Pallavi C., 2259
Patel, Ravi, 1018
Patel, Sandip, 1531
Patel, Sheetal, 2259
Patel, Sheila, 4026
Patel, Shilen, 2259
Patel, Tushar, 1239
Patenaude, Wayne, 3972
Pater, Jason, 4365
Paternot, Madeleine, 6158
Paternot, Stephan, 6158
Paterson, Allan G., 9205
Paterson, Allan G., Jr., 9139
Paterson, Basil A., 6527
Paterson, Jane R., 2946
Patience, Diane, 3204
Patience, John, 3204
Patillo, Bree, 2475
Patillo, Kathleen B., 2477
Patillo, Katy, 2432
Patino, Douglas X., 4510, 9596
Patke, Susan, 2829
Patmon, Charles G., 417
Patmon, Dorothy N., 417
Patnoe, Tom, 4732
Patricelli, Robert E., 1652
Patricia, Jenny, 6544
Patrick, Brian, 5013
Patrick, Charles F., 428
Patrick, Dan, 905
Patrick, Donna, 9796
Patrick, Howard, 2036
Patrick, John J., Jr., 1537
Patrick, Joseph E., Jr., 2477
Patrick, Laney, 7850
Patrick, Lois, 500
Patrick, Marilyn M., 2722
Patrick, Michael L., 8716
Patrick, Mike, 1110
Patrick, Shari L., 6724
Patrick, Susie, 8521
Patrick, Thomas H., 2722
Patrick, Todd, 9621
Patrick, Victoria, 1565
Patrick-Philip, Mary Karen, 2722
Patrimonio, Alicia, 5642
Patrino, Melissa, 959
Patt, Pauline, 8438
Patt, Richard A., 5357
Patten, Harry S., 4208
Patten, Kathryn M., 7620
Patterson Trust No. 2, Robert, 1669
Patterson Trust, Cissy, The, 8489
Patterson Trust, Dorothy C., 2260
Patterson Trust, Proctor, 7613
Patterson, Andy, 8521
Patterson, Anne, 3735, 3736
Patterson, Anne A., 3876
Patterson, Arthur C., 1831
Patterson, Aubrey, 4822
Patterson, Aubrey Abbott, 3521
Patterson, Clara Guthrie, 1669
Patterson, Deborah J., 4945
Patterson, Dorothy Clarke, 2260
Patterson, Douglas "Pete", 4828
Patterson, Frances, 8474
Patterson, H. Donald, 7627
Patterson, Harry, 9277
Patterson, Jack, 4485
Patterson, James J., 2260
Patterson, Jane, 4374
Patterson, Jane S., 7298
Patterson, Jeanne, 2261
Patterson, John A., 5068
Patterson, Joyce, 8475
Patterson, Katheryn C., 6273
Patterson, Linda B., 4412
Patterson, Louise M., 1831
Patterson, Melissa, 4511
Patterson, Neal, 2261
Patterson, Richard B., 3141, 3217
Patterson, Robert Leet, 1669
Patterson, Roger Chip, Jr., 2432
Patterson, Susan W., 7192
Patterson, Tom, 3201
Patterson, William, Dr., 1488
Patti, Patricia, 857
Patti, Robert, 1646
Pattillo Split Interest Trust, 2530
Pattillo, H.G., 2475
Pattillo, Janet, 4056
Pattillo-Cohen, Lynn L., 2530
Pattock, Susan D., 2791, 3010
Patton, Cynthia, 238
Patton, Douglas, 4395
Patton, Henry, Dr., 2533
Patton, James B., 2420
Patton, Michael B., 6
Patton, Patty, 11
Patton, Phillip, 7823
Patton, Robert W., III, 7823
Patton, Sara L., 7704
Patton, Sharyle, 1188
Patton, Susan, 78
Patton, Thomas J., 7627
Patton, Tina, 3289
Patuzzi, Cole, 3298
Patyrak, Robert S., 9147
Patzer, Faye A., 9838
Paukert, Maureen, 7383
Paul, Andrew S., 1711
Paul, David C., 8283
Paul, Douglas L., 5826
Paul, Josephine Bay, 5652
Paul, Kathryn, 1397
Paul, Robert A., 7384, 8030
Paul, Sonali, 8283
Paul, Thomas, 4785
Paul, Toni H., 2892
Paul, Weiss, Rifkind, Wharton & Garrison LLP, 1771
Pauley, Dorothy A., 9505
Pauley, Matt, 7474
Pauley, Stanley F., 9505
Paulin, Peggy, 5158
Pauline Austin Neuhoff Foundation, 8766
Paulseen, Ron, 3555
Paulsen, Thomas R., 3437
Paulson, Amanda Clark, 2707
Paulson, Bob, 8511
Paulson, Hank M., Jr., 5684
Paulson, Henry M., Jr., 2707
Paulson, Henry Merritt, III, 2707
Paulson, John, 6620
Paulson, Ken, 1907
Paulson, Richard A., 7721
Paulson, Wendy J., 2707
Pauly, Katie Kavanaugh, 9604
Pausic, Michael A., 9005
Pauwels, Franky, 7931
Pava, Jeremy, 4080
Pavelich, Gerald W., 9838
Pavicic, Kevin, 4937
Pavlatos, Plato, 7671
Pavlicek, Michele, 4585
Pavlock, Darlene, 7489
Pavloff, Andrew, 5806
Pavloff, Jonathan, 7579
Pawelski, Donald R., 3081
Pawelski, Tracy, 4297
Pax, David, 7567
Paxton, Jim, 415
Paxton, Joseph, 9411
Payette River Foundation, 389
Paykel, Neela, 570
Payne, Amy A., 4458
Payne, Bond, 7781
Payne, Brian, 3272
Payne, Carol, 9396
Payne, James O., 7386
Payne, John, 5106
Payne, John G., 8819
Payne, Jon, 2559
Payne, L. Robert, 1021
Payne, Marilyn, 432
Payne, Martha B., 2408
Payne, Michael C., 3295
Payne, Nona S., 9086
Payne, Patricia L., 1021
Payne, Richard, 4784
Payne, Seba B., 3073
Payne, Sharon L., 1021
Payne, Susan K., 9405
Payne, Susan M., 1021
Payne, William P., 2408
Payne, William Porter, 2514
Payne-Welborn, Ernestine, 9267
Paynter, Larry, 3319
Payson George Fundind Trust, Edward, 4068
Payson, Charles S., Mrs., 7080
Payson, Jonathan, 4039
Payson, Melinda B., 4125
Payson, Norman C., 4125
PB Americas Inc., 6621
PB Services Inc., 6621
PBM Products, 9476
PCCS, Inc., 9702
Peabody, Amelia, 4209, 4210
Peabody, Betty, 1040
Peabody, John W., 384
Peaceworks Holdings, LLC, 6563
Peach, Richard, 2826
Peacock, A., 777
Peacock, Albert E., III, 777
Peacock, David, 4853
Peacock, Deborah, 5511
Peacock, Henry B., Jr., 2263
Peacock, Jonathan M., 238
Peak, Martha H., 3711
Peak, William A., 9434
Pean, Jean Christophe, 886
Pearce, Gary B., 8918
Pearce, J. James, Jr., 3358
Pearce, M. Lee, 2264
Pearce, Rick, 7570
Pearl Assocs., 9249
Pearl Caslow Irrevocable Trust, 2736
Pearl Management Company, 3468
Pearl, Paul, 1942
Pearlman, Jeanne, 8228
Pearlman, Lowell R., 7182
Pearsall, Erika, 9975
Pearson Financial Group, 7873
Pearson, Andrall E., 6623
Pearson, Bruce, 3517
Pearson, Clint, 3543
Pearson, David, 2853
Pearson, Dwight W., 8470
Pearson, Eric, 8825
Pearson, Jackie, 8660
Pearson, James F., 7455
Pearson, Jim, 3277
Pearson, Joanne P., 6623
Pearson, Jonathan R., 5305
Pearson, Kevin J., 6406
Pearson, Mark, 5629
Pearson, Michael K., 8239
Pearson, Molly Jane, 3238
Pearson, Robert S., 7179
Pearson, Ruth B., 5735
Pease, Deborah S., 4174
Pease, Roland F., Jr., 4174
Pease, Roland F., Sr., 4174
Peatman, Joseph G., 566
Peavy, Kyle, 9241
Peca, Michael, 5726
Pecheone, Ray, 991
Pechter Family Foundation, 2265
Pechter Irrev. Trust, Melissa, The, 2265
Pechter, Coley, LP, 2265
Pechter, Danielle, LP, 2265
Pechter, Jack H., 2265
Pechter, Jeffrey S., 2265
Pechter, Lisa, 2265
Pechter, Marilyn A., 2265
Pechter, Martin H., 2265
Pechter, Marty, 2265
Pechter, Melissa, 2265
Pechter, Richard S., 2526
Pechter, Zach, LP, 2265
Peck, Art, 563
Peck, Bernard, 9918
Peck, Bob, 294, 296

Peck, Gary, 8040
Peck, J. Lane, 3567
Peck, Jodi, 9918
Peck, Katherine, 1421
Peck, M. Elaine, 3373
Peck, Miriam, 9918
Peck, Natalie, 5296
Peck, Robert, 1890
Peckham, Eugene, 6578
Peckham, Judith C., 6286
Peckham, Thomas, 1770
Pecoraro, Alice G., 3623
Pecos, Regis, 5530
Pedas, James, 1938
Pedas, Theodore, 1938
Peddie, Susannah, 2036
Peddrick, Martha, 7180
Peden, Janet, 8878
Pedersen, Anne-Mare, 822
Pedersen, Chris, 118
Pedersen, Kathryn, 1528
Pedersen, Lisa, 118, 170
Pedersen, Mary Q., 6670
Pedersen, Penny, 79
Pedersen, Rena, 4984
Pederson, Boyd, 1392
Pederson, Chris, 118
Pederson, Sally, 4729
Pedicord, Lester D., 1367
Pedlow, Joyce, 9759
Pedowitz, David, 6538
Pedrick, Joan, 9697
Pedroso, Luis, 4152
Pedroza, Nivia, 5948
Peebles, Allison H., 48
Peebles, Jami S., 4872
Peebles, John D., 48
Peebles, Sue, 3397
Peek, David H., 2130
Peek, Donald C., 500
Peek, Dorsey, 3618
Peeples, Audrey R., 2746
Peeples, P.G., Sr., 3560
Peeps, Claire, 487
Peercy, Paul S., 9817
Peery Special Purpose Trust, Louis S., 9344
Peery Trust, Jeffrey Scowcroft, 9344
Peery, David, 1022
Peery, Dennis T., 1022
Peery, Janet P., 9344
Peery, Jason, 1022
Peery, Jennifer, 1022
Peery, Louis S., 9344
Peery, Mimi, 1022
Peery, Richard T., 1022
Peet, Shelly, 7596
Peete, David D., Jr., 9552
Peetz, Karen, 7945
Peetz, Sarah, 5063
Pefil, David, 1834
Pegues, Julius, 7807
Pehlke, Linda Olson, 3962
Peierls Charitable Lead Trust, Ethel F., 1475
Peierls, Brian E., 1475
Peierls, Brian Eliot, 1475
Peierls, E. Jeffrey, 1475
Peierls, Edgar S., 1475
Peierls, Ethel F., 1475
Peiffer, Garry L., 7453
Peirce, Joan, 8215
Peirce, Mary, 7659
Peirce, Robert N., Jr., 8215
Peirrepont, Consuelo D., 4581
Pejeau, Larry, 3269
Pekarek, Nancy J., 8061
Pekarek, Nancy K., 8060
Pekor, Allan J., 2210
Pelaez, Marc Y.E., 8105
Pelham Testamentary Charitable Lead Annuity Trust, Heyward Gibbes, 1832
Pelham Testamentary, Heyward Gibbes, 1832
Pelham, Richard T., 1832
Pelham, William H., 1832
Pelissero, Deborah S., 945
Pelissero, Goodwin J., 945
Pelissier, Jack E., 9997
Pelissier, Raymond G., 3994
Pelizzon, David, Col., 3091
Pell, Christopher T.H., 6144
Pell, Eda, 1023
Pell, Joseph, 1023
Pella Corp., 3473
Pelland, Melissa, 4715, 4757
Pellegrini, Margaret Lobeck, 7768
Pellegrini, Molly, 7807
Pellegrino, Frank, 8040
Pellegrino, James, 1934
Pelletier, David, 1566
Pelletier, Gary, 6634
Pelletier, Marc S., 1564
Pelletier, Michele, 861
Pelletier, Sandra, 5169
Pelletier, Sean, 3428
Pellett Foundation, 8465
Pellillo, Leslie Day, 105
Pelling, Katherine, 2527
Pelling, Patricia G., 2527
Pelling, Thomas, 2527
Pelo, Brad, 9328
Pelo, Melody, 9328
Pelosi, Paula, 6554
Pels, Donald A., 6625
Pelster, Carla, 9750
Peltekian, Elizabeth M., 1890
Peltier, James, Dr., 3658
Peltier, Richard, 3658
Peltier, Stephen, 3658
Peltier, Valerie, 6896
Peltier, Valerie S., 6544
Pelzer, Robert E., 6569
Pemberton, Gayle, 6105
Pemberton, Gregory L., 3397
Pemberton, Kristen G., 6497, 7027
Pemberton, Margaret A., 3178
PEMCO Corp., 9702
PEMCO Mutual Insurance Co., 9702
PEMCO Technology Services, Inc., 9702
Pen, Sophia, 822
Pena, Carlos Gonzalez, 8773
Pena, Rogelio, 1391
Penates Foundation, The, 1219
Pence, Margaret Hall, 4905
Pender, Michael R., Jr., 2038
Pendergast, Mary, 5194
Pendergraft, Neal R., 5143
Pendergrass, David S., 7038
Pendleton, A. Patterson, III, 5745
Pendleton, James B., 9703
Pendleton, Jen, 3279
Pendleton, Laird, 8062
Pendleton, Ryan, 7382
Pendon, Lucy, 8775
Pendrey, J.C., Jr., 2485
Pendry, David L., 7506
Pendry, Pamela, 7506
Penguin Group, 7214
Penguin Putnam Inc., 5718
Penix, Timothy, 5757
Penn Security Bank & Trust Co., 8218, 8275
Penn Southern LLC, 9452
Penn, J. Scottie, 7294
Penn, Magaly, 8474
Penn, Marian, 255
Penn, Robert, 4325
Pennekamp, Peter H., 4621
Pennell, Colleen, 825
Pennell, Karen, 8225
Penner, Carrie W., 211
Penner, Carrie Walton, 1387
Penney Co., J.C., Inc., 9089
Penney Corp., J.C., Inc., 9089
Penney, Kyle L., 8819
Penney, Ron, 4872
Pennfield, Edward B., 6389
Pennick, Aurie A., 2831
Penniman, Nicholas G., IV, 3358
Penniman, Russell S., IV, 1182
Pennington 1998 Charitable Trust, William N., The, 5139
Pennington 1999 Charitable Trust, William N., The, 5139
Pennington 2003 Charitable Remainder Unitrust, William N., 5139
Pennington 2008 Charitable Remainder Trust, The, 5139
Pennington 2010 Charitable Remainder Trust, William N., 5139
Pennington Charitable Remainder Unitrust, William N., 5139
Pennington Separate Property Trust, William N., 5139
Pennington, C.B., 3659
Pennington, Christopher, 6716
Pennington, Claude B., III, 3659
Pennington, Daryl B., Jr., 3659
Pennington, Daryl B., Sr., 3659
Pennington, Hilary, 5994
Pennington, Irene W., 3659
Pennington, Sabrina, 3400
Pennington, Sharon Palmer, 3659
Pennington, Susanne, 5108
Pennington, Terry A., 7627
Pennington, Thomas, 5724
Pennington, William N., 5139
Pennoyer, Christy, 5728, 6148
Pennoyer, Peter, 7079
Pennoyer, Robert, 5728
Pennoyer, Russell, 6093
Pennoyer, Russell P., 5549, 5692
Pennoyer, Tracy, 5728
Pennsylvania Electric Co., 7455
Pennsylvania State Bank, 8046
Penny, M. Ann, 1374
Pennycook, Jean, 257
Penoles Met-Mex La, 7349
Penrose, Spencer, 1406
Penrose, Spencer, Mrs., 1406
Pensabene, Anthony, 6491
Pensec, Bob, 3346
Penske, Gregory W., 4519
Penske, Jay C., 4519
Penske, Kathryn H., 4519
Penske, Mark H., 4519
Penske, Roger S., Jr., 4519
Penson, Andrew S., 6626
Penson, Shannon S., 6626
Pentair, Inc., 4739
Pentecost, Joe D., 4520
People Magazine, 7008
People's United Bank, 1671
Peoples Bank, The, 1562
Peoples Federal Savings Bank Foundation, 4212
Peoples Natural Gas Co., 9422
PeopleSoft and Workday, 486
Pepe, Cathy, 1116
Peperone, Michelle, 2734
Peperone, Renee, 2734
Pepin, Susan M., 152
Pepinsky, Cassandra W., 8129
Peppard, Denise, 9498
Peppas, Denise, 5831
Pepper Cos., Inc., The, 3074
Pepper Trust, Richard S., 3074
Pepper, Anthony M., 1676
Pepper, J. David, 3074
Pepper, Jane G., 8041
Pepper, Jonathan Sergeant, 8273
Pepper, Lisa, 3074
Pepper, Richard S., 3074
Pepper, Roxelyn M., 3074
Pepper, T. Sergeant, 8273
Peppers, Ann, 1024
Peppes, Greg, 3507
Pepsi, 9837
Pepsi Cola Company, 7012
Pepsi-Cola & National Brand Beverages, Ltd., 5303
Pepsi-Cola Bottling Co. of Corvallis, Inc., 7879
Pepsico, 7214, 9276, 9742
Pepsico, Inc., 476
PepsiCo, Inc., 6627, 9837
Perala, Michael A., 4716
Percival, John, 4943
Percontee, Inc., 3809
Percy, Karen R., 2544
Percy, R. Ryland, III, 3613
Percy, Roger D., 9652
Perdue Incorporated, 1672
Perdue, Franklin P., 1672
Perdue, James A., 1672
Perdue, Mary H., 1672
Pereira, John M., 4009
Perelman, Debra G., 6628
Perelman, Hope G., 6628
Perelman, Joshua G., 6628
Perelman, Raymond G., 8219
Perelman, Ronald O., 6628
Perelman, Steven G., 6628
Perenchio, A. Jerrold, 397
Perenchio, Margaret A., 397
Perennial Sports & Entertainment, LLC, 246
Perera, Frederica, 4172
Peretsman, Nancy B., 6822
Peretto, Bo, 1399
Peretz, Anne, 7017
Peretz, Anne L., 5786, 6844
Peretz, Evgenia S., 6844
Peretz, Jesse W., 6844
Perez, Beatriz, 2428
Perez, Deborah A., 8139
Perez, Debra Joy, 3745
Perez, Edith R., 3358
Perez, Eladio, 8708
Perez, Gloria, 4616, 4714
Perez, Hugo, 2865
Perez, John, Comm., 1020
Perez, Lillian, 4646
Perez, Paul, 2031

Perez, Ray, 3540
Perfection Products, Inc., 7214
Perfetto, Carlo M., 6913
Perforce Software, Inc., 1026
Perigo, Seth, 3330
Perille, Christopher, 2944
Perino, Robert, 4342
Perkett, Donna Metivier, 6057
Perkin, Christopher T., 4213
Perkin, Gladys T., 4213
Perkin, Nicolas R., 4213
Perkin, Richard S., 4213
Perkin, Richard S., II, 4213
Perkin, Robert S., 4213
Perkin, Thorne L., 4213
Perkins Charitable Lead Annuity Trust, Jane H., 5599
Perkins Trust, Nancy, 2927
Perkins Trust, Phillip, 2927
Perkins Trust, Robert H., 2927
Perkins Trust, Todd, 2927
Perkins, Anne Hollis, 8398
Perkins, Benjamin F., 9988
Perkins, David R., 3700
Perkins, Debbie, 1650
Perkins, Donald, 4830
Perkins, Elvin, 3514
Perkins, Floyd D., 2674, 2933
Perkins, George W., Jr., 7041
Perkins, Grace J., 406
Perkins, Hillery Head, 43
Perkins, Irene, 417
Perkins, Janice L., 4475
Perkins, Jill, 2927
Perkins, Jimmie, 7895
Perkins, Jonathan C., 406
Perkins, Kenneth V., 2927
Perkins, Laurie, 2927
Perkins, Leigh H., 7499, 7615
Perkins, Lois, 9090
Perkins, Maurice, 1650
Perkins, Nancy A., 2927
Perkins, Nancy Allison, 3075
Perkins, Nancy F., 7041
Perkins, Patrick, 2927
Perkins, Paul, 417
Perkins, Phil, 4943
Perkins, Phillip M., 2927
Perkins, Robert H., 2927
Perkins, Roy, 5599
Perkins, Susie, 3360
Perkins, Timothy, 5599
Perkins, Todd, 2927
Perkins, William C., 4451
Perkovich, George, 6551
Perl, Edward L., 3716
Perles, Claudia, 2266
Perles, Claudia Kendrew, 2266
Perles, Steven, 2266
Perlis, Vivian, 5814
Perlman, Adam, 5296
Perlman, Dana, 6637
Perlman, Harriette, 3076
Perlman, Harriette L., 3076
Perlman, Ira, 82
Perlman, Jeffrey F., 5411
Perlman, Marilyn, 3076
Perlman, Martin, 48
Perlman, Nancy, 3685, 6292
Perlman, Noah, 6379
Perlman, Theodore F., 3076
Perlmuth, William A., 6134
Perlmutter, Martin, 8509
Perlmutter, Steven P., 4248
Perlow, Charles, 8188
Perls, Amelia B., 4214
Perls, Katherine M., 4214
Perls, Klaus G., 4214
Permaul, Jane S., 841
Pernicano, Mary Lou, 4519
Perniconi, Mark J., 9700
Perocchi, William L., 936
Perot, Bette, 9092
Perot, H. Ross, 9092
Perot, H. Ross, Jr., 9092
Perot, Henry Ross, Jr., 9093
Perot, Margot B., 9092
Perot, Sarah F., 9093
Perpich, Joseph G., 6105
Perreault, Dale E., 3808
Perret, Hank, 3623
Perri, Ron, 9892
Perrigo Co., 4521
Perrin, Charles, 1673
Perrin, Charles R., 1673
Perrin, David B., 1673
Perrin, Geoffrey, 8993
Perrin, Jeffrey L., 1673
Perrin, Michelle, 9005
Perrin, Sheila, 1673
Perrin, Sheila A., 1673
Perrine, Esther M., 8857
Perrini, Sara Wolfe, 7719
Perritt Char. Trust, Richard A., 3077
Perron, William, 4762
Perrotte, Alisa, 3162
Perrotte, Andrew, 3162
Perrotty, P. Sue, 7939
Perry 2002 Charitable Lead Annuity Trust, The, 9507
Perry Capital Corp., 1557
Perry Partners, 6951
Perry, Alan W., 4832
Perry, Andrew, 2451
Perry, Anthony, 2769
Perry, April Russell, 3575
Perry, Brandon D., 9507
Perry, Charles W., 8971
Perry, Charley, 3423
Perry, Christopher D., 4211
Perry, Christopher J., 4442
Perry, David P., 581
Perry, Debra, 517
Perry, Debra D., 517
Perry, Debra J., 1474
Perry, Diane, 1243
Perry, E. Lee, 8398
Perry, Elliot, 8610
Perry, Hunter, 9506
Perry, J. Christopher, 9507
Perry, J. Douglas, 9507
Perry, Jeff, 3396
Perry, Jennifer S., 4368
Perry, John L., 9246
Perry, Kathy A., 3325
Perry, L. Paige, 9507
Perry, Lorraine F., 359
Perry, Lynne Bassett, 1714
Perry, Mark, 517
Perry, Marnette, 7531
Perry, Mauree Jane, 1886
Perry, Patricia W., 9507
Perry, Richard, 3923, 6898, 6951
Perry, Richard J., Jr., 9865
Perry, Roger, 4448
Perry, Roger L., 8490
Perry, Ruth, 4550
Perry, Sam, 5068
Perry, Slocumb Hollis, 8398
Perry, Spencer, 3759
Perry, Stephen, 422
Perry, Stephen A., 7673
Perry, Susan, 1135, 4039
Perry, Susan Jeanette Segerstrom, 1135
Perry, Wes, 8650
Pershan, Richard H., 8247
Pershing Square Capital Mgmt., 6629
Pershing, Richard, 1288
Persico, Joseph L., 8152
Persing, David H., 384
Persing, Melissa, 4800
Persinger, Darrell, 3284
Persinger, Kyle, 3280
Person, Bruce H., 3947
Person, Norma J., 527
Persson, Celia A., 3116
Persson, Vicky, 9715
Pertile, Anthony, 2747
Pertl, Jeff, 9897
Pertusati, Joseph, 9094
Pertzik, Marvin, 4669
Pertzik, Marvin J., 7236, 8435
Peruggi, Regina S., 6148
Pesantez, Pablo, 830
Peshek, Elizabeth, 5089
Pesky, Wendy S., 6928
Pestronk, Robert, 4511
Pesyna, Gail M., 6872
Pete-Swanson, Kris, 3420
Peter, Arthur L., 1203
Peter, Edward T., 1091
Peter, Georges, Dr., 3923
Peter, James B., Jr., 1203
Peter, Joan C., 1203
Peter, Joshua, 86
Peterich, Daniel J., 9908
Peterken, Faye L., 8597
Peterkin, George, 9248
Peterman, Donna C., 8230
Peters 2007 Trust, Ruth Scott, 7616
Peters Trust, Lovett C., 7616
Peters, Amy, 4562
Peters, Andrew, 5726
Peters, Ann, 5169
Peters, Barbara, 4609
Peters, Barry, 9578
Peters, C. Wilbur, 7280
Peters, Channice, 9578
Peters, Charles M., 3439
Peters, Dan, Dr., 1345
Peters, Daniel S., 7616
Peters, David, 1028
Peters, Deborah D., 3032
Peters, Dennis, 888
Peters, Elizabeth, 686, 6943
Peters, Erik, 7702
Peters, Gary, 4236
Peters, Jennifer Treeger, 6944
Peters, Johnny, 9115
Peters, Kathleen, 7616
Peters, Leon S., 1028
Peters, Lisa B., 7946
Peters, Lovett C., 7616
Peters, Mary Lou, 6507
Peters, Phillip H., 4510
Peters, Richard W., 4369
Peters, Robert G., Dr., 2594
Peters, Ron, 1028
Peters, Samuel K., 1028
Peters, Serena, 781
Peters, Sharon, 3367
Peters, Susan P., 1591
Peters, Suzanne Brown, 1581
Peters, Thomas, 877
Petersen Living Trust, Robert E. and Margaret M., 1029
Petersen, Ann, 3078
Petersen, Curt, 4675
Petersen, David A., 9352
Petersen, Esper A., 3078
Petersen, Gary R., 9097
Petersen, Ken, 414
Petersen, L.W., 5014
Petersen, Margaret M., 1029
Petersen, Richard W., 3689
Petersen, Robert, 1163
Petersen, Robert E., 1029
Petersen, William B., 6872
Petersmeyer, Pamela C., 4608
Peterson, Bart, 3340, 3375
Peterson, Brian, 9345
Peterson, Brooke R., 9525
Peterson, Bruce D., 4410
Peterson, Carolyn S., 9508
Peterson, Chad, 7357
Peterson, Charlie, 9095
Peterson, Christy L., 2233
Peterson, Dean, 9410
Peterson, E. Joel, 4030
Peterson, Erik, 2267
Peterson, Ethel B., 7617
Peterson, Hal, 8676, 9095
Peterson, Jack C., 861
Peterson, Jack S., 437
Peterson, James N., 1371
Peterson, Jane McCoy, 7557
Peterson, Jeanette F., 8842
Peterson, Jeffrey, 9345
Peterson, Jeffrey T., 4672
Peterson, Jen, 9375
Peterson, Jennifer, 5537
Peterson, Jon M., 9508
Peterson, Jonathan, 9345
Peterson, Julie, 9375
Peterson, Karen, 950
Peterson, Kate Butler, 4622
Peterson, Kathleen Nord, 7594
Peterson, Katie, 1130
Peterson, Lynette, 177
Peterson, Marcia, 9880
Peterson, Marica K., 9824
Peterson, Mark, 1634, 9345, 9932
Peterson, Martin G., 9346
Peterson, Michael, 6630
Peterson, Michael L., 3482
Peterson, Milton V., 9508
Peterson, Nancy, 9345
Peterson, Patricia, 3429
Peterson, Peter G., 6630
Peterson, Peter L., 3540
Peterson, R. Price, 2267
Peterson, Renee, 4780
Peterson, Reuben W., Jr., 9816
Peterson, Richard C., 3085
Peterson, Robert F., 2889
Peterson, Roger, 7280, 9566
Peterson, Ron, 2042
Peterson, Rudolph A., 2267
Peterson, Russ, 5039
Peterson, Steve, 9843
Peterson, Steven B., 9508
Peterson, Suzanne, 1393
Peterson, Temple, 4622
Peterson, Terry D., 4644
Peterson, Tina, 3278
Peterson, Wes, 9631

Peterson, William C., 4737
Peterson, William E., 9508
Petit-Moore, Jane, 9814
Petkau, Gerald, 7153
Petne Parkman & Co., Inc., 9053
Petracca, Maureen E., 4032
Petrarca, Emily B., 7401
Petrarca, Mark A., 9947
Petras, Michael, Jr., 7406
Petrazzuoli, Anthony, 4009
Petrelli, Charlene G., 8025
Petrello, Anthony G., 9096
Petrello, Cynthia A., 9096
Petrey, Clay, 8532
Petrick, Edward, 2814
Petricone, F. Robert, 1565
Petrie, Carroll, 6632
Petrie, Carroll M., 6631
Petrie, Dale, 3356
Petrie, Milton, 6632
Petrik, Michael T., 2581
Petro, Darin, 5226
Petroff, Kip A., 9058
Petroff, Suzi, 9058
Petropoulos, Gust, 2900
Petrosewicz, Norma Montalvo, 8997
Petrovich, Thomas, 1107
Petruniw, Josh, 3290
Petrus, Elaine J., 8776
Petshaft, David B., 6318
Pettee, Sheila, 1650
Pettee, Timothy, 1650
Pettett, Jeff, 98
Petticolas, Augustus A., Jr., 9474
Pettis, Faith Li, 9600
Pettit, Brooks, 2037
Pettit, Jane Bradley, 9919
Pettit, Peter R., 8615
Pettit, William O., III, 8380
Pettker, John D., 756
Pettus Jr., James T., 4954
Pettway, Sam, 2477
Petty, Bruce, 8724
Petty, Frank E., 3262
Petty, Stephen P., 987
Petty, William A., 8227
Petures, John T., Jr., 7367
Petway, Brette E., 2268
Petway, Elizabeth P., 2268
Petway, Thomas F., III, 2268
Petway, Thomas F., IV, 2268
Petz, Cordell, 2670
Petzold, Arthur, 1840
Pew, Curtis, 5396
Pew, J. Howard, 8220
Pew, J. Howard, II, 8220
Pew, J.N., IV, 8220
Pew, John, 4592
Pew, Joseph N., Jr., 8220
Pew, Mary Catherine, 8220
Pew, Mary Ethel, 8220
Pew, R. Anderson, 8220
Pew, Robert C., 4592
Pew, Robert C., III, 1403, 4547
Pew, Sandy Ford, 8220
Pew, Wendy, 5279
Pewitt, Donald, 98
Peyerl, Diane, 7357
Pezzimenti, Dennis, 5750
Pezzoli, Raymond J., 6037
Pezzullo, John A., III, 8383
Pfaelzer, Ellard, Jr., 3110
Pfaendtner, Kate, 9916
Pfaff, Laura King, 331
Pfaffinger, Frank X., 1030
Pfaltzgraff Co., The, 8310
Pfau, Ann, 7618
Pfau, Bruce N., 5349
Pfau, Daniel A., 7618
Pfau, Norman, 3362
Pfau, Susan L., 7618
Pfeifer, Jerry, 7474
Pfeifer, Lya Friedrich, 6247
Pfeiffer, Gustavus A., 5405
Pfeiffer, Jim, 7816
Pfeiffer, Karen M., 2152
Pfeiffer, Louise F., 5405
Pfeil, David, 1834
Pfeil, Mindy K., 1834
Pfeil, Richard, 3289
Pfenninger, Steve, 3320
Pfirrman, Drew J., 6406
Pfister, Thomas, 1133
Pfitzenmayer, Jill, 8429
Pfizer (Pharmacia) Corp., 9915
Pfizer Inc., 3833, 6024, 6633, 6634, 7012
Pfleger, George T., 1031
Pfleger, Lila K., 8636
Pfleger, Sandra B., 1031
Pfleger, Thomas G., 1031
Pfleiderer, Carol, 4792
Pflug, Dorothy, 5020
Pfluger, Karen, 9147
Pforzheimer, Carl H., III, 6635
Pforzheimer, Carol K., 6635
Pforzheimer, Elizabeth S., 6635
Pforzheimer, Gary M., 6635
Pfotenhauer, Jeanette, 4785
Pfriem, Norma F., 8490
Pfrommer, Jim, 5108
PG&E Corporation, 1033
PG&E Gas Transmission, Texas Corp., 1033
PGA of America, 3449
PGA Tour Charities, Inc., 1996
PGA Tour Inc., 9470
Phagan, Eric, 3285
Pham, Liz, 4775
Pharaoh, Andrew, 3244
Pharma, 7272
Pharmacia & Upjohn, Inc., 6024, 7012
Pharmacy Network National Corp., 7283
Pharmacy Network National Corporation Trust, 7283
Pheasant Hill Construction, 8108
Phelan, Daniel J., 8221
Phelan, Joseph, 6191
Phelan, Paul, 8524
Phelan, Scott, 2433
Phelps Dodge Corp., 112
Phelps Trust, Charles and Florence, 9882
Phelps Trust, Mary Caroline, 7014
Phelps, Andrea C., 7202
Phelps, Fred, 3426
Phelps, Irene S., 3162
Phelps, Martha, 8136
Phelps, Michael E., 1034
Phelps, Patricia E., 1034
Phelps, W.H., 7772
Phelps-Tointon, Inc., 1513
Phieffer, James W., 7501, 7641
Phight LLC, 7861
Philadelphia Foundation, 8267
Philadelphia Gear Corp., 7927
Philadelphia Insurance Company, 395
Philanthropic Collaborative, The, 6148
Philbin, Ann, 6002
Philbin, Charlotte P., 9090
Philbin, Marianne, 3080
Philbrick, Aileen, 5390
Philbrick, Melissa, 3990
Philbrick, Roger, 3955
Philipp, Alicia, 2432
Philipp, Larry, 417
Philipp, Linda, 417
Philippe, Alain, 6636
Philippe, Anne-Marie, 6636
Philippe, Beatrice, 6636
Philippe, Daniel, 6636
Philippe, Isabelle, 6636
Philippe, Pierre, 6636
Philippe-Grenier, Helene, 6636
Philippe-Vaysse, Anne, 6636
Philipps, Mike, 7659
Philips, Blaine T., Jr., 1780
Philips, Caryl, 7619
Philips, Jesse, 7619
Philips, Karin, 4741
Phillippe, Jamie, 2746
Phillips Charitable Lead Annuity Trust, Edward J., 4740
Phillips Charitable Trust, Waite and Genevieve, 5531
Phillips Irrevocable Trust, Jewel M., 7284
Phillips Revocable Trust, Samuel L., 7284
Phillips, Alexandria C., 955
Phillips, Arthur William, 8222
Phillips, Bessie Wright, 4218
Phillips, Blaine T., 1780, 1821
Phillips, C. Deborah, 4194
Phillips, Clarence, 2030
Phillips, Cloyd, 5146
Phillips, D. Martin, 9097
Phillips, Dean, 4740, 4741
Phillips, Deborah R., 5622
Phillips, Dennis, 540, 7474
Phillips, Dennis J., 1725
Phillips, Diana, 6850
Phillips, Donald, 3608
Phillips, Edward J., 4740
Phillips, Edwin, 4217
Phillips, Fred, 67
Phillips, G. Byron, 7284
Phillips, Genevieve, 5531
Phillips, George, 1036
Phillips, Gina A., 7284
Phillips, Hollyce J., 1108
Phillips, James K., 8964
Phillips, James M., 8634
Phillips, Jeanne, 4741
Phillips, Jerry, 75, 9023
Phillips, Jim, 8994
Phillips, Jim, Dr., 184
Phillips, Joelle J., 8550
Phillips, John M., 414
Phillips, Joy, 4830
Phillips, Karen F., 9281
Phillips, Lawrence, 4219
Phillips, Leslye F.M., 4740
Phillips, Liane M., 9097
Phillips, Madelyn, 4219
Phillips, Marian, 15
Phillips, Mark R., 3622
Phillips, Mary K., 2075
Phillips, Michael, 8959
Phillips, Nathaniel P., Jr., 3616
Phillips, Paul, 9191
Phillips, Reid L., 7180
Phillips, Robert J., 8012
Phillips, Samuel L., 7284
Phillips, Scott, 1533
Phillips, Scott E., 8472
Phillips, Seymour, 4219
Phillips, Shannon E., 898
Phillips, Steve, 8551
Phillips, Susan E., 8041
Phillips, Susan M., 3174
Phillips, Tamara S., 3264
Phillips, Tammy, 3262
Phillips, Travis R., 9133
Phillips, Tyler, 4741
Phillips, Typer, 4740
Phillips, Van, 7284
Phillips-Van Heusen Corp., 6637
Phillips-Van Heusen Foundation, Inc., 782
Philpot, Buddy D., 211
Philpott, Peter, 8964
Philpott, Susan, 4894
Philpotts, William G., 2617
Philpson, Lyle, 2123
Phinney, David G., 1144
Phinney, Jaimie Mayer, 5833
Phipps, Beulah G., 2030
Phipps, Harriet, 5406
Phipps, Howard, Jr., 5406
Phipps, Jane, 9148
Phipps, Lynie, 9998
Phipps, Mary S., 5549, 5692
Phipps, Robert J., 4520
Phish Mail Order, Inc., 9376
Phoenix Charitable Lead Unitrust No. 2, Anne and Julius, 5259
Phoenix Charitable Lead Unitrust, Anne and Julius, 5259
Phoenix Charitable Trust, 1677
Phoenix Charitable Trust, Anne and Julius, 5259
Phoenix Life Insurance Co., 607
Phoenix, Anne, 5259
Phoenix, Frank L., 5259
Phoenix, J. Stuart, 5259
Phoenix, James E., 5259
Phoenix, Joy, 5259
Phoenix, Kaola, 5259
Phoenix, Tricia, 5259
Phumaphi, Joy, 1557
Phung, Quan, 365
Phyllis Lindsey, 9670
Piana, Beth P., 2226
Piascinski, Michael J., 8073
Piassick, Joel B., 2479
Piatt, Rodney L., 8192
Piazza, Annese, 3061
Picard, Robert P., 4144
Picardi, Kenneth E., 8234
Picasso, Rocky, 277
Piccolello, Marcelle L., 8383
Piccone, Debbie, 1819
Picerne Real Estate Group, 9606
Picerne, John C., 9606
Picerne, John G., 9606
Pichon, Emily E., 3276
Pichon, John N., Jr., 3276
Pick, Albert, Jr., 3079
Pick, Joan M., 9920
Pick, Melitta S., 9920
Pickard, Cary, 7152
Pickard, Mary, 4614, 4763
Pickard, Vivian R., 4442
Pickard, William F., 4371
Pickens, T. Boone, 9099

Pickens, William B., 8478
Picker Revocable Trust, Harvey, 5703
Picker Trust, Harvey, 5703
Picker, Gale, 5703
Picker, Harvey, 5703
Pickering, Jeffrey R., 780
Pickering, Kenneth E., 3612
Pickering, Robert, 1392
Picket, David L., 6638
Picket, Joan R., 6638
Picket, Joel I., 6638
Picket, Rona J., 6638
Pickett, Michelle Lee, 1116
Pickett, Tamara, 85
Pickett-Erway, Carrie, 4472
Pickler, Irv, 239
Pickus, Katherine, 2649
Picotte, Brooke A., 6639
Picotte, John D., 6639
Picotte, John D., Jr., 6639
Picotte, Joseph M., 6510
Picotte, Kathleen, 6692
Picotte, Kathleen M., 6510
Picotte, Margaret Hines, 6639
Picotte, Margaret L., 6510
Picotte, Michael B., 6510
Picotte, Michelle H., 6510
Picotte, Nicole L., 6510
Picotte, Susan C., Esq., 5803
Picower, Barbara, 6243
Picower, Jeffrey M., 6243
Pidcock-Lester, Kerry, Rev., 8234
Piediscalzi, Nick, 847
Piedmont Natural Gas Co., Inc., 7285
Piedras, Alejandro H., 3420
Piell, Hilda Harris, 2755
Piepel, John D., 4602
Piepenbring, Mary L., 7195
Pieper, Scott, 2042
Pier, Nancy G., 6058
Pierce, Barbara P., 3036
Pierce, Charles E., 3788
Pierce, Charlie, 3083
Pierce, Daniel, 3923
Pierce, Debbie, 1399
Pierce, Denis, 3080
Pierce, Edna B., 1739
Pierce, Edwin A., 7672
Pierce, Elsie, 4389
Pierce, Eve, 8224
Pierce, Harold Whitworth, 4220
Pierce, J. Peter, 8224
Pierce, Janice, 4792
Pierce, Janice L., 7735
Pierce, Jenny, 5926
Pierce, Judy, 7540
Pierce, Kathleen F., 8224
Pierce, Larry S., 1439
Pierce, Leo W., Jr., 8224
Pierce, Leo W., Sr., 8224
Pierce, Marjorie L., 8224
Pierce, Martha V., 3080
Pierce, Mary, 8224
Pierce, Michael, 8224
Pierce, Molly, 8224
Pierce, Nancy L., 3801
Pierce, Peter, 4792
Pierce, Richard B., 3304
Pierce, Sarah Rob Colby, 2668
Pierce, Sharon, 3397
Pierce, Wanda L., 9384
Pierce, Watson, 4389
Piereson, James, 6643, 6859
Pierre, Jerry St., 3612
Pierre, Scott, 2872
Pierro, Jynnifer, 1423
Piersol, Lawrence, 8524
Pierson, Bonnie B.K. Hunt, 8100
Pierson, Claire A., 3830
Pierson, David A., 8203
Pierson, Joseph A., 6723
Pierson, Matthew, 5182
Pierson, Robert L., 3720, 3830
Pierson, W. Michel, 3720, 3830
Pietra, May Della, 5839
Pietrantozzi, Susan, 9769
Pietrini, Andrew G., 6342
Pietrini, Lauri, 6342
Pietruszynski, Mary Ellen, 9189
Pietsch, Brian J., 4714
Piette, Michael, 5801
Pietzner, Clemens, 4238, 8330
Pigatti, Leah, 4730
Pigg, Betty Lou, 9460
Piggott 2012 Charitable Lead Annuity Trust, James C., 9687
Pignone, Christopher, 5894
Pigott 2005 Charitable Lead Annuity Trust, James C., 9687
Pigott 2005 Charitable Lead Unitrust, James C., 9687
Pigott, Charles M., 9693
Pigott, Dana, 9693
Pigott, Gaye T., 9687
Pigott, James C., 9687, 9693
Pigott, Judy, 9728
Pigott, Mark C., 6904, 9698
Pigott, Mary, 9693, 9728
Pigott, Maureen, 9687
Pigott, Maureen "Dina", 9687
Pigott, Michael J., 9728
Pigott, Paul, 9687
Piha, Morris, 9725
Pike, Charles L., 1690
Pike, Colette P., 2274
Pike, Drummond, 3925
Pike, Laurel W., 6567
Pike, Stacy, 4693
Piker, Dave, 3396
Pilch, Michael, 9988
Pilch, Tom, 9998
Pilchard, A. Franklin, 3081
Pilcher, Patricia, 9460
Pilcher, Ronald H., 2415
Pildner, Henry, Jr., 8300
Pilegge, Robert J., 9020
Piletic, William, Rev., 473
Pilgrim Insurance Co., 4222
Pilgrim, Gary L., 8225
Pilkington, Robert, 6532
Pillai, Marie, 4661
Pillman, Sally A., 2835
Pillman, William R., 2835
Pillsbury, John, 4955, 4956
Pillsbury, Marian S., 3182
Pillsbury, Marnie, 6723
Pillsbury, Marnie S., 6643, 6725
Pillsbury, Nancy, 4955, 4956
Pillsbury, Ruth, 4955, 4956
Pillsbury-Wainwright, Mary, 4956
Pilnick, Gary H., 4475
Pilon, Mary Claudia Belk, 7146, 7148
Pilotte, John, 2650
PIM Holding Co., 6488
Pim, Matt, 419
PIMCO, 1037, 9916
Pinado, Jeanne, 3980, 4061
Pinch, Karen, 3243
Pinck Charitable Trust, Laurie, The, 5553
Pinck, Laurie, 5553
Pinck, Menachem, 5553
Pinckney, C. Cotesworth, 9529
Pincschmidt, Ellen McCance, 4165
Pincus, Aaron, 5407
Pincus, Claudio, 5407
Pincus, Daniel, 5407
Pincus, David N., 1836
Pincus, Geraldine, 1836
Pincus, Penny, 5407
Pinder, Martha, 3475
Pindred, R. John, 4417
Pindred, Robert John, 4417
Pindroh, Corene L., 1015
Pine Fund Corp., 2343
Pine Island Cranberry Co., Inc., 5289
Pine River Domestic Management L.P., 4742
Pine, Mark J., 4148
Pine, William D., 1044
Pineda, Patricia Salas, 7002
Pineiro, Rosa Garcia, 7908
Pines, Heather K., 2960
Pines, Joan, 3151
Pinewood Foundation, 234
Ping, Ryan, 4806
Pingeon, Hendon C., 1558
Pingree, Sally E., 5954
Pingrey, Brad, 3761
Pinheiro, Emily, 3929
Pinizzotto, Marie E., 5593
Pinkard, Gregory C., 3796
Pinkard, Robert M., 3796
Pinkard, Walter D., Jr., 3796, 3891
Pinkernell, Layne, 410
Pinkerton, Robert A., 6643
Pinkett, Kathleen, 4761
Pinkett, Preston D., III, 5243
Pinnacle Associates, 7876
Pinnick, Stan, 9631
Pinnock, Blondel A., 6361
Pino, Catherine, 5608
Pino, Dom, 2243
Pinsker, Diane, 7780
Pinsker, Neal D., 8622
Pinsky, David, 3992
Pinsof, William, 2825
Pinto, Antonio Paulo, 1566
Pinto, Elizabeth A., 6586
Pinto, Maurice E., 6586
Pinto, Michael P., 3726, 6406
Piombo, Daniel F., Jr., 1183
Pioneer Hi-Bred International, Inc., 3474
Pioneer Trust Bank, N.A., 7885
Pipe Distributors, Inc., 3106
Piper Construction, LLC, 8227
Piper Industries, Inc., 8740
Piper Jaffray Cos. Inc., 4743
Piper, Gretchen, 4714
Piper, Lynn, 8740, 9974
Piper, Mark, 4372
Piper, Mary, 9974
Piper, Minnie Stevens, 9101
Piper, Paul, 9974
Piper, Paul P., 9974
Piper, Paul P., Jr., 8740
Piper, Paul P., Mrs., 8740
Piper, Paul P., Sr., 8740
Piper, Paul, Jr., 8740, 8763
Piper, Paul, Sr., 8763
Piper, Randall G., 9101
Piper, Ronald K., 9974
Piper, Roy W., 8227
Piper, Shirley, 8740
Piper, Thomas, III, 6115
Piper, Virginia G., 152
Piper, William H., 4510
Pipher, Jacqueline, 2936
Pipkin, John, 3676
Pipoli, Katherine M., 4918
Piqunik Management Corp., 81
Piraino, Thomas A., 7611
Pircsuk, Cathy M., 6567
Pirelli Tire North America, 118
Piretti-Miller, Mary Jo, 3947
Pirkle, Greg, 4822
Pirkle, Linda L., 7384
Piro, James J., 7881
Piro, Lawrence D., 685
Pirone, William, 5879
Pirozzolo-Millowes, R. Jan, 9829
Pirtle, Terri A., 7783
Pisano, Carol, 6159
Pisano, Jane G., 664
Pissocra, Ronald L., 7627
Piszek, Edward J., Jr., 7998
Piszek, Edward J., Sr., 7998
Piszek, George W., 7998
Piszek, William P., 7998
Pitcairn Trust Co., 7949
Pitcairn, Dean, 8062
Pitcairn, Kean, 8062
Pitcairn, Raymond, 8062
Pitcairn, Robert A., Jr., 7528
Pitcher, George W., 5810
Pitino Foundation, Rick, 5478
Pitkin Inc., Winifred M., 5408
Pitkin, George M., 5408
Pitkin, Jo, 2429
Pitkin, Sarah, 9511
Pitluck, Wayne M., 2601
Pitluk, Marvin J., 2702
Pitman, Donne W., 7739, 7740
Pitman, Norman D., III, 52
Pitman, Norman D., Jr., 24
Pitney Bowes Inc., 1674
Pitre, Tanya Jean, 8990
Pitrone, Gina L., 9500
Pitt, Brad, 1791
Pitt, Pauline Baker, 1675
Pitt, Tom, 4332
Pitt, William H., 1675
Pittelman, Carole, 6380, 6545
Pittman, Dana W., 3444
Pittman, Tom, 4821
Pittman, V.S., II, 9399
Pitts, Billy, 2435
Pitts, Francis Murdock, 5803
Pitts, Knox, II, 9148
Pitts, Margaret A., 2529
Pitts, Rodney D., 3522
Pitts, William I.H., 2529
Pittsburgh Forgings Foundation, 8030
Pivar, Ruth A., 1790
Pivnick, Isadore, 1226
Piwetz, Eileen, 8852
Piziali, Melanie, 7888
Pizzuti, Linda, 2154
Plain, Brian, 3061
Planchard, John B., 8829
Plangere KCA Charitable Trust, The, 2270
Plangere KRDJ Charitable Trust, The, 2270
Plangere, Jules L., III, 2270
Plangere, Jules L., Jr., 2270
Plangere, Jules, Jr., 2270

Plank, Desiree Jacqueline, 3769
Plank, J. Scott, 3780
Plank, Kevin A., 3769
Plank, Lollie Benz, 9999
Plank, Michael, 1512
Plankenhorn, Harry, 8229
Plansoen, Hector L., 7286
Plansoen, Louis, 7286
Planters LifeSavers Co., 7296
Plaster Trust, Robert W., 4957
Plaster, Robert W., 4957
Plaster, Stephen R., 4957
Plastics Engineering Co., Inc., 9825
Plati, Crystal, 1419
Platinum Properties, 1308
Plato, William R., 7391
Platt, Daniel, 1053
Platt, David J., 60
Platt, H. Thomas, 2288
Platt, Heather B., 60
Platt, Melanie M., 2400
Platt, Susan, 3271
Platte Valley Medical Center, 1394
Platts, H. Gregory, 9537
Platts, Robin, 3782
Plauche, Mary M., 5526
Player's Grievance Trust, 1939
Playfair, Larry, 5726
Plaza Cleaning Service Co. II LP, 5982
Pledger, James E., Dr., 9007
Pleiad Partners, L.P., 58
Plepler, Andrew D., 7139
Pletka, Irene, 6646
Plevo, Frank, 5341
Plimpton, David L., 6148
Plisco, Mary Alice, 2105
Plitt, Clarence M., 3862
Ploetz, Jon, 4855
Plomgren, Ronald, 847
Plotkin, Amanda, 6809
Plotkin, Carolyn, 6809
Plotkin, David, 6918
Plotkin, Fred, 6809
Plotkin, Janet, 6809
Plotkin, Jonathan, 6809
Plotkin, Richard A., 8356
Plotkin, Roger B., 433
Plotts, David, 3760
Plough, Abe, 8615
Plough, Alonzo L., 4016
Plough, Maurice, Jr., 9297
PLP Associates Holdings Inc., 6779
Pluff, J. Daniel, 5757
Plukas, John M., 4030
Plum Creek Timber Co., Inc., 9704
Plum Creek Timber Co., L.P., 9704
Plum, Kathleen McBride, 7562
Plum, Susan Butler, 6121, 6868
Plumb, John K., 6195
Plumeri, Jay, 6649
Plumeri, Joseph J., 6649
Plumley, Mark, 999
Plummer, Dan, 1950
Plummer, Hellen Ingram, 5409
Plummer, Phyllis M. Parmer, 3069
Plummer, Shari Sant, 1950
Plump, Jim, 3284
Plung, Louis, 8055
Plunkett, Ann C., 8084
Plunkett, L. Richard, 2439
Plunkett, Linda, 8472, 8502
Pluss Poultry, 1508
Pluss, Robert J., 1297
Plymouth Rock Assurance Corporation, 4222
Plymouth Rock Company, Inc., 4222
PNC Advisors, 8275
PNC Bank, 7673, 8168
PNC Bank N.A., 7423, 7465
PNC Bank, N.A., 1755, 3299, 3343, 4472, 7404, 7428, 7613, 7618, 7621, 7622, 7635, 7679, 7693, 7708, 7940, 7953, 7961, 7987, 7993, 8006, 8007, 8018, 8023, 8026, 8046, 8056, 8063, 8095, 8096, 8104, 8110, 8154, 8155, 8157, 8162, 8165, 8186, 8188, 8209, 8210, 8211, 8228, 8230, 8231, 8252, 8258, 8269, 8271, 8274, 8291, 8319, 8322, 8341, 8345
PNC Delaware Trust Company, 8370
PNC Equity Partners, LP, 8230
PNC Financial Services Group, Inc., The, 8230
PNM Resources, Inc., 5532
Poage, Ray, 8696
Poage, Ray M., 8889
Pocalyko, Paul W., 8199
Pochal, Susan, 1563
Pocilujko, Bill, 633
Podd Survivor's Trust, George W., 131
Podd, Greg, 131
Podell, Justine, 1304
Podjasek, John F., III, 2733
Podlich, Bill, 1037
Podlipny, Ann R., 6158, 6731
Podlipny, Lucia Rose, 6158
Podlipny, Magda, 6158
Podnar, Lawrence, 9719
Podoll, Christopher J., 3491
Poe, Parker, 2531
Poe, Ronald F., 9435
Poepl, John F., 4744
Poepl, Mary Pat, 4744
Poff, Jim, 9715
Pogue Foundation, The, 8789
Pogue, Ann, 8789
Pogue, Blake, 8789
Pogue, Jack, 8789
Pogue, John L., 7705
Pogue, Richard W., 7532
Pohanka Trust, John J., 3863
Pohanka, Geoffrey, 3863
Pohanka, Geoffrey P., 3863
Pohanka, John J., 3863
Pohl, David F., 4752
Pohl, Jack, 4715, 4757
Pohl, Jerrol A., 1292
Pohl, John C., 9688
Pohl, Lynn, 4512
Pohl, Nicola, 157
Pohl, Susan W., 9688, 9693
Pohl, Susan Wyckoff, 9749
Pohlad, Carl R., 4745
Pohlad, Eloise O., 4745
Pohlad, James O., 4745
Pohlad, Rebecca, 9726
Pohlad, Robert C., 4745
Pohlad, William M., 4745
Pohle, Elizabeth Malott, 2996
Poindexter, John S., III, 2532
Poindexter, Katherine, 2532
Poinier, Carol, 8223
Poinsatte, Richard A., 3389
Poirot, James W., 1384
Pokryfki, Sammye, 89
Polack, Fernando P., 9353
Polaha, Lindarae, 924
Polaris Industries Inc., 4746
Poley, Barbara, 92, 5530
Polhamus, Beatriz, 3085
Poliak, Joan B., 9595
Policinski, Gene, 1907
Policky, David B., 5035
Poliner, Gary A., 9914
Poling, Donald, 4966
Polinger Family Foundation, Howard & Geraldine, 3898
Polinger Family Trust, Geraldine, 3864
Polinger, Arnold Lee, 3864
Polinger, David, 7425
Polinger, David Marc, 3864
Polinger, Geraldine, 3864
Polinger, Geraldine H., 3864
Polinger, Howard, 3864
Polinger, Jan, 3864
Polinger, Lorre Beth, 3864
Polisi, Joseph W., 6788, 7043
Politeo, Janet L., 9629
Polito, Robert, 3083
Politzer, Nancy, 7425
Polizzi-Keller, Anna, 4992
Polizzotto, Joseph, 5876
Polk Bros., Inc., 3084
Polk, Bill, 2995
Polk, Cheryl, 1046
Polk, David D., 3084
Polk, Eugene P., 129, 148, 5764
Polk, Harry, 3084
Polk, Howard J., 3084
Polk, Ira, 2752
Polk, Julie A., 4524
Polk, Kenneth H., 6, 62
Polk, Morris G., 3084
Polk, Ralph L., 4524
Polk, Samuel H., 3084
Polk, Sol, 3084
Polk, Stephen R., 4524
Polk, Thomas E., 148
Polk, William L., Jr., 4952
Polk, William M., 3971
Polk, Winifred E., 4524
Pollack, Andrea S., 1501
Pollack, Carol, 1567
Pollack, Cintra, 1501
Pollack, Teddy, 6580
Pollak, Margot, 6745
Pollak, Mark, 9417
Pollard, Alison, 4362
Pollard, Brian, 5757
Pollard, C. William, 2933
Pollard, Lewis B., 9560
Pollard, Norval, 8994
Pollard, O. Miles, 3618
Pollard, Richard, 378
Pollet, Paula D., 1478
Polley, William, 1198
Polli, John M., 8351
Pollock, Channing, 5585
Pollock, John V., 3784
Pollock, Jonathan D., 7117
Pollock, Larry, 7406
Pollock, Lawrence S., III, 9103
Pollock, Lawrence S., Jr., 9103
Pollock, Lawrence S., Sr., 9103
Pollock, Richard, 9103
Pollock, Robert, 5621
Pollock, Robert G., 9103
Pollpeter, Susan C., 7178
Polly, Linda, 9769
Polo Ralph Lauren Corp., 6651
Polsky Investment Trust, Jack, 2653
Polsky Trust, Richard M., 2653
Polsky, Alex, 744
Polsky, Charles, 2653
Polsky, George, 2653, 2893
Polsky, Jack, 2653, 2893, 3125
Polsky, James, 2653
Polsky, Jean, 2653, 2893
Polsky, Larry, 7255
Polsky, Richard, 2653
Polsky, Virginia H., 2653
Polstein, Matthew, 3698
Polster, Bryan C., 1193
Poltack, Rupal M., 5178
Poma, Frank, 4373
Pomar, Christine, 1658
Pomer, Frank A., 1549
Pomerantz, Jane Weed, 248
Pomerleau Family LLC., 9369
Pomerleau, Antonio B., 9369
Pomerleau, Ernest A., 9369
Pomerleau, Patricia M., 9369
Pomerleau, Rita M., 9369
Pomeroy, Bob, 7731
Pomeroy, Claire, 6333
Pomeroy, Claire, Dr., 1163
Pomeroy, Katherine, 1566
Pomeroy, Sandra, 6652
Pomeroy, William G., 6652
Pompa, Delia, 1014
Pompetzki, George, 5437
Pon, Joseph M., 249
Ponce, Ana Marie, 414
Pond, Alethea Marder, 8231
Pond, Charles B., III, 9538
Pond, Charles N., Jr., 8231
Pond, Donna S., 8231
Pond, Randy, 402
Pong, Kathryn, 5422
Ponozzo, Dave, 9602
PonTell, Steve, 366
Ponting, Wendy, 9907
Pontius, Gil, 3297
Pontius, John, 8584
Pontius, John M., 5879
Pontius-Caves, Teresa, 9277
Pontzer, Deborah Dick, 8295
Ponzio, Craig, 1482
Ponzio, June, 1482
Pool, Peggy Cook, 8779
Pool, Philip B., Jr., 6967
Poole, Bob, 2631
Poole, Chris, 744
Poole, Joe, 9559
Poole, John S., 8501
Poole, Ron, 5807
Poole, Stephen H., 7922
Poole, Steven W., 4443
Poonai, Anila, 2271
Poonai, Parmanand V., 2271
Poonai, Premnath, 2271
Poonawala, Akbar, 5876
Poore, Christina Bezos, 9585
Poore, Gary, 3518
Poore, Stephen S., 9585
Poorman, Kevin, 3098
Poorvu, Lia G., 4224
Poorvu, William J., 4224
Popa, Nancy A., 4376
Pope Life Foundation, Lois, The, 2215
Pope Revocable Trust, Louis T. and Bobbie M., 9108
Pope, Amanda Joyce, 7288

Pope, Catherine E., 6653
Pope, David, 350, 4461
Pope, David Anthony, 6653
Pope, Deborah A., 5919
Pope, Ed, Rev., 9413
Pope, Edith A., 6653
Pope, Elizabeth J., 2533
Pope, Ellen, 3698
Pope, Generoso, 6653
Pope, James Arthur, 7288, 9819
Pope, Joyce W., 7288
Pope, Kathy, 4438
Pope, Lawrence J., 8884
Pope, Lois B., 2215, 2272
Pope, Lona, 2525
Pope, Marsha, 3552
Pope, Paul D., 2215
Pope, Stephen, 5807
Popejoy, Connie, 4936
Popejoy, Kevin, 4936
Popenhagen, Nancy K., 1291
Popeo, Helen B., 1952
Popeo, John W., 1952
Poplar Foundation, The, 8610
Poplava, Sharman, 8505
Popof, Al, 662
Popoff, Frank P., 5587
Popovich, David, 2728
Popovich, J. Kristoffer, 699
Popovich, Jane H., 699
Popovsky, Stacey, 6345
Poppell, Ed, 9800
Popsicle Playwear, Ltd., 5557
Popular Community Bank, 3085
Popular Community Foundation, Inc., 3085
Porch, Stanley, 8522
Porche, Denise, 4109
Porges, Evan, 1211
Porges, Leigh Simon, 6859
Poritz, Deborah T., Hon., 5270
Port, Clyde W., 8507
Port, Neil, 7971
Portago, Carolina, 6631
Portago, Theodora, 6631
Portanova, Zeb, 3361
Portaro, Sam A., Jr., Rev., 3100
Portcullis Partners, L.P., 9038
Portenoy, Winifred Riggs, 1901
Porter Charitable Trust, Lucile, 3036
Porter, A. Alex, 6116
Porter, Andrew C., 6093
Porter, Barbara, 4755
Porter, Betty Robins, 9523
Porter, Biggs C., 8851
Porter, Catherine, 234
Porter, Charles, 8055
Porter, Charles W., Jr., 32
Porter, Christian, 7217
Porter, David, 8676
Porter, David L., 3826
Porter, David, III, 8649
Porter, E, 1769
Porter, E., 1769
Porter, Ellen, 1838
Porter, Frances G., 7211
Porter, Grant, 6967
Porter, Haigh, 8461
Porter, James Hyde, 2533
Porter, Joanna O., 3826
Porter, John, 8522
Porter, John E., 2955
Porter, John L., 9380
Porter, Kathryn A., 1424, 3358
Porter, Kieren, 7829
Porter, Laurel, 3826
Porter, Martha A., 3178
Porter, Martin F., 3826
Porter, Mary L., 6797
Porter, Patricia A., 8959
Porter, Reid, 1838
Porter, Richard A., 4538
Porter, Richard, Jr., 4538
Porter, Robert C., Jr., 7405
Porter, Robert, III, 7405
Porter, Sharon, 4538
Porter, Susan J., 7659
Porter, Wayne, 3253
Porter, William, 2041
Portera, Malcolm, 4844
Porterfield, Mark J., 1037
Porteus, Beccy, 7421
Portlance, Karen, 3866
Portland General Electric Co., 7881
Portman, John C., Jr., 2454
Portnoi, Lee, 8649
Portnoy, Fern, 4102
Portnoy, James, 3034
Portnoy, Scott, 4628
Portoghese, Joseph D., 2390
Portovesme SRL E, 7349
Portrait Homes-North Carolina, LLC, 3071
Portugal, Susan, 7139
Portwood, Barbara, 4694
Portz, Jay J., 4796
Porzecanski, Arturo C., 6983
Posada, Julian G., 3172
Posch, Marty, 3303
Poses, Frederic, 6655
Posey, Jill M., 9104
Posey, Lee, 9104
Posey, Sally, 9104
Posey, Samuel F., 1645
Posillico Foundation, 6205
Posillico, Paul, 6205
Posin, Esther, 5620
Posner, David, 9922
Posner, Frederic G., 9922
Posner, Gene, 9922
Posner, Helen M., 8233
Posner, Henry, III, 8233
Posner, Henry, Jr., 8233
Posner, James T., 8233
Posner, Mary M., 4957
Posner, Paul M., 8233
Posner, Ruth, 9922
Posoff, Mindy M., 8221
Poss, Ellen M., Dr., 4226
Poss, Todd, 9889
Post Traditional High Yield Fund, 9916
Post, Carolyn, 1879
Post, Dave, 4370
Post, Dennis D., 3295
Post, Helen, 7286
Post, John, 7289
Post, John A., 7289
Post, Lawrence, 1041
Post, Lawrence A., 1041
Post, Margaret, 7289
Post, Martin R., 6243
Post, Ron, 7873
Post, Sandra, 1041
Post, Stephen G., 8313
Post, William J., 143
Post-Newsweek Stations, 9445
Poster, Dennis B., 1538
Postlethwait, Caitlin L., 3395
Postlethwait, Kathleen D., 3395
Postlethwait, Megan L., 3395
Postlethwait, Robert N., 3395
Postma, Pat, 8560
Poteat, Jennifer, 4340
Poteat-Flores, Jennifer R., 4557
Potenziani, A.F., 861
Potenziani, Cheryl L., 861
Potenziani, Cyrena K., 861
Potenziani, Frank A., 861
Potenziani, Frederick A., 861
Potenziani, Martha M., 861
Potenziani, William, 861
Poterba, James, 6872
Poteshman, Michael, 2363
Potesta, Ron L., 9780
Potiker, Brian, 1042
Potiker, Jori, 1042
Potiker, Lowell, 1042
Potiker, Sheila, 1042
Potomic Edison, 7455
Potpan, Michelle, 1549
Potricinos Mexico, 8834
Pottash, Carter, 6383
Potter 2003 Charitable Lead Annuity Trust, Susan S., 2170
Potter Inc., 1791
Potter, Clare P., 2739
Potter, Earl, Dr., 4679
Potter, Holly, 938
Potter, Kathleen Stowers, 3550
Potter, Kevin, 7731
Potter, Nancy, 5807
Potter, Trevor, 3182
Potter-Talbert, Elaine T., 3249
Pottruck, Emily Scott, 9341
Potts Trust, Beatrice P., 5409
Potts, Cheryl, 23
Potts, J. Brian, 3923
Potts, Robert, 2264
Potts, Robert J., 8809
Potts, Thomas S., Jr., 23
Poucher, John S., 1000
Pouliot, Rebecca R., 4012
Poulos, Catherine M. Creticos, 3217
Poulos, Gregory T., 4766
Poulos, James A., 3840, 3842
Poulos, Sara J. Slaggie, 4766
Poulson, Richard J.M., 1925
Pouschine, Tatiana, 5549, 5692
Povich, Maurice R., 7008
Powder Mill Apartments LLC, 9452
Powell Company, 1548
Powell, Ann, 7742
Powell, Ann Lavelle, Esq., 8275
Powell, Ben H., Jr., 9105
Powell, Ben H., V, 9105
Powell, Ben H., VI, 9105
Powell, Beverly J., 4996
Powell, Charlie, 9241
Powell, Christopher, 3861
Powell, Dina H., 6070
Powell, E. Bryson, 9529
Powell, Earl A., III, 1890
Powell, Francis R., 1616
Powell, Gary, 4872
Powell, Gregory, 3678, 3679
Powell, Jacklen E., 1849
Powell, John B., Jr., 3724, 3836
Powell, Karen, 2761
Powell, Kendall J., 4661
Powell, Kitty King, 9105
Powell, Kris, 4829
Powell, Laurence, 8601
Powell, Liz, 9924
Powell, M. Cleland, III, 3648
Powell, Meredith, 3861
Powell, Myrtis H., 1940
Powell, Paul W., 9138
Powell, Rodney O., 1609
Powell, Scott, 3570
Powell, Stephen, 67
Powell, Todd, 9704
Powell, Weldon, 1572
Power Equipment Distributors, Inc., 4580
Power Family Limited Partnership, The, 779
Power III 2008 Charitable Lead Annuity Trust, James D., 779
Power III 2008 Charitable Lead Unitrust, James D., 779
Power, Carla, 8649
Power, Christopher, 3524
Power, James D., III, 779
Power, James D., IV, 779
Power, James M., 9838
Power, Jeff, 4465
Power, Jeffrey B., 4403, 4592
Power, Jonathan P., 779
Power, Julie, 779
Power, Mary E., 779
Power, Mary H., 3971
Power, Susan H., 4017
Powers, Angela, 1562
Powers, Bill, 1037
Powers, Fred, 3313
Powers, Janice, 3287
Powers, Joe, 4755
Powers, John, 1578, 1839
Powers, John J., 6656
Powers, John P., 1779, 1839
Powers, Judith, 2269
Powers, Kathryn A., 3556
Powers, Linda E., 6656
Powers, Norma, 7287
Powers, Pamela E., 8981
Powers, Paula, 1053
Powers, Robert P., 7368
Powers, William J., 5717
Pownall-Gray, Lisa W., 5829
Poynor, Ed, 3426
Poynter, Henrietta M., 2332
Poynter, Nelson, 2332
Pozen, David E., 3928
Pozen, Elizabeth K., 3928
Pozen, Joanna R., 3928
Pozen, Robert C., 3928, 5800
Poznanski, Dorothy, 7882
Poznanski, Robert, 7882
PPG Industries, Inc., 8235
Pradere, John M., 9997
Pradhan, Dora, 9413
Pradhan, Geeta, 3956
Prager, Yossi, 5628, 8131
Prague, Andrew P., 3963
Prairie Pizza, 3245
Prairie, Pam, 4448
Praise Assembly, 3517
Prancia, Pete, 8610
Pranger, Leigh, 3359
Pranschke, Leonard J., 4861
Pranzo, Gene, 1964
Prassas, Jerome R., 2884
Prather, Eddie, 4822
Prather, John E., 7670
Prather, Lisa L., 7670
Prather, N. King, 7153

Prather, Pam, 7181
Pratnicki, Marylee M., 5324
Prato, Greg, 6852
Pratt, Andy, 7569
Pratt, Brent K., 3792
Pratt, Carolyn M., 4540
Pratt, Charles J., 9577
Pratt, Christine, 3833
Pratt, Deborah R., 4243
Pratt, G. Michael, 7570
Pratt, Harold I., 4220
Pratt, Larry C., 7280
Pratt, Mike, 6546, 6804
Pratt, Richard W., 1745
Pratt, Roger, 5441
Pratt, Sandra Zita, 7811
Pratt, Scott T., 777
Pratt, Timothy A., 3957
Pratt-Clarke, Menah, 2765
Praxair, Inc., 1676
Pray, Barbara H., 7733
Pray, Donald E., 7733
Pray, Joe E., 4357
Prazeres, Joseph, 4026
Prchal, Douglass, 7357
Preble, Bob, 9631
Prechter Charitable Lead Trust, Heinz C., 4594
Prechter, Heinz C., 4594
Prechter, Patricia M., 3612
Prechter, Paul, 4594
Prechter, Stephanie, 4594
Prechter, Waltraud, 4594
Prechter, Waltraud E., 4594
Precision Signs Lighting Inc., 8834
Precision Strip, Inc., 7840
Precourt, Amanda J., 1483
Precourt, Jay A., 1483
Precourt, Jay Anthony, Jr., 1483
Precourt, Walt, 4722
Predhomme, Michael J., 4401
Predolin Revocable Trust, Henry, 9923
Predolin, Henry, 9923
Preece, Aaron, 9795
Preece, William H., 2648
Prehn, Toby, 2626
Preik, Austin, 2273
Preik, Curtis, 2273
Preik, Jennifer, 2273
Preik, Reinhold, 2273
Preimesberger, David G., 471
Preisman-Beriro, 118
Prejean, Jerry, 3623
Premier Bank and Trust, 9773
Premier Bank, N.A., 9845
Premier Designs, 8789
Premier Radio, 7638
Premier Resource Group, 1268
Premier Store Fixtures, 6756
Prempas Trust, Helen, 2769
Prendergast, E. James, 9547
Prendergast, Michael, 9059
Prendergast, S. Lawrence, 5483
Preneta, Megan, 1614
Prentice Revocable Trust, Abra, 3088
Prentice, Bryant H., III, 2274
Prentice, Bryant, III, 2274
Prentice, Cynthia R., 9107
Prentice, F. David, 9107
Prentice, F. David, Mrs., 9107
Prentice, James S., 8996
Prentice, Joan P., 2274
Prentice, Margaret V., 5232
Prentice, Nathaniel S., 5808
Prentiss, Amanda, 1391
Prentiss, Carol W., 8549
Prentiss, Elisabeth Severance, 7621
Prentiss, John K., Dr., 5995
Presbyterian Communities and Svcs. Fdn., 9108
Prescott, Heidi, 7091
Presentation specialists technologies, 9193
Preservati, N. Karen, 9790
Preservati, Richard G., 9790
Presley, Cecilia DeMille, 459
Presley, Kimberley, 971
Presley, Steven, 965, 9056
Presnell, Lacy M., III, 7328
Presser Foundation, Theodore, 8236
Presser, Theodore, 8236
Pressley, Kirk, 8, 9
Pressley, Monica, 1109
Pressley-Brown, Scarlet, 7191
Pressman, Erica, 3864
Prestia, Carmine, 7973
Prestolite Wire Corp., 5185
Preston Ctr., 8649
Preston, Af, 8438
Preston, Hattie L., 3596
Preston, Jennifer, 2191
Preston, Kent, 3596
Preston, Raymond B., 3596
Preston, Robert J., 7840, 7847
Preston, Seymour S., III, 7928
Pretto, Christina L., 5563
Previn, Andre, 917
Prevost, Patrick M., 3966
Prevratil, Joseph F., 253
Prewitt, Edward K., Jr., 7169
Prewitt, Jennifer D., 7436
Prewitt, Kenneth, 6093
Pricara, 5327
Price 2006 Family Trust, 6657
Price Associates, T. Rowe, Inc., 3865
Price Group, T. Rowe, Inc., 3865
Price, Aimee Gamble, 562
Price, Allen L., 9146
Price, Allison, 1043
Price, Andrew Francis, 8927
Price, Anne Sage, 4531
Price, Barbara, 722
Price, Calvin K., 1630
Price, Clement A., 5243
Price, David, 2553
Price, Dean, 3422
Price, Deirdra, 9346
Price, Doug, 5750
Price, Eileen, 2553
Price, Ella C., 1015
Price, Fred D., 5839
Price, Glenda D., Dr., 4371
Price, Gregory T., 562
Price, Harold, 1484
Price, Helen, 1043
Price, Helen Smith, 2428
Price, Herb, Dr., 3271
Price, Jennifer C., 6659
Price, JoAnn H., 1609
Price, Jody, 4579
Price, John, 9346
Price, John Steven, 9346
Price, Jordan M., 6659
Price, Kim S., 7179
Price, Kimberly F., 4597
Price, Louis, 1484
Price, Marcia, 9346
Price, Margaret, 8681
Price, Mary B., 1044
Price, Mary Barbara, 1044
Price, Maxie, Jr., 2433
Price, Michael, 1518
Price, Michael F., 6659
Price, Michael R., 917
Price, Paula, 4297
Price, R. Gary, 2123
Price, Richard, 5517
Price, Robert, 1043, 6657
Price, Scott, 9380
Price, Sheila, 3061
Price, Sol, 1043
Price, Steven, 6657
Price, Susan, 3373, 8927
Price, Thomas, 6352
Price, Tina, 6657
Price, Todd, 8927
Price, Wayne Hollomon, 8914
Price, William, 8866
Price, William O., 3569
Pricer, Robert, 9852
PricewaterhouseCoopers, 7012
Prichard, Peter S., 1907
Prichard, Shelly Chenowith, 3555
Prickett Fund, Lynne R. and Karl E., 7218
Prickett, Caroline D., 1754
Prickett, Lynn R., 7290
Prickett, Peter, 9916
Priddy, Ashley H., 9109
Priddy, Robert T., 9109, 9277
Priddy, Swannanoa H., 9109
Priddy, Walter M., 9109
Pridham, Herbert H., 7403
Pridmore, Ken, 986
Pridmore, Melissa T., 9224
Pridmore, Tim, 8994
Priebe, Daniel, 4677
Priem, Curtis, 1045
Priem, Susan, 5533
Priem, Veronica, 1045
Pries, Kendall R., 977
Priest, Eric, 8313
Priest, Michael A., 7563
Priest, William W., Jr., 6199
Priestap, Gary, 4359
Priester, Brian, 4357
Priester, Susan, 8474
Prieto, Jose, 9083
Prill, Terry, 9603
Prim Ventures, Inc., 5140
Prim, Billy, 7563
Prim, Wayne L., 5140
Prim, Wayne L., Jr., 5140
Primary Health Management, Ltd., 9098
Primary Health, Inc., 9098
Prime A Investments, LLC, 461
Prime, Meredith, 7069
Primerica Inc., 2534
Primes, David M., 613
PrimeVest, 385
Prina, Dean, 1487
Prince & Co., F.H., Inc., 3090
Prince Capital, 6042
Prince Charitable Remainder Unitrust, 4525
Prince Corp., 4525
Prince Foundation, 4418
Prince Holding Corp., 4545
Prince Living Trust, Elsa D., 4525
Prince Remainder Trust, Eleanor Wood, 3083
Prince, Charles, 5780
Prince, Edgar D., 4525
Prince, Elizabeth, 8386
Prince, Elsa D., 4525
Prince, Erik D., 4525
Prince, Ethan A., 8383
Prince, Frederick Henry, 3089, 3090
Prince, Frederick Henry, IV, 3089
Prince, John, III, 2437
Prince, Larry L., 2561
Prince, Michael, 635
Prince, Ruth, 4107
Prince-Troutman, Stacey, 2015
Princeton Biomeditech Corporation, 5363
Princeton University, 5412
Principal Life Insurance Co., 3476
Principe, Gerald, 1992
Pringle, David, 5155
Pringle, Mary, 9603
Pringle, Rob, 2631
Prinster, Tony, 1520
Printpack Inc., 2508
Prinz, Beth Terdo, 2000
Prinz, Robert, 5073
Prior, Cornelius B., Jr., 9378
Prior, Gertrude J., 9378
Prior, Michael, 4039
Prior, Trudie J., 9377
Priour, Kyle, 9095
Prisk, Simon H., Esq., 6898
Prisyon, Maxine D., 6265
Pritchard, Elizabeth, 2519
Pritchard, Margaret Beck, 9559
Pritchard, Robert O., 7285
Pritchard, Ruth, 9775
Pritchett, Mark, 2142
Pritzker Cousins Foundation, 1691, 3091, 3092, 3095
Pritzker Foundation, 1691, 2981, 3091, 3092, 3095
Pritzker Foundation, Jay, 3094
Pritzker's Cousin Foundation, 9088
Pritzker's Foundation, 9088
Pritzker, Adam Nicholas, 1046
Pritzker, Anthony N., 3092, 3095
Pritzker, Daniel F., 9110
Pritzker, Irene, 2932
Pritzker, Isaac, 2981
Pritzker, Jacob, 2981
Pritzker, James, 3091
Pritzker, James N., 3094
Pritzker, Jay Robert, 3092, 3095
Pritzker, Jeanne, 3092
Pritzker, John, 997
Pritzker, John A., 1046
Pritzker, Joseph, 2981
Pritzker, Karen, 1691, 3094
Pritzker, Karen M., 9110
Pritzker, Linda, 1691, 9052, 9088, 9111
Pritzker, Lisa, 1046
Pritzker, Margot, 3093
Pritzker, Mary Kathryn, 3095
Pritzker, Mayari S., 3094
Pritzker, Nicholas J., 2875, 2981, 3096
Pritzker, Noah Stone, 1046
Pritzker, Penny, 3098
Pritzker, Rachel, 9111
Pritzker, Regan, 2981
Pritzker, Rhoda, 2981
Pritzker, Roland, 9111
Pritzker, Roland B., 9088
Pritzker, Rosemary, 9088
Pritzker, Susan S., 2981
Pritzker, Tal Hava, 3091

Pritzker, Thomas J., 3093, 3096
Pritzlaff, Mary Dell, 3036
Private One of NY, LLC, 6434
Private Trust Co., 665
Privett, Elizabeth, 8598
Privett, Tony, 8994
Privett, Wade C., 8598
Prizer, Robert, 6749
Pro Performance Sports, LLC, 7012
Probasco, Lloyd, 5036
Probert, Tim, 8884
Probst, Dave, 7563
Probst, Sonia M., 8200
Procello Maddox, Alicia, 272
Prochnow, Lisa V., 7218, 7290
Procop, Robert, 1791
Procter & Gamble, 3201
Procter & Gamble Co., The, 2294
Procton, Erica, 7180
Proctor and Gamble, 1771
Proctor Trust, E.C.W., 8617
Proctor, Elizabeth C., 8617
Proctor, Elizabeth Craig Weaver, 8617
Proctor, Enola, 3036
Proctor, Karen, 3122
Proctor, Martin, 2037
Proctor, Mattina R., 4227
Proctor, Pamela, 6932
Proenza, Theresa, 7579
Proffitt, Kathy, 8527
Progressive Casualty Insurance Co., 7623
Progressive Specialty Insurance Company, 7623
Prohaska, Beth, 2769
Prohaska, Thomas, 3113
Proietti, Alice A., 211
ProLogis, 1485
Promotions Network, The, 7012
Prophet Corp., The, 4680
Propolanis, Patricia J., 453
Propp, Ephraim, 5620
Propp, Gail, 6662
Propp, Morris S., 6662
Propper, Susan, 1511
Propst, Beverly L., 4898
Propst, Luther, 9992
Prosperity Bank, 9267
Prosser, John W., Jr., 738
Prosser, Michael H., 3480
Prosser, Sheri R., 9836
Protective Life Insurance Co., 59
Prothero, Alexander Loeffler, 7380
Prothro, Caren, 9067
Prothro, Caren H., 8912, 9112
Prothro, Charles B., 9277
Prothro, Charles N., 9090
Prothro, Elizabeth P., 9090
Prothro, Joe N., 9090
Prothro, Mark H., 9090
Prothro, Vincent H., 9112
Protz, Edward L., 9063
Proulx, Dana K., 3801
Prout, Curtis, 4084
Provencher, Kenneth, 7878
Providence Development Partners, LLC, 7280
Provident Bank Charitable Foundation, 5806
Provident Bank, The, 7404
Provident Financial Services, Inc., 5414
Provident Trust Company, 5087, 5088
Providential, LLC, 3408
Provision Trust, 8619
Provizer, Marlene, 6546
Provorse, Laura, 5085
Provost, David T., 4371
Prudential Equity Group, LLC, 5415
Prudential Financial, 7012
Prudential Insurance Co. of America, The, 5415
Prudholme, Marvin, 1273
Prudhomme, Florence, 1788
Pruet, Chesley, 4842
Prueter, Beverly, 7376
Pruett, Greg S., 1033
Pruett, J. Curtis, 2481
Pruett, Virginia S., 2481
Pruitt, Chris, 7939
Pruitt, Christopher, 8350
Pruitt, Larry, 7767
Pruner, Dave, 8916
Prusak, Robert, 9998
Prusoff Charitable Lead Annuity Trust, William H., 1678
Prusoff, Alvin, 1678
Prusoff, Laura, 1678
Prussian, Gordon S., 3084
Pruzan, Lucy, 9725
Prybylo, Martha, 4076
Pryce, Jennifer, 1916
Pryde, Jim, 4996
Pryne, Jane, 9635
Pryor, Emilie Mead, 3948
Pryor, Katherine A., 6445
Pryor, Marcus Q., 5803
Pryor, Stephen D., 6445
Przewrocki, Shelley S., 8631
Przybyl, Kimberly T., 9543
PSL Health Care Corporation, 1390
PTI Investments Inc., 7320
Public Service Co. of New Hampshire, 1656
Public Service Co. of New Mexico, 5532
Public Service Electric and Gas Co., 5416
Public Service Enterprise Group, Inc., 5416
Pucci Revocable Trust, Lawrence M., 3099
Puccio, M. Shawn, 8260
Pucillo, Deborah Dale, 2032
Puck, Robert J., 2102, 2161
Pucker, Gigi Pritzker, 3096
Pucker, GiGi Pritzker, 3097
Pucker, Michael, 3097
Puckett, John P., III, 8795
Puckett, Julie Phillips, 5531
Puckett, Kate, 1367
Puckett, Katherine M., 1367
Puckett, Lela Phillips, 5531
Puckett, Mark D., 8594
Puckett, Rick D., 7318
Puentes, George J., 7870
Puerzer, Paul, 4701
Puett Mortgage Co., Nelson, 9114
Puett, Caroline C., 9114
Puett, Nelson Harwood, 9114
Puett, Ruth B., 9114
Puff, Randy, 4443
Puff, Robert C., 2166
Puffer, Richard A., 8462
Puget Energy, 9705
Pugh, Dwight L., 3249
Pugh, Larry, 3678
Pugh, Will J., 8560
Pulcini, John, 3402
Puleo, Lenore, 6912
Pulido, Maria Begona, 2829
Pulitzer, Ceil, 4959
Pulitzer, Emily, 6271
Pulitzer, Michael E., 4959
Puliz, Vicki, 5124
Pullen, Donna S., 8468
Pullen-Venema, Elena, 9616
Pulles, Joanne, 8582
Pulliam, Eugene C., 8804
Pulliam, Jane B., 3371
Pulliam, Larry, 7812
Pulliam, Larry A., 7743, 7798
Pulliam, Myrta, 3272
Pulliam, Myrta J., 3371
Pullin, Randolph L., 9200
Pulling, Thomas L., 6398
Pullman, George Mortimer, 3100
Pullman, Harriet Sanger, 3100
Pulsifer, Ted, 8691
PUMA, 3303
Puma, Patricia, 5670
Pumphrey, Steven C., 9600
Pung, Steve, 4512
Pungello, Elizabeth, 9821
Pungello, Elizabeth P., 7156
Puno, Michael M., 7425
Puntureri, Albert R., 7994
Pura, Robert, Dr., 3992
Purce, Thomas L., 9605
Purcell, Anne McNamara, 3017
Purcell, Carolann P., 3101
Purcell, David P., 3017
Purcell, Lisa, 7340
Purcell, Michael J., 3017
Purcell, Patricia W., 3101
Purcell, Paul E., 3101, 9811
Purcell, Paul E., Jr., 3101
Purcell, Paul M., 3017
Purcell, Philip J., 3017
Purcell, Thomas W., Jr., 1717
Purdue Pharma, Inc., 6779
Purdue, Starr, 2533
Purdy, James A., 6535
Purich, Todd, 7306
Purington, William D., 3680
Purkerson, Mabel L., 2536
Purkey, Sheila L., 3803
Purks, Robert K., 4848
Purnell, Katharine J., 1320
Purnell, Kelley H., 1320
Purnell, Mark L., 1320
Purnell, Mary L., 1320
Purnell, Molly, 1320
Purnell, Richard W., 8105
Purnell, Susan K., 3760
Purohit, Manju, 23
Purohit, Sanjay, 1223
Purser, Craig, 3714
Purugganan, Michael, 6872
Purvis, Debbie, 4843
Purvis, E. Gail, 9240
Purvis, Edgar, Jr., 2822
Purvis, Randy, 4467
Puterbaugh, Jay Garfield, 7786
Puterbaugh, Leela Oliver, 7786
Puth, Betsey L., 6668
Puth, David W., 6668
Puth, John W., 6668
Puth, Leslie A., 6668
Putman, Gerald E., 5863
Putnam, Beth, 5006
Putnam, David F., 5186
Putnam, David F., Jr., 5186
Putnam, Deborah D., 4288, 4289
Putnam, Frederick A., 5186
Putnam, George, 3931
Putnam, James A., 5186
Putnam, Larry, 3514
Putnam, Louisa, 5186
Putnam, Nancy, 3931
Putnam, Richard, 5081
Putnam, Rosamond, 5186
Putnam, Theodore I., 5832
Putnam, Thomas P., 5186
Putnam, Tim, 2123
Putnam-Walkerly, Kris, 7412
Putney, Carolyn Davidow, 452
Putney, Charles H., 7871
Putzel, Henry "Pete", 3948
Puzo, Michael, 4109
PW Financial Partners, 8337
PWH Trust, 9706
Pycik, John M., 3338
Pye, Elisa Stude, 8731
Pyes, Margo, 3817
Pyle, Bruce, 7937
Pyle, Ida M., 9258
Pyle, Joe, 8267
Pyles, John C., 6945
Pyles, Todd, 3762
Pyott, David E.I., 228, 1047
Pyott, David I., 1047
Pyott, Julianna, 1047
Pzena, Jeffrey, 6669
Pzena, Richard, 6669
Pzena, Robin, 6669

Qep Energy Company, 9049
Qiu, Jackie, 4340
QLT, Inc., 9915
Quackenbush, Derek J., 1108
Quad/Graphics, Inc., 9968
Quadracci, Elizabeth E., 9968
Quadracci, J. Joel, 9968
Quadrant Capital, 6042
Quaid, John J., 8325
Quaker Oates Co., 7012
Quaker Oats, 3245
Qualcomm Incorporated, 1048
Qualkinbush, Andrea, 9266
Quandt, Carol, 5067
Quane, Cindy, 347
Quantum Realtors Inc., 720
Quaresma, Laure, 9588
Quarles, Orage, III, 1907
Quarles, Roger, 2626
Quarles, Tracey L., 4067
Quatman, G. William, 4866
Quatrini, Vincent J., Jr., 8228
Quatrochi, Danielle, 3303
Quattrini, Raymond J., 5806
Quattrocchi, Lisa, 5664
Quattrocchi, Lisa Benenson, 5665
Quattrone, Frank P., 1049
Quattrone, Michael, 6725
Quazzo, M. W., 295
Qubein Samuel, Nido, 7231
Queally Family Foundation, 1843
Queally, Anne-Marie, 1843
Queally, Paul, 1843
Queally, Paul B., 1843
Queen's Medical Centers, The, 2604
Queen's Medical, The, 9250
Queen, Megan, 7558
Queens Nassau Nursing Home, 6287, 6288, 6763
Quenon, Robert H., 4914

Querrey, Kimberly, 2277
Quesada Charitable Lead Trust, Kate D. P., 3687
Quesada, Anthony C., 3687
Quesada, Charlotte R., 3687
Quesada, Emily P., 3687
Quesada, Kate Davis P., 3687
Quesada, Peter W., 3687
Quesada, Strand O., 3687
Quesada, T. Ricardo, 3687
Questrom, Allen I., 9116
Questrom, Carol L., 9116
Questrom, Kelli, 9116
Quick Charitable Lead Trust, Leslie and Regina, 6670
Quick Charitable Trust Foundation, Leslie C. Quick, Jr. and Regina A., 2514
Quick, Christopher C., 6670
Quick, Elizabeth L., 7169, 7227, 7228
Quick, John B., 3321
Quick, Leslie C., III, 6670
Quick, Leslie C., Jr., 6670
Quick, Patricia C., 7673
Quick, Peter, 6670
Quick, Regina A., 6670
Quick, Thomas C., 6670
Quigg, Peter, 7992
Quigg, Tom, 9631
Quigley, Eliza Kempner, 8952
Quigley, Ellen White, 3301
Quigley, Jill, 3507
Quill, Thomas H., Jr., 4144
Quillon, Robin, 7990
Quilter, James F., 3015
Quilty, Kevin J., 5808
Quimby, Hannah, 3686, 3705
Quimby, Jane, 1520
Quimby, Rachelle, 3705
Quimby, Roxanne, 3686, 3705
Quin, J. Marvin, 7659
Quinlan, Annamarie, 6127
Quinlan, Frank, 339
Quinlan, Michael J., 3701
Quinlan, Thomas E., 8025
Quinlan, Thomas J., 2801
Quinn, Andrew, 7524
Quinn, Barbara, 8224
Quinn, Dean, 8728
Quinn, Eileen S., 3866
Quinn, George J., Jr., 3866
Quinn, John, 611, 3122
Quinn, Kathleen M., 3866
Quinn, M.L., 9799
Quinn, Patrick, 8834
Quinn, R. Patrick, 6543
Quinn, Sarah, 8224
Quinn, Thomas S., 3948
Quinn, Tim, 1002
Quinn, Todd, 365
Quinn, Tom, 5019
Quinn, Tricia, 9704
Quinney, David E., 9347
Quinney, David E., III, 9347
Quinney, S.J., 9347
Quinones, David Belena, 8780
Quinones, Margarita, 7412
Quint, Brian, 9715
Quintana, Kimberley M., 3675
Quintella, Antonio, 5826
Quirk, John, 5046
Quirk, Kathleen L., 112
Quirk, Neal, 2426
Quirk, Thomas V., 4081
Quirk, Tom, 8341
Quiroz, Lisa Garcia, 6982
Quisenberry, Cynthia, 2594
Quistad, Janice E., 690
Quistgaard, Jon, 4730
Quitkin, Megan, 656
Qwest Communications International Inc., 1750

R G I Group Incorporated, 6628
Raab, Emily, 8242
Raab, Isabel, 8242
Raab, Karen, 3291
Raab, Mary, Dr., 7217
Raab, Norman, 8242
Raab, Sara, 8242
Raab, Stephen, 8242
Raab, Whitney, 8242
Raabe, Bruce J., 1189
Raabe, Dave, 3280
Rabb, Bruce, 5779
Rabb, James M., 3913
Rabb, Jane M., 3913
Rabb, Lori, 1609
Rabb, Nancy, 8873
Rabbe, Lars, 486
Rabe, Travis, 5114
Raben, John R., Jr., 1854
Raben, Lucynda, 3507
Raber, Phillip, 7526
Rabert, Dean F., 8229
Rabin, Mira, 8193
Rabino, Kaynan, 1972
Rabinowitz, Dovid Isaac, 6671
Rabinowitz, Hannah, 6682
Rabinowitz, Rivka, 6671
Rabinowtish, Steve, 420
Rabksa, Don, 492
Rabon, Lori, 5412
RAC Funding LLC C/O Ken Slutsky Tax Exempt Inst Grp, 5455
Racette, Karen, 4472
Rachal, Ed, 9117
Racher, Susan, 2047, 2048
Rachlin, Theodore, 2587
Racine, Andrew D., 6003
Racine, Peter M., 2167
Racing Rest of America II Inc., 1850
Rackes, Barbara, 8468
Rackley Family Foundation, Tripp and Blair, The, 2514
Rackoff, Nancy L., 7966, 8228
Ractliffe, Wende B., 7102
Ractliffe, Wende Biggs, 7102
RAD Investments Inc., 8893
Radandt, Andre, 2743
Radandt, Andre M., 2743
Radandt, Lisa, 2743
Radar, Benjamin J., 6070
Radar, Roger, 4523
Radcliffe, Steve, 9738
Rader, Benjamin, 9656
Rader, Greg C., 4813
Rader, Gregory C., 4813
Rader, Kae, 1478
Rader, Welissa W., 4813
Radey, D. Neil, 5826
Radford, Nina, 8808
Radford, Phil, 6477
Radia, Suku, 3420
Radiator Specialty Co., 7154
Radin, Amy, 5629
Radin, Edward, 6722
Radin, Edward C., III, 6754
Radine, Gary D., 458
RadiOhio, Inc., 7719
Radler 2000, 9118
Radler 2000 Limited Partnership, 9118
Radler, Geoff, 9118
Radler, Graham C., 9118
Radler, Michael Evan, 9118
Radler, Michael G., 9118
Radler, Reinke, 9118
Radley, Jeanne R., 4963
Rado, Annette, 536
Rados, Stephan A., 1186
Radosevich, Rod, 4646
Radparvar, Wendy Milstein, 930
Radtke, Beth, 4926
Radtke, Catherine, 4580
Radtke, Edward, 4580
Radtke, Elizabeth, 4871
Radtke, Gerald W., 4355
Radtke, Janelle M., 4355
Radvan, Martin, 3244
Rae, Mimi, 4772
Rae, Nancy A., 4366
Rae, Wenche M., 1222
Raether, Paul E., 6673
Raether, Wendy S., 6673
Rafal, Alex, 9005
Rafal, Dyanne, 1563
Raff, Doug, 9591
Raff, Martin, 504
Raffa, Alec J., 7580
Raffa, Louise M., 7580
Raffel, Corey, 1619
Raffel, Kathleen Keefe, 1619
Rafferty, Emily, 5734
Rafferty, Stephen J., 4966
Raffin, Margaret, 730
Raft 1999 Charitable Lead Annuity Trust, 8519
Raft 2003 Charitable Lead Annuity Trust, 8519
Raft Charitable Foundation, 8519
Raftery, Betsy K., 1657
Raftis, Theresa, 5750
Raga, Tom, 7429
Ragains, Ronald J., 3393
Ragan, John, 9126
Ragauss, Peter A., 8679
Rager, R. Russell, 8663
Ragin, Shirley, 5532
Ragland, Cynthia, 992
Ragland, John, 3362
Ragland, W. Trent, III, 7273
Ragland, W. Trent, Jr., 7273
Ragon, Phillip T., 4228
Ragon, Susan M., 4228
Ragone, Daniel J., 8252
Ragone, David V., 6398
Ragusa, Philip, 6024
RAH Limited Partnership, 7493
Rahal, William, 5216
Rahjes, Doyle D., 3518
Rahm, Susan Berkman, 3945
Rahn, James, 9880
Rahn, James C., 1387
Rahr, Stewart J., 6674
Raiff, Robert M., 6675
Raikes, Jeffrey S., 9708
Raikes, Patricia M., 9708
Rail Investment Co., 9496
Railsback, R. Sherman, 330
Raim, Nina Ellenbogen, Dr., 2235
Rainbolt, David, 7766
Rainbolt, David E., 7781
Rainbolt, H.E. Gene, 7742
Rainbolt-Forbes, Leslie, 7742
Rainbow Apparel Companies, 5768
Rainbow Store, Inc., 5768
Rainer Arnhold Trust, 952
Rainer Fruit, 3245
Raines, Ann Haggerty, 8136
Raines, Jodee Fishman, 4415
Raines, Karol Willy, 3249
Raines, Valerie, 7721
Rainey, Craig L., 7814
Rainey, David, 197
Rainey, Esther S., 2418, 2419
Rainey, Gregory P., 1644
Rainey, Robert M., 8478
Rainger, Charles W., 7444
Rainin Charitable Lead Annuity Trust 1, Kenneth, 1051
Rainin Charitable Lead Annuity Trust 2, Kenneth, 1051
Rainin Charitable Lead Annuity Trust 3, Kenneth, 1051
Rainin, Jennifer Anne, 1051
Rainin, Kenneth, 1051
Raining Data US, Inc., 7638
Rains, Cameron, 3781
Rainwater, Courtney E., 9119
Rainwater, Matthew J., 9119
Rainwater, R. Todd, 9119
Rainwater, Richard, 8903
Rainwater, Richard E., 8488, 9119
Rainwater, Walter James, Jr., 9119
Raisbeck, James D., 9709
Raisbeck, Sherry L., 9709
Raitt, John, 2910
Raitt, Mary, 2910
Raja, Atul, 1294
Rajakulendran, Jerry, 2615
Rajchenbach, Jack, 3103
Rajchenbach, Judith, 3103
Rajen, Jaswa, 2271
Raker, Tim, 4461
Rakhlin, Serge, 701
Rakoczy, Mary J,, 6966
Rakofsky, Steven M., 8934
Rakow, Thomas S., 2818
Rakowich, Walter C., 1485
Raleigh Linen Svc., Inc., 2444
Rales, Joshua B., 1942
Rales, Mitchell P., 1942, 9513
Rales, Norman R., 1942
Rales, Steven M., 1942, 7424
Rall, Gina H., 2033
Rallo, Eduardo, 1166
Ralmondi, Josephine A., 1741
Ralph Lauren Media Polo.com, 6651
Ralsten, John, 9789
Ralston Purina Co., 4948
Ralston Purina Trust Fund, 2824
Ralston, Aaron, 3456
Ralston, Craig, 1489
Ralston, Hugh J., 549
Ralston, Jeannie, 8938
Ralston, Mary E., 3456
Ramaker, Dave, 4502
Ramaker, David, 4407
Ramanathan, Prakash, 6286
Ramdas, Kavita, 6723
Ramer, Daniel E., 7620
Ramer, Heber, 3542
Ramer, Jarrod, 3359
Ramill, Arthur C., Jr., 7891
Ramirez, Agustin A., Jr., 9926
Ramirez, M. Carmen, 1287

Ramirez, Maria Fiorini, 5718
Ramirez, Rebecca Page, 9926
Ramirez, Tawnya, 1387
Ramlo, Randy A., 3485
Ramming, James Christopher, 4314
Ramming, Shari, 8873
Ramnath, Marna, 7572
Ramos, Pedro, 8107
Ramos, Yulian, 6888
Ramoth, Diana, 88
Ramp, Steve, Dr., 4829
Rampone, David F., 8432
Ramsay, Betsy, 2414
Ramsay, Doug, Dr., 7585
Ramsay, Nonie B., 294, 296
Ramsay, Susan, 1405
Ramsay-Naile, Ashley, 24
Ramsburg, J. Ray, III, 3758
Ramsdell, Joe, 229
Ramsey, Bob, 90
Ramsey, Caroline, 7490
Ramsey, David L., III, 8621
Ramsey, Douglas T., 9460
Ramsey, George, 3282
Ramsey, Henry, Jr., Hon., 1088
Ramsey, Margaret, 4056
Ramsey, MariBen, 8676
Ramsey, Paul G., 6414
Ramsey, Robert J., 3972
Ramsey, Sammy Joe, 8980
Ramsey, Sandy, 2018
Ramsey, Sharon, 8621
Ramstad, Edie, 4730
Ramstad, Peter M., 4780
Ramunno, Charles A., 1437
Ramunno, Lou, 7640
Ranch Fiduciary Corp., 7493
Rancho Road Development, 5982
Rancho Santa Fe Thrift, 8070
Rand Realty and Development Co., 3084
Rand-Whitney Packaging Corp., 4128
Randa Accessories Leather Goods, 6676
Randa Corp., 6676
Randa Luggage, 6676
Randall Charitable Remainder Trust, Keith H., 1085
Randall Group, Inc., The, 7883
Randall Realty Corp., 7883
Randall, Brenda, 7883
Randall, Eleanor, 1054
Randall, Gail T., 3921
Randall, Glenn, 3955
Randall, James H., 1054
Randall, Kay Marie Boissicat, 1085
Randall, Keith H., 1085
Randall, Marcia H., 7883
Randall, Robert, 5093
Randall, Robert D., 7883
Randall-Mach, Cheryl, 3929
Randel, Don Michael, 5747
Randel, Jane, 5976
Randel, Vickie, 3509
Randhawa, Jessie, 9767
Randjelovic, Slobodan, 5608
Randle, Kathryn A., 2019
Randles, Steven G., 7585
Randmand, Ken, 1201
Randolph, Carter, Dr., 7590
Randolph, Guy, Jr., 7590
Randolph, James R., 7638
Randolph, Jane R., 7590
Randolph, Peter B., Dr., 3971
Randolph, Robert M., 4218
Randolph, Strother, 2525
Randolph, Whitney, 9135
Random, Cindee L., 2019
Rands, Amelia R., 4229
Rands, Robert D., 4229
Randt, Virginia, 6155, 6156
Randy Weil Trust, 262
Raneri, Stephanie A., 7014
Range, Larry, 4583
Rangel, Mary, 4438
Ranger Investments, L.P., 5884
Ranger, Michael W., 8243
Ranger, Thomas F., 4337
Ranger, Virginia R., 8243
Rangos, Alexander, 8244
Rangos, Jenica, 8244
Rangos, Jill, 8244
Rangos, John G., Jr., 8244
Rangos, John G., Sr., 8244
Rangwalla, Jaimin, 5791
Rani, Uma, 219
Ranier, Drew, 3651
Ranier, Gialberto, 4366
Ranjani, Rakesh, 686
Rankin, Beth O., 7406
Rankin, Evelyn Gordy, 2472
Rankin, R. Alex, 3563
Rankin, Richard E., Jr., Dr., 7179
Rankin, Susan B., 3902
Rankin, Thomas S., 4846
Ranney, Ann P., 7499
Ranney, George A., Jr., 2831
Ranney, Phillip A., 7667
Ransing Trust, Ruben and Elizabeth, 5514
Ransom Irrevocable Trust, Christiana, 3240
Ransom, Christiana L., 3240
Ransom, Earl, 3240
Ransom, Gail, 9701
Ransom, Mark, 3279
Ranton, Ashley M., 9028
Rantz, Michael G., 6678
Rantz, Paula Anne, 6678
Ranzetta, Tim, 581
Rao, Amy, 1125
Rao, Pravin, 3061
Rapaport, Jonathan, 4230
Rapaport, Marvin, 382
Raphael, Bob, 9715
Rapier, George M., III, 9121
Rapier, Hutson Hardwick, 9121
Rapier, Kymberly Ann, 9121
Rapoport, Audre, 9122
Rapoport, Bernard, 9122
Rapoport, Bernard O., 6395
Rapoport, Emily, 9122
Rapoport, Patricia, 9122
Rapoport, Ronald B., 9122
Rapp, Derek K., 4945
Rapp, Kathleen, 3447
Rapp, Marcia, 4447
Rappaport, Alan H., 1687, 6623
Rappaport, Jerome Lyle, 4230
Rappaport, Jill P., 6623
Rappaport, Jim, 4230
Rappaport, Nancy, 4230
Rappaport, Phyllis, 4230
Rappleyea, Holly, 6191
Rappuhn, Terry, 8591
Raps Industries, LLP, 1151
Rapson, Rip, 4479
Rardin, Jacob C., IV, 5893
Rasanen, Andrew, 5724
Rasch, Jennifer, 7357
Rashford, John, Dr., 2800
Raskin, Roy, 5824
Raskin, Shelley, 5824
Raskind, Peter E., 7509
Raskob, Christopher R., 1845
Raskob, Helena, 1845
Raskob, J. Max, 1845
Raskob, John J., 1845
Raskob, Kathleen, 5511
Raskob, Richard G., 1845
Raskob, T. Mark, 1845
Raskob, Timothy T., 1845
Raskopf, Karen, 4026
Rasmuson, Cathryn, 89
Rasmuson, Edward, 82
Rasmuson, Edward B., 89
Rasmuson, Elmer, 7293
Rasmuson, Elmer E., 89
Rasmuson, Jenny, 89
Rasmuson, Judy, 89
Rasmuson, Mary Louise, 89
Rasmussen, Anna, 4231
Rasmussen, Astrid Kann, 6679
Rasmussen, Hans Kann, 6679
Rasmussen, Jay, 9356
Rasmussen, Jessie, 5027
Rasmussen, Judy, 2645
Rasmussen, Kristian Kann, 6679
Rasmussen, Kristin, 4802
Rasmussen, Neil, 4231
Rasmussen, Paul E., 4765
Rasmussen, Stephen S., 7587
Rasmussen, Steven, 8541
Rasmussen, Teresa J., 9956
Rasmussen, Tom, 3757
Rasor, Linda, 8660
Raspberry, Jim, 4829
Rassas, Theresa, 3166
Rastin, Thomas, 7377
Rasulo, Jay, 467
Ratchford, David, 7179
Ratchford, Eleanor Knobloch, 8965
Ratcliff, Mike, RADM., 8179
Ratcliffe, Carole R., 2278
Ratcliffe, David M., 2514
Ratcliffe, Philip E., 2278
Ratcliffe, Richard, 7742
Rateliff, Charles, 186
Rath, Kimberly, 5072
Rath, Tom, 9652
Rath, V. Duane, 9927
Rathbone, John P., 9496
Rathbun, Sherry, 5076
Rathbun-Gunn, Betsy, 9375
Rathburn, Richard, 4393
Rathert, Terry W., 9060
Rathjen, Carolyn P., 9092
Rathmann, George, 3867
Rathmann, James Louis, 3867
Rathmann, Joy, 3867
Rathmann, Laura Jean, 3867
Rathmann, Margaret Crosby, 3867
Rathmann, Richard G., 3867
Rathmann-Noonan, Alexandra Joy, 3867
Ratliff, A.M., 9514
Ratliff, Troy, 2953
Ratner, Albert, 7626
Ratner, Albert B., 7626
Ratner, Audrey, 1691, 7626
Ratner, Brian, 7626
Ratner, Charles A., 1846
Ratner, Chuck, 1846
Ratner, Dennis F., 9515
Ratner, Donald, 3186
Ratner, Ilana Horowitz, 1846
Ratner, James A., 7406
Ratner, Jeffrey, 351
Ratner, Mathew, 1847
Ratner, Sarah, 1847
Ratner, Warren A., 9515
Rattner 2000 LT Trust, Steven, The, 6680
Rattner, Amy, 1805
Rattner, Andrew, 1805
Rattner, Justin, 7853
Rattner, Mark, 5589
Rattner, Steven L., 6680
Ratzlaff, Cyndi, 3534
Rau, Anita, 8775
Rau, John, 2791, 3010
Rau, Steven G., 1301
Rauch, Louis J., 6681
Rauch, Philip, 6681
Rauch, Philip J., 6681
Rauch, Philip J., Jr., 6681
Rauch, Ruth T., 6681
Raucher, Dana, 5715
Raudenbush, Stephen, 3171
Rauenhorst, Gerald, 4664
Rauenhorst, Gia, 4614
Rauenhorst, Jeff, 4763
Rauenhorst, Joe, 4731
Rauenhorst, Joseph J., 4664
Rauenhorst, Kristine, 8518
Rauenhorst, Kristine W., 4763
Rauenhorst, Loretta, 8518
Rauenhorst, Mark, 4664
Rauenhorst, Mark H., 4731
Rauenhorst, Matt, 4664
Rauenhorst, Matthew G., 4614
Rauenhorst, Michael, 8518
Rauert, Kent, 5098
Rauh, James M., 7156
Rauner, Bruce V., 3105
Rauner, Diana M., 3105
Rauscher, D. Lea, 1166
Rauscher, Leslie C., 8809
Rausing Trust, Sigrid, 5514
Rautenberg Trust, Erwin, 1056
Rauter, Kristie, 9867
Rauzi, Robert L., 7413
Rav-Noy, Varda, 1057
Rav-Noy, Zeev, 1057
Rava, Susan R., 4894
Ravarino, Helen, 4960
Ravarino, Mirella, 4960
Ravenel, Ramsay, 4077
Ravenscroft, Gretchen F., 125
Ravenscroft, Robert B., 125
Raver, Bill, 1110
Raver, C. Cybele, 3171
Raver, Mark, 3391
Ravitich, Donald N., 1857
Ravitz Revocable Living Trust, Edward, The, 4526
Ravitz, Edward, 4526
Ravitz, Robert, 6103
Rawins, Randa, 4971
Rawl, Julian, 7214
Rawley, Joe, 7231
Rawley, Stanley T., 3106
Rawlings and Assocs., PLLC, 2279
Rawlings Co., LLC, The, 2279
Rawlings, Beverly S., 2279
Rawlings, George R., 2279
Rawlings, Herbert M., 2279
Rawlings, Jane L., 1504

Rawlings, John, 2279
Rawlings, Lynn D., 4931
Rawlings, Steve, 4448
Rawlinson, Marion Clapp, 9682
Rawlinson, Maureen E., 359
Rawlinson, Rex J., 359
Rawls, Kaki, 2015
Rawls, S. Waite, III, 9399
Ray Foundation, Rachael, 674
Ray Plastic, Inc., 2208
Ray, Adele Richardson, 1679
Ray, Adele Rirchardson, 1679
Ray, Chester, 4334
Ray, Christine N., 9048
Ray, Christopher, 9053
Ray, Cynthia Sineath, 7979
Ray, Gilbert T., 664
Ray, Gloria S., 8634
Ray, H., 777
Ray, Helen, 2525
Ray, James Widener, 9711
Ray, Jim, 3320
Ray, Lisa, 186
Ray, Louise, 3253
Ray, R.H., 9399
Ray, Rob, 5726
Ray, Ronald D., 8930
Ray, Tabitha, 8775
Ray, Teresa, 3319
Ray, Tom, 9704
Ray, William K., 4811
Rayl, Anabeth, 3391
Rayl, Kristina, 1774
Rayle, Terry, 3295
Raymer, James H., 9501
Raymo, Greg, 4768
Raymond Charitable Lead Trust, Mary R., 155
Raymond Foundation, Robert, Inc., 155
Raymond James Trust Co., 2269
Raymond, Bob, 9149
Raymond, Carolyn M., 8169
Raymond, Dawn, 7349
Raymond, Elizabeth K., 155
Raymond, Jim W., 9146
Raymond, Jonathan, 1225
Raymond, Mary R., 155
Raymond, Robert, 155
Raymond, Scott H., 3497
Raymond, Shirley, 3314
Rayner, Carolyn K., 4807
Raynes, Martin, 5496
Raynolds, Robert, Dr., 1530
Raynor, Gene, 3880
Raynor, Geoffrey P., 9070
Raynor, Kim, 9070
Rayonier Inc., 2281
Raza, Syed K., 224
RB Associates, LLC, 5937
RB Nordick Foundation, The, 7846
RBC Capital Markets Corp., 4748
RBC Dain Rauscher Corp., 4748
RBC Dain Rauscher Inc., 1120
RBM Shopping Centers, Inc., 8605
RBS Citizens, N.A., 8374, 8406, 8432
RCI North American, 7214
RCK Properties, 2852
RCS II, LLC, 9534
RDV Foundation, 4541
Rea, Bayard D., 5892
Rea, Jeffrey, 3289
Rea, Nancy, 4316
Reabold, Melissa, 3761
Read 2009 Qtip Trust, 2240
Read Trust, Isabel Collier, 2240
Read, Charlie H., 8887
Read, Cheryl, 8582
Read, Gilan M., 999
Read, James P., Jr., 999
Read, Lauren Rispone, 3662
Read, Roger T., 7420
Read, William A., 111
Readey, B. John, III, 4990
Reagan, Richard S., 6564
Real Page, 9606
Reali, Heidi, 6658
Realnetworks Foundation, 9652
RealNetworks, Inc., 9712
Realty Investment Company, Inc., 3756
Reams, Fred W., 8493
Reams, Karen A., 8493
Reams, Matthew D., 8493
Reardon, Daniel C., 4620
Reardon, Edward J., II, 4871
Reardon, Joseph F., 4920
Reardon, Michael D., 5072
Reardon, Michele, 8257
Reardon, Robert P., 3972
Reaud, Jon A., 9124
Reaud, Wayne A., 9124
Reaume, Came, 4359
Reaves, Donald J., 8356
Reban, Alicia, 5108
Rebber, Stan, 3283
Rebelo, John G., Jr., 303
Rebholtz, Dorothy, 2640
Rebholtz, Thomas M., 2640
Rebmann, David, 9487
Rebozo, Charles F., 2282
Rebozo, Charles G., 2282
Rebozo, Michael, 2282
Rebozo, Thomas, Jr., 2282
Rebozo, William, Jr., 2282
Recasner, Anthony, 3656
Rechler, Bennett, 6682
Rechler, Beverley, 6682
Rechler, Deborah, 6799
Rechler, Morton, 6682
Rechler, Scott, 6799
Rechler-Newman, Yvetta, 6682
Rechnitz, Joan, 6541
Recht, Arthur M., 9772
Rechter, Ben R., 8550
Recinos, M. Suzette, 1581
Reckitt Benckiser Pharmaceuticals, Inc., 9516
Reckitt Benckiser PLC, 3201
Reckling, Isla C., 9203
Reckling, James S., 9203, 9243
Reckling, John B., 9203
Reckling, Stephen M., 9203, 9243
Reckling, T.R. "Cliff", IV, 9203
Reckling, T.R., III, 9203
Reckling, Thomas K., 9203
Reckseen, Donna, 846
Records, George, 7766
Records, Jeff, 7788
Records, Martha, 7788
Records, Nancy, 7788
Recreational Equipment Inc., 9713
Rector, Andrew, 8989
Rector, Ed, 4473
Rector, Jane, 8989
Rector, Linda, 8989
Rector, S.R., 9607
Recycled Paper Greetings, Inc., 2847
Red Man Charitable Trust, 7765
Red Wing Shoe Co., Inc., 4749
Redbeck Trust, Eleanor, 3556
Redd, Ellis S., 3402
Redd, Rainey D., 8015
Redden, D. Michael, 9046
Redden, Greg, 8333
Redden, Nigel, 8502
Redding, John P., 1555, 1556
Reddy, Lakshmi, 3396
Reddy, Lata N., 5415
Reddy, Madhava G., 4480
Reddy, Mina, 3971
Reddy, Prem, 461
Reddy, Prem N., 461
Reddy, Sobha, 4480
Reddy, Sunitha, 461
Reddy, Sushma, Dr., 4373
Redfern, Jerry L., 4947
Redford, Jan L., 9105
Redick, John R., 9405
Redlich, Catherine, 6188
Redman, Paula A., 7371
Redmond, Jerry, 4601
Redmond, Robin, 3100
Redpoint Management LLP, 1268
Redstone, Sumner M., 4233
Redwine, Morgan R., Jr., 2656
Redwood Contracting, 6205
Redwood, Yanique, 1894
Reebok International Ltd., 3303, 4234
Reece, Charlie, 9704
Reece, Heather K., 3135
Reece, Ken G., 7273
Reece, Patty, 2826
Reece, Sandra, 3135
Reece, Sandra M., 3135
Reece, Thomas L., 3135
Reed, Bruce, 347, 9664
Reed, Burton, 3271
Reed, Catharine N., 309
Reed, Charles C., 1270
Reed, Cynthia, 3109, 8429
Reed, Deanna, 2943
Reed, Donald E., 8200
Reed, Doug, 5019
Reed, Elaine, 7220
Reed, George, 7295
Reed, Glenn W., 8327
Reed, J. Brad, 8607
Reed, J. N., 4898
Reed, Jack, Sr., 4822
Reed, Jackie, 153
Reed, Jim, 3294
Reed, Joanne, 675
Reed, Joel, 2523
Reed, John S., 3109
Reed, Juanita, 2351
Reed, Julie, 4173
Reed, Kori E., 5029, 5030
Reed, Lawrence, 4528
Reed, Lee, 4347
Reed, Linda F., 2098
Reed, Marsha L., 467
Reed, Mary, 2768
Reed, Michael E., 2747
Reed, Michele, 3631
Reed, Rhoda Newberry, 4527
Reed, Robert, 921
Reed, Stacy, 2762
Reed, Susan, 7052
Reed, Sydney, 9341
Reed, Thomas, 7934
Reed, Thomas M., 9704
Reed, Winthrop B., III, 4966
Reeder, Mable Dorn, 2536
Reeder, Paul A., 4235
Reeder, Paul A., III, 4235
Reeder, Robert, 8229
Reeder, Ted, 3761
Reeder, William, 9280
Reedy, Jennifer Ford, 4621
Reeg, Chris, 500
Reeg, Linda A., 3641
Reen, Mary, 6552
Rees, John Nesbit, 8245
Rees, Nigel A., 903
Rees, Sarah Henne, 8245
Rees-Jones, Janice M., 9125
Rees-Jones, Trevor, 9125
Reese, Beth, 2400
Reese, Caleb F., 156
Reese, David E., 156
Reese, Eleanor Steele, 6915
Reese, Emmet P., 6915
Reese, Everett, 156
Reese, Everett D., 156
Reese, Everett D., II, 156
Reese, Gary W., 8685, 8688
Reese, J. Gilbert, 7540
Reese, Louise F., 156
Reese, Louise R., 156
Reese, Mauri, 396
Reese, Mike, 8776
Reese, Phyllis, 3846
Reese, Richard J., 9263
Reese, Tamela, 283
Reese, West, 283
Reese, William, 5190
Reeve, Brenda, 3554
Reeves, Bill, 7016
Reeves, Christy Oliver, 3615
Reeves, Helen F., 7627
Reeves, Hope, 6820
Reeves, J.E., Jr., 5420
Reeves, James C., 3249
Reeves, John E., III, 5420
Reeves, John E., Jr., 5420
Reeves, Katherine Mercer, 5420
Reeves, Katherine P., 9092
Reeves, Margaret J., 7627
Reeves, Marsha Y., 3726
Reeves, Olivia, 3403
Reeves, Robert K., 8661
Reeves, Samuel J., 7627
Reeves, Samuel T., 9470
Reeves, Steven, 3317
Reeves, William H., 2610
Reeves, William Huntington, 7016
Reffett, Terry L., 3578
Regal Energy LLC, 9001
Regal Entertainment Group, 8622
Regal Marine, 2283
Regal Marine Industries, Inc., 2283
Regan, Amy H., 5293
Regan, Andrew W., 2139
Regan, Ann, 3859
Regan, Barbara, 5618
Regan, Grace O'Neil, 3859
Regan, Harold, 7087
Regan, James S., 5293
Regan, James S., III, 5293
Regan, Jane, 3859
Regan, Kathleen, 5800
Regan, Mary, 3859
Regan, Michael J., 1144
Regan, Patrick H., 5293
Regan, William, 7281
Reganato, Joseph P., 6490
Regelbrugge, Laurie, 1935

Regen, Albert J., 6568
Regence Group, The, 7829
Regenstein, Helen, 3111
Regenstein, Joseph, 3111
Regenstein, Joseph, III, 3111
Regenstein, Susan L., 3111
Regents Park Trust, 2754
Reger, Gerald, 5801
Reger, James Randall, 4781
Reger, James Russell, 4781
Reger, Michael, 4781
Regiero, Angel, 9
Regino, Rita, 3809
Regions Bank, 11, 21, 26, 28, 43, 48, 53, 61, 72, 76, 3624, 4966, 8528
Regions Bank Trust Dept., 44, 2150
Regions Financial Corp., 61
Regions Morgan Keegan Trust, 61, 2269
Regions Trust Dept., 65
Regis Corp., 4750
Regis, Inc., 4750
Regnier, Robert D., 4920
Rehig, Cynthia J., 3249
Rehrig, Brian H., 4046
Rehwald, Rachel, 1151
Reich, Allan J., 2961
Reich, Carol F., 6666
Reich, David, 2688
Reich, Deborah, 6666
Reich, Elaine M., 6187
Reich, Harvey, 5247
Reich, Joseph H., 6666
Reich, Lawrence A., 2688
Reich, Seymour D., 6380
Reichard, James, 7214
Reichardt, Doug, 3420
Reiche, Nancy, 3992
Reichel, Aaron I., Rabbi, 5980
Reichel, Hillel, Rabbi, 5980
Reicher, Rita L., 5757
Reichert, Albert P., 2435
Reichert, Melissa McNair, 9017
Reichert, Robert, Mayor, 2533
Reichling, Jerald L., 3482
Reichman, Chaya, 6030
Reichman, Esther, 5759
Reichman, Harry, 6030
Reichman, John H., 5296
Reichman, Simon, 6030
Reid Survivors Trust, Jean, 3112
Reid, Bruce, 1933
Reid, Carter M., 9422
Reid, Christopher, 3583
Reid, Dan, 9588
Reid, Daniel, 7079
Reid, David F., 7439
Reid, Delia, 921
Reid, E. Lewis, 690
Reid, Elizabeth, 3971
Reid, Ella Hancock, 1060
Reid, Emilie, 78
Reid, J. Russell, 8776
Reid, Janet B., 7404
Reid, Jennifer, 8429
Reid, Lee, 3644
Reid, Lew, 420
Reid, Linda Bacon, 1370
Reid, Marjorie A., 3583
Reid, Miller David, 4840
Reid, R. Miller, 4840
Reid, Ralph, 3549
Reid, Robert J., 5528
Reid, Suzanne, 7649
Reid, Vernon A., Jr., 3865
Reid, Will J., 1060
Reiden, Tony Inder, 5946
Reidy, Anne Marie, 22
Reif, Mary Nell, 9834
Reifsteck, Shawn, 1131
Reign Print Soutions, 3201
Reilly, Dennis W., 387
Reilly, Edward A., 5912
Reilly, George, 4611
Reilly, Joanne S., 1757
Reilly, Joseph, 5182
Reilly, Mary Ann, 2040
Reilly, Rosemary, 1504
Reilly, Thom, 5106
Reilly, Ulla, 998
Reilly, William, II, 2766
Reily Foods Co., 3661
Reily, Robert D., 3661
Reily, William B., III, 3661
Reiman, Eric M., 111
Reiman, Roberta M., 9929
Reiman, Roy J., 9929
Reiman, Scott J., 9929
Reimer, Doug, 4691
Reimers, Arthur J., III, 6371
Reimers, Caitlin L., 6371
Reimers, Lindsay J.H., 6371
Reimers, Megan C., 6371
Reimers, Sarah E.M., 6371
Rein, Harry, 1650
Rein, Susan, 1650
Reinalt-Thomas Corp., 170
Reinalt-Thomas Corporation, 118
Reinberger, Clarence T., 7628
Reinberger, Louise F., 7628
Reinberger, William C., 7628
Reindl, Dana, 7788
Reinecke, David W., 9945
Reiner, John P., 6389
Reiner, Robert M., 3884
Reinertson, Tara, 1774
Reingold, Daniel, 5964
Reinhard, Ian, 1061
Reinhard, Myra, 1061
Reinhard, Neil, 1061
Reinhardt, J. Alec, 7453
Reinhardt, Richard, 517
Reinhart Enterprises, D.B., 9930
Reinhart Institutional Foods, 9930
Reinhart Partners, 9916
Reinhart Revocable Trust, Marjorie A., 9930
Reinhart, Carmen, Dr., 1679
Reinhart, James E., 2514
Reinhart, Leon, 888
Reinhart, M.H., 7967
Reinhart, Marjorie A., 9930
Reinhart, Myron H., 9517
Reinhart, Peter S., 5232
Reinhart, Randlyn, 888
Reinhart, William L., 9517
Reinharz, Jehuda, 6981
Reinhold, Henry, 6179
Reiniche, Dominique, 2428
Reinis, Richard G., 596
Reinke, Donald, 490
Reinke, Kristin, 615
Reinking, Craig, 9833
Reinsch 2009 Charitable Lead Annuity Trust, Dolores G., 9518
Reinsch Charitable Lead Annuity Trust 2, Dolores G., 9518
Reinsch Charitable Lead Annuity Trust, Dolores G., 9518
Reinsch Foundation, Emergon G. & Dolores G., 9518
Reinsch, Lola C., 9518
Reinstadler, Ruppert, 7893
Reintzel, Warren A., 8329
Reis & Chandler, Inc., 1062
Reis, Curtis S., 1062
Reis, Jerry D., 9214
Reis, Judson, 6093
Reis, Kevin Michael, 9206
Reis, Kyle C., 1062
Reis, L. Sanford, 1062
Reis, Pamela P., 1062
Reis, Pamela Petre, 1062
Reischman, Ann, 7721
Reischman, Anna A., 9055
Reischmann, Janis A., 2601
Reischour, Patricia, 6636
Reiser, Blake, 5311
Reiser, Hans, 581
Reiser, Margaret C., 2477
Reiser, Robert E., Jr., 2477
Reisman, Barbara, 5441
Reisman, Dorothy, 6686
Reisman, Lonny, 1531
Reisman, Marshall M., 6686
Reiss, Helene, 6687
Reiss, Mahir A., 6687
Reiss, Vicki, 6850
Reissner, James, 4744
Reister, Ruth, 4787
REIT Management Corp. 401K, 6089
REIT Management Corp. Pension, 6089
Reiten, Pat, 7877
Reiter, Bernard, 828
Reiter, Cody N., 4802
Reiter, Hayley M., 4802
Reiter, Kyle W., 4802
Reiter-Faragalli, Robin, 2263
Reitermann, Michael, 5454
Reith, John H., 661
Reithmeier, Roger, 2766
Reitz, Peter, 2752
Reitz, Sidney A., 3533
Reitz, Susan N., 3533
Reitz, Susy, 3540
ReliaStar Bankers Security Life Insurance Co., 7038
ReliaStar Financial Corp., 7038
ReliaStar Life Insurance Co., 7038
ReliaStar United Services Life Insurance Co., 7038
Remala, Rao V., 9714
Remala, Satya K., 9714
ReMax of Georgia, 6042
Rembe, Toni, 1283
Remey, Don, 1518
Remick, John D., 4751
Remick, Robert, 4751
Remillard, Arthur J., III, 4236
Remillard, Arthur J., Jr., 4236
Remillard, Regan P., 4236
Remillard, Robert P., 4236
Remmey, Virginia Hintz, 2911
Remo, Dee Ann, 9416, 9521
Remondi, Dorothy A., 4237
Remondi, John F., 4237
Remondi, John J., 4237
Remondi, Stephen A., 4237
Renaissance Charitable Foundation, Inc., 4458, 9652
Renard, Henry P., 6275
Renard, James S., 8705
Renard, Sabine, 6275
Renda, Susan, 9487
Render, Cecilia H., 7596
Rendulic, Mark, 5979
Renfert, Blaine, 9897
Renfield, Beatrice, 6688
Renfield, Joseph, 6688
Renfield, Robert, 6688
Renfield-Miller, D. Carrington, 6688
Renfield-Miller, Jean, 6688
Renfro, John F., Jr., 8485
Renfro, Robert, 2645
Rengel, Paula J., 7444
Renjen, Punit, 1572
Renken, Keith W., 1270
Renkes, Dean A., 9229
Rennebohm, Oscar, 9931
Rennels, Deborah, 5710
Rennels, Kathay, 1393
Renner, Christopher, 1578
Renner, Jill, 1578
Renner, Sue, 1459, 1460
Renner, Todd, 1578
Renner, Tom, 860
Renner, Trevor, 1578
Renner, Troy A., 8520
Rennert, Ari E.Y.M., 6772
Rennert, Ingeborg, 6772
Rennert, Ira Leon, 6772
Rennie, Renate, 6983
Renoux, Kelly, 1511
Renovitch, Sheila, 5976
Renschler, Scott, 3756
Renshaw, Jeannette W., 4309
Renshaw, Judith S., 9990
Renterghem, Lemont, 4452
Rentrop, Gary, 4337
Rentschler, Bryan, 5093
Rentschler, Thomas, Jr., 7481
Rentz, Becky, 8774
Renuart, Victor Eugene, Jr., Genl., 1406
Renwick, Glenn M., 7623
Renzi, Jude, 6567
Repass, Rob, 8676
Repensek, Jane, 9731
Repine, John E., 1376
Repole, Maria A., 6563
Repole, Michael, 6563
Repp, Chris, 9414
Reppas, John, Dr., 3232
Repplinger, William M., 1419
Republic Die & Tool Co., 5356
Resch, Marion G., 7629
Research Corporation Technologies, Inc., 103
Reseign, Christopher E., 6621
Residential Warranty Corp., 8212
ResMed Inc., 1063
Resnansky, Kristin, 6609
Resnick & Sons, Jack, Inc., 5660
Resnick Charitable Trust No. 2, Jack and Pearl, 6689
Resnick Family Foundation, Inc., 1064
Resnick, Burton P., 6689
Resnick, Eric, 1518
Resnick, Ira M., 6690
Resnick, Judith B., 6689
Resnick, Judith P., 6689
Resnick, Lynda, 927
Resnick, Lynda R., 1064
Resnick, Paula S., 6690
Resnick, Stewart A., 579, 1064
Resnik, Denise, 92
Resnik, Leslie, 7584
Ressler, Alison, 1065

Ressler, Antony, 1066
Ressler, April, 7971
Ressler, Richard, 1065
Restrepo, Robert P., 7674
Restuccia, Robert, 3953
Results Direct Marketing, 8834
Retail Apparel Service Corp., 5446
Retail Credit Co., 2455
Reth Trust, Eva, 7906
Retsinas, Nicolas, 9435
Rett Syndrome Research Foundation, 3833
Retta, Hector, 9083
Rettaliata, Caryl Pucci, 3099
Rettenmier, Ross, 9616, 9617
Retter, Betty, 6745
Retter, Daniel, 6745
Retter, Marcus, 6745
Retter, Ronny S., 3738
Retting, Don, 7607
Rettler, Tom, 9903
Reuben-Cooke, Wilhelmina M., 7195
Reuland, Timothy J., 2767
Reusch, Belinda, 6396
Reuss, Henry, 8247
Reuss, Mark L., 4442
Reuter, David, 8613
Reutter, Randall C., 3436
Reveley, W. Taylor, III, 6470
Revelle, Charles L., III, 7303
Revelle, Geoffrey, 9684
Revels, Carey, 4811
Revere, Elspeth A., 2989
Revolution Studios, 6904
Revson, Charles H., 6693
Revson, Charles H., Jr., 6693
Reward Oil, 3208
Rewinski, Jon L., 956
Rex Veneer Co., 7835
Rex, Ben, 8468
Rex, Gloria Ortega, 2032
Rexnord Industries LLC, 9932
Rexon, Robert, 5275
Rey, Lilli J., 1067
Rey-Hernandez, Cesar A., 8353
Rey-Murphy, Ramona, 643
Reyes, Anne N., 3114
Reyes, Elsie, 9773
Reyes, J. Christopher, 3114
Reyes, Jerome, 8462
Reyes, Juan J., 8353
Reyes, Lori W., 3239
Reyes, M. Jude, 3239
Reykdal, Chris, 9600
Reymond, Inez O., 9243
Reyna Foundation, Claudio, The, 5967
Reynolds American, 7296
Reynolds Irrevocable Trust, David P., 9519
Reynolds Tobacco Co., R.J., 7296
Reynolds Trust, Robert J., 1848
Reynolds, A. Sheffield, 8438
Reynolds, Alice, 78
Reynolds, Andrea L., 5808
Reynolds, Bobbie Ann, 2481
Reynolds, Brian, 919
Reynolds, C. Lockwood, 9537
Reynolds, David P., 9519
Reynolds, Diane, 8736
Reynolds, Dianne, 22
Reynolds, Donald W., 5143
Reynolds, Dudley C., 32
Reynolds, Edith, 1566
Reynolds, Emily J., 8634
Reynolds, Fairfax, 7180
Reynolds, Gerald A., 3586
Reynolds, Golda, 3376
Reynolds, Janet L., 7377
Reynolds, John, 713
Reynolds, Jonathan, 1578, 8763
Reynolds, Julia L., 9519
Reynolds, Kate B., 7297
Reynolds, Kaye, 2459
Reynolds, Kent, 8763
Reynolds, Kent, Mrs., 8763
Reynolds, Larry, 5062
Reynolds, Laura Caro, 6694
Reynolds, Libby Holman, 4238
Reynolds, Marshall T., 1773
Reynolds, Mary B., 4308
Reynolds, Nancy R., 1880
Reynolds, Nancy S., 7298
Reynolds, Pamela, 1537, 7860
Reynolds, Pearl G., 4961
Reynolds, Philip R., 1547
Reynolds, Randolph N., 9519
Reynolds, Richard J., III, 7299
Reynolds, Richard J., Jr., 2546, 7298
Reynolds, Richard M., 4549
Reynolds, Richard S., III, 9519
Reynolds, Robert H., 3361
Reynolds, Robert J., 877
Reynolds, Robert L., 6694
Reynolds, Sigrid S., 9537
Reynolds, Thillia, 3271
Reynolds, Timothy T., 7806
Reynolds, W. Ann, 2041
Reynolds, W. Noah, 7298
Reynolds, William N., 7298
Reynolds-Cane, Dianne L., 9416
Rezendes, Vic, 3762
RF Investors, LLC, 2323
RFP Sr. 1982 Irrev Trust, 4254
Rhea, Martha, 3540
Rhea, Randall R., 9415
Rheault, Wendy, 2900
Rhee, Barbara R., 6343
Rhee, John, 6343
Rhine, Diane F., 5394
Rhines, Steven, 7780
Rhinesmith, Steffanie, 3301, 3397
Rhino LP, Black, 9226
Rhoades, Alice, 3253
Rhoades, Hazel T., 3115
Rhoades, Mary, 9137
Rhoades, Otto L., 3115
Rhoades, Scott, 1127
Rhoads Jr. Charitable Lead Annuity Trust, Jay, 8248
Rhoads Jr. f/b/o P.F. Young Charitable Remainder Unitrust, Jay, 8248
Rhoads Trust, Jay R., Jr., 8248
Rhoads, Jennifer, 9603
Rhoads, Katheryn V., 2908
Rhoads, Paul K., 2908
Rhoads, Samuel V., 8267
Rhode Island Foundation, The, 8391
Rhodehamel, William A., 3319
Rhodenbaugh, Laura, 3520
Rhodes, Adam J., 1349
Rhodes, Bryce W., 1349
Rhodes, Carleen K., 4616, 4715, 4757
Rhodes, Charlotte, 8660
Rhodes, Emery W., 1349
Rhodes, Greg, 9605
Rhodes, Jack, 9832
Rhodes, Marcia A., 4975, 4976
Rhodes, Robert, 7564
Rhodes, Winifred W., 1349
Rhome, Joan W., 8338
RHP, Inc., 6615
Rhymes, Josephine, 4821
Rhynes, Lisa, 7808
Rhynhart, Erich, 4282
Riband, Herb F., 4712
Riccardi, Michael, 1711
Ricchuiti, Anthony, 5838
Ricchuito, David A., 8209
Ricci, A. Leo, 1643
Ricci, Arthur O., 4247
Ricci, Joann, 3656
Ricci, Shawn A., 9550
Ricciardi, Louis M., 3960
Riccobene, Mary, 9784
Rice, Ada, 3116
Rice, Arthur, 9716
Rice, Arthur L., Jr., 9716
Rice, Bill, 7990
Rice, Carolyn, 2479
Rice, Charles L., Jr., 3656
Rice, Christopher B., 9168
Rice, Daniel F., 3116
Rice, Derica W., 3340
Rice, Edward Hart, 6696
Rice, Elizabeth, 5533
Rice, Emily, 4109
Rice, Eve Hart, 6696
Rice, Gina, 9520
Rice, Gwendolyn M., 3079
Rice, Hanna O., 2386
Rice, Henry F., 2617
Rice, Henry Hart, 6696
Rice, Jeffery, 2039
Rice, Jim, 9999
Rice, Joanne, 9147
Rice, John, 1650, 8035
Rice, John G., 1591
Rice, Joseph A., 6116
Rice, Katherine D., 4677
Rice, Kathryn, 6802
Rice, Lela G., 4862
Rice, Leona Egeland, 471
Rice, Linda, 7777
Rice, Linda M., 9448
Rice, Lois Dickson, 6115
Rice, Lynn D., 9716
Rice, Margaret S., 6696
Rice, Martin, 6802
Rice, Mary E., 4677
Rice, Mary H., 4677
Rice, Molly E., 4677
Rice, Nell M., 7224
Rice, Norm B., 9595
Rice, Pat, 1650
Rice, Paul, 9520
Rice, Robert R., 2386
Rice, Terrie L., 7501, 7641
Rice, Tim, 7429
Rice, Ulysses, Deacon, 1879
Riceberg, Louis J., 384
Ricedorf, Charles W., 8272
Rich & Co., D.W., Inc., 1600
Rich Products Corp., 6697
Rich's, Inc., 2537
Rich, Barbara, 5845
Rich, David A., Jr., 4845
Rich, David A., Sr., 4845
Rich, David Barrett, 3948
Rich, Grace E., 4845
Rich, Harvey S., 5357
Rich, Ivor, 2135
Rich, Jack, 8774
Rich, Linda, 2123, 3249
Rich, MaryLisabeth, 7307
Rich, Melinda, 6697
Rich, Randy, 1034
Rich, Robert E., 7485
Rich, Robert E., Jr., 6697
Rich, Robert E., Sr., 6697
Rich, Robert S., 1364
Rich, Stuart, 7963
Rich, Suzy, 3279
Rich, Terry, 3249
Rich, Zan McKenna, 8166
Richard Associates, 3773
Richard T. Clark Living Trust, Jr., 8048
Richard, Alison, 5783
Richard, Alison F., Dame, 3818
Richard, D. Eugene, 472
Richard, Duayne, 3623
Richard, Robert J., 3490
Richard, Ronald B., 7406
Richards Charitable Trust, Mary Lea Johnson, 1985
Richards, Avis, 6699
Richards, Bob, 1263
Richards, Brian F., 2863
Richards, Bruce, 6699
Richards, Carol A., 348
Richards, Cecile, 5994
Richards, Charles, 6408
Richards, Christopher R., 9517
Richards, Cynthia, 5622
Richards, Cynthia R., 9517
Richards, David, 9221
Richards, David K., 348
Richards, Edgar G., 1697
Richards, Elizabeth, 2440
Richards, Eric, 7807, 7819
Richards, Erin, 4314
Richards, Florence, 1697
Richards, Gail, 3330, 7818, 7819
Richards, Grahame, 7912, 8138
Richards, James R., 9474
Richards, James W., 282
Richards, Jennifer, 4342
Richards, John W., III, 2538
Richards, John W., Jr., 2538
Richards, Jose E. Fernandez, 8352
Richards, Larry, 7902
Richards, Laura, 4512
Richards, Mabel Wilson, 1068
Richards, Martha S., 7871
Richards, Martin, 7139
Richards, Michael S., 9221
Richards, Nancy, 2538
Richards, Nancy T., 9221
Richards, Rachael K., 2641
Richards, Rebecca, 7819
Richards, Ron, 116
Richards, Roy, 2539
Richards, Roy, Jr., 2539
Richards, Thomas S., 6722
Richards, William Earl, 62
Richardson Carbon and Gasoline Co., Sid, 8686
Richardson Foundation Inc., Smith, 6532
Richardson Foundation, Smith, 7301
Richardson Jr. Charitable Lead Trust, L., 7232
Richardson, Anne S., 9131
Richardson, Barbara, 2658, 9600
Richardson, Barbara B., 7184
Richardson, Chester A., 2603
Richardson, Christine, 1394

Richardson, Connie, 3418
Richardson, Curtis R., 1473
Richardson, Danforth K., 8096
Richardson, David M., 2356
Richardson, Dean, 7915
Richardson, Eudora L., 7232
Richardson, Frank E., 6700
Richardson, Frank E., III, 6700
Richardson, Gale, 9109
Richardson, Grace Jones, 1679, 7301
Richardson, H. Smith, 7300
Richardson, H.S., Sr., 1679
Richardson, James, 4087
Richardson, James Lunsford, 7232
Richardson, Janie D., 3624
Richardson, Jannie, 1478
Richardson, Jeffrey, 2559
Richardson, Jill, 3298
Richardson, John, 1532
Richardson, Katherine G., 2602
Richardson, Kelly C., 1039
Richardson, Leah Beveridge, 3950
Richardson, Louise, 5747
Richardson, Lunsford, Jr., 1679, 7232
Richardson, M. Catherine, 6049
Richardson, Marge, 8096
Richardson, Mary D., 3317
Richardson, Michael, 7255
Richardson, Nancy, 3422
Richardson, Nancy A., 1473
Richardson, Nicolas, 7300
Richardson, P.L., 7301
Richardson, Paige, 9764
Richardson, Peggy, 9384
Richardson, Pete, 1473
Richardson, Peter L., 1679, 7300
Richardson, R. Randolph, 6677
Richardson, Rande S., 6567
Richardson, S.S., 7301
Richardson, Sarah, 7780
Richardson, Sarah Beinecke, 6663, 6895
Richardson, Schuyler, 9509
Richardson, Sid W., 9130
Richardson, Stuart S., 1679
Richardson, Sue, 9795
Richardson, Susan H., 6184
Richardson, Timothy L., 3358
Richardson, Tyler, 1679
Richardson, Tyler B., 7300, 7301
Richardson, Williamson C., 2827
Richardson-Lowry, Mary B., 2746
Richel, Victor, 5253
Richenthal Trust, 6701
Richenthal, David, 6701
Richer, Bob, 9341
Richert-Motullo, Kerstin, 669
Riches, Scott, 849
Richeson, Kathleen B., 4413
Richie, Beth E., 3242
Richins, Kent, 9999
Richland Trust Co., The, 7610
Richloom Fabrics Group, Inc., 6702
Richloom Sales Corp., 6702
Richman, Ellen S., 1680
Richman, Fred, 6702
Richman, James, 6702
Richman, Larry, 3186
Richman, Lawrence, 2886
Richman, Martin F., 6635
Richman, Richard P., 1680
Richman, Rita, 6702
Richmand, Frederick A., 485
Richmond County Financial Corp., 6703
Richmond Foundation, The, 6704
Richmond Hockey Fights Cancer, 6528
Richmond Memorial Hospital Foundation, 7302
Richmond Organization Inc., The, 6704
Richmond, Bradford C., 2051
Richmond, Christian T., 7895
Richmond, Frank, 6704
Richmond, Henry R., 7895
Richmond, Howard S., 6704
Richmond, J. Walker, III, 9404
Richmond, Jim, 4817
Richmond, John A., 7174
Richmond, Joseph W. "Rick", Jr., 9405
Richmond, Joseph W., Jr., 9404
Richmond, Katherine K., 7174
Richmond, Lawrence, 6704
Richmond, Lawrence S., 6704
Richmond, Matthew D., 7174
Richmond, Merritt C., 7174
Richmond, Michael H., 9290
Richmond, Phillip, 6704
Richmond, Robert, 6704
Richmond, Robert M., 6704
Richmond, Ruth B., 7895
Richmond, Sarah, 4467
Richmond, Vicki, 9290
Richmond, William L., 2368
Richmond-Schulman, Elizabeth, 6704
Richstone, Mitchell, 1091
Richter Trust, J. Edward, 8430
Richter, Bill, 3532
Richter, Catherine, 1790
Richter, Sid, 6191
Richter, Theodore E., 1790
Rick, Emilie Robinson, 8553
Rick, Kimberly, 5125
Rickard, Carol, 78
Rickard, F.W., 3578
Rickard, Jean J., 1888
Rickard, Polly Piper, 8740
Ricke, Beatrice, 4779
Rickeman, Norman, 4714
Ricker, Michell, 3481
Rickert, Luann, 3424
Rickert, Mary, 1154
Rickertson, Curt, 5062
Ricketts, Bob, 7973
Ricketts, Dorothy, 2768
Ricketts, John J., 1486
Rickey and Daughters Foundation, Dave, 1071
Rickey, Brenda, 1071
Rickey, Brenda Sjodin, 1070
Rickey, David M., 1070, 1071
Rickey, Michael, 237
Ricks, David A., 3340
Ricks, Mary, 5404
Ricksen, John C., 292
Rico, Victoria B., 8719
RICOH, 9149
Ridaught, Kyle Y., 6538
Riddle, Pamela Cogan, 3988
Ridenour, Julie, 4547
Rideout, Stephen, 9380
Rider, Anne, 2152
Rider, C. Anthony, 6153
Rider, Cynthia A., 4467
Rider, G. William, 9063
Rider, Grace F., 8885
Rider, Mike, 855
Ridgefield Foundation, The, 6349
Ridgefield High School Student Activity Account, 1850
Ridgewood, Inc., 7161
Ridgon, Henry, 2525
Ridgway, Anne, 9461
Ridgway, Curt, 9215
Ridihalgh, James R., 3469
Ridings, Dorothy S. "Dot", 3569
Ridings, Scott, 10
Ridino, Robert, 418
Ridlen, Mark, 8383
Ridlen, Sue, Dr., 3271
Ridley, Eleanor H., 2573
Ridley, Fred S., 2514
Ridloff, Elena, 9005
Ridolfi, Kaye, 7406
Ridout, Kyle, 3288
Riech, Allan J., 2974
Rieck, Amy Crossed, 5830
Riecker, Margaret Ann, 4557
Riecker, Steven Towsley, 4557
Riedel, Debra, 2632
Riedel, Walter G., III, 9198
Rieder, Corinne H., 6144
Riedman Corp., 6706
Riedman, John R., 6706
Riedman, Richard J., 6722
Rief, Frank J., III, 2069
Riegel, Amanda J.T., 6975
Riegel, Steve, 4636
Rieger, Abraham, 6707
Rieger, Abraham Jacob, 6707
Rieger, David, 6707
Rieger, John A., 7749
Rieger, Kathryn K., 1622
Rieger, Merri, Dr., 9715
Rieger, Rachel, 6707
Riehl, Margie, 3826
Riehl, Michael, 3826
Rieman, Richard, 2700
Riemer, Terrin S., 9929
Riemke, John, 3276
Rients, Cheryl Holthe, 4751
Riepe, Christina N., 3869
Riepe, Gail P., 3869
Riepe, James S., 3869
Ries, Edith, 5396
Riesch, Kenneth P., 9965
Riese, Dennis L., 6708
Riese, Lauren, 6708
Riese, Randi, 6708
Riese, Victoria, 6708
Riesen, Mark, 7798
Rieser, Len, 8035
Rietz, Bonnie Besse, 4617
Rifai, Dana, 3337
Rife, John A., 3462
Rife, William, 9514
Rifkin, Ariela, 3339
Rifkin, Daniel M., 3378
Rifkin, Francine, 4532
Rifkin, Leonard, 3339
Rifkin, Martin S., 3378, 9660
Rifkin, Richard, 3339
Rifkin, Richard S., 3378
Rifkin, Susan, 2868
Rifkind, Richard A., 6116, 7092
Rigby, Kevin, 5393
Rigby, Nancy K., 2425, 2445, 2560
Rigg, Robert E., 7979
Riggio Foundation, The, 6661
Riggio, Leonard, 6661, 6709
Riggio, Louise, 6661, 6709
Riggs Tractor Co., J.A., 196
Riggs Trust, Lamar W., 196
Riggs, David W., 7288
Riggs, Earl, 2327
Riggs, Earl, Mrs., 2327
Riggs, Edwin Keith, 196
Riggs, Gail, 4548
Riggs, Jack, III, 196
Riggs, John A., III, 196
Riggs, Judson T., 1244
Riggs, Lamar W., 196
Riggs, Lisa, 8135
Riggs, Peggy, Dr., 4947
Riggs, Sheila, 3490
Riggs, Susan G., 9060
Right Thing an ADP Company, The, 9470
Rightmire, Karen, 8350
Rigler, James, 1074
Rigler, Lloyd E., 1074
Rikfin, Martin S., 9660
Riley, Amelia Q., 7995
Riley, Barbara W., 7995
Riley, Bernard E., 4044
Riley, Brigid A., 6710
Riley, Calvin, 7180
Riley, Charles E., 9632
Riley, Christine, 4026, 4844
Riley, Courtney, 6710
Riley, Daniel P., 581
Riley, Ellen C., 6710
Riley, Emily C., 7995
Riley, Gail W., 4844
Riley, Gerun, 347
Riley, Heather A., 3616
Riley, J. Michael, 6406
Riley, James P., 9965
Riley, James P., Jr., 6710
Riley, Jennie, 4253
Riley, Joseph P., Jr., 8502
Riley, Katherine Murphy, 2522
Riley, Kathleen, 2519
Riley, Keith, 7579
Riley, Kerrylynn, 6710
Riley, Lane, 2414
Riley, Lane M., 2438
Riley, Mabel Louise, 4239
Riley, Margaret M., 2054
Riley, Mark B., 2499
Riley, Mary Ann, 4844
Riley, Odell, 1750
Riley, Richard F., Jr., 4844
Riley, Robert G. "Bob", Jr., 3420
Riley, Shannon C., 6710
Riley, Spud, 2768
Riley, Thomas A., 7995
Riley-Chew, Dorothy, 5834
Rimdo Properties Inc., 3878
Rimel, Rebecca W., 8220
Rimer, Kirk, 9279
Rimes, Leanne, 8554
RIMI, 8383
Rimmer, David, 6025
Rinard, Ronald E., 8755
Rindal, Edie Fleishhacker, 534
Rinde, Lisa, 9950
Rinder, Lawrence, 7050
Rine, Jasper, 3833
Rinehart, Marsha, 7413
Rinella, Bernard B., 3015
Ring, David, 5979
Ring, Norma, 1075
Ring, Timothy M., 5202
Ringel, Betsy, 3736
Ringel, Betsy F., 3735, 3816, 3873
Ringel, Deborah Taper, 1237
Ringel, Neil, 4282
Ringelman, Roger, 9961

Ringenberg, Nicole M., 4945
Ringness, Edward, 9642
Ringness, Marjorie, 9642
Rinker, Christopher R., 2286
Rinker, David B., 2174, 2286
Rinker, David S., 2286
Rinker, John J., 2285
Rinker, Leighan R., 2286
Rinker, M.E., Sr., 2286
Rinker, Sheila A., 2285
Rinkol, Randy, 5067
Rinn, Stefan, 1549
Riopel, Joseph, 5396
Riordan Fund, The, 5746
Riordan, Michael T., 9933
Riordan, Richard, 1818
Rios, Richard, 2040
Rios, Tim, 727
Ripacy Ltd., 7371
Ripkey, Dawn, 9835
Ripley, Richard L., 9295
Rippeto, Doug, 1518
Rippey, James F., 7854
Rippey, Jeffrey L., 7854
Rippey, Shirley K., 7854
Rippey, Timothy M., 7854
Rippy, Mary L., 4633
Risch, Frank A., 8773
Riser, Mary Martin, 66
Rishagen, Nancy, 917
Rishel, Philip S., 7991
Rising Starr Energy, LLC, 9053
Rising Sun Regional Foundation, 3293
Rising, Nelson, 774
Risinger, B.F., 8818, 9054
Risk, Colleen M., 9250
Riskin, Steven M., 422
Riso, Anthony, 1771
Risor, Bob, 208
Rispone, Edward L., 3662
Rispone, Kevin J., 3662
Rispone, Linda L., 3662
Rispone, Phyllis M., 3662
Rispone, Thad E., 3662
Rist, Judith L., 7112
Ristau, Sherry, 3424, 4768
Ristine, Thomas H., 3301
Ristorcelli, Peter J., 2085
Ritchie LLC, Park, 9452
Ritchie, Allen W., 4
Ritchie, Daniel L., 1381
Ritchie, Gregg W., 1333
Ritchie, Lee C., 8671
Ritschard, Mike, 1423
Ritschel, Debbie, 2763
Rittenhouse, Linda, 5613
Ritter, George W., 7633
Ritter, Gerald, 6712
Ritter, Geralyn S., 1929, 5379, 5380
Ritter, Mary C., 4327
Ritter, May Ellen, 6712
Ritter, Michele, 2272
Ritter, William D., 61
Rittgers, Rebecca, 556
Rittling, Mary E., 7266
Ritts Trust of 1998, Herb, The, 1076
Ritz, David, 2253
Ritz, Gordon H., Jr., 1624
Ritz, Margot L., 1624
Ritz, Susan Z., 1624
Ritzel, Nancy, 6876
Ritzen, Jason, 9019
Rivard, Laurie, 4626
Rivas, Jose, 4755
Rivas-Ramos, Marti, 3337
Rivel, David, 6546
River City Petrolium, 5119
Rivera, Chris, 9731
Rivera, Clara, 1850
Rivera, Errica, 7674
Rivera, Felipe, 9375
Rivera, Holli B., 3878
Rivera, Mariano, 1850
Rivera, Ron J., 5511
Rivera, Ruben Morales, 8353
Rivera, Victor R., 3939
Rivero, Jose, 5948
Rivers, Beth, 8776
Rivers, Glenn "Doc", 2008
Riverside Health System, Inc., 3539
Riverview Property LLC, 6394
Rives, Browder, 2150
Rives, Harold, III, 1567
Rives, S. Bradford, 3586
Rivet, Jeannine, 4685
Rivet, Jeannine M., 4685
Rivitz, Jan, 3890
Rivlin, Alice M., 1890
Rivlin, Jay E., 6853
Rix, Lynn M., 6006
Rizavi, Shaiza, 6834
Rizk, Andrew, 6211
Rizk, Richard H., 9558
Rizley, Jerry W., 1425
Rizor, Kathy, 4343
Rizzo, Cindy, 5608
Rizzo, Guy, 2182
Rizzo, Mario, 2657
Rizzo, Stephen, 6014
Rizzo, Susan P., 1041
Rizzuto, Leandro P., 6714
RJB Contracting, 5482
RJH Investment Partners, L.P., 6200
RJR Acquisition Corp., 7296
RJR Nabisco Holdings Corp., 7296
RJR Tobacco Intl., 7296
RLC Investments LLC, 1556
RLTS II, 6277
RMW 2012 Charitable Trust, 4634
Roach, Alexis, 1240
Roach, Dennis A., 1240
Roach, Jean W., 9132
Roach, Jill J., 1240
Roach, Joe, 9108
Roach, John L., 8889
Roach, John V., 9132
Roach, Kelly, 8889
Roach, Lori Anne, 9132
Roach, Michele C., 2019
Roach, Morgan, 647
Roach, Scott, 9775
Roach, Stephanie, 1240
Roan, Caroline, 6633
Roane, Caroline, 6634
Roane, Gay A., 9175
Roanoke-Chowan Hospital, 7303
Roark, Annmarie, 4152
Roark, Bill, 22
Roarty, Susan, 3782
Robak, Kim, 5031
Robb, Brad, 8663
Robb, Harry, 2654
Robb, J.Y., III, 9092, 9093
Robb, Neal S., 777
Robb, Patty, 2654
Robb, Richard G., 6615
Robb, Sandy, 2654
Robb, Sue, 2654
Robb, Trish, 2654
Robb, Walter E., IV, 9276
Robbins Doctoroff, Alisa, 302
Robbins, Allison S., 2337
Robbins, Amy L., 6533
Robbins, Ashley, 3560
Robbins, Beverly, 1681
Robbins, Bob, 4448
Robbins, Cathy, 1406, 7760
Robbins, Clifton S., 1681
Robbins, Diane H., 4063
Robbins, Edwin, 1681
Robbins, Eve, 4139
Robbins, Heidi, 128
Robbins, Jerome, 6716
Robbins, Larry, 1681, 3552, 6533
Robbins, Lawrence, 6715
Robbins, N. Clay, 3342
Robbins, Patricia H., 8485
Robbins, Peter, 3701
Robbins, Robert C., 9268
Robbins, William C., III, 292
Robbins, William D., 6752
Robenalt, Susan, 7431
Robers, Frank P., 7601
Roberson, Ed, 8528
Roberson, Joseph, 4438
Roberston Fund, Jeanne and Sanford, 720
Robert Wood Johnson Foundation, 3953
Robert, Pilar Crespi, 6893
Robert, Stephen, 6893
Roberts Charitable Lead Annuity Trust I, Nora, 5422
Roberts Charitable Lead Annuity Trust II, Nora, 5422
Roberts Charitable Lead Trust, Martha F., 8388
Roberts Children 1987 Trust f/b/o Eric, 1080
Roberts Foundation, 2514
Roberts Foundation, Aileen K. and Brian L., The, 2514
Roberts Fund, H. Clay and Sherry, 9578
Roberts Trust, Roy, 3120
Roberts, Adam J., 2290
Roberts, Aileen K., 8251
Roberts, Alfred M., Jr., 6717
Roberts, Andrew, 6115
Roberts, Anne M., 7789
Roberts, Anne W., 3120
Roberts, Annie Lee, 9213
Roberts, Bettina, 5423
Roberts, Betty, 3274
Roberts, Bradley A., 5574
Roberts, Brian L., 2514, 8251
Roberts, Carla, 4438
Roberts, Carol, 8952
Roberts, Carol L., 8585, 8633
Roberts, Christopher L., 3763
Roberts, Courtney A., 1081
Roberts, Cynthia Vagelos, 6641
Roberts, David, 3120
Roberts, Desmond, 1942
Roberts, Don, 434
Roberts, Dora, 3121
Roberts, Ellen Fales, 9990
Roberts, Elyse Meredith, 3118
Roberts, Emily Goodrich, 3370
Roberts, Eric B., 1080, 1081
Roberts, Frank, 2792
Roberts, George, 1080
Roberts, George R., 1081
Roberts, Gilroy, 8250
Roberts, J. David, 2290
Roberts, J. Haley, Jr., 2514
Roberts, Jack, 4357
Roberts, Jennifer P., 3612
Roberts, Jennifer S.D., 3974
Roberts, Jill D., 2290
Roberts, John, 3336, 3398
Roberts, John B., 7030
Roberts, John H., 3120
Roberts, John J., 3763
Roberts, John T., 8250
Roberts, Karen, 3532
Roberts, Katherine, 9137
Roberts, Kathleen, 744, 2038
Roberts, Kathleen A., 2290
Roberts, Kenneth L., 8568
Roberts, Kimberley I., 1414
Roberts, Kristen, 4240
Roberts, Larry, 7742
Roberts, Leanne B., 1081
Roberts, Lillian, 8250
Roberts, Lisa S., 8232
Roberts, Lon E., 9803
Roberts, Lorraine M., 5808
Roberts, Margaret A., 3119
Roberts, Mark, 2763
Roberts, Mark B., 1081
Roberts, Martha F., 8388
Roberts, Mary Reed, 5115
Roberts, Megan E., 2290
Roberts, Michael J., 3119
Roberts, Michele L., 3960
Roberts, Nora, 5422
Roberts, Norman, 5423
Roberts, Phillip E., 4828
Roberts, Ralph, 8232
Roberts, Ralph J., 7989
Roberts, Ralph J., Jr., 1414
Roberts, Raymond J., 3118
Roberts, Rebecca, 3120
Roberts, Rebecca B., 3763
Roberts, Ronald L., 2160, 9373
Roberts, Ryan, 3543
Roberts, Scott D., 2290
Roberts, Sue Marshall, 8155
Roberts, Susan Bass, 4612
Roberts, Susan Shawn, 3119
Roberts, Suzanne, 8232
Roberts, Tempie, 5062
Roberts, Thomas, 7062
Roberts, Thomas H., III, 3119
Roberts, Thomas S., 4240
Roberts, Virgil, 727
Roberts, William, 4172
Roberts, William L., Jr., 9559
Roberts-Suskin, Catherine, 3119
Robertshaw, Darren, 2327
Robertson Foundation, 5390, 6719
Robertson, Alex T., 7305
Robertson, Alexander Tucker, 6718
Robertson, Alexandra, 6718
Robertson, Beth, 5046
Robertson, Cathy, 4822
Robertson, Charles S., 5200
Robertson, Corbin J., III, 9072
Robertson, David, 7881
Robertson, Duncan, 1109
Robertson, Eddie, 2559
Robertson, Emily M., 3
Robertson, Geoffrey S., 5200, 5424
Robertson, Gloria J., 4503
Robertson, Gregory B., 9457
Robertson, Harold G., 8583
Robertson, Jeanne, 1082

Robertson, Joe, 7845
Robertson, John J., 4047
Robertson, Josephine T., 5602
Robertson, Julia, 5200
Robertson, Julian H., Jr., 5602, 6718, 6719, 6980, 7305
Robertson, Julian Hart, III, 6718
Robertson, Julian Spencer, 6718
Robertson, Kathy, 4968
Robertson, Lindsey, 4684
Robertson, Marie H., 5200
Robertson, Mark, 7766, 9377
Robertson, Russell B., 74
Robertson, Sanford R., 1082
Robertson, Sarah, 6718
Robertson, Spencer R., 7305
Robertson, Stuart, 8813
Robertson, W. Scott, 111
Robertson, Wilhelmina E., 8792, 9268
Robertson, Will, 8901
Robertson, William J., 7704
Robertson, William R., 7621
Robertson, William S., 5200
Robertson, Wyndham, 7305, 7322
Robes Revocable Trust, Martha, 3965
Robes, Martha S., 3965
Robeson, Mark D., 7578
Robfogel, Nathan J., 5969
Robicheaux, Michael R., 3623
Robinett, Bruce, 7769
Robinett, P. Ward, Jr., 9391
Robins Marital Trust, E.C., 7198
Robins Revocable Trust, L., 1769
Robins, Ann Carter, 9524
Robins, E. Claiborne, 9523
Robins, E. Claiborne, Jr., 7198, 9523
Robins, Gregory C., 9523
Robins, Kaplan, Miller & Ciresi L.L.P., 4754
Robins, M. Bruce, 9524
Robinsin, Roger W., Jr., 8266
Robinson Family, 3122
Robinson Pipe Cleaning Co., 2735
Robinson Worldwide, Inc., C.H., 8520
Robinson, Ann, 1110
Robinson, Barbara Paul, 6144, 6612, 6967, 7022
Robinson, Bob, 9773
Robinson, Branden, 4649
Robinson, Brenda, 5068
Robinson, Bruce, 9054
Robinson, Cheryl R., 359
Robinson, Chuck, 9759
Robinson, Coleman, 7752
Robinson, Craig P., 6531
Robinson, Curtis, 877
Robinson, Danielle, 4357
Robinson, Dawn H., 8472
Robinson, Dennis W., 4146
Robinson, Diane, 1014
Robinson, Donald G., 91
Robinson, Donna Marie, 1108
Robinson, Dorna M., 2592
Robinson, Dorothy J., 3352
Robinson, Doug, 7557
Robinson, Dwight, 9435
Robinson, E.B., Jr., 4843
Robinson, Edward H., 1845
Robinson, Edward O., 3598
Robinson, Elizabeth P., 3787
Robinson, Emilie W., 4326
Robinson, Florence L., 3122
Robinson, Frank Brooks, 7966
Robinson, George, 8409
Robinson, Jack, 1398
Robinson, Jack A., 4371
Robinson, James A., 7789
Robinson, James D., III, 6720
Robinson, James D., IV, 2514
Robinson, James Dixon, III, 2514
Robinson, Janet L., 5747
Robinson, Jean, 8047
Robinson, Jean A., 7956
Robinson, Jeffery P., 592
Robinson, Jesse, 3271
Robinson, Jill R., 3735, 3736, 3816, 3876
Robinson, Jim, 9833
Robinson, John H., 8752, 8753
Robinson, John R., 7081
Robinson, Jon, 4467
Robinson, Jonathan, 1750
Robinson, Joseph R., 4511
Robinson, Judy, 9083
Robinson, Katie Jacobs, 2514
Robinson, Kenneth, 8549
Robinson, Kenneth S., Dr., 8538
Robinson, Kirk, 3360
Robinson, Kristy H., 8913
Robinson, Linda G., 6720
Robinson, Linda Gosden, 6720
Robinson, Lori E., 5950
Robinson, M., 7299
Robinson, M. Bruce, 5294
Robinson, Malcolm Ari, 5294
Robinson, Margaret, 7808
Robinson, Margaret A., 8617
Robinson, Maria R., 1845
Robinson, Martha T., 8535
Robinson, Marty, 8548
Robinson, Maurice R., 3122
Robinson, Melanie, 1074, 3782
Robinson, Michael, 3285
Robinson, Michael J., 4442
Robinson, N., 7299
Robinson, Nicole R., 3034
Robinson, R. Avery, 6721
Robinson, Ray Charles, 396
Robinson, Reggie, 3509
Robinson, Robert, 7483
Robinson, Robert A., 5727
Robinson, Robert D., 3317
Robinson, Roger W., Jr., 7968
Robinson, Rowland P., 7081
Robinson, Russell M., II, 7195
Robinson, Ruth, 8495
Robinson, Sally, 7179
Robinson, Sandy, 2327
Robinson, Stacy, 3423
Robinson, Stephanie, 3370
Robinson, Steve, 9604
Robinson, Sylvia B., 7081
Robinson, Tamara Leona, 5294
Robinson, Teresa, 442, 1299
Robinson, Theresa G., 1845
Robinson, Thomas E., 7688
Robinson, Torrence H., 8851
Robinson, Velma Lee, 9133
Robinson, William A., 690
Robinson, William C. E., 3801
Robinson, William P., 9744
Robinson, Winnie M., 6721
Robinson, Zelig, 3880
Robison, Annette S., 312
Robison, Barbara, 3431
Robison, Eric, 2826
Robison, Laurie, 4357
Robison, M. LaVoy, 1365
Robison, Mark A., 3268
Robison, Paul L., Jr., 9208
Robledo, Patricia, 8560
Roblee Trust, Florence, 4963
Robles, Josue, Jr., 9245
Robo, James L., 2251
Robson, Edward D., 7790
Robson, Jack, 9923
Robson, Janet K., 7790
Roby, Carolyn H., 1312
Roby, David, 8267
Roby, John C., 7630
Roby, Katherine W., 7088
Roby, Riley, 19
Rocamora, Larry, 7328
Roche Laboratories Inc., 1083
Roche, Cathy, 566
Roche, George, 6333
Roche, George A., 3865
Rochel, Tim, Sr., 8135
Rochelle, Anne Zachry, 9296
Rochelle, Deborah, 8779
Rochelle, Michael, 98
Rochester Gas and Electric Corp., 3693
Rochkind, David, 607
Rochlin Trust, Heidemarie, 5144
Rochlin, Abraham, 5144
Rochlin, Heidemarie, 5144
Rochlin, Sonia, 5144
Rock S Corp., Arthur, 1084
Rock, Arthur, 1084, 1283
Rock, Douglas, 9134
Rock, Julie, 9134
Rock, Kimberly A., 4108
Rock, Patricia, 4256
Rock, Toni Rembe, 1084
Rockdale Industries, Inc., 2530
Rockefeller Brothers Fund, 5718
Rockefeller Charitable Trust, 1665
Rockefeller Charitable Trust, A.R., 6606
Rockefeller Foundation, The, 3982
Rockefeller Philanthropy Advisors, 6864
Rockefeller Trust Co., 6544
Rockefeller Trust Co., N.A., 1949
Rockefeller Trust, A.M., 1665, 6606
Rockefeller, Avery, III, 1665
Rockefeller, Camilla, 6725
Rockefeller, David, 6723, 6725
Rockefeller, David, Jr., 3670, 6724
Rockefeller, John D., III, 6723
Rockefeller, John D., Jr., 6723
Rockefeller, John D., Sr., 6724
Rockefeller, Justin, 6723
Rockefeller, Laurance S., 6723
Rockefeller, Lisenne, 197
Rockefeller, Martha Baird, 6723
Rockefeller, Monica, 1665
Rockefeller, Nelson A., 6723
Rockefeller, Steven C., 6723
Rockefeller, Susan Cohn, 6725
Rockefeller, Winthrop, 197, 198, 6723
Rockey, Chaz, 5661, 6500
Rockmont Mgmt. Partners, 7012
Rockville Bank, 1682
Rockway, Dennis, 636
Rockwell Automation, 9934
Rockwell Collins, Inc., 3477
Rockwell International Corporation Trust, 9934
Rockwern, S. Sumner, 7634
Roday, Leon E., 9441
Rodde, Wendy, 21
Roddenberry Trust, Majel, 1086
Roddenberry, Eugene, 1086
Roddenberry, Gene, 1086
Roddenberry, Heidi, 1086
Roddenberry, Majel Barrett, 1086
Roddey, James C., 8161, 8228, 8266
Roddick Foundation, Andrew S., The, 8649
Roddy, R. Tom, 8702
Rodecker, Julie, 4396
Roden, Elizabeth, 7932
Rodenbach, Edward F., 1588, 3058
Rodenbeck, Eric, 1051
Rodenbeek, James, 3543
Rodewall, Jeffrey P., 3200
Rodgers, Brooke, 3826
Rodgers, Charles, 7380
Rodgers, David A., 7380
Rodgers, Elizabeth Killam, 4241
Rodgers, Gary, 1511
Rodgers, Jane, 864
Rodgers, Jim, 7742
Rodgers, Leola, 6153
Rodgers, Lynn, 7380
Rodgers, Mary Anne, 1006
Rodgers, Michael, 3826
Rodgers, Pamela, 4371
Rodgers, Pat, 7202
Rodgers, Patrick A., 3826
Rodgers, Thomas A., III, 4242
Rodgers, Thomas A., Jr., 4242
Rodgers, W. Ralph, Jr., 2437
Rodin, Judith, Dr., 6724
Rodkin, Barbara, 5030
Rodkin, Gail, 237
Rodkin, Gary M., 5030
Rodman, Rica, 1300
Rodney, Clare, 4528
Rodney, James M., 4528
Rodney, Leigh, 4528
Rodney, Leign, 4528
Rodnick, Amie, 8904
Rodrigo, Rohan, 1890
Rodriguez & Associates, G.E., 9149
Rodriguez, Aida, 6546
Rodriguez, Aileen, 1771
Rodriguez, Al, 1116
Rodriguez, Amy, 4344
Rodriguez, Arlene, 6571
Rodriguez, Armando, 549
Rodriguez, Edwin "Rod", Jr., 3656
Rodriguez, Edwin R., Jr., 3654
Rodriguez, Jon Paul, 9656
Rodriguez, Jose R., 5349
Rodriguez, Karyn E., 272
Rodriguez, Kristy Sampson, 3878
Rodriguez, Nadia K., 5307
Rodriguez, Nidia Maldonado, 2280
Rodriguez, Ramon A., 2034
Rodriguez, Raul C., 414
Rodriguez, Raul F., 2280
Rodriguez, Raul Francisco, 2280
Rodriguez, Ray, 2191
Rodriguez, Ref, 1014
Rodriguez, Sylvia C., 9246
Rodriguez-Howard, Mayra, 3987
Roe, John J., III, 6296
Roe, Shirley W., 8494
Roe, Thomas A., 8494
Roeder, Richard W., 8245
Roeder, Susan, 4601
Roediger, Anne, 101
Roegiers, Stephen, 2476
Roehl, Jerrald J., 5511
Roehlk, Thomas M., 2363

Rose Foundation, Susan and Elihu, Inc., 6562
Rose Trust, 1020
Rose, Aaron, 6158
Rose, Adam, 6733
Rose, Adam R., 6733, 6736
Rose, Alexandra, 6158
Rose, Ann C., 1821
Rose, Barbara, 4795, 9780
Rose, Beth, 79
Rose, Billy, 6734
Rose, Christy, 7636
Rose, Clayton S., 3818
Rose, Daniel, 6738
Rose, David, 1360
Rose, David C., 1894
Rose, David H., 6158, 6731
Rose, Deborah, 6735, 6736
Rose, Deedie, 8912
Rose, Diana C., 6394
Rose, Elihu, 6737
Rose, Ella, 1389
Rose, Ellen Mackey, 4108
Rose, Eugene S., 7636
Rose, Frederick P., 6736
Rose, Gary D., 5270
Rose, Gina, 6158
Rose, Jacqueline T., 7636
Rose, James A., 6158, 6731
Rose, Jason, 9768
Rose, Jean H., 9201
Rose, Jean Weinberg, 7066
Rose, John, 9600
Rose, Jonathan F.P., 6394, 6736
Rose, Kelly, 7767
Rose, Kim, 7413
Rose, Laila, 830
Rose, Marian, 6158
Rose, Marian H., 6731
Rose, Marianne Curtis, 3282
Rose, Marshall, 6732
Rose, Marya M., 3292
Rose, Matthew K., 8706
Rose, Mike, 9290
Rose, Sandra, 6394
Rose, Sandra P., 6733, 6735
Rose, Sandra Priest, 6736
Rose, Sandy, 415
Rose, Sarah R. Frey, 4440
Rose, Simon, 6158
Rose, Simon M., 6731
Rose, Sonia, 6158
Rose, Stuart A., 7636
Rose, Susan, 900, 6737
Rose, Susan W., 6737
Rose, Suzanne, 7767
Rose, Tricia, 5833
Rose, Walter B., 1013
Roseman, Wilma S., 3599
Rosemore, Inc., 3873
Rosen Family Charitable Trust, 2351
Rosen Foundation Inc., Harris, The, 2351
Rosen Foundation, Abner, Inc., The, 6741
Rosen Hotels & Resorts, Inc., 2294
Rosen, Benjamin M., 6739
Rosen, Bruce A., 6665
Rosen, D., 6225
Rosen, Donna, 6739
Rosen, Elaine D., 4479
Rosen, Harris, 2294, 2351
Rosen, Jack, 6664
Rosen, Jeanette D., 6740
Rosen, Jeannette, 6741
Rosen, Jonathan P., 6740, 6741
Rosen, Judy, 3151
Rosen, Julia, 92
Rosen, Leizor, 1514
Rosen, Marni, 234, 1188
Rosen, Martin M., 4973
Rosen, Marvin S., 6052
Rosen, Maurice, 6189
Rosen, Miriam N., 6740
Rosen, Sarah, 5834, 6740
Rosen, Selma, 5296
Rosen, Seth D., 2354
Rosen, Sheri, 1195
Rosenau, Brett, 4693
Rosenau, Mark O., 3506
Rosenau, Paul, 4693
Rosenau, Susan, 4693
Rosenbaum Advisors, 118
Rosenbaum Trust, Gabriella, 2974
Rosenbaum, Gabriella, 2974
Rosenbaum, Jeffrey N., 5803
Rosenbaum, Lisa, 4052
Rosenberg Associates, Gene, 1548
Rosenberg Jr. Family Foundation, Louise & Claude, 1853
Rosenberg, Abraham, 6743
Rosenberg, Ann, 4245
Rosenberg, Brian C., 4792
Rosenberg, Chany, 6756
Rosenberg, Cheryl, 2545
Rosenberg, Deborah, 3155
Rosenberg, Dianne M., 7404
Rosenberg, Donald, 4245
Rosenberg, Dorothy L., 3874
Rosenberg, Douglas C., 1853
Rosenberg, Dulcy D., 2544
Rosenberg, Ellen A., 1853
Rosenberg, Eugene, 1548
Rosenberg, Frank B., 3874
Rosenberg, Gene, 1548
Rosenberg, Geoffrey, 6099
Rosenberg, H. Alan, 2544
Rosenberg, H. Jerome, III, 2544
Rosenberg, Henry A., Jr., 3873, 3874
Rosenberg, J. David, 7511
Rosenberg, James, 4245
Rosenberg, James M., 5740
Rosenberg, Jennifer, 4245
Rosenberg, Jessica, 7910
Rosenberg, Joe, 3560
Rosenberg, John, 4245
Rosenberg, Julie Goldsmith, 3804
Rosenberg, Karen, 2544, 5019
Rosenberg, Kenneth, 2544
Rosenberg, Max L., 1088
Rosenberg, Michael, 4245, 6756
Rosenberg, Michael N., Dr., 2238
Rosenberg, Michele, 2544
Rosenberg, Norman, 1932
Rosenberg, Patricia, 5533
Rosenberg, Robert, 4245
Rosenberg, Ruth Blaustein, 3873
Rosenberg, Sheli Z., 2987
Rosenberg, Sonia, 6743
Rosenberg, Stanley, 8702
Rosenberg, Stephen, 2545
Rosenberg, Stuart, 7711
Rosenberg, Tara-Lynn Boreham, 4245
Rosenberg, Vicki, 4334
Rosenberg, William, 4245
Rosenberg, William F., 6556
Rosenberger, David M., 4558
Rosenberger, Gary, 7874
Rosenberry Charitable Term Trust, 4802
Rosenberry Jones Charitable Tust, Lucy, 4802
Rosenblatt, C., 6745
Rosenblatt, Lief D., 5628, 6744
Rosenblatt, Richard A., 6573
Rosenblatt, Ruth, 6899
Rosenblatt, Stanley M., 2099, 2295
Rosenblatt, Susan, 2099, 2295
Rosenblatt, Toby, 411
Rosenbloom, Anita S., 5822
Rosenbloom, Ben, 3875
Rosenbloom, Dale C., 1751
Rosenbloom, Esther, 3875
Rosenbloom, Howard, 3875
Rosenbloom, Keith, 3875
Rosenbloom, Michelle G., 3875
Rosenbloom, Robert, 3875
Rosenblum, Daniel, 6746, 7093
Rosenblum, Ivan S., 5707
Rosenblum, Leonard, 6746
Rosenblum, Richard M., 2603
Rosenburg Fdn., Rueben, 6998
Rosenfeld, Barry, 5393
Rosenfeld, Gerald, 6693
Rosenfeld, Michael, 6747
Rosenfeld, Monica Hasten, 3316
Rosenfeld, Rachel, 6111
Rosenfeld, Shea, 6111
Rosenfeld, Tom, 3265
Rosenfeldt, Paul, 9843
Rosenfield, Barry, 6569
Rosenfield, Bruce A., 7955, 8203
Rosenfield, Patricia, 6115
Rosengard, Ariella M., 4179
Rosenkrantz, Dana, 662
Rosenkranz, Nicholas Quinn, 6748
Rosenkranz, Robert, 6748
Rosenkranz, Roberto, 1325
Rosenmiller, W. David, 4060
Rosenow, Penny, 2792
Rosenstein, Anita, 1213
Rosenstein, Anita May, 476, 5132
Rosenstein, Brian, 5132
Rosenstein, Carl, 5417
Rosenstein, Neal, 5417
Rosenstein, Perry, 5417
Rosenstein, Ronald S., 1565
Rosenstiel, Blanka A., 8254
Rosenstiel, Lewis S., 8254
Rosenstock, Jeffrey, 5612
Rosensweig, David, 1708
Rosenthal & Rosenthal, Inc., 6749
Rosenthal Trust A, Samuel, 2784
Rosenthal, Babette H., 2784
Rosenthal, David O., 9547
Rosenthal, Donald B., 5296
Rosenthal, Edward D., 2326
Rosenthal, Eric, 6749
Rosenthal, Hilary Kirk, 2056
Rosenthal, James A., 6507
Rosenthal, Jonathan, 6479
Rosenthal, Leighton A., 7637
Rosenthal, Lynne, 2882
Rosenthal, Marie-Louise, 2784
Rosenthal, Marion, 9525
Rosenthal, Monica, 1089
Rosenthal, Morris H., 6525
Rosenthal, Nancy, 9525
Rosenthal, Nancy Stephens, 1684
Rosenthal, Noah, 1684
Rosenthal, Philip, 1089
Rosenthal, Rick, 1684
Rosenthal, Robert M., 9525
Rosenthal, Ruth B., 2933
Rosenthal, Samuel L., 2784
Rosenthal, Samuel R., 2784
Rosenthal, Stephen, 6749
Rosenthal, Steven P., 4250
Rosenwald Family Fund Inc., William, 6483, 6751
Rosenwald Family Fund, William, 5547
Rosenwald, Alice, 6751
Rosenwald, Cindy, 5169
Rosenwald, Edward John, Jr., 6750
Rosenwald, Nina, 5547
Rosenwald, Patricia, 6750
Rosenzweig, Dora, 4379
Rosenzweig, Harry, 4379
Rosenzweig, Herschel, 4379
Rosenzweig, James, 6708
Rosenzweig, Joseph, 4379
Rosenzweig, Leonard, 4379
Rosenzweig, Newton, 92
Rosequist, Ronald V., 444
Roser, Eleanor, 9305
Rosetti Handbags, Ltd., 6166
Rosetti, Desila, 3369
Rosewood Corp., The, 9140
Rosholt, A.M., 6532
Rosica, A. Joseph, 3014
Rosica, Daniel, 3014
Rosica, Gregory A., 2040
Rosica, Kathryn, 3014
Rosica, Mark, 3014
Rosin, Katharine S., 6804
Rosing, Wayne E., 821, 842
Roskam, Don, 4529
Roskam, Donald O., 4529
Roskam, Robert O., 4529
Roskamp Charities, Inc., 2296
Roskamp, Diane Sampson, 2296
Roskamp, Robert G., 2296
Roske, Mary Grace, 9731
Rosloniec, James, 4541
Rosloniec, Michael, 4447
Roslyn Bancorp, Inc., 6543
Rosmarino, Claudine, 742
Rosner, June, 6752
Rosner, Myron, 5206
Ross Foundation, Arthur, 6218, 6608
Ross Fund, Sada, 9578
Ross Revocable Trust, Robert A., 1091
Ross Stores, Inc., 977
Ross Trust, Barbara M., 1090
Ross, Alexander B., 5644
Ross, Alfred F., 6753
Ross, Arthur, 6218, 6608, 6753
Ross, Barbara, 1260
Ross, Becky, 1069
Ross, Bill, 5055
Ross, Billie D., 6755
Ross, Catherine, 1423
Ross, Deborah, 7064
Ross, Dorothea Haus, 6754
Ross, Edward, 3123
Ross, Erika M., 7316
Ross, Esther C., 199
Ross, Everlena B., 9421
Ross, Ford, 3552
Ross, Gary, 5045
Ross, George H., 6755
Ross, George M., 8255
Ross, Gwen E., 3674
Ross, Ilene, 3123
Ross, J.R., 2087
Ross, Jack, 9467
Ross, James J., 6393

Ross, Jan, 3671
Ross, Jane, 199, 6753
Ross, Janet C., 6218
Ross, Jay, 3267
Ross, Karen C., 5146
Ross, Libby, 9384
Ross, Lyn M., 8255
Ross, M., 7809
Ross, Mary Caslin, 5323
Ross, Mary June, 159
Ross, Melissa, 9792
Ross, Merry, 8255
Ross, Michael, 8255
Ross, N. Barry, 6746
Ross, Nanci, 6755
Ross, Nina, 3984
Ross, R. Ian, 5152
Ross, R. J., Rev., 1390
Ross, Renee, 3123
Ross, Richard, Jr., 2876
Ross, Robert J., 7749, 7760
Ross, Robert K., 366
Ross, Samuel B., II, 9792
Ross, Samuel B., III, 9792
Ross, Samuel D., Jr., 8129
Ross, Sarane H., 5644
Ross, Spencer B., 9792
Ross, Stan, 339
Ross, Stephen B., 5644
Ross, Stephen M., 5656
Ross, Susan S., 9792
Ross, Terry, 777
Ross, Walter M., 2233
Ross, William, 3123
Ross, William J., 7749, 7760
Rosse, Earle, 5162
Rossi, Anthony T., 1974
Rossi, Deborah, 972
Rossi, Ellen E., 9331, 9347
Rossi, Frank H., Msgr., 9243
Rossi, Joseph H., 1651
Rossi, Moira Forbes, Countess, 5821
Rossi, Nicola, 5506
Rossi, Sharon, 5484
Rossi, WJ, 2036
Rossin, Ada E., 8256
Rossin, Peter C., 8256
Rossing, Wayne E., 842
Rossiter, Lois F., 9558
Rossiter, Rob, 4451
Rossiter, Scott, 4327
Rossley, Paul R., 4168
Rosso, Christine Hehmeyer, 2933
Rost, Rynthia M., 3801
Rost, Shawn, 5009
Rosta, Fannie, 5372
Rostan, James H., 7178
Roswaski, Chaim Z., 6336
Roswell, Arthur E., 3735, 3876
Roswell, Barbara S., 3876
Roswell, David I., 3876
Roswell, Elizabeth B., 3735, 3876
Roswell, Marjorie B., 3876
Roswell, Michael E., 3876
Roswell, Robert A., 3876
Roswick, John T., 7353
Rotan, Caroline P., 8838
Rotary Club of Elmbrook, 9961
Rotary Club of Greensboro, The, 7162
Rotatori, David J., 1616
Rotchild, Walter W., 8566
Rotella, Robert P., 9721
Rotella, Rosemarie C., 9721
Rotella, William J., 2380
Rotenberg, Robin, 7383
Roth and Co., Louis, 1093
Roth, Bernard B., 1094
Roth, David E., 7783
Roth, David H.O., 8719
Roth, David M., 2081
Roth, Elaine, 5813
Roth, Fannie, 1093
Roth, Florence, 1094
Roth, Harry, 1093
Roth, James, 4988
Roth, James J., 6518
Roth, Janet E., 8320
Roth, Linda, 2081
Roth, Linda H., 2081
Roth, Louis, 1093
Roth, Mark B., 3833
Roth, Michael P., 1093
Roth, Millicent, 1908
Roth, Rachel, 1093
Roth, Richard, 1094
Roth, Robert S., 1094
Roth, Robert W., 4447
Roth, Sarah, 1093
Roth, Steven, 5426
Roth, Steven F., 1094
Roth, Walter, 3154, 3173
Roth-Fedida, Andrea, 1093
Rothamel, Paul E., 8834
Rothberg Trust, Samuel, 3108
Rothberg, Emily, 9380
Rothberg, Heidi B., 3108
Rothberg, Henry M., 2297
Rothberg, Jean, 3108
Rothberg, Jean C., 3108
Rothberg, Jennifer Hoos, 5942
Rothberg, Jonathan M., 2297
Rothberg, Lee Patrick, 3108
Rothberg, Lilliam R., 2297
Rothberg, Michael, 3108
Rothberg, Michael J., 2297
Rothberg, Richard S., 6069
Rothberg, Samuel, 3108
Rothblatt, Ben, 2983
Rothchild, Emily, 5922
Rothe, Anne Richards, 2256
Rothenberg, Ann, 4111
Rothenberg, Daniel E., 4111
Rothenberg, Edward, 4111
Rothenberg, Lawrence, 2195
Rothenberg, Susan, 494, 4111
Rothenberger, Steve, 3283
Rothermel, Amy H., 2476
Rothermel, Andrew, 2476
Rothermel, Andrew J., 1742
Rothermel, Elizabeth B., 1742
Rothermel, Honea H., 8900
Rothfeld, Alan C., 6222
Rothkopf, Dick, 1518
Rothman Foundation, 2045
Rothman Foundation, The, 2298
Rothman, Howard, 2349, 6050
Rothman, Marc, 3042
Rothman, Margaret, 2298
Rothman, Robert, 2298
Rothman, Terry, 9833
Rothrock, Allyson, 9450
Rothrock, Donna, 7294
Rothschild Foundation, 6336
Rothschild, Alan F., Jr., 2460
Rothschild, Hulda B., 3124
Rothschild, Nathaniel, 6685
Rothschild, Peter, 3698
Rothschild, Steven, 4714
Rothschild, Susan, 3929
Rothstein, Andrew, 4073
Rothstein, Scott, 6518
Rothstein, William, 5582
Rothstein-Schwimmer, Susan, 5582
Rothweiler, Todd, 323
Rothwell, Sharon, 4497, 4557
Rottenberg, Alan, 4296
Rottenberg, Alan W., 3943
Rotter, Adam, 6757
Rotter, Robin, 6757
Rotter, Steven J., 6689, 6757
Rottinghaus, Stacy Suskin, 9747
Rottman, Burton, 2890
Rottman, Howard, 2890
Rottman, Michael, 2890
Rotuck, Scott, 9799
Rotunno, L. Charles, Jr., 1845
Rotz, Ann Marie, 3761
Roubal, James, 5076
Roumani, Nadia, 1903
Rounds, Bruce, 9916
Rounds, Charlie, 4723
Roundy's Supermarkets, Inc., 9936
Roundy's, Inc., 9936
Roundy, Deeann, 9768
Rounsavall, Robert W., III, 3563
Rountree, Paul, 2039
Rountree, Stephen D., 222
Rouse, Christopher, 5814
Rouse, Deidre, 2439
Rouse, Dudley L., Jr., 9019
Rouse, Elizabeth Meadows, 9019
Rouse, Eloise Meadows, 9019
Rouse, James, 3560
Rouse, Joseph P., 7718
Rouse, Michael, 7002
Roush, G. James, 9565
Roush, Galen, 7465
Roush, Nancy, 4332
Roush, Ruth C., 7465
Roush, William Morgan, 9565
Rouson, Janine, 1591
Roussel, Jane, 3610
Roux, Henry, 849
Roux, Tina, 7060
Rovecamp, Monica, 3894
Roven, Charles V., 5150
Roven, Rose Webb, 1092, 1304
Roven, Talia, 1304
Rover, Edward, 6431
Rover, Edward F., 5845, 6322
Rover, Mike, 309
Rovezzi, Guy, 1565
Rowan, Carolyn, 6758
Rowan, Eleanor, 5427
Rowan, Helen, 2281
Rowan, Henry M., 5427
Rowan, Marc, 6758
Rowan, Marcus, 8794
Rowan, Pamela Wallace, 8553
Rowan, Stephen, 7406
Rowan, Virginia, 3636
Rowe, Bradley M., 9782
Rowe, Connie, 7640
Rowe, Daphne C., 7903
Rowe, George, Jr., 6497
Rowe, J. S., 9548
Rowe, Jeanne M., 6759
Rowe, John W., 2746, 2827, 6724, 6759
Rowe, Karen Okamura, 9621
Rowe, Marshall, 5169
Rowe, Ramona C., 7182
Rowe, Rebecca, 3705
Rowe, Sara M., 9782
Rowe, Steven, 5169
Rowe, Thomas W., 9782
Rowe, William J., 6759
Rowe-Collins, Jodi, 3575
Rowell, Virginia, 2269
Rowland, Benjamin A., Jr., 9370
Rowland, Daniel B., 9370
Rowland, G. Joyce, 1140
Rowland, Marilyn, 2523
Rowland, Pleasant T., 9937
Rowland, Robert, 8446
Rowland, Ronny, 4822
Rowland, Wendy G., 9370
Rowley, Jim, 101
Rowley, Lynn, 3346
Rowley, Richard, 7580
Rowling, Robert B., 9141
Rowling, Robert B., Jr., 9141
Rowling, Terry H., 9141
Rowling, Travis Blake, 9141
Roxane Laboratories, Inc., 1549
Roy, Adelard A., 4247
Roy, Brittany D., 5899
Roy, C. R., 9932
Roy, Dillon, 5899
Roy, J. Steven, 31
Roy, Judy, 4730
Roy, Kathryn, 3980
Roy, Lisa, 1454
Roy, Ruby, M.D., 2769
Royal Blue Jeans, 5488
Royal Brand Roofing, Inc., 4875
Royal Dutch Shell PLC, 4254
Royal Oak Foundation, 5707
Royal Wine Corp., 5272
Royal, Amy, 2123
Royal, Nina, 5514
Royal, Pamela J., 9416
Royal, Susan B., 7926
Royals Charities Inc., 1850
Royalty, Andy, 3284
Royce, Charles M., 1685
Royce, Edgar, 6595
Royce, Ginna, 9799
Royce, Joseph W., 9011, 9187
Royster, R. Randall, Esq., 5511
Rozeboom, Leon D., 3480
Rozek, Alexander Buffett, 7324
Rozek, Gary, 3449
Rozell, Denise, 1879
Rozen, Michael R., 6918
Rozen, Neil, 6918
Rozen, Toby S., 6918
Rozen, Toby Stein, 6918
Rozenshteyn, Gary, 6628
Rozie-Battle, Judy, 1609
RPC Charitable Lead Annuity Trust, 6692
RSVP Advisory Council, 9652
Ruan Transport Corp., 3478
Ruan, Janis, 3420
Ruan, John, III, 3478
Ruane, William J., 5746
Rubacka, Kristen E., 5950
Rubbermaid Commercial Products, 3201
Rubega, Margaret, 3709
Rubel, John H., 850
Rubell, Michelle Simkins, 2321
Ruben, Harvey, 7751
Ruben, Lawrence, 6761
Ruben, Lenore, 6761
Ruben, Richard, 6761
Ruben, Sally, 5098

Ruben, Selma, 6761
Rubenfeld, Abraham, 6664
Rubenstein, Andrew, 5428
Rubenstein, Anne C., 4248
Rubenstein, Barry, 6762
Rubenstein, Beverly, 5428
Rubenstein, Brian, 6762
Rubenstein, Ernest, 6121
Rubenstein, Frederic A., 6739
Rubenstein, Jonathan, 3786
Rubenstein, Joshua S., 2951
Rubenstein, Lawrence J., 4248
Rubenstein, Marilyn, 6762
Rubenstein, Rebecca, 6762
Rubenstein, Steven, 5428
Rubenstein, Terry M., 3848, 3849
Rubenstein, William H., 4603
Rubin and Sons, Joseph, Inc., 4249
Rubin Foundation, Samuel, Inc., 6764
Rubin Trust UAD, 2300
Rubin Trust, Randi, 2300
Rubin Trust, Richard, 2300
Rubin Trust, Roberta, 2300
Rubin Trust, Ronald, 2300
Rubin, Burton, 169
Rubin, David M., 8303
Rubin, Donald, 6765
Rubin, Dorothy, 6763
Rubin, Gerald M., 3818
Rubin, Hank, 6722
Rubin, Howard, 6766
Rubin, Jacob M., 2299
Rubin, Jane Gregory, 6684
Rubin, Judith, 6338
Rubin, Judith O., 6544
Rubin, Kate, 4785
Rubin, L., 6287
Rubin, L. M., 8833
Rubin, Lara R., 6684
Rubin, Liebel, 6763
Rubin, Lucille, 2300
Rubin, Maia A., 6684
Rubin, Marsha, 3201
Rubin, Martin A., 2015
Rubin, Marvin, 6763
Rubin, Michael, 239, 8257
Rubin, Paulette, 8257
Rubin, Peter L., 6684
Rubin, Reed, 6684
Rubin, Richard, 5864
Rubin, Robert, 1648
Rubin, Roberta, 4061
Rubin, Rochelle A., 5577
Rubin, Sally L., 4225
Rubin, Samuel, 6684, 6764
Rubin, Shelley, 2210, 6765
Rubin, Solomon, 6763
Rubin, Steven A., 1397
Rubin, Steven I., 5577
Rubin, Steven M., 7144
Rubin, Walter, 2300
Rubinelli, Joseph O., Jr., 3007
Rubinelli, Mary Jane, 3007
Rubinfield, Louis, 3820
Rubini, John, 79
Rubino, Nick, 5976
Rubinow, Laurence P., 1690
Rubinstein, Joshua M., 374
Rubinstein, Wade, 4298
Rubinsztein-Dunlop, Halina, 298
Rubio, Luis, 6983
Ruble, Blaire, 7009
Ruble, Cindy S., 4350
Rubschlager, Joan S., 3126
Rubschlager, Paul A., 3126
Ruby Pipeline, 7848
Ruby, Burton B., 3393
Ruby, Diane, 972
Ruby, Kenneth A., 1095
Ruby, Paul J., 374
Ruby, Wendy, 1095
Ruby, Wendy L., 1095
Ruch, Joshua, 6231
Ruch, Julia M., 6231
Ruch, Susan, 3695
Ruckelshaus, William D., 9591
Rucker, Bill, 9617
Rucker, Geri, 7202
Rucker, Janet, 3356
Ruckle, James E., 3397
Rudd, Alexandra H., 1096
Rudd, Andrew T., 1096
Rudd, Christopher A., 1096
Rudd, David, 4410
Rudd, Natalie A., 1096
Rudd, Nicholas S., 1096
Rudd, Virginia A., 1096
Ruddy, James J., 5573, 5885, 5921
Rude-Willson, Janice, 5108
Rudel, Jack N., 594
Rudell, Michael, 6608
Rudenstine, Neil, 579
Ruderman, Jay Seth, 4250
Ruderman, Marcia, 4250
Ruderman, Morton E., 4250
Ruderman, Todd Adam, 4250
Rudick, Ian, 9799
Rudin Estates Co., LP, 6768
Rudin, Eric C., 6767, 6768, 6769
Rudin, Jack, 6767, 6768, 6769
Rudin, Katherine L., 6767, 6769
Rudin, Michael P.H., 6767
Rudin, Samantha Mia, 6767, 6769
Rudin, William C., 6767, 6768, 6769
Rudner, Diane R., 8615
Rudner, Jocelyn P., 8615
Rudner, William, 8615
Rudnick, A.J., 24
Rudnick, M. Jack, 5757
Rudolph, Alexander S., 3178
Rudolph, Geoffrey E., 3178
Rudolph, Phillip H., 736
Rudy Luther Toyota, 4698
Rudy, Ike, 5768
Rudy, Paul, III, 8351
Rudyak, Rada, 4251
Rudyak, Semen, 4251
Rudzik, John A., 7970
Rueckert, William Dodge, 5892
Rueffert, Brenda, 1233
Ruehle, Lyndsey, 1392
Ruesch, Jeanette Weaver, 5429
Ruesch, Matthew, 5429
Ruesga, G. Albert, Dr., 3656
Ruest, Michelle, 8548
Rueter, Marci, 9961
Ruettgers, Abagail, 4252
Ruettgers, Christopher, 4252
Ruettgers, Maureen, 4252
Ruettgers, Michael, 4252
Ruff, Gwendolyn H., 2438
Rugeley, Virginia, 9780
Ruggles Charitable Lead Annuity Trust A, Ruth C., 3127
Ruggles, Rudy, Jr., 3127
Ruh, William J., 1053
Ruhe, Thom, 4921
Ruhl, Roger L., 7426
Ruhlman, Barbara P., 7617
Ruhlman, Randall M., 7617
Ruhlman, Robert G., 7617
Ruiz, David, Dr., 9603
Ruiz, Gisel, 210
Ruiz, Jesse H., 2746
Rulon-Miller, William, 5345
Rumbarger, David, 4822
Rumbough, J. Wright, Jr., 2385
Rumelhart, Judith D., 4557
Rumelt Family Trust, 6687
Rumer, Rebecca W., 2556
Rummel, Mason B., 3563
Rummler, Greg S., 503
Rumore, Carol Ann Bruno, 17
Rumore, Phillip, 17
Rumsey, David, 6308
Rumsey, Dexter, III, 9503
Rumsey, John, 3293
Rumsey, Todd C., 3304
Rumsfeld Foundation, Joyce and Donald, 1943
Rumsfeld, Donald H., 1943, 3128
Rumsfeld, Joyce P., 1943, 3128
Rundorff, Jim, 9704
Rundquist, Rebecca, 3705
Runestad, Mary, 1665
Runestad, Rodney, 1665
Runge, Amy, 9566
Runkel, John, 8083
Runnells, Clive, III, 8878
Runyon Erectors, Inc., 5482
Runyon, Richard M., 6876
Runzheimer Internatioanl Ltd., 9938
Ruof, Mark, 1028
Ruopp, Frederick J., 956
Rupani, Amirali, 8795
Rupar, Anita, 3356
Rupe, Arthur N., 1097
Rupp, Adrienne, 5169
Rupp, Chris, 3281
Rupp, Christina D., 6771
Rupp, George, 6414
Rupp, George E., 6398
Rupp, Gerald E., 7030
Rupp, Richard W., 6771
Rupp, Susan S., 6771
Rupp, William R., 6771
Ruppel, Phillip, 3421
Rupprecht, Mark, 3420
Rurik, Dion, 9722
Rusakov, Vitaliy V., 7908
Rusche, Joseph A., 4796
Rusczek, Fred, 8397
Rush, Amy, 9411
Rush, Mike, 4502
Rush, Scott R., 4521
Rush, Sherri, 3280
Rush, Walter K., III, 1397
Rushing, Coretha, 2455
Rushing, Don, 8994
Rushing, Roger, 2516
Rushing, Ted, 8994
Ruskin, Florita, 1334
Rusnak, Jeffrey, 9111
Rusnock, Beth, 9368
Russ, Jack, 860
Russ, Randy J., 4450
Russel, Marjorie, 6495
Russell 94 Char Lead Trust, M.H., 557
Russell, Archie E., 9386
Russell, Benjamin, 63
Russell, Bernadette, 6437
Russell, Brian P., 3321
Russell, C. David, 5123
Russell, Chris, 22
Russell, Christine H., 557
Russell, Cristine, 5800
Russell, Dave, 1295
Russell, Deborah L., 2035
Russell, Eric, 9722
Russell, G. Richard, 5057
Russell, George F., Jr., 9722
Russell, Grover B., 3751, 3784
Russell, Hollis, Esq., 1826
Russell, Ida H., 2418
Russell, Ida Hudson, 2419
Russell, Jackie, 3363
Russell, James, 288
Russell, Jan Jarboe, 9079
Russell, Jane Haake, 288
Russell, Jane T., 9722
Russell, Jenny, 4171
Russell, Jileen, 9722
Russell, Joe, 8603
Russell, John A., 8129
Russell, John G., 4376
Russell, Joseph W., 6567
Russell, Josephine Schell, 8258
Russell, Julie, 1233
Russell, June, 1395
Russell, Justine V.R., 1851, 6487
Russell, Kimberly, 9416
Russell, Marion B., 9386
Russell, Melissa R., 8620
Russell, Richard, 3521, 9722
Russell, Robert, 2301
Russell, Sean, 1233
Russell, T. Alan, 3311
Russell, Tim, 8594
Russell, Todd, 2033
Russell, Tracy A., 1198
Russell, Vann, 6
Russell, William F., 9386
Russell, Zac, 9722
Russi, Christopher H., 9381
Russo, Daniel, 254
Russo, Marcy, 6228
Russo, Ralph D., 7453
Russo, Robert J., 685
Russo, Thomas A., 5967
Rust, Edward B., Jr., 3174
Rust, John M., 9509
Rust, Mary L., 7517
Rust, Randy, 9631
Rust, Rosemary, 8941
Rusted, Dale, 2264
Ruth McC Tankersley Trust, 169
Ruth, David A., 4036
Rutherfoord, Thomas D., 1944
Rutherford, Ira A., 4372
Rutherford, James, 4827
Rutherford, John R., 8822
Rutherford, Mary, 5013
Rutherford, Peter, 9604
Rutherfurd, Winthrop, 7101
Rutherfurd, Winthrop, Jr., 5734, 5913, 7612
Rutkoff, Mally Z., 3110
Rutkowski, Lawrence R., 7051
Rutkowski, Walter F., 7966
Rutledge, Amanda D., 6784
Rutledge, Edward, 9939
Rutledge, Gary L., 4853
Rutledge, Kathleen, 5096
Rutledge, Peter L., 6784
Rutledge, Sarah J., 6784
Rutledge, Stephen G., 2

Saic General Motors Sales Co., 1791
Saich, Anthony J., 3982
Said, Abdul Aziz, 1903
Saigh, Fred M., 4965
Saika, Peggy, 1109
Saikami, Duane, 722
Saiki, Curtis, 2602
Sailer, Jim, 5194
Sailer, William, 1048
Sailey, Joseph M., 6487
Sain, Steve, 239
Saint James, Susan, 1512
Saint, David, 6338
Saint-Amand, Alexander, 4818
Saint-Amand, Cynthia C., 4818
Saint-Amand, Elisabeth, 4818
Saint-Amand, Nathan, 8373
Saint-Amand, Nathan E., 4818
Saint-Gobain Autover USA, Inc., 7638
Saint-Gobain Corporation, 8260
Saiontz, Leslie, 2241
SAISD, 9149
Saito, Kenichi, 9881
Sajdak, Robert A., 4358
Sajevic, Joe, 5039
Sajjad, Nabeela, 224
Sak, Elizabeth, 5827
Saka, Charles, 5432
Saka, Jeffrey, 5432
Saka, Raymond, 5432
Saka, Sammy, 5432
Sakacs, Linda, 6276
Sakaida, Hideya, 6997
Sakar International Inc., 5432
Sakellaris, Harry, 9480
Sakmar, Thomas, 7080
Sakowicz, Adrian, 2803
Sakrison, James S., 95
Saks, Howard J., 1184
Saks, Jane M., 5833
Saks, Mark, 5855, 5952, 5977, 6036, 6207, 6524, 7028, 7110, 7124
Saks, Mark W., 5562, 5655, 5789, 6576, 6622
Sala, Angelica, 5889
Salah, James M., 1855
Salamatof Native Association, 85
Salanitri, Marie, 5372
Salatino, Cicely, 237
Salazar, Carlos, 4937
Salazar, Kathleen H., 1270
Saldana, Rafael, 2238
Saldanha, Anna, 5801
Sale, Anne, 8619
Saleeby, Amy, 1648
Saleh, William B., 516
Salem, Albert, Jr., 2151
Salem, Paul J., 8434
Salenger, Stuart, 6044
Salerno, Judith G., 4056
Salesforce, 9652
Salgado, Rose, 419
Salgado, Sandy, 9
Salgado, Sebastio, 5526
Saligman, Alice, 8261
Saligman, Carolyn, 8261
Saligman, Ira, 8261
Saligman, Laury, 8261
Saligman, Robert, 8261
Salimi, Hisham, 5934
Salina, Paul G., 1564
Salinas Valley Community Church, 9118
Salisbury, Tod P., Esq., 3758
Salizzoni, Frank L., 4902
Salkin, Alexandra Derby, 877
Salkind, Louis, 5710
Sall, Elizabeth A., 3132
Sall, English, 3132
Sall, John Phillip, 3132
Sall, Leslie C., 3132
Sall, Virginia B., 3132
Sall, William, 3132
Sallee, Jaclyn, 85
Sallick, Richard M., 6635
Sallin, Timothee, 2039
Salmon, Gene A., 3133
Salmon, Walter, 4057
Salo, Lynn D., 228
Salomon, Arthur R., 3560
Salomon, Charles, 6119
Salomon, Christina, 6785
Salomon, David, 6785
Salomon, Edna, 6785
Salomon, Jennifer, 6785
Salomon, Lionel J., 6546
Salomon, Richard B., 6785
Salomon, Richard E., 6785
Salomon, Staci, 6398
Salous, Omaima, 4330
Salquist, Gary, 7363
Salsa, Domenick A., 2370
Salsberg, Eric P., 9178
Salsbery, Phil, 3296
Salsman, Gloria, 3481
Salta Charitable Lead Trust, 1105
Salta, Gabriel Farao, 1105
Salta, Jan, 1105
Salta, Janet Lyn, 1105
Salta, Mike, 1105
Salta, Steven J., 1105
Salter, Lee W., 898
Saltiel, Karen Fine, 2433, 2534
Saltonstall, Alice W., 4174
Saltonstall, G. West, 4174
Saltonstall, Mary "Polly", 3698
Saltonstall, Mary R., 4254
Saltonstall, Patrick G., 4174
Saltonstall, Richard, 4254
Saltonstall, Timothy, 4174
Saltonstall, William L., Jr., 4174
Saltsgiver, Joann, 8262
Saltsgiver, Thomas M., 8262
Saltus Grammar School, 6925
Saltz Charitable Lead Annuity Trust, Leonard, 6786
Saltz Charitable Lead Annuity Trust, Ronald, 6786
Saltz Charitable Lead Annuity Trust, Susan, 6786
Saltz, Anita, 6786, 6787
Saltz, Jack, 6786, 6787
Saltz, Leonard, 6786
Saltz, Leonard B., 6787
Saltz, Ronald, 6786
Saltz, Ronald I., 6787
Saltz, Susan, 6786, 6787
Saltzman, Esther E., 3720
Saltzman, Rob, 324
Salva, Gary P., 1644
Salvador Imaging, Inc., 1491
Salvaggio, Anthony, 8263
Salvaggio, Norene L., 8263
Salvaggio, Thomas A., 8263
Salvatori, Kurt, 8332
Salvo, Calogero, 4681
Salyer, Meg, 7766
Salyer, Richard, 1210
Salzberg, Deborah Ratner, 1931, 7626
Salzer, Richard L., Jr., 6105
Salzman, Ruth, 5206
Salzmann, Benjamin M., 9801
Sam and Janet Sato, 3303
Sam, Albert D., II, 3613
Sam, Ellen H., 1342
Sam, Wah-Pui, 1342
Samad, Sam, 7398
Samaris, Shirley, 1643
Samaritan's Purse, 2087
Samberg, Arthur, 9527
Samberg, Rebecca, 9527
Samborsky, Ronald, 569
Sambroak, Barbara F., 8026
Sambucci, Lisa M., 4183
Sambunaris, Victoria, 6644
Samburg Family Foundation, 7791
Samerian Foundation, 3317
Samford, Janet, 8809
Samil, Dimek, 5136
Samloff, Harold, 7099
Sammis, Cheri, 4532
Samolczyk, Mark J., 7673
Samosky, Kristen, 7921
Sampaio, Jorge, 5747
Sample, Anne, 9956
Sample, Carolyn, 4737
Sample, Carolyn P., 4737
Sample, Kristina Lloyd, 1980
Sampson Foundation, Twila, 3878
Sampson, Cynthia, 3682
Sampson, Elbert, 8175
Sampson, Holly C., 4649
Sampson, J. Faye, 3878
Sampson, Mathew L., Esq., 8001
Sampson, Morris E., 1942
Sampson, Myles D., 3878
Sampson, Patricia, 7945
Sampson, Tim, 8994
Sams, Alfred, III, 2431
Sams, Earl C., 9145
Samson Charitable Lead Annuity Trust, Marvin, 5434
Samson, David, 2238
Samson, Lori, 7905
Samson, Marvin, 5434
Samsung Telecommunications America, 782
Samuel, Deena Qubein, 7231
Samueli 1995 Family Trust, The, 1106
Samueli Charitable Trust No. 00-1, 1106
Samueli, Henry, 349, 1106
Samueli, Susan, 1106
Samuelian, Steve, 1025
Samuels, Barbara, 3180
Samuels, Fan Fox, 6788
Samuels, Ivan A., 872
Samuels, Joseph T., Jr., 9405
Samuels, Laurel M., 872
Samuels, Leslie R., 6788
Samuels, Lourdes Peri, 4298
Samuels, Maurice, 4298
Samuels, Robert, 4057
Samuels, Sidney P., 872
Samuels, Theodore R., 375
Samuelsson, Ada, 6016
Samulski, Joseph M., 6052, 6375
San Diego Union Shoe Fund, 428
San Francisco Film Society, 5779
San Francisco Foundation, 5114
San Inocencio, Victor Garcia, 8353
San Joaquin County Office of Education Educational Foundation, 417
San Pedro, Claudia, 7742
Sanborn, Candace, 3698
Sanbrano, Angela, 6151
Sanchez Charitable Lead Annuity Trust, Alicia M., 9150
Sanchez, Alicia M., 9150
Sanchez, Ana Lee, 9150
Sanchez, Antonio R., III, 9150
Sanchez, Antonio R., Jr., 9150
Sanchez, Eduardo, 9150
Sanchez, Frank I., 7588
Sanchez, Frank M., 809, 1270
Sanchez, George & Mary Ann, 7659
Sanchez, Manolo, 9
Sanchez, Maria J., 9150
Sanchez, Marisol, 3272
Sanchez, Miren duPont, 1814
Sanchez, Patricio, 9150
Sanchez, Philip, 6982
Sanchez, Richard, 989
Sanchez, Sally, 3514
Sanchez, Thomasa, 2015
Sanchez, Tony, 5136
Sanchez, Tricia Grigsby, 3640
Sanchez, Yvonne, 9722
Sand, Carolyn H., 1955
Sand, Richard, 6945
Sand, Wesley, 7845
Sandak, Jay H., 1860
Sandak, Mary E., 1860
Sandberg, Michael, 5398
Sandbulte, Arend J., 4649
Sandefer Capital Partners, LP, 8822
Sandefer, Jeff, 7616
Sandefer, Jeff D., 8822
Sandefer, Laura, 8822
Sandefur, Charles C., 1288
Sander, Daniel J., 7481
Sander, Marcia, 848
Sandercock, Tara McKenzie, 7180
Sanderhoff, Steen, 9924
Sanders, 8756
Sanders Enterprises, Lawrence, 2305
Sanders Rev. Trust, Lawrence A., 2305
Sanders Trust, Lawrence A., 2305
Sanders, Anthony, 8834
Sanders, Bryan L., 1041
Sanders, Carol P., 9944
Sanders, Charles A., 2448, 7274
Sanders, Chris, 9152
Sanders, Corey, 2875
Sanders, Daniel, 7886
Sanders, David, 4869, 7671, 9595
Sanders, Deen Day, 2448
Sanders, Derial H., 8042
Sanders, Don A., 9152
Sanders, H. Walker, 7180
Sanders, Herman R., 7481
Sanders, Joseph, 956
Sanders, Julie G., 3821
Sanders, Lanny, 7771
Sanders, Machelle, 8363
Sanders, Melinda, 3527
Sanders, Melinda Lawrence, 8591
Sanders, Molly, 7886
Sanders, Olive Jane, 7886
Sanders, Paul, 9069
Sanders, Robert C., 7886
Sanders, Robert Deutch Petery, 6229
Sanders, Robert T., 7886
Sanders, Samuel, 7886
Sanders, Steven L., 8221
Sanders, Sue, 3288
Sanders, Susan N., 8492
Sanders, Theresa, 9615

Sanders, Tom, 4694
Sanders, Victoria B., 9377
Sanders, W.F., Jr., 46
Sanders, William C., 8922
Sanderson, Bill, 633
Sanderson, Brogann, 6115
Sanderson, Carolyn, 5411
Sanderson, Don, 4461
Sanderson, Peggy, 9733
Sanderson, Veronica, 4684
Sandhurst Associates, 5982
Sandler, Barbara, 1068
Sandler, David P., 7918
Sandler, Ellen, 927
Sandler, Harvey, 2306
Sandler, Herman, 5839
Sandler, Mara, 6789
Sandler, Neil, 6320
Sandler, Phyllis, 2306
Sandler, Richard, 927
Sandler, Ricky, 6789
Sandler, Susan Rule, 263
Sandler, Wendy, 6320
Sandlin, Larry, 9003
Sandlin, Maria Louisa, 9003
Sandlin, Mary Jo, 9052, 9088, 9111
Sandman, Brent, 3265
Sandman, Dan D., 7966
Sandman, David, 6549
Sandman, James, 1931
Sandner, John F., 2756
Sandness, Paul K., 7354
Sandorf, Julie, 7276
Sandorf, Julie A., 6693
Sandoval, Arturo, 1419
Sandoval, Niki, 1116
Sandow, Darren, 6127
Sandoz Corp., 6569
Sandridge, Leonard W., Jr., 9405
Sands, Christine, 3336
Sands, Elizabeth, 5435
Sands, Estelle M., 5435
Sands, George H., 5435
Sands, J. Clayton, 9140
Sands, Jeffrey H., 5435
Sands, Marilyn, 6790
Sands, Patrick B., 9140
Sands, Richard, 6790
Sands, Robert, 6790
Sands, Stephen, 9140
Sands, Susan J., 4616
Sands, Tim, 1039
Sands, Vincent V., 7946
Sandstrom, Constance, 3699
Sandvik, Helvi, 88
Sandy, George H., 1113
Sanford, Brenda, 2632
Sanford, Bruce W., 3600
Sanford, G.W., Jr., 8674
Sanford, Jo Anne, 7321
Sanford, Kay, 8759
Sanford, Rachael, 9421
Sanford, Shelton, 8102
Sanfrey, Janis, 7705
Sanger, Abbie W., 5940
Sanger, Alexander C., 7687
Sanger, James R., 9927
Sanger, Linda M., 5940
Sanger, Martha F.S., 8049
Sanger, Terence D., 5940
Sanger, Victoria, 5940
Sangiacomo, Angelo, 1115
Sangiacomo, James, 1115
Sangiacomo, Maria, 1115
Sangiacomo, Mark, 1115
Sangiacomo, Mia, 1115
Sangiacomo, Sandro, 1115
Sangiacomo, Susan, 1115
Sangiacomo, Yvonne, 1115
Sangiacomo-Iacomini, Maryanne, 1115
Sangster, Claudia, 968
Sankary, Scott, 8776
Sankey, Beth H., 7643
Sankey, James K., 7643
Sanna, Polly Weintz, 6132
Sannes, Aaron, 3423
Sannes, Heather E., 3142
Sanofi-Aventis US, LLC, 5437
Sans, Henri L., 4194
Sansing, Peggy L., 2307
Sansing, Robert C., 2307
Sansom, Andrew H., 8904
Sansone, Daniel F., 73
Sansone, Peter, 648
Sansone, Philip, 9276
Sant, Chrissie, 1950
Sant, Kristin, 1950
Sant, Leo M., 7808
Sant, Lex, 1950
Sant, Maralynn V., 7808
Sant, Michael, 1950
Sant, Roger, 1950
Sant, Stephen R., 8098
Sant, Victoria P., 1893, 1950
Sant-Johnson, Ali, 1950
Santamaria, Manuel, 1166
Santanello, Nancy C., 1929
Santangelo, Joseph A., 5611
Santangelo, Luly, 6640
Santarelli, Marino J., 1682
Sante, B. Joanne, 2654
Sante, Mike, 2654
Santen, Inc., 9915
Santhera Pharmaceuticals, 6898
Santi, Ernest Scott, 2934
Santiago, Arline, 5960
Santiago, Jose, 2823
Santilli, Vincent E., 1671
Santini, Alex, 7931
Santini, Leonard, 2327
Santis, Jorge H., 5438
Santmann, Theresa M., 6793
Santona, Gloria, 3012
Santoni, Roland J., 1314
Santori, Mary Beth, 4732
Santoro, Barbara A., 5314
Santoro, Christiane, 1114
Santos, Frank, 2294
Santos, John F., 3113
Santos, Peta Smit, 7112
Santos, Rudy, 8775
Santulli, Margaret, 6760
Santulli, Richard T., 6760
Sanyal, Subir K., 5765
Sanzi, James, 8429
SAP Global Marketing, Inc., 1153
Saper, Carol, 6794
Saper, Lawrence, 6794
Saperstein, Jill, 1004
Saperstein, Shira, 1950
Sapienza, Anne, 1650
Sapiro, Lisa, 670
Sapiro, Mark, 670
Sapirstein, Jacob, 7644
Sapoch, Jamie Kyte, 5220
Sapp, Adam, 8208
Sapp, Nancy Ware, 8208
Sapp, Richard, 1053
Sapp, Richard A., 6796
Sapp, Shari M., 6796
Sapper, Jon, 714
Saqi, Vinay, 9005
Sar, Ali, 701
Saravia, Nancy G., 2871
Sardone, Frank, 4472
Sargeant, Kimon Howland, 8313
Sargent Revocable Trust, Ellen, 1836
Sargent, Barbara, 761
Sargent, D. Thomas, 761
Sargent, Judith L., 5152
Sargent, Melaney, 3319
Sargent, Sara Ann, 7990
Sarin, Arun, 1519
Saris, Patti B., 3997
Sarkeys, S.J., 7793
Sarkowsky, Cathy, 9727
Sarkowsky, Faye, 9727
Sarkowsky, Herman, 9727
Sarkowsky, Steve, 9727
Sarles, Daniel G., 4029
Sarles, H. Jay, 4029
Sarles, Marilyn D., 4029
Sarli Crat, Ralph S., 3541
Sarli, Mary Helen, 3541
Sarli, Ralph, 3541
Sarmiento, Gil M., 2946
Sarna, Judith Eigen, 6870
Sarnat Charitable Lead Trust II, 1117
Sarnat, Bernard G., 1117
Sarnat, Joan E., 1117
Sarnat, Rhoda G., 1117
Sarofim, Allison, 6797
Sarofim, Christopher, 6797
Sarofim, Christopher B., 8731, 9154
Sarofim, Fayez, 476, 9154
Sarofim, Louisa S., 6797
Sarofim, Louisa Stude, 6797, 8731, 9154
Saroki, Stephanie, 7616
Sarosdy, Emma, 8095
Sarpin Developments, LP, 5773
Sarpolis, Keith, 2826
Sarra, Jon J., 5802
Sarratt, Mark, 5062
Sarrel, Lloyd, 3193
Sartor, C. Lane, 3673
Sarver, James H., 9779
Sarver, James H., II, 9779
Sarver, Jay, 4995
Sarver, Robert G., 175
Sasaki, Nancy L., 229
SASL, 9228
Sass, Steven D., Esq., 3759
Sasscer, Brian, 1891
Sasser, Barbara, 8952
Sasser, Leslie E., 8826
Sasson, Albert, 5488
Sasson, Sam N., 5488
Sasson, Samantha, 5488
Sastri, Candace J., 4197
Sastri, Rakhal Dev, 4197
Sastri, Suri A., Dr., 4197
Satchell, Ernest R., 3760
Satlof, Mark, 6022, 6023
Satloff, James, 5604
Sato, Akihiro, 281
Satre, Jennifer A., 5108
Satter Foundation, 6898
Satter, Muneer, 6898
Satter, Muneer A., 3136
Satterfield, B.K., 9770, 9794
Satterfield, L. Kent, 9444
Satterfield, Travis, 4823
Satterfield, William, 9774
Satterlee, Ellen, 4579
Satterwhite, Scott, 7244
Saucedo, Mary Carmen, 8825
Saucerman, Kristi, 4107
Sauer Group Inc., 5482
Sauer, Diane, 7415
Sauer, William, 1100
Sauerman, Dick, 3291
Sauers, Kim, 3393
Sauget, Richard A., 4966
Sauke, Leon, 7010
Saul, Andrew, 5601
Saul, Denise, 5601
Saul, Dianne P., 3036
Saul, Harry I., 2547
Saul, Julian D., 2547
Saul-Sena, Linda, 2040
Sauls, David L., 7319
Saulson, Eli, 4390
Saunders, Anita Ford, 1589
Saunders, Barry, 8462
Saunders, Barry L., 8500
Saunders, Carolyn, 3626
Saunders, Christine, 1118
Saunders, Joseph W., 1118
Saunders, Kay A., 4920
Saunders, Michael, 2142
Saunders, Nancy A., 4239
Saunders, R.R., 3626
Saunders, Rob, 4768
Saunders, Ruby Lee, 2308
Saunders, Sharon P., 1118
Saunders, Shirley R., 2113
Saunders, Steve, 8676
Saunders, Thomas J., 1118
Saunders, Whitney G., 9391, 9538
Saunders, William N., 2308
Saurage, Donna M., 3671
Sauvayre, Sarah Chubb, 5490
Savage, C. Jack, 9772
Savage, Cheri, 1116
Savage, Harriet, 7041
Savage, Lois, 136
Savage, Michael D., 5721
Savage, Philip, IV, 419
Savage, Sarah, 22
Savannah Electric Foundation, Inc., 2468
Savarese, Dorothy A., 3973
Savas, Paul G., 6628
Savedoff, Stuart H., 2223
Savido, Evelyn D., 8043
Saviers, Vicki, 197
Savignano, Whitney, 3127
Saving, Kay L., 2933
Savings Bank of Manchester Foundation, Inc., 1690
Savino, Frank, 5641
Savran, Bella, 5290
Sawczuk, Cornelia Urban, 3489
Sawicki, Tracy A., 7000
Sawrey, Barbara A., 1108
Sawtell, Sarah, 5533
Sawyer, Adrian, 523
Sawyer, Bo, 2524
Sawyer, Caren, 492
Sawyer, Gail L., 5147
Sawyer, John, 3594
Sawyer, L. Diane, 5842
Sawyer, Martha J., 2186
Sawyer, Raymond T., 7409
Sawyer, Wayne K., 9538

Sax, Ellen, 5803
Saxton, Carolyn, 3337
Saybrook, Inc., 7859
Sayers, Donald D., 7342
Sayers, Linda Rohrerrohrer, 8252
Sayfer, Steven M., 6414
Saykaly, Ronald, Dr., 3560
Sayler, Elizabeth Jubitz, 7859
Saylor, Clifford W., 149
Saylor, James L., II, 2279
Saylors, Charlotte, 172
Sayrafe, Kristine, 5400
Sayre, Richard H., 3980
Sayre, Sharon A., 9206
Sazerac Co., Inc., 3638, 3672
SB Westridge, Inc., 3142
SBC Communications Inc., 8675
SBH Intimates Inc., 6131
Scaglione, Janice F., 2111
Scagliotti, Nackey & Robert, 7659
Scaife, David N., 8017
Scaife, Frances G., 8017
Scaife, Jennie K., 2309
Scaife, Richard M., 7911, 7968, 8266
Scaife, Sara D., 8017
Scaife, Sarah Mellon, 2309, 8266
Scaife, Walter B., 973
Scalamandre, Ernest, 8721
Scaler Foundation, Inc., 1788
Scales, Julie, 2269
Scallon, Theodore J., 6153
Scalvino, Pauline C., 8327
Scammahorn, Kamala Lightner, 8985
Scangas, Christopher, 4070
Scanlan, John McAllen, 9156
Scanlan, Mary, 1368
Scanlan, Mary Bucksbaum, 3137
Scanlan, Patrick, 3137
Scanlan, William, 8886
Scanlan, William J., 19
Scanlan, William, Jr., 8868, 9156
Scanlan, Wilson M., 9156
Scanlon, Jennifer F., 3200
Scanlon, Patrick, 8218
Scanlon, William, 8885
Scannell, Michael, 4285
Scannelli, Sandi, 2033
ScanSource, Inc., 8495
Scantlebur, Joseph, 4474
Scarafile, Judy Walden, 4329
Scarborough, Christopher, 5291
Scardina, Julie, 2315
Scardino, Frank P., 917
Scardino, Marjorie M., 2989
Scarff, Bill, 7671
Scarfone, Anthony C., 4644
Scarlett, Andrew S., 8624
Scarlett, Catherine M., 5802
Scarlett, Clifford, 5927
Scarlett, Dorothy F., 8624
Scarlett, Jennifer, 8624
Scarlett, Joseph H., Jr., 8624
Scarlett, Tara Anne, 8624
Scarpa, John F., 2310
Scarpello, Fred, 5139
Scarritt, John D., 1634
Scarsella, Julie, 7415
Scarver, Michelle R., 9148
Scavo, Alton J., 3877
Scears, Michael A., 7796
Schaaf, Renee, 3476
Schaap, A. Paul, 4533
Schaap, Carol C., 4533
Schack, Paul, 2156
Schacter, Barbara, 6935
Schadt, Deborah O., 8530
Schaedler, Barbara M., 7930
Schaefer, Barbara, 7396
Schaefer, Barbara W., 5090
Schaefer, Carol, 5451
Schaefer, Charles V., III, 5451
Schaefer, Charles V., IV, 5451
Schaefer, Charles V., Jr., 5451
Schaefer, David A., 3531
Schaefer, Eileen Bonnie, 2311
Schaefer, Emily K., 7184
Schaefer, Gary L., 9931
Schaefer, Jamie C., 9834
Schaefer, John, 103
Schaefer, John P., 95, 157
Schaefer, Katheryn D., 3531
Schaefer, Lynne, 3759
Schaefer, R. Gregory, 4855
Schaefer, Robert, 9677
Schaefer, Rowland, 2311
Schaefer, William Donald, 3880
Schaeffer Family Foundation, 1121
Schaeffer, Donald M., 5873
Schaeffer, George, 1121
Schafale, Mark A., 2824
Schafer, Amanda, 4512
Schafer, Betty R., 3913
Schafer, Judi, 9715
Schafer, Maureen, 5134
Schaffer, Cathie, 5979
Schaffer, Jan, 7749
Schaffer, Kyle, 4056
Schaffer, Marianna, 6725
Schaffer, Tammy, 3403
Schaffert, Kim, 5045
Schaffler, Charles D., 8530
Schaffner Family Foundation, 6800
Schaffner, Elizabeth B., 6800
Schaffner, Mary E., 1312
Schaffner, Patrick, 6621
Schaffner, Timothy, 6800
Schaffner, Valentine, 6800
Schain, Howard, 5612
Schair, Justin, 3695
Schalk, Bill, 4347
Schalk, John, 9510
Schaller, George, 5783
Schaller, Sandra J., 3311
Schalon, Edward I., 4534
Schalon, Marcella J., 4534
Schalon, Scott, 4534
Schalon, Susan K., 4534
Schamp, Niceas Baron, 6007
Schankler, Noah, 6498
Schankweiler, David, 8046
Schantz Trust, Susan, 3863
Schanzer, Ken, 1518
Schapira, Daniel, 5398
Schapiro Charitable Unitrust, Morris A., 6801
Schapiro, Daniel E., 6801
Schapiro, Morris A., 6801
Schapperle, John F., 2606
Scharbauer, Clarence, 9157
Scharbauer, Clarence, III, 8650
Scharbauer, Clarence, Jr., 9157
Scharf Family Trust, David, 5759
Scharf Trust f/b/o Manuel, Leon, 5951
Scharf, Asher, 5759
Scharf, Charles, 5773
Scharf, Chava, 5951
Scharf, Ester, 5773
Scharf, Esther, 5773
Scharf, Irene, 5937
Scharf, Leon, 5937
Scharf, Manuel, 5951
Scharf, Moses, 5759
Scharf, Scharf, & Beer, 5937
Scharf, Sharon, 5773
Scharf, Yisroel, 5951
Scharff, Matthew D., 7080
Scharmann, Jo-Anne, 1521
Schastok, Sara L., 2826
Schatz, Adrienne, 1496
Schatz, David, 1496
Schatz, Douglas S., 1496
Schatz, Jill E., 1496
Schatz, Jill M., 1496
Schatz, Sanford L., 8383
Schatz, Susan, 6228
Schauder, Kenneth, 8062
Schauer, Laura, 4716
Schauer, W. E., 9932
Schaul, Mark H., 9780
Schaupp, Mary G., 9836
Schaures, Lisa, 9652
Schawk, Clarence W., 3138
Schawk, Marilyn G., 3138
Schear, Lee, 7645
Schear, Patricia, 7645
Schechner, Amy, 5296
Schechtel, Andrew J., 5455
Schechter, Leroy, 5439
Scheck, Jeff, 3201
Schecter, Aaron, 2320
Schecter, Julie, 2320
Schecter, Laurie, 2320
Schecter, Leroy, 5439
Schecter, Martha, 2320
Scheder-Bieschien, Dietrich, 8829
Scheef, David, 9196
Scheef, Marisa L., 9196
Scheef, Samuel R., 9196
Scheel, Fred B., 7359
Scheel, James E., 7814
Scheel, Steve D., 7359
Scheel, Steve M., 7359
Scheeler, C. Ron, 7273
Scheeler, Charles B., 3781
Scheer, Brick, 3507
Scheer, Dana, 2100
Scheer, Elizabeth L., 3612
Scheer, Jeffrey, 2135
Schefer, Norman A., 6372
Scheffel, William N., 4870
Scheflen, Janna E., 1786
Scheflen, John W., 1786
Scheflen, Marcia W., 1786
Scheiber, Fred, 3324
Scheiber, Jim, 3324
Scheich, Adrienne M., 3923
Scheid, Peter, 7515
Scheidel, Henry, 9528
Scheidel, Herbert, 9528
Scheidel, Miki, 9528
Scheidel, Miyuki, 9528
Scheidt, E. Elkan, 8625
Scheidt, Helen H., 8625
Scheidt, Kathleen, 2650
Scheidt, Kurt, 673
Scheidt, Rudi E., 8625
Scheidt, Rudi E., Jr., 8625
Scheine, Elizabeth Montgomery, 2518
Schejola, Linda, 1856
Schejola, Linda S., 2547
Schejola, Lisa, 1856
Schell, Charles E., 7646
Schell, Jacquelyn A., 6567
Scheller, Ernest, Jr., 8268
Scheller, Lisa, 8268
Scheller, Richard H., 571
Scheller, Roberta, 8268
Schellhorn, Charles, 4893
Schemel, Elizabeth A., 2312
Schemel, Gregory S., 2312
Schemel, Richard G., 2312
Schemel, Robert G., 2312
Schemel, Robert G., II, 2312
Schenck, Lillian Pitkin, 8269
Schenck, Todd, 9313
Schendel, Richard, 9117
Schendel, Walter G., III, 5598
Schenk Charitable Lead Unitrust, Kathleen H., 9793
Schenk Charitable Remainder Annuity Trust, 9793
Schenk, Daniel, 3402
Schenk, Deborah M., 7459
Schenk, Julie, 7808
Schenker Family Foundation, 7012
Schenker, Curtis, 6803
Schenker, Leo, 6803
Schenker, Livia, 6803
Scheper, Charles R., 7404
Schepps, A.I., 9158
Schepps, Barbara, 8383
Schepps, Manet, 9158
Schepps, Mitchell D., 2265
Scherer, Aaron, 6189
Scherer, Thomas W., 8530
Scherle, Joseph S., 2146
Schermer, Betty A., 1492
Schermer, Gregory P., 3457
Schermer, Lloyd G., 1492
Scherr, Jacob, 8914
Schervish, Thomas W., 7673
Scherzer, Mitchell, 6155, 6156
Scherzinger, Steve, 7483
Scheuer, Judith, 6390
Scheuer, Susan, 6390
Scheufler, Wes, 9528
Scheumann, Theiline P., 9693
Schewel, Marc A., 9474
SCHI, 5251
Schiavoni, Mark A., 91
Schick, Kevin, 849
Schick, Thomas, 5588
Schickler, Paul E., 3474
Schieffelin, Sarah I., 8270
Schiek, Frederick, 3428
Schield, Darren, 1218
Schiele, George, 6334, 6337
Schier, Irene Reynolds, 2546
Schierbeek, Robert H., 4398, 4399, 4400, 4418, 4559, 4572
Schierl, Carol A., 9836
Schierl, Michael J., 9836
Schierl, Paul J., 9836
Schiewetz, Richard F., 7647
Schiff Charitable Lead Annuity Trust Accounts, Robert C., 7648
Schiff Food Products Co., 5413
Schiff, Andrew N., 6805
Schiff, David T., 6805
Schiff, Edith B., 6805
Schiff, James A., 7648
Schiff, John J., 7649
Schiff, John M., 6805
Schiff, Mary R., 7649
Schiff, Patricia Palmer, 2871
Schiff, Peter G., 6805

Schiff, Robert C., 7648
Schiff, Robert C., Jr., 7648
Schiff, Stacy, 6116
Schiff, Thomas R., 7649
Schiffer, Karen, 601
Schiffman, Theodore, 5592
Schill, Michael H., 6868
Schiller, J.R., 2628
Schilling, Carol P., 3372
Schilling, Dean, 3347
Schilling, Frank, 3347
Schilling, Frank E., 3347
Schilling, Gregory, 3347
Schilling, Jeffrey, 3347
Schilling, Joe, 9521
Schilling, Mike, 1511
Schilling, Richard J., 2488
Schilling, Shirley, 3347
Schilling, Todd, 3347
Schilling, Vicki, 7762
Schillinger, Sara, 7877
Schiltz, Laura A., 3480
Schimberg, Alice, 3110
Schimmel, Rosalba, 1122
Schimmel, Stephen Harold, 1122
Schindele, Carrie, 5725
Schindhelm, Klaus, 1063
Schindler-Johnson, Elizabeth, 437
Schineller, Glenn, 7214
Schinke, Rick, 9832
Schipper, Kathy, 3456
Schippers, Phyllis, 9967
Schirmer Estate, The, 8492
Schirmer, Henry, 5484
Schisler, Kurt E., 7413
Schlachter, Harry, 6968
Schlappi, Art, 9412
Schlatter, Martin, 3244
Schleck, Mark T., 9729
Schlegel, Theodore F., 1374
Schlehuber, Michelle M., 4766
Schlehuber, Thomas M., 4766
Schleicher, William T., 2760
Schleicher, William T., Jr., 2761
Schlemmer, Robert N., 7688
Schlesinger, Harvey E., Hon., 2031
Schlesinger, Mark, 557
Schlesinger, Mark L., 557
Schlesinger, R. Diane, 241
Schlesinger, Steven R., 6055
Schlesinger, Stuart, 6287
Schlesinger, Thaleia, 4051
Schlesinger, William H., 5917, 5918, 5919
Schlessinger, Burd B., 7457
Schley, Scott, 5295, 5368
Schleyer, William T., 5188
Schlichter, Susan, 4888
Schlichting, Nancy M., 4479
Schlicker, Carl, 4297
Schlieder, Edward G., 3665
Schliesman, Paul, 4671
Schliesman, Paul D., 7353
Schlifske, John E., 9914
Schlimgen, Leesa D., 9839
Schlinger Foundation, Warren & Katherine, 1123
Schlinger Trust, Michael S., 1123
Schlinger, Greg S., 1123
Schlinger, Leanne M., 1123
Schlinger, Michael S., 1124
Schlinger, Michael Stewart, 1123
Schlinger, Norman W., 1124
Schlinger, Stacy, 1123
Schlinger, Warren G., 1124
Schlink, Albert G., 7650
Schlink, Olive H., 7650
Schlitz, Timothy D., 7492
Schloenbach, Steven, 7367
Schloesser, Jack, 9916
Schlosberg, Richard T., 9148
Schloss, Barry I., 3908
Schloss, Herta, 6907
Schloss, Jeffrey P., 8313
Schloss, Neil M., 4430
Schlossberg, Eli, 2258
Schlosser, Cheryl, 7597
Schlossman, Carol, 7351
Schlosstein, Ralph L., 6807
Schlott, Robert, 3447
Schlotterbeck, Steven T., 8025
Schlough, Joyce, 4631
Schlue, Larry, 3459
Schlueter, Richard, 2822
Schmank, James, 3552
Schmeltekopf, Lawrence M., 9246
Schmeltz, Amy, 6634
Schmetterer, Robert, 2253
Schmid, Chris, 7592
Schmid, Jeffrey R., 5071
Schmid, Karen M., 8189
Schmider, Ernie, 1037
Schmidhauser, Eric, 8649
Schmidhauser, Lucie, 8649
Schmidlapp, Jacob G., 7651
Schmidlkofer, Kathleen, 4715, 4757
Schmidt Irrevocable Charitable Lead Annuity Trust, Jareen E., 8824
Schmidt Revocable Trust, Jareen E., 8824
Schmidt, Allison, 9957
Schmidt, Andrew, 9957
Schmidt, Arthur J., 9957
Schmidt, Barbara M., 3139
Schmidt, Benno C., Jr., 4921
Schmidt, Buzz, 6164
Schmidt, Carl, 4758
Schmidt, Carl G., 3457
Schmidt, Catherine B., 3139
Schmidt, Charles E., 3139
Schmidt, Chris, 9566
Schmidt, Daniel P., 9819
Schmidt, Diane, 9394
Schmidt, Emily, 9957
Schmidt, Eric, 1125
Schmidt, Gerry, 9799
Schmidt, Gladys, 5514
Schmidt, Janet, 9384
Schmidt, Jareen E., 8824
Schmidt, Jennifer L., 7647
Schmidt, Joseph, 2803
Schmidt, Kris, 4485
Schmidt, Linda, 5440
Schmidt, Lynn D., 8235
Schmidt, Mary, 3174
Schmidt, Oscar, 6479
Schmidt, Ralph, 5440
Schmidt, Raymond, 9957
Schmidt, Richard L., 3139
Schmidt, Richard W., 1389
Schmidt, Ronald, 8694
Schmidt, Ryan, 5440
Schmidt, Sophie, 1125
Schmidt, Thomas A., 9957
Schmidt, Tracy G., 2025
Schmidt, Verna, 4758
Schmidt, Wendy, 1125
Schmidt, William, 9957
Schmieding Produce Co., H.C., Inc., 200
Schmieding Revocable Trust, L.H., 200
Schmieding, H.C., 200
Schmieding, Helen, 200
Schmieding, L.H., 200
Schmit, Aaron, 7357
Schmitt, Alfons J., 7008
Schmitt, Arthur J., 3140
Schmitt, Caroline, 7224
Schmitt, Caroline F., 6808
Schmitt, Edward H., Jr., 2767
Schmitt, Kilian J., 6808
Schmitt, Susan J., 9934
Schmitz, Jeff J., 1493
Schmitz, Marilyn J., 1493
Schmitz, Martin J., 1493
Schmitz, Richard, 1493
Schmitz, Richard V., 1493
Schmitz, Vincent N., 1493
Schmoke, Kurt, 6868
Schmoke, Kurt L., 3818, 5747
Schmolka, Leo L., 2912
Schmotter, James, 1581
Schmoyer, Terry K., Jr., 8468
Schnabel, Rockwell, Hon., 756
Schneickert, Michael D., 1015
Schneider Irrevocable Trust, Louis and Anne, 8271
Schneider National, Inc., 9942
Schneider, Charlene, 5068
Schneider, Eric C., 5800
Schneider, Joe, 3294
Schneider, John, 3422
Schneider, Kathryn, 7905
Schneider, Katie, 5801
Schneider, Louis, 8271
Schneider, Martin H., 5577
Schneider, Melvyn H., 3162
Schneider, Michael I., 6621
Schneider, Mildred, 5927
Schneider, Milton S., 8238
Schneider, Pam H., 8238
Schneider, Pamela S., 2346
Schneider, Richard, 9635
Schneider, Richard A., 2573
Schneider, Scott N., 1708
Schneider, Stanley B., 258, 270
Schneidman, Richard, 6050, 7086
Schnettler, Thomas P., 4743
Schniedwind, Joan Lavezzorio, 3007
Schnitzer Investment Corp., 7888
Schnitzer, Arlene, 7887
Schnitzer, Gary, 7888
Schnitzer, Gilbert, 7888
Schnitzer, Harold J., 7887
Schnitzer, Jordan D., 7887
Schnitzer, Thelma, 7888
Schnitzler, Robb, 5067
Schnurmacher, Adolph, 6809
Schnurmacher, Charles M., 6810
Schnurmacher, Ruth, 6809
Schnurr, Andrew V., Jr., 5330
Schnurr, Don, 3419
Schoch, Arch K., IV, 7327
Schock, Clarence, 8272
Schoeffler, Mike, 3298
Schoelkopf, Grace G., 3977
Schoen, Jeffrey, 9456
Schoen, Julie, 133
Schoen, Laurie G., 4260
Schoen, Nancy Bernstein, 1887
Schoen, Robert, 1887
Schoen, Scott A., 4260
Schoenbaum, Alex, 2313
Schoenbaum, Betty Jane, 2313
Schoenbaum, Emily, 2313
Schoenbaum, Jeffry F., 2313
Schoenbaum, Raymond D., 2313
Schoenberger, Frances, 701
Schoenbrodt, Frederick K., II, 5232
Schoenecker, Barbara, 4759
Schoenecker, David, 4759
Schoenecker, Guy L., 4759
Schoenecker, Larry, 4759
Schoeneckers, Inc., 4759
Schoenfeld, Michael, 7328
Schoenhofen, Christa, 9818
Schoenrich, Edyth H., 3844
Schoenthaler, Sue, 1081
Schoenthaler, Susan P., 260
Schoessel, Carl, 4342
Schoettler, Gail S., 1390
Schoferig, S., 5937
Schokking, Ronald, 9178
Scholastic Inc., 3122
Scholl, Barry, 5800
Scholl, Daniel, 3141
Scholl, Dennis, 2191, 9079
Scholl, Jeanne M., 3141
Scholl, Pamela, 3141
Scholl, Susan, 3141
Scholl, William M., 3141
Scholler, F.C., 8273
Schollmaier, Edgar H., 9159
Schollmaier, Rama L., 9159
Schollmaier, Taylor, 9159
Scholsberg, Richard T., 760
Scholvinck, Marc, 321
Scholz, Denise Lienemann, 5020
Schon, Anna, 6811
Schon, Baron, 6811
Schon, Henry A., 6811
Schonbek, Alexandra, 9364
Schonbek, Alice J., 9364
Schonbek, Amelia, 9364
Schonbek, Andrew J., 9364
Schonbek, Charlotte, 9364
Schonbek-Beer, Eileen, 9364
Schonberger, A., 6812
Schonberger, Alfred, 6812
Schonberger, J., 6812
Schoneman, Debra L., 4743
Schonherr, Mike, 1002
Schonwald, Joseph, 5144
School Employees Credit Union of Washington, 9702
School Futures Research Foundation, 1387
Schooler, Edith, 7421
Schooler, Seward, 7421
Schooley, Susan, 4498
Schools, Bob, 3690
Schoon, Rodney, 3359
Schoonmaker, Judith D., 1644
Schoonmaker, Peter, 9998
Schoonmaker, Trevor, 7050
Schoppa, Paul, Jr., 8726
Schorr, Deb, 5063
Schorr, Diane, 9212
Schoshinski, James J., 9836
Schott, Cathy, 1393
Schott, Harold C., 7479
Schott, John W., 8313
Schott, Joseph J., 7652
Schott, Margaret U., 7653
Schott, Michael A., 8872
Schott, Michael F., 3641
Schott, Milton B., Jr., 7479

Schottco Corp., 7653
Schottenstein Stores Corp., 7435
Schottenstein, Geraldine, 7435
Schottenstein, Jay, 7654
Schottenstein, Jeffrey, 7654
Schottenstein, Jonathan, 7654
Schottenstein, Joseph, 7654
Schottenstein, Robert H., 7550
Schottenstein, Thomas H., 7655
Schow, Howard, 1126
Schow, Melanie J., 1126
Schow, Nan, 1126
Schow, Roger, 1126
Schow, Steven, 1126
Schowalter, J.A., 3542
Schrafft, Bertha E., 4263
Schrafft, William E., 4263
Schrag, Fred, 3534
Schrage, Stephanie, 3291
Schrager, Harley, 5079
Schrager, Jack, 5079
Schrager, Jeffrey, 5079
Schrager, Phillip G., 5079
Schrager, Richard A., 5079
Schrager, Terri, 5079
Schrager, Terri L., 5079
Schrager, Timothy, 5079
Schragg, Jeff, 9497
Schraibman, Michael, 8468
Schram, Gus W., III, 3619
Schram, Jessica S., 3883
Schramka, E.G., 9852
Schramm, James, 647
Schramm, Lee J., 4644
Schramm, Loren, 7417
Schrayer, Max R., II, 3110
Schreck, Daniel, 5776
Schreck, Edward, D.O., 7605
Schreder, Carleen, 3247
Schreiber, Brian T., 5563
Schreiber, John G., 3142
Schreiber, Kathleen A., 3142
Schreiber, Mark, 3514
Schreiber, Mary, 6745
Schreiber, Richard, 9558
Schreibman, Robert M., DMD, 1567
Schreier, Bradley, 4777
Schreier, Edward G., 6573
Schreiner, Linda V., 9484
Schrenck, Niklas, 9392
Schreyer, Chara, 1304
Schreyer, L.J., 6779
Schrier, Derek, 496
Schrier, Derek C., 496
Schrirfer, Barbara, 1932
Schrock, Bob, 3298
Schrock, Bonnie, 3570
Schrock, Charles A., 9970
Schroder, Rod, 8660
Schroder, Soren, 4865
Schroeder, Charles G., 7428
Schroeder, Denise, 4357
Schroeder, Donna L., 4873
Schroeder, Emily, 588
Schroeder, Fu, 877
Schroeder, Harry L., 4873
Schroeder, James L., 2933
Schroeder, John C., 3402
Schroeder, Mark, 488
Schroeder, Marybeth, 2826
Schroeder, Patricia, 9596
Schroeder, Sherrie, 2007, 7742
Schroeder, Sonya, 488
Schroeder, Steve, 9950
Schroeder, Steven, 877
Schroeder, Steven A., 727, 4753
Schroff, Becky, 598
Schroffel, Bruce, 1401
Schroffel, Judy, 3092
Schron, Avi, 5449
Schron, Eli, 5449
Schron, Mark, 5449
Schroth Ireevocable Trust, Mary Louise, 8274
Schroth, Virginia Cowles, 5234
Schrum, R.P., 8500
Schrum, Roger, 8468
Schrunk, Irene, 8517
Schryver, Caitlyn, 7005
Schubert, Alan, 8751
Schubert, Arthur H., 4599
Schubert, Gage A., 4599
Schubert, Helen D., 4599
Schubert, John Dwan, 4599
Schubert, Leland, 4599
Schubert, Leland W., 4599
Schuberth, Kenneth, 3909
Schueler, Kelley Christopher, 2748
Schuenemann, Latisha Bernard, 7939
Schuerman, Janice, 4943
Schuerman, Joan Parker, 108
Schuette, William D., 4444, 4517
Schuetz, Gerald, 7272
Schuetz, Joachim, 5779
Schuetz, Stephanie J., 6437
Schuh, Kevin, 9903
Schuiteman, Norma, 9605
Schul, Carole, 7570
Schulaner, Felice, 5790
Schuleit, Fran, 4452
Schuler, Beth, 5108
Schuler, Christopher T., 2614
Schuler, Dana D., 4406
Schuler, E. Carroll, 9203
Schuler, G.L., 979
Schuler, George, 979
Schuler, Hunt, 979
Schuler, Jack W., 3143
Schuler, James K., 2614
Schuler, Larry, 4347
Schuler, Mark J., 2614
Schuler, Mary Jo, 3061
Schuler, Patricia T., 2614
Schuler, Renate R., 3143
Schuler, Rosalie, 979
Schuler, Rosalie T., 979
Schuler, Scott D., 979
Schuler, Tino H., 3143
Schuler, Wendy R., 9801
Schull, E. Gunner, 2591
Schullinger, John N., 5248
Schulman, Alvin H., 6511
Schulman, Carol, 3076
Schulman, Charles R., 5616
Schulman, David, 3076
Schulman, Elizabeth, 6704
Schulman, Elizabeth R., 6704
Schulman, Joanna, 6395
Schulman, Michael, 1106
Schulson, Rachel, 8548
Schulte, Catherine, 8777
Schulte, Kathy, 1650
Schulte, Laura, 7202
Schulte, Robert L., 195
Schulten, Warren, 929
Schultheiss, Elizabeth N., 4332
Schults, Robert, 198
Schultz Family Foundation, 9742
Schultz Family Foundation, Howard & Leslie, 7791
Schultz, Adam, 3313
Schultz, Allen, 7682
Schultz, Allison, 5865
Schultz, Arthur B., 2641
Schultz, Carol, 161
Schultz, Chris, 9002
Schultz, Donald, 4587
Schultz, Erik B., 2641
Schultz, Howard D., 9730
Schultz, James, 3169
Schultz, Ken, 7816
Schultz, Kenneth M., 161
Schultz, Kristin Kellner, 9877
Schultz, Lisa Oppenheim, 6594
Schultz, Michael, 4921
Schultz, Mike, 3569
Schultz, Patricia Parker, 9828
Schultz, Roger E., 9559
Schultz, Sheri K., 9730
Schultz, Stephen, 3201
Schultz, Steven D., 1488
Schultz, Timothy W., 1374
Schultz, Valerian, 3004
Schultz, Wendy, 9485
Schulz, Cindy, 1455
Schulz, David, 3409
Schulz, Jean, 420
Schulz, Paul, 365
Schulze, Charles T., 5674
Schulze, Elizabeth, 3761
Schulze, Katherine E., 1362
Schulze, Maureen, 4760
Schulze, Peter B., 5674
Schulze, Richard L., 2875
Schulze, Richard M., 4760
Schulze, Rogert Ervin, 1120
Schumacher, Jeffrey, 5085
Schumacher, Kyle, 1512
Schumacher, Laura, 5085
Schumacher, Lillian, Dr., 7682
Schumacher, Robert, 4443
Schumacker, Bill, 7417
Schumaker, Kevina A., 3321
Schuman, Dale N., 9650
Schumann Foundation, Florence and John, 5441
Schumann, Florence, 5441
Schumann, Florence F., 6813
Schumann, John, 5441
Schumann, John J., Jr., 6813
Schumann, R. Ford, 6813
Schumann, W. Ford, 6813
Schumeister, Steven A., 4754
Schundler, Eloise T., 7026
Schupp, Joseph E., 4256
Schur, Howard, 2646
Schur, Michael, 6158
Schureman, Dave, 9659
Schurr, Dan, 4636
Schurr, Susan Korman, 8132
Schuss, Deena, 6290
Schuster, Donald, 4512
Schuster, Elaine, 4264
Schuster, Gerald, 4264
Schuster, Kenneth, 6569
Schuster, Mike, 5044
Schusterman Family Foundation, Charles and Lynn, 5717, 7734
Schusterman Revocable Trust, Stacy, 7734
Schusterman, Charles, 7794
Schusterman, Lynn, 7791, 7794
Schusterman, Stacy, 1387, 7791
Schusterman, Stacy H., 7734, 7794
Schut, Evert, 986
Schut, Mark A., 4536
Schutjer, April T., 9316
Schutt, Aaron, 89
Schutt, Clarence, 4162
Schutt, Laurisa S., 1765
Schutt, Paul, 4340
Schutte, Caroline, 9160
Schutter, Mark, 7474
Schutz, Ronald J., 4754
Schuur, Hendrik, 4467
Schwab & Co., Charles, Inc., 1127
Schwab Charitable Trust, 9652
Schwab Corp., Charles, The, 1127
Schwab, Charles R., 1127, 1128
Schwab, Helen O., 1128
Schwab, Jack, 7860
Schwab, Katie, 1128
Schwab, Maria, 8223
Schwab, Roger, 672
Schwab-Pomerantz, Carrie, 1127
Schwabacher, Christopher C., 6068
Schwabauer, Mary L., 1287
Schwager, Joni S., 8296
Schwan's Home Services, 7214
Schwan, Barry, 3555
Schwanfelder, Craig, 5516
Schwanfelder, Kevin, 5516
Schwanfelder, Nancy H., 9315
Schwanfelder, Nancy Healy, 5516
Schwart, Amy, 5171
Schwartz Charitable Lead Unitrust, Alvin, 5442
Schwartz Charitable Remainder Trust, Sheila, 162
Schwartz Foundation, Donna and Marvin, The, 6538
Schwartz, Abby I., 162
Schwartz, Abe, 6998
Schwartz, Adam, 4457
Schwartz, Alan, 2839, 2995
Schwartz, Alan D., 6815
Schwartz, Alan E., 4371
Schwartz, Alan G., 2839
Schwartz, Alan U., 376
Schwartz, Alexander, 4265
Schwartz, Alvin, 5442
Schwartz, Amy, 1411
Schwartz, Andrew, 1587
Schwartz, Barnard, 5953
Schwartz, Barry F., 6628
Schwartz, Bernard, 4265, 5443
Schwartz, Bernard L., 1857
Schwartz, Beth, 7008
Schwartz, Carol L., 9537
Schwartz, Carolyn, 1561
Schwartz, Daniel, 6818
Schwartz, David, 975, 1561
Schwartz, David A., 5484
Schwartz, Deborah, 6818
Schwartz, Denise D., 1866
Schwartz, Donna, 6819
Schwartz, Dorothy, 3701
Schwartz, Edward, 2892
Schwartz, Eleanor, 3144
Schwartz, Emil, 4968
Schwartz, Eric, 1561
Schwartz, Eric A., 1857
Schwartz, Eric S., 6816
Schwartz, Erica, 6816
Schwartz, Erika, 5953
Schwartz, Eugenie, 2777

Seawell, Marjorie B., 3614
Seawell, Marjorie Beaird, 3614
Seawell, Susie, 3614
SeaWorld Parks and Entertainment, 2315
Seay, George E., III, 8766, 9163
Seay, Mason, 3277
Seay, Nancy Clements, 8766, 9050, 9163
Seay, Nicky, 9414
Seay, Susan F., 7750
Seay, Yvonne D., 9769
Sebade, Norbert, 8522
Sebastian, Audrey M., 4535
Sebastian, David S., 4535
Sebastian, James R., 4535
Sebastian, John O., 4535
Sebastian, Rona, 231
Sebastian, Teresa, 2051
Sebastiani, Dan, 673
Sebring, Penny Bender, 2980
SEC Grandchildren Trust, 888
Secchia, Peter F., 4536
Sechrest, Vita, 700
Seckel, Douglas, 8788
Seckinger, Mark R., 7605
Second Childrens Charitable Trust, The, 9455
Second Grandchildren's Charitable Trust, The, 9455
Secor, Dennis, 635
Secrest, Tish, 7139
Secunda, Cynthia, 6827
Secunda, Thomas F., 6827
Securian Holding Co., 4761
Security Benefit Life Insurance Co., 3544
Security National Bank, 3432
Security National Trust Co., 9773, 9777
Sed, Karen Winner, 7994
Sedgwick, Michael B., 697
Sedlacek, Bill, 7496
Sedwick, Dru A., 8276
Sedwick, Helen, 280
Sedwick, Jay L., 8276
Sedwick, Laurie, 8276
Sedwick, Linda, 8276
Sedzmak, Donna, 7640
Sedzmak, Joseph, 7640
Sedzmak, Joseph P., 7640
SEE-USA, 341
Seeber, Kristen, 8819
Seebold, Rhonda, 7972
Seed the Dream Foundation, 7486
Seed, Harris W., 1267
Seedworks, 6127
Seeger, Vicky, 9516
Seegers, Jacob P., 9164
Seegers, Paul Ray, 9164
Seegers, Phyllis Ann, 9164
Seegers, Scott R., 9164
Seegers, Steven P., 9164
Seelbach, William R., 7409
Seeley, Dana M., 9990
Seeley, Halsted H., 9990
Seeley, Laurel H., 9990
Seeley, Lynne A., 7450
Seeley, Miles P., 9990
Seeley, Nancy, 7450
Seeley, W. Scott, 2251
Seelinger, Nita, 3474
Seely, Margaret, 9375
Seestrom, Susan, 5518
Sefton, Brian, 4598
Sefton, Claudia, 4598
Sefton, Donna K., 1134
Sefton, Harley, 1134
Sefton, J.W., Jr., 1134
Sefton, Maureen, 4598
Sefton, Stephen R., 4598
Segal Family Trust, 3147
Segal Income Trust, Gordon I., 3147
Segal, Barry, 5262, 5446
Segal, Carole B., 3147
Segal, Christopher S., 3147
Segal, Dolly, 5262, 5446
Segal, Frederick M., 1273
Segal, George, 5447
Segal, Gordon, 3147
Segal, Greg, 6418
Segal, Helen, 5447
Segal, Leanne, 1273
Segal, Margaret, 6232
Segal, Martin, 5262, 5446
Segal, Michael, 611, 1273
Segal, Rena, 5447
Segal, Richard, 5262, 5446
Segal, Richard D., 6418
Segal, Robert, 3147
Segal, Rosalind, 6232
Segal, Susan L., 6983
Segal, Tina, 1273
Segarra, Ann, 5979
Segarra, Joseph W., 6697
Segel Foundation, 8250
Segel, Arthur I., 3997
Segerstrom & Sons, C. J., 1136
Segerstrom Residuary Trust, Harold T., 1136
Segerstrom Trust, Nellie R., 1136
Segerstrom, Anton, 1136
Segerstrom, Clark, 1198
Segerstrom, Henry T., 1136
Segerstrom, Jeanette, 1136
Segerstrom, Jeanette E., 1135
Segerstrom, Sally, 1135
Segerstrom, Sally Eileen, 1135
Segerstrom, Ted, 1136
Segerstrom, Theodore Walter, 1135
Seget, A., 6225
Seget, Alan D., 5910
Seggio, Kim, 6703
Segreto, Tony, 2034
Segworth, Lorranine M., 7674
Seib, Karl E., 5786
Seibel, Abe, 9165
Seibel, Annie, 9165
Seiber, John, 466
Seiberlich, William C., 8260
Seibert, Jody, 5279
Seibert, John, 2110
Seid, Barre, 3148
Seiden, Barbara, 5448
Seiden, Mark, 5448
Seiden, Norman, 5206, 5448
Seiden, Pearl, 5448
Seiden, Stephen, 5206, 5448
Seidenberg, Douglas, 1692
Seidenberg, Ivan, 1692
Seidenberg, Phyllis, 1692
Seider, William M., 2038
Seidle, Charlene, 828
Seidler, Charles J., Jr., 5799
Seidler, Evelyn G., 3479
Seidler, Lee J., 6850
Seidler, Stanley B., 3479
Seidler, Terry, Mrs., 473
Seidner, Mary, 1563
Seifert, Kathi, 9832
Seifert, Shelley J., 8230
Seifert, Stephen, 1401
Seifert-Russell, Margaret, 3285
Seigel, Fred, 5185
Seigel, Lisa, 2089
Seiger, Joseph R., 1137
Seiger, Randee, 1137
Seiler, Lena, 6828
Seiler, Nathan, 6828
Seiling, Ric, 5726
Seilstad, Carl, 5006
Seiple, Robert, 3505
Seirer, Darren, 6829
Seitchik, Adam D., 4103
Seitter, Dellmer B., III, 2508
Seitz, Charles E., 2791
Seitz, Cindy, 3290
Seitz, Colins J., Jr., 1800
Seitz, Howard G., 6924
Seitz, Michelle S., 2699
Seiwald, Christopher, 1026
Seiwald, Trudi, 1026
Sekston, Angela, 2650
Selak, George, 3207
Selak, Martin M., 3207
Selander, Crosby, 1693
Selander, Mary L., 9891
Selander, Nancy Cross, 1693
Selander, Robert W., 1693
Selander, Russell, 1693
Selbo, Paul G., 9826
Selby, Charles W., 7769
Selby, Leland C., 1576, 1654, 1655
Selby, Marie, 2316
Selby, Sandra F., Rev., 7367
Selby, William G., 2316
Selden, Jo Hershey, 7487
Selecky, Mary C., 9615
Select Energy, Inc., 1656
Select Equity Group, Inc., 6829
Selevan, Andrew, 2317
Selevan, Jack, 2317
Selevan, Marc, 2317
Selevan, Russell, 2317
Seleznow, Steven G., 92
Self, Catherine, 8533
Self, Furman C., 8496
Self, J.C., III, 8496
Self, James C., 8496
Self, Leslie Smith, 9992
Self, Sally E., 8496
Self, Sam, 8832
Self, W.M., 8496
Selfe, Jane B., 20
Selian, Paul, 4285
Selig Enterprises Inc., 2549
Selig, Cathy, 2549
Selig, Charles, Jr., 6918
Selig, Charles, Jr., Mrs., 6918
Selig, Linda, 2406
Selig, S. Stephen, III, 2549
Seliger, Nancy, 8660
Seligman, Cathy, 6332
Seligman, Thomas K., 399
Seligson, Aaron, 6238
Selim, Francine, 416
Selim, Karen W., 8768
Selinger, Maurice A., Jr., 5579
Selinger, Sam, 9615
Seljeskog, Peg, 8522
Selkowitz, Adam, 1694
Selkowitz, Arthur, 1694
Selkowitz, Betsey, 1694
Selkowitz, Jed, 1694
Sell, Bradley N., 3761
Sell, Ed S., III, 2403
Sellars, John, 9946
Sellers, Gene, 3623
Sellers, M. Edward, 8460
Sellier, Victor F., 9530
Sells, Carol B., 5105
Selman, Peter, 6904
Selsor, David, 7688
Seltzer, David, 8232
Seltzer, Karen, 9297
Seltzer, Marian Keidan, 4396
Selvidge, Becca A., 1452
Selvig, Janet, 3046
Selz Foundation, Inc., The, 7394
Selz, Bernard T., 6830
Selz, Lisa, 6830
Selzer, Herbert, 6042
Seman, Rebecca Colin, 5797
Seman, Robert J., 5747
Semans, James D.B.T., 7150
Semedo, Tony B., 4712
Semegen, Susan F., 5260
Semel, Jane, 1138
Semel, Terry, 1138
Semerdjian, Dickra, 279
Semiconductor Industry Association, 7307
Semiconductor Research Corp., 7307
Seminoff, Nancy Wiseman, 4495
Seminole Hard Rock Hotel & Casino, 7012
Seminole Management Co., Inc., 6842
Semler, Bernard, 2648
Semler, Jerry D., 3272
Semlitz, Stephen M., 6831
Semmes, Douglas R., 9166
Semmes, Douglas R., Jr., 9166
Semmes, Julia Yates, 9166
Semmes, Patricia A., 9166
Semmes, Thomas R., 9061, 9166
Semnani, Ghazelah, 9350
Semnani, Khosrow, 9350
Semnani, Khosrow B., 9350
Semnani, Taymour, 9350
Semple, Louise Taft, 7660
Sempra Energy, 1140
Semrau, Kelly M., 9874
Sena, Debbie, 5400
Sena, Kathryn E., 7913
Sender, Milton, 4057
Senders, Jane Gural, 6117
Seneca Foods Corp., 6832
Seneff, James M., Jr., 2025
Seneff, Timothy J., 2025
Senegal, Pam, 7328
Senekjian, Harry, 9313
Senerchia, Diane, 6568
Senft, Daniel, 5791
Seng, Kate, 4731
Seng, Orris, 3165
Seng, Tom, 3313
Senior, David M., 9357
Senkler, Robert L., 4761
Sennett, Nancy, 3356
Senor, Dan, 6862
Sens, Gene, 9715
Sensient Technologies Corp., 9943
Senske, Michael, 9880
Sentara Healthcare, 9500
Sentry Insurance, 9944
Sentry Trust Co., 8046
Senturia, Brenda Baird, 5635

Sepulveda, Eugene, 8949
Serbin, Daniel S., 7611
Serck-Hanssen, Eilif, 1867
Seretean, M.B., 1142
Seretean, Tracy, 1142
Sergi, Deborah K., 2948
Sergi, Theodore S., 1609
Sergi, Vincent A.F., 2951
Serino, Jim, 4467
Serko, Tracey, 5873
Serota, Susan P., 6776
Serotta, Abram, 2434
Serpe, Ralph M., 3726
Serr, Erik, 4411
Serr, Erik E., 4573
Serr, Erik H., 4530, 4573
Serritslev, Duane, 1100
Sertori, Catherine A., 519
Seruma, Larry, 5446
Servillo, Gene, 2826
Servisfirst Bank, 45
Servitex, Inc., 2444
Sessel Family Foundation, Sussman, 7425
Sessions, Kathy, 1188
Seter, Arthur H., 6548
Seth, Maruti, 3205
Sethi, Neerja, 2067
Sethre, Earl, 1393
Setlow, Carolyn E., 1566
Seto, Amy T., 3726
Settich, John, 7811
Settle, Ernest, 4369
Setton International Foods of Brooklyn, 6833
Setton's International Foods, Inc., 6833
Setton, Joshua, 6833
Setton, Morris, 6833
Setzer, David E., 7305
Seubert, Pat, 9916
Seuthe, Brenda, 243
Seven Mile Lane LP, 9452
Seventh Generation, 9276
Severietti, Yvonne B., 315
Severn Plumbing, 9606
Severns, Helen A., 1143
Severns, Jerr, 3570
Severns, Robert L., 1143
Severns, Sharon L., 1143
Severson, Eugene, 3459
Severson, Katherine, 9750
Severson, Lawrence, 4752
Severson, Sarah K., 3040
Seville Charitable Trust, 4305
Sevrin, Alexander, 6007
Sewall, Elmina B., 3708
Sewell, John L., 4815
Sewell, Stace, 8824
Sewell, Stan, 8824
Sexauer, John A., 8280
Sexter, Allan S., 5955
Sexton, Gwendolyn W., 1144
Sexton, Leah Ann, 25
Sexton, Richard, 6904
Sexton, Timothy, 3289
Sexworth, Beth, 9128
Seydel, J. Rutherford, II, 2563, 2581
Seydel, Laura Lee Turner, 2563
Seydel, Laura Turner, 4561
Seyle, David, 2529
Seymour, Alan, 7416
Seymour, James, 2674
Seymour, Robert, 4837
Seymour, Silas B., 7141
SFA Systems LLC, 9193
SFP, Inc., 9093
SFX Escrow - Blood PSA, 3449
SG Milazzo, 5482
Shabel, Fred A., 8292
Shabet, Rose, 1717
Shabshelowitz, Andrew, 4079
Shackelton, Scott, 753
Shaddock/Sotherby Homes, 8756
Shade, Nancy, 5216
Shadur, Craig, 6138, 6139
Shadwick, Gerald, 1394
Shadwick, Jeannine, 1394
Shafer, Julie, 518
Shafer, Susan, 7378
Shaffer Administration Trust, Ula G., 4549
Shaffer, Cecile, 8281
Shaffer, David, 8281
Shaffer, Jack M., 8281
Shaffer, James D., 1145
Shaffer, John, 7401
Shaffer, Michael A., 6637
Shaffer, Penelope S., 2101
Shaffer, Penny S., 2238
Shaffer, Quentin, 6982
Shaffer, Rebecca, 5419
Shaffer, Rose, 8281
Shaffer, Susan, 8281
Shaffer, Tanya L., 1145
Shaffir, Melvyn L., 6895
Shafir, Eldar, 5252
Shafir, Robert S., 5826
Shagren, Erin, 9690
Shaheen, David, 5148
Shaheen, David M., 5148
Shaheen, Kari, 4532
Shaheen, Linda F., 5148
Shailor, Barbara A., 6308
Shain, Paul S., 9817
Shales, Jack, 2818
Shallenberger, Anne M., 9011
Shallenberger, Anne McCullough, 9187
Shallenberger, Martin, 3595
Shalom, David, 5991
Shalom, Kaaren P., 7804
Shaltz, T. Ardele, 4372
Shama, Fatima, 6546
Shamah, Amy, 9728
Shamel, Marlene, 7188
Shammo, Francis J., 5489
Shamos, Jeremy, 1498
Shamos, Susan, 1498
Shamrock Industries, Inc., 4656
Shan, Helen, 1674
Shanahan, Jessica, 5830
Shanahan, Michael, 2823
Shanahan, Robert Michael, 1146
Shanbrom, Edward, 1147
Shanbrom, Helen, 1147
Shanbrom, William J., 1147
Shands, H.J., III, 9223
Shane, Barb, 5093
Shane, David N., 3342
Shane, W. John, 3205
Shaner, Diane, 7672
Shaner, Troy K., 3419
Shank, Donna, 3524
Shank, Matthew D., Dr., 9384
Shank, Walter T., 9231
Shanken Communications, M., Inc., 6837
Shanken, Marvin R., 6837
Shankland, Darcy, 8472
Shanks, Deb, 3271
Shanley, Frank E., 1554
Shanley, Gilbert R., Jr., 3657
Shanley, Kevin, 5490
Shanley, Patricia, 8683
Shanley, Richard, 2769
Shannon, Darryl, 5726
Shannon, David J., 3545
Shannon, James C., III, 4152
Shannon, Janet A., 3545
Shannon, Kathleen E., 5563
Shannon, Kathleen T., 1020
Shannon, Ken, 3545
Shannon, Kenneth F., 3545
Shannon, Kirsten, 3545
Shannon, Michael, 1518
Shannon, Patrick, 9146
Shannon, Paul B., 8129, 8294
Shannon, Sue-Ann Gerald, 8468
Shannon, Wendy, 4755
Shanor, Susan McRae, 4836
Shapell 2009 Charitable Lead Trust, David, 1148
Shapell 2009 Charitable Lead Trust, Fela, 1148
Shapell 2009 Trust, David, 1149
Shapell Industries, 1150
Shapell Lead Unitrust, David & Fela, The, 1149
Shapell Lead Unitrust, David and Fela, The, 1159
Shapell Lead Unitrust, Nathan, The, 1150
Shapell, Benjamin, 1148, 1149
Shapell, David, 1148
Shapell, Fela, 1148
Shapell, Irvin N., 1148
Shapell, Nathan, 1150
Shapell, Rochelle, 1148, 1159
Shaper, C. Park, 1439
Shapira, Cynthia, 8282
Shapira, David, 8055
Shapira, David S., 7946, 8282
Shapira, Deborah B., 8282
Shapira, Edith L., 8228
Shapira, Jeremy M., 8282
Shapira, Karen A., 8282
Shapiro Family Foundation, Soretta and Henry, 3152
Shapiro Revocable Trust, Gwen, 9945
Shapiro, Alexandra E. F., 3152
Shapiro, Alison, 1151
Shapiro, Alison D., 1151
Shapiro, Alison I., 3927
Shapiro, Barbara J., 1152
Shapiro, Barry R., 6884
Shapiro, Benjamin M., 3152
Shapiro, Brenda M., 3152
Shapiro, Carl, 4267
Shapiro, Carol S., 9511
Shapiro, Charles, 3151
Shapiro, Daniel, 3150, 8303
Shapiro, Earl W., 3152
Shapiro, Edward L., 1152
Shapiro, Florence, Hon., 8773
Shapiro, Gwendolyn H., 9945
Shapiro, Henry M., 5984
Shapiro, Howard, 3153
Shapiro, Isaac, 5724, 7009
Shapiro, J. Mark, 3872
Shapiro, Jane, 3925
Shapiro, Joel, 850
Shapiro, John M., 6838
Shapiro, Judith R., 6967
Shapiro, L. Dennis, 3927
Shapiro, Lester, 3150
Shapiro, Linda Grass, 8068
Shapiro, Marc J., 9287
Shapiro, Mary, 3151
Shapiro, Matthew I., 3152
Shapiro, Michael, 3186
Shapiro, Molly, 3151
Shapiro, Morris R., 3151
Shapiro, Nathan, 3150
Shapiro, Norman, 2434, 3153
Shapiro, Norman, Mrs., 2434
Shapiro, Norton, 3150
Shapiro, Peter W., 1151
Shapiro, Rachel, 8066
Shapiro, Rachel T., 3927
Shapiro, Ralph J., 1151
Shapiro, Richard, Esq., 5806
Shapiro, Robert, 3150
Shapiro, Robert N., 3997, 4301, 5542
Shapiro, Ruth, 4267
Shapiro, Sarah H., 3816
Shapiro, Scott, 9731
Shapiro, Sharon Ellen, 4250
Shapiro, Shirley, 1151
Shapiro, Soretta, 3152
Shapiro, Stephen L., 7704
Shapiro, Stephen R., 1358
Shapiro, Steven, 3150
Shapiro, Susan R., 3927
Shapiro, Zachary, 3927
Shapley, Rick, 2037
Shar, Albert O., 5329
Shara, Gary T., 1160
Share, Charles Morton, 7795
Share, Hugh, 2315
Sharf, Frederic A., 4268
Sharf, Jean S., 4268
Sharfin, Ira, 7589
Sharkey, Christopher, 3756
Sharkey, Jackie, 9957
Sharkey, Stevens, 8965
Sharko, Emily C., 6063
Sharko, Matthew, 3170
Sharko, Michelle, 3170
Sharma, Deven, 6963
Sharma, Janet, 5486
Sharman, Tanya E., 3143
Sharon, Ingrid, 8927
Sharp Foundation, Ruth & Charles, 6864
Sharp, Charles S., 9167
Sharp, Eli R., 1806
Sharp, Evelyn, 6839
Sharp, Joan L., 1765
Sharp, Karen, 2041
Sharp, Lisa, 4465
Sharp, Nancy, 9755
Sharp, Phillip A., 3833
Sharp, Richard, 535
Sharp, Ruth Collins, 9167
Sharp, Susan F., 9167
Sharp, Tom, 1528
Sharp, Tracie J., 8494
Sharp, William M.W., Mrs., 1821
Sharp, Winifred J., 406
Sharpe, Ann M., Esq., 5803
Sharpe, Daniel, 3202
Sharpe, Douglas B., 8437
Sharpe, Henry D., III, 8437
Sharpe, Henry D., Jr., 8437
Sharpe, Lynn Ann, 2085
Sharpe, Mary Elizabeth, 8437
Sharpe, Peggy B., 8437
Sharpe, Peggy Boyd, 8437

Sharpe, Sarah A., 8437
Sharra, Sue, 2032
Shashack, Will, 2817
Shashaty, Yolanda, 6489
Shattuck, Mayo A., II, 3868
Shattuck, Mayo A., IV, 1197
Shatz, Carla, 7164
Shatz, Carla J., 4708
Shaughnessy, Daniel G., 4969
Shaughnessy, James A., 4969
Shaughnessy, Jeannie, 9380
Shaughnessy, Joseph F., 4969
Shaughnessy, Kimberly B., 3866
Shaughnessy, Paul J., 4969
Shaughnessy, Rosemary E., 4969
Shauk, Gazala, 225
Shaul, Cheryl, 1423
Shaulson, Abraham, 6756, 6811
Shavel, Leonard, 5675
Shaver, Thomas, 4731
Shaw Charitable Lead Annuity Trust, Mary L., 1499
Shaw, Arch W., 4970
Shaw, Arch W., II, 4970
Shaw, Barbara E., 4778
Shaw, Beth K., 6840
Shaw, Bruce P., 4970
Shaw, Carol, 2768
Shaw, Christopher, 9295
Shaw, Cindy, 4830, 4839
Shaw, David E., 6840
Shaw, Dorothy, 4830
Shaw, Eric, 9311
Shaw, Eric W., 3813
Shaw, Gardiner Howland, 4270
Shaw, George, 3570
Shaw, George T., 3698
Shaw, H., 6779
Shaw, Harold, 1499
Shaw, Harry, 7264
Shaw, Irene R., 9940
Shaw, Jack R., 3375
Shaw, James W., 8501
Shaw, Jean Young, 3154
Shaw, Jeff, 1504
Shaw, Jeffrey W., 5149
Shaw, Joe, 5556
Shaw, Kathleen, 2031
Shaw, L Stanley, 9606
Shaw, Lani A., 1419
Shaw, Louise, 1499
Shaw, Mark W., 6090
Shaw, Minor M., 8460, 8476
Shaw, Minor Mickel, 7195
Shaw, Norman, 1999
Shaw, Patricia, 9057
Shaw, Patrick, 2730
Shaw, Perry L., 9057
Shaw, Richard, 7934
Shaw, Roger D., Jr., 4872, 4970
Shaw, Ronald L., 2619
Shaw, Run Run, Sir, 2615
Shaw, Ruth, 7202
Shaw, Sarah, 573
Shaw, Steve, 77
Shaw, T.R., Jr., 4343
Shaw, Terry, 1141
Shaw, Walden W., 3154
Shaw, William W., 4970
Shay, Robert P., Jr., 7342
Shea Co., J.F., Inc., 1155, 1156
Shea Megale Fund Corp., The, 6898
Shea, Carey C., 6661
Shea, E. Stewart, III, 3623
Shea, Edmund H., Jr., 1156
Shea, Gerald M., 3923
Shea, Greg, 5055
Shea, John F., 1155
Shea, Judith K., 8119
Shea, Julia V., 5579, 8086
Shea, Lindsay, 6864
Shea, Lindsay D., 7101
Shea, Mary S., 1156
Shea, Natalie, 9005
Shea, Patrick Kelly, 9635
Shea, Peter O., 1155
Shea-Ballay, Kathleen, 8308
Sheafe, Michael, 5740
Sheahan, Casey, 1017
Sheahan, E. Thomas, 9892
Sheahan, Patrick M., 3242
Sheahan, Tim, 1411
Sheaks, MaryAnn, 7672
Shean, Christopher W., 1448
Shear, Jack, 6271
Shearer, Barry, 7280
Shearer, Charles L., 3579
Sheba, Ron, 7991
Sheble-Hall, Alexander, 8295
Sheboygan Beverage, Inc., 9888
Shechtel, Andrew J., 5455, 5464
Shechtel, Raquel, 5455, 5464
Shedd, John, 4332
Sheehan, Chris, 4271
Sheehan, Elizabeth, 4271
Sheehan, Gerald V., 4271
Sheehan, Jim, 9683
Sheehan, John, 4271
Sheehan, Juliette K., 2592
Sheehan, Leo, 9663
Sheehan, Margaret, 4271
Sheehan, May, 7752
Sheehan, Robert C., 5989, 6868
Sheehan, Tanya M., 6605
Sheehan, Timothy, 4271
Sheely, William Wallace, 9206
Sheeran, Tim, 7417
Sheerer, Marilyn, 7321
Sheerin, Charles, 3354
Sheerin, Michael, 5297
Sheets, Alice, 2513
Sheets, Laura, 3283
Sheetz, Brenda A., 3369
Sheetz, Darryl, 794
Sheffer, Gary, 1591
Sheffield, Bill, 79
Sheffield, Edwin, 6202
Shehebar, Isaac, 5768, 5769
Shehi, Betty, 448
Sheiber, Sandra, 4217
Sheiffer, Steve, 9835
Sheikh, Kashif, 662
Sheils, Geoffery S., 3575
Shein, Jefferies, 5476
Sheinberg, Eric P., 1695
Sheinman, Jessica R., 6938
Shelby Cullom Davis & Co., 9437
Shelby, Sabina E., 1608
Shelby, Susan, 4061
Shelby, Timothy, 9059
Shelden, Allan, III, 4537
Shelden, Elizabeth Warren, 4537
Shelden, Virginia Durand, 7254
Shelden, W. Warren, 4537
Shelden, William W., Jr., 4371, 4498, 4537
Shelden, William Warren, 7254
Sheldon Trust, Isabella M., 6841
Sheldon, Dan, 5214
Sheldon, Donald, 7594
Sheldon, Isabell M., 6841
Sheldon, James, 9565
Sheldon, Roy C., 841
Sheldon, Sally S., 4537
Shelhamer, Betty S., 596
Shell Exploration & Production, 9168
Shell Offshore, Inc., 9049
Shell Oil Co., 81, 9168
Shell, Frederick E., 4410
Shell, Greg, 3956
Shell, John, 3330
Shellenberger, Lauren, 4359
Sheller, Lee, 3781
Shelman, Alicia J., 3599
Shelman, Linda K., 3599
Shelnitz, Mark A., 3807
Shelor, Cynthia M., 9415
Shelter Mutual Insurance Co., 4971
Shelto, Audrey, 3953
Shelton Cos., The, 7310
Shelton, Andrew B., 9169
Shelton, Bruce, 141
Shelton, Charles M., 7310
Shelton, John, 4532
Shelton, R. Edwin, 7310
Shelton, Ralph, 7335
Shelton, Robert, 157
Shelton, Ruby W., 9169
Shelton, Ruth, 8839
Shelton, Sandra Waller, 2826
Shelton, Todd, 3201
Shen Family 2003 Charitable Lead Trust, The, 5450
Shen, Carla, 5450
Shen, Katherine, 2021
Shen, Theodore P., 5450
Shenefelt, Jamie Lampros, 166
Shenfeld, Steven, 6089
Shenfeld, Wendy, 6089
Shenfield, Lauren Katzowitz, 6193
Shenk, Janet, 1880
Shenk, Willis W., 8299, 8300
Shenkman, Barry A., 5732
Shenkman, Jamie, 5732
Shennan, Jamie, 5019
Shenton, Robert, 569
Shepard, James D., 290, 1005
Shepard, John A., Jr., 9370
Shepard, Julia Sparkman, 1890
Shepard, Karen P., 290
Shepard, Larry, 5036
Shepard, Mikki, 6477
Shepard, Todd D., 1567
Shepherd, Anne H., 8888
Shepherd, Constance D., 838
Shepherd, Danny R., 73
Shepherd, Gary, 4194
Shepherd, Kimberely, 699
Shepherd, Matthew, 208
Shepherd, Nina S., 473
Sheppard, Julie R.G., 3516
Sheppard, Michael R., 7509
Sheppard-Hern, Donna L., 8936
Sheraton Corp., The, 4284
Sherbin, David, 4394
Sherbrooke, Ross E., 5170
Sherburne, Philip S., 4639
Sherck, Cary B., 7152
Shere, Helene O'Neil, 3859
Sherer, Christine, 6603
Sherer, Frank Alexei, Dr., 6603
Sherer, Ruth O., 6603
Sheridan County YMCA, 9998
Sheridan Foundation, James & Chantel, 6898
Sheridan, Brenda, 5452
Sheridan, Brian T., 5018
Sheridan, Chris R., 2502
Sheridan, Chris R., Jr., 2435
Sheridan, Don, 3481
Sheridan, Edward, 1512
Sheridan, Eileen F., 1116
Sheridan, Elizabeth M., 3883
Sheridan, Howard, 5452
Sheridan, John J., 2712
Sheridan, Mary Katherine, 6454
Sheridan, R. Kelly, 8370
Sheridan, Thomas B., 3883
Sheriff, Edd, 8454
Sherman & Sterling, 6904
Sherman, Andrew, 5662
Sherman, Bruce S., 2318
Sherman, Cindy, 7050
Sherman, Cynthia L., 2318
Sherman, Donald A., 6748
Sherman, Ernest, 9725
Sherman, George M., 2319
Sherman, Heather, 1980
Sherman, Howard B., 8509
Sherman, Jane F., 4423
Sherman, John, 4921, 4972
Sherman, John, Jr., 9505
Sherman, Mark, 9704
Sherman, Marny, 4937
Sherman, Mary, 4972
Sherman, Michael, 5718
Sherman, Michael B., 4030
Sherman, Nachum, 6301
Sherman, Richard, 567
Sherman, Sandra Brown, 5339
Sherman, Scott D., 228
Sherman, Stephanie, 5296
Sherman, Susan E., 8107
Sherman, Tom, 3625
Sherman, Winchester, 3791
Sherrer, Terrence, 7570
Sherrill, Edmund K., II, 1785
Sherrill, H. Sinclair, 1785
Sherrill, Joe, 9277
Sherrill, Stephen C., 7080
Sherry, Andrew, 2191
Sherry, Christine, 1228
Sherwell, Jon P., 3814
Sherwin, Heather, 8468
Sherwin-Williams Co., The, 7661
Sherwood Foundation, The, 5027
Sherwood Griswold Foundation, Lillian, 794
Sherwood, Arthur, Dr., 7992
Sherwood, Dick, 4606
Sherwood, Dolly, 9780
Sheser Creek LLC, 7314
Sheth, Adria, 9153
Sheth, Brian, 9153
Sheth, Jagdish, 2432
Shetter, Allison M., 3005
Sheval Lev Hatorah, 889
Shevlin, David A., 5653
Shevlin, Patricia A., 3140
Shi, Theodore, 297
Shibata, Christy Rupert, 6531
Shibata, Myles, 2602
Shiebler, Christina, 4762
Shiebler, Jason, 4762
Shiebler, Joanne, 4762
Shiebler, William, 4762

Shield, Fred W., 9170
Shield, Robin R., 9523
Shield-Taylor, Juliet E., 9523
Shields Living Trust, George L., 3884
Shields, Charlie, 4996
Shields, David D., 1821
Shields, Elaine H., 8479
Shields, George L., 3884
Shields, Joyce, 5784
Shields, Kathleen A., 5520
Shields, Laura S., 3665
Shields, Margaret M., 7988
Shields, Marsha M., 9009
Shields, Maury Flowers, 2459
Shields, Patrick, 9685
Shields, Robert E., 4333
Shields, W. Donald, 9087
Shiely, J.S., 9822
Shiffick, Margaret, 3156
Shiffick, William, 3156
Shifflett, Todd, 8462
Shiflett, Laura, 9240
Shifman, Arnold, 4526
Shifman, Burton R., 4526
Shifman, Pamela, 6570
Shih, Daphne, 5653
Shiley, Darlene, 1040
Shiley, Darlene V., 1157
Shiley, Donald P., 1157
Shillman, Robert J., 1158
Shilo Inn, 385
Shimer, Pete, 9731
Shimizu, Kazuo, 9881
Shimon, Miriam, 6317
Shin, Charley, 7362
Shin, Clara J., 1088
Shin, Nan C., 2616
Shin, Patrick N.C., 2616
Shine, Jane, 3266
Shine, John B., 3266
Shiner, Bethany, 3026
Shingle, Alice K., 2592
Shingleton Trust, Barbara, 4458
Shingleton, Barbara, 4458
Shinick, Mary, 7103
Shining, Stewart, 6427
Shinkman, Gillian C., 3765
Shinn & Assocs., George, Inc., 8627
Shinn, Chad, 8627
Shinn, Chris, 8627
Shinn, Denise, 8627
Shinn, George, 8627
Shinn, Susan, 8627
Shinnyo-En Foundation, 4420
Shiota, Renee, 570
Shiozaki, Richard, 4395
Shipley 1993 Trust, Lucia, 4272
Shipley, Allison P., 2238, 6843
Shipley, Barbara S., 6843
Shipley, Charles R., Jr., 4272
Shipley, Dorothy S., 6843
Shipley, John P., 6843
Shipley, Judith L., 6843
Shipley, Karen L., 4272
Shipley, Lucia H., 4272
Shipley, Pamela J., 6843
Shipley, Richard C., 4272
Shipley, Seth, 3757
Shipley, Walter V., 6843
Shipley, William S., III, 8351
Shipman, Steve, 784
Shipp, Pam, 1478
Shipp, William "Bill", 1893
Shipper, Earliene, 5904
Shipton, Natalie, 7276
Shira, Carol, 2123
Shirai, Sandra, 1572
Shiraki, Seiji, 6490
Shirato, Hideki, 6492
Shire Pharmaceuticals, 6231
Shireman, joe, 3314
Shires, Dana, 4816
Shirey, Angela, 179
Shirk, Betty J., 3158
Shirk, Christopher C., 4405
Shirk, Cynthia L., 3158
Shirk, Gerald, 2469
Shirk, James A., 3158
Shirk, Lia Valerio, 3158
Shirk, Linda S., 3158
Shirk, Russell O., 3158
Shirkey, Jennifer, 9411
Shirley, Carl, 5325
Shirley, Carl, Mrs., 5325
Shirley, E. Mary L., 9734
Shirley, Janet A., 2431
Shirley, Johnna, 8462
Shirley, Jon A., 9734
Shirley, Linda C., 7746
Shiva, Alexandra, 6845
Shiva, Andrew, 6845
Shivdarsan, Hemraj, 2271
Shiver, Michael W., 2358
Shiverick, Elizabeth, 6842
Shiverick, Paul, 6842
Shiverick, Paul C., 5786
Shivers, Anna S. "Candy", 7182
Shladovsky, David, 240
Shleifer, Elena, 5924
Shleifer, Scott L., 5924
Shmerling, Michael D., 8550
Shoaff, Thomas, 8341
Shoaff, Thomas M., 3352, 3401
Shock, Ellen, 5129
Shockley, Scott, 3262
Shoemaker Trust, Thomas H. and Mary Williams, 8284
Shoemaker, D. Charles, 5046
Shoemaker, Dale, 4539
Shoemaker, Dale A., 4539
Shoemaker, Edwin J., 4481, 4539
Shoemaker, Eric C., 4539
Shoemaker, James R., Esq., 3758
Shoemaker, Linda J., 1378
Shoemaker, Marcy Abramson, 1963
Shoemaker, Mary Williams, 8284
Shoemaker, Robert L., 4539
Shoemaker, Thomas H., 8284
Shofe, Allen, 1903
Shogren, Beth, 5662
Sholler, Andrea, 6477
Shon, Mordechai, 5282
Shonk, Brian, 7445
Shoof, Thomas, 2204
Shook, Charlie, 3282
Shook, Eric, 7682
Shook, Mark L., Rabbi, 4991
Shook, Steve, 8676
Shoolman, Edith Glick, 6846
Shoop, Jennifer Nurmi, 3713
Shoop, Landon, 3713
Shoos, John, 3684
Shooshan, John G., 9384
Shorb, Jack, 8351
Shore, Lesley, 3205
Shore, Melanie, 2036
Shore, William, 8061
Shorenstein, Douglas, 1858
Shorenstein, Douglas W., 1858
Shorenstein, Lydia, 1858
Shores, Gary H., 9277
Shores, Shirley A., 3758
Short, Jean R., 7311
Short, Marianne, 4628, 4785
Short, Marianne D., 4753
Short, Patricia A., 1375
Short, Rick A., 4887
Short, Tracy, 9924
Short, William R., 2433
Shorter, Kim, 8135
Shortino, Leo M., 1160
Shotley, Marsha, 4618
Shott, Hugh I., Jr., 9794
Shott, James H., III, 9794
Shott, John H., 9794
Shott, Michael R., 9794
Shoulson, Bruce, 5296
Shoup, John, 3283
Shovelin, Julia, 7179
Shover Kackley, Lisa, 3372
Showalter, Craig R., 9999
Shrack, Jordan, 8495
Shreiber, Gerald B., 5453
Shrem, Jan, 1330
Shrem, Maria, 1330
Shreve, Christine A., 3794, 3797
Shreve, Kevin, 5807
Shreve, Sandra, 1401
Shreves, Catherine, 4714
Shriber, Steve, 7401
Shriram, Kavitark R., 463
Shriram, Vidjealatchoumy, 463
Shriver, Elizabeth, 3444
Shriver, Michael F., 7139
Shrock, Kelly, 3286
Shroff, Chandrakant C., 9495
Shryock, Larry L., 8838
SHS Trust, 6848
Shtesl, Ascher, 6849
Shtesl, Joel, 6849
Shtohryn, Dmytro, 2907
Shuayb, Ahd, 224
Shuayb, Husam, 224
Shubert, J.J., 6850
Shubert, Lee, 6850
Shubert, Norman A., 3151
Shuck, V. DeWitt, 1012
Shue, Chikong, 4266
Shue, Susan, 4266
Shuey, Maura, 8156
Shuff, Lillian, 4102
Shuff, Rodney, 4102
Shuford, Alex, 2800
Shuford, Karen L., 8773, 8912
Shuler, Arlene, 6723, 7009
Shull, Brian, 9411
Shulman, Alison Bernstein, 1886
Shulman, Barbara J., 6020
Shulman, Donald L., 4073
Shulman, Joel, 4490
Shulman, Stanley, 6431
Shulruff, Stuart P., 2951
Shulsky, Rena, 6851
Shulsky, Rubin, 6851
Shults, Betsy, 6841
Shultz, Gary, 8854
Shultz, Herbert L., Jr., 6802
Shumaker, Albert L., 23
Shumaker, Dianne C., 3546
Shumaker, Eric A., 3546
Shumaker, Megan I., 3546
Shumaker, Paul K., 3546
Shumaker, Ronn, 3287
Shuman, Alfred J., 7089
Shuman, Bonney Stamper, 2431
Shuman, David M., 4056
Shuman, Erik, Esq., 2033
Shuman, Jeffrey S., 2149
Shuman, John R., 517
Shuman, Josephine R., 517
Shuman, Robert, 517
Shuman, Stanley, 1518, 6748
Shuman, Stanley S., 6124
Shuman, Stephanie, 7089
Shuman, Stephanie J., 7089
Shuman, Sydney, 6748
Shuman, Sydney R., 6124
Shumate, Greg, 2433
Shumate, Helen B., 1742
Shumate, Jonathan, 1742
Shumate, Kenneth, 9101
Shumate, Susan, 9780
Shumski, Edward, 4814
Shumway Mayer, Helen, 8439
Shumway, Brooks, 1257
Shumway, Frank R., Jr., 8439
Shure, Alice, 5254
Shurling, F. Tredway, 2435
Shurts, Steve, 4679
Shute, Benjamin R., Jr., 1600
Shute, Sharon, 7488
Shutt, John J., 9133
Shuttleworth, Tim, 8026
Shutts, Norma, 1527
Shuvo Yisroel Charity, 6336
Shvat Charitable Lead Trust, 5553
SI Bank & Trust, 6912
Si, Flora R., 6400
Sia, Christopher T., 6872
Siart, William E.B., 579
Sias, Thelma, 9969
Sibert, Ron, 3284
Sibley, Horace, 2580
Sibley, James M., 2571, 2579
SIBSCO, LLC, 4536
Sickler, Judi, 5055
Sickler, Lisa K., 7868
Sidamon-Eristoff, Anne P., 5406
Sidden, Curt, 9865
Sidden, Jennifer, 9865
Siddons, Ernest G., 8030
Sidford, James A., 5803
Sidgmore, John W., 3885
Sidgmore, Randi, 3885
Sidhu, Sanjiv, 9172
Sidman, Hope, 4273
Sidman, Mathew K., 4273
Sidman, Paula L., 4141
Sidman, Paula M., 4273
Sidnam, Caroline N., 6448
Sidney Casino, Inc., 5016
Sidoti, Paul A., M.D., 6339
Sidwell Materials, Inc., 7662
Sidwell, Adam, 7662
Sidwell, E.R., 8960
Sidwell, Jeffrey, 7662
Sidwell, Jennie, 7662
Sie, Anna M., 1500
Sie, John J., 1500
Siebel, Kenneth F., 938
Siebel, Stacey, 1162
Siebel, Thomas M., 1162
Siebels, Jane M., 8313
Siebens, Stewart, 8967
Siebens, Stewart D., 6853
Siebens, W. Carter, 6853

Siebert, A.F., 9946
Siebert, Reginald L., 9946
Siedow, Linda, 1488
Siegal, Edward G., 3991
Siegel Charitable Lead Trust, Naomi L., 7997
Siegel Family Foundation, 5446
Siegel, Alan, 6975
Siegel, Alan M., 5897
Siegel, Bary, 378
Siegel, Deborah, 635
Siegel, Herb M., 6913
Siegel, Herbert J., 5845
Siegel, Howard J., 2756
Siegel, John E., 5926
Siegel, Kenneth S., 4284
Siegel, Lynne F., 9662
Siegel, Mark S., 579
Siegel, Stuart C., 9416
Siegel, Sydney, 5446
Siegel, Thomas I., 8012
Siegel, William, 5446
Sieger, Diana R., 4447
Siegert, Kenneth V., 4148
Siegert, Robert F., 9924
Siegrist Construction, 1394
Siegrist, Greg, 1903
Sielak, George, 81
Sieman, Kathryn, 9832
Siemens Corp., 5454
Siemens, Richard, 1942
Siemer, Barbara, 7411
Siemer, Richard, 3169
Siemers, Stephan, 975
Siering, Tom, 4742
Sierra Enterprises Group LLC, 5455, 5464
Sierra Pacific Industries, 1164
Sierra Pacific Resources, 5136
Sierra Towers & Fresh Meadows, LLP, 6160
Sierra, Luis, 8718
Sieting, Janet, 4448
Sietsma, David, 2269
Sieve, Marty, 4730
Sieve, Richard, 1279
Sievers, Kimberly R., 7563
Sievers, Mary B., 9617
Sievertsen, Craig, 9588
Sieving, Charles E., 2251
Sifferlen, Ned J., 7429
Sigafoos, Kamilla, 7445
Sigelbaum, Harvey, 6765
Sigelman, Alice R., 6751
Sigfred, Sture, 9503
Sigler, Rose, 5317
Sigmon, Anthony, 7179
SIGroup, Inc., 7104
Sigsbee, Jill, 3298
Sikes, E. Larry, 3623
Sikes, Suzanne, 2740
Sikora, Katherine, 8639
Sikorski, Brad, 186
Silacci, Mike, 1287
Silagy, Eric E., 2251
Silard, Timothy P., 1088
Silber, Eva, 5761
Silber, Harry, 5761
Silber, Mark, 6861
Silberberg, Bernice, 526
Silberberg, Veronica, 9975
Silberfeld, Roman M., 4754
Silberman, Claire, 5718
Silberman, Samuel "Buddy", 5628
Silbermann, Julie A., 5456
Silbermann, Karen S., 5456
Silbermann, M. Steven, 5456
Silbermann, Rosanne H., 5456
Silbermann, S. David, 5456
Silberstein, Bruce, 6854
Silberstein, Paul, 1165
Silberstein, S., 6409
Silberstein, Stephen M., 1165
Silberstein, Sylvia, 6854
Silberstein, William, 6854
Silbert, Andrea, 4037
Silbiger, Shloime, 6169
Siler, James G., 517
Siler, Susan, 517
Silgar, Karen, 9793
Silge, Christopher, 2717
Silhavy, Thomas, 3833
Silicon Valley Community Foundation, 720
Silk, Andrew, 7757
Silk, Fred F., 7663
Silk, Stephen, 1167
Silk, Susan, 1167
Sill, Valerie J., 1765
Sillcox, Leslie C., 6996
Sillcox, Mark, 6996
Sillcox, Mark E., 6996
Sillerman, Laura Baudo, 6995
Sillerman, Robert F.X., 6995
Silliman, N. Reed, 3352
Sillin, Elizabeth H., 3992
Sills Charitable Trust, 9371
Sills Remainder Trust, 9371
Sills, Arthur S., 9371
Sills, Gregory, 6768
Sills, John L., 6768
Sills, John W., III, 9412
Sills, Larry, 9371
Sills, M., 9371
Sills, Peter, 9371
Sills, Peter S., 9371
Silten, Bobbi, 563
Silva, Gil V., 8280
Silva, Jo Ann Anixter, 2664
Silva, Kevin D., 6451, 7038
Silva, Kim, 1191
Silver & Black Give Back, 9149
Silver Bow Lounge Corp., 5016
Silver Line Building Products Corp., 5459
Silver Spring Towers Apartments LLC, 9452
Silver, B., 5688
Silver, Barbara, 1696
Silver, Chelsea Hoopes, 1725
Silver, Cindy Zoller, 936
Silver, David, 1885
Silver, Eli, 5628
Silver, Gerald L., 167
Silver, Jan Levit, 8982
Silver, Jane, 5882
Silver, Jean, 3929
Silver, Julie B., 1885
Silver, Julie Bender, 1885
Silver, Justin P., 5457
Silver, M., 5688
Silver, Melissa, 5332
Silver, Patti, 2882
Silver, Paul A., 8359, 8416
Silver, Peter Milo, 1696
Silver, Philip, 1696
Silver, Philip Tyler, 1696
Silver, R. Philip, 1696
Silver, Rhonda A., 5457
Silver, Richard, 744
Silver, Robert H., 5457
Silver, Sarah, 6870
Silver, Stuart, 6349, 6705
Silver, Todd D., 9744
Silverberg, Shonni J., 6838
Silverleaf Foundation, 6864
Silverman, Allison, 6855
Silverman, Amy Rose, 6562
Silverman, Andrew, 4034
Silverman, Barton M., 8107
Silverman, Brittany, 5459
Silverman, Claudia, 5459
Silverman, Daniel Olias, 727
Silverman, Fred, 877
Silverman, Greg, 6982
Silverman, Harold, 6542
Silverman, Jeffrey, 6562
Silverman, Kenneth, 5459
Silverman, Lorin, 6855
Silverman, Marty, 6855
Silverman, Richard J., 4108
Silverman, Robert, 3210
Silverman, Ross O., 2951
Silverman, Seth, 6855
Silverson, Donald, 8234
Silverstein 2003 Charitable Lead Annuity Trust, JM, 2170
Silverstein 2003 Charitable Lead Annuity Trust, Mark S., 2170
Silverstein, Barry, 2170
Silverstein, Carol, 4245
Silverstein, Flori, 6856
Silverstein, Jacob, 2170
Silverstein, Lawrence I., 4130, 4131
Silverstein, Molly, 2170
Silverstein, Raine, 6856
Silverstein, Stanley, 6856
Silverstein, Trudy, 2170
Silverstone, Harvey J., 3147
Silverthorne, Iain, 959
Silverton Partners, LP, 9235
Silvestri, Charles, 5134
Silvian, Cindy, 6858
Silvian, David L., 4112
Silwkowski, Mary B., 571
Simches, Michael, 6187
Simensky, Edward, 3684
Simental, Santiago, 416
Simer, William A., 9650
Simic, Curt, 3303
Simkins, Albert, 2321
Simkins, David, 2321
Simkins, Lawrence R., 5018
Simkins, Leon J., 2321
Simkins, Michael, 2321
Simkins, N. Turner, 2434
Simkins, Ronald, 2321
Simmer, Mike, 9854
Simmermon, Marcia, 3346
Simmers, Terry, 2123
Simmonds, Allean, 8495
Simmonds, Sidney G., 9518
Simmons Browder Gianaris Angelides, 3159
Simmons Charitable Lead Trust No. 1, Roy W., 9351
Simmons Charitable Lead Trust No. 2, Roy W., 9351
Simmons, Adele, 175
Simmons, Angelica C., 966
Simmons, Bryan E., 5608
Simmons, Cecelia, 2983
Simmons, David, 6633
Simmons, David E., 9351
Simmons, David P., 4211
Simmons, Edward M., 3648
Simmons, Elizabeth E., 9173
Simmons, Frederick L., 494
Simmons, G. McKittrick, Jr., 2479
Simmons, Gwen, 8332
Simmons, Harold, 9174
Simmons, Harris, 9305
Simmons, Harris H., 9351
Simmons, Hildy, 5718
Simmons, Hildy J., 6202
Simmons, Jeffrey, 2769
Simmons, Jeffrey N., 3340
Simmons, John, 3159
Simmons, Karen, 7979
Simmons, Karen A., 7979
Simmons, Kay, 8603
Simmons, L.E., 9173, 9351
Simmons, Liesel Pritzker, 2932
Simmons, Lisa K., 9174
Simmons, Mary, 5136
Simmons, Matthew R., 9351
Simmons, Michael, 3272
Simmons, Omar, 4103
Simmons, Peter, 5917, 5918, 5919
Simmons, Richard P., 8285
Simmons, Ronald D., 3497
Simmons, Roy W., 9351
Simmons, Sabrina, 563
Simmons, Sylvia, 4286
Simmons, Teisha, 86
Simmons, Todd, 4716
Simmons, Virginia W., 9173
Simmons, William T., 7942
Simmons-Parks, Karen, 8511
Simms, Cleo, 9415
Simms, Josh, 1169
Simms, Leon, 7743
Simms, Marsha, 6723
Simms, Nancy Gordy, 2472
Simms, Rick, 1412
Simms, Ronald A., 1169
Simms, Ruth, 5526
Simms, Steven H., 2472
Simms, Stuart O., 3726
Simms, Victoria Mann, 1169
Simon 10 Year Charitable Lead Annuity Trust, 3384
Simon 12 Year Charitable Lead Annuity Trust, 3384
Simon 15 Year Charitable Lead Annuity Trust, 3384
Simon 5 Year Charitable Lead Annuity Trust, 3384
Simon and Associates, Melvin, Inc., 3387
Simon Charitable Trust, Douglas, 1170
Simon Charitable Trust, Eric, 1170
Simon Foundation, Sidney, Milton & Leoma, 2322
Simon Foundation, William E., Inc., 5460
Simon, Albert, III, 3160
Simon, Albert, Jr., 3160
Simon, Allison S., 9201
Simon, Arnold, 1947
Simon, Bren, 3386, 3387
Simon, Cynthia L., 5460
Simon, Daniel L., 3149
Simon, David E., 3385
Simon, Deborah, 3317, 3386
Simon, Donald, 1170
Simon, Donald Ellis, 1170
Simon, Douglas, 1170

Skirvin, Brandi, 3560
Skiva International, 5768
Skjerven, Wendy, 4783
Skjodt, Cynthia Simon, 3272, 3384, 3386
Skjodt, Erik, 3384
Skjodt, Ian, 3384
Skjodt, Paul, 3384
Skjodt, Samantha, 3384
Sklar, Jo Ann, 139
Sklar, Linda, 2137
Sklar, Mark N., 139
Skoda, Gerald J., 5806
Skogen, Mark, 9854, 9855
Skoglund, Adelaide, 2253
Skoglund, Linda, 9950
Skoglund, Peter, 5826
Skoglund, William B., 2767
Skogman, Chris, 3417
Skolaski, Steven F., 9931
Skoll, Jeffrey S., 1175, 1176
Skolnick, Allen, 5741
Skolnick, Barry, 5741
Skolnick, Connie, 5741
Skopil, Trace, 9566
Skoug, John L., 9851
Skoulas, Caren F., 3083
Skrutskie, Mike, 821
Skydell, Harry, 6536
Skyler, Edward, 5780
Slack, Henry R., 6532
Slade, Christopher L., 3334
Slade, Jennifer K., 3334
Slade, Nicholas, 4729
Slager Trust, Donald M., 1178
Slager, David, 6685
Slaggie, Amanda, 4766
Slaggie, Barbara J., 4766
Slaggie, Lindsay, 4766
Slaggie, Matthew S., 4766
Slaggie, Michael J., 4766
Slaggie, Stephen M., 4766
Slaggie, Steve, 4766
Slagle, Frederick, 2511
Slagle, Richard, 7698
Slaight, Thomas L., 4947
Slamar, Charles, Jr., 2905
Slaney, Barbara L., 8266
Slaninka, Beth, 3274
Slate, C. Philip, 8700
Slate, Todd, 7340
Slater, Barbara, 6359
Slater, Colleen M., 1502
Slater, Craig D., 1365, 1502
Slater, Tammy, 3403
Slater, Thomas C., 7990
Slaton, Melanie V., 2438
Slattery, Anne, 1566
Slaughter, Charles L., 6072
Slaughter, Chris, 1116
Slaughter, Howard B., Jr., 8228
Slaughter, Lynn, 6909
Slaughter, R. James, 6072
Slaughter, Robert E., 4752
Slaughter, Thomas R., 6072
Slaughter, William A., 6072
Slavin, Susan C., 5603
Slavish, Timothy M., 8056
Slavitt, Andrew, 4785
Slawson, Kathryn Aicher, 3677
Sleasman, Dan, 6510
Slechta, Janna, 9024
Sledd, Herbert D., 3579
Sledd, Robert C., III, 9416
Sleeman, John, 3714
Sleik, Tom, 9889
Slemp, C. Bascom, 7665
Slette, Gary, 4796
Slichta, Amber L., 6153
Slick Revocable Trust, Earl F., 7313
Slick, Earl F., 7313
Slick, Rex, 3320
Slicker, John K., 182
Slifer, Rodney, 1518
Slifka, Alan B., 6870
Slifka, Barbara, 6871
Slifka, Barbara S., 6871
Slifka, Joseph, 6871
Slifka, Marlee, 9895, 9896
Slifka, Sylvia, 6870, 6871
Sligar, James, 6725
Sligar, Shelly, 9793
Slitka, Riva Ritro, 6870
Slivia, Raymond, 4612
Slivka, Alex, 79
Sliwkowski, Mary, 570
SLM Holding Corp., 3345
Sloan, Alfred P., Jr., 6872
Sloan, Cliff, 1940
Sloan, Florence, 1179
Sloan, Harry E., 1179
Sloan, Irene Jackson, 6872
Sloan, Jake, 6157
Sloan, Jon E., 8873
Sloan, Jr. Charitable Lead Trust, O. Temple, 7314
Sloan, Mark, 7314
Sloan, O. Temple, III, 7314
Sloan, O. Temple, Jr., 7314
Sloan, Robert, 3811
Sloan, Stephen R., 9341
Sloan, Steve, 7971
Sloan, Stuart M., 9736
Sloan, Sue, 8235
Sloan, Todd, 7973
Sloane, Alexander, 6157
Sloane, Edward G., Jr., 9772
Sloane, Howard G., 6157
Sloane, M. David, 202
Sloane, Nessia, 6157
Sloane, Virginia, 6157
Sloate, Laura J., 6163
Slocum, John J., Jr., 892
Sloenaker, James, 1120
Slomka, Stella Louise, Sr., 3113
Slonaker, David, 2627
Slone, Deck S., 4855
Sloneker, James, 973
Sloot, Alexander, 8152
Slosburg, D. David, 5083
Slosburg, Jacob, 5083
Slosburg, Richard H., 5083
Sloss, Deborah, 534
Sloss, Laura, 534
Slosser, Charles O., 718
Sloyan, Teresa, 8584
Sluder, Greenfield, 3967
Sluder, Hendrika, 3967
Sluis, Gordon, 4848
Slumberland, Inc., 2203
Slutsky, Kenneth J., 5228, 5421
Slutsky, Lorie A., 6544
Sluzewski, James A., 7552
Sly, Helen, 4986
Sly, Helen S., 4986
Sly, Patrick, 2822
Slyker, Kate, 79
Smadbeck, Arthur J., 6157
Smadbeck, Jeffrey, 6157
Smadbeck, Lou, 6157
Smadbeck, Louis, Jr., 6157
Smadbeck, Mark, 6157
Smadbeck, Paul, 6157
Smagala-DeVane, Colleen, 239
Small, Anna H., 8483
Small, Clarence, 3556
Small, Cornelia, 6967
Small, Eric L., 1252
Small, Glenn R., 6406
Small, J. Robert, 6046, 6219
Small, James, 9924
Small, John, Jr., 3348
Small, Leslie A., 4975, 4976
Small, Mario, 3171
Small, Nicole, 8908
Small, Nicole G., 8773
Smalley Family Foundation, 3877
Smalley, Alison, 7743
Smalley, Martha, 4432
Smallhouse, Sarah B., 97
Smallsreed, Timothy H., 490
Smallwood, Charlotte Houghteling, 4246
Smallwood, Clay, 2074
Smallwood, Edward, 4246
Smallwood, Guy, 4246
Smallwood, Thomas L., 9819, 9861
Smallwood, Valerie, 4246
Smart, Allen J., 7297
Smart, David A., 1697
Smart, John, 1697
Smart, Mary, 1697
Smart, Paul R., 7302
Smart, Raymond L., 1697
SMBC Capital Markets, Inc., 6873
SMC Limited Partnership, 9452
Smead, Ann, 1518
Smead, Larry H., 8579, 8623
Smead, Laurence H., 8579
Smead, Preston, 8623
Smead, Preston J., 8579
Smedley, Mike, 1395
Smedley, Robert “Bob”, 3569
Smeed, Ralph E., 2644
Smeltzer, David P., 7917
Smerch, Cathy, 2669
Smet, Cynthia Lee, 1181
Smet, John H., 1181
SMI International, Inc., 9024
Smigelski, Alex, 4026
Smiley, Butch, 9412
Smiley, Karl, 2223
Smiley, Martha, 9128
Smiley, Neil, 4100
Smilow, Joel E., 1698
Smirensky, Nick, 6549
Smirnov, Maxim, 7908
Smit, Johan J., 7112
Smit, Johan J., Mrs., 7112
Smit, Lisa, 7112
Smit, Sheila M., 7112
Smit, Stephen C., 7112
Smith 1994 Revocable Trust, Charles E., 3139
Smith Charitable Lead Annuity Trust, Andrea L., 3978
Smith Charitable Lead Annuity Trust, Beth K., 4990
Smith Charitable Lead Annuity Trust, Jennifer L., 3978
Smith Charitable Lead Annuity Trust, Rachel A., 3978
Smith Charitable Lead Trust, Sherman E., 7797
Smith Charitable Lead Unitrust, Beth K., 4990
Smith Charitable Lead Unitrust, Elizabeth G., 5461
Smith Charitable Remainder Unitrust, Floyd, 9460
Smith Charitable Remainder Unitrust, Nancy M., 4859
Smith Charitable Trust, Sherman E., 7797
Smith Corp., A.O., 9947
Smith Corp., J M, 8499
Smith Family Foundation, Charles E., 9464, 9534
Smith Family Foundation, Joyce, The, 1233
Smith Investment LP, Robert & Pamela, 1035
Smith Joint Charitable Remainder Unitrust, 4859
Smith Jr. Foundation, Edward W., 9915
Smith Marital Trust, Robert Brookings, 4859
Smith Memorial Fund, 1563
Smith Mgmt., Charles E., Inc., 9464
Smith Revocable Trust, Nancy Morrill, 4859
Smith Richardson Foundation, Inc., 7300
Smith Trust, Barry M., 2211
Smith Trust, Charles E., 9532
Smith Trust, E. Newbold, 8315
Smith Trust, Margaret D., 8315
Smith Wholesale Drug Corp., H.D., 3164
Smith, Adrian, 7180
Smith, Alfred, 8548
Smith, Andrea L., 3978
Smith, Andrew, 3164
Smith, Andy, 9227
Smith, Anita S., 3310
Smith, Anne Shen, 1140
Smith, Anne U., 3886
Smith, April L., 4338
Smith, Argile, 4814
Smith, B. Thomas, 4522
Smith, Banks M., 9238
Smith, Barbara, 101, 1188
Smith, Barbara L., 8245
Smith, Barry H., 6304
Smith, Benjamin M., 9552
Smith, Benjamin M., Jr., 9552
Smith, Bernadette Eyler, 8043
Smith, Bertie Deming, 3627
Smith, Beth K., 4990
Smith, Bob, 9023
Smith, Bonnie B., 8689
Smith, Bonnie H., 2130
Smith, Bradford K., 6983
Smith, Bradley, 7556
Smith, Bradley S., 7554, 7555
Smith, Brenda J., 1406
Smith, Brent, 9889
Smith, Brian, 3298
Smith, Brian J., 8332
Smith, Bridget, 4532
Smith, Bruce G., 3886
Smith, Bruce M., 9947
Smith, Byron, 2269
Smith, Camilla M., 6877
Smith, Caroline, 8660
Smith, Catherine Murray, 8396
Smith, Cathy, 210, 8120

Smith, Charles E., 9532
Smith, Charles W., 697
Smith, Cherida C., 7836
Smith, Chris, 3570
Smith, Christina Ittleson, 6217
Smith, Christine, 7428
Smith, Christine B., Dr., 8614
Smith, Christine J., 8287
Smith, Christopher, 4907
Smith, Christopher B., 2693, 7315, 9639
Smith, Cindy, 4474
Smith, Clara Blackford, 9179
Smith, Clarice R., 9532, 9534
Smith, Corey, 4452
Smith, Corey R., 8236
Smith, Corinne R., 5757
Smith, Cynthia, 8475
Smith, D. Andrew, 3164
Smith, D. Scarborough, III, 6873
Smith, Dana W., 4277
Smith, Darnell, 2101
Smith, David, 3407, 7431
Smith, David B., 2693, 9532, 9534
Smith, David F., 6526
Smith, David H., Dr., 3978
Smith, David L., 8650
Smith, David N., 7564
Smith, David S., 6561
Smith, David, II, 1407
Smith, Dean DuBose, 2450
Smith, Deborah, 1894
Smith, Deborah Alicia, 1312
Smith, Deborah M., 4990
Smith, Demaurice, 1939
Smith, Denise, 2632
Smith, Derek, 5726
Smith, Don, 1650
Smith, Donald, 6874
Smith, Donald R., 5377
Smith, Donna, 9789
Smith, Donna D., 1
Smith, Douglas H., 1185
Smith, Douglas I., 3886
Smith, Duane, 5095
Smith, Dwight, 229
Smith, Dwight E., 5026, 7411
Smith, E., 7690
Smith, E. Kendrick, 2462
Smith, E.B., Jr., 2955
Smith, E.J. Noble, 6561
Smith, E.N., Jr., 9222
Smith, Edward C., Jr., 7315
Smith, Edward N., 6561
Smith, Eileen O., 7942
Smith, Eleanor, 3743
Smith, Eliza, 9304
Smith, Elizabeth, 4974
Smith, Elizabeth B., 4103
Smith, Elizabeth G., 5461
Smith, Elizabeth W., 7067
Smith, Elizabeth Weinberg, 7066
Smith, Ellen Austin, 7380
Smith, Ellen Hauck, 4908
Smith, Erin, 3330
Smith, Ethel Sergeant Clark, 7317
Smith, Eva S., 3547
Smith, Evan, 8676
Smith, Evonne E., 9182
Smith, Fern, 744
Smith, Forrester M., III, 9238
Smith, Fred W., 5143
Smith, G. Blake, 5126
Smith, G. Boone, III, 2435
Smith, Garrett K., 3480
Smith, Gary, 7491, 9635, 9738
Smith, Gary L., 7789
Smith, Gavin H., 8916
Smith, Geoffrey A., 5879
Smith, Geoffrey J., 3990
Smith, George D., Jr., 6877
Smith, George D., Sr., 6877
Smith, George G., 5461
Smith, George G., III, 5461
Smith, Gerald C., 5142
Smith, Gerald H., 8865
Smith, Gordon V., 3886
Smith, Grant, 2429
Smith, Gregg, 4448
Smith, H. B., 9548
Smith, H. Bronson, 2450
Smith, H. Harrison, 8289
Smith, H. Russell, 1185
Smith, H.T., 8819
Smith, Harold Byron, Jr., 2693
Smith, Harriet T., 4974
Smith, Harry, 1184
Smith, Helen C., 3886
Smith, Henry B. duPont, 8315
Smith, Henry D., 8499
Smith, Henry Dale, Jr., 3164
Smith, Henry J., 9167
Smith, Hillary, 9524
Smith, Hilton C., Jr., 2066, 8502
Smith, Homer, 5685
Smith, Howard I., 6911
Smith, Hugh, Dr., 4755
Smith, Hunter J., 9533
Smith, Irving, 3955
Smith, J. Bradford, 9621
Smith, J. Burleson, 9101
Smith, J. Melvin, 3228
Smith, J. Michael, 2084
Smith, Jack, 860
Smith, Jacqueline, 5095
Smith, Jada P., 1184
Smith, James, 744, 7445
Smith, James Allen, 5785
Smith, James Campbell, 7665
Smith, James Christopher, 3164
Smith, James D., 4990
Smith, Jane, 8762
Smith, Janet, 3231, 5461
Smith, Jean Bixby, 365
Smith, Jean K., 9184
Smith, Jeanne Hoffman, 7760, 7766
Smith, Jeanne R., 1185
Smith, Jeff, 2233
Smith, Jefferson V., Jr., 8498
Smith, Jeffrey, 5220
Smith, Jeffrey O., 9558
Smith, Jennifer L., 3978
Smith, Jeremy T., 6561
Smith, Jerry M., 2528
Smith, Jerry V., 9046
Smith, Jesse W., 6663
Smith, Jill W., 6228
Smith, Jim, 1563
Smith, Jo A., 7315
Smith, Joan, 1035
Smith, Joan Irvine, 1182
Smith, Joan M., 3978
Smith, Joanne E., 2660
Smith, Jodi Alexander, 1965
Smith, Joe Mac, 6
Smith, John Cash, 9198
Smith, John F., 4442
Smith, John I., 8498
Smith, John W., 174
Smith, Jolene, 1948
Smith, Jonathan, 5143
Smith, Jordan V., 6561
Smith, Joseph, 8014
Smith, Joseph L., 3272
Smith, Joyce, 2662
Smith, Judith, 4374
Smith, Judith E., 4990
Smith, Judy, 5044
Smith, Julia A., 3016
Smith, Julie, 6874
Smith, June A., 3991
Smith, Karen, 7453
Smith, Kathleen D., 1845
Smith, Kathy, 1297, 8809
Smith, Kay, 3596
Smith, Kelly, 992
Smith, Kelvin, 7668
Smith, Ken Jennifer, 6
Smith, Kenneth L., 3547
Smith, Kenneth W., 9245
Smith, Kevin, 9737
Smith, Kim, 8135
Smith, Kirsten D., 9704
Smith, Kurtwood, 1035
Smith, Kyle, 9738
Smith, Kyle T., 9182
Smith, Langhorne B., 7982
Smith, Larry, 2511
Smith, LaTida, 7639
Smith, Laura, 6874, 7202
Smith, Laura A., 868
Smith, Lawrence S., 8287
Smith, Lawton R., 8472
Smith, Leo A., 3175
Smith, Leonard W., 4424
Smith, Lesley Stockard, Hon., 1675
Smith, Lesly S., 2105
Smith, Lesly Stockard, 2106
Smith, Lester, 68, 8721
Smith, Lester H., 9185
Smith, Lillian Strecker, 7557
Smith, Linda, 5108
Smith, Linda J., 9181
Smith, Lisle H., 7441
Smith, Logan, 1965
Smith, Lois E. H., 6679
Smith, Lola, 3290
Smith, Lorene, 8799
Smith, Lori, 5055
Smith, Lorraine, 3321
Smith, Lucy, 7786
Smith, Lunsford R., 7232
Smith, M. Catherine, 7253
Smith, Maggie, 5806
Smith, Manning J., III, 5427
Smith, Margaret Thompson, 8628
Smith, Marian, 4162, 4277
Smith, Marian R., 3578
Smith, Maribeth, 6561
Smith, Marie, 9148
Smith, Mark Clay, 9181
Smith, Mark D., 5800
Smith, Mark Douglas, 253
Smith, Markalan, 9832
Smith, Martha Scott, 8468
Smith, Mary, 9739
Smith, Mary B., 2638
Smith, Mary Ippoliti, 486
Smith, Mary L., 8288
Smith, Mary Rose, 6505
Smith, Mathew, 6037
Smith, Matt, Jr., 4375
Smith, Matthew, 6875
Smith, May, 1183, 1189
Smith, Melinda Hoag, 697
Smith, Melissa, 4395
Smith, Melissa W., 3858
Smith, Michael, 7038, 9304
Smith, Michael L., 3345
Smith, Michelle, 9534
Smith, Mike, Dr., 3391
Smith, Munson, 8941
Smith, Nancey Edmonds, 7665
Smith, Nancy, 3265, 3302, 3649
Smith, Nancy B., 4144
Smith, Nancy M., 4859
Smith, Nancy S., 4247
Smith, Neil T., 4974
Smith, Norm, 7414
Smith, Norton, 1188
Smith, Orin C., 9737
Smith, Orville D., 7776
Smith, Overton T., 8628
Smith, Pat, 3189, 3267
Smith, Patricia G., 4833
Smith, Patrick, 9859
Smith, Paul J., 3174
Smith, Paula, 6874
Smith, Peter, 3055, 3306, 4061, 5749
Smith, Peter F., 3985
Smith, Phil, 4714
Smith, Philip J., 6850
Smith, Phillips, 5995
Smith, Pierce, 9903
Smith, R. Lee, Jr., 2434
Smith, R.E., 9183
Smith, R.J., 5806
Smith, R.J., Mr., 5806
Smith, R.J., Mrs., 5806
Smith, Rachel A., 3978
Smith, Ralph, 3745, 8333
Smith, Ralph L., 4974
Smith, Randolph C.H., 9639
Smith, Randy, 9889
Smith, Raymond C., Jr., 8472
Smith, Raymond L., Jr., 8622
Smith, Richard, 2038
Smith, Richard A., 4275, 4277, 5674
Smith, Richard F., 2455
Smith, Richard G., 9558
Smith, Richard G., III, 7232
Smith, Richard J., 46
Smith, Richard M., 6643
Smith, Rick, 3283
Smith, Rick B., 1107
Smith, Rita M., 9524
Smith, Robert A., 4277
Smith, Robert A., III, 473
Smith, Robert B., 4859
Smith, Robert B., II, 4859
Smith, Robert B., III, 4859
Smith, Robert C., 6876
Smith, Robert E., 3858, 7591
Smith, Robert G., 6549
Smith, Robert H., 9532, 9534
Smith, Robert Lee, 3340
Smith, Robert R., 50
Smith, Roberta, 7942
Smith, Robin, 9984
Smith, Roderick, 3619
Smith, Roger S., 9947
Smith, Rogers, 3164
Smith, Ron, 4496
Smith, Ronnie, 4843
Smith, Rufus, 4830
Smith, Russell, 4070

Smith, Ruth McNair, 9017
Smith, S.M., 9185
Smith, S.W., 4397
Smith, Sadie Herzstein, 8905
Smith, Sarah, 6
Smith, Sarah A., 6877
Smith, Sarah N., 6561
Smith, Scott R., 9184
Smith, Shannon G., 8860
Smith, Sharon, 3391
Smith, Shelby L., 3657
Smith, Sherwood H., Jr., 7273
Smith, Sidney W., Jr., 4397
Smith, Stella B., 201
Smith, Stephanie H., 3569
Smith, Stephen B., 2693
Smith, Stephen P., S, 7591
Smith, Steve, 1108, 5062
Smith, Steven, 1511
Smith, Steven J., 9901
Smith, Stewart R., 756, 1185
Smith, Stockton N., 8315
Smith, Stuart P., 9533
Smith, Sue, 3284
Smith, Sue A., 9185
Smith, Susan F., 4275, 4277
Smith, Susan M., 9907
Smith, Susanne, 8922
Smith, Sybil H., 66
Smith, Taylor, 9470
Smith, Terry, 186, 3265, 9655
Smith, Thad, 2650
Smith, Thelma G., 7667
Smith, Thomas, 8819
Smith, Thomas A., 2213, 9182
Smith, Thomas W., 2365
Smith, Tim, 3698, 9104
Smith, Timothy A., 8803
Smith, Timothy R., 6
Smith, Todd, 7012
Smith, Tom, 9182
Smith, Tom E., 7202
Smith, Tony, 3180
Smith, Tracy, 6875
Smith, Trish, 7876
Smith, Ty, 2406
Smith, Valerie, 5532
Smith, Victoria, 7791
Smith, Vincent, 1242
Smith, Virgil L., 7298
Smith, Virginia, 2032
Smith, Virginia N., 9552
Smith, Virginia Rowan, 5427
Smith, Virginia V., 4859
Smith, Vivian L., 9183, 9186
Smith, W. Fred, Jr., 8819
Smith, W. Hinckle, 8289
Smith, Wallace H., 4859
Smith, Walt, 9629
Smith, Walter H., 8228
Smith, Wayne T., 3606
Smith, Wendy, 7762
Smith, Wes, 49, 5143
Smith, Willard, II, 1184
Smith, William, 5611
Smith, William A., 9187
Smith, William A., Rev., 8001
Smith, William G., 1357
Smith, William L.R., 7232
Smith, William Sherman, 7797
Smith, William Wikoff, 8288
Smith, William Z., 6561
Smith, Zeke W., 1
Smith-Hams, Denise, 571
Smith-Petersen, Douglas R., 4157
Smith-Rosario, Toni, 1589
Smitham, Peter, 5622
Smithe, Maureen, 7971
Smithers Foundation, Christopher D., 7012
Smithers, Les, 7671
Smithers-Fornaci, Adele, 7012
Smithfield Foods, Inc., 9535
Smithfield Trust Co., 8114
SmithKline Beecham Corp., 8060, 8061
Smithson, Mark, 4683
Smithsonian, 2300
Smits, James, 4402
Smits, Kerri Sue, 4402
Smitson, Patricia, 7394
Smitson, Patricia Mann, 7404
Smitson, Robert M., 3264
Smock, Laura L., 8290
Smokler Trust, Toba, 2190
Smokler, Carol S., 2190
Smokler, Irving A., 2190
Smolens, H. Marcia, 921
Smoot, J. Thomas, Jr., 5248
Smotherman, Patricia D., 4415
Smoyer, Donald, 466
Smucker Co., J.M., The, 7669
Smucker, Richard K., 7669
Smucker, Timothy P., 7669
Smulders, Patrick, 7001
Smulian, Rob, 2432
Smullin, Patricia C., 1190
Smullin, Patricia D., 1190
Smullin, William B., 1190
Smyers, Robyn Minter, 7478
Smysor, Catherine H., 3165
Smysor, John L., 3165
Smyth, Geralynn D., 3826
Smyth, John C., 3826
Smyth, Patrick J., 3826
Smyth, Peggy, 3826
Smyth, Sylvia, 1572
Snapp, David, 3502
Snead, Cheryl W., 8356
Snead, George C., Jr., 9382
Snead, Lauren R., 9536
Snead, Thomas G., Jr., 9416, 9536
Snead, Vickie M., 9536
Snearly-Vosberg, Sandra, 3337
Sneden Foundation, Robert W. and Margaret D., 4389
Sneden, Kathleen, 4389
Sneden, Marcia A., 4389
Snee, Katherine E., 8291
Sneed, Michael. E., 5326
Snell Contractor, E.R., Inc., 2552
Snell, Brian T., 2552
Snell, David E., 2552
Snell, Fred B., Jr., 2552
Snell, George B., 6012
Snell, Glen, 3534
Snell, Melissa, 3481
Snell, Nancy, 9384
Snell, Robin J., 2552
Snell, Sara Jane, 9109, 9277
Snider Holdings, LLC, 6695
Snider, Amy, 8282
Snider, Arnold H., 6695
Snider, Arnold M., 6401
Snider, Charles W., 8887
Snider, Craig, 8292
Snider, David, 7202
Snider, Don P., 111
Snider, Edward M., 8292
Snider, Jody, 1889
Snider, John D., 4855
Snider, Karen F., 8046
Snider, Katherine M., 6401, 6695
Sniderman, Howard, 7445
Snidow, Robin, 1419
Snite, Fred B., 3166
Snoddy, Brian, 6
Snodgrass, Larry, 8653
Snodgrass, Max V., 3515
Snook, Gregory I., 3791
Snook, Marjorie Y., 68
Snook, Todd, 3761
Snow Foundation, Phoebe, 1130
Snow, Adam B., 2553
Snow, Catherine, 1934
Snow, Chris, 9578
Snow, Denise, 2553
Snow, Doyle, 8797
Snow, Hal, 7876
Snow, Jeffrey, 2553
Snow, John Ben, 6878
Snow, Jonathan L., 6878
Snow, Kerri, 2553
Snow, Kerri K., 2553
Snow, R. Anthony, 8026
Snow, Sidney H., 3974
Snow, Susan, 7850
Snow, Sylvia, 2553
Snowden, James M., Jr., 4966
Snowden, W. Scott, 744
Snowdon Charitable Lead Unitrust, Edward, 1915
Snowdon, Andrew L., 1915
Snowdon, Ariana, 1915
Snowdon, Edward W., Jr., 1915, 6879
Snowdon, Margo, 9975
Snowdon, Marguerite, 1915
Snowdon, Richard W., 6879
Snowdon, Richard, III, 1915
Snowdon, Roger S., 3301
Snowe, Parker, 8284
Snows Hill, LLC, 4083
Snyder Family Living Trust, The, 1192
Snyder, Amy M., 7995
Snyder, Ann Marie, 5815
Snyder, B. Lee, 9775
Snyder, Beryl L., 6880
Snyder, Beth, 9059
Snyder, Bette, 9280
Snyder, Beverly B., 9188
Snyder, Brian, 6880
Snyder, Brian S., 6880
Snyder, Charles, 5815
Snyder, Cheryl L., 7610
Snyder, Dudley R., 9188
Snyder, Frost, 9739
Snyder, Harold, 6880
Snyder, Harold B., Sr., 5462
Snyder, Harry D., 6886
Snyder, Jack, 3375
Snyder, James D., 9382
Snyder, James M., 3217
Snyder, James T., 5394
Snyder, Jay, 6880
Snyder, Jay T., 6880
Snyder, Jeffrey L., 5074
Snyder, John C., 9188
Snyder, Kate, 4357
Snyder, Kim, 8774
Snyder, Loren, 3330
Snyder, Lynsi, 666
Snyder, Marcus M., 9188
Snyder, Margaret, 9739
Snyder, Paul L., 4715, 4757
Snyder, Phillip, 9280
Snyder, Phyllis Johnson, 5462
Snyder, Randy, 1192
Snyder, Rex, 7421
Snyder, Richard G., 7921
Snyder, Robert E., 5166
Snyder, Roy, 1389
Snyder, Solomon H., 3833, 6333
Snyder, Stephen, 3336
Snyder, Susan, 1192, 5815
Snyder, Todd, 9188
Snyder, Valerie, 4361
Snyder, William, 4102
Snyder, William A., 2034
So Charitable Trust, 5759
Soang, Joseph, III, 8392
Soape, Roger, 9049
Soape, Roger A., 9269
Soares, Gregory M., 8383
Sobeck, Tom, 4370
Sobel, Denise R., 844
Sobel, Jonathan, 6882
Sobel, Karen, 6883
Sobel, Naomi J., 844
Sobel, Robert J., 6883
Sobic, Dan D., 9698
Sobkowski, Gregory, 3369
Soboroff, Steven L., 1307
Sobrato Charitable Capital Trust, 1193
Sobrato Charitable Lead Trust I, 1193
Sobrato Charitable Lead Trust II, 1193
Sobrato Charitable Lead Trust III, 1193
Sobrato Charitable Lead Trust IV, 1193
Sobrato Trust Estate, Ann, 1193
Sobrato, John A., 1193
Sobrato, John M., 1193
Sobrato, Lisa, 1193
Sobrato, Sheri J., 1193
Sobrato, Susan, 1193
Soby, Dayton, 4796
Society Capital Corp., 7523
Society Corp., 7523
Sockabasin, Lisa, 3699
Sockabasin, Lisa J., 3708
Socorro, Julia, 8352
Soda Trust, Y. Charles, 1194
Soda, Helen C., 1194
Soda, Rosemary, 1194
Soda, Y. Charles, 1194
Sodano, Simone, 7425
Soderberg, Elsa A., 5575
Soderberg, Jon, 5575
Soderberg, Libby, 5575
Soderberg, Maureen, Dr., 5575
Soderberg, Peer Allyn, 5575
Soderberg, Peter H., 5575
Soderlund, Clea Newman, 1652
Soderquist Charitable Lead Annuity Trust, 202
Soderquist, Donald G., 202
Soderquist, Jeffrey, 202
Soderquist, Joann, 202
Soderquist, Mark, 202
Soderquist-Togami, Wendy, 202
Soderstrom, Carl D., 3167
Soderstrom, Carl W., 3167
Soderstrom, Carl W., Jr., 3167
Soderstrom, Robert W., 3167
Sodestrom, Calvin, 970
Sodestrom, Julie, 970
Sofaer, Abraham D., 801
Soffer, Marsha, 2095
Sofka, Paul, 8775

Soful, Michael G., 7401
Sognefast, Peter, 8105
Sohn Charitable Lead Trust, Fred & Frances, 7844
Sohn, Frances F., 7844
Sohn, Howard F., 7844
Sohn, Robert C., 6884
Sohn, Ruth, 7844
Sohn, Tina, 6884
Soicher Trust, Estelle, The, 1195
Soiland, Marlene, 420
Soileau, Eddie, 3623
Soimar, Michael S., 4369
Sokolof, Phil, 5084
Sokolove, Jennifer, 3709
Sola Scriptura, 2872
Sola, Dan, 1318
Sola, Richard, 1318
Sola, Tamara, 1318
Solana, Nancy J., 8844
Solanova, LLC, 216
Solari, Bruce, 239
Solari, John, 5108
Solari, Mary C., 1196
Solari, Richard C., 1196
Solberg, Jeffrey M., 2881
Solberg, Michael, 4621
Soldan, David R., 4405
Soldivieri, Susan I., 5232
Solek, Ellen Coote, 1647
Soles, Jeffrey, 8109
Solheim, Allan, 163
Solheim, Allan, Jr., 163
Solheim, Andrew, 163
Solheim, Barbara R., 132
Solheim, David, 163
Solheim, Joy, 163
Solheim, Karsten, 163
Solheim, Karsten L., 132
Solheim, Karsten Louis, 163
Solheim, Louise, 163
Solheim, Louise C., 163
Solid Rock Trust, 1409
Solinger, Hope G., 6053
Sollazzo, Jack, 5948
Sollins, Karen R., 6804
Solmes, David, 4342
Solnica-Krezel, Lila, 2995
Soloman, Susan G., 6887
Solomon Charitable Remainder Unitrust, Peter J., 6885
Solomon Investment Partnership, 7919
Solomon Trust, Jeanette R., 6885
Solomon, Alfred L., 6886
Solomon, Andrew, 2989
Solomon, Dana Bass, 9753
Solomon, Daniel, 3754
Solomon, Darlene, 220
Solomon, David, 3754
Solomon, Gerald R., 1106
Solomon, Geula R., 6379
Solomon, Jacob, 2301
Solomon, Jane, 3754
Solomon, Jeffrey, 5717
Solomon, Jeffrey R., 828
Solomon, Jerry, 5875
Solomon, Lillian Cohen, 3754
Solomon, Murray L., 2438
Solomon, Peter J., 6379, 6885
Solomon, Phyllis, 421
Solomon, Steven J., 2827
Solomon, T.J., 7179
Solomon, William T., 8912
Solomon, William T., Jr., 8795
Solon Investments, LP, 2407
Solot, Claire, 875
Solot, Claire M., 932
Solot, Edwin, 875
Solot, Edwin L., Jr., 932
Solow, Mark G., 5394
Solow, Steven P., 2951
Soloway, Howard B., 9417
Solso, Theodore M., 3292
Solstice Trust, 4305
Solt, Dana D., 3468
Solt, Robert H., 3468
Soltani, Atossa, 399
Solvang, Susan Lubar, 9894
Somasekar, Suchi, 1358
Somerlott, Bambi, 4461
Somers, Bonnie, 927
Somers, Carolyn, 6489
Somers, Jerome, 302
Somerset Trust Co., 8335
Somma, Anthony D., 3553
Somma, Robert, 4085
Sommer, Alfred, 5684, 6333
Sommer, Bruce A., 2762
Sommer, Lorraine G., 7466
Sommer, Melanie S., 5178
Sommerhauser, Peter M., 9812, 9862, 9879
Sommers, Josh, 5806
Sommers, Judith, 7650
Sommers, Sharon, 3336
Sonatori, Leslie Fancelli, 2092
Sondhe, Ratanjit S., 7406
Sondland, Gordon D., 9740
Sondregger, Leona, 9931
Sonenstein, Jeffrey, 1634
Sones, Betty, 5068
Sones, Randall D., 3719, 3733
Sonet, Steven G., 5897
Sonfield, Anita D., 3249
Song, Julie, 8383
Song, Unmi, 2849
Songer, Marty, 3267
Sonksen, Carl, 3418
Sonne, Christian R., 6514
Sonneborn, Dirk, 6049
Sonntag, Steve, 3330
Sonoco Foundation, 8505
Sonoco Products Co., 8500
Sonsini, Lisa Sobrato, 1193
Sonsini, Matt, 1193
Sontag, Frederick B., 2325
Sontag, Frederick T., 2325
Sontag, Susan T., 2325
Sony Corp., 6904
Sony Corp. of America, 6581
Sony Pictures Entertainment, 1184
SONY Playstation, 1153
Soo Hoo, Frank, 2746
Soo, Arpad, 8527
Sooch, Navdeep S., 9189
SooHoo, Richard, 378
Soon-Shiong, Michele, 391
Soon-Shiong, Patrick, 391
Soon-Shiong, Patrick, Dr., 391
Sopher, Raeman P., 9365
Sopris Foundation, 1367
Sordoni, Matthew, 7992
Sordoni, Susan F., 7425
Soref Foundation, Samuel and Helene, 9190
Soref Operating Trust, 9948
Soref, Jeffrey B., 5740
Sorensen, Arlo G., 423, 918, 1349
Sorensen, Catherine A., 793
Sorensen, Gergory, 5454
Sorensen, Harvey L., 1200
Sorensen, Jerry, 9704
Sorensen, Maud C., 1200
Sorensen, Ole M., 7184
Sorensen, R. Michael, 9511
Sorenson Legacy Foundation, The, 9303
Sorenson, Beverley, 9303
Sorenson, Cynthia K., 2592
Sorenson, James, 9303
Sorenson, Joseph, 9303
Sorenson, Richard W., 2326
Sorenson, Steve, 9916
Sorey, John F., III, 2035
Sorge, Bob, 9897
Sorgente Investments LLC, 2613
Sorgente No. 3 Trust, 2613
Sorgi, Peter, 4184
Soria, Carolina, 3539
Soria, Lorenzo, 701
Sorin, Gretchen Sullivan, Dr., 1530
Sorokanich, Mary Ann, 8275
Sorokes, Larry, 5750
Sorokin, Sharon L., 8236
Soroko, John J., 8010
Soros 1982 Charitable Lead Trust, George, 6213
Soros Charitable Foundation, 6891
Soros Foundation, 6213
Soros Foundation-Hungary, 6891
Soros, Alexander, 6889, 6891
Soros, Andrea, 7003, 7010
Soros, Daisy, 6888
Soros, George, 6004, 6213, 6593, 6891, 7003
Soros, Jonathan, 6004, 6593, 6890
Soros, Jonathan Allan, 6891
Soros, Melissa Schiff, 5956
Soros, Paul, 6888
Soros, Robert, 5956, 6891
Soros, Susan, 6213
Soros, Susan Weber, 6213
Sorrell, Martin, 5684
Sorrentino, Matthew R., Esq., 8136
Sorrick, Marcia, 3535
Sorrick, Marcia A., 3501
Sosa, Katherine, 9149
Sosa, Lionel, 9149
Sosa, Liz, 3554
Soskin, W. H., 909
Soskin, William H., 255
Sosland Revocable Trust, Vivan J., 4975
Sosland Trust B, Hymie J., 4977
Sosland, Blanche E., 4977
Sosland, Charles S., 4977
Sosland, David N., 4977
Sosland, Estelle, 4950
Sosland, Estelle G., 4977
Sosland, Jeanne, 4937
Sosland, L. Joshua, 4977
Sosland, Meyer J., 4977
Sosland, Morton I., 4902, 4905, 4977
Sosland, Neil N., 4977
Sosland-Edelman, Deborah, 4975, 4976, 4977
Sosnick, Aaron, 1799
Sosnoff, Martin T., 6892
Sosnoff, Toni, 6892
Sotheby's, Inc., 6844
Sotherden, Lucile, 5927
Sotirhos Nicholson, Pelagia, 6223
Sotiros, Diane, 2849
Soto, Javier Alberto, 2238
Soto-Harmon, Lidia, 1931
Sotos, Marybeth M., 1930
Soucheray, Diane, 1391
Souder Charitable Lead Trust, Susanna, 3168
Souder, Granger, Jr., 7686
Souder, Jeff, 3398
Souder, Jr. Charitable Lead Trust, William F., 3168
Souder, Susanna J., 3168
Souder, William F., Jr., 3168
Souede, Rachel, 6833
Souers, Tom M., 8889
Soukenik, Anthony J., 4928
Soukenik, Tony, 4928
Soulliere, Anne-Marie, 5170, 5178
Sound Around, Corp., 5699
Soupata, Lea N., 3745
Soupe, Roger A., Inc., 9049
Sources of Hope Foundation, 6042
Sousa, Barbara, 5476
Sousa, Jan, 2631
Sousou, Ramez, 7001
South Asian Advocates, 7846
South Jersey Financial Corp., Inc., 5463
South Pacific Trust, 8715
South Point Hotel Casino, 5119
South Texas Money Management, 8914
South, Scott, 9603
Southampton Memorial Hospital Endowment Fund, 9434
Southcentral Foundation, 85
Southeastern Asset Management, Inc., 8616
Southeastern Asset Mgmt., Inc., 8620
Southern Area of The Links, Inc., 2294
Southern Bancshares, Inc., 7319
Southern Bank & Trust Co., 7319
Southern Co., The, 2554
Southern Crushed Concrete, Inc., 4578
Southern Furniture Co. of Conover, Inc., 7155
Southern Industrial Corp., 2337
Southern Poultry Science Society, 2565
Southern States Brokerage, 9290
Southern Wine & Spirits of America, Inc., 782, 2347
Southern Wine & Spirits of Florida, Inc., 2294
Southern, Bill, 3521
Southland Enterprises Inc., 9369
Southport Trust, The, 8715, 9226
Southview Apartments LLC, 9452
Southwest Business Corp., 9217
Southwest Gas Corp., 5149
Southwestern Bell Corp., 8675
Southworth, Louis B., 9780
Soutter, Anne, 2534
Soutus, Sonya, 2428
Souza, Cynthia, 417
Souza, Tracy Hamilton, 3321
Sovereign Bank, 4256
Sovern, Michael I., 5622, 6850
Sovey, Mara L., 2790
Soward, Nancy, 7341
Sowell, Elizabeth, 9192
Sowell, James E., 9192
Sowell, Jerry, 98
Sowers, George, 9290
Space Center, Inc., 4701
Space Mark Inc., 80
Spacesaver Corp., 9813
Spacinsky, Charlotte L., 2192
Spadorcia, Doreen, 4783

Spady, Bob, 5068
Spafford, Pat, 419
Spagnol, Tracy E., 7931
Spagnoletti, Joe, 5223
Spain, James, 3317
Spain, John, 3613
Spain, Melissa, 7217
Spain, Tara N., 4783
Spalding, Charles C., Jr., 2597
Spalten, Marlene, 2040
Spanbock, Marion, 6228
Spangenberg, Audrey, 9193
Spangle, Morgan, 5864
Spangler Construction Co., C.D., 7320
Spangler, Abigail R., 7320
Spangler, C.D., 7320
Spangler, C.D., Jr., 7320
Spangler, Meredith R., 7320
Spangler-Crawford, Diana, 7178
Spanier, David B., 6460
Spanier, Jonathan G., 6460
Spanier, Maury L., 6460
Spaniolo, James, 4357
Spanton, Elisabeth, 3578
Spanx, Inc., 2412
Spar, Debora, 6431
Spar, Debora L., 7043
Sparaco, Jim, 1153
Sparber, Roy M., 6068
Sparby, David, 4808
Sparkle Sugar Corp., 4652
Sparks, Amy, 5529
Sparks, Annette M., 295
Sparks, Ben, 1405
Sparks, Candace "Candy", 1398
Sparks, Don, 3576
Sparks, George, 1401
Sparks, Gil, 9604
Sparks, Greg, 8558
Sparks, Jackie, 5169
Sparks, Justice Keith F., Hon., 1039
Sparks, Kit, 357
Sparks, Laura, 8216
Sparks, Mary Lee, 2986
Sparks, Nancy, 3576
Sparks, Pauline, 1699
Sparks, Philip L., 9506
Sparks, Robert D., 8629
Sparks, Tamara S., 7374
Sparks, Willard D., 8629
Sparks, William, 7425
Sparling, Alfred H., Jr., 4101
Sparrow, Bradford, 3677
Sparrow, Marvin, 3943
Sparrow, Paul, 1907
Sparrow, William, 4359
Spartan Light Metal Products, Inc., 4919
Spartan Organization, Inc., 8116
Spartan Stores Inc., 4544
Spartz, Margaret A., 3393
Spataro, Jodi, 3298
Spaulding Trust, Ruth E., 7670
Spaulding, Jean G., 7195
Spaulding, Karen Lee, 6584
Speakman-Yerick, Linda, 3359
Spear, Alexander, 392
Spear, R.D., 2448
Spearin, Preston and Burrows, Inc., 6205
Spearman, Grace H., 1201
Spears, Janet Y., 490
Spears, Larry Lee, 3072
Spears, Marcum A., 3072
Spears, Ron, 936
Speas Co., 4978, 4979
Speas Unitrust, Alice J., 4978
Speas, Effie E., 4978, 4979
Speas, Victor E., 4978, 4979
Spec's Family Partners, Ltd., 9195
Specht, Brian, 1627
Speciale, William G., 3597
Specialized Maintenance Services, 2735
Speck, David, 9380
Speck, David G., 9497
Speck, Samuel, III, 7412
Spector, Alfred, 615
Spector, Deborah, 221
Spector, Nancy, 1108
Spector, Robie, 631
Spector, Steven, 618
Spector, Warren J., 1874
Spedden, Sandra, 1672
Speed, James H., Jr., 7328
Speed, Linda S., 3288
Speedway Children's Charities, 7214
Speedy, Jerry, 4526
Speer Mechanical, 5482
Speer, John F., 9791
Speer, Lisa, 205
Speer, Lynnda L., 2328
Speer, Mark, 3540
Speer, R. Wayne, 8630
Speer, Richard M., 2328
Speer, Roy M., 2328
Speers, Jennifer, 9338
Speers, Jennifer P., 7041
Speh, Albert J., IV, 3170
Speh, Albert J., Jr., 3170
Speh, Claire R., 3170
Speh, Jonathan, 3170
Speh, Michael, 3170
Speilman, Amy, 5442
Speir, Shannon G., 19
Spellings, J. M., 8833
Spellings, Margaret, 9625
Spellman, Christina, 6448
Spellman, Neil, 5102
Spelsberg, Nancy T., 2819
Spelsberg, Thomas C., 2819
Spelsberg, Thomas C., Jr., 2819
Spence, Ann B., 6235
Spence, Bryan, 3987
Spence, Kathryn Curtiss, 4405
Spence, Kenneth F., III, 4783
Spence, Steve, 9697
Spencer Foundation, 1934
Spencer, Aaron, 4278
Spencer, Barbara G., 3617
Spencer, Dana, 8539
Spencer, David B., 3617
Spencer, David Paul, 3617
Spencer, Denise K., 8475
Spencer, Diana Davis, 3887
Spencer, Diana K., 3014
Spencer, Don, 4361
Spencer, Earnhart A., Jr., 9510
Spencer, George C., 7841
Spencer, J. Kyle, 2460
Spencer, J.M., 7688
Spencer, James, 6285
Spencer, Laura, 2038
Spencer, Letitia A., 5049
Spencer, Lyle M., 3171
Spencer, M. Hunter, 5899
Spencer, Marabeth, 4592
Spencer, Margaret Beale, 1934, 6003
Spencer, Mark, 4278
Spencer, Marni E., 8180
Spencer, Mary M., 2329
Spencer, Megan, 3534
Spencer, Patricia, 8383
Spencer, Phyllis, 2512
Spencer, Rebecca L., Rev., 8370
Spencer, Richard, 516
Spencer, Robert D., 5899
Spencer, Ronald P., 3617
Spencer, Samuel, 8001
Spencer, Steve R., 1
Spencer, Terry K., 7783
Spencer, William M., III, 5899
Spensley, Michael S., 6947
Speranza, Elisa M., 1384
Speranza, Paul S., Jr., 7061
Sperber, Burton S., 1205
Sperber, Charlene M., 1205
Sperling, John G., 94
Sperling, Laurene M., 4279
Sperling, Scott M., 4279
Spero, Suzanne M., 5377
Spero, Thomas L., 9907
Speyer, Jerry I., 6896
Speyer, Robert, 6896
Spicer, Barbara Ann, 2201
Spicer, Joyce, 4332
Spicer, Marian, 7414
Spiece, Trey, 109
Spiegal, Brad, 4394
Spiegel, Audrey, 6676
Spiegel, Debra, 1020
Spiegel, Eric A., 5454
Spiegel, Grace, 6676
Spiegel, Helene, 5150
Spiegel, Jeffrey, 6676
Spiegel, Judy, 850
Spiegel, Justin, 6676
Spiegel, Steven, 4750
Spiegel, Thomas, 5150
Spiehs, Marcia, 5045
Spiel, Norton, 6918
Spielberg Family Living Trust, 1073
Spielberg, Steven A., 1073, 1348
Spielman, Amy, 5442
Spielman, Richard, 5474
Spielman, Robert, 6918
Spielman, Ronald, 9835
Spielman, Susan, 5474
Spier, Michelle, 9012
Spiers, Mark, 1511
Spiggle, Wayne, Dr., 3762
Spika, Nicholas C., 9620, 9732, 9744
Spilker, Diane, 6897
Spilker, Marc, 6897
Spillane, Richard, 4159
Spiloto, Saundra L., 3228
Spilove, Elaina S., 7425
Spina, David A., 4280
Spina, Kimberly V., 6437
Spina, Stephanie H., 4280
Spinazzo, Gary, 4727
Spindler, Susan A., 1364
Spingold, Frances, 6899
Spingold, Nathan Breither, 6899
Spinks, Steve, 8474
Spinnato, John, 5437
Spinner, Joshua, Rabbi, 6336
Spinosa, Suzie A., 8263
Spira, David, 6111
Spira, Joel, 8151
Spira, Ruth, 8151
Spire, Henry, 8279
Spire, Linda J., 8279
Spire, William Bruce, 8279
Spirer, Kenneth, 3684
Spitaletta, Sabrina, 5437
Spitters, Laurence L., 851
Spitters, Louis, 851
Spitz, Edward A., 8478
Spitz, Julia, 5926
Spitz, Lauren, 4080
Spitzer Trust, Doreen, 5743
Spitzer, A. Travis, 1206
Spitzer, Anne, 6900
Spitzer, Arthur, 1206
Spitzer, Bernard, 6900
Spitzer, Daniel Evan, 6900
Spitzer, Eliot Laurence, 6900
Spitzer, N.B., 6916
Spitzer, Robert R., Ph.D., 9881
Spitzfaden, Thomas, 2790
Spivak, Hillary, 5412
Spivey, Anita, 5281
Spivey, Anita V., 5310
Spivey, Scott W., 2435
Splawn, Robert, M.D., 1270
Splinter, Michael R., 249
Spoelhof, John, 4545
Spoelhof, Judith, 4545
Spoelhof, Judy, 4545
Spoelhof, Scott, 4545
Spoelhof, Scott Alan, 4374
Spoelman, Roger, 986, 4369
Spogli, Ronald P., 546, 579
Spokane Chronicle Co., 9607
Spolter, Jerry, 744
Spoltman, John, 7490
Spooner, Dighton, 3698
Spooner, Rebecca L., 3094
Sport Fun, Inc., 7012
Sports Products of America LLC, 5559
Spotanski, Micheal R., 4931
Spotted Leopard Trust, 8715
Spottswood, Robert, 2041
Spradlin, Charles B., Jr., 3496
Spradlin, James, 2881
Spradling, T. Scott, 7781
Spraggins, Joe, Genl., 4830
Sprague, James B., 3774
Sprague, Norman F., III, 951, 1207
Sprague, Seth, 6901
Sprain, Robert A., Jr., 15
Spraker, Michael W., 9563
Sprangers, Rosie, 9832
Sprankle, Brenda Lynn, 8063
Sprankle, Carolyn Ann, 8063
Sprankle, Joseph F., III, 8063
Sprankle, Melissa F, 8063
Sprauve-Martin, Margaret, 9377
Spray, Donna & Ed, 7659
Spray, Jane, 370, 532, 977
Spreitler, Danny J., 4828
Sprenger, Paul, 6326
Spring, M. Edward, 1043
Springcreek Advisors, 1208
Springer, Fred, 315
Springer, J. William, 7444
Springer, Michael W., 8853
Springer, Thad, 7835
Springfield Financial Asset Mgmt., Inc., 4183
Springfield, James, 8615
Springgate, Susan, 4472
Springhouse Realty Co., 8047
Springs Company, The, 8506
Springs Creative Products Group, 8506
Springs Industries, Inc., 8506

Springs Window Fashions, Inc., 8506
Springs, Elliott W., 8504
Springs, Frances Ley, 8504
Springsted, Kirk, 4671
Sprint Communications Co., LP, 3549
Sprint Corp., 3549
Sprint Nextel, 7214
Sprint Nextel Corp., 3549
Sproul, Curt, 1039
Sproul, Rebecca P., 5349
Sproule, Martha S., 5273
Spruance, W. Halsey, Jr., 1780
Spruce 2007 Charitable Trust, 608
Sprung, Gilda, 9158
Sprunt, Gloria C., 7171
Spurgeon, Edward D., 328
Spurgeon, Mark, 9604
Spurgeon, Michael, 328
Spurgeon, Stephen, 328
Spurgeon, William, 2803
Spurlino, Cyrus W., 2330
Spurlock, Doug, 1077
Spurlock, Joyce, 1077
Spurlock, Sandra, 9632
Spurrier, Clinton, 3481
Spurs Sports & Entertainment, 9149
Spychala, Darlene A., 6406
Spytek, Eryk, 2944
Squadron, Anne S., 6918
Squeri, Stephen J., 5588
Squibb & Sons, E.R., Inc., 5712
Squibb & Sons, E.R., L.L.C., 5712
Squibb, Bristol Meyers, 5412
Squibb, James G., Jr., 9773
Squiers, Laura L., 9223
Squire Trust, Morris B., 7791
Squires, James A., 9496
Squires, Paul, 3958
SRB Corp., 4222
Sreeram, A., 4404
Srinivasan, Laverne Evans, 5747
Srinivasan, Raj, 272
Srinivasan, Vidya, 5160
Srochi-Meyerhoff, Lenel, 3726
Srodes, Ellen, 8043
Sroufe, Jon, 3335
SRYZ Corp., 1099
SSR Charitable Lead Annuity Trust 2004, 3854
St Albans Shoping Center Inc., 9369
St. Amant, Carol, 2853
St. Andrews Presbyterian College, 7314
St. Angelo, Steve, 7002
St. Arnaud, Shirley, 3354
St. Catherine's Island Foundation, Inc., 6561
St. Clair, Charles, 271
St. Clair, James W., 3575
St. Clair, Lucas, 3686
St. Clair, Margaret N., 4210
St. Clair, Yemana, 3705
St. Clair., Lucas, 3705
St. Francis Hospital, 3317
St. James Church, 6205
St. John Properties, Inc., 3888
St. John's Health Center Foundation, 1132
St. John's J1 Descendants Trust, 9459
St. John's J2 Descendants Trust, 9459
St. John's J3 Descendants Trust, 9459
St. John, Cornelia, 8350
St. John, Edward A., 3888
St. John, Emmett, 6070
St. John, Kellay, 3888
St. John, Morgan W., 1284
St. Johns Lutheran Church, 9807
St. Joseph Hill Academy, 5718
St. Joseph's Hospital, 2151
St. Jude Medical, CRM Div., 2151
St. Jude Medical, Inc., 4770
St. Lawrence, Dale, 4072
St. Leger, Judy, 2315
St. Louis Trust Company, The, 4909
St. Louis-San Francisco Railroad, 2576
St. Luke Medical Staff, 1020
St. Omer, Denise, 4920
St. Paul Companies, Inc., The, 4783
St. Paul Foundation, 4792
St. Paul Travelers Companies, Inc., The, 4783
St. Wrba, John A., 9174
Staab, Valari, 6531
Staadt, Gary, 3366
Staats Bibliotek Berlin, 5707
Stabler, Amelia Taper, 1237
Stabler, Margaretta K., Jr., 1872
Stabler, W. Laird, III, 1872
Stabler-Cordis, Sarah, 2763
Stache Trust, Emil, 1209
Stack, Candice, 1037
Stack, Edward W., 5786, 5975
Stack, Lauren, 9380
Stack, Richard L., 449
Stack, Sarah, 3948
Stackhouse, Lucinda, 81
Stackner, Irene M., 9951
Stackner, John S., 9951
Stackpole Carbon Co., 8295
Stackpole, Adelaide, 8295
Stackpole, Alice, 6802
Stackpole, Harrison C., 8295
Stackpole, J. Hall, 8295
Stackpole, R. Dauer, 8295
Stacy Charitable Trust, Helen, 2333
Stacy Family Trust, 7734
Stacy, Festus, 2333
Stacy, Julia K., 8951
Stadleman, Kelly, 9796
Stadler, Christopher, 5465
Stadler, Christopher J., 5465
Stadler, Gabrielle, 5465
Stadler, Julia C., 7425
Stadler, Julie Carell, 8540
Stadler, Loretta, 5465
Stadler, Loretta M., 5465
Stadler, Tom, 1650
Stadtmauer, Marisa, 5466
Stadtmauer, Richard, 5466
Stadtmueller, Gerald, 9888
Staebler, Rebecca, 9605
Staeck, Michael P., 9924
Staelin, Steve, 7572
Staffieri, Victor A., 3586
Stafford, Brian J., 4152
Stafford, Charles T., 2482
Stafford, George, 849
Stafford, Gwen, 8994
Stafford, William P., 9779
Stafford, William, II, 9779
Stafslien, Joan B., 377
Staggers, Barbara C., 368
Staggs, Melanie, 365
Stahl, Nancy, 2531
Stahl, Ralph, 3256
Stahler, Brian, 9277
Stahr, Don, 3518
Stai, Dian Graves Owen, 9076
Stainman, Arthur J., 6906
Stainman, Evan, 6906
Stainman, Lois, 6906
Stairs, Michael, 8236
Stakeley, Winifred, 78
Stakely, Margaret, 8599
Staley, Chuck, 3346
Staley, Franklin E.W., 4900
Staley, Mary Lynn, 1507
Staley, Roger, 7302
Staley, Sally J., 7639
Staley, Steven K., 7620
Staley, Walter G., III, 4900
Staley, Warren, 1507
Stall, Susan L., 3645
Stallard, Meg, 1103
Stallard, Troy, 9780
Staller, Levine, 5291
Stallings, Ann Parks, 9081
Stalonas, Michael, 7053
Stam, Deirdre C., 5871
Stamas, Stephen, 9051
Stamats, Amy, 4485
Stambaugh, Craig, 9559
Stambaugh, Jason, 3757
Stambaugh, Phillip F., 3990
Stamelman, Andrew, 5204
Stamelman, Andrew J., 5211
Stamm, Doug, 7870
Stammel, Laura, 5462
Stammerjohn, Lindsey, 598
Stamp, Greg, 7417
Stamp, Joan Corson, 9773
Stamp, Lisa Collins, 2256
Stamp, Trent, 499
Stamps, E. Roe, IV, 2191, 4281
Stamps, James L., 1210
Stamps, Penelope, 4281
Stamps, Penelope W., 4281
Stanaland, Andrea, 9212
Stanback, Bruce, 7302
Stanback, Elizabeth, 2584
Stanback, Fred J., Jr., 7305
Stancati, Joe, 4386
Stancil, Mike, 9604
Standard Textile Co., Inc., 7486
Standford Endowment, John, 9710
Standiford, Jessica, 673
Standing, Carolyn T., 7898
Standish, Christine, 5803
Standley, Don, 535
Stanek, Bernard, 7210
Stanek, Karen, 1714
Stanek, Mary Ellen, 9811
Stanfield, Bill, 8472
Stanfield, Mary, 3338
Stange Trust, Mary G., 4546
Stangis, Dave, 5223
Stangler, Dane, 4921
Stangler, Gary, 4869
Stanicki, Robert R., 5218
Stanislaw, Ann A., 8659
Stankevich, Dimitri, 9697
Stanley Foundation, The, 3444
Stanley Foundation, Theodore and Veda, 1650
Stanley Smith Barney Global, Morgan, 6044
Stanley Sussman, Janice, 7425
Stanley, Amanda G., 1710
Stanley, David, 2390, 3468
Stanley, David M., 3468
Stanley, Edmund A., Jr., 3897
Stanley, Elizabeth L., 7219
Stanley, James A., 2464, 2535
Stanley, Janet T., 1710
Stanley, Jean Leu, 3468
Stanley, Jennifer, 3897
Stanley, Jill Hammer, 1888
Stanley, Jim L., 7591
Stanley, John D., 7907
Stanley, Jonathan A., 1700
Stanley, Joseph H., 3444
Stanley, Justin A., Jr., 2747
Stanley, Karen W., 3698
Stanley, Lincoln, 3444
Stanley, Lisa A., 3897
Stanley, Lynne E., 3444
Stanley, Marianne, 9417
Stanley, Morgan, 1943
Stanley, Philip T., 1710
Stanley, Richard H., 3444
Stanley, Sarah, 3444
Stanley, Susan D., 1671
Stanley, Tamiko L., 8043
Stanley, Themla, 5371
Stanley, Theodore R., 1700
Stannard, William B., 667
Stansbury, Charles, 9774
Stansbury, Tayloe, 723
Stansell, Paula Harris, 3580
Stansky, Jill, 4298
Stansky, Jill M., 4299
Stansky, Michael, 4298
Stanton 2002 Trust, Frank, The, 6908
Stanton, Charles E., 1376
Stanton, David, 5486
Stanton, Elizabeth, 6907
Stanton, Frank, 6908
Stanton, Janet E., 1817
Stanton, John, 9731
Stanton, John W., 9575
Stanton, Marjorie, 1563
Stanton, Oliver K., 6907
Stanton, Paul E., 8634
Stanton, Robert E., 1376
Stanton, Ronald P., 6907
Stanton, Susan, 4893, 4937
Stanton, Thomas J., III, 5395
Stanton, Tom, 9122
Stanton, William E., 7087
Stanulis, Vincent, 1565
Staples Center Foundation, 396
Staples, David M., 4544
Staples, Inc., 4282
Staples, John N., III, 1118
Stapleton, Craig R., 1410
Stapleton, Jenna, 1410
Stapleton, Katharine H., 1410
Stapleton, Steven, 3341
Star Enterprises, 5797
Star Financial Bank, 3380
Star Scientific, 2296
Star, Elizabeth, 2335
Star, Elizabeth A., 2335
Star, Larry Morning, 8840
Star, Richard, 2335
Star, Sara Crown, 2781
Star, Stanley A., 2335
Star-Telegram Employees Fund, 8752
Starbucks Coffee Co., 9742
Starbucks Corp., 9742
Stare, David S., 4283
Stare, Fredrick A., 4283
Stare, Fredrick J., 4283
Stark Carpet Corp., 7008
Stark Revocable Trust, Ray, 1213
Stark Revocable Trust, Ray & Frances, 1213

Stark, Charles, 3555
Stark, Cynthia H., 2828
Stark, Dave, 9897
Stark, David, 6133
Stark, Donna, 3745
Stark, George, 7992
Stark, H. Allan, 3115
Stark, H.J. Lutcher, 9198
Stark, Jay W., 8133
Stark, Jessica, 3470
Stark, John K., 8133
Stark, Kenneth J., 9876
Stark, Kimberly, Dr., 7558
Stark, Mary, 7604
Stark, Michael, 7604
Stark, Michael R., 7536
Stark, Nelda C., 9198
Stark, Patrick E., 4856, 4919
Stark, Pearl, 5543
Stark, Peter, 5766
Stark, Ray, 1213
Starke, Debbie, 4920
Starke, Frank, 4796
Starke, Lydia, 2525
Starker, Farrel, 6910
Starker, Ray, 6910
Starker, Steven, 6910
Starkey, Claire, 9377
Starkey, John, 2565
Starks, Brooke Didier, 2765
Starks, Daniel J., 4770
Starks, Marvin L., 8497
Starling, Frank M., 9199
Starmack, Carol, 6340
Starner, Margaret C., 2223
Starnlicht Family Foundation, The, 9470
Starr Foundation, 5563, 6904
Starr Foundation, The, 1900
Starr, Cornelius V., 6911
Starr, Kathryn M., 1355
Starr, Loren M., 5564
Starr, Marilyn, 6529
Starr, Seth, 5846
Starr, Todd, 1395
Starry Night Foundation, 6864
Starshak, Michael J., 3113
Starwood Hotels & Resorts Worldwide, Inc., 4284
Staryk, Ted, 4709
Starzyk, Edward, 4094
Starzyk, Maria, 4094
Stasch, Julia, 2989
Stasiak, John, 3889
Staszewski, Emily, 8066
State Automobile Mutual Insurance Co., 7674
State Bank & Trust Co., 7351
State Farm, 9149
State Farm Mutual Auto Insurance Co., 2761
State Farm Mutual Automobile Insurance Co., 3174
State of Illinois Dept. of Human Services, 2761
State of Wisconsin Dept. of Adm., 9969
State Street Bank & Trust Co., 4285, 8446
Staten Island Savings Bank, 6912
States, Jean, 5068
Stathas, Judith Holz, 9864
Statler, Ellsworth Milton, 6913
Staton, Jimmy D., 7591
Statter, Amy P., 6645
Staub, Edwin, 2478
Staub, Jonathan, 3845
Staub, Jonathan E., 2592
Staub, Wanda, 3845
Stauber, Karl, 9421
Stauch, John L., 4739
Staufenberger, Dick, 529
Stauffer, John, 1214
Stauffer, Lu, 7372
Stauffer, M.J., 7439, 7444
Stauffer, Melvyn J., 7464
Stauffer, W. David, 647
Staunch, Linda J., 7273
Stautberg, Matt, 7552
Stautberg, Timothy E., 7659
Stava, Jeff, 7807
Stavropoulos, I. Linda, 2336
Stavropoulos, S. William, 2336
Stavropoulos, William S., 4444
Steadley Irrevocable Trust, K.D. & M.L., 8442
Steadman, Libby, 8472
Steadman, Mary Jane, 9147
Steakley, John, 8582
Steals, Melvin H., Ph.D., 7934
Steans, Harrison, 3175
Steans, Harrison I., 3175
Steans, Heather, 3175
Steans, Jennifer, 3175
Steans, Jennifer W., 3175
Steans, Lois, 3175
Steans, Lois M., 3175
Steans, Robin, 3175
Steans, Robin M., 3175
Stearns, Anna B., 4286
Stearns, Nancy, 8229
Stebbins, Richard, 6564
Stec, Randy, 4562
Stec, Vicki L., 8200
Stecher, Frederick William, 3950
Steckel, Willard, 9673
Stedham, Brenda S., 23
Stedman, Betty Ann West, 9200
Stedman, Stuart West, 9200
Steed, Zachary, 2439
Steeg, Robert, 3672
Steeger, Dean H., 6150
Steel Dynamics, Inc., 3389
Steel Family, Robert K., 6914
Steel, Corinne, 5652
Steel, Gillian, 6914
Steel, Gillian V., 6914
Steel, Joan E., 2783
Steel, Robert K., 6914
Steelcase Inc., 4547
Steele, Amy, 7696
Steele, Claude, 1934
Steele, Claude M., 2989, 6782
Steele, Daniel G., 3468
Steele, Ethel, 165
Steele, George, 141
Steele, Horace, 165
Steele, J. Donald, Jr., 7972
Steele, James M., 9320
Steele, John M., 8582
Steele, Katherine, 989
Steele, Linda A., 3468
Steele, Mike, 9604
Steele, Ray, Jr., 549
Steele, Richard B., Jr., 3992
Steele, Shelby, 9819
Steele, William G., Jr., 5164
Steen, Michael, 7585
Steenberg, Russell W., 6333
Steenbergen, Ewout, 7038
Steendam, Jan, 3826
Steenkamp, Zaldeus, 986
Steenrod, Mitch, 8560
Steere, Lynda, 1701
Steere, William C., 1701
Steere, William C., Jr., 6633
Steere, William, Jr., 1701
Steers, William C., 2670
Steet, Franklin, 7488
Stefan, Amanda May, 5132
Stefani Luckow Trust, 6399
Stefanik, Paul, 7675
Stefano, Ralph, 5784
Stefanski, Ashley, 7675
Stefanski, Marc A., 7675, 7681
Stefanski, Rhonda I., 7675
Stefansky, Meir, 6916
Stefansky, Ruth, 6916
Steffan, Brian J., 9384
Steffel, Sheila, 4446
Steffen, Carolyn, 365
Steffen, Linda, 9833
Steffens, John L., 6917
Steffens, Louise C., 6917
Steffens, Marian, 3122
Steffens, Roger S., 2468, 2554
Steffensen, Britt, 9171
Stegall, Hugh H., Dr., 25
Stege, Bill, 4448
Stegeman, Klaus P., 5454
Stegman, Harold, 4512
Stehling, James, 9095
Stehy, R. Charles, 8122
Steider, Norman D., 3297
Steiger, Debra R., 9448
Steiger, Heidi L., 7425
Steiger, John, 4056
Steiger, Paul, 2191
Steiger, Rod, 7704
Steigerwalt, Eric, 6479
Steigleder, Bert L., 9952
Steill, Laurie, 3407
Stein Charitable Lead Trust No. 2, Doris, 6845
Stein Charitable Lead Trust No. 2, Doris Jones, 987
Stein Charitable Lead Trust No. 4, Doris, 6845
Stein Charitable Lead Trust No. 4, Doris Jones, 987
Stein Revocable Trust, Elaine S., 6918
Stein, Amy B., 2749
Stein, Andrew M., Dr., 7378
Stein, Anne-Marie, 4291
Stein, Arlyne, 6919
Stein, Ben, 5290
Stein, Bessie, 8297
Stein, Daniel, 6972
Stein, David A., 2337
Stein, Edith Carol, 6331
Stein, Elaine S., 6918
Stein, Eric, 4296
Stein, Eric C., 6063
Stein, Eugene P., 1215
Stein, Gary S., 121
Stein, Gerda, 4296
Stein, Gideon, 1932
Stein, Gretchen, 9950
Stein, Gretchen M., 4782
Stein, Henry, 5290
Stein, Isaac, 727
Stein, Jane, 4296, 5442
Stein, Jason, 2393
Stein, Jay, 2338
Stein, Jennifer Shilling, 481
Stein, John S., 7
Stein, Joyce, 427, 1036
Stein, Ken, 1520
Stein, Kenneth L., 5930, 6063
Stein, Lewis, 2292, 2314
Stein, Linda, 2337
Stein, Linda B., 2337
Stein, Louis, 8297
Stein, Marilyn L., 1215
Stein, Martin, 2337, 6919
Stein, Martin A., 2588
Stein, Mary Ann, 1932
Stein, Michael R., 7029
Stein, Myron, 6994
Stein, Nancy C., 5930, 6063, 6331
Stein, Noah, 1932
Stein, Peter C., 6063
Stein, Rhoda, 2393
Stein, Richard H., 8915
Stein, Roger, 6918
Stein, Ronald, 5616
Stein, Ronald J., 6147
Stein, Roni L., 6918
Stein, Ronnit, 2393
Stein, Sarah, 1088, 1109
Stein, Stein & Engel, 8297
Stein, Steven N., 6919
Stein, Stuart M., 6918
Stein, Susan S., 6331
Stein, Sydney, Jr., 6331
Stein, Ted, 385
Stein, Ted, Mrs., 385
Stein, Tracey, 2337
Steinbach, William, 9809
Steinberg, Cornelia, 4287
Steinberg, Diane H., 6920
Steinberg, Gregory M., 7370
Steinberg, Harold, 6921
Steinberg, James D., 6921
Steinberg, Joan E., 6507
Steinberg, Joseph S., 6920
Steinberg, Judith Zee, 1368
Steinberg, Larry, 8303
Steinberg, Michael A., 6921
Steinberg, Neil, 8429
Steinberg, Randall, 4287
Steinberg, Robert, 6588, 6922
Steinberg, Stan, 670
Steinberg, Stephen P., 4287
Steinberg, Suzanne, 6922
Steinbock, R. Ted, 3563
Steinbright, Edith C., 7918
Steinbright, Marilyn Lee, 7918
Steinbrook, William J., Jr., 2424
Steinbrook, William M., Jr., 7893
Steiner 1999 Trust, Syliva, 5467
Steiner Foods Inc., 1771
Steiner Sports, 1850
Steiner Sports Memorabilia, 7012
Steiner, Anna B., 1723
Steiner, Brent, 7704
Steiner, Daniel L., 6587
Steiner, David S., 5467
Steiner, Elizabeth, 6587
Steiner, Ernest F., 1723
Steiner, Jeff, 633
Steiner, Joshua, 6587
Steiner, Joshua L., 6587
Steiner, Judith, 7456
Steiner, Katherine R., 5181
Steiner, Kathy, 3534
Steiner, Kellie, 4749
Steiner, Lisa A., 7080

Steiner, Martin, 1103
Steiner, Melissa, 3645
Steiner, Michael, 9606
Steiner, Prudence L., 6587
Steiner, Rebecca A., 1790
Steiner, Ruth, 952
Steiner, Sylvia, 5467
Steiner, William K., 517
Steines, Ann Munson, 7552
Steinfield, Frank, 3962
Steinfirst, Jane K., 7463
Steinford, Sherri Adams, 8653
Steinhafel, Gregg W., 4776
Steinhardt Foundation, Judy and Michael, 5717
Steinhardt, Judith, 6923
Steinhardt, Michael, 1695
Steinhardt, Michael H., 6923
Steinharter, Avrohom, 5242
Steinhauer, Bruce W., 4498
Steinhaus, David M., 4712
Steiniger, Joseph, 5556
Steininger, Don, 3281
Steinkraus, Eric M., 1731
Steinkraus, Helen Z., 1731
Steinkraus, Philip C., 1731
Steinman, Alan D., 4369
Steinman, Beverly R., 8299
Steinman, James Hale, 8299
Steinman, Jeffrey, 6768, 6769
Steinman, John Frederick, 8300
Steinman, Peter D., 6769
Steinman, Robert, 6768
Steinman, Shirley W., 8300
Steinmann, Jennifer, 1572
Steinmetz, Ann Marie, 1216
Steinmetz, Charles William, 1216
Steinmetz, Mary L., 1216
Steinmetz, William, 1216
Steinour, Patti, 7589
Steinschneider, Jean M., 1615
Steinwand, Todd, 7353
Steitz, Charles, 5482
Steitz, J., 3609
Steitz, Janet, 5482
Steitz, Joan A., Dr., 1558
Steitz, John M., 3609
Stella, Frank, 6554
Stellmacher, Jon, 9832
Stellmon, John, 7829
Stelzner, Dianna, 3443
Stembler, Bill, 2431
Stemler, R., 777
Stemler, Robert, 846
Stemler, Robert J., 777
Stemmerman, Marc, 5804
Stempel, Calvin B., 6925
Stempel, Ernest E., 6925
Stempel, Neil F., 6925
Stempler, Carolyn, 4327
Stenberg, Dave, 5062
Stender, Bruce, 4617
Stengel, William R., Jr., 2787
Stenham Trustees Limited, 6336
Stenhaug, Carmen R., 3440
Stenman, Eric G., 283
Stenson, Diane M., 3342
Stenson, Margo, 5045
Stepanek Revocable Trust, Elaine, 4771
Stepanek, Elaine F., 4771
Stepanian, Mariam, 549
Stepanian, Tania W., 440
Stepelman, Chaim, 5980
Stepelman, Deborah, 5980
Stepelton, Brett S., 2333, 2334
Stepelton, Douglas A., 2333, 2334
Stepelton, Sean D., 2333, 2334
Stepelton, Virlee S., 2334
Stepelton, Virlee Stacy, 2333
Stephan, Lynn, 3555
Stephans, Joan R., 8256
Stephans, Peter N., 8256
Stephany, Elizabeth G., 2380
Stephen, Cathy, 3287
Stephen, Ron, 3539
Stephenitch, Mark, 2883
Stephens Foundation, 6864
Stephens, Barb, 3481
Stephens, Bess C., 203
Stephens, Bess Chisum, 195
Stephens, Beth, 2653, 3125
Stephens, C. Austin, 2055
Stephens, Charles, 500
Stephens, Charles P., 2055
Stephens, Christopher J., Jr., 1542
Stephens, David B., 4589
Stephens, Elton B., 69
Stephens, Elton B., Jr., 69
Stephens, Eugene, 8537
Stephens, Gerald D., 3176
Stephens, Harriet, 204
Stephens, Harriet C., 204
Stephens, Helen M., 3176
Stephens, James T., 69
Stephens, Janet, 3176
Stephens, Jeffrey, 3176
Stephens, John, 8675
Stephens, Kathy Fong, 1264
Stephens, Lawton, 2576
Stephens, Louise, 1006
Stephens, Mel, 4482
Stephens, Michael D., 697
Stephens, R. Terry, 3762
Stephens, Rick, 2123
Stephens, Robert W., 9784
Stephens, Sandra D., 2055
Stephens, Scott R., 2055
Stephens, W.R., Jr., 203
Stephens, Warren A., 204
Stephenson Equity Co., 7799
Stephenson, Barbara, 1217
Stephenson, Betty L., 7805
Stephenson, Beverly, 419
Stephenson, Charles C., Jr., 7799
Stephenson, Craig, 212
Stephenson, Ed, 415
Stephenson, Erin Kendrick, 21
Stephenson, Jack, 4609
Stephenson, Jody, 2540
Stephenson, John W., 2420, 2441
Stephenson, Keith, 4380
Stephenson, Peggy C., 7799
Stephenson, Thomas F., 1217
Stephenson, Tom, 419
Stepka, Mathew, 615
Stepleton, Benjamin F., III, 1410
Sterchi, Anne, 2464, 2535
Steriliz LLC, 6945
Sterkenburg, Ryan, 4448
Sterkx, Mamie, 3627
Sterling, Donald T., 1218
Sterling, Lillie, 9202
Sterling, Marsha, 1721
Sterling, Michelle, 1048
Sterling, Peter, Dr., 2267
Sterling, Ray, 4550
Sterling, Rochelle H., 1218
Sterling, Vanessa, 3295
Sterling-Shaffer, Tanya L., 1145
Stermer, Audrey M., 1362
Stermer, Richard A., 1362
Stermer, Richard C., 1362
Stern Foundation, Gustav and Irene, 6929
Stern Foundation, William A., 7162
Stern, A. Joseph, 5468
Stern, Aaron, 6570, 6718, 9052
Stern, Aaron, Dr., 6719
Stern, Abraham J., 2838
Stern, Adam, 1219
Stern, Ann B., 8917
Stern, Beatrice, 6579
Stern, Bernice, 6928
Stern, Charles A., 2785
Stern, Daniel, 6716, 6926
Stern, David A., 1861
Stern, Denise, 6927
Stern, Denise R., 6927
Stern, Edward A., 7360
Stern, Eli, 5468
Stern, Elisabeth Ellen, 6579
Stern, Erika, 1219
Stern, Eva, 1219
Stern, Eva S., 1219
Stern, Frieda, 5468
Stern, H. Peter, 6579
Stern, Irvin, 3177
Stern, Joan O., 6579
Stern, John Peter, 6579
Stern, Joseph A., 6403
Stern, Julian N., 566, 1325
Stern, Lawrence, 8301
Stern, Lynn S., 6053
Stern, Marc I., 1219
Stern, Michael, 6928
Stern, Michael K., 4945
Stern, Nanna, 6926
Stern, Nathan, 6169
Stern, Nechama, 6169
Stern, Nicholas S.G., 6053
Stern, Patricia, 7244
Stern, Peter, 6928
Stern, Rebecca, 8301
Stern, Richard, 498
Stern, Richard J., 4980
Stern, Robert, 6928
Stern, Rochelle, 5468
Stern, Roy, 2339
Stern, S. Sidney, 9204
Stern, Sam, 7360
Stern, Steven, 2339
Stern, Steven E., 2339
Stern, Thomas D., 6927
Stern, Walter, 5562, 5655, 5789, 5855, 5952, 5977, 6036, 6207, 6524, 6576, 6622, 7028, 7110, 7124
Stern, William, 7360
Sternberg, David, 4714
Sternberg, Lisa, 6930
Sternberg, Paul, Jr., 41
Sternberg, Stuart L., 6930
Sternberg, William M., 4714
Sternberger, Sigmund, 7326
Sternleib, David F., 6148
Sternlicht, Barry, 1861
Sternlicht, Miriam Klein, 1861
Sternlieb, David, 5622
Stershic, Michael, 8136
Stesch, Irene Alisa, 3740
Stetsenko, Elena, 2191
Stetson, Anne, 4172
Stetson, Daniel T., 968
Stetson, Donald W., 9589
Stetson, E. William, III, 1679, 7300
Stetson, Jane W., 3218
Steuer, Gary P., 1376
Steuerle, Gene, 9380
Steuert, Varina M., 2078
Stevens 1997 Trust, Georgiana G., The, 580
Stevens, Abbot, 4288
Stevens, Alexandra Marie, 9206
Stevens, Audra, 5750
Stevens, Carrie Ann, 6024
Stevens, Carroll, 6064
Stevens, Colin Michael, 9206
Stevens, Derek, 4367
Stevens, Dorothy W., 5968
Stevens, Elizabeth, 4367
Stevens, Gene, 7453
Stevens, George C., 8472
Stevens, Georgiana G., 580
Stevens, Gregory, 4367
Stevens, H. Allen, 3938
Stevens, J. Whitney, 5968
Stevens, Jackie, 8960
Stevens, James, 3955
Stevens, James J., 2998
Stevens, James M., Jr., 2464, 2535
Stevens, James W., 5243
Stevens, Janet, 8960
Stevens, Jeff Allan, 9206
Stevens, John M., 3774
Stevens, Karen, 7604
Stevens, Lehrue, Dr., 3625
Stevens, Lon, 3278
Stevens, Marcella M., 4918, 4941
Stevens, Michael J., 2285
Stevens, Nancy E., 1143
Stevens, Nathaniel, 4289
Stevens, Randall, Dr., 3396
Stevens, Robert T., 5968
Stevens, Ruby, 9205
Stevens, Scott, 3093, 3097
Stevens, Sharon Ann, 9206
Stevens, Simon, 5800
Stevens, Sylvia L., 4211
Stevens, Tara, 9799
Stevens, W. Chandler, 7630
Stevens, Whitney, 5968
Stevens, William C., III, 8199
Stevens, William J., 18
Stevenson, Adair, 8709
Stevenson, Anne, 9743
Stevenson, Bayne, 2142
Stevenson, Charles P., Jr., 6116, 6971
Stevenson, Fredericka O., 4290
Stevenson, Howard H., 4290
Stevenson, Jane Hetland, 9950
Stevenson, Karen, 1650
Stevenson, Mary H., 9743
Stevenson, Sharon, 1650
Stevenson, Susan K., 1904
Stevenson-Colley, Ann, 6500
Steves, Frank, 2822
Steward Manor LLC, 9452
Steward, David L., 4981, 5002
Steward, Larry E., 4410
Steward, Thelma E., 4981
Stewart, Alan M., 8792
Stewart, Anna Mae, 5927
Stewart, Barbara M., 2520
Stewart, Bill, 3554, 5062, 9631
Stewart, Catharine P., 3286
Stewart, Chester French, 5511
Stewart, Christina, 382

Stewart, Clent, 7731
Stewart, Colleen, 417
Stewart, Craig W., 9574
Stewart, Diane P., 1862
Stewart, Dorothy I., 1015
Stewart, Douglas Bitonti, 4423
Stewart, Douglas G., 2698
Stewart, Elizabeth, 406
Stewart, Elizabeth D.S., 166
Stewart, James A., 7328
Stewart, Jay, 9293
Stewart, Jimmy, 3278
Stewart, John C., Jr., 3604
Stewart, Joseph M., 4474
Stewart, Julie, 9704
Stewart, Kimberly Louis, 2985
Stewart, Louise Ferry, 2764
Stewart, Luther, 4562
Stewart, Mamie Kanfer, 7542
Stewart, Marise M.M., 4510
Stewart, Marise Meynet, 442, 1299
Stewart, Mark, 3321
Stewart, Mary E., 1949
Stewart, Max, Jr., 3523, 8945
Stewart, Melanie, 9605
Stewart, Michael, 186
Stewart, Michael R., 4521
Stewart, Renee, 3396
Stewart, Robert, 4075
Stewart, Robert G., 3970
Stewart, Russell O., 8628
Stewart, Samuel S., Jr., 1862
Stewart, Susie, 3288
Stewart, Tim, 535
Stewart, Verlena, 7570
Stewart, William, 7565
Stewart, William C., 8276
Steyer, Hume R, 1831
Steyer, Hume R., 5858
Steyer, Thomas, 1256
Steyer, Thomas F., 1257
Stichler, Jeff, 9225
Stichman, Bennett, 1896
Stick, Elizabeth W., 8130
Stickney, George, 2476
Stickney, James W., IV, 7182
Stickney, Lara J., 2476
Stickney, Webster F., Jr., 8674
Stiefel, Barbara A., 2387
Stiefel, Christine, 2387
Stiefel, Christine E., 2387
Stiefel, Ernst C., 6931
Stiefel-Francis, Cheryl, 7569
Stieg, Edward C., 4358
Stieg, Elizabeth A., 4358
Stiehl, Cynthia F. Moeller, 9908
Stieren, Amy, 8769
Stierwalt, Mary, 3481
Stifler, Lawrence T.P., 4292
Stiftung Auxilium, 5837
Stiles, Jean McCullough, 899
Stiles, Leslie H., 4633
Still, David, 6722
Still, Susan K., 9415
Stiller, Christine, 9372
Stiller, Robert P., 9372
Stiller, Shale, 3781
Stiller, Shale D., 3766, 3891
Stilley, Patricia "Pat", 9243
Stilley, Patricia Moser, 9203
Stillman, Denise, 9385
Stillman, Katherine, 5921
Stillman, Waddell W., 6116
Stillwater, 5752
Stillwater Farms, Inc., 6044
Stillwell, Logan W., 149
Stillwell, Robert L., 9099
Stilwell, Brett, 3314
Stimpel, Richard J., 898
Stimpert, Cathy, 7630
Stimson, Paul, 6500
Stine, Curtis L., 2927
Stine, David J., 8302
Stine, Harry H., 3482
Stine, Helen A., 8272
Stine, James M., 8302
Stine, Kay A., 9448
Stine, Lindsay, 8302
Stine, Margaret V., 8302
Stine, Molly S., 3482
Stine, Robert, 1053
Stinehart, William, Jr., 392, 951, 5111
Stingley, Mark, 1974
Stinner, Charles G., 7907
Stinnett, Maggie, 9251
Stinnett, William, III, 8475
Stinnett-Brown, Kristen, 689
Stinson, Alan L., 2104
Stinson, Gayle, 9225
Stinson, GeorgAnn, 9924
Stinson, Ken, 5033
Stinson, Marion, 9007
Stinson, Terry, 8472
Stipe, Beth A., 9604
Stirk, Patti, 8351
Stirling, Cory, 10000
Stirling, Renee D., 10000
Stitch, Richard, 9704
Stith, Melvin T., 2243
Stitt, Carol, 5750
Stitzer, Lucy, 4700
Stivelman, William, 978
Stiwinter, Karen, 7273
Stobbe, April, 7742
Stobbs, Larry, 5068
Stobert, Troy, 4448
Stock, Georgia L., 9953
Stock, Jim, 3293
Stock, John P., 1280
Stock, Kenneth C., 9953
Stock, Steven, 9953
Stockamp, Dale R., 7873
Stockamp, Gail, 7873
Stockbridge, Gary, 1765
Stockdale, Caroline, 4712
Stocker, Beth K., 7676
Stocker, Laura, 5180
Stocker, Les, 1015
Stockham, Douglas A., 2032
Stockholm, Charles M., 573
Stockholm, Maryanna G., 573
Stockman, Allison A., 6932
Stockman, Charles C., 6932
Stockman, Hervey S., 6932
Stockman, Hervey S., Jr., 6932
Stockman, Robert P., 6932
Stockman, Sarah A., 6932
Stockton, Dmitri, 1591
Stockton, Richard, 5801
Stockwell, John, Dr., 8501
Stockwell, Lance, 7735
Stocky, Tom, 1166
Stoddard, Harry G., 4293
Stoddard, Jenny B., 3235
Stodden, Michael, 980
Stoeckel, Emily Heisley, 2902
Stoering, Mark E., 4808
Stoffer, Brad, 1373
Stoffregen, Michael L., 3422
Stoga, Alan, 6983
Stoico, Robert, 4242
Stoico, Robert F., 4294
Stoika, John R., 8755
Stoika, Lisa A., 8755
Stokar, Suzanne, 3652
Stokely, Clayton F., 8631
Stokely, Kay H., 8631
Stokely, William B., III, 8631
Stokely, William B., IV, 8631
Stoker, Philip, 106
Stokes, Gary, 9615
Stokes, Lucy, 1515
Stokes, Paul M., 2356
Stokes, Stacy S., 8468
Stoler, Peggy, 7645
Stoll, David, 1604
Stoll, David J., 6631
Stollenwerk, Robert T., 9891
Stoller, Cathy A., 7891
Stoller, Craig, 7642
Stoller, Philip, 9673
Stoller, Russell, 7642
Stoller, Susan B., 9673
Stoller, Todd, 7642
Stoller, William H., 7891
Stollings, Juanita, 3598
Stolper, Edward, 221
Stolper, Michael, 4921
Stommes, Eric, 4679
Stone Irrevocable Trust, Irving I., 7677
Stone Mountain Industrial Park, Inc., 2530
Stone Oversight Trust, Irving, 7677
Stone, Albert, 4194
Stone, Alison, 3675
Stone, Amy M., 3180
Stone, Barbara S., 9954
Stone, Barbara West, 3180
Stone, Bill, 2439
Stone, Carolyn, 9091
Stone, Christopher, 6593
Stone, Clifford W., 7801
Stone, David, 986, 1697, 3180, 4578
Stone, David C., 4546
Stone, David L., Jr., 9450
Stone, Deborah, 3180
Stone, Edward C., Jr., 774
Stone, Eric P., 9954
Stone, Erica, 321
Stone, Ethol, 4334
Stone, Haydee T., 3675
Stone, Helen, 7677
Stone, Henry, 8438
Stone, Holly, 3809
Stone, Howard L., 3225
Stone, Hugh Lamar, III, 9147
Stone, Irving, 5066
Stone, Irving I., 7677
Stone, James D., 3822
Stone, Jay, 6567
Stone, Jennifer, 3180, 8670
Stone, Jennifer Lynn, 3179
Stone, Jerry, 7182
Stone, Jessie V., 3180
Stone, Karen, 1863
Stone, Kathryn W., 4824
Stone, Kent, 4784
Stone, Lacie, 8548
Stone, Lauren Gail, 3179
Stone, Loren R., 3225
Stone, Mary R., 2304
Stone, Maximilian Dana, 6426
Stone, Michael A., 3180
Stone, Michael R., 1863
Stone, Nan, 3971
Stone, Norah Sharpe, 3180
Stone, Norman C., 3180
Stone, Peter E., 9954
Stone, Phil C., 9411
Stone, Roe, 2762
Stone, Roger, 3179
Stone, S. Adam, 9954
Stone, S. M., 4898
Stone, Samuel C., 7801
Stone, Sandra, 3180
Stone, Sara, 3180
Stone, Sheldon M., 365
Stone, Steven, 744, 3180
Stone, Steven L., 4194
Stone, Susan, 3179
Stone, Theresa M., 3678
Stone, Todd, 8618
Stone, W. Clement, 3180
Stone, William C., 2304
Stoneburner, Gresham, 2288
Stonecorner Corp., 4183
Stoneman, James M., 4295
Stoneman, Miriam, 4296
Stoneman, Sidney, 4296
Stoneman, Thea, 4295
Stoner, Alden, 3896
Stoner, Chelle, 3896
Stoner, Joan, 972
Stoner, Katharine E., 3896
Stoner, Thomas H., 3896
Stonerock, Barbra, 7428
Stoney, Mike, 9631
Stoneyfield Farm, 3245
Stonisch, Glorie, 4548
Stonisch, Helen, 4548
Stonisch, Mary Sue, 4548
Stonitsch, Joan, 7570
Stonkus, Jim, 7382
Stookey, John Hoyt, 5785, 5786
Stooks, Bryant, 165
Stop & Shop Cos., Inc., The, 3913
Stop & Shop Supermarket Co. LLC, The, 4297
Stop & Shop Supermarket Co., The, 3913, 4297
Stopak, Aaron, 3905
Stophel, Glenn C., 8614
Stopler, Jon, 7752
Storbeck, Cora, 4906
Storen, Stephen J., 6904
Storer, Dede, 9992
Storer, Elizabeth, 9992
Storer, Peter, Jr., 9992
Storer, Robert, 87
Storey, Barry L., 2434, 2514
Storey, Charles P., 8909
Storey, Lucille Amen, 9108
Storkerson, Christopher W., 2032
Storm, William, 3424
Stormer, JoAnn, 4755
Stormont-Vail Foundation, 9250
Storms, John W., 8996, 9225
Storr, Janet M., 9935
Stortz, Lowell, 4611, 4714
Story, Bernard J., 8136
Story, Christina E., 7251
Story, Janice K., 7251
Story, Thomas E., IV, 7251
Storz, Robert Herman, 5086
Stoskopf, Rita F., 4520
Stotsenberg, Henry, Jr., 1221

Stotsenberg, Pauline, 1221
Stotz-Ghosh, Suprotik, 4472
Stouder, A.G., 7688
Stoughton, Daphne, 1574
Stout, C., 777
Stout, Cameron G., 777
Stout, Catheryne, 8052
Stout, Charles J., 8021
Stout, Conrad, 1035
Stout, Coy, 586
Stout, Fred L., 7284
Stout, Jean C., 6194
Stout, Joan K., 6194
Stout, Joan M., 6194
Stout, John K., 6194
Stout, Lynne, 8332
Stout, Michael Ward, 6427
Stout, Patricia, 9509
Stout, Ray E., 6194
Stovall, Guy F., III, 8878
Stover, Betsy, 4565
Stover, David, 7288
Stover, Joan C., 1222
Stover, Susan J., 1222
Stover, W. Robert, 1222
Stowe, Daniel Harding, 7309
Stowe, Julie, 8548
Stowe, Richmond Harding, 7309
Stowe, Robert L., III, 7309
Stowers, James E., 3550
Stowers, James E., III, 3550
Stowers, James, IV, 3550
Stowers, Layne, 3550
Stowers, Linda, 3550
Stowers, Ryan, 7893
Stowers, Virginia G., 3550
Stoy, Kevin, 3390
Strachan, Camille Jones, 3637
Strachan, Stephen M., 2791
Strack, Denise, 938
Strader, Jim, 9789
Stradley, Jackie, 2457
Strafford, Maureen, 1708
Strahs, Kenneth, 298
Straka, Gordon, 2110
Strake, George W., 8905
Strake, George W., Jr., 9208
Strake, George W., Sr., 9208
Strake, Gregory P., 9208
Strake, Susan K., 9208
Straleu and Co., 1116
Stranahan, Abby, 7588
Stranahan, Ann, 7588
Stranahan, Daniel, 7588
Stranahan, Frank D., 7678
Stranahan, Mark, 7678
Stranahan, Mary C., 7588
Stranahan, Patrick, 7678
Stranahan, Patti, 7588
Stranahan, Robert, 7678
Stranahan, Robert A., 7678
Stranahan, Sarah, 7678
Strand, Eric H., 3991
Strand, Jeff, 8521
Strandell, Peter, 3857
Strandjord, Jeannine, 4920, 4921
Strange, Carol Martin, 8156
Strange, H. Lawrence, 8156
Strange, Karla, 9250
Strange, Lawrence, 8156
Strange, Peter S., 7404
Strangfeld, John R., Jr., 5415
Stranghoener, Lawrence, 4722
Strangie, Thomas, 4195
Strasburg, Robert, 4724
Strasburger Price, 8834
Strasfield, Janice E., 7723
Strasner, Sherry L., 8718
Strassburger, John, 8138
Strasser, Jonathan, 5689
Strassfield, Christina Mossaides, 7031
Strassler, Abbie, 5647
Strassler, Alan, 5647
Strassler, David, 5647
Strassler, David H., 5647
Strassler, Gary, 5647
Strassler, Karen, 5647
Strassler, Lorna, 5647
Strassler, Matthew, 5647
Strassler, Robert, 5647
Strassler, Robert B., 5647
Strassler, Samuel A., 5647
Strategic Resources Group, 7846
Stratton, Arlene, 8304
Stratton, F.P., Jr., 9822
Stratton, James W., 8304
Stratton, Robert "Bob" A., Col., 9501
Straub Lincoln Mercury, 7012
Straub, Maximilian, 4354
Strauch, Hans, 947, 948
Strauch, Kevin, 1029
Strauch, Mary Helen, 3761
Strauch, Roger, 947, 948
Straus Family Trust, 528
Straus, Daniel E., 5469
Straus, David, 1702
Straus, Donald Roy, 6934
Straus, Faye, 528
Straus, Harry H., Sr., 1702
Straus, Katherine Bea, 6934
Straus, Kim, 5516
Straus, Lee E., 9071
Straus, Lynn G., 6934
Straus, Michael, 7050
Straus, Moshael J., 5469
Straus, Oscar S., III, 7014
Straus, Philip A., 6934
Straus, Sandor, 528
Straus, Zahava, 5469
Strausbaugh, Mark, 8001
Strauss & Co., Levi, 1223
Strauss, Barbara Bachmann, 5632
Strauss, Diana, 8993
Strauss, Howard E., 5470
Strauss, Iris Lynn, 1040
Strauss, Judith, 5470
Strauss, Maurice L., 7323
Strauss, Mildred B., 5585
Strauss, Robert Perry, 7323
Strauss, Thomas W., 5632, 7019
Strautman, Jon, 3293
Stravitz, Richard Todd, 5723
Straw, Nancy, 4800
Strawbridge Foundation, Margaret Dorrance, 8305
Strawbridge, George, Jr., 8305
Strawbridge, R. Stewart, 8305
Strawbridge, Robin, 534
Strawn, Kathryn A., 9484
Strawn, Mary, 7773
Strayer University Educational Foundation, 1976
Strayer, Kelly, 3504
Strayer, Laurie, 1888
Strayer, Raquel, 9832
Strayer, Steve, 7367
Straz, David A., Jr., 2341
Straz, David A., Sr., 2341
Strear Farms Co., Inc., 1508
Strear, Irma, 1508
Strear, Leonard, 1508
Streator, Amy Kellerman, 3379
Streb, Elizabeth, 4681
Stredde, Sharon, 2767
Streep, Mary B. Simon, 6859
Street, Bryan, 7698
Street, David A., 9546
Street, Fay H., 9546
Street, James E., 1439
Street, Nicholas D., 9546
Streeter, Bill, 4943
Streeter, Mary Alice, 7704
Strehle, Donald, 9410
Strehle, Glenn, 1926
Streid, Amy W., 4803
Streiff, David R., 789
Streim, Edward, 5771
Streim, Lynn, 5771
Strein, Stefan, 3745
Streinger, Peter, 5598
Streisand, Barbra, 1224
Streit, Alan E., 3504
Streitmatter, David, 9108
Strelow, Jackie, 9938
Stremlau, Carolyn, 1881
Stremsterfer, John, 2762
Strench, Bill, 3569
Streng, William P., 8979
Stretz, James, 4451
Strever, Harold B., Jr., 3437
Stribling, Clay, 8660
Stribling, Jera G., 15
Stribling, Suzanna, 2471
Strickland, Buff, 9137
Strickland, Kyle, 7846
Strickland, R. Michael, 2285
Strickland, Ruth, 2433
Strickland, Sandra, 2433
Strickland, William, 8228
Strickland, William E., Jr., 7946
Strickler, Jan, 4512
Stride Rite Charitable Foundation, 3912
Stried, Amy W., 4802
Strietmann, William H., 7405
Strimbu, William J., 7994
Strimmenos, Sarah, 3304
Stringer, Diane T., 4009
Stringer, Edward, 4600
Stringer, Howard L., 8550
Stringer, Howard, Sir, 6904
Stringfellow, Ladson F., 8470
Strisofksy, Pamela A., 8041
Stritzke, Jerry, 5790, 9713
Strmecki, Marin J., 1679
Strnad, Audrey, 9948
Strobel, Barbara, 8887
Strobel, Kathy, 3597
Stroble, Jim, 7401
Stroer, Glenn, 3540
Stroh, Debra Tawney, 9675
Stroh, John, III, 4802
Stroh, Vivian Day, 4371
Strom, John D., 2325
Stroman, Diane, 1714
Stroman, Kent, 7731
Stromberg, Benjamin, 4732
Stromberg, Bernice, 166
Stromberg, Jean Gleason, 686
Stromberg, Richard, 166
Stromberg, William C., 166
Stromer, Malka, 525
Strong, Alicia, 1733
Strong, Bente, 9537
Strong, Caroline, 5420
Strong, Daniel, 1733
Strong, Elliot, 1733
Strong, Emily A., 3178
Strong, Gary, 1103
Strong, Hattie M., 9537
Strong, Henry L., 9537
Strong, Jeffrey D., 960
Strong, John D., Jr., 7733
Strong, John O., 667
Strong, L. Corrin, 9537
Strong, Laurel Durst, 5922
Strong, Leslie M., 1733
Strong, Lester, 974
Strong, Peter D., 1733
Strong, Robert A., 3680
Strong, Wendi E., 9245
Strosacker, Charles J., 4549
Strosser, Ted, 8040
Stroud, Brandy, 3614
Strough, Michael A., 2030
Strouse, Evelyn P., 4268
Strouse, Robert H., 7927
Strout, Arthur E., 4068
Strowger, Dick, 5556
Struck, Laurie, 1243
Struck, Richard, 7103
Structure, 975
Strueber, Michael M., 7986
Struewing, Herman, 3379
Strumpf, Linda B., 6160
Strunk, Bruce, 3442
Strunk, Janet Helpenstell, 3442
Strunk, Thomas W., 5002
Struse, Robert, 159
Struthers, Richard K., 1865
Struthers, Sharon M., 1865
Struyk, Robert J., 4709
Stryker, Jon L., 5608
Stryker, Mark, 8649
Stryker, Pat, 1375
Stryker, Ronda E., 4469
Strynchuk, Lynne, 2033
Stuart Revocable Trust, Harold C., 7802
Stuart, Alexander D., 3182
Stuart, Brett Fullerton, 1509
Stuart, Bridge, 5138
Stuart, Connie Bond, 1755
Stuart, Debra E., 5151
Stuart, Duncan, 4502
Stuart, Dwight L., Jr., 1225
Stuart, Elbridge A., 1225
Stuart, Elbridge H., 1225, 5151
Stuart, Elbridge H., III, 1225
Stuart, Frances Langford, 2202
Stuart, George B., 8307
Stuart, Harold C., 7802
Stuart, James M., 3182
Stuart, Joan S., 7802
Stuart, Jon R., 7802
Stuart, Lisa G., 6937
Stuart, Loraine, 959
Stuart, Maren M., 3182
Stuart, Marion Butler, 1509
Stuart, Mark F., 4496
Stuart, Mary H., 1225
Stuart, Nan M., 1509
Stuart, Paula, 5396
Stuart, Paulette, 1504
Stuart, Robert A., Jr., 3358
Stuart, Robert D., Jr., 3182
Stuart, Scott M., 6937
Stuart, Susan W., 6832

Stubbing, Holly K. Welch, 7202
Stubbins, Brent A, 7565
Stubblefield, Joseph L., 9745
Stubbs, R. John, 8199
Stubsten, Douglas, 9651
Stuchell, Harry, 9617
Stuckey, Charles L., 7771
Stuckey, Perry, 8561
Stuckey, Trenton, 3295
Stuckman, Jane, 7567
Stucky, Cathy, 3253
Stucky, Steven, 5814
Stude, Herman L., 8731
Studnicky, Daniel, 1893
Stueber, Frederick G., 7584
Stuedli, Thea, 989
Stufflebeaum, Cheryl, 3426
Stuhrling Original, 5981
Stuk, Steve, 3302
Stukes, Barbara D. Thorne, 74
Stulb, Marilyn H., 9538
Stuller, CeCe, 3668
Stuller, Matthew G., Sr., 3668
Stulman, James K., 6938
Stulman, Leonard, 3891
Stulman, Stephen L., 6938
Stulsaft Testamentary Trust, Morris, The, 1226
Stumberg, Diana M., 9210
Stumberg, Eric B., 9210
Stumberg, Louis H., 9210
Stumberg, Louis H., Jr., 9210
Stumberg, Mary Pat, 9210
Stump, Donald G., 7378
Stumpe, Karen, 2763
Stumpf, Kathryn, 9824
Stumpf, Melinda, 8136
Stuntz, Elizabeth, 6939
Stuntz, Mayo, 6939
Stuntz, Mayo S., Jr., 6939
Stupak, Libby, 1840
Stupp Bridge Co., 4982
Stupp Bros. Bridge & Iron Co., 4982
Stupp, John P., Jr., 4982
Stupp, Norman J., 4983
Stupp, Robert P., 4982
Sturdivant, Mike, Jr., 4823
Sturgeon, Nancy G., 7296
Sturges, Caren V., 7503
Sturges, Hale, 3923
Sturgis, Christine, 205, 9211
Sturgis, Roy, 205
Sturm, David, 8925
Sturm, Donald L., 1510
Sturm, Susan M., 1510
Stute, Natalie, 4684
Stutts, David, 9069
Stutzman, Jacki, 3369
Stutzman, Sandra, 1055
Stuver, Tom, 1520
Styberg, Ernest C., Jr., 9924
Styer, Elizabeth, 8199
Styers, Beth, 3348
Styre, Ryan W., 1435
Styres, Belinda, 4849
Styslinger, Kelly, 2514
Styslinger, Lee J., III, 4, 2514
Styslinger, Lee J., Jr., 4
Su, Jane Jin Wen, 321
Suares, Rahamin "Rocky", 253
Suarez, Kiko, 3345
Subaru of America, Inc., 5471
Subler, Matthew, 3253
Sublett, Tarn, 1261
Subotnick, Stuart, 6850
Subramaniam Family Foundation, 8393
Subramaniam, Shivan S., 8393
Subramanian, Meghna, 538
Subramanian, Nita, 538
Subramanian, Nita, Dr., 538
Subramanian, Priyal, 538
Subramanian, Sandhya, 7412
Subramanian, Srinivasan, 538
Succop, Benjamin S., 7178
Suchecki, Tomek, 3244
Suchomel, Frank, Jr., 1871
Sudakoff, Roberta L., 2342
Sudbeck, Carol R., 1003
Sudderth, Leisa, 2099
Sudderth, Robert J., Jr., 8535
Suddes, Adele J., 8446
Suder, Aaron, 9212
Suder, Deborah, 9212
Suder, Eric, 9212
SUDIA, 3245
Sudireddy, Ramakrishna R., 4300
Sudireddy, Santha K., 4300
Sudler 2003 Trust, Claire, 5472
Sudler, Claire E., 5472
Sudler, Peter, 5472
Sudler, Samuel, 5472
Sudow, Ellen L., 3871
Suebpetch, Artis, 830
Suess, David, 3317
Sugarbaker, David J., 4984
Sugarbaker, Everett V., 4984
Sugarbaker, Geneva V., 4984
Sugarbaker, Paul, 4984
Sugarbaker, Stephen P., 4984
Sugarman, Jay, 6940
Sugarman, Kelly, 6940
Suggs, D. Gray, 8478
Suggs, Michael, 3337
Suggs, Sean, 4822
Sugiyama, Alan, 9652
Suglia, Robert P., 8356
Sugura, Yasuyuki, 6490
Suh, Peters, 1519
Suhowatsky, Stephen J., 6153
Suisman, Joel, 5365
Suits, Brenda L., 7139
Suki, Lenora, 6571
Sukolsky, Bob, 2033
Sukup Mfg. Co., 3483
Sukup Trust, Eugene, 3483
Sukup Trust, Mary E., 3483
Sukup, Charles, 3483
Sukup, Eugene, 3483
Sukup, Mary, 3483
Sukup, Steven, 3483
Suleski, Steven R., 9838
Sulkin, Howard A., 3079
Sullivan Trust, Pauline G., 8767
Sullivan, Algernon Sydney, Mrs., 4846
Sullivan, Amy, 3290
Sullivan, Barbara, 4298
Sullivan, Brian C., 2820
Sullivan, Carol, 9916
Sullivan, Carol H., 3140
Sullivan, Carrie E., 2820
Sullivan, Chris, 7012
Sullivan, D. Harold, 4015
Sullivan, Daniel J., Jr., 6941
Sullivan, Daniel L., 1048
Sullivan, Dorothy G., 222
Sullivan, George Hammond, 4846
Sullivan, Irene, 2269
Sullivan, Jack, 9916
Sullivan, James F., Sr., 6083
Sullivan, James G., 7282
Sullivan, James M., 9876
Sullivan, Jane, 1109
Sullivan, Jill, 2253
Sullivan, Joanna, 2618
Sullivan, Joanne M., 3962
Sullivan, John, 4714
Sullivan, John M., 8744, 8745
Sullivan, John, Mrs., 4057
Sullivan, Joseph A., 3828
Sullivan, Joseph D., 2343
Sullivan, Joseph D., Jr., 2343
Sullivan, Joseph F., 8460
Sullivan, Katherine, 7224
Sullivan, Kathleen, 8397
Sullivan, Kerry H., 7139
Sullivan, Kevin, 59
Sullivan, Leonard W., 3991
Sullivan, Marisa Moran, 2242
Sullivan, Marjorie O., 6941
Sullivan, Mark E., 3954
Sullivan, Marsha Joy, 5801
Sullivan, Martin, 6904
Sullivan, Martin J., 6951
Sullivan, Mary, 3189, 5170
Sullivan, Mary Lou, 3996
Sullivan, Mary Sneden, 4389
Sullivan, Maurice H., Jr., 4212
Sullivan, Michael F., 4734
Sullivan, Michelle, 2738, 9989
Sullivan, Nancy, 9559
Sullivan, Patricia, 9032
Sullivan, Patrick, 4256
Sullivan, Patrick J., 3947
Sullivan, Patrick W., 9209
Sullivan, Peter B., 6841
Sullivan, Pike, 9994
Sullivan, R. Michael, 101
Sullivan, Ray H., 1703
Sullivan, Richard M., 3947
Sullivan, Robert, 5404
Sullivan, Sallie, 7615
Sullivan, Sallie P., 7615
Sullivan, Sandra H., 2343
Sullivan, Sara O'Neill, 7602
Sullivan, Susan, 3522, 9994
Sullivan, Susan P., 4966
Sullivan, T. Dennis, 3171, 6105
Sullivan, Terence C., 8831
Sullivan, Thomas, 4512
Sullivan, William, 4389
Sullivan, William P., 220
Sullivan, Yolanda N., 21
Sulzberger, Arthur Hays, 6942
Sulzberger, Arthur Ochs, 6942
Sulzberger, Cathy, 6333
Sulzberger, Iphigene Ochs, 6942
Sulzberger, Judith P., 6942
Sumberg, Richard, 4039
Sumerford, Rees, 2431
Sumitomo, 7272
Sumitomo Bank Capital Markets, Inc., 6873
Sumitomo Corporation of America "SCOA", 6943
Sumitomo Metal Mining AP, 7349
Summa Holdings, 7695
Summer Assocs., 6881
Summerfield, Elaine, 9416
Summerfield, Estelle M., 3712
Summerfield, Solon E., 6944
Summerour, Robert B., Dr., 8527
Summers Foundation, James and Barbara, The, 5291
Summers, Brett, 3851
Summers, Dale T., 3758
Summers, Douglas J., 6945
Summers, Jayne C., 6945
Summers, John M., 6945
Summers, Juliana, 3470
Summers, Lloyd R., 7869
Summers, Nita, 8560
Summers, Stran, 7153
Summers, Todd D., 6945
Summerset Roll, Jody, 101
Summit Business Mgmt., 1089
Summit Crest LLC, 9452
Summit Fund, LLC, The, 9546
Summit Hills LLC, 9452
Summit Investors, 154
Sumner, Ernest W., 7179
Sumner, Martha S., 2762
Sumney, Larry W., 7307
Sump, Scott, 3418
Sun Valley Center, 396
Sun, David, 1227
Sun, Diana, 1227
Sunbeam Development Corp., 1969
Sunbeam Properties, Inc., 1969
Sunbeam Television Corp., 1969
Suncoast Investment Holdings, 390
Sunday, C.W., 9036
Sundbeck, Milton, 4822
Sundberg, Dennis, 634
Sundberg, Susanne, 634
Sunde, Melisa, 5074
Sunderland, Charles, 3551
Sunderland, Charles T., 3492
Sunderland, James P., 3551
Sunderland, Kent, 3551
Sunderland, Kenton W., 3492
Sunderland, Lester T., 3551
Sunderland, Paul, 3551
Sunderland, Phil, 9380
Sunderland, William, 3551
Sundet, Leland N., 4774
Sundet, Louise C., 4774
Sundet, Sam, 9916
Sundet-Meeker, Carol, 4774
Sundin, Vanessa, 972
Sundram, Clarence J., 7023, 7024
Sundvold, Stephen, 744
Sung, Charley C., 3759
Sungard, 8834
Sunnen Products Co., 4986
Sunnen, Joseph, 4986
Sunoco, Inc., 8308
Sunquist, Scott, 4432
Sunrise, Bruce, 961
Sunroof Express, 7638
SunTrust Bank, 2056, 2125, 2225, 2235, 2269, 2324, 2345, 2377, 2400, 2421, 2427, 2453, 2458, 2463, 2470, 2529, 2561, 7340, 8615, 9474, 9539
SunTrust Bank Middle GA, N.A., 2533
SunTrust Bank, N.A., 2066
SunTrust Banks, Inc, 2376
SunTrust Banks, Inc., 2004, 2083
Suntrust Banks, Inc., 2103
SunTrust Banks, Inc., 2116, 2291, 2368
Sunwise Technologies Inc., 6491
Sunyecz, John A., 7991
Supahan, Terry, 714
Supcoe, Don C., 1404

Supera Charitable Lead Trust 1, Michael, 3183
Supera Charitable Lead Trust 2, Michael, 3183
Supera, John, 3183
Supera, Michael, 3183
Supera, Roslynne, 3183
Superior Metal Products, Inc., 7376
Superior Ready Mix Concrete, LP, 1220
Superior Tube Co., 8119
Supermarkets Inc., Ronetco, 5418
Superpac, Inc., 8171
SUPERVALU INC., 4775
Suplisson, Angela "Angie" W., 9501
Supplee, Henderson, III, 8236
Supranowicz, Dianne M., 3947
Supron, Wendy, 5232
Suquet, Ileana, 3656
Surdellpartners LLC, 8834
Surgala, M.J., 8309
Surls, Courtney L., 1907
Surma, John, 7563
Surma, John P., 8325
Suro, Robert, 664
Surplus Line Association of Arizona, The, 167
Surrey, Mary P., 1901
Surrey, Sara R., 1901
Susik, W. Daniel, 2302
Suski, Richard, 1690
Suskin, Margie, 9747
Suskin, Stephanie, 6755
Suskin, Steven C., 9747
Susman, Ellen S., 9216
Susman, Harry P., 9216
Susman, Sally, 6633
Susman, Stephen D., 9216
Susquehanna Bank, 8046
Susquehanna Cable Co., 8310
Susquehanna Motel Corp., 6032
Susquehanna Pfaltzgraff Co., 8310
Susquehanna Radio Corp., 8310
Sussman Family Foundation, The, 6990
Sussman, Andrea, 4056
Sussman, Charles, 8586
Sussman, David, 5251
Sussman, Paul, 331
Sussman, Richard, 2276
Sussman, S. Donald, 6990
Sussman, Ted, 3699
Susswein, Philip M., 5857
Sustic, Mark, 5483
Sutariya, Urvi, 237
Suter, Ben, 777
Suter, Tim, 2792
Sutherland, Barbara H., 7978
Sutherland, Guy, 7731
Sutherland, James, 2806
Sutherland, L. Frederick, 7978
Sutherland, Nancy, 5330
Sutherlin, Michael W., 9876
Suthern, Paul C., 5496
Sutkowski, Edward F., 3176
Sutland, Frank, 3808
Sutland, Josephine, 3808
Sutphin Charitable Lead Annuity Trust, Jean, 7679
Sutphin Charitable Lead Remainder Trust, Jean W., 7679
Sutphin Trust, Jean W., 7679
Sutphin, Charles P., 3272
Sutphin, Jean Webber, 7679
Sutphin, Richard H., 7679
Sutphin, Stuart B., III, 7679
Sutter, Nedra, 3280
Suttle, J. Linton, 7194
Suttles, Denise, 4438
Sutton Foundation, Joe and Eileen, 7109
Sutton Holdings GP, 6949
Sutton Ira First Clearing Corp., David, 6949
Sutton National Financial Services, Ruth, 6949
Sutton Warehousing, 5488
Sutton, Albert J., 6950
Sutton, David, 1002, 6949
Sutton, Deborah E., 8803
Sutton, Dianna, 2041
Sutton, Donald R., 7461
Sutton, E.S., Inc., 6950
Sutton, Eileen, 6950
Sutton, Elliot, 5558
Sutton, Heather, 6157
Sutton, Jeff, 6948
Sutton, Laurie, 5558
Sutton, Marion Mulligan, 7421
Sutton, Mark, 8585
Sutton, Mark S., 8633
Sutton, Mary, 1627
Sutton, Melissa, 6950
Sutton, Paul, 6949
Sutton, Rusty, 5062
Sutton, Ruth, 6949
Sutton, Steven, 6949
Sutton, Zook, 1120
Sutton, Zook, Hon., 973
Suver, Susan M., 8325
Suzman, Mark, 9625
Suzor, Sandra Scott, 9989
Suzuki, Marcia, 809
Suzuki, Nancie, 3840
Suzuki, Sheryl Lynn, 730
Suzuki, Wendy, 4708
Sveen, David E., 2799
Sveen, Donald E., 2799
Sveen, Marjorie L., 2799
Svendsen, John, 4550
Svenson, Roy, 2687
Sverre-Cullman, Nikken C., 5831
Svob, Robert S., 95
Svoboda, John A., 3172
Swaback Charities, Mitchell, Inc., 7214
Swaback, Brad, 7214
Swagelok Manufacturing Company, 7545
Swager, Duane, II, 7942
Swaim, Doris, 8669
Swaim, Kathie O., 3295
Swaim, M. Mort, 68
Swain, Joyce, 2390
Swain, Laura Taylor, Hon., 6148
Swalm, Beth, 9299
Swalm, Dave, 9299
Swamy, Dorothy, 1932
Swan, Andy, 3354
Swan, Lori, 3243
Swan, Philip A., 1024
Swan, Philip V., 611, 1015, 1024
Swan, Stephen, 8837
Swan, Steve, 9759
Swaney, Nancy C., 4363
Swaney, Richard G., 4363
Swaney, William C., 4363
Swank, Alma K., 1866
Swanson Charitable Remainder Unitrust, 1228
Swanson Revocable Trust, A.L., 98
Swanson, Beth, 2946
Swanson, Celia, 186
Swanson, E. William, 645
Swanson, Erica, 1228
Swanson, Frances L., 3399
Swanson, Gordon, 1012, 1053
Swanson, James R., 2744
Swanson, Jeff, 992
Swanson, Jill, 9807
Swanson, John W., II, 4369
Swanson, Judy C., 1228
Swanson, Kai, 2787
Swanson, Laura, 3418
Swanson, Linda V., 6841
Swanson, Lynwood W., 9689
Swanson, Marc G., 2315
Swanson, Marilyn, 9887
Swanson, Mark, 1504
Swanson, Mark T., 2744
Swanson, Marti, 3393
Swanson, Nancy, 842
Swanson, Robert, Rev., 7990
Swanson, Terry, 9887
Swanson, Vernon H., 9892
Swantek, Sandra, 2702
Swantek, Shauna, 4342
Swapp, Laura, 9713
Swarthout, Andrew T., 1503
Swarthout, Gerard, III, 64
Swartling, Barbara, 9578
Swartling, Tricia, 2632
Swarts, James L., 4871
Swartz, David B., 5542
Swartz, Diana Castellanos, 5542
Swartz, James R., 6954
Swartz, Jerome, Dr., 6953
Swartz, Judith W., 4301
Swartz, Julie, 4090
Swartz, Lonnie, 4732
Swartz, Margaret Z., 8351
Swartz, Sidney W., 4301
Swartz, Steven R., 6155, 6156
Swartz, Sydney, 4301
Swary, Mark F., 7410, 7527
Swarzman, Howard, 6380, 6545
SWAT, 5161
Swayne, Keith, 992
Swearer, Dell Marie Shanahan, 3521
Sweasay, Carol, 4749
Sweasy, William J., 4749
Sween, Susan, 4645
Sweeney, Aileen, 877
Sweeney, C. Jeanne, 2346
Sweeney, Eileen, 3042
Sweeney, Gerard J., 5594
Sweeney, Gregory, 2346
Sweeney, Janet, 3359
Sweeney, Jennifer, 9834
Sweeney, John J., III, 8260
Sweeney, Linda Porr, 8135
Sweeney, Lois Irene, 973
Sweeney, Mary S., 2346
Sweeney, Michael A., 7420
Sweeney, Michael J., III, 2482
Sweeney, Michelle, 7671
Sweeney, Mike, 7367
Sweeney, Paul, 7934
Sweeney, Ralph, 8474
Sweeney, Randall J., 5766
Sweeney, Timothy M., 4152
Sweeney-LeVecke, Marguente, 835
Sweeny, Jack C., 9223
Sweers, Kim, 2034
Sweet, Howard A., 9852
Sweet, John H.K., 5338
Sweet, Judith V., 5805
Sweet, Midge, 2546
Sweet, Robert W., Hon., 6148
Sweet, William R., 5338
Sweeters, Martha, 1650
Sweetland, Ralph C., 4159
Sweets Co. of America, Inc., The, 4249
Swegler, Jeffrey F., 4303
Sweigart Irrevocable Trust, Anne B., 7954
Swenson, Erik, 2227
Swenson, Galen, 3540
Swenson, James I., 1229
Swenson, James R., 5308
Swenson, Judy P., 9728
Swenson, Scott, 7357
Swenson, Susan G., 1229
Swensrud, Anthony S., 4303
Swensrud, Leslie R., 4303
Swensrud, S. Blake, II, 4303
Swensson, Macy D., 8592
Swerdlick, Eileen L., 1581
Swets, Joel B., 4003, 4199
Swezey, Carroll, 6296
Swezey, Dorothy, 6296
Swezey, John, 6296
Swezey, Nancy, 6296
SWFF, 393
Swickard, Sherri D., 59
Swider, Sandy, 4284
Swieca 2001 Charitable Trust, Henry, 6955
Swieca 2002 Charitable Trust, Henry, 6955
Swieca 2003 Charitable Trust, Henry, 6955
Swieca 2007 Charitable Trust, Henry, 6955
Swieca, Esther, 6955
Swieca, Henry, 6955
Swienton, Gregory T., 2302
Swift, Beth, 4502
Swift, Jack, 23
Swift, James L., 9718
Swift, John, 1230
Swift, Karen, 1230
Swift, Lauren, 9718
Swift, Mathews D., 2438
Swift, Nancy T., 3923
Swift, P., 1782
Swift, Peter, 1782
Swift, Phelps H., 3181
Swift, Sonja, 1230
Swift, T. Cody, 9718
Swig, Benjamin H., 1231
Swig, Steven, 1231
Swigert, Dorn, 7841
Swigert, Ernest C., 7841
Swigert, Hank, 9748
Swigert, Henry T., 7841
Swilley, Reginald, 271
Swim, Katherine, 9322
Swim, Lauralyn, 9322
Swim, Lauralyn B., 9322
Swim, Stanford, 9322
Swimmer, Joshua, 7991
Swindells, Ann, 7892
Swindells, Charles, 7892
Swindells, William, 7892
Swindells, William R., 7871
Swindells, William R., III, 7892
Swinden, James I., 1182
Swindle, P.W., 7809
Swindle, Stephen D., 9976

Swinford, Troy, 3027
Swink, Henry, 8461
Swinney, Edward F., 9218
Swinney, R. Andrew, 8221
Swisher International Inc., 9470
Swisher, Charles, 1939
Swiss, Rachel, 4361
Swistro, Christine, 3987
Switzer, Cathy R., 3583
Switzer, Elise, 3709
Switzer, Jessica, 3709
Switzer, Patricia, 3709
Switzer, Patricia D., 3709
Switzer, Paula M., 8080
Switzer, Robert, 3709
Switzer, Robert L., 3012
Swope, Patricia G., 3569, 3603
Swope, Samuel G., 3603
Swope, Susan, 3603
Swope, W. Chandler, 9794
Sword, Elizabeth, 3765
Sword, Leslie Lewis, 6365
Swyer, Edward P., 6956
SYB, Inc., 7
Sydney, Kristen J., 7576
Syed, Faizah, 2665
Sygielski, John J., Ed.D, 8351
Sykes, Frances P., 5403
Sykes, Gene T., 6957
Sykes, James W., Jr., 6106
Sykes, Tracy M., 6957
Sylvan Learning Systems, Inc., 1867
Sylvester, Dan, 7585
Sylvester, Harcourt M., 2348
Sylvester, Harcourt M., II, 2348
Sylvester, Leon, 1714
Sylvester, Virginia W., 2348
Symchych, Anne, 5561
Symchych, Catherine, 5561
Symchych, Christine, 5561
Symchych, Stephen, 5561
Symington, Ann H., 3218
Symington, J. Fife, III, 8049
Symmes, F.W., 7325
Symmonds, Bob, 3514
Symms, Dan, 2628, 2644
Symms, Steve, 2644
Symon, Bob, 9108
Symonik, Beverly, 1046
Syms, Lynn Tamarkin, 5475
Syms, Robert, 5475
Syms, Sy, 5475
Symson, Adam, 7659
Sync Inc., 5425
Synergy Resource Group, 7846
Synn, Alan, 1390
Synopsys Inc., 1232
Synor, Susan M., 4456
Synovus Financial Corp., 2556
Synovus Trust Co., 2269
Synovus Trust Co. N.A., 2410
Synthes, 7916
Synthes, Inc., 7915
Sypher, Eleanor, 7023
Sypher, Eleanor K., 7024
Syrek, Richard, 4532
Syrmis, Pamela Lee, 6217
Syrmis, Victor, 6217
Syrop, Arnold, 6830
Syrvalin, Kristine G., 7601
Sysko, David, 1800
Sytman, Alex, 9725
Sytsema, John M., 4369
Sytz, Ronald M., 7179
Syudio Ray, LLC, 5287
Syversen, Susan K., 4309
Syvertsen, John, 2873
Szabo, Cindy L., 1765
Szalai, Veronika, 157
Szapary, Gladys V., 892
Sze, Julia, 877
Sze, Stanley, 776
Szews, Charles L., 9917
Szoke, Charles J., 7698
Szokol, Pam F., 2892
Szoldatits, Linda, 6896
Szumowski, Marcia, 4342
Szutu, Peter C., 253
Szwarc, Bernardo Pedro, 2020
Szymanski, Stephen, 1628

T and Company Moriarty, 6205
T-L Irrigation Co., 5089
T-Twelve Legacy Trust, 1239
Tabah, Mimi, 7088
Tabankin and Assocs., Margery, 1089
Tabankin, Margery, 1073, 1224
Tabankin, Margery A., 1880, 5889
Tabasgo Foundation, 842
Tabasgo Foundation, The, 821
Tabat, Dawn, 9880
Taber, Jonathan, 6038
Taber, Nancy, 4350
Taber, Richard, Jr., 1584
Tabin, Clifford, Dr., 6693
Tablada, Marco, 1632
Tabler, Michael Rex, 9667, 9668
Tabor, A. Wellford, 7745
Tabor, Albert S., 9105
Tabor, Kristin, 5019
Taccolini, Fred, 4495
Tachau, David, 3569
Tackett, Maureen, 4386
Taczak, Janet S., 9414
Tada, Pierre Y., 1287
Taddonio, William, 8234
Tadlock, Lynn, 9410
Tadros, Niveen, 1101, 1340
Taft, Bill, 7217
Taft, Don, 2349
Taft, Dudley S., 7660
Taft, John, 4748
Taft, Kathy, 7287
Taft, Thomas Woodall, 7660
Taggart, Kenneth M., 8694
Tahari Ltd., Elie, 6958
Tahari, Elie, 6958
Tai & Co., J.T., Inc., 6959, 6960
Tai, Jun Tsei, 6959
Tai, Pin, 385
Tai, Ping Y., 6960
Taicher, Jaime, 6154
Tailwind, Ross, 9792
Tainer, Francis H., Jr., 5825
Taisey, Robert D., 2939
Taishoff, Laurie B., 2350
Taishoff, Martha, 2350
Taishoff, Robert P., 2350
Tait, Bryan, 8228
Tajima, Yoshihiro, 6961
Takach, Deborah E., 8332
Takaki, Donald M., 2588
Takami, Andrew, 3288
Takamiya, Katsuya, 9487
Takanishi, Ruby, 6003
Takashima, Makoto, 6873
Take 2 Interactive, 7012
Takeda, Donna, 2595
Taketa, Kelvin H., 2602
Takian, John, Jr., 8438
Takiff, Lionel, 2833
Takiff, Rosella, 2833
Takla-O'Reilly, Aida, Dr., 701
Takton, Marjorie J., 9830
Takumi, Larry, 2591
Talbert, Julie A., 1233
Talbert, Lloyd W., 1233
Talbert, Tukea, 3578
Talbot, Cliff, 8729
Talbot-Metz, Molly, 8459
Talbott, Natalie, 855
Taliaferro, Lilton R., Jr., 8106
Taliaferro, Roberta, 7631
Talkington, Margaret K., 9219
Tallant, Kevin, 2525
Tallardy, Gayle, 2253
Tallarida, Louisa, 673
Tallent, Charles, 5611
Tallerico, Joe, 1154
Talley, Chris L., 3311
Talley, Johnnie, 1110
Talley, Mike, 8874, 9123
Tallichet, George, 8681
Tallman, Lori, 4372
Tallon, James R., 5800
Talmage, Daniel B., 7680
Talmage, Joan S., 7680
Talmage, Ralph W., 7680
Talmage, Scott W., 7680
Talmide Chidishei Harim, 6287
Talpas, Jeffery, 9
Talsma, Kelly, 5019
Talton, Jimmy, 7295
Talton, Neal, 2435
Talton, Patricia, 9750
Tam, Nana, 6087
Tam, Raymond J., 2596
Tam, Richard, 5152
Tamboli, Kaizad, Dr., 4830
Tambour Foundation, The, 865
Tamko Asphalt Products, Inc., 4875
Tan, Lydia, 434
Tanabe, Barbara J., 2588
Tanabe, Charles Y., 1448
Tanaka Ikubikai Educational Corp., 6961
Tanaka, Atsushi, 6997
Tanaka, Kenji, 6961
Tanaka, Kimiko, 6961
Tanaka, Makiko, 6961
Tanaka, Susan, 6630
Tanaka, Taeko, 6961
Tanakeyowma, Lilia M., 667
Tananbaum, Lisa, 6962
Tananbaum, Steve A., 6962
Tancredi, David, 8976
Tancredi, Laura Sackler, 6778
Tandon, Chandrika, 6963
Tandon, Lita, 6963
Tandon, Ranjan, 6963
Tandy, Anne Burnett, 8737
Tandy, Daniel W., 6573
Tanen, Jeffrey, 7258
Tanenbaum, Ann, 6228
Tanenbaum, Charles J., 6642
Tanenbaum, Marla L., 3831
Tanenbaum, Robert K., 3831
Tanenbaum, Szlvia Szmuk, 6642
Tang Industries, Inc., 5153
Tang, Cindy, 9835
Tang, Cyrus, 5153
Tang, H.C., 711
Tang, Haeyoung K., 1235
Tang, Kevin C., 1235
Tang, Michael, 2746
Tang, Oscar, 1518
Tang, Patricia, 5534
Tang, Susan, 1628
Tang, Timothy, 772
Tang, Wilson, 385
Tangvik, Beverly J., 3926
Tani, Daniel, 7019
Taniguchi, Barry K., 2602
Tanimura, Gary K., 1236
Tanimura, George M., 1236
Tanimura, George T., 1236
Tanimura, Robert T., 1236
Tanimura, Sheila C., 1236
Tanimura, Tom T., 1236
Tank, David, 3484, 4708
Tannehill, Jean, 9632
Tannehill, Rocky, 9632
Tannenbaum, Allison Atlas, 266
Tannenbaum, David, 266
Tannenbaum, Jeanne L., 7326
Tannenbaum, Leah Louise B., 7326
Tannenbaum, Nancy B., 7326
Tannenbaum, Sigmund I., 7326
Tannenbaum, Susan M., 7326
Tanner Co., O.C., 9352
Tanner Recognition Company, O.C., 9352
Tanner, David A., 6555
Tanner, Estelle Newman, 6555
Tanner, Harold, 6555
Tanner, James M., 6555
Tanner, Jim, 3400
Tanner, Kim, 8932
Tanner, L. Gene, 3361
Tanner, Laurence A., 1537, 1564
Tanner, Obert C., 9352
Tanner, Robin C., 9537
Tanoue, Donna A., 2588
Tanous, Peter, 739
Tansey, Andrew L., 5676
Tansey, William A., III, 5317
Tanski, Ronald J., 6526
Tantillo, Richard, 5805
Tanzman, Norman, 5476
Tanzman, Roy H., 5476
Taormina, William, 239
Tapani, Traci, 4679
Taper, S. Mark, 1237
Tapiero, Jacques, 3340
Tappan, Philip, 179
Taradash, Bernard A.G., 4079
Tarakji, Bilal, 4551
Tarakji, Lama, 4551
Tarakji, N., 4551
Tarakji, Nael, 4551
Taraskas, Janice, 6215
Tarbell, Stephanie L., 3835
Tarble, Jan, 1238
Tardi, Joseph, 6802
Tarella, David R., 1850
Target Corp., 4776
Tarica, James, 6965
Tarica, Lawrence, 6965
Tarica, Mark E., 235
Tarica, Pamela, 6965
Tarica, Samuel, 235
Tarkiewicz, Tom, 4496
Tarleton, George, 1197
Tarlton, Gregg, 633
Tarnacki, Duane L., 4424
Tarnoff, Michael B., 3110

Tarnok, Robert C., 6479
Tarola, Jeffrey, 623
Taroni, John C., 5629
Tarpey, Randy, 7971
Tarpley, Billy, 184
Tarr, Jeff C., 6227
Tarr, Jeff, Jr., 6227
Tarr, Jefferson, 9428
Tarr, Jennifer, 6227
Tarr, Patricia G., 6227
Tarrant, Amy E., 2352
Tarrant, Brian, 2352
Tarrant, Cornelia, 1869
Tarrant, Deborah L., 9373
Tarrant, Jeffrey, 1869, 6221
Tarrant, Jeremiah, 2352
Tarrant, Richard E., 9373
Tarrant, Richard E., Jr., 2352
Tarrats, Nelson Colon, 8353
Tarta, Joy, 8138
Tartaglino, Jerry, 9221
Tartaglino, Nancy G., 9221
Tartar, Joy, 7912, 8137
Tartt, Hope Pierce, 9222
Tarullo, Michael, 7431
Tarver, Sarah T., 8562
Tarwater, Dwight, 8560
Tash, Paul, 2332
Tashjian, Elizabeth, 9311
Tashman, Hal, 92
Task, Robert, 5690
Tassone, Patricia, 2880
Tasto, Kellie E., 4781
Tatar, Jerome F., 7428
Tatar, Myrna, 7677
Tatar, Steven, 7644
Tate, Bryan K., 8351
Tate, Charles W., 9268
Tate, Deborah Taylor, 8550
Tate, Frank, 9277
Tate, Liz, 3272
Tate, Lloyd P., Jr., 7298
Tate, Louise F., 7485
Tate, Michael A., 4339
Tate, Ralph, 3992
Tate, Sherman, 181
Tate, Victoria E., 6556
Tate, William A., 25
Tatem, Sandra, 6956
Tateuchi, Atsuhiko, 9751
Tateuchi, Ina, 9751
Tatge, Jacklyn, 8731
Tatlock, Anne, 5747
Tatlock, Anne M., 3818, 5684
Tatman, Eula, 23
Tatna, Meher, 701
Tattersall, Fred T., 9505
Tattersall, T. Kirk, 9416
Tatum, Linda L., 833
Tatum, Lisa Skeete, 5411
Tatum, Nenetta Carter, 8753
Tatum, Susanne, 9062
Taub Revocable Trust, Henry, 5477
Taub, Arlene, 5478
Taub, H. Ben, 9287
Taub, Henry, 5477, 5628
Taub, Henry J.N., 9287
Taub, Henry J.N., II, 9287
Taub, Ira, 5477
Taub, Joseph, 5478
Taub, Marilyn, 5477
Taub, Miles, 2867
Taub, Sandra, 5478
Taub, Steven, 5477
Taube Foundation for Jewish Life, The, 6336
Taube, Dianne M., 1241
Taube, Tad, 801
Taube, Thaddeus N., 1241
Tauber, Alfred I., 3893
Tauber, Ingrid D., 3893
Tauber, Laszlo N., 3893
Tauber, Ron, 6260
Taubert, Bob, 4768
Taubman Restated Rev. Trust, A. Alfred, 4552, 4553
Taubman, A. Alfred, 4552, 4553
Taubman, Anne C., 7804
Taubman, Deborah, 7804
Taubman, Eugenia L., 9540
Taubman, H. Perry, 7804
Taubman, Herman P., 7804
Taubman, Hilary L., 7804
Taubman, Lawrence, 7804
Taubman, Nicholas F., 9540
Taubman, Robert S., 4553
Taubman, Sophia, 7804
Taubman, William S., 4552, 4553
Tauck, Arthur C., III, 1706
Tauck, Arthur C., Jr., 1706
Tauck, Chuck, 1706
Tauck, Peter, 1706
Tauck, Robin, 1706
Tauck, Tyler, 1706
Taunton, Michael J., 6527
Taus, Ellen, 6724
Taussig, Brenda, 849
Tavares, Jose, 6148
Tavares, Jose A., 6148
Tavernise, Peter, 402
Tavitian, Assadour, 5479
Tavlin, Michael J., 5096
Tawes, Greg, 3760
Tawresy, Alice, 9659
Tax Education Support Organization, 3468
Tayler, Jimmy, 3121
Tayler, Michele, 9110
Tayloe, Edward D., II, 9506
Taylor Char. Trust, Elizabeth, 3195
Taylor Charitable Lead Trust, Galen D., 2353
Taylor Charitable Trust, Glen A., 4777
Taylor Corp., 4777
Taylor Development Corp., 2354
Taylor Energy Co., 3669
Taylor Estates, Inc., 6768
Taylor Trust, Charlotte, 9612
Taylor, Alex, 3431
Taylor, Alexander C., 2425, 2445
Taylor, Alexander S., 8312
Taylor, Andrew C., 4987
Taylor, Anne C., 9398
Taylor, Betsy, 3897
Taylor, Blair, 9742
Taylor, Bruce C., 654
Taylor, C. Fred, 5455
Taylor, Carl D., 7303
Taylor, Caroline E., 8311
Taylor, Catherine H., 9955
Taylor, Charlotte L., 9612
Taylor, Cheryl K., 3304
Taylor, Christine, 6628
Taylor, Collette, 2675
Taylor, Connie, 5474
Taylor, Danny W., 9277
Taylor, David, 9069
Taylor, David H., 5850
Taylor, David H., Jr., 5850
Taylor, David S., 2638
Taylor, Debra, 4777
Taylor, Diem Chau, 2353
Taylor, Donald K., 3760
Taylor, Douglas F., 5850
Taylor, Ed, 9600
Taylor, Edward C., 5474
Taylor, Edward L., III, 7751
Taylor, Edward L., IV, 7751
Taylor, Edward N., 5474
Taylor, Eleanor H., 2447
Taylor, Elizabeth, 2354
Taylor, Elizabeth M., 9272
Taylor, Eloise Canter, 3121
Taylor, Emma Scott, 9529
Taylor, Eric W., 3569
Taylor, Fran, 3560
Taylor, French, 5349
Taylor, Galen D., 2353
Taylor, Gary, 744, 7445
Taylor, Gary J., 3630
Taylor, Gerald, 2353
Taylor, Glen, 4777
Taylor, Glenn, 25
Taylor, Grant, 3277
Taylor, Harold G., 8700
Taylor, Heather Butler, 780
Taylor, Helen W., 9510
Taylor, Howard, 7875
Taylor, J., 777
Taylor, Jack, 2354
Taylor, Jack C., 4887, 4987
Taylor, Jacqueline M., 6788
Taylor, James H., 3569
Taylor, James Kahea, 4724
Taylor, Jamie T., 3184
Taylor, Jane, 4724
Taylor, Janet C., 3916
Taylor, Jean, 4777
Taylor, Jeff, 986
Taylor, Jeremy P., 3195
Taylor, Jerry, 4943
Taylor, John L., Jr., 2422
Taylor, John R., 8085
Taylor, Julie Johns, 5524
Taylor, Kathryn, 1256
Taylor, Kathryn A., 1257
Taylor, Kelly, 3356
Taylor, Kenneth H., Jr., 8311
Taylor, Kenneth N., 3195
Taylor, Kris, 9604
Taylor, Kris J., 4651
Taylor, L.F., Maj. Gen., 3669
Taylor, Lance, 200
Taylor, Larry, 4777
Taylor, Lauren C., 3760
Taylor, Linda, 654
Taylor, Linda Davis, 411
Taylor, Louis H., 3760
Taylor, Marjorie, 1153
Taylor, Mark D., 3195
Taylor, Mark H., 4866
Taylor, Martha A., 9897
Taylor, Mary F., 7421
Taylor, Melaine Ann, 1841
Taylor, Michael, 4451, 4694
Taylor, Michelle A., 1765
Taylor, Mitchell, 2354
Taylor, Nancy W., 7178
Taylor, Norton, 6285
Taylor, Oather, 3417
Taylor, Patrick F., 3669
Taylor, Perry, 3293
Taylor, Peter, 760, 3698
Taylor, Peter J., 579
Taylor, Peter W., 3195
Taylor, Philip, 9955
Taylor, Phillipa P., 1940
Taylor, Phyllis M., 3669
Taylor, R. Bruce, 3980
Taylor, Richard G. A., 7853
Taylor, Rise, 3281
Taylor, Robert A., 3184
Taylor, Robert C., Jr., 993, 8599
Taylor, Robert K., 340, 682
Taylor, Robert M., 8878
Taylor, Robert N., 3304
Taylor, Russel G., 3306
Taylor, Sharon C., 5415
Taylor, Shelley E., 6782
Taylor, Stephen J., 7751
Taylor, Steven W., 7786
Taylor, Sue, 7919, 9651
Taylor, Susan H., 1403
Taylor, Suzanne, 7751
Taylor, Teresa Jane, 5881
Taylor, Thomas A., 8356
Taylor, Tommy, 2142
Taylor, Virginia C., 5474
Taylor, W.H., 207
Taylor, Walker, IV, 1776
Taylor, William, 8506
Taylor, William G., 8504
TC Electric LLC, 6205
TCF Financial Corp., 4778
TCF National Bank, 4778
TCF National Bank Minnesota, 4778
TCIF Fund, 1557
TCIFM UK LLP, 1557
TD Bank, N.A., 5173, 6057
TD Banknorth Inc., 3710
Tea Ranch (June Goldston Family Trust), 3249
Teachers Foundation, 9702
Teagarden, Becky, 3399
Teagle, Walter C., III, 6967
Teague, Syd, 8723
Teague, Thomas, 8723
Teague, Wil, 3277
Teahan, Marlaine, 4357
Teal, James C., 4687
TEAM Industries, Inc., 4779
Teamer, Cheryl R., 3656
Teammates for Kids Foundation, 977
Teamup Team of Stars, 3898
Tebay, John, 9789
Tebbetts, Jennell, 3514
Tech Dev, 9193
Techmeier, Heather, 4693
Technologia Tecnomet Sa De Cv Mexic, 8834
Technology Media Group, 8834
Teck Resources Ltd, 7349
Tecklenburg, Dorothy, 8332
TECT, 7210
Ted Arison Charitable Trust, 1972
Tedesco, Francis, 2482
Tedesco, Francis J., M.D., 2427
Teel, Jim, 1243
Teel, Joyce, 1243
Teel, K. Roger, Jr., 19
Teel, Mike, 1243
Teeter, Geoff, 570, 571
Tefft, Tom M., 4712
Tegman, Deyonne, 9663
Tehan, Jean C., 9834, 9856
Tehan, Timothy P., 8858

Teibel, Steve, 3347
Teich, Jerome, 6296
Teicher, Florence E., 5958
Teicher, Seth, 5958
Teichert & Son, A., Inc., 1244
Teichert, Frederick A., 1244
Teichert, Inc., 1244
Teichert, Melita M., 1244
Teitelbaum, Helene, 5759
Teixeira, Frank, 3960
Teixeira, Paulo L., 8549
Tektronix, Inc., 7894
Telecom Capital Partners II LP, 1965
Telfer, Steve, 3285
Telfer, William, 8341
Tellabs, Inc., 3185
Teller Property Inc., 685
Telles, Cynthia, 365
Tellez, Lorenzo, 8805
Telliez, Jean-Luc, 5526
Tellis, Ashley, Dr., 1679
Tellor, Nancy JS, 4760
Tempel, William C., 3556
Tempero, Stephen, 3552
Temple B'nai Israel, 9165
Temple, Arthur, III, 9223
Temple, Cassie L., 7805
Temple, Charlotte, 9223
Temple, David E., 7805
Temple, Diane E., 9541
Temple, Katherine S., 9223
Temple, L. Peter, Esq., 7979
Temple, Leslie P., 8040
Temple, Nancy, 9541
Temple, Pamela Y., 8497
Temple, Paul N., 9541
Temple, Paulina, 9541
Temple, Robin, 9541
Temple, Ruth K., 9656
Temple, Thomas, 9541
Temple-Inland Forest Products Corp., 8633
Temple-Inland Inc., 8633
Templeson Trust for Robert Templeson, Herbert A., 7895
Templeton Cust Trust JMT, J.M., Jr., 8237
Templeton Religious Trust, 8313
Templeton World Charity Foundation, 8313
Templeton, D. Jeffrey, 3946
Templeton, Esther, 3872
Templeton, Harvey M., III, 8313
Templeton, Herbert A., 7895
Templeton, John M., Jr., 3358, 8237
Templeton, John Marks, Jr., 8313
Templeton, John Marks, Sir., 8313
Templeton, John, Dr., 5776
Templeton, Josephine "Pina", 8313
Templeton, Josephine J., 8237
Templeton, Josephine, Dr., 5776
Templeton, Mary, 6969
Templeton, Richard, 6969
Templeton, Steven A., 2032
Templin, Daniel P., 2792
Templin, Robert G., Jr., 1931
Ten Pas, Paul H., 9884
Tenenbaum Co., A., Inc., 206
Tenenbaum, Harold, 206
Tenenbaum, J.M., 206
Tenenbaum, Matityahu, 6664
Tenenblatt, Anna, 1245
Tenenblatt, William, 1245
Tenet Healthcare Foundation, 1389
Teng, Fred, 5346, 6382
Tennant, T. Michael, 2433
Tennery, Frances E., 3787
Tennessee Higher Education Assn., 8532
Tenney, Jay, Rev., 2481
Tenney, Judy E., 6124
Tenney, Justine D., 5822
Tennille, Jocelyn D., 2791
Tennison, Lee Lupton, 8730
Tennity, Marilyn S., 9718
Tenny, Barron "Buzz", 6544
Tennyson, Clark, 199
Tenula, Kathy, 2844
Tenula, Peter, 2844
Tenzer, David, 9443
Tenzer, Melissa, 5412
Teplicky, J. William, Jr., 9680
Tepper, David A., 5193, 5480
Tepper, Michael S., 2749
Teramo, Michelle, 6135
Terashi, Shigeki, 7002
Terni, Diane D., 8469
Terra, Daniel J., 3186
Terra, James D., 3186
Terra, Jean Lim, 238
Terra, Karen, 9975
Terracina, Christopher, 3650
Terracina, Roy, 9048
Terre Haute Gas Corp., 3327
Terrell, Fred, 5826
Terrell, Holly J., 8942
Terrill, Marc B., 3726, 3803
Terrill, Thomas, 7012
Terry, Anne, 8162
Terry, Carl E., 8001
Terry, Carry P., 3960
Terry, Charles R., Jr., 40
Terry, Charles R., Sr., 40
Terry, Frederick A., Jr., 1928
Terry, Howard L., 9225
Terry, Jessie W., 9936
Terry, Keith, 2826
Terry, Lee Ellen, 1563
Terry, Mary D., 9224
Terry, Michael F., 9224
Terry, Nancy M., 9225
Terry, Randall B., Jr., 7327
Terry, Scott, 8819
Terry, Verlan, 9307
Terwilliger, J. Ronald, 1900
Terzi, Elliot, 5991
Tesher, Robert, Dr., 2393
Tesjia, Kathee, 4776
Teske, T.J., 9822
Teskey, Kristen, 7146
Teskey, Kristen L., 7139
Tesoriero, Jean T., 6527
Tessier, Janice M., 4368
Tessler, Karla, 9975
Tessler, N., 6812
Testerman, Patricia, 3866
Teter, Betsy, 8459
Teter, Jeff, 9276
Tetler, George A., 4327
Tetreault, Melissa, 4282
Teuber, Andy, 79
Teunon, Jennifer, 9682
Teuton, Gary, 975
Teutsch, Peter, 9766
Tevlin, Beth A.A., 3396
Tevrizian, Dickran, 744
Tewnion, Lesley A., 8061
Tewnion, Lewsley A., 8060
Texas Instruments Inc., 1316, 9227
Texas Longhorn Breeders Association of America, 9151
Texas Stadium Corp, 8943
Texas Tech University, 3209
Textile Benefit Assn., 2419
Textiles From Europe, Inc., 5792
Textor, Donald F., 6973
Textor, Elaine R., 6973
Textron Inc., 8446
TFS Financial Corp., 7681
TFS Key Trust Donations, 7675
Thacher, Carry, 959
Thacker, Bradley D., 8613
Thacker, James L., Jr., 9398
Thacker, Pat, 9277
Thain, Carmen M., 5192
Thain, John, 5192
Thain, John A., 5192
Thaler, Richard H., 6782
Thalheimer, Louis B., 3894
Thalhimer, Robert, 9416
Thalhimer, Robert L., 9521
Thalhimer, Sallie, 9485
Thames, Brenda, 8474
Thames, Sydney E., 9145
Thane, Janet, 4562
Thanhouser, Sally P., 3783
Thao, Terri, 4616
Tharp, Allesandra, 8613
Tharp, Donald, 7496
Tharpe Irrevocable Trust, Max B., 2355
Thatcher Irrevocable Trust, Mary, 2356
Thatcher, Bill, 3419
Thatcher, Diane, 1248
Thatcher, George A., 1248
Thatcher, Georgia R., 1248
Thatcher, John W., 2356
Thatcher, K. Blake, 3063
Thatcher, Mary W., 2356
Thatcher, Nancy J., 1248
Thatcher, Thomas D., II, 6148
Thatcher-Keller, Becky, 7357
Thaw, Clare Eddy, 5534
Thaw, Eugene Victor, 5534
Thawer, Amyn, 493
Thawerbhoy, Nazim G., 738
Thaxter, Shaun, 9516
Thaxton, Greg, 7596
Thayer, Douglas, 3376
Thayer, Gladys Brooks, 5719
Thayer, Larry R., 3974
Thayer, Lisa, 5044
Thayer, Richard M., 384
The Grand Manse Events & Lodging, 5040
Theam, Sophie, 4207
Theders, Jonathan, 7417
Thedford, Mary H., 9133
Theile, Kevin, 3278
Theiler, Robert J., 4647, 4807
Theisen, Jim, 3421
Themides, James, 2040
Theobald, Jon A., 4672, 4782
Theobald, Stephen B., 6974
Theobald, Thomas C., 6974
Theofilactidis, Alexis, 6841
Theosophical Book Gift Institute, The, 2958
Theosophical Order of Service, 2958
Theosophical Society in America, 2958
Therakos, Inc., 5327
Theriot, Julie, 7080
Thermofoil Doors Inc., 6229
Thernstrom, Abigail, 7893
Thewes Charitable Annuity Lead Trust, The, 4483
Thewes Trust, The, 4483
Thewes, Beverly A., 4554
Thibault, George E., 6414
Thibault, Matthew A., 8448
Thibault, Susan, 3703
Thibodeau, Laurie, 8314
Thibodeau, Mia, 4649
Thiede, Patty, 2817
Thiel, Carsten, 238
Thiel, Karen, 9802
Thiel, paul, 1053
Thiel, Peter, 1249
Thielhelm, Jennifer, 406
Thieman, Frederick W., 7956
Thiemann, Frank H., III, 3588
Thieriot, Julia, 2739
Thigpen, Richard T., 5416
Thille, Nick, 1110
Thilo, Sue, 2632
Third Federal Savings and Loan Association, MHC, 7675, 7681
Third Point LLC, 6383
Thistle, J. Jeffrey, 2213
Thivierge, Ann D., 6713
Thivierge, Arthur, 6713
Thode, Mary Ann, 471
Thoele, Blake, 2757
Thoeni, Ruedi F., 2609
Thogerson, Lynn, 2482
Thom, David, 5089
Thom, David W., 5089
Thom, James, 5046, 5089
Thom, James L., 5089
Thom, Jean E., 5089
Thom, LeRoy W., 5089
Thom, Michael, 5089
Thom, Thomas, 5089
Thom, Thomas A., 5089
Thoma, Marilynn, 3186
Thoman, Brent, 3265
Thoman, Lynn B., 6395
Thoman, Richard, 9437
Thomas, Angela, 3602
Thomas, Anna, 8397
Thomas, Bart, 9227
Thomas, Bernie, 9600
Thomas, Billie D., 9231
Thomas, Blythe, 3524
Thomas, Carl M., 3577
Thomas, Catherine M., 2385
Thomas, Cherryl T., 3084
Thomas, Cheryl, 1473
Thomas, Colleen, 9804
Thomas, David, 5663, 8564
Thomas, Deborah, 8403, 9232
Thomas, Debra, 7103
Thomas, Dee, 4621
Thomas, Emily, 2357
Thomas, Frank, 983
Thomas, George I., 9757
Thomas, Geri, 2009
Thomas, Glenn E., 3584
Thomas, H. Gillis, 9231
Thomas, Harold, 2645
Thomas, Harold E., 2645
Thomas, Helen S., 2357
Thomas, J. Darrell, 9859
Thomas, J. Grover, Jr., 3193
Thomas, Jack, 1345, 9704
Thomas, James, 3955
Thomas, James A., 1013

Tice, Richard L., 5355
Tichenor, Lisa, 9115
Tichenor, McHenry "Mac" T., Jr., 9115
Tichenor, McHenry "Taylor" T., III, 9115
Tichenor, Taylor, 9115
Ticketmaster Group, Inc., 1153
Tickle, John D., 9542
Ticktin, Richard M., 6393
Tidd, John, 3356
Tides Foundation, 3682, 6864
Tidewater Transit, 7225
Tidmarsh, Karen MaCausland, 7145
Tidwell, Doris H., 8459
Tidwell, Sharon L., 3523
Tiede, Rob, 8462
Tiedemann, Susan L., 9834
Tieken Charitable Lead Trust, Elizabeth Babson, 2883
Tieken, Nancy B., 2883
Tieken, Theodore D., Jr., 2883
Tieman, Douglas, 2476
Tienda, Marta, 6872
Tienor, Lawrence J., 1840
Tierney, Brian X., 7368
Tierney, Cathie, 9832
Tierney, Joseph E., III, 9921
Tierney, Karen E., 3513
Tierney, Kevin M., Sr., 4039
Tietze, Albert J., Jr., 8694
TIFF ARP III, 9916
Tiffany & Co., 6978
Tiffany, Bob, 415
Tifft, Douglas, 5804
Tiger Asia Management, 6090
Tiger Conservation Fund, 5545
Tigerman, Charles S., 917
Tighe, J. Hagood, 8468
Tighe, Jack, 8275
Tighe, Lisa, 4152
Tijerina, Hortensia C., 9234
Tijerina, Raul, Jr., 9234
Tilden Mining Co., 7407
Tilghman, Shirley M., 3833
Tillander, John, 6080
Tillander, Thomas, 6080
Tilleman, Paul J., 9841, 9935, 9951, 9952
Tilles, Cap Andrew, 4991
Tilley, Bruce, 9148
Tilley, Donna, 8546
Tillman, Brenda, 3354
Tillman, Michael, 2236
Tillotson, Sandra N., 9340
Tillou, Sandra S., 3791
Tillson, David, 6157
Tilman, Audrey, 2399
Tilney, Elizabeth A., 8916
Tilney, Katherine R., 4677
Tilos, Mari, 398
Tilos, Mari Grace, 398
Tilton, Sumner, 8405
Tilton, Sumner B., Jr., 4035, 4088, 4168
Timberlake, Laurel Sewell, 3575
Timberlake, William, 8473
Timberman, Terri L., 349
Timblin, Danny, 8634
Time Insurance Co., 5621
Time Warner Cable, 246
Time Warner Inc., 6982
Time, Inc., 7012
Timemax International, Ltd., 6651
Times Publishing Co., 2332
Times-World Corp., 9467
Timesworks Worldwide, 5981
Timken Co., The, 3188, 7683
Timken Company Charitable Trust of NH, 7683
Timken, Joy A., 7684
Timken, W. J., Jr., 7683
Timken, W. R., Jr., 7684
Timken, W.J., Jr., 7684
Timken, Ward J., 7684
Timm, Terry, 9956
Timmer, Steve, 7481
Timmerman, Tim, 8873
Timmins, Norm, 894
Timmons, Brenda, 2765
Timmons, Diane K., 7428
Timmons, Jr. Testamentary Charitable Lead Annuity Trust, William R., 8466
Timmons, Poe A., 7719
Timmons, William R., III, 8466
Tinanoff, Norman A., 4016
Tindall Corp., 4154
Tindol, Perry, 2433
Tiner, Stan, 4830
Ting, Carol, 1225
Tingley, Chad, 3180
Tingley, Tyler, 5995
Tinkelman, Steven, 5808
Tinker, Douglas, 334
Tinker, Edward Larocque, 6983
Tinkey, Jim, 3335
Tinkler, Philip, 3247
Tinnen, Brenda, 4920
Tinney, Barbara, 1600
Tinney, Linda, 8698
Tinnin, Derek, 7702
Tint, Barbara, 7844
Tint, Lawrence, 5345
Tipper, Charles F., 7549
Tipper, Katharine Nason, 7549
Tippetts, J. Edward, 921
Tippie, Henry, 2543
Tippit 1992 Charitable Lead Trust, 7685
Tippit, Carl J., 7685
Tips, Karen Kodosky, 8966
Tipsord, Michael L., 3174
Tipton, Dayle, 8734
Tipton, Gwen I., 3276
Tipton, Tracy, 3276
Tirre, Lois, 7287
Tirrell, David A., 661
Tirrell, Matthew V., 5912
Tisch Hotels, Inc., 6988
Tisch, Alice M., 6986
Tisch, Andrew H., 6388, 6987, 6988, 6992
Tisch, Ann R., 6987
Tisch, Bonnie J., 5844
Tisch, Daniel R., 5844, 6988, 6992
Tisch, Dean H., 2872
Tisch, Elizabeth S., 6984
Tisch, James S., 6988, 6989, 6992
Tisch, Joan H., 6984, 6985, 6988, 6990
Tisch, Jonathan M., 6984, 6988
Tisch, Laurence A., 5844, 6986, 6987, 6989
Tisch, Laurie M., 6988, 6990
Tisch, Merryl H., 6989
Tisch, Preston R., 6985
Tisch, Preston Robert, 6990
Tisch, Steven E., 6985, 6988, 6991
Tisch, Thomas J., 6986, 6988, 6992
Tisch, Wilma S., 5844, 6986, 6987, 6988, 6989, 6992
Tisdahl, Elizabeth, 2692
Tisdale, Stephen, 212
Tishman Family Foundation, 4298
Tishman Speyer Properties, LP, 6896
Tishman, Dan, 1512
Tishman, Daniel R., 6993
Tishman, Sheryl C., 6993
Tison, Anne Marie, 2481
Tison, Kelley H., 2481
Tisone, Joseph J., 2824
Tissot-Colle, Catherine, 7272
Tissue, Phillip, 9780
Titcomb, Daniel L., 4802
Titcomb, Frederick W., 4802
Titcomb, John W., Jr., 4802
Titley, Robert J.K., 6904
Titmus, Edward B., 9543
Titmus, Edward H., III, 9543
Titmus, Edward Hutson, Jr., 9543
Titmus, Edward Hutson, Sr., 9543
Titus, Brian, 3169
Titus, Rexford W., III, 9965
Titzman, Donna Marie, 9246
Tivadar Charitable Lead Trust, 6213
Tjian, Robert, 3818, 3833, 6333
TJX Cos., Inc., The, 4308
Toal, Margaret L., 122
Toan, Barrett, 5536
Tobbe, N., 7537
Toben, Steve, 536
Tober, Barbara, 6994
Tober, Donald G., 6994
Tobey, David, 2145
Tobias, David, 1708
Tobin Endowment, The, 9149
Tobin Trust, Robert Batts, 9236
Tobin, Alan J., 7643
Tobin, David J., 82
Tobin, Gail, 7496
Tobin, Haley, 1139
Tobin, John, 3994, 4516
Tobin, John H., 1616
Tobin, Joyce, 3994
Tobin, Mark, 1212
Tobin, Philip, 7496
Tobin, Robert L.B., 9236
Tobin, Steven, 1201
Tobin, Susannah Barton, 4211
Toblert, Bryan, 8883
Tobolowsky, George, 9297
Toburen, Jim, 4342
Tocci, Michele C., 5667
Tocker, Barbara, 9237
Tocker, Darryl, 9237
Tocker, Phillip, 9237
Tocker, Phillip, Mrs., 9237
Tocker, Robert, 9237
Tocker, Terry, 9237
Todd Established Foundation, Ruth Davis, 4992
Todd, Albert John, IV, 4507
Todd, Bob, 3503
Todd, Brynley Zorich, 9301
Todd, C. B., 8192
Todd, Chris, 1913
Todd, David M., 790
Todd, Jane B., 4507
Todd, Jeremy, 3403
Todd, Kristin, 1399
Todd, Mary, 1035
Todd, Rick, 1035
Todd, Sharon, 3503
Todd, Stephen J., 6567
Toebben, Del, 5036
Toele, Patience E., 4993
Toelle, Michael, 4636
Toepfer, Robert A., 9785
Tofle, Marla B., 959
Tognazzini, Roland, Jr., 1335
Toigo, Marla, 3390
Tointon, Betty L., 1513
Tointon, Bryan E., 1513
Tointon, Robert G., 1513
Tointon, William I., 1513
Tokarsky, Michelle, Esq., 7990
Tokioka, Franklin M., 2606
Tokioka, Lionel Y., 2606
Tokioka, Tyler M., 2606
Tokyo Club, 9587
Tol-O-Matic, 4777
Tolbert, Bernard A., 6913
Tolbert, Susan M., 3353
Toledo Edison Co., The, 7455
Tolefson, Darla, 9226
Tolf, Leslie A., 1953
Toll, Bruce E., 8316
Toll, Jennifer Bauer, 1543
Toll, Martha A., 1889
Toll, Robert I., 8317
Toll, Sylvia S., 8317
Tollefson, Bennett H., 2361
Tollefson, Darla, 8715
Tollefson, Louise B., 2361
Tollerson, Ernest, 5833
Tolley, Evangeline, 4984
Tolsma, Cynthia, 8046
Tolzin, Jeff R., 4648
Tom, Carol L., 2617
Tom, Cindy, 669
Tom, Kip, 3336
Tomarchio, Jack T., 8289
Tomasky, Susan, 7368
Tomassi, Kathy, 9999
Tombros, Ann C., 1707
Tombros, Peter G., 1707
Tomc, Richard W., 1630, 1644
Tomchin, Cheryl, 215
Tome, Jennifer, 7497
Tomei, Paula, 968
Tomera, Fred M., 3228
Tomich, Geraldine, 5134
Tomlin, Debora, 421
Tomlin, Richard E., Jr., 393, 5161
Tomlins, Paula, 3540
Tomlinson, Tommy, 4822
Tomorrow Foundation, The, 8586
Tompkins, Andy, 3524
Tompkins, Douglas R., 426, 542
Tompkins, Kristine M., 426
Tompkins, Kristine McDivitt, 542, 5733
Tompkins, Marjorie B., 5745
Tompkins, Maureen C., 2152
Tompkins, Mercedes, 3939
Tompkins, P. Kelly, 7407
Tompkins, Rachel, 6151
Tompkins, Richard, 7421
Tompkins, Sue, 2166
Tomsich, Robert J., 7625
Tonder, Daniel L., 4716
Toner, Kevin, 6214
Tonn, Sheri, 9750
Tonti, John E., 7640
Tontini, Nevio, 9604
Toohey, Linda G., 3458
Toohey, Maureen, 5168
Tooker Charitable Lead Annuity Trust, Gary L., The, 171
Tooker, Diane R., 171
Tooker, Gary L., 171

Tooker, Michael R., 171
Toole, James D., 154
Toole, James D., II, 154
Toole, James D., III, 154
Toole, Molly C., 154
Toole, Thomas D., 154
Toole, Timothy J., 154
Toone, Mark, 9354
Tootsie Roll Industries, Inc., 4249
Topa Insurance Group, 243
Topek, Nathan H., 8905
Topfer, Alan, 9239
Topfer, Angela, 9239
Topfer, Mort, 9239
Topfer, Morton, 9239
Topfer, Richard, 9239
Topham, Roy B., 8947
Toplitzky, Holly, 251
Topp, Richard, 4829
Topp, Robert E., 464
Topping, Robert G., 9559
Topps Us, 1850
Toran, Kay, 7876
Torbert, Clay, 19
Torbert, Dorothy Dann Collins, 8772
Torcivia, Benedict J., Jr., 5257
Torcivia, Benedict J., Sr., 5257
Torcivia, Joseph, 5257
Toren, Rob, 9725
Toretti, Christine J., 8266
Torgersen, Carolyn, 8475
Torgow, Gary, 4371
Tormey, Jill O'Donnell, 6912
Tormohlen, Tamara, 1368
Tornborg, Kay, 1252
Toro Co., The, 4780
Toro Development Company, 3878
Torrance, Mark, 9753
Torrance, Susan, 9753
Torres, Christine, 863
Torres, Ernest C., Hon., 8429
Torres, Esther B. Wiskemann, 908
Torres, Gerald, 1882
Torres, Margarita V., 1567
Torres, Robert, 8333
Torres, Wendel P., 1478
Torres-Barron, Benjamin, 9083
Torres-Spelliscy, Clara, 6477
Torrey, Kate, 7079
Torrington Area Foundation, 1558
Torrington Savings Bank, 1565
Torsone, Johnna G., 1674
Tortelli, Michele, 6489
Tortora, Leslie C., 6996
Tortorella, Vincent, 5791
Tortorelli, Joseph L., 1003
Tosh, Joseph N., II, 7934
Toshiba America, Inc., 6997
Toshiba Corporation, 6997
Total System Services, Inc., 2556
Toth, Kirstin S., 7465
Totusek, Jeffrey P., 5090
Touche, Peter, 5511
Touff, Michael, 1450
Tougas, Carol B., 361
Toulmin, Virginia B., 7687
Toulouse, Sarah, 7932
Toulouse, Srah, 7931
Touma, Douglas S., 4373
Toups, Roland M., 3613
Touro University, 3209
Tousley, Carol, 3469
Toussaint, Claudia S., 1542
Tow, Andrew, 1708
Tow, Claire, 1708
Tow, Frank, 1708
Tow, Leonard, 1708
Towbes, Gail, 1260
Towbes, Lynn C., 1260
Towbes, Michael, 1260
Towell, Todd, 1363
Tower Assocs., Peter, LP, 6999
Tower Bank, 3368
Tower Capital, LLC, 3715
Tower Land Co, LLC, 3619
Tower Living Trust, Peter, 7000
Tower Trust Company, 3382
Tower, Elizabeth C., 7000
Tower, Peter, 6999, 7000
Tower, Peter, Inc., 7000
Tower, Phil, 4452
Towerbrook Capital Partners LP, 7001
Towers, Katy, 2288
Towle, Christopher D., 4993
Towle, J. Ellwood, 4993
Towle, Robin D., 4993
Towle, Terri, 9832
Towler, Fred, 8585
Towler, Fred A., 8633
Towler, Jeri, 7742
Towler, Susan B., 2101
Towles, Amor, 6829
Towles, Amor H., 7043
Town Pump of Ennis, Inc., 5016
Town Pump of Northwest Missoula, Inc., 5016
Town Pump of Rocker, Inc., 5016
Town Pump of Townsend, Inc., 5016
Town, Cassandra, 9681
Town, Denice M., 9702
Towne, Curtis D., 3205
Townes, Charles H., 157
Townley, F. Bradford, 4114
Townley, Martha R. Gerry, 4114
Townsend, Camilla, 596
Townsend, Christopher, 6479
Townsend, John W., IV, 5579
Townsend, Margaret W., 8599
Townsend, Michele A., 1003
Townsend, Polly J., 8110
Townsend, Raymond C., 2515
Townsend, Rich, 1650
Townsend, Robert, 4395
Townsend, Ronald, 7202
Townsend, Tyler A., 2438
Townsley, Karen, 4468
Towsley, Margaret D., 4557
Towson, G. Edward, II, 7182
Toy, Andrew, 8175
Toyoda Machinety USA, 4779
Toyota Financial Svcs., 783
Toyota Motor Manufacturing North America, Inc., 7002
Toyota Motor Sales, U.S.A., Inc., 7002
Tozer, David, 4782
TP Land, LLC, 62
TPE Inc., 6450
TPG Axon Capital, 6898
TPG Holding LP, 6898
Trace Foundation, 6005, 7010
Tracey, Martha C., 7746
Trachimowicz, Richard J., 1682
Trachtenberg, Ilene C., 9554
Tracy Fund, Emmet and Frances, 4558
Tracy Industries, Inc., 4558
Tracy, Alex, 3189
Tracy, Cynthia, 4558
Tracy, Don, 3189
Tracy, Elizabeth L., 1449
Tracy, Erma Jean, 4558
Tracy, Jane, 3189
Tracy, Linda, 3189
Tracy, Liz, 3189
Tracy, Michael, 3781
Tracy, Philip R., 7164
Tracy, Rob, 3189
Tracy, Sr. Survivor's Trust, Thomas J., 4558
Tracy, Thomas J., 4558
Tradewind Capital Group Inc., 2606
Trading Partners I, 1930
Trading Partners II, 1930
Traeger, Michele O'Shaughnessy, 4734
Traeger, Peter A., 2818
Trafelet, Remy W., 6160
Trafton, Adelaide F., 8049
Trafton, Peter, 7915
Traggio, Anna, 7478
Traggio, Anna L., 7476
Trahan, Anne, 4344
Trainer, B. Douglas, 8234
Trainer, Francis H., 5825
Trainer, Francis H., Jr., 5825
Trainer, Jeanne A., 5825
Trainor, Cassandra, 335
Trainor, Rhonda, 8495
Trammell, Ann Gordon, 8853
Trammell, Harper B., 8853
Tran, Minh, 7285
Trandahl, Jeff, 5608
Trandotcom Solutions, 8834
Tranel, Inc., 6741
Trani, Carol A., 6098
Trani, John M., 6098
Trannel, Jerald A., 2872
Tranquada, Robert E., 611, 1013
Transammonia, Inc., 6907
Transcontinental Realty Investors, Inc., 385
Transmerica Financial Life Insurance Co., 3409
Transnetyx, 8579
Transport, Robyn S., 6785
Trant, Pat, 3403
Tranter, Thomas, Jr., 5804
Trapani, Kevin, 7138
Trapasso, Joseph "Jody", 4366
Trapp, Ann, 9768
Trask, Grover, Hon., 419
Traub, Barry, 1797
Traub, Bernadette, 1815
Traub, Jean, 9380
Traub, Lester G., 135
Traub, Marjorie, 1797
Traubert, Brian S., 3096
Traubert, Bryan, 3098
Traubert, Bryan S., 3098, 3172
Traugott, Joe, 5520
Trautman, David, 7540
Trautman, David L., 7610
Trautman, Dawn M., 1003
Trautmann, Kristy, 8043
Travelers Companies, Inc., The, 4783
Travelli Trust, Emma R., 4310
Travelli, Charles I., 4310
Travelli, Emma R., 4310
Traver, Charles, 4316
Travers, Charles N., 1261
Travers, Elizabeth, 1261
Travers, Gayle, 1261
Travers, Martin, 5437
Travers, Todd, 1261
Travinsky, Kathleen B., 5229
Travis, Anne, 4816
Travis, Carol, 5807
Travis, Dempsey J., 7004
Travis, Jeanette, 8637
Travis, John C., 2634
Travis, June, 1399
Travis, Moselynne E., 7004
Travis, Robert, 5726
Travis, Tracey, 6408
Travis, Tracy, 6651
Trawick, Carol, 3898
Trawick, James, 3898
Trawick, Ken W., 9117
Traylor Brothers, Inc., 293
Traylor, Michael T., 293
Traylor, Travis, Jr., 8716
Traylor, Wilhelmina B., 9000
Traynham, Andrew, 9768
Traynor, Michael, 2548
Treacy Co., 5017
Treacy, Dennis H., 9535
Treadway, Brandy, 9089
Treadwell Charitable Trust, Nora Eccles, 1262
Treadwell, Joseph, 71
Treadwell, Pam, 7742
Treakle, Kay, 9640
Tredway, Dana, 1528
Tredway, Doug, 1392
Tredway, Phillip M., 8200
Treeger, Thomas C., 6944
Trees Trust, Edith L., 8319
Trees, George S., Jr., 2747
Trefz, Christian C., 1709
Trefz, Ernest C., 1709
Trefz, Joan M., 1709
Trefz, Linda M., 1709
Trefz, Paul D., 1709
Trego, Mary, 8669
Tregoning, Daniel K., 3758
Trehan, Ranvir, 9544
Treiber, John, 6681
Treiber, John A., 9951
Treiber, Phillip J., 9951
Treier, Merike, 6049
Treiger, Irwin L., 9725
Treiger, Louis, 9727
Treister, Diane, 396
Tremaine, Burton G., III, 1710
Tremaine, Burton G., Jr., 1710
Tremaine, Burton G., Sr., 1710
Tremaine, Emily Hall, 1710
Tremaine, John M., 1710
Tremaine, John M., Jr., 1710
Tremaine, Sarah C., 1710
Tremaine, Susan C., 1710
Tremblay, Diane D., 4442
Tremblay, Wade, 9506
Trembly, Jeff, 9916
Tremondt, Mary J., 2904
Trenary, Bradford, 9711
Trenary, Lloyd R., 7767
Trent, B. Keith, 7196
Trent, Ken, 9866
Trent, Thomas, 3281
Trenz, Alan R., 7418
Tressider, Susan Jackson, 8047
Tressler, Connie, 7972
Tressler, Trinna, 1423
Treumper, Mark, 2811
Treutel, David, Jr., 4830
Trevelyan-Hall, Kate, 904
Trew, Betsie, 8332

Trexler, Harry C., 8320
Trexler, Mary M., 8320
Treyball, Inc., 1184
Trezise, Robert L., Jr., 4357
Tri State Quality Ford Dealers, 7012
Trianfo, Victor, Dr., 7416
Triangle Towers LLC, 9452
Triangle Trust, 6707
Triano, Victoria, The Rev., 1564
Triantafillopoulos, Nick, 7601
Tribble, J. Lee, 2579
Tribull, Cynthia, 611
Tribune-Star Publishing Co., 3327
Trice, Thomas L., IV, 3814
Trice, Win, 3851
Tricon Global Restaurants, Inc., 3608
Trieu, Elizabeth, 9115
Trigeant, Ltd., 8936
Trimble, Arch E., III, 8614
Trimble, Joan W., 1541
Trinchero, Lilli, 5108
Trinity GST Exempt Trust, 1493
Trinity Logistics Corp., 2397
Tripeny, Tony, 5804
Triple C Securities & Investment Ltd., 8754
Triple Five VIII, LLC, 5274
Triplet Investments Co., LLC, 5228
Triplett, Deborah, 1035
Triplett, R. Faser, 4837
Triplett, Tim, 1035
Triplett, Vera, Dr., 3656
Triplett-Brady, Sheila, 7160
Tripp, Ann K., 4086
Tripp, Valerie, 9937
Tritsch, Mary Jane, 7785, 7817
Tritsch, Robert C., 7817
Triumph MC LP, 8680
Trivette, Christen S., 9536
Trochet, Glennah, 378
Trock, Tamara L., 2836
Troderman, Diane, 4080
Trojanowski, Robert S., 1564
Tromberg, Bruce, 685
Trone, David, 3899
Trone, David J., 3899
Trone, Julia E., 3899
Trone, June, 3899
Trone, June S., 3899
Trone, Michelle C., 3899
Trone, Natalie R., 3899
Troop, Keith, M.D., 7798
Tropical Foods, 1771
Tropin, Kathleen O., 1663
Tropin, Kenneth G., 1663
Troska, Patrick J., 4741
Trosky, Ben, 1037
Trost, Cathy, 1907
Trost, Charles A., 8550
Trotman, Mark, 3521
Trott, Byron D., 3192
Trott, James C., 8650
Trott, Tina L., 3192
Trotta, F.P., 1628
Trotta, Frank, 1628
Trotter, James B., 2434
Trotter, John, 744
Trotter, Mark C., 1012
Trottier, David, 7357
Troubetzkoy Trust, Ms., 7678
Troubh, Jean L., 6632
Trout, Kenny, 5047
Trout, Lisa, 5047
Trout, Ltd., 8648
Troutman, Deanna, 7704
Trowbridge, Alice, 8040
Trowbridge, Katie, 2806
Troxel, David B., 471
Troxel, Douglas D., 1386
Troxel, Kenneth D., 1386
Troxel, Michael Douglas, 1386
Troxel, Sergei George, 1386
Troxell, William, 6876
Troy Financial Corp., 7006
Troy Savings Bank, The, 7006
Troy, Elizabeth Thornton, 1252
Troy, Ronnie, 3539
Troyer, Julie, 3390
TRT Equity Advisors, LLC, 9141
TRT Holdings, Inc., 9141
Truck Rental Co., 2444
Trudell, Cynthia M., 6627
True Oil LLC, 9995
True, Bill, 9765
True, Calvin E., 3703
True, H. A., III, 9995
True, H. A., Jr., 9995
True, H.A., III, 9995
True, Jean D., 9995
True, Lawrence, 1951, 9754
Trueb, Martin, 8403
Truemper, Mark E., 2767
TrueNorth Companies, 3449
Truist, 7638
Truitt, Michael P., 3760
Truland Systems Corp., 9545
Truland, Mary W., 9545
Truland, Robert W., 9545
Trulaske Charitable Trust No. 1, R.J. Trulaske, Sr. & G.M., 4995
Trulaske, Sarah, 4995
Trull, Florence M., 9240
Trull, R. Scott, 9240
Trull, R.B., 9240
Trulock, James, 3317
Truman, Darlene, 9775
Truman, Mildred Faulkner, 7007
Trumble, Susan McCune, 900
Trumbull, Margaret, 4565
Trump Park Ave., LLC, 7008
Trump, Donald J., 7008
Trump, Donald J., Jr., 7008
Trump, Eric F., 7008
Trump, Ivanka M., 7008
Trunek, Bob, 9759
Truong, Martin, 4985
Trust A U/A of Ellison S. Mckissick, Jr., 8486
Trust Co. of Connecticut, 1609
Trust Co. of Oklahoma, The, 7775
Trust Co. of Sterne, Agee and Leach, The, 21
Trust Company of Oklahoma, The, 7732, 7803
Trust Company of Vermont, 9359
Trust For Alfie, 4007
Trust Point, 9853
Trust Point Inc., 9807
Trust, David, 5189
Trust, Diane, 5189
Trust, Laura, 5189
Trust, Lewis Elkins, 8175
Trust, Martin, 5189
Trustco Bank, 6802
Trustees of the Eastern Star Hall, 5927
Trustmark Insurance Co., 3193
Trustmark National Bank, 71
Trusty, David, 7285
TRW Charitable Annuity Remainder Trust, 9253
Trzcinski, Cheryl, 7689
Trzcinski, Ronald, 7689
Tsang, Chui L., 841
Tschanz, Melissa, 5108
Tschirhart, Mary, 3132
Tse, Stephen, 1103
Tseng, Vivian, 6093
TSI Holding Co., 4908
Tsimbinos, John M., 6543
Tsokris, Sue, 6627
Tsoumas, Richard, 4350
Tsoumas, Richard M., 4474
Tsui, John K., 2596, 9971, 9972
Tsuji, Ryohei, Ph.D., 9881
Tsujii, Tim, 7180
Tsuruta, Naoki, 6490
TT Trust, The, 4483
TTC, 7425
Tu, Darwin, 721
Tu, John, 1265
Tu, Mary, 1265
Tubb, Marilyn, 2036
Tubbs, Barbara, 7993
Tubergen, Jerry L., 4398, 4399, 4400, 4418, 4559, 4572
Tubergen, Marcia D., 4559
Tuchman, Debra Mautner, 1514
Tuchman, Kenneth D., 1514
Tuck, Kenneth, 9415
Tuck, Lucy, 3226
Tucker Foundation, Max and Rose, 7896
Tucker, Bruce R., 1759
Tucker, Carol, 3709
Tucker, Donald F., 4451
Tucker, Elmer D., 9320
Tucker, Eva Camunez, 9241
Tucker, Greg, 3409
Tucker, James, Rep., 3612
Tucker, Lane, 79
Tucker, Larry C., 9398
Tucker, Mary M., 24
Tucker, Robert A., 1759
Tucker, Rose E., 7896
Tucker, Royster, 7231
Tucker, Ruth, 1244
Tucker, Scott, 3335
Tucker, Stacy, 105
Tucker, William E., 8730
Tucker, William H., 2434
Tuckey, Leigh H., 9844
Tudor Arbitrage Partners, 1711
Tudor Group Holdings, LLC, 1711
Tudor Investment Corp., 1711
Tudor Proprietary Trading, LLC, 1711
Tudor, Fiona, 1063
Tudor, Katherine J., 8638
Tudzin, Ellis, 8936
Tuegel, William, 3845
Tuel, Leslie, 1200
Tuetken, Doug, 3426
Tufano, Paul A., 8106
Tuffli, Don L., 1266
Tuffli, Martha T., 1266
Tuft, Diane H., 7011
Tuft, Thomas E., 7011
Tufts, 3953
Tufts, Patrick, 8397
Tuggle, Charles T., Jr., 8565
Tuggle, Clyde C., 2428
Tuggle, Reginald, 6681
Tuininga, Heather, 9674
Tulalip Tribes Charitable Fund, 9652
Tulaney, Thomas P., 8227
Tulchinsky, Igor, 1726
Tulchinsky, Mina Joy, 1726
Tulipana, Peter, 3447
Tull Metal and Supply Co., J.M., Inc., 2561
Tull, Doug, 8797
Tull, J.M., 2561
Tullar, Jill, 3277
Tullgren, Estella, 179
Tullis, Jon, 9612
Tullius, Raymond L., Jr., 7770
Tully, Sally Gipson, 6977
Tulsky, James A., 6105
Tung, Glenn, 8383
Tung, Joseph, 711
Tung, Sherif, 711
Tunick, Andrew J., 6261
Tunick, Carrie Elston, 6663
Tunney, Christine, 2811
Tunquist, Eric, 736
Tuohy, Alice Tweed, 1267
Tuohy, Sean, 8610
Tupancy, Oswald A., 4312
Tupper, Christopher, 4109
Tupper, Helen "Cricket", 4109
Tupper, Margaret C., 1565
Tupperware Brands Corp., 2363, 6532
Tupperware U.S., Inc., 2363
Turani, Will, 9773
Turchiano, Dayvin, 1114
Turcik, John J., 8173
Turcotte, Jean Claire, 8768
Turer, Clarice Soref, 9805
Turer, Harris J., 9805
Turino, Mary, 1815
Turino, William, 1815
Turissini, Christina H., 1418
Turkel, Bruce, 2238
Turley, Elizabeth C., 9198
Turley, Stewart, 1518
Turman, John, 7825
Turmon, Henry, 1980
Turn 2 Enterprises, Inc., 7012
Turn 2, Inc., 7012
Turnage, Roxanne, 442, 1299
Turnas, Jeff, 9276
Turnbow, Walter, 186
Turnbull, Paula E., 4183
Turner 97 Trust, Harry M., 7691
Turner Construction Co., 4041, 5482
Turner for Employees/Guests, 5482
Turner, Barbara, 8946
Turner, Barbara A., 2562
Turner, Beau, 2563
Turner, Bernard, 5334
Turner, Betty M., 8632
Turner, Billy G., 2438
Turner, Cal, Sr., 8639
Turner, Caroline, 7276
Turner, Carolyn, 8321
Turner, Christi, 8641
Turner, Courtney S., 9242
Turner, D.A., 2414
Turner, Deborah F., 8550
Turner, Donna, 2792, 4640
Turner, Elizabeth B., 2414
Turner, Greg, 3422
Turner, H. Callister, Jr., 8640
Turner, Hoyt J., 2562
Turner, Hurley C., III, 8640
Turner, Isla Carroll, 9203
Turner, Jack B., 8550
Turner, James C., 2562

Van Cleave, Paul R., 7025
Van Clief, Mary Ann, 5419
Van Cott, Eleanor, 1267
Van Daele Family Trust, Mike and Linda, 1281
Van Daele, Linda, 1281
Van Daele, Mike, 1281
Van de Wal, Eve, 5805
Van den Bergh Foods Co., 5484
Van Der Hyde, Whitney M., 1672
Van Deuren, Richard A., 9880
Van Devender, Mollie M., 4847
Van Devender, William J., 4847
van Dijk, Pieter Eenkema, 1715
Van Dijk-Francois, Yvette Eenkema, 1715
Van Dongen, Robert, 4571
Van Doren, James E., 4531
Van Dusen, Amanda, 4463
Van Dusen, Barbara C., 4371
Van Dyck, Mary Liz, 4211
Van Dyke, James L, 9442
Van Dyke, Kathryn, 9921
Van Dyke, Polly H., 9921
Van Dyke, William D., 9921
Van Dyke, William D., III, 9921
Van Eekeren, Bridget, 3202
Van Eekeren, David, 3202
Van Eekeren, Donna, 3202
Van Eekeren, Kevin, 3202
Van Eekeren-Sharpe, Kathryn, 3202
Van Ekeren, Philip T., 3428
Van Elslander, Archie A., 4569
Van Elslander, Debra A., 4569
Van Elslander, Kenneth, 4569
Van Elslander, Mary Ann, 4569
Van Every, Philip, 7329
Van Fossen, E. Jane, 7431
van Gorden, Mary, 9896
Van Gordon, Mary, 9895
Van Gorp, Stacy, 3461
Van Handel, Michael J., 9899
Van Haren, W. Michael, 4579
van Heck, Deb, 4402
Van Hengel, Drusilla R., 6903
Van Hoene, William A., Jr., 2827
van Hoof, J., 1614
Van Horn, Stacy, 3865
Van Houten, Amy, 4972
Van Houten, Stella C., 7330
Van Huss, Edith H.L., 375
Van Kampen, Judith, 2872
Van Kampen, Robert, 2872
Van Kampen-Pierre, Karla, 2872
Van Konynenburg, Claire, 1282
Van Konynenburg, D. Michael, 1282
Van Lee, Reggie, 6408
van Loben Sels, Ernst D., 1283
Van Lopik, William Harold, 9910
Van Milligen, Nancy, 3421
Van Natta, Jennifer M., 720
Van Nelson, Robert, 4646
Van Ness, Paula, 1566
Van Noord, Andrew, 4571
Van Noord, Gladys, 4571
Van Nortwick, Terry, 2036
Van Nuys Trust, Emily, 1284
Van Nuys Trust, J. Benton, 1284
Van Nuys, Emily, 1284
Van Nuys, J. Benton, 1284
Van Orden, Alan, 2632
Van Osdol, John, 2796
Van Ranst, Al, 3956
Van Ribbink, Steve, 2604
Van Riper, Carolyn Dircks, 5241
Van Riper, Jeffrey L., 6832
Van Rossum, Anton, 6007
van Scherrenburg, May, 932
Van Scoyoc, Sandi, 5175
Van Sickle Trust, Hettie, 5155
Van Sickle Trust, Jack, 5155
van Straaten, Tom, 1368
Van Tassel, Ann, 4369
Van Velson, Glenn, 5068
Van Vleck, James, 2031
Van Vleet, Harriet Smith, 2368
Van Voorhis, John A., 2369
Van Voorhis, Julie A., 2369
Van Voorhis, Samuel D., 2369
Van Vugt, Eric J., 9926
Van Waeyenberge, Piet Baron, 6007
Van Wagoner, Randy, 5805
Van Winkle, Barbara, 3759
Van Winter, Jerrold A., 3901
van Wyngarden, Allison, 3486
Van Zante, Mary A., 3473
Van, Sue, 2047, 2048
Vana, Kent, 4393
Vanatta, Pam, 1528
Vanberg Charitable Lead Trust, Harold, 9247
Vanberg, Anne M., 9247
Vanberg, Harold E., Sr., 9247
Vance, Brian, 9605
Vance, Douglas B., 4372
Vance, Douglass A., 309
Vance, James J., 9845
Vance, Lucy C., 2573
Vance, Patricia H., 8294
Vance, Robert C., 8450
Vance, Tim, 7421
VanCura, Sam, 7630
Vandemark, Jim, 7412
vanden Heuvel, Melinda Fuller, 5172
Vanden Heuvel, Wendy, 6640
Vandenberg, Anne, 3422
Vandenberg, Bill, 1419
Vander Haar, Anne, 871
Vander Hart, Ginny, 4398, 4399, 4418
Vander Lans, Judy, 846
Vander Leest, Mary, 4775
Vander Maten, Larry D., 4989
Vander Ploeg, Mark, 3171
Vander Zanden, Dave, 9832
Vanderbilt, Hugh B., Jr., 7331
Vanderbilt, Paul, 7331
Vanderheiden, Deb, 5045
Vanderhoef, Eunice Taylor, 4112
Vanderhoef, Sheila, 3974
Vanderhoof, Joe, 5806
Vanderkloot, Barbara Block, 2701
Vanderkloot, Mathew, 2701
Vanderkolk, Jon, 4402
Vanderkolk, Lisa, 4402
Vanderkooi, Joel, 4473
Vanderlaan, Michelle, 3061
VanderRoest, Stan M., 4443
Vanderslice, Michael, 8698
Vanderslice, Vicki, 8698
Vandervalk, James M., 5398
Vanderveen, Debra, 4393
Vanderweide, Hannah J., 4572
Vanderweide, Katelyn S., 4572
Vanderweide, Suzanne C. Devos, 4572
Vanderweide, Suzanne DeVos, 4572
Vandevelde, Doug, 4475
VanDeventer, Larry, 5162
Vandever, James D., 1004
VanDuyne, AnnMarie, 4372
Vanech, Dean N., 5487
Vanech, Denise, 5487
VanEtten, Donald, 6721
VanEtten, Jack, 3354
VanGelder, Kim, 6722
Vanguard, 9916
Vanguard Charitable Endowment Program, 2296
Vanguard Group, 8136
Vanguard Group, Inc., The, 8327
Vanguard Group, The, 8289
Vanguard Intermediate Tax Exempt Fund, 4254
VanHaren, Julie M., 9227
VanHaren, Shirley, 4381
Vanhatten, Mary, 5711
Vanhoose, Robert W., 3604
VanHouten Minogue, Karen, 5806
VanHoy, Henry P., 7188
VanHuss, Susie H., 8468
Vankavage, Ledy, 5601
VanMeter, Griffin, 3560
Vann, Aurom R., 5813
Vann, Avrom, 5813
Vann, E.J., IV, 2437
Vann, Thomas H., Jr., 2572
Vannatta, Mark E., 7551
Vanneck, Barbara Bailey, 2370
Vanneck, John, 2370
Vanneck, William P., 2370
Vanni d'Archirafi, Francesco, 5780
Vanosdol, Thomas G., 3305
Vanosky, Robert, 1053
Vansessen, Kimberly, 3355
Vapor Thrift Stores, 62
Varady, Eric, 1121
Varela, Kathryn Lewis, 2980
Varet, David R., 6483
Varet, Elizabeth R., 6483, 7913
Varet, Joseph R., 6483
Varet, Michael A., 5589, 6483
Varet, Sarah R., 6483
Varey, Downey R., 3113
Vargas, Adrienne, 1108
Vargas, Belen, 1307
Vargas, Bogen, 6099
Vargas, Carmen M., 8825
Vargas, Marcos, 900
Vargas, Sandra L., 4792
Vargas, Sandy L., 4714
Varian, Nancy A., 7673
Varki Investments, Inc., 1369
Varley, Molly McGlynn, 4706
Varma, Vivek, 9742
Varmus, Harold, 9625
Varnell, Henry, 8584
Varnell, Jeanne, 8584
Varner, Pamela, 8364
Varner, Sean, 419
Varney, Kerry, 1236
Varns Investments, Ltd., 6779
Varnum, Philip, 7865
Varoquiers, Carrie J., 903
Vars, Amy S., 6722
Vartanian, Christabel, 2181
Varus Trust, The, 6779
Vary, George, 7349
Vasan, Regina B., 3837
Vasan, Usha, Dr., 9789
Vasel, Marta, 8718
Vasoli, Sandra C., 8199
Vasquez, Carlos J., 3085
Vasquez, Dolores, 9060
Vasquez, Felicia & Virginia, 7659
Vasquez, Francisco, Ph.D., 5801
Vasquez, Gilbert R., 809
Vasquez, Misael, 720
Vasquez, Ricardo A., 5745
Vasseur, Ernest, 2900
Vassiliou, Ann, 3472
Vasudevan, Damayanti P., 2801
Vaswani, Sanjay, 1166
Vath, Bradley, 7569
Vatnsdal, Lisa, 7351
Vatterott, Joan M., 2371
Vatterott, John C., 2371, 7560
Vatterott, John C., Jr., 2371
Vatterott, Patrick, 2371
Vatterott, Timothy, 2371
Vaughan, Chris, 4340
Vaughan, Curtis T., III, 8806
Vaughan, Frances, 617, 4421
Vaughan, Frances E., 4420
Vaughan, Jennie, 3278
Vaughan, Patricia A., 8946
Vaughan, Shirley, 8946
Vaughan, Timothy R., 3236
Vaughn, Cathryn E., 5164
Vaughn, David, 417
Vaughn, Doug, 3283
Vaughn, Edgar H., 3203
Vaughn, John, 2074
Vaughn, Lashell, 8549
Vaughn, Lillie Mae, 3203
Vaughn, Mark D., 5920
Vaughn, Robert W., 2811
Vaughn-Fowler, John Brandan, 4178
Vaupel, Ronald, 4454
Vavyad, Keren Klein, 1648
Vawter, Paul E., 1713
Vaysee, Anne B., 6636
Vaysse, Jacques, 6636
Vaysse, Jacques B., 6636
Vazouez, Carlos, 3085
Vazquez, Alani, 246
Vazquez, Desiree, 6967
Vazquez, George, 8613
Vazquez, Gilbert, 6133
Vazquez-Dedelow, Alexis, 3337
VBS Holdings LLC, 5228
Veale, Carolyn, 3277
Veale, Harriet Ernst, 7694
Veale, Tinkham, II, 7694
Vear, Tom, 4495
Veasey, Zoe, 4316
Veazey, Samuel J., 7743
Vecchie-Campbell, Donn, 3285
Vectren Corp., 3394
Veden Trust, Frank, 4787
Veeder, Sybil P., 7966
Veeser, Peggy I., 8530
Vega-Marquis, Luz, 9596
Vega-Pestana, Miguel, 9625
Vegesna, Anatakoti Raju, 1286
Vegesna, Bala, 1286
Veilbell, Cody, 9354
Veitch, Christopher O., 1001
Veitch, Frederick A., III, 1499
Veitch, Heather K., 1499
Veitch, Julie, 1001
Veitch, Kelly A., 1499
Veitch, Robert D., 1499
Veitch, Sally Louise, 1499
Velamoor, Sesh, 9622
Velasco, Caridad, 1983
Velasco, Horacio Matta, 5222
Velaski, Paul, 1166

Velasquez, Amy, 2439
Velasquez, Carmen, 2673
Velasquez, Christian A., 4405
Velasquez, Erika R., 3536
Velay, Christophe, 7022
Velay, Christopher J., 6612
Velay, Frances A., 6612, 7022
Veld Kamp, Theresa, 1220
Velde, Gretchen Swanson, 5087, 5088
Veldkamp, Arnold, 1220
Veldman, Anita, 3259
Veldman, Anita J., 3259
Veldman, Peter, 3259
Veldman, Thomas F., 3259
Veldman, Wilma, 3259
Velie, Carroll, 4439
Vella, James G., 4430
Vella, Nancy M., 3010
Veller, Kevin S., 9373
Vellines, Wilson F., Jr., 9412
Velo, Kenneth J., 2783
Velsicol Corporation, 3111
Velux Trust, The, 6679
Vena, Charlotte, 2154
Venhuizen, John, 3040
Veniskey, David P., 6722
Venkataraman, Bala, 7704
Venkatesan, Ravi, 6724
Venker, Thomas E., Jr., 4901
Vento, Maria Lopez, 9810
Ventura Foods, 9837
Venture Strategy Group, 1268
Venturella, John, 7570
Ventures, Seneca, 6762
Veon, Greg, 3457
Ver Brugge, William, 9973
Vera, Francesca, 417
Vera, George, 582
Vera, John R., 417
Vera, Ronald T., 365
Verble, Kay W., 2325
Verdin, Mary, 1110
Verdone, Martha, 3994
Verdoorn, Carol, 4788
Verdoorn, Daryl, 4788
Verdoorn, Daryl R., 4788
Verdoorn, Jay, 4788
Verdoorn, Jeff, 4788
Verduzco, Joseph, 3306
Vereb, Karen A., 7554, 7555, 7556
Vergara Trust, Lamar Bruni, 8880
Vergara, Lamar Bruni, 9249
Verhasselt, Randy P., 9834
Verhulp, Linda, 939, 940
Vering, Toni, 5039
Verizon Communications Inc., 5489
Verkaik, Brett, 2743
Verkamp, John R., 7653
Verme, Alberto, 5780
Vermeer Farms, Inc., 3486
Vermeer Manufacturing Co., 3486
Vermeer, David, 3486
Vermeer, Lois J., 3486
Vermeer, Matilda, 3486
Vermeer, Robert, 3486
Vermeer, Tricia, 3486
Vermer, Cendrine, 8495
Vermeulen, Steven, 7607
Vermie, Craig, 3449
Vermie, Craig D., 3409
Vermillion, Bill, 7824
Vermillion, Dennis, 9576
Vermillion, Rod, 7824
Vermilye, W. Moorhead, 3851
Verner, Elizabeth H., 4846
Verner, Myrna, 9219
Verney, E. Geoffrey, 3990
Vernof, Ruben R., 2694
Vernon, Joe, 8899
Vernon, Miles Hodsdon, 7026
Vernon, Molly, 2159
Vero Beach Florida 32963, 2183
Veron, Heidi, 4965
Veroneau, Vincent P., 3680
Verplank, Monica, 4446
Versa Cace Inc., 8527
Verslues, Ernie, 4943
Versluis, Joyce, 4465
Versten, E., 3025
Vertuca, Jeff, 478
Vescovo, Stephen W., 8630
Vesledahl, Dale, 4796
Veson, Eva D., 6681
Vesper Corp., 7695
Vespoli, Leila L., 7455
Vessey, Michael, 402
Vest, Lee Diane Collins, 7836
Vestal, Richard, 5309
Vester, Linda J., 6102
Veth, Debra, 4105
Vetlesen, George Unger, 7027
Vetlesen, Maude Monell, 6497
Vetter Holding, Inc, 5091
Vetter Leasing Services, 5091
Vetter, Denith D., 5091
Vetter, Eldora D., 5091
Vetter, Jack D., 5091
Vetter, Roman, 9869
Vetter, Todd, 5091
Vettori, Diane S. A., Hon., 7415
Vezeris, David J., 5837
VF Services, 1850
VF Services, Inc., 7638
Vh Arquitectos Asociados Sa De Cv M, 8834
VHA Gulf States, 9250
VHA Inc., 9250
VHA Southeast, 9250
Via Chip Technologies, Inc., 514
Vice, Cynthia M., 18
Vicente, Harriet G., 7029
Vick, Patricia P., 861
Vick, Ross, 9115
Vickar, L. Kerry, 7333
Vickar, Simone D., 7333
Vickerman, Sue, 9605
Vickers, Clark L., 1407
Vickers, Guy, 6637
Vickter Trust, David, 1289
Vickter, David, 1289
Victory Memorial Park Foundation, 5209
Victory Wind-Down Company, 2900
Vidal, Kara K., 8958
Vidalakis, George N., 1290
Vidalakis, John N., 1290
Vidalakis, Nancy G., 1290
Vidalakis, Nick S., 1290
Vidalakis, Nicole N., 1290
Vidalakis, Perry N., 1290
Videla, Ignacio, 1521
Video Indiana, Inc., 7719
Video Industrial Services, 2735
Video Pipe Services, 2735
Viebig, V. Richard, Jr., 8681
Viehland, Thomas, 2838
Vienna Beef, 9837
Vienna Park LLC, 9452
Viera, Antonio Escudero, 8353
Viera, Beatrice F. "Bia", 8221
Vierk, Rich, 5063
Vierk, Richard J., 5031
Viersen, Sam K., Jr., 7808
Vietor, Lynn A., 714
Vietor, Vera P., 714
Viets, Hermann, 9880
Vig, Ritu, 3244
Vigdor, Justin, 5591
Vigdor, Robert, 5591
Vigeland, Julie, 7855
Viglio, Howard Martin, 4178
Vigness, Mary Katherine, 9115
Vignos, Edith Ingalls, 7503
Vigoda, Robert A., 4056
Vigue, Peter G., 3683
Vijay, Madhu, 1003
Vijayakumar, James, 4432
Viking Global Investors LP, 1717
Vila, Bob, 5987
Vila, Christopher, 5987
Vilcek, Jan, 7031
Vilcek, Marica, 7031
Vill, Carrie, 4565
Villa, Daniel, 6285
Villa, David, 9596
Villafranco, William S., 7687
Village Pantry, 7214
Villages of Hope Africa, 9118
Villagra, Victor, M.D., 1567
Villaire, Michael, 722
Villani, Allison, 4609
Villanueva, Maritza Rojas de, 8708
Villanueva, Marland, 3319
Villari, Alexander, 5718
Villarosa, Lorelei, 6151
Villarreal, Lydia M., 727
Villasuso, Raul, 3228
Villegas, Luis, 1116
Villeneuve, James, 4853
Villenueve, James, 3714
Villere, St. Denis J., 3631
Villone, Heather, 7289
Villone, Rich, 7289
Vilmure, Richard, 953
Vinardi, John J., 4640
Vinay, Michael, 7382
Vincent Foundation, Thomas J., 2619
Vincent, Anne B., 1852
Vincent, C. Alec, 8706
Vincent, Edward, 1852
Vincent, James L., 4315
Vincent, Loree A., 1818
Vincent, Richard A., 7605
Vincent, Steve, 9576
Vincent, Thomas J., 2619
Vincent, Valerie, 1852
Vincent, William, 1852
Vincente Revocable Trust, Harriet, 7029
Vincer, Julia, 3011
Vinciguerra, Maggie, 5803
Viner, Edward, 5345
Viney, Jo, 8363
Vineyard, Sinskey, 1174
Viniar, Barbara A., 3851
Vinik, Jeffrey N., 2372
Vinik, Mary Penny, 2372
Vining, Dick, 3396
Vining, James L., 8549
Vinitsky, Elyse, 3730
Vinnell, Wilhelmina McLane, 7566
Vinney, Betty De, 8634
Vinolus, Peter A., 6913
Vinovich, William N., 3255
Vinson, Benjamin, 55
Vinson, Frank B., Jr., 55
Vinson, Kenneth G., 55
Viola, Roger K., 3552
Violet, John R., 472
Violich, Deanne Gillette, 1335
Vion-Hasenaur, Cheryl, 7374
Viotti, Dave, 1873
Viragh Foundation, Skip, 5135
Viragh, Albert P., 3902
Viragh, Katherine A., 3902, 5135, 5156
Viragh, Mark S., 3902, 5135, 5156
Viragh, Robert J., 3902
Virden, Mary Lee J., 9201
Virgin, Tom, 3277
Virginia Capital Bancshares, Inc., 9436
Virginia Scrap Iron & Metal Co., Inc., 9443
Virginian-Pilot, The, 9467
Virgne, Joanna Ford, 4560
Virkler, Laura H., 5339
Virmani, Yash Paul, 8933
Viropharma Inc., 8328
Virostek, Steve, 1518
Visaggio, Joe, 5393
Visbal, J. Malcolm, 568
Viscardi, Molly Kreider, 8267
Visher, Melva D., 6153
Vishnoi, Rohit, 2921
Visnich Trust, Virginia Casey, 3746
Viso, Olga, 7050
Visser, Anna, 1035
Vissicchio, John A., 6993
Vista Metals Corp., 230
Vistakon Pharmaceutical, 5327
Visual Architectural Designs, 7012
Vit, Paul, 994
Vitale, Jim, 2730
Vitale, Terri, 2038
Viti, Alissa M., 6406
Vitti, Bonnie, 1484
Viveiros, Cecilia, 4294
Vivinetto, Jack, 6994
Vivino, Paul, Dr., 3991
Vivint, 9354
Vizanko, Jim, 4732
Vizza, Robert, 5895, 5896
Vizza, Robert F., 5873
VLM Charitable Lead Annuity Trust, The, 5781, 6647
Vlock, Michael, 1691, 3094
Voboril, Joe, 7887
Vodafone Americas Inc., 1519
Voelkel, Alice K., 3826
Voelkel, Emmett, 3826
Voelkle, William, 5707
Voelz, Shelley D., 3333
Vogel Paint & Wax, 3487
Vogel, Benjamin Charles, 9964
Vogel, Bob, 4485
Vogel, Charles, 744
Vogel, Charles H.E., 9964
Vogel, Diana G., 3977
Vogel, Frank, 3487
Vogel, Judith, 3466
Vogel, Kenneth E., 3521
Vogel, Lee M., 4961
Vogel, Paul L., 4929
Vogel, Rhona E., 9937
Vogel, Robert J., 5232
Vogel, Sarah, 4729
Vogeler, Deb, 3484
Vogelheim, Katie, 652
Vogelheim, Mary, 652

Vogelsang, Peter J., 663
Vogelstein Revocable Trust, John L., 7034
Vogelstein, Andrew, 6228
Vogelstein, Andrew A., 7034
Vogelstein, Barbara Manfrey, 7034
Vogelstein, Deborah H., 3816
Vogelstein, Hans A., 7034
Vogelstein, John L., 7034
Vogen, Kristin Carlson, 2905
Voges, William J., 2293
Vogl, Marc, 932
Vogler, Emily Crean, 439
Vogler, Suzy Brodie, 3235
Vogt, Mary Anschuetz, 3036
Vogt, Susan J., 4355
Vohtz, Erik, 9108
Voichcik, Sarah Jane, 9936
Voigt, William, 108
Voiland, Eugene J., 780
Vojta, Christopher, 5607
Vojta, George, 5607
Vojta, Timothy, 5607
Vojvoda, Antoinette P., 3825
Vokolos-Zias, Ourania, 6157
Volcker, James P., 7035
Volcker, Paul A., 7035
Volckhausen, Alexander Louis, 6979
Volentine Admin. Trust, Mary G., 1291
Volentine, Mary G., 1291
Volentine, Myatt W., 1291
Volf, Chris, 8472
Volgenau, Ernst, 9549
Volgenau, Lisa, 9549
Volgenau, Sara L., 9549
Volgenau, Sara Lane, 9549
Volk, Edward, 3393
Volk, Norman H., 6144
Volk, Tim, 9375
Volk, William, 8676
Volkema, Michael A., 4470
Volkerts, Drake, 1276
Volkerts, Keith, 1276
Volkerts, Linda L., 1276
Volkman, Toby, 6398
Volland, Patricia J., 5579
Vollintine, Leona S., 3208
Vollmer, Alberto F., 2373
Vollmer, Gustavo A., 2373
Vollmer, Gustavo J., 2373
Vollmer-Eseverri, Carolina, 2373
Vollrath, David A., 7416
Volpe, Michelle, 3939
Volpe, Mike, 8834
Volpe-Seyler, Autumn, 7921
Volpert, Barry S., 7036
Volpert, Teri C., 7036
Voltz, Susan A., 6451
Von Arx, Carol, 4963
Von Arx, Jeffrey Allen, 4963
Von Arx, Robyn Ann, 4963
Von Behran, Thomas R., Fr., 9706
von Bostel, Sylvia, 9410
von Bucher, Judy, 6722
von der Heyden, Eric M., 7037
von der Heyden, Heike, 7037
von der Heyden, Ingolf M., 7037
von der Heyden, Karl M., 7037
von der Heyden, Mary Ellen, 7037
Von Furstenberg, Alexandre, 5884
Von Furstenberg, Diane, 5884
Von Furstenberg, Tatiana, 5884
Von Gehr, Barbara, 9726
von Gillern, Jeffry H., 4784
von Hassel, George A., 6148
von Hess, Louise Steinman, 8299
von Hess, Richard C., 8329
von Imhof, Natasha, 89
Von Kurnatowski, Beverly, 8709
von Notzing, Niklas Schrenck, 9392
Von Rohr, Jason, 1388
Von Voigtlander, Jeffrey P., 4574
Vona, Kenneth, 4056
VonCannon, Theresa, 7285
Vonder Hoya, Margaret Bright, 8756
Vondra, Shawn, 4461
Vongphakdy, Manee, 9834
Vonkannon, John, 5301
vonRosenberg, Sarah, 8775
VonRosenstiel, Elaine, 9578
Voorhees, Adeline J., 9780
Voorhis, Caspar J., 6202
Vorhees, Charles A., 2712
Vorhees, Marianne, 3286
Vorhis, David A., 3760
Voris, Scott, 2767
Vorys Sater Seymour and Please, LLP, 7638
Vorys, Sater, Seymour & Pease, 7563
Vosburg, Tammie, 5229
Voskuil, Steven E., 8957
Voss, Annabelle K., 1292
Voss, David, 420
Voss, Francois, 6481
Voss, Jayna, 8521
Voss, Omer G., 1292
Voss, Omer G., Jr., 1292
Voss, Shiela, 2315
Vossler, Jeff, 7672
Voth, Douglas, 7816
Votorantim Metals Cajamarquilla, 7349
Votorantim Metals Ltd, 7349
Vouras, Peter, Jr., 1643
Voutsinas, Gerry, 6543
Vowel, Max R., 7778
Vowell, Cameron M., 21
Vozar, Bonnie, 9239
Vradenburg, Alissa, 1954
Vradenburg, George A., III, 1954
Vradenburg, Patricia L., 1954
Vradenburg, Trish, 1954
Vradenburg, Tyler, 1954
Vraney, Inge L., 2192
Vraney, Jeffrey, 2192
Vraney, Lawrence E., Jr., 2192
Vraney, Lori A., 2192
Vraney, Maura J., 2192
Vranos, Michael, 1718
Vreeland, John, 2123
Vrenna, Cathy, 7411
Vroman, Gary J., 9890
Vroman, Rich, 9631
Vruwink, Dawn, 9867
VTP Enterprises, 736
Vucurevich, John T., 8524
Vucurevich, Thomas, 8524
Vujovich, Tom, 3321
Vukasin, George, 973, 1120
Vukusich, Jillian C., 2032
Vulcan Lands Inc., 73
Vulcan Materials Co., 73
Vulgamore, Myles, 3543
Vyskocil, Mary Kay, 6544
Vyskocil, Nancy, 4730

W B Investors, LLC, 880
W. Durham, Charles W., 8817
W.M.G., Inc., 2867
Waara, Jonny, 4375
Wachenfeld, William T., 6859
Wachenheim, Chris A., 7039
Wachenheim, Edgar, III, 7039
Wachenheim, Lance R., 7039
Wachenheim, Sue W., 7039
Wachovia Bank, N.A., 21, 1562, 2269, 8046, 9474
Wachovia Corp., 8333
Wachs, Joel, 7050
Wachtel, Gail K., 804
Wachtel, Marcy, 6752
Wachtell, Herbert M., 7040
Wachtell, Lipton, Rosen & Katz, 7040
Wachtell, Thomas, 611
Wachtell, Wendy, 484
Wachter, Renee, 4649
Wachter-Campbell, Christine, 1749
Wack, Catherine M., 9414
Wacker Michigan Corporation, 3099
Wacker Springfield Corporation, 3099
Wacker, Richard F., 2603
Wackowski-Faria, Barbara, 3929
Waclawek, Nancy, 2332
Waddell, Arin, 9989
Waddell, Catherine Hughes, 6193
Waddell, Chauncey L., 6193
Waddell, Ellen, 950
Waddell, Katherine J., 2492
Waddell, Sandra, 6193
Waddell, Sandra H., 6193
Waddell, Theodore H., 6193
Waddell, William R., 7205
Waddell, Wright, 2492
Waddill, David, 6500
Wade's World Foundation Inc., 2351
Wade, Angela, 1293
Wade, Anne, 6164
Wade, Brian, 8408
Wade, Charles, 1293
Wade, Chris, 1293
Wade, Dennis, 8507
Wade, Diana, 1293
Wade, Gerald T., 1160
Wade, James L., 2764
Wade, Jason, 4461
Wade, Jim, 9415
Wade, Katherine M., 9011
Wadge, Gordon R., 3637
Wadhams, Timothy J., 4497
Wadhwani, Kathleen E., 1294
Wadhwani, Romesh T., 1294
Wadhwani, Romesh T., Dr., 1294
Wadleigh, George C., 4316
Wadsworth Golf Construction Company-Midwest, 7698
Wadsworth, Brenton H., 7698
Wadsworth, Erminia, 3611
Wadsworth, James M., 6584
Wadsworth, Jean, 7698
Wadsworth, Leslie, 7698
Waechter, Joseph W., 690
Waeschle, Karen, 1805
Waestman, Loraine, 901
Wafle, Benjamin, 9414
Wagaman, Marcia J., 7425
Wageman, Patrick A., 9245
Wagenberg, Ellen R., 5296
Wagener, Jean, 6349, 6705
Wages, Barbara, 1725
Wages, Page, 1725
Wages, Randy, 2437
Waggaman, Donald E., Jr., 1651
Waggoner, Crystelle, 9252
Waggoner, Don, 2374
Waggoner, Jami, 4852
Waggoner, Lynda S., 7991
Waggoner, Tom, 7374
Waggoner, Zelma, 2374
Wagler Homes of Akron, Inc., 7699
Wagler Homes of Cleveland, Inc., 7699
Wagler, Phil, 7699
Wagler, Theresa E., 3389
Wagley, Anne Paxton, 9082
Wagley, James F.P., 9082
Wagley, Sue, 9082
Wagman, Joseph G., 8351
Wagman, Kim Wachenheim, 7039
Wagner Family Foundation, The, 5795
Wagner, Brian, 7585
Wagner, C.J., 8077
Wagner, Carol, 9277
Wagner, Charlotte R. Cramer, 4317
Wagner, Clarie Chiaramonte, 9407
Wagner, Daphne, 5420
Wagner, Elizabeth B., 5411
Wagner, Emile A., III, 3674
Wagner, Eric, 3749
Wagner, Fred A., 1426
Wagner, Gregory R., 3774
Wagner, Harry, 5491
Wagner, Herbert S., III, 4317
Wagner, James, 2009
Wagner, Jay R., 6506
Wagner, Jay R., Esq., 7939
Wagner, Jean D., 3508
Wagner, Jeffry, 7627
Wagner, Jody M., 9448
Wagner, John, 222
Wagner, Judith B., 1374
Wagner, Kay, 4502
Wagner, Kevin, 3463
Wagner, Leon, 5491
Wagner, Lou, 9023
Wagner, Marilyn Dymond, 9977
Wagner, Mark, 4475
Wagner, Marsha, 5491
Wagner, Matthew L., 9910
Wagner, Merle, 4800
Wagner, Peter F., 7627
Wagner, Phyllis, 2411
Wagner, Rich, 9715
Wagner, Richard G., 3480
Wagner, Richard H., 9961
Wagner, Robert, 3368
Wagner, Roberta L., 9961
Wagner, Sally E., 5950
Wagner, Sean, 5067
Wagner, Shari S., 9963
Wagner, Sylvia, 5621
Wagner, Thomas E., 7391
Wagner, Todd R., 9253
Wagner, William J., 8200
Wagnon, Carolyn, 2475
Wagoner, Pamela, 3807
Wahl, Kristina, 7928
Wahl, Michael, 6016
Wahlen, Eric S., 2568
Wahlstrom, Jeff, 3699
Wahlstrom, Richard, 8511
Waid, John M., 3665
Waide, Patrick J., Jr., 6116
Wainscott, James L., 7366
Waintrup, Linda S., 4267
Wainwright, Donald, 4956
Wainwright, Mary, 4955
Wainwright, Susan, 2414

Warren, James A., 60
Warren, Jean M., 7809
Warren, John, 3336, 4234, 8371
Warren, John-Kelly C., 7809
Warren, Judith, 539
Warren, Kirk, 9300
Warren, Laurie A., 1854
Warren, Leslie, 4044
Warren, Linda, 9341
Warren, Linda M., 7564
Warren, Nani S., 9748
Warren, Richard F., Jr, 8637
Warren, Shirley, 5850
Warren, Stephen K., 7809
Warren, Taylor F., 5850
Warren, Thomas H., Sr., 5074
Warren, Vivian, 8734
Warren, W.K., Jr., 7809
Warren, Wendy, 7841
Warren, William C., IV, 2420
Warren, William K., 7809
Warren, William K., Mrs., 7809
Warrick, Meghan, 2015
Warring, John, 9631
Warrington, Elsie H., 7703
Warsavsky, Michael S., 791
Warsh, Herman, 442
Warsh, Herman E., 1299
Warsh, Michael, 442, 1299
Warshaw, Milton, 6265
Warshaw, Robert S., 2918, 7029
Warth, Robert, 9711
Wartman, Carl, 9867
Wartner, A.L., 3055
Warwar, Rebecca, 1003
Warwick, Robert F., 7170
Wasden, Tracy, 9362
Wasdin, Gelon, 2439
Wasem, Penny, 7445
Wasescha, Anna M., 1644
Washabaugh, Cathy, 4344
Washburn, Earl, Dr., 1163
Washburn, Steve, Dr., 8789
Washington Corporations, 5018
Washington Legal Foundation, 1952
Washington Magazine, Inc., 3847
Washington Post Co., The, 9445
Washington School Employees Credit Union, 9702
Washington Speakers Bureau, 1268
Washington State Diary Council, 3245
Washington Trust Bank, 9662
Washington, A. Eugene, 5329
Washington, Alandra, 4474
Washington, Dana, 5071
Washington, Dennis, 5018
Washington, Don, 3623
Washington, Eugene, 368
Washington, Kevin, 9731
Washington, Lara E., 7956
Washington, Marc, 1064
Washington, Marie Brooks, 365
Washington, Pamela, 3657
Washington, Perry, 8475
Washington, Phyllis J., 5018
Washington, Reginald L., 1390
Washington, Reginald L., M.D., 1381
Washington, Walt, 9659
Washington, Willie, 3649
Washington-Lacey, Bonita, 3400
Washkewicz, Donald E., 7611
Wasie, Donald A., 4794
Wasie, Marie F., 4794
Wasie, Stanley L., 4794
Wasily Irrevocable Trust, Anne V., 1871
Wasily, Anne V., 1871
Wason, Paul K., 8313
Wasserman, Alvin, 4576
Wasserman, Bert W., 7055
Wasserman, Casey, 1300
Wasserman, Debra, 7055
Wasserman, Edith B., 1300
Wasserman, Edith L., 4576
Wasserman, Ellen W.P., 3906
Wasserman, Gary L., 4576
Wasserman, George, 3905
Wasserman, Lew R., 1300
Wasserman, Linda, 4568
Wasserman, Lynne, 1300
Wasserman, Rodger D., 4576
Wasserman, Sandra K., 7055
Wasserman, Steven F., 6220
Wasson, Nathaniel P., 2812
Waste Mangement, 9149
Waste, Laura, 517
Waste, William, 517
Watabe, Shinichi, 6943
Watanabe, Jeffrey N., 2603
Watchowsky, Dale L., 4371
Water Project, Inc., The, 9118
Water Street Advisors, LLC, 9279
Water Street Capital, 1993
Waterbury Companies, Inc., 3201
Waterbury, James B., 3461
Watercress, Inc., 4183
Waterfield, Anne K., 3399
Waterfield, J. Randall, 3399
Waterfield, Jill L., 3399
Waterfield, Richard D., 3399
Waterfield, Richard R., 3399
Waterman Charitable Lead Unitrust, Mary H., 3446
Waterman Trust, Mary H., 3446
Waterman, Ann E., 3446
Waterman, C. Dana, III, 3446
Waterman, Darci, 9604
Waterman, David F., 7686
Waterman, Larned A., Jr., 3446
Waterman, Mary H., 3446
Waterman, Robert E., 157
Waterman, Robert V.P., Jr., 3446
Watermark Estate Mgmt. Svcs., 9746
Waters, Barbara, 7810
Waters, Dana, 3502
Waters, Eloise, 3121
Waters, Feron, 7810
Waters, James H., 6099
Waters, James L., 4369
Waters, Judy, 2433
Waters, Judy Gayle, 7810
Waters, Nina M., 2031
Waters, Richard C., 9487
Waters, Susan, 5556
Waters, Thomas J., 7922
Waterston, Lynn, 7057
Waterston, Samuel, 7057
Waterstone Foundation, 8725
Watkins Associated Industries, Inc., 2568
Watkins, Amy A., 8659
Watkins, Barbara, 3061
Watkins, Betty J., 9553
Watkins, Bill, 2568
Watkins, C. Scott, 9356
Watkins, Carol, 9356
Watkins, Carole, 7398
Watkins, Edward G., 2379
Watkins, Gary, 9356
Watkins, George C., 2568
Watkins, Gregg D., 4396
Watkins, H. Craig, 8097
Watkins, H. Thomas, III, 9553
Watkins, Hays T., 9553
Watkins, Jane G., 9505
Watkins, Jerry W., 193
Watkins, John C., 2568
Watkins, Joy R., 2037
Watkins, Julia S., 9351
Watkins, Julie, 1423
Watkins, Kate, 8630
Watkins, Kimberly, 2568
Watkins, Linda, 2632
Watkins, Michael L., 2568
Watkins, Richard, 9627
Watkins, Ruth Ann, 3113
Watkins, Susan, 1231
Watkins, Tony, 3570
Watkins, Wendy R., 9553
Watlington, Stuart, 9413
Watnabe, Jun, 8613
Watro, Lonny J., 3762
Watsa, V. Prem, 9178
Watson Clinic Foundation, 2151
Watson Foundation, Thomas J., 3218
Watson Marital Trust, Olive C., 3219
Watson Trust, William J., 2747
Watson, Ann, 9731
Watson, Anne, 9320
Watson, Arthur K., 7058
Watson, Arthur K., Jr., 3218
Watson, Ashley B., 687
Watson, Ben, 1423
Watson, Bill, 5138
Watson, Bud, 3560
Watson, Charles, 4846
Watson, Charles L., 8836
Watson, Christopher J., 2416
Watson, David J., 3218
Watson, Douglas, 4109
Watson, Eliza Jane, 5310
Watson, Emmanuel, 3164
Watson, F. Jean, 9611
Watson, George E., 5521
Watson, Geraldine F., 6723
Watson, Hiram W., 3249
Watson, Jamie, 959
Watson, Jared, 9731
Watson, Jeannette K., 7058
Watson, Jennie Lehua, 643
Watson, Jo-Ann, 4109
Watson, John C., 2416
Watson, John S., Jr., 5411
Watson, Joseph W., 411
Watson, Karl H., Jr., 8757
Watson, Keith, 8446
Watson, Kim R., 8836
Watson, Lenna, 1488
Watson, Melissa, 2764
Watson, Philip B., Jr., 4848
Watson, Roslyn M., 4103
Watson, Sol, 6564
Watson, Solomon, IV, 6868
Watson, Stanley W., 4320
Watson, Stephen, 7182
Watson, Stuart, 7058
Watson, Stuart H., 3218
Watson, Thomas J., III, 3219, 7058
Watson, Thomas J., Jr., 3219, 7058
Watson, Tim, 9291
Watson, Wendy K., 4608
Watt, Alston, 2437
Watt, Alston Parker, Mrs., 2572
Watt, Debra S., 7202
Watt, Robert, 8947
Watt, Robert A. "Bob", 9595
Watterson, Barbara N., 3986
Wattis Foundation, Paul L., 1302
Wattles, Alexander B., 5653
Wattles, Charles D., 4445
Wattles, Gurdon B., 5653
Wattles, Gurdon S., 5653
Wattles, John C., 4507
Wattlesworth, Roberta, 3490
Wattley, M.A., 3209
Watts, C. Gregory, 5355
Watts, David, 618
Watts, Gary, 4806
Watts, Linda, 4830
Watts, Mitchell W., 7283
Watts, Ray, 21
Watts, Robb, 2009
Watts, Susan P., 9836
Watts, Wayne, 8675
Watts, William R., Sr., 2380
Watumull Bros., Ltd., 2620
Watumull, Gulab, 2620
Watumull, Jaidev, 2620
Watumull, Jhamandos, 2620
Watumull, Jyoti, 2620
Watumull, Vikram, 2620
Waugh, Marie, 5486
Waugh, Seth, 5876
Waughtal, Bill, 9896
Waughtal, William, 9895
Wavering, Emer H., 3220
Waverly Plastics, Inc., 3437
Wax, Sharon B., 277
Waxenberg, Jay D., 5688
Waxman, Harvey L., 5297
Waxman, Mitchell, 1842
Way, Charles, 3517
Way, Griffith, 9587
Way, Joni B., 3578
Way, Paul, 4646
Wayburn, Cynthia, 9565
Waycaster, Mitch, 4822
Wayne, Bob, 8040
Wayne, Daren, 2525
Wayne, Debra Ann, 1631
Wayne, Valerie Rockefeller, 6723
Wayser, Joshua D., 2951
Wayside of Virginia Inc., 1886
WBAP Radio, 8753
WBH Evansville, Inc., 3402
WBI Energy Midstream, LLC, 7354
WBI Energy Transmission, Inc., 7354
WBI Energy, Inc., 7354
WBNS-TV, Inc., 7719
WCKLC-2, L.C., 3452
WDI Corporation, 2147
WDKMP LLC, 4003
WEA Enterprises Co., Inc., 7106
Weake, Gay, 5015
Weakley, Joan, 6002
Weakley, Wendell W., Sr., 4837
Wean, Gordon B., 7415, 7705
Wean, Raymond John, Sr., 7705
Wean, Susanne C., 7966
Wearing, Betsy, 3540
Weary Trust, Dale J., 7706
Weary Trust, Robert K., 7706
Weary, Dale J., Mrs., 7706
Weary, Daniel C., 9242
Weary, Gifford, 7706
Weary, Robert K., 7706
Weary, Robert K., Jr., 7706

Weatherbie, Matthew A., 4321
Weatherbie, Susan B., 4321
Weatherhead Charitable Trust, 7707
Weatherhead, Albert J., Jr., 7707
Weatherhead, Celia J., 7707
Weatherhead, David Parmely, 3987
Weatherup, Constance K., 173
Weatherup, Craig E., 173
Weatherwax Trust I, K.A., 4577
Weaver Charitable Trust, William M., 9261
Weaver Living Trust, Everett, 2691
Weaver Popcorn Co., Inc., 3401
Weaver, Akilah L., 7316
Weaver, Alyson A., 8744
Weaver, Annamarie F., 2691
Weaver, Annemarie, 2691
Weaver, Claire S., 8351
Weaver, Dale M., 8324
Weaver, Dorothy Collins, 8772
Weaver, E.H., 7335
Weaver, Edith M., 8324
Weaver, Elizabeth Eudora, 9260
Weaver, Everett P., 2691
Weaver, Galbraith McF., 9260
Weaver, George, 5219
Weaver, H. Michael, 7335
Weaver, H. Mike, 7335
Weaver, Irene M., 8324
Weaver, James D., 7268, 8744
Weaver, James K., 8744
Weaver, Jim, 8729
Weaver, John F., 4476
Weaver, Karen Williams, 4372
Weaver, Katherine, 7335
Weaver, Margaret, 8296
Weaver, Margaret W., 7268, 8745
Weaver, Marjorie, 2691
Weaver, Martha, 2691
Weaver, Martha J., 2691
Weaver, Michael D., 8152
Weaver, Michael E., 3401
Weaver, Monte, 8594
Weaver, Nathan, 4659
Weaver, Paul, 2691
Weaver, Paul J., 4451
Weaver, R.H., 3121
Weaver, Rebecca J., 3401
Weaver, Rebecca S., 4966
Weaver, Robert, 2691
Weaver, Robert P., 2691
Weaver, Sharon L., 8234
Weaver, Sharyn A., 8744
Weaver, Shirley, 3699
Weaver, Victor F., 8324
Weaver, W.H., 7335
Weaver, Warren W., 4950
Weaver, William, 2691
Weaver, William C., IV, 8617
Weaver, William M., 3401
Weaver, William R., 9260
Weaver, William T., 2691
Webb Charitable Lead Trust, Max, 1092
Webb, Angela, 8474
Webb, Arthur, 5894
Webb, Cindy, 4839
Webb, Del E., 174
Webb, Donald, 3639
Webb, Fred K., Jr., 9480
Webb, George, 7188
Webb, Greg, 3625
Webb, Irene C., 1303
Webb, J. David, 3351
Webb, John H., 9468
Webb, Joyce A., 2812
Webb, Kevin, 1303
Webb, Kevin R., 9487
Webb, Lessie E., 9480
Webb, Lewis W., III, 9465
Webb, Lewis, Jr., 309
Webb, Linda Gavel, 8469
Webb, Louis A., 1015
Webb, Marion L., 1015
Webb, Marjorie, 9449
Webb, Martha, 4999
Webb, Max, 1092, 1304
Webb, Maynard G., Jr., 1303
Webb, Mike, 8499
Webb, Raymond, 3139
Webb, Robert, 2517
Webb, Robert D., 4004
Webb, Susan, 9509
Webb, Susan Mott, 76
Webb, Thomas J., 4376
Webb-Waring Foundation, 1374
Webber, Eloise, 4463
Webber, Erica, 9262
Webber, Joan, 4578
Webber, Josh, 5006
Webber, Larry D., 4900
Webber, Neil, 8649, 9262
Webber, Richard, 4463
Webber, Russ, 8499
Webber, Thomas L., 6087
Webber, W. Temple, III, 9223
Webber, Wayne, 4578
Webber-McLeod, Gwen, 5757
Weber, A.M., 912
Weber, Al, 7939
Weber, Arnold, 2781
Weber, Bere, 5631
Weber, Charles R., Mrs., 7059
Weber, David, 9604
Weber, David G., 3027
Weber, Donald, 9842
Weber, Doron, 6872
Weber, Edward, 7572
Weber, Elizabeth F., 9842
Weber, Gene, 7405
Weber, Heather, 7018
Weber, Hugh, 8627
Weber, Jay, 54
Weber, Jeff, 3049
Weber, Jennifer L., 7196
Weber, John M., 9396
Weber, Joseph F., 2570
Weber, Karl, 4495
Weber, Kelly, 3576
Weber, Mark, 5074
Weber, Melissa, 3244
Weber, Murray, 6213
Weber, Nicholas Fox, 1532
Weber, Robert, 54
Weber, Robert W., 3548
Weber, Scott, 2817
Weber, Shen, 4646
Weber, Tammy A., 8040
Weber, W. Erik, 3295
Weber, Warren, 3447
Weber, Wayne E., 3256, 3351
Weberg, Claudia, 3221
Weberg, Gary, 3221
Weberg, Jacqueline, 3221
Weberg, John P., 3221
WebMD Health Corp., 5425
Webster Bank, N.A., 1643
Webster, Alec J., 1305
Webster, Binyomin, 6835
Webster, Curtis M., 5376
Webster, Cynthia F., 7454
Webster, David C., 8308
Webster, Edwin S., 4322
Webster, Elizabeth McGraw, 5376
Webster, Helen E., 1305
Webster, Jeffrey, 8613
Webster, Jim, 5108
Webster, John W., 5050
Webster, June Norcross, 6564
Webster, Kyshun, 3644
Webster, Norma, 5108
Webster, Richard B., 1305
Webster, Ronald S., 9269
Webster, Susan, 3354
Webster, Theo M., 5376
Webster, Wilton W., Jr., 1305
Webster, Wilton, Jr., 1305
Wechsler, Dan, 5639
Wechsler, Joseph, 6798
Wechsler, Samuel, 6798
Wechter, Gerald, 5894
Wede, J. Scott, 167
WEDGE Group Incorporated, 9263
WEDGE Holdings, Inc., 9263
Wedgeworth, Robert, 3083
Wedum, John A., 4796
Wedum, Maynard C., 4796
Wee, Esther, 385
Weeber, Steve, 3422
Weed, David, 3298
Weeden Fund, Frank, 7060
Weeden, Alan N., 7060
Weeden, Bob, 7060
Weeden, Donald A., 7060
Weeden, Donald E., 7060
Weeden, Frank, 7060
Weeden, H. Leslie, 7060
Weeden, Jack D., 7060
Weeden, Jennifer, 5006
Weeden, John D., 7060
Weeden, Norman, 7060
Weeden, William, 7060
Weeden, William F., 7060
Weekes, Elizabeth B., 8028
Weekley Homes, David, 8756
Weekley Homes, L.P., 8756
Weekley, Bonnie S., 9264
Weekley, Daniel A., 9422
Weekley, Dave, 8777
Weekley, David M., 9264
Weeks, A. Ray, Jr., 2433
Weeks, Kenneth Durham, Jr., 7195
Weeks, R. Thomas, 6109
Weeks, Wendell P., 5818
Weems, Alonzo, 3341
Weems, Carrie Mae, 7050
Weems, Diane Zabak, 2482
Weems, Katharine Lane, 5585
Weese, Elizabeth Grass, 8066, 8067, 8068
Weese-Mayer, Debra, 3124
Wefald, Susan, 5889
Wegdam, Bernardus, 9509
Wege, Christopher M., 4579
Wege, Diana, 4579
Wege, Jonathan M., 4579
Wege, Peter M., 4579
Wege, Peter M., II, 4579
Wegener, Marlou, 3497
Wegman, Daniel R., 7061
Wegman, Danny, 6945
Wegman, Joe, 3422
Wegman, Margaret F., 7061
Wegman, Robert B., 7061
Wehl, Phil, 8120
Wehle, Kathy, 760
Wehling, Katharine, 3369
Wehmeier, Sutter, 1774
Wehr, C. Frederic, 9966
Wehrle, E. Gaines, 9783
Wehrle, Elizabeth Marie, 9797
Wehrle, H. Bernard, III, 9797
Wehrle, Henry B., Jr., 9797
Wehrle, Lisa, 3541
Wehrle, Melinda, 3541
Wehrle, Michael H., 9783
Wehrle, Stephen D., 9797
Wehrle-Zande, Lynne, 9797
Wehrly, Jennifer, 8775
Wehrman, Jim, 7490
Wehrwein, Sven, 4714
Wei, James, 2602
Weiant, William S., 7441
Weich, Erika Hansen, 5291
Weichers-Marshall, Ana, 686
Weichert, James A., 4687
Weideman, William H., 4404
Weidenbach, Joseph L., 2812
Weidenfeld, Edward L., 1920
Weider Health and Fitness, 1306
Weider, Eric, 1306
Weider, Joe, 1306
Weidert, Steve, 3320
Weidlein, Peter K., 5892
Weidman, John N., 8272
Weidman, Shiela, 2469
Weidman, Steven C., 5955
Weidner, Ellen, 9800
Weidner, Jared, 3348
Weidner, Thomas P., 5411
Weiffenbach, B., 7520
Weigand, Scott, 5106
Weigard, Gregory E., 7907
Weigel Broadcasting Co., 3153
Weigel Verwaltung BMBH GO, 7349
Weigel, Bonnie, 1287
Weigel, Karel, 4755
Weil, Amanda, 6565
Weil, Amanda E., 6173
Weil, Andrew, 175
Weil, Anna Elizabeth C., 4953
Weil, Christopher, 739
Weil, David M., 6898
Weil, Denie S., 6173
Weil, Frank A., 6173
Weil, Gotshal & Manges LLP, 7062
Weil, Gottshalk & Manges, 2912
Weil, John D., 4953
Weil, Paul P., 4991
Weil, Richard L., 6451
Weil, Sandison E., 6173
Weil, Sharon, 262
Weil, William S., 6173
Weiland, John H., 5202
Weiland, Margaret E., 9736
Weiler Trust, Theodore R., 7063
Weiler, Barbara, 7112
Weiler, John, 6546
Weiler, Karen Buglisi, 6408
Weiler, Skip, 7431
Weiler, Theodore R., 7063
Weilnau, Sparky, 7444
Wein, George, 5612, 7064
Weinberg, A.J., 7175
Weinberg, Adam D., 7050
Weinberg, Charlotte Cohen, 3752
Weinberg, David B., 3223

Wellness, Charlene A., 295
Wellnitz, Joel F., 7812
Wellnitz, Paul, 7214
Wellons, Elizabeth Hobgood, 7273
WellPoint, Inc., 3257
Wells Annuity Trust, Ruth L., 7073
Wells Capital Management, 7876
Wells Fargo, 8046, 8136
Wells Fargo & Co., 1312, 4254
Wells Fargo bank, 720
Wells Fargo Bank, 1005, 7221, 7286
Wells Fargo Bank Iowa, N.A., 5066
Wells Fargo Bank Minnesota, N.A., 4714, 4757, 7236
Wells Fargo Bank Nebraska, N.A., 3446
Wells Fargo Bank Nevada, N.A., 964
Wells Fargo Bank Northwest, N.A., 127, 9309, 9317
Wells Fargo Bank Texas, N.A., 8874
Wells Fargo Bank West, N.A., 122
Wells Fargo Bank, N.A., 155, 166, 549, 614, 1116, 1841, 2406, 2513, 2580, 5009, 5024, 5043, 5219, 7131, 7132, 7133, 7145, 7149, 7157, 7159, 7165, 7167, 7168, 7175, 7176, 7177, 7190, 7193, 7197, 7203, 7206, 7207, 7224, 7226, 7235, 7238, 7240, 7250, 7256, 7261, 7262, 7263, 7270, 7277, 7279, 7281, 7285, 7293, 7297, 7304, 7308, 7311, 7312, 7317, 7323, 7325, 7330, 7337, 7339, 7343, 7344, 7351, 7638, 8142, 8288, 8290, 8678, 8891, 8894, 9080, 9123, 9148, 9312, 9318, 9320
Wells Fargo Commercial Banking Office, 1233
Wells Fargo Financial Alaska, Inc., 89
Wells Fargo Private Client Services, 9717
Wells Fargo, N.A., 2316, 7340
Wells Foundation, Joseph H. & Miriam F., Inc., 5944
Wells Marital Trust, Frank, 7073
Wells, Albert, 234
Wells, Ann D., 9236
Wells, Barbara S., 2383
Wells, Carri Baker, 9149
Wells, Carrie, 1368
Wells, Christopher, 3861
Wells, David, 4917
Wells, Dawn E., 5157
Wells, DeAngeloa, 7881
Wells, Della A., 2506
Wells, Frank G., 508
Wells, Helen, 78
Wells, J. Kent, 7354
Wells, James M., III, 9539
Wells, Jeff, 3298
Wells, Jeremy, 4715, 4757
Wells, Jo, 3475
Wells, John, 1311
Wells, Karen, 7412
Wells, Kevin, 508
Wells, Leeroy, Jr., 4376
Wells, Lindsey B., 3861
Wells, Luanne C., 508
Wells, Lyndon, 3522, 3555
Wells, Marilyn, 1311
Wells, Mike, 7340
Wells, Nancy, 3373
Wells, Owen W., 3696
Wells, Paula, 8613
Wells, Peter, 7539
Wells, Preston A., Jr., 2383
Wells, Richard G., Jr., 3994
Wells, Robert G., 508
Wells, Robert J., 7661
Wells, Susan, 85
Wells, Terry Lee, 5157
Wells, Thomas, 5207
Wells, William, 6002
Welp, Holly Hughes, 9793
Welsch, Tim, 4664
Welsh, Carol A., 2384
Welsh, David, 8695
Welsh, David D., 8695
Welsh, Eric A., 2384
Welsh, Jack, 7459
Welsh, Jay, 744
Welsh, John J., 744
Welsh, Kathleen, 4221
Welsh, Michael J., 7164
Welsh, Patrick J., 2384
Welsh, Tim, 4757
Welsh, Timothy, 4715
Welsh-Loveman, Jeremy, 4221
Welsh-Loveman, Monica, 4221
Welstead, Marvin G., 5039
Welty, Claudia Scott, 4649
Welty, John D., 367
Welty, Joseph S., 3723
Welu, Kevin, 3417
Wenco, Inc. of North Carolina, 7856
Wenco, Inc. of Ohio, 7856
Wendel, Clyde F., 4942
Wendel, Katie, 4893
Wendel, Michael, 9538
Wendele, Mindy, 8777
Wendelken, Cherie, 3963
Wendeln, Karen S., 7620
Wendeln, Tony, 7620
Wender, Nancy L., 5539
Wendler, William F., II, 3865
Wendling, Cheryl J., 3294
Wendling, Mike, 4373
Wendt Family Revocable Trust, 9758
Wendt, Henry, III, 9758
Wendt, Henry, IV, 9758
Wendt, Holly P., 9758
Wendt, Margaret L., 7074
Wendt, Nancy J., 7856
Wendt, Roderick C., 7856
Wendtland, Debra, 9997
Wenger, Consuelo S., 4581
Wenger, Howard, 7704
Wenick-Kutz, Bonnie, 4375
Wennberg, David, 4107
Wennberg, John "Jack" E., 4107
Wenner, David L., 157
Wenner-Gren, Axel L., 7075
Wensinger, Arnie, 666
Wenske Enterprises, Inc., 3225
Wenske, Florence, 3225
Wenske, Herbert C., 3225
Wentcher, Ernest C., 3226
Wente, Tom, 4755
Wentling, Thomas L., Jr., 7966
Wentworth, Cynthia, 5165
Wentworth, Steve, 9049
Wentz, Richard E.H., 9510
Wenzel, Anne, 1520
Wenzel, Don, 8863
Wenzel, John, 6681
Wepsic, Eric, 6964
Werber, Suzanne E., 4225
Werblow, Nina W., 7076
Werderman, D.V., 634
Werdiger, Esther, 5498
Werdiger, Solomon, 5498
Werdlow, Sean K., 4371
Wereszczak, Chrysta, 2907
Werking, Helen, 2288
Werlinich, Greg, 5544
Werlinich, Lucille, 5544
Werly, Charles M., 2213, 4257
Werly, Jane E., 2213
Werly, John, 4257
Werly, Scott, 4257
Werner, Adrienne, 5094
Werner, Amanda, 1313
Werner, Carolyn, 1313
Werner, Clarence L., 5094
Werner, Edward, 1313
Werner, Holly, 6673
Werner, Jeff, 9832
Werner, Jill, 1313
Werner, Jill Troy, 1313
Werner, Mark, 7274
Werner, Mary C., 7686
Werner, Mary Leach, 3625
Werner, Mary R., 5094
Werner, Rick S., 9653
Werner, Robert "Bob", 8914
Werner, Rolland, 3502
Werner, Sarah R., 9653
Werner, Susan K., 4881
Werner, Thomas, 1313
Werner, William N., 3217
Werner-Robertson, Gail M., 5094
Wernig, Raymond R., 7420
Wernig, Ruth, 366
Werring, Eden, 1706
Werth, Pamela, 1719
Werth, Peter J., III, 1719
Werth, Peter J., Jr., 1719
Werth, Suzanne, 1719
Wertheimer, Marvin, 5296
Wertz, Richard, 3330
Wertz, Robert C., 6024
Wes-Tex Drilling Co., 8875
WesBanco Bank, Inc., 9780
WesBanco Bank, N.A., 9781
WesBanco Trust & Investment Services, Inc., 9773
Wesby, Meridith D., 8380
Wescombe, Gary T., 297
Wesel, Marcy, 7557
Wesley, Gregory, 9901
Wesley, John W., 8957
Wesley, Thomas G., 6099
Wesolowski, Timothy M., 7659
Wesr, Rod, 8558
Wessels, Kenneth, 5019
Wessels, Patrick, 4928
Wessels, Pete, 3424
Wessler, Susan, 3833
Wessner, David K., 3227
Wessner, Norma C., 3227
Wessner, Patricia A., 3227
West Baking Co., 8644
West Co., Inc., The, 8334
West Penn Power, 7455
West Pharmaceutical Services, Inc., 8334
West Trusts, E. & J., 973
West, Andrew L., 9270
West, Brenda, 4996
West, Bryce L., 2005
West, Christopher R., 3909
West, Ellen B., 9270
West, Emily A., 3404
West, Florence G., 8644
West, Gary L., 1314
West, Gordon T., 9270
West, Gordon T., Jr., 9270
West, James S., 7484
West, John Dunham, 9967
West, Joseph F., 3110
West, Kathryn, 7322
West, Ken, 1504
West, Kristen, 9615
West, Laura, 9324
West, Lucy W., 4122
West, M. Rudolph, 9494
West, Madeline D., 3656
West, Mary Beth, 7043, 8560
West, Mary E., 1314
West, Mary G., 1763
West, Mary L., 1314
West, Matt, 9324
West, Nancy, 1136
West, Neal S., Esq., 8046
West, Neva Watkins, 9200
West, Phyllis M., 3404
West, Richard A., 8644
West, Robert H., 9184
West, Rod K., 3630
West, Ruth St. John, 9967
West, Sarah, 2414
West, Sharon Kelly, 7182
West, Stephen R., 3404
West, Stuart B., 9270
West, Terri L., 9227
West, Terry W., 7793
West, Thomas H., 4101
West, Thomas H., Jr., 4101
West, W. Richard, Jr., 760
West, Wesley, 9200
West-Scantlebury, Sherece Y., 197
Westar Energy, Inc., 3553
Westbrook, E.M., 1060
Westbrook, Elizabeth Moore, 1060
Westbrook, Mary, 1136, 3422
Westbrook, Tracey, 2031
Westby, David, Dr., 9631
Westcom Investment, LLC, 4989
Westcott, Bruce J., 6443
Westcott, Helen D., 6443
Westcott, Vicki, 5075
Wester, Nelson G., 8393
Westergaard, Steadman, 7023, 7024
Westergaard, Steadman H., 5623
Westergom, Andrea P., 1985
Westerhold, Mary, 2817
Westerlage, Joe N., 8739
Westerland, Maureen, 1511
Westerling, Richard S., 8622
Westerman, Laura J., 7811
Westerman, Lene, 7811
Westerman, Samuel L., 4582
Westermann, Mariet, 6470
Western & Southern Life Insurance Co., The, 7710
Western Asset Management Co., 1315
Western Catering Services, Inc., 5016
Western Dairy Association, 3245
Western Digital Corp., 1316
Western Digital Technologies, Inc., 1316
Western Massachusetts Electric Co., 1656
Western Oilfield Supply Co., 815
Western Pacific Mutual Insurance Co., 8212
Western Resources, Inc., 3553

Western Union Co., 1521
Western, David, Dr., 5783
Westfall, Heath, 9304
Westfall, Rebekah, 9304
Westfeldt, Thomas D., 3665
Westfield Group Foundation, 7711
Westfield Insurance Co., 7711
Westfield National Insurance Co., 7711
Westheimer, Jerome M., 7812
Westheimer, Jerome M., Jr., 7812
Westhodd, Sandra, 5006
Westhues, Barbara A., 4951
Westlake Hospital, 3228
Westlake, James L., 5000
Westlake, Lisa Simone, 6499
Westlake, Nellie M., 5000
Westlund, Janice, 2766
Westly, Anita, 1873
Westly, Steve, 1873
Westly, Steven P., 1873
Westman, Paul J., 2865
Westminster Motor Co., 3829
Weston Properties, Sam, Inc., 2168
Weston, Eric, 5499
Weston, Graham, 9064
Weston, Josh S., 5499
Weston, Judy, 5499
Weston, Peter, 3950
Weston, Ron, 5499
Weston, Sharon R., 5171
Weston-Murphy, Dotty, 1562
Westra, Laurie, 5253
Westreich, Anthony, 1317
Westreich, Ruth, 1317
Westreich, Stanley I., 1317
Westriech, Lauren, 1317
Westrope, 9606
Westrum, Megan C., 9873
Wetherill, Edward B, 8370
Wetmore, Brooke, 9793
Wetmore, Lu Ann, 3502
Wetterau, Mark S., 633
Wettergren, David, 4782, 9950
Wetzel, Barbara A., 1318
Wetzel, Mark R., 4035
Wetzel, Todd H., 4035
Wetzler, Charles E., 3506
Wexner Charitable Fund, Leslie H., The, 7713
Wexner Charitable Remainder Unitrust, Bella, 5562, 5655, 5789, 5855, 5952
Wexner Family Charitable Fund, 7713
Wexner Revocable Trust, Susan, 5562, 5655, 5789, 5855, 5952, 6207, 7124
Wexner Revocable Trust, Susan R., 7028
Wexner, Abigail, 7713
Wexner, Abigail S., 7712
Wexner, Bella, 7028
Wexner, Leslie H., 7712, 7713
Wexner, Susan, 5977, 6036, 6207, 7124
Wexner, Susan R., 5562, 5655, 5789, 5855, 5952, 6524, 6576, 6622, 7028, 7110
Weyehaeuser, Ian, 4802
Weyenberg, Tim, 9854
Weyeneth, Ernest L., 5059
Weyeneth, Len, 5059
Weyerhaeuser Corporation, 325
Weyerhaeuser Irrevocable Trust, C. Davis, 9744
Weyerhaeuser Trust, C.L., 4803
Weyerhaeuser, Annette B., 9620
Weyerhaeuser, Benjamin D., 9732
Weyerhaeuser, C. Davis, 9620, 9732
Weyerhaeuser, Charles A., 4634
Weyerhaeuser, Daniel J., 4803
Weyerhaeuser, F.T., 9732
Weyerhaeuser, Frederick T., 4600, 4803
Weyerhaeuser, Gail T., 9620, 9732, 9744
Weyerhaeuser, George H., 4802
Weyerhaeuser, Ginnie, 4803
Weyerhaeuser, Henry G., 4634
Weyerhaeuser, Ian, 4802
Weyerhaeuser, Leilee, 4802
Weyerhaeuser, Robert M., 4634, 4802
Weyerhaeuser, W. Drew, 4802
Weyerhaeuser, Wendy, 4802
Weyerhaeuser, William T., 9620, 9732, 9744
Weyerhaeuser-Johnson, Jane, 4802
Weyerhauser, George H., Mrs., 4802
Weyers, Russell C., 9924
Weymouth, George, 7911
Weymouth, John, 8475
Weymouth, Theodore S., 3084
Weywrhaeuser, W. Drew, 9732
WF Foundation, 7846
Whalen, George T., Jr., 6485
Whalen, George, III, 6485
Whalen, Michael, 1076
Whalen, Michael S., 1214
Whalen, Robert W., 6485
Whalen, Robert, Jr., 6159
Whaley, Darlene K., 3355
Whaley, J. Patrick, 611
Whaley, James, 5454
Whaley, Patricia, 9932
Whaling, Tom, 9789
Whalley, Lawrence G., 9272
Whalley, Mary, 9272
Whalton, Michael, 9775
Wham, S. Smith, 8478
Wharff, Carol B., 7557
Wharton, Clifton R., 5786
Wharton, Daniel B., 9789
Wharton, James H., Dr., 3669
Whatley, Jon, 8768
WHDH-TV, Inc., 1969
Whealy, Kent, 4632
Wheat, Warren, 186
Wheelan, Belle S., 3345
Wheeler Bros., Inc., 8335
Wheeler Revocable Trust, Don M., 7336
Wheeler, Charles B., 9760
Wheeler, Christopher, 7566
Wheeler, Coleman H., 9760
Wheeler, Coleman H., Jr., 9760
Wheeler, Connie, 7336
Wheeler, Cornelia T., 9760
Wheeler, David L., 8335
Wheeler, Don M., 7336
Wheeler, Hank, 4838
Wheeler, Harold W., 8335
Wheeler, Harold W., III, 8335
Wheeler, Henry H., Jr., 1319
Wheeler, Henry Hugh, III, 1319
Wheeler, James G., Jr., 9375
Wheeler, Janet P., 7340
Wheeler, Joan M., 8335
Wheeler, John C., 9760
Wheeler, John R.C., 4362
Wheeler, Kathryn A., 4286
Wheeler, Ken, 3570
Wheeler, Kevin J., 8550
Wheeler, Max E., 2800
Wheeler, Mimi, 2800
Wheeler, Nyri Antia, 1319
Wheeler, Paul, 8335
Wheeler, Paul J., 8335
Wheeler, Robert L., 4512
Wheeler, Stacy, 8335
Wheeler, Steve, 5009
Wheeler, Steven M., 111
Wheeler, Thomas K., 9760
Wheelock, Brad, 4631
Wheelock, Pam, 4757
Wheelock, Pamela, 4715
Wheelock, Pamela A., 4618
Wheels Pros, 118
Whelan, Catherine P., 9468
Whelan, Mary C., 3586
Whelan, Matthew, 1186
Whelan, Sidney S., Jr., 6202
Wheless, Nicholas Hobson, Jr., 3673
Whelton, Joan M., 3968
Wherry, Roger S., 4700
Whetsell, Joann, 7375
Whetstone, Scott F., 7427
Whetzel, Michelle, 1765
Whico, Inc., 2904
Whipple, Dan, 3319
Whipple, Earl D., 8313
Whipple, Gretchen, 3929
Whipple, Ken, 4371
Whipple, Mary, 199
Whipple, Mary Margaret, Hon., 9384
Whipple, Scott, 2627
Whirlpool Corp., 4583
Whisler, Ardyce, 5019
Whitacre, Edward E., 9273
Whitacre, Edward E., Jr., 9273
Whitacre, Linda Lawrence, 9273
Whitaker, Anne, 5437
Whitaker, Darla H., 9227
Whitaker, Janice M., 7274
Whitaker, Mae M., 5001
Whitaker, Mary Ann, 8971
Whitaker, Shannon McNeely, 4710
Whitaker, Vivian, 3373
Whitbeck, Carl, 3948
Whitcombe, Kimberly S., 979
Whitcup, Scott M., M.D., 228
White Living Trust, Betty D., 1321
White, A. Dennis, 6479
White, A. Scott, 2327
White, Andrea A., 8631
White, Andrew J., 9543
White, Andrew S., 8961
White, Andy, 7444
White, Anna Seim, 3274
White, Anne, 9604
White, Annette F., 3632
White, Barbara, 4139
White, Barbara E., 3406
White, Barrie M., 1819
White, Benjamin T., 2432, 2506, 2580
White, Beth, 2792
White, Betty D., 1321
White, Bill, 3288, 3549, 9775
White, Bruce W., 3405
White, Bryan, 6898, 9724
White, C. Cody, Jr., 3639
White, C. Edward, Jr., 4455
White, Calvin, 197
White, Carolee, 1321
White, Carolyn A., 9447
White, Catherine M., 7374
White, Charles B., 9474
White, Charles E., 7635
White, Chris, 3337
White, Christine, 6898, 9724
White, Christopher, 3406
White, Christopher M., 6437
White, Chuck, 9277
White, Claire Mott, 4455, 4466
White, Craig, 3406
White, Cris, 3855
White, Cyrus, 4667
White, David, 3748
White, David E., 1738
White, Dean V., 3406
White, Diana, 9685
White, Diane L., 780
White, E., 8833
White, E.G., 3342
White, Eddie, 9538
White, Edward L., Jr., 2448
White, Elizabeth E., 3405
White, G.R., 3230
White, George, 8873
White, George W., 8545
White, Graham, 8182
White, Gregory, 1934
White, Gregory D., 4476
White, H. Hunter, Jr., 3616
White, Hazel B., 3229
White, Henry S., 4139
White, Hugh W., 3268
White, J. Austin, 212
White, Jaleigh J., 3402
White, James, 3556
White, Jared, 4139
White, Jim, 7231
White, JoAnn, 7554, 7555, 7556
White, JoAnn D., 8012
White, Jodi, 4334
White, John D., 9117
White, John W., 2577
White, Julie, 7417
White, Justin F., 6437
White, Karen, 972
White, Katherine, 2783
White, Kathleen M., 8768
White, Kathryn A. Weitz, 5051
White, Kathryn W., 5092
White, Keith, 3632, 8527
White, Keith, Mrs., 3632
White, Kim, 4502
White, Larry J., 3789
White, Lee, 3272
White, Lisa Holder, Hon., 2764
White, Lynn T., 4557
White, Marcus, 9907
White, Margaret R., 7232
White, Mark, 4667
White, Melovee, 9274
White, Michael, Jr., 2766
White, Miles D., 2649
White, Miranda, 4139
White, Miriam deQuadros, 904
White, Nancy G., 4900
White, P. Maureen, 6680
White, Pamela, 1819
White, Pat, 9299
White, Paul, 1315
White, Philip O., 3229
White, R. Elton, 2142
White, R. Marc, 3632
White, Rachel, 1384
White, Randy, 3390
White, Raye G., 9154
White, Richard, 2036

White, Richard L., 8332
White, Ridgeway H., 4466
White, Ridgway H., 4455, 4510
White, Robbie T., 2447
White, Robert N., 3632
White, Roger B., 3229
White, Rosalyn, 9503
White, Russell E., 595
White, Sharon, 7594
White, Shelby, 6363, 6364, 6748
White, Steve, 5223
White, Steven A., 7989
White, Steven R., 3229
White, Susie, 7782
White, Teresa, 2399
White, Thomas H., 7715
White, Thomas W., 8685, 8688
White, Thurman V., Jr., 1166
White, Valerie, 9299
White, Vickie, 9007
White, Wayne, Dr., 5162
White, William P., 3229
White, William P., III, 3229
White, William S., 4455, 4466, 4510
White-Longworth, Stephenie, 3313
White-Seals, Beverly, 3759
White-Spunner, John, 11
Whitecap Investments G.P., 2661
Whited-Howell, Mary Amelia, 5519
Whitehall Casino, Inc., 5016
Whitehead, Andy, 3
Whitehead, Baruch, 5807
Whitehead, Cindy, 8994
Whitehead, Joseph B., Jr., 2571
Whitehead, Mark, 5063
Whitehead, Susan M., 3
Whitehill, Jim, 4461
Whitehurst, Grover J., Dr., 1679
Whitelaw, Jeff, 9487
Whiteleather, John, 3407
Whiteley, Sherry, 723
Whiteman, Jeffery S., 2614
Whiteman, John O., 92
Whiteman, Lance, 7921
Whiteman, Lawrence E., 8295
Whitener, C. Cleve, III, 9275
Whitener, Mary Rebecca, 9275
Whitener, Sarah Ford, 7365
Whiteside, Carol, 1163
Whiteside, Jeffrey W., 3394
Whiteside, Jennifer Tolle, 7273
Whitesman, Guy E., 2327
Whitfield Familt Charitable Trust, 8492
Whitfield, Ed, 7204
Whitfield, Lewis, 4822
Whitfield, Sue Trammell, 8853
Whitfield, W. Elliott, 9434
Whitfield, W. Trammell, 8853
Whitfield, William F., Jr., 8853
Whitham, Mark, 7523
Whiting, Amy, 9019
Whiting, Giles, Mrs., 7079
Whiting, Laura L., 8809
Whiting, Len, 7971
Whiting, Macauley, Jr., 4407
Whiting, Michael, 1395
Whiting-Turner Construction Company, The, 3810
Whitley, Henry C., 9133
Whitley, Steven R., 2327
Whitley, Tracee, 3560
Whitlock, John D., 9556
Whitlock, Jonathan, 2766
Whitlow, Allan, 3297
Whitlow, Jennifer M., 3837
Whitlow, Katherine, 430
Whitman Charitable Remainder Trust, Catherine A., 4313
Whitman, C. Thomas, 8530, 8556
Whitman, Frederick C., 1322
Whitman, Lois Q., 6516
Whitman, Margaret C., 6143
Whitman, Martin J., 6516, 7083, 8193
Whitman, Sara G., 4313
Whitman, Thomas I., 8193
Whitmire, Elbert N., III, 2562
Whitmire, Julia, 9277
Whitmore, John, 1925
Whitmore, Lynn, 3418
Whitmore, Peter J., 6567
Whitmore, Richard, 411
Whitney Bank, 3667
Whitney National Bank, 2777
Whitney, Ben, 4714
Whitney, Cynthia M., 1966
Whitney, Donald W., 6242
Whitney, Edward A., 9998
Whitney, Jean S., 4267
Whitney, Kathleen P., 2871
Whitney, Michael, 5164
Whitney, Todd, 5806
Whitney, Willis R., 6802
Whitridge, David, 440
Whitridge, Serena, 4171
Whitridge, Serena M., 4172
Whitsitt, Jan, 9731
Whitsitt, Steve, 2765
Whitson, Betty, 1394
Whittaker, Jim, 9384
Whittaker, Joan Gibney, 9362
Whittaker, Robert, 9362
Whittemore, Denise, 8621
Whitten, Michelle S., 1500
Whittenberg, Russell T., 263
Whittenburg, J. Vernon, 5462
Whittied, Peter, 1397
Whittier Charitable Lead Trust, N. Paul, 423
Whittier, Brian, 918
Whittier, Cheyenna, 423
Whittier, Dorothy, 3938
Whittier, Kimberly, 423
Whittier, Leland K., 1323
Whittier, N. Paul, 423
Whittier, Paul Michael, 423
Whittingham, Andrew, 1720
Whittingham, C. Anthony, 1720
Whittingham, Cecil A., 1720
Whittingham, Jean, 1720
Whittington, Ro, 3321
Whittle, Polly K., 8958
Whittle, Rob, 9380
Whitton, Margaret, 1874
Whitwam, Barbara L., 2737
Whitwam, David R., 2737
Whitwam, Mark D., 2737
Whitwell, Sara E., 7813
Whitwell, Thomas D., 7813
Whitworth, William B., 8768
Whole Foods Market Services, Inc., 9276
Whorton, Brett, 2577
Whyte, Paul W., 8392
Wi-Fi Wheeling and Dealing, LLC, 2866
Wiancko, Cynthia, 9761
Wiancko, R. Dennis, 9761
Wiancko, Sibyl S., 9761
Wiancko, Thomas H., 9761
Wiancko-Chasman, Anna K., 9761
Wiberg, Alexandra T., 4213
Wice, David H., 8035
Wichmann, David, 4785
Wick, Adele, 5269
Wick, Emily R., 1710
Wick, Mieka, 1892
Wickersham, Theodore S., 6043
Wickert, Marilyn, 3360
Wickes, Harvey Randall, 4585
Wicks, John R., 4771
Wicks, Tom, 4830
Widdowson, Gayle W., 3760
Widdowson, Julia H., 8892
Wideman, Frank J., III, 8496
Widener Memorial Foundation 2, 8336
Widener Memorial School Endowment, 8336
Widener, Peter A.B., 8336
Widga, Sidney L., 5045
Widger Trust, Leon P., 5162
Widing, J. William, III, 7939
Widman, Stephen, 1616
Widoff, Lissa, 3709
Width, Richard, 5253
Wiebe, Nancy, 3507
Wieberg, Fred, 4968
Wieberg, Julie, 4968
Wieboldt, Anna Krueger, 3231
Wieboldt, Nancy, 3231
Wieboldt, William A., 3231
Wiechmann, Marcus, 4725
Wieder, Jane, 3859
Wiederhold, Jane A., 1721
Wiederspan, Nancy, 5063
Wiedlea, John, 4550
Wiefling, Bridgette, 6099
Wiegand, Ann K., 5159
Wiegand, Ben, 8337
Wiegand, Edwin L., 5159
Wiegand, Paul, 9705
Wiegand, Phillips, 8337
Wiegand, Phillips, Jr., 8337
Wiegand, Ruth, 8337
Wiegers, Betsy, 1518
Wiegers, E. Alexander, 7082
Wiegers, Elizabeth C., 7082
Wiegers, George A., 7082
Wieland, Clyde, 2913
Wieland, Jennifer Thornton, 1252
Wieland, John S., 2913
Wieland, Julie, 2913
Wielenga, Terilea J., 228
Wieler, Scott A., 3883
Wieman, Russell G., 2877
Wien, Anita, 6748
Wien, Byron, 6748
Wiener, Ann, 6571
Wiener, Carolyn S., 7083, 8109
Wiener, Donald B., 3670
Wiener, Ian, 231
Wiener, Judy, 4820
Wiener, Malcolm H., 7083, 8109
Wiener, William B., Jr., 3670
Wierda, Emilie, 4525
Wierman, Scott F., 7340
Wiese, David R., 7178
Wiese, Joseph F. "Ted", 3264
Wiese, Ronald O., 9890
Wiesner, Jeffrey D., 9965
Wietlisbach, Binney H.C., 7955
Wiggins, Anthony A., 1722
Wiggins, Barrie L., 7173
Wiggins, Matthew Maxwell, 1722
Wiggins, Stephen F., 1722
Wight, Russell, Jr., 5501
Wightman, Gail, 5062
Wightman, John, 5062
Wightman, Sage, 4881
Wightmen, Orrin Sage, IV, 4881
Wigton, Kent, 420
Wiita, Kaycee, 9603
Wikstrom, Francis M., 9323
Wilbanks, Karen C., 2451
Wilber, John, 7915
Wilbratte, Chris, 8721
Wilcox, Daniel, 1324
Wilcox, George N., 2621
Wilcox, Joseph, 1324
Wilcox, Linda, 3287
Wilcox, Margaret, 1324
Wilcox, Ronald C., 621
Wilcox, Stephen, 1324
Wilcox, Steven, 9950
Wilcox, Thomas, 1324
Wilcox, Thomas E., 3726
Wild Wings Foundation, 6606
Wild, Marc W., 9791
Wilday, Ward, 5750
Wilde, Benna, 3083
Wilde, John R., 9970
Wilde, Katrin, 9597
Wilde, Sara, 8495
Wildecroft Terrace LLC, 9452
Wildenthal, Kern, 8889, 8912
Wilder Trust, Eleanor, 5422
Wilder, Abigail H., 440
Wilder, H. Rodger, 4830
Wilder, Roger, 4830
Wildrick, Eve B., 1889
Wilds, Deborah J., 9600
Wildwood Charitable Lead Annuity Trust, 7084
Wildwood Trust, 7084
Wilen, Julie, 3097
Wiles, Rhonda, 3319
Wiles, Stephanie, 5807
Wiley, C. Matthew, 3758
Wiley, Donna L., Dr., 3275
Wiley, J. Michael, 8229
Wiley, Jennifer Volgenau, 9549
Wiley, Jim, 9108
Wiley, Lewis S., 9560
Wiley, Mary L.F., 9560
Wiley, Richard R., 7382
Wiley, Tom, 7570
Wilf Charitable Lead Trust, Alex H., 5352
Wilf Charitable Lead Trust, Harley Ryan, 5352
Wilf Charitable Lead Trust, Harrison, 5352
Wilf Charitable Lead Trust, Jenna, 5352
Wilf Charitable Lead Trust, Judith, 5352
Wilf Charitable Trust II, Halle, 5352
Wilf Charitable Trust, Halle, 5352
Wilf Charitable Trust, Zygmunt, 5504
Wilf, Audrey, 5504
Wilf, Beth, 5352
Wilf, Elizabeth, 5502, 5503
Wilf, Harry, 5502
Wilf, Jason, 5502, 5503
Wilf, Jeffrey, 5502, 5503
Wilf, Jonathan, 5502, 5503
Wilf, Joseph, 5502, 5503, 5504
Wilf, Judith, 5352
Wilf, Leonard, 5502, 5503
Wilf, Leonard A., 5352
Wilf, Mark, 5502, 5503, 5504

Wilf, Orin, 5352, 5502
Wilf, Zygmunt, 5352, 5502, 5503, 5504
Wilfong, Diane, 5106
Wilford, Dan S., 8816
Wilfrid, Thomas N., 5391
Wilharm, John H., Jr., 7509
Wilhelm, Ed, 3303
Wilhelm, Roberta, 5081
Wilhelm, Steven R., 4877
Wilhelm, Suzanne A., 3408
Wilhoite, Charles, 7870
Wilke, Jeffrey Allan, 1875
Wilke, Liesl D., 1875
Wilken, James, 3088
Wilkens, Michael T., 3485
Wilkerson, Betsy, 9650
Wilkerson, Bonnie, 2638
Wilkerson, Debbie, 4920
Wilkerson, Dick, 8474
Wilkerson, Ernest L., Jr., 7406
Wilkerson, Justin, 2638
Wilkerson, Walker, 2123
Wilkes, Andrea B., 1922
Wilkes, Elizabeth W., 5653
Wilkes, J. Larry, 7773
Wilkes, Robert W., 8478
Wilkie, Margot, 1532
Wilkie, Valleau, Jr., 8685
Wilkin, Abra Prentice, 3088
Wilkins, Elizabeth, 1786
Wilkins, Jaci, 5015
Wilkins, Jan, 9775
Wilkins, John W., Jr., 8839
Wilkins, Laura G. Batterman, 9813
Wilkins, Roger, 1888
Wilkinson, Amy, 1650
Wilkinson, Ann, 3618
Wilkinson, Cathy, 4373
Wilkinson, Darla J., 4846
Wilkinson, F. McKinnon, 7325
Wilkinson, Frank W., 9770, 9794
Wilkinson, George D., 4372
Wilkinson, James, 6627
Wilkinson, Jill Matthews, 8810, 8955
Wilkinson, Joe B., 9147
Wilkinson, Julia Matthews, 9207
Wilkinson, Leslie, 8606
Wilkinson, Margie, 9421
Wilkinson, Marie, 2648
Wilkinson, Mary S., 4283
Wilkinson, R.W., 9770, 9794
Wilkinson, Sue, 5023, 5063
Wilkinson, Teresa D., 8959
Wilkinson, Walter, 5303
Wilkinson, Whitney A., 5304
Wilkinson-Fannin, Lisa, 111
Wilkinston, Steven, 7349
Wilks, Barbara, 7716
Wilks, Craig, 7481
Wilks, Dan H., 8897
Wilks, Farris, 9230
Wilks, Farris C., 9230
Wilks, Harry T., 7716
Wilks, JoAnn, 9230
Wilks, Sandra, 3206
Wilks, Staci, 8897
Will, Dean, 7908
Will, George F., 9819
Willard, Kirk, 9867
Willcox, Thomas L., Jr., 8494
Willens, Liliane, 3705
Willet, Linda A., 5305
Willett, Boyd Ryan, Jr., 1523
Willett, Harry L., 1523
Willett, Jeffrey, 3524
Willett, Kathryn A., 2661
Willett, Lynne, 9557
Willett, William G., 9557
Willey, Stephanie T., 3760
Willgerodt, Penny Fujiko, 6663
Willhardt, Gary D., 3021
William Companies, Inc., 8670
William, Susan Krenbiel, 3552
Williams Charitable Trust, Caroline, 2747
Williams Charitable Trust, George J., 2747
Williams Co., Gary, The, 1480
Williams Cos., Inc., The, 7814
Williams Energy Corp., Gary, 1480
Williams Family Trust, The, 1325
Williams Trust, Elmer, 3556
Williams Trust, Hobart W., 2747
Williams, A. Damon, 9415
Williams, A. Morris, Jr., 8226
Williams, A.F., 1524
Williams, A.F., Mrs., 1524
Williams, Abigail, 9279
Williams, Alex L., 2575
Williams, Allysunn, 549
Williams, Andrea M., 8043
Williams, Andrew K., 4586
Williams, Andrew L., 2575
Williams, Angela, 3841, 4419
Williams, Angela H., 2575
Williams, Ann Claire, 5747
Williams, Anthony, 8774
Williams, Arlen, 7742
Williams, Arthur L., Jr., 2575
Williams, Arthur R., III, 2575
Williams, Arthur R., IV, 2575
Williams, Ashlyn W., 2572
Williams, Bailey, 7171
Williams, Benjamin, 4270, 7698
Williams, Benjamin J., Jr., 4216
Williams, Bennie G., 2572
Williams, Bruce, 7877
Williams, C. Wayne, 5803
Williams, Carolyn H., Hon., 4472
Williams, Catherine, 8267
Williams, Catherine Merrill, 3847
Williams, Charles A., 8657, 8658
Williams, Charles F., 7743, 7812
Williams, Charles K., II, 8339
Williams, Christel G., 4586
Williams, Christopher, 2238
Williams, Christopher H., 9416
Williams, Churchill, 3469
Williams, Clarence, 1103
Williams, Clyde, 6408
Williams, Constance Hess, 5298
Williams, Craig M., 4256
Williams, Cynthia, 7340
Williams, Dale F., 4586
Williams, Dale L., 4586
Williams, Dale L., M.D., 4586
Williams, Darrell, 8260
Williams, Dave, 9833
Williams, David, 2288, 4996
Williams, David F., 2388
Williams, David, II, 8550
Williams, Debbie, 9652
Williams, Debra W., 5493
Williams, Dennis K., 7913
Williams, Dianne E., 1563
Williams, Donna J., 2767
Williams, Doris Carson, 8092
Williams, Dorothy L., 2449
Williams, Dwight, 9750
Williams, Edna Sproull, 2388
Williams, Elise, 4419
Williams, Elizabeth, 9682
Williams, Elizabeth G., 8861
Williams, Elrick, 3234
Williams, Emelie Melton, 6878
Williams, Ethel Isaacs, 2276
Williams, Eva C., 7184
Williams, Evan, 1326, 3509
Williams, Frantz, Jr., 1644
Williams, Georgeanne, 2110
Williams, Greg, 194
Williams, Grice E., 2648
Williams, H.L. "Sandy", Jr., 4822
Williams, J. McDonald, 8912
Williams, James B., 2571, 2579
Williams, James M., 579
Williams, James M., Jr., 2574
Williams, James P., 4746
Williams, Jan, 3390
Williams, Jay, 4461
Williams, Jeffrey R., 3982
Williams, Jennifer, 2040
Williams, Jerry B., 8550
Williams, Jim, 1039
Williams, Joel T., Jr., 8778
Williams, John, 3049
Williams, John A., 2061
Williams, Johnathan, 1014
Williams, Jon, 960
Williams, Joseph Neel, 2572
Williams, Julie Jones, 3036
Williams, Karen R., 9335
Williams, Kate, 1053
Williams, Kathryn, 7328
Williams, Kenna, 208
Williams, Khalif, 5652
Williams, Kim, 7659
Williams, Kimberley S., 5808
Williams, L. Neil, Jr., 2581
Williams, Laird M., 2449
Williams, Lance, 3166, 4829
Williams, Lawrence, IV, 2864
Williams, Leonard E., 2061
Williams, Linda Sue, 2574
Williams, Lindsey, 4394
Williams, Lisa B., 2519
Williams, Lon R., Jr., 9214
Williams, Lorelei, 6864
Williams, M. Nancy, 8770
Williams, Margaret Alkek, 8658
Williams, Margaret V., 8657
Williams, Marguerite N., 2572
Williams, Mark, 8949
Williams, Mark K., 8529
Williams, Marla J., 1385
Williams, Marva E., 2702
Williams, Marvall, 3469
Williams, Mary, 9605
Williams, Mary Alice, 4439
Williams, Mary E., 4442
Williams, Max, 7876
Williams, Michael J., 9944
Williams, Nancy, 3422
Williams, Nat Chioke, Ph.D., 1915
Williams, Noel Brown, 8582
Williams, Pam, 7597
Williams, Patricia, 200, 8953
Williams, Patrick M., 2388
Williams, Paul, 4616
Williams, Paul A., 7493
Williams, Paula Virgah, 3902
Williams, Pete, 7531
Williams, Peter H., 4586
Williams, Randa Duncan, 8657, 8658
Williams, Ray R., Jr., 8465
Williams, Raymond H., 1358
Williams, Richard, 399
Williams, Richard J., 2742
Williams, Richard Tyrone, 7196
Williams, Richard, Dr., 7188
Williams, Robert G., 8220
Williams, Robert H., 8438
Williams, Robert J., 11
Williams, Robert R., 157
Williams, Ronald K., 4441
Williams, Ronald W., 1481
Williams, Rosa Sternberger, 7326
Williams, Ruth E., 3528
Williams, Ruth W., 8226
Williams, S.R., 9399
Williams, Sandra Jo, 9279
Williams, Sara, 1326
Williams, Sarah, Esq., 2269
Williams, Scott, 1907, 4327
Williams, Scott W., 8152
Williams, Sean, 4419
Williams, Sharon, 4996
Williams, Sherwin, 9606
Williams, Stacey, 3061
Williams, Stephen T., 7577
Williams, Susan B., 4586
Williams, Tammy, 9832
Williams, Tamra, 960
Williams, Terry Tempest, 422
Williams, Thomas, 1374
Williams, Thomas L., 7443, 7710
Williams, Thomas L., III, 2572
Williams, Thomas Lyle, IV, 2572
Williams, Todd, 9104
Williams, Todd A., 9279
Williams, Tom, 4438
Williams, Tyler, 9354
Williams, Vivien, 4755
Williams, Walter E., 9406
Williams, Worth, 2414
Williams-Puccio, Kelly, 2275
Williamson Gangi, Emily, 7178
Williamson, Alexandra Bowes, 333
Williamson, Brett, 193
Williamson, Brett J., 1182
Williamson, Brian R., 7688
Williamson, Debra, 7522
Williamson, Debra L., 7520
Williamson, Donald G., 4474
Williamson, Douglas E., 7520
Williamson, Greg, 3186
Williamson, Heather, 4772
Williamson, Heidi, 7939
Williamson, James G., 1564
Williamson, James J., 9888
Williamson, Judith Cole, 4343
Williamson, Kate J., 2289
Williamson, Keith H., 4870
Williamson, Leslie G., 7520
Williamson, Martin, Brooke Family Foundation, 14
Williamson, Mary F., 2609
Williamson, Parker, 1222
Williamson, R. Mark, 2506
Williamson, Richard S., 143
Williamson, S.K., 7520
Williamson, Scott T., 4815
Williamson, Susan, 23
Williamson, Susan K., 7520, 7522
Williamson, Tom A., 3548
Williamson, W. Bland, 7733

Williamson, Wayne, 1572
Williamson, Wendy, 6193
Williard, Coy O., 7231
Williard, David B., 3973
Willis Family Trust, Bruce, 396
Willis North America, Inc., 293
Willis, Ann D., 7294
Willis, Daniel, 2959
Willis, David S., 4254
Willis, Duane Scott, 2959
Willis, Dudley H., 4254
Willis, Gracia T., 6504
Willis, Hilda M., 8340
Willis, Janet, 2959
Willis, Kathryn, 2433
Willis, Lois Cross, 6504
Willis, Mark, 3294
Willis, Robert M., 7221
Willis, Sally S., 4254
Willis, Scott, 2959
Willis, Toby, 2959
Willits, Harris L., 5505
Willkie, Wendell L., II, 9484
Willman, Jeffrey, 229
Willoughby, Jack, 8040
Wills, Charles, 9045
Wills, Don, 9045
Wills, Rosemary C., 2074
Willson, Janet, 1431
Willson, Victoria, 5137
Willumstad, Carol A., 7085
Willumstad, Robert B., 7085
Wilmans, Carlie, 1302
Wilmers, Gertrude, 6210
Wilmers, Robert G., 6210, 6406, 7077
Wilmington Trust Co., 1745, 1746, 1763, 1764, 1768, 1778, 1851, 5522
Wilner, Myron, 4242
Wilson Biodiversity Foundation, E.O., 2629
Wilson Co., H.W., Inc., The, 7087
Wilson Family Foundation, Thomas Henry, 7338
Wilson, Adrian N., 7171
Wilson, Albert W., III, 2636
Wilson, Alfred G., 4589
Wilson, Andrea, 798, 1246
Wilson, Andrew, 4658
Wilson, Angelina M., 3671
Wilson, Anthony L., 2468
Wilson, Betty H., 3317
Wilson, Blair J., 3237, 8645
Wilson, Boyd, Jr., 7160
Wilson, Carol, 9650
Wilson, Catherine, 3475
Wilson, Charles, 2787
Wilson, Charles K., Jr., 8646
Wilson, Charles L., III, 4581
Wilson, Chris, 7088
Wilson, Christina P., 1053
Wilson, Clarence A., 9558
Wilson, Colleen, 571
Wilson, Dan, 7249
Wilson, Dan L., 6109
Wilson, David, 798, 3803, 7338
Wilson, Denver C., 3671
Wilson, Derek, 1328
Wilson, Diane Wenger, 4581
Wilson, Donald R., Jr., 2807
Wilson, Dorothy Cheney, 9019
Wilson, Douglas A., 7465
Wilson, Dwayne A., 8851
Wilson, E. Miles, 4447
Wilson, Edwin G., Jr., 7294
Wilson, Elisa Gabelli, 5120
Wilson, Frances W., Mrs., 2576
Wilson, Frazier, 9168
Wilson, Fred B., 2576
Wilson, Fred W., 798, 1246
Wilson, Frederick R., 6887
Wilson, Gary, 7453
Wilson, Gary L., 1328
Wilson, Gayle, 1013
Wilson, George C., 3956
Wilson, Gloria, 857
Wilson, H.S., 4432
Wilson, H.W., 7087
Wilson, H.W., Mrs., 7087
Wilson, Henry, 7338
Wilson, Henry, III, 7338
Wilson, Howard O., 1024, 9204
Wilson, Huey J., 3671
Wilson, J. Bradley, 7153
Wilson, Jack D., Mrs., 3236
Wilson, James C., Jr., 8499
Wilson, James E., 7421
Wilson, Jane, 350, 5585
Wilson, Janet, 7338
Wilson, Janet D., 3934
Wilson, Janice, 9280
Wilson, Janice J., 8588
Wilson, Jasper L., 3236
Wilson, Jeff, 9280
Wilson, Jennifer, 5422, 8040
Wilson, Jennifer D., 8040
Wilson, Jennifer H., 3181
Wilson, Jennifer L., 3339
Wilson, Jim, 9280
Wilson, Jo, 3762
Wilson, Joanne S., 6887
Wilson, John, 4561
Wilson, John H., 71
Wilson, John H., II, 9101
Wilson, John K., 5033
Wilson, John S. (Tripp), 7296
Wilson, Joseph, 7088
Wilson, Joseph C., 7088
Wilson, June, 9707
Wilson, Justin P., 3237
Wilson, Karen Gail Miller, 9335
Wilson, Katherine C., 2414
Wilson, Katherine M., 7088
Wilson, Kathleen H., 7194
Wilson, Kenneth, 399
Wilson, Kent R., 1258
Wilson, Kerrie B., 1931
Wilson, Kevin, 2944
Wilson, Lana L., 1258
Wilson, Lars G., 7152
Wilson, Linda, 798
Wilson, Linde B., 8645
Wilson, Lisa, 3419
Wilson, Lisa W., 9217
Wilson, Lloyd R., 21
Wilson, Lynn N., 2281
Wilson, M., 1258
Wilson, Maria, 9280
Wilson, Marie C., 7088
Wilson, Mark, 7335
Wilson, Mark L., 4715, 4757
Wilson, Mary K., 7743
Wilson, Mary M., 4588
Wilson, Matilda R., 4589
Wilson, Matthew, 8156
Wilson, Melanie R., 7676
Wilson, Michael G., 350
Wilson, Michael J., 5182
Wilson, Norman L., 1369
Wilson, Pamela, 1246
Wilson, Perry, 4846
Wilson, Pete, Hon., 339
Wilson, Peter A., 4120
Wilson, Raiann, 1154
Wilson, Ralph, 9280
Wilson, Ralph C., Jr., 4588
Wilson, Randall, 4684
Wilson, Rebecca, 3195
Wilson, Richard A., 424
Wilson, Robert, 8613
Wilson, Robert A., 8646
Wilson, Robert A., Dr., 8265
Wilson, Robert C., III, 9072
Wilson, Robert F., 3822
Wilson, Robert L., 857
Wilson, Robert M., 3972
Wilson, Robert W., 7086
Wilson, Roger, Dr., 8511
Wilson, Rosine M., 9258
Wilson, Roxanne, 1133
Wilson, Russ, 9566
Wilson, Sarah F., 4658
Wilson, Scott, 7088
Wilson, Scott L., 3466
Wilson, Sharon, 9280
Wilson, Sherry A., 9026
Wilson, Spence, 8538
Wilson, Spence L., 8646
Wilson, Stephen, 4372, 7702
Wilson, Steve, 4440
Wilson, Steven, 8655
Wilson, Sunny, 9280
Wilson, Suzanne M., Dr., 5345
Wilson, T., 1258
Wilson, Terri, 9280
Wilson, Terry, 3424
Wilson, Thomas, 3909
Wilson, Thomas J., 2657
Wilson, Thomas L., 9188
Wilson, Tim, 106
Wilson, Tricia, 9444
Wilson, Ursula, 2818
Wilson, V. Otis, Jr., 7178
Wilson, Vera, 8236
Wilson, Wayne, 809, 9421
Wilson, William M., 3237
Wilson-Moore, Elizabeth, 8646
Wilson-Oyelaran, Eileen B., Dr., 4472
Wilson-Scott, Dalila, 6244
Wilson-Taylor, Marti, 4103
Wilson-Walker, Dianne, 3671
Wilson-West, Carol, 8646
Wilt Family Foundation, Toby S., 2514
Wilt, Gary, 8527
Wilt, Priscilla, 7414
Wilton, Jane L., 6544
Wiltse, Tom, 4448
Wiltsek, Nancy, 1283
Wiltshire, Albert, 6527
Wiltshire, Lisa, 8603
Wiltz, James W., 4738
Wimberg, Judith, 7419
Wimberg, Mary J., 1457
Wimberley, Ruby J., 9198
Wimer, Allan, 2041
Wimer, Ross, 2873
Winant, Joan, 5957
Winant, John, 5957
Winblad, Ann, 4760
Winchcole, Dorothy C., 3751
Winchell, Jean Rogers, 9139
Winchester-Vega, Michele, Dr., 5806
Wincrest Ventures LP, 8836
Wind River Holdings, LP, 7927
Winder, Charles, 2633
Winder, Phoebe, 4121
Windham, Diann, 8994
Windheim, Justin, 7910
Windheim, Randi, 7910
Windhorst, John, Jr., 4795
Windhorst, Peter, 4795
Window to Asia, 1346
Windreich, David, 1724
Winds of Change Foundation, 6864
Windsor, David L., 95
Windsor, Robert G., Rev., 1396
Wine, Scott W., 4746
Wineberg, Richard, 7425
Winer, Elizabeth Star, 2335
Winestock, Jim, 3745
Winetroub, Elizabeth H., 3519
Winfrey, Oprah, 3067
Winfrey, Oprah G., 3067
Wing, Edward J., 8383
Wing, Keith M., 7934
Wingate, Jo Stott, 2437
Wingate, Roy S., 9198
Wingens, Gay M., 5490
Winger, Rodger, 3373
Wingerter, Lori, 4442
Wingfield, W.T., 2576
Wingo, Nancy Brent, 8078
Wingo, Sherril L., 7287
Winhusen, Stephen M., 7632
Winiarski, Barbara, 1332
Winiarski, Warren, 1332
Winick Realty Group, LLC, 1771
Winkel, Rick, 2765
Winkelried, Abby, 7090
Winkelried, Jon, 7090
Winkhaus, Gwenn S., 7515
Winkler, Candace, 79
Winkler, Clifford E., 8789
Winkler, David J., 564
Winkler, Dean, 9280
Winkler, Margaret O., 9281
Winkler, Matthew M., 9281
Winkowski, Daniel, 3078
Winn, Carie, 9833
Winn, Christopher S., 9282
Winn, Heather M., 9282
Winn, Jack, 3269
Winn, Melinda G., 9282
Winn, Stephen T., 9282
Winn-Dixie Stores, Inc., 1996
Winnell, Todd, 4522
Winner, Donna, 7994
Winner, Leslie J., 7298
Winnick, Adam, 1333
Winnick, Alex, 1333
Winnick, Gary, 1333
Winnick, Karen, 1333
Winnitex Ltd., 6651
Winokur, Herbert, 9087
Winowiecki, Ronald L., 4521
Winship, Susan, 4152
Winship, William B., 5676
Winslow Tech Group, 9606
Winslow, Julia D., 1525
Winsor, Curtin, Jr., Hon., 5899
Winsor, Henry, 8175
Winsor, Monica, 5899
Winsor, Rebecca D., 5899
Winston Foundation, N.K., Inc., The, 7092
Winston, Bert F., III, 9203

Winston, Blake W., 9203
Winston, Frank, 8571
Winston, Harry, Inc., 7093
Winston, Hathily Johnson, 753
Winston, Jim, 2031
Winston, Joni R., 9929
Winston, L. David, 9203
Winston, Norman K., 7092
Winston, Patrick H., 9382
Winston, Phillip W., 9243
Winter, Alison, 3059
Winter, Arthur, 3177
Winter, David, 8808
Winter, David K., 945
Winter, Dorothy, 3177
Winter, Emma, 3177
Winter, Laura, 7876
Winter, Marlene, 9715
Winter, Mathew E., 2657
Winter, Nancy C.H., 2888
Winter, Nancy H.C., 2888
Winter, Susan W., 4231
Winter, William, Hon., 4827
Wintermann Marital Trust, 9283
Wintermann, Eula G., 9283
Winters, Barbara, 3348
Winters, Harold D., 7094
Winters, Judith, 7094
Winters, Laura, 7094
Winters, Maryann M., 5757
Winters, Peter, 2530
Winters, Vernon, 7340
Winterthur, 5707
Winthrop Trust, Amory, 7091
Winthrop, Grant, 864
Winthrop, Inc., 5185
Winthrop, Phoebe Jane, 3852
Wintrob, Jay S., 579
Wintrode, David C., 5394
Wintrode, Victoria L., 1031
Wipple, Ross M., 199
Wirginis, Terrence L., 7942
Wirshba, Lewis H., 5826
Wirshup, David, 1159
Wirshup, Rochelle Shapell, 1159
Wirth, Anton, 5095
Wirth, Christopher, 1525
Wirth, Doris, 5095
Wirth, Dyann, 7164
Wirth, John, 5095
Wirth, Kelsey, 1525
Wirth, Paul, 5095
Wirth, Wren Winslow, 1525
Wirtz, Mary, 9867
Wirz, Henry, 1103
Wisbey, Ron, 1288
Wischer, Irene S., 9284
Wischmeier, Curt, 8522
Wischmeier, Priscilla, 3284
Wischmeier, Shawn, 4627
Wisconsin Energy Corp., 9969
Wisconsin Power and Light Co., 9804
Wisconsin Public Service Corp., 9970
Wisconsin Sports Development Corporation, 9913
Wisdom, Andrew, 3663
Wisdom, Grace, 7816
Wisdom, Peggy, 7816
Wise, Carol, 3644
Wise, Catherine J., 6346
Wise, Craig E., 7688
Wise, Deborah, 6346
Wise, Henry Stephen, 4813
Wise, Janelle A., 2630
Wise, Mary Ann, 3312
Wise, Phyllis M., 5329
Wise, Robert G., 5029, 5030
Wise, Watson W., 9285
Wisehart, Lucie, 1394
Wiseman, Eric C., 7332
Wiseman, Joan, 3354
Wiseman, Mary Whitten, 3575
Wiseman, Michael L., 7581
Wiseman, Robert A., 7576
Wisen, Kristen, 2872
Wisenburg, Ralph, 7421
Wiser, Bob, 9561
Wiser, Wanda G., 9417
Wish You Were Here Productions, 1850
Wishard Hospital, 3317
Wishcamper, Carol, 3708
Wishkoff, Marc, 9410
Wishnafski, Diane, 1651
Wishnak, Stevie, 2253
Wishnew, Robert, 6222
Wishnia, Steve, 8615
Wishnick, Lisa, 2646
Wishnick, William, 2646
Wisinski, Pamela, 3196
Wiskemann, Christine Y., 908
Wiskemann, Elizabeth, 908
Wiskemann, Rico M., 908
Wismann, David, 3293
Wismer, Joan M., 8343
Wisnom, Craig, 101
Wispelwey, June C., 9547
Wiss & Co, 6918
Wisse, Ruth R., 5628
Wissinger, Nancy M., 8111
Wissink, Margaret Kean, 8950
Wistar, Christy, 2648
Wistreich, Kenneth, 1771
Wit, Jerry, 3888
Witcher, Doug, 7231
With, Jacob, 1392
Withee, Jody, 420
Witherbee, Victoria, 1334
Witherby, Brenten, 2766
Witherington, Hunter, 8538
Witherington, James D., Jr., 8538
Withers, Suzanne, 3960
Withers, Timothy C., 4007
Witherspoon, Gary D., 9030
Witherspoon, John, 3698
Withrow, William J., 9382
Witkovski, Vicki F., 5058
Witmer, Charles H., 5395
Witmer, Chuck, 7973
Witmer, Jean Hudson, 4463
Witorsch, Rafael, Dr., 9457
Witorsch, Raphael, 9447
Witt, Bruce, 3507
Witt, John, 5019
Witt, Judith D., 539
Witt, Judy, 2826
Witt, Kyle D., 2767
Witt, Richard A., 5071
Witt, Susan E. Ahrens, 3410
Wittchow, Scott, 9843
Witteman, Mike, 4314
Witten, Elizabeth, 7095
Witten, Elizabeth H., 7095
Witten, Richard E., 7095
Wittenbach, Jo Ann, 3289
Wittenberg, Carol, 744
Wittenberg, Joel R., 4474
Wittenborn, Christopher Dirk, 5224
Witter & Co., Dean, 1335
Witter, Dean, 1335
Witter, Dean, III, 1200, 1335
Witter, Dean, Mrs., 1335
Witter, Malcolm G., 1335
Witter, William P., 1335
Witthoefft, Charles F., 9504
Witting, Paul, 4361
Wittink, Alicia P., 6615
Wittler, Don, 5095
Wittlin, Lori, 8718
Witzer, Lawrence L., 381
Wizig-Barrios, Renee, 8916
WJ Foundation, The, 8590
WJS Trust, 1184
WLD Trust, 2081
WMG, Inc. Pension Plan, 2867
Wo, Robert W., Jr., 2588, 2613
Woburn Properties LLP, 4003
Wochok, Taras M., 8020
Wockner, Frances A., 9763
Wockner, Irene, 9763
Wockner, William E., 9763
Wodetzki, Tom, 3205
Woehrer, Patricia, 9960
Woerner, John R., 1469
Woerner, Otto H., 7178
Woetzel, Kurt, 7945
Wohl, Alexander D., 7097
Wohl, Allison K., 7097
Wohl, Diane, 7097
Wohl, Frank, 5348
Wohl, Howard, 7097
Wohl, Pamela B., 7097
Wohlers, Albert H., 3238
Wohlers, Janet L., 3238
Wohlford, Mary M., 1336
Wohlford, Sheryl L., 3555
Wohlgelernter, Myriam, 644
Wohlgemuth, David C., 5404
Wohlgemuth, Jay, 7820
Wohlleban, Robin, 9443
Wohlstetter, John, 6734
Woidke, Eric, 7412
Wojan, Connie, 4361
Wojcicki, Anne, 343
Wojcik, Tim, 5044
Wolanksy, Paul, 1596
Wolchock, Carey, 6536
Wolcott, Arthur S., 6832
Wolcott, Gregory, 5969
Wold, Clark, 8523
Wold, Diana J., 1985
Wold, Elaine J., 1985, 6698
Wold, Keith C., Jr., 1985
Wolden, Wayne, 4679
Woldenberg, Malcolm, 3672
Woldert, Thomas M., 8819
Woleske, Christine, 9854
Wolf Family Trust, 6246
Wolf, Alan, 1234
Wolf, Ben, 9676
Wolf, Brian J., 7629
Wolf, Chaim, 5962
Wolf, Charles B., 2998
Wolf, Christopher, 1337
Wolf, Cindy, 8784
Wolf, Daniel, 1957
Wolf, David, 1099
Wolf, David M., 1684
Wolf, Deborah, 5962
Wolf, Don A., 8341
Wolf, Elaine, 1526
Wolf, Frank, 6241, 7058
Wolf, Gerald, 7971
Wolf, Greg, 2927
Wolf, Jamie R., 1684
Wolf, Kate, 1684
Wolf, Leon M., 3642
Wolf, Linda S., 2746
Wolf, May H., 3642
Wolf, Melvin, 1526
Wolf, Nidia, 4332
Wolf, Peter, 2998
Wolf, Randall A., 1337
Wolf, Rebecca Medeiros, 415
Wolf, Richard, 3955
Wolf, Robert, 6246
Wolf, Robert B., 2718
Wolf, Sandra, 1526
Wolf, Saul, 5962
Wolf, Shimon, 5705
Wolf, Thomas M., 7444
Wolf, Wendy J., 3698, 3699
Wolfberg, David A., 2223
Wolfe Administrative Trust, Betty K., 2391
Wolfe Charitable Remainder Unitrust 1997, Tiffany T., 169
Wolfe Charitable Remainder Unitrust 1999, Tiffany T., 169
Wolfe, Albert, 9789
Wolfe, Andrew Frey, 4658
Wolfe, Betty K., 2391
Wolfe, Carol F., 4658
Wolfe, D. Jay, 5067
Wolfe, Dana, 6748
Wolfe, Daniel T., 4658
Wolfe, David W., 5394
Wolfe, Jessica, 5987
Wolfe, Joan M., 6419
Wolfe, Johanna L., 6419
Wolfe, John F., 7719
Wolfe, John J., 4859
Wolfe, Judson A., 6419
Wolfe, Katherine Cassels, 8467
Wolfe, Katherine I, 7719
Wolfe, Lawrence A., 4471
Wolfe, Mark, 1497
Wolfe, Marueen, 5960
Wolfe, Merle D., 8635
Wolfe, Molly Frey, 4658
Wolfe, Olivia L., 6419
Wolfe, Patricia A., 7963
Wolfe, Peggy, 1497
Wolfe, Ray, 2632
Wolfe, Rita J., 7719
Wolfe, Wendy, 1511
Wolfen, Mary G., 1338
Wolfen, Werner F., 1338
Wolfensohn, Adam R., 5696, 7098
Wolfensohn, Elaine R., 5696, 7098
Wolfensohn, James, 5747
Wolfensohn, James D., 5696, 7098
Wolfensohn, Naomi R., 5696, 7098
Wolfensohn, Sara R., 5696, 7098
Wolff, Avery C., 2505
Wolff, Christoph J., 1007
Wolff, Curtis, 9286
Wolff, Cyvia G., 9286
Wolff, Drew, 9578
Wolff, Frances Klitsner, 9810
Wolff, Gregory S., 1690
Wolff, Holly, 5556
Wolff, J. Marshall, 8136
Wolff, Jean, 4590
Wolff, John, 9410
Wolff, Kari, 977
Wolff, Keith, 4590

Wolff, Kevin, 4590
Wolff, L. Thomas, 6153
Wolff, Laura, 5785
Wolff, Lewis, 4590
Wolff, Luther H., III, 2505
Wolff, Margaret L., 6144
Wolff, Melvyn L., 9286
Wolff, Paula, 2946
Wolff, Robert L., Jr., 4310
Wolff, Steven A., 1581
Wolfington, J. Eustace, 8029
Wolfman, Darren, 8692
Wolford, Kate, 4708, 4709
Wolfrum Capital Management Group, 3388
Wolfson, Jeri Louise Waxenberg, 2392
Wolfson, Louis E., 4325
Wolfson, Louis, III, 2392
Wolfson, Mitchell, Jr., 2392
Wolfson, Nancy Abramson, 1963
Wolfson, Stephen S., 4603
Wolfson, Warren, 6285
Wolfzorn, E. John, 7659
Wolgamott, Steve, 7437
Wolk, David M., 7099
Wolk, Jeremy J., 7099
Wolk, Louis S., 7099
Wolk, Marvin L., 7099
Wolkomir, Mary Ann, 944
Wollberg, Maria Elena, 1828
Wollen, Carolyn S., 5676
Wollenberg, Christopher, 1339
Wollenberg, David A., 1339
Wollenberg, H.L., 1339
Wollenberg, Richard, 9603
Wollenberg, Richard H., 1339
Wollowick, Gladys, 2393
Wollowick, Janet Amy, 2393
Wolman, Paul C., 3726
Wolohan, Angela M., 4591
Wolohan, Christine M., 4591
Wolohan, James L., 4591
Wolohan, Michael, 4591
Wolohan, Michael J., 4591
Wolohan, Richard P., 4591
Wolohan, Richard V., 4591
Wolohan, Sharon, 4591
Wolohan, Sharon L., 4591
Woloshyn, Sonya, 5483
Woloszyk, Carl, 4370
Wolsey, Randy, 9118
Wolslager, J.W., 9288
Wolslager, J.W., III, 9288
Wolslager, J.W., Jr., 9288
Wolslager, Josephine S., 9288
Wolslager, Stephen J., 9288
Wolstencroft, Catherine, 7100
Wolstencroft, Tracy, 7100
Wolszczak, Jay, 2147
Wolter, Gary J., 9898
Wolters, Kate, 1403
Wolters, Kate Pew, 4547, 4592
Wolters, Richard, 4592
Wolverine Sign Works, 4377
Wolverine World Wide, 4593
Wolverton, David, 9109
Wolz, John F., 1397
Womac, Joe, 1203
Womack, Christopher C., 2554
Womack, Fred D., 8560
Womack, Walter C., 4866
Womble, Bill R., 9184
Womble, Ralph H., 7221
Women's Center of San Joaquin County, 417
Women's Project Foundation, 7472
Wommack, Kent W., 3708
Wonacott, Jeff, 4448
Wonders, Clare Atkinson, 8768
Wong, Dennis Jason, 1341
Wong, Emily, 9599
Wong, Frances, 5263
Wong, Francis, 309
Wong, Harry C., 2622
Wong, Huey, 841
Wong, Irwin, 385
Wong, Kirk, 877
Wong, Natasha, 273
Wong, Nee-Chang Chock, 2622
Wong, Pausang, 841
Wong, Phillip W., 3973
Wong, Shannon Elizabeth, 1341
Wong, Sharon, 2585
Wong, Sheyl, 1109
Wong, William H., 1936
Wong, Winston F., 366
Wong-Avery, Sally Tsui, 273
Woo, Michael, 841
Woo, Myong Shin, 512
Woo, Richard, 9722
Wood 2004 Charitable Remainder Unitrust, William M., 8452
Wood III Trust, William M., 8452
Wood, Anthony C., 6217
Wood, Brandon C., 9695
Wood, Brenda K., 9695
Wood, Brian K., 3605
Wood, Carla, 2253
Wood, Charles O., III, 4326
Wood, Charles R., 1725
Wood, Clay, 9289
Wood, Cynthia, 1344
Wood, Danny Lee, 8647
Wood, Daphne F., 2459
Wood, David, 3962, 4296
Wood, David L., 1425
Wood, David S., 4326
Wood, Dean, 4375
Wood, Donald E., 9289
Wood, Donald R., III, 9695
Wood, E. Jenner, III, 2499, 2529, 2573, 2579
Wood, Edna, 6802
Wood, Elizabeth, 7051
Wood, Erica, 1166
Wood, Frank Martin, 8767
Wood, Franklin Jerry, 3910
Wood, Gregory, 9289
Wood, Irene, 177
Wood, J. Kurt, 2390
Wood, Jack, 9289
Wood, James, 6228
Wood, Jeff, 5808
Wood, Jenner, 9539
Wood, John F., 4900
Wood, Karen, 3419
Wood, Kate B., 5310
Wood, Kathryn, 3910
Wood, Kristin K., 2755
Wood, Louise, 9289
Wood, Minnie Rhea, 8835
Wood, Miriam M., 4326
Wood, Nora, 1749
Wood, Norman, 8775
Wood, Patti Jo Peck, 8647
Wood, Phoebe A., 3577
Wood, Robert A., 4900
Wood, Robin, 5803
Wood, Rodney P., 4331, 4425, 4426, 4427, 4428, 4429
Wood, Roger, 9925
Wood, Ross, 9634
Wood, Sarah Hager, 3597
Wood, Sylvia Upton, 4565
Wood, William P., 9235
Wood, William, III, 8452
Wood, Willis, 221
Wood, Willis B., Jr., 664
Wood-Prince, Patrick, 3090
Wood-Prince, Patrick B., 3089
Woodall, Timothy, 958
Woodard, Andrew, 7899
Woodard, Billy T., 7273
Woodard, Carlton, 7899
Woodard, Diondra, 2351
Woodard, Elizabeth H., 9405
Woodard, Joan, 7188
Woodard, Joan B., 157
Woodard, Joan C., 420
Woodard, Joy, 7899
Woodard, Kim, 7899
Woodard, Kristen A., 7899
Woodard, Sandra, 7303
Woodard, Tod, 7899
Woodard, Tyson, 7899
Woodard, Walter A., 7899
Woodbourne Foundation, 6380
Woodbranch Associates, 3773
Woodbridge Forest Apartments LLC, 9452
Woodburn, Connie, 7398
Woodbury, J. J., 8833
Woodbury, Richard L., 7170
Woodcliff, Inc., 5444
Woodeshick, Kevin D., 7972
Woodford, Buckner, IV, 3560
Woodforest National Bank, 9290
Woodham, Denise "Dee" A., 21
Woodham, John, 2569
Woodhouse, Charles E., 583
Woodhouse, Lorenzo E., 9361
Woodin, John H., 9892
Woodin, Peter, 744
Woodland Landing LP, 9452
Woodland Venture Fund, 6762
Woodling, Nancy Elizabeth, 7676
Woodriff, Jaffray P., 8241
Woodring, Juji, 8324
Woodrow Foundation, 9615
Woodruff Law Firm PA, 7425
Woodruff, Barbara McBeth, 894
Woodruff, Carolyn, 7425
Woodruff, Christopher S., 2578
Woodruff, Dina, 2578
Woodruff, Ethel I., 2578
Woodruff, J. Barnett, 2578
Woodruff, James W., 2578
Woodruff, James W., III, 2578
Woodruff, Judy, 5747, 7195
Woodruff, Judy C., 1907
Woodruff, Katherine F., 2578
Woodruff, Robert W., 2579
Woods Charitable Fund, Inc., 3242
Woods, Alfred, 5501
Woods, Alfred L., 9559
Woods, Alison, 1563
Woods, Bethany, 4211
Woods, Bonnie, 5805
Woods, Brent V., 226
Woods, C. Patrick, 3552
Woods, Clancy, 93
Woods, Cynthia R., 5013
Woods, David W., 293
Woods, Donald McG., 1374
Woods, Donna W., 5096
Woods, Emily L., 4155
Woods, Francine, 966
Woods, Frank H., 5096
Woods, Frank H., Jr., 5096
Woods, Gary V., 9009
Woods, Hank, 5063, 5096
Woods, Henry C., 5096
Woods, Henry Clay, III, 8618
Woods, J. Eric, 8475
Woods, James F., 4362
Woods, Jane, 9497
Woods, Janet, 9655
Woods, Joan Jarrett, 3241
Woods, Laura-Lee Whittier, 845, 1323
Woods, Marilyn J., 226
Woods, Matthew B., 8490
Woods, Milton, 9622
Woods, Nelle C., 5096
Woods, Pam, 8745
Woods, Richard A., 9400
Woods, Robert J., 3241
Woods, Ronald L., 5463
Woods, Skye, 894
Woods, Susanne, 2041
Woods, Thomas C., IV, 5096
Woods, Thomas C., Jr., 5096
Woods, Ward W., 1006
Woods, Wendee, 4496
Woods, William S., 9413
Woodson Trust Co., Margaret C., 7342
Woodson, Cheryl, 3113
Woodson, Margaret C., 7342
Woodson, Paul B., Jr., 7342
Woodsum, Stephen G., 4151
Woodward Charitable Lead Trust, Helen, 1349
Woodward Governor Co., 3243
Woodward, Brad, 3341
Woodward, Elizabeth M., 1845
Woodward, Helen W., 1349
Woodward, Inc., 3243
Woodward, Josephine, 6375
Woodward, Kay E., Dr., 8501
Woodward, Robert B., 157
Woodward, Robert G., 2480
Woodword, Joan K., 4783
Woodworth, Patricia, 579
Woodyard Trust, Dorothy M., 2742
Woodzell, Bruce, 9405
Wooldredge, William D., 7496
Woolever, Elizabeth S., 8003
Wooley, Dudley, 4820
Wooley, Ken, 888
Woolf, Geraldine H., 3673
Woolf, William C., 3673
Woolfolk, Bill, 2844
Woolfolk, Kristy, 2844
Woolfolk, William C., III, 2460
Woolford, Linda, 4058
Woolhiser, Dale, 5013
Woolhiser, Michael, 4517
Woollam Co., John A., Inc., 5097
Woollam, John A., 5097
Woollam, Olivia, 3663
Woollam, Philip, 3636
Woollam, Tina Freeman, 3636
Woolley Fund, 1387
Woolley, R.B., Jr., 591
Woolley, Scott, 591
Woolley, Vasser, 2581

Woolls, Betty O'Shaughnessy, 1345
Woolsey, Holly, 2033
Woolsey, R. James, 1679
Woolsey, Ted, 9587
Woolsey, William T., 4877
Woolway, Paul, 1127
Woosley, Christopher K., 7735
Wooten, David, 7183
Wooten, Lamont, 7217
Wooten, Lynn, 7180
Wooten, McKinley, 7321
Wooten, Rosalie O'Reilly, 4872
Wooten, Wilma, 3366
Wootten, Emily L., 45
Wootton, Connie J., 5531
Wootton, Earle, 7992
Worboys-Turner, Mary, 6722
Word at Work Foundation, The, 9961
Worden, John T., 8560
Worden, Margaret, 1868
Worden, Richard, 1650
Worden, Trish, 1650
Workman, Carolyn, 4735
Workman, Nicole, 7558
Workman, Russ, 9321
Workman, Rusty, 9045
Worland, Brooke, 3330
World Childrens Fund-Europe (CH), 1346
World Events, LLC, 396
World Harvest Church, 1346
World Reach, 7398
World Trade Ventures, Ltd., 2494
World Union for Progressive Judaism, 341
World Wide Technology Holding Co. Inc., 5002
World Wrestling Entertainment, 7008
World Zionist Organization, 6229
Worldbridge LLC, 9587
WorldCom, Inc., 1153
Worley, Dana, 9291
Worley, Karen, 8994
Worley, Peyton, 8506
Worley, Richard B., 8183
Worley, Thomas D., 9291
Worls, G. Randolph, 7935
Worman, Nancy H., 7456
Wornall, Kearney, 5003
Worner, Jacob, 7700
Worner, Rebecca, 4800
Worrell 1989 Charitable Lead Unitrust, T. Eugene, 9440
Worrell Charitable Lead Trust, Shaffer, The, 2395
Worrell, Anne R., 9440
Worrell, Odette A., 2395
Worrell, T. Eugene, 9440
Worrell, Thomas E., Jr., 2395
Worsham, Gary, 9022
Worsoe, Johannes, 5724
Worster, Bruce, 1347
Worster, Susan, 1347
Worth, Carolyn A., 1280
Worth, Robert, 4562
Worth, Sherry, 7295
Wortham, Gus S., 9292
Wortham, Lee, 6343
Wortham, Lyndall F., 9292
Wortham, Maxine, Dr., 2763
Wortham, R.W., III, 9292
Worthen, Diana Gonzalez, 197
Worthington Industries, 7563
Worthington, John, 3014
Worthington, T.H., 9114
Wos, Aldona Z., 7345
Wott, Robert, 3166
Wozniak, Julie, 7591
Wray, Cecil, 5556
Wray, Gay F., 5260
Wray, Ronald D., 3096, 3098
Wray, Timothy F., 5260
Wren, John, 5583
Wren, Marvin F., 9764
Wren, Michele M., 9764
Wren, William C., 2442
Wrenn, Frank, 7191
Wrenn, Peter J., 3140
Wright, Andrew, 3398
Wright, Anne L., 9382
Wright, Barbara P., 1007
Wright, Bernard H., Jr., 7544
Wright, Bob, 3651
Wright, Carolyn, 9367
Wright, Celeste Hank, 2828
Wright, Charles B., III, 9765
Wright, Christopher, 6951
Wright, Cleveland A., 9398
Wright, David, 85
Wright, David C., 7268
Wright, Earl L., 1427
Wright, Eldon S., 7629
Wright, Hubert, 3851
Wright, Jack W., 8768
Wright, James, 3788
Wright, James D., 2278
Wright, James W., 9474
Wright, Jason H., 6544
Wright, Jennifer R., 8133
Wright, Jill, 7295
Wright, Jim, 3481
Wright, Johnie E., 9293
Wright, Joseph, 1894
Wright, Karen Buchwald, 7377, 7413
Wright, Katherine B., 3911
Wright, Katie, 9341
Wright, Kenneth R., 414
Wright, Lucy B., 3911
Wright, Marcy, 7287
Wright, Martha C., 7174
Wright, Mary, 3690
Wright, Meg, 2755
Wright, Merrill, 9765
Wright, Minturn T., III, 1849
Wright, Pearl, 9321
Wright, Peter A., 1727
Wright, Prentice "Bing", 9765
Wright, Randy L., 8944
Wright, Renee, 1527
Wright, Richard L., 5270
Wright, Stephen C., 3923
Wright, Stephen J., 5766, 6195
Wright, Suzanne, 4306
Wright, Thomas, 3058, 4599, 6395
Wright, Thomas D., 3381
Wright, Tim, 9802
Wright, Timothy, 9625
Wright, Ursula, 1014
Wright, V. Orville, 3014
Wright, Vernon H.C., 3911
Wright, Virginia B., 9765
Wright, W. Haig, II, 74
Wright, W.R., 2056
Wright, Wendy, 1727
Wright, Wilhelmina, Hon., 4703
Wright, William, 1390
Wright, William H., II, 6414
Wright, William L., 6195
Wright, William T., II, 8133
Wright, Zach, 7188
Wrigley, 1771
Wrigley Jr. Co., Wm., 3244
Wrigley, Drew, 7352
Wrigley, Julie A., 9766
Wrigley, Julie Ann, 9766
Wrigley, Mark D., 5229
Wrinkle, Briggen, 1395
Wriston, Kathryn D., 6144
Wrobleski, Paul, 5881
Wroblewski, Jeff, 4659
Wroclawski, John, 6804
Wronski, Maria, 349
Wrubel, Rob, 1478
Wruble, Brian, 2041
WSCR LLC, 4003
WTVF-News Channel 5 Network, 9467
Wu, Danke, 1351
Wu, Hueyling, 5507
Wu, Kathleen J., 8975
Wu, Lambert, 3552
Wu, Peter, 385
Wu, Simone, 3748
Wu, Whiting, 6382
Wu, Yi-Ching, 721
Wu, Yuyi, 1351
Wu, Yvonne W., 9353
Wubbena, Robert, 9605
Wuebbels, Brian, 4985
Wuebker, Dean, 4605
Wuerthner, George, 426
Wuest, Karen A., 9843
Wulf, Cap, 9925
Wulf, Jerold W., 4602
Wulff, Susan, 2717
Wulfsohn, Michael, 586
Wuliger Charitable Lead Unitrust, Patricia, 7722
Wuliger, E. Jeffrey, 7722
Wuliger, Ernest M., 7722
Wuliger, Gregory, 7722
Wuliger, Timothy F., 7722
Wunderkinder Foundation, The, 1073
Wunderman, Deborah, 5161
Wunderman, Michael, 5161
Wunderman, Nathan, 5161
Wunsch, Eric M., 7106
Wunsch, Ethel, 7106
Wunsch, Joseph W., 7106
Wunsch, Peter, 7106
Wunsch, Samuel, 7106
Wurm, Jamen, 743
Wurm, Robert, 5542
Wurmb, Robert O., 4943
Wurmfeld, Sanford, 6159
Wurster, Hans, 1511
Wurth, Megan, 6644
Wurtz, Rebecca M., 3172
Wurzer, Henry "Buzz", 2166
Wurzer, Marvin A., 8793, 9155, 9271
WV Culture and Arts Grant, 9795
WWF, Ltd., 9555
WWP/Young & Rubicam, 6904
Wyant, Dom H., 2406
Wyatt, Jane, 4714
Wyatt, Joe, 7810
Wyatt, Kim, 9054
Wyatt, Mary F., 3896
Wyatt, Natalie, 9401
Wyatt, Oscar S., Jr., 8804
Wyckoff, Ann P., 9749
Wyckoff, Ann Pigott, 9693
Wyckoff, Christy, 9693
Wyckoff, Martha, 9749
Wyckoff, Paul L., 9749
Wyckoff, T. Evans, 9749
Wyckoff-Dickey, Sheila, 9749
Wycoff, Dorothy, 5068
Wyeth, 3833
Wyeth, Judy, 3319
Wyeth, Phyllis M., 1754
Wyett, Pamela Applebaum, 4341
Wygod, Emily, 5425
Wygod, Martin J., 5425, 5496
Wygod, Max, 5425
Wygod, Pamela, 5425, 5496
Wyks, Philip M., 5398
Wylde, Lynn, 3929
Wylie, Ann C., 1424
Wylie, D.C., 8470
Wylie, Elizabeth A., 1636
Wylie, J. Michael, 8690
Wyllie, Ed, 1198
Wyly, Evan A., 9005
Wyman, Beth, 9916
Wyman, Bill, 9916
Wyman, Francis S., 2208
Wymer, Anne, 919
Wyndham Championship, 9470
Wyndham Worldwide Corp., 5506
Wyndsor Custom Homes, 8756
Wynkoop, Derrik, 5806
Wynn, Bee, 1350
Wynn, Brenda, 8603
Wynn, Carl, 1350
Wynn, David, 2763
Wynn, Deryl W., 4920
Wynn, Hope Mead, 6466
Wynn, John R., 3, 46
Wynn, Mark, 3285
Wynn, Tom, 4806
Wynne, Jennifer, 2379
Wynne, John, 7727
Wynne, John O. "Dubby", 9448
Wyrick, Cynthia G., 2588
Wysard, Paul L., 2617
Wyse, Duncan, 7876
Wyskiel, Christy, 9005
Wysong, Kathryn Lyman, 4734
Wyss, Amy E., 9983
Wyss, Hansjoerg, 1958, 1959
Wyszynski, Kathy A., 3818
Wytana, Inc., 5056
Wythes, Carol Krause, 9886

Xbox, 3245
Xcel Energy Inc., 4808
Xerox Corp., 1728
XFMRS Inc., 3326
Xie Children's Irrevocable Trust, 1351
Xie, Bing, 1351
Xie, Ken, 1351
Xie, Michael, 1351
Xing, Jing, 3201
Xstrata Zinc, 7349

Yablon, Andrea Rozran, 3110
Yabu, Irene, 1107
Yackira, Michael W., 5136
Yacktman, Steve, 541
Yackulic, Corrie, 9565
Yacoby, Alicia Kaylie, 6263
Yad Hanadiv, 5651
Yadao, Elisa, 2604
Yaeger, William J., Jr., 9773
Yaffa, Earle, 5989
Yagoda, Eva Dabah, 5840

Yagoda, Scott, 5265
Yahgulanaas, Michael Nicoll, 399
Yahng, Christopher D., 721
Yake, Byron, 5396
Yakes, Gary, 9916
Yakes, Gary R., 4809
Yakey, Ace, 3342
Yale New Haven Health, 9250
Yale University, 1729
Yale, Camille, 9146
Yalich, Barbara L., 7760
Yamaato, Joyce, 2513
Yamada, Albert M., 2598
Yamada, Sayuri, 5532
Yamagata, Gene H., 9357
Yamamoto, Andrew Yutaka, 4432
Yamamoto, John M., 458
Yamanishi, Kenichiro, 9487
Yamate, Gordon, 1166
Yamazaki, Akiko, 1059
Yamba, A. Zachary, 5490
Yamin, Alice, 6085
Yanarella, Mark C., 1616
Yance, Gordon E., 7413
Yancey, Scott, Dr., 7558
Yanchura, Marc P., 2989
Yanders, Elise Roby, 8043
Yang Living Trust, Jerry, 1059
Yang, Amy, 1353
Yang, Frank, 1352
Yang, Geoffrey, 1353
Yang, Gina, 9889
Yang, Henry T., 771
Yang, Jackson, 1352
Yang, Jennifer, 1352
Yang, Jerry, 936, 1059
Yang, Jimmy, 1352
Yang, Julie, 1352
Yang, Linda, 1352
Yang, Peter, 1352
Yanis, Caren, 2781
Yankee Gas Services Company, 1656
Yankie, Karen, 4332
Yanko, Mary, 7401
Yanko, Sara Casey, 9793
Yanney, Charese E., 3480
Yanni, Catherine, 744
Yannucci, Michael P., 7620
Yano, James A., 7674
Yanotta, Patrick, 6714
Yanta, Joyce A., 9101
Yantz, Jeff, 4344
Yao, Lily K., 2598
Yaphe, Dana, 2128
Yar, Margaret Hille, 7759
Yarborough Applegate Law Firm, 8492
Yarborough KRI, Inc., 9294
Yarborough, Linda B., 9294
Yarborough, Martha, 7231
Yarborough, Susan K., 9294
Yarborough, W.B., 9294
Yarbrough, Brian G., 9225
Yardi, 9606
Yarmolinsky, Alex, 876
Yarnevich, George W., 3548
Yaroma, Laura, 7490
Yarter, David L., 9447, 9457
Yartz, Larry J., 8347
Yaschik, Henry, 8509
Yass, Jeff, 9408
Yates Trust, S.P., 5537
Yates, Brooks, 9049
Yates, C. Daniel, 3256
Yates, Ellanor, 8853
Yates, Emily, 8853
Yates, Estelle H., 5537, 5538
Yates, Jim, 3360
Yates, Kelsy, 5537
Yates, Lloyd, 7196
Yates, Mary Beth, 5537
Yates, Michelle Crozier, 1734
Yates, Peter, 9411
Yates, Peyton, 5537
Yates, Richard, 8446
Yates, Richard Martin, 5538
Yates, S.P., 5537
Yates, Sam, 43
Yates, St. Clair Peyton, Jr., 5538
Yavitz, Jerome A., 2396
Yaw, Nancy, 3397
Yawkey, Jean R., 4329
Yazoo Investment Corp., 4832
Yeager, Barbara Coit, 9317
Yeager, Coye, 64
Yeager, Jerry, 3336
Yeager, Judy, 3265
Yeager, K. Elizabeth, 9090
Yeager, Kathi, 8935
Yeager, Kathryn P., 9090
Yeager, Kathryn Prothro, 9090
Yeager, Kay, 9277
Yeaman, Eric K., 2593, 2602
Yeamans, David G., 4866
Yeargan, Flora, 7346
Yeargan, Rowann, 7346
Yeargan, Sherman, 7346
Yearout, Kevin, 5511
Yeater, Royce, 9869
Yedlin, Nancy, 1575
Yedlin, Samuel, 3809
Yee Tung Garment Co., Ltd., 6651
Yee, James, 1035
Yee, Sylvia, 643
Yeh, Charlotte S., 3953
Yehling, Mary Kleine, 3195
Yeiser, Charles F., 7485
Yeiser, Eric B., 7485
Yelen, Jan, 2184
Yeley, Brian D., 3278
Yellin, Eric, 603
Yellott, Kinloch N., III, 3909
Yen, Tai Hwa, 5507
Yen, Victor, 6881
Yen, Vincent, 6881
Yenawine, Philip, 612
Yerger, Wirt, Jr., 4820
Yes Network, 1850
Yeshiva B'nai Zion, 6763
Yeshiva Imrei Yosef, 5668
Yeshiva Imrei Yosef Spinka, 5699
Yeshiva Novominsk, 5668
Yeshiva Tov V'Chesed, 7107
Yesod Fund, 913, 8384
Yett, Jane, 248
Yeung, Michael, 3244
Yevich, Cynthia, 8275
Yhang, Kacie E., 721
Yi-Ching, Jennie Lee Mui, 841
Yien, Valentine, 2648
Ying Foundation, Tse, 5114
Yingling, Beth, 6813
Yingling, Earl, 8001
Yingling, Sue, 3757
Yip, Alex, 5190
Yip, Trea C., 6864
Yishan, Wu, 4036
Yitchok, Zichran, 5937
Yochim, Maryann C., 8026
Yockey, Laura, 4532
Yocum, Bob, 2730
Yoder, Lewis, 7402
Yoder, Linda K., 3348
Yoder, Peggy L., 7378
Yoder, Tom, 2658
Yohlin, Joseph M., 1963
Yoho, Terri, 9884
Yokohama Tire Corporation, 118
Yokota, Bonita A.T., 1236
Yokota, Ronald, 1236
Yonekura, Lynn, 611
Yonkers, Suzanne C., 7741
Yoo, Don Chan, 8383
Yoo, Tae, 402
Yoon, Kyung, 6546
Yoor, Brian, 2648
Yorba, Jonathan Lorenzo, 419
York Cable Television Co., 8310
York Home Care, LLC, 5890
York Investments LC, 9508
York, Tommy, 4509
Yoshida, Masao, 2675
Yoshida, Rika, 3000
Yoshikawa, Hirokazu, 6003
Yoshitani, Tay, 9731
Yost, Clayton, 8993
Yost, Richard A., 7702
Youckton, Rodney, 9605
Youde, Jim, Dr., 9603
Youga, Anthony L., 561
Youmans, Richard Y., 2490
Young, Aaron, 1005
Young, Allan C., 1005
Young, Amy Jo, 9304
Young, Anne, 7111
Young, Barbara A., 3369
Young, Beatriz Palomino, 1140
Young, Brian D., 7111
Young, Byrnes M., 3674
Young, Candace, Dr., 9603
Young, Caprice, 8672
Young, Carol, Dr., 7416
Young, Caroline McKissick, 8486
Young, Carolyn A., 2192
Young, Chad, 9304
Young, Christopher, 3593
Young, Dan, 3319
Young, Dennis, 849
Young, Donald, 4204
Young, Doreen, 810
Young, Ellen, 3423
Young, Emily, 1108
Young, Fay Cameron, 9295
Young, G., 777
Young, Gay, 6544
Young, George, 9295
Young, George V., 3656
Young, Glenn, 2315
Young, Herbert D., Jr., 8545
Young, J. Stephen, 777
Young, J.D., 3283
Young, James H., II, 3706
Young, Jan, Dr., 8530
Young, Jane H., 2582
Young, Jennifer, 9833
Young, Johanna, 7286
Young, John, 6446
Young, John R., 6088, 6192
Young, Joseph P., 3174
Young, Juan, 7901
Young, Julie, 7191
Young, Juliet M., 3618
Young, Kristi, 530
Young, Laura, 3698
Young, Laura Koenig, 8819
Young, Lindsay, 8529
Young, Logan, 9413
Young, Margaret, 8593
Young, Margaret Morton, 944
Young, Marie, 1166
Young, Marilyn F., 3607
Young, Marlene B., 3778
Young, Michael, 744
Young, Michael D., 1116, 2145
Young, Neil, 2409
Young, Patricia L., 2099
Young, Patty, 9109
Young, Paul, 1140, 3710
Young, Rachel P., 8529
Young, Rick, 3461
Young, Robert S., III, 8529
Young, Roger E., 3902, 5135, 5156
Young, S. Zachary, 2420
Young, Samuel H., 2747
Young, Sherry, 5182
Young, Stephen F., 7780
Young, Sue, 8040, 9362
Young, Susan, 3540
Young, Tricia, 4779
Young, Tyler, 4311
Young, William A., Jr., 9543
Young, William B., 9436
Young, William D., 2582
Young, William D., Sr., 2582
Young, William P., Jr., 3791
Young, William R., III, 3607
Young, William T., Jr., 3593
Youngblood, Joseph, II, 6003
Youngblood, Kaye, 7181
Younger, Charles M., 8650
Younger, Gil, 395
Younggren, Dave, 1480
Younggren, David J., 1481
Youngman, JoAnn C., 9919
Youngren, Faye L., 8519
Youngs, Lisa Pepicelli, Esq., 8001
Younker, Kathy, 7336
Yount, Benny, 7348
Yount, Cherrie, 7348
Yount, Lisa, 7348
Younts, Charles, 2421
Younts, Rosemary, 378
Younts, Willie Camp, 2421
Youth Football Fund, Inc., 9855
Youth Hope Enterprises, LLC, 4809
Youth With A Mission, 2283
Youthworks!, 4791
Youtie, Philip, 8027
Yowan, David L., 5587
Yoxall, James R., 3493
Yoxall, Richard R., 3493
Ypma, Ellie, 3373
YSA Holdings LLC, 4163
Yslas, Stephen D., 222
Yu, Anita W., 1873
Yu, Emily, 1891
Yu, Karen, 6693
Yu, Pauline, 6967
Yuan, Grace T., 9731
Yudelson Foundation, 3642
Yudichak, John T., 8152
Yuditsky, Robert J., 2632
Yudnich, Nishka M., 417
Yudof, Mark G., 3345
Yue, Drina, 1521
Yuk Chun Tiu, Celia, 7425
Yuknat, David A., 3823

Zigdon, Ketti, 7542
Ziger, Steven G., 3725, 3726
Zigler, Fred B., 3676
Zigler, Ruth B., 3676
Zigmant, James R., 6506
Zigulis, Carol, 570
Zilber Marital Trust, Vera, 9971
Zilber, Joseph J., 9972
Zilber, Ltd., 9972
Zilber, Marilyn, 9971, 9972
Zilber, Vera J., 9972
Zilkha & Sons, Inc., 7125
Zilkha, Cecile E., 7125
Zilkha, Cornelia O'Leary, 9062
Zilkha, Donald, 7125
Zilkha, Ezra K., 5385, 7125
Zilkha, Michael, 9062
Zill, Anne, 1948
Zillmer, Chelsea M., 2726
Zillmer, John, 3201
Zima, Janis Volcker, 7035
Ziman, Richard, 585
Zimdars, John, 9946
Ziminski, Jeff, 2824
Zimlich, Cheryl, 1375
Zimlich, Joe, 1375
Zimmer, Bernadine, 9967
Zimmer, Donna, 9300
Zimmer, George, 9300
Zimmer, Ida, 7557
Zimmer, Mary, 4748
Zimmer, Max, 1361
Zimmer, Rick, 4562
Zimmer, Robert E., 9300
Zimmer-Meyer, Heidi N., 6722
Zimmerman Family Trust, No. 1, 3491
Zimmerman, Anne D., 10000
Zimmerman, Clara, 2624
Zimmerman, Collin, 10000
Zimmerman, Craig, 1260
Zimmerman, David, 6528
Zimmerman, Eva M., 10000
Zimmerman, Gail D., 10000
Zimmerman, Hans, 2624
Zimmerman, Jacob, 6836
Zimmerman, Jane, 7973
Zimmerman, Kenneth, 5441
Zimmerman, Landis, 1940, 3818
Zimmerman, Lee E., 1511
Zimmerman, Lily, 10000
Zimmerman, Michael D., 10000
Zimmerman, Mitchel D., 10000
Zimmerman, Myron, 862
Zimmerman, Raymond, 5131
Zimmerman, Rhonda S., 10000
Zimmerman, Richard A., 8294
Zimpleman, Larry, 3476
Zimski, Patrick, 8255
Zinck, Amy, 3186
Zineddin, Mohamed, 3589
Zingale, Daniel, 366
Zink, Anne B., 4697
Zink, Darton J., 7821
Zink, Frank, 1805
Zink, Harold L., 2035
Zink, Jacqueline A., 7821
Zink, Jamie, 7821
Zink, John Steele, 7821
Zink, Phillip L., 4697
Zink, Robby, 200
Zinke 2004 Irrevocable Trust, Ernest E., 3793
Zinke, Christy, 3793
Zinke, Douglas E., 3793
Zinke, Ernest Edward, 3793
Zinke, J., 777
Zinke, Leonora Anne, 3793
Zinn, Douglas, 7248
Zinniel, Mimi, 3569
Zinsmeyer, Jeffrey W., 5889
Zip-A-Dee-Doo-Dah Charitable Lead Annuity Trust, 1228
Zipkin, Jeffrey, 7511
Zipperly, Cynthia H., 24
Zipursky, S. Lawrence, 7080
Zirkin, Harold, 3772
Zischke, Marian, 517
Zischke, Peter H., 517
Zitzelsberger, Terrie, 4512
Zivley, Walter P., 9152
Zizelmann, Joe, 6506
Zobel, Katie Allen, 3992
Zoberman, Yehudit, 7108
Zobrist, Richard, 888
Zoccola, William L., 8530
Zoe, Benjamin, 5416
Zoerb, Don, 79
Zoffer, Jerome, 5667
Zoghbi, Huda Yahya, 4708
Zoley, George C., 2120
Zoll, David L., 5457
Zollett, Scott, 7570
Zollo, Margaret G., 2528
Zolot, Andrew, 8202
Zolot, Stanley L., 8202
Zondervan Corp., 4417
Zonis, Jonathan, 8829
Zopp, Andrea, 2827
Zoretic, Richard C., 9383
Zorich, Barbara L., 9301
Zorich, Bret A., 9301
Zorich, Robert L., 9301
Zorich, Robert M., 9301
Zorn, Edward L., 1524
Zornoza, Simon, 4285
Zovko, Gregory A., 8325
Zubay, Cori, 2487
Zubia, Maria, 1401
Zubrow, Barry L., 7126
Zubrow, Jan Rock, 7126
Zuccaro, Edward J., 5220
Zuccaro, Teri, 3421
Zucco, Donato, Dr., 7990
Zuccotti, John, 5918, 5919
Zuccotti, John E., 5917
Zuccotti, Margaret M., 8428
Zucker, Adam, 5509
Zucker, Anita, 8472
Zucker, Anita G., 8510
Zucker, Barbara Hrbek, 7127
Zucker, Benjamin, 5620
Zucker, Donald, 7127
Zucker, Jerry, 8510
Zucker, Jonathan, 5509
Zucker, Jonathan M., 8510
Zucker, Uzi, 5509
Zuckerberg, Barbara, 7128
Zuckerberg, Dina R., 7128
Zuckerberg, Lloyd P., 7128
Zuckerberg, Roy, 2032
Zuckerberg, Roy J., 7128
Zuckerman Investments, LLC, 178
Zuckerman, Amy, 178
Zuckerman, Enid, 178
Zuckerman, Heather P., 6538
Zuckerman, Jane L., 5802
Zuckerman, Jay, 178
Zuckerman, Mel, 178
Zuckerman, Michael H., 6167
Zuckerman, Sherwin A., 3048
Zuckerwar Trust, Marjorie, 4295
Zuckerwar, Marjorie R., 4295
Zugazagoitia, Julian, 7050
Zuhayll, Fatema, 3589
Zuieback, Michael, 118, 170
Zuieback, Michael S., 118
Zuieback, Sheila, 118
Zuill, Cummings V., 5622
Zukerman, Ed, 6993
Zuleba, Kimberly, 8208
Zultowsky, Diane, 6226
Zumiez Inc., 9768
Zumstein, Ron, 3609
Zunick, Robert, 179
Zuppas, Nitsa, 1162
Zurbay, Donald, 4770
Zurek, Thomas M., 3364
Zurich Insurance Sevices Inc., 2268
Zuskin, Lauren, 1578
Zuskin, Morey, 1578
Zweibel, Beth, 6556
Zweifler, Michael, Dr., 184
Zweig, Barbara, 7130
Zweig, Marcia, 5273
Zweig, Martin, 7130
Zwiers, James D., 4593
Zwilich, Ellen Taaffe, 5814, 6116
Zwirn, Randy H., 5454
Zygala, Mary, 5188
Zygielbaum, Michelle, 420
Zylstra, Betty, 4412
Zylstra, Joel M., 4450
Zyndorf, Mark, 7686
Zyskind, Barry, 6968
Zyskind, Esther, 6968
Zyskind, Frady, 5668
Zywiec, David A., 2309

GEOGRAPHIC INDEX

Foundations in boldface type make grants on a national or international basis; the others generally limit giving to the city or state in which they are located. For local funders with a history of giving in another state, consult the "see also" references at the end of each state section.

ALABAMA

Alexander City: Russell 63
Andalusia: Dixon 30
Anniston: Community 23
Birmingham: Alabama 1, Altec 4, Arlington 6, Bashinsky 7, BBVA 8, BBVA 9, Bolden 12, Brock 13, Brooke 14, Bruno 15, Bruno 16, Bruno-Rumore 17, Caring 18, Comer 20, Community 21, Daniel 27, Energen 32, Friedman 35, Goodrich 36, Hess 39, **International 41**, Jernigan 42, Kaul 43, Mayer 49, McWane 51, Meyer 53, Nabers 56, Pleiad 58, Protective 59, Psalm 60, Richards 62, Stephens 69, Thompson 70, Turner 72, Vulcan 73
Brewton: Finlay 33, McMillan 50
Dothan: Dove 31, Wiregrass 77
Fairhope: Mapp 47
Florence: Anderson 5
Foley: Snook 68
Huntsville: Alpha 3, Community 22, Lowe 46
Indian Springs: Smith 67
Jasper: Walker 74
Mobile: Bedsole 11, Community 24, Crampton 26, Davenport-Spiva 28, Hearin 38, May 48, Meyer 52, Mitchell 54, Mitchell 55, Nelson 57, Regions 61, Smith 66, Treadwell 71, Webb 76
Montgomery: Alfa 2, Central 19, **Flack 34**, King 44, Lowder 45, Smith 65, Working 78
Mountain Brook: Hill 40
Northport: Community 25
Opelika: **Scott 64**
Spanish Fort: DeBakey 29
Tuscaloosa: Bean 10, Harrison 37, Warner 75

see also 188, 569, 854, 1933, 1996, 2173, 2211, 2275, 2307, 2410, 2420, 2438, 2469, 2490, 2505, 2509, 2517, 2518, 2554, 2565, 2657, 2694, 2914, 3296, 3606, 3629, 4078, 4547, 4817, 4861, 5156, 5245, 5409, 6829, 7138, 7148, 7279, 7280, 7337, 7407, 7531, 7960, 8178, 8235, 8325, 8718, 8833, 9181, 9290, 9499, 9606, 9704, 9822

ALASKA

Anchorage: Alaska 79, Aleut 80, Arctic 81, Atwood 82, Carr 83, Chugach 84, CIRI 85, Rasmuson 89
Fairbanks: Doyon 86
Juneau: Gaguine 87
Kotzebue: Newlin 88

see also 854, 907, 1131, 1183, 1264, 2657, 3003, 7098, 7293, 7523, 8718, 8833, 8851, 9565, 9567, 9590, 9591, 9594, 9606, 9621, 9640, 9642, 9661, 9681, 9689, 9762

AMERICAN SAMOA

see 2588, 5327

ARIZONA

Carefree: Jazzbird 125
Chandler: **Johnson 126**
Flagstaff: Whale 176
Fountain Hills: Schultz 161
Gilbert: Neely 149
Glendale: Delta 106, Least 132
Kingman: Rouha 160
Mesa: **Hickey 121**
Paradise Valley: Barrett 96, Kiita 130, KMB 131, Linde 135, Reese 156
Phoenix: Anderson 90, APS 91, Arizona 92, Arizona 93, Aurora 94, Canyon 98, Day 105, Emerald 108, Flinn 111, Freeport-McMoRan 112, Grace 116, Hill 122, Jones 127, Levine 133, Lodestar 136, Long 137, Marco 139, Marley 140, McCain 143, Moreno 147, Ottosen 150, Piper 152, Pivotal 153, Raymond 155, Schwartz 162, Solheim 163, Steele 165, Stewart 166, University 172
Prescott: **Kieckhefer 129**, Morris 148, Webb 174
Scottsdale: Caris 99, Cooper 102, Dorrance 107, Farrington 110, Giving 114, Globe 115, Halle 118, Herberger 119, Ivy 123, Matricaria 142, Moeller 145, Parsons 151, Rodel 158, Stardust 164, Surplus 167, Thomarie 170, Tooker 171, Weatherup 173
Tempe: Fulton 113, JSC 128, Lewis 134, Lord's 138, Wood 177
Tucson: Baird 95, Brown 97, Click 100, Community 101, Cottrell 103, Davis 104, Every 109, Green 117, Hermundslie 120, Jasam 124, Marshall 141, McDonald 144, Mooney 146, Pocono 154, **Research 157**, Ross 159, SVL 168, Tankersley 169, Weil 175, Zuckerman 178

see also 9, 286, 349, 532, 590, 619, 669, 723, 857, 909, 942, 1123, 1183, 1212, 1456, 1472, 1521, 1531, 1774, 1958, 2185, 2227, 2413, 2469, 2582, 2587, 2649, 2657, 2679, 2710, 2729, 2738, 2743, 2942, 2950, 2984, 3002, 3056, 3058, 3218, 3257, 3372, 3488, 3520, 3582, 3748, 4026, 4038, 4366, 4368, 4406, 4430, 4506, 4623, 4663, 4695, 4712, 4731, 4778, 4784, 4948, 5030, 5040, 5090, 5106, 5107, 5137, 5149, 5159, 5260, 5415, 5471, 5587, 5588, 6244, 6258, 6260, 6507, 7002, 7250, 7307, 7531, 7553, 7587, 7669, 7676, 7853, 7873, 8334, 8344, 8364, 8447, 8493, 8495, 8527, 8794, 8906, 9206, 9245, 9288, 9362, 9383, 9439, 9456, 9530, 9569, 9657, 9762, 9766, 9816, 9859, 9860, 9994

ARKANSAS

Arkadelphia: Ross 199
Bentonville: Glass 190, Wal-Mart 210, Walton 211
Conway: Nabholz 194
El Dorado: El Dorado 185, Murphy 193, Union 208
Eudora: White 212
Fayetteville: Walker 209
Fort Smith: Carson 183
Gurdon: Cabe 182
Little Rock: Arkansas 179, Bailey 180, Blue 181, Fox 187, Frueauff 188, George 189, Jesus 191, Jonsson 192, Oliver 195, Riggs 196, Rockefeller 197, Rockefeller 198, Smith 201, Stephens 203, Stephens 204, Sturgis 205, Tenenbaum 206
Rogers: Soderquist 202
Sherwood: Delta 184
Siloam Springs: **Windgate 213**
Springdale: Endeavor 186, Schmieding 200, Tyson 207

see also 569, 633, 854, 1750, 1774, 2410, 2469, 2565, 2582, 2657, 2738, 2778, 3409, 3492, 3551, 3580, 3609, 3630, 4481, 4691, 4784, 4827, 4842, 4863, 4971, 5030, 5090, 5143, 5787, 6236, 7022, 7138, 7368, 7398, 7531, 7739, 7764, 7770, 8235, 8499, 8530, 8537, 8549, 8610, 8673, 8860, 8959, 9211, 9214, 9704, 9815

CALIFORNIA

Agoura Hills: **Hilton 692**
Alameda: Chintu 398, **Duffield 486**, Perforce 1026
Aliso Viejo: Downey 477, Nicholas 969
Altadena: Webster 1305
Anaheim: Anaheim 239, Ellis 503, Hanson 653, Schlinger 1123, Schlinger 1124
Angwin: Woolls 1345
Aptos: Community 418
Arcadia: BayTree 289
Atherton: Hoag 696, Lamond 817, Welch 1310
Auburn: Muskavitch 958, Placer 1039
Bakersfield: **Bolthouse 325**, Gombos 610, Grimm 626, Grimm 627, Kern 780, Lake 815, Lindsey 839, **Patel 1018**
Bayside: Humboldt 714
Belmont: Taube 1241
Belvedere: Silberstein 1165
Berkeley: **Arkay 255**, La 808, Marmor 881, Mosse 947, Mosse 948, Smullin 1190, Springcreek 1208
Beverly Hills: Ahmanson 222, Apatow-Mann 247, Arbus 251, Barth 285, Begin 299, Black 317, Bohnett 324, Brandman 337, Brooks 351, Copses 429, Douglas 476, Edgerton 495, Eisner 499, Field 522, Goldsmith 608, Gordon 616, Greenberg 623, **Guthy-Jackson 638**, Hauptman 662, Horwich 706, i.am.angel 720, Israel 731, JG 750, Karsh 767, Kestenbaum 781, Lear 824, Lee 826, Leichtman 829, Marciano 873, Marciano 874, McAlister 891, Moss 946, Oppenheimer 987, Padway 1008, Post 1041, Ritts 1076, Schaeffer 1121, Semel 1138, Shapell 1148, **Shapell 1149**, Shapell 1150, Shapiro 1151, Simms/Mann 1169, Smith 1186,

5201, 5222, 5223, 5225, 5259, 5260, 5264, 5338, 5343, 5346, 5349, 5350, 5364, 5379, 5384, 5415, 5424, 5425, 5433, 5442, 5460, 5471, 5481, 5489, 5491, 5496, 5506, 5513, 5515, 5520, 5523, 5541, 5560, 5565, 5568, 5571, 5587, 5588, 5599, 5602, 5606, 5609, 5641, 5645, 5697, 5710, 5711, 5723, 5775, 5794, 5814, 5826, 5872, 5884, 5899, 5906, 5908, 5911, 5947, 5976, 6000, 6017, 6069, 6090, 6098, 6103, 6110, 6132, 6143, 6151, 6183, 6198, 6203, 6216, 6232, 6236, 6237, 6244, 6248, 6253, 6265, 6272, 6282, 6305, 6334, 6408, 6417, 6439, 6440, 6460, 6466, 6478, 6479, 6491, 6494, 6499, 6503, 6507, 6512, 6518, 6528, 6531, 6551, 6553, 6589, 6595, 6602, 6607, 6609, 6619, 6629, 6642, 6651, 6655, 6664, 6670, 6678, 6679, 6695, 6704, 6783, 6786, 6795, 6796, 6810, 6829, 6832, 6840, 6859, 6868, 6869, 6877, 6889, 6898, 6901, 6935, 6937, 6953, 6954, 6957, 6966, 6985, 6991, 6997, 7002, 7010, 7017, 7031, 7038, 7045, 7048, 7051, 7060, 7065, 7067, 7118, 7133, 7145, 7176, 7203, 7206, 7226, 7239, 7247, 7261, 7277, 7290, 7307, 7323, 7356, 7364, 7380, 7430, 7450, 7470, 7472, 7493, 7517, 7531, 7552, 7587, 7596, 7603, 7609, 7615, 7616, 7669, 7676, 7720, 7774, 7791, 7804, 7828, 7833, 7843, 7845, 7847, 7853, 7873, 7875, 7877, 7882, 7888, 7890, 7926, 7932, 7989, 8005, 8052, 8093, 8100, 8139, 8162, 8197, 8207, 8235, 8242, 8292, 8330, 8343, 8363, 8369, 8403, 8430, 8441, 8554, 8579, 8613, 8622, 8623, 8651, 8655, 8665, 8667, 8673, 8683, 8712, 8714, 8718, 8748, 8780, 8788, 8815, 8831, 8833, 8842, 8843, 8851, 8883, 8891, 8906, 8948, 8957, 8983, 9015, 9022, 9038, 9052, 9080, 9082, 9084, 9088, 9094, 9098, 9102, 9106, 9110, 9111, 9119, 9142, 9178, 9204, 9244, 9253, 9278, 9300, 9325, 9340, 9362, 9372, 9379, 9383, 9385, 9425, 9428, 9456, 9481, 9482, 9487, 9525, 9535, 9569, 9571, 9586, 9596, 9597, 9598, 9599, 9606, 9618, 9638, 9647, 9649, 9657, 9676, 9692, 9700, 9712, 9713, 9721, 9728, 9736, 9748, 9751, 9755, 9758, 9766, 9871, 9912, 9990, 9993, 9996

COLORADO

Aspen: Aspen 1367, Aspen 1368, Doolin 1402, Fullerton 1415, Furlotti 1416, **General 1419**, Gildor 1420, Hitchcock 1430, Schermer 1492
Avon: Staley 1507, Vail 1518
Boulder: Boedecker 1373, Bowana 1377, Brett 1378, Brown 1379, Community 1391, Jumping 1434, Left 1445, Neuman 1470
Breckenridge: Summit 1511
Broomfield: Ball 1371, Charter 1387
Brush: Petteys 1477
Carbondale: Twelve 1515
Castle Rock: McDonnell 1458
Colorado: Munger 1467
Colorado Springs: Bruni 1380, **Crowell 1398**, Edmondson 1405, El Pomar 1406, Kane 1435, Lane 1443, Pikes 1478, Sachs 1489, **Salvador 1491**, Seay 1495, Shaw 1499, SSB 1506, Whispering 1522
Crested Butte: YPI 1529
Denver: Anschutz 1364, **Anschutz 1365**, Armstrong 1366, Bernstein 1372, Boettcher 1374, Bonfils 1376, Buell 1381, Carson 1382, Catto 1383, Chambers 1385, **Chipotle 1388**, Colorado 1390, Coors 1396, COPIC 1397, Daniels 1399, Davis 1400, Denver 1401, ECA 1404, Encana 1407, Foundation 1411, Fox 1412, Fulcrum 1414, Galena 1417, Gates 1418, **Gill 1421**, Goldstein 1422, Harvey 1428, Hawley 1429, Janus 1432, JFM 1433, KBK 1437, Kern 1438, King 1440, Larrk 1444, Lipscomb 1449, M.D.C./Richmond 1450, Maffei 1451, Maggieegeorge 1452, Marquez 1454, Marsico 1455, Martin 1456, Mizel 1461, Mizel 1462, Morgridge 1466, Nagel 1468, **National 1469**, PB&K 1474, Pioneer 1479, Piton 1480, Piton 1481, ProLogis 1485, Ricketts 1486, Rose 1487, Saeman 1490, Schmitz 1493, Scurci 1494, Shamos 1498, Sie 1500, Singer 1501, Slater 1502, Sprout 1505, Strear 1508, Sturm 1510, U'Brocha 1517, Vodafone 1519, Willett 1523, Wolf 1526
Durango: Community 1395
Eaton: Monfort 1465
Edwards: Precourt 1483
Englewood: CH2M 1384, Fishback 1410, Fries 1413, Hansen 1427, Lewis 1447, Libertygives 1448, **Malone 1453**, Mayer 1457, Merage 1459, **Merage 1460**, Tuchman 1514, **Western 1521**
Erie: Change 1386
Evergreen: Kaufmann 1436, Ponzio 1482
Fort Collins: Bohemian 1375, Community 1393, Griffin 1425, Monfort 1464, Otter 1473, Serimus 1496
Fort Morgan: Williams 1524
Glendale: Hunter 1431
Golden: Peierls 1475, Pema 1476
Grand Junction: Bacon 1370, Colorado 1389, Saccomanno 1488, Western 1520
Greeley: Community 1394, Tointon 1513
Greenwood Village: Find 1409
Gunnison: Community 1392
Highlands Ranch: Mol 1463
Lakewood: Animal 1363, **Avenir 1369**, **Kinder 1439**
Littleton: Leptas 1446, Servant 1497, Society 1503, TYL 1516
Longmont: Stuart 1509, Wolf 1527
Louisville: Price 1484, **Winslow 1525**
Loveland: Erion 1408, Kroh 1442
Manitou Springs: Norwood 1471
Ophir: Halton 1426
Pueblo: Southern 1504
Ridgway: Ottens 1472
Steamboat Springs: Yampa 1528
Telluride: Telluride 1512
Westcliffe: 6/S 1362
Westminster: Green 1424
Winter Park: Grand 1423
Woody Creek: Dornick 1403
Wray: Kitzmiller 1441

see also 9, 60, 64, 112, 118, 122, 145, 158, 163, 188, 220, 238, 300, 349, 370, 607, 618, 638, 738, 751, 806, 854, 871, 910, 1006, 1017, 1121, 1127, 1183, 1206, 1222, 1230, 1291, 1316, 1735, 1750, 1774, 1779, 1820, 1825, 1839, 1855, 1875, 1920, 1958, 1961, 1975, 2022, 2062, 2176, 2191, 2211, 2321, 2378, 2410, 2447, 2483, 2619, 2655, 2657, 2671, 2678, 2685, 2724, 2743, 2754, 2815, 2838, 2844, 2883, 2891, 2921, 2942, 2947, 3014, 3034, 3058, 3137, 3190, 3208, 3243, 3257, 3503, 3537, 3545, 3549, 3558, 3582, 3745, 3748, 3813, 3827, 3835, 3837, 3884, 3984, 4097, 4129, 4142, 4191, 4272, 4282, 4366, 4466, 4486, 4506, 4609, 4636, 4712, 4724, 4743, 4778, 4781, 4784, 4801, 4808, 4819, 4835, 4853, 4855, 4869, 4925, 4948, 4971, 5030, 5087, 5088, 5090, 5200, 5273, 5376, 5433, 5471, 5609, 5819, 5857, 5862, 5899, 6056, 6137, 6244, 6417, 6465, 6478, 6500, 6528, 6551, 6784, 7038, 7051, 7082, 7227, 7238, 7301, 7380, 7389, 7422, 7441, 7454, 7470, 7473, 7523, 7531, 7563, 7587, 7594, 7596, 7706, 7737, 7760, 7764, 7788, 7872, 7873, 8093, 8197, 8226, 8232, 8337, 8489, 8508, 8510, 8512, 8598, 8600, 8636, 8645, 8661, 8833, 8908, 8983, 8990, 9245, 9383, 9475, 9515, 9526, 9754, 9808, 9820, 9929, 9983, 9984

CONNECTICUT

Bethany: **Albers 1532**
Bloomfield: Daniell 1570, Kohn 1622, Rogow 1683
Branford: McLeod 1641, Sassafras 1688, Seedlings 1691
Bridgeport: People's 1671, Trefz 1709
Bristol: Barnes 1542, Main 1634
Brooklyn: Beagary 1544
Canaan: Bok 1550
Cheshire: Alexion 1533
Cos Cob: Grossman 1602, Vervane 1716
Danbury: Maranatha 1636, **Praxair 1676**
Darien: Brightwater 1552, George 1592, Goodnow 1598, Heimbold 1612, Pay 1670, Seidenberg 1692, Silver 1696, Wiggins 1722, **Ziegler 1731**
Derby: Valley 1714
East Hartford: Sparks 1699
Enfield: Lego 1627
Essex: Kitchings 1621
Fairfield: **Educational 1578**, **GE 1591**, Neuberger 1649, Perdue 1672, Prusoff 1678, Wood 1725, ZOOM 1732
Farmington: **Newman's 1652**
Georgetown: Rubin-Ladd 1686
Glastonbury: Ensworth 1580, Matthies 1639, Palmer 1666, Patterson 1669, Sullivan 1703, Twenty-Seven 1712
Green Farms: Fisher 1586
Greens Farms: Allison 1535
Greenwich: ALFA 1534, Allwin 1536, Baker 1540, Baldwin 1541, Citrin 1559, Cohen 1560, Common 1561, Davis 1571, Donchian 1576, Foster 1588, Goergen 1595, Grossman 1601, Grossman 1603, Hack 1604, **Halvorsen 1606**, Jeffe 1617, Keefe 1619, Lehrman 1628, **Lone 1632**, Lowenstein 1633, Marx 1638, O'Connell 1658, Ohnell 1661, Olson 1662, Pasculano 1668, Provident 1677, Richman 1680, Robbins 1681, Royce 1685, Sage 1687, Selander 1693, **Tudor 1711**, Viking 1717, Windreich 1724, Wright 1727
Guilford: Huisking 1615
Hamden: Graustein 1600
Hartford: Aetna 1531, Chase 1555, Chase 1556, Connecticut 1567, Fund 1589, Glover 1594, **Hampshire 1608**, Hartford 1609, Northeast 1656, Say 1689, Zachs 1730
Madison: Summer 1704
Manchester: Bob's 1548, SBM 1690
Middletown: Liberty 1630, Middlesex 1644
Milford: DeLuca 1573
Mystic: Hamm 1607
Naugatuck: Ion 1616
New Britain: American 1537, Community 1564
New Canaan: Bullfrogs 1553, **Calder 1554**, Martino 1637, New Canaan 1650, Sheinberg 1695, Swordspoint 1705, Tow 1708
New Haven: Childs 1558, Community 1562, Eder 1577, Ellis 1579, Levine 1629, NewAlliance 1651, **Tremaine 1710**, Yale 1729
New London: Community 1563
Newington: Mandell 1635
Newtown: Berbecker 1545, **October 1659**
Norwalk: Culpeper 1568, Fairfield 1581, Fink 1583, Orchard 1663, Stanley 1700, Tauck 1706, Xerox 1728
Norwarlk: Pitt 1675
Old Greenwich: Laverack 1625, **Niles 1654**, Niles 1655, Oaklawn 1657, Vranos 1718, WorldQuant 1726
Old Lyme: Panoram 1667
Pomfret Center: 1772 1530
Redding: Link 1631
Ridgefield: Boehringer 1549, Bossidy 1551, Goldstone 1597, Perrin 1673, Tombros 1707
Riverside: Berger 1546
Roxbury: Diebold 1574
Salisbury: MJPM 1645
Shelton: Hubbell 1614

Sherman: Goldring 1596
South Windsor: Rockville 1682
Southport: Foley 1587
Stamford: First 1584, Garden 1590, Heidenreich 1611, JJJ 1618, Lee 1626, McGraw 1640, McMahon 1642, Ner 1648, Niblack 1653, O'Herron 1660, Pitney 1674, Rosenthal 1684, Selkowitz 1694, Straus 1702, Whittingham 1720, Windmill 1723
Torrington: Community 1565, Wiederhold 1721
Wallingford: Farid 1582
Waterbury: Connecticut 1566, Meriden 1643
West Hartford: Ayer 1539, Bissell 1547, **Children's 1557**, Donaghue 1575, Fisher 1585, Hartman 1610, Hoffman 1613, Larsen 1624, Mortensen 1647, Ossen 1664, Owenoke 1665, Valentine 1713
Weston: Hahn 1605
Westport: Aronson 1538, Dalio 1569, Georgescu 1593, Gorab 1599, Kelly 1620, Kossak 1623, Morris 1646, **Richardson 1679**, Smilow 1698, Steere 1701, van Dijk 1715
Wilton: Bauer 1543, Deloitte 1572, Smart 1697
Woodbridge: Werth 1719

---

see also 112, 188, 244, 375, 446, 447, 586, 854, 886, 955, 1118, 1509, 1741, 1748, 1811, 1813, 1830, 1843, 1852, 1854, 1860, 1861, 1863, 1910, 1964, 1984, 2022, 2081, 2133, 2145, 2153, 2200, 2214, 2237, 2297, 2304, 2326, 2360, 2361, 2365, 2370, 2382, 2448, 2501, 2504, 2649, 2657, 2710, 2770, 2788, 2802, 2824, 2841, 2859, 2997, 3016, 3050, 3088, 3178, 3257, 3273, 3344, 3582, 3677, 3691, 3709, 3710, 3745, 3825, 3857, 3866, 3921, 3926, 3935, 3948, 3984, 4012, 4025, 4046, 4047, 4100, 4120, 4151, 4165, 4170, 4176, 4186, 4192, 4193, 4209, 4213, 4218, 4241, 4245, 4256, 4260, 4284, 4297, 4302, 4310, 4328, 4422, 4428, 4630, 4718, 4783, 4869, 5100, 5111, 5173, 5200, 5223, 5246, 5292, 5320, 5346, 5365, 5392, 5395, 5409, 5415, 5458, 5497, 5506, 5539, 5552, 5593, 5598, 5614, 5616, 5653, 5677, 5697, 5711, 5719, 5725, 5728, 5762, 5814, 5844, 5853, 5872, 5877, 5932, 5936, 5965, 5979, 5997, 6025, 6040, 6051, 6071, 6086, 6093, 6095, 6097, 6102, 6125, 6132, 6137, 6154, 6158, 6161, 6167, 6184, 6187, 6216, 6225, 6244, 6273, 6275, 6294, 6305, 6323, 6344, 6349, 6371, 6422, 6425, 6451, 6468, 6469, 6502, 6504, 6509, 6513, 6531, 6539, 6553, 6560, 6589, 6591, 6592, 6594, 6606, 6607, 6616, 6645, 6646, 6658, 6673, 6679, 6688, 6691, 6696, 6704, 6705, 6726, 6728, 6735, 6752, 6770, 6784, 6809, 6817, 6824, 6837, 6838, 6840, 6854, 6857, 6887, 6891, 6922, 6933, 6937, 6938, 6946, 6953, 6963, 6975, 6985, 6996, 7001, 7038, 7045, 7048, 7065, 7066, 7081, 7083, 7084, 7100, 7111, 7118, 7172, 7253, 7301, 7331, 7343, 7381, 7615, 7684, 7751, 7981, 8005, 8096, 8235, 8253, 8315, 8357, 8359, 8362, 8365, 8366, 8367, 8374, 8376, 8377, 8378, 8414, 8430, 8431, 8436, 8440, 8441, 8443, 8450, 8453, 8469, 8490, 8587, 8701, 8965, 8998, 9053, 9131, 9244, 9362, 9378, 9383, 9422, 9482, 9553, 9982, 9987, 9990, 9996

DELAWARE

Bear: Rivera 1850
Dover: **Progress 1842**
Greenville: Nor'Easter 1824, Struthers 1865
Hockessin: Mount 1821, Patterson 1831
Montchanin: Crystal 1758
Newark: David 1760
St. Georges: Tarrant 1869
Wilmington: Berlin 1743
Wilmington: 9:7 1733, **Adobe 1734**, AEC 1735, Anderson 1736, Aster 1737, **AstraZeneca 1738**, Bennett 1739, Bere 1740, Berkley 1741, Berkshire 1742, **Birch 1744**, Bishop 1745, Bishop 1746, Brill 1747, Bucks 1748, Campbell 1749, CenturyLink-Clarke 1750, CGLC 1751, Chapman 1752, Chase 1753, **Chichester 1754**, Common 1755, Corkins 1756, Crestlea 1757, CTW 1759, Davis 1761, Davis 1762, Day 1763, Day 1764, Delaware 1765, Desich 1766, Detkin 1767, Devonwood 1768, Doctorbird 1769, Draper 1770, Duane 1771, Dwoskin 1772, Edwards 1773, Edwards 1774, Enoch 1775, Eshelman 1776, Esperance 1777, Etnier 1778, Ettinger 1779, Fair 1780, First 1781, G.D.S 1782, Ganatra 1783, **Gloria 1784**, Good 1785, Gospel 1786, Griswold 1787, **Gynesis 1788**, James 1789, Johnson 1790, **Jolie-Pitt 1791**, Joynor 1792, JP's 1793, Kendeda 1794, Khan 1795, Kirby 1796, Klein 1797, Kohl 1798, La Vida 1799, Laffey 1800, Landenberger 1801, Lefrak 1802, LeFrak 1803, Lefrak 1804, Lennox 1805, Longwood 1806, Lourie 1807, Lucas 1808, Mackenzie 1809, MacMahon 1810, Mancheski 1811, Margolis 1812, **Marks 1813**, Marmot 1814, Mastronardi 1815, Matthews 1816, McDonald 1817, McHugh 1818, **Memton 1819**, Mordecai 1820, Natembea 1822, Nobari 1823, Oak 1825, O'Neil 1826, Orr 1827, Ortega 1828, Parker 1829, Parrish 1830, Pelham 1832, Pere 1833, Pfeil 1834, Phillips 1835, Pincus 1836, Planet 1837, Prairie 1838, Prentice 1839, Presto 1840, Price 1841, Queally 1843, Quitiplas 1844, **Raskob 1845**, Ratner 1846, Ratner 1847, Reynolds 1848, Reynolds 1849, Romill 1851, Rose 1852, Rosenberg 1853, Rossi 1854, Salah 1855, Schejola 1856, Schwartz 1857, Shorenstein 1858, Singer 1859, Singer 1860, Sternlicht 1861, Stewart 1862, Stone 1863, **Stratus 1864**, Swank 1866, Sylvan 1867, Tapeats 1868, Victory 1870, Wasily 1871, Welfare 1872, Westly 1873, Whitton-Spector 1874, Wilke 1875, Yavanna 1876

---

see also 188, 210, 220, 1096, 1459, 1460, 1615, 1628, 1979, 1985, 2075, 2469, 2510, 2535, 2657, 3476, 3695, 3710, 3734, 3797, 3825, 3868, 4256, 5226, 5379, 5391, 5593, 5719, 6236, 6244, 6406, 6462, 6507, 6925, 7038, 7066, 7201, 7985, 8020, 8138, 8145, 8230, 8235, 8236, 8333, 8339, 8374, 8688, 9499

DISTRICT OF COLUMBIA

Washington: Abramson 1877, Agua 1878, Aid 1879, **Arca 1880**, **Banyan 1881**, Bauman 1882, Bedford 1883, Beech 1884, Bender 1885, Bernstein 1886, Bernstein 1887, Block 1888, **Butler 1889**, Cafritz 1890, **Case 1891**, **CityBridge 1892**, Community 1893, Consumer 1894, Coors 1895, Coyne 1896, CrossCurrents 1897, **Davis 1898**, DeLaski 1899, Dole 1900, **Dreyfus 1901**, Dweck 1902, **El-Hibri 1903**, Flamboyan 1904, Forster 1905, Forsythia 1906, **Freedom 1907**, Friedman-French 1908, Gewirz 1909, Goldman 1910, Gottesman 1911, Gudelsky 1912, Hansen 1913, Hillside 1914, **Hill 1915**, **Hitachi 1916**, HRH 1917, Jones 1918, Kaplan 1919, Kaye 1920, Kimsey 1921, Kiplinger 1922, Lavin 1923, Lehrman 1924, Loughran 1925, **Lounsbery 1926**, Ludwig 1927, McIntosh 1928, **Merck 1929**, Merriman 1930, Meyer 1931, **Moriah 1932**, Munson 1933, **National 1934**, **NDPI 1935**, **New 1936**, Palmer 1937, Pedas 1938, Professional 1939, **Public 1940**, Quetzal 1941, Rales 1942, Rumsfeld 1943, Rutherfoord 1944, **San Giacomo 1945**, **Searle 1946**, Seter 1947, Spectemur 1948, Stewart 1949, **Summit 1950**, True 1951, U.S. 1952, **Union 1953**, Vradenburg 1954, **Wallace 1955**, Wallace 1956, Wolf 1957, Wyss 1958, **Wyss 1959**, Zients 1960

---

see also 54, 123, 158, 172, 188, 210, 218, 251, 268, 274, 281, 289, 295, 302, 305, 306, 316, 335, 341, 369, 383, 446, 467, 532, 569, 582, 583, 586, 615, 624, 649, 656, 675, 687, 702, 723, 733, 738, 744, 788, 813, 824, 842, 884, 886, 897, 909, 931, 957, 965, 976, 1016, 1041, 1061, 1082, 1085, 1101, 1131, 1138, 1165, 1171, 1176, 1180, 1188, 1199, 1339, 1342, 1383, 1384, 1400, 1436, 1462, 1467, 1475, 1521, 1531, 1569, 1572, 1591, 1601, 1617, 1628, 1633, 1659, 1674, 1700, 1702, 1741, 1770, 1772, 1779, 1780, 1782, 1789, 1791, 1794, 1827, 1833, 1839, 1844, 1857, 1859, 1975, 1990, 2003, 2014, 2022, 2043, 2046, 2048, 2065, 2072, 2089, 2119, 2133, 2136, 2138, 2147, 2157, 2159, 2178, 2207, 2230, 2249, 2264, 2340, 2350, 2387, 2391, 2428, 2461, 2465, 2469, 2516, 2555, 2564, 2629, 2649, 2657, 2663, 2685, 2700, 2706, 2707, 2739, 2752, 2804, 2815, 2845, 2846, 2847, 2856, 2858, 2892, 2902, 2906, 2909, 2943, 3012, 3014, 3034, 3042, 3043, 3089, 3104, 3128, 3132, 3179, 3184, 3444, 3526, 3528, 3584, 3587, 3670, 3693, 3710, 3713, 3715, 3720, 3730, 3736, 3739, 3743, 3746, 3750, 3751, 3753, 3754, 3756, 3764, 3769, 3772, 3778, 3784, 3785, 3786, 3788, 3794, 3795, 3797, 3801, 3813, 3821, 3831, 3832, 3839, 3841, 3842, 3843, 3845, 3847, 3854, 3857, 3859, 3863, 3864, 3866, 3870, 3871, 3884, 3887, 3892, 3896, 3901, 3905, 3928, 3984, 3989, 4026, 4034, 4059, 4073, 4077, 4119, 4154, 4176, 4188, 4214, 4225, 4238, 4258, 4261, 4284, 4296, 4297, 4303, 4309, 4311, 4366, 4397, 4422, 4475, 4487, 4580, 4594, 4596, 4605, 4645, 4694, 4723, 4770, 4785, 4794, 4819, 4854, 4875, 4913, 5015, 5027, 5029, 5113, 5154, 5159, 5160, 5196, 5240, 5255, 5285, 5293, 5301, 5306, 5320, 5340, 5341, 5347, 5348, 5349, 5379, 5391, 5429, 5431, 5453, 5471, 5478, 5484, 5489, 5547, 5563, 5569, 5587, 5588, 5599, 5629, 5648, 5674, 5683, 5695, 5697, 5711, 5715, 5732, 5762, 5776, 5787, 5812, 5823, 5826, 5836, 5859, 5870, 5872, 5900, 5932, 5964, 5966, 5998, 6004, 6069, 6086, 6110, 6139, 6140, 6146, 6152, 6201, 6237, 6244, 6281, 6291, 6326, 6369, 6389, 6406, 6417, 6418, 6431, 6437, 6439, 6442, 6468, 6479, 6500, 6517, 6518, 6531, 6551, 6576, 6589, 6591, 6603, 6612, 6614, 6615, 6627, 6629, 6651, 6679, 6696, 6735, 6738, 6744, 6770, 6780, 6816, 6827, 6840, 6844, 6862, 6868, 6874, 6914, 6942, 6946, 6957, 6961, 6970, 6973, 6982, 7002, 7035, 7090, 7091, 7093, 7098, 7140, 7177, 7191, 7220, 7288, 7301, 7339, 7374, 7424, 7435, 7436, 7441, 7593, 7602, 7616, 7720, 7764, 7792, 7875, 7898, 7900, 7920, 7968, 7981, 8034, 8236, 8266, 8286, 8310, 8346, 8384, 8433, 8446, 8489, 8651, 8687, 8693, 8708, 8718, 8790, 8831, 8833, 8856, 8861, 8910, 8914, 8948, 8965, 8981, 9022, 9098, 9111, 9172, 9263, 9278, 9342, 9346, 9386, 9387, 9400, 9406, 9409, 9431, 9435, 9438, 9439, 9445, 9458, 9459, 9463, 9464, 9466, 9475, 9477, 9481, 9484, 9487, 9491, 9499, 9513, 9515, 9518, 9525, 9526, 9530, 9532, 9534, 9537, 9539, 9544, 9545, 9553, 9554, 9582, 9595, 9597, 9647, 9657, 9721, 9758, 9761, 9766, 9798, 9865, 9875, 9949, 9958, 9978, 9985, 9994

FLORIDA

Amelia Island: Amos 1967, Gemunder 2119
Ave Maria: LaMothe 2199
Aventura: **Arison 1972**, Deshe 2062, Fine 2095
Bal Harbour: Gann 2113, Greenburg 2137
Bay Harbor: **Lampert 2200**
Belle Glade: Hill 2158
Boca Raton: Alexander 1965, Bay 1985, Bernstein 1995, Cammarata 2010, **Catholic 2014**, Cobb 2027, **Cornell 2046**, Esman 2088, Geo 2120, Gutin 2143, Henry 2154, **Katz 2177**, **Kazma 2179**, Kazma 2180, KMD 2190, Krouse 2196, Leder 2209, Levitetz 2211, Lynn 2221, Newman 2250, Pechter 2265, Rubin 2300, Sanders 2305,

GEORGIA

Atlanta: AGL 2400, Anderson 2404, Argo 2405, Atlanta 2406, Beard-Payne 2408, Blakely 2412, Blank 2413, Brain 2416, Bunzl 2417, Campbell 2420, Camp-Younts 2421, Carlos 2422, **Challenge 2424**, Chambers 2425, CLC 2426, **Coca 2428**, Collins 2429, Community 2432, Correll 2440, Courts 2441, Cousins 2442, Cousins 2443, Covenant 2444, Cox 2445, Cox 2446, Dobbs 2449, DuBose 2450, Ellis 2452, English 2453, Entelechy 2454, Equifax 2455, Fitzgerald 2457, Fleming 2458, Franklin 2462, Fraser 2463, Fuqua 2464, Gaby 2465, Galloway 2467, Georgia 2468, **Georgia 2469**, Glenn 2470, Glenn 2471, Gordy 2472, **Hanley 2476**, Harland 2477, Harris 2479, Harrison 2481, Healthcare 2482, Holder 2485, **Imlay 2487**, Kahn 2493, Katz 2494, Kennedy 2495, **Keough 2496**, Klaus 2497, Lanier 2499, Lender 2501, Loridans 2506, Love 2508, Lowder 2509, Ma-Ran 2510, Marcus 2511, MARTA 2512, Mason 2513, McKenna 2516, Montgomery 2518, Moore 2519, Moore 2520, Morgens 2521, Murphy 2522, Murray 2523, Pechter 2526, Pelling 2527, Pitts 2529, Realan 2535, Reeder 2536, Rich 2537, Rockdale 2540, Rollins 2542, Rollins 2543, Rosenberg 2544, **Rosenberg 2545**, Selig 2549, Servant's 2550, Snow 2553, Southern 2554, Spring 2555, Thunder 2558, Trailsend 2560, Tull 2561, **Turner 2563**, Turner 2564, **UPS 2566**, Watkins 2568, Weber 2570, Whitehead 2571, Williams 2573, WinShape 2577, Woodruff 2579, Woodward 2580, Woolley 2581, Young 2582, Zaban 2583, Zeist 2584

Augusta: Community 2434, Creel-Harison 2447, Masters 2514, Richards 2538

Bainbridge: Jackson 2490

Bartow: Harrison 2480

Brunswick: Sapelo 2546

Canton: Addison 2398, **Thoresen 2557**

Carrollton: Community 2439, Richards 2539

Columbus: Aflac 2399, Amos 2401, Amos 2402, Belcher 2410, Beloco 2411, Bradley 2414, Community 2438, Fort 2460, Jordan 2492, Lockwood 2505, **Pickett 2528**, Synovus 2556, Woodruff 2578

Conyers: Beech 2409

Cumming: Bagwell 2407, Brady 2415

Dalton: Community 2436, Saul 2547

Decatur: **Guanacaste 2475**

Duluth: Community 2433, Hudgens 2486, NCR 2524, Primerica 2534, Williams, 2575

Ellerslie: Loudermilk 2507

Gainesville: North 2525

Hoschton: Walker 2567

Kennesaw: Invisible 2489

LaGrange: Callaway 2418, Callaway 2419

Lookout Mountain: Indiana 2488

Macon: Anderson 2403, Community 2435, Griffith 2473, Jones 2491, Lewis 2502, McAfee 2515, Porter 2533

Marietta: Foundation 2461, Mohawk 2517

Menlo: Tillotson-Menlo 2559

Norcross: Day 2448, Helton 2483

Peachtree City: Cawood 2423

Roswell: Harris 2478

Saint Simons Island: Communities 2431

Savannah: Colonial 2430, Gaines 2466, Layton 2500, Lewis 2503, LittleJohn 2504, Poindexter 2532, Savannah 2548

Sharpsburg: Cobb 2427

Smyrna: Dunn 2451, Hertz 2484

Snellville: Snell 2552

Stone Mountain: Pittulloch 2530

Thomasville: Community 2437, Flowers 2459, Poe 2531, Singletary 2551, Williams 2572

Thomson: Knox 2498, Watson 2569

Tucker: Grizzard 2474, U.S. 2565, Wilson 2576

---

see also 54, 55, 61, 65, 128, 132, 145, 176, 188, 210, 349, 396, 402, 409, 546, 633, 704, 723, 839, 854, 1005, 1085, 1142, 1356, 1499, 1531, 1591, 1674, 1699, 1733, 1735, 1747, 1786, 1790, 1856, 1870, 1967, 1977, 1990, 1996, 2009, 2047, 2063, 2083, 2163, 2171, 2191, 2204, 2205, 2273, 2275, 2281, 2283, 2302, 2314, 2369, 2377, 2657, 2668, 2694, 2726, 2738, 2786, 2790, 2821, 3034, 3042, 3043, 3188, 3257, 3409, 3549, 3582, 3602, 3745, 3801, 3825, 3837, 3870, 3966, 4281, 4282, 4285, 4354, 4356, 4388, 4417, 4470, 4561, 4647, 4651, 4659, 4661, 4853, 4869, 4906, 4945, 4948, 5030, 5040, 5148, 5225, 5281, 5284, 5304, 5318, 5409, 5454, 5471, 5587, 5588, 5607, 5710, 5826, 6135, 6244, 6259, 6396, 6518, 6561, 6601, 6796, 7038, 7048, 7138, 7145, 7148, 7157, 7175, 7191, 7193, 7201, 7204, 7244, 7245, 7263, 7267, 7356, 7441, 7452, 7454, 7531, 7552, 7587, 7596, 7601, 7684, 7751, 7964, 8102, 8226, 8235, 8401, 8495, 8499, 8503, 8562, 8573, 8588, 8600, 8613, 8655, 8693, 8718, 8744, 8833, 9253, 9266, 9275, 9290, 9321, 9383, 9386, 9470, 9481, 9496, 9499, 9539, 9704, 9746, 9822, 9885, 9929, 9974, 9978

GUAM

---

see 1953, 2588, 5327, 5381

HAWAII

Honolulu: Atherton 2586, Baldwin 2587, Bank 2588, Cades 2591, Castle 2594, Central 2595, Ching 2596, Cooke 2597, First 2598, Geist 2600, Hau'oli 2601, Hawaii 2602, Hawaiian 2603, HMSA 2604, Hughes 2605, Island 2606, Kosasa 2607, Lange 2609, Learning 2610, LGA 2611, McInerny 2612, Moh 2613, Schuler 2614, **Shaw 2615**, Shin 2616, Strong 2617, Sullivan 2618, **Watumull 2620**, Wilcox 2621, Wong 2622, Zimmerman 2624

Kahului: Frost 2599

Kailua: Castle 2593

Kailua Kona: **Burke 2590**

Kailua-Kona: Zierk 2623

Kamuela: Kutler 2608

Kaneohe: **Albrecht 2585**, Vincent 2619

Kapolei: Campbell 2592

Lahaina: Buehner 2589

---

see also 315, 335, 373, 512, 528, 544, 573, 584, 586, 728, 821, 847, 848, 878, 910, 1060, 1082, 1183, 1386, 2144, 2657, 2886, 3908, 4599, 4632, 4954, 5103, 5122, 5515, 6598, 7031, 7290, 7602, 7804, 7850, 9357, 9526, 9528

IDAHO

Boise: Albertson 2626, Cunningham 2630, Idaho 2632, Jeker 2633, Jeker 2634, Lightfoot 2636, **Micron 2637**, Morrison 2638, Rebholtz 2640, Simplot 2643, Thomas 2645

Caldwell: Smeed 2644

Eagle: Nagel 2639

Fruitland: Adiuvo 2625

Idaho Falls: Carr 2629, **Gorongosa 2631**

Ketchum: **Schultz 2641**

Meridian: Blue 2627

Nampa: Brandt 2628, Kleiner 2635

Ponderay: Wishnick 2646

Twin Falls: Seagraves 2642

---

see also 709, 735, 1114, 1183, 1318, 1534, 1750, 1774, 1958, 2365, 2589, 2657, 3003, 3163, 3457, 3492, 3551, 4363, 4388, 4636, 4691, 4695, 4729, 4784, 4796, 4945, 5030, 5090, 5104, 5159, 5336, 5376, 6244, 6832, 6915, 6928, 7523, 7829, 7843, 7864, 7877, 7878, 8100, 8688, 9138, 9321, 9326, 9327, 9362, 9470, 9567, 9576, 9590, 9591, 9594, 9621, 9640, 9642, 9650, 9661, 9689, 9762, 9766, 9860

ILLINOIS

Abbott Park: **Abbott 2649**, **Abbvie 2650**

Alton: Simmons 3159

Arlington Heights: Eisenberg 2819, Johnson 2943, Magnus 2993

Aurora: Community 2767, Dunham 2811, H.B.B. 2883, Sheba 3155

Bannockburn: Clark 2751, Ellis 2820, Leibowitz 2973, Miller 3024

Barrington: Perritt 3077, Roberts 3118

Batavia: Hansen 2889

Bloomington: Brewer 2713, Dew 2794, Growmark 2881, Mirza 3032, Shirk 3158, **State 3174**

Buffalo Grove: Miller 3025, Miller 3026, Night 3057, REAM 3107

Burr Ridge: Hermann 2908, McDaniel 3011

Carlyle: Maddux 2991

Carol Stream: **Tyndale 3195**

Champaign: Community 2765, Meyer 3023, Salmon 3133

Charleston: Charleston 2742

Chicago: 2010 2647, Ackermann 2652, Adjuvant 2653, Allen 2656, Alphawood 2658, Alsdorf 2659, Angell 2663, Anixter 2664, Anschel 2666, Aon 2667, Appleby 2668, ArcelorMittal 2670, Archer 2671, Ashley 2674, Austin 2677, Bacca 2678, Barnett 2680, Barnett 2681, Barney 2682, Baskes 2683, Baskes 2684, Baskin 2685, Bass 2686, Bauer 2687, Bauer 2688, Baum 2689, Beidler 2692, Bellebyron 2693, Berner 2694, Bernick 2695, Bersted 2696, Best 2697, Blair 2699, Blair 2700, Blue 2703, Bluhm 2704, Blum 2705, Blum 2706, Bobolink 2707, Bondi 2710, Brach 2712, **Brinson 2715**, Brooker 2716, Bryce 2719, Buchbinder 2721, Bucksbaum 2723, Bucksbaum 2724, Buder 2725, Carrus 2734, **Carylon 2735**, Catch 2737, Cedar 2739, Chaddick 2740, Chao 2741, Chartered 2744, Cheney 2745, Chicago 2746, Children's 2747, Clapham 2750, Clearing 2752, Clinton 2754, CME 2755, CME 2756, Code 2757, Coleman 2759, Comer 2760, Comer 2761, Conduit 2770, Cooney 2771, Corboy 2773, **Cornwell 2775**, Cox 2776, Coypu 2777, Crain-Maling 2778, Crown 2780, Crown 2781, Crump 2782, Cuneo 2783, D and R 2784, Davee 2785, Davis 2786, de Kay 2788, Dean 2789, Deering 2791, Delany 2793, Dickenson 2795, Dimon 2797, DiSomma 2798, Donnelley 2800, Donnelley 2801, Donnelley 2802, Driehaus 2805, **Driskill 2806**, DRW 2807, Dryer 2808, Edlis-Neeson 2815, Ellis 2821, Emerson 2822, Ende 2823, Energizer 2824, Epstein 2825, Exelon 2827, Feinberg 2830, Field 2831, Fogelson 2836, Foglia 2837, Fossett 2838, Franke 2841, Frankel 2842, Frankel 2843, Frechette 2844, Friedman 2846, Friedmann 2847, Froehlich 2848, Fry 2849, Fulk 2850, Galvin 2857, Galvin 2858, Gates 2859, Genius 2861, Gidwitz 2862, Gies 2863, Goodyear 2870, Gore 2871, **Graham 2873**, Grand 2875, Grant 2877, Gray 2878, Gregory 2879, Guthman 2882, Haerther 2884, Halligan 2886, Hamel 2887, Hamill 2888, Hanson 2890, **Harder 2891**, Harris 2892, **Harris 2893**, Harrison 2895, Harrison 2896, Hazan 2899, Heerey 2901, **Heisley 2902**, Heller 2903, Heller 2904, Hendrickson 2905, Heritage 2907, Herr 2909, Herro 2910, Hintz 2911, Hirschl 2912, Hoehn 2916, Hoffritz 2917, **Hofmann 2918**, Homan 2919, Hudson 2923, Hull 2925, Hunter 2926, Hunter 2927, Huntington 2928, Hurley 2929, I and G 2931, **IDP 2932**, Ingersoll 2935, Jackson 2937, Jephson 2939, JNT 2940, Johnson 2942, Jordan 2945, **Joyce 2946**, Kaplan 2948, Katten 2951, Keith 2952, Kellman 2953, **Kemper 2955**, Kendall 2956, Kensington 2957, Kern 2958, Khesed 2959, **Klaff 2961**, Kott 2963, Kovler 2964, Kreyling 2965,

Landau 2966, Lasky 2968, Lefkofsky 2971, Lehmann 2972, Leonian 2974, Lewis 2979, Libra 2981, Liebmann 2982, Logan 2983, Louis 2984, Louis 2985, Lurie 2987, Lynn 2988, **MacArthur 2989**, Madigan 2992, Makray 2994, Malott 2996, Manaaki 2997, Mander 2998, **Manitoba 2999**, Mansueto 3000, Marks 3001, Martin 3002, Martin 3003, Mayer 3005, Mayer 3006, Mazza 3007, McCaskey 3009, McCormick 3010, McDougal 3013, McGowan 3014, McQueen 3018, Medlock 3020, Melman 3022, Mirman 3031, Montgomery 3035, Morrison 3037, Morrison 3038, Morse 3039, Morton 3040, Mosher 3041, MRB 3044, Munson 3045, Neisser 3048, Nerenberg 3050, Nesbitt 3051, NIB 3053, Nierling 3055, Nierling, 3056, Northern 3059, Nygren 3060, Offield 3062, Oppenheimer 3065, Oppenheimer 3066, Oprah 3067, Parr 3070, Payne 3073, Pepper 3074, Pick, 3079, Pierce 3080, **Ploughshares 3082**, **Poetry 3083**, Polk 3084, Potishman 3086, Potter 3087, Prentice 3088, Prince 3089, Prince 3090, Pritzker 3091, Pritzker 3092, Pritzker 3093, Pritzker 3094, Pritzker 3095, Pritzker 3096, Pritzker 3097, Pritzker 3098, Pucci 3099, Pullman 3100, R H 3102, Rawley 3106, Reed 3109, Reese 3110, Regenstein 3111, Reid 3112, **Retirement 3113**, Rhoades 3115, Richards 3117, Roberts 3119, Roberts 3120, Roberts 3121, Robinson 3122, Ross 3123, **Rothschild 3124**, Rotonda 3125, Rubschlager 3126, Ruggles 3127, Rumsfeld 3128, Ryan 3130, Sall 3132, **Santreece 3135**, Satter 3136, Scanlan 3137, Schmidt 3139, Schwartz 3144, Schwartz 3145, Seabury 3146, Seid 3148, SF 3149, Shapiro 3151, Shapiro 3152, Shapiro 3153, Shaw 3154, Shiffick 3156, Shipman 3157, Sinsheimer 3161, Siragusa 3162, Sirius 3163, Souder 3168, **Spencer 3171**, Sprague 3172, Square 3173, Steans 3175, Stern 3177, Stewart 3178, STS 3181, Supera 3183, **Terra 3186**, **Thome 3187**, Timken 3188, Tricord 3190, Trott 3192, Tulsa 3194, United 3199, United 3200, Vaughn 3203, **Ventana 3204**, VNA 3206, Walker 3211, Walsh 3212, Walter 3213, **Ward 3215**, Ward 3216, Washington 3217, Watson 3218, Watson 3219, Wavering 3220, Weberg 3221, Weezie 3222, Weinberg 3223, Weiss 3224, Wenske 3225, Wentcher 3226, Wessner 3227, White 3230, Wieboldt 3231, Wilemal 3232, Williams 3233, Williams 3234, Wilson 3236, Wilson 3237, Wohlers 3238, **Woodbury 3240**, Woods 3242, **Wrigley 3244**, Yulman 3246, Zell 3247, Zita 3249, **Zuhlke 3250**

Countryside: FDC 2829
Danville: Vermilion 3205
Decatur: **Buffett 2726**, Community 2764, Millikin 3027, Ullrich 3198
Deerfield: **Baxter 2690**, Cole-Crone 2758, **Mondelez 3034**, United 3201, Walgreen 3209, **Walgreens 3210**
DeKalb: Ryan 3129
Des Plaines: Atherton 2676, Bruning 2717, Frank 2840, Schawk 3138
Downers Grove: Dover 2803, Kolschowsky 2962, Perlman 3076
Dundee: Fischer 2834
Edwardsville: Edwardsville 2817
Effingham: Southeastern 3169
Elgin: EFS 2818
Elk Grove Village: Voice 3207
Evanston: Evanston 2826, Finnegan 2832, Jahn 2938, Lewis 2980, New 3052
Flossmoor: Perkins 3075
Franklin Park: Brunner 2718
Galesburg: Galesburg 2853, Larson 2967
Geneva: Grace 2872
Glen Carbon: Mallinckrodt 2995
Glencoe: Cooper 2772, Goldschmidt 2867, **Goodman 2869**, Simon 3160, Ubben 3196
Glenview: Abt 2651, Ansari 2665, Caslow 2736, Illinois 2934, Johnson 2944, Lea 2970, Levin 2978
Godfrey: Monticello 3036, Nelson 3049
Grayslake: Petersen 3078
Gurnee: **Abbott 2648**
Harwood Heights: Block 2701
Herrin: Harrison 2894
Highland Park: Buffett 2727, First 2833, Kaplan 2947, Kaplan 2949, Mills 3029, Sacks 3131, Shapiro 3150
Hinsdale: Charlevoix 2743, Community 2769, Purcell 3101
Hoffman Estates: Natural 3046
Homewood: Buckeye 2722
Inverness: Canning 2733
Itasca: Boler 2708, Gallagher 2854, **Gallagher 2855**
Jacksonville: Henry 2906, Hobbs 2914
Kenilworth: Gavin 2860, McIntosh 3016
LaGrange: Schmitt 3140
Lake Forest: Buchanan 2720, Bunning 2728, **Grainger 2874**, Grant 2876, Hospira 2921, **Kapoor 2950**, Mills 3028, Schreiber 3142, Schuler 3143, Stuart 3182, Trustmark 3193, Uihlein 3197
Lake Zurich: Allegretti 2655
Lansing: Van Eekeren 3202
Libertyville: **Motorola 3042**
Lincoln: Woods 3241
Lincolnshire: **Bright 2714**
Lincolnwood: Hartman 2898, Rajchenbach 3103
Lisle: Levin 2977
Mattoon: Lumpkin 2986, Smysor 3165
Minooka: ARIA 2672
Moline: **Deere 2790**, Johnson 2941, Moline 3033, Sangre 3134
Monmouth: Community 2768, Mellinger 3021, Pattee 3072
Mossville: His 2913
Mount Carroll: Willow 3235
Mount Sterling: Tracy 3189
Mundelein: Medline 3019
Naperville: Albert 2654, Calamos 2731, **Tellabs 3185**
Niles: **MacArthur 2990**
Northbrook: Allstate 2657, **Astellas 2675**, Boyer 2711, Cless 2753, Cressey 2779, Dunard 2810, **Foundation 2839**, Galashiels 2852, Hochberg 2915, Hurvis 2930, Lerner 2975, McGraw 3015, Negaunee 3047, **Scholl 3141**, Segal 3147, Stone 3179, Waraich 3214
Northfield: Circle 2749, Cornell 2774, Hagenah 2885, Snite 3166, White 3229
Oak Brook: Duchossois 2809, Houlsby 2922, Huizenga 2924, Illinois 2933, King 2960, McDonald's 3012
Oak Lawn: Opler 3064
Oak Park: Eddema 2814, Master 3004, Oak Park 3061, Stone 3180
Oakbrook Terrace: Westlake 3228
Orland Park: Andrew 2661, Andrew 2662
Palatine: Pilchard 3081
Palos Heights: Owens 3068
Paris: Lawless 2969
Park Ridge: Butler 2729
Peoria: Caterpillar 2738, Community 2763, Flynn 2835, Gilmore 2864, Redhill 3108, Soderstrom 3167, Stephens 3176
Peoria Heights: Bielfeldt 2698
Pontiac: Camp 2732
Richmond: Full 2851
Riverside: Arthur 2673
Rock Island: Day 2787
Rockford: C.W.B. 2730, Community 2766, Woodward 3243
Rosemont: MB 3008, Popular 3085, Reyes 3114, Speh 3170, Wonderful 3239, Youth 3245
Schaumburg: Blowitz 2702, **Motorola 3043**, Omron 3063
Skokie: Friedman 2845, **Glenner 2866**, **Goodman 2868**, Rice 3116
Springfield: Community 2762, Hartke 2897, Hoogland 2920, Levi 2976, Smith 3164, Vollintine 3208
St. Charles: Norris 3058
Sterling: Dillon 2796
Sycamore: DeKalb 2792
Teutopolis: Zerrusen 3248
Watseka: Miner 3030
Waukegan: Healthcare 2900
Wayne: Ranch 3104
West Chicago: Ball 2679
Westchester: Irwin 2936
Western Springs: Christopher 2748, Grohne 2880
Westmont: Amicus 2660, Farnham 2828
Wheaton: Bond 2709, **Domanada 2799**, DuPage 2812
Willowbrook: Pasquinelli 3071
Wilmette: Appleton 2669
Winfield: McNamara 3017
Winnetka: Bechtner 2691, Doyle 2804, Dury 2813, Edwardson 2816, Galvin 2856, Kemper 2954, Nichols 3054, Parmer 3069, Rauner 3105, Taylor 3184, Trio 3191
Woodridge: GKN 2865

---

see also 115, 131, 138, 160, 188, 202, 385, 428, 465, 471, 525, 546, 563, 633, 646, 652, 688, 738, 742, 744, 839, 854, 970, 1085, 1104, 1129, 1167, 1292, 1356, 1387, 1456, 1470, 1521, 1531, 1572, 1591, 1601, 1697, 1705, 1761, 1774, 1790, 1795, 1816, 1848, 1889, 1937, 1957, 1998, 2014, 2016, 2048, 2063, 2119, 2133, 2179, 2180, 2194, 2206, 2212, 2277, 2312, 2358, 2364, 2370, 2383, 2387, 2400, 2469, 2478, 2619, 3350, 3357, 3363, 3392, 3402, 3405, 3416, 3424, 3432, 3442, 3443, 3446, 3456, 3457, 3470, 3473, 3570, 3581, 3582, 3781, 3884, 3966, 4016, 4120, 4249, 4281, 4283, 4285, 4330, 4354, 4363, 4366, 4394, 4397, 4417, 4430, 4475, 4531, 4538, 4605, 4636, 4651, 4659, 4661, 4691, 4739, 4743, 4778, 4784, 4804, 4851, 4855, 4886, 4906, 4926, 4930, 4932, 4945, 4960, 4963, 4966, 4970, 4971, 4984, 4989, 4992, 5027, 5029, 5030, 5069, 5090, 5092, 5106, 5223, 5278, 5369, 5379, 5415, 5454, 5471, 5480, 5482, 5484, 5513, 5576, 5587, 5588, 5644, 5719, 5811, 5826, 5827, 6025, 6069, 6084, 6138, 6139, 6158, 6181, 6188, 6223, 6233, 6244, 6248, 6258, 6280, 6474, 6479, 6491, 6507, 6518, 6531, 6535, 6547, 6627, 6668, 6715, 6759, 6829, 6832, 6868, 6974, 6997, 7002, 7004, 7090, 7279, 7372, 7383, 7398, 7422, 7452, 7528, 7531, 7603, 7616, 7698, 7828, 7842, 8073, 8134, 8177, 8179, 8192, 8196, 8230, 8235, 8325, 8358, 8364, 8369, 8374, 8389, 8418, 8427, 8718, 8736, 8833, 9085, 9087, 9110, 9239, 9290, 9321, 9364, 9422, 9459, 9481, 9487, 9553, 9582, 9596, 9716, 9806, 9814, 9815, 9820, 9857, 9858, 9859, 9869, 9873, 9875, 9891, 9936

INDIANA

Anderson: Madison 3346
Angola: Steuben 3390
Auburn: DeKalb 3295, MTI 3357, Rick 3377
Avon: Hendricks 3319
Batesville: Ripley 3379
Bloomington: Community 3278, National 3358
Bluffton: Wells 3403
Camby: Imburgia 3326
Carmel: Noyes 3361, Saltsburg 3383, Samerian 3384, Simon 3385, Simon 3386, Simon 3387
Columbia City: Whitley 3407
Columbus: **Cummins 3292**, Heritage 3321, Reeves 3374
Corydon: Harrison 3314
Crawfordsville: Montgomery 3356
Crown Point: Crown Point 3291

Decatur: Adams 3253
East Chicago: Foundations 3306
Elkhart: Elkhart 3298, Martin 3350
Ellettsville: Smithville 3388
Evansville: Community 3277, Hamman 3312, Holiday 3322, Indiana 3327, Koch 3334, Old 3363, Vectren 3394, Welborn 3402
Fishers: Annis 3256
Fort Wayne: Auer 3260, Brotherhood 3268, Cole 3276, Community 3281, English 3299, Foellinger 3304, Journal-Gazette 3332, Len-Ari 3339, Lincoln 3344, McMillen 3352, Parrish 3367, Peabody 3368, Rifkin 3378, Roehm 3380, Rolland 3381, Rothschild 3382, Steel 3389, Waterfield 3399
Franklin: Johnson 3330
Greencastle: Putnam 3373
Greenfield: Hancock 3313
Huntington: Huntington 3324
Indianapolis: **Ackerman 3252**, Anthem 3257, Apgar 3258, Central 3272, Champagne 3273, Clowes 3274, Clowes 3275, DeHaan 3294, Eskenazi 3300, Fairbanks 3301, Fehsenfeld 3302, Finish 3303, Glick 3310, **Goodrich 3311**, **Hasten 3315**, **Hasten 3316**, Health 3317, Hoover 3323, Indiana 3328, Jackson 3329, Jordan 3331, **Lilly 3340**, **Lilly 3341**, **Lilly 3342**, Lilly 3343, **Lumina 3345**, Marten 3349, Met 3353, OneAmerica 3364, Pulliam 3371, Pulliam 3372, Regenstrief 3375, Transformation 3392, Walther 3397, West 3404
Jeffersonville: Bales 3261, Ogle 3362
Kendallville: Dekko 3296
Kokomo: Community 3283
Lafayette: Community 3282, McAllister 3351
Lawrenceburg: Dearborn 3293
Lebanon: Community 3279
Ligonier: Noble 3359
Logansport: Cass 3271
Madison: Community 3285
Marion: Community 3280
Merrillville: Gagan 3308, Legacy 3337, White 3405, White 3406
Michigan City: Duneland 3297, Michigan 3354, Unity 3393
Mishawaka: Garatoni 3309
Mooresville: Kendrick 3333
Muncie: Ball 3262, Ball 3263, Ball 3264, Community 3286
Nashville: Brown 3269
New Albany: Blue 3266, Community 3288
New Castle: Henry 3320
Noblesville: Weaver 3401
North Manchester: Community 3290
Osgood: Reynolds 3376
Paoli: Orange 3365
Plymouth: Marshall 3348
Portland: Portland 3370
Richmond: Wayne 3400
Riley: Hux 3325
Rochester: Northern 3360
Rockville: Parke 3366
Salem: Washington 3398
Seymour: Community 3284
Shelbyville: Blue 3265
South Bend: 1st 3251, Asante 3259, Carmichael 3270, Community 3289, Leighton 3338
St. John: Marian 3347
Terre Haute: Froderman 3307, Wabash 3396
Tipton: Tipton 3391
Upland: Boren 3267
Valparaiso: Anderson 3255, Porter 3369
Wabash: Ford 3305
Warsaw: Kosciusko 3335, Kosciusko 3336
Westfield: **Word 3408**
Winchester: Community 3287
Winona Lake: Miller 3355
Zionsville: ADL 3254, Helping 3318, Volo 3395

---

see also 188, 560, 1127, 1345, 1615, 1712, 1858, 2150, 2191, 2212, 2304, 2336, 2469, 2649, 2657, 2658, 2670, 2690, 2738, 2828, 2852, 2946, 2965, 2988, 3011, 3075, 3113, 3134, 3212, 3411, 3431, 3457, 3542, 3581, 3582, 3745, 3834, 3837, 3857, 3957, 4066, 4359, 4366, 4380, 4394, 4405, 4484, 4523, 4598, 4614, 4636, 4651, 4661, 4691, 4699, 4712, 4778, 4784, 4869, 4932, 4971, 5030, 5106, 5438, 5506, 5644, 5711, 5719, 6244, 6356, 6505, 7196, 7214, 7216, 7230, 7368, 7372, 7374, 7404, 7430, 7436, 7441, 7452, 7480, 7500, 7523, 7531, 7591, 7642, 7646, 7711, 7792, 8117, 8230, 8271, 8290, 8321, 8325, 8341, 8411, 8434, 8493, 8536, 8537, 8654, 8665, 8678, 8718, 8725, 8856, 8954, 9199, 9290, 9383, 9422, 9439, 9466, 9815, 9869, 9943

IOWA

Adel: Stine 3482
Bettendorf: Community 3424, Helpenstell 3442
Cedar Rapids: AEGON 3409, Cedar Rapids 3417, Hall-Perrine 3439, Johnson 3449, Mansfield 3459, **Rockwell 3477**, United 3485, Wallace 3488
Chariton: South 3481
Clarinda: Clarinda 3418
Clinton: Durgin 3427
Council Bluffs: Iowa 3447
Davenport: Bechtel 3412, Bechtel 3413, Hubbell 3446, Lee 3457
Des Moines: Community 3420, Dahl 3425, EMC 3428, Glazer 3433, Glazer 3434, Hubbell 3445, Levitt 3458, Meredith 3463, Meredith 3464, MidAmerican 3465, Mid-Iowa 3466, **Ochylski 3470**, Pappajohn 3472, Principal 3476, Ruan 3478, Seidler 3479, Weathertop 3489, Wellmark 3490
Dubuque: Butler 3415, Community 3421
Fairfield: Global 3435, Zimmerman 3491
Forest City: Hanson 3441
Fort Dodge: Community 3419
Grinnell: Ahrens 3410, Poweshiek 3475
Hampton: Sukup 3483
Iowa City: Community 3422
Johnston: **Pioneer 3474**
Manchester: Delaware 3426
Marion: Giacoletto 3431
Marshalltown: Tye 3484
Mason City: Kinney-Lindstrom 3451
Montezuma: Brownell 3414
Mount Vernon: McIntyre 3462
Muscatine: Carver 3416, HNI 3443, Holthues 3444, Kent 3450, New 3468
New Hampton: Hansen 3440
Newton: Maytag 3460
North Liberty: Gerdin 3430
Oelwein: Northeast 3469
Ogden: Good 3436
Orange City: Vogel 3487
Pella: Kuyper 3456, Pella 3473, Vermeer 3486
Sioux City: Gilchrist 3432, Siouxland 3480
Urbandale: Gabus 3429
Waterloo: Community 3423, Guernsey 3437, McElroy 3461
Wayland: On 3471
West Des Moines: Aviva 3411, GuideOne 3438, Jacobson 3448, Knapp 3452, Koehn 3453, Krause 3454, Kruidenier 3455, Nelson 3467

---

see also 112, 376, 1018, 1386, 1492, 1539, 1741, 1750, 2467, 2469, 2657, 2787, 2790, 2889, 2940, 3033, 3034, 3113, 3292, 3296, 3551, 3715, 3745, 3832, 4601, 4636, 4647, 4661, 4676, 4691, 4695, 4729, 4746, 4784, 4869, 4945, 4948, 4971, 5024, 5050, 5057, 5059, 5060, 5066, 5070, 5071, 5074, 5080, 5090, 5106, 5415, 6067, 6853, 7587, 8235, 8420, 8515, 8541, 9182, 9535, 9651, 9804, 9815, 9820, 9838, 9869, 9873, 9882, 9929

KANSAS

Dodge City: Community 3502
Emporia: Emporia 3514, Jones 3523
Fairway: Kirk 3527
Garden City: Western 3554
Gardner: HANDinHAND 3517
Gridley: French 3515
Hays: Dreiling 3511
Hutchinson: Hutchinson 3521
Kansas City: Wyandotte 3556
Lawrence: Beach 3494, Douglas 3509, Rice 3538
Leawood: Deffenbaugh 3506, Stowers 3550
Liberal: Baughman 3493, Cooper 3503
Logan: Hansen 3518
Manhattan: Manhattan 3532
McPherson: McPherson 3534
Mission Hills: Hartley 3519
Newton: Schowalter 3542
Olathe: Kao 3525, Kelly 3526, **Shumaker 3546**
Overland Park: Ash 3492, Cohen 3499, Cohen 3500, Deramus 3508, Dreiseszun 3512, Elliott 3513, **Lloyd 3530**, Mader 3531, Smith 3547, Sprint 3549, Sunderland 3551
Pittsburg: Coleman 3501, Miller 3535
Prairie Village: Sarli 3541
Salina: Horejsi 3520, McCune 3533, Salina 3540, Smoot 3548
Scott City: Scott 3543
Shawnee Mission: Morgan 3536
Topeka: Blue 3497, Capitol 3498, Damon 3504, Morris 3537, Security 3544, Topeka 3552, Westar 3553
Wichita: Beren 3495, Beren 3496, DeBoer 3505, Delta 3507, Downing 3510, Garvey 3516, INTRUST 3522, Kansas 3524, Koch 3528, Koch 3529, Riverside 3539, Shannon 3545, Wichita 3555

---

see also 145, 188, 209, 319, 854, 1513, 1572, 2191, 2204, 2261, 2469, 2654, 2657, 2738, 2790, 2921, 3014, 3075, 3119, 3257, 3411, 4031, 4636, 4691, 4739, 4743, 4784, 4865, 4868, 4876, 4896, 4902, 4906, 4912, 4913, 4920, 4921, 4922, 4926, 4940, 4942, 4950, 4962, 4971, 4974, 4977, 4979, 5080, 5090, 5523, 6251, 7531, 7706, 7764, 7770, 7783, 7801, 7873, 7932, 8446, 8495, 8693, 8761, 8791, 8884, 8919, 8945, 9160, 9214, 9242, 9383, 9606, 9990

KENTUCKY

Ashland: Foundation 3575, Jain 3585, Vanhoose 3604
Bellevue: Orleton 3594
Brandenburg: Roseman 3599
Covington: Durr 3572
Crestview Hills: Smith 3601
Crestwood: Good 3578
Florence: Mercy 3589
Fort Mitchell: Fischer 3574, Scripps 3600
Henderson: Preston 3596
La Grange: Horn 3581
Lexington: Blue 3560, Hagan 3579, Mt. 3590, Opera 3593, Robinson 3598, Spray 3602
Louisville: Augusta 3557, Barzun 3559, Bond 3561, Brown 3562, Brown 3563, Brown 3564, Brown 3565, C.E. 3566, Coffey 3568, Community 3569, Cralle 3571, Gheens 3577, Harris 3580, Humana 3582, J & L 3584, LG&E 3586, Lift 3587, Marshall 3588, Norton 3592, Owsley 3595, Swope 3603, Ventas 3605, WCA 3606, Yum! 3608
Madisonville: Badgett 3558
Mayfield: Gardner 3576

Owensboro: Independence 3583, Public 3597, Young 3607
Paducah: Carson-Myre 3567, Community 3570, Eckstein 3573
Somerset: Newell 3591

see also 188, 238, 288, 571, 854, 1591, 1793, 2027, 2079, 2191, 2279, 2347, 2416, 2469, 2625, 2650, 2657, 2738, 2824, 3113, 3257, 3261, 3334, 3362, 3363, 3402, 3409, 3443, 3456, 3457, 3473, 3745, 3868, 4386, 4388, 4405, 4533, 4570, 4659, 4739, 4749, 4784, 4855, 4971, 5688, 5842, 6244, 6915, 7138, 7172, 7196, 7201, 7216, 7248, 7292, 7296, 7347, 7368, 7376, 7389, 7395, 7396, 7398, 7404, 7405, 7419, 7443, 7452, 7480, 7483, 7498, 7510, 7523, 7531, 7618, 7624, 7642, 7646, 7656, 7724, 7960, 8025, 8075, 8230, 8235, 8305, 8499, 8539, 8546, 8571, 8635, 8639, 8851, 9290, 9383, 9482, 9483, 9487, 9499, 9557, 9815, 9822, 9947

LOUISIANA

Alexandria: Coughlin 3626, Deming 3627, Huie 3643
Baton Rouge: Albemarle 3609, Baton Rouge 3613, Blue 3615, Burden 3618, Clement 3622, Grigsby 3640, Lamar 3647, Pennington 3659, Rispone 3662, Wilson 3671
Broussard: Stuller 3668
Coushatta: Cason 3620
Jennings: Zigler 3676
Lafayette: Community 3623, Pinhook 3660
Lake Charles: Burton 3619, Community 3625, Dore' 3629, Louisiana 3651
Metairie: Brown 3617, Eye 3631, Goldring 3638, Lupin 3652, Marshall 3653, **Woldenberg 3672**
Minden: Frazier 3635
Monroe: Scott 3666
Morgan City: Sanford 3664, Young 3674
New Iberia: Factor 3632
New Orleans: Almar 3610, Azby 3611, Baptist 3612, Booth 3616, Chambers 3621, Diboll 3628, Entergy 3630, Fertel 3633, Freeman 3636, German 3637, Helis 3641, Heymann 3642, Institute 3644, Jones 3645, Keller 3646, Libby-Dufour 3648, McIlhenny 3654, Moffett 3655, New Orleans 3656, Reily 3661, RosaMary 3663, Schlieder 3665, Seal 3667, Taylor 3669, Zemurray 3675
Ruston: Lincoln 3649
Shreveport: Beaird 3614, Community 3624, Franks 3634, Grayson 3639, Noel 3657, Wiener 3670, Woolf 3673
Thibodaux: Lorio 3650, Peltier 3658

see also 32, 112, 144, 188, 854, 1412, 1452, 1591, 1790, 1996, 2150, 2469, 2484, 2657, 2777, 2790, 2929, 3249, 3257, 3577, 3582, 3966, 4140, 4474, 4651, 4722, 4827, 4854, 4945, 4971, 5030, 5090, 5106, 5121, 5415, 5452, 5519, 5542, 5580, 5616, 5719, 6098, 6244, 6391, 6489, 6661, 7138, 7368, 8235, 8337, 8670, 8702, 8779, 8833, 8869, 8884, 9214, 9260, 9290, 9383, 9400, 9606, 9704, 9815

MAINE

Augusta: Maine 3699, MELMAC 3700
Bangor: Bangor 3680, King 3694, Nichols 3703
Belfast: Switzer 3709
Boothbay Harbor: **Walter 3711**
Ellsworth: Maine 3698
Farmington: **Sandy 3707**
Freeport: Sewall 3708
Fryeburg: Mulford 3702
Harrison: Aicher 3677
New Gloucester: Iberdrola 3693
Old Town: Elliotsville 3686
Pittsfield: Cianbro 3683
Portland: Alfond 3678, Alfond 3679, **Catalyst 3682**, Cohen 3684, Davis 3685, Fore 3687, Glickman 3688, Gorman 3689, Hannaford 3690, Horizon 3691, Hungarian-American 3692, Lerner 3695, Libra 3696, Lunder 3697, Morton 3701, Quimby 3705, Redco 3706, TD 3710
Rockport: Cascade 3681
South Portland: Orchard 3704

see also 175, 854, 1499, 1530, 1531, 1541, 1668, 1671, 1741, 1768, 1805, 1831, 1864, 1984, 2224, 2227, 2416, 2440, 2448, 2531, 2657, 2839, 3218, 3257, 3275, 3823, 3825, 3915, 3916, 3921, 3931, 3932, 3935, 3963, 3965, 3968, 4046, 4047, 4100, 4109, 4112, 4132, 4160, 4168, 4171, 4186, 4187, 4189, 4192, 4193, 4203, 4209, 4218, 4227, 4292, 4302, 4310, 4324, 4328, 4466, 4609, 4654, 4695, 4869, 5171, 5179, 5188, 5325, 5343, 5542, 5676, 5703, 5719, 5733, 5881, 5885, 5921, 6158, 6256, 6425, 6725, 6747, 6774, 6901, 7081, 7100, 7216, 7331, 7343, 7423, 7450, 7523, 7612, 7695, 7803, 7987, 8096, 8100, 8181, 8248, 8305, 8310, 8611, 8687, 8715, 9362, 9383, 9464, 9486, 9704

MARIANAS (COMMONWEALTH OF)

see 2588, 5327

MARYLAND

Annapolis: Fusco 3800, Jacobsohn 3819, Seale 3881, TKF 3896, Wood 3910
Arnold: Cromwell 3767, Rathmann 3867
Baltimore: Abell 3712, Adalman-Goodwin 3716, Adams 3718, Angelos 3721, Attman 3722, Baker 3724, Baker 3725, Baltimore 3726, **Bearman 3728**, Berger 3729, **Blaustein 3735**, Blaustein 3736, Blum 3737, **Boehm 3738**, Brown 3740, **Casey 3745**, Cohen 3752, Concordia 3763, Cordish 3764, Crane 3766, Cupid 3769, Dahan 3770, Davison 3773, DiCarlo 3780, **DLA 3781**, Dresher 3782, France 3796, Goldseker 3803, Goldsmith 3804, Gorn 3806, Hackerman 3810, Hahn 3811, Hirschhorn 3816, Hoffberger 3817, Knott 3826, Legg 3828, Legum 3829, Life 3833, Lockhart 3836, Merrill 3847, Meyerhoff 3848, Meyerhoff 3849, Middendorf 3850, Myers 3856, Plitt 3862, Price 3865, Rembrandt 3868, Rollins 3872, Rosenberg 3873, Rosenberg 3874, Rosenbloom 3875, Roswell 3876, Schaefer 3880, St. John 3888, Stasiak 3889, Straus 3890, Stulman 3891, **Thalheimer 3894**, Tzedakah 3900, Wareheim 3903, Wasserman 3906, Wilson 3909
Bel Air: **ABMRF 3714**
Beltsville: Cohen 3753
Bethesda: **Brown 3741**, Clark 3750, Clark 3751, **Cohen 3754**, Cornell 3765, **de Beaumont 3774**, **England 3785**, Fowler 3795, Jacobson 3820, Lockheed 3837, Mann 3839, Marriott 3840, Marriott 3841, Marriott 3842, Marriott 3843, Mead 3845, Millstream 3852, **Morningstar 3854**, Rock 3870, Sampson 3878, Spencer 3887, Sunrise 3892, Trawick 3898, Wasserman 3905
Butler: Riepe 3869
Capitol Heights: Pohanka 3863
Chestertown: **Shared 3882**
Chevy Chase: Abell 3713, **Deerbrook 3776**, Dekelboum 3777, **Ewing 3787**, Fairchild 3788, GEICO 3801, **Hughes 3818**, Johnston 3821, O'Neil 3859, Polinger 3864, Quinn 3866, Rocking 3871
Cockeysville: Nextgen 3858
Columbia: Church 3749, Community 3759, **Grace 3807**, Viragh 3902
Crownsville: Helena 3812
Cumberland: Community 3762
Davidsonville: Decesaris 3775
Easton: Fisher 3790, Kerr 3823, Mid-Shore 3851, Town 3897
Elkton: Thorn 3895
Ellicott City: Higgins-Hussman 3815
Frederick: Ausherman 3723, Community 3758, Cross 3768, Delaplaine 3778
Fulton: Foundation 3794
Gaithersburg: Ceres 3747, Eaton 3784
Glyndon: Colhoun 3755
Hagerstown: Community 3761, Fletcher 3791
Hanover: Allegis 3719, Bisciotti 3733, Davis 3771
Hunt Valley: Bunting 3742, Bunting 3743, Little 3835, Sheridan 3883
Jarrettsville: Calvin 3744
Lutherville: Rouse 3877
North Bethesda: Macklin 3838, Tauber 3893
Olney: Friedman 3799
Owings: **Murray 3855**
Owings Mills: Klein 3824, **Weinberg 3908**
Pasadena: Mechanic 3846
Phoenix: Maryland 3844
Potomac: Adams 3717, Brickman 3739, Gordon 3805, **Sidgmore 3885**, **Smith 3886**, Trone 3899
Preston: Blades 3734
Riderwood: Battye 3727, Gross 3808
Rockville: Abramson 3715, **Berman 3730**, **Berman 3731**, Bethesda 3732, Casey 3746, Choice 3748, Davis 3772, Epstein 3786, Foulger 3792, Freeman 3797, Lerner 3831, Levitt 3832, NASDAQ 3857, Shields 3884, Van 3901
Salisbury: Community 3760, Henson 3814
Silver Spring: Commonweal 3756, Felburn 3789, Foundation 3793, Gudelsky 3809, Hendricks 3813
Smithsburg: Washington 3904
Sparks: **Lawless 3827**, Mirmiran 3853, Wright 3911
St. Michaels: Knapp 3825
Sykesville: Kahlert 3822
Timonium: Glazer 3802, Weinberg 3907
Towson: **Ames 3720**, Deutsch 3779, Dupkin 3783, Frenkil 3798, Leidy 3830, Linehan 3834, Orokawa 3860, Osprey 3861, Samuelson 3879
Westminster: Community 3757

see also 90, 163, 188, 210, 246, 295, 349, 373, 854, 1162, 1184, 1197, 1362, 1369, 1424, 1531, 1591, 1638, 1702, 1780, 1801, 1844, 1867, 1877, 1879, 1885, 1888, 1890, 1893, 1894, 1895, 1902, 1905, 1908, 1912, 1914, 1925, 1931, 1932, 1933, 1937, 2046, 2079, 2089, 2138, 2201, 2258, 2265, 2278, 2297, 2319, 2350, 2400, 2527, 2657, 2721, 2726, 2827, 2839, 3042, 3043, 3187, 3244, 3257, 3273, 3409, 3582, 3710, 3954, 4001, 4016, 4026, 4053, 4078, 4256, 4322, 4366, 4388, 4553, 4596, 4605, 4661, 4664, 4691, 5135, 5156, 5212, 5237, 5269, 5285, 5379, 5391, 5422, 5424, 5429, 5471, 5522, 5541, 5547, 5553, 5571, 5617, 5719, 5826, 5831, 5885, 5961, 6113, 6318, 6353, 6406, 6413, 6437, 6612, 6651, 6681, 6784, 6827, 6898, 7002, 7091, 7093, 7102, 7140, 7172, 7201, 7339, 7424, 7455, 7472, 7475, 7587, 7602, 7699, 7843, 7847, 7985, 8066, 8082, 8165, 8178, 8194, 8210, 8211, 8230, 8236, 8242, 8244, 8279, 8291, 8302, 8323, 8371, 8433, 8536, 8579, 8692, 8765, 9055, 9290, 9383, 9400, 9407, 9409, 9422, 9428, 9431, 9435, 9438, 9452, 9464, 9466, 9476, 9477, 9482, 9495, 9499, 9508, 9515, 9525, 9532, 9539, 9545, 9606, 9796

MASSACHUSETTS

Acton: Dunn 4027, Steinberg-Lalli 4287
Agawam: Grinspoon 4080
Allston: Hamilton 4085
Amherst: Colombe 3989

6714, 6721, 6727, 6730, 6735, 6747, 6751, 6774, 6776, 6783, 6814, 6824, 6829, 6844, 6846, 6847, 6851, 6868, 6884, 6898, 6901, 6908, 6920, 6927, 6928, 6941, 6946, 6953, 6954, 6966, 6974, 6976, 6991, 6999, 7000, 7001, 7008, 7017, 7038, 7047, 7048, 7056, 7067, 7077, 7081, 7095, 7111, 7123, 7140, 7145, 7214, 7218, 7278, 7343, 7434, 7477, 7502, 7543, 7559, 7594, 7596, 7601, 7612, 7615, 7712, 7748, 7815, 7853, 7890, 7944, 7967, 7989, 8000, 8034, 8072, 8076, 8080, 8096, 8100, 8117, 8134, 8145, 8181, 8193, 8260, 8264, 8315, 8318, 8355, 8357, 8359, 8363, 8372, 8374, 8380, 8382, 8384, 8392, 8394, 8398, 8403, 8404, 8405, 8407, 8411, 8416, 8419, 8421, 8422, 8424, 8428, 8434, 8437, 8448, 8503, 8555, 8687, 8701, 8895, 8933, 8948, 8965, 8975, 8977, 9052, 9110, 9167, 9215, 9263, 9362, 9366, 9371, 9383, 9387, 9419, 9422, 9431, 9481, 9484, 9487, 9525, 9597, 9599, 9654, 9657, 9686, 9724, 9788, 9808, 9873, 9902

MICHIGAN

Ada: Korth 4478, Silverwing 4541, Van Andel 4567
Adrian: Hickman 4460, Merillat 4500
Albion: Albion 4332
Allegan: Allegan 4334, Perrigo 4521
Alma: Leppien 4486
Alpena: Besser 4349, Community 4370
Ann Arbor: Ann Arbor 4340, Cascade 4359, Duffy 4411, **Earhart 4413**, Ferrantino 4419, Knight 4477, Mosaic 4509, RNR 4527, Saddle 4530, Vaughan 4573
Auburn Hills: BorgWarner 4353, Chrysler 4366, Guardian 4454
Battle Creek: Battle Creek 4343, Binda 4350, **Kellogg 4473**, **Kellogg 4474**, **Kellogg's 4475**, Miller 4503
Bay City: Bay 4344
Benton Harbor: Whirlpool 4583
Berkley: Molinello 4505
Bingham Farms: Blumenstein 4351, Hough 4462
Birmingham: Alix 4333, Frankel 4436, Lewis 4488, Polk 4524, Thewes 4554, Two 4563
Bloomfield Hills: Applebaum 4341, Carls 4358, Davis 4391, Devereaux 4397, **Erb 4415**, Frankel 4434, Helppie 4456, Legion 4483, Penske 4519, Taubman 4552, Taubman 4553, Tracy 4558, Wasserman 4576, Westerman 4582
Bridgeport: Andersen 4339
Brighton: Johnson 4468, Sage 4531
Caro: Tuscola 4562
Chelsea: Chelsea 4362
Clinton Township: Webber 4578
Dearborn: Ford 4430, Levy 4487
Detroit: Alandt 4331, Comerica 4368, Community 4371, Dewey 4401, DTE 4410, Firestone 4422, Flinn 4424, Ford 4425, Ford 4426, Ford 4427, Ford 4428, Ford 4429, General 4442, Grosfeld 4453, Herrick 4459, Hudson 4463, Jubilee 4470, Mardigian 4494, McGregor 4498, Schaap 4533, Skillman 4543, Turner 4561, Willmas 4587, Wilson 4589, Wolff 4590
East Jordan: Charlevoix 4361
East Lansing: Heritage 4458, Pentecost 4520
Escanaba: Community 4375
Farmington Hills: Bosch 4354, Zatkoff 4595
Flint: Community 4372, Eddy 4414, Harding 4455, **Isabel 4466**, **Mott 4510**, Mott 4511, Whiting 4584
Frankfort: Dow 4406
Fremont: Fremont 4438, **Gerber 4443**
Fruitport: Van 4570
Gladstone: Besse 4348
Grand Blanc: Mackey 4489
Grand Haven: Grand Haven 4446
Grand Rapids: Christian 4365, Cook 4378, **Coopersmith 4379**, Cornucopia 4381, Davenport 4389, Dayenu 4392, DeVos 4398, DeVos 4399, DeVos 4400, Doornink 4403, Dyer 4412, Family 4417, Family 4418, Frey 4439, Frey 4440, G. 4441, Grand Rapids 4447, Idema 4465, Meijer 4499, MSJ 4513, Rordor 4529, Sebastian 4535, Secchia 4536, Spartan 4544, Steelcase 4547, **Tubergen 4559**, Van Andel 4566, Van Andel 4568, Van Noord 4571, VanderWeide 4572, Wege 4579, Williams 4586, Wolters 4592
Greenville: Greenville 4452
Grosse Point Farms: Stonisch 4548
Grosse Pointe Farms: Shelden 4537, Wilson 4588
Hastings: Barry 4342, DeCamp 4393
Highland: Beard 4345
Hillsdale: Hillsdale 4461, **Moller 4506**
Holland: Anchor 4338, Chinnick 4363, Community 4374, DeWitt 4402, **Foundation 4432**, **Myers 4515**, Prince 4525, Spoelhof 4545
Howell: Von 4574
Jackson: Alro 4336, Consumers 4376, Hurst 4464, Jackson 4467, Sigmund 4540, Weatherwax 4577
Kalamazoo: Dalton 4385, Fabri 4416, **Fetzer 4420**, Gilmore 4445, Johnston 4469, Kalamazoo 4472, Parish 4518, Ravitz 4526, Upjohn 4564
Lansing: Capital 4357, Granger 4449, Granger 4450, Great 4451
Manistee: Foster 4431
Marquette: Marquette 4495
Marshall: Cronin 4383, Marshall 4496
Mason: Dart 4388
Midland: **Allen 4335**, **Dow 4404**, Dow 4405, Dow 4407, Dow 4408, Gerstacker 4444, Midland 4502, **Pardee 4517**, Strosacker 4549, Towsley 4557
Milford: Bretzlaff 4355
Monroe: Knabusch 4476, La-Z-Boy 4481
Mount Pleasant: Mount Pleasant 4512
Muskegon: Community 4369
New Buffalo: Pokagon 4523
Niles: Leighton 4484
North Muskegon: Walker 4575
Northville: Manat 4490
Novi: Americana 4337, **Cooper-Standard 4380**
Orchard Lake: Tuktawa 4560
Oscoda: Shepherds 4538
Owosso: Cook 4377
Paw Paw: Charboneau 4360
Petoskey: Petoskey 4522
Plymouth: Thompson 4555, Thompson 4556
Port Huron: Community 4373
Portage: Brown 4356, Monroe 4507
Rockford: Wolverine 4593
Royal Oak: Here 4457
Saginaw: Saginaw 4532, Wickes 4585, Wolohan 4591
Saint Joseph: Berrien 4347
Schoolcraft: Fetzer 4421
Shelby Township: Weingartz 4580
Southfield: **Berman 4346**, Cummings 4384, Davidson 4390, **DENSO 4395**, DeRoy 4396, **Fisher 4423**, Lear 4482, **Rodney 4528**, Tarakji 4551
St. Clair Shores: Boll 4352, Cracchiolo 4382
St. Joseph: Schalon 4534, Upton 4565
Sturgis: Sturgis 4550
Taylor: Manoogian 4491, Manoogian 4492, Manoogian 4493, Masco 4497
Tecumseh: Lenawee 4485
Traverse City: Christ 4364, Grand 4448, Oleson 4516
Trenton: World 4594
Troy: Danto 4387, Delphi 4394, Frankel 4433, Frankel 4435, **Frankel 4437**, **Kresge 4479**, **Lachimi 4480**, Shoemaker 4539, Stange 4546
Van Buren Township: Dana 4386
Warren: Cold 4367, Kahn 4471, Van Elslander 4569
West Bloomfield: Dresner 4409
White Lake: Wenger 4581
Whitmore Lake: Skilling 4542
Winn: Morey 4508
Zeeland: **Micah 4501**, Miller 4504, Mulder 4514

see also 124, 276, 525, 640, 707, 763, 854, 1463, 1674, 1777, 2060, 2190, 2191, 2199, 2336, 2364, 2469, 2613, 2654, 2657, 2737, 2808, 2814, 2872, 2920, 2924, 2938, 2946, 3062, 3080, 3120, 3168, 3187, 3190, 3247, 3263, 3363, 3405, 3582, 3609, 3793, 3820, 3837, 3886, 3966, 4086, 4154, 4281, 4330, 4636, 4661, 4691, 4778, 4804, 4808, 4869, 5030, 5097, 5129, 5152, 5264, 5313, 5356, 5382, 5386, 5608, 6138, 6188, 6244, 6438, 6528, 7012, 7368, 7372, 7374, 7380, 7388, 7407, 7441, 7452, 7512, 7523, 7531, 7751, 8080, 8230, 8235, 8334, 8374, 8536, 8579, 8613, 8670, 8725, 8811, 9214, 9343, 9439, 9487, 9704, 9820, 9823, 9858, 9869, 9969, 9970

MINNESOTA

Austin: Hormel 4676
Bagley: TEAM 4779
Bayport: **Andersen 4601**, **Andersen 4602**, Andersen 4603
Bemidji: Neilson 4725, Northwest 4730
Bloomington: Eagle 4650, Kopp 4688, O'Rourke 4733, **O'Shaughnessy 4734**, **Toro 4780**
Buffalo: Hageman 4670
Burnsville: Shiebler 4762
Byron: Koskovich 4690
Duluth: Duluth 4649, Johnson 4683, Minnesota 4716, Mitchell 4717, Ordean 4732
Eagan: Blue 4618
Eden Prairie: Cargill 4627, St. 4769, Sundet 4774, Verdoorn 4788
Edina: Annexstad 4606, Charlson 4633, Edelstein 4652, Maas 4699, Mooty 4719, Mossier 4723, NFC 4727, Oswald 4735, Veritas 4789
Fergus Falls: West 4800
Golden Valley: **Pentair 4739**
Grand Rapids: Blandin 4617, Grand Rapids 4667
Hutchinson: Southwest 4768
Inver Grove Heights: CHS 4636
Lakefield: Remick 4751
Little Falls: Initiative 4679
Long Lake: Carlson 4629, Nelson 4726
Mankato: Andreas 4604, Andreas 4605
Maple Grove: Engdahl 4654
Medina: **Polaris 4746**
Minneapolis: A Better 4598, AHS 4599, Athwin 4607, Bakken 4608, Beim 4609, Beverly 4615, Buuck 4623, Campbell 4626, Cargill 4628, Carolyn 4630, Christianson 4635, Ciresi 4637, Cloverfields 4638, Cox 4639, Dayton 4643, Donaldson 4646, Dorea 4647, Evert 4655, Fiterman 4656, Frey 4658, **Gallagher 4660**, General 4661, George 4662, Gesner 4663, Graco 4666, Greystone 4668, Holmes 4675, Jennings 4680, Jostens 4684, **King 4687**, Leonard 4694, Leuthold 4695, Lored 4697, MacMillan 4700, Marbrook 4702, McGuire 4707, **McKnight 4708**, McKnight 4709, **Medtronic 4712**, Minneapolis 4714, Mooty 4720, **Mortenson 4721**, Patch 4737, Phillips 4740, Phillips 4741, Piper 4743, Pohlad 4745, Prospect 4747, RBC 4748, Regis 4750, Robina 4753, Robins 4754, Sabes 4756, Schoeneckers 4759, Schulze 4760, Sit 4764, Sit 4765, Stevens 4772, Stone 4773, SUPERVALU 4775, Target 4776, U.S. 4784, Valspar 4786, W.M. 4790, Wallestad 4791, Wallin 4792, Wallin 4793, Wedum 4796, Weiser 4798, WEM 4799, Westcliff 4801, WSDC 4807, Xcel 4808, **Youth 4809**
Minnetonka: **Better 4614**, GHR 4664, McVay 4711, Opus 4731, Pine 4742, Sieben 4763, United 4785, WCA 4795
Minnetrista: K.A.H.R. 4685
North Mankato: Taylor 4777
North Oaks: Hardenbergh 4672
Northfield: Ceres 4632

Plymouth: Cummins 4641, Foundation 4657, Martin 4704, **Mosaic 4722**
Red Wing: Red Wing 4749
Richfield: Best 4612
Rochester: Hiawatha 4674, Rochester 4755, Schmidt 4758
Saint Cloud: Central 4631
Saint Paul: 1988 4596, Bendorf 4610, Davis 4642, Stepanek 4771, Weyerhaeuser 4804
Savage: Cade 4625
Shoreview: Deluxe 4644
St. Louis Park: Luther 4698, Smikis 4767
St. Paul: 3M 4597, Alliss 4600, Bethel 4613, Bigelow 4616, Bremer 4620, Bush 4621, Butler 4622, C C 4624, Cherbec 4634, Criss 4640, Driscoll 4648, Ecolab 4651, Edwards 4653, **Fuller 4659**, Griggs 4669, Hallett 4671, Hersey 4673, HRK 4677, Hubbard 4678, Jerome 4681, Jewett 4682, Kelley 4686, Koran 4689, Land 4691, Lilly 4696, Manitou 4701, Mardag 4703, McCarthy 4705, McNeely 4710, Minnesota 4715, Musser 4724, Nicholson 4728, Northwest 4729, **Patterson 4738**, Saint Paul 4757, Securian 4761, **St. Jude 4770**, Travelers 4783, Veden 4787, Weesner 4797, **Weyerhaeuser 4802**, Weyerhaeuser 4803, Whiteside 4805
Stillwater: Rivers 4752, Tozer 4782
Vermillion: Poepl 4744
Waseca: Legacy 4693
Wayzata: Bentson 4611, Brandenborg 4619, Deziel 4645, Larson 4692, McGlynn 4706, Melrose 4713, Mithun 4718, Pagel 4736, TCF 4778, Total 4781, Wasie 4794
Winona: Gostomski 4665, Slaggie 4766, Winona 4806

see also 144, 260, 295, 315, 349, 398, 600, 831, 854, 988, 1229, 1267, 1316, 1345, 1420, 1470, 1507, 1602, 1624, 1662, 1750, 1760, 1789, 2011, 2044, 2057, 2191, 2200, 2245, 2469, 2490, 2640, 2657, 2670, 2738, 2819, 2880, 2946, 3034, 3056, 3138, 3149, 3167, 3178, 3292, 3296, 3405, 3430, 3443, 3444, 3448, 3457, 3777, 3838, 3857, 3867, 3957, 4137, 4198, 4890, 4932, 5008, 5043, 5080, 5090, 5358, 5415, 5471, 5489, 5607, 5629, 6230, 6244, 6554, 6651, 6832, 6851, 7038, 7214, 7236, 7351, 7356, 7360, 7407, 7577, 7641, 7761, 8426, 8435, 8512, 8519, 8520, 8569, 9084, 9085, 9087, 9263, 9482, 9641, 9643, 9716, 9804, 9807, 9815, 9820, 9869, 9912, 9923, 9936, 9950, 9956, 9962, 9963

MISSISSIPPI

Amory: Gilmore 4828
Biloxi: Biloxi 4814
Columbia: McLean 4835
Columbus: BBB 4813
Flowood: Blue 4815, Morgan 4840
Gulfport: Gulf 4830, Mississippi 4839
Hattiesburg: Asbury 4811, Greater 4829
Hernando: Community 4821, Maddox 4834
Jackson: Community 4819, Community 4820, Ergon 4824, Feild 4825, Ford 4826, Foundation 4827, Hearin 4832, McRae 4836, Pruet 4842, Regions 4843, Risen 4845, Van Devender 4847
Laurel: Chisholm 4818
Madison: Mississippi 4838
Meridian: Hardin 4831, Riley 4844
Natchez: **Armstrong 4810**
Oxford: Sullivan 4846
Ridgeland: Bower 4816, C Spire 4817, Luckyday 4833, Walker 4849
Stoneville: Delta 4823
Tupelo: BancorpSouth 4812, CREATE 4822, Oakwood 4841
University: Mississippi 4837
Vicksburg: Vicksburg 4848

see also 28, 47, 188, 211, 277, 854, 1996, 2191, 2469, 2554, 2565, 2657, 2738, 3617, 3630, 3667, 4388, 4395, 4474, 4481, 4651, 4691, 4971, 5030, 5106, 6151, 7138, 7470, 7531, 7601, 8373, 8495, 8530, 8549, 8572, 8610, 8613, 8629, 8779, 8851, 8997, 9290, 9499, 9704

MISSOURI

Augusta: Kooyumjian 4930
Birch Tree: Shaw 4970
Chesterfield: Brauer 4860
Clayton: Apex 4854, Baer 4857, Brown 4862, Busch 4867, Cox 4874, Duesenberg 4880, Dula 4881, Graybar 4898, Green 4899, Pott 4958, Rosewood 4964, Stupp 4983, Taylor 4987, Tilles 4991
Columbia: Hagan 4903, Hagan 4904, Laurie 4933, Lichtenstein 4936, MFA 4943, Shelter 4971
Crestwood: Concorde 4873
Creve Coeur: Pettus 4954
Hazelwood: Dierberg 4879
Independence: Truman 4996
Jefferson City: Mayer 4939, Schwartze 4968, Sugarbaker 4984
Joplin: Craig 4875, Humphreys 4913
Kansas City: American 4852, Burns 4866, Carter 4868, Commerce 4871, Cray 4876, Dunn 4882, **Francis 4893**, Goppert 4896, Gottlieb 4897, Green 4900, H & R 4902, Hall 4905, Hallmark 4906, Hulston 4911, Humphreys 4912, Kansas 4920, **Kauffman 4921**, Kauffman 4922, Kemper 4923, Kemper 4924, Kemper 4925, Kemper 4926, Kemper 4927, Loose 4937, McDonnell 4940, McGee 4942, Moulton 4946, Nichols 4949, Oppenstein 4950, Reynolds 4961, Rhoden 4962, Sherman 4972, Smith 4974, Sosland 4975, Sosland 4976, Sosland 4977, Speas 4978, Speas 4979, Stern 4980, Ten-Ten 4990, Ward 4998, Wornall 5003
Kirkwood: Ladner 4932
Lebanon: Plaster 4957
Moberly: Orscheln 4951
Neosho: Farber 4889
Saint Louis: Breen 4861, Buder 4864, Interco 4914, Jubel 4919, Kienstra 4928, Pershing 4953, Saint Louis 4966
Springfield: Community 4872, Hammons 4907, Musgrave 4947
St. Clair: Ferring 4891
St. Joseph: Taylor 4988
St. Louis: Albrecht 4850, Ameren 4851, Anheuser 4853, Arch 4855, Baer 4856, Ballmann 4858, Bellwether 4859, Brunner 4863, Bunge 4865, Casey 4869, Centene 4870, Cruse 4877, **Deer 4878**, Edison 4883, Edison 4884, Emerson 4885, Engelhardt 4886, **Enterprise 4887**, Express 4888, Feraldo 4890, Fox 4892, Gateway 4894, Goldfarb 4895, Grigg 4901, Hauck 4908, Hecker 4909, Holekamp 4910, Jacobsen 4915, Jones 4916, Jordan 4917, JSM 4918, Koman 4929, Laclede 4931, Lay 4934, Lemons 4935, Lopata 4938, **McDonnell 4941**, Millstone 4944, **Monsanto 4945**, Nestle 4948, Pershing 4952, Pillsbury 4955, Pillsbury 4956, Pulitzer 4959, Ravarino 4960, Roblee 4963, Saigh 4965, Sander 4967, Shaughnessy 4969, Simon 4973, Steward 4981, Stupp 4982, Sunnen 4986, Ten 4989, Todd 4992, Towle 4993, Trio 4994, Trulaske 4995, Waldheim 4997, Webb 4999, Westlake 5000, Whitaker 5001, World 5002
St. Peters: SunEdison 4985

see also 65, 116, 188, 209, 514, 633, 738, 854, 1543, 1750, 1774, 1791, 1796, 2004, 2047, 2261, 2279, 2302, 2371, 2469, 2518, 2536, 2654, 2657, 2709, 2725, 2738, 2822, 2824, 2838, 2923, 2969, 2972, 2995, 3034, 3113, 3125, 3211, 3257, 3334, 3492, 3506, 3508, 3512, 3525, 3526, 3527, 3531, 3535, 3536, 3537, 3541, 3546, 3547, 3549, 3550, 3551, 3556, 3581, 3582, 3835, 4166, 4285, 4466, 4481, 4636, 4647, 4661, 4691, 4743, 4749, 4784, 4807, 5080, 5090, 5106, 5266, 5314, 5338, 5371, 5536, 5601, 5722, 6185, 6244, 6310, 6597, 6853, 7279, 7280, 7348, 7452, 7552, 7590, 7624, 7690, 7764, 7765, 7770, 7800, 7801, 7806, 7932, 8104, 8230, 8400, 8413, 8442, 8697, 8783, 8791, 8919, 8925, 8990, 8991, 9018, 9059, 9098, 9160, 9218, 9242, 9247, 9383, 9386, 9466, 9657, 9815, 9822, 9859, 9869, 9929, 9943, 9990

MONTANA

Alder: Scoob 5015
Billings: Bair 5004, Bair 5005, First 5009
Bozeman: Cross 5007, Gianforte 5010, Gilhousen 5011
Butte: Town 5016
Helena: Montana 5013, Treacy 5017
Kalispell: Oro 5014
Lewistown: Central 5006
Missoula: Heman 5012, Washington 5018
Red Lodge: Edwards 5008
Whitefish: Whitefish 5019

see also 249, 778, 1017, 1183, 1277, 1723, 1794, 1958, 1997, 2072, 2104, 2106, 2240, 2563, 2657, 2802, 3003, 3457, 3492, 3551, 3813, 4114, 4609, 4636, 4661, 4690, 4729, 4784, 5090, 5159, 5301, 5622, 6158, 6356, 6391, 6915, 7314, 7389, 7615, 7729, 7738, 8714, 8831, 8833, 9121, 9315, 9372, 9567, 9576, 9590, 9591, 9594, 9621, 9640, 9642, 9661, 9689, 9704, 9762, 9984, 9989, 9996

NEBRASKA

Atkinson: Weller 5093
Aurora: Hamilton 5045
Central City: Merrick 5067
Chappell: Buckley 5026
Elkhorn: Vetter 5091
Fremont: Fremont 5039
Grand Island: Grand Island 5044
Hastings: Hastings 5046, Thom 5089
Holdrege: Phelps 5075
Kearney: Cope 5032, Hirschfeld 5049, Kearney 5055
Lexington: Lexington 5062
Lincoln: Abbott 5020, Abel 5021, Acklie 5022, Ameritas 5023, Cooper 5031, Dillon 5035, Dunklau 5036, Froehlich 5040, Kimmel 5059, Lincoln 5063, Nelnet 5072, Rogers 5077, St. Anthony 5085, Woods 5096, Woollam 5097
Nebraska City: Wirth 5095
North Platte: Mid-Nebraska 5068
Oakland: Nielsen 5073
Omaha: Beer 5024, Boyer 5025, Buffett 5027, **Buffett 5028**, ConAgra 5029, ConAgra 5030, Daugherty 5033, Davis 5034, Family 5038, Gaughan 5042, Graham 5043, Hawks 5047, Heider 5048, Hitchcock 5050, Holland 5051, Hubbard 5054, Kiewit 5056, Kiewit 5057, Kim 5058, Kind 5060, Lauritzen 5061, Linder 5064, Lozier 5065, Mapes 5066, Moglia 5069, Muchemore 5070, Mutual 5071, Omaha 5074, Robinson 5076, Ryan 5078, Schrager 5079, Scoular 5080, Sherwood 5081, Simon 5082, Slosburg 5083, Sokolof 5084, Storz 5086, Swanson 5087, Swanson 5088, Union 5090, Weitz 5092, Werner 5094
Sidney: Eagle 5037
South Bend: Hubbard 5053
Wakefield: Gardner 5041
York: Holthus 5052, York 5098

see also 144, 188, 1003, 1291, 1314, 1397, 1486, 1750, 1789, 2399, 2518, 2657, 2727, 3215, 3344, 3429, 3447, 3457, 3459, 3476, 3480,

3487, 3492, 3551, 4114, 4624, 4636, 4640, 4676, 4691, 4780, 4784, 4869, 4887, 4948, 4971, 5128, 5379, 6439, 7587, 8334, 8362, 8515, 8817, 8830, 8950, 9214

NEVADA

Carson City: Mallory 5129
Crystal Bay: Prometheus 5141, Shaheen 5148
Henderson: Crescere 5112, EBV 5116, Findlay 5119, Guidry 5121, Kagi 5125, Sawyer 5147
Incline Village: Buck 5105, Castleman 5107, Parasol 5138, Stuart 5151
Las Vegas: Adelson 5099, AJA 5100, Bennett 5101, Caesars 5106, Engelstad 5117, Lee 5127, Lied 5128, Mann 5130, M-K 5133, Nevada 5134, O'Bannon 5137, **Reynolds 5143**, Ruvo 5145, Southwest 5149, Spiegel 5150, Tam 5152, **Tang 5153**, White 5158, **World 5160**, Wunderman 5161
Minden: Fairweather 5118
Reno: Bretzlaff 5103, **Browning 5104**, Community 5108, Connor 5109, Cord 5110, Cordelia 5111, Crystal 5113, Davidson 5114, Doyle 5115, Gabelli 5120, Hart 5122, Hawkins 5123, Joseph 5124, Keyser 5126, Mathewson 5131, May 5132, Nova 5135, NV 5136, Pennington 5139, Redfield 5142, Rochlin 5144, Safe 5146, Tusher 5154, Van Sickle 5155, Viragh 5156, Wells 5157, Wiegand 5159
Stateline: Berner 5102
Zephyr Cove: Prim 5140

---

see also 174, 385, 723, 753, 1183, 1238, 1329, 1958, 2210, 2347, 2469, 2657, 2801, 3014, 3257, 3334, 3457, 3582, 3918, 4245, 4756, 4784, 4971, 5042, 5090, 5341, 5454, 6244, 6433, 6518, 6598, 6878, 7531, 7609, 8235, 8983, 9098, 9383, 9467

NEW HAMPSHIRE

Concord: Alexander 5162, Butler 5165, Endowment 5169, Gifford 5173, HNH 5175, New Hampshire 5182
Hampton: Penates 5185
Hanover: Barrette 5163, Byrne 5166
Keene: Panjandrum 5184, Putnam 5186
Loudon: Mosaic 5181
Manchester: Bean 5164, Cogswell 5167, DEKA 5168, Hunt 5177, Lindsay 5179
New London: Hopeman 5176
Newport: Malool 5180, Oberkotter 5183
Portsmouth: Foundation 5171, Haas 5174
Rye Beach: Fuller 5172, Schleyer 5188
Salem: **Fidelity 5170**, Johnson 5178, Trust 5189
Warner: Quinlan 5187

---

see also 188, 380, 452, 854, 1451, 1536, 1559, 1570, 1625, 1646, 1653, 1656, 1660, 1671, 1823, 1883, 1913, 1984, 2010, 2133, 2448, 2469, 2649, 2657, 2852, 2887, 3105, 3188, 3257, 3275, 3344, 3630, 3690, 3709, 3710, 3784, 3788, 3825, 3921, 3926, 3932, 3935, 3936, 3942, 3965, 3969, 4022, 4029, 4046, 4047, 4078, 4079, 4100, 4107, 4142, 4148, 4151, 4169, 4171, 4186, 4192, 4193, 4206, 4209, 4218, 4243, 4246, 4256, 4302, 4310, 4318, 4321, 4322, 4328, 4853, 4910, 5160, 5227, 5541, 5719, 5971, 6082, 6158, 6197, 6373, 6425, 6433, 6437, 6438, 6658, 6750, 6917, 6927, 6937, 7026, 7343, 7684, 7695, 8076, 8093, 8096, 8100, 8248, 8374, 8397, 8406, 8416, 8430, 9055, 9362, 9363, 9383, 9704, 9996

NEW JERSEY

Avenel: Haber 5287
Basking Ridge: Gibson 5277, **Verizon 5489**
Bayonne: Galanta 5272
Bedminster: Mushett 5388
Berkeley Heights: Mazer 5375
Bernardsville: Gagnon 5271, Jockey 5325
Bridgewater: **Sanofi 5437**
Caldwell: Orenstein 5397
Camden: Campbell 5223
Chatham: Golden 5280, Kemmerer 5336, Mario 5370, O'Neill 5395, Sudler 5472
Cherry Hill: **GHH 5275**, Heart 5297, Hummingbird 5309, Katz 5332, Lackner 5354, Samson 5434, Subaru 5471
Clark: Werdiger 5498
Clifton: Berger 5205, Cooperman 5233, Family 5258
Cologne: Hansen 5291
Cranbury: Stern 5468
Cranford: Delano 5240
Cresskill: Kauffmann 5334
Dayton: Klingenstein 5343
Deal: V'Emunah 5488
East Hanover: **Novartis 5393**, Schwartz 5442
East Rutherford: Ghermezian 5274
Eatontown: Sunup 5474
Edgewater: Balazs 5199
Edison: Parnes 5402, Saka 5432
Egg Harbor: Haines 5289
Elizabeth: Elizabethtown 5253
Elmwood Park: Lewis 5362, Rose 5425, WebMD 5496
Englewood: Atran 5197, C 5221, Katz 5333
Englewood Cliffs: **Crane 5235**, Kolatch 5347, Oster 5399, Palestroni 5400, Straus 5469, Unilever 5484
Fairfield: Roberts 5423
Far Hills: Gem 5273, Gibson 5276, Goldberg 5279
Flemington: Large 5355
Florham Park: Eckerson 5246, Give 5278, Kushner 5351, Stadtmauer 5466, Wagner 5491
Fort Lee: Mack 5366, Mack 5367, Syms 5475
Franklin Lakes: Boye 5212, De Nicola 5239, Stadler 5465
Freehold: Matthews 5374
Glen Ridge: Samaritan 5433
Glen Rock: L.F.H. 5353
Green Brook: **Perrin 5404**
Green Pond: Nicolais 5392
Hackensack: Buehler 5219, Creamer 5236, Pitkin 5408
Hamburg: Levitt 5361
Hamilton: Atlantic 5196, Johnson 5328
Harrington Park: United 5486
Hopewell: Bunbury 5220, Smith 5461
Iselin: **Siemens 5454**
Jamesburg: Seiden 5448
Jersey City: Broadridge 5214, Eisenreich 5251, Fortune 5263, **Guarini 5283**, Provident 5414
Kearny: Schecter 5439
Lafayette: **Yin 5507**
Lakewood: Dirshu 5242, SFF 5449
Lambertville: Bridge 5213, Hickory 5299
Lawrenceville: Bacchetta 5198, Dow 5244, Martinson 5373, Princeton 5411
Ledgewood: R. 5418
Linden: Brozowski 5218
Little Falls: Rubenstein 5428
Livingston: Friedman 5268, Gurwin 5286, Hawthorne 5295, Isdell 5318, James 5322, Maher 5368, Shen 5450, Silbermann 5456, Taub 5478, Tepper 5480
Long Branch: Brothers 5215
Long Valley: Borgenicht 5210
Madison: Milano 5384
Mahwah: Jaffe 5320
Marlton: Danellie 5237, Levitt 5360
Mendham: Barer 5203, Carolan 5225, Kirby 5340
Merchantville: JMP 5324
Midland Park: Hope 5304
Millburn: Healthcare 5296
Millville: Frankino 5266, Frankino 5267
Monmouth Junction: LifeCare 5363
Montclair: McMullen 5378, Schumann 5441, Silver 5457, Turrell 5483, Wall 5492, Weston 5499
Montvale: KPMG 5349, Turner 5482
Moorestown: Knowles 5344, **Knowles 5345**
Morristown: Charles 5227, Clare 5230, Community 5232, Dodge 5243, Isermann 5319, Kirby 5339, MCJ 5377, Sandy 5436, Silver 5458, Simon, 5460, Vanech 5487, Zurs 5510
Mount Laurel: Schwartz 5443
Mountain Lakes: Dircks 5241
Mountainside: L.A.W. 5352, Schwarz 5444, Wilf 5503, Wilf 5504
Murray Hill: **Alcatel 5190**, Bard 5202, Willits 5505
Neptune: Grove 5282
New Brunswick: **Johnson 5326**, **Johnson 5327**
Newark: **Edison 5248**, Horizon 5305, **IDT 5311**, Martini 5372, Newark 5390, **Prudential 5415**, PSEG 5416, Victoria 5490, Wight 5501
North Brunswick: Segal 5447
North Plainfield: Levin 5359
Oak Ridge: Sansom 5438
Ocean: Lipman 5364
Ocean View: Messner 5383
Oldwick: Cape 5224
Paramus: Indian 5313, Point 5410, Roth 5426, Zucker 5509
Parsippany: Wishes 5506
Pennington: Antz 5192, Brougher 5217, Dunbar 5245, Elias 5252, Fenwick 5259, Firestone 5260, Frohring 5269, Hanson 5292, Holmes 5302, James 5321, Kerr 5338, Kish 5341, Kresa 5350, Lasko 5356, Lenzmeier 5358, Lord 5365, Marsh 5371, Merillat 5382, Mohler 5386, Mosakowski 5387, Parker 5401, Plummer 5409, Roberts 5422, Ruesch 5429, Schmidt 5440, Scott 5445, Sheridan 5452, Touchpoint 5481, Weitzman 5497
Pennsauken: Honickman 5303, Shreiber 5453
Piscataway: Ingersoll-Rand 5314, Wicks 5500
Pittstown: Catholic 5226
Plainsboro: **Fish 5261**, Integra 5315
Point Pleasant: Barber 5201
Princeton: **Allen 5191**, Atkinson 5195, Bonner 5208, D'Angelo 5238, Evans 5254, Fund 5270, Gund 5285, Harbourton 5293, Holman 5301, **JM 5323**, **Johnson 5329**, Karma 5331, Kovner 5348, McGraw 5376, **Milbank 5385**, **Newcombe 5391**, Princeton 5412, RuthMarc 5431, Sands 5435, Sierra 5455, ST2 5464
Pt. Pleasant: Cabin 5222
Rancocas: Rowan 5427
Randolph: IGH 5312
Red Bank: Banbury 5200, Family 5257, Hovnanian 5307, Kelly 5335, Pascale 5403, Robertson 5424, Snyder 5462
Ridgewood: Bolger 5207, Holloway 5300, Marcon 5369, Shepherd 5451
Ringwood: Brotherton 5216
Roseland: CHDI 5228, Hess 5298, Laurie 5357, Renewable 5421, Steiner 5467
Rumson: Borden 5209, Cowles 5234, Strauss 5470
Saddle Brook: **Wang 5495**
Secaucus: Cole 5231
Short Hills: Appaloosa 5193, Edelste 5247, Investors 5317, **Pfeiffer 5405**, Rummel 5430, Silverman 5459, Wilf 5502
Somerset: Koguan 5346
South Orange: Harris 5294, Orange 5396
Springfield: Halpern 5290
Summit: Bouras 5211, Fournier 5264, Hugin 5308, Pincus 5407, Reeves 5420, Summit 5473
Teaneck: **Berrie 5206**, Hahn 5288, **Puffin 5417**, **Ramapo 5419**, Taub 5477, Yosef 5508
Tenafly: Kaplen 5330, Kennedy 5337
Teterboro: Klatskin 5342

Tinton Falls: **Hovnanian 5306**
Toms River: OceanFirst 5394
Totowa: Providence 5413
Township of Washington: OritaniBank 5398
Union: Eisenberg 5250
Voorhees: South 5463
Wall: New Jersey 5389
Warren: **Chubb 5229**, Grassmann 5281, Gulton 5284, Hyde 5310, Union 5485
Watchung: Focus 5262, **Segal 5446**
Wayne: **International 5316**
West Caldwell: Frankel 5265
West Orange: Benjamin 5204, Wallerstein 5493, Wallerstein 5494
Westfield: Fairbanks 5255
Whippany: **ARCH 5194**
Whitehouse Station: **Merck 5379**, Merck 5380, **Merck 5381**
Woodbridge: Phipps 5406, Tanzman 5476
Woodcliff Lake: Eisai 5249, Tavitian 5479
Wyckoff: Falcon 5256

---

see also 112, 188, 349, 385, 425, 467, 631, 854, 893, 1032, 1083, 1219, 1475, 1494, 1530, 1531, 1590, 1596, 1615, 1631, 1632, 1646, 1689, 1697, 1713, 1759, 1768, 1778, 1810, 1816, 1839, 1875, 1975, 2110, 2144, 2156, 2197, 2220, 2231, 2247, 2270, 2310, 2384, 2387, 2400, 2469, 2526, 2545, 2650, 2657, 2750, 2751, 2788, 2866, 2994, 3034, 3042, 3043, 3102, 3109, 3199, 3257, 3549, 3582, 3691, 3710, 3718, 3763, 3813, 3825, 3868, 3876, 3921, 4049, 4066, 4097, 4119, 4240, 4256, 4282, 4285, 4297, 4425, 4458, 4599, 4601, 4661, 4841, 4853, 4918, 5106, 5555, 5559, 5573, 5630, 5640, 5649, 5653, 5672, 5677, 5692, 5711, 5719, 5731, 5739, 5753, 5758, 5810, 5815, 5819, 5826, 5834, 5842, 5866, 5870, 5906, 5918, 5921, 5939, 5975, 5976, 6010, 6011, 6035, 6060, 6075, 6093, 6098, 6108, 6113, 6119, 6150, 6152, 6166, 6176, 6188, 6196, 6201, 6204, 6206, 6224, 6240, 6244, 6259, 6269, 6270, 6274, 6279, 6282, 6338, 6342, 6375, 6413, 6443, 6451, 6468, 6478, 6498, 6517, 6535, 6536, 6537, 6547, 6558, 6568, 6599, 6602, 6605, 6629, 6651, 6659, 6770, 6774, 6783, 6829, 6840, 6843, 6873, 6878, 6881, 6891, 6917, 6929, 6933, 6953, 6977, 6981, 6997, 7015, 7021, 7026, 7035, 7062, 7083, 7090, 7126, 7140, 7149, 7159, 7267, 7286, 7289, 7330, 7389, 7455, 7472, 7475, 7596, 7687, 7932, 7936, 7943, 7962, 7975, 7976, 7984, 8078, 8081, 8138, 8142, 8162, 8185, 8207, 8216, 8230, 8231, 8236, 8239, 8243, 8249, 8252, 8269, 8322, 8333, 8369, 8374, 8393, 8411, 8420, 8446, 8503, 8506, 8826, 8833, 8999, 9263, 9383, 9400, 9532, 9758, 9862, 9982, 9987

NEW MEXICO

Albuquerque: Albuquerque 5511, Albuquerque 5512, Hammersley 5520, **Johns 5524**, Karakin 5525, PNM 5532
Artesia: Chase 5517, Yates 5537, Yates 5538
Hobbs: Maddox 5528
Los Alamos: Delle 5518
Ruidoso: Hubbard 5523
Santa Fe: Altman 5513, Angelica 5514, Aurora 5515, Brindle 5516, Frost 5519, Hankins 5521, **Lannan 5526**, **Levinson 5527**, McCune 5529, New Mexico 5530, Phillips 5531, Santa Fe 5533, **Thaw 5534**, Thornburg 5535, Toan-O'Brien 5536
Taos: Healy 5522

---

see also 9, 32, 112, 175, 569, 854, 893, 961, 1001, 1171, 1183, 1369, 1399, 1472, 1498, 1750, 1958, 2469, 2563, 2657, 2890, 3128, 3257, 3852, 4002, 4191, 4458, 4474, 4506, 4661, 4808, 5090, 6183, 6389, 6731, 6774, 6797, 7002, 7031, 7398, 7676, 7764, 7770, 7853, 8541, 8593, 8663, 8707, 8724, 8813, 8851, 9052, 9053, 9080, 9083, 9091, 9098, 9214, 9288, 9315, 9321, 9383, 9512, 9570, 9762

NEW YORK

Albany: Albert 5567, Armstrong 5613, Bachmann 5632, Community 5803, Falcon 5966, Gross 6110, Ingrassia 6208, Lipp 6377, Maguire 6415, Maguire 6416, Massry 6444, Morse 6510, Mozilo 6512, O'Sullivan 6601, O'Toole 6602, Parke 6616, Pearson 6623, Picotte 6639, Puth 6668, Review 6692, Reynolds 6694, Rowe 6759, Swyer 6956, Templeton 6969, Ward 7049, Water 7056, Weir 7069, Willumstad 7085
Amherst: Alfiero 5570, **Buffalo 5726**, Lee 6343
Armonk: **IBM 6203**, MBIA 6451, Park 6614
Astoria: Elmezzi 5948
Auburn: Emerson 5950
Babylon: Santmann 6793, Sun 6946
Bangall: Animal 5601
Barneveld: Bugher 5727
Bedford: Naomi 6523, Newman 6553, Rice 6696
Bedford Hills: Amsterdam 5595, Sidewalk 6852, **Weeden 7060**
Bellmore: Levy 6362
Binghamton: Decker 5863, Klee 6286, Link 6374, Mee 6467
Bohemia: Lane 6325
Briarcliff Manor: **Gutfleish 6120**
Bridgehampton: Mallah 6424
Bronx: DOJ 5894, Equipart 5959, New Yankee 6542
Bronxville: Demartini 5872
Brooklyn: A M 5543, ACE 5548, American 5590, B & S 5631, Basch 5649, B'Chaya 5654, Berkowitz 5668, BFF 5672, Blue 5685, Brach 5699, Brooklyn 5718, Chaim 5761, Chehebar 5768, Chehebar 5769, Cohen 5792, Cornerstone 5817, **Discount 5889**, Donner 5898, Dovid 5905, Drizin 5914, Educational 5937, Eisenberg 5944, Elbogen 5945, Emes 5951, Empire 5953, ETZ 5962, Fischer 5981, **Ford 5995**, Frank 6008, Fuchs 6028, Fund 6030, Gross 6111, H & M 6122, H. & Y. 6123, Hartman 6145, **Jewish 6229**, K.W. 6246, **Klein 6287**, Kleinman 6290, Kohn 6301, Kornfeld 6304, L.E. 6317, Langer 6328, Leibowitz 6348, Lichtenstein 6366, M&E 6407, Ma'asim 6409, Marmurstein 6434, Mazel 6450, Moore 6502, Ohel 6580, Parkview 6617, Providence 6664, Radif 6671, Rieger 6707, Ritter 6712, Rostrust 6756, Rubin 6763, Schon 6811, Schonberger 6812, Shaarei 6835, Shaindel 6836, Shtesl 6849, United 7020, Walentas 7042, Whiting 7079, Wilson 7086, Yad 7108, Yashar 7109, Zichron 7120, Zvi 7129
Brookville: Rubenstein 6762
Buffalo: Arrison 5618, Baird 5635, Baird 5636, Ciminelli 5778, Community 5801, **Cummings 5832**, First 5979, Health 6153, Knox 6299, Lapine 6330, **M & T 6406**, McCormick 6458, Miller 6486, Oishei 6584, Rich 6697, Rupp 6771, Statler 6913, TE 6966, Tower 6999, Truman 7007, Wells 7073, Wendt 7074, Western 7078
Cambria: Moore 6503
Campbell Hall: **Ottaway 6603**
Canajoharie: Arkell 5611
Canandaigua: Schwartz 6817
Center Moriches: Island 6215
Centerport: Pulier 6665
Chappaqua: Clinton 5787, **David 5852**, Edelman 5930, Frog 6026, Goldie 6063, Hettinger 6170, Meyer 6481, Warner 7052
Churchville: Davison 5854
Clarence: Galasso 6032
Cold Spring Harbor: Lessing 6355
College Point: IF 6205
Commack: Boxer 5698, Setton 6833
Corning: Corning 5818
Corona: **Edhi 5934**, **Klein 6288**
Dewitt: **Reisman 6686**
Dix Hills: **Jaffe 6222**
Dobbs Ferry: Tensor 6970
East Hampton: Sabin 6775
East Norwich: Hoffman 6182
East Quogue: Harnisch 6135
Elmira: Aequus 5560, Bishop 5679
Floral Park: Brennan 5706
Flushing: Deutsch 5875, Kupferberg 6312, Kupferberg 6313, YAD 7107
Forest Hills: Cwierzyk 5838
Garden City: Biddle 5674, Brooks 5719, Dancing 5846, Effron 5938, **Gitenstein 6055**, Khatib 6278, Overhills 6606, Rauch 6681
Garrison: Waterston 7057
Getzville: Tower 7000
Glen Head: Banfi 5641, Barker 5644, DeMatteis 5873
Glens Falls: Glens Falls 6057
Gouverneur: Kinney 6285
Great Neck: Bass 5650, Butler 5733, Butler 5734, Gould 6089, Katz 6255, Levian 6358, Neuwirth 6539
Harrison: Jandon 6226, Kuflik 6311, Lanza 6329
Hauppauge: Brach 5700
Hewlett Harbor: Ross 6755
Hicksville: National 6527
Hobart: O'Connor 6578
Horseheads: Community 5804
Hudson: Hudson 6191
Hudson Falls: Sandy 6791
Huntington: Friedlander 6018
Ithaca: Community 5807, Park 6615, Triad 7005
Jamestown: Chautauqua 5766, Gebbie 6038, Hultquist 6195, Sheldon 6841
Jericho: Alpern 5577, Aron 5616, **Ashner 5619**, BMS 5688, Coudert 5820, Cullman 5831, Feinstein 5974, **Krupa 6310**, Rechler 6682
Johnson City: Community 5802
Katonah: Adelson 5555, Lostand 6394
Kings Point: Kaylie 6263
Lake Placid: Adirondack 5556
Lake Success: Mack 6412
Lakewood: Lenna 6352
Larchmont: Chernow 5771, Hendel 6161
Latham: WSB 7105
Lawrence: C & Y 5739, Edelman 5931, Ganger 6033, L. & L. 6316
Liberty: Gerry 6044
Lloyd Harbor: Shoreland 6847, Swartz 6953
Lockport: Grigg 6109
Locust Valley: Rogers 6727
Long Island City: **Citi 5780**, Milliken 6487, Steiniger 6924, Travis 7004
Mamaroneck: Goldberg 6061, Kushel 6315, Nias 6556, Silberstein 6854, **Straus 6934**
Manhasset: Colin 5797, Lachman 6318
Marion: Seneca 6832
Melville: Androcles 5599, Greater 6098, Kanas 6249, Lerner 6353, **Pershing 6629**, Sebonack 6826, Silvian 6858, Tahari 6958
Middle Village: Bnai 5689, **Friends 6024**
Mill Neck: Big 5675, Wohl 7097
Millbrook: Dyson 5923, Millbrook 6485
Mineola: Cross 5829
Monroe: Tova 6998
Monsey: Bais 5637, Fishoff 5984, Gold 6060, Hertz 6169, **Stefansky 6916**
Montgomery: Community 5806
Mount Kisco: East 5925, **Kohlberg 6300**, **Mathers 6446**, Santa 6792
Mountainville: Ogden 6579
New City: Cooper 5813, **Whitney 7080**, Work 7103

Riese 6708, Riggio 6709, Riley 6710, Ripple 6711, Riversville 6713, Rizzuto 6714, Robbins 6715, Robbins 6716, Roberts 6717, **Robertson 6718**, Robertson 6719, **Rockefeller 6723**, **Rockefeller 6724**, Rockefeller 6725, Roepers 6726, Rogers 6728, Rohatyn 6729, Rohr 6730, Rose 6732, Rose 6733, Rose 6735, Rose 6736, Rose 6737, Rose 6738, Rosen 6739, Rosen 6740, Rosen 6741, Rosen 6742, Rosenberg 6743, Rosenblatt 6744, Rosenblatt 6745, Rosenblum 6746, Rosenfeld 6747, Rosenkranz 6748, Rosenthal 6749, Rosenwald 6750, Rosenwald 6751, Ross 6753, Rotter 6757, Rowan 6758, Ruben 6761, **Rubin 6764**, **Rubin 6765**, Rubin 6766, Rudin 6767, Rudin 6768, Rudin 6769, Ruffin 6770, **Ruth 6772**, RZH 6773, Sackler 6776, Sackler 6777, Sackler 6778, Sackler 6779, Sackler 6780, Safra 6781, **Sage 6782**, Sagner 6783, Salmon 6784, Salomon 6785, Saltz 6786, Saltz 6787, Samuels 6788, Sandler 6789, **Saper 6794**, **Sapling 6795**, Sapp 6796, Sarofim 6797, **Sato 6798**, Schaffner 6800, Schapiro 6801, Schenker 6803, Scherman 6804, Schiff 6805, Schlosstein 6807, Schnurmacher 6809, Schnurmacher 6810, Schumann 6813, Schwartz 6814, Schwartz 6815, Schwartz 6816, Schwartz 6818, Schwartz 6819, Sculco 6821, Scully 6822, SDA 6823, Sealark 6824, Seaver 6825, Secunda 6827, Select 6829, Selz 6830, Semlitz 6831, Seven 6834, Shanken 6837, Shapiro 6838, Sharp 6839, **Shaw 6840**, Shelter 6842, Shipley 6843, Shippy 6844, Shiva 6845, Shoolman 6846, SHS 6848, **Shubert 6850**, Shulsky 6851, Siebens 6853, Silverman 6855, Silverstein 6856, Silverweed 6857, Simon 6859, **Simons 6860**, Simons 6861, Singer 6862, Sirus 6863, Sister 6864, Sitt 6866, SJS 6867, Skirball 6869, Slifka 6870, Slifka 6871, **Sloan 6872**, **SMBC 6873**, Smith 6874, Smith 6875, Smith 6877, Snowdon 6879, Snyder 6880, SO 6881, Sobel 6882, Sohn 6884, Solomon 6885, Solomon 6887, **Soros 6888**, Soros 6889, Soros 6890, Soros 6891, Source 6893, **Sparkplug 6894**, Sperry 6895, Speyer 6896, Spilker 6897, Spinal 6898, Spingold 6899, Spitzer 6900, Sprague 6901, **Spunk 6902**, St. George's 6904, St. Giles 6905, Stainman 6906, Stanton 6907, Stanton 6908, Starfish 6909, Starker 6910, **Starr 6911**, Steel 6914, Steele 6915, Steffens 6917, Stein 6919, Steinberg 6920, Steinberg 6921, Steinberg 6922, Steinhardt 6923, **Stempel 6925**, Stern 6926, Stern 6927, Stern 6928, Stern 6929, Stiefel 6931, **Stockman 6932**, Stony 6933, Stringer 6935, Stulman 6938, Stuntz 6939, Sugarman 6940, Sullivan 6941, Sulzberger 6942, Sumitomo 6943, **Summerfield 6944**, **Surdna 6947**, Sutton 6948, Sutton 6949, Sutton 6950, **Sutton 6951**, SVM 6952, Swartz 6954, Swieca 6955, **Tai 6959**, Tai 6960, **Tanaka 6961**, Tandon 6963, Tansy 6964, Teagle 6967, Teferes 6968, Terra 6971, Terumah 6972, Textor 6973, Theobald 6974, Thompson 6975, Three 6976, Tiffany 6978, Tiger 6979, Tiger 6980, **Tikvah 6981**, Time 6982, **Tinker 6983**, Tisch 6984, Tisch 6985, Tisch 6986, Tisch 6987, Tisch 6988, Tisch 6989, Sussman 6990, Tisch 6991, Tisch 6992, Tishman 6993, Tober 6994, Tomorrow 6995, Tortora 6996, **Toshiba 6997**, **Towerbrook 7001**, Toyota 7002, **Trace 7003**, **Trust 7009**, **Tsadra 7010**, Tuft 7011, Turn 7012, Turner 7013, Tuttle 7014, Unanue 7015, **Unbound 7016**, Union 7017, United 7018, **United 7019**, Unterberg 7021, Uphill 7022, van Ameringen 7023, van Ameringen 7024, Van Cleave 7025, Vetlesen 7027, **VHIV 7028**, **Vicente 7029**, Vidda 7030, Vilcek 7031, Viola 7032, **Vital 7033**, Vogelstein 7034, Volcker 7035, Volpert 7036, von der Heyden 7037, Voya 7038, Wachtell, 7040, Walbridge 7041, **Wallace 7043**, Walsh 7045, Walter 7046, Wang 7047, Warburg 7048, **Warhol 7050**, Warnaco 7051, Warner 7053, Wasserman 7055, **Watson 7058**, Weber 7059, Weil, 7062, Wein 7064, Weinberg 7065, Weinberg 7066, Weinberg 7067, Weinstein 7068, Weisberg 7070, **Wenner 7075**, Werblow 7076, West 7077, Wiegers 7082, Wiener 7083, Wildwood 7084, Wilson 7087, Windmill 7089, Winkelried 7090, Winston 7092, **Winston 7093**, Winters 7094, Witten 7095, WLC 7096, **Wolfensohn 7098**, Wolstencroft 7100, Woodcock 7101, **Woodshouse 7102**, Wunsch 7106, **YLRY 7110**, Young 7111, **Youths' 7112**, Zalaznick 7113, Zankel 7114, Zaro 7115, Zegar 7116, Zegarac-Pollock 7117, Zehner 7118, Zeides 7119, Ziff 7121, Ziff 7122, Ziff 7123, **ZIIZ 7124**, Zilkha 7125, Zubrow 7126, Zucker 7127, Zuckerberg 7128, Zweig 7130

North Creek: St. Faith's 6903

North Merrick: Lindner 6372

North Tonawanda: East 5926

Norwich: Smith 6876

Old Westbury: Berg 5666, D'Addario 5841

Olean: Cattaraugus 5750

Oneonta: Dewar 5879, Warren 7054

Oriskany: Eastern 5927

Ossining: Homcrest 6185

Oyster Bay: Bahnik 5634

Patchogue: Knapp 6296

Pearl River: Duncan 5920, Hunter 6196

Pelham: Countess 5821

Pelham Manor: Strypemonde 6936

Penfield: Davenport 5850

Pittsford: Ames 5591, Golisano 6077

Plainview: Sykes 6957

Pleasantville: Burns 5732

Port Chester: Seiler 6828

Port Jefferson: Frey 6014

Port Washington: Dejana 5868, Scotts 6820

Poughkeepsie: Community 5808, McCann 6453, Nuhn 6572, Schlobach 6806

Purchase: Abeles 5544, Alpert 5578, Baker 5638, Central 5756, Dove 5903, Dove 5904, Essel 5961, Hochfelder 6177, Leventhal 6357, **PepsiCo 6627**, Sobel 6883, Tananbaum 6962, Wachenheim 7039, Wallach 7044

Queens: Augustine 5625

Rego Park: Ammon 5594, Goldstein 6074

Rhinebeck: Sosnoff 6892

Riverdale: Bravmann 5705

Riverhead: Corey 5816, Laurents/Hatcher 6338

Rochester: Crossed 5830, DiMino 5887, ESL 5960, Farash 5969, Greater 6099, Jones 6242, Levine 6359, Riedman 6706, Rochester 6722, **Ross 6754**, Schmitt 6808, Summers 6945, Wegman 7061, Wilson 7088, Wolk 7099

Rockville Centre: Rose 6734, Winley 7091

Roslyn: Mallah 6423, New York 6543

Roslyn Harbor: Hagedorn 6127

Rye: Flinn, 5988, Mack 6411, Sternberg 6930, Weissman 7071

Rye Brook: Andor 5598, Landegger 6323, Lisabeth 6378, Moore 6501

Sands Point: Plum 6648, Tarica 6965

Saranac Lake: Keet 6266

Saratoga Springs: Ammon 5593, Anderson 5597, Berkowitz 5669, Bright 5710, Caudill 5751, Harsh, 6143, Kaye 6262, Kilts 6280, Longwell 6391, Many 6426, Neidich 6534, Plumeri 6649, Robinson 6720, RTS 6760, S & G 6774, Solomon 6886, Stuart 6937

Scarborough: Curran 5835

Scarsdale: Doolittle 5901, Heyer 6171, Marx 6441, Sitchin 6865

Schenectady: Golub 6079, Price 6658, Schenectady 6802, Wright 7104

Sherrill: Gorman 6083

Shoreham: Dreams 5909

Skaneateles: Allyn 5575

Sleepy Hollow: Glickenhaus 6058, Vernon 7026

Southampton: JAF 6221

Spencertown: Kelly 6271

Spring Valley: Inzlicht 6212

Stamford: Robinson 6721

Staten Island: Geary 6037, Northfield 6568, Richmond 6703, Staten 6912

Suffern: Chada 5759, Horwitz 6188, New Brook 6540

Syosset: Brunckhorst 5723, Knott 6298, Weiler 7063

Syracuse: Central 5757, Gifford 6049, Pomeroy 6652, Snow 6878

Tarrytown: **Diamond 5881**, Donner 5899

Troy: McCarthy 6454, Troy 7006

Tuckahoe: Pope 6653

Tuxedo Park: Mulford 6514

Unadilla: Tianaderrah 6977

Uniondale: Gutenstein 6119, Lemle 6351, Save 6799, Widgeon 7081

Utica: Community 5805

Valhalla: **NBI 6532**, Paley 6610

Vestal: Hershaft 6167

Victor: Sands 6790

Watertown: Northern 6567

Westbury: McCarthy 6456

White Plains: All 5572, Barnett 5645, Barrington 5647, **Mailman 6418**, Rosner 6752, **Skadden 6868**, Stein 6918, Weissman 7072

Whitestone: Foundation 6000, Nonna's 6563

Williamsville: National 6526

Woodbury: Cramer 5824, Dolan 5895, Dolan 5896, Nazarian 6530, Trump 7008

Woodsburgh: Hershman 6168

Yonkers: Carvel 5749

York: Rose 6731

---

see also 9, 54, 75, 87, 102, 136, 170, 173, 188, 210, 251, 256, 268, 281, 299, 306, 333, 341, 343, 346, 351, 353, 354, 355, 362, 370, 371, 375, 379, 385, 386, 394, 397, 406, 435, 436, 444, 450, 455, 467, 532, 544, 563, 567, 574, 582, 583, 586, 599, 607, 612, 615, 619, 624, 628, 631, 633, 644, 656, 662, 683, 702, 704, 705, 710, 723, 724, 729, 738, 757, 758, 770, 781, 782, 792, 798, 802, 803, 811, 813, 834, 843, 844, 854, 873, 876, 886, 889, 910, 913, 914, 922, 926, 928, 932, 933, 939, 941, 948, 950, 952, 957, 965, 1017, 1037, 1038, 1045, 1057, 1058, 1065, 1070, 1071, 1074, 1076, 1078, 1085, 1089, 1096, 1099, 1101, 1111, 1121, 1131, 1138, 1142, 1148, 1150, 1158, 1162, 1165, 1179, 1180, 1184, 1219, 1223, 1235, 1249, 1258, 1274, 1277, 1278, 1306, 1328, 1330, 1333, 1340, 1348, 1356, 1361, 1369, 1400, 1436, 1445, 1459, 1470, 1475, 1514, 1515, 1517, 1521, 1527, 1529, 1530, 1531, 1532, 1534, 1535, 1536, 1538, 1546, 1550, 1551, 1552, 1553, 1559, 1560, 1569, 1571, 1574, 1583, 1590, 1591, 1593, 1594, 1595, 1596, 1597, 1601, 1612, 1615, 1617, 1618, 1623, 1624, 1626, 1628, 1631, 1632, 1633, 1638, 1646, 1648, 1649, 1653, 1654, 1658, 1660, 1661, 1662, 1663, 1668, 1669, 1671, 1674, 1677, 1680, 1681, 1683, 1684, 1685, 1686, 1687, 1689, 1692, 1693, 1694, 1695, 1697, 1698, 1700, 1701, 1702, 1707, 1708, 1709, 1711, 1713, 1716, 1718, 1723, 1724, 1725, 1734, 1739, 1741, 1743, 1748, 1759, 1761, 1771, 1775, 1778, 1779, 1781, 1782, 1789, 1794, 1797, 1799, 1802, 1803, 1807, 1813, 1815, 1816, 1817, 1823, 1826, 1827, 1830, 1833, 1836, 1837, 1839, 1850, 1854, 1856, 1857, 1859, 1860, 1861, 1869, 1871, 1874, 1882, 1889, 1897, 1910, 1911, 1912, 1917, 1919, 1920, 1926, 1941, 1947, 1948, 1957, 1965, 1970, 1972, 1973, 1984, 1992, 1998, 2003, 2005, 2017, 2018, 2021, 2022, 2047, 2049, 2053, 2062, 2066, 2077, 2086, 2095, 2100, 2104, 2107, 2110, 2119, 2121, 2126, 2128, 2132, 2133, 2135, 2137, 2139, 2141, 2143, 2145, 2147, 2157, 2175, 2176, 2178, 2183, 2189, 2190, 2193, 2195, 2196, 2197, 2207, 2216, 2217, 2222, 2226, 2229, 2231, 2234, 2239, 2240, 2242, 2247, 2252, 2258, 2264, 2266, 2272, 2274, 2277, 2295, 2303, 2306, 2309, 2311, 2318, 2320, 2338,

2339, 2341, 2344, 2347, 2350, 2360, 2361, 2362, 2365, 2370, 2382, 2387, 2392, 2399, 2425, 2428, 2467, 2469, 2494, 2497, 2526, 2541, 2545, 2649, 2652, 2653, 2657, 2664, 2666, 2668, 2672, 2677, 2680, 2683, 2684, 2685, 2703, 2707, 2710, 2716, 2722, 2727, 2728, 2729, 2734, 2739, 2750, 2751, 2754, 2755, 2758, 2770, 2778, 2781, 2788, 2795, 2797, 2801, 2810, 2815, 2824, 2832, 2841, 2842, 2848, 2866, 2869, 2890, 2891, 2911, 2912, 2917, 2918, 2919, 2923, 2926, 2939, 2945, 2948, 2950, 2961, 2999, 3014, 3016, 3034, 3042, 3043, 3044, 3050, 3063, 3065, 3076, 3085, 3093, 3104, 3108, 3109, 3122, 3125, 3128, 3136, 3137, 3144, 3149, 3151, 3152, 3159, 3161, 3177, 3178, 3180, 3196, 3199, 3222, 3234, 3246, 3257, 3292, 3315, 3316, 3404, 3409, 3411, 3444, 3457, 3495, 3496, 3528, 3549, 3565, 3582, 3630, 3642, 3652, 3653, 3670, 3677, 3681, 3690, 3693, 3704, 3710, 3715, 3720, 3729, 3730, 3731, 3736, 3738, 3763, 3770, 3786, 3788, 3790, 3799, 3801, 3808, 3810, 3813, 3820, 3825, 3837, 3848, 3852, 3857, 3859, 3868, 3871, 3884, 3907, 3908, 3921, 3928, 3936, 3941, 3945, 3946, 3948, 3963, 3978, 3981, 3988, 4004, 4007, 4008, 4020, 4026, 4029, 4032, 4046, 4052, 4078, 4082, 4087, 4097, 4111, 4119, 4128, 4131, 4139, 4143, 4154, 4156, 4165, 4171, 4179, 4183, 4191, 4198, 4213, 4214, 4225, 4226, 4232, 4238, 4249, 4250, 4251, 4256, 4259, 4262, 4266, 4271, 4273, 4278, 4284, 4285, 4296, 4297, 4302, 4307, 4309, 4311, 4322, 4323, 4341, 4351, 4366, 4379, 4384, 4387, 4390, 4394, 4422, 4423, 4437, 4458, 4466, 4471, 4490, 4493, 4509, 4526, 4530, 4552, 4553, 4570, 4580, 4581, 4588, 4652, 4661, 4669, 4673, 4681, 4723, 4740, 4742, 4743, 4785, 4798, 4809, 4818, 4852, 4853, 4854, 4857, 4865, 4884, 4913, 4915, 4948, 4959, 4970, 5008, 5024, 5037, 5082, 5100, 5111, 5113, 5116, 5120, 5135, 5144, 5158, 5159, 5168, 5170, 5173, 5181, 5185, 5190, 5192, 5195, 5196, 5197, 5198, 5199, 5200, 5201, 5203, 5204, 5205, 5206, 5211, 5216, 5224, 5225, 5228, 5231, 5233, 5234, 5238, 5246, 5247, 5250, 5251, 5252, 5254, 5258, 5264, 5268, 5272, 5273, 5274, 5280, 5282, 5283, 5284, 5285, 5286, 5287, 5288, 5292, 5293, 5294, 5298, 5299, 5300, 5307, 5310, 5311, 5313, 5319, 5320, 5322, 5324, 5325, 5328, 5330, 5332, 5333, 5334, 5335, 5337, 5342, 5343, 5347, 5348, 5349, 5351, 5352, 5353, 5354, 5359, 5361, 5362, 5364, 5366, 5367, 5368, 5377, 5379, 5384, 5385, 5388, 5390, 5391, 5392, 5395, 5397, 5399, 5402, 5403, 5406, 5409, 5410, 5415, 5420, 5421, 5422, 5423, 5424, 5426, 5427, 5428, 5433, 5436, 5438, 5439, 5442, 5444, 5446, 5448, 5449, 5450, 5455, 5456, 5457, 5458, 5461, 5464, 5466, 5467, 5469, 5470, 5472, 5475, 5477, 5478, 5479, 5480, 5484, 5487, 5489, 5491, 5493, 5495, 5496, 5499, 5502, 5503, 5504, 5509, 5510, 5513, 5515, 5525, 7132, 7136, 7140, 7145, 7149, 7150, 7172, 7216, 7218, 7220, 7248, 7290, 7301, 7307, 7331, 7343, 7349, 7381, 7470, 7472, 7476, 7477, 7493, 7505, 7518, 7523, 7529, 7530, 7538, 7552, 7554, 7559, 7587, 7595, 7602, 7612, 7613, 7626, 7644, 7654, 7677, 7687, 7695, 7707, 7712, 7720, 7726, 7734, 7737, 7755, 7804, 7868, 7875, 7908, 7910, 7912, 7919, 7920, 7926, 7938, 7962, 7964, 7965, 7967, 7975, 7997, 8003, 8006, 8027, 8034, 8045, 8052, 8057, 8066, 8067, 8086, 8093, 8115, 8134, 8145, 8149, 8162, 8177, 8181, 8193, 8196, 8197, 8201, 8202, 8207, 8226, 8233, 8237, 8242, 8243, 8247, 8254, 8257, 8270, 8278, 8280, 8287, 8297, 8298, 8306, 8309, 8316, 8317, 8323, 8326, 8330, 8347, 8354, 8357, 8369, 8373, 8374, 8384, 8392, 8396, 8404, 8407, 8408, 8411, 8415, 8422, 8425, 8426, 8439, 8441, 8443, 8489, 8503, 8551, 8579, 8611, 8613, 8665, 8685, 8705, 8708, 8711, 8713, 8718, 8732, 8736, 8757, 8765, 8793, 8794, 8804, 8807, 8831, 8833, 8840, 8854, 8860, 8871, 8895, 8906, 8914, 8966, 8969, 8981, 8999, 9005, 9062, 9085, 9111, 9116, 9155, 9172, 9176, 9178, 9190, 9193, 9199, 9216, 9244, 9263, 9276, 9278, 9290, 9297, 9314, 9359, 9362, 9371, 9383, 9400, 9404, 9409, 9422, 9428, 9439, 9458, 9464, 9468, 9481, 9486, 9493, 9517, 9526, 9527, 9532, 9540, 9547, 9577, 9585, 9612, 9657, 9660, 9712, 9798, 9800, 9812, 9815, 9857, 9865, 9929, 9976, 9980, 9982, 9987, 9994

NORTH CAROLINA

Ahoskie: Roanoke 7303
Asheville: Community 7182, Glass 7210
Belmont: Seven 7309
Burlington: Hunt 7237
Cary: Curran 7185, Goodnight 7212
Chapel Hill: Brady 7156, Bryson 7163, **Carlson 7172**, Hesburgh-Yusko 7230, Ireland 7239, Kenan 7248, **Morehead-Cain 7268**, **Oak 7276**, Randleigh 7292, Rominger 7306, Warner 7334
Charlotte: 25th 7131, Adams 7132, Allen 7134, **Bank 7139**, Baxter 7142, Beckman 7145, Belk 7146, Belk 7147, Belk 7148, Bergen 7149, Bissell 7152, Blumenthal 7154, Branan 7157, Byrum 7166, Campbell 7168, Carnrick 7173, Chatham 7175, Christopher 7176, Dalton 7187, Deaver 7190, Delta 7191, Dickson 7192, Duke 7195, Duke 7196, E. 7198, Foundation 7202, Gibbs 7207, Giles 7208, Goodrich 7213, Gorelick 7215, Gratis 7216, Hallowell 7220, Hanes 7221, Harris 7223, Harvest 7224, Hayes 7227, Hayworth, 7228, Humphrey 7236, Jolley 7240, Josef 7244, Kahn 7245, Keith 7247, Kimbrell 7249, Kramer 7250, Levine 7255, Lewis 7256, Lewis 7257, Luddy 7259, McCausland 7262, McEachern 7263, Murphy 7270, Nucor 7275, Oechsle 7278, Olin 7279, Palm Beach 7281, Phillips 7284, Piedmont 7285, Plansoen 7286, Post 7289, Provident 7291, Richmond 7302, Short 7311, Simpson 7312, Smith 7316, Smith 7317, Snyder's-Lance 7318, Spangler 7320, Strauss 7323, Symmes 7325, Van Every 7329, Van Houten 7330, Vanderbilt 7331, Vickar 7333, Wheeler 7336, Woodward 7343
Concord: Cannon 7169, Gordon 7214
Conover: Bolick 7155
Dobson: Shelton 7310
Durham: Biddle 7150, BIN 7151, Blue 7153, **Nickel 7272**, Triangle 7328, Zinc 7349
Fayetteville: Cumberland 7184, McLean 7264
Garner: Yeargan 7346
Gastonia: Community 7179
Goldsboro: Bryan 7161
Greensboro: Anonymous 7135, Armfield 7137, Bryan 7162, Cemala 7174, Community 7180, Fund 7204, Gunzenhauser-Chapin 7218, Haley 7219, Hillsdale 7232, Prickett 7290, Richardson 7300, Richardson 7301, Tannenbaum 7326, VF 7332, Weaver 7335
Greenville: Greenville 7217, Smith 7315
Hendersonville: Baruch 7140, Community 7181, Leever 7253
Hickory: George 7205, Yount 7348
High Point: High Point 7231, Terry 7327, Wilson 7338, Wos 7345
Huntersville: Merancas 7267
Kinston: Harvey 7225
Lake Toxaway: Love 7258
Laurel Hill: Morgan 7269
Lenoir: Broyhill 7160, Jonas 7241
Madison: McMichael 7265
Marion: Corpening 7183
Matthews: P & B 7280
Mocksville: Davie 7188, Mebane 7266
Morehead City: **Sunshine 7324**
Morganton: Community 7178
Mount Olive: Southern 7319
New Bern: Bate 7141
North Wilkesboro: Herring 7229
Norwood: Kean/Hartquist 7246
Oakboro: Jordan 7243
Raleigh: Anonymous 7136, Capital 7171, Curtis 7186, Finley 7199, Gipson 7209, Jones 7242, **Lynch 7260**, North Carolina 7273, Perkins 7282, Pharmacy 7283, Pope 7288, Rex 7295, Reynolds 7299, Sloan 7314, State 7321, Stewards 7322
Reidsville: Reidsville 7294
Research Triangle Park: **Burroughs 7164**, North 7274, **S.R.C. 7307**
Salisbury: Food 7201, Robertson 7305, Woodson 7342
Shelby: Dover 7194
Smithfield: Holding 7233, Holding 7234
Tryon: Polk 7287
Wadesboro: Braswell 7158
Wilkesboro: Kulynych 7251, Kulynych 7252
Wilmington: Cape Fear 7170, Davis 7189, Women's 7341
Wilson: BB&T 7143, BB&T 7144, Neviaser 7271, Young 7347
Winston-Salem: Adams 7133, Babcock 7138, Brauninger 7159, Butler 7165, Caine 7167, Clamer 7177, Dobbs 7193, Duke 7197, Flow 7200, French 7203, Ghidotti 7206, Glenn 7211, Hanes 7222, Havens 7226, Hommer 7235, Hunter 7238, Legatus 7254, Mayr 7261, Odell 7277, Rasmuson 7293, Reynolds 7296, Reynolds 7297, Reynolds 7298, Roberts 7304, Schumacker 7308, Slick 7313, Wilson 7337, Winslow 7339, Winston-Salem 7340, Woodward 7344

see also 6, 187, 188, 349, 380, 390, 402, 501, 633, 767, 854, 871, 880, 1174, 1328, 1403, 1426, 1427, 1515, 1531, 1545, 1553, 1569, 1625, 1646, 1768, 1776, 1783, 1809, 1810, 1832, 1839, 1841, 1855, 1900, 1937, 1996, 2027, 2061, 2073, 2079, 2163, 2191, 2230, 2335, 2358, 2420, 2464, 2469, 2517, 2532, 2613, 2657, 2700, 2738, 2740, 2753, 2790, 2824, 2872, 2895, 2921, 3127, 3188, 3232, 3292, 3344, 3443, 3582, 3710, 3821, 3825, 3827, 3845, 3857, 4048, 4221, 4315, 4380, 4388, 4405, 4481, 4546, 4634, 4651, 4654, 4739, 5106, 5176, 5223, 5259, 5314, 5339, 5370, 5379, 5420, 5423, 5425, 5506, 5664, 5738, 5742, 5751, 5826, 5832, 5836, 5920, 6067, 6084, 6095, 6158, 6236, 6411, 6528, 6615, 6651, 6719, 6815, 6890, 6966, 7005, 7037, 7452, 7470, 7493, 7587, 7613, 7614, 7643, 7684, 7873, 7932, 7967, 8226, 8235, 8334, 8363, 8411, 8430, 8447, 8479, 8484, 8486, 8491, 8499, 8506, 8528, 8552, 8573, 8579, 8604, 8627, 9290, 9386, 9413, 9421, 9422, 9441, 9460, 9467, 9470, 9476, 9480, 9486, 9499, 9500, 9535, 9539, 9543, 9606, 9828, 9947

NORTH DAKOTA

Bismarck: Leach 7353, MDU 7354, North Dakota 7357
Fargo: Barry 7350, Fargo 7351, Larson 7352, Offutt 7358, Scheels 7359, Stern 7360, Wanzek 7361
Grand Forks: Myra 7355
West Fargo: Nordick 7356

see also 854, 1750, 2191, 2657, 2738, 2790, 3056, 3457, 3748, 4620, 4621, 4636, 4691, 4694, 4716, 4729, 4784, 4796, 4808, 5008, 8541

OHIO

Akron: Akron 7367, Berlin 7385, Boutell 7388, Children's 7401, Corbin 7420, FirstEnergy 7455, FirstMerit 7456, GAR 7465, Haslinger 7482, Lehner 7536, Lippman 7542, Northern 7597,

Oelschlager 7598, Orr 7604, Sankey 7643, Sisler 7664
Amherst: Nord 7594
Ashland: Ashland 7378
Ashtabula: Ashtabula 7379, Morrison 7580
Barberton: Barberton 7382
Bay Village: Jenkins 7508
Beachwood: BASF 7383, Gund 7475, Krause 7530, Lozick 7545, Maltz 7553
Bratenahl: Howley 7494
Brecksville: Vesper 7695
Brooklyn: Dermitt 7432, Fasenmyer 7448, Fenn 7449, Ford 7459, Goatie 7472, Gund 7477, Hoover 7491, Lincoln 7541, Scott 7658, Smith 7666, Wade 7697, Women's 7720
Canton: David 7427, Hoover 7492, Stark 7673, **Timken 7684**
Celina: Mercer 7567
Chagrin Falls: **Geisse 7468**
Chesterland: Fairmount 7446
Cincinnati: A Good 7363, Anderson 7373, Broussard 7389, Budig 7392, Buenger 7393, Building 7394, Burleigh 7395, Butler 7396, Castellini 7399, Cincinnati 7404, Cincinnati 7405, Clouse 7408, Conn 7418, Conway 7419, Covenant 7422, Dater 7426, DeWine 7434, Dornette 7440, Emery 7443, Fifth 7452, Fleischmann 7457, Friedlander 7463, Haile, 7480, Hatton 7483, Hayfields 7485, Heiman 7486, Hubert 7495, Hunt 7498, Hutton 7500, Ima/ Mickey 7502, J. & H. 7504, Jacobs 7505, Jergens 7510, Jewish 7511, Kaplan 7516, Keeler 7517, Kersten 7519, Knowlton 7528, Kroger 7531, Lapp 7534, Luedeking 7547, Luther 7548, Macy's 7552, Mayerson 7561, McLane 7566, Meshewa 7568, Nippert 7590, Ohio 7599, Oliver 7600, Peters 7616, Pfau 7618, Pulley 7624, Rockwern 7634, Schell 7646, Schiff 7648, Schiff 7649, Schmidlapp 7651, Schott 7653, Schulze 7656, Scripps 7659, Semple 7660, Slemp 7665, Spaulding 7670, Sutphin 7679, Warrington 7703, Western 7710, Wodecroft 7717, Wohlgemuth 7718, Zembrodt 7724
Cleveland: Abar 7364, Abington 7365, American 7369, American 7370, Austin 7380, Bailey 7381, **Bingham 7387**, Bruening 7391, Cleveland 7406, Cliffs 7407, Codrington 7409, Cole 7410, DBJ 7430, **Eaton 7442**, Ferry 7451, Firman 7454, Green 7473, Gund 7478, H.C.S. 7479, Humphrey 7497, Huntington 7499, Jennings 7509, Jochum 7513, Keithley 7518, KeyBank 7523, Knight 7527, Kramer 7529, Kulas 7532, Lennon 7537, Mandel 7554, **Mandel 7555**, Mandel 7556, Mather 7559, McBride 7562, McGregor 7564, Miller 7571, MJH 7573, Murch 7582, Murphy 7584, O'Neill 7602, Park 7609, Parker 7611, Partridge 7612, **Patterson 7613**, Payne 7614, Perkins 7615, Peterson 7617, Prentiss 7621, Price 7622, Ratner 7626, Reinberger 7628, Rosenthal 7637, Saint 7639, **Sapirstein-Stone-Weiss 7644**, Schott 7652, Sherwin-Williams 7661, Smith 7667, Smith 7668, Stefanski 7675, Stone 7677, Third 7681, Tippit 7685, Vair 7693, Warmenhoven 7701, Weisbrod 7708, White 7715, Woodruff 7721
Columbus: **58 7362**, American 7368, Columbus 7411, Diamond 7435, Ferguson 7450, Fleming 7458, Gelbman 7469, Gerlach 7471, IHS 7501, Lancaster 7533, M/I 7550, Macbea 7551, McConnell 7563, Montei 7574, Moores 7576, Motorists 7581, Nationwide 7587, NiSource 7591, Osteopathic 7605, Safelite 7638, Salem 7641, Schottenstein 7654, Schottenstein 7655, State 7674, Talmage 7680, Weary 7706, Wolfe 7719
Concord Township: Hershey 7487
Coshocton: Coshocton 7421, Montgomery 7575
Dayton: Berry 7386, Dayton 7428, Dayton 7429, **Kettering 7520**, Kettering 7521, Kettering 7522, Levin 7539, Mathile 7560, Parents 7608, Philips 7619, Rose 7636, Schear 7645, Schiewetz 7647, Toulmin 7687, Wallace 7700
Delaware: Jegs 7507
Dover: Kimble 7526, Reeves 7627
Dublin: **Cardinal 7398**
East Liverpool: Gund 7476
Eaton: Home 7488
Elyria: Community 7412, Stocker 7676
Euclid: Wellman 7709
Fairlawn: **OMNOVA 7601**
Fairview Park: Ridgecliff 7631
Findlay: Findlay 7453
Gates Mills: Kalberer 7515
Hamilton: Hamilton 7481, Wilks 7716
Hartville: Christ 7402
Haviland: Samaritan 7642
Highland Heights: **Lerner 7538**
Hudson: Hudson 7496, Morgan 7578, Morgan 7579, Murdough 7583
Jefferson: Androse 7375
Kirtland Hills: Kiebach 7524
Lancaster: Fairfield 7445, Fox 7461
Lebanon: Loeb 7544, Warren 7702
Lima: Ar-Hale 7376
Louisville: Silk 7663
Mansfield: Richland 7630
Marietta: Marietta 7557
Marion: Marion 7558
Marysville: Community 7416, Honda 7490
Mason: Farmer 7447, Gardner 7466
Maumee: Anderson 7372, Andersons 7374
Mayfield Heights: Ames 7371, Danaher 7424, Fowler 7460, Horvitz 7493, R.T. 7625, Weatherhead 7707
Mayfield Village: Progressive 7623
Middletown: Middletown 7570, Wadsworth 7698
Moreland Hills: Wuliger 7722
Mount Vernon: Ariel 7377, Community 7413
New Albany: New Albany 7589, Wexner 7712, **Wexner 7713**
New Bremen: Dicke 7436
Newark: Licking 7540, Park 7610
North Canton: Deuble 7433, Diebold 7437, **Timken 7683**
North Royalton: Trzcinski 7689
Norwalk: Schlink 7650, Twenty 7692
Novelty: Outcalt 7606
Oberlin: Nord 7595
Orrville: Smucker 7669
Pepper Pike: CPB 7423, LZ 7549, Veale 7694
Perrysburg: Charities 7400, Vortex 7696
Piqua: Brown 7390, Miami 7569, Piqua 7620
Portsmouth: Scioto 7657
Powell: Dance 7425, Delaware 7431
Rome: Dodero 7438
Salem: Salem 7640
Sandusky: Dorn 7439, Erie 7444, Frost 7464
Shaker Heights: Ingalls 7503, Jordan 7514
Sidney: Community 7414
Springfield: Llewellyn 7543, Springfield 7671, TSF 7690, Turner 7691
St. Marys: St. Marys 7672
Steubenville: Berkman 7384
Streetsboro: Geis 7467
Sylvania: LaValley 7535
Terrace Park: Riley 7632
Tiffin: National 7586, Tiffin 7682
Toledo: France 7462, **Generation 7470**, Jobst 7512, Miniger 7572, **Needmor 7588**, Ormond 7603, Owens 7607, Ritter 7633, Stranahan 7678, Toledo 7686, White 7714
Troy: Troy 7688
Uniontown: Wagler 7699
Wapakoneta: Hauss 7484
Warren: Wean 7705
West Chester: AK Steel 7366, Community 7417
Westerville: Durell 7441
Westfield Center: Westfield 7711
Westlake: Nonneman 7593, Nordson 7596
Wickliffe: Lubrizol 7546
Wooster: **Noble 7592**, Wayne 7704
Xenia: Greene 7474, Jamestown 7506
Yellow Springs: Morgan 7577
Youngstown: Cafaro 7397, Christman 7403, Community 7415, Home 7489, Kikel 7525, Resch 7629, Youngstown 7723
Zanesville: McIntire 7565, Muskingum 7585, Roggecora 7635, Sidwell 7662

see also 156, 273, 274, 428, 471, 576, 854, 884, 1071, 1127, 1158, 1531, 1573, 1591, 1693, 1732, 1737, 1755, 1766, 1773, 1774, 1846, 1855, 1876, 1961, 1984, 2011, 2062, 2119, 2136, 2148, 2191, 2241, 2302, 2343, 2346, 2386, 2461, 2469, 2494, 2518, 2524, 2616, 2649, 2657, 2660, 2722, 2786, 2824, 2860, 2946, 3188, 3192, 3199, 3257, 3292, 3332, 3394, 3395, 3456, 3489, 3542, 3572, 3574, 3575, 3581, 3582, 3594, 3609, 3945, 4007, 4114, 4197, 4235, 4266, 4355, 4359, 4366, 4380, 4386, 4390, 4395, 4417, 4423, 4444, 4458, 4466, 4570, 4588, 4599, 4636, 4661, 4666, 4691, 4735, 4739, 4744, 4784, 4853, 4948, 5030, 5170, 5223, 5266, 5267, 5269, 5471, 5541, 5719, 5844, 5986, 6244, 6260, 6367, 6507, 6611, 6675, 6942, 6974, 7059, 7117, 7196, 7280, 7307, 7817, 7840, 7847, 7873, 7906, 7951, 7976, 7994, 8014, 8055, 8100, 8226, 8230, 8235, 8258, 8274, 8277, 8293, 8312, 8331, 8374, 8398, 8537, 8626, 8651, 8718, 8757, 8833, 9085, 9193, 9199, 9290, 9321, 9383, 9422, 9439, 9461, 9484, 9487, 9651, 9653, 9720, 9773, 9784, 9789, 9815, 9859, 9866, 9869, 9934, 9992

OKLAHOMA

Alva: Wisdom 7816
Ardmore: Community 7743, McCrory 7773, Noble 7780, Southern 7798, Westheimer 7812
Bartlesville: Bartlesville 7731, Lyon 7769
Duncan: McCasland 7772
Edmond: Grace 7754, Masonic 7771, **Westerman 7811**
Lawton: McMahon 7776
McAlester: Puterbaugh 7786
Norman: Liddell 7767, Sarkeys 7793
Oklahoma City: Allen 7727, American 7728, Bowen 7736, Brown 7737, Browning-Kimball 7738, Communities 7742, Crawley 7746, Dobson 7747, **Ethics 7749**, Gaylord 7753, Harris 7757, Inasmuch 7760, Jones 7762, Kerr 7764, Kirkpatrick 7766, McGee 7774, Meinders 7777, Oklahoma City 7781, Oklahoma 7782, Rapp 7787, Records 7788, Share 7795, Simmons 7796, Wilshire 7815
Tulsa: Adams 7725, Adelson 7726, Asbjornson 7729, Barthelmes 7730, Bartlett 7732, Bernsen 7733, Bezalel 7734, Bovaird 7735, Chapman 7739, Chapman 7740, Collins 7741, Coretz 7744, Craft 7745, Dotson 7748, Flint 7750, Foundation 7751, Frank 7752, Gussman 7755, Hardesty 7756, Helmerich 7758, Hille 7759, Jackson 7761, Kaiser 7763, Ketchum 7765, Lobeck 7768, Mabee 7770, McGill 7775, Miller 7778, Nelson 7779, ONEOK 7783, Oxley 7784, Oxley 7785, Robinson 7789, Robson 7790, **ROI 7791**, Rooney 7792, **Schusterman 7794**, Smith 7797, Stephenson 7799, Stevens 7800, Stone 7801, Stuart 7802, Tandy 7803, Taubman 7804, Temple 7805, Titus 7806, Tulsa 7807, Viersen 7808, Warren 7809, Waters 7810, Whitwell-Meyer 7813, Williams 7814, Yot 7817, Zarrow 7818, Zarrow 7819, Zarrow 7820, Zink 7821

see also 145, 183, 188, 209, 466, 854, 1142, 1462, 1573, 2007, 2469, 2518, 2657, 3020, 3194, 3211, 3493, 4008, 4388, 4433, 4506, 4636, 4932, 4948, 4971, 5090, 5143, 5531, 6244, 6307, 7031, 7368, 7376, 7527, 7656, 8629,

8661, 8663, 8679, 8811, 8833, 8836, 8875, 8884, 8960, 9007, 9010, 9044, 9060, 9085, 9099, 9109, 9182, 9214, 9260, 9606, 9704, 9815, 9981

OREGON

Alsea: Clemens 7835
Beaverton: Clark 7834, Knight 7861, **NIKE 7875**, Tektronix 7894
Bend: Greater 7848, Macdonald 7866
Corvallis: Benton 7825, Hull 7852, Pastega 7879, Simple 7889
Eugene: Haugland 7849, PacificSource 7878, Tykeson 7897, Woodard 7899
Hillsboro: **Intel 7853**
Klamath Falls: Jeld 7856
Lake Oswego: Crabby 7838, Metolius 7869, Sky 7890, TeamCFA 7893
Medford: Carpenter 7831, Fjarli 7842, Fjarli 7843, Morris 7874
Milwaukie: Dieringer 7839, Kinsman 7860
Portland: Adler 7822, Autzen 7823, Braemar 7826, Burning 7827, Cambia 7829, Campbell 7830, **Chiles 7833**, Collins 7836, Collins 7837, **Eiting 7840**, Esco 7841, Healy 7850, Hedinger 7851, J.F.R. 7854, Jackson 7855, John 7857, Jubitz 7859, Krueger 7862, Lazar 7864, **Lemelson 7865**, MDEKFSE 7867, Meyer 7870, Miller 7871, Miller 7872, Oregon 7876, PacifiCorp 7877, Peterson 7880, PGE 7881, Randall 7883, Renaissance 7884, Schnitzer 7887, Schnitzer 7888, Swindells 7892, Templeton 7895, Tucker 7896, Vibrant 7898, Yarg 7900, Young 7901, Zidell 7902
Redmond: Johnson 7858
Roseburg: Caddock 7828, **Fohs 7844**, Ford 7845
Salem: Salem 7885
Sherwood: Merrill 7868
Springfield: Chambers 7832
Tigard: **Foreign 7846**, Glory 7847, Mission 7873
Tualatin: Stoller 7891
West Linn: Sanders 7886
Wilsonville: Bauman 7824, Lamfrom 7863, Poznanski 7882

---

see also 94, 282, 301, 373, 457, 466, 471, 571, 588, 633, 778, 854, 907, 951, 1114, 1183, 1190, 1339, 1384, 1696, 1750, 1796, 2469, 2636, 2649, 2657, 3003, 3005, 3042, 3154, 3323, 3456, 3457, 3473, 3477, 3492, 3551, 4012, 4636, 4691, 4729, 4743, 4784, 5030, 5090, 5159, 5321, 5471, 6244, 6587, 6893, 7523, 7531, 7609, 8093, 8145, 8277, 8362, 8430, 8964, 9329, 9362, 9567, 9570, 9576, 9588, 9590, 9591, 9593, 9598, 9601, 9621, 9638, 9640, 9642, 9643, 9644, 9661, 9689, 9704, 9719, 9723, 9738, 9740, 9743, 9748, 9755, 9760, 9761, 9762

PENNSYLVANIA

Allentown: Air 7907, Baker 7926, Century 7974, Jones 8113, Kline 8128, Lehigh Valley 8136, Salvaggio 8263, Trexler 8320
Altoona: Central 7971
Ambler: Copernicus 7998
Ardmore: 1675 7903, Erlbaum 8027
Bala Cynwyd: Clayman 7984, Miller 8179, Perelman 8219, Saligman 8261, Stein 8297
Beaver: Beaver 7934
Bensalem: Rubin 8257
Berwick: Central 7972
Berwyn: Ametek 7913, Poor 8232
Bethlehem: Keystone 8122, Shaffer 8281
Blue Bell: Genuardi 8053, Henkels 8089, Stratton 8304
Boyertown: Biesecker 7941
Bridgeville: II-VI 8105, Massey 8158
Bryn Mawr: Aqua 7917, **Cardone 7964**, Coulson 8000, **Diiriye 8011**, Fishman 8044, Gray 8069, Ingerman 8108, Miller 8183, Psalm 8237
Butler: Sedwick 8276
Canonsburg: CentiMark 7970, Mylan 8192
Carlisle: Long 8149, Stuart 8307
Chalfont: Lomax 8148
Chester Springs: Quaker 8240
Coatesville: Huston 8102
Collegeville: Smith 8287
Colmar: North 8199
Concordville: Abessinio 7904
Conshohocken: Feldman 8034, Green 8070, Roberts 8250
Coopersburg: Lutron 8151
Cranberry Township: Mine 8184
Devon: Chatham 7978
Downingtown: Smith 8289
Du Bois: Mengle 8174
East Earl: Pilgrim 8225
East Petersburg: Crels 8002
Elverson: Firstfruits 8042
Ephrata: Brossman 7954, Hibshman 8091
Erdenheim: Kind 8125
Erie: Carnahan 7965, Erie 8026, Surgala 8309
Erwinna: Woodtiger 8346
Exton: Seed 8277, **Viropharma 8328**, West 8334
Fairless Hills: Katz 8117
Fort Washington: Argus 7920, Gitlin 8058, Greenfield 8072, Karabots 8116, Withington 8344
Ft. Washington: Alexander 7910
Gladwyne: Angelakis 7914, Miller 8180, Pine 8226, Seed 8278
Gwynedd Valley: Barrist 7929
Harrisburg: Foundation 8046, Grass 8068, Hoverter 8097, Kline 8129, Kunkel 8133, Parmer 8212, Stabler 8294
Haverford: Presser 8236
Hazleton: Scheller 8268
Hermitage: Kavanagh 8118
Hershey: Falcone 8031, Glatfelter 8059
Holicong: Raab 8242
Horsham: Toll 8316, Toll 8317
Huntingdon Valley: Linlundh 8143, Neubauer 8196
Indiana: S & T 8259
Jenkintown: Brickman 7949, Caplan 7962, Glencairn 8062
Johnstown: Community 7990, Pasquerilla 8213
King of Prussia: Ball 7927, Eustace 8029, Morgan 8187
Kittanning: Armstrong 7921
Lahaska: Franklin 8048
Lancaster: Armstrong 7922, Ferree 8036, Gunterberg 8073, Hughes 8099, Lancaster 8135, Steinman 8299, Steinman 8300
Latrobe: **Kennametal 8120**, McFeely 8163, McKenna 8166
Lebanon: Dixon 8012
Luzerne: Luzerne 8152
Malvern: Field 8037, King 8126, Vanguard 8327
McMurray: Rossin 8256
Meadville: Crawford 8001
Mechanicsburg: Grass 8066, Grass 8067, Ortenzio 8205, Ortenzio 8206
Media: **Botstiber 7947**, Measey 8170
Merion: Elias 8022
Milford: Nichols 8197
Montrose: Community 7992
Moon Township: Baker 7925
Mount Joy: Schock 8272
Narberth: Kelly 8119
Narbeth: Kohelet 8131
New Castle: Hoyt 8098
Newtown: Alderbaugh 7909
Newtown Square: Davis 8004, Mullen 8190, Ujala 8323
Norristown: Arcadia 7918
North Wales: Patriarch 8214, Teva 8314
Nottingham: Herr 8090
Oakmont: Wiegand 8337
Oil City: Phillips 8222
Oxford: Oxford 8208
Paoli: **AO 7915**, Aospine 7916, DuPont 8020, Kim 8123, Thornedge 8315, Turner 8321
Philadelphia: **ACE 7905**, Arete 7919, Beneficial 7936, Britton 7951, Brodsky 7952, Buck 7955, **Cardiovascular 7963**, Carpenter 7967, Cassett 7969, CIGNA 7981, Cochran 7985, Comcast 7989, **Davis 8005**, Dietrich 8010, Dolfinger 8013, Drumcliff 8016, Ellis 8023, Farber 8032, Fels 8035, First 8041, Garfield 8052, GlaxoSmithKline 8060, GlaxoSmithKline 8061, Greenfield 8071, Haldeman 8076, Harding 8080, Head 8081, Hocker 8094, Independence 8106, Independence 8107, **Institute 8109**, Kahn 8115, Kimmel 8124, La Vea 8134, Lenfest 8137, Lenfest 8138, Leonard 8139, Lindback 8142, Locks 8147, Mandell 8153, Martin 8156, McCutchen 8162, Merchants 8175, Metcalf 8178, MKM 8185, Nararo 8193, Novotny 8202, **Oberkotter 8203**, Penn 8216, Penn 8217, Pew 8220, Philadelphia 8221, Pond 8231, Public 8239, Quantitative 8241, Roberts 8251, Rohrer 8252, Rosenstiel 8254, Ross 8255, Sargent 8265, Scattergood 8267, Schenck 8269, Scholler 8273, Seraph 8279, Shoemaker 8284, Smock 8290, Snider 8292, Stein/Bellet 8298, Stine 8302, Stoneleigh 8303, Strawbridge 8305, Sunoco 8308, **Tecovas 8312**, Tyler 8322, Vague 8326, von Hess 8329, **Waldorf 8330**, Warburton 8331, Wells 8333, Wismer 8343, Wolf 8345, Wyncote 8349
Phoenixville: Phoenixville 8223, **Shiloh 8283**
Pittsburgh: Adam 7906, **Alcoa 7908**, Allegheny 7911, Avs 7924, Bayard 7930, **Bayer 7931**, Bayer 7932, Beatty 7933, Benedum 7935, Benter 7937, Berkman 7938, Bernheim 7940, Birmingham 7942, Blanchard 7943, Blanchard 7944, **BNY 7945**, BNY 7946, Bozzone 7948, Briggs 7950, Brooks 7953, Buhl 7956, Buncher 7957, Burke 7958, Burke 7959, Campbell 7960, Campbell 7961, **Carnegie 7966**, **Carthage 7968**, Cestone 7975, Cestone 7976, Chosky 7980, Clapp 7983, **Colcom 7986**, Colket 7987, Constandy 7996, Cooper 7997, Davis 8006, Davis 8007, Degenstein 8008, Dickson 8009, Dollar 8014, Donahue 8015, DSF 8017, Duff 8018, Dull 8019, Eden 8021, England 8024, EQT 8025, Fair 8030, Federated 8033, Fine 8039, FISA 8043, Fitch 8045, **Frick 8049**, Frick 8050, Fulton 8051, Gerber 8054, Giant 8055, Gibson 8056, Giop 8057, Gospel 8063, Grable 8064, Guthrie 8074, Haggin 8075, Hecht 8082, **Heinz 8083**, Heinz 8084, **Heinz 8085**, Heinz 8086, Helping 8088, Highmark 8092, Hillman 8093, Hodge 8095, Hopwood 8096, Hunt 8100, Hutton 8104, Jackson 8110, Jordan 8114, Levis 8140, Lipsitz 8144, **Little 8145**, Lockhart 8146, Maplewood 8154, Mason 8157, McCune 8160, McCune 8161, McGinley 8164, McKaig 8165, **McKenna 8167**, McKinney 8168, Mellon 8172, Mellon 8173, Mertz 8177, Miller, 8182, **Moore 8186**, Morris 8188, Musser 8191, Nimick 8198, Noteman 8201, O-Parker 8204, O'Toole 8207, Palumbo 8209, Pangborn 8210, Pangborn 8211, Peirce 8215, Pittsburgh 8228, PNC 8230, Posner 8233, **PPG 8235**, Ranger 8243, Rangos 8244, Reeser 8246, Reuss 8247, Rhoads,Jr. 8248, Russell 8258, Scaife 8266, Schieffelin 8270, Schneider 8271, Schroth 8274, Sexauer 8280, Shapira 8282, Simon 8286, Snee 8291, Staunton 8296, Stern 8301, Strelsin 8306, Torch 8318, Trees 8319, United 8325, Williams 8338, **Williams 8339**, Willis 8340, Wilson 8341, Winstar 8342, Wright 8347, Wright 8348
Plymouth Meeting: Claneil 7982, Fieldstone 8038, Kestenbaum 8121, PTS 8238, Sand 8264, Springbank 8293, Widener 8336
Pocopson: Davenport 8003
Pottstown: Pottstown 8234
Radnor: McCausland 8159, Mosi 8189, Nelson 8195

Reading: Berks 7939, Miller 8181
Scranton: Peoples 8218, Scranton 8275
Seven Valleys: Kinsley 8127
Sewickley: Hansen 8079, Marshall 8155, Simmons 8285
Sharon: Community 7994
Shrewsbury: United 8324
Sinking Spring: Jerlyn 8112
Somerset: Wheeler 8335
Southampton: Medleycott 8171
Springtown: Hurd 8101
St. Marys: Stackpole 8295
State College: Centre 7973, Hamer 8077
Stroudsburg: ESSA 8028
Titusville: Rees 8245
Trevose: Korman 8132
Tunkhannock: Piper 8227
Uniontown: Community 7991
Valley Forge: Saint 8260
Villanova: Cotswold 7999, Rorer 8253
W. Conshohocken: Pierce 8224
Warren: Community 7993, Northwest 8200
Washington: Washington 8332
Wayne: Barra 7928, Charter 7977, Hamilton 8078, Helen's 8087, Huston 8103, Lily 8141, McLean 8169
West Chester: Chester 7979, RJM 8249
West Conshohocken: Allerton 7912, Connelly 7995, Lotman 8150, Smith 8288, **Templeton 8313**
Wilkes Barre: Mericle 8176
Williamsport: First 8040, Plankenhorn 8229, Saltsgiver 8262
Willow Grove: Asplundh 7923, Fourjay 8047
Wyalusing: Taylor 8311
Wyomissing: Colonial 7988, Janssen 8111, Wyomissing 8350
York: Graham 8065, Knipel 8130, Naylor 8194, **Susquehanna 8310**, York 8351

see also 167, 188, 295, 311, 349, 371, 463, 501, 854, 883, 909, 933, 1062, 1146, 1184, 1222, 1249, 1404, 1409, 1463, 1492, 1531, 1550, 1571, 1591, 1595, 1596, 1599, 1602, 1620, 1689, 1698, 1707, 1741, 1742, 1757, 1758, 1778, 1801, 1806, 1836, 1849, 1858, 1865, 1870, 1872, 1889, 1923, 1959, 1963, 2014, 2044, 2107, 2121, 2146, 2155, 2188, 2191, 2194, 2196, 2205, 2207, 2212, 2297, 2309, 2310, 2314, 2323, 2334, 2347, 2362, 2367, 2469, 2562, 2657, 2810, 2827, 2977, 2995, 3014, 3034, 3042, 3073, 3159, 3164, 3224, 3344, 3383, 3405, 3409, 3456, 3457, 3473, 3582, 3602, 3609, 3710, 3771, 3825, 3867, 3868, 3869, 3876, 3878, 3908, 3921, 3945, 3966, 4026, 4053, 4089, 4114, 4158, 4176, 4179, 4248, 4256, 4285, 4309, 4326, 4354, 4388, 4390, 4394, 4416, 4466, 4475, 4634, 4691, 4693, 4910, 4913, 4948, 5030, 5054, 5083, 5106, 5176, 5188, 5195, 5217, 5223, 5226, 5244, 5257, 5297, 5303, 5309, 5313, 5324, 5332, 5339, 5340, 5343, 5360, 5379, 5380, 5391, 5415, 5434, 5436, 5443, 5453, 5471, 5480, 5510, 5547, 5587, 5588, 5640, 5679, 5687, 5719, 5730, 5750, 5826, 5869, 5909, 5915, 5955, 5978, 5979, 5993, 6078, 6081, 6119, 6171, 6174, 6187, 6208, 6223, 6244, 6248, 6303, 6322, 6326, 6353, 6362, 6389, 6406, 6415, 6416, 6437, 6439, 6443, 6451, 6452, 6458, 6464, 6465, 6466, 6467, 6479, 6480, 6486, 6495, 6499, 6506, 6507, 6526, 6531, 6602, 6612, 6658, 6691, 6728, 6755, 6760, 6770, 6826, 6832, 6898, 6954, 6966, 6973, 7023, 7024, 7026, 7038, 7047, 7048, 7059, 7073, 7083, 7110, 7126, 7131, 7177, 7190, 7201, 7207, 7209, 7220, 7235, 7278, 7304, 7317, 7323, 7344, 7356, 7376, 7383, 7384, 7424, 7452, 7455, 7458, 7475, 7587, 7596, 7601, 7609, 7708, 7711, 7737, 7751, 7754, 8374, 8404, 8419, 8499, 8536, 8561, 8579, 8655, 8665, 8669, 8884, 8990, 9244, 9266, 9290, 9327, 9350, 9408, 9422, 9486, 9487, 9688, 9711, 9812, 9815, 9859, 9940, 9973

PUERTO RICO

San Juan: Kinesis 8352, Puerto Rico 8353

see also 9, 238, 1828, 1904, 1953, 2138, 2649, 4712, 5327, 5379, 5381, 5588, 6634, 7398, 8379

RHODE ISLAND

Cranston: Champlin 8370, **Feinstein 8390**, **Feinstein 8391**, Shriners 8438
East Providence: Diagnostic 8383
Johnston: **FM 8393**
Lincoln: Amica 8356
Newport: EJMP 8386, Newport 8423, **SVF 8444**, van Beuren 8449
Pawtucket: Fain 8388, Hasbro 8403
Providence: Acton 8354, Alpert 8355, Armour 8358, Bafflin 8359, Barrus 8360, **Bingham 8361**, Binney 8362, Biogen 8363, Buehler 8364, Capewell 8365, Capewell 8366, Capewell 8367, Carter 8368, Chamberlain 8369, Charlesmead 8371, Charlton 8372, Chisholm 8373, Combined 8375, Corning 8376, Crary, 8377, Cuno 8378, Daniels 8380, Dexter 8382, **Dorot 8384**, Dunphy 8385, Elms 8387, Falk 8389, Felicia 8392, Foster 8394, Fox 8395, Freeman 8396, Greene 8398, **Grinnell 8399**, Guth 8400, Hallett 8401, Harris 8402, Hassenfeld 8404, Hoche-Scofield 8405, HPB 8407, IMA 8408, Kaplan 8409, Knoop 8411, Koonce 8412, Luehrmann 8413, M. 8414, Manning 8415, McAdams 8416, McCurdy 8417, McNeil 8418, Mercer 8419, Middendorf 8420, Murray 8421, Nelson 8422, Noonan 8424, O'Brien 8425, Osborn 8426, Patten 8427, **Rainbow 8428**, Rhode Island 8429, Richter 8430, Roraback 8431, **Ryan 8433**, Salem 8434, Scrooby 8435, Seymour 8436, Sharpe 8437, Shumway 8439, Smith 8440, Statter 8441, Steadley 8442, Stone 8443, Swanson 8445, Textron 8446, Thompson 8447, TriMix 8448, Vance 8450, Wille 8451, Wood 8452, Woodward 8453
Riverside: Citizens 8374, De Ramel 8381, Gale 8397, Hosser 8406, Routhier 8432
Westerly: Apple 8357, Kimball 8410
Woonsocket: CVS 8379

see also 188, 238, 244, 575, 854, 892, 1065, 1118, 1502, 1560, 1593, 1646, 1658, 1759, 1864, 2185, 2204, 2205, 2227, 2365, 2448, 2653, 2657, 3089, 3219, 3709, 3710, 3745, 3825, 3921, 3922, 3935, 3960, 3986, 4012, 4025, 4029, 4046, 4047, 4079, 4082, 4100, 4109, 4144, 4171, 4186, 4192, 4193, 4209, 4218, 4242, 4256, 4294, 4302, 4310, 4328, 4581, 4739, 4869, 5170, 5349, 5370, 5410, 5578, 5653, 5665, 5677, 5719, 5731, 5795, 5844, 5971, 5993, 6021, 6091, 6120, 6367, 6425, 6436, 6667, 6675, 6676, 6717, 6774, 6785, 6794, 6857, 7059, 7292, 7343, 7596, 7615, 8096, 8145, 8315, 8506, 9082, 9136, 9154, 9422

SOUTH CAROLINA

Anderson: Abney 8454, Foothills 8478
Charleston: Ceres 8469, Coastal 8472, Patterson 8489, Post 8492, Reams 8493, Spaulding-Paolozzi 8502, Speedwell 8503, Yaschik 8509
Chester: Chester 8470
Clinton: Bailey 8458
Columbia: Blue 8460, Central 8468, First 8477
Darlington: Coker 8473
Easley: McKissick 8486
Florence: Bruce 8461
Fort Mill: Springs 8504
Fountain Inn: **AVX-Kyocera 8457**
Gaffney: Fullerton 8479
Greenville: Campbell 8463, Campbell 8464, Campbell 8465, Canal 8466, Community 8474, Daniel 8476, Graham 8481, Hartness 8482, Hipp 8483, Roe 8494, **ScanSource 8495**, WLT 8508
Greenwood: Self 8496
Greer: Smith 8498
Hartsville: Byerly 8462, Sonoco 8500, Teach 8505
Hilton Head: Pfriem 8490
Hilton Head Island: Community 8475
Inman: Inman 8485
Lake City: Moore 8488
Lancaster: Sims 8497, TSC 8506
Lexington: Cassels 8467
Murrells Inlet: Waccamaw 8507
North Charleston: Zucker 8510
Rock Hill: Hopewell 8484
Spartanburg: Arkwright 8456, Black 8459, Gibbs 8480, Montgomery 8487, Phifer 8491, Smith 8499, Spartanburg 8501
Summerville: Childrens 8471
West Columbia: Agape 8455

see also 188, 327, 633, 738, 805, 816, 854, 1449, 1832, 1851, 1852, 1914, 1996, 2135, 2191, 2210, 2275, 2347, 2374, 2399, 2413, 2420, 2434, 2469, 2487, 2505, 2517, 2538, 2539, 2563, 2569, 2657, 2738, 2800, 3188, 3292, 3456, 3457, 3582, 3609, 3710, 3825, 3899, 4154, 4171, 4328, 4391, 4416, 4565, 4909, 5080, 5200, 5733, 5742, 6487, 6966, 7084, 7091, 7138, 7195, 7196, 7201, 7202, 7224, 7240, 7256, 7257, 7279, 7283, 7285, 7312, 7325, 7329, 7383, 7461, 7594, 7601, 7613, 7652, 7684, 7696, 7926, 8235, 8265, 8277, 8396, 8561, 8851, 8926, 9290, 9321, 9383, 9426, 9460, 9484, 9499, 9539, 9551, 9704, 9947

SOUTH DAKOTA

Aberdeen: South Dakota 8523
Brookings: Larson 8516
Huron: Hofer 8515
North Sioux City: Nylen 8517
Pierre: South Dakota 8522
Rapid City: Black 8511, Dakota 8514, Vucurevich 8524
Sioux Falls: Branches 8512, Brenden-Mann 8513, **Opus 8518**, Raft 8519, Robinson 8520, Sioux Falls 8521

see also 188, 1750, 2191, 3457, 3480, 3487, 3490, 4621, 4636, 4666, 4691, 4694, 4729, 4746, 4778, 4784, 4808, 5008, 5009, 5094, 7133, 8541, 9182, 9514, 9868

TENNESSEE

Brentwood: Beaman 8534, Dobberpuhl 8557, Hart 8578, Johnson 8589, Lewis 8598, Martin 8606, Massey 8607, Ramsey 8621
Bristol: Gatton 8571, Lazarus 8596, Master's 8608
Chattanooga: Alumni 8527, Benwood 8535, Christian 8544, Community 8548, Hamico 8576, Hurlbut 8583, Lebovitz 8597, Lyndhurst 8599, MacLellan 8600, **Maclellan 8601**, Maclellan 8602, Osborne 8614, Tennessee 8634, Tucker 8638, **Westwood 8644**
Cleveland: Johnson 8588
Collierville: Martin 8604
Cookeville: Seme 8626
Eads: Glenn 8572
Franklin: Campbell 8539, Johnson's 8590, Nissan 8613, Shinn 8627
Goodlettsville: Dollar 8558

Hendersonville: CIC 8546
Kingsport: Eastman 8561
Knoxille: Stokely 8631
Knoxville: Aslan 8529, Charis 8542, Clayton 8547, East 8560, Elgin 8562, Goodfriend 8574, Haslam 8580, Haslam 8581, Provision 8619, Regal 8622, Thompson 8635, Thompson 8636
Maryville: Lange 8593
Memphis: American 8528, Assisi 8530, Briggs 8538, Children's 8543, Community 8549, Compton 8551, Day 8556, First 8565, Formanek 8566, Great 8575, Hardin 8577, Hartwell 8579, Hyde 8584, **International 8585**, Jeniam 8587, Lansky 8594, Martin 8605, Memphis 8610, Plough 8615, Poplar 8616, Pyramid 8620, Sasco 8623, Scheidt 8625, Sparks 8629, Speer 8630, Temple 8633, Wilson 8646
Murfreesboro: Adams 8525, Adams 8526, Christy 8545
Nashville: Atticus 8531, Baptist 8533, Bridgestone 8537, Carell 8540, Carlton 8541, Community 8550, Cook 8552, Craig 8553, Curb 8554, Davis 8555, Dugas 8559, Eskind 8563, Ezell 8564, Frist 8567, Frist 8568, Fritch 8569, **Gardner 8570**, Goldstein 8573, HCA 8582, Jeckyl 8586, Kharis 8591, Maddox 8603, Melkus 8609, Midler 8611, Msb 8612, Proctor 8617, **Scarlett 8624**, Smith 8628, T & T 8632, Travis 8637, Turner 8639, Turner 8640, Turner 8641, Wallace 8642, Washington 8643, Wilson 8645
Parsons: Ayers 8532
Union City: Kirkland 8592, Latimer 8595, Promethean 8618
Vonore: Blankemeyer 8536

see also 5, 57, 61, 188, 210, 362, 569, 854, 1001, 1142, 1479, 1529, 1553, 1850, 1858, 1990, 1996, 2000, 2079, 2080, 2116, 2275, 2279, 2364, 2368, 2400, 2420, 2469, 2479, 2504, 2505, 2532, 2547, 2555, 2657, 2711, 2790, 2880, 2902, 2920, 3087, 3192, 3237, 3257, 3292, 3581, 3582, 4040, 4261, 4395, 4430, 4481, 4661, 4712, 4784, 4817, 4834, 4835, 4863, 4869, 4971, 4984, 5030, 5277, 5304, 5379, 5719, 5872, 5886, 6518, 6933, 6997, 7104, 7132, 7138, 7201, 7247, 7256, 7279, 7285, 7291, 7368, 7380, 7398, 7423, 7452, 7531, 7587, 7590, 7684, 7689, 8088, 8230, 8337, 8401, 8487, 8495, 8702, 9136, 9181, 9321, 9342, 9383, 9418, 9467, 9481, 9482, 9483, 9487, 9499, 9514, 9535, 9539, 9542, 9546, 9557, 9815, 9947, 9973

TEXAS

Abilene: Community 8774, Dodge 8810, Greathouse 8875, Kickapoo 8955, Legett 8978, Owen 9076, Shelton 9169, Whitener 9275
Addison: Pinon 9100
Amarillo: Amarillo 8660, Brumley 8734, Engler 8830, Ware 9259
Angleton: Community 8775
Austin: **A Glimmer 8649**, Albany 8654, Anderson 8663, Austin 8676, Badger 8678, Booth 8712, Booth 8713, Brownsville 8733, Cain 8743, **Dell 8805**, Eby 8820, Ed 8822, Ezcorp 8834, Fath 8840, Greathouse 8874, Harris 8891, Harvey 8894, Jamail 8928, Kahng 8948, KDK-Harman 8949, KLE 8961, Kodosky 8966, Link 8986, Lowe 8993, MFI 9025, O'Hare 9068, **Paloheimo 9080**, Puett 9114, Rea 9123, Reynolds 9127, **RGK 9128**, Roddy-Holden 9136, Sangreal 9153, Shield 9170, Shivers 9171, Smith 9182, Sooch 9189, Stern 9204, Still 9207, Tapestry 9220, **Tingari-Silverton 9235**, Tocker 9237, Topfer 9239, Webber 9262, Weir 9265, **Whole 9276**, Winkler 9281, Wright 9293
Avinger: Simpson 9177
Beaumont: Brock 8727, Gale 8859, Morgan 9037, Reaud 9124, Ward 9258
Bedford: Adams 8653
Bellaire: Schepps 9158, Sterling 9202
Big Spring: Broughton 8729
Boerne: Branch 8720
Bryan: Gibson 8866
Buda: Johnson 8939
Centerville: Wallrath 9255
Cisco: Heavenly 8897
Cleburne: Marti 9001
Colleyville: Beneski 8701, **Caris 8749**
Corpus Christi: Coastal 8768, Kennedy 8953, Moore 9034, Rachal 9117, Sams 9145
Corsicana: Eady 8818, Navarro 9054
Dallas: Ackerman 8651, Adams 8652, Andrews 8667, Armentrout 8671, AT&T 8675, Baron 8682, Barrow 8684, Bass 8689, Bass 8690, Beals, 8697, Beasley 8698, **Bell 8700**, Bickel 8705, Boeckman 8707, Boone 8710, Booth 8711, Buck 8735, Buford 8736, Cameron 8747, Campbell 8748, Carlson 8750, Clements 8766, Clements 8767, Collins 8771, Collins 8772, Communities 8773, Constantin 8778, Cowden 8783, Cox 8784, Craig, 8786, Criswell 8789, Crowell 8791, Dahan 8794, Dallas 8795, Daniel 8796, Dean 8803, Diener 8807, Discovery 8808, Doswell 8814, Duda 8815, Durham 8817, Embrey 8828, Enrico 8831, Fikes 8844, Ford 8854, Gayden 8861, Haggerty 8881, Halbert 8882, Hamon 8889, Hawn 8896, Higgins 8906, Hill 8908, Hillcrest 8909, Hirsch 8910, Hoblitzelle 8912, Hoglund 8913, Hunt 8923, Ingram 8925, **Jiv 8933**, JKL 8935, Jones 8945, King 8959, Korenvaes 8969, Kurth 8971, Lebowitz-Aberly 8975, Lesley 8980, Lightner 8985, Litman 8987, Littauer 8988, Loose 8991, Lyman 8995, Mankoff 8998, Marsh 8999, Martin 9002, Maverick 9005, McDermott 9013, McGrath 9015, McIntyre 9016, Meadows 9019, Miller 9027, Mitchell 9030, Moneygram 9032, Morning 9040, Moss 9043, Murchison 9045, Murchison 9046, NAH 9047, Napier 9050, Nearburg 9055, Nestle 9056, New Hope 9058, O'Donnell 9067, Partnership 9082, Patton 9084, Patton 9085, Pediatric 9087, Pertusati 9094, Pickens 9099, Pollock 9103, Posey 9104, Presbyterian 9108, Prothro 9112, QuadW 9115, Questrom 9116, Rees-Jones 9125, Rhodes 9129, Richardson 9131, Rogers 9137, Rosewood 9140, Saada 9142, Schutte 9160, Seay 9163, Seegers 9164, Sidhu 9172, Simmons 9174, **Simonian 9176**, Smith 9179, Smith 9181, Smith 9184, Sowell 9192, Spangenberg 9193, Sparrow 9194, Stuart 9209, Sturgis 9211, Summerlee 9213, Sumners 9214, Sunnyside 9215, Swinney 9218, Tartaglino 9221, Terry 9224, Texas 9227, Thank 9229, Thomas 9231, Thomas 9232, Thompson 9233, Turner 9242, TurningPoint 9244, Vanberg 9247, Wagner 9253, Wal 9254, Weaver 9260, West 9270, Williams 9279, Winn 9282, Young 9295, Zale 9297
Decatur: Dixon 8809
Diboll: Grum 8876
Eagle Lake: Wintermann 9283
Eastland: Thirteen 9230
Edna: Robinson 9133
El Paso: Bowling 8717, El Paso 8825, Hunt 8922, **Paso 9083**, Stevens 9206
Fairview: Martinez 9003
Forney: Nasher 9051
Fort Worth: Alcon 8655, Andrews, 8668, Bass 8685, Bass 8686, Bass 8687, Bass 8688, BNSF 8706, Bratton 8722, Bridge 8724, Brown 8730, Burnett 8737, Carter 8752, Carter 8753, Community 8776, Cornerstone 8780, Davis 8799, Doss 8812, Edwards 8824, Fischer 8847, Fleming 8850, Justin 8947, Kessler 8954, Klabzuba 8960, Kleinheinz 8964, Lard 8972, Live 8989, Miles 9026, Moncrief 9031, Morris 9041, Nape 9049, Once 9070, **Radler 9118**, Rainwater 9119, Richardson 9130, Roach 9132, Sand 9151, Schollmaier 9159, Scott 9161, Snyder 9188, Waggoner 9252, Walsh 9256, Wildcat 9278
Frisco: Brentwood 8723, Hall 8883, Johnson 8940, Masters 9004
Galveston: Kempner 8952, Moody 9033, Northen 9063, Seibel 9165
Georgetown: Lord 8992
Glen Rose: Pleroma 9102
Grapevine: Janszen 8930, Kohl 8967
Hallettsville: Dickson-Allen 8806
Henderson: Sadler 9143
Houston: Alexander 8656, Alkek 8657, Alkek 8658, Allison 8659, Anchorage 8662, Anderson 8664, Andras 8666, **Arnold 8672**, Astros 8674, **Baker 8679**, Barnhart 8681, Barr 8683, Bauer 8691, Bauer 8692, Baxter 8695, **Bolivar 8708**, Bookout 8709, Borick 8714, Bosarge 8715, **Bovay 8716**, **BP 8718**, Brass 8721, Brookshire 8728, Brown 8731, Cain 8744, Cain 8745, Carruth 8751, Castex 8755, CEMEX 8757, CFP 8758, Cizik 8764, Clayton 8765, Cockrell 8770, Cook 8779, Crane 8788, Cullen 8792, **Cultural 8793**, Davis 8798, Davis 8800, DeBakey 8804, Dunn 8816, Eckel 8821, Elkins 8826, Ellwood 8827, Eugene 8832, Family 8836, Fant 8837, Farish 8838, Favrot 8842, Finger 8845, Fish 8848, Fleming 8849, Fondren 8853, Frees 8857, Gallagher 8860, Getz 8864, GHS Foun 8865, Glasscock 8867, Goodman 8870, Goradia 8871, Hachar 8880, Halliburton 8884, Hamill 8887, Hamman 8888, Hankamer 8890, Hawkins 8895, Hershey 8904, Herzstein 8905, Hildebrand 8907, Hobby 8911, Holthouse 8915, **Houston 8916**, Houston 8917, Huffington 8920, Inspiration 8926, **International 8927**, Jamail 8929, JKJ 8934, JLH 8936, Johnson 8937, Kean 8950, Kilroy 8956, Kinder 8958, Knobloch 8965, Lawrence 8973, **Leducq 8976**, **Levant 8981**, Levit 8982, Liatis 8983, Looper 8990, Lyons 8996, **Marshall 9000**, McCullough 9011, McGovern 9014, McNair 9017, Medallion 9020, Miller 9028, Moran 9036, Morgan 9038, Morian 9039, Mulva 9044, **Natem 9052**, Nightingale 9062, **Notsew 9064**, **Oldham 9069**, Onstead 9071, O'Quinn 9072, Oshman 9074, Owsley 9078, Pema 9088, Petrello 9096, Powell 9105, Pritzker 9110, Pritzker 9111, Reliant 9126, Rockwell 9135, Sanders 9152, Sarofim 9154, **Scaler 9155**, Scurlock 9162, Shell 9168, Simmons 9173, Simmons 9175, Smith 9180, Smith 9183, Smith 9185, Smith 9186, Smith 9187, Soref-Breslauer 9190, Spec's 9195, Star 9197, Starling 9199, Stedman 9200, Sterling 9203, Strake 9208, Susman 9216, Terry 9225, Texas 9226, Turner 9243, Vaughan 9248, Walter 9257, WEDGE 9263, Weekley 9264, Welch 9268, West 9269, **Westbury 9271**, Whalley 9272, Wolff 9286, Wolff 9287, Wortham 9292, Zimmer 9300, Zorich 9301
Irving: B.E.L.I.E.F. 8677, Chasdrew 8762, **ExxonMobil 8833**, Feldman 8843, Fluor 8851, Hersh 8903, **Jenesis 8932**, Jones 8943, Kimberly 8957, Natural 9053, Rowling 9141, Stemmons 9201, **VHA 9250**
Jersey Village: Baugh 8693
Jonesville: Jonesville 8946
Katy: Ballard 8680, **Mehta 9021**
Keller: Hudson 8919
Kerrville: Butt 8738, Cailloux 8741, Cailloux 8742, Community 8777, Peterson 9095, Stevens 9205
Kingsville: Kleberg 8963
Kingwood: New Hope 9059, Tijerina, 9234
La Pryor: Jones 8942
Laredo: De Llano 8802, Sanchez 9150, **South 9191**, Vergara 9249
Lewisville: Castle 8756, **Six 9178**
Liberty: Humphreys 8921
Livingston: Bergman 8703
Longview: Crain 8787, Worley 9291
Lubbock: Cash 8754, CH 8759, Jones 8944, Lubbock 8994, SS 9196, Talkington 9219, Welborn 9267
Lufkin: Henderson 8900, Temple 9223
Marshall: Tartt 9222
Midland: 1687 8647, Abell 8650, Beal 8696, Brown, 8732, Chaparral 8760, Cox 8785, Davidson 8797, Fasken 8839, FMH 8852, Moore 9035, Morrow

9042, Permian 9091, Prairie 9106, Scharbauer 9157, Yarborough 9294
Mineola: Meredith 9023
Odessa: Weaver 9261, Wood 9289
Orange: Stark 9198
Palacios: Trull 9240
Pampa: Payne 9086
Paris: Lennox 8979, Ram 9120
Plano: Anderson 8665, Penney 9089, Perot 9092, Perot 9093, **Suder 9212**
Poolville: Dogwood 8811
Port Neches: Hebert 8899
Porter: **New Beginning 9057**
Post: Franklin 8855
Richardson: Fruhman 8858, Owen 9077
Richmond: Belin 8699, George 8863, Henderson 8901, Madison 8997
Rockport: Howell 8918
Round Rock: Greater 8873
Round Top: Bybee 8739
Salado: Angela 8669
San Angelo: San Angelo 9146, San Angelo 9147, Tucker 9241, Wolslager 9288
San Antonio: 80/20 8648, Baumberger 8694, Benson 8702, Brackenridge 8719, Coates 8769, Covenant 8781, Cowden 8782, Franklin 8856, Goldsbury 8868, Gorman 8872, Guenther 8877, H.E.B. 8879, Halsell 8885, Halsell 8886, Harte 8892, Hartman 8893, Hollomon 8914, Impetus 8924, Kelleher 8951, Kleberg 8962, Kolitz 8968, Kronkosky 8970, Lawson 8974, Lee 8977, Light 8984, Mays 9008, McCombs 9009, McNutt 9018, Najim 9048, Newman 9061, NuStar 9065, Orsinger 9073, Pace 9079, Piper 9101, Prentice 9107, Pryor 9113, Rapier 9121, Rogers 9139, Saint 9144, San Antonio 9148, San Antonio 9149, Scanlan 9156, Semmes 9166, Stumberg 9210, SWBC 9217, Tobin 9236, Tomerlin 9238, USAA 9245, Valero 9246, Whitacre 9273, White 9274, Wischer 9284, Zachry 9296, Zeller 9298
San Marcos: Crook 8790
Sealy: Chapman 8761
Seminole: Doss 8813
Sherman: Mayor 9007, **PHM 9098**
Sugar Land: Beyer 8704, Bridges 8725, Day 8801, Gonsoulin 8869, Parks 9081, Phillips 9097
Temple: Callaway 8746, Mayborn 9006, Wilson 9280
Texarkana: Arnold 8673, Texas 9228
Texas City: McDaniel 9012
The Colony: Sharp 9167
The Woodlands: Anadarko 8661, Arena 8670, Endowment 8829, Mitchell 9029, Newfield 9060, Rockjensen 9134, Woodforest 9290
Tyler: East 8819, Faulconer 8841, Fisch 8846, Genecov 8862, Herd 8902, Jarvis 8931, Owen 9075, Rogers 9138, Wise 9285
Victoria: Johnson 8941, **Merali 9022**, O'Connor 9066
Waco: C.I.O.S. 8740, Christian 8763, Heavin 8898, Meyer 9024, Rapoport 9122, Waco 9251
Wellington: Zephyr 9299
Westworth Village: Weiser 9266
Wharton: Gulf 8878
Wichita Falls: Bridwell 8726, Edwards 8823, Fain 8835, Johnson 8938, McCoy 9010, Perkins 9090, Priddy 9109, Wichita 9277

see also 8, 9, 32, 60, 98, 112, 138, 163, 169, 182, 188, 190, 210, 219, 228, 240, 249, 277, 283, 349, 375, 385, 402, 541, 546, 586, 723, 738, 752, 806, 821, 887, 1127, 1167, 1183, 1366, 1383, 1387, 1402, 1404, 1407, 1434, 1475, 1523, 1527, 1531, 1572, 1626, 1642, 1659, 1674, 1700, 1762, 1793, 1834, 1838, 1868, 1905, 1965, 2185, 2204, 2210, 2273, 2279, 2283, 2302, 2370, 2400, 2428, 2490, 2518, 2541, 2565, 2567, 2644, 2647, 2649, 2657, 2719, 2738, 2741, 2782, 2789, 2827, 2921, 2923, 2952, 3018, 3034, 3042, 3045, 3050, 3058, 3063, 3070, 3086, 3106, 3121, 3156, 3167, 3185, 3199, 3203, 3230, 3236, 3257, 3292, 3334, 3409, 3473, 3477, 3484, 3495, 3549, 3582, 3590, 3609, 3629, 3630, 3635, 3653, 3655, 3745, 3777, 3793, 3801, 3837, 3857, 3868, 3911, 3966, 4319, 4366, 4368, 4388, 4390, 4430, 4466, 4475, 4539, 4541, 4636, 4651, 4691, 4712, 4780, 4808, 4853, 4863, 4887, 4906, 4989, 5030, 5088, 5090, 5170, 5223, 5379, 5392, 5424, 5440, 5445, 5454, 5471, 5517, 5523, 5525, 5531, 5532, 5587, 5588, 5597, 5660, 5674, 5711, 5727, 5826, 5936, 6176, 6234, 6236, 6244, 6391, 6439, 6474, 6507, 6518, 6531, 6619, 6627, 6797, 6824, 6829, 6853, 6969, 6997, 7002, 7031, 7038, 7104, 7209, 7368, 7398, 7436, 7531, 7546, 7587, 7602, 7609, 7707, 7734, 7739, 7746, 7764, 7765, 7770, 7783, 7804, 7828, 7873, 7926, 7932, 7967, 8042, 8192, 8235, 8312, 8345, 8412, 8430, 8554, 8561, 8579, 8613, 8632, 8633, 9383, 9400, 9418, 9481, 9704, 9798, 9838, 9859, 9947, 9974

UTAH

Alpine: Peterson 9345
Farmington: Simmons 9351
Kaysville: Dumke 9315, Dumke, 9316
Lehi: Yamagata 9357
Linden: Noorda 9339
Lindon: Ashton 9304
North Salt Lake: Bertin 9308
Ogden: Dialysis 9313, Hall 9324
Orem: Bastian 9306
Park City: Park 9341
Pleasant Grove: GFC 9322
Provo: I Am 9328, **Nu 9340**, Rose 9349, Vivint 9354
Salt Lake City: ALSAM 9302, Art 9303, Bamberger 9305, Burton 9309, Call 9310, Community 9311, Dee 9312, Doctorow 9314, Eccles 9317, Eccles 9318, Eccles 9319, Eccles 9320, EnergySolutions 9321, Gillmor 9323, Harman 9325, Hemingway 9326, Huntsman 9327, Kirk 9329, Lawson 9330, Lawson 9331, McCarthey 9332, Meldrum 9333, Miller 9336, Miller 9337, My 9338, Parrish 9342, Patel 9343, Peery 9344, Price 9346, Quinney 9347, RLC 9348, Semnani 9350, Tanner 9352, **Thrasher 9353**, Wagner 9355, Watkins 9356
Sandy: Miller 9334, Miller 9335
St. George: Beesley 9307

see also 127, 155, 166, 210, 359, 541, 569, 789, 854, 1183, 1399, 1472, 1488, 1615, 1734, 1750, 1862, 1958, 1959, 1997, 2589, 2625, 2646, 2657, 3257, 3551, 3582, 3792, 3840, 4636, 4762, 4784, 4855, 5007, 5090, 5104, 5159, 5170, 5223, 5321, 5540, 5587, 5588, 5715, 6244, 6507, 6694, 6954, 6991, 7041, 7118, 7167, 7336, 7364, 7523, 7531, 7829, 7867, 7877, 8466, 8689, 8833, 9090, 9362, 9459, 9608, 9762, 9976

VERMONT

Brattleboro: **Daly 9359**
Burlington: General 9361, Isaiah 9364, Mill 9367, Pomerleau 9369, Stiller 9372, Waterwheel 9376
Middlebury: Vermont 9375
Montpelier: National 9368
Putney: McKenzie 9366
Richmond: Sills 9371
Shelburne: Lintilhac 9365
South Burlington: **Ben 9358**, Gibney 9362
South Londonderry: Rowland 9370
Stowe: Evslin 9360, Three 9374
White River Junction: Gilman 9363
Winooski: Tarrant 9373

see also 188, 244, 482, 1624, 1660, 1671, 1782, 1823, 1863, 1951, 2152, 2160, 2205, 2240, 2352, 2370, 2448, 2657, 2802, 3075, 3164, 3275, 3630, 3690, 3709, 3710, 3825, 3921, 3932, 3935, 3946, 3965, 4046, 4047, 4100, 4171, 4180, 4186, 4192, 4193, 4209, 4218, 4302, 4307, 4310, 4322, 4328, 5008, 5163, 5166, 5179, 5183, 5428, 5474, 5483, 5719, 5743, 5853, 5872, 5972, 6012, 6137, 6239, 6285, 6425, 6658, 6700, 6774, 6784, 6933, 6946, 7343, 7450, 7523, 7549, 7573, 7615, 8038, 8051, 8096, 8192, 8374, 8395, 9704, 9808

VIRGIN ISLANDS

Charlotte Amalie: Community 9377
St. Thomas: Prior 9378

see also 1953, 3965, 4032, 5324, 5327, 5381, 5936, 6634

VIRGINIA

Alexandria: ACT 9380, Chiaramonte 9407, Hirst 9453, Nirman 9495, Northern 9497
Arlington: Arlington 9384, Graham 9445, Koch 9463, Kogod 9464, Mitsubishi 9487, Reinsch 9518, Rosenthal 9525, Samberg 9527, **Scheidel 9528**, Smith 9532, Smith 9534, Washington 9552, Weissberg 9554
Bristol: McGlothlin 9482, McGlothlin 9483, Tickle 9542, United 9546
Casanova: Evans 9428
Catlett: Wiser 9561
Charlottesville: **Bellarmin 9392**, **Blue 9394**, Charles 9404, Charlottesville 9405, **Chase 9406**, Elmo 9425, Fife 9429, **Friends 9437**, Genan 9440, Gilliam 9442, Manning 9476, MLG 9488, Newman 9493, Oak 9499, Perry 9506, Rimora 9522, Smith 9533, Wardle 9551, **WestWind 9555**
Chesapeake: Agena 9381
Clifton: Three 9541
Covington: Alleghany 9382
Dale City: Hylton 9455
Danville: Carrington, 9402, Community 9413, Danville 9420, Danville 9421, Maude 9480
Doswell: Flippo 9430
Fairfax: **ICE 9456**, **Loyola 9471**, Moore 9489, Peterson 9508
Falls Church: Lambert 9466, **Mustard 9492**, **Northrop 9498**, **Olmsted 9501**
Franklin: Camp 9399, Franklin 9434
Fredericksburg: Community 9414, Fredericksburg 9436
Galax: Matthews 9479
Goochland: Herndon 9451
Great Falls: Sellier 9530
Harrisonburg: Community 9411
Herndon: Balsells 9385, Claws 9408, Colburn 9409, Hobbs 9454, Launders 9468, Mousetrap 9491
Keswick: Craig 9418
Lansdowne: **Cooke 9417**
Lynchburg: Easley 9424, English 9426, Lynchburg 9474
Manakin Sabot: Scott 9529
Manakin-Sabot: Harrison 9449
Manassas: Breeden 9396, Kellar 9461
Marshall: **Bosack 9395**, Luminescence 9473, Wise 9560
Martinsville: Harvest 9450, Keesee 9460
Mathews: Owens 9503
Mc Lean: Bansal 9387, Rales 9513
McLean: Capital 9400, Folger 9431, Freddie 9435, Funger 9438, **Gannett 9439**, Malek 9475, Mars 9477, Trehan 9544, Volgenau 9549
Middleburg: Piedmont 9509
Midlothian: Watkins 9553

Mineral: Whitlock 9556
Newport News: Goodman 9444
Norfolk: Batten 9388, Batten 9389, Batten 9390, Dalis 9419, Hampton 9448, Lafayette 9465, Landmark 9467, Norfolk 9496, Perry 9507, Shearwater 9531
Oak Hill: Willett 9557
Oakton: Community 9410
Petersburg: Cameron 9398
Portsmouth: Beazley 9391, Portsmouth 9510
Potomac Falls: United 9547
Reston: MAXIMUS 9481, **Truland 9545**
Richmond: 4G 9379, Cabell 9397, CarMax 9401, Carter 9403, Community 9416, Dominion 9422, Estes 9427, Foster 9432, **Genworth 9441**, Guilford 9446, Gwathmey 9447, Jeffress 9457, Lipman 9469, Love 9470, Luck 9472, Massey 9478, MeadWestvaco 9484, Memorial 9485, Millhiser 9486, Morgan, 9490, NewMarket 9494, Parsons 9504, Pauley 9505, Reckitt 9516, Reinhart 9517, Reynolds 9519, Richmond 9521, Robins 9523, Robins 9524, Snead 9536, SunTrust 9539, Universal 9548
Roanoke: Community 9415, Fralin 9433, Golden 9443, Kirk 9462, Taubman 9540
Shawsville: Waldron 9550
Smithfield: Smithfield 9535
Springfield: Strong 9537
Staunton: Community 9412
Suffolk: Birdsong 9393, Obici 9500, Suffolk 9538
Sutherland: Titmus 9543
Tazewell: Ratcliffe 9514
The Plains: Johnson 9458, **Sacharuna 9526**, Wrinkle 9562
Vienna: Hillman 9452, Kanter 9459, Ratner 9515
Virginia Beach: AMERIGROUP 9383, Dreyfus 9423
Warrenton: Rice 9520
West Point: Olsson 9502
Williamsburg: Bangs-Russell 9386, Williamsburg 9558, Williamsburg 9559
Winchester: Proteus 9512
Woodbridge: Potomac 9511
Wytheville: Wythe-Bland 9563

---

see also 105, 145, 188, 204, 210, 295, 343, 369, 373, 471, 525, 569, 582, 586, 628, 633, 723, 730, 738, 754, 769, 792, 854, 909, 952, 1016, 1038, 1122, 1174, 1249, 1355, 1463, 1509, 1572, 1591, 1659, 1674, 1704, 1748, 1772, 1780, 1794, 1837, 1843, 1878, 1888, 1890, 1893, 1894, 1895, 1899, 1917, 1920, 1925, 1931, 1932, 1933, 1937, 1976, 2030, 2046, 2072, 2075, 2103, 2111, 2116, 2173, 2198, 2237, 2249, 2262, 2279, 2291, 2345, 2350, 2365, 2387, 2389, 2391, 2395, 2400, 2421, 2428, 2469, 2517, 2637, 2649, 2657, 2665, 2707, 2789, 2844, 2846, 2856, 2883, 2895, 2903, 2979, 3034, 3038, 3044, 3046, 3132, 3188, 3190, 3197, 3244, 3257, 3258, 3392, 3433, 3565, 3568, 3581, 3582, 3620, 3629, 3682, 3710, 3744, 3756, 3784, 3789, 3795, 3797, 3801, 3813, 3822, 3825, 3837, 3847, 3850, 3870, 3884, 3886, 3887, 3903, 3922, 3936, 4066, 4077, 4114, 4129, 4202, 4238, 4282, 4284, 4322, 4394, 4397, 4484, 4575, 4601, 4645, 4739, 4790, 4835, 4841, 4853, 4875, 4910, 4913, 4948, 4957, 5097, 5118, 5141, 5200, 5246, 5294, 5301, 5340, 5379, 5454, 5471, 5525, 5569, 5570, 5648, 5710, 5723, 5733, 5742, 5858, 5899, 5900, 5985, 5998, 6106, 6107, 6176, 6224, 6279, 6389, 6400, 6406, 6439, 6440, 6474, 6582, 6583, 6601, 6619, 6627, 6649, 6770, 6795, 6829, 7022, 7091, 7136, 7138, 7168, 7191, 7198, 7200, 7201, 7216, 7256, 7262, 7280, 7288, 7308, 7311, 7327, 7339, 7368, 7424, 7470, 7531, 7538, 7573, 7587, 7593, 7596, 7602, 7615, 7616, 7623, 7665, 7684, 7847, 7967, 8025, 8030, 8048, 8230, 8241, 8257, 8262, 8266, 8343, 8441, 8446, 8469, 8499, 8571, 8579, 8635, 8724, 8833, 8911, 9063, 9193, 9229, 9245, 9266, 9290, 9622, 9653, 9712, 9737, 9746, 9758, 9770, 9791, 9794, 9949, 9987, 9990

WASHINGTON

Bainbridge Island: Ames 9570, Bainbridge 9578, Rice 9716
Battle Ground: Chou 9599
Bellevue: **444S 9565**, Apex 9574, Aven 9575, Benaroya 9583, Bradley 9589, Bushnell 9592, Danz 9609, Ellison 9614, Glaser 9629, Greenstein 9633, Hanson 9639, Jones 9655, Lalji 9665, Lie 9669, **Luke 9674**, Oki 9694, PACCAR 9698, **PAH 9699**, Pendleton 9703, Puget 9705, Remala 9714, Rotella 9721, Sunbridge 9746
Bellingham: 25 9564, Whatcom 9759
Cle Elum: McMillen 9681
Deer Harbor: Anders 9571
Eastsound: Orcas 9697
Edmonds: Corvias 9606
Ephrata: Columbia 9602, Lauzier 9667, Lauzier 9668
Everett: Everett 9616, Evertrust 9617, Fuchs 9624, Intermec 9651
Fircrest: Names 9690
Friday Harbor: San Juan 9726, Wendt 9758
Gig Harbor: Russell 9722
Hoquiam: Grays 9631
Kirkland: Anderson 9572, Foster 9621, **Hotes 9646**, Lafromboise 9663, McCaw 9676, Riverstyx 9718, Suskin 9747
Langley: George 9626
Lynnwood: Zumiez 9768
Medina: Eggnog 9613, Lochland 9670
Mercer Island: Bezos 9585, Giuliani 9628, Lockwood 9671
Montesano: Kelsey 9658
Olympia: Community 9605, **Haugland 9643**
Prescott: **Vista 9756**
Redmond: **Foundation 9622**
Renton: First 9619, Renton 9715
Sammamish: Wren 9764
Seattle: Adams 9566, Allen 9567, **Allen 9568**, Almi 9569, Anduin 9573, B&E 9577, Barton 9581, Berwick 9584, Biller 9586, Blakemore 9587, **Brainerd 9590**, **Bullitt 9591**, **Campion 9594**, Casey 9595, Casey 9596, **Channel 9597**, College 9600, Crystal 9608, Discuren 9611, Edgebrook 9612, Fabert 9618, **Gates 9625**, Giddens, 9627, **Glaser 9630**, Green 9632, Hanauer 9636, Handsel 9638, Harvest 9642, Horizons 9645, Howard 9647, Hughes 9648, Hussey 9649, Invested 9652, **Islands 9653**, **Jain 9654**, JRS 9656, Kaphan 9657, **Kongsgaard 9661**, **Laird 9664**, Laurel 9666, Loeb 9672, Lucky 9673, McCaw 9675, McEachern 9678, McKinstry 9680, Medina 9682, Miller 9684, Miller 9685, Miller 9686, Moccasin 9687, Moraine 9688, Nesholm 9691, Neukom 9692, Norcliffe 9693, OneFamily 9695, Opportunities 9696, Peach 9701, PEMCO 9702, Plum 9704, PWH 9706, **Quixote 9707**, Raikes 9708, Raisbeck 9709, Raven 9710, Raynier 9711, RealNetworks 9712, Richardson 9717, Roma 9719, Roots 9720, Safeco 9723, Sahsen 9724, **Samis 9725**, Sarkowsky 9727, Satterberg 9728, Scan 9729, Schultz 9730, Seattle 9731, Shirley 9734, Simonyi 9735, Sloan 9736, Smith 9737, Smith 9738, Sondland 9740, Spark 9741, **Starbucks 9742**, Stevenson 9743, T.E.W. 9749, **Goodwin 9751**, **Torrance 9753**, True 9754, **Tyler 9755**, Washington 9757, Wiancko 9761, **Wilburforce 9762**, Wockner 9763, Wright 9765, Wrigley 9766
Sequim: Haller 9635
Shoreline: Hanauer 9637, McIntyre 9679
Silverdale: Kitsap 9659
Spokane: Avista 9576, Cowles 9607, Empire 9615, Hagan 9634, Inland 9650
Steilacoom: Thompson 9752
Sumner: REI 9713
Tacoma: Bamford 9580, Bates 9582, Cheney 9598, Dimmer 9610, Forest 9620, Harder 9640, Honzel 9644, Milgard 9683, Sequoia 9732, Snyder 9739, **Stewardship 9744**, Tacoma 9750
Tukwila: Harnish 9641
Vancouver: Cameron 9593, Colson 9601, Community 9603, KMR 9660, Kuni 9662, McClaskey 9677, Murdock 9689, Pankow 9700, Wheeler 9760
Vashon: Baker 9579
Walla Walla: Blue 9588, Sherwood 9733, Stubblefield 9745
Washougal: Swigert-Warren 9748
Wenatchee: Community 9604, Foundation 9623
Yakima: Yakima 9767

---

see also 84, 98, 238, 349, 385, 392, 471, 569, 633, 704, 726, 798, 853, 854, 907, 957, 989, 1164, 1183, 1225, 1282, 1288, 1339, 1384, 1531, 1674, 1696, 1733, 1734, 1750, 1875, 1959, 2133, 2188, 2281, 2347, 2469, 2614, 2645, 2657, 3003, 3112, 3120, 3257, 3275, 3392, 3443, 3457, 3476, 3492, 3551, 3745, 4388, 4466, 4609, 4614, 4636, 4659, 4661, 4663, 4691, 4712, 4729, 4743, 4784, 4818, 5030, 5090, 5104, 5121, 5151, 5159, 5223, 5257, 5321, 5471, 5711, 5996, 6244, 6512, 6795, 6832, 6909, 7145, 7279, 7369, 7523, 7531, 7676, 7804, 7827, 7829, 7838, 7840, 7841, 7843, 7853, 7858, 7860, 7864, 7870, 7873, 7877, 7886, 7887, 8145, 8235, 8242, 8393, 8403, 8495, 8623, 8851, 9053, 9199, 9206, 9209, 9321, 9325, 9362, 9383, 9947

WEST VIRGINIA

Beckley: Beckley 9769
Bluefield: Bowen 9770, Shott, 9794
Charleston: Brickstreet 9771, Daywood 9774, Kanawha 9780, Maier 9782, Wehrle 9797
Elkins: Myles 9787
Hansford: Hamilton, 9776
Huntington: Prichard 9791, Teubert 9795, Weisberg 9798
Lansing: Martha 9783
Lewisburg: Hollowell 9778
Martinsburg: Eastern 9775
Morgantown: McQuain 9785, Your 9799
Parkersburg: McDonough 9784, Meagel 9786, Parkersburg 9789, Ross 9792
Parsons: Tucker 9796
Princeton: Hunnicutt 9779, Preservati 9790
Wheeling: Chambers 9772, Community 9773, Hess 9777, Laughlin 9781, Nutting 9788, Schenk 9793

---

see also 188, 854, 1404, 1773, 2000, 2024, 2313, 2469, 2657, 3334, 3575, 3581, 3797, 4651, 4855, 4948, 5422, 6244, 7138, 7144, 7201, 7368, 7407, 7452, 7455, 7531, 7557, 7563, 7609, 7935, 8025, 8165, 8192, 8235, 8291, 8655, 9290, 9383, 9422, 9491, 9499, 9653, 9704

WISCONSIN

Altoona: Integrity 9868
Appleton: Community 9832, Mercy 9905, Thrivent 9956, U.S. 9957
Arcadia: Wanek 9962, Wanek 9963, Wanek 9964
Belleville: Mortenson 9909
Beloit: Beloit 9814, Neese 9911
Black River Falls: Lunda 9895, Lunda 9896
Brookfield: Fotsch 9846, Ladish 9891, Rowland 9937, Siebert 9946, Vine 9960
Brownsville: Michels 9906
Chippewa Falls: Rutledge 9939
De Pere: Meng 9904

Elm Grove: Benidt 9816, Helfaer 9861, Ladish 9890
Fond du Lac: Fond du Lac 9843, Sadoff 9941, Stone 9954
Fort Atkinson: Fort 9845
Glendale: Krause 9886
Green Bay: Cornerstone 9836, Green Bay 9854, Green Bay 9855, Kress 9887, **Schneider 9942**, Stock 9953, Wisconsin 9970
Green Lake: Riordan 9933
Hudson: St. Croix 9950
Janesville: Community 9835, Jeffris 9869, Rath 9927
Kimberly: MMG 9908
Kohler: Kohler 9884
La Crosse: Antioch 9807, Cleary 9831, Family 9842, Gordon 9853, La Crosse 9889, Reinhart 9930
Lyons: **Wagner 9961**
Madison: Alliant 9804, Batterman 9813, Bradshaw 9820, Clark 9830, CUNA 9838, Frautschi 9847, Fund 9849, Goodman 9852, Hands 9858, Hovde 9865, Johnson 9873, Madison 9897, Madison 9898, Ocular 9915, Predolin 9923, RDK 9928, Rennebohm 9931, Shapiro 9945, **Taylor 9955**
Manitowoc: West 9967
Marathon: Goldbach 9851
Mayville: Bachhuber 9809
Mequon: Brookby 9823, Nicholas 9913, Ryan 9940
Middleton: Berbeewalsh 9817, Frautschi 9848
Milwaukee: 1923 9800, Anon 9805, Argosy 9808, Bader 9810, **Baird 9811**, Baker 9812, **Bradley 9819**, Brady 9821, Casper 9827, Caxambas 9828, Charter 9829, Eder 9840, Evinrude 9841, Godfrey 9850, Griffiss 9857, Harley 9859, Heil 9860, Herma 9862, Herzfeld 9863, Holz 9864, Iddings 9866, Johnson 9870, Johnson 9871, Jordan 9875, Joy 9876, Kelben 9877, Kellogg 9879, Klein 9882, Kohl 9883, Kohler 9885, Lubar 9894, ManpowerGroup 9899, Marcus 9900, McBeath 9901, Milwaukee 9907, Northwestern 9914, Peck 9918, Pick 9920, Pollybill 9921, Posner 9922, Ramirez 9926, Reiman 9929, Rexnord 9932, Rockwell 9934, Roundy's 9936, Sensient 9943, Smith 9947, Soref 9948, Stackner 9951, Steigleder 9952, Uihlein 9958, Uihlein 9959, Wisconsin 9969, Zilber 9971, Zilber 9972
Mount Horeb: DeAtley 9839
Nashotah: Rolfs 9935
Neenah: Bemis 9815, Keller 9878, Menasha 9903
Oshkosh: Kuenzl 9888, Oshkosh 9916, Oshkosh 9917
Pewaukee: Loehrke 9893
Port Edwards: Alexander 9802
Prairie du Sac: Culver's 9837
Prescott: Nelson 9912
Racine: Johnson 9872, Johnson 9874, Mound 9910, Racine 9924
Shawano: Bleser 9818
Sheboygan: Acuity 9801, Brotz 9825
Stevens Point: Community 9833, Sentry 9944
Stoughton: Bryant 9826
Sturgeon Bay: Raibrook 9925
Sussex: Windhover 9968
Thiensville: Lakeview 9892
Walworth: Kikkoman 9881
Waterford: Runzheimer 9938
Waukesha: Brookhill 9824, Kern 9880, Waukesha 9965
Waupaca: Anthony 9806
Wausau: Alexander 9803, Community 9834, Forester 9844, Greenheck 9856, Spire 9949
Wauwatosa: Briggs 9822, Pettit 9919, Wehr 9966
Wisconsin Rapids: Incourage 9867, Mead 9902

---

see also 345, 633, 854, 1055, 1229, 1278, 1313, 1482, 1591, 1674, 1835, 1840, 1876, 1889, 1937, 2063, 2341, 2364, 2469, 2654, 2656, 2657, 2738, 2790, 2910, 2915, 2916, 2921, 2923, 2938, 2946, 3005, 3034, 3041, 3060, 3075, 3101, 3113, 3168, 3213, 3243, 3257, 3292, 3347, 3457, 3476, 3573, 3582, 3744, 3745, 3901, 4271, 4366, 4601, 4602, 4603, 4620, 4636, 4649, 4651, 4661, 4664, 4665, 4676, 4677, 4691, 4693, 4694, 4733, 4739, 4746, 4778, 4780, 4784, 4796, 4808, 4948, 4970, 5090, 5165, 5223, 5767, 5799, 6006, 6130, 6244, 6318, 6518, 6789, 6832, 6938, 7145, 7398, 7596, 7601, 7603, 7641, 7716, 8042, 8230, 8235, 8579, 8811, 9044, 9383, 9422, 9704, 9716, 9729

WYOMING

Casper: Ellbogen 9977, Martin 9984, McMurry 9986, True 9995, Zimmerman 10000
Cheyenne: Allen 9973
Jackson: Community 9975, Cumming 9976, Friess 9978, Hessel 9980, Liana 9982, LOR 9983, McKinnell 9985, Niner 9987, Storer 9992, Stuart 9993, Sullivan 9994
Laramie: Wyoming 9999
Sheridan: Griffith 9979, Perkins 9988, Scott 9989, Seven 9991, Watt 9997, Whitney 9998
Teton Village: Tyrrell 9996
Wilson: Christian 9974, Kerr 9981, Seeley 9990

---

see also 105, 122, 742, 1017, 1183, 1399, 1400, 1425, 1486, 1529, 1687, 1750, 1770, 1958, 2469, 2657, 2668, 2947, 3334, 3339, 3405, 3457, 3479, 4636, 4784, 4855, 5009, 5057, 5087, 5090, 5336, 5379, 7098, 7877, 8345, 8489, 8638, 8833, 8965, 9315, 9342, 9640, 9717

INTERNATIONAL GIVING INDEX

List of terms: Names of countries, continents, or regions used in this index are drawn from the complete list below. Terms may appear on the list but not be present in the index.

Index: In the index itself, foundations are listed under the countries, continents, or regions in which they have demonstrated giving interests or made charitable contributions. Within these country or regional groupings, foundations are arranged by state location, abbreviated name, and sequence number.

Afghanistan
Africa
Albania
Algeria
Andorra
Angola
Anguilla
Antarctica
Antigua & Barbuda
Arctic Region
Argentina
Armenia
Aruba
Asia
Australia
Austria
Azerbaijan
Bahamas
Bahrain
Balkans, The
Bangladesh
Barbados
Belarus
Belgium
Belize
Benin
Bermuda
Bhutan
Bolivia
Bonaire
Bosnia-Herzegovina
Botswana
Brazil
British Virgin Islands
Brunei
Bulgaria
Burkina Faso
Burma (Myanmar)
Burundi
Cambodia
Cameroon
Canada
Cape Verde
Caribbean
Cayman Islands
Central Africa
Central Africa Republic
Central America
Central Asia and the Caucasus
Chad
Chile
China
Colombia
Commonwealth of the Northern Mariana Islands
Comoros
Congo
Costa Rica
Croatia
Cuba
Curacao
Cyprus
Czech Republic
Democratic Republic of the Congo
Denmark
Developing countries
Djibouti
Dominica
Dominican Republic
East Africa/Horn of Africa
East Asia
East Jerusalem
East Timor
Eastern & Central Europe
Ecuador
Egypt
El Salvador
England
Equatorial Guinea
Eritrea
Estonia
Ethiopia
Europe
Federated States of Micronesia
Fiji
Finland
France
French Guiana
Gabon
Gambia
Georgia (Republic of)
Germany
Ghana
Gibraltar
Global programs
Greater Antilles
Greece
Greenland
Grenada
Guadeloupe
Guatemala
Guernsey
Guinea
Guinea-Bissau
Guyana
Haiti
Honduras
Hong Kong
Hungary
Iceland
India
Indonesia
Iran
Iraq
Ireland
Isle of Man
Israel
Italy
Ivory Coast
Jamaica
Japan
Jersey
Jordan
Kazakhstan
Kenya
Kiribati
Kosovo
Kuwait
Kyrgyzstan
Laos
Latin America
Latvia
Lebanon
Leeward Islands
Lesotho
Lesser Antilles
Liberia
Libya
Liechtenstein
Lithuania
Luxembourg
Macau
Macedonia
Madagascar
Malawi
Malaysia
Maldives
Mali
Malta
Marshall Islands
Martinique
Mauritania
Mauritius
Mexico
Middle East
Moldova
Monaco
Mongolia
Montenegro
Montserrat
Morocco and the Western Sahara
Mozambique
Namibia
Nauru
Nepal
Netherlands
Netherlands Antilles
New Caledonia
New Zealand
Nicaragua
Niger
Nigeria
North Korea
North Africa
Northern Ireland
Norway
Oceania
Oman
Pakistan
Palau
Panama
Papua New Guinea
Paraguay
Peru
Philippines
Poland
Portugal
Qatar
Romania
Russia
Rwanda
Saint Kitts-Nevis
Saint Lucia
Saint Vincent & the Grenadines
Samoa
Sao Tome and Principe
Saudi Arabia
Scandinavia
Scotland
Senegal

Serbia
Seychelles
Sierra Leone
Singapore
Slovakia
Slovenia
Solomon Islands
Somalia, Somaliland and Puntland
South Africa
South America
South Asia
South Korea
South Sudan
Southeast Asia
Southern Africa
Soviet Union (Former)
Spain
Sri Lanka
Sub-Saharan Africa
Sudan
Suriname
Swaziland
Sweden
Switzerland
Syria
Tahiti
Taiwan
Tajikistan
Tanzania, Zanzibar and Pemba
Thailand
Togo
Tonga
Trinidad & Tobago
Tunisia
Turkey
Turkmenistan
Turks & Caicos Islands
Tuvalu
Uganda
Ukraine
United Arab Emirates
United Kingdom
Uruguay
Uzbekistan
Vanuatu
Vatican City
Venezuela
Vietnam
Wales
West Bank/Gaza
Western Africa
Windward Islands
Yemen
Yugoslavia (Former)
Zambia
Zimbabwe

Afghanistan
Illinois: Abbott 2649, Motorola 3042

Africa
Arizona: Hickey 121
California: Alalusi 224, Annenberg 245, Egg 496, Gilead 586, Hilton 692, Manasseh's 870, Open 986, Roth 1093, Sangham 1114, Stamps 1210, Strauss 1223
Connecticut: GE 1591
District of Columbia: Banyan 1881
Florida: Stacy 2333, Working 2394
Georgia: Coca 2428, Georgia 2469
Hawaii: Burke 2590
Illinois: Abbott 2649, Deere 2790, IDP 2932, King 2960, Libra 2981
Indiana: West 3404
Kansas: Lloyd 3530
Maine: Catalyst 3682
Massachusetts: Alchemy 3920, Grand 4076
Minnesota: Medtronic 4712, Oswald 4735
Missouri: Monsanto 4945
New Jersey: Merck 5379, Segal 5446
New York: Abraham 5545, Arcus 5608, Bristol 5711, Carnegie 5747, Claiborne 5783, Clark 5785, Ford 5994, Foundation 6001, Goldman 6070, IBM 6203, JPMorgan 6244, Nduna 6533, Neuberger 6538, Open 6593, PepsiCo 6627, Rockefeller 6724, Schaffner 6800, Unbound 7016
North Carolina: Oak 7276
Oregon: Lemelson 7865, NIKE 7875
Pennsylvania: Alcoa 7908, Heinz 8083, Huston 8103, PPG 8235
Tennessee: International 8585, Maclellan 8601, Westwood 8644
Texas: ExxonMobil 8833, Whole 9276
Virginia: Loyola 9471, Mustard 9492
Washington: Colson 9601, Gates 9625, JRS 9656, Laird 9664, Starbucks 9742
Wisconsin: Johnson 9871, Wagner 9961

Albania
New York: Trust 7009

Algeria
New York: Citi 5780

Angola
New York: Flowers 5990
Texas: Baker 8679, International 8927

Antarctica
New York: Tinker 6983

Argentina
California: Conservation 426, Foundation 542, Mattel 886
Colorado: Western 1521
Illinois: Mondelez 3034, Motorola 3042, Motorola 3043
Iowa: Pioneer 3474
Maryland: Hughes 3818
Massachusetts: Cabot 3966
Minnesota: Mosaic 4722
Missouri: Monsanto 4945
New York: American 5588, Citi 5780, Deutsche 5876, JPMorgan 6244
Texas: Bolivar 8708, Whole 9276

Armenia
California: Gogian 598, Karisma 766
Michigan: Manoogian 4493
New Jersey: Hovnanian 5306
New York: Nazarian 6530, Trust 7009
Texas: Simonian 9176

Asia
California: Alalusi 224, Annenberg 245, Christensen 399, Flextronics 535, Hilton 692, Open 986, Spencer 1204, Strauss 1223
Connecticut: Praxair 1676, Richardson 1679
Florida: Stacy 2333
Georgia: Georgia 2469
Hawaii: Burke 2590
Illinois: Libra 2981, Terra 3186
Massachusetts: China 3982, Grand 4076
Missouri: Monsanto 4945
New York: Abraham 5545, Claiborne 5783, Ford 5994, Foundation 6001, Freeman 6012, Goldman 6070, IBM 6203, JPMorgan 6244, Neuberger 6538, Open 6593, PepsiCo 6627, Schaffner 6800, SMBC 6873, Starr 6911, United 7019
North Carolina: Oak 7276
Ohio: Timken 7683
Oregon: Lemelson 7865
Pennsylvania: Alcoa 7908, PPG 8235
Tennessee: Maclellan 8601, Westwood 8644
Texas: Whole 9276
Virginia: Blue 9394, Loyola 9471, Mustard 9492
Washington: Gates 9625, Laird 9664, Starbucks 9742

Australia
California: Christensen 399, Las 821, Mattel 886, ResMed 1063
Colorado: Western 1521
Connecticut: Tudor 1711
Florida: Jaffer 2168
Georgia: Coca 2428
Illinois: Mondelez 3034
Maryland: Hughes 3818
Massachusetts: State 4285
Michigan: Kellogg 4473
Minnesota: Medtronic 4712, Toro 4780
New York: American 5588, Citi 5780, Commonwealth 5800, Wolfensohn 7098
Pennsylvania: Alcoa 7908, Pew 8220, Susquehanna 8310
Texas: BP 8718, Tingari-Silverton 9235

Austria
Colorado: Avenir 1369, Western 1521
Illinois: Wrigley 3244
Iowa: Rockwell 3477
Massachusetts: State 4285
Michigan: Kellogg's 4475
Minnesota: Medtronic 4712
New York: Kade 6247, Lauder 6336
Pennsylvania: Alcoa 7908, Botstiber 7947
Virginia: Genworth 9441

Azerbaijan
New York: Trust 7009

Bahamas
District of Columbia: Merriman 1930
New York: Citi 5780, Credit 5826
Pennsylvania: Little 8145

Bahrain
New York: Citi 5780

Bangladesh
Maryland: Hughes 3818
Minnesota: Mortenson 4721
New York: Citi 5780, PepsiCo 6627
Oregon: NIKE 7875
Pennsylvania: Heinz 8083
Texas: Merali 9022, Whole 9276

Belarus
New York: Lauder 6336, Trust 7009

Belgium
California: Broadcom 349
Illinois: Motorola 3043
Massachusetts: Cabot 3966, State 4285
Minnesota: Medtronic 4712
New York: Citi 5780, Debbane 5859, Francqui 6007, Sato 6798

Belize
District of Columbia: Summit 1950
Texas: Caris 8749
Wisconsin: Wagner 9961

Bermuda
New York: Stempel 6925
Virginia: Truland 9545
Wisconsin: Wagner 9961

Bolivia
Minnesota: Oswald 4735
Wisconsin: Wagner 9961

Bosnia and Herzegovina
New York: Trust 7009

Brazil
California: Avery 272, Mattel 886, Thiel 1249
Colorado: Western 1521
Connecticut: Praxair 1676
Georgia: UPS 2566
Hawaii: Albrecht 2585
Illinois: Abbott 2649, Mondelez 3034, Motorola 3042, Motorola 3043
Indiana: Cummins 3292
Iowa: Pioneer 3474
Maryland: Hughes 3818
Massachusetts: Cabot 3966

Michigan: Kellogg 4474
Minnesota: Medtronic 4712, Mosaic 4722
Missouri: Monsanto 4945
New Jersey: Prudential 5415
New York: Buck 5725, Citi 5780, Credit 5826, Deutsche 5876, JPMorgan 6244, MetLife 6479, Overbrook 6604
Ohio: Timken 7683, Timken 7684
Oregon: Intel 7853, NIKE 7875
Pennsylvania: Alcoa 7908
South Dakota: Opus 8518

Brunei
New York: Citi 5780

Bulgaria
Maryland: Hughes 3818
New York: Citi 5780, Lauder 6336, Trust 7009
North Carolina: Oak 7276

Burkina Faso
Missouri: Monsanto 4945

Burundi
New Jersey: Segal 5446

Cambodia
Idaho: Schultz 2641
Massachusetts: Grinspoon 4080
Minnesota: McKnight 4709, Mortenson 4721
New York: Johnson 6233, Matisse 6447

Cameroon
New York: Citi 5780

Canada
Alabama: Flack 34
California: Agilent 220, Agouron 221, Amgen 238, Burkle 355, Cisco 402, Fineberg 525, Ing 721, Kingfisher 788, Mattel 886, Neilsen 964, ResMed 1063, Sea 1131, Seaver 1132, Smith 1183, Strauss 1223, Thiel 1249, Vadasz 1275, Weider 1306
Colorado: Kinder 1439, Western 1521
Connecticut: GE 1591, October 1659
Delaware: Adobe 1734
District of Columbia: Union 1953
Florida: Jaffer 2168, Lampert 2200
Georgia: UPS 2566
Illinois: Astellas 2675, Joyce 2946, Mondelez 3034, Motorola 3043, State 3174
Iowa: Pioneer 3474, Rockwell 3477
Maryland: ABMRF 3714, Grace 3807, Hughes 3818, Lawless 3827
Massachusetts: Cabot 3966, Krieble 4129, Rodgers 4241, Rosenberg 4245, State 4285, Sweet 4302
Michigan: Cooper-Standard 4380, DENSO 4395, Erb 4415, Kellogg 4473, Kellogg's 4475
Minnesota: Andersen 4601, Medtronic 4712, Mosaic 4722, Patterson 4738, Polaris 4746
Missouri: Enterprise 4887, Francis 4893, Monsanto 4945
New Hampshire: Fidelity 5170
New Jersey: Crane 5235
New York: American 5588, Bronfman 5717, Buffalo 5726, Citi 5780, Commonwealth 5800, Credit 5826, Cummings 5832, Deutsche 5876, Elishis 5946, Guggenheim 6116, IBM 6203, JPMorgan 6244, LaSalle 6331, Lupus 6401, M & T 6406, M.A.C. 6408, Mayday 6448, Norcross 6564, PepsiCo 6627, Rheuminations 6695, Tsadra 7010, Whitney 7080
North Carolina: Burroughs 7164, Morehead-Cain 7268, Nickel 7272
Ohio: OMNOVA 7601, Patterson 7613, Timken 7684
Pennsylvania: Alcoa 7908, AO 7915, Carnegie 7966, Pew 8220, Waldorf 8330
Rhode Island: FM 8393
South Carolina: ScanSource 8495
Texas: Six 9178, Summerlee 9213
Vermont: Daly 9359
Virginia: Chase 9406, Genworth 9441, Sacharuna 9526
Washington: 444S 9565, Brainerd 9590, Bullitt 9591, Campion 9594, Islands 9653, Kongsgaard 9661, Starbucks 9742, Torrance 9753, Wilburforce 9762
Wisconsin: Schneider 9942

Caribbean
California: Linked 842
Colorado: General 1419
Illinois: Henry 2906
New York: Ford 5994, Guggenheim 6116, Open 6593, Reed 6684
Pennsylvania: Alcoa 7908
Virginia: Loyola 9471, WestWind 9555

Cayman Islands
Massachusetts: State 4285

Central America
California: Arntz 259, Atkinson 265, Bergstrom 310, S.G. 1100
Colorado: General 1419
Florida: Peterson 2267
Hawaii: Burke 2590
Idaho: Schultz 2641
New Mexico: Aurora 5515
New York: Claiborne 5783
Ohio: Geisse 7468
Pennsylvania: Alcoa 7908
Washington: Laird 9664, Vista 9756
Wisconsin: Wagner 9961

Central Asia
New York: Open 6593

Chile
California: Allende 227, Conservation 426, Foundation 542, Marisla 878, Mattel 886
Georgia: Coca 2428
Iowa: Pioneer 3474
Maryland: Hughes 3818, Shared 3882
Massachusetts: Grand 4076
Minnesota: Mosaic 4722
Missouri: Monsanto 4945
New York: Deutsche 5876, JPMorgan 6244, Weeden 7060
Washington: Tyler 9755

China
California: Agilent 220, Alalusi 224, Applied 249, Avery 272, Broadcom 349, Cisco 402, Hewlett 686, Lingnan 841, Mattel 886, Strauss 1223, Zee 1357
Colorado: Western 1521
Connecticut: GE 1591
Delaware: Adobe 1734
District of Columbia: New 1936
Georgia: Coca 2428, UPS 2566
Hawaii: Shaw 2615
Illinois: Baxter 2690, Mondelez 3034, Motorola 3042, Motorola 3043, Tellabs 3185, Wrigley 3244
Indiana: Cummins 3292
Iowa: Pioneer 3474
Kansas: Lloyd 3530
Massachusetts: Cabot 3966, China 3982, Grand 4076, Lincoln 4146
Michigan: Foundation 4432
Minnesota: Fuller 4659, Medtronic 4712, Mosaic 4722
Missouri: Monsanto 4945
Nevada: Tang 5153
New Jersey: Merck 5379, Wang 5495
New York: American 5588, Bristol 5711, Carnegie 5747, Citi 5780, Jiang 6230, PepsiCo 6627, Rockefeller 6723, Trace 7003
Ohio: 58 7362, Cardinal 7398, OMNOVA 7601, Timken 7683, Timken 7684
Oregon: Intel 7853
Pennsylvania: Alcoa 7908, Heinz 8083
Texas: BP 8718, Caris 8749
Utah: Nu 9340
Virginia: Blue 9394
Washington: Starbucks 9742
Wisconsin: Schneider 9942

Colombia
California: Fund 556, Swift 1230
Georgia: Coca 2428
Massachusetts: Cabot 3966, Hunt 4102
Missouri: Monsanto 4945
New York: Citi 5780, Genesis 6042, JPMorgan 6244
South Dakota: Opus 8518

Congo, Democratic Republic of the
New Jersey: Segal 5446
New York: Citi 5780

Congo, Republic of the
Massachusetts: Bresky 3958
New York: Bristol 5711
Texas: Caris 8749

Costa Rica
Colorado: Western 1521
Florida: Community 2036
Georgia: Guanacaste 2475
Massachusetts: Grand 4076
New York: Citi 5780
Oregon: Intel 7853
Texas: Whole 9276
Washington: Islands 9653

Cote d'Ivoire
New York: Citi 5780

Croatia
New York: Trust 7009

Cuba
Massachusetts: Reynolds 4238

Czech Republic
Maryland: Hughes 3818
Massachusetts: Cabot 3966
Minnesota: Medtronic 4712
New York: Citi 5780, Lauder 6336, Trust 7009
Ohio: Timken 7684
South Carolina: AVX-Kyocera 8457

Denmark
California: Agouron 221, Broadcom 349
Minnesota: Medtronic 4712
New York: Citi 5780

Developing Countries
California: Catalysis 384, First 530, Rivendell 1077, Saje 1104
Connecticut: Children's 1557
Idaho: Schultz 2641
Massachusetts: Conservation 3993
New Jersey: International 5316
New York: Claiborne 5783, Gould 6086
Ohio: Geisse 7468
Oregon: Lemelson 7865, NIKE 7875
Tennessee: Lazarus 8596
Texas: ExxonMobil 8833, PHM 9098, Whole 9276
Vermont: Evslin 9360
Virginia: Loyola 9471
Washington: Gates 9625
Wisconsin: Taylor 9955

Dominican Republic
Arizona: Hickey 121
California: S.G. 1100
New York: Citi 5780
Ohio: Cardinal 7398, Marion 7558
Washington: Vista 9756

East Jerusalem
Idaho: Schultz 2641
New York: Sparkplug 6894

Eastern Africa
North Carolina: Oak 7276
Texas: Radler 9118

Eastern Asia
Massachusetts: China 3982
New York: Luce 6398, Soros 6891

Eastern Europe
Illinois: Domanada 2799
Michigan: Mott 4510
New York: Johnson 6235, Lauder 6336, Open 6593, Trust 7009
Ohio: Timken 7683
Tennessee: Maclellan 8601

Ecuador
California: Fund 556
New Hampshire: Butler 5165
New York: Citi 5780, Overbrook 6604
Oregon: Vibrant 7898
Texas: Caris 8749, New Beginning 9057

Egypt
Colorado: Western 1521
Massachusetts: Grand 4076
New York: Citi 5780
Oregon: Intel 7853

El Salvador
Florida: Kazma 2179
New York: Citi 5780
South Carolina: AVX-Kyocera 8457
Washington: Vista 9756

England
California: Broccoli 350, Guthy-Jackson 638
Connecticut: Lone 1632, Tudor 1711
Delaware: Adobe 1734
District of Columbia: Butler 1889
Florida: Griffin 2138, Jaffer 2168
Georgia: UPS 2566
Illinois: Buffett 2726, Cornwell 2775, Goodman 2869, Manitoba 2999, Motorola 3042, Motorola 3043
Massachusetts: Grantham 4077, Min 4178, University 4314
Michigan: Kellogg 4473, Tubergen 4559
Nevada: Browning 5104
New York: Belvedere 5661, Berg 5667, Brice 5708, Flowers 5990, Goldman 6064, Hayden 6149, Mead 6466, Mehra 6469, Moody's 6499, Neuberger 6538, New 6551, Saper 6794, Sapling 6795, Sutton 6951, Tanaka 6961, Wolfensohn 7098
North Carolina: Morehead-Cain 7268
Ohio: Generation 7470, Lerner 7538
South Carolina: ScanSource 8495
Texas: A Glimmer 8649

Estonia
Maryland: Hughes 3818
New York: Lauder 6336, Trust 7009

Ethiopia
California: Christensen 399
Florida: Ephraim 2087
Massachusetts: Barr 3937
New York: Bristol 5711
North Carolina: Oak 7276
Texas: A Glimmer 8649, Caris 8749, Rees-Jones 9125, Whole 9276
Utah: Nu 9340

Europe
California: Amgen 238, Annenberg 245, Applied 249, Flextronics 535, Strauss 1223
Connecticut: GE 1591, Richardson 1679
Florida: Stacy 2333
Georgia: Coca 2428, Georgia 2469
Illinois: Libra 2981, Terra 3186
Indiana: West 3404
Maryland: Thalheimer 3894
Massachusetts: Grand 4076, Lincoln 4146, State 4285
Missouri: Monsanto 4945
New York: Bristol 5711, Goldman 6070, IBM 6203, Johnson 6235, JPMorgan 6244, Kade 6247, Kress 6308, Lauder 6336
North Carolina: Nickel 7272, Oak 7276
Pennsylvania: Alcoa 7908, Pew 8220, PPG 8235
Texas: BP 8718
Virginia: Bellarmin 9392, Genworth 9441, Mustard 9492
Washington: Gates 9625, Starbucks 9742

Finland
Illinois: Tellabs 3185
New York: Citi 5780, Towerbrook 7001
Texas: Paloheimo 9080

France
California: Broadcom 349, Mattel 886, ResMed 1063, Thiel 1249
Colorado: Fishback 1410
Connecticut: Albers 1532
Delaware: Gynesis 1788
District of Columbia: Lounsbery 1926
Illinois: Mondelez 3034, Motorola 3043, Ward 3215
Iowa: Rockwell 3477
Maryland: Hughes 3818
Massachusetts: American 3923, Cabot 3966, State 4285
Minnesota: Medtronic 4712
New York: American 5588, Citi 5780, David 5852, de Rothschild 5857, Gould 6088, Lurcy 6402, Philippe 6636, Tsadra 7010, Woodshouse 7102
Ohio: OMNOVA 7601, Timken 7684
South Carolina: ScanSource 8495
Texas: Cultural 8793, Leducq 8976, Scaler 9155, Westbury 9271
Washington: Jain 9654

Georgia
New York: Trust 7009

Germany
California: Agilent 220, Mattel 886
Illinois: Hofmann 2918, Mondelez 3034
Maryland: Hughes 3818
Massachusetts: Cabot 3966, State 4285
Minnesota: Medtronic 4712
New York: American 5588, Citi 5780, Kade 6247, Lauder 6336, Leir 6349, Ridgefield 6705
Ohio: Timken 7684
Oregon: Chiles 7833
South Carolina: ScanSource 8495
Texas: BP 8718, Natem 9052
Washington: Allen 9568

Ghana
Colorado: Western 1521
Florida: Worrell 2395
Illinois: IDP 2932
Minnesota: Mortenson 4721
New York: Citi 5780, PepsiCo 6627
Ohio: Noble 7592
Oregon: Vibrant 7898

Global Programs
California: Hilton 692, Packard 1006
Colorado: Society 1503, Western 1521
Delaware: Raskob 1845
District of Columbia: Case 1891
Florida: Working 2394
Illinois: Deere 2790, IDP 2932
New York: Clark 5785, International 6211, Open 6593, Rockefeller 6724

Greece
California: Broadcom 349
Maryland: Hughes 3818
Massachusetts: Gerondelis 4070
New York: Citi 5780
Pennsylvania: Institute 8109, Williams 8339

Guatemala
California: Maya 888
Colorado: Western 1521
District of Columbia: Palmer 1937, Summit 1950
Maryland: Shared 3882
Minnesota: Mortenson 4721
Missouri: Monsanto 4945
New Jersey: Danellie 5237
New York: Citi 5780, Gould 6086
Oregon: Eiting 7840, Vibrant 7898
Tennessee: Ezell 8564
Texas: Caris 8749, International 8927, New Beginning 9057, Whole 9276
Washington: Vista 9756

Guinea
Maryland: Hughes 3818

Haiti
Arizona: Hickey 121, Parsons 151
California: S.G. 1100, Strauss 1223
Colorado: Western 1521
Florida: May 2230
Illinois: Abbott 2649
Massachusetts: Barr 3937
Michigan: Kellogg 4474
New Jersey: Danellie 5237
Oregon: Vibrant 7898
Texas: Caris 8749, International 8927, New Beginning 9057, Whole 9276
Washington: Vista 9756

Holy See
Iowa: Ochylski 3470

Honduras
Alabama: Scott 64
District of Columbia: Summit 1950
Minnesota: Mortenson 4721, Pentair 4739
Missouri: Monsanto 4945
New York: Citi 5780
Ohio: Noble 7592
Tennessee: Ezell 8564
Texas: International 8927, Whole 9276

Hong Kong
California: KLA-Tencor 792, Lingnan 841, Mattel 886, Zee 1357
Connecticut: Lone 1632
Hawaii: Shaw 2615
Massachusetts: China 3982
New York: American 5588, Citi 5780

Hungary
California: Mattel 886
Maryland: Hughes 3818
Minnesota: Medtronic 4712
New York: Citi 5780, Lauder 6336, Rockefeller 6723, Trust 7009

India
California: AAM 216, Agilent 220, Amar 236, Applied 249, Avery 272, Broadcom 349, Cisco 402, Hewlett 686, Ing 721, Mattel 886, Patel 1018, Sangham 1114, Tarsadia 1239, Vegesna 1286, Wadhwani 1294
Colorado: Western 1521
Connecticut: GE 1591, Praxair 1676
Delaware: Adobe 1734
Florida: Catholic 2014, Jaffer 2168, Patel 2259
Hawaii: Watumull 2620
Illinois: Abbott 2649, Heisley 2902, Kapoor 2950, MacArthur 2989, Mondelez 3034, Wrigley 3244
Indiana: Cummins 3292
Iowa: Pioneer 3474
Kansas: Lloyd 3530
Maryland: Hughes 3818
Massachusetts: Barr 3937, Cabot 3966, State 4285
Michigan: Lachimi 4480
Minnesota: Medtronic 4712, Mosaic 4722
Missouri: Monsanto 4945
Nevada: World 5160
New Jersey: Prudential 5415
New York: American 5588, Bloomberg 5684, Bristol 5711, Chatterjee 5765, Citi 5780, Krupa 6310, MetLife 6479, Neuberger 6538, PepsiCo 6627, Tandon 6963, Tsadra 7010
North Carolina: Oak 7276
Ohio: OMNOVA 7601, Timken 7683, Timken 7684
Oregon: Foreign 7846, Intel 7853, NIKE 7875
Pennsylvania: Heinz 8083, Pilgrim 8225
Tennessee: Westwood 8644
Texas: Dell 8805, Jiv 8933, Oldham 9069, Rees-Jones 9125, Whole 9276
Virginia: ICE 9456, Trehan 9544
Washington: Foundation 9622, Vista 9756

Indonesia
California: Mattel 886
Colorado: Western 1521
Illinois: Mondelez 3034
Iowa: Pioneer 3474
Massachusetts: Cabot 3966, China 3982
Michigan: Foundation 4432
Missouri: Monsanto 4945
New York: Citi 5780
Oregon: Vibrant 7898
Texas: Caris 8749, Whole 9276

Iraq
Massachusetts: Reynolds 4238

Ireland
Illinois: Baxter 2690, Wrigley 3244
Massachusetts: State 4285
Minnesota: Medtronic 4712
New Jersey: McMullen 5378
New York: Citi 5780, Curran 5835
Texas: A Glimmer 8649

Israel
California: Applied 249, Berman 311, Broadcom 349, Davis 455,

Italy

Jamaica

Japan

Jordan

Kazakhstan

Kenya

Kosovo

Kuwait

Kyrgyz Republic

Laos

Latin America

Latvia

Lebanon

Lesotho

Liberia

Lithuania

Luxembourg

Macedonia

Malawi

Malaysia

Mexico

Middle East

New York: Arcus 5608, Clark 5785, Dodge 5892, Ford 5994, Goldman 6070, Hauser 6147, JPMorgan 6244, Olayan 6585, Slifka 6870
Pennsylvania: PPG 8235
Tennessee: Maclellan 8601
Virginia: Mustard 9492
Washington: Starbucks 9742

Moldova
New York: Lauder 6336, Trust 7009
North Carolina: Oak 7276

Mongolia
New York: Trust 7009

Montenegro
New York: Rockefeller 6723, Trust 7009

Morocco
Colorado: Western 1521
New York: Citi 5780
South Dakota: Opus 8518

Mozambique
California: Gilead 586
Idaho: Gorongosa 2631
Minnesota: Mortenson 4721

Myanmar
California: Kee 776
North Carolina: Oak 7276

Namibia
Delaware: Jolie-Pitt 1791
Massachusetts: Grand 4076
New York: Flowers 5990
Ohio: Noble 7592

Nepal
California: McConnell 898
Massachusetts: Hunt 4102
New York: Simons 6860, Tsadra 7010
Texas: Whole 9276

Netherlands
California: Sea 1131, Thiel 1249
Illinois: Foundation 2839
Kansas: Lloyd 3530
Massachusetts: Cabot 3966, State 4285
Minnesota: Medtronic 4712, Youth 4809
New York: American 5588, Citi 5780
Washington: Channel 9597, Jain 9654
Wisconsin: Schneider 9942

New Zealand
Colorado: Western 1521
New York: Aotearoa 5602, Citi 5780, Commonwealth 5800

Nicaragua
Minnesota: Mortenson 4721
New York: Citi 5780
Ohio: Noble 7592
Texas: Whole 9276

Niger
Oregon: Vibrant 7898

Nigeria
Colorado: Western 1521
District of Columbia: NDPI 1935
Illinois: MacArthur 2989
New York: Citi 5780
Oregon: NIKE 7875
Tennessee: Ezell 8564

North Korea
Massachusetts: China 3982
New Jersey: Prudential 5415

Norway
California: ResMed 1063
Connecticut: Halvorsen 1606
Massachusetts: Cabot 3966
New York: Citi 5780

Oceania
California: Packard 1006
Missouri: Monsanto 4945
New York: Claiborne 5783

Pakistan
California: Al-Ameen 225
Colorado: Western 1521
Maryland: Shared 3882
New York: Citi 5780, Edhi 5934

Panama
Florida: Peterson 2267
Maryland: Shared 3882
New York: Citi 5780

Papua New Guinea
California: Christensen 399
Maryland: Shared 3882

Paraguay
Missouri: Monsanto 4945
New York: Citi 5780
Oregon: NIKE 7875

Peru
California: Fund 556
Colorado: Western 1521
Connecticut: Hampshire 1608
Maryland: Shared 3882
Massachusetts: Grand 4076
Minnesota: Oswald 4735
New York: Citi 5780, Deutsche 5876, JPMorgan 6244, MetLife 6479
Texas: Whole 9276
Washington: Foundation 9622

Philippines
Arizona: Hickey 121
California: Jerome 749, Wade 1293
Colorado: Western 1521
District of Columbia: CityBridge 1892
Georgia: Coca 2428, UPS 2566
Illinois: Mondelez 3034
Iowa: Pioneer 3474
Massachusetts: China 3982
Missouri: Monsanto 4945
New York: Alvarez 5584, Citi 5780
Texas: BP 8718, Caris 8749, International 8927
Wisconsin: Wagner 9961

Poland
California: Mattel 886
Illinois: Motorola 3043
Iowa: Ochylski 3470
Maryland: Hughes 3818
Massachusetts: State 4285
Minnesota: Medtronic 4712
New York: Citi 5780, Lauder 6336, Trust 7009
Ohio: Timken 7683, Timken 7684
Pennsylvania: Copernicus 7998, Rosenstiel 8254

Portugal
Minnesota: Medtronic 4712
New York: Citi 5780

Qatar
Massachusetts: State 4285
New York: Citi 5780

Romania
Colorado: Western 1521
Delaware: Adobe 1734
New York: Citi 5780, Lauder 6336, Trust 7009
Ohio: Timken 7683, Timken 7684

Russia
Colorado: Western 1521
Georgia: Coca 2428
Illinois: Bright 2714, MacArthur 2989, Mondelez 3034
Maryland: Hughes 3818, Thalheimer 3894
Massachusetts: Rudyak 4251
Michigan: Mott 4510
Minnesota: Medtronic 4712
New Mexico: Thaw 5534
New York: Carnegie 5747, Citi 5780, Trust 7009, Weeden 7060
North Carolina: Oak 7276
Oregon: Intel 7853
Pennsylvania: Alcoa 7908
Rhode Island: Ryan 8433

Rwanda
Idaho: Schultz 2641
Massachusetts: Hunt 4102, Ruettgers 4252
Michigan: Williams 4586
New Jersey: Segal 5446

Scotland
Georgia: Imlay 2487
Illinois: Driehaus 2805
Michigan: Myers 4515
Ohio: Patterson 7613

Senegal
Minnesota: Mortenson 4721
New York: Citi 5780

Serbia
New York: Rockefeller 6723, Trust 7009

Sierra Leone
Maine: Catalyst 3682
Minnesota: Mortenson 4721

Singapore
California: Applied 249, Broadcom 349, Wong 1342
Idaho: Micron 2637
Illinois: Motorola 3043
Massachusetts: China 3982, State 4285
New York: American 5588, Citi 5780

Slovakia
Maryland: Hughes 3818
New York: Citi 5780, Lauder 6336, Trust 7009

Slovenia
New York: Trust 7009

Somalia
Pennsylvania: Diiriye 8011

South Africa
California: Bickerstaff 313, Gilead 586, Kaiser 760
Colorado: Western 1521
District of Columbia: CityBridge 1892
Georgia: UPS 2566
Indiana: Cummins 3292
Maryland: Hughes 3818
Massachusetts: Karp 4117, State 4285
Michigan: Mott 4510
Minnesota: Gallagher 4660, Medtronic 4712
Missouri: Monsanto 4945
New York: Bristol 5711, Citi 5780, Gould 6086, Mellon 6470, NBI 6532
Ohio: Noble 7592, Timken 7683, Timken 7684

South America
California: Foundation 542, Smith 1189
Connecticut: Praxair 1676
Georgia: Georgia 2469
Illinois: Terra 3186
Indiana: West 3404
Massachusetts: Garfield 4065, Grand 4076
New Mexico: Aurora 5515
New York: Claiborne 5783
North Carolina: Oak 7276
Pennsylvania: Alcoa 7908
Virginia: Blue 9394, Mustard 9492
Washington: Gates 9625
Wisconsin: Wagner 9961

South Korea
California: Applied 249, Broadcom 349, Kim 785
Delaware: Marks 1813
Massachusetts: China 3982, State 4285
New Jersey: Prudential 5415
New York: Citi 5780, MBK 6452, MetLife 6479

South Sudan
Texas: Radler 9118

Southeastern Asia
California: Open 986, Stamps 1210
Connecticut: GE 1591
District of Columbia: Banyan 1881
Massachusetts: China 3982
New York: Arcus 5608, Luce 6398, Open 6593, Rockefeller 6724
Virginia: Loyola 9471

Southern Africa
Illinois: Klaff 2961
Michigan: Kellogg 4474
New York: NBI 6532

Southern Asia
California: Hewlett 686, Packard 1006, Stamps 1210

Soviet Union
Connecticut: Richardson 1679
District of Columbia: Wallace 1955
Maryland: Weinberg 3908

Spain
California: Broadcom 349, Mattel 886
Illinois: Mondelez 3034
Massachusetts: Cabot 3966
Minnesota: Medtronic 4712
New York: American 5588, Citi 5780, de Rothschild 5857, Vicente 7029
North Carolina: Carlson 7172

Sri Lanka
California: Sangiacomo 1115
Massachusetts: Hunt 4102
New York: Citi 5780, Gorman 6083

Sub-Saharan Africa
California: Firelight 529, Hewlett 686, Packard 1006
Connecticut: GE 1591
Massachusetts: Barr 3937
New Jersey: Segal 5446
New York: Bristol 5711, Carnegie 5747

Sudan
Massachusetts: Hunt 4102

Swaziland
New York: Bristol 5711

Sweden
California: Lund 857, ResMed 1063
Minnesota: Medtronic 4712
New York: Citi 5780
Ohio: Generation 7470

Switzerland
California: Foundation 543
District of Columbia: Wyss 1959
Illinois: Harder 2891
Maryland: Hughes 3818
Massachusetts: Cabot 3966, State 4285
Minnesota: Medtronic 4712
New York: Bloomberg 5684, Citi 5780, de Rothschild 5857, Glades 6056, International 6211, Polo 6651
North Carolina: Oak 7276
Texas: Levant 8981
Virginia: Friends 9437

Taiwan
California: Agilent 220, Applied 249, Broadcom 349, KLA-Tencor 792, Sun 1227
Maryland: Hughes 3818
Massachusetts: China 3982, State 4285
New Jersey: Prudential 5415, Yin 5507
New York: American 5588, Bristol 5711, Citi 5780
Virginia: Scheidel 9528

Tajikistan
California: Christensen 399
New York: Trust 7009
Texas: Merali 9022

Tanzania
California: Wade 1293
Florida: DeMoss 2059, Jaffer 2168
Idaho: Schultz 2641
Illinois: Abbott 2649
Maryland: Smith 3886
Massachusetts: Grand 4076
Minnesota: Better 4614, King 4687, McKnight 4709, Mortenson 4721, Oswald 4735
New Jersey: Segal 5446
New York: Bristol 5711, Citi 5780
North Carolina: Oak 7276
Oregon: NIKE 7875
Pennsylvania: Heinz 8083

Thailand
California: Leonard 830, Mattel 886
Massachusetts: China 3982, Grand 4076
Missouri: Monsanto 4945
New York: Bristol 5711, Citi 5780
Ohio: OMNOVA 7601
Texas: Whole 9276
Washington: Haugland 9643

Timor-Leste
Texas: Tingari-Silverton 9235

Trinidad and Tobago
New York: Citi 5780

Turkey
California: Christensen 399
Iowa: Pioneer 3474
Massachusetts: Grand 4076
Minnesota: Gallagher 4660
New York: Citi 5780
Oregon: Intel 7853

Turkmenistan
New York: Trust 7009

Uganda
Colorado: Western 1521
District of Columbia: Wolf 1957
Florida: DeMoss 2059
Maryland: Hughes 3818
Minnesota: McKnight 4709, Oswald 4735
Missouri: Monsanto 4945
New Jersey: Segal 5446
New York: Citi 5780
North Carolina: Oak 7276
Oregon: NIKE 7875
Texas: Rees-Jones 9125
Utah: Nu 9340
Washington: Luke 9674, Vista 9756

Ukraine
Illinois: Heritage 2907
Maryland: Hughes 3818
Massachusetts: Rudyak 4251
Michigan: Mott 4510
New York: Citi 5780, Lauder 6336, Trust 7009

United Arab Emirates
Colorado: Western 1521
Massachusetts: Cabot 3966
New York: Citi 5780

United Kingdom
California: Broadcom 349, Google 615, Mattel 886, Pyott 1047, Swift 1230, Thiel 1249
District of Columbia: Butler 1889, Lounsbery 1926
Illinois: Mondelez 3034
Iowa: Rockwell 3477
Kansas: Lloyd 3530
Maryland: Hughes 3818
Massachusetts: Hendrickson 4093, Foundation 4107, State 4285
Michigan: Kellogg 4473, Kellogg's 4475, Moller 4506
Minnesota: Medtronic 4712
Missouri: Enterprise 4887, Monsanto 4945
New Jersey: Crane 5235
New Mexico: Thaw 5534
New York: American 5588, Belvedere 5661, Citi 5780, Commonwealth 5800, Diamond 5881, Goldman 6070, Iris 6213, Lehman 6346, New 6551, PepsiCo 6627, St. George's 6904, Tanaka 6961, Towerbrook 7001, Unbound 7016
Ohio: 58 7362, Timken 7684
Texas: BP 8718, Notsew 9064
Virginia: Bosack 9395, Gannett 9439
Washington: Jain 9654, Starbucks 9742

Uruguay
Maryland: Hughes 3818
Missouri: Monsanto 4945
New York: Citi 5780

Uzbekistan
New York: Trust 7009

Vanuatu
California: Christensen 399

Venezuela
Florida: Vollmer 2373
Maryland: Hughes 3818
Massachusetts: Cabot 3966
New York: Citi 5780
Texas: Bolivar 8708

Vietnam
Idaho: Schultz 2641
Massachusetts: Alchemy 3920
Minnesota: McKnight 4709
New York: Citi 5780

Wales
Massachusetts: Cabot 3966

West Bank/Gaza (Palestinian Territories)
Arizona: Hickey 121
Idaho: Schultz 2641
New York: Sparkplug 6894

Zambia
Michigan: Fisher 4423
Minnesota: Mortenson 4721
New Jersey: Segal 5446
New York: Citi 5780, Flowers 5990
Oregon: NIKE 7875
Texas: Caris 8749

Zimbabwe
California: Gilead 586
Massachusetts: Grand 4076
New York: Bristol 5711, Flowers 5990
Pennsylvania: Pilgrim 8225

TYPES OF SUPPORT INDEX

List of terms: Terms for the major types of support used in this index are listed below with definitions.

Index: In the index itself, foundation entries are arranged under each term by state location, abbreviated name, and sequence number. Foundations in boldface type make grants on a national or international basis. The others generally limit giving to the state or city in which they are located.

Advocacy: cash grants for services related to advocacy, including advocating for better assistance in various program areas (for example school reform, full access to health care, legal reform, environmental clean-up work, etc.) and providing assistance in planning advocacy campaigns.

Annual campaigns: any organized effort by a nonprofit to secure gifts on an annual basis; also called annual appeals.

Building/renovation: money raised for construction, renovation, remodeling, or rehabilitation of buildings; may be part of an organization's capital campaign.

Camperships: funding to organizations to provide partial or full tuition subsidies to enable participants who would not otherwise be financially able to participate in fee-based camping programs.

Capital campaigns: a campaign, usually extending over a period of years, to raise substantial funds for enduring purposes, such as building or endowment funds.

Cause-related marketing: linking gifts to charity with marketing promotions. This may involve donating products which will then be auctioned or given away in a drawing with the proceeds benefiting a charity. The advertising campaign for the product will be combined with the promotion for the charity. In other cases it will be advertised that when a customer buys the product a certain amount of the proceeds will be donated to charity. Often gifts made to charities stemming from cause-related marketing are not called charitable donations and may be assigned as expenses to the department in charge of the program. Public affairs and marketing are the departments usually involved.

Computer technology: grants to acquire, upgrade or develop computer technology. Includes hardware, software, peripherals, systems, networking components and mobile devices.

Conferences/seminars: a grant to cover the expenses of holding a conference or seminar.

Consulting services: professional staff support provided by the foundation to a nonprofit to consult on a project of mutual interest or to evaluate services (not a cash grant).

Continuing support: a grant that is renewed on a regular basis.

Curriculum development: grants to schools, colleges, universities, and educational support organizations to develop general or discipline-specific curricula.

Debt reduction: also known as deficit financing. A grant to reduce the recipient organization's indebtedness; frequently refers to mortgage payments.

Donated equipment: surplus furniture, office machines, paper, appliances, laboratory apparatus, or other items that may be given to charities, schools, or hospitals.

Donated land: land or developed property. Institutions of higher education often receive gifts of real estate; land has also been given to community groups for housing development or for parks or recreational facilities.

Donated products: companies giving away what they make or produce. Product donations can include periodic clothing donations to a shelter for the homeless or regular donations of pharmaceuticals to a health clinic resulting in a reliable supply.

Emergency funds: a one-time grant to cover immediate short-term funding needs on an emergency basis.

Employee matching gifts: a contribution to a charitable organization by a corporate employee which is matched by a similar contribution from the employer. Many corporations support employee matching gift programs in higher education to stimulate their employees to give to the college or university of their choice. In addition, many foundations support matching gift programs for their officers and directors.

Employee volunteer services: an ongoing coordinated effort through which the company promotes involvement with nonprofits on the part of employees. The involvement may be during work time or after hours. (Employees may also volunteer on their own initiative; however, that is not described as corporate volunteerism). Many companies honor their employees with awards for outstanding volunteer efforts. In making cash donations, many favor the organizations with which their employees have worked as volunteers. Employee volunteerism runs the gamut from school tutoring programs to sales on work premises of employee-made crafts or baked goods to benefit nonprofits. Management of the programs can range from fully-staffed offices of corporate volunteerism to a part-time coordinating responsibility on the part of one employee.

Employee-related scholarships: a scholarship program funded by a company-sponsored foundation usually for children of employees; programs are frequently administered by the National Merit Scholarship Corporation which is responsible for selection of scholars.

Endowments: a bequest or gift intended to be kept permanently and invested to provide income for continued support of an organization.

Equipment: a grant to purchase equipment, furnishings, or other materials.

Exchange programs: usually refers to funds for educational exchange programs for foreign students.

Faculty/staff development: grants to institutions or organizations to train or further educate staff or faculty members

Fellowships: usually indicates funds awarded to educational institutions to support fellowship programs. A few foundations award fellowships directly to individuals.

Film/video/radio: grants to fund a specific film, video, or radio production.

General/operating support: a grant made to further the general purpose or work of an organization, rather than for a specific purpose or project; also called unrestricted grants.

Grants to individuals: awards made directly by the foundation to individuals rather than to nonprofit organizations; includes aid to the needy. (See also "Fellowships," "Scholarships—to individuals," and "Student loans—to individuals.")

In-kind gifts: a contribution of equipment, supplies, or other property as distinct from a monetary grant. Some organizations may also donate space or staff time as an in-kind contribution.

Income development: grants for fundraising, marketing, and to expand audience base.

Internship funds: usually indicates funds awarded to an institution or organization to support an internship program rather than a grant to an individual.

Land acquisition: a grant to purchase real estate property.

Lectureships: see "Curriculum development."

Loaned talent: an aspect of employee volunteerism. It differs from the usual definition of such in that it usually involves loaned professionals and executive staff who are helping a nonprofit in an area involving their particular skills. Loaned talents can assist a nonprofit in strategic planning, dispute resolution or negotiation services, office administration, real estate technical assistance, personnel policies, lobbying, consulting, fundraising, and legal and tax advice.

Loans: see "Program-related investments/ loans" and "Student loans—to individuals."

Loans—to individuals: assistance distributed directly to individuals in the form of loans.

Management development/capacity building: grants for salaries, staff support, staff training, strategic and long-term planning, capacity building, budgeting and accounting.

Matching/challenge support: a grant which is made to match funds provided by another donor. (See also "Employee matching gifts.")

Mission-related investments/loans: Market-rate loans or other investments (as distinguished from grants) to organizations to finance projects related to the foundation's stated charitable purpose and interests. Organizations invested in may be for-profit entities.

Operating budgets: see "General/operating support."

Pro bono services: pro bono services rendered by a company, professional services firm, intermediary,association or individual professional leveraging the core competencies and expertise of the professional(s) engaged to meet the client's need.

Pro bono services-advocacy: pro bono consulting assistance related to advocacy, including advocating for better services in various program areas (for example school reform, full access to health care, legal reform, environmental clean-up work, etc.) and providing assistance in planning advocacy campaigns that will follow current legal guidelines preventing certain kinds of advocacy by nonprofits

Pro bono services-board: pro bono consulting assistance in board effectiveness assessment, board recruitment process design, board reporting, meeting facilitation, executive coaching, and performance review.

Pro bono services-communications/public relations: pro bono consulting assistance in external communications and public relations, including but not limited to assistance with the development of an annual report, brochure, newsletter design, and/or public service announcement.

Pro bono services-financial management: pro bono consulting assistance in financial management, including but not limited to program cost analysis, financial audit, financial controls assessment and design, budgeting process design, pricing strategy, and purchase and supply chain audit.

Pro bono services-fundraising: Pro bono consulting assistance in programs or projects directly relating to fundraising. These may include event planning and production, executive fundraising coaching, donor segmentation, in-kind opportunity assessment, capital campaign design and management, and the development of capital campaign materials.

Pro bono services-human resources: pro bono consulting assistance in the area of human resources, including a strategic assessment and recommendations for a human resources plan, organizational diversity plan, performance management system, back office systems implementation, staff compensation and incentive plan, staff training and development plan, and an internal communications plan.

Pro bono services-interactive/website technology: pro bono consulting assistance in website technology, including the design and development of a basic website, interactive website, intranet, and extranet.

Pro bono services-legal: pro bono consulting assistance in the area of legal support, including donation of legal services in court situations, review of various legal documents, including those related to incorporation and other law, justice, and counsel issues.

Pro bono services-marketing/branding: pro bono consulting assistance in marketing and branding. Programs or projects may cover issues such as a program marketing, organizational positioning and key messages, visual identity or re-naming.

Pro bono services-medical: pro bono consulting assistance in the medical area, including donation of medical services and equipment.

Pro bono services-strategic management: pro bono consulting assistance in the area of strategic management, including the development of a strategic plan, refined mission, environmental and sustainability policy and plan, internal capacity assessment, strengths, weaknesses, opportunities, and threats analysis, competitive analysis, earned income business plan, geographic expansion plan, and logic model design

Pro bono services-technology infrastructure: pro bono consulting assistance in technology infrastructure such as donor database implementation, the development of an organizational IT plan, installation of office networking, remote IT access set up, and program database implementation.

Professorships: a grant to an educational institution to endow a professorship or chair.

Program development: grants to support specific projects or programs as opposed to general purpose grants.

Program evaluation: grants to evaluate a specific project or program; includes awards both to agencies to pay for evaluation costs and to research institutes and other program evaluators.

Program-related investments/loans: a loan is any temporary award of funds that must be repaid. A program-related investment is a loan or other investment (as distinguished from a grant) made by a foundation to another organization for a project related to the foundation's stated charitable purpose and interests.

Public relations services: may include printing and duplicating, audio-visual and graphic arts services, helping to plan special events such as festivals, piggyback advertising (advertisements that mention a company while also promoting a nonprofit), and public service advertising.

Publication: a grant to fund reports or other publications issued by a nonprofit resulting from research or projects of interest to the foundation.

Renovation projects: see "Building/renovation."

Research: usually indicates funds awarded to institutions to cover costs of investigations and clinical trials. Research grants for individuals are usually referred to as fellowships.

Scholarship funds: a grant to an educational institution or organization to support a scholarship program, mainly for students at the undergraduate level. (See also "Employee-related scholarships.")

Scholarships—to individuals: assistance awarded directly to individuals in the form of educational grants or scholarships. (See also "Employee-related scholarships.")

Seed money: a grant or contribution used to start a new project or organization. Seed grants may cover salaries and other operating expenses of a new project. Also known as "start-up funds."

Special projects: see "Program development."

Sponsorships: endorsements of charities by corporations; or corporate contributions to all or part of a charitable event.

Student aid: see "Fellowships," "Scholarships—to individuals," and "Student loans—to individuals."

Student loans—to individuals: assistance awarded directly to individuals in the form of educational loans.

Technical assistance: operational or management assistance given to nonprofit organizations; may include fundraising assistance, budgeting and financial planning, program planning, legal advice, marketing, and other aids to management. Assistance may be offered directly by a foundation staff member or in the form of a grant to pay for the services of an outside consultant.

Travel awards: funding to organizations to provide awards to individuals to cover transportation and/or out-of-town living expenses while attending a conference or completing a period of studt or special project. Enrollment in a college or university is not a requirement.

Use of facilities: this may include rent free office space for temporary periods, dining and meeting facilities, telecommunications services, mailing services, transportation services, or computer services.

Advocacy

California: Ross 1090, Small 1180
Georgia: Community 2432
Illinois: Allegretti 2655, Oak Park 3061
Indiana: Duneland 3297
Nebraska: Cooper 5031
Texas: Fath 8840

Annual campaigns

Alabama: BBVA 9, Brock 13, Friedman 35, Hess 39, Kaul 43, Protective 59, Smith 66, Vulcan 73, Webb 76

Arizona: Freeport-McMoRan 112, Globe 115, Green 117, **Kieckhefer 129**, Mooney 146, Stewart 166

Arkansas: Cabe 182, Endeavor 186, Frueauff 188, Jonsson 192, Murphy 193

California: Applied 249, Aratani 250, Atlas 266, Bechtel 294, Bechtel, 296, Bengier 304, Boswell 330, Bowes 334, Brenner 340, Center 388, Clif 405, Community 414, Community 417, Davidson 453, Desert 461, Disney 467, Dolby 474, Eisenberg 498, Eucalyptus 510, Foothills 537, Garb 564, Garland 565, **Geffen 567**, Gellert 568, Getty 578, GGS 580, Goldman 605, Goldsmith 608, Goldwyn 609, Gruber 632, Haas 641, Hofmann 700, Hutton 718, Jacobs 738, JL 751, Jones 755, Koret 801, Laural 823, Littlefield 844, Lucas 855, Maxfield 887, Mendelson 912, Moore 937, Morgan 940, Norris 971, Outhwaite 1000, Parker 1012, Philibosian 1036, Price 1043, Reid 1060, **ResMed 1063**, **Saban 1101**, Simpson 1173, Smith 1187, Sorensen 1200, Synopsys 1232, Taper 1237, Ueberroth 1268, **Vadasz 1275**, Wells 1312, Wood 1344

Colorado: Community 1391, Community 1395, Daniels 1399, **Gill 1421**, Halton 1426, Lipscomb 1449, Peierls 1475, Price 1484, Saeman 1490, Shamos 1498, Summit 1511, Telluride 1512, Yampa 1528

Connecticut: Baldwin 1541, Barnes 1542, Community 1562, Culpeper 1568, Garden 1590, Hubbell 1614, JJJ 1618, Larsen 1624, Meriden 1643, Neuberger 1649, Ohnell 1661, Rockville 1682, Rogow 1683, Rosenthal 1684, Zachs 1730, **Ziegler 1731**

Delaware: **Adobe 1734**, **AstraZeneca 1738**, Bennett 1739, CenturyLink-Clarke 1750, Crestlea 1757, Duane 1771, Griswold 1787, Laffey 1800, Lennox 1805, McDonald 1817, **Memton 1819**, Schwartz 1857, Sylvan 1867, Tapeats 1868

District of Columbia: Aid 1879, Bender 1885, Bernstein 1887, Gewirz 1909, Kiplinger 1922, Loughran 1925, Zients 1960

Florida: Beaver 1986, **Believers 1989**, Bi-Lo 1996, Brown 2004, Burns 2006, **Chester 2020**, Community 2041, Engelberg 2086, Gooding 2130, Greenburg 2137, Haller 2146, Indian 2166, **Katz 2177**, Klorfine 2188, Rayonier 2281, **Russell 2301**, Ryder 2302, Sack 2303, Straz 2341, SWS 2347, Thomas 2357, Watts 2380, Wollowick 2393

Georgia: Aflac 2399, AGL 2400, Callaway 2419, Camp-Younts 2421, Colonial 2430, Community 2434, Cousins 2442, Cox 2446, DuBose 2450, Franklin 2462, Georgia 2468, **Georgia 2469**, Harrison 2481, **Imlay 2487**, Knox 2498, Mohawk 2517, Moore 2519, Moore 2520, Rich 2537, Rollins 2542, Sapelo 2546, Southern 2554, Synovus 2556, Wilson 2576, Woolley 2581, Zeist 2584

Hawaii: Atherton 2586, Bank 2588, First 2598

Idaho: Blue 2627, Wishnick 2646

Illinois: Alsdorf 2659, Andrew 2661, Blair 2699, Brach 2712, Brunner 2718, Butler 2729, Caterpillar 2738, Charleston 2742, Circle 2749, Clinton 2754, CME 2755, Crown 2781, **Deere 2790**, Dillon 2796, Donnelley 2802, Duchossois 2809, Dunard 2810, Emerson 2822, Franke 2841, Frankel 2842, Gray 2878, Halligan 2886, Hansen 2889, Harris 2892, Hermann 2908, Illinois 2934, Keith 2952, King 2960, Logan 2983, Louis 2985, Lumpkin 2986, Mallinckrodt 2995, McGraw 3015, Northern 3059, Potishman 3086, Reed 3109, Souder 3168, Speh 3170, Stuart 3182, Tracy 3189, United 3199, United 3200, White 3229, Woodward 3243

Indiana: **Ackerman 3252**, Anderson 3255, Ball 3262, Brotherhood 3268, Central 3272, Crown Point 3291, **Cummins 3292**, DeHaan 3294, Fairbanks 3301, Ford 3305, Huntington 3324, Jordan 3331, Koch 3334, **Lilly 3340**, **Lilly 3342**, Miller 3355, Montgomery 3356, Noyes 3361, Rolland 3381, Samerian 3384, Simon 3386, Tipton 3391, Waterfield 3399, West 3404

Iowa: Guernsey 3437, Kuyper 3456, Maytag 3460, Meredith 3463, Meredith 3464, MidAmerican 3465, Principal 3476

Kansas: Beren 3496, Capitol 3498, Hutchinson 3521, McPherson 3534, Security 3544, Sprint 3549, Sunderland 3551, Topeka 3552

Kentucky: Brown 3562, Brown 3564, Community 3569, Community 3570, Humana 3582, LG&E 3586, Spray 3602, Yum! 3608

Louisiana: Albemarle 3609, Community 3623, Freeman 3636, Goldring 3638, Huie 3643, Jones 3645, RosaMary 3663

Maine: Alfond 3678, Alfond 3679, Bangor 3680, Lunder 3697, TD 3710

Maryland: **Bearman 3728**, Blades 3734, **Cohen 3754**, Davis 3772, Delaplaine 3778, **England 3785**, **Ewing 3787**, Foundation 3794, Freeman 3797, Gudelsky 3809, Henson 3814, Hirschhorn 3816, Jacobsohn 3819, Levitt 3832, Linehan 3834, Meyerhoff 3848, Meyerhoff 3849, Millstream 3852, **Morningstar 3854**, Riepe 3869, Rollins 3872, Rosenberg 3873, Roswell 3876, Rouse 3877, Straus 3890, Washington 3904, Wasserman 3905

Massachusetts: Barker 3936, **Barr 3937**, Bayrd 3938, Berkshire 3946, Beveridge 3950, Cabot 3968, Cambridge 3972, Cape Cod 3974, Carney 3975, Davis 4011, Demoulas 4014, Donahue 4023, Eastern 4030, Ellsworth 4035, Evans 4040, Finch 4048, Fuller 4063, Grayson 4078, Grinspoon 4080, Highland 4098, Hopedale 4101, Institution 4108, Linde 4147, Miller 4177, Pappas 4204, Perkin 4213, **Phillips 4219**, Poss 4226, Proctor 4227, Rodgers 4242, Santander 4256, Shapiro 4267, Sharf 4268, Smith 4277, Stoddard 4293, Stoico 4294, Tupancy 4312

Michigan: Barry 4342, Chrysler 4366, Cook 4377, Dana 4386, Dart 4388, Davis 4391, DeRoy 4396, DeVos 4398, DeVos 4400, Dow 4408, Family 4418, **Fisher 4423**, Ford 4430, General 4442, Gerstacker 4444, Gilmore 4445, Granger 4449, Harding 4455, Herrick 4459, Hudson 4463, **Isabel 4466**, Leighton 4484, Masco 4497, Miller 4503, Monroe 4507, Oleson 4516, Pentecost 4520, Sage 4531, Shelden 4537, Spartan 4544, Towsley 4557, **Tubergen 4559**, Upton 4565, Van Andel 4567, VanderWeide 4572, Walker 4575, Weatherwax 4577, Wege 4579, Wickes 4585

Minnesota: **Andersen 4601**, Andersen 4603, Butler 4622, Buuck 4623, Carlson 4629, Charlson 4633, CHS 4636, Davis 4642, Deluxe 4644, Donaldson 4646, Frey 4658, **Fuller 4659**, Greystone 4668, Griggs 4669, Hardenbergh 4672, Hormel 4676, HRK 4677, Kelley 4686, Kopp 4688, Leonard 4694, Lilly 4696, Maas 4699, Marbrook 4702, Martin 4704, **Medtronic 4712**, Melrose 4713, Minnesota 4715, Minnesota 4716, Nelson 4726, Opus 4731, **O'Shaughnessy 4734**, RBC 4748, Regis 4750, Securian 4761, Sit 4765, Tozer 4782, Valspar 4786, Weyerhaeuser 4804, Winona 4806

Mississippi: C Spire 4817, Community 4820, Ergon 4824, Ford 4826, McLean 4835, McRae 4836, Mississippi 4839, Regions 4843, Walker 4849

Missouri: Ameren 4851, Brown 4862, Burns 4866, Centene 4870, Commerce 4871, Community 4872, Cox 4874, Cray 4876, Dierberg 4879, Edison 4883, H & R 4902, JSM 4918, Kemper 4926, Laclede 4931, Lichtenstein 4936, Lopata 4938, Millstone 4944, Musgrave 4947, Nestle 4948, Orscheln 4951, Pershing 4952, Pott 4958, Reynolds 4961, Shaw 4970, Sosland 4977, Stupp 4982, Ward 4998

Montana: Washington 5018

Nebraska: Ameritas 5023, Dunklau 5036, Fremont 5039, Kiewit 5056, Kind 5060, Lozier 5065, Nelnet 5072, Scoular 5080, Storz 5086

Nevada: **Browning 5104**, NV 5136, Parasol 5138

New Hampshire: Hunt 5177, Penates 5185

New Jersey: Atran 5197, Banbury 5200, Cowles 5234, **Crane 5235**, Firestone 5260, Goldberg 5279, Golden 5280, **Johnson 5326**, Karma 5331, Kirby 5339, McGraw 5376, OceanFirst 5394, Sudler 5472, Wallerstein 5494, Wilf 5502

New Mexico: Angelica 5514, Hubbard 5523, McCune 5529, New Mexico 5530, Santa Fe 5533

New York: Abeles 5544, Abrons 5546, Adirondack 5556, Allen 5573, Allyn 5575, American 5587, **American 5588**, Aron 5616, **Ashner 5619**, Bahnik 5634, Barker 5644, Barrington 5647, Barth 5648, Bayne 5653, Berg 5667, Botwinick 5696, Burns

5732, Charina 5763, Charina 5764, Community 5807, Curran 5835, Demartini 5872, Dewar 5879, Diamond 5880, **Diamond 5881**, Dillon 5885, Doolittle 5901, Dunwalke 5921, Dyson 5923, Emerson 5950, **Engelhard 5954**, Englander 5955, Fanwood 5968, Farash 5969, Fifth 5976, Fisher 5982, **Ford 5995**, Four 6006, Freed 6011, Galasso 6032, Gebbie 6038, Gerry 6043, Gilder 6050, Goldman 6068, Goldstein 6076, **Harriman 6136**, Harriman 6137, **Hauser 6147**, Hoerle 6180, Hughes 6193, Hultquist 6195, Icahn 6204, IFF 6206, Joelson 6232, Johnson 6239, Kaplan 6250, Katzenberger 6258, Kaufman 6259, Kautz 6260, Kennedy 6274, Kinney 6285, Klein 6289, Knapp 6296, **Kohlberg 6300**, Lang 6326, Lauder 6337, Lehman 6346, Lenna 6352, Loews 6388, Lubo 6396, **M & T 6406**, McCann 6453, McCarthy 6454, McGonagle 6460, Monell 6497, Monteforte 6498, **Moody's 6499**, Moore 6501, Morse 6509, Moses 6511, Mulford 6514, National 6526, **New 6551**, Normandie 6566, Northern 6567, NYSE 6573, O'Connor 6578, Ohrstrom 6582, Paley 6610, Phillips 6637, Picotte 6639, Price 6658, Raiff 6675, Rich 6697, Richmond 6703, Ritter 6712, Rose 6732, Rose 6737, Rubenstein 6762, Ruffin 6770, Schaffner 6800, Scherman 6804, Schiff 6805, Schmitt 6808, Schnurmacher 6809, Semlitz 6831, Sheldon 6841, **SMBC 6873**, Solomon 6885, Spingold 6899, Steel 6914, **Straus 6934**, Strypemonde 6936, Sulzberger 6942, Swyer 6956, Thompson 6975, **Towerbrook 7001**, Vetlesen 7027, Vidda 7030, **Vital 7033**, Wachenheim 7039, Wachtell, 7040, Warburg 7048, Weinberg 7066, Weissman 7071, **Wolfensohn 7098**

North Carolina: BB&T 7143, Belk 7148, BIN 7151, Blumenthal 7154, Bolick 7155, Broyhill 7160, Bryan 7161, Campbell 7168, Chatham 7175, Dover 7194, Duke 7196, Finley 7199, Goodrich 7213, Gorelick 7215, Greenville 7217, Hanes 7221, Hanes 7222, Leever 7253, Mebane 7266, Merancas 7267, Morgan 7269, Olin 7279, Piedmont 7285, Reynolds 7296, Southern 7319, Triangle 7328, Weaver 7335

North Dakota: MDU 7354, North Dakota 7357, Stern 7360

Ohio: AK Steel 7366, American 7369, Anderson 7372, Ar-Hale 7376, Ashtabula 7379, Budig 7392, Cliffs 7407, Codrington 7409, Dater 7426, Diamond 7435, Fifth 7452, Firman 7454, FirstEnergy 7455, Fox 7461, France 7462, GAR 7465, **Geisse 7468**, Gund 7477, Home 7489, Hoover 7492, Humphrey 7497, Jochum 7513, **Kettering 7520**, Kettering 7521, KeyBank 7523, Kramer 7529, Kulas 7532, Lennon 7537, Lubrizol 7546, Luther 7548, Macy's 7552, Maltz 7553, Marion 7558, Mather 7559, Mayerson 7561, Montgomery 7575, Moores 7576, Murch 7582, Murdough 7583, Murphy 7584, National 7586, Nationwide 7587, Nippert 7590, NiSource 7591, Nordson 7596, Ohio 7599, **OMNOVA 7601**, Parker 7611, Progressive 7623, Pulley 7624, Reinberger 7628, Salem 7640, Sherwin-Williams 7661, Smith 7668, St. Marys 7672, Tiffin 7682, Western 7710, Wodecroft 7717, Wolfe 7719, Wuliger 7722

Oklahoma: Adams 7725, American 7728, Bovaird 7735, Chapman 7739, Chapman 7740, Hille 7759, Kaiser 7763, Masonic 7771, McGee 7774, McMahon 7776, Meinders 7777, Nelson 7779, Oklahoma 7782, Oxley 7785, Puterbaugh 7786, Records 7788, **Schusterman 7794**, Southern 7798, Stone 7801, Tandy 7803, Tulsa 7807, Zarrow 7820, Zink 7821

Oregon: Benton 7825, Carpenter 7831, Esco 7841, Kinsman 7860, Macdonald 7866, Metolius 7869, PacifiCorp 7877, Schnitzer 7887, Schnitzer 7888, Tektronix 7894, Woodard 7899

Pennsylvania: 1675 7903, Air 7907, **Alcoa 7908**, Alexander 7910, Allerton 7912, Ametek 7913, Arcadia 7918, Arete 7919, Armstrong 7922, Baker 7926, Ball 7927, Beneficial 7936, Britton 7951, Buncher 7957, Cassett 7969, Centre 7973, Century 7974, CIGNA 7981, Clapp 7983, **Colcom 7986**, Colonial 7988, Community 7991, Drumcliff 8016, Federated 8033, Ferree 8036, Graham 8065, Grass 8068, Hamer 8077, Hamilton 8078, **Heinz 8083**, Hopwood 8096, Hoyt 8098, Hunt 8100, Hurd 8101, Huston 8103, Kavanagh 8118, Kelly 8119, Kline 8129, Lenfest 8138, Lindback 8142, **Little 8145**, Mandell 8153, Marshall 8155, Martin 8156, McFeely 8163, McKenna 8166, Mellon 8172, Mine 8184, Nichols 8197, O'Toole 8207, Plankenhorn 8229, Pottstown 8234, **PPG 8235**, Rangos 8244, Rees 8245, Roberts 8250, S & T 8259, Saint 8260, Stackpole 8295, Steinman 8299, Steinman 8300, Washington 8332, West 8334, Wheeler 8335, Willis 8340, Wyomissing 8350

Rhode Island: Amica 8356, Biogen 8363, Carter 8368, Charlesmead 8371, Daniels 8380, Freeman 8396, TriMix 8448, Vance 8450

South Carolina: Abney 8454, Roe 8494, Springs 8504

South Dakota: Larson 8516

Tennessee: Beaman 8534, Bridgestone 8537, Carlton 8541, Cook 8552, First 8565, Frist 8567, HCA 8582, Martin 8606, Stokely 8631, T & T 8632, Thompson 8636, Tucker 8638, Wilson 8646

Texas: Abell 8650, Austin 8676, Bass 8689, Bauer 8691, Bickel 8705, BNSF 8706, Boeckman 8707, Brown 8731, Cailloux 8742, Carter 8752, CFP 8758, CH 8759, Coates 8769, Cockrell 8770, Community 8775, Cullen 8792, Eady 8818, Fikes 8844, Fisch 8846, Fish 8848, Fleming 8850, Fluor 8851, Genecov 8862, Halliburton 8884, Halsell 8885, Hamill 8887, Hamman 8888, Herzstein 8905, Hirsch 8910, Hoglund 8913, **Houston 8916**, Houston 8917, Huffington 8920, Kempner 8952, Kilroy 8956, Kinder 8958, Kodosky 8966, Liatis 8983, Light 8984, Lightner 8985, Lyons 8996, Mankoff 8998, **Marshall 9000**, Martinez 9003, McDermott 9013, Miller 9028, Moore 9034, Moss 9043, Navarro 9054, O'Connor 9066, Once 9070, Owen 9076, Owsley 9078, Penney 9089, Puett 9114, Rosewood 9140, Sams 9145, San Antonio 9148, Scott 9161, Scurlock 9162, Shield 9170, Simmons 9174, Smith 9183, Smith 9184, Smith 9186, Sterling 9203, Stern 9204, Still 9207, Strake 9208, Stumberg 9210, Terry 9224, Texas 9227, Trull 9240, Tucker 9241, Vaughan 9248, Waggoner 9252, Wal 9254, Weaver 9260, Weekley 9264, Wortham 9292, Young 9295, Zachry 9296

Utah: Burton 9309, Dee 9312, Eccles 9319, Patel 9343

Vermont: Tarrant 9373

Virginia: ACT 9380, Community 9411, Dominion 9422, Kanter 9459, Landmark 9467, Mars 9477, Massey 9478, MeadWestvaco 9484, Norfolk 9496, Perry 9506, Reynolds 9519, SunTrust 9539, Titmus 9543, Universal 9548, Washington 9552

Washington: Bates 9582, Cameron 9593, Dimmer 9610, Everett 9616, Fuchs 9624, **Gates 9625**, Harder 9640, **Kongsgaard 9661**, Lucky 9673, McKinstry 9680, Milgard 9683, Norcliffe 9693, Oki 9694, PACCAR 9698, Shirley 9734

West Virginia: Daywood 9774, Eastern 9775, Maier 9782, McDonough 9784, Shott, 9794

Wisconsin: Alliant 9804, Argosy 9808, **Baird 9811**, Bemis 9815, **Bradley 9819**, Briggs 9822, Charter 9829, Cleary 9831, Cornerstone 9836, Evinrude 9841, Johnson 9870, Johnson 9874, Kelben 9877, Kikkoman 9881, Krause 9886, Kress 9887, Ladish 9890, Mead 9902, Neese 9911, Northwestern 9914, Oshkosh 9917, Peck 9918, Pettit 9919, Pick 9920, Roundy's 9936, Smith 9947, Stock 9953, U.S. 9957, Waukesha 9965, West 9967, Windhover 9968, Wisconsin 9970

Wyoming: Ellbogen 9977, Seeley 9990, Zimmerman 10000

Building/renovation

Alabama: Alabama 1, Bedsole 11, Community 21, Community 23, Community 24, Crampton 26, Dixon 30, Friedman 35, Hearin 38, Hess 39, Hill 40, Kaul 43, Meyer 53, Smith 66, Walker 74, Webb 76

Alaska: Rasmuson 89

Arizona: APS 91, Arizona 92, Globe 115, Green 117, **Hickey 121**, **Johnson 126**, Jones 127, **Kieckhefer 129**, Linde 135, Marshall 141, McDonald 144, Morris 148, Piper 152, Stewart 166, Webb 174

Arkansas: Cabe 182, Endeavor 186, Frueauff 188, Jonsson 192, Ross 199, Schmieding 200, Walker 209, White 212

California: **Agilent 220**, Ahmanson 222, Aratani 250, Ayrshire 276, Baxter 288, Beaver 292, Bechtel 294, Bechtel, 296, Bothin 331, Bowes 334, Campini 374, Carsey 380, Caruso 382, Center 388, Chandler 392, Collins 412, Community 414, Community 417, Copley 428, Cowell 434, Dachs 446, Darling 449, **DJ & T 469**, Doheny 473, Dolby 474, Eisner 499, Ellis 503, Eucalyptus 510, Factor 513, Finley 527, Firedoll 528, **Firelight 529**, **First 530**, Fremont 548, Garb 564, Garland 565, Gasser 566, Gellert 568, Gilmore 588, Gogian 598, Gold 600, Goldman 605, Goldman 606, Goldsmith 608, Gruber 632, GSF 633, Haas 641, Haas 642, Hannon 650, Hannon 651, Hayden 663, Hayward 665, Hedco 672, Herbst 682, Hewlett 687, **Hilton 692**, Hind 693, Hoag 697, Hope 702, Humboldt 714, Hutton 718, Irwin 728, Jackson 737, JL 751, Jones 756, **Keck 774**, Kern 780, **Kim 785**, Kvamme 807, LA84 809, Laural 823, Lesher 833, **Lingnan 841**, Littlefield 844, Long 847, Los Altos 849, Lucas 855, Ludwick 856, **Lund 857**, Lytel 860, Mabie 863, Marin 877, McBean 892, **McConnell 898**, McMillen 905, Mericos 918, Milken 926, Miller 929, Monroe 935, Monterey 936, Moore 937, Norris 971, Outhwaite 1000, Parker 1012, Parsons 1013, Pasadena 1015, Patron 1020, Perforce 1026, Peters 1028, PG&E 1033, Rancho 1053, **Saban 1101**, Sacramento 1103, Samuelsson 1107, San Luis 1110, Santa Barbara 1116, Severns 1143, Shasta 1154, Sobrato 1193, Sonora 1198, Sorensen 1200, Springcreek 1208, Stauffer 1214, Taper 1237, Taube 1241, Tuohy 1267, Ueberroth 1268, Valley 1280, Van Nuys 1284, Weingart 1307, Wohlford 1336, Wood 1344

Colorado: Animal 1363, Aspen 1368, Boettcher 1374, Bohemian 1375, Bonfils 1376, Buell 1381, Community 1391, Community 1395, Coors 1396, Daniels 1399, Denver 1401, Edmondson 1405, El Pomar 1406, Foundation 1411, Gates 1418, Griffin 1425, King 1440, Kitzmiller 1441, Lipscomb 1449, Marquez 1454, Ottens 1472, Rose 1487, Seay 1495, Summit 1511, **Western 1521**, Yampa 1528

Connecticut: 1772 1530, American 1537, Baldwin 1541, Barnes 1542, **Calder 1554**, Community 1562, Community 1563, Community 1564, Community 1565, Connecticut 1566, Culpeper 1568, Fund 1589, Garden 1590, Hartford 1609, Hubbell 1614, Huisking 1615, Liberty 1630, Main 1634, Matthies 1639, New Canaan 1650, NewAlliance 1651, Ohnell 1661, **Praxair 1676**, Rosenthal 1684, Zachs 1730

Delaware: AEC 1735, **Chichester 1754**, Crestlea 1757, Crystal 1758, Delaware 1765, Esperance 1777, Fair 1780, Griswold 1787, Laffey 1800, Lennox 1805, Longwood 1806, Marmot 1814, Matthews 1816, McDonald 1817, **Memton 1819**, Phillips 1835, **Raskob 1845**, Schwartz 1857, Tapeats 1868, Welfare 1872

District of Columbia: Aid 1879, Bender 1885, Gewirz 1909, Gottesman 1911, Gudelsky 1912, Kiplinger 1922

Florida: Amaturo 1966, Bank 1979, **Barbour 1980**, Baroco 1981, Bi-Lo 1996, Bush 2008, Columbus 2030, Community 2035, Community 2039, Community 2041, Conn 2042, **Davis 2056**, Duckwall 2069, Ebert 2079, Engelberg 2086, Goodes 2129, Gooding 2130, Hersh 2156, Hough 2162, Indian 2166, Kennedy 2182, Klorfine 2188, **Knight 2191**, Magruder 2225, Miami 2238, Pinellas 2269, Publix 2275, Quantum 2276, Rinker 2285, **Russell 2301**, Ryder 2302, Sack 2303, Saunders 2308, Selby 2316, Southwest 2327, St. Joe 2331, Straz 2341, Sylvester 2348, Thomas 2357, Watts 2380, Wells 2383

Georgia: AGL 2400, Amos 2401, Atlanta 2406, Bagwell 2407, Callaway 2418, Callaway 2419, Campbell 2420, Community 2433, Community 2435, Courts 2441, Cousins 2442, Cox 2446, Day 2448, DuBose 2450, English 2453, Equifax 2455, EZ 2456, Franklin 2462, **Georgia 2469, Hanley 2476**, Harland 2477, Harrison 2481, **Imlay 2487**, Knox 2498, Lanier 2499, Lockwood 2505, Loridans 2506, Mohawk 2517, Moore 2519, Moore 2520, Pitts 2529, Porter 2533, Rich 2537, Rollins 2543, Synovus 2556, **Thoresen 2557**, Tillotson-Menlo 2559, Trailsend 2560, Tull 2561, Watson 2569, Whitehead 2571, Williams 2572, Wilson 2576, Woodruff 2579, Woodward 2580, Woolley 2581, Zeist 2584

Hawaii: Atherton 2586, Bank 2588, Campbell 2592, Castle 2594, Ching 2596, Cooke 2597, First 2598, McInerny 2612, **Watumull 2620**, Wilcox 2621

Idaho: Cunningham 2630, Idaho 2632

Illinois: **Abbott 2649**, Andrew 2661, Arthur 2673, Bersted 2696, Blair 2699, Brach 2712, Brunner 2718, Butler 2729, Camp 2732, Caterpillar 2738, Chaddick 2740, Charleston 2742, Chicago 2746, Circle 2749, CME 2755, Coleman 2759, Community 2765, Community 2767, Crown 2781, Cuneo 2783, Day 2787, **Deere 2790**, DeKalb 2792, Dillon 2796, Donnelley 2802, DuPage 2812, Edwardsville 2817, Field 2831, Frankel 2842, **Grainger 2874**, Hamel 2887, Hansen 2889, Harris 2892, Hermann 2908, Hobbs 2914, Illinois 2933, Illinois 2934, Jackson 2937, Keith 2952, Kemper 2954, King 2960, Levi 2976, Logan 2983, Louis 2985, Martin 3003, Munson 3045, Northern 3059, Omron 3063, Payne 3073, Petersen 3078, Prentice 3088, Pritzker 3091, Reed 3109, Regenstein 3111, Souder 3168, Speh 3170, **Tellabs 3185**, Timken 3188, United 3200, Walter 3213, White 3230, **Woodbury 3240, Wrigley 3244**

Indiana: **Ackerman 3252**, Bales 3261, Ball 3262, Ball 3264, Blue 3265, Brotherhood 3268, Brown 3269, Central 3272, Clowes 3274, Cole 3276, Community 3278, Community 3280, Community 3281, Community 3283, Community 3284, Community 3285, Community 3286, Community 3288, Community 3289, Community 3290, **Cummins 3292**, Dearborn 3293, DeKalb 3295, Dekko 3296, Elkhart 3298, Fairbanks 3301, Finish 3303, Ford 3305, Foundations 3306, Froderman 3307, Harrison 3314, Hendricks 3319, Henry 3320, Heritage 3321, Huntington 3324, Johnson 3330, Jordan 3331, Koch 3334, Kosciusko 3335, Kosciusko 3336, Legacy 3337, **Lilly 3342**, Lincoln 3344, Madison 3346, Marshall 3348, McMillen 3352, Michigan 3354, Montgomery 3356, Noble 3359, Northern 3360, Ogle 3362, Orange 3365, Peabody 3368, Portland 3370, Putnam 3373, Rolland 3381, Steel 3389, Steuben 3390, Tipton 3391, Unity 3393, Wabash 3396, Washington 3398, Waterfield 3399, Welborn 3402, Wells 3403

Iowa: AEGON 3409, Ahrens 3410, Carver 3416, Cedar Rapids 3417, Clarinda 3418, Community 3420, Community 3423, Community 3424, Guernsey 3437, Hall-Perrine 3439, HNI 3443, Hubbell 3446, Iowa 3447, Kinney-Lindstrom 3451, Kuyper 3456, Lee 3457, Mansfield 3459, Maytag 3460, McElroy 3461, Meredith 3464, MidAmerican 3465, Pella 3473, Principal 3476, Ruan 3478, Siouxland 3480, Tye 3484, Vermeer 3486, Vogel 3487

Kansas: Baughman 3493, Beach 3494, Beren 3496, Capitol 3498, Cooper 3503, Delta 3507, Douglas 3509, Dreiling 3511, Garvey 3516, Hansen 3518, INTRUST 3522, McPherson 3534, Rice 3538, Sunderland 3551, Topeka 3552, Wyandotte 3556

Kentucky: Blue 3560, Brown 3563, Brown 3564, Community 3569, Cralle 3571, Foundation 3575, Gheens 3577, Horn 3581, Humana 3582, LG&E 3586, Orleton 3594, Preston 3596, Robinson 3598, Young 3607

Louisiana: Albemarle 3609, Baton Rouge 3613, Beaird 3614, Booth 3616, Burden 3618, Community 3623, Community 3624, Coughlin 3626, Diboll 3628, Entergy 3630, Freeman 3636, Goldring 3638, Huie 3643, Jones 3645, Libby-Dufour 3648, Pennington 3659, Reily 3661, RosaMary 3663, Wilson 3671, **Woldenberg 3672**, Woolf 3673, Zigler 3676

Maine: Alfond 3678, Bangor 3680, Hannaford 3690, King 3694, Libra 3696, Morton 3701, **Sandy 3707**

Maryland: Abell 3712, **Ames 3720**, Baker 3724, Blades 3734, **Blaustein 3735**, Clark 3751, **Cohen 3754**, Community 3758, Community 3759, Davis 3772, Dresher 3782, Eaton 3784, **England 3785**, Fowler 3795, France 3796, **Grace 3807**, Gudelsky 3809, Hahn 3811, Henson 3814, **Hughes 3818**, Jacobsohn 3819, Kerr 3823, Knott 3826, Leidy 3830, Linehan 3834, Meyerhoff 3848, Meyerhoff 3849, Middendorf 3850, Mid-Shore 3851, Rembrandt 3868, Riepe 3869, Rollins 3872, Rosenberg 3873, Rouse 3877, Sheridan 3883, **Smith 3886**, Straus 3890, **Thalheimer 3894**, Trone 3899, Wasserman 3905, **Weinberg 3908**

Massachusetts: Alden 3921, Barker 3936, **Barr 3937**, Bayrd 3938, Berkman 3945, Berkshire 3948, Beveridge 3950, Bristol 3960, **Cabot 3966**, Cabot 3968, Cape Cod 3973, Charlesbank 3980, Clipper 3987, Community 3991, Community 3992, Danversbank 4009, Davis 4011, DentaQuest 4016, Dusky 4028, Eastern 4030, Ellsworth 4035, Farnsworth 4043, Finch 4048, Fletcher 4054, Foundation 4056, Fuller 4063, **Grand 4076**, Hall 4084, Hanover 4086, Highland 4098, Institution 4108, Jebediah 4112, Levy 4144, Linde 4147, Ludcke 4157, Lynch 4159, Mifflin 4175, Miller 4177, New England 4193, Pappas 4204, Pardoe 4206, Parker 4207, Peabody 4210, Perkin 4213, Pierce 4220, Proctor 4227, Riley 4239, Rodgers 4242, **Rosenberg 4245**, Roy 4247, Santander 4256, Shapiro 4267, Smith 4275, Smith 4277, Stevens 4288, Stevens 4289, Stoddard 4293, Stoico 4294, Thompson 4307, Tupancy 4312, Wadleigh 4316, Webster 4322

Michigan: Albion 4332, Allegan 4334, Alro 4336, Americana 4337, Andersen 4339, Barry 4342, Battle Creek 4343, Bay 4344, Besser 4349, Capital 4357, Chrysler 4366, Community 4369, Community 4373, Community 4374, Consumers 4376, Cook 4377, Cronin 4383, Dalton 4385, Dana 4386, Dart 4388, Davenport 4389, Davis 4391, **DENSO 4395**, DeRoy 4396, DeVos 4398, DeVos 4400, Dow 4405, Dow 4406, Dow 4407, Ford 4427, Ford 4430, Fremont 4438, Gerstacker 4444, Gilmore 4445, Grand Rapids 4447, Grand 4448, Greenville 4452, Herrick 4459, Hudson 4463, Hurst 4464, Idema 4465, **Isabel 4466**, Jackson 4467, Johnson 4468, Kahn 4471, **Kellogg's 4475**, Knight 4477, La-Z-Boy 4481, Leighton 4484, Lenawee 4485, Manoogian 4491, Marquette 4495, Marshall 4496, Masco 4497, McGregor 4498, Merillat 4500, Midland 4502, Miller 4503, Monroe 4507, Mount Pleasant 4512, Oleson 4516, Pentecost 4520, Perrigo 4521, Petoskey 4522, Pokagon 4523, Sage 4531, Saginaw 4532, Schalon 4534, Secchia 4536, Shelden 4537, Spartan 4544, Spoelhof 4545, Steelcase 4547, Strosacker 4549, Sturgis 4550, Towsley 4557, Tuscola 4562, Upton 4565, VanderWeide 4572, Weatherwax 4577, Wege 4579, Wickes 4585, Wilson 4589

Minnesota: AHS 4599, **Andersen 4601**, Andersen 4603, Beverly 4615, Bigelow 4616, Bremer 4620, Central 4631, Christianson 4635, Deluxe 4644, Donaldson 4646, **Fuller 4659**, Gesner 4663, Graco 4666, Greystone 4668, Griggs 4669, Hardenbergh 4672, Hormel 4676, Johnson 4683, **King 4687**, Land 4691, Lilly 4696, Maas 4699, Marbrook 4702, Mardag 4703, Martin 4704, McKnight 4709, Minnesota 4715, Minnesota 4716, Neilson 4725, Opus 4731, Regis 4750, Rochester 4755, Saint Paul 4757, TEAM 4779, Tozer 4782, Valspar 4786, Wasie 4794, WCA 4795

Mississippi: Blue 4815, Community 4820, Maddox 4834, Mississippi 4839, Riley 4844

Missouri: Ameren 4851, Anheuser 4853, Apex 4854, Baer 4856, Brown 4862, Centene 4870, Commerce 4871, Community 4872, Dierberg 4879, Dunn 4882, Edison 4883, **Enterprise 4887**, Gateway 4894, Goppert 4896, Green 4899, Green 4900, H & R 4902, Hall 4905, Hallmark 4906, Jordan 4917, JSM 4918, Jubel 4919, Kansas 4920, Kemper 4926, Laclede 4931, Musgrave 4947, Nestle 4948, Oppenstein 4950, Orscheln 4951, Pillsbury 4956, Reynolds 4961, Rhoden 4962, Shaw 4970, Sosland 4977, Speas 4978, Stern 4980, Stupp 4983, Trio 4994, Whitaker 5001

Montana: First 5009, Washington 5018, Whitefish 5019

Nebraska: Abel 5021, Buckley 5026, Cope 5032, Dunklau 5036, Fremont 5039, Gardner 5041, Hastings 5046, Hirschfeld 5049, Hitchcock 5050, Kearney 5055, Kiewit 5056, Kiewit 5057, Kind 5060, Lexington 5062, Lincoln 5063, Lozier 5065, Mid-Nebraska 5068, Mutual 5071, Omaha 5074, Phelps 5075, Scoular 5080, Storz 5086, Union 5090, Wirth 5095

Nevada: Bretzlaff 5103, **Browning 5104**, Caesars 5106, Cord 5110, Fairweather 5118, Gabelli 5120, Hawkins 5123, Pennington 5139, **Reynolds 5143**, **Tang 5153**, Wiegand 5159

New Hampshire: Alexander 5162, Bean 5164, **Fidelity 5170**, Hunt 5177, Johnson 5178, Lindsay 5179, Penates 5185

New Jersey: Atlantic 5196, Banbury 5200, Borden 5209, Buehler 5219, Bunbury 5220, Campbell 5223, Cape 5224, Charles 5227, Clare 5230, Cowles 5234, Danellie 5237, Frankino 5266, Frohring 5269, Golden 5280, Grassmann 5281, Healthcare 5296, Hyde 5310, Johnson 5328, Karma 5331, Kirby 5339, Laurie 5357, **Merck 5379**, OceanFirst 5394, **Perrin 5404**, Provident 5414, Robertson 5424, Smith 5461, Snyder 5462, South 5463, Sudler 5472, Summit 5473, Turrell 5483, Union 5485, **Verizon 5489**, Victoria 5490, Wallerstein 5494, Wilf 5502

New Mexico: Chase 5517, Hubbard 5523, **Lannan 5526**, Maddox 5528, McCune 5529, PNM 5532

New York: Abrons 5546, Adirondack 5556, **Alavi 5566**, Allen 5573, Allyn 5575, American 5587, **Arcus 5608**, Arkell 5611, Aron 5616, **Ashner 5619**, Barker 5644, Botwinick 5696, Bravmann 5705, Brooks 5719, Carvel 5749, Cattaraugus 5750, Central 5757, Chadwick 5760, Charina 5763, Charina 5764, Chautauqua 5766, Chazen 5767, Clark 5786, Community 5802, Community 5804, Community 5805, Community 5807, Corning 5818, **Cummings 5832**, Curran 5835, Davenport 5850, Decker 5863, DeMatteis 5873, **Deutsche 5876**, Dewar 5879, **Diamond 5881**, Dillon 5885, Dodge 5892, Dolan 5895, Dolan 5896, Dunwalke 5921, Dyson 5923, East 5926, EHA 5940, Emerson 5950, **Engelhard 5954**, Englander 5955, **Ford 5995**, Four 6006, Freed 6011, Galasso 6032, Gebbie 6038, Gerry 6043, Gifford 6049, Gilman 6052, Glens Falls 6057, Goldman 6068, Goldstein 6076, Golisano 6077, Gorman 6083, Grigg 6109, Hayden 6150, Health 6153, Hudson 6191, Hultquist 6195, Icahn 6204, Jaharis 6223, Jones 6242, **JPMorgan 6244**, Kennedy 6274, Kinney 6285, Knapp 6296, **Lauder 6336**, Lehman 6346, Lemberg 6350, Lenna 6352, Lindner 6372, **M & T 6406**, Manton 6425, MBIA 6451, McCann 6453, Monell 6497, Morse 6509, Mulford 6514, **Nash 6525, Neuberger 6538, Norcross 6564**, Northern 6567, Northfield 6568, Nuhn 6572, O'Connor 6578, Ohrstrom 6582, **Pfizer 6633**, Price 6658, **Reisman 6686**, Richmond 6703, Ritter 6712, Robinson 6721, Rochester 6722, Rose 6737, **Ross 6754**, Rubenstein 6762, Schaffner 6800, Schenectady 6802, Semlitz 6831, Seneca 6832, Sheldon 6841, Siebens 6853, Snow 6878, Solomon 6885, Sosnoff 6892, **Starr 6911**, Statler 6913, **Straus 6934**, Sulzberger 6942, Thompson 6975, Time 6982, Tisch 6988, Truman 7007, Tuttle 7014, Vetlesen 7027, Vidda 7030, **Vital 7033**, Wachenheim 7039, Warner 7053, Weinberg 7066, Western 7078, Widgeon 7081, Wright 7104

North Carolina: Adams 7133, BB&T 7143, Belk 7148, BIN 7151, Blumenthal 7154, Bolick 7155, Broyhill 7160, Bryan 7161, Campbell 7168, Cannon 7169, Cape Fear 7170, Cemala 7174, Chatham 7175, Community 7179, Community 7180, Dalton 7187, Davis 7189, Dover 7194, Duke 7195, Duke 7196, Finley 7199, French 7203, Glass 7210, Glenn 7211, Gorelick 7215, Hallowell 7220, Hanes 7221, Hanes 7222, High Point 7231, Jones 7242, Mebane 7266, Morgan 7269, North Carolina 7273, **Oak 7276**, Olin 7279, Polk 7287, Reidsville 7294, Reynolds 7297, Reynolds 7299, Robertson 7305, Smith 7317, Southern 7319, State 7321, Tannenbaum 7326, Van Houten 7330, Vanderbilt 7331, Weaver 7335, Winston-Salem 7340, Woodward 7343

North Dakota: Fargo 7351, Leach 7353, MDU 7354, Myra 7355, North Dakota 7357, Stern 7360

Ohio: Abington 7365, American 7368, Anderson 7372, Ar-Hale 7376, Ariel 7377, Ashland 7378, Ashtabula 7379, Austin 7380, Barberton 7382, **Bingham 7387**, Bruening 7391, Budig 7392, Christ 7402, Cincinnati 7404, Cliffs 7407, Columbus 7411, Community 7413, Community 7415, Corbin 7420, Coshocton 7421, Covenant 7422, Dater 7426, David 7427, Dayton 7428, Delaware 7431, Diamond 7435, Dicke 7436, Dodero 7438, **Eaton 7442**, Emery 7443, Erie 7444, Fairfield 7445, Farmer 7447, Fifth 7452, Findlay 7453, Firman 7454, FirstEnergy 7455, Ford 7459, Fowler 7460, Frost 7464, GAR 7465, Greene 7474, H.C.S. 7479, Haslinger 7482, Hatton 7483, Hershey 7487, Honda 7490, Humphrey 7497, Ingalls 7503, Jewish 7511, Jochum 7513, Kettering 7522, Kimble 7526, Kulas 7532, Lehner 7536, Lennon 7537, Levin 7539, Licking 7540, Lubrizol 7546, Maltz 7553, Marietta 7557, Marion 7558, Mather 7559, Mayerson 7561, Miami 7569, Middletown 7570, Montgomery 7575, Morgan 7577, Murch 7582, Murdough 7583, Murphy 7584, Muskingum 7585, Nippert 7590, NiSource 7591, Nord 7594, Nordson 7596, Ohio 7599, **OMNOVA 7601**, Parker 7611, Payne 7614, Piqua 7620, Prentiss 7621, Reeves 7627, Reinberger 7628, Richland 7630, Saint 7639, Salem 7640, Schear 7645, Schlink 7650, Scripps 7659, Semple 7660, Silk 7663, Sisler 7664, Slemp 7665, Smith 7668, Spaulding 7670, Stark 7673, Stocker 7676, Sutphin 7679, **Timken 7684**, Troy 7688, Turner 7691, Twenty 7692, Warren 7702, Wayne 7704, Western 7710, Westfield 7711, White 7715, Wodecroft 7717, Wolfe 7719, Wuliger 7722, Youngstown 7723, Zembrodt 7724

Oklahoma: Adams 7725, Bartlesville 7731, Bernsen 7733, Bovaird 7735, Chapman 7739, Chapman 7740, Community 7743, Gaylord 7753, Helmerich 7758, Hille 7759, Kaiser 7763, Kerr 7764, Mabee 7770, McCasland 7772, McCrory 7773, McGee 7774, McMahon 7776, Noble 7780, Oklahoma 7782, ONEOK 7783, Puterbaugh 7786, Rapp 7787, Robinson 7789, Sarkeys 7793, **Schusterman 7794**, Share 7795, Southern 7798, Stevens 7800, Tandy 7803, Taubman 7804, Titus 7806, Tulsa 7807, Viersen 7808, Warren 7809, Williams 7814, Zink 7821

Oregon: Adler 7822, Autzen 7823, Benton 7825, Braemar 7826, Carpenter 7831, Chambers 7832, Clark 7834, Collins 7836, Esco 7841, Ford 7845, Haugland 7849, Hedinger 7851, Jeld 7856, Kinsman 7860, Macdonald 7866, Metolius 7869, Meyer 7870, Oregon 7876, PacifiCorp 7877, Schnitzer 7887, Schnitzer 7888, Swindells 7892, Tucker 7896, Woodard 7899, Young 7901

Pennsylvania: 1675 7903, **Alcoa 7908**, Alexander 7910, Allerton 7912, Ametek 7913, Arcadia 7918, Armstrong 7922, Beatty 7933, Beneficial 7936, Blanchard 7944, Brossman 7954, Buncher 7957, Carnahan 7965, Cassett 7969, Central 7972, Centre 7973, Century 7974, Cestone 7975, Cestone 7976, Chester 7979, Claneil 7982, Clapp 7983, Colket 7987, Colonial 7988, Community 7991, Community 7993, Community 7994, Connelly 7995, Crawford 8001, Crels 8002, Drumcliff 8016, DSF 8017, Eden 8021, Erie 8026, Federated 8033, Ferree 8036, First 8040, FISA 8043, Fourjay 8047, Glencairn 8062, Graham 8065, Grass 8068, Gray 8069, Hamer 8077, **Heinz 8083, Heinz 8085**, Hodge 8095, Hopwood 8096, Hoyt 8098, Hunt 8100, Hurd 8101, Huston 8102, Kelly 8119, **Kennametal 8120**, Keystone 8122, Kline 8128, Kline 8129, Lehigh Valley 8136, **Little 8145**, Mandell 8153, McCune 8160, McCune 8161, McFeely 8163, McKenna 8166, McLean 8169, Mellon 8172, Mellon 8173, **Moore 8186**, Morris 8188, Mylan 8192, Nichols 8197, O'Toole 8207, Penn 8216, Phillips 8222, Phoenixville 8223, Pierce 8224, Plankenhorn 8229, PNC 8230, Pottstown 8234, **PPG 8235**, Presser 8236, Rees 8245, Rossin 8256, Russell 8258, S & T 8259, Saint 8260, Schenck 8269, Seraph 8279, Shoemaker 8284, Smith 8289, Snee 8291, Stackpole 8295, Steinman 8299, Steinman 8300, Trexler 8320, Tyler 8322, United 8324, **Waldorf 8330**, Washington 8332, West 8334, Widener 8336, Willis 8340, Wyomissing 8350

Rhode Island: Amica 8356, Bafflin 8359, Carter 8368, Champlin 8370, CVS 8379, Daniels 8380, Hasbro 8403, Kimball 8410, McNeil 8418, Rhode Island 8429, Textron 8446, van Beuren 8449, Vance 8450

South Carolina: Abney 8454, Bruce 8461, Byerly 8462, Coastal 8472, Community 8475, Daniel 8476, Graham 8481, Roe 8494, Sims 8497, Spartanburg 8501, Springs 8504

South Dakota: Larson 8516, Robinson 8520, South Dakota 8522, Vucurevich 8524

Tennessee: American 8528, Beaman 8534, Benwood 8535, Bridgestone 8537, Briggs 8538, Carlton 8541, Christy 8545, CIC 8546, Community 8548, Cook 8552, East 8560, First 8565, Frist 8567, Frist 8568, HCA 8582, Hyde 8584, Jeniam 8587, Johnson 8588, Lyndhurst 8599, Martin 8606, Osborne 8614, Plough 8615, Thompson 8635, Tucker 8638, Wilson 8646

Texas: Abell 8650, Alkek 8658, Amarillo 8660, Anderson 8664, Astros 8674, Austin 8676, Bass 8686, Bass 8688, Bass 8689, Bass 8690, Bauer 8691, Beasley 8698, Beneski 8701, BNSF 8706, Boeckman 8707, **Bolivar 8708**, Boone 8710, Bridwell 8726, Brown 8731, Cailloux 8742, Cameron 8747, Carter 8752, CFP 8758, CH 8759, Clayton 8765, Coates 8769, Cockrell 8770, Collins 8771, Communities 8773, Community 8774, Community 8775, Community 8777, Constantin 8778, Cowden 8783, Cullen 8792, Dallas 8795, Davis 8799, Dickson-Allen 8806, Doss 8812, Doss 8813, Eady 8818, Edwards 8823, Elkins 8826, Embrey 8828, Favrot 8842, Fikes 8844, Fisch 8846, Fish 8848, Fluor 8851, Fondren 8853, Greathouse 8874, Guenther 8877, Gulf 8878, Haggerty 8881, Halsell 8885, Hamman 8888, Hebert 8899, Henderson 8900, Herzstein 8905, Hillcrest 8909, Hoblitzelle 8912, Hoglund 8913, **Houston 8916**, Houston 8917, Huffington 8920, Hunt 8922, Johnson 8941, Kelleher 8951, Kempner 8952, Kinder 8958, King 8959, Klabzuba 8960, Kodosky 8966, Kronkosky 8970, Liatis 8983, Light 8984, Lightner 8985, Littauer 8988, Lowe 8993, Lubbock 8994, Lyons 8996, Mankoff 8998, **Marshall 9000**, Martinez 9003, Mayborn 9006, Mayor 9007, McDermott 9013, McGovern 9014, McNutt 9018, Meadows 9019, Moody 9033, Moss 9043, Navarro 9054, Nearburg 9055, Northen 9063, O'Connor 9066, **Oldham 9069**, Owen 9076, Owen 9077, Owsley 9078, Payne 9086, Perkins 9090, Perot 9093, Peterson 9095, Priddy 9109, Pryor 9113, Puett 9114, Rachal 9117, Rees-Jones 9125, Reynolds 9127, Richardson 9130, Rogers 9138, Rosewood 9140, Sams 9145, San Angelo 9146, San Angelo 9147, San Antonio 9148, Sarofim 9154, **Scaler 9155**, Schutte 9160, Scott 9161, Scurlock 9162, Shield 9170, Simmons 9174, Simmons 9175, Smith 9179, Smith 9184, Smith 9186, Stedman 9200, Stemmons 9201, Sterling 9203, Stern 9204, Still 9207, Strake 9208, Sturgis 9211, Summerlee 9213, Temple 9223, Terry 9224, Texas 9227, Tobin 9236, Topfer 9239, Tucker 9241, Valero 9246, Vanberg 9247, Vaughan 9248, Waco 9251, Waggoner 9252, Ward 9258, WEDGE 9263, Wichita 9277, Wolslager 9288, Wright 9293, Young 9295, Zachry 9296, Zephyr 9299

Utah: ALSAM 9302, Burton 9309, Dee 9312, Eccles 9317, Eccles 9319, Hemingway 9326, **Nu 9340**, Patel 9343

Vermont: Tarrant 9373, Vermont 9375

Virginia: Alleghany 9382, AMERIGROUP 9383, Beazley 9391, **Bosack 9395**, Cabell 9397, Cameron 9398, Carter 9403, Community 9411, Dominion 9422, Folger 9431, Fralin 9433, Graham 9445, Gwathmey 9447, Hampton 9448, Kanter 9459, Landmark 9467, **Loyola 9471**, Lynchburg 9474, Mars 9477, McGlothlin 9483, Morgan, 9490, Norfolk 9496, Parsons 9504, Perry 9506, Potomac 9511, Reynolds 9519, Robins 9523, Scott 9529, SunTrust 9539, Titmus 9543, United 9546, Washington 9552

Washington: Allen 9567, Anderson 9572, Bainbridge 9578, Bates 9582, Cameron 9593, Cheney 9598, Columbia 9602, Community 9604, Dimmer 9610, Evertrust 9617, Foster 9621, Fuchs 9624, Grays 9631, Green 9632, Harvest 9642, Inland 9650, Kitsap 9659, Lucky 9673, McEachern 9678, Medina 9682, Milgard 9683, Murdock 9689, Names 9690, Nesholm 9691, Norcliffe 9693, PACCAR 9698, Plum 9704, Renton 9715, **Samis 9725**, San Juan 9726, Seattle 9731, Sherwood 9733

West Virginia: Beckley 9769, Chambers 9772, Community 9773, Daywood 9774, Eastern 9775, Hamilton, 9776, Hollowell 9778, Kanawha 9780, Maier 9782, McDonough 9784, Parkersburg 9789, Schenk 9793, Shott, 9794

Wisconsin: Alexander 9803, Alliant 9804, Antioch 9807, Bachhuber 9809, Bader 9810, Beloit 9814, Bemis 9815, **Bradley 9819**, Briggs 9822, Brotz 9825, Clark 9830, Community 9833, Community 9834, Community 9835, Cornerstone 9836, CUNA 9838, Evinrude 9841, Goldbach 9851, Helfaer 9861, Herzfeld 9863, Holz 9864, Iddings 9866, Incourage 9867, Jeffris 9869, Johnson 9870, Johnson 9874, Kelben 9877, Krause 9886, Kress 9887, Lakeview 9892, Lunda 9896, Madison 9897, Mead 9902, Milwaukee 9907, Neese 9911, Northwestern 9914, Oshkosh 9916, Pettit 9919, Pick 9920, Rennebohm 9931, Rexnord 9932, Smith 9947, Stackner 9951, Steigleder 9952, Stock 9953, **Taylor 9955**, U.S. 9957, West 9967, Wisconsin 9970

Wyoming: Community 9975, Kerr 9981, Martin 9984, McMurry 9986, Storer 9992

Capital campaigns

Alabama: Alabama 1, Bedsole 11, Brock 13, Bruno 15, Community 21, Crampton 26, Daniel 27, Dove 31, Friedman 35, Hearin 38, Hess 39, Hill 40, Kaul 43, McWane 51, Meyer 53, Protective 59, Smith 66, Vulcan 73, Walker 74, Webb 76

Alaska: Rasmuson 89

Arizona: Globe 115, Green 117, **Hickey 121, Johnson 126**, Linde 135, Marshall 141, Morris 148, Piper 152, Stewart 166, Webb 174

Arkansas: Cabe 182, Endeavor 186, Frueauff 188, Jonsson 192, Ross 199, Walker 209

California: Ahmanson 222, Aratani 250, Ayrshire 276, Bechtel 294, Bechtel, 296, Bothin 331, Bowes 334, California 365, Chandler 392, Collins 412, Community 414, Community 417, Copley 428, Cowell 434, Crail 437, Dachs 446, Daly 447, Darling 449, Davies 454, Disney 467, **DJ & T 469**, Doheny 473, Dolby 474, Eisner 499, Eucalyptus 510, Femino 521, Firedoll 528, Foothills 537, Fremont 548, Garb 564, Garland 565, Gasser 566, **Geffen 567**, Gellert 568, Geschke 576, Gold 600, Goldman 605, Goldman 606, Goldsmith 608, Gruber 632, GSF 633, Haas 641, Haas 642, Hale

645, Hannon 650, Hannon 651, Harden 654, Hayden 663, **Hilton 692**, Hind 693, Hoag 697, Hofmann 700, Humboldt 714, Hutton 718, Irwin 728, Jackson 737, JL 751, Jones 756, **Keck 774**, Kern 780, LA84 809, Laural 823, Lesher 833, Littlefield 844, Long 847, Los Altos 849, **Lund 857**, M & T 861, Mabie 863, Marin 877, McBean 892, McCarthy 895, **McConnell 898**, Miller 929, Monterey 936, Moore 937, Morgan 940, Newhall 966, Osher 997, Outhwaite 1000, Pacific 1002, Pacific 1003, Parsons 1013, Pasadena 1015, Patron 1020, Payne 1021, Samuelsson 1107, Sangham 1114, Santa Barbara 1116, Schlinger 1124, Schwab 1128, Sefton 1134, Shortino 1160, Smullin 1190, Sobrato 1193, Sonora 1198, Springcreek 1208, **Strauss 1223**, Taper 1237, Teichert 1244, Tesuque 1246, Towbes 1260, Tuohy 1267, Ueberroth 1268, Valley 1279, Valley 1280, Van Nuys 1284, Wasserman 1300, Weingart 1307, Wood 1344

Colorado: Boettcher 1374, Bohemian 1375, Buell 1381, Chambers 1385, Community 1391, Daniels 1399, Edmondson 1405, El Pomar 1406, Gates 1418, Halton 1426, Kitzmiller 1441, Lipscomb 1449, Marquez 1454, Piton 1480, Rose 1487, Shamos 1498, Summit 1511, Telluride 1512, Yampa 1528

Connecticut: American 1537, Baldwin 1541, **Calder 1554**, Community 1562, Community 1564, Community 1565, Connecticut 1566, Culpeper 1568, Fund 1589, Garden 1590, Hartford 1609, Hubbell 1614, Keefe 1619, Larsen 1624, Liberty 1630, Matthies 1639, McLeod 1641, New Canaan 1650, NewAlliance 1651, O'Herron 1660, Ohnell 1661, Rogow 1683, Zachs 1730

Delaware: AEC 1735, Crestlea 1757, Crystal 1758, Delaware 1765, Esperance 1777, Lennox 1805, Longwood 1806, Marmot 1814, Mastronardi 1815, Matthews 1816, McDonald 1817, **Memton 1819**, Schwartz 1857, Sylvan 1867, Tapeats 1868, Welfare 1872, Westly 1873

District of Columbia: Aid 1879, Bender 1885, Bernstein 1886, Bernstein 1887, **El-Hibri 1903**, Gewirz 1909, Gottesman 1911, Gudelsky 1912, Kiplinger 1922

Florida: Baroco 1981, Batchelor 1983, Brown 2004, Bush 2008, **Chester 2020**, Community 2041, Conn 2042, **Davis 2056**, Duckwall 2069, Dunspaugh-Dalton 2073, Engelberg 2086, Florescue 2100, Florida 2101, GiveWell 2123, Gooding 2130, Haller 2146, Harris 2149, Hersh 2156, Hough 2162, Indian 2166, Jacksonville 2167, **Katz 2177**, Kennedy 2182, Klorfine 2188, **Knight 2191**, NextEra 2251, Publix 2275, Quantum 2276, Rayonier 2281, Rinker 2285, Rinker 2286, **Russell 2301**, Ryder 2302, Sack 2303, Selby 2316, Southwest 2327, St. Joe 2331, St. Petersburg 2332, Straz 2341, Sylvester 2348, Thomas 2357, Tupperware 2363, Watts 2380, Wells 2383

Georgia: Aflac 2399, AGL 2400, Amos 2402, Atlanta 2406, Beloco 2411, Brain 2416, Callaway 2418, Callaway 2419, Campbell 2420, Camp-Younts 2421, Community 2433, Community 2434, Community 2435, Courts 2441, Cousins 2442, Cox 2445, Cox 2446, Day 2448, DuBose 2450, English 2453, Equifax 2455, Franklin 2462, Fraser 2463, Georgia 2468, **Georgia 2469**, **Hanley 2476**, Harland 2477, Harrison 2481, **Imlay 2487**, Jordan 2492, Knox 2498, Lanier 2499, Moore 2519, Moore 2520, Rich 2537, Singletary 2551, Southern 2554, Synovus 2556, **Thoresen 2557**, Trailsend 2560, Tull 2561, Watson 2569, Whitehead 2571, Wilson 2576, Woodruff 2579, Woodward 2580, Woolley 2581, Zeist 2584

Hawaii: Atherton 2586, Bank 2588, Castle 2594, Ching 2596, Cooke 2597, First 2598, Hawaiian 2603, Island 2606, McInerny 2612, **Watumull 2620**

Idaho: Wishnick 2646

Illinois: Alsdorf 2659, Andrew 2661, Blair 2699, Blowitz 2702, Butler 2729, Caterpillar 2738, Chicago 2746, Circle 2749, Coleman 2759, Community 2763, Community 2767, Crown 2781, Day 2787, Dillon 2796, Donnelley 2802, Driehaus 2805, Duchossois 2809, Eisenberg 2819, Field 2831, Franke 2841, Frankel 2842, **Grainger 2874**, Gray 2878, Hamill 2888, Hansen 2889, Harris 2892, Hobbs 2914, Illinois 2934, Irwin 2936, Keith 2952, King 2960, Louis 2985, Mallinckrodt 2995, Miller 3025, Northern 3059, Potishman 3086, Prince 3089, Pritzker 3091, Reed 3109, Regenstein 3111, Southeastern 3169, Speh 3170, Stuart 3182, Tracy 3189, United 3200, VNA 3206, Walter 3213, Ward 3216, Woodward 3243

Indiana: **Ackerman 3252**, Ball 3262, Ball 3264, Blue 3265, Boren 3267, Brotherhood 3268, Brown 3269, Central 3272, Community 3282, Community 3283, Community 3285, Community 3286, Community 3288, Community 3289, Crown Point 3291, DeKalb 3295, Dekko 3296, Fairbanks 3301, Finish 3303, Ford 3305, Foundations 3306, Glick 3310, Hamman 3312, Harrison 3314, Henry 3320, Heritage 3321, Jordan 3331, Journal-Gazette 3332, Koch 3334, Kosciusko 3335, Kosciusko 3336, **Lilly 3340**, **Lilly 3342**, Madison 3346, McMillen 3352, Michigan 3354, Montgomery 3356, Noble 3359, Noyes 3361, Old 3363, Porter 3369, Portland 3370, Rolland 3381, Samerian 3384, Steel 3389, Tipton 3391, Vectren 3394, Wabash 3396, Washington 3398, Waterfield 3399, Welborn 3402, West 3404, Whitley 3407

Iowa: AEGON 3409, Ahrens 3410, Carver 3416, Cedar Rapids 3417, Community 3423, Community 3424, Guernsey 3437, Hall-Perrine 3439, HNI 3443, Hubbell 3446, Iowa 3447, Kuyper 3456, Lee 3457, Maytag 3460, McElroy 3461, Meredith 3463, Meredith 3464, MidAmerican 3465, Pella 3473, Principal 3476, **Rockwell 3477**, Tye 3484

Kansas: Capitol 3498, Hutchinson 3521, INTRUST 3522, **Lloyd 3530**, Manhattan 3532, McPherson 3534, Rice 3538, Salina 3540, Security 3544, **Shumaker 3546**, Sunderland 3551, Topeka 3552

Kentucky: Brown 3562, Brown 3563, Brown 3564, C.E. 3566, Coffey 3568, Community 3570, Cralle 3571, Gheens 3577, Humana 3582, Spray 3602, Young 3607

Louisiana: Baton Rouge 3613, Beaird 3614, Booth 3616, Community 3623, Community 3624, Coughlin 3626, Diboll 3628, Freeman 3636, Goldring 3638, Huie 3643, Jones 3645, Keller 3646, Libby-Dufour 3648, Pennington 3659, Reily 3661, RosaMary 3663, Schlieder 3665, Wilson 3671, **Woldenberg 3672**, Woolf 3673

Maine: Alfond 3678, Alfond 3679, Bangor 3680, Cianbro 3683, Hannaford 3690, King 3694, Libra 3696, Lunder 3697, Morton 3701, Sewall 3708

Maryland: Abell 3712, Blades 3734, **Blaustein 3735**, **Cohen 3754**, Community 3758, Concordia 3763, Davis 3772, **Deerbrook 3776**, Delaplaine 3778, Dresher 3782, **England 3785**, **Ewing 3787**, France 3796, **Grace 3807**, Gudelsky 3809, Hahn 3811, Helena 3812, Henson 3814, Hirschhorn 3816, Jacobsohn 3819, Kerr 3823, Knott 3826, Linehan 3834, Lockhart 3836, Meyerhoff 3848, Meyerhoff 3849, Middendorf 3850, Mid-Shore 3851, Millstream 3852, **Morningstar 3854**, Price 3865, Rathmann 3867, Rembrandt 3868, Riepe 3869, Rosenberg 3873, Rouse 3877, Sheridan 3883, Straus 3890, **Thalheimer 3894**, Washington 3904, **Weinberg 3908**

Massachusetts: Alden 3921, Barker 3936, **Barr 3937**, Bayrd 3938, Berkman 3945, Berkshire 3946, Beveridge 3950, **Cabot 3966**, Cabot 3967, Cabot 3968, Cape Cod 3973, Carney 3975, Clipper 3987, Community 3992, Danversbank 4009, Davis 4011, Donahue 4023, Dusky 4028, Eastern 4030, Essex 4039, Farnsworth 4043, Fields 4046, Fireman 4049, Fletcher 4054, Foundation 4056, Fuller 4063, Harrington 4088, Highland 4098, Hopedale 4101, Institution 4108, Island 4109, Levy 4144, Liberty 4145, Linde 4147, Ludcke 4157, Lynch 4159, Mifflin 4175, Miller 4177, Pardoe 4206, Parker 4207, Peabody 4209, Peabody 4210, Perkin 4213, **Phillips 4219**, Pierce 4220, Poss 4226, Riley 4239, **Rosenberg 4245**, Roy 4247, Schooner 4261, Shapiro 4267, Sharf 4268, Smith 4275, Smith 4277, Stevens 4288, Stevens 4289, Stoddard 4293, Stoico 4294, Swartz 4301, Thompson 4307, Tupancy 4312, Webster 4322

Michigan: Andersen 4339, Barry 4342, Bay 4344, Besser 4349, Capital 4357, Carls 4358, Comerica 4368, Community 4374, Community 4375, Consumers 4376, Cook 4377, Dalton 4385, Dana 4386, Dart 4388, Davenport 4389, Davis 4391, **DENSO 4395**, DeVos 4398, DeVos 4399, DeVos 4400, Doornink 4403, Dow 4405, Dow 4406, Dow 4408, DTE 4410, Family 4418, **Fisher 4423**, Ford 4430, Fremont 4438, Frey 4440, Gerstacker 4444, Gilmore 4445, Grand Haven 4446, Grand Rapids 4447, Granger 4449, Greenville 4452, Herrick 4459, Hickman 4460, Hudson 4463, Idema 4465, **Isabel 4466**, Jackson 4467, Knight 4477, Lenawee 4485, Marquette 4495, Masco 4497, McGregor 4498, Miller 4503, Monroe 4507, Oleson 4516, Polk 4524, Sage 4531, Shelden 4537, Silverwing 4541, Steelcase 4547, Sturgis 4550, Towsley 4557, **Tubergen 4559**, Upton 4565, Van Andel 4567, VanderWeide 4572, Weatherwax 4577, Webber 4578, Wege 4579, Wolters 4592, World 4594

Minnesota: 3M 4597, AHS 4599, **Andersen 4601**, **Andersen 4602**, Andersen 4603, Athwin 4607, Best 4612, **Better 4614**, Beverly 4615, Bigelow 4616, Bremer 4620, Cargill 4628, Charlson 4633, Deluxe 4644, Donaldson 4646, Driscoll 4648, Edwards 4653, General 4661, Graco 4666, Griggs 4669, Hardenbergh 4672, Hubbard 4678, Kelley 4686, **King 4687**, Kopp 4688, Land 4691, Marbrook 4702, Mardag 4703, Martin 4704, McKnight 4709, McVay 4711, Melrose 4713, Minneapolis 4714, Minnesota 4715, Minnesota 4716, **Mosaic 4722**, Nelson 4726, Opus 4731, **O'Shaughnessy 4734**, **Patterson 4738**, Piper 4743, Pohlad 4745, Regis 4750, Saint Paul 4757, Securian 4761, Slaggie 4766, Smikis 4767, Tozer 4782, Travelers 4783, U.S. 4784, Wasie 4794, WCA 4795

Mississippi: Community 4820, Maddox 4834, McRae 4836, Mississippi 4839, Regions 4843, Walker 4849

Missouri: Ameren 4851, Apex 4854, Arch 4855, Brown 4862, Centene 4870, Commerce 4871, Community 4872, Cox 4874, Edison 4883, **Enterprise 4887**, Express 4888, Goppert 4896, H & R 4902, Hall 4905, Hallmark 4906, Jordan 4917, JSM 4918, Kansas 4920, Kauffman 4922, Kemper 4926, Lichtenstein 4936, Lopata 4938, McGee 4942, Musgrave 4947, Nestle 4948, Oppenstein 4950, Pershing 4952, Pillsbury 4956, Reynolds 4961, Shaw 4970, Sosland 4977, Speas 4978, Stern 4980, Stupp 4983, Sunnen 4986, Trio 4994, Ward 4998, Whitaker 5001

Montana: First 5009, Whitefish 5019

Nebraska: Abel 5021, Ameritas 5023, Buckley 5026, Cope 5032, Dunklau 5036, Fremont 5039, Gardner 5041, Hirschfeld 5049, Hitchcock 5050, Kiewit 5056, Kiewit 5057, Kimmel 5059, Kind 5060, Lexington 5062, Lincoln 5063, Lozier 5065, Merrick 5067, Mid-Nebraska 5068, Mutual 5071, Scoular 5080, Storz 5086, Union 5090

Nevada: **Browning 5104**, Caesars 5106, Fairweather 5118, Nevada 5134, NV 5136, Parasol 5138

New Hampshire: Alexander 5162, Bean 5164, **Fidelity 5170**, Hunt 5177, Johnson 5178, Lindsay 5179, Penates 5185, Putnam 5186

New Jersey: Banbury 5200, Borden 5209, Brotherton 5216, Bunbury 5220, Campbell 5223, Charles 5227, Cowles 5234, Danellie 5237, Firestone 5260, Golden 5280, Grassmann 5281, Harbourton 5293, Hyde 5310, Investors 5317, Isermann 5319, Karma 5331, Kirby 5339, Laurie 5357, McMullen 5378, OceanFirst 5394, Orange 5396, Pitkin 5408, Provident 5414, **Prudential 5415**, Reeves 5420, Snyder 5462, South 5463, Turrell 5483, Union 5485, Victoria 5490, Wilf 5502

New Mexico: Frost 5519, Maddox 5528

New York: Abrons 5546, Adirondack 5556, Allen 5573, Allyn 5575, **Arcus 5608**, Aron 5616, Auchincloss 5623, Bahnik 5634, Baird 5636, Barker 5644, Barrington 5647, Bayne 5653, Bingham 5676, Botwinick 5696, Bravmann 5705, Brooklyn 5718, Burns 5732, Butler 5733, Central 5757, Chadwick 5760, Charina 5763, Charina 5764, Chazen 5767, **Citi 5780**, Clark 5786, Community 5802, Community 5804, Community 5805, Community 5807, Corning 5818, **Cummings 5832**, Curran 5835, Davenport 5850, DeCamp 5861, Decker 5863, **Diamond 5881**, Dillon 5885, Dolan 5895, Doolittle 5901, Dreyfus 5913, Dunwalke 5921, Dyson 5923, Emerson 5950, **Engelhard 5954**, Englander 5955, Farash 5969, **Ford 5995**, Four 6006, **Frankenberg 6009**, Freed 6011, Galasso 6032, Gebbie 6038, Gerry 6043, Gifford 6049, Gilder 6050, Glens Falls 6057, Goldman 6068, Goldstein 6076, Golisano 6077, Grigg 6109, Hagedorn 6128, **Harriman 6136**, Harriman 6137, **Hauser 6147**, **Hearst 6155**, **Hearst 6156**, **Heron 6164**, Hudson 6191, Hultquist 6195, Joelson 6232, Kautz 6260, Kennedy 6274, Kinney 6285, Lauder 6337, Lehman 6346, Lenna 6352, Lerner 6353, **M & T 6406**, Manton 6425, McCarthy 6454, Millbrook 6485, Monell 6497, Moore 6501, Morse 6509, Mulford 6514, National 6526, **Neuberger 6538**, New York 6543, Nicholas 6557, Northern 6567, NYSE 6573, O'Connor 6578, **Ohga 6581**, **Ottaway 6603**, Price 6658, **Prospect 6663**, **Reisman 6686**, Richmond 6703, Riggio 6709, Ritter 6712, Roberts 6717, Rose 6737, Rubenstein 6762, Ruffin 6770, Schaffner 6800, Schenectady 6802, Schiff 6805, Schmitt 6808, Semlitz 6831, Sheldon 6841, Simons 6861, Solomon 6885, **Starr 6911**, Steel 6914, **Straus 6934**, **Summerfield 6944**, Swyer 6956, **Tanaka 6961**, Time 6982, Troy 7006, Truman 7007, Vetlesen 7027, **Vital 7033**, Wachenheim 7039, Weinberg 7066, Weissman 7071, Western 7078, Widgeon 7081, **Wolfensohn 7098**, Wright 7104

North Carolina: BB&T 7143, Belk 7148, Blue 7153, Blumenthal 7154, Bolick 7155, Brady 7156, Broyhill 7160, Bryan 7161, Campbell 7168, Cannon 7169, Cape Fear 7170, **Carlson 7172**, Cemala 7174, Chatham 7175, Community 7179, Community 7180, Dalton 7187, Davis 7189, Dover 7194, Duke 7195, Glass 7210, Gorelick 7215, Hanes 7221, Hanes 7222, Harvest 7224, High Point 7231, Jolley 7240, Leever 7253, Levine 7255, Mebane 7266, Merancas 7267, Morgan 7269, North Carolina 7273, North 7274, Olin 7279, Polk 7287, Reidsville 7294, Reynolds 7296, Reynolds 7297, Robertson 7305, Simpson 7312, Sloan 7314, Smith 7317, Southern 7319, State 7321, Tannenbaum 7326, Triangle 7328, Van Houten 7330, VF 7332, Weaver 7335, Winston-Salem 7340, Woodward 7343, Wos 7345

North Dakota: Fargo 7351, Leach 7353, MDU 7354, Stern 7360

Ohio: Abington 7365, American 7368, Anderson 7372, Ar-Hale 7376, Ariel 7377, Ashland 7378, Austin 7380, Barberton 7382, **Bingham 7387**, Bruening 7391, Budig 7392, Cincinnati 7404, Cleveland 7406, Cliffs 7407, Codrington 7409, Columbus 7411, Community 7413, Community 7414, Community 7415, Coshocton 7421, Covenant 7422, David 7427, Dayton 7428, Delaware 7431, Diamond 7435, **Eaton 7442**, Emery 7443, Erie 7444, Fairfield 7445, Farmer 7447, Fifth 7452, Findlay 7453, Firman 7454, Fox 7461, Frost 7464, H.C.S. 7479, Hershey 7487, Home 7489, Hoover 7492, Ingalls 7503, Jewish 7511, Jochum 7513, **Kettering 7520**, Kettering 7521, Kettering 7522, KeyBank 7523, Kroger 7531, Kulas 7532, Lehner 7536, Lennon 7537, Levin 7539, Licking 7540, Lubrizol 7546, Macy's 7552, Maltz 7553, Marion 7558, Mayerson 7561, Miami 7569, Middletown 7570, Miniger 7572, Montgomery 7575, Moores 7576, Morgan 7577, Murch 7582, Murphy 7584, Muskingum 7585, National 7586, Nationwide 7587, Nippert 7590, **Noble 7592**, Nord 7594, Nordson 7596, Ohio 7599, **OMNOVA 7601**, Park 7609, Parker 7611, Payne 7614, Piqua 7620, Reeves 7627, Reinberger 7628, Richland 7630, Saint 7639, Schlink 7650, Scioto 7657, Scripps 7659, Semple 7660, Sherwin-Williams 7661, Silk 7663, Sisler 7664, Smith 7668, Spaulding 7670, St. Marys 7672, Stark 7673, Sutphin 7679, Tiffin 7682, **Timken 7684**, Troy 7688, Twenty 7692, Wallace 7700, Wayne 7704, Western 7710, Westfield 7711, White 7715, Wodecroft 7717, Wuliger 7722, Youngstown 7723

Oklahoma: Adams 7725, Bernsen 7733, Bovaird 7735, Chapman 7739, Chapman 7740, Community 7743, **Ethics 7749**, Hardesty 7756, Helmerich 7758, Hille 7759, Inasmuch 7760, Kaiser 7763, Lyon 7769, Mabee 7770, Masonic 7771, McGee 7774, McMahon 7776, Nelson 7779, Noble 7780, ONEOK 7783, Oxley 7785, Puterbaugh 7786, Rapp 7787, Records 7788, Sarkeys 7793, **Schusterman 7794**, Southern 7798, Stevens 7800, Tandy 7803, Tulsa 7807, Viersen 7808, Williams 7814, Zink 7821

Oregon: Benton 7825, Carpenter 7831, Collins 7836, Esco 7841, Ford 7845, Haugland 7849, Jackson 7855, Jeld 7856, John 7857, Kinsman 7860, Macdonald 7866, Meyer 7870, Mission 7873, Oregon 7876, Randall 7883, Schnitzer 7887, Schnitzer 7888, Swindells 7892, Tucker 7896, Woodard 7899, Young 7901

Pennsylvania: Alexander 7910, Allerton 7912, Arcadia 7918, Baker 7926, Ball 7927, Bayer 7932, Beatty 7933, Beneficial 7936, Berks 7939, Blanchard 7944, Brossman 7954, Buncher 7957, Carnahan 7965, CentiMark 7970, Centre 7973, Century 7974, Cestone 7975, Cestone 7976, Chester 7979, CIGNA 7981, Claneil 7982, Clapp 7983, **Colcom 7986**, Colonial 7988, Community 7991, Community 7993, Connelly 7995, Crels 8002, Degenstein 8008, Drumcliff 8016, Eden 8021, Erie 8026, ESSA 8028, Federated 8033, Ferree 8036, First 8040, FISA 8043, Graham 8065, Grass 8068, Gray 8069, Hamer 8077, **Heinz 8083**, **Heinz 8085**, Hillman 8093, Hopwood 8096, Hoyt 8098, Hunt 8100, Hurd 8101, Huston 8102, Jerlyn 8112, Kelly 8119, Keystone 8122, Kline 8128, Kline 8129, Lehigh Valley 8136, Lenfest 8137, Lenfest 8138, Lindback 8142, Mandell 8153, Marshall 8155, Martin 8156, McCune 8160, McCune 8161, McFeely 8163, McKenna 8166, McKinney 8168, McLean 8169, Mellon 8172, Mellon 8173, Mengle 8174, **Moore 8186**, Morris 8188, Nichols 8197, O'Toole 8207, Penn 8216, Peoples 8218, Phillips 8222, Phoenixville 8223, Pierce 8224, PNC 8230, **PPG 8235**, Rees 8245, Roberts 8250, Russell 8258, S & T 8259, Saint 8260, Seraph 8279, Shaffer 8281, Shoemaker 8284, Simmons 8285, Smith 8289, Stackpole 8295, Steinman 8299, Steinman 8300, **Susquehanna 8310**, Trexler 8320, Tyler 8322, United 8325, Washington 8332, West 8334, Wheeler 8335, Willis 8340, Withington 8344, Wyomissing 8350

Rhode Island: Amica 8356, Carter 8368, Champlin 8370, Charlesmead 8371, Daniels 8380, Hasbro 8403, Hoche-Scofield 8405, Kimball 8410, McAdams 8416, Rhode Island 8429, Textron 8446, van Beuren 8449, Vance 8450

South Carolina: Bruce 8461, Byerly 8462, Coastal 8472, Daniel 8476, Foothills 8478, Gibbs 8480, Graham 8481, Roe 8494, Sims 8497, Smith 8498, Sonoco 8500, Springs 8504

South Dakota: Larson 8516, **Opus 8518**, Robinson 8520, South Dakota 8522, Vucurevich 8524

Tennessee: American 8528, Assisi 8530, Beaman 8534, Benwood 8535, Bridgestone 8537, Briggs 8538, Carlton 8541, Community 8548, Cook 8552, Eastman 8561, Ezell 8564, First 8565, Frist 8567, Frist 8568, HCA 8582, Hyde 8584, Jeniam 8587, Lyndhurst 8599, Martin 8606, Osborne 8614, Plough 8615, Regal 8622, Stokely 8631, Thompson 8635, Tucker 8638, Wilson 8646

Texas: Abell 8650, Alkek 8658, Astros 8674, Austin 8676, Bass 8686, Bass 8689, Beals, 8697, Beasley 8698, Boeckman 8707, Boone 8710, Booth 8711, Bridwell 8726, Brown 8731, Brumley 8734, Burnett 8737, Cailloux 8742, Carter 8752, CFP 8758, CH 8759, Clements 8767, Coates 8769, Cockrell 8770, Communities 8773, Community 8774, Community 8775, Community 8777, Constantin 8778, Cook 8779, Cowden 8783, Cullen 8792, Dallas 8795, Davis 8799, Eady 8818, Edwards 8823, Edwards 8824, Elkins 8826, Embrey 8828, Fain 8835, Fikes 8844, Fisch 8846, Fish 8848, Fluor 8851, Fondren 8853, George 8863, Gulf 8878, Haggerty 8881, Hall 8883, Hamill 8887, Hamman 8888, Herzstein 8905, Hillcrest 8909, Hirsch 8910, Hoblitzelle 8912, Hoglund 8913, **Houston 8916**, Houston 8917, Huffington 8920, Hunt 8922, Jamail 8929, Johnson 8941, Kelleher 8951, Kempner 8952, Kilroy 8956, Kimberly 8957, Kinder 8958, Klabzuba 8960, Kodosky 8966, Liatis 8983, Light 8984, Lightner 8985, Lowe 8993, Lubbock 8994, Lyons 8996, Mankoff 8998, **Marshall 9000**, Martinez 9003, Mayborn 9006, McDermott 9013, McNutt 9018, Meadows 9019, Miller 9028, Moody 9033, Moran 9036, Moss 9043, Navarro 9054, Northen 9063, Owen 9076, Owen 9077, Payne 9086, Perot 9093, Priddy 9109, Pryor 9113, Puett 9114, Rachal 9117, Rees-Jones 9125, Reynolds 9127, Richardson 9131, Rosewood 9140, San Angelo 9146, San Angelo 9147, Schutte 9160, Scott 9161, Scurlock 9162, Shield 9170, Simmons 9174, Simmons 9175, Smith 9179, Smith 9183, Smith 9184, Smith 9186, Smith 9187, Stedman 9200, Stemmons 9201, Sterling 9203, Still 9207, Strake 9208, Stumberg 9210, Sturgis 9211, Summerlee 9213, SWBC 9217, Temple 9223, Terry 9224, Texas 9227, Thomas 9231, Tobin 9236, Topfer 9239, Turner 9242, TurningPoint 9244, Valero 9246, Vanberg 9247, Vaughan 9248, Waco 9251, Waggoner 9252, Wal 9254, Ward 9258, Weekley 9264, **Whole 9276**, Wichita 9277, Wilson 9280, Wolslager 9288, Wortham 9292, Young 9295, Zachry 9296, Zeller 9298, Zephyr 9299

Utah: Eccles 9317, Eccles 9319, Patel 9343

Vermont: Gibney 9362, Lintilhac 9365, Tarrant 9373

Virginia: Alleghany 9382, Beazley 9391, Cabell 9397, Cameron 9398, Carter 9403, Community 9411, Dominion 9422, Freddie 9435, **Gannett 9439**, Graham 9445, Gwathmey 9447, Hampton 9448, Hylton 9455, Kanter 9459, Lambert 9466, Landmark 9467, Lynchburg 9474, MeadWestvaco 9484, Norfolk 9496, Parsons 9504, Reynolds 9519, Robins 9523, Scott 9529, SunTrust 9539, Titmus 9543, **Truland 9545**, United 9546, Universal 9548, Washington 9552, Wrinkle 9562

Washington: Allen 9567, Avista 9576, Bainbridge 9578, Bates 9582, Cameron 9593, Cheney 9598, Columbia 9602, Cowles 9607, Danz 9609, Dimmer 9610, Evertrust 9617, Fuchs 9624, Grays 9631, Green 9632, Harvest 9642, Horizons 9645, Inland 9650, Laurel 9666, Lauzier 9667, Lucky 9673, McEachern 9678, Milgard 9683, Nesholm 9691, Norcliffe 9693, Oki 9694, PACCAR 9698, Puget 9705, Safeco 9723, San Juan 9726, Seattle 9731, Sherwood 9733, Spark 9741, **Goodwin 9751**, Wiancko 9761, **Wilburforce 9762**, Wright 9765

West Virginia: Beckley 9769, Chambers 9772, Daywood 9774, Eastern 9775, Hollowell 9778, Kanawha 9780, Maier 9782, McDonough 9784, Parkersburg 9789, Schenk 9793, Shott, 9794

Wisconsin: Alexander 9802, Alexander 9803, Bader 9810, **Baird 9811**, Beloit 9814, Bemis 9815, Benidt 9816, Briggs 9822, Charter 9829, Clark 9830, Cleary 9831, Community 9834, Community 9835, Cornerstone 9836, CUNA 9838, Evinrude 9841, Harley 9859, Herzfeld 9863, Holz 9864, Iddings 9866, Johnson 9870, Johnson 9871, Johnson 9874, Kelben 9877, Krause 9886, Kress 9887, La Crosse 9889, Ladish 9890, Lakeview 9892, Lubar 9894, Lunda 9896, Mead 9902, Milwaukee 9907, Neese 9911, Northwestern 9914, Oshkosh 9916, Peck 9918, Pettit 9919, Pick 9920, Roundy's 9936, **Schneider 9942**, Smith 9947, Stackner 9951, Stock 9953, Wisconsin 9969, Wisconsin 9970, Zilber 9972

Wyoming: Community 9975, Ellbogen 9977, Martin 9984, McMurry 9986, Seeley 9990, Zimmerman 10000

Cause-related marketing

California: CAA 362
Georgia: Aflac 2399
Illinois: Allstate 2657
Michigan: Chrysler 4366
New York: Doolittle 5901, Voya 7038

Computer technology

Massachusetts: Beveridge 3950
Pennsylvania: First 8040
Wisconsin: Green Bay 9854

Conferences/seminars

Alabama: Community 23, **International 41**, Walker 74
Alaska: CIRI 85
Arizona: **Johnson 126, Kieckhefer 129**
Arkansas: Arkansas 179, Cabe 182, Endeavor 186
California: **Agilent 220**, Aratani 250, Archstone 253, Atlas 266, Ayrshire 276, Blue 320, California 366, California 368, **Christensen 399**, Community 414, Community 417, **Compton 422, CS 442**, Doctors 471, El Dorado 500, **Ellison 504, First 530, Foundation 542, Fund 556**, Gaia 557, **Gilead 586**, Girard 591, **Glenn 594**, Hannon 650, Jacobs 739, **Kalliopeia 761, Kapor 764**, Koret 801, **Lingnan 841**, Littlefield 844, Los Altos 849, Mabie 863, Marin 877, Mental 914, Milken 926, **Moore 938**, North 972, Orange 992, Pacific 1003, Placer 1039, **Saban 1101**, Samuelsson 1107, Schwab 1127, Silicon 1166, Sonora 1198, **Special 1202**, Stuart 1225, Taper 1237, Thornton 1252, Towbes 1260, True 1264, Ueberroth 1268, Ventura 1287, **Warsh 1299**, Wohlford 1336
Colorado: Animal 1363, Community 1391, Community 1395, COPIC 1397, Foundation 1411, **General 1419, Gill 1421**, Piton 1480, Summit 1511, **Winslow 1525**, Yampa 1528
Connecticut: Aetna 1531, Community 1562, Connecticut 1566, Connecticut 1567, Deloitte 1572, Graustein 1600, Main 1634, Middlesex 1644, New Canaan 1650, Palmer 1666, **Richardson 1679**, Rosenthal 1684
Delaware: AEC 1735, **Raskob 1845**
District of Columbia: **Arca 1880**, Bauman 1882, Bernstein 1886, Coyne 1896, Gudelsky 1912, **Moriah 1932**, Munson 1933, **Searle 1946**
Florida: **Believers 1989**, Bi-Lo 1996, Community 2032, Community 2039, Community 2041, Conn 2042, Darden 2051, duPont 2075, Engelberg 2086, **Koch 2192**, Rayonier 2281, Wells 2383, Winter 2390
Georgia: **Challenge 2424**, Communities 2431, DuBose 2450, Georgia 2468, **Georgia 2469**, Healthcare 2482, Lewis 2502, Pitts 2529, Savannah 2548, Watson 2569, Zeist 2584
Idaho: Albertson 2626
Illinois: **Abbott 2649**, Allstate 2657, Bauer 2687, Brach 2712, Chaddick 2740, Coleman 2759, Community 2763, Coypu 2777, Edwardsville 2817, Frankel 2842, Harris 2892, Henry 2906, Heritage 2907, **Joyce 2946, Kemper 2955**, Mallinckrodt 2995, McDougal 3013, **Tellabs 3185, Tyndale 3195**
Indiana: Ball 3262, Brown 3269, Central 3272, Community 3280, Community 3285, Community 3286, Community 3288, Dekko 3296, **Goodrich 3311**, Hancock 3313, Harrison 3314, Health 3317, Henry 3320, Heritage 3321, Huntington 3324, **Lilly 3342, Lumina 3345**, Montgomery 3356, Noble 3359, Orange 3365, Steuben 3390, Tipton 3391, Unity 3393, Washington 3398, Wayne 3400, Welborn 3402
Iowa: Ahrens 3410, Carver 3416, Cedar Rapids 3417, Community 3423, Community 3424, Guernsey 3437, Maytag 3460, **Pioneer 3474**, Siouxland 3480
Kansas: Capitol 3498, Cooper 3503, Hutchinson 3521, McPherson 3534, Salina 3540
Louisiana: Community 3624, Institute 3644
Maine: Horizon 3691, Maine 3699
Maryland: Abell 3712, **Bearman 3728, Casey 3745**, Community 3759, Community 3760, **de Beaumont 3774, Deerbrook 3776**, Meyerhoff 3849, Rathmann 3867, Rembrandt 3868, **Thalheimer 3894**
Massachusetts: **Barr 3937**, Berkshire 3948, Cape Cod 3974, **China 3982**, Community 3992, Foundation 4056, **Hunt 4102, Iacocca 4104**, Lowell 4153, Melville 4170, Merck 4171, Parker 4207, Reynolds 4238, Schott 4262, Sheehan 4271
Michigan: Americana 4337, Ann Arbor 4340, Barry 4342, Battle Creek 4343, Community 4370, Community 4375, Dow 4408, **Earhart 4413, Fetzer 4420, Fisher 4423**, Fremont 4438, Gilmore 4445, Hillsdale 4461, Lenawee 4485, Marshall 4496, **Mott 4510**, Mount Pleasant 4512, Pokagon 4523, Weatherwax 4577
Minnesota: Bremer 4620, Central 4631, CHS 4636, Grand Rapids 4667, Greystone 4668, **Medtronic 4712**, Northwest 4729, Northwest 4730, Southwest 4768, **St. Jude 4770**, Winona 4806
Mississippi: **Armstrong 4810**, Community 4820, Foundation 4827, Hardin 4831, Maddox 4834
Missouri: Commerce 4871, Community 4872, Green 4900, **Kauffman 4921**, Kemper 4926, **Monsanto 4945**, Rhoden 4962
Nebraska: Dunklau 5036, Hastings 5046, Mid-Nebraska 5068, Omaha 5074
Nevada: Nevada 5134
New Hampshire: Alexander 5162, Bean 5164, Endowment 5169, **Fidelity 5170**, Hunt 5177
New Jersey: **Allen 5191**, Atran 5197, Brotherton 5216, Clare 5230, Fund 5270, Integra 5315, Kirby 5339, **Knowles 5345**, KPMG 5349, **Merck 5379**, Merck 5380, **Milbank 5385**, Pascale 5403, **Ramapo 5419**, Summit 5473
New Mexico: Frost 5519, **Levinson 5527**, McCune 5529, New Mexico 5530, **Thaw 5534**
New York: Achelis 5549, Allen 5573, **American 5588, Arcus 5608, AVI 5628**, Bay 5652, Berg 5667, Bodman 5692, **Bronfman 5717**, Burns 5732, **Carnegie 5747**, Chautauqua 5766, Community 5802, Community 5804, Community 5805, Cricket 5827, **Cummings 5833, Dedalus 5864, Delmas 5871, Engelhard 5954, Ford 5995, Foundation 6003**, Gifford 6049, Glens Falls 6057, **Goldman 6066, Grant 6093**, Grigg 6109, **Hartford 6144, Hauser 6147**, Health 6153, Hermione 6163, **Isdell 6214, JPMorgan 6244**, Klingenstein 6292, **Kress 6308**, Lang 6326, **Macy 6414**, McCann 6453, **Mitsubishi 6490**, Mitsui 6491, Northern 6567, O'Connor 6578, **Peterson 6630, Philippe 6636, Porticus 6654**, Rauch 6681, **Reisman 6686**, Richmond 6703, Rochester 6722, **Rockefeller 6724**, Rosner 6752, **Sage 6782**, Schaffner 6800, **Sparkplug 6894, Tinker 6983**, Triad 7005, Vilcek 7031, Voya 7038, **Wallace 7043, Warhol 7050, Wenner 7075**, Western 7078, Widgeon 7081, Wilson 7088
North Carolina: **Bank 7139**, Biddle 7150, Blue 7153, Blumenthal 7154, Brady 7156, Cemala 7174, Community 7180, Cumberland 7184, Duke 7195, French 7203, Glass 7210, Greenville 7217, Hanes 7222, North Carolina 7273, Polk 7287, Robertson 7305, Tannenbaum 7326
North Dakota: North Dakota 7357
Ohio: Anderson 7372, Barberton 7382, **Bingham 7387, Cardinal 7398**, Community 7413, Coshocton 7421, Durell 7441, Gund 7478, Hamilton 7481, Hatton 7483, **Kettering 7520**, Kulas 7532, Levin 7539, Licking 7540, Marietta 7557, Marion 7558, Miami 7569, Morgan 7578, Morgan 7579, Muskingum 7585, Nord 7594, O'Neill 7602, Scioto 7657, Scripps 7659, Tiffin 7682, Wallace 7700
Oklahoma: Bernsen 7733, Bovaird 7735, **Ethics 7749**, Inasmuch 7760, Kirkpatrick 7766, Oklahoma City 7781, **Schusterman 7794**, Zarrow 7818
Oregon: Carpenter 7831, **Intel 7853**, Kinsman 7860
Pennsylvania: **Alcoa 7908**, Alexander 7910, Arete 7919, Baker 7926, Bayer 7932, Berks 7939, **Carthage 7968**, Centre 7973, Chester 7979, CIGNA 7981, Claneil 7982, Comcast 7989, Copernicus 7998, Crawford 8001, Dolfinger 8013, First 8040, FISA 8043, Grable 8064, Hopwood 8096, Morris 8188, Pottstown 8234, Scaife 8266, Scranton 8275, Staunton 8296, **Templeton 8313**, United 8324, **Waldorf 8330**, York 8351
Puerto Rico: Puerto Rico 8353
Rhode Island: Rhode Island 8429
South Carolina: Community 8474, Roe 8494, Spartanburg 8501
South Dakota: Sioux Falls 8521
Tennessee: Assisi 8530, Benwood 8535, East 8560, First 8565
Texas: Austin 8676, Community 8774, Community 8777, Favrot 8842, Halliburton 8884, **Houston 8916**, Houston 8917, Hudson 8919, Kempner 8952, Kodosky 8966, McGovern 9014, Moody 9033, Moore 9034, Owen 9076, **RGK 9128**, Richardson 9130, San Angelo 9147, Simmons 9174, Sterling 9203, Summerlee 9213, Sumners 9214, Tocker 9237, Vanberg 9247, Yarborough 9294
Utah: Eccles 9320, Hemingway 9326, Patel 9343
Vermont: Lintilhac 9365
Virginia: ACT 9380, **Bosack 9395**, Dominion 9422, Freddie 9435, **Gannett 9439**, Koch 9463, Moore 9489, **WestWind 9555**
Washington: **Brainerd 9590**, George 9626, **Glaser 9630**, Grays 9631, Harvest 9642, Jones 9655, JRS 9656, **Kongsgaard 9661**, Miller 9684, **Quixote 9707**
West Virginia: Beckley 9769, Community 9773
Wisconsin: Alliant 9804, Argosy 9808, Bader 9810, **Bradley 9819**, Bradshaw 9820, Community 9832, Community 9833, Community 9835, Harley 9859, Oshkosh 9916, Racine 9924, St. Croix 9950, Thrivent 9956
Wyoming: Community 9975, Ellbogen 9977, Wyoming 9999

Consulting services

Alabama: Smith 66
Arizona: **Johnson 126**, Steele 165
Arkansas: Ross 199
California: Atlas 266, California 365, Clif 405, Community 414, Community 417, Community 420, **Compton 422**, Cowell 434, **Fund 556**, Gerbode 573, Girard 591, Heller 676, Humboldt 714, Jacobs 739, **Kapor 764**, Kern 780, Littlefield 844, Marin 877, Miller 929, Mosher 945, North 972, **Packard 1006**, Placer 1039, San Luis 1110, Sangham 1114, Sonora 1198, **Thrive 1255**, Truckee 1263, True 1264, Wohlford 1336
Colorado: Bohemian 1375, Community 1391, Denver 1401, Foundation 1411, **Gill 1421**, Rose 1487, Telluride 1512
Connecticut: American 1537, Community 1562, Community 1563, Community 1564, Community 1565, Connecticut 1566, Connecticut 1567, Graustein 1600, Hartford 1609, Palmer 1666
Delaware: **Raskob 1845**
District of Columbia: Meyer 1931
Florida: Bush 2008, Community 2031, Community 2032, Community 2040, Conn 2042, **Davis 2056**, duPont 2075, Greenburg 2137, Gulf 2142, Miami 2238, Quantum 2276, Southwest 2327, Winter 2390
Georgia: **Challenge 2424**, Communities 2431, Community 2432, Zeist 2584
Hawaii: Cooke 2597, Geist 2600, Hawaii 2602
Idaho: Jeker 2634

Illinois: **Abbott 2648**, Chicago 2746, Community 2769, Edwardsville 2817, Frankel 2842, Mander 2998, Oak Park 3061, Speh 3170

Indiana: Ball 3262, Blue 3265, Central 3272, Community 3281, Community 3284, Community 3285, Community 3286, Dekko 3296, Foellinger 3304, Hancock 3313, Harrison 3314, Health 3317, Henry 3320, Heritage 3321, Huntington 3324, Johnson 3330, **Lilly 3342, Lumina 3345**, Marshall 3348, Noble 3359, Northern 3360, Orange 3365, Putnam 3373, Tipton 3391, Washington 3398

Iowa: Cedar Rapids 3417, Community 3421, Community 3424, Iowa 3447

Kansas: McPherson 3534

Kentucky: Blue 3560, C.E. 3566, Foundation 3575, Young 3607

Maryland: Baker 3725, **Casey 3745**, Community 3759, Community 3760, Fowler 3795, Goldseker 3803, Straus 3890

Massachusetts: **Barr 3937**, Berkshire 3948, Beveridge 3950, Boston 3956, Cape Cod 3974, Clipper 3987, Davis 4011, Essex 4039, Foundation 4056, Melville 4170, Parker 4207, Schooner 4261, Sudbury 4299

Michigan: Barry 4342, Charlevoix 4361, Community 4369, Dyer 4412, Fremont 4438, Gilmore 4445, Hudson 4463, Jackson 4467, Marquette 4495, Midland 4502, Miller 4503, Mount Pleasant 4512, Pokagon 4523, Sturgis 4550, Weatherwax 4577

Minnesota: Beverly 4615, Butler 4622, Duluth 4649, Northwest 4730, Phillips 4741, Rochester 4755

Mississippi: Foundation 4827, Riley 4844

Missouri: Community 4872, Saint Louis 4966

Nebraska: Hastings 5046, Kind 5060, Lincoln 5063, Woods 5096

Nevada: Nevada 5134

New Hampshire: Alexander 5162, Bean 5164, **Fidelity 5170**, New Hampshire 5182

New Jersey: **Allen 5191**, Clare 5230, Pascale 5403, Victoria 5490

New York: Abrons 5546, Allyn 5575, **Arcus 5608, Bronfman 5717**, Brooklyn 5718, Central 5757, **Clark 5784**, Community 5802, Community 5804, Community 5805, Community 5807, Cricket 5827, Cummings 5834, Dyson 5923, **Friends 6024**, Health 6153, New York 6544, Petrie 6632, **Porticus 6654**, Rauch 6681, Rochester 6722, Wilson 7088

North Carolina: Blue 7153, Community 7180, Duke 7195, North Carolina 7273, Reidsville 7294, Weaver 7335, Winston-Salem 7340

Ohio: Ar-Hale 7376, Cleveland 7406, Dater 7426, Dayton 7428, Findlay 7453, Kulas 7532, Morgan 7579, Murphy 7584, Muskingum 7585, O'Neill 7602, Saint 7639, Scioto 7657, Stark 7673

Oklahoma: Communities 7742, Hille 7759, Kirkpatrick 7766, Oklahoma City 7781, Sarkeys 7793, **Schusterman 7794**, Tulsa 7807

Oregon: Carpenter 7831, Kinsman 7860, Mission 7873, Woodard 7899

Pennsylvania: Barra 7928, Berks 7939, Central 7972, Chester 7979, Claneil 7982, Grable 8064, Luzerne 8152, North 8199, Penn 8216, Pottstown 8234, Scranton 8275, York 8351

Puerto Rico: Puerto Rico 8353

Rhode Island: Rhode Island 8429

South Carolina: Byerly 8462, Coastal 8472, Community 8475, Self 8496, Spartanburg 8501

Tennessee: Assisi 8530, Carlton 8541, East 8560, Frist 8568, Hyde 8584, Jeniam 8587, **Maclellan 8601**

Texas: Austin 8676, Community 8774, Community 8776, Community 8777, Davis 8799, **Houston 8916**, Kronkosky 8970, Meadows 9019, Northen 9063, Owen 9076, San Angelo 9147

Utah: Hemingway 9326

Vermont: Gibney 9362, Vermont 9375

Virginia: Alleghany 9382, Arlington 9384, Cameron 9398, Community 9412, Freddie 9435, Lambert 9466, Robins 9523, Weissberg 9554

Washington: Community 9605, Fuchs 9624, Handsel 9638, **Quixote 9707**, Tacoma 9750, Whatcom 9759, **Wilburforce 9762**

West Virginia: Beckley 9769, Community 9773

Wisconsin: Community 9832, Siebert 9946, St. Croix 9950

Wyoming: Community 9975

Continuing support

Alabama: Alabama 1, Kaul 43, McMillan 50, Meyer 53, Protective 59, Regions 61, Vulcan 73, Webb 76

Alaska: CIRI 85

Arizona: Arizona 92, Freeport-McMoRan 112, Globe 115, Jones 127, **Kieckhefer 129**, McDonald 144, Piper 152, Webb 174

Arkansas: Arkansas 179, Cabe 182, Frueauff 188, Jonsson 192, Schmieding 200, Walker 209, Walton 211

California: Altman 234, **Amado 235, American 237, Amgen 238**, Anderson 241, Applied 249, Aratani 250, Arrillaga 261, AS&F 263, Atkinson 265, Atlas 266, **Avery 272**, Barker 282, Beaver 292, Bechtel, 296, Benbough 303, Berry 312, Blue 320, Boswell 330, **Broadcom 349**, California 365, California 368, Campbell 373, Caruso 382, **Christensen 399, Cisco 402**, Collins 412, Community 414, Community 417, Community 418, Community 420, **Compton 422, CS 442**, Danford 448, Disney 467, **DJ & T 469**, Doctors 471, Doheny 473, East 490, Eisenberg 498, Eisner 499, El Dorado 500, Eucalyptus 510, Firedoll 528, **Firelight 529, Flextronics 535, Foundation 542**, Fresno 549, **Fund 556**, Gaia 557, Garb 564, Garland 565, Gellert 568, Genentech 571, Getty 578, GGS 580, Gilmore 588, Girard 591, Gold 600, Goldman 606, Goldsmith 608, Gross 629, Gruber 632, Gumbiner 636, Haas 641, Haas 642, Hannon 651, Hayden 663, Hayward 665, Heller 676, Hewlett 686, **Hilton 692**, James 742, **Kapor 764, Karisma 766**, Kern 780, **Kim 785**, Kirchgessner 790, Koret 801, Kvamme 807, Laural 823, Lesher 833, **Lingnan 841**, Lucas 855, Lytel 860, Marin 877, Masimo 884, McKesson 903, Mendelson 912, Mental 914, Milken 927, Miller 929, Morgan 940, Murphy 956, Norris 971, Noyce 974, Orange 992, Pacific 1002, Pacific 1003, **Packard 1006**, Parker 1012, Patron 1020, Peppers 1024, PG&E 1033, Philibosian 1036, Placer 1039, Quest 1050, Rancho 1053, Reid 1060, Reinhard 1061, **ResMed 1063, Righteous 1073**, Roberts 1081, Rogers 1087, Rosenberg 1088, Ryan 1098, **S.G. 1100, Saban 1101**, San Luis 1110, Sandy 1113, Sangham 1114, Schwab 1127, Schwab 1128, Silicon 1166, **Smith 1183**, Smith 1188, Sobrato 1193, Soda 1194, Sonora 1198, **Special 1202, Strauss 1223**, Streisand 1224, Stuart 1225, Stulsaft 1226, Taube 1241, Teichert 1244, Thornton 1252, **Thrive 1255**, Truckee 1263, Union 1271, **Vadasz 1275**, Valley 1279, vanLoben 1283, Van Nuys 1284, **Warsh 1299**, Wells 1312, Wood 1344, Zellerbach 1358

Colorado: Aspen 1368, Bohemian 1375, Brett 1378, Buell 1381, Chambers 1385, Colorado 1390, Community 1391, Community 1395, Edmondson 1405, El Pomar 1406, Fishback 1410, **Gill 1421**, Janus 1432, KBK 1437, **Kinder 1439**, Kitzmiller 1441, Lipscomb 1449, Marquez 1454, Ottens 1472, Pikes 1478, Price 1484, Summit 1511, Vodafone 1519, **Western 1521, Winslow 1525**, Yampa 1528

Connecticut: American 1537, Community 1562, Community 1564, Community 1565, Culpeper 1568, First 1584, **GE 1591**, Hartford 1609, Huisking 1615, Morris 1646, Neuberger 1649, NewAlliance 1651, Northeast 1656, Perrin 1673, Rockville 1682, Rosenthal 1684, Valentine 1713, Xerox 1728, **Ziegler 1731**

Delaware: **Adobe 1734, AstraZeneca 1738**, CenturyLink-Clarke 1750, Day 1763, Delaware 1765, Edwards 1774, Griswold 1787, Lennox 1805, Mastronardi 1815, McDonald 1817, **Memton 1819**, Schwartz 1857, Tapeats 1868

District of Columbia: **Arca 1880, Banyan 1881**, Bauman 1882, Bernstein 1887, Consumer 1894, Coors 1895, Gudelsky 1912, Kiplinger 1922, Loughran 1925, McIntosh 1928, **Moriah 1932, Public 1940**, Stewart 1949, **Summit 1950, Wallace 1955**

Florida: Amaturo 1966, Aurora 1974, **Barbour 1980**, Batchelor 1983, Beaver 1986, **Believers 1989**, Bi-Lo 1996, Brown 2004, Community 2041, Conn 2042, **Davis 2056**, Dunspaugh-Dalton 2073, Engelberg 2086, Florescue 2100, Florida 2101, Gooding 2130, Greenburg 2137, Henderson 2152, Hough 2162, Jacksonville 2167, **Katz 2177**, Klorfine 2188, Kramer 2195, Macdonald 2223, Magruder 2225, Moran 2243, Peacock 2263, Pinellas 2269, Rayonier 2281, **Russell 2301, SeaWorld 2315**, SunTrust 2345, Thomas 2357, **Vollmer 2373**, Watts 2380, Wells 2383

Georgia: Beloco 2411, Brain 2416, Callaway 2419, **Coca 2428**, Cox 2446, Day 2448, Franklin 2462, Fraser 2463, Georgia 2468, **Georgia 2469**, Harris 2479, **Keough 2496**, Knox 2498, Pitts 2529, Sapelo 2546, Southern 2554, **Turner 2563, UPS 2566**, Wilson 2576, WinShape 2577

Hawaii: Bank 2588, Campbell 2592, First 2598, Hawaiian 2603, Island 2606, McInerny 2612, Wong 2622

Idaho: Blue 2627, Idaho 2632, Jeker 2634, **Micron 2637, Schultz 2641**

Illinois: **Abbott 2648, Abbott 2649**, Arthur 2673, Bauer 2687, **Baxter 2690**, Bersted 2696, Blair 2699, Blowitz 2702, **Brinson 2715**, Brunner 2718, Butler 2729, Chaddick 2740, Chicago 2746, Circle 2749, Comer 2760, Community 2769, Crown 2781, Cuneo 2783, **Deere 2790**, Dillon 2796, Donnelley 2802, Dunard 2810, EFS 2818, Emerson 2822, Energizer 2824, Frankel 2842, Fry 2849, Galashiels 2852, **Grainger 2874**, Grand 2875, Guthman 2882, Halligan 2886, Hamill 2888, Harris 2892, Houlsby 2922, Illinois 2934, **Joyce 2946**, Keith 2952, Kemper 2954, King 2960, Landau 2966, Louis 2985, Martin 3003, McDougal 3013, McGowan 3014, McGraw 3015, **Mondelez 3034**, Morse 3039, Negaunee 3047, New 3052, Northern 3059, Omron 3063, Pick, 3079, Polk 3084, Popular 3085, Potishman 3086, Prince 3089, Reed 3109, Schmitt 3140, **Scholl 3141**, Seabury 3146, Siragusa 3162, Speh 3170, Steans 3175, Stern 3177, Stuart 3182, United 3200, White 3229, Wieboldt 3231, Woods 3242, Woodward 3243, **Wrigley 3244**

Indiana: **Ackerman 3252**, Anderson 3255, Anthem 3257, Bales 3261, Brown 3269, Cole 3276, Community 3281, Community 3290, Crown Point 3291, **Cummins 3292**, DeHaan 3294, Dekko 3296, Elkhart 3298, Fairbanks 3301, Foellinger 3304, Harrison 3314, Health 3317, Hendricks 3319, Henry 3320, **Lilly 3340, Lilly 3342, Lumina 3345**, Noyes 3361, Old 3363, Samerian 3384, Waterfield 3399

Iowa: Aviva 3411, Community 3423, Community 3424, Guernsey 3437, Maytag 3460, Nelson 3467, Principal 3476, **Rockwell 3477**, Wellmark 3490

Kansas: Capitol 3498, Cooper 3503, Hansen 3518, Hutchinson 3521, INTRUST 3522, Kansas 3524, Koch 3529, McPherson 3534, Security 3544, Smith 3547, Sprint 3549, Sunderland 3551, Topeka 3552, Wyandotte 3556

Kentucky: Community 3569, Cralle 3571, Humana 3582, Norton 3592, Robinson 3598, Yum! 3608

Louisiana: Baptist 3612, Beaird 3614, Brown 3617, Community 3623, Community 3624, Coughlin 3626, Goldring 3638, Grigsby 3640, Huie 3643, Institute 3644, Jones 3645, Reily 3661, RosaMary 3663, Wilson 3671, **Woldenberg 3672**, Woolf 3673

Maine: Libra 3696, Morton 3701, **Sandy 3707**

Maryland: Blades 3734, Blaustein 3736, Commonweal 3756, Community 3759, Davis 3772, **Deerbrook 3776**, Delaplaine 3778, Deutsch 3779, **England**

3785, Ewing 3787, Fowler 3795, Freeman 3797, Henson 3814, Meyerhoff 3848, Meyerhoff 3849, Millstream 3852, NASDAQ 3857, Polinger 3864, Price 3865, Rathmann 3867, Rembrandt 3868, Riepe 3869, **Shared 3882**, TKF 3896, Town 3897, Wasserman 3905

Massachusetts: Arbella 3926, Barker 3936, Berkshire 3946, Blue 3953, **Cabot 3966**, Cape Cod 3973, Cape Cod 3974, Clipper 3987, Community 3992, Danversbank 4009, Davis 4011, DentaQuest 4016, Donahue 4023, Dusky 4028, Ellsworth 4035, Finch 4048, Fireman 4049, Fuller 4063, **Grand 4076**, Hall 4084, Highland 4098, Hyams 4103, Institution 4108, Levy 4144, Liberty 4145, Lowell 4153, Ludcke 4157, Merck 4171, MetroWest 4173, New 4189, New England 4193, Pappas 4204, Perkin 4213, Poss 4226, Reynolds 4238, **Rosenberg 4245**, Santander 4256, Schott 4262, Schrafft 4263, Shaw 4270, Sheehan 4271, **State 4285**, Stearns 4286, Stevens 4288, Stevens 4289, Stoddard 4293, Stoico 4294, TJX 4308

Michigan: Allegan 4334, Besser 4349, Chrysler 4366, Community 4375, Consumers 4376, Dalton 4385, Dana 4386, Dart 4388, Davis 4391, DeRoy 4396, DeVos 4398, DeVos 4400, Dow 4405, Dow 4406, Dow 4408, DTE 4410, Family 4418, Ford 4430, Fremont 4438, General 4442, Gerstacker 4444, Gilmore 4445, Harding 4455, Herrick 4459, Hudson 4463, **Isabel 4466**, Leighton 4484, Manoogian 4491, McGregor 4498, **Mott 4510**, Mott 4511, Oleson 4516, Pokagon 4523, Sage 4531, Shelden 4537, Skillman 4543, Strosacker 4549, Towsley 4557, VanderWeide 4572, Walker 4575, Westerman 4582, Whirlpool 4583

Minnesota: Andersen 4603, Best 4612, **Better 4614**, Blandin 4617, Blue 4618, Bremer 4620, Butler 4622, Buuck 4623, Cargill 4628, Davis 4642, Deluxe 4644, Donaldson 4646, George 4662, Greystone 4668, Griggs 4669, Hardenbergh 4672, Hormel 4676, HRK 4677, Jerome 4681, Kelley 4686, Lilly 4696, Marbrook 4702, Martin 4704, McNeely 4710, **Medtronic 4712**, Minneapolis 4714, Minnesota 4715, **Mosaic 4722**, Ordean 4732, **O'Shaughnessy 4734**, Oswald 4735, **Patterson 4738**, RBC 4748, **St. Jude 4770**, TEAM 4779, Tozer 4782, United 4785, Wedum 4796, Winona 4806

Mississippi: **Armstrong 4810**, Blue 4815, Community 4820, Community 4821, Foundation 4827, Gulf 4830, McRae 4836, Mississippi 4839, Riley 4844

Missouri: Ameren 4851, Anheuser 4853, Arch 4855, Centene 4870, Commerce 4871, Community 4872, Cox 4874, Cray 4876, Express 4888, **Francis 4893**, Graybar 4898, H & R 4902, Hallmark 4906, Interco 4914, Jordan 4917, Kansas 4920, Kemper 4926, Laclede 4931, Millstone 4944, **Monsanto 4945**, Musgrave 4947, Nestle 4948, Orscheln 4951, Pettus 4954, Pillsbury 4955, Pillsbury 4956, Pott 4958, Reynolds 4961, Shaw 4970, Sosland 4977, Stern 4980, Truman 4996

Montana: Edwards 5008, Montana 5013, Treacy 5017, Washington 5018

Nebraska: Ameritas 5023, Buckley 5026, Dunklau 5036, Hastings 5046, Kind 5060, Lozier 5065, Omaha 5074, Phelps 5075, Union 5090, Weitz 5092

Nevada: **Browning 5104**, Buck 5105, Caesars 5106, Fairweather 5118, NV 5136, Pennington 5139

New Hampshire: Alexander 5162, Fuller 5172, Hunt 5177, Penates 5185

New Jersey: **Alcatel 5190, Allen 5191**, Atran 5197, Banbury 5200, **Berrie 5206**, Bonner 5208, Borden 5209, Cowles 5234, **Crane 5235**, Creamer 5236, Danellie 5237, Dodge 5243, **Edison 5248**, Firestone 5260, Fund 5270, Horizon 5305, Investors 5317, **Johnson 5326**, Kirby 5339, **Knowles 5345**, KPMG 5349, McGraw 5376, McMullen 5378, **Merck 5379**, OceanFirst 5394, Pascale 5403, **Perrin 5404**, Princeton 5411, Provident 5414, PSEG 5416, Roberts 5423, Schumann 5441, Silbermann 5456, South 5463, Subaru 5471, Sudler 5472, Turrell 5483, Victoria 5490, **Yin 5507**

New Mexico: Albuquerque 5511, Frost 5519, McCune 5529, New Mexico 5530, Santa Fe 5533, Thornburg 5535

New York: Abrons 5546, Adirondack 5556, **Alavi 5566**, Allen 5573, Altschul 5582, **American 5588, Ashner 5619**, Badgeley 5633, Bahnik 5634, Barker 5644, Barth 5648, Bay 5652, **Benenson 5663**, Berg 5667, Botwinick 5696, **Bristol 5711, Carnegie 5747**, Cattaraugus 5750, Century 5758, Chadwick 5760, Charina 5763, Charina 5764, Chautauqua 5766, Chernow 5771, **Citi 5780, Claiborne 5783, Clark 5784, Clark 5785**, Clark 5786, Coach 5790, Community 5802, Copper 5815, Countess 5821, Cricket 5827, Curran 5835, Daphne 5848, Deerfield 5865, **Delmas 5871, Deutsche 5876**, Dewar 5879, **Diamond 5881**, Dillon 5885, Dunwalke 5921, Dyson 5923, East 5925, Edlow 5935, EHA 5940, **Engelhard 5954**, Englander 5955, **Ford 5994, Foundation 6003**, Four 6006, Galasso 6032, Gebbie 6038, Gilder 6050, Gilman 6052, Gimbel 6053, **Goldman 6066**, Goldman 6068, **Goldman 6070**, Gorman 6083, Greve 6106, Grigg 6109, Guttman 6121, Haring 6133, Harriman 6137, **Hartford 6144**, Hayden 6150, Hermione 6163, **Heron 6164**, Hughes 6193, Hultquist 6195, Joelson 6232, Johnson 6238, Johnson 6239, **JPMorgan 6244**, Kaplan 6250, **Kaplan 6252**, Katzenberger 6258, Kautz 6260, Kennedy 6274, Klingenstein 6292, Knapp 6296, Kopf 6302, Lang 6326, **Lauder 6336**, Lauder 6337, Lehman 6346, Lincoln 6368, Link 6374, Link 6375, Lubo 6396, **Mayer 6449**, MBIA 6451, McCann 6453, McCarthy 6454, **Mellon 6470, Mertz 6477, MetLife 6479, Mitsubishi 6490**, Mizuho 6492, Monell 6497, **Moody's 6499**, Moore 6501, Morgan 6507, Moses 6511, Mulford 6514, **Neuberger 6538**, New York 6543, New York 6546, New York 6548, **New 6551**, Nias 6556, Noble 6561, **Norman 6565**, Normandie 6566, **Noyes 6571**, O'Connor 6578, Ohrstrom 6582, **Open 6593**, Ostrovsky 6600, **Ottaway 6603**, Paley 6610, Park 6615, **PepsiCo 6627**, Petrie 6632, **Pfizer 6633**, Phillips 6637, Price 6658, **Reed 6684, Revson 6693**, Rich 6697, Ritter 6712, Roberts 6717, **Rockefeller 6724**, Rockefeller 6725, Rosenberg 6743, Rubenstein 6762, Santa 6792, Schaffner 6800, Scherman 6804, Schnurmacher 6809, Schnurmacher 6810, Schumann 6813, Semlitz 6831, Sirus 6863, Slifka 6870, Spingold 6899, St. Faith's 6903, **Starr 6911**, Stern 6928, Stiefel 6931, **Straus 6934**, Strypemonde 6936, Sulzberger 6942, **Surdna 6947**, Tiffany 6978, Tiger 6980, Tisch 6988, Troy 7006, Tuttle 7014, Vetlesen 7027, Vidda 7030, **Vital 7033**, Voya 7038, Warner 7053, **Watson 7058, Weeden 7060**, Weissman 7071, Wilson 7088, **Wolfensohn 7098**

North Carolina: Adams 7133, **Bank 7139**, Belk 7148, Blue 7153, Brady 7156, Bryan 7161, Caine 7167, Cape Fear 7170, Community 7180, Delta 7191, Dover 7194, Duke 7195, Finley 7199, Food 7201, Goodrich 7213, High Point 7231, Mebane 7266, Morgan 7269, North Carolina 7273, **Oak 7276**, Olin 7279, Piedmont 7285, Polk 7287, Randleigh 7292, Reidsville 7294, Reynolds 7296, Reynolds 7298, Robertson 7305, Triangle 7328, Warner 7334, Weaver 7335

North Dakota: Leach 7353, MDU 7354, Stern 7360

Ohio: AK Steel 7366, American 7368, American 7369, Ar-Hale 7376, Austin 7380, **Bingham 7387**, Budig 7392, **Cardinal 7398**, Codrington 7409, Columbus 7411, Community 7415, Community 7416, Community 7417, Coshocton 7421, Covenant 7422, Dater 7426, Dayton 7429, Delaware 7431, Diamond 7435, **Eaton 7442**, Fairfield 7445, Fifth 7452, Fowler 7460, France 7462, GAR 7465, **Geisse 7468**, Gund 7478, Hoover 7491, Humphrey 7497, Jennings 7509, KeyBank 7523, Kulas 7532, Lennon 7537, Lubrizol 7546, Macy's 7552, Mercer 7567, Morgan 7579, Murphy 7584, Nationwide 7587, Nippert 7590, NiSource 7591, Nord 7594, Nordson 7596, **OMNOVA 7601**, Prentiss 7621, Reeves 7627, Salem 7640, Sisler 7664, Smith 7668, Spaulding 7670, Stranahan 7678, Twenty 7692, Wallace 7700, Wayne 7704, Weisbrod 7708, Western 7710, Wolfe 7719

Oklahoma: Bartlesville 7731, Bovaird 7735, Community 7743, Harris 7757, Hille 7759, Kaiser 7763, Kirkpatrick 7766, Nelson 7779, Oklahoma City 7781, Oklahoma 7782, Puterbaugh 7786, **Schusterman 7794**, Southern 7798, Stevens 7800, Stone 7801, Tandy 7803, Viersen 7808, Zink 7821

Oregon: Autzen 7823, Benton 7825, Caddock 7828, Carpenter 7831, Chambers 7832, Collins 7836, Esco 7841, Jackson 7855, Johnson 7858, Kinsman 7860, PacifiCorp 7877, PGE 7881, Schnitzer 7887, Tektronix 7894, Templeton 7895

Pennsylvania: Air 7907, **Alcoa 7908**, Allerton 7912, Arcadia 7918, Arete 7919, Baker 7925, Baker 7926, Bayer 7932, Britton 7951, Burke 7958, Burke 7959, Carnahan 7965, **Carnegie 7966**, Central 7972, Century 7974, Cestone 7975, Claneil 7982, Clapp 7983, **Colcom 7986**, Colonial 7988, Comcast 7989, Community 7990, Community 7993, Connelly 7995, Copernicus 7998, Dollar 8014, Drumcliff 8016, Fels 8035, First 8040, First 8041, FISA 8043, Fourjay 8047, Grable 8064, Grass 8068, Gray 8069, Heinz 8084, Highmark 8092, Hillman 8093, Hopwood 8096, Hoyt 8098, Hunt 8100, Jerlyn 8112, Kavanagh 8118, Kelly 8119, **Kennametal 8120**, Kind 8125, Kline 8129, Lenfest 8137, Lenfest 8138, **Little 8145**, Mandell 8153, Martin 8156, McCune 8160, McFeely 8163, **McKenna 8167**, Mellon 8172, Mellon 8173, Mine 8184, Morris 8188, Nichols 8197, O'Toole 8207, Pew 8220, Philadelphia 8221, Phoenixville 8223, PNC 8230, **PPG 8235**, Rees 8245, Roberts 8250, Rosenstiel 8254, Saint 8260, Scaife 8266, Schieffelin 8270, Scholler 8273, Scranton 8275, Shoemaker 8284, Smith 8289, Trexler 8320, Washington 8332, West 8334, Wheeler 8335, Withington 8344, Wyomissing 8350

Puerto Rico: Puerto Rico 8353

Rhode Island: Amica 8356, Biogen 8363, Carter 8368, CVS 8379, Daniels 8380, **Dorot 8384**, Freeman 8396, Hasbro 8403, Hoche-Scofield 8405, Textron 8446, TriMix 8448

South Carolina: Abney 8454, Black 8459, Bruce 8461, Byerly 8462, Central 8468, Daniel 8476, Foothills 8478, Roe 8494, Sims 8497, Smith 8499, Sonoco 8500, Spartanburg 8501

South Dakota: Larson 8516, Robinson 8520, Vucurevich 8524

Tennessee: Baptist 8533, Beaman 8534, Benwood 8535, Bridgestone 8537, Eastman 8561, Ezell 8564, Hamico 8576, Lyndhurst 8599, Martin 8606, **Scarlett 8624**, Stokely 8631, Wilson 8646

Texas: Abell 8650, Anderson 8663, Austin 8676, Bass 8690, Bauer 8691, Brown 8731, Cailloux 8742, Carter 8752, CFP 8758, Clayton 8765, Coates 8769, Community 8777, Covenant 8781, Davis 8799, Dean 8803, Eady 8818, Embrey 8828, Fikes 8844, Fisch 8846, Fish 8848, Fleming 8850, Fondren 8853, Frees 8857, Genecov 8862, Greathouse 8875, Halliburton 8884, Hamman 8888, Herzstein 8905, Hirsch 8910, **Houston 8916**, Houston 8917, **Jenesis 8932**, KDK-Harman 8949, Kempner 8952, Kimberly 8957, Kinder 8958, Kodosky 8966, Kohl 8967, Kronkosky 8970, Light 8984, Lubbock 8994, Lyons 8996, **Marshall 9000**, Martinez 9003, McDermott 9013, McGovern 9014, Meadows 9019, Moore 9034, Moran 9036, Northen 9063, O'Connor 9066, Orsinger 9073, Owen 9076, Owsley 9078, **Paloheimo 9080**, Parks 9081, Richardson 9130, Rockwell 9135, Rosewood 9140, Sams 9145, San Antonio 9148, **Scaler 9155**, Scott 9161, Scurlock 9162, Simmons 9174, Simmons 9175, Smith 9183, Smith 9184, Smith 9186, Strake 9208, Sumners 9214, Swinney 9218, Texas 9227, Tobin 9236, Topfer 9239, Trull 9240, Valero 9246, Waggoner 9252, Wal 9254,

Walsh 9256, Weaver 9260, Wichita 9277, Wortham 9292, Wright 9293, Young 9295, Zephyr 9299

Utah: Bamberger 9305, Burton 9309, Eccles 9320, Hemingway 9326, **Nu 9340**

Vermont: Lintilhac 9365

Virginia: Alleghany 9382, AMERIGROUP 9383, Arlington 9384, Cameron 9398, Capital 9400, CarMax 9401, Community 9410, Community 9411, Community 9416, Dominion 9422, Freddie 9435, Landmark 9467, Mars 9477, Moore 9489, Norfolk 9496, Samberg 9527, Washington 9552, Weissberg 9554, **WestWind 9555**, Williamsburg 9558

Washington: Blue 9588, **Brainerd 9590, Bullitt 9591**, Casey 9595, Columbia 9602, Dimmer 9610, Evertrust 9617, **Foundation 9622**, Fuchs 9624, **Gates 9625**, George 9626, Handsel 9638, Harder 9640, Harvest 9642, Kitsap 9659, **Kongsgaard 9661**, Laurel 9666, Lockwood 9671, Miller 9684, Oki 9694, PACCAR 9698, **Quixote 9707**, Raikes 9708, RealNetworks 9712, Renton 9715, Safeco 9723, **Samis 9725, Starbucks 9742, Stewardship 9744**, Tacoma 9750, Wiancko 9761, **Wilburforce 9762**

West Virginia: Daywood 9774, Eastern 9775, Kanawha 9780, Tucker 9796

Wisconsin: Acuity 9801, Alexander 9802, Alliant 9804, Bemis 9815, **Bradley 9819**, Community 9833, Cornerstone 9836, CUNA 9838, Evinrude 9841, Green Bay 9854, Green Bay 9855, Holz 9864, Johnson 9870, Kelben 9877, Krause 9886, Kress 9887, La Crosse 9889, McBeath 9901, Mead 9902, Milwaukee 9907, Northwestern 9914, Oshkosh 9916, Oshkosh 9917, **Schneider 9942**, Sentry 9944, Smith 9947, Stock 9953, U.S. 9957, Vine 9960, Waukesha 9965, Windhover 9968, Wisconsin 9970

Wyoming: Community 9975, McMurry 9986, Scott 9989, Seeley 9990, Wyoming 9999, Zimmerman 10000

Curriculum development

Alabama: BBVA 9, Community 21, Community 23, Community 24, Friedman 35, Kaul 43, Meyer 53, Walker 74, Webb 76

Alaska: Rasmuson 89

Arizona: Freeport-McMoRan 112, Globe 115, Steele 165, Webb 174

Arkansas: Cabe 182, Endeavor 186, Jonsson 192, Walton 211

California: **Agilent 220**, Alliance 229, **Amado 235, American 237, Amgen 238**, Applied 249, Aratani 250, Archstone 253, Atlas 266, **Avery 272**, Bechtel 294, Bechtel, 296, Bickerstaff 313, Caruso 382, Center 388, **Cisco 402**, Collins 412, Cowell 434, Crail 437, Eucalyptus 510, **First 530**, Fleishhacker 534, Garland 565, Gasser 566, GenCorp 569, Genentech 571, **Gilead 586**, Girard 591, Goldman 605, Goldman 606, Haas 641, Heller 676, **Hilton 692**, Hughes 713, **Kalliopeia 761, Kapor 764, Keck 774**, Kern 780, **Lingnan 841**, Marin 877, Miller 929, Monroe 935, Noyce 974, **Oracle 991**, Payne 1021, Rancho 1053, Reinhard 1061, **Righteous 1073, Rivendell 1077**, Roche 1083, **Rupe 1097, Saban 1101**, Severns 1143, Sonora 1198, **Special 1202**, Taper 1237, **Thrive 1255**, Ueberroth 1268, UniHealth 1270, Van Nuys 1284, Versacare 1288, Wohlford 1336

Colorado: Animal 1363, Aspen 1368, Community 1394, **Crowell 1398**, ECA 1404, Janus 1432, **Kinder 1439**, Ottens 1472, Piton 1480, Rose 1487, Summit 1511, Yampa 1528

Connecticut: **Calder 1554**, Community 1562, Community 1564, Connecticut 1566, Deloitte 1572, **GE 1591**, Hartford 1609, Larsen 1624, Main 1634, Pitney 1674, Xerox 1728

Delaware: **Memton 1819, Raskob 1845**

District of Columbia: Bauman 1882, Bender 1885, Block 1888

Florida: Amaturo 1966, **Believers 1989**, Burns 2006, **Chatlos 2019**, Community 2040, Community 2041, **Davis 2056**, duPont 2075, Engelberg 2086, Henderson 2152, **Johnson 2174, Knight 2191, Koch 2192**, NextEra 2251, St. Joe 2331, Thomas 2357

Georgia: **Challenge 2424**, Communities 2431, Cox 2446, Harrison 2481, **Imlay 2487**, Zeist 2584

Hawaii: Atherton 2586, Campbell 2592, Castle 2594, Wong 2622

Idaho: Albertson 2626, Blue 2627, Idaho 2632, **Micron 2637**

Illinois: **Abbott 2649**, Allstate 2657, Arthur 2673, Caterpillar 2738, Chaddick 2740, Chicago 2746, Coleman 2759, Crump 2782, Edwardsville 2817, Evanston 2826, Field 2831, Frankel 2842, Fry 2849, Kemper 2954, **Kemper 2955**, Kendall 2956, King 2960, Logan 2983, Martin 3003, McDougal 3013, Miller 3025, **Motorola 3042, Motorola 3043**, Polk 3084, Robinson 3122, Seabury 3146, Speh 3170, Sprague 3172, Steans 3175, Stone 3180, **Tellabs 3185**, Tracy 3189

Indiana: Bales 3261, Ball 3262, Blue 3265, Central 3272, Community 3284, Community 3286, Community 3287, Community 3290, **Cummins 3292**, Dekko 3296, Hancock 3313, Harrison 3314, Hendricks 3319, Huntington 3324, **Lilly 3340, Lilly 3342**, Madison 3346, Old 3363, Orange 3365, Pulliam 3372, Steuben 3390, Tipton 3391, Washington 3398, Welborn 3402

Iowa: Carver 3416, Cedar Rapids 3417, Iowa 3447, Maytag 3460, Principal 3476, Tye 3484, Wellmark 3490

Kansas: Blue 3497, Douglas 3509, Hutchinson 3521, McPherson 3534, **Shumaker 3546**

Kentucky: Good 3578, Humana 3582

Louisiana: Albemarle 3609, Baptist 3612, Community 3624

Maine: Horizon 3691, Libra 3696

Maryland: Abell 3712, Community 3759, **de Beaumont 3774**, Deutsch 3779, **Hughes 3818**, Kerr 3823, Meyerhoff 3849, Mid-Shore 3851, NASDAQ 3857, Polinger 3864, Rathmann 3867, **Thalheimer 3894**, Wright 3911

Massachusetts: Boston 3957, Cambridge 3971, Clarke 3986, Donahue 4023, Essex 4039, Foundation 4056, **Grand 4076**, Island 4109, Liberty 4145, Linde 4147, Lowell 4153, Poss 4226, Riley 4239, Rodgers 4242, Rubenstein 4248, Santander 4256, Sheehan 4271, Smith 4277, Staples 4282

Michigan: Albion 4332, Allegan 4334, Barry 4342, Battle Creek 4343, Bay 4344, Binda 4350, Chrysler 4366, Community 4374, Community 4375, Consumers 4376, Dart 4388, Davenport 4389, Dow 4405, DTE 4410, Dyer 4412, **Earhart 4413**, Flinn 4424, Ford 4430, **Foundation 4432**, Fremont 4438, Grand 4448, Greenville 4452, Herrick 4459, Marshall 4496, Mount Pleasant 4512, Oleson 4516, Pokagon 4523, Tuscola 4562, Weatherwax 4577, Wege 4579

Minnesota: 3M 4597, Best 4612, Bremer 4620, Cargill 4628, CHS 4636, Duluth 4649, Ecolab 4651, Grand Rapids 4667, **Medtronic 4712, O'Shaughnessy 4734**, Phillips 4741, West 4800, Xcel 4808

Mississippi: Blue 4815, Community 4820, Foundation 4827, Hardin 4831

Missouri: Commerce 4871, Community 4872, Green 4900, Kansas 4920, **Kauffman 4921**, Kemper 4926, **Monsanto 4945**, Oppenstein 4950, Pershing 4952, Sosland 4977

Nebraska: Dunklau 5036, Hirschfeld 5049, Mid-Nebraska 5068

New Hampshire: **Fidelity 5170**

New Jersey: **Allen 5191**, Dircks 5241, Dodge 5243, Elizabethtown 5253, Horizon 5305, KPMG 5349, **Merck 5379**, Merck 5380, **Perrin 5404**, Princeton 5411, Provident 5414, **Verizon 5489**

New Mexico: Frost 5519, Maddox 5528

New York: Achelis 5549, Adirondack 5556, **Arcus 5608, AVI 5628**, Berg 5667, Bodman 5692, **Bristol 5711, Bronfman 5717**, Burns 5732, **Carnegie 5747**, Cattaraugus 5750, Central 5757, Charina 5763, Charina 5764, Community 5802, Community 5804, Community 5805, Community 5807, Corning 5818, Curran 5835, **Delmas 5871, Deutsche 5876**, Flom 5989, **Ford 5995**, Freeman 6012, **Friends 6024**, Frog 6026, **Fuld 6029, Genesis 6042**, Gifford 6049, Gilman 6052, Gould 6087, Haring 6133, Harkness 6134, **Hartford 6144**, Heckscher 6157, **Johnson 6235, JPMorgan 6244**, Kornfeld 6304, Lehman 6346, **M & T 6406, Macy 6414, Mailman 6418**, Mars 6437, Monell 6497, New York 6548, Oishei 6584, **Ottaway 6603, Peterson 6630**, Petrie 6632, **Pfizer 6633, Porticus 6654, Reisman 6686, Rockefeller 6724**, Rose 6732, Rosenberg 6743, Schnurmacher 6809, Schnurmacher 6810, Semlitz 6831, Slifka 6870, Snow 6878, **Sparkplug 6894, Straus 6934**, Toyota 7002, Troy 7006, **United 7019, Vital 7033**, Warner 7053

North Carolina: BB&T 7143, BIN 7151, Blue 7153, Brady 7156, Broyhill 7160, Caine 7167, Cape Fear 7170, Community 7179, Community 7180, Community 7182, Duke 7195, Finley 7199, Greenville 7217, Mebane 7266, North Carolina 7273, North 7274, Olin 7279, Piedmont 7285, Polk 7287, Robertson 7305

North Dakota: Leach 7353

Ohio: Ar-Hale 7376, Ashtabula 7379, Barberton 7382, **Bingham 7387**, Community 7416, Coshocton 7421, Diamond 7435, Fairfield 7445, Fowler 7460, GAR 7465, Hershey 7487, Hoover 7492, Jennings 7509, **Kettering 7520**, KeyBank 7523, Licking 7540, Marion 7558, Miami 7569, Middletown 7570, Morgan 7578, Morgan 7579, Murphy 7584, Nippert 7590, Nordson 7596, O'Neill 7602, Saint 7639, Scioto 7657, Scripps 7659, Sisler 7664, Slemp 7665, Springfield 7671, St. Marys 7672, Stocker 7676, Troy 7688, Wallace 7700

Oklahoma: Bovaird 7735, **Ethics 7749**, Hille 7759, Inasmuch 7760, Kerr 7764, Kirkpatrick 7766, ONEOK 7783, **Schusterman 7794**, Tulsa 7807, Zink 7821

Oregon: Braemar 7826, Carpenter 7831, Chambers 7832, Collins 7836, Esco 7841, **Fohs 7844, Intel 7853**, Kinsman 7860, PacifiCorp 7877, PGE 7881

Pennsylvania: **Alcoa 7908**, Alexander 7910, Baker 7926, Bayer 7932, Buhl 7956, Carnahan 7965, Cestone 7975, Cestone 7976, Claneil 7982, Community 7994, Crawford 8001, Erie 8026, Fels 8035, Grable 8064, Highmark 8092, Hurd 8101, Kind 8125, Kline 8129, PNC 8230, Pottstown 8234, Rees 8245, Scaife 8266, Schenck 8269, Scranton 8275, Shoemaker 8284, Staunton 8296, **Templeton 8313**

Puerto Rico: Puerto Rico 8353

Rhode Island: McNeil 8418, TriMix 8448

South Carolina: Byerly 8462, Community 8475, Daniel 8476, Spartanburg 8501

South Dakota: Sioux Falls 8521, South Dakota 8522

Tennessee: Assisi 8530, **International 8585**, Jeniam 8587, **Scarlett 8624**, Wilson 8646

Texas: Alcon 8655, AT&T 8675, Bass 8688, Boeckman 8707, Brown 8731, CH 8759, Coates 8769, Community 8774, Community 8777, Cullen 8792, Fasken 8839, Fluor 8851, Halliburton 8884, **Houston 8916**, Houston 8917, Hudson 8919, Kempner 8952, Kimberly 8957, Kodosky 8966, Light 8984, **Marshall 9000**, McDermott 9013, McGovern 9014, McNair 9017, Meadows 9019, Northen 9063, Orsinger 9073, Powell 9105, Reynolds 9127, Rockwell 9135, San Antonio 9148, Simmons 9174, Stemmons 9201, Sterling 9203, Still 9207, Summerlee 9213, Sumners 9214, Terry 9224, Texas 9227, Waggoner 9252, Wichita 9277, Wolslager 9288, Young 9295

Utah: Hemingway 9326

Vermont: Gibney 9362, Vermont 9375

Virginia: Alleghany 9382, Arlington 9384, Beazley 9391, Cameron 9398, Community 9412, Community 9414, Dominion 9422, Landmark 9467, Memorial

9485, Mitsubishi 9487, Samberg 9527, Strong 9537, Weissberg 9554
Washington: Blue 9588, Grays 9631, Harvest 9642, Jones 9655, Kitsap 9659, Lucky 9673, Norcliffe 9693, **Quixote 9707**, Safeco 9723, True 9754
West Virginia: Eastern 9775, Tucker 9796
Wisconsin: **Bradley 9819**, Bradshaw 9820, Community 9832, Community 9833, Community 9834, Community 9835, Green Bay 9854, Harley 9859, Helfaer 9861, Kelben 9877, La Crosse 9889, Lakeview 9892, Northwestern 9914, Stock 9953, Thrivent 9956, Waukesha 9965
Wyoming: Community 9975, Scott 9989

Debt reduction

Arizona: Morris 148
Arkansas: Cabe 182
California: Ahmanson 222, Garland 565, Gasser 566, Marin 877
Delaware: AEC 1735
Florida: **Chatlos 2019**, Watts 2380
Georgia: Zeist 2584
Illinois: Frankel 2842, Hamill 2888, Keith 2952
Kansas: Hutchinson 3521
Kentucky: Community 3570
Louisiana: Booth 3616
Maryland: Blades 3734, Meyerhoff 3848
Massachusetts: Donahue 4023, Ellsworth 4035, Stoico 4294
Michigan: Dalton 4385, Gilmore 4445, Johnson 4468, Knight 4477
Minnesota: Slaggie 4766
Missouri: Dunn 4882, McGee 4942
New Jersey: Banbury 5200, Hyde 5310
New York: Charina 5763, Charina 5764, **Vital 7033**
North Carolina: Cannon 7169, Cape Fear 7170, Mebane 7266, Morgan 7269, Southern 7319, Weaver 7335
Ohio: Ashtabula 7379, Covenant 7422, GAR 7465, St. Marys 7672
Oregon: Kinsman 7860
Pennsylvania: Century 7974, Crels 8002, McFeely 8163, Trees 8319
South Carolina: Bruce 8461
Tennessee: Martin 8606
Texas: Cullen 8792, Herzstein 8905, **Houston 8916**, Kronkosky 8970, Lightner 8985, Meadows 9019, Once 9070, Sterling 9203
Washington: Lucky 9673
West Virginia: Daywood 9774
Wisconsin: Cornerstone 9836, Kelben 9877, West 9967

Donated equipment

California: Gap 563, **KLA-Tencor 792**
Idaho: Blue 2627
Kansas: Sprint 3549
Massachusetts: Berkshire 3946
Missouri: Ameren 4851
Wisconsin: **Schneider 9942**

Donated land

Minnesota: Remick 4751
Missouri: Ameren 4851

Donated products

Arizona: Delta 106
California: Clif 405, **Clorox 407**, Gap 563, **Genentech 570**, Oakland 977, Western 1316
Connecticut: Alexion 1533, Boehringer 1549
Delaware: Duane 1771
Florida: Glazer 2124
Illinois: **Abbvie 2650, Mondelez 3034, Walgreens 3210**
Indiana: **Lilly 3340, Lilly 3341**
Kansas: Delta 3507
Massachusetts: **Genzyme 4067**
Michigan: **Dow 4404**
Minnesota: Hormel 4676, **Medtronic 4712, Mosaic 4722**, NFC 4727
Nebraska: ConAgra 5030
New Jersey: **ARCH 5194, Johnson 5327, Merck 5381, Novartis 5393, Sanofi 5437**
New York: **Bristol 5712, Pfizer 6634**, Price 6658
Ohio: **Cardinal 7398**
Pennsylvania: **Bayer 7931**, GlaxoSmithKline 8061, Teva 8314, **Viropharma 8328**
Tennessee: Memphis 8610
Virginia: Reckitt 9516
Wisconsin: Roundy's 9936

Emergency funds

Alabama: Community 23, Community 24, McMillan 50, Walker 74, Webb 76
Arizona: Arizona 92, Green 117, **Kieckhefer 129**, Mooney 146, Webb 174
Arkansas: Cabe 182, Frueauff 188, Ross 199, Wal-Mart 210
California: Anaheim 239, AS&F 263, Barker 282, Campbell 373, Center 388, Change 393, Community 414, Community 416, Community 419, Community 420, Cowell 434, Crail 437, Desert 461, eBay 493, Firedoll 528, **Flextronics 535**, Garb 564, Garland 565, Goldman 605, Goldman 606, Green 621, Gumbiner 636, **Hilton 692**, Hughes 713, Humboldt 714, Irmas 725, **Kee 776**, Marin 877, Mendelson 912, Parker 1012, PIMCO 1037, Rancho 1053, Sacramento 1103, Santa Barbara 1116, Sobrato 1193, Sonora 1198, Taper 1237, **Vadasz 1275**, Van Nuys 1284, Ventura 1287, Wohlford 1336
Colorado: Animal 1363, Aspen 1368, Community 1391, Community 1394, Edmondson 1405, El Pomar 1406, **General 1419, Gill 1421**, Halton 1426, King 1440, M.D.C./Richmond 1450, Yampa 1528
Connecticut: Baldwin 1541, Community 1562, Community 1563, Community 1564, Community 1565, Hartford 1609, Main 1634, New Canaan 1650, Ohnell 1661, Xerox 1728
Delaware: Laffey 1800, **Raskob 1845**
District of Columbia: Aid 1879, Block 1888, Gottesman 1911, Gudelsky 1912, **Moriah 1932**
Florida: Amaturo 1966, Bush 2008, Community 2031, Community 2035, Community 2038, Community 2040, Community 2041, Conn 2042, Engelberg 2086, Greenburg 2137, Gulf 2142, Klorfine 2188, **Knight 2191**, Miami 2238, **Peterson 2267**, Quantum 2276, **Skelly 2324**, Southwest 2327, SWS 2347, Taylor 2353, Winter 2390, Wollowick 2393
Georgia: AGL 2400, Brain 2416, Camp-Younts 2421, **Coca 2428**, Community 2433, Day 2448, Georgia 2468, Loridans 2506, Mohawk 2517, Moore 2519, Savannah 2548, Southern 2554, Woolley 2581
Hawaii: Bank 2588, Hughes 2605
Idaho: Idaho 2632
Illinois: **Abbott 2648**, Allstate 2657, CME 2755, Community 2766, Day 2787, **Deere 2790**, Dillon 2796, Driehaus 2805, Edwardsville 2817, Field 2831, Frankel 2842, Herr 2909, Houlsby 2922, Illinois 2933, Keith 2952, King 2960, Landau 2966, Libra 2981, Owens 3068, Siragusa 3162, Speh 3170, Woodward 3243
Indiana: Anthem 3257, Brown 3269, Central 3272, Community 3278, Community 3280, Community 3281, Community 3282, Community 3284, Community 3285, Community 3286, Community 3288, Crown Point 3291, **Cummins 3292**, Elkhart 3298, Finish 3303, Harrison 3314, Hendricks 3319, Henry 3320, Heritage 3321, Johnson 3330, **Lilly 3342**, Madison 3346, Marshall 3348, Noble 3359, Northern 3360, Porter 3369, Rolland 3381, Steuben 3390, Tipton 3391, Wabash 3396, Waterfield 3399, Wells 3403, Whitley 3407
Iowa: Cedar Rapids 3417, Community 3423, Community 3424, Guernsey 3437, GuideOne 3438, Maytag 3460, McElroy 3461, United 3485
Kansas: Beren 3496, Capitol 3498, Cooper 3503, Douglas 3509, McPherson 3534, Salina 3540, Sunderland 3551, Topeka 3552, Wyandotte 3556
Kentucky: C.E. 3566, Community 3569, Community 3570, Foundation 3575, Independence 3583
Louisiana: Baton Rouge 3613, Community 3624, Coughlin 3626, Goldring 3638, New Orleans 3656, Wilson 3671, **Woldenberg 3672**
Maine: Iberdrola 3693, Libra 3696
Maryland: **Bearman 3728**, Blades 3734, Blaustein 3736, Community 3758, Community 3759, Community 3760, Davis 3772, Knott 3826, Meyerhoff 3848, Meyerhoff 3849, Mid-Shore 3851, Washington 3904
Massachusetts: **Barr 3937**, Bayrd 3938, Berkman 3945, Berkshire 3948, Beveridge 3950, Cambridge 3971, Cape Cod 3974, Clipper 3987, Community 3991, Davis 4011, Ellsworth 4035, Essex 4039, Fields 4046, Fireman 4049, Fuller 4063, **Phillips 4219**, Rubenstein 4248, Santander 4256, Stevens 4289, Stoddard 4293, Thompson 4307
Michigan: Allegan 4334, Ann Arbor 4340, Battle Creek 4343, Bay 4344, Charlevoix 4361, Chrysler 4366, Community 4369, Community 4373, Community 4374, Community 4375, Dalton 4385, Dana 4386, **Fisher 4423**, Ford 4430, Fremont 4438, General 4442, Gerstacker 4444, Gilmore 4445, Greenville 4452, Herrick 4459, Kalamazoo 4472, **Kellogg 4473**, Manoogian 4491, Miller 4503, Mount Pleasant 4512, Pokagon 4523, Saginaw 4532, Tuscola 4562, Weatherwax 4577
Minnesota: **Andersen 4601**, Beverly 4615, Bremer 4620, Deluxe 4644, Duluth 4649, Ecolab 4651, Grand Rapids 4667, Greystone 4668, Kopp 4688, Northwest 4730, Rochester 4755, WCA 4795, Winona 4806
Missouri: Ameren 4851, Commerce 4871, Community 4872, **Enterprise 4887**, Green 4900, H & R 4902, Hall 4905, Kansas 4920, **Kauffman 4921**, Lopata 4938, Millstone 4944, Oppenstein 4950, Pershing 4952, Pillsbury 4955, Reynolds 4961, Shaw 4970, Speas 4978, Stern 4980
Montana: Edwards 5008, Montana 5013, Whitefish 5019
Nebraska: Buckley 5026, Grand Island 5044, Hirschfeld 5049, Kearney 5055, Lincoln 5063, Mutual 5071, Omaha 5074, Phelps 5075
Nevada: Cord 5110, Fairweather 5118, Nevada 5134
New Hampshire: Endowment 5169, Fuller 5172, Hunt 5177, Penates 5185
New Jersey: **Allen 5191**, Banbury 5200, **Berrie 5206**, Carolan 5225, Cowles 5234, Delano 5240, Karma 5331, Kirby 5339, OceanFirst 5394, Pascale 5403, Princeton 5411, **Prudential 5415**, Roberts 5423, Sudler 5472, Summit 5473, Victoria 5490, Weston 5499
New Mexico: McCune 5529, Santa Fe 5533
New York: Abeles 5544, **AIG 5563, American 5588**, Bravmann 5705, Brooklyn 5718, Charina 5763, Charina 5764, Chautauqua 5766, Community 5802, Community 5804, Community 5805, Community 5807, Diamond 5880, Edouard 5936, Emerson 5950, Farash 5969, Gifford 6049, Glens Falls 6057, Glickenhaus 6058, Gorman 6083, **Gottlieb 6085**, Grigg 6109, Hermione 6163, Hoerle 6180, Katzenberger 6258, Kennedy 6274, Lehman 6346, Lubo 6396, Mulford 6514, **Neuberger 6538**, O'Connor 6578, Ohrstrom 6582, Petrie 6632, Phillips 6637, Raiff 6675, Rockefeller 6725, **Ross 6754**, Schaffner 6800, Schnurmacher 6809, Schnurmacher 6810, Semlitz 6831, Sheldon 6841, Siebens 6853, Smith 6876, St. George's 6904, **Starr 6911, Straus 6934**, Sulzberger 6942, Truman 7007, **Vital 7033**, Warner 7053, **Weeden 7060**, Weissman 7071, Wells 7073, Western 7078, Wilson 7088

North Carolina: BB&T 7143, Belk 7148, Blumenthal 7154, Cemala 7174, Community 7179, Community 7180, Community 7181, Dover 7194, Duke 7195, Hanes 7221, Hanes 7222, North Carolina 7273, Piedmont 7285, Reidsville 7294, Robertson 7305, Smith 7317, Tannenbaum 7326, Triangle 7328, Weaver 7335, Winston-Salem 7340

North Dakota: Fargo 7351, Leach 7353, Stern 7360

Ohio: Anderson 7372, Ar-Hale 7376, Ashtabula 7379, Butler 7396, Cincinnati 7404, Community 7417, Covenant 7422, Diamond 7435, Fairfield 7445, **Generation 7470**, Gund 7478, Hamilton 7481, Humphrey 7497, Jewish 7511, Levin 7539, Mayerson 7561, Middletown 7570, Miniger 7572, National 7586, Nationwide 7587, Nordson 7596, Richland 7630, Saint 7639, Scripps 7659, Sherwin-Williams 7661, Slemp 7665, Spaulding 7670, Stark 7673, Stocker 7676, Tiffin 7682, Troy 7688, Twenty 7692, Wallace 7700, Wayne 7704, White 7715, Woodruff 7721, Wuliger 7722, Youngstown 7723

Oklahoma: Bernsen 7733, Community 7743, Hille 7759, Masonic 7771, McMahon 7776, Robinson 7789, Sarkeys 7793, **Schusterman 7794**, Tandy 7803, Tulsa 7807, Viersen 7808

Oregon: Chambers 7832, Esco 7841, Johnson 7858, Kinsman 7860, Meyer 7870, PacifiCorp 7877, Schnitzer 7887, Templeton 7895

Pennsylvania: **Alcoa 7908**, Beneficial 7936, Blanchard 7944, Britton 7951, Centre 7973, Cestone 7975, Cestone 7976, Colonial 7988, Community 7991, Community 7994, Dixon 8012, Dolfinger 8013, Erie 8026, Fourjay 8047, **Heinz 8083**, Hopwood 8096, Hurd 8101, Huston 8103, Kline 8129, Lehigh Valley 8136, **Little 8145**, McFeely 8163, Merchants 8175, O'Toole 8207, Philadelphia 8221, **PPG 8235**, Saint 8260, Smith 8288, Steinman 8300, Tyler 8322, West 8334, Wheeler 8335, Wyomissing 8350

Puerto Rico: Puerto Rico 8353

Rhode Island: Carter 8368, Daniels 8380, Kimball 8410, Rhode Island 8429

South Carolina: Abney 8454, Bruce 8461, Coastal 8472, Community 8474, **ScanSource 8495**, Self 8496, Smith 8498, Spartanburg 8501

South Dakota: Vucurevich 8524

Tennessee: Assisi 8530, Baptist 8533, Bridgestone 8537, Dollar 8558, Frist 8568, Wilson 8646

Texas: Amarillo 8660, Anderson 8663, **BP 8718**, Cailloux 8742, Carter 8752, Communities 8773, Community 8774, Community 8775, Cowden 8783, Dallas 8795, Edwards 8824, Elkins 8826, Embrey 8828, Fikes 8844, Fleming 8850, Greathouse 8875, Hamill 8887, **Houston 8916**, Hudson 8919, Kempner 8952, Kinder 8958, Kronkosky 8970, Light 8984, Lubbock 8994, Lyons 8996, **Marshall 9000**, McGovern 9014, Meadows 9019, Moore 9034, Owsley 9078, Parks 9081, Payne 9086, Permian 9091, Rachal 9117, San Angelo 9147, San Antonio 9148, Scurlock 9162, Shield 9170, Simmons 9174, Simmons 9175, Sterling 9203, Stern 9204, Stumberg 9210, Sunnyside 9215, Temple 9223, Tucker 9241, Waggoner 9252, Wal 9254, Wichita 9277, Wortham 9292

Utah: Burton 9309, Hemingway 9326, Simmons 9351

Vermont: Evslin 9360, Vermont 9375

Virginia: Arlington 9384, **Bosack 9395**, Community 9410, Community 9411, Community 9415, Community 9416, Landmark 9467, Lynchburg 9474, Titmus 9543, Washington 9552

Washington: Allen 9567, **Brainerd 9590**, **Bullitt 9591**, Cheney 9598, Community 9605, Fuchs 9624, Grays 9631, Green 9632, Horizons 9645, Invested 9652, Kitsap 9659, **Kongsgaard 9661**, Lockwood 9671, **Quixote 9707**, **Samis 9725**, **Starbucks 9742**, Tacoma 9750

West Virginia: Daywood 9774, Kanawha 9780, McDonough 9784, Parkersburg 9789, Your 9799

Wisconsin: Alexander 9803, Alliant 9804, Argosy 9808, Beloit 9814, Community 9832, Community 9835, Cornerstone 9836, Green Bay 9854, Incourage 9867, Johnson 9870, Kelben 9877, Mead 9902, Milwaukee 9907, Northwestern 9914, Oshkosh 9916, Pick 9920, **Schneider 9942**, **Taylor 9955**, U.S. 9957

Wyoming: Community 9975, Kerr 9981, McMurry 9986

Employee matching gifts

Alabama: Energen 32, Protective 59, Regions 61

Arizona: Freeport-McMoRan 112, Globe 115, Piper 152

Arkansas: Union 208, Wal-Mart 210

California: **Agilent 220**, **Amgen 238**, **Avery 272**, Bechtel 294, **Bechtel 295**, Bechtel, 296, **Beckman 297**, California 365, California 366, Campbell 373, **Capital 375**, **Cisco 402**, **Clorox 407**, College 411, Copley 428, Coulter 433, Crail 437, Disney 467, Gap 563, GenCorp 569, **Getty 579**, Haas 642, **Haas 643**, Hewlett 686, Hewlett 687, **Hilton 692**, Hofmann 700, Intuit 723, Irvine 727, Jacobs 739, **Keck 774**, **KLA-Tencor 792**, Marin 877, **Mattel 886**, **McConnell 898**, McKesson 903, Monterey 936, **Omidyar 984**, Orfalea 994, Pacific 1003, **Packard 1006**, PG&E 1033, PIMCO 1037, San Diego 1108, San Francisco 1109, Schwab 1127, Schwab 1128, Sempra 1140, Sierra 1163, **Strauss 1223**, Stuart 1225, Synopsys 1232, Teichert 1244, UniHealth 1270, **Waitt 1295**, Weingart 1307, Wells 1312, Western 1316

Colorado: Chambers 1385, Colorado 1390, Community 1391, ECA 1404, El Pomar 1406, Encana 1407, **Gill 1421**, Janus 1432, **Kinder 1439**, Piton 1480, ProLogis 1485, Vodafone 1519, **Western 1521**

Connecticut: Aetna 1531, Barnes 1542, Deloitte 1572, **GE 1591**, Hubbell 1614, Lego 1627, NewAlliance 1651, Northeast 1656, Pitney 1674, **Praxair 1676**, Xerox 1728

Delaware: CenturyLink-Clarke 1750

District of Columbia: Coyne 1896, Kiplinger 1922, **Public 1940**

Florida: Bi-Lo 1996, Bush 2008, Darden 2051, **Davis 2056**, Haller 2146, Harris 2149, **Johnson 2174**, **Knight 2191**, NextEra 2251, Publix 2275, Quantum 2276, Ryder 2302, St. Petersburg 2332, SWS 2347

Georgia: Blank 2413, **Coca 2428**, Colonial 2430, Equifax 2455, Georgia 2468, Mohawk 2517, **UPS 2566**

Hawaii: Hawaiian 2603, Island 2606

Idaho: **Micron 2637**

Illinois: **Abbott 2649**, Allstate 2657, Aon 2667, **Baxter 2690**, Caterpillar 2738, Chicago 2746, CME 2755, Community 2763, Crown 2781, **Deere 2790**, Donnelley 2800, Duchossois 2809, Energizer 2824, Field 2831, **Gallagher 2855**, Grand 2875, **Harris 2893**, Illinois 2934, **Joyce 2946**, Lumpkin 2986, **MacArthur 2989**, McGraw 3015, **Mondelez 3034**, **Motorola 3042**, Munson 3045, Northern 3059, Omron 3063, Pasquinelli 3071, Polk 3084, Prince 3089, Prince 3090, Siragusa 3162, **Spencer 3171**, **State 3174**, Tracy 3189, United 3200, **Wrigley 3244**

Indiana: Anthem 3257, **Cummins 3292**, Koch 3334, **Lilly 3340**, **Lilly 3342**, Lincoln 3344, **Lumina 3345**, Old 3363, Unity 3393, Vectren 3394

Iowa: AEGON 3409, Aviva 3411, Meredith 3463, MidAmerican 3465, Pella 3473, **Pioneer 3474**, Principal 3476, **Rockwell 3477**

Kansas: Capitol 3498, Delta 3507, McPherson 3534, Security 3544, Sprint 3549, Topeka 3552

Kentucky: Community 3569, Humana 3582, LG&E 3586, Yum! 3608

Louisiana: Albemarle 3609, Booth 3616, Community 3624

Maine: TD 3710

Maryland: Abell 3712, Allegis 3719, **Blaustein 3735**, Choice 3748, Freeman 3797, GEICO 3801, **Grace 3807**, Kerr 3823, Knott 3826, Lockheed 3837, Mid-Shore 3851, Price 3865, Rembrandt 3868

Massachusetts: Arbella 3926, Boston 3956, Eastern 4030, **Elsevier 4036**, **Grand 4076**, Liberty 4145, Reebok 4234, Santander 4256, **State 4285**

Michigan: Chrysler 4366, Consumers 4376, Dana 4386, **Dow 4404**, DTE 4410, **Fetzer 4420**, Ford 4430, Fremont 4438, Frey 4440, General 4442, Gilmore 4445, Grand Rapids 4447, Hudson 4463, Kalamazoo 4472, **Kellogg 4474**, **Kellogg's 4475**, **Kresge 4479**, Masco 4497, McGregor 4498, Miller 4503, **Mott 4510**, Skillman 4543, Steelcase 4547, Towsley 4557, Whirlpool 4583, Wolverine 4593

Minnesota: 3M 4597, Blandin 4617, Deluxe 4644, Donaldson 4646, Ecolab 4651, **Fuller 4659**, General 4661, Graco 4666, Hormel 4676, HRK 4677, Jostens 4684, Land 4691, McKnight 4709, McNeely 4710, **Medtronic 4712**, Northwest 4729, **Pentair 4739**, Piper 4743, Pohlad 4745, RBC 4748, Securian 4761, **St. Jude 4770**, SUPERVALU 4775, TCF 4778, Travelers 4783, U.S. 4784, Valspar 4786, Wallestad 4791, Xcel 4808

Mississippi: Mississippi 4839, Regions 4843

Missouri: Ameren 4851, American 4852, Anheuser 4853, Bunge 4865, Emerson 4885, Express 4888, Graybar 4898, H & R 4902, Hallmark 4906, Kansas 4920, **Kauffman 4921**, Kauffman 4922, Laclede 4931, **Monsanto 4945**, Shelter 4971, Sosland 4977

Montana: First 5009

Nebraska: ConAgra 5030, Lincoln 5063, Lozier 5065, Mutual 5071, Nelnet 5072

Nevada: NV 5136, **Reynolds 5143**

New Hampshire: **Fidelity 5170**

New Jersey: Bard 5202, Campbell 5223, Clare 5230, Dodge 5243, Horizon 5305, **IDT 5311**, Ingersoll-Rand 5314, **JM 5323**, **Johnson 5326**, **Johnson 5329**, KPMG 5349, **Merck 5379**, **Milbank 5385**, OceanFirst 5394, **Prudential 5415**, PSEG 5416, Subaru 5471, Unilever 5484, **Verizon 5489**

New Mexico: **Lannan 5526**, PNM 5532

New York: Altman 5579, American 5587, **Arcus 5608**, Assurant 5621, AXA 5629, **Bristol 5711**, **Bronfman 5717**, Brooklyn 5718, **Carnegie 5747**, Central 5757, **Clark 5785**, Coach 5790, Corning 5818, **Dana 5845**, **Deutsche 5876**, Dodge 5892, **Duke 5917**, Fifth 5976, **Ford 5994**, Galasso 6032, **Guggenheim 6115**, **Harriman 6136**, **Hartford 6144**, Hazen 6151, **Heron 6164**, **IBM 6203**, IFF 6206, **JPMorgan 6244**, **Kress 6308**, Littauer 6379, Loews 6388, **Luce 6398**, **Macy 6414**, MBIA 6451, **MetLife 6479**, Mitsui 6491, Mizuho 6492, **Moody's 6499**, Mutual 6518, New York 6544, New York 6548, Novartis 6569, NYSE 6573, **Open 6593**, Park 6615, **PepsiCo 6627**, **Pfizer 6633**, Price 6658, **Prospect 6663**, **Rockefeller 6723**, **Rockefeller 6724**, **Sage 6782**, Select 6829, Simon 6859, **SMBC 6873**, **Starr 6911**, Staten 6912, **Surdna 6947**, Triad 7005, Voya 7038, **Wallace 7043**

North Carolina: **Bank 7139**, Delta 7191, Duke 7196, Goodrich 7213, Olin 7279, Reynolds 7296, Reynolds 7298, Spangler 7320, Triangle 7328, VF 7332, Weaver 7335

North Dakota: MDU 7354

Ohio: AK Steel 7366, **Cardinal 7398**, Charities 7400, Cliffs 7407, Coshocton 7421, Dorn 7439, **Eaton 7442**, FirstEnergy 7455, GAR 7465, Hoover 7492, KeyBank 7523, Lubrizol 7546, Macy's 7552, Middletown 7570, Nationwide 7587, Nord 7594, Nordson 7596, Ohio 7599, **OMNOVA 7601**, Parker 7611, Progressive 7623, Scripps 7659, Sherwin-Williams 7661, St. Marys 7672, Western 7710

Oklahoma: American 7728, McCasland 7772, Noble 7780, Oklahoma 7782, ONEOK 7783

Oregon: Ford 7845, **Intel 7853**, Meyer 7870, Mission 7873, PacifiCorp 7877, Tektronix 7894

Pennsylvania: **ACE 7905**, Air 7907, **Alcoa 7908**, Armstrong 7922, Baker 7925, **BNY 7945**, Buhl 7956, CIGNA 7981, Connelly 7995, GlaxoSmithKline 8060, **Heinz 8083**, McCune 8161, Penn 8216, Pew 8220, PNC 8230, **PPG 8235**,

Rees 8245, Saint 8260, United 8325, Vanguard 8327, West 8334
Rhode Island: Amica 8356, Biogen 8363, Citizens 8374, **FM 8393**, Hasbro 8403, Textron 8446
South Carolina: Sonoco 8500
South Dakota: Larson 8516, Robinson 8520
Tennessee: Bridgestone 8537, First 8565, Frist 8568, HCA 8582, Hyde 8584, **International 8585**, Lyndhurst 8599
Texas: Abell 8650, AT&T 8675, **Baker 8679**, BNSF 8706, **BP 8718**, Brown 8731, **ExxonMobil 8833**, Fluor 8851, Halliburton 8884, **Houston 8916**, Houston 8917, Kimberly 8957, Meadows 9019, NuStar 9065, Rachal 9117, Rees-Jones 9125, Rosewood 9140, Shell 9168, Simmons 9174, Temple 9223, Texas 9227, Wichita 9277
Vermont: **Ben 9358**
Virginia: AMERIGROUP 9383, Capital 9400, CarMax 9401, Dominion 9422, Freddie 9435, **Gannett 9439**, **Genworth 9441**, MeadWestvaco 9484, Mitsubishi 9487, Norfolk 9496, **Northrop 9498**, SunTrust 9539
Washington: Apex 9574, Avista 9576, **Bullitt 9591**, Casey 9596, Everett 9616, **Gates 9625**, Intermec 9651, Murdock 9689, PACCAR 9698, Plum 9704, Puget 9705, RealNetworks 9712, Russell 9722, Safeco 9723, **Starbucks 9742**
West Virginia: McDonough 9784
Wisconsin: Alliant 9804, **Baird 9811**, Bemis 9815, CUNA 9838, Harley 9859, Johnson 9870, Johnson 9874, Keller 9878, Mead 9902, Menasha 9903, Northwestern 9914, Rexnord 9932, Rockwell 9934, Sentry 9944, Smith 9947, Thrivent 9956, U.S. 9957, Windhover 9968, Wisconsin 9969, Wisconsin 9970, Zilber 9972
Wyoming: Community 9975, Scott 9989

Employee volunteer services

Alabama: Vulcan 73
Arizona: Freeport-McMoRan 112
Arkansas: Wal-Mart 210
California: **Agilent 220**, Allergan 228, **Amgen 238**, **Avery 272**, **Bechtel 295**, **Broadcom 349**, CAA 362, **Capital 375**, CareFusion 377, **Cisco 402**, **Clorox 407**, Coulter 433, eBay 493, **Flextronics 535**, Gap 563, GenCorp 569, GSF 633, Intuit 723, **KLA-Tencor 792**, **Mattel 886**, McKesson 903, Schwab 1127, Sempra 1140, **Strauss 1223**, Wells 1312, Western 1316
Colorado: COPIC 1397, **Western 1521**
Connecticut: Aetna 1531, Barnes 1542, Boehringer 1549, Lego 1627, Pitney 1674, **Praxair 1676**, Rockville 1682, Xerox 1728
Delaware: CenturyLink-Clarke 1750
District of Columbia: **Hitachi 1916**
Florida: Darden 2051, NextEra 2251, Ryder 2302
Georgia: Aflac 2399, **Georgia 2469**, **UPS 2566**
Hawaii: First 2598, Hawaiian 2603
Idaho: **Micron 2637**
Illinois: Allstate 2657, Aon 2667, **Baxter 2690**, Caterpillar 2738, **Deere 2790**, Donnelley 2801, Illinois 2934, **Mondelez 3034**, **Motorola 3042**, **Motorola 3043**, Northern 3059, **State 3174**, Trustmark 3193, United 3199, **Wrigley 3244**
Indiana: Anthem 3257, Koch 3334, **Lilly 3340**, Lincoln 3344, Vectren 3394
Iowa: AEGON 3409, Aviva 3411, Meredith 3463, Pella 3473, Wellmark 3490
Kansas: Capitol 3498, Sprint 3549
Kentucky: Humana 3582, Yum! 3608
Louisiana: Albemarle 3609, Blue 3615
Maine: TD 3710
Maryland: Choice 3748, Lockheed 3837, Price 3865, Rembrandt 3868
Massachusetts: Arbella 3926, Berkshire 3946, Boston 3957, **Grand 4076**, Hanover 4086, Liberty 4145, New England 4193, Starwood 4284, **State 4285**
Michigan: Chrysler 4366, Consumers 4376, DTE 4410, Ford 4430, General 4442, **Kellogg's 4475**, Whirlpool 4583
Minnesota: 3M 4597, Deluxe 4644, General 4661, Graco 4666, Land 4691, **Medtronic 4712**, **Mosaic 4722**, NFC 4727, RBC 4748, Securian 4761, Travelers 4783, Xcel 4808
Missouri: American 4852, Anheuser 4853, Commerce 4871, Emerson 4885, H & R 4902, Hallmark 4906
Montana: First 5009
Nebraska: Mutual 5071
Nevada: Caesars 5106, NV 5136
New Jersey: **Alcatel 5190**, Campbell 5223, Horizon 5305, Ingersoll-Rand 5314, **Merck 5379**, PSEG 5416, **Verizon 5489**
New Mexico: PNM 5532
New York: American 5587, **Bristol 5711**, Coach 5790, **Credit 5826**, **Deutsche 5876**, First 5979, IFF 6206, **JPMorgan 6244**, **M & T 6406**, MBIA 6451, **MetLife 6479**, **Mitsubishi 6490**, Mitsui 6491, Mizuho 6492, **Moody's 6499**, Morgan 6507, **Neuberger 6538**, New York 6548, NYSE 6573, **PepsiCo 6627**, **Pfizer 6633**, **Polo 6651**, TE 6966, Voya 7038
North Carolina: **Bank 7139**, Duke 7196, Goodrich 7213, Piedmont 7285, VF 7332
North Dakota: MDU 7354
Ohio: **Cardinal 7398**, Dayton 7429, **Eaton 7442**, KeyBank 7523, Kroger 7531, Lubrizol 7546, Macy's 7552, Nationwide 7587, Nordson 7596, **OMNOVA 7601**, Scripps 7659, Westfield 7711
Oklahoma: American 7728, ONEOK 7783
Oregon: **Intel 7853**
Pennsylvania: **ACE 7905**, Air 7907, **Alcoa 7908**, Armstrong 7922, CIGNA 7981, Comcast 7989, EQT 8025, **Heinz 8083**, **Kennametal 8120**, **PPG 8235**
Rhode Island: Amica 8356, Citizens 8374, CVS 8379, **FM 8393**
South Carolina: Blue 8460, **ScanSource 8495**, Sonoco 8500
Tennessee: First 8565, HCA 8582, **International 8585**
Texas: AT&T 8675, **BP 8718**, **ExxonMobil 8833**, Fluor 8851, Halliburton 8884, Kimberly 8957, Penney 9089, Texas 9227, **Whole 9276**
Virginia: CarMax 9401, Freddie 9435, **Genworth 9441**, MeadWestvaco 9484, Mitsubishi 9487
Washington: Intermec 9651, Plum 9704, Puget 9705, RealNetworks 9712, **Starbucks 9742**
Wisconsin: Alliant 9804, **Baird 9811**, CUNA 9838, Harley 9859, Menasha 9903, Northwestern 9914, **Schneider 9942**, Smith 9947, Thrivent 9956, Wisconsin 9970

Employee-related scholarships

Alabama: Alabama 1, Bashinsky 7, BBVA 9, Protective 59, Vulcan 73
Arizona: Freeport-McMoRan 112
Arkansas: Wal-Mart 210
California: **Bechtel 295**, Blue 320, **Clorox 407**, Disney 467, GenCorp 569, Heffernan 673, Jacobs 738, **Mattel 886**, McKesson 903, Mosher 945, Sacramento 1103, Sierra 1164
Connecticut: Barnes 1542, Garden 1590, **GE 1591**, Northeast 1656, Xerox 1728
Delaware: Presto 1840
Florida: Community 2032, Kelly 2181, Rayonier 2281, Ryder 2302
Georgia: **Georgia 2469**, **UPS 2566**
Illinois: **Abbott 2648**, Andrew 2662, **Baxter 2690**, Donnelley 2801, Illinois 2934, Omron 3063, Speh 3170, **State 3174**, Trustmark 3193
Indiana: Community 3284, Harrison 3314, Koch 3334, Miller 3355
Iowa: Nelson 3467, Pella 3473, Siouxland 3480, Vermeer 3486
Kansas: Koch 3529, Topeka 3552
Kentucky: Blue 3560, Humana 3582, LG&E 3586
Louisiana: Albemarle 3609
Maine: Cianbro 3683, Hannaford 3690
Maryland: Choice 3748, GEICO 3801, Lockheed 3837
Massachusetts: Boston 3957, Hanover 4086, Santander 4256
Michigan: Chrysler 4366, Community 4374, **Cooper-Standard 4380**, Dana 4386, Fabri 4416, Ford 4430, Grand Rapids 4447, Lenawee 4485, Steelcase 4547, Whirlpool 4583
Minnesota: Donaldson 4646, General 4661, Graco 4666, Hormel 4676, Jostens 4684, McNeely 4710, **Patterson 4738**, Valspar 4786
Missouri: Arch 4855, Emerson 4885, H & R 4902, Hall 4905, Kansas 4920, Orscheln 4951, Shelter 4971
Montana: Montana 5013, Washington 5018
Nebraska: ConAgra 5030, Nelnet 5072
New Jersey: Campbell 5223, **Chubb 5229**, **Siemens 5454**, Subaru 5471, Unilever 5484, **Verizon 5489**
New Mexico: Chase 5517
New York: **AIG 5564**, American 5587, AXA 5629, **Bristol 5711**, Central 5756, Community 5803, Community 5804, Hunter 6196, Loews 6388, **MetLife 6479**, Mitsui 6491, **Moody's 6499**, New York 6548, **PepsiCo 6627**, **Starr 6911**
North Carolina: **Bank 7139**, Community 7180, Duke 7196, Giles 7208, Goodrich 7213, North Carolina 7273, Nucor 7275, Reynolds 7296, Triangle 7328
North Dakota: MDU 7354
Ohio: AK Steel 7366, **Cardinal 7398**, Cliffs 7407, Fairfield 7445, Fifth 7452, Macy's 7552, National 7586, **OMNOVA 7601**, Scripps 7659, Sherwin-Williams 7661, **Timken 7683**
Oklahoma: Noble 7780, Tulsa 7807, Williams 7814
Pennsylvania: **Alcoa 7908**, Armstrong 7922, Berks 7939, Community 7993, Community 7994, **PPG 8235**, Steinman 8299, United 8325, West 8334
Rhode Island: CVS 8379, Textron 8446
South Carolina: Inman 8485, Spartanburg 8501
South Dakota: Robinson 8520
Tennessee: Bridgestone 8537, Temple 8633
Texas: BNSF 8706, Carter 8753, Community 8775, Dallas 8795, Fluor 8851, Halliburton 8884, **Houston 8916**, Kimberly 8957, Nestle 9056, Simmons 9175
Utah: Miller 9334
Virginia: Community 9410, Lynchburg 9474, Norfolk 9496, Smithfield 9535
Washington: Columbia 9602, Intermec 9651, Plum 9704, **Vista 9756**
West Virginia: Tucker 9796
Wisconsin: Alliant 9804, Bemis 9815, Briggs 9822, Culver's 9837, Johnson 9870, Johnson 9874, ManpowerGroup 9899, Rexnord 9932, Sentry 9944, Stock 9953, Windhover 9968, Wisconsin 9970
Wyoming: True 9995

Endowments

Alabama: Alabama 1, Brock 13, Crampton 26, Daniel 27, Hearin 38, Hill 40, Vulcan 73, Webb 76
Arizona: Globe 115, Green 117, **Kieckhefer 129**, Linde 135, Morris 148, Piper 152, Stardust 164, Stewart 166
Arkansas: Arkansas 179, Cabe 182, Endeavor 186, Frueauff 188, Murphy 193, Ross 199, Walker 209, White 212
California: Aratani 250, Ayrshire 276, Barker 282, **Beavers 293**, **Berman 311**, Bickerstaff 313, Bren 339, Campini 374, Center 388, Community 416, Community 417, Community 420, Copley 428, Croul 441, Dachs 446, Danford 448, Davies 454, Davis 455, El Dorado 500, Eucalyptus 510, Finley 527, Fremont 548, Garland 565, Gellert 568, Geschke 576, Goldsmith 608, Haas 641, **Hilton 692**, Hutton 718, Jacobs 739, Jones 756, Kern 780, Kirchgessner 790, Koshland 804, Lucas 855, Mabie 863, McBean 892, **McConnell 898**, McMillen 905, Mosher 945, Norris 971, North 972,

Payne 1021, Peppers 1024, Philibosian 1036, Rogers 1087, Rudd 1096, Smith 1182, Smith 1187, Smullin 1190, Stanislaus 1211, Stauffer 1214, Tesuque 1246, Thornton 1252, Tuohy 1267, Ueberroth 1268, **Vadasz 1275**, Wasserman 1300, Wollenberg 1339

Colorado: Chambers 1385, Community 1391, Community 1393, Community 1395, Halton 1426, Lipscomb 1449, M.D.C./Richmond 1450, **Malone 1453**, Peierls 1475, Pioneer 1479, Summit 1511, Yampa 1528

Connecticut: Community 1562, Community 1565, Garden 1590, Huisking 1615, NewAlliance 1651, Oaklawn 1657, Ohnell 1661, Zachs 1730

Delaware: Devonwood 1768, Good 1785, **Memton 1819**, Parker 1829, Phillips 1835, Schwartz 1857

District of Columbia: Bender 1885, **Davis 1898**, Gewirz 1909, Gudelsky 1912, Kiplinger 1922, **Moriah 1932**

Florida: Batchelor 1983, Community 2031, Community 2039, **Davis 2056**, Duckwall 2069, Dunspaugh-Dalton 2073, Gooding 2130, Greenburg 2137, Indian 2166, **Johnson 2174**, Kennedy 2182, Klorfine 2188, **Knight 2191**, Magruder 2225, Miami 2238, NextEra 2251, Rinker 2286, Southwest 2327, St. Joe 2331, Sylvester 2348, Thomas 2357, Van Vleet 2368, Watts 2380, Wells 2383

Georgia: Aflac 2399, AGL 2400, Campbell 2420, Courts 2441, Cousins 2442, DuBose 2450, Glenn 2470, Harris 2479, Knox 2498, Lanier 2499, Lewis 2502, Loridans 2506, Moore 2520, Rich 2537, Savannah 2548, **UPS 2566**

Hawaii: Bank 2588, First 2598, **Watumull 2620**

Idaho: Cunningham 2630, Wishnick 2646

Illinois: Alsdorf 2659, Arthur 2673, Bauer 2687, Blair 2699, Butler 2729, Crown 2781, Dillon 2796, Donnelley 2802, Dunard 2810, Emerson 2822, Frankel 2842, **Grainger 2874**, Gray 2878, Hamill 2888, Hermann 2908, Keith 2952, King 2960, Logan 2983, Louis 2985, Lurie 2987, Miller 3025, Monticello 3036, Munson 3045, Negaunee 3047, Northern 3059, Omron 3063, **Woodbury 3240**

Indiana: **Ackerman 3252**, Ball 3262, Blue 3265, Community 3279, Community 3285, Community 3290, **Cummins 3292**, Dekko 3296, Fairbanks 3301, Ford 3305, Henry 3320, Huntington 3324, **Lilly 3342**, McMillen 3352, Northern 3360, Ogle 3362, Rolland 3381, Steuben 3390, Unity 3393, Wabash 3396, Waterfield 3399, Whitley 3407

Iowa: Community 3423, Guernsey 3437, Kuyper 3456, Lee 3457, Maytag 3460, Meredith 3464, Poweshiek 3475, Wallace 3488

Kansas: Baughman 3493, Beach 3494, Community 3502, Garvey 3516, Hutchinson 3521, Salina 3540, Sunderland 3551

Kentucky: Blue 3560, C.E. 3566, Community 3570, Cralle 3571, Public 3597, Spray 3602

Louisiana: Almar 3610, Baton Rouge 3613, Booth 3616, Community 3623, Community 3624, Diboll 3628, Freeman 3636, Huie 3643, Jones 3645, New Orleans 3656, RosaMary 3663

Maine: Alfond 3678, Alfond 3679, King 3694, Libra 3696, Maine 3698

Maryland: Baltimore 3726, **Blaustein 3735**, Delaplaine 3778, Helena 3812, Henson 3814, Hirschhorn 3816, Jacobsohn 3819, Knott 3826, Meyerhoff 3848, Meyerhoff 3849, Middendorf 3850, Rathmann 3867, Riepe 3869, Sheridan 3883, Wasserman 3905

Massachusetts: Alden 3921, Barker 3936, **Barr 3937**, Berkman 3945, Berkshire 3948, Cabot 3968, **China 3982**, DeFreitas 4013, Demoulas 4014, Donahue 4023, Eastern 4030, Fields 4046, Foundation 4056, Grinspoon 4080, Highland 4098, Linde 4147, Lynch 4159, North 4194, Pappas 4204, Perkin 4213, **Phillips 4219**, Pierce 4220, **Rosenberg 4245**, Schooner 4261, Stevens 4288, Stevens 4289, Webster 4322

Michigan: Barry 4342, BorgWarner 4353, Charlevoix 4361, Community 4375, Dow 4406, Dow 4407, Dow 4408, **Fisher 4423, Frankel 4437**, Fremont 4438, Gerstacker 4444, Grand 4448, Greenville 4452, Herrick 4459, Hickman 4460, Leighton 4484, Lenawee 4485, Manoogian 4491, Mount Pleasant 4512, Pentecost 4520, Ravitz 4526, Sage 4531, Shelden 4537, Strosacker 4549, Sturgis 4550, Towsley 4557, Wege 4579, Westerman 4582, Wilson 4589, Wolters 4592

Minnesota: AHS 4599, Grand Rapids 4667, Griggs 4669, Lilly 4696, Marbrook 4702, Martin 4704, Minnesota 4715, Opus 4731, **O'Shaughnessy 4734**, TEAM 4779, Weyerhaeuser 4804

Mississippi: C Spire 4817, Chisholm 4818, Community 4820, Community 4821, CREATE 4822, Hardin 4831, Maddox 4834, Riley 4844, Sullivan 4846, Vicksburg 4848

Missouri: Burns 4866, Centene 4870, Community 4872, Goppert 4896, Green 4900, Jordan 4917, JSM 4918, Kansas 4920, Kauffman 4922, Kooyumjian 4930, Lay 4934, Lopata 4938, Reynolds 4961, Saigh 4965, Sander 4967, Shaw 4970, Sosland 4977, Ward 4998

Montana: Whitefish 5019

Nebraska: Fremont 5039, Gardner 5041, Hastings 5046, Hitchcock 5050, Kind 5060, Merrick 5067

Nevada: Bretzlaff 5103, **Browning 5104**, Parasol 5138

New Hampshire: Johnson 5178, Putnam 5186

New Jersey: **Allen 5191**, Atran 5197, Banbury 5200, Brotherton 5216, Charles 5227, Cowles 5234, Grassmann 5281, Kirby 5339, Lipman 5364, McMullen 5378, **Newcombe 5391**, Taub 5478, Union 5485, Wilf 5502

New Mexico: Hubbard 5523, **Lannan 5526**, New Mexico 5530

New York: Abeles 5544, Adirondack 5556, **Arcus 5608**, Barrington 5647, Barth 5648, **Benenson 5663**, Brooklyn 5718, Brooks 5719, Cattaraugus 5750, Charina 5763, Charina 5764, Community 5804, Community 5805, Community 5806, Dewar 5879, Dillon 5885, Dodge 5892, Dunwalke 5921, Eastern 5927, Elmezzi 5948, Emerson 5950, **Engelhard 5954**, Fanwood 5968, **Ford 5994, Ford 5995, Foundation 6003**, Four 6006, **Fuld 6029**, Gebbie 6038, Gerry 6043, Gilder 6050, Glickenhaus 6058, Goldman 6068, Greve 6106, **Harriman 6136, Hauser 6147, Hearst 6155, Hearst 6156**, Heineman 6158, Hermione 6163, Jaharis 6223, Kaplan 6250, Kautz 6260, Kennedy 6274, Lehman 6346, Lemberg 6350, Littauer 6379, Manton 6425, Markle 6431, McGonagle 6460, **Mellon 6470**, Moore 6501, Moses 6511, New York 6543, Noble 6561, Nuhn 6572, O'Connor 6578, Ohrstrom 6582, **Pforzheimer 6635, Reed 6684**, Richmond 6703, Ritter 6712, Rose 6732, Rose 6737, Ruffin 6770, Schmitt 6808, Shoreland 6847, Siebens 6853, Simons 6861, Solomon 6885, **Starr 6911**, Steel 6914, Steele 6915, **Straus 6934**, Sulzberger 6942, **Summerfield 6944, Tanaka 6961**, Vetlesen 7027, Vidda 7030, **Vital 7033**, Weinberg 7066, Weissman 7071, Widgeon 7081

North Carolina: BB&T 7143, Belk 7148, Blumenthal 7154, Broyhill 7160, Bryan 7161, Capital 7171, Chatham 7175, Community 7180, Community 7182, Dalton 7187, Deaver 7190, Dover 7194, Duke 7195, Finley 7199, Gorelick 7215, Greenville 7217, Hanes 7221, Hanes 7222, Kenan 7248, Levine 7255, Mebane 7266, Morgan 7269, North Carolina 7273, Vanderbilt 7331, Weaver 7335, Winston-Salem 7340, Woodward 7343

North Dakota: North Dakota 7357

Ohio: American 7368, Ar-Hale 7376, **Bingham 7387**, Budig 7392, Community 7415, Diamond 7435, Dorn 7439, Fairfield 7445, Findlay 7453, GAR 7465, Gund 7477, H.C.S. 7479, Haslinger 7482, Hershey 7487, Humphrey 7497, **Kettering 7520**, Kettering 7522, Kramer 7529, Maltz 7553, Marietta 7557, Marion 7558, Mather 7559, Morgan 7578, Murch 7582, Muskingum 7585, Oelschlager 7598, **OMNOVA 7601**, Osteopathic 7605, Parker 7611, Richland 7630, Schlink 7650, Schmidlapp 7651, Scripps 7659, Semple 7660, Silk 7663, Sisler 7664, Slemp 7665, Stocker 7676, Wayne 7704, Weatherhead 7707

Oklahoma: Bovaird 7735, Communities 7742, Harris 7757, Hille 7759, Masonic 7771, McGee 7774, Oxley 7785, Puterbaugh 7786, Rapp 7787, Records 7788, Sarkeys 7793, Stevens 7800, Tulsa 7807, Viersen 7808, Warren 7809, Westheimer 7812

Oregon: Benton 7825, Jackson 7855, Jeld 7856, John 7857, Kinsman 7860, Macdonald 7866

Pennsylvania: Alexander 7910, Ametek 7913, Arcadia 7918, Britton 7951, Chester 7979, Claneil 7982, Clapp 7983, **Colcom 7986**, Copernicus 7998, Eden 8021, Farber 8032, Ferree 8036, Fourjay 8047, Grass 8068, Greenfield 8071, Hansen 8079, **Heinz 8083, Heinz 8085**, Hillman 8093, Hopwood 8096, Hunt 8100, Kelly 8119, Lancaster 8135, Luzerne 8152, McCune 8160, McCune 8161, McFeely 8163, McKenna 8166, McKinney 8168, McLean 8169, Phoenixville 8223, Pierce 8224, Rees 8245, Seraph 8279, Shaffer 8281, Shoemaker 8284, Simmons 8285, Trees 8319, Wyomissing 8350

Rhode Island: Amica 8356, van Beuren 8449

South Carolina: Abney 8454, Bruce 8461, Central 8468, Daniel 8476, Gibbs 8480, Graham 8481, Smith 8498, Springs 8504

South Dakota: Larson 8516, South Dakota 8522

Tennessee: Assisi 8530, Bridgestone 8537, Carlton 8541, Eastman 8561, First 8565, Johnson 8588, Plough 8615, Proctor 8617, Stokely 8631, Tucker 8638, Wilson 8646

Texas: Alkek 8658, Bass 8688, Brackenridge 8719, Cain 8743, Carter 8752, Cockrell 8770, Community 8774, Community 8775, Community 8777, Constantin 8778, Cook 8779, Cullen 8792, Doss 8813, Dunn 8816, Edwards 8823, Elkins 8826, Fikes 8844, Fish 8848, Fluor 8851, Franklin 8855, Gulf 8878, Herzstein 8905, Hoglund 8913, **Houston 8916**, Houston 8917, Huffington 8920, Jamail 8929, Johnson 8941, Kinder 8958, Klabzuba 8960, Kodosky 8966, Kronkosky 8970, Light 8984, Lyman 8995, Lyons 8996, Marsh 8999, Mayborn 9006, McCullough 9011, McDermott 9013, McGovern 9014, Moss 9043, Perkins 9090, Reynolds 9127, Richardson 9130, Schutte 9160, Scurlock 9162, Shield 9170, Smith 9184, Starling 9199, Sterling 9203, Stern 9204, Still 9207, Stumberg 9210, Sturgis 9211, Sumners 9214, Terry 9224, Tobin 9236, TurningPoint 9244, Waggoner 9252, WEDGE 9263, Wortham 9292, Young 9295, Zeller 9298

Utah: Dee 9312

Virginia: Cabell 9397, Community 9410, Community 9411, Community 9412, Community 9414, Fife 9429, Folger 9431, Herndon 9451, Kanter 9459, Mars 9477, Norfolk 9496, Northern 9497, Reynolds 9519, Robins 9523, Titmus 9543, Washington 9552

Washington: Blue 9588, Community 9604, Cowles 9607, Danz 9609, Dimmer 9610, Everett 9616, Harder 9640, Milgard 9683, Miller 9684, Norcliffe 9693, Renton 9715, Sherwood 9733

West Virginia: Eastern 9775, Maier 9782, Tucker 9796, Your 9799

Wisconsin: Cleary 9831, Community 9835, Cornerstone 9836, Johnson 9871, Johnson 9874, Krause 9886, Lubar 9894, Mead 9902, Neese 9911, Oshkosh 9916, Pick 9920, Racine 9924, St. Croix 9950, Stock 9953, West 9967, Wisconsin 9969

Wyoming: Community 9975, Ellbogen 9977, McMurry 9986, Seeley 9990, Storer 9992

Equipment

Alabama: Community 21, Community 23, Community 24, Crampton 26, Daniel 27, Dixon 30, Hearin 38, Hill 40, **International 41**, Kaul 43, Meyer 53, Smith 66, Walker 74, Webb 76

Alaska: Alaska 79, Rasmuson 89

New York: Achelis 5549, Allyn 5575, Arkell 5611, Badgeley 5633, Baird 5636, Barker 5644, **Bat 5651**, Berg 5667, Bodman 5692, Brooklyn 5718, Brooks 5719, Cattaraugus 5750, Central 5757, Charina 5764, Chautauqua 5766, Community 5802, Community 5804, Community 5805, Community 5807, Community 5808, Corning 5818, **Cummings 5832**, Davenport 5850, Decker 5863, DeMatteis 5873, Dodge 5892, Dolan 5895, Dolan 5896, **Dreyfus 5912**, Dyson 5923, East 5926, Emerson 5950, **Ford 5995**, Freed 6011, Gebbie 6038, **Genesis 6042**, Gifford 6049, Glens Falls 6057, Golisano 6077, Greater 6099, Grigg 6109, Hayden 6150, Hudson 6191, Hugoton 6194, Hultquist 6195, Kinney 6285, Klee 6286, Lehman 6346, Lenna 6352, Loewy 6389, **M & T 6406**, McCann 6453, McGonagle 6460, Monell 6497, **Moody's 6499**, National 6528, New York 6543, **Norcross 6564**, Northern 6567, Northfield 6568, Nuhn 6572, O'Connor 6578, Ohrstrom 6582, **Porticus 6654**, **Reisman 6686**, Richmond 6703, Ritter 6712, Robinson 6721, Rochester 6722, **Ross 6754**, Schenectady 6802, Schmitt 6808, Schnurmacher 6809, Schnurmacher 6810, Semlitz 6831, Sheldon 6841, Snow 6878, St. Giles 6905, Statler 6913, Steele 6915, Strypemonde 6936, Tisch 6988, **Toshiba 6997**, **Towerbrook 7001**, Toyota 7002, Troy 7006, Truman 7007, Tuttle 7014, Vetlesen 7027, Warner 7053, Wells 7073, Western 7078, Widgeon 7081, Wilson 7088, Wright 7104

North Carolina: Adams 7133, BIN 7151, Blue 7153, Brady 7156, Cannon 7169, Cape Fear 7170, Cemala 7174, Community 7179, Community 7180, Community 7181, Community 7182, Duke 7195, Finley 7199, French 7203, Ghidotti 7206, Glass 7210, Hanes 7221, Hanes 7222, High Point 7231, Leever 7253, North Carolina 7273, **Oak 7276**, Olin 7279, Piedmont 7285, Polk 7287, Reidsville 7294, Reynolds 7297, Robertson 7305, Smith 7317, Southern 7319, Tannenbaum 7326, Van Houten 7330, Weaver 7335, Woodward 7343

North Dakota: Fargo 7351, Leach 7353, MDU 7354, Myra 7355, North Dakota 7357, Stern 7360

Ohio: Ariel 7377, Ashland 7378, Ashtabula 7379, Barberton 7382, **Bingham 7387**, Boutell 7388, Bruening 7391, Cincinnati 7404, Codrington 7409, Community 7413, Community 7414, Community 7415, Corbin 7420, Coshocton 7421, Covenant 7422, Dater 7426, David 7427, Dayton 7428, Delaware 7431, Dorn 7439, **Eaton 7442**, Emery 7443, Erie 7444, Fairfield 7445, Fifth 7452, Fowler 7460, Frost 7464, GAR 7465, **Geisse 7468**, Greene 7474, Haslinger 7482, Hershey 7487, Home 7489, Hoover 7491, Hoover 7492, Humphrey 7497, Jewish 7511, Jochum 7513, **Kettering 7520**, Kettering 7521, Kettering 7522, Kulas 7532, Lehner 7536, Lennon 7537, Levin 7539, Licking 7540, Loeb 7544, Lubrizol 7546, Marietta 7557, Marion 7558, Mathile 7560, Miami 7569, Middletown 7570, Miniger 7572, Montgomery 7575, Morgan 7577, Murphy 7584, Muskingum 7585, National 7586, Nordson 7596, Orr 7604, Piqua 7620, Prentiss 7621, Reeves 7627, Reinberger 7628, Richland 7630, Saint 7639, Salem 7640, Schlink 7650, Schmidlapp 7651, Schott 7652, Scioto 7657, Scripps 7659, Semple 7660, Sisler 7664, Slemp 7665, Spaulding 7670, Springfield 7671, Stark 7673, Stocker 7676, Sutphin 7679, Tiffin 7682, **Timken 7684**, Troy 7688, Wallace 7700, Wayne 7704, Westfield 7711, White 7715, Wodecroft 7717, Wolfe 7719, Youngstown 7723

Oklahoma: Bartlesville 7731, Bernsen 7733, Bovaird 7735, Chapman 7740, Community 7743, Hardesty 7756, Harris 7757, Helmerich 7758, Hille 7759, Inasmuch 7760, Kaiser 7763, Kerr 7764, Kirkpatrick 7766, Mabee 7770, McGee 7774, McMahon 7776, Noble 7780, Oklahoma City 7781, Oklahoma 7782, ONEOK 7783, Puterbaugh 7786, Rapp 7787, Sarkeys 7793, Share 7795, Southern 7798, Stone 7801, Tulsa 7807, Viersen 7808

Oregon: Adler 7822, Autzen 7823, Benton 7825, Braemar 7826, Carpenter 7831, Chambers 7832, Collins 7836, Collins 7837, Esco 7841, Ford 7845, Jeld 7856, Johnson 7858, Kinsman 7860, Lamfrom 7863, Meyer 7870, Mission 7873, Oregon 7876, Randall 7883, Schnitzer 7887, Swindells 7892, Tektronix 7894, Tucker 7896, Young 7901

Pennsylvania: **Alcoa 7908**, Alexander 7910, Ametek 7913, Arcadia 7918, Baker 7926, Bayer 7932, Beneficial 7936, Blanchard 7944, Carnahan 7965, Central 7972, Centre 7973, Century 7974, Cestone 7975, Cestone 7976, Claneil 7982, **Colcom 7986**, Community 7990, Community 7991, Community 7993, Community 7994, Connelly 7995, Crawford 8001, Crels 8002, Degenstein 8008, Dixon 8012, DSF 8017, Eden 8021, Erie 8026, ESSA 8028, Fels 8035, First 8040, First 8041, FISA 8043, Foundation 8046, Fourjay 8047, Gray 8069, **Heinz 8085**, Highmark 8092, Hurd 8101, Huston 8102, Huston 8103, Kavanagh 8118, **Kennametal 8120**, Keystone 8122, Kline 8129, Lehigh Valley 8136, **Little 8145**, McCune 8161, McFeely 8163, McKenna 8166, McLean 8169, Mellon 8172, Mellon 8173, **Moore 8186**, Morris 8188, Nelson 8195, Nichols 8197, Penn 8216, Phillips 8222, Phoenixville 8223, **PPG 8235**, Presser 8236, Rees 8245, Russell 8258, Schenck 8269, Seraph 8279, Smith 8288, Smith 8289, Snee 8291, Stackpole 8295, Trees 8319, Trexler 8320, Tyler 8322, Washington 8332, Wells 8333, Widener 8336, Wyomissing 8350, York 8351

Puerto Rico: Puerto Rico 8353

Rhode Island: Buehler 8364, Champlin 8370, Daniels 8380, Hoche-Scofield 8405, McNeil 8418, Rhode Island 8429, Textron 8446

South Carolina: Abney 8454, Blue 8460, Bruce 8461, Byerly 8462, Central 8468, Coastal 8472, Community 8474, Community 8475, Daniel 8476, Graham 8481, Roe 8494, Self 8496, Sims 8497, Smith 8499, Spartanburg 8501, Springs 8504

South Dakota: Sioux Falls 8521, Vucurevich 8524

Tennessee: Assisi 8530, Benwood 8535, Christy 8545, Community 8548, East 8560, Ezell 8564, First 8565, Frist 8568, HCA 8582, **International 8585**, Jeniam 8587, Johnson 8588, Martin 8606, Plough 8615, Thompson 8636

Texas: Abell 8650, Amarillo 8660, Anderson 8664, Austin 8676, Bass 8690, **Bolivar 8708**, Bridwell 8726, Brumley 8734, Cailloux 8742, Cameron 8747, Carter 8752, CH 8759, Coastal 8768, Communities 8773, Community 8774, Community 8776, Community 8777, Constantin 8778, Cowden 8783, Cullen 8792, Dallas 8795, Davis 8799, Doss 8813, Eady 8818, Edwards 8823, Edwards 8824, El Paso 8825, Elkins 8826, Embrey 8828, Farish 8838, Fikes 8844, Fisch 8846, Fluor 8851, Gulf 8878, Haggerty 8881, Halliburton 8884, Halsell 8885, Hamman 8888, Herzstein 8905, Hillcrest 8909, Hoblitzelle 8912, Hoglund 8913, **Houston 8916**, Houston 8917, Johnson 8941, Jones 8944, Kempner 8952, King 8959, Klabzuba 8960, Kronkosky 8970, Light 8984, Lightner 8985, Lubbock 8994, Lyons 8996, **Marshall 9000**, Martinez 9003, McDermott 9013, Meadows 9019, Meredith 9023, Moody 9033, Moore 9034, Moss 9043, Newman 9061, **Oldham 9069**, Once 9070, Orsinger 9073, Owen 9077, Payne 9086, Penney 9089, Peterson 9095, Priddy 9109, Pryor 9113, Puett 9114, Rachal 9117, Rapoport 9122, Reynolds 9127, Richardson 9130, Saada 9142, Sams 9145, San Angelo 9147, San Antonio 9148, Scott 9161, Simmons 9174, Simmons 9175, Smith 9179, Smith 9184, Smith 9186, Stemmons 9201, Sterling 9203, Stern 9204, Strake 9208, Stumberg 9210, Sturgis 9211, Summerlee 9213, Swinney 9218, Temple 9223, Tobin 9236, Tocker 9237, Trull 9240, Waco 9251, Waggoner 9252, Ward 9258, Wichita 9277, Wolslager 9288, Wright 9293, Zachry 9296, Zephyr 9299

Utah: Ashton 9304, Bamberger 9305, Burton 9309, Dee 9312, Dumke 9315, Dumke, 9316, Eccles 9317, Eccles 9319, Hemingway 9326, **Nu 9340**

Vermont: Gibney 9362, Tarrant 9373, Vermont 9375

Virginia: Alleghany 9382, Beazley 9391, **Bosack 9395**, Cabell 9397, Cameron 9398, Carter 9403, Community 9410, Community 9412, Community 9414, Community 9415, Community 9416, Dominion 9422, Fralin 9433, **Gannett 9439**, Graham 9445, Gwathmey 9447, Landmark 9467, **Loyola 9471**, Lynchburg 9474, Mars 9477, McGlothlin 9483, Memorial 9485, Morgan, 9490, Norfolk 9496, Parsons 9504, Perry 9506, Robins 9523, Scott 9529, SunTrust 9539, Titmus 9543, Washington 9552, Weissberg 9554

Washington: Anderson 9572, Avista 9576, Bainbridge 9578, Blue 9588, Cheney 9598, Columbia 9602, Community 9604, Dimmer 9610, Everett 9616, Evertrust 9617, Forest 9620, Foster 9621, Fuchs 9624, Grays 9631, Handsel 9638, Inland 9650, Intermec 9651, Kitsap 9659, **Kongsgaard 9661**, Lauzier 9667, Lockwood 9671, Lucky 9673, McEachern 9678, Milgard 9683, Miller 9684, Murdock 9689, Nesholm 9691, Norcliffe 9693, Pendleton 9703, Plum 9704, **Quixote 9707**, Renton 9715, Seattle 9731, Tacoma 9750, **Wilburforce 9762**, Yakima 9767

West Virginia: Beckley 9769, Chambers 9772, Community 9773, Daywood 9774, Eastern 9775, Hamilton, 9776, Kanawha 9780, Maier 9782, McDonough 9784, Parkersburg 9789, Schenk 9793, Your 9799

Wisconsin: Alexander 9803, Alliant 9804, Bachhuber 9809, Beloit 9814, **Bradley 9819**, Bradshaw 9820, Clark 9830, Community 9832, Community 9833, Community 9834, Community 9835, Cornerstone 9836, Evinrude 9841, Green Bay 9854, Green Bay 9855, Holz 9864, Iddings 9866, Incourage 9867, Johnson 9874, La Crosse 9889, Lakeview 9892, Lunda 9896, Madison 9897, Mead 9902, Milwaukee 9907, Oshkosh 9916, Racine 9924, Rennebohm 9931, **Schneider 9942**, Stock 9953, **Taylor 9955**, U.S. 9957, **Wagner 9961**, Waukesha 9965, West 9967, Wisconsin 9969, Wisconsin 9970

Wyoming: Community 9975, Kerr 9981, McMurry 9986, Seeley 9990

Exchange programs

California: Aratani 250, **Lingnan 841**

Colorado: Summit 1511, Yampa 1528

Illinois: Charleston 2742

Indiana: Henry 3320, Waterfield 3399

Iowa: Clarinda 3418, Community 3423

Kansas: McPherson 3534

Maryland: Wasserman 3905

Massachusetts: Island 4109, Reynolds 4238

Michigan: Community 4369

Minnesota: Oswald 4735

New Jersey: Atran 5197, McMullen 5378

New York: Berg 5667, **Clark 5785**, Freeman 6012, **Kade 6247**, **Lauder 6336**, Mitsui 6491, **Philippe 6636**, **Reed 6684**, **Starr 6911**, **Tai 6959**, **Trust 7009**

North Carolina: Community 7180, Smith 7317

Ohio: Fox 7461, Murphy 7584

Oklahoma: Puterbaugh 7786

Pennsylvania: Alexander 7910, Ametek 7913

Texas: **Houston 8916**, Lyons 8996

Washington: **Samis 9725**

Faculty/staff development

Connecticut: **GE 1591**

Illinois: **Abbott 2649**

Louisiana: Blue 3615

New Hampshire: **Fidelity 5170**

New York: **Citi 5780**

Fellowships

Alabama: **International 41**, Kaul 43
Alaska: CIRI 85, Rasmuson 89
Arizona: Piper 152
California: **Alpert 231**, Aratani 250, Baxter 288, Capote 376, **Christensen 399**, Clif 405, Connell 424, **Draper 481**, Eucalyptus 510, Fleishhacker 534, Genentech 571, **Getty 579**, Giannini 581, **Glenn 594**, Haynes 664, Hellman 678, Hewitt 685, Hillblom 690, **Hilton 692**, Jones 756, Koret 801, **Lingnan 841**, Mericos 918, Morgan 940, **Packard 1006**, Parsons 1013, Price 1043, **Righteous 1073, Rupe 1097**, San Francisco 1109, Schlinger 1124, Sefton 1134, Stauffer 1214, Synopsys 1232, Taube 1241, **Thrive 1255**, Towbes 1260, **Vadasz 1275**
Connecticut: Childs 1558, Community 1562, Deloitte 1572, Larsen 1624, Lehrman 1628, **Newman's 1652, Richardson 1679**, Rosenthal 1684
Delaware: Schwartz 1857
District of Columbia: Aid 1879, Gudelsky 1912, **National 1934, Searle 1946**
Florida: **Barbour 1980, Davis 2056**, Engelberg 2086, Haller 2146, **Knight 2191, Larson 2203, Russell 2301, Skelly 2324**, St. Joe 2331, St. Petersburg 2332, Van Vleet 2368
Georgia: Aflac 2399, **Coca 2428**, Watson 2569
Hawaii: **Watumull 2620**
Idaho: **Micron 2637**
Illinois: Arthur 2673, Blair 2699, **Brinson 2715**, Butler 2729, Crown 2781, Frankel 2842, **Grainger 2874**, Irwin 2936, **MacArthur 2989**, Monticello 3036, **Poetry 3083**, Schmitt 3140, **Scholl 3141**, Siragusa 3162, **Spencer 3171, Terra 3186**, Washington 3217
Indiana: Fairbanks 3301, **Lilly 3342**
Iowa: Maytag 3460, McElroy 3461
Kansas: Beren 3496, Capitol 3498, McPherson 3534
Kentucky: Good 3578
Louisiana: Jones 3645
Maine: Hungarian-American 3692, Switzer 3709
Maryland: **Casey 3745, de Beaumont 3774, Deerbrook 3776**, Deutsch 3779, **Hughes 3818**, Life 3833, Meyerhoff 3848, NASDAQ 3857, Rathmann 3867
Massachusetts: **American 3923, Barr 3937**, Berkman 3945, Blue 3953, Boston 3957, Cabot 3968, **China 3982, Iacocca 4104**, King 4122, **Lincoln 4146**, Pappas 4204, Perkin 4213, Rappaport 4230, Schooner 4261
Michigan: **Earhart 4413, Fisher 4423, Kellogg 4474**, Manoogian 4491
Minnesota: Bush 4621, Buuck 4623, Jerome 4681, McKnight 4709, **Medtronic 4712, St. Jude 4770**
Mississippi: Hardin 4831
Missouri: **Francis 4893, Kauffman 4921**, Sosland 4977
Montana: Washington 5018
Nebraska: Kimmel 5059
New Hampshire: New Hampshire 5182
New Jersey: **Allen 5191, Berrie 5206, JM 5323, Knowles 5345**, McMullen 5378, **Merck 5379**, Merck 5380, **Milbank 5385, Newcombe 5391, Puffin 5417**
New Mexico: Frost 5519, **Lannan 5526**
New York: Avery 5627, Berg 5667, Charina 5763, Charina 5764, **Commonwealth 5800**, Community 5805, Corning 5818, **Cummings 5833, Dedalus 5864, Delmas 5871, Diamond 5881, Dreyfus 5912**, Dunwalke 5921, EHA 5940, **Foundation 6003**, Freeman 6012, **Friends 6024**, Gilder 6050, Gilman 6052, Goldman 6068, **Grant 6093, Guggenheim 6115, Guggenheim 6116**, Haas 6124, **Hartford 6144**, Health 6153, **Hearst 6155, Hearst 6156**, Heineman 6158, **IBM 6203**, Jewish 6228, Kaplan 6250, Kautz 6260, Kennedy 6274, Klee 6286, Klingenstein 6292, Kopf 6302, **Kress 6308**, Lang 6326, Lemberg 6350, Lindner 6372, Link 6374, Loewy 6389, **Luce 6398**, Lurcy 6402, **Macy 6414**, McCann 6453, **Mellon 6470**, Mitsui 6491, **Moody's 6499**, Morgan 6507, New York 6544, **Open 6593, Overbrook 6604, Pforzheimer 6635, Philippe 6636, Reed 6684, Revson 6693**, Ritter 6712, **Rockefeller 6724, Skadden 6868**, Snow 6878, **Soros 6888**, Soros 6891, **Starr 6911, Tai 6959, Trace 7003**, Triad 7005, **Tsadra 7010, Vital 7033, Warhol 7050, Watson 7058, Wenner 7075, Whitney 7080**, Wilson 7088
North Carolina: Biddle 7150, Cemala 7174, Community 7180, Dover 7194, Duke 7195, Finley 7199, **Nickel 7272**, North Carolina 7273, **S.R.C. 7307**
Ohio: Ar-Hale 7376, Lubrizol 7546, Morgan 7579, Muskingum 7585, Scripps 7659, **Wexner 7713**
Oklahoma: Hille 7759, Kerr 7764, **Schusterman 7794**, Tulsa 7807
Oregon: Ford 7845, Haugland 7849, Oregon 7876
Pennsylvania: Berks 7939, Central 7971, Independence 8107, Lindback 8142, Measey 8170, Presser 8236, Scaife 8266, Steinman 8300, Stoneleigh 8303, **Templeton 8313, Williams 8339**
Rhode Island: **Bingham 8361, Dorot 8384**, Rhode Island 8429
South Carolina: Abney 8454
Tennessee: Hartwell 8579
Texas: Anchorage 8662, Coastal 8768, Cockrell 8770, Cullen 8792, Hankamer 8890, **Houston 8916**, Houston 8917, Kempner 8952, Liatis 8983, Puett 9114, QuadW 9115, Reynolds 9127, Starling 9199, Sterling 9203, Summerlee 9213, Sumners 9214, WEDGE 9263, Wichita 9277
Utah: Burton 9309, Eccles 9317, Eccles 9320
Vermont: Lintilhac 9365, Rowland 9370
Virginia: **Mustard 9492**, Olsson 9502, Weissberg 9554
Washington: Blakemore 9587, Blue 9588, **Bullitt 9591**, George 9626, Norcliffe 9693, **Quixote 9707**, Russell 9722
Wisconsin: **Bradley 9819**, Milwaukee 9907
Wyoming: Ellbogen 9977

Film/video/radio

Alabama: Kaul 43, Meyer 53
Arizona: Every 109
California: Ayrshire 276, Center 388, **Compton 422**, Fleishhacker 534, Noyce 974, **Peery 1022, Righteous 1073, Special 1202**, Wohlford 1336
Connecticut: American 1537, Community 1562, Graustein 1600, Rosenthal 1684
Delaware: **Raskob 1845**
District of Columbia: **Arca 1880**
Florida: **Davis 2056**
Illinois: Allstate 2657
Indiana: Brown 3269, **Lumina 3345**, Orange 3365
Michigan: Battle Creek 4343, Marquette 4495, Mount Pleasant 4512, Pokagon 4523
Minnesota: Duluth 4649, Jerome 4681
Montana: Whitefish 5019
New Hampshire: Hunt 5177
New York: Community 5807, **Engelhard 5954, Fledgling 5987, M & T 6406**, Park 6615, **Rubin 6764**, Schaffner 6800
North Carolina: Community 7180, Robertson 7305
Ohio: Ar-Hale 7376
Oregon: Chambers 7832
Pennsylvania: Baker 7926, Fine 8039, Hurd 8101, Washington 8332
Rhode Island: Rhode Island 8429
Texas: Community 8777, **Houston 8916**, Meadows 9019, Moore 9034, Summerlee 9213
Utah: Eccles 9320
Vermont: Vermont 9375
Wisconsin: Bradshaw 9820

General/operating support

Alabama: Alabama 1, Arlington 6, Bashinsky 7, BBVA 9, Bedsole 11, Brock 13, Caring 18, Community 23, Community 24, Crampton 26, Daniel 27, Dove 31, Energen 32, Finlay 33, Hearin 38, Jernigan 42, Kaul 43, Lowe 46, Mayer 49, McWane 51, Meyer 52, Meyer 53, Protective 59, Regions 61, Russell 63, **Scott 64**, Stephens 69, Treadwell 71, Vulcan 73, Walker 74, Webb 76
Alaska: Alaska 79, CIRI 85, Doyon 86
Arizona: Anderson 90, APS 91, Arizona 92, Aurora 94, Day 105, Every 109, Freeport-McMoRan 112, Globe 115, Grace 116, Green 117, **Hickey 121**, Jones 127, **Kieckhefer 129**, Linde 135, Lord's 138, Marley 140, Matricaria 142, McDonald 144, Moeller 145, Morris 148, Piper 152, Stardust 164, Steele 165, University 172, Webb 174
Arkansas: Arkansas 179, Blue 181, Cabe 182, Endeavor 186, Frueauff 188, Jonsson 192, Murphy 193, Riggs 196, Rockefeller 198, Ross 199, Schmieding 200, Walton 211, White 212
California: Achieving 218, **Agilent 220**, Ahmanson 222, **Alalusi 224, Allende 227**, Alliance 229, Alpert 230, **Alpert 231**, Altman 234, **Amado 235, American 237, Amgen 238**, Anaheim 239, Anderson 241, **Appleton 248**, Aratani 250, Archer 252, **Arkay 255**, Arnold 258, Arntz 259, AS&F 263, Atkinson 265, Atlas 266, Auen 269, Avant! 271, **Avery 272**, Barker 282, Bauer 287, Beaver 292, Bechtel 294, **Bechtel 295**, Bechtel, 296, Bella 301, **ben Joseph 302**, Benbough 303, Bengier 304, Berry 312, Blue 320, Bohnett 324, Boswell 330, Bower 332, Bowes 334, Brenner 340, Brewster 342, Broad 346, **Broccoli 350**, CAA 362, Cale 364, California 365, California 366, California 368, Campbell 373, Campini 374, **Capital 375**, Carsey 380, Carson 381, Caruso 382, Cathay 385, Center 388, Chandler 392, Chapman 395, **Cisco 402**, Clif 405, Clive 406, **Clorox 407**, Colburn 410, College 411, Collins 412, Community 414, Community 416, Community 417, Community 418, Community 420, **Compton 422**, Coulter 433, Cowell 434, Craigslist 436, Crail 437, Crankstart 438, Crean 439, Croul 441, **CS 442**, Daly 447, Davies 454, Davis 455, Day 457, Disney 467, Disney 468, **DJ & T 469**, Doctors 471, Doheny 473, Douglas 476, **Draper 481**, Drown 484, **Duffield 486**, Durfee 487, East 490, eBay 493, Eisner 499, El Dorado 500, Ellis 503, **Environment 508**, Eucalyptus 510, Farese 518, Faucett 520, Field 522, Finley 527, Firedoll 528, **Firelight 529, First 530**, Five 533, Fleishhacker 534, **Flextronics 535**, Foothills 537, **Foundation 542**, Freeberg 545, Freidenrich 547, Fremont 548, Friedman 550, Fry 555, **Fund 556**, Gaia 557, Gamble 562, Gap 563, Garland 565, **Geffen 567**, Gellert 568, Genentech 571, Geschke 576, Getty 578, **Gilead 586**, Gilmore 588, Gogian 598, Gold 600, Goldman 606, Good 611, Good 612, **Google 615**, Green 621, Gross 629, Grout 630, Gruber 632, GSF 633, Guess? 635, Gumbiner 636, Haas 641, Haas 642, **Haas 643**, Hager 644, Hale 645, Hammer 648, Hannon 651, Harden 654, Hayward 665, Heffernan 673, Heller 676, Hellman 677, Henley 680, Herbst 682, Hewlett 686, Hewlett 687, **Hilton 692**, Hoag 697, Hodges 698, Hoffman 699, Hofmann 700, Hope 702, Hughes 713, Humboldt 714, **Hume 715**, Hurtt 716, Hutton 718, Intuit 723, Irvine 727, Jack 736, Jackson 737, Jacobs 738, Jacobs 739, Jameson 743, JL 751, JMM 752, Johnson 753, **Kalliopeia 761, Kapor 764, Karisma 766**, Kern 780, King 787, **Kingfisher 788**, Kingsley 789, Kirchgessner 790, **KLA-Tencor 792**, Koret 801, Kvamme 807, Lake 815, Langendorf 819, Laural 823, Lear 824, Lee 826, Leichtman 829, Leonetti/O'Connell 832, Lesher 833, Levine 836, Lilly's 838, **Lingnan 841**, Littlefield 844, Los Altos 849, Luberski 852, Lucas 855, **Lund 857**, Lytel 860, M & T 861, March 872, Marcled 875, Marin 877, **Marisla 878**, Masimo 884, Matsui 885, **Mattel 886**, McBean 893, McCarthy 895, **McConnell 898**, McCune 900, McKay 902, McKesson 903, Mendelson 912, Mental 914, **Mercer 917**, Mericos 918, Milken 926, Milken 927, Miller 929, Milstein 930, Moca 932, Monroe 935, Monterey 936, Moore 937, Morgan 940, Mosher 945, Mudd 951, Murphy 956, Muskavitch 958, Napa 959, Neeley 963, Nestle

965, Newhall 966, Norris 971, North 972, Noyce 974, Oak 976, Oakland 977, **Omidyar 984**, Oppenheimer 987, Orange 992, Orfalea 994, Osher 997, Outhwaite 1000, Pacific 1002, Pacific 1003, **Packard 1006**, Panda 1010, Parker 1012, Parsons 1013, Patagonia.org 1017, Patron 1020, **Peery 1022**, Pell 1023, Peppers 1024, Perforce 1026, Peters 1028, Pfaffinger 1030, PG&E 1033, Post 1041, Quest 1050, Rancho 1053, Ransom 1055, Reid 1060, **Righteous 1073**, **Rivendell 1077**, Roberts 1081, Roche 1083, Rogers 1087, Rosenberg 1088, Roth 1093, Roth 1094, Rudd 1096, Ryan 1098, **S.G. 1100**, **Saban 1101**, Sacchi 1102, Sacramento 1103, Samuelsson 1107, San Diego 1108, San Francisco 1109, San Luis 1110, Sandy 1113, Sangham 1114, Schimmel 1122, Schwab 1127, Schwab 1128, Sefton 1134, Sempra 1140, Shapell 1150, Shapiro 1151, Shasta 1154, Shea 1155, Sierra 1164, Silberstein 1165, Silicon 1166, Simon 1171, Simpson 1173, Sinskey 1174, Skoll 1175, Slager 1178, Smet 1181, **Smith 1183**, Smith 1186, Smith 1188, **Smith 1189**, Smullin 1190, Sobrato 1193, Soda 1194, Solid 1197, Sonora 1198, Soref 1199, **Special 1202**, Springcreek 1208, Sterling 1218, Stotsenberg 1221, **Strauss 1223**, Streisand 1224, Stuart 1225, Stulsaft 1226, Taper 1237, Taube 1241, Teichert 1244, Tesuque 1246, Thornton 1252, Three 1254, **Thrive 1255**, Towbes 1260, Treadwell 1262, Truckee 1263, True 1264, Ueberroth 1268, Union 1271, **Vadasz 1275**, Valley 1279, Valley 1280, Van Konynenburg 1282, vanLoben 1283, Van Nuys 1284, Ventura 1287, **Warsh 1299**, Webb 1303, Weingart 1307, Welch 1310, Wells 1312, Werner 1313, Western 1315, Wohlford 1336, Wollenberg 1339, **Wong 1342**, Wood 1344, WWW 1349, Yellow 1354, Zable 1355, **Zee 1357**, Zellerbach 1358, Zelman 1359

Colorado: Animal 1363, Anschutz 1364, **Anschutz 1365**, Aspen 1368, Bernstein 1372, Bohemian 1375, Brett 1378, Brown 1379, Bruni 1380, Buell 1381, Chambers 1385, Charter 1387, Colorado 1390, Community 1391, Community 1393, Community 1394, Community 1395, Coors 1396, **Crowell 1398**, Daniels 1399, Denver 1401, Doolin 1402, Edmondson 1405, El Pomar 1406, Fishback 1410, Foundation 1411, **General 1419**, **Gill 1421**, Halton 1426, Hunter 1431, Jumping 1434, KBK 1437, King 1440, Lewis 1447, Libertygives 1448, Lipscomb 1449, M.D.C./Richmond 1450, Marquez 1454, Martin 1456, Monfort 1465, Norwood 1471, Ottens 1472, Pikes 1478, Piton 1480, Ponzio 1482, Price 1484, ProLogis 1485, Rose 1487, Saeman 1490, **Salvador 1491**, Seay 1495, Serimus 1496, Slater 1502, Sprout 1505, Summit 1511, Telluride 1512, Vodafone 1519, Western 1520, **Winslow 1525**, Wolf 1526, Yampa 1528

Connecticut: Allison 1535, Baldwin 1541, Barnes 1542, Beagary 1544, Bissell 1547, Bob's 1548, Boehringer 1549, Bossidy 1551, Bullfrogs 1553, Community 1562, Community 1563, Community 1564, Community 1565, Connecticut 1567, Culpeper 1568, DeLuca 1573, Fairfield 1581, Farid 1582, Fink 1583, First 1584, Fisher 1585, Fund 1589, Goergen 1595, Graustein 1600, Grossman 1602, Grossman 1603, Hartford 1609, Hoffman 1613, Hubbell 1614, Huisking 1615, JJJ 1618, Keefe 1619, Lehrman 1628, Liberty 1630, **Lone 1632**, Lowenstein 1633, Main 1634, Matthies 1639, Meriden 1643, Middlesex 1644, Morris 1646, Neuberger 1649, New Canaan 1650, NewAlliance 1651, **Newman's 1652**, Northeast 1656, **October 1659**, O'Herron 1660, Panoram 1667, Perrin 1673, Pitney 1674, Pitt 1675, **Praxair 1676**, Rockville 1682, Rogow 1683, Rosenthal 1684, Rubin-Ladd 1686, Seedlings 1691, Selander 1693, Sheinberg 1695, Smart 1697, Tow 1708, Valentine 1713, Valley 1714, Vervane 1716, Whittingham 1720, Wood 1725, Wright 1727, Xerox 1728, **Ziegler 1731**

Delaware: **Adobe 1734**, AEC 1735, **AstraZeneca 1738**, Berkley 1741, Berlin 1743, Bishop 1745, CenturyLink-Clarke 1750, **Chichester 1754**, Common 1755, Day 1763, Devonwood 1768, Draper 1770, Duane 1771, Dwoskin 1772, Edwards 1774, Esperance 1777, Ettinger 1779, Good 1785, Griswold 1787, Johnson 1790, Lennox 1805, Longwood 1806, **Marks 1813**, Mastronardi 1815, Matthews 1816, McDonald 1817, **Memton 1819**, Ortega 1828, Parker 1829, Phillips 1835, Presto 1840, **Raskob 1845**, Romill 1851, Salah 1855, Schwartz 1857, Struthers 1865, Sylvan 1867, Tapeats 1868, Victory 1870, Wasily 1871, Westly 1873

District of Columbia: Aid 1879, **Arca 1880**, **Banyan 1881**, Bauman 1882, Bender 1885, Bernstein 1886, Bernstein 1887, Block 1888, **Butler 1889**, Cafritz 1890, Community 1893, Coors 1895, Coyne 1896, Dole 1900, **Dreyfus 1901**, **El-Hibri 1903**, Forsythia 1906, Gottesman 1911, Gudelsky 1912, **Hill 1915**, Jones 1918, Kaye 1920, Kimsey 1921, Kiplinger 1922, Lehrman 1924, Loughran 1925, McIntosh 1928, Meyer 1931, **Moriah 1932**, Munson 1933, **Public 1940**, Rutherfoord 1944, Stewart 1949, **Summit 1950**, Vradenburg 1954, **Wallace 1955**, Wallace 1956, Wyss 1958

Florida: Amos 1967, Ansin 1969, Aurora 1974, **Barbour 1980**, Baroco 1981, Batchelor 1983, Beaver 1986, **Believers 1989**, Bernstein 1995, Blank 1997, Bradley 2001, Bronfman 2003, Brown 2004, **Chatlos 2019**, **Chester 2020**, Cobb 2026, Colen 2029, Columbus 2030, Community 2036, Community 2039, Community 2041, Conn 2042, Dallepezze 2049, Darden 2051, Davis 2055, **Davis 2056**, Diermeier 2063, Dunspaugh-Dalton 2073, duPont 2074, duPont 2075, Ebert 2079, Engelberg 2086, Ferguson 2093, FIS 2097, Florida 2101, Gooding 2130, Goodwin 2131, Greenburg 2137, Gronewaldt 2139, Hahn 2144, Hard 2147, Harris 2149, Henry 2154, Hill 2158, Hoehl 2160, Hough 2162, Indian 2166, Jacksonville 2167, **Jaffer 2168**, Kelly 2181, Kennedy 2182, Klorfine 2188, Klurman 2189, **Knight 2191**, **Koch 2192**, KPS 2194, Kramer 2195, **Larson 2203**, Lattner 2204, Lattner 2205, Leclerc 2208, Lennar 2210, Levitetz 2211, Lewis 2212, Lichtenberger 2214, Lynn 2221, Macdonald 2223, Magruder 2225, May 2230, McMurtry 2236, Miami 2238, Mill 2240, Moran 2243, Newman 2250, **Patel 2259**, Peacock 2263, **Peterson 2267**, Pinellas 2269, Publix 2275, Quantum 2276, Rawlings 2279, Rayonier 2281, Rooms 2292, Root 2293, Roskamp 2296, **Russell 2301**, Ryder 2302, Sage 2304, Scaife 2309, **SeaWorld 2315**, Sherman 2319, Sontag 2325, Star 2335, Sullivan 2343, SunTrust 2345, SWS 2347, Tangelo 2351, Taylor 2353, Thomas 2357, Tupperware 2363, TWS 2365, **Vollmer 2373**, Walter 2375, Wardlaw 2377, Watts 2380, Wells 2383, Wildflower 2386, Wolfe 2391, Wollowick 2393

Georgia: Aflac 2399, Amos 2402, Atlanta 2406, Beech 2409, Beloco 2411, Bradley 2414, Brain 2416, Bunzl 2417, Callaway 2419, Camp-Younts 2421, CLC 2426, **Coca 2428**, Colonial 2430, Community 2432, Community 2435, Cousins 2442, Cousins 2443, Cox 2446, Day 2448, Dunn 2451, Equifax 2455, EZ 2456, Flowers 2459, Franklin 2462, Fraser 2463, Georgia 2468, **Georgia 2469**, Harland 2477, Harris 2479, Healthcare 2482, Holder 2485, **Imlay 2487**, Jordan 2492, **Keough 2496**, Knox 2498, Lanier 2499, Love 2508, Mohawk 2517, Moore 2519, Moore 2520, North 2525, Pitts 2529, Primerica 2534, Rich 2537, **Rosenberg 2545**, Sapelo 2546, Saul 2547, Southern 2554, Synovus 2556, **Turner 2563**, U.S. 2565, Watson 2569, Williams 2572, Wilson 2576, Woodruff 2579, Zeist 2584

Hawaii: Bank 2588, Central 2595, Ching 2596, Hau'oli 2601, Hawaiian 2603, HMSA 2604, McInerny 2612, Schuler 2614, Sullivan 2618, **Watumull 2620**, Wilcox 2621, Wong 2622

Idaho: Cunningham 2630, Idaho 2632, Jeker 2634, Rebholtz 2640, **Schultz 2641**, Smeed 2644, Wishnick 2646

Illinois: **Abbott 2649**, Abt 2651, Adjuvant 2653, Allstate 2657, Alphawood 2658, Andrew 2661, Andrew 2662, Aon 2667, Appleby 2668, ArcelorMittal 2670, Arthur 2673, Atherton 2676, Baskin 2685, Bauer 2687, Berner 2694, Bersted 2696, Blair 2699, Blowitz 2702, Blum 2706, Boler 2708, Brach 2712, **Brinson 2715**, Bruning 2717, Brunner 2718, Butler 2729, Calamos 2731, Camp 2732, Caterpillar 2738, Charleston 2742, Chicago 2746, Circle 2749, Clinton 2754, CME 2755, Coleman 2759, Comer 2760, Comer 2761, Community 2763, Community 2769, Cooper 2772, Cressey 2779, Crown 2781, Cuneo 2783, Davee 2785, Day 2787, **Deere 2790**, Deering 2791, Delany 2793, Dillon 2796, Donnelley 2800, Donnelley 2801, Donnelley 2802, Driehaus 2805, DRW 2807, Dryer 2808, Duchossois 2809, Dunard 2810, DuPage 2812, Eisenberg 2819, Energizer 2824, Farnham 2828, Field 2831, Frankel 2842, Frechette 2844, Fry 2849, Full 2851, Galashiels 2852, **Glenner 2866**, Gore 2871, **Grainger 2874**, Grand 2875, Grant 2876, Grant 2877, Gray 2878, Growmark 2881, Guthman 2882, Hagenah 2885, Halligan 2886, Hamel 2887, Hamill 2888, Harris 2892, **Harris 2893**, Harrison 2894, Heller 2904, Heritage 2907, Hermann 2908, Herr 2909, His 2913, Homan 2919, Hurvis 2930, Illinois 2934, Jahn 2938, **Joyce 2946**, Kaplan 2947, Kaplan 2948, Katten 2951, Keith 2952, Kellman 2953, Kemper 2954, Kendall 2956, Khesed 2959, King 2960, Kolschowsky 2962, Kovler 2964, Landau 2966, Lea 2970, Levi 2976, Libra 2981, Logan 2983, Louis 2985, Lumpkin 2986, **MacArthur 2989**, **MacArthur 2990**, Mander 2998, Martin 3003, Master 3004, MB 3008, McCormick 3010, McGowan 3014, McGraw 3015, Miller 3025, Millikin 3027, **Mondelez 3034**, Morse 3039, Mosher 3041, **Motorola 3042**, **Motorola 3043**, Munson 3045, Negaunee 3047, Nelson 3049, New 3052, Northern 3059, Oak Park 3061, Omron 3063, Oppenheimer 3065, Owens 3068, Pattee 3072, Payne 3073, Pepper 3074, Petersen 3078, Pick, 3079, Pierce 3080, **Ploughshares 3082**, Polk 3084, Popular 3085, Prentice 3088, Prince 3089, Prince 3090, Pritzker 3093, Purcell 3101, Rawley 3106, Redhill 3108, Reed 3109, Reese 3110, Rice 3116, Roberts 3119, Roberts 3121, **Santreece 3135**, Schmidt 3139, Schmitt 3140, Shapiro 3152, Shirk 3158, Siragusa 3162, Souder 3168, Speh 3170, Sprague 3172, **State 3174**, Steans 3175, Stern 3177, Stone 3180, Stuart 3182, **Thome 3187**, Timken 3188, Tracy 3189, Trustmark 3193, **Tyndale 3195**, Ubben 3196, Ullrich 3198, United 3199, United 3200, Vaughn 3203, VNA 3206, Ward 3216, Wentcher 3226, White 3229, White 3230, Wieboldt 3231, **Woodbury 3240**, Woods 3242, Woodward 3243, **Wrigley 3244**, Zerrusen 3248

Indiana: 1st 3251, **Ackerman 3252**, Anderson 3255, Anthem 3257, Apgar 3258, Ball 3262, Blue 3266, Boren 3267, Brotherhood 3268, Central 3272, Clowes 3274, Cole 3276, Community 3279, Community 3281, Community 3286, Community 3290, Crown Point 3291, **Cummins 3292**, DeHaan 3294, DeKalb 3295, Dekko 3296, Elkhart 3298, Fairbanks 3301, Foellinger 3304, Ford 3305, Foundations 3306, Glick 3310, **Goodrich 3311**, Hamman 3312, Harrison 3314, Health 3317, Hux 3325, Indiana 3327, Johnson 3330, Jordan 3331, Journal-Gazette 3332, **Lilly 3340**, **Lilly 3342**, **Lumina 3345**, Madison 3346, Miller 3355, Noble 3359, Northern 3360, Noyes 3361, OneAmerica 3364, Parke 3366, Pulliam 3372, Reynolds 3376, Ripley 3379, Rolland 3381, Rothschild 3382, Samerian 3384, Simon 3386, Steel 3389, Steuben 3390, Vectren 3394, Volo 3395, Wabash 3396, Waterfield 3399, Weaver 3401, West 3404, White 3405

Iowa: AEGON 3409, Aviva 3411, Community 3421, Community 3423, EMC 3428, Gilchrist 3432, Glazer 3433, Glazer 3434, Guernsey 3437, GuideOne 3438, HNI 3443, Iowa 3447, Kruidenier 3455, Mansfield 3459, Maytag 3460, McElroy 3461, Meredith 3463, Mid-Iowa 3466, Principal

3476, **Rockwell 3477**, Ruan 3478, Seidler 3479, Stine 3482, Tye 3484, United 3485, Wallace 3488, Weathertop 3489

Kansas: Baughman 3493, Beach 3494, Beren 3496, Blue 3497, Capitol 3498, Cooper 3503, Damon 3504, DeBoer 3505, Dreiling 3511, Garvey 3516, Hansen 3518, Hutchinson 3521, INTRUST 3522, Kansas 3524, Koch 3529, McPherson 3534, Rice 3538, Salina 3540, Sprint 3549, Sunderland 3551, Topeka 3552, Wyandotte 3556

Kentucky: Barzun 3559, Blue 3560, Brown 3564, C.E. 3566, Community 3569, Community 3570, Cralle 3571, Gheens 3577, Good 3578, Horn 3581, Humana 3582, Independence 3583, LG&E 3586, Mercy 3589, Norton 3592, Orleton 3594, Preston 3596, Robinson 3598, Spray 3602, Swope 3603, Ventas 3605, Young 3607, Yum! 3608

Louisiana: Albemarle 3609, Almar 3610, Baptist 3612, Beaird 3614, Blue 3615, Brown 3617, Burden 3618, Burton 3619, Coughlin 3626, Diboll 3628, German 3637, Goldring 3638, Grigsby 3640, Huie 3643, Institute 3644, Jones 3645, Keller 3646, New Orleans 3656, Pennington 3659, Pinhook 3660, Reily 3661, RosaMary 3663, Taylor 3669, Wilson 3671, **Woldenberg 3672**, Woolf 3673, Young 3674, Zigler 3676

Maine: Cohen 3684, Fore 3687, King 3694, Libra 3696, Morton 3701, Quimby 3705, **Sandy 3707**, Sewall 3708

Maryland: Abell 3712, Abell 3713, Abramson 3715, Adalman-Goodwin 3716, Allegis 3719, **Ames 3720**, Ausherman 3723, Baker 3724, Battye 3727, Blades 3734, **Blaustein 3735**, Blaustein 3736, Blum 3737, **Casey 3745**, Casey 3746, Ceres 3747, Choice 3748, Church 3749, Clark 3750, Clark 3751, **Cohen 3754**, Colhoun 3755, Commonweal 3756, Community 3759, Concordia 3763, Davis 3772, **de Beaumont 3774, Deerbrook 3776**, Delaplaine 3778, Deutsch 3779, Dresher 3782, Eaton 3784, **England 3785**, Epstein 3786, **Ewing 3787**, Foundation 3794, Fowler 3795, Freeman 3797, GEICO 3801, Goldsmith 3804, Gordon 3805, **Grace 3807**, Helena 3812, Hendricks 3813, Hirschhorn 3816, Hoffberger 3817, Jacobsohn 3819, Klein 3824, Knott 3826, Legg 3828, Leidy 3830, Lerner 3831, Lockhart 3836, Lockheed 3837, Mead 3845, Meyerhoff 3848, Meyerhoff 3849, Middendorf 3850, Mid-Shore 3851, Millstream 3852, **Morningstar 3854**, O'Neil 3859, Osprey 3861, Polinger 3864, Price 3865, Rathmann 3867, Rembrandt 3868, Rocking 3871, Rollins 3872, Rosenberg 3873, Roswell 3876, Rouse 3877, **Shared 3882, Smith 3886**, St. John 3888, Straus 3890, Stulman 3891, Sunrise 3892, Town 3897, Washington 3904, Wasserman 3905, **Weinberg 3908**, Wright 3911

Massachusetts: Abrams 3914, Adams 3916, Adams 3917, Arbella 3926, Atchinson 3930, Babson 3933, Balfour 3935, Barker 3936, **Barr 3937**, Benson 3942, Berkman 3945, Berkshire 3946, Berkshire 3947, Boston 3956, **Cabot 3966**, Cabot 3967, Cabot 3968, Cambridge 3971, Cambridge 3972, Cape Cod 3974, Carney 3975, Cedar 3978, Chorus 3984, Clarke 3986, Clipper 3987, Community 3991, Cosette 3997, Danversbank 4009, Davis 4011, Demoulas 4014, Donahue 4023, Dunkin' 4026, Dusky 4028, Eaglemere 4029, Eastern 4030, Ellsworth 4035, **Elsevier 4036**, Essex 4039, Evans 4040, Farnsworth 4043, Finch 4048, Fireman 4049, Fish 4051, Fletcher 4054, Foundation 4056, **Garfield 4065**, Garrison 4066, **Germeshausen 4069**, Gordon 4074, Grayson 4078, Grinspoon 4080, Hall 4084, Hanover 4086, Harrington 4088, Higgins 4096, Highland 4098, Hopedale 4101, **Hunt 4102**, Hyams 4103, Inavale 4106, Institution 4108, Island 4109, Janey 4111, Jebediah 4112, Josetta 4114, Keel 4120, Kendall 4121, Kingsbury 4123, Kittredge 4124, Klarman 4126, Lauring 4138, Levy 4144, Liberty 4145, Linde 4147, Linden 4148, Ludcke 4157, Lynch 4159, Melville 4170, Merck 4171, **Merck 4172**, Mifflin 4175, Miller 4177, **Min 4178**, New 4189, New England 4193, North 4194, Ory 4200, Peabody 4210, Perkin 4213, Perpetual 4215, **Phillips 4219**, Pierce 4220, Popplestone 4225, Poss 4226, Proctor 4227, Rappaport 4230, Reebok 4234, Reynolds 4238, Rodgers 4242, Rogers 4243, **Rosenberg 4245**, Rowland 4246, Roy 4247, Rubenstein 4248, Santander 4256, Schooner 4261, Schott 4262, Shapiro 4267, Shaw 4270, Sheehan 4271, Smith 4277, Starwood 4284, **State 4285**, Stearns 4286, Stevens 4288, Stevens 4289, Stifler 4292, Stoddard 4293, Stoico 4294, Stoneman 4296, Swartz 4301, TJX 4308, Wallace 4318, Weatherbie 4321, Webster 4322

Michigan: Alro 4336, Americana 4337, Barry 4342, Bay 4344, Beard 4345, Besse 4348, Besser 4349, Boll 4352, BorgWarner 4353, Capital 4357, Christian 4365, Chrysler 4366, Cold 4367, Comerica 4368, Community 4372, Consumers 4376, Cook 4377, Cook 4378, **Cooper-Standard 4380**, Cracchiolo 4382, Cummings 4384, Dalton 4385, Dana 4386, Dart 4388, DeRoy 4396, Devereaux 4397, DeVos 4398, DeVos 4399, DeVos 4400, Dewey 4401, Doornink 4403, Dow 4406, Dow 4407, Dow 4408, DTE 4410, **Erb 4415**, Family 4418, **Fetzer 4420**, Fetzer 4421, Firestone 4422, **Fisher 4423**, Ford 4427, Fremont 4438, General 4442, Gerstacker 4444, Gilmore 4445, Greenville 4452, Harding 4455, Herrick 4459, Hudson 4463, Hurst 4464, Idema 4465, **Isabel 4466**, Jackson 4467, Johnson 4468, Jubilee 4470, Kahn 4471, Kalamazoo 4472, **Kellogg 4474, Kellogg's 4475**, Knight 4477, **Kresge 4479**, La-Z-Boy 4481, Lear 4482, Legion 4483, Leighton 4484, Lenawee 4485, Manoogian 4491, Manoogian 4492, Marshall 4496, Masco 4497, McGregor 4498, Merillat 4500, Miller 4503, Miller 4504, Mosaic 4509, **Mott 4510**, Mott 4511, Oleson 4516, Parish 4518, Perrigo 4521, Pokagon 4523, Polk 4524, Prince 4525, Sage 4531, Shelden 4537, Silverwing 4541, Skillman 4543, Spartan 4544, Spoelhof 4545, Steelcase 4547, Sturgis 4550, Thompson 4555, Towsley 4557, **Tubergen 4559**, Tuktawa 4560, Upton 4565, Van Andel 4566, Van Andel 4567, VanderWeide 4572, Von 4574, Walker 4575, Weatherwax 4577, Wege 4579, Weingartz 4580, Westerman 4582, Whirlpool 4583, Whiting 4584, Wilson 4588, Wilson 4589, Wolters 4592, Wolverine 4593, World 4594

Minnesota: 1988 4596, 3M 4597, AHS 4599, **Andersen 4601, Andersen 4602**, Andersen 4603, Athwin 4607, Bakken 4608, Best 4612, Bethel 4613, **Better 4614**, Beverly 4615, Blandin 4617, Bremer 4620, Butler 4622, Buuck 4623, Cade 4625, Cargill 4628, Carlson 4629, Carolyn 4630, Charlson 4633, Christianson 4635, CHS 4636, Davis 4642, Deluxe 4644, Driscoll 4648, Duluth 4649, Ecolab 4651, Edwards 4653, Fiterman 4656, Foundation 4657, Frey 4658, **Fuller 4659**, General 4661, George 4662, Greystone 4668, Griggs 4669, Hardenbergh 4672, Hiawatha 4674, Holmes 4675, Hormel 4676, HRK 4677, Hubbard 4678, Initiative 4679, Jennings 4680, Jerome 4681, Johnson 4683, Jostens 4684, Kelley 4686, **King 4687**, Kopp 4688, Koran 4689, Land 4691, Leonard 4694, Lilly 4696, Marbrook 4702, Martin 4704, McCarthy 4705, McGlynn 4706, McKnight 4709, McVay 4711, Melrose 4713, Minneapolis 4714, Minnesota 4715, Minnesota 4716, **Mortenson 4721, Mosaic 4722**, Nelson 4726, NFC 4727, Northwest 4729, Opus 4731, Ordean 4732, **O'Shaughnessy 4734**, Oswald 4735, **Pentair 4739**, Phillips 4741, Pine 4742, Piper 4743, Pohlad 4745, **Polaris 4746**, RBC 4748, Regis 4750, Rivers 4752, Robins 4754, Securian 4761, Sieben 4763, Sit 4765, Smikis 4767, St. 4769, **St. Jude 4770**, Stevens 4772, Sundet 4774, SUPERVALU 4775, Target 4776, TCF 4778, TEAM 4779, Tozer 4782, Travelers 4783, U.S. 4784, Valspar 4786, Veritas 4789, Wasie 4794, WCA 4795, Weyerhaeuser 4804, Winona 4806, Xcel 4808

Mississippi: **Armstrong 4810**, BancorpSouth 4812, Blue 4815, C Spire 4817, Chisholm 4818, Community 4819, Community 4820, Community 4821, Ergon 4824, Feild 4825, Foundation 4827, Gulf 4830, Maddox 4834, Mississippi 4839, Regions 4843, Riley 4844, Risen 4845, Sullivan 4846, Walker 4849

Missouri: Ameren 4851, American 4852, Anheuser 4853, Apex 4854, Arch 4855, Brown 4862, Bunge 4865, Burns 4866, Centene 4870, Commerce 4871, Community 4872, Concorde 4873, Cox 4874, Cray 4876, Dierberg 4879, Dula 4881, Dunn 4882, Emerson 4885, **Enterprise 4887**, Express 4888, Farber 4889, **Francis 4893**, Graybar 4898, H & R 4902, Hall 4905, Hallmark 4906, Interco 4914, Jordan 4917, Kansas 4920, **Kauffman 4921**, Kauffman 4922, Kemper 4923, Kemper 4925, Kemper 4926, Laclede 4931, Lay 4934, Lopata 4938, MFA 4943, Millstone 4944, **Monsanto 4945**, Musgrave 4947, Nestle 4948, Oppenstein 4950, Orscheln 4951, Pershing 4952, Pettus 4954, Pillsbury 4955, Pillsbury 4956, Plaster 4957, Pott 4958, Reynolds 4961, Rhoden 4962, Rosewood 4964, Saint Louis 4966, Sander 4967, Schwartze 4968, Shaw 4970, Shelter 4971, Sosland 4977, Speas 4978, Speas 4979, Stern 4980, Stupp 4982, SunEdison 4985, Ten 4989, Trio 4994, Truman 4996, Wornall 5003

Montana: Bair 5004, Edwards 5008, Gilhousen 5011, Oro 5014, Whitefish 5019

Nebraska: Abel 5021, Acklie 5022, Ameritas 5023, Boyer 5025, Buckley 5026, **Buffett 5028**, Cooper 5031, Eagle 5037, Grand Island 5044, Hirschfeld 5049, Hitchcock 5050, Holthus 5052, Kiewit 5056, Kiewit 5057, Kind 5060, Lincoln 5063, Linder 5064, Lozier 5065, Mutual 5071, Nelnet 5072, Omaha 5074, Phelps 5075, Scoular 5080, Sherwood 5081, Swanson 5088, Union 5090, Weitz 5092, Wirth 5095, Woods 5096

Nevada: Adelson 5099, Bennett 5101, Bretzlaff 5103, Buck 5105, Caesars 5106, Community 5108, Cord 5110, Crystal 5113, Fairweather 5118, Gabelli 5120, Hawkins 5123, Nevada 5134, NV 5136, Parasol 5138, Pennington 5139, Tam 5152

New Hampshire: Alexander 5162, Bean 5164, Butler 5165, Byrne 5166, Foundation 5171, Fuller 5172, HNH 5175, Hunt 5177, Malool 5180, New Hampshire 5182, Panjandrum 5184, Putnam 5186, Quinlan 5187

New Jersey: **Alcatel 5190**, Antz 5192, Atlantic 5196, Atran 5197, Bacchetta 5198, Banbury 5200, Bard 5202, **Berrie 5206**, Bolger 5207, Borden 5209, Brozowski 5218, Bunbury 5220, Campbell 5223, Cape 5224, Cole 5231, Cooperman 5233, Cowles 5234, Creamer 5236, Danellie 5237, Dodge 5243, **Edison 5248**, Elias 5252, Firestone 5260, Frankino 5266, Frohring 5269, Fund 5270, Galanta 5272, Gibson 5276, Goldberg 5279, Golden 5280, Harbourton 5293, Holmes 5302, Honickman 5303, Horizon 5305, **IDT 5311**, Ingersoll-Rand 5314, Integra 5315, Investors 5317, Isermann 5319, **Johnson 5326**, Johnson 5328, Karma 5331, Kerr 5338, Kirby 5339, Martini 5372, McGraw 5376, MCJ 5377, McMullen 5378, Merck 5380, OceanFirst 5394, Orange 5396, **Perrin 5404**, Pitkin 5408, Plummer 5409, Princeton 5411, Provident 5414, **Prudential 5415**, Roberts 5422, Roberts 5423, Rubenstein 5428, Saka 5432, **Sanofi 5437**, Sansom 5438, Schmidt 5440, Schumann 5441, Schwarz 5444, Scott 5445, **Segal 5446**, Sheridan 5452, **Siemens 5454**, South 5463, Subaru 5471, Sunup 5474, Syms 5475, Tanzman 5476, Taub 5478, Tepper 5480, Touchpoint 5481, Turner 5482, Turrell 5483, Unilever 5484, **Verizon 5489**, Victoria 5490, Weitzman 5497, Wight 5501, Wilf 5504, Willits 5505

New Mexico: Albuquerque 5511, Brindle 5516, Chase 5517, Delle 5518, **Lannan 5526, Levinson 5527**, Maddox 5528, McCune 5529, New Mexico 5530, PNM 5532, Santa Fe 5533, Thornburg 5535, Yates 5537

New York: A M 5543, Abeles 5544, Abrons 5546, Achelis 5549, Adelman 5554, Adirondack 5556, Aequus 5560, Albert 5567, Alfiero 5570, Allen

5573, Allen 5574, Altman 5580, Altschul 5582, American 5587, **American 5588**, American 5590, Ammon 5593, Ammon 5594, Amsterdam 5595, Anderson 5596, Animal 5601, Appel 5603, Arbesfeld 5605, **Arcus 5608**, Aron 5616, Assurant 5621, Auchincloss 5623, AXA 5629, Badgeley 5633, Baird 5636, Barker 5644, Barth 5648, **Bat 5651**, Bay 5652, Benedict 5662, Benenson 5664, Berg 5667, Biddle 5674, Bingham 5676, Blank 5682, Block 5683, Bodman 5692, Botwinick 5696, Boxer 5698, Brach 5699, Branta 5703, Bright 5710, **Bristol 5711**, Brodsky 5714, Bronfman 5715, **Bronfman 5717**, Brooklyn 5718, BTMU 5724, Buck 5725, **Buffalo 5726**, Butler 5733, Butler 5734, **Bydale 5738**, C & Y 5739, **Carnegie 5747**, Carson 5748, Cattaraugus 5750, Central 5756, Century 5758, Chadwick 5760, Challenger 5762, Charina 5763, Charina 5764, Chautauqua 5766, Chazen 5767, Chernow 5771, Chiang 5774, **Clark 5784**, Clark 5786, Coach 5790, Community 5802, Community 5803, Community 5807, Copland 5814, Corning 5818, Countess 5821, **Credit 5826**, Cricket 5827, **Cummings 5833**, Curran 5835, D'Addario 5841, Daedalus 5842, Daphne 5848, Dean 5858, Deerfield 5865, Dejana 5868, **Delmas 5871**, Demartini 5872, **Deutsche 5876**, Devlin 5877, Diamond 5880, Dillon 5885, **Discount 5889**, Dobkin 5891, Donner 5899, Dreitzer 5910, Dreyfus 5913, Duke 5918, Dunwalke 5921, Dyson 5923, East 5925, Edelman 5932, **Edhi 5934**, Edouard 5936, Effron 5938, EHA 5940, **Engelhard 5954**, Englander 5955, Equipart 5959, ESL 5960, Essel 5961, Fanwood 5968, Farash 5969, Fifth 5976, Fischel 5980, Fisher 5982, Fisher 5983, Flaherty 5986, **Ford 5994**, **Foundation 6003**, Frank 6008, Freed 6011, Freeman 6012, **Friends 6024**, Froelich 6025, Galasso 6032, **GBRG 6036**, Gebbie 6038, Gerry 6043, Gifford 6049, Gilder 6050, Gilman 6052, Gimbel 6053, **Gitenstein 6055**, **Goldman 6066**, Goldman 6068, Golisano 6077, Golub 6079, Gorman 6083, Gorter 6084, Greene 6103, Greve 6106, Griffin 6108, Grigg 6109, Guttman 6121, H & M 6122, H. & Y. 6123, Haas 6124, Hagedorn 6128, Harkness 6134, **Harriman 6136**, Harriman 6137, Harris 6139, Harrison 6142, **Hartford 6144**, Hazen 6151, **Hearst 6155**, **Hearst 6156**, Heineman 6158, Hermione 6163, **Heron 6164**, Hettinger 6170, Hillman 6174, Hochstein 6178, Hoerle 6180, Horncrest 6185, Horowitz 6186, Hudson 6191, Hultquist 6195, Hurford 6199, Hutchins 6202, **IBM 6203**, Icahn 6204, IFF 6206, **Iris 6213**, **Isdell 6214**, Israel 6216, Jacoff 6220, **Jaffe 6222**, JAM 6224, Joelson 6232, **Johnson 6235**, Johnson 6238, Johnson 6239, Jones 6242, **JPMorgan 6244**, Kaplan 6250, **Kaplan 6252**, Katzenberger 6258, Kaufman 6259, Kaylie 6263, Keet 6266, Kennedy 6274, Khatib 6278, Kinney 6285, Klein 6289, Klingenstein 6292, Knapp 6295, Knox 6299, Kopf 6302, Kraus 6305, Kravis 6306, Kupferberg 6313, Landau 6322, Lang 6326, **Lauder 6336**, Lauder 6337, Lavelle 6339, Lehman 6346, Lenna 6352, Lerner 6353, Levine 6359, Link 6375, Litwin 6380, Liu 6381, Liu 6382, Lortel 6393, Lowenstein 6395, Lubo 6396, Luce 6397, **Luce 6398**, Lui 6400, Lurie 6403, **M & T 6406**, Marks 6432, Mars 6437, **Mathers 6446**, Mazel 6450, McCarthy 6454, McNeil 6464, **Mertz 6477**, Mesdag 6478, **MetLife 6479**, Meyer 6481, Millbrook 6485, Milliken 6487, **Mitsubishi 6490**, Monell 6497, **Moody's 6499**, Moore 6501, Morgan 6507, Moses 6511, Mule 6513, Mulford 6514, Mutual 6518, Nakash 6522, **Nash 6525**, National 6528, NBC 6531, **Neuberger 6538**, New York 6543, New York 6546, New York 6547, New York 6548, **New 6551**, Nicholas 6557, Noble 6561, **Norman 6565**, Normandie 6566, Northfield 6568, **Noyes 6571**, Nuhn 6572, NYSE 6573, **Ohga 6581**, Ohrstrom 6582, Ohrstrom 6583, Oishei 6584, Old 6586, Olive 6587, **Open 6593**, **Ottaway 6603**, **Overbrook 6604**, Paley 6610, Park 6615, Peco 6624, Pels 6625, **PepsiCo 6627**, **Pfizer 6633**, Phillips 6637, Pine 6642, Pinkerton 6643, Plumeri 6649, **Polo 6651**, Pope 6653, **Porticus 6654**, Price 6658, **Prospect 6663**, Raether 6673, Rasmussen 6679, Rauch 6681, **Reed 6684**, Regals 6685, **Reisman 6686**, Rich 6697, Richardson 6700, Richmond 6703, Riedman 6706, Riggio 6709, Riley 6710, Ritter 6712, Rochester 6722, **Rockefeller 6723**, **Rockefeller 6724**, Rockefeller 6725, Rohatyn 6729, Rose 6732, Rosenberg 6743, Rosenfeld 6747, **Rubin 6764**, Rudin 6767, Ruffin 6770, Rupp 6771, S & G 6774, Sackler 6778, Sackler 6779, Sackler 6780, Salomon 6785, Sandy 6791, Santa 6792, Santmann 6793, **Saper 6794**, Schaffner 6800, Schenectady 6802, Schenker 6803, Scherman 6804, Schiff 6805, Schmitt 6808, Schnurmacher 6809, Schnurmacher 6810, Schumann 6813, Select 6829, Selz 6830, Seneca 6832, Shaarei 6835, Shanken 6837, Sheldon 6841, Shoolman 6846, Shoreland 6847, **Shubert 6850**, Siebens 6853, Simon 6859, **Simons 6860**, Simons 6861, Sirus 6863, Slifka 6870, **SMBC 6873**, Smith 6875, Sohn 6884, Soros 6889, Soros 6891, Sosnoff 6892, Spilker 6897, Spingold 6899, Spitzer 6900, Sprague 6901, **Spunk 6902**, St. Giles 6905, **Starr 6911**, Staten 6912, Steel 6914, Steele 6915, Stein 6918, Stiefel 6931, Strypemonde 6936, Sulzberger 6942, Sumitomo 6943, **Summerfield 6944**, **Surdna 6947**, Sutton 6949, Sykes 6957, **Tai 6959**, Tai 6960, **Tanaka 6961**, TE 6966, Terra 6971, Thompson 6975, Tiffany 6978, Tiger 6980, Time 6982, **Towerbrook 7001**, Triad 7005, **Tsadra 7010**, Tuttle 7014, United 7018, van Ameringen 7023, van Ameringen 7024, Vetlesen 7027, Vidda 7030, **Vital 7033**, Wachtell, 7040, **Wallace 7043**, Walsh 7045, Wang 7047, Warburg 7048, Warner 7053, **Watson 7058**, **Weeden 7060**, Weil, 7062, Wein 7064, Weinberg 7066, Weinberg 7067, Weissman 7071, Widgeon 7081, Wilson 7088, Winston 7092, Wohl 7097, **Wolfensohn 7098**, Wolstencroft 7100, **Youths' 7112**, Zehner 7118, Zichron 7120, Zilkha 7125, Zvi 7129

North Carolina: Adams 7133, Babcock 7138, **Bank 7139**, BB&T 7143, BB&T 7144, Belk 7148, Blue 7153, Blumenthal 7154, Bolick 7155, Brady 7156, Bryan 7161, Bryson 7163, Caine 7167, Cape Fear 7170, **Carlson 7172**, Cemala 7174, Chatham 7175, Community 7180, Cumberland 7184, Curtis 7186, Davie 7188, Delta 7191, Dickson 7192, Dover 7194, Duke 7195, Finley 7199, Fund 7204, Glenn 7211, Goodrich 7213, Greenville 7217, Hallowell 7220, Hanes 7222, Harvest 7224, Holding 7234, Jones 7242, Lewis 7256, Mebane 7266, North Carolina 7273, **Oak 7276**, Olin 7279, P & B 7280, Piedmont 7285, Plansoen 7286, Polk 7287, Prickett 7290, Provident 7291, Randleigh 7292, Rasmuson 7293, Reidsville 7294, Reynolds 7298, Richardson 7301, Roanoke 7303, Robertson 7305, Shelton 7310, Smith 7317, Snyder's-Lance 7318, Southern 7319, Tannenbaum 7326, Terry 7327, Vanderbilt 7331, VF 7332, Warner 7334, Weaver 7335, Wheeler 7336, Winston-Salem 7340, Woodson 7342, Woodward 7344, Wos 7345

North Dakota: Leach 7353, MDU 7354, Myra 7355, North Dakota 7357, Scheels 7359, Stern 7360

Ohio: A Good 7363, AK Steel 7366, American 7368, American 7369, American 7370, Ames 7371, Anderson 7372, Anderson 7373, Ar-Hale 7376, Ariel 7377, Austin 7380, BASF 7383, **Bingham 7387**, Budig 7392, Burleigh 7395, Butler 7396, Cafaro 7397, Charities 7400, Christ 7402, Cliffs 7407, Codrington 7409, Community 7412, Community 7415, Community 7416, Corbin 7420, Covenant 7422, Danaher 7424, Dater 7426, Dayton 7429, DBJ 7430, Diamond 7435, Dicke 7436, Dodero 7438, Dorn 7439, Durell 7441, **Eaton 7442**, Fairfield 7445, Farmer 7447, Fifth 7452, Findlay 7453, Firman 7454, FirstEnergy 7455, Fleischmann 7457, Fowler 7460, France 7462, Friedlander 7463, Frost 7464, GAR 7465, **Geisse 7468**, Gerlach 7471, Gund 7476, Gund 7477, Gund 7478, H.C.S. 7479, Haslinger 7482, Hatton 7483, Hayfields 7485, Honda 7490, Hoover 7492, Howley 7494, Hubert 7495, Humphrey 7497, Hutton 7500, Jegs 7507, Jochum 7513, Kaplan 7516, **Kettering 7520**, Kettering 7521, KeyBank 7523, Kimble 7526, Knowlton 7528, Kramer 7529, Krause 7530, Kulas 7532, LaValley 7535, Lennon 7537, Lincoln 7541, Lippman 7542, Lubrizol 7546, Macy's 7552, Maltz 7553, Mandel 7554, **Mandel 7555**, Marietta 7557, Marion 7558, Mather 7559, Mathile 7560, Mayerson 7561, McBride 7562, Mercer 7567, Miller 7571, Moores 7576, Morgan 7577, Morgan 7578, Morgan 7579, Morrison 7580, Murch 7582, Murdough 7583, Murphy 7584, Muskingum 7585, National 7586, Nationwide 7587, **Needmor 7588**, Nippert 7590, **Noble 7592**, Nord 7594, Nord 7595, Ohio 7599, **OMNOVA 7601**, Orr 7604, Park 7609, Park 7610, Parker 7611, Payne 7614, Peterson 7617, Prentiss 7621, Progressive 7623, Reinberger 7628, Richland 7630, Ritter 7633, Saint 7639, Samaritan 7642, Sankey 7643, **Sapirstein-Stone-Weiss 7644**, Schear 7645, Schott 7652, Schottenstein 7654, Scripps 7659, Sherwin-Williams 7661, Silk 7663, Sisler 7664, Smith 7668, Spaulding 7670, Springfield 7671, St. Marys 7672, Stark 7673, State 7674, Stocker 7676, Third 7681, Trzcinski 7689, Turner 7691, Twenty 7692, Veale 7694, Vesper 7695, Wagler 7699, Warren 7702, Weary 7706, Weatherhead 7707, Weisbrod 7708, Western 7710, Westfield 7711, Wolfe 7719, Wuliger 7722, Youngstown 7723, Zembrodt 7724

Oklahoma: Adams 7725, American 7728, Asbjornson 7729, Bartlesville 7731, Bovaird 7735, Brown 7737, Chapman 7739, Collins 7741, Communities 7742, Community 7743, Coretz 7744, Hille 7759, Inasmuch 7760, Ketchum 7765, Kirkpatrick 7766, Masonic 7771, McCasland 7772, McCrory 7773, McGee 7774, Meinders 7777, Miller 7778, Nelson 7779, Noble 7780, Oklahoma City 7781, Oklahoma 7782, ONEOK 7783, Oxley 7785, Records 7788, **Schusterman 7794**, Simmons 7796, Southern 7798, Stevens 7800, Stuart 7802, Tandy 7803, Taubman 7804, Titus 7806, Tulsa 7807, Viersen 7808, Warren 7809, Westheimer 7812, Williams 7814, Zarrow 7818, Zarrow 7819, Zarrow 7820, Zink 7821

Oregon: Benton 7825, Braemar 7826, Burning 7827, Caddock 7828, Carpenter 7831, Chambers 7832, Collins 7836, Esco 7841, **Fohs 7844**, Ford 7845, Hedinger 7851, **Intel 7853**, Jeld 7856, Johnson 7858, Kinsman 7860, Lamfrom 7863, Lazar 7864, Macdonald 7866, Meyer 7870, Mission 7873, Morris 7874, **NIKE 7875**, Oregon 7876, PacifiCorp 7877, PacificSource 7878, PGE 7881, Randall 7883, Renaissance 7884, Schnitzer 7887, Tektronix 7894, Templeton 7895, Tucker 7896, Woodard 7899

Pennsylvania: 1675 7903, **ACE 7905**, Air 7907, Alexander 7910, Allegheny 7911, Allerton 7912, Ametek 7913, Angelakis 7914, Arcadia 7918, Armstrong 7922, Baker 7925, Baker 7926, Ball 7927, Barra 7928, Beatty 7933, Beaver 7934, Birmingham 7942, Blanchard 7944, **BNY 7945**, Bozzone 7948, Britton 7951, Brossman 7954, Buncher 7957, Campbell 7960, Carnahan 7965, **Carthage 7968**, CentiMark 7970, Central 7972, Centre 7973, Century 7974, Cestone 7975, Cestone 7976, Chester 7979, CIGNA 7981, Claneil 7982, Clapp 7983, **Colcom 7986**, Colket 7987, Colonial 7988, Comcast 7989, Community 7994, Connelly 7995, Cotswold 7999, Crels 8002, Dollar 8014, Drumcliff 8016, DSF 8017, Eden 8021, ESSA 8028, Farber 8032, Federated 8033, Feldman 8034, Fels 8035, Ferree 8036, Fieldstone 8038, First 8040, First 8041, Firstfruits 8042, FISA 8043, Fishman 8044, Foundation 8046, Fourjay 8047, Genuardi 8053, Gerber 8054, Glencairn 8062, Grable 8064, Graham 8065, Grass 8067, Grass 8068, Gray 8069, Hamer 8077, Hamilton 8078, Hansen 8079, **Heinz 8083**, Heinz 8084, Henkels 8089, Highmark 8092, Hopwood 8096, Hoverter 8097, Hughes 8099, Hunt 8100, Huston 8102, Huston 8103, Independence 8106, Independence 8107, Jerlyn 8112, Karabots 8116, Kavanagh 8118, Kelly 8119, **Kennametal 8120**,

Keystone 8122, Kind 8125, Kunkel 8133, Lenfest 8137, Lenfest 8138, Lindback 8142, Lipsitz 8144, **Little 8145**, Lomax 8148, Mandell 8153, Marshall 8155, Martin 8156, McCausland 8159, McCune 8160, McFeely 8163, McKenna 8166, **McKenna 8167**, McKinney 8168, Mellon 8172, Mellon 8173, Mengle 8174, Miller, 8182, Mine 8184, Morgan 8187, Morris 8188, Mullen 8190, Mylan 8192, Nelson 8195, **Oberkotter 8203**, Ortenzio 8205, O'Toole 8207, Parmer 8212, Penn 8216, Philadelphia 8221, Phoenixville 8223, Pierce 8224, Pilgrim 8225, Pine 8226, Plankenhorn 8229, PNC 8230, Pottstown 8234, **PPG 8235**, Raab 8242, Rees 8245, Roberts 8250, Rosenstiel 8254, Rossin 8256, S & T 8259, Saint 8260, Scaife 8266, Schenck 8269, Scholler 8273, Scranton 8275, Sedwick 8276, Sexauer 8280, Shaffer 8281, Shoemaker 8284, Simmons 8285, Smith 8289, Stein/Bellet 8298, Steinman 8300, Toll 8317, Torch 8318, Trees 8319, Trexler 8320, United 8324, United 8325, Vanguard 8327, Warburton 8331, Washington 8332, West 8334, Williams 8338, Wilson 8341, Wyomissing 8350

Puerto Rico: Puerto Rico 8353

Rhode Island: Amica 8356, Biogen 8363, Buehler 8364, Carter 8368, Charlesmead 8371, Citizens 8374, Cuno 8378, Daniels 8380, **Dorot 8384, FM 8393**, Freeman 8396, Greene 8398, Hasbro 8403, Kimball 8410, Koonce 8412, McAdams 8416, McNeil 8418, Rhode Island 8429, Seymour 8436, Shriners 8438, Statter 8441, Textron 8446, TriMix 8448, van Beuren 8449

South Carolina: Abney 8454, **AVX-Kyocera 8457**, Black 8459, Blue 8460, Byerly 8462, Campbell 8463, Cassels 8467, Central 8468, Coastal 8472, Gibbs 8480, Inman 8485, McKissick 8486, Patterson 8489, Roe 8494, **ScanSource 8495**, Sims 8497, Smith 8498, Smith 8499, Sonoco 8500, Springs 8504

South Dakota: **Opus 8518**, Robinson 8520, Sioux Falls 8521, Vucurevich 8524

Tennessee: Adams 8525, Alumni 8527, American 8528, Assisi 8530, Baptist 8533, Beaman 8534, Bridgestone 8537, Briggs 8538, CIC 8546, Cook 8552, Curb 8554, East 8560, Eastman 8561, Ezell 8564, First 8565, Frist 8568, Hamico 8576, Hart 8578, HCA 8582, Hyde 8584, **International 8585**, Johnson 8588, Johnson 8589, Lyndhurst 8599, Martin 8606, Memphis 8610, Nissan 8613, Proctor 8617, Ramsey 8621, Regal 8622, **Scarlett 8624**, Seme 8626, Shinn 8627, Speer 8630, Stokely 8631, Temple 8633, Tennessee 8634, Thompson 8635, Thompson 8636, Tucker 8638, Washington 8643, **Westwood 8644**, Wilson 8646

Texas: 80/20 8648, Abell 8650, Adams 8652, Albany 8654, Alexander 8656, Alkek 8658, Anchorage 8662, Anderson 8663, Angela 8669, Armentrout 8671, **Arnold 8672**, Astros 8674, Baron 8682, Bass 8686, Bass 8687, Bass 8688, Bass 8689, Bass 8690, Bauer 8691, Baugh 8693, Beal 8696, Beals, 8697, Beasley 8698, **Bell 8700**, Bickel 8705, Boeckman 8707, Borick 8714, **Bovay 8716, BP 8718**, Bridwell 8726, Brown 8731, Brumley 8734, Buford 8736, Burnett 8737, Butt 8738, Cailloux 8742, Cameron 8747, **Caris 8749**, Carter 8752, Carter 8753, Cash 8754, CEMEX 8757, CFP 8758, CH 8759, Chaparral 8760, Chapman 8761, Clayton 8765, Clements 8766, Clements 8767, Coastal 8768, Coates 8769, Cockrell 8770, Collins 8771, Community 8774, Community 8777, Cook 8779, Covenant 8781, Cox 8784, Cullen 8792, Dallas 8795, Davis 8799, Dean 8803, Dickson-Allen 8806, Dixon 8809, Dodge 8810, Doss 8812, Doss 8813, Durham 8817, Eady 8818, Edwards 8824, El Paso 8825, Ellwood 8827, Embrey 8828, Enrico 8831, **ExxonMobil 8833**, Fain 8835, Fasken 8839, Favrot 8842, Fikes 8844, Fisch 8846, Fish 8848, Fleming 8850, Fluor 8851, Frees 8857, George 8863, Goldsbury 8868, Goodman 8870, Greathouse 8874, Greathouse 8875, Guenther 8877, Gulf 8878, Hachar 8880, Haggerty 8881, Halliburton 8884, Hamill 8887, Hamman 8888, Hankamer 8890, Harvey 8894, Heavin 8898, Hebert 8899, Henderson 8900, Herzstein 8905, Hoglund 8913, **Houston 8916**, Houston 8917, Huffington 8920, Hunt 8922, Hunt 8923, Ingram 8925, **International 8927**, Jamail 8929, **Jenesis 8932**, JKJ 8934, Johnson 8938, Jones 8943, Jones 8944, KDK-Harman 8949, Kelleher 8951, Kempner 8952, Kickapoo 8955, Kilroy 8956, Kimberly 8957, Kinder 8958, Kodosky 8966, Kohl 8967, Kronkosky 8970, Lightner 8985, Littauer 8988, Lowe 8993, Lubbock 8994, Lyman 8995, Lyons 8996, Marsh 8999, **Marshall 9000**, Martinez 9003, Maverick 9005, Mayborn 9006, Mayor 9007, McCullough 9011, McDermott 9013, McGovern 9014, McNutt 9018, Meadows 9019, Meredith 9023, Miller 9028, Moncrief 9031, Moore 9034, Morgan 9038, Murchison 9046, Napier 9050, Natural 9053, Navarro 9054, Nearburg 9055, **New Beginning 9057**, Newman 9061, Northen 9063, NuStar 9065, O'Connor 9066, Once 9070, Orsinger 9073, Owen 9076, Owen 9077, Owsley 9078, Pace 9079, Parks 9081, Payne 9086, Penney 9089, Perkins 9090, Perot 9093, Peterson 9095, **PHM 9098**, Powell 9105, Priddy 9109, QuadW 9115, Rachal 9117, Rapoport 9122, Rees-Jones 9125, Reynolds 9127, Richardson 9130, Richardson 9131, Rockwell 9135, Rogers 9138, Rosewood 9140, Saada 9142, Sadler 9143, Sams 9145, San Angelo 9146, San Angelo 9147, San Antonio 9148, Sanchez 9150, **Scaler 9155**, Schepps 9158, Scurlock 9162, Seegers 9164, Sharp 9167, Shell 9168, Shield 9170, Simmons 9174, Simmons 9175, **Six 9178**, Smith 9183, Smith 9184, Smith 9186, Smith 9187, Snyder 9188, Starling 9199, Stedman 9200, Sterling 9203, Stern 9204, Still 9207, Strake 9208, Sturgis 9211, **Suder 9212**, Sumners 9214, Talkington 9219, Temple 9223, Terry 9224, Texas 9227, Tobin 9236, Topfer 9239, Trull 9240, TurningPoint 9244, USAA 9245, Valero 9246, Vanberg 9247, Vaughan 9248, **VHA 9250**, Waggoner 9252, Walsh 9256, Weaver 9260, WEDGE 9263, Weekley 9264, Welborn 9267, **Whole 9276**, Wichita 9277, Wilson 9280, Winkler 9281, Wolslager 9288, Wood 9289, Woodforest 9290, Wortham 9292, Yarborough 9294, Young 9295, Zale 9297, Zeller 9298, Zephyr 9299, Zimmer 9300

Utah: Ashton 9304, Bamberger 9305, Dee 9312, Eccles 9317, Eccles 9319, Eccles 9320, Gillmor 9323, Hemingway 9326, Lawson 9330, **Nu 9340**, Parrish 9342, Quinney 9347, Simmons 9351

Vermont: **Ben 9358**, Evslin 9360, Gibney 9362, Lintilhac 9365, McKenzie 9366, Tarrant 9373, Vermont 9375, Waterwheel 9376

Virginia: AMERIGROUP 9383, Arlington 9384, Balsells 9385, Bangs-Russell 9386, Beazley 9391, Birdsong 9393, **Blue 9394**, Breeden 9396, Cameron 9398, Capital 9400, Charles 9404, Charlottesville 9405, **Chase 9406**, Community 9410, Community 9411, Community 9412, Community 9414, Community 9415, Community 9416, **Cooke 9417**, Danville 9421, Dominion 9422, English 9426, Estes 9427, Evans 9428, Fife 9429, Flippo 9430, Folger 9431, Freddie 9435, Fredericksburg 9436, Golden 9443, Goodman 9444, Herndon 9451, Hylton 9455, Koch 9463, Luck 9472, Massey 9478, MAXIMUS 9481, MeadWestvaco 9484, Memorial 9485, Mitsubishi 9487, Moore 9489, Norfolk 9496, Northern 9497, **Olmsted 9501**, Potomac 9511, Ratner 9515, Robins 9523, Rosenthal 9525, **Sacharuna 9526**, Samberg 9527, Smithfield 9535, Strong 9537, SunTrust 9539, Tickle 9542, Titmus 9543, **Truland 9545**, United 9546, Universal 9548, Washington 9552, Weissberg 9554, **WestWind 9555**, Williamsburg 9558, Wrinkle 9562

Washington: **444S 9565**, Adams 9566, Anders 9571, Aven 9575, Avista 9576, Bainbridge 9578, Baker 9579, Blue 9588, **Brainerd 9590, Bullitt 9591**, Cameron 9593, **Campion 9594**, Casey 9595, Casey 9596, **Channel 9597**, Cheney 9598, Columbia 9602, Community 9604, Community 9605, Corvias 9606, Dimmer 9610, Everett 9616, Evertrust 9617, First 9619, Forest 9620, Fuchs 9624, **Gates 9625, Glaser 9630**, Grays 9631, Hagan 9634, Haller 9635, Handsel 9638, Harder 9640, Harnish 9641, Harvest 9642, **Haugland 9643**, Horizons 9645, **Hotes 9646**, Inland 9650, Kitsap 9659, **Kongsgaard 9661, Laird 9664**, Laurel 9666, Lochland 9670, Lockwood 9671, Lucky 9673, McKinstry 9680, Medina 9682, Milgard 9683, Names 9690, Norcliffe 9693, OneFamily 9695, Orcas 9697, PEMCO 9702, **Quixote 9707**, Raikes 9708, REI 9713, Remala 9714, Renton 9715, Russell 9722, Safeco 9723, Sahsen 9724, **Samis 9725**, Seattle 9731, Shirley 9734, Sloan 9736, **Starbucks 9742, Stewardship 9744**, Stubblefield 9745, Suskin 9747, Tacoma 9750, **Goodwin 9751**, Whatcom 9759, Wheeler 9760, **Wilburforce 9762**

West Virginia: Bowen 9770, Daywood 9774, Eastern 9775, Hamilton, 9776, Hollowell 9778, Maier 9782, McDonough 9784, Prichard 9791, Tucker 9796, Weisberg 9798

Wisconsin: Acuity 9801, Antioch 9807, Bachhuber 9809, Bader 9810, **Baird 9811**, Bemis 9815, Benidt 9816, **Bradley 9819**, Bradshaw 9820, Briggs 9822, Casper 9827, Charter 9829, Community 9832, Community 9833, Community 9835, Cornerstone 9836, CUNA 9838, Eder 9840, Evinrude 9841, Fort 9845, Frautschi 9847, Goldbach 9851, Green Bay 9855, Griffiss 9857, Herzfeld 9863, Holz 9864, Johnson 9870, Johnson 9871, Johnson 9874, Kelben 9877, Keller 9878, Kikkoman 9881, Krause 9886, Kuenzl 9888, La Crosse 9889, Ladish 9890, Loehrke 9893, ManpowerGroup 9899, Marcus 9900, McBeath 9901, Mead 9902, Menasha 9903, Neese 9911, Northwestern 9914, Ocular 9915, Oshkosh 9916, Oshkosh 9917, Peck 9918, Pettit 9919, Pick 9920, Rockwell 9934, Roundy's 9936, Rutledge 9939, **Schneider 9942**, Sentry 9944, Smith 9947, St. Croix 9950, Stackner 9951, Steigleder 9952, Stock 9953, Thrivent 9956, U.S. 9957, Uihlein 9959, Vine 9960, Wanek 9964, Waukesha 9965, Windhover 9968, Wisconsin 9969, Wisconsin 9970, Zilber 9972

Wyoming: Community 9975, Ellbogen 9977, Friess 9978, Griffith 9979, Kerr 9981, Martin 9984, McMurry 9986, Perkins 9988, Scott 9989, Seeley 9990, Storer 9992, True 9995, Whitney 9998, Wyoming 9999, Zimmerman 10000

Grants to individuals

Alaska: CIRI 85, Rasmuson 89

Arkansas: Wal-Mart 210

California: **Alalusi 224, Alpert 231**, Bickerstaff 313, California 368, Change 393, Doctors 471, Durfee 487, **Ellison 504**, Fleishhacker 534, **Foundation 542, Getty 579**, Guzik 639, Herbst 682, Humboldt 714, Jack 736, Luberski 852, **Lund 857**, Oakley 978, Rancho 1053, Sempra 1140, Sonora 1198

Colorado: Colorado 1389, Sachs 1489, Society 1503

Connecticut: Boehringer 1549, Main 1634, New Canaan 1650

Delaware: **Adobe 1734, AstraZeneca 1738**, CenturyLink-Clarke 1750, Common 1755

District of Columbia: Professional 1939

Florida: **Believers 1989**, Community 2031, duPont 2074, Hard 2147, Ryder 2302, **SeaWorld 2315**, Wolfe 2391

Georgia: Lockwood 2505, **Rosenberg 2545**, Southern 2554

Idaho: Lightfoot 2636, Rebholtz 2640

Illinois: **Abbott 2648, Abbvie 2650**, Allstate 2657, de Kay 2788, Driehaus 2805, Ende 2823, Gore 2871, **Graham 2873**, Morton 3040, **Poetry 3083**, Walgreen 3209, **Walgreens 3210**

Indiana: Blue 3265, Elkhart 3298, Hendricks 3319, **Lilly 3341**, Samerian 3384

Iowa: United 3485

Kansas: Damon 3504, HANDinHAND 3517, Jones 3523, McPherson 3534, Salina 3540

Kentucky: Gardner 3576, Independence 3583, Yum! 3608
Louisiana: Young 3674
Maine: Lerner 3695, Maine 3698
Maryland: **Casey 3745**, GEICO 3801, **Hughes 3818**
Massachusetts: Association 3929, Berkshire 3948, Cape Cod 3974, Fallon 4041, **Genzyme 4067**
Michigan: **Earhart 4413**, **Fetzer 4420**, Ford 4430, Here 4457, **Kellogg 4473**
Minnesota: Ecolab 4651, Jerome 4681, Koran 4689
Mississippi: CREATE 4822
Missouri: Arch 4855, Shelter 4971
New Jersey: **ARCH 5194**, **Knowles 5345**, **Merck 5381**, Orenstein 5397, **Puffin 5417**, **Sanofi 5437**, Segal 5447, Silbermann 5456
New Mexico: **Lannan 5526**
New York: BFF 5672, **Bristol 5712**, Campbell 5742, Chazen 5767, Collins 5798, Community 5804, **Dedalus 5864**, Dove 5903, Ebb 5928, **Gottlieb 6085**, **Guggenheim 6115**, Havens 6148, Hutchins 6202, **Jaffe 6222**, Klingenstein 6292, **Lasker 6333**, **Lauder 6336**, **Luce 6398**, Mitchell 6489, Newhouse 6550, **Open 6593**, **Philippe 6636**, **Pollock 6650**, **Skadden 6868**, **Soros 6888**, **Sparkplug 6894**, St. George's 6904, **Stefansky 6916**, SVM 6952, **Trace 7003**, Tuttle 7014, **Wenner 7075**
North Carolina: Beckman 7145, Corpening 7183, Foundation 7202, Smith 7316
Ohio: A Good 7363, Diamond 7435, Ford 7459, Loeb 7544, Marietta 7557, National 7586, **Patterson 7613**, Samaritan 7642, Scripps 7659, St. Marys 7672, Twenty 7692, **Wexner 7713**
Pennsylvania: Armstrong 7922, **Bayer 7931**, Berks 7939, **Cardiovascular 7963**, **Carnegie 7966**, Community 7994, England 8024, GlaxoSmithKline 8061, **Heinz 8085**, **Institute 8109**, Merchants 8175, Presser 8236, Smock 8290, **Templeton 8313**
Rhode Island: Alpert 8355, Rhode Island 8429
Tennessee: Dollar 8558, Hurlbut 8583, Lazarus 8596
Texas: Astros 8674, Boeckman 8707, Carter 8753, Ingram 8925, **New Beginning 9057**, Penney 9089, Perot 9092, Sunnyside 9215, **VHA 9250**, West 9270
Utah: Peterson 9345
Vermont: Vermont 9375
Virgin Islands: Community 9377
Virginia: Arlington 9384, Community 9416, **Cooke 9417**, Reckitt 9516
Washington: George 9626, Plum 9704, Russell 9722, Stubblefield 9745
Wisconsin: **Wagner 9961**
Wyoming: Perkins 9988

Income development

Alabama: Central 19
Arizona: Steele 165
California: Aratani 250, Atkinson 265, McKay 902, **Peery 1022**, Placer 1039, Sangham 1114, **Special 1202**, Truckee 1263
Colorado: Pikes 1478
District of Columbia: **Moriah 1932**, Vradenburg 1954
Georgia: Healthcare 2482
Idaho: **Schultz 2641**
Illinois: Arthur 2673, Chicago 2746, Coleman 2759, Evanston 2826, Oak Park 3061, Timken 3188
Indiana: Community 3284, Putnam 3373, Tipton 3391
Kansas: Capitol 3498, McPherson 3534
Kentucky: C.E. 3566
Maine: **Sandy 3707**
Maryland: Baker 3725, Baltimore 3726, Straus 3890
Massachusetts: Adams 3916, **Garfield 4065**, Lowell 4152, Schooner 4261
Michigan: Ann Arbor 4340
Minnesota: Wasie 4794, West 4800
Nebraska: Dunklau 5036
New Hampshire: New Hampshire 5182
New Jersey: Johnson 5328, Pascale 5403
New York: Charina 5763, Charina 5764, Community 5803, Demartini 5872, **M & T 6406**, New York 6544, O'Connor 6578, **Vital 7033**, Western 7078
North Carolina: Cape Fear 7170, Community 7180, Community 7182, Cumberland 7184, Warner 7334, Winston-Salem 7340
Ohio: Lennon 7537, Morgan 7577, O'Neill 7602, Wean 7705
Oregon: **Fohs 7844**, Kinsman 7860, Meyer 7870, Mission 7873
Pennsylvania: Centre 7973, Erie 8026, Hurd 8101, McCune 8161, United 8324
South Dakota: South Dakota 8522
Texas: **Houston 8916**, Littauer 8988, **Marshall 9000**, Meadows 9019, Once 9070, Rockwell 9135, **Scaler 9155**, TurningPoint 9244
Vermont: Gibney 9362, Vermont 9375
Virginia: ACT 9380, Robins 9523
Washington: Allen 9567, Bainbridge 9578, **Brainerd 9590**, Casey 9596, Grays 9631, **Quixote 9707**, Satterberg 9728, **Vista 9756**

In-kind gifts

Alabama: Community 24, Walker 74
Arizona: Delta 106
Arkansas: Union 208
California: CAA 362, Gap 563, James 742, **Kapor 764**, **KLA-Tencor 792**, **Mattel 886**, **McConnell 898**, Monterey 936, North 972, Oakland 977, Orfalea 994, PIMCO 1037, Schwab 1127, Sierra 1163, Western 1316, **World 1346**
Colorado: Community 1391, El Pomar 1406, Saeman 1490, Summit 1511
Connecticut: Alexion 1533, Boehringer 1549, SBM 1690
District of Columbia: **Moriah 1932**
Florida: Darden 2051, Florescue 2100, Glazer 2124, Jacksonville 2167, Magruder 2225, Ryder 2302, **Stacy 2333**
Georgia: Callaway 2419, **Georgia 2469**, Savannah 2548, **UPS 2566**
Illinois: Community 2763, Dillon 2796, **Mondelez 3034**, Trustmark 3193, **Walgreens 3210**
Indiana: Ball 3262, Blue 3265, Community 3286, Elkhart 3298, Noble 3359, Old 3363, Steuben 3390
Kansas: Sprint 3549, Topeka 3552
Maryland: Henson 3814, Mid-Shore 3851
Massachusetts: Cape Cod 3974, Highland 4098, New England 4193, Starwood 4284
Michigan: Community 4374, **Dow 4404**, Hillsdale 4461, Walker 4575
Minnesota: 3M 4597, Hormel 4676, **Mosaic 4722**, Northwest 4730, **Polaris 4746**, U.S. 4784, Valspar 4786
Missouri: Ameren 4851, Truman 4996
Nebraska: ConAgra 5029, ConAgra 5030, Fremont 5039, Hastings 5046, Mutual 5071
Nevada: Parasol 5138
New Jersey: Clare 5230, New Jersey 5389, **Novartis 5393**
New Mexico: **Lannan 5526**, New Mexico 5530
New York: **Bristol 5711**, **Dedalus 5864**, **MetLife 6479**, **PepsiCo 6627**, **Pfizer 6634**
North Carolina: Cumberland 7184, Duke 7196, Goodrich 7213, Mebane 7266, Triangle 7328
North Dakota: Fargo 7351
Ohio: **Cardinal 7398**, Community 7416, **Eaton 7442**, Muskingum 7585, **OMNOVA 7601**, Stark 7673
Oklahoma: Kerr 7764, **Schusterman 7794**, Stone 7801, Zink 7821
Pennsylvania: Air 7907, Buck 7955, EQT 8025, **Heinz 8083**, Teva 8314
Puerto Rico: Puerto Rico 8353
South Carolina: Community 8474, Spartanburg 8501
Tennessee: **International 8585**, Memphis 8610, Regal 8622
Texas: **Houston 8916**, Jones 8943, **Marshall 9000**, Sams 9145, Simmons 9174
Utah: Hemingway 9326
Virginia: ACT 9380, Community 9410, Danville 9420, Dominion 9422, Peterson 9508
Washington: Community 9605, Grays 9631, Kitsap 9659, **Quixote 9707**, San Juan 9726, Whatcom 9759
Wisconsin: Community 9835, Roundy's 9936, **Schneider 9942**, Wisconsin 9969
Wyoming: Community 9975

Internship funds

Alabama: Webb 76
Alaska: CIRI 85, Doyon 86
Arizona: Freeport-McMoRan 112
California: Connell 424, **Getty 579**, Goldman 605, **Lingnan 841**, Monroe 935, Parsons 1013, **Rupe 1097**, Van Nuys 1284, Wohlford 1336
Colorado: Lipscomb 1449, Ottens 1472
Connecticut: Larsen 1624
Delaware: **Memton 1819**, Schwartz 1857
District of Columbia: Aid 1879, Munson 1933
Florida: Community 2031, Community 2035, **Davis 2056**, Greenburg 2137, Haller 2146, **Skelly 2324**
Georgia: DuBose 2450, Zeist 2584
Illinois: Arthur 2673, Blair 2699, Butler 2729, Comer 2760, Frankel 2842, Harris 2892, **Kemper 2955**, King 2960, Lumpkin 2986, Monticello 3036, Robinson 3122, **Scholl 3141**, Speh 3170
Indiana: **Lilly 3342**
Iowa: Maytag 3460, McElroy 3461
Kansas: Capitol 3498, McPherson 3534
Kentucky: C.E. 3566
Maine: Horizon 3691, Morton 3701
Maryland: Deutsch 3779, Rathmann 3867
Massachusetts: Foundation 4056, Island 4109
Michigan: Americana 4337, Bay 4344, Cook 4377, Ford 4430
Minnesota: Bremer 4620
Mississippi: Hardin 4831
New Jersey: Brotherton 5216, Buehler 5219, **JM 5323**, **Merck 5379**, Merck 5380, **Newcombe 5391**
New Mexico: New Mexico 5530
New York: Avery 5627, Brooklyn 5718, **Dedalus 5864**, Emerson 5950, Gilman 6052, Goldman 6068, **Kress 6308**, Lang 6326, Levitt 6361, **Luce 6398**, Morgan 6507, Noble 6561, **Open 6593**, **Peterson 6630**, **Pforzheimer 6635**, **Philippe 6636**, **Revson 6693**, Schnurmacher 6810, Sulzberger 6942, Triad 7005
North Carolina: **Bank 7139**, Community 7180, Duke 7195, **Morehead-Cain 7268**, North 7274, Polk 7287, Tannenbaum 7326
Ohio: Gund 7478, Humphrey 7497, Lennon 7537, Levin 7539, Morgan 7578, Muskingum 7585, Nippert 7590, Scripps 7659
Oklahoma: Kerr 7764, **Schusterman 7794**
Oregon: Benton 7825, Kinsman 7860, Macdonald 7866
Pennsylvania: Centre 7973, Fels 8035, **Heinz 8083**, Independence 8106, **Institute 8109**, Seraph 8279, United 8324
Rhode Island: **Dorot 8384**, Textron 8446
South Carolina: Abney 8454, Community 8474
Tennessee: **Scarlett 8624**, Tucker 8638
Texas: Community 8777, Covenant 8781, Edwards 8823, **Houston 8916**, Lyons 8996, QuadW 9115, Summerlee 9213, Sumners 9214
Washington: Blue 9588, George 9626, Miller 9684
West Virginia: Eastern 9775
Wisconsin: **Bradley 9819**, Community 9835

Land acquisition

Alabama: Kaul 43, Meyer 53
Alaska: Rasmuson 89
Arizona: **Johnson 126**, **Kieckhefer 129**, Morris 148, Webb 174
Arkansas: Cabe 182
California: Ahmanson 222, Ayrshire 276, Community 419, **Compton 422**, Cowell 434, Firedoll 528, **Foundation 542**, Gasser 566, Gold 600, Hedco 672, Hind 693, Irwin 728, Long 847, Marin 877, McBean 892, McMillen 905, Mead 907, Monterey 936, **Moore 938**, Morgan 940, **Packard 1006**, Parker 1012, Rancho 1053, Reid 1060, San Diego 1108, Santa Barbara 1116, Tuohy 1267
Colorado: Boettcher 1374, Edmondson 1405, El Pomar 1406, Gates 1418, Summit 1511
Connecticut: Baldwin 1541, Fund 1589, Hartford 1609, Larsen 1624, Vervane 1716
Delaware: AEC 1735, Crystal 1758, Fair 1780, Laffey 1800, Lennox 1805, Longwood 1806, Marmot 1814, **Raskob 1845**
District of Columbia: **Wallace 1955**
Florida: Bush 2008, Gooding 2130, Hersh 2156, Miami 2238, **Peterson 2267**, Rinker 2285, Selby 2316
Georgia: Callaway 2419, Campbell 2420, Courts 2441, DuBose 2450, English 2453, Equifax 2455, Loridans 2506, **Thoresen 2557**, Whitehead 2571, Wilson 2576, Woodruff 2579, Woolley 2581, Zeist 2584
Illinois: Bauer 2687, Chicago 2746, Dillon 2796, Edwardsville 2817, Field 2831, Frankel 2842, Grand 2875, Jahn 2938, Keith 2952, Martin 3003, Nelson 3049, Reed 3109
Indiana: Auer 3260, Brown 3269, Central 3272, Cole 3276, Community 3281, Dekko 3296, Harrison 3314, Hendricks 3319, Heritage 3321, Huntington 3324, Kendrick 3333, **Lilly 3342**, Noble 3359, Ogle 3362, Steuben 3390, Unity 3393, Waterfield 3399
Iowa: Maytag 3460
Kansas: Cooper 3503, McPherson 3534, Sunderland 3551
Kentucky: Brown 3563, Brown 3564, C.E. 3566
Louisiana: Community 3624
Maine: King 3694, Libra 3696, Maine 3698, Morton 3701
Maryland: Abell 3712, Blades 3734, Concordia 3763, Knott 3826, Meyerhoff 3848, Mid-Shore 3851, Riepe 3869
Massachusetts: **Barr 3937**, Beveridge 3950, Cape Cod 3974, Community 3992, Davis 4011, Ellsworth 4035, Fields 4046, Fletcher 4054, Fuller 4063, **Garfield 4065**, Island 4109, Merck 4171, Mifflin 4175, Parker 4207, **Phillips 4219**, Proctor 4227, Sheehan 4271, Stoddard 4293, **Sweet 4302**
Michigan: Battle Creek 4343, Dalton 4385, Frey 4440, Gerstacker 4444, Gilmore 4445, Grand Haven 4446, Grand Rapids 4447, Herrick 4459, Jackson 4467, Johnson 4468, Mount Pleasant 4512, Oleson 4516, Pokagon 4523
Minnesota: Buuck 4623, Greystone 4668, **King 4687**, Lilly 4696, Marbrook 4702
Mississippi: Maddox 4834
Missouri: Cox 4874, Green 4900, Hall 4905, Reynolds 4961, Sander 4967
Nebraska: Hirschfeld 5049, Kiewit 5057, Kind 5060, Lincoln 5063, Mid-Nebraska 5068
New Hampshire: Fuller 5172, Hunt 5177, Panjandrum 5184, Penates 5185
New Jersey: Cape 5224, Charles 5227, Delano 5240, Grassmann 5281, Hyde 5310, Kirby 5339, Union 5485, Victoria 5490
New Mexico: **Lannan 5526**, Maddox 5528
New York: Adirondack 5556, Brooklyn 5718, Charina 5763, Charina 5764, Community 5805, **Cummings 5832**, Dolan 5895, Fanwood 5968, Freeman 6012, Gerry 6043, Gifford 6049, Glens Falls 6057, Hayden 6150, Hultquist 6195, **Kohlberg 6300**, LaSalle 6331, Mars 6437, McCann 6453, **Mitsubishi 6490**, **Norcross 6564**, Northern 6567, O'Connor 6578, Ohrstrom 6582, **Prospect 6663**, Schaffner 6800, Schenectady 6802, Steele 6915, Thompson 6975, **Vital 7033**, **Weeden 7060**, Western 7078
North Carolina: Cape Fear 7170, Community 7180, Glass 7210, Hanes 7221, Hanes 7222, Robertson 7305, Tannenbaum 7326, Weaver 7335
Ohio: Ashtabula 7379, Barberton 7382, Columbus 7411, Covenant 7422, Dayton 7428, Fairfield 7445, GAR 7465, Gund 7478, Kulas 7532, Maltz 7553, Muskingum 7585, Richland 7630, Salem 7640, Schmidlapp 7651, Semple 7660, Stark 7673, **Timken 7684**, Wayne 7704
Oklahoma: Chapman 7740, Community 7743, Helmerich 7758, Hille 7759, Inasmuch 7760, McGee 7774, McMahon 7776, Stone 7801, Viersen 7808
Oregon: Carpenter 7831, Collins 7836, Esco 7841, Kinsman 7860, Oregon 7876, Swindells 7892, Tucker 7896, Woodard 7899
Pennsylvania: Blanchard 7944, Claneil 7982, **Colcom 7986**, Erie 8026, First 8040, Kline 8129, Martin 8156, McCune 8161, McFeely 8163, McKenna 8166, McLean 8169, Mellon 8173, Nichols 8197, Penn 8216, Seraph 8279, Steinman 8300, Trexler 8320
Rhode Island: Bafflin 8359, Champlin 8370, Daniels 8380, Rhode Island 8429, Seymour 8436, van Beuren 8449
South Carolina: Abney 8454, Bruce 8461, Coastal 8472, Roe 8494
Tennessee: Benwood 8535, Carlton 8541, Community 8548, Lyndhurst 8599, Plough 8615, Tucker 8638
Texas: Amarillo 8660, Austin 8676, Brown 8731, Cailloux 8742, Carter 8752, Cockrell 8770, Communities 8773, Constantin 8778, Cowden 8783, Cullen 8792, Halsell 8885, Herzstein 8905, Hillcrest 8909, Hoblitzelle 8912, **Houston 8916**, Houston 8917, Johnson 8941, Kinder 8958, Kronkosky 8970, McDermott 9013, Meadows 9019, Moody 9033, Richardson 9130, San Angelo 9147, San Antonio 9148, Scurlock 9162, Shield 9170, Sterling 9203, Stern 9204, Summerlee 9213, Vanberg 9247
Utah: Dumke 9315, Eccles 9317
Vermont: Lintilhac 9365
Virginia: Alleghany 9382, Cameron 9398, Fralin 9433, Hylton 9455, McGlothlin 9483, Robins 9523, Titmus 9543, **WestWind 9555**
Washington: Community 9604, Grays 9631, Green 9632, Horizons 9645, Kitsap 9659, **Kongsgaard 9661**, Murdock 9689, Norcliffe 9693, **Quixote 9707**, Sherwood 9733, Tacoma 9750
West Virginia: Eastern 9775
Wisconsin: Alexander 9803, Community 9833, Iddings 9866, Lunda 9896, Madison 9897, Milwaukee 9907, Stock 9953, U.S. 9957, West 9967

Loaned talent

Illinois: Allstate 2657

Loans—to individuals

Florida: Hill 2158
Minnesota: Northwest 4730, Southwest 4768
North Carolina: Smith 7316
Ohio: Loeb 7544, Samaritan 7642

Management development/capacity building

Alabama: BBVA 9, Central 19, Community 23, Community 24, Kaul 43, Meyer 53, Walker 74
Alaska: Rasmuson 89
Arizona: Freeport-McMoRan 112, **Hickey 121**, **Johnson 126**, Piper 152, Steele 165
Arkansas: Cabe 182, Rockefeller 197, Wal-Mart 210, Walton 211
California: Alliance 229, **Alpert 231**, **Amgen 238**, Aratani 250, Atkinson 265, Atlas 266, Bechtel 294, Bechtel, 296, Blue 320, California 365, California 366, Campbell 373, Clif 405, Community 414, Community 416, Community 417, Community 418, Cowell 434, **Draper 481**, East 490, Eisner 499, **Firelight 529**, Fresno 549, **Fund 556**, Gap 563, Gerbode 573, **Gilead 586**, Girard 591, Goldman 606, Haas 642, **Hilton 692**, Humboldt 714, Hutton 718, **Kapor 764**, **Kee 776**, Kern 780, Koret 801, Lesher 833, **Lingnan 841**, Long 847, Mabie 863, McCune 900, McKay 902, Monterey 936, Morgan 940, Napa 959, North 972, Noyce 974, Orange 992, Pacific 1002, Pacific 1003, **Packard 1006**, **Peery 1022**, PIMCO 1037, Placer 1039, Rancho 1053, **Righteous 1073**, **Rivendell 1077**, Rosenberg 1088, Sacramento 1103, San Luis 1110, Sangham 1114, Schwab 1127, Schwab 1128, Silicon 1166, **Smith 1183**, Soda 1194, Sonora 1198, **Special 1202**, **Strauss 1223**, Stuart 1225, Truckee 1263, UniHealth 1270, Union 1271, Ventura 1287, Weingart 1307, Wells 1312, Wohlford 1336
Colorado: Aspen 1368, Bonfils 1376, Chambers 1385, **Crowell 1398**, ECA 1404, Lipscomb 1449, Ottens 1472, Pikes 1478, Rose 1487, Summit 1511
Connecticut: American 1537, Community 1562, Community 1563, Connecticut 1566, Connecticut 1567, Fairfield 1581, Fund 1589, **GE 1591**, Graustein 1600, Hartford 1609, Liberty 1630, Main 1634, Middlesex 1644, New Canaan 1650, NewAlliance 1651, **Newman's 1652**, Valley 1714
Delaware: Edwards 1774, Longwood 1806, **Raskob 1845**
District of Columbia: **Arca 1880**, Cafritz 1890, Community 1893, Consumer 1894, **El-Hibri 1903**, Meyer 1931, **Moriah 1932**, Vradenburg 1954, Wallace 1956
Florida: Bush 2008, Central 2015, Community 2032, Community 2033, Community 2034, Community 2041, Conn 2042, duPont 2075, Florida 2101, Henderson 2152, Indian 2166, **Knight 2191**, Miami 2238, **Peterson 2267**, Quantum 2276, Southwest 2327, St. Joe 2331, Wells 2383, Winter 2390
Georgia: Camp-Younts 2421, Communities 2431, Community 2432, Community 2435, Equifax 2455, **Georgia 2469**, Healthcare 2482, Moore 2519, North 2525, Primerica 2534, **UPS 2566**, Woodruff 2579
Hawaii: Atherton 2586, Castle 2593, Cooke 2597, First 2598, Hawaii 2602
Idaho: Idaho 2632, **Schultz 2641**
Illinois: **Abbott 2649**, Allstate 2657, Arthur 2673, **Brinson 2715**, Chicago 2746, Circle 2749, Community 2766, Community 2769, Evanston 2826, Grand 2875, Guthman 2882, Kaplan 2947, King 2960, Libra 2981, Lumpkin 2986, Mander 2998, Morse 3039, Oak Park 3061, Pierce 3080, Polk 3084, Speh 3170, Steans 3175, Stone 3180, **Tellabs 3185**, Tracy 3189
Indiana: Ball 3262, Community 3277, Community 3279, Community 3281, Community 3284, Community 3285, Community 3288, Community 3289, Dekko 3296, Elkhart 3298, Fairbanks 3301, Foellinger 3304, Foundations 3306, Harrison 3314, Health 3317, Heritage 3321, Huntington 3324, Johnson 3330, Kosciusko 3336, **Lilly 3342**, **Lumina 3345**, Noble 3359, Porter 3369, Pulliam 3372, Steuben 3390, Tipton 3391, Washington 3398
Iowa: Community 3420, Community 3421, Community 3423, Community 3424, Iowa 3447, Wellmark 3490
Kansas: Capitol 3498, Douglas 3509, Kansas 3524, McPherson 3534, Salina 3540, **Shumaker 3546**
Kentucky: Blue 3560, C.E. 3566
Louisiana: Beaird 3614, Blue 3615, Community 3624, Keller 3646, New Orleans 3656, Wilson 3671
Maine: Cohen 3684, Maine 3698, Maine 3699, **Sandy 3707**, Sewall 3708, TD 3710

Maryland: Baker 3725, Baltimore 3726, **Bearman 3728, Casey 3745**, Community 3760, **de Beaumont 3774, Deerbrook 3776**, France 3796, Knott 3826, Mid-Shore 3851

Massachusetts: Adams 3916, **Barr 3937**, Berkshire 3948, Blue 3953, Cape Cod 3974, Community 3991, Community 3992, Cosette 3997, Davis 4011, DentaQuest 4016, Essex 4039, Foundation 4056, **Garfield 4065, Hunt 4102**, Lowell 4152, Melville 4170, Smith 4277, Stevens 4288, Sudbury 4299

Michigan: Albion 4332, Ann Arbor 4340, Capital 4357, Community 4369, Community 4372, Community 4373, **Erb 4415**, Fremont 4438, Greenville 4452, Knight 4477, Lenawee 4485, Miller 4503, **Mott 4510**, Mott 4511, Mount Pleasant 4512, Pokagon 4523, Steelcase 4547, Upton 4565

Minnesota: Athwin 4607, Beverly 4615, Blue 4618, Bremer 4620, Carlson 4629, Graco 4666, **Medtronic 4712**, Northwest 4729, Northwest 4730, Oswald 4735, Phillips 4741, Rochester 4755, Winona 4806

Mississippi: Community 4821, Foundation 4827

Missouri: Bellwether 4859, Community 4872, Kauffman 4922, Saint Louis 4966

Montana: Edwards 5008, Oro 5014, Whitefish 5019

Nebraska: ConAgra 5030, Cooper 5031, Fremont 5039, Lincoln 5063, Omaha 5074, Union 5090

Nevada: Community 5108

New Hampshire: **Fidelity 5170**, Hunt 5177, New Hampshire 5182

New Jersey: **Allen 5191**, Atlantic 5196, **Berrie 5206**, Dircks 5241, Dodge 5243, Elias 5252, Fund 5270, **JM 5323, Merck 5379**, Merck 5380, Pascale 5403, Provident 5414, **Prudential 5415**, PSEG 5416, Victoria 5490

New Mexico: Brindle 5516, Santa Fe 5533

New York: Altman 5579, **American 5588, Arcus 5608**, Blue 5685, **Bristol 5711**, Brooklyn 5718, Central 5757, **Citi 5780, Clark 5784**, Clark 5786, Community 5802, Community 5803, Community 5804, Community 5805, Community 5807, Community 5808, Corning 5818, **Credit 5826**, Cricket 5827, **Cummings 5833**, DeCamp 5861, **Deutsche 5876**, Dyson 5923, Elmezzi 5948, **Ford 5994, Frankenberg 6009, Genesis 6042**, Gould 6087, **Hartford 6144**, Health 6153, **Isdell 6214**, Johnson 6239, **JPMorgan 6244**, Lenna 6352, Link 6375, **M & T 6406, MetLife 6479**, Mizuho 6492, **Moody's 6499, Nash 6525**, New York 6544, New York 6546, O'Connor 6578, Oishei 6584, Park 6615, **PepsiCo 6627, Pfizer 6633**, Pinkerton 6643, **Porticus 6654, Reisman 6686**, Richmond 6703, Rochester 6722, Schnurmacher 6810, **Sparkplug 6894, Starr 6911**, Staten 6912, Steele 6915, **Surdna 6947**, Tiger 6980, Tower 7000, Triad 7005, van Ameringen 7024, Warner 7053

North Carolina: **Bank 7139**, Blue 7153, Brady 7156, Cape Fear 7170, Cemala 7174, Community 7180, Community 7181, Community 7182, Cumberland 7184, Davie 7188, Duke 7196, Goodrich 7213, High Point 7231, North Carolina 7273, **Oak 7276**, Piedmont 7285, Reidsville 7294, Rex 7295, Robertson 7305, Tannenbaum 7326, Triangle 7328, Warner 7334, Weaver 7335, Winston-Salem 7340

North Dakota: Fargo 7351

Ohio: Abington 7365, Ar-Hale 7376, **Bingham 7387**, Dayton 7428, Erie 7444, Fairfield 7445, Fifth 7452, Findlay 7453, Fowler 7460, GAR 7465, Kettering 7521, Lennon 7537, Maltz 7553, Mayerson 7561, Miami 7569, Morgan 7577, Morgan 7579, O'Neill 7602, Osteopathic 7605, Reinberger 7628, Richland 7630, Saint 7639, Scioto 7657, Spaulding 7670, Wayne 7704, Wean 7705, Youngstown 7723

Oklahoma: Community 7743, Hille 7759, Inasmuch 7760, Ketchum 7765, Kirkpatrick 7766, Oklahoma City 7781, Sarkeys 7793, Viersen 7808

Oregon: Cambia 7829, Carpenter 7831, Chambers 7832, Collins 7836, **Fohs 7844**, Ford 7845, Kinsman 7860, Meyer 7870, Mission 7873, **NIKE 7875**

Pennsylvania: **Alcoa 7908**, Armstrong 7921, Baker 7926, Barra 7928, Benedum 7935, Buhl 7956, Chester 7979, Claneil 7982, **Colcom 7986**, Crawford 8001, Eden 8021, Erie 8026, First 8041, Heinz 8084, Highmark 8092, Hurd 8101, Independence 8106, Lancaster 8135, Lehigh Valley 8136, McCune 8161, North 8199, Penn 8216, Phoenixville 8223, Pittsburgh 8228, Pottstown 8234, Staunton 8296

Puerto Rico: Puerto Rico 8353

Rhode Island: CVS 8379, Rhode Island 8429

South Carolina: Black 8459, Central 8468, Community 8475, Daniel 8476, Sims 8497

South Dakota: Sioux Falls 8521, Vucurevich 8524

Tennessee: Assisi 8530, Benwood 8535, Community 8548, Community 8549, Frist 8568, Plough 8615, **Scarlett 8624**

Texas: Alcon 8655, Amarillo 8660, **Arnold 8672**, BNSF 8706, Booth 8711, Community 8774, Community 8777, Dallas 8795, Davis 8799, El Paso 8825, Favrot 8842, **Houston 8916**, Hudson 8919, KDK-Harman 8949, King 8959, Kronkosky 8970, Meadows 9019, Orsinger 9073, Powell 9105, Priddy 9109, Rees-Jones 9125, **RGK 9128**, Rockwell 9135, San Angelo 9147, Simmons 9175, Terry 9224, Tocker 9237, Trull 9240, Waco 9251

Vermont: **Ben 9358**, Gibney 9362, Vermont 9375

Virginia: ACT 9380, Arlington 9384, Cameron 9398, Capital 9400, Danville 9421, Freddie 9435, **Genworth 9441**, MeadWestvaco 9484, Northern 9497, Robins 9523, Samberg 9527, Weissberg 9554, Williamsburg 9558

Washington: Allen 9567, Blue 9588, **Brainerd 9590, Bullitt 9591, Campion 9594**, Casey 9596, Community 9604, Grays 9631, Handsel 9638, Inland 9650, JRS 9656, Kitsap 9659, **Laird 9664**, Medina 9682, Murdock 9689, **Quixote 9707**, Satterberg 9728, Sherwood 9733, Tacoma 9750, Whatcom 9759, **Wilburforce 9762**

West Virginia: Eastern 9775, Parkersburg 9789

Wisconsin: Community 9832, Community 9835, Green Bay 9854, Incourage 9867, Johnson 9874, Madison 9897, Milwaukee 9907, Oshkosh 9916, St. Croix 9950, Thrivent 9956, Vine 9960, Zilber 9972

Wyoming: Community 9975, Scott 9989, Wyoming 9999

Matching/challenge support

Alabama: Alabama 1, BBVA 9, Bruno 15, Central 19, Community 21, Community 23, Community 24, Friedman 35, Hearin 38, Hill 40, **International 41**, Kaul 43, McWane 51, Meyer 53, Smith 66, Vulcan 73, Walker 74

Alaska: Alaska 79, Rasmuson 89

Arizona: Arizona 92, Community 101, Delta 106, Every 109, Freeport-McMoRan 112, Globe 115, Grace 116, **Hickey 121**, Hill 122, **Johnson 126, Kieckhefer 129**, Linde 135, Morris 148, Piper 152, Steele 165, Stewart 166, Webb 174

Arkansas: Cabe 182, Frueauff 188, Jonsson 192, Rockefeller 197, Ross 199, Walker 209, Wal-Mart 210, Walton 211, **Windgate 213**

California: Ahmanson 222, **Alpert 231, American 237, Amgen 238**, AS&F 263, Atlas 266, Auen 269, Ayrshire 276, **Beavers 293**, Bechtel, 296, Benbough 303, California 365, Campbell 373, **Christensen 399**, Colburn 410, Collins 412, Community 414, Community 416, Community 419, Community 420, **Compton 422**, Confidence 423, Cowell 434, Crail 437, Crocker 440, **CS 442**, Darling 449, Doheny 473, Drown 484, East 490, Eisner 499, **Environment 508**, Field 523, Firedoll 528, **First 530**, Garland 565, Gasser 566, Gerbode 573, Getty 578, **Getty 579**, Girard 591, Gogian 598, Goldman 605, Goldman 606, Goldsmith 608, Good 612, Green 621, Gruber 632, Gumbiner 636, Haas 640, Haas 641, Haas 642, **Haas 643**, Hale 645, Harden 654, Hayward 665, Hedco 672, Hewlett 686, **Hilton 692**, Humboldt 714, Hutton 718, Irvine 727, Irwin 728, Jack 736, Jacobs 738, Jacobs 739, JL 751, Jones 756, **Kapor 764, Keck 774**, Kern 780, Kirchgessner 790, Koret 801, Kvamme 807, LA84 809, Lesher 833, Littlefield 844, Long 847, Los Altos 849, **Lund 857**, Lytel 860, Mabie 863, Marcled 875, Marin 877, McBean 892, McCarthy 895, **McConnell 898**, Mead 907, Mericos 918, Miller 929, Monterey 936, Morgan 940, Newhall 966, Norris 971, North 972, Noyce 974, Oakland 977, Orfalea 994, Outhwaite 1000, Oxnard 1001, **Packard 1006**, Parker 1012, Parsons 1013, Perforce 1026, Placer 1039, **Righteous 1073, Rivendell 1077**, Rogers 1087, Roth 1093, **S.G. 1100, Saban 1101**, Sacramento 1103, San Diego 1108, San Luis 1110, Sangham 1114, Santa Barbara 1116, Schwab 1127, Sempra 1140, Severns 1143, Smith 1182, Sobrato 1193, Sonora 1198, Sorensen 1200, **Special 1202, Spencer 1204, Stamps 1210**, Stauffer 1214, Stulsaft 1226, Taper 1237, Thornton 1252, Towbes 1260, True 1264, Tuohy 1267, **Vadasz 1275**, Valley 1279, Valley 1280, Ventura 1287, Versacare 1288, **Warsh 1299**, Weingart 1307, WHH 1320, Whittier 1323, WWW 1349

Colorado: Aspen 1368, Boettcher 1374, Bohemian 1375, Chambers 1385, Colorado 1389, Colorado 1390, Community 1393, Community 1394, Daniels 1399, Denver 1401, ECA 1404, Edmondson 1405, Gates 1418, **Gill 1421**, Halton 1426, JFM 1433, KBK 1437, King 1440, Kitzmiller 1441, Lipscomb 1449, Marquez 1454, Ottens 1472, Pikes 1478, Price 1484, Rose 1487, Serimus 1496, Summit 1511, Telluride 1512, Western 1520, **Western 1521, Winslow 1525**

Connecticut: Aetna 1531, American 1537, Baldwin 1541, **Calder 1554**, Community 1562, Community 1564, Community 1565, Connecticut 1566, Culpeper 1568, Ensworth 1580, Fairfield 1581, Fund 1589, Graustein 1600, Hartford 1609, Lego 1627, Liberty 1630, Main 1634, Matthies 1639, Middlesex 1644, New Canaan 1650, NewAlliance 1651, **Newman's 1652**, Palmer 1666, Rockville 1682, Rosenthal 1684

Delaware: AEC 1735, Edwards 1774, Ettinger 1779, Laffey 1800, Lennox 1805, Longwood 1806, Marmot 1814, Prentice 1839, **Raskob 1845**, Welfare 1872

District of Columbia: **Arca 1880, Banyan 1881**, Bauman 1882, Bender 1885, Block 1888, Cafritz 1890, Community 1893, **Hitachi 1916**, Kimsey 1921, Loughran 1925, **Lounsbery 1926**, Meyer 1931, **Moriah 1932**, Munson 1933, Palmer 1937, **Summit 1950, Wallace 1955**, Wallace 1956

Florida: Amaturo 1966, Bank 1979, **Barbour 1980**, Batchelor 1983, Bi-Lo 1996, Bush 2008, **Chatlos 2019**, Community 2031, Community 2032, Community 2034, Community 2035, Community 2039, Community 2040, Community 2041, Conn 2042, Darden 2051, **Davis 2056**, Duckwall 2069, Dunspaugh-Dalton 2073, duPont 2075, GiveWell 2123, Gronewaldt 2139, Henderson 2152, Hersh 2156, Indian 2166, Jacksonville 2167, **Johnson 2174**, Kennedy 2182, **Knight 2191, Koch 2192**, Miami 2238, Peacock 2263, Quantum 2276, Rayonier 2281, **Russell 2301**, Saunders 2308, **Skelly 2324**, Southwest 2327, St. Petersburg 2332, **Stacy 2333**, SWS 2347, Sylvester 2348, Thomas 2357, Wells 2383, Winter 2390, Wollowick 2393

Georgia: Anderson 2403, Brain 2416, Callaway 2418, Callaway 2419, Campbell 2420, **Challenge 2424**, Community 2434, Community 2435, Community 2436, Day 2448, Equifax 2455, **Hanley 2476**, Harland 2477, Harris 2479, Knox 2498, Loridans 2506, Mohawk 2517, Moore 2519, Moore 2520, North 2525, Porter 2533, Sapelo 2546, Singletary 2551, **Thoresen 2557, Turner 2563**, Watson 2569, Williams 2572, Woolley 2581, Zeist 2584

Hawaii: Atherton 2586, Bank 2588, Castle 2594, Ching 2596, Cooke 2597, Island 2606, McInerny 2612, Wilcox 2621

Idaho: Blue 2627, Idaho 2632, Jeker 2634, **Schultz 2641**

Illinois: Arthur 2673, Brunner 2718, Butler 2729, Caterpillar 2738, Chicago 2746, Children's 2747, Circle 2749, Clinton 2754, Coleman 2759, Community 2763, Community 2766, Community 2767, Community 2769, Crown 2781, Cuneo 2783, DeKalb 2792, Dillon 2796, Donnelley 2802, Driehaus 2805, Dunard 2810, DuPage 2812, Field 2831, Frankel 2842, Grant 2876, Guthman 2882, Hamill 2888, Hansen 2889, **Harris 2893**, Henry 2906, Keith 2952, King 2960, Libra 2981, Logan 2983, Lumpkin 2986, **MacArthur 2989**, Martin 3003, McGowan 3014, McGraw 3015, Morse 3039, Oak Park 3061, Pritzker 3091, **Rothschild 3124**, Schmidt 3139, Seabury 3146, Speh 3170, Steans 3175, **Tyndale 3195**, VNA 3206, Washington 3217, Woods 3241

Indiana: Bales 3261, Ball 3262, Ball 3264, Blue 3265, Boren 3267, Brown 3269, Cass 3271, Central 3272, Clowes 3274, Cole 3276, Community 3279, Community 3280, Community 3281, Community 3283, Community 3284, Community 3285, Community 3286, Community 3288, Community 3289, Community 3290, **Cummins 3292**, Dearborn 3293, DeHaan 3294, DeKalb 3295, Dekko 3296, Elkhart 3298, Fairbanks 3301, Glick 3310, Hancock 3313, Harrison 3314, Hendricks 3319, Henry 3320, Heritage 3321, Huntington 3324, Johnson 3330, Jordan 3331, Koch 3334, Kosciusko 3335, Kosciusko 3336, Legacy 3337, **Lilly 3340**, **Lilly 3342**, Lincoln 3344, **Lumina 3345**, Madison 3346, Marshall 3348, McMillen 3352, Miller 3355, Montgomery 3356, Noble 3359, Northern 3360, Ogle 3362, Portland 3370, Putnam 3373, Ripley 3379, Rolland 3381, Steuben 3390, Tipton 3391, Wabash 3396, Wayne 3400, Welborn 3402, Wells 3403, West 3404, Whitley 3407

Iowa: Ahrens 3410, Cedar Rapids 3417, Community 3420, Community 3423, Community 3424, Hall-Perrine 3439, Hanson 3441, Iowa 3447, Maytag 3460, McElroy 3461, **Pioneer 3474**, Tye 3484

Kansas: Capitol 3498, Community 3502, Douglas 3509, HANDinHAND 3517, Hutchinson 3521, Kansas 3524, McPherson 3534, Topeka 3552, Wichita 3555, Wyandotte 3556

Kentucky: Blue 3560, Brown 3563, Community 3569, Cralle 3571, Foundation 3575, Humana 3582, LG&E 3586, Robinson 3598, Spray 3602, Young 3607

Louisiana: Baptist 3612, Baton Rouge 3613, Blue 3615, Booth 3616, Brown 3617, Community 3624, German 3637, Goldring 3638, Huie 3643, Institute 3644, Jones 3645, Keller 3646, New Orleans 3656, Wilson 3671, Zigler 3676

Maine: Alfond 3678, Bangor 3680, Cohen 3684, Gorman 3689, Horizon 3691, Iberdrola 3693, King 3694, Lunder 3697, Maine 3698, **Sandy 3707**, Sewall 3708, **Walter 3711**

Maryland: Abell 3712, Abell 3713, Baltimore 3726, **Bearman 3728**, Blades 3734, **Blaustein 3735**, Commonweal 3756, Community 3759, **Deerbrook 3776**, Dresher 3782, **England 3785**, Fowler 3795, France 3796, Freeman 3797, Goldseker 3803, Henson 3814, Jacobsohn 3819, Kerr 3823, Knapp 3825, Knott 3826, Meyerhoff 3848, Meyerhoff 3849, Middendorf 3850, Mid-Shore 3851, Plitt 3862, Polinger 3864, Rathmann 3867, Rembrandt 3868, Rosenberg 3873, **Shared 3882**, Sheridan 3883, Stulman 3891, TKF 3896, Town 3897, **Weinberg 3908**, Wright 3911

Massachusetts: Barker 3936, **Barr 3937**, Berkman 3945, Bristol 3960, Cabot 3968, Cape Cod 3974, Clarke 3986, Clipper 3987, Community 3992, Davis 4011, Donahue 4023, Fields 4046, Finch 4048, Foundation 4056, Fuller 4063, **Garfield 4065**, Highland 4098, Hyams 4103, **Iacocca 4104**, Island 4109, Linden 4148, Lowell 4153, Ludcke 4157, Lynch 4159, Melville 4170, Merck 4171, Mifflin 4175, Miller 4177, New 4189, Parker 4207, Peabody 4210, Perkin 4213, **Phillips 4219**, Poss 4226, Riley 4239, Schooner 4261, Sheehan 4271, Smith 4277, Stearns 4286, Stevens 4288, Stevens 4289, Stoddard 4293, Sudbury 4299, **Sweet 4302**, Thompson 4307

Michigan: Albion 4332, Allegan 4334, Americana 4337, Ann Arbor 4340, Barry 4342, Battle Creek 4343, Bay 4344, Besser 4349, Capital 4357, Community 4369, Community 4372, Community 4373, **Cooper-Standard 4380**, Dalton 4385, Dart 4388, DeVos 4398, DeVos 4400, Dow 4405, Dow 4407, **Erb 4415**, **Fetzer 4420**, **Fisher 4423**, Fremont 4438, General 4442, Gerstacker 4444, Gilmore 4445, Grand Haven 4446, Grand 4448, Greenville 4452, Herrick 4459, Hillsdale 4461, Hudson 4463, Jackson 4467, Kalamazoo 4472, **Kellogg 4474**, Leighton 4484, Manoogian 4491, Marshall 4496, Midland 4502, Miller 4503, Monroe 4507, **Mott 4510**, Mott 4511, Mount Pleasant 4512, Oleson 4516, Petoskey 4522, Pokagon 4523, Ravitz 4526, Sage 4531, Saginaw 4532, Sturgis 4550, Towsley 4557, Tuscola 4562, VanderWeide 4572, Weatherwax 4577, Wege 4579, Whirlpool 4583, Wilson 4589

Minnesota: Bigelow 4616, Blandin 4617, Bremer 4620, Carlson 4629, Charlson 4633, Frey 4658, **Fuller 4659**, Griggs 4669, Hardenbergh 4672, HRK 4677, Initiative 4679, **King 4687**, Kopp 4688, Land 4691, Lilly 4696, Marbrook 4702, Mardag 4703, Martin 4704, McKnight 4709, McNeely 4710, Minnesota 4715, Minnesota 4716, Neilson 4725, Northwest 4730, Ordean 4732, **O'Shaughnessy 4734**, Oswald 4735, Pohlad 4745, Rochester 4755, Saint Paul 4757, Slaggie 4766, Wasie 4794, Wedum 4796, Winona 4806

Mississippi: Chisholm 4818, Community 4820, Community 4821, Foundation 4827, Gulf 4830, Hardin 4831, Maddox 4834, Riley 4844

Missouri: Ameren 4851, Anheuser 4853, Brown 4862, Community 4872, Fox 4892, Gateway 4894, Goppert 4896, Green 4900, H & R 4902, JSM 4918, Kansas 4920, **Kauffman 4921**, Kauffman 4922, Lichtenstein 4936, **Monsanto 4945**, Musgrave 4947, Pillsbury 4955, Saigh 4965, Saint Louis 4966, Sander 4967, Speas 4978, Stupp 4983, Sunnen 4986, Truman 4996

Montana: Edwards 5008, First 5009, Washington 5018, Whitefish 5019

Nebraska: Acklie 5022, Buckley 5026, Daugherty 5033, Dunklau 5036, Fremont 5039, Grand Island 5044, Hastings 5046, Hirschfeld 5049, Hitchcock 5050, Kearney 5055, Kiewit 5057, Kimmel 5059, Kind 5060, Lexington 5062, Lincoln 5063, Lozier 5065, Mutual 5071, Omaha 5074, Phelps 5075, Scoular 5080, Storz 5086, Woods 5096

Nevada: Buck 5105, Cord 5110, Fairweather 5118, Hawkins 5123, Nevada 5134, NV 5136, Parasol 5138, **Tang 5153**

New Hampshire: Bean 5164, **Fidelity 5170**, Fuller 5172, HNH 5175, Hunt 5177, Lindsay 5179

New Jersey: Atlantic 5196, **Berrie 5206**, Borden 5209, Brotherton 5216, Buehler 5219, Bunbury 5220, Campbell 5223, Carolan 5225, Clare 5230, Cowles 5234, Delano 5240, Dodge 5243, Fund 5270, Golden 5280, Hyde 5310, Investors 5317, **JM 5323**, Johnson 5328, **Johnson 5329**, Lipman 5364, Martini 5372, MCJ 5377, **Newcombe 5391**, OceanFirst 5394, Pascale 5403, Provident 5414, **Ramapo 5419**, Roberts 5423, Snyder 5462, Summit 5473, Turrell 5483, Victoria 5490, Wallerstein 5494

New Mexico: Brindle 5516, Delle 5518, Frost 5519, Hubbard 5523, **Johns 5524**, **Lannan 5526**, Maddox 5528, McCune 5529, New Mexico 5530, Santa Fe 5533, **Thaw 5534**

New York: Achelis 5549, Adirondack 5556, Allyn 5575, **Arcus 5608**, Auchincloss 5623, Baird 5636, Bay 5652, Bodman 5692, Brooklyn 5718, **Bydale 5738**, Carvel 5749, Cattaraugus 5750, Central 5757, Charina 5763, Charina 5764, Chautauqua 5766, **Claiborne 5783**, Community 5802, Community 5804, Community 5805, Community 5807, **Credit 5826**, **Cummings 5832**, Cummings 5834, Demartini 5872, DeMatteis 5873, **Deutsche 5876**, Dodge 5892, **Doherty 5893**, Dolan 5895, Dolan 5896, Dreyfus 5913, Dyson 5923, EHA 5940, Emerson 5950, **Engelhard 5954**, Fifth 5976, **Ford 5995**, Freeman 6012, Galasso 6032, Gebbie 6038, Gerry 6043, Gifford 6049, Gilman 6052, Glens Falls 6057, Golisano 6077, Greve 6106, Grigg 6109, **Harriman 6136**, **Hartford 6144**, Hayden 6150, Health 6153, **Hearst 6155**, **Hearst 6156**, Heckscher 6157, **Heron 6164**, Hoerle 6180, Horncrest 6185, Icahn 6204, **Ittleson 6217**, Jaharis 6223, Joelson 6232, **Johnson 6235**, Johnson 6239, Jones 6242, Kaylie 6263, Kopf 6302, Langeloth 6327, LaSalle 6331, Lenna 6352, Lincoln 6368, Link 6375, Littauer 6379, Lowenstein 6395, Lubo 6396, **Luce 6398**, **M & T 6406**, **Macy 6414**, Manton 6425, McCarthy 6454, **Mellon 6470**, **Mertz 6477**, Monell 6497, Moses 6511, Mulford 6514, **New 6551**, Noble 6561, **Norman 6565**, Northern 6567, Nuhn 6572, O'Connor 6578, Ohrstrom 6582, Oishei 6584, Park 6615, **Pforzheimer 6635**, Pinkerton 6643, **Porticus 6654**, **Prospect 6663**, Rauch 6681, **Reed 6684**, Richmond 6703, Robinson 6721, **Rockefeller 6723**, **Ross 6754**, Schaffner 6800, Schenectady 6802, Scherman 6804, Schnurmacher 6809, Schnurmacher 6810, Schumann 6813, Sheldon 6841, Simon 6859, Slifka 6870, Snow 6878, Sprague 6901, St. Faith's 6903, **Starr 6911**, Staten 6912, Steele 6915, Stiefel 6931, **Summerfield 6944**, Tower 7000, Triad 7005, Troy 7006, Truman 7007, **United 7019**, van Ameringen 7023, **Vital 7033**, Western 7078, Wright 7104

North Carolina: BB&T 7143, Belk 7148, Biddle 7150, BIN 7151, Blue 7153, Blumenthal 7154, Brady 7156, Cannon 7169, Cape Fear 7170, **Carlson 7172**, Cemala 7174, Community 7180, Community 7181, Community 7182, Cumberland 7184, Davie 7188, Dover 7194, Duke 7195, Duke 7196, Finley 7199, Foundation 7202, French 7203, Fund 7204, Glass 7210, Goodrich 7213, Greenville 7217, Hanes 7221, Hanes 7222, High Point 7231, Kenan 7248, Leever 7253, Levine 7255, Mebane 7266, Morgan 7269, North 7274, **Oak 7276**, Polk 7287, Reidsville 7294, Reynolds 7297, Reynolds 7298, Robertson 7305, Simpson 7312, Smith 7317, **Sunshine 7324**, Tannenbaum 7326, Triangle 7328, Warner 7334, Weaver 7335

North Dakota: Fargo 7351, Leach 7353, North Dakota 7357, Stern 7360

Ohio: Akron 7367, Anderson 7372, Ar-Hale 7376, Ashland 7378, Ashtabula 7379, Austin 7380, Barberton 7382, **Bingham 7387**, Butler 7396, **Cardinal 7398**, Charities 7400, Cincinnati 7404, Cleveland 7406, Columbus 7411, Community 7412, Community 7413, Community 7415, Conway 7419, Corbin 7420, Coshocton 7421, Covenant 7422, Delaware 7431, Diamond 7435, **Eaton 7442**, Erie 7444, Fairfield 7445, Farmer 7447, Ferguson 7450, GAR 7465, **Geisse 7468**, Gund 7478, Hoover 7491, Hoover 7492, Humphrey 7497, Jennings 7509, Jewish 7511, **Kettering 7520**, KeyBank 7523, Kramer 7529, Kulas 7532, Lehner 7536, Lennon 7537, Levin 7539, Licking 7540, Luther 7548, Macy's 7552, Maltz 7553, Marietta 7557, Mathile 7560, Mayerson 7561, Mercer 7567, Middletown 7570, Miniger 7572, Montgomery 7575, Morgan 7577, Morgan 7578, Morgan 7579, Murphy 7584, Muskingum 7585, Nationwide 7587, Nord 7594, O'Neill 7602, Prentiss 7621, Reeves 7627, Reinberger 7628, Richland 7630, Saint 7639, Scioto 7657, Scripps 7659, Semple 7660, Sisler 7664, Stark 7673, Stocker 7676, Stranahan 7678, Tiffin 7682, **Timken 7684**, Toledo 7686, Troy 7688, Turner 7691, Wayne 7704, Wolfe 7719

Oklahoma: Adams 7725, Bernsen 7733, Bovaird 7735, Chapman 7739, Chapman 7740, Communities 7742, Hardesty 7756, Harris 7757, Hille 7759, Kerr 7764, Masonic 7771, McCasland 7772,

McGee 7774, McMahon 7776, Noble 7780, ONEOK 7783, Puterbaugh 7786, Rapp 7787, Sarkeys 7793, **Schusterman 7794**, Southern 7798, Stone 7801, Tulsa 7807, Williams 7814, Zink 7821

Oregon: Adler 7822, Autzen 7823, Carpenter 7831, Chambers 7832, Collins 7836, Collins 7837, Esco 7841, Ford 7845, **Intel 7853**, Jeld 7856, Johnson 7858, Kinsman 7860, Macdonald 7866, Meyer 7870, Mission 7873, Oregon 7876, PacifiCorp 7877, Schnitzer 7887, Swindells 7892, Tucker 7896

Pennsylvania: 1675 7903, **Alcoa 7908**, Ametek 7913, Baker 7926, Benedum 7935, Berks 7939, Blanchard 7944, Buncher 7957, Carnahan 7965, Central 7972, Centre 7973, Century 7974, Cestone 7975, Claneil 7982, Clapp 7983, **Colcom 7986**, Community 7993, Community 7994, Connelly 7995, Degenstein 8008, Dolfinger 8013, Drumcliff 8016, DSF 8017, EQT 8025, Erie 8026, Fels 8035, First 8040, First 8041, FISA 8043, Foundation 8046, Fourjay 8047, Grable 8064, Gray 8069, Hamilton 8078, Highmark 8092, Hopwood 8096, Huston 8102, Huston 8103, Independence 8107, Keystone 8122, Kind 8125, Kline 8129, Lehigh Valley 8136, Levis 8140, Lindback 8142, **Little 8145**, Martin 8156, McFeely 8163, McKinney 8168, McLean 8169, Mellon 8173, Nichols 8197, North 8199, **Oberkotter 8203**, O'Toole 8207, Penn 8216, Philadelphia 8221, Phillips 8222, Phoenixville 8223, PNC 8230, Pottstown 8234, Presser 8236, Rees 8245, Roberts 8250, Saint 8260, Scranton 8275, Seraph 8279, Stackpole 8295, Staunton 8296, **Templeton 8313**, Trexler 8320, **Waldorf 8330**, West 8334, Wyomissing 8350, York 8351

Puerto Rico: Puerto Rico 8353

Rhode Island: Amica 8356, Bafflin 8359, Carter 8368, Champlin 8370, Daniels 8380, **Dorot 8384**, Kimball 8410, McNeil 8418, Murray 8421, Rhode Island 8429, Textron 8446

South Carolina: Bruce 8461, Byerly 8462, Central 8468, Community 8474, Community 8475, Daniel 8476, Fullerton 8479, Graham 8481, Roe 8494, Self 8496, Sims 8497, Spartanburg 8501, Springs 8504

South Dakota: Larson 8516, Sioux Falls 8521, South Dakota 8522, Vucurevich 8524

Tennessee: Assisi 8530, Benwood 8535, Bridgestone 8537, Carlton 8541, Christy 8545, Davis 8555, Day 8556, East 8560, Frist 8568, HCA 8582, Hyde 8584, Jeniam 8587, Lyndhurst 8599, **Maclellan 8601**, Martin 8606, Osborne 8614, Plough 8615, Thompson 8636, Wilson 8646

Texas: Abell 8650, Amarillo 8660, Anderson 8663, Anderson 8664, AT&T 8675, Austin 8676, Bass 8690, BNSF 8706, Brown 8731, Brumley 8734, Cailloux 8742, Carter 8752, CH 8759, Cockrell 8770, Communities 8773, Community 8774, Community 8777, Constantin 8778, Cook 8779, Cullen 8792, Dallas 8795, Davis 8799, Dunn 8816, Eady 8818, Edwards 8824, El Paso 8825, Embrey 8828, Fasken 8839, Fikes 8844, Fisch 8846, Fish 8848, George 8863, Goldsbury 8868, Gulf 8878, Haggerty 8881, Hamman 8888, Hillcrest 8909, Hoblitzelle 8912, Hoglund 8913, **Houston 8916**, Hudson 8919, **Jenesis 8932**, Kempner 8952, Kinder 8958, Klabzuba 8960, Kleberg 8962, Kodosky 8966, Kronkosky 8970, Liatis 8983, Lightner 8985, Littauer 8988, Lubbock 8994, Lyons 8996, Mankoff 8998, **Marshall 9000**, Mayor 9007, McDermott 9013, McGovern 9014, McNutt 9018, Meadows 9019, Moody 9033, Navarro 9054, Once 9070, Orsinger 9073, Owen 9076, Owsley 9078, **Paloheimo 9080**, Parks 9081, Payne 9086, Permian 9091, Peterson 9095, Powell 9105, Priddy 9109, Rapoport 9122, Rees-Jones 9125, **RGK 9128**, Richardson 9130, Rockwell 9135, Rogers 9138, Rosewood 9140, Sams 9145, San Angelo 9147, San Antonio 9148, Scurlock 9162, Shield 9170, Simmons 9174, Simmons 9175, Smith 9184, Sterling 9203, Stern 9204, Still 9207, Strake 9208, Sturgis 9211, Summerlee 9213, Sumners 9214, Swinney 9218, Temple 9223, Terry 9224, Tobin 9236, Tomerlin 9238, Topfer 9239, Trull 9240, Turner 9242, Vanberg 9247, Vaughan 9248, Waco 9251, Wichita 9277, Wolslager 9288, Wortham 9292, Young 9295, Zachry 9296, Zephyr 9299

Utah: Burton 9309, Dee 9312, Dumke 9315, Dumke, 9316, Eccles 9317, Eccles 9319, Eccles 9320, Patel 9343, Simmons 9351

Vermont: Evslin 9360, Gibney 9362, Lintilhac 9365

Virginia: ACT 9380, Alleghany 9382, Beazley 9391, **Blue 9394**, Cabell 9397, Cameron 9398, Carter 9403, Charlottesville 9405, Community 9410, Community 9411, Community 9416, Dominion 9422, Graham 9445, Gwathmey 9447, Kanter 9459, Landmark 9467, **Loyola 9471**, Lynchburg 9474, Mars 9477, Moore 9489, Morgan, 9490, **Mustard 9492**, Norfolk 9496, Perry 9506, Potomac 9511, Reynolds 9519, Samberg 9527, Titmus 9543, Washington 9552, Weissberg 9554, **WestWind 9555**

Washington: **444S 9565**, Allen 9567, **Brainerd 9590**, **Bullitt 9591**, **Campion 9594**, Columbia 9602, Community 9604, Community 9605, Dimmer 9610, Evertrust 9617, Forest 9620, Foster 9621, Fuchs 9624, George 9626, Glaser 9629, Grays 9631, Harder 9640, Invested 9652, **Kongsgaard 9661**, Lucky 9673, Medina 9682, Milgard 9683, Miller 9684, Murdock 9689, Nesholm 9691, Norcliffe 9693, **Quixote 9707**, Raikes 9708, **Samis 9725**, San Juan 9726, Sherwood 9733, **Stewardship 9744**, Tacoma 9750, **Goodwin 9751**, **Vista 9756**, Wiancko 9761, **Wilburforce 9762**

West Virginia: Beckley 9769, Chambers 9772, Community 9773, Daywood 9774, Eastern 9775, Hollowell 9778, Kanawha 9780, Maier 9782, McDonough 9784, Parkersburg 9789, Your 9799

Wisconsin: Alexander 9803, Alliant 9804, Antioch 9807, Argosy 9808, Beloit 9814, **Bradley 9819**, Community 9833, Community 9835, Cornerstone 9836, Green Bay 9854, Herzfeld 9863, Iddings 9866, Incourage 9867, Jeffris 9869, Keller 9878, La Crosse 9889, Lunda 9896, Madison 9897, McBeath 9901, Milwaukee 9907, Northwestern 9914, Oshkosh 9916, Racine 9924, Rowland 9937, Siebert 9946, St. Croix 9950, **Taylor 9955**, Thrivent 9956, U.S. 9957, Vine 9960, West 9967, Zilber 9972

Wyoming: Community 9975, Friess 9978, Kerr 9981, Martin 9984, Scott 9989, Storer 9992, Wyoming 9999

Mission-related investments/loans

Alaska: Rasmuson 89

Arkansas: Rockefeller 197

California: California 365, California 366, **Compton 422**, Cowell 434, **Environment 508**, Gasser 566, Jacobs 739, **Kapor 764**, McCune 900, Silicon 1166, Skoll 1175, Springcreek 1208

Colorado: **General 1419**

Connecticut: Fink 1583, Graustein 1600

District of Columbia: Consumer 1894, **Hitachi 1916**

Florida: duPont 2075, **Knight 2191**

Georgia: Community 2432

Illinois: Donnelley 2800

Indiana: Central 3272

Kentucky: Community 3569

Louisiana: Baton Rouge 3613, Beaird 3614, Community 3624

Maine: Maine 3698, Switzer 3709

Maryland: **Casey 3745**

Massachusetts: Boston 3956, Hyams 4103, **Merck 4172**, Reynolds 4238, Stoneman 4296

Michigan: **Fetzer 4420**, Kalamazoo 4472, **Kellogg 4474**

Minnesota: McKnight 4709, West 4800

Missouri: Community 4872

New Hampshire: New Hampshire 5182, Putnam 5186

New Jersey: **Prudential 5415**

New York: **Deutsche 5876**, Hazen 6151, **Heron 6164**, **Mitsubishi 6490**, **Noyes 6571**, Oishei 6584, Park 6615, **Prospect 6663**, Rasmussen 6679

North Carolina: Babcock 7138

Ohio: Cleveland 7406, Columbus 7411, Gund 7478, Stranahan 7678, Toledo 7686

Oregon: Meyer 7870

Pennsylvania: Kind 8125, Lancaster 8135

Texas: KDK-Harman 8949

Vermont: Vermont 9375

Virginia: **Blue 9394**, Northern 9497

Washington: Russell 9722, Seattle 9731

Pro bono services

California: PIMCO 1037

Illinois: Allstate 2657

Pro bono services - advocacy

Tennessee: Hyde 8584

Pro bono services - communications/public relations

Illinois: Allstate 2657

Pro bono services - financial management

Illinois: Allstate 2657

Pro bono services - human resources

Illinois: Allstate 2657

Pro bono services - interactive/website technology

Illinois: Allstate 2657

Pro bono services - legal

Illinois: Allstate 2657, Polk 3084

Maine: Cohen 3684

Pro bono services - marketing/branding

Illinois: Allstate 2657

Pro bono services - medical

Maine: Cohen 3684

Pro bono services - strategic management

Illinois: Allstate 2657

Pro bono services - technology infrastructure

Illinois: Allstate 2657

Professorships

Alabama: Hill 40, Kaul 43

Arizona: Globe 115, Stewart 166

California: Ayrshire 276, Bauer 287, Baxter 288, Bren 339, Davis 455, Eucalyptus 510, Field 523, Garb 564, Goldsmith 608, Gruber 632, Irmas 725, Jones 756, **Kavli 771**, Kirchgessner 790, **Lingnan 841**, Mabie 863, Norris 971, **Rupe 1097**, Schlinger 1124, Springcreek 1208, Stauffer 1214, Thornton 1252, Treadwell 1262, Wohlford 1336

Connecticut: Deloitte 1572, Larsen 1624, Xerox 1728

Delaware: AEC 1735, Bennett 1739, Good 1785

Program development

2433, Community 2435, Community 2436, Cousins 2442, Cousins 2443, Cox 2445, Cox 2446, EZ 2456, Georgia 2468, **Georgia 2469**, Glenn 2470, **Hanley 2476**, Harland 2477, Harris 2479, Harrison 2481, Healthcare 2482, **Imlay 2487**, Knox 2498, Lanier 2499, Lockwood 2505, Love 2508, Mason 2513, North 2525, Primerica 2534, Sapelo 2546, Southern 2554, **Thoresen 2557**, Trailsend 2560, **Turner 2563**, U.S. 2565, **UPS 2566**, Watson 2569, Whitehead 2571, Williams 2572, Woodruff 2579

Hawaii: Atherton 2586, Bank 2588, Campbell 2592, Castle 2593, Castle 2594, Central 2595, Ching 2596, Cooke 2597, First 2598, Geist 2600, Hawaii 2602, Hawaiian 2603, Hughes 2605, Island 2606, Lange 2609, McInerny 2612, **Watumull 2620**, Wilcox 2621

Idaho: Albertson 2626, Blue 2627, Cunningham 2630, Idaho 2632, Jeker 2634, **Micron 2637**, Nagel 2639, **Schultz 2641**

Illinois: **Abbott 2649**, Allegretti 2655, Allen 2656, Allstate 2657, Aon 2667, ArcelorMittal 2670, Arthur 2673, **Baxter 2690**, Blowitz 2702, Boler 2708, Brach 2712, **Brinson 2715**, Butler 2729, Caterpillar 2738, Chaddick 2740, Cheney 2745, Chicago 2746, CME 2755, Coleman 2759, Comer 2760, Comer 2761, Community 2763, Community 2766, Community 2769, Coypu 2777, Crown 2781, **Deere 2790**, Dillon 2796, Donnelley 2800, Driehaus 2805, DRW 2807, Dunard 2810, DuPage 2812, Edwardsville 2817, EFS 2818, Energizer 2824, Evanston 2826, Exelon 2827, Field 2831, Frankel 2842, Fry 2849, **Graham 2873**, **Grainger 2874**, Grand 2875, Guthman 2882, **Harris 2893**, Henry 2906, Heritage 2907, Hermann 2908, Hospira 2921, Houlsby 2922, Illinois 2933, Illinois 2934, Irwin 2936, **Joyce 2946**, Kaplan 2947, Kemper 2954, **Kemper 2955**, Kendall 2956, King 2960, Landau 2966, Levi 2976, Lumpkin 2986, **MacArthur 2989**, **MacArthur 2990**, Mander 2998, Martin 3003, Mayer 3005, MB 3008, McDougal 3013, McGowan 3014, Miller 3025, **Mondelez 3034**, Morse 3039, **Motorola 3042**, **Motorola 3043**, Nelson 3049, New 3052, Northern 3059, Oak Park 3061, Omron 3063, Pick, 3079, Polk 3084, Popular 3085, Prince 3089, Pritzker 3091, Pullman 3100, Reed 3109, Reese 3110, Regenstein 3111, Robinson 3122, **Rothschild 3124**, **Santreece 3135**, **Scholl 3141**, Seabury 3146, Siragusa 3162, Southeastern 3169, Speh 3170, Sprague 3172, Steans 3175, Stern 3177, Stone 3180, **Tellabs 3185**, **Terra 3186**, Tracy 3189, Trustmark 3193, **Tyndale 3195**, United 3199, United 3200, VNA 3206, Walter 3213, Washington 3217, White 3229, Woods 3242, **Wrigley 3244**

Indiana: Anderson 3255, Anthem 3257, Ball 3262, Ball 3264, Blue 3265, Brotherhood 3268, Brown 3269, Cass 3271, Central 3272, Clowes 3274, Community 3277, Community 3278, Community 3279, Community 3280, Community 3281, Community 3283, Community 3285, Community 3286, Community 3287, Community 3288, Community 3290, **Cummins 3292**, Dearborn 3293, DeHaan 3294, DeKalb 3295, Dekko 3296, Elkhart 3298, Fairbanks 3301, Finish 3303, Foellinger 3304, Glick 3310, **Goodrich 3311**, Hancock 3313, Harrison 3314, Health 3317, Hendricks 3319, Henry 3320, Heritage 3321, Huntington 3324, Johnson 3330, Koch 3334, Kosciusko 3335, Kosciusko 3336, Legacy 3337, **Lilly 3342**, Lincoln 3344, **Lumina 3345**, Madison 3346, Marshall 3348, McMillen 3352, Michigan 3354, Miller 3355, Montgomery 3356, Noble 3359, Northern 3360, Noyes 3361, Ogle 3362, Old 3363, Orange 3365, Parke 3366, Porter 3369, Portland 3370, Pulliam 3371, Pulliam 3372, Putnam 3373, Rolland 3381, Steuben 3390, Tipton 3391, Unity 3393, Vectren 3394, Washington 3398, Waterfield 3399, Wayne 3400, Welborn 3402, Wells 3403

Iowa: AEGON 3409, Ahrens 3410, Carver 3416, Cedar Rapids 3417, Clarinda 3418, Community 3420, Community 3423, GuideOne 3438, Iowa 3447, Maytag 3460, McElroy 3461, Meredith 3463, Mid-Iowa 3466, Pella 3473, **Pioneer 3474**, Poweshiek 3475, Principal 3476, **Rockwell 3477**, Siouxland 3480, Tye 3484, United 3485, Wellmark 3490

Kansas: Baughman 3493, Blue 3497, Capitol 3498, Delta 3507, Douglas 3509, Hutchinson 3521, Kansas 3524, Koch 3529, **Lloyd 3530**, Manhattan 3532, McPherson 3534, Salina 3540, Sprint 3549, Topeka 3552, Western 3554, Wyandotte 3556

Kentucky: Blue 3560, C.E. 3566, Community 3569, Community 3570, Cralle 3571, Foundation 3575, Gheens 3577, Humana 3582, Independence 3583, LG&E 3586, Norton 3592, Public 3597, Spray 3602, Ventas 3605, Young 3607, Yum! 3608

Louisiana: Albemarle 3609, Baptist 3612, Baton Rouge 3613, Beaird 3614, Blue 3615, Community 3624, Coughlin 3626, Entergy 3630, Freeman 3636, German 3637, Goldring 3638, Grigsby 3640, Huie 3643, Institute 3644, Jones 3645, New Orleans 3656, Pennington 3659, Reily 3661, RosaMary 3663, Wilson 3671, **Woldenberg 3672**, Woolf 3673, Zigler 3676

Maine: Bangor 3680, Cianbro 3683, Cohen 3684, Hannaford 3690, Horizon 3691, Iberdrola 3693, King 3694, Libra 3696, Maine 3698, Maine 3699, Morton 3701, Sewall 3708, TD 3710

Maryland: Abell 3712, Abell 3713, Allegis 3719, **Ames 3720**, Baker 3724, Baker 3725, Baltimore 3726, **Bearman 3728**, Blades 3734, **Blaustein 3735**, Blaustein 3736, **Casey 3745**, Choice 3748, Commonweal 3756, Community 3758, Community 3759, Community 3760, Community 3761, Concordia 3763, **de Beaumont 3774**, **Deerbrook 3776**, Delaplaine 3778, Deutsch 3779, **England 3785**, Freeman 3797, Goldseker 3803, **Grace 3807**, Hoffberger 3817, **Hughes 3818**, Jacobsohn 3819, Kerr 3823, Knott 3826, Legg 3828, Leidy 3830, Lockhart 3836, Lockheed 3837, Mead 3845, Meyerhoff 3848, Meyerhoff 3849, Mid-Shore 3851, NASDAQ 3857, O'Neil 3859, Polinger 3864, Price 3865, Rathmann 3867, Rembrandt 3868, Rocking 3871, Rouse 3877, **Shared 3882**, Sheridan 3883, St. John 3888, Straus 3890, **Thalheimer 3894**, TKF 3896, Town 3897, Washington 3904, Wasserman 3905, **Weinberg 3908**, Wilson 3909, Wright 3911

Massachusetts: Adams 3916, **Alchemy 3920**, Arbella 3926, Babson 3933, Balfour 3935, Barker 3936, **Barr 3937**, Bayrd 3938, Berkman 3945, Berkshire 3946, Berkshire 3947, Beveridge 3950, Blue 3953, Boston 3956, Boston 3957, Bristol 3960, Brookline 3962, **Cabot 3966**, Cabot 3967, Cabot 3968, Cambridge 3971, Cape Cod 3973, **China 3982**, Clarke 3986, Clipper 3987, Community 3991, Community 3992, **Conservation 3993**, Cosette 3997, Danversbank 4009, Davis 4011, Demoulas 4014, DentaQuest 4016, Eastern 4030, Essex 4039, Farnsworth 4043, Filene 4047, Finch 4048, Foundation 4056, **Garfield 4065**, **Grand 4076**, Grinspoon 4080, Hall 4084, Hanover 4086, Harrington 4088, Highland 4098, **Hunt 4102**, Hyams 4103, Institution 4108, Island 4109, Kendall 4121, Liberty 4145, Linde 4147, Linden 4148, Lynch 4159, Melville 4170, Merck 4171, **Merck 4172**, MetroWest 4173, Mifflin 4175, Miller 4177, New 4191, New England 4193, Pardoe 4206, Parker 4207, Peabody 4210, Perkin 4213, Perpetual 4215, Reebok 4234, Riley 4239, **Rosenberg 4245**, Rubenstein 4248, Santander 4256, Schooner 4261, Schott 4262, Shapiro 4267, Sharf 4268, Shaw 4270, Smith 4277, Staples 4282, Starwood 4284, **State 4285**, Stearns 4286, Stevens 4288, Stevens 4289, Stoneman 4296, Sudbury 4299, Swartz 4301, Thompson 4307, TJX 4308, Webster 4322, Worcester 4327

Michigan: Albion 4332, Allegan 4334, Alro 4336, Americana 4337, Ann Arbor 4340, Barry 4342, Battle Creek 4343, Bay 4344, Berrien 4347, Binda 4350, Capital 4357, Charlevoix 4361, Chrysler 4366, Comerica 4368, Community 4369, Community 4370, Community 4371, Community 4372, Community 4373, Community 4374, Cook 4377, **Cooper-Standard 4380**, Cronin 4383, Dalton 4385, Dart 4388, Davenport 4389, Delphi 4394, **DENSO 4395**, DeRoy 4396, DeVos 4398, DeVos 4399, DeVos 4400, Dewey 4401, Doornink 4403, **Dow 4404**, Dow 4405, Dow 4406, Dow 4407, DTE 4410, Dyer 4412, Eddy 4414, **Erb 4415**, **Fetzer 4420**, Flinn 4424, Ford 4430, **Frankel 4437**, Fremont 4438, Frey 4440, General 4442, Gilmore 4445, Grand Haven 4446, Grand Rapids 4447, Grand 4448, Greenville 4452, Herrick 4459, Hudson 4463, Hurst 4464, Idema 4465, **Isabel 4466**, Jackson 4467, Johnson 4468, Kalamazoo 4472, **Kellogg 4474**, **Kellogg's 4475**, Knight 4477, **Kresge 4479**, Lear 4482, Lenawee 4485, Marquette 4495, Marshall 4496, McGregor 4498, Miller 4503, Monroe 4507, **Mott 4510**, Mott 4511, Mount Pleasant 4512, Pentecost 4520, Perrigo 4521, Petoskey 4522, Pokagon 4523, Sage 4531, Saginaw 4532, Skillman 4543, Steelcase 4547, Strosacker 4549, Sturgis 4550, Thompson 4556, Towsley 4557, Tuscola 4562, Upjohn 4564, Upton 4565, Van Andel 4567, VanderWeide 4572, Wege 4579, Westerman 4582, Whirlpool 4583, Whiting 4584, Wilson 4589, Wolters 4592, World 4594

Minnesota: 3M 4597, AHS 4599, **Andersen 4601**, **Andersen 4602**, Andersen 4603, Athwin 4607, Beim 4609, Best 4612, **Better 4614**, Beverly 4615, Bigelow 4616, Blandin 4617, Blue 4618, Bremer 4620, Bush 4621, Butler 4622, Cargill 4628, Carlson 4629, Carolyn 4630, Central 4631, CHS 4636, Deluxe 4644, Duluth 4649, Ecolab 4651, Edwards 4653, Frey 4658, **Fuller 4659**, General 4661, George 4662, Graco 4666, Greystone 4668, Hardenbergh 4672, Hormel 4676, HRK 4677, Initiative 4679, Jerome 4681, Johnson 4683, Jostens 4684, Kelley 4686, Lilly 4696, Marbrook 4702, Mardag 4703, Martin 4704, McKnight 4709, McNeely 4710, **Medtronic 4712**, Minneapolis 4714, Minnesota 4715, Minnesota 4716, **Mortenson 4721**, **Mosaic 4722**, Musser 4724, Neilson 4725, NFC 4727, Northwest 4729, Northwest 4730, Opus 4731, Ordean 4732, **O'Shaughnessy 4734**, Oswald 4735, **Patterson 4738**, **Pentair 4739**, Phillips 4741, Piper 4743, **Polaris 4746**, RBC 4748, Robins 4754, Saint Paul 4757, Securian 4761, Smikis 4767, Southwest 4768, Stevens 4772, SUPERVALU 4775, TCF 4778, TEAM 4779, Travelers 4783, U.S. 4784, United 4785, Valspar 4786, WCA 4795, West 4800, **Weyerhaeuser 4802**, Winona 4806, Xcel 4808

Mississippi: **Armstrong 4810**, Blue 4815, C Spire 4817, Chisholm 4818, Community 4820, Community 4821, CREATE 4822, Foundation 4827, Hardin 4831, Maddox 4834, Mississippi 4839

Missouri: Ameren 4851, American 4852, Anheuser 4853, Apex 4854, Baer 4856, Baer 4857, Bellwether 4859, Bunge 4865, Burns 4866, Centene 4870, Commerce 4871, Community 4872, Cox 4874, Cray 4876, **Deer 4878**, Emerson 4885, **Enterprise 4887**, Express 4888, Fox 4892, **Francis 4893**, Green 4900, H & R 4902, Hall 4905, Hallmark 4906, JSM 4918, Kansas 4920, **Kauffman 4921**, Kauffman 4922, Kemper 4926, Laclede 4931, Loose 4937, Lopata 4938, **Monsanto 4945**, Musgrave 4947, Nestle 4948, Oppenstein 4950, Pershing 4952, Pillsbury 4956, Rhoden 4962, Saigh 4965, Saint Louis 4966, Shaw 4970, Simon 4973, Sosland 4977, Speas 4978, Speas 4979, Stern 4980, Stupp 4982, Stupp 4983, Sunnen 4986, Trio 4994, Truman 4996, Whitaker 5001

Montana: Edwards 5008, First 5009, Washington 5018, Whitefish 5019

Nebraska: Abel 5021, Ameritas 5023, ConAgra 5029, ConAgra 5030, Cooper 5031, Fremont 5039, Grand Island 5044, Hastings 5046, Hirschfeld 5049, Kiewit 5057, Kind 5060, Lexington 5062, Lincoln 5063, Mid-Nebraska 5068, Mutual 5071, Omaha 5074, Phelps 5075, Scoular 5080, Union 5090, Woods 5096, York 5098

South Carolina: Black 8459, Blue 8460, Byerly 8462, Central 8468, Coastal 8472, Community 8474, Community 8475, Daniel 8476, Fullerton 8479, Gibbs 8480, Inman 8485, Roe 8494, Self 8496, Sims 8497, Smith 8499, Springs 8504

South Dakota: Larson 8516, **Opus 8518**, Robinson 8520, Sioux Falls 8521, Vucurevich 8524

Tennessee: Assisi 8530, Baptist 8533, Benwood 8535, Bridgestone 8537, Carlton 8541, CIC 8546, Community 8548, Community 8549, Community 8550, Davis 8555, East 8560, Eastman 8561, First 8565, Frist 8568, HCA 8582, Hyde 8584, **International 8585**, Lyndhurst 8599, **Maclellan 8601**, Maddox 8603, Memphis 8610, Nissan 8613, Plough 8615, Regal 8622, **Scarlett 8624**, Tennessee 8634, Thompson 8635, Wilson 8646

Texas: Abell 8650, Alcon 8655, Amarillo 8660, Anchorage 8662, **Arnold 8672**, Astros 8674, AT&T 8675, Austin 8676, Baron 8682, Bass 8690, Beals, 8697, Bickel 8705, BNSF 8706, Boeckman 8707, **Bolivar 8708**, Boone 8710, Borick 8714, **BP 8718**, Brackenridge 8719, Bridwell 8726, Brown 8731, Burnett 8737, Cailloux 8742, Carter 8752, Clayton 8765, Coastal 8768, Coates 8769, Cockrell 8770, Communities 8773, Community 8774, Community 8775, Community 8777, Constantin 8778, Cowden 8783, Cox 8784, Cullen 8792, Dallas 8795, Davis 8799, Dean 8803, Eady 8818, El Paso 8825, Elkins 8826, Embrey 8828, **ExxonMobil 8833**, Fain 8835, Farish 8838, Fasken 8839, Favrot 8842, Fikes 8844, Fisch 8846, Fish 8848, Fleming 8850, Fluor 8851, Fondren 8853, Frees 8857, George 8863, Goldsbury 8868, Greathouse 8874, Greathouse 8875, Gulf 8878, Halliburton 8884, Hillcrest 8909, Hoblitzelle 8912, Hoglund 8913, **Houston 8916**, Houston 8917, Hudson 8919, **Jenesis 8932**, KDK-Harman 8949, Kempner 8952, Kimberly 8957, Kinder 8958, King 8959, Klabzuba 8960, Kleberg 8962, Kodosky 8966, Kronkosky 8970, Light 8984, Lightner 8985, Littauer 8988, Lubbock 8994, Lyons 8996, Marsh 8999, **Marshall 9000**, Martinez 9003, Maverick 9005, McDermott 9013, McNair 9017, Meadows 9019, Moody 9033, Moore 9034, Morgan 9038, Northen 9063, **Oldham 9069**, Once 9070, Orsinger 9073, Owen 9076, Owen 9077, **Paloheimo 9080**, **Paso 9083**, Penney 9089, Permian 9091, Powell 9105, Priddy 9109, Puett 9114, QuadW 9115, Rapoport 9122, Rees-Jones 9125, Reynolds 9127, **RGK 9128**, Richardson 9130, Richardson 9131, Rockwell 9135, Rosewood 9140, Sams 9145, San Angelo 9146, San Angelo 9147, San Antonio 9148, **Scaler 9155**, Scott 9161, Shield 9170, Simmons 9174, Simmons 9175, Smith 9179, Smith 9184, Stemmons 9201, Sterling 9203, Stern 9204, Still 9207, Strake 9208, Sturgis 9211, Summerlee 9213, Sumners 9214, Swinney 9218, Temple 9223, Terry 9224, Texas 9227, Tocker 9237, Topfer 9239, Trull 9240, Tucker 9241, Turner 9242, TurningPoint 9244, USAA 9245, Valero 9246, **VHA 9250**, Waco 9251, Waggoner 9252, Wichita 9277, Wolslager 9288, Woodforest 9290, Wright 9293, Yarborough 9294, Young 9295, Zachry 9296

Utah: Ashton 9304, Burton 9309, Dee 9312, Dumke, 9316, Eccles 9319, Eccles 9320, Hemingway 9326, Simmons 9351

Vermont: **Ben 9358**, Gibney 9362, Lintilhac 9365, Tarrant 9373, Vermont 9375

Virginia: Alleghany 9382, AMERIGROUP 9383, Arlington 9384, Beazley 9391, **Blue 9394**, **Bosack 9395**, Cameron 9398, Capital 9400, CarMax 9401, Community 9410, Community 9412, Community 9414, Community 9415, Community 9416, Danville 9421, Dominion 9422, Freddie 9435, **Gannett 9439**, **Genworth 9441**, Golden 9443, Graham 9445, Gwathmey 9447, Hampton 9448, Kanter 9459, Koch 9463, Landmark 9467, Luck 9472, Lynchburg 9474, MAXIMUS 9481, McGlothlin 9483, MeadWestvaco 9484, Memorial 9485, Mitsubishi 9487, Moore 9489, Norfolk 9496, **Northrop 9498**, Portsmouth 9510, Potomac 9511, Ratner 9515, Robins 9523, Rosenthal 9525, Samberg 9527, Scott 9529, Smithfield 9535, Strong 9537, United 9546, Universal 9548, Washington 9552, Weissberg 9554, **WestWind 9555**, Williamsburg 9558, Wrinkle 9562, Wythe-Bland 9563

Washington: **444S 9565**, Allen 9567, Avista 9576, Blue 9588, **Brainerd 9590**, **Bullitt 9591**, **Campion 9594**, Casey 9595, Casey 9596, Cheney 9598, Community 9604, Community 9605, Danz 9609, Dimmer 9610, Everett 9616, Evertrust 9617, Forest 9620, Foster 9621, **Foundation 9622**, Fuchs 9624, **Gates 9625**, George 9626, Glaser 9629, **Glaser 9630**, Grays 9631, Handsel 9638, Horizons 9645, Inland 9650, Jones 9655, JRS 9656, Kitsap 9659, **Kongsgaard 9661**, **Laird 9664**, Laurel 9666, Lucky 9673, McKinstry 9680, Medina 9682, Milgard 9683, Miller 9684, Murdock 9689, Nesholm 9691, Norcliffe 9693, Orcas 9697, PEMCO 9702, Plum 9704, Puget 9705, **Quixote 9707**, Raikes 9708, RealNetworks 9712, Renton 9715, Russell 9722, Safeco 9723, **Samis 9725**, **Starbucks 9742**, **Stewardship 9744**, Tacoma 9750, True 9754, **Vista 9756**, Whatcom 9759, Wiancko 9761, **Wilburforce 9762**

West Virginia: Beckley 9769, Chambers 9772, Community 9773, Eastern 9775, Kanawha 9780, Maier 9782, McDonough 9784, Parkersburg 9789, Schenk 9793, Tucker 9796, Your 9799

Wisconsin: Acuity 9801, Alexander 9803, Alliant 9804, Argosy 9808, Bader 9810, **Baird 9811**, Beloit 9814, Bemis 9815, **Bradley 9819**, Bradshaw 9820, Briggs 9822, Community 9832, Community 9833, Community 9834, Community 9835, Cornerstone 9836, CUNA 9838, Fond du Lac 9843, Green Bay 9854, Green Bay 9855, Harley 9859, Herzfeld 9863, Iddings 9866, Incourage 9867, Johnson 9870, Johnson 9874, Kelben 9877, Keller 9878, Kern 9880, Kohler 9884, Kress 9887, La Crosse 9889, Ladish 9890, Lakeview 9892, Madison 9897, Marcus 9900, McBeath 9901, Milwaukee 9907, Northwestern 9914, Oshkosh 9916, Oshkosh 9917, Pettit 9919, Racine 9924, Rexnord 9932, Rockwell 9934, Roundy's 9936, Rowland 9937, Rutledge 9939, **Schneider 9942**, Siebert 9946, Smith 9947, Stackner 9951, Stock 9953, **Taylor 9955**, Thrivent 9956, Waukesha 9965, West 9967, Wisconsin 9969, Wisconsin 9970, Zilber 9972

Wyoming: Community 9975, Ellbogen 9977, Martin 9984, McMurry 9986, Scott 9989, True 9995, Wyoming 9999

Program evaluation

Alabama: Community 23, Community 24, Kaul 43, Meyer 53, Walker 74

Alaska: Rasmuson 89

Arizona: **Johnson 126**, Steele 165

Arkansas: Blue 181, Endeavor 186, Rockefeller 197, Walton 211

California: **Agilent 220**, Alliance 229, **Amgen 238**, Anderson 241, Archstone 253, Atlas 266, Bechtel, 296, Blue 320, California 365, California 366, California 367, California 368, **Christensen 399**, Community 418, Community 419, Community 420, East 490, Firedoll 528, **First 530**, **Fund 556**, **Geffen 567**, Girard 591, Goldman 606, Haas 642, **Haas 643**, Hayward 665, Heller 676, **Hilton 692**, **Hume 715**, Hutton 718, Irvine 727, Johnson 753, **Kapor 764**, Kern 780, Koret 801, Laural 823, Los Altos 849, Marcled 875, Marin 877, Miller 929, Monterey 936, Morgan 940, Mosher 945, Noyce 974, Orange 992, **Packard 1006**, **Peery 1022**, Placer 1039, Price 1043, Reid 1060, **Righteous 1073**, Sacramento 1103, San Diego 1108, Shortino 1160, Sierra 1163, Sobrato 1193, Soda 1194, Sonora 1198, **Special 1202**, Stuart 1225, **Thrive 1255**, UniHealth 1270, Ventura 1287, Wohlford 1336, Zellerbach 1358

Colorado: Aspen 1368, Bohemian 1375, Buell 1381, Chambers 1385, Colorado 1390, Daniels 1399, **National 1469**, Piton 1480, Rose 1487, Serimus 1496, Summit 1511

Connecticut: Community 1562, Community 1564, Connecticut 1566, Connecticut 1567, Graustein 1600, Hartford 1609, Middlesex 1644

Delaware: **Raskob 1845**

District of Columbia: **Arca 1880**, Block 1888, Cafritz 1890, **CityBridge 1892**, Community 1893, Consumer 1894, **Moriah 1932**, **Summit 1950**, Wallace 1956

Florida: Community 2032, Community 2035, Conn 2042, **Davis 2056**, duPont 2075, Engelberg 2086, Indian 2166, **Knight 2191**, Macdonald 2223, Miami 2238, Quantum 2276, Winter 2390

Georgia: **Challenge 2424**, Communities 2431, Community 2438, Cousins 2442, Healthcare 2482, North 2525, Zeist 2584

Hawaii: Atherton 2586, Castle 2593, Castle 2594, Cooke 2597, Geist 2600

Idaho: Blue 2627

Illinois: Arthur 2673, Bauer 2687, Chicago 2746, Community 2766, Community 2769, Evanston 2826, Fry 2849, Illinois 2933, **Joyce 2946**, King 2960, Libra 2981, Lumpkin 2986, Mander 2998, Morse 3039, Polk 3084, Reese 3110, **Retirement 3113**, Steans 3175, Stone 3180, VNA 3206

Indiana: Ball 3262, Central 3272, Clowes 3274, Community 3277, Community 3281, Community 3284, Community 3290, Fairbanks 3301, Foellinger 3304, Harrison 3314, Health 3317, Huntington 3324, Johnson 3330, **Lilly 3342**, **Lumina 3345**, Orange 3365, Steuben 3390

Iowa: Community 3423, Principal 3476

Kansas: Delta 3507, Douglas 3509, Kansas 3524, McPherson 3534, **Shumaker 3546**

Louisiana: Baptist 3612, Beaird 3614, Blue 3615, Institute 3644, New Orleans 3656, Wilson 3671

Maine: Horizon 3691, Maine 3699, **Sandy 3707**

Maryland: **Bearman 3728**, **Blaustein 3735**, **Casey 3745**, **Cohen 3754**, Community 3759, **de Beaumont 3774**, **Deerbrook 3776**, **England 3785**, **Hughes 3818**, Knott 3826, Meyerhoff 3849, Rathmann 3867, Straus 3890

Massachusetts: **Barr 3937**, Beveridge 3950, Community 3992, Davis 4011, Essex 4039, Melville 4170, Miller 4177, Schott 4262, Sheehan 4271, Smith 4277, Sudbury 4299, Worcester 4327

Michigan: Barry 4342, Battle Creek 4343, Community 4372, Community 4374, **Fetzer 4420**, Flinn 4424, Fremont 4438, Gilmore 4445, Greenville 4452, Hudson 4463, Jackson 4467, **Kellogg 4474**, **Mott 4510**, Mott 4511, Mount Pleasant 4512, Weatherwax 4577

Minnesota: Beverly 4615, Bremer 4620, CHS 4636, Duluth 4649, McKnight 4709, Northwest 4730, Phillips 4741, Sieben 4763, WCA 4795, Winona 4806

Mississippi: Hardin 4831, Riley 4844

Missouri: Community 4872, Hall 4905, Hallmark 4906, **Kauffman 4921**, **Monsanto 4945**, Sosland 4977

Nebraska: ConAgra 5029, Lincoln 5063, Woods 5096

New Hampshire: Alexander 5162, Bean 5164

New Jersey: **Allen 5191**, Dircks 5241, Dodge 5243, Elizabethtown 5253, **Johnson 5329**, Karma 5331, Pascale 5403, Wallerstein 5494

New York: Achelis 5549, Altman 5579, **Arcus 5608**, Bodman 5692, **Bristol 5711**, **Carnegie 5747**, **Clark 5784**, **Commonwealth 5800**, Community 5802, Community 5804, Community 5805, Community 5807, Corning 5818, **Cummings 5833**, Dyson 5923, **Ford 5994**, Frog 6026, Gifford 6049, **Goldman 6066**, Golisano 6077, Gould 6087, **Grant 6093**, Greater 6099, **Hartford 6144**, Health 6153, Heckscher 6157, **Isdell 6214**, Johnson 6239, **Kohlberg 6300**, Kornfeld 6304, Langeloth 6327, LaSalle 6331, **Macy 6414**, McCarthy 6454, **MetLife 6479**, **Neuberger 6538**, New York 6544, Oishei 6584, **Pfizer 6633**, Rauch 6681, Rochester 6722, **Rockefeller 6723**, Rosenberg 6743, Samuels 6788, Slifka 6870, **Sloan 6872**,

Sparkplug 6894, Tiger 6980, Tower 7000, Toyota 7002, Voya 7038, **Wallace 7043**, Warner 7053, Wilson 7088

North Carolina: Blue 7153, Brady 7156, Cemala 7174, Community 7180, Community 7181, Community 7182, Cumberland 7184, Mebane 7266, North Carolina 7273, **Oak 7276**, Reidsville 7294, Rex 7295, Reynolds 7297, Robertson 7305, Tannenbaum 7326, Weaver 7335, Winston-Salem 7340

Ohio: Community 7413, Erie 7444, Findlay 7453, Jennings 7509, Kettering 7522, Kramer 7529, Levin 7539, Marion 7558, Miami 7569, Morgan 7579, O'Neill 7602, Saint 7639, Scioto 7657, Springfield 7671, Stranahan 7678, Wean 7705

Oklahoma: American 7728, Chapman 7739, Community 7743, Hardesty 7756, Kerr 7764, Sarkeys 7793, Tulsa 7807

Oregon: Caddock 7828, Carpenter 7831, Kinsman 7860

Pennsylvania: Barra 7928, Buhl 7956, Chester 7979, Claneil 7982, **Colcom 7986**, Crawford 8001, DSF 8017, Eden 8021, Erie 8026, Fine 8039, First 8041, FISA 8043, Genuardi 8053, Grable 8064, Heinz 8084, Hunt 8100, Mellon 8173, Penn 8216, Phoenixville 8223, Staunton 8296, Wells 8333

Rhode Island: **Dorot 8384**, Rhode Island 8429

South Carolina: Black 8459, Byerly 8462, Community 8475, Daniel 8476

South Dakota: Sioux Falls 8521

Tennessee: Assisi 8530, East 8560, Hyde 8584, **Maclellan 8601**, Plough 8615, **Scarlett 8624**, Wilson 8646

Texas: Cailloux 8742, Community 8776, Community 8777, Favrot 8842, Fikes 8844, **Houston 8916**, Hudson 8919, Kronkosky 8970, Meadows 9019, Orsinger 9073, Owen 9076, **Paso 9083**, Rockwell 9135, Rosewood 9140, San Angelo 9147, Swinney 9218, Terry 9224

Utah: Eccles 9320

Vermont: Vermont 9375

Virginia: Cameron 9398, Community 9412, Community 9414, Koch 9463, Robins 9523, Samberg 9527, Scott 9529, Weissberg 9554, Williamsburg 9558

Washington: Allen 9567, **Campion 9594**, Casey 9595, Casey 9596, Handsel 9638, Inland 9650, Kitsap 9659, Lucky 9673, Medina 9682, Miller 9684, **Quixote 9707**, Raikes 9708, Tacoma 9750, **Wilburforce 9762**

West Virginia: Kanawha 9780

Wisconsin: Community 9832, Community 9835, Green Bay 9854, Milwaukee 9907, St. Croix 9950, Zilber 9972

Wyoming: Ellbogen 9977, Wyoming 9999

Program-related investments/loans

Alabama: Community 24

Alaska: Rasmuson 89

Arkansas: Cabe 182, Rockefeller 197, Walton 211

California: Ahmanson 222, Auen 269, Benbough 303, Benificus 305, **Broad 347**, Burns 359, California 365, California 366, Community 420, **Conservation 426**, Cowell 434, **Environment 508**, Fresno 549, Friedman 550, Haas 642, **Hilton 692**, Hutton 718, Irmas 725, Jacobs 739, Los Altos 849, Marin 877, **Moore 938**, Mosher 945, Napa 959, Noyce 974, **Omidyar 984**, Oppenheimer 987, **Packard 1006, Peery 1022**, Reid 1060, San Francisco 1109, Scripps 1129, Skoll 1175, Specialty 1203, Springcreek 1208, Taper 1237, Tuohy 1267, UniHealth 1270, **Waitt 1295**, Weingart 1307

Colorado: Aspen 1368, Charter 1387, Community 1391, Denver 1401, Gates 1418

Connecticut: Community 1562, Dalio 1569, Fink 1583, Graustein 1600, Hartford 1609, Royce 1685, Smart 1697

Delaware: **Raskob 1845**

District of Columbia: **Case 1891**, Consumer 1894, **Moriah 1932**

Florida: Broad 2002, Bush 2008, Colen 2029, Community 2031, duPont 2075, **Knight 2191**, Miami 2238, Rawlings 2279

Georgia: Callaway 2419, Community 2432, Lanier 2499, Marcus 2511

Idaho: **Schultz 2641**

Illinois: **Abbott 2648**, Adjuvant 2653, Blowitz 2702, Butler 2729, Children's 2747, Circle 2749, Coleman 2759, Community 2766, Crump 2782, Donnelley 2800, Dunham 2811, Khesed 2959, Landau 2966, **MacArthur 2989**, Prince 3089, Robinson 3122, Steans 3175, Washington 3217, Wieboldt 3231

Indiana: Community 3278, Community 3282, Huntington 3324, Putnam 3373, Reynolds 3376

Kansas: McPherson 3534, Security 3544

Kentucky: C.E. 3566

Louisiana: Baton Rouge 3613, Brown 3617

Maine: Libra 3696, Maine 3699, **Sandy 3707**

Maryland: Abell 3712, **Blaustein 3735, Casey 3745**, Ceres 3747, Community 3759, **England 3785**, Epstein 3786, Goldseker 3803, Knott 3826, Plitt 3862, Rathmann 3867

Massachusetts: Berkman 3945, Cedar 3978, Fireman 4049, Grinspoon 4080, Highland 4098, **Hunt 4102**, Hyams 4103, Island 4109, Melville 4170, Pardoe 4206, Parker 4207, **Phillips 4219**, Stevens 4288

Michigan: Battle Creek 4343, Community 4369, Community 4373, Family 4418, Fremont 4438, Grand Rapids 4447, Kalamazoo 4472, **Kellogg 4474, Kresge 4479**, Meijer 4499, Miller 4503, Mosaic 4509, **Mott 4510**, Pokagon 4523, Skillman 4543, Thompson 4555

Minnesota: Blandin 4617, Bremer 4620, Initiative 4679, Jerome 4681, Leonard 4694, McKnight 4709, Minneapolis 4714, Northwest 4729, Northwest 4730, Ordean 4732, Oswald 4735, Pohlad 4745, Southwest 4768, Wallestad 4791, West 4800

Mississippi: Regions 4843

Missouri: Baer 4856, Community 4872, Farber 4889, Hall 4905, Kansas 4920, **Kauffman 4921**, Saint Louis 4966

Montana: Edwards 5008, Gilhousen 5011

Nebraska: Hawks 5047, Kiewit 5057, Woods 5096

New Hampshire: HNH 5175, New Hampshire 5182, Putnam 5186

New Jersey: Community 5232, Golden 5280, **IDT 5311, Johnson 5329**, Pascale 5403, **Prudential 5415**, Sansom 5438

New Mexico: **Lannan 5526**, Maddox 5528, McCune 5529

New York: **Alavi 5566**, Altman 5579, **AVI 5628**, Benedict 5662, **Bloomberg 5684**, Brooklyn 5718, Buck 5725, Clark 5786, Community 5802, Community 5805, Community 5807, **Deutsche 5876**, Dyson 5923, Einhorn 5942, **Ford 5994**, Gebbie 6038, Gerry 6044, Gorman 6083, Greater 6099, Hermione 6163, **Heron 6164, JPMorgan 6244, Kaplan 6252, Kohlberg 6300**, Lindner 6372, **Mellon 6470, Mertz 6477, MetLife 6479, Mitsubishi 6490, Norcross 6564**, O'Connor 6578, Oishei 6584, **Open 6593**, Park 6615, Planning 6644, **Revson 6693, Rockefeller 6723, Rockefeller 6724**, Rockefeller 6725, Silverman 6855, **Surdna 6947**, van Ameringen 7024, **Weeden 7060**, Weinberg 7066, Western 7078, Wilson 7086

North Carolina: Babcock 7138, Bryan 7162, Community 7180, P & B 7280, Triangle 7328, Warner 7334

Ohio: Barberton 7382, Cleveland 7406, Covenant 7422, Diamond 7435, Findlay 7453, **Geisse 7468**, Gund 7478, Hamilton 7481, Hubert 7495, Marietta 7557, Morgan 7579, Murphy 7584, Muskingum 7585, Nord 7594, Richland 7630, Saint 7639, St. Marys 7672, Turner 7691, Wean 7705

Oklahoma: Hardesty 7756, Inasmuch 7760, Tulsa 7807, Warren 7809

Oregon: Collins 7836, **Lemelson 7865**, Meyer 7870, Schnitzer 7887

Pennsylvania: Berks 7939, Buhl 7956, Central 7972, Community 7990, First 8040, Firstfruits 8042, Grable 8064, Hansen 8079, Hillman 8093, Hopwood 8096, Kind 8125, McCune 8161, Mellon 8173, Penn 8216, Pew 8220, Pittsburgh 8228, PNC 8230, Roberts 8250, United 8324

Puerto Rico: Puerto Rico 8353

Rhode Island: Charlesmead 8371, Rhode Island 8429

Tennessee: Benwood 8535, Curb 8554, East 8560, Jeniam 8587, Plough 8615, Tucker 8638

Texas: **Arnold 8672**, Baugh 8693, Burnett 8737, C.I.O.S. 8740, Christian 8763, **Houston 8916**, Kempner 8952, Meadows 9019, Orsinger 9073, **PHM 9098**, Rees-Jones 9125, Richardson 9130, Rockwell 9135, San Antonio 9148, Temple 9223, Wagner 9253

Utah: ALSAM 9302, Eccles 9319, Huntsman 9327

Vermont: Evslin 9360, Gibney 9362, Vermont 9375

Virginia: **Blue 9394**, English 9426, Robins 9523, Weissberg 9554

Washington: **Bullitt 9591, Gates 9625, Laird 9664**, Lucky 9673, Miller 9684, Murdock 9689, Russell 9722, Tacoma 9750, Washington 9757

Wisconsin: Alexander 9803, Bader 9810, **Bradley 9819**, Incourage 9867, Kellogg 9879, Oshkosh 9916

Wyoming: Community 9975, Friess 9978, Kerr 9981, Whitney 9998

Public relations services

Rhode Island: Citizens 8374

Publication

Alabama: Bedsole 11, Community 21, Community 23, Community 24, Hill 40, Kaul 43, Meyer 53, Webb 76

Alaska: Rasmuson 89

Arizona: Arizona 92, **Kieckhefer 129**, Linde 135

Arkansas: Arkansas 179, Ross 199

California: California 368, **Compton 422, CS 442**, El Dorado 500, Ellis 503, **Foundation 542**, Gellert 568, **Getty 579**, Guess? 635, Heller 676, **Hilton 692, Lingnan 841**, Littlefield 844, McCarthy 895, Mental 914, Monterey 936, Noyce 974, Parker 1012, Rancho 1053, **ResMed 1063**, Sacramento 1103, Sangham 1114, **Smith 1189**, Sonora 1198, **Strauss 1223**, Stuart 1225, Taper 1237, Truckee 1263, **Warsh 1299**, Witter 1335

Colorado: Bohemian 1375, Colorado 1390, **Crowell 1398**, Rose 1487, Society 1503

Connecticut: **Albers 1532**, Community 1562, Community 1565, Connecticut 1566, **GE 1591**, Hartford 1609, Matthies 1639, Palmer 1666, **Richardson 1679, Ziegler 1731**

Delaware: AEC 1735, **Raskob 1845**

District of Columbia: Aid 1879, **Arca 1880**, Bauman 1882, **Public 1940, Searle 1946**

Florida: **Believers 1989, Chatlos 2019, Davis 2056**, duPont 2075, **Koch 2192**, Miami 2238, St. Joe 2331

Georgia: Healthcare 2482, **UPS 2566**, Watson 2569

Illinois: Brach 2712, Driehaus 2805, Frankel 2842, **Graham 2873**, Henry 2906, Heritage 2907, Logan 2983, **MacArthur 2990**, Pritzker 3091, **Rothschild 3124**, Sprague 3172, **Tyndale 3195**

Indiana: Ball 3262, Brown 3269, Central 3272, Clowes 3274, **Cummins 3292**, Froderman 3307, Harrison 3314, Henry 3320, Heritage 3321, Huntington 3324, **Lilly 3342, Lumina 3345**, Marshall 3348, Orange 3365, Wayne 3400

Iowa: Cedar Rapids 3417, Community 3423, Community 3424, Maytag 3460, Wellmark 3490

Kansas: Douglas 3509, Hansen 3518, McPherson 3534, Salina 3540, Wyandotte 3556

Kentucky: Community 3569

Louisiana: Booth 3616
Maryland: **Casey 3745**, Community 3758, **de Beaumont 3774, England 3785**, Kerr 3823, Meyerhoff 3848
Massachusetts: Berkshire 3946, Berkshire 3948, **Cabot 3966, China 3982**, Community 3992, Foundation 4056, **Lincoln 4146**, Melville 4170, Schott 4262, Sharf 4268
Michigan: Albion 4332, Americana 4337, Ann Arbor 4340, Battle Creek 4343, Community 4373, Dart 4388, Dyer 4412, **Earhart 4413**, Ford 4430, Gilmore 4445, Greenville 4452, Hillsdale 4461, Mount Pleasant 4512, Saginaw 4532
Minnesota: Duluth 4649, Greystone 4668, Jerome 4681, Lilly 4696, **Medtronic 4712**, United 4785
Mississippi: **Armstrong 4810**, Hardin 4831
Missouri: Kemper 4926, Reynolds 4961
Montana: Whitefish 5019
Nebraska: Omaha 5074, Phelps 5075
Nevada: Nevada 5134
New Hampshire: **Fidelity 5170**, Hunt 5177
New Jersey: Atran 5197, Dircks 5241, Fund 5270, **JM 5323**, Merck 5380, **Milbank 5385, Puffin 5417**, Wallerstein 5494
New Mexico: Frost 5519, **Lannan 5526, Levinson 5527**, New Mexico 5530, Santa Fe 5533, **Thaw 5534**
New York: Achelis 5549, Adirondack 5556, **Arcus 5608**, Berg 5667, Bodman 5692, Brooklyn 5718, **Carnegie 5747**, Central 5757, Chautauqua 5766, **Clark 5785**, Community 5804, Community 5807, **Dedalus 5864**, Dillon 5885, **Engelhard 5954, Foundation 6003, Grant 6093, Hartford 6144**, Heineman 6158, IFF 6206, **Isdell 6214, Ittleson 6217**, Johnson 6239, **Kaplan 6252**, Klingenstein 6292, **Kress 6308**, Littauer 6379, Lubo 6396, **M & T 6406, Macy 6414, Mailman 6418, Mapplethorpe 6427**, McCann 6453, **MetLife 6479**, New York 6544, **Norcross 6564**, Northern 6567, O'Connor 6578, **Open 6593, Pforzheimer 6635**, Richmond 6703, Rochester 6722, **Rockefeller 6724, Ross 6754**, Sackler 6777, **Sage 6782**, Schaffner 6800, Schnurmacher 6810, Snow 6878, **Sparkplug 6894, Trace 7003, United 7019, Wallace 7043, Warhol 7050**, Warner 7053, Weissman 7071, **Wenner 7075**, Western 7078, Widgeon 7081
North Carolina: BB&T 7143, Blumenthal 7154, Brady 7156, Cape Fear 7170, Community 7180, Cumberland 7184, Duke 7195, Hanes 7222, North Carolina 7273, Polk 7287, Reynolds 7298, Richardson 7300
North Dakota: North Dakota 7357
Ohio: Anderson 7372, Columbus 7411, Dayton 7428, Fairfield 7445, Gund 7478, **Kettering 7520**, Levin 7539, Marion 7558, Mather 7559, Miami 7569, Murphy 7584, Muskingum 7585, Nord 7594, Saint 7639, Scioto 7657, Springfield 7671
Oklahoma: Kirkpatrick 7766, **Schusterman 7794**
Oregon: Carpenter 7831, Kinsman 7860
Pennsylvania: Arete 7919, Centre 7973, Claneil 7982, Comcast 7989, Copernicus 7998, Crawford 8001, Dolfinger 8013, Erie 8026, Fine 8039, Foundation 8046, Fourjay 8047, Lehigh Valley 8136, McLean 8169, PNC 8230, Scaife 8266, Scranton 8275, Shoemaker 8284, **Templeton 8313**, Washington 8332
Puerto Rico: Puerto Rico 8353
Rhode Island: **Dorot 8384**, Rhode Island 8429
South Carolina: Coastal 8472, Roe 8494
South Dakota: South Dakota 8522
Tennessee: Assisi 8530, East 8560
Texas: Austin 8676, CH 8759, Community 8774, Community 8777, Covenant 8781, Halsell 8885, **Houston 8916**, Houston 8917, Kempner 8952, McGovern 9014, Meadows 9019, Moody 9033, Moore 9034, **Paloheimo 9080**, Payne 9086, Richardson 9130, San Antonio 9148, Simmons 9174, Sterling 9203, Summerlee 9213, Trull 9240, Waggoner 9252
Vermont: Gibney 9362, Vermont 9375
Virginia: Alleghany 9382, Community 9414, Freddie 9435, Weissberg 9554
Washington: **Gates 9625**, George 9626, Kitsap 9659, Miller 9684, **Quixote 9707, Samis 9725**
West Virginia: Kanawha 9780
Wisconsin: **Bradley 9819**, U.S. 9957
Wyoming: Community 9975

Research

Alabama: BBVA 9, Brock 13, Community 23, Dixon 30, Hill 40, **International 41**, Kaul 43, Meyer 53, Protective 59
Alaska: CIRI 85, Rasmuson 89
Arizona: Arizona 92, Community 101, Flinn 111, Freeport-McMoRan 112, Globe 115, Hermundslie 120, **Hickey 121, Johnson 126, Kieckhefer 129**, Linde 135, McDonald 144, **Research 157**, Steele 165, Stewart 166, University 172, Webb 174
Arkansas: Arkansas 179, Blue 181, Cabe 182, Jonsson 192, Rockefeller 197, Ross 199
California: **Agilent 220, Amgen 238, Arkay 255**, Bauer 287, Baxter 288, Bechtel, 296, **Beckman 297**, Beckman 298, **ben Joseph 302**, Benbough 303, Bengier 304, **Berman 311**, Bickerstaff 313, Blue 320, **Broadcom 349**, California 365, California 367, California 368, Campini 374, Center 388, **Christensen 399, Compton 422, CS 442**, Danford 448, Davidson 453, Early 489, East 490, Eisenberg 498, **Ellison 504**, Eucalyptus 510, Factor 513, Femino 521, **First 530**, Fremont 548, Garland 565, Gellert 568, Genentech 571, **Getty 579**, Giannini 581, Girard 591, **Glenn 594**, Goldsmith 608, Goldwyn 609, Haas 642, Haynes 664, Hayward 665, Heart 670, Heller 676, Hellman 678, Hillblom 690, **Hilton 692**, Hoag 697, **Hume 715**, Irvine 727, Irwin 728, Jameson 743, Johnson 753, **Kalliopeia 761, Kavli 771, Keck 774**, Kirchgessner 790, Koret 801, Kvamme 807, Laural 823, **Lingnan 841**, Littlefield 844, Lucas 853, M & T 861, Mabie 863, Marcled 875, Marin 877, Maxfield 887, McCarthy 895, McKesson 903, Mead 907, Mental 914, Milken 926, Milken 927, Moore 937, **Moore 938**, Morgan 940, **Neilsen 964**, Norris 971, North 972, Noyce 974, Oxnard 1001, Pacific 1003, **Packard 1006**, Parker 1012, Parsons 1013, Patron 1020, **ResMed 1063**, Rudd 1096, **Rupe 1097, Saban 1101**, Samuelsson 1107, San Diego 1108, Saw 1119, Scripps 1129, **Seaver 1133**, Sefton 1134, Severns 1143, Smith 1182, **Smith 1189, Special 1202, Strauss 1223**, Stuart 1225, Taper 1237, **Thrive 1255**, Torrey 1258, Towbes 1260, Treadwell 1262, Ueberroth 1268, Valley 1279, Valley 1280, **Waitt 1295, Warsh 1299**, Wasserman 1300, Whittier 1323, Witter 1335, Wohlford 1336, WWW 1349, **Zee 1357**
Colorado: Bohemian 1375, Bonfils 1376, Bruni 1380, Chambers 1385, Colorado 1390, Kaufmann 1436, **Malone 1453, National 1469**, Rose 1487, Saccomanno 1488, Williams 1524, **Winslow 1525**
Connecticut: Aetna 1531, Boehringer 1549, Childs 1558, Community 1562, Community 1564, Connecticut 1566, Connecticut 1567, Deloitte 1572, Donaghue 1575, **GE 1591**, Graustein 1600, Hartford 1609, Huisking 1615, Larsen 1624, Lehrman 1628, Morris 1646, Mortensen 1647, Palmer 1666, Patterson 1669, **Richardson 1679**, Rosenthal 1684, Smart 1697, Tow 1708, Xerox 1728, **Ziegler 1731**
Delaware: AEC 1735, Landenberger 1801, Marmot 1814, Mastronardi 1815, Matthews 1816, Phillips 1835, Schwartz 1857, Wasily 1871
District of Columbia: Aid 1879, **Arca 1880**, Bauman 1882, Bender 1885, **CityBridge 1892**, Community 1893, Coyne 1896, Gewirz 1909, Lehrman 1924, **Public 1940, Searle 1946**, Stewart 1949, True 1951, **Wallace 1955**, Wyss 1958
Florida: Amaturo 1966, Bailey 1976, **Barbour 1980**, Bi-Lo 1996, Community 2032, Community 2034, Coulter 2047, **Davis 2056**, Duckwall 2069, Duda 2070, duPont 2075, **Geyer 2122**, Greenburg 2137, Haller 2146, Hard 2147, Hayward 2150, **McKnight 2235**, Miami 2238, Peacock 2263, Rothberg 2297, **SeaWorld 2315, Skelly 2324**, St. Joe 2331, Sylvester 2348, **Vollmer 2373**, Wells 2383, **Whitehall 2385**, Winter 2390, Wollowick 2393
Georgia: Aflac 2399, Blank 2413, DuBose 2450, Franklin 2462, Harris 2478, Healthcare 2482, **Imlay 2487**, Mason 2513, Rich 2537, **Thoresen 2557, Turner 2563**, U.S. 2565, **UPS 2566**, Watson 2569, Zeist 2584
Hawaii: Atherton 2586, Ching 2596, Geist 2600, Hawaii 2602, Schuler 2614
Idaho: Blue 2627, **Micron 2637**, Wishnick 2646
Illinois: **Abbott 2649**, Allstate 2657, Arthur 2673, Bauer 2687, Blowitz 2702, **Brinson 2715**, Brunner 2718, Butler 2729, Chaddick 2740, Chicago 2746, CME 2755, Coleman 2759, Community 2766, Coypu 2777, Crump 2782, Davee 2785, **Deere 2790**, Duchossois 2809, Frankel 2842, **Graham 2873, Grainger 2874**, Hirschl 2912, Illinois 2933, **Joyce 2946**, Kemper 2954, Kovler 2964, Logan 2983, **MacArthur 2989**, Mallinckrodt 2995, McGowan 3014, McGraw 3015, Petersen 3078, Pritzker 3091, Redhill 3108, Reese 3110, Regenstein 3111, **Retirement 3113, Rothschild 3124, Scholl 3141**, Sinsheimer 3161, **Spencer 3171**, Sprague 3172, **Tellabs 3185**, United 3199, United 3200, Washington 3217, Woods 3242
Indiana: Anderson 3255, Anthem 3257, Ball 3262, Clowes 3274, Fairbanks 3301, Foellinger 3304, **Goodrich 3311**, Harrison 3314, Hendricks 3319, Henry 3320, Heritage 3321, Koch 3334, **Lilly 3342, Lumina 3345**, Marshall 3348, Orange 3365, Regenstrief 3375, Rolland 3381, Walther 3397
Iowa: Carver 3416, Community 3420, Community 3423, Maytag 3460, McElroy 3461, **Pioneer 3474**, Siouxland 3480, Wallace 3488
Kansas: Cooper 3503, Koch 3528, Koch 3529, McPherson 3534, Rice 3538
Kentucky: Brown 3563, C.E. 3566, Community 3569, Gheens 3577, Good 3578, Public 3597
Louisiana: Baptist 3612, Baton Rouge 3613, Blue 3615, Booth 3616, Brown 3617, Community 3624, Grigsby 3640, Huie 3643, Institute 3644, New Orleans 3656, Schlieder 3665, **Woldenberg 3672**, Woolf 3673, Zigler 3676
Maine: Alfond 3678, Cohen 3684, King 3694, Libra 3696, Maine 3699, Morton 3701
Maryland: **ABMRF 3714, Bearman 3728**, Blades 3734, **Casey 3745**, Choice 3748, Davis 3772, **de Beaumont 3774, Deerbrook 3776**, Deutsch 3779, **Ewing 3787**, Gudelsky 3809, **Hughes 3818**, Kerr 3823, Life 3833, Meyerhoff 3848, Meyerhoff 3849, NASDAQ 3857, Rathmann 3867, **Shared 3882**, Sunrise 3892, Wasserman 3905, Wilson 3909, Wright 3911
Massachusetts: Barker 3936, **Barr 3937**, Berkman 3945, Berkshire 3948, Beveridge 3950, **China 3982, Conservation 3993**, Fuller 4063, **Garfield 4065**, Hall 4084, Harris 4089, Higgins 4096, Hood 4100, **Iacocca 4104**, Island 4109, King 4122, **Krieble 4129**, Levy 4144, **Lincoln 4146**, Ludcke 4157, Lynch 4159, Melville 4170, New 4189, Pappas 4204, Parker 4207, Peabody 4211, Perkin 4213, **Phillips 4219**, Pierce 4220, Proctor 4227, **Rosenberg 4245**, Rowland 4246, Schott 4262, Shapiro 4267, Smith 4277, Webster 4322
Michigan: Ann Arbor 4340, Barry 4342, Battle Creek 4343, Bay 4344, Community 4369, Dalton 4385, Dart 4388, Davis 4391, Dow 4406, Dow 4407, **Earhart 4413, Fetzer 4420**, Fetzer 4421, Flinn 4424, Frey 4440, General 4442, **Gerber 4443**, Gerstacker 4444, Herrick 4459, **Kellogg's 4475, Kresge 4479**, Manoogian 4491, Mount Pleasant 4512, **Pardee 4517**, Pokagon 4523, Sage 4531, Shelden 4537, Stonisch 4548, Strosacker 4549, Towsley 4557, Upjohn 4564, Upton 4565, Walker 4575, Westerman 4582, Whirlpool 4583, Wilson 4589

Minnesota: **Better 4614**, Buuck 4623, CHS 4636, Duluth 4649, Greystone 4668, Jerome 4681, Lilly 4696, Marbrook 4702, **McKnight 4708**, Northwest 4730, **O'Shaughnessy 4734**, **St. Jude 4770**, Wasie 4794, West 4800

Mississippi: **Armstrong 4810**, Hardin 4831, McLean 4835

Missouri: Baer 4857, Bellwether 4859, Community 4872, Cox 4874, Edison 4883, **Enterprise 4887**, JSM 4918, Kansas 4920, **Kauffman 4921**, Kemper 4926, **McDonnell 4941**, Millstone 4944, **Monsanto 4945**, Pershing 4952, Reynolds 4961, Saigh 4965, Shaw 4970, Sosland 4977, Speas 4978, Speas 4979, Stupp 4983

Montana: Whitefish 5019

Nebraska: ConAgra 5029, ConAgra 5030, Kind 5060, Lincoln 5063, Weitz 5092

Nevada: Caesars 5106, Cord 5110, Fairweather 5118, **Reynolds 5143**, Wiegand 5159

New Hampshire: Butler 5165, Endowment 5169, Hunt 5177, Johnson 5178

New Jersey: **Allen 5191**, Atran 5197, Banbury 5200, **Berrie 5206**, Brotherton 5216, Buehler 5219, Cape 5224, Carolan 5225, Dircks 5241, **Edison 5248**, Elias 5252, Frankino 5266, Fund 5270, Goldberg 5279, Horizon 5305, Hummingbird 5309, Hyde 5310, **JM 5323**, **Johnson 5329**, Karma 5331, Kirby 5339, **Knowles 5345**, **Merck 5379**, Merck 5380, **Milbank 5385**, Pascale 5403, Provident 5414, **Ramapo 5419**, Silbermann 5456, Sudler 5472, Summit 5473, Tavitian 5479, Wallerstein 5494

New Mexico: Delle 5518, Maddox 5528, **Thaw 5534**

New York: Abrons 5546, Achelis 5549, Alpern 5577, Altschul 5582, Amsterdam 5595, Appleman 5604, Aron 5616, **AVI 5628**, Badgeley 5633, Baird 5636, Bay 5652, Berg 5667, Bodman 5692, Botwinick 5696, Brach 5699, **Bristol 5711**, **Bronfman 5717**, Brooklyn 5718, Bugher 5727, Burch 5729, Butler 5733, **Carnegie 5747**, Carvel 5749, Central 5757, Chadwick 5760, Charina 5763, Charina 5764, Chernow 5771, **Citi 5780**, **Clark 5785**, **Commonwealth 5800**, Community 5804, **Cummings 5832**, **Cummings 5833**, Curran 5835, **Dana 5845**, **Dedalus 5864**, **Delmas 5871**, DeMatteis 5873, Diller 5884, **Doherty 5893**, Dolan 5895, Dolan 5896, **Dreyfus 5912**, Dunwalke 5921, Edouard 5936, Emerson 5950, **Engelhard 5954**, **Eppley 5957**, Essel 5961, **Ford 5995**, **Foundation 6003**, Freeman 6012, Gerschel 6045, Gifford 6049, Gilman 6052, **Gitenstein 6055**, Glens Falls 6057, Glickenhaus 6058, **Goldman 6066**, Goldman 6068, **Grant 6093**, Grateful 6094, **Greenwall 6105**, Grigg 6109, **Guggenheim 6115**, **Hartford 6144**, **Hearst 6155**, **Hearst 6156**, Heineman 6158, Hermione 6163, Hugoton 6194, **Isdell 6214**, **Ittleson 6217**, Jaharis 6223, Johnson 6238, Johnson 6239, Kaplan 6250, **Kaplan 6252**, Klein 6289, Klingenstein 6292, Kornfeld 6304, **Kress 6308**, Lemberg 6350, Link 6374, Littauer 6379, Litwin 6380, Loewenberg 6387, Loewy 6389, **Luce 6398**, **M & T 6406**, **Mailman 6418**, Manton 6425, **Mapplethorpe 6427**, Marsh 6439, **Mathers 6446**, **Mayday 6448**, **Mayer 6449**, McGonagle 6460, **Mellon 6470**, **MetLife 6479**, Meyer 6481, **Mitsubishi 6490**, Monell 6497, **Moody's 6499**, Moses 6511, New York 6544, **New 6551**, NYSE 6573, O'Connor 6578, Oishei 6584, **Open 6593**, **Peterson 6630**, **Philippe 6636**, Phillips 6637, Pinkerton 6643, **Porticus 6654**, **Reed 6684**, **Revson 6693**, Richmond 6703, Ritter 6712, **Rockefeller 6724**, Rose 6734, Rosenberg 6743, **Sage 6782**, Saltz 6786, Schaffner 6800, Schenectady 6802, Schnurmacher 6809, Schnurmacher 6810, Seaver 6825, Semlitz 6831, Shanken 6837, Simons 6861, Slifka 6870, **Sloan 6872**, Smith 6877, **Sparkplug 6894**, Spinal 6898, **Spunk 6902**, St. Giles 6905, **Starr 6911**, Statler 6913, Stiefel 6931, Strypemonde 6936, Sumitomo 6943, **Tai 6959**, TE 6966, Tiffany 6978, **Tinker 6983**, Tisch 6988, **Trace 7003**, Triad 7005, **United 7019**, Vernon 7026, Vetlesen 7027, Vidda 7030, Vilcek 7031, **Vital 7033**, Voya 7038, **Wallace 7043**, **Warhol 7050**, Warner 7053, Weinberg 7066, **Wenner 7075**, Wilson 7087, Wilson 7088, **Wolfensohn 7098**

North Carolina: Blumenthal 7154, Brady 7156, Broyhill 7160, Bryan 7161, **Burroughs 7164**, Community 7180, Dover 7194, Duke 7195, Duke 7196, Finley 7199, French 7203, Goodrich 7213, Hanes 7222, Jones 7242, Mebane 7266, **Nickel 7272**, North Carolina 7273, **Oak 7276**, Olin 7279, Richardson 7300, Rominger 7306, **S.R.C. 7307**, Smith 7317, Triangle 7328

North Dakota: North Dakota 7357, Stern 7360

Ohio: Akron 7367, Anderson 7372, **Cardinal 7398**, Cleveland 7406, Codrington 7409, Corbin 7420, Covenant 7422, David 7427, Diamond 7435, Dodero 7438, Farmer 7447, France 7462, Gund 7478, Hatton 7483, Hoover 7491, Humphrey 7497, Ingalls 7503, Jegs 7507, **Kettering 7520**, Kettering 7521, Kettering 7522, Kulas 7532, Lennon 7537, Levin 7539, Lozick 7545, Maltz 7553, Marietta 7557, Marion 7558, Murphy 7584, Muskingum 7585, Nippert 7590, Prentiss 7621, Reinberger 7628, Saint 7639, Schlink 7650, Schott 7652, Scioto 7657, Scripps 7659, Springfield 7671, St. Marys 7672, Stark 7673, Wayne 7704, Weatherhead 7707, Women's 7720, Woodruff 7721

Oklahoma: Adams 7725, American 7728, Bovaird 7735, Chapman 7739, Chapman 7740, Community 7743, Hardesty 7756, Hille 7759, Kerr 7764, McGee 7774, Noble 7780, Sarkeys 7793, **Schusterman 7794**, Taubman 7804, Warren 7809, Williams 7814

Oregon: Cambia 7829, Chambers 7832, **Chiles 7833**, Collins 7837, Esco 7841, **Fohs 7844**, **Intel 7853**, Jackson 7855, Kinsman 7860, Schnitzer 7888, Swindells 7892

Pennsylvania: 1675 7903, **Alcoa 7908**, Alexander 7910, Ametek 7913, **AO 7915**, Arcadia 7918, Arete 7919, Beaver 7934, Berks 7939, Blanchard 7944, Britton 7951, Buhl 7956, **Cardiovascular 7963**, Centre 7973, Cestone 7975, Cestone 7976, Chester 7979, Claneil 7982, **Colcom 7986**, Crawford 8001, Dickson 8009, DSF 8017, Eden 8021, Erie 8026, Farber 8032, Ferree 8036, Fine 8039, Grable 8064, Gray 8069, Hopwood 8096, Hurd 8101, Huston 8103, **Institute 8109**, Kavanagh 8118, Kline 8129, Mandell 8153, McLean 8169, Mellon 8172, Mellon 8173, Nichols 8197, **Oberkotter 8203**, O'Toole 8207, Penn 8216, Pew 8220, Pittsburgh 8228, Pottstown 8234, Raab 8242, Rossin 8256, Scaife 8266, Scranton 8275, Seraph 8279, Sexauer 8280, Smith 8288, **Templeton 8313**, **Waldorf 8330**, West 8334, Widener 8336, **Williams 8339**

Puerto Rico: Puerto Rico 8353

Rhode Island: Alpert 8355, Amica 8356, **Bingham 8361**, Buehler 8364, Carter 8368, McNeil 8418

South Carolina: Abney 8454, Blue 8460, Central 8468, Roe 8494, Sims 8497

South Dakota: Sioux Falls 8521, South Dakota 8522

Tennessee: Assisi 8530, Bridgestone 8537, Community 8549, Davis 8555, Frist 8567, Hartwell 8579, Jeniam 8587, Temple 8633, Wilson 8646

Texas: Abell 8650, Alcon 8655, Alexander 8656, Alkek 8658, Anchorage 8662, Anderson 8664, Armentrout 8671, **Arnold 8672**, Austin 8676, Bass 8690, **BP 8718**, Brackenridge 8719, Brown 8731, Cain 8743, Cameron 8747, Carter 8752, CH 8759, Coates 8769, Cockrell 8770, Collins 8771, Communities 8773, Community 8777, Cullen 8792, Dunn 8816, Edwards 8824, Elkins 8826, Ellwood 8827, Farish 8838, Favrot 8842, Fikes 8844, Fish 8848, Fleming 8850, Fluor 8851, Franklin 8855, Haggerty 8881, Halsell 8885, Hamill 8887, Hamman 8888, Hirsch 8910, Hoglund 8913, **Houston 8916**, Houston 8917, Hudson 8919, Hunt 8922, Jones 8944, Kempner 8952, Klabzuba 8960, Kleberg 8962, Kronkosky 8970, Light 8984, Lightner 8985, Lowe 8993, **Marshall 9000**, Mayor 9007, McDermott 9013, McGovern 9014, McNair 9017, Meadows 9019, Miller 9028, Moody 9033, Moore 9034, Moss 9043, Parks 9081, Puett 9114, QuadW 9115, Reynolds 9127, Richardson 9130, Rosewood 9140, San Angelo 9147, San Antonio 9148, Scurlock 9162, Simmons 9174, **Six 9178**, Smith 9184, Smith 9186, Stedman 9200, Sterling 9203, Stern 9204, Strake 9208, Stumberg 9210, Sturgis 9211, Summerlee 9213, Sumners 9214, Temple 9223, Texas 9227, Tobin 9236, TurningPoint 9244, Waggoner 9252, Wal 9254, Welch 9268

Utah: ALSAM 9302, Burton 9309, Dee 9312, Dialysis 9313, Eccles 9317, Eccles 9319, Eccles 9320, Hemingway 9326, **Nu 9340**, Simmons 9351, **Thrasher 9353**

Vermont: Evslin 9360, Lintilhac 9365

Virginia: AMERIGROUP 9383, **Bosack 9395**, Freddie 9435, Jeffress 9457, Koch 9463, Mars 9477, Reynolds 9519, Rosenthal 9525, Samberg 9527, Three 9541, Titmus 9543, Williamsburg 9558

Washington: Allen 9567, Anderson 9572, Casey 9595, Casey 9596, Dimmer 9610, Foster 9621, **Foundation 9622**, Fuchs 9624, **Gates 9625**, George 9626, Handsel 9638, **Jain 9654**, JRS 9656, Kitsap 9659, **Laird 9664**, Lockwood 9671, Miller 9684, Murdock 9689, Norcliffe 9693, Pankow 9700, Pendleton 9703, **Quixote 9707**, **Samis 9725**, True 9754, Washington 9757, **Wilburforce 9762**

West Virginia: Hamilton, 9776, Kanawha 9780

Wisconsin: Alliant 9804, Argosy 9808, Benidt 9816, **Bradley 9819**, Bradshaw 9820, Clark 9830, Community 9833, Helfaer 9861, Herzfeld 9863, Incourage 9867, Johnson 9871, Kress 9887, Ladish 9890, Milwaukee 9907, Northwestern 9914, Pettit 9919, Rennebohm 9931, Thrivent 9956, Wisconsin 9970

Wyoming: Community 9975, Ellbogen 9977, Seeley 9990, Storer 9992, Zimmerman 10000

Scholarship funds

Alabama: Alabama 1, BBVA 9, Bedsole 11, Central 19, Comer 20, Community 23, Community 24, Daniel 27, Finlay 33, Hearin 38, Hill 40, Kaul 43, Lowe 46, McWane 51, Meyer 53, Protective 59, Russell 63, Vulcan 73

Alaska: Alaska 79, CIRI 85

Arizona: Arizona 92, Community 101, Flinn 111, Freeport-McMoRan 112, Grace 116, Hill 122, Linde 135, Marshall 141, Matricaria 142, Morris 148, Stardust 164, Steele 165, Stewart 166, University 172, Webb 174

Arkansas: Arkansas 179, Cabe 182, Endeavor 186, Frueauff 188, Jonsson 192, Riggs 196, Ross 199, Walker 209, Wal-Mart 210, White 212

California: Ahmanson 222, Allergan 228, **Alpert 231**, **American 237**, Anderson 243, Aratani 250, Argyros 254, Atkinson 265, **Avery 272**, Ayrshire 276, Barker 282, Baxter 288, **Beavers 293**, Bechtel 294, **Bechtel 295**, Bechtel, 296, Benbough 303, Berry 312, Blue 320, Borchard 328, Boswell 330, Bowes 334, **Broccoli 350**, Burnand-Partridge 356, CAA 362, California 365, California 368, Center 388, Change 393, **Clorox 407**, Colburn 410, College 411, Community 416, Community 417, Community 419, Community 420, Copley 428, Cortopassi 430, Coyne 435, Dachs 446, Danford 448, Darling 449, Davidson 453, Davies 454, Davis 455, Disney 467, Drown 484, El Dorado 500, Eucalyptus 510, Factor 513, Femino 521, Field 523, Finley 527, **Flextronics 535**, Freeberg 545, Fremont 548, Gap 563, Garland 565, Gasser 566, Gellert 568, GenCorp 569, Girard 591, Goldman 605, Goldwyn 609, Green 621, Guess? 635, Haas 640, Hale 645, Hannon 650, Hannon 651, Heffernan 673, Heller 676, **Hilton 692**, Hoag 697, Humboldt 714, Hutton 718, Jacobs 738, Jacobs 739, Jameson 743, Jenkins 747, Jones 756, **Kee 776**, **Kim 785**, Kingsley 789, Kirchgessner 790, Koret 801, Koshland 804, Langendorf 819, Laural 823, Leonetti/O'Connell 832, Lesher 833, **Lingnan**

841, Lucas 855, **Lund 857**, Lytel 860, M & T 861, MacKenzie 866, Marin 877, **Mattel 886, McConnell 898**, McCullough 899, McKesson 903, McMicking 904, Milken 926, Milken 927, Miller 929, Monroe 935, Morgan 939, Morgan 940, Mosher 945, Napa 959, Newhall 966, Norris 971, North 972, Orange 992, Orfalea 994, Parsons 1013, Peppers 1024, Peters 1028, PG&E 1033, Philibosian 1036, PIMCO 1037, Placer 1039, Price 1043, Rancho 1053, Reis 1062, Richards 1068, Ring 1075, **Rivendell 1077**, Rogers 1087, **Rupe 1097, Saban 1101**, Sacramento 1103, Sandy 1113, Santa Barbara 1116, Saw 1119, Schlinger 1124, Schwab 1127, Scripps 1129, Shasta 1154, Shortino 1160, Silicon 1166, Simpson 1173, Slager 1178, Smet 1181, Smith 1187, Smullin 1190, Solid 1197, Sonora 1198, **Special 1202**, Stauffer 1214, Stotsenberg 1221, **Strauss 1223**, Swenson 1229, Synopsys 1232, Taper 1237, Thornton 1252, Towbes 1260, Tuohy 1267, UniHealth 1270, Union 1271, Valley 1280, Van Nuys 1284, Ventura 1287, Versacare 1288, Wasserman 1300, Zable 1355, **Zee 1357**

Colorado: Boettcher 1374, Community 1391, Community 1393, Community 1394, Community 1395, COPIC 1397, **Crowell 1398**, ECA 1404, El Pomar 1406, Fishback 1410, Halton 1426, Janus 1432, Kaufmann 1436, King 1440, Lipscomb 1449, M.D.C./Richmond 1450, Ottens 1472, Peierls 1475, Petteys 1477, ProLogis 1485, Saccomanno 1488, Summit 1511, Telluride 1512, Vodafone 1519, **Western 1521**, Williams 1524

Connecticut: Aetna 1531, Community 1562, Community 1563, Community 1565, Connecticut 1566, Culpeper 1568, Deloitte 1572, Fairfield 1581, First 1584, Garden 1590, **GE 1591**, Hartford 1609, Huisking 1615, Larsen 1624, Liberty 1630, Main 1634, McLeod 1641, Morris 1646, New Canaan 1650, Oaklawn 1657, Palmer 1666, Pitt 1675, **Praxair 1676**, Rogow 1683, Sullivan 1703, Xerox 1728, Zachs 1730

Delaware: **Adobe 1734**, Bennett 1739, Duane 1771, Etnier 1778, Matthews 1816, **Memton 1819**, O'Neil 1826, Ortega 1828, Phillips 1835

District of Columbia: Bender 1885, Cafritz 1890, Gottesman 1911, Gudelsky 1912, Lehrman 1924, Loughran 1925, **Union 1953**

Florida: Amaturo 1966, Amos 1967, Ansin 1969, Bi-Lo 1996, Central 2015, **Chatlos 2019, Chester 2020**, Community 2031, Community 2032, Community 2035, Community 2036, Community 2038, Community 2039, Community 2040, Community 2041, Conn 2042, Darden 2051, **Davis 2056**, Duckwall 2069, Egan 2082, Florida 2101, Goodwin 2131, Greenburg 2137, Gulf 2142, Indian 2166, Jacksonville 2167, **Johnson 2174**, Kelly 2181, Kennedy 2182, Macdonald 2223, Magruder 2225, Miami 2238, Moran 2243, **Peterson 2267**, Pinellas 2269, Rayonier 2281, Rosen 2294, Rubin 2299, **Russell 2301**, Ryder 2302, Saunders 2308, Schoenbaum 2313, **Skelly 2324**, Southwest 2327, St. Joe 2331, St. Petersburg 2332, Star 2335, Thomas 2357, TWS 2365, Van Vleet 2368, Van Voorhis 2369, Watts 2380, Wells 2383, Winter 2390, Wolfson 2392

Georgia: Aflac 2399, AGL 2400, **Challenge 2424**, CLC 2426, **Coca 2428**, Colonial 2430, Community 2432, Community 2434, Community 2435, Dunn 2451, Equifax 2455, EZ 2456, Franklin 2462, Georgia 2468, **Georgia 2469**, Glenn 2470, Harrison 2481, **Imlay 2487, Keough 2496**, Lewis 2502, Lockwood 2505, Loridans 2506, Love 2508, Moore 2519, Moore 2520, Pitts 2529, Rollins 2543, Savannah 2548, **Thoresen 2557, UPS 2566**, Watson 2569, Wilson 2576, Woolley 2581

Hawaii: Bank 2588, Campbell 2592, Castle 2594, Ching 2596, Hawaii 2602, HMSA 2604, McInerny 2612, Moh 2613, **Watumull 2620**, Wilcox 2621, Wong 2622

Idaho: Cunningham 2630, Idaho 2632, **Micron 2637**, Nagel 2639, **Schultz 2641**

Illinois: **Abbott 2649**, Abt 2651, Andrew 2661, Appleby 2668, ArcelorMittal 2670, Arthur 2673, Atherton 2676, Blair 2699, Brach 2712, **Brinson 2715**, Butler 2729, Calamos 2731, Caterpillar 2738, Chaddick 2740, Charleston 2742, CME 2755, Coleman 2759, Community 2763, Community 2765, Community 2766, Community 2767, Crown 2781, Crump 2782, Cuneo 2783, Day 2787, **Deere 2790**, Dillon 2796, Dunard 2810, Dunham 2811, DuPage 2812, EFS 2818, Energizer 2824, Frankel 2842, **Grainger 2874**, Growmark 2881, Harris 2892, Hermann 2908, Hirschl 2912, Hospira 2921, Houlsby 2922, Illinois 2934, Irwin 2936, Jephson 2939, Kemper 2954, King 2960, Mallinckrodt 2995, McGowan 3014, McGraw 3015, Miller 3025, Moline 3033, Monticello 3036, Omron 3063, Owens 3068, Pepper 3074, Pilchard 3081, Polk 3084, Popular 3085, Pullman 3100, Redhill 3108, Robinson 3122, Schmidt 3139, Schmitt 3140, **Scholl 3141**, Seabury 3146, Shirk 3158, Siragusa 3162, Speh 3170, **State 3174**, Stone 3180, Tracy 3189, United 3199, United 3200, Vollintine 3208, Ward 3216, Washington 3217, White 3229, White 3230, **Wrigley 3244**

Indiana: Adams 3253, Anderson 3255, Anthem 3257, Ball 3264, Blue 3265, Brown 3269, Central 3272, Community 3278, Community 3279, Community 3281, Community 3282, Community 3283, Community 3284, Community 3285, Community 3286, Community 3287, Community 3288, Community 3290, Crown Point 3291, **Cummins 3292**, Elkhart 3298, Finish 3303, Foundations 3306, Froderman 3307, Hancock 3313, Henry 3320, Heritage 3321, Huntington 3324, Hux 3325, Johnson 3330, Journal-Gazette 3332, Kosciusko 3335, Legacy 3337, **Lilly 3340, Lilly 3342**, Lincoln 3344, Madison 3346, Miller 3355, Montgomery 3356, Noble 3359, Northern 3360, Noyes 3361, Ogle 3362, Parke 3366, Portland 3370, Pulliam 3371, Pulliam 3372, Putnam 3373, Rolland 3381, Simon 3386, Steuben 3390, Tipton 3391, Unity 3393, Wabash 3396, Washington 3398, Waterfield 3399, Wayne 3400

Iowa: Aviva 3411, Carver 3416, Cedar Rapids 3417, Clarinda 3418, Community 3420, Community 3421, Community 3423, Glazer 3434, Kuyper 3456, Mansfield 3459, Maytag 3460, McElroy 3461, MidAmerican 3465, Northeast 3469, Pella 3473, **Pioneer 3474**, Poweshiek 3475, Principal 3476, **Rockwell 3477**, Seidler 3479, Siouxland 3480, Tye 3484, Vermeer 3486, Vogel 3487

Kansas: Baughman 3493, Capitol 3498, Delta 3507, Dreiling 3511, Garvey 3516, Hansen 3518, Hutchinson 3521, Koch 3529, **Lloyd 3530**, McPherson 3534, Rice 3538, Salina 3540, Sprint 3549, Topeka 3552

Kentucky: Blue 3560, C.E. 3566, Community 3569, Community 3570, Cralle 3571, Foundation 3575, Gheens 3577, Good 3578, Humana 3582, Independence 3583, LG&E 3586, Norton 3592, Orleton 3594, Robinson 3598, Young 3607

Louisiana: Almar 3610, Booth 3616, Community 3624, Coughlin 3626, Entergy 3630, Grigsby 3640, Huie 3643, Jones 3645, Noel 3657, Scott 3666, Taylor 3669

Maine: Alfond 3678, Alfond 3679, Cianbro 3683, Lunder 3697, Morton 3701

Maryland: Abell 3712, Allegis 3719, Baltimore 3726, Blades 3734, Choice 3748, Commonweal 3756, Community 3758, Community 3759, Community 3761, Concordia 3763, Davis 3772, **de Beaumont 3774, Deerbrook 3776**, Dresher 3782, Eaton 3784, Goldsmith 3804, **Grace 3807**, Gudelsky 3809, Henson 3814, Jacobsohn 3819, Johnston 3821, Leidy 3830, Linehan 3834, Lockheed 3837, Meyerhoff 3848, Meyerhoff 3849, Mid-Shore 3851, Osprey 3861, Price 3865, Rathmann 3867, Rembrandt 3868, Riepe 3869, **Smith 3886**, St. John 3888, Straus 3890, Sunrise 3892, Wasserman 3905, Wood 3910

Massachusetts: Arbella 3926, Ayling 3932, Babson 3933, Bayrd 3938, Berkman 3945, Berkshire 3946, Berkshire 3948, Bristol 3960, **Cabot 3966**, Cabot 3968, Cambridge 3971, Cape Cod 3974, **China 3982**, Clarke 3986, Community 3991, Croll 4000, Cummings 4003, Danversbank 4009, Demoulas 4014, Donahue 4023, Dunkin' 4026, Eastern 4030, Essex 4039, Finch 4048, Foundation 4056, Fuller 4063, Gerondelis 4070, Gordon 4074, Grinspoon 4080, Hanover 4086, Highland 4098, Institution 4108, Jordan 4113, Levy 4144, Liberty 4145, Linde 4147, Lowell 4153, Lynch 4159, Mifflin 4175, Mooney 4181, New 4189, New England 4193, North 4194, Pappas 4204, Pierce 4220, Rappaport 4230, Rogers 4243, Rubenstein 4248, Schooner 4261, Schrafft 4263, Sheehan 4271, Starwood 4284, Stoico 4294, Travelli 4310, Worcester 4327, Yawkey 4329

Michigan: Albion 4332, Alro 4336, Andersen 4339, Ann Arbor 4340, Barry 4342, Battle Creek 4343, Bay 4344, Binda 4350, BorgWarner 4353, Bretzlaff 4355, Charlevoix 4361, Chrysler 4366, Comerica 4368, Community 4369, Community 4370, Community 4371, Community 4372, Community 4373, Community 4374, Community 4375, Consumers 4376, Cook 4377, Dart 4388, DeRoy 4396, Dow 4405, Dow 4406, **Fisher 4423**, Ford 4427, Ford 4430, Fremont 4438, General 4442, Gilmore 4445, Grand Haven 4446, Grand 4448, Greenville 4452, Harding 4455, Herrick 4459, Hickman 4460, Hillsdale 4461, Idema 4465, Johnson 4468, Jubilee 4470, Kahn 4471, Kalamazoo 4472, **Kellogg's 4475**, Lear 4482, Lenawee 4485, Manoogian 4491, Marquette 4495, Marshall 4496, Midland 4502, Miller 4503, Morey 4508, Mount Pleasant 4512, Perrigo 4521, Petoskey 4522, Pokagon 4523, Sage 4531, Saginaw 4532, Secchia 4536, Steelcase 4547, Sturgis 4550, Thompson 4556, Tuscola 4562, Upjohn 4564, Van Andel 4567, Walker 4575, Wege 4579, Westerman 4582, Whirlpool 4583, Wilson 4589, Wolverine 4593

Minnesota: 3M 4597, Alliss 4600, Best 4612, **Better 4614**, Blandin 4617, Buuck 4623, Cade 4625, Central 4631, Christianson 4635, CHS 4636, Davis 4642, Donaldson 4646, Duluth 4649, General 4661, Graco 4666, Griggs 4669, Hormel 4676, Kelley 4686, Kopp 4688, Koran 4689, Maas 4699, Marbrook 4702, McVay 4711, **Medtronic 4712**, Minnesota 4716, Nelson 4726, NFC 4727, Northwest 4730, Opus 4731, Ordean 4732, **O'Shaughnessy 4734, Pentair 4739**, Pohlad 4745, Regis 4750, Robins 4754, Slaggie 4766, Smikis 4767, SUPERVALU 4775, Travelers 4783, U.S. 4784, United 4785, WCA 4795, Wedum 4796, West 4800

Mississippi: C Spire 4817, Community 4820, Community 4821, CREATE 4822, Gulf 4830, Maddox 4834, McRae 4836, Mississippi 4838, Mississippi 4839, Regions 4843, Riley 4844, Sullivan 4846, Vicksburg 4848

Missouri: Ameren 4851, Anheuser 4853, Apex 4854, Baer 4856, Buder 4864, Centene 4870, Commerce 4871, Community 4872, Edison 4883, **Enterprise 4887**, Feraldo 4890, Goppert 4896, Green 4900, H & R 4902, Humphreys 4912, Interco 4914, Jones 4916, Kansas 4920, Lay 4934, Mayer 4939, MFA 4943, Millstone 4944, Musgrave 4947, Orscheln 4951, Pershing 4952, Pettus 4954, Pott 4958, Saigh 4965, Saint Louis 4966, Shaw 4970, Shelter 4971, Simon 4973, Sosland 4977, Stupp 4982, Tilles 4991, Truman 4996

Montana: Edwards 5008, First 5009, Treacy 5017, Washington 5018, Whitefish 5019

Nebraska: Acklie 5022, Ameritas 5023, Buckley 5026, Dunklau 5036, Grand Island 5044, Hamilton 5045, Hastings 5046, Hirschfeld 5049, Hitchcock 5050, Kiewit 5056, Kimmel 5059, Kind 5060, Lincoln 5063, Muchemore 5070, Nelnet 5072, Omaha 5074, Phelps 5075, Scoular 5080

Nevada: Bretzlaff 5103, Caesars 5106, Community 5108, Cord 5110, Hawkins 5123, Mallory 5129, Nevada 5134, NV 5136, Parasol 5138, Pennington 5139, **Tang 5153**, Viragh 5156

New Hampshire: Alexander 5162, Fuller 5172, Lindsay 5179, New Hampshire 5182, Penates 5185

New Jersey: **Allen 5191**, Atran 5197, Bard 5202, Berger 5205, Brotherton 5216, Cape 5224, Charles 5227, Community 5232, **Crane 5235**, Creamer 5236, Dircks 5241, Frohring 5269, Give 5278, **IDT 5311**, Ingersoll-Rand 5314, Integra 5315, Investors 5317, Isermann 5319, **Johnson 5326**, Karma 5331, KPMG 5349, McMullen 5378, **Merck 5379**, **Newcombe 5391**, OceanFirst 5394, Orange 5396, Princeton 5411, Provident 5414, **Siemens 5454**, Summit 5473, Syms 5475, Tavitian 5479, Turner 5482, Turrell 5483, Unilever 5484, **Verizon 5489**, Victoria 5490, Wilf 5502

New Mexico: Albuquerque 5511, Chase 5517, Hubbard 5523, McCune 5529, New Mexico 5530, Santa Fe 5533

New York: Abrons 5546, Achelis 5549, Adirondack 5556, Allyn 5575, **Alvarez 5584**, Ammon 5594, Arkell 5611, **Ashner 5619**, Avery 5627, AXA 5629, Bahnik 5634, Barrington 5647, Berg 5667, Bishop 5679, Bodman 5692, Botwinick 5696, Bravmann 5705, Brooklyn 5718, Brooks 5719, **Buffalo 5726**, Carvel 5749, Central 5757, Charina 5763, Charina 5764, Chazen 5767, Coach 5790, Community 5802, Community 5804, Community 5805, Community 5806, Community 5808, Curran 5835, Davenport 5850, **Dedalus 5864**, **Delmas 5871**, Devlin 5877, Dewar 5879, **Diamond 5881**, Donghia 5897, Dyson 5923, EHA 5940, Emerson 5950, **Engelhard 5954**, Farash 5969, Fisher 5982, **Ford 5995**, Freeman 6012, **Fuld 6029**, Galasso 6032, Gebbie 6038, Gilder 6050, Goldman 6068, Gorman 6083, Harkness 6134, **Hartford 6144**, Health 6153, **Hearst 6155**, **Hearst 6156**, Hermione 6163, Hettinger 6170, Hoerle 6180, Horncrest 6185, Hudson 6191, Jaharis 6223, Kaplan 6250, Kennedy 6274, Knapp 6295, Knapp 6296, Kopf 6302, Lang 6326, Lanza 6329, Lavelle 6339, Lemberg 6350, Lenna 6352, Lightfighter 6367, Lincoln 6368, Link 6375, Loews 6388, Loewy 6389, **Luce 6398**, Lurie 6403, **M & T 6406**, McCann 6453, McCarthy 6454, McGonagle 6460, Mesdag 6478, **MetLife 6479**, Millbrook 6485, Mitsui 6491, Monell 6497, **Moody's 6499**, Moore 6501, Morgan 6506, Morgan 6507, Moses 6511, National 6526, National 6527, National 6528, New York 6543, New York 6544, New York 6547, Northern 6567, Northfield 6568, NYSE 6573, O'Connor 6578, **Ohga 6581**, Oishei 6584, **Open 6593**, Park 6615, **Pforzheimer 6635**, Phillips 6637, **Polo 6651**, Price 6658, **Reed 6684**, **Reisman 6686**, Ritter 6712, Robinson 6721, Rochester 6722, Rosner 6752, Rudin 6769, Ruffin 6770, Schaffner 6800, Schenectady 6802, Schnurmacher 6809, Schnurmacher 6810, Select 6829, Semlitz 6831, Seneca 6832, Siebens 6853, Simon 6859, **SMBC 6873**, Snow 6878, Solomon 6885, Soros 6891, **Starr 6911**, Steele 6915, **Straus 6934**, Sulzberger 6942, **Summerfield 6944**, **Tai 6959**, **Tanaka 6961**, **Towerbrook 7001**, **Trace 7003**, Truman 7007, Vernon 7026, Vetlesen 7027, **Vital 7033**, Voya 7038, Wachenheim 7039, Wachtell, 7040, Warner 7053, Weil, 7062, Wilson 7087, Wilson 7088, **Youths' 7112**

North Carolina: Adams 7133, BB&T 7143, Belk 7148, Bergen 7149, Biddle 7150, Brady 7156, Broyhill 7160, Bryan 7161, Caine 7167, Campbell 7168, Cemala 7174, Community 7180, Community 7182, Cumberland 7184, Davie 7188, Dickson 7192, Dover 7194, Duke 7195, Duke 7196, Finley 7199, Foundation 7202, French 7203, Goodrich 7213, Greenville 7217, Harvest 7224, High Point 7231, Holding 7234, Leever 7253, Mayr 7261, Mebane 7266, North Carolina 7273, North 7274, Olin 7279, Polk 7287, Reynolds 7296, Robertson 7305, Snyder's-Lance 7318, Southern 7319, Tannenbaum 7326, Triangle 7328, Van Houten 7330, Weaver 7335, Winslow 7339, Winston-Salem 7340, Woodward 7343

North Dakota: Fargo 7351, Leach 7353, MDU 7354, Myra 7355, North Dakota 7357, Stern 7360

Ohio: Akron 7367, American 7368, Anderson 7372, Ariel 7377, Ashland 7378, Barberton 7382, BASF 7383, Butler 7396, **Cardinal 7398**, Charities 7400, Cleveland 7406, Cliffs 7407, Columbus 7411, Community 7412, Community 7413, Community 7414, Coshocton 7421, Dater 7426, Delaware 7431, Diamond 7435, **Eaton 7442**, Erie 7444, Fairfield 7445, Farmer 7447, Ferguson 7450, Fifth 7452, Findlay 7453, Firman 7454, France 7462, Frost 7464, GAR 7465, Greene 7474, Gund 7477, Gund 7478, H.C.S. 7479, Hamilton 7481, Haslinger 7482, Home 7489, Honda 7490, Hoover 7491, Hoover 7492, Huntington 7499, Hutton 7500, Jamestown 7506, Kettering 7521, Kettering 7522, KeyBank 7523, Kramer 7529, LaValley 7535, Lennon 7537, Licking 7540, Lincoln 7541, Lubrizol 7546, Macy's 7552, Maltz 7553, Marietta 7557, Marion 7558, McConnell 7563, Mercer 7567, Miami 7569, Middletown 7570, Montgomery 7575, Moores 7576, Morgan 7578, Murch 7582, Muskingum 7585, National 7586, Nippert 7590, Nordson 7596, **OMNOVA 7601**, Park 7609, Park 7610, Parker 7611, Resch 7629, Richland 7630, Saint 7639, Salem 7640, Schlink 7650, Schott 7652, Scioto 7657, Silk 7663, Sisler 7664, Slemp 7665, St. Marys 7672, Stark 7673, Tiffin 7682, Troy 7688, Vesper 7695, Wayne 7704, Western 7710, Wolfe 7719, Zembrodt 7724

Oklahoma: Bovaird 7735, Communities 7742, Community 7743, Hille 7759, McGee 7774, McMahon 7776, Oklahoma City 7781, Oklahoma 7782, Oxley 7785, Puterbaugh 7786, Rapp 7787, Records 7788, Sarkeys 7793, **Schusterman 7794**, Share 7795, Southern 7798, Stevens 7800, Stone 7801, Tulsa 7807, Williams 7814, Zarrow 7820, Zink 7821

Oregon: Autzen 7823, Benton 7825, Carpenter 7831, Chambers 7832, **Chiles 7833**, Clemens 7835, Collins 7837, Haugland 7849, Hedinger 7851, **Intel 7853**, Jeld 7856, John 7857, Macdonald 7866, Merrill 7868, Morris 7874, Oregon 7876, PacifiCorp 7877, PGE 7881, Renaissance 7884, Schnitzer 7887, Swindells 7892, Tucker 7896

Pennsylvania: **ACE 7905**, **Alcoa 7908**, Alexander 7910, Ametek 7913, Arcadia 7918, Arete 7919, Armstrong 7922, Baker 7925, Baker 7926, Bayer 7932, Beaver 7934, Beneficial 7936, Berks 7939, **Botstiber 7947**, Britton 7951, Brossman 7954, Buncher 7957, Carnahan 7965, Centre 7973, Century 7974, Cestone 7975, Chester 7979, CIGNA 7981, Claneil 7982, Comcast 7989, Community 7991, Community 7994, Connelly 7995, Crawford 8001, Dixon 8012, Dollar 8014, Duff 8018, Eden 8021, Ellis 8023, EQT 8025, Federated 8033, First 8040, Foundation 8046, Fourjay 8047, Genuardi 8053, Graham 8065, Greenfield 8071, Hamilton 8078, **Heinz 8083**, Henkels 8089, Hopwood 8096, Independence 8106, Independence 8107, Kavanagh 8118, **Kennametal 8120**, Keystone 8122, Kline 8129, Lancaster 8135, Lehigh Valley 8136, Lenfest 8137, **Little 8145**, Luzerne 8152, McFeely 8163, Measey 8170, Mine 8184, **Moore 8186**, Mullen 8190, Nichols 8197, Ortenzio 8206, Peoples 8218, Philadelphia 8221, Phillips 8222, Pilgrim 8225, Pittsburgh 8228, **PPG 8235**, Presser 8236, Rees 8245, Roberts 8250, S & T 8259, Schock 8272, Scranton 8275, Seraph 8279, Shoemaker 8284, Simmons 8285, Smith 8288, Smith 8289, United 8325, **Waldorf 8330**, Washington 8332, **Williams 8339**, York 8351

Rhode Island: Amica 8356, Carter 8368, Citizens 8374, Cuno 8378, CVS 8379, Daniels 8380, **FM 8393**, McNeil 8418, Middendorf 8420, Murray 8421, Rhode Island 8429, Textron 8446

South Carolina: Abney 8454, Bruce 8461, Central 8468, Coastal 8472, Community 8474, Foothills 8478, Gibbs 8480, McKissick 8486, **ScanSource 8495**, Smith 8498, Smith 8499, Spartanburg 8501, Waccamaw 8507

South Dakota: Larson 8516, Sioux Falls 8521, South Dakota 8523, Vucurevich 8524

Tennessee: American 8528, Benwood 8535, Bridgestone 8537, CIC 8546, Community 8548, Community 8549, Cook 8552, Davis 8555, East 8560, Eastman 8561, First 8565, Frist 8567, HCA 8582, Johnson 8588, Kirkland 8592, Osborne 8614, Promethean 8618, Regal 8622, Shinn 8627, Stokely 8631, Thompson 8635, Travis 8637, Tucker 8638, Wilson 8646

Texas: Abell 8650, Alkek 8658, Amarillo 8660, Armentrout 8671, Astros 8674, AT&T 8675, B.E.L.I.E.F. 8677, **Baker 8679**, Bass 8688, Bauer 8691, Baumberger 8694, Bickel 8705, BNSF 8706, **BP 8718**, Brackenridge 8719, Brown 8731, Brumley 8734, Cailloux 8742, Cain 8743, Carter 8752, CH 8759, Clayton 8765, Coastal 8768, Cockrell 8770, Communities 8773, Community 8774, Community 8775, Community 8777, Constantin 8778, Cook 8779, Cullen 8792, Dallas 8795, Dickson-Allen 8806, Doss 8813, El Paso 8825, Ellwood 8827, Fasken 8839, Fisch 8846, Fish 8848, Fluor 8851, Franklin 8855, Genecov 8862, George 8863, GHS Foun 8865, Greathouse 8874, Haggerty 8881, Hamill 8887, Hamman 8888, Herzstein 8905, Hoglund 8913, **Houston 8916**, Houston 8917, Huffington 8920, Jamail 8929, Johnson 8941, Jones 8944, Kempner 8952, Kinder 8958, Klabzuba 8960, Kleberg 8962, Kodosky 8966, Liatis 8983, Lubbock 8994, Lyman 8995, **Marshall 9000**, Marti 9001, Martinez 9003, Maverick 9005, Mayborn 9006, McCullough 9011, McDermott 9013, McGovern 9014, McNair 9017, Meredith 9023, Miller 9028, Moody 9033, Moore 9034, Morgan 9038, Murchison 9046, Navarro 9054, Newman 9061, Owen 9076, Owsley 9078, Payne 9086, Penney 9089, Permian 9091, Powell 9105, Priddy 9109, Puett 9114, QuadW 9115, Rees-Jones 9125, Robinson 9133, Rogers 9138, San Antonio 9148, Simmons 9174, **Six 9178**, Smith 9184, Smith 9187, Starling 9199, Sterling 9203, Stern 9204, Still 9207, Strake 9208, Sturgis 9211, **Suder 9212**, Sumners 9214, Tartt 9222, Temple 9223, Terry 9224, Terry 9225, Texas 9227, Trull 9240, Tucker 9241, TurningPoint 9244, Waco 9251, Waggoner 9252, Wal 9254, Wallrath 9255, Weaver 9260, West 9270, Wolslager 9288, Wood 9289, Young 9295, Zephyr 9299

Utah: ALSAM 9302, Bamberger 9305, Burton 9309, Dee 9312, Eccles 9317, Eccles 9319, Eccles 9320, Patel 9343, Simmons 9351

Vermont: Gibney 9362, Lintilhac 9365, McKenzie 9366, Tarrant 9373

Virginia: ACT 9380, Arlington 9384, Beazley 9391, Charlottesville 9405, Community 9410, Community 9411, Community 9412, Community 9413, Community 9414, Community 9415, **Cooke 9417**, Folger 9431, **Gannett 9439**, Goodman 9444, Herndon 9451, Kanter 9459, Kogod 9464, Landmark 9467, Lynchburg 9474, Memorial 9485, Moore 9489, **Mustard 9492**, Norfolk 9496, **Northrop 9498**, Potomac 9511, Reynolds 9519, Rosenthal 9525, Smithfield 9535, Strong 9537, Titmus 9543, United 9546, Universal 9548, Washington 9552, Weissberg 9554

Washington: Anderson 9572, Avista 9576, Bainbridge 9578, Bates 9582, Cameron 9593, Casey 9595, **Channel 9597**, Cheney 9598, Columbia 9602, Community 9605, Dimmer 9610, Everett 9616, Evertrust 9617, Foster 9621, **Gates 9625**, George 9626, Lafromboise 9663, Lochland 9670, Lockwood 9671, Lucky 9673, McKinstry 9680, McMillen 9681, Milgard 9683, Norcliffe 9693, PACCAR 9698, PEMCO 9702, Puget 9705, PWH 9706, Renton 9715, **Samis 9725**, San Juan 9726, Whatcom 9759

West Virginia: Beckley 9769, Bowen 9770, Community 9773, Kanawha 9780, Maier 9782, Parkersburg 9789, Prichard 9791, Schenk 9793, Tucker 9796, Your 9799

Wisconsin: Alliant 9804, Argosy 9808, Bachhuber 9809, Benidt 9816, **Bradley 9819**, Clark 9830, Cleary 9831, Community 9833, Community 9835, CUNA 9838, Fond du Lac 9843, Green Bay 9854,

Harley 9859, Holz 9864, Incourage 9867, Johnson 9870, Johnson 9871, Johnson 9874, Kelben 9877, Kern 9880, Kikkoman 9881, Kress 9887, La Crosse 9889, Ladish 9890, Lunda 9896, ManpowerGroup 9899, Mead 9902, Milwaukee 9907, Neese 9911, Northwestern 9914, Oshkosh 9916, Rockwell 9934, **Schneider 9942**, Sentry 9944, Shapiro 9945, Smith 9947, St. Croix 9950, Stock 9953, **Wagner 9961**, West 9967, Wisconsin 9969, Wisconsin 9970

Wyoming: Community 9975, Ellbogen 9977, Martin 9984, McMurry 9986, Scott 9989, True 9995

Scholarships—to individuals

Alabama: Bashinsky 7, Bedsole 11, Central 19, Finlay 33, Smith 67

Alaska: Aleut 80, Arctic 81, Chugach 84, CIRI 85, Doyon 86, Newlin 88

Arizona: Community 101, Freeport-McMoRan 112, Grace 116, Lewis 134

Arkansas: El Dorado 185, Endeavor 186, Murphy 193, Tyson 207, Union 208

California: Anaheim 239, Avant! 271, Bickerstaff 313, Change 393, Community 418, Community 420, Desert 461, Downey 477, El Dorado 500, Fansler 516, Field 523, Gogian 598, Humboldt 714, James 742, Kern 780, Leavey 825, Los Altos 849, Marin 877, Matsui 885, Northern 973, Oakland 977, Ohana 983, Orange 992, Price 1043, Price 1044, Sacramento 1103, San Diego 1108, San Francisco 1109, San Luis 1110, Santa Barbara 1116, Scaife 1120, Shasta 1154, Silicon 1166, Simon 1171, Sonora 1198, Stanislaus 1211, Ventura 1287

Colorado: Colorado 1389, Community 1391, Daniels 1399, Griffin 1425, Norwood 1471, Saccomanno 1488, Sachs 1489, Seay 1495, Telluride 1512, Western 1520, **Western 1521**, Yampa 1528

Connecticut: American 1537, Community 1563, Community 1564, Community 1565, Connecticut 1566, Fairfield 1581, First 1584, Garden 1590, Hartford 1609, Liberty 1630, Main 1634, Meriden 1643, New Canaan 1650, Ohnell 1661, Rockville 1682, Rogow 1683, SBM 1690, Sullivan 1703

Delaware: Etnier 1778, Ortega 1828

District of Columbia: **Freedom 1907**, **Union 1953**

Florida: Abramson 1963, Bailey 1976, Central 2015, Columbus 2030, Community 2032, Community 2034, Community 2038, Community 2039, Community 2041, Kelly 2181, Life 2215, Miami 2238, **Patel 2259**, Pinellas 2269, Rayonier 2281, Selby 2316, Southwest 2327, St. Petersburg 2332, Sudakoff 2342

Georgia: Beech 2409, Callaway 2418, Cobb 2427, Community 2432, Community 2437, Lewis 2502, Lockwood 2505, Savannah 2548, Watson 2569, WinShape 2577

Hawaii: Atherton 2586, Geist 2600, Hawaii 2602, **Watumull 2620**, Zimmerman 2624

Idaho: Jeker 2633, **Micron 2637**

Illinois: **Abbott 2648**, Berner 2694, Brewer 2713, Community 2766, Community 2767, Dover 2803, Edwardsville 2817, Gore 2871, Hansen 2889, Harrison 2894, Hartke 2897, Liebmann 2982, Master 3004, Mellinger 3021, Munson 3045, Oak Park 3061, Ranch 3104, Schuler 3143, Smysor 3165, Voice 3207, **Woodbury 3240**

Indiana: Adams 3253, Blue 3265, Brown 3269, Cass 3271, Central 3272, Cole 3276, Community 3277, Community 3278, Community 3281, Community 3282, Community 3283, Community 3284, Community 3285, Community 3286, Community 3288, Community 3289, Community 3290, Crown Point 3291, Dearborn 3293, DeKalb 3295, Elkhart 3298, Foundations 3306, Harrison 3314, Hendricks 3319, Huntington 3324, Johnson 3330, Kendrick 3333, Kosciusko 3336, Legacy 3337, Madison 3346, Marshall 3348, Montgomery 3356, Noble 3359, Orange 3365, Parke 3366, Portland 3370, Samerian 3384, Steuben 3390, Tipton 3391, Wabash 3396, Washington 3398, Wayne 3400, Weaver 3401, Wells 3403, Whitley 3407

Iowa: Clarinda 3418, Community 3420, Delaware 3426, Iowa 3447, Northeast 3469, **Pioneer 3474**, Poweshiek 3475, Seidler 3479, Siouxland 3480

Kansas: Community 3502, Douglas 3509, French 3515, Hansen 3518, Hutchinson 3521, Jones 3523, McPherson 3534, Salina 3540, Topeka 3552, Wichita 3555

Kentucky: Blue 3560, Community 3569, Independence 3583

Louisiana: Baton Rouge 3613, Burton 3619, Zigler 3676

Maine: Hungarian-American 3692, Maine 3698, MELMAC 3700

Maryland: Baltimore 3726, Choice 3748, Community 3758, Community 3759, Community 3760, Foulger 3792, GEICO 3801, Jacobsohn 3819

Massachusetts: Berkshire 3946, Cambridge 3972, Cape Cod 3974, Community 3992, Cummings 4003, Essex 4039, Gerondelis 4070, Hanover 4086, Hopedale 4101, Institution 4108, MetroWest 4173, Phillips 4218, Sudbury 4299, Worcester 4327

Michigan: Battle Creek 4343, Charlevoix 4361, Community 4370, Community 4371, Community 4373, Community 4375, **Earhart 4413**, Fremont 4438, **Gerber 4443**, Grand Haven 4446, Grand Rapids 4447, Grand 4448, Hillsdale 4461, Jackson 4467, Kalamazoo 4472, Legion 4483, Marquette 4495, Marshall 4496, Miller 4504, Mount Pleasant 4512, Petoskey 4522, Pokagon 4523, Saginaw 4532, Sigmund 4540, Sturgis 4550

Minnesota: Bakken 4608, Blandin 4617, Central 4631, CHS 4636, Duluth 4649, **Gallagher 4660**, Grand Rapids 4667, Hiawatha 4674, Initiative 4679, Land 4691, Minnesota 4715, Minnesota 4716, Northwest 4730, Wallin 4792, Whiteside 4805, Winona 4806

Mississippi: Community 4820

Missouri: Ballmann 4858, Kansas 4920, MFA 4943, Orscheln 4951, Pershing 4952, Shelter 4971, Westlake 5000

Montana: Bair 5004, Central 5006, Montana 5013, Washington 5018

Nebraska: **Buffett 5028**, Fremont 5039, Grand Island 5044, Hamilton 5045, Hawks 5047, Kearney 5055, Lexington 5062, Merrick 5067, Mid-Nebraska 5068, Nelnet 5072, Weller 5093, York 5098

Nevada: Berner 5102, Community 5108, Doyle 5115, NV 5136

New Hampshire: Alexander 5162, Butler 5165, Foundation 5171, New Hampshire 5182, Oberkotter 5183

New Jersey: **Knowles 5345**, KPMG 5349, Lasko 5356, LifeCare 5363, Merck 5380, Princeton 5411, **Siemens 5454**, Tavitian 5479, Wight 5501, Willits 5505

New Mexico: Albuquerque 5511, Chase 5517, Delle 5518, Hubbard 5523, Maddox 5528

New York: Adirondack 5556, AXA 5629, **Buffalo 5726**, Cattaraugus 5750, Central 5757, Chautauqua 5766, Chazen 5767, Community 5802, Community 5804, Community 5806, Druckenmiller 5915, Gilman 6052, Glens Falls 6057, JAM 6224, Jandon 6226, Mitchell 6489, Mitsui 6491, Morgan 6507, Northern 6567, **Open 6593**, **PepsiCo 6627**, Pope 6653, Price 6658, **Rockefeller 6724**, Sperry 6895

North Carolina: Armfield 7137, Butler 7165, Community 7179, Community 7180, Community 7181, Community 7182, Cumberland 7184, Davie 7188, Deaver 7190, Ghidotti 7206, **Morehead-Cain 7268**, North Carolina 7273, Nucor 7275, Polk 7287, **S.R.C. 7307**, Sloan 7314, State 7321, Tannenbaum 7326, Triangle 7328, Winston-Salem 7340, Young 7347

North Dakota: Fargo 7351, North Dakota 7357

Ohio: AK Steel 7366, Ar-Hale 7376, Ariel 7377, Ashland 7378, Ashtabula 7379, Cafaro 7397, Cleveland 7406, Community 7412, Community 7413, Community 7414, Community 7416, Community 7417, Coshocton 7421, David 7427, Delaware 7431, Diamond 7435, Fairfield 7445, Ford 7459, Hauss 7484, Howley 7494, Hutton 7500, Jamestown 7506, Marietta 7557, Marion 7558, McIntire 7565, Mercer 7567, Middletown 7570, Muskingum 7585, National 7586, Parents 7608, **Patterson 7613**, Piqua 7620, Richland 7630, Ritter 7633, Salem 7641, Samaritan 7642, Scripps 7659, Slemp 7665, Springfield 7671, St. Marys 7672, Stark 7673, **Wexner 7713**

Oklahoma: Bartlett 7732, Masonic 7771, Stevens 7800, Tulsa 7807

Oregon: Adler 7822, Benton 7825, Clemens 7835, Ford 7845, Merrill 7868, Oregon 7876

Pennsylvania: Beatty 7933, Beaver 7934, Berks 7939, Blanchard 7944, **Botstiber 7947**, **Carnegie 7966**, Central 7972, Chester 7979, Comcast 7989, Community 7990, Community 7991, Community 7992, Community 7993, Community 7994, Ellis 8023, England 8024, EQT 8025, Erie 8026, Foundation 8046, Hoyt 8098, II-VI 8105, Kimmel 8124, Lenfest 8138, Lutron 8151, Luzerne 8152, McKaig 8165, Phoenixville 8223, Piper 8227, Schock 8272, Steinman 8299, Washington 8332, West 8334

Puerto Rico: Puerto Rico 8353

Rhode Island: Cuno 8378, Hosser 8406, Rhode Island 8429, Shriners 8438

South Carolina: **AVX-Kyocera 8457**, Community 8475, Spartanburg 8501

South Dakota: Sioux Falls 8521, South Dakota 8522

Tennessee: Alumni 8527, CIC 8546, Community 8548, **Scarlett 8624**

Texas: Astros 8674, Baumberger 8694, Bergman 8703, BNSF 8706, Brookshire 8728, Castle 8756, Chapman 8761, Communities 8773, Community 8774, Cook 8779, Eady 8818, Fant 8837, Fasken 8839, Faulconer 8841, Hachar 8880, Hamman 8888, Klabzuba 8960, Marti 9001, Nearburg 9055, Piper 9101, San Angelo 9146, San Antonio 9148, Sand 9151, Sunnyside 9215, Thomas 9231, Wichita 9277, Wintermann 9283, Wood 9289, Zimmer 9300

Utah: Bamberger 9305, Harman 9325, Miller 9334

Vermont: General 9361, Rowland 9370

Virginia: Arlington 9384, Community 9410, Community 9411, Community 9413, Community 9414, Community 9416, **Cooke 9417**, Hampton 9448, Lynchburg 9474, Maude 9480, **Mustard 9492**, **Olmsted 9501**, Perry 9507, United 9546, Wythe-Bland 9563

Washington: Baker 9579, Blakemore 9587, Blue 9588, **Channel 9597**, Columbia 9602, Community 9604, Corvias 9606, Everett 9616, George 9626, Grays 9631, Haller 9635, Kelsey 9658, KMR 9660, Lauzier 9668, Lochland 9670, McMillen 9681, **PAH 9699**, PEMCO 9702, Tacoma 9750

West Virginia: Bowen 9770, Eastern 9775, Kanawha 9780, Parkersburg 9789, Tucker 9796

Wisconsin: Alliant 9804, Casper 9827, Community 9832, Community 9835, Fort 9845, Fund 9849, Goldbach 9851, Green Bay 9854, Green Bay 9855, Incourage 9867, Kelben 9877, Kohler 9884, La Crosse 9889, Menasha 9903, Milwaukee 9907, Oshkosh 9916, Racine 9924, Ramirez 9926, St. Croix 9950, Wisconsin 9970

Wyoming: Community 9975, Wyoming 9999

Seed money

Alabama: Alabama 1, Bruno 15, Central 19, Community 21, Community 23, Community 24, Hill 40, Kaul 43, Vulcan 73, Walker 74

Alaska: Rasmuson 89

Arizona: Arizona 92, Delta 106, Flinn 111, **Johnson 126**, Webb 174

Arkansas: Arkansas 179, Cabe 182, Endeavor 186, Ross 199

7453, GAR 7465, **Generation 7470**, Gund 7478, Hamilton 7481, Hershey 7487, Hoover 7492, Jennings 7509, Kettering 7522, Kroger 7531, Lennon 7537, Levin 7539, Licking 7540, Macy's 7552, Marietta 7557, Marion 7558, Mayerson 7561, Miami 7569, Middletown 7570, Montgomery 7575, Moores 7576, Morgan 7578, Muskingum 7585, Nationwide 7587, Nord 7594, Nordson 7596, Piqua 7620, Prentiss 7621, Richland 7630, Saint 7639, Schmidlapp 7651, Scioto 7657, Scripps 7659, Sisler 7664, Slemp 7665, Springfield 7671, St. Marys 7672, Stark 7673, Stocker 7676, Toledo 7686, Troy 7688, Warren 7702, Wayne 7704, White 7715, Woodruff 7721

Oklahoma: American 7728, Communities 7742, **Ethics 7749**, Inasmuch 7760, Kirkpatrick 7766, Noble 7780, Rapp 7787, **Schusterman 7794**

Oregon: Autzen 7823, Carpenter 7831, Chambers 7832, Collins 7837, **Fohs 7844**, Johnson 7858, Kinsman 7860, Lazar 7864, Meyer 7870, **NIKE 7875**, Oregon 7876, Templeton 7895, Woodard 7899

Pennsylvania: Allegheny 7911, Allerton 7912, Benedum 7935, Berks 7939, Blanchard 7944, Buhl 7956, Carnahan 7965, Central 7972, Centre 7973, Century 7974, Cestone 7975, Claneil 7982, **Colcom 7986**, Dolfinger 8013, DSF 8017, EQT 8025, Fels 8035, Fine 8039, First 8040, FISA 8043, Foundation 8046, Fourjay 8047, Grable 8064, **Heinz 8083**, Hopwood 8096, Hoyt 8098, Huston 8102, Huston 8103, Lehigh Valley 8136, Lenfest 8137, Lindback 8142, Martin 8156, McCune 8160, McCune 8161, McFeely 8163, McKenna 8166, McLean 8169, Mellon 8172, Mellon 8173, **Moore 8186**, Nelson 8195, O'Toole 8207, Penn 8216, Philadelphia 8221, Phoenixville 8223, Pittsburgh 8228, Presser 8236, Rosenstiel 8254, Russell 8258, Saint 8260, Scaife 8266, Scholler 8273, Scranton 8275, Shaffer 8281, Shoemaker 8284, Stackpole 8295, Staunton 8296, United 8324, Widener 8336, Wyomissing 8350, York 8351

Rhode Island: **Dorot 8384**, Freeman 8396, Hoche-Scofield 8405, Kimball 8410, Rhode Island 8429, TriMix 8448

South Carolina: Abney 8454, Black 8459, Bruce 8461, Byerly 8462, Coastal 8472, Community 8474, Community 8475, Daniel 8476, Fullerton 8479, Roe 8494, Self 8496, Sims 8497, Spartanburg 8501, Springs 8504

South Dakota: Robinson 8520, Sioux Falls 8521, South Dakota 8522

Tennessee: Benwood 8535, Community 8548, Community 8549, Davis 8555, Day 8556, East 8560, Hyde 8584, **International 8585**, Jeniam 8587, Lyndhurst 8599, Martin 8606, Osborne 8614, Plough 8615, **Scarlett 8624**, Wilson 8646

Texas: Abell 8650, Amarillo 8660, Anderson 8664, **Arnold 8672**, Austin 8676, Burnett 8737, Cailloux 8742, Carter 8752, Coastal 8768, Communities 8773, Community 8774, Community 8775, Covenant 8781, Cowden 8783, El Paso 8825, Embrey 8828, Fikes 8844, Fish 8848, George 8863, Halsell 8885, Hoblitzelle 8912, **Houston 8916**, **Jenesis 8932**, Kempner 8952, Kodosky 8966, Kronkosky 8970, Lubbock 8994, **Marshall 9000**, McDermott 9013, Meadows 9019, Moody 9033, Navarro 9054, Owsley 9078, **Paloheimo 9080**, Permian 9091, Peterson 9095, Rapoport 9122, Richardson 9130, Rockwell 9135, San Angelo 9147, San Antonio 9148, **Scaler 9155**, Simmons 9175, Sterling 9203, Still 9207, Summerlee 9213, Swinney 9218, Tomerlin 9238, Trull 9240, Tucker 9241, Turner 9242, Waco 9251, Waggoner 9252, Ward 9258, Wortham 9292, Zale 9297

Vermont: Lintilhac 9365, Vermont 9375

Virginia: Arlington 9384, Cameron 9398, Charlottesville 9405, Community 9415, Community 9416, Graham 9445, Koch 9463, Landmark 9467, Lynchburg 9474, Memorial 9485, Mitsubishi 9487, Samberg 9527, Scott 9529, Washington 9552, Weissberg 9554, Wrinkle 9562

Washington: Avista 9576, **Brainerd 9590**, Cheney 9598, Community 9604, Foster 9621, **Foundation 9622**, Glaser 9629, Grays 9631, Handsel 9638, Harder 9640, Inland 9650, Jones 9655, **Kongsgaard 9661**, Lucky 9673, Miller 9684, **Quixote 9707**, **Samis 9725**, **Starbucks 9742**, Tacoma 9750, **Goodwin 9751**, Washington 9757, **Wilburforce 9762**

West Virginia: Beckley 9769, Chambers 9772, Community 9773, Daywood 9774, Eastern 9775, Kanawha 9780, Parkersburg 9789, Schenk 9793, Tucker 9796, Your 9799

Wisconsin: Alexander 9803, Alliant 9804, Beloit 9814, Bradshaw 9820, Community 9833, Community 9835, Fond du Lac 9843, Green Bay 9854, Iddings 9866, Incourage 9867, Johnson 9870, Johnson 9874, Kelben 9877, Kohler 9884, La Crosse 9889, Lunda 9896, Madison 9897, McBeath 9901, Mead 9902, Milwaukee 9907, Oshkosh 9916, Racine 9924, Siebert 9946, St. Croix 9950, Thrivent 9956, U.S. 9957

Wyoming: Community 9975, Martin 9984, McMurry 9986, Seeley 9990, Wyoming 9999

Sponsorships

Alabama: BBVA 9, Protective 59

Arizona: Delta 106, University 172

Arkansas: Wal-Mart 210

California: **Agilent 220**, Allergan 228, Applied 249, **Broadcom 349**, Coulter 433, Doctors 471, Gap 563, GSF 633, Guess? 635, Hofmann 700, Jack 736, Jacobs 738, **Mattel 886**, Oakland 977, Schwab 1127, Sierra 1164, **Strauss 1223**, Synopsys 1232

Connecticut: Aetna 1531, Bob's 1548, Deloitte 1572, NewAlliance 1651, Northeast 1656, Pitney 1674, Rockville 1682, Xerox 1728

Delaware: Duane 1771, Sylvan 1867

Florida: Beaver 1986, Ryder 2302, SWS 2347

Georgia: AGL 2400, **Coca 2428**, Colonial 2430, Georgia 2468, **Georgia 2469**

Hawaii: First 2598

Idaho: Blue 2627, **Micron 2637**

Illinois: **Abbott 2649**, Caterpillar 2738, CME 2755, Donnelley 2801, **Mondelez 3034**

Indiana: Anthem 3257, Brotherhood 3268, **Cummins 3292**, Koch 3334, Lincoln 3344, Miller 3355, Steel 3389, Vectren 3394

Iowa: GuideOne 3438, MidAmerican 3465, Vermeer 3486

Kentucky: Independence 3583

Louisiana: Blue 3615

Maine: Iberdrola 3693, TD 3710

Maryland: GEICO 3801

Massachusetts: Berkshire 3946, Blue 3953, Cape Cod 3973, DentaQuest 4016, Eastern 4030, Institution 4108, Starwood 4284, **State 4285**

Michigan: Chrysler 4366, DTE 4410, Ford 4430, General 4442

Minnesota: CHS 4636, Hormel 4676, **Medtronic 4712**, Minnesota 4716, **Mosaic 4722**, Opus 4731, Robins 4754, **St. Jude 4770**, SUPERVALU 4775, TEAM 4779, Travelers 4783, Valspar 4786

Mississippi: Blue 4815, C Spire 4817

Missouri: Ameren 4851, Arch 4855, Bunge 4865, Centene 4870, Emerson 4885, Nestle 4948, SunEdison 4985

Nebraska: Ameritas 5023, Scoular 5080

Nevada: Caesars 5106, NV 5136

New Jersey: Bard 5202, Creamer 5236, Danellie 5237, Horizon 5305, **IDT 5311**, Integra 5315, KPMG 5349, OceanFirst 5394, **Verizon 5489**

New York: American 5587, Brooklyn 5718, Century 5758, **Deutsche 5876**, Doolittle 5901, First 5979, IFF 6206, **JPMorgan 6244**, Kinney 6285, **M & T 6406**, MBIA 6451, **Mitsubishi 6490**, Mitsui 6491, National 6528, New York 6543, Northfield 6568, NYSE 6573, **Pfizer 6633**, Price 6658, Rich 6697, Richmond 6703, Staten 6912, Sumitomo 6943, Voya 7038

North Carolina: Belk 7148, Delta 7191, Goodrich 7213

Ohio: Home 7489, KeyBank 7523, National 7586, Ohio 7599, Western 7710

Oklahoma: American 7728, Oklahoma 7782

Oregon: **Intel 7853**, PGE 7881

Pennsylvania: **Alcoa 7908**, Baker 7925, Comcast 7989, EQT 8025, Graham 8065, Keystone 8122, S & T 8259

Rhode Island: Biogen 8363, Citizens 8374, Textron 8446

South Carolina: **AVX-Kyocera 8457**

Tennessee: American 8528, Bridgestone 8537, First 8565, Regal 8622

Texas: Astros 8674, **BP 8718**, Kimberly 8957, Penney 9089, Valero 9246, WEDGE 9263

Virginia: AMERIGROUP 9383, Freddie 9435, Norfolk 9496, United 9546

Washington: Evertrust 9617

Wisconsin: Acuity 9801, Johnson 9874, Kikkoman 9881, Northwestern 9914, Sentry 9944, Smith 9947, Wisconsin 9969

Student loans—to individuals

California: Santa Barbara 1116, Shasta 1154

Colorado: Colorado 1389, Community 1391

Connecticut: Sullivan 1703

Georgia: **Pickett 2528**

Illinois: Mellinger 3021

Indiana: Whitley 3407

Kentucky: Gardner 3576

Maryland: Plitt 3862, Thorn 3895

Massachusetts: Cape Cod 3974, Community 3992, Hopedale 4101

Michigan: Eddy 4414, Mount Pleasant 4512, Sturgis 4550

Mississippi: Feild 4825

Missouri: Speas 4978

New Hampshire: New Hampshire 5182

New York: **Alavi 5566**, Community 5806

North Carolina: Winston-Salem 7340

Ohio: Ashland 7378, Mercer 7567, St. Marys 7672, Stark 7673

Pennsylvania: Community 7994, Gibson 8056

Rhode Island: Cuno 8378

South Carolina: Springs 8504

Tennessee: Latimer 8595

Texas: Hachar 8880, Ingram 8925, Marti 9001, Piper 9101, Seibel 9165, Wintermann 9283

Virginia: **Cooke 9417**

Washington: George 9626

West Virginia: Laughlin 9781

Wyoming: Perkins 9988, Whitney 9998

Technical assistance

Alabama: Bruno 15, Central 19, Community 23, Hill 40, Kaul 43, Meyer 53, Walker 74, Webb 76

Alaska: Rasmuson 89

Arizona: Arizona 92, Every 109, Piper 152, Steele 165

Arkansas: Arkansas 179, Frueauff 188, Rockefeller 197, Walton 211

California: Ahmanson 222, Alliance 229, Archstone 253, **Arkay 255**, Atkinson 265, Atlas 266, **Berman 311**, Blue 320, California 365, California 366, California 368, Community 414, Community 416, Community 418, Community 420, Cowell 434, **CS 442**, **Draper 481**, East 490, Firedoll 528, **Firelight 529**, Fleishhacker 534, **Fund 556**, Gellert 568, Gerbode 573, Girard 591, Goldman 605, Goldman 606, Gumbiner 636, Haas 642, **Haas 643**, Heller 676, **Hilton 692**, Humboldt 714, Irvine 727, Jacobs 739, Johnson 753, **Kapor 764**, Kern 780,

Kirchgessner 790, Koret 801, Lesher 833, Los Altos 849, Marin 877, **Mattel 886, Maya 888, McConnell 898**, McCune 900, McKay 902, Mendelson 912, Miller 929, Monterey 936, Napa 959, North 972, Noyce 974, Orange 992, Parsons 1013, **Peery 1022**, Placer 1039, Rancho 1053, **Righteous 1073**, Sacramento 1103, San Francisco 1109, San Luis 1110, Sierra 1163, Sobrato 1193, Soda 1194, Sonora 1198, **Strauss 1223**, Stuart 1225, Truckee 1263, True 1264, UniHealth 1270, Valley 1279, Van Nuys 1284, Ventura 1287, **Warsh 1299**, Wohlford 1336, Zellerbach 1358

Colorado: Animal 1363, Anschutz 1364, Aspen 1368, Bohemian 1375, Bonfils 1376, Brett 1378, Buell 1381, Chambers 1385, Colorado 1390, Community 1391, **Crowell 1398**, Denver 1401, Edmondson 1405, **General 1419**, Ottens 1472, Piton 1480, Rose 1487, Summit 1511, Telluride 1512

Connecticut: American 1537, Community 1562, Community 1563, Community 1564, Community 1565, Connecticut 1566, Connecticut 1567, Ensworth 1580, Fairfield 1581, Graustein 1600, Hartford 1609, Liberty 1630, Main 1634, Middlesex 1644, Mortensen 1647, New Canaan 1650, Valentine 1713, Xerox 1728

Delaware: AEC 1735, Delaware 1765, Edwards 1774, **Raskob 1845**

District of Columbia: Bauman 1882, Cafritz 1890, Community 1893, Consumer 1894, Kimsey 1921, Meyer 1931, **Moriah 1932, Summit 1950**

Florida: **Barbour 1980, Believers 1989**, Burns 2006, Bush 2008, **Chatlos 2019**, Community 2031, Community 2032, Community 2034, Community 2035, Community 2040, Conn 2042, **Davis 2056**, duPont 2075, Florida 2101, Henderson 2152, Kennedy 2182, **Knight 2191**, Macdonald 2223, Miami 2238, Quantum 2276, Southwest 2327

Georgia: **Challenge 2424**, Communities 2431, Community 2432, Equifax 2455, Healthcare 2482, North 2525, Rich 2537, **Thoresen 2557, Turner 2563, UPS 2566**, Zeist 2584

Hawaii: Atherton 2586, Bank 2588, Castle 2593, Castle 2594, Cooke 2597, Hawaii 2602

Illinois: Allstate 2657, Bersted 2696, **Brinson 2715**, Chicago 2746, Community 2766, Community 2769, Field 2831, Frankel 2842, Fry 2849, Grand 2875, Guthman 2882, King 2960, Lumpkin 2986, McGowan 3014, Morse 3039, Pick, 3079, Polk 3084, Prince 3089, Reese 3110, **Retirement 3113**, Siragusa 3162, Speh 3170, Sprague 3172, Steans 3175, United 3200

Indiana: Ball 3262, Blue 3265, Brown 3269, Central 3272, Community 3279, Community 3280, Community 3281, Community 3284, Community 3285, Community 3286, Community 3290, **Cummins 3292**, DeKalb 3295, Dekko 3296, Elkhart 3298, Fairbanks 3301, Foellinger 3304, Hancock 3313, Health 3317, Henry 3320, Heritage 3321, Huntington 3324, Johnson 3330, Legacy 3337, **Lilly 3342, Lumina 3345**, Marshall 3348, Noble 3359, Orange 3365, Putnam 3373, Steuben 3390, Unity 3393, Wells 3403

Iowa: Ahrens 3410, Cedar Rapids 3417, Community 3420, Community 3421, Community 3424, Maytag 3460, Mid-Iowa 3466

Kansas: Capitol 3498, Cooper 3503, Hutchinson 3521, Kansas 3524, McPherson 3534, Wyandotte 3556

Kentucky: Blue 3560, C.E. 3566, Community 3569, Foundation 3575, Public 3597, Robinson 3598

Louisiana: Baptist 3612, Beaird 3614, Community 3624, Institute 3644, New Orleans 3656, Wilson 3671

Maine: Libra 3696, Maine 3698, Maine 3699

Maryland: Baker 3725, Baltimore 3726, **Bearman 3728, Blaustein 3735, Casey 3745**, Community 3759, Community 3760, Dresher 3782, France 3796, Freeman 3797, Goldseker 3803, Knott 3826, **Shared 3882**, Straus 3890, TKF 3896, Wasserman 3905

Massachusetts: **Barr 3937**, Berkshire 3948, Boston 3956, Cambridge 3971, Cape Cod 3974, **China 3982**, Clipper 3987, Community 3991, Community 3992, **Conservation 3993**, Davis 4011, DentaQuest 4016, Essex 4039, Farnsworth 4043, Foundation 4056, **Garfield 4065**, Hyams 4103, Island 4109, Melville 4170, MetroWest 4173, Reynolds 4238, Riley 4239, Schott 4262, Shapiro 4267, Shaw 4270, Sheehan 4271, Stevens 4288, Stevens 4289, **Sweet 4302**, Worcester 4327

Michigan: Albion 4332, Americana 4337, Barry 4342, Battle Creek 4343, Bay 4344, Capital 4357, Charlevoix 4361, Community 4370, Community 4371, Community 4372, Community 4373, Community 4374, Community 4375, Dyer 4412, Fremont 4438, Frey 4440, Gilmore 4445, Grand Rapids 4447, Grand 4448, Jackson 4467, Kalamazoo 4472, **Kellogg 4474, Kellogg's 4475, Kresge 4479**, Marquette 4495, Marshall 4496, Midland 4502, **Mott 4510**, Mott 4511, Mount Pleasant 4512, Oleson 4516, Petoskey 4522, Saginaw 4532, Weatherwax 4577

Minnesota: Blandin 4617, Blue 4618, Bremer 4620, Central 4631, Duluth 4649, Graco 4666, Grand Rapids 4667, Initiative 4679, Jerome 4681, McKnight 4709, Minneapolis 4714, Northwest 4729, Northwest 4730, Rochester 4755, Saint Paul 4757, Securian 4761, Southwest 4768, United 4785, Wasie 4794, West 4800, Winona 4806

Mississippi: Foundation 4827, Gulf 4830, Maddox 4834, Riley 4844

Missouri: Community 4872, Gateway 4894, Hall 4905, Hallmark 4906, Kansas 4920, Kemper 4926, Loose 4937, Oppenstein 4950, Roblee 4963, Saint Louis 4966, Stupp 4983

Montana: Whitefish 5019

Nebraska: ConAgra 5029, Lexington 5062, Lincoln 5063, Omaha 5074, Woods 5096

Nevada: Nevada 5134

New Hampshire: Alexander 5162, Endowment 5169, **Fidelity 5170**, Foundation 5171, New Hampshire 5182

New Jersey: Dircks 5241, Dodge 5243, Fund 5270, Harbourton 5293, Horizon 5305, **Johnson 5329**, Karma 5331, MCJ 5377, Princeton 5411, **Prudential 5415**, Summit 5473, **Verizon 5489**, Victoria 5490

New Mexico: Brindle 5516, Frost 5519, **Lannan 5526**, McCune 5529, New Mexico 5530, Santa Fe 5533, **Thaw 5534**

New York: Abrons 5546, Achelis 5549, Adirondack 5556, Altman 5579, **Arcus 5608**, Bay 5652, Bodman 5692, **Bristol 5711, Bronfman 5717**, Brooklyn 5718, **Carnegie 5747**, Central 5757, **Citi 5780, Clark 5784**, Clark 5786, Community 5802, Community 5803, Community 5804, Community 5805, Community 5807, Corning 5818, Cricket 5827, Cummings 5834, **Deutsche 5876**, Dyson 5923, Elmezzi 5948, Fifth 5976, **Foundation 6003**, Gifford 6049, **Hartford 6144**, Health 6153, **Hearst 6155, Hearst 6156**, Heineman 6158, **Heron 6164, Ittleson 6217**, Jones 6242, **JPMorgan 6244, Kaplan 6252**, Lenna 6352, **Mailman 6418, Mertz 6477**, Mizuho 6492, New York 6544, New York 6546, Northern 6567, O'Connor 6578, **Open 6593, Pfizer 6633**, Pinkerton 6643, **Porticus 6654**, Rauch 6681, Richmond 6703, Rochester 6722, **Rockefeller 6723, Rockefeller 6724**, Scherman 6804, Schnurmacher 6810, **Sparkplug 6894**, Staten 6912, Tiger 6980, Tower 7000, Triad 7005, Tuttle 7014, van Ameringen 7024, **Wallace 7043**, Western 7078, Wilson 7088, **Wolfensohn 7098**

North Carolina: Blue 7153, Brady 7156, Cape Fear 7170, Community 7180, Community 7181, Community 7182, Cumberland 7184, Duke 7195, North Carolina 7273, **Oak 7276**, Reidsville 7294, Rex 7295, Reynolds 7297, Reynolds 7298, Robertson 7305, Smith 7317, Triangle 7328, Warner 7334, Weaver 7335, Winston-Salem 7340

North Dakota: Fargo 7351, Leach 7353, Stern 7360

Ohio: Ar-Hale 7376, Barberton 7382, **Bingham 7387**, Cincinnati 7404, Cleveland 7406, Columbus 7411, Community 7412, Community 7415, Dayton 7428, Fairfield 7445, Findlay 7453, **Generation 7470**, Gund 7478, Humphrey 7497, **Kettering 7520**, Kettering 7522, Marietta 7557, Marion 7558, Mayerson 7561, Morgan 7577, Morgan 7579, Muskingum 7585, Nord 7594, Nordson 7596, O'Neill 7602, Richland 7630, Saint 7639, Schmidlapp 7651, Scioto 7657, Scripps 7659, Springfield 7671, Stark 7673, Stocker 7676, Tiffin 7682, Wean 7705

Oklahoma: Communities 7742, **Ethics 7749**, Hille 7759, Inasmuch 7760, Sarkeys 7793, **Schusterman 7794**, Tulsa 7807

Oregon: Cambia 7829, Carpenter 7831, Ford 7845, Kinsman 7860, Meyer 7870, Oregon 7876

Pennsylvania: Ametek 7913, Baker 7926, Benedum 7935, Beneficial 7936, Birmingham 7942, Buhl 7956, Central 7972, Centre 7973, Cestone 7975, Cestone 7976, Claneil 7982, **Colcom 7986**, Community 7991, Connelly 7995, Dixon 8012, Erie 8026, Fels 8035, Ferree 8036, FISA 8043, Foundation 8046, Genuardi 8053, Grable 8064, **Heinz 8083**, Heinz 8084, Hopwood 8096, Hurd 8101, Huston 8102, Huston 8103, Luzerne 8152, McCune 8161, Mellon 8173, Merchants 8175, North 8199, Penn 8216, Pew 8220, Philadelphia 8221, Phoenixville 8223, Pittsburgh 8228, Scranton 8275, Wells 8333, York 8351

Puerto Rico: Puerto Rico 8353

Rhode Island: **Dorot 8384**, Rhode Island 8429, Textron 8446, TriMix 8448

South Carolina: Black 8459, Byerly 8462, Central 8468, Coastal 8472, Community 8474, Community 8475, Self 8496

South Dakota: Robinson 8520, Sioux Falls 8521, South Dakota 8522

Tennessee: Assisi 8530, Baptist 8533, Benwood 8535, Carlton 8541, Community 8548, Community 8549, East 8560, Frist 8568, Hyde 8584, Lyndhurst 8599, Memphis 8610

Texas: **Arnold 8672**, Austin 8676, Burnett 8737, Cailloux 8742, Chasdrew 8762, Communities 8773, Community 8774, Community 8776, Community 8777, Davis 8799, Edwards 8824, El Paso 8825, Halsell 8885, **Houston 8916, Jenesis 8932**, KDK-Harman 8949, Kronkosky 8970, Meadows 9019, Moody 9033, Moore 9034, Orsinger 9073, **Paso 9083**, Priddy 9109, Rockwell 9135, San Angelo 9147, Simmons 9175, Stemmons 9201, Summerlee 9213, Swinney 9218, Trull 9240, Waco 9251, Wichita 9277, Zale 9297

Utah: Dumke 9315, Dumke, 9316

Vermont: Evslin 9360, Gibney 9362, Vermont 9375

Virginia: Alleghany 9382, Arlington 9384, Cameron 9398, Community 9414, Community 9416, Freddie 9435, Landmark 9467, Lynchburg 9474, Northern 9497, Portsmouth 9510, Samberg 9527, Weissberg 9554

Washington: Allen 9567, Blue 9588, **Brainerd 9590, Bullitt 9591**, Casey 9595, Casey 9596, Community 9604, Fuchs 9624, **Gates 9625, Glaser 9630**, Inland 9650, Kitsap 9659, **Kongsgaard 9661**, Miller 9684, Murdock 9689, **Quixote 9707, Samis 9725**, Sherwood 9733, Tacoma 9750, Whatcom 9759, **Wilburforce 9762**

West Virginia: Beckley 9769, Chambers 9772, Community 9773, Kanawha 9780, Tucker 9796

Wisconsin: Alexander 9803, Bader 9810, Community 9832, Community 9835, Green Bay 9854, Incourage 9867, Madison 9897, McBeath 9901, Milwaukee 9907, St. Croix 9950, Stock 9953, Vine 9960, Waukesha 9965

Wyoming: Community 9975, McMurry 9986, Wyoming 9999

Travel awards

Hawaii: Hawaii 2602

Use of facilities

SUBJECT INDEX

List of terms: Terms used in this index conform to the Foundation Center's Grants Classification System's comprehensive subject area coding scheme. The alphabetical list below represents the complete list of subject terms found in this edition. "See also" references to related subject areas are also provided as an additional aid in accessing the giving interests of foundations in this volume.

Index: In the index itself, foundation entries are arranged under each term by state location, abbreviated name, and sequence number. Foundations in boldface type make grants on a national or international basis. The others generally limit giving to the state or city in which they are located.

Accessibility/universal design
Adult education—literacy, basic skills & GED
Adult/continuing education
Adults
Adults, men
Adults, women
African Americans/Blacks
Aging
Aging, centers/services
Agriculture
Agriculture, community food systems
Agriculture, farm bureaus/granges
Agriculture, farmlands
Agriculture, livestock issues
Agriculture, sustainable programs
Agriculture/food
Agriculture/food, alliance/advocacy
Agriculture/food, association
Agriculture/food, formal/general education
Agriculture/food, public education
Agriculture/food, public policy
Agriculture/food, reform
Agriculture/food, research
AIDS
see also AIDS, people with
AIDS research
AIDS, people with
Alcoholism
Allergies
Allergies research
ALS
ALS research
Alzheimer's disease
Alzheimer's disease research
American Red Cross
American studies
Anatomy (human)
Anesthesiology
Animal population control
Animal welfare
Animals/wildlife
Animals/wildlife, association
Animals/wildlife, bird preserves
Animals/wildlife, clubs
Animals/wildlife, endangered species
Animals/wildlife, equal rights
Animals/wildlife, fisheries
Animals/wildlife, formal/general education
Animals/wildlife, preservation/protection
Animals/wildlife, public education
Animals/wildlife, public policy
Animals/wildlife, reform
Animals/wildlife, research
Animals/wildlife, sanctuaries
Animals/wildlife, special services
Animals/wildlife, training
Animals/wildlife, volunteer services
Anthropology/sociology
Anti-slavery/human trafficking
Aquariums
Art & music therapy
Art history
Arthritis
Arthritis research
Arts
see also dance; film/video; museums; music; performing arts; theater; visual arts
Arts councils
Arts education
Arts, administration/regulation
Arts, alliance/advocacy
Arts, artist's services
Arts, association
Arts, cultural/ethnic awareness
Arts, equal rights
Arts, ethics
Arts, folk arts
Arts, formal/general education
Arts, fund raising/fund distribution
Arts, government agencies
Arts, information services
Arts, management/technical assistance
Arts, multipurpose centers/programs
Arts, public education
Arts, public policy
Arts, research
Arts, services
Arts, single organization support
Arts, volunteer services
Asians/Pacific Islanders
Assistive technology
Asthma
Astronomy
Athletics/sports, academies
Athletics/sports, amateur competition
Athletics/sports, amateur leagues
Athletics/sports, baseball
Athletics/sports, basketball
Athletics/sports, equestrianism
Athletics/sports, football
Athletics/sports, golf
Athletics/sports, Olympics
Athletics/sports, professional leagues
Athletics/sports, racquet sports
Athletics/sports, school programs
Athletics/sports, soccer
Athletics/sports, Special Olympics
Athletics/sports, training
Athletics/sports, water sports
Athletics/sports, winter sports
Autism
Autism research
Big Brothers/Big Sisters
Biology/life sciences
Biomedicine
Biomedicine research
Bisexual
Blind/visually impaired
Botanical gardens
Botanical/horticulture/landscape services
Boy scouts
Boys
Boys & girls clubs
Boys clubs
Brain disorders
Brain research
Breast cancer
Breast cancer research
Buddhism
Business school/education
Business/industry
Camp Fire
Cancer
Cancer research
Cancer, leukemia
Cancer, leukemia research
Catholic agencies & churches
Catholic federated giving programs
Cemeteries/burial services
Cerebral palsy
Cerebral palsy research

Foundations (private independent)
Foundations (private operating)
Foundations (public)
Fraternal societies
Gay men
Genetic diseases and disorders
Genetic diseases and disorders research
Geology
Geriatrics
Geriatrics research
Gerontology
Girl scouts
Girls
Girls clubs
Goodwill Industries
Government/public administration
Graduate/professional education
Health care
Health care, administration/regulation
Health care, alliance/advocacy
Health care, association
Health care, blood supply
Health care, burn centers
Health care, clinics/centers
Health care, cost containment
Health care, emergency transport services
Health care, EMS
Health care, equal rights
Health care, ethics
Health care, financing
Health care, formal/general education
Health care, fund raising/fund distribution
Health care, government agencies
Health care, HMOs
Health care, home services
Health care, infants
Health care, information services
Health care, insurance
Health care, management/technical assistance
Health care, organ/tissue banks
Health care, patient services
Health care, public policy
Health care, reform
Health care, research
Health care, rural areas
Health care, single organization support
Health care, support services
Health care, volunteer services
Health organizations
Health organizations, administration/regulation
Health organizations, association
Health organizations, fund raising/fund distribution
Health organizations, public education
Health organizations, public policy
Health organizations, reform
Health organizations, research
Health organizations, single organization support
Health organizations, volunteer services
Health sciences school/education
Heart & circulatory diseases
Heart & circulatory research
Hemophilia
Hemophilia research
Higher education
Higher education reform
Higher education, college
see also higher education
Higher education, college (community/junior)
see also higher education
Higher education, university
see also higher education
Hinduism
Hispanics/Latinos
Historic preservation/historical societies
Historical activities
Historical activities, centennials
Historical activities, genealogy
Historical activities, war memorials
History/archaeology
Holistic medicine
Homeless
Homeless, human services
see also economically disadvantaged; food services; housing/shelter, homeless
Horticulture/garden clubs
Hospitals (general)
Hospitals (specialty)
Housing/shelter
Housing/shelter, aging
Housing/shelter, alliance/advocacy
Housing/shelter, development
Housing/shelter, expense aid
Housing/shelter, formal/general education
Housing/shelter, home owners
Housing/shelter, homeless
Housing/shelter, information services
Housing/shelter, management/technical assistance
Housing/shelter, owner/renter issues
Housing/shelter, public education
Housing/shelter, public housing
Housing/shelter, reform
Housing/shelter, rehabilitation
Housing/shelter, repairs
Housing/shelter, research
Housing/shelter, search services
Housing/shelter, services
Housing/shelter, single organization support
Housing/shelter, SROs
Housing/shelter, temporary shelter
Human services
Human services, alliance/advocacy
Human services, emergency aid
Human services, equal rights
Human services, financial counseling
Human services, gift distribution
Human services, information services
Human services, mind/body enrichment
Human services, personal services
Human services, public policy
Human services, reform
Human services, self-help groups
Human services, single organization support
Human services, transportation
Human services, victim aid
Human services, volunteer services
Humanities
see also history/archaeology; language/linguistics; literature; museums
Immigrants/refugees
Immunology
Immunology research
Independent housing for people with disabilities
Independent living, disability
Indigenous peoples
Infants/toddlers
Infants/toddlers, female
Infants/toddlers, male
Insurance, providers
Interactive games
International affairs
see also arms control; international peace/security
International affairs, arms control
see also international affairs; international peace/security
International affairs, association
International affairs, equal rights
International affairs, foreign policy
International affairs, goodwill promotion
International affairs, information services
International affairs, national security
International affairs, public policy
International affairs, research
International affairs, U.N.
International affairs, volunteer services
International agricultural development
International conflict resolution
International democracy & civil society development
International development
International economic development
International economics/trade policy
International exchange
International exchange, arts
International exchange, students
International human rights
International migration/refugee issues
International peace/security
International relief
International relief, 2004 tsunami
International studies
International terrorism
Intersex
Islam
Jewish agencies & synagogues
Jewish federated giving programs
Journalism school/education
Kidney diseases
Labor rights
Landscaping
Language (foreign)
Language/linguistics
Law school/education
Law/international law
Leadership development
see also youth development, services
Learning disorders
Legal services
Legal services, public interest law
Lesbians
LGBTQ
Libraries (academic/research)
Libraries (law)
Libraries (public)
Libraries (school)
Libraries (special)
Libraries, archives
Libraries/library science
Literature
Liver disorders
Lung diseases
Lung research
Lupus
Lupus research
Marine science
Mathematics
Media, film/video
Media, journalism
Media, print publishing
Media, radio
Media, television
Media/communications
Medical care, bioethics
Medical care, community health systems
Medical care, in-patient care
Medical care, outpatient care
Medical care, rehabilitation
Medical research
Medical research, association
Medical research, formal/general education
Medical research, information services
Medical research, institute

Medical school/education
see also dental school/education; nursing school/education
Medical specialties
Medical specialties research
Medicine/medical care, public education
Men
Mental health, addictions
Mental health, association
Mental health, clinics
Mental health, counseling/support groups
Mental health, depression
Mental health, disorders
Mental health, eating disorders
Mental health, grief/bereavement counseling
Mental health, schizophrenia
Mental health, smoking
Mental health, treatment
Mental health/crisis services
Mental health/crisis services, association
Mental health/crisis services, formal/general education
Mental health/crisis services, hot-lines
Mental health/crisis services, public education
Mental health/crisis services, public policy
Mental health/crisis services, rape victim services
Mental health/crisis services, research
Mental health/crisis services, single organization support
Mental health/crisis services, suicide
Mentally disabled
Microfinance/microlending
Middle schools/education
Migrant workers
Military/veterans
Military/veterans' organizations
Minorities
see also African Americans/Blacks; Asians/Pacific Islanders; civil/human rights, minorities; Hispanics/Latinos; Native Americans/American Indians
Minorities/immigrants, centers/services
Mobile media
Mormon agencies & churches
Multiple sclerosis
Multiple sclerosis research
Muscular dystrophy
Muscular dystrophy research
Museums
Museums (art)
Museums (children's)
Museums (ethnic/folk arts)
Museums (history)
Museums (marine/maritime)
Museums (natural history)
Museums (science/technology)
Museums (specialized)
Museums (sports/hobby)
Native Americans/American Indians
Neighborhood centers
Nerve, muscle & bone diseases
Nerve, muscle & bone research
Neuroscience
Neuroscience research
Nonprofit management
Nursing care
Nursing home/convalescent facility
Nursing school/education
Nutrition
Obstetrics/gynecology
Offenders/ex-offenders
Offenders/ex-offenders, bail issues
Offenders/ex-offenders, prison alternatives
Offenders/ex-offenders, probation/parole
Offenders/ex-offenders, rehabilitation
Offenders/ex-offenders, services
Offenders/ex-offenders, transitional care
Optometry/vision screening
Organ research
Orthodox agencies & churches
Orthopedics
Orthopedics research
Palliative care
Parasitic diseases
Parasitic diseases research
Parkinson's disease
Parkinson's disease research
Pediatrics
Pediatrics research
Pensions
Performing arts
Performing arts (multimedia)
Performing arts centers
Performing arts, ballet
Performing arts, circus arts
Performing arts, dance
Performing arts, education
Performing arts, music
Performing arts, music (choral)
Performing arts, music composition
Performing arts, music ensembles/groups
Performing arts, opera
Performing arts, orchestras
Performing arts, theater
Performing arts, theater (musical)
Performing arts, theater (playwriting)
Personal assistance services (PAS)
Pharmacy/prescriptions
Philanthropy/voluntarism
Philanthropy/voluntarism, administration/regulation
Philanthropy/voluntarism, alliance/advocacy
Philanthropy/voluntarism, association
Philanthropy/voluntarism, fund raising/fund distribution
Philanthropy/voluntarism, information services
Philanthropy/voluntarism, management/technical assistance
Philanthropy/voluntarism, public policy
Philanthropy/voluntarism, research
Philosophy/ethics
Physical therapy
Physical/earth sciences
Physically disabled
Physics
Planetarium
Political science
Population studies
Poverty studies
Pregnancy centers
Prostate cancer
Prostate cancer research
Protestant agencies & churches
Protestant federated giving programs
Psychology/behavioral science
Public affairs
Public affairs, alliance/advocacy
Public affairs, association
Public affairs, citizen participation
Public affairs, election regulation
Public affairs, equal rights
Public affairs, ethics
Public affairs, finance
Public affairs, formal/general education
Public affairs, government agencies
Public affairs, information services
Public affairs, political organizations
Public affairs, public education
Public affairs, reform
Public affairs, research
Public health
Public health school/education
Public health, bioterrorism
Public health, clean water supply
Public health, communicable diseases
Public health, environmental health
Public health, epidemiology
Public health, hygiene
Public health, obesity
Public health, occupational health
Public health, physical fitness
Public health, sanitation
Public health, STDs
Public policy, research
Public utilities, sewage
Public utilities, water
Recreation
Recreation, adaptive sports
Recreation, association
Recreation, camps
Recreation, centers
Recreation, community
Recreation, country clubs
Recreation, fairs/festivals
Recreation, parks/playgrounds
Recreation, public policy
Recreation, single organization support
Recreation, social clubs
Religion
see also Jewish agencies & temples; Protestant agencies & churches; Catholic agencies & churches
Religion, association
Religion, formal/general education
Religion, fund raising/fund distribution
Religion, interfaith issues
Religion, management/technical assistance
Religion, public policy
Religion, research
Religion, single organization support
Religious federated giving programs
Reproductive health
Reproductive health, family planning
Reproductive health, OBGYN/Birthing centers
Reproductive health, prenatal care
Reproductive health, sexuality education
Residential/custodial care
Residential/custodial care, group home
Residential/custodial care, hospices
Residential/custodial care, senior continuing care
Rural development
Safety, automotive safety
Safety, education
Safety, poisons
Safety/disasters
Safety/disasters, research
Safety/disasters, volunteer services
Salvation Army
Scholarships/financial aid
Science
see also biological sciences; chemistry; computer science; engineering/technology; marine science; physical/earth sciences
Science, administration/regulation
Science, association
Science, formal/general education
Science, information services
Science, public education
Science, public policy
Science, reform
Science, research
Science, single organization support
Secondary school/education

see also elementary/secondary education
Self-advocacy services, disability
Sex workers
SIDS (Sudden Infant Death Syndrome) research
Single parents
Skin disorders
Skin disorders research
Social entrepreneurship
Social sciences
see also anthropology/sociology; economics; political science; psychology/behavioral science
Social sciences, equal rights
Social sciences, ethics
Social sciences, formal/general education
Social sciences, government agencies
Social sciences, interdisciplinary studies
Social sciences, public policy
Social sciences, research
Space/aviation
Speech/hearing centers
Spine disorders
Spine disorders research
Spirituality
Student services/organizations
Students, sororities/fraternities
Substance abuse, prevention
Substance abuse, services
Substance abuse, treatment
Substance abusers
Supported living
Surgery
Surgery research
Teacher school/education
Terminal illness, people with
Theological school/education
Theology
Transgender and gender nonconforming
Transition planning
Transportation
Tropical diseases
United Ways and Federated Giving Programs
Urban/community development
Utilities
Venture philanthropy
Veterinary medicine
Veterinary medicine, hospital
Visual arts
Visual arts, architecture
Visual arts, art conservation
Visual arts, design
Visual arts, painting
Visual arts, photography
Visual arts, sculpture
Vocational education
Vocational education, post-secondary
Vocational school, secondary
Voluntarism promotion
Volunteers of America
Web-based media
Welfare policy/reform
Women
see also civil/human rights, women; reproductive rights
Women's studies
Women, centers/services
YM/YWCAs & YM/YWHAs
Young adults
Young adults, female
Young adults, male
Youth
Youth development
Youth development, adult & child programs
Youth development, agriculture
Youth development, alliance/advocacy
Youth development, business
Youth development, centers/clubs
Youth development, citizenship
Youth development, community service clubs
Youth development, equal rights
Youth development, intergenerational programs
Youth development, public policy
Youth development, reform
Youth development, religion
Youth development, research
Youth development, scouting agencies (general)
Youth development, services
Youth development, single organization support
Youth, pregnancy prevention
Youth, services
Zoos/zoological societies

Accessibility/universal design
Ohio: Nordson 7596

Adult education—literacy, basic skills & GED
Alabama: Community 24
Arizona: Arizona 92
California: Ahmanson 222, Atkinson 265, Marin 877, Pacific 1003, Richmond 1069, Sacramento 1103, San Diego 1108, San Francisco 1109, Union 1271, Weingart 1307
Colorado: Anschutz 1364, El Pomar 1406
Connecticut: People's 1671, Pitney 1674
Delaware: Marmot 1814, **Memton 1819**
District of Columbia: Block 1888, Cafritz 1890, Jones 1918, Meyer 1931
Florida: Bank 1979, Community 2032, Community 2035
Georgia: Atlanta 2406, Harland 2477
Hawaii: Wilcox 2621
Illinois: Community 2763, Field 2831, Polk 3084, Seabury 3146
Indiana: Ball 3262, Community 3281, Harrison 3314, Lincoln 3344, Old 3363, Wayne 3400
Iowa: Siouxland 3480
Kentucky: Hagan 3579
Louisiana: Booth 3616, Community 3624
Maryland: Baltimore 3726, Fowler 3795, Rosenberg 3873
Massachusetts: Berkshire 3946, Boston 3956, Community 3992, **State 4285**, TJX 4308, Yawkey 4329
Michigan: Battle Creek 4343, Greenville 4452, Jackson 4467, Knight 4477
Minnesota: Bigelow 4616, Mardag 4703, RBC 4748, Saint Paul 4757
Missouri: Fox 4892, H & R 4902
Nevada: Nevada 5134
New Jersey: Roberts 5422
New Mexico: McCune 5529, Santa Fe 5533
New York: Central 5757, Community 5803, Cummings 5834, Dreyfus 5913, First 5979, **Hearst 6155**, **Hearst 6156**, **Pforzheimer 6635**, **Rubin 6765**, Stringer 6935
North Carolina: Triangle 7328
Ohio: Columbus 7411, Findlay 7453, **OMNOVA 7601**, Reinberger 7628, Richland 7630, **Timken 7684**
Oregon: Carpenter 7831, Johnson 7858, Oregon 7876
Pennsylvania: Dolfinger 8013, Fourjay 8047, Hurd 8101, McCune 8161, Stackpole 8295
South Carolina: Central 8468
Tennessee: Aslan 8529
Texas: Booth 8711, Coastal 8768, Fisch 8846, George 8863, Hoblitzelle 8912, Kempner 8952, King 8959, Lubbock 8994, Meadows 9019, San Antonio 9148, Sterling 9203, Tapestry 9220, Trull 9240, Wright 9293
Virginia: Arlington 9384, Moore 9489, Strong 9537
Washington: Blue 9588, Community 9604, Grays 9631, Norcliffe 9693, Renton 9715
West Virginia: Parkersburg 9789
Wisconsin: Cornerstone 9836

Adult/continuing education
Arizona: Freeport-McMoRan 112
California: Applied 249, Cathay 385, **Cisco 402**, Fromm 553, Marcled 875, Sand 1112
Colorado: El Pomar 1406
Connecticut: Connecticut 1566, Donchian 1576, Liberty 1630, Palmer 1666, Pitney 1674
District of Columbia: Cafritz 1890
Florida: Martin 2229
Hawaii: Hawaii 2602
Illinois: Coleman 2759, Community 2763, **Deere 2790**, Polk 3084, White 3229
Indiana: Lincoln 3344, Old 3363, Wayne 3400
Louisiana: Albemarle 3609
Maryland: Thorn 3895
Massachusetts: Boston 3956, Community 3992, Hyams 4103, **State 4285**
Michigan: Comerica 4368, Midland 4502, Miller 4503
Missouri: Truman 4996
Nevada: Nevada 5134
New Jersey: **Newcombe 5391**, Provident 5414
New Mexico: McCune 5529
New York: **JPMorgan 6244**
North Carolina: Cumberland 7184, Goodrich 7213, Triangle 7328
Ohio: Richland 7630
Oregon: Carpenter 7831
Pennsylvania: **Alcoa 7908**, Arcadia 7918, Connelly 7995, Dolfinger 8013, EQT 8025, Stackpole 8295
South Carolina: Spartanburg 8501
Texas: Constantin 8778, Edwards 8824, Hillcrest 8909, Hoblitzelle 8912, Meadows 9019, San Antonio 9148, Temple 9223
Vermont: Vermont 9375
Washington: Community 9604, Renton 9715, Seattle 9731, Tacoma 9750, Yakima 9767
Wisconsin: Alexander 9803, Clark 9830, Johnson 9870, Milwaukee 9907, Wisconsin 9970

Adults
Alabama: Comer 20, Kaul 43, Meyer 53
Arizona: Webb 174
Arkansas: Rockefeller 197, Ross 199
California: Ahmanson 222, **Alpert 231**, Aroha 260, Atkinson 265, Center 388, Community 414, **Geffen 567**, Gerbode 573, Giannini 581, Gogian 598, Green 621, Hellman 678, Lesher 833, Marcled 875, McMillen 905, Napa 959, Newhall 966, Patron 1020, Payne 1021, Rogers 1087, Schwab 1127, Sefton 1134, Silicon 1166, **Special 1202**, Taper 1237, Tuohy 1267, **Vadasz 1275**, Weingart 1307
Colorado: Colorado 1390, Community 1391, Fishback 1410, King 1440, Rose 1487, Summit 1511, **Western 1521**
Connecticut: Community 1562, Community 1563, Community 1564, Connecticut 1567
Delaware: **Raskob 1845**
District of Columbia: **CityBridge 1892**, Consumer 1894, **Union 1953**
Florida: Hough 2162, Pinellas 2269, Quantum 2276, Winter 2390

Adults, men

Adults, women

African Americans/Blacks

Aging

Connecticut: Community 1562, Community 1563, Community 1564, Connecticut 1566, NewAlliance 1651, Palmer 1666
Delaware: Crystal 1758, Delaware 1765, McDonald 1817, **Raskob 1845**
District of Columbia: Agua 1878, Cafritz 1890, Community 1893, Lehrman 1924
Florida: Bank 1979, Bush 2008, Central 2015, Community 2031, Community 2032, Community 2033, Community 2036, Community 2038, Community 2040, duPont 2074, Greenburg 2137, **McKnight 2235**, Miami 2238, Moran 2243, Ocean 2253, Patterson 2260, Pinellas 2269, Selby 2316, Winter 2390
Georgia: AGL 2400, Callaway 2419, Community 2433, Pitts 2529, Rich 2537, **Thoresen 2557**, Whitehead 2571, Woodruff 2579
Hawaii: Hawaii 2602, Hughes 2605
Illinois: **Abbott 2648**, Allegretti 2655, **Baxter 2690**, Blowitz 2702, Butler 2729, Chicago 2746, Community 2762, Community 2763, Community 2765, de Kay 2788, Evanston 2826, Field 2831, Logan 2983, Oak Park 3061, Reese 3110, **Rothschild 3124**, Shipman 3157, Siragusa 3162, **Thome 3187**, Washington 3217
Indiana: **Ackerman 3252**, Blue 3265, Community 3279, Community 3281, Community 3285, Community 3286, Community 3287, Elkhart 3298, Harrison 3314, Heritage 3321, **Lilly 3342**, Lincoln 3344, Putnam 3373, Steuben 3390, Wayne 3400
Iowa: Community 3421, Meredith 3463, Principal 3476, Siouxland 3480
Kansas: Community 3502, Cooper 3503, Delta 3507, Hutchinson 3521, Manhattan 3532
Kentucky: Cralle 3571, Humana 3582
Louisiana: Baton Rouge 3613, Blue 3615, Booth 3616, Community 3624, Entergy 3630
Maine: Gorman 3689, **Walter 3711**
Maryland: Baltimore 3726, **Bearman 3728**, Community 3759, Community 3761, Fowler 3795, Hoffberger 3817, Stulman 3891, Washington 3904, **Weinberg 3908**
Massachusetts: Association 3929, Boston 3956, Brookline 3962, Cambridge 3971, Clipper 3987, Community 3992, Essex 4039, Farnsworth 4043, **Grand 4076**, Hall 4084, MetroWest 4173, Wadleigh 4316, Worcester 4327
Michigan: Ann Arbor 4340, Bay 4344, Berrien 4347, Charlevoix 4361, Chrysler 4366, Community 4373, Community 4374, Fremont 4438, Gerstacker 4444, Grand Rapids 4447, Hillsdale 4461, Marshall 4496, Midland 4502, Mount Pleasant 4512, Prince 4525, Saginaw 4532, Steelcase 4547, Tuscola 4562, Van Andel 4567
Minnesota: **Andersen 4601**, Beim 4609, Bremer 4620, Mardag 4703, Minneapolis 4714, Northwest 4730, Ordean 4732, Rivers 4752, Rochester 4755, Southwest 4768, Stevens 4772, TEAM 4779
Mississippi: Community 4821, Foundation 4827
Missouri: Ameren 4851, Community 4872, Dunn 4882, Humphreys 4912, Saint Louis 4966, Simon 4973, Truman 4996
Montana: Oro 5014
Nebraska: Dunklau 5036, Hamilton 5045, Kearney 5055, Lincoln 5063, Woods 5096
Nevada: Caesars 5106, Fairweather 5118, Nevada 5134
New Jersey: Danellie 5237, **GHH 5275**, Horizon 5305, **Johnson 5329**, Kirby 5339, **Ramapo 5419**, Summit 5473, **Verizon 5489**, Wallerstein 5493
New Mexico: Frost 5519, Maddox 5528, McCune 5529, New Mexico 5530, Santa Fe 5533
New York: Abrons 5546, Altman 5579, **Bristol 5711**, **Clark 5785**, **Commonwealth 5800**, Community 5802, Community 5803, Corey 5816, **Cummings 5832**, Diamond 5880, Dreyfus 5913, Eastern 5927, Glickenhaus 6058, Hagedorn 6128, **Hartford 6144**, Health 6153, **Hearst 6155**, **Hearst 6156**, Hoerle 6180, Jones 6242, Litwin 6380, McGonagle 6460, **MetLife 6479**, Monell 6497, **Nash 6525**, New York 6546, Noble 6560, O'Connor 6578, Ritter 6712, Rochester 6722, Samuels 6788, Silverman 6855, **Skadden 6868**, **Starr 6911**, Tuttle 7014, van Ameringen 7024, Western 7078
North Carolina: Blue 7153, Community 7180, Community 7181, French 7203, North Carolina 7273, Reidsville 7294, Robertson 7305, Triangle 7328, Van Houten 7330
North Dakota: MDU 7354, North Dakota 7357, Stern 7360
Ohio: Abington 7365, Akron 7367, Bruening 7391, **Cardinal 7398**, Cincinnati 7404, Cincinnati 7405, Cleveland 7406, Community 7416, Fairfield 7445, Ford 7459, GAR 7465, Loeb 7544, McGregor 7564, Mercer 7567, Middletown 7570, Muskingum 7585, O'Neill 7602, Price 7622, Richland 7630, Saint 7639, Schlink 7650, Sisler 7664, Stark 7673, Toledo 7686, Youngstown 7723
Oklahoma: Hille 7759, Masonic 7771
Oregon: Collins 7836, Oregon 7876, Poznanski 7882
Pennsylvania: Arcadia 7918, Armstrong 7921, Beneficial 7936, Berks 7939, Birmingham 7942, Campbell 7961, Clapp 7983, Community 7994, Connelly 7995, Dolfinger 8013, EQT 8025, First 8041, Highmark 8092, Independence 8107, Keystone 8122, McCune 8160, McLean 8169, Morris 8188, North 8199, Pew 8220, Phoenixville 8223, Pierce 8224, Roberts 8250, Scranton 8275, Smith 8288, Smith 8289, Snee 8291, York 8351
Rhode Island: Kimball 8410
South Carolina: Agape 8455, Self 8496
South Dakota: Sioux Falls 8521
Tennessee: Baptist 8533, Community 8550, Wilson 8646
Texas: Anderson 8663, Bass 8690, Baxter 8695, Carter 8752, CH 8759, Coastal 8768, Cockrell 8770, Community 8774, Community 8776, Community 8777, Dallas 8795, Embrey 8828, Favrot 8842, Frees 8857, Genecov 8862, Hillcrest 8909, Hoblitzelle 8912, King 8959, Kronkosky 8970, Lightner 8985, McDermott 9013, Meadows 9019, Moody 9033, Orsinger 9073, Permian 9091, San Antonio 9148, Sterling 9203, Stevens 9205, Turner 9243, Wright 9293
Utah: Eccles 9320
Virginia: AMERIGROUP 9383, Arlington 9384, Beazley 9391, Community 9410, Community 9411, **Genworth 9441**, Lynchburg 9474, Suffolk 9538, Williamsburg 9558
Washington: Avista 9576, Community 9604, Glaser 9629, Harvest 9642, Inland 9650, Murdock 9689, Norcliffe 9693, Tacoma 9750, Yakima 9767
Wisconsin: Community 9832, Green Bay 9854, Keller 9878, La Crosse 9889, Madison 9897, McBeath 9901, Milwaukee 9907, Oshkosh 9916, Racine 9924, Stock 9953, West 9967
Wyoming: McMurry 9986

Aging, centers/services

Alabama: Community 21, Community 24, Community 25, Mitchell 54, Walker 74
Alaska: Rasmuson 89
Arizona: Piper 152
Arkansas: Wal-Mart 210
California: Anaheim 239, Atkinson 265, Auen 269, Black 317, Bothin 331, California 365, California 368, Cathay 385, Doelger 472, Doheny 473, Edelstein 494, Gellert 568, Gogian 598, Gross 629, Hale 645, Harden 654, Lytel 860, **McConnell 898**, Parsons 1013, Placer 1039, Ross 1090, Sacramento 1103, San Francisco 1109, Santa Barbara 1116, Sonora 1198, **Vadasz 1275**, Van Nuys 1284
Colorado: El Pomar 1406, Gates 1418, Summit 1511
Connecticut: Community 1563, Community 1564, Community 1565, Connecticut 1566, Hartford 1609, Palmer 1666, Say 1689
Delaware: Crystal 1758, McDonald 1817, Reynolds 1849
District of Columbia: Cafritz 1890, Consumer 1894, Jones 1918, Lehrman 1924
Florida: Bank 1979, Community 2031, Community 2040, duPont 2074, Fireman 2096, Florman 2102, GiveWell 2123, Greenburg 2137, Gulf 2142, Moran 2243, NextEra 2251, Patterson 2260, Pinellas 2269, Selby 2316, Stein 2337, Tarrant 2352
Georgia: Callaway 2419, Community 2434, Hudgens 2486, Pitts 2529, Whitehead 2571, Woodruff 2579
Hawaii: Hawaii 2602, Hughes 2605, Wilcox 2621
Illinois: Allen 2656, Archer 2671, Chicago 2746, Community 2763, Eisenberg 2819, Evanston 2826, Field 2831, Keith 2952, Logan 2983, Omron 3063, **Retirement 3113**, **Rothschild 3124**, Siragusa 3162
Indiana: Adams 3253, Blue 3265, Central 3272, Community 3280, Elkhart 3298, Heritage 3321, Portland 3370
Iowa: Siouxland 3480
Kansas: Cooper 3503, Hutchinson 3521
Kentucky: Durr 3572
Louisiana: Baton Rouge 3613, Booth 3616, Community 3624
Maine: Maine 3698
Maryland: Community 3758, Community 3759, Fowler 3795, Hoffberger 3817, **Weinberg 3908**
Massachusetts: Boston 3956, Cape Cod 3973, Clipper 3987, Community 3992, Farnsworth 4043, Hall 4084, Hanover 4086, Institution 4108, Linn 4149, Wadleigh 4316, Worcester 4327
Michigan: Ann Arbor 4340, Fremont 4438, Gerstacker 4444, Hillsdale 4461, Prince 4525, Upjohn 4564
Minnesota: **Andersen 4601**, **Andersen 4602**, Mardag 4703, Rivers 4752, Rochester 4755, Stevens 4772, TEAM 4779, WCA 4795, Wedum 4796
Missouri: Truman 4996
Nebraska: Hirschfeld 5049, Lincoln 5063
Nevada: Caesars 5106, Fairweather 5118, Nevada 5134
New Hampshire: Foundation 5171
New Jersey: **GHH 5275**, Healthcare 5296, Hyde 5310, **Johnson 5329**, Laurie 5357, **Merck 5379**, OceanFirst 5394, **Ramapo 5419**, Tanzman 5476, Wallerstein 5493
New Mexico: Frost 5519, Maddox 5528, McCune 5529, PNM 5532, Santa Fe 5533
New York: Abrons 5546, Altman 5579, Auchincloss 5623, Benedict 5662, Brown 5720, BTMU 5724, Charina 5763, Community 5803, Community 5805, Community 5806, Coudert 5820, **Cummings 5832**, Dreyfus 5913, Gifford 6049, Grigg 6109, **Hartford 6144**, Kinney 6285, Moses 6511, New York 6544, New York 6546, Noble 6560, Silverman 6855, Spingold 6899, Tuttle 7014, van Ameringen 7023, Vidda 7030, Western 7078
North Carolina: Community 7181, Cumberland 7184, Foundation 7202, French 7203, Triangle 7328
North Dakota: North Dakota 7357, Stern 7360
Ohio: AK Steel 7366, Akron 7367, Bruening 7391, Cincinnati 7405, Cleveland 7406, Community 7415, Fairfield 7445, Greene 7474, Macy's 7552, Marietta 7557, McGregor 7564, Ohio 7599, Parker 7611, Richland 7630, Riley 7632, Schlink 7650, Schmidlapp 7651, Stark 7673, Toledo 7686, Youngstown 7723
Oklahoma: Lyon 7769, Oklahoma City 7781, Zarrow 7820
Oregon: Benton 7825, Macdonald 7866, Meyer 7870, Oregon 7876, PacifiCorp 7877, PGE 7881
Pennsylvania: Arcadia 7918, Century 7974, Connelly 7995, Dolfinger 8013, Fourjay 8047, Huston 8102, McLean 8169, Morris 8188, Pew 8220, Rossin 8256, Shaffer 8281, Smith 8288, Smith 8289, Smock 8290, Snee 8291, Trexler 8320, Wright 8347
Rhode Island: Gale 8397, Kimball 8410
South Carolina: Self 8496, Springs 8504
Tennessee: American 8528, Community 8550, Hart 8578
Texas: Abell 8650, Amarillo 8660, Anderson 8663, Anderson 8664, Bass 8690, Carter 8752, Coastal 8768, Communities 8773, Frees 8857, Hankamer 8890, Heavin 8898, Hillcrest 8909, Hoblitzelle 8912, Johnson 8941, King 8959, Levit 8982, Meadows 9019, San Antonio 9148, Smith 9180, Turner 9243, Woodforest 9290, Wright 9293, Young 9295
Utah: Eccles 9320

Agriculture

Agriculture, community food systems

Agriculture, farm bureaus/granges

Agriculture, farmlands

Agriculture, livestock issues

Agriculture, sustainable programs

Agriculture/food

Agriculture/food, alliance/advocacy

Agriculture/food, association

Agriculture/food, formal/general education

Agriculture/food, public education

Agriculture/food, public policy

Agriculture/food, reform

Agriculture/food, research

AIDS

AIDS research

Ohio: Cleveland 7406, Columbus 7411, Gund 7478, Macy's 7552, Stark 7673
Pennsylvania: Dolfinger 8013, Philadelphia 8221, Smith 8288
Texas: Meadows 9019, Moody 9033, San Antonio 9148, Sterling 9203
Washington: Norcliffe 9693, Pendleton 9703, Tacoma 9750

AIDS, people with

Alabama: Community 24, Kaul 43, Meyer 53
Arizona: Webb 174
California: Bickerstaff 313, Community 414, **Geffen 567**, Green 621, **Hilton 692**, Patron 1020, Ritts 1076, Small 1180, Taper 1237, Weingart 1307
Connecticut: Community 1562, Community 1563
Delaware: AEC 1735, **Raskob 1845**
District of Columbia: Cafritz 1890, Consumer 1894
Florida: duPont 2075, Fortin 2106, Miami 2238, Southwest 2327, Sylvester 2348
Georgia: Community 2432, Rich 2537
Illinois: Field 2831, Fry 2849, Siragusa 3162, Washington 3217
Indiana: Community 3281, Health 3317
Louisiana: Wilson 3671
Maryland: Abell 3712
Massachusetts: TJX 4308, Worcester 4327
Michigan: **Fisher 4423**
Minnesota: Bremer 4620, HRK 4677, Phillips 4741
Missouri: Saint Louis 4966
New Hampshire: Lindsay 5179
New Jersey: Danellie 5237, Fund 5270, Healthcare 5296, Hyde 5310, Kirby 5339, MCJ 5377
New Mexico: Santa Fe 5533
New York: **Ford 5994**, Haring 6133, New York 6546, **Open 6593**, Ritter 6712, **Sparkplug 6894**
North Carolina: Community 7180, North Carolina 7273, Robertson 7305
Ohio: Akron 7367, Levin 7539, Saint 7639, White 7715
Oklahoma: Hille 7759
Pennsylvania: Beneficial 7936, First 8041
Tennessee: Baptist 8533
Texas: Abell 8650, Dallas 8795, Embrey 8828, McDermott 9013, Sterling 9203
Utah: Eccles 9320
Washington: **Gates 9625**, Norcliffe 9693
Wisconsin: Cornerstone 9836, Green Bay 9854, Milwaukee 9907, Stock 9953

Alcoholism

California: Atkinson 265, Norris 971, Sacramento 1103, San Francisco 1109, Sierra 1163, Sonora 1198
Colorado: Daniels 1399
Connecticut: Palmer 1666
Georgia: **Hanley 2476**
Illinois: Community 2763
Iowa: Siouxland 3480
Maryland: **ABMRF 3714**
Minnesota: Ordean 4732
Nevada: Fairweather 5118
New Jersey: Borden 5209
New Mexico: McCune 5529, Santa Fe 5533
New York: Achelis 5549, Badgeley 5633, Monell 6497, O'Connor 6578, Western 7078
North Carolina: Triangle 7328
North Dakota: Stern 7360
Ohio: Coshocton 7421, Hamilton 7481, Murphy 7584, Woodruff 7721, Youngstown 7723
Pennsylvania: Connelly 7995, Dolfinger 8013, Stackpole 8295
Tennessee: Davis 8555
Texas: Coastal 8768, Franklin 8855, Hoblitzelle 8912, Meadows 9019, San Antonio 9148, Wright 9293
Utah: Eccles 9320
Vermont: Vermont 9375
Washington: Community 9604, Norcliffe 9693
Wisconsin: McBeath 9901

Allergies

Illinois: Bunning 2728

Allergies research

Maryland: **Sidgmore 3885**

ALS

California: Vickter 1289
Delaware: Duane 1771
New York: Barnett 5645, Tarica 6965

ALS research

Arizona: Fulton 113
California: Vickter 1289
Connecticut: Tow 1708
Kentucky: Roseman 3599
New York: Rosenfeld 6747
Oklahoma: Adams 7725

Alzheimer's disease

California: Hoag 696, Oakley 978, Shiley 1157, Smullin 1190
District of Columbia: Vradenburg 1954
Florida: Albert 1964, Esman 2088, Graff 2133, Lichtenberger 2214, Miami 2238
Georgia: Jones 2491
Illinois: McQueen 3018, Miller 3024
Indiana: Met 3353
Massachusetts: TJX 4308
Michigan: Bay 4344
Missouri: Orscheln 4951
Nevada: Caesars 5106
New Jersey: Evans 5254
New York: Goldman 6069, Johnson 6233, **MetLife 6479**, Parsons 6619
Ohio: Warmenhoven 7701
Pennsylvania: Mertz 8177
Texas: King 8959, Smith 9180
Virginia: **Genworth 9441**, Richmond 9521
Wisconsin: Bader 9810, Green Bay 9854

Alzheimer's disease research

California: Coates 408, Zander 1356
Colorado: Kaufmann 1436
Delaware: Rosenberg 1853
Florida: Goodes 2129, Morby 2244
Illinois: Miller 3024
Kentucky: Roseman 3599
Maryland: Dekelboum 3777
Massachusetts: Saltonstall 4254
Michigan: Dart 4388, **Erb 4415**
Mississippi: Chisholm 4818
New Jersey: Atkinson 5195
New York: Beene 5658, D'Agostino 5843, **MetLife 6479**, Neuwirth 6539
Oklahoma: Hille 7759
Pennsylvania: Sexauer 8280

American Red Cross

Arkansas: Wal-Mart 210
California: Coulter 433, GenCorp 569, Goldwyn 609, Hewlett 687, Keesal 777, Lucas 855, Meadowview 908, Nestle 965, Pacific 1003, Panda 1010, Perforce 1026, PG&E 1033, Ray 1058, Ross 1090, Sempra 1140, **Strauss 1223**, Synopsys 1232, Tanimura 1236, Tuffli 1266, Western 1315
Colorado: KBK 1437, **Western 1521**
Connecticut: Barnes 1542, Bob's 1548, O'Herron 1660
Florida: Bedford 1988, Bi-Lo 1996, Darden 2051, Do 2065, James 2169, Johnson 2172, Langford 2202, Lichtenberger 2214, May 2230, McKeen 2234, Rayonier 2281, Ryder 2302, Taylor 2354, Wollowick 2393
Georgia: Gaines 2466, Poindexter 2532, **UPS 2566**
Hawaii: Central 2595
Illinois: **Abbott 2649**, Aon 2667, Caterpillar 2738, Cox 2776, **Deere 2790**, Illinois 2934, Ingersoll 2935, JNT 2940, **Mondelez 3034**, **Motorola 3043**, Munson 3045, Omron 3063, Sprague 3172, United 3200, **Wrigley 3244**, **Zuhlke 3250**
Indiana: Anthem 3257, Bales 3261, **Lilly 3340**, Michigan 3354, OneAmerica 3364, Vectren 3394
Iowa: AEGON 3409, EMC 3428, Gilchrist 3432, GuideOne 3438
Kansas: Sprint 3549
Kentucky: Ventas 3605
Louisiana: Chambers 3621, Community 3624
Massachusetts: Institution 4108, Liberty 4145, Peters 4216, Remillard 4236, TJX 4308
Michigan: Chrysler 4366, Dana 4386, **DENSO 4395**, DTE 4410, General 4442, Johnson 4468, **Kellogg's 4475**, Perrigo 4521, Whirlpool 4583
Minnesota: Carlson 4629, CHS 4636, **Pentair 4739**, Valspar 4786
Mississippi: Mississippi 4839
Missouri: Anheuser 4853, Busch 4867, Commerce 4871, Cruse 4877, Emerson 4885, Interco 4914
Nebraska: Nelnet 5072, Scoular 5080
Nevada: Caesars 5106
New Jersey: Eisai 5249, Frankino 5267, Honickman 5303, Ingersoll-Rand 5314, **Johnson 5326**, Kresa 5350, **Merck 5379**
New York: **AIG 5563**, American 5587, **American 5588**, **Bristol 5711**, Coach 5790, **Credit 5826**, Dauman 5849, Diamond 5880, IFF 6206, **International 6211**, Johnson 6237, Kinney 6285, **M & T 6406**, **Moody's 6499**, Morgan 6507, Phillips 6637, Schmitt 6808, Solomon 6886
North Carolina: Delta 7191, Duke 7196, Murphy 7270, Reynolds 7296, VF 7332
Ohio: AK Steel 7366, Andersons 7374, Christ 7402, Cliffs 7407, Dayton 7429, Dodero 7438, Dornette 7440, **Eaton 7442**, Fifth 7452, Nationwide 7587, Nonneman 7593, Ohio 7599, Samaritan 7642, Western 7710
Oklahoma: Gaylord 7753
Pennsylvania: **ACE 7905**, **Alcoa 7908**, Ametek 7913, Armstrong 7922, Bayer 7932, CIGNA 7981, Dickson 8009, Eden 8021, Jackson 8110, Knipel 8130, MKM 8185, Pond 8231, **PPG 8235**, Sexauer 8280, Wilson 8341
Rhode Island: Swanson 8445
South Carolina: McKissick 8486, TSC 8506
South Dakota: Raft 8519, Robinson 8520
Tennessee: Beaman 8534, Regal 8622, Tennessee 8634
Texas: 80/20 8648, Bass 8690, BNSF 8706, **BP 8718**, Dean 8803, Kimberly 8957, Penney 9089, USAA 9245, Valero 9246, Wal 9254, WEDGE 9263
Virginia: Bangs-Russell 9386, Chiaramonte 9407, Fredericksburg 9436, SunTrust 9539, Universal 9548
Washington: PEMCO 9702, Plum 9704, REI 9713
West Virginia: Daywood 9774, Hess 9777
Wisconsin: Anthony 9806, **Baird 9811**, Jordan 9875, Northwestern 9914, Windhover 9968

American studies

Massachusetts: Linn 4149

Anatomy (human)

Pennsylvania: Winstar 8342

Anesthesiology

New York: **Simons 6860**

Animal population control

California: **DJ & T 469**, **Duffield 486**
Colorado: Animal 1363
Indiana: Pulliam 3372
Louisiana: Lorio 3650

New York: Schnurmacher 6810
Texas: Chapman 8761

Animal welfare

Alabama: Community 21, Community 24, Mapp 47
Arizona: Day 105, McDonald 144, Morris 148, Tankersley 169
Arkansas: Arkansas 179
California: **Annenberg 245**, Blume 322, California 365, Clive 406, Community 414, Conte 427, Danford 448, Davidson 453, DeMille 459, Doelger 472, **Duffield 486**, Eagle 488, Eichenbaum 497, Foothills 537, Found 540, Gershman 575, Glide 595, Grand 619, Greenbaum 622, Greenberg 623, Harden 654, Hayward 665, Heigl 674, Issa 732, Lewis 837, Ludwick 856, Marcus 876, McBeth 894, Otter 999, Perforce 1026, Pfleger 1031, Pfleger 1032, Philanthropy 1035, Roberts 1080, Roberts 1081, Santa Barbara 1116, Schlinger 1123, Sonora 1198, Tosa 1259, Travers 1261, WWW 1349
Colorado: Animal 1363, Aspen 1367, Dornick 1403, Monfort 1464, Stuart 1509, Whispering 1522
Connecticut: Baker 1540, Community 1563, Community 1565, Huisking 1615, **October 1659**, Wiederhold 1721
Delaware: Bishop 1746, JP's 1793, **Memton 1819**, Parker 1829, Rossi 1854
District of Columbia: Bedford 1883
Florida: Beaver 1986, Community 2033, Community 2034, Community 2036, Corbett 2045, Darden 2051, Do 2065, Graff 2133, Huizenga 2165, Kislak 2187, Litowitz 2218, Martin 2229, McFarlane 2233, Miami 2238, Nanci's 2249, NextEra 2251, Pinellas 2269, Pope 2272, Scaife 2309, **SeaWorld 2315**, Southwest 2327
Georgia: Chambers 2425, Community 2435, Community 2436, Jordan 2492, Turner 2562
Hawaii: Schuler 2614
Idaho: Seagraves 2642, Wishnick 2646
Illinois: ArcelorMittal 2670, Brach 2712, Chao 2741, Community 2763, Energizer 2824, Levin 2978, Natural 3046, Payne 3073, Perkins 3075, Rice 3116, **Zuhlke 3250**
Indiana: Blue 3266, Community 3285, Fehsenfeld 3302, Parke 3366, Portland 3370, Pulliam 3372, Wayne 3400
Iowa: Gilchrist 3432, Wallace 3488
Kansas: Downing 3510, Morris 3537, **Shumaker 3546**
Kentucky: Blue 3560, Swope 3603
Maine: Sewall 3708
Massachusetts: Copeland 3994, Eaglemere 4029, Elfers 4033, Fels 4045, Josetta 4114, Raymond 4232
Michigan: Battle Creek 4343, Bay 4344, Dewey 4401, Dresner 4409, Duffy 4411, Hillsdale 4461, Korth 4478, **Moller 4506**, Two 4563, Vaughan 4573
Minnesota: Duluth 4649, Leuthold 4695, Minnesota 4715, Shiebler 4762
Mississippi: Morgan 4840
Missouri: Ballmann 4858, Brown 4862, Busch 4867, Nestle 4948
Nebraska: Ameritas 5023, Hitchcock 5050, Mapes 5066
Nevada: Castleman 5107, Hawkins 5123, Lied 5128, Nevada 5134
New Jersey: Brougher 5217, Brozowski 5218, Isdell 5318, James 5321, JMP 5324, Kish 5341, Levitt 5360, **Merck 5379**, Stadler 5465, Strauss 5470
New Mexico: Brindle 5516, Frost 5519, Hankins 5521, McCune 5529, **Thaw 5534**
New York: **Abraham 5545**, Adirondack 5556, Androcles 5599, Animal 5601, Arnhold 5614, Baird 5636, Bass 5650, **Bobst 5690**, Brunckhorst 5723, Butler 5733, Community 5804, Community 5808, DeGeorge 5867, East 5926, **Frankenberg 6009**, Freed 6011, Geary 6037, Goldberg 6061, Johnson 6233, Kaufman 6259, Malkin 6422, Marcus 6428, Monell 6497, Neu 6537, O'Connor 6578, Panaphil 6612, Park 6615, Petrie 6631, Roberts 6717, Sarofim 6797, Schiff 6805, Sidewalk 6852, Stanton 6908, Stringer 6935, Vidda 7030, Winley 7091, **Woodshouse 7102**
North Carolina: Capital 7171, Plansoen 7286, Simpson 7312, Triangle 7328
Ohio: American 7369, Columbus 7411, Dayton 7428, J. & H. 7504, Morrison 7580, Muskingum 7585, National 7586, Schiff 7649, Scott 7658
Oklahoma: Communities 7742, Kirkpatrick 7766
Pennsylvania: Allerton 7912, Arcadia 7918, Century 7974, Cestone 7975, Coulson 8000, Dolfinger 8013, EQT 8025, Giop 8057, Head 8081, Scranton 8275, Washington 8332, Woodtiger 8346
Rhode Island: Chamberlain 8369, Kimball 8410, Rhode Island 8429, Stone 8443, TriMix 8448
South Carolina: Waccamaw 8507
Tennessee: Aslan 8529, Carlton 8541, Community 8550
Texas: Austin 8676, Bridge 8724, Cailloux 8741, Cailloux 8742, Coastal 8768, Cowden 8782, Crowell 8791, Dahan 8794, Dallas 8795, Dodge 8810, El Paso 8825, Embrey 8828, Henderson 8901, Hollomon 8914, Kronkosky 8970, Lubbock 8994, McNutt 9018, Mitchell 9030, Moncrief 9031, O'Connor 9066, San Antonio 9148, Stevens 9205, Summerlee 9213, Temple 9223, Thompson 9233, Young 9295, Zeller 9298
Virginia: **Bosack 9395**, Community 9412, Kellar 9461, Robins 9524, Suffolk 9538, Wise 9560
Washington: Blue 9588, Community 9604, Dimmer 9610, **Glaser 9630**, Handsel 9638, Kitsap 9659, Rotella 9721, Suskin 9747, Tacoma 9750, Wrigley 9766
West Virginia: Hamilton, 9776, Parkersburg 9789
Wisconsin: Bemis 9815, Johnson 9874, Milwaukee 9907

Animals/wildlife

Alabama: Alabama 1, Altec 4, Vulcan 73, Webb 76
Arizona: Barrett 96, **Johnson 126**, Mooney 146, Raymond 155, Schultz 161, SVL 168
California: Bakar 278, **Beagle 291**, Bowman 335, **Duffield 486**, El Dorado 500, **Google 615**, Greenberg 623, Hennings 681, Laulhere 822, Lear 824, Meadowview 908, Michelson 923, Placer 1039, Roddenberry 1086, Scripps 1129, Shasta 1154, Sierra 1164, Valentine 1277, Warren 1298, Winnick 1333, Witter 1335
Colorado: Community 1392
Connecticut: Goergen 1595, JJJ 1618, Keefe 1619, Main 1634, Matthies 1639, Middlesex 1644, Niles 1655, Twenty-Seven 1712
Delaware: Chase 1753, Delaware 1765, Draper 1770, G.D.S 1782, Johnson 1790, Kendeda 1794, **Memton 1819**, Tapeats 1868
District of Columbia: **Dreyfus 1901**
Florida: Alexander 1965, **Barbour 1980**, Batchelor 1983, Bedford 1988, Clark 2022, Community 2038, Community 2040, Life 2215, Morby 2244, NextEra 2251, **SeaWorld 2315**
Georgia: Communities 2431, **Turner 2563**
Idaho: Idaho 2632
Illinois: Blair 2700, Cedar 2739, Coypu 2777, GKN 2865, Halligan 2886, Hamill 2888, Levin 2978, Makray 2994, McGraw 3015, Stewart 3178, Uihlein 3197
Indiana: Elkhart 3298, McAllister 3351, Orange 3365, Pulliam 3371, Putnam 3373, Unity 3393, Wells 3403
Iowa: Community 3422
Kansas: McPherson 3534
Louisiana: Community 3624, Wiener 3670
Maine: Libra 3696, Quimby 3705
Maryland: Colhoun 3755, Community 3759, Mid-Shore 3851
Massachusetts: Beveridge 3950, Cedar 3977, Harris 4089, Peters 4216, Sims/Maes 4274, Yawkey 4329
Michigan: Mosaic 4509, Sturgis 4550, Tuktawa 4560, Wasserman 4576
Minnesota: Cargill 4627, Leuthold 4695, Schmidt 4758, Xcel 4808
Missouri: Brown 4862, Buder 4864, Hagan 4904, Taylor 4987
Montana: Cross 5007, Whitefish 5019
Nebraska: Hubbard 5054, Lincoln 5063, Swanson 5088
Nevada: Kagi 5125, NV 5136, O'Bannon 5137, Tusher 5154
New Hampshire: Butler 5165, Haas 5174
New Jersey: Falcon 5256, Sheridan 5452
New York: 2A 5540, A Kinder 5542, **Abraham 5545**, Alexander 5569, Butler 5733, Community 5801, Donner 5899, Fanwood 5968, **Gould 6086**, Harriman 6137, Harris 6140, Lehman 6346, **Pfizer 6633**, Planning 6644, Selz 6830, Walter 7046, WSB 7105, Zucker 7127
North Carolina: Hunt 7237, Love 7258, McCausland 7262, North Carolina 7273, Winston-Salem 7340
North Dakota: Fargo 7351
Ohio: Community 7415, Fleming 7458, Goatie 7472, Maltz 7553, Springfield 7671, Tiffin 7682, Wellman 7709
Oklahoma: Chapman 7739
Oregon: Clark 7834, Hedinger 7851, Jubitz 7859, Kinsman 7860
Pennsylvania: Allerton 7912, Berks 7939, Hamer 8077, Jordan 8114, Lindback 8142
Rhode Island: Corning 8376, Textron 8446
South Carolina: Arkwright 8456, Central 8468, TSC 8506
Tennessee: Atticus 8531, Community 8550
Texas: Bass 8690, Cizik 8764, Communities 8773, Community 8774, Davidson 8797, Favrot 8842, Hershey 8904, Lesley 8980, Newfield 9060, Prentice 9107, Sanders 9152, Sangreal 9153, Waco 9251, Wildcat 9278
Utah: Park 9341
Washington: Bainbridge 9578, Inland 9650, Renton 9715, San Juan 9726, Seattle 9731
West Virginia: Ross 9792
Wisconsin: Wisconsin 9970
Wyoming: Community 9975

Animals/wildlife, association

California: Greenberg 623
Florida: Bay 1985
Massachusetts: Foundation 4058
North Carolina: Terry 7327

Animals/wildlife, bird preserves

Delaware: Reynolds 1849
Illinois: Bobolink 2707
Massachusetts: Gruben 4082
Mississippi: Walker 4849
New York: Ford 5993, Kelly 6271

Animals/wildlife, clubs

Pennsylvania: Feldman 8034

Animals/wildlife, endangered species

Arizona: McDonald 144
Maryland: **Shared 3882**
Nebraska: Abel 5021
New Jersey: Delano 5240
New York: **Arcus 5608**
North Carolina: Duke 7196
Rhode Island: **SVF 8444**
Texas: **ExxonMobil 8833**

Animals/wildlife, equal rights

Florida: Nanci's 2249

Animals/wildlife, fisheries

California: Campbell 373, Firedoll 528, Kern 780, Mead 907, **Packard 1006**, Patagonia.org 1017, **Waitt 1295**
District of Columbia: Munson 1933
Florida: **SeaWorld 2315**
Illinois: Martin 3003

Maine: Hannaford 3690
New York: Riedman 6706
Oregon: Burning 7827

Animals/wildlife, formal/general education
Louisiana: Lorio 3650

Animals/wildlife, preservation/protection
Alabama: Vulcan 73
California: Begin 299, **Foundation 542**, Glide 595, Hind 693, Hofmann 700, Hopper-Dean 704, McBean 893, McCaw 897, Menard 911, Mental 914, Roberts 1081, Sorensen 1200, Truckee 1263
Colorado: Hawley 1429
Connecticut: Baker 1540, Baldwin 1541, Foster 1588, Larsen 1624, Orchard 1663, Swordspoint 1705
Delaware: Fair 1780, Presto 1840
Florida: Batchelor 1983, Martin 2229, **SeaWorld 2315**, Spurlino 2330
Georgia: Chambers 2425, Sapelo 2546, **Thoresen 2557**, **Turner 2563**, Williams 2572
Illinois: Allegretti 2655, Appleby 2668, Bobolink 2707, Community 2763, Donnelley 2802, DuPage 2812, Grohne 2880, Henry 2906, Huntington 2928, Reed 3109, Tricord 3190
Indiana: Marshall 3348, Met 3353
Kansas: **Shumaker 3546**
Maine: Fore 3687, Quimby 3705, Sewall 3708
Maryland: Felburn 3789, Knapp 3825, **Shared 3882**
Massachusetts: Community 3992, **Conservation 3993**, Island 4109, Keane 4119, Peabody 4209, **Sweet 4302**, Yawkey 4328
Michigan: Devereaux 4397, Saddle 4530, Turner 4561
Minnesota: Robina 4753, W.M. 4790
Missouri: Nestle 4948
Nebraska: Mapes 5066
New Hampshire: Fuller 5172
New Jersey: Delano 5240, James 5322, Mushett 5388, Phipps 5406, Stadler 5465
New Mexico: McCune 5529, Santa Fe 5533
New York: Alexander 5569, Brunckhorst 5723, Chadwick 5760, **Claiborne 5783**, **Duke 5917**, **Engelhard 5954**, Ford 5993, **Frankenberg 6009**, Freed 6011, Gilman 6052, Goldberg 6061, Knox 6299, LaSalle 6331, Linden 6369, Marsh 6439, **Norcross 6564**, O'Connor 6578, Schenectady 6802, **Trust 7009**, Unterberg 7021, Vidda 7030, Winley 7091, Wolstencroft 7100
North Carolina: Bryan 7161, Cumberland 7184, Duke 7196, Richardson 7301, Triangle 7328
Ohio: CPB 7423, Muskingum 7585, Perkins 7615
Oklahoma: Kirkpatrick 7766
Pennsylvania: Arcadia 7918, Nichols 8197, Pew 8220, Schieffelin 8270, Wolf 8345, Woodtiger 8346
Rhode Island: Bafflin 8359, **SVF 8444**
South Dakota: Sioux Falls 8521
Tennessee: Carlton 8541, Jeniam 8587, Maddox 8603
Texas: Borick 8714, Hollomon 8914, Kleberg 8962, Kleberg 8963, Meadows 9019, Northen 9063, San Antonio 9148, Summerlee 9213
Utah: ALSAM 9302, My 9338
Virginia: **Sacharuna 9526**, Wrinkle 9562
Washington: **444S 9565**, Community 9604, Hughes 9648, Moccasin 9687, Norcliffe 9693, Raynier 9711, Rotella 9721, Wiancko 9761
Wyoming: Kerr 9981

Animals/wildlife, public education
Florida: **SeaWorld 2315**

Animals/wildlife, public policy
California: **Duffield 486**

Animals/wildlife, reform
California: **Duffield 486**

Animals/wildlife, research
Florida: **SeaWorld 2315**
Illinois: **Harder 2891**
New York: **Eppley 5957**
Texas: Kleberg 8963

Animals/wildlife, sanctuaries
California: Campbell 373, **Waitt 1295**
Florida: **SeaWorld 2315**
Illinois: Martin 3003
New York: **Arcus 5608**, Winley 7091
Ohio: Broussard 7389
Texas: Kronkosky 8970

Animals/wildlife, special services
California: Dickinson 466
Colorado: Stuart 1509
Michigan: Duffy 4411
Missouri: Nestle 4948
New York: **Arcus 5608**

Animals/wildlife, training
Arizona: **Johnson 126**
Minnesota: **Patterson 4738**
Missouri: Nestle 4948

Animals/wildlife, volunteer services
Minnesota: **Patterson 4738**

Anthropology/sociology
California: Getty 578
New York: **Guggenheim 6115**, **Wenner 7075**

Anti-slavery/human trafficking
California: **Google 615**

Aquariums
California: Breslauer-Soref 341, Keesal 777, Union 1271
Illinois: Bellebyron 2693, Fossett 2838, Haerther 2884, Souder 3168, Stewart 3178
Massachusetts: **Karp 4117**
Missouri: Hecker 4909
Nebraska: Union 5090
Pennsylvania: **PPG 8235**
Rhode Island: Buehler 8364

Art & music therapy
California: **Smith 1183**, Smith 1188
New York: Community 5803, Dannheisser 5847
Rhode Island: CVS 8379

Art history
California: **Getty 579**
Wyoming: Hessel 9980

Arthritis
Florida: Community 2034, Patterson 2260
Illinois: Nerenberg 3050
Minnesota: Wasie 4794
Nebraska: Boyer 5025
New Jersey: Hummingbird 5309
New York: Rantz 6678, Sculco 6821
Ohio: Anderson 7373, Marion 7558

Arthritis research
California: Treadwell 1262
Florida: Sontag 2325
Minnesota: Wasie 4794
Oklahoma: Foundation 7751

Arts
Alabama: Alabama 1, Altec 4, Anderson 5, BBVA 9, Bedsole 11, Bruno 15, Central 19, Comer 20, Community 21, Community 23, Community 24, Community 25, Crampton 26, Daniel 27, Dove 31, Energen 32, Finlay 33, Goodrich 36, Hearin 38, Hess 39, Hill 40, Kaul 43, Lowder 45, Mapp 47, May 48, McWane 51, Meyer 53, Nabers 56, Pleiad 58, Protective 59, Regions 61, Smith 66, Stephens 69, Thompson 70, Walker 74, Webb 76, Working 78
Alaska: Carr 83, CIRI 85, Rasmuson 89
Arizona: Arizona 92, Community 101, Dorrance 107, Flinn 111, Freeport-McMoRan 112, Green 117, Halle 118, Herberger 119, Hill 122, Jones 127, **Kieckhefer 129**, Levine 133, Long 137, Marco 139, Marshall 141, Mooney 146, Morris 148, Neely 149, Piper 152, Pivotal 153, Stardust 164, Stewart 166, Zuckerman 178
Arkansas: Arkansas 179, Cabe 182, Jonsson 192, Murphy 193, Ross 199, Wal-Mart 210
California: 1011 214, 2005 215, Ahmanson 222, Allergan 228, Alpert 230, **Alpert 231**, Altman 233, **Amado 235**, **Amgen 238**, Anaheim 239, Angell 244, **Annenberg 245**, Applied 249, Argyros 254, Atkinson 264, Attias 268, Auen 269, Autry 270, Ayrshire 276, Baker 280, Barker 282, Bartman 286, Bauer 287, **Bechtel 295**, Begin 299, Bell 300, Bergen 308, Berger 309, Berry 312, Bilger 314, Black 317, Bloomfield 319, Blum 321, Booth 326, Borchard 328, Bowes 333, Brenner 340, Brittingham 345, Broad 346, **Broad 347**, **Broccoli 350**, Buckhantz 354, Burnham 357, CAA 362, California 365, Campbell 372, Campini 374, **Capital 375**, Carolands 379, Carsey 380, Cathay 385, Caufield 386, Center 388, Chamberlin 389, Chartwell 397, Clif 405, Clive 406, **Clorox 407**, Community 414, Community 415, Community 416, Community 418, Community 419, Community 420, Connell 424, Conte 427, Copley 428, Cortopassi 430, Coyne 435, Daly 447, Danford 448, Davidow 452, Davis 455, Day 456, Day 457, Deutsch 462, Dickinson 466, Disney 467, Disney 468, Douglas 476, Draper 480, Drown 484, Ducommun 485, Durfee 487, East 490, East 491, Edgerton 495, Eichenbaum 497, El Dorado 500, Ellis 503, Engemann 506, Eucalyptus 510, Farallon 517, Farrell 519, Faucett 520, Field 522, Finley 527, Fleishhacker 534, Fremont 548, Fresno 549, Friedman 551, Friend 552, Galen 558, Gallo 561, Garland 565, Gasser 566, **Geffen 567**, Gensler 572, Gerbode 573, **Getty 579**, Gillespie 587, Glide 595, Gluck 596, Gold 599, Goldman 605, Goldsmith 608, Goldwyn 609, Good 612, **Google 615**, Gould 618, Grand 619, Green 621, Greene 625, Gross 629, Grout 630, Gruber 632, GSF 633, Guzik 639, Haas 642, Hammer 648, Harden 654, Harman 655, Harman 656, Harrington 657, Harris-Johnson 658, Hauptman 662, Heller 676, Hellman 677, Hench 679, Hewlett 686, Hills 691, Hitz 694, Hoag 697, Hoffman 699, Hollywood 701, Horwich 706, Humboldt 714, Hutton 718, Ishiyama 730, Israel 731, Jackson 737, Jameson 743, Janeway 745, JL 751, Katzenberg 769, Kaufman 770, Kayne 773, **Keck 774**, Keesal 777, Kelley 778, Kern 780, King 787, Kingsley 789, KLM 795, Koret 801, Kvamme 807, La 808, Lamond 817, Langendorf 819, Lantz 820, Laulhere 822, Lear 824, Lee 826, Lehrer 827, Leonetti/O'Connell 832, Lesher 833, Leslie 834, Littlefield 844, LLWW 845, Long 848, Los Altos 849, LS 851, Lucas 855, Ludwick 856, **Lund 857**, Lyons 859, Lytel 860, Marciano 873, Marcus 876, Marin 877, Markkula 879, Marmor 881, Martindale 883, **Mattel 886**, Mazza 890, McBean 893, McBeth 894, **McConnell 898**, Menard 911, Mental 914, **Mercer 917**, Mericos 918, Merrill 920, Middleton 924, Milias 925, Miller 929, Milstein 930, Moca 932, Mohn 934, Monterey 936, Mosher 945, Moss 946,

3383, Simon 3387, Steuben 3390, Tipton 3391, Transformation 3392, Unity 3393, Wabash 3396, Washington 3398, Wayne 3400, Wells 3403, White 3406, Whitley 3407

Iowa: AEGON 3409, Ahrens 3410, Aviva 3411, Bechtel 3412, Bechtel 3413, Brownell 3414, Butler 3415, Cedar Rapids 3417, Community 3419, Community 3420, Community 3422, Community 3423, Community 3424, Dahl 3425, EMC 3428, Gilchrist 3432, Hall-Perrine 3439, Hanson 3441, Helpenstell 3442, HNI 3443, Hubbell 3445, Hubbell 3446, Koehn 3453, Krause 3454, Kruidenier 3455, Kuyper 3456, Lee 3457, Levitt 3458, Maytag 3460, McElroy 3461, McIntyre 3462, Meredith 3463, Meredith 3464, Pella 3473, Poweshiek 3475, Principal 3476, **Rockwell 3477**, Ruan 3478, Siouxland 3480, South 3481, Tye 3484, Vogel 3487, Weathertop 3489

Kansas: Baughman 3493, Beach 3494, Cohen 3499, Cohen 3500, Cooper 3503, Douglas 3509, Dreiseszun 3512, Emporia 3514, Garvey 3516, Hartley 3519, Hutchinson 3521, INTRUST 3522, Kirk 3527, Koch 3528, Koch 3529, Mader 3531, Manhattan 3532, McCune 3533, McPherson 3534, Rice 3538, Salina 3540, Security 3544, Smoot 3548, Sprint 3549, Sunderland 3551, Topeka 3552, Wichita 3555

Kentucky: Augusta 3557, Barzun 3559, Blue 3560, Brown 3562, Brown 3564, Brown 3565, Community 3569, Community 3570, Durr 3572, Foundation 3575, Gheens 3577, Humana 3582, LG&E 3586, Owsley 3595, Preston 3596, Robinson 3598, Scripps 3600, Ventas 3605, Young 3607, Yum! 3608

Louisiana: Albemarle 3609, Azby 3611, Baton Rouge 3613, Beaird 3614, Booth 3616, Community 3624, Coughlin 3626, Deming 3627, Freeman 3636, Goldring 3638, Grigsby 3640, Heymann 3642, Jones 3645, Keller 3646, Lamar 3647, Libby-Dufour 3648, Lupin 3652, New Orleans 3656, RosaMary 3663, Taylor 3669, **Woldenberg 3672**, Zemurray 3675, Zigler 3676

Maine: Alfond 3678, Bangor 3680, Cianbro 3683, Cohen 3684, Elliotsville 3686, Glickman 3688, Hannaford 3690, King 3694, Libra 3696, Lunder 3697, Maine 3698, Morton 3701, Quimby 3705, **Walter 3711**

Maryland: Abell 3712, Abramson 3715, Adalman-Goodwin 3716, Angelos 3721, Ausherman 3723, Baker 3725, Baltimore 3726, **Blaustein 3735**, Blum 3737, Brown 3740, Bunting 3742, Casey 3746, Clark 3750, Clark 3751, Cohen 3753, Community 3757, Community 3758, Community 3759, Community 3760, Community 3761, Concordia 3763, Cordish 3764, Davis 3772, Delaplaine 3778, Fairchild 3788, Foundation 3794, France 3796, Freeman 3797, Goldsmith 3804, Gordon 3805, **Grace 3807**, Hahn 3811, Helena 3812, Henson 3814, Jacobsohn 3819, Klein 3824, Knott 3826, Legg 3828, Leidy 3830, Lerner 3831, Levitt 3832, Linehan 3834, Lockheed 3837, Marriott 3841, Marriott 3842, Mechanic 3846, Merrill 3847, Meyerhoff 3848, Mid-Shore 3851, Millstream 3852, **Morningstar 3854**, Myers 3856, Pohanka 3863, Price 3865, Rathmann 3867, Riepe 3869, Rosenberg 3873, Rouse 3877, Sampson 3878, Sheridan 3883, Shields 3884, Straus 3890, TKF 3896, Trawick 3898, Wasserman 3905, Wasserman 3906, Wright 3911

Massachusetts: A.M. 3912, Abrams 3914, **Alchemy 3920**, AMG 3924, Arbella 3926, Arzak 3927, Ausolus 3931, Babson 3933, Barker 3936, **Barr 3937**, Bayrd 3938, Beal 3940, Bergstrom 3944, Berkshire 3946, Berkshire 3948, Beveridge 3950, Black 3952, Boston 3956, Brookline 3962, Brooks 3963, Cabbadetus 3965, Cabot 3967, Cabot 3968, Cambridge 3971, Cambridge 3972, Cape Cod 3973, Cape Cod 3974, Casty 3976, Chafetz 3979, Chorus 3984, Cogan 3988, Community 3990, Community 3991, Community 3992, Crane 3998, Cutler 4006, Danversbank 4009, Davis 4011, Donahue 4023, Doran 4024, Dusky 4028, Elfers 4033, Ellsworth 4035, Essex 4039, Fallon 4041, Feigenbaum 4044, Filene 4047, Fletcher 4054, Foundation 4056, Fuller 4063, Golden 4073, Grayson 4078, Grimshaw 4079, Grinspoon 4080, Hamilton 4085, Hanover 4086, Harrington 4088, Hermann 4094, Hershey 4095, Highland 4098, Hopedale 4101, Inavale 4106, Institution 4108, Janey 4111, Jebediah 4112, Keane 4118, Krupp 4130, Ladd 4132, Ladera 4133, Leventhal 4141, Levy 4144, Liberty 4145, Linde 4147, Liswhit 4150, Lovett 4151, Lowell 4152, Lowell 4153, Lubin 4155, Lucretia 4156, Lurie 4158, Lynch 4159, Marks 4162, Massiah 4163, McDonnell 4166, McDonough 4167, **Middlecott 4174**, Milikowsky 4176, Miller 4177, Mittelman 4180, Nathan 4188, New England 4192, North 4194, OneWorld 4199, Ory 4200, Overly 4201, Palace 4203, Pappas 4204, Pappas 4205, Parker 4207, Perkin 4213, **Phillips 4219**, Poorvu 4224, Poss 4226, Proctor 4227, Rappaport 4230, Raymond 4232, Riley 4239, Rowland 4246, Roy 4247, Santander 4256, Saquish 4257, Sarnoff 4258, Schoen 4260, Schooner 4261, Schrafft 4263, Schwartz 4265, Shapiro 4267, Shaver 4269, Sidman 4273, Sims/Maes 4274, Smith 4277, Stamps 4281, Stare 4283, Stevens 4288, Stevens 4289, Stevenson 4290, Stoddard 4293, Stoico 4294, Sudbury 4299, Thompson 4307, Two 4313, Vincent 4315, Webster 4322, Windover 4324, Wood 4326, Worcester 4327, Yawkey 4328, Yawkey 4329

Michigan: Albion 4332, Allegan 4334, Ann Arbor 4340, Applebaum 4341, Barry 4342, Battle Creek 4343, Bay 4344, Berrien 4347, Besser 4349, Binda 4350, Blumenstein 4351, Boll 4352, Brown 4356, Charlevoix 4361, Chrysler 4366, Community 4369, Community 4370, Community 4371, Community 4372, Community 4373, Community 4374, Consumers 4376, Cook 4378, Cornucopia 4381, Cronin 4383, Cummings 4384, Dalton 4385, Dana 4386, Danto 4387, DeVos 4398, DeVos 4400, Dewey 4401, Dow 4406, Dow 4407, Dow 4408, Dresner 4409, DTE 4410, Duffy 4411, Dyer 4412, Eddy 4414, **Erb 4415**, Fabri 4416, Family 4418, Firestone 4422, **Fisher 4423**, Ford 4426, Ford 4427, Ford 4430, Frankel 4434, Fremont 4438, Frey 4440, General 4442, Gilmore 4445, Grand Haven 4446, Grand Rapids 4447, Grand 4448, Greenville 4452, Grosfeld 4453, Harding 4455, Hickman 4460, Hillsdale 4461, Hudson 4463, Hurst 4464, **Isabel 4466**, Jackson 4467, Johnston 4469, Jubilee 4470, **Kellogg's 4475**, Knight 4477, **Kresge 4479**, Lear 4482, Leighton 4484, Lenawee 4485, Manoogian 4491, Manoogian 4492, Mardigian 4494, Marquette 4495, Marshall 4496, Masco 4497, McGregor 4498, Midland 4502, Miller 4503, Miller 4504, Monroe 4507, Mosaic 4509, Mott 4511, Mount Pleasant 4512, Perrigo 4521, Petoskey 4522, Pokagon 4523, Polk 4524, Sage 4531, Saginaw 4532, Schalon 4534, Sebastian 4535, Shelden 4537, Skillman 4543, Steelcase 4547, Sturgis 4550, Towsley 4557, **Tubergen 4559**, Turner 4561, Upjohn 4564, Van 4570, Vaughan 4573, Walker 4575, Weatherwax 4577, Wenger 4581, Westerman 4582, Whirlpool 4583, Whiting 4584, Wickes 4585, Wilson 4589, Wolters 4592, Wolverine 4593

Minnesota: 3M 4597, AHS 4599, **Andersen 4601**, **Andersen 4602**, Andersen 4603, Athwin 4607, Beim 4609, Bigelow 4616, Butler 4622, Buuck 4623, Cargill 4627, Cargill 4628, Carolyn 4630, Central 4631, Ciresi 4637, Cox 4639, Criss 4640, Davis 4642, Driscoll 4648, Duluth 4649, Ecolab 4651, **Fuller 4659**, General 4661, Grand Rapids 4667, Greystone 4668, Griggs 4669, Hardenbergh 4672, Hubbard 4678, Jerome 4681, Jewett 4682, Johnson 4683, Kelley 4686, Land 4691, Leonard 4694, Lilly 4696, MacMillan 4700, Manitou 4701, Marbrook 4702, Mardag 4703, Martin 4704, McCarthy 4705, McGuire 4707, McKnight 4709, McVay 4711, **Medtronic 4712**, Melrose 4713, Minneapolis 4714, Minnesota 4716, Mitchell 4717, Musser 4724, Neilson 4725, Nicholson 4728, Northwest 4730, Oswald 4735, Piper 4743, Pohlad 4745, **Polaris 4746**, Prospect 4747, RBC 4748, Red Wing 4749, Regis 4750, Remick 4751, Rivers 4752, Robins 4754, Rochester 4755, Sabes 4756, Saint Paul 4757, Schmidt 4758, Securian 4761, Shiebler 4762, Sit 4764, Sit 4765, **St. Jude 4770**, Stepanek 4771, Stone 4773, Target 4776, TCF 4778, Travelers 4783, U.S. 4784, Valspar 4786, Weesner 4797, Weiser 4798, WEM 4799, Westcliff 4801, Winona 4806, Xcel 4808

Mississippi: Chisholm 4818, Community 4820, Feild 4825, Ford 4826, Gulf 4830, McLean 4835, Mississippi 4839, Regions 4843, Riley 4844, Risen 4845, Walker 4849

Missouri: Ameren 4851, Arch 4855, Baer 4856, Bellwether 4859, Brauer 4860, Bunge 4865, Burns 4866, Carter 4868, Centene 4870, Commerce 4871, Community 4872, Cox 4874, Dula 4881, Edison 4884, Emerson 4885, Engelhardt 4886, Express 4888, Ferring 4891, Fox 4892, **Francis 4893**, Gateway 4894, Gottlieb 4897, Graybar 4898, Grigg 4901, H & R 4902, Hall 4905, Hallmark 4906, Hauck 4908, Interco 4914, Jordan 4917, JSM 4918, Kansas 4920, Kauffman 4922, Kemper 4923, Kemper 4924, Kemper 4925, Kemper 4926, Kemper 4927, Laclede 4931, Lopata 4938, McDonnell 4940, **Monsanto 4945**, Musgrave 4947, Oppenstein 4950, Pershing 4953, Pillsbury 4955, Saint Louis 4966, Shaughnessy 4969, Shaw 4970, Smith 4974, Sosland 4975, Sosland 4977, Stern 4980, Steward 4981, Stupp 4983, Taylor 4988, Ten-Ten 4990, Trio 4994, Truman 4996, Whitaker 5001, World 5002, Wornall 5003

Montana: First 5009, Gilhousen 5011, Montana 5013, Oro 5014, Washington 5018, Whitefish 5019

Nebraska: Abbott 5020, Abel 5021, Ameritas 5023, Cooper 5031, Cope 5032, Davis 5034, Family 5038, Fremont 5039, Froehlich 5040, Grand Island 5044, Hamilton 5045, Hastings 5046, Hawks 5047, Hitchcock 5050, Holland 5051, Kearney 5055, Kiewit 5056, Kiewit 5057, Kind 5060, Lauritzen 5061, Lexington 5062, Lincoln 5063, Merrick 5067, Mid-Nebraska 5068, Omaha 5074, Phelps 5075, Scoular 5080, Sherwood 5081, Simon 5082, Slosburg 5083, Storz 5086, Swanson 5087, Weitz 5092, Woods 5096, York 5098

Nevada: Bretzlaff 5103, **Browning 5104**, Buck 5105, Community 5108, Fairweather 5118, Hawkins 5123, Lee 5127, Lied 5128, Mathewson 5131, Nevada 5134, NV 5136, Parasol 5138, Southwest 5149, Wells 5157, Wiegand 5159

New Hampshire: Bean 5164, Butler 5165, Cogswell 5167, **Fidelity 5170**, Fuller 5172, Hunt 5177, Johnson 5178, Mosaic 5181, New Hampshire 5182, Penates 5185, Putnam 5186, Quinlan 5187, Trust 5189

New Jersey: **Allen 5191**, Atlantic 5196, Atran 5197, Berger 5205, **Berrie 5206**, Borden 5209, Boye 5212, Brougher 5217, Bunbury 5220, Campbell 5223, Cape 5224, Cole 5231, Community 5232, Cooperman 5233, Cowles 5234, Dodge 5243, **Edison 5248**, Eisenberg 5250, Fairbanks 5255, Fenwick 5259, Firestone 5260, Frankino 5266, Friedman 5268, Goldberg 5279, Golden 5280, Grassmann 5281, Gulton 5284, Gund 5285, Harbourton 5293, Hawthorne 5295, Honickman 5303, Horizon 5305, Hummingbird 5309, Hyde 5310, Investors 5317, Isdell 5318, Isermann 5319, Jaffe 5320, James 5322, **Johnson 5326**, Karma 5331, Kerr 5338, Kirby 5339, Kirby 5340, Kovner 5348, L.A.W. 5352, L.F.H. 5353, Laurie 5357, Levin 5359, Levitt 5361, Lipman 5364, Mack 5366, Martini 5372, Mazer 5375, McGraw 5376, **Merck 5379**, Milano 5384, OceanFirst 5394, Parker 5401, Pincus 5407, Plummer 5409, Provident 5414, **Prudential 5415**, **Puffin 5417**, Roberts 5422, Rose 5425, Roth 5426, Scott 5445, Seiden 5448, Shen 5450, Silver 5458, Summit 5473, Syms 5475, Tavitian 5479, Union 5485, **Verizon 5489**, Weston 5499, Zurs 5510

New Mexico: Albuquerque 5511, Brindle 5516, Hankins 5521, **Lannan 5526**, McCune 5529, Phillips 5531,

Oklahoma: Adams 7725, American 7728, Barthelmes 7730, Bartlesville 7731, Bernsen 7733, Bovaird 7735, Chapman 7739, Communities 7742, Crawley 7746, Gaylord 7753, Gussman 7755, Harris 7757, Helmerich 7758, Jones 7762, Kerr 7764, Kirkpatrick 7766, Lobeck 7768, Lyon 7769, McCasland 7772, McGee 7774, McGill 7775, McMahon 7776, Oklahoma City 7781, Oklahoma 7782, ONEOK 7783, Oxley 7785, Records 7788, Sarkeys 7793, **Schusterman 7794**, Simmons 7796, Smith 7797, Stone 7801, Tandy 7803, Taubman 7804, Titus 7806, Viersen 7808, Westheimer 7812, Williams 7814, Zarrow 7818, Zarrow 7820, Zink 7821

Oregon: Autzen 7823, Bauman 7824, Benton 7825, Braemar 7826, Carpenter 7831, Chambers 7832, **Chiles 7833**, Clark 7834, Collins 7836, Crabby 7838, J.F.R. 7854, Jackson 7855, Jeld 7856, Kinsman 7860, Macdonald 7866, Meyer 7870, Miller 7871, Oregon 7876, PacifiCorp 7877, PGE 7881, Renaissance 7884, Schnitzer 7888, Swindells 7892, Templeton 7895, Tucker 7896, Tykeson 7897, Vibrant 7898, Woodard 7899, Zidell 7902

Pennsylvania: 1675 7903, Abessinio 7904, Adam 7906, Air 7907, Alderbaugh 7909, Ametek 7913, Aqua 7917, Arete 7919, Argus 7920, Armstrong 7921, Asplundh 7923, Ball 7927, Barra 7928, Bayer 7932, Beatty 7933, Beaver 7934, Berkman 7938, Berks 7939, Biesecker 7941, Bozzone 7948, Britton 7951, Brodsky 7952, Brossman 7954, Buncher 7957, Burke 7958, Carpenter 7967, Cassett 7969, Central 7971, Central 7972, Centre 7973, Century 7974, Cestone 7976, Chester 7979, Chosky 7980, Claneil 7982, Clapp 7983, Colket 7987, Community 7990, Community 7991, Connelly 7995, Coulson 8000, Crawford 8001, Davenport 8003, Degenstein 8008, Dolfinger 8013, Drumcliff 8016, DuPont 8020, Eden 8021, EQT 8025, Erie 8026, ESSA 8028, Federated 8033, Fels 8035, Fieldstone 8038, Fine 8039, First 8040, Fishman 8044, Foundation 8046, **Frick 8049**, Gerber 8054, Giant 8055, Giop 8057, Gitlin 8058, Glatfelter 8059, Graham 8065, Grass 8066, Grass 8068, Gray 8069, Greenfield 8071, Greenfield 8072, Hansen 8079, Head 8081, Hecht 8082, **Heinz 8083**, Heinz 8084, **Heinz 8085**, Heinz 8086, Hillman 8093, Hodge 8095, Hopwood 8096, Hoyt 8098, Hunt 8100, Hurd 8101, Huston 8102, Huston 8103, Independence 8107, Jerlyn 8112, Kavanagh 8118, Kelly 8119, Keystone 8122, Kim 8123, Kline 8129, Korman 8132, Lancaster 8135, Lehigh Valley 8136, Lenfest 8137, Lenfest 8138, Lindback 8142, **Little 8145**, Lomax 8148, Lotman 8150, Lutron 8151, Luzerne 8152, Mandell 8153, Massey 8158, McCausland 8159, McCune 8161, McCutchen 8162, McFeely 8163, McKenna 8166, McKinney 8168, Miller 8180, Miller 8181, Miller 8183, Mine 8184, Morgan 8187, Mylan 8192, O-Parker 8204, Peirce 8215, Penn 8216, Penn 8217, Pew 8220, Philadelphia 8221, Pittsburgh 8228, PNC 8230, Poor 8232, **PPG 8235**, Rees 8245, Roberts 8250, Roberts 8251, Rosenstiel 8254, Ross 8255, Rossin 8256, Rubin 8257, Russell 8258, Saint 8260, Saligman 8261, Scheller 8268, Schenck 8269, Schieffelin 8270, Scranton 8275, Seed 8278, Simmons 8285, Snee 8291, Snider 8292, Steinman 8299, Steinman 8300, Surgala 8309, Taylor 8311, Thornedge 8315, Toll 8317, Trexler 8320, United 8325, Vague 8326, Vanguard 8327, von Hess 8329, Washington 8332, West 8334, Willis 8340, Wilson 8341, Wyomissing 8350, York 8351

Rhode Island: Amica 8356, Biogen 8363, Carter 8368, Charlesmead 8371, Chisholm 8373, Daniels 8380, Elms 8387, Greene 8398, Harris 8402, Hoche-Scofield 8405, Kimball 8410, McAdams 8416, McNeil 8418, Nelson 8422, Newport 8423, Osborn 8426, Rhode Island 8429, Sharpe 8437, Textron 8446, TriMix 8448

South Carolina: Bruce 8461, Canal 8466, Central 8468, Coastal 8472, Community 8474, Community 8475, First 8477, Foothills 8478, Graham 8481, Hipp 8483, Inman 8485, Montgomery 8487, Patterson 8489, Phifer 8491, Self 8496, Smith 8498, Spartanburg 8501, TSC 8506, Waccamaw 8507, Yaschik 8509

South Dakota: Black 8511, Brenden-Mann 8513, Larson 8516, Raft 8519, Sioux Falls 8521, South Dakota 8522

Tennessee: Adams 8525, Atticus 8531, Benwood 8535, Bridgestone 8537, Briggs 8538, Carell 8540, Clayton 8547, Community 8549, Community 8550, Curb 8554, Day 8556, East 8560, Eastman 8561, Eskind 8563, First 8565, Formanek 8566, Frist 8568, Great 8575, Hamico 8576, Haslam 8580, Haslam 8581, HCA 8582, Hyde 8584, Jeniam 8587, Johnson 8588, Kharis 8591, Lyndhurst 8599, Martin 8605, Martin 8606, Massey 8607, Melkus 8609, Midler 8611, Msb 8612, Plough 8615, Poplar 8616, Regal 8622, Scheidt 8625, Stokely 8631, Temple 8633, Thompson 8636, Wallace 8642

Texas: Abell 8650, Amarillo 8660, Anchorage 8662, AT&T 8675, Austin 8676, **Baker 8679**, Barrow 8684, Bass 8686, Bass 8688, Bass 8689, Bass 8690, Beals, 8697, Beasley 8698, Bergman 8703, BNSF 8706, Bookout 8709, Booth 8711, Booth 8712, Booth 8713, Borick 8714, Bosarge 8715, Brass 8721, Bridwell 8726, Brown 8730, Brown 8731, Brown, 8732, Brownsville 8733, Burnett 8737, Carlson 8750, Carter 8752, Cash 8754, CFP 8758, Chapman 8761, Cizik 8764, Clayton 8765, Clements 8766, Coastal 8768, Coates 8769, Cockrell 8770, Collins 8771, Collins 8772, Communities 8773, Community 8774, Community 8775, Community 8776, Community 8777, Constantin 8778, Cowden 8782, Cowden 8783, Crane 8788, Cullen 8792, **Cultural 8793**, Dallas 8795, Day 8801, Dickson-Allen 8806, Dodge 8810, Dogwood 8811, Durham 8817, Eady 8818, East 8819, Eckel 8821, Edwards 8823, El Paso 8825, Embrey 8828, Eugene 8832, Ezcorp 8834, Fain 8835, Family 8836, Fasken 8839, Favrot 8842, Fish 8848, Fondren 8853, Glasscock 8867, Goldsbury 8868, Goodman 8870, Greater 8873, Guenther 8877, H.E.B. 8879, Haggerty 8881, Halsell 8885, Halsell 8886, Hamman 8888, Harris 8891, Hawn 8896, Henderson 8900, Herd 8902, Herzstein 8905, Hirsch 8910, Hoblitzelle 8912, **Houston 8916**, Houston 8917, Hudson 8919, Huffington 8920, Hunt 8922, Jamail 8929, Johnson 8940, Jones 8943, Jones 8944, Kelleher 8951, Kempner 8952, Kimberly 8957, Kinder 8958, King 8959, Klabzuba 8960, Kleberg 8962, Kodosky 8966, Kohl 8967, Lard 8972, Levit 8982, Liatis 8983, Link 8986, Littauer 8988, Lubbock 8994, Madison 8997, Mankoff 8998, Mayborn 9006, McCombs 9009, McDermott 9013, McIntyre 9016, McNair 9017, McNutt 9018, Meadows 9019, Meredith 9023, MFI 9025, Miller 9028, Moncrief 9031, Moody 9033, Murchison 9045, Napier 9050, Nightingale 9062, Northen 9063, NuStar 9065, O'Connor 9066, O'Donnell 9067, Once 9070, Orsinger 9073, Owen 9076, Owsley 9078, Partnership 9082, Penney 9089, Perkins 9090, Permian 9091, Perot 9093, Petrello 9096, Pollock 9103, Powell 9105, Prairie 9106, Priddy 9109, Prothro 9112, Pryor 9113, Questrom 9116, Rapoport 9122, Rea 9123, Reynolds 9127, Rhodes 9129, Richardson 9130, Roach 9132, Rogers 9137, Rogers 9138, Rogers 9139, Rosewood 9140, Saint 9144, San Angelo 9146, San Angelo 9147, San Antonio 9148, Scanlan 9156, Scharbauer 9157, Schollmaier 9159, Schutte 9160, Scott 9161, Scurlock 9162, Sharp 9167, Shelton 9169, Shield 9170, Sidhu 9172, Simmons 9173, Simmons 9174, **Six 9178**, Smith 9182, Smith 9184, Smith 9185, Smith 9186, Smith 9187, Stedman 9200, Stemmons 9201, Sterling 9203, Stern 9204, Stuart 9209, Stumberg 9210, Sturgis 9211, Susman 9216, Swinney 9218, Talkington 9219, Temple 9223, Terry 9224, Texas 9227, Tijerina, 9234, Tobin 9236, Turner 9242, TurningPoint 9244, USAA 9245, Valero 9246, Vaughan 9248, Waco 9251, Waggoner 9252, Wichita 9277, Wilson 9280, Wise 9285, Wood 9289, Wortham 9292, Wright 9293, Zachry 9296

Utah: Ashton 9304, Bastian 9306, Beesley 9307, Bertin 9308, Community 9311, Dee 9312, Doctorow 9314, Dumke 9315, Eccles 9319, Eccles 9320, Gillmor 9323, Hall 9324, Hemingway 9326, Lawson 9330, Meldrum 9333, Miller 9337, Park 9341, Patel 9343, Price 9346, Quinney 9347, Tanner 9352

Vermont: Evslin 9360, Lintilhac 9365, Mill 9367, National 9368, Vermont 9375, Waterwheel 9376

Virginia: Arlington 9384, Batten 9390, Birdsong 9393, Cabell 9397, Cameron 9398, Carrington, 9402, Charlottesville 9405, Community 9410, Community 9411, Community 9412, Community 9413, Community 9414, Community 9415, Community 9416, Dalis 9419, Dominion 9422, Easley 9424, Fife 9429, Foster 9432, Fralin 9433, Funger 9438, **Gannett 9439**, Golden 9443, Graham 9445, Guilford 9446, Gwathmey 9447, Hampton 9448, Herndon 9451, Johnson 9458, Kanter 9459, Kellar 9461, Lafayette 9465, Landmark 9467, Luminescence 9473, Lynchburg 9474, Malek 9475, Mars 9477, Massey 9478, MAXIMUS 9481, McGlothlin 9482, McGlothlin 9483, MeadWestvaco 9484, Memorial 9485, Millhiser 9486, Morgan, 9490, Newman 9493, Norfolk 9496, Olsson 9502, Owens 9503, Parsons 9504, Piedmont 9509, Rosenthal 9525, Smith 9533, Smith 9534, Suffolk 9538, SunTrust 9539, Taubman 9540, Titmus 9543, United 9546, Universal 9548, Volgenau 9549, Washington 9552, Weissberg 9554, Williamsburg 9559

Washington: Allen 9567, Ames 9570, Anders 9571, Bainbridge 9578, Barton 9581, Bates 9582, Biller 9586, Blakemore 9587, Blue 9588, Cheney 9598, Columbia 9602, Community 9603, Community 9604, Community 9605, Dimmer 9610, Eggnog 9613, Empire 9615, Everett 9616, Foster 9621, Fuchs 9624, Grays 9631, Green 9632, Greenstein 9633, **Haugland 9643**, Horizons 9645, Hughes 9648, Inland 9650, Intermec 9651, Kaphan 9657, Kitsap 9659, Lafromboise 9663, Lalji 9665, Lochland 9670, Loeb 9672, Moccasin 9687, Moraine 9688, Murdock 9689, Norcliffe 9693, Oki 9694, PACCAR 9698, **PAH 9699**, Plum 9704, Raisbeck 9709, Raven 9710, Raynier 9711, RealNetworks 9712, Renton 9715, Rice 9716, Riverstyx 9718, Safeco 9723, San Juan 9726, Sarkowsky 9727, Seattle 9731, Shirley 9734, Simonyi 9735, Spark 9741, Stevenson 9743, Sunbridge 9746, Swigert-Warren 9748, Tacoma 9750, True 9754, Whatcom 9759, Wheeler 9760, Wright 9765, Yakima 9767

West Virginia: Beckley 9769, Community 9773, Daywood 9774, Eastern 9775, Hamilton, 9776, Hollowell 9778, Kanawha 9780, Parkersburg 9789, Prichard 9791, Schenk 9793, Your 9799

Wisconsin: Acuity 9801, Alexander 9803, Alliant 9804, Anon 9805, Argosy 9808, **Baird 9811**, Baker 9812, Beloit 9814, Bemis 9815, **Bradley 9819**, Briggs 9822, Caxambas 9828, Charter 9829, Clark 9830, Cleary 9831, Community 9832, Community 9833, Community 9834, Community 9835, CUNA 9838, Eder 9840, Family 9842, Fond du Lac 9843, Fort 9845, Frautschi 9847, Frautschi 9848, Green Bay 9854, Harley 9859, Helfaer 9861, Herzfeld 9863, Iddings 9866, Incourage 9867, Johnson 9870, Johnson 9874, Joy 9876, Kikkoman 9881, Kohl 9883, Kohler 9884, Krause 9886, Kress 9887, La Crosse 9889, Ladish 9890, Ladish 9891, Lubar 9894, Lunda 9896, Madison 9897, Madison 9898, Marcus 9900, Mead 9902, Menasha 9903, Milwaukee 9907, MMG 9908, Nicholas 9913, Northwestern 9914, Oshkosh 9916, Oshkosh 9917, Peck 9918, Pettit 9919, Pick 9920, Posner 9922, Racine 9924, Rexnord 9932, Rockwell 9934, Rowland 9937, Ryan 9940, Sadoff 9941, **Schneider 9942**, Sensient 9943, Sentry 9944, Smith 9947, Soref 9948, St. Croix 9950, Steigleder 9952, U.S. 9957, Uihlein 9958, Waukesha 9965, West 9967, Windhover 9968, Wisconsin 9969, Wisconsin 9970

Wyoming: Community 9975, Cumming 9976, Hessel 9980, Liana 9982, McMurry 9986, Scott 9989, Seeley 9990, Storer 9992, Wyoming 9999

Arts councils

Alabama: Smith 66
California: Irvine 727
Delaware: Romill 1851
Florida: Brown 2004
Indiana: Community 3278
Louisiana: Woolf 3673
New Jersey: Sands 5435
North Carolina: Reynolds 7296
North Dakota: MDU 7354
Ohio: Park 7610
Oregon: PacifiCorp 7877
Pennsylvania: Hurd 8101
Tennessee: Eastman 8561
Texas: Jones 8945
Wisconsin: Wanek 9964

Arts education

Alabama: Stephens 69
Arkansas: **Windgate 213**
California: **Alpert 231**, **Burkle 355**, Eisner 499, **Getty 579**, Gluck 596, Goldwyn 609, Greenberg 624, Haas 642, Hale 645, Hench 679, JL 751, Parsons 1013, Smith 1184, Stotsenberg 1221, United 1272, **Wadhwani 1294**
Colorado: **Kinder 1439**
Connecticut: Hamm 1607, Kohn 1622
Delaware: **Birch 1744**, Wasily 1871
District of Columbia: Bernstein 1886
Florida: Becker 1987, Bush 2008, Peacock 2263
Georgia: Community 2432
Hawaii: Bank 2588
Illinois: Alphawood 2658, Community 2763, Eddema 2814, Edlis-Neeson 2815, Franke 2841, Guthman 2882, Jahn 2938, Lea 2970, Nichols 3054, Northern 3059, Oppenheimer 3066, REAM 3107, Seabury 3146, Stewart 3178, **Terra 3186**, Wilemal 3232, Wilson 3237
Indiana: Lincoln 3344
Iowa: **Rockwell 3477**, Siouxland 3480
Kentucky: Norton 3592, Opera 3593
Louisiana: Albemarle 3609, Fertel 3633
Maine: Horizon 3691
Maryland: **Blaustein 3735**, Hoffberger 3817, Legg 3828, Mead 3845
Massachusetts: Filene 4047, Klarman 4126, Stewart 4291
Michigan: Community 4369, Weatherwax 4577
Minnesota: Driscoll 4648, Ecolab 4651, McNeely 4710, **Pentair 4739**, Travelers 4783, U.S. 4784, Xcel 4808
Missouri: **Monsanto 4945**
Nebraska: Kimmel 5059
New Hampshire: Fuller 5172
New Jersey: Horizon 5305, Provident 5414, **Prudential 5415**, Victoria 5490
New Mexico: Santa Fe 5533
New York: Avery 5627, Bay 5652, BTMU 5724, Dannheisser 5847, **de Rothschild 5857**, **Dedalus 5864**, First 5979, Gelman 6041, Haring 6133, **Hearst 6155**, **Hearst 6156**, Heckscher 6157, **JPMorgan 6244**, Knox 6299, Lauder 6334, Loewe 6386, Milliken 6487, Mitsui 6491, Paestum 6608, Sharp 6839, **Summerfield 6944**, **Surdna 6947**, Tiffany 6978
North Carolina: Bergen 7149, Woodward 7344
Ohio: Cleveland 7406, Dorn 7439, Hershey 7487, IHS 7501, State 7674
Oklahoma: Kirkpatrick 7766
Oregon: PGE 7881
Pennsylvania: Baker 7926, Carpenter 7967, Eden 8021, England 8024, Grable 8064, Hurd 8101, PNC 8230, Presser 8236, von Hess 8329, Washington 8332
South Carolina: Arkwright 8456
Tennessee: HCA 8582, Wilson 8645
Texas: Bass 8690, Borick 8714, King 8959, Loose 8991, NuStar 9065, Wal 9254
Utah: Art 9303
Vermont: McKenzie 9366
Virginia: CarMax 9401, Hampton 9448
Washington: Harvest 9642, **Laird 9664**, Renton 9715, Tacoma 9750
West Virginia: Eastern 9775
Wisconsin: Harley 9859, Herzfeld 9863, Northwestern 9914
Wyoming: Hessel 9980, Kerr 9981

Arts, administration/regulation

Connecticut: **Albers 1532**
Oregon: Ford 7845
Tennessee: Jeniam 8587

Arts, alliance/advocacy

California: Parsons 1013
Georgia: Camp-Younts 2421
Illinois: Robinson 3122
Maryland: Baker 3725
New York: Diller 5884, Michaels 6482, O'Connor 6578, **Rockefeller 6723**, Rudin 6768, **Surdna 6947**
Washington: Rice 9716
Wisconsin: Stock 9953

Arts, artist's services

Alabama: Community 21
California: Community 420, San Francisco 1109
Connecticut: **Albers 1532**
Michigan: **Kresge 4479**
New York: **Warhol 7050**
Texas: Northen 9063

Arts, association

Florida: CNL 2025
New York: Bialkin 5673, Goldberg 6062, Loewe 6386, **Ohga 6581**, **Surdna 6947**
Ohio: Nord 7595, Ohio 7599, Ratner 7626
Pennsylvania: Hurd 8101
Rhode Island: Greene 8398
Tennessee: Jeniam 8587

Arts, cultural/ethnic awareness

Alabama: Alabama 1
Alaska: Aleut 80, CIRI 85, Doyon 86
Arizona: Freeport-McMoRan 112
California: **Berman 311**, **Christensen 399**, **Getty 579**, Irvine 727, **Packard 1006**, Panda 1010, Pell 1023, San Francisco 1109
Connecticut: Community 1562
District of Columbia: Coyne 1896
Florida: Community 2035, Goel 2127, Wells 2383
Hawaii: Lange 2609
Illinois: Omron 3063
Indiana: Central 3272, Lincoln 3344, Noble 3359, Old 3363, Pulliam 3372, Waterfield 3399
Iowa: Principal 3476
Kentucky: Community 3570
Massachusetts: **Grand 4076**, Morningside 4183
Michigan: Chrysler 4366, DTE 4410, Mott 4511, Whirlpool 4583
Minnesota: 3M 4597, HRK 4677, Marbrook 4702, **Medtronic 4712**, **Pentair 4739**, RBC 4748, Travelers 4783
Nebraska: Lincoln 5063
Nevada: NV 5136
New Jersey: Horizon 5305, **Hovnanian 5306**, Koguan 5346
New York: American 5587, Assael 5620, **Hearst 6155**, **Hearst 6156**, Pope 6653, **Rockefeller 6723**, **Rubin 6765**, Shoreland 6847, Steinberg 6920, Sumitomo 6943, **Surdna 6947**, **Trace 7003**, Warburg 7048
North Carolina: Foundation 7202
Ohio: American 7368, Nordson 7596, **OMNOVA 7601**, Partridge 7612, Tiffin 7682
Oklahoma: Kirkpatrick 7766
Oregon: PacifiCorp 7877
Pennsylvania: Argus 7920, Benter 7937, Berks 7939, EQT 8025, Federated 8033, Hurd 8101, Pittsburgh 8228
Rhode Island: **Dorot 8384**
Tennessee: Nissan 8613
Texas: Kleinheinz 8964, **Levant 8981**, **Paloheimo 9080**, WEDGE 9263
Utah: Semnani 9350
Virginia: **Gannett 9439**
Washington: Miller 9685, PACCAR 9698, **Goodwin 9751**
Wisconsin: Green Bay 9854, Wisconsin 9970

Arts, equal rights

Iowa: Principal 3476
Minnesota: Xcel 4808
Pennsylvania: **PPG 8235**

Arts, ethics

Minnesota: Evert 4655

Arts, folk arts

California: Irvine 727
Pennsylvania: Pasquerilla 8213
Texas: Morgan 9038
Washington: Yakima 9767

Arts, formal/general education

California: Aroha 260, Field 523
Florida: Burns 2006
Louisiana: Community 3624
Maryland: Cohen 3752
Massachusetts: Abrams 3914
Michigan: Webber 4578
Minnesota: HRK 4677
New Jersey: Johnson 5328, Point 5410
New York: Schapiro 6801
Oklahoma: Simmons 7796
Oregon: Esco 7841
Washington: McMillen 9681

Arts, fund raising/fund distribution

Ohio: Oliver 7600
Texas: Tobin 9236
Virginia: Lafayette 9465

Arts, government agencies

Alabama: Finlay 33

Arts, information services

Connecticut: **Albers 1532**

Arts, management/technical assistance

Connecticut: **Albers 1532**
New Jersey: Johnson 5328

Arts, multipurpose centers/programs

California: Epstein 509, Frank 544, Green 621, Irvine 727
Colorado: Gates 1418
Connecticut: Community 1562
Florida: Columbus 2030, James 2169, Johnson 2173, Miami 2238
Illinois: Hoogland 2920, **Terra 3186**
Kansas: Downing 3510
Louisiana: Franks 3634

Maine: Quimby 3705
Maryland: Levitt 3832
Massachusetts: Mannion 4161, Peabody 4209
Minnesota: McGuire 4707, Stone 4773, U.S. 4784, Winona 4806
Nebraska: Linder 5064
Nevada: Mallory 5129
New Jersey: Wilf 5504
New York: Levy 6364, Nuhn 6572, Plant 6645, Riggio 6709, Windmill 7089
Ohio: Dorn 7439
Oregon: Schnitzer 7887
Pennsylvania: Hurd 8101, Piper 8227
Texas: Doss 8812, Kronkosky 8970, Still 9207, Tucker 9241
Utah: Art 9303
Wisconsin: Kohler 9885, RDK 9928

Arts, public education
Connecticut: **Albers 1532**
Kansas: **Shumaker 3546**
Tennessee: Tucker 8638

Arts, public policy
New Jersey: Atlantic 5196

Arts, research
California: **Getty 579**
Connecticut: **Albers 1532**
New York: **Dedalus 5864**, Rose 6734

Arts, services
California: Knapp 796, Parsons 1013
Connecticut: **Albers 1532**
Illinois: Morrison 3037

Arts, single organization support
California: James 742, Zellerbach 1358
Connecticut: **Albers 1532**
Illinois: **Zuhlke 3250**
Louisiana: Community 3624
Minnesota: HRK 4677
New Jersey: Atlantic 5196
New York: 291 5539, First 5979, Parsons 6619
Pennsylvania: Hurd 8101
Wisconsin: Frautschi 9848

Arts, volunteer services
Pennsylvania: Hurd 8101

Asians/Pacific Islanders
Alabama: Community 24, Kaul 43
Arizona: Webb 174
California: Atkinson 265, California 365, California 368, Community 414, Cowell 434, East 490, Fleishhacker 534, Gerbode 573, Lesher 833, Panda 1010, Small 1180, **Sun 1227**, Taper 1237, Weingart 1307
Connecticut: Community 1562
Delaware: **Raskob 1845**
District of Columbia: Cafritz 1890, **CityBridge 1892**, **Union 1953**
Florida: Chia 2021
Illinois: Allstate 2657, Chicago 2746, Fry 2849
Indiana: **Lumina 3345**
Iowa: Siouxland 3480
Maryland: **Hughes 3818**
Massachusetts: Hyams 4103
Michigan: Chrysler 4366, Grand Rapids 4447, **Kellogg 4474**
Minnesota: Bremer 4620, Minneapolis 4714, Phillips 4741
Nebraska: Woods 5096
New Hampshire: Lindsay 5179
New Jersey: **Allen 5191**
New Mexico: Santa Fe 5533
New York: **Ford 5994**, **MetLife 6479**, **Noyes 6571**, **Sparkplug 6894**
North Carolina: Community 7180, North Carolina 7273
Ohio: Community 7412, GAR 7465, O'Neill 7602, Parents 7608
Pennsylvania: Beneficial 7936, First 8041
Texas: Community 8777, Stern 9204
Washington: Norcliffe 9693
Wisconsin: Community 9835, La Crosse 9889, West 9967

Assistive technology
Massachusetts: Liberty 4145
Rhode Island: CVS 8379

Asthma
California: HealthCare 667
Connecticut: **GE 1591**
District of Columbia: **Merck 1929**
New Jersey: **Merck 5379**, **Verizon 5489**
Rhode Island: CVS 8379

Astronomy
Arizona: **Research 157**
California: **Las 821**
Montana: Edwards 5008

Athletics/sports, academies
California: **Easton 492**
Florida: Moskowitz 2247
Massachusetts: New 4189

Athletics/sports, amateur competition
Colorado: Aspen 1367

Athletics/sports, amateur leagues
California: **Foundation 543**, LA84 809, **Mattel 886**, Oakland 977
Colorado: Daniels 1399, M.D.C./Richmond 1450
Connecticut: Rockville 1682
Florida: Glazer 2124
Illinois: Abt 2651
Indiana: Finish 3303
Michigan: Alro 4336, **Kellogg's 4475**
Mississippi: C Spire 4817
Missouri: Centene 4870
New York: National 6528, New Yankee 6542, Truman 7007
Ohio: Parker 7611
Tennessee: First 8565, Hamico 8576, Memphis 8610
Texas: Jones 8943, Valero 9246
Wisconsin: Johnson 9874

Athletics/sports, baseball
California: Hofmann 700, Oakland 977
Florida: Copham 2044
Maryland: Legg 3828
Massachusetts: Davis 4010
Ohio: Ar-Hale 7376
Pennsylvania: ESSA 8028
Texas: Astros 8674
Wisconsin: Helfaer 9861

Athletics/sports, basketball
California: Anthony 246
Delaware: Singer 1859
Tennessee: Memphis 8610

Athletics/sports, equestrianism
California: Ellis 503, Lewis 837, McCarthy 896, Pfleger 1032
Florida: Carmichael 2011, Johnson 2173
Illinois: Hamill 2888, Roberts 3118
Michigan: Leighton 4484, Van 4570
Nebraska: Swanson 5088
New Hampshire: Mosaic 5181
New York: Fernleigh 5975
Ohio: Broussard 7389, Philips 7619
Oklahoma: Oxley 7785
Pennsylvania: Naylor 8194
Texas: 1687 8647, Dogwood 8811, Sand 9151

Athletics/sports, football
Florida: Glazer 2124
Illinois: Jordan 2945
Oregon: Stoller 7891

Athletics/sports, golf
Georgia: Masters 2514
Iowa: AEGON 3409
Maryland: Rembrandt 3868
New Jersey: Wishes 5506
New York: Fisher 5982, Reynolds 6694
Ohio: Wadsworth 7698
Texas: Cox 8785, NuStar 9065

Athletics/sports, Olympics
California: Keesal 777

Athletics/sports, professional leagues
Wisconsin: Stock 9953

Athletics/sports, racquet sports
Connecticut: Georgescu 1593
Georgia: Kennedy 2495
New York: Gordon 6082, O'Toole 6602, Walter 7046
Tennessee: Hamico 8576

Athletics/sports, school programs
California: **Easton 492**, Eisner 499, **Foundation 543**, Gifford 584, Sierra 1164, Zable 1355
Connecticut: DeLuca 1573, Provident 1677
Illinois: Martin 3003, Munson 3045
Maryland: Cupid 3769
North Carolina: Blue 7153
Ohio: Piqua 7620
Oklahoma: Ketchum 7765
Rhode Island: CVS 8379
Tennessee: Hamico 8576
Texas: Johnson 8940, McCombs 9009
Washington: Names 9690
West Virginia: Preservati 9790
Wisconsin: Bemis 9815

Athletics/sports, soccer
California: Perforce 1026
Maryland: Hendricks 3813
Pennsylvania: Poor 8232

Athletics/sports, Special Olympics
California: Anaheim 239, **Mattel 886**
Minnesota: NFC 4727, **Patterson 4738**, Robins 4754
Montana: Town 5016, Washington 5018
Texas: H.E.B. 8879, O'Quinn 9072

Athletics/sports, training
California: **Easton 492**, LA84 809
Indiana: Waterfield 3399

Texas: Moore 9034

Athletics/sports, water sports

California: Western 1315
Florida: Community 2036
Massachusetts: Wallace 4318
Michigan: **Kellogg's 4475**
New York: Mesdag 6478, Warnaco 7051
Ohio: Coshocton 7421
Oregon: Benton 7825
Wisconsin: Goldbach 9851

Athletics/sports, winter sports

California: Sharks 1153
Colorado: Vail 1518
Maine: Libra 3696
Massachusetts: Gross 4081
Minnesota: Hubbard 4678, Shiebler 4762
New York: National 6528, Reynolds 6694

Autism

California: Barry 284, Gogian 598
Connecticut: Cohen 1560
Florida: Gemcon 2118
Illinois: Norris 3058
Maryland: **Bearman 3728**
Massachusetts: Marks 4162
Minnesota: Luther 4698
New Jersey: Focus 5262, Healthcare 5296, Karma 5331
New York: Karmazin 6254, Kupferberg 6312, McCarthy 6456
Ohio: Warmenhoven 7701
Pennsylvania: FISA 8043
Texas: O'Quinn 9072

Autism research

California: JL 751
Connecticut: Berbecker 1545
Massachusetts: Marks 4162
New Jersey: Focus 5262
New York: Luckow 6399, Seaver 6825, Simons 6861
North Carolina: Ireland 7239
Pennsylvania: Allerton 7912, Mosi 8189
Tennessee: Thompson 8635
Texas: Higgins 8906

Big Brothers/Big Sisters

California: GSF 633, Jack 736, M & T 861, Melaleuca 909
Colorado: Libertygives 1448
Connecticut: Bob's 1548
Delaware: Stone 1863
Florida: Moran 2243
Georgia: **Coca 2428**
Illinois: Jackson 2937, Reed 3109
Iowa: Ruan 3478
Kansas: Capitol 3498, Sprint 3549
Minnesota: Carlson 4629
New Jersey: **Alcatel 5190**
New York: Alper 5576, **Credit 5826**, First 5979, Liu 6382, Weber 7059
Ohio: American 7368, Dayton 7429, Dorn 7439, Nationwide 7587
Pennsylvania: Comcast 7989, **Heinz 8083**, Sexauer 8280
Texas: Sumners 9214, Valero 9246
West Virginia: Prichard 9791
Wisconsin: CUNA 9838, Oshkosh 9917

Biology/life sciences

Arizona: Flinn 111
California: **Agilent 220**, **Agouron 221**, **Beckman 297**, **Christensen 399**, **Ellison 504**, **Glenn 594**, **Keck 774**, Pacific 1003, Stauffer 1214
Connecticut: Foster 1588
District of Columbia: Bernstein 1887
Florida: Maren 2227, **Whitehall 2385**
Illinois: Schwartz 3144
Maryland: **Hughes 3818**, Life 3833
Massachusetts: **Cabot 3966**, Island 4109, **Sweet 4302**
Michigan: Hillsdale 4461
Missouri: Kansas 4920
Nevada: Fairweather 5118, Wiegand 5159
New Jersey: **Allen 5191**, Balazs 5199, Banbury 5200
New York: CAMBR 5741, Chernow 5771, **Eppley 5957**, **Guggenheim 6115**, **Kade 6247**, Landau 6322, **Lasker 6333**, Levy 6364, **Mathers 6446**, McGonagle 6460, Newman 6553, O'Connor 6578, **Revson 6693**, Vetlesen 7027
North Carolina: **Burroughs 7164**
Ohio: Schlink 7650
Pennsylvania: Cotswold 7999, Pew 8220
Texas: Dunn 8816, Elkins 8826, Kleberg 8962
Washington: JRS 9656

Biomedicine

California: **Beckman 297**, **Broad 347**, **Ellison 504**, Sierra 1163
Connecticut: Rosenthal 1684
Florida: Coulter 2047
Iowa: Carver 3416
Louisiana: Booth 3616
Maryland: **Hughes 3818**
Nevada: Fairweather 5118
New Jersey: Kirby 5339, **Merck 5379**
New York: **Cummings 5832**, **Engelhard 5954**, **Eppley 5957**, **Kade 6247**, **Lasker 6333**, McGonagle 6460, Smith 6877
North Carolina: Van Houten 7330
Oregon: Collins 7837
Pennsylvania: DSF 8017, Nichols 8197, Pew 8220
Texas: Franklin 8855, Hill 8908
Utah: Eccles 9320
Virginia: Jeffress 9457
Washington: Norcliffe 9693
Wisconsin: McBeath 9901

Biomedicine research

California: **Ellison 504**, Merkin 919
District of Columbia: Kaye 1920, **Lounsbery 1926**
Florida: O'Keeffe 2254
Illinois: Mallinckrodt 2995
Louisiana: Schlieder 3665
Massachusetts: **Adelson 3919**
New York: New York 6544
Rhode Island: Wood 8452
Texas: Halsell 8886, Newman 9061
Virginia: Claws 9408
Washington: McKinstry 9680

Bisexual

California: Weingart 1307
Illinois: Allstate 2657
Michigan: Grand Rapids 4447

Blind/visually impaired

Alabama: Community 25, Kaul 43, Meyer 53
Arizona: **Johnson 126**, Webb 174
California: Bartman 286, Center 388, Colombo 413, Community 414, Danford 448, **Hilton 692**, Jackson 737, Kirchgessner 790, Lesher 833, Ludwick 856, McBeth 894, Monroe 935, Patron 1020, Rogers 1087, Sandy 1113, **Smith 1183**, Smith 1186, Taper 1237, Ullman 1269, Weingart 1307
Colorado: Hunter 1431, King 1440
Connecticut: Bissell 1547, Community 1562, **Ziegler 1731**
Delaware: **Raskob 1845**
District of Columbia: Aid 1879, Cafritz 1890, **Union 1953**
Florida: Garfield 2115, Greenburg 2137, Pinellas 2269, Southwest 2327, Thomas 2357, Watts 2380
Georgia: Franklin 2462, Rich 2537, **Thoresen 2557**
Illinois: Arthur 2673, Butler 2729, Chicago 2746, Cuneo 2783, Dryer 2808, Medlock 3020, Opler 3064, Perkins 3075, Siragusa 3162, Vollintine 3208
Indiana: Community 3281, Pulliam 3372
Kansas: Emporia 3514
Kentucky: Cralle 3571
Maryland: Adams 3718, **Bearman 3728**
Massachusetts: Baldwin 3934, JSJN 4115, Phillips 4217
Michigan: Chrysler 4366, Grand Rapids 4447, Molinello 4505
Minnesota: Bremer 4620
Missouri: Saint Louis 4966
Nebraska: Dunklau 5036
Nevada: Nevada 5134
New Hampshire: Lindsay 5179
New Jersey: Atkinson 5195, Hyde 5310, Wallerstein 5493
New York: Bass 5650, Blum 5686, Central 5756, Community 5803, D'Agostino 5843, deForest 5866, Hagedorn 6128, **Open 6593**, Puth 6668, Ritter 6712, **Ross 6754**, **Starr 6911**, Warner 7053
North Carolina: Community 7180, Cumberland 7184, North Carolina 7273
North Dakota: Leach 7353
Ohio: Anderson 7373, Cincinnati 7404, Fairfield 7445, Gund 7475, Licking 7540, O'Neill 7602, Spaulding 7670, Springfield 7671
Oklahoma: Hardesty 7756, Hille 7759
Oregon: Carpenter 7831
Pennsylvania: Beneficial 7936, Connelly 7995, Dolfinger 8013, First 8041, O'Toole 8207, Phoenixville 8223
Rhode Island: Stone 8443, Wood 8452
Texas: Abell 8650, Alcon 8655, Community 8774, Community 8777, Crowell 8791, Dallas 8795, Lyman 8995, McDermott 9013, Moore 9034
Utah: Eccles 9320
Vermont: Gibney 9362
Virginia: Memorial 9485
Washington: Norcliffe 9693, Roma 9719
West Virginia: Weisberg 9798
Wisconsin: Cornerstone 9836, Green Bay 9854, Helfaer 9861, Kellogg 9879, La Crosse 9889, Ladish 9890, Nicholas 9913, Stock 9953, West 9967

Botanical gardens

Arizona: Ottosen 150
California: Lantz 820, McCarthy 896, Schimmel 1122, **Smith 1189**, Union 1271
Connecticut: Steere 1701
Delaware: Mordecai 1820
Florida: Batchelor 1983, Chabraja 2016, DiMare 2064, Johnson 2172, Sherman 2318, Vanneck-Bailey 2370
Georgia: **Imlay 2487**, Reeder 2536
Illinois: **Astellas 2675**, Bellebyron 2693, Dickenson 2795, Froehlich 2848, **Goodman 2869**, Harris 2892, Illinois 2934, Kemper 2954, Lehmann 2972, Louis 2985, Regenstein 3111, Rice 3116, Sirius 3163
Iowa: Guernsey 3437, Weathertop 3489
Kentucky: Brown 3565
Maryland: Casey 3746
Massachusetts: McEvoy 4168, Stoddard 4293
Michigan: Meijer 4499
Minnesota: Davis 4642
Missouri: Bellwether 4859, Jordan 4917, Lichtenstein 4936, Lopata 4938
Nebraska: Union 5090
New Jersey: Antz 5192
New York: Butler 5733, Everett 5964, **Goldman 6064**, Goldman 6067, Hagedorn 6128, J. 6218, **Mitsubishi 6490**, Rose 6733, Schnurmacher 6810, Steinberg 6920, Widgeon 7081, Ziff 7121
North Carolina: Kimbrell 7249, Seven 7309
Ohio: Dornette 7440, Ferry 7451, Vesper 7695
Oklahoma: Miller 7778

Oregon: Salem 7885
Pennsylvania: Bernheim 7940, Blanchard 7943, Feldman 8034, Mine 8184
Rhode Island: Buehler 8364, Daniels 8380, Mercer 8419
Tennessee: Carell 8540, Msb 8612
Texas: Bass 8690, Waggoner 9252
Washington: Miller 9684, **Goodwin 9751**
Wisconsin: Heil 9860, West 9967
Wyoming: Niner 9987

Botanical/horticulture/landscape services

Missouri: **Monsanto 4945**
New York: Levy 6364, Tiffany 6978
Ohio: American 7369
Texas: Richardson 9131
Wisconsin: Harley 9859

Boy scouts

Alabama: Caring 18
California: AS&F 263, Deutsch 462, Freeberg 545, GSF 633, Halsell 647, Keesal 777, MacNaughton 868, Martin 882, Smith 1186, Tanimura 1236
Colorado: ProLogis 1485
Connecticut: Diebold 1574
District of Columbia: Forster 1905, Merriman 1930
Florida: Batchelor 1983, Brown 2004, CNL 2025, Lichtenberger 2214, Ryder 2302
Georgia: CLC 2426, Love 2508, Turner 2562
Illinois: Frechette 2844
Indiana: Met 3353, Weaver 3401
Iowa: HNI 3443
Kansas: Sprint 3549
Kentucky: Swope 3603
Maryland: Rosenberg 3874
Massachusetts: Bristol 3960
Michigan: Dow 4405, Lear 4482, Perrigo 4521
Minnesota: Sit 4765, Xcel 4808
Missouri: Centene 4870, Graybar 4898, Humphreys 4913, Musgrave 4947
Nebraska: Ameritas 5023, Boyer 5025, Scoular 5080
New Jersey: Scott 5445
New York: Landy 6324, National 6528
North Carolina: Belk 7148, Bolick 7155, Rasmuson 7293
Ohio: AK Steel 7366, Dayton 7429, Ohio 7599, Parker 7611, Schiewetz 7647, Western 7710
Oklahoma: Meinders 7777
Pennsylvania: Armstrong 7922, Benter 7937, ESSA 8028
South Carolina: Campbell 8464, TSC 8506
Tennessee: Adams 8526, Beaman 8534, Proctor 8617
Texas: BNSF 8706, Owen 9077, Puett 9114, Simmons 9173, Strake 9208, Valero 9246
Virginia: Moore 9489, Tickle 9542, United 9546
Washington: McKinstry 9680
Wisconsin: **Baird 9811**

Boys

Alabama: Comer 20, Community 24, Meyer 53
Arizona: Webb 174
California: California 368, Center 388, **Clorox 407**, Community 417, Cowell 434, Danford 448, Goldman 605, Gumbiner 636, **Hume 715**, Lesher 833, McMillen 905, Monroe 935, Patron 1020, Simpson 1173, Weingart 1307
Colorado: King 1440, Lipscomb 1449
Connecticut: Community 1562
Delaware: **Raskob 1845**
District of Columbia: **Union 1953**
Florida: Fortin 2106
Illinois: Chicago 2746, Evanston 2826, Fry 2849, Medlock 3020, Steans 3175, Tulsa 3194
Indiana: **Lilly 3342**
Kentucky: Cralle 3571
Maryland: Washington 3904
Massachusetts: Stevens 4289
Michigan: Chrysler 4366, Grand Rapids 4447
Minnesota: Bremer 4620, **O'Shaughnessy 4734**
Mississippi: Community 4821
Missouri: Saigh 4965
New Jersey: **Allen 5191**, Hyde 5310
New York: Altman 5579, Community 5802, Heckscher 6157, Hoerle 6180, Lenna 6352, **MetLife 6479**, O'Connor 6578, Ritter 6712, **Ross 6754**, Warner 7053
North Carolina: Community 7180
Ohio: Fairfield 7445, GAR 7465, Hershey 7487, O'Neill 7602, Parents 7608, St. Marys 7672
Oklahoma: Hardesty 7756, Hille 7759
Oregon: J.F.R. 7854
Pennsylvania: Beneficial 7936, Birmingham 7942, Heinz 8084, Pilgrim 8225
Tennessee: **Scarlett 8624**, Wilson 8646
Texas: Bass 8690, McDermott 9013, Moore 9034, Orsinger 9073, Rockwell 9135
Washington: **Gates 9625**, Norcliffe 9693
Wisconsin: Lakeview 9892, West 9967

Boys & girls clubs

Alabama: Lowe 46, Working 78
Arizona: Arizona 92, Click 100, Davis 104, Moreno 147
Arkansas: Bailey 180, Wal-Mart 210
California: AS&F 263, Bauer 287, Beaver 292, California 368, Doelger 472, Doheny 473, Dr. Bronners 479, Gap 563, Halsell 647, Heffernan 673, House 707, Issa 732, J & J 734, Jackson 737, Keesal 777, Laulhere 822, Macfarlane 865, Markkula 879, Munzer 955, Nestle 965, OneWest 985, Pacific 1002, Pacific 1004, Pacific 1005, Perforce 1026, Quest 1050, Rickey 1071, Samuelsson 1107, Schwab 1127, Sharks 1153, Teichert 1244, Ueberroth 1268, Warnack 1297, Witherbee 1334, WWW 1349
Colorado: Carson 1382, Libertygives 1448, Monfort 1464, ProLogis 1485
Connecticut: First 1584, McMahon 1642, Meriden 1643, Pitt 1675, Selander 1693
Delaware: Berkley 1741, Mordecai 1820, Presto 1840, Salah 1855, Schejola 1856
District of Columbia: Merriman 1930
Florida: Ansin 1969, Basham 1982, Becker 1987, Bi-Lo 1996, Darden 2051, Fortin 2105, Garfield 2115, Goodes 2129, Goodwin 2131, Henry 2154, Huizenga 2165, Johnson 2172, Lacy 2198, Martin 2229, McCann 2232, Rebozo 2282, Tupperware 2363, Walter 2375, Watts 2380
Georgia: Correll 2440, Franklin 2462, Grizzard 2474, Thunder 2558, Turner 2562, **UPS 2566**, Woodruff 2578
Illinois: Camp 2732, Chartered 2744, Donnelley 2801, EFS 2818, Energizer 2824, Goldschmidt 2867, Hobbs 2914, Illinois 2934, Jahn 2938, Katten 2951, Trio 3191, Ubben 3196
Indiana: Anthem 3257, Lilly 3343, Michigan 3354, National 3358
Iowa: Glazer 3434, Levitt 3458
Kansas: Capitol 3498, Sprint 3549
Kentucky: Young 3607
Louisiana: Community 3624
Maryland: Clark 3751, Community 3761, Davis 3772, Fletcher 3791, GEICO 3801
Massachusetts: Boston 3957, Bristol 3960, Demoulas 4014, Demoulas 4015, Duniry 4025, Eastern 4030, Edgerley 4031, Epker 4038, Foundation 4058, Harrington 4088, Institution 4108, JSJN 4115, Keane 4118, Knez 4127, Liberty 4145, Lovett 4151, Narada 4187, New England 4193, Staples 4282, Webster 4322
Michigan: Consumers 4376, Dana 4386, Dart 4388, Hickman 4460, Mackey 4489, **Micah 4501**, Mulder 4514, Whirlpool 4583
Minnesota: Best 4612, Deluxe 4644, Mitchell 4717, Opus 4731
Missouri: Centene 4870, Dierberg 4879, Hammons 4907, Interco 4914, Musgrave 4947, Nestle 4948, Waldheim 4997
Nebraska: Muchemore 5070, Union 5090, Werner 5094
Nevada: Mann 5130, Van Sickle 5155
New Jersey: Campbell 5223, **Crane 5235**, Gibson 5276, Holmes 5302, Katz 5332, Kish 5341, Lenzmeier 5358, Rose 5425
New York: Bahnik 5634, Baird 5636, Coudert 5820, Dauman 5849, DeGeorge 5867, Dunwalke 5921, Finneran 5978, First 5979, Goings 6059, Kellogg 6269, Knapp 6296, Knott 6298, Loeb 6384, McDonnell 6459, Milliken 6487, Mule 6513, New York 6548, Phillips 6637, Raether 6673, Turn 7012, Walter 7046, Wells 7073
North Carolina: Belk 7148, High Point 7231, Stewards 7322
Ohio: American 7368, Cliffs 7407, Dorn 7439, Nationwide 7587, Third 7681
Oklahoma: McCrory 7773, Puterbaugh 7786
Oregon: Autzen 7823, Esco 7841, J.F.R. 7854, Schnitzer 7887
Pennsylvania: Armstrong 7922, Briggs 7950, Comcast 7989, Quantitative 8241
South Carolina: McKissick 8486, Smith 8499
Tennessee: Adams 8526, Clayton 8547, Martin 8604, Memphis 8610, Regal 8622, Smith 8628, Temple 8633
Texas: Andras 8666, Astros 8674, BNSF 8706, De Llano 8802, Holthouse 8915, Jones 8943, Kimberly 8957, Mayborn 9006, Owen 9076, Patton 9084, Perkins 9090, Valero 9246, Wolslager 9288, Woodforest 9290
Virginia: Agena 9381, Batten 9388, Fredericksburg 9436, Hylton 9455, Reinhart 9517, Reynolds 9519, United 9546
Washington: Evertrust 9617, McIntyre 9679, McKinstry 9680, Names 9690, PEMCO 9702
Wisconsin: Alliant 9804, Anon 9805, **Baird 9811**, Briggs 9822, Brookhill 9824, CUNA 9838, Gordon 9853, Heil 9860, Incourage 9867, Kohl 9883, Kress 9887, Lakeview 9892, Northwestern 9914, Riordan 9933, Rockwell 9934, **Schneider 9942**, Sentry 9944, Soref 9948, Stock 9953, Wisconsin 9969, Zilber 9972
Wyoming: Zimmerman 10000

Boys clubs

California: Samuelsson 1107
Delaware: Eshelman 1776
Florida: Jenkins 2171
Georgia: Franklin 2462
Minnesota: Mooty 4719
New York: Widgeon 7081
Rhode Island: Chamberlain 8369, Kimball 8410, Osborn 8426
Texas: Bratton 8722
West Virginia: Prichard 9791

Brain disorders

Nevada: Ruvo 5145

Brain research

Arizona: Ivy 123
California: Case 383, Hillblom 690
Connecticut: Selander 1693
Florida: **McKnight 2235**, Sontag 2325
Massachusetts: **Adelson 3919**
Missouri: **McDonnell 4941**
Nevada: Mathewson 5131
New York: **Dana 5845**
Texas: McNair 9017

Breast cancer

California: HealthCare 667, Oakland 977, Perforce 1026, Valentine 1277
Connecticut: Lee 1626, McMahon 1642
Delaware: **AstraZeneca 1738**, Duane 1771
Illinois: Caterpillar 2738, Omron 3063
Maryland: **Bearman 3728**, GEICO 3801
Massachusetts: Arbella 3926, Boston 3957
Nevada: Shaheen 5148

New Jersey: Honickman 5303, Wall 5492
New York: Coach 5790, IFF 6206, PB 6621, **Polo 6651**, Tisch 6985, Warnaco 7051
North Carolina: 25th 7131, Belk 7148, Blue 7153
Ohio: Kroger 7531, Macy's 7552
Pennsylvania: CIGNA 7981, Fieldstone 8038
Texas: Carter 8753

Breast cancer research

Florida: **Lampert 2200**
Indiana: Miller 3355
Nevada: Shaheen 5148
New York: Goldstein 6076, Lauder 6334
Texas: McNair 9017, Smith 9185

Buddhism

California: McBean 893, Panda 1010, Paramitas 1011, Tanimura 1236, Yang 1352, **Zee 1357**
Illinois: Chao 2741
Maryland: Gorn 3806
Michigan: Ford 4425
Missouri: Pillsbury 4955
New Jersey: **Yin 5507**
New Mexico: Altman 5513
New York: **Tsadra 7010**
Washington: Almi 9569

Business school/education

Alabama: Energen 32, Mitchell 54
Alaska: CIRI 85
California: **Bechtel 295**, Copses 429, Halperin 646, Littlefield 844, **Pyott 1047**, Tuffli 1266, Union 1271
Colorado: Halton 1426
Connecticut: Allison 1535, Deloitte 1572, **GE 1591**, Jeffe 1617, O'Herron 1660, Richman 1680, Rosenthal 1684, Wiggins 1722
Illinois: Coleman 2759, Cressey 2779, Illinois 2934
Indiana: Community 3281, Steel 3389
Iowa: Principal 3476, United 3485
Kansas: Sprint 3549
Maine: Bangor 3680
Maryland: Macklin 3838
Massachusetts: Higgins 4096, Jordan 4113, Keane 4118, O'Donnell 4196, Sperling 4279
Michigan: Chrysler 4366, Comerica 4368, Consumers 4376, DTE 4410, Grand Haven 4446, Whirlpool 4583
Minnesota: 3M 4597, Deluxe 4644, McNeely 4710
Nebraska: Kimmel 5059
Nevada: Gabelli 5120, Wiegand 5159
New Hampshire: Penates 5185
New Jersey: Cooperman 5233, Friedman 5268, KPMG 5349
New Mexico: Frost 5519
New York: Charina 5763, Charina 5764, Foundation 5999, Kaufman 6259, Kopf 6302, **Moody's 6499**, O'Connor 6578, Pearson 6623, PLM 6647, Roepers 6726, Seven 6834, Statler 6913, Wiegers 7082
North Dakota: MDU 7354
Ohio: Broussard 7389, Fifth 7452, Morgan 7578, Stark 7673, Third 7681, Troy 7688, Western 7710
Oregon: **Intel 7853**, Woodard 7899
Pennsylvania: Haldeman 8076, United 8325
South Carolina: McKissick 8486
Texas: **A Glimmer 8649**, Abell 8650, Ed 8822, Fluor 8851, Franklin 8855, Hillcrest 8909, Lawrence 8973
Utah: Huntsman 9327
Virginia: Dominion 9422, Snead 9536, SunTrust 9539
Washington: Jones 9655, PACCAR 9698
Wisconsin: Baker 9812, Wisconsin 9970

Business/industry

Alabama: BBVA 9, Vulcan 73
Arizona: Freeport-McMoRan 112
California: **Avery 272**, eBay 493, **Flextronics 535**, Guess? 635, **Strauss 1223**
Colorado: **Western 1521**
Connecticut: Donchian 1576, People's 1671
Delaware: Sylvan 1867
Georgia: AGL 2400, Holder 2485
Illinois: Popular 3085
Indiana: **Cummins 3292**, Lincoln 3344
Iowa: AEGON 3409, EMC 3428
Maine: Bangor 3680
Michigan: Chrysler 4366, Comerica 4368, DTE 4410, General 4442
Minnesota: Graco 4666, Securian 4761, Xcel 4808
Mississippi: **Armstrong 4810**
New Jersey: Cole 5231, KPMG 5349, **Sanofi 5437**
New York: Central 5756, **Citi 5780**, Coach 5790, **Deutsche 5876**, NYSE 6573, Phillips 6637, TE 6966
North Carolina: Duke 7196
North Dakota: Scheels 7359
Ohio: Lincoln 7541, State 7674, Western 7710, Wolfe 7719
Oregon: **Lemelson 7865**
Pennsylvania: Ametek 7913, EQT 8025, PNC 8230
Tennessee: Bridgestone 8537, Eastman 8561
Texas: BNSF 8706, **ExxonMobil 8833**, Penney 9089, Texas 9227
Virginia: Dominion 9422, Norfolk 9496
Washington: PEMCO 9702
Wisconsin: Wisconsin 9969

Camp Fire

California: Reid 1060
Kansas: Sprint 3549
Texas: BNSF 8706, Carter 8753
Washington: PEMCO 9702

Cancer

Arizona: Ross 159
Arkansas: Fox 187, Riggs 196
California: Alpert 230, **Beckman 297**, Bickerstaff 313, Colombo 413, Curci 444, Davidow 451, Early 489, Frank 544, Genentech 571, Gross 629, Jaffe 741, James 742, Lee 826, McKesson 903, Milken 926, Neeley 963, Norris 971, Oakland 977, O'Connell 982, Outhwaite 1000, **Patel 1018**, San Francisco 1109, Shapiro 1152, Talbert 1233, White 1321, Wolfen 1338, Zander 1356
Colorado: Halton 1426, M.D.C./Richmond 1450
Connecticut: Barnes 1542, Bauer 1543, Bob's 1548, Gorab 1599, Kelly 1620, Robbins 1681
Delaware: **AstraZeneca 1738**, Davis 1762, Ortega 1828
District of Columbia: Stewart 1949
Florida: Albert 1964, Beaver 1986, Bi-Lo 1996, Clermont 2023, Cobb 2027, Community 2034, Duckwall 2069, Fireman 2096, Gerstner 2121, Greenburg 2137, Huizenga 2165, **Lampert 2200**, Lennar 2210, Lichtenberger 2214, Rothman 2298, Star 2335, Stein 2337, Vanneck-Bailey 2370
Georgia: Aflac 2399, Amos 2402, Colonial 2430, Georgia 2468
Hawaii: Buehner 2589, Schuler 2614
Illinois: Abt 2651, Andrew 2662, Atherton 2676, Blair 2699, Clapham 2750, Coleman 2759, Community 2763, Cox 2776, Fogelson 2836, Harrison 2895, Hospira 2921, **Kapoor 2950**, Katten 2951, Lea 2970, Medlock 3020, Oppenheimer 3065, Potter 3087, Shaw 3154, Waraich 3214
Indiana: Anthem 3257, Kosciusko 3335, **Lilly 3340**
Kansas: Dreiling 3511, Kelly 3526, **Lloyd 3530**, Security 3544
Louisiana: Booth 3616, Marshall 3653, Moffett 3655
Maine: Gorman 3689
Maryland: Decesaris 3775, **Ewing 3787**, GEICO 3801, Mirmiran 3853
Massachusetts: Boston 3957, Cedar 3977, Community 3992, Demoulas 4014, Kittredge 4124, Levine 4142, Lubin 4155, Morningside 4183, Sharf 4268, Sims/Maes 4274, Smith 4275, Wilderness 4323
Michigan: **Cooper-Standard 4380**, Dana 4386, Herrick 4459, **Pardee 4517**, Perrigo 4521, Spartan 4544, Van 4570, Whiting 4584, Wolverine 4593
Minnesota: **Medtronic 4712**, Sit 4765, Stepanek 4771, Total 4781, Wasie 4794
Mississippi: Ergon 4824, Mississippi 4839, Pruet 4842
Missouri: Hulston 4911, SunEdison 4985
Nevada: Fairweather 5118, Nevada 5134, Nova 5135, Pennington 5139
New Jersey: Benjamin 5204, Brozowski 5218, **Crane 5235**, Healthcare 5296, Horizon 5305, Hyde 5310, **IDT 5311**, Ingersoll-Rand 5314, **Johnson 5326**, L.F.H. 5353, Schecter 5439, Shen 5450, Tanzman 5476, Wall 5492
New Mexico: McCune 5529, Santa Fe 5533
New York: Alfiero 5570, Baldwin 5639, Belfer 5660, **Bobst 5690**, **Bristol 5711**, Carvel 5749, Crisp 5828, Dechman 5862, Dejana 5868, Diller 5884, Friedman 6019, Glickenhaus 6058, **Goldman 6066**, Goldman 6069, Grayer 6096, Hagedorn 6128, IFF 6206, **Jaffe 6222**, Johnson 6240, Kinney 6285, Lane 6325, Liu 6382, **Mayer 6449**, McGonagle 6460, Mys 6519, Naddisy 6520, National 6528, Neuwirth 6539, New York 6544, Nonna's 6563, **Olayan 6585**, Palette 6609, **Pfizer 6633**, Phillips 6637, Plum 6648, **Polo 6651**, Rizzuto 6714, Roepers 6726, Rosenthal 6749, Sabin 6775, Schwartz 6817, Select 6829, Singer 6862, Walsh 7045
North Carolina: Baxter 7142, Blue 7153, Bryan 7161, Gordon 7214, Oechsle 7278
Ohio: AK Steel 7366, BASF 7383, Cafaro 7397, Dorn 7439, **Eaton 7442**, IHS 7501, Jegs 7507, Park 7609, Western 7710
Oregon: Collins 7837
Pennsylvania: Ametek 7913, Bayer 7932, Fourjay 8047, Gitlin 8058, Highmark 8092, Kim 8123, Kimmel 8124, McCausland 8159, Miller 8180, Miller 8181, Nichols 8197, Ross 8255, Sexauer 8280, Snee 8291, Stein 8297, Strawbridge 8305
Rhode Island: Chamberlain 8369, Foster 8394, Freeman 8396, Osborn 8426
Tennessee: Davis 8555, Hart 8578, Hurlbut 8583, Johnson 8589, Regal 8622, Thompson 8635
Texas: Anadarko 8661, Arnold 8673, Astros 8674, Cox 8785, Dunn 8816, Edwards 8824, Franklin 8855, Guenther 8877, Hillcrest 8909, Justin 8947, Korenvaes 8969, Owen 9076, Penney 9089, San Antonio 9148, Sterling 9203, Weaver 9260, Wolff 9286, Zeller 9298
Virginia: Evans 9428, Lipman 9469, Malek 9475, Massey 9478, **Scheidel 9528**, SunTrust 9539, Titmus 9543, **Truland 9545**, Universal 9548
Washington: Moccasin 9687, Norcliffe 9693, Suskin 9747
Wisconsin: Acuity 9801, Northwestern 9914

Cancer research

Arizona: Ivy 123
Arkansas: Jonsson 192
California: Arbus 251, Bartman 286, **Beckman 297**, Burnham 357, Chambers 390, Cusenza 445, Davidow 451, Deutsch 462, Early 489, Eisenberg 498, Freidenrich 547, Goldhirsh-Yellin 603, Gross 629, Katzenberg 769, Maxfield 887, Merkin 919, Milken 926, Morton 943, Norris 971, Oxnard 1001, **Patel 1018**, Petersen 1029, Samuelsson 1107, Saw 1119, Swanson 1228, Tallen 1234
Colorado: Halton 1426, Kaufmann 1436
Connecticut: Bossidy 1551, Childs 1558, Tow 1708, Vranos 1718, Whittingham 1720
Delaware: Pere 1833, Schwartz 1857, Wasily 1871
District of Columbia: **San Giacomo 1945**
Florida: Amaturo 1966, Applebaum 1970, Diermeier 2063, Donaldson 2066, Egan 2082, Fredman 2108, Greenburg 2137, Paiko 2255, **Pariser 2258**, Rooms 2292
Georgia: Aflac 2399, **Thoresen 2557**
Hawaii: LGA 2611
Illinois: Bacca 2678, Blair 2699, Block 2701, Boyer 2711, Chaddick 2740, Coleman 2759, Community 2763, **Cornwell 2775**, Irwin 2936, **Kapoor 2950**,

Nerenberg 3050, Perritt 3077, Shaw 3154, Simmons 3159, Weinberg 3223, Wilson 3236, Zell 3247
Indiana: Walther 3397, Wayne 3400
Iowa: Gerdin 3430
Kansas: **Lloyd 3530**
Kentucky: Mt. 3590
Louisiana: Booth 3616
Maryland: Abramson 3715, Viragh 3902
Massachusetts: **Adelson 3919**, Grinspoon 4080, Gross 4081, Jordan 4113, Leaves 4139, Leventhal 4140, Redstone 4233, Shapiro 4267, Stoneman 4295
Michigan: Devereaux 4397, General 4442, Hickman 4460, Levy 4487, **Pardee 4517**
Minnesota: Cade 4625, Sabes 4756
Mississippi: McLean 4835
Missouri: **McDonnell 4941**
Nevada: Fairweather 5118, Nevada 5134, Nova 5135, O'Bannon 5137, Ruvo 5145, Wiegand 5159
New Hampshire: Byrne 5166
New Jersey: Banbury 5200, Cooperman 5233, Frankino 5266, Hope 5304, Ingersoll-Rand 5314, Kauffmann 5334, Kirby 5339, Mushett 5388, Snyder 5462, Stadler 5465, Summit 5473, Wagner 5491
New York: Alpern 5577, Baker 5638, Beene 5658, **Bristol 5711**, Demartini 5872, Diamond 5880, Diker 5883, IFF 6206, Island 6215, Jacoff 6220, Kaylie 6263, Lynch 6404, Mack 6412, Marron 6435, McGonagle 6460, Mnuchin 6494, Moore 6503, Mule 6513, Parsons 6619, **Philippe 6636**, Robbins 6715, Rosen 6741, Salomon 6785, **Saper 6794**, Schwartz 6819, SDA 6823, Shelter 6842, Thompson 6975, **Vital 7033**, **Wolfensohn 7098**
North Carolina: Bryan 7161, **Carlson 7172**, Gordon 7214, Plansoen 7286
Ohio: AK Steel 7366, CPB 7423, Haile, 7480, Jegs 7507, Partridge 7612, R.T. 7625, Warmenhoven 7701
Oregon: Collins 7837
Pennsylvania: Dickson 8009, Kimmel 8124, Nichols 8197, Pasquerilla 8213, Sand 8264, Scheller 8268, Seraph 8279, Smith 8288, Toll 8316, Tyler 8322
Rhode Island: Foster 8394, Freeman 8396
Tennessee: Davis 8555, Hurlbut 8583
Texas: Dunn 8816, Edwards 8824, Ellwood 8827, Franklin 8855, Hersh 8903, Hudson 8919, McNair 9017, **Mehta 9021**, O'Quinn 9072, QuadW 9115, San Antonio 9148, Shivers 9171, Simmons 9173, Smith 9185, Smith 9187, Sterling 9203, Stuart 9209, Tobin 9236, Tomerlin 9238, Zeller 9298
Utah: Eccles 9320
Virginia: Malek 9475, NewMarket 9494, Smithfield 9535, Titmus 9543
Washington: Anduin 9573, B&E 9577, Biller 9586, Giuliani 9628, Hughes 9648, Kuni 9662, Norcliffe 9693
Wisconsin: Frautschi 9847

Cancer, leukemia

Colorado: M.D.C./Richmond 1450
Florida: Beaver 1986
Illinois: Katten 2951
Missouri: SunEdison 4985
New Jersey: **Crane 5235**
New York: IFF 6206, Pomeroy 6652, Singer 6862
Ohio: AK Steel 7366
Virginia: Evans 9428

Cancer, leukemia research

California: Maxfield 887
Louisiana: Lupin 3652
Maryland: Orokawa 3860
New York: Diller 5884

Catholic agencies & churches

Alabama: Bruno 16, Bruno-Rumore 17
Alaska: Carr 83
Arizona: Anderson 90, Caris 99, Farrington 110, Halle 118, Hill 122, Moeller 145, Pocono 154
Arkansas: Nabholz 194, Sturgis 205
California: Achieving 218, Angell 244, Bauer 287, Burns 358, Burns 359, Cale 364, Caruso 382, Colombo 413, Connolly 425, Curci 443, Danford 448, Davies 454, Doheny 473, Gallo 559, Gallo 561, Hannon 650, Hannon 651, Hayden 663, Hope 702, J.A.N.S. 735, Jameson 743, KLM 795, Koontz 800, MacMurray 867, Martindale 883, McCullough 899, McDonald 901, Menard 911, Milias 925, Muller 953, Murphy 956, Philanthropy 1035, Rickey 1070, **Sangiacomo 1115**, Shea 1155, Shea 1156, Soda 1194, Specialty 1203, Steinmetz 1216, Valley 1280
Colorado: Fox 1412, Pema 1476, Saeman 1490, Schmitz 1493, Staley 1507
Connecticut: Eder 1577, Foley 1587, Goodnow 1598, Hoffman 1613, Huisking 1615, Link 1631, Martino 1637, Meriden 1643, O'Herron 1660, Straus 1702, Sullivan 1703
Delaware: **Birch 1744**, Johnson 1790, Laffey 1800, Mastronardi 1815, O'Neil 1826, Queally 1843, **Raskob 1845**, Rose 1852, Wasily 1871
District of Columbia: Bedford 1883, Rales 1942
Florida: Amaturo 1966, Baroco 1981, Bell 1990, Bradley 2001, Burton 2007, **Catholic 2014**, Demetree 2058, Do 2065, duPont 2074, Faigen 2089, Fortin 2106, Gerstner 2121, **Griffin 2138**, **Kazma 2179**, Kazma 2180, **Koch 2192**, LaMothe 2199, Leclerc 2208, Lewis 2212, Maren 2227, Martin 2228, McFarlane 2233, McKeen 2234, Morrison 2245, Sanders 2305, Welch 2382
Georgia: **Keough 2496**, Lewis 2502, Lowder 2509
Illinois: Ackermann 2652, Blair 2699, Brunner 2718, Clapham 2750, Corboy 2773, Cuneo 2783, Delany 2793, Gallagher 2854, Gavin 2860, Goodyear 2870, Heerey 2901, **Heisley 2902**, **Hofmann 2918**, Hudson 2923, Kensington 2957, Madigan 2992, Mazza 3007, McIntosh 3016, Morton 3040, Parmer 3069, Ryan 3130, Sangre 3134, Schreiber 3142, Smith 3164, Snite 3166, Stewart 3178, Tracy 3189, Walsh 3212
Indiana: Garatoni 3309, Hux 3325, Marten 3349
Iowa: Krause 3454, **Ochylski 3470**
Kansas: Miller 3535
Kentucky: Eckstein 3573, Fischer 3574
Louisiana: Booth 3616, Coughlin 3626, Diboll 3628, Dore' 3629, Lorio 3650, Peltier 3658, Pinhook 3660, Rispone 3662, Sanford 3664, Young 3674
Maine: Mulford 3702
Maryland: Bisciotti 3733, Bunting 3742, Bunting 3743, Clark 3750, Clark 3751, Davis 3771, Decesaris 3775, Knott 3826, Linehan 3834, O'Neil 3859, Quinn 3866, Van 3901
Massachusetts: Carney 3975, Cedar 3977, Duniry 4025, Flatley 4053, Lauring 4138, Lynch 4159, Rodgers 4242
Michigan: Cold 4367, Cracchiolo 4382, Legion 4483, Mackey 4489, Sage 4531, Secchia 4536, Stonisch 4548, Thewes 4554, Tracy 4558, Two 4563, Van Elslander 4569, Willmas 4587, Wolohan 4591
Minnesota: 1988 4596, A Better 4598, AHS 4599, Andreas 4605, **Better 4614**, Cade 4625, Christianson 4635, Ciresi 4637, Cloverfields 4638, Fiterman 4656, GHR 4664, Kopp 4688, Maas 4699, Manitou 4701, McGlynn 4706, Poepl 4744, Sieben 4763, Slaggie 4766
Missouri: Busch 4867, Dierberg 4879, Kienstra 4928, Ladner 4932, Lay 4934, McDonnell 4940, Orscheln 4951, Ravarino 4960, Schwartze 4968, Todd 4992, World 5002
Nebraska: Acklie 5022, Buckley 5026, Dillon 5035, Eagle 5037, Heider 5048, Ryan 5078, St. Anthony 5085, Werner 5094, Wirth 5095
Nevada: Engelstad 5117, Ruvo 5145
New Hampshire: Gifford 5173
New Jersey: Clare 5230, Family 5257, Frankino 5266, Grassmann 5281, Kelly 5335, L.F.H. 5353, Marcon 5369, Mohler 5386, Mosakowski 5387, Roberts 5423, Ruesch 5429, Sandy 5436, Union 5485
New York: Altman 5581, Chiaroscuro 5776, Curran 5835, Dolan 5895, **Doty 5902**, Dowling 5907, Dreams 5909, East 5925, Fearons, 5972, Finneran 5978, Gaisman 6031, Galasso 6032, Gillespie 6051, Gordon 6082, Gross 6110, Hansen 6130, Healey 6152, Heisman 6159, Hollyhock 6183, Hugoton 6194, Ingrassia 6208, Johnson 6237, Johnson 6238, Lee 6343, Link 6375, Longwell 6391, Luckow 6399, Lynch 6404, Maguire 6416, McCarthy 6454, Millbrook 6485, Moore 6505, Mozilo 6512, Naddisy 6520, O'Connor 6577, Pope 6653, **Porticus 6654**, Purchase 6667, Quick 6670, Riley 6710, Ritter 6712, RTS 6760, Rudin 6768, Santa 6792, Shelter 6842, Smith 6876, Steiniger 6924, Templeton 6969, Weir 7069, Young 7111
North Carolina: Adams 7133, Anonymous 7135, Baxter 7142, Kramer 7250, Luddy 7259, **Lynch 7260**, Murphy 7270, Odell 7277, Post 7289, Symmes 7325
North Dakota: Wanzek 7361
Ohio: Ar-Hale 7376, Bruening 7391, Burleigh 7395, Butler 7396, Cafaro 7397, Conway 7419, Gardner 7466, H.C.S. 7479, LaValley 7535, Lehner 7536, McBride 7562, Miller 7571, Nonneman 7593, Roggecora 7635, Smith 7666, Stefanski 7675, Trzcinski 7689, Twenty 7692, Warmenhoven 7701, Wohlgemuth 7718, Zembrodt 7724
Oklahoma: Brown 7737, Collins 7741, Grace 7754, McGill 7775, Robinson 7789, **Westerman 7811**
Oregon: **Eiting 7840**, John 7857, Salem 7885
Pennsylvania: Bozzone 7948, CentiMark 7970, Clayman 7984, Connelly 7995, Copernicus 7998, Donahue 8015, Eustace 8029, Falcone 8031, Franklin 8048, Hutton 8104, Jones 8113, Kavanagh 8118, Kim 8123, Ortenzio 8206, O'Toole 8207, Palumbo 8209, Pangborn 8211, Salvaggio 8263, Simon 8286, Stackpole 8295, Stine 8302
Rhode Island: Knoop 8411
South Carolina: Pfriem 8490
South Dakota: Dakota 8514, Hofer 8515
Tennessee: Carell 8540
Texas: Barrow 8684, Bass 8689, Benson 8702, Branch 8720, Brown, 8732, Cameron 8747, Coates 8769, Davis 8798, Davis 8800, Finger 8845, Gonsoulin 8869, Haggerty 8881, Hebert 8899, Kennedy 8953, Kinder 8958, Kleinheinz 8964, Lyons 8996, Mulva 9044, Owen 9075, Spec's 9195, Sterling 9203, Strake 9208, Terry 9224, Tucker 9241, Whalley 9272
Utah: ALSAM 9302, Meldrum 9333
Vermont: Pomerleau 9369
Virginia: **Bellarmin 9392**, Hirst 9453, **Loyola 9471**, Willett 9557
Washington: Honzel 9644, Lauzier 9667, Snyder 9739, Swigert-Warren 9748, T.E.W. 9749
Wisconsin: Bleser 9818, Goldbach 9851, Kohl 9883, Ladish 9891, Mercy 9905, Michels 9906, Reinhart 9930, Riordan 9933, Ryan 9940, **Wagner 9961**, Wanek 9963
Wyoming: Niner 9987

Catholic federated giving programs

Arizona: Hill 122
California: Burns 359, Gross 629, Hayden 663, Smet 1181
Colorado: Saeman 1490, Whispering 1522
Connecticut: O'Herron 1660, Straus 1702
Delaware: **Raskob 1845**
Florida: Amaturo 1966, **Griffin 2138**, **Kazma 2179**
Illinois: Ackermann 2652, Kensington 2957, Morton 3040
Maryland: Clark 3751, Linehan 3834, Van 3901
Minnesota: Ciresi 4637, Sieben 4763
Nevada: Lied 5128, Ruvo 5145
New Hampshire: Hopeman 5176
New Jersey: De Nicola 5239, Maher 5368
New York: Island 6215, Maguire 6416, McCarthy 6454, Ritter 6712, Steiniger 6924, Wegman 7061
North Carolina: **Lynch 7260**
Ohio: Ford 7459
Oklahoma: Warren 7809
Oregon: Glory 7847
Pennsylvania: Cochran 7985, Stine 8302
South Dakota: **Opus 8518**

Texas: Enrico 8831, Waggoner 9252
Utah: ALSAM 9302
Washington: Honzel 9644
Wisconsin: Ryan 9940

Cemeteries/burial services
Indiana: Parke 3366

Cerebral palsy
California: Fansler 516
Colorado: COPIC 1397
New Jersey: Tanzman 5476

Cerebral palsy research
California: Arbus 251

Charter schools
California: Applied 249, Fisher 532, Partners 1014, Quest 1050
Colorado: Charter 1387
Connecticut: People's 1671
Louisiana: Albemarle 3609, **Woldenberg 3672**
Massachusetts: Boston 3956
Michigan: Ford 4430, Skilling 4542
New Jersey: Newark 5390
New Mexico: PNM 5532
New York: Ward 7049
Ohio: Lincoln 7541, Lubrizol 7546
Texas: Brackenridge 8719, Maverick 9005
Wisconsin: CUNA 9838

Chemistry
Arizona: **Research 157**
California: **Agilent 220**, **Beckman 297**, **Keck 774**, Stauffer 1214
Florida: Rayonier 2281
Idaho: **Micron 2637**
Massachusetts: **Cabot 3966**
Michigan: **Dow 4404**
Nevada: Wiegand 5159
New Jersey: **Siemens 5454**
New York: **Dreyfus 5912**, **Eppley 5957**, **Kade 6247**
Ohio: BASF 7383, Lubrizol 7546
Pennsylvania: **PPG 8235**
Texas: Welch 9268
Virginia: Jeffress 9457

Child development, education
Alabama: Community 23
Arizona: Arizona 92
Arkansas: Walton 211
California: Atkinson 265, Atlas 266, Crail 437, Field 523, Gross 629, Mosse 948, Sacramento 1103, San Francisco 1109, Sierra 1163, Sonora 1198, Weingart 1307
Colorado: Chambers 1385, El Pomar 1406, Kaufmann 1436
Connecticut: Community 1564, Connecticut 1566, Fund 1589, Lego 1627, Rosenthal 1684
District of Columbia: Cafritz 1890, Jones 1918, Meyer 1931
Florida: Bank 1979, Community 2038, Henderson 2152, Selby 2316
Georgia: Whitehead 2571, WinShape 2577
Illinois: Chicago 2746, Community 2763, **Harris 2893**, Polk 3084, Seabury 3146
Indiana: Portland 3370
Iowa: Community 3423, McElroy 3461, Principal 3476, Siouxland 3480
Kansas: Beach 3494
Louisiana: Baton Rouge 3613, Booth 3616, Community 3624
Maryland: Abell 3712, Commonweal 3756, **England 3785**, Fowler 3795
Massachusetts: Boston 3956, Community 3991, Peabody 4210, Santander 4256
Michigan: Battle Creek 4343, Berrien 4347, Hillsdale 4461, Skillman 4543
Minnesota: Bigelow 4616, Blue 4618, Bremer 4620, Duluth 4649, HRK 4677, Mardag 4703, Minneapolis 4714, Rochester 4755
Missouri: Hall 4905, Hallmark 4906, Pettus 4954, Sunnen 4986
Nebraska: Buffett 5027, Lincoln 5063
New Jersey: Borden 5209, Hyde 5310, **Johnson 5329**, MCJ 5377
New Mexico: McCune 5529, Santa Fe 5533
New York: Central 5757, Drexler 5911, Farber 5970, Fordham 5996, New York 6544, New York 6548, O'Connor 6578, Rochester 6722, **Ross 6754**, Shoolman 6846, **Spunk 6902**, Western 7078
North Carolina: Broyhill 7160, Cemala 7174, Community 7181, Cumberland 7184, Reynolds 7296, Reynolds 7298, Smith 7317, Triangle 7328, Van Houten 7330
North Dakota: Leach 7353, Stern 7360
Ohio: Columbus 7411, Coshocton 7421, Dater 7426, Hershey 7487, Jergens 7510, Nord 7594, Richland 7630, Schmidlapp 7651, Stark 7673, Stocker 7676, **Timken 7684**, Toledo 7686, Troy 7688, Youngstown 7723
Oregon: Carpenter 7831, Meyer 7870
Pennsylvania: Arcadia 7918, Buhl 7956, Connelly 7995, Dolfinger 8013, Grable 8064, Nelson 8195, Penn 8216, Pew 8220, PNC 8230, Scranton 8275
South Carolina: Central 8468, Coastal 8472, **ScanSource 8495**
Tennessee: Community 8548
Texas: Anderson 8663, Austin 8676, Bass 8690, Carruth 8751, Edwards 8824, Elkins 8826, George 8863, **Jenesis 8932**, Kempner 8952, King 8959, Meadows 9019, Morris 9041, San Antonio 9148, Scott 9161, Sterling 9203, Trull 9240, Wright 9293
Utah: Dee 9312
Vermont: Vermont 9375
Virginia: Memorial 9485
Washington: Community 9604, Renton 9715, Tacoma 9750
West Virginia: Parkersburg 9789
Wisconsin: Milwaukee 9907, Siebert 9946

Child development, services
Arizona: Arizona 92
California: Atkinson 265, Atlas 266, Bella 301, Bothin 331, Crail 437, Gross 629, Mosse 948, **Packard 1006**, Sacramento 1103, San Diego 1108, San Francisco 1109, Sierra 1163, Sonora 1198, Weingart 1307
Colorado: El Pomar 1406, Kaufmann 1436, Norwood 1471, Rose 1487, Telluride 1512
Connecticut: Community 1564, Connecticut 1566, Fund 1589, Rosenthal 1684
Delaware: Mastronardi 1815
District of Columbia: Bernstein 1887, Cafritz 1890, Meyer 1931
Florida: Bank 1979, Kennedy 2182, Selby 2316
Georgia: Harland 2477, Whitehead 2571, WinShape 2577
Hawaii: Castle 2594
Illinois: Chicago 2746, Community 2763, Community 2766, **Harris 2893**, Polk 3084, Siragusa 3162
Iowa: Community 3423, McElroy 3461, Siouxland 3480
Kansas: Hutchinson 3521
Louisiana: Baton Rouge 3613, Booth 3616
Maryland: Adams 3718, Commonweal 3756, Fowler 3795, Freeman 3797
Massachusetts: Boston 3956, Community 3991, Peabody 4210, Rubenstein 4248
Michigan: Battle Creek 4343, Hillsdale 4461, **Mott 4510**, Skillman 4543
Minnesota: Bigelow 4616, Bremer 4620, Duluth 4649, Mardag 4703, McKnight 4709, Minneapolis 4714, Rochester 4755
Missouri: Hall 4905, Pettus 4954, Sunnen 4986
Nebraska: Lincoln 5063
New Jersey: Borden 5209, Hyde 5310, **Johnson 5329**, MCJ 5377, Wishes 5506
New Mexico: McCune 5529, New Mexico 5530, Santa Fe 5533
New York: Central 5757, Cummings 5834, **Guggenheim 6115**, NoVo 6570, O'Connor 6578, Rochester 6722, **Ross 6754**, Schenectady 6802, Shoolman 6846, Sirus 6863, **Spunk 6902**
North Carolina: Community 7181, Cumberland 7184, Smith 7317, Triangle 7328, Van Houten 7330
North Dakota: Leach 7353, Stern 7360
Ohio: Columbus 7411, Coshocton 7421, Dater 7426, Hershey 7487, Nord 7594, Richland 7630, Schmidlapp 7651, Stark 7673, **Timken 7684**, Toledo 7686, Troy 7688, Wean 7705, Youngstown 7723
Oregon: Carpenter 7831, Meyer 7870
Pennsylvania: Arcadia 7918, Buhl 7956, Connelly 7995, Dolfinger 8013, Nelson 8195, Pew 8220, Scranton 8275, York 8351
Texas: Austin 8676, Bass 8690, Edwards 8824, Elkins 8826, George 8863, Hoglund 8913, **Jenesis 8932**, Kempner 8952, Meadows 9019, Morris 9041, San Antonio 9148, Sterling 9203, Trull 9240, Wright 9293
Utah: Dee 9312
Vermont: Vermont 9375
Virgin Islands: Community 9377
Virginia: Memorial 9485
Washington: Blue 9588, Community 9604, Norcliffe 9693, Tacoma 9750
West Virginia: Parkersburg 9789
Wisconsin: McBeath 9901, Milwaukee 9907, Siebert 9946

Children
Alabama: Caring 18, Comer 20, Kaul 43, Meyer 53
Arizona: Steele 165, Webb 174
Arkansas: Cabe 182
California: **AAM 216**, Allergan 228, Alliance 229, Bechtel 294, Brandman 337, **Clorox 407**, Community 414, Community 417, Confidence 423, Cowell 434, Deutsch 462, Douglas 476, East 490, Eisner 499, El Dorado 500, Field 523, Fleishhacker 534, Goldman 605, Gumbiner 636, **Hilton 692**, **Hume 715**, Jack 736, Kelley 778, Leonetti/O'Connell 832, Lesher 833, Lucas 855, Ludwick 856, **Mattel 886**, McKesson 903, McMicking 904, Monroe 935, Moxie 950, Nestle 965, Newman 967, Noll 970, Oakland 977, Outhwaite 1000, Panda 1010, Patron 1020, Payne 1021, Perkins 1027, Rogers 1087, Sangham 1114, Sefton 1134, Simpson 1173, Stanislaus 1211, Stulsaft 1226, Teichert 1244, Ueberroth 1268, Weingart 1307
Colorado: Buell 1381, Chambers 1385, Colorado 1390, ECA 1404, Halton 1426, Hunter 1431, King 1440, Lipscomb 1449, Munger 1467, Piton 1480, **Western 1521**
Connecticut: Aetna 1531, Bob's 1548, Community 1562, Community 1563, Connecticut 1567, Eder 1577, Fund 1589, Graustein 1600, Lego 1627, Mortensen 1647, **Newman's 1652**
Delaware: **Raskob 1845**, Salah 1855
District of Columbia: **Banyan 1881**, Bernstein 1887, **CityBridge 1892**, Jones 1918, **Union 1953**
Florida: Conn 2042, Florescue 2100, Florida 2101, Fortin 2106, Geo 2120, Gooding 2130, Greenburg 2137, Hough 2162, Kennedy 2182, Quantum 2276, Southwest 2327, Watts 2380
Georgia: Camp-Younts 2421, EZ 2456, Franklin 2462, Pelling 2527, Pitts 2529, **Thoresen 2557**, **Turner 2563**, Williams 2573, WinShape 2577
Hawaii: Castle 2594
Idaho: Blue 2627
Illinois: **Abbott 2649**, Arthur 2673, Boyer 2711, Butler 2729, Chicago 2746, Community 2766, Ende 2823, Fry 2849, **IDP 2932**, Illinois 2933, King 2960, Logan 2983, Lurie 2987, Miller 3025, **Mondelez 3034**, Nierling, 3056, Northern 3059, Prince 3089, REAM 3107, Siragusa 3162, Steans 3175

Indiana: Community 3286, **Lilly 3342**, Lincoln 3344, Michigan 3354, Rolland 3381, Simon 3387, Steuben 3390, Wayne 3400
Iowa: Johnson 3449, McElroy 3461, Meredith 3463, Wellmark 3490
Kansas: Delta 3507, Mader 3531, Sarli 3541
Louisiana: Beaird 3614, Community 3624, Entergy 3630, Institute 3644
Maryland: **Casey 3745**, Stulman 3891, Washington 3904, Wright 3911
Massachusetts: **Barr 3937**, Berkshire 3947, Davis 4011, DentaQuest 4016, Dunkin' 4026, Eos 4037, Leaves 4139, **Min 4178**, New 4189, Peabody 4210, Phillips 4217, Stevens 4288, Stevens 4289, TJX 4308, Worcester 4327
Michigan: Chrysler 4366, Community 4369, Community 4375, **Cooper-Standard 4380**, **Gerber 4443**, Grand Rapids 4447, Johnson 4468, **Kellogg 4474**, Midland 4502, Mount Pleasant 4512, Pentecost 4520, Skillman 4543, Sturgis 4550, Tuscola 4562
Minnesota: **Better 4614**, Blue 4618, Bremer 4620, Cargill 4628, Foundation 4657, **O'Shaughnessy 4734**, RBC 4748, Rivers 4752, Rochester 4755, Total 4781, U.S. 4784, **Youth 4809**
Mississippi: Blue 4815, Community 4821, Gulf 4830, Hardin 4831
Missouri: Brown 4862, Centene 4870, Express 4888, Green 4900, Jordan 4917, **Monsanto 4945**, Pettus 4954, Saigh 4965, Saint Louis 4966
Montana: Oro 5014, Washington 5018
Nebraska: ConAgra 5030, Kearney 5055, Merrick 5067, Woods 5096
Nevada: Mann 5130
New Hampshire: DEKA 5168, HNH 5175, Lindsay 5179
New Jersey: **Allen 5191**, Danellie 5237, Dodge 5243, Healthcare 5296, Horizon 5305, Hyde 5310, **Johnson 5326**, Karma 5331, Orange 5396, Schumann 5441, Turrell 5483, **Verizon 5489**, Victoria 5490
New Mexico: Brindle 5516
New York: Abeles 5544, Abrons 5546, Altman 5579, **Ashner 5619**, Bouncer 5697, **Bristol 5711**, Canaday 5743, Charina 5763, Charina 5764, Community 5802, Countess 5821, Deerfield 5865, First 5979, **Foundation 6003**, Gorman 6083, Greater 6099, Haring 6133, Harriman 6137, Health 6153, Heckscher 6157, Johnson 6233, Lang 6326, Levine 6359, Lewis 6365, MBIA 6451, Morgan 6507, **Neuberger 6538**, New York 6548, NYSE 6573, O'Connor 6578, O'Malley 6589, **Open 6593**, **Overbrook 6604**, Phillips 6637, Pinkerton 6643, Price 6659, Ritter 6712, Rochester 6722, **Ross 6754**, **Rubin 6765**, Schenectady 6802, Schnurmacher 6810, Shoolman 6846, St. Faith's 6903, **Starr 6911**, **Straus 6934**, Ward 7049, Warner 7053, **Youths' 7112**
North Carolina: Allen 7134, Brady 7156, Cemala 7174, Community 7180, French 7203, Hunter 7238, Roberts 7304, Robertson 7305, Zinc 7349
Ohio: **Cardinal 7398**, Children's 7401, Cincinnati 7404, Fairfield 7445, GAR 7465, Hershey 7487, Home 7489, Jergens 7510, Keeler 7517, Mathile 7560, Mercer 7567, Nord 7594, O'Neill 7602, Parents 7608, Pfau 7618, Richland 7630, Ridgecliff 7631, Saint 7639, St. Marys 7672, Warmenhoven 7701, Youngstown 7723
Oklahoma: Hardesty 7756, Hille 7759
Oregon: Ford 7845, Haugland 7849, Healy 7850, J.F.R. 7854, Lamfrom 7863
Pennsylvania: Beaver 7934, Beneficial 7936, Connelly 7995, Dolfinger 8013, First 8041, Highmark 8092, Independence 8106, Independence 8107, **Oberkotter 8203**, Philadelphia 8221, Phoenixville 8223, Pilgrim 8225, PNC 8230, Rangos 8244, Smith 8289, Staunton 8296
Rhode Island: CVS 8379, Hasbro 8403
South Carolina: Blue 8460, Childrens 8471, Graham 8481, **ScanSource 8495**, Waccamaw 8507
Tennessee: Bridgestone 8537, **International 8585**, **Maclellan 8601**, Ramsey 8621, Regal 8622, **Scarlett 8624**, Seme 8626, Tennessee 8634, Wilson 8646
Texas: Anderson 8663, Bass 8690, Baxter 8695, Community 8774, Community 8776, Cook 8779, Hartman 8893, **Jenesis 8932**, McDermott 9013, Moore 9034, Moran 9036, Najim 9048, O'Hare 9068, Orsinger 9073, **Paso 9083**, Pediatric 9087, Powell 9105, **RGK 9128**, Rockwell 9135, Spangenberg 9193, Sterling 9203, Still 9207, Sumners 9214, Temple 9223, Terry 9224, Waco 9251
Utah: **Thrasher 9353**
Vermont: Mill 9367, Waterwheel 9376
Virginia: Community 9411, Memorial 9485, Mitsubishi 9487, MLG 9488, Portsmouth 9510, Strong 9537, Trehan 9544
Washington: Everett 9616, **Gates 9625**, Kitsap 9659, Norcliffe 9693, Raikes 9708, Sunbridge 9746
West Virginia: Chambers 9772, Eastern 9775
Wisconsin: Beloit 9814, Green Bay 9854, Lakeview 9892, Madison 9897, Reiman 9929, St. Croix 9950, West 9967
Wyoming: McMurry 9986, Scott 9989

Children's rights

Indiana: Duneland 3297

Children, adoption

Georgia: Singletary 2551
Kansas: HANDinHAND 3517
Maine: **Sandy 3707**
Massachusetts: TJX 4308
Michigan: Family 4417
New York: **Youths' 7112**
Texas: **International 8927**
Virginia: Freddie 9435
Washington: Anduin 9573

Children, day care

Alabama: Community 24
California: Santa Barbara 1116, Stulsaft 1226, Union 1271
Colorado: Buell 1381, Telluride 1512
Connecticut: Liberty 1630
Florida: duPont 2075, Fortin 2106
Idaho: Blue 2627
Indiana: Community 3282
Iowa: Sukup 3483
Massachusetts: Brookline 3962
Nebraska: Buckley 5026
New York: Lenna 6352, St. Faith's 6903
Ohio: Akron 7367
Pennsylvania: Hurd 8101
Tennessee: Promethean 8618
Texas: **Dell 8805**, Waco 9251
Virginia: Capital 9400
Wyoming: Christian 9974

Children, foster care

California: Chapman 395, Gogian 598, Guess? 635, Stulsaft 1226, Western 1315
Florida: Community 2034, Lennar 2210
Indiana: Pulliam 3372
Missouri: Casey 4869
New York: DeCamp 5861, Warner 7053
Virginia: Freddie 9435
Washington: Casey 9595

Children, services

Alabama: Anderson 5, McWane 51
Arizona: Canyon 98, Caris 99, Lewis 134
Arkansas: Riggs 196, Wal-Mart 210
California: Begin 299, Bella 301, **Capital 375**, **Cisco 402**, Dhanam 463, Draper 480, Gallo 561, **Google 615**, GSF 633, Leichtman 829, Lucas 855, Markkula 879, McBeth 894, Morton 943, Pacific 1003, Panda 1010, Ray 1058, **Saban 1101**, Semel 1138, Siebel 1162
Colorado: M.D.C./Richmond 1450, Rose 1487
Connecticut: Levine 1629, Perrin 1673, Provident 1677, Rockville 1682, Vranos 1718, Wood 1725
Delaware: Davis 1762, **Jolie-Pitt 1791**, Mastronardi 1815, Singer 1859, Stone 1863, Victory 1870
Florida: Amos 1967, Beaver 1986, Corbett 2045, Egleston 2083, Garfield 2115, **Kazma 2179**, **Knight 2191**, Libra 2213, McFarlane 2233, Publix 2275, Walter 2375
Georgia: Community 2434, EZ 2456, Griffith 2473, Love 2508, Rockdale 2540
Hawaii: HMSA 2604
Idaho: Seagraves 2642
Illinois: Beidler 2692, Crump 2782, Hamel 2887, Houlsby 2922, JNT 2940, Johnson 2944, Lumpkin 2986, Parr 3070, Ross 3123, Walsh 3212, Williams 3233, **Woodbury 3240**
Indiana: OneAmerica 3364, Samerian 3384
Iowa: Guernsey 3437, United 3485
Kansas: Shannon 3545
Kentucky: Humana 3582
Maine: Gorman 3689
Maryland: Adams 3718, Community 3761, GEICO 3801, Straus 3890, Washington 3904
Massachusetts: Adams 3916, Association 3929, Chafetz 3979, Child 3981, Community 3991, Davis 4010, Dunkin' 4026, Eastern 4030, One 4198, TJX 4308
Michigan: Ford 4425, Helppie 4456, **Mott 4510**, Spartan 4544
Minnesota: Mooty 4719, Robins 4754, Schmidt 4758, TEAM 4779, **Weyerhaeuser 4802**, **Youth 4809**
Missouri: Brown 4862, Centene 4870, Community 4872, Express 4888, Ferring 4891, Simon 4973
Nebraska: Ameritas 5023, Mutual 5071, Union 5090
Nevada: AJA 5100, Hart 5122
New Jersey: Hope 5304, Horizon 5305, Hummingbird 5309, **Johnson 5326**, L.F.H. 5353, **Merck 5379**, Summit 5473
New York: **AHBA 5562**, AJG 5565, Assael 5620, Coach 5790, Cranaleith 5825, Hagedorn 6127, Haring 6133, Hearst 6154, IFF 6206, Jones 6242, Kaylie 6263, Kingdon 6284, Lehman 6346, **Leir 6349**, **PepsiCo 6627**, **Pfizer 6633**, Richmond 6704, Riggio 6709, Scotts 6820, Select 6829, SO 6881, Tisch 6986, Warner 7053, Wegman 7061, Weiler 7063
North Carolina: Lewis 7257, VF 7332
Ohio: Levin 7539, Montei 7574, Park 7609, Sankey 7643
Oklahoma: Hille 7759
Oregon: Glory 7847
Pennsylvania: Baker 7925, Clayman 7984, **Davis 8005**, Degenstein 8008, Federated 8033, Lehigh Valley 8136, Marshall 8155, Mine 8184, Phoenixville 8223, Poor 8232, Saligman 8261, Wells 8333
South Carolina: McKissick 8486, **ScanSource 8495**, TSC 8506
Tennessee: Bridgestone 8537, Children's 8543, Seme 8626
Texas: Bass 8690, Baxter 8695, Carter 8753, Craig, 8786, Davis 8799, Gorman 8872, **International 8927**, Kinder 8958, Lyman 8995, Mitchell 9030, Natural 9053, Tobin 9236
Utah: **Nu 9340**
Virginia: AMERIGROUP 9383, Rales 9513, SunTrust 9539, Trehan 9544
Washington: Community 9603, Giddens, 9627, Oki 9694, PEMCO 9702, Renton 9715, Rotella 9721, **Tyler 9755**
Wisconsin: Herma 9862, Pettit 9919, Reiman 9929, Sentry 9944, Wisconsin 9969

Children/youth

Alabama: Central 19, Community 24, Community 25, Kaul 43, Meyer 53, Walker 74
Arizona: **Hickey 121**, Steele 165, Webb 174
Arkansas: Rockefeller 197, Ross 199
California: Ahmanson 222, **Alpert 231**, Aroha 260, Atkinson 265, Ayrshire 276, Bechtel, 296, **ben**

Children/youth, services

Shea 1155, Shea 1156, Sierra 1163, Silver 1168, Smith 1184, Smith 1186, Snyder 1192, Solari 1196, Solid 1197, Sonora 1198, Soref 1199, Springcreek 1208, Stark 1213, Stein 1215, Steinmetz 1216, Stephenson 1217, Streisand 1224, Stuart 1225, Stulsaft 1226, Swig 1231, Taper 1237, Teichert 1244, Truckee 1263, Tuohy 1267, Ueberroth 1268, United 1273, Valley 1280, Van Nuys 1284, Volentine 1291, Weingart 1307, Weisman 1309, Wells 1311, Western 1315, WHH 1320, Williams 1327, Wilson 1328, Witherbee 1334, Wolf 1337, Wolfen 1338, Wood 1344, **World 1346**, Wunderkinder 1348, WWW 1349, Wynn 1350, Ziegler 1360

Colorado: 6/S 1362, Anschutz 1364, Bacon 1370, Boedecker 1373, Boettcher 1374, Bohemian 1375, Bowana 1377, Buell 1381, Carson 1382, Change 1386, Community 1395, ECA 1404, Edmondson 1405, El Pomar 1406, Fishback 1410, Galena 1417, Hunter 1431, Janus 1432, JFM 1433, Lewis 1447, Libertygives 1448, Maggiegeorge 1452, McDonnell 1458, Peierls 1475, Pikes 1478, Pioneer 1479, Precourt 1483, Price 1484, ProLogis 1485, Saeman 1490, Shaw 1499, Sie 1500, Staley 1507, Sturm 1510, Summit 1511, Telluride 1512, Vodafone 1519, Wolf 1526, Wolf 1527

Connecticut: **Albers 1532**, Allwin 1536, Bauer 1543, Bissell 1547, Bob's 1548, Bossidy 1551, Community 1563, Community 1564, Community 1565, Connecticut 1566, Connecticut 1567, Culpeper 1568, Daniell 1570, Fairfield 1581, First 1584, Foley 1587, Fund 1589, Glover 1594, Goodnow 1598, Hartford 1609, Heidenreich 1611, Heimbold 1612, Keefe 1619, Kitchings 1621, Larsen 1624, Liberty 1630, McMahon 1642, Meriden 1643, Morris 1646, New Canaan 1650, NewAlliance 1651, **Newman's 1652**, Niles 1655, Orchard 1663, Palmer 1666, Robbins 1681, Rogow 1683, Say 1689, SBM 1690, Selkowitz 1694, Silver 1696, Smilow 1698, **Tudor 1711**, Werth 1719

Delaware: **Adobe 1734**, Berkley 1741, Bishop 1745, CenturyLink-Clarke 1750, **Chichester 1754**, Crystal 1758, Delaware 1765, Duane 1771, Ettinger 1779, Johnson 1790, Laffey 1800, Marmot 1814, McDonald 1817, **Memton 1819**, Parker 1829, Queally 1843, **Raskob 1845**, Rose 1852, Salah 1855, Sternlicht 1861, Sylvan 1867, Tapeats 1868, Wasily 1871, Westly 1873

District of Columbia: Cafritz 1890, **CityBridge 1892**, Community 1893, Consumer 1894, **Hill 1915**, Kimsey 1921, Loughran 1925, Meyer 1931, Rales 1942, Stewart 1949, Zients 1960

Florida: Abraham 1962, Amaturo 1966, Applebaum 1970, **Arison 1972**, Asofsky 1973, Bank 1979, Basham 1982, Batchelor 1983, Bay 1985, Berg 1993, Blum 1999, Broad 2002, Bronfman 2003, Burns 2006, Bush 2008, Central 2015, **Chatlos 2019**, Community 2031, Community 2032, Community 2034, Community 2035, Community 2038, Community 2040, Darden 2051, Davis 2054, Davis 2055, Demetree 2058, DiMare 2064, DuBow 2068, Ebert 2079, Einstein 2084, Fireman 2096, Florman 2102, Flournoy 2103, Fortin 2105, Fortin 2106, Funkhouser 2111, Gay 2117, Glazer 2124, Goodes 2129, Gooding 2130, Goodwin 2131, GPD 2132, Graff 2133, Green 2134, Gronewaldt 2139, Harris 2149, Henderson 2152, Hersh 2156, Hoehl 2160, Horvitz 2161, Hudson 2164, Katcher 2176, Kennedy 2182, Lacy 2198, Langford 2202, Lennar 2210, Mangurian 2226, Maren 2227, Miami 2238, Miller 2241, Moran 2243, Palank 2256, Pechter 2265, Pinellas 2269, Pope 2272, Publix 2275, Rayonier 2281, Rebozo 2282, River 2287, Rooms 2292, Rosenblatt 2295, Sack 2303, Sansing 2307, Southwest 2327, Spurlino 2330, **Stacy 2333**, Tarrant 2352, Taylor 2353, Thomas 2357, Vanneck-Bailey 2370, **Vollmer 2373**, Waggoner 2374, **Wardlaw 2376**, Welch 2382, Wells 2383, Welsh 2384

Georgia: Aflac 2399, Anderson 2403, Beech 2409, Beloco 2411, Campbell 2420, Community 2436, Community 2438, Correll 2440, Courts 2441, Cousins 2442, Dunn 2451, Flowers 2459, Franklin 2462, Gaines 2466, Gordy 2472, Harland 2477, Harris 2479, Holder 2485, **Imlay 2487**, Kahn 2493, Lockwood 2505, Loudermilk 2507, Murphy 2522, Primerica 2534, Realan 2535, Rich 2537, Rollins 2543, Tillotson-Menlo 2559, Tull 2561, **UPS 2566**, Whitehead 2571, Wilson 2576, WinShape 2577, Woodruff 2578, Woodruff 2579

Hawaii: Cades 2591, Campbell 2592, First 2598, Geist 2600, Hau'oli 2601, Hughes 2605, Kosasa 2607, Lange 2609, Schuler 2614, Wilcox 2621

Idaho: Cunningham 2630, Jeker 2633, Nagel 2639

Illinois: Allegretti 2655, Andrew 2661, Andrew 2662, Anixter 2664, Appleby 2668, Archer 2671, ARIA 2672, Austin 2677, Barnett 2681, Baskes 2684, Beidler 2692, Bersted 2696, Blair 2699, Blair 2700, Blowitz 2702, Bluhm 2704, Blum 2706, Brach 2712, **Bright 2714**, Brunner 2718, Buckeye 2722, Buder 2725, Camp 2732, Cedar 2739, Chaddick 2740, Charleston 2742, Chicago 2746, Children's 2747, Christopher 2748, Circle 2749, Clark 2751, CME 2755, Code 2757, Comer 2760, Community 2763, Community 2767, Corboy 2773, Cox 2776, Cuneo 2783, Day 2787, Dillon 2796, Dimon 2797, Donnelley 2801, Donnelley 2802, **Driskill 2806**, DuPage 2812, Eisenberg 2819, Energizer 2824, Evanston 2826, Field 2831, Foglia 2837, Frank 2840, Frankel 2842, Frankel 2843, Frechette 2844, Galvin 2857, Galvin 2858, Gates 2859, Genius 2861, Gies 2863, Guthman 2882, H.B.B. 2883, Hanson 2890, Harris 2892, Harrison 2896, His 2913, Hobbs 2914, Hunter 2927, I and G 2931, Ingersoll 2935, Johnson 2942, Katten 2951, Keith 2952, Kemper 2954, **Klaff 2961**, Kolschowsky 2962, Kovler 2964, Leibowitz 2973, Levi 2976, Levin 2978, Lewis 2980, Louis 2984, Madigan 2992, Malott 2996, Marks 3001, Mayer 3005, Mazza 3007, McCormick 3010, McDaniel 3011, McDonald's 3012, McQueen 3018, Melman 3022, Meyer 3023, Mills 3028, Montgomery 3035, Morrison 3037, Morse 3039, Mosher 3041, Munson 3045, Nesbitt 3051, Nierling 3055, Nygren 3060, Opler 3064, Oppenheimer 3065, Payne 3073, Perritt 3077, Polk 3084, Potishman 3086, Prince 3089, Prince 3090, Pritzker 3095, Rauner 3105, Rawley 3106, Reese 3110, Regenstein 3111, Reyes 3114, Rhoades 3115, Rice 3116, Roberts 3118, Ryan 3129, Ryan 3130, Sacks 3131, Schmidt 3139, Schreiber 3142, Schuler 3143, Shaw 3154, Sheba 3155, Sirius 3163, Speh 3170, Stone 3179, Taylor 3184, Tracy 3189, Trustmark 3193, United 3200, Vaughn 3203, Walter 3213, Ward 3216, Weiss 3224, Wenske 3225, White 3229, Willow 3235, Woodward 3243, **Wrigley 3244**, Youth 3245

Indiana: Adams 3253, Anderson 3255, Auer 3260, Bales 3261, Ball 3262, Ball 3263, Blue 3265, Boren 3267, Central 3272, Community 3278, Community 3279, Community 3280, English 3299, Foellinger 3304, Foundations 3306, Glick 3310, Health 3317, Henry 3320, Heritage 3321, Hux 3325, McMillen 3352, Michigan 3354, Miller 3355, National 3358, Noyes 3361, Portland 3370, Pulliam 3372, Putnam 3373, Reeves 3374, Rifkin 3378, Simon 3385, Steel 3389, Unity 3393, Vectren 3394, Wayne 3400, Weaver 3401, Wells 3403, White 3406

Iowa: AEGON 3409, Community 3420, Community 3423, EMC 3428, Gilchrist 3432, Guernsey 3437, GuideOne 3438, Hanson 3441, Helpenstell 3442, Johnson 3449, Kinney-Lindstrom 3451, Knapp 3452, Levitt 3458, McElroy 3461, Meredith 3463, Meredith 3464, New 3468, **Ochylski 3470**, On 3471, Ruan 3478, Siouxland 3480

Kansas: Coleman 3501, Douglas 3509, Downing 3510, Dreiseszun 3512, HANDinHAND 3517, Hutchinson 3521, INTRUST 3522, Jones 3523, Kansas 3524, Koch 3529, Morris 3537, Rice 3538, Sarli 3541, Security 3544, Smoot 3548, Sunderland 3551, Topeka 3552

Kentucky: Blue 3560, Cralle 3571, Fischer 3574, Harris 3580, J & L 3584, Marshall 3588, Norton 3592, Spray 3602

Louisiana: Albemarle 3609, Baton Rouge 3613, Beaird 3614, Coughlin 3626, Frazier 3635, German 3637, Marshall 3653, Moffett 3655, Woolf 3673, Zigler 3676

Maine: Alfond 3678, Hannaford 3690, Maine 3698, Nichols 3703, Sewall 3708

Maryland: Abell 3712, **Casey 3745**, Ceres 3747, Clark 3750, Commonweal 3756, Community 3759, Crane 3766, Dekelboum 3777, DiCarlo 3780, **DLA 3781**, Eaton 3784, **England 3785**, Fowler 3795, Gross 3808, Henson 3814, Higgins-Hussman 3815, Levitt 3832, Marriott 3840, Orokawa 3860, Osprey 3861, Rathmann 3867, Rembrandt 3868, Shields 3884, Spencer 3887, Van 3901, Viragh 3902, Wareheim 3903, Wilson 3909

Massachusetts: A.M. 3912, Abrams 3914, Arbella 3926, Bayrd 3938, Benson 3942, Berkman 3945, Bilezikian 3951, Boston 3956, Boston 3957, Byrnes 3964, Caldwell 3970, Cambridge 3971, Cape Cod 3973, Carney 3975, Clarke 3986, Clipper 3987, Cogan 3988, Community 3991, Community 3992, Copeland 3994, Crimson 3999, Cutler 4005, DentaQuest 4016, Devonshire 4017, Egan 4032, Elfers 4033, Ellsworth 4035, Fletcher 4054, Gildea 4071, Gordon 4074, Gross 4081, Hermann 4094, Hopedale 4101, Jacobson 4110, Jordan 4113, JSJN 4115, Kittredge 4124, Klarman 4126, Knez 4127, Landry 4134, Levy 4144, Linde 4147, Lovett 4151, Lubin 4155, Lurie 4158, Mazar 4164, Merck 4171, **Middlecott 4174**, Morrison 4184, OneWorld 4199, Pappas 4204, Parker 4207, Peabody 4210, Peabody 4211, Phillips 4217, Plymouth 4222, Rasmussen 4231, Riley 4239, **Rosenberg 4245**, Rowland 4246, Rubenstein 4248, Santander 4256, Schoen 4260, Schrafft 4263, Schwartz 4265, Smith 4277, Stearns 4286, Stevens 4288, Stevens 4289, Stoddard 4293, Stoneman 4295, Stoneman 4296, Strategic 4298, Thompson 4307, TripAdvisor 4311, Tupancy 4312, Webster 4322, Worcester 4327, Yawkey 4329

Michigan: Albion 4332, Allegan 4334, Ann Arbor 4340, Barry 4342, Battle Creek 4343, Beard 4345, Besser 4349, Brown 4356, Capital 4357, Carls 4358, Charlevoix 4361, Community 4369, Community 4370, Community 4372, Community 4374, **Cooper-Standard 4380**, Cracchiolo 4382, Dana 4386, Dart 4388, Davis 4391, DeRoy 4396, DeVos 4398, Doornink 4403, Duffy 4411, Family 4417, Family 4418, **Fetzer 4420**, Ford 4426, Frankel 4436, Fremont 4438, Frey 4440, General 4442, Gerstacker 4444, Greenville 4452, Herrick 4459, Hickman 4460, Hillsdale 4461, Jackson 4467, Kahn 4471, **Kellogg's 4475**, Leppien 4486, Manat 4490, Manoogian 4492, Mardigian 4494, Marquette 4495, **Micah 4501**, Miller 4503, Mott 4511, Polk 4524, Secchia 4536, Skillman 4543, **Tubergen 4559**, Turner 4561, Van Andel 4567, Van 4570, Wege 4579, Westerman 4582, Whiting 4584, Wickes 4585, Wilson 4588, Wolohan 4591, Wolters 4592, Wolverine 4593, World 4594

Minnesota: Andersen 4603, Andreas 4605, Athwin 4607, Beverly 4615, Bremer 4620, Carlson 4629, Charlson 4633, Christianson 4635, Cloverfields 4638, Criss 4640, Davis 4642, Duluth 4649, Ecolab 4651, Engdahl 4654, Fiterman 4656, **Fuller 4659**, Hersey 4673, HRK 4677, Hubbard 4678, Initiative 4679, Kelley 4686, **King 4687**, Kopp 4688, Larson 4692, Leuthold 4695, Lilly 4696, Marbrook 4702, Mardag 4703, McKnight 4709, McNeely 4710, Minneapolis 4714, Mitchell 4717, Neilson 4725, NFC 4727, Ordean 4732, Oswald 4735, Phillips 4740, Sabes 4756, Saint Paul 4757, Schulze 4760, Sit 4765, Stone 4773, Sundet 4774, Valspar 4786, Wallestad 4791, WCA 4795, West 4800

Mississippi: Community 4820, Ergon 4824, Feild 4825, Ford 4826, Foundation 4827, Mississippi 4839, Walker 4849

Missouri: Albrecht 4850, American 4852, Apex 4854, Ballmann 4858, Brauer 4860, Brown 4862, Burns

4866, Busch 4867, Cruse 4877, Dula 4881, Engelhardt 4886, Express 4888, Goldfarb 4895, Graybar 4898, Green 4900, Hallmark 4906, Hauck 4908, Holekamp 4910, Humphreys 4912, Jordan 4917, Kansas 4920, Kemper 4927, Lay 4934, Lemons 4935, Loose 4937, Musgrave 4947, Oppenstein 4950, Orscheln 4951, Pettus 4954, Pott 4958, Reynolds 4961, Rhoden 4962, Roblee 4963, Rosewood 4964, Saigh 4965, Sander 4967, Sosland 4975, Speas 4978, Stupp 4983, SunEdison 4985, Sunnen 4986, Tilles 4991, Truman 4996

Montana: Edwards 5008, Gianforte 5010, Gilhousen 5011, Oro 5014

Nebraska: Buckley 5026, ConAgra 5029, Davis 5034, Hastings 5046, Hawks 5047, Kim 5058, Kind 5060, Lexington 5062, Moglia 5069, Omaha 5074, Robinson 5076, Rogers 5077, Scoular 5080, Sherwood 5081, Werner 5094, Woods 5096, York 5098

Nevada: Bennett 5101, Crescere 5112, Engelstad 5117, Fairweather 5118, Gabelli 5120, Hawkins 5123, Keyser 5126, Lied 5128, Mallory 5129, Mathewson 5131, May 5132, Nevada 5134, O'Bannon 5137, Pennington 5139, Ruvo 5145, Van Sickle 5155, Wells 5157

New Hampshire: Cogswell 5167, HNH 5175, Hunt 5177, Lindsay 5179, Putnam 5186

New Jersey: Atkinson 5195, Bolger 5207, Borden 5209, Broadridge 5214, Brotherton 5216, Bunbury 5220, Campbell 5223, Clare 5230, Danellie 5237, D'Angelo 5238, Dircks 5241, Dow 5244, Fenwick 5259, Firestone 5260, Frankino 5266, Grassmann 5281, Harbourton 5293, Hyde 5310, **IDT 5311**, Jaffe 5320, **JM 5323**, **Johnson 5329**, Katz 5332, Kauffmann 5334, Kemmerer 5336, Kresa 5350, Laurie 5357, Levitt 5361, Martini 5372, MCJ 5377, Milano 5384, OceanFirst 5394, Orange 5396, OritaniBank 5398, Rose 5425, Schumann 5441, Schwarz 5444, Simon, 5460, Taub 5477, Turrell 5483, Unilever 5484, Union 5485, **Verizon 5489**, Victoria 5490, **Wang 5495**, WebMD 5496

New Mexico: Albuquerque 5511, Frost 5519, Hubbard 5523, Karakin 5525, Maddox 5528, McCune 5529, Phillips 5531, Santa Fe 5533

New York: A Kinder 5542, Abrons 5546, Achelis 5549, Acquavella 5550, Adirondack 5556, Alfiero 5570, Allen 5574, Allyn 5575, Alpern 5577, Altman 5580, Altman 5581, **American 5588**, Ames 5591, Ammon 5594, Andor 5598, Auchincloss 5623, Bahnik 5634, Baird 5636, Baker 5638, Barker 5644, Bass 5650, Berkowitz 5669, Bialkin 5673, Biddle 5674, Blue 5685, **Bobst 5690**, Bodman 5692, Bullitt 5728, Butler 5734, Butler 5735, Campbell 5742, Canaday 5743, Carmel 5746, Carvel 5749, Chautauqua 5766, Ckew 5782, Clark 5786, **CLRC 5789**, Cohn 5793, Cole 5795, Community 5803, Community 5805, Copper 5815, Coydog 5823, Crisp 5828, **Cummings 5832**, Cummings 5834, Daedalus 5842, D'Agostino 5843, Daphne 5848, Dauman 5849, Davenport 5850, DeGeorge 5867, **Deutsche 5876**, Devlin 5877, Dewar 5879, Diker 5883, Diller 5884, Dodge 5892, Dove 5904, Downs 5908, Dreitzer 5910, Dreyfus 5913, Dunwalke 5921, Durst 5922, Dyson 5923, Edouard 5936, Elmezzi 5948, Emerson 5950, Feil 5973, **FIMF 5977**, Finneran 5978, First 5979, **Fledgling 5987**, Flom 5989, **Fridolin 6016**, Friedberg 6017, Friedman 6022, Frog 6026, **GBRG 6036**, Gebbie 6038, Gifford 6049, **Glades 6056**, Glickenhaus 6058, Golub 6079, Gorter 6084, Gould 6089, Grateful 6094, Great 6097, Greenberg 6102, Greene 6103, Haje 6129, **Harriman 6136**, Harriman 6137, Harris 6141, Hayden 6150, **Hearst 6155**, **Hearst 6156**, Henle 6162, Heyman-Merrin 6172, Horwitz 6188, Hurdus 6198, Hurford 6199, Icahn 6204, **IIMI 6207**, JAF 6221, Jandon 6226, Joelson 6232, Johnson 6233, Johnson 6234, **JPMorgan 6244**, Karmazin 6254, Katzenberger 6258, Kautz 6260, Kazickas 6264, Kellogg 6269, Kellogg 6270, King 6283, Kinney 6285, Klee 6286, Klingenstein 6293, **Kohlberg 6300**, Kurz 6314, Landy 6324, Lane 6325, Lanza 6329, Lee 6343, Leibowitz 6348, Lemberg 6350, Letterman 6356, Leventhal 6357, Levitt 6361, Lincoln 6368, Lindner 6372, Link 6375, Lipp 6377, Lisabeth 6378, Litwin 6380, Loeb 6383, Maguire 6416, Mai 6417, Malkin 6422, Mariposa 6429, Marks 6432, Marrus 6436, Marx 6441, McCann 6453, McManus 6463, McNulty 6465, **Mead 6466**, **MetLife 6479**, Millbrook 6485, Milliken 6487, Moore 6502, Moore 6504, Morse 6510, Moses 6511, Mutual 6518, National 6528, National 6529, Neidich 6534, **Neuberger 6538**, New York 6544, New York 6546, Newhouse 6550, Nias 6556, Northfield 6568, O'Connor 6578, O'Neill 6591, Orthwein 6597, O'Toole 6602, Pearson 6623, Phillips 6637, Pinkerton 6643, **Polo 6651**, Poses 6655, Price 6657, Price 6659, Pumpkin 6666, Regals 6685, Resnick 6690, Richards 6698, Riedman 6706, Riese 6708, Ripple 6711, Riversville 6713, Rochester 6722, Rosenberg 6743, **Ross 6754**, RTS 6760, Rubenstein 6762, Rubin 6766, Sabin 6775, Sagner 6783, Salmon 6784, Saltz 6786, Saltz 6787, Sandler 6789, Sandy 6791, Schenker 6803, Schiff 6805, Schwartz 6815, Selz 6830, Semlitz 6831, Seneca 6832, Shapiro 6838, Siebens 6853, Simon 6859, Snow 6878, Soros 6891, **Spunk 6902**, St. Faith's 6903, St. Giles 6905, Starker 6910, Steele 6915, Stein 6918, Stern 6928, Stringer 6935, Strypemonde 6936, Stuart 6937, Sugarman 6940, Sumitomo 6943, **Summerfield 6944**, Tiger 6980, Tisch 6987, Tisch 6989, Tomorrow 6995, Tower 6999, Triad 7005, Tuft 7011, Turn 7012, Uphill 7022, Vernon 7026, Vidda 7030, Vogelstein 7034, Voya 7038, Warren 7054, Water 7056, Weber 7059, Weinberg 7065, Weissman 7072, Wendt 7074, Western 7078, **Youths' 7112**

North Carolina: Bate 7141, Belk 7148, BIN 7151, Blue 7153, Branan 7157, Campbell 7168, Cannon 7169, **Carlson 7172**, Carnrick 7173, Cemala 7174, Community 7180, Community 7182, Cumberland 7184, Curran 7185, Dalton 7187, Duke 7195, Foundation 7202, French 7203, Ghidotti 7206, Glenn 7211, Gordon 7214, Hanes 7221, Harris 7223, Herring 7229, High Point 7231, Hillsdale 7232, Jolley 7240, Jones 7242, Kulynych 7252, Mebane 7266, North 7274, Odell 7277, Olin 7279, Piedmont 7285, Prickett 7290, Provident 7291, Richmond 7302, Rominger 7306, Smith 7315, Smith 7317, Stewards 7322, Strauss 7323, Symmes 7325, Terry 7327, Triangle 7328, Van Houten 7330, Vickar 7333, Weaver 7335, Woodson 7342

North Dakota: Fargo 7351, Leach 7353, North Dakota 7357, Stern 7360

Ohio: AK Steel 7366, Akron 7367, American 7369, Anderson 7372, Andersons 7374, Boutell 7388, Bruening 7391, Cafaro 7397, Castellini 7399, Charities 7400, Children's 7401, Cincinnati 7404, Cliffs 7407, Codrington 7409, Community 7413, Community 7415, Corbin 7420, Coshocton 7421, Dater 7426, David 7427, Dayton 7428, DeWine 7434, Dodero 7438, **Eaton 7442**, Fairfield 7445, France 7462, Gund 7478, Hamilton 7481, Hershey 7487, Hoover 7492, Horvitz 7493, IHS 7501, Jergens 7510, Lancaster 7533, Licking 7540, Llewellyn 7543, Luedeking 7547, Luther 7548, Marietta 7557, Mathile 7560, Moores 7576, Murphy 7584, Muskingum 7585, Nippert 7590, Nord 7594, Nordson 7596, Ohio 7599, Parker 7611, Perkins 7615, Pfau 7618, Pulley 7624, Reeves 7627, Reinberger 7628, Richland 7630, Ridgecliff 7631, Riley 7632, Safelite 7638, Salem 7640, Samaritan 7642, Schiff 7648, Schmidlapp 7651, Schott 7652, Schott 7653, Sisler 7664, Spaulding 7670, Stark 7673, State 7674, Toledo 7686, Toulmin 7687, Troy 7688, TSF 7690, Turner 7691, Twenty 7692, Wade 7697, Warrington 7703, Weisbrod 7708, Wellman 7709, Western 7710, White 7715, Wodecroft 7717, Wolfe 7719, Wuliger 7722, Youngstown 7723

Oklahoma: American 7728, Bartlett 7732, Bernsen 7733, Browning-Kimball 7738, Dobson 7747, Hardesty 7756, Harris 7757, Lyon 7769, McGill 7775, ONEOK 7783, Oxley 7785, Puterbaugh 7786, **Schusterman 7794**, Stephenson 7799, Taubman 7804, Temple 7805, Titus 7806, Viersen 7808, Yot 7817

Oregon: Autzen 7823, Bauman 7824, Braemar 7826, Campbell 7830, Carpenter 7831, Collins 7836, Ford 7845, J.F.R. 7854, Jackson 7855, Johnson 7858, Jubitz 7859, Lamfrom 7863, Meyer 7870, Mission 7873, Oregon 7876, PacifiCorp 7877, PGE 7881, Renaissance 7884, Templeton 7895, Tucker 7896, Tykeson 7897, Young 7901

Pennsylvania: **Alcoa 7908**, Arcadia 7918, Armstrong 7922, Avs 7924, Barrist 7929, Biesecker 7941, Bozzone 7948, Buhl 7956, Carnahan 7965, CentiMark 7970, Century 7974, CIGNA 7981, Comcast 7989, Community 7990, Community 7993, Community 7994, Connelly 7995, Cooper 7997, Dolfinger 8013, DSF 8017, ESSA 8028, Eustace 8029, Ferree 8036, Fitch 8045, Fourjay 8047, **Heinz 8083**, Heinz 8084, Helping 8088, Hoverter 8097, Hoyt 8098, Hurd 8101, Huston 8102, Jackson 8110, Kavanagh 8118, Kline 8129, La Vea 8134, Lancaster 8135, Mandell 8153, Massey 8158, McLean 8169, Mellon 8173, Mengle 8174, Nelson 8195, Nichols 8197, Nimick 8198, O-Parker 8204, Peirce 8215, Pew 8220, Phillips 8222, Plankenhorn 8229, Pond 8231, Public 8239, Rangos 8244, Rohrer 8252, Russell 8258, Schenck 8269, Schieffelin 8270, Scranton 8275, Shaffer 8281, Simmons 8285, Simon 8286, Smith 8287, Smith 8288, Smith 8289, Snee 8291, Stackpole 8295, Staunton 8296, Steinman 8299, Steinman 8300, Trees 8319, Trexler 8320, Wheeler 8335, Widener 8336, Wilson 8341

Rhode Island: Binney 8362, Capewell 8365, Capewell 8366, Capewell 8367, Chamberlain 8369, Dexter 8382, **Grinnell 8399**, Guth 8400, Hoche-Scofield 8405, Kaplan 8409, Kimball 8410, McNeil 8418, Nelson 8422, Osborn 8426, Rhode Island 8429, Shriners 8438, Woodward 8453

South Carolina: Abney 8454, Blue 8460, Canal 8466, Cassels 8467, Ceres 8469, Coastal 8472, Community 8474, Self 8496, Spartanburg 8501, Speedwell 8503, WLT 8508, Zucker 8510

South Dakota: Larson 8516, Robinson 8520, Vucurevich 8524

Tennessee: Adams 8525, Adams 8526, American 8528, Aslan 8529, Atticus 8531, Beaman 8534, Briggs 8538, Campbell 8539, Charis 8542, Clayton 8547, Cook 8552, Day 8556, Dobberpuhl 8557, Dugas 8559, East 8560, Hamico 8576, Haslam 8581, Kirkland 8592, Lewis 8598, Maclellan 8602, Martin 8605, Martin 8606, Massey 8607, Melkus 8609, Midler 8611, Osborne 8614, Poplar 8616, Sasco 8623, Smith 8628, Stokely 8631, T & T 8632, Temple 8633, Thompson 8635, Thompson 8636, Turner 8640, Wilson 8646

Texas: 1687 8647, **A Glimmer 8649**, Abell 8650, Amarillo 8660, Anchorage 8662, Anderson 8663, Andrews, 8668, Arena 8670, Arnold 8673, Bass 8690, Beal 8696, Beasley 8698, Boone 8710, Booth 8711, Borick 8714, Branch 8720, Bridwell 8726, Brumley 8734, Cailloux 8742, Cameron 8747, Carlson 8750, Castex 8755, Chaparral 8760, Chapman 8761, Clayton 8765, Clements 8766, Coastal 8768, Cockrell 8770, Collins 8771, Community 8774, Community 8776, Community 8777, Constantin 8778, Cowden 8782, Cowden 8783, Cox 8785, Crain 8787, De Llano 8802, **Dell 8805**, Dickson-Allen 8806, Doss 8813, Duda 8815, Elkins 8826, Ellwood 8827, Family 8836, Fasken 8839, Fikes 8844, Fisch 8846, Fish 8848, Ford 8854, Franklin 8856, Frees 8857, George 8863, Goldsbury 8868, Goodman 8870, Greathouse 8874, Greathouse 8875, Gulf 8878, H.E.B. 8879, Halsell 8886, Hamill 8887, Hamman 8888, Harvey 8894, Hawn 8896, Hebert 8899, Herd 8902, Hillcrest 8909, Hirsch 8910, Hoblitzelle 8912, Holthouse 8915, Hudson 8919, Hunt 8922, Impetus 8924, Jamail 8928, **Jenesis 8932**, Johnson 8937, Johnson 8938, Jones 8943, Jonesville 8946, Kimberly 8957, King 8959, Kolitz 8968, Lard 8972, Lennox 8979, Levit 8982, Liatis

8983, Lightner 8985, Littauer 8988, Looper 8990, Lowe 8993, Lubbock 8994, Lyons 8996, Madison 8997, Maverick 9005, McDermott 9013, McGovern 9014, McGrath 9015, Meadows 9019, Medallion 9020, Meredith 9023, MFI 9025, Moore 9034, Morgan 9037, Morning 9040, Morris 9041, Murchison 9045, Najim 9048, O'Connor 9066, Once 9070, O'Quinn 9072, Owen 9075, Owen 9076, Owen 9077, Owsley 9078, Pertusati 9094, Phillips 9097, Pinon 9100, Prairie 9106, Rachal 9117, Ram 9120, Rapier 9121, Reaud 9124, Rees-Jones 9125, Richardson 9131, Roach 9132, Robinson 9133, Rockwell 9135, Rosewood 9140, Saint 9144, Sams 9145, San Antonio 9148, Scanlan 9156, Schollmaier 9159, Scurlock 9162, Seegers 9164, Sharp 9167, Shelton 9169, Simmons 9173, Simmons 9174, Simmons 9175, Simpson 9177, Smith 9179, Star 9197, Stemmons 9201, Sterling 9203, Stern 9204, Stevens 9205, Strake 9208, Stuart 9209, Swinney 9218, Terry 9224, Thomas 9232, Thompson 9233, Tijerina, 9234, Topfer 9239, Trull 9240, Turner 9242, Valero 9246, Vanberg 9247, Vergara 9249, Waco 9251, Waggoner 9252, Wagner 9253, Wal 9254, Ward 9258, Weaver 9260, WEDGE 9263, Weir 9265, Whalley 9272, Whitacre 9273, Wichita 9277, Wise 9285, Woodforest 9290, Wright 9293, Young 9295, Zale 9297

Utah: Bamberger 9305, Call 9310, Dee 9312, Dumke 9315, Eccles 9319, Eccles 9320, Hall 9324, Hemingway 9326, Lawson 9331, Miller 9336, Noorda 9339, Peery 9344, Price 9346, Simmons 9351, Wagner 9355, Watkins 9356

Vermont: McKenzie 9366, Sills 9371, Three 9374, Vermont 9375

Virgin Islands: Community 9377

Virginia: AMERIGROUP 9383, Arlington 9384, Camp 9399, Chiaramonte 9407, Claws 9408, Community 9410, Community 9415, Community 9416, Franklin 9434, Freddie 9435, Fredericksburg 9436, Genan 9440, Herndon 9451, Lynchburg 9474, Malek 9475, MAXIMUS 9481, Memorial 9485, NewMarket 9494, Olsson 9502, Perry 9506, Reinhart 9517, Robins 9523, Samberg 9527, Snead 9536, Suffolk 9538, Titmus 9543, United 9546, Universal 9548, Wardle 9551, Washington 9552

Washington: Anderson 9572, Aven 9575, Barton 9581, Bezos 9585, Blue 9588, Cameron 9593, Casey 9596, Community 9604, Crystal 9608, Discuren 9611, Foster 9621, Glaser 9629, **Haugland 9643**, **Islands 9653**, Kaphan 9657, Lafromboise 9663, Lauzier 9667, Lie 9669, Lucky 9673, **Luke 9674**, McEachern 9678, McKinstry 9680, Medina 9682, Milgard 9683, Miller 9685, Norcliffe 9693, OneFamily 9695, Plum 9704, Raikes 9708, Raven 9710, Roma 9719, San Juan 9726, Satterberg 9728, Schultz 9730, Seattle 9731, Smith 9738, Stubblefield 9745, Suskin 9747, Tacoma 9750, Whatcom 9759, Wheeler 9760, Wockner 9763, Zumiez 9768

West Virginia: Chambers 9772, Daywood 9774, Eastern 9775, Kanawha 9780, McQuain 9785, Meagel 9786, Parkersburg 9789, Prichard 9791, Schenk 9793, Wehrle 9797

Wisconsin: Alexander 9803, Bader 9810, **Baird 9811**, Beloit 9814, Casper 9827, Clark 9830, Cleary 9831, DeAtley 9839, Eder 9840, Evinrude 9841, Helfaer 9861, Holz 9864, Iddings 9866, Incourage 9867, Johnson 9873, Kellogg 9879, Kohl 9883, Kress 9887, La Crosse 9889, Ladish 9890, McBeath 9901, Michels 9906, Milwaukee 9907, MMG 9908, Mortenson 9909, Nelson 9912, Nicholas 9913, Oshkosh 9916, Pettit 9919, Pollybill 9921, Reinhart 9930, Rexnord 9932, Riordan 9933, Ryan 9940, **Schneider 9942**, Soref 9948, Stackner 9951, Stone 9954, **Wagner 9961**, Wehr 9966, Windhover 9968

Wyoming: Allen 9973, Ellbogen 9977, Martin 9984, McMurry 9986, Scott 9989, Storer 9992, Wyoming 9999

Chiropractic

Georgia: Harris 2478

Christian agencies & churches

Alabama: Arlington 6, Bean 10, Dove 31, Hearin 38, May 48, Nabers 56, Richards 62, Thompson 70, Webb 76, Working 78

Arizona: Canyon 98, Cooper 102, Hermundslie 120, Jasam 124, Jazzbird 125, JSC 128, Least 132, Long 137, Lord's 138, Ross 159, Solheim 163, Surplus 167, Tooker 171

Arkansas: Carson 183, Glass 190, Riggs 196, Soderquist 202

California: Berry 312, **Bolthouse 325**, Chao 394, Chapman 395, Day 457, El 501, Ellis 503, **First 530**, God's 597, Grimm 626, Hammer 648, Harrington 657, Healing 666, Herwaldt 684, Ho 695, Hofmann 700, Hoppe 703, Hurtt 716, Issa 732, It 733, Johnson 754, Kay 772, Keck 775, Kroner 806, Kvamme 807, Lindsey 839, Lindsey 840, Maranatha 871, Martin 882, Mourier 949, Narrow 960, Noll 970, North 972, Oarsmen 979, Oates 980, **Open 986**, Orthodox 995, Padway 1008, Peters 1028, Philanthropy 1035, Philibosian 1036, Rogers 1087, Ryan 1098, Saje 1104, Salta 1105, **Samueli 1106**, Schimmel 1122, Schlinger 1124, Semloh 1139, Silk 1167, Smith 1184, **Stamps 1210**, Stewardship 1220, Stover 1222, TF 1247, Van Daele 1281, Van Konynenburg 1282, **Wade 1293**, White 1321, **Wong 1342**

Colorado: Bowana 1377, Bruni 1380, **Crowell 1398**, Galena 1417, King 1440, Lane 1443, Leptas 1446, Lewis 1447, McDonnell 1458, Mol 1463, Norwood 1471, **Salvador 1491**, Seay 1495, TYL 1516, Willett 1523

Connecticut: Bullfrogs 1553, Daniell 1570, Hack 1604, Laverack 1625, Ohnell 1661, Wiggins 1722

Delaware: 9:7 1733, Bennett 1739, Chase 1753, **Gloria 1784**, Gospel 1786, Prairie 1838, Rivera 1850, Struthers 1865

District of Columbia: Rutherfoord 1944

Florida: 100 1961, Abraham 1962, Albert 1964, Aurora 1974, Basham 1982, Bay 1985, **Believers 1989**, Burns 2006, Chabraja 2016, Clermont 2023, CNL 2025, Demetree 2058, **DeMoss 2059**, DiMare 2064, Duda 2070, duPont 2074, Durkee 2076, Eagle 2078, Ebert 2079, Einstein 2084, Free 2109, Galloway 2112, Garrott 2116, Gay 2117, Gronewaldt 2139, Hahn 2144, Herr 2155, Jenkins 2171, Kings 2185, Kirbo 2186, Lacy 2198, Langford 2202, **Larson 2203**, Lattner 2204, Magruder 2225, Pamphalon 2257, Rawlings 2279, Regal 2283, Sansing 2307, **Stacy 2333**, Stacy 2334, Taishoff 2350, Thatcher 2356, Thornburgh 2360, Usher 2367, Waggoner 2374, Walter 2375, Williams 2388, Zehnder 2397

Georgia: Amos 2401, Bagwell 2407, Belcher 2410, Callaway 2419, Campbell 2420, Courts 2441, Cousins 2442, Day 2448, Ellis 2452, Flowers 2459, Gaby 2465, Gordy 2472, Helton 2483, Jackson 2490, Lewis 2503, Lockwood 2505, Loudermilk 2507, Love 2508, McAfee 2515, Poindexter 2532, Reeder 2536, Richards 2538, Servant's 2550, Spring 2555, Walker 2567, Watkins 2568, Williams, 2575, WinShape 2577

Hawaii: Vincent 2619, Wong 2622

Idaho: Brandt 2628, Seagraves 2642, Thomas 2645

Illinois: Andrew 2662, Archer 2671, Atherton 2676, Bacca 2678, Baum 2689, Block 2701, Boyer 2711, Chaddick 2740, Code 2757, Cornell 2774, Davis 2786, **Domanada 2799**, Dury 2813, Emerson 2822, **Gallagher 2855**, Gilmore 2864, Grace 2872, Hamill 2888, Harrison 2896, Hartke 2897, Hendrickson 2905, His 2913, Hobbs 2914, Huizenga 2924, Hunter 2927, Johnson 2941, Johnson 2943, Kemper 2954, Khesed 2959, Madigan 2992, Miner 3030, Pepper 3074, Rhoades 3115, Roberts 3119, Ryan 3129, Salmon 3133, Schawk 3138, Tricord 3190, **Tyndale 3195**, Vaughn 3203, Wessner 3227, Zerrusen 3248

Indiana: ADL 3254, Blue 3266, Brotherhood 3268, Community 3278, English 3299, Froderman 3307, Holiday 3322, Jackson 3329, Rick 3377, Saltsburg 3383, **Word 3408**

Iowa: Brownell 3414, GuideOne 3438, Knapp 3452, Nelson 3467, New 3468, Sukup 3483, Vermeer 3486, Vogel 3487, Weathertop 3489

Kansas: DeBoer 3505, Deffenbaugh 3506, **Lloyd 3530**, Shannon 3545

Kentucky: Carson-Myre 3567, Harris 3580, Lift 3587, Preston 3596, Swope 3603

Louisiana: Coughlin 3626, Factor 3632, Frazier 3635, Huie 3643, Moffett 3655, Stuller 3668, Woolf 3673

Maryland: Angelos 3721, Blades 3734, Calvin 3744, Fusco 3800, **Lawless 3827**, Little 3835, Rock 3870, **Smith 3886**

Massachusetts: Boston 3955, Byrnes 3964, Copeland 3994, Davis 4010, De Ganahl 4012, DeFreitas 4013, Elfers 4033, Fels 4045, Gildea 4071, Grayson 4078, Imago 4105, Keane 4119, Lucretia 4156, Mifflin 4175, Morningside 4183, Ragon 4228, Rogers 4243, Romney 4244, Roy 4247, Spina 4280, Wallace 4318

Michigan: Anchor 4338, Boll 4352, Brown 4356, Christ 4364, Christian 4365, Cook 4378, Cornucopia 4381, DeVos 4398, DeVos 4399, DeWitt 4402, Dow 4406, Family 4417, Family 4418, Foster 4431, G. 4441, Granger 4449, Granger 4450, Heritage 4458, Johnson 4468, Jubilee 4470, Legion 4483, Leppien 4486, Mardigian 4494, Merillat 4500, **Micah 4501**, Miller 4504, Molinello 4505, Mulder 4514, **Myers 4515**, Oleson 4516, Polk 4524, Prince 4525, Rordor 4529, Silverwing 4541, Spoelhof 4545, Stonisch 4548, **Tubergen 4559**, Upjohn 4564, Van Andel 4566, Van Noord 4571, VanderWeide 4572, Zatkoff 4595

Minnesota: AHS 4599, Andreas 4604, Andreas 4605, Campbell 4626, Carlson 4629, Christianson 4635, Deziel 4645, Dorea 4647, Engdahl 4654, Evert 4655, Hersey 4673, Luther 4698, McVay 4711, Mooty 4719, Mooty 4720, Nicholson 4728, Pagel 4736, Patch 4737, Rivers 4752, Sundet 4774, Verdoorn 4788, Veritas 4789, Wallestad 4791

Mississippi: C Spire 4817, Ergon 4824, Feild 4825, McRae 4836, Oakwood 4841, Walker 4849

Missouri: Concorde 4873, Moulton 4946, Musgrave 4947, Pershing 4952, Pillsbury 4955, Rosewood 4964, Shaughnessy 4969, Sosland 4976, Steward 4981, Sugarbaker 4984, Ten 4989

Montana: Gianforte 5010, Gilhousen 5011

Nebraska: Family 5038, Hamilton 5045, Hawks 5047

Nevada: Crescere 5112, Gabelli 5120

New Hampshire: Hunt 5177, Penates 5185, Quinlan 5187

New Jersey: Bolger 5207, Bonner 5208, Brougher 5217, Carolan 5225, Danellie 5237, Dunbar 5245, **GHH 5275**, Holmes 5302, Hope 5304, Hovnanian 5307, IGH 5312, James 5322, Kish 5341, Merillat 5382, Messner 5383, **Perrin 5404**, Plummer 5409, R. 5418, Roberts 5423, Samaritan 5433

New Mexico: **Johns 5524**

New York: Ames 5591, Aresty 5610, Armstrong 5613, Baldwin 5640, Campbell 5742, Chiaroscuro 5776, Conard-Davis 5809, D'Addario 5841, Doolittle 5901, Dove 5903, Dove 5904, Eveillard 5963, Fanwood 5968, **Flowers 5990**, Gorter 6084, Great 6097, Greater 6098, His 6176, Kanas 6249, Link 6375, Linville 6376, MBIA 6451, McCann 6453, Melly 6471, Millbrook 6485, O'Connor 6578, Pearson 6623, Puth 6668, Review 6692, S & G 6774, Seven 6834, Sister 6864, SJS 6867, Soros 6891, Swartz 6954, **Tai 6959**, Vernon 7026, Zehner 7118

North Carolina: Bolick 7155, Braswell 7158, Bryan 7161, Carnrick 7173, Curran 7185, Curtis 7186, Finley 7199, Harvest 7224, Hayes 7227, Jordan 7243, Kahn 7245, Keith 7247, P & B 7280, Randleigh 7292, Richardson 7301, Sloan 7314, Stewards 7322, Wilson 7338, Wos 7345, Yount 7348

North Dakota: Nordick 7356

Ohio: **58 7362**, Androse 7375, Ar-Hale 7376, Ashtabula 7379, Christ 7402, Clouse 7408, Conn 7418,

Covenant 7422, Dater 7426, Dorn 7439, Durell 7441, Gardner 7466, **Generation 7470**, Hubert 7495, Orr 7604, Park 7609, Piqua 7620, Samaritan 7642, Sankey 7643, Talmage 7680, Vortex 7696, Wagler 7699
Oklahoma: Craft 7745, Gaylord 7753, Jones 7762, Liddell 7767, Lobeck 7768, Oxley 7785, Temple 7805, Waters 7810, Yot 7817
Oregon: Bauman 7824, Caddock 7828, Dieringer 7839, Fjarli 7843, John 7857, Merrill 7868, Mission 7873, Poznanski 7882
Pennsylvania: Arcadia 7918, Asplundh 7923, Beaver 7934, Brickman 7949, Burke 7958, Burke 7959, Campbell 7961, **Cardone 7964**, Carnahan 7965, Chatham 7978, Clayman 7984, Crels 8002, Degenstein 8008, Dickson 8009, England 8024, Eustace 8029, Federated 8033, Firstfruits 8042, Glencairn 8062, Gospel 8063, Gunterberg 8073, Haldeman 8076, Herr 8090, Huston 8102, Huston 8103, Jackson 8110, Linlundh 8143, Long 8149, Marshall 8155, McCausland 8159, Medleycott 8171, Mosi 8189, Parmer 8212, Pilgrim 8225, Psalm 8237, Rangos 8244, Saltsgiver 8262, Schieffelin 8270, Sedwick 8276, Seed 8277, Sexauer 8280, **Shiloh 8283**, Snee 8291, Stratton 8304, Wiegand 8337, Wilson 8341
Rhode Island: Chisholm 8373, Knoop 8411, Koonce 8412, McAdams 8416, Middendorf 8420, Routhier 8432, Swanson 8445, Thompson 8447
South Carolina: Abney 8454, Cassels 8467, Community 8474, Hopewell 8484, McKissick 8486, Smith 8498, Smith 8499, Springs 8504, TSC 8506, WLT 8508
South Dakota: Branches 8512, Hofer 8515
Tennessee: Adams 8525, Adams 8526, American 8528, Beaman 8534, Blankemeyer 8536, Christian 8544, Cook 8552, Dobberpuhl 8557, Elgin 8562, **Gardner 8570**, Glenn 8572, Haslam 8580, Johnson's 8590, Latimer 8595, Lazarus 8596, MacLellan 8600, **Maclellan 8601**, Maclellan 8602, Osborne 8614, Poplar 8616, Proctor 8617, Provision 8619, Seme 8626, Shinn 8627, Speer 8630, Thompson 8636, Washington 8643
Texas: Albany 8654, Angela 8669, Arnold 8673, Astros 8674, Baxter 8695, **Bell 8700**, Beyer 8704, Boone 8710, Brentwood 8723, Buford 8736, Butt 8738, C.I.O.S. 8740, **Caris 8749**, Chapman 8761, Cockrell 8770, Cornerstone 8780, Covenant 8781, Criswell 8789, Crowell 8791, Eady 8818, Ed 8822, Edwards 8824, Elkins 8826, Fleming 8849, Gallagher 8860, Gorman 8872, Hamill 8887, Hankamer 8890, Hawn 8896, Heavenly 8897, Heavin 8898, Howell 8918, Janszen 8930, JKL 8935, Johnson 8940, Jones 8943, Justin 8947, Kahng 8948, Kessler 8954, Kohl 8967, Lard 8972, Looper 8990, Madison 8997, Marsh 8999, Martin 9002, Martinez 9003, Mays 9008, McCoy 9010, McGrath 9015, McNutt 9018, Mitchell 9030, Moore 9034, Morning 9040, Morrow 9042, Murchison 9045, Murchison 9046, **New Beginning 9057**, Onstead 9071, Owen 9075, Owen 9076, Owen 9077, Patton 9085, Payne 9086, **PHM 9098**, Pinon 9100, Rachal 9117, Ram 9120, Reaud 9124, Rees-Jones 9125, Roach 9132, Rockjensen 9134, Rowling 9141, Sadler 9143, Scanlan 9156, Scurlock 9162, Seay 9163, Seegers 9164, Shelton 9169, Simpson 9177, Smith 9186, Snyder 9188, Sowell 9192, Sparrow 9194, Sterling 9202, Stumberg 9210, Thirteen 9230, Thomas 9232, Vergara 9249, Walter 9257, Ware 9259, WEDGE 9263, Weekley 9264, Weiser 9266, Welborn 9267, Whitacre 9273, White 9274, Whitener 9275, Wise 9285, Zeller 9298, Zorich 9301
Utah: Bertin 9308, Quinney 9347
Virginia: Bangs-Russell 9386, Batten 9390, English 9426, Hobbs 9454, **ICE 9456**, Lambert 9466, **Mustard 9492**, Robins 9524, Scott 9529, Sellier 9530, Three 9541, Titmus 9543, **Truland 9545**, Watkins 9553, Willett 9557
Washington: Anduin 9573, B&E 9577, Foundation 9623, Green 9632, Hughes 9648, Hussey 9649, Lie 9669, **Luke 9674**, Norcliffe 9693, OneFamily 9695, Smith 9738, **Stewardship 9744**, Zumiez 9768
West Virginia: Hamilton, 9776, Hess 9777
Wisconsin: Bachhuber 9809, Batterman 9813, Bleser 9818, Fotsch 9846, Hovde 9865, Integrity 9868, Johnson 9872, Johnson 9873, Kress 9887, Loehrke 9893, Mortenson 9909, Nelson 9912, Rolfs 9935, Vine 9960, Windhover 9968
Wyoming: Christian 9974, Friess 9978, Martin 9984, Seven 9991, Stuart 9993, Zimmerman 10000

Civil liberties, advocacy

California: Hitz 694, McCune 900, Streisand 1224, **Warsh 1299**
District of Columbia: Block 1888
Illinois: Libra 2981
Massachusetts: Golden 4073
Minnesota: Kelley 4686
Missouri: **Deer 4878**
New York: **Cummings 5833**, Levy 6364, **Overbrook 6604**
Pennsylvania: Brodsky 7952, Federated 8033
Virginia: Proteus 9512

Civil liberties, death penalty issues

California: **Fund 556**
District of Columbia: **Butler 1889**
New York: Soros 6890

Civil liberties, due process

California: vanLoben 1283
Georgia: Sapelo 2546
Illinois: Libra 2981

Civil liberties, first amendment

District of Columbia: Block 1888, **Freedom 1907**
New York: Klingenstein 6292, Smith 6874
Ohio: Scripps 7659
Virginia: **Gannett 9439**
Washington: RealNetworks 9712

Civil liberties, freedom of information

District of Columbia: **Freedom 1907**

Civil liberties, freedom of religion

Georgia: Richards 2538

Civil liberties, reproductive rights

California: Dolby 474, Gerbode 573, Goldman 606, Grove 631, Gumbiner 636, **Packard 1006**, Taper 1237, Wohlford 1336
Colorado: **General 1419**
Connecticut: **Educational 1578**
Delaware: Ettinger 1779
District of Columbia: Cafritz 1890, Kaye 1920
Illinois: Buffett 2727, Libra 2981, New 3052
Maryland: **Cohen 3754**, Millstream 3852
Michigan: Grand Rapids 4447
Minnesota: Martin 4704, Phillips 4741
Missouri: **Deer 4878**, Roblee 4963, Sunnen 4986
Nebraska: **Buffett 5028**
New Jersey: Balazs 5199
New York: **Bydale 5738**, **Clark 5785**, Gimbel 6053, New York 6544, New York 6546, **Noyes 6571**, **Overbrook 6604**, Scherman 6804
North Carolina: Reynolds 7298
Pennsylvania: Claneil 7982
Texas: Fikes 8844
Washington: **Quixote 9707**

Civil liberties, right to life

California: McDonald 901
Delaware: **Gloria 1784**
Massachusetts: Firstgreen 4050, Flatley 4053
Minnesota: Christianson 4635
Ohio: Gardner 7466
Pennsylvania: Federated 8033
Texas: Dodge 8810

Civil rights, race/intergroup relations

Alabama: BBVA 9
California: Akonadi 223, California 365, Humboldt 714, Irvine 727, Orange 992
Colorado: Peierls 1475
Connecticut: Larsen 1624, **Praxair 1676**
District of Columbia: Meyer 1931
Florida: Community 2032, **Knight 2191**
Illinois: Allstate 2657, Field 2831, **Ploughshares 3082**, Polk 3084, Stuart 3182
Indiana: Heritage 3321
Kentucky: Bond 3561
Maryland: Hirschhorn 3816
Massachusetts: Hyams 4103, One 4198, TJX 4308
Michigan: Community 4371, Grand Rapids 4447, **Mott 4510**
Minnesota: Bremer 4620, Duluth 4649, Initiative 4679, Minneapolis 4714, Musser 4724, Saint Paul 4757
Missouri: **Deer 4878**, Kansas 4920, Roblee 4963
New Mexico: Santa Fe 5533
New York: **Ford 5994**, **Guggenheim 6115**, New York 6546, Soros 6891
North Carolina: Cumberland 7184, Reynolds 7298, Triangle 7328
Ohio: Columbus 7411, Gund 7478, Richland 7630
Pennsylvania: Dolfinger 8013
Texas: Kempner 8952, Meadows 9019
Vermont: **Ben 9358**
Wisconsin: Milwaukee 9907

Civil rights, voter education

California: **Arkay 255**, Bohnett 324, Goldman 606, Streisand 1224
New York: **Carnegie 5747**, **Cummings 5833**, **Rockefeller 6723**

Civil/human rights

Alabama: Protective 59
Arkansas: Rockefeller 197
California: **Arkay 255**, Bowes 334, Craigslist 436, **CS 442**, Davis 455, **Draper 481**, **Geffen 567**, Gerbode 573, Gibson 583, Goldman 606, Handleman 649, Hidden 689, JMM 752, Lear 824, McCune 900, Meyer 922, Mohn 934, Morton 943, San Francisco 1109, Silberstein 1165, Skoll 1176, **Strauss 1223**, Streisand 1224, vanLoben 1283, Ventura 1287, Yellow 1354
Connecticut: **Newman's 1652**
Delaware: Berkshire 1742
District of Columbia: **Arca 1880**, Block 1888, Cafritz 1890, Meyer 1931, **Moriah 1932**, **Wyss 1959**
Florida: Miami 2238, SHIFT 2320, Wolfe 2391
Georgia: Sapelo 2546, **UPS 2566**
Illinois: Community 2763, Epstein 2825, Katten 2951, Landau 2966, Lefkofsky 2971, Libra 2981, **MacArthur 2990**, Satter 3136, Williams 3234
Indiana: **Cummins 3292**
Iowa: Holthues 3444
Kansas: Hutchinson 3521, **Shumaker 3546**
Maine: Lerner 3695
Maryland: **Cohen 3754**, **DLA 3781**
Massachusetts: A.M. 3912, Bell 3941, Berkman 3945, Beveridge 3950, Boston 3956, Community 3992, Eastern 4030, Kahn 4116, TJX 4308
Michigan: General 4442, Shoemaker 4539, Walker 4575
Minnesota: Bremer 4620, Minneapolis 4714, Rochester 4755
Missouri: Community 4872, Humphreys 4913, JSM 4918
New Hampshire: Panjandrum 5184
New Jersey: Elias 5252

New York: **Arcus 5608**, Baird 5635, Bullitt 5728, **Bydale 5738**, Crossed 5830, Diamond 5882, **Ford 5994**, **Foundation 6001**, Hughes 6193, Levy 6363, Marx 6442, **Mitsubishi 6490**, Mullen 6516, **New 6551**, **Norman 6565**, Normandie 6566, **Open 6593**, **Overbrook 6604**, Randolph 6677, **Reed 6684**, **Rubin 6764**, Scherman 6804, Select 6829, **Skadden 6868**, Spingold 6899, **Straus 6934**
North Carolina: Cumberland 7184, Reynolds 7298
Oregon: **Fohs 7844**
Pennsylvania: Argus 7920, FISA 8043, Miller 8179, Philadelphia 8221
South Carolina: Coastal 8472, Roe 8494
Texas: Alexander 8656, Embrey 8828, Rapoport 9122, Simmons 9174, Stern 9204
Vermont: **Ben 9358**, Vermont 9375
Virginia: Proteus 9512
Washington: Kaphan 9657, **Quixote 9707**, RealNetworks 9712

Civil/human rights, advocacy
California: Angell 244, **Fund 556**, Grove 631, **Righteous 1073**, **Strauss 1223**
Colorado: Chambers 1385
Connecticut: Valentine 1713
District of Columbia: **Arca 1880**, Community 1893, **Hill 1915**
Illinois: Libra 2981
New Jersey: **Allen 5191**, Elias 5252
New York: **Cummings 5833**, **Fledgling 5987**, Kaplan 6250, **Overbrook 6604**, Rockefeller 6725, Scherman 6804, **Skadden 6868**
Ohio: Akron 7367
Pennsylvania: CIGNA 7981
Texas: Fikes 8844

Civil/human rights, aging
District of Columbia: Cafritz 1890
Maryland: Stulman 3891
Michigan: Grand Rapids 4447
Minnesota: Bremer 4620, Minneapolis 4714
New Mexico: Santa Fe 5533
New York: New York 6544, New York 6546

Civil/human rights, alliance/advocacy
California: **Fund 556**
Illinois: Libra 2981
Massachusetts: Beveridge 3950
New York: Cricket 5827, New York 6546

Civil/human rights, association
New Jersey: Hickory 5299
New York: Wilson 7086

Civil/human rights, disabled
Illinois: Reese 3110
Kansas: Beach 3494
Michigan: Grand Rapids 4447
Minnesota: Bremer 4620, Minneapolis 4714
New Mexico: Santa Fe 5533
New York: New York 6544, New York 6546, Rantz 6678
Pennsylvania: FISA 8043
Texas: Stern 9204

Civil/human rights, equal rights
Alabama: Alabama 1
Arkansas: Wal-Mart 210
California: Pacific 1003, **Strauss 1223**
Florida: Florida 2101
Georgia: **UPS 2566**
Illinois: Allstate 2657, Donnelley 2801, Exelon 2827
Massachusetts: New England 4193
Michigan: Chrysler 4366, Comerica 4368, DTE 4410, Ford 4430
New York: **Cummings 5833**, Hagedorn 6127, **IBM 6203**, Morgan 6507, NoVo 6570, **PepsiCo 6627**
North Carolina: Delta 7191, Foundation 7202
Ohio: KeyBank 7523
Pennsylvania: Air 7907, CIGNA 7981, **Heinz 8083**
Texas: BNSF 8706
Virginia: Dominion 9422, **Gannett 9439**
Wisconsin: Alliant 9804, **Baird 9811**

Civil/human rights, formal/general education
North Carolina: Reynolds 7298

Civil/human rights, fund raising/fund distribution
Pennsylvania: Air 7907

Civil/human rights, government agencies
New York: **Rockefeller 6723**

Civil/human rights, immigrants
Arkansas: Endeavor 186
California: Firedoll 528, **Haas 643**, Rosenberg 1088, vanLoben 1283
District of Columbia: Cafritz 1890
Massachusetts: Berkshire 3946
Michigan: Grand Rapids 4447
Minnesota: Bremer 4620, Minneapolis 4714, Phillips 4741
New Mexico: Santa Fe 5533
New York: **Carnegie 5747**, New York 6544, New York 6546, Speyer 6896
Vermont: **Ben 9358**

Civil/human rights, LGBTQ
California: Bohnett 324, **Haas 643**, Small 1180, vanLoben 1283
Colorado: **Gill 1421**
Florida: Miami 2238
Maryland: Rocking 3871
Massachusetts: Harmsworth 4087
Michigan: Grand Rapids 4447
Minnesota: Bremer 4620, Phillips 4741
New Mexico: Santa Fe 5533
New York: **Arcus 5608**, Habib 6126, Johnson 6239, New York 6544, New York 6546, Snowdon 6879

Civil/human rights, minorities
California: vanLoben 1283
District of Columbia: Cafritz 1890
Florida: Miami 2238
Maryland: Rock 3870
Massachusetts: Golden 4073
Michigan: Grand Rapids 4447
Minnesota: Bremer 4620, Minneapolis 4714, Phillips 4741
New Jersey: Elias 5252, Victoria 5490
New Mexico: Santa Fe 5533
New York: New York 6544, New York 6546, Scherman 6804
North Carolina: Foundation 7202, Reynolds 7298

Civil/human rights, public policy
Illinois: Libra 2981, **Retirement 3113**
Minnesota: Westcliff 4801
New York: **Rockefeller 6723**

Civil/human rights, reform
Illinois: Libra 2981

Civil/human rights, single organization support
Massachusetts: Krupp 4131
New York: Pels 6625

Civil/human rights, women
California: Linked 842, vanLoben 1283
District of Columbia: Cafritz 1890
Michigan: Grand Rapids 4447
Minnesota: Bremer 4620, Minneapolis 4714
New Mexico: Santa Fe 5533
New York: **Bydale 5738**, New York 6544, New York 6546, NoVo 6570
North Carolina: Reynolds 7298
Washington: **Channel 9597**

Community development, business promotion
Arkansas: Wal-Mart 210
Connecticut: People's 1671
Georgia: Colonial 2430
Illinois: **Deere 2790**, MB 3008
Indiana: Central 3272
Missouri: **Kauffman 4921**
New Jersey: Give 5278, KPMG 5349
North Carolina: Olin 7279
Ohio: Dayton 7429
Pennsylvania: Merchants 8175
Texas: Sterling 9203, **Whole 9276**
Virginia: SunTrust 9539
Wisconsin: Wanek 9964

Community development, citizen coalitions
California: California 368
Colorado: Colorado 1390
Florida: Gulf 2142
Illinois: Mander 2998, Woods 3242
New Mexico: Santa Fe 5533
New York: Cricket 5827, Loeb 6384, **Mertz 6477**
Ohio: **Needmor 7588**

Community development, civic centers
Iowa: EMC 3428
Michigan: Consumers 4376, General 4442
Minnesota: Larson 4692
Texas: Herzstein 8905
Washington: Miller 9685

Community development, men's clubs
Virginia: SunTrust 9539

Community development, neighborhood associations
Illinois: Woods 3242
Indiana: Community 3280
Michigan: Dyer 4412
New York: Loeb 6384

Community development, neighborhood development
Alabama: Alabama 1, BBVA 9, Finlay 33, Goodrich 36
California: Cathay 385, Eucalyptus 510, Germanacos 574, Herbst 682, Irvine 727, Ludwick 856, North 972, Silver 1168
Colorado: Pikes 1478
Connecticut: Community 1562, Middlesex 1644, People's 1671
Delaware: Reynolds 1849
Florida: Community 2040, Gulf 2142, **Knight 2191**, Miami 2238, NextEra 2251, Stein 2337
Georgia: Communities 2431, Community 2432, Community 2434, Georgia 2468
Idaho: Idaho 2632

Community development, public/private ventures

Community development, real estate

Community development, service clubs

Community development, small businesses

Community development, women's clubs

Community/economic development

Douglas 3509, Hutchinson 3521, Manhattan 3532, Scott 3543, Sprint 3549, Stowers 3550, Topeka 3552

Kentucky: Augusta 3557, Barzun 3559, Blue 3560, Community 3569, Community 3570, Cralle 3571, Durr 3572, Independence 3583, Public 3597, Young 3607

Louisiana: Albemarle 3609, Baton Rouge 3613, Brown 3617, Community 3623, Community 3624, Community 3625, Dore' 3629, Grigsby 3640, Helis 3641, Jones 3645, Keller 3646, Lorio 3650, New Orleans 3656, RosaMary 3663, Scott 3666, Young 3674

Maine: Alfond 3679, Gorman 3689, Maine 3698, Mulford 3702, TD 3710

Maryland: Abell 3712, Choice 3748, Colhoun 3755, Community 3758, Community 3759, Community 3760, Delaplaine 3778, France 3796, Legg 3828, Lockheed 3837, Mid-Shore 3851, NASDAQ 3857, Price 3865, **Sidgmore 3885**, St. John 3888, TKF 3896

Massachusetts: Adams 3916, Arbella 3926, **Barr 3937**, Bayrd 3938, BCLF 3939, Benson 3942, Berkshire 3946, Berkshire 3947, Boston 3956, **Bresky 3958**, Bristol 3960, Brookline 3962, Brooks 3963, **Cabot 3966**, Cambridge 3971, Cape Cod 3974, Clarke 3986, Clipper 3987, Community 3990, Community 3991, Community 3992, Copeland 3994, Demoulas 4015, Dunn 4027, Eos 4037, Fletcher 4054, **Garfield 4065**, Hanover 4086, Highland 4098, Hyams 4103, Island 4109, Janey 4111, Ladd 4132, Liberty 4145, Lowell 4152, McEvoy 4168, Miller 4177, MWC 4186, North 4194, Parker 4207, Riley 4239, Rogers 4243, Santander 4256, Starwood 4284, Stoddard 4293, Sudbury 4299, Thompson 4307, Worcester 4327

Michigan: Albion 4332, Alro 4336, Ann Arbor 4340, Barry 4342, Battle Creek 4343, Bay 4344, Berrien 4347, Besse 4348, Brown 4356, Capital 4357, Charlevoix 4361, Chrysler 4366, Comerica 4368, Community 4369, Community 4371, Community 4373, Community 4374, Consumers 4376, **Cooper-Standard 4380**, Cronin 4383, DeVos 4399, **Dow 4404**, Dow 4405, Dow 4407, Dow 4408, DTE 4410, Eddy 4414, Ford 4430, Fremont 4438, Frey 4440, General 4442, Gilmore 4445, Grand Haven 4446, Grand Rapids 4447, Grand 4448, Greenville 4452, Helppie 4456, Hillsdale 4461, Hurst 4464, Jackson 4467, Johnston 4469, Kalamazoo 4472, **Kellogg 4473**, **Kellogg 4474**, **Kresge 4479**, Lenawee 4485, Manoogian 4492, Marshall 4496, Midland 4502, **Mott 4510**, Mott 4511, **Myers 4515**, Petoskey 4522, Pokagon 4523, Saginaw 4532, Steelcase 4547, Strosacker 4549, Sturgis 4550, Van Andel 4567, VanderWeide 4572, Wasserman 4576, Wege 4579, Whirlpool 4583, Whiting 4584

Minnesota: Blandin 4617, Blue 4618, Bremer 4620, Buuck 4623, Duluth 4649, Ecolab 4651, Grand Rapids 4667, Hallett 4671, Hersey 4673, HRK 4677, Initiative 4679, Johnson 4683, Land 4691, Leonard 4694, Marbrook 4702, McKnight 4709, McNeely 4710, Minneapolis 4714, Minnesota 4715, Minnesota 4716, Mooty 4720, **Mosaic 4722**, Neilson 4725, Northwest 4729, Opus 4731, Oswald 4735, **Pentair 4739**, RBC 4748, Rochester 4755, Saint Paul 4757, Securian 4761, Southwest 4768, **St. Jude 4770**, Target 4776, TCF 4778, TEAM 4779, Travelers 4783, U.S. 4784, Valspar 4786, Veden 4787, West 4800, Xcel 4808

Mississippi: CREATE 4822, Foundation 4827, Greater 4829, Gulf 4830, Hardin 4831, Mississippi 4839, Riley 4844

Missouri: Albrecht 4850, American 4852, Anheuser 4853, Centene 4870, Community 4872, Dunn 4882, H & R 4902, Hall 4905, JSM 4918, Kansas 4920, Kemper 4926, Musgrave 4947, Saint Louis 4966, Schwartze 4968, Stupp 4983, Taylor 4987, Truman 4996

Montana: Central 5006, Edwards 5008, First 5009, Washington 5018

Nebraska: Abel 5021, Buckley 5026, Grand Island 5044, Hamilton 5045, Hastings 5046, Kearney 5055, Kiewit 5056, Kiewit 5057, Lexington 5062, Merrick 5067, Mid-Nebraska 5068, Omaha 5074, Phelps 5075, Slosburg 5083, Union 5090, Weitz 5092, Wirth 5095, Woods 5096, York 5098

Nevada: Bretzlaff 5103, Community 5108, Hart 5122, Nevada 5134, Parasol 5138

New Hampshire: Butler 5165, **Fidelity 5170**

New Jersey: **Allen 5191**, Barber 5201, Bolger 5207, Campbell 5223, Community 5232, Danellie 5237, Elias 5252, Fund 5270, L.F.H. 5353, Levitt 5361, Mazer 5375, MCJ 5377, **Merck 5379**, Phipps 5406, Princeton 5411, Princeton 5412, PSEG 5416, **Sanofi 5437**, South 5463, Strauss 5470, Summit 5473, Sunup 5474, Unilever 5484, **Verizon 5489**, Victoria 5490

New Mexico: Chase 5517, McCune 5529, Santa Fe 5533

New York: Abrons 5546, Adirondack 5556, Allyn 5575, Altman 5581, American 5587, **American 5588**, Assurant 5621, Bahnik 5634, Bischoff 5678, Blue 5685, Brooklyn 5718, BTMU 5724, Carson 5748, Cattaraugus 5750, Central 5757, Charina 5764, Chautauqua 5766, **Citi 5780**, **Clark 5785**, Community 5802, Copper 5815, Crisp 5828, Curran 5835, Dancing 5846, **Deutsche 5876**, Dewar 5879, DiMenna 5886, DiMino 5887, **Discount 5889**, Dyson 5923, Elmezzi 5948, ESL 5960, Fisher 5983, **Ford 5994**, **Foundation 6001**, Gebbie 6038, Gerry 6044, Glens Falls 6057, **Goldman 6070**, Green 6101, Grigg 6109, Hagedorn 6128, Herrnstein 6165, **Hickrill 6173**, Hudson 6191, Jones 6242, **JPMorgan 6244**, **Kaplan 6252**, Kelly 6271, Klingenstein 6293, Kurz 6314, Lanza 6329, Lenna 6352, Makioka 6421, MBIA 6451, McManus 6463, **Mertz 6477**, **MetLife 6479**, Milliken 6487, Mitsui 6491, Mizuho 6492, Mys 6519, National 6526, NBC 6531, New York 6543, New York 6544, New York 6546, Nicholson 6558, **Norman 6565**, Normandie 6566, Northfield 6568, NoVo 6570, NYSE 6573, O'Connor 6578, Oishei 6584, O'Sullivan 6601, **Ottaway 6603**, **Pershing 6629**, **Polo 6651**, Rauch 6681, Richmond 6703, Riedman 6706, Robinson 6721, Rochester 6722, **Rockefeller 6724**, Rockefeller 6725, Rosner 6752, Rudin 6768, Sandy 6791, Schenectady 6802, Scherman 6804, Schwartz 6819, Sheldon 6841, Snow 6878, Solomon 6887, **Sparkplug 6894**, Spingold 6899, Stanton 6908, Staten 6912, Sumitomo 6943, **Surdna 6947**, TE 6966, Thompson 6975, Tianaderrah 6977, Vidda 7030, Wegman 7061, Weinberg 7067, Wells 7073, Wendt 7074, Western 7078, Wilson 7088, Wright 7104, Zeides 7119

North Carolina: Babcock 7138, **Bank 7139**, Bate 7141, BB&T 7143, Beckman 7145, Biddle 7150, Branan 7157, Community 7178, Community 7179, Community 7180, Community 7181, Community 7182, Cumberland 7184, Dalton 7187, Finley 7199, George 7205, Goodrich 7213, Greenville 7217, Hanes 7222, Legatus 7254, Morgan 7269, Perkins 7282, Polk 7287, Reynolds 7296, Reynolds 7297, Reynolds 7298, Robertson 7305, Shelton 7310, Smith 7317, Tannenbaum 7326, Triangle 7328, VF 7332, Weaver 7335, Winston-Salem 7340

North Dakota: Fargo 7351, Larson 7352, MDU 7354, North Dakota 7357

Ohio: Akron 7367, American 7368, Anderson 7372, Ariel 7377, Ashland 7378, Ashtabula 7379, Cincinnati 7404, Cleveland 7406, Columbus 7411, Community 7413, Community 7414, Community 7417, Coshocton 7421, Dayton 7429, Delaware 7431, Dorn 7439, **Eaton 7442**, Erie 7444, Fairfield 7445, Fifth 7452, FirstEnergy 7455, Frost 7464, Geis 7467, Gund 7478, Haile, 7480, Hamilton 7481, Haslinger 7482, Honda 7490, Hubert 7495, Hudson 7496, Lancaster 7533, Lehner 7536, Lincoln 7541, Luther 7548, Macbea 7551, **Mandel 7555**, Marietta 7557, Mercer 7567, Middletown 7570, Montgomery 7575, Morrison 7580, Murdough 7583, Murphy 7584, Muskingum 7585, National 7586, Nationwide 7587, New Albany 7589, NiSource 7591, Nord 7595, Northern 7597, Orr 7604, Parker 7611, Piqua 7620, Richland 7630, Roggecora 7635, Scioto 7657, Sherwin-Williams 7661, Silk 7663, Stark 7673, Stranahan 7678, Third 7681, **Timken 7684**, Toledo 7686, Troy 7688, Turner 7691, Warren 7702, Wayne 7704, Wean 7705, Western 7710, Westfield 7711, Wolfe 7719, Youngstown 7723

Oklahoma: American 7728, Asbjornson 7729, Bartlesville 7731, Bovaird 7735, Dotson 7748, Helmerich 7758, Hille 7759, Inasmuch 7760, Jones 7762, Masonic 7771, McCasland 7772, McMahon 7776, Oklahoma City 7781, ONEOK 7783, Share 7795, Southern 7798, Tulsa 7807, Williams 7814

Oregon: Adler 7822, Benton 7825, Carpenter 7831, **Fohs 7844**, Ford 7845, Jeld 7856, Lamfrom 7863, Meyer 7870, Miller 7872, Oregon 7876, PacifiCorp 7877, Sky 7890, Tucker 7896, Woodard 7899

Pennsylvania: Adam 7906, Air 7907, Ametek 7913, Armstrong 7921, Armstrong 7922, Baker 7925, Bayer 7932, Benedum 7935, Beneficial 7936, Berks 7939, BNY 7946, Central 7971, Centre 7973, Century 7974, Chatham 7978, CIGNA 7981, Claneil 7982, **Colcom 7986**, Community 7990, Community 7991, Community 7992, Community 7994, Connelly 7995, Crawford 8001, Davis 8007, Degenstein 8008, Dietrich 8010, **Diiriye 8011**, Dolfinger 8013, Dollar 8014, EQT 8025, Erie 8026, ESSA 8028, Fels 8035, First 8040, First 8041, Foundation 8046, Hunt 8100, Huston 8102, Kinsley 8127, Lancaster 8135, Lehigh Valley 8136, Luzerne 8152, McFeely 8163, Mellon 8173, Northwest 8200, Oxford 8208, Philadelphia 8221, Pittsburgh 8228, PNC 8230, **PPG 8235**, Saint 8260, Scranton 8275, Simon 8286, Snee 8291, Stackpole 8295, United 8324, Vanguard 8327, West 8334, York 8351

Puerto Rico: Puerto Rico 8353

Rhode Island: Amica 8356, Carter 8368, Citizens 8374, Elms 8387, **FM 8393**, Hoche-Scofield 8405, Rhode Island 8429, Steadley 8442, Textron 8446, TriMix 8448

South Carolina: Bailey 8458, Byerly 8462, Central 8468, Coastal 8472, Community 8475, Foothills 8478, Graham 8481, Hipp 8483, Moore 8488, Post 8492, **ScanSource 8495**, Sonoco 8500, Spartanburg 8501, Springs 8504, Waccamaw 8507

South Dakota: Black 8511, Dakota 8514, Sioux Falls 8521, South Dakota 8522

Tennessee: Assisi 8530, Christy 8545, Clayton 8547, Community 8548, Community 8550, East 8560, Eastman 8561, Frist 8568, Haslam 8581, Lansky 8594, Lyndhurst 8599, Shinn 8627, Turner 8639, Wilson 8646

Texas: Abell 8650, Ackerman 8651, Alcon 8655, Alexander 8656, AT&T 8675, Austin 8676, Badger 8678, Ballard 8680, Bass 8688, Bass 8689, Bickel 8705, BNSF 8706, Boeckman 8707, Booth 8711, **BP 8718**, Cailloux 8742, Coastal 8768, Collins 8771, Community 8774, Community 8775, Community 8776, Community 8777, **Dell 8805**, Dickson-Allen 8806, Doss 8813, Eady 8818, East 8819, El Paso 8825, Embrey 8828, **ExxonMobil 8833**, Fluor 8851, Frees 8857, Greater 8873, H.E.B. 8879, Herzstein 8905, Hoblitzelle 8912, Hunt 8922, Ingram 8925, Jarvis 8931, Johnson 8940, Johnson 8941, Kempner 8952, Kessler 8954, Kilroy 8956, Kinder 8958, Kurth 8971, Lawrence 8973, Lightner 8985, Lubbock 8994, Mayor 9007, McDermott 9013, McNair 9017, Meadows 9019, Meredith 9023, Moody 9033, Murchison 9045, **Natem 9052**, Navarro 9054, Northen 9063, NuStar 9065, Once 9070, Permian 9091, Priddy 9109, Rapoport 9122, Rees-Jones 9125, Robinson 9133, Rockwell 9135, Sams 9145, San Angelo 9146, San Angelo 9147, San Antonio 9148, Sharp 9167, Shell 9168, Simmons 9174, Simmons 9175, Smith 9179, Smith 9181, Smith 9184, Sterling 9203, Swinney 9218, Temple 9223, Texas 9227, Tijerina, 9234, Trull 9240,

Turner 9242, Vanberg 9247, Waco 9251, Weaver 9261, Wintermann 9283, Woodforest 9290
Utah: Huntsman 9327, Park 9341
Vermont: **Ben 9358**, Lintilhac 9365, National 9368, Tarrant 9373, Vermont 9375
Virgin Islands: Community 9377
Virginia: Alleghany 9382, AMERIGROUP 9383, Arlington 9384, Beazley 9391, Cabell 9397, Cameron 9398, Capital 9400, Carrington, 9402, Charlottesville 9405, Community 9410, Community 9411, Community 9416, Danville 9421, Dominion 9422, Dreyfus 9423, Franklin 9434, Fredericksburg 9436, **Gannett 9439**, Harvest 9450, Launders 9468, Love 9470, Lynchburg 9474, MAXIMUS 9481, MeadWestvaco 9484, Norfolk 9496, Perry 9506, Piedmont 9509, Proteus 9512, SunTrust 9539, Universal 9548, Waldron 9550, Williamsburg 9559, Wythe-Bland 9563
Washington: Avista 9576, **Campion 9594**, Casey 9596, Columbia 9602, Community 9603, Community 9604, Community 9605, Corvias 9606, First 9619, Forest 9620, **Gates 9625**, Grays 9631, Haller 9635, Inland 9650, Kitsap 9659, **Luke 9674**, Norcliffe 9693, Orcas 9697, Plum 9704, RealNetworks 9712, Renton 9715, Sahsen 9724, San Juan 9726, Seattle 9731, Sherwood 9733, **Starbucks 9742**, **Stewardship 9744**, Tacoma 9750, **Vista 9756**, Yakima 9767
West Virginia: Chambers 9772, Community 9773, Daywood 9774, Hollowell 9778, Kanawha 9780, McDonough 9784, McQuain 9785, Parkersburg 9789, Ross 9792, Shott, 9794, Wehrle 9797
Wisconsin: Alexander 9802, Alexander 9803, Alliant 9804, Bader 9810, **Baird 9811**, Bryant 9826, Community 9832, Community 9834, CUNA 9838, Fond du Lac 9843, Fort 9845, Green Bay 9854, Harley 9859, Helfaer 9861, Herzfeld 9863, Holz 9864, Incourage 9867, Johnson 9870, Johnson 9874, Kohl 9883, Kress 9887, Kuenzl 9888, Lunda 9895, Madison 9897, Milwaukee 9907, Northwestern 9914, Oshkosh 9916, Oshkosh 9917, Pettit 9919, Racine 9924, Raibrook 9925, **Schneider 9942**, Sentry 9944, Smith 9947, St. Croix 9950, Stackner 9951, Stone 9954, U.S. 9957, Wanek 9964, Waukesha 9965, Wisconsin 9969, Wisconsin 9970, Zilber 9971
Wyoming: Scott 9989, True 9995, Whitney 9998, Wyoming 9999

Community/economic development, alliance/advocacy

New York: Cricket 5827, Scherman 6804

Community/economic development, association

Florida: Community 2039

Community/economic development, equal rights

New York: **Mertz 6477**

Community/economic development, formal/general education

California: Weingart 1307

Community/economic development, government agencies

Georgia: Tillotson-Menlo 2559

Community/economic development, management/technical assistance

California: Irvine 727
Connecticut: People's 1671
Louisiana: Entergy 3630
New York: **Citi 5780**, Mizuho 6492, **Trace 7003**

Community/economic development, public education

California: JAMS 744
New York: **Revson 6693**

Community/economic development, public policy

California: JAMS 744, Soda 1194
Illinois: Grand 2875, Woods 3242
Missouri: Graybar 4898

Community/economic development, single organization support

Pennsylvania: PTS 8238

Computer science

California: Craigslist 436, **Google 615**, **Keck 774**, **Omidyar 984**, Western 1316
Connecticut: Larsen 1624
Delaware: **Adobe 1734**
Idaho: **Micron 2637**
Iowa: Principal 3476
Maryland: Adams 3717
Massachusetts: **Cabot 3966**
New Jersey: **Siemens 5454**, **Verizon 5489**
New York: **IBM 6203**
Ohio: **Timken 7684**
Pennsylvania: Comcast 7989
Texas: San Antonio 9148, Wagner 9253
Washington: Norcliffe 9693

Consumer protection

Ohio: Akron 7367

Courts/judicial administration

California: JAMS 744, Opperman 988
Illinois: Bauer 2687
Maryland: Wareheim 3903
New York: **Prospect 6663**
Oregon: PacifiCorp 7877
Texas: **Arnold 8672**

Crime/abuse victims

Alabama: Community 25, Kaul 43, Meyer 53
Arizona: Webb 174
California: Atkinson 265, Bickerstaff 313, Community 414, Community 417, **Fund 556**, Gogian 598, Green 621, Gumbiner 636, Lesher 833, Monroe 935, Simpson 1173, Weingart 1307, Wetzel 1318
Colorado: Halton 1426, Hunter 1431
Connecticut: Community 1562, Selander 1693
Delaware: **Raskob 1845**
District of Columbia: Cafritz 1890, **CityBridge 1892**
Florida: Bush 2008, Miami 2238, Southwest 2327
Illinois: Butler 2729, Field 2831
Indiana: Community 3281
Kentucky: Cralle 3571
Maryland: Ceres 3747, Community 3759, Community 3761, Washington 3904
Michigan: Grand Rapids 4447, Midland 4502, Sturgis 4550
Minnesota: Bremer 4620
Missouri: Saint Louis 4966
Montana: Oro 5014
Nebraska: Woods 5096
New Hampshire: Foundation 5171, Lindsay 5179
New Jersey: Hyde 5310
New York: Community 5802, Ritter 6712, Schnurmacher 6810, van Ameringen 7024
North Carolina: Community 7180, North Carolina 7273, Reidsville 7294, Robertson 7305
North Dakota: Leach 7353
Ohio: Fairfield 7445, GAR 7465, Levin 7539, Mercer 7567, O'Neill 7602, Ridgecliff 7631, Saint 7639, Spaulding 7670, Springfield 7671, Youngstown 7723
Oregon: J.F.R. 7854
Pennsylvania: Beneficial 7936, Birmingham 7942, Huston 8102, Phoenixville 8223, Staunton 8296
Tennessee: Baptist 8533, Wilson 8646
Texas: Abell 8650, Community 8774, Community 8777, Dallas 8795, Embrey 8828, Fluor 8851, Hoglund 8913, McDermott 9013, Moore 9034, Terry 9224
Utah: Eccles 9320
Virginia: Memorial 9485
Washington: Horizons 9645, Norcliffe 9693
Wisconsin: Cornerstone 9836, Green Bay 9854, West 9967

Crime/law enforcement

Arkansas: Wal-Mart 210
California: Caruso 382, **Draper 481**, **Manasseh's 870**, Norris 971, Seretean 1142
Delaware: McDonald 1817
Florida: Sweeney 2346
Hawaii: Wilcox 2621
Louisiana: Booth 3616, Louisiana 3651, New Orleans 3656
Maryland: GEICO 3801
Massachusetts: Beveridge 3950, Community 3992
Michigan: Grand Haven 4446, Hillsdale 4461
Minnesota: Athwin 4607, Deziel 4645, Leonard 4694, Robins 4754
Missouri: Todd 4992
Montana: Oro 5014
Nebraska: Nielsen 5073
New Jersey: **Verizon 5489**
New Mexico: McCune 5529
New York: Goldman 6068, **Guggenheim 6115**, **Open 6593**, **Vital 7033**, Western 7078
North Carolina: Triangle 7328
Ohio: Coshocton 7421, Gund 7478, Stark 7673
Oregon: PacifiCorp 7877
Pennsylvania: Community 7993, Dolfinger 8013, Federated 8033
South Carolina: Central 8468
Tennessee: Shinn 8627
Texas: Bickel 8705, Kempner 8952, Meadows 9019
Wisconsin: Alexander 9803

Crime/law enforcement, correctional facilities

New York: van Ameringen 7023

Crime/law enforcement, counterterrorism

Pennsylvania: **Carthage 7968**

Crime/law enforcement, DWI

Iowa: GuideOne 3438

Crime/law enforcement, government agencies

Indiana: Dearborn 3293

Crime/law enforcement, police agencies

California: Stark 1213
Iowa: Guernsey 3437
New York: Brownstone 5722, Fisher 5982, IFF 6206
Ohio: Loeb 7544
Pennsylvania: Clayman 7984
Wisconsin: Alliant 9804

Crime/law enforcement, reform

District of Columbia: **Butler 1889**, **Public 1940**
Massachusetts: Shaw 4270
Texas: **Arnold 8672**

Crime/violence prevention

Alabama: Community 24
California: Alliance 229, California 368, **Cisco 402**, Humboldt 714, Oakland 977, Richmond 1069, Taper 1237, Union 1271
Colorado: Anschutz 1364
Connecticut: American 1537
Florida: duPont 2075
Illinois: **Joyce 2946**, Oak Park 3061
Indiana: 1st 3251, Crown Point 3291, Foundations 3306, Welborn 3402
Iowa: Community 3419
Louisiana: Baptist 3612
Maryland: Abell 3712
Massachusetts: One 4198
Michigan: Hudson 4463
Minnesota: Duluth 4649
Missouri: Emerson 4885, Roblee 4963, Truman 4996
New Jersey: **Johnson 5329**
New York: Gifford 6049
North Carolina: Piedmont 7285
Ohio: **OMNOVA 7601**
Pennsylvania: United 8325
Tennessee: Plough 8615
Texas: Greater 8873
Washington: PEMCO 9702

Crime/violence prevention, abuse prevention

Alabama: Community 24
California: Bickerstaff 313, Drown 484, Eisner 499, Fremont 548
Connecticut: Bissell 1547
Florida: Pinellas 2269
Illinois: Community 2765, **Santreece 3135**
Maryland: Abell 3713
Massachusetts: Worcester 4327
Michigan: **Cooper-Standard 4380**
Nevada: Prim 5140
New York: Community 5803, **Ford 5994**, Seneca 6832
North Carolina: **Oak 7276**
Ohio: **Timken 7684**
Pennsylvania: First 8041
Texas: Bass 8690, **Dell 8805**, King 8959, Meadows 9019, **RGK 9128**, Stevens 9205
Wisconsin: Acuity 9801

Crime/violence prevention, child abuse

Arizona: Freeport-McMoRan 112
California: Fansler 516, Fremont 548, Gold 600, Gumbiner 636, McCarthy 895, Van Nuys 1284
Colorado: M.D.C./Richmond 1450
Delaware: Delaware 1765
Florida: Miami 2238, Ware 2378
Georgia: Turner 2562
Illinois: **Baxter 2690**, **Driskill 2806**
Indiana: Wayne 3400
Maryland: Abell 3713
Nebraska: Ameritas 5023, Davis 5034
New York: Cummings 5834, **Duke 5917**, Seneca 6832, **Spunk 6902**
North Carolina: **Oak 7276**
Ohio: Montei 7574, National 7586, Women's 7720
Oklahoma: **Schusterman 7794**
Oregon: Ford 7845
Pennsylvania: Claneil 7982
Tennessee: Regal 8622
Texas: Arena 8670, BNSF 8706, Dallas 8795, **Dell 8805**, Goldsbury 8868, King 8959, Kronkosky 8970, Maverick 9005, Meadows 9019, Najim 9048, **RGK 9128**, Topfer 9239
Vermont: Mill 9367
Virginia: MAXIMUS 9481
Washington: Renton 9715

Crime/violence prevention, domestic violence

Arizona: Freeport-McMoRan 112, Kiita 130
California: Ahmanson 222, **Allende 227**, Blue 320, Fremont 548, Gogian 598, Gumbiner 636, Van Nuys 1284
Colorado: Anschutz 1364
Connecticut: Bissell 1547, Community 1564, Culpeper 1568, Fund 1589
District of Columbia: Jones 1918
Florida: Bush 2008
Illinois: **Baxter 2690**, Morton 3040, Polk 3084, Washington 3217
Indiana: Kosciusko 3335
Iowa: Siouxland 3480
Kansas: **Shumaker 3546**
Massachusetts: Stevens 4288, Stevens 4289, TJX 4308
Michigan: Ann Arbor 4340, Duffy 4411
Minnesota: Bremer 4620, Minneapolis 4714
Missouri: Roblee 4963
Nebraska: Lozier 5065, Woods 5096
New Jersey: Healthcare 5296, MCJ 5377, **Verizon 5489**
New Mexico: Chase 5517, Santa Fe 5533
New York: Murphy 6517, New York 6544, Phillips 6637
North Carolina: **Oak 7276**, Reynolds 7298
Ohio: White 7715
Oklahoma: Robinson 7789
Pennsylvania: Claneil 7982, FISA 8043, Staunton 8296
Texas: BNSF 8706, CH 8759, Cockrell 8770, Fikes 8844, King 8959, Meadows 9019, **RGK 9128**, San Antonio 9148, Sterling 9203
Virginia: Reinhart 9517, Titmus 9543
Washington: Horizons 9645, Renton 9715

Crime/violence prevention, gun control

Illinois: **Joyce 2946**
New Jersey: MCJ 5377
New York: D'Addario 5841

Crime/violence prevention, sexual abuse

Illinois: **Baxter 2690**
North Carolina: **Oak 7276**
Pennsylvania: FISA 8043
Tennessee: Melkus 8609

Crime/violence prevention, youth

California: Anaheim 239, Atkinson 265, San Francisco 1109, Sierra 1163, Union 1271, Weingart 1307
Connecticut: Tow 1708
Florida: Bank 1979
Georgia: Sapelo 2546
Hawaii: Wilcox 2621
Illinois: Allstate 2657, Community 2763, **MacArthur 2989**
Indiana: Wayne 3400
Massachusetts: Boston 3956, Community 3992, Shaw 4270
Michigan: Hillsdale 4461, Skillman 4543
Minnesota: Bremer 4620, Ordean 4732
Nebraska: Mutual 5071
Nevada: Prim 5140
New Jersey: Borden 5209, Victoria 5490
New Mexico: McCune 5529
New York: Achelis 5549, Cummings 5834, O'Connor 6578
North Carolina: Cumberland 7184, Reynolds 7298, Triangle 7328
Ohio: Dater 7426
Oregon: Meyer 7870
Pennsylvania: Dolfinger 8013, Highmark 8092, Hunt 8100
South Carolina: Central 8468
Texas: Constantin 8778
Wisconsin: Milwaukee 9907

Cystic fibrosis

Illinois: Atherton 2676
Maryland: **Bearman 3728**
Ohio: Piqua 7620
Virginia: **Truland 9545**
Wisconsin: **Baird 9811**

Cystic fibrosis research

New York: Randolph 6677

Deaf/hearing impaired

Alabama: Kaul 43, Meyer 53
Arizona: Webb 174
California: Center 388, Green 621, Gumbiner 636, Lesher 833, Patron 1020, **Smith 1183**, Taper 1237, Weingart 1307
Colorado: Hunter 1431, King 1440
Connecticut: Community 1562
Delaware: **Raskob 1845**
District of Columbia: Cafritz 1890, **Union 1953**
Florida: Garfield 2115, Pinellas 2269, Southwest 2327
Georgia: Franklin 2462, **Thoresen 2557**
Illinois: Arthur 2673, Butler 2729, Rawley 3106
Indiana: Community 3281, Community 3284
Kansas: Emporia 3514
Kentucky: Cralle 3571
Massachusetts: Phillips 4217
Michigan: Fremont 4438, Grand Rapids 4447, Midland 4502
Minnesota: Bremer 4620, WSDC 4807
Missouri: Saint Louis 4966
New Hampshire: Lindsay 5179
New Jersey: Hyde 5310, Kirby 5339
New York: Community 5803, Harriman 6137, **Ross 6754**, Schnurmacher 6810, Shulsky 6851, **Starr 6911**, Warner 7053
North Carolina: Community 7180, North Carolina 7273
Ohio: Cincinnati 7404, Fairfield 7445, O'Neill 7602, Pulley 7624, Saint 7639, Spaulding 7670, Springfield 7671
Oklahoma: Hardesty 7756, Hille 7759
Pennsylvania: Connelly 7995, Dolfinger 8013, First 8041, Huston 8102, Phoenixville 8223
Rhode Island: Guth 8400
Tennessee: Baptist 8533, Wilson 8646
Texas: Abell 8650, Baxter 8695, Community 8774, Community 8777, Cook 8779, Dallas 8795, McDermott 9013, Moore 9034
Utah: Eccles 9320
Virginia: Memorial 9485
Washington: Norcliffe 9693
Wisconsin: Kellogg 9879, La Crosse 9889, West 9967

Dental care

Arizona: Delta 106
Arkansas: Blue 181, Delta 184, Wal-Mart 210
California: California 368, Pacific 1003, Patron 1020
Colorado: COPIC 1397
Connecticut: Connecticut 1567
Florida: Florida 2101
Georgia: Cobb 2427, Williams 2573
Illinois: **Baxter 2690**, Community 2769, Healthcare 2900, Illinois 2933, VNA 3206, **Wrigley 3244**
Indiana: Elkhart 3298
Iowa: Wellmark 3490
Kansas: Delta 3507
Massachusetts: DentaQuest 4016
Minnesota: **Patterson 4738**
Montana: Washington 5018
New Hampshire: Endowment 5169, HNH 5175
New York: New York 6549
North Carolina: Blue 7153, Piedmont 7285
Oregon: Ford 7845
Pennsylvania: Genuardi 8053, Highmark 8092
Texas: Hillcrest 8909, Meadows 9019
Virginia: Hampton 9448
Washington: Norcliffe 9693
West Virginia: Kanawha 9780
Wisconsin: McBeath 9901

Dental school/education

California: California 368
Illinois: Roberts 3120
Kansas: Delta 3507
Massachusetts: DentaQuest 4016
Minnesota: **Patterson 4738**

Developmentally disabled, centers & services

California: Cathay 385, Gogian 598, GSF 633, **Smith 1183**, **Special 1202**
Colorado: Daniels 1399
Connecticut: NewAlliance 1651, People's 1671, Rockville 1682
Florida: Bi-Lo 1996, Colen 2029, Pinellas 2269, Rosenblatt 2295, Walter 2375
Georgia: Jordan 2492
Illinois: Abt 2651, Hartke 2897, Omron 3063, Popular 3085, **Zuhlke 3250**
Indiana: Anderson 3255, Henry 3320, Miller 3355
Iowa: Ruan 3478, United 3485
Kentucky: Young 3607
Maryland: **Murray 3855**
Massachusetts: Danversbank 4009, Liberty 4145, TJX 4308
Michigan: Consumers 4376, Jubilee 4470, Perrigo 4521
Minnesota: Cargill 4628, Fiterman 4656
Missouri: Centene 4870, Orscheln 4951
Nevada: Caesars 5106
New York: Kinney 6285
North Carolina: Ireland 7239, Piedmont 7285
Ohio: AK Steel 7366, Ohio 7599
Oregon: PGE 7881
Pennsylvania: CentiMark 7970, CIGNA 7981
Tennessee: American 8528, Hamico 8576
Texas: Anderson 8663, Heavin 8898, Penney 9089, Valero 9246
Virginia: AMERIGROUP 9383, MAXIMUS 9481
Washington: Everett 9616, McKinstry 9680, Safeco 9723
Wisconsin: **Schneider 9942**, Wisconsin 9970

Diabetes

Arkansas: Blue 181
California: Cathay 385, Colombo 413, Guess? 635, Hillblom 690, McKesson 903, Mead 907, Rotasa 1092
Connecticut: **GE 1591**
Delaware: Berkley 1741, Duane 1771
Florida: Patterson 2260
Illinois: **Abbott 2649**, **Abbvie 2650**, Energizer 2824, FDC 2829, Frechette 2844, Harrison 2896, Kovler 2964
Indiana: Anthem 3257, **Lilly 3340**
Kentucky: Yum! 3608
Massachusetts: **Iacocca 4104**, Linn 4149
Michigan: Wolverine 4593
Minnesota: **Medtronic 4712**, SUPERVALU 4775
Nevada: Wells 5157
New Jersey: Healthcare 5296, Horizon 5305, Kelly 5335, **Merck 5379**, **Verizon 5489**
New York: **Bristol 5711**, Elkes 5947, Helmsley 6160, MBIA 6451, New York 6549
North Carolina: Baxter 7142, Blue 7153, VF 7332
Ohio: AK Steel 7366
Pennsylvania: Ametek 7913, Bayer 7932, Highmark 8092, **Oberkotter 8203**
Rhode Island: CVS 8379
Tennessee: Compton 8551, Regal 8622
Texas: Coastal 8768, San Antonio 9148, Young 9295
Wisconsin: Green Bay 9854, Ladish 9890

Diabetes research

Alabama: Dove 31
Arkansas: Fox 187
California: Altman 233, Coates 408, Gleis 593, Oakland 977, Treadwell 1262
Florida: Batchelor 1983, Dunn 2071, Egan 2082, Fireman 2096, Johnson 2172, Simkins 2321
Illinois: Abt 2651, Bernick 2695, Ross 3123
Kentucky: Lift 3587
Massachusetts: **Iacocca 4104**
Michigan: General 4442
New Jersey: Schwartz 5442
New York: Helmsley 6160, Ingrassia 6208, Saltz 6787, Stern 6927
Ohio: Licking 7540, Warrington 7703
Oklahoma: Hille 7759
Pennsylvania: Cooper 7997, Lotman 8150, **Oberkotter 8203**
Texas: McNair 9017, Parks 9081
Virginia: Guilford 9446
Washington: Benaroya 9583, McKinstry 9680
Wisconsin: Kellogg 9879, Milwaukee 9907

Digestive diseases

New York: Helmsley 6160, New York 6545

Disabilities, people with

Alabama: Community 25, Kaul 43, Meyer 53
Arizona: Arizona 92, McDonald 144, Morris 148, Webb 174
Arkansas: Ross 199
California: Ahmanson 222, Arbus 251, Atkinson 265, Ayrshire 276, Barker 282, Bothin 331, California 365, Carson 381, Center 388, Community 414, Community 417, El Dorado 500, Fansler 516, Gilmore 588, Goldman 605, Green 621, Gross 629, Gumbiner 636, **Hilton 692**, Lesher 833, Ludwick 856, Lytel 860, Marin 877, Moxie 950, **Neilsen 964**, Newhall 966, Norris 971, Oakland 977, Pasadena 1015, Patron 1020, PG&E 1033, Sacramento 1103, San Diego 1108, San Francisco 1109, San Luis 1110, Sandy 1113, **Smith 1183**, Sonora 1198, **Special 1202**, Taper 1237, True 1264, Van Nuys 1284, Weingart 1307, Weisman 1309, Wood 1344, Wynn 1350
Colorado: Anschutz 1364, Community 1391, Community 1395, Daniels 1399, El Pomar 1406, Halton 1426, Hunter 1431, King 1440, Maggiegeorge 1452, Summit 1511
Connecticut: Bissell 1547, Community 1562, Community 1563, Community 1564, Connecticut 1566, Culpeper 1568, People's 1671, Pitney 1674, **Tudor 1711**
Delaware: Laffey 1800, McDonald 1817, **Raskob 1845**
District of Columbia: Aid 1879, Cafritz 1890, Consumer 1894, Loughran 1925, **Union 1953**
Florida: **Arison 1972**, Bank 1979, Bush 2008, Community 2035, Community 2038, Gooding 2130, **Johnson 2174**, Pinellas 2269, Southwest 2327, Thomas 2357
Georgia: Community 2435, Franklin 2462, Harland 2477, Rich 2537, **Thoresen 2557**
Idaho: **Schultz 2641**
Illinois: Allstate 2657, Aon 2667, Arthur 2673, **Baxter 2690**, Blowitz 2702, Brach 2712, Butler 2729, Chicago 2746, Coleman 2759, Community 2762, Community 2763, Community 2765, Community 2766, Evanston 2826, Field 2831, **Gallagher 2855**, Gore 2871, Northern 3059, Oak Park 3061, Omron 3063, Polk 3084, Reese 3110, Rhoades 3115, Siragusa 3162, Washington 3217, Woodward 3243
Indiana: Blue 3265, Brown 3269, Central 3272, Community 3279, Community 3281, Community 3286, Finish 3303, Henry 3320, **Lilly 3342**, Montgomery 3356, Noyes 3361, Old 3363, Parrish 3367, Portland 3370, Pulliam 3372, Rolland 3381, Steuben 3390, Waterfield 3399, Wayne 3400
Iowa: Maytag 3460, Meredith 3463, Siouxland 3480
Kansas: Beach 3494, Hansen 3518, Hutchinson 3521, Topeka 3552
Kentucky: Cralle 3571, Gheens 3577
Louisiana: Baton Rouge 3613, Community 3624, Lupin 3652, Wilson 3671
Maryland: **Bearman 3728**, Community 3759, Community 3761, Dresher 3782, Gross 3808, Leidy 3830, Washington 3904, **Weinberg 3908**
Massachusetts: Boston 3956, Clipper 3987, Community 3992, Essex 4039, Hyams 4103, Liberty 4145, Peabody 4211, Ruderman 4250, Shapiro 4267, Stevens 4288, Stevens 4289, TJX 4308, Worcester 4327
Michigan: Chrysler 4366, Fremont 4438, Grand Rapids 4447, Johnson 4468, Midland 4502, Steelcase 4547, Sturgis 4550
Minnesota: **Andersen 4601**, Beim 4609, Bremer 4620, Duluth 4649, Edwards 4653, Kelley 4686, Kopp 4688, Minneapolis 4714, Ordean 4732, Phillips 4741, Rivers 4752, Rochester 4755
Mississippi: Gulf 4830
Missouri: Dunn 4882, Pettus 4954, Saint Louis 4966, Simon 4973, Sunnen 4986, Trio 4994
Montana: Oro 5014, Washington 5018
Nebraska: Merrick 5067, Woods 5096
Nevada: Fairweather 5118, Nevada 5134
New Hampshire: Foundation 5171, Lindsay 5179
New Jersey: Danellie 5237, Hyde 5310, **Johnson 5329**, Karma 5331, MCJ 5377, **Milbank 5385**, **Newcombe 5391**, OceanFirst 5394, Summit 5473, **Verizon 5489**
New Mexico: McCune 5529, Santa Fe 5533
New York: Achelis 5549, Baird 5636, Barker 5644, Bodman 5692, **Commonwealth 5800**, Community 5802, Community 5803, Cranaleith 5825, Edouard 5936, Goldman 6068, Golisano 6077, Harriman 6137, **IBM 6203**, Lavelle 6339, Litwin 6380, **MetLife 6479**, Mitsui 6491, Monell 6497, Morgan 6507, Moses 6511, **Nash 6525**, New York 6544, New York 6546, Newhouse 6550, Noble 6560, **Open 6593**, Ritter 6712, **Skadden 6868**, Snow 6878, St. Giles 6905, **Starr 6911**, Staten 6912, Tower 7000, **Vital 7033**, Ward 7049, Warner 7053, Warren 7054, Wegman 7061, Western 7078
North Carolina: **Bank 7139**, Biddle 7150, Blue 7153, Community 7180, Cumberland 7184, North Carolina 7273, Reidsville 7294, Robertson 7305, Smith 7317, Triangle 7328
North Dakota: Leach 7353, Stern 7360
Ohio: Akron 7367, Bruening 7391, Cincinnati 7404, Columbus 7411, Dater 7426, Fairfield 7445, Hatton 7483, Licking 7540, Marion 7558, Mercer 7567, Murphy 7584, O'Neill 7602, Parents 7608, Pfau 7618, Richland 7630, Saint 7639, Salem 7640, Schlink 7650, Sisler 7664, Spaulding 7670, Springfield 7671, Stark 7673, White 7715, Youngstown 7723
Oklahoma: Hardesty 7756, Hille 7759, Zarrow 7820, Zink 7821
Oregon: Benton 7825, Carpenter 7831, Tucker 7896
Pennsylvania: Arcadia 7918, Armstrong 7921, Avs 7924, Beneficial 7936, Birmingham 7942, Community 7994, Connelly 7995, Dolfinger 8013, First 8041, FISA 8043, Fourjay 8047, Genuardi 8053, Highmark 8092, Huston 8102, Independence 8107, Keystone 8122, Lancaster 8135, Nichols 8197, North 8199, Philadelphia 8221, Phoenixville 8223, **PPG 8235**, Smith 8289, Snee 8291, Stackpole 8295, Staunton 8296, Steinman 8300, Trexler 8320, Widener 8336
Rhode Island: CVS 8379, Kimball 8410
South Dakota: Sioux Falls 8521
Tennessee: Baptist 8533, Community 8548, Wilson 8646
Texas: Abell 8650, Anderson 8663, Baxter 8695, CH 8759, Cockrell 8770, Community 8774, Community 8776, Community 8777, Constantin 8778, Dallas 8795, Davis 8799, Hartman 8893, Hillcrest 8909, Hoblitzelle 8912, McDermott 9013, Moody 9033, Moore 9034, Najim 9048, Nearburg 9055, Orsinger 9073, Rees-Jones 9125, Stern 9204, Stevens 9205, Still 9207, Strake 9208, Waco 9251, Wichita 9277, Wright 9293
Utah: Eccles 9320
Vermont: Gibney 9362
Virginia: AMERIGROUP 9383, Beazley 9391, Lynchburg 9474, Memorial 9485, Mitsubishi 9487, Williamsburg 9558

Washington: Casey 9596, Community 9604, Glaser 9629, Murdock 9689, Norcliffe 9693, Safeco 9723, Tacoma 9750
West Virginia: Eastern 9775, Kanawha 9780, Ross 9792, Schenk 9793, Teubert 9795
Wisconsin: Community 9832, Cornerstone 9836, Evinrude 9841, Green Bay 9854, La Crosse 9889, Milwaukee 9907, Pettit 9919, Racine 9924, Stackner 9951, Stock 9953, West 9967
Wyoming: McMurry 9986, Storer 9992

Disasters, 9/11/01
Florida: Miami 2238
New Jersey: O'Neill 5395
New York: Andor 5598, Hunter 6196, Riggio 6709, Time 6982

Disasters, fire prevention/control
Florida: Klorfine 2188
Georgia: **Georgia 2469**
Idaho: Seagraves 2642
Illinois: **Motorola 3043**, White 3230
Indiana: Parke 3366, Reynolds 3376
Iowa: HNI 3443
Louisiana: Entergy 3630
Maine: Nichols 3703
Massachusetts: Dunkin' 4026
Minnesota: Land 4691, Schmidt 4758
Missouri: **Monsanto 4945**, Schwartze 4968
Nebraska: Hastings 5046
New York: Fisher 5982, Kinney 6285
North Carolina: Olin 7279
Ohio: Akron 7367, Loeb 7544, Park 7609
Pennsylvania: Degenstein 8008, ESSA 8028, Mine 8184, Taylor 8311
Tennessee: Thompson 8635
Texas: Bridwell 8726
Virginia: Wise 9560
Washington: Plum 9704, Renton 9715
Wisconsin: Alliant 9804, Johnson 9872

Disasters, floods
California: Hewlett 687, **Wadhwani 1294**

Disasters, Hurricane Katrina
Alabama: Community 25
Arizona: Arizona 92
California: Angell 244, King 787, Los Altos 849
Florida: James 2169
Iowa: Community 3423
Kentucky: Blue 3560
Louisiana: Almar 3610, Baton Rouge 3613, Community 3624, Helis 3641, Scott 3666
Maryland: Osprey 3861
Minnesota: Minneapolis 4714
Mississippi: Community 4820, Foundation 4827, Gulf 4830
Nebraska: Kearney 5055
New York: Keet 6266, Project 6661
North Carolina: Community 7181, Foundation 7202
Ohio: Akron 7367, Cincinnati 7404, Cleveland 7406, Columbus 7411
Pennsylvania: Community 7990
Tennessee: Thompson 8636
Texas: Austin 8676, Communities 8773, San Antonio 9148
Virginia: Arlington 9384
Washington: Community 9603

Disasters, preparedness/services
Alabama: Community 21, Community 24
Arizona: Freeport-McMoRan 112
Arkansas: Wal-Mart 210
California: **Agilent 220**, Allergan 228, **Amgen 238**, Applied 249, **Cisco 402**, **Clorox 407**, eBay 493, **Flextronics 535**, **Google 615**, Hewlett 687, **Mattel 886**, Panda 1010, PG&E 1033, Schwab 1127, Sempra 1140, **Strauss 1223**, Western 1316, **Wong 1342**
Colorado: M.D.C./Richmond 1450, **Western 1521**
Connecticut: Boehringer 1549, Community 1562, **GE 1591**, **Newman's 1652**, **Praxair 1676**
Delaware: **AstraZeneca 1738**
District of Columbia: Agua 1878
Florida: Bi-Lo 1996, Fortin 2106, Gulf 2142, Lennar 2210, Ryder 2302
Georgia: **Coca 2428**, **Georgia 2469**, Southern 2554, **UPS 2566**
Illinois: **Abbott 2649**, Allstate 2657, Aon 2667, ArcelorMittal 2670, Caterpillar 2738, CME 2755, **Deere 2790**, **Mondelez 3034**, **Motorola 3042**, **Motorola 3043**, Omron 3063, United 3199, **Wrigley 3244**
Indiana: Anthem 3257, **Cummins 3292**, Johnson 3330, Kosciusko 3335, **Lilly 3340**
Iowa: AEGON 3409, GuideOne 3438, HNI 3443, Principal 3476
Kentucky: Humana 3582, Yum! 3608
Louisiana: Albemarle 3609, Pennington 3659
Maine: **Sandy 3707**
Maryland: Battye 3727, **de Beaumont 3774**, NASDAQ 3857
Massachusetts: Arbella 3926, Clipper 3987, Community 3991, New 4189, Starwood 4284, TJX 4308, TripAdvisor 4311
Michigan: Chrysler 4366, **DENSO 4395**, General 4442, Here 4457, **Kellogg's 4475**, Whirlpool 4583
Minnesota: 3M 4597, **Andersen 4601**, Best 4612, CHS 4636, **Fuller 4659**, General 4661, Hormel 4676, **Medtronic 4712**, **Mosaic 4722**, **St. Jude 4770**, Xcel 4808
Mississippi: C Spire 4817
Missouri: Anheuser 4853, Emerson 4885, **Enterprise 4887**, Nestle 4948, SunEdison 4985
Nevada: Caesars 5106
New Jersey: **Alcatel 5190**, Ingersoll-Rand 5314, **Merck 5379**, PSEG 5416
New York: **AIG 5563**, American 5587, **American 5588**, **Citi 5780**, Coach 5790, Community 5803, Corning 5818, **Credit 5826**, **Deutsche 5876**, **Moody's 6499**, Morgan 6507, Mutual 6518, New York 6548, **PepsiCo 6627**, Phillips 6637, Sumitomo 6943, TE 6966, Voya 7038
North Carolina: Goodrich 7213, Merancas 7267
Ohio: **Cardinal 7398**, Community 7417, **Eaton 7442**, Nationwide 7587, **OMNOVA 7601**, Samaritan 7642
Oklahoma: Tulsa 7807
Oregon: **Intel 7853**
Pennsylvania: **ACE 7905**, **Alcoa 7908**, **PPG 8235**
Rhode Island: CVS 8379, Hasbro 8403
Tennessee: Bridgestone 8537, Tennessee 8634
Texas: Amarillo 8660, AT&T 8675, **Bolivar 8708**, **BP 8718**, Coastal 8768, Dean 8803, Fluor 8851, Kimberly 8957, Penney 9089, Simmons 9174, Texas 9227
Utah: **Nu 9340**
Vermont: Evslin 9360
Virginia: Batten 9389, **Gannett 9439**, MAXIMUS 9481, SunTrust 9539
Washington: Puget 9705, **Starbucks 9742**
Wisconsin: Alliant 9804, Incourage 9867, Northwestern 9914, Rockwell 9934, **Schneider 9942**, Wisconsin 9969

Disasters, search/rescue
California: Hewlett 687, Slager 1178
Connecticut: Donchian 1576

Diseases (rare)
Texas: **International 8927**

Diseases (rare) research
Wyoming: McKinnell 9985

Dispute resolution
California: JAMS 744, Los Altos 849, Union 1271
New York: Coach 5790

Down syndrome
California: Gogian 598, Noll 970
Colorado: M.D.C./Richmond 1450
Illinois: Van Eekeren 3202
Ohio: AK Steel 7366
Texas: Turner 9243

Down syndrome research
Colorado: Sie 1500

Ear, nose & throat diseases
Louisiana: Eye 3631
Pennsylvania: Fourjay 8047

Ear, nose & throat research
California: Caruso 382
Florida: Egan 2082
Illinois: Schwartz 3144
Maryland: **Sidgmore 3885**
New Jersey: **Pfeiffer 5405**
Pennsylvania: **Oberkotter 8203**

Economic development
Alabama: Bedsole 11, Kaul 43
Arizona: Freeport-McMoRan 112
California: **Broadcom 349**, **Cisco 402**, Community 416, Craigslist 436, **CS 442**, **Draper 481**, eBay 493, Fresno 549, Friedman 550, Haas 642, Intuit 723, Irvine 727, Jack 736, Linked 842, North 972, **Omidyar 984**, Roberts 1081, Roth 1093, Silicon 1166, Sobrato 1193, Soda 1194, Wells 1312
Colorado: Anschutz 1364, Chambers 1385, Pikes 1478, **Salvador 1491**, **Western 1521**
Connecticut: Community 1562, Community 1564, Connecticut 1566, Fairfield 1581, NewAlliance 1651, Northeast 1656, People's 1671
District of Columbia: Bauman 1882, **Hill 1915**, **NDPI 1935**
Florida: Community 2032, Community 2037, duPont 2075, **Knight 2191**, Miami 2238, NextEra 2251
Georgia: AGL 2400, **Coca 2428**, Community 2434, Community 2435, Community 2439, North 2525, Whitehead 2571, Woodruff 2579
Hawaii: Bank 2588
Idaho: **Schultz 2641**
Illinois: Allstate 2657, Austin 2677, Chicago 2746, Community 2766, Driehaus 2805, Moline 3033
Indiana: Central 3272, Community 3280, Community 3286, Community 3287, Community 3290, Heritage 3321, Lincoln 3344, Madison 3346, Old 3363, Putnam 3373, Steel 3389, Vectren 3394, Wells 3403
Iowa: Community 3424
Kansas: Community 3502, Hutchinson 3521
Kentucky: Blue 3560, Robinson 3598
Louisiana: Community 3624, New Orleans 3656
Maine: Bangor 3680
Maryland: **Ames 3720**, Rembrandt 3868
Massachusetts: Babson 3933, Boston 3956, Cape Cod 3973, Cape Cod 3974, Community 3991, Eastern 4030, **Garfield 4065**, **Grand 4076**, Island 4109, Lowell 4152, Melville 4170, North 4194, Santander 4256
Michigan: Albion 4332, Ann Arbor 4340, Brown 4356, Charlevoix 4361, Chrysler 4366, Community 4369, Community 4371, Community 4373, Community 4375, Jackson 4467, Kalamazoo 4472, Midland 4502, Miller 4503, **Mott 4510**, Petoskey 4522, Saginaw 4532, Steelcase 4547
Minnesota: Bigelow 4616, Blandin 4617, Duluth 4649, Initiative 4679, Johnson 4683, Minneapolis 4714, Northwest 4730, Saint Paul 4757, Securian 4761,

Southwest 4768, U.S. 4784, West 4800, Xcel 4808
Mississippi: Foundation 4827, Riley 4844
Missouri: Anheuser 4853, H & R 4902, Kooyumjian 4930
Montana: First 5009, Montana 5013
Nebraska: Grand Island 5044, Hastings 5046, Kearney 5055, Lincoln 5063
Nevada: Nevada 5134
New Jersey: Campbell 5223, **International 5316**, **Prudential 5415**, PSEG 5416
New Mexico: Maddox 5528, PNM 5532, Santa Fe 5533
New York: **American 5588**, **Citi 5780**, Community 5805, **DBID 5855**, Fifth 5976, First 5979, **Ford 5994**, Gilder 6050, Gimbel 6053, **Heron 6164**, **JPMorgan 6244**, Mizuho 6492, **Moody's 6499**, NBC 6531, **Norman 6565**, **PepsiCo 6627**, **Surdna 6947**, Vidda 7030, Voya 7038, **ZIIZ 7124**
North Carolina: BB&T 7143, Community 7178, Cumberland 7184, Duke 7196, Foundation 7202, Piedmont 7285, VF 7332
North Dakota: Scheels 7359
Ohio: Cleveland 7406, Columbus 7411, Community 7412, Community 7415, Erie 7444, Findlay 7453, Greene 7474, Lennon 7537, Nordson 7596, **OMNOVA 7601**, Richland 7630, Third 7681
Oklahoma: Williams 7814
Oregon: **Lemelson 7865**, **NIKE 7875**
Pennsylvania: Armstrong 7921, Bayer 7932, Beaver 7934, Benedum 7935, Berks 7939, Blanchard 7944, **BNY 7945**, Buhl 7956, Chester 7979, Community 7991, First 8040, Heinz 8084, McCune 8161, Pittsburgh 8228, PNC 8230, **PPG 8235**, **Templeton 8313**, Vanguard 8327, Washington 8332, Wells 8333, York 8351
Rhode Island: Citizens 8374, Textron 8446
South Carolina: Byerly 8462
South Dakota: Black 8511, Sioux Falls 8521, South Dakota 8522
Tennessee: Benwood 8535, First 8565, HCA 8582, Plough 8615, Tennessee 8634
Texas: **ExxonMobil 8833**, Fluor 8851, **Tingari-Silverton 9235**, USAA 9245, **Whole 9276**
Utah: **Nu 9340**
Vermont: Evslin 9360, Vermont 9375
Virginia: **Blue 9394**, Cameron 9398, Dominion 9422, **Gannett 9439**, MeadWestvaco 9484
Washington: Blue 9588, Casey 9596, Forest 9620, **Gates 9625**, Inland 9650, Kitsap 9659, Medina 9682, Seattle 9731, Yakima 9767
West Virginia: Community 9773, Eastern 9775, Kanawha 9780, Parkersburg 9789
Wisconsin: Alexander 9803, Alliant 9804, Wisconsin 9969

Economic development, visitors/convention bureau/tourism promotion

Arizona: Freeport-McMoRan 112
Indiana: Central 3272
Iowa: Principal 3476
Maryland: Choice 3748, Community 3761
Pennsylvania: Community 7991
Rhode Island: **FM 8393**
Wisconsin: Northwestern 9914

Economically disadvantaged

Alabama: Alabama 1, BBVA 9, Comer 20, Community 21, Community 24, Community 25, Kaul 43, McMillan 50, Meyer 53
Arizona: Arizona 92, Delta 106, Freeport-McMoRan 112, Kiita 130, Morris 148, Steele 165, University 172, Webb 174
Arkansas: Cabe 182, Rockefeller 197, Wal-Mart 210
California: **AAM 216**, Ahmanson 222, Allergan 228, Alliance 229, Applied 249, Aroha 260, Atkinson 265, Avant! 271, **Avery 272**, Blue 320, Borchard 328, California 365, California 366, California 368, Carson 381, Cathay 385, Center 388, **Cisco 402**, **Clorox 407**, Community 414, Community 416, Community 417, Confidence 423, Cowell 434, Crail 437, Croul 441, Danforth 448, Drown 484, East 490, eBay 493, Eisner 499, El Dorado 500, Eucalyptus 510, Farese 518, Five 533, Fleishhacker 534, **Flextronics 535**, Friedman 550, Gap 563, **Geffen 567**, GenCorp 569, **Genentech 570**, **Gilead 586**, Gilmore 588, Goldman 605, **Google 615**, Green 621, Grove 631, Gumbiner 636, **Hilton 692**, Hughes 713, Humboldt 714, **Hume 715**, i.am.angel 720, Intuit 723, Irvine 727, Jacobs 739, James 742, Johnson 753, **Kaiser 760**, Klein 793, Leonetti/O'Connell 832, Lesher 833, Ludwick 856, Marcled 875, McCune 900, McKesson 903, McMillen 905, Milken 927, Monroe 935, Norris 971, Oakland 977, **Omidyar 984**, Pacific 1002, Pacific 1003, Parsons 1013, **Patel 1018**, Patron 1020, **Peery 1022**, Perfect 1025, Pfaffinger 1030, PG&E 1033, Price 1043, Roberts 1080, Roberts 1081, Rogers 1087, Rosenberg 1088, Roth 1093, **S.G. 1100**, Sacramento 1103, San Diego 1108, San Francisco 1109, San Luis 1110, Sandy 1113, **Sangiacomo 1115**, Schwab 1127, Sharks 1153, Silicon 1166, **Smith 1183**, Soda 1194, Solid 1197, Sonora 1198, **Strauss 1223**, Taper 1237, Union 1271, **Vadasz 1275**, Van Nuys 1284, Ventura 1287, Weingart 1307, Weisman 1309, Wells 1312, Western 1316, Wynn 1350, Yellow 1354, Zellerbach 1358
Colorado: Anschutz 1364, **Anschutz 1365**, Aspen 1368, Boettcher 1374, Bonfils 1376, Colorado 1389, Colorado 1390, Coors 1396, Daniels 1399, Denver 1401, El Pomar 1406, Halton 1426, Hunter 1431, Janus 1432, King 1440, Libertygives 1448, Marquez 1454, Morgridge 1466, Rose 1487, **Salvador 1491**, Summit 1511, **Western 1521**
Connecticut: Aetna 1531, Alexion 1533, Bissell 1547, Boehringer 1549, Cohen 1560, Community 1562, Community 1563, Community 1564, Connecticut 1566, Connecticut 1567, Culpeper 1568, Fairfield 1581, First 1584, Fund 1589, **GE 1591**, Graustein 1600, Lego 1627, Liberty 1630, NewAlliance 1651, **Newman's 1652**, Niles 1655, Orchard 1663, People's 1671, Perrin 1673, Pitt 1675, Tauck 1706, Windreich 1724
Delaware: Crystal 1758, **Gloria 1784**, **Raskob 1845**, Reynolds 1849
District of Columbia: Agua 1878, **Banyan 1881**, Bernstein 1887, Block 1888, Cafritz 1890, **CityBridge 1892**, Consumer 1894, **Hill 1915**, **Hitachi 1916**, Jones 1918, Ludwig 1927, Meyer 1931, Professional 1939, Stewart 1949, **Union 1953**
Florida: Bank 1979, Batchelor 1983, Bay 1985, Bush 2008, Community 2032, Community 2036, Community 2038, Conn 2042, duPont 2074, duPont 2075, Einstein 2084, Florescue 2100, Florida 2101, Glazer 2124, Gooding 2130, Green 2134, Jacksonville 2167, **Johnson 2174**, Kennedy 2182, Lennar 2210, Miami 2238, Moran 2243, NextEra 2251, Pinellas 2269, Quantum 2276, Rosenblatt 2295, Southwest 2327, Sylvester 2348, Watts 2380
Georgia: AGL 2400, Beech 2409, Community 2435, Equifax 2455, Fitzgerald 2457, Franklin 2462, Hudgens 2486, Lockwood 2505, **Pickett 2528**, Primerica 2534, Rich 2537, Rockdale 2540, **Rosenberg 2545**, Tull 2561, **UPS 2566**, Williams 2572
Hawaii: Bank 2588, Castle 2594, Ching 2596, Hawaii 2602, Hughes 2605
Idaho: Blue 2627, Cunningham 2630, **Schultz 2641**
Illinois: **Abbott 2648**, **Abbott 2649**, **Abbvie 2650**, Allegretti 2655, Allstate 2657, Aon 2667, Arthur 2673, **Baxter 2690**, Blowitz 2702, Brach 2712, Butler 2729, Caterpillar 2738, Chicago 2746, Coleman 2759, Community 2763, Community 2765, Community 2766, **Deere 2790**, EFS 2818, Ende 2823, Energizer 2824, Evanston 2826, Field 2831, Fry 2849, Gore 2871, Grant 2876, Guthman 2882, Healthcare 2900, Hospira 2921, **IDP 2932**, King 2960, Landau 2966, Libra 2981, Mander 2998, Master 3004, MB 3008, McGowan 3014, Northern 3059, Owens 3068, Polk 3084, Prince 3089, Seabury 3146, SF 3149, Siragusa 3162, VNA 3206, Walgreen 3209, **Walgreens 3210**, White 3229, Woodward 3243
Indiana: Community 3279, Community 3281, Community 3286, **Cummins 3292**, Finish 3303, Foellinger 3304, Health 3317, Henry 3320, Hoover 3323, **Lilly 3340**, **Lilly 3341**, **Lilly 3342**, Lincoln 3344, Noyes 3361, Old 3363, Pulliam 3372, Rolland 3381
Iowa: Community 3421, Meredith 3463, Siouxland 3480
Kansas: Damon 3504, Delta 3507, Hutchinson 3521, Jones 3523, Security 3544
Kentucky: Cralle 3571, Gardner 3576, Gheens 3577, Humana 3582, Norton 3592
Louisiana: Baton Rouge 3613, Beaird 3614, Blue 3615, Booth 3616, Community 3624, Entergy 3630, Eye 3631
Maine: Gorman 3689, Maine 3698, TD 3710, **Walter 3711**
Maryland: Abell 3712, **Bearman 3728**, **Casey 3745**, Ceres 3747, **Cohen 3754**, Community 3761, **DLA 3781**, Dresher 3782, **England 3785**, Fowler 3795, Hoffberger 3817, Jacobsohn 3819, Rathmann 3867, Rembrandt 3868, St. John 3888, Stulman 3891, Sunrise 3892, Tauber 3893, Viragh 3902, Washington 3904, **Weinberg 3908**, Wright 3911
Massachusetts: Association 3929, **Barr 3937**, Berkshire 3946, Berkshire 3947, Boston 3956, Boston 3957, Brookline 3962, Cape Cod 3974, Community 3992, Danversbank 4009, Davis 4011, DentaQuest 4016, Essex 4039, Fireman 4049, **Genzyme 4067**, Hyams 4103, Josetta 4114, Liberty 4145, Linden 4148, Ludcke 4157, Merck 4171, Mifflin 4175, New 4189, Pardoe 4206, Parker 4207, Phillips 4218, Santander 4256, Schrafft 4263, Shapiro 4267, Smith 4277, Staples 4282, **State 4285**, Stevens 4288, Stevens 4289, Stoico 4294, TJX 4308, Worcester 4327, Yawkey 4329
Michigan: Chrysler 4366, Comerica 4368, Community 4371, Community 4372, Dart 4388, **Fisher 4423**, Fremont 4438, Grand Rapids 4447, Great 4451, Helppie 4456, Here 4457, Hillsdale 4461, Johnson 4468, Jubilee 4470, **Kellogg 4473**, **Kellogg 4474**, **Kresge 4479**, Mackey 4489, Masco 4497, Midland 4502, Molinello 4505, **Mott 4510**, Skillman 4543, Steelcase 4547, Sturgis 4550, Tuscola 4562, Van Andel 4567
Minnesota: 3M 4597, **Andersen 4601**, Andersen 4603, Best 4612, **Better 4614**, Bigelow 4616, Blue 4618, Bremer 4620, Cargill 4628, Carolyn 4630, Charlson 4633, Deluxe 4644, Duluth 4649, Ecolab 4651, Engdahl 4654, General 4661, McKnight 4709, McNeely 4710, **Medtronic 4712**, Minneapolis 4714, NFC 4727, Northwest 4729, Northwest 4730, Ordean 4732, **O'Shaughnessy 4734**, **Pentair 4739**, Phillips 4741, Pohlad 4745, RBC 4748, Securian 4761, TCF 4778, Travelers 4783, U.S. 4784, United 4785, Valspar 4786, Xcel 4808
Mississippi: Community 4821, Gulf 4830
Missouri: American 4852, Anheuser 4853, Brown 4862, **Enterprise 4887**, Fox 4892, Goppert 4896, H & R 4902, Humphreys 4912, Jones 4916, Loose 4937, **Monsanto 4945**, Musgrave 4947, Nestle 4948, Roblee 4963, Saint Louis 4966, Sander 4967, Speas 4978, Sunnen 4986, Trio 4994
Montana: Edwards 5008, First 5009, Oro 5014, Washington 5018
Nebraska: Dunklau 5036, Lozier 5065, Weitz 5092, Woods 5096, York 5098
Nevada: Fairweather 5118, Nevada 5134, Ruvo 5145, Shaheen 5148, Wells 5157
New Hampshire: Foundation 5171, Lindsay 5179
New Jersey: **Alcatel 5190**, **Allen 5191**, **ARCH 5194**, Borden 5209, Community 5232, **Crane 5235**, Danellie 5237, D'Angelo 5238, Dodge 5243, Elias 5252, Fund 5270, Healthcare 5296, Hyde 5310, **Johnson 5326**, **Johnson 5327**, Karma 5331, Kirby 5339, MCJ 5377, **Merck 5379**, **Merck 5381**, **Newcombe 5391**, **Novartis 5393**, OceanFirst 5394, Orange 5396, Pascale 5403, Princeton

Economics

Education

Factor 3632, Fertel 3633, Franks 3634, Frazier 3635, Goldring 3638, Grayson 3639, Grigsby 3640, Jones 3645, Keller 3646, Lamar 3647, Libby-Dufour 3648, Lupin 3652, McIlhenny 3654, Moffett 3655, New Orleans 3656, Reily 3661, Rispone 3662, RosaMary 3663, Schlieder 3665, Stuller 3668, Wilson 3671, Zemurray 3675

Maine: Alfond 3679, Bangor 3680, Cianbro 3683, Cohen 3684, Fore 3687, Glickman 3688, Hannaford 3690, Horizon 3691, Hungarian-American 3692, Iberdrola 3693, King 3694, Lerner 3695, Libra 3696, Maine 3698, Morton 3701, Mulford 3702, Quimby 3705, Redco 3706, TD 3710, **Walter 3711**

Maryland: Abramson 3715, Adalman-Goodwin 3716, Adams 3717, Allegis 3719, **Ames 3720**, Attman 3722, Baker 3724, Baltimore 3726, **Bearman 3728**, Berger 3729, **Berman 3730**, **Berman 3731**, Bethesda 3732, Bisciotti 3733, Blades 3734, Blaustein 3736, Blum 3737, **Boehm 3738**, Brickman 3739, Brown 3740, **Brown 3741**, Bunting 3742, **Casey 3745**, Ceres 3747, Choice 3748, Clark 3750, Cohen 3752, Colhoun 3755, Community 3757, Community 3758, Community 3759, Community 3760, Community 3761, Community 3762, Concordia 3763, Cordish 3764, Cornell 3765, Crane 3766, Cromwell 3767, Cross 3768, Cupid 3769, Davison 3773, DiCarlo 3780, **DLA 3781**, Dupkin 3783, Eaton 3784, Epstein 3786, Foundation 3794, France 3796, Freeman 3797, Frenkil 3798, Friedman 3799, Fusco 3800, Glazer 3802, Goldseker 3803, Goldsmith 3804, **Grace 3807**, Hahn 3811, Hendricks 3813, **Hughes 3818**, Jacobsohn 3819, Klein 3824, Legg 3828, Levitt 3832, Linehan 3834, Little 3835, Lockhart 3836, Lockheed 3837, Mann 3839, Marriott 3841, Marriott 3843, Mechanic 3846, Middendorf 3850, Mid-Shore 3851, **Morningstar 3854**, Myers 3856, NASDAQ 3857, Nextgen 3858, Orokawa 3860, Plitt 3862, Pohanka 3863, Price 3865, Rathmann 3867, Rembrandt 3868, Riepe 3869, Rock 3870, Rollins 3872, Rosenberg 3873, Rosenberg 3874, Rouse 3877, Samuelson 3879, Spencer 3887, St. John 3888, **Thalheimer 3894**, Tzedakah 3900, Van 3901, Viragh 3902, Wareheim 3903, Wasserman 3906, **Weinberg 3908**, Wood 3910

Massachusetts: A.M. 3912, Aaron 3913, Abrams 3914, Acorn 3915, **Alchemy 3920**, Alden 3921, Aloha 3922, Arbella 3926, Arzak 3927, Ausolus 3931, Babson 3933, Baldwin 3934, Balfour 3935, Barker 3936, **Barr 3937**, Beal 3940, Benson 3942, Berenson 3943, Bergstrom 3944, Berkshire 3946, Berkshire 3947, Berkshire 3948, Beveridge 3950, Bilezikian 3951, Black 3952, BOSE 3954, Boston 3956, Boston 3957, Bressler 3959, Bristol 3960, Brookline 3962, Byrnes 3964, Cabbadetus 3965, **Cabot 3966**, Cabot 3967, Cabot 3968, Cambridge 3971, Cambridge 3972, Cape Cod 3973, Cape Cod 3974, Carney 3975, Casty 3976, Cedar 3977, Chafetz 3979, Clarke 3986, Cogan 3988, Community 3990, Community 3991, Community 3992, Copeland 3994, Corkin 3996, Cosette 3997, Croll 4000, Cross 4001, Crotty 4002, Cummings 4003, Cutler 4005, Cutler 4006, Dalessandro 4007, Dana 4008, Danversbank 4009, Davis 4010, De Ganahl 4012, Demoulas 4014, Demoulas 4015, Dintersmith 4020, Doe 4022, Donahue 4023, Doran 4024, Duniry 4025, Dunn 4027, Dusky 4028, Eaglemere 4029, Eastern 4030, Egan 4032, Ellsworth 4035, **Elsevier 4036**, Eos 4037, Epker 4038, Essex 4039, Evans 4040, Fallon 4041, Family 4042, Fels 4045, Filene 4047, Fish 4051, Fisher 4052, Fletcher 4054, Fradian 4059, Fresh 4062, Garrison 4066, George 4068, Gerondelis 4070, Gildea 4071, Glass 4072, Golden 4073, Gordon 4074, **Grand 4076**, **Grantham 4077**, Grimshaw 4079, Grinspoon 4080, Gross 4081, Gruben 4082, Hanover 4086, Harmsworth 4087, Heide 4091, High 4097, Highland 4098, Hildreth 4099, Inavale 4106, Institution 4108, Island 4109, Jacobson 4110, Jordan 4113, Josetta 4114, JSJN 4115, Keane 4118, Kingsbury 4123, Kittredge 4124, Klarman 4126, Knez 4127, **Krieble 4129**, Krupp 4130, Ladd 4132, Ladera 4133, Larson 4137, Leaves 4139, Leventhal 4140, Levine 4142, Levovitz 4143, Levy 4144, Liberty 4145, Linde 4147, Liswhit 4150, Lovett 4151, Lowell 4152, Lowndes 4154, Lucretia 4156, Ludcke 4157, Lurie 4158, Lynch 4159, Maine 4160, Mannion 4161, Massiah 4163, McCance 4165, McDonough 4167, McEvoy 4168, **Middlecott 4174**, Mifflin 4175, Milikowsky 4176, **Mirowski 4179**, Mooney 4181, Morgan 4182, Moseley 4185, New 4189, New 4190, New 4191, New England 4192, New England 4193, North 4194, O'Donnell 4196, OneWorld 4199, Ory 4200, Overly 4201, Palace 4203, Pappas 4204, Pappas 4205, Pardoe 4206, Parker 4207, Patten 4208, Peabody 4210, Peoples 4212, Perkin 4213, Perpetual 4215, Peters 4216, Phillips 4218, **Phillips 4219**, Pierce 4220, Play 4221, Pomegranate 4223, Popplestone 4225, Poss 4226, Ragon 4228, Rands 4229, Rappaport 4230, Rasmussen 4231, Reebok 4234, Reeder 4235, Riley 4239, Roberts 4240, Rogers 4243, **Rosenberg 4245**, Rubin 4249, Ruderman 4250, Ruettgers 4252, Saltonstall 4254, Santander 4256, Saquish 4257, Sarnoff 4258, Schoen 4260, Schooner 4261, Schott 4262, Schwartz 4265, Shapiro 4267, Sharf 4268, Sheehan 4271, Sims/Maes 4274, Smith 4276, Smith 4277, Spencer 4278, Spina 4280, Stamps 4281, Staples 4282, Stare 4283, Starwood 4284, Steinberg-Lalli 4287, Stevens 4288, Stevens 4289, Stevenson 4290, Stifler 4292, Stoddard 4293, Stoico 4294, Stoneman 4295, Stoneman 4296, Strategic 4298, Sudireddy 4300, Thompson 4307, TJX 4308, Towards 4309, Travelli 4310, Two 4313, **University 4314**, Wang 4319, Watson 4320, Webster 4322, Wilderness 4323, Worcester 4327, Yawkey 4328, Yawkey 4329

Michigan: Alandt 4331, Albion 4332, Allegan 4334, Alro 4336, Anchor 4338, Andersen 4339, Ann Arbor 4340, Applebaum 4341, Barry 4342, Battle Creek 4343, Bay 4344, Berrien 4347, Besse 4348, Besser 4349, Binda 4350, Blumenstein 4351, BorgWarner 4353, Brown 4356, Capital 4357, Carls 4358, Charboneau 4360, Charlevoix 4361, Chelsea 4362, Chinnick 4363, Christ 4364, Christian 4365, Chrysler 4366, Comerica 4368, Community 4369, Community 4370, Community 4371, Community 4372, Community 4373, Community 4374, Consumers 4376, Cook 4377, **Cooper-Standard 4380**, Cornucopia 4381, Cracchiolo 4382, Cronin 4383, Dana 4386, Dart 4388, Davidson 4390, Delphi 4394, **DENSO 4395**, DeVos 4398, Dewey 4401, Doornink 4403, Dow 4406, Dow 4407, DTE 4410, Dyer 4412, Eddy 4414, Fabri 4416, Family 4418, **Fetzer 4420**, Firestone 4422, **Fisher 4423**, Ford 4425, Ford 4426, Ford 4428, Ford 4429, Ford 4430, Frankel 4433, Frankel 4435, **Frankel 4437**, Fremont 4438, General 4442, Gilmore 4445, Grand Haven 4446, Grand Rapids 4447, Grand 4448, Greenville 4452, Grosfeld 4453, Hickman 4460, Hillsdale 4461, Jackson 4467, Johnston 4469, Jubilee 4470, Kahn 4471, Kalamazoo 4472, **Kellogg 4474**, **Kellogg's 4475**, La-Z-Boy 4481, Lear 4482, Legion 4483, Lenawee 4485, Manoogian 4492, Marquette 4495, Marshall 4496, McGregor 4498, Midland 4502, Miller 4504, **Moller 4506**, Monroe 4507, Morey 4508, **Mott 4510**, Mount Pleasant 4512, Mulder 4514, Penske 4519, Perrigo 4521, Petoskey 4522, Pokagon 4523, Polk 4524, **Rodney 4528**, Sage 4531, Saginaw 4532, Sebastian 4535, Secchia 4536, Shelden 4537, Skillman 4543, Spartan 4544, Steelcase 4547, Sturgis 4550, Taubman 4553, Thompson 4555, Thompson 4556, Towsley 4557, **Tubergen 4559**, Turner 4561, Tuscola 4562, Van 4570, VanderWeide 4572, Walker 4575, Webber 4578, Wenger 4581, Westerman 4582, Whirlpool 4583, Whiting 4584, Wickes 4585, Willmas 4587, Wilson 4588, Wolff 4590, Wolverine 4593, Zatkoff 4595

Minnesota: 3M 4597, A Better 4598, AHS 4599, **Andersen 4601**, Andreas 4605, Athwin 4607, Bakken 4608, Beim 4609, Best 4612, Bethel 4613, Beverly 4615, Blandin 4617, Blue 4618, Brandenborg 4619, Bush 4621, Buuck 4623, Cade 4625, Campbell 4626, Cargill 4628, Carlson 4629, Central 4631, Cherbec 4634, CHS 4636, Ciresi 4637, Cloverfields 4638, Cox 4639, Criss 4640, Dayton 4643, Deziel 4645, Donaldson 4646, Driscoll 4648, Duluth 4649, Ecolab 4651, Edelstein 4652, Evert 4655, Fiterman 4656, Foundation 4657, **Fuller 4659**, General 4661, Gesner 4663, GHR 4664, Graco 4666, Grand Rapids 4667, Hallett 4671, Hardenbergh 4672, Hormel 4676, HRK 4677, Hubbard 4678, Jewett 4682, Johnson 4683, Jostens 4684, K.A.H.R. 4685, Koran 4689, Koskovich 4690, Land 4691, MacMillan 4700, Manitou 4701, Marbrook 4702, Mardag 4703, Martin 4704, McCarthy 4705, McNeely 4710, McVay 4711, **Medtronic 4712**, Minneapolis 4714, Minnesota 4716, Mitchell 4717, Mithun 4718, **Mortenson 4721**, **Mosaic 4722**, Nicholson 4728, Northwest 4730, Opus 4731, Ordean 4732, Oswald 4735, Pagel 4736, **Pentair 4739**, Phillips 4740, Phillips 4741, Pine 4742, Poepl 4744, Prospect 4747, RBC 4748, Regis 4750, Remick 4751, Robina 4753, Robins 4754, Rochester 4755, Saint Paul 4757, Schoeneckers 4759, Securian 4761, Shiebler 4762, Sit 4765, Smikis 4767, St. 4769, Stepanek 4771, Stone 4773, Sundet 4774, Taylor 4777, TCF 4778, TEAM 4779, **Toro 4780**, Tozer 4782, Travelers 4783, U.S. 4784, Valspar 4786, Veden 4787, Verdoorn 4788, Wallin 4793, WCA 4795, Wedum 4796, WEM 4799, West 4800, Winona 4806, WSDC 4807, Xcel 4808, **Youth 4809**

Mississippi: BancorpSouth 4812, BBB 4813, Biloxi 4814, C Spire 4817, Chisholm 4818, Community 4821, CREATE 4822, Delta 4823, Ergon 4824, Feild 4825, Ford 4826, Foundation 4827, Gilmore 4828, Gulf 4830, Hardin 4831, Maddox 4834, McRae 4836, Mississippi 4837, Mississippi 4839, Oakwood 4841, Pruet 4842, Regions 4843, Riley 4844, Van Devender 4847, Walker 4849

Missouri: Albrecht 4850, Ameren 4851, Anheuser 4853, Apex 4854, Baer 4856, Ballmann 4858, Bellwether 4859, Brauer 4860, Brown 4862, Buder 4864, Bunge 4865, Burns 4866, Busch 4867, Carter 4868, Centene 4870, Commerce 4871, Community 4872, Cruse 4877, Duesenberg 4880, Dula 4881, Dunn 4882, Edison 4883, Edison 4884, Emerson 4885, Engelhardt 4886, Express 4888, Ferring 4891, **Francis 4893**, Goldfarb 4895, Goppert 4896, Gottlieb 4897, Green 4900, H & R 4902, Hagan 4903, Hagan 4904, Hall 4905, Hallmark 4906, Hauck 4908, Hecker 4909, Holekamp 4910, Humphreys 4913, Interco 4914, Jones 4916, Jordan 4917, Jubel 4919, **Kauffman 4921**, Kemper 4923, Kemper 4924, Kemper 4925, Kemper 4926, Kemper 4927, Laclede 4931, Ladner 4932, Lay 4934, Lemons 4935, Lopata 4938, Mayer 4939, McDonnell 4940, McGee 4942, MFA 4943, Millstone 4944, **Monsanto 4945**, Nestle 4948, Oppenstein 4950, Orscheln 4951, Pershing 4952, Pettus 4954, Plaster 4957, Pott 4958, Reynolds 4961, Rhoden 4962, Rosewood 4964, Saigh 4965, Saint Louis 4966, Sander 4967, Shaughnessy 4969, Shaw 4970, Shelter 4971, Sherman 4972, Smith 4974, Sosland 4976, Speas 4979, Stupp 4982, Stupp 4983, Sugarbaker 4984, Towle 4993, Trio 4994, Truman 4996, World 5002

Montana: Central 5006, Edwards 5008, First 5009, Gianforte 5010, Gilhousen 5011, Heman 5012, Montana 5013, Oro 5014, Scoob 5015, Town 5016, Washington 5018, Whitefish 5019

Nebraska: Abbott 5020, Abel 5021, Acklie 5022, Ameritas 5023, Beer 5024, Buckley 5026, Buffett 5027, Cooper 5031, Cope 5032, Daugherty 5033, Davis 5034, Dillon 5035, Family 5038, Fremont 5039, Froehlich 5040, Grand Island 5044, Hamilton 5045, Hastings 5046, Hawks 5047, Heider 5048, Hitchcock 5050, Holland 5051, Hubbard 5053, Kearney 5055, Kiewit 5057, Kind 5060, Lexington 5062, Merrick 5067,

Mid-Nebraska 5068, Moglia 5069, Mutual 5071, Nelnet 5072, Omaha 5074, Phelps 5075, Robinson 5076, Ryan 5078, Schrager 5079, Scoular 5080, Union 5090, Weitz 5092, Werner 5094, Wirth 5095, Woods 5096, York 5098

Nevada: Bennett 5101, **Browning 5104**, Community 5108, Connor 5109, Cordelia 5111, Engelstad 5117, Fairweather 5118, Gabelli 5120, Guidry 5121, Hart 5122, Hawkins 5123, Mann 5130, Mathewson 5131, May 5132, M-K 5133, Nevada 5134, NV 5136, Parasol 5138, Prim 5140, Prometheus 5141, Ruvo 5145, Sawyer 5147, Southwest 5149, Stuart 5151, **Tang 5153**, Van Sickle 5155, Wells 5157, **World 5160**

New Hampshire: Alexander 5162, Bean 5164, Cogswell 5167, **Fidelity 5170**, Fuller 5172, Haas 5174, Hunt 5177, Lindsay 5179, New Hampshire 5182, Penates 5185, Putnam 5186, Quinlan 5187, Schleyer 5188, Trust 5189

New Jersey: **Alcatel 5190**, Atkinson 5195, Bacchetta 5198, Banbury 5200, Barber 5201, Bard 5202, Berger 5205, Bolger 5207, Bonner 5208, Borden 5209, Borgenicht 5210, Broadridge 5214, Brothers 5215, Brotherton 5216, Brougher 5217, Bunbury 5220, C 5221, Cabin 5222, Campbell 5223, Cape 5224, Catholic 5226, Charles 5227, CHDI 5228, **Chubb 5229**, Clare 5230, Community 5232, Cooperman 5233, Cowles 5234, **Crane 5235**, Creamer 5236, Danellie 5237, D'Angelo 5238, De Nicola 5239, Dircks 5241, Dodge 5243, **Edison 5248**, Evans 5254, Fairbanks 5255, Falcon 5256, Family 5258, Fenwick 5259, Firestone 5260, **Fish 5261**, Fournier 5264, Frankino 5266, Friedman 5268, Fund 5270, Gagnon 5271, Gem 5273, Ghermezian 5274, Give 5278, Grassmann 5281, Gund 5285, Haber 5287, Haines 5289, Halpern 5290, Hanson 5292, Harris 5294, Hickory 5299, Holloway 5300, Holmes 5302, Honickman 5303, Horizon 5305, **Hovnanian 5306**, Hugin 5308, Hyde 5310, **IDT 5311**, Indian 5313, Ingersoll-Rand 5314, **International 5316**, Investors 5317, Jaffe 5320, James 5322, Jockey 5325, **Johnson 5326**, Kaplen 5330, Karma 5331, Katz 5332, Kelly 5335, Kemmerer 5336, Kirby 5340, Kish 5341, Klatskin 5342, Klingenstein 5343, Knowles 5344, **Knowles 5345**, Kolatch 5347, Kovner 5348, Kresa 5350, L.A.W. 5352, L.F.H. 5353, Large 5355, Lenzmeier 5358, Lord 5365, Mario 5370, Martinson 5373, Mazer 5375, McGraw 5376, MCJ 5377, **Merck 5379**, Milano 5384, New Jersey 5389, OceanFirst 5394, Orange 5396, Orenstein 5397, OritaniBank 5398, Oster 5399, Palestroni 5400, Parker 5401, Princeton 5411, Provident 5414, **Prudential 5415**, R. 5418, Roberts 5422, Roberts 5423, Robertson 5424, Rose 5425, Roth 5426, Rowan 5427, Ruesch 5429, Rummel 5430, Saka 5432, Samson 5434, Sands 5435, Sandy 5436, **Sanofi 5437**, Schmidt 5440, Schumann 5441, Schwartz 5443, Sheridan 5452, **Siemens 5454**, Sierra 5455, Silver 5457, Silver 5458, Simon, 5460, Smith 5461, Stadler 5465, Stadtmauer 5466, Strauss 5470, Subaru 5471, Summit 5473, Sunup 5474, Syms 5475, Taub 5477, Taub 5478, Touchpoint 5481, Turrell 5483, Unilever 5484, Union 5485, United 5486, Vanech 5487, **Verizon 5489**, Victoria 5490, Wall 5492, **Wang 5495**, Weitzman 5497, Weston 5499, Wight 5501, Wilf 5502, Wilf 5503, **Yin 5507**, Zurs 5510

New Mexico: Albuquerque 5511, Altman 5513, Aurora 5515, Frost 5519, Hankins 5521, Healy 5522, Hubbard 5523, Maddox 5528, McCune 5529, New Mexico 5530, Phillips 5531, PNM 5532, Santa Fe 5533, Thornburg 5535, Toan-O'Brien 5536, Yates 5538

New York: 5 51 5541, A M 5543, Abrons 5546, AD 5551, Adams 5552, Adelson 5555, Adirondack 5556, Adjmi 5558, **AHBA 5562**, **Alavi 5566**, Albert 5567, Alfiero 5570, All 5572, Allen 5573, Allen 5574, Allyn 5575, Alper 5576, Alpern 5577, Alpert 5578, Altman 5579, Altman 5581, Altschul 5582, Altus 5583, American 5587, **American 5588**, Ames 5591, Amicus 5592, Ammon 5594, Amsterdam 5595, Androcles 5599, Angel 5600, **Aotearoa 5602**, Appel 5603, Appleman 5604, Arbesfeld 5605, Archangel 5606, Arctos 5607, Aresty 5609, Aresty 5610, Arkell 5611, Armstrong 5612, Arnhold 5614, Aron 5616, Assael 5620, Assurant 5621, Auchincloss 5623, August 5624, Augustine 5625, **AVI 5628**, Azrak 5630, Bachmann 5632, Badgeley 5633, Baird 5636, Bais 5637, Baker 5638, Baldwin 5639, Barakett 5642, Barrington 5647, Basch 5649, Bay 5652, Bayne 5653, Bechtle 5657, Beker 5659, Belfer 5660, **Belvedere 5661**, **Benenson 5663**, Benenson 5665, Berkowitz 5668, Berkowitz 5669, Betesh 5671, Bialkin 5673, Big 5675, Bingham 5676, Birkelund 5677, Black 5681, Block 5683, **Bloomberg 5684**, Blue 5685, Blum 5686, Blutt 5687, Bodini 5691, Bogen 5694, Boisi 5695, Botwinick 5696, Bouncer 5697, Boxer 5698, Brach 5699, Braddock 5701, Braka 5702, Braufman 5704, Bravmann 5705, Brennan 5706, Brice 5708, Bricker 5709, **Bristol 5711**, Brodsky 5714, Bronfman 5716, **Bronfman 5717**, Brooklyn 5718, Brown 5720, Brownington 5721, Brownstone 5722, Brunckhorst 5723, Buck 5725, Burch 5729, Burke 5730, Burns 5732, Butler 5734, Butler 5735, Buttenwieser 5736, CAMBR 5741, Campbell 5742, Canary 5744, **Carey 5745**, Carmel 5746, Cattaraugus 5750, Cayre 5752, Cayre 5753, Cayre 5755, Central 5757, Century 5758, Chadwick 5760, Chaim 5761, Challenger 5762, Charina 5764, Chatterjee 5765, Chautauqua 5766, Chernin 5770, Chiara 5775, Ckew 5782, Clark 5786, Coach 5790, Cole 5795, Coleman 5796, Colin 5797, Collins 5799, Community 5801, Community 5802, Community 5804, Community 5805, Community 5808, Conway 5811, Cooper 5812, Cooper 5813, Corey 5816, Corning 5818, Corzine 5819, Coudert 5820, Countess 5821, Cramer 5824, **Credit 5826**, Crisp 5828, Cross 5829, Crossed 5830, Curran 5835, Curry 5836, Cushman 5837, Cypress 5839, **Dabah 5840**, Daedalus 5842, Damial 5844, Dauman 5849, Davenport 5850, Davison 5854, Dean 5858, **Debbane 5859**, Debs 5860, Dechman 5862, Decker 5863, Deerfield 5865, deForest 5866, Dejana 5868, Delaney 5869, Demartini 5872, DeMatteis 5873, **Deutsche 5876**, Dewar 5879, **Diamond 5881**, Diller 5884, Dillon 5885, DiMenna 5886, Dinan 5888, Donner 5899, Donovan 5900, **Doty 5902**, Dove 5903, Dove 5904, Dow 5906, Dreams 5909, Dreitzer 5910, Drexler 5911, Dreyfus 5913, Duke 5918, Dunwalke 5921, Durst 5922, Dyson 5923, E & SS 5924, East 5926, Edelman 5931, Edelman 5932, Edelstein 5933, Edlow 5935, Effron 5938, EGL 5939, EHA 5940, Ehrenkranz 5941, Einhorn 5943, Elmezzi 5948, Emes 5951, Empire 5953, Epstein 5958, Equipart 5959, Everett 5964, Fairfield 5965, Falcon 5966, Falconwood 5967, Fanwood 5968, Farber 5970, Fascitelli 5971, Fearons, 5972, **FIMF 5977**, First 5979, Fischel 5980, Fisher 5983, Fitt 5985, Flinn, 5988, Foop 5991, Ford 5993, **Ford 5994**, Fordham 5996, Foundation 5999, **Foundation 6002**, Foundation 6004, Four 6006, Frankfort 6010, Fribourg 6015, **Fridolin 6016**, Friedberg 6017, Friedman 6020, Friedman 6022, Froelich 6025, Fuchs 6028, **Fuld 6029**, Fund 6030, Galasso 6032, Ganzi 6034, Garschina 6035, Gebbie 6038, Gellert 6040, **Genesis 6042**, Gershwind 6046, Gerson 6047, Gilder 6050, Gillespie 6051, Gilman 6052, Gindi 6054, Glickenhaus 6058, Gold 6060, Goldberg 6062, Goldie 6063, Goldman 6065, Goldman 6067, Goldman 6068, Goldman 6069, **Goldman 6070**, Goldsmith 6071, Goldstein 6075, Gordon 6080, Gordon 6081, Gordon 6082, Gorman 6083, Gould 6089, Grace 6090, Granoff 6091, Grauer 6095, Grayer 6096, Great 6097, Green 6100, Green 6101, Greenberg 6102, Greene 6103, Greve 6106, Griffin 6107, Grigg 6109, Gross 6111, Grubman 6113, Gural 6117, Gurwin 6118, Gutenstein 6119, H & M 6122, Haas 6124, Habe 6125, Habib 6126, Hagedorn 6128, Haje 6129, Hansen 6130, Harbor 6132, Harnisch 6135, **Harriman 6136**, Harriman 6137, Harris 6141, Harsh, 6143, **Hayden 6149**, Hayden 6150, Healey 6152, Hearst 6154, Heisman 6159, Helmsley 6160, Henle 6162, Hersh 6166, Hettinger 6170, Heyer 6171, Hochstein 6178, Hoerle 6180, Hoffman 6181, Hollyhock 6183, Horwitz 6188, Huberfeld 6190, Hudson 6191, Hughes 6193, Hunter 6196, Hunter 6197, Hurst 6200, Hutchins 6201, IF 6205, IFF 6206, **IIMI 6207**, Ingrassia 6208, Inzlicht 6212, JAF 6221, Jaharis 6223, JAM 6224, Jandon 6226, JCT 6227, **Jiang 6230**, Joelson 6232, Johnson 6233, **Johnson 6235**, Johnson 6236, Johnson 6237, Johnson 6238, Johnson 6239, **JPMorgan 6244**, Kadrovach 6248, Kanas 6249, Kaplan 6250, Kapnick 6253, Katz 6255, Kaufman 6259, Kautz 6260, Kaye 6262, Kaylie 6263, Kearns 6265, Keet 6266, Kellogg 6269, Kellogg 6270, Kemp 6272, Kempner 6273, Kent 6275, **Keren 6276**, Kiernan 6279, Kimmel 6281, Kimmelman 6282, King 6283, **Klein 6288**, Klein 6289, Klingenstein 6291, Klingenstein 6293, Klingenstein 6294, Knapp 6295, Knapp 6296, Knipe 6297, Knott 6298, Knox 6299, Kraus 6305, Kravis 6306, **Krupa 6310**, Kuflik 6311, Kupferberg 6312, Kupferberg 6313, Kushel 6315, L.E. 6317, Lambert 6321, Landegger 6323, Landy 6324, Lang 6326, Lanza 6329, Lauder 6335, **Lauder 6336**, Laurents/Hatcher 6338, Lebensfeld 6342, Leeds 6344, Leffell 6345, Lehman 6346, Lemle 6351, Lenna 6352, Lerner 6353, Leshkowitz 6354, Lessing 6355, Letterman 6356, Levian 6358, Lewis 6365, Lichtenstein 6366, Lincoln 6368, Lindsay 6373, Litwin 6380, Loeb 6383, Loeb 6385, Loews 6388, Longwell 6391, Lopatin 6392, Lostand 6394, Lowenstein 6395, Lubo 6396, Luckow 6399, Lynch 6404, Lynton 6405, **M & T 6406**, Mack 6411, Mack 6412, Maguire 6415, Maguire 6416, Mai 6417, Mailman 6419, Makioka 6421, Malkin 6422, Manton 6425, Mariposa 6429, Mark 6430, Marron 6435, Marrus 6436, Marx 6443, Massry 6444, **Matisse 6447**, MBIA 6451, McCann 6453, McCarthy 6454, McCarthy 6456, McClelland 6457, McDonnell 6459, McNeil 6464, McNulty 6465, **Mead 6466**, Mee 6467, Meehan 6468, **Mehra 6469**, Melly 6471, Mercy 6475, Meringoff 6476, **MetLife 6479**, Meyer 6480, Michaels 6482, Millard 6484, Milliken 6487, Mitsui 6491, Mnuchin 6493, Mnuchin 6494, Model 6495, Monell 6497, Monteforte 6498, **Moody's 6499**, Moore 6500, Moore 6502, Moore 6504, Morgan 6507, Morse 6509, Morse 6510, Mullen 6515, Mullen 6516, Murphy 6517, Mutual 6518, Naddisy 6520, Naomi 6523, **NAON 6524**, National 6527, National 6528, Nazarian 6530, NBC 6531, Nduna 6533, Neidich 6534, Nesharim 6536, Neu 6537, **Neuberger 6538**, New Yankee 6542, New York 6543, New York 6544, New York 6547, New York 6548, Newman 6552, Nias 6556, Nicholas 6557, Nicholson 6558, Niehaus 6559, Noble 6561, Nola 6562, Northern 6567, Northfield 6568, Novartis 6569, **OCLO 6576**, Ogden 6579, Ohel 6580, Ohrstrom 6582, Old 6586, Olive 6587, Olshan 6588, O'Malley 6589, O'Neill 6591, **Open 6593**, Oppenheim 6594, O'Reilly 6595, O'Shea 6599, O'Sullivan 6601, O'Toole 6602, **Ottaway 6603**, Overdeck 6605, Overhills 6606, Overlook 6607, Paley 6610, Palm 6611, Pannonia 6613, Park 6614, Parkview 6617, Parsons 6618, Paulson 6620, PB 6621, **PBHP 6622**, Pearson 6623, Peco 6624, **PepsiCo 6627**, **Pershing 6629**, **Pfizer 6633**, **Pforzheimer 6635**, Phillips 6637, Picotte 6639, Pindaros 6641, Plant 6645, PLM 6647, Plumeri 6649, **Polo 6651**, Pope 6653, Poses 6655, Powers 6656, Price 6658, **Prospect 6663**, Providence 6664, Pumpkin 6666, Purchase 6667, Pzena 6669, Rahr 6674, Randa 6676, Randolph 6677, Rantz 6678, Rattner 6680, Rechler 6682, Red 6683, **Reed 6684**, Regals 6685, Renfield 6688, Resnick 6690, Resource 6691, Review 6692, **Revson 6693**, Rich 6697, Richards 6699, Richardson 6700, Richenthal 6701, Richmond 6703, Richmond 6704, **Ridgefield 6705**, Riedman 6706, Riese 6708, Ritter 6712, Riversville 6713, Robbins 6715, Roberts 6717, **Robertson 6718**, Robinson 6720, Rochester 6722, Rockefeller 6725, Roepers 6726, Rogers 6727, Rogers 6728,

8187, Mosi 8189, Mullen 8190, Musser 8191, Mylan 8192, Naylor 8194, Neubauer 8196, Nichols 8197, Nimick 8198, Novotny 8202, O-Parker 8204, O'Toole 8207, Oxford 8208, Pangborn 8210, Pangborn 8211, Peirce 8215, Penn 8217, Peoples 8218, Pew 8220, Philadelphia 8221, Phillips 8222, Pilgrim 8225, Pine 8226, Piper 8227, Pittsburgh 8228, Poor 8232, Posner 8233, Pottstown 8234, **PPG 8235**, Public 8239, Quaker 8240, Quantitative 8241, Raab 8242, RJM 8249, Roberts 8251, Rorer 8253, Ross 8255, S & T 8259, Saint 8260, Saligman 8261, Salvaggio 8263, Sand 8264, Scaife 8266, Scattergood 8267, Scheller 8268, Schieffelin 8270, Scholler 8273, Scranton 8275, Seed 8277, Seed 8278, Simmons 8285, Simon 8286, Smith 8289, Snee 8291, Snider 8292, Springbank 8293, Stabler 8294, Stackpole 8295, Steinman 8299, Steinman 8300, Stuart 8307, Sunoco 8308, Taylor 8311, Thornedge 8315, Torch 8318, Trexler 8320, Turner 8321, Ujala 8323, Vanguard 8327, Washington 8332, West 8334, Wilson 8341, Withington 8344, York 8351

Puerto Rico: Kinesis 8352, Puerto Rico 8353

Rhode Island: Amica 8356, Apple 8357, Biogen 8363, Carter 8368, Champlin 8370, Charlesmead 8371, Daniels 8380, De Ramel 8381, Dexter 8382, **Dorot 8384**, Elms 8387, **Feinstein 8391**, **FM 8393**, Greene 8398, **Grinnell 8399**, Guth 8400, Hallett 8401, Harris 8402, HPB 8407, IMA 8408, Kaplan 8409, Kimball 8410, McAdams 8416, McNeil 8418, Middendorf 8420, Murray 8421, **Rainbow 8428**, Rhode Island 8429, Routhier 8432, **Ryan 8433**, Salem 8434, Shumway 8439, Smith 8440, Textron 8446, Thompson 8447, TriMix 8448, van Beuren 8449, Vance 8450, Wille 8451, Wood 8452, Woodward 8453

South Carolina: Arkwright 8456, **AVX-Kyocera 8457**, Bruce 8461, Byerly 8462, Central 8468, Ceres 8469, Chester 8470, Coastal 8472, Community 8474, Community 8475, First 8477, Foothills 8478, Graham 8481, Hipp 8483, Hopewell 8484, Inman 8485, McKissick 8486, Montgomery 8487, Pfriem 8490, Phifer 8491, Reams 8493, Roe 8494, **ScanSource 8495**, Self 8496, Sims 8497, Smith 8498, Smith 8499, Sonoco 8500, Spartanburg 8501, Speedwell 8503, Teach 8505, TSC 8506, Waccamaw 8507

South Dakota: Black 8511, Dakota 8514, **Opus 8518**, Robinson 8520, Sioux Falls 8521, South Dakota 8522, South Dakota 8523, Vucurevich 8524

Tennessee: Adams 8526, Alumni 8527, American 8528, Assisi 8530, Atticus 8531, Bridgestone 8537, Briggs 8538, Carell 8540, Charis 8542, Christian 8544, CIC 8546, Clayton 8547, Community 8548, Community 8549, Community 8550, Compton 8551, Davis 8555, Day 8556, Dobberpuhl 8557, Dugas 8559, East 8560, Elgin 8562, Ezell 8564, First 8565, Formanek 8566, Frist 8567, Frist 8568, Goldstein 8573, Hamico 8576, Hardin 8577, Haslam 8580, Haslam 8581, HCA 8582, Hyde 8584, **International 8585**, Jeckyl 8586, Latimer 8595, MacLellan 8600, Maclellan 8602, Martin 8604, Martin 8605, Martin 8606, Massey 8607, Memphis 8610, Midler 8611, Nissan 8613, Osborne 8614, Poplar 8616, Proctor 8617, Provision 8619, Regal 8622, **Scarlett 8624**, Seme 8626, Shinn 8627, Smith 8628, Sparks 8629, Temple 8633, Thompson 8635, Thompson 8636, Tucker 8638, Turner 8639, Turner 8640, Turner 8641, Wallace 8642, Washington 8643, Wilson 8645

Texas: Ackerman 8651, Alcon 8655, Amarillo 8660, Anchorage 8662, Anderson 8664, Anderson 8665, Andrews 8667, Astros 8674, AT&T 8675, Austin 8676, B.E.L.I.E.F. 8677, **Baker 8679**, Ballard 8680, Barnhart 8681, Baron 8682, Barrow 8684, Bass 8687, Bass 8689, Bass 8690, Bauer 8691, Bauer 8692, Baugh 8693, Beal 8696, Beasley 8698, Bergman 8703, Bickel 8705, BNSF 8706, Boeckman 8707, Bookout 8709, Booth 8711, Booth 8712, Booth 8713, Borick 8714, **Bovay 8716**, **BP 8718**, Brackenridge 8719, Branch 8720, Bratton 8722, Brock 8727, Brookshire 8728, Brown 8731, Brown, 8732, Brownsville 8733, Burnett 8737, Bybee 8739, Cailloux 8741, Cailloux 8742, Cain 8744, Cain 8745, Campbell 8748, **Caris 8749**, Carruth 8751, Carter 8752, Carter 8753, Castle 8756, CEMEX 8757, CFP 8758, Clayton 8765, Coastal 8768, Coates 8769, Communities 8773, Community 8774, Community 8775, Community 8777, Constantin 8778, Cowden 8782, Cowden 8783, Crain 8787, Crook 8790, Cullen 8792, Dallas 8795, Day 8801, De Llano 8802, Dean 8803, **Dell 8805**, Dickson-Allen 8806, Diener 8807, Dodge 8810, Dogwood 8811, Doss 8812, Duda 8815, Eady 8818, East 8819, Ed 8822, El Paso 8825, Elkins 8826, Ellwood 8827, Embrey 8828, Engler 8830, Eugene 8832, **ExxonMobil 8833**, Family 8836, Farish 8838, Favrot 8842, Feldman 8843, Fikes 8844, Fisch 8846, Fish 8848, Fleming 8849, Fluor 8851, FMH 8852, Franklin 8855, Franklin 8856, Frees 8857, Gale 8859, Gayden 8861, Genecov 8862, George 8863, Glasscock 8867, Goldsbury 8868, Gorman 8872, Greater 8873, Greathouse 8874, Greathouse 8875, H.E.B. 8879, Haggerty 8881, Hall 8883, Halliburton 8884, Halsell 8885, Halsell 8886, Hamill 8887, Hamman 8888, Harris 8891, Hawkins 8895, Hawn 8896, Heavin 8898, Hebert 8899, Hersh 8903, Herzstein 8905, Hillcrest 8909, Hirsch 8910, Hobby 8911, Hoblitzelle 8912, Hoglund 8913, Holthouse 8915, **Houston 8916**, Houston 8917, Hudson 8919, Huffington 8920, Impetus 8924, Ingram 8925, Inspiration 8926, Jamail 8929, **Jiv 8933**, JKJ 8934, Johnson 8937, Johnson 8938, Johnson 8939, Johnson 8941, Jones 8943, Jones 8945, Kahng 8948, Kean 8950, Kempner 8952, Kilroy 8956, Kimberly 8957, Kinder 8958, King 8959, Klabzuba 8960, KLE 8961, Kleinheinz 8964, Knobloch 8965, Kohl 8967, Kurth 8971, Lard 8972, Lawrence 8973, Lee 8977, Legett 8978, Lennox 8979, **Levant 8981**, Levit 8982, Liatis 8983, Lightner 8985, Littauer 8988, Live 8989, Looper 8990, Lubbock 8994, Lyons 8996, **Marshall 9000**, Maverick 9005, Mayor 9007, Mays 9008, McCoy 9010, McDermott 9013, McGovern 9014, McNair 9017, McNutt 9018, Meadows 9019, Medallion 9020, **Mehta 9021**, **Merali 9022**, Meredith 9023, Meyer 9024, MFI 9025, Miller 9028, Mitchell 9030, Moncrief 9031, Moody 9033, Morning 9040, Morris 9041, Murchison 9046, NAH 9047, Najim 9048, Navarro 9054, Nearburg 9055, New Hope 9058, Newman 9061, Nightingale 9062, Northen 9063, NuStar 9065, O'Connor 9066, O'Donnell 9067, Once 9070, Onstead 9071, Orsinger 9073, Oshman 9074, Owen 9075, Owen 9076, Owen 9077, Owsley 9078, **Paloheimo 9080**, Parks 9081, Partnership 9082, Patton 9084, Payne 9086, Penney 9089, Perkins 9090, Permian 9091, Perot 9093, Pinon 9100, Piper 9101, Posey 9104, Prairie 9106, Priddy 9109, Pritzker 9110, Prothro 9112, Pryor 9113, Puett 9114, **Radler 9118**, Rainwater 9119, Rapier 9121, Rapoport 9122, Rea 9123, Reaud 9124, Rees-Jones 9125, Reliant 9126, Reynolds 9127, Rhodes 9129, Richardson 9130, Roach 9132, Roddy-Holden 9136, Rogers 9137, Rosewood 9140, Saada 9142, Saint 9144, San Angelo 9147, San Antonio 9148, Sanchez 9150, Sand 9151, Sangreal 9153, Sarofim 9154, Scanlan 9156, Scharbauer 9157, Schepps 9158, Schollmaier 9159, Schutte 9160, Scurlock 9162, Seay 9163, Semmes 9166, Shelton 9169, Shield 9170, Simmons 9174, Simmons 9175, **Simonian 9176**, **Six 9178**, Smith 9182, Smith 9183, Smith 9184, Smith 9185, Smith 9186, Smith 9187, Sooch 9189, **South 9191**, Spangenberg 9193, SS 9196, Stedman 9200, Stemmons 9201, Sterling 9202, Sterling 9203, Still 9207, Stumberg 9210, Sturgis 9211, Sunnyside 9215, SWBC 9217, Talkington 9219, Tapestry 9220, Tartaglino 9221, Temple 9223, Terry 9224, Texas 9227, Texas 9228, Thank 9229, Thompson 9233, Tijerina, 9234, **Tingari-Silverton 9235**, Trull 9240, Turner 9242, TurningPoint 9244, USAA 9245, Valero 9246, Vanberg 9247, Vaughan 9248, Vergara 9249, Waco 9251, Waggoner 9252, Wagner 9253, Wal 9254, Wallrath 9255, Ward 9258, Ware 9259, Weaver 9260, Webber 9262, Welborn 9267, West 9269, West 9270, Whalley 9272, Whitacre 9273, Wichita 9277, Williams 9279, Winkler 9281, Wise 9285, Wolff 9286, Worley 9291, Wright 9293, Yarborough 9294, Young 9295, Zale 9297, Zeller 9298, Zephyr 9299, Zimmer 9300, Zorich 9301

Utah: ALSAM 9302, Ashton 9304, Beesley 9307, Burton 9309, Community 9311, Dee 9312, Doctorow 9314, Eccles 9317, Eccles 9318, EnergySolutions 9321, GFC 9322, Hall 9324, Hemingway 9326, McCarthey 9332, Miller 9335, Miller 9336, Miller 9337, My 9338, **Nu 9340**, Park 9341, Patel 9343, Peterson 9345, Quinney 9347, Rose 9349, Semnani 9350, Vivint 9354, Wagner 9355

Vermont: Evslin 9360, Gilman 9363, Lintilhac 9365, Mill 9367, Pomerleau 9369, Rowland 9370, Sills 9371, Stiller 9372, Vermont 9375

Virgin Islands: Community 9377, Prior 9378

Virginia: 4G 9379, Alleghany 9382, AMERIGROUP 9383, Arlington 9384, Batten 9390, Beazley 9391, Birdsong 9393, Cameron 9398, Camp 9399, Capital 9400, CarMax 9401, Carrington, 9402, Carter 9403, Charlottesville 9405, Chiaramonte 9407, Community 9410, Community 9411, Community 9412, Community 9413, Community 9415, Community 9416, **Cooke 9417**, Craig 9418, Dalis 9419, Danville 9420, Danville 9421, Dominion 9422, Dreyfus 9423, Easley 9424, Elmo 9425, English 9426, Estes 9427, Evans 9428, Flippo 9430, Folger 9431, Foster 9432, Fralin 9433, Franklin 9434, Freddie 9435, Funger 9438, **Gannett 9439**, Genan 9440, **Genworth 9441**, Gilliam 9442, Goodman 9444, Graham 9445, Guilford 9446, Gwathmey 9447, Hampton 9448, Harrison 9449, Harvest 9450, Hirst 9453, Hylton 9455, Kanter 9459, Keesee 9460, Kellar 9461, Landmark 9467, Love 9470, Luck 9472, Luminescence 9473, Lynchburg 9474, MAXIMUS 9481, McGlothlin 9482, MeadWestvaco 9484, Memorial 9485, Millhiser 9486, Mitsubishi 9487, MLG 9488, Moore 9489, Morgan, 9490, NewMarket 9494, Nirman 9495, Norfolk 9496, **Northrop 9498**, **Olmsted 9501**, Olsson 9502, Owens 9503, Parsons 9504, Perry 9506, Peterson 9508, Piedmont 9509, Rales 9513, Ratcliffe 9514, Ratner 9515, Reinsch 9518, Reynolds 9519, Rice 9520, Rimora 9522, Robins 9524, Rosenthal 9525, Samberg 9527, Scott 9529, Shearwater 9531, Smith 9534, Smithfield 9535, Strong 9537, Suffolk 9538, SunTrust 9539, Three 9541, Titmus 9543, **Truland 9545**, United 9546, Universal 9548, Volgenau 9549, Washington 9552, **WestWind 9555**, Whitlock 9556, Williamsburg 9559, Wise 9560, Wrinkle 9562

Washington: Adams 9566, Allen 9567, Ames 9570, Anders 9571, Anderson 9572, Apex 9574, Avista 9576, Bainbridge 9578, Bamford 9580, Barton 9581, Bates 9582, Berwick 9584, Bezos 9585, Biller 9586, Blue 9588, Bradley 9589, Cheney 9598, College 9600, Colson 9601, Columbia 9602, Community 9603, Community 9604, Community 9605, Corvias 9606, Dimmer 9610, Discuren 9611, Ellison 9614, Empire 9615, Everett 9616, Evertrust 9617, Foster 9621, **Foundation 9622**, Foundation 9623, Fuchs 9624, **Gates 9625**, George 9626, Grays 9631, Hagan 9634, Haller 9635, **Haugland 9643**, Honzel 9644, Howard 9647, Hughes 9648, Inland 9650, Intermec 9651, Invested 9652, **Islands 9653**, Jones 9655, Kelsey 9658, Kitsap 9659, **Kongsgaard 9661**, Lauzier 9667, Lochland 9670, Lockwood 9671, Loeb 9672, Lucky 9673, McEachern 9678, McKinstry 9680, Medina 9682, Milgard 9683, Miller 9685, Moccasin 9687, Moraine 9688, Murdock 9689, Nesholm 9691, Norcliffe 9693, Oki 9694, OneFamily 9695, Opportunities 9696, **PAH 9699**, PEMCO 9702, Plum 9704, Puget 9705, PWH 9706, Raikes 9708, Raven 9710, RealNetworks 9712, Renton 9715, Rice 9716, Riverstyx 9718, Roots 9720, Safeco 9723, **Samis 9725**, San Juan 9726,

Satterberg 9728, Schultz 9730, Seattle 9731, Shirley 9734, Simonyi 9735, Sloan 9736, Smith 9738, Snyder 9739, Sondland 9740, **Starbucks 9742**, Stubblefield 9745, Swigert-Warren 9748, Tacoma 9750, **Torrance 9753**, True 9754, **Tyler 9755**, **Vista 9756**, Wendt 9758, Whatcom 9759, Wockner 9763, Wren 9764, Yakima 9767, Zumiez 9768
West Virginia: Beckley 9769, Bowen 9770, Brickstreet 9771, Chambers 9772, Community 9773, Daywood 9774, Eastern 9775, Hess 9777, Hunnicutt 9779, Kanawha 9780, Maier 9782, Martha 9783, Myles 9787, Nutting 9788, Parkersburg 9789, Ross 9792, Schenk 9793, Shott, 9794, Tucker 9796, Wehrle 9797, Weisberg 9798, Your 9799
Wisconsin: Acuity 9801, Alexander 9803, Alliant 9804, Antioch 9807, Argosy 9808, **Baird 9811**, Batterman 9813, Bemis 9815, Benidt 9816, Bleser 9818, **Bradley 9819**, Brady 9821, Briggs 9822, Brookhill 9824, Brotz 9825, Bryant 9826, Caxambas 9828, Charter 9829, Clark 9830, Community 9832, Community 9833, Community 9834, Community 9835, CUNA 9838, Eder 9840, Evinrude 9841, Family 9842, Fond du Lac 9843, Fort 9845, Fotsch 9846, Frautschi 9847, Frautschi 9848, Godfrey 9850, Goldbach 9851, Green Bay 9854, Green Bay 9855, Greenheck 9856, Hands 9858, Harley 9859, Herzfeld 9863, Iddings 9866, Incourage 9867, Johnson 9870, Johnson 9871, Johnson 9872, Johnson 9874, Kelben 9877, Kern 9880, Kikkoman 9881, Kohl 9883, Kohler 9884, Krause 9886, Kress 9887, La Crosse 9889, Ladish 9890, Lakeview 9892, Lunda 9895, Lunda 9896, Madison 9897, Madison 9898, ManpowerGroup 9899, Marcus 9900, Mead 9902, Menasha 9903, Meng 9904, Michels 9906, Milwaukee 9907, MMG 9908, Nelson 9912, Nicholas 9913, Northwestern 9914, Oshkosh 9916, Peck 9918, Pettit 9919, Pollybill 9921, Posner 9922, Racine 9924, Raibrook 9925, Rath 9927, RDK 9928, Reiman 9929, Rennebohm 9931, Rexnord 9932, Riordan 9933, Rockwell 9934, Rolfs 9935, Roundy's 9936, Rowland 9937, Runzheimer 9938, Rutledge 9939, **Schneider 9942**, Sentry 9944, Siebert 9946, Soref 9948, St. Croix 9950, Steigleder 9952, Thrivent 9956, U.S. 9957, Uihlein 9958, Uihlein 9959, **Wagner 9961**, Waukesha 9965, Windhover 9968, Wisconsin 9969, Wisconsin 9970, Zilber 9971
Wyoming: Allen 9973, Community 9975, Ellbogen 9977, Friess 9978, McMurry 9986, Niner 9987, Scott 9989, Sullivan 9994, True 9995, Tyrrell 9996, Wyoming 9999, Zimmerman 10000

Education, administration/regulation

West Virginia: Hunnicutt 9779

Education, alliance/advocacy

New Jersey: **Segal 5446**
Pennsylvania: Stratton 8304

Education, alumni groups

California: Hwang 719
Texas: Johnson 8938

Education, association

Colorado: Halton 1426
Georgia: **Challenge 2424**
Illinois: Trott 3192
Massachusetts: Hopedale 4101
Michigan: Hillsdale 4461
Mississippi: Hardin 4831
New Jersey: Harbourton 5293
New York: Kautz 6260, Silverman 6855, Tisch 6989
North Carolina: Cemala 7174, Dickson 7192
Ohio: Anderson 7372, Columbus 7411, Jennings 7509, Kulas 7532, Youngstown 7723
Pennsylvania: **Waldorf 8330**
Texas: Booth 8711, Sterling 9203
Washington: Norcliffe 9693
Wisconsin: Cornerstone 9836

Education, community/cooperative

Louisiana: Community 3624
Minnesota: CHS 4636
New York: **Genesis 6042**, **Wallace 7043**
Pennsylvania: Hurd 8101
Texas: Herzstein 8905

Education, computer literacy/technology training

California: **Oracle 991**, Union 1271, Western 1316
Delaware: **Adobe 1734**
Illinois: Seabury 3146
Massachusetts: Eastern 4030
New York: **Genesis 6042**
Oregon: **Intel 7853**
Pennsylvania: Comcast 7989

Education, continuing education

Connecticut: Pitney 1674
Indiana: Old 3363
New York: **IBM 6203**
Ohio: Fairfield 7445
Washington: Renton 9715

Education, drop-out prevention

Alabama: Community 21
California: Hauptman 662
Georgia: **Coca 2428**, Primerica 2534
Illinois: Seabury 3146, **State 3174**
Indiana: Foundations 3306, Lincoln 3344
Massachusetts: **Grand 4076**
Michigan: Ford 4430
Minnesota: Jostens 4684
Nebraska: Mutual 5071
New Mexico: Santa Fe 5533
New York: **Genesis 6042**, Seneca 6832
Oregon: PGE 7881
Pennsylvania: Chester 7979, Keystone 8122
Texas: AT&T 8675, Topfer 9239
Virginia: CarMax 9401, Hampton 9448
Washington: Discuren 9611

Education, e-learning

California: **Oracle 991**
New Jersey: **Alcatel 5190**, **Verizon 5489**
New York: **Deutsche 5876**, **Genesis 6042**
Pennsylvania: Comcast 7989

Education, early childhood education

Arizona: Arizona 92, Freeport-McMoRan 112
Arkansas: Rockefeller 197
California: Aroha 260, Atlas 266, California 365, Confidence 423, Crail 437, Drown 484, East 490, Fansler 516, Haas 641, **Haas 643**, Hutto 717, Moxie 950, Orange 992, Orfalea 994, **Packard 1006**, Packard 1007, Parsons 1013, Richmond 1069, Rotasa 1092, San Francisco 1109, Sexton 1144, Sonora 1198, Weingart 1307
Colorado: Boettcher 1374, Buell 1381, Chambers 1385, Daniels 1399, **Merage 1460**, Serimus 1496, Summit 1511
Connecticut: Connecticut 1566, Fairfield 1581, Fund 1589, Graustein 1600, Liberty 1630, Main 1634, People's 1671, Pitney 1674
District of Columbia: Cafritz 1890, Meyer 1931
Florida: Bank 1979, Community 2032, Community 2035, Henderson 2152, Martin 2229
Georgia: **Challenge 2424**, Communities 2431, Cox 2445, Harland 2477, Moore 2519, Pittulloch 2530
Hawaii: Castle 2594
Idaho: Albertson 2626
Illinois: Caterpillar 2738, Community 2763, Evanston 2826, FDC 2829, Field 2831, Grand 2875, **Harris 2893**, McGowan 3014, Polk 3084, Prince 3089, Seabury 3146, Tracy 3189
Indiana: Adams 3253, Community 3281, Community 3283, Dekko 3296, Heritage 3321, Lincoln 3344, Noyes 3361, Old 3363
Iowa: McElroy 3461, Siouxland 3480
Kansas: Beach 3494, Hutchinson 3521, **Shumaker 3546**, Topeka 3552
Kentucky: Blue 3560, Norton 3592
Louisiana: Blue 3615, Booth 3616
Maryland: Abell 3712, Rollins 3872
Massachusetts: **Barr 3937**, Berkshire 3946, Berkshire 3947, Brookline 3962, **Cabot 3966**, Davis 4011, Santander 4256, Sheehan 4271, Smith 4277
Michigan: Consumers 4376, General 4442, Hillsdale 4461, **Kellogg 4474**, Skillman 4543, Steelcase 4547, Towsley 4557
Minnesota: 3M 4597, **Better 4614**, Bigelow 4616, Cargill 4628, Fiterman 4656, Frey 4658, Graco 4666, Hiawatha 4674, Hubbard 4678, **King 4687**, Minneapolis 4714, Opus 4731, **O'Shaughnessy 4734**, Saint Paul 4757, TEAM 4779
Mississippi: Community 4821, Foundation 4827, Hardin 4831
Missouri: Fox 4892, H & R 4902, Hall 4905
Montana: Washington 5018
Nebraska: Buffett 5027, Mutual 5071
New Jersey: Borden 5209, Hyde 5310, **Johnson 5326**, MCJ 5377, **Merck 5379**, Schumann 5441, Turrell 5483, Victoria 5490
New Mexico: McCune 5529
New York: Altman 5579, Community 5808, **Foundation 6003**, **Genesis 6042**, Goldman 6068, Guttman 6121, **IBM 6203**, Jones 6242, Lang 6326, **Mailman 6418**, O'Connor 6578, Rauch 6681, Rochester 6722, Seneca 6832, Sirus 6863, Sobel 6883, Tower 7000
North Carolina: Community 7178, Duke 7196, Mebane 7266, Merancas 7267, Reynolds 7297, Reynolds 7298, Smith 7317, Triangle 7328, Van Houten 7330, Weaver 7335
North Dakota: Leach 7353
Ohio: American 7368, Bruening 7391, Cincinnati 7404, Fairfield 7445, GAR 7465, Gund 7478, Hershey 7487, Hoover 7492, Middletown 7570, Nord 7594, Ohio 7599, Reinberger 7628, Richland 7630, Stark 7673, Stocker 7676, **Timken 7684**, Wean 7705, White 7715
Oklahoma: American 7728
Oregon: Carpenter 7831, PacifiCorp 7877, Templeton 7895
Pennsylvania: Arcadia 7918, Claneil 7982, Community 7994, Connelly 7995, Dolfinger 8013, Harding 8080, Hurd 8101, Huston 8102, Mellon 8173, PNC 8230
Rhode Island: Textron 8446
South Carolina: Central 8468, Community 8474, Springs 8504
Tennessee: Benwood 8535, Davis 8555, Plough 8615
Texas: Bass 8690, George 8863, **Jenesis 8932**, Kempner 8952, King 8959, McDermott 9013, Meadows 9019, Powell 9105, Rainwater 9119, San Antonio 9148, Smith 9187, Wright 9293
Vermont: Vermont 9375
Virginia: Capital 9400, Freddie 9435, Graham 9445, Hampton 9448, Norfolk 9496
Washington: Community 9604, Renton 9715, Seattle 9731, Yakima 9767
West Virginia: Kanawha 9780
Wisconsin: Alexander 9803, Herzfeld 9863, McBeath 9901, Milwaukee 9907, Northwestern 9914, Siebert 9946, Thrivent 9956
Wyoming: Christian 9974

Education, equal rights

Iowa: Principal 3476
New York: **Genesis 6042**
Virginia: Mitsubishi 9487

Education, ESL programs

California: Cathay 385, Union 1271
Colorado: **Western 1521**
Connecticut: People's 1671
Illinois: Arthur 2673, Seabury 3146
Indiana: Lincoln 3344, Old 3363
Maine: TD 3710
Massachusetts: TJX 4308
New York: RTS 6760
North Carolina: Merancas 7267
Pennsylvania: Hurd 8101
Rhode Island: Textron 8446
Tennessee: **International 8585**
Washington: Seattle 9731

Education, ethics

California: **Rupe 1097**
Colorado: Daniels 1399

Education, formal/general education

Florida: **Chester 2020**
Illinois: **Motorola 3043**
Louisiana: Community 3624
New Jersey: **Segal 5446**
New York: **Genesis 6042**
Rhode Island: Felicia 8392
Texas: KDK-Harman 8949, **RGK 9128**

Education, fund raising/fund distribution

Alabama: Snook 68
Arizona: McCain 143, Pivotal 153
California: Dhanam 463, Skywords 1177
Colorado: Monfort 1465
Connecticut: Zachs 1730
Louisiana: Booth 3616
Massachusetts: Community 3992
Missouri: Kooyumjian 4930
Nebraska: Gardner 5041
New Jersey: Merck 5380
New York: Michaels 6482
North Carolina: Delta 7191
Ohio: Kulas 7532, Schlink 7650
Pennsylvania: Dixon 8012, Stackpole 8295, West 8334
Texas: Rogers 9138, Sterling 9203
Washington: Norcliffe 9693
Wisconsin: Berbeewalsh 9817

Education, gifted students

Colorado: **Malone 1453**
Nevada: Davidson 5114

Education, management/technical assistance

California: Girard 591, Ressler 1066
Hawaii: Castle 2593
New York: **Genesis 6042**, Kornfeld 6304
Texas: Legett 8978, Texas 9227

Education, public education

Arizona: Arizona 92
California: Begin 299, CAA 362, Noyce 974, Stuart 1225
Colorado: **National 1469**
Florida: Maren 2227
Hawaii: Castle 2593
Illinois: Dryer 2808, **MacArthur 2989**, Reese 3110
Louisiana: Community 3624
Maryland: **Blaustein 3735**
Massachusetts: Colombe 3989, Duniry 4025, Schott 4262
Nebraska: Union 5090
New Mexico: Santa Fe 5533
New York: Freeman 6012, Hazen 6151, New York 6544
Ohio: Greene 7474, **Noble 7592**
South Carolina: Foothills 8478
Tennessee: Atticus 8531, Plough 8615
Texas: **Arnold 8672**, Meadows 9019, **Paso 9083**, Powell 9105
Washington: **Gates 9625**

Education, public policy

California: **Rupe 1097**, Severns 1143, Stuart 1225
Colorado: Foundation 1411
Hawaii: Castle 2593
Maryland: Straus 3890
Massachusetts: Cosette 3997
Michigan: Frey 4439
Missouri: **Kauffman 4921**
New York: Cricket 5827
Texas: KDK-Harman 8949

Education, reading

Alabama: Community 21, Protective 59
Arizona: Arizona 92, Freeport-McMoRan 112
Arkansas: Wal-Mart 210
California: Ahmanson 222, **American 237**, Applied 249, **Capital 375**, **Cisco 402**, Crail 437, Goldman 606, **Mattel 886**, Nestle 965, Quest 1050, Sacramento 1103, San Diego 1108, San Francisco 1109, Sharks 1153, Steinmetz 1216, Union 1271, Weingart 1307
Colorado: El Pomar 1406, Morgridge 1466
Connecticut: NewAlliance 1651, People's 1671, Pitney 1674, Rockville 1682, Seedlings 1691
Delaware: Marmot 1814
Florida: Bank 1979, Community 2032, Florida 2101, Glazer 2124, Green 2136, Indian 2166, Jacksonville 2167, Martin 2229, Moran 2243, Rayonier 2281
Georgia: AGL 2400, Atlanta 2406, **Georgia 2469**, Pittulloch 2530, **UPS 2566**
Hawaii: Hawaii 2602, Wilcox 2621
Illinois: Community 2763, Donnelley 2801, Levi 2976, Polk 3084
Indiana: Ball 3262, Foundations 3306, Lincoln 3344, Old 3363, Unity 3393, Vectren 3394, Wayne 3400
Iowa: AEGON 3409, Community 3419, Siouxland 3480
Kentucky: Blue 3560, Norton 3592
Louisiana: Booth 3616, Community 3624, Entergy 3630
Maine: TD 3710
Maryland: Fowler 3795
Massachusetts: **Cabot 3966**, Community 3992, **Grand 4076**, Hanover 4086, Staples 4282, Starwood 4284
Michigan: Battle Creek 4343, Grand Rapids 4447, Jackson 4467, Pokagon 4523, Skillman 4543, Spartan 4544
Minnesota: Bigelow 4616, Deluxe 4644, Jostens 4684, Mardag 4703, NFC 4727, RBC 4748, Saint Paul 4757, TEAM 4779
Missouri: Express 4888
Nevada: Nevada 5134
New Jersey: KPMG 5349, Subaru 5471, **Verizon 5489**
New Mexico: McCune 5529, PNM 5532
New York: BTMU 5724, **Carnegie 5747**, Daphne 5848, Dreyfus 5913, **Genesis 6042**, **IBM 6203**, **JPMorgan 6244**, Kornfeld 6304, New York 6548, **PepsiCo 6627**, **Pforzheimer 6635**, Stringer 6935, Warburg 7048
North Carolina: Cemala 7174, Davie 7188, Duke 7196, North 7274, Piedmont 7285, Triangle 7328
Ohio: Charities 7400, Columbus 7411, Nordson 7596, **OMNOVA 7601**, Richland 7630, Scripps 7659, **Timken 7684**
Oregon: Benton 7825, Carpenter 7831, Metolius 7869, Oregon 7876, PacifiCorp 7877, PGE 7881
Pennsylvania: Comcast 7989, Dolfinger 8013, EQT 8025, Nichols 8197, Stackpole 8295
Rhode Island: Textron 8446
South Carolina: Central 8468
Tennessee: Eastman 8561, **International 8585**
Texas: Astros 8674, Booth 8711, Coastal 8768, George 8863, Hoblitzelle 8912, Jones 8943, Kempner 8952, Lubbock 8994, Meadows 9019, San Antonio 9148, Sterling 9203, Tapestry 9220, Wright 9293
Utah: **Nu 9340**
Virginia: Arlington 9384, Capital 9400, MAXIMUS 9481, **Northrop 9498**, Strong 9537, SunTrust 9539
Washington: Community 9604, Norcliffe 9693, PACCAR 9698, Safeco 9723, Seattle 9731
West Virginia: Parkersburg 9789
Wisconsin: Northwestern 9914, **Schneider 9942**, Sentry 9944

Education, reform

Alabama: Vulcan 73
California: Johnson 753, **Rupe 1097**, Stuart 1225
Colorado: Daniels 1399, Foundation 1411
Connecticut: **GE 1591**
Hawaii: Castle 2593
Maryland: **Blaustein 3735**
Massachusetts: Boston 3956
Minnesota: **Medtronic 4712**, Travelers 4783
Missouri: Roblee 4963
New Jersey: **Prudential 5415**
New York: Achelis 5549, Bodman 5692, **Carnegie 5747**, Cricket 5827, **Foundation 6003**, **Genesis 6042**, **JPMorgan 6244**
North Carolina: Goodrich 7213
Ohio: Nordson 7596
Tennessee: Hyde 8584
Texas: **Arnold 8672**

Education, research

Arizona: University 172
California: **Samueli 1106**, Stuart 1225
Colorado: **National 1469**
Connecticut: Larsen 1624
District of Columbia: **National 1934**
Idaho: **Micron 2637**
Illinois: **Spencer 3171**
Indiana: **Lilly 3342**
Louisiana: Community 3624
Maryland: Abell 3712
Michigan: Heritage 4458, Mount Pleasant 4512, **Rodney 4528**
Mississippi: **Armstrong 4810**, Hardin 4831
Missouri: Craig 4875
New York: Bay 5652, Charina 5763, **Ford 5994**, **Grant 6093**, **Vital 7033**
Ohio: Gund 7478
Oklahoma: Rapp 7787
Pennsylvania: Pew 8220
Texas: Franklin 8855, Northen 9063, San Antonio 9148, Sterling 9203
Wisconsin: **Bradley 9819**

Education, services

Alabama: Alabama 1
Arizona: University 172
California: Girard 591, **Mattel 886**, **Oracle 991**, Quest 1050, Union 1271
Colorado: **Kinder 1439**
Connecticut: Liberty 1630, NewAlliance 1651, Pitney 1674, Trefz 1709
Florida: Ansin 1969, Community 2035, Darden 2051, Lennar 2210, Sack 2303
Georgia: **Coca 2428**
Illinois: Energizer 2824, Tracy 3189
Indiana: **Cummins 3292**, Lincoln 3344, Vectren 3394, Wayne 3400
Iowa: HNI 3443
Maine: Bangor 3680, TD 3710
Massachusetts: **Barr 3937**, Danversbank 4009, Eastern 4030, Liberty 4145, Yawkey 4329
Michigan: DTE 4410
Minnesota: 3M 4597, **Andersen 4601**, Cargill 4628, Deluxe 4644, RBC 4748, Wedum 4796, Xcel 4808
Missouri: **Kauffman 4921**, Nestle 4948
Montana: Washington 5018
Nebraska: Union 5090
New Jersey: **Merck 5379**, Provident 5414, PSEG 5416, Subaru 5471, **Verizon 5489**

Education, single organization support

Education, special

Electronic communications/Internet

Elementary school/education

Elementary/secondary education

Elementary/secondary school reform

Employment

Hawaii: Vincent 2619
Idaho: **Micron 2637**
Illinois: **Abbott 2649**, Caterpillar 2738, **Deere 2790**, **Motorola 3042**, **Motorola 3043**
Indiana: Blue 3266, **Cummins 3292**, **Lilly 3340**
Iowa: **Rockwell 3477**
Louisiana: Albemarle 3609, Marshall 3653
Maryland: Lockheed 3837, Rembrandt 3868
Massachusetts: Ashurst 3928, **Cabot 3966**, **Technical 4306**
Michigan: Chrysler 4366, Consumers 4376, Dart 4388, Delphi 4394, **DENSO 4395**, Dow 4405, Dow 4407, DTE 4410, General 4442
Minnesota: 3M 4597, **Andersen 4601**, Best 4612, **Fuller 4659**, **Medtronic 4712**, Minnesota 4716, **Pentair 4739**, **St. Jude 4770**, TEAM 4779, Xcel 4808
Missouri: Burns 4866
New Jersey: Banbury 5200, **Berrie 5206**, Buehler 5219, **Edison 5248**, Golden 5280, **Merck 5379**, Merck 5380, PSEG 5416, **Siemens 5454**, **Verizon 5489**
New York: **Deutsche 5876**, **IBM 6203**, Link 6374, **Luce 6398**, NBC 6531, PB 6621, Schenectady 6802, **Sloan 6872**, TE 6966, Vetlesen 7027
North Carolina: Duke 7196, Goodrich 7213, **Nickel 7272**, Piedmont 7285
Ohio: Cliffs 7407, FirstEnergy 7455, Huntington 7499
Oregon: **Intel 7853**, **Lemelson 7865**, PGE 7881
Pennsylvania: **Alcoa 7908**, Baker 7925, Bayer 7932, Buhl 7956, EQT 8025, **Kennametal 8120**, **PPG 8235**, West 8334
Rhode Island: Biogen 8363, Textron 8446
Tennessee: Eastman 8561
Texas: AT&T 8675, **BP 8718**, East 8819, Elkins 8826, Fluor 8851, Moody 9033, Sturgis 9211, Texas 9227, Zachry 9296
Virginia: **Bosack 9395**, CarMax 9401, Dominion 9422, Norfolk 9496, **Northrop 9498**, United 9547
Washington: Avista 9576, Bainbridge 9578, Harvest 9642
Wisconsin: Bemis 9815, Rockwell 9934

Environment

Alabama: Alabama 1, BBVA 9, Community 21, Community 24, Community 25, Kaul 43, Meyer 52, Meyer 53, Protective 59, Psalm 60, Thompson 70, Vulcan 73, Walker 74
Arizona: APS 91, Arizona 92, Community 101, Freeport-McMoRan 112, **Johnson 126**, Morris 148
Arkansas: Arkansas 179
California: 2005 215, Altman 234, **American 237**, Anaheim 239, **Annenberg 245**, **Appleton 248**, Applied 249, Arntz 259, Art 262, **Avery 272**, Ayrshire 276, Barker 282, BayTree 289, **Beagle 291**, Bechtel 294, Bechtel, 296, Begin 299, Bell 300, Booth 326, Borchard 328, Boswell 330, Bothin 331, Bower 332, Brittingham 345, Caldwell 363, Campbell 373, **Capital 375**, Carolands 379, Center 388, Chamberlin 389, Chartwell 397, **Christensen 399**, Clif 405, Community 414, Community 415, Community 416, Community 418, Community 420, Connell 424, Craigslist 436, Crocker 440, Disney 467, **Draper 481**, East 490, Edgerton 495, El Dorado 500, Eucalyptus 510, Factor 513, **Foundation 542**, Frank 544, Fremont 548, Fresno 549, Gaia 557, Gamble 562, Gasser 566, Gerbode 573, Goldhirsh-Yellin 603, **Goldman 604**, Goldman 606, Good 612, Greenberg 624, Gruber 632, Guess? 635, Harden 654, Healthy 668, Heffernan 673, Heising-Simons 675, Hewlett 686, Hitz 694, Horn 705, Ishiyama 730, JDH 746, **Kapor 764**, Kern 780, **Kingfisher 788**, La 808, Laural 823, Lear 824, Lehrer 827, Long 847, Ludwick 856, March 872, Marin 877, McAlister 891, **McConnell 898**, McKay 902, Mead 907, Mental 914, Merrill 920, Monterey 936, **Moore 938**, Morgan 939, Morgan 940, Morton 943, Moxie 950, Mulago 952, Newhall 966, Orange 992, Osher 997, Pacific 1002, Pacific 1003, **Packard 1006**, Page 1009, Parker 1012, Pasadena 1015, Passport 1016, Patagonia.org 1017, PG&E 1033, Pisces 1038, Reis 1062, Roche 1083, Roth 1093, Sacramento 1103, San Diego 1108, San Francisco 1109, San Luis 1110, Sand 1112, Santa Barbara 1116, Schmidt 1125, **Seaver 1132**, Sefton 1134, Sempra 1140, Shasta 1154, Smith 1182, Smith 1188, Sonora 1198, Springcreek 1208, Stanislaus 1211, Stephenson 1217, Streisand 1224, **Swift 1230**, Tang 1235, Taper 1237, Teichert 1244, Thornton 1253, Tomkat 1256, TomKat 1257, Tosa 1259, Truckee 1263, True 1264, Union 1271, **Vadasz 1275**, Valhalla 1278, Wasserman 1300, Welch 1310, Western 1316
Colorado: Aspen 1367, CH2M 1384, Community 1391, Community 1392, Edmondson 1405, El Pomar 1406, Fulcrum 1414, Grand 1423, Hitchcock 1430, KBK 1437, Neuman 1470, Pikes 1478, Ricketts 1486, Summit 1511, Telluride 1512, Vail 1518, Vodafone 1519, Western 1520, Yampa 1528
Connecticut: Barnes 1542, Common 1561, Community 1562, Community 1563, Community 1564, Community 1565, **Educational 1578**, Ensworth 1580, Fairfield 1581, Fink 1583, Heidenreich 1611, Larsen 1624, Main 1634, Middlesex 1644, New Canaan 1650, NewAlliance 1651, Northeast 1656, Palmer 1666, Perdue 1672, **Praxair 1676**, Sage 1687, **Tremaine 1710**, Vervane 1716
Delaware: AEC 1735, Davis 1761, Delaware 1765, Draper 1770, Esperance 1777, G.D.S 1782, Ganatra 1783, Kendeda 1794, Longwood 1806, Marmot 1814, **Memton 1819**, Nor'Easter 1824, Orr 1827, Prentice 1839, Shorenstein 1858, Tapeats 1868, Welfare 1872, Yavanna 1876
District of Columbia: Bauman 1882, Cafritz 1890, Community 1893, **Dreyfus 1901**, Forsythia 1906, Munson 1933, Palmer 1937, **Summit 1950**, Wallace 1956
Florida: Bank 1979, Batchelor 1983, Blank 1997, Community 2032, Community 2033, Community 2034, Community 2035, Community 2036, Community 2037, Community 2038, Community 2040, Community 2041, Corbett 2045, Darden 2051, Gardener 2114, GiveWell 2123, Glenn 2125, Gulf 2142, Indian 2166, Kelly 2181, Kennedy 2183, Klorfine 2188, Lattner 2204, Lattner 2205, Litowitz 2218, Maren 2227, Martin 2229, Miami 2238, NextEra 2251, Ocean 2253, Pinellas 2269, Rayonier 2281, River 2287, **SeaWorld 2315**, Southwest 2327, Thomas 2357, Thornburgh 2360, Ware 2378, Wildflower 2387
Georgia: Aflac 2399, Blank 2413, Communities 2431, Community 2434, Community 2435, Community 2436, Community 2439, Dobbs 2449, Fort 2460, Georgia 2468, **Georgia 2469**, Glenn 2470, Kennedy 2495, Lanier 2499, Murphy 2522, North 2525, Rich 2537, Southern 2554, **Thoresen 2557**, Tull 2561, **UPS 2566**, Whitehead 2571, Williams 2572, Woodruff 2579
Hawaii: Atherton 2586, Castle 2593, Cooke 2597, Hau'oli 2601, Hawaii 2602, Hawaiian 2603, McInerny 2612
Idaho: **Gorongosa 2631**, Idaho 2632
Illinois: Angell 2663, Aon 2667, Appleby 2668, ARIA 2672, Austin 2677, Brach 2712, Bruning 2717, Buchanan 2720, **Buffett 2726**, Butler 2729, Caterpillar 2738, Chicago 2746, Community 2763, Community 2764, Community 2765, Coypu 2777, Crown 2781, DeKalb 2792, Donnelley 2800, DuPage 2812, Edwardsville 2817, Evanston 2826, Exelon 2827, Field 2831, Frankel 2842, **Gallagher 2855**, H.B.B. 2883, Hamill 2888, **Harder 2891**, Hull 2925, Hunter 2926, Illinois 2934, **Joyce 2946**, Kaplan 2947, Louis 2985, Malott 2996, McGraw 3015, Morrison 3038, Mosher 3041, **Motorola 3042**, MRB 3044, NIB 3053, Northern 3059, Oak Park 3061, Oppenheimer 3066, **Ploughshares 3082**, Prince 3089, Rice 3116, Seabury 3146, Siragusa 3162, Stewart 3178, **Tellabs 3185**, White 3230, **Wrigley 3244**
Indiana: Ball 3262, Ball 3264, Brown 3269, Community 3277, Community 3279, Community 3282, Community 3284, Community 3285, Community 3287, Community 3288, Community 3290, Crown Point 3291, **Cummins 3292**, Dearborn 3293, DeKalb 3295, Elkhart 3298, Harrison 3314, Hendricks 3319, Huntington 3324, Johnson 3330, Kosciusko 3336, Legacy 3337, Marshall 3348, Montgomery 3356, National 3358, Northern 3360, Orange 3365, Parrish 3367, Porter 3369, Putnam 3373, Ripley 3379, Samerian 3384, Steuben 3390, Unity 3393, Vectren 3394, Waterfield 3399, Wayne 3400, Wells 3403
Iowa: Cedar Rapids 3417, Community 3419, Community 3422, Community 3423, Community 3424, McElroy 3461, Pella 3473, Poweshiek 3475, Principal 3476, **Rockwell 3477**
Kansas: Douglas 3509, Koch 3529, Manhattan 3532, McPherson 3534, Salina 3540, **Shumaker 3546**, Sprint 3549, Topeka 3552, Wichita 3555
Kentucky: Blue 3560, Community 3569, Community 3570
Louisiana: Baton Rouge 3613, Booth 3616, Community 3624, Grigsby 3640, New Orleans 3656
Maine: Cascade 3681, Cianbro 3683, Iberdrola 3693, Maine 3698, Morton 3701, Orchard 3704, **Sandy 3707**, Sewall 3708, Switzer 3709, TD 3710
Maryland: Abell 3712, Baker 3724, Baltimore 3726, Bunting 3742, **Cohen 3754**, Colhoun 3755, Community 3759, Community 3760, France 3796, **Grace 3807**, Hendricks 3813, Legg 3828, Lockhart 3836, Lockheed 3837, Merrill 3847, Mid-Shore 3851, **Morningstar 3854**, Rathmann 3867, Rembrandt 3868, **Shared 3882**, Shields 3884, Town 3897
Massachusetts: Adams 3916, Ausolus 3931, **Barr 3937**, Berkshire 3948, Beveridge 3950, Brookline 3962, Cabot 3967, Cabot 3968, Cambridge 3971, Cape Cod 3973, Cape Cod 3974, Cedar 3977, Cedar 3978, Chorus 3984, Community 3990, Community 3991, Community 3992, **Conservation 3993**, Currents 4004, Doran 4024, Eaglemere 4029, Essex 4039, Fields 4046, Foundation 4056, Foundation 4058, Fresh 4062, **Germeshausen 4069**, **Grantham 4077**, Island 4109, Lowell 4152, Maine 4160, Merck 4171, **Merck 4172**, Miller 4177, MWC 4186, Nathan 4188, New 4189, New 4191, North 4194, Parker 4207, Perls 4214, Pierce 4220, Roy 4247, Santander 4256, Saquish 4257, Sims/Maes 4274, Stearns 4286, Stevens 4289, Stifler 4292, Stoddard 4293, Sudbury 4299, Towards 4309, Worcester 4327, Yawkey 4328, Yawkey 4329
Michigan: Albion 4332, Americana 4337, Ann Arbor 4340, Bay 4344, Binda 4350, Capital 4357, Charlevoix 4361, Community 4369, Community 4370, Community 4371, Community 4372, Community 4374, Community 4375, Consumers 4376, Cook 4377, Danto 4387, **Dow 4404**, Dow 4405, DTE 4410, Dyer 4412, Ford 4430, Fremont 4438, General 4442, Grand Haven 4446, Grand Rapids 4447, Grand 4448, Greenville 4452, Hickman 4460, Hillsdale 4461, Jackson 4467, Jubilee 4470, Kalamazoo 4472, **Kresge 4479**, Marshall 4496, Masco 4497, Midland 4502, Mosaic 4509, Mount Pleasant 4512, Oleson 4516, Petoskey 4522, Pokagon 4523, Saginaw 4532, Steelcase 4547, Upjohn 4564, Wolverine 4593
Minnesota: 3M 4597, Beim 4609, Beverly 4615, Blue 4618, Butler 4622, Buuck 4623, Cargill 4627, Carolyn 4630, Central 4631, Cox 4639, Duluth 4649, Ecolab 4651, Grand Rapids 4667, Johnson 4683, Leuthold 4695, Lilly 4696, MacMillan 4700, Marbrook 4702, Martin 4704, McKnight 4709, McNeely 4710, Minnesota 4715, Minnesota 4716, **Mortenson 4721**, **Mosaic 4722**, Musser 4724, Northwest 4730, Red Wing 4749, Remick 4751, Rochester 4755, Smikis 4767, SUPERVALU 4775, **Weyerhaeuser 4802**, Weyerhaeuser 4803, Winona 4806, Xcel 4808
Mississippi: Community 4820, Community 4821, Maddox 4834, McLean 4835, Mississippi 4839, Walker 4849
Missouri: Arch 4855, Brauer 4860, Burns 4866, Community 4872, Cox 4874, **Deer 4878**, Laclede 4931, **Monsanto 4945**, Saint Louis 4966, Sander 4967, Taylor 4987, Trio 4994
Montana: Cross 5007, Scoob 5015, Whitefish 5019

Environment, administration/regulation

Environment, air pollution

Environment, alliance/advocacy

Environment, association

Environment, beautification programs

Environment, climate change/global warming

Environment, energy

Environment, ethics

Environment, forests

Environment, formal/general education

Environment, government agencies

Environment, information services

Environment, land resources

Environment, legal rights

Environment, natural resources

Environment, plant conservation

Environment, pollution control

Environment, public education

Environment, public policy

Environment, radiation control

Environment, recycling

Environment, reform

Environment, research

Environment, single organization support

Environment, toxics

Environment, waste management

Environment, water pollution

Michigan: Community 4369
Minnesota: Initiative 4679
Missouri: **Monsanto 4945**
New York: **PepsiCo 6627**
Pennsylvania: Woodtiger 8346
South Dakota: Sioux Falls 8521
Tennessee: **International 8585**
Washington: **Bullitt 9591**, Seattle 9731

Environment, water resources

Alabama: Alabama 1
Arizona: Freeport-McMoRan 112
California: **Avery 272**, Borch 327, Campbell 373, **Conservation 426**, Firedoll 528, **Google 615**, **Hilton 692**, Pacific 1003, Patagonia.org 1017, Pisces 1038, San Diego 1108, Sangham 1114, Sempra 1140
Colorado: **Salvador 1491**
Connecticut: Common 1561, Gorab 1599, Northeast 1656, Swordspoint 1705
Delaware: Davis 1761, Fair 1780, **Raskob 1845**
District of Columbia: Munson 1933
Florida: Clark 2022, Darden 2051, Lennar 2210, **SeaWorld 2315**, Ware 2378, **Worrell 2395**
Georgia: **Coca 2428**, Sapelo 2546, **Turner 2563**
Hawaii: Castle 2593
Illinois: **Abbott 2649**, Caterpillar 2738, Froehlich 2848, Grand 2875, Henry 2906, **Tellabs 3185**
Indiana: Blue 3266, **Cummins 3292**
Iowa: **Rockwell 3477**
Maryland: Legg 3828
Massachusetts: Bilezikian 3951, Bristol 3960, Lowell 4152, **Sweet 4302**
Michigan: Consumers 4376, **Erb 4415**, Jubilee 4470
Minnesota: Land 4691, **Mosaic 4722**, **Pentair 4739**, Xcel 4808
Mississippi: Mississippi 4839
Missouri: Anheuser 4853
Nebraska: Vetter 5091
New Jersey: Klingenstein 5343, OceanFirst 5394, Unilever 5484
New Mexico: Healy 5522
New York: Auchincloss 5623, Butler 5733, Coudert 5820, Heineman 6158, **Mitsubishi 6490**, Park 6615, **PepsiCo 6627**, Scherman 6804, Select 6829, Tensor 6970, Tiffany 6978, Triad 7005
North Carolina: **Oak 7276**
Ohio: Vesper 7695
Oregon: Burning 7827
Pennsylvania: **ACE 7905**, **Alcoa 7908**, Martin 8156, Sand 8264
Tennessee: Thompson 8635
Texas: Shield 9170
Washington: **Bullitt 9591**, Fabert 9618, **Laird 9664**, **Starbucks 9742**
Wisconsin: Brookby 9823, Kohler 9885

Environmental and resource rights

Illinois: Libra 2981
New York: **Cummings 5833**

Environmental education

Alabama: BBVA 9
Arizona: Freeport-McMoRan 112
California: Applied 249, Campbell 373, Community 420, Kimball 786, Lurie 858, Pacific 1002, Pacific 1003, PG&E 1033, Sacramento 1103, Sempra 1140, Small 1180, Steinmetz 1216, Union 1271, Wynn 1350
Colorado: **Kinder 1439**
District of Columbia: **Wallace 1955**
Florida: Darden 2051, Gulf 2142, NextEra 2251, Peacock 2263, Rayonier 2281, **SeaWorld 2315**
Georgia: **Georgia 2469**, Singletary 2551, **UPS 2566**
Hawaii: Hawaii 2602
Illinois: DuPage 2812, **Motorola 3042**, **Tellabs 3185**, **Wrigley 3244**
Indiana: Pulliam 3372, Vectren 3394
Louisiana: Grigsby 3640
Maine: Horizon 3691, Quimby 3705
Maryland: Middendorf 3850, Rembrandt 3868
Massachusetts: Berkshire 3946, Gruben 4082
Michigan: Consumers 4376, DTE 4410, General 4442
Minnesota: 3M 4597, Ecolab 4651, Xcel 4808
Missouri: Anheuser 4853
Nebraska: Swanson 5088
New Jersey: PSEG 5416, Subaru 5471, **Verizon 5489**
New Mexico: PNM 5532
New York: Auchincloss 5623, Butler 5733, Canaday 5743, de Coizart 5856, Johnson 6239, **Mitsubishi 6490**, **Rockefeller 6723**
North Carolina: Duke 7196, Piedmont 7285
Ohio: American 7368, Lubrizol 7546
Oklahoma: Kirkpatrick 7766
Oregon: Burning 7827
Pennsylvania: **Alcoa 7908**, Bayer 7932, EQT 8025, McLean 8169, **PPG 8235**
Tennessee: Carlton 8541, **International 8585**
Texas: Fluor 8851
Virginia: Dominion 9422, Hampton 9448, Landmark 9467
Washington: Plum 9704
Wisconsin: Alliant 9804, Brookby 9823, Harley 9859, Wisconsin 9969

Epilepsy research

New York: Klingenstein 6292
Texas: Pediatric 9087

Ethnic studies

New York: Nazarian 6530

Eye diseases

California: **Beckman 297**, Campbell 372, Danford 448, Doheny 473, Gleis 593, Kirchgessner 790
Connecticut: **Ziegler 1731**
District of Columbia: Aid 1879
Florida: Ueltschi 2366
Illinois: **Foundation 2839**, Perkins 3075
Indiana: Len-Ari 3339, Pulliam 3372, Reeves 3374
Louisiana: Eye 3631
New Jersey: Gund 5285
New York: Burch 5729, de Coizart 5856, **Friends 6024**, Lavelle 6339
Ohio: Marion 7558
Pennsylvania: Fourjay 8047, Mertz 8177, Reuss 8247
Texas: Alcon 8655
West Virginia: Teubert 9795
Wyoming: Cumming 9976

Eye research

Alabama: **International 41**
California: Argyros 254, **Beckman 297**, Doheny 473, Fortisure 538, Foster 539, Hillblom 690, JVK 758, Kirchgessner 790, Silk 1167, Sinskey 1174
Connecticut: **Ziegler 1731**
District of Columbia: Aid 1879
Florida: Kennedy 2183, Spencer 2329
Illinois: **Foundation 2839**
Indiana: Glick 3310
Maryland: Jacobson 3820
Nevada: Wiegand 5159
New Jersey: Frankino 5266, **Pfeiffer 5405**
New York: Block 5683, Burch 5729, de Coizart 5856
Oregon: Bauman 7824
Pennsylvania: Lotman 8150, Sexauer 8280
Rhode Island: McCurdy 8417
Texas: Alcon 8655, Barr 8683, Smith 9187, Tomerlin 9238, West 9269, Young 9295
Virginia: Manning 9476
Wisconsin: Ocular 9915

Family resources and services, disability

California: **Smith 1183**

Family services

Alabama: Central 19, Community 21, Community 24, Kaul 43, Lowder 45, Working 78
Arizona: Arizona 92, Click 100, Freeport-McMoRan 112, Kiita 130, Long 137, Stardust 164
Arkansas: Blue 181, **Windgate 213**
California: Anderson 241, Atkinson 265, Barker 282, Begin 299, Bella 301, Bickerstaff 313, Bothin 331, Brandes 336, California 368, **Capital 375**, Carson 381, Community 419, Confidence 423, Cortopassi 430, Crail 437, Danford 448, Doheny 473, Eagle 488, Edelstein 494, Eichenbaum 497, Eustace-Kwan 511, Galen 558, Gasser 566, Goldman 605, GSF 633, Gumbiner 636, Gumpert 637, Haas 640, Hale 645, Harden 654, Harrington 657, HealthCare 667, Heffernan 673, Hughes 713, Humboldt 714, Hutto 717, Hutton 718, It 733, Jacobs 739, James 742, Johnson 753, Jones 755, Laulhere 822, Lear 824, Leichtman 829, Lesher 833, Lindsey 840, Long 847, Ludwick 856, Lurie 858, Marcled 875, McCarthy 896, Napa 959, Newhall 966, Norris 971, O'Connell 982, Orange 992, Oschin 996, Outhwaite 1000, Pacific 1003, **Packard 1006**, Parsons 1013, Pasadena 1015, Pfleger 1032, PG&E 1033, Quest 1050, Reinhard 1061, Roberts 1081, **S.G. 1100**, Sacramento 1103, San Francisco 1109, Sand 1112, Sangham 1114, Sempra 1140, Sharks 1153, Sierra 1163, Smith 1186, Snyder 1192, Sonora 1198, Soref 1199, Talbert 1233, Taper 1237, Ventura 1287, Weingart 1307, Western 1316, Wood 1344, Wynn 1350
Colorado: 6/S 1362, Anschutz 1364, Bernstein 1372, Colorado 1390, Edmondson 1405, El Pomar 1406, Halton 1426, Libertygives 1448, Maggiegeorge 1452, Marquez 1454, Piton 1480, Rose 1487, Saeman 1490, Singer 1501, Summit 1511, Vodafone 1519
Connecticut: Bissell 1547, Bob's 1548, Community 1563, Community 1564, Connecticut 1566, Ensworth 1580, First 1584, Fund 1589, Keefe 1619, Larsen 1624, Liberty 1630, Matthies 1639, New Canaan 1650, Palmer 1666, Wiggins 1722, Windreich 1724
Delaware: Crystal 1758, Ettinger 1779, **Memton 1819**, Reynolds 1848, Singer 1860, Wasily 1871
District of Columbia: Cafritz 1890, **Hill 1915**, Meyer 1931
Florida: Bank 1979, Brown 2004, Burns 2006, Community 2033, Community 2034, Community 2036, Community 2037, Community 2038, Community 2039, Community 2040, Conn 2042, Florida 2101, Galloway 2112, GiveWell 2123, Indian 2166, Jacksonville 2167, Kennedy 2182, Kennedy 2183, **Knight 2191**, Libra 2213, Martin 2229, Moran 2243, Pinellas 2269, Tarrant 2352, Usher 2367, **Wardlaw 2376**
Georgia: Campbell 2420, Community 2432, Community 2434, Hudgens 2486, Primerica 2534, Williams 2572, WinShape 2577
Hawaii: Buehner 2589, Hawaiian 2603, Hughes 2605, Lange 2609, **Watumull 2620**, Wilcox 2621
Idaho: Nagel 2639
Illinois: **Abbott 2649**, ARIA 2672, Blair 2700, Blum 2705, Chartered 2744, Christopher 2748, Community 2763, Community 2766, Evanston 2826, Hansen 2889, Harris 2892, Huizenga 2924, Kemper 2954, MB 3008, Mirza 3032, Northern 3059, Oak Park 3061, Pierce 3080, Polk 3084, Popular 3085, SF 3149, Speh 3170, Tracy 3189
Indiana: Ball 3262, Central 3272, Community 3278, Community 3280, Community 3281, Duneland 3297, Foellinger 3304, Foundations 3306, Marshall 3348, Michigan 3354, Noyes 3361, Portland 3370, Pulliam 3372, Steel 3389
Iowa: AEGON 3409, Community 3423, Guernsey 3437, Johnson 3449, Meredith 3463, New 3468, Principal 3476, Ruan 3478, Siouxland 3480
Kansas: Topeka 3552
Kentucky: Community 3569, Horn 3581, Humana 3582, J & L 3584, Lift 3587, Norton 3592, Ventas 3605

Louisiana: Albemarle 3609, Booth 3616, Community 3624, Entergy 3630, Frazier 3635, Grigsby 3640, Institute 3644
Maine: **Sandy 3707**
Maryland: Abell 3712, Ceres 3747, Community 3759, Community 3761, Cupid 3769, Davis 3772, **DLA 3781**, Mead 3845, Polinger 3864, Price 3865, Roswell 3876, Spencer 3887, Straus 3890, Viragh 3902
Massachusetts: Arbella 3926, Association 3929, Bayrd 3938, Community 3991, Eastern 4030, Foundation 4056, Franklin 4061, Gruben 4082, Hyams 4103, Leaves 4139, Liberty 4145, Linden 4148, New 4189, New England 4193, Riley 4239, Stearns 4286, TJX 4308, Worcester 4327
Michigan: Ann Arbor 4340, Charlevoix 4361, Community 4373, Consumers 4376, DeRoy 4396, DeVos 4399, Family 4418, Fremont 4438, Frey 4440, Grand Rapids 4447, Hillsdale 4461, Kalamazoo 4472, Knight 4477, Prince 4525, Saginaw 4532, Skillman 4543, Upjohn 4564, VanderWeide 4572, Whirlpool 4583, Williams 4586, Wolverine 4593
Minnesota: Andersen 4603, **Better 4614**, Blue 4618, Butler 4622, Cargill 4627, Central 4631, Charlson 4633, Duluth 4649, Fiterman 4656, General 4661, Grand Rapids 4667, HRK 4677, Initiative 4679, **King 4687**, Larson 4692, Minneapolis 4714, Mithun 4718, NFC 4727, Ordean 4732, **Pentair 4739**, Phillips 4741, RBC 4748, Rochester 4755, Slaggie 4766, Target 4776, Valspar 4786, Wallestad 4791, WCA 4795, West 4800
Mississippi: Community 4819, Community 4820, Ergon 4824, Foundation 4827
Missouri: Centene 4870, Emerson 4885, Express 4888, Goldfarb 4895, Hall 4905, Hallmark 4906, Jordan 4917, Kansas 4920, Loose 4937, Pott 4958, Roblee 4963, Sunnen 4986
Montana: Edwards 5008, Gianforte 5010
Nebraska: Ameritas 5023, Dunklau 5036, Hawks 5047, Kind 5060, Lincoln 5063, Mutual 5071, Wirth 5095, Woods 5096
Nevada: Nevada 5134, O'Bannon 5137
New Hampshire: Alexander 5162
New Jersey: Borden 5209, Brougher 5217, Bunbury 5220, Community 5232, **Crane 5235**, Frankino 5266, Friedman 5268, Healthcare 5296, Hyde 5310, **Johnson 5329**, Lord 5365, **Merck 5379**, Merillat 5382, Orange 5396, Pascale 5403, **Sanofi 5437**, Schwarz 5444, Scott 5445, Wicks 5500, Wishes 5506
New Mexico: Brindle 5516, Frost 5519, McCune 5529, New Mexico 5530
New York: Abrons 5546, Achelis 5549, Allyn 5575, Altman 5579, Anderson 5596, Andor 5598, Assurant 5621, Bahnik 5634, Bayne 5653, Bodman 5692, Canaday 5743, **Clark 5785**, **CLRC 5789**, Coach 5790, Cole 5795, Community 5805, **Credit 5826**, Daphne 5848, Deerfield 5865, deForest 5866, Dove 5903, Dove 5904, Gilman 6052, Grauer 6095, **Hearst 6155**, **Hearst 6156**, IF 6205, **JPMorgan 6244**, Kaylie 6263, Lee 6343, Lindner 6372, Massry 6444, MBIA 6451, Melly 6471, **MetLife 6479**, Moore 6502, Morse 6510, New York 6543, New York 6544, Phillips 6637, Poses 6655, Rauch 6681, Resource 6691, Rochester 6722, RTS 6760, Sagner 6783, Save 6799, Siebens 6853, Sirus 6863, **Sloan 6872**, **Spunk 6902**, St. Faith's 6903, Steele 6915, Tiger 6980, Wendt 7074, Western 7078
North Carolina: **Bank 7139**, Cumberland 7184, Glenn 7211, Gordon 7214, Robertson 7305, Stewards 7322, Triangle 7328, VF 7332
North Dakota: Stern 7360
Ohio: Akron 7367, American 7369, Ar-Hale 7376, Children's 7401, Cleveland 7406, Community 7414, Dater 7426, **Eaton 7442**, Fifth 7452, Friedlander 7463, Greene 7474, Lancaster 7533, Mathile 7560, Middletown 7570, Nationwide 7587, Nordson 7596, O'Neill 7602, Richland 7630, Saint 7639, Scripps 7659, Spaulding 7670, Stark 7673, Stocker 7676, Sutphin 7679, Weisbrod 7708, White 7715, Youngstown 7723
Oklahoma: American 7728, McCrory 7773, ONEOK 7783, Taubman 7804, Williams 7814
Oregon: Carpenter 7831, Jubitz 7859, Meyer 7870, Oregon 7876, PGE 7881, Salem 7885
Pennsylvania: Arcadia 7918, Armstrong 7922, CentiMark 7970, CIGNA 7981, Claneil 7982, Dolfinger 8013, ESSA 8028, First 8040, Fourjay 8047, Hansen 8079, **Heinz 8083**, Heinz 8084, Highmark 8092, Huston 8102, Jackson 8110, Mellon 8173, Morris 8188, Nichols 8197, Pew 8220, Philadelphia 8221, Pilgrim 8225, Pittsburgh 8228, Saligman 8261, Staunton 8296, Wells 8333, Wiegand 8337
Rhode Island: Capewell 8365, M. 8414, Rhode Island 8429, Textron 8446
South Carolina: Canal 8466, Coastal 8472, **ScanSource 8495**, Springs 8504
South Dakota: Robinson 8520, Sioux Falls 8521
Tennessee: American 8528, Aslan 8529, Atticus 8531, Beaman 8534, HCA 8582, Plough 8615, Seme 8626
Texas: Abell 8650, Amarillo 8660, Baron 8682, Bass 8690, Boone 8710, Brumley 8734, Cailloux 8742, Coastal 8768, Community 8777, Doss 8813, Fikes 8844, Fluor 8851, Frees 8857, George 8863, Getz 8864, Greathouse 8875, Heavin 8898, Holthouse 8915, Jones 8943, Kimberly 8957, King 8959, Kurth 8971, Levit 8982, Lowe 8993, Lubbock 8994, Lyons 8996, Maverick 9005, McGovern 9014, Meadows 9019, Murchison 9045, Owen 9076, Rees-Jones 9125, Rockwell 9135, Saint 9144, San Antonio 9148, Simmons 9173, Sterling 9203, Tapestry 9220, Thompson 9233, Trull 9240, Valero 9246, Waco 9251, Wal 9254, Ward 9258, Welborn 9267, Wright 9293, Young 9295
Utah: Dee 9312, Eccles 9320, Hemingway 9326
Vermont: Three 9374, Vermont 9375
Virgin Islands: Community 9377
Virginia: AMERIGROUP 9383, CarMax 9401, Community 9410, Community 9412, Community 9415, Freddie 9435, Lynchburg 9474, MAXIMUS 9481, MLG 9488, Piedmont 9509, Rimora 9522, Samberg 9527
Washington: Blue 9588, Casey 9596, Community 9604, Danz 9609, Discuren 9611, Evertrust 9617, Giddens, 9627, Glaser 9629, Green 9632, Laurel 9666, Lucky 9673, Medina 9682, Murdock 9689, Norcliffe 9693, Roma 9719, Safeco 9723, Satterberg 9728, Smith 9738, Tacoma 9750, Thompson 9752, Whatcom 9759, Zumiez 9768
West Virginia: Daywood 9774, Eastern 9775, Kanawha 9780, Parkersburg 9789, Your 9799
Wisconsin: Alexander 9802, Anthony 9806, Beloit 9814, CUNA 9838, Evinrude 9841, Incourage 9867, Kress 9887, La Crosse 9889, Lubar 9894, McBeath 9901, Milwaukee 9907, Northwestern 9914, Raibrook 9925, **Schneider 9942**, Soref 9948, Stackner 9951

Family services, adolescent parents

Alabama: Community 21
Indiana: Miller 3355
New Mexico: Santa Fe 5533
New York: Bodman 5692
Pennsylvania: FISA 8043
Tennessee: Thompson 8635
Texas: Topfer 9239
Washington: Horizons 9645

Family services, counseling

New York: Save 6799
Pennsylvania: Staunton 8296
Washington: Horizons 9645

Family services, domestic violence

Alabama: Central 19
Arizona: Freeport-McMoRan 112
California: Al-Ameen 225, Blue 320, **Capital 375**, Cathay 385, Eagle 488, Heffernan 673, Shea 1155, Simpson 1173, Wetzel 1318
Colorado: Tuchman 1514
Connecticut: Liberty 1630
Florida: Community 2035, Dallepezze 2049
Georgia: **Georgia 2469**
Illinois: Allstate 2657, Alphawood 2658, JNT 2940, Woodward 3243
Indiana: Community 3280, Lincoln 3344, Weaver 3401
Massachusetts: Eastern 4030, Franklin 4061, TJX 4308
Michigan: Consumers 4376
Minnesota: NFC 4727
Missouri: American 4852, Truman 4996
Nebraska: Mutual 5071
New Jersey: OceanFirst 5394, **Verizon 5489**
New Mexico: Santa Fe 5533
New York: Coach 5790, Fifth 5976, van Ameringen 7023, Wolk 7099
North Carolina: **Sunshine 7324**
Ohio: Reinberger 7628
Oregon: PacifiCorp 7877, PGE 7881
Pennsylvania: FISA 8043, Lily 8141
Texas: Heavin 8898, **RGK 9128**, Valero 9246
Virginia: CarMax 9401, Obici 9500
Washington: Horizons 9645, OneFamily 9695
Wisconsin: CUNA 9838, Johnson 9874

Family services, parent education

Alabama: Community 21
California: Valentine 1277
Connecticut: Liberty 1630
Georgia: Community 2432
Hawaii: **Burke 2590**
Indiana: Noble 3359
Iowa: Wellmark 3490
Michigan: **Mott 4510**
New Jersey: **Verizon 5489**
New York: Cummings 5834, Downs 5908, MBIA 6451
North Carolina: Blue 7153
Ohio: **OMNOVA 7601**
Oregon: PGE 7881
Rhode Island: CVS 8379
Texas: Kronkosky 8970, Topfer 9239
Washington: Yakima 9767
Wisconsin: Thrivent 9956

Family services, single parents

District of Columbia: **Moriah 1932**

Financial services

California: Marcled 875, Sand 1112, Schwab 1127, Soda 1194, **Strauss 1223**
New York: **Citi 5780**, **JPMorgan 6244**, **MetLife 6479**
Texas: Pema 9088
Washington: **Gates 9625**, Roots 9720

Financial services, credit unions

California: Marcled 875

Food banks

Alabama: Protective 59
Arizona: Farrington 110, Halle 118, Raymond 155, Surplus 167
Arkansas: Wal-Mart 210
California: **Amgen 238**, Applied 249, BayTree 289, Brewster 342, California 368, Cathay 385, Croul 441, Dhont 464, Genentech 571, Goodman 613, Grove 631, GSF 633, Heffernan 673, Hoven 708, Kelley 778, Oak 976, Perforce 1026, Roche 1083, Wetzel 1318
Colorado: King 1440
Connecticut: Aetna 1531, Liberty 1630, NewAlliance 1651, Orchard 1663, Ossen 1664, Owenoke 1665, People's 1671

Delaware: **Adobe 1734**, Berkley 1741, CenturyLink-Clarke 1750, Johnson 1790
Florida: Bi-Lo 1996, Darden 2051, Moskowitz 2247
Georgia: Snow 2553
Idaho: Jeker 2634
Illinois: **Abbott 2649**, **Deere 2790**, **Goodman 2868**, Hartke 2897, Illinois 2934, **Kapoor 2950**, **Mondelez 3034**, Nesbitt 3051, Omron 3063, Rhoades 3115, Woodward 3243
Indiana: Foundations 3306, Lincoln 3344, Pulliam 3372
Iowa: GuideOne 3438
Kentucky: Harris 3580, Yum! 3608
Louisiana: Albemarle 3609
Maine: TD 3710
Maryland: Battye 3727, Shields 3884
Massachusetts: Arbella 3926, Cape Cod 3973, Clipper 3987, Davis 4010, Dunkin' 4026, Eastern 4030, Liberty 4145, Morrison 4184
Michigan: Consumers 4376, Ford 4430, General 4442, **Kellogg 4473**, **Kellogg's 4475**, Mackey 4489, Pokagon 4523
Minnesota: Ecolab 4651, General 4661, Hageman 4670, Hormel 4676, Land 4691, NFC 4727, Sit 4765, SUPERVALU 4775
Missouri: Hagan 4904, Waldheim 4997
Montana: Town 5016, Washington 5018
Nebraska: ConAgra 5029, ConAgra 5030, Mutual 5071, Rogers 5077
Nevada: Bennett 5101
New Jersey: Hummingbird 5309, Ingersoll-Rand 5314, **Merck 5379**, OceanFirst 5394, Provident 5414, Tepper 5480, Unilever 5484
New Mexico: PNM 5532
New York: **American 5588**, **Credit 5826**, First 5979, Jacoff 6220, MBIA 6451, **MetLife 6479**, Morgan 6507, **PepsiCo 6627**, Richmond 6703, Schnurmacher 6810, Siebens 6853, Sprague 6901, Stainman 6906, Wegman 7061
North Carolina: **Bank 7139**, Food 7201, Josef 7244, Stewards 7322
Ohio: American 7368, Dayton 7429, Ferry 7451, Kroger 7531, Macy's 7552, Marion 7558, Moores 7576, Nationwide 7587, Reinberger 7628, Samaritan 7642
Oklahoma: McCrory 7773
Oregon: PGE 7881
Pennsylvania: **ACE 7905**, Armstrong 7922, Bayer 7932, BNY 7946, CentiMark 7970, **Heinz 8083**, Hurd 8101, Trexler 8320, Wheeler 8335
Rhode Island: **Feinstein 8391**, Hasbro 8403, Kimball 8410, Textron 8446
South Dakota: Robinson 8520
Tennessee: American 8528, Fritch 8569, Regal 8622, Speer 8630
Texas: Bass 8690, Brumley 8734, Coastal 8768, Cowden 8783, Dean 8803, Doswell 8814, Fisch 8846, Johnson 8938, King 8959, Lesley 8980, Maverick 9005, Natural 9053, USAA 9245, Valero 9246, Welborn 9267, Woodforest 9290
Utah: Wagner 9355, Watkins 9356
Vermont: Three 9374, Waterwheel 9376
Virginia: Dominion 9422, Fredericksburg 9436, **Genworth 9441**, Hampton 9448, Landmark 9467, Morgan, 9490, Norfolk 9496, United 9546
Washington: Cameron 9593, Evertrust 9617, Intermec 9651, Plum 9704, Renton 9715
Wisconsin: Bemis 9815, Johnson 9873, Ladish 9890, Windhover 9968

Food distribution, groceries on wheels

New York: **Jaffe 6222**, Klein 6289
Oregon: Metolius 7869
Texas: Anderson 8663, King 8959

Food distribution, meals on wheels

Arkansas: Wal-Mart 210
California: California 368, JVK 758, Macfarlane 865
Connecticut: People's 1671
Florida: Bi-Lo 1996, Walter 2375
Indiana: Michigan 3354
Michigan: Dana 4386, DTE 4410
Minnesota: Stevens 4772
Missouri: Ballmann 4858
Nevada: Caesars 5106
New Jersey: **Merck 5379**
New York: **American 5588**, First 5979, Loeb 6384, Semlitz 6831, Tisch 6985
North Carolina: Food 7201, Stewards 7322
Pennsylvania: Armstrong 7922, CentiMark 7970, Genuardi 8053, Wheeler 8335
South Carolina: Smith 8499
Texas: Anderson 8663, Bass 8690, Tucker 9241
Wisconsin: Acuity 9801

Food services

Arkansas: Wal-Mart 210
California: Applied 249, Atkinson 265, **Cisco 402**, Clif 405, Genentech 571, Grand 619, GSF 633, Healthy 668, Heffernan 673, Hope 702, Humboldt 714, Nestle 965, Norris 971, Pacific 1003, **Packard 1006**, Sacramento 1103, Sangham 1114, Sonora 1198, Webster 1305, Weingart 1307, Wolf 1337, Zelman 1359
Colorado: Anschutz 1364, El Pomar 1406, Fulcrum 1414, Jumping 1434
Connecticut: Aetna 1531, **Children's 1557**, Culpeper 1568, First 1584, Glover 1594, Liberty 1630, MJPM 1645, NewAlliance 1651
Delaware: **Adobe 1734**, CenturyLink-Clarke 1750, Crystal 1758, Duane 1771
District of Columbia: Cafritz 1890
Florida: Baroco 1981, Batchelor 1983, Bi-Lo 1996, Community 2033, Community 2035, Community 2039, Copham 2044, Darden 2051, Glazer 2124, Indian 2166, Moran 2243
Georgia: Colonial 2430, **UPS 2566**, Watkins 2568
Hawaii: Bank 2588
Idaho: Blue 2627
Illinois: **Abbott 2649**, Bunning 2728, Caterpillar 2738, Community 2763, **Deere 2790**, Field 2831, Illinois 2934, **Mondelez 3034**, Northern 3059, Petersen 3078, Stern 3177, United 3199, Woodward 3243
Indiana: Community 3281, Community 3282, Foundations 3306, Lincoln 3344, Parrish 3367
Iowa: **Pioneer 3474**, Wellmark 3490
Kansas: **Lloyd 3530**, Security 3544
Kentucky: Lift 3587, Yum! 3608
Louisiana: Booth 3616, Brown 3617
Maine: **Sandy 3707**
Maryland: Abell 3712, Abell 3713, Choice 3748, Fowler 3795, **Grace 3807**, Leidy 3830, **Weinberg 3908**
Massachusetts: Arbella 3926, Clipper 3987, Copeland 3994, Dunkin' 4026, Hanover 4086, Hershey 4095, Institution 4108, TJX 4308
Michigan: Consumers 4376, **Cooper-Standard 4380**, Dow 4405, Ford 4430, General 4442, Hillsdale 4461, Jubilee 4470, **Kellogg's 4475**, Masco 4497, Pokagon 4523, Skillman 4543, Spartan 4544
Minnesota: Deluxe 4644, Duluth 4649, Ecolab 4651, General 4661, Hormel 4676, Land 4691, Minnesota 4716, **Mosaic 4722**, NFC 4727, Ordean 4732, RBC 4748, Sit 4765, SUPERVALU 4775, Target 4776, TEAM 4779
Mississippi: Morgan 4840
Missouri: **Monsanto 4945**
Montana: First 5009
Nebraska: ConAgra 5029, ConAgra 5030, Mutual 5071
Nevada: Caesars 5106, Nevada 5134
New Jersey: Bonner 5208, Campbell 5223, **Johnson 5326**, **Merck 5379**, Provident 5414, Unilever 5484
New Mexico: Frost 5519, McCune 5529, PNM 5532, Santa Fe 5533
New York: American 5587, **American 5588**, Androcles 5599, BTMU 5724, Community 5808, **Credit 5826**, Doolittle 5901, Jacoff 6220, **JPMorgan 6244**, **M.A.C. 6408**, Mnuchin 6494, **Moody's 6499**, Morgan 6507, New York 6543, New York 6544, **PepsiCo 6627**, Richmond 6703, Solomon 6886
North Carolina: **Bank 7139**, Blue 7153, Food 7201, George 7205, Merancas 7267, Stewards 7322, Triangle 7328
Ohio: American 7368, Hoover 7492, Kroger 7531, Macy's 7552, Marion 7558, Mathile 7560, Nationwide 7587, Riley 7632, Schmidlapp 7651, Stark 7673, Wagler 7699, Weisbrod 7708
Oklahoma: Bartlesville 7731
Oregon: PGE 7881
Pennsylvania: **ACE 7905**, Arcadia 7918, Armstrong 7922, CentiMark 7970, Community 7994, Dolfinger 8013, Fourjay 8047, North 8199, Pierce 8224, Smith 8288, **Tecovas 8312**
Rhode Island: Daniels 8380, **Feinstein 8390**, **Feinstein 8391**, Hasbro 8403, HPB 8407, Textron 8446
South Carolina: Smith 8499
South Dakota: Robinson 8520
Tennessee: HCA 8582, **International 8585**, Lazarus 8596, Melkus 8609, Speer 8630, Thompson 8635, Thompson 8636
Texas: Coastal 8768, Dahan 8794, Dean 8803, Edwards 8824, Fikes 8844, Fluor 8851, Hillcrest 8909, **International 8927**, Kempner 8952, Maverick 9005, Shield 9170, Sterling 9203, Sturgis 9211, Trull 9240
Utah: ALSAM 9302, Eccles 9320
Vermont: Vermont 9375
Virginia: AMERIGROUP 9383, Arlington 9384, CarMax 9401, Dominion 9422, **Genworth 9441**, Hampton 9448, Lynchburg 9474, MAXIMUS 9481, United 9546, Universal 9548
Washington: Community 9604, Evertrust 9617, Haller 9635, Medina 9682, Norcliffe 9693, Safeco 9723, Tacoma 9750
Wisconsin: Anthony 9806, Bemis 9815, Evinrude 9841, Harley 9859, Ladish 9890, Madison 9897, Milwaukee 9907, Rexnord 9932, Stackner 9951, Windhover 9968

Food services, congregate meals

California: Bergen 308
Nebraska: ConAgra 5029, ConAgra 5030
Texas: King 8959, Wolslager 9288

Foundations (community)

Alabama: Community 21, Jernigan 42
Arizona: APS 91, Aurora 94, Halle 118, Lodestar 136, Moreno 147, Stardust 164, Zuckerman 178
Arkansas: Oliver 195, Ross 199
California: Attias 268, Avery-Tsui 273, Bauer 287, **Beagle 291**, Borina 329, Breslauer-Soref 341, **Capital 375**, Cavalletto 387, Chamberlin 389, DMK 470, East 490, eBay 493, Edgerton 495, Falling 515, Gallo 560, Gimbel 589, Haas 640, Hennings 681, Irvine 727, Jones 755, Kelley 778, Lampert 818, Lowitz 850, Marks 880, Morgan 940, Muskavitch 958, Native 961, Neeley 963, Oschin 996, Quest 1050, Red 1059, Reid 1060, Shapell 1148, Smullin 1190, Sobrato 1193, Solari 1196, Stein 1215, Teach 1242, Tuffli 1266, Valentine 1277, Wallis 1296, Warnack 1297, Wolf 1337, Wonner 1343
Colorado: Goldstein 1422, Left 1445, Sprout 1505
Connecticut: Chase 1556, Fink 1583, Fisher 1586, Kitchings 1621, MJPM 1645, Seedlings 1691
Delaware: Ettinger 1779, Kirby 1796, Klein 1797
District of Columbia: Vradenburg 1954
Florida: Arison 1971, Blum 1999, Brown 2004, Burton 2007, Duckwall 2069, Gardener 2114, Garrott 2116, Goldstein 2128, Riverside 2288, Sanders 2305, Simkins 2321, **Stacy 2333**, Stein 2337, Taylor 2353, **Worrell 2395**
Georgia: **Imlay 2487**, Ma-Ran 2510, Richards 2539, Rockdale 2540, Rollins 2543, Zeist 2584
Hawaii: First 2598, Frost 2599, Learning 2610
Illinois: Eddema 2814, Harrison 2896, Kaplan 2949, Lea 2970, Mirza 3032, Morrison 3038
Indiana: 1st 3251, Glick 3310, Martin 3350, MTI 3357, Peabody 3368, Smithville 3388, Vectren 3394, White 3405

Foundations (corporate)

Foundations (private grantmaking)

Foundations (private independent)

Foundations (private operating)

Foundations (public)

Massachusetts: Dalessandro 4007, Heartstone 4090, **Mirowski 4179**, Owens 4202, SDSC 4266, Steinberg-Lalli 4287, Strategic 4298
Michigan: RNR 4527, Walker 4575
Minnesota: Brandenborg 4619, Cloverfields 4638, Manitou 4701, Mossier 4723
Mississippi: Riley 4844
New Jersey: Barer 5203, De Nicola 5239, Family 5257
New Mexico: Angelica 5514
New York: Bright 5710, Butters 5737, Daedalus 5842, Dancing 5846, Davis 5853, Dinan 5888, Greater 6098, Greenberg 6102, Hollyhock 6183, Katz 6257, Kiernan 6279, Lightfighter 6367, Lone 6390, Ohrstrom 6583, Palm 6611, Parke 6616, **Pershing 6629**, Rohr 6730, Sternberg 6930, Sulzberger 6942, Trump 7008, Zegar 7116
Ohio: American 7370, Gund 7477, Rosenthal 7637, Stefanski 7675
Oklahoma: Allen 7727
Pennsylvania: Benter 7937, CIGNA 7981, Simon 8286, Toll 8316
South Carolina: Reams 8493
Tennessee: Clayton 8547, Sasco 8623
Texas: 80/20 8648, Anderson 8665, Bass 8685, Cash 8754, Davidson 8797, Hunt 8923, **Jiv 8933**, Sharp 9167, Stevens 9205, Whitacre 9273
Utah: Semnani 9350
Vermont: Sills 9371
Virginia: Bansal 9387, Batten 9388, Dalis 9419
Washington: Edgebrook 9612
Wyoming: Zimmerman 10000

Fraternal societies

Delaware: Johnson 1790
Missouri: Schwartze 4968

Gay men

California: Weingart 1307
Illinois: Allstate 2657
Michigan: Grand Rapids 4447
New York: Klein 6289, Schnurmacher 6810

Genetic diseases and disorders

Massachusetts: TJX 4308
New Jersey: **Johnson 5326**
New York: IFF 6206
Pennsylvania: CIGNA 7981

Genetic diseases and disorders research

Arizona: Tooker 171
Illinois: Buchbinder 2721
New York: Diamond 5880, Seaver 6825

Geology

Arizona: Freeport-McMoRan 112
Colorado: Society 1503
New York: Tiffany 6978
North Carolina: Olin 7279
Ohio: Cliffs 7407

Geriatrics

California: Archstone 253, Hillblom 690
Colorado: Daniels 1399
Illinois: **Retirement 3113**, **Thome 3187**
Iowa: Principal 3476
New Jersey: Healthcare 5296
New York: Elmezzi 5948, **Hartford 6144**
Ohio: McGregor 7564
Texas: Wolslager 9288
Virginia: Charles 9404, Richmond 9521

Geriatrics research

California: Gensler 572, **Glenn 594**
Illinois: **Retirement 3113**
New Jersey: **Pfeiffer 5405**

Gerontology

California: Archstone 253, **Ellison 504**
Illinois: **Retirement 3113**
Maryland: Stulman 3891

Girl scouts

California: Bechtel, 296
Georgia: **Coca 2428**, **Keough 2496**, Turner 2562, **UPS 2566**
Kansas: Sprint 3549
Maryland: GEICO 3801
Michigan: Lear 4482, Perrigo 4521
Missouri: Graybar 4898
New Jersey: **Alcatel 5190**, Cole 5231, Holmes 5302, Ingersoll-Rand 5314, Nicolais 5392, Phipps 5406
New York: **MetLife 6479**, Mutual 6518, Wells 7073
Ohio: Dayton 7429, Parker 7611
Pennsylvania: **Alcoa 7908**, FISA 8043
Tennessee: Atticus 8531
Texas: Glasscock 8867, Halsell 8885, Valero 9246
Washington: Plum 9704

Girls

Alabama: Comer 20, Community 24, Kaul 43, Meyer 53
Arizona: Freeport-McMoRan 112, Webb 174
California: **Allende 227**, Beaver 292, California 368, Center 388, **Cisco 402**, **Clorox 407**, Community 417, Cowell 434, Danford 448, El Dorado 500, Fleishhacker 534, GenCorp 569, Gerbode 573, Goldman 605, **Google 615**, Gumbiner 636, **Hume 715**, LA84 809, Leonetti/O'Connell 832, Lesher 833, **Mattel 886**, McMillen 905, Monroe 935, Patron 1020, **Peery 1022**, PG&E 1033, Roth 1093, San Luis 1110, Sangham 1114, Simpson 1173, Ventura 1287, Weingart 1307
Colorado: Community 1394, Halton 1426, King 1440, Lipscomb 1449, Summit 1511
Connecticut: Community 1562, **GE 1591**
Delaware: **Raskob 1845**
District of Columbia: Cafritz 1890, **Summit 1950**, **Union 1953**
Florida: Community 2036, Tupperware 2363
Georgia: **Turner 2563**
Idaho: **Schultz 2641**
Illinois: Buffett 2727, Caterpillar 2738, Chicago 2746, Community 2762, Crown 2780, Evanston 2826, Field 2831, Fry 2849, **Harris 2893**, **Motorola 3043**, Siragusa 3162, Steans 3175
Indiana: **Lilly 3342**, Noble 3359, Steuben 3390
Kentucky: Cralle 3571
Maryland: Community 3759, Community 3760, Washington 3904
Massachusetts: Essex 4039, Imago 4105, One 4198, Stearns 4286, Stevens 4288, Stevens 4289
Michigan: Chrysler 4366, Community 4372, Fremont 4438, Frey 4439, Grand Rapids 4447, Knight 4477, Midland 4502, Mount Pleasant 4512
Minnesota: Bremer 4620, Mithun 4718, **O'Shaughnessy 4734**
Mississippi: Community 4821
Missouri: Saigh 4965
Montana: Montana 5013, Oro 5014
Nebraska: Lozier 5065, Weitz 5092
New Jersey: **Allen 5191**, Hyde 5310
New York: Altman 5579, Community 5802, Heckscher 6157, Hoerle 6180, Lenna 6352, **MetLife 6479**, New York 6544, NoVo 6570, O'Connor 6578, **Open 6593**, **Overbrook 6604**, **PepsiCo 6627**, Ritter 6712, Rochester 6722, **Ross 6754**, Warner 7053
North Carolina: Community 7180, Community 7182
Ohio: Fairfield 7445, Hershey 7487, O'Neill 7602, Parents 7608, Richland 7630, St. Marys 7672, Youngstown 7723
Oklahoma: Hardesty 7756, Hille 7759
Oregon: Haugland 7849, J.F.R. 7854, Lamfrom 7863, **NIKE 7875**
Pennsylvania: **Alcoa 7908**, Beneficial 7936, Birmingham 7942, Connelly 7995, Ellis 8023, FISA 8043, Heinz 8084, Phoenixville 8223, Pilgrim 8225, Staunton 8296
Rhode Island: Buehler 8364
Tennessee: **Scarlett 8624**, Wilson 8646
Texas: Bass 8690, Community 8777, Embrey 8828, Frees 8857, Jonesville 8946, McDermott 9013, Moore 9034, Orsinger 9073, Rockwell 9135, **South 9191**, Texas 9227
Washington: **Gates 9625**, Norcliffe 9693, Tacoma 9750, **Vista 9756**
West Virginia: Community 9773
Wisconsin: Community 9835, Lakeview 9892, Milwaukee 9907, Oshkosh 9916, West 9967

Girls clubs

California: Samuelsson 1107, Simpson 1173
Colorado: Libertygives 1448
Nebraska: Sherwood 5081
New York: Voya 7038

Goodwill Industries

Arkansas: Wal-Mart 210
Illinois: Tulsa 3194
Iowa: United 3485
Louisiana: Community 3624
Michigan: Leighton 4484
Ohio: Wolfe 7719
Wisconsin: Wisconsin 9969

Government/public administration

Arizona: Arizona 92
California: Eisenberg 498, Fresno 549, Gross 629, Lytel 860, Sacramento 1103, San Francisco 1109, Taper 1237
Colorado: Kitzmiller 1441, Petteys 1477, Williams 1524
Connecticut: Palmer 1666, **Richardson 1679**
Delaware: **Birch 1744**, CGLC 1751, Prentice 1839, Welfare 1872
Florida: Community 2040, NextEra 2251
Georgia: Community 2434, Whitehead 2571, Williams 2572
Illinois: Blair 2699, Charleston 2742, Chicago 2746, Community 2763, Dillon 2796
Indiana: Central 3272, Cole 3276, Harrison 3314, Henry 3320, Marshall 3348, Noble 3359
Iowa: Siouxland 3480
Kansas: Hansen 3518, Topeka 3552
Louisiana: Freeman 3636, RosaMary 3663
Massachusetts: Worcester 4327
Michigan: Charlevoix 4361, Community 4370, Community 4371, Fremont 4438, Gerstacker 4444, Greenville 4452, La-Z-Boy 4481
Minnesota: Duluth 4649, Rochester 4755
Mississippi: **Armstrong 4810**
Missouri: Saint Louis 4966, Sosland 4977
Nebraska: Fremont 5039, Grand Island 5044, Omaha 5074
Nevada: Nevada 5134
New Hampshire: Putnam 5186
New Jersey: Fund 5270, Kirby 5339
New York: Aequus 5560, Chautauqua 5766, **Clark 5785**, **Ford 5994**, **Guggenheim 6115**, **Hauser 6147**, Johnson 6237, Millbrook 6485, New York 6544, O'Connor 6578, **Pforzheimer 6635**, **Revson 6693**, Robinson 6721, **Tinker 6983**, **United 7019**
North Carolina: Community 7180, Triangle 7328
North Dakota: Fargo 7351
Ohio: Anderson 7372, Cleveland 7406, Columbus 7411, Community 7417, Coshocton 7421, Gund 7478, Murphy 7584, Reeves 7627, Richland 7630, Salem 7640, St. Marys 7672, Stark 7673, Wellman 7709
Oklahoma: Kerr 7764, Lyon 7769
Oregon: Carpenter 7831, Oregon 7876
Pennsylvania: **Carthage 7968**, Dolfinger 8013, Pew 8220
Rhode Island: Rhode Island 8429

Graduate/professional education

Health care

6092, Greater 6099, Greene 6103, Hagedorn 6128, Haring 6133, **Harriman 6136**, **Hartford 6144**, **Hayden 6149**, Healey 6152, Health 6153, Heckscher 6157, Heineman 6158, Helmsley 6160, Herrnstein 6165, Hudson 6191, Hugoton 6194, Hunter 6197, Hurdus 6198, Hurst 6200, Hutchins 6202, **IBM 6203**, IFF 6206, Island 6215, Jacobson 6219, Jacoff 6220, Jana 6225, Joelson 6232, Johnson 6236, Johnson 6241, Kadrovach 6248, Kaplan 6250, Kaylie 6263, Kennedy 6274, Khatib 6278, Kinney 6285, Klee 6286, Knapp 6295, Knipe 6297, Knott 6298, Knox 6299, Kornfeld 6304, Kupferberg 6313, Kushel 6315, Laffont 6319, Lambert 6321, Lang 6326, Langeloth 6327, **Lasker 6333**, Lauder 6334, Lauder 6335, Lee 6343, Lehman 6346, Levine 6360, Lindner 6372, Lindsay 6373, Longwell 6391, Lowenstein 6395, **M & T 6406**, MacMillan 6413, **Macy 6414**, Mallah 6423, Manton 6425, Many 6426, Marx 6442, Marx 6443, Massry 6444, MBIA 6451, McCann 6453, McGonagle 6460, McGraw 6461, McGraw 6462, Melly 6471, **MetLife 6479**, Meyer 6480, Monell 6497, **Moody's 6499**, Moore 6503, Moore 6504, Morgan 6507, Morse 6509, Mullen 6515, Mullen 6516, Mutual 6518, National 6528, Nduna 6533, New Yankee 6542, New York 6543, New York 6544, New York 6545, New York 6547, New York 6549, Nias 6556, Noble 6560, Northern 6567, Northfield 6568, **Oceanic 6574**, Oishei 6584, Olive 6587, O'Shea 6599, Paley 6610, **PBHP 6622**, **PepsiCo 6627**, **Pfizer 6633**, Phillips 6637, PLM 6647, Price 6658, Propp 6662, **Reisman 6686**, Rice 6696, Rich 6697, Ritter 6712, Robinson 6720, Robinson 6721, Rochester 6722, **Rockefeller 6724**, Rockefeller 6725, Rosen 6741, Rosenwald 6751, **Ross 6754**, Save 6799, Schenectady 6802, Schiff 6805, Schlobach 6806, Schmitt 6808, Sealark 6824, Select 6829, Semlitz 6831, Shiva 6845, Siebens 6853, **Simons 6860**, Singer 6862, Snowdon 6879, SO 6881, Sohn 6884, Solomon 6886, Soros 6891, Spingold 6899, Sprague 6901, St. George's 6904, Starker 6910, **Starr 6911**, Staten 6912, Steel 6914, Steele 6915, Steinberg 6920, Stern 6929, Sternberg 6930, **Summerfield 6944**, **Tai 6959**, TE 6966, Tisch 6984, Tishman 6993, Trump 7008, van Ameringen 7023, Viola 7032, **Vital 7033**, Volcker 7035, Wachenheim 7039, Wachtell, 7040, Wallach 7044, Wang 7047, Warburg 7048, Warner 7052, Weisberg 7070, Weissman 7072, Wells 7073, Werblow 7076, Wolk 7099, Wright 7104, Wunsch 7106, **Youths' 7112**

North Carolina: 25th 7131, Anonymous 7135, BB&T 7143, BB&T 7144, Belk 7148, Blue 7153, Blumenthal 7154, Bolick 7155, Branan 7157, Bryan 7161, Cape Fear 7170, Capital 7171, Community 7178, Community 7180, Community 7181, Cumberland 7184, Davis 7189, Delta 7191, Duke 7195, Foundation 7202, Ghidotti 7206, Goodrich 7213, Gordon 7214, Gratis 7216, Hanes 7221, Hanes 7222, Hayes 7227, High Point 7231, Holding 7233, Kulynych 7251, Kulynych 7252, Leever 7253, Levine 7255, McMichael 7265, Merancas 7267, **Nickel 7272**, North Carolina 7273, North 7274, Oechsle 7278, Olin 7279, Phillips 7284, Piedmont 7285, Polk 7287, Reidsville 7294, Rex 7295, Reynolds 7297, Richardson 7301, Richmond 7302, Roanoke 7303, Robertson 7305, Southern 7319, State 7321, Stewards 7322, **Sunshine 7324**, Tannenbaum 7326, Triangle 7328, Van Every 7329, Van Houten 7330, Vanderbilt 7331

North Dakota: Barry 7350, Fargo 7351, Leach 7353, MDU 7354, North Dakota 7357

Ohio: Abington 7365, AK Steel 7366, Akron 7367, American 7368, Ames 7371, Ar-Hale 7376, Ashland 7378, Austin 7380, Berkman 7384, **Bingham 7387**, Brown 7390, Building 7394, **Cardinal 7398**, Charities 7400, Cincinnati 7404, Cleveland 7406, Cliffs 7407, Columbus 7411, Community 7412, Community 7413, Community 7414, Community 7415, Community 7416, Community 7417, Coshocton 7421, Danaher 7424, Dayton 7428, Dayton 7429, Delaware 7431, Dermitt 7432, Dicke 7436, **Eaton 7442**, Emery 7443, Erie 7444, Fairfield 7445, Fairmount 7446, Ferguson 7450, Fifth 7452, Findlay 7453, Firman 7454, FirstEnergy 7455, FirstMerit 7456, Fowler 7460, Friedlander 7463, Gerlach 7471, Greene 7474, Gund 7475, Gund 7476, H.C.S. 7479, Hamilton 7481, Hayfields 7485, Home 7489, Humphrey 7497, Jacobs 7505, Jenkins 7508, Jordan 7514, Keeler 7517, **Kettering 7520**, Kettering 7521, Kettering 7522, KeyBank 7523, Kikel 7525, Kramer 7529, Kroger 7531, Lennon 7537, Licking 7540, Lozick 7545, Luther 7548, M/I 7550, Maltz 7553, Marietta 7557, Marion 7558, Mayerson 7561, Mercer 7567, Middletown 7570, Murch 7582, Murphy 7584, Muskingum 7585, National 7586, Nationwide 7587, New Albany 7589, Nord 7594, Northern 7597, Osteopathic 7605, Park 7609, Park 7610, Parker 7611, Perkins 7615, Piqua 7620, Prentiss 7621, Reeves 7627, Reinberger 7628, Richland 7630, Ridgecliff 7631, Riley 7632, Saint 7639, Schlink 7650, Schmidlapp 7651, Schott 7652, Scioto 7657, Sherwin-Williams 7661, Sidwell 7662, Sisler 7664, Smith 7666, Smith 7668, Smucker 7669, Spaulding 7670, Springfield 7671, St. Marys 7672, Stark 7673, Sutphin 7679, Tiffin 7682, **Timken 7684**, Tippit 7685, Toledo 7686, Troy 7688, Turner 7691, Veale 7694, Wade 7697, Wayne 7704, Weisbrod 7708, Wellman 7709, Western 7710, Wolfe 7719, Youngstown 7723

Oklahoma: American 7728, Bartlesville 7731, Bovaird 7735, Bowen 7736, Chapman 7739, Chapman 7740, Communities 7742, Community 7743, Flint 7750, Frank 7752, Helmerich 7758, Kerr 7764, Noble 7780, Oklahoma City 7781, ONEOK 7783, Records 7788, Sarkeys 7793, Stone 7801, Titus 7806, Tulsa 7807, Warren 7809, Waters 7810, Westheimer 7812, Williams 7814, Yot 7817, Zarrow 7818, Zarrow 7819, Zarrow 7820

Oregon: Autzen 7823, Benton 7825, Cambia 7829, Carpenter 7831, Collins 7836, Glory 7847, Jackson 7855, Jeld 7856, John 7857, Knight 7861, Macdonald 7866, Meyer 7870, **NIKE 7875**, Oregon 7876, PacifiCorp 7877, PacificSource 7878, Pastega 7879, Peterson 7880, PGE 7881, Poznanski 7882, Salem 7885, Tucker 7896, Young 7901, Zidell 7902

Pennsylvania: 1675 7903, **ACE 7905**, Adam 7906, Air 7907, Aospine 7916, Arcadia 7918, Argus 7920, Armstrong 7921, Armstrong 7922, Baker 7925, Ball 7927, **Bayer 7931**, Beaver 7934, Benedum 7935, Beneficial 7936, Berks 7939, Biesecker 7941, Birmingham 7942, Blanchard 7944, BNY 7946, Britton 7951, Brooks 7953, Buncher 7957, **Cardone 7964**, CentiMark 7970, Central 7972, Centre 7973, Cestone 7976, Charter 7977, Chester 7979, CIGNA 7981, Claneil 7982, Cochran 7985, Community 7990, Community 7991, Connelly 7995, Crawford 8001, Davis 8006, Davis 8007, Degenstein 8008, Dickson 8009, Dixon 8012, Dolfinger 8013, DSF 8017, Eden 8021, Erie 8026, ESSA 8028, Falcone 8031, Ferree 8036, Fine 8039, First 8040, First 8041, FISA 8043, Fishman 8044, Foundation 8046, Fourjay 8047, Fulton 8051, Genuardi 8053, Gibson 8056, GlaxoSmithKline 8061, Grass 8066, Gray 8069, Green 8070, Gunterberg 8073, Guthrie 8074, **Heinz 8083**, Henkels 8089, Highmark 8092, Hillman 8093, Hodge 8095, Hunt 8100, Hurd 8101, Huston 8102, Huston 8103, Hutton 8104, Independence 8106, Independence 8107, Kahn 8115, Katz 8117, Kestenbaum 8121, Keystone 8122, Kind 8125, Kinsley 8127, Kunkel 8133, La Vea 8134, Lancaster 8135, Lehigh Valley 8136, Luzerne 8152, Mandell 8153, Massey 8158, McCune 8160, McCune 8161, Medleycott 8171, Mellon 8172, Metcalf 8178, Mine 8184, Musser 8191, Mylan 8192, North 8199, Pangborn 8211, Peirce 8215, Pew 8220, Philadelphia 8221, Phoenixville 8223, Pittsburgh 8228, Pottstown 8234, Psalm 8237, Public 8239, Raab 8242, Rangos 8244, Rees 8245, Rubin 8257, Russell 8258, S & T 8259, Saint 8260, Scholler 8273, Schroth 8274, Scranton 8275, Snee 8291, Springbank 8293, Stabler 8294, Steinman 8299, Steinman 8300, **Templeton 8313**, United 8325, Vanguard 8327, **Viropharma 8328**, Warburton 8331, Washington 8332, West 8334, York 8351

Rhode Island: Amica 8356, Barrus 8360, Capewell 8366, Champlin 8370, Charlton 8372, Combined 8375, Crary, 8377, Cuno 8378, CVS 8379, Dunphy 8385, Elms 8387, Hallett 8401, Hasbro 8403, Hoche-Scofield 8405, HPB 8407, Kimball 8410, M. 8414, McNeil 8418, Noonan 8424, Patten 8427, Rhode Island 8429, Smith 8440, Textron 8446, van Beuren 8449

South Carolina: Abney 8454, Arkwright 8456, **AVX-Kyocera 8457**, Black 8459, Blue 8460, Bruce 8461, Canal 8466, Coastal 8472, Community 8474, Community 8475, Foothills 8478, Fullerton 8479, Gibbs 8480, Graham 8481, Hopewell 8484, Phifer 8491, **ScanSource 8495**, Self 8496, Sims 8497, Spartanburg 8501, Springs 8504

South Dakota: Robinson 8520, Sioux Falls 8521, South Dakota 8522, Vucurevich 8524

Tennessee: American 8528, Aslan 8529, Assisi 8530, Baptist 8533, Charis 8542, Christy 8545, Clayton 8547, Community 8548, Community 8549, Community 8550, Craig 8553, Davis 8555, Eastman 8561, First 8565, Frist 8568, Fritch 8569, Hamico 8576, Hardin 8577, Haslam 8581, HCA 8582, Martin 8604, Massey 8607, Plough 8615, Poplar 8616, Proctor 8617, Regal 8622, Smith 8628, Stokely 8631, Temple 8633, Tennessee 8634, Thompson 8635, Thompson 8636

Texas: Abell 8650, Alexander 8656, Amarillo 8660, Anderson 8664, Andrews, 8668, Arena 8670, Astros 8674, AT&T 8675, Austin 8676, **Baker 8679**, Ballard 8680, Bass 8690, Beasley 8698, Bickel 8705, BNSF 8706, **Bolivar 8708**, Brass 8721, Bridwell 8726, Brown, 8732, Cailloux 8742, Cain 8743, Carter 8752, Carter 8753, Clements 8766, Clements 8767, Coastal 8768, Communities 8773, Community 8774, Community 8775, Community 8776, Community 8777, Constantin 8778, Crain 8787, Crook 8790, Cullen 8792, Dahan 8794, Dallas 8795, Davis 8799, **Dell 8805**, Dodge 8810, Dunn 8816, East 8819, Edwards 8824, El Paso 8825, **ExxonMobil 8833**, Ezcorp 8834, Fikes 8844, Fondren 8853, Ford 8854, Frees 8857, George 8863, Gorman 8872, Gulf 8878, H.E.B. 8879, Haggerty 8881, Halliburton 8884, Hamman 8888, Harris 8891, Hawn 8896, Heavenly 8897, Heavin 8898, Herzstein 8905, Higgins 8906, Hillcrest 8909, Hoblitzelle 8912, Hoglund 8913, **Houston 8916**, Houston 8917, Inspiration 8926, **International 8927**, **Jiv 8933**, JKJ 8934, JLH 8936, Johnson 8939, Johnson 8940, Johnson 8941, Jones 8945, Kempner 8952, Kennedy 8953, Kimberly 8957, Klabzuba 8960, KLE 8961, Kleberg 8962, Lard 8972, Lee 8977, Link 8986, Littauer 8988, Lubbock 8994, Lyman 8995, Lyons 8996, Maverick 9005, McCoy 9010, McCullough 9011, McDermott 9013, McGovern 9014, McNutt 9018, Meadows 9019, Meredith 9023, Moody 9033, Mulva 9044, Murchison 9046, Najim 9048, Nearburg 9055, Newfield 9060, O'Hare 9068, Once 9070, Owen 9076, Parks 9081, **Paso 9083**, Penney 9089, Perkins 9090, Permian 9091, Peterson 9095, Pickens 9099, Powell 9105, Priddy 9109, Rapoport 9122, Rees-Jones 9125, **RGK 9128**, Richardson 9130, Roach 9132, Roddy-Holden 9136, Rogers 9138, Saint 9144, Sams 9145, San Angelo 9147, San Antonio 9148, Scharbauer 9157, Scott 9161, Semmes 9166, Shield 9170, Simmons 9174, Simmons 9175, **Six 9178**, Smith 9179, Smith 9180, Smith 9184, Spangenberg 9193, Stedman 9200, Sterling 9203, Stern 9204, Still 9207, Strake 9208, Stumberg 9210, Sturgis 9211, Temple 9223, Texas 9227, Tijerina, 9234, USAA 9245, Valero 9246, **VHA 9250**, Waco 9251, WEDGE 9263, Weiser 9266, Whalley 9272, Wise 9285, Wolslager 9288, Woodforest 9290, Wright 9293, Young 9295, Zachry 9296, Zeller 9298

Utah: Bamberger 9305, Burton 9309, Community 9311, Dee 9312, Dumke 9315, Dumke, 9316, Eccles 9317, Eccles 9319, Eccles 9320, Miller 9337, Noorda 9339, **Nu 9340**, Park 9341, Peterson 9345, Vivint 9354, Watkins 9356
Vermont: Lintilhac 9365, National 9368, Vermont 9375
Virgin Islands: Community 9377
Virginia: 4G 9379, Alleghany 9382, AMERIGROUP 9383, Arlington 9384, Beazley 9391, Breeden 9396, Cameron 9398, Camp 9399, Charlottesville 9405, Chiaramonte 9407, Community 9410, Community 9411, Community 9412, Community 9415, Craig 9418, Danville 9421, Dominion 9422, Elmo 9425, **Gannett 9439**, **Genworth 9441**, Gilliam 9442, Golden 9443, Guilford 9446, Hampton 9448, Harvest 9450, Hirst 9453, Kellar 9461, Lynchburg 9474, Mars 9477, Massey 9478, MAXIMUS 9481, McGlothlin 9483, Morgan, 9490, Nirman 9495, Norfolk 9496, Northern 9497, Obici 9500, Pauley 9505, Perry 9506, Piedmont 9509, Portsmouth 9510, Potomac 9511, Ratcliffe 9514, Reckitt 9516, Richmond 9521, Rosenthal 9525, Samberg 9527, **Scheidel 9528**, Sellier 9530, Snead 9536, Suffolk 9538, SunTrust 9539, Titmus 9543, **Truland 9545**, United 9546, Universal 9548, Weissberg 9554, Williamsburg 9558, Williamsburg 9559, Wythe-Bland 9563
Washington: Bainbridge 9578, Blue 9588, Cheney 9598, Columbia 9602, Community 9603, Community 9604, Community 9605, Dimmer 9610, Eggnog 9613, Everett 9616, Evertrust 9617, Foster 9621, **Gates 9625**, Glaser 9629, Grays 9631, Green 9632, Haller 9635, Harnish 9641, Howard 9647, Hughes 9648, Inland 9650, Intermec 9651, Kitsap 9659, Lauzier 9667, Lockwood 9671, McKinstry 9680, Milgard 9683, Nesholm 9691, Norcliffe 9693, OneFamily 9695, PACCAR 9698, Plum 9704, Raynier 9711, Renton 9715, Rice 9716, Safeco 9723, San Juan 9726, Satterberg 9728, Seattle 9731, **Starbucks 9742**, Tacoma 9750, Wheeler 9760, Wrigley 9766, Yakima 9767
West Virginia: Community 9773, Eastern 9775, Kanawha 9780, Martha 9783, McDonough 9784, Parkersburg 9789, Schenk 9793, Tucker 9796, Your 9799
Wisconsin: Alexander 9803, Alliant 9804, Argosy 9808, **Baird 9811**, Baker 9812, Beloit 9814, Bemis 9815, Briggs 9822, Charter 9829, Community 9832, Community 9833, Community 9834, Community 9835, Cornerstone 9836, CUNA 9838, Evinrude 9841, Fond du Lac 9843, Green Bay 9854, Green Bay 9855, Greenheck 9856, Harley 9859, Heil 9860, Incourage 9867, Johnson 9870, Kelben 9877, Keller 9878, Klein 9882, La Crosse 9889, Lubar 9894, Lunda 9896, McBeath 9901, Mead 9902, Menasha 9903, Milwaukee 9907, Northwestern 9914, Pettit 9919, Posner 9922, Racine 9924, Reiman 9929, Rolfs 9935, Sadoff 9941, **Schneider 9942**, Smith 9947, Soref 9948, St. Croix 9950, Stackner 9951, **Taylor 9955**, Thrivent 9956, Wanek 9962, Wanek 9963, Wanek 9964, Waukesha 9965, Windhover 9968, Wisconsin 9970
Wyoming: Cumming 9976, Liana 9982, McKinnell 9985, Scott 9989, Wyoming 9999

Health care, administration/regulation

Florida: **Johnson 2174**
New York: **Cummings 5833**

Health care, alliance/advocacy

Florida: Florida 2101
New York: **Cummings 5833**

Health care, association

Arkansas: Nabholz 194
California: Versacare 1288
Illinois: Parr 3070
Iowa: Aviva 3411
Minnesota: Patch 4737
New York: Planning 6644, Tai 6960
North Carolina: North 7274
Rhode Island: Manning 8415
Texas: WEDGE 9263

Health care, blood supply

Colorado: COPIC 1397
Texas: Carter 8753, Shivers 9171

Health care, burn centers

California: Peters 1028

Health care, clinics/centers

Arizona: Delta 106
Arkansas: Blue 181, Delta 184, Nabholz 194, Wal-Mart 210
California: Blue 320, California 368, CareFusion 377, Chapman 395, Disney 467, Doctors 471, **Gilead 586**, Irmas 726, **Mattel 886**, McKesson 903, Patron 1020, Shea 1155, Sierra 1164, Weisman 1309, Western 1315
Colorado: COPIC 1397
Connecticut: Aetna 1531, Bob's 1548, Boehringer 1549, **GE 1591**
Delaware: **AstraZeneca 1738**, Duane 1771, Presto 1840
Florida: Beaver 1986, Brown 2004, Florida 2101, Glazer 2124, Martin 2229
Georgia: Aflac 2399
Illinois: **Abbott 2649**, Boler 2708, Community 2769, Hospira 2921, Illinois 2934, Levi 2976, **Tellabs 3185**, Trustmark 3193, Woodward 3243
Indiana: Duneland 3297, Pulliam 3372, Vectren 3394, White 3405
Iowa: HNI 3443, Mid-Iowa 3466
Kansas: Blue 3497, Delta 3507
Kentucky: Harris 3580
Louisiana: Blue 3615, RosaMary 3663
Maine: Hannaford 3690
Maryland: GEICO 3801, Legg 3828, Linehan 3834
Massachusetts: Blue 3953, Boston 3957, Clarke 3986, Danversbank 4009, DentaQuest 4016, Eastern 4030, Golden 4073, Higgins 4096
Michigan: Leighton 4484
Minnesota: Blue 4618, Fiterman 4656, Hormel 4676, Hubbard 4678, Martin 4704, Robins 4754, United 4785
Missouri: Apex 4854
Nebraska: Scoular 5080
Nevada: Caesars 5106, Castleman 5107, Viragh 5156
New Jersey: **Berrie 5206**, Creamer 5236, Horizon 5305, Integra 5315, **Johnson 5326**, **Merck 5379**, **Verizon 5489**
New York: Anderson 5596, **Bristol 5711**, **Credit 5826**, Deerfield 5865, Gerry 6044, Kinney 6285, Leeds 6344, McCarthy 6455, Morgan 6507, National 6528, New York 6543, New York 6549, Northfield 6568, **Pfizer 6634**, Phillips 6637, Warburg 7048
North Carolina: BB&T 7144, Blue 7153, Reynolds 7297
Ohio: AK Steel 7366, **Cardinal 7398**, Charities 7400, Miller 7571, Oelschlager 7598, Park 7609, Parker 7611, R.T. 7625
Oklahoma: McCrory 7773
Oregon: Cambia 7829, Ford 7845
Pennsylvania: BNY 7946, CIGNA 7981, ESSA 8028, Highmark 8092, Hughes 8099, Independence 8106, Schneider 8271, Sedwick 8276
Rhode Island: CVS 8379
South Carolina: **AVX-Kyocera 8457**, Blue 8460
South Dakota: Robinson 8520
Tennessee: American 8528, First 8565, HCA 8582, Ramsey 8621, Tennessee 8634
Texas: Anderson 8663, **Bolivar 8708**, Dean 8803, **Dell 8805**, **International 8927**, King 8959, Maverick 9005, Simmons 9174, WEDGE 9263, Wolff 9286, Woodforest 9290
Utah: Semnani 9350
Virginia: Fredericksburg 9436, Hampton 9448, Mousetrap 9491, Norfolk 9496, United 9546
Washington: McKinstry 9680, PACCAR 9698, Safeco 9723
Wisconsin: CUNA 9838, Ladish 9890, Wanek 9964

Health care, cost containment

California: Blue 320
Connecticut: Aetna 1531
Illinois: **Baxter 2690**
New Jersey: **Johnson 5329**
New York: Achelis 5549, Bodman 5692, New York 6549, **Peterson 6630**

Health care, emergency transport services

Minnesota: **Medtronic 4712**

Health care, EMS

Indiana: Kosciusko 3335
Minnesota: **King 4687**, **Medtronic 4712**
New York: Kinney 6285
Pennsylvania: Hurd 8101

Health care, equal rights

Alabama: BBVA 9
Arkansas: Wal-Mart 210
California: **Amgen 238**, California 368, McKesson 903
Connecticut: Aetna 1531, Boehringer 1549, Connecticut 1567
District of Columbia: Consumer 1894
Florida: Florida 2101
Iowa: Principal 3476
Massachusetts: Blue 3953, DentaQuest 4016
Minnesota: Blue 4618
New Jersey: Healthcare 5296, **Merck 5379**, OceanFirst 5394
New York: **Bristol 5711**, **Cummings 5833**
Pennsylvania: CIGNA 7981, Highmark 8092
Rhode Island: CVS 8379

Health care, ethics

New York: Kornfeld 6304

Health care, financing

Arizona: Hill 122
California: Blue 320
District of Columbia: Consumer 1894
Florida: Florida 2101
New York: **Commonwealth 5800**, New York 6549, **Peterson 6630**

Health care, formal/general education

California: California 368, **Gilead 586**, Patron 1020, Smullin 1190
Florida: Klorfine 2188
Illinois: DiSomma 2798, Healthcare 2900
Louisiana: Lincoln 3649
Massachusetts: MetroWest 4173
Michigan: Binda 4350
Ohio: Osteopathic 7605
Virginia: Moore 9489

Health care, fund raising/fund distribution

Colorado: Monfort 1465
Illinois: Bunning 2728
Michigan: Leighton 4484

Health care, government agencies

California: Patron 1020

Health care, HMOs

California: California 367
Texas: **Dell 8805**

Health care, home services

California: California 368, **Smith 1183**
Illinois: **Retirement 3113**, VNA 3206
Maryland: Maryland 3844
New York: Community 5803, Kinney 6285
Ohio: Corbin 7420, Reinberger 7628, Weary 7706
Pennsylvania: McLean 8169, Surgala 8309
Virginia: MAXIMUS 9481

Health care, infants

Arizona: Halle 118
Arkansas: Blue 181
California: Patron 1020
Colorado: Kaufmann 1436
Connecticut: Aetna 1531, **GE 1591**, Liberty 1630
District of Columbia: Stewart 1949
Illinois: **Abbott 2649**
Indiana: Anthem 3257
Massachusetts: TJX 4308
Michigan: **Gerber 4443**
New Hampshire: Foundation 5171
New Jersey: **Johnson 5326**
Tennessee: Tennessee 8634
Texas: **Dell 8805**, Topfer 9239
Washington: **Gates 9625**

Health care, information services

California: **Amgen 238**
Illinois: Natural 3046
New Jersey: Horizon 5305, **Verizon 5489**
Ohio: Osteopathic 7605

Health care, insurance

Alabama: Community 24
California: Blue 320, California 367, **Packard 1006**
Illinois: **Baxter 2690**
Indiana: Anthem 3257
Kansas: Blue 3497
Massachusetts: Blue 3953, DentaQuest 4016
Missouri: Express 4888
New Hampshire: HNH 5175
New Jersey: **Johnson 5329**
New York: New York 6549
North Carolina: Reynolds 7297
Oregon: Cambia 7829
South Carolina: Blue 8460
Tennessee: Tennessee 8634
Virginia: AMERIGROUP 9383

Health care, management/technical assistance

Massachusetts: DentaQuest 4016

Health care, organ/tissue banks

Georgia: Mason 2513
Texas: **Bolivar 8708**

Health care, patient services

Arkansas: Blue 181
California: Allergan 228, **Amgen 238**, CareFusion 377, Doctors 471, Genentech 571, **Gilead 586**, GSF 633, McKesson 903, Nestle 965, Patron 1020
Colorado: COPIC 1397, ProLogis 1485
Connecticut: Aetna 1531, Bob's 1548, **GE 1591**
Delaware: **AstraZeneca 1738**, Duane 1771
Florida: Florida 2101, Glazer 2124, Lennar 2210
Illinois: **Rothschild 3124**
Kansas: Blue 3497
Maryland: Maryland 3844
Minnesota: HRK 4677, **Medtronic 4712**, United 4785
Missouri: American 4852, Express 4888, Farber 4889
Nevada: Caesars 5106
New Jersey: **Crane 5235**
New York: Mutual 6518, National 6528, **Pfizer 6633**, Phillips 6637
North Carolina: Blue 7153, Olin 7279, Piedmont 7285
Ohio: **Cardinal 7398**, **Eaton 7442**, Samaritan 7642, Western 7710
Oregon: Cambia 7829
Pennsylvania: CIGNA 7981, Highmark 8092, North 8199, Rossin 8256
Rhode Island: CVS 8379
South Carolina: Blue 8460
South Dakota: Robinson 8520
Tennessee: Regal 8622, Tennessee 8634
Texas: **Bolivar 8708**, Coastal 8768, **Dell 8805**, Valero 9246, WEDGE 9263, Woodforest 9290
Wisconsin: Ladish 9890

Health care, public policy

Arkansas: Blue 181
California: Blue 320, **Kaiser 760**
Connecticut: Aetna 1531
Florida: Florida 2101
Indiana: Transformation 3392
Maine: Maine 3699
Massachusetts: Blue 3953, Boston 3956, DentaQuest 4016
New Jersey: **Merck 5379**, **Milbank 5385**
New York: **Bristol 5711**, **Cummings 5833**, Mollylou 6496, New York 6549, **Pfizer 6633**

Health care, reform

Arkansas: Blue 181
California: **Amgen 238**, Blue 320
Illinois: Sprague 3172
Michigan: **Kellogg 4474**
New York: **Cummings 5833**
Pennsylvania: North 8199

Health care, research

California: Mead 907
Louisiana: Lincoln 3649
Maryland: Attman 3722
Massachusetts: Blue 3953, Lynch 4159
Michigan: Dresner 4409
North Carolina: Broyhill 7160
Virginia: AMERIGROUP 9383

Health care, rural areas

California: California 368
Illinois: **Abbott 2649**
New York: **Friends 6024**, New York 6549
North Carolina: Reynolds 7297
Texas: King 8959
Washington: Murdock 9689

Health care, single organization support

Illinois: Blum 2705
Michigan: Heritage 4458
New Jersey: LifeCare 5363
New York: Zegarac-Pollock 7117
Ohio: Bailey 7381, **Lerner 7538**

Health care, support services

California: Patron 1020
Illinois: VNA 3206
Maryland: Maryland 3844
Massachusetts: Peabody 4209
Minnesota: **King 4687**
New York: Samuels 6788, Witten 7095
Rhode Island: Daniels 8380
Texas: **Bolivar 8708**, Hudson 8919, **International 8927**, **Paso 9083**
Washington: Sondland 9740

Health care, volunteer services

California: Perforce 1026
Illinois: Katten 2951
New York: Warburg 7048
Ohio: AK Steel 7366

Health organizations

Alabama: Arlington 6, Bean 10, Bolden 12, Jernigan 42, Meyer 52, Thompson 70
Arizona: **Kieckhefer 129**, Pivotal 153
Arkansas: George 189, Jonsson 192, Walker 209
California: Archer 252, Autry 270, Bagley 277, Cale 364, Campini 374, Caufield 386, Chambers 390, Copses 429, Cortopassi 430, Crean 439, Curci 444, Danford 448, Day 456, Desert 461, Dolby 474, Drollinger 483, Eagle 488, El Dorado 500, Eustace-Kwan 511, Faucett 520, Foster 539, Fremont 548, Fry 555, Gallo 559, Gallo 561, Gillespie 587, Goldhirsh 602, Goodwin 614, Gordon 616, Gould 618, Grand 619, Hansen 652, Hartley 659, Hauptman 662, Hodges 698, Hoffman 699, Hope 702, Hsu 711, Ishiyama 730, Keesal 777, Khachaturian 783, Lehrer 827, Leonetti/O'Connell 832, Lilly's 838, Lippman 843, Marmor 881, Martindale 883, Mellam 910, Metta 921, Morris 942, Napa 959, O'Connell 982, Padway 1008, Pfleger 1032, Potiker 1042, **ResMed 1063**, Roche 1083, Roddenberry 1086, Salta 1105, Schlinger 1123, Shapiro 1151, Snow 1191, Spearman 1201, Stark 1213, Tallen 1234, Teach 1242, Thatcher 1248, Tuffli 1266, Vickter 1289, Voss 1292, Wallis 1296, Westreich 1317, Williams 1325, Yang 1352, Yang 1353
Colorado: Aspen 1367, Boedecker 1373, McDonnell 1458
Connecticut: Daniell 1570, Grossman 1603, Link 1631, O'Connell 1658, Owenoke 1665, Rogow 1683
Delaware: **AstraZeneca 1738**, Day 1763, Detkin 1767, First 1781, **Marks 1813**, Pincus 1836, Reynolds 1848, Wasily 1871, Whitton-Spector 1874
District of Columbia: Bedford 1883, Cafritz 1890, Coyne 1896, Forsythia 1906, Meyer 1931, True 1951, Vradenburg 1954, Zients 1960
Florida: Bailey 1977, Becker 1987, Blank 1997, Bradley 2001, Cobb 2027, Copham 2044, Dallepezze 2049, Davis 2054, Esman 2088, Faigen 2089, Fine 2095, Fortin 2106, Fredman 2108, Garrott 2116, Global 2126, Goodwin 2131, **Griffin 2138**, Hard 2147, Kaplan 2175, Langenfelder 2201, Lichtenberger 2214, McCahill 2231, McFarlane 2233, Melville 2237, Muss 2248, Perles 2266, Preik 2273, Rothberg 2297, Rubin 2300, Seaman 2314, Simkins 2321, Speer 2328, Sun 2344, Taylor 2354, Tollefson 2361, Welch 2382, Wells 2383, Yavitz 2396
Georgia: Lowder 2509, McKenna 2516, Richards 2538, Woodward 2580
Idaho: Blue 2627
Illinois: Allen 2656, Bass 2686, Beidler 2692, Bersted 2696, Block 2701, Blum 2706, Bryce 2719, Carrus 2734, Clark 2751, Dimon 2797, Doyle 2804, Duchossois 2809, Feinberg 2830, Finnegan 2832, Frechette 2844, Friedmann 2847, Full 2851, Genius 2861, Grohne 2880, Hamel 2887, Harrison 2895, Harrison 2896, Heller 2903, Hintz 2911, Johnson 2943, Larson 2967, Medlock 3020, Meyer 3023, Mills 3028, Mirman 3031, Nierling 3055, Norris 3058, Perkins 3075, Pritzker 3097, Reid 3112, Reyes 3114, Roberts 3120, Schreiber 3142, Schwartz 3145, Soderstrom 3167, Stern 3177, Stone 3179, Willow 3235, Wohlers 3238
Indiana: Ball 3263, Helping 3318, Rifkin 3378, Rothschild 3382, Simon 3385, Simon 3387, Volo 3395
Iowa: Butler 3415, Weathertop 3489
Kansas: Sarli 3541

Louisiana: Cason 3620, Wiener 3670
Maine: Davis 3685
Maryland: Abramson 3715, Allegis 3719, Berger 3729, Brickman 3739, Cordish 3764, Crane 3766, DiCarlo 3780, Higgins-Hussman 3815, Linehan 3834, **Murray 3855**, Osprey 3861, Pohanka 3863, **Smith 3886**, Wasserman 3906
Massachusetts: Baldwin 3934, Casty 3976, Chirag 3983, Crane 3998, Crotty 4002, Ellison 4034, **Elsevier 4036**, Gildea 4071, Haley 4083, Inavale 4106, **Karp 4117**, Keane 4119, Landry 4134, Lovett 4151, McCance 4165, McDonough 4167, Milikowsky 4176, Peters 4216, Ragon 4228, Redstone 4233, Roy 4247, Saquish 4257, Schaffer 4259, Schooner 4261, Shaver 4269, Stamps 4281, Two 4313
Michigan: Chinnick 4363, Devereaux 4397, **Fisher 4423**, Frankel 4435, Helppie 4456, Rordor 4529, Thewes 4554, Van 4570, Von 4574, Walker 4575, Wilson 4588, Wolters 4592
Minnesota: GHR 4664, Jennings 4680, Luther 4698, Pine 4742, Schulze 4760, **St. Jude 4770**, Taylor 4777, Wasie 4794
Mississippi: Biloxi 4814, Feild 4825
Missouri: Albrecht 4850, Baer 4856, Craig 4875, Dula 4881, Gottlieb 4897, Koman 4929, Rosewood 4964, Shelter 4971, Speas 4978, Tilles 4991
Montana: Oro 5014
Nebraska: Kim 5058, Robinson 5076, York 5098
Nevada: Lee 5127
New Hampshire: Foundation 5171
New Jersey: Catholic 5226, Frankel 5265, Harbourton 5293, Healthcare 5296, **Hovnanian 5306**, **International 5316**, James 5322, Kish 5341, **Merck 5379**, New Jersey 5389, Oster 5399, Silverman 5459, Taub 5478, Turner 5482, Union 5485
New York: AJG 5565, All 5572, Altman 5579, Altman 5581, Ames 5591, Anderson 5596, Bass 5650, Belfer 5660, Block 5683, **Bristol 5711**, Brodsky 5714, Brownington 5721, Buttenwieser 5736, Chernow 5771, Colin 5797, Corzine 5819, Cypress 5839, **Dana 5845**, Elkes 5947, Fisher 5983, Four 6006, Friedman 6023, Goldie 6063, Goldsmith 6071, Goldstein 6074, Gordon 6081, Greene 6104, Harbor 6132, Harris 6139, Harsh, 6143, Haseltine 6146, Hermione 6163, Hettinger 6170, Hoffman 6181, Horowitz 6186, **Jaffe 6222**, Jana 6225, Kanas 6249, Klingenstein 6291, Knapp 6295, Landy 6324, **Lasker 6333**, Lear 6341, Lebensfeld 6342, Leeds 6344, Mai 6417, Mee 6467, Mercer 6474, Meringoff 6476, Moore 6500, National 6526, National 6529, Newman 6553, **OCLO 6576**, Omer 6590, O'Neill 6591, Overlook 6607, Palette 6609, Parsons 6619, PB 6621, Pels 6625, **Pershing 6629**, Powers 6656, Raether 6673, Rogers 6728, Rosen 6739, Rosenblum 6746, Rosenthal 6749, Rosenwald 6750, Sackler 6779, Safra 6781, Schapiro 6801, Secunda 6827, Semlitz 6831, Shulsky 6851, Sobel 6883, Solomon 6885, Speyer 6896, Stanton 6907, **Summerfield 6944**, Sykes 6957, Tisch 6992, Tortora 6996, Trump 7008, Union 7017, Van Cleave 7025, Warner 7052, Wolk 7099
North Carolina: Allen 7134, Bate 7141, Braswell 7158, **Carlson 7172**, Curran 7185, Hanes 7222, Hillsdale 7232, Jolley 7240, Reynolds 7299, Simpson 7312, Southern 7319, Wilson 7338, Winston-Salem 7340
Ohio: Gardner 7466, Haile, 7480, Hayfields 7485, Mandel 7554, Piqua 7620, Ratner 7626, Schiff 7648, Schulze 7656, Sidwell 7662, Wadsworth 7698, White 7714
Oklahoma: Adams 7725, Browning-Kimball 7738, Jackson 7761, Ketchum 7765, McCasland 7772
Oregon: Meyer 7870
Pennsylvania: Asplundh 7923, Berkman 7938, Britton 7951, Cassett 7969, Cooper 7997, Fieldstone 8038, Fitch 8045, Giant 8055, Gitlin 8058, Highmark 8092, Kahn 8115, Kline 8129, McGinley 8164, Mengle 8174, Mullen 8190, RJM 8249, Saligman 8261, Simmons 8285, Wismer 8343
Rhode Island: Charlesmead 8371, Dexter 8382, Guth 8400, Hassenfeld 8404, Routhier 8432
South Carolina: Blue 8460, Ceres 8469, Gibbs 8480
South Dakota: Nylen 8517
Tennessee: Compton 8551, Johnson 8588, Sasco 8623
Texas: Alkek 8657, Bass 8687, Brass 8721, Cailloux 8742, Cox 8785, Doss 8812, Edwards 8823, Ellwood 8827, Eugene 8832, Fasken 8839, Fleming 8849, Heavenly 8897, Johnson 8938, Litman 8987, Madison 8997, Mankoff 8998, Mays 9008, Morris 9041, Patton 9085, Pediatric 9087, **Radler 9118**, Rainwater 9119, Reaud 9124, Sharp 9167, Sterling 9202, Thompson 9233, TurningPoint 9244, Whitacre 9273
Utah: Beesley 9307, Dumke, 9316
Vermont: Mill 9367, Vermont 9375
Virginia: Breeden 9396, Foster 9432, Funger 9438, Lipman 9469, Millhiser 9486, Newman 9493, Olsson 9502, Owens 9503, Scott 9529
Washington: Berwick 9584, Fabert 9618, Greenstein 9633, Honzel 9644, Lauzier 9667, Names 9690, Roma 9719, Shirley 9734
West Virginia: Wehrle 9797
Wisconsin: Antioch 9807, Clark 9830, Incourage 9867, Steigleder 9952, Uihlein 9959

Health organizations, administration/ regulation

Illinois: **Rothschild 3124**

Health organizations, association

Alabama: BBVA 8, Dove 31, Friedman 35, Harrison 37, Hill 40, McMillan 50, Meyer 53, Mitchell 54, Mitchell 55, Nelson 57, Stephens 69
Arizona: Arizona 92, Farrington 110, Halle 118, Hermundslie 120, Hill 122, Jasam 124, Marshall 141, McDonald 144, Moreno 147, Raymond 155, Stewart 166
Arkansas: Carson 183, Schmieding 200, Smith 201
California: Alpert 232, Apatow-Mann 247, Arbus 251, Arrillaga 261, Auen 269, Bakar 278, Barker 282, Bartman 286, Bell 300, Berger 309, Bickerstaff 313, Bilger 314, Blum 321, Blume 322, Booth 326, Boswell 330, Bower 332, Burnham 357, Ciocca 401, Danford 448, Davidow 451, Davidson 453, Day 457, Eichenbaum 497, Eisenberg 498, Engemann 506, Fansler 516, Femino 521, Galen 558, Gibson 583, Gleis 593, Gold 599, Gold 601, Goldwyn 609, Greenberg 624, Gross 629, Haas 640, Hedco 672, **Hilton 692**, Issa 732, Jackson 737, Jennings 748, Katzenberg 769, Kayne 773, Kenrose 779, King 787, Kissick 791, Kvamme 807, Lantz 820, Lear 824, Lewis 837, Lytel 860, M & T 861, MacNaughton 868, Marks 880, McAlister 891, McBeth 894, Meadowview 908, Mendelson 912, Milken 926, Moelis 933, Monterey 936, Morton 943, Morton 944, Moss 946, Muller 953, Munzer 955, **Nazarian 962**, Oberndorf 981, Philanthropy 1035, Post 1041, Pritzker 1046, Quattrone 1049, Reinhard 1061, Ressler 1066, Rey 1067, Rickey 1071, Sacramento 1103, San Francisco 1109, Semel 1138, Shapell 1148, Shapiro 1152, Shea 1156, Sierra 1163, Simon-Strauss 1172, Smith 1184, Smith 1186, Smith 1187, Sonora 1198, Spitzer 1206, Stephenson 1217, Swig 1231, Tanimura 1236, Taube 1241, Thornton 1252, Treadwell 1262, Ueberroth 1268, **Vadasz 1275**, Valente 1276, Van Nuys 1284, Ventura 1287, Volentine 1291, Wells 1311, West 1314, Winnick 1333, Wohlford 1336, Wood 1344, Wunderkinder 1348, Zander 1356
Colorado: Bacon 1370, Boettcher 1374, Brown 1379, Colorado 1390, El Pomar 1406, Fishback 1410, Monfort 1465, Norwood 1471, Peierls 1475, Saeman 1490, Strear 1508, Summit 1511, Wolf 1526, Yampa 1528
Connecticut: Aronson 1538, Chase 1556, Community 1564, Connecticut 1566, Culpeper 1568, Dalio 1569, Davis 1571, Ensworth 1580, Foley 1587, Foster 1588, Goergen 1595, Goldring 1596, Goldstone 1597, Grossman 1601, Huisking 1615, Kitchings 1621, Kohn 1622, Kossak 1623, Mandell 1635, Meriden 1643, O'Herron 1660, Orchard 1663, Palmer 1666, Robbins 1681, Smilow 1698, Straus 1702, Trefz 1709, Wiggins 1722
Delaware: Bishop 1745, Brill 1747, Crystal 1758, Delaware 1765, Esperance 1777, Ettinger 1779, Klein 1797, Lefrak 1802, Marmot 1814, Mastronardi 1815, Phillips 1835, Schwartz 1857, Westly 1873
District of Columbia: Bender 1885, Bernstein 1887, Community 1893, DeLaski 1899, Lehrman 1924, Rales 1942
Florida: Abraham 1962, Applebaum 1970, Bank 1979, Bauman 1984, Bay 1985, Berg 1993, Blum 1999, **Chatlos 2019**, Cobb 2026, Community 2032, Community 2038, DeHaan 2057, Denison, 2060, DiMare 2064, Eagle 2078, Fireman 2096, Florescue 2100, Florman 2102, Gay 2117, Goldstein 2128, Harrington 2148, Hersh 2156, Hudson 2164, Johnson 2172, Johnson 2173, **Katz 2177**, Kennedy 2183, Kirbo 2186, Klurman 2189, LaMothe 2199, Leclerc 2208, Lewis 2212, Miami 2238, Peacock 2263, Pechter 2265, Pope 2272, Riverside 2288, Rooms 2292, Sansing 2307, Saunders 2308, Scarpa 2310, Schaefer 2311, Sherman 2319, Simon 2322, Spurlino 2330, Taishoff 2350, Thomas 2357, TWS 2365, Williams 2388, Wollowick 2393
Georgia: Bradley 2414, Callaway 2418, Callaway 2419, Camp-Younts 2421, Chambers 2425, Cousins 2442, Franklin 2462, Gaines 2466, Harrison 2481, Lewis 2503, Ma-Ran 2510, Pechter 2526, Rich 2537, Rosenberg 2544, Savannah 2548, Selig 2549, **Thoresen 2557**, Whitehead 2571, Wilson 2576, Woodruff 2578, Zeist 2584
Hawaii: Atherton 2586, Cooke 2597, HMSA 2604, McInerny 2612, Wilcox 2621
Idaho: Jeker 2633
Illinois: Andrew 2662, Appleby 2668, **Astellas 2675**, Baum 2689, Bernick 2695, Bluhm 2704, Brunner 2718, Buder 2725, Canning 2733, Chaddick 2740, Circle 2749, Clapham 2750, Code 2757, Cole-Crone 2758, Community 2763, Community 2765, Community 2767, Corboy 2773, Cornell 2774, Cox 2776, Crump 2782, Cuneo 2783, Davee 2785, Day 2787, Delany 2793, Ellis 2820, Evanston 2826, Friedman 2845, Galvin 2858, Goldschmidt 2867, **Goodman 2869**, H.B.B. 2883, Harris 2892, Hazan 2899, Hendrickson 2905, Hermann 2908, Hobbs 2914, Hoehn 2916, Houlsby 2922, Huntington 2928, Kemper 2954, Kolschowsky 2962, Leibowitz 2973, Madigan 2992, Magnus 2993, Mazza 3007, Morrison 3037, Mosher 3041, Natural 3046, Neisser 3048, Opler 3064, Oppenheimer 3065, Pasquinelli 3071, Polk 3084, Potishman 3086, Potter 3087, Pritzker 3092, Pritzker 3095, Pucci 3099, Rawley 3106, Roberts 3119, Ross 3123, Rotonda 3125, Rubschlager 3126, Satter 3136, Schmidt 3139, Segal 3147, Shapiro 3151, Sheba 3155, Shirk 3158, Sirius 3163, Square 3173, Supera 3183, Trott 3192, Vaughn 3203, Wenske 3225, Wonderful 3239
Indiana: **Ackerman 3252**, Asante 3259, Ball 3262, Central 3272, Community 3281, Community 3285, English 3299, Eskenazi 3300, Froderman 3307, Gagan 3308, Heritage 3321, Hux 3325, McMillen 3352, Northern 3360, Noyes 3361, Parke 3366, Samerian 3384, Wayne 3400, White 3406
Iowa: Knapp 3452, Maytag 3460, New 3468, Siouxland 3480, Vogel 3487
Kansas: Deramus 3508, Dreiseszun 3512, Hutchinson 3521, Morgan 3536, Riverside 3539
Kentucky: Blue 3560, Gheens 3577
Louisiana: Baton Rouge 3613, Booth 3616, Factor 3632, Franks 3634, Helis 3641, Lupin 3652, Moffett 3655
Maine: Alfond 3678, King 3694, Maine 3698
Maryland: Angelos 3721, Battye 3727, Blades 3734, Blum 3737, **Brown 3741**, Davis 3772, Decesaris 3775, Glazer 3802, Leidy 3830, Levitt 3832, Mechanic 3846, Meyerhoff 3849, Mirmiran 3853,

Orokawa 3860, Rathmann 3867, Riepe 3869, Sampson 3878
Massachusetts: Bayrd 3938, Beveridge 3950, Bromley 3961, Cambridge 3971, Carney 3975, Chafetz 3979, **China 3982**, Community 3992, Copeland 3994, Cutler 4005, Egan 4032, Gordon 4075, Grimshaw 4079, Hall 4084, Harrington 4088, Ladd 4132, Landsman 4136, Lubin 4155, McEvoy 4168, **Middlecott 4174**, **Mirowski 4179**, Nathan 4188, Pappas 4204, Pappas 4205, Plymouth 4222, **Rosenberg 4245**, Rubin 4249, Schuster 4264, Spina 4280, Stare 4283, Stoddard 4293, Stoneman 4295, Worcester 4327
Michigan: Ann Arbor 4340, Battle Creek 4343, Blumenstein 4351, Brown 4356, Cold 4367, Community 4369, Community 4370, Community 4371, Cook 4378, Cracchiolo 4382, Dart 4388, DeRoy 4396, DeVos 4398, Dow 4408, Frankel 4436, Fremont 4438, Gerstacker 4444, Grand Rapids 4447, Hillsdale 4461, **Kellogg 4474**, Lenawee 4485, Levy 4487, Manat 4490, Manoogian 4492, Mardigian 4494, Marquette 4495, Marshall 4496, McGregor 4498, Prince 4525, Sage 4531, Secchia 4536, Turner 4561, Westerman 4582, World 4594
Minnesota: Brandenborg 4619, Bremer 4620, Campbell 4626, Christianson 4635, Foundation 4657, George 4662, Hardenbergh 4672, Leuthold 4695, Mitchell 4717, Nicholson 4728, Prospect 4747, Sabes 4756, Saint Paul 4757, Schmidt 4758
Mississippi: Chisholm 4818, Community 4820, Ford 4826
Missouri: Brauer 4860, Edison 4884, Lemons 4935, Lopata 4938, McDonnell 4940, Pillsbury 4956, Reynolds 4961, Sosland 4977, World 5002
Nebraska: Hawks 5047, Moglia 5069, Omaha 5074, Rogers 5077, Slosburg 5083
Nevada: Fairweather 5118, Mathewson 5131, May 5132, Nevada 5134
New Hampshire: Bean 5164
New Jersey: Atkinson 5195, Benjamin 5204, Borden 5209, Broadridge 5214, Cooperman 5233, Cowles 5234, Eisai 5249, Evans 5254, Fournier 5264, Frankino 5266, Frankino 5267, Gagnon 5271, Grassmann 5281, **Guarini 5283**, Gulton 5284, Gund 5285, Hyde 5310, Indian 5313, Jaffe 5320, Kaplen 5330, Katz 5332, Kauffmann 5334, L.F.H. 5353, Levitt 5361, Mack 5366, Martini 5372, Mazer 5375, MCJ 5377, Mushett 5388, **Ramapo 5419**, Roberts 5422, Rose 5425, Roth 5426, Rummel 5430, Sandy 5436, Schecter 5439, Seiden 5448, Silver 5457, Strauss 5470, Sudler 5472, Syms 5475, Tepper 5480, Wagner 5491, Wallerstein 5493, WebMD 5496, Wilf 5502, Wilf 5503
New Mexico: Frost 5519, Hubbard 5523, McCune 5529, New Mexico 5530, Phillips 5531, Santa Fe 5533
New York: Albert 5567, Alison 5571, Alpert 5578, Altman 5580, Altus 5583, Ammon 5593, Aron 5616, Bachmann 5632, Baker 5638, Baldwin 5639, Baldwin 5640, Banfi 5641, Beker 5659, **Benenson 5663**, Benenson 5664, Berkowitz 5669, Boxer 5698, Braufman 5704, **Buffalo 5726**, Butler 5735, Campbell 5742, Challenger 5762, Chazen 5767, Chernin 5770, Chiara 5775, Clinton 5787, Cole 5795, Cooper 5812, **Cummings 5833**, Daedalus 5842, D'Agostino 5843, Damial 5844, Davenport 5850, Davidson 5851, Dechman 5862, DeGeorge 5867, Dewar 5879, Diller 5884, Dobkin 5891, Drexler 5911, Edouard 5936, ESL 5960, Fascitelli 5971, Feil 5973, Feinstein 5974, Finneran 5978, Fitt 5985, Ford 5993, Frey 6014, Fribourg 6015, Friedberg 6017, Glickenhaus 6058, Goldberg 6062, **Goldman 6064**, Goldman 6065, Goldman 6068, Golub 6079, Gorter 6084, Gould 6089, **Grant 6092**, Grateful 6094, Grauer 6095, Greene 6103, Gross 6112, Gural 6117, Haas 6124, Harnisch 6135, **Harriman 6136**, Harriman 6137, Harris 6138, **Hayden 6149**, Heisman 6159, Hendel 6161, Henle 6162, Hershaft 6167, Hochfelder 6177, Holtzmann 6184, Hurdus 6198, Icahn 6204, Israel 6216, Johnson 6237, Katz 6255, Kautz 6260, Kayden 6261, Kaye 6262, Kellogg 6269, King 6283, Kingdon 6284, Knapp 6296, **Kohlberg 6300**, Kriendler 6309, Landegger 6323, Lang 6326, Lauder 6334, Leibowitz 6348, Lerner 6353, Letterman 6356, Lindner 6372, Lisabeth 6378, Litwin 6380, Loeb 6384, Loeb 6385, Lubo 6396, Luckow 6399, Lynton 6405, Mack 6411, Maguire 6416, Malkin 6422, Mallah 6423, Mark 6430, Marx 6442, Marx 6443, McGraw 6461, **Mead 6466**, Mercy 6475, Middle 6483, Monell 6497, Morse 6509, Mullen 6515, Murphy 6517, Neuwirth 6539, New York 6544, Nola 6562, Nonna's 6563, Olive 6587, Oppenheim 6594, O'Toole 6602, Pearson 6623, Perelman 6628, Plant 6645, Plum 6648, Poses 6655, Pulier 6665, Pumpkin 6666, Purchase 6667, Quick 6670, Red 6683, Regals 6685, Resnick 6690, Richardson 6700, Richmond 6704, Riggio 6709, Riley 6710, Rose 6737, Rosen 6741, **Ross 6754**, Rubenstein 6762, Sabin 6775, Saltz 6787, Sandler 6789, Sandy 6791, Schenker 6803, Schlosstein 6807, Schnurmacher 6809, Schwartz 6815, Schwartz 6819, Silberstein 6854, Silverman 6855, Snow 6878, SO 6881, Sobel 6882, Soros 6891, Spitzer 6900, Starker 6910, **Starr 6911**, Steel 6914, Steele 6915, Stein 6918, Sternberg 6930, Sugarman 6940, Summers 6945, Textor 6973, Thompson 6975, Tianaderrah 6977, Tisch 6986, Tisch 6989, Tuft 7011, Vogelstein 7034, Walbridge 7041, Walsh 7045, Water 7056, Weber 7059, Weiler 7063, Weinberg 7067, Werblow 7076, Winkelried 7090, **Youths' 7112**, Zankel 7114, Zuckerberg 7128
North Carolina: Baruch 7140, Bryan 7161, Carnrick 7173, Community 7180, Dickson 7192, Dover 7194, Foundation 7202, French 7203, Glass 7210, Haley 7219, Herring 7229, Jones 7242, Kulynych 7251, Kulynych 7252, Lewis 7257, **Nickel 7272**, Odell 7277, Smith 7315, Smith 7317, Triangle 7328, Van Every 7329, Van Houten 7330
North Dakota: Fargo 7351
Ohio: Akron 7367, American 7369, Barberton 7382, Berlin 7385, Berry 7386, Butler 7396, Cafaro 7397, Castellini 7399, Cleveland 7406, Columbus 7411, Community 7412, Community 7413, Community 7414, DBJ 7430, Dodero 7438, Dorn 7439, Dornette 7440, Fairfield 7445, Fairmount 7446, Fox 7461, France 7462, Gund 7476, Hamilton 7481, Hatton 7483, Heiman 7486, Horvitz 7493, Hutton 7500, IHS 7501, Kersten 7519, Miller 7571, Moores 7576, Murphy 7584, Nord 7594, Prentiss 7621, Pulley 7624, R.T. 7625, Reeves 7627, Richland 7630, Ridgecliff 7631, Schmidlapp 7651, **Timken 7684**, Toledo 7686, TSF 7690, Wallace 7700, Wodecroft 7717, Wuliger 7722
Oklahoma: Bartlett 7732, Bernsen 7733, Bovaird 7735, Chapman 7739, Gussman 7755, Hardesty 7756, Kaiser 7763, Lobeck 7768, McGill 7775, Meinders 7777, Oklahoma City 7781, Oxley 7785, Robinson 7789, Smith 7797, Taubman 7804, Titus 7806, Zarrow 7818
Oregon: Benton 7825, Crabby 7838, Oregon 7876, Schnitzer 7887, Tykeson 7897
Pennsylvania: Aqua 7917, Arcadia 7918, Bozzone 7948, Briggs 7950, Central 7971, Clayman 7984, Community 7990, Community 7991, Dolfinger 8013, Erlbaum 8027, Foundation 8046, Fourjay 8047, Hopwood 8096, Huston 8102, Jerlyn 8112, La Vea 8134, Luzerne 8152, Mandell 8153, Massey 8158, McCutchen 8162, Miller 8180, MKM 8185, Morgan 8187, Phillips 8222, Psalm 8237, Rohrer 8252, Rosenstiel 8254, Ross 8255, Schieffelin 8270, Scranton 8275, Sexauer 8280, Snee 8291, Snider 8292, Stein/Bellet 8298, Steinman 8299, Stine 8302, Taylor 8311, Toll 8316
Rhode Island: Champlin 8370, Hoche-Scofield 8405, Kimball 8410, Nelson 8422, Rhode Island 8429, Salem 8434, Swanson 8445, Woodward 8453
South Carolina: Arkwright 8456, Hipp 8483, Reams 8493, Spartanburg 8501, TSC 8506
South Dakota: South Dakota 8522
Tennessee: Beaman 8534, Christy 8545, Clayton 8547, Community 8550, Davis 8555, Martin 8605, Martin 8606, Massey 8607, Melkus 8609, Speer 8630, Stokely 8631, T & T 8632
Texas: Alexander 8656, Andrews 8667, Bass 8689, Bridwell 8726, Brown 8730, Cailloux 8741, Cameron 8747, Cash 8754, Clayton 8765, Collins 8772, Communities 8773, Community 8776, Cullen 8792, Dallas 8795, Davis 8799, Dodge 8810, Duda 8815, Dunn 8816, Elkins 8826, Engler 8830, Family 8836, Gayden 8861, Hall 8883, Halsell 8885, Hamill 8887, Hawn 8896, Hebert 8899, Henderson 8901, Hillcrest 8909, Hoglund 8913, Holthouse 8915, Howell 8918, Johnson 8941, Jones 8942, Kinder 8958, Kolitz 8968, Levit 8982, Lightner 8985, Lubbock 8994, Lyman 8995, McDermott 9013, McGrath 9015, Medallion 9020, Meyer 9024, Moran 9036, Murchison 9045, Nightingale 9062, O'Connor 9066, O'Quinn 9072, Owen 9076, Owen 9077, Perkins 9090, Prairie 9106, Puett 9114, Rachal 9117, Richardson 9130, Roach 9132, San Antonio 9148, Schutte 9160, Scurlock 9162, Seegers 9164, Shelton 9169, Simmons 9173, Smith 9185, Soref-Breslauer 9190, Sparrow 9194, Stedman 9200, Stern 9204, Stuart 9209, Sturgis 9211, Swinney 9218, Waggoner 9252, Walsh 9256, Ware 9259, Weaver 9260, Weekley 9264, **Westbury 9271**, Wichita 9277, Wise 9285, Wright 9293, Zorich 9301
Utah: Ashton 9304, Burton 9309, Eccles 9320, Semnani 9350, Watkins 9356
Virginia: Beazley 9391, Carrington, 9402, Community 9415, Evans 9428, Folger 9431, Franklin 9434, Harrison 9449, Herndon 9451, Kellar 9461, Malek 9475, Newman 9493, Peterson 9508, Rales 9513, Reynolds 9519, Three 9541, Titmus 9543, Washington 9552
Washington: Cheney 9598, Crystal 9608, Foster 9621, Glaser 9629, McEachern 9678, Nesholm 9691, Norcliffe 9693, **PAH 9699**, Raven 9710, Rice 9716, Schultz 9730, Seattle 9731, Swigert-Warren 9748, Tacoma 9750
West Virginia: Beckley 9769
Wisconsin: Bleser 9818, Community 9834, DeAtley 9839, Evinrude 9841, Frautschi 9847, Helfaer 9861, Johnson 9873, Kellogg 9879, Kohl 9883, Kress 9887, McBeath 9901, Meng 9904, Milwaukee 9907, Nicholas 9913, Peck 9918, Pettit 9919, Posner 9922, Riordan 9933, U.S. 9957, Zilber 9972
Wyoming: Allen 9973, Wyoming 9999

Health organizations, fund raising/fund distribution

Illinois: Crump 2782

Health organizations, public education

California: California 367
Iowa: Principal 3476
Minnesota: **St. Jude 4770**
Nebraska: ConAgra 5029, ConAgra 5030
New York: Overlook 6607
South Carolina: Black 8459

Health organizations, public policy

California: California 367

Health organizations, reform

California: Blue 320

Health organizations, research

Michigan: **Gerber 4443**
Nebraska: ConAgra 5029, ConAgra 5030
Texas: **Arnold 8672**
Washington: McMillen 9681

Health organizations, single organization support

Texas: Weir 9265

Health organizations, volunteer services

Vermont: Waterwheel 9376

Health sciences school/education

Alaska: CIRI 85
California: **Cisco 402**
Mississippi: Ergon 4824
New York: Lachman 6318, **Macy 6414**
Pennsylvania: Knipel 8130
Virginia: AMERIGROUP 9383

Heart & circulatory diseases

California: Barker 282, **Beckman 297**, Gross 629, Guess? 635, Hearst 669, Heart 670, Treadwell 1262
Colorado: Halton 1426
Connecticut: Connecticut 1566, **GE 1591**
Delaware: **AstraZeneca 1738**
District of Columbia: Vradenburg 1954
Florida: Greenburg 2137, **Lampert 2200**, Miami 2238, Speer 2328, Stein 2337
Georgia: Love 2508
Illinois: Community 2763, Katten 2951, Omron 3063, United 3200
Indiana: Anthem 3257
Massachusetts: Community 3992
Michigan: **Cooper-Standard 4380**
Minnesota: **Medtronic 4712**, **St. Jude 4770**
Mississippi: Mississippi 4839
Nevada: Fairweather 5118, Nevada 5134, Wiegand 5159
New Jersey: Horizon 5305, Snyder 5462
New Mexico: McCune 5529
New York: Kinney 6285, Wegman 7061
North Carolina: Blue 7153
Ohio: AK Steel 7366
Pennsylvania: Highmark 8092, Sexauer 8280, Tyler 8322
Rhode Island: CVS 8379
South Carolina: **AVX-Kyocera 8457**
Texas: Astros 8674, Moss 9043, NuStar 9065, San Antonio 9148, Sterling 9203, Wright 9293
Utah: **Nu 9340**
Virginia: **Truland 9545**
Washington: Corvias 9606, McMillen 9681

Heart & circulatory research

California: Barker 282, **Beckman 297**, Gross 629, Heart 670, Khachaturian 783, Treadwell 1262
Colorado: Halton 1426
Florida: Amaturo 1966
Illinois: Community 2763, McGowan 3014
Indiana: Leighton 3338
Maryland: **Sidgmore 3885**
Massachusetts: Stare 4283
Michigan: General 4442, **Tubergen 4559**
Nevada: Fairweather 5118, Nevada 5134, Wiegand 5159
New Jersey: Heart 5297
New York: Bugher 5727, Gilman 6052
Pennsylvania: **Cardiovascular 7963**, Smith 8288
Texas: Goldsbury 8868, **Leducq 8976**, Moss 9043, San Antonio 9148, Sarofim 9154, Sterling 9203, Tomerlin 9238
Wisconsin: Wanek 9963

Hemophilia

Louisiana: Wilson 3671
Michigan: Cascade 4359

Hemophilia research

Michigan: Cascade 4359

Higher education

Alabama: Alabama 1, Anderson 5, Arlington 6, BBVA 9, Bedsole 11, Brock 13, Brooke 14, Comer 20, Community 21, Community 24, Daniel 27, DeBakey 29, Dixon 30, Energen 32, Finlay 33, **Flack 34**, Harrison 37, Hearin 38, Hess 39, Hill 40, Lowe 46, May 48, McWane 51, Mitchell 55, Nelson 57, Pleiad 58, Protective 59, Russell 63, Smith 65, Smith 66, Smith 67, Thompson 70, Treadwell 71, Vulcan 73
Alaska: Aleut 80, Arctic 81, Atwood 82, Carr 83, Chugach 84, CIRI 85, Doyon 86
Arizona: APS 91, Arizona 92, Aurora 94, Baird 95, Barrett 96, Canyon 98, Cottrell 103, Emerald 108, Farrington 110, Flinn 111, Freeport-McMoRan 112, Globe 115, Grace 116, Halle 118, Herberger 119, **Hickey 121**, Hill 122, Jazzbird 125, **Kieckhefer 129**, Lewis 134, Linde 135, Marley 140, Marshall 141, McDonald 144, Moeller 145, Mooney 146, Moreno 147, Morris 148, Neely 149, Ottosen 150, Raymond 155, Reese 156, Rodel 158, Schultz 161, Stardust 164, Stewart 166, Tankersley 169, University 172, Weatherup 173, Weil 175, Whale 176, Wood 177, Zuckerman 178
Arkansas: Arkansas 179, Bailey 180, Cabe 182, Carson 183, Fox 187, Frueauff 188, Glass 190, Jonsson 192, Murphy 193, Nabholz 194, Riggs 196, Rockefeller 197, Ross 199, Schmieding 200, Smith 201, Soderquist 202, Sturgis 205, Tyson 207, Walker 209, Wal-Mart 210
California: **Agilent 220**, **Agouron 221**, Ahmanson 222, Albatross 226, Altman 233, **American 237**, **Amgen 238**, Anderson 242, Angell 244, Arbus 251, Arnold 258, Arrillaga 261, Atkinson 265, Atol 267, Auen 269, Avant! 271, **Avery 272**, Avery-Tsui 273, Ax 275, Bagley 277, Bakar 278, Barker 282, Barth 285, Bartman 286, Bauer 287, BayTree 289, BCM 290, **Beavers 293**, **Bechtel 295**, Beckman 298, Begin 299, Bell 300, Benificus 305, Berger 309, Bickerstaff 313, Bilger 314, Bilinski 315, Binder 316, Bloomfield 318, Bloomfield 319, Blum 321, Blume 322, Booth 326, Borchard 328, Bowes 334, Brandman 337, Bren 339, Brenner 340, **Broadcom 349**, **Broccoli 350**, **Burkle 355**, Burnham 357, Burns 359, C.E.B. 361, Cale 364, California 368, **Capital 375**, Capote 376, Caruso 382, Cathay 385, Center 388, Chamberlin 389, Chambers 390, Charles 396, Chartwell 397, Chrysopolae 400, Ciocca 401, Cisneros 403, Clayes 404, Coates 408, College 411, Connolly 425, Cotsen 432, Coulter 433, Craigslist 436, Crean 439, Dachs 446, Danford 448, Davidow 451, Davidow 452, Davies 454, Davis 455, Day 456, Day 457, DeMille 459, Denney 460, Desert 461, Deutsch 462, Dhanam 463, Dhont 464, Dialynas 465, Doelger 472, Doheny 473, Dolby 474, Dougherty 475, Douglas 476, Downey 477, Drew 482, Ducommun 485, Early 489, Eisenberg 498, Engemann 506, **Enlight 507**, Femino 521, Field 522, Field 523, Fisher 532, **Flextronics 535**, Fortisure 538, Foster 539, Freeman 546, Fromm 553, Fry 555, Gallo 560, Gallo 561, Gellert 568, GenCorp 569, Genentech 571, Gensler 572, Geschke 576, Gifford 584, **Gilbert 585**, Gluck 596, Gold 599, Gold 601, Goldwyn 609, Goodman 613, **Google 615**, Gould 618, Grand 619, Graziadio 620, Greenberg 624, Grimm 626, Grimm 627, Gross 629, Grove 631, Gruber 632, Guzik 639, Haas 640, Halperin 646, Halsell 647, Hammer 648, Hannon 651, Hansen 652, Harman 655, Harrington 657, Harwit 660, Heffernan 673, Heller 676, Hellman 677, Hench 679, Henley 680, Herwaldt 684, Hewlett 686, Hexberg 688, Hitz 694, Hoffman 699, Hofmann 700, Horn 705, Horwich 706, Hsieh 710, Hutto 717, Irmas 725, Irwin 728, Ishiyama 730, Issa 732, J & J 734, Jackson 737, Jacobs 740, Jameson 743, Janeway 745, Jenkins 747, JG 750, JL 751, Johnson 754, Jones 755, Jones 756, Kalmanovitz 762, **Kapor 764**, Karsh 767, Katz 768, Katzenberg 769, Kay 772, **Keck 774**, Keck 775, Kelley 778, Kenrose 779, Kilroy 784, King 787, **Kingfisher 788**, Kingsley 789, Kissick 791, **KLA-Tencor 792**, KLM 795, Knossos 798, Koret 801, Kornwasser 802, Krause 805, Lamond 817, Lantz 820, Lear 824, Leichtman 829, Leonard 831, **Lingnan 841**, Lippman 843, Littlefield 844, Los Altos 849, LS 851, Lucas 855, **Lund 857**, Lurie 858, Lytel 860, M & T 861, Mabie 863, **MacDonald 864**, Marcled 875, Martin 882, Martindale 883, Matsui 885, McAlister 891, McBeth 894, McDonald 901, McKesson 903, McMicking 904, Meadowview 908, Mericos 918, Merkin 919, Merrill 920, Milken 926, Mitchell 931, Moelis 933, Mohn 934, Monroe 935, Moore 937, Morris 942, Mosher 945, Moss 946, Mosse 947, Mosse 948, Moxie 950, Mudd 951, Mulago 952, Muller 953, Munger 954, Murphy 956, Nestle 965, Norris 971, Oak 976, Oberndorf 981, OneWest 985, Oppenheimer 987, Opperman 988, Orfalea 994, Osher 997, **Osher 998**, Pacific 1004, Padway 1008, Panda 1010, Parsons 1013, Perforce 1026, Perkins 1027, Peters 1028, Phelps 1034, Price 1044, Pritzker 1046, Quest 1050, Raintree 1052, Randall 1054, Reid 1060, Reis 1062, Ressler 1065, Rickey 1070, Rickey 1071, Ring 1075, RJM 1078, Robertson 1082, Roche 1083, Rogers 1087, Ruby 1095, Rudd 1096, Sacramento 1103, San Diego 1108, San Francisco 1109, San Simeon 1111, Saunders 1118, Saw 1119, Scaife 1120, Schlinger 1124, Schow 1126, Semel 1138, Sence 1141, Shanahan 1146, Shanbrom 1147, Shapell 1148, Shapell 1150, Shapiro 1151, Shasta 1154, Shea 1156, Shiley 1157, Shortino 1160, Simms/Mann 1169, Sinskey 1174, Slager 1178, Smet 1181, Smith 1182, Smith 1185, Smith 1187, Smullin 1190, Snow 1191, Solari 1196, Soref 1199, Specialty 1203, Spitzer 1206, Sprague 1207, Springcreek 1208, Stache 1209, Stanley 1212, Stark 1213, Stauffer 1214, Stein 1215, Steinmetz 1216, Stephenson 1217, Stern 1219, Swenson 1229, Swig 1231, Tang 1235, **Tarsadia 1239**, Taube 1241, TF 1247, Thompson 1250, Thornton 1251, Thornton 1252, Thornton 1253, Tosa 1259, Towbes 1260, Travers 1261, Tu 1265, Tuffli 1266, **Vadasz 1275**, Valente 1276, Valley 1280, Van Nuys 1285, Voss 1292, Wallis 1296, Wasserman 1300, Webb 1304, Weingart 1307, Welch 1310, Western 1315, Westreich 1317, Wheeler 1319, Whittier 1323, Williams 1326, Wilson 1328, Wine 1330, Winnick 1333, Witherbee 1334, Wolf 1337, Wolfen 1338, Wollenberg 1339, Wong 1341, Worster 1347, Wynn 1350, Zable 1355, Zander 1356, **Zee 1357**, Zelman 1359, Zimmer 1361
Colorado: Armstrong 1366, Boedecker 1373, Boettcher 1374, Bowana 1377, Carson 1382, Change 1386, Colorado 1389, Davis 1400, Dornick 1403, El Pomar 1406, Fishback 1410, Gildor 1420, Green 1424, Griffin 1425, Hitchcock 1430, Kane 1435, Kaufmann 1436, KBK 1437, **Kinder 1439**, King 1440, Lewis 1447, Libertygives 1448, M.D.C./Richmond 1450, Maffei 1451, Marquez 1454, Marsico 1455, Monfort 1464, Nagel 1468, Peierls 1475, Petteys 1477, Ponzio 1482, Precourt 1483, ProLogis 1485, Saccomanno 1488, Schermer 1492, Scurci 1494, Seay 1495, Shamos 1498, Shaw 1499, Sie 1500, SSB 1506, Sturm 1510, Telluride 1512, Tointon 1513, Twelve 1515, Vodafone 1519
Connecticut: **Albers 1532**, ALFA 1534, Allwin 1536, Barnes 1542, Bauer 1543, Berbecker 1545, Boehringer 1549, Chase 1555, Citrin 1559, Community 1565, Connecticut 1566, Culpeper 1568, Dalio 1569, Daniell 1570, Davis 1571, Deloitte 1572, Diebold 1574, Ellis 1579, Fairfield 1581, First 1584, Fisher 1585, Foley 1587, Foster 1588, **GE 1591**, George 1592, Glover 1594, Goergen 1595, Goldring 1596, Grossman 1601, **Halvorsen 1606**, Hamm 1607, Heidenreich 1611, Heimbold 1612, Hoffman 1613, Huisking 1615, Keefe 1619, Kossak 1623, Larsen 1624, Laverack 1625, Lee 1626, Lehrman 1628, Liberty 1630, Link 1631, Main 1634, McLeod 1641, McMahon 1642, Morris 1646, Mortensen 1647, Neuberger 1649,

McCune 8161, McCutchen 8162, McKaig 8165, McKenna 8166, **McKenna 8167**, Mengle 8174, Metcalf 8178, Miller 8179, Miller 8180, Miller 8181, Miller 8183, Mine 8184, Morgan 8187, Naylor 8194, Neubauer 8196, Nichols 8197, Nimick 8198, Ortenzio 8205, Ortenzio 8206, O'Toole 8207, Palumbo 8209, Parmer 8212, Peirce 8215, Perelman 8219, Phillips 8222, Pine 8226, **PPG 8235**, Presser 8236, PTS 8238, Quantitative 8241, Ranger 8243, Rangos 8244, Rees 8245, Reeser 8246, Reuss 8247, Roberts 8250, Roberts 8251, Rohrer 8252, Rosenstiel 8254, Ross 8255, Saligman 8261, Sand 8264, Sargent 8265, Scaife 8266, Scheller 8268, Schock 8272, Schroth 8274, Scranton 8275, Sedwick 8276, Seraph 8279, Sexauer 8280, Shapira 8282, Simmons 8285, Simon 8286, Smith 8287, Smith 8288, Stackpole 8295, Stein 8297, Steinman 8299, Taylor 8311, Toll 8316, Toll 8317, Trexler 8320, Turner 8321, Ujala 8323, United 8325, Vague 8326, Vanguard 8327, **Waldorf 8330**, Warburton 8331, West 8334, Williams 8338, Willis 8340, Withington 8344, Wyomissing 8350

Rhode Island: Acton 8354, Alpert 8355, **Bingham 8361**, Binney 8362, Biogen 8363, Buehler 8364, Champlin 8370, Charlesmead 8371, Charlton 8372, Chisholm 8373, Cuno 8378, CVS 8379, Dexter 8382, Diagnostic 8383, Fain 8388, **Feinstein 8391**, Foster 8394, Freeman 8396, Greene 8398, Hallett 8401, Hassenfeld 8404, Hoche-Scofield 8405, HPB 8407, IMA 8408, Luehrmann 8413, Manning 8415, McAdams 8416, McCurdy 8417, Murray 8421, Osborn 8426, Richter 8430, Salem 8434, Sharpe 8437, **SVF 8444**, Swanson 8445, Textron 8446, Vance 8450, Woodward 8453

South Carolina: Abney 8454, Arkwright 8456, **AVX-Kyocera 8457**, Campbell 8465, Canal 8466, Cassels 8467, Community 8474, Daniel 8476, Fullerton 8479, Hipp 8483, Hopewell 8484, McKissick 8486, Patterson 8489, Phifer 8491, Smith 8498, Smith 8499, Spartanburg 8501, Speedwell 8503

South Dakota: Dakota 8514, Larson 8516, Raft 8519, South Dakota 8523

Tennessee: American 8528, Atticus 8531, Ayers 8532, Beaman 8534, Bridgestone 8537, Carell 8540, Charis 8542, Christian 8544, Clayton 8547, Community 8548, Curb 8554, Eastman 8561, Eskind 8563, First 8565, Fritch 8569, **Gardner 8570**, Gatton 8571, Great 8575, Hamico 8576, Hardin 8577, Hart 8578, Haslam 8580, Haslam 8581, Jeniam 8587, Johnson 8588, Johnson 8589, Lange 8593, Massey 8607, Msb 8612, Regal 8622, **Scarlett 8624**, Scheidt 8625, Smith 8628, Speer 8630, Stokely 8631, Temple 8633, Tennessee 8634, Thompson 8636, Turner 8639, Washington 8643, Wilson 8645, Wilson 8646

Texas: Abell 8650, Adams 8652, Adams 8653, Alexander 8656, Alkek 8657, Alkek 8658, Anadarko 8661, Anderson 8665, Andras 8666, Armentrout 8671, AT&T 8675, B.E.L.I.E.F. 8677, Badger 8678, Bass 8687, Bass 8688, Bass 8689, Bauer 8692, Baugh 8693, Baumberger 8694, Belin 8699, Beneski 8701, Benson 8702, Bickel 8705, BNSF 8706, Booth 8711, Booth 8712, Booth 8713, **BP 8718**, Bratton 8722, Bridwell 8726, Brookshire 8728, Broughton 8729, Brown 8730, Buck 8735, Buford 8736, Cain 8743, Callaway 8746, Cameron 8747, **Caris 8749**, Carlson 8750, Carter 8752, Carter 8753, Cash 8754, CFP 8758, CH 8759, Chaparral 8760, Chapman 8761, Cizik 8764, Clayton 8765, Clements 8766, Coastal 8768, Coates 8769, Cockrell 8770, Collins 8771, Collins 8772, Communities 8773, Community 8775, Constantin 8778, Cook 8779, Cox 8784, Cox 8785, Craig, 8786, Crane 8788, Criswell 8789, Daniel 8796, Davidson 8797, De Llano 8802, Dickson-Allen 8806, Doss 8812, Doss 8813, Duda 8815, Edwards 8823, Elkins 8826, Engler 8830, **ExxonMobil 8833**, Fain 8835, Faulconer 8841, Fikes 8844, Fisch 8846, Fish 8848, Fleming 8849, Fluor 8851, Fondren 8853, Ford 8854, Franklin 8855, Gale 8859, Greathouse 8874, Grum 8876, Gulf 8878, Hachar 8880, Halliburton 8884, Halsell 8885, Hamill 8887, Hamman 8888, Hamon 8889, Hawkins 8895, Heavin 8898, Hebert 8899, Henderson 8900, Herd 8902, Hersh 8903, Higgins 8906, Hillcrest 8909, Hirsch 8910, Hobby 8911, Hoblitzelle 8912, Hudson 8919, Huffington 8920, Hunt 8922, Impetus 8924, Jamail 8929, Johnson 8937, Johnson 8939, Johnson 8940, Johnson 8941, Jones 8942, Jones 8943, Jones 8944, Jones 8945, Justin 8947, Kean 8950, Kempner 8952, Kennedy 8953, Kessler 8954, Kilroy 8956, Kimberly 8957, Kleberg 8962, Kleberg 8963, Kodosky 8966, Lard 8972, Lawrence 8973, Lebowitz-Aberly 8975, Legett 8978, Lennox 8979, Lesley 8980, Levit 8982, Loose 8991, Lord 8992, Lyman 8995, Madison 8997, Mankoff 8998, Marsh 8999, Martinez 9003, Maverick 9005, Mayborn 9006, McCombs 9009, McCoy 9010, McCullough 9011, McDaniel 9012, McDermott 9013, McNair 9017, McNutt 9018, Meyer 9024, MFI 9025, Miles 9026, Miller 9027, Moncrief 9031, Moore 9034, Morgan 9037, Morgan 9038, Mulva 9044, Murchison 9045, Murchison 9046, Nestle 9056, Newman 9061, Nightingale 9062, **Notsew 9064**, NuStar 9065, O'Donnell 9067, O'Hare 9068, Onstead 9071, O'Quinn 9072, Owen 9075, Owen 9076, Owsley 9078, **Paloheimo 9080**, Parks 9081, Patton 9084, Payne 9086, Penney 9089, Perkins 9090, Perot 9092, Perot 9093, Peterson 9095, Pinon 9100, Piper 9101, Pritzker 9110, QuadW 9115, Rachal 9117, Ram 9120, Rea 9123, Reaud 9124, Richardson 9130, Roach 9132, Robinson 9133, Rogers 9138, Rosewood 9140, Rowling 9141, San Angelo 9146, San Antonio 9148, Sanchez 9150, Schollmaier 9159, Scurlock 9162, Seegers 9164, Sharp 9167, Shelton 9169, Simmons 9173, Simmons 9174, Smith 9179, Smith 9181, Smith 9185, Smith 9187, Spec's 9195, Stedman 9200, Sterling 9203, Stern 9204, Stevens 9206, Still 9207, Strake 9208, Stumberg 9210, **Suder 9212**, Sumners 9214, Talkington 9219, Tartt 9222, Temple 9223, Terry 9225, Texas 9228, Thomas 9231, Tobin 9236, Trull 9240, Turner 9242, USAA 9245, Valero 9246, Vaughan 9248, Vergara 9249, Wal 9254, Wallrath 9255, Walsh 9256, Ware 9259, WEDGE 9263, Weir 9265, Whitacre 9273, Wichita 9277, Wintermann 9283, Wischer 9284, Wise 9285, Wood 9289, Wright 9293, Zachry 9296, Zimmer 9300

Utah: Bamberger 9305, Beesley 9307, Bertin 9308, Burton 9309, Dee 9312, Dumke 9315, Dumke, 9316, Eccles 9317, Eccles 9319, Eccles 9320, GFC 9322, Harman 9325, Huntsman 9327, Lawson 9330, McCarthey 9332, Meldrum 9333, Miller 9334, Miller 9337, Noorda 9339, Price 9346, Quinney 9347, RLC 9348, Semnani 9350, Simmons 9351, Tanner 9352, Watkins 9356, Yamagata 9357

Vermont: General 9361, McKenzie 9366, Tarrant 9373, Vermont 9375

Virgin Islands: Prior 9378

Virginia: Agena 9381, AMERIGROUP 9383, Balsells 9385, Bangs-Russell 9386, Batten 9388, Beazley 9391, **Bosack 9395**, Cabell 9397, Carrington, 9402, Carter 9403, **Cooke 9417**, Craig 9418, English 9426, Estes 9427, Fife 9429, Folger 9431, **Friends 9437**, Funger 9438, Gilliam 9442, Hampton 9448, Herndon 9451, Hillman 9452, Keesee 9460, Kellar 9461, Lambert 9466, Landmark 9467, Launders 9468, Lipman 9469, Luck 9472, Manning 9476, Massey 9478, Maude 9480, McGlothlin 9483, MeadWestvaco 9484, Millhiser 9486, Moore 9489, Morgan, 9490, NewMarket 9494, Norfolk 9496, **Northrop 9498**, Olsson 9502, Pauley 9505, Perry 9507, Ratcliffe 9514, Reinhart 9517, Reynolds 9519, Rice 9520, Rimora 9522, Shearwater 9531, Smith 9534, Smithfield 9535, Snead 9536, SunTrust 9539, Tickle 9542, **Truland 9545**, United 9546, Universal 9548, Waldron 9550, Watkins 9553, Willett 9557, Wise 9560

Washington: Ames 9570, Anderson 9572, Aven 9575, Avista 9576, Baker 9579, Bamford 9580, Bates 9582, Benaroya 9583, Bezos 9585, Biller 9586, Blakemore 9587, Blue 9588, Cameron 9593, **Channel 9597**, Cheney 9598, Community 9604, Cowles 9607, Crystal 9608, Danz 9609, Dimmer 9610, Discuren 9611, Evertrust 9617, Foster 9621, Fuchs 9624, Green 9632, Jones 9655, KMR 9660, Lafromboise 9663, Lauzier 9667, Lauzier 9668, Lockwood 9671, Lucky 9673, McCaw 9676, McKinstry 9680, Miller 9684, Murdock 9689, Neukom 9692, Norcliffe 9693, Oki 9694, PACCAR 9698, **PAH 9699**, PEMCO 9702, Plum 9704, Raikes 9708, Raven 9710, Remala 9714, Rice 9716, Richardson 9717, Scan 9729, Shirley 9734, Smith 9737, Snyder 9739, Spark 9741, Sunbridge 9746, Swigert-Warren 9748, Tacoma 9750, Washington 9757, Wendt 9758, Wheeler 9760, Wrigley 9766, Yakima 9767

West Virginia: Bowen 9770, Daywood 9774, Hess 9777, Hollowell 9778, Kanawha 9780, Maier 9782, Meagel 9786, Nutting 9788, Parkersburg 9789, Preservati 9790, Prichard 9791, Schenk 9793, Shott, 9794, Wehrle 9797

Wisconsin: 1923 9800, Alexander 9803, Alliant 9804, **Baird 9811**, Beloit 9814, Bemis 9815, Bleser 9818, **Bradley 9819**, Briggs 9822, Brookhill 9824, Brotz 9825, Casper 9827, Charter 9829, Clark 9830, Cleary 9831, Culver's 9837, CUNA 9838, Family 9842, Frautschi 9847, Fund 9849, Helfaer 9861, Herma 9862, Holz 9864, Incourage 9867, Johnson 9870, Johnson 9871, Johnson 9872, Johnson 9874, Kelben 9877, Kohl 9883, Kohler 9884, Kohler 9885, Krause 9886, Kress 9887, La Crosse 9889, Ladish 9890, Ladish 9891, Loehrke 9893, Lubar 9894, Mead 9902, Menasha 9903, Michels 9906, Milwaukee 9907, MMG 9908, Neese 9911, Nelson 9912, Northwestern 9914, Oshkosh 9916, Pettit 9919, Predolin 9923, Ramirez 9926, Rath 9927, RDK 9928, Reinhart 9930, Rennebohm 9931, Rexnord 9932, Rolfs 9935, Ryan 9940, **Schneider 9942**, Sentry 9944, Siebert 9946, Smith 9947, Steigleder 9952, Uihlein 9958, West 9967, Windhover 9968, Wisconsin 9969, Wisconsin 9970, Zilber 9972

Wyoming: Allen 9973, Cumming 9976, Ellbogen 9977, Griffith 9979, Liana 9982, Martin 9984, Niner 9987, Perkins 9988, Storer 9992, Stuart 9993, Watt 9997, Whitney 9998

Higher education reform

Louisiana: Community 3624

Higher education, college

Arizona: Dorrance 107
California: California 368, Deutsch 462, Yellow 1354
Colorado: Ottens 1472
Delaware: MacMahon 1810
Florida: May 2230, Ratcliffe 2278, Wolfson 2392
Georgia: Poindexter 2532
Idaho: Brandt 2628
Illinois: Hurley 2929, **Kemper 2955**, Stewart 3178
Iowa: Durgin 3427
Louisiana: Community 3624
Maryland: Stasiak 3889
Massachusetts: Alden 3921, Gildea 4071, Rands 4229
Minnesota: Alliss 4600
Missouri: Pershing 4953
Nebraska: Sherwood 5081
New Jersey: Barer 5203
New York: Conard-Davis 5809, Gould 6087, Hunter 6197, Jacoff 6220, Johnson 6233, Raether 6673, Reynolds 6694, Wolstencroft 7100
North Carolina: McEachern 7263
Oregon: **Intel 7853**
Pennsylvania: Burke 7959, Haldeman 8076, Mertz 8177, Miller, 8182, Mosi 8189, Rorer 8253, Stabler 8294
Rhode Island: Knoop 8411
South Carolina: Coker 8473, Foothills 8478

Higher education, college (community/junior)

Higher education, university

Hinduism

Hispanics/Latinos

Historic preservation/historical societies

Oleson 4516, Petoskey 4522, Tuktawa 4560, Whiting 4584
Minnesota: Hersey 4673, Larson 4692, Manitou 4701, Marbrook 4702, Nicholson 4728, Schmidt 4758, Sit 4765, Slaggie 4766, U.S. 4784
Mississippi: Greater 4829, Gulf 4830
Missouri: Apex 4854, Burns 4866, Dierberg 4879, Kooyumjian 4930, Truman 4996
Montana: Town 5016
Nebraska: Hastings 5046, Union 5090
New Hampshire: Johnson 5178, Putnam 5186
New Jersey: Brotherton 5216, **Edison 5248**, Grassmann 5281, Honickman 5303, James 5322, Jockey 5325, Kirby 5339, L.F.H. 5353
New Mexico: Albuquerque 5511, **Lannan 5526**, McCune 5529
New York: Adams 5552, Adirondack 5556, American 5587, **American 5588**, Auchincloss 5623, Baird 5636, Bayne 5653, Berg 5667, Butler 5733, Central 5757, Debs 5860, Gerry 6043, Grigg 6109, Hudson 6191, J. 6218, **Kaplan 6252**, Kellogg 6270, Klingenstein 6294, **Lauder 6336**, Lenna 6352, Malkin 6422, Miller 6486, New York 6544, O'Connor 6578, Peco 6624, **Pershing 6629**, Pomeroy 6652, Resource 6691, Roberts 6717, Rochester 6722, Rockefeller 6725, Rose 6737, Rosenwald 6751, Snow 6878, **Stockman 6932**, Thompson 6975, Tianaderrah 6977, Truman 7007, **Trust 7009**, Weinberg 7066, Weinberg 7067, Weisberg 7070, Wendt 7074, Wilson 7086
North Carolina: E. 7198, Foundation 7202, Hanes 7221, Robertson 7305, Slick 7313, Smith 7317, Tannenbaum 7326, Triangle 7328, Vanderbilt 7331
North Dakota: Stern 7360
Ohio: Akron 7367, Christman 7403, Columbus 7411, Community 7415, Dater 7426, Fleischmann 7457, Gelbman 7469, Hudson 7496, Ingalls 7503, Kersten 7519, LZ 7549, Montgomery 7575, Murphy 7584, Nordson 7596, Richland 7630, Schiewetz 7647, Schiff 7649, Stark 7673, **Timken 7684**, Troy 7688, Turner 7691, Youngstown 7723
Oklahoma: Allen 7727, Communities 7742, Kirkpatrick 7766, McGee 7774, ONEOK 7783
Oregon: Kinsman 7860, PacifiCorp 7877
Pennsylvania: Allegheny 7911, Arcadia 7918, Argus 7920, Armstrong 7921, Berks 7939, Century 7974, Claneil 7982, Community 7991, Federated 8033, Fieldstone 8038, First 8040, Hurd 8101, Huston 8102, Jackson 8110, Janssen 8111, Lehigh Valley 8136, McCune 8161, McLean 8169, Pew 8220, Quaker 8240, Rees 8245, Scranton 8275, Steinman 8299, von Hess 8329
Rhode Island: Champlin 8370, Daniels 8380, Felicia 8392, Freeman 8396, Rhode Island 8429, Scrooby 8435, Shumway 8439, van Beuren 8449
South Carolina: Graham 8481, Spartanburg 8501
South Dakota: Sioux Falls 8521
Tennessee: Atticus 8531, Community 8550, Haslam 8581
Texas: Bass 8687, Clements 8766, Collins 8771, Dogwood 8811, East 8819, Edwards 8823, George 8863, Herzstein 8905, Hoblitzelle 8912, Johnson 8939, Kelleher 8951, Kempner 8952, Lubbock 8994, McCombs 9009, McDermott 9013, Meadows 9019, Northen 9063, Owen 9076, **Paloheimo 9080**, San Antonio 9148, Sharp 9167, Smith 9180, Sterling 9203, Stuart 9209, Summerlee 9213, Ward 9258, Wichita 9277, Wortham 9292
Utah: Eccles 9318
Vermont: Vermont 9375
Virginia: Cabell 9397, Cameron 9398, Community 9411, Community 9412, Folger 9431, Genan 9440, Gwathmey 9447, Morgan, 9490, Parsons 9504, Reynolds 9519, Shearwater 9531, Smith 9534, SunTrust 9539, **Truland 9545**, Universal 9548, Williamsburg 9559
Washington: Blue 9588, Community 9604, Grays 9631, Inland 9650, Norcliffe 9693, Renton 9715, Seattle 9731, Tacoma 9750
West Virginia: Community 9773, Kanawha 9780, Parkersburg 9789
Wisconsin: Bachhuber 9809, Bemis 9815, Caxambas 9828, Community 9834, Community 9835, Green Bay 9854, Incourage 9867, Jeffris 9869, Johnson 9874, Kress 9887, Mead 9902, Milwaukee 9907, Nicholas 9913, Raibrook 9925, Rowland 9937, Spire 9949, Waukesha 9965

Historical activities

Alabama: Protective 59
Arkansas: Carson 183
California: **Ing 721**, **Shapell 1149**
Colorado: Fishback 1410
Connecticut: Lehrman 1628, New Canaan 1650
Florida: Walter 2375
Georgia: Franklin 2462
Hawaii: Castle 2594
Idaho: Seagraves 2642
Illinois: Pritzker 3091
Indiana: Orange 3365, Washington 3398
Iowa: Hanson 3441
Kansas: Cohen 3499
Massachusetts: Peabody 4209
Michigan: Ford 4430
Mississippi: **Armstrong 4810**
New Jersey: Kirby 5340
New York: Alfiero 5570, Aresty 5610, Manton 6425, Solomon 6886, Weir 7069
North Carolina: Bolick 7155, Delta 7191
North Dakota: North Dakota 7357
Oregon: Kinsman 7860, Swindells 7892
Pennsylvania: Ferree 8036
South Carolina: Bruce 8461
Tennessee: HCA 8582
Texas: King 8959
Utah: Miller 9335, Miller 9336, Parrish 9342
Virginia: Proteus 9512

Historical activities, centennials

North Carolina: Delta 7191

Historical activities, genealogy

New York: Rogers 6727

Historical activities, war memorials

California: Wunderkinder 1348
Pennsylvania: Lotman 8150, Smith 8289

History/archaeology

Alaska: CIRI 85
California: Goldhirsh-Yellin 603, Packard 1007
Georgia: Watson 2569
Michigan: **Earhart 4413**
New Mexico: McCune 5529
New York: **Grant 6092**, **Guggenheim 6115**, **Kress 6308**, Levy 6364, Littauer 6379, O'Connor 6578, **Wenner 7075**
North Carolina: Cumberland 7184
Ohio: Fleischmann 7457, Murphy 7584
Oregon: PGE 7881
Pennsylvania: **Institute 8109**, **Williams 8339**
Texas: Austin 8676, Clements 8766, Coastal 8768, Kempner 8952, Meadows 9019, Northen 9063, Summerlee 9213
Washington: Community 9604
Wisconsin: **Bradley 9819**

Holistic medicine

Arizona: Steele 165, Weil 175
Tennessee: Baptist 8533

Homeless

Alabama: Community 24, Kaul 43, Meyer 53, Webb 76
Arizona: Arizona 92, **Hickey 121**, Hill 122, Morris 148, Steele 165, Webb 174
Arkansas: Cabe 182
California: Ahmanson 222, Alliance 229, Atkinson 265, California 365, California 368, **Cisco 402**, Community 414, Community 417, Croul 441, Deutsch 462, El Dorado 500, Five 533, **Geffen 567**, Gilmore 588, Goldman 605, Gombos 610, Green 621, Grove 631, Gumbiner 636, **Hilton 692**, Lesher 833, Ludwick 856, Marin 877, McCarthy 895, McMillen 905, Parsons 1013, Patron 1020, Roberts 1081, Ross 1090, Sacramento 1103, San Diego 1108, San Francisco 1109, San Luis 1110, Silicon 1166, Sonora 1198, Taper 1237, Van Nuys 1284, Weingart 1307, Wetzel 1318, Wynn 1350
Colorado: Boettcher 1374, Colorado 1390, Daniels 1399, Denver 1401, El Pomar 1406, Halton 1426, Hunter 1431, King 1440, Rose 1487, Summit 1511
Connecticut: Community 1562, Community 1563, Connecticut 1566, Culpeper 1568, Fund 1589, Lowenstein 1633, Mortensen 1647
Delaware: Crystal 1758, Marmot 1814, **Raskob 1845**
District of Columbia: **Butler 1889**, Cafritz 1890, **Hill 1915**, Jones 1918, Ludwig 1927
Florida: Baldwin 1978, Bank 1979, Bush 2008, Community 2036, Community 2040, duPont 2075, Indian 2166, Miami 2238, Pinellas 2269, Southwest 2327, Wardlaw 2377
Georgia: Community 2432, EZ 2456, Franklin 2462, Primerica 2534, Rich 2537, **Thoresen 2557**, Tull 2561, Woolley 2581
Idaho: Jeker 2634
Illinois: Chicago 2746, Community 2763, Community 2765, Day 2787, Evanston 2826, Field 2831, **Kapoor 2950**, Levi 2976, Owens 3068, Pierce 3080, **Ploughshares 3082**, Polk 3084, Prince 3089, Siragusa 3162, VNA 3206, Washington 3217, Woodward 3243
Indiana: Community 3281, Community 3284, Community 3286, Henry 3320, **Lilly 3342**, Pulliam 3372, Rolland 3381, Steuben 3390
Iowa: Siouxland 3480
Kansas: Security 3544, Topeka 3552
Kentucky: Cralle 3571, Horn 3581
Louisiana: Booth 3616, Brown 3617, Community 3624, Wilson 3671
Maryland: Abell 3712, Abell 3713, Battye 3727, **Bearman 3728**, Ceres 3747, **Cohen 3754**, Community 3759, Community 3761, **DLA 3781**, Dresher 3782, Fowler 3795, O'Neil 3859, Washington 3904
Massachusetts: Boston 3956, Boston 3957, Clipper 3987, Essex 4039, Fireman 4049, Liberty 4145, Linden 4148, Melville 4170, Mifflin 4175, Smith 4277, Worcester 4327
Michigan: Ann Arbor 4340, Chrysler 4366, Grand Rapids 4447, McGregor 4498, Midland 4502, Skillman 4543, Sturgis 4550, Tuscola 4562, Van Andel 4567
Minnesota: Andersen 4603, Bremer 4620, Duluth 4649, Frey 4658, Minneapolis 4714, Phillips 4741
Missouri: Fox 4892, Roblee 4963, Saint Louis 4966
Montana: Oro 5014, Washington 5018
Nebraska: Dunklau 5036, Lozier 5065, Woods 5096
Nevada: Nevada 5134
New Hampshire: Foundation 5171, Lindsay 5179
New Jersey: Borden 5209, Danellie 5237, Dodge 5243, Hyde 5310, **Johnson 5329**, Karma 5331, MCJ 5377, Orange 5396
New Mexico: Frost 5519, McCune 5529, Santa Fe 5533
New York: Abrons 5546, Central 5757, **Clark 5785**, Community 5802, Cummings 5834, **Discount 5889**, Gorman 6083, **Hearst 6155**, **Hearst 6156**, Langeloth 6327, Litwin 6380, **MetLife 6479**, Mulford 6514, New York 6546, NYSE 6573, Ritter 6712, Schnurmacher 6810, Sidewalk 6852, Staten 6912, Troy 7006, van Ameringen 7024, Western 7078
North Carolina: Cemala 7174, Community 7180, Community 7181, Cumberland 7184, North

Carolina 7273, Reidsville 7294, Robertson 7305, Stewards 7322, Triangle 7328
North Dakota: Leach 7353, North Dakota 7357, Stern 7360
Ohio: Akron 7367, Bruening 7391, Cincinnati 7404, Columbus 7411, Fairfield 7445, GAR 7465, Hatton 7483, Levin 7539, Marion 7558, Mercer 7567, Nord 7594, Nordson 7596, O'Neill 7602, Osteopathic 7605, Saint 7639, Springfield 7671, Stark 7673, Toledo 7686, White 7715
Oklahoma: Hardesty 7756, Hille 7759, Robinson 7789
Oregon: Benton 7825, Carpenter 7831, Collins 7836, J.F.R. 7854, John 7857
Pennsylvania: Beneficial 7936, Connelly 7995, Dolfinger 8013, First 8041, Fourjay 8047, Huston 8102, Independence 8107, Morris 8188, North 8199, Pew 8220, Phoenixville 8223, Smith 8288, Snee 8291, Staunton 8296, Surgala 8309
Rhode Island: Kimball 8410
South Carolina: Coastal 8472
Tennessee: Baptist 8533, Thompson 8636, Wilson 8646
Texas: Abell 8650, Baron 8682, Baxter 8695, Coastal 8768, Community 8774, Community 8776, Community 8777, Cullen 8792, Dallas 8795, Davis 8799, Embrey 8828, Fluor 8851, Frees 8857, Hoblitzelle 8912, Kennedy 8953, King 8959, McDermott 9013, Meadows 9019, Moore 9034, Orsinger 9073, Rees-Jones 9125, Rockwell 9135, Sterling 9203, Still 9207, Sturgis 9211, Terry 9224, Waco 9251, Wolslager 9288, Wright 9293, Zale 9297
Utah: ALSAM 9302, Eccles 9320
Virginia: Beazley 9391, Community 9410, Freddie 9435, Launders 9468, Lynchburg 9474
Washington: **Campion 9594**, Community 9604, **Gates 9625**, Giddens, 9627, KMR 9660, Norcliffe 9693, Raikes 9708, Safeco 9723, Tacoma 9750
West Virginia: Eastern 9775, Kanawha 9780
Wisconsin: Cornerstone 9836, Green Bay 9854, La Crosse 9889, Milwaukee 9907, Pettit 9919, Stock 9953, West 9967

Homeless, human services

Alabama: Alpha 3, McMillan 50
Arizona: Arizona 92, Canyon 98, Morris 148, Stardust 164
California: Ahmanson 222, Applied 249, Atkinson 265, Autry 270, Bothin 331, California 368, Community 420, Danford 448, Fremont 548, Grove 631, **Hilton 692**, Keck 775, McCarthy 895, McKay 902, Norris 971, Pacific 1003, Parsons 1013, Perforce 1026, Roberts 1081, Sacramento 1103, San Francisco 1109, Siebel 1162, Sterling 1218, Weingart 1307, Wetzel 1318
Colorado: Anschutz 1364, Boettcher 1374, Daniels 1399, Edmondson 1405, El Pomar 1406, Halton 1426, M.D.C./Richmond 1450
Connecticut: Community 1564, Connecticut 1566, Donchian 1576, Ensworth 1580, First 1584, Fund 1589, Liberty 1630, NewAlliance 1651, Orchard 1663
Delaware: **Adobe 1734**, CenturyLink-Clarke 1750, Crystal 1758
District of Columbia: Cafritz 1890, Meyer 1931
Florida: Bank 1979, Baroco 1981, Batchelor 1983, Cohen 2028, **Ephraim 2087**, Gutin 2143, Lennar 2210, Miami 2238, NextEra 2251, **Wardlaw 2376**
Georgia: Community 2432, Hudgens 2486, Rich 2537, Tull 2561
Illinois: **Abbott 2649**, Brach 2712, Chicago 2746, Community 2763, Day 2787, Evanston 2826, Field 2831, His 2913, Levi 2976, Pierce 3080, Polk 3084, Siragusa 3162, Stern 3177, Woodward 3243
Indiana: Community 3281, Lincoln 3344, Michigan 3354
Kansas: Topeka 3552
Louisiana: Booth 3616, Brown 3617, Community 3624
Maryland: Abell 3713, Fowler 3795, O'Neil 3859
Massachusetts: Arbella 3926, Clipper 3987, Fireman 4049, Hanover 4086, Liberty 4145, Linden 4148, Melville 4170, Rubenstein 4248, Schoen 4260, Smith 4277, Worcester 4327
Michigan: Ann Arbor 4340, Consumers 4376, Masco 4497, Perrigo 4521, Skillman 4543, Steelcase 4547
Minnesota: Bremer 4620, Duluth 4649, NFC 4727, Ordean 4732, Sit 4765
Mississippi: Ergon 4824
Missouri: Cruse 4877, Hall 4905, Interco 4914, Orscheln 4951, Pott 4958
Nebraska: Lozier 5065, Mutual 5071
Nevada: Nevada 5134
New Jersey: Borden 5209, Danellie 5237, Harbourton 5293, Hyde 5310, **Johnson 5329**, OceanFirst 5394, Provident 5414
New Mexico: Frost 5519, McCune 5529, Santa Fe 5533
New York: Charina 5763, Community 5803, Cwierzyk 5838, Deerfield 5865, **Deutsche 5876**, Dreitzer 5910, **Hearst 6155**, **Hearst 6156**, Lake 6320, Mizuho 6492, Mulford 6514, Mutual 6518, New York 6544, New York 6546, Sidewalk 6852, St. Faith's 6903, **Vital 7033**
North Carolina: **Bank 7139**, Community 7181, Cumberland 7184, Piedmont 7285, Stewards 7322, Triangle 7328, Weaver 7335
North Dakota: Stern 7360
Ohio: Charities 7400, Columbus 7411, Hatton 7483, Mathile 7560, Nationwide 7587, Osteopathic 7605, Stark 7673, Toledo 7686, White 7715
Oklahoma: Robinson 7789
Oregon: PGE 7881
Pennsylvania: CentiMark 7970, Community 7994, Connelly 7995, Dolfinger 8013, Fourjay 8047, Hurd 8101, Huston 8102, Morris 8188, Pew 8220, Smith 8288
Rhode Island: Kimball 8410, Rhode Island 8429, Textron 8446
South Carolina: Central 8468, Coastal 8472
South Dakota: Robinson 8520
Texas: Boone 8710, Carter 8753, Coastal 8768, Davis 8799, Fikes 8844, Fluor 8851, Goldsbury 8868, Kempner 8952, Meadows 9019, NuStar 9065, San Antonio 9148, Simmons 9174, Sterling 9203, Sturgis 9211, Texas 9227, Trull 9240, USAA 9245, Valero 9246, Woodforest 9290, Wright 9293, Zale 9297
Utah: ALSAM 9302, Eccles 9320
Vermont: Vermont 9375
Virginia: Beazley 9391, Dominion 9422, Fredericksburg 9436, Landmark 9467, Lynchburg 9474, MAXIMUS 9481, Norfolk 9496
Washington: Blue 9588, Community 9604, Foster 9621, Grays 9631, Medina 9682, Renton 9715, Safeco 9723, Seattle 9731, Tacoma 9750
West Virginia: Kanawha 9780
Wisconsin: Evinrude 9841, Johnson 9874, Keller 9878, Milwaukee 9907, Stackner 9951, Thrivent 9956

Horticulture/garden clubs

Florida: Colen 2029
Illinois: Hagenah 2885, Illinois 2934
Louisiana: Burden 3618
Michigan: Meijer 4499
Nebraska: Kearney 5055, Kimmel 5059
Pennsylvania: EQT 8025, Miller 8183

Hospitals (general)

Alabama: Caring 18, Crampton 26, Energen 32, McMillan 50, Meyer 53, Protective 59, Russell 63
Arizona: Freeport-McMoRan 112, Globe 115, Hill 122, Jasam 124, Matricaria 142
Arkansas: Blue 181, Cabe 182, Frueauff 188, Nabholz 194, Riggs 196, Wal-Mart 210
California: Al-Ameen 225, Allergan 228, Anderson 242, Arnold 257, Autry 270, Barker 282, Barnhart 283, Bauer 287, Berger 309, Binder 316, Booth 326, Bower 332, **Broccoli 350**, Brooks 352, Buckhantz 354, Burns 359, Caldwell 363, California 368, **Capital 375**, CareFusion 377, Chandler 392, Chapman 395, Chartwell 397, Colombo 413, Copses 429, Crean 439, Curci 443, Danford 448, Davidow 451, Day 457, Denney 460, Dhont 464, Doelger 472, Doheny 473, Douglas 476, Ducommun 485, Eisenberg 498, Engemann 506, Field 524, **Fineberg 525**, Garland 565, Gasser 566, Gellert 568, Gershman 575, **Gilead 586**, Gleis 593, Goldsmith 608, Good 611, Greene 625, Gross 629, Grout 630, Guenther 634, HealthCare 667, Hedco 672, Hills 691, Hoag 697, Hoffman 699, Hofmann 700, Jack 736, Jackson 737, **Jerome 749**, JVK 758, Kalmanovitz 762, Katzenberg 769, Kingsley 789, Kissick 791, Knee 797, Koontz 800, Lamond 817, Laulhere 822, Lewis 837, Lurie 858, Lytel 860, Mabie 863, Marciano 874, Martindale 883, **Mattel 886**, McAlister 891, Meadowview 908, Menard 911, Metta 921, Milias 925, Milstein 930, Mitchell 931, Mulago 952, Munger 954, Munzer 955, Nestle 965, Norris 971, Oakland 977, O'Connell 982, OneWest 985, Pacific 1004, Panda 1010, Patron 1020, Perforce 1026, Perkins 1027, Philanthropy 1035, Pritzker 1046, Reinhard 1061, **ResMed 1063**, Robertson 1082, Schaeffer 1121, Schow 1126, Scripps 1129, Sence 1141, Shapell 1148, Smith 1185, Solari 1196, Sonora 1198, Sorensen 1200, Sprague 1207, Stauffer 1214, Tallen 1234, Thatcher 1248, Ueberroth 1268, UniHealth 1270, United 1272, **Vadasz 1275**, Van Nuys 1284, Van Nuys 1285, Versacare 1288, Wasserman 1300, Weingart 1307, Western 1315, Williams 1325, WWW 1349, Wynn 1350, Zander 1356, **Zee 1357**
Colorado: Bacon 1370, Davis 1400, El Pomar 1406, Fishback 1410, Kaufmann 1436, Ottens 1472, Petteys 1477, ProLogis 1485, Shaw 1499, Tuchman 1514, Williams 1524
Connecticut: Aetna 1531, Allwin 1536, Aronson 1538, Ayer 1539, Baldwin 1541, Cohen 1560, Community 1564, Community 1565, Culpeper 1568, Daniell 1570, Davis 1571, Diebold 1574, Foster 1588, Georgescu 1593, Goergen 1595, Goldring 1596, Hoffman 1613, Huisking 1615, Larsen 1624, Link 1631, Meriden 1643, Morris 1646, Mortensen 1647, Ossen 1664, Palmer 1666, **Praxair 1676**, SBM 1690, Seidenberg 1692, Sheinberg 1695, Smart 1697, Smilow 1698, Straus 1702, Wiggins 1722, Windreich 1724, Wood 1725, Zachs 1730
Delaware: Crystal 1758, Edwards 1773, Eshelman 1776, Good 1785, Laffey 1800, Lefrak 1802, LeFrak 1803, Lucas 1808, Marmot 1814, Mastronardi 1815, McDonald 1817, O'Neil 1826, Ortega 1828, Pere 1833, Pincus 1836, Presto 1840, **Progress 1842**, Reynolds 1849, Schejola 1856, Singer 1860, Wasily 1871, Welfare 1872, Whitton-Spector 1874
District of Columbia: Aid 1879, Bedford 1883, **Dreyfus 1901**, Gottesman 1911, Hillside 1914, **Merck 1929**, Rales 1942
Florida: Abramson 1963, Andersen 1968, Ansin 1969, Applebaum 1970, Batchelor 1983, Bauman 1984, Bay 1985, Beaver 1986, Bi-Lo 1996, Block 1998, Broad 2002, Brown 2004, **Chatlos 2019**, Clermont 2023, Community 2036, Connors 2043, **Cornell 2046**, Demetree 2058, Dunspaugh-Dalton 2073, Edgemer 2081, Ellmar 2085, Funkhouser 2111, Gay 2117, Glazer 2124, Greenburg 2137, Gronewaldt 2139, Haller 2146, Harrington 2148, Henry 2154, Hersh 2156, Huizenga 2165, Kimmelman 2184, KMD 2190, Kramer 2195, Lynn 2221, Mangurian 2226, McCahill 2231, McKeen 2234, Moran 2242, Morby 2244, Ocean 2253, **Pariser 2258**, Peacock 2263, Pearce 2264, Pechter 2265, Rayonier 2281, Rooms 2292, Ryder 2302, Sandler 2306, Seaman 2314, **Skelly 2324**, Sorenson 2326, Speer 2328, Stein 2337, Straz 2341, Taishoff 2350, Vanneck-Bailey 2370, Walter 2375, Watkins 2379, Welch 2382, Wells 2383, Welsh 2384, Williams 2388, Wolfson 2392, Wollowick 2393
Georgia: Atlanta 2406, Callaway 2418, Callaway 2419, Camp-Younts 2421, **Coca 2428**, Ellis 2452, Fort 2460, Harris 2479, **Imlay 2487**, Katz 2494, Rich 2537, Williams, 2575
Hawaii: Ching 2596, First 2598, HMSA 2604

Idaho: Blue 2627
Illinois: **Abbott 2649**, Adjuvant 2653, Andrew 2662, Bacca 2678, Baum 2689, Bellebyron 2693, Blair 2699, Buchanan 2720, Buckeye 2722, Buffett 2727, C.W.B. 2730, **Carylon 2735**, Caterpillar 2738, Chao 2741, Children's 2747, Cole-Crone 2758, Comer 2760, Comer 2761, Community 2767, Cox 2776, Davee 2785, Delany 2793, Dickenson 2795, Dimon 2797, **Domanada 2799**, Donnelley 2802, Eisenberg 2819, Foglia 2837, Frank 2840, Galvin 2858, Goodyear 2870, Gregory 2879, Hagenah 2885, Harris 2892, Harrison 2896, Hoffritz 2917, Hunter 2926, Huntington 2928, Illinois 2934, Irwin 2936, Katten 2951, Kolschowsky 2962, Madigan 2992, Malott 2996, Martin 3002, Mazza 3007, McCormick 3010, McNamara 3017, Melman 3022, Morrison 3038, Munson 3045, Nierling, 3056, Offield 3062, Opler 3064, Parr 3070, Payne 3073, Pepper 3074, Perritt 3077, Prince 3089, Pritzker 3092, Pritzker 3096, Rawley 3106, Rhoades 3115, Rice 3116, Satter 3136, Schawk 3138, Schmidt 3139, Segal 3147, Shaw 3154, Shipman 3157, Siragusa 3162, Sirius 3163, Souder 3168, **Tellabs 3185**, Tricord 3190, United 3200, Vaughn 3203, Vermilion 3205, Ward 3216, Wenske 3225, Wilemal 3232, **Zuhlke 3250**
Indiana: 1st 3251, Adams 3253, Anthem 3257, Bales 3261, Ball 3262, Cole 3276, Community 3278, Community 3283, Dearborn 3293, English 3299, Hux 3325, Marshall 3348, Noyes 3361
Iowa: Brownell 3414, HNI 3443, Kinney-Lindstrom 3451, Kuyper 3456
Kansas: Dreiseszun 3512, Hansen 3518, Morgan 3536, Riverside 3539, Smith 3547, Sunderland 3551
Kentucky: Carson-Myre 3567, Preston 3596, Swope 3603
Louisiana: Albemarle 3609, Blue 3615, Booth 3616, Brown 3617, Dore' 3629, Lupin 3652, McIlhenny 3654, Seal 3667
Maine: Alfond 3678, Hannaford 3690, Nichols 3703
Maryland: Berger 3729, Blades 3734, Clark 3750, Clark 3751, Davis 3772, Dekelboum 3777, GEICO 3801, Glazer 3802, **Grace 3807**, Gross 3808, Helena 3812, Henson 3814, Kahlert 3822, Sampson 3878, Shields 3884
Massachusetts: Abrams 3914, Arbella 3926, Baldwin 3934, Blue 3953, Boston 3957, Bristol 3960, Calderwood 3969, Cape Cod 3973, Community 3992, Copeland 3994, Croll 4000, Dana 4008, Davis 4010, Demoulas 4014, Demoulas 4015, Devonshire 4017, Duniry 4025, Dunkin' 4026, Elfers 4033, Ellison 4034, Fireman 4049, Ford 4055, Foundation 4057, Golden 4073, Heitman 4092, Higgins 4096, Hopedale 4101, **Iacocca 4104**, **Foundation 4107**, **Karp 4117**, Keane 4118, Kittredge 4124, Kiva 4125, Klarman 4126, Leaves 4139, Leventhal 4141, Levine 4142, Linn 4149, Lovett 4151, Lubin 4155, Lurie 4158, Lynch 4159, Marks 4162, Massiah 4163, **Middlecott 4174**, Mittelman 4180, Moseley 4185, New 4189, New 4190, New England 4192, O'Donnell 4196, Pappas 4204, Peters 4216, Rappaport 4230, Redstone 4233, Rogers 4243, **Rosenberg 4245**, Saltonstall 4254, Saquish 4257, Schoen 4260, Shapiro 4267, Sharf 4268, Smith 4277, Spencer 4278, Sperling 4279, Stare 4283, Stoneman 4295, Tupancy 4312, Wagner 4317, Wang 4319, Webster 4322, Windover 4324, Yawkey 4329, Zakat 4330
Michigan: **Allen 4335**, Battle Creek 4343, Carls 4358, Cracchiolo 4382, Cronin 4383, Dart 4388, Davis 4391, Dow 4405, Duffy 4411, Ford 4426, Foster 4431, Gerstacker 4444, Herrick 4459, Hickman 4460, Hillsdale 4461, Morey 4508, Perrigo 4521, Shelden 4537, Spartan 4544, Taubman 4553, Tracy 4558, Tuktawa 4560, Van Andel 4567, Webber 4578, Wege 4579, Westerman 4582, Wickes 4585, Wilson 4588, Wilson 4589
Minnesota: **Andersen 4601**, **Andersen 4602**, Andreas 4605, Bakken 4608, Bentson 4611, Campbell 4626, Driscoll 4648, Edwards 4653, Fiterman 4656, Greystone 4668, Hardenbergh 4672, Hubbard 4678, **King 4687**, Land 4691, Legacy 4693, Maas 4699, MacMillan 4700, **Medtronic 4712**, Prospect 4747, Rivers 4752, Robina 4753, Robins 4754, Stone 4773, TEAM 4779, WEM 4799
Mississippi: Biloxi 4814, Ergon 4824, Hearin 4832, Mississippi 4838, Oakwood 4841
Missouri: Ameren 4851, American 4852, Apex 4854, Brown 4862, Centene 4870, Cox 4874, Dierberg 4879, Dula 4881, Edison 4883, Emerson 4885, Goppert 4896, Gottlieb 4897, Green 4900, Hallmark 4906, Holekamp 4910, Nichols 4949, Shaw 4970, Speas 4979
Montana: Bair 5004
Nebraska: Abbott 5020, Ameritas 5023, Buckley 5026, Gardner 5041, Hirschfeld 5049, Hubbard 5053, Kearney 5055, Union 5090, Werner 5094
Nevada: Caesars 5106, Fairweather 5118, Joseph 5124, Keyser 5126, Mallory 5129
New Hampshire: Gifford 5173
New Jersey: Antz 5192, **Berrie 5206**, Catholic 5226, Charles 5227, Cowles 5234, **Crane 5235**, Creamer 5236, D'Angelo 5238, **Edison 5248**, Family 5257, Fortune 5263, Frankino 5267, Gagnon 5271, Grassmann 5281, Hess 5298, Holmes 5302, Hovnanian 5307, Hugin 5308, Hummingbird 5309, Hyde 5310, **IDT 5311**, Integra 5315, Jockey 5325, **Johnson 5326**, **Johnson 5329**, Kaplen 5330, Kauffmann 5334, Kennedy 5337, Mack 5367, McGraw 5376, Palestroni 5400, Point 5410, Provident 5414, Schwartz 5442, Schwarz 5444, Shreiber 5453, Strauss 5470, Tanzman 5476, Taub 5477, Union 5485, **Verizon 5489**, Wagner 5491, Wilf 5502, Willits 5505
New Mexico: Hubbard 5523, McCune 5529, Phillips 5531
New York: Abeles 5544, Abrons 5546, **AHBA 5562**, Allen 5573, Allen 5574, Alper 5576, Altus 5583, **American 5588**, Ames 5591, Amicus 5592, Ammon 5594, Appleman 5604, Armstrong 5612, Aron 5616, **Ashner 5619**, Bachmann 5632, Bahnik 5634, Baird 5636, Baker 5638, Baldwin 5640, Banfi 5641, Barakett 5642, Barakett 5643, Bass 5650, Beal 5656, Berkowitz 5669, Bishop 5679, Block 5683, **Bobst 5690**, Boxer 5698, Braufman 5704, **Bristol 5711**, Brooks 5719, Brownstone 5722, Butler 5735, Campbell 5742, Carvel 5749, Central 5756, Challenger 5762, Charina 5763, Charina 5764, Chernow 5771, Chronic 5777, CJM 5781, Coach 5790, Cohn 5793, Coleman 5796, Colin 5797, Community 5802, Community 5805, Corning 5818, Cramer 5824, **Cummings 5832**, Cummings 5834, D'Addario 5841, Daedalus 5842, Damial 5844, Davenport 5850, **David 5852**, **DBID 5855**, Deerfield 5865, Derfner 5874, **Deutsche 5876**, Dewar 5879, Diamond 5880, Diller 5884, Dillon 5885, DiMenna 5886, DiMino 5887, Dinan 5888, Dolan 5896, Donghia 5897, Dowling 5907, Drexler 5911, Dubin 5916, Ehrenkranz 5941, Emerald 5949, Enterprise 5956, Falconwood 5967, Fanwood 5968, Feil 5973, Feinstein 5974, Finneran 5978, Fisher 5982, Frey 6014, Fribourg 6015, **Fridolin 6016**, Friedman 6021, Gaisman 6031, **Gelb 6039**, Gershwind 6046, Gibbs 6048, Gifford 6049, Gillespie 6051, **Gitenstein 6055**, Goldberg 6062, Goldstein 6074, Goldstein 6075, Goldstein 6076, Golub 6079, Gorter 6084, Grateful 6094, Greater 6098, Green 6100, Gross 6110, Gural 6117, Gutenstein 6119, Haas 6124, **Harriman 6136**, Harriman 6137, **Hearst 6155**, **Hearst 6156**, Helmsley 6160, Hermione 6163, Hillman 6174, Hochfelder 6177, Hudson 6191, Hugoton 6194, Hunter 6197, Hurdus 6198, Icahn 6204, IFF 6206, Israel 6216, Jacobson 6219, Jacoff 6220, JAF 6221, Jaharis 6223, Johnson 6240, Kaufman 6259, Kaye 6262, Kearns 6265, Keidan 6267, Kellogg 6269, Kempner 6273, Kinney 6285, Klingenstein 6292, Klingenstein 6293, Knapp 6296, Kopf 6302, Kraus 6305, Kurz 6314, Lane 6325, Lang 6326, Lasdon 6332, Lenna 6352, Levy 6363, Lindner 6372, Link 6375, Litwin 6380, Lui 6400, Mack 6411, Mallah 6423, Mallah 6424, Marcus 6428, Mariposa 6429, Marlon 6433, Marrus 6436, Marx 6441, McCann 6453, McCarthy 6454, McGonagle 6460, Mee 6467, **Menschel 6473**, Mercy 6475, Meyer 6480, Millbrook 6485, Mnuchin 6493, Mnuchin 6494, Monell 6497, **Moody's 6499**, Moore 6500, Morgan 6506, Morgan 6507, Morse 6509, Moses 6511, Mozilo 6512, Mule 6513, Murphy 6517, Mys 6519, National 6528, Neu 6537, Neuwirth 6539, New York 6543, New York 6545, Newhouse 6550, Nias 6556, Noble 6560, Northfield 6568, Och 6575, O'Connor 6578, O'Malley 6589, Oppenheim 6594, Orthwein 6597, Pannonia 6613, Pearson 6623, Perelman 6628, **Pfizer 6634**, Picket 6638, Picotte 6639, **Polo 6651**, Price 6658, Price 6659, Raiff 6675, Regals 6685, Review 6692, **Rheuminations 6695**, Richardson 6700, Richmond 6703, Richmond 6704, Riedman 6706, Riggio 6709, Riley 6710, Ritter 6712, Rizzuto 6714, **Robertson 6718**, Rosner 6752, Rubenstein 6762, Rudin 6768, Saltz 6787, Sandy 6791, Santmann 6793, Schapiro 6801, Schnurmacher 6810, Schwartz 6814, Sculco 6821, SDA 6823, Seaver 6825, Sharp 6839, **Shaw 6840**, Sheldon 6841, Shulsky 6851, Silberstein 6854, Silverman 6855, **Simons 6860**, Snyder 6880, Sosnoff 6892, Speyer 6896, St. Giles 6905, Steffens 6917, Stein 6918, Steinberg 6921, **Stempel 6925**, Stern 6926, Sullivan 6941, **Summerfield 6944**, Tai 6960, Tisch 6986, Tisch 6992, Trump 7008, Tuft 7011, Unterberg 7021, Van Cleave 7025, **Vital 7033**, Vogelstein 7034, Warburg 7048, Warren 7054, Wegman 7061, Weiler 7063, Weinberg 7066, Weinberg 7067, Weir 7069, Weissman 7072, Winston 7092, Witten 7095, Zankel 7114, Zegar 7116, Ziff 7122, Zucker 7127, Zuckerberg 7128, Zweig 7130
North Carolina: Armfield 7137, **Bank 7139**, Baxter 7142, BB&T 7144, Belk 7148, Cannon 7169, Dickson 7192, Duke 7195, French 7203, Holding 7234, Kean/Hartquist 7246, Lewis 7256, Phillips 7284, Plansoen 7286, Provident 7291, Reynolds 7299, Roanoke 7303, Slick 7313, Sloan 7314, Southern 7319, Strauss 7323, Van Houten 7330, Vanderbilt 7331, Woodward 7343
North Dakota: Leach 7353, MDU 7354
Ohio: AK Steel 7366, American 7368, Austin 7380, Bailey 7381, Berry 7386, **Cardinal 7398**, Children's 7401, Cliffs 7407, Codrington 7409, Corbin 7420, Coshocton 7421, Dater 7426, Dermitt 7432, Deuble 7433, Dodero 7438, **Eaton 7442**, Fairfield 7445, Gund 7477, Hatton 7483, Hoover 7492, Horvitz 7493, Humphrey 7497, Ima/Mickey 7502, Ingalls 7503, Kimble 7526, **Lerner 7538**, Lincoln 7541, McBride 7562, Miami 7569, Moores 7576, Murch 7582, Murphy 7584, Muskingum 7585, National 7586, Nationwide 7587, Ohio 7599, **OMNOVA 7601**, Outcalt 7606, Park 7610, Parker 7611, Prentiss 7621, Price 7622, Reeves 7627, Reinberger 7628, Richland 7630, Ritter 7633, Schiff 7649, **Timken 7684**, Troy 7688, Vesper 7695, Vortex 7696, Wade 7697, Wellman 7709, Wodecroft 7717, Wolfe 7719
Oklahoma: Lyon 7769, Mabee 7770, McCrory 7773, Nelson 7779, ONEOK 7783, Oxley 7785, Robson 7790, Share 7795, Southern 7798, Stone 7801, Taubman 7804, Titus 7806
Oregon: Cambia 7829, Jeld 7856, Schnitzer 7888, Stoller 7891, Tykeson 7897
Pennsylvania: Ametek 7913, **AO 7915**, Arcadia 7918, Armstrong 7922, Asplundh 7923, Baker 7925, Berkman 7938, Caplan 7962, Carnahan 7965, CentiMark 7970, Charter 7977, Colket 7987, Crels 8002, Davenport 8003, Dolfinger 8013, Franklin 8048, Haggin 8075, Head 8081, Highmark 8092, Hopwood 8096, Hoyt 8098, Hurd 8101, Jackson 8110, Katz 8117, Keystone 8122, Leonard 8139, Levis 8140, Lindback 8142, Lockhart 8146, Lutron 8151, Mandell 8153, Mason 8157, McFeely 8163, McLean 8169, Medleycott 8171, Miller 8180, Mine 8184, Neubauer 8196, Nichols 8197, Nimick 8198, Novotny 8202, Palumbo 8209, Pond 8231, Quantitative 8241, RJM 8249, Roberts 8250, Roberts 8251, Rossin 8256, Sand 8264, Schenck 8269, Schieffelin 8270, Scholler 8273, Sexauer 8280, Smith 8289, Steinman 8300, Stine 8302,

Surgala 8309, Toll 8316, Toll 8317, West 8334, Williams 8338, Withington 8344
Rhode Island: Alpert 8355, Armour 8358, Capewell 8365, Capewell 8366, Capewell 8367, Champlin 8370, Combined 8375, Corning 8376, CVS 8379, Diagnostic 8383, Foster 8394, Fox 8395, Greene 8398, Hasbro 8403, Kimball 8410, Manning 8415, McAdams 8416, McCurdy 8417, Murray 8421, O'Brien 8425, Roraback 8431, Routhier 8432, Sharpe 8437, Shriners 8438, Shumway 8439, Steadley 8442, Swanson 8445, Textron 8446, Vance 8450, Woodward 8453
South Carolina: **AVX-Kyocera 8457**, Canal 8466, Daniel 8476, Pfriem 8490, Reams 8493
South Dakota: Brenden-Mann 8513, Robinson 8520
Tennessee: Christy 8545, First 8565, Hamico 8576, Melkus 8609, Regal 8622, Speer 8630, Tennessee 8634, Wilson 8646
Texas: Anderson 8664, BNSF 8706, **Bolivar 8708**, Bookout 8709, Cailloux 8741, Cameron 8747, Carter 8752, CH 8759, Coastal 8768, Cockrell 8770, Communities 8773, Constantin 8778, Crowell 8791, Cullen 8792, Davis 8799, Dunn 8816, East 8819, Edwards 8823, Elkins 8826, Fasken 8839, Finger 8845, Fish 8848, Franklin 8855, Hamman 8888, Hawn 8896, Heavin 8898, Hebert 8899, Henderson 8900, Hillcrest 8909, Hobby 8911, Hoblitzelle 8912, Hudson 8919, Hunt 8922, JLH 8936, Johnson 8941, Kimberly 8957, Knobloch 8965, Levit 8982, Loose 8991, Lyman 8995, Madison 8997, Marsh 8999, McDermott 9013, McGrath 9015, McIntyre 9016, Moncrief 9031, Murchison 9046, **Notsew 9064**, Once 9070, Owen 9076, Pertusati 9094, Pryor 9113, Rogers 9137, Sanchez 9150, Schollmaier 9159, Scurlock 9162, Sharp 9167, Simmons 9173, Simmons 9174, Smith 9183, Sowell 9192, Sterling 9203, Stern 9204, Strake 9208, Sturgis 9211, Temple 9223, Turner 9242, USAA 9245, Valero 9246, West 9269, Zale 9297, Zimmer 9300
Utah: Dee 9312, Dumke 9315, Eccles 9319, Eccles 9320, Watkins 9356
Virginia: Batten 9388, Beazley 9391, Charles 9404, Chiaramonte 9407, Folger 9431, Fredericksburg 9436, Funger 9438, Hylton 9455, Massey 9478, Proteus 9512, Reinsch 9518, Rosenthal 9525, Smith 9534, SunTrust 9539, **Truland 9545**, Universal 9548
Washington: Anderson 9572, Cheney 9598, Community 9604, Danz 9609, Dimmer 9610, McKinstry 9680, Moccasin 9687, Norcliffe 9693, PACCAR 9698, **PAH 9699**, Plum 9704, Suskin 9747, Tacoma 9750
West Virginia: McQuain 9785
Wisconsin: Alexander 9802, **Baird 9811**, Bleser 9818, Briggs 9822, Brotz 9825, Bryant 9826, Charter 9829, Clark 9830, Green Bay 9855, Incourage 9867, Johnson 9870, Kelben 9877, Kress 9887, Ladish 9890, Ladish 9891, Michels 9906, Neese 9911, Pettit 9919, Smith 9947, Stock 9953, Windhover 9968, Wisconsin 9970
Wyoming: Allen 9973, Griffith 9979, Storer 9992, Watt 9997

Hospitals (specialty)

Alabama: Nelson 57
Arizona: Emerald 108, Halle 118, Ottosen 150, Tankersley 169
Arkansas: Cabe 182, Delta 184, Nabholz 194, Smith 201, Stephens 203
California: Barth 285, Binder 316, Chambers 390, Dialynas 465, Dickinson 466, Dougherty 475, Edelstein 494, Found 540, Foundation 541, Freeberg 545, Gleis 593, Hanson 653, Harrington 657, HealthCare 667, Hoffman 699, Irmas 725, Issa 732, James 742, Kenrose 779, Leonetti/O'Connell 832, **Lund 857**, Mudd 951, Patron 1020, Perkins 1027, Pritzker 1046, Randall 1054, **Saban 1101**, Semel 1138, Shanahan 1146, Shapiro 1152, Simms/Mann 1169, Soicher 1195, Tallen 1234, Tang 1235, UniHealth 1270
Colorado: Fox 1412, Pioneer 1479, Ponzio 1482, Sie 1500, Wolf 1526
Connecticut: ALFA 1534, Aronson 1538, Eder 1577, Meriden 1643, Robbins 1681, Steere 1701
Delaware: Pere 1833, Pincus 1836
District of Columbia: Coyne 1896
Florida: Arison 1971, Demetree 2058, DiMare 2064, Edgemer 2081, Gerstner 2121, Horvitz 2161, Hudson 2164, Langford 2202, Speer 2328, Van Vleet 2368
Georgia: Addison 2398
Illinois: Barnett 2681, Bluhm 2704, Buckeye 2722, Bunning 2728, de Kay 2788, DiSomma 2798, Eisenberg 2819, Gates 2859, Hanson 2890, Hirschl 2912, Louis 2984, Lurie 2987, Mazza 3007, Mills 3028, Opler 3064, Parr 3070, Perritt 3077, Regenstein 3111, Reid 3112, Shaw 3154, Sheba 3155, Trio 3191, Walsh 3212, Wonderful 3239
Kansas: Dreiseszun 3512, Koch 3528, Mader 3531, Sarli 3541
Kentucky: Fischer 3574
Maryland: Adams 3718, Cohen 3752, Decesaris 3775, Dekelboum 3777, Jacobson 3820
Massachusetts: Baldwin 3934, Beal 3940, Berthiaume 3949, Corkin 3996, Crimson 3999, Dinovi 4019, Egan 4032, Family 4042, Gildea 4071, Jordan 4113, **Karp 4117**, McDonnell 4166, Peabody 4211, Peters 4216, Proctor 4227, Rasmussen 4231, Spencer 4278, Stevenson 4290, Stoneman 4295, Swensrud 4303
Michigan: DeVos 4398, Helppie 4456, Levy 4487, Rordor 4529, Secchia 4536, Van 4570, World 4594
Minnesota: Criss 4640, Foundation 4657, Kelley 4686, Legacy 4693, Phillips 4740, Schmidt 4758, Weyerhaeuser 4803
Mississippi: Feild 4825
Missouri: Ballmann 4858, Dula 4881, Holekamp 4910, Kemper 4927, Millstone 4944, Rosewood 4964
New Jersey: Firestone 5260, Frankino 5266, Healthcare 5296, Holloway 5300, Kauffmann 5334, Mushett 5388, Shen 5450, Silbermann 5456
New Mexico: Hubbard 5523
New York: Adelman 5554, Alfiero 5570, Andor 5598, Beene 5658, Burke 5730, Butler 5735, Carvel 5749, Colin 5797, Cooper 5813, Coydog 5823, Cramer 5824, Fanwood 5968, Friedman 6019, Greene 6103, Greene 6104, Israel 6216, Johnson 6240, Kautz 6260, King 6283, Levine 6359, Loeb 6384, Many 6426, Marrus 6436, National 6529, Niehaus 6559, Nonna's 6563, **Olayan 6585**, O'Malley 6589, O'Neill 6591, Orthwein 6597, **Rheuminations 6695**, Robbins 6715, Roepers 6726, Rosen 6739, Rosenthal 6749, Rosenwald 6751, Ross 6755, **Shaw 6840**, Sobel 6882, Solomon 6885, St. Giles 6905, Three 6976, Windmill 7089, Winters 7094, **ZIIZ 7124**
North Carolina: Bissell 7152, Christopher 7176, Gordon 7214, Lewis 7256, Roberts 7304
Ohio: Gerlach 7471, Haslinger 7482, Jenkins 7508, Keeler 7517, Kersten 7519, Lancaster 7533, Luther 7548, Nippert 7590, Schear 7645, Schiff 7648, Stefanski 7675, TSF 7690, Wodecroft 7717
Oklahoma: Bezalel 7734, Oxley 7785
Oregon: Miller 7872
Pennsylvania: Biesecker 7941, Colket 7987, Greenfield 8071, Helping 8088, Hoverter 8097, Ingerman 8108, Kahn 8115, Marshall 8155, PTS 8238, Simmons 8285, Stein/Bellet 8298, Wheeler 8335
Rhode Island: Capewell 8365, Foster 8394, Guth 8400, Manning 8415, Roraback 8431, Swanson 8445
South Carolina: Childrens 8471
Tennessee: Children's 8543, Goodfriend 8574, Martin 8605, Melkus 8609
Texas: Alcon 8655, Andras 8666, Clements 8767, Crane 8788, Harvey 8894, Jones 8942, Justin 8947, Kinder 8958, Korenvaes 8969, Liatis 8983, Lyman 8995, Madison 8997, McGrath 9015, MFI 9025, Morris 9041, Murchison 9046, Once 9070, Owen 9076, Owen 9077, Petrello 9096, Saada 9142, Smith 9183, Smith 9185, Wolff 9287
Utah: Lawson 9331, Miller 9335, Noorda 9339
Virginia: Claws 9408, Ratcliffe 9514
Washington: Anderson 9572, Oki 9694, Sunbridge 9746
Wisconsin: Bleser 9818, Herma 9862, Nicholas 9913, Predolin 9923
Wyoming: Allen 9973

Housing/shelter

Alabama: BBVA 9, Central 19
Arizona: Arizona 92, Freeport-McMoRan 112, Giving 114
Arkansas: Wal-Mart 210
California: Allergan 228, Applied 249, Cathay 385, **Cisco 402**, Clif 405, Community 414, Community 420, Coto 431, Cowell 434, **Draper 481**, Foster 539, Freeberg 545, Genentech 571, Glide 595, Gombos 610, GSF 633, Guess? 635, Heffernan 673, **Hilton 692**, Humboldt 714, i.am.angel 720, Macpherson 869, McMinn 906, **Packard 1006**, Rotasa 1092, Santa Barbara 1116, Union 1271, Ventura 1287, Weingart 1307, Wells 1312, Wilcox 1324
Colorado: Anschutz 1364, Community 1394, Fox 1412, Halton 1426, Pikes 1478, Vodafone 1519
Connecticut: American 1537, Community 1562, Community 1565, Donchian 1576, Fairfield 1581, First 1584, Fisher 1585, Liberty 1630, NewAlliance 1651, SBM 1690
Delaware: **Adobe 1734**, Bucks 1748, Longwood 1806, Orr 1827, Salah 1855
District of Columbia: **Butler 1889**, Cafritz 1890, Community 1893
Florida: Albert 1964, Baldwin 1978, Bush 2008, Community 2032, Community 2033, Community 2036, Community 2037, Copham 2044, Gardener 2114, GiveWell 2123, McCahill 2231, Miami 2238, NextEra 2251, Pinellas 2269, Zehnder 2397
Georgia: Community 2432, **Georgia 2469**, NCR 2524, Primerica 2534
Hawaii: Bank 2588
Idaho: Lightfoot 2636
Illinois: Allegretti 2655, Brach 2712, Caterpillar 2738, Community 2766, Dunham 2811, EFS 2818, FDC 2829, MB 3008, Morse 3039, Northern 3059, Oak Park 3061, Pierce 3080, Popular 3085, Woodward 3243
Indiana: Central 3272, Community 3282, Crown Point 3291, **Lilly 3342**, Lincoln 3344, Pulliam 3372, Unity 3393, Vectren 3394, Waterfield 3399
Iowa: AEGON 3409, MidAmerican 3465, Principal 3476
Kansas: Capitol 3498, Douglas 3509
Kentucky: Blue 3560
Louisiana: Beaird 3614, Community 3624, Entergy 3630, New Orleans 3656
Maine: TD 3710
Maryland: Choice 3748, Community 3758, Rouse 3877, **Weinberg 3908**
Massachusetts: Berkshire 3946, Beveridge 3950, Cambridge 3972, Charlesbank 3980, Community 3991, Danversbank 4009, Eastern 4030, Hamilton 4085, Hanover 4086, Santander 4256, Yawkey 4329
Michigan: Bay 4344, Berrien 4347, Comerica 4368, Community 4374, Dyer 4412, Ferrantino 4419, Great 4451, Masco 4497, Two 4563
Minnesota: **Andersen 4601**, Blue 4618, Ecolab 4651, Frey 4658, Marbrook 4702, Minneapolis 4714, Northwest 4730, Opus 4731, Ordean 4732, Pohlad 4745, Target 4776, TCF 4778, Travelers 4783, U.S. 4784, Valspar 4786
Mississippi: Mississippi 4839
Missouri: Anheuser 4853, Concorde 4873, Emerson 4885, Fox 4892, H & R 4902, Roblee 4963, Stupp 4983
Montana: First 5009, Oro 5014, Town 5016
Nebraska: Holthus 5052, Weitz 5092
New Jersey: Cabin 5222, Catholic 5226, Investors 5317, OceanFirst 5394, OritaniBank 5398, Provident 5414
New Mexico: Santa Fe 5533
New York: Assurant 5621, Brennan 5706, **Deutsche 5876**, Dyson 5923, **Fledgling 5987**, Hagedorn 6128, **Hearst 6155**, **Hearst 6156**, Island 6215,

JPMorgan 6244, LCU 6340, **MetLife 6479**, Mizuho 6492, **Moody's 6499**, Mulford 6514, New York 6543, NYSE 6573, Project 6661, Richmond 6703, Siebens 6853, Staten 6912, Troy 7006, van Ameringen 7023, Wilson 7088
North Carolina: Babcock 7138, **Bank 7139**, BB&T 7143, High Point 7231, Merancas 7267, Reynolds 7297
North Dakota: Fargo 7351
Ohio: American 7368, Columbus 7411, Corbin 7420, **Eaton 7442**, Fairfield 7445, Fifth 7452, Home 7488, Nationwide 7587, Nordson 7596, Westfield 7711
Oklahoma: Bartlesville 7731
Oregon: Simple 7889
Pennsylvania: Bayer 7932, BNY 7946, CentiMark 7970, Claneil 7982, Dollar 8014, DuPont 8020, ESSA 8028, Genuardi 8053, Keystone 8122, North 8199, Phoenixville 8223, PNC 8230, Saint 8260, Scranton 8275, Wells 8333
Puerto Rico: Puerto Rico 8353
Rhode Island: Citizens 8374, Crary, 8377, Daniels 8380, Rhode Island 8429, Textron 8446
South Dakota: Robinson 8520
Tennessee: East 8560, Goldstein 8573, HCA 8582, Thompson 8635
Texas: Baron 8682, Coastal 8768, Cornerstone 8780, Davis 8799, Fisch 8846, Fluor 8851, King 8959, Littauer 8988, New Hope 9058, New Hope 9059, Permian 9091, Puett 9114, **Radler 9118**, Rees-Jones 9125
Utah: ALSAM 9302
Vermont: Vermont 9375
Virginia: Arlington 9384, Capital 9400, Community 9412, Freddie 9435, Fredericksburg 9436, **Genworth 9441**, Graham 9445
Washington: Bainbridge 9578, **Campion 9594**, Evertrust 9617, Lockwood 9671, Medina 9682, Miller 9685, Renton 9715, Seattle 9731, Thompson 9752, Yakima 9767
West Virginia: Laughlin 9781
Wisconsin: Alliant 9804, Madison 9897, Thrivent 9956

Housing/shelter, aging

California: Union 1271
Illinois: **Retirement 3113**
New York: Samuels 6788
Ohio: Christman 7403
Pennsylvania: Fitch 8045
Texas: Topfer 9239
Virginia: **Genworth 9441**

Housing/shelter, alliance/advocacy

Minnesota: Phillips 4741
South Carolina: Cassels 8467

Housing/shelter, development

Alabama: Community 21
Arizona: Arizona 92, Mooney 146
California: Borch 327, California 365, **Cisco 402**, Heffernan 673, Irmas 725, Marin 877, Norris 971, Parsons 1013, Richmond 1069, Sacramento 1103, San Francisco 1109, Schwab 1128, Taper 1237, Wells 1312
Colorado: El Pomar 1406, Twelve 1515
Connecticut: Community 1562, Connecticut 1566, Ensworth 1580, Fund 1589, Goldstone 1597, Liberty 1630, People's 1671
Delaware: **Adobe 1734**, Crystal 1758, Delaware 1765, Kendeda 1794, Marmot 1814
District of Columbia: Cafritz 1890
Florida: Batchelor 1983, Bi-Lo 1996, Community 2040, Goodes 2129, Lacy 2198, Magruder 2225, Martin 2229, Pamphalon 2257, Selby 2316, Tarrant 2352, Waggoner 2374
Georgia: Atlanta 2406, Community 2432, EZ 2456, **Georgia 2469**, Tull 2561
Illinois: Chicago 2746, Day 2787, Driehaus 2805, Energizer 2824, Evanston 2826, Full 2851, MB 3008, Omron 3063, Owens 3068, Payne 3073, Popular 3085, White 3229
Indiana: Brotherhood 3268, Vectren 3394, Waterfield 3399
Iowa: GuideOne 3438
Kansas: Hutchinson 3521
Kentucky: Harris 3580
Louisiana: Albemarle 3609, Entergy 3630, Lorio 3650, RosaMary 3663
Maine: TD 3710
Maryland: Abell 3712, Community 3759, Fowler 3795, Rembrandt 3868
Massachusetts: Boston 3956, Cambridge 3971, Clipper 3987, Community 3992, Farnsworth 4043, Hyams 4103, Melville 4170, Parker 4207, Riley 4239, Steinberg-Lalli 4287, Stoico 4294, Worcester 4327
Michigan: General 4442, Grand Rapids 4447, Kalamazoo 4472, Knight 4477, Masco 4497, Whiting 4584, Wolverine 4593
Minnesota: Bigelow 4616, Bremer 4620, Butler 4622, Duluth 4649, Fiterman 4656, Frey 4658, McKnight 4709, Rochester 4755, Schmidt 4758, U.S. 4784, Valspar 4786
Mississippi: Oakwood 4841
Missouri: Anheuser 4853, Hall 4905, Truman 4996
Nebraska: Boyer 5025, Weitz 5092, Woods 5096
Nevada: Viragh 5156
New Hampshire: Bean 5164
New Jersey: Borden 5209, Danellie 5237, Fund 5270, Ingersoll-Rand 5314, **Segal 5446**, Victoria 5490
New Mexico: McCune 5529
New York: Altman 5579, Androcles 5599, Brooklyn 5718, BTMU 5724, Chautauqua 5766, **Citi 5780**, **Credit 5826**, **Deutsche 5876**, First 5979, **Ford 5994**, **JPMorgan 6244**, Letterman 6356, New York 6544, New York 6546, O'Connor 6578, **Polo 6651**, Western 7078
North Carolina: BIN 7151, Cemala 7174, Community 7180, Cumberland 7184, Stewards 7322, Triangle 7328, Weaver 7335
North Dakota: Stern 7360
Ohio: American 7368, Cleveland 7406, **Eaton 7442**, Gund 7478, Hamilton 7481, Hubert 7495, Morgan 7577, National 7586, Ohio 7599, Stark 7673, Westfield 7711
Oklahoma: McMahon 7776
Oregon: Carpenter 7831, Crabby 7838, Meyer 7870
Pennsylvania: Armstrong 7922, Briggs 7950, EQT 8025, Huston 8102, McCune 8161, Pew 8220, Philadelphia 8221, Pine 8226, Smith 8288, Wells 8333
Rhode Island: Citizens 8374
South Carolina: Central 8468, Coastal 8472, Reams 8493, **ScanSource 8495**
South Dakota: Larson 8516, Vucurevich 8524
Tennessee: American 8528, Bridgestone 8537, Community 8550, Davis 8555, HCA 8582, Lyndhurst 8599, Thompson 8635
Texas: Carter 8753, Constantin 8778, Fikes 8844, Frees 8857, Hillcrest 8909, Hoblitzelle 8912, Kempner 8952, Meadows 9019
Utah: Eccles 9320
Virginia: Bangs-Russell 9386, Community 9416, **Genworth 9441**, Oak 9499
Washington: Community 9604, Norcliffe 9693, Satterberg 9728, Tacoma 9750, **Vista 9756**
West Virginia: Kanawha 9780
Wisconsin: Charter 9829, Community 9834, DeAtley 9839, Milwaukee 9907, Oshkosh 9917, **Schneider 9942**

Housing/shelter, expense aid

Georgia: Primerica 2534

Housing/shelter, formal/general education

New York: First 5979

Housing/shelter, home owners

California: Wells 1312
Connecticut: Liberty 1630, People's 1671
Hawaii: Central 2595
Illinois: EFS 2818
Indiana: Old 3363
Massachusetts: Berkshire 3946, Santander 4256
Minnesota: U.S. 4784
New York: First 5979, **JPMorgan 6244**, Mizuho 6492, New York 6543
North Carolina: **Bank 7139**
Ohio: Cincinnati 7404
Pennsylvania: Lancaster 8135, PNC 8230
Virginia: Capital 9400
Wisconsin: Thrivent 9956

Housing/shelter, homeless

California: Bickerstaff 313, California 368, Doheny 473, Firedoll 528, JVK 758, Union 1271
Colorado: Daniels 1399
Connecticut: Bissell 1547, Donchian 1576, Orchard 1663
Florida: Community 2035, Egan 2082
Illinois: Community 2769
Indiana: Community 3282, Unity 3393
Iowa: AEGON 3409
Kentucky: Blue 3560
Massachusetts: Berkshire 3946, Fireman 4049
Michigan: Mackey 4489
Minnesota: NFC 4727
Nevada: Viragh 5156
New Jersey: OceanFirst 5394
New York: Dreyfus 5913, Mulford 6514
North Carolina: **Oak 7276**
Ohio: Osteopathic 7605, Wagler 7699
Pennsylvania: North 8199
Tennessee: Plough 8615
Texas: Meadows 9019
Virginia: Freddie 9435, Hampton 9448
Washington: **Hotes 9646**
Wisconsin: Thrivent 9956

Housing/shelter, information services

New York: First 5979

Housing/shelter, management/technical assistance

New York: First 5979

Housing/shelter, owner/renter issues

California: Cathay 385
Minnesota: **Andersen 4601**
North Carolina: **Bank 7139**

Housing/shelter, public education

New York: First 5979, Mulford 6514

Housing/shelter, public housing

North Carolina: Reynolds 7298

Housing/shelter, reform

Pennsylvania: North 8199

Housing/shelter, rehabilitation

Connecticut: People's 1671
Florida: Hill 2158
Illinois: MB 3008
Indiana: Old 3363
Maine: TD 3710
Minnesota: U.S. 4784
New York: First 5979
North Carolina: Hayes 7227

Housing/shelter, repairs
Mississippi: Mississippi 4839

Housing/shelter, research
Washington: Pankow 9700

Housing/shelter, search services
Maryland: Goldseker 3803
Minnesota: Phillips 4741

Housing/shelter, services
California: Ludwick 856, Schwab 1128, **Smith 1183**, Wells 1312
Connecticut: People's 1671
Illinois: Community 2769
Maryland: Viragh 3902
Massachusetts: Franklin 4061, Melville 4170, Santander 4256
Minnesota: Smikis 4767
New York: Sagner 6783
Pennsylvania: North 8199
Texas: Rockwell 9135
Washington: **Channel 9597**

Housing/shelter, single organization support
Colorado: Staley 1507
New York: First 5979

Housing/shelter, SROs
Virginia: Hampton 9448

Housing/shelter, temporary shelter
California: California 368, Community 420, Doheny 473, Gogian 598, Union 1271
Connecticut: Liberty 1630
Illinois: Community 2769
Indiana: Lincoln 3344
Massachusetts: Berkshire 3946, TJX 4308
Minnesota: **Andersen 4601**
New York: Source 6893
North Carolina: Piedmont 7285
Ohio: Nationwide 7587, Reinberger 7628
Pennsylvania: PNC 8230
Virginia: Freddie 9435, **Genworth 9441**, Hampton 9448

Human services
Alabama: Alabama 1, Alfa 2, Alpha 3, Anderson 5, Arlington 6, Bashinsky 7, BBVA 8, BBVA 9, Bedsole 11, Bolden 12, Brock 13, Brooke 14, Bruno 15, Caring 18, Central 19, Comer 20, Community 21, Community 23, Community 24, Community 25, Crampton 26, Daniel 27, Davenport-Spiva 28, DeBakey 29, Dixon 30, Energen 32, Finlay 33, Friedman 35, Harrison 37, Hearin 38, Hess 39, Hill 40, Kaul 43, King 44, Lowder 45, Lowe 46, Mapp 47, May 48, Mayer 49, McMillan 50, Meyer 52, Meyer 53, Mitchell 55, Nabers 56, Nelson 57, Pleiad 58, Protective 59, Psalm 60, **Scott 64**, Smith 65, Smith 66, Thompson 70, Treadwell 71, Walker 74, Webb 76, Working 78
Alaska: Carr 83, Chugach 84, Gaguine 87, Rasmuson 89
Arizona: Arizona 92, Barrett 96, Caris 99, Click 100, Community 101, Cooper 102, Davis 104, Day 105, Delta 106, Emerald 108, Farrington 110, Freeport-McMoRan 112, Globe 115, Green 117, Halle 118, Hill 122, Jasam 124, Jones 127, **Kieckhefer 129**, Kiita 130, Least 132, Levine 133, Lodestar 136, Long 137, Marshall 141, McDonald 144, Moeller 145, Mooney 146, Moreno 147, Morris 148, Neely 149, Ottosen 150, Parsons 151, Pivotal 153, Pocono 154, Raymond 155, Reese 156, Ross 159, Rouha 160, Solheim 163, Stardust 164, Stewart 166, Surplus 167, SVL 168, Tankersley 169, Tooker 171, Weatherup 173
Arkansas: Arkansas 179, Bailey 180, Cabe 182, Carson 183, Endeavor 186, Frueauff 188, Glass 190, Jonsson 192, Murphy 193, Nabholz 194, Schmieding 200, Smith 201, Soderquist 202, Stephens 203, Sturgis 205, Tenenbaum 206, Union 208, Wal-Mart 210, White 212
California: 1011 214, 2005 215, Abrams 217, Ahmanson 222, Al-Ameen 225, Allergan 228, Alpert 230, Altman 233, Amar 236, **Amgen 238**, Anaheim 239, Anderson 240, Anderson 242, Anderson 243, Angell 244, Apatow-Mann 247, **Appleton 248**, Applied 249, Arbus 251, Archer 252, **Arkay 255**, Arrillaga 261, AS&F 263, Atkinson 264, Atkinson 265, Atol 267, Attias 268, Auen 269, Autry 270, Avery-Tsui 273, Bagley 277, Bakar 278, Baker 280, Barry 284, Barth 285, Bartman 286, Bauer 287, BCM 290, Bechtel 294, **Bechtel 295**, Bell 300, Bergen 308, Berry 312, Bickerstaff 313, Bilger 314, Black 317, Bloomfield 319, Blum 321, Blume 322, Bohnett 324, Borchard 328, Borina 329, Bothin 331, Bower 332, Bowman 335, Brandes 336, Brandman 337, Branson 338, Brenner 340, Breslauer-Soref 341, Brewster 342, Brin 343, Brittingham 345, **Broadcom 349**, **Broccoli 350**, Buckhantz 354, **Burkle 355**, Burnham 357, Burns 358, Burns 359, Byer 360, CAA 362, Cale 364, California 365, Call 369, Campbell 371, Campini 374, **Capital 375**, Carolands 379, Carsey 380, Carson 381, Caruso 382, Cathay 385, Caufield 386, Center 388, Change 393, Chao 394, Chapman 395, Charles 396, Chartwell 397, Chintu 398, Chrysopolae 400, Ciocca 401, **Cisco 402**, Clif 405, Clive 406, Coit 409, Collins 412, Colombo 413, Community 414, Community 415, Community 418, Community 419, Community 420, Community 421, Confidence 423, Connolly 425, Conte 427, Cortopassi 430, Coto 431, Cowell 434, Craigslist 436, Crean 439, Crocker 440, Croul 441, Curci 443, Cusenza 445, Dachs 446, Daly 447, Danford 448, Dart-L 450, Davidow 451, Davidow 452, Davidson 453, Davies 454, Davis 455, Day 456, Day 457, Delta 458, DeMille 459, Desert 461, Deutsch 462, Dhont 464, Dialynas 465, Dickinson 466, Disney 468, DMK 470, Doelger 472, Dolby 474, Douglas 476, DPR 478, Dr. Bronners 479, Draper 480, **Draper 481**, Drew 482, Drollinger 483, Drown 484, Eagle 488, Eagle 488, East 491, Edelstein 494, Edgerton 495, Eichenbaum 497, El Dorado 500, El 501, Elbaz 502, Ellis 503, Engemann 506, **Enlight 507**, Eucalyptus 510, Eustace-Kwan 511, Everlasting 512, Factor 513, Farese 518, Farrell 519, Faucett 520, Field 522, Field 524, Finley 527, **Firelight 529**, Fischmann 531, Foothills 537, Foster 539, Foundation 541, Freeberg 545, Fremont 548, Fresno 549, Friedman 551, Friend 552, Fromm 553, Fruth 554, Fry 555, Galen 558, Gallo 561, Gap 563, Garb 564, Garland 565, Gasser 566, Gellert 568, Gershman 575, Getty 577, Gifford 584, **Gilbert 585**, Gillespie 587, Gilmore 588, Gimbel 589, Glide 595, Gluck 596, God's 597, Gold 599, Gold 601, Goldhirsh 602, Goldman 605, Goldsmith 608, Goldwyn 609, Goodman 613, Goodwin 614, **Google 615**, Gordon 617, Gould 618, Grand 619, Graziadio 620, Green 621, Greenbaum 622, Greenberg 624, Greene 625, Grinold 628, Gross 629, Grout 630, Gruber 632, Guenther 634, Guess? 635, Gumbiner 636, Gumpert 637, Guzik 639, Haas 640, Halperin 646, Halsell 647, Hammer 648, Handleman 649, Hannon 650, Hanson 653, Harden 654, Harman 655, Harman 656, Harrington 657, Hartley 659, Harwit 660, Hauptman 662, Hayden 663, Hayward 665, HealthCare 667, Hedco 672, Heffernan 673, Hellman 677, Herbst 682, Herwaldt 684, Hewlett 687, Hexberg 688, Hills 691, **Hilton 692**, Hitz 694, Hoag 696, Hoag 697, Hoffman 699, Hofmann 700, Hollywood 701, Hope 702, Horwich 706, House 707, Hoven 708, HRH 709, Hsieh 710, Hsu 711, Hughes 713, Humboldt 714, Hurtt 716, Hutto 717, Hutton 718, Hwang 719, Intuit 723, Irmas 725, Irmas 726, Irwin 728, Ishiyama 730, Israel 731, Issa 732, It 733, J & J 734, J.A.N.S. 735, Jack 736, Jackson 737, Jacobs 738, Jacobs 739, Jaffe 741, Jameson 743, Jennings 748, **Jerome 749**, JL 751, JMM 752, Jones 755, Kahle 759, **Kalliopeia 761**, Karatz 765, Karsh 767, Katzenberg 769, Kayne 773, **Kee 776**, Keesal 777, Kelley 778, Kern 780, Keys 782, Kilroy 784, King 787, Kingsley 789, **KLA-Tencor 792**, Kling 794, KLM 795, Knossos 798, Koshland 804, Krause 805, Kroner 806, La 808, Lai 810, Lainer 813, Lamond 817, Langendorf 819, Lantz 820, Lear 824, Leavey 825, Lee 826, Lehrer 827, **Leichtag 828**, Leichtman 829, **Leonard 830**, Leonard 831, Leonetti/O'Connell 832, Leslie 834, LeVecke 835, Lewis 837, Lilly's 838, Linked 842, Lippman 843, Long 848, Luberski 852, Lucas 855, **Lund 857**, Lurie 858, Lyons 859, Lytel 860, M.Z. 862, Mabie 863, Macfarlane 865, MacMurray 867, MacNaughton 868, Macpherson 869, **Manasseh's 870**, Marciano 873, Marcus 876, Marin 877, Markkula 879, Marks 880, Marmor 881, Martindale 883, **Mattel 886**, **Maya 888**, Mazza 890, McAlister 891, McBean 893, McDonald 901, McKay 902, McMinn 906, Meadowview 908, Melalucca 909, Menard 911, Mendelson 912, Merage 915, **Mercer 917**, Mericos 918, Merrill 920, Metta 921, Meyer 922, Middleton 924, Milias 925, Milken 926, Milken 927, **Miller 928**, Mitchell 931, Moca 932, Moelis 933, Mohn 934, Monterey 936, Moore 937, Morris 942, Morton 943, Morton 944, Moss 946, Mosse 947, Mourier 949, Moxie 950, Mulago 952, Muller 953, Munzer 955, Murphy 956, Narrow 960, **Nazarian 962**, Nestle 965, Newhall 966, Newman 967, Nicholas 969, Noll 970, Norris 971, North 972, NuVasive 975, Oak 976, Oarsmen 979, Oberndorf 981, O'Connell 982, OneWest 985, Oppenheimer 987, Opperman 988, Opus 989, Orange 992, Orfalea 994, Pacific 1003, Packard 1007, Padway 1008, Page 1009, Parsons 1013, Pasadena 1015, Pathways 1019, Peppers 1024, Perfect 1025, Perforce 1026, Peters 1028, Petersen 1029, Pfaffinger 1030, Pfleger 1031, Pfleger 1032, PG&E 1033, Philanthropy 1035, Philibosian 1036, Placer 1039, Plaza 1040, Post 1041, Price 1044, Pritzker 1046, **Qualcomm 1048**, Quest 1050, Raintree 1052, Rancho 1053, Ransom 1055, Rautenberg 1056, Ray 1058, Reid 1060, Reis 1062, Ressler 1065, Rey 1067, Rickey 1071, Ritts 1076, RJM 1078, Rmlow 1079, Roberts 1080, Robertson 1082, Roche 1083, Rock 1084, Rock 1085, Rogers 1087, Rosenthal 1089, Ross 1090, Ross 1091, Ross 1091, Rudd 1096, Ryan 1098, Sacchi 1102, Sacramento 1103, Saje 1104, **Samueli 1106**, Samuelsson 1107, San Diego 1108, San Francisco 1109, San Luis 1110, Sand 1112, Sandy 1113, **Sangiacomo 1115**, Santa Barbara 1116, Saw 1119, Schaeffer 1121, Schlinger 1123, Schlinger 1124, Schow 1126, Schwab 1127, Schwab 1128, Scripps 1129, Scully 1130, Seiger 1137, Semel 1138, Sempra 1140, Sence 1141, Seretean 1142, Shanahan 1146, Shapiro 1151, Shapiro 1152, Shasta 1154, Shea 1155, Shea 1156, Shillman 1158, Shoresh 1159, Shortino 1160, Sierra 1163, Sierra 1164, Silicon 1166, Simon 1171, Sinskey 1174, Skoll 1176, Skywords 1177, Small 1180, Smet 1181, **Smith 1183**, Smith 1184, Smith 1186, Smith 1187, Snow 1191, Sobrato 1193, Solari 1196, Sonora 1198, Soref 1199, Sorensen 1200, Spearman 1201, Sperber 1205, Spitzer 1206, Springcreek 1208, Stanislaus 1211, Stark 1213, Steinmetz 1216, Stern 1219, Stotsenberg 1221, Stover 1222, **Strauss 1223**, Stulsaft 1226, Swig 1231, Taper 1237, **Tarsadia 1239**, Taub 1240, Taube 1241, Teach 1242, Teichert 1244, TF 1247, Thatcher 1248, **Thiel 1249**, Thompson 1250, Three 1254, TomKat 1257, Torrey 1258, Tosa 1259, Truckee 1263, Truckee 1263, Tu 1265, Tuohy 1267, Ueberroth 1268, United 1273, **Vadasz 1275**, Valente 1276, Valhalla 1278, Valley 1280, Van Daele 1281, Van Konynenburg 1282, Van Nuys 1284, Van Nuys 1285, Ventura 1287, Vickter 1289, Volentine 1291, **Wadhwani 1294**, Wallis 1296, Warnack 1297, Warren 1298, Wasserman

1300, Waterford 1301, Webb 1303, Webb 1304, Webster 1305, **Weider 1306**, Weingart 1307, Weisman 1309, Wells 1311, Wells 1312, Werner 1313, West 1314, Western 1315, Westreich 1317, Wetzel 1318, WHH 1320, White 1321, Whitman 1322, Wilcox 1324, Williams 1325, Williams 1326, Williams 1327, Wilson 1328, Wings 1331, Witherbee 1334, Wohlford 1336, Wolf 1337, Wolfen 1338, Womens 1340, Wong 1341, **Wong 1342**, Wood 1344, WWW 1349, Wynn 1350, Xie 1351, Zable 1355, Zander 1356, Zellerbach 1358, Zelman 1359, Ziegler 1360

Colorado: 6/S 1362, Anschutz 1364, Aspen 1367, Aspen 1368, Bacon 1370, Ball 1371, Bernstein 1372, Boedecker 1373, Boettcher 1374, Bonfils 1376, Bowana 1377, Brown 1379, Bruni 1380, Carson 1382, Catto 1383, CH2M 1384, Change 1386, Community 1391, Community 1392, Community 1393, Community 1394, Community 1395, COPIC 1397, Davis 1400, Denver 1401, Doolin 1402, Dornick 1403, El Pomar 1406, Encana 1407, Erion 1408, Find 1409, Fox 1412, Fries 1413, Fulcrum 1414, Gates 1418, Grand 1423, Green 1424, Halton 1426, Hansen 1427, Hunter 1431, Kern 1438, King 1440, Kitzmiller 1441, Larrk 1444, Lewis 1447, Libertygives 1448, M.D.C./Richmond 1450, Maffei 1451, Maggiegeorge 1452, Marquez 1454, Marsico 1455, McDonnell 1458, Monfort 1464, Nagel 1468, Neuman 1470, Norwood 1471, PB&K 1474, Pikes 1478, Pioneer 1479, Precourt 1483, Price 1484, ProLogis 1485, Rose 1487, Saeman 1490, **Salvador 1491**, Schermer 1492, Scurci 1494, Seay 1495, Servant 1497, Shaw 1499, Slater 1502, Southern 1504, Sprout 1505, Strear 1508, Summit 1511, Telluride 1512, Tointon 1513, Tuchman 1514, TYL 1516, Vail 1518, Vodafone 1519, Western 1520, **Western 1521**, Whispering 1522, Willett 1523, Wolf 1526, Yampa 1528, YPI 1529

Connecticut: Allison 1535, American 1537, Aronson 1538, Bissell 1547, Bob's 1548, Boehringer 1549, Bossidy 1551, Brightwater 1552, Bullfrogs 1553, Chase 1555, Cohen 1560, Common 1561, Community 1563, Community 1563, Community 1564, Community 1565, Connecticut 1566, Culpeper 1568, Dalio 1569, Daniell 1570, Davis 1571, Diebold 1574, Donchian 1576, Eder 1577, Ellis 1579, Ensworth 1580, Fairfield 1581, Farid 1582, First 1584, Fisher 1585, Fisher 1586, Foley 1587, Fund 1589, Garden 1590, **GE 1591**, George 1592, Georgescu 1593, Glover 1594, Goergen 1595, Goldring 1596, Goldstone 1597, Goodnow 1598, Grossman 1601, Grossman 1602, Hack 1604, **Hampshire 1608**, Hartford 1609, Hartman 1610, Heidenreich 1611, Hoffman 1613, Hubbell 1614, Huisking 1615, Ion 1616, Keefe 1619, Kitchings 1621, Kohn 1622, Lehrman 1628, Liberty 1630, Link 1631, Lowenstein 1633, Main 1634, Maranatha 1636, Marx 1638, Matthies 1639, Meriden 1643, Middlesex 1644, MJPM 1645, Mortensen 1647, New Canaan 1650, NewAlliance 1651, Niblack 1653, **Niles 1654**, **October 1659**, O'Herron 1660, Ohnell 1661, Olson 1662, Orchard 1663, Ossen 1664, Owenoke 1665, Pay 1670, Perdue 1672, Pitt 1675, Provident 1677, Prusoff 1678, Richman 1680, Robbins 1681, Rockville 1682, Rogow 1683, Rosenthal 1684, Sage 1687, Say 1689, SBM 1690, Seedlings 1691, Sheinberg 1695, Silver 1696, Smilow 1698, Stanley 1700, Steere 1701, Straus 1702, Sullivan 1703, Tombros 1707, Trefz 1709, **Tudor 1711**, Viking 1717, Vranos 1718, Werth 1719, Wiggins 1722, Windmill 1723, Windreich 1724, WorldQuant 1726, Xerox 1728

Delaware: 9:7 1733, **Adobe 1734**, Bennett 1739, Bere 1740, Berkley 1741, Berlin 1743, **Birch 1744**, Bishop 1745, Brill 1747, Bucks 1748, CenturyLink-Clarke 1750, Chapman 1752, Chase 1753, **Chichester 1754**, Common 1755, Crestlea 1757, Crystal 1758, Davis 1761, Davis 1762, Day 1763, Day 1764, Delaware 1765, Detkin 1767, Devonwood 1768, Duane 1771, Ettinger 1779, First 1781, Good 1785, Gospel 1786, JP's 1793, Klein 1797, Kohl 1798, Laffey 1800, Lefrak 1802, LeFrak 1803, Lennox 1805, Longwood 1806, Mackenzie 1809, **Marks 1813**, Marmot 1814, Mastronardi 1815, Matthews 1816, McDonald 1817, **Memton 1819**, Mordecai 1820, Nobari 1823, O'Neil 1826, Parker 1829, Parrish 1830, Patterson 1831, Pere 1833, Pfeil 1834, Phillips 1835, Pincus 1836, Planet 1837, Prentice 1839, Presto 1840, Price 1841, Quitiplas 1844, **Raskob 1845**, Reynolds 1848, Reynolds 1849, Rose 1852, Rossi 1854, Salah 1855, Schwartz 1857, Sternlicht 1861, **Stratus 1864**, Struthers 1865, Tapeats 1868, Wasily 1871, Welfare 1872, Westly 1873, Whitton-Spector 1874

District of Columbia: Agua 1878, Bedford 1883, Beech 1884, Bender 1885, Bernstein 1887, Cafritz 1890, Community 1893, Coyne 1896, CrossCurrents 1897, **Davis 1898**, Dole 1900, **Dreyfus 1901**, Forsythia 1906, Gewirz 1909, Goldman 1910, Gottesman 1911, Gudelsky 1912, Hansen 1913, **Hill 1915**, Kaye 1920, Kiplinger 1922, Lehrman 1924, Loughran 1925, Ludwig 1927, Merriman 1930, Meyer 1931, **NDPI 1935**, Palmer 1937, Pedas 1938, Rales 1942, Rumsfeld 1943, Rutherfoord 1944, Seter 1947, Spectemur 1948, True 1951, **Union 1953**, Wolf 1957, Zients 1960

Florida: 100 1961, Abraham 1962, Abramson 1963, Alexander 1965, Amaturo 1966, Applebaum 1970, **Arison 1972**, Asofsky 1973, Azeez 1975, Baldwin 1978, Bank 1979, Baroco 1981, Basham 1982, Batchelor 1983, Bauman 1984, Bay 1985, Beaver 1986, Becker 1987, Bedford 1988, Bell 1990, Bell 1991, Bennett 1992, Berg 1993, Berman 1994, Bernstein 1995, Bi-Lo 1996, Blank 1997, Blum 1999, Bradley 2001, Broad 2002, Bronfman 2003, Brown 2004, Bryce 2005, Burns 2006, Burton 2007, Bush 2008, **Catholic 2014**, Central 2015, **Chatlos 2019**, **Chester 2020**, Chia 2021, Cobb 2026, Cobb 2027, Cohen 2028, Community 2032, Community 2033, Community 2034, Community 2035, Community 2036, Community 2037, Community 2038, Community 2040, Community 2041, Conn 2042, Connors 2043, Dallepezze 2049, Danial 2050, Darden 2051, Davis 2054, Davis 2055, Demetree 2058, Denison, 2060, Densch 2061, Diermeier 2063, DiMare 2064, DuBow 2068, Duckwall 2069, Dunspaugh-Dalton 2073, duPont 2075, E.J.N.R.A. 2077, Ebert 2079, Einstein 2084, Ellmar 2085, Engelberg 2086, Falic 2091, Fancelli 2092, Ferguson 2093, Ferraro 2094, FIS 2097, Fites 2098, Florida 2101, Florman 2102, Flournoy 2103, Fortin 2105, Fortin 2106, Franklin 2107, French 2110, Funkhouser 2111, Galloway 2112, Gardener 2114, Garfield 2115, Garrott 2116, Gay 2117, Gemcon 2118, GiveWell 2123, Glazer 2124, Glenn 2125, Global 2126, Goldstein 2128, Goodes 2129, Gooding 2130, GPD 2132, Green 2134, Green 2135, Green 2136, Greenburg 2137, **Griffin 2138**, Gronewaldt 2139, Gruss 2141, Gulf 2142, Gutin 2143, Haller 2146, Harrington 2148, Harris 2149, Henriksen 2153, Henry 2154, Hersh 2156, Hill 2158, Hillenbrand 2159, Hoehl 2160, Hudson 2164, Huizenga 2165, Indian 2166, Jacksonville 2167, **Jaffer 2168**, Johnson 2172, **Katz 2177**, Katzman 2178, **Kazma 2179**, Kelly 2181, Kennedy 2182, Kennedy 2183, Kirbo 2186, Klurman 2189, KMD 2190, KPS 2194, Kramer 2195, Krouse 2196, Lacy 2198, LaMothe 2199, **Lampert 2200**, Langenfelder 2201, Langford 2202, Lattner 2205, Lavin 2206, Leclerc 2208, Lennar 2210, Lewis 2212, Libra 2213, Life 2215, Lindemann 2217, Lynn 2221, Macdonald 2223, Magruder 2225, Mangurian 2226, Maren 2227, Martin 2229, McCahill 2231, McCann 2232, McFarlane 2233, McMurtry 2236, Melville 2237, Miami 2238, Michaan 2239, Mill 2240, Miller 2241, Moran 2242, Moran 2243, Newman 2250, NextEra 2251, Ocean 2253, Palank 2256, Pamphalon 2257, **Pariser 2258**, **Patel 2259**, Patterson 2260, Patterson 2261, Peacock 2263, Pearce 2264, Pechter 2265, Petway 2268, Pinellas 2269, Plangere 2270, Pope 2272, Preik 2273, Ratcliffe 2278, Rawlings 2279, Rayonier 2281, Rebozo 2282, Regal 2283, Rinker 2285, Roberts 2290, Rooms 2292, Root 2293, Rosenblatt 2295, Rubin 2299, Rubin 2300, Ryder 2302, Sack 2303, Sanders 2305, Sandler 2306, Sansing 2307, Saunders 2308, Scarpa 2310, Schaefer 2311, Schemel 2312, Schoenbaum 2313, Selby 2316, Selevan 2317, Sherman 2318, Sherman 2319, Simon 2322, Sontag 2325, Southwest 2327, St. Petersburg 2332, **Stacy 2333**, Stavropoulos 2336, Stein 2337, Stein 2338, Stern 2339, Straz 2341, Sullivan 2343, Sun 2344, SWS 2347, Sylvester 2348, Taft 2349, Tarrant 2352, Taylor 2353, Taylor 2354, Thomas 2357, Thornburgh 2360, Tollefson 2361, Tsunami 2362, TWS 2365, Usher 2367, Vatterott 2371, Vinik 2372, Waggoner 2374, Walter 2375, Ware 2378, Weisman 2381, Welch 2382, Welsh 2384, Wildflower 2386, Wildflower 2387, Winter 2390, Wolfe 2391, Wollowick 2393, **Worrell 2395**, Yavitz 2396, Zehnder 2397

Georgia: Addison 2398, Aflac 2399, Amos 2401, Anderson 2403, Atlanta 2406, Beard-Payne 2408, Beech 2409, Belcher 2410, Beloco 2411, Blakely 2412, Bradley 2414, Brady 2415, Brain 2416, Callaway 2418, Campbell 2420, Camp-Younts 2421, Chambers 2425, Collins 2429, Colonial 2430, Communities 2431, Community 2432, Community 2433, Community 2434, Community 2435, Community 2436, Community 2437, Community 2438, Community 2439, Correll 2440, Cousins 2442, Cousins 2443, Covenant 2444, Cox 2445, Creel-Harison 2447, Dunn 2451, Ellis 2452, Equifax 2455, EZ 2456, Fleming 2458, Flowers 2459, Fuqua 2464, Gaby 2465, Gaines 2466, Galloway 2467, Georgia 2468, Glenn 2470, Glenn 2471, Gordy 2472, Griffith 2473, Grizzard 2474, Harris 2479, Holder 2485, Hudgens 2486, **Imlay 2487**, Indiana 2488, Invisible 2489, Jackson 2490, Jones 2491, Kahn 2493, Kennedy 2495, Knox 2498, Lanier 2499, Lewis 2503, Lockwood 2505, Loridans 2506, Loudermilk 2507, Love 2508, Lowder 2509, Ma-Ran 2510, McKenna 2516, Moore 2520, Morgens 2521, Murray 2523, NCR 2524, North 2525, Pechter 2526, Pelling 2527, Pitts 2529, Pittulloch 2530, Poe 2531, Porter 2533, Primerica 2534, Realan 2535, Rich 2537, Rockdale 2540, Rosenberg 2544, Savannah 2548, Servant's 2550, Snell 2552, Synovus 2556, Tull 2561, Turner 2564, U.S. 2565, **UPS 2566**, Watkins 2568, Weber 2570, Williams 2574, Williams, 2575, Woodruff 2578, Woodruff 2579, Woodward 2580, Young 2582, Zaban 2583, Zeist 2584

Hawaii: **Albrecht 2585**, Atherton 2586, Bank 2588, Cades 2591, Campbell 2592, Cooke 2597, First 2598, Geist 2600, Hawaii 2602, HMSA 2604, Hughes 2605, Kosasa 2607, Learning 2610, LGA 2611, McInerny 2612, Schuler 2614, Shin 2616, Strong 2617, **Watumull 2620**, Wilcox 2621, Wong 2622, Zierk 2623

Idaho: Cunningham 2630, Idaho 2632, Jeker 2633, Jeker 2634, Kleiner 2635, Lightfoot 2636, Nagel 2639, Rebholtz 2640, Seagraves 2642, Simplot 2643, Smeed 2644, Wishnick 2646

Illinois: 2010 2647, **Abbott 2648**, **Abbott 2649**, Abt 2651, Ackermann 2652, Allegretti 2655, Allen 2656, Amicus 2660, Andrew 2661, Andrew 2662, Anixter 2664, Anschel 2666, Aon 2667, Appleby 2668, Appleton 2669, Archer 2671, Ashley 2674, **Astellas 2675**, Atherton 2676, Austin 2677, Ball 2679, Barnett 2681, Baskes 2683, Baskes 2684, Baskin 2685, Baum 2689, Bechtner 2691, Beidler 2692, Berner 2694, Bersted 2696, Blair 2699, Blair 2700, Block 2701, Blowitz 2702, Bluhm 2704, Blum 2705, Blum 2706, Boler 2708, Bondi 2710, Boyer 2711, Brach 2712, Brunner 2718, Bryce 2719, Buchanan 2720, Buckeye 2722, Bucksbaum 2723, Bucksbaum 2724, Buder 2725, **Buffett 2726**, Buffett 2727, Butler 2729, C.W.B. 2730, Camp 2732, Canning 2733, Carrus 2734, **Carylon 2735**, Caslow 2736, Caterpillar 2738, Cedar 2739, Chaddick 2740, Chartered 2744, Chicago 2746, Children's 2747, Christopher 2748, Circle 2749, Clapham 2750, Clark 2751, Clearing 2752, CME 2755, CME 2756, Cole-Crone 2758,

Coleman 2759, Comer 2760, Community 2763, Community 2765, Community 2765, Community 2766, Community 2767, Cooney 2771, Corboy 2773, **Cornwell 2775**, Cox 2776, Cressey 2779, Crown 2781, Cuneo 2783, D and R 2784, Davee 2785, Davis 2786, Day 2787, Dean 2789, **Deere 2790**, Deering 2791, DeKalb 2792, Dew 2794, Dickenson 2795, Dillon 2796, Dimon 2797, **Domanada 2799**, Donnelley 2801, Dover 2803, Doyle 2804, Driehaus 2805, Dryer 2808, Duchossois 2809, DuPage 2812, Dury 2813, Edlis-Neeson 2815, Edwardson 2816, Edwardsville 2817, EFS 2818, Eisenberg 2819, Ellis 2820, Energizer 2824, Evanston 2826, FDC 2829, Feinberg 2830, Field 2831, Finnegan 2832, First 2833, Foglia 2837, Fossett 2838, Frank 2840, Frankel 2842, Frankel 2843, Frechette 2844, Friedman 2846, Friedmann 2847, Fulk 2850, Full 2851, **Gallagher 2855**, Galvin 2857, Gates 2859, Gavin 2860, Genius 2861, Gidwitz 2862, Gilmore 2864, Goldschmidt 2867, **Goodman 2869**, Goodyear 2870, **Grainger 2874**, Grohne 2880, Guthman 2882, H.B.B. 2883, Hamel 2887, Hamill 2888, Hanson 2890, Harris 2892, **Harris 2893**, Hartke 2897, Hazan 2899, Heerey 2901, Hendrickson 2905, Heritage 2907, Hermann 2908, Herr 2909, Hintz 2911, Hirschl 2912, His 2913, Hobbs 2914, Hochberg 2915, Hoehn 2916, Huizenga 2924, Hull 2925, Hunter 2926, Hunter 2927, Huntington 2928, Hurvis 2930, I and G 2931, Illinois 2934, Ingersoll 2935, Irwin 2936, Jackson 2937, JNT 2940, Johnson 2942, Johnson 2943, Johnson 2944, Kaplan 2948, Kaplan 2949, **Kapoor 2950**, Katten 2951, Keith 2952, Kemper 2954, Kendall 2956, Kensington 2957, King 2960, **Klaff 2961**, Kolschowsky 2962, Kott 2963, Kovler 2964, Kreyling 2965, Landau 2966, Lea 2970, Leibowitz 2973, Lerner 2975, Levi 2976, Levin 2978, Lewis 2980, Louis 2984, Louis 2985, Lumpkin 2986, Madigan 2992, Magnus 2993, Malott 2996, Mander 2998, **Manitoba 2999**, Martin 3002, Master 3004, Mazza 3007, MB 3008, McCaskey 3009, McCormick 3010, McDaniel 3011, McGowan 3014, McGraw 3015, McIntosh 3016, McQueen 3018, Melman 3022, Meyer 3023, Miller 3025, Millikin 3027, Mills 3028, Mills 3029, Mirman 3031, Moline 3033, **Mondelez 3034**, Morrison 3037, Morse 3039, Morton 3040, Mosher 3041, **Motorola 3042**, **Motorola 3043**, MRB 3044, Munson 3045, Negaunee 3047, Nerenberg 3050, Nesbitt 3051, New 3052, NIB 3053, Nichols 3054, Nierling 3055, Nierling, 3056, Night 3057, Northern 3059, Nygren 3060, Oak Park 3061, Omron 3063, Opler 3064, Oppenheimer 3066, Owens 3068, Parmer 3069, Pasquinelli 3071, Perkins 3075, Perlman 3076, Perritt 3077, Petersen 3078, Pick, 3079, Pierce 3080, **Ploughshares 3082**, Polk 3084, Popular 3085, Potishman 3086, Potter 3087, Prentice 3088, Prince 3089, Pritzker 3092, Pritzker 3094, Pritzker 3095, Pritzker 3096, Rajchenbach 3103, Rauner 3105, REAM 3107, Redhill 3108, Regenstein 3111, Reid 3112, Rhoades 3115, Rice 3116, Richards 3117, Roberts 3118, Roberts 3119, Roberts 3120, Roberts 3121, Rotonda 3125, Rubschlager 3126, Rumsfeld 3128, Ryan 3129, Ryan 3130, Sacks 3131, **Santreece 3135**, Satter 3136, Scanlan 3137, Schawk 3138, Schmidt 3139, Schmitt 3140, Schreiber 3142, Schuler 3143, Schwartz 3144, Schwartz 3145, Segal 3147, Seid 3148, SF 3149, Shapiro 3151, Shirk 3158, Simon 3160, Siragusa 3162, Sirius 3163, Smith 3164, Snite 3166, Souder 3168, Southeastern 3169, Square 3173, Stern 3177, Stone 3179, Supera 3183, **Thome 3187**, Timken 3188, Tracy 3189, Trott 3192, Trustmark 3193, Tulsa 3194, **Tyndale 3195**, Ullrich 3198, United 3199, United 3200, United 3201, Vaughn 3203, **Ventana 3204**, Voice 3207, Walsh 3212, Walter 3213, Ward 3216, Weezie 3222, Weinberg 3223, Weiss 3224, White 3229, White 3230, Wilemal 3232, Willow 3235, Wilson 3237, Wohlers 3238, Wonderful 3239, **Woodbury 3240**, Woods 3241, Woodward 3243, Yulman 3246, Zell 3247, Zerrusen 3248

Indiana: 1st 3251, **Ackerman 3252**, Adams 3253, ADL 3254, Anderson 3255, Annis 3256, Apgar 3258, Asante 3259, Auer 3260, Bales 3261, Ball 3262, Ball 3264, Blue 3265, Brotherhood 3268, Brown 3269, Carmichael 3270, Cass 3271, Central 3272, Clowes 3275, Community 3277, Community 3278, Community 3279, Community 3280, Community 3281, Community 3282, Community 3283, Community 3284, Community 3285, Community 3286, Community 3287, Community 3288, Community 3289, Community 3290, Crown Point 3291, **Cummins 3292**, Dearborn 3293, DeKalb 3295, Duneland 3297, Elkhart 3298, English 3299, Eskenazi 3300, Fairbanks 3301, Fehsenfeld 3302, Finish 3303, Ford 3305, Foundations 3306, Froderman 3307, Gagan 3308, Garatoni 3309, Glick 3310, Hamman 3312, Hancock 3313, Harrison 3314, Health 3317, Helping 3318, Hendricks 3319, Henry 3320, Heritage 3321, Holiday 3322, Hoover 3323, Huntington 3324, Hux 3325, Indiana 3327, Jackson 3329, Johnson 3330, Journal-Gazette 3332, Koch 3334, Kosciusko 3336, Legacy 3337, Leighton 3338, **Lilly 3342**, Lincoln 3344, Madison 3346, Marshall 3348, Marten 3349, Martin 3350, McAllister 3351, Michigan 3354, Miller 3355, Montgomery 3356, MTI 3357, National 3358, Noble 3359, Noble 3359, Northern 3360, Noyes 3361, Ogle 3362, OneAmerica 3364, Orange 3365, Parke 3366, Parrish 3367, Porter 3369, Portland 3370, Pulliam 3372, Putnam 3373, Reeves 3374, Reynolds 3376, Rifkin 3378, Ripley 3379, Rolland 3381, Rothschild 3382, Saltsburg 3383, Simon 3385, Simon 3386, Steuben 3390, Tipton 3391, Transformation 3392, Unity 3393, Volo 3395, Wabash 3396, Wayne 3400, Weaver 3401, Wells 3403, West 3404, White 3406, Whitley 3407

Iowa: AEGON 3409, Ahrens 3410, Aviva 3411, Bechtel 3413, Butler 3415, Cedar Rapids 3417, Clarinda 3418, Community 3419, Community 3420, Community 3422, Community 3423, Community 3424, Dahl 3425, EMC 3428, Gilchrist 3432, Glazer 3434, Good 3436, GuideOne 3438, Hall-Perrine 3439, Hanson 3441, Helpenstell 3442, HNI 3443, Holthues 3444, Hubbell 3445, Hubbell 3446, Iowa 3447, Jacobson 3448, Johnson 3449, Kent 3450, Kinney-Lindstrom 3451, Knapp 3452, Kruidenier 3455, Lee 3457, Mansfield 3459, Maytag 3460, McElroy 3461, McIntyre 3462, Meredith 3463, MidAmerican 3465, New 3468, Northeast 3469, **Ochylski 3470**, On 3471, Pella 3473, Poweshiek 3475, Principal 3476, Ruan 3478, Seidler 3479, Siouxland 3480, South 3481, Stine 3482, Sukup 3483, Tye 3484, United 3485, Vermeer 3486, Vogel 3487, Weathertop 3489, Zimmerman 3491

Kansas: Ash 3492, Baughman 3493, Beach 3494, Beren 3495, Beren 3496, Capitol 3498, Coleman 3501, Cooper 3503, Damon 3504, DeBoer 3505, Deramus 3508, Douglas 3509, Downing 3510, Dreiseszun 3512, Elliott 3513, Emporia 3514, Garvey 3516, Hartley 3519, Hutchinson 3521, INTRUST 3522, Kelly 3526, Kirk 3527, Manhattan 3532, McCune 3533, McPherson 3534, Miller 3535, Morgan 3536, Rice 3538, Salina 3540, Sarli 3541, Security 3544, Shannon 3545, Smoot 3548, Topeka 3552, Westar 3553, Wichita 3555, Wyandotte 3556

Kentucky: Augusta 3557, Blue 3560, Brown 3563, Carson-Myre 3567, Community 3569, Community 3570, Cralle 3571, Durr 3572, Fischer 3574, Gardner 3576, Gheens 3577, Hagan 3579, Harris 3580, Horn 3581, Humana 3582, J & L 3584, Jain 3585, LG&E 3586, Lift 3587, Marshall 3588, Newell 3591, Norton 3592, Owsley 3595, Preston 3596, Public 3597, Robinson 3598, Roseman 3599, Scripps 3600, Smith 3601, Spray 3602, Swope 3603, Vanhoose 3604, Ventas 3605, Young 3607, Yum! 3608

Louisiana: Albemarle 3609, Azby 3611, Baton Rouge 3613, Beaird 3614, Booth 3616, Brown 3617, Clement 3622, Community 3624, Community 3625, Coughlin 3626, Deming 3627, Diboll 3628, Dore' 3629, Factor 3632, Franks 3634, Frazier 3635, Freeman 3636, Goldring 3638, Grayson 3639, Grigsby 3640, Helis 3641, Heymann 3642, Huie 3643, Keller 3646, Libby-Dufour 3648, Lorio 3650, Louisiana 3651, Lupin 3652, New Orleans 3656, Peltier 3658, Pennington 3659, Pinhook 3660, Reily 3661, Rispone 3662, RosaMary 3663, Scott 3666, Stuller 3668, Wiener 3670, Wilson 3671, **Woldenberg 3672**, Woolf 3673, Young 3674, Zemurray 3675, Zigler 3676

Maine: Alfond 3678, Cascade 3681, Elliotsville 3686, Fore 3687, Glickman 3688, Hannaford 3690, Iberdrola 3693, King 3694, Libra 3696, Maine 3698, Mulford 3702, Nichols 3703, Sewall 3708, TD 3710, **Walter 3711**

Maryland: Abell 3713, Abramson 3715, Adalman-Goodwin 3716, Adams 3718, Allegis 3719, Angelos 3721, Ausherman 3723, Baltimore 3726, Battye 3727, **Bearman 3728**, **Berman 3730**, **Berman 3731**, Bisciotti 3733, Blades 3734, Blum 3737, **Boehm 3738**, Brickman 3739, Brown 3740, **Brown 3741**, Bunting 3742, Bunting 3743, **Casey 3745**, Ceres 3747, Choice 3748, Clark 3750, Clark 3751, Cohen 3753, **Cohen 3754**, Commonweal 3756, Community 3757, Community 3758, Community 3759, Community 3760, Community 3761, Crane 3766, Dahan 3770, Davis 3772, Davison 3773, **Deerbrook 3776**, Dekelboum 3777, DiCarlo 3780, **DLA 3781**, Dresher 3782, Dupkin 3783, Eaton 3784, Fairchild 3788, Foundation 3794, Fowler 3795, France 3796, Freeman 3797, Fusco 3800, Glazer 3802, Goldseker 3803, Goldsmith 3804, **Grace 3807**, Hahn 3811, Higgins-Hussman 3815, Hirschhorn 3816, Kahlert 3822, Kerr 3823, Klein 3824, Knott 3826, **Lawless 3827**, Legg 3828, Leidy 3830, Lerner 3831, Levitt 3832, Linehan 3834, Lockheed 3837, Marriott 3840, Marriott 3841, Meyerhoff 3848, Middendorf 3850, Mid-Shore 3851, Mirmiran 3853, **Morningstar 3854**, **Murray 3855**, O'Neil 3859, Orokawa 3860, Osprey 3861, Pohanka 3863, Price 3865, Riepe 3869, Rollins 3872, Rosenberg 3874, Rosenbloom 3875, Roswell 3876, Rouse 3877, Sampson 3878, Shields 3884, **Sidgmore 3885**, Spencer 3887, St. John 3888, Straus 3890, Tauber 3893, **Thalheimer 3894**, Trawick 3898, Van 3901, Viragh 3902, Wareheim 3903, Washington 3904, Wasserman 3905, Weinberg 3907, **Weinberg 3908**

Massachusetts: A.M. 3912, Aaron 3913, Abrams 3914, Acorn 3915, Adams 3916, **Adelson 3918**, **Alchemy 3920**, Aloha 3922, AMG 3924, Anthony 3925, Arbella 3926, Bayrd 3938, Benson 3942, Bergstrom 3944, Berkman 3945, Berkshire 3946, Berkshire 3948, Beveridge 3950, Bilezikian 3951, BOSE 3954, Boston 3957, **Bresky 3958**, Bristol 3960, Bromley 3961, Brookline 3962, Byrnes 3964, Cabbadetus 3965, **Cabot 3966**, Cabot 3967, Cabot 3968, Caldwell 3970, Cambridge 3971, Cambridge 3972, Cape Cod 3973, Cape Cod 3974, Carney 3975, Casty 3976, Chafetz 3979, Chirag 3983, Citizens 3985, Clarke 3986, Clipper 3987, Cogan 3988, Community 3990, Community 3991, Community 3992, Copeland 3994, Corcoran 3995, Corkin 3996, Cosette 3997, Crane 3998, Croll 4000, Cross 4001, Crotty 4002, Cummings 4003, Currents 4004, Cutler 4005, Cutler 4006, Dalessandro 4007, Dana 4008, Danversbank 4009, Davis 4011, Demoulas 4014, Dibner 4018, Dinovi 4019, Dintersmith 4020, Doran 4024, Duniry 4025, Dunkin' 4026, Dunn 4027, Dusky 4028, Eaglemere 4029, Eastern 4030, Edgerley 4031, Egan 4032, Ellsworth 4035, **Elsevier 4036**, Eos 4037, Epker 4038, Essex 4039, Evans 4040, Fallon 4041, Feigenbaum 4044, Fels 4045, Finch 4048, Fireman 4049, Firstgreen 4050, Fish 4051, Fisher 4052, Flatley 4053, Fletcher 4054, Foundation 4056, Foundation 4058, Fradian 4059, Frances 4060, Fuller 4063, George 4068, **Germeshausen 4069**, Gildea 4071, Golden 4073, Gordon 4074, **Grand 4076**, Grinspoon 4080, Gross

4081, Haley 4083, Hanover 4086, Harmsworth 4087, Heide 4091, Hermann 4094, Hershey 4095, Hildreth 4099, Hyams 4103, Imago 4105, Inavale 4106, Institution 4108, Jacobson 4110, Janey 4111, Jebediah 4112, Jordan 4113, JSJN 4115, **Karp 4117**, Keane 4118, Kingsbury 4123, Klarman 4126, Knez 4127, Krupp 4130, Ladd 4132, Landry 4134, Larson 4137, Lauring 4138, Leventhal 4140, Levine 4142, Levovitz 4143, Levy 4144, Liberty 4145, Liswhit 4150, Lovett 4151, Lowell 4152, Lowndes 4154, Lubin 4155, Lucretia 4156, Ludcke 4157, Lurie 4158, Marks 4162, Massiah 4163, Mazar 4164, McCance 4165, McEvoy 4168, **Middlecott 4174**, Mifflin 4175, Miller 4177, **Mirowski 4179**, Mooney 4181, Morgan 4182, Morrison 4184, Moseley 4185, MWC 4186, Narada 4187, New 4189, New 4190, New 4191, New England 4192, North 4194, O'Brien 4195, O'Donnell 4196, OneWorld 4199, Overly 4201, Palace 4203, Pappas 4204, Pappas 4205, Pardoe 4206, Parker 4207, Patten 4208, Peoples 4212, Perpetual 4215, Peters 4216, Play 4221, Plymouth 4222, Popplestone 4225, Poss 4226, Ragon 4228, Rasmussen 4231, Raymond 4232, Redstone 4233, Reebok 4234, Remillard 4236, Reynolds 4238, Riley 4239, Roberts 4240, Rodgers 4242, Rogers 4243, Romney 4244, **Rosenberg 4245**, Rowland 4246, Roy 4247, Rubin 4249, **Rudyak 4251**, Ruettgers 4252, Saltonstall 4254, Samantha, 4255, Santander 4256, Saquish 4257, Sarnoff 4258, Schaffer 4259, Schoen 4260, Schooner 4261, Schott 4262, Schwartz 4265, Shapiro 4267, Shaver 4269, Sidman 4273, Sims/ Maes 4274, Spina 4280, Stamps 4281, Stare 4283, Stevens 4288, Stevens 4289, Stevenson 4290, Stifler 4292, Stoddard 4293, Stoneman 4296, Stop 4297, Strategic 4298, Sudbury 4299, Swartz 4301, Swensrud 4303, Taunton 4304, Thompson 4307, Travelli 4310, TripAdvisor 4311, Tupancy 4312, Wadleigh 4316, Wagner 4317, Webster 4322, Wilderness 4323, Windover 4324, Wood 4326, Worcester 4327, Yawkey 4328, Yawkey 4329

Michigan: Alix 4333, Allegan 4334, Alro 4336, Andersen 4339, Ann Arbor 4340, Barry 4342, Battle Creek 4343, Bay 4344, Beard 4345, Berrien 4347, Besser 4349, Binda 4350, Boll 4352, BorgWarner 4353, Bosch 4354, Brown 4356, Capital 4357, Charboneau 4360, Charlevoix 4361, Chelsea 4362, Chinnick 4363, Christ 4364, Christian 4365, Chrysler 4366, Community 4369, Community 4370, Community 4371, Community 4372, Community 4373, Community 4374, Community 4375, Consumers 4376, Cook 4377, Cook 4378, **Cooper-Standard 4380**, Cornucopia 4381, Cracchiolo 4382, Cronin 4383, Dalton 4385, Dana 4386, Dart 4388, Davis 4391, **DENSO 4395**, DeRoy 4396, Devereaux 4397, DeVos 4398, DeVos 4399, Dewey 4401, DeWitt 4402, Doornink 4403, Dow 4406, Dow 4407, Dow 4408, DTE 4410, Duffy 4411, Dyer 4412, Eddy 4414, Ferrantino 4419, Firestone 4422, **Fisher 4423**, Ford 4425, Ford 4428, Ford 4429, Frankel 4434, Frankel 4435, Fremont 4438, Frey 4439, Frey 4440, General 4442, Gerstacker 4444, Gilmore 4445, Grand Haven 4446, Grand Rapids 4447, Granger 4449, Granger 4450, Grosfeld 4453, Harding 4455, Helppie 4456, Heritage 4458, Herrick 4459, Hickman 4460, Hillsdale 4461, Hough 4462, Hurst 4464, Idema 4465, Jackson 4467, Johnston 4469, Jubilee 4470, Kahn 4471, **Kellogg's 4475**, Knabusch 4476, Knight 4477, Korth 4478, **Kresge 4479**, La-Z-Boy 4481, Lear 4482, Lenawee 4485, Mackey 4489, Manat 4490, Manoogian 4491, Manoogian 4492, Manoogian 4493, Mardigian 4494, Marquette 4495, Marshall 4496, Masco 4497, McGregor 4498, Merillat 4500, **Micah 4501**, Midland 4502, Miller 4503, Miller 4504, Molinello 4505, Monroe 4507, Morey 4508, Mosaic 4509, **Mott 4510**, Mount Pleasant 4512, Mulder 4514, **Myers 4515**, Oleson 4516, Perrigo 4521, Petoskey 4522, Pokagon 4523, Polk 4524, RNR 4527, **Rodney 4528**, Rordor 4529, Saddle 4530, Sage 4531, Saginaw 4532, Schalon 4534, Sebastian 4535, Shelden 4537, Shepherds 4538, Shoemaker 4539, Silverwing 4541, Skillman 4543, Spartan 4544, Spoelhof 4545, Stange 4546, Steelcase 4547, Stonisch 4548, Strosacker 4549, Sturgis 4550, Taubman 4553, Thewes 4554, Towsley 4557, **Tubergen 4559**, Tuktawa 4560, Tuscola 4562, Van Andel 4567, Van Elslander 4569, Van 4570, Van Noord 4571, VanderWeide 4572, Vaughan 4573, Von 4574, Wasserman 4576, Weatherwax 4577, Webber 4578, Wege 4579, Westerman 4582, Whirlpool 4583, Wickes 4585, Wilson 4588, Wilson 4589, Wolff 4590, Wolohan 4591, Wolters 4592, World 4594

Minnesota: 1988 4596, A Better 4598, AHS 4599, **Andersen 4601**, Andersen 4603, Andreas 4604, Andreas 4605, Athwin 4607, Bakken 4608, Beim 4609, Best 4612, Bethel 4613, **Better 4614**, Beverly 4615, Bigelow 4616, Blue 4618, Bremer 4620, Butler 4622, C C 4624, Campbell 4626, Cargill 4627, Carlson 4629, Central 4631, Cherbec 4634, Christianson 4635, Ciresi 4637, Cox 4639, Criss 4640, Davis 4642, Deluxe 4644, Driscoll 4648, Duluth 4649, Duluth 4649, Edwards 4653, Engdahl 4654, Evert 4655, Fiterman 4656, Foundation 4657, Frey 4658, **Fuller 4659**, General 4661, GHR 4664, Gostomski 4665, Graco 4666, Greystone 4668, Griggs 4669, Hageman 4670, Hallett 4671, Hardenbergh 4672, Hormel 4676, Hubbard 4678, Initiative 4679, Jennings 4680, Jewett 4682, Johnson 4683, Kelley 4686, Kopp 4688, Koskovich 4690, Land 4691, Leuthold 4695, Lilly 4696, Lored 4697, Luther 4698, Maas 4699, Manitou 4701, Marbrook 4702, Mardag 4703, McCarthy 4705, McGlynn 4706, McNeely 4710, McVay 4711, **Medtronic 4712**, Minneapolis 4714, Minnesota 4715, Minnesota 4716, Mitchell 4717, Mithun 4718, **Mosaic 4722**, Neilson 4725, Nicholson 4728, Opus 4731, Ordean 4732, Oswald 4735, Pagel 4736, Patch 4737, Phillips 4740, Phillips 4741, Pine 4742, Piper 4743, Poepl 4744, Pohlad 4745, Prospect 4747, RBC 4748, Red Wing 4749, Regis 4750, Remick 4751, Robins 4754, Rochester 4755, Sabes 4756, Saint Paul 4757, Schmidt 4758, Schulze 4760, Securian 4761, Shiebler 4762, Sieben 4763, Sit 4764, Sit 4765, Slaggie 4766, **St. Jude 4770**, Stepanek 4771, Sundet 4774, Target 4776, Taylor 4777, TCF 4778, TEAM 4779, **Toro 4780**, Valspar 4786, Veden 4787, Wallestad 4791, WCA 4795, Wedum 4796, Weesner 4797, Weiser 4798, Westcliff 4801, Weyerhaeuser 4803, Winona 4806, WSDC 4807

Mississippi: BancorpSouth 4812, BBB 4813, C Spire 4817, Chisholm 4818, Community 4820, CREATE 4822, Ergon 4824, Feild 4825, Gilmore 4828, Gulf 4830, Maddox 4834, McLean 4835, McRae 4836, Mississippi 4837, Mississippi 4839, Morgan 4840, Oakwood 4841, Riley 4844, Risen 4845, Walker 4849

Missouri: Albrecht 4850, Ameren 4851, American 4852, Anheuser 4853, Apex 4854, Ballmann 4858, Brauer 4860, Brown 4862, Brunner 4863, Burns 4866, Busch 4867, Carter 4868, Casey 4869, Centene 4870, Commerce 4871, Community 4872, Cruse 4877, Dierberg 4879, Dula 4881, Dunn 4882, Edison 4883, Edison 4884, Emerson 4885, Engelhardt 4886, Farber 4889, Fox 4892, Goldfarb 4895, Goppert 4896, Gottlieb 4897, Graybar 4898, Green 4900, H & R 4902, Hall 4905, Hallmark 4906, Hammons 4907, Hauck 4908, Hecker 4909, Holekamp 4910, Humphreys 4912, Interco 4914, Jones 4916, Kemper 4925, Kemper 4926, Kemper 4927, Laclede 4931, Ladner 4932, Laurie 4933, Lemons 4935, Lopata 4938, McDonnell 4940, McGee 4942, Millstone 4944, **Monsanto 4945**, Moulton 4946, Musgrave 4947, Oppenstein 4950, Orscheln 4951, Pershing 4952, Pershing 4953, Pettus 4954, Pillsbury 4955, Pillsbury 4956, Pott 4958, Pulitzer 4959, Reynolds 4961, Rhoden 4962, Rosewood 4964, Saint Louis 4966, Shaughnessy 4969, Shaw 4970, Shelter 4971, Smith 4974, Sosland 4975, Sosland 4977, Speas 4978, Speas 4979, Steward 4981, Stupp 4982, Stupp 4983, Taylor 4988, Ten 4989, Tilles 4991, Towle 4993, Trio 4994, Trulaske 4995, Truman 4996, Waldheim 4997, Ward 4998, Webb 4999, World 5002, Wornall 5003

Montana: Central 5006, Edwards 5008, First 5009, Gianforte 5010, Gilhousen 5011, Montana 5013, Oro 5014, Town 5016, Treacy 5017, Washington 5018, Whitefish 5019

Nebraska: Abbott 5020, Abel 5021, Acklie 5022, Ameritas 5023, Buckley 5026, Cooper 5031, Cope 5032, Dillon 5035, Eagle 5037, Family 5038, Fremont 5039, Grand Island 5044, Hamilton 5045, Hastings 5046, Hawks 5047, Heider 5048, Hirschfeld 5049, Hitchcock 5050, Holland 5051, Hubbard 5053, Kearney 5055, Kiewit 5056, Kiewit 5057, Kim 5058, Kimmel 5059, Lexington 5062, Lincoln 5063, Lozier 5065, Merrick 5067, Mid-Nebraska 5068, Mutual 5071, Omaha 5074, Phelps 5075, Robinson 5076, Rogers 5077, Ryan 5078, Sherwood 5081, Sokolof 5084, Storz 5086, Swanson 5087, Swanson 5088, Union 5090, Vetter 5091, Weitz 5092, Werner 5094, Wirth 5095, Woods 5096, York 5098, York 5098

Nevada: Adelson 5099, AJA 5100, Bretzlaff 5103, **Browning 5104**, Caesars 5106, Community 5108, Cord 5110, Crescere 5112, Crystal 5113, Doyle 5115, Engelstad 5117, Fairweather 5118, Gabelli 5120, Hawkins 5123, Keyser 5126, Lee 5127, Mallory 5129, Mathewson 5131, May 5132, Nevada 5134, NV 5136, O'Bannon 5137, Parasol 5138, Pennington 5139, Prim 5140, **Reynolds 5143**, Rochlin 5144, Ruvo 5145, Safe 5146, Sawyer 5147, Tam 5152, **Tang 5153**, Wells 5157

New Hampshire: Alexander 5162, Bean 5164, Cogswell 5167, **Fidelity 5170**, Haas 5174, Hunt 5177, Lindsay 5179, Malool 5180, New Hampshire 5182, Penates 5185, Schleyer 5188

New Jersey: Antz 5192, Atkinson 5195, Bacchetta 5198, Banbury 5200, Bard 5202, **Berrie 5206**, Bolger 5207, Borden 5209, Borgenicht 5210, Bouras 5211, Boye 5212, Broadridge 5214, Brotherton 5216, Brougher 5217, Brozowski 5218, C 5221, Cabin 5222, Campbell 5223, Catholic 5226, Clare 5230, Community 5232, Cooperman 5233, Cowles 5234, **Crane 5235**, Creamer 5236, Danellie 5237, D'Angelo 5238, De Nicola 5239, Dircks 5241, Dow 5244, Dunbar 5245, Eckerson 5246, Eisai 5249, Eisenberg 5250, Evans 5254, Fairbanks 5255, Falcon 5256, Fenwick 5259, Firestone 5260, Fournier 5264, Frankino 5266, Friedman 5268, Frohring 5269, Gagnon 5271, Galanta 5272, Gibson 5276, Gibson 5277, Goldberg 5279, Grassmann 5281, Gulton 5284, Gund 5285, Hahn 5288, Haines 5289, Hanson 5292, Harbourton 5293, Hawthorne 5295, Healthcare 5296, Hess 5298, Hickory 5299, Holmes 5302, Hugin 5308, Hummingbird 5309, Hyde 5310, **IDT 5311**, IGH 5312, Indian 5313, Ingersoll-Rand 5314, **International 5316**, Investors 5317, Isermann 5319, Jaffe 5320, JMP 5324, Jockey 5325, **Johnson 5326**, Kaplen 5330, Karma 5331, Katz 5332, Katz 5333, Kauffmann 5334, Kelly 5335, Kemmerer 5336, Kennedy 5337, Kirby 5340, Kish 5341, Klatskin 5342, Klingenstein 5343, Kolatch 5347, Kresa 5350, L.A.W. 5352, L.F.H. 5353, Lackner 5354, Large 5355, Lenzmeier 5358, Levin 5359, Levitt 5360, Levitt 5361, Lord 5365, Mack 5366, Mack 5367, Marcon 5369, Mario 5370, Martini 5372, McGraw 5376, MCJ 5377, McMullen 5378, **Merck 5379**, Merillat 5382, Messner 5383, Mosakowski 5387, Mushett 5388, OceanFirst 5394, Orange 5396, Orenstein 5397, OritaniBank 5398, Oster 5399, Palestroni 5400, Parker 5401, Pascale 5403, Phipps 5406, Plummer 5409, Point 5410, Princeton 5411, Provident 5414, **Ramapo 5419**, Roberts 5422, Roberts 5423, Roth 5426, Rowan 5427, Rummel 5430, Samaritan 5433, Sands 5435, Sandy 5436, **Sanofi 5437**, Sansom 5438, Schecter 5439, Schmidt 5440, Schumann 5441, Schwartz 5443, Scott 5445, **Segal 5446**, Seiden 5448, Shepherd 5451, Silver 5457, Silver 5458, Silverman 5459,

Simon, 5460, Smith 5461, Snyder 5462, South 5463, Stadler 5465, Strauss 5470, Subaru 5471, Sudler 5472, Syms 5475, Taub 5477, Tepper 5480, Touchpoint 5481, Turner 5482, Turrell 5483, Unilever 5484, Union 5485, United 5486, Vanech 5487, Victoria 5490, Wagner 5491, Wall 5492, **Wang 5495**, WebMD 5496, Weston 5499, Wicks 5500, Wilf 5502, Wilf 5503, Wilf 5504, Wishes 5506, **Yin 5507**, Zurs 5510

New Mexico: Albuquerque 5511, Altman 5513, Angelica 5514, Chase 5517, Delle 5518, Frost 5519, Hubbard 5523, Maddox 5528, McCune 5529, Phillips 5531, PNM 5532, Santa Fe 5533, Santa Fe 5533, Thornburg 5535, Yates 5537

New York: 291 5539, A Kinder 5542, A M 5543, Abeles 5544, **Abraham 5545**, Abrons 5546, Acquavella 5550, AD 5551, Adams 5552, Adelman 5554, Adelson 5555, Adirondack 5556, Adjmi 5557, Adjmi 5558, **AIG 5563**, AJG 5565, **Alavi 5566**, Albert 5567, Alexander 5568, Alfiero 5570, All 5572, Allen 5573, Allen 5574, Allyn 5575, Alper 5576, Alpern 5577, Altman 5579, Altman 5580, Altman 5581, Altschul 5582, Altus 5583, American 5587, **American 5588**, Ames 5591, Amicus 5592, Ammon 5593, Ammon 5594, Amsterdam 5595, Anderson 5596, Anderson 5597, Andor 5598, Androcles 5599, Appel 5603, Appleman 5604, Arbesfeld 5605, Arctos 5607, Aresty 5609, Aresty 5610, Armstrong 5613, Arnhold 5614, Arnow 5615, Aron 5616, Arrison 5618, **Ashner 5619**, Assurant 5621, Atlantic 5622, Auchincloss 5623, Avalon 5626, **AVI 5628**, Bachmann 5632, Badgeley 5633, Bahnik 5634, Baird 5636, Baker 5638, Baldwin 5639, Banfi 5641, Barker 5644, Barth 5648, Bass 5650, **Bat 5651**, Bayne 5653, Beker 5659, Belfer 5660, **Belvedere 5661**, **Benenson 5663**, Benenson 5665, Berkowitz 5669, Berne 5670, Bialkin 5673, Biddle 5674, Birkelund 5677, Bischoff 5678, Blank 5682, Block 5683, Blum 5686, **Bobst 5690**, Bogen 5694, Boisi 5695, Botwinick 5696, Bouncer 5697, Boxer 5698, Braddock 5701, Braka 5702, Branta 5703, Braufman 5704, Bravmann 5705, Bright 5710, **Bristol 5711**, Brodsky 5714, Bronfman 5716, **Bronfman 5717**, Brooklyn 5718, Brownington 5721, Brownstone 5722, Buck 5725, Bullitt 5728, Burch 5729, Burns 5732, Butler 5734, Butler 5735, Buttenwieser 5736, CAMBR 5741, Campbell 5742, Canary 5744, Carmel 5746, Carson 5748, Carvel 5749, Cattaraugus 5750, Caudill 5751, Cayre 5752, Cayre 5753, Cayre 5755, Central 5757, Century 5758, Chadwick 5760, Chaim 5761, Challenger 5762, Chatterjee 5765, Chautauqua 5766, Chazen 5767, Chernow 5771, Chiara 5775, Chiaroscuro 5776, CJM 5781, Ckew 5782, **Clark 5785**, Clark 5786, Clinton 5787, **CLRC 5789**, Coatue 5791, Cohn 5793, Colad 5794, Cole 5795, Colin 5797, Collins 5799, Community 5801, Community 5802, Community 5804, Community 5805, Community 5808, Conway 5811, Cooper 5812, Copper 5815, Corey 5816, Cornerstone 5817, Corning 5818, Corzine 5819, Coydog 5823, Cranaleith 5825, **Credit 5826**, Cross 5829, **Cummings 5832**, Cummings 5834, Curry 5836, Cushman 5837, Cypress 5839, D'Addario 5841, Daedalus 5842, D'Agostino 5843, Damial 5844, Dauman 5849, Davenport 5850, Davidson 5851, Davis 5853, **de Rothschild 5857**, Dean 5858, **Debbane 5859**, Debs 5860, Dechman 5862, Decker 5863, Deerfield 5865, deForest 5866, Dejana 5868, Demartini 5872, DeMatteis 5873, Derfner 5874, **Deutsche 5876**, Devlin 5877, Dewar 5879, Diamond 5880, Diker 5883, Diller 5884, Dillon 5885, DiMenna 5886, DiMino 5887, Dobkin 5891, **Doherty 5893**, Dolan 5895, Dolan 5896, Donner 5899, Doolittle 5901, **Doty 5902**, Dove 5903, Dove 5904, Dow 5906, Dowling 5907, Downs 5908, Dreams 5909, Dreitzer 5910, Drexler 5911, Dreyfus 5913, **Duke 5919**, Durst 5922, Dyson 5923, E & SS 5924, East 5925, Eastern 5927, Eberstadt-Kuffner 5929, Edelman 5930, Edelman 5932, Edelstein 5933, Edlow 5935, Edouard 5936, Effron 5938, EHA 5940, Ehrenkranz 5941, Einhorn 5943, Emerson 5950, Emes 5951, Englander 5955, Enterprise 5956, Epstein 5958, ESL 5960, Eveillard 5963, Everett 5964, Falcon 5966, Falconwood 5967, Farash 5969, Farber 5970, Fascitelli 5971, Feil 5973, Fernleigh 5975, Fifth 5976, **FIMF 5977**, Finneran 5978, Fischer 5981, Fishoff 5984, Fitt 5985, Flaherty 5986, Flom 5989, **Flowers 5990**, Ford 5993, **Ford 5994**, Forst 5997, **Foundation 6001**, **Foundation 6002**, Foundation 6004, Frankfort 6010, French 6013, Frey 6014, Fribourg 6015, **Fridolin 6016**, Friedberg 6017, Friedman 6019, Friedman 6021, Friedman 6022, Ganzi 6034, **GBRG 6036**, Gebbie 6038, Gellert 6040, Gerry 6044, Gerson 6047, Gibbs 6048, Gifford 6049, **Gitenstein 6055**, **Glades 6056**, Glens Falls 6057, Glickenhaus 6058, Goldberg 6061, Goldberg 6062, Goldie 6063, **Goldman 6064**, Goldman 6065, Goldman 6068, Goldman 6069, Goldsmith 6071, Goldstein 6074, Goldstein 6076, Golkin 6078, Golub 6079, Gorman 6083, Gorter 6084, Gould 6089, Grace 6090, Grateful 6094, Grauer 6095, Grayer 6096, Great 6097, Greater 6098, Green 6101, Greenberg 6102, Greene 6103, Griffin 6108, Grigg 6109, Gross 6110, Grubman 6113, Gruss 6114, Gural 6117, Gurwin 6118, **Gutfleish 6120**, Hagedorn 6128, Haje 6129, Hansen 6130, Harary 6131, Harbor 6132, **Harriman 6136**, Harriman 6137, Harris 6138, Harris 6139, Harris 6141, Harrison 6142, Haseltine 6146, **Hayden 6149**, Healey 6152, Hearst 6154, **Hearst 6155**, **Hearst 6156**, Heisman 6159, Helmsley 6160, Hendel 6161, Henle 6162, Hermione 6163, Herrnstein 6165, Hershaft 6167, Hettinger 6170, Heyer 6171, Hirsch 6175, Hochfelder 6177, Hochstein 6178, Hoerle 6180, Hoffman 6182, Hollyhock 6183, Holtzmann 6184, Horowitz 6186, Horwitz 6188, Howard 6189, Huberfeld 6190, Hugoton 6194, Hultquist 6195, Hunter 6196, Hunter 6197, Hurdus 6198, Hurford 6199, Hurst 6200, Hutchins 6202, **IBM 6203**, IF 6205, IFF 6206, **IIMI 6207**, Inmaat 6209, Inzlicht 6212, Island 6215, Israel 6216, Jacobson 6219, Jacoff 6220, JAF 6221, **Jaffe 6222**, Jaharis 6223, JAM 6224, Jana 6225, Jandon 6226, JCT 6227, Joelson 6232, Johnson 6233, Johnson 6237, Johnson 6238, Johnson 6239, Johnson 6240, Johnson 6241, Kadrovach 6248, Kanas 6249, **Kaplan 6252**, Kapnick 6253, Karmazin 6254, Katz 6255, Katz 6257, Katzenberger 6258, Kaufman 6259, Kautz 6260, Kaylie 6263, Kazickas 6264, Kearns 6265, Keet 6266, Kellogg 6269, Kemp 6272, Kennedy 6274, Kent 6275, Kimmelman 6282, King 6283, Kingdon 6284, Kinney 6285, Klee 6286, **Klein 6287**, Klingenstein 6293, Knapp 6296, Knipe 6297, Knox 6299, Kraus 6305, Kravis 6306, Kriendler 6309, Kuflik 6311, Kurz 6314, Kushel 6315, Laffont 6319, Lambert 6321, Landegger 6323, Landy 6324, Lanza 6329, Lauder 6334, Laurents/Hatcher 6338, Lear 6341, Lee 6343, Leeds 6344, Leffell 6345, Lehman 6346, Leibowitz 6348, **Leir 6349**, Lemberg 6350, Lenna 6352, Lerner 6353, Leshkowitz 6354, Letterman 6356, Leventhal 6357, Levine 6360, Levy 6362, Levy 6363, Lincoln 6368, Lindenbaum 6370, Lindner 6372, Lindsay 6373, Link 6375, Lipp 6377, Lisabeth 6378, Litwin 6380, Liu 6382, Loeb 6383, Loeb 6384, Loeb 6385, Loews 6388, Longwell 6391, Lopatin 6392, Lostand 6394, Lubo 6396, Luckow 6399, **M & T 6406**, M&E 6407, **M.A.C. 6408**, Ma'asim 6409, Mack 6411, Mack 6412, MacMillan 6413, Maguire 6415, Maguire 6416, Mai 6417, Mailman 6419, Mailman 6420, Malkin 6422, Mallah 6424, Marcus 6428, Mariposa 6429, Mark 6430, Marks 6432, Marlon 6433, Marron 6435, Martin 6440, Marx 6441, Marx 6442, Marx 6443, Massry 6444, MBIA 6451, McCann 6453, McCarthy 6454, McCarthy 6456, McClelland 6457, McCormick 6458, McDonnell 6459, McGonagle 6460, McGraw 6461, McGraw 6462, McManus 6463, McNulty 6465, Mee 6467, Meehan 6468, **Mehra 6469**, Melly 6471, **Menschel 6473**, Mercer 6474, Mercy 6475, **MetLife 6479**, Meyer 6481, Michaels 6482, Milliken 6487, **Mitsubishi 6490**, Mitsui 6491, Mnuchin 6493, Model 6495, Monell 6497, Monteforte 6498, **Moody's 6499**, Moore 6500, Moore 6501, Moore 6502, Moore 6504, Moore 6505, Morgan 6506, Morgan 6507, Morse 6509, Morse 6510, Moses 6511, Mule 6513, Mullen 6515, Mullen 6516, Murphy 6517, Mutual 6518, Naddisy 6520, Nadler 6521, **Nash 6525**, National 6526, Neidich 6534, Neiman 6535, New Brook 6540, New Yankee 6542, New York 6543, New York 6544, New York 6546, New York 6547, Newhouse 6550, **New 6551**, Newman 6553, Newman 6555, Nias 6556, Nicholas 6557, Nicholson 6558, Nola 6562, Northern 6567, Northfield 6568, Nuhn 6572, NYSE 6573, Och 6575, O'Connor 6578, Ohrstrom 6582, Ohrstrom 6583, Oishei 6584, **Olayan 6585**, Olive 6587, Olshan 6588, Omer 6590, O'Neill 6591, Oppenheim 6594, O'Reilly 6595, Orentreich 6596, Orthwein 6597, O'Shea 6599, O'Sullivan 6601, O'Toole 6602, **Ottaway 6603**, Overlook 6607, Palette 6609, Panaphil 6612, Pannonia 6613, Parsons 6618, Paulson 6620, **PBHP 6622**, Pearson 6623, Peco 6624, Pels 6625, Perelman 6628, **Pershing 6629**, Phillips 6637, Picotte 6639, Plant 6645, PLM 6647, Plum 6648, Plumeri 6649, Pope 6653, Price 6657, Price 6658, Propp 6662, Providence 6664, Pulier 6665, Pumpkin 6666, Purchase 6667, Raether 6673, Randolph 6677, Rattner 6680, Rechler 6682, Red 6683, **Reed 6684**, Regals 6685, Renfield 6688, Resnick 6690, Resource 6691, Review 6692, Rice 6696, Rich 6697, Richards 6699, Richardson 6700, Richenthal 6701, Richmond 6703, Richmond 6704, **Ridgefield 6705**, Riggio 6709, Riley 6710, Ritter 6712, Riversville 6713, Rochester 6722, Rohatyn 6729, Rose 6732, Rose 6735, Rose 6736, Rose 6737, Rose 6738, Rosen 6741, Rosenblatt 6745, Rosenblum 6746, Rosenfeld 6747, Rosenthal 6749, Rosner 6752, Rowan 6758, RTS 6760, Rubin 6766, Rudin 6767, Rudin 6768, Ruffin 6770, Rupp 6771, **Ruth 6772**, Sabin 6775, Sagner 6783, Salomon 6785, Saltz 6786, Saltz 6787, Samuels 6788, Sandler 6789, Sands 6790, Sandy 6791, Santa 6792, Santmann 6793, **Saper 6794**, Save 6799, Schaffner 6800, Schenker 6803, Scherman 6804, Schiff 6805, Schlobach 6806, Schlosstein 6807, Schmitt 6808, Schnurmacher 6809, Schwartz 6814, Schwartz 6815, Schwartz 6816, Schwartz 6817, Schwartz 6819, Scully 6822, SDA 6823, Sebonack 6826, Seiler 6828, Select 6829, Semlitz 6831, Shanken 6837, Sheldon 6841, Shipley 6843, Siebens 6853, Silberstein 6854, Silverman 6855, Silverstein 6856, Silverweed 6857, Simon 6859, Singer 6862, Sitchin 6865, Skirball 6869, **SMBC 6873**, Smith 6875, Snowdon 6879, Snyder 6880, SO 6881, Sohn 6884, Solomon 6885, Soros 6889, Soros 6890, Soros 6891, Source 6893, Speyer 6896, Spilker 6897, Spingold 6899, Sprague 6901, Stainman 6906, Stanton 6907, Stanton 6908, Starfish 6909, Starker 6910, **Starr 6911**, Staten 6912, Steele 6915, Steffens 6917, Stein 6918, Steinberg 6921, Steinhardt 6923, **Stempel 6925**, Stern 6928, Sternberg 6930, Stiefel 6931, Stony 6933, **Straus 6934**, Stringer 6935, Strypemonde 6936, Stuart 6937, Stulman 6938, Stuntz 6939, Sugarman 6940, Sumitomo 6943, **Summerfield 6944**, Summers 6945, Sun 6946, Sutton 6950, Swartz 6954, Swieca 6955, Sykes 6957, Tahari 6958, Tai 6960, Tananbaum 6962, Tarica 6965, TE 6966, Teagle 6967, Terra 6971, Textor 6973, Theobald 6974, Thompson 6975, Tiger 6979, Tiger 6980, Tisch 6986, Tisch 6987, Tisch 6988, Tisch 6989, Sussman 6990, Tisch 6992, Tomorrow 6995, Tova 6998, Tower 6999, Triad 7005, Troy 7006, Truman 7007, Trump 7008, Tuft 7011, Turn 7012, Turner 7013, **Unbound 7016**, Unterberg 7021, Uphill 7022, Van Cleave 7025, Vernon 7026, **Vicente 7029**, Vidda 7030, Viola 7032, **Vital 7033**, Vogelstein 7034, Volpert 7036, von der Heyden 7037, Wachenheim 7039, Wachtell, 7040, Walbridge 7041, Wallach 7044, Walter 7046, Warburg 7048, Warren 7054, Water 7056,

Waterston 7057, Wegman 7061, Weil, 7062, Weiler 7063, Weinberg 7065, Weinberg 7066, Weinberg 7067, Weir 7069, Weisberg 7070, Weissman 7071, Weissman 7072, Wells 7073, Wendt 7074, Werblow 7076, Western 7078, Widgeon 7081, Windmill 7089, Winters 7094, Witten 7095, WLC 7096, Wohl 7097, Wolk 7099, Woodcock 7101, **Woodshouse 7102**, Wright 7104, WSB 7105, **Youths' 7112**, Zankel 7114, Zegar 7116, Zeides 7119, Ziff 7122, Ziff 7123, Zilkha 7125, Zuckerberg 7128

North Carolina: 25th 7131, Adams 7132, Adams 7133, Anonymous 7135, **Bank 7139**, Baruch 7140, Bate 7141, Baxter 7142, BB&T 7143, BB&T 7144, Belk 7147, Belk 7148, BIN 7151, Bissell 7152, Blumenthal 7154, Bolick 7155, Branan 7157, Braswell 7158, Brauninger 7159, Broyhill 7160, Bryan 7161, Campbell 7168, Cannon 7169, Cape Fear 7170, Capital 7171, **Carlson 7172**, Camrick 7173, Cemala 7174, Chatham 7175, Community 7178, Community 7180, Community 7181, Community 7182, Cumberland 7184, Curran 7185, Dalton 7187, Davis 7189, Dickson 7192, Dover 7194, Duke 7196, Finley 7199, Flow 7200, Foundation 7202, Ghidotti 7206, Giles 7208, Gipson 7209, Glass 7210, Glenn 7211, Goodnight 7212, Goodrich 7213, Gordon 7214, Gratis 7216, Gunzenhauser-Chapin 7218, Haley 7219, Hallowell 7220, Hanes 7221, Harris 7223, Harvey 7225, Hayes 7227, High Point 7231, Hillsdale 7232, Humphrey 7236, Hunter 7238, Ireland 7239, Jolley 7240, Jones 7242, Jordan 7243, Keith 7247, Kramer 7250, Kulynych 7251, Kulynych 7252, Leever 7253, Legatus 7254, Levine 7255, Love 7258, Luddy 7259, McCausland 7262, McMichael 7265, Merancas 7267, Murphy 7270, Neviaser 7271, North Carolina 7273, Odell 7277, Olin 7279, Palm Beach 7281, Perkins 7282, Phillips 7284, Piedmont 7285, Plansoen 7286, Polk 7287, Post 7289, Prickett 7290, Provident 7291, Reynolds 7297, Reynolds 7299, Richardson 7301, Short 7311, Simpson 7312, Slick 7313, Smith 7315, Smith 7317, Snyder's-Lance 7318, Spangler 7320, State 7321, Stewards 7322, Strauss 7323, **Sunshine 7324**, Symmes 7325, Tannenbaum 7326, Triangle 7328, Van Every 7329, Van Houten 7330, Vanderbilt 7331, VF 7332, Vickar 7333, Weaver 7335, Wheeler 7336, Wilson 7338, Winslow 7339, Winston-Salem 7340, Woodson 7342, Woodward 7343, Wos 7345, Zinc 7349

North Dakota: Fargo 7351, Leach 7353, MDU 7354, Myra 7355, North Dakota 7357, Stern 7360, Wanzek 7361

Ohio: **58 7362**, A Good 7363, Abar 7364, Abington 7365, AK Steel 7366, Akron 7367, American 7368, American 7369, Ames 7371, Anderson 7372, Andersons 7374, Androse 7375, Ar-Hale 7376, Ariel 7377, Ashland 7378, Ashtabula 7379, Austin 7380, Bailey 7381, Berry 7386, **Bingham 7387**, Boutell 7388, Broussard 7389, Brown 7390, Bruening 7391, Building 7394, Burleigh 7395, Butler 7396, Cafaro 7397, Castellini 7399, Charities 7400, Children's 7401, Christ 7402, Christman 7403, Cincinnati 7404, Cleveland 7406, Cliffs 7407, Clouse 7408, Cole 7410, Columbus 7411, Community 7412, Community 7413, Community 7414, Community 7415, Community 7417, Conway 7419, Corbin 7420, Dater 7426, Dayton 7428, Dayton 7429, DBJ 7430, Delaware 7431, Deuble 7433, DeWine 7434, Diebold 7437, Dodero 7438, Dorn 7439, Dornette 7440, Durell 7441, **Eaton 7442**, Emery 7443, Erie 7444, Fairfield 7445, Fairmount 7446, Farmer 7447, Fasenmyer 7448, Ferguson 7450, Ferry 7451, Fifth 7452, Findlay 7453, Firman 7454, FirstEnergy 7455, Fleming 7458, Fox 7461, France 7462, Friedlander 7463, Frost 7464, GAR 7465, Gardner 7466, Geis 7467, Gelbman 7469, Gerlach 7471, Goatie 7472, Green 7473, Gund 7477, Gund 7478, H.C.S. 7479, Haile, 7480, Hamilton 7481, Haslinger 7482, Hatton 7483, Hayfields 7485, Heiman 7486, Home 7489, Honda 7490, Hoover 7491, Horvitz 7493, Hudson 7496, Hutton 7500, IHS 7501, Jacobs 7505, Jegs 7507, Jenkins 7508, Jochum 7513, Jordan 7514, Kalberer 7515, Kaplan 7516, Kersten 7519, **Kettering 7520**, Kettering 7521, Kettering 7522, KeyBank 7523, Kiebach 7524, Kimble 7526, Kulas 7532, LaValley 7535, Lehner 7536, Levin 7539, Licking 7540, Lincoln 7541, Llewellyn 7543, Lozick 7545, Lubrizol 7546, Luedeking 7547, Luther 7548, LZ 7549, Maltz 7553, Mather 7559, Mayerson 7561, McBride 7562, McGregor 7564, McLane 7566, Mercer 7567, Meshewa 7568, Miami 7569, Middletown 7570, Miller 7571, Miniger 7572, MJH 7573, Montei 7574, Moores 7576, Morgan 7577, Morrison 7580, Motorists 7581, Murch 7582, Murdough 7583, Murphy 7584, Muskingum 7585, National 7586, Nationwide 7587, New Albany 7589, Nippert 7590, NiSource 7591, **Noble 7592**, Nonneman 7593, Nord 7594, Nord 7595, Nordson 7596, Northern 7597, Ohio 7599, **OMNOVA 7601**, Orr 7604, Outcalt 7606, Owens 7607, Park 7609, Park 7610, Parker 7611, **Patterson 7613**, Perkins 7615, Philips 7619, Piqua 7620, Price 7622, Pulley 7624, R.T. 7625, Reeves 7627, Richland 7630, Riley 7632, Ritter 7633, Safelite 7638, Saint 7639, Salem 7641, Samaritan 7642, Sankey 7643, **Sapirstein-Stone-Weiss 7644**, Schiff 7648, Schlink 7650, Schmidlapp 7651, Schott 7652, Schott 7653, Scioto 7657, Scripps 7659, Sherwin-Williams 7661, Silk 7663, Sisler 7664, Smith 7667, Smith 7668, Smucker 7669, Spaulding 7670, Springfield 7671, Stark 7673, State 7674, Stefanski 7675, Stranahan 7678, Sutphin 7679, Talmage 7680, Tiffin 7682, Tippit 7685, Toledo 7686, Toulmin 7687, Troy 7688, TSF 7690, Twenty 7692, Veale 7694, Wade 7697, Wadsworth 7698, Wagler 7699, Warmenhoven 7701, Warrington 7703, Wayne 7704, Weary 7706, Weisbrod 7708, Wellman 7709, Western 7710, Westfield 7711, **Wexner 7713**, White 7715, Wilks 7716, Wodecroft 7717, Wohlgemuth 7718, Wolfe 7719, Wuliger 7722, Youngstown 7723, Zembrodt 7724

Oklahoma: Adams 7725, American 7728, Bartlesville 7731, Bartlett 7732, Bernsen 7733, Bovaird 7735, Bowen 7736, Brown 7737, Browning-Kimball 7738, Chapman 7739, Collins 7741, Communities 7742, Community 7743, Coretz 7744, Crawley 7746, Dobson 7747, Flint 7750, Frank 7752, Gaylord 7753, Hardesty 7756, Harris 7757, Hille 7759, Inasmuch 7760, Jackson 7761, Kaiser 7763, Kerr 7764, Ketchum 7765, Lobeck 7768, Lyon 7769, Mabee 7770, Masonic 7771, McCasland 7772, McCrory 7773, McGill 7775, McMahon 7776, Meinders 7777, Miller 7778, Noble 7780, Oklahoma City 7781, Oklahoma 7782, ONEOK 7783, Oxley 7784, Oxley 7785, Puterbaugh 7786, Records 7788, Robinson 7789, Sarkeys 7793, **Schusterman 7794**, Share 7795, Simmons 7796, Southern 7798, Stephenson 7799, Stevens 7800, Stuart 7802, Tandy 7803, Temple 7805, Titus 7806, Tulsa 7807, Viersen 7808, Warren 7809, Waters 7810, Williams 7814, Yot 7817, Zarrow 7818, Zarrow 7819, Zarrow 7820

Oregon: Autzen 7823, Bauman 7824, Braemar 7826, Campbell 7830, Carpenter 7831, Chambers 7832, Clark 7834, Collins 7836, Dieringer 7839, **Eiting 7840**, Fjarli 7842, Fjarli 7843, **Foreign 7846**, Glory 7847, Hull 7852, J.F.R. 7854, Jackson 7855, Jeld 7856, John 7857, Jubitz 7859, Macdonald 7866, Meyer 7870, Mission 7873, Oregon 7876, PacifiCorp 7877, PacificSource 7878, Pastega 7879, PGE 7881, Poznanski 7882, Randall 7883, Renaissance 7884, Salem 7885, Schnitzer 7887, Schnitzer 7888, Swindells 7892, Templeton 7895, Tucker 7896, Tykeson 7897, Vibrant 7898, Woodard 7899

Pennsylvania: 1675 7903, Air 7907, Alexander 7910, Ametek 7913, Angelakis 7914, Aqua 7917, Arcadia 7918, Arete 7919, Armstrong 7921, Armstrong 7922, Asplundh 7923, Avs 7924, Baker 7925, Barra 7928, Bayer 7932, Beatty 7933, Beaver 7934, Benedum 7935, Beneficial 7936, Berkman 7938, Biesecker 7941, Birmingham 7942, Blanchard 7944, **BNY 7945**, BNY 7946, Bozzone 7948, Brickman 7949, Briggs 7950, Britton 7951, Brodsky 7952, Brooks 7953, Brossman 7954, Buck 7955, Buncher 7957, Burke 7958, Burke 7959, Campbell 7960, **Cardone 7964**, Carnahan 7965, **Carnegie 7966**, Cassett 7969, CentiMark 7970, Central 7972, Centre 7973, Century 7974, Cestone 7976, Charter 7977, Chester 7979, CIGNA 7981, Claneil 7982, Clapp 7983, Clayman 7984, Cochran 7985, Colket 7987, Colonial 7988, Community 7990, Community 7991, Connelly 7995, Cooper 7997, Cotswold 7999, Coulson 8000, Crels 8002, Davenport 8003, Degenstein 8008, Dietrich 8010, Dolfinger 8013, Dollar 8014, Donahue 8015, Drumcliff 8016, DSF 8017, Eden 8021, Elias 8022, Erie 8026, Erlbaum 8027, ESSA 8028, Eustace 8029, Farber 8032, Federated 8033, Fieldstone 8038, Fine 8039, First 8040, First 8041, FISA 8043, FISA 8043, Foundation 8046, Fourjay 8047, Franklin 8048, **Frick 8049**, Garfield 8052, Gerber 8054, Giant 8055, Graham 8065, Grass 8066, Grass 8068, Gray 8069, Greenfield 8072, Gunterberg 8073, Head 8081, Hecht 8082, **Heinz 8083**, Helen's 8087, Henkels 8089, Herr 8090, Hillman 8093, Hodge 8095, Hopwood 8096, Hoverter 8097, Hoyt 8098, Hughes 8099, Hunt 8100, Hurd 8101, Huston 8102, Huston 8103, Hutton 8104, Independence 8107, Jackson 8110, Janssen 8111, Jerlyn 8112, Jordan 8114, Katz 8117, Kavanagh 8118, Keystone 8122, Kind 8125, King 8126, Kinsley 8127, Kline 8128, Kline 8129, Kunkel 8133, La Vea 8134, Lancaster 8135, Lehigh Valley 8136, Lenfest 8137, Leonard 8139, Lily 8141, Lindback 8142, Linlundh 8143, Lipsitz 8144, **Little 8145**, Lomax 8148, Lutron 8151, Luzerne 8152, Mandell 8153, Maplewood 8154, Mason 8157, Massey 8158, McCausland 8159, McCune 8160, McCune 8161, McCutchen 8162, McFeely 8163, McGinley 8164, McKinney 8168, Mellon 8172, Mellon 8173, Mengle 8174, Mericle 8176, Metcalf 8178, Miller 8180, Miller 8181, Miller 8183, MKM 8185, Morgan 8187, Mullen 8190, Musser 8191, Nararo 8193, Nichols 8197, North 8199, Northwest 8200, Novotny 8202, O'Toole 8207, Oxford 8208, Palumbo 8209, Pangborn 8210, Pangborn 8211, Peirce 8215, Penn 8217, Peoples 8218, Perelman 8219, Pew 8220, Philadelphia 8221, Phillips 8222, Phoenixville 8223, Pierce 8224, Pine 8226, Piper 8227, Plankenhorn 8229, PNC 8230, Pond 8231, Posner 8233, **PPG 8235**, PTS 8238, Public 8239, Raab 8242, Ranger 8243, Rees 8245, Roberts 8250, Roberts 8251, Rohrer 8252, Rosenstiel 8254, Ross 8255, Rubin 8257, Russell 8258, Saint 8260, Saligman 8261, Saltsgiver 8262, Salvaggio 8263, Sand 8264, Scheller 8268, Schenck 8269, Schieffelin 8270, Scholler 8273, Schroth 8274, Scranton 8275, Sedwick 8276, Shaffer 8281, **Shiloh 8283**, Simmons 8285, Smith 8287, Smock 8290, Snider 8292, Springbank 8293, Stabler 8294, Stackpole 8295, Staunton 8296, Stein 8297, Steinman 8299, Steinman 8300, Stern 8301, Stratton 8304, Strelsin 8306, Stuart 8307, Sunoco 8308, Surgala 8309, **Susquehanna 8310**, Taylor 8311, **Tecovas 8312**, Thornedge 8315, Toll 8317, Trexler 8320, Turner 8321, Tyler 8322, Ujala 8323, United 8325, Vanguard 8327, Washington 8332, West 8334, Wheeler 8335, Wiegand 8337, Wilson 8341, Wismer 8343, Withington 8344, Wolf 8345, Wyomissing 8350, York 8351

Rhode Island: Amica 8356, Biogen 8363, Buehler 8364, Capewell 8365, Capewell 8367, Carter 8368, Champlin 8370, Charlesmead 8371, Charlton 8372, Citizens 8374, Corning 8376, Crary, 8377, Cuno 8378, Daniels 8380, De Ramel 8381, Dexter 8382, Fain 8388, **Feinstein 8391**, **FM 8393**, Greene 8398, **Grinnell 8399**, Guth 8400, Harris 8402, Hoche-Scofield 8405, HPB 8407, Kaplan 8409, Kimball 8410, Knoop 8411, Koonce 8412, M. 8414, Manning 8415, McAdams 8416, McNeil 8418, Murray 8421, Nelson 8422, Newport 8423, Noonan 8424, Rhode Island 8429, Salem

8434, Scrooby 8435, Steadley 8442, Textron 8446, TriMix 8448, van Beuren 8449, Wille 8451, Woodward 8453

South Carolina: Abney 8454, Arkwright 8456, Bailey 8458, Bruce 8461, Campbell 8465, Canal 8466, Cassels 8467, Central 8468, Ceres 8469, Chester 8470, Coastal 8472, Community 8474, Community 8475, Daniel 8476, Gibbs 8480, Graham 8481, Hipp 8483, Hopewell 8484, Inman 8485, Montgomery 8487, Patterson 8489, Phifer 8491, Post 8492, Reams 8493, **ScanSource 8495**, Smith 8498, Smith 8499, Sonoco 8500, Spartanburg 8501, Speedwell 8503, TSC 8506, Yaschik 8509, Zucker 8510

South Dakota: Black 8511, Branches 8512, Dakota 8514, Hofer 8515, Larson 8516, Nylen 8517, **Opus 8518**, Raft 8519, Robinson 8520, Sioux Falls 8521, South Dakota 8522, Vucurevich 8524

Tennessee: Adams 8525, Adams 8526, American 8528, Assisi 8530, Atticus 8531, Ayers 8532, Beaman 8534, Bridgestone 8537, Briggs 8538, Campbell 8539, Charis 8542, Children's 8543, CIC 8546, Clayton 8547, Community 8548, Community 8549, Community 8550, Cook 8552, Curb 8554, Dugas 8559, Eastman 8561, Elgin 8562, Eskind 8563, First 8565, Frist 8567, Frist 8568, Gatton 8571, Hamico 8576, Haslam 8580, Haslam 8581, **International 8585**, Johnson 8588, Johnson's 8590, Kharis 8591, Lansky 8594, Latimer 8595, Lazarus 8596, Lebovitz 8597, Lewis 8598, Martin 8604, Martin 8605, Martin 8606, Massey 8607, Master's 8608, Melkus 8609, Memphis 8610, Midler 8611, Osborne 8614, Plough 8615, Poplar 8616, Provision 8619, Regal 8622, Sasco 8623, Smith 8628, Sparks 8629, Speer 8630, T & T 8632, Temple 8633, Tennessee 8634, Thompson 8635, Thompson 8636, Tucker 8638, Turner 8639, Turner 8640, Turner 8641, Wallace 8642, Washington 8643, Wilson 8645

Texas: 1687 8647, **A Glimmer 8649**, Abell 8650, Adams 8652, Alcon 8655, Alkek 8657, Allison 8659, Amarillo 8660, Anderson 8664, Anderson 8665, Andrews 8667, Angela 8669, Arena 8670, Armentrout 8671, Arnold 8673, AT&T 8675, Austin 8676, **Baker 8679**, Baron 8682, Barr 8683, Bass 8687, Bass 8690, Beal 8696, Beasley 8698, Belin 8699, Bergman 8703, BNSF 8706, **Bolivar 8708**, Bookout 8709, Booth 8711, Booth 8712, Booth 8713, Bosarge 8715, **Bovay 8716**, Bowling 8717, **BP 8718**, Branch 8720, Brentwood 8723, Bridges 8725, Bridwell 8726, Broughton 8729, Brown 8730, Brown 8731, Brownsville 8733, Brumley 8734, Burnett 8737, C.I.O.S. 8740, Cailloux 8741, Cain 8744, Cain 8745, Cameron 8747, **Caris 8749**, Carter 8752, Carter 8753, Cash 8754, Castex 8755, CEMEX 8757, CFP 8758, CH 8759, Chaparral 8760, Chapman 8761, Chasdrew 8762, Christian 8763, Clayton 8765, Clements 8766, Clements 8767, Coastal 8768, Cockrell 8770, Collins 8771, Collins 8772, Communities 8773, Community 8774, Community 8775, Community 8776, Community 8777, Constantin 8778, Cowden 8782, Cowden 8783, Cox 8784, Crane 8788, Crook 8790, Cullen 8792, Dallas 8795, Davidson 8797, Davis 8799, Davis 8800, Day 8801, De Llano 8802, Dickson-Allen 8806, Diener 8807, Doswell 8814, Duda 8815, Durham 8817, Eady 8818, East 8819, Eckel 8821, Ed 8822, Edwards 8823, Edwards 8824, El Paso 8825, Ellwood 8827, Embrey 8828, Engler 8830, Enrico 8831, **ExxonMobil 8833**, Ezcorp 8834, Fain 8835, Family 8836, Farish 8838, Fasken 8839, Favrot 8842, Feldman 8843, Fikes 8844, Finger 8845, Fisch 8846, Fish 8848, Fleming 8849, Fluor 8851, FMH 8852, Fondren 8853, Ford 8854, Franklin 8856, Fruhman 8858, Gale 8859, Gallagher 8860, Gayden 8861, Genecov 8862, George 8863, GHS Foun 8865, Glasscock 8867, Gonsoulin 8869, Gorman 8872, Greater 8873, Greathouse 8874, Greathouse 8875, H.E.B. 8879, Haggerty 8881, Halbert 8882, Hall 8883, Halliburton 8884, Halsell 8885, Halsell 8886, Hamill 8887, Hamman 8888, Hawkins 8895, Hawn 8896, Heavenly 8897, Heavin 8898, Hebert 8899, Henderson 8900, Henderson 8901, Herd 8902, Hersh 8903, Hershey 8904, Herzstein 8905, Hillcrest 8909, Hirsch 8910, Hobby 8911, Hoblitzelle 8912, Hoglund 8913, Holthouse 8915, **Houston 8916**, Houston 8917, Howell 8918, Hudson 8919, Huffington 8920, Hunt 8922, Jamail 8928, Jamail 8929, Janszen 8930, **Jenesis 8932**, **Jiv 8933**, JKJ 8934, JKL 8935, Johnson 8937, Johnson 8938, Johnson 8939, Johnson 8941, Jones 8942, Jones 8943, Jones 8944, Jonesville 8946, Justin 8947, Kahng 8948, Kelleher 8951, Kempner 8952, Kennedy 8953, Kickapoo 8955, Kimberly 8957, Kinder 8958, King 8959, Kurth 8971, Lard 8972, Lebowitz-Aberly 8975, Lee 8977, Legett 8978, Lennox 8979, Levit 8982, Liatis 8983, Light 8984, Lightner 8985, Link 8986, Litman 8987, Littauer 8988, Live 8989, Looper 8990, Loose 8991, Lord 8992, Lowe 8993, Lubbock 8994, Lyman 8995, Lyons 8996, Madison 8997, Marsh 8999, **Marshall 9000**, Martinez 9003, Maverick 9005, Mayor 9007, Mays 9008, McCoy 9010, McCullough 9011, McGrath 9015, McIntyre 9016, McNutt 9018, Meadows 9019, Medallion 9020, Meredith 9023, Meyer 9024, MFI 9025, Miles 9026, Miller 9027, Miller 9028, Mitchell 9030, Moncrief 9031, Moody 9033, Moore 9034, Moore 9035, Morgan 9037, Morning 9040, Morris 9041, Morrow 9042, Murchison 9045, Murchison 9046, NAH 9047, Nape 9049, **Natem 9052**, Navarro 9054, **New Beginning 9057**, New Hope 9059, Newman 9061, Nightingale 9062, **Notsew 9064**, NuStar 9065, O'Connor 9066, O'Hare 9068, Once 9070, Onstead 9071, O'Quinn 9072, Orsinger 9073, Owen 9075, Owen 9076, Owen 9077, Owsley 9078, Partnership 9082, **Paso 9083**, Patton 9084, Payne 9086, Pema 9088, Penney 9089, Perkins 9090, Permian 9091, Perot 9092, Perot 9093, Pertusati 9094, Petrello 9096, Phillips 9097, Pickens 9099, Pollock 9103, Powell 9105, Prairie 9106, Priddy 9109, Prothro 9112, Pryor 9113, Puett 9114, Rachal 9117, Rainwater 9119, Ram 9120, Rapier 9121, Reaud 9124, Rees-Jones 9125, Reliant 9126, Rhodes 9129, Richardson 9130, Roach 9132, Robinson 9133, Rockjensen 9134, Rockwell 9135, Roddy-Holden 9136, Rogers 9137, Rosewood 9140, Rowling 9141, Saint 9144, San Angelo 9146, San Angelo 9147, San Antonio 9148, Sanchez 9150, Sanders 9152, Sangreal 9153, **Scaler 9155**, Scanlan 9156, Scharbauer 9157, Schepps 9158, Schollmaier 9159, Scurlock 9162, Seegers 9164, Sharp 9167, Shelton 9169, Shield 9170, Sidhu 9172, Simmons 9173, Simmons 9174, Simmons 9175, **Simonian 9176**, Simpson 9177, **Six 9178**, Smith 9179, Smith 9185, Smith 9187, Snyder 9188, Sooch 9189, Sowell 9192, Sparrow 9194, SS 9196, Stedman 9200, Stemmons 9201, Sterling 9202, Stern 9204, Stevens 9205, Strake 9208, Stuart 9209, Stumberg 9210, Sturgis 9211, Susman 9216, SWBC 9217, Swinney 9218, Talkington 9219, Tartaglino 9221, Temple 9223, Terry 9224, Texas 9227, Thomas 9231, Thomas 9232, Tijerina, 9234, **Tingari-Silverton 9235**, Trull 9240, Turner 9242, USAA 9245, Valero 9246, Vanberg 9247, Vaughan 9248, Vergara 9249, Waco 9251, Waggoner 9252, Wal 9254, Walsh 9256, Walter 9257, Ward 9258, Ware 9259, Weaver 9260, Welborn 9267, West 9269, **Westbury 9271**, Whalley 9272, Whitacre 9273, White 9274, Wichita 9277, Williams 9279, Wise 9285, Wolff 9286, Wood 9289, Woodforest 9290, Worley 9291, Wright 9293, Young 9295, Zachry 9296, Zale 9297, Zeller 9298, Zephyr 9299

Utah: ALSAM 9302, Bamberger 9305, Bastian 9306, Beesley 9307, Bertin 9308, Community 9311, Dee 9312, Doctorow 9314, Eccles 9317, Eccles 9318, Eccles 9319, Eccles 9320, GFC 9322, Gillmor 9323, Hall 9324, Kirk 9329, Lawson 9331, McCarthey 9332, My 9338, Noorda 9339, **Nu 9340**, Park 9341, Peery 9344, Peterson 9345, Price 9346, Quinney 9347, RLC 9348, Semnani 9350, Simmons 9351, Tanner 9352, Vivint 9354, Watkins 9356

Vermont: **Ben 9358**, Mill 9367, Pomerleau 9369, Sills 9371, Tarrant 9373, Three 9374, Vermont 9375, Waterwheel 9376

Virginia: Arlington 9384, Bangs-Russell 9386, Bansal 9387, Batten 9390, Breeden 9396, Cabell 9397, Cameron 9398, Camp 9399, CarMax 9401, Carrington, 9402, Carter 9403, Charlottesville 9405, Chiaramonte 9407, Community 9411, Community 9412, Community 9413, Community 9414, Community 9415, Dalis 9419, Danville 9420, Danville 9421, Dominion 9422, Easley 9424, Elmo 9425, English 9426, Estes 9427, Fife 9429, Folger 9431, Foster 9432, Fralin 9433, Fredericksburg 9436, Funger 9438, **Gannett 9439**, **Genworth 9441**, Gilliam 9442, Graham 9445, Guilford 9446, Gwathmey 9447, Hampton 9448, Harrison 9449, Herndon 9451, Hobbs 9454, Hylton 9455, Johnson 9458, Kellar 9461, Kogod 9464, Launders 9468, Love 9470, Luminescence 9473, Lynchburg 9474, Malek 9475, Mars 9477, Massey 9478, Maude 9480, MAXIMUS 9481, McGlothlin 9483, Memorial 9485, Millhiser 9486, Morgan, 9490, Newman 9493, NewMarket 9494, Nirman 9495, Norfolk 9496, Obici 9500, Olsson 9502, Owens 9503, Parsons 9504, Perry 9506, Perry 9507, Peterson 9508, Piedmont 9509, Rales 9513, Reynolds 9519, Rimora 9522, Robins 9524, **Scheidel 9528**, Scott 9529, Shearwater 9531, Smith 9532, Smith 9533, Snead 9536, Suffolk 9538, SunTrust 9539, Three 9541, Titmus 9543, Trehan 9544, United 9546, Universal 9548, Volgenau 9549, Wardle 9551, Washington 9552, **WestWind 9555**, Whitlock 9556, Williamsburg 9559, Wise 9560

Washington: Adams 9566, Allen 9567, Ames 9570, Anderson 9572, Aven 9575, Avista 9576, B&E 9577, Bainbridge 9578, Bamford 9580, Barton 9581, Benaroya 9583, Biller 9586, Blue 9588, Bradley 9589, Bushnell 9592, Cameron 9593, Cheney 9598, Colson 9601, Columbia 9602, Community 9603, Community 9604, Community 9604, Community 9605, Cowles 9607, Crystal 9608, Dimmer 9610, Eggnog 9613, Everett 9616, Evertrust 9617, Fabert 9618, First 9619, Foster 9621, Foundation 9623, Foundation 9623, Fuchs 9624, **Gates 9625**, Giuliani 9628, Glaser 9629, Grays 9631, Green 9632, Greenstein 9633, Haller 9635, Hanauer 9636, Harnish 9641, Harvest 9642, **Haugland 9643**, Honzel 9644, Horizons 9645, Howard 9647, Hughes 9648, Hussey 9649, Inland 9650, Invested 9652, Kaphan 9657, Kelsey 9658, Kitsap 9659, Lalji 9665, Laurel 9666, Lauzier 9667, Lie 9669, Lockwood 9671, Lucky 9673, **Luke 9674**, McCaw 9676, McEachern 9678, McKinstry 9680, McMillen 9681, Milgard 9683, Miller 9686, Moccasin 9687, Moraine 9688, Murdock 9689, Nesholm 9691, Norcliffe 9693, Oki 9694, OneFamily 9695, PACCAR 9698, **PAH 9699**, PEMCO 9702, Plum 9704, Puget 9705, PWH 9706, Raikes 9708, Raisbeck 9709, Raven 9710, Raynier 9711, RealNetworks 9712, Remala 9714, Renton 9715, Roma 9719, Rotella 9721, Safeco 9723, San Juan 9726, Satterberg 9728, Schultz 9730, Seattle 9731, Sherwood 9733, Shirley 9734, Smith 9738, Snyder 9739, Spark 9741, Stubblefield 9745, Sunbridge 9746, Suskin 9747, Swigert-Warren 9748, T.E.W. 9749, Tacoma 9750, **Torrance 9753**, True 9754, **Tyler 9755**, Wockner 9763, Wrigley 9766, Yakima 9767, Zumiez 9768

West Virginia: Beckley 9769, Chambers 9772, Community 9773, Daywood 9774, Hamilton, 9776, Hollowell 9778, Hunnicutt 9779, Kanawha 9780, McDonough 9784, McQuain 9785, Meagel 9786, Myles 9787, Parkersburg 9789, Ross 9792, Schenk 9793, Shott, 9794, Your 9799

Wisconsin: Alexander 9802, Alexander 9803, Alliant 9804, Anon 9805, Anthony 9806, Antioch 9807, Argosy 9808, Bachhuber 9809, Bader 9810, **Baird 9811**, Baker 9812, Beloit 9814, Bemis 9815, Benidt 9816, Berbeewalsh 9817, Bleser 9818, Brady 9821, Briggs 9822, Brookhill 9824, Brotz 9825, Bryant 9826, Casper 9827, Clark 9830, Cleary 9831, Community 9832, Community 9833,

Community 9834, Community 9835, Cornerstone 9836, CUNA 9838, DeAtley 9839, Eder 9840, Evinrude 9841, Family 9842, Fond du Lac 9843, Fort 9845, Fotsch 9846, Frautschi 9847, Goldbach 9851, Goodman 9852, Gordon 9853, Green Bay 9854, Green Bay 9855, Greenheck 9856, Hands 9858, Harley 9859, Heil 9860, Helfaer 9861, Herma 9862, Hovde 9865, Iddings 9866, Incourage 9867, Johnson 9870, Johnson 9871, Johnson 9873, Johnson 9874, Jordan 9875, Joy 9876, Kelben 9877, Keller 9878, Kellogg 9879, Kikkoman 9881, Kohl 9883, Kohler 9885, Kress 9887, Kuenzl 9888, La Crosse 9889, Ladish 9890, Loehrke 9893, Lubar 9894, Madison 9897, Madison 9898, Marcus 9900, McBeath 9901, Mead 9902, Meng 9904, Mercy 9905, Michels 9906, Milwaukee 9907, MMG 9908, Mound 9910, Neese 9911, Nelson 9912, Nicholas 9913, Northwestern 9914, Peck 9918, Pettit 9919, Pick 9920, Pollybill 9921, Racine 9924, Raibrook 9925, RDK 9928, Reinhart 9930, Rennebohm 9931, Rexnord 9932, Riordan 9933, Rockwell 9934, Rolfs 9935, Runzheimer 9938, Rutledge 9939, Ryan 9940, Sadoff 9941, **Schneider 9942**, Sensient 9943, Siebert 9946, Smith 9947, Soref 9948, St. Croix 9950, Stackner 9951, Steigleder 9952, Stone 9954, **Taylor 9955**, Thrivent 9956, U.S. 9957, Uihlein 9958, Uihlein 9959, **Wagner 9961**, Wanek 9964, Waukesha 9965, Wehr 9966, West 9967, Windhover 9968, Wisconsin 9969, Wisconsin 9970, Zilber 9971, Zilber 9972
Wyoming: Allen 9973, Community 9975, Griffith 9979, Kerr 9981, Liana 9982, Martin 9984, McMurry 9986, Niner 9987, Scott 9989, Seeley 9990, Storer 9992, True 9995, Tyrrell 9996, Watt 9997, Wyoming 9999, Zimmerman 10000

Human services, alliance/advocacy

Ohio: Nordson 7596

Human services, emergency aid

Alabama: Community 21, Community 24
California: Anaheim 239
Connecticut: Community 1565
Florida: Copham 2044
Idaho: Idaho 2632
Indiana: Central 3272, Portland 3370
Iowa: Community 3419
Maryland: O'Neil 3859, Price 3865
Minnesota: Evert 4655, Koran 4689
Pennsylvania: Genuardi 8053, Hurd 8101, Plankenhorn 8229
Rhode Island: Guth 8400, Rhode Island 8429
Texas: Fluor 8851
Washington: Horizons 9645
Wisconsin: Brookby 9823

Human services, equal rights

New York: NoVo 6570

Human services, financial counseling

Alabama: BBVA 9
Arkansas: Wal-Mart 210
California: Cathay 385, **Cisco 402**, Fremont 548, Intuit 723, Schwab 1127, **Strauss 1223**, Union 1271, Wells 1312
Colorado: **Western 1521**
Connecticut: Liberty 1630, People's 1671
Georgia: Primerica 2534, **UPS 2566**
Hawaii: Bank 2588
Illinois: Allstate 2657, MB 3008
Indiana: Foundations 3306, Lincoln 3344, Old 3363
Iowa: AEGON 3409, Principal 3476
Louisiana: Entergy 3630
Maine: TD 3710
Maryland: NASDAQ 3857
Massachusetts: Berkshire 3946, Eastern 4030, Santander 4256
Michigan: Comerica 4368
Minnesota: Deluxe 4644, RBC 4748, TCF 4778, U.S. 4784
Nebraska: Mutual 5071
New Jersey: KPMG 5349, Provident 5414
New York: **Citi 5780**, **Deutsche 5876**, **JPMorgan 6244**, **MetLife 6479**, Mizuho 6492, **Neuberger 6538**, NYSE 6573, Voya 7038
North Carolina: **Bank 7139**
Ohio: KeyBank 7523
Oregon: **NIKE 7875**
Pennsylvania: **BNY 7945**, BNY 7946, PNC 8230, **PPG 8235**
Tennessee: First 8565
Virginia: Capital 9400, **Genworth 9441**, SunTrust 9539
Wisconsin: Johnson 9870, Thrivent 9956

Human services, gift distribution

Tennessee: Regal 8622

Human services, information services

Pennsylvania: Hurd 8101

Human services, mind/body enrichment

Arkansas: Wal-Mart 210
California: Altman 234, **Smith 1183**, Smith 1188, United 1273
Connecticut: Ayer 1539
Massachusetts: Hershey 4095, Imago 4105
Michigan: Cook 4378, Fetzer 4421, **Lachimi 4480**
Nevada: Caesars 5106
New York: Hultquist 6195
Pennsylvania: **Waldorf 8330**

Human services, personal services

California: Santa Barbara 1116
Ohio: Nordson 7596

Human services, public policy

Illinois: **Retirement 3113**

Human services, reform

California: Rosenberg 1088
Ohio: Nordson 7596

Human services, self-help groups

Pennsylvania: Genuardi 8053

Human services, single organization support

Maryland: **Sidgmore 3885**
Pennsylvania: Hurd 8101

Human services, transportation

California: **Smith 1183**
Ohio: Marion 7558

Human services, victim aid

Connecticut: Selander 1693
New York: Schnurmacher 6810

Human services, volunteer services

New Jersey: Dircks 5241

Humanities

Alabama: Community 25, Walker 74
Arkansas: Arkansas 179
California: Ahmanson 222, Community 420, Drown 484, El Dorado 500, **Getty 579**, Osher 997, Pasadena 1015, Sacramento 1103, San Francisco 1109, Sonora 1198
Colorado: Bonfils 1376, Chambers 1385, Community 1393, El Pomar 1406, Gates 1418
Connecticut: Community 1564, Connecticut 1566
Delaware: Welfare 1872
Florida: Bank 1979, Community 2038, Lattner 2204, Wells 2383
Hawaii: Atherton 2586, Cooke 2597
Idaho: Idaho 2632
Illinois: Chicago 2746, Community 2763, Community 2765, Community 2766, Community 2767, Franke 2841, McGraw 3015, Siragusa 3162
Indiana: Ball 3262, Brown 3269, Clowes 3274, Community 3277, Community 3282, **Goodrich 3311**, Orange 3365, Wayne 3400
Iowa: Tye 3484
Kansas: Manhattan 3532, Wichita 3555
Kentucky: Community 3569, Robinson 3598
Louisiana: Baton Rouge 3613, Beaird 3614, Grigsby 3640
Maine: Maine 3698
Maryland: Knott 3826
Massachusetts: Ayling 3932, Cape Cod 3974, Perkin 4213, Stevens 4288, Stevens 4289, Worcester 4327
Michigan: Capital 4357, Community 4370, Community 4372, Dyer 4412, Jackson 4467, Midland 4502
Minnesota: Andersen 4603, Bigelow 4616, Grand Rapids 4667, Minnesota 4715, Saint Paul 4757
Nebraska: Abel 5021, Cooper 5031, Hastings 5046, Kimmel 5059, Woods 5096
New Hampshire: Trust 5189
New Jersey: **Allen 5191**, Hyde 5310, **Newcombe 5391**
New Mexico: Santa Fe 5533
New York: Achelis 5549, Central 5757, Community 5801, Community 5802, Community 5804, **Delmas 5871**, **Guggenheim 6116**, Littauer 6379, **Luce 6398**, **Mellon 6470**, Steele 6915, Vidda 7030, Whiting 7079, Wiener 7083
North Carolina: Blumenthal 7154, Broyhill 7160, Community 7178, Community 7180, Cumberland 7184, North Carolina 7273, Polk 7287, Triangle 7328
Ohio: Columbus 7411, Community 7413, Community 7415, Dayton 7428, New Albany 7589, Reinberger 7628, Semple 7660, Tiffin 7682, Wayne 7704
Oklahoma: Hardesty 7756, Williams 7814
Oregon: Collins 7836, Jeld 7856, Kinsman 7860, Meyer 7870, Swindells 7892
Pennsylvania: Argus 7920, Community 7990, Dolfinger 8013, Foundation 8046, Pew 8220, Washington 8332
Rhode Island: Amica 8356
South Carolina: Spartanburg 8501
South Dakota: Sioux Falls 8521
Tennessee: Benwood 8535, Community 8550, Tucker 8638
Texas: Constantin 8778, East 8819, El Paso 8825, Kempner 8952, Meadows 9019, Permian 9091, Zachry 9296
Utah: Eccles 9320
Vermont: Vermont 9375
Virginia: Arlington 9384, Charlottesville 9405, Lynchburg 9474, Suffolk 9538
Washington: Blue 9588, Community 9603, Community 9604, Inland 9650, Rice 9716, Seattle 9731, Tacoma 9750
West Virginia: Kanawha 9780
Wisconsin: Alliant 9804, **Bradley 9819**, Johnson 9874
Wyoming: McMurry 9986, Scott 9989

Immigrants/refugees

Alabama: Kaul 43
Arizona: Webb 174
Arkansas: Rockefeller 197
California: Atkinson 265, California 365, California 368, Community 414, El Dorado 500, Gerbode 573, Grove 631, **Hume 715**, Marcled 875, McMillen 905, Merage 915, Napa 959, Rosenberg 1088, San

Francisco 1109, Silicon 1166, Soda 1194, Weingart 1307, Zellerbach 1358
Colorado: Aspen 1368, Colorado 1390, Denver 1401, King 1440, Summit 1511, **Western 1521**
Connecticut: Community 1562
Delaware: **Raskob 1845**
District of Columbia: Cafritz 1890, Consumer 1894, Kimsey 1921
Florida: Community 2032, Green 2134, Miami 2238, Southwest 2327
Georgia: Franklin 2462
Illinois: Arthur 2673, Chicago 2746, Field 2831, Fry 2849, Landau 2966, Reese 3110, Siragusa 3162, Washington 3217
Indiana: Community 3281, **Lumina 3345**, Pulliam 3372
Kentucky: Cralle 3571
Maryland: Meyerhoff 3848
Massachusetts: Boston 3956, Hyams 4103, Mifflin 4175, Parker 4207, Shapiro 4267, Stevens 4288, Stevens 4289, Swensrud 4303
Michigan: Grand Rapids 4447, **Kellogg 4474**
Minnesota: Blue 4618, Bremer 4620, Marbrook 4702, Minneapolis 4714, Northwest 4729, Phillips 4741
Nebraska: Woods 5096
New Hampshire: Lindsay 5179
New Jersey: Healthcare 5296, Hyde 5310
New Mexico: Santa Fe 5533
New York: Altman 5579, **Deutsche 5876**, **Discount 5889**, **Ford 5994**, **Foundation 6003**, Gorman 6083, Langeloth 6327, New York 6546, **Noyes 6571**, **Open 6593**, Ritter 6712, **Soros 6888**, **Sparkplug 6894**, **Starr 6911**, Staten 6912, **Straus 6934**, **Unbound 7016**, van Ameringen 7024
North Carolina: Community 7180, North Carolina 7273, Weaver 7335
Ohio: Akron 7367, GAR 7465
Oklahoma: Hille 7759
Oregon: Collins 7836
Pennsylvania: Beneficial 7936, Connelly 7995, Independence 8107
South Carolina: Patterson 8489
Tennessee: Baptist 8533, Community 8548
Texas: Community 8774, Community 8777, Dallas 8795, Embrey 8828, Frees 8857, Moore 9034, Stern 9204, Still 9207
Utah: Eccles 9320
Washington: Biller 9586, Norcliffe 9693
Wisconsin: La Crosse 9889

Immunology

Maryland: **de Beaumont 3774**

Immunology research

Washington: **Gates 9625**

Independent housing for people with disabilities

California: Union 1271

Independent living, disability

Arizona: Reese 156
California: Gogian 598, Koontz 800, **Smith 1183**
Illinois: C.W.B. 2730
Indiana: Lincoln 3344
Massachusetts: TJX 4308
Minnesota: **Andersen 4601**
Rhode Island: CVS 8379
Texas: Anderson 8663, El Paso 8825, Lyman 8995
Virginia: AMERIGROUP 9383, Mitsubishi 9487

Indigenous peoples

Alabama: Kaul 43
Alaska: Newlin 88
Arizona: Webb 174
California: California 368, **Christensen 399**, Community 414, Gerbode 573, McMillen 905, Weingart 1307
Colorado: King 1440
Delaware: **Raskob 1845**
Hawaii: Bank 2588
Illinois: Chicago 2746, King 2960
Maryland: **Shared 3882**
Michigan: Chrysler 4366, Grand Rapids 4447, **Kellogg 4474**
Minnesota: Bremer 4620, Northwest 4729
Montana: Edwards 5008, Oro 5014
New York: **Ford 5994**, **Noyes 6571**, **Open 6593**, **Overbrook 6604**, Ritter 6712, **Sparkplug 6894**, Yad 7108
North Carolina: Community 7180, North Carolina 7273
Oklahoma: Hille 7759
Tennessee: **Maclellan 8601**
Texas: Community 8774, Community 8777, Hollomon 8914, McDermott 9013, Orsinger 9073
Utah: Eccles 9320
Virginia: **Sacharuna 9526**
Washington: Norcliffe 9693

Infants/toddlers

Alabama: Community 25, Kaul 43, Meyer 53
Arizona: Steele 165, Webb 174
California: Aroha 260, Atkinson 265, Community 414, Cowell 434, Deutsch 462, El Dorado 500, Goldman 605, Green 621, Gumbiner 636, **Hilton 692**, Ludwick 856, Patron 1020, Sangham 1114, Weingart 1307
Colorado: Aspen 1368, Buell 1381, King 1440, Lipscomb 1449, Summit 1511
Connecticut: Community 1562, Community 1564, Connecticut 1567, Fund 1589, Graustein 1600
Delaware: **Raskob 1845**
District of Columbia: Cafritz 1890, **CityBridge 1892**
Florida: Community 2031, Fortin 2106, Kennedy 2182, Southwest 2327, Sylvester 2348
Georgia: Franklin 2462
Illinois: Evanston 2826, **Harris 2893**, Johnson 2944, Seabury 3146, Siragusa 3162, Steans 3175, **Walgreens 3210**
Indiana: Community 3281, Henry 3320, **Lilly 3342**
Iowa: McElroy 3461, Principal 3476
Kentucky: Blue 3560
Maryland: Community 3761, Fowler 3795, Washington 3904
Massachusetts: Brookline 3962, Cabot 3967, Cambridge 3971, Davis 4011
Michigan: Chrysler 4366, Community 4369, Community 4375, **Fisher 4423**, **Gerber 4443**, Grand Rapids 4447, **Kellogg 4474**, Midland 4502
Minnesota: Bremer 4620, Northwest 4730
Mississippi: Gulf 4830
Missouri: Saint Louis 4966
Montana: Edwards 5008, Oro 5014, Washington 5018
New Hampshire: Lindsay 5179
New Jersey: Fund 5270, Healthcare 5296, Hyde 5310, Orange 5396, Schumann 5441
New Mexico: Brindle 5516
New York: Altman 5579, Community 5802, Heckscher 6157, Lenna 6352, **Mailman 6418**, Ritter 6712, **Ross 6754**, St. Faith's 6903, Staten 6912, **Straus 6934**, van Ameringen 7024, Warner 7053, Western 7078
North Carolina: Cemala 7174, Community 7180, Community 7182, Reidsville 7294, Robertson 7305
Ohio: Fairfield 7445, GAR 7465, Hershey 7487, Mathile 7560, Parents 7608, Saint 7639, Springfield 7671
Oklahoma: Hardesty 7756, Hille 7759
Oregon: Ford 7845, J.F.R. 7854, Lamfrom 7863
Pennsylvania: Birmingham 7942, Connelly 7995, Mellon 8173, **Oberkotter 8203**, Pilgrim 8225, Smith 8288, Staunton 8296
Tennessee: Baptist 8533, Wilson 8646
Texas: Bass 8690, Community 8774, Community 8776, Community 8777, Dallas 8795, Embrey 8828, Hoglund 8913, Moore 9034, Orsinger 9073, Rees-Jones 9125, Still 9207, Terry 9224, Waco 9251, Wolslager 9288, Wright 9293
Utah: Eccles 9320, **Thrasher 9353**
Virginia: ACT 9380, Memorial 9485, Strong 9537, Williamsburg 9558
Washington: **Gates 9625**, Norcliffe 9693
West Virginia: Eastern 9775
Wisconsin: Green Bay 9854, West 9967
Wyoming: McMurry 9986, Scott 9989

Infants/toddlers, female

Alabama: Kaul 43, Meyer 53
Arizona: Webb 174
California: Gumbiner 636, Patron 1020, Sangham 1114, Weingart 1307
Colorado: King 1440, Lipscomb 1449
Connecticut: Community 1562
Delaware: **Raskob 1845**
District of Columbia: Cafritz 1890
Illinois: Steans 3175
Indiana: **Lilly 3342**
Massachusetts: Phillips 4217
Michigan: Chrysler 4366, Midland 4502
Minnesota: Bremer 4620
New York: Community 5802, **Straus 6934**
North Carolina: Community 7180
Ohio: Fairfield 7445, Hershey 7487, Parents 7608
Oklahoma: Hardesty 7756
Oregon: Ford 7845, J.F.R. 7854
Pennsylvania: Beneficial 7936, Pilgrim 8225
Tennessee: Wilson 8646
Texas: Bass 8690, Moore 9034, Orsinger 9073
Vermont: Gibney 9362
Washington: **Gates 9625**, Norcliffe 9693
Wisconsin: West 9967

Infants/toddlers, male

Alabama: Kaul 43, Meyer 53
Arizona: Webb 174
California: Gumbiner 636, Patron 1020, Sangham 1114, Weingart 1307
Colorado: King 1440, Lipscomb 1449
Connecticut: Community 1562
Delaware: **Raskob 1845**
Illinois: Steans 3175
Indiana: **Lilly 3342**
Massachusetts: Phillips 4217
Michigan: Chrysler 4366, Midland 4502
Minnesota: Bremer 4620
New York: Altman 5579, Community 5802, **Straus 6934**
North Carolina: Community 7180
Ohio: Fairfield 7445, Hershey 7487, Parents 7608
Oklahoma: Hardesty 7756, Hille 7759
Oregon: J.F.R. 7854
Pennsylvania: Beneficial 7936, Pilgrim 8225
Tennessee: Wilson 8646
Texas: Bass 8690, Moore 9034
Vermont: Gibney 9362
Washington: **Gates 9625**, Norcliffe 9693
Wisconsin: West 9967

Insurance, providers

Illinois: Rawley 3106

Interactive games

Minnesota: Best 4612

International affairs

Arizona: Barrett 96, Solheim 163
California: Amar 236, **Appleton 248**, **Bergstrom 310**, **Foundation 542**, Gap 563, Hitz 694, Hoppe 703, Macfarlane 865, **Saban 1101**, Saje 1104, Skoll 1176, Tosa 1259, **Wadhwani 1294**, **Wong 1342**
Connecticut: Allison 1535, **GE 1591**, Pasculano 1668, **Richardson 1679**
Florida: SHIFT 2320
Hawaii: **Burke 2590**
Illinois: Pritzker 3093, Ranch 3104
Indiana: Transformation 3392

Iowa: Holthues 3444, Hubbell 3445
Kansas: Shannon 3545
Massachusetts: Flatley 4053, Hershey 4095, Reynolds 4238, Schooner 4261
Michigan: Jubilee 4470, **Myers 4515**
Minnesota: Kelley 4686, Oswald 4735
New Jersey: Barber 5201, **Hovnanian 5306**, **Johnson 5326**
New York: Altman 5581, Berkowitz 5669, Birkelund 5677, Cone 5810, **Debbane 5859**, Donner 5899, Einhorn 5942, **Fledgling 5987**, **Ford 5994**, **Guggenheim 6115**, Hurford 6199, **Isdell 6214**, Kriendler 6309, Loeb 6385, **M.A.C. 6408**, Mesdag 6478, Mitsui 6491, Nduna 6533, Ogden 6579, Randa 6676, **Saper 6794**, **Sapling 6795**, Schaffner 6800, Slifka 6870, **Sparkplug 6894**, **Tinker 6983**, **United 7019**, Volcker 7035, Warburg 7048
Ohio: Danaher 7424, Partridge 7612
Pennsylvania: Ametek 7913, Benter 7937, **Botstiber 7947**, **Carthage 7968**, Clayman 7984, Scaife 8266
Rhode Island: **Dorot 8384**
Texas: **A Glimmer 8649**, Marsh 8999
Washington: 25 9564, Scan 9729
Wisconsin: Argosy 9808, **Bradley 9819**, Kohler 9885

International affairs, arms control
Delaware: James 1789
New York: **Carnegie 5747**, **Guggenheim 6115**, **New 6551**, **Prospect 6663**, **Rubin 6764**

International affairs, association
California: Caufield 386

International affairs, equal rights
California: **Draper 481**
New Mexico: Karakin 5525
Washington: **Channel 9597**

International affairs, foreign policy
Connecticut: **Richardson 1679**
Delaware: James 1789
District of Columbia: **Arca 1880**
Illinois: Madigan 2992
Missouri: Jacobsen 4915
New York: Abstraction 5547, **Guggenheim 6115**, **Hauser 6147**, Hurford 6199, Ross 6753, **Rubin 6764**, Salomon 6785, **Tinker 6983**, **United 7019**, Wiener 7083, Zilkha 7125
Ohio: Veale 7694
Pennsylvania: Cotswold 7999, Mine 8184
Texas: Marsh 8999
Wisconsin: **Bradley 9819**

International affairs, goodwill promotion
California: Chao 394, Stephenson 1217
District of Columbia: Kaye 1920
Florida: **Wardlaw 2376**
Illinois: Stuart 3182
Kentucky: C.E. 3566
Maine: Hungarian-American 3692, **Walter 3711**
Minnesota: Duluth 4649, Sit 4765
New Jersey: Borgenicht 5210, Fairbanks 5255
New York: Banfi 5641, Freeman 6012, Gerschel 6045, Greve 6106, Soros 6891, **Tinker 6983**, Wiener 7083
Ohio: Partridge 7612
Washington: Scan 9729

International affairs, information services
Massachusetts: Colombe 3989

International affairs, national security
District of Columbia: **Arca 1880**
New York: **Carnegie 5747**, **Peterson 6630**

International affairs, public policy
District of Columbia: Kimsey 1921
Minnesota: WEM 4799
New York: Abstraction 5547, Alexander 5568, Interlaken 6210

International affairs, research
District of Columbia: Rumsfeld 1943

International affairs, U.N.
California: Wilson 1328
Colorado: **Western 1521**
Connecticut: **GE 1591**
New Jersey: **Johnson 5326**

International affairs, volunteer services
Delaware: **Jolie-Pitt 1791**

International agricultural development
Florida: **Working 2394**
Maine: **Sandy 3707**

International conflict resolution
District of Columbia: **El-Hibri 1903**, Zients 1960
Illinois: **Buffett 2726**

International democracy & civil society development
California: Egg 496
District of Columbia: **El-Hibri 1903**
Maryland: Spencer 3887
New York: Clinton 5787
Pennsylvania: Argus 7920

International development
California: **Google 615**, Handleman 649, Rock 1085, Roth 1093, Tosa 1259
Connecticut: **Children's 1557**, Vranos 1718
Delaware: Sylvan 1867
District of Columbia: **CityBridge 1892**
Florida: Green 2134, **Patel 2259**, **Stacy 2333**
Illinois: **IDP 2932**
Maryland: O'Neil 3859, Sampson 3878
Massachusetts: Mazar 4164
Michigan: Williams 4586
Minnesota: Minneapolis 4714, **Weyerhaeuser 4802**
New Jersey: **Johnson 5326**
New York: Assael 5620, Donner 5899, Fitt 5985, **IIMI 6207**, Nduna 6533, **Pfizer 6633**, Phillips 6637, **Trace 7003**, **Tsadra 7010**, Warburg 7048
Ohio: **Geisse 7468**
Oregon: Vibrant 7898
Pennsylvania: **ACE 7905**
Rhode Island: Koonce 8412
Tennessee: Lazarus 8596
Texas: Goradia 8871, **Merali 9022**, **Whole 9276**
Virginia: Mousetrap 9491, Three 9541, Trehan 9544
Washington: **Gates 9625**, Kaphan 9657, McKinstry 9680
Wisconsin: Hovde 9865

International economic development
California: Atkinson 265, **Draper 481**, Hewlett 686, Linked 842, **Omidyar 984**, Saje 1104
Connecticut: **Children's 1557**, Donchian 1576, **Hampshire 1608**
District of Columbia: **NDPI 1935**
Florida: **Working 2394**
Illinois: Weberg 3221
Indiana: West 3404
New York: **Ford 5994**, Kaye 6262, **Open 6593**, **Rockefeller 6724**, Select 6829, **United 7019**
Texas: **PHM 9098**, **Whole 9276**
Vermont: Evslin 9360
Washington: Crystal 9608, **Glaser 9630**, **Starbucks 9742**, **Stewardship 9744**

International economics/trade policy
Connecticut: **GE 1591**

International exchange
District of Columbia: **San Giacomo 1945**
New York: **Trust 7009**
Washington: Bezos 9585

International exchange, arts
District of Columbia: **San Giacomo 1945**
New York: Ross 6753

International exchange, students
Massachusetts: **Rodgers 4241**
Michigan: Levy 4487
New York: Mitsui 6491

International human rights
California: **Alalusi 224**, Benjamin 306, Falling 515, **Google 615**, Jennings 748, San Francisco 1109
Colorado: **General 1419**
Connecticut: Valentine 1713
Delaware: James 1789, **Jolie-Pitt 1791**
District of Columbia: **Arca 1880**, **El-Hibri 1903**, Kimsey 1921, **Moriah 1932**, **Summit 1950**
Florida: **Patel 2259**, **Wardlaw 2376**
Illinois: Libra 2981, **MacArthur 2989**, Magnus 2993
Iowa: Holthues 3444
Maine: **Catalyst 3682**
Maryland: **Blaustein 3735**, Blaustein 3736, **Cohen 3754**
Minnesota: Mossier 4723
New Jersey: Harbourton 5293
New Mexico: Angelica 5514, **Levinson 5527**
New York: Edouard 5936, Epstein 5958, **Ford 5994**, Gellert 6040, **Gould 6086**, **Guggenheim 6115**, **Hauser 6147**, Mullen 6516, **Open 6593**, **Overbrook 6604**, **Rubin 6764**, **Sparkplug 6894**, Speyer 6896
North Carolina: **Oak 7276**
Pennsylvania: Nararo 8193, Scranton 8275
Texas: McDermott 9013
Washington: **Channel 9597**

International migration/refugee issues
Georgia: Rockdale 2540
Massachusetts: **Alchemy 3920**
New Jersey: **Johnson 5326**
New York: Adelson 5555, **Kaplan 6252**, Model 6495, **Sparkplug 6894**

International peace/security
California: Craigslist 436, Firedoll 528, Lainer 813
Colorado: **General 1419**
District of Columbia: **El-Hibri 1903**, **Wyss 1959**
Florida: SHIFT 2320, **Wardlaw 2376**
Hawaii: **Burke 2590**
Illinois: **MacArthur 2989**
Iowa: Global 3435, Holthues 3444
Kansas: **Shumaker 3546**
Maine: **Catalyst 3682**
Maryland: **Morningstar 3854**, Town 3897
Massachusetts: Colombe 3989, One 4198, Schooner 4261
Minnesota: Duluth 4649, **Weyerhaeuser 4802**

International relief

International relief, 2004 tsunami

International studies

International terrorism

Intersex

Islam

Jewish agencies & synagogues

Nebraska: Schrager 5079, Slosburg 5083
Nevada: Mann 5130, M-K 5133, Rochlin 5144, Spiegel 5150
New Hampshire: Trust 5189
New Jersey: **Berrie 5206**, Brothers 5215, C 5221, Cole 5231, Cooperman 5233, Dirshu 5242, Edelste 5247, Eisenberg 5250, Eisenreich 5251, Evans 5254, Family 5258, Frankel 5265, Friedman 5268, Ghermezian 5274, Grove 5282, Haber 5287, Hahn 5288, Halpern 5290, Healthcare 5296, Hess 5298, **IDT 5311**, Indian 5313, Isermann 5319, Jaffe 5320, Kaplen 5330, Karma 5331, Katz 5332, Katz 5333, Kerr 5338, Klatskin 5342, Kolatch 5347, Kushner 5351, L.A.W. 5352, Lackner 5354, Laurie 5357, Lewis 5362, Mack 5366, Mack 5367, Milano 5384, Orenstein 5397, Oster 5399, Parnes 5402, Providence 5413, **Ramapo 5419**, Roberts 5423, Roth 5426, Rubenstein 5428, Samson 5434, Schecter 5439, Schwartz 5442, Schwartz 5443, Schwarz 5444, Scott 5445, Seiden 5448, SFF 5449, Sierra 5455, Silver 5457, Stadtmauer 5466, Steiner 5467, Stern 5468, Sudler 5472, Syms 5475, Tanzman 5476, Taub 5477, Tepper 5480, V'Emunah 5488, Wagner 5491, Werdiger 5498, Wilf 5502, Wilf 5503, Wilf 5504, Yosef 5508
New Mexico: **Levinson 5527**
New York: A Kinder 5542, A M 5543, Abrons 5546, Abstraction 5547, ACE 5548, Adar 5553, Adelman 5554, Adelson 5555, Adjmi 5557, Adjmi 5558, **Adjmi 5559**, **AHBA 5562**, AJG 5565, Albert 5567, Alpern 5577, Alpert 5578, Altschul 5582, American 5590, Ames 5591, Appleman 5604, Arbesfeld 5605, Aresty 5609, Arnow 5615, Aronson 5617, Assael 5620, August 5624, Augustine 5625, Azrak 5630, B & S 5631, Bachmann 5632, Bais 5637, Baker 5638, Baron 5646, Barrington 5647, Basch 5649, Bass 5650, B'Chaya 5654, **BCHB 5655**, Beker 5659, Belfer 5660, **Benenson 5663**, Benenson 5664, Benenson 5665, Berg 5667, Berkowitz 5668, Berkowitz 5669, Betesh 5671, BFF 5672, Bialkin 5673, BL 5680, Blank 5682, Blum 5686, Blutt 5687, Bnai 5689, Bodner 5693, Botwinick 5696, Boxer 5698, Brach 5699, Brach 5700, Braka 5702, Braufman 5704, Bravmann 5705, Bricker 5709, Bronfman 5715, **Bronfman 5717**, Burns 5732, Butler 5735, C & Y 5739, CAMBR 5741, Canary 5744, Cayre 5752, Cayre 5754, Cayre 5755, Century 5758, Chada 5759, Chaim 5761, Charina 5764, Chazen 5767, Chehebar 5768, Chehebar 5769, Chernow 5771, Chesed 5772, Chesed 5773, Cohen 5792, Cohn 5793, Cooper 5812, Cooper 5813, Cornerstone 5817, Cowin 5822, Cramer 5824, **Dabah 5840**, Damial 5844, Dejana 5868, Derfner 5874, Deutsch 5875, Diker 5883, Ditmars 5890, Dobkin 5891, Donner 5898, Dovid 5905, Drexler 5911, Drizin 5914, Edelman 5930, Edelman 5931, Edelstein 5933, Edlow 5935, Edouard 5936, Educational 5937, EGL 5939, Ehrenkranz 5941, Einhorn 5942, Einhorn 5943, Eisenberg 5944, Elbogen 5945, **Elishis 5946**, Elkes 5947, **EMLE 5952**, Empire 5953, Englander 5955, Epstein 5958, Equipart 5959, ETZ 5962, Everett 5964, Farash 5969, Feil 5973, Feinstein 5974, **FIMF 5977**, Fischel 5980, Fischer 5981, Fisher 5982, Fishoff 5984, Foop 5991, Foundation 6000, Frankfort 6010, Fribourg 6015, Friedman 6019, Friedman 6020, Friedman 6021, Friedman 6022, Fruchthandler 6027, Fuchs 6028, Fund 6030, Ganger 6033, **GBRG 6036**, Gershwind 6046, Gerson 6047, Gindi 6054, Glickenhaus 6058, Gold 6060, Goldberg 6062, Goldie 6063, Goldman 6065, **Goldman 6066**, Goldsmith 6071, Goldstein 6073, Goldstein 6074, Goldstein 6075, Goldstein 6076, Gould 6089, **Grant 6092**, Grayer 6096, Green 6100, Green 6101, Greene 6103, Gross 6111, Gross 6112, Gruss 6114, Gural 6117, Gurwin 6118, Gutenstein 6119, H & M 6122, H. & Y. 6123, Harary 6131, Harris 6138, Harris 6141, Hartman 6145, Hendel 6161, Hermione 6163, Hersh 6166, Hershaft 6167, Hershman 6168, Hertz 6169, Heyer 6171, Heyman-Merrin 6172, Hillman 6174, Hirsch 6175, Hochfelder 6177, Hochstein 6178, Hod 6179, Holtzmann 6184, Horowitz 6186, Howard 6189, Huberfeld 6190, Hurst 6200, Icahn 6204, **IIMI 6207**, Inzlicht 6212, Jacobson 6219, **Jaffe 6222**, Jana 6225, **Jewish 6229**, Joelson 6232, K.W. 6246, Kaplan 6250, Kaplan 6251, Katz 6255, Katz 6257, Kaufman 6259, Kayden 6261, Kaye 6262, Kaylie 6263, Keidan 6267, Keshet 6277, Kimmel 6281, Kingdon 6284, **Klein 6287**, **Klein 6288**, Kleinman 6290, Klingenstein 6291, Klingenstein 6293, Kohn 6301, Korman 6303, Kraus 6305, Kriendler 6309, Kuflik 6311, Kupferberg 6312, Kurz 6314, L. & L. 6316, L.E. 6317, Lake 6320, Lambert 6321, Langer 6328, Lasdon 6332, Lauder 6334, **Lauder 6336**, Leffell 6345, **Leir 6349**, Lemberg 6350, Lerner 6353, Leshkowitz 6354, Leventhal 6357, Levian 6358, Levine 6359, Levine 6360, Lichtenstein 6366, Lindenbaum 6370, Littauer 6379, Litwin 6380, Loeb 6385, Loewe 6386, Loewenberg 6387, Lone 6390, Lopatin 6392, Lostand 6394, Lubo 6396, M&E 6407, Ma'asim 6409, Mab 6410, Mack 6412, Mallah 6423, Mark 6430, Marmurstein 6434, Marrus 6436, Marx 6442, Massry 6444, Melohn 6472, Mercy 6475, Meyer 6480, Middle 6483, Milstein 6488, Mnuchin 6494, Mullen 6516, Mys 6519, Nadler 6521, Nakash 6522, Naomi 6523, **NAON 6524**, **Nash 6525**, Neidich 6534, Nesharim 6536, New Brook 6540, Nias 6556, Nola 6562, **OCLO 6576**, Ohel 6580, Olive 6587, Olshan 6588, Oppenheim 6594, Orentreich 6596, Parkview 6617, **PBHP 6622**, Penson 6626, Perelman 6628, **Pershing 6629**, Pletka 6646, PLM 6647, Plum 6648, Poses 6655, Price 6657, Prins 6660, Propp 6662, Providence 6664, Pulier 6665, Pzena 6669, Radif 6671, Raiff 6675, Rechler 6682, Red 6683, Regals 6685, Reiss 6687, Resnick 6689, Resnick 6690, Richmond 6704, **Ridgefield 6705**, Rieger 6707, Riese 6708, Rose 6732, Rose 6737, Rosen 6741, Rosen 6742, Rosenblatt 6744, Rosenblatt 6745, Rosenblum 6746, Rosenfeld 6747, Rosenwald 6750, Rosner 6752, Rostrust 6756, Rowan 6758, Rubenstein 6762, Rubin 6763, RZH 6773, Sabin 6775, Safra 6781, Sagner 6783, Saltz 6786, Saltz 6787, **Saper 6794**, **Sato 6798**, Schenker 6803, Schnurmacher 6810, Schon 6811, Schwartz 6816, Schwartz 6818, Schwartz 6819, SDA 6823, Seaver 6825, Seiler 6828, Semlitz 6831, Setton 6833, Shaarei 6835, Shapiro 6838, **Shaw 6840**, Shtesl 6849, Silverstein 6856, Silverweed 6857, Silvian 6858, Singer 6862, Sitt 6866, Skirball 6869, Slifka 6870, SO 6881, Sobel 6882, Sobel 6883, Solomon 6885, Solomon 6886, Soros 6889, Soros 6891, Speyer 6896, Spilker 6897, Stanton 6907, Starker 6910, **Stefansky 6916**, Stein 6918, Stein 6919, Steinberg 6920, Steinberg 6922, Steinhardt 6923, Stulman 6938, Stuntz 6939, Sun 6946, Sutton 6949, Sutton 6950, SVM 6952, Swieca 6955, Tahari 6958, Tananbaum 6962, Tarica 6965, Teferes 6968, Terumah 6972, **Tikvah 6981**, Tisch 6986, Tisch 6987, Tisch 6988, Tisch 6989, Tova 6998, United 7020, **VHIV 7028**, Vogelstein 7034, Volpert 7036, Wallach 7044, Wasserman 7055, Weber 7059, Weiler 7063, Winkelried 7090, Witten 7095, Wohl 7097, **Wolfensohn 7098**, Wolk 7099, YAD 7107, Yad 7108, Yashar 7109, Zaro 7115, Zeides 7119, Zichron 7120, **ZIIZ 7124**, Zilkha 7125, Zubrow 7126, Zucker 7127
North Carolina: Baruch 7140, Blumenthal 7154, Gorelick 7215, High Point 7231, Levine 7255
Ohio: Berlin 7385, Diamond 7435, Heiman 7486, Horvitz 7493, Jewish 7511, Kaplan 7516, Kramer 7529, Krause 7530, **Lerner 7538**, Levin 7539, Mandel 7554, **Mandel 7555**, Mandel 7556, Mayerson 7561, Miller 7571, Ratner 7626, Rosenthal 7637, **Sapirstein-Stone-Weiss 7644**, Schear 7645, Schottenstein 7654, Schottenstein 7655, Stone 7677, Wexner 7712, **Wexner 7713**, Wuliger 7722
Oklahoma: Bezalel 7734, Gussman 7755, Kaiser 7763, Oxley 7785, **ROI 7791**, Taubman 7804, Zarrow 7819
Oregon: **Fohs 7844**, Renaissance 7884, Schnitzer 7887, Schnitzer 7888, Zidell 7902
Pennsylvania: Alexander 7910, Arete 7919, Brodsky 7952, Buncher 7957, Caplan 7962, Cassett 7969, Chosky 7980, Clayman 7984, Davis 8006, Davis 8007, Erlbaum 8027, Farber 8032, Feldman 8034, Fine 8039, Fishman 8044, Giant 8055, Gitlin 8058, Grass 8066, Grass 8067, Grass 8068, Kline 8128, Kohelet 8131, Levis 8140, Lipsitz 8144, Lotman 8150, Mandell 8153, Miller 8180, Morgan 8187, Morris 8188, Neubauer 8196, Novotny 8202, Posner 8233, Roberts 8250, Roberts 8251, Ross 8255, Saligman 8261, Scheller 8268, Schneider 8271, Seed 8278, Shapira 8282, Snider 8292, Stein 8297, Toll 8316, Toll 8317
Rhode Island: Alpert 8355, Elms 8387, Fain 8388
South Carolina: Yaschik 8509, Zucker 8510
Tennessee: Eskind 8563, Goodfriend 8574, Lebovitz 8597, Scheidt 8625
Texas: Ackerman 8651, Alexander 8656, Diener 8807, Feldman 8843, Finger 8845, Fruhman 8858, Gale 8859, Genecov 8862, Getz 8864, Hall 8883, Hersh 8903, Hirsch 8910, Kempner 8952, Kolitz 8968, Levit 8982, Litman 8987, Mankoff 8998, Nightingale 9062, **PHM 9098**, Pollock 9103, Schepps 9158, Smith 9185, Soref-Breslauer 9190, Sterling 9203, Susman 9216, Wolff 9286, Zale 9297
Virginia: Colburn 9409, Funger 9438, Kanter 9459, Kogod 9464, Lipman 9469, Newman 9493, Ratner 9515, Rosenthal 9525, Smith 9532, Smith 9534
Washington: B&E 9577, Danz 9609, Loeb 9672, **Samis 9725**, Sarkowsky 9727, Sondland 9740
West Virginia: Weisberg 9798
Wisconsin: Eder 9840, Goodman 9852, Kohl 9883, Lubar 9894, Peck 9918, Posner 9922, Soref 9948

Jewish federated giving programs

Alabama: Friedman 35
Arizona: Levine 133, Marco 139, Schwartz 162, Zuckerman 178
Arkansas: Tenenbaum 206
California: Alpert 230, Arnall 256, Bilger 314, Black 317, Brandman 337, Breslauer-Soref 341, Buckhantz 354, Byer 360, Campini 374, Davidow 451, Davis 455, Day 457, Edelstein 494, Eichenbaum 497, Emerson 505, **Fineberg 525**, Friend 552, Fromm 553, Garb 564, Gibson 583, Gold 599, Goldrich 607, Goldsmith 608, Goodman 613, Hellman 677, Horwich 706, Irmas 725, Israel 731, Jaffe 741, June 757, Karatz 765, Karsh 767, Katz 768, Kayne 773, Koret 801, Lainer 812, Lainer 813, Lainer 814, Lehrer 827, **Leichtag 828**, Leslie 834, Menlo 913, Merage 916, Merkin 919, Milken 926, Milken 927, Mitchell 931, Morton 943, **Nazarian 962**, Oschin 996, Post 1041, Potiker 1042, Pritzker 1046, Reinhard 1061, Sarnat 1117, Seiger 1137, Semel 1138, Shapell 1150, Shillman 1158, Shoresh 1159, Simms/Mann 1169, Snyder 1192, Soref 1199, Stern 1219, Swig 1231, Tenenblatt 1245, Wasserman 1300, Webb 1304, Weisman 1308, Winnick 1333, Wolfen 1338, Ziegler 1360
Colorado: Bernstein 1372, Merage 1459, **Merage 1460**, Mizel 1462, Schermer 1492, Singer 1501, Strear 1508, Sturm 1510, Tuchman 1514
Connecticut: Chase 1555, Davis 1571, Kohn 1622, Lowenstein 1633, Ner 1648, Provident 1677, Robbins 1681, Rogow 1683, Rosenthal 1684, Say 1689, Straus 1702, Windreich 1724, Wright 1727
Delaware: Brill 1747, **Marks 1813**, Natembea 1822, Phillips 1835, Ratner 1846, Sternlicht 1861, Whitton-Spector 1874
District of Columbia: Abramson 1877, Bender 1885, Bernstein 1887, Dweck 1902, Friedman-French 1908, Gewirz 1909, Gottesman 1911, Gudelsky 1912, Kaplan 1919, Lehrman 1924, Rales 1942, Seter 1947
Florida: Abramson 1963, Applebaum 1970, **Arison 1972**, Azeez 1975, Beaver 1986, Berman 1994, Bi-Lo 1996, Blank 1997, Block 1998, Bronfman 2003, Brown 2004, **Chester 2020**, Edelman 2080,

Edgemer 2081, Einstein 2084, Fairholme 2090, Falic 2091, Florman 2102, Franklin 2107, Gann 2113, Global 2126, Goldstein 2128, Greenburg 2137, Hertog 2157, Kaplan 2175, Katcher 2176, **Katz 2177**, Katzman 2178, Klurman 2189, KMD 2190, Korf 2193, Kramer 2195, Laber 2197, Lindemann 2217, Lyons 2222, Michaan 2239, Miller 2241, Muss 2248, Newman 2250, RJKB 2289, Rosen 2294, Rosenblatt 2295, Rubin 2300, **Russell 2301**, Sandler 2306, Schaefer 2311, Schoenbaum 2313, Seaman 2314, Selevan 2317, Stein 2337, Stein 2338, Stern 2339, Sun 2344, Wollowick 2393

Georgia: Argo 2405, Covenant 2444, Rosenberg 2544, Saul 2547, Selig 2549, Weber 2570, Zaban 2583

Idaho: Wishnick 2646

Illinois: Abt 2651, Anixter 2664, Anschel 2666, Austin 2677, Baskes 2683, Baskes 2684, Baskin 2685, Bass 2686, Bernick 2695, Blum 2705, Blum 2706, **Carylon 2735**, Cole-Crone 2758, Crain-Maling 2778, D and R 2784, Feinberg 2830, First 2833, Frankel 2842, Friedman 2845, Gidwitz 2862, **Glenner 2866**, **Goodman 2868**, **Goodman 2869**, Harris 2892, **Harris 2893**, Hazan 2899, Heller 2904, Hirschl 2912, Hochberg 2915, I and G 2931, Kovler 2964, Landau 2966, Lasky 2968, Leibowitz 2973, Lerner 2975, Levin 2977, Mander 2998, **Manitoba 2999**, Mills 3028, Oppenheimer 3065, Oppenheimer 3066, Perlman 3076, Polk 3084, Pritzker 3092, Pritzker 3095, Redhill 3108, Ross 3123, Rotonda 3125, Sacks 3131, Seid 3148, Shapiro 3151, Shapiro 3152, Shapiro 3153, Sheba 3155, Sirius 3163, Square 3173, Stern 3177, Stone 3179, Supera 3183, Weinberg 3223, Wenske 3225, Yulman 3246

Indiana: **Ackerman 3252**, **Hasten 3316**, Rifkin 3378, Simon 3385, Simon 3387

Iowa: Glazer 3433

Kansas: Beren 3496, Dreiseszun 3512, Morgan 3536

Louisiana: Goldring 3638, Heymann 3642, Lupin 3652, **Woldenberg 3672**

Maryland: Abramson 3715, **Bearman 3728**, Berger 3729, **Berman 3731**, **Blaustein 3735**, Blum 3737, **Brown 3741**, Cohen 3752, Cohen 3753, Crane 3766, Dahan 3770, Davison 3773, Dupkin 3783, Epstein 3786, Freeman 3797, Glazer 3802, Hackerman 3810, Hirschhorn 3816, Jacobson 3820, Leidy 3830, Lerner 3831, Levitt 3832, Meyerhoff 3848, **Morningstar 3854**, Myers 3856, Polinger 3864, Rosenberg 3873, Rosenberg 3874, Rosenbloom 3875, Wasserman 3905, Wasserman 3906, Weinberg 3907

Massachusetts: A.M. 3912, Aaron 3913, Abrams 3914, Berkman 3945, Chafetz 3979, Cosette 3997, Cutler 4005, Dana 4008, Feigenbaum 4044, Fisher 4052, Ford 4055, Golden 4073, Gordon 4074, Heartstone 4090, Jacobson 4110, Kahn 4116, **Karp 4117**, Klarman 4126, Kraft 4128, Krupp 4131, Marks 4162, Rappaport 4230, **Rosenberg 4245**, Ruderman 4250, Schuster 4264, Shapiro 4267, Sharf 4268, Sidman 4273, Spencer 4278, Sperling 4279, Starwood 4284, Stoneman 4295, Swartz 4301

Michigan: Applebaum 4341, Blumenstein 4351, **Coopersmith 4379**, Danto 4387, Davidson 4390, DeRoy 4396, **Fisher 4423**, Frankel 4433, Frankel 4434, Frankel 4435, Frankel 4436, **Frankel 4437**, Grosfeld 4453, Kahn 4471, Levy 4487, Lewis 4488, Manat 4490, Taubman 4552

Minnesota: Beverly 4615, Edelstein 4652, Foundation 4657, Regis 4750, Sabes 4756

Missouri: Edison 4883, Edison 4884, Gottlieb 4897, Millstone 4944, Oppenstein 4950, Sosland 4975, Sosland 4976, Sosland 4977

Nebraska: Schrager 5079, Slosburg 5083, Sokolof 5084

Nevada: Crystal 5113, Rochlin 5144, Spiegel 5150

New Jersey: **Allen 5191**, Atran 5197, Bacchetta 5198, Cooperman 5233, Gurwin 5286, Halpern 5290, **IDT 5311**, Isermann 5319, Jaffe 5320, Katz 5333, Kauffmann 5334, Kushner 5351, L.A.W. 5352, Levitt 5361, Lewis 5362, Mack 5367, Oster 5399, Renewable 5421, Roberts 5423, Roth 5426, Schecter 5439, Schwartz 5442, Schwartz 5443, Schwarz 5444, Seiden 5448, SFF 5449, ST2 5464, Stadtmauer 5466, Stern 5468, Strauss 5470, Sudler 5472, Syms 5475, Tanzman 5476, Taub 5477, Wagner 5491, Wilf 5502, Wilf 5503, Yosef 5508, Zucker 5509

New Mexico: Altman 5513

New York: Abstraction 5547, Adar 5553, Adelman 5554, Adelson 5555, Adjmi 5557, **AHBA 5562**, Alpern 5577, Alpert 5578, Ames 5591, Appleman 5604, Aresty 5609, Aron 5616, Aronson 5617, **Ashner 5619**, August 5624, **AVI 5628**, Azrak 5630, Bachmann 5632, Baker 5638, Baron 5646, **BCHB 5655**, Beker 5659, Belfer 5660, Benenson 5665, Berg 5666, Berkowitz 5669, Betesh 5671, Bialkin 5673, Black 5681, Blank 5682, Blum 5686, Braka 5702, Braufman 5704, Bravmann 5705, Bronfman 5715, Butler 5735, Buttenwieser 5736, Canary 5744, Cayre 5752, Central 5756, Century 5758, Chazen 5767, Chehebar 5768, Chernow 5771, Chesed 5772, **CLRC 5789**, Cohn 5793, Cooper 5812, Cornerstone 5817, Damial 5844, **David 5852**, Derfner 5874, Diamond 5880, Diker 5883, Ditmars 5890, Dobkin 5891, Drexler 5911, E & SS 5924, Edelman 5930, Edlow 5935, EGL 5939, Einhorn 5943, Englander 5955, Everett 5964, Farash 5969, Feil 5973, Feinstein 5974, Fischer 5981, Fisher 5982, Friedman 6019, Friedman 6020, Friedman 6021, Fuchs 6028, Ganger 6033, **GBRG 6036**, Gershwind 6046, Gerson 6047, Gindi 6054, Goldberg 6062, Goldstein 6074, Goldstein 6075, Goldstein 6076, Golub 6079, Gould 6089, Granoff 6091, **Grant 6092**, Green 6101, Greene 6103, Gural 6117, Harary 6131, Harris 6138, Harris 6141, Hartman 6145, Hendel 6161, Hersh 6166, Hershaft 6167, Hershman 6168, Heyman-Merrin 6172, Hochfelder 6177, Hochstein 6178, Holtzmann 6184, Horowitz 6186, Hurst 6200, **IIMI 6207**, Jacobson 6219, JJR 6231, Joelson 6232, Kaplan 6250, Kaplan 6251, Katz 6257, Kaufman 6259, Kayden 6261, Kaylie 6263, Keidan 6267, Kingdon 6284, **Klein 6287**, Korman 6303, Lake 6320, Lane 6325, Lasdon 6332, Leffell 6345, **Leir 6349**, Lemberg 6350, Lerner 6353, Leshkowitz 6354, Leventhal 6357, Levine 6359, Levy 6362, Levy 6363, Lindner 6372, Loewenberg 6387, Lopatin 6392, Lostand 6394, Lurie 6403, Malkin 6422, Mark 6430, Marx 6442, Massry 6444, Melohn 6472, Meyer 6480, Meyer 6481, Millard 6484, Milstein 6488, Mnuchin 6493, Morse 6509, Moses 6511, National 6528, Neidich 6534, Neuwirth 6539, New Brook 6540, New Tamarind 6541, Newhouse 6550, Newman 6555, Nias 6556, Och 6575, Olshan 6588, Oppenheim 6594, Ostrovsky 6600, Parkview 6617, **Pershing 6629**, Picket 6638, Price 6657, Propp 6662, Pulier 6665, Pzena 6669, Rechler 6682, Regals 6685, Reiss 6687, Richman 6702, **Ridgefield 6705**, Robbins 6715, Rose 6732, Rose 6737, Rose 6738, Rosen 6741, Rosenfeld 6747, Rosenthal 6749, Rosenwald 6750, Rosner 6752, Rotter 6757, Rubenstein 6762, Rudin 6767, Rudin 6768, Sackler 6776, Safra 6781, Sagner 6783, Saltz 6787, Sandler 6789, **Sato 6798**, Schenker 6803, Schnurmacher 6810, Schwartz 6816, Schwartz 6818, Schwartz 6819, SDA 6823, Secunda 6827, Seiler 6828, Shapiro 6838, Silverweed 6857, Sitt 6866, Skirball 6869, Slifka 6871, SO 6881, Sobel 6883, Solomon 6885, Spilker 6897, Spitzer 6900, Stanton 6907, Starker 6910, Stein 6918, Steinberg 6920, Steinberg 6921, Steinberg 6922, Steinhardt 6923, Stern 6927, Stulman 6938, Sun 6946, Sutton 6948, SVM 6952, Tananbaum 6962, Teferes 6968, Tisch 6986, Tisch 6987, Tisch 6988, Tisch 6989, Tova 6998, Tuft 7011, Unterberg 7021, **VHIV 7028**, **Vicente 7029**, Volpert 7036, Wasserman 7055, Weiler 7063, Weinstein 7068, Winkelried 7090, Wohl 7097, Wunsch 7106, **YLRY 7110**, Zilkha 7125, Zubrow 7126, Zuckerberg 7128

North Carolina: Baruch 7140, Blumenthal 7154, Strauss 7323, Vickar 7333

Ohio: American 7370, Diamond 7435, Friedlander 7463, Heiman 7486, Horvitz 7493, Kaplan 7516, **Lerner 7538**, Levin 7539, Mandel 7554, **Mandel 7555**, Mandel 7556, Mayerson 7561, Miller 7571, Philips 7619, Rockwern 7634, Rose 7636, **Sapirstein-Stone-Weiss 7644**, Schear 7645, Schottenstein 7654, Stone 7677, **Wexner 7713**, Wuliger 7722

Oklahoma: Coretz 7744, Kaiser 7763, **ROI 7791**, Taubman 7804

Oregon: Zidell 7902

Pennsylvania: Arete 7919, Barrist 7929, Berkman 7938, BNY 7946, Buncher 7957, Cassett 7969, Chosky 7980, Clayman 7984, Cooper 7997, Elias 8022, Erlbaum 8027, Farber 8032, Feldman 8034, Fine 8039, Fishman 8044, Grass 8067, Hecht 8082, Kestenbaum 8121, Kimmel 8124, Kline 8128, Levis 8140, Lipsitz 8144, Lotman 8150, Mandell 8153, Miller 8180, Morgan 8187, Novotny 8202, Posner 8233, Roberts 8250, Ross 8255, Saligman 8261, Scheller 8268, Schneider 8271, Shapira 8282, Snider 8292, Stein 8297, Toll 8316, Toll 8317

Rhode Island: Elms 8387, Fain 8388, Hassenfeld 8404

South Carolina: Zucker 8510

Tennessee: Great 8575, Lebovitz 8597

Texas: Diener 8807, Feldman 8843, Gale 8859, Hall 8883, Hirsch 8910, Kolitz 8968, Levit 8982, Mankoff 8998, Rapoport 9122, Schepps 9158, Soref-Breslauer 9190, Sterling 9202, Wolff 9287

Virginia: Colburn 9409, Funger 9438, Kanter 9459, Newman 9493, Ratner 9515, Rosenthal 9525, Samberg 9527, Smith 9532

Washington: Benaroya 9583, Loeb 9672, **PAH 9699**, Sarkowsky 9727, Schultz 9730, Sloan 9736

Wisconsin: Anon 9805, Goodman 9852, Kohl 9883, Lubar 9894, Peck 9918, Posner 9922, Soref 9948, Zilber 9972

Journalism school/education

Illinois: Logan 2983
Iowa: Meredith 3463
North Carolina: Curtis 7186
Ohio: Scripps 7659
Oklahoma: **Ethics 7749**
Virginia: **Gannett 9439**

Kidney diseases

Mississippi: Bower 4816
New York: Select 6829

Labor rights

New York: **Cummings 5833**
Vermont: **Ben 9358**

Landscaping

Alabama: Alabama 1
New York: Richmond 6703
Pennsylvania: Rhoads,Jr. 8248

Language (foreign)

Washington: Blakemore 9587

Language/linguistics

California: **Ing 721**
Connecticut: Rosenthal 1684
Illinois: **Tyndale 3195**
New York: **Kade 6247**, Littauer 6379, **Pforzheimer 6635**, **Wenner 7075**
North Carolina: Cumberland 7184

Law school/education

California: Caruso 382, Darling 449, Greenberg 624, Irmas 725, Irmas 726, Lamond 817, Leichtman 829, Mabie 863, Munger 954, Ressler 1065
Colorado: Monfort 1464
Connecticut: Meriden 1643, Richman 1680
Delaware: Salah 1855
Florida: Bradley 2001, Engelberg 2086, James 2169, Scarpa 2310, Star 2335
Georgia: Watson 2569
Illinois: Austin 2677, Blum 2705, Cressey 2779, Katten 2951, Montgomery 3035
Louisiana: Louisiana 3651
Michigan: Leighton 4484
Minnesota: Kelley 4686, Mooty 4720, Robins 4754
Mississippi: Hearin 4832
Missouri: Hulston 4911
Nevada: Lee 5127, Wiegand 5159
New Jersey: Goldberg 5279, L.A.W. 5352, Sudler 5472
New York: Burns 5732, D'Agostino 5843, Dauman 5849, Dowling 5907, Feil 5973, Green 6100, Haje 6129, Hughes 6193, Katz 6257, Leventhal 6357, Levy 6362, MBIA 6451, Moore 6505, **Shaw 6840**, Silverweed 6857, **Skadden 6868**, **Stempel 6925**, Sun 6946
North Carolina: Bryan 7162
Ohio: Ferry 7451, Stark 7673
Pennsylvania: Dickson 8009, Haldeman 8076, Stein/Bellet 8298
Texas: Bickel 8705, O'Quinn 9072, Sumners 9214
Virginia: Lipman 9469

Law/international law

California: JAMS 744
Illinois: Mirza 3032
Maryland: **DLA 3781**
Michigan: **Fetzer 4420**
New York: **Ford 5994**, **Guggenheim 6115**, **Hauser 6147**, **Open 6593**, Swyer 6956
Pennsylvania: Scaife 8266

Leadership development

Alabama: BBVA 9
Arizona: Freeport-McMoRan 112, Rodel 158
California: Applied 249, Bechtel, 296, Blue 320, California 368, **Capital 375**, Cathay 385, Confidence 423, Egg 496, Germanacos 574, **Haas 643**, Johnson 753, Los Altos 849, Morgan 940, Pacific 1003, Panda 1010, Placer 1039, Sacramento 1103, San Francisco 1109, Shasta 1154, Sierra 1163, Weingart 1307, Whitman 1322
Colorado: Piton 1480, Vodafone 1519
Connecticut: Community 1564, Donchian 1576, **GE 1591**, **Newman's 1652**
Delaware: Sylvan 1867
District of Columbia: **Hill 1915**, Meyer 1931, **Moriah 1932**
Florida: Florida 2101, **Katz 2177**
Georgia: AGL 2400, Pittulloch 2530, **UPS 2566**
Hawaii: Hawaii 2602
Illinois: Caterpillar 2738, Chicago 2746, Community 2763, Evanston 2826, Logan 2983, Polk 3084, Tracy 3189
Indiana: Community 3281, Community 3283, Lincoln 3344, Old 3363, OneAmerica 3364, Vectren 3394, Wayne 3400
Iowa: AEGON 3409, McElroy 3461
Kansas: Kansas 3524, Sprint 3549
Maine: Horizon 3691, Maine 3698
Maryland: Abell 3712
Massachusetts: Blue 3953, Boston 3956, Community 3991, **Germeshausen 4069**, Liberty 4145
Michigan: Community 4371, Community 4372, Consumers 4376, DTE 4410, Hillsdale 4461, **Kellogg 4474**, **Mott 4510**, RNR 4527
Minnesota: Best 4612, Blandin 4617, Bush 4621, CHS 4636, **Fuller 4659**, George 4662, Hubbard 4678, Land 4691, Minnesota 4715, Travelers 4783, West 4800
Mississippi: Foundation 4827
Missouri: Truman 4996
Montana: First 5009
New Jersey: Community 5232, Dodge 5243, **Johnson 5329**, Kirby 5339, **Prudential 5415**, Victoria 5490
New Mexico: McCune 5529
New York: American 5587, **American 5588**, **Citi 5780**, **Ford 5994**, **JPMorgan 6244**, **MetLife 6479**, **Pershing 6629**, Seneca 6832, **Skadden 6868**, **Wallace 7043**
North Carolina: **Bank 7139**, Blue 7153, Cumberland 7184, Duke 7196, Foundation 7202, Piedmont 7285, Reynolds 7298, Triangle 7328, Weaver 7335
Ohio: Coshocton 7421, **Mandel 7555**, Middletown 7570, Murphy 7584, Muskingum 7585, Stark 7673, **Timken 7684**, **Wexner 7713**, Youngstown 7723
Oregon: Meyer 7870, Oregon 7876
Pennsylvania: CIGNA 7981, Comcast 7989, Dolfinger 8013, Keystone 8122, Pew 8220, Scranton 8275, Stackpole 8295, **Templeton 8313**
Rhode Island: Rhode Island 8429
Tennessee: Hyde 8584
Texas: AT&T 8675, Buford 8736, Dean 8803, **Jenesis 8932**, Meadows 9019
Virginia: Alleghany 9382, CarMax 9401, Landmark 9467, Luck 9472, Mitsubishi 9487, SunTrust 9539
Washington: **Bullitt 9591**, **Stewardship 9744**, Tacoma 9750
Wisconsin: Alliant 9804

Learning disorders

California: Schwab 1128
Georgia: Rollins 2543
Minnesota: Cargill 4628
North Carolina: **Oak 7276**
Ohio: Park 7609

Legal services

Arizona: Arizona 92
California: Gibson 583, Jennings 748, Marin 877, Mendelson 912, Napa 959, Parsons 1013, Rosenberg 1088, Sacramento 1103, San Francisco 1109, **Strauss 1223**, vanLoben 1283, Weingart 1307
Connecticut: Ossen 1664, Palmer 1666
Delaware: Berkley 1741
District of Columbia: Beech 1884, Meyer 1931
Florida: Liman 2216
Georgia: Flowers 2459, McKenna 2516
Illinois: Austin 2677, Katten 2951, New 3052, Polk 3084
Louisiana: Louisiana 3651
Maryland: **DLA 3781**, Wareheim 3903
Massachusetts: Beveridge 3950, Golden 4073, Mifflin 4175
Minnesota: Bremer 4620, Leonard 4694, Robins 4754
Missouri: Ten-Ten 4990
Montana: Oro 5014
New Jersey: Cole 5231, Evans 5254
New York: Abrons 5546, Berg 5667, Calamus 5740, Charina 5764, Daphne 5848, **Ford 5994**, Gimbel 6053, Hughes 6193, New York 6544, Rosenfeld 6747, Scherman 6804, Starfish 6909, Western 7078
North Carolina: Reynolds 7298, Triangle 7328
North Dakota: Stern 7360
Ohio: Nonneman 7593
Oregon: Carpenter 7831
Pennsylvania: Dolfinger 8013, Independence 8107, Philadelphia 8221, United 8325
Rhode Island: Rhode Island 8429
Texas: Bickel 8705, Fikes 8844, Maverick 9005, Stern 9204, Wright 9293
Virginia: Koch 9463, Mousetrap 9491
Washington: Norcliffe 9693
Wisconsin: Milwaukee 9907

Legal services, public interest law

California: vanLoben 1283
Georgia: Sapelo 2546
Illinois: Landau 2966
Michigan: **Moller 4506**
New Jersey: Evans 5254, RuthMarc 5431
Pennsylvania: Independence 8107, Jackson 8110
Vermont: Waterwheel 9376
Virginia: Claws 9408

Lesbians

California: Weingart 1307
Pennsylvania: Staunton 8296

LGBTQ

Arizona: Webb 174
California: Atkinson 265, Bohnett 324, California 365, California 368, Community 414, East 490, Fleishhacker 534, **Geffen 567**, Gerbode 573, Gumbiner 636, Lesher 833, PG&E 1033, San Luis 1110, Small 1180, Weingart 1307, Wunderkinder 1348
Colorado: Community 1391, **Gill 1421**
Connecticut: Community 1562
Delaware: **Raskob 1845**
District of Columbia: Cafritz 1890, **Union 1953**
Florida: Burns 2006, Miami 2238
Illinois: Allstate 2657, ARIA 2672, Chicago 2746, Community 2765, Day 2787, Field 2831, Logan 2983, Washington 3217
Indiana: Community 3281
Massachusetts: Community 3992, Currents 4004, Harmsworth 4087, Hyams 4103, Two 4313
Michigan: Chrysler 4366, Grand Rapids 4447
Minnesota: Bremer 4620, Mossier 4723, Phillips 4741
Missouri: Saint Louis 4966
Montana: Montana 5013
New Hampshire: Foundation 5171
New Jersey: Hyde 5310
New Mexico: McCune 5529, Santa Fe 5533
New York: **Arcus 5608**, Calamus 5740, Dechman 5862, **Ford 5994**, Haring 6133, Johnson 6239, Langeloth 6327, Luce 6397, McCarthy 6455, **MetLife 6479**, New York 6546, **Open 6593**, **Overbrook 6604**, Palette 6609, Snowdon 6879, **Sparkplug 6894**
North Carolina: Community 7180, Triangle 7328
Ohio: Akron 7367, KeyBank 7523
Oklahoma: Hille 7759
Oregon: Carpenter 7831, Collins 7836
Pennsylvania: First 8041, Staunton 8296
Texas: Chasdrew 8762, Dallas 8795, Richardson 9131
Utah: Bastian 9306
Virginia: Luminescence 9473
Wisconsin: La Crosse 9889, Milwaukee 9907

Libraries (academic/research)

California: Steinmetz 1216
Illinois: Brooker 2716
Massachusetts: Calderwood 3969, Ragon 4228

Libraries (law)

Texas: Fleming 8849

Libraries (public)

Alabama: Hearin 38
California: **Capital 375**, Engemann 506, Farese 518, Genentech 571, Klein 793, Milias 925, Nestle 965, Simpson 1173, Tanimura 1236, Thornton 1251, WHH 1320
Colorado: Janus 1432, **Kinder 1439**
Connecticut: New Canaan 1650, **Praxair 1676**, Rockville 1682, Sheinberg 1695
Delaware: Presto 1840
Florida: Glazer 2124, Green 2136, Hertog 2157
Georgia: Aflac 2399, Singletary 2551
Illinois: **Abbott 2649**, Donnelley 2801, Energizer 2824, Hamel 2887, Lumpkin 2986, Maddux 2991, Munson 3045

Libraries (school)

Libraries (special)

Libraries, archives

Libraries/library science

Literature

Liver disorders

Lung diseases

Lung research

Lupus

Lupus research

Marine science

Mathematics

Minnesota: 3M 4597, **Andersen 4601**, **Fuller 4659**, **Medtronic 4712**, **Pentair 4739**, Securian 4761, **St. Jude 4770**, TEAM 4779, Xcel 4808
Missouri: Burns 4866, Express 4888, **Kauffman 4921**, **Monsanto 4945**
New Jersey: **Knowles 5345**, **Merck 5379**, Merck 5380, PSEG 5416, **Siemens 5454**, Subaru 5471, **Verizon 5489**
New York: **Deutsche 5876**, **IBM 6203**, **Moody's 6499**, **Pfizer 6633**, Simons 6861, TE 6966, Tensor 6970, **Toshiba 6997**, Toyota 7002
North Carolina: Duke 7196, Goodrich 7213, Piedmont 7285
Ohio: FirstEnergy 7455, Jennings 7509, Nordson 7596, **OMNOVA 7601**
Oklahoma: Oklahoma 7782
Oregon: **Intel 7853**, PGE 7881
Pennsylvania: **Alcoa 7908**, Bayer 7932, EQT 8025, PNC 8230, **PPG 8235**
Rhode Island: Biogen 8363
Tennessee: Eastman 8561
Texas: AT&T 8675, **BP 8718**, **ExxonMobil 8833**, Fluor 8851, O'Donnell 9067, Texas 9227
Virginia: CarMax 9401, Dominion 9422, Norfolk 9496, **Northrop 9498**
Washington: Avista 9576, Norcliffe 9693
Wisconsin: Bemis 9815, Brookhill 9824, Rockwell 9934

Media, film/video

Arizona: Schultz 161
California: Arbus 251, CAA 362, Craigslist 436, DeMille 459, Disney 467, Fleishhacker 534, Goldwyn 609, Katzenberg 769, Lucas 855, Pacific 1004, Packard 1007, Reinhard 1061, Skywords 1177
Colorado: Summit 1511
Connecticut: Mandell 1635, Rosenthal 1684
Delaware: Devonwood 1768, Dwoskin 1772, Tarrant 1869
District of Columbia: Kaye 1920
Florida: Bank 1979, **Davis 2056**, Gulf 2142
Illinois: **MacArthur 2989**
Indiana: Simon 3386
Minnesota: Best 4612, Jerome 4681, Land 4691
Nevada: Mann 5130, Mathewson 5131
New Jersey: Evans 5254, **Puffin 5417**
New York: Amicus 5592, Burns 5732, Cinereach 5779, **Cummings 5833**, **Fledgling 5987**, **Ford 5994**, Greenberg 6102, Greve 6106, Mack 6411, **Mayer 6449**, Piece 6640, Stern 6926, Time 6982, Tisch 6991, **Trace 7003**, Vilcek 7031
Ohio: Akron 7367
Pennsylvania: Crawford 8001
Tennessee: Regal 8622
Texas: **Cultural 8793**
Washington: Seattle 9731

Media, journalism

California: Craigslist 436, Oakland 977
Florida: **Knight 2191**
Iowa: Meredith 3463
Minnesota: Martin 4704
New York: **Cummings 5833**, Time 6982
Pennsylvania: Wyncote 8349

Media, print publishing

Connecticut: Rosenthal 1684
Florida: **Knight 2191**, St. Petersburg 2332
Iowa: Meredith 3463
Minnesota: Hubbard 4678
New Jersey: Cole 5231
New York: **Cummings 5833**, Newhouse 6550, **Ottaway 6603**, Park 6615, Snow 6878
Ohio: Scripps 7659
Pennsylvania: Pew 8220
Texas: **PHM 9098**
Virginia: **Gannett 9439**

Media, radio

California: Avis 274, Barry 284, **Capital 375**, Center 388, Greenberg 624, Hoppe 703, Ishiyama 730, Mohn 934, Oakland 977, Roth 1093, Western 1315
Colorado: Catto 1383
Florida: Graff 2133, Litowitz 2218
Illinois: Chaddick 2740, Clinton 2754, Morrison 3038
Maryland: Sunrise 3892, Town 3897
Michigan: Mosaic 4509, Schaap 4533
Minnesota: Ciresi 4637, **Medtronic 4712**, Valspar 4786
Missouri: Centene 4870
Nebraska: Union 5090, Weitz 5092
New York: 2A 5540, Albert 5567, Baldwin 5639, **Cummings 5833**, Greene 6104, Harriman 6137, Solomon 6885
Ohio: Morgan 7577
Tennessee: Atticus 8531, Bridgestone 8537
Texas: Criswell 8789, Heavin 8898
Virginia: Bansal 9387
Washington: Seattle 9731
Wisconsin: Johnson 9870

Media, television

Arizona: Stewart 166
California: Arbus 251, **Capital 375**, Center 388, Disney 467, Goldwyn 609, Katzenberg 769, Lyons 859
Colorado: KBK 1437
Delaware: Dwoskin 1772
Florida: Brown 2004, Graff 2133
Illinois: Boyer 2711, Clinton 2754, Heller 2904
Indiana: 1st 3251, Miller 3355, Wayne 3400
Iowa: Aviva 3411
Maryland: Town 3897
Massachusetts: Filene 4047, Keane 4118
Michigan: Devereaux 4397, Polk 4524
Minnesota: Land 4691
Nebraska: Union 5090
New Jersey: Syms 5475
New York: Burns 5732, **Cummings 5833**, D'Agostino 5843, Eberstadt-Kuffner 5929, Harriman 6137, **MetLife 6479**, Park 6615, Radio 6672, Smith 6877, Stern 6926, Time 6982, Walter 7046
Ohio: Lincoln 7541
Rhode Island: TriMix 8448
Tennessee: Atticus 8531, Bridgestone 8537, Travis 8637
Texas: Heavin 8898, Rea 9123
Washington: PEMCO 9702
Wisconsin: Johnson 9870

Media/communications

California: Bohnett 324, Carsey 380, Disney 467, Ducommun 485, **Google 615**, Hitz 694, Rotasa 1092, Roth 1093, San Francisco 1109, Small 1180
Connecticut: Berger 1546, Huisking 1615, Rosenthal 1684
Delaware: **Adobe 1734**
District of Columbia: Quetzal 1941
Florida: Cohen 2028, Jacksonville 2167, Martin 2229, St. Petersburg 2332
Illinois: Logan 2983, **MacArthur 2989**, Manaaki 2997, Oppenheimer 3066, Stuart 3182
Massachusetts: Bell 3941, Lowell 4153, Ruettgers 4252, Saltonstall 4254, Santander 4256, Tupancy 4312
Michigan: **Moller 4506**
Minnesota: **Andersen 4601**, Best 4612, Mooty 4719, Robins 4754, Veritas 4789
Missouri: Emerson 4885
New Jersey: Dodge 5243, Gulton 5284, Hickory 5299
New Mexico: **Johns 5524**
New York: Alfiero 5570, Cloud 5788, Corning 5818, **Cummings 5833**, Diller 5884, **Ford 5994**, **Hauser 6147**, Kellen 6268, Mercer 6474, Milliken 6487, Newhouse 6550, **Open 6593**, Park 6615, **Revson 6693**, Schumann 6813, Skirball 6869, Time 6982, van Ameringen 7023, Walter 7046
Ohio: Reinberger 7628
Oklahoma: **Ethics 7749**, Williams 7814
Pennsylvania: Federated 8033, Saltsgiver 8262, Vanguard 8327, Wyncote 8349
Rhode Island: Koonce 8412
Texas: Gale 8859, Meadows 9019, San Antonio 9148, Thank 9229, Wright 9293
Virginia: **Gannett 9439**
Washington: **Allen 9568**, Community 9604, **Glaser 9630**, Yakima 9767
Wisconsin: Acuity 9801

Medical care, bioethics

Colorado: Pema 1476
New York: Cranaleith 5825, **Greenwall 6105**, Klingenstein 6291, Littauer 6379

Medical care, community health systems

California: California 368, Patron 1020
Illinois: **Abbott 2649**, Healthcare 2900
Indiana: Kosciusko 3335
Iowa: Mid-Iowa 3466
Massachusetts: Chafetz 3979, George 4068, MetroWest 4173
Michigan: Rordor 4529
Minnesota: **Medtronic 4712**
New Jersey: **Merck 5379**
New York: **Bristol 5711**, Health 6153, New York 6549, **Pfizer 6633**
North Carolina: Blue 7153
Ohio: **Cardinal 7398**, Osteopathic 7605
Oregon: Cambia 7829
Pennsylvania: Noteman 8201, Phoenixville 8223, Pottstown 8234
Tennessee: Hamico 8576
Texas: Discovery 8808, Murchison 9045
Virginia: Hampton 9448, Northern 9497, SunTrust 9539, Williamsburg 9558

Medical care, in-patient care

Alabama: Hearin 38
Connecticut: Heimbold 1612
Illinois: Morrison 3037
Massachusetts: Peabody 4209
Michigan: Ford 4427, McGregor 4498
New York: Countess 5821, Vidda 7030
Oregon: Cambia 7829

Medical care, outpatient care

California: Community 415, Patron 1020
Hawaii: HMSA 2604
Minnesota: **King 4687**
New York: Kellen 6268, Klein 6289, Korman 6303, New York 6549, Samuels 6788

Medical care, rehabilitation

California: Anaheim 239, Patron 1020, Sierra 1163, Teichert 1244, Weingart 1307
Colorado: Boettcher 1374
District of Columbia: Cafritz 1890
Florida: Martin 2229
Illinois: Coleman 2759, Community 2763, Eisenberg 2819, Harris 2892, Prince 3089, Wonderful 3239
Indiana: Kosciusko 3335
Maryland: **Ewing 3787**, GEICO 3801
Massachusetts: Beveridge 3950, Community 3992, Demoulas 4014, Janey 4111
Michigan: Fremont 4438
Minnesota: Ordean 4732, **Patterson 4738**
Nevada: Nevada 5134
New Jersey: Hyde 5310, **Milbank 5385**, Snyder 5462
New Mexico: McCune 5529
New York: Achelis 5549, Charina 5763, Charina 5764, Cummings 5834, Four 6006, **Hearst 6155**, **Hearst 6156**, Noble 6560, NYSE 6573, **Ross 6754**, Ross 6755, **Vital 7033**, Western 7078
North Carolina: Cumberland 7184, Triangle 7328

Medical research

Medical research, association

Medical research, formal/general education

Medical research, information services

Medical research, institute

Quick 6670, Raether 6673, Raiff 6675, Rasmussen 6679, Regals 6685, Rosen 6741, Rosenblum 6746, Rosenthal 6749, Rowan 6758, Rubenstein 6762, Saltz 6787, Schenker 6803, Schnurmacher 6810, Schwartz 6819, SDA 6823, Semlitz 6831, Shulsky 6851, Smith 6877, Starker 6910, Stuart 6937, **Summerfield 6944**, Sun 6946, Tai 6960, Tisch 6987, Tisch 6988, Trump 7008, Turner 7013, Vilcek 7031, **Vital 7033**, Walsh 7045, Wasserman 7055, Weinberg 7066, Zaro 7115
North Carolina: Bryan 7161, **Burroughs 7164**, Foundation 7202, Gordon 7214, Plansoen 7286, Slick 7313, Van Every 7329, Van Houten 7330
Ohio: Akron 7367, Berlin 7385, Brown 7390, Cleveland 7406, Dodero 7438, Horvitz 7493, Ingalls 7503, Jobst 7512, **Kettering 7520**, Licking 7540, McBride 7562, Miller 7571, Murch 7582, Philips 7619, Prentiss 7621, Rosenthal 7637, Schlink 7650, Warrington 7703, Wodecroft 7717
Oklahoma: Foundation 7751, Gaylord 7753, Kerr 7764, Noble 7780, Puterbaugh 7786, Simmons 7796, Warren 7809
Oregon: **Chiles 7833**, Collins 7837, Poznanski 7882
Pennsylvania: **AO 7915**, Buncher 7957, Fine 8039, Gitlin 8058, Kimmel 8124, Lotman 8150, Lutron 8151, Mandell 8153, Massey 8158, McCune 8161, Rohrer 8252, Springbank 8293, Wheeler 8335, Widener 8336, Withington 8344
Rhode Island: Alpert 8355, Charlesmead 8371, Falk 8389
South Carolina: Abney 8454, TSC 8506
Tennessee: Children's 8543, Davis 8555, Hartwell 8579, Massey 8607, Midler 8611
Texas: Ackerman 8651, Alexander 8656, Alkek 8657, Alkek 8658, Anadarko 8661, Cain 8743, Chapman 8761, Coates 8769, Cullen 8792, DeBakey 8804, Dunn 8816, Edwards 8824, Elkins 8826, Ellwood 8827, Fikes 8844, Fish 8848, Franklin 8855, Gibson 8866, Halsell 8885, Hamill 8887, Hamman 8888, Hankamer 8890, Hawn 8896, Herd 8902, Hillcrest 8909, Kleberg 8962, Knobloch 8965, Kronkosky 8970, Lightner 8985, McCombs 9009, McDermott 9013, Moody 9033, Moss 9043, Murchison 9046, **Notsew 9064**, Once 9070, Owsley 9078, Parks 9081, Reliant 9126, Reynolds 9127, San Antonio 9148, Shivers 9171, Smith 9183, Smith 9185, Smith 9187, Stedman 9200, Strake 9208, Sturgis 9211, Waco 9251, Wichita 9277, Wolff 9287
Utah: ALSAM 9302, Dee 9312, Dialysis 9313, Eccles 9319, Eccles 9320, McCarthey 9332, Semnani 9350, **Thrasher 9353**
Virginia: Carter 9403, Claws 9408, Jeffress 9457, Manning 9476, NewMarket 9494, Titmus 9543
Washington: Anderson 9572, Apex 9574, Biller 9586, Dimmer 9610, Kuni 9662, Norcliffe 9693, Wheeler 9760
Wisconsin: Bleser 9818, Helfaer 9861, Hovde 9865, Kohl 9883
Wyoming: Zimmerman 10000

Medical school/education

Alabama: Turner 72
Arizona: Morris 148, Weil 175
California: Baxter 288, California 368, Early 489, Femino 521, Genentech 571, **Gilead 586**, Gleis 593, Hastings 661, Hodges 698, MacKenzie 866, McKesson 903, Pacific 1004, Saunders 1118, Shapell 1150, Sidell-Kagan 1161, Wollenberg 1339
Colorado: COPIC 1397, Williams 1524
Connecticut: Aetna 1531, Culpeper 1568, Larsen 1624, Lee 1626, O'Herron 1660, Prusoff 1678, Steere 1701, Yale 1729
Delaware: O'Neil 1826
District of Columbia: Aid 1879
Florida: Applebaum 1970, Coulter 2048, **Davis 2056**, Kimmelman 2184, Macdonald 2223, Speer 2328
Georgia: Cobb 2427, Harris 2478, Harrison 2480, Katz 2494, Reeder 2536
Hawaii: **Burke 2590**
Illinois: Arthur 2673, Hirschl 2912, Homan 2919, Jahn 2938, Miller 3024, Perritt 3077, Prentice 3088, Pritzker 3096, Roberts 3120, Sinsheimer 3161, Washington 3217
Indiana: Ball 3262, Kendrick 3333, Reeves 3374
Iowa: Siouxland 3480
Louisiana: Baton Rouge 3613, Marshall 3653
Maryland: Adalman-Goodwin 3716, Angelos 3721, **Hughes 3818**, Kerr 3823
Massachusetts: Baldwin 3934, Boston 3957, **China 3982**, Foundation 4057, Kiva 4125, **Mirowski 4179**, Wolfson 4325, Worcester 4327
Michigan: MSJ 4513, Ravitz 4526, Towsley 4557, Wolverine 4593
Minnesota: United 4785
Missouri: Express 4888, Gottlieb 4897, Speas 4978
Nevada: Wiegand 5159
New Hampshire: Gifford 5173
New Jersey: Atran 5197, Carolan 5225, Healthcare 5296, Hyde 5310, Integra 5315, **Johnson 5329**, **Pfeiffer 5405**, **Ramapo 5419**, Silbermann 5456, WebMD 5496
New York: Alpern 5577, Archangel 5606, Baker 5638, Baron 5646, Belfer 5660, **Bristol 5711**, Brodsky 5714, Charina 5764, Collins 5798, Community 5803, **Cummings 5832**, Dowling 5907, Friedman 6019, Glickenhaus 6058, **Goldman 6066**, Goldstein 6073, Gural 6117, Horncrest 6185, Hugoton 6194, Jaharis 6223, Kanas 6249, Kempner 6273, Kennedy 6274, Klingenstein 6293, Knapp 6295, Kornfeld 6304, Lurie 6403, Lynch 6404, **Macy 6414**, McGonagle 6460, Mesdag 6478, Mollylou 6496, Plumeri 6649, Rantz 6678, Resnick 6689, Rosenwald 6751, Ruben 6761, Rudin 6769, Sackler 6780, Saltz 6787, **Shaw 6840**, Sosnoff 6892, **Tai 6959**, Vilcek 7031, Werblow 7076, Winston 7092
North Carolina: Love 7258, Van Houten 7330, Winslow 7339
Ohio: Cleveland 7406, Schlink 7650
Oregon: Collins 7837, Esco 7841, Swindells 7892
Pennsylvania: **AO 7915**, Aospine 7916, Briggs 7950, Fieldstone 8038, Garfield 8052, Kahn 8115, Measey 8170, Perelman 8219, Piper 8227, Sand 8264
Rhode Island: Alpert 8355, CVS 8379
South Carolina: Abney 8454
Tennessee: Tennessee 8634
Texas: Alcon 8655, Alexander 8656, Alkek 8658, CH 8759, DeBakey 8804, Elkins 8826, Ellwood 8827, Fikes 8844, Franklin 8855, Gulf 8878, Hankamer 8890, Hobby 8911, Hoblitzelle 8912, Hudson 8919, Huffington 8920, Kempner 8952, Meadows 9019, Medallion 9020, Moody 9033, San Antonio 9148, Star 9197, Wintermann 9283
Utah: Bamberger 9305, Eccles 9320
Vermont: Evslin 9360
Virginia: Beazley 9391, Lipman 9469, Moore 9489, Olsson 9502
Washington: Foundation 9623, McMillen 9681, Stevenson 9743
Wisconsin: Charter 9829, McBeath 9901, Peck 9918, Rath 9927, Shapiro 9945

Medical specialties

Illinois: Siragusa 3162
Michigan: VanderWeide 4572
New Jersey: Bard 5202
Oklahoma: Oxley 7785
Pennsylvania: Stein 8297
Texas: Anderson 8664

Medical specialties research

Louisiana: Pennington 3659
Maryland: **Sidgmore 3885**

Medicine/medical care, public education

California: Patron 1020
Illinois: Healthcare 2900
Louisiana: Blue 3615
Massachusetts: DentaQuest 4016, MetroWest 4173
Missouri: Express 4888
New York: **Pfizer 6633**
North Dakota: Leach 7353
Rhode Island: CVS 8379

Men

Alabama: Kaul 43, Meyer 53
Arizona: Webb 174
California: California 368, Gerbode 573, Lesher 833, McMillen 905, Patron 1020, Weingart 1307
Colorado: Community 1391, King 1440
Connecticut: Community 1562
Delaware: **Raskob 1845**
District of Columbia: **Union 1953**
Georgia: Lewis 2502
Illinois: Chicago 2746, Fry 2849
Indiana: Community 3286, Henry 3320, **Lilly 3342**, Steuben 3390
Kansas: Hutchinson 3521
Kentucky: Cralle 3571
Michigan: Chrysler 4366, Grand Rapids 4447, Midland 4502
Minnesota: Bremer 4620
Mississippi: Community 4821, Gulf 4830
Montana: Oro 5014
Nevada: Mann 5130
New Jersey: **Allen 5191**, Fund 5270, Hyde 5310
New York: Altman 5579, Community 5802, Greater 6099, **Hearst 6155**, **Hearst 6156**, **MetLife 6479**, Ritter 6712
North Carolina: Community 7180, Reidsville 7294
Ohio: Cincinnati 7404, Fairfield 7445, O'Neill 7602, Parents 7608, St. Marys 7672
Oklahoma: Hardesty 7756, Hille 7759
Pennsylvania: Beneficial 7936, Birmingham 7942, Phoenixville 8223, Staunton 8296
Tennessee: Wilson 8646
Texas: Community 8774, Community 8777, McDermott 9013, Orsinger 9073, Rockwell 9135
Washington: **Gates 9625**, Norcliffe 9693
Wisconsin: West 9967

Mental health, addictions

Illinois: **Retirement 3113**
Oklahoma: Liddell 7767

Mental health, association

Maryland: **Murray 3855**, Stulman 3891
Missouri: Baer 4857
New York: Lopatin 6392, Mule 6513
Oklahoma: Browning-Kimball 7738, Helmerich 7758
Texas: O'Quinn 9072

Mental health, clinics

Illinois: Community 2769

Mental health, counseling/support groups

California: **Smith 1183**, Smith 1188
Florida: Florida 2101
Illinois: Community 2769, Healthcare 2900
Massachusetts: TJX 4308
New Jersey: OceanFirst 5394
New York: Freed 6011
Texas: Rockwell 9135
Washington: Renton 9715

Mental health, depression

California: Mental 914
Indiana: **Lilly 3340**
Michigan: Frankel 4436
Minnesota: RBC 4748
New Jersey: Horizon 5305
Rhode Island: HPB 8407

Mental health, disorders

Maryland: Tauber 3893
Michigan: Flinn 4424, World 4594
Minnesota: RBC 4748
New Jersey: **Johnson 5329**
New York: Freed 6011
Texas: Rockwell 9135

Mental health, eating disorders

Pennsylvania: **Davis 8005**

Mental health, grief/bereavement counseling

Maryland: **Bearman 3728**
New York: New York 6548
Pennsylvania: Highmark 8092
Wisconsin: **Baird 9811**

Mental health, schizophrenia

Indiana: **Lilly 3340**
Maryland: Stulman 3891
Minnesota: Wasie 4794

Mental health, smoking

Idaho: Blue 2627
Indiana: Anthem 3257
New Jersey: **Johnson 5329**

Mental health, treatment

Alabama: Community 23
California: Hughes 713
Connecticut: Connecticut 1567
Florida: Diermeier 2063, Indian 2166
Georgia: Marcus 2511, Pittulloch 2530
Hawaii: Hawaii 2602
Illinois: Healthcare 2900, Houlsby 2922, Shaw 3154
Maryland: **Blaustein 3735**, Stulman 3891
Massachusetts: Community 3991
Michigan: Flinn 4424
Minnesota: RBC 4748, **Weyerhaeuser 4802**
New York: **Bristol 5711**, Schnurmacher 6810, Tower 7000, van Ameringen 7024
North Carolina: Reynolds 7297
Ohio: Reinberger 7628
Pennsylvania: Staunton 8296, Steinman 8300
Texas: O'Quinn 9072, Rockwell 9135
Virginia: Hampton 9448
West Virginia: Schenk 9793

Mental health/crisis services

Arizona: Arizona 92, Freeport-McMoRan 112, Morris 148
California: Aroha 260, Atkinson 265, Atlas 266, Barker 282, Cathay 385, Fremont 548, HealthCare 667, **Hilton 692**, Hughes 713, Melalucca 909, Norris 971, Pacific 1003, Patron 1020, Sacramento 1103, San Francisco 1109, Sand 1112, Sierra 1163, Sonora 1198, Truckee 1263, Wood 1344
Colorado: Anschutz 1364, Colorado 1390, Summit 1511
Connecticut: American 1537, Community 1563, Community 1564, Community 1565, Connecticut 1566, Foster 1588, Stanley 1700
District of Columbia: Cafritz 1890, Lavin 1923, Meyer 1931
Florida: Bank 1979, Community 2035, Community 2038, Florida 2101, Gulf 2142, Macdonald 2223, Martin 2229, Peacock 2263, Pinellas 2269, Roskamp 2296, Southwest 2327, Walter 2375
Georgia: Harrison 2481, Williams 2573
Illinois: **Baxter 2690**, Blowitz 2702, Community 2763, DuPage 2812, Field 2831, Henry 2906, Illinois 2933, MB 3008, Polk 3084, **Retirement 3113**, Stern 3177, Woodward 3243
Indiana: Central 3272, Community 3280, Community 3282, Henry 3320, Kosciusko 3335, **Lilly 3340**, Unity 3393, Wayne 3400
Iowa: Ruan 3478, Siouxland 3480
Kansas: Hutchinson 3521, Manhattan 3532, McPherson 3534
Kentucky: Gheens 3577
Louisiana: Booth 3616, Community 3624, Institute 3644
Maine: Bangor 3680, Gorman 3689
Maryland: Blaustein 3736
Massachusetts: Beveridge 3950, Cambridge 3971
Michigan: Gerstacker 4444, Miller 4504, Zatkoff 4595
Minnesota: **Andersen 4601**, Blue 4618, Bremer 4620, Deluxe 4644, Edwards 4653, Ordean 4732, Oswald 4735, RBC 4748
Missouri: Apex 4854, H & R 4902, Pott 4958
Nebraska: Kearney 5055, Kim 5058, Mutual 5071
Nevada: Caesars 5106, Kagi 5125, Nevada 5134
New Hampshire: Alexander 5162, Foundation 5171
New Jersey: Borden 5209, Healthcare 5296, Horizon 5305, Hyde 5310, **Johnson 5329**, McGraw 5376, OceanFirst 5394, Provident 5414
New Mexico: Frost 5519, McCune 5529, Santa Fe 5533
New York: Altman 5579, Barker 5644, **Bristol 5711**, Carmel 5746, Cummings 5834, Goldman 6068, **Ittleson 6217**, Meehan 6468, Monell 6497, New York 6544, Plumeri 6649, Spingold 6899, Tower 7000, van Ameringen 7023, van Ameringen 7024, Western 7078
North Carolina: Cumberland 7184, High Point 7231, Piedmont 7285, Reynolds 7297, Smith 7317, Triangle 7328
North Dakota: North Dakota 7357
Ohio: Akron 7367, Columbus 7411, Coshocton 7421, Fairfield 7445, Licking 7540, Morgan 7579, Motorists 7581, Richland 7630, Ridgecliff 7631, Spaulding 7670, Toledo 7686, Western 7710, Wodecroft 7717, Woodruff 7721
Oklahoma: Bartlesville 7731, Bernsen 7733, Dotson 7748, Zarrow 7818, Zarrow 7819
Oregon: Carpenter 7831, Simple 7889
Pennsylvania: Armstrong 7921, Central 7972, Dolfinger 8013, FISA 8043, Fourjay 8047, Genuardi 8053, Highmark 8092, Phoenixville 8223, Scattergood 8267, Schenck 8269, Scranton 8275, Sexauer 8280, Stackpole 8295, Staunton 8296, Steinman 8300
Rhode Island: Daniels 8380, Hasbro 8403
South Carolina: Blue 8460
South Dakota: Sioux Falls 8521, Vucurevich 8524
Tennessee: Baptist 8533
Texas: Alexander 8656, Butt 8738, Fikes 8844, Fisch 8846, Gulf 8878, Henderson 8901, Kempner 8952, Meadows 9019, **Paso 9083**, Rees-Jones 9125, Sterling 9203, Swinney 9218, Temple 9223, Waco 9251
Utah: Doctorow 9314, Eccles 9320
Vermont: Vermont 9375
Virginia: Community 9410
Washington: Casey 9595, Community 9604, Grays 9631, Norcliffe 9693, Seattle 9731, Tacoma 9750, Whatcom 9759, Yakima 9767
West Virginia: Parkersburg 9789
Wisconsin: CUNA 9838, Evinrude 9841, Harley 9859, Keller 9878, McBeath 9901, Milwaukee 9907, Stackner 9951, Wisconsin 9970

Mental health/crisis services, association

California: Brooks 352, Jackson 737
Oklahoma: Nelson 7779
Texas: Rockwell 9135

Mental health/crisis services, formal/general education

California: McMillen 905

Mental health/crisis services, hot-lines

California: California 368
Texas: NAH 9047

Mental health/crisis services, public education

Minnesota: RBC 4748, Weyerhaeuser 4803

Mental health/crisis services, public policy

California: Alliance 229
Illinois: **MacArthur 2989**

Mental health/crisis services, rape victim services

California: Gershman 575
Pennsylvania: FISA 8043

Mental health/crisis services, research

Maryland: Tauber 3893

Mental health/crisis services, single organization support

Illinois: Buffett 2727, **Zuhlke 3250**

Mental health/crisis services, suicide

Texas: Baxter 8695

Mentally disabled

Alabama: Community 24, Community 25, Kaul 43, Meyer 53
Arizona: Webb 174
California: Atkinson 265, Ayrshire 276, Center 388, Gogian 598, Green 621, Gumbiner 636, Lesher 833, McMillen 905, Patron 1020, **Smith 1183**, Taper 1237, Tuohy 1267, Van Nuys 1284, Weingart 1307
Colorado: Hunter 1431, King 1440, Summit 1511
Connecticut: Community 1562, Community 1563, Connecticut 1566, Connecticut 1567
Delaware: **Raskob 1845**
District of Columbia: Cafritz 1890
Florida: Pinellas 2269, Southwest 2327, Wells 2383
Georgia: Franklin 2462
Illinois: Arthur 2673, Blowitz 2702, Butler 2729, Master 3004, Siragusa 3162
Indiana: Community 3281, **Lilly 3342**
Kansas: Beach 3494, Topeka 3552
Kentucky: Cralle 3571
Louisiana: Wilson 3671
Maryland: Abell 3713, Community 3761, Dresher 3782, Fowler 3795, Higgins-Hussman 3815, Stulman 3891, Tauber 3893, Washington 3904
Massachusetts: Phillips 4217, Stevens 4289
Michigan: Bay 4344, Flinn 4424, Fremont 4438, Midland 4502, Sturgis 4550
Minnesota: Beim 4609, Bremer 4620, Rochester 4755
Mississippi: Gulf 4830
Missouri: Saint Louis 4966
Montana: Oro 5014
New Hampshire: Lindsay 5179
New Jersey: Danellie 5237, Hyde 5310, Karma 5331, Wallerstein 5493
New York: BTMU 5724, Community 5802, Langeloth 6327, **Nash 6525**, **Open 6593**, Ritter 6712, **Ross 6754**, Staten 6912, **Straus 6934**, Tower 7000, van Ameringen 7024, Warner 7053, Western 7078
North Carolina: Community 7180, North Carolina 7273, Reidsville 7294, Robertson 7305
North Dakota: Leach 7353
Ohio: Bruening 7391, Cincinnati 7404, Fairfield 7445, Mercer 7567, O'Neill 7602, Ridgecliff 7631, Saint 7639, Spaulding 7670, Springfield 7671, Youngstown 7723
Oklahoma: Hardesty 7756, Hille 7759
Oregon: Benton 7825, Carpenter 7831, Collins 7836

Pennsylvania: Beneficial 7936, Connelly 7995, First 8041, FISA 8043, Huston 8102, North 8199, Pew 8220, Phoenixville 8223, Snee 8291, Trees 8319
Tennessee: Baptist 8533, Wilson 8646
Texas: Abell 8650, Baxter 8695, Community 8774, Community 8777, Dallas 8795, Hartman 8893, Hoblitzelle 8912, Hoglund 8913, McDermott 9013, Moore 9034, Orsinger 9073, Rees-Jones 9125, Rockwell 9135, Stevens 9205, Terry 9224
Utah: Eccles 9320
Virginia: Beazley 9391
Washington: Everett 9616, Kuni 9662, Norcliffe 9693
Wisconsin: Cornerstone 9836, Green Bay 9854, Keller 9878, Racine 9924, Stock 9953, West 9967

Microfinance/microlending
California: Amar 236, **Cisco 402**, eBay 493, **Google 615**, Union 1271
Colorado: **Salvador 1491**
Connecticut: People's 1671
Georgia: **UPS 2566**
Indiana: Old 3363
New York: **Citi 5780**, **Credit 5826**, **JPMorgan 6244**, **MetLife 6479**, **Moody's 6499**, NYSE 6573
Oregon: **NIKE 7875**
Texas: **Whole 9276**
Washington: McKinstry 9680, **Starbucks 9742**

Middle schools/education
Arkansas: Wal-Mart 210
California: Applied 249, **Capital 375**, Jack 736
Connecticut: **GE 1591**
Florida: Darden 2051, Lennar 2210
Illinois: Seabury 3146
Louisiana: Community 3624
Maryland: Hoffberger 3817
New Mexico: PNM 5532
New York: Ward 7049
North Carolina: Reynolds 7297
Rhode Island: Biogen 8363
Tennessee: Maddox 8603
Texas: **Arnold 8672**, Fluor 8851
Washington: **Gates 9625**

Migrant workers
Alabama: Kaul 43
Arizona: Webb 174
California: Atkinson 265, California 368, Community 414, San Luis 1110, **Vadasz 1275**, Weingart 1307
Colorado: King 1440, **Western 1521**
Delaware: **Raskob 1845**
Florida: Community 2032
Illinois: Chicago 2746
Minnesota: Bremer 4620
New Jersey: Fund 5270
New York: New York 6546, **Noyes 6571**, **Open 6593**
North Carolina: Community 7180
Pennsylvania: Independence 8107
Texas: Abell 8650, Community 8777

Military/veterans
Alabama: Kaul 43, Meyer 53
Arizona: Webb 174
Arkansas: Wal-Mart 210
California: **Annenberg 245**, California 368, Center 388, Green 621, Lesher 833, McMillen 905, Schwab 1127, Small 1180, Weingart 1307, Western 1316, Wings 1331
Colorado: King 1440
Connecticut: Community 1562, **Newman's 1652**
Delaware: **Raskob 1845**
District of Columbia: Agua 1878, Cafritz 1890, Jones 1918
Florida: Bush 2008
Georgia: Hudgens 2486, **Thoresen 2557**
Illinois: Allegretti 2655, **Baxter 2690**, King 2960, Reese 3110, Siragusa 3162
Indiana: **Lilly 3342**
Massachusetts: Berkshire 3946
Michigan: Chrysler 4366, Johnson 4468, Midland 4502
Minnesota: K.A.H.R. 4685
Mississippi: Community 4821
Missouri: Express 4888, Jones 4916, Saint Louis 4966, Sander 4967
Nevada: EBV 5116
New Jersey: Healthcare 5296, Kirby 5339
New York: Achelis 5549, Andor 5598, **Ashner 5619**, Bodman 5692, **Bristol 5711**, Cattaraugus 5750, Hoerle 6180, Knapp 6296, **MetLife 6479**, Ritter 6712, **Starr 6911**, van Ameringen 7024
North Carolina: **Bank 7139**, Community 7180, North Carolina 7273
Ohio: Community 7416, Fairfield 7445, Hatton 7483, Youngstown 7723
Oklahoma: Hardesty 7756
Oregon: Benton 7825
Pennsylvania: Beneficial 7936, Genuardi 8053, Hocker 8094, Phoenixville 8223, Staunton 8296
Tennessee: Baptist 8533, Wilson 8646
Texas: 1687 8647, AT&T 8675, Community 8774, Community 8777, Dallas 8795, Orsinger 9073, San Antonio 9148, Terry 9224, Texas 9226
Virginia: Community 9410
Wisconsin: Green Bay 9854, Milwaukee 9907

Military/veterans' organizations
Arizona: Day 105
Arkansas: Wal-Mart 210
California: California 368, Call 369, Craigslist 436, Hearst 669, **Smith 1183**, West 1314, Western 1316, Wunderkinder 1348
Colorado: Jumping 1434
Connecticut: **Newman's 1652**
District of Columbia: Rumsfeld 1943, **Union 1953**
Florida: Life 2215, Pope 2272, Sack 2303, Zehnder 2397
Illinois: Allegretti 2655
Maryland: GEICO 3801, Lockheed 3837
Massachusetts: Arbella 3926, Dunkin' 4026, Josetta 4114
Michigan: General 4442, Masco 4497
Minnesota: Evert 4655, Sit 4764, Sit 4765
Missouri: Anheuser 4853, Express 4888, Hallmark 4906
Montana: Scoob 5015
New York: **Bristol 5711**, Fisher 5982, Jacoff 6220
North Carolina: Cumberland 7184
Pennsylvania: Comcast 7989
Texas: Valero 9246
Virginia: **Olmsted 9501**
Wisconsin: Harley 9859

Minorities
Alabama: Alabama 1, BBVA 9, Community 24, Kaul 43, Meyer 53
Arizona: Arizona 92, Webb 174
Arkansas: Rockefeller 197, Wal-Mart 210
California: **Agilent 220**, Ahmanson 222, **Alpert 231**, **American 237**, Atkinson 265, **Broadcom 349**, California 366, California 368, Center 388, **Cisco 402**, Confidence 423, Cowell 434, East 490, Fleishhacker 534, **Geffen 567**, GenCorp 569, Gerbode 573, **Getty 579**, Goldman 605, Green 621, Gumbiner 636, Hewlett 686, **Hume 715**, **Kaiser 760**, Lesher 833, Ludwick 856, McMillen 905, Monroe 935, Patron 1020, PG&E 1033, Rosenberg 1088, Sacramento 1103, San Diego 1108, San Francisco 1109, Simpson 1173, **Smith 1183**, Weingart 1307
Colorado: Colorado 1390, Community 1391, El Pomar 1406, King 1440, Peierls 1475, Rose 1487, **Western 1521**
Connecticut: Aetna 1531, Community 1562, Community 1563, Connecticut 1566, Connecticut 1567, Culpeper 1568, Fund 1589, Graustein 1600, Palmer 1666, People's 1671, Pitney 1674
Delaware: Ortega 1828, **Raskob 1845**
District of Columbia: Cafritz 1890, Consumer 1894, **Hill 1915**, Jones 1918, **Union 1953**
Florida: Bank 1979, Florida 2101, Southwest 2327, St. Petersburg 2332
Georgia: Aflac 2399, AGL 2400, Franklin 2462, **Georgia 2469**, **UPS 2566**
Illinois: **Abbott 2649**, Allstate 2657, Aon 2667, Chicago 2746, Community 2763, Day 2787, **Deere 2790**, Evanston 2826, Field 2831, Fry 2849, **Harris 2893**, Mander 2998, **Motorola 3043**, Oak Park 3061, Polk 3084, Prince 3089, Siragusa 3162, Steans 3175, Washington 3217, White 3229
Indiana: Community 3281, Health 3317, **Lilly 3342**, **Lumina 3345**, Noyes 3361, Rolland 3381
Iowa: Siouxland 3480
Kentucky: Cralle 3571
Louisiana: Beaird 3614
Maryland: Abell 3712, **Cohen 3754**, Commonweal 3756, Community 3761, Fowler 3795, **Hughes 3818**
Massachusetts: **Barr 3937**, Boston 3956, Clipper 3987, Community 3992, Davis 4011, Essex 4039, Mifflin 4175, Parker 4207, Riley 4239, Schrafft 4263, Smith 4277, Stevens 4288, Stevens 4289, Webster 4322
Michigan: Battle Creek 4343, Chrysler 4366, DTE 4410, Ford 4430, Grand Rapids 4447, **Kellogg 4474**, Midland 4502, **Mott 4510**
Minnesota: 3M 4597, Bigelow 4616, Blue 4618, Bremer 4620, Duluth 4649, General 4661, Graco 4666, Mardag 4703, **Medtronic 4712**, Minneapolis 4714, **O'Shaughnessy 4734**, Phillips 4741, Rochester 4755, Saint Paul 4757, Travelers 4783
Mississippi: Community 4821, Foundation 4827, Gulf 4830, Hardin 4831
Missouri: Anheuser 4853, Centene 4870, Dunn 4882, **Enterprise 4887**, Goppert 4896, Saigh 4965, Saint Louis 4966
Montana: Montana 5013, Oro 5014
Nebraska: Dunklau 5036, Lozier 5065, Woods 5096
Nevada: Nevada 5134
New Hampshire: Lindsay 5179
New Jersey: **Allen 5191**, Bonner 5208, Fund 5270, Hyde 5310, **Johnson 5329**, KPMG 5349, MCJ 5377, **Merck 5379**, Princeton 5411, **Siemens 5454**, Victoria 5490
New Mexico: Frost 5519, McCune 5529, Santa Fe 5533
New York: Altman 5579, AXA 5629, **Citi 5780**, **Commonwealth 5800**, Cummings 5834, **Deutsche 5876**, **Discount 5889**, **Ford 5994**, Greater 6099, **Guggenheim 6115**, Haring 6133, **Hearst 6155**, **Hearst 6156**, **IBM 6203**, Langeloth 6327, **Macy 6414**, **MetLife 6479**, **Moody's 6499**, Morgan 6507, New York 6546, **Norman 6565**, **Noyes 6571**, NYSE 6573, **Open 6593**, **PepsiCo 6627**, Price 6658, Ritter 6712, Rochester 6722, Ruffin 6770, Scherman 6804, **Sparkplug 6894**, Staten 6912, **Straus 6934**, Voya 7038, Western 7078
North Carolina: Babcock 7138, Cemala 7174, Community 7180, Cumberland 7184, Duke 7196, Mayr 7261, North Carolina 7273, North 7274, Reynolds 7298, Robertson 7305, **S.R.C. 7307**, Triangle 7328, Warner 7334
North Dakota: Stern 7360
Ohio: Cincinnati 7404, Fairfield 7445, GAR 7465, Gund 7478, KeyBank 7523, Kroger 7531, Macy's 7552, Morgan 7577, Nord 7594, O'Neill 7602, Parents 7608, Richland 7630, Saint 7639, Stark 7673, White 7715
Oklahoma: Hardesty 7756, Hille 7759
Oregon: Benton 7825, Collins 7836, **Fohs 7844**, **Intel 7853**, PGE 7881
Pennsylvania: **Alcoa 7908**, Bayer 7932, Beneficial 7936, Birmingham 7942, Buhl 7956, Connelly 7995, Dolfinger 8013, First 8041, **Heinz 8083**, Highmark 8092, Huston 8102, Philadelphia 8221, Pilgrim 8225, **PPG 8235**
Rhode Island: Textron 8446
South Carolina: Coastal 8472
South Dakota: South Dakota 8522
Tennessee: Baptist 8533, Wilson 8646
Texas: AT&T 8675, BNSF 8706, Community 8774, Community 8777, Embrey 8828, Frees 8857,

Minorities/immigrants, centers/services

Mobile media

Mormon agencies & churches

Multiple sclerosis

Multiple sclerosis research

Muscular dystrophy

Muscular dystrophy research

Museums

6882, **Stockman 6932**, Stony 6933, **Straus 6934**, Theobald 6974, Thompson 6975, Three 6976, Tiffany 6978, Time 6982, Tisch 6988, Trump 7008, **Trust 7009**, **Vital 7033**, Volpert 7036, **Warhol 7050**, Weiler 7063, Wein 7064, Western 7078, Wunsch 7106, Zucker 7127, Zuckerberg 7128
North Carolina: BB&T 7143, Cumberland 7184, Dalton 7187, Gorelick 7215, North 7274, Smith 7315, Smith 7317, Spangler 7320, Triangle 7328, VF 7332, Woodson 7342
North Dakota: MDU 7354, Stern 7360
Ohio: AK Steel 7366, Akron 7367, Castellini 7399, Christman 7403, Codrington 7409, Cole 7410, Community 7413, Conway 7419, Coshocton 7421, Dorn 7439, Gund 7476, Ingalls 7503, Kaplan 7516, Kersten 7519, Krause 7530, Kulas 7532, Lapp 7534, Lozick 7545, Lubrizol 7546, Murphy 7584, Nord 7595, Ohio 7599, Oliver 7600, Perkins 7615, Philips 7619, Reinberger 7628, Schiff 7648, Schlink 7650, State 7674, Troy 7688, Vesper 7695, Western 7710, Wodecroft 7717, Youngstown 7723
Oklahoma: American 7728, Browning-Kimball 7738, Helmerich 7758, Kerr 7764, Kirkpatrick 7766, Lobeck 7768, Oxley 7785, Simmons 7796, Stuart 7802, Williams 7814
Oregon: Campbell 7830, PacifiCorp 7877, Schnitzer 7887
Pennsylvania: **ACE 7905**, Ametek 7913, Bayer 7932, Berkman 7938, Bozzone 7948, Carpenter 7967, Colket 7987, Dolfinger 8013, Drumcliff 8016, EQT 8025, Federated 8033, **Heinz 8085**, Heinz 8086, Hurd 8101, Jackson 8110, Karabots 8116, Keystone 8122, Lindback 8142, Lomax 8148, Mandell 8153, McCune 8161, McLean 8169, Miller 8181, Mine 8184, Neubauer 8196, Pew 8220, Poor 8232, Ross 8255, Toll 8316, Vanguard 8327, Williams 8338
Rhode Island: Biogen 8363, Charlesmead 8371, Daniels 8380, **FM 8393**, Kaplan 8409, Osborn 8426, Sharpe 8437, Shumway 8439, Vance 8450
South Carolina: **AVX-Kyocera 8457**, McKissick 8486, Pfriem 8490
South Dakota: Sioux Falls 8521
Tennessee: Briggs 8538, First 8565, **International 8585**, Jeniam 8587, Nissan 8613, Stokely 8631, Temple 8633, Thompson 8636, Wilson 8646
Texas: Andrews, 8668, Bass 8690, BNSF 8706, Boeckman 8707, Booth 8711, Bratton 8722, Burnett 8737, Cain 8744, Carter 8752, Carter 8753, CH 8759, Clements 8766, Coastal 8768, Coates 8769, Cockrell 8770, Collins 8772, Constantin 8778, Cox 8785, Crane 8788, Dickson-Allen 8806, Fikes 8844, Glasscock 8867, Goodman 8870, Halsell 8886, Hamill 8887, Hudson 8919, Jones 8944, Kempner 8952, Kilroy 8956, Kinder 8958, Kohl 8967, Kronkosky 8970, Kurth 8971, McDermott 9013, Meadows 9019, Moran 9036, Natural 9053, Northen 9063, Once 9070, Rogers 9139, San Antonio 9148, Semmes 9166, Sharp 9167, Smith 9185, Sterling 9203, Strake 9208, Texas 9227, Trull 9240, Valero 9246, Wal 9254, Ward 9258, **Westbury 9271**, Wortham 9292, Wright 9293
Utah: Eccles 9320
Virginia: Dominion 9422, Estes 9427, Folger 9431, Gwathmey 9447, Landmark 9467, MeadWestvaco 9484, Morgan, 9490, Norfolk 9496, Olsson 9502, Parsons 9504, Ratner 9515, Reynolds 9519, Samberg 9527, Scott 9529, Smith 9534, SunTrust 9539, Watkins 9553
Washington: Allen 9567, Bamford 9580, Blakemore 9587, Cheney 9598, Community 9604, Dimmer 9610, Miller 9684, Murdock 9689, PACCAR 9698, Plum 9704, Renton 9715, Shirley 9734, Swigert-Warren 9748, Tacoma 9750
West Virginia: Daywood 9774, Kanawha 9780, Parkersburg 9789
Wisconsin: Baker 9812, Frautschi 9847, Johnson 9870, Johnson 9874, Krause 9886, Ladish 9890, Lubar 9894, Northwestern 9914, Pick 9920, Pollybill 9921, Raibrook 9925, Soref 9948, Steigleder 9952, Wisconsin 9969, Wisconsin 9970

Museums (art)

Alabama: Warner 75
Arizona: Halle 118, Ottosen 150, Thomarie 170, Weatherup 173
California: Albatross 226, Bakar 278, Bloomfield 319, Broad 346, Camp 370, **Capital 375**, Chandler 392, Clayes 404, Clive 406, Davies 454, Davis 455, Falling 515, Friedman 551, Galen 558, Good 612, Greenberg 624, Hauptman 662, Hsieh 710, Irmas 725, Isambard 729, James 742, Janeway 745, Kayne 773, Lainer 811, Lamond 817, Munzer 955, Neeley 963, **Osher 998**, Pritzker 1046, Red 1059, Ressler 1066, Ritts 1076, Simpson 1173, Sloan 1179, Small 1180, Sprague 1207, Stark 1213, Tarble 1238, Taub 1240, Teel 1243, Weisman 1309, Wine 1330, Winnick 1333, Zander 1356
Colorado: Bonfils 1376, Mayer 1457, Precourt 1483, Sie 1500
Connecticut: Chase 1555, Goergen 1595, Sheinberg 1695
Delaware: Lefrak 1804, Schejola 1856, Stewart 1862, Stone 1863, Victory 1870
District of Columbia: Coyne 1896, DeLaski 1899, HRH 1917, Vradenburg 1954
Florida: Ansin 1969, Brown 2004, Connors 2043, Eagle 2078, Edelman 2080, Edgemer 2081, Garrott 2116, Hudson 2164, James 2169, Katcher 2176, Kislak 2187, Miller 2241, Moran 2242, Root 2293, Rothman 2298
Georgia: Bunzl 2417, Holder 2485, Selig 2549
Illinois: Appleton 2669, Bluhm 2704, Buchbinder 2721, Bucksbaum 2724, Edlis-Neeson 2815, Edwardson 2816, Energizer 2824, Fogelson 2836, Franke 2841, Heller 2903, Keith 2952, Leonian 2974, McCormick 3010, Pritzker 3092, Pritzker 3093, Reed 3109, Rhoades 3115, Rotonda 3125, Sacks 3131, Scanlan 3137, **Terra 3186**, Trott 3192, Yulman 3246, Zell 3247
Indiana: Simon 3387
Kansas: Downing 3510
Kentucky: Barzun 3559, Young 3607
Louisiana: Chambers 3621, Deming 3627, Diboll 3628, Helis 3641
Maine: Glickman 3688
Maryland: Adams 3717, Baker 3725, Fletcher 3791, Legum 3829, Middendorf 3850, Price 3865, Riepe 3869, Wasserman 3906
Massachusetts: Acorn 3915, Bressler 3959, Calderwood 3969, Croll 4000, Doran 4024, Duniry 4025, Heide 4091, Keane 4118, Landry 4135, Lubin 4155, McLane/Harper 4169, **Middlecott 4174**, Nathan 4188, Ruettgers 4252, Sharf 4268, Stewart 4291, Stoddard 4293, Weatherbie 4321
Michigan: Dana 4386, DeVos 4398, Dow 4406, Meijer 4499, Taubman 4553, Wolters 4592
Minnesota: Deluxe 4644, Griggs 4669, Martin 4704
Mississippi: Mississippi 4839, Walker 4849
Missouri: Arch 4855, Brauer 4860, Edison 4884, Ferring 4891, Interco 4914, Jacobsen 4915, Kemper 4923, Kemper 4925, Lopata 4938, Pershing 4953
Nebraska: Scoular 5080, Swanson 5087
Nevada: Prim 5140
New Jersey: Cole 5231, Gulton 5284, Levin 5359, McMullen 5378, Point 5410, Sansom 5438, Segal 5447, Wall 5492
New Mexico: Hammersley 5520, Phillips 5531
New York: Abeles 5544, Acquavella 5550, All 5572, American 5586, Assurant 5621, Bachmann 5632, Baker 5638, Bayne 5653, Belfer 5660, Birkelund 5677, Brice 5708, Brodsky 5713, Buttenwieser 5736, Carson 5748, Chazen 5767, Cowin 5822, D'Agostino 5843, Dannheisser 5847, **David 5852**, Debs 5860, Dechman 5862, Demartini 5872, **Deutsche 5876**, Diker 5883, Dowling 5907, Effron 5938, Foundation 6000, Friedberg 6017, Gelman 6041, Goldberg 6061, Great 6097, Gural 6117, Horowitz 6186, Horowitz 6187, IFF 6206, **Iris 6213**, Johnson 6233, Johnson 6237, **JPMorgan 6244**, Katz 6256, Kelly 6271, Klein 6289, Kraus 6305, Kravis 6307, Lauder 6335, **Leir 6349**, Lindenbaum 6370, Link 6375, Loeb 6383, Loeb 6384, **M & T 6406**, Mack 6412, Mailman 6419, Marron 6435, **Matisse 6447**, McGraw 6462, Melly 6471, Mesdag 6478, **MetLife 6479**, Mnuchin 6494, Neidich 6534, Orentreich 6596, Parsons 6618, Peco 6624, Pels 6625, Petrie 6631, PLM 6647, **Reed 6684**, Richardson 6700, Riggio 6709, Rosen 6739, Rosenwald 6750, Sackler 6777, Sackler 6778, Salomon 6785, Schapiro 6801, Shoreland 6847, Speyer 6896, Tananbaum 6962, Tisch 6985, Tisch 6986, Sussman 6990, Tuft 7011, **Vicente 7029**, Vogelstein 7034, Volpert 7036, Wallach 7044, Weiler 7063, Weinberg 7066, Weir 7069, West 7077, Widgeon 7081, Wiegers 7082, Wiener 7083, Wilson 7086, Wunsch 7106
North Carolina: Belk 7147, Hanes 7222, North 7274, Richardson 7301, Woodward 7344
Ohio: American 7368, Charities 7400, CPB 7423, **Eaton 7442**, Fleischmann 7457, Gund 7475, Gund 7477, Haslinger 7482, IHS 7501, Keithley 7518, Kersten 7519, Lehner 7536, **Lerner 7538**, Mandel 7554, Ohio 7599, Outcalt 7606, Payne 7614, Ritter 7633, Schiff 7649, Schott 7652, State 7674, Warrington 7703
Oklahoma: Collins 7741, Lobeck 7768, Oklahoma 7782, Oxley 7785, Stephenson 7799, Stone 7801
Oregon: Esco 7841
Pennsylvania: Arete 7919, Century 7974, Cotswold 7999, Dietrich 8010, Fine 8039, Hecht 8082, Hurd 8101, Kim 8123, Locks 8147, Poor 8232, Rossin 8256, Saligman 8261, Sargent 8265, Stein/Bellet 8298, Strelsin 8306, von Hess 8329, Wilson 8341
Rhode Island: Bafflin 8359, Greene 8398, Mercer 8419, Murray 8421
South Carolina: **AVX-Kyocera 8457**, Phifer 8491
Tennessee: Atticus 8531, Regal 8622
Texas: Barnhart 8681, Beals, 8697, Bookout 8709, Booth 8712, Campbell 8748, Ford 8854, Guenther 8877, Halsell 8885, Hamon 8889, Hudson 8919, Jarvis 8931, Jones 8943, Kahng 8948, Kolitz 8968, Lawrence 8973, Lawson 8974, Marsh 8999, Mays 9008, McNutt 9018, Moncrief 9031, Nightingale 9062, Owsley 9078, Pace 9079, Questrom 9116, Sarofim 9154, Simmons 9174, Stedman 9200, Stuart 9209, Susman 9216, Tobin 9236, Tucker 9241, Valero 9246, Vaughan 9248, Wolff 9286
Virginia: Fralin 9433, Funger 9438, Pauley 9505, Rales 9513, Rosenthal 9525, SunTrust 9539, United 9546
Washington: McKinstry 9680, Miller 9684, **PAH 9699**, Sarkowsky 9727, Shirley 9734, Sondland 9740, Stevenson 9743, T.E.W. 9749, Wright 9765
Wisconsin: **Baird 9811**, Caxambas 9828, CUNA 9838, Forester 9844, Incourage 9867, Rexnord 9932, Spire 9949, Windhover 9968

Museums (children's)

California: Albatross 226, Hoffman 699, Milias 925
Colorado: Marsico 1455
Connecticut: Provident 1677
District of Columbia: Hillside 1914
Florida: Hudson 2164
Illinois: Beidler 2692, Christopher 2748, Galvin 2858, Harrison 2895, Souder 3168
Massachusetts: Lovett 4151
Mississippi: Ford 4826
Nebraska: Ameritas 5023
New York: Hayden 6150, Kazickas 6264, Richmond 6704, Save 6799
Oklahoma: Taubman 7804
Pennsylvania: Hurd 8101
Tennessee: Briggs 8538, Jeniam 8587
Texas: Diener 8807, Impetus 8924, Kodosky 8966, Zeller 9298
Washington: Dimmer 9610

Museums (ethnic/folk arts)

California: Lainer 811, Shoresh 1159

Colorado: Edmondson 1405
Florida: Azeez 1975, Katcher 2176
Illinois: Herr 2909
Maryland: Cohen 3753
New York: Belfer 5660, Goldberg 6062, Goldman 6069, Greene 6104, Korman 6303, Parsons 6618, Resnick 6689, Robbins 6715, Rubenstein 6762, **Rubin 6765**, Sitt 6866, Tananbaum 6962, Unanue 7015, Volpert 7036, Weiler 7063
Ohio: Mandel 7554
Pennsylvania: Berkman 7938, Hurd 8101, Kestenbaum 8121, Saligman 8261, Toll 8316
Washington: **Goodwin 9751**

Museums (history)
Colorado: Edmondson 1405
Florida: Colen 2029, Galloway 2112, Rothman 2298, Saunders 2308
Georgia: Fleming 2458
Illinois: Galvin 2857, Illinois 2934, White 3230
Indiana: 1st 3251
Massachusetts: Grayson 4078
Michigan: Americana 4337, Parish 4518
Nebraska: Kimmel 5059
New York: **Debbane 5859**
Ohio: Schott 7652
Oklahoma: Gaylord 7753
Pennsylvania: Harding 8080, Hurd 8101
Rhode Island: Felicia 8392
South Carolina: Phifer 8491
Virginia: Ratcliffe 9514
Washington: Peach 9701

Museums (marine/maritime)
California: Outhwaite 1000
Delaware: **Stratus 1864**
Florida: Gardener 2114, Kislak 2187, Langford 2202
Massachusetts: Wallace 4318
Nebraska: Lincoln 5063
New York: **Stempel 6925**, Weinberg 7067
Pennsylvania: McCausland 8159
Virginia: **Truland 9545**
Wisconsin: Evinrude 9841

Museums (natural history)
California: San Simeon 1111
Connecticut: Sage 1687
Delaware: Draper 1770, Reynolds 1849
Florida: Gerstner 2121
Illinois: Angell 2663, Comer 2761, Ward 3216
New Jersey: Golden 5280, Isdell 5318, Phipps 5406
New York: Altman 5581, Burke 5731, D'Agostino 5843, Habe 6125, J. 6218, Keet 6266, Klingenstein 6293, Klingenstein 6294, Lostand 6394, Parsons 6618, Saltz 6786, Schwartz 6817, Seven 6834, Shipley 6843, Speyer 6896, Walter 7046, Wildwood 7084
Ohio: American 7369, Murch 7582
Pennsylvania: DuPont 8020
Texas: Carruth 8751
Utah: Bamberger 9305
Washington: Stevenson 9743

Museums (science/technology)
Alabama: Energen 32, McWane 51
Arizona: Dorrance 107
California: Bengier 304, **Broccoli 350**
Connecticut: Northeast 1656
Florida: James 2169, Saunders 2308
Illinois: **Abbott 2649**, Dover 2803, Illinois 2934, **Motorola 3043**
Massachusetts: Gordon 4075
Michigan: DTE 4410, Lear 4482
Minnesota: 3M 4597, Cargill 4628, Foundation 4657, **Medtronic 4712**, Valspar 4786, Weesner 4797
Missouri: Burns 4866, SunEdison 4985
Nebraska: Union 5090
New Jersey: Buehler 5219, Smith 5461
New York: Riedman 6706
North Carolina: Goodrich 7213, McLean 7264, VF 7332
Ohio: Cliffs 7407, Pulley 7624
Pennsylvania: Bayer 7932, Hurd 8101, **PPG 8235**
Rhode Island: Biogen 8363, Scrooby 8435
Tennessee: Turner 8641
Texas: Brown 8730, Morian 9039
Virginia: Charles 9404, Hobbs 9454

Museums (specialized)
Arizona: Halle 118, Levine 133
California: Arbus 251, Dickinson 466, Greenberg 624, House 707, Otter 999, Petersen 1029
Colorado: **Avenir 1369**, Martin 1456
Delaware: Berlin 1743, Nor'Easter 1824
District of Columbia: Hillside 1914
Florida: Kislak 2187, Morby 2244
Georgia: Carlos 2422
Illinois: Johnson 2943, Leonian 2974
Kentucky: Bond 3561, Young 3607
Massachusetts: Stevens 4289
Michigan: Firestone 4422, Penske 4519, Van Andel 4568
Minnesota: **Patterson 4738**
New Jersey: Kerr 5338, Oster 5399
New York: Alison 5571, Haas 6124, Lemle 6351, **New 6551**, Orthwein 6597, Pulier 6665, Rosner 6752, Solomon 6886, Sulzberger 6942, Swyer 6956, **Winston 7093**
Ohio: Schott 7652
Oklahoma: Dobson 7747
Pennsylvania: Hurd 8101, Kunkel 8133
Rhode Island: Wood 8452
Texas: Moncrief 9031, Texas 9226
Virginia: Moore 9489
Washington: Anders 9571, Hanson 9639
Wisconsin: Johnson 9873, Zilber 9972
Wyoming: Kerr 9981

Museums (sports/hobby)
California: Hope 702, McBean 892
Delaware: **Birch 1744**
Florida: Ebert 2079
Michigan: Wilson 4588

Native Americans/American Indians
Alabama: Kaul 43
Alaska: Aleut 80, Arctic 81, Chugach 84, CIRI 85, Doyon 86, Rasmuson 89
Arizona: Freeport-McMoRan 112, Webb 174
California: California 365, California 368, Center 388, **Christensen 399**, Community 414, Cowell 434, Fleishhacker 534, Gumbiner 636, Weingart 1307, Wunderkinder 1348
Colorado: King 1440, Ottens 1472
Connecticut: Community 1562, Connecticut 1567, Culpeper 1568
Delaware: **Raskob 1845**
District of Columbia: **Union 1953**
Florida: Thomas 2357
Illinois: Allstate 2657, Carrus 2734, Chicago 2746, King 2960, Siragusa 3162
Indiana: **Lilly 3342**, **Lumina 3345**
Iowa: Siouxland 3480
Maryland: **Hughes 3818**
Massachusetts: Community 3992
Michigan: Chrysler 4366, Grand Rapids 4447, **Kellogg 4474**, Pokagon 4523
Minnesota: Blue 4618, Bremer 4620, Bush 4621, Cargill 4627, Duluth 4649, Land 4691, Minneapolis 4714, Northwest 4729, Phillips 4741
Mississippi: Community 4821
Missouri: Saint Louis 4966
Montana: Edwards 5008, Montana 5013, Oro 5014, Washington 5018
Nebraska: Dunklau 5036, Woods 5096
New Hampshire: Lindsay 5179
New Jersey: **Allen 5191**, **Johnson 5329**, KPMG 5349
New Mexico: Frost 5519, **Lannan 5526**, McCune 5529, New Mexico 5530, Santa Fe 5533
New York: Atlantic 5622, **Hearst 6155**, **Hearst 6156**, Langeloth 6327, **Macy 6414**, **MetLife 6479**, **Noyes 6571**, **Ross 6754**, Ruffin 6770, Schnurmacher 6810, **Sparkplug 6894**
North Carolina: Community 7180, Cumberland 7184, North Carolina 7273, Reynolds 7298, **S.R.C. 7307**, Triangle 7328
North Dakota: Leach 7353, Stern 7360
Ohio: Parents 7608
Oklahoma: Stephenson 7799
Oregon: Benton 7825, **Intel 7853**
Pennsylvania: First 8041, **Moore 8186**
South Dakota: South Dakota 8522
Tennessee: Baptist 8533
Texas: BNSF 8706, Community 8777, McDermott 9013, Stern 9204
Utah: ALSAM 9302, Eccles 9320
Vermont: Gibney 9362
Virginia: Arlington 9384
Washington: Allen 9567, Norcliffe 9693
Wisconsin: Community 9835, Green Bay 9854

Neighborhood centers
Alabama: Community 21, Community 24
California: **Smith 1183**
Missouri: Simon 4973
New York: Auchincloss 5623, McCarthy 6455, Stern 6928
Pennsylvania: Hurd 8101
Virginia: Proteus 9512
Washington: Renton 9715
Wisconsin: Lunda 9895
Wyoming: LOR 9983

Nerve, muscle & bone diseases
California: Danford 448
Indiana: **Lilly 3340**
Pennsylvania: Highmark 8092

Nerve, muscle & bone research
Pennsylvania: **AO 7915**
Wisconsin: Milwaukee 9907

Neuroscience
Florida: Greenburg 2137
Illinois: Frechette 2844
Minnesota: McKnight 4709
New York: **Dana 5845**
Pennsylvania: Aospine 7916, DSF 8017

Neuroscience research
California: Coates 408
Massachusetts: **Adelson 3919**
Minnesota: Cherbec 4634, **McKnight 4708**
New Jersey: Barer 5203, Integra 5315
New York: Essel 5961, Harsh, 6143, Klingenstein 6292
Pennsylvania: Field 8037
Texas: **Leducq 8976**, Pediatric 9087
Virginia: Three 9541

Nonprofit management
Alabama: Central 19, Community 21
California: California 368, **Draper 481**, Germanacos 574, **Haas 643**, Irvine 727, Placer 1039, San Luis 1110, Shasta 1154
Connecticut: Fairfield 1581
District of Columbia: Community 1893
Florida: Bush 2008, Community 2035
Georgia: **UPS 2566**
Hawaii: Hawaii 2602
Illinois: Chicago 2746, **Retirement 3113**
Louisiana: Community 3624

Maine: Maine 3698
Massachusetts: Cape Cod 3974
Michigan: Knight 4477
Minnesota: Initiative 4679, West 4800
Mississippi: Mississippi 4839
Missouri: Saint Louis 4966
New Mexico: Santa Fe 5533
New York: **American 5588**, Community 5808, Union 7017
North Carolina: Community 7182
Ohio: **Mandel 7555**
Oklahoma: Oklahoma City 7781
Rhode Island: Rhode Island 8429
Texas: Buford 8736, King 8959, Rockwell 9135
Virginia: ACT 9380, Alleghany 9382, Lynchburg 9474

Nursing care
California: Norris 971, Patron 1020, Weingart 1307
Delaware: **AstraZeneca 1738**
Illinois: **Thome 3187**, VNA 3206, Washington 3217
Iowa: Siouxland 3480
Massachusetts: **China 3982**, MetroWest 4173, Proctor 4227
Michigan: Willmas 4587
Missouri: Musgrave 4947
Nebraska: Weller 5093
Nevada: Fairweather 5118
New Jersey: **Johnson 5329**, Snyder 5462
New York: **Bristol 5711**, **Fuld 6029**, O'Connor 6578, **Pforzheimer 6635**
North Carolina: Van Houten 7330
Ohio: Community 7413, Murphy 7584, Schlink 7650
Oregon: Johnson 7858
Pennsylvania: Arcadia 7918, Dolfinger 8013, Fourjay 8047, Independence 8107
South Carolina: Blue 8460
Tennessee: Christy 8545
Texas: Abell 8650, Armentrout 8671, Davidson 8797, Franklin 8855, Gulf 8878, Johnson 8941, Meadows 9019, Pollock 9103
Utah: Bamberger 9305, Eccles 9320
West Virginia: Kanawha 9780
Wisconsin: McBeath 9901

Nursing home/convalescent facility
California: **Smith 1183**
Illinois: Washington 3217
Kentucky: WCA 3606
Maryland: Wasserman 3905
Michigan: **Isabel 4466**
New York: DOJ 5894, Fernleigh 5975
Pennsylvania: Dull 8019, McLean 8169
Rhode Island: Capewell 8366, M. 8414
Washington: Danz 9609

Nursing school/education
California: California 368, Dickinson 466, McKesson 903
Connecticut: Culpeper 1568
Florida: **Chatlos 2019**, Florida 2101
Idaho: Blue 2627
Illinois: Arthur 2673, Walter 3213, Washington 3217
Indiana: Duneland 3297
Louisiana: Baton Rouge 3613
Maryland: Johnston 3821
Massachusetts: Worcester 4327
Mississippi: Biloxi 4814
Missouri: Ballmann 4858, Musgrave 4947
New York: Community 5803, **Fuld 6029**, Hillman 6174, Hugoton 6194, Kennedy 6274, Lincoln 6368, **Macy 6414**, Orvis 6598, Renfield 6688, Rudin 6769
North Carolina: Van Houten 7330
Ohio: Wellman 7709
Oregon: Collins 7837, Johnson 7858, Peterson 7880
Pennsylvania: Arcadia 7918, Independence 8106, Independence 8107, Saligman 8261
Tennessee: Travis 8637
Texas: Abell 8650, CH 8759, Johnson 8941, Mayborn 9006, San Antonio 9148

Utah: Watkins 9356
Virginia: Lambert 9466, Moore 9489, Richmond 9521
Wisconsin: Meng 9904, Shapiro 9945

Nutrition
Arizona: Freeport-McMoRan 112, Parsons 151
Arkansas: Wal-Mart 210
California: California 368, Cathay 385, Fremont 548, Hughes 713, **Saban 1101**, Sierra 1163, Thornton 1252
Colorado: Anschutz 1364, El Pomar 1406
Connecticut: Aetna 1531, **Children's 1557**, **Newman's 1652**
Delaware: Delaware 1765
Florida: Florida 2101, Jacksonville 2167
Georgia: **Coca 2428**
Idaho: Blue 2627
Illinois: **Abbott 2649**, Caterpillar 2738, Community 2763, FDC 2829, Hospira 2921, **Kapoor 2950**, **Mondelez 3034**, Trustmark 3193, **Wrigley 3244**, Youth 3245
Indiana: Health 3317, Welborn 3402
Iowa: AEGON 3409, **Pioneer 3474**, Principal 3476, Wellmark 3490
Kentucky: Humana 3582
Louisiana: Blue 3615, Community 3624
Massachusetts: Boston 3956, Eastern 4030, New 4189
Michigan: **Allen 4335**, **Gerber 4443**, **Kellogg's 4475**
Minnesota: **Better 4614**, Blue 4618, Bremer 4620, General 4661, Land 4691, **Mosaic 4722**, NFC 4727, SUPERVALU 4775, TEAM 4779
Mississippi: Blue 4815, Community 4821
Missouri: **Monsanto 4945**
Nebraska: ConAgra 5029, ConAgra 5030
Nevada: Bennett 5101, Caesars 5106
New Jersey: Campbell 5223, Horizon 5305, **Merck 5379**, **Pfeiffer 5405**, Unilever 5484
New Mexico: McCune 5529
New York: Assurant 5621, Dreyfus 5913, Freed 6011, Levitt 6361, Morgan 6507, NYSE 6573, Palette 6609, **PepsiCo 6627**
North Carolina: **Bank 7139**, Blue 7153, Cumberland 7184
Pennsylvania: Dolfinger 8013, **Heinz 8083**, Highmark 8092, Independence 8106, North 8199
Rhode Island: Citizens 8374
South Carolina: Central 8468
Tennessee: Christy 8545
Texas: Dean 8803, Meadows 9019, **Paso 9083**
Virginia: AMERIGROUP 9383, CarMax 9401, MAXIMUS 9481, MLG 9488
Washington: **Gates 9625**, Norcliffe 9693, **Starbucks 9742**
Wisconsin: McBeath 9901, Milwaukee 9907

Obstetrics/gynecology
California: California 368, HealthCare 667

Offenders/ex-offenders
Alabama: Kaul 43, Meyer 53
Arizona: Webb 174
California: Atkinson 265, California 368, Community 414, **Fund 556**, Rosenberg 1088, Taper 1237, Weingart 1307
Connecticut: Community 1562
Delaware: **Raskob 1845**
District of Columbia: Cafritz 1890
Illinois: Chicago 2746, Field 2831, Siragusa 3162
Indiana: Community 3281, Waterfield 3399
Louisiana: Wilson 3671
Maryland: Abell 3712, Washington 3904
Massachusetts: Essex 4039, Shaw 4270
Minnesota: Bremer 4620
New Jersey: Danellie 5237, Fund 5270, Kirby 5339
New York: Abrons 5546, Achelis 5549, Bodman 5692, Langeloth 6327, **Open 6593**, Ritter 6712, Rockefeller 6725, van Ameringen 7024
North Carolina: Community 7180, North Carolina 7273, Reidsville 7294

Ohio: O'Neill 7602
Oklahoma: Hardesty 7756, Hille 7759
Pennsylvania: Huston 8102, Pew 8220
Tennessee: Baptist 8533
Texas: Orsinger 9073, Wichita 9277
Wisconsin: Milwaukee 9907

Offenders/ex-offenders, bail issues
District of Columbia: **Public 1940**

Offenders/ex-offenders, prison alternatives
California: California 368, **Fund 556**
District of Columbia: **Public 1940**
New York: Achelis 5549

Offenders/ex-offenders, probation/parole
California: California 368

Offenders/ex-offenders, rehabilitation
California: California 368
Connecticut: Bissell 1547
Massachusetts: Shaw 4270
Ohio: Reinberger 7628
Pennsylvania: Genuardi 8053
Rhode Island: Daniels 8380

Offenders/ex-offenders, services
California: California 368
Florida: Usher 2367
Louisiana: Wilson 3671
Maryland: Abell 3712
Texas: Wichita 9277

Offenders/ex-offenders, transitional care
California: California 368
District of Columbia: Consumer 1894
Pennsylvania: Genuardi 8053

Optometry/vision screening
District of Columbia: Aid 1879
Florida: Florida 2101, Glazer 2124
Illinois: Healthcare 2900
New York: **Deutsche 5876**
Pennsylvania: Phoenixville 8223
Texas: Alcon 8655

Organ research
Georgia: Mason 2513

Orthodox agencies & churches
California: Orthodox 995
Connecticut: Hoffman 1613
Massachusetts: Demoulas 4015, Pappas 4204
Nevada: Joseph 5124
New Jersey: Bouras 5211
New York: Jaharis 6223, Parsons 6619, United 7018

Orthopedics
District of Columbia: **Wyss 1959**
Louisiana: Marshall 3653
North Carolina: Christopher 7176
Pennsylvania: Aospine 7916, Widener 8336

Orthopedics research
Colorado: Gildor 1420
Massachusetts: Harris 4089
Pennsylvania: **AO 7915**
Tennessee: Compton 8551

Palliative care

California: Archstone 253, Hofmann 700, UniHealth 1270
New Jersey: Healthcare 5296, **Johnson 5329**, **Milbank 5385**
New York: Altman 5579, **Bristol 5711**, Chiang 5774, Kornfeld 6304, Littauer 6379, **Open 6593**, Samuels 6788
North Carolina: Duke 7195
Oregon: Cambia 7829
Texas: **Jiv 8933**

Parasitic diseases

Texas: **ExxonMobil 8833**

Parasitic diseases research

Illinois: **Cornwell 2775**
Washington: **Gates 9625**

Parkinson's disease

California: Barry 284, Brin 343
Ohio: Marion 7558
Wisconsin: Milwaukee 9907

Parkinson's disease research

California: Oxnard 1001
New York: Barakett 5643, **Jaffe 6222**

Pediatrics

California: Campini 374, Genentech 571, HealthCare 667, Issa 732
Florida: Applebaum 1970
Illinois: Trio 3191, Trustmark 3193
Maryland: Decesaris 3775
Massachusetts: Proctor 4227
Michigan: **Gerber 4443**
Minnesota: Legacy 4693
New Jersey: **Johnson 5326**, **Merck 5379**, **Sanofi 5437**, **Verizon 5489**
New York: Morgan 6507, **Ross 6754**
North Carolina: Gordon 7214
Pennsylvania: Biesecker 7941, Rangos 8244
Rhode Island: CVS 8379, Hasbro 8403, Kaplan 8409
Texas: **Jiv 8933**, Topfer 9239
Virginia: Richmond 9521
Washington: Foster 9621

Pediatrics research

California: Musk 957
Colorado: Kaufmann 1436
Illinois: Sprague 3172
Massachusetts: Hood 4100
Michigan: **Gerber 4443**
Minnesota: Legacy 4693
New Jersey: **Pfeiffer 5405**
New York: D'Addario 5841, Steinberg 6922
Texas: Pediatric 9087
Utah: **Thrasher 9353**

Pensions

Texas: **Arnold 8672**

Performing arts

Alabama: Alabama 1, Hearin 38, Smith 66
Alaska: Atwood 82, CIRI 85
Arizona: Arizona 92, Halle 118, Herberger 119, Morris 148, Raymond 155, Stewart 166
Arkansas: Smith 201
California: Ahmanson 222, Arbus 251, Bauer 287, Bell 300, **Capital 375**, **Clorox 407**, Danford 448, Davis 455, Douglas 476, Field 522, Fleishhacker 534, Fremont 548, Getty 578, Gillespie 587, Grand 619, Gross 629, Grout 630, Grove 631, Guzik 639, Hellman 677, Hewlett 686, Irvine 727, Isambard 729, Lehrer 827, LLWW 845, March 872, **McConnell 898**, Miller 929, Norris 971, Opperman 988, Osher 997, **Packard 1006**, Parker 1012, Parsons 1013, Placer 1039, Potiker 1042, Priem 1045, Rigler 1074, Rock 1084, Sacramento 1103, San Francisco 1109, Segerstrom 1136, Simpson 1173, Small 1180, Sonora 1198, Spitzer 1206, Springcreek 1208, Stern 1219, Thornton 1253, Towbes 1260, Tu 1265, Wallis 1296, Wasserman 1300, Wattis 1302, WHH 1320, Witherbee 1334, Zellerbach 1358
Colorado: Boettcher 1374, El Pomar 1406, Fullerton 1415, Gates 1418, Halton 1426, M.D.C./Richmond 1450, Summit 1511, Vodafone 1519
Connecticut: **Albers 1532**, Bissell 1547, Chase 1555, Community 1565, Fisher 1585, Garden 1590, Huisking 1615, Kohn 1622, Kossak 1623, Neuberger 1649, NewAlliance 1651, Palmer 1666
Delaware: Bennett 1739, Berkley 1741, Common 1755, **Memton 1819**, Whitton-Spector 1874
District of Columbia: Bender 1885, Bernstein 1887, Cafritz 1890, Coors 1895, DeLaski 1899, **Dreyfus 1901**, Kaye 1920
Florida: Bank 1979, Columbus 2030, Community 2040, Connors 2043, Dunspaugh-Dalton 2073, Edgemer 2081, Goldstein 2128, James 2169, Kramer 2195, Life 2215, Lindemann 2217, Pearce 2264, Rayonier 2281, Ryder 2302, Sack 2303, Selby 2316, Simon 2322, Stein 2337, Stern 2339, Windsor 2389
Georgia: Community 2433, Love 2508, Tull 2561, Williams 2572, Woolley 2581
Hawaii: Cades 2591
Illinois: Appleby 2668, Baskes 2683, Buchanan 2720, Buchbinder 2721, Chicago 2746, Community 2763, Dickenson 2795, EFS 2818, Franke 2841, Frankel 2843, Gray 2878, Heller 2904, Hunter 2926, Illinois 2934, Jephson 2939, Katten 2951, Keith 2952, King 2960, Malott 2996, Martin 3003, Munson 3045, Neisser 3048, Polk 3084, REAM 3107, Rhoades 3115, Ryan 3130, United 3200
Indiana: Auer 3260, Clowes 3275, Noyes 3361, Waterfield 3399, Wayne 3400
Iowa: AEGON 3409, Aviva 3411, Helpenstell 3442, McElroy 3461, Meredith 3463, Ruan 3478
Kansas: Garvey 3516, Hutchinson 3521, Salina 3540, Security 3544, Sprint 3549, Topeka 3552
Kentucky: Opera 3593
Louisiana: Booth 3616, Community 3624, Grigsby 3640, Stuller 3668
Maryland: Baker 3725, Community 3759, Davis 3772, Fairchild 3788, Fisher 3790, Freeman 3797, Hahn 3811, Polinger 3864, Rouse 3877, Sunrise 3892
Massachusetts: **Barr 3937**, Berkman 3945, Boston 3956, Community 3992, Fresh 4062, Haley 4083, Hanover 4086, Institution 4108, Jebediah 4112, New England 4192, Santander 4256
Michigan: Ann Arbor 4340, Bay 4344, Consumers 4376, Dalton 4385, DTE 4410, **Fisher 4423**, Ford 4427, Ford 4430, Frankel 4435, Fremont 4438, Gilmore 4445, Grand Rapids 4447, Hillsdale 4461, Leighton 4484, Manoogian 4492, Masco 4497, Mosaic 4509, Pokagon 4523, Skillman 4543, Van Andel 4566, Weatherwax 4577, Wege 4579
Minnesota: AHS 4599, **Andersen 4601**, Athwin 4607, Deluxe 4644, Duluth 4649, General 4661, Jerome 4681, Land 4691, Marbrook 4702, McVay 4711, Prospect 4747, Robins 4754, Sit 4765, U.S. 4784, Xcel 4808
Mississippi: Community 4820, Feild 4825
Missouri: Apex 4854, Burns 4866, Centene 4870, Duesenberg 4880, Dula 4881, Emerson 4885, Gateway 4894, Grigg 4901, Hall 4905, Hallmark 4906, **Monsanto 4945**, Oppenstein 4950, Orscheln 4951, Reynolds 4961, Sosland 4977, Stern 4980, Ten-Ten 4990
Montana: Edwards 5008
Nebraska: Abel 5021, Holland 5051, Kearney 5055, Phelps 5075, Rogers 5077, Weitz 5092, Woods 5096
Nevada: Buck 5105, Cordelia 5111, Fairweather 5118, Wiegand 5159
New Hampshire: Fuller 5172, Johnson 5178, Trust 5189
New Jersey: Bridge 5213, Cowles 5234, Creamer 5236, Dodge 5243, Hess 5298, Horizon 5305, Hyde 5310, Jaffe 5320, James 5322, Jockey 5325, Kirby 5339, Levitt 5361, McGraw 5376, Point 5410, Roth 5426, Shepherd 5451, Vanech 5487
New Mexico: Hankins 5521, Maddox 5528, McCune 5529, Santa Fe 5533
New York: Abeles 5544, Altus 5583, American 5587, **American 5588**, Arnhold 5614, Assael 5620, Bachmann 5632, Baird 5636, Barth 5648, Bechtle 5657, Benenson 5664, Berkowitz 5669, Blum 5686, Braddock 5701, Burns 5732, Canary 5744, **Clark 5785**, Cullman 5831, Curry 5836, Davenport 5850, Debs 5860, **Delmas 5871**, Diamond 5880, **Duke 5917**, Enterprise 5956, Finneran 5978, Fitt 5985, **Ford 5994**, Friedberg 6017, Gellert 6040, Gibbs 6048, Gilman 6052, Goldman 6068, **Gould 6086**, Granoff 6091, Great 6097, Greene 6104, Greve 6106, Haas 6124, Haje 6129, Harkness 6134, Harriman 6137, **Hauser 6147**, **Hearst 6155**, **Hearst 6156**, Hillman 6174, Joelson 6232, Lang 6326, Lauder 6334, Laurents/Hatcher 6338, Lemberg 6350, Lindner 6372, Loeb 6384, Loewe 6386, Lostand 6394, Lubo 6396, **M & T 6406**, Malkin 6422, Marcus 6428, Mars 6437, McCormick 6458, **Mellon 6470**, Mercy 6475, Meringoff 6476, Morse 6509, Moses 6511, Mozilo 6512, Nias 6556, Northfield 6568, O'Connor 6578, Peco 6624, **Pforzheimer 6635**, Pumpkin 6666, **Reed 6684**, Resnick 6690, Resource 6691, Richardson 6700, Riggio 6709, Rose 6734, Rose 6736, Rose 6737, Rosenkranz 6748, Sagner 6783, Samuels 6788, Scherman 6804, Secunda 6827, Sharp 6839, Sheldon 6841, Shiva 6845, **Shubert 6850**, Snow 6878, Sosnoff 6892, Speyer 6896, Steinberg 6921, Sumitomo 6943, Swartz 6954, Tisch 6986, Sussman 6990, **Trust 7009**, Weiler 7063, Weinberg 7066, Weinberg 7067, West 7077, Western 7078, Zalaznick 7113
North Carolina: Adams 7133, Cemala 7174, Cumberland 7184, Love 7258, Odell 7277, Smith 7317, Triangle 7328, Wheeler 7336, Woodward 7343
North Dakota: Leach 7353, Stern 7360
Ohio: Akron 7367, Bailey 7381, Budig 7392, Christman 7403, Cleveland 7406, Codrington 7409, Columbus 7411, Dayton 7429, Emery 7443, Frost 7464, Haile, 7480, Hayfields 7485, IHS 7501, Ingalls 7503, Kaplan 7516, **Kettering 7520**, Kettering 7522, Kulas 7532, Middletown 7570, Miniger 7572, Morgan 7577, Murphy 7584, Muskingum 7585, Nordson 7596, **OMNOVA 7601**, Park 7610, Partridge 7612, Payne 7614, Reinberger 7628, Stark 7673, Toulmin 7687, Wohlgemuth 7718, Youngstown 7723
Oklahoma: Bartlesville 7731, Helmerich 7758, Kerr 7764, Kirkpatrick 7766, Zink 7821
Oregon: Autzen 7823, Benton 7825, Carpenter 7831, Haugland 7849, Jackson 7855, Meyer 7870, PacifiCorp 7877
Pennsylvania: Aqua 7917, Arete 7919, Armstrong 7921, Baker 7926, Carnahan 7965, Carpenter 7967, Claneil 7982, Colket 7987, Coulson 8000, Dolfinger 8013, EQT 8025, Ferree 8036, Garfield 8052, Hecht 8082, Hurd 8101, Huston 8102, Independence 8107, Keystone 8122, Mandell 8153, Massey 8158, McCune 8161, McLean 8169, Miller 8183, Neubauer 8196, Penn 8216, Pew 8220, Pine 8226, **PPG 8235**, Schroth 8274, Toll 8316, United 8325, Vanguard 8327, von Hess 8329, Washington 8332
Rhode Island: Charlesmead 8371, Chisholm 8373, Daniels 8380, Rhode Island 8429, Vance 8450
South Carolina: Graham 8481
Tennessee: Atticus 8531, Benwood 8535, Curb 8554, Eastman 8561, Frist 8568, Massey 8607, Nissan 8613, Scheidt 8625, Temple 8633
Texas: BNSF 8706, Boeckman 8707, Bratton 8722, Carter 8752, Carter 8753, Fikes 8844, Fish 8848,

Fleming 8850, Ford 8854, Hoblitzelle 8912, Hudson 8919, Humphreys 8921, Johnson 8939, Jones 8943, Kempner 8952, Kilroy 8956, King 8959, Kodosky 8966, Littauer 8988, Madison 8997, Marsh 8999, McIntyre 9016, Moody 9033, Nearburg 9055, Owen 9076, Payne 9086, Perot 9093, Petrello 9096, Reynolds 9127, Richardson 9130, Rogers 9139, Rosewood 9140, San Antonio 9148, Scurlock 9162, Smith 9187, Sterling 9203, Texas 9227, Tobin 9236, Vanberg 9247, Walsh 9256, Wortham 9292, Wright 9293
Utah: Bastian 9306, Dee 9312, Eccles 9319, Eccles 9320, Lawson 9330, Lawson 9331, Quinney 9347, Tanner 9352
Virginia: Arlington 9384, Folger 9431, Lafayette 9465, Malek 9475, Norfolk 9496, Pauley 9505, Reinsch 9518, Reynolds 9519, Rimora 9522, Rosenthal 9525, Universal 9548, Weissberg 9554
Washington: Allen 9567, Apex 9574, Blue 9588, Community 9604, Foster 9621, McCaw 9675, McEachern 9678, McIntyre 9679, Nesholm 9691, Norcliffe 9693, Plum 9704, Renton 9715, Safeco 9723, Sarkowsky 9727, Sherwood 9733, Tacoma 9750, Yakima 9767
West Virginia: Kanawha 9780, Tucker 9796
Wisconsin: **Baird 9811**, Baker 9812, Briggs 9822, Charter 9829, Frautschi 9847, Hands 9858, Heil 9860, Incourage 9867, Johnson 9870, Johnson 9874, Kohler 9884, Ladish 9890, Lubar 9894, Mead 9902, Milwaukee 9907, Northwestern 9914, Pick 9920, Rockwell 9934, Sentry 9944, Steigleder 9952, Uihlein 9958, Wisconsin 9969, Wisconsin 9970

Performing arts (multimedia)

Illinois: Alphawood 2658
New York: **Cummings 5833**
Pennsylvania: Hurd 8101

Performing arts centers

Alabama: Stephens 69
California: Bower 332, Clayes 404, Fry 555, Gallo 560, Irvine 727, Jackson 737, Pacific 1003, Randall 1054, **Samueli 1106**, San Simeon 1111, Schlinger 1123, Shanbrom 1147
Connecticut: Chase 1555, Kohn 1622, Pasculano 1668, Tow 1708
District of Columbia: Gudelsky 1912, HRH 1917
Florida: **Patel 2259**, Saunders 2308, Straz 2341
Illinois: Keith 2952
Kansas: Capitol 3498
Kentucky: Young 3607
Maryland: Baker 3725, Dekelboum 3777, Fisher 3790, Freeman 3797
Massachusetts: Feigenbaum 4044, Fireman 4049, Leventhal 4141
Missouri: Centene 4870, Nichols 4949
Nebraska: Kind 5060
Nevada: Bennett 5101, Ruvo 5145
New Hampshire: Penates 5185
New Jersey: Cole 5231, Cooperman 5233, Creamer 5236, Honickman 5303, Shen 5450, Smith 5461
New York: Armstrong 5612, Belfer 5660, Braddock 5701, Diamond 5880, Diker 5883, Dinan 5888, Effron 5938, Ehrenkranz 5941, Finneran 5978, Fisher 5982, Fisher 5983, Gural 6117, Harris 6138, Harris 6139, Harrison 6142, IFF 6206, JAM 6224, Katzenberger 6258, Kravis 6307, Lauder 6334, Lauder 6337, Morse 6509, Newman 6552, Northfield 6568, Pels 6625, Picket 6638, Sosnoff 6892, Steinberg 6920, Stern 6926, **Tanaka 6961**, Sussman 6990, Wegman 7061, Ziff 7121
Ohio: Wodecroft 7717
Pennsylvania: Field 8037, Knipel 8130, Schroth 8274
Rhode Island: Scrooby 8435
Tennessee: Carlton 8541
Texas: Bass 8690, Carlson 8750, Collins 8772, MFI 9025, TurningPoint 9244, Wood 9289
Utah: Price 9346

Virginia: Funger 9438, Hylton 9455, SunTrust 9539, Trehan 9544
Washington: McIntyre 9679, Wright 9765

Performing arts, ballet

California: Baker 280, Caldwell 363, Irvine 727, Martin 882, Ross 1091, San Simeon 1111, Sloan 1179
Colorado: PB&K 1474
Florida: Ansin 1969
Georgia: Holder 2485
Illinois: McIntosh 3016, NIB 3053, United 3199, Vaughn 3203
Kentucky: Opera 3593
Maryland: Abell 3713
Massachusetts: Kiva 4125
Michigan: DeVos 4398
Missouri: Centene 4870, Laurie 4933, Wornall 5003
Nevada: Buck 5105
New Jersey: Point 5410
New York: Buttenwieser 5736, Friedberg 6017, Granoff 6091, **Hughes 6192**, Lear 6341, Lipp 6377, McGraw 6462, Richardson 6700, Robbins 6716, Sands 6790, Slifka 6871, Sosnoff 6892, Vogelstein 7034, Ziff 7122
Ohio: State 7674
Oklahoma: Miller 7778, Robinson 7789
Pennsylvania: Benter 7937, Mine 8184
Tennessee: Fritch 8569
Texas: Barr 8683, Beals, 8697, Carlson 8750, Fischer 8847, Humphreys 8921
Utah: Bastian 9306, Meldrum 9333
Washington: **PAH 9699**
Wisconsin: **Baird 9811**, Heil 9860

Performing arts, circus arts

New York: Zankel 7114

Performing arts, dance

California: Fleishhacker 534, Hewlett 686, Irvine 727, Kaufman 770, Osher 997, **Rainin 1051**, San Francisco 1109
Colorado: Gates 1418, Halton 1426, Vail 1518
Connecticut: Allison 1535, Lee 1626, Provident 1677
District of Columbia: Cafritz 1890
Florida: Bank 1979
Illinois: Alphawood 2658, Cheney 2745, Clinton 2754, Community 2763, Prince 3090, Taylor 3184
Iowa: Siouxland 3480
Kentucky: Opera 3593
Louisiana: Community 3624
Maryland: Mann 3839
Massachusetts: One 4198, Shapiro 4267
Minnesota: Jerome 4681
Missouri: Kauffman 4922
New Jersey: Dodge 5243, **Puffin 5417**
New Mexico: McCune 5529
New York: Baldwin 5639, **Clark 5785**, Dannheisser 5847, Diker 5883, **Duke 5917**, **Ford 5994**, Gilman 6052, Harkness 6134, Lindenbaum 6370, **Mayer 6449**, **Mertz 6477**, Morse 6509, Moses 6511, Robbins 6716, Samuels 6788, Scherman 6804, SHS 6848, **Shubert 6850**, **Trust 7009**, Unanue 7015, **Vital 7033**, Western 7078, Ziff 7122
North Carolina: Biddle 7150, Triangle 7328
North Dakota: Stern 7360
Ohio: Coshocton 7421, Dance 7425, Gund 7476, Murphy 7584
Oregon: Esco 7841
Pennsylvania: Dolfinger 8013, Pew 8220, Philadelphia 8221
South Dakota: Sioux Falls 8521
Texas: Bass 8689, Kempner 8952, San Antonio 9148, Simmons 9174
Utah: Eccles 9320
Virginia: Millhiser 9486
Washington: Seattle 9731
West Virginia: Kanawha 9780
Wisconsin: Bemis 9815, Milwaukee 9907

Performing arts, education

California: Colburn 410, Lehrer 827, Roth 1093
Delaware: Esperance 1777
Illinois: Dunard 2810
Indiana: Community 3282
New York: Butler 5734, **Hearst 6155**, **Hearst 6156**, McClelland 6457, Morse 6509, **Shubert 6850**
North Dakota: Larson 7352
Pennsylvania: Hurd 8101
Tennessee: Tucker 8638
Vermont: McKenzie 9366

Performing arts, music

Alaska: Carr 83
Arizona: Morris 148
California: **Alpert 231**, Colburn 410, Femino 521, Field 522, Fleishhacker 534, Fresno 549, Getty 578, Hale 645, Heller 676, Hewlett 686, Hind 693, **Mercer 917**, Osher 997, Packard 1007, Ross 1090, Roth 1093, Sonora 1198, Stotsenberg 1221, Thornton 1252, **Wadhwani 1294**, Wood 1344
Colorado: Bernstein 1372, Boettcher 1374, El Pomar 1406, Gates 1418, Halton 1426, Summit 1511, Vail 1518
Connecticut: Daniell 1570, Fisher 1586, Kossak 1623
Delaware: Crystal 1758
District of Columbia: Bernstein 1887, Cafritz 1890
Florida: Clark 2022, Colen 2029, Global 2126, Katcher 2176
Georgia: Katz 2494
Hawaii: Ching 2596
Illinois: Alphawood 2658, Barnett 2680, Cheney 2745, Clinton 2754, Community 2763, Dunard 2810, Gray 2878, Morrison 3037, Morrison 3038, Negaunee 3047, Neisser 3048, Ryan 3129, Seid 3148, United 3199, Wilson 3237
Indiana: Clowes 3275, Community 3282, Lincoln 3344
Iowa: AEGON 3409, Siouxland 3480
Kansas: Morris 3537
Kentucky: Opera 3593, Preston 3596
Maryland: Community 3759, Fisher 3790
Massachusetts: Klarman 4126, Proctor 4227, Shapiro 4267, Weatherbie 4321
Michigan: Dalton 4385, Ford 4430, Harding 4455, Westerman 4582
Minnesota: **Andersen 4601**, Duluth 4649, Jerome 4681, RBC 4748, Xcel 4808
Missouri: Kauffman 4922, Sosland 4977, Stern 4980
Montana: Scoob 5015, Washington 5018
Nevada: Buck 5105, Fairweather 5118, Wiegand 5159
New Jersey: Dodge 5243, OceanFirst 5394
New Mexico: McCune 5529, Santa Fe 5533
New York: Armstrong 5612, Bayne 5653, Botwinick 5696, Butler 5734, Buttenwieser 5736, Carvel 5749, **Clark 5785**, Community 5803, Cone 5810, Copland 5814, **Deutsche 5876**, **Duke 5917**, **Ford 5994**, **Grant 6092**, **Hauser 6147**, Heineman 6158, Hermione 6163, Hillman 6174, Kellen 6268, Mailman 6419, Marcus 6428, McNeil 6464, Mesdag 6478, Moore 6504, Morse 6509, Moses 6511, Newhouse 6550, Noble 6561, Orvis 6598, Puth 6668, Samuels 6788, Sarofim 6797, Scherman 6804, Seven 6834, Stiefel 6931, **Trust 7009**, **Vital 7033**, Western 7078, Ziff 7121
North Carolina: Adams 7133, Bergen 7149, Biddle 7150, Gibbs 7207, Triangle 7328
Ohio: American 7368, Gund 7476, Kulas 7532, Licking 7540, Muskingum 7585, Ratner 7626, Youngstown 7723
Oklahoma: Barthelmes 7730
Pennsylvania: Arcadia 7918, Central 7971, Dolfinger 8013, Drumcliff 8016, Field 8037, Giop 8057, Greenfield 8071, Pew 8220, Presser 8236, Rosenstiel 8254, Steinman 8299
Rhode Island: **Bingham 8361**
South Dakota: Sioux Falls 8521
Texas: Bass 8689, Fikes 8844, Johnson 8939, **Scaler 9155**, Starling 9199
Utah: Doctorow 9314
Vermont: McKenzie 9366

Performing arts, music (choral)

Performing arts, music composition

Performing arts, music ensembles/groups

Performing arts, opera

Performing arts, orchestras

Performing arts, theater

Texas: Community 8775, Hersh 8903, Humphreys 8921, Jamail 8929, Jones 8943, Kempner 8952, Meredith 9023, Natural 9053, San Antonio 9148, Simmons 9174, Sterling 9203
Utah: Doctorow 9314, Eccles 9320, Meldrum 9333
Washington: Biller 9586, Community 9604, Norcliffe 9693, Tacoma 9750, Wright 9765
West Virginia: Eastern 9775
Wisconsin: Acuity 9801, Bemis 9815, Incourage 9867, Mead 9902, Nicholas 9913

Performing arts, theater (musical)

Louisiana: Community 3624
New Jersey: Shreiber 5453
New York: Ebb 5928, Snowdon 6879
Pennsylvania: Hurd 8101

Performing arts, theater (playwriting)

New York: Cohn 5793, Steinberg 6921
Pennsylvania: Hurd 8101
Washington: George 9626

Personal assistance services (PAS)

California: **Smith 1183**

Pharmacy/prescriptions

California: Patron 1020
Colorado: El Pomar 1406
Connecticut: Alexion 1533
Indiana: Kosciusko 3335
Maryland: Hoffberger 3817
Missouri: Express 4888
New Jersey: WebMD 5496
New York: **Bristol 5711**, **Pfizer 6634**
North Carolina: Piedmont 7285
Ohio: **Cardinal 7398**
Pennsylvania: **Viropharma 8328**
Rhode Island: CVS 8379
Virginia: Reckitt 9516

Philanthropy/voluntarism

Alaska: Alaska 79
Arizona: Kiita 130, KMB 131, Linde 135, Lodestar 136
California: Briskin 344, Broad 348, Buchheit 353, Case 383, Coit 409, **Draper 481**, **Draper 481**, Gerbode 573, Germanacos 574, Hewlett 686, Irvine 727, Kern 780, Kohl 799, **Packard 1006**, Saw 1119, Schwab 1127, Springcreek 1208, Valhalla 1278, **Wadhwani 1294**, Woolls 1345, Yellow 1354
Colorado: Anschutz 1364, Chambers 1385, **Gill 1421**, M.D.C./Richmond 1450, Merage 1459, **Merage 1460**
Connecticut: Cohen 1560, **Newman's 1652**, Summer 1704, Valley 1714, ZOOM 1732
Delaware: Dwoskin 1772, La Vida 1799
Florida: Community 2035, Community 2036, Deshe 2062, Huizenga 2165, Roberts 2290, SHIFT 2320
Georgia: North 2525
Illinois: Amicus 2660, Logan 2983, Mansueto 3000, Pritzker 3093, Pritzker 3096
Indiana: Central 3272, Community 3280, Crown Point 3291, Legacy 3337, **Lilly 3342**
Iowa: Community 3424
Kansas: Elliott 3513, McPherson 3534
Louisiana: Grayson 3639
Maryland: Blum 3737
Massachusetts: Adams 3916, Beveridge 3950, Corcoran 3995, Crimson 3999, Cummings 4003, Devonshire 4017, Leaves 4139, Levine 4142, Mannion 4161, Sims/Maes 4274
Michigan: **Fetzer 4420**, Frey 4440, Granger 4450
Minnesota: Bendorf 4610, Butler 4622, Southwest 4768
Missouri: Saint Louis 4966
New Hampshire: Byrne 5166, New Hampshire 5182
New Jersey: Holman 5301, **Johnson 5326**, KPMG 5349
New Mexico: Chase 5517
New York: Berne 5670, Bingham 5676, **Bloomberg 5684**, BMS 5688, **Breslauer 5707**, Cole 5795, DeGeorge 5867, Donner 5899, **Ford 5994**, Foundation 6004, Helmsley 6160, Kaplan 6251, LaSalle 6331, Loeb 6383, Paestum 6608, **Pfizer 6633**, Raiff 6675, Randa 6676, Tisch 6987, **Trace 7003**, **Unbound 7016**, Zehner 7118, Zvi 7129
Ohio: Columbus 7411, Gund 7477, Hunt 7498, Rosenthal 7637
Oklahoma: Coretz 7744, Zink 7821
Pennsylvania: Chatham 7978, Davis 8004, Helen's 8087, Stern 8301
Rhode Island: Hasbro 8403
Tennessee: Community 8549, Jeniam 8587
Texas: McCombs 9009, Pema 9088, Pleroma 9102, Wilson 9280
Utah: Miller 9336
Virginia: ACT 9380
Washington: Almi 9569, Remala 9714, Yakima 9767
Wisconsin: Mound 9910

Philanthropy/voluntarism, administration/ regulation

California: Irvine 727

Philanthropy/voluntarism, alliance/advocacy

Washington: **Gates 9625**

Philanthropy/voluntarism, association

California: Irvine 727, Los Altos 849

Philanthropy/voluntarism, fund raising/fund distribution

Arizona: Lodestar 136
Colorado: Mizel 1461

Philanthropy/voluntarism, information services

California: Irvine 727

Philanthropy/voluntarism, management/ technical assistance

California: **Packard 1006**
Colorado: Mizel 1461
New York: Dyson 5923, Ohrstrom 6582
Pennsylvania: York 8351
Tennessee: Frist 8568
Texas: Pleroma 9102, Pritzker 9111
Washington: Roots 9720

Philanthropy/voluntarism, public policy

Massachusetts: Boston 3956

Philanthropy/voluntarism, research

Florida: Wells 2383
Indiana: **Lilly 3342**

Philosophy/ethics

Alaska: CIRI 85
California: **Rupe 1097**
Michigan: **Earhart 4413**

Physical therapy

California: McCarthy 896
Florida: Maren 2227
Idaho: **Schultz 2641**
Indiana: Kosciusko 3335
Minnesota: **Patterson 4738**
Rhode Island: CVS 8379

Physical/earth sciences

Arizona: Freeport-McMoRan 112
California: **American 237**, **Beckman 297**, **Keck 774**
Colorado: Harvey 1428
Florida: Selby 2316
Illinois: **Brinson 2715**
New York: **Eppley 5957**, **Kade 6247**, Monell 6497, Vetlesen 7027
North Carolina: Woodward 7344
Virginia: Jeffress 9457
Washington: Avista 9576, Murdock 9689

Physically disabled

Alabama: Community 25, Kaul 43, Meyer 53
Arizona: **Johnson 126**, Webb 174
Arkansas: Cabe 182
California: Ahmanson 222, Atkinson 265, Center 388, Community 414, El Dorado 500, Green 621, Gumbiner 636, Lesher 833, McMillen 905, Outhwaite 1000, Patron 1020, Rogers 1087, San Luis 1110, Sandy 1113, **Smith 1183**, Tuohy 1267, Weingart 1307
Colorado: Fishback 1410, Halton 1426, Hunter 1431, King 1440, Summit 1511
Connecticut: Community 1562, Mortensen 1647
Delaware: **Raskob 1845**
District of Columbia: Cafritz 1890, **Union 1953**
Florida: **Peterson 2267**, Southwest 2327
Georgia: Franklin 2462, Rich 2537, **Thoresen 2557**
Idaho: **Schultz 2641**
Illinois: Arthur 2673, Blowitz 2702, Butler 2729, King 2960, Master 3004, Siragusa 3162
Indiana: Brown 3269, Community 3281, Henry 3320, **Lilly 3342**, Rolland 3381, Waterfield 3399
Iowa: Community 3421
Kansas: Community 3502, Security 3544
Kentucky: Cralle 3571
Louisiana: Wilson 3671
Maryland: **Bearman 3728**, Community 3761, Fowler 3795
Massachusetts: Shapiro 4267, Stevens 4288
Michigan: Chrysler 4366, Fremont 4438, Johnson 4468, Midland 4502
Minnesota: Bremer 4620
Missouri: Saigh 4965, Saint Louis 4966
Montana: Oro 5014, Washington 5018
Nebraska: Dunklau 5036
New Hampshire: Foundation 5171, Lindsay 5179
New Jersey: Hyde 5310
New York: Achelis 5549, Bodman 5692, BTMU 5724, Community 5802, Diamond 5880, **MetLife 6479**, **Nash 6525**, O'Connor 6578, Ritter 6712, **Ross 6754**, Schnurmacher 6810, Staten 6912, Ward 7049, Warner 7053
North Carolina: Community 7180, North Carolina 7273, Reidsville 7294, Robertson 7305
North Dakota: Leach 7353
Ohio: Bruening 7391, Cincinnati 7404, Fairfield 7445, Hatton 7483, KeyBank 7523, O'Neill 7602, Parents 7608, Pfau 7618, Richland 7630, Saint 7639, Spaulding 7670, Springfield 7671, Youngstown 7723
Oklahoma: Hardesty 7756, Hille 7759, Zink 7821
Oregon: Benton 7825, Carpenter 7831, Collins 7836, J.F.R. 7854, Poznanski 7882
Pennsylvania: Beneficial 7936, Connelly 7995, First 8041, Huston 8102, Independence 8107, North 8199, Pew 8220, Phoenixville 8223, Snee 8291
Tennessee: Baptist 8533, Thompson 8636, Wilson 8646
Texas: Abell 8650, Bass 8690, Community 8774, Community 8777, Dallas 8795, Hartman 8893, McDermott 9013, Moore 9034, Orsinger 9073, Rees-Jones 9125, Stevens 9205, Terry 9224
Utah: Eccles 9320
Vermont: Gibney 9362
Virginia: Beazley 9391, Mitsubishi 9487
Washington: Norcliffe 9693
Wisconsin: Benidt 9816, Green Bay 9854, La Crosse 9889, Stock 9953, West 9967

Physics

Arizona: **Research 157**
California: **Beckman 297**
Nevada: Wiegand 5159
New Jersey: **Siemens 5454**
New York: **IBM 6203**
Pennsylvania: Brodsky 7952

Planetarium

Illinois: Clark 2751, Cressey 2779, Ward 3216

Political science

Connecticut: **Richardson 1679**
Indiana: **Goodrich 3311**
Massachusetts: Colombe 3989
Michigan: Consumers 4376, **Earhart 4413**
New York: Aequus 5560, **Guggenheim 6115**, Littauer 6379, Monell 6497, Sackler 6779, **Tinker 6983**
Pennsylvania: **Carthage 7968**, Scaife 8266
Texas: Sumners 9214
Wisconsin: **Bradley 9819**

Population studies

California: Hewlett 686, **Packard 1006**
Colorado: **Winslow 1525**
Florida: Martin 2229
Georgia: **Turner 2563**
New York: Dodge 5892, **New 6551**, **Weeden 7060**
North Carolina: Cumberland 7184
Pennsylvania: **Colcom 7986**

Poverty studies

California: Rosenberg 1088
Texas: **Marshall 9000**

Pregnancy centers

Arizona: Hermundslie 120
California: California 368, Smullin 1190
Indiana: Miller 3355
Kansas: Shannon 3545
Massachusetts: Josetta 4114
Pennsylvania: CentiMark 7970
Texas: Fath 8840, Thomas 9232

Prostate cancer

Florida: Moran 2242
New Jersey: Evans 5254
New York: Foundation 6000, **Shaw 6840**
Virginia: Evans 9428

Prostate cancer research

California: Graziadio 620
Kansas: Koch 3528
New York: Mack 6412, Thompson 6975
Washington: Sunbridge 9746

Protestant agencies & churches

Alabama: Alpha 3, Arlington 6, Bean 10, **Flack 34**, Jernigan 42, King 44, May 48, Mitchell 55, Nabers 56, Nelson 57, Stephens 69
Arizona: Jazzbird 125, Long 137, Neely 149
Arkansas: Cabe 182, George 189, Schmieding 200, Smith 201, Sturgis 205, Union 208
California: Boeckmann 323, Brewster 342, Draper 480, El 501, **First 530**, Grimm 626, Henley 680, JDH 746, Kay 772, Leonard 831, Markkula 879, Philanthropy 1035, Raintree 1052, Schlinger 1123, Semloh 1139, Smith 1184, Smullin 1190, Ullman 1269, Valhalla 1278, Versacare 1288, Voss 1292
Colorado: Armstrong 1366, Bowana 1377, Edmondson 1405, Lane 1443, Norwood 1471, TYL 1516, Whispering 1522
Connecticut: Georgescu 1593, Glover 1594, Lee 1626, Meriden 1643, Royce 1685, Twenty-Seven 1712
Delaware: Chase 1753, Day 1764, Gospel 1786, James 1789, Pelham 1832, Reynolds 1849
Florida: Bank 1979, **Believers 1989**, Bell 1991, Berg 1993, Booth 2000, Cobb 2026, Dallepezze 2049, Do 2065, Duda 2070, duPont 2074, Eagle 2078, Gay 2117, Hahn 2144, Herr 2155, Jenkins 2171, Maren 2227, Pamphalon 2257, Patton 2262, Robinson 2291, Sansing 2307, Speer 2328, Tharpe 2355, Vanneck-Bailey 2370
Georgia: Amos 2401, Amos 2402, Beard-Payne 2408, Campbell 2420, Camp-Younts 2421, CLC 2426, Day 2448, Griffith 2473, Grizzard 2474, Harrison 2481, Indiana 2488, Jackson 2490, Jordan 2492, Layton 2500, Lewis 2503, Loudermilk 2507, Ma-Ran 2510, Montgomery 2518, Morgens 2521, Pitts 2529, Rod 2541, Rollins 2542, Rollins 2543, Williams 2574, Williams, 2575, Young 2582
Hawaii: Atherton 2586, Wilcox 2621
Illinois: Andrew 2662, Barnett 2681, Butler 2729, Christopher 2748, Clark 2751, Clinton 2754, Cornell 2774, Cressey 2779, Delany 2793, Emerson 2822, Flynn 2835, Hobbs 2914, Hunter 2926, Ingersoll 2935, Kolschowsky 2962, Nierling, 3056, Norris 3058, Pierce 3080, Roberts 3121, Schawk 3138, Smith 3164, Souder 3168, **Tyndale 3195**, Vaughn 3203, Wenske 3225, White 3230, Wonderful 3239
Indiana: Bales 3261, Community 3278, Hux 3325, Met 3353, Parke 3366
Iowa: Gabus 3429, Helpenstell 3442, Krause 3454, New 3468, Sukup 3483
Kansas: Hartley 3519, McCune 3533, Morris 3537, Schowalter 3542
Kentucky: Coffey 3568, Newell 3591
Louisiana: Burton 3619, Cason 3620, Chambers 3621, Coughlin 3626, Diboll 3628, Factor 3632, Franks 3634, Frazier 3635, Huie 3643, Jones 3645, Lorio 3650, McIlhenny 3654, Scott 3666, Seal 3667
Maine: Mulford 3702
Maryland: Adams 3718, Clark 3751, Osprey 3861, Rock 3870, Sampson 3878, **Smith 3886**
Massachusetts: Boston 3955, Finch 4048, Inavale 4106, Linn 4149
Michigan: Boll 4352, Chinnick 4363, Ford 4427, Helppie 4456, Hurst 4464, Mackey 4489, Mulder 4514, Pentecost 4520, Turner 4561, VanderWeide 4572, Willmas 4587
Minnesota: AHS 4599, Andreas 4604, Bakken 4608, Driscoll 4648, Gesner 4663, Koskovich 4690, Stone 4773
Mississippi: BBB 4813, Community 4819, Luckyday 4833, Mississippi 4837, Pruet 4842
Missouri: Breen 4861, Duesenberg 4880, Humphreys 4912, Pillsbury 4956, Plaster 4957, Rhoden 4962, Rosewood 4964, Webb 4999
Montana: Bair 5004, Treacy 5017
Nebraska: Acklie 5022, Beer 5024, Buckley 5026, Dunklau 5036, Hawks 5047, Lauritzen 5061, Mapes 5066, Vetter 5091, Werner 5094
New Hampshire: Hopeman 5176
New Jersey: Bolger 5207, Cowles 5234, Dunbar 5245, Kish 5341, Lasko 5356, Nicolais 5392, Point 5410
New Mexico: **Johns 5524**
New York: Campbell 5742, Caudill 5751, Clinton 5787, deForest 5866, Delaney 5869, Dewar 5879, Duncan 5920, Dunwalke 5921, Gordon 6081, Grace 6090, Gross 6110, Grubman 6113, Habib 6126, IF 6205, Kanas 6249, Kellen 6268, Landegger 6323, Liu 6381, Michaels 6482, Millbrook 6485, Miller 6486, Mule 6513, Nuhn 6572, O'Connor 6578, Park 6614, Rantz 6678, Resource 6691, **Robertson 6718**, Roepers 6726, Rogers 6728, Steel 6914, Van Cleave 7025, Vidda 7030, Warren 7054
North Carolina: Baxter 7142, Belk 7147, Branan 7157, Braswell 7158, Brauninger 7159, Byrum 7166, Cannon 7169, Community 7178, Dalton 7187, Dover 7194, Duke 7195, Gibbs 7207, Giles 7208, Gipson 7209, Glenn 7211, Harvey 7225, Hayes 7227, Herring 7229, Hillsdale 7232, Holding 7233, Hommer 7235, Humphrey 7236, Jonas 7241, Keith 7247, Kimbrell 7249, Kulynych 7251, Kulynych 7252, Lewis 7256, McEachern 7263, McMichael 7265, Morgan 7269, P & B 7280, Perkins 7282, Plansoen 7286, Simpson 7312, Sloan 7314, Smith 7315, Stewards 7322, Yount 7348
Ohio: Austin 7380, Christman 7403, Fenn 7449, Fox 7461, IHS 7501, Jobst 7512, Jordan 7514, Knight 7527, Miller 7571, Riley 7632, Ritter 7633, Talmage 7680, Wade 7697, Warrington 7703, White 7714
Oklahoma: Bernsen 7733, Crawley 7746, Jackson 7761, McGill 7775, Nelson 7779, Stephenson 7799, Stone 7801
Oregon: Metolius 7869, Salem 7885
Pennsylvania: Arcadia 7918, Biesecker 7941, Brickman 7949, Buck 7955, Century 7974, Community 7993, Connelly 7995, Firstfruits 8042, Fitch 8045, Harding 8080, Hughes 8099, Huston 8103, Mason 8157, McFeely 8163, Nimick 8198, Oxford 8208, Pond 8231, Quaker 8240, Schieffelin 8270, Smock 8290, Stackpole 8295, Taylor 8311, Turner 8321, Williams 8338
Rhode Island: Binney 8362, Capewell 8366, Fox 8395, Knoop 8411, M. 8414, Manning 8415, McCurdy 8417, Stone 8443
South Carolina: Abney 8454, Arkwright 8456, Campbell 8463, Canal 8466, Hipp 8483, Hopewell 8484, Montgomery 8487, Pfriem 8490, Phifer 8491, TSC 8506
South Dakota: Branches 8512, Hofer 8515
Tennessee: Atticus 8531, Clayton 8547, Curb 8554, Ezell 8564, Kharis 8591, Lewis 8598, MacLellan 8600, **Maclellan 8601**, Martin 8604, Martin 8605, Stokely 8631, Wallace 8642, Washington 8643, Wilson 8645, Wilson 8646
Texas: Allison 8659, Armentrout 8671, Badger 8678, Bass 8689, Baugh 8693, Bratton 8722, Brock 8727, Brown, 8732, C.I.O.S. 8740, Cain 8743, Christian 8763, Coates 8769, Cox 8784, Craig, 8786, Crain 8787, Criswell 8789, Crowell 8791, Doss 8812, Family 8836, Gayden 8861, Grum 8876, Halbert 8882, Hawn 8896, Henderson 8900, Henderson 8901, Herd 8902, Jamail 8928, JKL 8935, Johnson 8937, Johnson 8938, Jones 8942, Live 8989, Looper 8990, Lyman 8995, Marsh 8999, Meyer 9024, Miller 9027, Morgan 9037, Morning 9040, Morris 9041, NAH 9047, Napier 9050, **Notsew 9064**, O'Connor 9066, O'Hare 9068, **Oldham 9069**, Perkins 9090, Perot 9092, Perot 9093, Phillips 9097, Ram 9120, Robinson 9133, Rogers 9138, Rowling 9141, Scurlock 9162, Sharp 9167, Shelton 9169, Sparrow 9194, Sterling 9203, Sunnyside 9215, Thomas 9231, Tucker 9241, Vanberg 9247, Walter 9257, Ward 9258, Ware 9259, Weaver 9261, Whitacre 9273, White 9274, Zorich 9301
Utah: Lawson 9330
Vermont: Isaiah 9364
Virginia: Balsells 9385, Carter 9403, English 9426, Flippo 9430, Foster 9432, Kirk 9462, Love 9470, Owens 9503, Perry 9507, Reinsch 9518, Reynolds 9519, Titmus 9543, Whitlock 9556
Washington: Bamford 9580, Bushnell 9592, Colson 9601, Hughes 9648, Rice 9716, Spark 9741
West Virginia: Hunnicutt 9779
Wisconsin: Alexander 9802, Antioch 9807, Frautschi 9847, Gordon 9853, Johnson 9873, Kellogg 9879, Kern 9880, Kohl 9883, Siebert 9946, Thrivent 9956, Wanek 9963
Wyoming: Christian 9974, Griffith 9979

Protestant federated giving programs

Illinois: Ackermann 2652
Iowa: Gabus 3429
North Carolina: Curtis 7186
Pennsylvania: Reeser 8246
Texas: **Scaler 9155**
Wisconsin: Siebert 9946

Psychology/behavioral science
Michigan: Fetzer 4421
New York: **Grant 6093**, **Guggenheim 6115**
Ohio: Ridgecliff 7631
Pennsylvania: Staunton 8296, Steinman 8300

Public affairs
Alabama: Community 21, Energen 32
Arizona: Arizona 92, Freeport-McMoRan 112
California: Allergan 228, **Bechtel 295**, Blum 321, Community 419, **Draper 481**, Genentech 571, Gerbode 573, Jacobs 738, **Omidyar 984**, Pacific 1003, San Francisco 1109, Silicon 1166, **Strauss 1223**, Teichert 1244
Colorado: **Anschutz 1365**, Community 1391, Pikes 1478, Vodafone 1519, **Western 1521**
Connecticut: Barnes 1542, Larsen 1624, Rosenthal 1684
Delaware: **Gloria 1784**, Quitiplas 1844, Romill 1851
District of Columbia: **Arca 1880**, Dole 1900, **Searle 1946**, U.S. 1952, Wallace 1956
Florida: Community 2034, Community 2040, Community 2041, Dunn's 2072, Gulf 2142, Harris 2149, Hertog 2157, Martin 2229, Rayonier 2281, Ryder 2302
Georgia: Love 2508, Woodruff 2579
Hawaii: Learning 2610
Illinois: Beidler 2692, Blair 2699, Crown 2781, Exelon 2827, Field 2831, Friedmann 2847, Galvin 2856, Landau 2966, MB 3008, Stern 3177, United 3200, Williams 3234, Woods 3242
Indiana: 1st 3251, Ball 3262, Crown Point 3291, Heritage 3321, Koch 3334, Kosciusko 3336, Legacy 3337, Madison 3346, Noble 3359, Tipton 3391, Vectren 3394, Wells 3403, Whitley 3407
Iowa: AEGON 3409, Aviva 3411, Clarinda 3418, Maytag 3460, Pella 3473, Poweshiek 3475, Principal 3476, Tye 3484
Kansas: Koch 3528, Sprint 3549
Kentucky: Blue 3560, Humana 3582
Louisiana: Lamar 3647, New Orleans 3656
Maine: Bangor 3680, Hannaford 3690
Maryland: **Casey 3745**, Community 3758, **Grace 3807**, Lockheed 3837
Massachusetts: Ashurst 3928, Cabot 3967, Cabot 3968, Chorus 3984, Clipper 3987, Community 3992, Liberty 4145, Nathan 4188, Parker 4207, Swensrud 4303, Worcester 4327
Michigan: Ann Arbor 4340, Battle Creek 4343, Capital 4357, Community 4371, Dart 4388, Hillsdale 4461, Masco 4497, **Rodney 4528**, Van Noord 4571
Minnesota: Central 4631, Hersey 4673, Land 4691, **Medtronic 4712**, **Mosaic 4722**, RBC 4748, Rochester 4755, Securian 4761, **St. Jude 4770**, Winona 4806
Mississippi: C Spire 4817
Missouri: Ameren 4851, Commerce 4871, Emerson 4885, Hallmark 4906, **Monsanto 4945**, Todd 4992
Nebraska: Grand Island 5044, Lincoln 5063, Merrick 5067, Union 5090
Nevada: Caesars 5106, **Reynolds 5143**, Wiegand 5159
New Jersey: Community 5232, Fund 5270, Hickory 5299, Kirby 5340, Provident 5414, Schumann 5441, **Verizon 5489**, Victoria 5490
New Mexico: McCune 5529, Santa Fe 5533
New York: American 5587, **American 5588**, **Clark 5785**, Cloud 5788, Community 5805, Crossed 5830, Donner 5899, Fairfield 5965, Falcon 5966, Foundation 5998, **Guggenheim 6115**, **Isdell 6214**, Johnson 6239, Jones 6242, **JPMorgan 6244**, **M & T 6406**, McNulty 6465, **Mellon 6470**, **MetLife 6479**, Model 6495, **Moody's 6499**, NBC 6531, **Norman 6565**, Northfield 6568, Novartis 6569, Randolph 6677, **Revson 6693**, **Ruth 6772**, Sagner 6783, Schnurmacher 6809, Smith 6874
North Carolina: Beckman 7145, Community 7181, Foundation 7202, North Carolina 7273, Reynolds 7298, Richardson 7300, Triangle 7328
North Dakota: Fargo 7351, Larson 7352
Ohio: Akron 7367, Cliffs 7407, Columbus 7411, Dayton 7428, Dayton 7429, Delaware 7431, Findlay 7453, FirstEnergy 7455, Gund 7478, Honda 7490, KeyBank 7523, Murphy 7584, Nordson 7596, **OMNOVA 7601**, Parker 7611, Partridge 7612, Scripps 7659, Springfield 7671, Toledo 7686
Oklahoma: Allen 7727, American 7728, Williams 7814
Oregon: Carpenter 7831, **Fohs 7844**, Jeld 7856, PacifiCorp 7877
Pennsylvania: Community 7990, Dolfinger 8013, Elias 8022, Hunt 8100, McKinney 8168, Mellon 8172, Miller 8179, Pew 8220, Philadelphia 8221, **PPG 8235**, Scranton 8275, United 8325, Vanguard 8327, York 8351
Rhode Island: Rhode Island 8429, Seymour 8436
Tennessee: Eastman 8561
Texas: AT&T 8675, Booth 8711, Bosarge 8715, Brown 8731, Brownsville 8733, Covenant 8781, **ExxonMobil 8833**, Fikes 8844, **Houston 8916**, Meadows 9019, Penney 9089, Permian 9091, Pritzker 9111, Scharbauer 9157, Scurlock 9162, Simmons 9174
Utah: Park 9341
Vermont: Vermont 9375
Virginia: **Chase 9406**, Dominion 9422, Fife 9429, SunTrust 9539, Waldron 9550
Washington: Plum 9704, RealNetworks 9712, Seattle 9731
Wisconsin: Alliant 9804, Argosy 9808, Bemis 9815, **Bradley 9819**, Green Bay 9855, Rockwell 9934, Smith 9947, West 9967
Wyoming: Community 9975

Public affairs, alliance/advocacy
Pennsylvania: Federated 8033
Tennessee: Hyde 8584

Public affairs, association
Maryland: Goldseker 3803
New York: Gilder 6050, Johnson 6237

Public affairs, citizen participation
California: **Arkay 255**, **Kapor 764**, Patagonia.org 1017, Santa Barbara 1116
Colorado: Vodafone 1519
Delaware: **Memton 1819**
District of Columbia: Block 1888
Florida: Gulf 2142, James 2170, **Knight 2191**
Illinois: Evanston 2826
Indiana: Putnam 3373
Louisiana: Baptist 3612, Community 3624
Massachusetts: Brookline 3962
Michigan: Ann Arbor 4340
Minnesota: Bremer 4620, RBC 4748
Missouri: **Deer 4878**, Roblee 4963
Nevada: Nevada 5134
New Mexico: McCune 5529, Santa Fe 5533
New York: **Ford 5994**, **Peterson 6630**, **Pforzheimer 6635**, Schumann 6813, **Surdna 6947**
North Carolina: Reynolds 7298
Ohio: Coshocton 7421, Middletown 7570, Nordson 7596
Pennsylvania: Pew 8220
Rhode Island: **Dorot 8384**
South Dakota: South Dakota 8522
Texas: **Arnold 8672**
Vermont: **Ben 9358**
Washington: **Bullitt 9591**
Wisconsin: **Bradley 9819**, McBeath 9901

Public affairs, election regulation
New York: **Rockefeller 6723**
Pennsylvania: Pew 8220

Public affairs, equal rights
California: Silberstein 1165
Connecticut: **Newman's 1652**

Public affairs, ethics
District of Columbia: Spectemur 1948
Illinois: Clearing 2752
New York: Adelson 5555

Public affairs, finance
Illinois: **Joyce 2946**
New York: **Peterson 6630**
Ohio: Peters 7616
Washington: Roots 9720

Public affairs, formal/general education
Michigan: **Moller 4506**

Public affairs, government agencies
Alabama: Dixon 30
Iowa: Good 3436, Hanson 3441
Massachusetts: Ladd 4132
North Carolina: Yeargan 7346
Texas: Owen 9077

Public affairs, information services
California: **Omidyar 984**
Massachusetts: **Lincoln 4146**

Public affairs, political organizations
District of Columbia: Kimsey 1921
Illinois: **Joyce 2946**
Michigan: **Moller 4506**

Public affairs, public education
California: Travers 1261
Massachusetts: Hershey 4095, **Lincoln 4146**

Public affairs, reform
California: East 490, Rosenberg 1088
Illinois: Grand 2875

Public affairs, research
California: **Kingfisher 788**
Florida: Dunn's 2072
Massachusetts: A.M. 3912, **Lincoln 4146**
Michigan: **Moller 4506**
New Jersey: Atlantic 5196, Holman 5301
South Carolina: Reams 8493
Washington: Rotella 9721

Public health
Alabama: BBVA 9
Arkansas: Wal-Mart 210
California: Allergan 228, **Annenberg 245**, California 366, California 368, Fremont 548, McCarthy 896, McKesson 903, Patron 1020, **ResMed 1063**, Richmond 1069, Santa Barbara 1116, Shortino 1160, **Strauss 1223**, Thornton 1252, UniHealth 1270
Colorado: COPIC 1397
Connecticut: Aetna 1531, **GE 1591**, Liberty 1630, Tow 1708
Delaware: **Gloria 1784**
District of Columbia: Bauman 1882, **CityBridge 1892**, Consumer 1894, Palmer 1937
Florida: Florida 2101, Green 2136
Georgia: Healthcare 2482, Rollins 2543
Idaho: Blue 2627

Illinois: Comer 2760, Eisenberg 2819, Hospira 2921, Pritzker 3098, Reese 3110, Sprague 3172, **Tellabs 3185**, Youth 3245
Indiana: Anthem 3257, Foundations 3306, Legacy 3337, **Lilly 3340**
Iowa: Principal 3476, Wellmark 3490
Kansas: Blue 3497, Kansas 3524, Topeka 3552
Kentucky: Community 3569, Community 3570
Louisiana: Blue 3615, Community 3624
Maryland: **de Beaumont 3774**
Massachusetts: Blue 3953, Boston 3956, MetroWest 4173
Minnesota: **Andersen 4601**, Blue 4618, **Medtronic 4712**
Mississippi: Blue 4815, Community 4821
Missouri: Express 4888
Nebraska: Scoular 5080
New Jersey: Healthcare 5296, Horizon 5305, **Johnson 5329**, **Merck 5379**, **Verizon 5489**
New York: **Bloomberg 5684**, **Bristol 5711**, Brownstone 5722, Carson 5748, Four 6006, **Friends 6024**, **Hearst 6155**, **Hearst 6156**, **MetLife 6479**, New York 6549, **Open 6593**, **PepsiCo 6627**
North Carolina: Blue 7153, North 7274
Ohio: **Cardinal 7398**, Osteopathic 7605
Oregon: Cambia 7829, PacificSource 7878
Pennsylvania: CIGNA 7981, Highmark 8092, Independence 8106, North 8199, Pew 8220, Phoenixville 8223, Pottstown 8234, United 8325
Rhode Island: Textron 8446
South Carolina: Black 8459, Blue 8460
Tennessee: Tennessee 8634
Texas: **International 8927**, Rockwell 9135
Virginia: AMERIGROUP 9383, Northern 9497
Washington: **Gates 9625**
Wisconsin: Harley 9859

Public health school/education

California: California 368
Florida: Hubert 2163
New York: Kinney 6285, **Macy 6414**
North Dakota: Leach 7353
Texas: Pollock 9103
Virginia: Northern 9497

Public health, bioterrorism

Maryland: **de Beaumont 3774**
Mississippi: Mississippi 4838

Public health, clean water supply

California: **Cisco 402**, **Hilton 692**
Connecticut: **GE 1591**
District of Columbia: **Wallace 1955**
Georgia: **Coca 2428**
Illinois: **Buffett 2726**
Minnesota: **Pentair 4739**
Missouri: **Monsanto 4945**
New York: **PepsiCo 6627**
Washington: **Gates 9625**, **Laird 9664**, **Starbucks 9742**, **Stewardship 9744**

Public health, communicable diseases

California: California 368
Indiana: Anthem 3257, **Lilly 3340**
Maryland: **de Beaumont 3774**
New York: **Bristol 5711**

Public health, environmental health

California: California 368
Illinois: Natural 3046
Massachusetts: Blue 3953
Minnesota: Blue 4618
New Jersey: **Johnson 5329**
New York: **Cummings 5833**

Public health, epidemiology

Maryland: **de Beaumont 3774**

Public health, hygiene

California: **Hilton 692**, **Strauss 1223**

Public health, obesity

California: Anaheim 239, Cathay 385, **Cisco 402**
Connecticut: Aetna 1531
Florida: Florida 2101
Georgia: **Coca 2428**
Idaho: Blue 2627
Illinois: Feinberg 2830, **Mondelez 3034**
Indiana: Anthem 3257, Putnam 3373
Iowa: Wellmark 3490
Kansas: Blue 3497
Kentucky: Humana 3582
Louisiana: Blue 3615, Community 3624
Massachusetts: New 4189
Michigan: **Kellogg's 4475**
Mississippi: Blue 4815
New Hampshire: Foundation 5171, HNH 5175
New Jersey: Healthcare 5296, Horizon 5305, **Johnson 5329**, **Verizon 5489**
North Carolina: Blue 7153, Reynolds 7297
Ohio: Marion 7558
Pennsylvania: **Heinz 8083**, Highmark 8092, Independence 8106
South Carolina: Blue 8460
Tennessee: Tennessee 8634
Texas: Maverick 9005
Virginia: CarMax 9401

Public health, occupational health

California: California 368

Public health, physical fitness

Arizona: Freeport-McMoRan 112
California: Cathay 385, Oakland 977
Connecticut: Aetna 1531
Florida: Florida 2101, Jacksonville 2167
Georgia: **Coca 2428**, Cox 2445
Idaho: Blue 2627
Illinois: **Abbott 2649**, Galesburg 2853, **Mondelez 3034**, **Wrigley 3244**
Indiana: Anthem 3257
Iowa: Wellmark 3490
Kansas: Blue 3497
Kentucky: Humana 3582
Louisiana: Blue 3615, Community 3624
Maine: Bangor 3680
Massachusetts: New 4189
Michigan: **Kellogg's 4475**
Minnesota: General 4661
Mississippi: Blue 4815
Nebraska: ConAgra 5030
New Jersey: Healthcare 5296, Horizon 5305, **Johnson 5329**, Unilever 5484
New York: **PepsiCo 6627**
North Carolina: Blue 7153
Ohio: **Cardinal 7398**
Pennsylvania: Highmark 8092, Independence 8106, Pottstown 8234
Rhode Island: CVS 8379
Wisconsin: Bemis 9815, **Schneider 9942**

Public health, sanitation

California: **Hilton 692**
Connecticut: **GE 1591**
Georgia: **Coca 2428**
Missouri: **Monsanto 4945**
Washington: **Gates 9625**, **Laird 9664**, **Starbucks 9742**

Public health, STDs

California: California 368
New York: **Bristol 5711**

Public policy, research

Arizona: Rodel 158
Arkansas: Rockefeller 197
California: Blum 321, Confidence 423, East 490, Freeman 546, Freidenrich 547, Gibson 583, Haynes 664, Hewlett 686, **Hume 715**, Irvine 727, **Kingfisher 788**, McKay 902, Rosenberg 1088, **Rupe 1097**, Sacramento 1103, San Francisco 1109, **Strauss 1223**, Stuart 1225, Wasserman 1300
Colorado: Brett 1378, Vodafone 1519
Connecticut: **GE 1591**, Ohnell 1661, **Richardson 1679**
Delaware: Berkley 1741, James 1789, Sylvan 1867
District of Columbia: **Arca 1880**, Bauman 1882, **Wallace 1955**
Florida: Dunn's 2072, Engelberg 2086, SHIFT 2320, TWS 2365
Illinois: Caterpillar 2738, Chicago 2746, Field 2831, Hermann 2908, **MacArthur 2989**, Malott 2996, Montgomery 3035, Uihlein 3197, Woods 3242
Indiana: Anthem 3257, **Lilly 3340**, **Lilly 3342**
Kansas: Hansen 3518
Maryland: Straus 3890, Sunrise 3892
Massachusetts: A.M. 3912, Community 3992, Island 4109, Swensrud 4303
Michigan: Chrysler 4366, DeVos 4398, DeVos 4400, Family 4418, Heritage 4458, **Kresge 4479**, Morey 4508, Van Andel 4567
Minnesota: Minneapolis 4714
Missouri: Humphreys 4913
New Jersey: Fund 5270, Golden 5280, Holman 5301, **JM 5323**, Kirby 5339, Klingenstein 5343, Kovner 5348, RuthMarc 5431
New York: Achelis 5549, Aequus 5560, Bodman 5692, Bright 5710, **Clark 5785**, **Discount 5889**, Dunwalke 5921, **Foundation 6003**, Garschina 6035, **Grant 6093**, **Guggenheim 6115**, **Hauser 6147**, **IBM 6203**, Klingenstein 6292, Leffell 6345, **Luce 6398**, **M & T 6406**, Markle 6431, Monell 6497, **Revson 6693**, **Tinker 6983**, Tisch 6986, **United 7019**, Vetlesen 7027, Zilkha 7125
North Carolina: Pope 7288, Reynolds 7298
Ohio: Berry 7386, Peters 7616
Oregon: Jeld 7856
Pennsylvania: **Carthage 7968**, CIGNA 7981, Feldman 8034, Huston 8103, **McKenna 8167**, Philadelphia 8221, Scaife 8266, Sedwick 8276, United 8325
Rhode Island: **FM 8393**
Texas: Anderson 8664, Bickel 8705, **ExxonMobil 8833**, Fikes 8844, Hirsch 8910, WEDGE 9263
Vermont: **Ben 9358**
Virginia: Koch 9463, Trehan 9544
Washington: Rotella 9721
Wisconsin: **Bradley 9819**, McBeath 9901, Milwaukee 9907

Public utilities, sewage

California: **Hilton 692**

Public utilities, water

California: **Hilton 692**

Recreation

Alabama: Community 24, Community 25, Walker 74
Alaska: Rasmuson 89
Arizona: Community 101, Freeport-McMoRan 112
Arkansas: Wal-Mart 210
California: Aratani 250, Campbell 371, Community 416, **Easton 492**, Goldman 605, Goldman 606, Hofmann 700, Humboldt 714, **McConnell 898**, Pacific 1002, San Luis 1110, Santa Barbara 1116, Shasta 1154, Sierra 1164, Sonora 1198, Truckee 1263, Weingart 1307, Yang 1353

Recreation, adaptive sports

Recreation, association

Recreation, camps

Recreation, centers

Recreation, community

Recreation, country clubs

Recreation, fairs/festivals

Recreation, parks/playgrounds

Recreation, public policy

Recreation, single organization support

Recreation, social clubs

Religion

Everlasting 512, Faith, 514, Gallo 560, Gordon 616, Graziadio 620, **Hilton 692**, Hoven 708, Hsu 711, Kohl 799, Lehrer 827, **Leonard 830**, LeVecke 835, Marcus 876, Marin 877, **Rivendell 1077**, Rmlow 1079, Ryan 1098, Salta 1105, Spearman 1201, Vidalakis 1290, Webb 1303, Western 1315
Colorado: Bruni 1380, **Crowell 1398**, Lane 1443
Connecticut: Ion 1616, Mortensen 1647, Palmer 1666
Delaware: Bere 1740, Joynor 1792, Laffey 1800, Margolis 1812, Pfeil 1834, Presto 1840, **Raskob 1845**, Ratner 1847
District of Columbia: Bernstein 1887, Merriman 1930, Pedas 1938
Florida: Bernstein 1995, Community 2036, duPont 2075, Egan 2082, Grundy 2140, **Jaffer 2168**, Kirbo 2186, Lattner 2204, LeBow 2207, McFarlane 2233, Pinellas 2269, Poonai 2271, Preik 2273, Rinker 2286, Stacy 2334, Thompson 2358
Georgia: Bradley 2414, Carlos 2422, Community 2434, Community 2436, Fraser 2463, Love 2508, North 2525, Savannah 2548, Snell 2552, Snow 2553, Wilson 2576, WinShape 2577
Hawaii: First 2598, Wilcox 2621
Idaho: Simplot 2643
Illinois: Bauer 2688, Cooper 2772, Eisenberg 2819, Farnham 2828, Fogelson 2836, GKN 2865, Hermann 2908, Kern 2958, Larson 2967
Indiana: Brotherhood 3268, Crown Point 3291, Imburgia 3326, Indiana 3327, Koch 3334, **Lilly 3342**, Marian 3347, Roehm 3380, Wabash 3396, Welborn 3402
Iowa: Hansen 3440, Kruidenier 3455, Pappajohn 3472, Seidler 3479
Kansas: McPherson 3534, Westar 3553
Kentucky: Blue 3560, Brown 3562, WCA 3606
Louisiana: Almar 3610, Baton Rouge 3613, Booth 3616, Brown 3617
Maryland: **Ames 3720**, **Berman 3730**, Community 3758, Cromwell 3767, Frenkil 3798, Gordon 3805
Massachusetts: Arzak 3927, Beal 3940, Beveridge 3950, BOSE 3954, Cross 4001, Demoulas 4014, **Hendrickson 4093**, Highland 4098, Josetta 4114, Kittredge 4124, Levovitz 4143, Milikowsky 4176, Morgan 4182, Pomegranate 4223, Rands 4229
Michigan: Alix 4333, Dayenu 4392, DeVos 4400, Fabri 4416, Korth 4478, Manoogian 4491, Shepherds 4538, Weingartz 4580, Westerman 4582
Minnesota: Athwin 4607, Bendorf 4610, Bethel 4613, Deziel 4645, Fiterman 4656, GHR 4664, **Toro 4780**
Mississippi: Foundation 4827, Maddox 4834, Van Devender 4847
Missouri: Concorde 4873, Dunn 4882, Green 4900, Interco 4914, Jubel 4919, Stupp 4982, Sugarbaker 4984
Nebraska: Daugherty 5033, Froehlich 5040, Simon 5082, Thom 5089, York 5098
New Jersey: Bacchetta 5198, Bonner 5208, Brotherton 5216, Catholic 5226, **Fish 5261**, Galanta 5272, Haines 5289, Hyde 5310, McGraw 5376, **Perrin 5404**, Pincus 5407, Saka 5432, Sierra 5455, Straus 5469, **Yin 5507**
New York: Achelis 5549, Bayne 5653, Blutt 5687, Brennan 5706, Cushman 5837, Dejana 5868, **Engelhard 5954**, Frey 6014, **Klein 6287**, **Lauder 6336**, Littauer 6379, **Mater 6445**, MBIA 6451, **Mehra 6469**, Nakash 6522, O'Connor 6578, Resource 6691, Ritter 6712, Rotter 6757, Sackler 6777, Simon 6859, Sister 6864, Slifka 6870, Smith 6876, Soros 6889, Stern 6929, Tianaderrah 6977, Tishman 6993, United 7018, Weil, 7062, Wein 7064, Wendt 7074, Zvi 7129
North Carolina: Adams 7133, Capital 7171, Chatham 7175, Community 7178, Foundation 7202, Harvest 7224, Hayworth, 7228, Jordan 7243, North Carolina 7273, Shelton 7310, Woodward 7344
North Dakota: Offutt 7358
Ohio: Anderson 7372, Berkman 7384, Community 7415, Community 7416, Diebold 7437, FirstMerit 7456, Kaplan 7516, Kiebach 7524, Krause 7530, Lippman 7542, Owens 7607, Vesper 7695, Wolfe 7719
Oklahoma: Whitwell-Meyer 7813
Oregon: Collins 7836, Fjarli 7842, **Foreign 7846**, Mission 7873
Pennsylvania: Abessinio 7904, Arcadia 7918, Beneficial 7936, Central 7971, Cestone 7976, Chester 7979, Community 7990, Constandy 7996, Davis 8006, Dolfinger 8013, Fair 8030, Foundation 8046, Gospel 8063, Green 8070, Hopwood 8096, Hunt 8100, Morris 8188, Northwest 8200, Pangborn 8210, Peoples 8218, Scranton 8275, Smith 8287, Stern 8301, **Templeton 8313**, United 8324, Washington 8332
Rhode Island: Newport 8423, Noonan 8424
South Carolina: Bailey 8458, Chester 8470, Community 8475, First 8477, Post 8492
South Dakota: Sioux Falls 8521
Tennessee: American 8528, CIC 8546, Community 8549, Johnson's 8590, Lansky 8594, Ramsey 8621, Sparks 8629
Texas: Alexander 8656, Astros 8674, Community 8775, Davidson 8797, Edwards 8824, Elkins 8826, Franklin 8855, Franklin 8856, Getz 8864, Hamman 8888, Henderson 8901, Hildebrand 8907, **Houston 8916**, Inspiration 8926, Liatis 8983, Masters 9004, Moody 9033, New Hope 9059, Newfield 9060, Oshman 9074, **PHM 9098**, Pryor 9113, Puett 9114, Rogers 9138, San Antonio 9148, Scharbauer 9157, Sterling 9203, Strake 9208, Thank 9229, Trull 9240, Worley 9291, Young 9295
Utah: ALSAM 9302, Community 9311
Vermont: **Daly 9359**
Virginia: Beazley 9391, Birdsong 9393, Community 9411, Golden 9443, Peterson 9508, Titmus 9543, Washington 9552, Whitlock 9556
Washington: Berwick 9584, Lochland 9670, Miller 9685, Moccasin 9687, **Samis 9725**, Sondland 9740, Wren 9764
West Virginia: Schenk 9793
Wisconsin: Alexander 9802, Griffiss 9857, Roundy's 9936, Sensient 9943, Siebert 9946
Wyoming: McMurry 9986

Religion, association

Georgia: Turner 2562
Illinois: Ellis 2821
Tennessee: **Maclellan 8601**

Religion, formal/general education

New Jersey: Dirshu 5242
Virginia: Keesee 9460
Wisconsin: Vine 9960

Religion, fund raising/fund distribution

Wisconsin: Thrivent 9956

Religion, interfaith issues

Delaware: Sternlicht 1861
District of Columbia: **El-Hibri 1903**
Kansas: **Shumaker 3546**
Kentucky: J & L 3584
Maine: **Catalyst 3682**
Maryland: **Ames 3720**, Hirschhorn 3816
Minnesota: Cloverfields 4638
New Jersey: **Berrie 5206**
New York: **Cummings 5833**, **Ford 5994**, Slifka 6870
Tennessee: Lansky 8594
Texas: KLE 8961, **PHM 9098**
Utah: Semnani 9350

Religion, management/technical assistance

Wisconsin: Thrivent 9956

Religion, public policy

New York: Loeb 6385, **Tikvah 6981**
Pennsylvania: Pew 8220

Religion, research

Indiana: **Lilly 3342**
Pennsylvania: Pew 8220

Religion, single organization support

Texas: Davis 8800

Religious federated giving programs

Florida: Free 2109, Speer 2328
Georgia: Watkins 2568
Illinois: **Domanada 2799**, Pritzker 3096, **Tyndale 3195**
Michigan: Merillat 4500
Minnesota: Wallestad 4791
New York: O'Connor 6578
North Carolina: Stewards 7322
Pennsylvania: Dolfinger 8013
Tennessee: Proctor 8617
Texas: Perot 9092, Saada 9142

Reproductive health

California: California 368, **Kaiser 760**, **Packard 1006**, Roth 1093, **Strauss 1223**, Valentine 1277, Wohlford 1336
Colorado: **General 1419**
Connecticut: **GE 1591**
District of Columbia: **Moriah 1932**, **Summit 1950**
Illinois: Grant 2876, **Harris 2893**, **MacArthur 2989**
Iowa: Wellmark 3490
New Jersey: **Segal 5446**
New York: **Ford 5994**, **Open 6593**
Pennsylvania: Pilgrim 8225
Texas: Fath 8840, **Jiv 8933**, **PHM 9098**, Valero 9246
Virginia: AMERIGROUP 9383, Oak 9499

Reproductive health, family planning

Arizona: Morris 148
Arkansas: Jonsson 192
California: Atkinson 265, **Bergstrom 310**, California 368, Carson 381, Confidence 423, Gold 600, Goodman 613, Grove 631, Hewlett 686, Jennings 748, Lehrer 827, **Packard 1006**, San Francisco 1109, Springcreek 1208, Stark 1213, Wohlford 1336
Colorado: **Avenir 1369**, Boettcher 1374, **General 1419**, KBK 1437, Peierls 1475
Connecticut: Community 1564, **Educational 1578**, Palmer 1666
Delaware: Crystal 1758, Ettinger 1779, Marmot 1814
District of Columbia: Cafritz 1890, **Moriah 1932**, **Summit 1950**
Florida: Bank 1979, Bay 1985, Kennedy 2183, Martin 2229, **Wardlaw 2376**
Georgia: Moore 2520
Illinois: Appleby 2668, Bauer 2687, Blair 2700, Community 2763, Munson 3045, Prince 3089, **Zuhlke 3250**
Maine: Fore 3687
Maryland: Abell 3712, Rocking 3871
Massachusetts: Community 3992, Hall 4084, Rappaport 4230, Towards 4309
Minnesota: Bremer 4620, Kelley 4686, Prospect 4747
Missouri: Sunnen 4986
Nebraska: **Buffett 5028**
Nevada: Fairweather 5118
New Jersey: Borden 5209, **Segal 5446**
New Mexico: McCune 5529
New York: Abrons 5546, Baird 5635, Brunckhorst 5723, **Clark 5785**, Demartini 5872, Moore 6501, Noble 6561, **Prospect 6663**, Scherman 6804, Stringer 6935, Vogelstein 7034, Woodcock 7101
North Carolina: Cumberland 7184, Triangle 7328
Ohio: Columbus 7411, Hayfields 7485, Partridge 7612, Perkins 7615, Wexner 7712
Oklahoma: McGee 7774
Oregon: Johnson 7858
Pennsylvania: Claneil 7982, Dolfinger 8013, Nichols 8197

Texas: Boone 8710, Clayton 8765, Fikes 8844, Kempner 8952, San Antonio 9148, Vaughan 9248
Utah: Eccles 9320
Vermont: Vermont 9375
Virginia: Portsmouth 9510, **WestWind 9555**
Washington: Blue 9588, Community 9604, **Gates 9625**, Horizons 9645, Moccasin 9687, Wiancko 9761
Wisconsin: Iddings 9866, Milwaukee 9907, Windhover 9968

Reproductive health, OBGYN/Birthing centers

Illinois: **Abbott 2649**

Reproductive health, prenatal care

Alabama: Community 21
California: California 368
Florida: Burns 2006
Indiana: Anthem 3257
Iowa: Wellmark 3490
Massachusetts: TJX 4308
New Jersey: **Johnson 5326**
Pennsylvania: Genuardi 8053, Highmark 8092
Virginia: AMERIGROUP 9383

Reproductive health, sexuality education

California: California 368
District of Columbia: **Summit 1950**
Minnesota: HRK 4677
New York: **Ford 5994**

Residential/custodial care

California: **Smith 1183**
Delaware: Eshelman 1776
Florida: Magruder 2225, Walter 2375
Georgia: Pitts 2529, Tull 2561
Hawaii: Hawaii 2602
Illinois: Allegretti 2655, Baum 2689, Eisenberg 2819, Parr 3070
Iowa: Ruan 3478, United 3485
Kansas: Smith 3547
Maryland: Maryland 3844
Massachusetts: TJX 4308
Missouri: Ballmann 4858, Graybar 4898, SunEdison 4985
New Jersey: Frankel 5265
New York: First 5979
North Carolina: Curtis 7186, Hunter 7238
Ohio: DeWine 7434, Ohio 7599, State 7674
Oklahoma: Liddell 7767
South Carolina: Cassels 8467, **ScanSource 8495**
Texas: BNSF 8706, Craig, 8786, Doss 8813, Doswell 8814, Jonesville 8946, Presbyterian 9108, Valero 9246
Utah: Gillmor 9323
Virginia: Obici 9500, Universal 9548, Wiser 9561

Residential/custodial care, group home

California: Gogian 598
Illinois: **Ward 3215**
Mississippi: Ergon 4824
Virginia: Ratner 9515

Residential/custodial care, hospices

Alabama: Community 25
Arizona: Morris 148
Arkansas: Schmieding 200, Walker 209
California: Bower 332, Center 388, Gogian 598, Gross 629, Gumpert 637, Heffernan 673, **Keck 774**, Lytel 860, O'Connell 982, Sacramento 1103, Santa Barbara 1116, Scripps 1129, Smullin 1190, Sonora 1198, Volentine 1291, Weingart 1307
Colorado: Bacon 1370, Boettcher 1374, El Pomar 1406, Halton 1426, Summit 1511
Connecticut: Connecticut 1566, Culpeper 1568, Gorab 1599, Palmer 1666, Rosenthal 1684
Delaware: Crystal 1758, Marmot 1814
District of Columbia: Cafritz 1890
Florida: Bank 1979, Bedford 1988, Community 2038, Dallepezze 2049, DuBow 2068, Kennedy 2183, Petway 2268
Georgia: Community 2439, Gaines 2466, Hudgens 2486, Lewis 2503, Rich 2537
Hawaii: First 2598, Wilcox 2621
Illinois: Appleby 2668, Ashley 2674, Foglia 2837, Hansen 2889, Illinois 2934, Ryan 3130, Trustmark 3193, Willow 3235
Indiana: Kosciusko 3335
Iowa: Glazer 3434, United 3485
Kansas: Hutchinson 3521
Kentucky: Preston 3596
Maryland: Hahn 3811, Higgins-Hussman 3815
Massachusetts: **Cabot 3966**, Cape Cod 3973, Demoulas 4014, Institution 4108, Taunton 4304, TJX 4308
Michigan: Chinnick 4363, Hillsdale 4461, Pokagon 4523, Saddle 4530, Von 4574, Wilson 4588
Minnesota: Bremer 4620, TEAM 4779
Missouri: Dula 4881, Emerson 4885, Shaw 4970
New Hampshire: Penates 5185
New Jersey: Brozowski 5218, **Crane 5235**, Danellie 5237, **GHH 5275**, Provident 5414
New Mexico: Frost 5519, McCune 5529
New York: Albert 5567, **Bristol 5711**, Corning 5818, Lindner 6372, Marx 6442, McGraw 6461, Western 7078
North Carolina: Bolick 7155, Christopher 7176, Cumberland 7184, Davis 7189, Dickson 7192, Glenn 7211, Hillsdale 7232, Kimbrell 7249, Neviaser 7271, Reynolds 7299, Triangle 7328, VF 7332, Yeargan 7346
North Dakota: Stern 7360
Ohio: Ames 7371, Christman 7403, Luedeking 7547, McGregor 7564, Muskingum 7585, Oliver 7600, Parker 7611, Schlink 7650, Troy 7688, Youngstown 7723
Pennsylvania: Arcadia 7918, Carpenter 7967, ESSA 8028, Fourjay 8047, Huston 8102, McCutchen 8162, Ortenzio 8206
South Carolina: Abney 8454, TSC 8506
Tennessee: American 8528, Atticus 8531, Christy 8545, Thompson 8635
Texas: Bridwell 8726, Fisch 8846, Kempner 8952, Meadows 9019, San Antonio 9148, Sterling 9203, Temple 9223, Tucker 9241, Wal 9254, Wright 9293
Virginia: Peterson 9508, Smith 9533
Washington: Blue 9588, Community 9604, Cowles 9607, Norcliffe 9693, Renton 9715, Tacoma 9750, Wockner 9763
West Virginia: Kanawha 9780, Prichard 9791
Wisconsin: Acuity 9801, Green Bay 9854, McBeath 9901, Meng 9904, Wanek 9964, Windhover 9968

Residential/custodial care, senior continuing care

California: California 368, Center 388, Gogian 598
Colorado: KBK 1437
Florida: Patton 2262
Illinois: Boyer 2711, Lynn 2988, **Retirement 3113**, **Rothschild 3124**, Williams 3233
Iowa: Dahl 3425
New Jersey: **GHH 5275**, **Perrin 5404**
New York: Eastern 5927, Lapine 6330
Ohio: Knight 7527
Oklahoma: Titus 7806
Pennsylvania: DSF 8017, Mine 8184

Rural development

Arizona: Arizona 92
Arkansas: Rockefeller 197
California: **S.G. 1100**
Colorado: Boettcher 1374
Indiana: Old 3363
Maine: Bangor 3680, **Sandy 3707**
Massachusetts: **Grand 4076**
Michigan: **Kellogg 4474**, **Mott 4510**
Minnesota: Blandin 4617, Bremer 4620, CHS 4636, Land 4691, Minnesota 4715, Musser 4724
Nebraska: Kiewit 5057
New Jersey: **International 5316**, **Segal 5446**
New Mexico: McCune 5529, New Mexico 5530
New York: **Ford 5994**, **Hearst 6155**, **Hearst 6156**, O'Connor 6578, **Simons 6860**, Steele 6915
North Carolina: Blue 7153, Cumberland 7184, Reynolds 7298, Triangle 7328
Oregon: Carpenter 7831, Johnson 7858
Pennsylvania: Stackpole 8295
South Carolina: Coastal 8472
Texas: King 8959, Meadows 9019
Virginia: Wrinkle 9562
Wyoming: Wyoming 9999

Safety, automotive safety

Georgia: **UPS 2566**
Illinois: Allstate 2657
Iowa: GuideOne 3438
Maryland: GEICO 3801
Massachusetts: Arbella 3926
Michigan: Chrysler 4366, Ford 4430, General 4442
Ohio: Honda 7490, Progressive 7623, Westfield 7711
Tennessee: Bridgestone 8537

Safety, education

Alabama: Caring 18
Missouri: **Monsanto 4945**
Pennsylvania: United 8325
Virginia: Oak 9499

Safety, poisons

Minnesota: Valspar 4786

Safety/disasters

Alabama: McWane 51
Arizona: Freeport-McMoRan 112
California: Branson 338, Community 421, **Hilton 692**, Humboldt 714, Napa 959, Sempra 1140, Sharks 1153, Shasta 1154, **Wadhwani 1294**
Colorado: Community 1391
Connecticut: Hubbell 1614, Palmer 1666
Delaware: **Adobe 1734**
Florida: Glazer 2124, Southwest 2327
Georgia: **Georgia 2469**, **UPS 2566**
Illinois: Allstate 2657, **Motorola 3043**, Trustmark 3193
Indiana: Foundations 3306, **Lilly 3342**, Noble 3359
Iowa: Siouxland 3480
Kansas: Damon 3504, Manhattan 3532
Kentucky: C.E. 3566
Louisiana: Community 3623, Lamar 3647, New Orleans 3656
Massachusetts: Beveridge 3950, Community 3992, Dunkin' 4026, Liberty 4145
Michigan: Ann Arbor 4340, Weingartz 4580
Minnesota: **Andersen 4601**, Blue 4618
Mississippi: C Spire 4817, Greater 4829
Missouri: **Monsanto 4945**
New Jersey: New Jersey 5389
New York: Andor 5598, Freed 6011, Interlaken 6210, **PepsiCo 6627**, Phillips 6637, **Winston 7093**
North Carolina: Duke 7196, **Nickel 7272**, Smith 7316
North Dakota: Fargo 7351
Ohio: American 7368, **Cardinal 7398**, Coshocton 7421, NiSource 7591, **OMNOVA 7601**
Oregon: **NIKE 7875**
Pennsylvania: Air 7907, **Alcoa 7908**, Dixon 8012, Pittsburgh 8228
Texas: Coastal 8768, Elkins 8826, McNair 9017, Meadows 9019, New Hope 9058
Virginia: Arlington 9384, Community 9412

Safety/disasters, research

Safety/disasters, volunteer services

Salvation Army

Scholarships/financial aid

Science

Science, administration/regulation

Science, association

Science, formal/general education

Alabama: Vulcan 73
Arizona: Freeport-McMoRan 112
California: **Agilent 220**, **American 237**, **Amgen 238**, Coulter 433, Genentech 571, McCarthy 895, Musk 957, Roche 1083, Synopsys 1232
Colorado: Dornick 1403
Connecticut: Boehringer 1549
Georgia: AGL 2400
Idaho: **Micron 2637**
Illinois: **Motorola 3042**
Iowa: **Pioneer 3474**, **Rockwell 3477**
Kansas: Koch 3528
Massachusetts: TBL 4305
Michigan: Delphi 4394, Dow 4405
Minnesota: 3M 4597, **Medtronic 4712**, Xcel 4808
Missouri: **Monsanto 4945**
New Jersey: **Merck 5379**, Merck 5380, PSEG 5416, **Siemens 5454**, Subaru 5471
New York: Afognak 5561, **American 5589**, **IBM 6203**, **Pfizer 6633**, **Sloan 6872**, **Toshiba 6997**, Toyota 7002
Ohio: NiSource 7591, Nordson 7596
Oregon: **Intel 7853**
Pennsylvania: **Kennametal 8120**, **PPG 8235**
Texas: **ExxonMobil 8833**, Fluor 8851, KDK-Harman 8949
Virginia: Dominion 9422

Science, information services

New York: **Sloan 6872**

Science, public education

California: **Las 821**
Maryland: Rathmann 3867
New York: **Sloan 6872**
Washington: Simonyi 9735

Science, public policy

District of Columbia: **Lounsbery 1926**

Science, reform

North Dakota: Scheels 7359

Science, research

California: **Agouron 221**, **Ellison 504**, Maxfield 887, San Diego 1108, **Waitt 1295**
Florida: **Vollmer 2373**
Georgia: Franklin 2462
Illinois: Anixter 2664
Iowa: Carver 3416
Maryland: Rathmann 3867
Massachusetts: Beveridge 3950, Perkin 4213
Michigan: **Gerber 4443**
Missouri: JSM 4918, **McDonnell 4941**
New Jersey: **Berrie 5206**, Brotherton 5216, Rubenstein 5428
New Mexico: Delle 5518
New York: **American 5589**, **Mathers 6446**, Oishei 6584, Rose 6735, Simons 6861, **Sloan 6872**, Swartz 6953
Ohio: Community 7415
Oklahoma: Communities 7742
Pennsylvania: Central 7971
Utah: ALSAM 9302
Vermont: Lintilhac 9365
Washington: Murdock 9689, Washington 9757

Science, single organization support

California: Oschin 996, San Simeon 1111
New Jersey: Atlantic 5196

Secondary school/education

Alabama: Finlay 33, May 48
Arizona: Click 100, Schweitz 162, Tankersley 169
Arkansas: Oliver 195, Wal-Mart 210
California: Ahmanson 222, Atkinson 265, Barker 282, Burnham 357, **Capital 375**, Caruso 382, Confidence 423, Cortopassi 430, Crean 439, Day 457, Dhanam 463, Ducommun 485, Foothills 537, Gap 563, Gellert 568, Geschke 576, **Gleason 592**, Herbst 682, Hofmann 700, J.A.N.S. 735, Jack 736, **Kapor 764**, **Keck 774**, Kingsley 789, M & T 861, Martin 882, **McConnell 898**, Mosher 945, Muller 953, Murphy 956, Norris 971, Oakland 977, Oberndorf 981, Pacific 1004, Padway 1008, Parsons 1013, Perforce 1026, PG&E 1033, Quest 1050, **ResMed 1063**, Rickey 1071, San Diego 1108, Shea 1155, Sierra 1164, **Wadhwani 1294**, Weingart 1307, Zander 1356
Colorado: Saeman 1490, Summit 1511, **Western 1521**, Williams 1524
Connecticut: Community 1564, Connecticut 1566, Grossman 1603, Larsen 1624, McLeod 1641, Oaklawn 1657, Palmer 1666, Rockville 1682, Seedlings 1691, Smart 1697, Zachs 1730
Delaware: Crystal 1758, Laffey 1800, MacMahon 1810, Marmot 1814, Mastronardi 1815
District of Columbia: Cafritz 1890, Meyer 1931
Florida: Ansin 1969, Bank 1979, Berg 1993, Darden 2051, **Davis 2056**, duPont 2075, Galloway 2112, **Griffin 2138**, Kennedy 2183, Moran 2243, Schemel 2312, Selby 2316, Walter 2375
Georgia: AGL 2400, Callaway 2419, Campbell 2420, Camp-Younts 2421, **Challenge 2424**, Fraser 2463, Montgomery 2518, Primerica 2534, Tull 2561, Williams 2572, WinShape 2577
Idaho: **Micron 2637**, Seagraves 2642
Illinois: Ackermann 2652, Bond 2709, Brach 2712, Buchbinder 2721, Canning 2733, Chicago 2746, Coleman 2759, Community 2763, Donnelley 2801, Field 2831, Fry 2849, Galashiels 2852, Harrison 2896, Henry 2906, Jephson 2939, Levi 2976, Omron 3063, Owens 3068, Seabury 3146, SF 3149, Walsh 3212, White 3229, Williams 3234
Indiana: Adams 3253, Ball 3262, Dekko 3296, Harrison 3314, Marshall 3348, Miller 3355, Noyes 3361, Reeves 3374, Reynolds 3376, Weaver 3401
Iowa: AEGON 3409, McElroy 3461, Vogel 3487
Kansas: Dreiling 3511
Kentucky: Gheens 3577, Norton 3592
Louisiana: Baton Rouge 3613, Booth 3616, Community 3624, Pennington 3659, Sanford 3664, Scott 3666, Taylor 3669, Zigler 3676
Maine: MELMAC 3700
Maryland: Attman 3722, Commonweal 3756, Davis 3772, **Hughes 3818**, Johnston 3821, Knott 3826, Price 3865, Quinn 3866, Sheridan 3883, St. John 3888
Massachusetts: A.M. 3912, Boston 3956, Carney 3975, Croll 4000, Danversbank 4009, Grimshaw 4079, **Karp 4117**, Massiah 4163, O'Brien 4195, O'Donnell 4196, Remondi 4237, Rogers 4243, Schrafft 4263, Stevens 4288, Stevens 4289
Michigan: Cold 4367, General 4442, Herrick 4459, Hurst 4464, **Kellogg 4474**, MSJ 4513, Van Andel 4566
Minnesota: Alliss 4600, Bigelow 4616, Carlson 4629, Edelstein 4652, Greystone 4668, O'Rourke 4733, Slaggie 4766
Mississippi: C Spire 4817
Missouri: Apex 4854, Centene 4870, Cox 4874, Hall 4905, McDonnell 4940, Orscheln 4951, Sosland 4977
Montana: First 5009
Nebraska: Ameritas 5023, Gaughan 5042, Mutual 5071, Nelnet 5072, Scoular 5080, St. Anthony 5085
Nevada: Cord 5110, Mathewson 5131, Wiegand 5159
New Jersey: Cabin 5222, Dodge 5243, Give 5278, Hyde 5310, James 5322, **Knowles 5345**, KPMG 5349, Martini 5372, Ruesch 5429, **Siemens 5454**, Simon, 5460
New Mexico: McCune 5529
New York: Altman 5579, Baird 5635, Bay 5652, Carvel 5749, Cattaraugus 5750, Coach 5790, Community 5808, **Credit 5826**, Deerfield 5865, Della 5870, Dodge 5892, **Engelhard 5954**, **Ford 5994**, **Ford 5995**, Galasso 6032, **Gelb 6039**, **Genesis 6042**, Gordon 6080, Hayden 6150, Israel 6216, Kanas 6249, Kaylie 6263, Kellen 6268, Lambert 6321, Lincoln 6368, Link 6375, **M & T 6406**, Mars 6437, Milstein 6488, **Moody's 6499**, Morgan 6507, Mutual 6518, Naddisy 6520, NBC 6531, Newhouse 6550, Oishei 6584, **Pforzheimer 6635**, **Polo 6651**, Ruffin 6770, Select 6829, Strypemonde 6936, Templeton 6969, Tisch 6988, Turn 7012, **United 7019**, Vernon 7026, Wegman 7061, Western 7078, Winston 7092, **Youths' 7112**
North Carolina: **Bank 7139**, Belk 7148, Biddle 7150, Cannon 7169, Dickson 7192, Kenan 7248, Mayr 7261, Reynolds 7298, Smith 7317
North Dakota: MDU 7354
Ohio: Anderson 7372, Ar-Hale 7376, Buenger 7393, Charities 7400, Cleveland 7406, Cliffs 7407, Conway 7419, Coshocton 7421, Dayton 7429, Dodero 7438, **Eaton 7442**, GAR 7465, Gund 7478, Hoover 7492, Jennings 7509, **Noble 7592**, Nord 7594, Parker 7611, Piqua 7620, Richland 7630, Samaritan 7642, Schott 7653, Third 7681, **Timken 7684**, Vesper 7695, White 7715, Zembrodt 7724
Oklahoma: Meinders 7777, Rapp 7787, **Westerman 7811**
Oregon: Carpenter 7831, **NIKE 7875**, Sanders 7886, TeamCFA 7893
Pennsylvania: Claneil 7982, Connelly 7995, Dolfinger 8013, Ellis 8023, Federated 8033, Hamilton 8078, Kelly 8119, **Kennametal 8120**, McCune 8160, Nichols 8197, Ortenzio 8205, Ortenzio 8206, Penn 8216, Public 8239, Stackpole 8295, Steinman 8299
Rhode Island: Biogen 8363, Champlin 8370, Freeman 8396, Kimball 8410, Salem 8434
South Carolina: **AVX-Kyocera 8457**, Campbell 8465, Smith 8499
Tennessee: Adams 8526, Benwood 8535, Lyndhurst 8599, Maddox 8603, Memphis 8610, Regal 8622
Texas: Alexander 8656, AT&T 8675, Bass 8690, Booth 8711, Cain 8743, Carter 8753, Constantin 8778, Crain 8787, Fondren 8853, Hillcrest 8909, Hoblitzelle 8912, Kempner 8952, Maverick 9005, McDermott 9013, Morgan 9038, Peterson 9095, Rockwell 9135, Sanchez 9150, Scott 9161, Sterling 9203, Strake 9208, Texas 9227, Trull 9240
Vermont: Vermont 9375
Virginia: Beazley 9391, Carter 9403, Folger 9431, Freddie 9435, Massey 9478, Reynolds 9519, Strong 9537
Washington: Foundation 9623, **Gates 9625**, Invested 9652, PACCAR 9698, PEMCO 9702, Snyder 9739, T.E.W. 9749
West Virginia: Bowen 9770, Hunnicutt 9779, Preservati 9790
Wisconsin: **Baird 9811**, Briggs 9822, CUNA 9838, Green Bay 9855, Krause 9886, Ladish 9890, McBeath 9901, Milwaukee 9907, Pettit 9919, Runzheimer 9938, Ryan 9940, Siebert 9946, Wanek 9964
Wyoming: Stuart 9993

Self-advocacy services, disability

California: **Smith 1183**

Sex workers

California: Weingart 1307

SIDS (Sudden Infant Death Syndrome) research

Colorado: Kaufmann 1436

Single parents

Alabama: Community 24, Community 25, Kaul 43, Meyer 53
Arizona: Webb 174
California: Atkinson 265, Center 388, Community 414, Gumbiner 636, Leonetti/O'Connell 832, Lesher 833, Marcled 875, McMillen 905, Patron 1020, Rogers 1087, Weingart 1307
Colorado: King 1440, Summit 1511
Connecticut: Community 1562, Mortensen 1647
Delaware: **Raskob 1845**
District of Columbia: Cafritz 1890, **Union 1953**
Florida: Southwest 2327
Illinois: **Harris 2893**
Indiana: Community 3281
Kentucky: Cralle 3571
Louisiana: Wilson 3671
Maryland: Abell 3712, Community 3759, Community 3761, Jacobsohn 3819, Washington 3904
Michigan: Chrysler 4366, Grand Rapids 4447, **Kellogg 4474**, Midland 4502
Minnesota: Bremer 4620
Mississippi: Community 4821
Missouri: Saint Louis 4966
Nebraska: Dunklau 5036
New Jersey: Danellie 5237
New York: Community 5802, Ritter 6712
North Carolina: Community 7180, North Carolina 7273, Reidsville 7294, Robertson 7305
Ohio: Fairfield 7445, O'Neill 7602, Parents 7608, Youngstown 7723
Oklahoma: Hardesty 7756
Oregon: J.F.R. 7854
Pennsylvania: Beneficial 7936, First 8041, Phoenixville 8223, Pilgrim 8225
Tennessee: Wilson 8646
Texas: Community 8774, Community 8777, Embrey 8828, Hoglund 8913, McDermott 9013, Orsinger 9073, Rockwell 9135, Terry 9224
Utah: Eccles 9320
Virginia: ACT 9380
Washington: Norcliffe 9693
Wisconsin: Community 9835, Green Bay 9854, La Crosse 9889, West 9967

Skin disorders

Minnesota: Hubbard 4678
New York: Nonna's 6563

Skin disorders research

Utah: **Nu 9340**

Social entrepreneurship

California: **Cisco 402**, eBay 493, Moxie 950, **Omidyar 984**, **Peery 1022**, Skoll 1175
Colorado: **Western 1521**
Georgia: **Georgia 2469**, **UPS 2566**
Illinois: Crown 2780
Maine: Bangor 3680
Massachusetts: **Grand 4076**
Nevada: EBV 5116
New York: **MetLife 6479**, Niehaus 6559, **Pershing 6629**
North Dakota: Barry 7350
Oregon: **NIKE 7875**
Pennsylvania: Baker 7926
Texas: **PHM 9098**, **Whole 9276**
Washington: **Starbucks 9742**

Social sciences

California: BayTree 289, Buckhantz 354, Haynes 664, **Lingnan 841**, Sacramento 1103
Connecticut: Larsen 1624, **Richardson 1679**, Rosenthal 1684
District of Columbia: Kaye 1920, **San Giacomo 1945**, **Searle 1946**
Illinois: Community 2763, Edlis-Neeson 2815
Indiana: Community 3290
Maryland: **Ames 3720**, **Brown 3741**
Massachusetts: Frances 4060, Hopedale 4101, Marks 4162
Michigan: DeVos 4400, **Fetzer 4420**, **Rodney 4528**
New York: **Ford 5994**, **Grant 6093**, **Guggenheim 6115**, **Guggenheim 6116**, Littauer 6379, **Luce 6398**, **Sage 6782**, **Starr 6911**
North Carolina: Richardson 7300
Ohio: Peters 7616
Pennsylvania: Pew 8220
Texas: **Arnold 8672**
Virginia: Lynchburg 9474
Washington: Bainbridge 9578
West Virginia: Kanawha 9780

Social sciences, equal rights

Tennessee: Assisi 8530

Social sciences, ethics

California: **Rupe 1097**
Tennessee: Assisi 8530

Social sciences, formal/general education

Massachusetts: Colombe 3989

Social sciences, government agencies

Massachusetts: Colombe 3989

Social sciences, interdisciplinary studies

New York: **Grant 6093**
Virginia: Proteus 9512

Social sciences, public policy

Arizona: Rodel 158
California: Binder 316, Bren 339, Connolly 425, Geschke 576, Heising-Simons 675
Colorado: Catto 1383
Connecticut: Lehrman 1628
District of Columbia: CrossCurrents 1897, Spectemur 1948
Illinois: Galashiels 2852, Levin 2977
Maryland: Brickman 3739
Massachusetts: Colombe 3989, **Krieble 4129**, Stoneman 4296
Missouri: Craig 4875, Humphreys 4913
New Hampshire: Endowment 5169
New Jersey: Hickory 5299
New York: Hutchins 6201, Mercer 6474, Randolph 6677, Schlosstein 6807, Stanton 6908, Tisch 6989
North Carolina: Broyhill 7160
Pennsylvania: Jackson 8110
Texas: Owen 9076, Shield 9170, Sumners 9214
Virginia: **Chase 9406**
Washington: Bainbridge 9578

Social sciences, research

California: Dachs 446, Field 524, Friedman 551
Florida: Klorfine 2188
Illinois: Pritzker 3094
Michigan: **Fetzer 4420**
New York: Alison 5571, **Grant 6093**
Oregon: **Fohs 7844**
Pennsylvania: Jackson 8110
Virginia: **Chase 9406**

Space/aviation

California: Musk 957
Michigan: Parish 4518
Missouri: Busch 4867
New Jersey: Buehler 5219
New York: Link 6374
North Carolina: Goodrich 7213
Texas: Thompson 9233

Speech/hearing centers

California: Patron 1020
Georgia: Rollins 2543
Louisiana: Booth 3616
Massachusetts: Danversbank 4009
Michigan: Carls 4358
Nevada: Fairweather 5118
New York: Einhorn 5943
North Carolina: Smith 7317
Pennsylvania: **Oberkotter 8203**
Texas: **Bolivar 8708**

Spine disorders

Colorado: ProLogis 1485
New York: Spinal 6898

Spine disorders research

District of Columbia: **Wyss 1959**
Florida: Lynn 2221
Pennsylvania: Aospine 7916

Spirituality

California: Angell 244
Indiana: Transformation 3392
Kansas: Salina 3540
Maryland: Delaplaine 3778
Michigan: **Lachimi 4480**
Minnesota: Marbrook 4702
New York: Cranaleith 5825, **Cummings 5833**
North Dakota: Barry 7350
Texas: QuadW 9115

Student services/organizations

Indiana: Wayne 3400
Massachusetts: Brookline 3962
Washington: Grays 9631

Students, sororities/fraternities

California: Dr. Bronners 479

Substance abuse, prevention

Alabama: Community 21, Community 24
Arizona: Freeport-McMoRan 112
California: Community 414, GGS 580, Oakland 977
Colorado: Vodafone 1519
Delaware: Delaware 1765
Florida: Community 2036, Scaife 2309
Illinois: **Goodman 2868**
Michigan: Perrigo 4521
Minnesota: **Andersen 4601**
Missouri: Roblee 4963
New Mexico: Santa Fe 5533
New York: Achelis 5549, Bodman 5692, **Fledgling 5987**, Turn 7012
Ohio: Reinberger 7628
Pennsylvania: Staunton 8296
South Dakota: Sioux Falls 8521
Texas: Goldsbury 8868, Hebert 8899

Substance abuse, services

Arizona: Arizona 92
California: Anaheim 239, Atkinson 265, Drown 484, Ellis 503, Gellert 568, Guess? 635, Lytel 860, Norris 971, Patron 1020, San Francisco 1109, Santa Barbara 1116, Sierra 1163, Sonora 1198, Weingart 1307
Colorado: Daniels 1399, El Pomar 1406, Halton 1426

Connecticut: Community 1563, Community 1564, Connecticut 1566
District of Columbia: Cafritz 1890, Meyer 1931
Florida: Indian 2166, Pinellas 2269
Georgia: Hudgens 2486
Illinois: **Baxter 2690**, Cedar 2739, Community 2763, Community 2769, Field 2831, Grant 2876, **Woodbury 3240**, Woodward 3243
Indiana: Community 3281, Community 3282, Welborn 3402
Iowa: Principal 3476, Siouxland 3480
Kansas: Hutchinson 3521, Topeka 3552
Maryland: Abell 3712, Higgins-Hussman 3815
Massachusetts: Community 3992, Parker 4207, TJX 4308
Michigan: Fremont 4438, Jackson 4467, Skillman 4543
Minnesota: Butler 4622, Ordean 4732
Nevada: Fairweather 5118, Nevada 5134
New Hampshire: Fuller 5172
New Jersey: Borden 5209, Hansen 5291, Healthcare 5296, Hyde 5310, **Johnson 5329**, McGraw 5376, Princeton 5411
New Mexico: Chase 5517, Frost 5519, Maddox 5528, McCune 5529
New York: deForest 5866, New York 6544, O'Connor 6578, Tower 7000, Western 7078
North Carolina: Cumberland 7184, Jones 7242, Piedmont 7285, Reynolds 7297, Triangle 7328
North Dakota: Stern 7360
Ohio: Coshocton 7421, Hamilton 7481, Nationwide 7587, Richland 7630, Ridgecliff 7631, Stark 7673, Troy 7688, Woodruff 7721
Oregon: Carpenter 7831, PacifiCorp 7877
Pennsylvania: Armstrong 7922, Connelly 7995, Dolfinger 8013, Eden 8021, Fourjay 8047, Huston 8102, Snee 8291, Stackpole 8295, Staunton 8296
Tennessee: Davis 8555
Texas: Abell 8650, BNSF 8706, Coastal 8768, Constantin 8778, Hillcrest 8909, Kempner 8952, Meadows 9019, NAH 9047, San Antonio 9148, Sterling 9203, Temple 9223, Trull 9240, Wright 9293
Utah: Eccles 9320
Vermont: Vermont 9375
Virginia: Williamsburg 9558
Washington: Casey 9595, Community 9604, Norcliffe 9693, Tacoma 9750
West Virginia: Eastern 9775, Kanawha 9780
Wisconsin: McBeath 9901, Milwaukee 9907, Stackner 9951

Substance abuse, treatment

California: Auen 269, McMillen 905, Union 1271
Georgia: **Hanley 2476**
Illinois: **Woodbury 3240**
Louisiana: Lamar 3647
Nevada: Adelson 5099
New Jersey: Healthcare 5296
New York: Turn 7012
Ohio: Reinberger 7628
Pennsylvania: Armstrong 7922, Rosenstiel 8254, Staunton 8296
Texas: Heavenly 8897, **International 8927**, Wichita 9277
Wisconsin: Stone 9954

Substance abusers

Alabama: Kaul 43, Meyer 53
Arizona: Webb 174
California: Ahmanson 222, Atkinson 265, Center 388, Community 414, Green 621, Gumbiner 636, **Hilton 692**, Lesher 833, McMillen 905, Patron 1020, Weingart 1307
Colorado: King 1440, Summit 1511
Connecticut: Community 1562, Community 1563
Delaware: **Raskob 1845**
District of Columbia: Cafritz 1890
Florida: Indian 2166, Southwest 2327
Georgia: **Hanley 2476**
Indiana: Brown 3269, Community 3281
Kentucky: Cralle 3571
Louisiana: Wilson 3671
Maryland: Abell 3712, **Bearman 3728**, Community 3761
Michigan: Midland 4502, Pentecost 4520, Sturgis 4550, Tuscola 4562
Minnesota: Bremer 4620
Nebraska: Dunklau 5036
New Hampshire: Lindsay 5179
New Jersey: Danellie 5237, Fund 5270, Hyde 5310, Kirby 5339
New York: Achelis 5549, Bodman 5692, Community 5802, Langeloth 6327, **Open 6593**, Ritter 6712, Staten 6912, Tower 7000
North Carolina: Community 7180, North Carolina 7273, Reidsville 7294
North Dakota: Leach 7353
Ohio: Fairfield 7445, O'Neill 7602, Ridgecliff 7631, Saint 7639, Spaulding 7670
Oklahoma: Hardesty 7756, Hille 7759
Oregon: Carpenter 7831, Poznanski 7882
Pennsylvania: Beneficial 7936, Birmingham 7942, First 8041, Huston 8102, Phoenixville 8223, Staunton 8296
Tennessee: Baptist 8533, Wilson 8646
Texas: Abell 8650, Community 8774, Community 8777, Hoblitzelle 8912, McDermott 9013, Moore 9034, Orsinger 9073, Terry 9224, Wichita 9277
Utah: Eccles 9320
Virginia: Williamsburg 9558
Washington: Norcliffe 9693
Wisconsin: Cornerstone 9836, Green Bay 9854, La Crosse 9889, West 9967

Supported living

California: **Smith 1183**

Surgery

Minnesota: **St. Jude 4770**

Surgery research

New Jersey: Integra 5315

Teacher school/education

Alabama: Alabama 1, BBVA 9
Arizona: Freeport-McMoRan 112
California: **Amgen 238**, Roche 1083
Colorado: Vodafone 1519
Connecticut: People's 1671
Delaware: Sylvan 1867
Florida: **Peterson 2267**
Hawaii: Castle 2594
Idaho: **Micron 2637**
Illinois: McDougal 3013, Northern 3059
Massachusetts: Pierce 4220
Minnesota: **Medtronic 4712**, Travelers 4783
Missouri: Roblee 4963
New Jersey: **Knowles 5345**, Merck 5380, **Siemens 5454**, Subaru 5471
New York: **Carnegie 5747**, **Credit 5826**, **JPMorgan 6244**, Naomi 6523
Oregon: **Intel 7853**
Pennsylvania: **Alcoa 7908**, Hurd 8101, PNC 8230
Texas: Sumners 9214, Texas 9227
Vermont: Rowland 9370
Virginia: Moore 9489

Terminal illness, people with

Alabama: Comer 20, Community 25, Kaul 43, Meyer 53
Arizona: Webb 174
Arkansas: Cabe 182
California: Bickerstaff 313, Center 388, Community 414, Gilmore 588, Gogian 598, Green 621, Weingart 1307
Colorado: King 1440, Summit 1511
Connecticut: Community 1562
Delaware: **Raskob 1845**
Georgia: **Thoresen 2557**
Illinois: Blowitz 2702, Butler 2729, King 2960
Indiana: Community 3281, Orange 3365
Kentucky: Cralle 3571
Michigan: Chrysler 4366, Midland 4502
Minnesota: Bremer 4620
Missouri: Saint Louis 4966
New York: Altman 5579, Diamond 5880, **Open 6593**, Ritter 6712, Warner 7053
North Carolina: Community 7180, North Carolina 7273, Reidsville 7294
Ohio: Fairfield 7445, O'Neill 7602, Saint 7639
Oklahoma: Hardesty 7756, Hille 7759
Pennsylvania: First 8041, Phoenixville 8223
Tennessee: Baptist 8533, Wilson 8646
Texas: Community 8774, Community 8777, McDermott 9013, Orsinger 9073
Utah: Eccles 9320
Virginia: Beazley 9391
Washington: Norcliffe 9693
Wisconsin: Green Bay 9854, Stock 9953, West 9967

Theological school/education

Alabama: Mitchell 54
Arizona: Jazzbird 125
California: **Bolthouse 325**, Gold 599, Menlo 913, **Rivendell 1077**, Shea 1156, Stewardship 1220
Colorado: **Crowell 1398**, Mol 1463
Florida: **Chatlos 2019**, **Davis 2056**, Edelman 2080, Patton 2262, Williams 2388
Georgia: Love 2508
Hawaii: Atherton 2586
Idaho: Brandt 2628
Illinois: Ackermann 2652, Bryce 2719, Butler 2729, Clark 2751, Crump 2782, Davis 2786, **Domanada 2799**, Hartman 2898, Huizenga 2924, Leibowitz 2973, Levin 2977, Nerenberg 3050, Rajchenbach 3103, Salmon 3133, Segal 3147, Uihlein 3197
Indiana: **Lilly 3342**
Kansas: Morris 3537
Louisiana: Booth 3616, Cason 3620
Maryland: **Berman 3731**, Calvin 3744, Foundation 3793, **Smith 3886**
Massachusetts: DeFreitas 4013, Sudireddy 4300
Michigan: **Foundation 4432**, **Frankel 4437**, Granger 4450, Jubilee 4470, **Micah 4501**, Mulder 4514, **Myers 4515**, Schaap 4533
Minnesota: McVay 4711
Mississippi: Ergon 4824
Missouri: Breen 4861
New Jersey: **IDT 5311**, Roth 5426
New York: ACE 5548, Adar 5553, Arbesfeld 5605, Century 5758, Damial 5844, Eisenberg 5944, Englander 5955, Grace 6090, Habib 6126, **Hearst 6155**, **Hearst 6156**, Hendel 6161, Horowitz 6186, Kaplan 6250, Kaplan 6251, Lopatin 6392, **Luce 6398**, **Nash 6525**, New Brook 6540, Park 6614, **PBHP 6622**, Propp 6662, Rose 6732, Shaarei 6835, Sister 6864, SO 6881, Steiniger 6924, Wendt 7074
North Carolina: Bolick 7155, Byrum 7166, Woodson 7342
Ohio: **Sapirstein-Stone-Weiss 7644**, Schottenstein 7654
Oklahoma: Crawley 7746, Oxley 7785
Pennsylvania: Carpenter 7967, Dolfinger 8013, Firstfruits 8042, Jackson 8110, Neubauer 8196
Rhode Island: Knoop 8411, Wood 8452, Woodward 8453
South Carolina: Hopewell 8484, Smith 8498
Tennessee: Latimer 8595, Maclellan 8602
Texas: Baugh 8693, Butt 8738, C.I.O.S. 8740, Clements 8766, Criswell 8789, Grum 8876, Henderson 8901, Looper 8990, Patton 9084, Sadler 9143, Seegers 9164, Simpson 9177, Trull 9240, Weiser 9266
Virgin Islands: Prior 9378
Virginia: Keesee 9460, **Mustard 9492**, SunTrust 9539
Wyoming: Christian 9974

Theology
New York: **Luce 6398**

Transgender and gender nonconforming
California: Weingart 1307

Transition planning
California: **Smith 1183**

Transportation
Arizona: Freeport-McMoRan 112
California: Craigslist 436, Teichert 1244
Colorado: El Pomar 1406
Connecticut: Palmer 1666
Illinois: Grand 2875
Indiana: Putnam 3373
Maryland: Baltimore 3726
Minnesota: McKnight 4709, Phillips 4741, Weyerhaeuser 4804
Missouri: Truman 4996
Pennsylvania: **Alcoa 7908**, Dolfinger 8013
Texas: Meadows 9019
Washington: **Bullitt 9591**

Tropical diseases
California: Smith 1184
Connecticut: **GE 1591**
Illinois: **Abbott 2649**
Texas: **Jiv 8933**

United Ways and Federated Giving Programs
Alabama: Alabama 1, Anderson 5, BBVA 8, BBVA 9, Brock 13, Brooke 14, Caring 18, Community 25, Energen 32, Mapp 47, Protective 59, Smith 65, Snook 68, Thompson 70
Arizona: Day 105, Freeport-McMoRan 112, Least 132, Stardust 164, Stewart 166, Surplus 167
Arkansas: Murphy 193, Riggs 196, Ross 199, Wal-Mart 210
California: Agarwal 219, Allergan 228, Anderson 243, **Avery 272**, Bagley 277, Bakar 278, **Bechtel 295**, Bennett 307, Burnham 357, Caruso 382, Case 383, Gibson 583, Glide 595, Heavensent 671, Hewlett 687, Jack 736, Jennings 748, Kling 794, McKesson 903, Mitchell 931, Mosse 948, Nestle 965, Sempra 1140, Shapiro 1151, Shea 1155, Sinskey 1174, Smith 1185, Smith 1186, Taube 1241, Volentine 1291, Western 1316, Worster 1347, Zable 1355
Colorado: Carson 1382, Green 1424, Lewis 1447, Monfort 1465, Staley 1507
Connecticut: Barnes 1542, Boehringer 1549, Chase 1555, Common 1561, Ellis 1579, First 1584, **GE 1591**, Grossman 1603, Heimbold 1612, Huisking 1615, Kitchings 1621, Liberty 1630, McLeod 1641, Meriden 1643, **October 1659**, **Praxair 1676**, Rogow 1683, SBM 1690, Trefz 1709, Zachs 1730
Delaware: Bishop 1745, CenturyLink-Clarke 1750, Chase 1753, Laffey 1800, Mancheski 1811, Natembea 1822, Ortega 1828, Parker 1829, Presto 1840, Ratner 1846, Reynolds 1848, Romill 1851, Struthers 1865, Sylvan 1867, Wasily 1871, Wilke 1875
District of Columbia: Merriman 1930
Florida: Ansin 1969, Baldwin 1978, Basham 1982, Batchelor 1983, Bauman 1984, Beaver 1986, Bedford 1988, Bi-Lo 1996, Brown 2004, Coulter 2047, Dallepezze 2049, Darden 2051, DuBow 2068, Eagle 2078, Florescue 2100, Fortin 2106, Galloway 2112, Garrott 2116, Harris 2149, James 2169, Katcher 2176, Kirbo 2186, Kislak 2187, Lennar 2210, Lichtenberger 2214, Lindemann 2217, Martin 2229, Miller 2241, Morby 2244, NextEra 2251, Nommontu 2252, Publix 2275, Rayonier 2281, Ryder 2302, Sage 2304, Sanders 2305, Selevan 2317, Sherman 2319, Spurlino 2330, Stein 2337, Sylvester 2348, Watts 2380
Georgia: Aflac 2399, AGL 2400, Anderson 2404, Atlanta 2406, CLC 2426, Colonial 2430, Correll 2440, Covenant 2444, Franklin 2462, **Georgia 2469**, **Guanacaste 2475**, Holder 2485, Klaus 2497, Lewis 2503, Love 2508, Lowder 2509, MARTA 2512, Morgens 2521, Saul 2547, Turner 2562, **UPS 2566**, Zaban 2583
Hawaii: Buehner 2589, First 2598
Illinois: **Abbott 2649**, ArcelorMittal 2670, Atherton 2676, Austin 2677, Beidler 2692, Bielfeldt 2698, Blum 2705, Buchanan 2720, Buder 2725, Caterpillar 2738, Charleston 2742, Community 2763, Donnelley 2801, Emerson 2822, Energizer 2824, Frank 2840, Galvin 2857, Harris 2892, Hirschl 2912, Illinois 2934, Katten 2951, Lea 2970, Malott 2996, Meyer 3023, Mills 3028, **Motorola 3042**, New 3052, Nygren 3060, Omron 3063, Purcell 3101, Redhill 3108, Ryan 3130, Schawk 3138, Trustmark 3193, Ullrich 3198, United 3199, United 3200, Vaughn 3203, Woodward 3243, **Wrigley 3244**, Yulman 3246
Indiana: 1st 3251, **Ackerman 3252**, Anderson 3255, Brotherhood 3268, Champagne 3273, **Cummins 3292**, Len-Ari 3339, **Lilly 3340**, Lincoln 3344, Miller 3355, Transformation 3392, Vectren 3394, White 3405
Iowa: AEGON 3409, Aviva 3411, Bechtel 3412, EMC 3428, Giacoletto 3431, GuideOne 3438, HNI 3443, Hubbell 3445, Johnson 3449, Kent 3450, Koehn 3453, Krause 3454, McIntyre 3462, Meredith 3463, Nelson 3467, New 3468, United 3485, Vogel 3487, Weathertop 3489, Wellmark 3490
Kansas: Baughman 3493, Capitol 3498, Douglas 3509, Hutchinson 3521, INTRUST 3522, Kao 3525, Morris 3537, Shannon 3545, Smoot 3548
Kentucky: Yum! 3608
Louisiana: Entergy 3630, Helis 3641, Huie 3643, Keller 3646, McIlhenny 3654, Moffett 3655, Pinhook 3660, Rispone 3662
Maine: Alfond 3679, Bangor 3680, Cascade 3681, Hannaford 3690, King 3694, TD 3710
Maryland: Angelos 3721, Blum 3737, Brown 3740, Bunting 3742, Community 3761, GEICO 3801, **Grace 3807**, **Lawless 3827**, Legg 3828, Leidy 3830, Linehan 3834, Price 3865, Rembrandt 3868, Sampson 3878, Straus 3890
Massachusetts: Aaron 3913, Adams 3916, Arbella 3926, Bristol 3960, Brooks 3963, **Cabot 3966**, Casty 3976, Cogan 3988, Crane 3998, Cutler 4005, Duniry 4025, Eastern 4030, Edgerley 4031, Ellsworth 4035, Epker 4038, Golden 4073, Grayson 4078, Hopedale 4101, Island 4109, Jordan 4113, Knez 4127, Leventhal 4141, Levy 4144, Lubin 4155, Mazar 4164, New 4189, New England 4193, One 4197, One 4198, Peters 4216, Plymouth 4222, Rodgers 4242, Rubin 4249, Saltonstall 4254, Sidman 4273, Sims/Maes 4274, Spina 4280, Webster 4322
Michigan: Alro 4336, Bosch 4354, Brown 4356, Consumers 4376, Dana 4386, Doornink 4403, **Dow 4404**, Dow 4405, **Fisher 4423**, Ford 4425, Ford 4426, Ford 4428, Ford 4430, Frankel 4435, General 4442, **Kellogg 4473**, **Kellogg's 4475**, La-Z-Boy 4481, Lear 4482, Manoogian 4492, MSJ 4513, Oleson 4516, Perrigo 4521, **Rodney 4528**, Shelden 4537, Sigmund 4540, Spartan 4544, Strosacker 4549, Taubman 4552, VanderWeide 4572, Von 4574, Weatherwax 4577, Whirlpool 4583, Whiting 4584, Wolverine 4593, Zatkoff 4595
Minnesota: 3M 4597, AHS 4599, Best 4612, **Better 4614**, Cargill 4628, Dayton 4643, Deluxe 4644, Donaldson 4646, Driscoll 4648, Ecolab 4651, Foundation 4657, General 4661, Graco 4666, Greystone 4668, Hormel 4676, Kelley 4686, Land 4691, McGlynn 4706, **Medtronic 4712**, Minnesota 4715, Minnesota 4716, Mitchell 4717, Mooty 4720, Opus 4731, **Pentair 4739**, Prospect 4747, Regis 4750, Robins 4754, Securian 4761, Sit 4765, Stone 4773, Target 4776, U.S. 4784, Valspar 4786, Veden 4787, Weesner 4797, Xcel 4808
Mississippi: Mississippi 4839, Riley 4844
Missouri: Albrecht 4850, Ameren 4851, American 4852, Anheuser 4853, Brauer 4860, Burns 4866, Centene 4870, Commerce 4871, Dierberg 4879, Emerson 4885, **Enterprise 4887**, Graybar 4898, Hallmark 4906, Hauck 4908, Hulston 4911, Interco 4914, Laclede 4931, Lopata 4938, Nestle 4948, Nichols 4949, Orscheln 4951, Pershing 4953, Pott 4958, Ten-Ten 4990
Nebraska: Abel 5021, Buffett 5027, Grand Island 5044, Lauritzen 5061, Linder 5064, Mutual 5071, Nelnet 5072, Sherwood 5081
Nevada: Community 5108, Nevada 5134, NV 5136
New Jersey: Bard 5202, Brougher 5217, Campbell 5223, **Crane 5235**, Gund 5285, Hickory 5299, Ingersoll-Rand 5314, **Johnson 5326**, Kirby 5340, Kresa 5350, L.F.H. 5353, MCJ 5377, Simon, 5460, Smith 5461, Wagner 5491
New Mexico: Altman 5513, McCune 5529, Phillips 5531
New York: Albert 5567, All 5572, American 5587, Barakett 5642, Benenson 5664, Central 5756, Corning 5818, **Credit 5826**, Davidson 5851, Diker 5883, Donovan 5900, Doolittle 5901, Dreams 5909, Dunwalke 5921, Edouard 5936, Emerson 5950, ESL 5960, Fitt 5985, Friedberg 6017, Gerson 6047, Goings 6059, Goldstein 6074, Golub 6079, Gorter 6084, Great 6097, Hultquist 6195, IFF 6206, Island 6215, Kellogg 6269, Knox 6299, Lebensfeld 6342, Lindsay 6373, **M & T 6406**, Marsal 6438, Massry 6444, Meyer 6480, Milliken 6487, Mutual 6518, National 6527, Neiman 6535, Newhouse 6550, **OCLO 6576**, O'Connor 6578, **PepsiCo 6627**, Perelman 6628, **Pfizer 6633**, Phillips 6637, Price 6658, Resource 6691, Review 6692, Richmond 6704, Sandy 6791, Schwartz 6819, Semlitz 6831, Seneca 6832, Tai 6960, TE 6966, Templeton 6969, Walter 7046, Wegman 7061, Weinberg 7067, West 7077, Wildwood 7084, Wohl 7097
North Carolina: Anonymous 7135, **Bank 7139**, Baxter 7142, BB&T 7143, BB&T 7144, Belk 7148, Branan 7157, Dickson 7192, Duke 7196, Flow 7200, Food 7201, Glass 7210, Glenn 7211, Goodrich 7213, Harvest 7224, Jonas 7241, Leever 7253, Olin 7279, Piedmont 7285, Post 7289, Reynolds 7296, Richardson 7301, Sloan 7314, Van Every 7329, Wos 7345
Ohio: AK Steel 7366, Anderson 7372, Ariel 7377, Ashtabula 7379, BASF 7383, Berlin 7385, Broussard 7389, Budig 7392, Castellini 7399, Charities 7400, Cliffs 7407, Community 7413, Conway 7419, Dayton 7429, Deuble 7433, **Eaton 7442**, Fifth 7452, FirstEnergy 7455, Gelbman 7469, Gerlach 7471, H.C.S. 7479, Haile, 7480, Home 7489, Hoover 7492, Kaplan 7516, KeyBank 7523, Kimble 7526, Kroger 7531, Lincoln 7541, Macy's 7552, Mandel 7554, **Mandel 7555**, Miller 7571, Murphy 7584, National 7586, NiSource 7591, Nonneman 7593, Ohio 7599, Oliver 7600, Ormond 7603, Outcalt 7606, Park 7610, Parker 7611, Perkins 7615, Piqua 7620, Sankey 7643, State 7674, Weary 7706, Weisbrod 7708, Western 7710, Westfield 7711, Wexner 7712, Wolfe 7719, Wuliger 7722
Oklahoma: American 7728, Brown 7737, Collins 7741, Coretz 7744, Ketchum 7765, McCrory 7773, McMahon 7776, Oklahoma 7782, ONEOK 7783, Oxley 7785, Williams 7814, Wilshire 7815, Zarrow 7818, Zarrow 7820
Oregon: **Intel 7853**, Jeld 7856, PacifiCorp 7877, PGE 7881
Pennsylvania: **ACE 7905**, Air 7907, Ametek 7913, Aqua 7917, Baker 7925, Baker 7926, Briggs 7950, Burke 7958, Burke 7959, Comcast 7989, Community 7993, Degenstein 8008, Dixon 8012, Farber 8032, Federated 8033, Haldeman 8076, Janssen 8111, Kline 8129, Kunkel 8133, Lutron 8151, Mengle 8174, Mine 8184, Morris 8188, **PPG 8235**, Salvaggio 8263, Sargent 8265, Scheller 8268, Steinman 8299, Steinman 8300, Stine 8302, Taylor 8311, Vanguard 8327, West 8334, Wyomissing 8350

Rhode Island: Amica 8356, Charlton 8372, Cuno 8378, **FM 8393**, Greene 8398, Hoche-Scofield 8405, McAdams 8416, Middendorf 8420, Murray 8421, Osborn 8426, Roraback 8431, Sharpe 8437, Stone 8443, Textron 8446, Vance 8450
South Carolina: Canal 8466, Community 8474, Foothills 8478, McKissick 8486, Smith 8499
South Dakota: Dakota 8514, Larson 8516, Robinson 8520, South Dakota 8522, Vucurevich 8524
Tennessee: Atticus 8531, Bridgestone 8537, Charis 8542, Clayton 8547, Eastman 8561, First 8565, Frist 8568, Goodfriend 8574, Hamico 8576, Hart 8578, Haslam 8580, HCA 8582, Johnson 8588, Martin 8604, Melkus 8609, Osborne 8614, Regal 8622, Shinn 8627, Wilson 8646
Texas: Astros 8674, BNSF 8706, Bookout 8709, Brownsville 8733, Collins 8772, Dodge 8810, Durham 8817, Fain 8835, Family 8836, Gayden 8861, Goodman 8870, Goradia 8871, Herd 8902, Hirsch 8910, Jarvis 8931, Jones 8942, Kimberly 8957, McDermott 9013, Miller 9027, Miller 9028, Moncrief 9031, Moran 9036, NuStar 9065, Owsley 9078, Penney 9089, Rea 9123, Roach 9132, **Scaler 9155**, Schepps 9158, Sharp 9167, Shell 9168, Simmons 9174, Smith 9187, Snyder 9188, Stumberg 9210, Texas 9227, Tobin 9236, USAA 9245, Valero 9246, Ware 9259, Wichita 9277, Wise 9285, Wolff 9286, Wood 9289, Wright 9293
Utah: Miller 9337
Vermont: Mill 9367
Virginia: AMERIGROUP 9383, Charles 9404, Foster 9432, **Genworth 9441**, Landmark 9467, Luminescence 9473, Newman 9493, Norfolk 9496, Peterson 9508, **Scheidel 9528**, Shearwater 9531, SunTrust 9539, Three 9541, Tickle 9542, Universal 9548, Watkins 9553, Whitlock 9556
Washington: Aven 9575, Bamford 9580, Ellison 9614, Evertrust 9617, Foster 9621, Haller 9635, Hughes 9648, McCaw 9675, Neukom 9692, Norcliffe 9693, PACCAR 9698, **PAH 9699**, PEMCO 9702, Raisbeck 9709, Remala 9714, Rice 9716, Safeco 9723, Sarkowsky 9727, Schultz 9730, Shirley 9734, Smith 9737
West Virginia: Hess 9777
Wisconsin: Acuity 9801, Alliant 9804, Anon 9805, **Baird 9811**, Bemis 9815, Briggs 9822, Charter 9829, Cleary 9831, CUNA 9838, Frautschi 9847, Goodman 9852, Greenheck 9856, Harley 9859, Heil 9860, Helfaer 9861, Johnson 9870, Johnson 9874, Kellogg 9879, Kohl 9883, Kress 9887, Ladish 9890, ManpowerGroup 9899, Mortenson 9909, Neese 9911, Nicholas 9913, Northwestern 9914, Oshkosh 9917, Predolin 9923, Rexnord 9932, Rockwell 9934, Ryan 9940, **Schneider 9942**, Sentry 9944, Smith 9947, Uihlein 9958, Windhover 9968, Wisconsin 9969

Urban/community development

Alabama: Alabama 1, Webb 76
California: Hewlett 686, Price 1043, Sacramento 1103, San Francisco 1109
Colorado: Colorado 1390
Connecticut: Fairfield 1581, People's 1671
District of Columbia: Meyer 1931
Florida: Bank 1979
Illinois: Comer 2761, Community 2763, Community 2765, Morrison 3038, Polk 3084, Wieboldt 3231
Indiana: Old 3363
Kentucky: Brown 3563, C.E. 3566
Louisiana: Community 3624
Maine: Maine 3698
Maryland: **Casey 3745**
Massachusetts: Berkshire 3946, Boston 3956, Hyams 4103, McDonnell 4166
Michigan: Community 4369, DTE 4410, Hudson 4463, Monroe 4507, **Mott 4510**, Wolverine 4593
Missouri: Gateway 4894, H & R 4902, Hall 4905, Hallmark 4906, Kansas 4920
New Jersey: Community 5232, **International 5316**, PSEG 5416, Victoria 5490
New York: BTMU 5724, **Citi 5780**, **Clark 5785**, **Ford 5994**, **JPMorgan 6244**, **MetLife 6479**, **NBI 6532**, Scherman 6804, **Surdna 6947**, Tiffany 6978
North Carolina: Triangle 7328
Ohio: Barberton 7382, Boutell 7388, Cleveland 7406, Gund 7478, **Mandel 7555**, Murphy 7584, Nord 7594, **OMNOVA 7601**, Stark 7673, Youngstown 7723
Oregon: PacifiCorp 7877
Pennsylvania: **Alcoa 7908**, Dolfinger 8013, McCune 8161, Mellon 8173, Philadelphia 8221, Washington 8332, Wells 8333
Tennessee: Benwood 8535, Midler 8611
Texas: Meadows 9019, Swinney 9218
Virginia: SunTrust 9539
Wisconsin: Johnson 9870, Milwaukee 9907

Utilities

California: PG&E 1033
Connecticut: Liberty 1630
Oklahoma: ONEOK 7783
Washington: Avista 9576

Venture philanthropy

New York: Blue 5685

Veterinary medicine

California: McBeth 894
Colorado: Stuart 1509
Connecticut: Twenty-Seven 1712
Massachusetts: Peabody 4209
Minnesota: **Patterson 4738**
Nevada: Guidry 5121
North Carolina: Terry 7327
Oklahoma: Kirkpatrick 7766
Rhode Island: TriMix 8448
Virginia: Waldron 9550

Veterinary medicine, hospital

New York: Acquavella 5550, **Bobst 5690**

Visual arts

Alabama: Alabama 1
Alaska: CIRI 85
California: Ahmanson 222, **Avery 272**, **Christensen 399**, **Clorox 407**, Femino 521, Fleishhacker 534, **Getty 579**, Gross 629, Hind 693, LLWW 845, Marmor 881, Miller 929, Osher 997, Parker 1012, Placer 1039, Rotasa 1092, Sacramento 1103, Sonora 1198, Wattis 1302
Colorado: Boettcher 1374, El Pomar 1406, Gates 1418, Summit 1511
Connecticut: **Albers 1532**, Kossak 1623, Neuberger 1649
Delaware: **Adobe 1734**
Florida: Bank 1979, Community 2040, Miami 2238, Selby 2316
Georgia: Moore 2519, Williams 2572
Illinois: Alphawood 2658, Cheney 2745, Chicago 2746, Community 2763, **Graham 2873**, Lea 2970, Martin 3003, **Terra 3186**
Indiana: Wayne 3400
Iowa: Aviva 3411, McElroy 3461, Meredith 3463
Kansas: Hutchinson 3521, Salina 3540, Sprint 3549
Louisiana: Booth 3616, Grigsby 3640
Maryland: Fairchild 3788, Rouse 3877
Massachusetts: Hanover 4086, Peabody 4209, Santander 4256
Michigan: Ann Arbor 4340, Bay 4344, Fremont 4438, Hillsdale 4461, Skillman 4543
Minnesota: **Andersen 4601**, Athwin 4607, Duluth 4649, Jerome 4681, Land 4691, Marbrook 4702, RBC 4748, Xcel 4808
Missouri: Gateway 4894, **Monsanto 4945**
Montana: Edwards 5008
Nebraska: Kearney 5055, Woods 5096
Nevada: Wiegand 5159
New Hampshire: Johnson 5178, Trust 5189
New Jersey: Atlantic 5196, Dodge 5243, Honickman 5303
New Mexico: **Lannan 5526**, McCune 5529, Santa Fe 5533
New York: **American 5585**, **American 5588**, Auchincloss 5623, Barker 5644, Charina 5763, **Clark 5785**, **Deutsche 5876**, **Gottlieb 6085**, **Guggenheim 6116**, **Hauser 6147**, **Kress 6308**, Lehman 6347, **Luce 6398**, Mars 6437, **Pollock 6650**, **Reed 6684**, Rose 6734, Sheldon 6841, Steinberg 6921, Tiffany 6978, **Trace 7003**, **Trust 7009**, **Vital 7033**, **Warhol 7050**, Western 7078, Wunsch 7106
North Carolina: Smith 7317, Triangle 7328
North Dakota: Leach 7353
Ohio: American 7370, Charities 7400, Cleveland 7406, **Kettering 7520**, Murphy 7584, Nordson 7596, Reinberger 7628, Stark 7673, Youngstown 7723
Oklahoma: Kerr 7764
Oregon: Carpenter 7831, Ford 7845, PacifiCorp 7877
Pennsylvania: Armstrong 7921, Baker 7926, Claneil 7982, Fine 8039, Hurd 8101, Independence 8107, Keystone 8122, Pew 8220, Washington 8332
Tennessee: Atticus 8531, First 8565, Frist 8568, HCA 8582
Texas: BNSF 8706, Hoblitzelle 8912, Hudson 8919, Kempner 8952, Reynolds 9127, San Antonio 9148, **Scaler 9155**, Sterling 9203, Wright 9293
Utah: Dee 9312, Eccles 9319, Eccles 9320
Virginia: Luck 9472
Washington: Blue 9588, Community 9604, McMillen 9681, Norcliffe 9693, Seattle 9731, Yakima 9767
West Virginia: Tucker 9796
Wisconsin: Heil 9860, Johnson 9870, Kohler 9884, Milwaukee 9907, Sentry 9944

Visual arts, architecture

Arizona: Arizona 92
California: **Getty 579**
Illinois: **Graham 2873**, Gray 2878
Indiana: **Cummins 3292**
Missouri: Gateway 4894
New York: O'Connor 6578
Rhode Island: Felicia 8392
Texas: Meadows 9019
Washington: Norcliffe 9693

Visual arts, art conservation

California: **Getty 579**
Kentucky: Ventas 3605
Michigan: Community 4374
Pennsylvania: Hurd 8101

Visual arts, design

California: **Avery 272**
Illinois: Driehaus 2805
New York: Donghia 5897, Tiffany 6978

Visual arts, painting

Connecticut: **Albers 1532**
New York: Avery 5627, **Gottlieb 6085**

Visual arts, photography

California: Hearst 669
New Jersey: Segal 5447
New York: Lubo 6396, **Mapplethorpe 6427**, Werblow 7076, Windmill 7089

Visual arts, sculpture

Missouri: **Deer 4878**, Lay 4934
New Jersey: Atlantic 5196
New York: Avery 5627, **Gottlieb 6085**
Texas: Nasher 9051

Vocational education

Vocational education, post-secondary

Vocational school, secondary

Voluntarism promotion

Volunteers of America

Web-based media

Welfare policy/reform

Women

Women's studies

Women, centers/services

Alaska: Rasmuson 89
California: **Allende 227**, California 368, Community 420, Douglas 476, Gumbiner 636, **Marisla 878**, Norris 971, Sonora 1198
Colorado: Boettcher 1374
Connecticut: Community 1563, Fairfield 1581, Windmill 1723
District of Columbia: Cafritz 1890, Meyer 1931, Zients 1960
Florida: Bank 1979, Community 2035, Martin 2229, Pinellas 2269
Georgia: Community 2432
Illinois: Chicago 2746, Polk 3084, Schuler 3143, Sirius 3163
Indiana: Asante 3259
Kentucky: Harris 3580
Louisiana: Baton Rouge 3613, Beaird 3614
Maryland: Ceres 3747
Massachusetts: Community 3992, Gruben 4082, Stearns 4286
Michigan: Knight 4477
Minnesota: Bremer 4620, Butler 4622, Minneapolis 4714
Missouri: Roblee 4963, Smith 4974, Ten-Ten 4990
Nebraska: Lozier 5065
Nevada: Nevada 5134
New Jersey: Borden 5209
New Mexico: Frost 5519, McCune 5529
New York: Coach 5790, Dobkin 5891, Dreyfus 5913, **Ford 5994**, Lanza 6329, Marrus 6436, New York 6544, NoVo 6570, O'Connor 6578, Rochester 6722, Sister 6864, Western 7078
North Carolina: Cumberland 7184, Reynolds 7298, Smith 7317, Triangle 7328
Ohio: Columbus 7411, Gund 7478, Kroger 7531, Murphy 7584, Richland 7630, Women's 7720, Youngstown 7723
Pennsylvania: Connelly 7995, Dolfinger 8013, Fieldstone 8038, FISA 8043, Hurd 8101, McGinley 8164, Pilgrim 8225, Smith 8288
Rhode Island: Hoche-Scofield 8405
South Carolina: Spaulding-Paolozzi 8502
Texas: Craig, 8786, Edwards 8824, Lowe 8993, O'Quinn 9072, Sidhu 9172, Simmons 9174, Simmons 9175, Waco 9251, Woodforest 9290
Utah: Eccles 9320
Vermont: Sills 9371
Virginia: Community 9414, Lynchburg 9474, Newman 9493
Washington: **Channel 9597**, Community 9604, Horizons 9645, OneFamily 9695
West Virginia: Kanawha 9780
Wisconsin: Milwaukee 9907, Pettit 9919, Windhover 9968

YM/YWCAs & YM/YWHAs

Alabama: Alabama 1, Comer 20, Energen 32, King 44, McWane 51, Protective 59, Smith 65
Arizona: Jones 127
California: Anderson 243, AS&F 263, Bauer 287, Burnham 357, California 368, Davidson 453, Halsell 647, Jack 736, Jackson 737, **Jerome 749**, Keesal 777, Klein 793, Martin 882, Munger 954, Opus 989, Ryan 1098, Sexton 1144, Silk 1167, Tanimura 1236, Ullman 1269, Volentine 1291, Werner 1313
Colorado: Jumping 1434
Connecticut: Beagary 1544, Cohen 1560, George 1592, Goergen 1595, McMahon 1642, Meriden 1643, New Canaan 1650, Rockville 1682
Delaware: Esperance 1777, Khan 1795, Presto 1840, Reynolds 1849
Florida: Batchelor 1983, Bedford 1988, Brown 2004, Densch 2061, Galloway 2112, GPD 2132, Hillenbrand 2159, Jacksonville 2167, McCann 2232, Sanders 2305, Spurlino 2330, Sudakoff 2342
Georgia: Brady 2415, Colonial 2430, Flowers 2459, Jordan 2492, Lockwood 2505, Singletary 2551, Turner 2562
Hawaii: Ching 2596
Idaho: Jeker 2634
Illinois: Barnett 2680, Beidler 2692, Davis 2786, Donnelley 2801, Foglia 2837, Gregory 2879, Hoogland 2920, Illinois 2934, Ingersoll 2935, Lynn 2988, McCormick 3010, McDaniel 3011, **Mondelez 3034**, Norris 3058, Pattee 3072, Potishman 3086, **Santreece 3135**, Shirk 3158, Tracy 3189, Tulsa 3194, Walker 3211, Walter 3213, Woodward 3243
Indiana: 1st 3251, Anthem 3257, Bales 3261, Holiday 3322, Michigan 3354, MTI 3357, Vectren 3394, Weaver 3401
Iowa: Bechtel 3412, Guernsey 3437, HNI 3443, Krause 3454, McIntyre 3462, United 3485
Kansas: Kirk 3527, Shannon 3545, Smoot 3548
Louisiana: Community 3624, Lamar 3647
Maine: Hannaford 3690
Maryland: Community 3761, Sampson 3878
Massachusetts: Bayrd 3938, Berkman 3945, Boston 3957, Bristol 3960, Caldwell 3970, Danversbank 4009, Ellsworth 4035, Foundation 4058, Gildea 4071, Institution 4108, McEvoy 4168, Wang 4319
Michigan: Boll 4352, Dalton 4385, Duffy 4411, Granger 4449, Granger 4450, Hickman 4460, Johnston 4469, **Kellogg's 4475**, MSJ 4513, Saddle 4530, Spartan 4544, Whirlpool 4583, Wolverine 4593
Minnesota: Cargill 4628, Deluxe 4644, Fiterman 4656, General 4661, Mooty 4719, Mooty 4720, Ordean 4732, Robins 4754, Valspar 4786
Missouri: Commerce 4871, Farber 4889, Graybar 4898, Orscheln 4951, Rosewood 4964, Taylor 4988
Montana: Town 5016
Nebraska: Abel 5021, Ameritas 5023, Hirschfeld 5049
New Hampshire: Cogswell 5167
New Jersey: Boye 5212, Brougher 5217, Gagnon 5271, Gibson 5277, Grassmann 5281, Horizon 5305, Ingersoll-Rand 5314, Large 5355, Orange 5396, Silver 5457, Simon, 5460, Union 5485
New York: American 5587, Berne 5670, Butler 5735, Corning 5818, Davenport 5850, **Deutsche 5876**, Goldman 6065, Hultquist 6195, **JPMorgan 6244**, Lenna 6352, Miller 6486, Milliken 6487, **Neuberger 6538**, Nola 6562, PLM 6647, Price 6658, Rantz 6678, Shipley 6843, Swartz 6954, Swyer 6956, Vernon 7026, Wells 7073, Wright 7104
North Carolina: 25th 7131, Armfield 7137, BB&T 7144, Belk 7148, Bissell 7152, Bolick 7155, Brauninger 7159, Dickson 7192, French 7203, Harvest 7224, Herring 7229, Humphrey 7236, Keith 7247, McLean 7264, Reynolds 7296, Reynolds 7299, Symmes 7325, Woodson 7342, Woodward 7343
Ohio: AK Steel 7366, Andersons 7374, Ar-Hale 7376, Ariel 7377, Ashtabula 7379, **Eaton 7442**, Fenn 7449, Haile, 7480, Home 7489, Hoover 7492, Luedeking 7547, McBride 7562, National 7586, Nippert 7590, Park 7610, Parker 7611, Philips 7619, Ritter 7633, Schiewetz 7647, Silk 7663, Warrington 7703, Weary 7706
Oklahoma: McCrory 7773, Viersen 7808
Pennsylvania: Aqua 7917, BNY 7946, Bozzone 7948, Carnahan 7965, Century 7974, CIGNA 7981, Comcast 7989, Degenstein 8008, Dickson 8009, Eden 8021, ESSA 8028, Hughes 8099, Janssen 8111, Kinsley 8127, Kunkel 8133, Long 8149, Mason 8157, Phillips 8222, Pottstown 8234, **PPG 8235**, Rossin 8256, Sedwick 8276, Sexauer 8280, Smith 8287, Wilson 8341, Wismer 8343
Rhode Island: Dexter 8382, Kaplan 8409, Kimball 8410, Roraback 8431
South Carolina: Canal 8466, Phifer 8491, **ScanSource 8495**, Smith 8498, Smith 8499
South Dakota: Robinson 8520
Tennessee: Bridgestone 8537, Clayton 8547, HCA 8582, Regal 8622, Thompson 8635, Turner 8640
Texas: Bass 8690, Beasley 8698, BNSF 8706, Brumley 8734, Carter 8753, Cowden 8783, Jones 8943, Moore 9034, Simmons 9174, Sterling 9203, Turner 9242, Valero 9246
Utah: Call 9310, Peery 9344
Vermont: Pomerleau 9369
Virginia: AMERIGROUP 9383, Flippo 9430, Fredericksburg 9436, Luck 9472, SunTrust 9539, United 9546, Universal 9548, Wardle 9551
Washington: Bamford 9580, Discuren 9611, Evertrust 9617, Foster 9621, McKinstry 9680, Names 9690, Oki 9694, REI 9713, Safeco 9723, Sondland 9740
West Virginia: Hess 9777
Wisconsin: Alliant 9804, **Baird 9811**, Briggs 9822, CUNA 9838, Green Bay 9855, Kress 9887, Ladish 9890, Loehrke 9893, Michels 9906, MMG 9908, Neese 9911, Oshkosh 9917, Raibrook 9925, Sentry 9944, Spire 9949, Stock 9953, Wisconsin 9969
Wyoming: Watt 9997

Young adults

Alabama: Community 24, Kaul 43, Meyer 53
Arizona: **Hickey 121**, Webb 174
Arkansas: Cabe 182, Rockefeller 197
California: Ahmanson 222, **Alpert 231**, Ayrshire 276, **ben Joseph 302**, Bickerstaff 313, California 368, Center 388, Community 414, Eisner 499, El Dorado 500, Five 533, **Geffen 567**, Gerbode 573, Gumbiner 636, **Hilton 692**, Johnson 753, Lesher 833, Ludwick 856, Marcled 875, McMillen 905, Napa 959, Patron 1020, San Luis 1110, Sangham 1114, Schwab 1127, **Smith 1183**, Taper 1237, Weingart 1307, Yellow 1354
Colorado: Colorado 1390, Community 1391, Fishback 1410, Halton 1426, King 1440, Summit 1511
Connecticut: Community 1562, Connecticut 1566, Pitt 1675
Delaware: **Raskob 1845**
District of Columbia: Cafritz 1890, **CityBridge 1892**, **Union 1953**
Florida: Bush 2008, Community 2034, Southwest 2327
Georgia: Camp-Younts 2421, Franklin 2462, **Thoresen 2557**, **Turner 2563**
Idaho: **Schultz 2641**
Illinois: Arthur 2673, Blowitz 2702, Chicago 2746, Fry 2849, Mellinger 3021, Seabury 3146, Siragusa 3162, Steans 3175
Indiana: Community 3281, Community 3286, **Lilly 3342**, **Lumina 3345**
Iowa: McElroy 3461
Kansas: Security 3544
Maryland: Abell 3712, Ceres 3747, Community 3761
Massachusetts: **Barr 3937**, Boston 3956, Essex 4039, MetroWest 4173, Shapiro 4267, Shaw 4270, Smith 4277, **State 4285**, Stevens 4288, Stevens 4289
Michigan: Chrysler 4366, Grand Rapids 4447, Midland 4502, **Mott 4510**, Sturgis 4550
Minnesota: Bremer 4620, CHS 4636, **O'Shaughnessy 4734**, Pohlad 4745, U.S. 4784
Mississippi: Community 4821, Gulf 4830
Missouri: Saint Louis 4966, Westlake 5000
Montana: Edwards 5008, Oro 5014
Nebraska: Merrick 5067
New Hampshire: Lindsay 5179
New Jersey: **Allen 5191**, **Chubb 5229**, Danellie 5237, Fund 5270, Hyde 5310, **Knowles 5345**
New York: Abeles 5544, Altman 5579, Canaday 5743, **Clark 5784**, **Clark 5785**, Clark 5786, Community 5802, Cummings 5834, First 5979, Gould 6087, **Nash 6525**, O'Connor 6578, Price 6659, Ritter 6712, **Sparkplug 6894**, Staten 6912
North Carolina: Cemala 7174, Community 7180, North Carolina 7273, Reidsville 7294
Ohio: Cincinnati 7404, Fairfield 7445, GAR 7465, Howley 7494, O'Neill 7602, Parents 7608, Ridgecliff 7631, Saint 7639, St. Marys 7672
Oklahoma: Hardesty 7756, Hille 7759
Oregon: J.F.R. 7854, Lamfrom 7863
Pennsylvania: Beneficial 7936, Birmingham 7942, Connelly 7995, Dolfinger 8013, Heinz 8084, Mellon 8173, Phoenixville 8223, Roberts 8250, Staunton 8296
Tennessee: Baptist 8533, **Maclellan 8601**, **Scarlett 8624**, Wilson 8646
Texas: Abell 8650, AT&T 8675, Community 8774, Community 8776, Hoglund 8913, **Jenesis 8932**, Jones 8944, McDermott 9013, Moore 9034, Orsinger 9073, Rockwell 9135, Sumners 9214, Terry 9224

Young adults, female

Young adults, male

Youth

Youth development

Youth development, adult & child programs

Youth development, agriculture

Youth development, alliance/advocacy

Youth development, business

Youth development, centers/clubs

Youth development, citizenship

Youth development, community service clubs

Youth development, equal rights

Youth development, intergenerational programs

Youth development, public policy

Youth development, reform

Youth development, religion

Youth development, research

Youth development, scouting agencies (general)

Youth development, services

Youth development, single organization support

Youth, pregnancy prevention

Youth, services

Finneran 5978, Grigg 6109, Heckscher 6157, Hudson 6191, Knapp 6296, **M & T 6406**, Ross 6753, Sheldon 6841, Snow 6878, Toyota 7002, Warburg 7048, Wegman 7061
North Carolina: Dickson 7192, Finley 7199, Holding 7234, Merancas 7267, Robertson 7305, Woodward 7343
North Dakota: MDU 7354
Ohio: Butler 7396, Cleveland 7406, Columbus 7411, Durell 7441, Erie 7444, FirstEnergy 7455, GAR 7465, Middletown 7570, National 7586, Nationwide 7587, Schiewetz 7647, Stranahan 7678
Oklahoma: Helmerich 7758, Kerr 7764, Mabee 7770, McMahon 7776, Waters 7810, Zarrow 7818
Oregon: Benton 7825, Burning 7827
Pennsylvania: Ametek 7913, Bayer 7932, First 8040, Grable 8064, Helen's 8087, Hopwood 8096, Phoenixville 8223, Sand 8264, Stuart 8307, Trees 8319
Rhode Island: Biogen 8363, Champlin 8370, TriMix 8448
South Carolina: Campbell 8464, Foothills 8478
Tennessee: First 8565, Maddox 8603, Plough 8615, Shinn 8627
Texas: Anderson 8664, Arnold 8673, **Baker 8679**, Bass 8690, Carter 8752, Communities 8773, Dodge 8810, East 8819, Edwards 8824, Fluor 8851, Fondren 8853, Halsell 8885, Kempner 8952, Mayor 9007, Miller 9028, Payne 9086, **PHM 9098**, Simmons 9174, Smith 9187, Sumners 9214, Talkington 9219, Texas 9227, Webber 9262, Weekley 9264
Vermont: **Ben 9358**, Vermont 9375
Virginia: Beazley 9391, Community 9412, **Genworth 9441**, Graham 9445, MeadWestvaco 9484, Obici 9500, Wiser 9561
Washington: Allen 9567, Bushnell 9592, Cheney 9598, Evertrust 9617, George 9626, Inland 9650, Kitsap 9659, REI 9713, **Stewardship 9744**
West Virginia: Your 9799
Wisconsin: Bemis 9815, Cornerstone 9836, Fond du Lac 9843, Johnson 9870, Johnson 9872, Johnson 9874, Mead 9902, Pick 9920, Rutledge 9939
Wyoming: Perkins 9988, Stuart 9993

Zoos/zoological societies

Alabama: Thompson 70
Arizona: Click 100, Globe 115, Marley 140
California: Doelger 472, Issa 732, Lehrer 827, McBeth 894, McCarthy 896, Outhwaite 1000, Winnick 1333
Colorado: Lane 1443, Shaw 1499, SSB 1506
Florida: Batchelor 1983, Stein 2337
Georgia: Carlos 2422, Holder 2485, Reeder 2536
Illinois: Bielfeldt 2698, Chaddick 2740, Comer 2760, Guthman 2882, Hamill 2888, Harris 2892, Hoehn 2916, Regenstein 3111, Stewart 3178
Indiana: Annis 3256, Auer 3260, Michigan 3354, OneAmerica 3364, White 3406
Kansas: Downing 3510
Maryland: **Brown 3741**
Massachusetts: Bristol 3960, Play 4221
Michigan: Consumers 4376, Idema 4465, **Kellogg 4473**, Mardigian 4494, Polk 4524, Wasserman 4576
Minnesota: Dayton 4643, Hubbard 4678, Weesner 4797
Missouri: Brauer 4860, Emerson 4885, Graybar 4898, Lichtenstein 4936
Nebraska: Hubbard 5053, Union 5090
New York: Alison 5571, Geary 6037, Riedman 6706, **Stempel 6925**
North Carolina: Slick 7313
Ohio: Dornette 7440, Lehner 7536, Reinberger 7628
Oklahoma: Bernsen 7733
Oregon: Clark 7834
Pennsylvania: Brodsky 7952, **PPG 8235**
Rhode Island: Felicia 8392, Hasbro 8403, Sharpe 8437
Tennessee: Carlton 8541, Hamico 8576
Texas: Brown 8730, Carlson 8750, Coastal 8768, Coates 8769, GHS Foun 8865, Kronkosky 8970, Lawson 8974, Once 9070, Onstead 9071, Simmons 9174, Strake 9208, Valero 9246, Zeller 9298
Utah: Lawson 9331
Washington: **Tyler 9755**
Wisconsin: Holz 9864, Ladish 9890

FOUNDATIONS NEW TO THE EDITION

The following foundations appear in this edition of *The Foundation Directory* but had not met criteria for inclusion in the previous edition. The entries for these foundations are highlighted with a star (☆) in the Descriptive Directory section. They are included in all indexes.

2010 McKaco Charitable Foundation Trust, IL, 2647

58 Partners Foundation, OH, 7362

6/S Foundation, CO, 1362

80/20 Fund, TX, 8648

A Kinder World Foundation, NY, 5542
Abraham Foundation, Alexander, The, NY, 5545
Abrams Family Foundation, McGrath, The, CA, 217
Abt Family Charitable Foundation, IL, 2651
Achieving America Family Foundation, CA, 218
Ackermann Memorial Fund, G.A., IL, 2652
AD Philanthropic Fund, Inc., The, NY, 5551
Adam Trust, E. Reginald Adam and Rhea H., PA, 7906
Adams County Community Foundation, IN, 3253
Adams Foundation, John and Patricia, The, TX, 8653
Adams Town Memorial Fund, H.T., M.T. and H.T., NY, 5552
Adelman Charitable Foundation, Inc., Ethel & Philip, NY, 5554
Aequus Institute, NY, 5560
Agape Senior Foundation, Inc., SC, 8455
Albion Civic Foundation, MI, *see* 4332
Albion Community Foundation, MI, 4332
Albuquerque Public Library, NM, 5512
Alderbaugh Foundation, PA, 7909
Allen Family Foundation, Bill and Sharon, NC, 7134
Allen Institute for Artificial Intelligence, WA, 9568
Allwin Family Foundation, The, CT, 1536
Alpert Foundation, Raymond and Barbara, CA, 232
Alumni Achievement Awards, Inc., TN, 8527
America's Children's Fund, NY, *see* 6503
American Center Foundation, NY, *see* 6002
Ames Family Foundation, WA, 9570
Ames-Amzalak Memorial Trust, NY, 5591
AMG Charitable Foundation, The, MA, 3924
Amsterdam Foundation, Jack and Mimi Leviton, The, NY, 5595
Anaheim Community Foundation, CA, 239
Anders Foundation, The, WA, 9571
Anderson Foundation, Annie Wallingford, OH, 7373
Anderson Foundation, OH, 7372
Andersons Inc. Charitable Foundation, The, OH, 7374
Androse Foundation, The, OH, 7375
Angelica Foundation, NM, 5514
Animal Farm Foundation, Inc., NY, 5601
Ansari Family Foundation, Inc., IL, 2665
Anschel Eilian Family Charitable Foundation, IL, 2666
Anthony Charitable Trust, Phyllis, MA, 3925
Anthony Foundation, Inc., Carmelo, CA, 246
Appaloosa Management Charitable Foundation, Inc., NJ, 5193
Ar-Hale Family Foundation, Inc., OH, 7376
Ar-Hale Foundation, Inc., OH, *see* 7376
Arbesfeld Foundation Inc., Hyman & Ann, NY, 5605
Arbus Foundation, Loreen, The, CA, 251
Arch Coal Foundation, MO, 4855
Archer Family Foundation, The, CA, 252
Arctos Foundation, NY, 5607
Armstrong Foundation, Inc., The, NY, 5613
Arnold Foundation Inc., John & Hilda, CA, 258
Aronson Family Foundation, The, CT, 1538
Asbjornson Foundation, OK, 7729
Atchinson Foundation, Robert and Michelle Cooke, The, MA, 3930
Atlantic Foundation of New York, The, NY, 5622
Attman Foundation Inc., Phyllis L. & Leonard J., The, MD, 3722
Auen Foundation, The, CA, 269
Auen-Bergen Foundation, The, CA, *see* 269
Augusta Brown Holland Philanthropic Foundation, Inc., The, KY, 3557
Aurora Foundation, The, FL, 1974
Aurora Ministries, The, FL, *see* 1974
Ausherman Family Foundation, Inc., MD, 3723
Ayer Family Foundation, Ramani and Louise D., CT, 1539

B & S Charity Foundation Inc, NY, 5631
B.E.L.I.E.F. Foundation, The, TX, 8677
Bacca Foundation, IL, 2678
Bacchetta Foundation, NJ, 5198
Baer Charitable Foundation, Arthur & Helen, MO, 4856
Bailey Family Foundation, AR, 180
Bailey Foundation, Inc., Bobbie, FL, 1977
Baker Family Foundation, Thomas E. and Linda O., WA, 9579
Baker Foundation, R. C., CA, 279
Baldwin Foundation, The, CT, 1541
Bales Foundation, Hazel & Walter T., IN, 3261
Ball Foundation, The, CO, 1371
Ballard Foundation, The, TX, 8680
Banco Popular Foundation, Inc., IL, *see* 3085
BancorpSouth Foundation, MS, 4812
Barakett Foundation, Brett and Patricia, The, NY, *see* 5642
Barakett Foundation, Brett, The, NY, 5642
Barber Foundation, Swain, NJ, 5201
Barer Family Foundation Inc., NJ, 5203
Barnhart Charitable Foundation, Douglas E. and Nancy J., CA, 283
Baroco Foundation, Inc., J. H., FL, 1981
Barrette Family Fund, NH, 5163
Barrist Family Foundation, The, PA, 7929
Barrow Foundation, James Purdy, TX, 8684
Barry Charitable Foundation, Richard Allan, CA, 284
Barton Family Foundation, WA, 9581
Barzun Philanthropic Foundation, Inc., Brooke Brown, The, KY, 3559
BASF Foundation USA, The, OH, 7383
Basham Foundation, Inc., Danker, FL, 1982
Bayard Cutting Arboretum Endowment Fund, PA, 7930
Bayer U.S. Patient Assistance Foundation, PA, 7931
BCLF Managed Assets Corporation, MA, 3939
Beagle Charitable Foundation, CA, 291
Beal Family Foundation, Bruce A. & Robert L., The, MA, 3940
Beal Family Foundation, NY, 5656
Bean Foundation, Inc., A. H., AL, 10
Beard Charitable Foundation, Robert F., MI, 4345
Beard-Payne Family Foundation, The, GA, 2408
Beatty Trust, Helen D. Groome, PA, 7933
Beckman Award Trust, Elizabeth Hurlock, NC, 7145
Belin Foundation, TX, 8699
Belvedere Charitable Foundation, NY, 5661
Bendorf Charitable Trust, Agnes M., MN, 4610
Benenson Foundation, Robert and Nettie, The, NY, 5664
Bennett Foundation, The, CA, 307
Bennett Foundation, The, NV, *see* 5125
Benton County Foundation, OR, 7825
Berbeewalsh Foundation, Inc., WI, 9817
Berger Foundation, James R. and Frances H., CT, 1546
Berger Fund, Leo V., MD, 3729
Bergstrom Foundation, The, MA, 3944
Berkley Corporation Charitable Foundation, W.R., DE, 1741
Berlin Family Foundation, DE, 1743
Berman Charitable Foundation, Sam, FL, 1994
Bernheim Trust, Isaac W., PA, 7940
Bernstein Family Foundation Inc., Steven E., The, FL, 1995
Bernstein Family Foundation, DC, 1886
Bernstein Family Foundation, Leo M., DC, *see* 1886
Bertin Family Foundation, UT, 9308
Berwick Degel Family Foundation, The, WA, 9584
Besse Foundation, John & Melissa, MI, 4348
Bethel College and Seminary Pooled Common Fund, MN, *see* 4613
Bethel University Foundation Pooled Common Fund, MN, 4613
Bethesda Foundation, The, MD, 3732
Biloxi Regional Medical Center, Inc., MS, 4814
Bischoff Foundation, Herbert & Diane, NY, 5678
Bistricer Foundation, Moric & Elsa, NY, *see* 6407
BL Squared Foundation, The, NY, 5680
Black Hills Area Community Foundation, SD, 8511
Blakely Foundation Inc., Sara, The, GA, 2412
Blank Foundation, Nancy & Robert S., NY, 5682
Block Family Foundation Inc., Ellen & Ronald, FL, 1998
Blodgett Foundation and Ferris Greeney Family Foundation, The, WI, *see* 9823
Blue Cross of Idaho Foundation for Health, Inc., ID, 2627
Blutt Family Foundation, Mitchell J. Blutt and Margo K., The, NY, 5687
Boeckman Family Foundation, The, TX, 8707
Boeckmann Charitable Foundation, CA, 323
Boehm Charity Fund, Hershel & Esther, MD, 3738
Bolden Charitable, Herman and Emmie, AL, 12
Bookout Family Foundation, The, TX, 8709
Booth Inc., Suzanne Deal and David G., TX, 8713
Borch Foundation, The, CA, 327
Bossidy Foundation, Lawrence A., The, CT, 1551
Bovay, Jr. Foundation, Harry E., TX, 8716
Bowen Charitable Foundation, Charles and Cassandra, OK, 7736
Bowen Foundation, Ethel N., WV, 9770
Bowes Family Foundation, CA, 333
Bowling Family Charitable Foundation, TX, 8717
Boxer Foundation, The, NY, 5698
Boyer Foundation, John K. & Lynne D., NE, 5025
Brach Foundation, NY, 5700
Brady Corporation Foundation Inc., WI, 9821
Braka Philanthropic Foundation, NY, 5702
Branson Family Foundation, CA, 338
Brass Family Foundation, TX, 8721

Bratton Family Foundation, The, TX, 8722
Bren Foundation, Donald, The, CA, 339
Breslauer Foundation, Inc., B. H., NY, 5707
Brickstreet Foundation, Inc., WV, 9771
Bridge Street Foundation, Inc., NJ, 5213
Bridges Evangelical Foundation, TX, 8725
Bright Future International NFP Inc., IL, 2714
Brill Charitable Trust, Ron and Lisa, DE, 1747
Brock Foundation, Harry B. & Jane H., The, AL, 13
Brock Foundation, The, AL, *see* 13
Brodsky Foundation, Julian A. and Lois G., The, PA, 7952
Brookby Foundation, The, WI, 9823
Brooker Foundation, T. Kimball, IL, 2716
Brooks Family Charitable Foundation, MA, *see* 3963
Brooks Family Foundation, MA, 3963
Brooks for Charities, Charles, PA, 7953
Brookshire Foundation, William A., TX, 8728
Brotherhood Mutual Foundation Inc., IN, 3268
Brown Foundation, OK, 7737
Brownington Foundation, Inc., NY, 5721
Brownstone Family Foundation, NY, 5722
Brownstone Foundation, Inc., Lucien & Ethel, NY, *see* 5722
Brownsville Foundation for Health and Education, TX, 8733
Bruni Foundation, Jerome V., CO, 1380
Bryce L. West Foundation, Inc., FL, 2005
Buchbinder Family Foundation, Henry and Gilda, The, IL, 2721
Buck Foundation, Caroline Alexander, PA, 7955
Bucks Creek Foundation, DE, 1748
Buehner - Joan B. Merrill Family Foundation, Paul & Irene, HI, 2589
Buehner Foundation, Paul & Irene, HI, *see* 2589
Building Healthy Lives Foundation, OH, 7394
Bullfrogs & Butterflies Foundation, CT, 1553
Burleigh Family Foundation, OH, 7395
Burns Foundation Inc., Donald A., FL, 2006
Burton Foundation, William T. and Ethel Lewis, The, LA, 3619
Bushnell Family Foundation, WA, 9592
Butler Family Foundation, Inc., Gilbert and Ildiko, The, NY, 5734
Butler Foundation, Alice, NC, 7165
Butler Memorial Scholarship Foundation, J. D. and Alice, NC, *see* 7165
Butters Foundation, The, NY, 5737
Bybee Foundation - A Trust, Faith P. & Charles L., TX, 8739
Byrum Charitable Trust, Porter B., NC, 7166

C.E.B. Foundation, The, CA, 361
C.W.B. Foundation, IL, 2730
Cabbadetus Foundation, MA, 3965
Cabin Road Foundation, NJ, 5222
Cade Foundation, The, MN, 4625
Call of Duty Endowment, The, CA, 369
Campbell Foundation, Betsy M., SC, 8463
CareFusion Foundation, CA, 377
Cares Foundation, CA, 378
Carlos Foundation, Inc., Thalia N. and Chris M., The, GA, 2422
Carolands Preservation Foundation, CA, 379
Carr Foundation, Gregory C., ID, see 2631
Carr Foundation, Inc., The, AK, 83
Caxambas Foundation Inc., WI, 9828
Cayre Foundation, Michael & Shirley, The, NY, 5754
Central Montana Foundation, MT, 5006
Central Pacific Bank Foundation, HI, 2595
Chafetz Family Charitable Trust, Irwin, MA, 3979
Chambers Memorial, James B., WV, 9772
Chaplin Family Foundation Inc., FL, see 2017
Chaplin Family Foundation, Paul & Karen, FL, 2017
Charlesmead Foundation, Inc., The, RI, 8371
Chartered Foundation, The, IL, 2744
Chase & Stuart Bear Family Foundation Inc., Cheryl, CT, 1555
Chatham Valley Foundation, Inc., The, NC, 7175
CHDI Foundation, Inc., NJ, 5228
CHDI, Inc., NJ, see 5228
Children's Family Care, Inc., OH, 7401
Chipotle Cultivate Foundation, CO, 1388
Chirag Foundation, The, MA, 3983
Christ Foundation, OH, 7402
Chronic Fatigue Initiative, Inc., NY, 5777
Church Home Corporation, MD, 3749
Cianbro Charitable Foundation, ME, 3683
Ciresi Foundation, Michael V. & Ann C., MN, 4637
Citrin Charitable Foundation, Rona and Jeffrey, CT, 1559
Clark Family Foundation, PA, see 8048
Clark Foundation, OR, 7834
Clayman Family Foundation, The, PA, 7984
Clements Foundation, B. Gill, The, TX, 8767
Clements Foundation, TX, 8766
Coatue Foundation, NY, 5791
Coffey Charitable Trust, Larry R., KY, 3568
Cognis Foundation, OH, see 7383
Coit Family Foundation, CA, 409
Colhoun Family Foundation, Inc., Howard P., MD, 3755
Collins Medical Trust, OR, 7837
Community Foundation for Nantucket, MA, 3990
Community Foundation of Jackson County, Inc., The, IN, 3284
Community Foundation of Northwest Connecticut, Inc., The, CT, 1565
Community Foundation of Orange and Sullivan, Inc., NY, see 5806
Community Foundation of Orange County, Inc., NY, 5806
Community Foundation of Randolph County, Inc., IN, 3287
Community Foundation of San Joaquin, CA, 417
Community Foundation of South Lake County, Inc., FL, 2039
Community Foundation, Inc., The, MS, 4819
Community Life Foundation of Owensboro, KY, The, KY, see 3597
Community Safety Foundation, CA, 421
Conn Family Foundation, The, OH, 7418
Connolly Foundation, G. L., CA, 425
Connors Foundation, Inc., The, FL, 2043
Constandy, Vaseleke H. Constandy, and C. Harry Constandy Memorial Trust, Harry K., PA, 7996
Conway Foundation, Robert M. & Lois, NY, see 5811
Conway Foundation, Robert M., The, NY, 5811
Cook Family Foundation, MI, 4377
Cooper Foundation, Abe and Ida, IL, 2772
Cooper-Standard Foundation Inc., MI, 4380
Copernicus Society of America, PA, 7998
COPIC Medical Foundation, CO, 1397
Copp Foundation, Inc., The, CT, see 1667
Coretz Family Foundation, OK, 7744
Cornell Douglas Foundation, Inc., MD, 3765
Cornucopia Family Foundation, MI, 4381
Cornwell and Peter Mann Foundation, Dominique, IL, 2775
Corzine Foundation, Joanne D., The, NY, 5819
Cosper Foundation, Judith McBean, The, CA, see 893
Coto Foundation, The, CA, 431
Cottage Health Care Foundation, IL, see 2853
Cousins Properties Foundation, Inc., GA, 2443
Coypu Foundation, IL, 2777
Craig Foundation, E. L., MO, 4875
Crary, Jr. Estate Trust, David, RI, 8377
Crawford Heritage Community Foundation, PA, 8001
Creamer Foundation, J. Fletcher, NJ, 5236
Cressey Foundation, Bryan C. & Christina I., The, IL, 2779
Crestar Bank Charitable Trust, FL, see 2345
Cromwell Foundation, Barbara and George, The, MD, 3767
Crook Foundation, Eleanor, TX, 8790
Cross Family Charitable Foundation, Theodore L., NY, 5829
Cross Foundation, The, MA, 4001
Cummings Foundation, Inc., MA, 4003
Cuno Foundation, RI, 8378
Curtis Foundation Inc., The, NC, 7186
Cutler Charitable Foundation, Melvin S., MA, 4005
Cutler Family Charitable Trust, Theodore H., MA, 4006

D'Addario Family Foundation, Inc., James, NY, 5841
Dabah Charitable Foundation, Inc., Renee & Ezra, NY, 5840
Dachs Foundation, A.M., CA, 446
Dahan Family Foundation, Inc., The, TX, 8794
Dalessandro Foundation, The, MA, 4007
Dalton Foundation, Inc., Harry L., NC, see 7187
Dalton-Brand Foundation, Inc., NC, 7187
Daly Foundation, Robert and Carole, CA, 447
Daly Foundation, Robert, CA, *see* 447
Daly Narthex Project CRUT, Helen E., VT, 9359
Damon Family Foundation, KS, 3504
Dana Foundation, MI, 4386
Danaher Foundation, OH, 7424
Danial Family Foundation, Inc., FL, 2050
Danville Foundation House, VA, 9420
Dattels and Kristine Johnson Foundation, Timothy, CA, *see* 788
Davie Community Foundation, Inc., NC, 7188
Davis Family Foundation, The, MA, 4010
Davis Foundation, Carl A. and Lois E., The, TX, 8798
Davis Foundation, Evelyn Y., The, DC, 1898
Davis Foundation, Inc., Sadie and Harry, ME, 3685
Davis Trust for Charity, Mirrel, PA, 8007
Davis Trust, Rebecca, PA, 8006
Day Foundation, James C. and Teresa K., TX, 8801
De Ganahl Family Foundation, Charles F., MA, 4012
De Llano Charitable Trust, Matias, TX, 8802
de Ramel Family Charitable Trust, Regis, The, DE, *see* 1864
Dean Foundation, Inc., The, IL, 2789
DeCamp Foundation, Douglas A. & Margaret E., MI, 4393
DeFreitas Charitable Foundation, V. Eugene and Rosalie, MA, 4013
Dejana Family Foundation, Peter and Jeri, The, NY, 5868
DEKA Foundation, The, NH, 5168
DeKalb County Community Foundation, Inc., IN, 3295
Delaware County Community Foundation, Greater, IA, 3426
Delle Foundation, The, NM, 5518
DeLuca Foundation, Inc., Frederick A., The, CT, 1573
Derfner Foundation, Harold and Helen, NY, see 5874
Derfner Foundation, The, NY, 5874
Dermitt Hospital, Jeanette, OH, 7432
Deshe Foundation, Ann and Ari, FL, 2062
Desich Foundation, Richard, DE, 1766
Detkin Family Foundation, Peter and Michelle, The, DE, 1767
Deutsch Foundation, Robert W., MD, 3779
Dew Foundation, IL, 2794
Dewan Foundation, The, NY, 5878
Dexter Trust, Henrietta F., RI, 8382
Deziel Family Foundation, Inc., George, MN, 4645
Dharma Foundation III, Inc., The, FL, *see* 2395
Diamond Family Foundation, Robert & Jennifer, The, NY, 5881
Dicke Family Foundation, OH, 7436
Dickson Memorial Trust, Conway Wing Dickson and Gertrude Finck, PA, 8009
Diiriye Foundation, Inc., Sidciyo Jaamac Suldaan, PA, 8011
DiMino Family Trust, Frank, The, NY, 5887
DiMino Memorial Foundation, Raymond, The, NY, *see* 5887
Dintersmith-Hazard Foundation, The, MA, 4020
Diomedes Foundation, The, MA, 4021
DLA Piper Foundation, The, MD, 3781
Dodero Trust for the Arts and Sciences, Corinne L., OH, 7438
Dole Charitable Foundation, Elizabeth, The, DC, 1900
Dollar Bank Foundation, PA, 8014
Donner Family Charitable Foundation, David, NY, 5898
Doolin Family Foundation, The, CO, 1402
Doolittle Foundation, Harry and Misook, NY, 5901
Dotson Family Foundation, The, OK, 7748
Dove Family Foundation, AL, 31
Dove Foundation, G. Mack and Nancy R., The, AL, *see* 31
Dover Foundation, The, IL, 2803
Dow Fund, Alden & Vada, MI, 4408
Dr. Bronners Family Foundation, CA, 479
Draper Charitable Foundation, Nancy-Carroll, DE, 1770
Dreiling Charitable Trust, Leo J. & Albina, KS, 3511
Dresner Foundation, MI, see 4409
Dresner Foundation, Vera and Joseph, MI, 4409

Drizin Charitable Foundation, Mmac, NY, 5914
Dryer Charitable Foundation, Edward T. & Ellen K., IL, 2808
Duane Reade Charitable Foundation, DE, 1771
Duckwall Foundation, Frank E., FL, 2069
Ducommun & Gross Foundation, CA, 485
Duda Foundation, Inc., Ferdinand & Anna, The, FL, 2070
Duke Foundation, Doris, NY, 5918
Duke University Medical School and Hospital Trust, NC, 7197
Dull Casper Trust, PA, 8019
Duneland Health Council, Inc., IN, 3297
Dunn Family Foundation, MO, 4882
DuPont Foundation, John E., PA, 8020
Durham Family Charitable Foundation, Steven H., TX, 8817
Durham Foundation I, Margre & Charles, TX, *see* 8817
Durham Foundation III, Margre & Charles, NE, *see* 5025
Durham Foundation IV, Margre & Charles, NE, *see* 5038
Dyer-Ives Foundation, MI, 4412
Dynamet Foundation, PA, *see* 8256

E & SS Foundation, Inc., The, NY, 5924
Eagle Foundation, Roy and Ida, CA, 488
East West Bank Foundation, CA, 491
Eby Foundation, George, TX, 8820
Eckerson Family Foundation, John and Jennifer, NJ, 5246
Einstein Fund, Albert E. & Birdie W., FL, 2084
Elgin Foundation, TN, 8562
Elizabethtown Healthcare Foundation, NJ, 5253
Elliotsville Plantation Inc, ME, 3686
Elmo Foundation, The, VA, 9425
Emerson Family Foundation, CA, 505
Entelechy Foundation, The, GA, 2454
Ephraim Project, Inc., The, FL, 2087
Eppley Foundation for Research, Inc., The, NY, 5957
Eshelman Foundation, The, DE, 1776
ETZ Chaim Charitable Trust, The, NY, 5962
Every Voice In Action Foundation, AZ, 109
Ezcorp Foundation, TX, 8834

Faith, Hope and Love Foundation, CA, 514
Falcon Fund Foundation, The, NY, 5966
Falling Leaves Foundation Inc., CA, 515
Fallon Family Charitable Foundation, MA, 4041
Family Foundation, Debby Durham, NE, 5038
Family Foundation, Inc., Weber, WI, 9842
Family Foundation, Torcivia, NJ, 5257
Faucett Catalyst Fund, CA, 520
Faucett Family Foundation, CA, *see* 520
Fearons, III Charitable Trust, George H., NY, 5972
Feigenbaum Foundation, Inc., The, MA, 4044
Fenwick Foundation, NJ, 5259
Feraldo Memorial Fund, William Pablo, MO, 4890
Ferry Family Foundation, The, OH, 7451
Findlay Education Foundation, NV, 5119
Fine & Greenwald Foundation, Inc., The, FL, 2095
Firelight Endowment, CA, 529
Firelight Foundation, CA, *see* 529
Fireman Charitable Foundation, Simon C., The, FL, 2096
First National Bank in Wichita Charitable Trust, KS, *see* 3522
Fisher Foundation, Eileen, NY, 5983
Fisher Foundation, Inc., CT, 1585
Fishman Foundation, Jill and Mark, The, PA, 8044
Fites Family Charitable Trust, FL, 2098
Fitt and James I. McLaren Foundation, Lawton W., NY, 5985
Flaherty Family Foundation, The, NY, 5986
Fleischmann Foundation, OH, 7457
Fleming Endowment, TX, 8849
Flextronics Foundation, CA, 535
Flippo Foundation, Jane and Arthur, The, VA, 9430
Florman Family Foundation Inc., The, FL, 2102
Flournoy Georgia Portsmouth Trust, FL, 2103
Flowers Foundation, J. C., NY, 5990
Foley Family Charitable Foundation, The, FL, 2104
Forchheimer Foundation, Leo and Julia, NY, 5992
Forchheimer Foundation, The, NY, *see* 5992
Ford Meter Box Foundation, Inc., IN, 3305
Foster Charitable Foundation, Diana K. and Lawrence T., OH, *see* 7696
Foster Family Foundation, MI, 4431
Foster Foundation Inc., VA, 9432
Fotsch Family Foundation, WI, 9846
Foundation for a Better World, Inc., GA, 2461
Foundation for Arts Initiatives, NY, 6002
Foundation for Global Sports Development, The, CA, 543
Foundation for Research in Cell Biology and Cancer, MA, *see* 4057
Foundation for Research in Cell Biology Cancer and Cardiology, MA, 4057
Foundation, Kellner, The, NY, 5999
Fox Family Foundation, CO, 1412
Frank Family Foundation, Herbert & Noemi, The, NY, 6008
Frankel Family Foundation, Stanley and Judith, MI, 4433
Franklin St. Giving Tree Foundation, PA, 8048
Free Enterprise Foundation, Inc., The, NJ, *see* 5412
Free Family Foundation Corp., FL, 2109
Frenkil Charitable Foundation, Dr. and Mrs. James, MD, 3798
Friedberg and Charlotte Moss Family Foundation, Barry, The, NY, 6017
Friedlander Family Foundation, Claire, The, NY, 6018
Friedman Jewish Learning Exchange Inc., Samuel & Zehava, MD, 3799
Froehlich Family Foundation, Monte L. and Lisa R., NE, 5040
Froelich Foundation, William, NY, 6025
Frost Family Foundation, HI, 2599
Frost-Parker Foundation, The, OH, 7464
Fulcrum Foundation, CO, 1414
Fuller Company Foundation, H.B., MN, 4659
Fund for Democratic Communities, The, NC, 7204
Fusco Family Foundation, Inc., MD, 3800
Fuss Fund, Tommy, The, MA, 4064

Gabus Family Foundation, IA, 3429
Gale Foundation, Inc., Mary, RI, 8397
Galesburg Community Foundation, IL, 2853
Gallagher Foundation, The, TX, 8860
Gallo Foundation, David E., CA, 559
Gamble Foundation, The, CA, 562
Ganatra Family Foundation, DE, 1783
Gardner Charitable Foundation, Eldon and Emma Belle, TN, 8570
Garfield Foundation, Eugene, The, PA, 8052
Garrison Charitable Foundation, Arnold, MA, *see* 4066
Garrison Foundation, Arnold, The, MA, 4066
Garrott Foundation, Thomas M., FL, 2116
Garschina Foundation, Story, The, NY, 6035
Geis Charitable Foundation, Erwin & Katherine, The, OH, 7467
Gelman Foundation Inc., Jacques & Natasha, NY, 6041
Gemunder Foundation, Joel F., FL, 2119
Genecov Foundation, A. S., TX, 8862
George Charitable Trust, Conway & Margaret, AR, 189
Gerber Foundation, Cindy & Murry, The, PA, 8054
German Protestant Orphan Asylum Association Foundation, LA, 3637
Getty Foundation, Aileen, The, CA, 577
Getz Foundation, Harry A. and Rose, TX, 8864
GHR Foundation, MN, 4664
Giacoletto Foundation, John P. and Lawrence J., IA, 3431
Giant Eagle Foundation, PA, 8055
Gibson Family Foundation, NJ, 5276
Giles Foundation, Edward C., The, NC, *see* 7208
Giles Foundation, Lucille P. and Edward C., The, NC, 7208
Gilmore Foundation, IL, 2864
Giuliani Family Foundation, David and Patricia, WA, 9628
Glass Charitable Foundation, MA, 4072
Glasscock Foundation, Melbern G. & Susanne M., TX, 8867
Glazer Foundation, Jeffrey W., The, IA, 3433
Gleis Foundation, Josephine Herbert, CA, 593
Glenn Family Foundation, NC, 7211
Glenn Family Foundation, The, TN, 8572
Godfrey Foundation Inc., Dudley and Constance, WI, 9850
Goings Foundation, Rick and Susan, NY, 6059
Goldman Family Foundation, Richard W., DC, 1910
Goldman Foundation, Robert I., NY, 6069
Goldstein Family Foundation, Arlene & Arnold, NY, 6074
Goldstein Private Foundation, Elliott & Harriet, The, TN, 8573
Gombos Family Charitable Foundation, The, CA, *see* 610
Gombos Foundation, Michael & Corlene, CA, 610
Goodman Foundation, Dixon Hughes, VA, 9444
Goodwin Family Memorial Trust, CA, 614
Gorab Foundation, Eugene A. & Suzanne H., CT, 1599
Goradia Charitable Foundation, Vijay and Marie, TX, 8871
Gordon Foundation, Betsy, The, CA, 617
Gordon Foundation, Inc., The, MD, 3805
Gorelick Family Foundation, William and Patricia, NC, 7215
Gorn Family Foundation, Inc., Stephen M., MD, 3806
Gorongosa Restoration Project, Inc., ID, 2631
Gospel Evangelism Foundation, PA, 8063
GPD Charitable Trust, FL, 2132
GPOA Foundation, LA, *see* 3637
Graff Irrevocable Trust, George H., FL, 2133
Gratis Foundation, NC, 7216
Gray Cary Foundation, The, MD, *see* 3781
Graybar Foundation, MO, 4898
Graziadio Foundation, George and Reva, CA, 620
Greater Round Rock Community Foundation, TX, 8873
Green Foundation, Daniel B. and Florence E., The, PA, 8070
Green Park Foundation, FL, 2136
Greenheck Foundation, B.A. and Esther, WI, 9856
Greenstein Family Foundation, WA, 9633
Griffiss Charitable Trust, James E., The, WI, 9857
Grim Foundation, S. T., NJ, *see* 5455
Gross Charitable Trust, Stella B., CA, 629
Guidry Foundation, Mark & Carolyn, NV, 5121
Gurwin Family Foundation, Inc., The, NJ, 5286
Gurwin Foundation Inc., J., NY, 6118
Gurwin Foundation, Inc., Joseph and Rosalind, NJ, *see* 5286
Gutin Charitable Foundation, Irving and Barbara C., FL, 2143

H. & Y. Charitable Foundation, Inc., NY, 6123
Habe Foundation, The, NY, 6125
Hagan Foundation, Cornelius and Lydiellen, WA, *see* 9634
Hagan Foundation, WA, 9634
Hagan Scholarship Foundation, The, MO, 4903
Hagan Trust, The, MO, 4904
Haller, Jr. Foundation, Henry E., FL, 2146
Hamer Foundation, The, PA, 8077
Hammersley Foundation, Frederick, NM, 5520
Hancock County Community Foundation, Inc., IN, 3313
HANDinHAND Christian Adoption, Inc., KS, 3517
Hankins Family Foundation Inc., Melville, The, NM, 5521
Hansen Charitable Foundation, William M. and Patricia A., IA, 3440
Hansen Foundation, Inc., NJ, 5291
Hanson Family Foundation, Alice G., IL, 2890
Hanson Family Foundation, WA, 9639
Hanson Foundation, Stanley E., The, CA, 653
Harder Declaration of Trust, Kenneth L., IL, 2891
Harman Family Foundation, CA, 656
Harman Foundation, Sidney and Jane, CA, *see* 656
Harnischfeger Industries Foundation, WI, *see* 9876
Harris Family Foundation, Matthew and Jennifer, NY, 6140
Harris Family Foundation, The, RI, 8402
Harris-Johnson Family Foundation, CA, 658
Harrison Foundation Trust, Francena T., NY, 6142
Harrison Foundation, Fred G., IL, 2894
Harte Charitable Foundation, TX, 8892
Hartford Family Fund Inc., Huntington, NY, *see* 5551
Hastings Community Foundation, Inc., NE, 5046
Hawkins Family Foundation, Russell and Diana, TX, 8895
Hayfields Foundation, OH, 7485
Head Family Charitable Foundation, PA, 8081
Healing Hearts & Nations, CA, 666
Hecker Family Foundation, MO, 4909
Heitman Foundation, Andrew David, MA, 4092

Helen's Hope Foundation, PA, 8087
Heller Foundation, Walter E., IL, 2904
Heman Foundation, Inc., Jane S., MT, 5012
Hench Foundation, John C., CA, 679
Henderson-Wessendorff Foundation, TX, 8901
Hendricks Charitable Foundation, John and Maureen, MD, 3813
Hendrickson Family Foundation, Carl R., IL, 2905
Hendrickson Foundation, Inc., Stephen J., The, MA, 4093
Henle Foundation, Joan C. & David L., The, NY, 6162
Henley Foundation, CA, 680
Hennings Foundation, Jeanette Bertea, The, CA, 681
Here to Help Foundation, MI, 4457
Heritage Foundation of First Security Federal Savings Bank, Inc., The, IL, 2907
Heritage Fund of Huntington County, Inc., IN, *see* 3324
Herr Foundation, The, IL, 2909
Herring Creek Foundation, Inc., NY, *see* 6390
Herrnstein Foundation Inc., Jim and Robin, The, NY, 6165
Hersey Foundation, MN, 4673
Hershaft Foundation, Arthur N., NY, 6167
Hershey Foundation, Jacob and Terese, TX, 8904
Hershman Family Foundation Inc., NY, 6168
Hertz Foundation Inc., The, NY, 6169
Herwaldt Foundation, CA, 684
Hesburgh-Yusko Scholars Foundation, The, NC, 7230
Higgins Foundation, Robert F., The, MA, 4096
Highland Vineyard Foundation, TN, *see* 8573
Hill Foundation, Lyda, The, TX, 8908
Hintz Family Fund, Inc., IL, 2911
Ho Foundation, C.K. & Kay, CA, 695
Hobbs Foundation, VA, 9454
Hochfelder Charitable Foundation, Inc., Peter & Stacy, NY, 6177
Hoffman Foundation, Jane and Michael, The, NY, 6181
Hollomon-Price Foundation, TX, 8914
Hollowell Foundation, Inc., WV, 9778
Hollowell-Ford Foundation, Inc., WV, *see* 9778
Hollywood Foreign Press Association Charitable Trust, CA, 701
Holman Foundation, Inc., NJ, 5301
Holthus Foundation, NE, 5052
Homan, Jr. Trust, B. H., IL, 2919
Hosser Scholarship Fund Trust, Edward Wagner and George, RI, 8406
Hubert Family Foundation, Inc., Ed & Joann, OH, 7495
Hughes Trust, Teresa F., HI, 2605
Hulston Family Foundation, The, MO, 4911
Hummingbird Foundation, Inc., NJ, 5309
Huntington County Community Foundation, Inc., IN, 3324
Hurd Foundation, Priscilla Payne, PA, 8101
Hurtt Family Foundation, CA, 716
Hutton & Jost Memorial Trust, PA, 8104

I Am A Leader Foundation, UT, 9328
i.am.angel Foundation, CA, 720
Icahn Foundation, Carl C., The, NY, 6204
Icarus Foundation, The, NY, *see* 5966
IGH Charitable Foundation, Inc., NJ, 5312
Ima/Mickey Family Foundation, OH, 7502
Imburgia Foundation Inc., IN, 3326
Indiana Charitable Trust, GA, 2488
Ingerman Foundation, Justin, PA, 8108
Inmaat Foundation, NY, 6209
Inman-Riverdale Foundation, SC, 8485
Inner Solutions Institute, VT, *see* 9372
Institute of Mental Hygiene of the City of New Orleans, LA, 3644
INTRUST Bank Charitable Trust, KS, 3522
Invisible Hand Foundation, Inc., The, GA, 2489
Inzlicht Heritage Foundation, The, NY, 6212

Jacobs Foundation, Paul and Stacy, CA, 740
Jacobsohn Foundation, Carol and Howard, MD, *see* 3819
Jacobsohn Foundation, Carol M., MD, 3819
JAF Foundation, NY, 6221
Jaffe Family Foundation, The, CA, 741
James Foundation, Inc., Thomas A. and Mary S., FL, 2169
James Foundation, Inc., William, The, FL, 2170
Janszen Charitable Trust, The, TX, 8930
JDH Family Foundation, CA, 746
Jeckyl Charitable Foundation, The, TN, 8586
Jeg's Quarter Mile Charities, OH, *see* 7507
Jegs Foundation, The, OH, 7507
Jenkins Charitable Trust, Tom H. and Anne H., The, OH, 7508
Jenkins Family Foundation, Matthew and Roberta, The, CA, 747
Jennings Family Foundation, Inc., The, MN, 4680
Jensen Foundation, Janet Jarie, TX, *see* 8677
Jewett Foundation, George F., The, MN, 4682
JHD Charity Foundation, The, NY, *see* 7107
Jiang Foundation, Yibing and Ping, NY, 6230
JKJ Charitable Foundation, TX, 8934
Johnson Charitable Foundation, Lowell N., IL, 2941
Johnson Custody Foundation, TN, *see* 8589
Johnson Family Foundation, Joe & Nan, TX, 8938
Johnson Foundation, Julie Ann, IL, 2943
Johnson Foundation, Keith & Nancy, The, TN, 8589
Johnson Foundation, Zach, IA, 3449
Johnson Street Foundation, The, NY, 6241
Johnson's Foundation, Willis and Reba, TN, 8590
Jones Family Foundation, Eugenie and Joseph, LA, 3645
Jones Foundation, PA, 8113
Jonesville Foundation, TX, 8946
Jordan Foundation, Arthur, IN, 3331
Jordan Foundation, Fred J. and Shirley H., PA, 8114
Joy Global Foundation, Inc., WI, 9876
Joynor Foundation Inc., Oluv C., DE, 1792
JRS Biodiversity Foundation, WA, 9656
Jubel Foundation, Henry A., The, MO, 4919
Justice for Athletes, CA, *see* 543

Kagi Foundation, Eleanor, The, NV, 5125
Kahlert Foundation, Inc., The, MD, 3822
Kahn Family Foundation, MI, *see* 4471
Kahn Foundation, D. Dan and Betty, The, MI, 4471
Kahn Foundation, Robert J, PA, 8115
Kalberer Foundation, Walter and Jean, The, OH, 7515
Kane Family Foundation, Inc., CO, 1435
Katz Family Foundation, The, PA, 8117
Kaufman Dance Foundation, Glorya, CA, 770
Kazma Family Foundation, FL, 2180
Kean Charitable Foundation Inc., Steven J. and Melissa C., TX, 8950
Kearns Foundation, William H., NY, 6265
Keefe Family Foundation, CT, 1619
Keeler Foundation, Robert T., OH, 7517
Keesal, Young & Logan Charitable Foundation, CA, 777
Keidan Family Foundation, Inc., NY, 6267
Kelly Family Foundation, CT, 1620
Kemp Foundation Inc, Barbara and Gil, The, NY, 6272
Kennedy Foundation, Ethel, FL, 2183
Kern Family Foundation, CO, 1438
Kerr Foundation Inc., The, OK, 7764
Kestenbaum Family Foundation, The, PA, 8121
Ketchum Charitable Foundation Inc., OK, 7765
Keys Family Foundation, Alicia, The, CA, 782
Kharis Foundation, TN, 8591
Khatib Foundation Inc., The, NY, 6278
Kienstra Foundation, Theodore A., The, MO, 4928
Kiernan Foundation, Peter and Eaddo, The, NY, 6279
Kiita Foundation, The, AZ, 130
Kim Foundation, Steve Y., The, CA, 785
Kimball Foundation, Horace A. Kimball and S. Ella, RI, 8410
Kinesis, Inc, PR, 8352
King Family Foundation, Jeffery & Cynthia, The, PA, 8126
King Trust, Annie Graham, AL, 44
Kingfisher Foundation, The, CA, 788
Kings Point Richmond Foundation, Inc., NY, *see* 6704
Kitsap Community Foundation, WA, 9659
Kittredge Foundation, The, MA, 4124
Klatskin Family Charitable Trust, Charles and Lynne, The, NJ, 5342
Kleiner Memorial Park Trust, Julius M., The, ID, 2635
KMB Charitable Foundation, AZ, 131
KMR Group Foundation, WA, 9660
Knapp Foundation Inc., The, NY, 6295
Knee Family Foundation, CA, 797
Knox Family Foundation, John and Linda, TX, *see* 8934
Kohler Foundation Inc., John M., WI, 9885
Kohn Foundation, Zichron Moshe Vesther, NY, 6301
Kolitz Foundation Inc., TX, 8968
Koman Family Foundation, Bill and Amy, MO, 4929
Kopf Family Foundation, NY, 6302
Kopf Foundation, Inc., NY, *see* 6302
Korth Family Foundation, Inc., The, MI, 4478
Koskovich Foundation, Jerome and Marlyce, MN, 4690
Kossak Foundation Inc., John & Evelyn, CT, 1623
Kramer Charitable Foundation, Milton A. & Charlotte R., OH, 7529
Krause Family Foundation, The, OH, 7530
Kreyling Charitable Foundation, Marcia Turner, IL, 2965
Kroh Charitable Trust, CO, 1442
Kuni Foundation, Wayne D. & Joan E., WA, 9662
Kushel Foundation, Gloria and Richard, NY, 6315

Labuda Family Foundation, NJ, *see* 5481
Lackner Family Foundation, NJ, 5354
Ladera Foundation, MA, 4133
Laffont Family Foundation, NY, 6319
Lai Foundation, Lily, CA, 810
Lamfrom Charitable Foundation, Marie, OR, 7863
Lamis Crown Foundation, Inc., FL, *see* 1998
Lamond Family Foundation, CA, 817
Landau Family Foundation, IL, 2966
Landry Charitable Foundation, G. Barrie, MA, 4134
Landy Family Foundation, NY, 6324
Larson Charitable Trust, Orville H. and Shirley I., IL, 2967
Larson Foundation, FL, 2203
Laurents Foundation, NY, *see* 6338
Laurents/Hatcher Foundation Inc, NY, 6338
Laurie Foundation for the Performing Arts, Inc., MO, 4933
Lauritzen Foundation, NE, 5061
Lauzier Scholarship Foundation, Paul, WA, 9668
Laverack Family Foundation, The, CT, 1625
Laverack Foundation, William and Cordelia, The, CT, *see* 1625
Lavin Family Foundation, Inc., The, DC, 1923
Learning Coalition, The, HI, 2610
Least Indeed Foundation, AZ, 132
Leducq Foundation for Cardiovascular Research, TX, 8976
Lee Charitable Fund, Quincy and Estine, TX, 8977
Lee Family Foundation, Inc., The, CT, 1626
Lee Family Foundation, Theodore and Doris, NV, 5127
Left Hand Foundation, CO, 1445
Lehrer Family Foundation, The, CA, 827
Lemons Charitable Trust, Jean, Jack, and Mildred, MO, 4935
Lender Family Foundation Inc., Murray, GA, 2501
Leshkowitz Memorial Foundation, Naftali Tzvi, NY, 6354
LeVecke Family Foundation, The, CA, 835
Levi, Ray & Shoup Foundation, IL, 2976
Levin Family Foundation, Donald, IL, 2978
Levine Family Charitable Trust, The, MA, 4142
Levine Foundation Inc., William S. & Ina, AZ, 133
Levine Foundation, William and Mildred, NY, 6359
Levitetz Family Foundation, Inc, FL, 2211
Levovitz Family Foundation Charitable Trust, Abraham and Marilyn, MA, 4143
Lewis Family Foundation, Richard H., CO, 1447
Lewis Family Foundation, Robert and Beverly, CA, 837
Lewis Foundation, TN, 8598
Lewis Scholarship Trust, J. Edward, IL, 2979
Lexington Community Foundation, NE, 5062
Libby-Dufour Fund, LA, 3648
Liddell Foundation, Robert Clay, OK, 7767
Liman Foundation, Inc., The, FL, 2216
Lincoln Fund, The, NY, 6368
Link Foundation, The, TX, 8986
Linked Foundation, CA, 842
Linville Family Foundation, NY, 6376
Liswhit Foundation, MA, 4150
Littauer Educational Trust, Helen Irwin, TX, 8988
Liu Foundation, Ernest and Joan, The, NY, 6381
Live Oak Foundation, TX, 8989
Locks Family Foundation, PA, *see* 8147
Locks Foundation, PA, 8147

Loeb Charitable Foundation, WA, 9672
Loeb Foundation, OH, 7544
Loeb, Jr. Foundation, John L., NY, 6385
Loewe Foundation, Inc., Frederick, NY, 6386
London Foundation Inc., FL, 2219
Lone Rock Foundation, Inc., The, NY, 6390
Lopatin Family Foundation, The, NY, 6392
Lord Foundation, Edward and Mary, NJ, 5365
Lord Foundation, Grogan, TX, 8992
Lored Foundation, MN, 4697
Loridans Foundation, Inc., Charles, GA, 2506
Lowitz Foundation, CA, 850
Lucas Foundation, Donald Lee and Sally Steadman, DE, 1808
Lunda Charitable Fund, Inc., WI, 9895
Lynch Foundation, The, MA, 4159
Lynton Foundation, The, NY, 6405
LZ Francis Foundation, OH, 7549

M&E Foundation, The, NY, 6407
Maas Foundation, MN, 4699
Macbea Foundation, The, OH, 7551
Mackenzie Foundation, Inc., Gloria C., FL, 2224
MacMillan Foundation, W. Duncan and Nivin, MN, 4700
MacMurray Foundation, Fred and June, The, CA, 867
Maddox Foundation, MS, 4834
Maddux Trust 819, Flora Ethel, IL, 2991
Maffei Foundation, CO, 1451
Maher Charitable Foundation, M. Brian and Sandra, NJ, *see* 5368
Maher Charitable Foundation, NJ, 5368
Main Street Community Foundation, CT, 1634
Maine Timberlands Charitable Trust, MA, 4160
Makioka Foundation, NY, 6421
Malool Family Foundation, Roy M., NH, 5180
Manasseh's Children, CA, 870
Mann-Paller Foundation, Inc., MD, 3839
Manning Family Foundation, VA, 9476
Mansueto Foundation, IL, 3000
Many Voices Foundation, NY, 6426
Mapes Charitable Trust, NE, 5066
Maranatha Charitable Foundation, The, CA, 871
March Foundation, The, CA, 872
Marian Wayside Shrine Foundation Inc., IN, 3347
Marquette Community Foundation, MI, *see* 4495
Marquette County Community Foundation, MI, 4495
Marriott Daughters Foundation, MD, 3840
Marsal Family Foundation, The, NY, 6438
Marsh Family Foundation, NJ, 5371
Marshall Foundation, Inc., Silver, NY, *see* 6295
Marten Charitable Trust, IN, 3349
Martha Gaines and Russell Wehrle Memorial Foundation, The, WV, 9783
Martin Family Foundation, Inc., Don and Faith, The, TX, 9002
Martin Family Foundation, Inc., FL, 2228
Martin Foundation, Gilbert J., The, CA, 882
Martino Family Foundation, The, CT, 1637
Marx Foundation, William, The, NY, 6442
Maryland Home & Community Care Foundation, MD, 3844
Matricaria Family Foundation, AZ, 142
Matthews Foundation, Jack M., The, VA, 9479
MAXIMUS Foundation, Inc., VA, 9481
May Foundation, Edwin and Jeanette, FL, 2230
May Foundation, Edwin J., The, FL, *see* 2230
Maya Relief Foundation, CA, 888
Mazel Charitable Trust, NY, 6450
McBean Foundation, Judith, The, CA, 893
McBride, Sr. Family Foundation, Arthur B., The, OH, 7562
McCain Institute Foundation, AZ, 143
McCarthy Foundation, Inc., Michael W., NY, 6456
McCaskey 2003 Charitable Trust, Raymond F. and Judith K., IL, 3009
McConnell Educational Foundation, The, OH, 7563
McDonald's Foundation, IL, 3012
McGlynn Family Foundation, MN, 4706
McIntyre Foundation, Shirley & William S., TX, 9016
McKinnell Foundation, Henry A., The, WY, 9985
McKinney Charitable Foundation, William V. and Catherine A., PA, 8168
McLeod Blue Skye Charitable Foundation, Inc., CT, 1641
McQueen Foundation, Adeline & George, IL, 3018
Mechanic Foundation, Inc., Morris A., MD, 3846
Medlock Trust, Mary L., IL, 3020
Meehan Foundation, NY, 6468
Mehra Family Foundation, The, NY, 6469
Meinders Foundation, The, OK, 7777
Meldrum Foundation, UT, 9333
MEMC Foundation, MO, *see* 4985
Memton Fund, Inc., The, DE, 1819
Mercer Trust, Martha Dana, RI, 8419
Merchants Fund, PA, 8175
Mercy Foundation, Inc., KY, 3589
Meredith Foundation, Edwin T., IA, 3464
Mericle Foundation, PA, 8176
Mesdag Family Foundation, The, NY, 6478
Miami County Foundation, OH, 7569
Middendorf Family Foundation, Frank J., RI, *see* 8420
Middendorf Family Foundation, RI, 8420
Milano Foundation, Inc., NJ, 5384
Milikowsky Family Foundation, Rebecca and Nathan, The, MA, 4176
Mill Foundation, Ltd., The, VT, 9367
Miller Center for Teaching America's Founding Principles and History, Jack, The, PA, 8179
Miller Charitable Foundation, Lou and Connie, OK, 7778
Miller Family Foundation, Glen and Wendy, IL, 3024
Miller Foundation, Hazel, WA, 9685
Miller Foundation, The, WA, 9686
Miller Trust, Pierson K., NY, 6486
Millstone Foundation, MO, 4944
Miner Charitable Foundation, Inc., IL, 3030
Mirman Family Foundation Trust, Stuart Frankel and Rita, The, IL, 3031
Mirmiran Foundation, The, MD, 3853
Mizel Foundation I, Flora and Morris, CO, 1461
Mizel Foundation II, Flora and Morris, CO, 1462
MKM Foundation, PA, 8185
Moca Foundation, The, CA, 932
Moffett Family Foundation, James R., The, LA, 3655
Moneygram Foundation, Inc, TX, 9032
Moore for Kids, NY, 6503
Mooty Foundation Trust, Jane N., MN, 4719
Mooty Foundation Trust, John W., MN, 4720
Moran Charitable Trust, John A., The, FL, 2242
Morby Family Charitable Foundation, Inc., The, FL, 2244
Morian Foundation, TX, 9039
Morris Family Foundation, OR, 7874
Morris Foundation, William C. and Susan F., The, NY, 6508
Morrison Center Endowment Foundation, Inc., ID, 2638
Morrow Family Foundation, Luke And Lori, TX, 9042
Morton Foundation, The, CA, 944
Morton-Kelly Charitable Trust, The, ME, 3701
Mosi Foundation, PA, 8189
Motorists Insurance Companies Foundation, The, OH, *see* 7581
Motorists Insurance Group Foundation, The, OH, 7581
Moulton Christmas Poor Fund, Judge C. F., MO, 4946
Mound Properties Inc., WI, 9910
Mount Pleasant Area Community Foundation, MI, 4512
Mount Pleasant Community Foundation, MI, *see* 4512
Moxie Foundation, Inc., The, CA, 950
MSJ Foundation, MI, 4513
Mule Family Foundation, NY, 6513
Mullen Family Foundation, The, PA, 8190, *see* 8190
Muller Charitable Foundation, Inc., Marisa, FL, *see* 2252
Munson Foundation, W. B., IL, 3045
Muskavitch Foundation, Charles & Gail, CA, 958
Myers Charitable Foundation, David G. & Carol P., MI, *see* 4515
Myers Foundation, David & Carol, MI, 4515
Myra Foundation, ND, 7355
Mys Family US Charitable Foundation Inc., NY, 6519

Naomi Prawer Kadar Foundation, Inc, The, NY, 6523
Nape Charities Fund, TX, 9049
Narrow Gate - A Charitable Foundation, The, CA, 960
Natembea Foundation, DE, 1822
Nathan Charitable Trust, Scott A., MA, 4188
National Endowment for Financial Education, CO, 1469
National Life Group Charitable Foundation, Inc., VT, 9368
Natural Gas Partners Foundation, TX, 9053
Nazarian Family Foundation, NY, 6530
Neda Foundation, The, DE, *see* 1823
Neeley Foundation, Lucille and Ronald, CA, 963
Neese Family Foundation, Inc., WI, 9911
NEFE, CO, *see* 1469
Nelson Foundation, The, IA, 3467
Neuman Foundation, Inc., Gerald David, NY, *see* 6540
New Albany Community Foundation, OH, 7589
New Beginning Resources, Inc., TX, 9057
New Brook Charitable Foundation, Inc., The, NY, 6540
New Hope Foundation, TX, 9058
New Horizons at Choate, Inc., MA, *see* 4003
New Tamarind Foundation, Inc., NY, 6541
New York Jets Foundation, Inc., NY, 6547
Newlin, Sr. Memorial Trust, Robert "Aqqaluk", AK, 88
Newman Family Foundation, Arthur and Eileen, The, VA, 9493
Newman Family Foundation, C. & R., CA, 967
Newman Foundation, Barnett and Annalee, The, NY, 6554
Newport Restoration Foundation, RI, 8423
Nextgen Foundation Charitable Trust, The, MD, 3858
Niblack Foundation, The, CT, 1653
Nicholas Family Charitable Trust, NY, 6557
Nielsen Foundation, Inc., Donald E., NE, 5073
Night Owl Foundation, IL, 3057
Nirman Foundation, VA, 9495
Nobari Foundation, Neda, DE, 1823
Nommontu Foundation, Inc., The, FL, 2252
Northwest Connecticut Community Foundation, Inc., CT, *see* 1565
Northwest Florida Improvement Foundation, Inc., FL, *see* 2331
Nova Foundation, Inc., NV, 5135
Novotny Charitable Trust, Yetta Deitch, PA, 8202
Nutting Foundation, The, WV, 9788
Nygren Charitable Foundation, William & Sara, IL, *see* 3060
Nygren Foundation, Bill, IL, 3060
Nylen Foundation, Inc., Mark and Mary Ellen, The, SD, 8517

O'Connor Family Foundation, NY, 6577
O'Hare Family Private Foundation, The, TX, 9068
O'Keeffe Charitable Foundation, Esther B., FL, 2254
O'Neill Foundation, Timothy J. and Linda D., The, NY, 6591
O'Rourke Family Charitable Trust, Dr. William James And Winifred Joyce, MN, 4733
Ocular Physiology Research and Education Foundation, Inc., WI, 9915
Ohana Foundation, Thomas, CA, 983
Old Boys Foundation, The, NY, 6586
Omer Foundation, NY, 6590
One World Fund, MA, 4198
OneFamily Foundation, WA, 9695
OneWorld Boston, Inc., MA, 4199
Opus Community Foundation, CA, 989
Oracle Education Foundation, CA, 991
Oracle Help Us Help Foundation, CA, *see* 991
Orr Family Foundation, DE, 1827
Orthodox Vision Foundation, CA, 995
Ory Charitable Trust, Linda Hammett & Andrew, The, MA, 4200
Oshkosh Corporation Foundation, Inc., WI, 9917
Oshkosh Truck Foundation, Inc., WI, *see* 9917
Oshman Foundation, TX, 9074
Ossen Family Foundation, Jeffrey P., CT, 1664
Oster Family Foundation, Inc., NJ, 5399
Overdeck Family Foundation, Inc., NY, 6605
Owens Foundation, Inc., William & Catherine, The, VA, 9503
Owsley Brown Ii Cockayne Fund, Inc., KY, 3595
Oxley Foundation, Mary K., OK, 7784
Oxnard Foundation, CA, 1001

Pagel Foundation, Jack W., MN, *see* 4736
Pagel Foundation, MN, 4736
Paiko Foundation, The, FL, 2255
Pangborn Trust, Thomas W., PA, 8211

Panoram Foundation Inc., CT, 1667
Pappajohn Scholarship Foundation, John & Mary, IA, 3472
Pardoe Foundation, Samuel P., MA, 4206
Park City Foundation, The, UT, 9341
Parke Foundation, Jim and Shirley, NY, 6616
Parmer Family Foundation Inc., PA, 8212
Parrish Foundation, Robert J. Harriet A. and David T., IN, 3367
Partnership Foundation, The, TX, 9082
Pasquerilla Foundation, Frank J. & Sylvia T., PA, 8213
Pastega Family Foundation, Mario and Alma, OR, 7879
Patel Foundation, Dinesh and Kalpana, UT, 9343
Pathways in Education, Inc., CA, 1019
Patterson Foundation, Cissy, The, SC, 8489
Patterson Foundation, The, FL, 2261
Patton Trust, George William, TX, 9085
Pay it Forward Foundation, The, CT, 1670
PB&K Family Foundation, CO, 1474
Pediatric Epilepsy Research Foundation, TX, 9087
Pelling Foundation Inc., Patricia G., GA, 2527
Pema Foundation, Inc., CO, 1476
Penn Treaty Special Services District, PA, 8217
Penseco Foundation, PA, see 8218
Penske Foundation, Inc., MI, 4519
Peoples Federal Savings Bank Charitable Foundation, MA, 4212
Peoples Security Charitable Foundation, PA, 8218
Pere Foundation, Kors Le, The, DE, 1833
Perforce Foundation, CA, 1026
Perles Family Foundation, Claudia and Steven, FL, 2266
Pershing Place Foundation, MO, 4953
Petersen Foundation, Esper A., IL, 3078
Peterson Foundation, Mark and Nancy, The, UT, 9345
Petway Family Foundation Inc., FL, 2268
Pfeiffer Research Foundation, Gustavus and Louise, NJ, 5405
Phillips Foundation, Waite and Genevieve, NM, 5531
Phillips-Green Foundation, Inc., MA, 4219
Phoenix Family Foundation, NJ, see 5259
Piece by Piece Productions Inc, NY, 6640
Piedmont Community Foundation, VA, 9509
Pincus Foundation, Claudio and Penny, NJ, 5407
Pindaros Foundation, Inc., The, NY, 6641
Pine River Foundation, The, MN, 4742
Pioneer Hi-Bred International, Inc. Foundation, IA, 3474
Piper Jaffray Foundation, MN, 4743
Piqua-Miami County Foundation, OH, see 7569
Pitkin Foundation Inc., Winifred M. & George P., NJ, 5408
Plankenhorn Foundation Inc., Harry, PA, 8229
Plansoen Charitable Trust, Louis M., NC, 7286
Plaza De Panama Committee, CA, 1040
Pletka Foundation, Kronhill, The, NY, 6646
Plitt Trust, Clarence Manger & Audrey Cordero, MD, 3862
Plumeri Foundation, Inc., Joe, NY, 6649
Plymouth Rock Foundation, The, MA, 4222
Pocono Charitable Foundation, The, AZ, 154
Poe Charitable Trust, Parker, GA, 2531
Pomegranate Foundation, MA, 4223
Poonai Charitable Foundation, Inc., Anila Sarswati and Parmanand Vijay, FL, 2271
Popular Community Bank Foundation, IL, 3085
Posey Family Foundation, TX, 9104
Posner Foundation, Inc., Gene & Ruth, WI, 9922
Prairie Creek Partners Charitable Foundation, DE, 1838
Prairie Foundation, The, TX, 9106
Prentice Foundation, The, TX, 9107
Price Family Foundation, Julian, DE, 1841
Princeton Regional Chamber of Commerce Foundation, Inc., NJ, 5412
Prins Foundation, Vivian G., NY, 6660
Proctor Charitable Foundation, Elizabeth Craig Weaver, TN, 8617
Prophet Corporation Foundation, The, MN, see 4680
Pruet Foundation, The, MS, 4842
Psalm 67 Foundation, The, AL, 60
Public Life Foundation of Owensboro, KY, 3597
Pulier Charitable Foundation Inc., Benjamin & Seema, NY, 6665
Pulliam Charitable Trust, Myrta J., IN, 3371
Purcell Charitable Foundation, IL, 3101
Puth Family Foundation, The, NY, 6668
Puth Foundation, John and Betsey, NY, see 6668
PWH Educational Foundation Inc., WA, 9706

Quinlan Foundation, Walter S., NH, 5187

Radif Chesed Foundation, NY, 6671
Ragon Foundation, Phillip and Susan, MA, 4228
Rainbow Foundation, The, RI, 8428
Ramsey Family Foundation Trust, TN, 8621
Randa Foundation, NY, 6676
Randall Family Foundation, The, CA, 1054
Rangos Charitable Foundation, John G., PA, 8244
Rapier Family Foundation, TX, 9121
Ratcliffe Foundation, Inc., Philip E. and Carole R., FL, 2278
Ratner Family Foundation, Horowitz, The, DE, 1846
Rautenberg Foundation, Erwin, The, CA, 1056
Regal Foundation Inc., FL, 2283
Reid Family Foundation, Robert and Jean, IL, 3112
Reinhart Foundation, CA, see 888
Remondi Family Foundation, MA, 4237
Resnick Foundation, Burton P. and Judith B., The, NY, 6689
Ressler Family Foundation, The, CA, 1065
Reynolds Family Foundation, NY, 6694
Reynolds Foundation, Gilmore & Golda, IN, 3376
Richards Family Foundation, GA, 2538
Richards Foundation, Inc., The, GA, 2539
Richards Private Foundation, Murray and Harriet, IL, 3117
Richards Scholarship Fund, Mabel Wilson, The, CA, 1068
Richards, Jr. Foundation for Charitable Giving, Roy, GA, see 2539
Richmond Children's Foundation, CA, see 1069
Richmond Community Foundation, CA, 1069
Richmond Foundation Inc., Anita B. and Howard S., The, NY, 6704
Rick L. and Vicki L .James Foundation Inc., IN, 3377
Ricketts Conservation Fund, CO, 1486
Rifkin Family Foundation, IN, 3378
Rimora Foundation, The, VA, 9522
Ring Foundation, CA, 1075
Ripley County Community Foundation, Inc., IN, 3379
Risen Son Foundation, Inc., MS, 4845
Rivera Foundation, Mariano, DE, 1850
Rizavi Friedland Foundation, Inc., NY, see 6834
RNR Foundation, Inc., MI, 4527
Robbins Family Foundation, The, CT, 1681
Robbins Foundation, Inc., CT, see 1681
Roberts Charitable Foundation, Gilroy & Lillian P., PA, 8250
Roberts Family Foundation, Inc, J. David and Kathleen A., FL, 2290
Robertson Foundation for Government Inc., NJ, 5424
Robinson Foundation, Inc., Jim and Linda, The, NY, 6720
Robinson Fund, Maurice R., IL, 3122
Rock Springs Foundation, The, MD, 3870
Roehm Charitable Trust, IN, 3380
Rohr Foundation, Inc., George, The, NY, 6730
Rominger Foundation, Phil & Gerry, The, NC, 7306
Root Family Foundation, FL, 2293
Roots and Wings, WA, 9720
Rose Family Foundation, NY, 6731
Rose Family Foundation, Stuart, OH, 7636
Rose Shield Fund, The, NY, see 6751
Roseman Foundation, Inc., Ephraim, KY, 3599
Rosenblatt Charitable Trust, The, NY, 6744
Rosenfeld Foundation, Inc., Max & Morton M., The, NY, 6747
Rosenwald Fund, Alice, NY, 6751
Ross Foundation Inc., Billie and George, NY, 6755
Rossin Foundation, PA, 8256
Rostrust Foundation, NY, 6756
Roth Family Foundation, Florence and Bernard B., The, CA, 1094
Rothberg Family Charitable Foundation for Children's Diseases, FL, 2297
Rotter Family Foundation, Steven J. and Robin, NY, 6757
Rouha Education & Welfare Foundation Inc., AZ, 160
Rubin Family Foundation, PA, 8257
Rudd Family Foundation, CA, 1096
Ruggles Family Foudation, IL, 3127
Rupp Foundation, Richard W., The, NY, 6771
RuthMarc Foundation, Inc., The, NJ, 5431

Saada Foundation, TX, 9142
Sackler Foundation, Arthur M., The, NY, 6777
Sadler Family Foundation, TX, 9143
Salem Lutheran Foundation, OH, 7641
Salta Foundation, Mike and Jan, CA, 1105
Samaritan Foundation, OH, 7642
Samerian Foundation, Inc., IN, 3384
Samuelson Foundation, Inc., Herman & Walter, MD, 3879
San Antonio Foundation for Excellence in Education, TX, 9149
Sanders Family Foundation, Don A., TX, 9152
Sangham Foundation, CA, 1114
Sapirstein Foundation of Cleveland, Jacob, The, OH, see 7644
Sapirstein-Stone-Weiss Foundation, OH, 7644
Sapp Family Foundation, The, NY, 6796
Sasco Foundation Corporation, TN, 8623
Satterberg Foundation, WA, 9728
Saul Foundation, Inc., Helen and Harry, GA, 2547
Scaife Scholarship Foundation, CA, 1120
Schalon Foundation, The, MI, 4534
Schear Family Foundation Inc., Lee and Patti, OH, 7645
Scheef Family Foundation, The, TX, see 9196
Schimmel Foundation, Inc., Stephen Harold, The, CA, 1122
Schmitt Foundation, Inc., Kilian J. and Caroline F., The, NY, 6808
Schmitz Family Foundation, CO, 1493
Schoeneckers Foundation, MN, 4759
Schonberger Family Foundation, Inc., A. and R., NY, 6812
Schott Foundation, Joseph J., OH, 7652
Schottenstein Foundation C, Saul, OH, 7655
Schultz Foundation, Ken & Carol, AZ, 161
Seal United Methodist Church Trust, Leo W., LA, 3667
Seaver Charitable Trust, Richard C., CA, 1132
Sebonack Foundation, NY, 6826
Seiger Family Foundation, The, CA, 1137
Selander Foundation, The, CT, 1693
Seme Foundation, Inc., TN, 8626
Semlitz/Glaser Foundation, NY, 6831
Sence Foundation, CA, 1141
Servant Leadership Foundation, The, CO, 1497
Seven Turns Fund, Inc., NY, 6834
Seymour Trust, George Dudley, RI, 8436
Shaffer Family Foundation, CA, 1145
Shanken Family Foundation, NY, 6837
Shannon Family Foundation, Ken and Jan, The, KS, 3545
Sharks Foundation, The, CA, 1153
Shea Company Foundation, J.F., CA, 1155
Shearwater Foundation Inc., VA, 9531
Shelton Foundation, The, NC, 7310
Sheridan Family Foundation, Dr. Howard and Brenda, NJ, 5452
Shiebler Family Foundation, MN, 4762
Shiley Foundation, The, CA, 1157
Shiloh Foundation, The, PA, 8283
Shin Foundation, Patrick N. C., The, HI, 2616
Shinn Foundation, Inc., George, TN, 8627
Shoemaker Fund, Thomas H. and Mary Williams, The, PA, 8284
Shtesl Family Foundation, The, NY, 6849
Shumway Foundation, Helen and Ritter, RI, 8439
Sidewalk Angels Foundation, NY, 6852
Sidgmore Family Foundation, MD, 3885
Sidwell Family Foundation, Jeff and Jennie, The, OH, 7662
Sierra Foundation Inc., NJ, 5455
Silk Family Foundation, The, CA, 1167
Silverstein Family Foundation, Inc., Raine & Stanley, The, NY, 6856
Simmons Family Foundation, R. P., PA, 8285
Simon Foundation, Lucille Ellis, CA, 1170
Simon-Strauss Foundation, CA, 1172
Simonian Foundation, Sam and Sylva, TX, 9176

Simple Actions Family Foundation, OR, 7889
Singhal Foundation, The, MA, *see* 3983
Sit Foundation, Eugene C. and Gail V., The, MN, 4764
Sitt 1986 Charitable Trust, Joseph Jack, NY, 6866
Slater Foundation, The, CO, 1502
Small Change Foundation, The, CA, 1180
SMBC Global Foundation Inc., NY, 6873
Smeed Memorial Foundation, ID, 2644
Smith and John G. Berylson Charitable Foundation, Amy, MA, 4276
Smith Charitable Trust, Christine and Lawrence, PA, 8287
Smith Family Foundation, Will and Jada, CA, 1184
Smith Foundation, Hoxie Harrison, PA, 8289
Smith Foundation, Matthew & Tracy, The, NY, 6875
Smith Foundation, The, PA, *see* 8289
Smith Foundation, Will, CA, *see* 1184
Smith Scholarship Foundation, Inc., J. Craig and Page T., AL, 67
Smithville Charitable Foundation, IN, 3388
Snow Family Private Foundation, Inc., Kerri and Jeffrey, The, GA, 2553
Snyder Foundation, Harold B. and Dorothy A., The, NJ, 5462
Solomon Wilson Family Foundation, Inc., The, NY, 6887
Sonoco Foundation, SC, 8500
South Jersey Charitable Foundation, NJ, 5463
South Jersey Savings Charitable Foundation, NJ, *see* 5463
South Lake County Community Foundation, Inc., FL, *see* 2039
Southeastern Illinois Community Foundation, IL, 3169
Spangenberg Family Foundation to Benefit Childrens Education and Healthcare, TX, 9193
Spark Charitable Foundation, WA, 9741
Sparkplug Foundation, The, NY, 6894
Sparks Foundation, John and Polly, The, CT, 1699
Sparks Foundation, The, TN, 8629
Spartan Stores Foundation, MI, 4544
Spearman Foundation, Grace Helen, The, CA, 1201
Spencer Foundation Inc., Mary M. and Sash A., FL, 2329
Spingold Foundation, Inc., Nate B. and Frances, NY, *see* 6899
Spingold Foundation, Inc., The, NY, 6899
SS Foundation, TX, 9196
St. Agnes Catholic Education Foundation, MN, 4769
St. Faith's House Foundation, NY, 6903
St. Joe Community Foundation Inc., The, FL, 2331
St. Marys Community Foundation, OH, 7672
Stache Charitable Trust, Emil J., CA, 1209
Stefanski Charitable Foundation, Ben S. & Gerome R., OH, *see* 7675
Stefanski Charitable Foundation, Marc A. and Rhonda L., The, OH, 7675
Stein Family Foundation, FL, *see* 2337
Stein Foundation Inc., David A., FL, 2337
Stephens Foundation, Gerald D. & Helen M., IL, 3176
Sterling Charitable Foundation, Donald T., The, CA, 1218
Sterling Family Foundation, TX, 9202
Stern Foundation, Joyce C., The, NY, 6929
Sternberg Charitable Trust, NY, 6930
Stevenson Family Charitable Trust, MA, 4290
Stevenson Foundation, Inc., Bruce and Mary, WA, 9743
Stevenson Foundation, Inc., Mary Hoyt, WA, *see* 9743
Steward Family Foundation, MO, 4981
Stewart Family Foundation, Sam & Diane, The, DE, 1862
Stewart Foundation, Genevieve McMillan-Reba, The, MA, 4291
Stewart Foundation, IL, 3178
Stifler Family Foundation, MA, 4292
Stiller Family Foundation, VT, 9372
Stone Family Foundation, Inc., Michael and Karen, The, DE, 1863
Storz Foundation, Robert Herman, NE, 5086
Stratton Foundation, PA, 8304
Stratus Foundation, DE, 1864
Strear Family Foundation, Inc., The, CO, 1508
Stuart Family Foundation, Inc., The, NY, 6937
Stumberg Foundation, Louis H. and Mary Patricia, TX, 9210
Sudireddy Foundation, Inc., MA, 4300
Suffolk Foundation, VA, 9538
Sugarbaker Foundation, Everett D. and Geneva V., MO, 4984
Sullivan Family Foundation, The, NY, 6941
Sullivan Family Fund, FL, 2343
Sullivan Foundation, Pike and Susan, WY, 9994
Sumitomo Bank Global Foundation, NY, *see* 6873
SunEdison Foundation, MO, 4985
Sunnyside Foundation, TN, *see* 8645
SunTrust Bank Charitable Trust, FL, 2345
Susquehanna Pfaltzgraff Foundation, PA, 8310
Sutton Foundation, Inc., Albert & Melissa, NY, 6950
SVF Foundation, RI, 8444
SVL Foundation, AZ, 168
SWBC Foundation, TX, 9217
Sweeney Foundation, Jake and Jeanne, The, FL, 2346

Tahari Family Foundation, The, NY, 6958
Tanimura Family Foundation, The, CA, 1236
Tarica Foundation, Pamela and Laurence, The, NY, 6965
Tartaglino-Richards Foundation, TX, 9221
Taubman Foundation for the Arts, VA, 9540
Taubman Foundation, Herman P. and Sophia, OK, 7804
Tauck Family Foundation, Inc., CT, 1706
Tauck Foundation, Inc., The, CT, *see* 1706
Taunton Female Charitable Association, MA, 4304
Taylor Charitable Trust, Jack DeLoss, WI, 9955
Teach A Man To Fish Foundation, CA, 1242
Teach Foundation, SC, 8505
TEAM Foundation, MN, 4779
Tecovas Foundation, PA, 8312
Tenenbaum Foundation, AR, 206
Texas Pioneer Arts Foundation, TX, *see* 8739
Thank Heaven Foundation, TX, 9229
Thatcher Foundation, CA, 1248
Theobald Foundation, NY, 6974
Thewes Family Foundation, MI, 4554
Thompson Foundation, The, WA, 9752
Thompson-Hartford Foundation, Inc., FL, 2359
Three Guineas Fund, CA, 1254
Tippit Charitable Trust, C. Carlisle and Margaret M., The, OH, 7685
Tisch Family Foundation, Lizzie and Jonathan, The, NY, 6984
Tisch Foundation, Wilma S. and Laurence A., The, NY, 6992
Toan-O'Brien Foundation, NM, 5536
Tointon Family Foundation, The, CO, 1513
Tollefson Family Foundation, Louise B. Blackman, FL, 2361
Tomar Foundation, Inc., NC, *see* 7306
TomKat Foundation, CA, 1257
Torch Foundation, Jordan, PA, 8318
Toshiba America Foundation, NY, 6997
Total Depth Foundation, MN, 4781
Touchpoint Foundation, NJ, 5481
Travis Foundation, Jeanette, TN, 8637
Travis Foundation, NY, 7004
Trio Foundation, IL, 3191
Trone Family Foundation, David and June, The, MD, 3899
Truman Foundation, Mildred Faulkner, NY, 7007
Tu Foundation, John and Mary, CA, 1265
Tuffli Family Foundation, The, CA, 1266
Tuscola County Community Foundation, MI, 4562
Tyler Perpetual Trust, Alice C., WA, 9755
Tyrrell Foundation, Inc., The, WY, 9996
Tzedakah Fund, The, MD, 3900

U.S. Bancorp Piper Jaffray Companies Foundation, MN, *see* 4743
Ujala Foundation, PA, 8323
Union County Community Foundation, Inc., AR, 208
Union Plus Education Foundation, DC, 1953
United Plankton Charitable Trust, CA, 1272
United Ten Foundation, Inc., The, NY, 7020
Universal Foundation, Inc., The, FL, *see* 2268
University Industry Research Corp., MA, 4314

Vague Foundation, Richard, The, PA, 8326
Vair Trust, Frances Bean, OH, 7693
Valley Community Foundation, CT, 1714
Valley Foundation, The, CA, 1279
Van Devender Family Foundation, MS, 4847
Van Devender Foundation, MS, *see* 4847
van Dijk Foundation, Pieter and Yvette Eenkema, CT, 1715
Van Houten Memorial Fund, Edward W. and Stella C., The, NC, 7330
Van Noord Foundation, Andrew and Gladys, MI, 4571
Van Voorhis Family Foundation, FL, 2369
Vanhoose Stewart Foundation, Inc., KY, 3604
Vanneck-Bailey Foundation, FL, 2370
Ventas Charitable Foundation, Inc., KY, 3605
Vernon Foundation, Inc., Miles Hodsdon, The, NY, 7026
Vibrant Village Foundation, The, OR, 7898
Vidalakis Family Foundation, CA, 1290
Viking Global Foundation Inc., CT, 1717
Viropharma Charitable Foundation, PA, 8328
Voice of Peace Foundation, Inc., IL, 3207
Voice of Peace, Inc., IL, *see* 3207
Volcker Family Foundation, Inc., The, NY, 7035
Volgenau Charitable Foundation, The, VA, 9549
Volo Non Valeo Foundation Inc., IN, 3395
Volpert Foundation, Barry and Teri, NY, 7036
von der Heyden Family Foundation, The, NY, 7037
Vortex Foundation, OH, 7696
Voss Charitable Trust, Omer G. & Annabelle K., The, CA, *see* 1292
Voss Family Foundation, Omer G., The, CA, 1292

Waldorf Educational Foundation, The, PA, 8330
Walentas Foundation, Ltd., NY, 7042
Wallace Charitable Memorial Foundation, Inc., Fred & Alice, OH, 7700
Walter Family Trust, Byron L., IL, 3213
Wang Family Charitable Foundation, The, NY, 7047
Warnack Foundation, The, CA, 1297
Wasserman Family Foundation, Alvin and Edith, The, MI, 4576
WaterWheel Foundation, The, VT, 9376
WCA Charitable Foundation, KY, 3606
Weaver Foundation, William M., TX, 9261
Webb Charitable Trust, Frank K., MO, 4999
Webb Family Charitable Foundation, Maynard and Irene, The, CA, *see* 1303
Webb Family Foundation, CA, 1303
Wehrle Foundation, H.B., WV, 9797
Weisberg Family Foundation, Inc., Arthur and Joan, WV, 9798
Weiser Family Foundation, MN, 4798
Weitzman Family Foundation, NJ, 5497
Weller Foundation, Inc., The, NE, 5093
Wells Foundation, Franklin H. & Ruth L., NY, 7073
Wells Foundation, Terry Lee, NV, 5157
Wentcher Educational Fund, Ernest, IL, 3226
West Foundation, Inc., IN, 3404
Whispering Fox Foundation, CO, 1522
White Horse Youth Ranch, NV, 5158
Whitehead Foundation, Joseph B., GA, 2571
Whitener Family Foundation, TX, 9275
Whitlock Foundation, W.W., VA, 9556
Whitwell-Meyer Foundation, The, OK, 7813
Wiegand Morning Star Foundation, Inc., PA, 8337
Wiegers Family Foundation, The, NY, 7082
Wight Foundation, Inc., The, NJ, 5501
Wildcat Foundation, The, TX, 9278
Wildflower Foundation, FL, 2386
Willett Charitable Foundation, William Gerald, The, VA, 9557
Williams Foundation, C. K., The, PA, 8338
Williams Foundation, Sara & Evan, CA, 1326
Wilson Charitable Trust "A", L.E., NC, 7337
Wilson Charitable Trust, Blair J., TN, 8645
Windom, Judy, GA, *see* 2539
Wine and Art Educational Foundation, Jan and Mitsuko, The, CA, 1330
Winston Hope Foundation, Inc., Harry, NY, 7093
Winters Family Fund, The, NY, 7094
Wishes By Wyndham Foundation, NJ, 5506
WLC and SBC Family Foundation, NY, 7096
Wohlgemuth Herschede Foundation, The, OH, 7718
Wolfe Foundation, Betty K., The, FL, 2391
Wolff Family Foundation, Jean & Lewis, MI, 4590
Wolff Foundation, Cyvia and Melvyn, TX, 9286

FOUNDATION NAME INDEX

Numbers following the foundation names refer to the entry sequence numbers in the Descriptive Directory section. The letter "A" following a name refers to Appendix A, which lists foundations that appeared in the previous edition of the *Directory* but no longer qualify.

Albert Charitable Trust, Anne & Leo N., FL, 1964
Albert Foundation, Sidney and Beatrice, NY, 5567
Albertson Foundation, Inc., J. A. & Kathryn, ID, 2626
Albion Civic Foundation, MI, *see* 4332
Albion Community Foundation, MI, 4332
Albrecht Family Charitable Foundation, The, MO, 4850
Albrecht Foundation, Lanie, The, HI, 2585
Albuquerque Community Foundation, NM, 5511
Albuquerque Public Library, NM, 5512
Alcatel-Lucent Foundation, NJ, 5190
Alchemy Foundation, The, MA, 3920
Alcoa Foundation, PA, 7908
Alcoholic Beverage Medical Research Foundation, MD, *see* 3714
Alcon Foundation, Inc., The, TX, 8655
Alden Trust, George I., The, MA, 3921
Alderbaugh Foundation, PA, 7909
Aleut Foundation, The, AK, 80
Alexander & Baldwin Foundation, HI, A
Alexander Charitable Foundation, Inc., WI, 9802
Alexander Eastman Foundation, NH, 5162
Alexander Family Foundation, The, NY, 5568
Alexander Foundation, Inc., Joseph, PA, 7910
Alexander Foundation, Inc., Judd S., WI, 9803
Alexander Foundation, Inc., Leslie L., FL, 1965
Alexander Foundation, Inc., NY, 5569
Alexander Foundation, Stanford & Joan, The, TX, 8656
Alexandria Community Trust, VA, *see* 9380
Alexion Complement Foundation, CT, 1533
Alfa Foundation, AL, 2
ALFA Foundation, The, CT, 1534
Alfiero Family Charitable Foundation, NY, 5570
Alfond Foundation, Harold, ME, 3678
Alfond Foundation, William and Joan, The, ME, 3679
Alfond Foundation, William L., ME, *see* 3679
Alice Manufacturing Company, Inc. Foundation, SC, *see* 8486
Alison Foundation, NY, 5571
Alix Foundation, Jay & Maryanne, MI, *see* 4333
Alix Foundation, The, MI, 4333
Alkek and Williams Foundation, The, TX, 8657
Alkek Foundation, Albert and Margaret, TX, 8658
All the Way Foundation, NY, 5572
Allchin Foundation, WA, *see* 9746
Allegan County Community Foundation, MI, 4334
Allegan County Foundation, MI, *see* 4334
Alleghany Foundation, The, VA, 9382
Allegheny Foundation, PA, 7911
Allegis Group Foundation, Inc., MD, 3719
Allegretti Foundation, Inc., Fred & Jean, IL, 2655
Allen Charitable Foundation, Andrew, The, WY, 9973
Allen Family Charitable Foundation, OK, 7727
Allen Family Foundation, Bill and Sharon, NC, 7134
Allen Family Foundation, Inc., The, NY, 5573
Allen Family Foundation, Paul G., The, WA, 9567
Allen Foundation, Herbert, The, NY, 5574
Allen Foundation, IL, 2656
Allen Foundation, Inc., MI, 4335
Allen Foundation, Inc., Rita, NJ, 5191
Allen Institute for Artificial Intelligence, WA, 9568
Allendale Insurance Foundation, RI, *see* 8393
Allende Foundation, Isabel, The, CA, 227
Allergan Foundation, The, CA, 228
Allerton Foundation, Inc., The, PA, 7912
Alliance Healthcare Foundation, CA, 229
Alliant Energy Foundation, Inc., WI, 9804
Allison Family Foundation, Inc., The, CT, *see* 1535
Allison Foundation Inc., CT, 1535
Allison, Jr. Family Foundation, Carolyn J. and Robert J., The, TX, 8659
Alliss Educational Foundation, Charles and Ellora, MN, *see* 4600
Alliss Educational Foundation, MN, 4600
Allmerica Financial Charitable Foundation, Inc., MA, *see* 4086
Allstate Foundation, The, IL, 2657
Allwin Family Foundation, The, CT, 1536
Allyn Foundation, Inc., NY, 5575
Almar Foundation, The, LA, 3610
Almi Foundation, Inc., WA, 9569
Aloha Foundation, MA, 3922
Alper Family Foundation, NY, 5576
Alpern Family Foundation, Inc., NY, 5577
Alpert & Alpert Foundation, The, CA, 230
Alpert Family Foundation, Inc., The, NY, 5578
Alpert Foundation, Herb, The, CA, 231
Alpert Foundation, Raymond and Barbara, CA, 232
Alpert Foundation, Warren, RI, 8355
Alpha & Omega Family Foundation, SD, *see* 8518
Alpha Foundation, Inc., AL, 3
Alpha Omega Foundation, Inc., MN, *see* 4614
Alphawood Foundation, IL, 2658
Alro Steel Foundation, The, MI, 4336
ALSAM Foundation, The, UT, 9302
Alsdorf Foundation, IL, 2659
Altec/Styslinger Foundation, AL, 4
Altman Family Foundation, Lisa & Steve, The, CA, 233
Altman Foundation, Inc., Jeffrey A., The, NY, 5580
Altman Foundation, Jenifer, The, CA, 234
Altman Foundation, Jonathan & Kathleen, NM, 5513
Altman Foundation, NY, 5579
Altman/Kazickas Foundation, NY, 5581
Altschul Foundation, The, NY, 5582
Altus One Fund, Inc., The, NY, 5583
Alumni Achievement Awards, Inc., TN, 8527
Alvarez Educational and Charitable Foundation Inc., The, NY, 5584
Amado Foundation, Maurice, CA, 235
Amar Foundation, CA, 236
Amarillo Area Foundation, Inc., TX, 8660
Amateur Athletic Foundation of Los Angeles, CA, *see* 809
Amaturo Family Foundation, Inc., The, FL, 1966
Ameren Corporation Charitable Trust, MO, 4851
America's Children's Fund, NY, *see* 6503
American Academy & Institute of Arts and Letters, NY, *see* 5585
American Academy of Arts and Letters, NY, 5585
American Art Foundation, Inc., The, NY, 5586
American Center Foundation, NY, *see* 6002
American Century Companies Foundation, MO, *see* 4852
American Century Investments Foundation, MO, 4852
American Contemporary Art Foundation, Inc., The, NY, *see* 5586
American Electric Power Foundation, OH, 7368
American Express Charitable Fund, NY, 5587
American Express Foundation, NY, 5588
American Fidelity Corporation Founders Fund, Inc., OK, *see* 7728
American Fidelity Foundation, OK, 7728
American Foundation Corporation, The, OH, 7369
American Foundation for Basic Research in Israel, NY, 5589
American Foundation for Courtesy and Grooming, NY, *see* 6356
American Friends of Tenuvas Sadie, NY, 5590
American Greetings Foundation, Inc., OH, 7370
American Honda Foundation, CA, 237
American Memorial Hospital, Inc., MA, 3923
American Savings Foundation of Connecticut, Inc., CT, *see* 1537
American Savings Foundation, CT, 1537
American Snuff Charitable Trust, TN, 8528
Americana Foundation, MI, 4337
AMERIGROUP Foundation, VA, 9383
Ameritas Charitable Foundation, NE, 5023
AmerUs Group Charitable Foundation, IA, *see* 3411
Ames Family Foundation, The, OH, *see* 7371
Ames Family Foundation, WA, 9570
Ames Foundation, B. Charles and Jay G., OH, 7371
Ames Foundation, Inc., Kathryn, The, MD, 3720
Ames-Amzalak Memorial Trust, NY, 5591
Ametek Foundation, Inc., PA, 7913
AMG Charitable Foundation, The, MA, 3924
Amgen Foundation, Inc., CA, 238
Amica Companies Foundation, RI, 8356
Amicus Foundation Inc., NY, 5592
Amicus Foundation, IL, 2660
Ammon Family Foundation, Inc., The, NY, *see* 5593
Ammon Foundation, Inc., Carol A., The, NY, 5593
Ammon Foundation, The, NY, 5594
Amos Family Foundation, Daniel P., GA, 2401
Amos Foundation, Inc., Daniel P. and Shannon L., GA, *see* 2401
Amos Foundation, Inc., Paul and Courtney, The, GA, 2402
Amos, Sr. Foundation, Inc., W. L., FL, 1967
Amos-Cheves Foundation, Inc., GA, *see* 2505
AMPCO-Pittsburgh Foundation II, Inc., PA, *see* 8030
AmSouth Foundation, MS, *see* 4843
Amsterdam Foundation, Jack and Mimi Leviton, The, NY, 5595
Anadarko Foundation, TX, 8661
Anaheim Community Foundation, CA, 239
Anchor Foundation, The, MI, 4338
Anchorage Charitable Fund, The, NY, *see* 6483
Anchorage Foundation of Texas, TX, 8662
Anders Foundation, The, WA, 9571
Andersen Corporate Foundation, MN, 4601
Andersen Foundation, Frank N., MI, 4339
Andersen Foundation, Fred C. and Katherine B., MN, 4602
Andersen Foundation, Hugh J., MN, 4603
Andersen Foundation, Martin Andersen-Gracia, FL, 1968
Andersen Foundation, MN, *see* 4602
Anderson Capital Advisors Foundation, Kayne, CA, 240
Anderson Charitable Foundation, Carl C. Anderson, Sr. and Marie Jo, TX, 8663
Anderson Children's Foundation, Irene W. & Guy L., CA, 241
Anderson Family Charitable Fund, NY, 5596
Anderson Family Foundation, A. Gary, CA, 242
Anderson Family Foundation, AZ, 90
Anderson Family Foundation, Charlie and Beth, The, AL, *see* 5
Anderson Family Foundation, Keith & Peggy, NY, 5597
Anderson Family Foundation, Miner, The, DE, 1736
Anderson Foundation, Annie Wallingford, OH, 7373
Anderson Foundation, Charlie & Moll, The, AL, 5
Anderson Foundation, Inc., Peyton, The, GA, 2403
Anderson Foundation, Inc., Ray C., GA, 2404
Anderson Foundation, John W., IN, 3255
Anderson Foundation, M. D., TX, 8664
Anderson Foundation, Marion & John E., CA, 243
Anderson Foundation, OH, 7372
Anderson Foundation, Rose-Marie and Jack R., TX, 8665
Anderson Foundation, WA, 9572
Andersons Inc. Charitable Foundation, The, OH, 7374
Andor Capital Management Foundation, NY, 5598
Andras Foundation, The, TX, 8666
Andreas Foundation, L. & N., MN, 4604
Andreas Foundation, The, MN, 4605
Andrew Family Foundation, IL, 2661
Andrew Foundation, Aileen S., IL, 2662
Andrews Family Fund, TX, *see* 8668
Andrews Trust, Selma E., TX, 8667
Andrews, Jr. Foundation, Paul E., TX, 8668
Androcles Foundation, Inc., The, NY, 5599
Androse Foundation, The, OH, 7375
Anduin Foundation, WA, 9573
Angel Foundation, NY, 5600
Angela Foundation, The, TX, 8669
Angelakis Family Foundation, PA, 7914
Angelica Foundation, NM, 5514
Angell Family Foundation, Paul M., IL, 2663
Angell Foundation, The, CA, 244
Angelos Foundation, Peter and Georgia, The, MD, 3721
Anheuser-Busch Foundation, MO, 4853
Animal Assistance Foundation, CO, 1363
Animal Farm Foundation, Inc., NY, 5601
Anixter Family Foundation, Lester and Edward, IL, 2664
Anixter Foundation, L. & R., IL, *see* 2664
Ann Arbor Area Community Foundation, MI, 4340
Ann Arbor Area Foundation, MI, *see* 4340
Anna Fund, Inc., The, FL, A
Anncox Foundation, Inc., GA, *see* 2425
Annenberg Foundation, CA, 245
Annexstad Family Foundation, The, MN, 4606
Annis Educational Foundation, R. B., The, IN, 3256
Anon Charitable Trust, WI, 9805
Anonymous Fund, The, NC, 7135
Anonymous Trust, NC, 7136
Ansari Family Foundation, Inc., IL, 2665
Anschel Eilian Family Charitable Foundation, IL, 2666
Anschutz Family Foundation, CO, 1364

Baer Charitable Foundation, Arthur & Helen, MO, 4856
Baer, Jr. Foundation, Sidney R., MO, 4857
Bafflin Foundation, RI, 8359
Bagley Foundation, J.W., CA, 277
Bagwell Family Foundation Inc., Chantal and Tommy, The, GA, 2407
Bahnik Foundation, Inc., The, NY, 5634
Bailey Charitable Trust, Cornelia T., OH, 7381
Bailey Family Foundation, AR, 180
Bailey Family Foundation, Inc., The, FL, 1976
Bailey Foundation, Inc., Bobbie, FL, 1977
Bailey Foundation, P. S. and Ouida C., SC, 8458
Bainbridge Community Foundation, WA, 9578
Bainbridge Island Community Endowment, WA, see 9578
Bair Memorial Trust, Charles M., MT, 5004
Bair Ranch Foundation, The, MT, 5005
Baird and Company Foundation, Inc., Robert W., WI, see 9811
Baird Foundation Inc., The, AZ, 95
Baird Foundation, Cameron and Jane, The, NY, 5635
Baird Foundation, Cameron, The, NY, see 5635
Baird Foundation, Inc., WI, 9811
Baird Foundation, The, NY, 5636
Bais Ephraim Charitable Foundation Trust, NY, 5637
Bakar Foundation, Gerson, CA, 278
Baker Corporation Foundation, Michael, PA, 7925
Baker Family Foundation, Mr. and Mrs. Robert C., NY, 5638
Baker Family Foundation, Thomas E. and Linda O., WA, 9579
Baker Foundation, Dexter F. and Dorothy H., PA, 7926
Baker Foundation, Elinor Patterson, The, CT, 1540
Baker Foundation, Inc., Pat and Jay, WI, 9812
Baker Foundation, R. C., CA, 279
Baker Hughes Foundation, TX, 8679
Baker Street Foundation, The, CA, 280
Baker Trust, Clayton, MD, 3724
Baker, Jr. Memorial Fund, William G., The, MD, 3725
Bakken Family WRC Foundation, MN, 4608
Balazs Foundation, Endre A., The, NJ, 5199
Baldwin Charitable Foundation, Inc., A. W., The, MA, 3934
Baldwin Charitable Foundation, Inc., MA, see 3934
Baldwin Foundation, George M., FL, 1978
Baldwin Foundation, Inc., Alec, The, NY, 5639
Baldwin Foundation, Inc., David M. & Barbara, The, NY, 5640
Baldwin Foundation, Priscilla and Michael, HI, 2587
Baldwin Foundation, The, CT, 1541
Bales Foundation, Hazel & Walter T., IN, 3261
Balfour Foundation, Lloyd G., MA, 3935
Ball Brothers Foundation, IN, 3262
Ball Family Foundation, G. Carl, IL, 2679
Ball Family Foundation, The, PA, 7927
Ball Foundation, George and Frances, IN, 3264
Ball Foundation, Inc., Edmund F. and Virginia B., IN, 3263
Ball Foundation, Russell C., PA, see 7927
Ball Foundation, The, CO, 1371
Ballard Foundation, The, TX, 8680
Ballmann Family Private Foundation, The, MO, 4858
Balsells Foundation, VA, 9385
Baltimore Community Foundation, The, MD, 3726
Bamberger and John Ernest Bamberger Memorial Foundation, Ruth Eleanor, UT, 9305
Bamford Foundation, The, WA, 9580
Banbury Fund, Inc., NJ, 5200
Banco Popular Foundation, Inc., IL, see 3085
Bancorp Hawaii Charitable Foundation, HI, see 2588
BancorpSouth Foundation, MS, 4812
Bandai Foundation, The, CA, 281
Banfi Vintners Foundation, The, NY, 5641
Bangor Savings Bank Foundation, ME, 3680
Bangs-Russell Foundation, VA, 9386
Bank of America Charitable Foundation, Inc., The, NC, 7139
Bank of America Client Foundation, FL, 1979
Bank of Hawaii Foundation, HI, 2588
Bank of New York Mellon Corporation Foundation, The, PA, see 7945
Bansal Foundation, The, VA, 9387
Banyan Tree Foundation, DC, 1881
Baptist Community Ministries, LA, 3612
Baptist Healing Hospital Trust, TN, 8533
Baptist Healing Trust, TN, see 8533
Barakett Foundation, Brett and Patricia, The, NY, see 5642
Barakett Foundation, Brett, The, NY, 5642
Barakett Foundation, Timothy and Michele, NY, 5643
Barber Foundation, Swain, NJ, 5201
Barberton Community Foundation, OH, 7382
Barbour Foundation, Inc., Bernice, FL, 1980
Bard Foundation, Inc., C. R., NJ, 5202
Barer Family Foundation Inc., NJ, 5203
Barker Foundation, Coeta and Donald, The, CA, 282
Barker Foundation, Donald R., The, CA, see 282
Barker Foundation, J. M. R., MA, 3936
Barker Welfare Foundation, The, NY, 5644
Barnes Group Foundation Inc., CT, 1542
Barnett Charitable Foundation, Inc., Lawrence & Isabel, NY, 5645
Barnett Family Foundation, A.N. and Pearl G., IL, 2680
Barnett Foundation, Gertrude A., IL, 2681
Barney Family Foundation, IL, 2682
Barnhart Charitable Foundation, Douglas E. and Nancy J., CA, 283
Barnhart Foundation, Joe, TX, 8681
Baroco Foundation, Inc., J. H., FL, 1981
Baron & Blue Foundation, TX, 8682
Baron Capital Foundation, NY, 5646
Barr Foundation, Inc., Melza M. and Frank Theodore, TX, 8683
Barr Foundation, MA, 3937
Barra Foundation, Inc., PA, 7928
Barrett Foundation, Craig and Barbara, AZ, 96
Barrette Family Fund, NH, 5163
Barrington Foundation, Inc., Greater, The, NY, 5647
Barrington Foundation, The, NY, see 5647
Barrist Family Foundation, The, PA, 7929
Barrow Foundation, James Purdy, TX, 8684
Barrus Medical Foundation, Avis & Clifford, RI, 8360
Barry Charitable Foundation, Richard Allan, CA, 284
Barry Community Foundation, MI, 4342
Barry Foundation, The, ND, 7350
Barsky Family Foundation, NY, see 5851
Barth Family Foundation, CA, 285
Barth Foundation, Inc., Theodore H., NY, 5648
Barthelmes Foundation, Inc., OK, 7730
Bartlesville Community Foundation, The, OK, 7731
Bartlett Foundation, Edward & Helen, OK, 7732
Bartlett Foundation, Edward E. Bartlett & Helen Turner, OK, see 7732
Bartman Foundation, The, CA, 286
Barton Family Foundation, WA, 9581
Baruch Fund, The, NC, 7140
Barzun Philanthropic Foundation, Inc., Brooke Brown, The, KY, 3559
Basch Foundation, Inc., Jack & Miriam, NY, 5649
BASF Foundation USA, The, OH, 7383
Basham Foundation, Inc., Danker, FL, 1982
Bashinsky Foundation, Inc., AL, 7
Baskes Charitable Trust, Julie and Roger, IL, 2683
Baskes Family Foundation, IL, 2684
Baskin Charitable Trust, Samuel J., IL, 2685
Bass & Edythe & Sol G. Atlas Fund, Inc., Sandra Atlas, NY, 5650
Bass Charitable Corporation, The, TX, 8685
Bass Corporation, Perry and Nancy Lee, TX, see 8685
Bass Foundation, Anne T. & Robert M., TX, 8687
Bass Foundation, Bill, The, IL, 2686
Bass Foundation, Lee and Ramona, TX, 8688
Bass Foundation, Richard D., TX, 8689
Bass Foundation, The, TX, see 8689
Bass Foundation, TX, 8686
Bass, Jr. Foundation, Harry W., TX, 8690
Bastian Foundation, B. W., The, UT, 9306
Bat Hanadiv Foundation No. 3, NY, 5651
Batchelor Foundation, Inc., The, FL, 1983
Bate Foundation, Inc., Harold H., The, NC, 7141
Bates Family Foundation, WA, 9582
Baton Rouge Area Foundation, LA, 3613
Batten Foundation, D. N., The, VA, 9388
Batten Foundation, The, VA, 9389
Batten, Jr. Foundation, Aimee & Frank, VA, 9390
Batten-Rolph Foundation, The, VA, see 9388
Batterman Family Foundation, Inc., Theodore W., WI, 9813
Battle Creek Community Foundation, MI, 4343
Battle Creek Foundation, Greater, MI, see 4343
Battye Charitable Trust, Kenneth S., The, MD, 3727
Bauer Family Foundation, Ruth & Ted, TX, 8691
Bauer Foundation, Charles T., TX, 8692
Bauer Foundation, Evalyn M., CA, 287
Bauer Foundation, M. R., CA, see 287
Bauer Foundation, M. R., IL, 2687
Bauer Foundation, Modestus, IL, 2688
Bauer Foundation, The, CT, 1543
Baugh Foundation, Eula Mae and John, TX, 8693
Baughman Foundation, KS, 3493
Baum Family Fund, Alvin H., The, IL, 2689
Bauman Family Foundation, Inc., DC, see 1882
Bauman Family Foundation, Inc., Robert & Patricia, The, FL, 1984
Bauman Foundation, The, DC, 1882
Bauman Foundation, William H. & Mary L., OR, 7824
Baumberger Endowment, TX, 8694
Baxter Allegiance Foundation, The, IL, see 2690
Baxter Foundation, Donald E. and Delia B., The, CA, 288
Baxter Foundation, Inc., George W. and Ruth R., NC, 7142
Baxter Foundation, Inc., George W., NC, see 7142
Baxter International Foundation, The, IL, 2690
Baxter Trust, The, TX, 8695
Bay and Paul Foundations, Inc., The, NY, 5652
Bay Area Community Foundation, MI, 4344
Bay Branch Foundation, The, FL, 1985
Bayard Cutting Arboretum Endowment Fund, PA, 7930
Bayer Foundation, PA, see 7932
Bayer U.S. Patient Assistance Foundation, PA, 7931
Bayer USA Foundation, PA, 7932
Bayne Fund, Howard, The, NY, 5653
Bayport Foundation of Andersen Corporation, The, MN, see 4601
Bayrd Foundation, Adelaide Breed, MA, 3938
BayTree Fund, CA, 289
BB&T Charitable Foundation, NC, 7143
BB&T West Virginia Foundation Inc., NC, 7144
BBB Foundation, MS, 4813
BBVA Compass Charity, AL, 8
BBVA Compass Foundation, AL, 9
BCHB, Inc., NY, 5655
BCLF Managed Assets Corporation, MA, 3939
BCM Foundation, CA, 290
Beach Foundation, Inc., Ross and Marianna, The, KS, 3494
Beagary Charitable Trust, The, CT, 1544
Beagle Charitable Foundation, CA, 291
Beaird Family Foundation, Carolyn W. and Charles T., LA, 3614
Beaird Foundation, Charles T., LA, see 3614
Beal Family Foundation, Bruce A. & Robert L., The, MA, 3940
Beal Family Foundation, NY, 5656
Beal Foundation, The, TX, 8696
Beals, III Charitable Trust, David T., TX, 8697
Beaman Foundation, Alvin and Sally, TN, 8534
Bean Foundation, Inc., A. H., AL, 10
Bean Foundation, Norwin S. and Elizabeth N., NH, 5164
Beard Charitable Foundation, Robert F., MI, 4345
Beard-Payne Family Foundation, The, GA, 2408
Bearman Foundation, Herbert, MD, 3728
Beasley Foundation, Inc., Theodore and Beulah, TX, 8698
Beatty Trust, Helen D. Groome, PA, 7933
Beaver County Foundation, The, PA, 7934
Beaver Foundation, The, CA, 292
Beaver Street Foundation, Inc., FL, 1986
Beavers Charitable Trust, CA, 293
Beazley Foundation, Inc., VA, 9391
Bechtel Charitable Trust, Harold R., IA, 3412
Bechtel Charitable Trust, Marie H., IA, 3413
Bechtel Foundation, CA, see 295
Bechtel Fund, Stephen, CA, 294
Bechtel Group Foundation, CA, 295
Bechtel, Jr. Charitable Foundation, Stephen D., CA, see 296
Bechtel, Jr. Foundation, S.D., CA, 296
Bechtle Foundation, Nancy & Joachim, NY, 5657

Bechtner Foundation, Paul, IL, 2691
Becker Charitable Foundation, Henry E. Becker and Pauline S., The, FL, 1987
Beckley Area Foundation, Inc., WV, 9769
Beckman Award Trust, Elizabeth Hurlock, NC, 7145
Beckman Foundation, Arnold and Mabel, CA, 297
Beckman Laser Institute & Medical Clinic, CA, 298
Bedford Falls Foundation, DC, 1883
Bedford Foundation, Edward T., FL, 1988
Bedminster Fund, Inc., The, NY, *see* 5573
Bedsole Foundation, J. L., The, AL, 11
Beech Foundation, Inc., GA, 2409
Beech Street Foundation, DC, 1884
Beene Foundation, Geoffrey, NY, 5658
Beer Trust, Paul, NE, 5024
Beesley Foundation, Brent and Bonnie Jean, UT, 9307
Begin Today for Tomorrow, CA, 299
Beidler Foundation, Francis, IL, 2692
Beim Foundation, The, MN, 4609
Beinecke Foundation, Inc., The, NY, *see* 7081
Beker Foundation, The, NY, 5659
Belcher, Jr. Private Foundation No. 2, S.E., GA, 2410
Belfer Family Foundation, Robert A. and Renee E., NY, 5660
Believers Foundation, Inc., The, FL, 1989
Belin Foundation, TX, 8699
Belk Educational Endowment, John M., NC, 7146
Belk Endowment, John M., NC, *see* 7146
Belk Foundation, Inc., Katherine and Thomas, The, NC, 7147
Belk Foundation, The, NC, 7148
Belk-Simpson Foundation, NC, *see* 7224
Bell Atlantic Foundation, NJ, *see* 5489
Bell Charitable Foundation, Helen W., FL, 1990
Bell Family Foundation, FL, 1991
Bell Family Foundation, Inc., CA, 300
Bell Foundation, Millicent and Eugene, MA, 3941
Bell Trust, TX, 8700
Bella Vista Foundation, CA, 301
Bellarmin Foundation, St. Roberto, VA, 9392
Bellebyron Foundation, IL, 2693
Bellwether Foundation, Inc., The, MO, 4859
Belo Foundation, The, TX, A
Beloco Foundation, Inc., GA, 2411
Beloit Foundation, Inc., WI, 9814
Belvedere Charitable Foundation, NY, 5661
Bemis Company Foundation, WI, 9815
Ben & Jerry's Foundation, Inc., VT, 9358
ben Joseph Foundation, Shimon, CA, 302
Benaroya Family Foundation, Larry, WA, 9583
Benbough Foundation, Legler, The, CA, 303
Bender Foundation, Inc., DC, 1885
Bendorf Charitable Trust, Agnes M., MN, 4610
Benedict Foundation, Inc., Helen Andrus, NY, 5662
Benedum Foundation, Claude Worthington, PA, 7935
Beneficial Foundation, Inc., DE, *see* 1759
Beneficial Foundation, The, PA, 7936
Benenson Foundation Inc., Edward H., The, NY, 5665
Benenson Foundation, Inc., Frances & Benjamin, NY, 5663
Benenson Foundation, Robert and Nettie, The, NY, 5664
Beneski Foundation, Ted and Laurie, The, TX, 8701
Bengier Foundation, The, CA, 304
Benidt Foundation, Inc., Charles E., WI, 9816
Benificus Foundation, The, CA, 305
Benjamin Charitable Foundation, Inc., Elizabeth and Barets O., The, NJ, 5204
Benjamin Fund, Inc., The, CA, 306
Bennett Family Foundation, Gertrude Josephine, FL, 1992
Bennett Family Foundation, The, NV, 5101
Bennett Foundation, C. E., DE, 1739
Bennett Foundation, The, CA, 307
Bennett Foundation, The, NV, *see* 5125
Benson Charitable Foundation, Gayle and Tom, TX, 8702
Benson Family Charitable Trust, The, MA, 3942
Benter Foundation, The, PA, 7937
Benton County Foundation, OR, 7825
Bentson Foundation, MN, 4611
Benwood Foundation, Inc., TN, 8535
Berbecker and Lille A. Webb Scholarship Fund, Walter J., CT, *see* 1545
Berbecker Scholarship Fund, Walter J. and Lille A., CT, 1545
Berbeewalsh Foundation, Inc., WI, 9817
Bere Foundation, David and Karen, DE, 1740
Beren Charitable Trust, Israel Henry, KS, 3495
Beren Foundation, Inc., Robert M., KS, 3496
Berenson Charitable Foundation, Theodore W. & Evelyn G., MA, 3943
Berg Family Charitable Foundation, FL, 1993
Berg Family Foundation, The, NY, 5666
Berg Foundation, Inc., David, The, NY, 5667
Bergen Foundation, CA, 308
Bergen Foundation, Frank and Lydia, NC, 7149
Berger Foundation, H. N. & Frances C., CA, 309
Berger Foundation, James R. and Frances H., CT, 1546
Berger Foundation, Sol & Margaret, NJ, 5205
Berger Fund, Leo V., MD, 3729
Bergman-Davison-Webster Charitable Trust, TX, 8703
Bergstrom Foundation, A Charitable Trust, Erik E. and Edith H., CA, 310
Bergstrom Foundation, The, MA, 3944
Berkley Corporation Charitable Foundation, W.R., DE, 1741
Berkman Charitable Trust, Allen H. and Selma W., The, MA, 3945
Berkman Foundation, Louis and Sandra, OH, 7384
Berkman Foundation, Sybiel B., PA, 7938
Berkowitz Family Charitable Trust, The, NY, 5668, *see* 5668
Berkowitz Foundation, Bruce and Tracey, FL, *see* 2090
Berkowitz Foundation, Judy & Howard, The, NY, 5669
Berks County Community Foundation, PA, 7939
Berkshire Bank Foundation -Legacy Region, Inc., MA, 3947
Berkshire Bank Foundation, Inc., MA, 3946
Berkshire Charitable Foundation, DE, 1742
Berkshire Taconic Community Foundation, MA, 3948
Berlin Family Charitable Corporation, OH, *see* 7385
Berlin Family Foundation, DE, 1743
Berlin Family Foundation, Inc., OH, 7385
Berman Charitable Foundation, Sam, FL, 1994
Berman Charitable Trust, MD, 3730
Berman Family Foundation Inc., Dennis, The, MD, 3731
Berman Foundation, Inc., Robin and Dennis, The, MD, *see* 3731
Berman Foundation, Madeleine and Mandell L., MI, *see* 4346
Berman Foundation, Mandell L. and Madeleine H., MI, 4346
Berman Foundation, Philip and Muriel, CA, 311
Berne Foundation, Robert, The, NY, 5670
Berner Charitable and Scholarship Foundation, The, IL, 2694
Berner Educational Trust No. 2, NV, 5102
Bernheim Trust, Isaac W., PA, 7940
Bernick Foundation, Howard B., The, IL, 2695
Bernsen Foundation, Grace & Franklin, OK, 7733
Bernstein Family Foundation Inc., Steven E., The, FL, 1995
Bernstein Family Foundation, DC, 1886
Bernstein Family Foundation, Leo M., DC, *see* 1886
Bernstein Foundation, Inc., Diane & Norman, DC, 1887
Bernstein Foundation, Paula & William, CO, 1372
Berrie Foundation, Russell, The, NJ, 5206
Berrien Community Foundation, Inc., MI, 4347
Berry Campbell Trust For Columbia Theological Seminary, Laura, FL, A
Berry Family Foundation, OH, 7386
Berry Foundation, Loren M., OH, *see* 7386
Berry Foundation, Lowell, The, CA, 312
Bersted Foundation, Alfred, IL, 2696
Berthiaume Family Foundation, Inc., MA, 3949
Bertin Family Foundation, UT, 9308
Berwick Degel Family Foundation, The, WA, 9584
Besse Foundation, John & Melissa, MI, 4348
Besser Foundation, MI, 4349
Best Buy Children's Foundation, MN, *see* 4612
Best Buy Foundation, MN, 4612
Best Portion Foundation, IL, 2697
Betesh Family Foundation, Inc., Eddie and Rachelle, The, NY, 5671
Bethel College and Seminary Pooled Common Fund, MN, *see* 4613
Bethel University Foundation Pooled Common Fund, MN, 4613
Bethesda Foundation, The, MD, 3732
Bethlehem Area Foundation, PA, *see* 8136
Better and Better Foundation, VT, A
Better Way Foundation, Inc., MN, 4614
Beveridge Family Foundation, The, MA, 3950
Beverly Foundation, The, MN, 4615
Beyer Foundation, Henry & Eileen, TX, 8704
Bezalel Foundation, The, OK, 7734
Bezos Family Foundation, WA, 9585
BFF Foundation, Inc., The, NY, 5672
BGB Foundation, WI, *see* 9826
Bi-Lo Holdings Foundation, Inc., FL, 1996
Bialkin Family Foundation, NY, 5673
Bickel & Brewer Foundation, TX, 8705
Bickel & Brewer Legal Foundation, TX, *see* 8705
Bickerstaff Family Foundation, CA, 313
Biddle Foundation, Margaret T., NY, 5674
Biddle Foundation, Mary Duke, The, NC, 7150
Bielfeldt Foundation, Gary K. and Carlotta J., The, IL, *see* 2698
Bielfeldt Foundation, The, IL, 2698
Biesecker Foundation, PA, 7941
Big Guy Foundation, Inc., NY, 5675
Bigelow Foundation, F. R., MN, 4616
Biggs Foundation, The, NY, *see* 7102
Bikoff Foundation, Jill & Darius, NY, *see* 6000
Bilezikian Family Foundation, Inc., MA, 3951
Bilger Foundation, The, CA, 314
Bilinski Educational Foundation, CA, 315
Biller Family Foundation, Sheri & Les, WA, 9586
Biloxi Regional Medical Center, Inc., MS, 4814
BIN Charitable Foundation, NC, 7151
Binda Foundation, Guido A. & Elizabeth H., MI, 4350
Binder Foundation, CA, 316
Bingham 2nd Betterment Fund, William, NY, 5676
Bingham Foundation, William, The, OH, 7387
Bingham Trust, The, RI, 8361
Bingham's Trust for Charity, Mr., RI, *see* 8361
Binney Charitable Fund, E. P., RI, 8362
Binney Charitable Trust, Elizabeth Peters, RI, *see* 8362
Biogen Foundation, Inc., RI, *see* 8363
Biogen Idec Foundation Incorporated, RI, 8363
Biomet Foundation, Inc., The, IN, *see* 3355
Birch Foundation, Inc., Stephen and Mary, DE, 1744
Birdsong Charitable Foundation, VA, 9393
Birkelund Fund, The, NY, 5677
Birmingham Foundation, Greater, The, AL, *see* 21
Birmingham Foundation, The, PA, 7942
Bischoff Foundation, Herbert & Diane, NY, 5678
Bisciotti Foundation, Inc., Stephen & Renee, The, MD, 3733
Bishop Foundation, Edward E. and Lillian H., DE, 1745
Bishop Scholarship Foundation, Donald F. and Edna G., NY, 5679
Bishop Scholarship Foundation, NY, *see* 5679
Bishop Trust A for the SPCA of Manatee County, Florida, Lillian H., DE, 1746
Bissell Foundation, Inc., J. Walton, CT, 1547
Bissell Foundation, NC, 7152
Bistricer Foundation, Moric & Elsa, NY, *see* 6407
BL Squared Foundation, The, NY, 5680
Black Family Foundation Inc., Leon, NY, 5681
Black Family Foundation, Stanley and Joyce, The, CA, 317
Black Foundation, Inc., Mary, SC, 8459
Black Foundation, Linda Cabot, MA, 3952
Black Hills Area Community Foundation, SD, 8511
Blades Foundation, A. T. & Mary H., MD, 3734
Blair & Company Foundation, William, IL, 2699
Blair County Community Endowment, PA, *see* 7971
Blair Foundation, IL, 2700
Blakely Foundation Inc., Sara, The, GA, 2412
Blakemore Foundation, WA, 9587
Blanchard III Trust- Dendroica Foundation, Peter P., PA, 7943
Blanchard Trust, Arthur F., PA, 7944
Blandin Foundation, Charles K., MN, 4617
Blank Family Foundation, Arthur M., The, GA, 2413
Blank Family Foundation, Inc., The, FL, 1997

Blank Foundation, Nancy & Robert S., NY, 5682
Blankemeyer Foundation Inc., TN, 8536
Blaustein Foundation, Inc., Jacob and Hilda, The, MD, 3735
Blaustein Foundation, Inc., Morton K. and Jane, The, MD, 3736
Bleser Family Foundation, Inc., WI, 9818
BLN Charitable Foundation, NE, see 5023
Block Family Foundation Inc., Ellen & Ronald, FL, 1998
Block Family Foundation, George and June, IL, 2701
Block Foundation, Herb, DC, 1888
Block Foundation, Inc., Adele and Leonard, NY, 5683
Blodgett Foundation and Ferris Greeney Family Foundation, The, WI, see 9823
Bloomberg Family Foundation, Inc., The, NY, see 5684
Bloomberg Philanthropies, NY, 5684
Bloomfield Family Foundation, CA, 318
Bloomfield Foundation, Sam & Rie, CA, 319
Bloomington Community Foundation, Inc., IN, see 3278
Blowitz-Ridgeway Foundation, The, IL, 2702
Blue & You Foundation for a Healthier Arkansas, AR, 181
Blue Cross & Blue Shield of Mississippi Foundation, MS, 4815
Blue Cross and Blue Shield of Florida Foundation, FL, see 2101
Blue Cross and Blue Shield of Kansas Foundation, Inc., KS, 3497
Blue Cross and Blue Shield of Louisiana Foundation, LA, 3615
Blue Cross and Blue Shield of Minnesota Foundation, Inc., MN, 4618
Blue Cross and Blue Shield of North Carolina Foundation, NC, 7153
Blue Cross and Blue Shield of South Carolina Foundation, SC, 8460
Blue Cross Blue Shield of Massachusetts Foundation, Inc. for Expanding Healthcare Access, MA, 3953
Blue Cross of Idaho Foundation for Health, Inc., ID, 2627
Blue Foundation, IL, 2703
Blue Grass Community Foundation, Inc., KY, 3560
Blue Grass Foundation, Inc., KY, see 3560
Blue Knight Foundation, The, IL, A
Blue Moon Fund, Inc., VA, 9394
Blue Mountain Area Foundation, WA, see 9588
Blue Mountain Community Foundation, WA, 9588
Blue Ridge Foundation New York, NY, 5685
Blue River Community Foundation, Inc., The, IN, 3265
Blue River Foundation, Inc., The, IN, see 3265
Blue Shield of California Foundation, CA, 320
Blue Sky Foundation, Inc., IN, 3266
Bluegrass Foundation, GA, see 2471
Bluhm Family Charitable Foundation, The, IL, 2704
Blum Family Foundation, CA, 321
Blum Foundation, Harry and Maribel G., IL, see 2964
Blum Foundation, Inc., Edith C., NY, 5686
Blum Foundation, Inc., Walter & Adi, FL, 1999
Blum Foundation, Lois and Irving, The, MD, 3737
Blum Fund, Nathan and Emily S., The, IL, 2705
Blum-Kovler Foundation, IL, 2706
Blume Foundation, CA, 322
Blumenstein Foundation Corporation, Harold & Penny B., MI, 4351
Blumenthal Foundation, The, NC, 7154
Blutt Family Foundation, Mitchell J. Blutt and Margo K., The, NY, 5687
BMS Family Foundation, NY, 5688
Bnai Jacob Foundation, The, NY, 5689
BNSF Foundation, TX, see 8706
BNSF Railway Foundation, TX, 8706
BNY Mellon Charitable Foundation, The, PA, see 7946
BNY Mellon Foundation of Southwestern PA, PA, 7946
BNY Mellon Foundation, Inc., PA, 7945
BOA Client Foundation, FL, see 1979
Bob's Discount Furniture Charitable Foundation, Inc., CT, 1548
Bobolink Foundation, The, IL, 2707
Bobst Foundation, Inc., Elmer and Mamdouha, NY, 5690
Bodini Charitable Foundation, Alexander, The, NY, see 5691
Bodini Foundation, Alexander, The, NY, 5691
Bodman Foundation, The, NY, 5692
Bodner Family Foundation, Inc., NY, 5693
Boeckman Family Foundation, The, TX, 8707
Boeckmann Charitable Foundation, CA, 323
Boedecker Foundation, The, CO, 1373
Boehm Charity Fund, Hershel & Esther, MD, 3738
Boehringer Ingelheim Cares Foundation, Inc., CT, 1549
Boettcher Foundation, CO, 1374
Bogen Charitable Foundation, Stanley and Roberta, The, NY, 5694
Bohemian Foundation, CO, 1375
Bohnett Foundation, David, CA, 324
Boisi Family Foundation, The, NY, 5695
Bok Family Foundation, The, CT, 1550
Bolden Charitable, Herman and Emmie, AL, 12
Bolden Foundation, Herman & Emmie, AL, A
Boler Company Foundation, The, IL, see 2708
Boler Family Foundation, The, IL, 2708
Bolger Foundation, NJ, 5207
Bolick Foundation, The, NC, 7155
Bolivar Foundation, Inc., Simon, TX, 8708
Boll Foundation, John A. & Marlene L., MI, 4352
Bolthouse Foundation, The, CA, 325
Bond Ashbourne Charitable Fund Inc., Ina B., KY, 3561
Bond Family Foundation, IL, 2709
Bondi Foundation, The, IL, 2710
Bonfils-Stanton Foundation, CO, 1376
Bonner Foundation, Inc., Corella & Bertram F., The, NJ, 5208
Bookout Family Foundation, The, TX, 8709
Boone Family Foundation, The, TX, 8710
Booth Ferris Foundation, TX, 8711
Booth Foundation, Inc., FL, 2000
Booth Foundation, Otis, The, CA, 326
Booth Heritage Foundation, Inc., TX, 8712
Booth Inc., Suzanne Deal and David G., TX, 8713
Booth-Bricker Fund, The, LA, 3616
Borch Foundation, The, CA, 327
Borchard Foundation, Inc., Albert & Elaine, CA, 328
Borden Memorial Foundation, Mary Owen, NJ, 5209
Boren Foundation, Inc., The, IN, 3267
Borgenicht Foundation, Inc., NJ, 5210
BorgWarner Foundation, MI, 4353
Borick Foundation, Louis L., TX, 8714
Borina Foundation, CA, 329
Bosack and Bette M. Kruger Charitable Foundation, Inc., Leonard X., VA, 9395
Bosarge Family Foundation, The, TX, 8715
Bosch Community Fund, MI, 4354
BOSE Foundation, Inc., MA, 3954
Bossidy Foundation, Lawrence A., The, CT, 1551
Boston Baptist Social Union, MA, 3955
Boston Foundation, Inc., MA, 3956
Boston Scientific Foundation, Inc., MA, 3957
Boswell Foundation, James G., The, CA, 330
Bothin Foundation, CA, 331
Botstiber Foundation, Dietrich W., The, PA, 7947
Botwinick-Wolfensohn Foundation, Inc., NY, 5696
Boulder Area Communities Foundation, CO, see 1391
Bouncer Foundation, Inc., The, NY, 5697
Bouras Foundation, Inc., Nicholas J. and Anna K., The, NJ, 5211
Boutell Memorial Fund, Arnold and Gertrude, OH, see 7388
Boutell Memorial Fund, OH, 7388
Bovaird Foundation, Mervin, The, OK, 7735
Bovay, Jr. Foundation, Harry E., TX, 8716
Bowana Foundation, CO, 1377
Bowen Charitable Foundation, Charles and Cassandra, OK, 7736
Bowen Foundation, Ethel N., WV, 9770
Bower Foundation, CA, see 332
Bower Foundation, Inc., The, MS, 4816
Bower Foundation, James G., CA, 332
Bowes Family Foundation, CA, 333
Bowes, Jr. Foundation, William K., CA, 334
Bowling Family Charitable Foundation, TX, 8717
Bowman Family Foundation, CA, 335
Boxer Foundation, The, NY, 5698
Boye Foundation, Inc., The, NJ, 5212
Boyer Foundation, John K. & Lynne D., NE, 5025
Boyer Foundation, Martin and Mary L., IL, 2711
Bozzone Family Foundation, PA, 7948
BP Amoco Foundation, Inc., TX, see 8718
BP Foundation, Inc., TX, 8718
Brach Family Foundation, Inc., NY, 5699
Brach Foundation, Helen V., IL, 2712
Brach Foundation, NY, 5700
Brackenridge Foundation, George W., TX, 8719
Braddock Family Foundation, Inc., Richard and Susan, The, NY, 5701
Bradley Collection Foundation, John Spencer, WA, 9589
Bradley Foundation, Inc., Lynde and Harry, The, WI, 9819
Bradley, Jr. Charitable Fund, Harry L., FL, 2001
Bradley-Turner Foundation, Inc., GA, 2414
Bradshaw-Knight Foundation, Inc., WI, 9820
Brady Charitable Foundation, Benjamin F., The, GA, 2415
Brady Corporation Foundation Inc., WI, 9821
Brady Education Foundation, Inc., NC, 7156
Brady Foundation, Inc., W.H., NC, see 7156
Braemar Charitable Trust, OR, 7826
Brain Foundation, Inc., Frances Hollis, GA, 2416
Brainerd Foundation, The, WA, 9590
Braka Philanthropic Foundation, NY, 5702
Branan Trust, Charles I., NC, 7157
Branch Trust, C. B. and Anita, TX, 8720
Branches Foundation, SD, 8512
Brandenborg Family Foundation, Douglass, The, MN, 4619
Brandes Foundation, Linda, CA, 336
Brandman Foundation, Saul, CA, 337
Brandt Foundation, John H. & Orah I., ID, 2628
Branson Family Foundation, CA, 338
Branta Foundation, Inc., NY, 5703
Brass Family Foundation, TX, 8721
Braswell Trust, James R. and Bronnie L., NC, 7158
Bratton Family Foundation, The, TX, 8722
Brauer Charitable Trust, Stephen F. and Camilla T., The, MO, 4860
Braufman Family Foundation, Inc., Daniel L. Nir & Jill E., NY, 5704
Brauninger Trust, George, NC, 7159
Bravmann Foundation, Inc., L., The, NY, 5705
Breeden Foundation, I. J. and Hilda M., VA, 9396
Breen Charitable Foundation, Marion I., MO, 4861
Bremer Foundation, Otto, MN, 4620
Bren Foundation, Donald, The, CA, 339
Brenden-Mann Foundation, Blythe, SD, 8513
Brenden-Mann Foundation, SD, see 8513
Brennan Charitable Foundation Inc., The, NY, 5706
Brennan Trust, Robert E., PA, A
Brenner Foundation, Inc., Mervyn L., The, CA, 340
Brentwood Foundation, TX, 8723
Bresky Foundation, MA, 3958
Breslauer Foundation, Inc., B. H., NY, 5707
Breslauer-Soref Foundation, CA, 341
Bressler Family Foundation, The, MA, 3959
Bressler Foundation, Alan S. Bressler and Lorraine D., The, MA, see 3959
Brett Family Foundation, CO, 1378
Bretzlaff Foundation, Inc., Hilda E., The, MI, 4355
Bretzlaff Foundation, Inc., The, NV, 5103
Brewer Family Foundation, Robert N., IL, 2713
Brewster West Foundation, CA, 342
Brice Foundation, Deborah Loeb, The, NY, 5708
Bricker Trust, William L., NY, 5709
Brickman Family Foundation, Scott and Patrice, The, MD, 3739
Brickman Foundation, PA, 7949
Brickstreet Foundation, Inc., WV, 9771
Bridge Foundation, Inc., The, TX, 8724
Bridge Street Foundation, Inc., NJ, 5213
Bridges Evangelical Foundation, TX, 8725
Bridgestone Americas Trust Fund, The, TN, 8537
Bridgestone/Firestone Trust Fund, The, TN, see 8537
Bridwell Foundation, J. S., The, TX, 8726
Briggs & Stratton Corporation Foundation, Inc., WI, 9822
Briggs Foundation, Inc., Thomas W., TN, 8538
Briggs Foundation, Margaret, PA, 7950
Bright Future International NFP Inc., IL, 2714
Bright Horizon Foundation, NY, 5710
Brightwater Fund, The, CT, 1552
Brill Charitable Trust, Ron and Lisa, DE, 1747

Brin Foundation, The, CA, *see* 343
Brin Wojcicki Foundation, The, CA, 343
Brindle Foundation, NM, 5516
Brinson Foundation, The, IL, 2715
Briskin Charitable Foundation, Judy and Bernard, The, CA, 344
Bristol County Savings Charitable Foundation Inc., MA, 3960
Bristol-Myers Fund, Inc., The, NY, *see* 5711
Bristol-Myers Squibb Foundation, Inc., The, NY, 5711
Bristol-Myers Squibb Patient Assistance Foundation, Inc., The, NY, 5712
Brittingham Family Foundation, CA, 345
Britton Fund, PA, 7951
Broad Art Foundation, The, CA, 346
Broad Foundation, Eli & Edythe, The, CA, 347
Broad Foundation, Inc., Shepard, The, FL, 2002
Broad Foundation, The, CA, *see* 347
Broad Reach Foundation, CA, 348
Broadcom Foundation, CA, 349
Broadridge Foundation, NJ, 5214
Broccoli Charitable Foundation, Dana & Albert R., CA, 350
Brock Family Foundation, Todd, The, TX, 8727
Brock Foundation, Harry B. & Jane H., The, AL, 13
Brock Foundation, The, AL, *see* 13
Brodsky Family Foundation, Daniel and Estrellita, The, NY, 5713
Brodsky Family Foundation, The, NY, 5714
Brodsky Foundation, Julian A. and Lois G., The, PA, 7952
Bromley Charitable Trust, The, MA, 3961
Bronfman Family Foundation, Inc., Edgar M., The, NY, *see* 5715
Bronfman Foundation, Ann L., FL, 2003
Bronfman Foundation, Samuel, The, NY, 5715
Bronfman Jr. Foundation, Clarissa and Edgar, The, NY, 5716
Bronfman Philanthropies, Inc., Andrea and Charles, The, NY, 5717
Brookby Foundation, The, WI, 9823
Brooke Family Foundation, AL, 14
Brooker Foundation, T. Kimball, IL, 2716
Brookhill Foundation, The, WI, 9824
Brookline Community Foundation, MA, 3962
Brooklyn Community Foundation, NY, 5718
Brooks Charitable Foundation, Diane, CA, *see* 352
Brooks Family Charitable Foundation, MA, *see* 3963
Brooks Family Foundation, MA, 3963
Brooks for Charities, Charles, PA, 7953
Brooks Foundation, Clarence S., The, CA, 351
Brooks Foundation, Diane and Dorothy, CA, 352
Brooks Foundation, Gladys, NY, 5719
Brookshire Foundation, William A., TX, 8728
Brossman Charitable Foundation, William & Jemima, PA, 7954
Brotherhood Mutual Foundation Inc., IN, 3268
Brothers Ashkenazi Foundation, Inc., The, NJ, 5215
Brotherton Charitable Foundation, Fred J., NJ, 5216
Brotherton Foundation, Inc., Fred J., NJ, *see* 5216
Brotz Family Foundation, Inc., Frank G. & Frieda K., WI, 9825
Brotz Family Foundation, Inc., Frank G., WI, *see* 9825
Brougher Foundation, Inc., W. Dale, The, NJ, 5217
Broughton Foundation Trust, G. C., TX, 8729
Broussard Charitable Foundation, OH, 7389
Broward Community Foundation, Inc., FL, *see* 2034
Brown Advisory Charitable Foundation Inc., MD, 3740
Brown and C. A. Lupton Foundation, Inc., T. J., TX, 8730
Brown Charitable Foundation, Owsley, KY, 3562
Brown Charitable Trust, Dana, MO, 4862
Brown Charitable Trust, Himan, NY, 5720
Brown Charitable Trust, Peter D. and Dorothy S., MI, *see* 4488
Brown County Community Foundation, Inc., IN, 3269
Brown Family Charitable Foundation, Alvin I. and Peggy S., MD, 3741
Brown Family Foundation, John and Rosemary, The, MI, 4356
Brown Family Private Foundation, Thomas R., AZ, 97
Brown Foundation, Inc., James Graham, KY, 3563
Brown Foundation, Inc., The, TX, 8731
Brown Foundation, Joe W. & Dorothy Dorsett, LA, 3617
Brown Foundation, L.P., CO, 1379
Brown Foundation, OK, 7737
Brown Foundation, W. L. Lyons, KY, 3564
Brown Group, Inc. Charitable Trust, FL, *see* 2004
Brown Jr. Family Foundation, Inc., Constance W. & James W., OH, 7390
Brown Shoe Co., Charitable Trust, FL, 2004
Brown, Jr. Charitable Foundation, W. L. Lyons, KY, 3565
Brown, Jr. Family Foundation, H.L., TX, 8732
Brownell Family Foundation, IA, 3414
Browning Foundation, Val A., NV, 5104
Browning Memorial Fund, L. L., OH, *see* 7624
Browning-Kimball Foundation, OK, 7738
Brownington Foundation, Inc., NY, 5721
Brownstone Family Foundation, NY, 5722
Brownstone Foundation, Inc., Lucien & Ethel, NY, *see* 5722
Brownsville Foundation for Health and Education, TX, 8733
Broyhill Family Foundation, Inc., NC, 7160
Brozowski Foundation, Inc., Robert & Marion Schamann, The, NJ, 5218
Bruce and Lee Foundation, Drs., SC, 8461
Bruening Foundation, Eva L. and Joseph M., OH, 7391
Brumley Foundation, The, TX, 8734
Brunckhorst Foundation, The, NY, 5723
Bruni Foundation, Jerome V., CO, 1380
Bruning Foundation, The, IL, 2717
Brunner Foundation, Fred J., IL, 2718
Brunner Foundation, The, MO, 4863
Bruno Charitable Foundation, Joseph S., The, AL, 15
Bruno Foundation, Lee, The, AL, 16
Bruno-Rumore Foundation, AL, 17
Bryan Foundation Inc., R. A., NC, 7161
Bryan Foundation of Greater Greensboro, Inc., Joseph M., The, NC, 7162
Bryant Foundation, Inc., Edwin E. and Janet L., The, WI, 9826
Bryce L. West Foundation, Inc., FL, 2005
Bryce Memorial Fund, William & Catherine, IL, 2719
Bryson Foundation Limited, NC, 7163
BT Foundation, NY, see 5876
BTL Foundation, IL, *see* 3193
BTM Foundation, Inc., The, NY, *see* 5724
BTMU Foundation, Inc., The, NY, 5724
Buchanan Family Foundation, The, IL, 2720
Buchbinder Family Foundation, Henry and Gilda, The, IL, 2721
Buchheit Foundation, CA, 353
Buck Charitable Trust, James & Catherine, TX, 8735
Buck Family Foundation, FL, A
Buck Foundation, Carol Franc, NV, 5105
Buck Foundation, Caroline Alexander, PA, 7955
Buck Foundation, Inc., Peter and Carmen Lucia, The, NY, 5725
Buckeye Foundation, IL, 2722
Buckhantz Foundation, Vladimir & Araxia, CA, 354
Buckley Trust, Thomas D., NE, 5026
Bucks Creek Foundation, DE, 1748
Bucksbaum Family Foundation, John & Jacolyn, IL, 2723
Bucksbaum Family Foundation, Matthew and Carolyn, IL, 2724
Bucksbaum Family Foundation, Matthew, IL, *see* 2724
Buder Charitable Foundation, G. A., Jr. and Kathryn M., MO, 4864
Buder Foundation Trust, Leo R., IL, 2725
Budig Family Foundation, Otto M., The, OH, 7392
Buehler Family Foundation, RI, 8364
Buehler Foundation, A. C., RI, *see* 8364
Buehler Perpetual Trust, Emil, NJ, 5219
Buehner - Joan B. Merrill Family Foundation, Paul & Irene, HI, 2589
Buehner Foundation, Paul & Irene, HI, *see* 2589
Buell Foundation, Temple Hoyne, CO, 1381
Buenger Foundation, Clement and Ann, OH, 7393
Buffalo Sabres Alumni Association, NY, 5726
Buffett Early Childhood Fund, NE, 5027
Buffett Foundation, Howard G., IL, 2726
Buffett Foundation, Rebecca Susan, IL, 2727
Buffett Foundation, Susan A., The, NE, *see* 5081
Buffett Foundation, Susan Thompson, The, NE, 5028
Buffett Foundation, The, NE, *see* 5028
Buford Foundation, TX, 8736
Bugher Foundation, Henrietta B. & Frederick H., NY, 5727
Bugher Foundation, NY, *see* 5727
Buhl Foundation, The, PA, 7956
Building Healthy Lives Foundation, OH, 7394
Bullfrogs & Butterflies Foundation, CT, 1553
Bullitt Foundation, Inc., William C., The, NY, 5728
Bullitt Foundation, The, WA, 9591
Bunbury Company, Inc., The, NJ, 5220
Buncher Family Foundation, PA, *see* 7957
Buncher Foundation, Jack, PA, 7957
Bunge Corporation Foundation, MO, *see* 4865
Bunge North America Foundation, MO, 4865
Bunning Family Foundation, IL, 2728
Bunting Family Foundation, The, MD, 3742
Bunting Foundation, Inc., Mary Catherine, The, MD, 3743
Bunzl Foundation, Walter and Frances, GA, 2417
Burch Family Foundation, The, NY, *see* 5729
Burch Foundation, The, NY, 5729
Burden Foundation, The, LA, 3618
Burke Family Foundation, NY, 5730
Burke Family Foundation, The, NY, 5731
Burke Family Foundation, The, PA, 7958
Burke Foundation, Julia, The, HI, 2590
Burke Foundation, The, PA, 7959
Burkle Foundation, Ronald W., CA, 355
Burleigh Family Foundation, OH, 7395
Burnand-Partridge Foundation, CA, 356
Burnett Foundation, The, TX, 8737
Burnett-Tandy Foundation, The, TX, *see* 8737
Burnham Foundation, The, CA, 357
Burning Foundation, The, OR, 7827
Burns & McDonnell Foundation, MO, 4866
Burns Family Foundation, CA, 358
Burns Foundation Inc., Donald A., FL, 2006
Burns Foundation, Fritz B., CA, 359
Burns Foundation, Inc., Jacob, NY, 5732
Burroughs Wellcome Fund, NC, 7164
Burton Foundation, Inc., FL, 2007
Burton Foundation, R. Harold, UT, 9309
Burton Foundation, William T. and Ethel Lewis, The, LA, 3619
Busch III Charitable Trust, August A., MO, 4867
Bush Charitable Foundation, Inc., Edyth, FL, 2008
Bush Foundation, MN, 4621
Bushnell Family Foundation, WA, 9592
Butler Conservation Fund, Inc., NY, 5733
Butler Family Foundation, IL, 2729
Butler Family Foundation, Inc., Gilbert and Ildiko, The, NY, 5734
Butler Family Foundation, Patrick and Aimee, MN, 4622
Butler Family Foundation, The, IA, 3415
Butler Family Fund, The, DC, 1889
Butler Foundation, Alice, NC, 7165
Butler Foundation, Inc., Gilbert & Ildiko, NY, *see* 5733
Butler Foundation, Inc., J. E. & Z. B., NY, 5735
Butler Foundation, The, NH, 5165
Butler Foundation, The, OH, 7396
Butler Memorial Foundation, Robert M., OH, *see* 7396
Butler Memorial Scholarship Foundation, J. D. and Alice, NC, *see* 7165
Butt Foundation, H. E., TX, 8738
Buttenwieser Foundation, Catherine & Paul, NY, 5736
Butters Foundation, The, NY, 5737
Buuck Family Foundation, MN, 4623
BWMF Farm, AR, *see* 212
Bybee Foundation - A Trust, Faith P. & Charles L., TX, 8739
Bydale Foundation, NY, 5738
Byer Foundation, CA, 360
Byerly Foundation, The, SC, 8462
Byrne Foundation, Inc., Jack and Dorothy, The, NH, 5166
Byrnes Family Foundation, The, MA, 3964
Byrum Charitable Trust, Porter B., NC, 7166

C & Y Foundation, Inc., NY, 5739
C C Criss Hattie B Munroe Foundation, MN, 4624
C Funding, NJ, 5221
C Spire Wireless Foundation, MS, 4817
C.E. & S. Foundation, Inc., The, KY, 3566
C.E.B. Foundation, The, CA, 361

CentiMark Foundation, PA, 7970
Central Alabama Community Foundation, Inc., AL, 19
Central Carolina Community Foundation, SC, 8468
Central Florida Foundation, Inc., FL, 2015
Central Indiana Community Foundation, Inc., IN, 3272
Central Minnesota Community Foundation, MN, 4631
Central Minnesota Initiative Fund, MN, *see* 4679
Central Montana Foundation, MT, 5006
Central National-Gottesman Foundation, The, NY, 5756
Central New York Community Foundation, Inc., NY, 5757
Central Pacific Bank Foundation, HI, 2595
Central Pennsylvania Community Foundation, PA, 7971
Central Susquehanna Community Foundation, PA, 7972
Central Texas Scholarship Foundation, TX, *see* 8746
Centre County Community Foundation, Inc., PA, 7973
Century 21 Associates Foundation, Inc., NY, 5758
Century Fund Trust, The, PA, 7974
CenturyLink-Clarke M. Williams Foundation, DE, 1750
Cephalon Cares Foundation, PA, *see* 8314
Ceres Foundation, Inc., The, SC, 8469
Ceres Foundation, MD, 3747
Ceres Trust, The, MN, 4632
Cestone Foundation, Inc., Michele and Agnese, PA, 7975
Cestone Foundation, Inc., Ralph M., The, PA, 7976
CF2 Foundation, Inc., FL, *see* 2011
CFGL, FL, *see* 2123
CFOV, WV, *see* 9773
CFP Foundation, TX, 8758
CFVI, VI, *see* 9377
CGLC Charitable Trust, DE, 1751
CH Foundation, The, TX, 8759
CH2M Hill Foundation, CO, 1384
Chabraja Foundation, Nicholas and Eleanor, FL, 2016
Chada Foundation, Inc., NY, 5759
Chaddick Foundation, Inc., Harry F. and Elaine, IL, 2740
Chadwick Fund, Dorothy Jordan, NY, 5760
Chafetz Family Charitable Trust, Irwin, MA, 3979
Chaim Foundation, NY, 5761
Challenge Foundation, The, GA, 2424
Challenger Foundation, NY, 5762
Challenger Oceanographic Foundation, IL, *see* 2838
Chamberlain Memorial Fund, Harry E. Chamberlain & Adrienne S., RI, 8369
Chamberlin Family Foundation, CA, 389
Chambers Charitable Foundation, LA, 3621
Chambers Family Foundation, CA, 390
Chambers Family Foundation, OR, 7832
Chambers Family Fund, CO, 1385
Chambers Foundation, Inc., Anne Cox, GA, 2425
Chambers Memorial, James B., WV, 9772
Champagne Family Charitable Trust, IN, 3273
Champlin Foundations, The, RI, 8370
Chan Soon-Shiong Family Foundation, CA, 391
Chanan Foundation, Inc., CO, A
Chandler Family Foundation, Camilla, CA, 392
Chandler Foundation, AL, *see* 38
Change a Life Foundation, CA, 393
Change Happens Foundation, CO, 1386
Channel Foundation, WA, 9597
Chao Family Foundation, Ping and Amy, CA, 394
Chao Foundation, Ting Tsung and Wei Fong, IL, 2741
Chaparral Foundation, TX, 8760
Chaplin Family Foundation Inc., FL, *see* 2017
Chaplin Family Foundation, Paul & Karen, FL, 2017
Chapman & Associates Foundation, CA, 395
Chapman Charitable Trust, H. A. and Mary K., OK, 7739
Chapman Foundation, Mark A., TX, 8761
Chapman Foundation, Mary K., OK, 7740
Chapman Hanson Foundation, DE, 1752
Charboneau Family Foundation, MI, 4360
Charina Endowment Fund, Inc., The, NY, 5763
Charina Foundation, Inc., NY, 5764
Charis Foundation Inc., TN, 8542
Charities Foundation, OH, 7400
Charles Charitable Trust Two, Roy R., VA, A
Charles Foundation, Inc., NJ, 5227
Charles Foundation, Inc., Ray, The, CA, 396
Charles Fund, Inc., The, VA, 9404
Charles G. Koch Charitable Foundation, VA, *see* 9463
Charlesbank Homes, MA, 3980
Charlesmead Foundation, Inc., The, RI, 8371
Charleston Area Charitable Foundation, IL, 2742
Charlevoix County Community Foundation, MI, 4361
Charlevoix Foundation, The, IL, 2743
Charlottesville Area Community Foundation, VA, 9405
Charlottesville-Albemarle Community Foundation, VA, *see* 9405
Charlson Foundation, MN, 4633
Charlton Charity Fund, Ida S., RI, 8372
Charter Foundation, The, PA, 7977
Charter Fund, Inc., CO, *see* 1387
Charter Manufacturing Company Foundation Inc., WI, 9829
Charter School Growth Fund, CO, 1387
Chartered Foundation, The, IL, 2744
Chartrand Foundation, Inc., The, FL, 2018
Chartwell Charitable Foundation, CA, 397
Chasdrew Fund, The, TX, 8762
Chase & Stuart Bear Family Foundation Inc., Cheryl, CT, 1555
Chase Family Foundation Inc., Rhoda & David, CT, 1556
Chase Family Foundation, DE, 1753
Chase Family Foundation, Inc., The, CT, *see* 1556
Chase Foundation of Virginia, VA, 9406
Chase Foundation, NM, 5517
Chase Manhattan Foundation, The, NY, *see* 6244
Chatham Foundation, The, PA, 7978
Chatham Valley Foundation, Inc., The, NC, 7175
Chatlos Foundation, Inc., The, FL, 2019
Chatterjee Charitable Foundation, NY, 5765
Chautauqua Region Community Foundation, Inc., NY, 5766
Chazen Foundation, The, NY, 5767
CHDI Foundation, Inc., NJ, 5228
CHDI, Inc., NJ, *see* 5228
Chehebar Family Foundation, Inc., NY, 5768
Chehebar Family Foundation, Joseph, NY, 5769
Chelsea Health and Wellness Foundation, The, MI, 4362
Cheney Foundation, Ben B., WA, 9598
Cheney Foundation, Elizabeth F., IL, 2745
Cherbec Advancement Foundation, MN, 4634
Chernin Family Foundation, Inc., The, NY, 5770
Chernow Trust, Michael, NY, 5771
Chesed Foundation of America, NY, 5772
Chesed Global Foundation, Inc., The, NY, 5773
Chester County Community Foundation, PA, 7979
Chester Foundation, IL, *see* 2682
Chester Foundation, Jack, FL, 2020
Chester Foundation, The, SC, 8470
Chia Family Foundation, Inc., FL, 2021
Chiang Foundation, Y.C. Ho/Helen & Michael, The, NY, 5774
Chiara Charitable Fund Inc., Judith L., NY, 5775
Chiaramonte Private Foundation, Dr. Francis P., The, VA, 9407
Chiaroscuro Foundation, NY, 5776
Chicago Community Trust, The, IL, 2746
Chichester duPont Foundation, Inc., DE, 1754
Chico Community Foundation, CA, *see* 972
Child Relief International Foundation, MA, 3981
Children's Care Foundation, The, IL, 2747
Children's Family Care, Inc., OH, 7401
Children's Foundation of Memphis, The, TN, 8543
Children's Healthcare Support Fund, FL, *see* 2083
Children's Investment Fund Foundation, The, CT, 1557
Childrens Cancer Cooperative, Inc., SC, 8471
Childs Memorial Fund for Medical Research, Jane Coffin, The, CT, 1558
Chiles Foundation, OR, 7833
China Medical Board of New York, Inc., MA, *see* 3982
China Medical Board, Inc., MA, 3982
Ching Foundation, Clarence T. C., The, HI, 2596
Chinnick Charitable Foundation, William, The, MI, 4363
Chintu Gudiya Foundation, CA, 398
Chipotle Cultivate Foundation, CO, 1388
Chirag Foundation, The, MA, 3983
Chisholm Charitable Trust, M. A., RI, 8373
Chisholm Foundation, The, MS, 4818
Choice Hotels International Foundation, MD, 3748
Chorus, Inc., The, MA, 3984
Chosky Charitable & Educational Foundation, Philip, The, PA, 7980
Chou Foundation, Sunlin and Priscilla, WA, 9599
Christ Cares for Kids Foundation, MI, 4364
Christ Foundation, OH, 7402
Christensen Fund, The, CA, 399
Christian Education Charitable Trust, TN, 8544
Christian Evangelical Foundation, MI, 4365
Christian Health Ministries, LA, *see* 3612
Christian Mission Concerns of Tennessee, Inc., WY, 9974
Christian Mission Concerns, TX, 8763
Christianson Foundation, W. G., MN, 4635
Christman Foundation, Anne Kilcawley, OH, 7403
Christopher Family Foundation, The, IL, 2748
Christopher Foundation, Jay and Doris, IL, *see* 2748
Christopher Memorial Charity Fund, Louis J., NC, 7176
Christy-Houston Foundation, Inc., TN, 8545
Chronic Fatigue Initiative, Inc., NY, 5777
Chrysler Foundation, The, MI, 4366
Chrysopolae Foundation, CA, 400
CHS Foundation, MN, 4636
Chubb Foundation, The, NJ, 5229
Chugach Heritage Foundation, AK, 84
Church Home Corporation, MD, 3749
Church of Christ Foundation, Inc., TN, *see* 8643
Cianbro Charitable Foundation, ME, 3683
CIC Foundation, Inc., TN, 8546
CIGNA Foundation, PA, 7981
Cimarron Foundation, The, TX, *see* 8922
Ciminelli Family Foundation, Louis P., NY, 5778
Cincinnati Foundation for the Aged, The, OH, 7405
Cincinnati Foundation, Greater, The, OH, 7404
Cinereach Ltd., NY, 5779
Ciocca Charitable Foundation, Arthur & Carlyse, CA, 401
Circle of Service Foundation, IL, 2749
Ciresi Foundation, Michael V. & Ann C., MN, 4637
CIRI Foundation, The, AK, 85
Cisco Systems Foundation, CA, 402
Cisneros Foundation, Gilbert and Jacki, The, CA, 403
Citi Foundation, NY, 5780
Citigroup Foundation, NY, *see* 5780
Citizens Charitable Foundation, RI, 8374
Citizens Programs Corporation, MA, 3985
Citrin Charitable Foundation, Rona and Jeffrey, CT, 1559
City of Hope-Workers Comp, CA, A
CityBridge Foundation, Inc., The, DC, 1892
Cizik Foundation, Robert & Jane, The, TX, 8764
CJM Foundation, NY, 5781
Ckew Foundation, NY, 5782
Claiborne & Art Ortenberg Foundation, Liz, NY, 5783
Clamer Foundation, Guilliam H., The, NC, 7177
Claneil Foundation, Inc., PA, 7982
Clapham Charitable Trust, Mary D., IL, 2750
Clapp Charitable and Educational Trust, Anne L. and George H., The, PA, 7983
Clapp Foundation, M. Roger and Anne Melby, The, MA, A
Clare Foundation, David R. Clare & Margaret C., NJ, 5230
Clarinda Foundation, The, IA, 3418
Clark Charitable Foundation, Inc., MD, 3750
Clark Charitable Foundation, James H., FL, 2022
Clark County Community Foundation, WA, *see* 9603
Clark Family Foundation, Emory T., WI, 9830
Clark Family Foundation, PA, *see* 8048
Clark Family Foundation, The, IL, 2751
Clark Foundation, Edna McConnell, The, NY, 5784
Clark Foundation, Inc., Robert Sterling, NY, 5785
Clark Foundation, OR, 7834
Clark Foundation, The, NY, 5786
Clark-Winchcole Foundation, MD, 3751
Clarke Trust, John, The, MA, 3986
Claws Foundation, VA, 9408
Clayes, III Charitable Trust, Joseph A.W., CA, 404
Clayman Family Foundation, The, PA, 7984
Clayton Family Foundation, The, TN, 8547
Clayton Fund, Inc., The, TX, 8765
CLC Foundation Inc., GA, 2426
Clearing Corporation Charitable Foundation, IL, 2752
Cleary Foundation, WI, *see* 9831
Cleary-Kumm Foundation, Inc., WI, 9831
Clemens Foundation, The, OR, 7835
Clement Foundation, Inc., Christen Elizabeth, LA, 3622
Clements Foundation, B. Gill, The, TX, 8767

Clements Foundation, TX, 8766
Clermont Charitable Trust, FL, 2023
Cless Family Foundation, IL, 2753
Cless Foundation, Karl, IL, *see* 2753
Cleveland Foundation, The, OH, 7406
Cleveland-Cliffs Foundation, The, OH, *see* 7407
Click Family Foundation, AZ, 100
Clif Bar Family Foundation, CA, 405
Cliffs Foundation, The, OH, 7407
Cline Family Foundation, Inc., The, FL, 2024
Clinton Family Foundation, The, NY, 5787
Clinton Family Fund, The, IL, 2754
Clipper Ship Foundation, Inc., MA, 3987
Clive Foundation, Winifred Johnson, CA, 406
Clorox Company Foundation, The, CA, 407
Cloud Mountain Foundation, NY, 5788
Clouse Trust, August, OH, 7408
Cloverfields Foundation, MN, 4638
Clowes Charitable Foundation, Inc., Allen Whitehill, IN, 3274
Clowes Fund, Inc., The, IN, 3275
CLRC, Inc., NY, 5789
CME Group Community Foundation, IL, 2755
CME Group Foundation, IL, 2756
CNA Foundation, IL, A
CNL Charitable Foundation, Inc., FL, 2025
Coach Foundation, Inc., NY, 5790
Coastal Bend Community Foundation, TX, 8768
Coastal Community Foundation of South Carolina, SC, 8472
Coates Charitable Foundation of 1992, Elizabeth Huth, TX, 8769
Coates Foundation, Vincent J., CA, 408
Coatue Foundation, NY, 5791
Cobb Educational Fund, Ty, GA, 2427
Cobb Family Foundation, Inc., FL, 2026
Cobb Foundation, FL, 2027
Coca-Cola Foundation, Inc., The, GA, 2428
Cochran Family Foundation, The, PA, 7985
Cockrell Foundation, The, TX, 8770
Code Family Foundation, The, IL, 2757
Codrington Charitable Foundation, George W., The, OH, 7409
Coffey Charitable Trust, Larry R., KY, 3568
Cogan Family Foundation, MA, 3988
Cognis Foundation, OH, *see* 7383
Cogswell Benevolent Trust, NH, 5167
Cohen Brothers Foundation, NY, 5792
Cohen Charitable Foundation, Inc., Ben & Zelda, MD, 3752
Cohen Charitable Fund Part II, Barton P. & Mary Davidson, KS, 3499
Cohen Charitable Fund Part One, Barton P. and Mary Davidson, KS, 3500
Cohen Family Foundation, Inc., Ryna and Melvin, The, MD, 3753
Cohen Foundation, Naomi and Nehemiah, MD, 3754
Cohen Foundation, Sam L., ME, 3684
Cohen Foundation, Steven A. and Alexandra M., CT, 1560
Cohen Trust, John and Golda, FL, 2028
Cohn Foundation Inc., Betsy & Alan D., The, NY, 5793
Coit Family Foundation, CA, 409
Coker College Foundation, SC, 8473
Colad Charitable Trust, NY, 5794
Colburn Family Foundation, The, VA, 9409
Colburn Foundation, CA, 410
Colcom Foundation, PA, 7986
Cold Heading Foundation, The, MI, 4367
Cole Charitable Trust, Helen C., OH, 7410
Cole Foundation, Inc., Olive B., IN, 3276
Cole Foundation, Kenneth, NY, 5795
Cole Productions Foundation, Kenneth, NJ, 5231
Cole Trust, Quincy, FL, *see* 2389
Cole-Crone Family Foundation, Inc., IL, 2758
Coleman Family Foundation, Inc., KS, 3501
Coleman Foundation, Chase and Stephanie, The, NY, 5796
Coleman Foundation, Inc., The, IL, 2759
Colen Foundation, Inc., The, FL, 2029
Colhoun Family Foundation, Inc., Howard P., MD, 3755
Colin Foundation, Simon and Eve, NY, 5797
Colket Foundation, Ethel D., PA, 7987
College Access Foundation of California, The, CA, 411
College Spark Washington, WA, 9600
Collins Family Foundation, Inc., Calvert K., TX, 8771
Collins Foundation, Carol and James, The, CA, 412
Collins Foundation, Fulton & Susie, OK, 7741
Collins Foundation, Inc., Calvert K., TX, *see* 8771
Collins Foundation, Inc., Susanne Marcus, GA, 2429
Collins Foundation, James M., The, TX, 8772
Collins Foundation, Joseph, NY, 5798
Collins Foundation, The, OR, 7836
Collins Fund, P. & C., NY, 5799
Collins Medical Trust, OR, 7837
Colombe Foundation, MA, 3989
Colombo Charitable Trust, CA, 413
Colombo Charitable Trust, Elsie T. & Josephine, CA, *see* 413
Colonial Foundation, Inc., GA, 2430
Colonial Oaks Foundation, PA, 7988
Colorado Masons Benevolent Fund Association, CO, 1389
Colorado Trust, The, CO, 1390
Colson Family Foundation, WA, 9601
Columbia Basin Foundation, WA, 9602
Columbia Charitable Foundation, NV, *see* 5150
Columbia Foundation, The, MD, *see* 3759
Columbia Gas Foundation, OH, *see* 7591
Columbia/HCA Healthcare Foundation, Inc., TN, *see* 8582
Columbine Foundation for the Grand Foundation, CO, *see* 1423
Columbus Foundation and Affiliated Organizations, The, OH, 7411
Columbus Foundation, The, OH, *see* 7411
Columbus Phipps Foundation, The, FL, 2030
Combined International Foundation, IL, *see* 2667
Combined Townsend Fund, RI, 8375
Comcast Foundation, The, PA, 7989
Comer Foundation, The, AL, 20
Comer Foundation, The, IL, 2760
Comer Science & Education Foundation, IL, 2761
Comerica Charitable Foundation, MI, 4368
Commerce Bancshares Foundation, MO, 4871
Commerce Foundation, The, MO, *see* 4871
Common Sense Fund Inc., The, CT, 1561
Common Stream, MA, *see* 4004
Common Wealth Trust, DE, 1755
Commonweal Foundation, Inc., MD, 3756
Commonwealth Fund, The, NY, 5800
Communities Foundation of Oklahoma, OK, 7742
Communities Foundation of Texas, Inc., TX, 8773
Communities of Coastal Georgia Foundation, Inc., GA, 2431
Community Fdn. of Delaware County, OH, *see* 7431
Community Foundation - Boulder County, The, CO, 1391
Community Foundation Alliance, Inc., IN, 3277
Community Foundation for Greater Atlanta, The, GA, 2432
Community Foundation for Greater Buffalo, NY, 5801
Community Foundation for Greater New Haven, The, CT, 1562
Community Foundation for Monterey County, CA, 414
Community Foundation for Muskegon County, MI, 4369
Community Foundation for Nantucket, MA, 3990
Community Foundation for Northeast Georgia, GA, 2433
Community Foundation for Northeast Michigan, MI, 4370
Community Foundation for Northern Virginia, VA, 9410
Community Foundation for Palm Beach and Martin Counties, Inc., FL, 2032
Community Foundation for San Benito County, CA, 415
Community Foundation for South Central New York, Inc., The, NY, 5802
Community Foundation for Southeast Michigan, MI, 4371
Community Foundation for Southeastern Michigan, MI, *see* 4371
Community Foundation for Southern Arizona, AZ, 101
Community Foundation for Southwest Washington, WA, 9603
Community Foundation for the Alleghenies, The, PA, 7990
Community Foundation for the Central Savannah River Area, GA, 2434
Community Foundation for the Fox Valley Region, Inc., WI, 9832
Community Foundation for the Greater Capital Region, Inc., The, NY, 5803
Community Foundation for the Land of Lincoln, IL, 2762
Community Foundation for the National Capital Region, The, DC, 1893
Community Foundation for the Ohio Valley, Inc., WV, 9773
Community Foundation in Jacksonville, The, FL, *see* 2031
Community Foundation of Abilene, TX, 8774
Community Foundation of Acadiana, LA, 3623
Community Foundation of Ardmore, Inc., OK, 7743
Community Foundation of Bloomington and Monroe County, Inc., IN, 3278
Community Foundation of Boone County, Inc., IN, 3279
Community Foundation of Brazoria County, Texas, The, TX, 8775
Community Foundation of Brevard County, Inc., FL, *see* 2033
Community Foundation of Brevard, FL, 2033
Community Foundation of Broward, FL, 2034
Community Foundation of Burke County, NC, 7178
Community Foundation of Cape Cod, The, MA, *see* 3974
Community Foundation of Carroll County, Inc., MD, 3757
Community Foundation of Central Florida, Inc., FL, *see* 2015
Community Foundation of Central Georgia, Inc., GA, 2435
Community Foundation of Central Illinois, IL, 2763
Community Foundation of Central Wisconsin, Inc., WI, 9833
Community Foundation of Champaign County, IL, *see* 2765
Community Foundation of Collier County, FL, 2035
Community Foundation of Decatur/Macon County, The, IL, 2764
Community Foundation of East Central Illinois, IL, 2765
Community Foundation of Eastern Connecticut, CT, 1563
Community Foundation of Elmira-Corning and the Finger Lakes, Inc., The, NY, 5804
Community Foundation of Fayette County, PA, 7991
Community Foundation of Fort Dodge and United Way, IA, 3419
Community Foundation of Frederick County, MD, Inc., The, MD, 3758
Community Foundation of Gaston County, Inc., NC, 7179
Community Foundation of Grant County, IN, 3280
Community Foundation of Greater Birmingham, AL, 21
Community Foundation of Greater Chattanooga, Inc., The, TN, 8548
Community Foundation of Greater Des Moines, IA, 3420
Community Foundation of Greater Dubuque, IA, 3421
Community Foundation of Greater Flint, MI, 4372
Community Foundation of Greater Fort Wayne, Inc., IN, 3281
Community Foundation of Greater Greensboro, Inc., NC, 7180
Community Foundation of Greater Jackson, MS, 4820
Community Foundation of Greater Johnstown, The, PA, *see* 7990
Community Foundation of Greater Lafayette, The, IN, 3282
Community Foundation of Greater Lakeland, Inc., The, FL, *see* 2123
Community Foundation of Greater Lorain County, The, OH, *see* 7412
Community Foundation of Greater Memphis, TN, 8549
Community Foundation of Greater New Britain, CT, 1564
Community Foundation of Greater South Wood County, Inc., WI, *see* 9867
Community Foundation of Greater Tampa, Inc., The, FL, *see* 2040
Community Foundation of Greenville, Inc., SC, 8474
Community Foundation of Gunnison Valley, CO, 1392
Community Foundation of Harrisonburg and Rockingham County, The, VA, 9411
Community Foundation of Henderson County, Inc., NC, 7181

Community Foundation of Herkimer & Oneida Counties, Inc., The, NY, 5805
Community Foundation of Howard County, Inc., The, IN, 3283
Community Foundation of Howard County, MD, 3759
Community Foundation of Huntsville/Madison County, AL, 22
Community Foundation of Jackson County, Inc., The, IN, 3284
Community Foundation of Jackson Hole, WY, 9975
Community Foundation of Johnson County, IA, 3422
Community Foundation of Lorain County, The, OH, 7412
Community Foundation of Louisville, Inc., The, KY, 3569
Community Foundation of Madison and Jefferson County, Inc., IN, 3285
Community Foundation of Mendocino County, Inc., The, CA, 416
Community Foundation of Metropolitan Tarrant County, The, TX, see 8776
Community Foundation of Middle Tennessee, Inc., TN, 8550
Community Foundation of Mount Vernon & Knox County, OH, 7413
Community Foundation of Muncie and Delaware County, Inc., The, IN, 3286
Community Foundation of New Jersey, NJ, 5232
Community Foundation of North Central Florida, Inc., FL, 2036
Community Foundation of North Central Washington, WA, 9604
Community Foundation of North Central Wisconsin, Inc., WI, 9834
Community Foundation of North Florida, Inc., The, FL, 2037
Community Foundation of North Louisiana, The, LA, 3624
Community Foundation of North Texas, TX, 8776
Community Foundation of Northeast Alabama, AL, 23
Community Foundation of Northeast Florida, Inc., The, FL, see 2031
Community Foundation of Northeast Iowa, IA, 3423
Community Foundation of Northern Colorado, CO, 1393
Community Foundation of Northern Illinois, IL, 2766
Community Foundation of Northwest Connecticut, Inc., The, CT, 1565
Community Foundation of Northwest Georgia, Inc., GA, 2436
Community Foundation of Northwest Mississippi, MS, 4821
Community Foundation of Orange and Sullivan, Inc., NY, see 5806
Community Foundation of Orange County, Inc., NY, 5806
Community Foundation of Portage County, Inc., WI, see 9833
Community Foundation of Randolph County, Inc., IN, 3287
Community Foundation of Riverside County, CA, see 419
Community Foundation of San Joaquin, CA, 417
Community Foundation of Santa Cruz County, The, CA, see 418
Community Foundation of Sarasota County, Inc., The, FL, 2038
Community Foundation of Shelby County, The, OH, 7414
Community Foundation of Shreveport-Bossier, LA, see 3624
Community Foundation of Sidney and Shelby County, The, OH, see 7414
Community Foundation of South Alabama, The, AL, 24
Community Foundation of South Georgia, Inc., GA, 2437
Community Foundation of South Lake County, Inc., FL, 2039
Community Foundation of South Puget Sound, The, WA, 9605
Community Foundation of Southeastern Connecticut, Inc., The, CT, see 1563
Community Foundation of Southeastern Massachusetts, MA, 3991
Community Foundation of Southern Indiana, IN, 3288
Community Foundation of Southern Wisconsin, Inc., WI, 9835
Community Foundation of Southwest Georgia, Inc., GA, see 2437
Community Foundation of Southwest Kansas, KS, 3502
Community Foundation of Southwest Louisiana, LA, 3625
Community Foundation of St. Clair County, MI, 4373
Community Foundation of St. Joseph County, IN, 3289
Community Foundation of Susquehanna and Wyoming Counties, PA, see 7992
Community Foundation of Tampa Bay, Inc., FL, 2040
Community Foundation of the Central Blue Ridge, The, VA, 9412
Community Foundation of the Chattahoochee Valley, GA, 2438
Community Foundation of the Chemung County Area and Corning Community Foundation, The, NY, see 5804
Community Foundation of the Dan River Region, VA, 9413
Community Foundation of the Eastern Shore, Inc., MD, 3760
Community Foundation of the Endless Mountains, PA, 7992
Community Foundation of the Florida Keys, Inc., FL, 2041
Community Foundation of the Fox River Valley, IL, 2767
Community Foundation of the Great River Bend, IA, 3424
Community Foundation of the Holland/Zeeland Area, The, MI, 4374
Community Foundation of the Lowcountry, SC, 8475
Community Foundation of the Mahoning Valley, OH, 7415
Community Foundation of the Ozarks, MO, 4872
Community Foundation of the Rappahannock River Region, Inc., VA, 9414
Community Foundation of the Texas Hill Country, TX, 8777
Community Foundation of the Upper Peninsula, MI, 4375
Community Foundation of the Virgin Islands, VI, 9377
Community Foundation of Tompkins County, NY, 5807
Community Foundation of Union County, Inc., OH, 7416
Community Foundation of Utah, The, UT, 9311
Community Foundation of Wabash County, IN, 3290
Community Foundation of Warren County, PA, 7993
Community Foundation of Washington County Maryland, Inc., MD, 3761
Community Foundation of Waterloo/Cedar Falls and Northeast Iowa, IA, see 3423
Community Foundation of West Alabama, AL, 25
Community Foundation of West Chester/Liberty, The, OH, 7417
Community Foundation of West Georgia, GA, 2439
Community Foundation of West Kentucky, KY, 3570
Community Foundation of Western Massachusetts, MA, 3992
Community Foundation of Western Nevada, NV, 5108
Community Foundation of Western North Carolina, Inc., The, NC, 7182
Community Foundation of Western Pennsylvania and Eastern Ohio, PA, 7994
Community Foundation of Western Virginia, VA, 9415
Community Foundation Santa Cruz County, CA, 418
Community Foundation Serving Coastal South Carolina, The, SC, see 8472
Community Foundation Serving Greeley and Weld County, CO, 1394
Community Foundation Serving Richmond & Central Virginia, The, VA, 9416
Community Foundation Serving Riverside and San Bernardino Counties, The, CA, 419
Community Foundation Serving Southwest Colorado, CO, 1395
Community Foundation Sonoma County, CA, 420
Community Foundation, Inc., MO, see 4872
Community Foundation, Inc., The, FL, 2031
Community Foundation, Inc., The, MS, 4819
Community Foundation, The, LA, see 3624
Community Foundations of the Hudson Valley, NY, 5808
Community Health Foundation of Warren, IL, 2768
Community Health Foundation of Western & Central New York, Inc., NY, see 6153
Community Life Foundation of Owensboro, KY, The, KY, see 3597
Community Memorial Foundation, IL, 2769
Community Safety Foundation, CA, 421
Community Trust Foundation, MD, 3762
Compass Bank Foundation, AL, see 9
Compton Family Foundation, Inc., TN, 8551
Compton Foundation, Inc., CA, 422
ConAgra Foods Feeding Children Better Foundation, NE, 5029
ConAgra Foods Foundation, NE, 5030
ConAgra Foundation, Inc., The, NE, see 5030
Conard-Davis Family Foundation, NY, 5809
Concorde Foundation, MO, 4873
Concordia Foundation, The, MD, 3763
Conduit Foundation, The, IL, 2770
Cone Foundation, Edward T., The, NY, 5810
Confidence Foundation, CA, 423
Conn Family Foundation, The, OH, 7418
Conn Memorial Foundation, FL, 2042
Connecticut Community Foundation, The, CT, 1566
Connecticut Health Foundation, Inc., CT, 1567
Connell Foundation, Michael J., CA, 424
Connelly Foundation, PA, 7995
Connolly Foundation, G. L., CA, 425
Connor Foundation, William E., The, NV, 5109
Connors Foundation, Inc., The, FL, 2043
Conservation Land Trust, The, CA, 426
Conservation, Food and Health Foundation, Inc., MA, 3993
Consolidated Natural Gas Company Foundation, VA, see 9422
Consolidated Papers Foundation, Inc., WI, see 9902
Constandy, Vaseleke H. Constandy, and C. Harry Constandy Memorial Trust, Harry K., PA, 7996
Constantin Foundation, Inc., The, TX, 8778
Constellation Energy Group Foundation, Inc., MD, see 3868
Consumer Health Foundation, DC, 1894
Consumers Energy Foundation, MI, 4376
Consumers Power Foundation, MI, see 4376
Conte Foundation, Sirpuhe & John, The, CA, 427
Conway Foundation, Inc., Ruth J. & Robert A., OH, 7419
Conway Foundation, Robert M. & Lois, NY, see 5811
Conway Foundation, Robert M., The, NY, 5811
Conwood Charitable Trust, TN, see 8528
Cook and Signe Ostby Charitable Foundation, Scott, The, CA, see 1278
Cook Charitable Foundation, MI, see 4378
Cook Family Foundation, MI, 4377
Cook Foundation, inc., Judith E. & Joseph C., Jr., The, TN, 8552
Cook Foundation, Peter C. and Emajean, MI, 4378
Cook Inlet Region, Inc. Foundation, The, AK, see 85
Cook, Sr. Charitable Foundation, Inc., Kelly Gene, TX, 8779
Cooke Foundation, Jack Kent, VA, 9417
Cooke Foundation, Ltd., HI, 2597
Cooney Family Foundation, Robert J. & Loretta W., IL, 2771
Cooper Family Foundation Inc., The, NY, 5812
Cooper Family Foundation, AZ, 102
Cooper Foundation, Abe and Ida, IL, 2772
Cooper Foundation, Harriet & Eli, NY, 5813
Cooper Foundation, Milton, NY, see 5812
Cooper Foundation, NE, 5031
Cooper Industries Foundation, TX, A
Cooper-Clark Foundation, The, KS, 3503
Cooper-Hohn Family Foundation, CT, see 1557
Cooper-Siegel Family Foundation, The, PA, 7997
Cooper-Standard Foundation Inc., MI, 4380
Cooperman Family Foundation, Leon and Toby, The, NJ, 5233
Cooperman Foundation, Leon & Toby, NJ, see 5233
Coopersmith Foundation, Rosenzweig, The, MI, 4379
Coors Foundation for the Performing Arts, Dallas Morse, DC, 1895
Coors Foundation, Adolph, CO, 1396
Cope Foundation, Ron and Carol, NE, 5032
Copeland Family Foundation, Inc., MA, 3994
Copernicus Society of America, PA, 7998
Copham Family Foundation, The, FL, 2044
COPIC Medical Foundation, CO, 1397
Copland Fund for Music, Inc., Aaron, The, NY, 5814
Copley Foundation, David C., CA, 428
Copley Foundation, James S., CA, see 428

Copp Foundation, Inc., The, CT, *see* 1667
Copper Beech Foundation, The, NY, 5815
Copses Family Foundation, The, CA, 429
Corbett Family Charitable Foundation Inc., The, FL, 2045
Corbin Foundation, Mary S. & David C., OH, 7420
Corboy Foundation, Philip H., IL, 2773
Corcoran Family Foundation, John and Mary, The, MA, 3995
Cord Foundation, E.L., The, NV, 5110
Cordelia Corp., NV, 5111
Cordish Family Foundation, Inc, MD, 3764
Coretz Family Foundation, OK, 7744
Corey Foundation, The, NY, 5816
Corkin Charitable Foundation, Robert Lloyd, MA, 3996
Corkins Family Foundation, DE, 1756
Cornell Douglas Foundation, Inc., MD, 3765
Cornell Foundation, Alverin M., IL, 2774
Cornell Memorial Foundation, Joseph and Robert, The, FL, 2046
Cornerstone Foundation of Northeastern Wisconsin Inc., WI, 9836
Cornerstone Foundation, NY, 5817
Cornerstone Project, The, TX, 8780
Corning Glass Works Foundation, NY, *see* 5818
Corning Incorporated Foundation, NY, 5818
Corning Trust, John J., RI, 8376
Cornucopia Family Foundation, MI, 4381
Cornwell and Peter Mann Foundation, Dominique, IL, 2775
Corpening, Jr. Memorial Foundation, Maxwell M., NC, 7183
Correll Family Foundation, Inc., The, GA, 2440
Corrigan Foundation, The, NY, *see* 5762
Cortopassi Family Foundation, The, CA, 430
Corvias Foundation, WA, 9606
Corzine Foundation, Joanne D., The, NY, 5819
Cosette Charitable Fund, The, MA, 3997
Coshocton Foundation, OH, 7421
Cosper Foundation, Judith McBean, The, CA, *see* 893
Coto Foundation, The, CA, 431
Cotsen Family Foundation, CA, 432
Cotswold Foundation, The, PA, 7999
Cottage Health Care Foundation, IL, *see* 2853
Cottrell Foundation, Frederick Gardner, AZ, 103
Coudert Foundation, Frederic R., NY, 5820
Coughlin-Saunders Foundation, Inc., LA, 3626
Coulson Foundation, Frank L. and Sarah Miller, The, PA, 8000
Coulter Foundation, Beckman, CA, 433
Coulter Foundation, Wallace H., FL, 2047
Coulter Trust, Wallace H., FL, 2048
Countess Moira Charitable Foundation, The, NY, 5821
Courts Foundation, Inc., GA, 2441
Cousins Foundation, Inc., The, GA, 2442
Cousins Properties Foundation, Inc., GA, 2443
Covenant Foundation, Inc., OH, 7422
Covenant Foundation, Inc., The, GA, 2444
Covenant Foundation, Inc., TX, 8781
Cowden Charitable Foundation, Faye L. and William L., TX, 8782
Cowden Foundation, Louetta M., TX, 8783
Cowell Foundation, S. H., CA, 434
Cowin Foundation, Joyce & Daniel, NY, 5822
Cowles Charitable Trust, The, NJ, 5234
Cowles Foundation, Harriet Cheney, WA, 9607
Cox Charity Trust, A. G., IL, 2776
Cox Family Foundation, Berry R., TX, 8784
Cox Family Fund, MN, 4639
Cox Foundation of Georgia, Inc., James M., The, GA, 2445
Cox Foundation, Inc., MO, 4874
Cox Foundation, John and Maurine, TX, 8785
Cox, Jr. Foundation, Inc., James M., GA, *see* 2560
Cox, Jr. Foundation, Jim, GA, 2446
Coydog Foundation, The, NY, 5823
Coyne Family Foundation, Richard & Jean, The, CA, 435
Coyne Foundation, Inc., Marshall B., DC, 1896
Coyote Foundation, Will E., TX, *see* 9070
Coypu Foundation, IL, 2777
CPB Foundation, OH, 7423
Crabby Beach Foundation, OR, 7838
Cracchiolo Foundation, Peter J. & Constance M., MI, 4382
Craft Foundation, Kathleen S., OK, 7745
Craig Foundation, E. L., MO, 4875
Craig Foundation, James P. and Rebecca T., VA, 9418
Craig II Family Foundation, C. A., TN, *see* 8553
Craig II Family Foundation, Deborah and C. A., TN, 8553
Craig, S.D. Heard and L.D. Heard Memorial Trust, T.E., The, TX, 8786
Craigslist Charitable Fund, CA, 436
Crail-Johnson Foundation, CA, 437
Crain Foundation, The, TX, 8787
Crain-Maling Foundation, IL, 2778
Cralle Foundation, Inc., The, KY, 3571
Cramer Family Foundation, Inc., Gerald and Daphna, The, NY, 5824
Cramer Family Foundation, Inc., Gerald B., NY, *see* 5824
Crampton Trust, AL, 26
Cranaleith Foundation, Inc., NY, 5825
Crane Family Foundation, Inc., Charles, The, MD, 3766
Crane Foundation, Inc., Josephine and Louise, MA, 3998
Crane Foundation, James R., TX, 8788
Crane Fund for Widows & Children, NJ, 5235
Crankstart Foundation, CA, 438
Crapo Charitable Foundation, Henry H., MA, A
Crary, Jr. Estate Trust, David, RI, 8377
Crawford Heritage Community Foundation, PA, 8001
Crawley Family Foundation, OK, 7746
Cray Foundation, Cloud L., MO, 4876
Creamer Foundation, J. Fletcher, NJ, 5236
Crean Foundation, The, CA, 439
Create Christian Research Education Action Technical Enterprise, Inc., MS, *see* 4822
CREATE Foundation, MS, 4822
Credit Suisse Americas Foundation, NY, 5826
Credit Suisse First Boston Foundation Trust, NY, *see* 5826
Creel Foundation, Inc., The, GA, *see* 2447
Creel-Harison Foundation Inc., GA, 2447
Crels Foundation, PA, 8002
Crescere Foundation, NV, 5112
Cressey Foundation, Bryan C. & Christina I., The, IL, 2779
Crestar Bank Charitable Trust, FL, *see* 2345
Crestlea Foundation, Inc., DE, 1757
Cricket Island Foundation, NY, 5827
Cricket Island Foundation, The, NY, *see* 5827
Crimson Lion Foundation, MA, 3999
Crippled Children's Foundation, TN, *see* 8543
Crisp Family Foundation, The, NY, 5828
Crisp Fund, Peter O., The, NY, *see* 5828
Criss Memorial Foundation, Dr. C.C. and Mabel L., MN, 4640
Criss Memorial Foundation, MN, *see* 4640
Criswell Foundation, Inc., W.A., TX, 8789
Crocker Trust, Mary A., CA, 440
Croll Foundation, The, MA, 4000
Cromwell Foundation, Barbara and George, The, MD, 3767
Cronin Foundation, MI, 4383
Crook Foundation, Eleanor, TX, 8790
Cross Charitable Foundation, Inc., MT, 5007
Cross Creek Foundation, Inc., CO, *see* 1403
Cross Family Charitable Foundation, Theodore L., NY, 5829
Cross Foundation, Inc., William E., MD, 3768
Cross Foundation, The, MA, 4001
CrossCurrents Foundation, Inc., DC, 1897
Crossed Foundation, Charles and Mary, The, NY, 5830
Crossroads Community Foundation, Inc., MA, *see* 4056
Crotty Family Foundation, Inc., The, MA, 4002
Croul Family Foundation, CA, 441
Crowell Trust f/b/o Charities, Renee C., TX, 8791
Crowell Trust, Henry P. and Susan C., CO, *see* 1398
Crowell Trust, The, CO, 1398
Crown Exchange Inc., Susan, IL, 2780
Crown Family Philanthropies, IL, *see* 2781
Crown Memorial, Arie and Ida, IL, 2781
Crown Point Community Foundation, IN, 3291
Crump Fund, Joe and Jessie, IL, 2782
Cruse Trust, Lee H., MO, 4877
Crystal Family Foundation, NV, 5113
Crystal Springs Foundation, WA, 9608
Crystal Trust, DE, 1758
CS Fund, CA, 442
CSRA Community Foundation, Inc., GA, *see* 2434
CTM Foundation, CO, *see* 1455
CTW Foundation, Inc., DE, 1759
Cullen Foundation, The, TX, 8792
Cullman Foundation, Inc., Lewis B. & Dorothy, NY, 5831
Culpeper Memorial Foundation, Inc., Daphne Seybolt, The, CT, 1568
Cultural Heritage Preservation Fund, The, TX, 8793
Culver's V.I.P. Foundation, Inc., WI, 9837
Culverhouse Family Foundation, Inc., FL, *see* 2232
Cumberland Community Foundation, Inc., NC, 7184
Cumming Foundation, WY, 9976
Cummings Family Foundation, Peter D. & Julie F., MI, 4384
Cummings Foundation, Inc., James H., NY, 5832
Cummings Foundation, Inc., MA, 4003
Cummings Foundation, Nathan, The, NY, 5833
Cummings Foundation, Peter & Julie Fisher, MI, *see* 4384
Cummings Memorial Fund, Frances L. & Edwin L., The, NY, 5834
Cummins Engine Foundation, IN, *see* 3292
Cummins Family Foundation, MN, 4641
Cummins Foundation, The, IN, 3292
CUNA Mutual Group Foundation, Inc., WI, 9838
CUNA Mutual Insurance Group Charitable Foundation, Inc., WI, *see* 9838
Cuneo Foundation, The, IL, 2783
Cunningham Foundation, Inc., Laura Moore, ID, 2630
Cuno Foundation, RI, 8378
Cupid Foundation, Inc., The, MD, 3769
Curb Family Foundation, Mike, TN, 8554
Curci Family Foundation, John, CA, 443
Curci Foundation, Shurl & Kay, The, CA, 444
Curran Charitable Foundation, John P. & Constance A., The, NY, 5835
Curran Family Foundation, Michael G., The, NC, 7185
Currents of Change, Inc., MA, 4004
Curry Foundation, Ravenel and Elizabeth, NY, 5836
Curry III Foundation, Ravenel B., NY, *see* 5836
Curtis Foundation Inc., The, NC, 7186
Curtis Fund, The, VT, *see* 9361
Curves Community Fund, Inc., The, TX, *see* 8898
Cusenza Family Foundation, John & Geraldine, CA, 445
Cushman Foundation, The, NY, 5837
Cutler Charitable Foundation, Melvin S., MA, 4005
Cutler Family Charitable Trust, Theodore H., MA, 4006
CVS Caremark Charitable Trust, Inc., RI, *see* 8379
CVS Health Foundation, RI, 8379
Cwierzyk and Sidney Gordon Trust Fund, Theresa A., NY, 5838
Cypress Foundation, Inc., NY, 5839
D & D Foundation, DC, see 1946
D and R Fund, IL, 2784
D'Addario Family Foundation, Inc., James, NY, 5841
D'Agostino Foundation, Filomena M., NY, 5843
D'Angelo Foundation, NJ, 5238
D.H.R. Foundation, IL, *see* 3128
Dabah Charitable Foundation, Inc., Renee & Ezra, NY, 5840
Dachs Foundation, A.M., CA, 446
Dade Community Foundation, FL, *see* 2238
Daedalus Foundation, Inc., NY, 5842
Dahan Family Foundation, Inc., The, TX, 8794
Dahan Foundation, Inc., Haron, The, MD, 3770
Dahl Trust, W. T. and Edna M., IA, 3425
DaimlerChrysler Corporation Fund, MI, *see* 4366
Dakota Charitable Foundation, Inc., SD, 8514
Dakota Foundation, Inc., The, NY, *see* 6224
Dalessandro Foundation, The, MA, 4007
Dalio Family Foundation, Inc., CT, *see* 1569
Dalio Foundation, Inc., CT, 1569
Dalis Foundation, The, VA, 9419
Dallas Foundation, The, TX, 8795
Dallepezze Foundation, Joanne & John, The, FL, 2049
Dalton Foundation, Inc., Dorothy U., MI, 4385
Dalton Foundation, Inc., Harry L., NC, *see* 7187
Dalton-Brand Foundation, Inc., NC, 7187
Daly Foundation, Robert and Carole, CA, 447

Desert Valley Charitable Foundation, CA, 461
Deshe Foundation, Ann and Ari, FL, 2062
Desich Foundation, Richard, DE, 1766
Detkin Family Foundation, Peter and Michelle, The, DE, 1767
Detroit Edison Foundation, MI, *see* 4410
Deuble Foundation, George H., The, OH, 7433
Deutsch Charity Foundation, Herman, The, NY, 5875
Deutsch Foundation, Carl & Roberta, CA, 462
Deutsch Foundation, Robert W., MD, 3779
Deutsche Bank Americas Foundation, NY, 5876
Devereaux Foundation, Richard C., The, MI, 4397
DeVito/Perlman Family Foundation, The, CA, A
Devlin Foundation, The, NY, 5877
Devonshire Associates, MA, *see* 4017
Devonshire Foundation, MA, 4017
Devonwood Foundation, DE, 1768
DeVos Foundation, Daniel and Pamella, MI, 4398
DeVos Foundation, Douglas & Maria, MI, 4399
DeVos Foundation, Richard and Helen, The, MI, 4400
Dew Foundation, IL, 2794
Dewan Foundation, The, NY, 5878
Dewar Foundation, Inc., NY, 5879
Dewey Marcks Foundation, Oliver, MI, 4401
DeWine Family Foundation, Inc., OH, 7434
DeWitt Families Conduit Foundation, MI, 4402
Dexter Trust, Henrietta F., RI, 8382
Deziel Family Foundation, Inc., George, MN, 4645
Dhanam Foundation, CA, 463
Dharma Foundation III, Inc., The, FL, *see* 2395
Dhont Family Foundation, The, CA, 464
Diagnostic Imaging Foundation, RI, 8383
Dialynas Family Foundation, Chris, CA, 465
Dialysis Research Foundation, UT, 9313
Diamond Charitable Trust, Miriam and Arthur, NY, 5880
Diamond Family Foundation, Jon & Susan, OH, 7435
Diamond Family Foundation, Robert & Jennifer, The, NY, 5881
Diamond Fund, Irene, NY, 5882
Dibner Charitable Trust of Massachusetts, The, MA, 4018
Diboll Private Foundation, Collins C., LA, 3628
DiCarlo Family Foundation, Inc., J.S. Plank & D.M., MD, 3780
Dicke Family Foundation, OH, 7436
Dickenson Foundation, Harriet F., The, IL, 2795
Dickenson Foundation, Harriet Ford, The, IL, *see* 2795
Dickinson Foundation, Donald C. & Elizabeth M., CA, 466
Dickson Foundation, Inc., The, NC, 7192
Dickson Foundation, Raymond, The, TX, *see* 8806
Dickson Memorial Trust, Conway Wing Dickson and Gertrude Finck, PA, 8009
Dickson-Allen Foundation, TX, 8806
Diebold Foundation, Inc., The, CT, 1574
Diebold Foundation, OH, 7437
Diener Foundation, Robert and Michelle, TX, 8807
Dierberg Foundation, The, MO, 4879
Dieringer Family Foundation, Bob and Evelyn, OR, 7839
Diermeier Family Foundation, FL, 2063
Dietrich Foundation, William B., PA, 8010
Diiriye Foundation, Inc., Sidciyo Jaamac Suldaan, PA, 8011
Diker Fund, Inc., Valerie & Charles, NY, 5883
Diller Foundation, The, NY, *see* 5884
Diller-von Furstenberg Family Foundation, The, NY, 5884
Dillon Foundation, IL, 2796
Dillon Foundation, NE, 5035
Dillon Fund, The, NY, 5885
Dillon, Jr. Foundation, Roderick H., OH, A
DiMare Foundation, Paul J., The, FL, 2064
DiMenna Family Foundation, Inc., The, NY, *see* 5886
DiMenna Foundation, Inc., The, NY, 5886
DiMino Family Trust, Frank, The, NY, 5887
DiMino Memorial Foundation, Raymond, The, NY, *see* 5887
Dimmer Family Foundation, The, WA, 9610
Dimon Foundation, James and Judith K., The, IL, 2797
Dinan Family Foundation, The, NY, 5888
Dinan Foundation, Inc., James G., NY, *see* 5888
Dinovi Family Foundation, The, MA, 4019
Dintersmith-Hazard Foundation, The, MA, 4020
Diomedes Foundation, The, MA, 4021
Dircks Foundation, Inc., Joan M., NJ, *see* 5241
Dircks Foundation, Inc., Robert and Joan, NJ, 5241
Dirshu International, Inc., NJ, 5242
Discount Foundation, The, NY, 5889
Discovery Foundation, The, TX, 8808
Discuren Charitable Foundation, WA, 9611
Disney Company Foundation, Walt, The, CA, 467
Disney Foundation, Lillian B., The, CA, *see* 468
Disney Foundation, Walt and Lilly, The, CA, 468
DiSomma Family Foundation, IL, 2798
Ditmars Foundation Inc., The, NY, 5890
Division Fund, IL, *see* 2862
Dixon Foundation, Francis J., The, PA, 8012
Dixon Foundation, Solon & Martha, AL, 30
Dixon Foundation, The, TX, *see* 8809
Dixon Water Foundation, The, TX, 8809
DJ & T Foundation, CA, 469
DLA Piper Foundation, The, MD, 3781
DMK Foundation, The, CA, 470
Do Unto Others Trust, Inc., FL, 2065
Dobberpuhl Foundation, Peter Hawkins, TN, 8557
Dobbs Foundation, Inc., Helen and Howard, GA, *see* 2449
Dobbs Trust, Samuel C., NC, 7193
Dobbs, Jr. Foundation, Inc., R. Howard, GA, 2449
Dobkin Family Foundation, NY, 5891
Dobson Family Foundation, OK, 7747
Doctorbird Foundation, DE, 1769
Doctorow Family Foundation, Jarvis and Constance, UT, 9314
Doctors Company Foundation, The, CA, 471
Dodero Trust for the Arts and Sciences, Corinne L., OH, 7438
Dodge City Area Foundation, KS, *see* 3502
Dodge Foundation, Inc., Cleveland H., NY, 5892
Dodge Foundation, Inc., Geraldine R., NJ, 5243
Dodge Jones Foundation, TX, 8810
Doe Family Foundation, The, MA, 4022
Doelger Charitable Trust, Thelma, CA, 472
Dogwood Foundation, The, TX, 8811
Doheny Foundation, Carrie Estelle, CA, 473
Doherty Charitable Foundation, Inc., Henry L. and Grace, The, NY, 5893
DOJ Support Organization, NY, 5894
Dolan Children's Foundation, NY, 5895
Dolan Family Foundation, NY, 5896
Dolby Family Foundation, CA, *see* 474
Dolby Family Fund, Ray and Dagmar, CA, 474
Dole Charitable Foundation, Elizabeth, The, DC, 1900
Dolfinger 2 Trust, PA, 8013
Dollar Bank Foundation, PA, 8014
Dollar General Employee Assistance Foundation, TN, 8558
Domanada Foundation, IL, 2799
Dominion Foundation, VA, 9422
Donaghue Foundation, The, CT, 1575
Donaghue Medical Research Foundation, Patrick and Catherine Weldon, The, CT, *see* 1575
Donahue Charitable Foundation, Richard K. & Nancy L., MA, 4023
Donahue Family Foundation, Inc., PA, 8015
Donaldson Charitable Trust, Oliver S. and Jennie R., FL, 2066
Donaldson Foundation, MN, 4646
Donchian Charitable Foundation, Inc., Richard D., CT, *see* 1576
Donchian Foundation, Inc., Richard Davoud, CT, 1576
Donghia Foundation, Inc., Angelo, NY, 5897
Donnelley Foundation, Gaylord and Dorothy, IL, 2800
Donnelley Foundation, R. R., IL, 2801
Donnelley Foundation, The, IL, 2802
Donner Family Charitable Foundation, David, NY, 5898
Donner Foundation, William H., The, NY, 5899
Donovan Foundation, NY, 5900
Doolin Family Foundation, The, CO, 1402
Doolittle Foundation, Harry and Misook, NY, 5901
Doornink Foundation, The, MI, 4403
Doran Family Charitable Trust, MA, 4024
Dore' Family Foundation, The, LA, 3629
Dorea Foundation, MN, 4647
Dorn Foundation, Randolph J. & Estelle M., OH, 7439
Dornette Foundation, Helen G., Henry F. & Louise T., OH, 7440
Dornick Foundation Inc., CO, 1403
Dorot Foundation, RI, 8384
Dorrance Family Foundation, AZ, 107
Doss Foundation, Inc., James & Dorothy, TX, 8812
Doss Foundation, Inc., M. S., The, TX, 8813
Doswell Foundation, H. J. & Florence A., TX, 8814
Dotson Family Foundation, The, OK, 7748
Doty Family Foundation, NY, 5902
Dougherty Family Foundation, CA, 475
Douglas Charitable Foundation, CA, *see* 476
Douglas County Community Foundation, KS, 3509
Douglas Foundation, CA, 476
Douglass Foundation, Terry D. and Rosann B., The, TN, A
Dove Family Foundation, AL, 31
Dove Foundation, G. Mack and Nancy R., The, AL, *see* 31
Dove Givings Foundation II, NY, 5904
Dove Givings Foundation, NY, 5903
Dover Foundation, Inc., NC, 7194
Dover Foundation, The, IL, 2803
Dovid Inc., Zichron Zvi, NY, 5905
Dow Chemical Company Foundation, The, MI, 4404
Dow Corning Foundation, MI, 4405
Dow Foundation, Christina and Robert, The, NJ, 5244
Dow Foundation, Herbert H. and Barbara C., MI, 4406
Dow Foundation, Herbert H. and Grace A., The, MI, 4407
Dow Fund, Alden & Vada, MI, 4408
Dow Jones Foundation, NY, 5906
Dowling Jr. Foundation, William C., NY, 5907
Downey Foundation, James E., The, CA, 477
Downing Foundation, Barry L. & Paula M., KS, 3510
Downs Miller Foundation, Inc., Doreen, NY, 5908
Doyle Foundation, Inc., Frank M., The, NV, 5115
Doyle Foundation, William and Kathy, IL, 2804
Doyon Foundation, The, AK, 86
DPC Community Foundation, VA, *see* 9413
DPR Foundation, CA, 478
Dr. Bronners Family Foundation, CA, 479
Draper Charitable Foundation, Nancy-Carroll, DE, 1770
Draper Foundation, CT, A
Draper Foundation, The, CA, 480
Draper Richards Foundation, The, CA, *see* 481
Draper Richards Kaplan Foundation, The, CA, 481
Dreams R US Foundation, NY, 5909
Dreiling Charitable Trust, Leo J. & Albina, KS, 3511
Dreiseszun Family Foundation, The, KS, 3512
Dreitzer Foundation Inc., NY, 5910
Dresher Foundation, Inc., The, MD, 3782
Dresner Foundation, MI, *see* 4409
Dresner Foundation, Vera and Joseph, MI, 4409
Drew Family Foundation, CA, 482
Drexler Foundation, Peggy and Millard, NY, 5911
Dreyfus Foundation, Inc., Camille and Henry, The, NY, 5912
Dreyfus Foundation, Inc., Jean and Louis, NY, 5913
Dreyfus Foundation, Inc., Max and Victoria, The, DC, 1901
Dreyfus Foundation, VA, 9423
Driehaus Foundation, Richard H., The, IL, 2805
Driscoll Foundation, MN, 4648
Driskill Charitable Foundation, Walter S. and Lucienne, IL, 2806
Drizin Charitable Foundation, Mmac, NY, 5914
Drollinger Family Charitable Foundation, CA, 483
Drown Foundation, Joseph, CA, 484
Druckenmiller Foundation, NY, 5915
Drumcliff Foundation, The, PA, 8016
DRW Trading Group Foundation, IL, 2807
Dryer Charitable Foundation, Edward T. & Ellen K., IL, 2808
DS Foundation, The, FL, 2067
DSF Charitable Foundation, PA, 8017
DTE Energy Foundation, MI, 4410
Duane Reade Charitable Foundation, DE, 1771
Dubin Family Foundation, G. & E., NY, 5916
DuBose Foundation, Inc., Frances and Beverly, The, GA, 2450
DuBow Family Foundation, Inc., FL, 2068
Duchossois Family Foundation, The, IL, 2809
Duchossois Foundation, The, IL, *see* 2809
Duckwall Foundation, Frank E., FL, 2069
Ducommun & Gross Foundation, CA, 485

Emerson Directors & Officers Charitable Trust, IL, 2822
Emerson Family Foundation, CA, 505
Emerson Foundation, Inc., Fred L., NY, 5950
Emery Memorial, Thomas J., The, OH, 7443
Emes Foundation, Inc., NY, 5951
EMLE, Inc., NY, 5952
Empire Health Foundation, WA, 9615
Empire State Foundation, NY, 5953
Employers Mutual Charitable Foundation, IA, *see* 3428
Emporia Community Foundation, KS, 3514
Empower Baltimore Management Corporation, MD, A
EnCana Cares (USA) Foundation, CO, 1407
Ende Menzer Walsh & Quinn Retirees' Widows' & Children's Assistance Fund, IL, 2823
Endeavor Foundation, AR, 186
Endesha Group, WA, *see* 9738
Endowment for Health, Inc., NH, 5169
Endowment for Regional Sustainability Science, TX, 8829
Energen Foundation, AL, 32
Energizer Charitable Trust, IL, 2824
Energy East Foundation, Inc., The, ME, *see* 3693
EnergySolutions Foundation, UT, 9321
Engdahl Family Foundation, The, MN, 4654
Engelberg Foundation, The, FL, 2086
Engelhard Foundation, Charles, The, NY, 5954
Engelhardt Family Foundation, MO, 4886
Engelstad Family Foundation, NV, 5117
Engemann Family Foundation, CA, 506
England Family Foundation, Inc., Lois & Richard, The, MD, 3785
England Foundation, Inc., Lois & Richard, The, MD, *see* 3785
England Trust, Elizabeth R., PA, 8024
Englander Foundation, Inc., NY, 5955
Engler Foundation, Paul F. and Virginia J., TX, 8830
English Foundation, W. C., VA, 9426
English Memorial Fund, Florence C. and Harry L., The, GA, 2453
English-Bonter-Mitchell Foundation, IN, 3299
Enlight Foundation, CA, 507
Enoch Foundation Charitable Trust, DE, *see* 1775
Enoch Foundation, The, DE, 1775
Enrico Foundation, Roger and Rosemary, The, TX, 8831
Ensworth Charitable Foundation, CT, 1580
Entelechy Foundation, The, GA, 2454
Entergy Charitable Foundation, LA, 3630
Enterprise Foundation Trust, NY, 5956
Enterprise Holdings Foundation, MO, 4887
Enterprise Rent-A-Car Foundation, MO, *see* 4887
Environment Now Foundation, CA, 508
Eos Foundation, MA, 4037
Ephraim Project, Inc., The, FL, 2087
Epker-Sinha Foundation, MA, 4038
Eppley Foundation for Research, Inc., The, NY, 5957
Epstein Family Foundation, CA, 509
Epstein Family Foundation, Dan J., IL, 2825
Epstein Family Foundation, Inc., Diana and Michael David, MD, 3786
Epstein Philanthropies, NY, *see* 5958
Epstein Teicher Philanthropies, NY, 5958
EQT Foundation, Inc., PA, 8025
Equifax Foundation, GA, 2455
Equinox Foundation, Inc., NY, *see* 6639
Equipart Foundation, The, NY, 5959
Equitable Foundation, Inc., The, NY, *see* 5629
Equitable Resources Foundation, Inc., PA, *see* 8025
Erb Family Foundation, Fred A. and Barbara M., MI, 4415
Erb Family Foundation, MI, *see* 4415
Ergon Foundation, Inc., MS, 4824
Erie Community Foundation, The, PA, 8026
Erie County Community Foundation, OH, 7444
Erion Foundation, CO, 1408
Erlbaum Family Foundation, PA, 8027
Esco Foundation, The, OR, 7841
Eshelman Foundation, The, DE, 1776
Eskenazi Family Foundation, Inc., IN, 3300
Eskind and Family Foundation, Jane and Richard, The, TN, 8563
ESL Charitable Foundation, NY, 5960
Esman Foundation, Inc., Saul and Theresa, The, FL, 2088
Esperance Family Foundation, The, DE, 1777
ESSA Bank & Trust Foundation, PA, 8028
Essel Foundation, Inc., NY, 5961
Essex County Community Foundation, Inc., MA, 4039
Estes Foundation, VA, 9427
Ethics & Excellence in Journalism Foundation, OK, 7749
Etnier Charitable Trust, Oliver, DE, 1778
Ettinger Foundation, Inc., The, DE, 1779
ETZ Chaim Charitable Trust, The, NY, 5962
Eucalyptus Foundation, The, CA, 510
Eugene McDermott Foundation, The, TX, 8832
Eustace Foundation, The, PA, 8029
Eustace-Kwan Family Foundation, CA, 511
Evans Family Foundation, The, MA, 4040
Evans Foundation, Charles, The, NJ, 5254
Evans Foundation, Edward P., VA, 9428
Evanston Community Foundation, IL, 2826
Eveillard Family Charitable Trust, NY, 5963
Everett Community Foundation, Greater, The, WA, 9616
Everett Foundation, Inc., NY, 5964
Everett Mutual Savings Bank Foundation, WA, *see* 9617
Everlasting Private Foundation, CA, 512
Evert Foundation, MN, 4655
Evertrust Foundation, WA, 9617
Every Voice In Action Foundation, AZ, 109
Evinrude Foundation, Inc., Ralph, WI, 9841
Evslin Family Foundation, Inc., The, VT, 9360
Ewing Foundation, Inc., Frank M., MD, 3787
Exelon Foundation, IL, 2827
Express Scripts Foundation, MO, 4888
ExxonMobil Foundation, TX, 8833
Eye, Ear, Nose and Throat Foundation, LA, 3631
EZ Agape Foundation, The, GA, 2456
Ezcorp Foundation, TX, 8834
Ezell Foundation, Inc., TN, 8564

Fabert Foundation, Martin, The, WA, 9618
Fabri-Kal Foundation, MI, 4416
Factor Family Foundation, Max, CA, 513
Factor Foundation, Ben E., The, LA, 3632
Faigen Family Foundation, Inc., FL, 2089
Fain Family Foundation, Norman and Rosalie, The, RI, 8388
Fain Foundation, The, TX, 8835
Fain Fund Trust, Norman & Rosalie, RI, *see* 8388
Fair Oaks Foundation, PA, 8030
Fair Play Foundation, DE, 1780
Fairbanks Family Foundation, The, NJ, 5255
Fairbanks Foundation, Inc., IN, *see* 3301
Fairbanks Foundation, Inc., Richard M., IN, 3301
Fairchild Foundation, Inc., Sherman, The, MD, 3788
Fairfield County Community Foundation, Inc., CT, *see* 1581
Fairfield County Foundation, OH, 7445
Fairfield County's Community Foundation, Inc., CT, 1581
Fairfield Foundation, The, NY, 5965
Fairholme Foundation, The, FL, 2090
Fairmount Minerals Foundation, The, OH, 7446
Fairweather Foundation, The, NV, 5118
Faith, Hope and Love Foundation, CA, 514
Falcon Foundation, Inc., NJ, 5256
Falcon Fund Foundation, The, NY, 5966
Falcone Trust, Anthony P., The, PA, 8031
Falconwood Foundation, Inc., NY, 5967
Falic Family Foundation, The, FL, 2091
Falk Medical Research Trust, Dr. Ralph and Marian, RI, 8389
Falling Leaves Foundation Inc., CA, 515
Fallon Family Charitable Foundation, MA, 4041
Family Christian Stores Foundation, MI, 4417
Family DeVos Foundation, Dick & Betsy, MI, 4418
Family Foundation Inc., M.W., NJ, 5258
Family Foundation, Debby Durham, NE, 5038
Family Foundation, Inc., Kelly, MA, 4042
Family Foundation, Inc., Weber, WI, 9842
Family Foundation, Torcivia, NJ, 5257
Family Foundation, Watson, TX, 8836
FAMRI, FL, *see* 2099
Fancelli Foundation, Inc., FL, 2092
Fanch Family Foundation, Inc., CO, *see* 1505
Fansler Foundation, CA, 516
Fant Foundation, The, TX, 8837
Fanwood Foundation, The, NY, 5968
Farallon Foundation, CA, 517
Farash Charitable Foundation, Max & Marian, NY, 5969
Farber Family Foundation Inc., PA, 8032
Farber Foundation, Gloria and Hilliard, The, NY, 5970
Farber Foundation, The, MO, 4889
Farese Family Foundation, The, CA, 518
Fargo-Moorhead Area Foundation, ND, 7351
Farid Foundation, CT, 1582
Farish Fund, William Stamps, The, TX, 8838
Farmer Family Foundation, OH, 7447
Farmhouse Foundation, The, DE, A
Farnham Foundation, IL, 2828
Farnsworth Trust, Charles H., MA, 4043
Farrell Family Foundation, CA, 519
Farrington Foundation, Alberta B., AZ, 110
Fascitelli Family Foundation, The, NY, 5971
Fasenmyer Foundation, Richard J., OH, 7448
Fasken Foundation, The, TX, 8839
Fath Charitable Foundation, Creekmore and Adele, TX, 8840
Faucett Catalyst Fund, CA, 520
Faucett Family Foundation, CA, *see* 520
Faulconer Scholarship Programs, The, TX, 8841
Favrot Fund, The, TX, 8842
FCCF, CT, *see* 1581
FDC Foundation, IL, 2829
Fearons, III Charitable Trust, George H., NY, 5972
Federated Department Stores Foundation, OH, *see* 7552
Federated Investors Foundation, Inc., PA, 8033
Fehsenfeld Family Foundation Inc., J.E., The, IN, 3302
Feigenbaum Foundation, Inc., The, MA, 4044
Feil Family Foundation, The, NY, 5973
Feil Foundation, Inc., Louis & Gertrude, NY, *see* 5973
Feild Co-Operative Association Inc., MS, 4825
Feinberg Foundation, Joseph and Bessie, IL, 2830
Feinstein Family Foundation, NY, *see* 5974
Feinstein Family Fund, RI, 8390
Feinstein Foundation, Inc., The, RI, 8391
Feinstein Foundation, Susan & Leonard, NY, 5974
Felburn Foundation, MD, 3789
Feldman Family Foundation, Moses, The, PA, 8034
Feldman Family Foundation, The, TX, 8843
Felicia Fund, Inc., RI, 8392
Fels Family Foundation, MA, 4045
Fels Fund, Samuel S., PA, 8035
Femino Foundation, CA, *see* 521
Femino Foundation, James J. and Sue, The, CA, 521
Fenn S P No. 1, OH, 7449
Fenwick Foundation, NJ, 5259
Feraldo Memorial Fund, William Pablo, MO, 4890
Ferguson Charitable Trust, Dan C., FL, 2093
Ferguson Foundation, Leonard C. & Mildred F., OH, 7450
Fernleigh Foundation, NY, 5975
Ferrantino Charitable Foundation, J., MI, 4419
Ferraro Family Foundation Inc., FL, 2094
Ferree Foundation, PA, 8036
Ferring Family Foundation, John and Alison, The, MO, 4891
Ferry Family Foundation, The, OH, 7451
Fertel Foundation, Ruth U., LA, 3633
Fetzer Foundation, Inc., John E., MI, *see* 4420
Fetzer Institute, Inc., John E., MI, 4420
Fetzer Memorial Trust Fund, John E., MI, 4421
Fidelity Foundation, NH, 5170
Field Family Foundation, Eris & Larry, CA, 522
Field Foundation of Illinois, Inc., The, IL, 2831
Field Foundation, Frances K. & Charles D., The, CA, 523
Field Foundation, Joseph and Marie, PA, 8037
Field Fund, Charles D. and Frances K., The, CA, 524
Fields Pond Foundation, Inc., MA, 4046
Fieldstone 1793 Foundation, PA, 8038
Fife Family Foundation, Eugene V., VA, 9429
Fifth & Pacific Foundation, NY, 5976
Fifth Third Foundation, The, OH, 7452
Fikes Foundation, Leland, TX, 8844
Filene Foundation, Inc., Lincoln and Therese, MA, 4047
FIMF, Inc., NY, 5977
Finch Foundation, Thomas Austin, MA, 4048
Find Us Faithful Foundation, CO, 1409
Findlay Education Foundation, NV, 5119

Findlay Hancock County Community Foundation, The, OH, 7453
Fine & Greenwald Foundation, Inc., The, FL, 2095
Fine Family Foundation, The, PA, see 8039
Fine Foundation, The, PA, 8039
Fineberg Foundation, CA, 525
Fineshriber Family Foundation, The, CA, 526
Finger Family Foundation, Marvy, TX, 8845
Finish Line Youth Foundation, Inc., IN, 3303
Fink Foundation, Betsy and Jesse, CT, 1583
Finlay Foundation Inc., Curtis, AL, 33
Finley Foundation, Ernest L. and Ruth W., CA, 527
Finley Foundation, Inc., A. E., NC, 7199
Finnegan Family Foundation, IL, 2832
Finnegan Foundation, IL, see 2832
Finneran Family Foundation, NY, 5978
Firedoll Foundation, CA, 528
Firelight Endowment, CA, 529
Firelight Foundation, CA, see 529
Fireman Charitable Foundation, Paul and Phyllis, The, MA, 4049
Fireman Charitable Foundation, Simon C., The, FL, 2096
Firestone Foundation, Roger S., NJ, 5260
Firestone, Jr. Foundation, Harvey, MI, 4422
Firman Fund, OH, 7454
First Bank of Highland Park Foundation, IL, 2833
First Citizens Foundation, Inc., SC, 8477
First Community Foundation Partnership of Pennsylvania, PA, 8040
First County Bank Foundation, Inc., CT, 1584
First Data Foundation, CO, A
First Eagle Investment Management Foundation, DE, 1781
First Financial Northwest Foundation, WA, 9619
First Fruit, Inc., CA, 530
First Hawaiian Bank Foundation, HI, 2598
First Hawaiian Foundation, HI, see 2598
First Horizon Foundation, TN, 8565
First Hospital Foundation, The, PA, 8041
First Interstate BancSystem Foundation, Inc., MT, 5009
First National Bank in Wichita Charitable Trust, KS, see 3522
First Niagara Bank Foundation, NY, see 5979
First Niagara Foundation, NY, 5979
First Tennessee Foundation, TN, see 8565
FirstEnergy Foundation, OH, 7455
Firstfruits Foundation, PA, 8042
Firstgreen Foundation, Inc., The, MA, 4050
FirstMerit Foundation, OH, 7456
FIS Foundation, Inc., FL, 2097
FISA Foundation, PA, 8043
Fisch Foundation, Ben & Maytee, TX, 8846
Fischel Foundation, Harry and Jane, NY, 5980
Fischer Charitable Trust, Andrew and Alice, IL, 2834
Fischer Family Foundation 2008, The, KY, 3574
Fischer Family Foundation, The, NY, 5981
Fischer Foundation, Friderika, The, NY, see 7031
Fischer Foundation, Jill and Charles, TX, 8847
Fischmann Family Foundation, CA, 531
Fish Charitable Foundation, Lawrence K., The, MA, see 4051
Fish Family Foundation, MA, 4051
Fish Foundation, Inc., NJ, 5261
Fish Foundation, Ray C., TX, 8848
Fishback Foundation Trust, Harmes C., CO, 1410
Fisher Brothers Foundation, Inc., The, NY, 5982
Fisher Education Fund, Doris & Donald, CA, see 532
Fisher Family Foundation, MA, 4052
Fisher Foundation Inc., Renee B., CT, 1586
Fisher Foundation, Doris & Donald, CA, see 370
Fisher Foundation, Eileen, NY, 5983
Fisher Foundation, Gramma, MD, 3790
Fisher Foundation, Inc., CT, 1585
Fisher Foundation, Inc., Max M. and Marjorie S., MI, 4423
Fisher Fund, Doris & Donald, CA, 532
Fishman Foundation, Jill and Mark, The, PA, 8044
Fishoff Family Foundation, The, NY, 5984
Fitch Trust, Lydia J., PA, 8045
Fiterman Family Foundation, Mike & Linda, MN, 4656
Fiterman Foundation, Jack and Bessie, The, MN, see 4656
Fites Family Charitable Trust, FL, 2098
Fitt and James I. McLaren Foundation, Lawton W., NY, 5985
Fitzgerald Foundation, Inc., Betty and Davis, GA, 2457
Five Bridges Foundation, CA, 533
Fjarli Foundation, Inc., Merlin and Jo Ann, The, OR, 7843
Fjarli Foundation, OR, 7842
Flack Foundation, Inc., J. Hunter, AL, 34
Flagg Creek Foundation, IL, see 2960
Flagler Foundation, The, VA, A
Flaherty Family Foundation, The, NY, 5986
Flamboyan Foundation, Inc., DC, 1904
Flatley Foundation, The, MA, 4053
Fledgling Fund, The, NY, 5987
Fleischmann Foundation, OH, 7457
Fleishhacker Foundation, CA, 534
Fleming Endowment, TX, 8849
Fleming Family Foundation, OH, 7458
Fleming Foundation, Porter, GA, 2458
Fleming Foundation, TX, 8850
Fletcher Foundation, Alice Virginia & David W., MD, 3791
Fletcher Foundation, The, MA, 4054
Flextronics Foundation, CA, 535
Flight Attendant Medical Research Institute, Inc., FL, 2099
Flinn Family Foundation, Ethel and James, MI, see 4424
Flinn Foundation, Ethel and James, MI, 4424
Flinn Foundation, The, AZ, 111
Flinn, Jr. Charitable Trust, Stephanie & Lawrence, NY, 5988
Flint Family Foundation, OK, 7750
Flippo Foundation, Jane and Arthur, The, VA, 9430
Flom Family Foundation, The, NY, 5989
Flora Family Foundation, CA, 536
Florescue Family Foundation, Inc., FL, 2100
Florida Blue Foundation, FL, 2101
Florman Family Foundation Inc., The, FL, 2102
Flournoy Georgia Portsmouth Trust, FL, 2103
Flow Foundation, Inc., NC, 7200
Flowers Foundation, J. C., NY, 5990
Flowers, Jr. Foundation, Inc., William Howard, GA, 2459
Fluor Foundation, Marjorie L. and J. Simon, CO, A
Fluor Foundation, The, TX, 8851
Flynn Foundation, J. & V., IL, 2835
FM Global Foundation, RI, 8393
FMH Foundation, TX, 8852
Focus Autism, Inc., NJ, 5262
Foellinger Foundation, Inc., IN, 3304
Fogelman Foundation, Martha and Robert, TN, see 8575
Fogelson Foundation, The, IL, 2836
Foglia Family Foundation, IL, 2837
Fohs Foundation, OR, 7844
Foley Family Charitable Foundation, The, FL, 2104
Foley Family Foundation Inc., Lawrence & Megan, CT, 1587
Folger Fund, Lee and Juliet, The, VA, 9431
Folger Fund, The, VA, see 9431
Fond du Lac Area Foundation, WI, 9843
Fondren Foundation, The, TX, 8853
Food Lion Charitable Foundation, Inc., NC, 7201
Foop Foundation, The, NY, 5991
Foothills Community Foundation, SC, 8478
Foothills Foundation, The, CA, 537
For HIS Adopted Children, Inc., GA, see 2550
Forbesway Foundation, PA, see 8198
Force for Good Foundation, The, UT, see 9340
Forchheimer Foundation, Leo and Julia, NY, 5992
Forchheimer Foundation, The, NY, see 5992
Ford Family Foundation, Gerald J., TX, 8854
Ford Family Foundation, The, NY, 5993
Ford Family Foundation, The, OR, 7845
Ford Family Foundation, TX, see 8854
Ford Foundation, David B. & Virginia M., The, NY, see 5993
Ford Foundation, Edward E., The, NY, 5995
Ford Foundation, Inc., Gertrude C., The, MS, 4826
Ford Foundation, Joseph F. and Clara, MA, 4055
Ford Foundation, NY, 5994
Ford Foundation, William & Lisa, MI, 4425
Ford Fund, Benson and Edith, MI, 4426
Ford Fund, Eleanor and Edsel, MI, 4427
Ford Fund, S.N. & Ada, OH, 7459
Ford Fund, William and Martha, MI, 4428
Ford II Fund, Henry, The, MI, 4429
Ford Meter Box Foundation, Inc., IN, 3305
Ford Motor Company Fund, MI, 4430
Fordham Street Foundation, NY, 5996
Fore River Foundation, ME, 3687
Foreign Mission Foundation, OR, 7846
Foreman Family Foundation, Peter and Virginia, IL, see 3163
Forest Foundation, WA, 9620
Forest Lawn Foundation, CA, see 263
Forester Charitable Trust, John & Alice, WI, 9844
Formanek Foundation, TN, 8566
Forst Family Foundation, NY, 5997
Forster Family Foundation, The, DC, 1905
Forsythia Foundation, DC, 1906
Fort Atkinson Community Foundation, WI, 9845
Fort Collins Area Community Foundation, CO, see 1393
Fort Foundation, Inc., Mildred Miller, GA, 2460
Fort Wayne Community Foundation, IN, see 3281
Fortin Foundation of Florida, Inc., The, FL, 2106
Fortin Foundation, Mary Alice, The, FL, 2105
Fortis Foundation, NY, see 5621
Fortisure Foundation, CA, 538
Fortune Education Foundation, Inc., NJ, 5263
Fossett Foundation, Peggy and Steve, IL, 2838
Foster Charitable Foundation, Diana K. and Lawrence T., OH, see 7696
Foster Family Foundation, Louis W. Foster and Gladyce L., The, CA, 539
Foster Family Foundation, MI, 4431
Foster Foundation Inc., VA, 9432
Foster Foundation, The, WA, 9621
Foster Trust, Alta W., RI, 8394
Foster-Davis Foundation, Inc., CT, 1588
Fotsch Family Foundation, WI, 9846
Fotsch Foundation, The, WI, A
Foulger Foundation, Inc., Sid & Mary, MD, 3792
Found Animals Foundation, Inc., CA, 540
Foundation 14, NY, 6000
Foundation for a Better World, Inc., GA, 2461
Foundation for a Just Society, NY, 6001
Foundation for Advancement of Chiropractic Education, Inc., GA, see 2478
Foundation for Adventist Education, The, MD, 3793
Foundation for Arts Initiatives, NY, 6002
Foundation for Better Education, CA, 541
Foundation for Child Development, NY, 6003
Foundation for Chronic Diseases Inc., Nancy Taylor, The, OK, 7751
Foundation for Deep Ecology, CA, 542
Foundation for Educational Excellence, CO, 1411
Foundation for Educational Research and Development, MN, 4657
Foundation for Enhancing Communities, The, PA, 8046
Foundation for Global Sports Development, The, CA, 543
Foundation for Informed Medical Decisions Foundation, MA, see 4107
Foundation for Maryland's Future, The, MD, 3794
Foundation for MetroWest, The, MA, 4056
Foundation for Research in Cell Biology and Cancer, MA, see 4057
Foundation for Research in Cell Biology Cancer and Cardiology, MA, 4057
Foundation for Retinal Research, IL, 2839
Foundation for Roanoke Valley, VA, see 9415
Foundation for Seacoast Health, NH, 5171
Foundation For The Carolinas, NC, 7202
Foundation for the Continuity of Mankind, The, OH, see 7526
Foundation for the Future, WA, 9622
Foundation for the Mid South, MS, 4827
Foundation for the National Capital Region, The, DC, see 1893
Foundation for the Tri-State Community, Inc., KY, 3575
Foundation for Theological Education in Southeast Asia, MI, 4432
Foundation Francqui Belgium, NY, see 6007
Foundation M, MA, 4058
Foundation Northwest, WA, see 9650
Foundation of Caring Fund, WA, 9623
Foundation of Greater Greensboro, Inc., The, NC, see 7180

Gardner Charitable Foundation, Eldon and Emma Belle, TN, 8570
Gardner Family Foundation, James J. and Joan A., The, OH, 7466
Gardner Family Foundation, OH, see 7466
Gardner Foundation, Annie, KY, 3576
Gardner Foundation, NE, 5041
Garfield Charitable Foundation Inc., Joseph & Sherrie, FL, 2115
Garfield Foundation, Eugene, The, PA, 8052
Garfield Foundation, The, MA, 4065
Garland Foundation, John Jewett & Helen Chandler, CA, 565
Garrison Charitable Foundation, Arnold, MA, see 4066
Garrison Foundation, Arnold, The, MA, 4066
Garrott Foundation, Thomas M., FL, 2116
Garschina Foundation, Story, The, NY, 6035
Garvey Fund, Jean and Willard, KS, 3516
Gary-Williams Foundation, The, CO, see 1481
Gasser Foundation, Peter A. & Vernice H., CA, 566
Gates Charitable Trust, IL, 2859
Gates Family Foundation, CO, 1418
Gates Foundation, Bill & Melinda, WA, 9625
Gates Foundation, CO, see 1418
Gates Foundation, William H., WA, see 9625
Gateway Foundation, MO, 4894
Gatton Foundation, Bill, The, TN, 8571
Gaughan Family Foundation, NE, 5042
Gaughan Foundation, Jackie & Bertie, NE, see 5042
Gauntlett Foundation, Inc., Barbara, The, NJ, see 5240
Gavin Foundation, James & Zita, IL, 2860
Gay Foundation, W. W. and Eloise D., FL, 2117
Gayden Family Foundation, TX, 8861
Gaylord Foundation, E. L. and Thelma, OK, 7753
GBRG, Inc., NY, 6036
GE Foundation, CT, 1591
GE Fund, CT, see 1591
Geary Foundation, Bruce G., NY, 6037
Gebbie Foundation, Inc., NY, 6038
Geds Help Fund Foundation, NY, see 6799
Geffen Foundation, David, The, CA, 567
GEICO Philanthropic Foundation, MD, 3801
Geis Charitable Foundation, Erwin & Katherine, The, OH, 7467
Geisse Foundation, John F. and Mary A., OH, 7468
Geisse Foundation, The, OH, see 7468
Geist Foundation, Victoria S. & Bradley L., HI, 2600
Gelb Foundation, Inc., Lawrence M., NY, 6039
Gelbman Charitable Trust, Frank & Pearl E., OH, 7469
Gellert Foundation, Carl Gellert and Celia Berta, The, CA, 568
Gellert Foundation, Carl, The, CA, see 568
Gellert Trust, Michael E., NY, 6040
Gelman Foundation Inc., Jacques & Natasha, NY, 6041
Gelman Trust, Jacques and Natasha, NY, A
Gem Foundation, Inc., NJ, 5273
Gemcon Family Foundation, FL, 2118
Gemunder Foundation, Joel F., FL, 2119
Genan Foundation, The, VA, 9440
GenCorp Foundation, Incorporated, CA, 569
Genecov Foundation, A. S., TX, 8862
Genentech Access To Care Foundation, CA, 570
Genentech Foundation, CA, 571
General Education Fund, Inc., VT, 9361
General Mills Foundation, MN, 4661
General Motors Foundation, Inc., MI, 4442
General Service Foundation, CO, 1419
Generation Trust, The, OH, 7470
Genesis Foundation Inc., NY, 6042
Genius Charitable Trust, Elizabeth Morse, IL, 2861
Gensler Family Foundation, CA, 572
Genuardi Family Foundation, PA, 8053
Genworth Foundation, VA, 9441
Genzyme Charitable Foundation, Inc., MA, 4067
Geo Group Foundation, Inc., The, FL, 2120
George Charitable Trust, Conway & Margaret, AR, 189
George Charitable Trust, Edward Payson, MA, 4068
George Family Foundation, Inc., Meredith and Whitney, The, CT, 1592
George Family Foundation, MN, 4662
George Foundation, Elizabeth, The, WA, 9626
George Foundation, Inc., NC, 7205
George Foundation, The, TX, 8863
Georgescu Family Foundation, The, CT, 1593
Georgia Power Foundation, Inc., GA, 2468
Georgia-Pacific Foundation, Inc., GA, 2469
Gerber Companies Foundation and The Gerber Baby Food Fund, The, MI, see 4443
Gerber Foundation, Cindy & Murry, The, PA, 8054
Gerber Foundation, The, MI, 4443
Gerbode Foundation, Wallace Alexander, CA, 573
Gerdin Charitable Foundation, The, IA, 3430
Gerlach Foundation, Inc., OH, 7471
German Protestant Orphan Asylum Association Foundation, LA, 3637
Germanacos Foundation, The, CA, 574
Germeshausen Foundation, Inc., MA, 4069
Gerondelis Foundation Inc., MA, 4070
Gerry Charitable Trust, NY, 6043
Gerry Charitable Trust, Peggy N. & Roger G., NY, see 6043
Gerry Foundation, Inc., NY, 6044
Gerschel Foundation, Patrick A., The, NY, 6045
Gershman Foundation, Ronald and Catherine, CA, 575
Gershwind Family Foundation, The, NY, 6046
Gerson Family Foundation, Inc., NY, 6047
Gerstacker Foundation, Rollin M., The, MI, 4444
Gerstner Family Foundation, The, FL, 2121
Geschke Foundation, Charles M. Geschke and Nancy A., CA, 576
Gesner-Johnson Foundation, MN, 4663
Getty Foundation, Aileen, The, CA, 577
Getty Foundation, Ann and Gordon, The, CA, 578
Getty Trust, J. Paul, CA, 579
Getz Foundation, Harry A. and Rose, TX, 8864
Gewirz Foundation, Inc., Bernard & Sarah, DC, 1909
Geyer Foundation, Charlotte, FL, 2122
GFC Foundation, The, UT, 9322
GGS Foundation, CA, 580
Gheens Foundation, Inc., The, KY, 3577
Ghermezian Foundation, Jacob and Miriam, NJ, 5274
GHH Foundation, Inc., NJ, 5275
Ghidotti Foundation, William & Marian, NC, 7206
GHR Foundation, MN, 4664
GHS Foundation, TX, 8865
Giacoletto Foundation, John P. and Lawrence J., IA, 3431
Gianforte Family Charitable Trust, MT, 5010
Giannini Family Foundation, CA, see 581
Giannini Foundation, A. P., CA, 581
Giannini Fund, Claire, CA, 582
Giant Eagle Foundation, PA, 8055
Gibbs Charitable Foundation, SC, 8480
Gibbs Foundation, Inc., Malcolm, NY, 6048
Gibbs Trust, NC, 7207
Gibney Family Foundation, Inc., The, VT, 9362
Gibson Family Foundation, Inc., NJ, 5277
Gibson Family Foundation, NJ, 5276
Gibson Foundation, Addison H., PA, 8056
Gibson Foundation, Inc., OH, see 7370
Gibson Hemostasis-Thrombosis Foundation, Mary Rodes, TX, 8866
Gibson, Dunn & Crutcher Foundation, The, CA, 583
Giddens, Jr. Charitable Foundation, Thomas V., WA, 9627
Gidwitz Memorial Foundation, Joseph L. & Emily K., IL, 2862
Gies Foundation, The, IL, 2863
Gifford Charitable Corporation, Rosamond, The, NY, 6049
Gifford Foundation, Inc., The, CA, 584
Gifford Foundation, The, NY, see 6049
Gifford Residuary Trust, Adelle, NH, 5173
Gilbert Foundation, Rosalinde and Arthur, The, CA, 585
Gilchrist Foundation, IA, 3432
Gildea Charitable Foundation, Edward & Janet, The, MA, 4071
Gilder Foundation, Inc., NY, 6050
Gildor Foundation, Ephraim F., CO, 1420
Gilead Foundation, CA, 586
Giles Foundation, Edward C., The, NC, see 7208
Giles Foundation, Lucille P. and Edward C., The, NC, 7208
Gilhousen Family Foundation, MT, 5011
Gill Foundation, The, CO, 1421
Gillespie Family Fund, Inc., The, NY, 6051
Gillespie Foundation, William, The, CA, 587
Gilliam Foundation, Richard and Leslie, The, VA, 9442
Gillmor Foundation, Edward Lincoln and Bessie Boyce, UT, see 9323
Gillmor Foundation, Florence J., UT, 9323
Gilman Foundation, Frank M. & Olive E., VT, 9363
Gilman Foundation, Inc., Howard, NY, 6052
Gilman Private Family Foundation, WA, see 9577
Gilmore Foundation, IL, 2864
Gilmore Foundation, Inc., MS, see 4828
Gilmore Foundation, Irving S., MI, 4445
Gilmore Foundation, William G., The, CA, 588
Gilmore Sanitarium, Inc., MS, 4828, see 4828
Gimbel Foundation, Inc., Bernard F. and Alva B., NY, 6053
Gimbel Foundation, S. L., CA, 589
Gindi Associates Foundation, Inc., NY, see 5758
Gindi Private Foundation, Ralph S., The, NY, 6054
Gingher State Auto Insurance Companies Foundation, Paul R., OH, see 7674
Ginn Family Foundation, CA, 590
Giop Charitable Foundation, Sonia Raiziss, PA, 8057
Gipson Family Foundation, NC, 7209
Girard Foundation, CA, 591
Gitenstein Foundation Inc., Kermit, NY, 6055
Gitlin Family Foundation, Harvey S., The, PA, see 8058
Gitlin Foundation, The, PA, 8058
Giuliani Family Foundation, David and Patricia, WA, 9628
Give Something Back Foundation, Inc., NJ, 5278
GiveWell Community Foundation, Inc., The, FL, 2123
Giving Hope Worldwide Foundation, AZ, 114
GKN Foundation, IL, 2865
Glades Foundation, The, NY, 6056
Glaser Foundation, Inc., WA, 9629
Glaser Foundation, The, WA, see 9630
Glaser Progress Foundation, WA, 9630
Glass Charitable Foundation, MA, 4072
Glass Family Foundation, AR, 190
Glass Family Foundation, Inc., NC, see 7210
Glass Foundation, Inc., NC, 7210
Glasscock Foundation, Melbern G. & Susanne M., TX, 8867
Glatfelter III Family Foundation, Anne & Philip, PA, 8059
Glaxo Wellcome Foundation, The, NC, see 7274
GlaxoSmithKline Foundation, PA, 8060
GlaxoSmithKline Patient Access Programs Foundation, PA, 8061
Glazer Family Foundation, Inc., FL, 2124
Glazer Family Foundation, Lowell & Harriet, MD, 3802
Glazer Family Foundation, Lowell R., MD, see 3802
Glazer Foundation, Jeffrey W., The, IA, 3433
Glazer Foundation, Madelyn L., IA, see 3458
Glazer Foundation, Susan J., IA, 3434
Gleason Family Foundation, CA, 592
Gleason Foundation, CA, see 592
Gleberman Foundation, Joseph & Carson, NY, see 6683
Gleis Foundation, Josephine Herbert, CA, 593
Glencairn Foundation, PA, 8062
Glenn Charitable Foundation, Jack and Anne, FL, 2125
Glenn Charitable Foundation, Jack and Anne, GA, 2470
Glenn Family Foundation, NC, 7211
Glenn Family Foundation, The, TN, 8572
Glenn Family Foundation, Wilbur and Hilda, The, GA, 2471
Glenn Foundation for Medical Research, Inc., CA, 594
Glenn Foundation for Medical Research, Inc., Paul F., CA, see 594
Glenn Foundation, Wadley R., SC, see 8508
Glenner Foundation, Sidney and Lisa, IL, 2866
Glens Falls Foundation, The, NY, 6057
Glenstone Foundation, The, VA, see 9513
Glick Foundation Corporation, Eugene and Marilyn, IN, 3310
Glickenhaus Foundation, The, NY, 6058
Glickman Family Foundation, Albert B., ME, 3688
Glide Foundation, Thornton S., Jr. and Katrina D., CA, 595
Global Invincibility Foundation, IA, 3435
Global Village Charitable Trust, FL, 2126
Globe Foundation, AZ, 115
Globe Foundation, The, WA, see 9580
Gloria Dei Foundation, DE, 1784

Hamilton, Jr. Family Foundation, Inc., Jeanne G. and Lawson W., The, WV, 9776
Hamm Family Foundation Inc., CT, 1607
Hamman Foundation, George and Mary Josephine, TX, 8888
Hamman Foundation, Inc., Cecil A. and Mabel Lene, IN, 3312
Hammel Foundation, Inc., Kenneth W., PA, *see* 8088
Hammer Foundation, Armand, The, CA, 648
Hammersley Foundation, Frederick, NM, 5520
Hammons Foundation, Inc., John Q., MO, 4907
Hamon Charitable Foundation, TX, 8889
Hampshire Foundation, The, CT, 1608
Hampton Roads Community Foundation, VA, 9448
Hanauer Foundation, Lenore, WA, 9636
Hanauer Foundation, Nick and Leslie, The, WA, 9637
Hancock County Community Foundation, Inc., IN, 3313
HANDinHAND Christian Adoption, Inc., KS, 3517
Handleman Charitable Foundation Trust B, Joseph & Sally, CA, *see* 649
Handleman Charitable Foundation, Lynn, CA, 649
Hands Foundation, Sally Mead, WI, 9858
Handsel Foundation, WA, 9638
Hanes Foundation, John W. and Anna H., The, NC, 7221
Hanes Memorial Fund, James G., NC, 7222
Hanes Memorial Fund/Foundation, James G., NC, *see* 7222
Hank, Jr. Charitable Trust, Bernard J. and Joyce M., IL, *see* 3134
Hankamer Foundation, Curtis & Doris K., TX, 8890
Hankins Family Foundation Inc., Melville, The, NM, 5521
Hanley Family Foundation, Inc., The, GA, 2476
Hannaford Charitable Foundation, ME, 3690
Hannon Foundation, Bill, CA, 650
Hannon Foundation, William H., CA, 651
Hanover Foundation, The, CA, *see* 1151
Hanover Insurance Group Foundation, Inc., The, MA, 4086
Hansen Charitable Foundation, William M. and Patricia A., IA, 3440
Hansen Family Foundation Inc., NY, 6130
Hansen Family Foundation, John and Katie, The, CA, 652
Hansen Foundation, Dane G., KS, 3518
Hansen Foundation, Inc., NJ, 5291
Hansen Foundation, Mark and Anne, The, DC, 1913
Hansen Foundation, PA, *see* 8079
Hansen Foundation, William Stucki, PA, 8079
Hansen Foundation, Zenon C. R., CO, 1427
Hansen-Furnas Foundation, Inc., IL, 2889
Hanson CGF, Inc., Alex and Laura, NJ, 5292
Hanson Family Foundation, Alice G., IL, 2890
Hanson Family Foundation, WA, 9639
Hanson Foundation, John K. & Luise V., The, IA, 3441
Hanson Foundation, Stanley E., The, CA, 653
Hanson Foundation, The, IA, *see* 3441
Happy Hollow Fund, IL, *see* 2888
Harary Foundation, Inc., Ralph J., NY, 6131
Harbers Family Foundation, Renee and Jeff, WA, *see* 9613
Harbor Lights Foundation, NY, 6132
Harbourton Foundation, NJ, 5293
Hard Rock Cafe Foundation, Inc., FL, 2147
Harden Foundation, CA, 654
Hardenbergh Foundation, MN, 4672
Harder Declaration of Trust, Kenneth L., IL, 2891
Harder Foundation, WA, 9640
Hardesty Family Foundation, Inc., The, OK, 7756
Hardin Charitable Trust, Helen and Jabie, TN, 8577
Hardin Foundation, Phil, MS, 4831
Harding Foundation, Charles Stewart, MI, 4455
Harding Foundation, The, PA, 8080
Haring Foundation, Inc., Keith, The, NY, 6133
Harkness Foundation for Dance, Inc., The, NY, 6134
Harland Charitable Foundation, Inc., John H. and Wilhelmina D., GA, 2477
Harley-Davidson Foundation, Inc., WI, 9859
Harman Family Foundation, CA, 655, 656
Harman Foundation, Leon & Arline, The, UT, 9325
Harman Foundation, Sidney and Jane, CA, *see* 656
Harmsworth 1997 Charitable Foundation, Esmond, MA, 4087
Harnisch Foundation Inc, William F., NY, 6135
Harnischfeger Industries Foundation, WI, *see* 9876
Harnish Foundation, WA, 9641
Harrah's Foundation, The, NV, *see* 5106
Harriman Foundation, Gladys and Roland, NY, 6136
Harriman Foundation, Mary W., NY, 6137
Harrington Family Foundation, The, FL, 2148
Harrington Foundation, Francis A. & Jacquelyn H., MA, 4088
Harrington Foundation, Mark H. & Blanche M., CA, 657
Harrington-McLaughlin Family Foundation, The, FL, *see* 2148
Harris Family Foundation Trust, Jeffrey and Jamie, The, NY, 6141
Harris Family Foundation, IL, 2892
Harris Family Foundation, Inc., J. Ira & Nicki, NY, 6138
Harris Family Foundation, Inc., J. Ira and Nicki, NY, 6139
Harris Family Foundation, John W., The, NC, 7223
Harris Family Foundation, Matthew and Jennifer, NY, 6140
Harris Family Foundation, The, RI, 8402
Harris Family Foundation, William M., GA, 2478
Harris Foundation A, Irving, IL, *see* 3125
Harris Foundation B, Irving, IL, *see* 2653
Harris Foundation Trust, Elisabeth Katte, TX, 8891
Harris Foundation, FL, 2149
Harris Foundation, Inc., Clarence E., GA, 2479
Harris Foundation, Inc., Claude and Betty, The, KY, 3580
Harris Foundation, Inc., J. Ira and Nicki, NY, *see* 6139
Harris Foundation, Inc., OK, 7757
Harris Foundation, Inc., Robinson, The, NJ, 5294
Harris Foundation, Irving, IL, 2893
Harris Foundation, The, IL, *see* 2893
Harris Foundation, William H., MA, 4089
Harris-Johnson Family Foundation, CA, 658
Harrisburg Foundation, Greater, The, PA, *see* 8046
Harrison County Community Foundation, Inc., IN, 3314
Harrison Family Foundation, James I., The, AL, 37
Harrison Foundation Inc., Helen M., IL, 2896
Harrison Foundation Trust, Francena T., NY, 6142
Harrison Foundation, Fred G., IL, 2894
Harrison Foundation, Inc., Dr. J. Harold, GA, 2480
Harrison Foundation, Inc., Luther & Susie, The, GA, 2481
Harrison Foundation, Mary A., The, IL, 2895
Harrison Foundation, VA, 9449
Harrisonburg Rockingham Community Foundation, VA, *see* 9411
Harron Family Foundation, PA, *see* 8214
Harsh, IV and Margaret C. Whitman Charitable Foundation, Griffith R., NY, 6143
Hart Foundation, Patricia and Rodes, TN, 8578
Hart Foundation, Thelma B. & Thomas P., The, NV, 5122
Harte Charitable Foundation, TX, 8892
Hartford Courant Foundation, Inc., The, CT, *see* 1589
Hartford Family Fund Inc., Huntington, NY, *see* 5551
Hartford Foundation for Public Giving, CT, 1609
Hartford Foundation, Inc., John A., The, NY, 6144
Hartke Community Foundation, Selma J., The, IL, 2897
Hartley Family Foundation, Fred L., CA, 659
Hartley Family Foundation, KS, 3519
Hartman Family Foundation, Gordon, The, TX, 8893
Hartman Family Foundation, IL, *see* 2898
Hartman Family Foundation, Robert & Debra F., The, IL, 2898
Hartman Family Foundation, Shamai & Richu, NY, 6145
Hartman Foundation, John and Kelly, CT, 1610
Hartness Foundation, The, SC, 8482
Hartquist Foundation, The, NC, *see* 7246
Hartwell Foundation, The, TN, 8579
Harvest Charities, NC, 7224
Harvest Foundation of the Piedmont, The, VA, 9450
Harvest Foundation, WA, 9642
Harvey Family Foundation, Hugh & Michelle, The, CO, 1428
Harvey Foundation, Inc., C. Felix, The, NC, 7225
Harvey Trust, J. H., TX, 8894
Harwit Z"L and Manya Harwit-Aviv Charitable Trust, J. Samuel, CA, 660
Hasbro Charitable Trust, Inc., RI, *see* 8403
Hasbro Children's Fund, Inc., RI, 8403
Haseltine Charitable Foundation, William A., NY, 6146
Haslam 3 Foundation, Inc., The, TN, 8580
Haslam Family Foundation, Inc., The, TN, 8581
Haslinger Family Foundation, Inc., Sandra L. and Dennis B., OH, 7482
Hassenfeld Foundation, RI, 8404
Hasten Family Foundation, Inc., Hart N. and Simona, IN, 3315
Hasten Family Foundation, Inc., Mark and Anna Ruth, IN, 3316
Hastings Community Foundation, Inc., NE, 5046
Hastings Foundation, CA, 661
Hatton Foundation, E. Kenneth & Esther Marie, OH, *see* 7483
Hatton Foundation, OH, 7483
Hau'oli Mau Loa Foundation, The, HI, 2601
Hauck Charitable Foundation, MO, 4908
Haugland Foundation, Richard P., WA, 9643
Haugland Foundation, Rosaria P., OR, 7849
Haugland Foundation, WA, *see* 9643
Hauptman Family Foundation, Inc., The, CA, 662
Hauser Foundation, Inc., The, NY, 6147
Hauss-Helms Foundation, Inc., The, OH, 7484
Havens Foundation, Weston, NC, 7226
Havens Relief Fund Society, The, NY, 6148
Hawaii Community Foundation, HI, 2602
Hawaii Medical Service Association Foundation, HI, *see* 2604
Hawaiian Electric Industries Charitable Foundation, HI, 2603
Hawaiian Foundation, The, HI, *see* 2602
Hawkins Family Foundation, Russell and Diana, TX, 8895
Hawkins Foundation, Robert Z., NV, 5123
Hawks Foundation, The, NE, 5047
Hawley Family Foundation, CO, 1429
Hawn Foundation, Inc., TX, 8896
Hawthorne Charitable Foundation, NJ, 5295
Hayden Family Foundation, NY, 6149
Hayden Foundation, Charles, NY, 6150
Hayden Foundation, William R. & Virginia, CA, 663
Hayden Foundation, William R., CA, see 663
Hayes Charitabe Trust, Mariam and Robert, NC, 7227
Hayfields Foundation, OH, 7485
Haynes Foundation, John Randolph Haynes and Dora, The, CA, 664
Hayward Family Foundation, CA, *see* 665
Hayward Family Foundation, Nancy Eccles and Homer M., CA, 665
Hayward Foundation, John T. and Winifred, FL, 2150
Hayworth Foundation, Charles E. & Pauline, The, NC, *see* 7228
Hayworth, Jr. Foundation, Charles E., NC, 7228
Hazan Family Foundation, Morris A., The, IL, 2899
Hazen Foundation, Inc., Edward W., The, NY, 6151
HCA Foundation, The, TN, 8582, *see* 8568
Head Family Charitable Foundation, PA, 8081
Healey Family Foundation, NY, 6152
Healing Hearts & Nations, CA, 666
Health Foundation For Western and Central New York, NY, 6153
Health Foundation of Greater Indianapolis, Inc., The, IN, 3317
HealthCare Foundation for Orange County, The, CA, 667
Healthcare Foundation of New Jersey, The, NJ, 5296
Healthcare Foundation of Northern Lake County, IL, 2900
Healthcare Georgia Foundation, Inc., GA, 2482
Healthy Earthworks Charitable Foundation, CA, 668
Healy Foundation, Bill, The, OR, 7850
Healy Foundation, NM, 5522
Hearin Foundation, Robert M., The, MS, 4832
Hearin-Chandler Foundation, AL, 38
Hearst Foundation, Austin & Gabriela, The, NY, 6154
Hearst Foundation, Austin, The, NY, *see* 6154
Hearst Foundation, Inc., The, NY, 6155
Hearst Foundation, William Randolph, NY, 6156
Hearst Jr. Foundation, David Whitmire, CA, 669
Heart Foundation, The, CA, 670
Heart Institute of Southern New Jersey, NJ, 5297
Heartbeat International of West Central Florida, FL, *see* 2151
Heartbeat International Worldwide, Inc., FL, 2151
Heartstone Foundation, The, MA, 4090

Holloway Foundation Inc., Charles & Marjorie, The, NJ, 5300
Hollowell Foundation, Inc., WV, 9778
Hollowell-Ford Foundation, Inc., WV, see 9778
Hollyhock Foundation, Inc., The, NY, 6183
Hollywood Foreign Press Association Charitable Trust, CA, 701
Holman Foundation, Inc., NJ, 5301
Holmes CSM Family Foundation, MN, 4675
Holmes Family Foundation, Inc., D., NJ, 5302
Holthouse Foundation for Kids, The, TX, 8915
Holthues Trust, IA, 3444
Holthus Foundation, NE, 5052
Holtzmann Foundation, Jacob L. and Lillian, NY, 6184
Holz Family Foundation, Jerome J. and Dorothy H., WI, 9864
Homan, Jr. Trust, B. H., IL, 2919
Home is the Foundation, OH, 7488
Home Savings Charitable Foundation, OH, 7489
Hommer Foundation Trust, NC, 7235
HON INDUSTRIES Charitable Foundation, IA, see 3443
Honda of America Foundation, OH, 7490
Honickman Charitable Fund, NJ, 5303
Honzel Family Foundation, The, WA, 9644
Hood Foundation, Charles H., MA, 4100
Hoogland Family Foundation, IL, 2920
Hoover Family Foundation, IN, 3323
Hoover Foundation, Herbert W., OH, 7491
Hoover Foundation, The, OH, 7492
Hope Charitable Foundation, Bob & Dolores, The, CA, 702
Hope Foundation, The, NJ, 5304
Hopedale Foundation, The, MA, 4101
Hopeman Foundation, Inc., Hank and Lynn, NH, 5176
Hopewell Foundation, Inc., SC, 8484
Hoppe Foundation, The, CA, 703
Hopper-Dean Foundation, CA, 704
Hopwood Charitable Trust, John M., PA, 8096
Horejsi Charitable Foundation, Inc., KS, 3520
Horizon Charitable Foundation, Inc., NJ, 5305
Horizon Foundation for New Jersey, The, NJ, see 5305
Horizon Foundation, Inc., ME, 3691
Horizons Foundation, WA, 9645
Hormel Foods Corporation Charitable Trust, MN, 4676
Horn Foundation, Mildred V., KY, 3581
Horn Foundation, The, CA, 705
Horncrest Foundation, Inc., NY, 6185
Horowitz Family Foundation, Inc., G. & B., The, NY, 6186
Horowitz Foundation for the Arts, Inc., Mr. and Mrs. Raymond J., The, NY, 6187
Horowitz Foundation, Gedale B. and Barbara S., NY, see 6186
Horvitz and Erica Hartman-Horvitz Foundation, Richard, OH, 7493
Horvitz Family Foundation, Inc., David & Francie, FL, 2161
Horvitz Foundation, Richard A., The, OH, see 7493
Horwich Family Foundation, James and Ada, CA, 706
Horwitz Foundation, Redlich, NY, 6188
Hospira Foundation, IL, 2921
Hosser Scholarship Fund Trust, Edward Wagner and George, RI, 8406
Hostetter Foundation, The, MA, see 3937
Hotes Foundation, Richard W., WA, 9646
Hough Family Foundation, Inc., The, FL, 2162
Hough Family Foundation, MI, 4462
Houlsby Foundation, John R., The, IL, 2922
House Family Foundation, CA, 707
House Family Foundation, Dave, CA, see 707
House of St. Giles the Cripple, The, NY, see 6905
Houston Community Foundation, Greater, TX, 8916
Houston Endowment Inc., TX, 8917
Hovde Foundation, Eric D. & Steven D., The, WI, 9865
Hoven Foundation, Melvin and Geraldine, CA, 708
Hoverter Charitable Foundation, Lawrence L. and Julia Z., PA, 8097
Hovnanian Foundation, Inc., Hirair and Anna, NJ, 5306
Hovnanian Foundation, Kevork and Sirwart, The, NJ, 5307
Howard Charitable Foundation, WA, 9647
Howard Memorial Foundation, Max and Sunny, NY, 6189
Howell Foundation, Laverne and Thomas, TX, 8918
Howley Family Foundation, The, OH, 7494
Hoyt Foundation, PA, 8098
HPB Foundation, RI, 8407
HRH Foundation, CA, 709
HRH Foundation, DC, 1917
HRK Foundation, MN, 4677
Hsieh Family Foundation, The, CA, 710
Hsu Foundation, Alice Wan-Tsen, CA, 711
Huang Foundation, Jen-Hsun & Lori, The, CA, 712
Hubbard Broadcasting Foundation, The, MN, 4678
Hubbard Family Foundation, Theodore F. and Claire M., NE, 5053
Hubbard Foundation, Claire M., NE, 5054
Hubbard Foundation, R.D. & Joan Dale, NM, 5523
Hubbard Foundation, The, MN, see 4678
Hubbell Foundation, Fred and Charlotte, IA, 3445
Hubbell Foundation, Harvey, CT, 1614
Hubbell-Waterman Foundation, IA, 3446
Huberfeld Family Foundation, Inc., NY, 6190
Hubert Charitable Trust, O. C., FL, 2163
Hubert Family Foundation, Inc., Ed & Joann, OH, 7495
Hudgens Family Foundation, Inc., Scott, The, GA, 2486
Hudson Charitable Trust, Hargrove, IL, 2923
Hudson Community Foundation, OH, 7496
Hudson Family Foundation, Inc., FL, 2164
Hudson Foundation, M. R. & Evelyn, The, TX, 8919
Hudson River Bancorp, Inc. Foundation, NY, 6191
Hudson-Webber Foundation, MI, 4463
Huffington Foundation, TX, 8920
Hughes Foundation, Inc., Geoffrey C., NY, 6192
Hughes Foundation, John C. & Karyl Kay, The, WA, 9648
Hughes Foundation, Mark, CA, 713
Hughes Foundation, R. Dale and Frances M., PA, 8099
Hughes Medical Institute, Howard, MD, 3818
Hughes Memorial Foundation, Inc., Charles Evans, The, NY, 6193
Hughes Trust, Teresa F., HI, 2605
Hugin Family Foundation Inc., NJ, 5308
Hugoton Foundation, NY, 6194
Huie-Dellmon Trust, LA, 3643
Huisking Foundation, Inc., The, CT, 1615
Huizenga Family Foundation, FL, 2165
Huizenga Foundation, IL, 2924
Hull Family Foundation, IL, 2925
Hull Foundation, Ralph, OR, 7852
Hulston Family Foundation, The, MO, 4911
Hultquist Foundation, Inc., NY, 6195
Humana Foundation, Inc., The, KY, 3582
Humanitas Foundation, The, NY, see 6654
Humboldt Area Foundation, The, CA, 714
Hume Foundation, Jaquelin, CA, 715
Hummingbird Foundation, Inc., NJ, 5309
Humphrey Foundation, James Daniel, NC, 7236
Humphrey Fund, George M. and Pamela S., OH, 7497
Humphreys Charitable Trust, Lewis H., MO, 4912
Humphreys Foundation, J. P., MO, 4913
Humphreys Foundation, TX, 8921
Hungarian-American Enterprise Scholarship Fund, ME, 3692
Hunnicutt Foundation, Inc., H. P. and Anne S., The, WV, 9779
Hunt Family Foundation, Swanee, MA, 4102
Hunt Family Foundation, The, TX, 8922
Hunt Foundation, Nancy Ann Hunt and Ray L., TX, see 8923
Hunt Foundation, Roy A., PA, 8100
Hunt Foundation, Samuel P., NH, 5177
Hunt Foundation, Vicky and Sam, NC, 7237
Hunt Philanthropic Fund, Nancy Ann Hunt and Ray L., TX, 8923
Hunt Trust, Margaretta W., OH, 7498
Hunter Charitable Trust, Estelle, NC, 7238
Hunter Douglas Foundation Inc., NY, 6196
Hunter Family Foundation, IL, 2926
Hunter Foundation, Perkins Malo, IL, 2927
Hunter Foundation, The, NY, 6197
Hunter Trust, Inc., A. V., CO, 1431
Huntington County Community Foundation, Inc., IN, 3324
Huntington Foundation, James, The, IL, 2928
Huntington Fund for Education, John, The, OH, 7499
Huntsman Foundation, Jon and Karen, The, UT, see 9327
Huntsman Foundation, The, UT, 9327
Hurd Foundation, Priscilla Payne, PA, 8101
Hurdus 1992 Charitable Trust, Syde, NY, see 6198
Hurdus Foundation, Inc., Syde, NY, 6198
Hurford Foundation, The, NY, 6199
Hurlbut Memorial Fund, Orion L. & Emma B., TN, 8583
Hurley Endowment Foundation, Gladys & Ed E., IL, 2929
Hurst Family Foundation, NY, 6200
Hurst Foundation, Robert J., The, NY, see 6200
Hurst Foundation, The, MI, 4464
Hurtt Family Foundation, CA, 716
Hurvis Charitable Foundation, Inc., IL, 2930
Hussey Foundation, The, WA, 9649
Huston Charitable Trust, Stewart, The, PA, 8102
Huston Foundation, The, PA, 8103
Hutchins Family Foundation, Inc., NY, 6201
Hutchins Foundation, Inc., Mary J., NY, 6202
Hutchinson Community Foundation, KS, 3521
Hutto Patterson Charitable Foundation, CA, 717
Hutton & Jost Memorial Trust, PA, 8104
Hutton Foundation, CA, see 718
Hutton Foundation, Edward L., The, OH, 7500
Hutton Parker Foundation, CA, 718, see 718
Hux Family Charitable Trust, The, IN, 3325
Hwang Foundation, Kyupin Philip & Gemma, CA, 719
Hwang Foundation, Kyupin Philip and C. Gemma, The, CA, see 719
HWG Fund, Inc., The, NY, see 5763
Hyams Foundation, Inc., The, MA, 4103
Hyams Fund, Sarah A., MA, see 4103
Hyde and Watson Foundation, The, NJ, 5310
Hyde Family Foundations, TN, 8584
Hylton Foundation, Inc., Cecil and Irene, The, VA, 9455

I Am A Leader Foundation, UT, 9328
I and G Charitable Foundation, IL, 2931
i.am.angel Foundation, CA, 720
Iacocca Family Foundation, The, MA, 4104
Iacocca Foundation, The, MA, see 4104
IASD Health Care Foundation, The, IA, see 3490
Iberdrola USA Foundation, Inc., The, ME, 3693
IBJ Foundation, Inc., The, NY, see 6492
IBM International Foundation, NY, 6203
IBM South Africa Projects Fund, NY, see 6203
Icahn Foundation, Carl C., The, NY, 6204
Icarus Foundation, The, NY, see 5966
ICE Charitable Foundation, VA, 9456
Idaho Community Foundation, ID, 2632
Iddings Benevolent Trust, WI, 9866
Iddings Foundation, WI, see 9866
Idema Foundation, Bill and Bea, MI, 4465
IDP Foundation, Inc., IL, 2932
IDT Charitable Foundation, The, NJ, 5311
IF Foundation, The, NY, 6205
IFF Foundation Inc., NY, 6206
IGH Charitable Foundation, Inc., NJ, 5312
IHS Foundation, OH, 7501
II-VI Foundation, PA, 8105
II-VI Incorporated Foundation, PA, see 8105
IIMI, Inc., NY, 6207
Illinois Children's Healthcare Foundation, IL, 2933
Illinois Tool Works Foundation, IL, 2934
IMA McQuade Family Foundation, RI, 8408
Ima/Mickey Family Foundation, OH, 7502
Imago Dei Fund, The, MA, 4105
Imburgia Foundation Inc., IN, 3326
Imlay Foundation, Inc., The, GA, 2487
IMMI Word & Deed Foundation, Inc., IN, see 3408
Impetus Foundation, TX, 8924
Inasmuch Foundation, OK, 7760
Inavale Foundation, Inc., MA, 4106
Incourage Community Foundation, Inc., WI, 9867
Independence Blue Cross Foundation, PA, 8106
Independence Community Foundation, MO, see 4996
Independence Community Foundation, NY, see 5718
Independence Foundation, Inc., KY, 3583
Independence Foundation, PA, 8107
Indian River Community Foundation, FL, 2166
Indian Trail Charitable Foundation, Inc., NJ, 5313
Indiana Charitable Trust, GA, 2488
Indiana Chemical Trust, IN, 3327
Indiana Energy Foundation, Inc., IN, see 3394
Indiana Pathology Endowment, Inc., IN, 3328

Informed Medical Decisions Foundation, Inc., MA, 4107
Ing Foundation, CA, 721
ING Foundation, NY, *see* 7038
Ingalls Foundation, Inc., Louise H. and David S., The, OH, 7503
Ingerman Foundation, Justin, PA, 8108
Ingersoll Trust, William P., IL, 2935
Ingersoll-Rand Charitable Foundation, NJ, 5314
Ingram Trust, Joe, TX, 8925
Ingrassia Foundation, Elizabeth & Frank, NY, 6208
Initiative Foundation, MN, 4679
Inland Northwest Community Foundation, WA, 9650
Inmaat Foundation, NY, 6209
Inman-Riverdale Foundation, SC, 8485
Inner Solutions Institute, VT, *see* 9372
Inspiration Charitable Foundation, TX, 8926
Institute for Aegean Prehistory, The, PA, 8109
Institute for Healthcare Advancement, CA, 722
Institute of Mental Hygiene of the City of New Orleans, LA, 3644
Institution for Savings Charitable Foundation, Inc., MA, 4108
Institution for Savings in Newburyport & Its Vicinity Charitable Foundation, Inc., MA, *see* 4108
Integra Foundation, Inc., The, NJ, 5315
Integrity Trust, WI, 9868
Intel Foundation, OR, 7853
Interco Charitable Trust, MO, 4914
Interlake Foundation, IL, *see* 2865
Interlaken Foundation, Inc., NY, 6210
Intermec Foundation, WA, 9651
International Federation of Red Cross and Red Crescent Societies at the United Nations, Inc., NY, 6211
International Foundation, The, NJ, 5316
International Medical Outreach, Inc., TX, 8927
International Paper Company Foundation, TN, 8585
International Retinal Research Foundation, Inc., AL, 41
INTRUST Bank Charitable Trust, KS, 3522
Intuit Foundation, The, CA, 723
Invested, WA, 9652
Investors Foundation, Inc., NJ, 5317
Investors Savings Bank Charitable Foundation, NJ, *see* 5317
Invisible Hand Foundation, Inc., The, GA, 2489
Inzlicht Heritage Foundation, The, NY, 6212
Ion Bank Foundation, Inc., CT, 1616
Iovino Family Foundation, The, NY, *see* 6205
Iowa Realty Charitable Foundation, IA, *see* 3452
Iowa West Foundation, IA, 3447
Irani Foundation, Ray R., The, CA, 724
Ireland Family Foundation, The, NC, 7239
Iris Foundation, The, NY, 6213
Irmas Charitable Foundation, Audrey & Sydney, CA, 725
Irmas Family Foundation, Audrey and Sydney, CA, *see* 726
Irmas Foundation for Social Justice, Audrey, CA, 726
Irvine Foundation, James, The, CA, 727
Irwin Charity Foundation, William G., The, CA, 728
Irwin Family Foundation, IL, 2936
Isaacs Brothers Foundation, The, CA, A
Isabel Foundation, The, MI, 4466
Isaiah 61 Foundation, VT, 9364
Isambard Kingdom Brunel Society of North America, The, CA, 729
Isdell Family Foundation, The, NJ, 5318
Isdell Foundation, NY, 6214
Isermann Family Foundation, Inc., NJ, 5319
Ishiyama Foundation, The, CA, 730
Island Foundation, Inc., MA, 4109
Island Insurance Foundation, HI, 2606
Island Outreach Foundation, Inc., NY, 6215
Islands Fund, WA, 9653
Israel Foundation, Inc., A. C., NY, 6216
Israel Foundation, Inc., Marcia, The, CA, 731
Israel Foundation, Marcia and Lawrence, The, CA, *see* 731
Issa Family Foundation, CA, 732
It Takes a Family Foundation, Inc., CA, 733
ITT Rayonier Foundation, The, FL, *see* 2281
Ittleson Foundation, Inc., NY, 6217
Ivy Foundation, Ben and Catherine, AZ, 123

J & J Family Foundation, CA, 734
J & L Foundation, The, KY, 3584
J. & AR Foundation, NY, 6218
J. & H. Bernard Foundation, Joanie, OH, 7504
J.A.N.S. Foundation, The, CA, 735
J.F.R. Foundation, OR, 7854
Jack in the Box Foundation, CA, 736
Jackson Charitable Foundation, Carroll & Carolynn, TX, *see* 9195
Jackson Charitable Trust, John E. & Sue M., PA, 8110
Jackson Charitable Trust, Marion Gardner, IL, 2937
Jackson Community Foundation, MI, 4467
Jackson County Community Foundation, The, MI, *see* 4467
Jackson Family Charitable Foundation Inc., Ethan and Joyce, The, IN, 3329
Jackson Family Foundation, Ann, The, CA, 737
Jackson Family Foundation, Stephen E. and Shelley S., The, OK, 7761
Jackson Foundation, Greater, MS, *see* 4820
Jackson Foundation, The, OR, 7855
Jackson Test Charitable Trust, Horace B., GA, 2490
Jacksonville Jaguars Foundation, FL, 2167
Jacobs Engineering Foundation, CA, 738
Jacobs Family Foundation, Inc., CA, 739
Jacobs Foundation, Carl, OH, 7505
Jacobs Foundation, David H. and Barbara M., The, OH, *see* 7430
Jacobs Foundation, Paul and Stacy, CA, 740
Jacobsen Foundation, Diane and Thomas, The, MO, 4915
Jacobsohn Foundation, Carol and Howard, MD, *see* 3819
Jacobsohn Foundation, Carol M., MD, 3819
Jacobson Family Foundation, The, NY, 6219
Jacobson Family Trust Foundation, The, MA, 4110
Jacobson Foundation, Inc., Richard O., IA, 3448
Jacobson Foundation, Jerome, MD, 3820
Jacoff Foundation, Inc., Richard & Natalie, NY, 6220
JAF Foundation, NY, 6221
Jaffe Family Foundation, The, CA, 741
Jaffe Family Foundation, The, NJ, 5320
Jaffe Foundation, Rona, The, NY, 6222
Jaffer Foundation, Mohsin & Fauzia, FL, 2168
Jaharis Family Foundation, Inc., The, NY, 6223
Jahn Foundation Trust, Reinhardt H. & Shirley R., IL, 2938
Jain Family Foundation, Inc., Dr. Kirti, KY, 3585
Jain Foundation, Inc., The, WA, 9654
JAM Anonymous Foundation, Inc., NY, 6224
Jamail Family Foundation, David & Sharon, TX, 8928
Jamail Foundation, Lee and Joseph D., The, TX, 8929
James Charitable Foundation, Roger, NJ, 5321
James Family Charitable Foundation, The, NJ, 5322
James Family Foundation, CA, 742
James Foundation, Inc., Thomas A. and Mary S., FL, 2169
James Foundation, Inc., William, The, FL, 2170
James Foundation, Robert & Ardis, DE, 1789
Jameson Foundation, J. W. and Ida M., CA, 743
Jamestown Area Foundation, Inc., The, OH, 7506
JAMS Foundation, CA, 744
Jana Foundation Inc., NY, 6225
Jandon Foundation, NY, 6226
Janeway Foundation, Elizabeth Bixby, CA, 745
Janey Fund Charitable Trust, The, MA, 4111
Janssen Foundation, Henry, PA, 8111
Janssen Ortho Patient Assistance Foundation, Inc., NJ, *see* 5327
Janszen Charitable Trust, The, TX, 8930
Janus Foundation, The, CO, 1432
Jarvis Foundation, Julietta, TX, 8931
Jasam Foundation Fund B, AZ, 124
Jay Stein Foundation Trust, FL, *see* 2338
Jazzbird Foundation, The, AZ, 125
JCK Foundation, Inc., GA, *see* 2495
JCM Foundation, TN, *see* 8607
JCT Foundation, The, NY, 6227
JDH Family Foundation, CA, 746
Jebediah Foundation, MA, 4112
Jeckyl Charitable Foundation, The, TN, 8586
JED Charitable Foundation, MA, *see* 4116
Jeffe Foundation, Robert A. & Elizabeth R., The, CT, 1617
Jeffress Memorial Trust, Thomas F. and Kate Miller, VA, 9457
Jeffris Family Foundation, Ltd., WI, 9869
Jeg's Quarter Mile Charities, OH, *see* 7507
Jegs Foundation, The, OH, 7507
Jeker Family Trust, ID, 2633
Jeker Foundation, Inc., Julius C., The, ID, 2634
Jeld-Wen Foundation, The, OR, 7856
Jeld-Wen, Wenco Foundation, OR, *see* 7856
Jenesis Group, The, TX, 8932
Jeniam Clarkson Foundation, The, TN, *see* 8587
Jeniam Foundation, The, TN, 8587
Jenkins Charitable Foundation, Victoria, FL, 2171
Jenkins Charitable Trust, Tom H. and Anne H., The, OH, 7508
Jenkins Family Foundation, Matthew and Roberta, The, CA, 747
Jenkins Foundation, Inc., George W., FL, *see* 2275
Jennings Family Foundation, Inc., The, MN, 4680
Jennings Foundation, Alan K. and Cledith M., The, CA, 748
Jennings Foundation, Martha Holden, The, OH, 7509
Jensen Foundation, Janet Jarie, TX, *see* 8677
Jephson Educational Trust No. 2, IL, 2939
Jergens Foundation, Andrew, The, OH, 7510
Jerlyn Foundation, PA, 8112
Jernigan Foundation, Thomas E., The, AL, 42
Jerome Foundation, CA, 749
Jerome Foundation, MN, 4681
Jesus Fund, The, AR, 191
Jet Foundation, The, NY, *see* 5948
Jewett Foundation, George F., The, MN, 4682
Jewish Foundation for Education of Women, NY, 6228
Jewish Foundation of Cincinnati, The, OH, 7511
Jewish Spirit, Inc., NY, 6229
JFM Foundation, The, CO, 1433
JG Foundation, CA, 750
JGFF, CA, *see* 598
JHD Charity Foundation, The, NY, *see* 7107
Jiang Foundation, Yibing and Ping, NY, 6230
Jiv Daya Foundation, TX, 8933
JJJ Charitable Foundation, CT, 1618
JJR Foundation, NY, 6231
JKJ Charitable Foundation, TX, 8934
JKL Foundation, The, TX, 8935
JL Foundation, CA, 751
JLH Foundation, TX, 8936
JM Foundation, The, NJ, 5323
JMM Charitable Foundation Inc., CA, 752
JMP Foundation Inc., NJ, 5324
JNT Foundation, IL, 2940
Jobst Foundation, Conrad & Caroline, OH, 7512
Jochum-Moll Foundation, The, OH, 7513
Jockey Hollow Foundation, Inc., The, NJ, 5325
Joelson Foundation, The, NY, 6232
John and Hasmik Foundation, CA, A
John Foundation, B. P. Lester & Regina, OR, 7857
John Foundation, B. P., OR, *see* 7857
Johns Family Foundation, NM, 5524
Johnson & Johnson Family of Companies Contribution Fund, NJ, *see* 5326
Johnson & Johnson Family of Companies Foundation, NJ, 5326
Johnson & Johnson Patient Assistance Foundation, Inc., NJ, 5327
Johnson Art and Education Foundation, NJ, 5328
Johnson Charitable Foundation, Lowell N., IL, 2941
Johnson Charitable Foundation, Willard and Ruth, The, TX, 8937
Johnson Charitable Trust No. 33, 1994 Christopher W., The, NY, 6234
Johnson Charitable Trust, 1994 Elizabeth R., The, NY, 6233
Johnson Charitable Trust, Christopher W., The, NY, *see* 6234
Johnson Controls Foundation, Inc., WI, 9870
Johnson Controls Foundation, WI, *see* 9870
Johnson County Community Foundation, Greater, IN, *see* 3330
Johnson County Community Foundation, Inc., IN, 3330
Johnson Custody Foundation, TN, *see* 8589
Johnson Endeavor Foundation, Christian A., NY, 6235

Kee Foundation, B. K., CA, 776
Keefe Family Foundation, CT, 1619
Keel Foundation, The, MA, 4120
Keeler Foundation, Robert T., OH, 7517
Keesal, Young & Logan Charitable Foundation, CA, 777
Keesee Educational Fund, Inc., Charles B., VA, 9460
Keet Foundation, Ernest and Nancy, The, NY, 6266
Keidan Family Foundation, Inc., NY, 6267
Keith Foundation Trust, Ben E., IL, 2952
Keith Foundation, Greg and India, The, NC, 7247
Keithley Foundation, Joseph and Nancy, OH, 7518
Kelben Foundation, Inc., WI, 9877
Kellar Family Foundation, The, VA, 9461
Kelleher Charitable Foundation, Joan and Herb, TX, 8951
Kellen Foundation, Inc., Anna-Maria & Stephen, NY, 6268
Keller Family Foundation, LA, 3646
Keller Foundation, George M. and Adelaide M., The, CO, A
Keller Foundation, Inc., J. J., WI, 9878
Keller Foundation, Inc., WI, see 9878
Kelley Family Foundation, Lora L. and Martin N., CA, 778
Kelley Foundation, Inc., Margaret H. and James E., MN, 4686
Kellman Family Foundation, Joseph, The, IL, 2953
Kellman Foundation, The, IL, see 2953
Kellogg Company 25-Year Employees Fund, Inc., MI, 4473
Kellogg Family Foundation, Inc., The, WI, 9879
Kellogg Foundation, Inc., J. C., NY, 6269
Kellogg Foundation, Peter R. & Cynthia K., NY, 6270
Kellogg Foundation, W. K., MI, 4474
Kellogg's Corporate Citizenship Fund, MI, 4475
Kelly Family Foundation, Brian & Joelle, NJ, 5335
Kelly Family Foundation, CT, 1620
Kelly Family Foundation, KS, 3526
Kelly Foundation, Inc., Ellsworth, NY, 6271
Kelly Foundation, Inc., FL, 2181
Kelly Foundation, Paul E., PA, 8119
Kelsey Foundation, Forest C. & Ruth V., The, WA, 9658
Kemmerer Family Foundation, Inc., The, NJ, 5336
Kemp Foundation Inc, Barbara and Gil, The, NY, 6272
Kemper Charitable Trust, R. C., MO, 4923
Kemper Charitable Trust, William T., MO, 4924
Kemper Educational and Charitable Fund, IL, 2954
Kemper Foundation, Enid and Crosby, MO, 4925
Kemper Foundation, James S., IL, 2955
Kemper Foundation, William T., MO, 4926
Kemper Memorial Foundation, David Woods, MO, 4927
Kempner Fund, Harris and Eliza, TX, 8952
Kempner Fund, Inc., Harris and Eliza, TX, see 8952
Kempner, Jr. Foundation, Thomas L., NY, 6273
Kenan, Jr. Charitable Trust, William R., NC, 7248
Kendall Foundation, George R., IL, 2956
Kendall Foundation, Henry P., The, MA, 4121
Kendeda Fund, The, DE, 1794
Kendrick Foundation, Inc., IN, 3333
Kendrick Memorial Hospital, Inc., IN, see 3333
Kennametal Foundation, PA, 8120
Kennedy Family Foundation, Inc., Ethel & W. George, The, FL, 2182
Kennedy Family Foundation, Louis and Clara, The, CA, A
Kennedy Foundation Inc., Quentin J., NJ, 5337
Kennedy Foundation, Dr. and Mrs. Hugh A., TX, 8953
Kennedy Foundation, Ethel, FL, 2183
Kennedy Foundation, Inc., J. C., GA, 2495
Kennedy Foundation, Karen A. & Kevin W., The, NY, 6274
Kennedy Funding Invitational Corporation, The, NY, A
Kenrose Kitchen Table Foundation, The, CA, 779
Kensington Square Foundation, The, IL, 2957
Kent Corporation Charitable Foundation, IA, 3450
Kent Foundation, Ada Howe, NY, 6275
Kent-Stein Foundation, IA, see 3450
Keough Foundation, Donald and Marilyn, GA, 2496
Keough Foundation, Donald R., GA, see 2496
Keren Keshet - The Rainbow Foundation, NY, 6276
Kern Community Foundation, The, CA, 780
Kern County Community Foundation, The, CA, see 780
Kern Family Foundation, CO, 1438
Kern Family Foundation, Inc., The, WI, 9880
Kern Foundation Trust, IL, 2958
Kerr Foundation Inc., The, OK, 7764
Kerr Foundation, Inc., Robert S. and Grayce B., The, WY, 9981
Kerr Foundation, William A., The, NJ, 5338
Kerr Fund, Inc., Grayce B., MD, 3823
Kerrville Area Community Trust, TX, see 8777
Kersten Charitable Trust, Dorothy M. M., OH, 7519
Kersten Family Foundation, IL, see 3173
Keshet Foundation, NY, 6277
Kessler Family Foundation, Carl E., TX, 8954
Kestenbaum Family Foundation, CA, 781
Kestenbaum Family Foundation, The, PA, 8121
Ketchum Charitable Foundation Inc., OK, 7765
Kettering Family Foundation, The, OH, 7520
Kettering Foundation, Virginia W., The, OH, 7521
Kettering Fund, The, OH, 7522
Ketterlinus Trust f/b/o University of Pennsylvania Hospital, E., PA, A
Key Community Foundation, OH, see 7417
Key Foundation, OH, see 7523
KeyBank Foundation, OH, 7523
Keys Family Foundation, Alicia, The, CA, 782
Keyser Foundation, Robert S. & Dorothy J., NV, 5126
KeySpan Foundation, The, NY, see 6527
Keystone Nazareth Charitable Foundation, PA, see 8122
Keystone Savings Foundation, PA, 8122
Khachaturian Foundation, The, CA, 783
Khan Foundation, Inc., The, DE, 1795
Kharis Foundation, TN, 8591
Khatib Foundation Inc., The, NY, 6278
Khesed Foundation, IL, 2959
Kickapoo Springs Foundation, TX, 8955
Kidney Care, Inc., MS, see 4816
Kiebach Foundation, Walter & Olivia, OH, 7524
Kieckhefer Foundation, J. W., AZ, 129
Kienstra Foundation, Theodore A., The, MO, 4928
Kiernan Foundation, Peter and Eaddo, The, NY, 6279
Kiewit Companies Foundation, NE, 5056
Kiewit Foundation, Peter, NE, 5057
Kiita Foundation, The, AZ, 130
Kikel Charitable Foundation, OH, 7525
Kikkoman Foods Foundation, Inc., WI, 9881
Kilroy Foundation, John B. and Nelly Llanos, The, CA, 784
Kilroy Foundation, William S. & Lora Jean, TX, 8956
Kilts Family Foundation, The, NY, 6280
Kim Foundation, Inc., James & Agnes, The, PA, 8123
Kim Foundation, NE, 5058
Kim Foundation, Steve Y., The, CA, 785
Kimball Foundation, Horace A. Kimball and S. Ella, RI, 8410
Kimball Foundation, Sara H. and William R., CA, see 786
Kimball Foundation, The, CA, 786
Kimberly-Clark Foundation, Inc., TX, 8957
Kimble Foundation, Doris & Floyd, OH, 7526
Kimbrell Family Foundation, W. Duke, The, NC, 7249
Kimmel Charitable Foundation, Inc., Richard P. Kimmel and Laurine, NE, 5059
Kimmel Family Foundation, The, NY, 6281
Kimmel Foundation, Martin S., NY, see 6281
Kimmel Foundation, Sidney, The, PA, 8124
Kimmelman Family Foundation, The, NY, 6282
Kimmelman Foundation, Eloise, FL, 2184
Kimsey Foundation, DC, 1921
Kind Family Foundation, Patricia, PA, 8125
Kind World Foundation, The, NE, 5060
Kinder Foundation, Inc., Richard D., TX, see 8958
Kinder Foundation, TX, 8958
Kinder Morgan Foundation, CO, 1439
Kinesis, Inc, PR, 8352
King Family Foundation, Jeffery & Cynthia, The, PA, 8126
King Family Foundation, Michael, The, CA, see 787
King Family Foundation, Peter J., MN, 4687
King Family Foundation, The, IL, 2960
King Foundation, Carl B. and Florence E., TX, 8959
King Foundation, Inc., Stephen and Tabitha, ME, 3694
King Foundation, Jena & Michael, The, CA, 787
King Foundation, Kenneth Kendal, CO, see 1440
King Foundation, Kenneth, The, CO, 1440
King Street Charitable Trust, The, NY, 6283
King Trust, Annie Graham, AL, 44
King Trust, Charles A., MA, 4122
Kingdon Fund, Mark and Anla Cheng, NY, 6284
Kingfisher Foundation, The, CA, 788
Kings Grant Foundation, FL, 2185
Kings Point Richmond Foundation, Inc., NY, see 6704
Kingsbury Road Charitable Foundation, MA, 4123
Kingsley Foundation, Lewis A., CA, 789
Kinney Drugs Foundation, Inc., NY, 6285
Kinney-Lindstrom Foundation Inc., IA, 3451
Kinsley Family Foundation, PA, 8127
Kinsman Foundation, OR, 7860
Kiplinger Foundation, The, DC, 1922
Kirbo Charitable Foundation, Thomas M. & Irene B., The, FL, 2186
Kirby Foundation, Inc., F. M., NJ, 5339
Kirby Foundation, The, DE, 1796
Kirby, Jr. Foundation Inc., A. P., NJ, 5340
Kirchgessner Foundation, Karl, The, CA, 790
Kirk Family Charitable Trust, KS, see 3527
Kirk Family Foundation, VA, 9462
Kirk Foundation, KS, 3527
Kirk Humanitarian, UT, 9329
Kirkland Foundation, Robert E. and Jenny D., TN, 8592
Kirkpatrick Foundation, OK, 7766
Kish Foundation, John C., NJ, 5341
Kish Foundation, NJ, see 5341
Kislak Family Fund, Inc., The, FL, 2187
Kissick Family Foundation, CA, 791
Kitchen Window Foundation, The, NC, A
Kitchings Family Foundation, Chester, The, CT, 1621
Kitchings Foundation, Chester W., The, CT, see 1621
Kitsap Community Foundation, WA, 9659
Kittredge Foundation, The, MA, 4124
Kitzmiller-Bales Trust, CO, 1441
Kiva Foundation, The, MA, 4125
KLA-Tencor Foundation, CA, 792
Klabzuba Family Foundation, TX, 8960
Klaff Family Foundation, IL, 2961
Klarman Family Foundation, MA, 4126
Klarman Foundation, Seth A. & Beth S., The, MA, see 4126
Klatskin Family Charitable Trust, Charles and Lynne, The, NJ, 5342
Klaus Family Foundation, The, GA, 2497
KLE Foundation, The, TX, 8961
Kleberg Foundation for Wildlife Conservation, Caesar, TX, 8963
Kleberg Foundation, Robert J. Kleberg, Jr. and Helen C., TX, 8962
Klee Foundation, Inc., Conrad and Virginia, The, NY, 6286
Klein Charitable Foundation, Reb Ephraim Chaim & Miriam Rochel, The, NY, 6287
Klein Family Foundation, Calvin, NY, 6289
Klein Family Foundation, Lloyd E. & Elisabeth H., The, CA, 793
Klein Family Foundation, NY, 6288
Klein Foundation Inc., Philip E. and Harriet J., The, MD, 3824
Klein Foundation, Inc., Calvin & Kelly, NY, see 6289
Klein Smith Charitable Trust, Edward P. and Mary, KY, see 3601
Klein Trust, F. Albert, WI, 9882
Klein, Jr. Foundation, David L., DE, 1797
Klein, Jr. Memorial Foundation, Inc., David L., DE, see 1797
Kleiner Memorial Park Trust, Julius M., The, ID, 2635
Kleinheinz Family Endowment for the Arts, TX, 8964
Kleinman Family Foundation, The, NY, 6290
Kline Foundation, Charles and Figa, PA, 8128
Kline Foundation, Inc., Josiah W. and Bessie H., PA, 8129
Kling Family Foundation, The, CA, 794
Klingenstein Family Fund Inc., Andrew & Julie, NY, 6291
Klingenstein Fund, Frederick & Sharon, NY, 6293
Klingenstein Fund, Inc., Esther A. & Joseph, The, NY, 6292
Klingenstein Fund, John & Patricia, NY, 6294
Klingenstein Fund, Thomas D., NJ, 5343
KLM Foundation, CA, 795
Klorfine Foundation, FL, 2188
Klurman Foundation, Inc., Samuel Aba and Sisel, The, FL, 2189

Klurman Foundation, Inc., The, FL, *see* 2189
KMB Charitable Foundation, AZ, 131
KMD Foundation, FL, 2190
KMR Group Foundation, WA, 9660
Knabusch Charitable Trust 2, Edward M. & Henrietta M., MI, 4476
Knabusch Charitable Trust No. 1, Edward M. and Henrietta M., MI, A
Knapp Charitable Foundation, William C., IA, 3452
Knapp Foundation Inc., The, NY, 6295
Knapp Foundation, Harry Bronson and Edith R., CA, 796
Knapp Foundation, Inc., The, MD, 3825
Knapp-Swezey Foundation, Inc., NY, 6296
Knee Family Foundation, CA, 797
Knez Family Charitable Foundation, MA, 4127
Knight Charitable Trust, OH, 7527
Knight Foundation, FL, *see* 2191
Knight Foundation, James A. and Faith, MI, 4477
Knight Foundation, John S. and James L., FL, 2191
Knight Foundation, OR, 7861
Knipe Charitable Trust, Alice F. & Cortland J., NY, 6297
Knipel, Harry V. and J. William Warehime Foundation, Airie, PA, 8130
Knobloch Family Foundation, TX, 8965
Knoop Trust, Rose, RI, 8411
Knossos Foundation, Inc., The, CA, 798
Knott Family Foundation, NY, 6298
Knott Foundation, Inc., Marion I. and Henry J., The, MD, 3826
Knowles Charitable Foundation a New Jersey Nonprofit Corporation, The, NJ, 5344
Knowles Foundation, Inc., Janet H. and C. Harry, NJ, 5345
Knowles Science Teaching Foundation (KSTF), NJ, *see* 5345
Knowlton Foundation Inc., Austin E., OH, 7528
Knox Family Foundation, John and Linda, TX, *see* 8934
Knox Foundation, Seymour H., The, NY, 6299
Knox Foundation, The, GA, 2498
Koch Charitable Foundation, David H., KS, 3528
Koch Foundation, Charles, VA, 9463
Koch Foundation, Fred C., The, KS, *see* 3529
Koch Foundation, Inc., FL, 2192
Koch Foundation, Inc., Fred C. and Mary R., The, KS, 3529
Koch Foundation, Inc., IN, 3334
Koch Sons Foundation, Inc., George, IN, *see* 3334
Kodosky Foundation, The, TX, 8966
Koehn Foundation, Thomas and Linda, IA, 3453
Kogod Family Foundation, Robert P. and Arlene R., The, VA, 9464
Koguan Foundation, Leo, The, NJ, 5346
Kohelet Foundation, The, PA, 8131
Kohl Charitable Foundation, Inc., Allen D., CA, 799
Kohl Charities, Inc., Herbert H., WI, 9883
Kohl Family Foundation, Jerry and Terri, DE, 1798
Kohl Family Foundation, Nicole F. and Atlee M., The, TX, *see* 8967
Kohl Family Foundation, The, TX, 8967
Kohlberg Foundation, Inc., The, NY, 6300
Kohler Foundation Inc., John M., WI, 9885
Kohler Foundation, Inc., WI, 9884
Kohn Foundation, Zichron Moshe Vesther, NY, 6301
Kohn-Joseloff Foundation, Inc., CT, 1622
Koinonia Foundation, MI, *see* 4586
Kolatch Family Foundation, NJ, 5347
Kolitz Foundation Inc., TX, 8968
Kolschowsky Foundation, Inc., Gerald A. & Karen A., IL, 2962
Koman Family Foundation, Bill and Amy, MO, 4929
Kongsgaard-Goldman Foundation, WA, 9661
Koonce Family Foundation, RI, 8412
Koontz Foundation, Dean & Gerda, CA, 800
Kooyumjian Family Trust, Thomas A., MO, 4930
Kopf Family Foundation, NY, 6302
Kopf Foundation, Inc., NY, *see* 6302
Kopp Family Foundation, MN, 4688
Koran Trust, Ida C., MN, 4689
Korenvaes Family Foundation, Harlan and Amy, TX, 8969
Koret Foundation, CA, 801
Korf Family Foundation, Inc., The, FL, 2193
Korman Family Foundation, Hyman, NY, 6303
Korman Family Foundation, Jane & Leonard, PA, 8132
Kornfeld Foundation, Emily Davie and Joseph S., NY, 6304
Kornwasser Charitable Foundation, CA, 802
Kornwasser Foundation, Jacob, CA, 803
Korth Family Foundation, Inc., The, MI, 4478
Kosasa Foundation, The, HI, 2607
Kosciusko 21st Century Foundation, Inc., IN, 3335
Kosciusko County Community Foundation, Inc., IN, 3336
Koshland Foundation, The, CA, 804
Koskovich Foundation, Jerome and Marlyce, MN, 4690
Kossak Foundation Inc., John & Evelyn, CT, 1623
Kott Memorial Charitable Trust, Russell & Josephine, IL, 2963
Kovler Family Foundation, IL, 2964
Kovner Foundation, The, NJ, 5348
KPMG Foundation, The, NJ, 5349
KPMG Peat Marwick Foundation, The, NJ, *see* 5349
KPS Charitable Foundation, The, FL, 2194
Kraft and J. Hiatt Foundation, Inc., Robert and Myra, MA, *see* 4128
Kraft Family Foundation, Inc., Robert and Myra, MA, 4128
Kraft Foods Foundation, The, IL, *see* 3034
Kramer Charitable Foundation, Milton A. & Charlotte R., OH, 7529
Kramer Charitable Trust, Victor W., NC, 7250
Kramer Foundation, Inc., C. L. C., FL, 2195
Kraus Family Foundation, The, NY, 6305
Krause Family Foundation, Inc., WI, 9886
Krause Family Foundation, The, OH, 7530
Krause Foundation, Charles A., WI, *see* 9886
Krause Foundation, The, CA, 805
Krause Gentle Foundation, IA, 3454
Kravis Foundation, Inc., Marie-Josee and Henry R., The, NY, 6306
Kravis Foundation, Raymond and Bessie, The, NY, 6307
Kresa Family Foundation, NJ, 5350
Kresge Foundation, The, MI, 4479
Kress Foundation, Inc., George, The, WI, 9887
Kress Foundation, Samuel H., NY, 6308
Kreyling Charitable Foundation, Marcia Turner, IL, 2965
Krieble Foundation, The, MA, 4129
Kriendler Charitable Trust, Jeannette & H. Peter, NY, 6309
Kroger Co. Foundation, The, OH, 7531
Kroh Charitable Trust, CO, 1442
Kroner Family Foundation, CA, 806
Kronkosky Charitable Foundation, Albert & Bessie Mae, TX, 8970
Krouse Family Foundation, Inc., FL, 2196
Krueger Scholarship Fund, Dale, OR, 7862
Kruidenier Charitable Foundation, IA, 3455
Krupa Foundation Inc., Guru, NY, 6310
Krupp Family Charitable Foundation, Judith & Douglas, The, MA, *see* 4131
Krupp Family Foundation, MA, 4130
Krupp Foundation, The, MA, 4131
Kruse Foundation, Anthony H., CO, *see* 1373
Kuenzl Foundation Inc., John E., The, WI, 9888
Kuflik Charitable Foundation, Mitchell and Karen, NY, 6311
Kulas Foundation, OH, 7532
Kulynych Family Foundation I, NC, *see* 7252
Kulynych Family Foundation II, Inc., NC, 7251
Kulynych Foundation Inc., Petro, NC, 7252
Kuni Foundation, Wayne D. & Joan E., WA, 9662
Kunkel Foundation, John Crain, PA, 8133
Kupferberg Family Foundation, Jesse and Joan, NY, 6312
Kupferberg Foundation, The, NY, 6313
Kurth, Jr. Charitable Foundation, Ernest L., TX, 8971
Kurz Family Foundation Ltd., The, NY, 6314
Kushel Foundation, Gloria and Richard, NY, 6315
Kushner Charitable Foundation, Charles and Seryl, NJ, 5351
Kutler Family Foundation, The, HI, 2608
Kuyper Foundation, Peter H. and E. Lucille Gaass, IA, 3456
Kvamme Foundation, Jean & E. Floyd, The, CA, 807

L. & L. Foundation, NY, 6316
L. and S. Milken Foundation, CA, *see* 926
L.A.W. Foundation, Inc., The, NJ, 5352
L.E. Charitable Trust, The, NY, 6317
L.F.H. Foundation Family Trust, NJ, 5353
La Crosse Community Foundation, WI, 9889
La Fetra Foundation, CA, 808
La Vea Charitable Foundation, James Annenberg, PA, 8134
La Vida Feliz Foundation, DE, 1799
La Vida Foundation, NM, *see* 5524
La-Z-Boy Chair Foundation, MI, *see* 4481
La-Z-Boy Foundation, MI, 4481
LA84 Foundation, CA, 809
Laber Foundation, Inc., The, FL, 2197
Labuda Family Foundation, NJ, *see* 5481
Lachimi Foundation, The, MI, 4480
Lachman Family Foundation Inc., The, NY, 6318
Lackner Family Foundation, NJ, 5354
Laclede Gas Charitable Trust, MO, *see* 4931
Laclede Group Foundation, The, MO, 4931
Lacy, Jr. Foundation, Constance C. and Linwood A., FL, 2198
Ladd Charitable Corporation, Helen & George, MA, 4132
Ladera Foundation, MA, 4133
Ladish Company Foundation, WI, 9890
Ladish Family Foundation, Inc., Herman W., WI, 9891
Ladner Family Foundation, Frank S. and Julia M., MO, 4932
Lafayette River Foundation, VA, 9465
Laffey-McHugh Foundation, DE, 1800
Laffont Family Foundation, NY, 6319
Lafromboise Foundation, Jean K., WA, 9663
Lai Foundation, Lily, CA, 810
Lainer Family Foundation, Alice and Nahum, CA, 811
Lainer Family Foundation, Ellie and Mark, CA, 812
Lainer Family Foundation, Lee And Luis, CA, 813
Lainer Family Foundation, Simha and Sara, CA, 814
Laird Norton Family Foundation, WA, 9664
Laird Norton Foundation, WA, *see* 9664
Lake Charitable Trust, Diane S., CA, 815
Lake Road Foundation, NY, 6320
Lakeside Foundation, CA, 816
Lakeview Foundation, Inc., The, WI, 9892
Lalji Foundation, Firoz and Najma, The, WA, 9665
Lamar Family Foundation, Charles, The, LA, 3647
Lambe Charitable Foundation, Claude R., KS, A
Lambert Charitable Foundation, Inc., Lucille and Bruce, The, VA, 9466
Lambert Family Foundation, NY, 6321
Lamfrom Charitable Foundation, Marie, OR, 7863
Lamis Crown Foundation, Inc., FL, *see* 1998
Lamond Family Foundation, CA, 817
LaMothe Foundation, Patricia A. & William E., FL, 2199
Lampert Family Foundation, CA, 818
Lampert Foundation, Edward and Kinga, The, FL, *see* 2200
Lampert Foundation, The, FL, 2200
Lancaster County Community Foundation, The, PA, 8135
Lancaster County Foundation, The, PA, *see* 8135
Lancaster Lens, Inc., OH, 7533
Land O'Lakes Foundation, MN, 4691
Landau Family Foundation, IL, 2966
Landau Foundation, Ralph, NY, 6322
Landegger Charitable Foundation, Inc., The, NY, 6323
Landenberger Research Foundation, Margaret Q., DE, 1801
Landmark Communications Foundation, VA, *see* 9467
Landmark Foundation, The, VA, 9467
Landry Charitable Foundation, G. Barrie, MA, 4134
Landry Charitable Foundation, Kevin, MA, 4135
Landsman Charitable Trust, The, MA, 4136
Landy Family Foundation, NY, 6324
Lane Foundation, Inc., Randi and Clifford, The, NY, 6325
Lane Foundation, John E. and Margaret L., The, CO, 1443
Lang Foundation, Eugene M., NY, 6326
Lange Foundation, Lura-Lee G. & William E., TN, 8593
Lange Foundation, Robert F., HI, 2609
Langeloth Foundation, Jacob and Valeria, The, NY, 6327
Langendorf Foundation, Stanley S., The, CA, 819
Langenfelder Charitable Trust, George H., FL, 2201

Langer Charitable Trust, Irving, NY, 6328
Langford Foundation, Frances, FL, 2202
Lanie Foundation, The, HI, *see* 2585
Lanier Family Foundation, Inc., Sartain, The, GA, 2499
Lannan Foundation, NM, 5526
Lansky Foundation, Irvin, TN, 8594
Lantz Foundation, Walter, The, CA, 820
Lanza Family Foundation, NY, 6329
Lapine Charitable Trust, A.B., NY, 6330
Lapp Foundation, Elma M., OH, 7534
Lard Trust, Mary Potishman, TX, 8972
Large Foundation, The, NJ, 5355
Larrk Foundation, CO, 1444
Larsen Fund, CT, 1624
Larson Charitable Trust, Orville H. and Shirley I., IL, 2967
Larson Family Foundation, MA, 4137
Larson Foundation, David & Janis, MN, 4692
Larson Foundation, Edson & Margaret, ND, 7352
Larson Foundation, FL, 2203
Larson Foundation, SD, 8516
Las Cumbres Observatory, Inc., CA, 821
LaSalle Adams Fund, NY, 6331
Lasdon Foundation, William & Mildred, NY, 6332
Lasker Foundation, Inc., Albert and Mary, NY, 6333
Lasko Foundation, John C., NJ, 5356
Lasky Foundation, Harry and Sadie, IL, 2968
Latimer Charitable Foundation, Bill and Carol, The, TN, 8595
Lattner Family Foundation, Inc., FL, 2204
Lattner Foundation, Forrest C. & Frances H., FL, 2205
Lauder Foundation Inc., NY, 6337
Lauder Foundation, Leonard and Evelyn, The, NY, 6334
Lauder Foundation, Ronald & Jo Carole, The, NY, 6335
Lauder Foundation, Ronald S., The, NY, 6336
Laughlin Trust, George A., WV, 9781
Laulhere Foundation, Cherese Mari, CA, 822
Launders Charitable Trust, Ruth and Hal, VA, 9468
Laural Foundation, CA, 823
Laurel Foundation, The, WA, 9666
Laurents Foundation, NY, *see* 6338
Laurents/Hatcher Foundation Inc, NY, 6338
Laurie Foundation for the Performing Arts, Inc., MO, 4933
Laurie Foundation, Inc., Blanche & Irving, NJ, 5357
Lauring Charitable Foundation, MA, 4138
Lauritzen Foundation, NE, 5061
Lauzier Charitable Foundation, Paul, WA, 9667
Lauzier Scholarship Foundation, Paul, WA, 9668
LaValley Foundation, The, OH, 7535
Lavelle Fund for the Blind, Inc., NY, 6339
Laverack Family Foundation, The, CT, 1625
Laverack Foundation, William and Cordelia, The, CT, *see* 1625
Lavin Family Foundation, FL, 2206
Lavin Family Foundation, Inc., The, DC, 1923
Lavin Foundation, Leonard H., FL, *see* 2206
Lawless Family Foundation, MD, 3827
Lawless Testamentary Trust B, John J., IL, 2969
Lawrence Family Foundation, TX, 8973
Lawson Charitable Trust, Geraldine G., TX, 8974
Lawson Foundation, Frederick Q., UT, 9330
Lawson Foundation, Janet Q., UT, 9331
Lay Family Foundation, The, MO, 4934
Layton Charitable Trust, Wade L., GA, 2500
Lazar Foundation, The, OR, 7864
Lazarus Foundation, Inc., The, TN, 8596
LCU Foundation, NY, *see* 6340
LCU Fund for Women's Education, NY, 6340
Lea Charitable Trust, IL, 2970
Leach Foundation Inc., Tom and Frances, The, ND, 7353
Leach Foundation, ND, *see* 7353
Leach II Foundation, Charles Henry, PA, A
Lear Corporation Charitable Foundation, MI, 4482
Lear Family Foundation, Inc., CA, 824
Lear Foundation, Frances, The, NY, 6341
Learning Coalition, The, HI, 2610
Least Indeed Foundation, AZ, 132
Leaves of Grass Fund, MA, 4139
Leavey Foundation, Thomas & Dorothy, CA, 825
Lebensfeld Foundation, The, NY, 6342
Lebovitz Charitable Trust, Moses and Leba, TN, *see* 8597
Lebovitz Family Charitable Trust, TN, 8597
LeBow Foundation Inc., Bennett and Geraldine, The, FL, 2207
Lebowitz-Aberly Family Foundation, TX, 8975
Leclerc Charity Fund, FL, 2208
Leder Foundation, Inc., Marc J., FL, 2209
Ledler Foundation, The, CA, *see* 1074
Leducq Foundation for Cardiovascular Research, TX, 8976
Lee Charitable Fund, Quincy and Estine, TX, 8977
Lee Family Foundation, Inc., The, CT, 1626
Lee Family Foundation, Theodore and Doris, NV, 5127
Lee Foundation, IA, 3457
Lee Foundation, Norman & Sadie, The, CA, 826
Lee Foundation, Patrick P., NY, 6343
Lee Foundation, Rowena, The, NY, A
Leeds Family Foundation, NY, 6344
Leeoma Charitable Trust, CO, A
Leever Foundation, The, NC, 7253
Leffell Family Foundation, Lisa and Michael, NY, 6345
Lefkofsky Family Foundation, The, IL, 2971
Lefrak Charitable Foundation, Inc., Richard S. and Karen, DE, 1802
LeFrak Charitable Foundation, Inc., Samuel J. & Ethel, The, DE, 1803
Lefrak Charitable Trust, Samuel J. and Ethel, DE, 1804
Left Hand Foundation, CO, 1445
Left Tilt Fund, The, CA, *see* 649
Legacy Banks Foundation, The, MA, *see* 3947
Legacy Foundation, Inc., IN, 3337
Legacy of Angels, The, MN, 4693
Legatus Foundation, NC, 7254
Legett Foundation, The, TX, 8978
Legg Mason Charitable Foundation, Inc., MD, 3828
Legion Foundation, The, MI, 4483
Lego Children's Fund, Inc., CT, 1627
Legum Foundation, Inc., MD, 3829
Lehigh Valley Community Foundation, PA, 8136
Lehman Brothers Foundation, The, NY, *see* 6538
Lehman Foundation, Inc., Edith and Herbert, NY, 6346
Lehman Foundation, Inc., Robert, NY, 6347
Lehmann Charitable Trust, John S., IL, 2972
Lehner Family Foundation, OH, 7536
Lehrer Family Foundation, The, CA, 827
Lehrman Foundation, Inc., Jacob and Charlotte, DC, 1924
Lehrman Institute, The, CT, 1628
Leibowitz and Greenway Family Charitable Foundation, NY, 6348
Leibowitz Foundation, Sheldon L. and Pearl R., IL, 2973
Leichtag Foundation, The, CA, 828
Leichtman and Arthur E. Levine Family Foundation, Lauren B., CA, 829
Leidy Foundation, Inc., John J., The, MD, 3830
Leighton Foundation, Inc., Judd, IN, 3338
Leighton-Oare Foundation, Inc., MI, 4484
Leir Foundation, Inc., The, NY, 6349
Lemberg Foundation, Inc., NY, 6350
Lemelson Foundation, The, OR, 7865
Lemle Family Foundation, Robert and Roni, NY, 6351
Lemons Charitable Trust, Jean, Jack, and Mildred, MO, 4935
Len-Ari Foundation, Inc., The, IN, 3339
Lenawee Community Foundation, MI, 4485
Lender Family Foundation Inc., Murray, GA, 2501
Lenfest Foundation, Inc., Brook J., The, PA, 8137
Lenfest Foundation, Inc., The, PA, 8138
Lenna Foundation, Inc., Reginald A. & Elizabeth S., NY, 6352
Lenna Foundation, The, NY, *see* 6352
Lennar Foundation, FL, 2210
Lennon Charitable Trust, Fred A., The, OH, 7537
Lennox Foundation, DE, 1805
Lennox Foundation, Martha, David & Bagby, TX, 8979
Lenzmeier Family Foundation, NJ, 5358
Leonard & Laila Rose Foundations, CA, 830
Leonard Charitable Foundation, George & Wilma, The, CA, 831
Leonard Family Foundation, PA, 8139
Leonard Street and Deinard Foundation, The, MN, 4694
Leonetti/O'Connell Family Foundation, The, CA, 832
Leonian Foundation, Phillip and Edith, IL, 2974
Leppien Foundation, The, MI, 4486
Leptas Foundation Trust, CO, 1446
Lerner Family Foundation Inc., Annette M. and Thdore N., The, MD, 3831
Lerner Family Foundation Inc., Eugene & Janet, IL, 975
Lerner Family Foundation, NY, 6353
Lerner Foundation, Emanuel & Pauline A., ME, 369
Lerner Foundation, The, OH, 7538
Lesher Foundation, Dean & Margaret, CA, 833
Leshkowitz Memorial Foundation, Naftali Tzvi, NY, 63
Lesley Family Foundation, Inc., TX, 8980
Leslie Family Foundation, CA, 834
Lessing Family Foundation, The, NY, 6355
Letterman Foundation for Courtesy and Grooming, The, NY, 6356
Leuthold Family Foundation, Steven C., MN, 4695
Levant Foundation, The, TX, 8981
LeVecke Family Foundation, The, CA, 835
Levee Charitable Foundation, James Annenberg, PA, *see* 8134
Leventhal Family Charitable Foundation, NY, 6357
Leventhal Family Foundation Inc., Muriel & Norman B., MA, 4141
Leventhal Family Foundation, Sherry and Alan, MA, 4140
Leventhal Foundation, Ira and Beth, NY, *see* 6357
Levi, Ray & Shoup Foundation, IL, 2976
Levian Charitable Foundation, Pary & Abdulrahim, The, NY, 6358
Levin Charitable Fund, Daniel, IL, 2977
Levin Family Foundation, Donald, IL, 2978
Levin Family Foundation, OH, 7539
Levin Family Foundation, The, OR, *see* 7884
Levin Foundation, Philip & Janice, The, NJ, 5359
Levine Family Charitable Trust, The, MA, 4142
Levine Family Foundation, Howard and Irene, CA, 836
Levine Foundation Inc., Laurence W., NY, 6360
Levine Foundation Inc., Tammy and Jay, The, CT, 1629
Levine Foundation Inc., William S. & Ina, AZ, 133
Levine Foundation, Leon, The, NC, 7255
Levine Foundation, William and Mildred, NY, 6359
Levinson Foundation, Max and Anna, NM, 5527
Levis Trust, PA, 8140
Levit Family Foundation, Joe, TX, 8982
Levitetz Family Foundation, Inc, FL, 2211
Levitt Family Charitable Foundation, Inc., Michael J. and Patricia, NJ, 5360
Levitt Foundation, Inc., Mortimer, NJ, 5361
Levitt Foundation, Inc., NY, 6361
Levitt Foundation, Madelyn M., IA, 3458
Levitt Foundation, Richard S., MD, *see* 3832
Levitt Foundation, The, MD, 3832
Levovitz Family Foundation Charitable Trust, Abraham and Marilyn, MA, 4143
Levy Family Foundation, Paul and Karen, The, NY, 6362
Levy Foundation, Edward C. and Linda Dresner, MI, 4487
Levy Foundation, Inc., June Rockwell, MA, 4144
Levy Foundation, Jerome, NY, 6363
Levy Foundation, Leon, NY, 6364
Levy, Jr. Foundation, Julie & Edward, MI, *see* 4487
Lewis Family Foundation, Richard H., CO, 1447
Lewis Family Foundation, Robert and Beverly, CA, 837
Lewis Family Trust, NJ, 5362
Lewis Family Trust, The, MI, 4488
Lewis Foundation, Inc., Dorothy V. & Logan, GA, 2502
Lewis Foundation, Inc., Frank J., FL, 2212
Lewis Foundation, Inc., J. C., GA, 2503
Lewis Foundation, Inc., Reginald F., NY, 6365
Lewis Foundation, T. W., AZ, 134
Lewis Foundation, TN, 8598
Lewis Jr. Charitable Foundation, Carol Sutton & William M., The, NY, A
Lewis Scholarship Trust, J. Edward, IL, 2979
Lewis Trust, J. Arnet and Mildred M., NC, 7256
Lewis, Jr. 2001 Foundation, George T., NC, 7257
Lewis-Sebring Family Foundation, IL, 2980
Lexington Community Foundation, NE, 5062
LG&E and KU Foundation Inc., KY, 3586
LGA Family Foundation, HI, 2611
Liana Foundation, Inc., WY, 9982
Liatis Foundation, TX, 8983
Libby-Dufour Fund, LA, 3648
Liberty Bank Foundation, Inc., CT, 1630

McKeen Fund, FL, 2234
McKenna Foundation, Inc., Katherine Mabis, PA, 8166
McKenna Foundation, Inc., Philip M., PA, 8167
McKenna Long & Aldridge Foundation, Inc., GA, 2516
McKenzie Family Charitable Trust, VT, 9366
McKesson Foundation, Inc., CA, 903
McKesson Foundation, OH, A
McKesson HBOC Foundation, Inc., CA, *see* 903
McKinnell Foundation, Henry A., The, WY, 9985
McKinney Charitable Foundation, William V. and Catherine A., PA, 8168
McKinstry Company Charitable Foundation, WA, 9680
McKissick Foundation, Ellison S. and Noel P., SC, 8486
McKnight Brain Research Foundation, Evelyn F., The, FL, 2235
McKnight Brain Research Foundation, FL, *see* 2235
McKnight Brain Research Foundation, The, FL, *see* 2235
McKnight Endowment Fund for Neuroscience, The, MN, 4708
McKnight Foundation, The, MN, 4709
McLane Foundation, George and Margaret, OH, 7566
McLane/Harper Charitable Foundation Inc., MA, 4169
McLean Contributionship, The, PA, 8169
McLean Foundation, Inc., Thomas R. & Elizabeth E., NC, 7264
McLean Foundation, MS, 4835
McLeod Blue Skye Charitable Foundation, Inc., CT, 1641
McMahon Family Foundation, Inc., Vince & Linda, CT, 1642
McMahon Foundation, The, OK, 7776
McManus Foundation Inc., D.J., The, NY, 6463
McMichael Family Foundation, The, NC, 7265
McMicking Foundation, CA, *see* 904
McMicking Foundation, Joseph R. & Mercedes, The, CA, 904
McMillan Foundation, D. W., AL, 50
McMillen Family Foundation, CA, 905
McMillen Foundation, Inc., IN, 3352
McMillen Foundation, Robert B., The, WA, 9681
McMinn Foundation, CA, 906
McMullen Family Foundation, NJ, 5378
McMurry Foundation, The, WY, 9986
McMurtry Family Foundation of 2003, FL, 2236
McMurtry Family Foundation, FL, *see* 2236
McNair Foundation, Robert and Janice, The, TX, 9017
McNamara Purcell Foundation, The, IL, 3017
McNeely Foundation, The, MN, 4710
McNeil Foundation, Colonel Stanley R., RI, 8418
McNeil Trust, Joanna, NY, 6464
McNulty Foundation, John P. & Anne Welsh, NY, 6465
McNutt Charitable Trust, Amy Shelton, TX, 9018
McPherson County Community Foundation, KS, 3534
McQuain Charitable Trust, Hazel Ruby, WV, 9785
McQueen Foundation, Adeline & George, IL, 3018
McRae Foundation, Inc., Selby and Richard, MS, 4836
McRae Foundation, MS, *see* 4836
McVaney Family Foundation Trust, Kevin E. & Colleen K., CO, *see* 1446
McVaney Family Foundation, CO, *see* 1516
McVay Foundation, MN, 4711
McWane Foundation, AL, 51
MDEKFSE Family Foundation, OR, 7867
MDU Resources Foundation, ND, 7354
Mead Family Foundation, Gilbert and Jaylee, MD, *see* 3845
Mead Family Foundation, MD, 3845
Mead Foundation, Giles W. and Elise G., CA, 907
Mead Foundation, Scott & Suling, The, NY, 6466
Mead Witter Foundation, Inc., WI, 9902
Meadowlark Foundation, CO, A
Meadows Foundation, Inc., The, TX, 9019
Meadowview Foundation, The, CA, 908
MeadWestvaco Foundation, The, VA, 9484
Meagel Charitable Trust, WV, 9786
Measey Foundation, Benjamin and Mary Siddons, The, PA, 8170
Mebane Charitable Foundation, Inc., NC, 7266
Mechanic Foundation, Inc., Morris A., MD, 3846
Medallion Foundation, Inc., TX, 9020
Medina Foundation, WA, 9682
Medleycott Family Foundation, The, PA, 8171
Medline Foundation, The, IL, 3019
Medlock Trust, Mary L., IL, 3020
Medtronic Foundation, The, MN, 4712
Mee Charitable Foundation, George and Margaret, NY, 6467
Meehan Foundation, NY, 6468
Mehra Family Foundation, The, NY, 6469
Mehta Family Foundation, Bhupat and Jyott, TX, *see* 9021
Mehta Family Foundation, The, TX, 9021
Meijer Foundation, The, MI, 4499
Meinders Foundation, The, OK, 7777
Meisels Family Foundation, Usher and Miriam, NY, *see* 5543
Melalucca Foundation, CA, 909
Meldrum Foundation, UT, 9333
Melkus Family Foundation, The, TN, 8609
Mellam Family Foundation, CA, 910
Mellinger Educational Foundation, Inc., Edward Arthur, IL, 3021
Mellon Family Foundation, R. K., PA, 8172
Mellon Foundation, Andrew W., The, NY, 6470
Mellon Foundation, Richard King, PA, 8173
Melly Foundation, Alice Pack and L. Thomas, The, NY, 6471
Melly Foundation, L. Thomas, NY, *see* 6471
MELMAC Education Foundation, ME, 3700
Melman Foundation, Richard & Martha, IL, 3022
Melohn Foundation, Inc., The, NY, 6472
Melrose Family Foundation, Kendrick B., MN, 4713
Melville Charitable Trust, The, MA, 4170
Melville Foundation, The, FL, 2237
MEMC Foundation, MO, *see* 4985
Memorial Foundation for Children, VA, 9485
Memphis Grizzlies Charitable Foundation, TN, 8610
Memton Fund, Inc., The, DE, 1819
Menard Family Foundation, CA, 911
Menasha Corporation Foundation, WI, 9903
Mendelson Foundation, Inc., Littler, CA, 912
Mendocino County Community Foundation, Inc., CA, *see* 416
Meng Inc., John and Engrid, WI, 9904
Mengle Foundation, Glenn and Ruth, PA, 8174
Menlo Foundation, Inc., CA, 913
Menschel Family Foundation, Robert and Joyce, The, NY, 6473
Menschel Foundation, Robert and Joyce, The, NY, *see* 6473
Mental Insight Foundation, The, CA, 914
Merage Family Foundation, Paul & Elisabeth, The, CA, 915
Merage Foundation of Nevada, Andre & Katherine, CA, 916
Merage Foundation, Andre & Katherine, CO, 1459
Merage Foundation, David and Laura, CO, 1460
Merali Foundation, Shirin Pandju, The, TX, 9022
Merancas Foundation, Inc., NC, 7267
Mercer County Civic Foundation, Inc., The, OH, 7567
Mercer Family Foundation, NY, 6474
Mercer Foundation, Johnny, The, CA, 917
Mercer Trust, Martha Dana, RI, 8419
Merchants Fund, PA, 8175
Merck Childhood Asthma Network, Inc., DC, 1929
Merck Company Foundation, The, NJ, 5379
Merck Family Fund, MA, 4171
Merck Fund, John, The, MA, 4172
Merck Institute for Science Education, Inc., NJ, 5380
Merck Patient Assistance Program, Inc., NJ, 5381
Mercy Foundation, Inc., KY, 3589
Mercy Works Foundation, Inc., WI, 9905
Mercy, Jr. Foundation, Inc., Sue and Eugene, The, NY, 6475
Meredith Corporation Foundation, IA, 3463
Meredith Foundation, Edwin T., IA, 3464
Meredith Foundation, TX, 9023
Meredith Private Foundation, TX, *see* 9025
Mericle Foundation, PA, 8176
Mericos Foundation, The, CA, 918
Meriden Foundation, The, CT, 1643
Merillat Foundation, Orville D. & Ruth A., MI, 4500
Merillat Private Foundation, Richard D. & Lynette S., NJ, 5382
Meringoff Family Foundation, Inc., The, NY, 6476
Merkin Family Foundation, CA, 919
Mermans Foundation, Inc., NC, *see* 7267
Merrick Foundation, Inc., NE, 5067
Merrill Family Foundation Inc., OR, 7868
Merrill Family Foundation, Steven L., The, CA, 92
Merrill Foundation, Inc., MD, 3847
Merriman Foundation, DC, 1930
Mertz Charitable Trust, The, PA, 8177
Mertz Gilmore Foundation, NY, 6477
Mertz-Gilmore Foundation, Joyce, NY, *see* 6477
Mesdag Family Foundation, The, NY, 6478
Meshewa Farm Foundation, OH, 7568
Messengers of Healing Winds Foundation, TN, *see* 854
Messner Foundation, Inc., NJ, 5383
Met Foundation, Inc., IN, 3353
Metavante Technologies Foundation, Inc., FL, *see* 2097
Metcalf Charitable Foundation, Dorothy A., The, PA, 8178
MetLife Foundation, NY, 6479
Metolius Trust, The, OR, 7869
MetroWest Community Health Care Foundation, Inc., MA, *see* 4173
MetroWest Health Foundation, MA, 4173
Metta Fund, CA, 921
Meyer Charitable Foundation, Barry and Wendy, The, CA, 922
Meyer Charitable Foundation, The, IL, 3023
Meyer Charitable Fund, Inc., Erie Hall, AL, 52
Meyer Charitable Trust, Fred, OR, *see* 7870
Meyer Family Foundation, Paul & Jane, TX, 9024
Meyer Family Foundation, Paul J., TX, *see* 9024
Meyer Foundation, Alice Kleberg Reynolds, TX, *see* 9127
Meyer Foundation, Eugene and Agnes E., DC, 1931
Meyer Foundation, Inc., Edward & Sandra, NY, 6480
Meyer Foundation, Robert R., AL, 53
Meyer Foundation, The, NY, 6481
Meyer Memorial Trust, OR, 7870
Meyerhoff Fund Inc., Harvey M., The, MD, 3849
Meyerhoff Fund, Inc., Joseph, The, MD, 3848
MFA Foundation, MO, 4943
MFI Foundation, TX, 9025
Miami County Foundation, OH, 7569
Miami Foundation, The, FL, 2238
Micah 6:8 Foundation, MI, 4501
Michaan Foundation, J. S. & S., The, FL, 2239
Michaels Family Foundation Inc., The, NY, 6482
Michaels Foundation, Inc., Lorne, The, NY, *see* 6482
Michels Family Foundation, Dale R. & Ruth L., WI, 9906
Michelson Foundation, The, CA, *see* 260
Michelson Medical Research Foundation, Inc., CA, 923
Michelson, M.D. Charitable Foundation, Inc., Gary Karlin, CA, *see* 923
Michigan Capital Fund for Non-Profit Housing Corporation, MI, *see* 4451
Michigan City Community Enrichment Corporation, IN, 3354
Micron Technology Foundation, Inc., ID, 2637
Mid-Iowa Health Foundation, IA, 3466
Mid-Nebraska Community Foundation, Inc., NE, 5068
Mid-Shore Community Foundation, Inc., MD, 3851
MidAmerican Energy Foundation, IA, 3465
Middendorf Family Foundation, Frank J., RI, *see* 8420
Middendorf Family Foundation, RI, 8420
Middendorf Foundation, Inc., MD, 3850
Middle Road Foundation, NY, 6483
Middlecott Foundation, MA, 4174
Middlesex County Community Foundation, Inc., CT, 1644
Middleton Foundation, The, CA, 924
Middletown Community Foundation, OH, 7570
Midland Area Community Foundation, MI, 4502
Midland Foundation, MI, *see* 4502
Midler Family Foundation, TN, 8611
Midwest Foundation, IA, *see* 3465
Mifflin Memorial Fund, George H. & Jane A., MA, 4175
Milano Foundation, Inc., NJ, 5384
Milbank Foundation for Rehabilitation, NJ, *see* 5385
Milbank Foundation, NJ, 5385
Miles Foundation, Inc., The, TX, 9026
Milgard Family Foundation, Gary & Carol, WA, *see* 9683
Milgard Family Foundation, Gary E., WA, 9683
Milias Foundation, The, CA, 925

Morrison Family Foundation, Harold M. and Adeline S., IL, 3038
Morrison Family Foundation, IL, 3037
Morrison Family Foundation, John M. & Susan, FL, 2245
Morrison Foundation, Robert S., OH, 7580
Morrow Family Foundation, Luke And Lori, TX, 9042
Morsani Foundation, Inc., Frank and Carol, FL, 2246
Morse Charitable Trust, Elizabeth, The, IL, 3039
Morse Family Foundation, Inc., NY, 6509
Morse Hill Foundation, Inc., NY, 6510
Morse, Jr. Foundation, Inc., Enid & Lester S., NY, *see* 6509
Mortensen Foundation, William & Alice, The, CT, 1647
Mortenson Family Foundation, The, MN, 4721
Mortenson Family Foundation, WI, 9909
Morton Foundation, Inc., Peter A., CA, 943
Morton Foundation, The, CA, 944
Morton Memorial Fund, Mark, IL, 3040
Morton-Kelly Charitable Trust, The, ME, 3701
Mosaic Company Foundation, MN, 4722
Mosaic Foundation of R. & P. Heydon, The, MI, 4509
Mosaic Fund, The, NH, 5181
Mosakowski Family Charitable Foundation, The, NJ, 5387
Mosakowski Family Foundation, NJ, *see* 5387
Mosbacher, Jr. Foundation, Inc., Emil, CA, *see* 1119
Moseley Foundation, Edward S. & Winifred G., MA, 4185
Moses Fund, Inc., Henry and Lucy, NY, 6511
Mosher Family Foundation, George & Julie, IL, 3041
Mosher Foundation, Samuel B. and Margaret C., CA, 945
Mosher Foundation, Samuel B., CA, *see* 945
Mosher Foundation, The, CA, *see* 945
Mosi Foundation, PA, 8189
Moskowitz Foundation, Cherna, FL, 2247
Moss Foundation, CA, 946
Moss Heart Trust, Harry S., TX, 9043
Mosse Foundation for Education and the Arts, The, CA, 948
Mosse Foundation, CA, 947
Mosse Foundation, Hilde L., The, CA, *see* 948
Mossier Foundation, Kevin J., MN, 4723
Motorists Insurance Companies Foundation, The, OH, *see* 7581
Motorists Insurance Group Foundation, The, OH, 7581
Motorola Foundation, IL, *see* 3042, *see* 3043
Motorola Mobility Foundation, IL, 3042
Motorola Solutions Foundation, IL, 3043
Mott Foundation, Charles Stewart, MI, 4510
Mott Foundation, Ruth, MI, 4511
Moulton Christmas Poor Fund, Judge C. F., MO, 4946
Mound Properties Inc., WI, 9910
Mount Cuba Center, Inc., DE, 1821
Mount Pleasant Area Community Foundation, MI, 4512
Mount Pleasant Community Foundation, MI, *see* 4512
Mount Vernon/Knox County Community Trust, The, OH, *see* 7413
Mourier Family Foundation, CA, 949
Mousetrap Foundation, The, VA, 9491
Moxie Foundation, Inc., The, CA, 950
Mozilo Family Foundation, The, NY, 6512
MRB Foundation, IL, 3044
Msb Cockayne Fund, Inc, TN, 8612
MSJ Foundation, MI, 4513
Mt. Brilliant Foundation, The, KY, 3590
MTI Foundation, Inc., IN, 3357
Muchemore Foundation, G. Robert, NE, 5070
Mudd Foundation, Mildred E. & Harvey S., CA, 951
Mulago Foundation, CA, 952
Mulder Foundation, Larry and Karen, MI, 4514
Mule Family Foundation, NY, 6513
Mulford Foundation, Vincent, The, NY, 6514
Mulford Trust, Clarence E., The, ME, 3702
Mullen Family Foundation, Inc., Donald R., NY, 6515
Mullen Family Foundation, The, PA, 8190, *see* 8190
Mullen Foundation, Hilda, The, NY, 6516
Muller Charitable Foundation, Inc., Marisa, FL, *see* 2252
Muller Family Foundation, CA, 953
Muller, Sr. Foundation, Frank, CA, *see* 953
Mulva Family Foundation, The, TX, 9044
Munger Family Foundation, CO, 1467
Munger Foundation, Alfred C., CA, 954
Munson Foundation, Curtis & Edith, DC, 1933
Munson Foundation, W. B., IL, 3045
Munzer Foundation, Rudolph J. & Daphne A., The, CA, 955
Murch Foundation, The, OH, 7582
Murchison Foundation, Ginger, The, TX, 9045
Murchison Foundation, Lupe, The, TX, 9046
Murdock Charitable Trust, M. J., WA, 9689
Murdough Foundation, OH, 7583
Murdough Foundation, Thomas G. & Joy P., OH, *see* 7583
Murphy Family Foundation, The, NY, 6517
Murphy Foundation, Dan, CA, 956
Murphy Foundation, Fred M. Klaus and Harold L., NC, 7270
Murphy Foundation, John P., OH, 7584
Murphy Foundation, Katherine John, GA, 2522
Murphy Foundation, Philip D. & Tammy S., The, NY, *see* 6517
Murphy Foundation, The, AR, 193
Murray Family Charitable Foundation, RI, 8421
Murray Foundation, Jerome S. & Grace H., MD, 3855
Murray Foundation, Stuart & Eulene, GA, 2523
Muse Foundation, The, OH, A
Musgrave Foundation, MO, 4947
Mushett Family Foundation, Inc., NJ, 5388
Musk Foundation, CA, 957
Muskavitch Foundation, Charles & Gail, CA, 958
Muskegon County Community Foundation, Inc., MI, *see* 4369
Muskingum County Community Foundation, OH, 7585
Muss Foundation, Inc., Stephen and Sandra, The, FL, 2248
Muss Foundation, Inc., Stephen, The, FL, *see* 2248
Musser Fund, Laura Jane, The, MN, 4724
Musser Fund, The, MN, *see* 4724
Musser Memorial Fund, Custer, PA, 8191
Mustard Seed Foundation, Inc., VA, 9492
Mutual of America Foundation, NY, 6518
Mutual of Omaha Foundation, NE, 5071
MWC Foundation, Inc., MA, 4186
My Good Fund, UT, 9338
Myer Foundation, Inc., Diane Lenfest, The, PA, *see* 7912
Myers Charitable Foundation, David G. & Carol P., MI, *see* 4515
Myers Foundation, David & Carol, MI, 4515
Myers Foundation, Israel & Mollie, MD, 3856
Mylan Charitable Foundation, The, PA, 8192
Myles Family Foundation, WV, 9787
Myra Foundation, ND, 7355
Mys Family US Charitable Foundation Inc., NY, 6519

Nabers Charitable Foundation, The, AL, 56
Nabholz Charitable Foundation, AR, 194
Naddisy Foundation, Inc., NY, 6520
Nadler Family Charitable Trust, Paul S., NY, 6521
Nagel Foundation, CO, 1468
Nagel Foundation, John F., The, ID, 2639
NAH Foundation, The, TX, 9047
Najafi Family Foundation, F. Francis, AZ, *see* 153
Najim Family Foundation, Harvey E., TX, 9048
Nakash Family Foundation, NY, 6522
Names Family Foundation, WA, 9690
Nanci's Animal Rights Foundation, Inc., FL, 2249
Nancy and John Foundation, TX, *see* 9188
Naomi Prawer Kadar Foundation, Inc, The, NY, 6523
NAON, Inc., NY, 6524
Napa Valley Community Foundation, CA, 959
Nape Charities Fund, TX, 9049
Napier Foundation, Margaret Gill Clements, The, TX, 9050
Narada Foundation, Creighton, The, MA, 4187
Nararo Foundation, The, PA, 8193
Narrow Gate - A Charitable Foundation, The, CA, 960
NASDAQ OMX Group Educational Foundation, Inc., MD, 3857
Nasdaq Stock Marked Educational Foundation, Inc., The, MD, *see* 3857
Nash Charitable Trust, Beth Nash & Joshua, NY, *see* 6062
Nash Family Foundation, NY, 6525
Nasher Foundation, The, TX, 9051
Nashville Community Foundation, Inc., TN, *see* 8550
Natem Foundation Inc., TX, 9052
Natembea Foundation, DE, 1822
Nathan Charitable Trust, Scott A., MA, 4188
National Academy of Education, The, DC, 1934
National Endowment for Financial Education, C
National Fuel Gas Company Foundation, NY, 65
National Grid Foundation, The, NY, 6527
National Hockey League Foundation, NY, 6528
National Life Group Charitable Foundation, Inc., V 9368
National Machinery Foundation Inc., OH, 7586
National Mah Jongg League Foundation, Inc., NY, 65
National Recreation Foundation, Inc., IN, 3358
Nationwide Foundation, OH, *see* 7587
Nationwide Insurance Foundation, OH, 7587
Native American Preparatory Scholarships, CA, 961
Natural Gas Partners Foundation, TX, 9053
Natural Health Research Foundation, IL, 3046
Naugatuck Savings Bank Foundation, Inc., CT, *see* 1616
Navarro Community Foundation, TX. 9054
Naylor Family Foundation, PA, 8194
Nazarian Family Foundation, NY, 6530
Nazarian Family Foundation, Y. & S., CA, 962
NBC Universal Foundation, NY, 6531
NBI Foundation, Inc., The, NY, 6532
NBI Healthcare Foundation, Inc., NJ, *see* 5296
NCR Foundation, GA, 2524
NDCF, ND, *see* 7357
NDPI Foundation, Inc., DC, 1935
Nduna Foundation, The, NY, 6533
Nearburg Foundation, Charles and Dana, The, TX, 9055
Neda Foundation, The, DE, *see* 1823
Needmor Fund, The, OH, 7588
Neeley Foundation, Lucille and Ronald, CA, 963
Neely Foundation, Otto & Edna, AZ, 149
Neese Family Foundation, Inc., WI, 9911
NEFE, CO, *see* 1469
Negaunee Foundation, The, IL, 3047
Neidich & Brooke Garber Foundation, Daniel M., NY, 6534
Neilsen Foundation, Craig H., CA, 964
Neilson Foundation, George W., MN, 4725
Neiman Foundation, Inc., LeRoy, NY, 6535
Neisser Family Foundation, The, IL, 3048
Nelnet Foundation, NE, 5072
Nelson Family Foundation, Inc., The, WI, 9912
Nelson Family Foundation, Jonathan M., RI, 8422
Nelson Family Foundation, Ruth, OK, 7779
Nelson Family Foundation, The, MN, 4726
Nelson Foundation, Grace S. & W. Linton, PA, 8195
Nelson Foundation, Hermoine & Glen, The, AL, 57
Nelson Foundation, James & Aune, IL, 3049
Nelson Foundation, The, IA, 3467
Ner Tzion Foundation, CT, 1648
Nerenberg 2000 Charitable Trust, Jerome, IL, 3050
Nesbitt Foundation, IL, 3051
Nesharim Foundation, Kanfei, NY, 6536
Nesholm Family Foundation, WA, 9691
Neslab Charitable Foundation, NH, *see* 5165
Nestle Purina PetCare Trust Fund, MO, 4948
Nestle Scholarship Foundation, TX, 9056
Nestle USA Foundation, CA, 965
Neu Family Foundation, Inc., John and Wendy, The, NY, 6537
Neubauer Family Foundation, The, PA, 8196
Neuberger Berman Foundation, The, NY, 6538
Neuberger Foundation, Inc., Roy R. and Marie S., CT, 1649
Neukom Family Foundation, WA, 9692
Neuman Family Foundation, CO, 1470
Neuman Foundation, Inc., Gerald David, NY, *see* 6540
Neuwirth Foundation, Inc., The, NY, 6539
Nevada Community Foundation, Inc., NV, 5134
Neviaser Charitable Foundation, Inc., NC, 7271
New Albany Community Foundation, OH, 7589
New Balance Foundation, MA, 4189
New Beginning Resources, Inc., TX, 9057
New Blank Family Foundation, Inc., The, FL, *see* 1997
New Breeze Foundation, MA, 4190
New Britain Foundation for Public Giving, CT, *see* 1564
New Brook Charitable Foundation, Inc., The, NY, 6540
New Canaan Community Foundation, Inc., CT, 1650
New Cycle Foundation, MA, 4191
New England Foundation, The, MA, 4192

Oarsmen Foundation, CA, 979
Oates Charitable Foundation, Marvin "Buzz", CA, 980
Oberkotter Family Foundation, Robert & Joyce, NH, 5183
Oberkotter Foundation, PA, 8203
Oberndorf Foundation, Bill and Susan, CA, 981
Oberndorf Foundation, CA, see 981
Obici Foundation, Inc., VA, see 9500
Obici Healthcare Foundation, Inc., VA, 9500
Occupational Physicians Scholarship Fund, IL, A
Ocean Federal Foundation, NJ, see 5394
Ocean Reef Community Foundation, Inc., FL, 2253
Ocean Reef Foundation, Inc., FL, see 2253
OceanFirst Foundation, NJ, 5394
Oceanic Heritage Foundation, The, NY, 6574
OCF, OR, see 7876
Och Family Foundation, Jane and Daniel, The, NY, 6575
Ochylski Family Foundation, IA, 3470
OCLO, Inc., NY, 6576
October Hill Foundation, The, CT, 1659
Ocular Physiology Research and Education Foundation, Inc., WI, 9915
Odell Fund, Robert S. & Helen P., NC, 7277
Odell Fund, Robert Stewart and Helen Pfeiffer, NC, see 7277
Oechsle Family Foundation, NC, 7278
Oehrli Charitable Trust, Diana, The, MA, see 4082
Oelschlager Foundation, Jim & Vanita, OH, 7598
Offield Family Foundation, The, IL, 3062
Offutt Family Foundation, Ronald D., ND, 7358
Ogden Foundation, Inc., Ralph E., NY, 6579
OGE Energy Corp. Foundation, OK, see 7782
Ogle Foundation, Inc., Paul, IN, 3362
Ohana Foundation, Thomas, CA, 983
Ohel Harav Yehoshua Boruch Foundation, Inc., NY, 6580
Ohga Foundation, Norio, NY, 6581
Ohio MedCenter Foundation, Inc., OH, see 7558
Ohio National Foundation, The, OH, 7599
Ohnell Family Foundation, The, CT, 1661
Ohrstrom Foundation, Inc., The, NY, 6582
Ohrstrom, Jr. Foundation, George L., NY, 6583
Oishei Foundation, John R., The, NY, 6584
Oki Charitable Foundation, The, WA, see 9694
Oki Foundation, WA, 9694
Oklahoma City Community Foundation, Inc., OK, 7781
Oklahoma Communities Foundation, Inc., OK, see 7742
Oklahoma Gas and Electric Company Foundation, Inc., OK, 7782
Olayan Charitable Trust, NY, 6585
Old Boys Foundation, The, NY, 6586
Old National Bank Foundation, Inc., IN, 3363
Oldham Little Church Foundation, TX, 9069
Olean Community Foundation, Greater, NY, see 5750
Oleson Foundation, MI, 4516
Olin Corporation Charitable Trust, NC, 7279
Olive Bridge Fund, NY, 6587
Oliver Charitable Corporation, AR, 195
Oliver Family Foundation, The, OH, 7600
Olmsted Foundation, George and Carol, The, VA, 9501
Olshan Foundation, Morton & Carole, NY, 6588
Olson Foundation, The, CT, 1662
Olsson Memorial Foundation, Elis, VA, 9502
Omaha Community Foundation, NE, 5074
Omer Foundation, NY, 6590
Omidyar Network Fund, Inc., CA, 984
OMNOVA Solutions Foundation, Inc., OH, 7601
Omron Foundation, Inc., IL, 3063
On His Path, IA, 3471
On Top of the World Foundation, Inc., The, FL, see 2029
Once Upon A Time Foundation, TX, 9070
One Life Foundation Inc., MA, 4197
One Valley Bank Foundation, Inc., NC, see 7144
One World Fund, MA, 4198
OneAmerica Foundation, Inc., The, IN, 3364
OneFamily Foundation, WA, 9695
ONEOK Foundation, Inc., OK, 7783
OneWest Foundation, CA, 985
OneWorld Boston, Inc., MA, 4199
Onstead Foundation, Robert R. & Kay M., TX, 9071
Opatrny Family Foundation, The, NY, 6592
Opatrny, Jr. Charitable Foundation, Donald C. and Judith T., NY, see 6592
Open Doors International, Inc., CA, 986
Open Society Institute, NY, 6593
Open Spaces, Sacred Places, MD, see 3896
Opera House Fund, Inc., KY, 3593
Opler Foundation, Edmond and Alice, IL, 3064
Opler Foundation, Edmond, IL, see 3064
Oppenheim Family Fund, Inc., NY, 6594
Oppenheimer and Flora Oppenheimer Haas Trust, Leo, IL, 3065
Oppenheimer Family Foundation, Gerald and Virginia, CA, see 987
Oppenheimer Family Foundation, Gerald, CA, 987
Oppenheimer Family Foundation, The, IL, 3066
Oppenstein Brothers Foundation, MO, 4950
Opperman Foundation, Dwight D., The, CA, 988
Opportunities for Education Foundation, WA, 9696
Oprah Winfrey Charitable Foundation, IL, 3067
Opus Community Foundation, CA, 989
Opus Foundation, CA, 990
Opus Foundation, MN, 4731
Opus Prize Foundation, SD, 8518
Oracle Education Foundation, CA, 991
Oracle Help Us Help Foundation, CA, see 991
Oral Health Services Foundation, Inc., MA, see 4016
Orange County Community Foundation, CA, 992
Orange County Community Foundation, Inc., IN, 3365
Orange Orphan Society, The, NJ, 5396
Orcas Island Community Foundation, WA, 9697
Orchard Farm Foundation, The, CT, 1663
Orchard Foundation, The, ME, 3704
Ordean Foundation, MN, 4732
Oreggia Family Foundation, CA, 993
Oregon Community Foundation, The, OR, 7876
Orenstein Foundation, Inc., Henry and Carolyn Sue, NJ, 5397
Orentreich Family Foundation, NY, 6596
Orfalea Family Foundation, The, CA, 994
Original Sorenson Legacy Foundation, UT, A
Oritani Savings Bank Charitable Foundation, NJ, see 5398
OritaniBank Charitable Foundation, NJ, 5398
Orleton Trust Fund, The, KY, 3594
Ormond Family Charitable Foundation, The, OH, 7603, see 7603
Oro y Plata Foundation, MT, 5014
Orokawa Foundation, Inc., The, MD, 3860
Orr Family Foundation, DE, 1827
Orr Family Foundation, Robert O. and AnnaMae, OH, 7604
Orscheln Industries Foundation Inc., MO, 4951
Orsinger Foundation, Genevieve and Ward, TX, 9073
Orsinger Foundation, Genevieve McDavitt, TX, see 9073
Ortega Charitable Foundation, DE, 1828
Ortenberg Foundation, The, NY, see 5783
Ortenzio Family Foundation, Robert and Angela, The, PA, 8205
Ortenzio Family Foundation, Rocco and Nancy, The, PA, see 8206
Ortenzio Foundation, Rocco and Nancy, The, PA, 8206
Orthodox Vision Foundation, CA, 995
Orthwein Foundation, William R. Orthwein, Jr. & Laura Rand, The, NY, 6597
Orvis Foundation, Arthur Emerton, The, NY, see 6598
Orvis Foundation, Inc., Arthur and Mae, The, NY, 6598
Ory Charitable Trust, Linda Hammett & Andrew, The, MA, 4200
Osborn Charitable Trust, Edward B., RI, 8426
Osborne Foundation, Inc., Weldon F., TN, 8614
Oschin Family Foundation, Mr. & Mrs. Samuel, CA, 996
Osher Foundation, Bernard, CA, 997
Osher Pro Suecia Foundation, Barbro, The, CA, 998
Oshkosh Area Community Foundation, WI, 9916
Oshkosh Corporation Foundation, Inc., WI, 9917
Oshkosh Foundation, WI, see 9916
Oshkosh Truck Foundation, Inc., WI, see 9917
Oshman Foundation, TX, 9074
Osprey Foundation, The, MD, 3861
Ossen Family Foundation, Jeffrey P., CT, 1664
Osteopathic Heritage Foundations, OH, 7605
Oster Family Foundation, Inc., NJ, 5399
Ostrovsky Family Fund, Inc., NY, 6600
Oswald Charitable Foundation, MN, see 4735
Oswald Family Foundation, MN, 4735
Ottaway Foundation, Inc., Nicholas B., NY, 66
Ottens Foundation, John and Sophie, The, CO,
Otter Cares Foundation, CO, 1473
Otter Cove Foundation, CA, 999
OtterCares Foundation, CO, see 1473
Ottley Trust-Atlanta, Marian W., GA, see 2580
Ottley Trust-Watertown, Marian W., NC, see 7343
Ottosen Family Foundation, The, AZ, 150
Our Community's Foundation, WV, see 9789
Our Family for Families First, Inc., WA, see 9606
Outcalt Charitable Fund, OH, see 7606
Outcalt Foundation, Jane and Jon, OH, 7606
Outhwaite Charitable Trust, June G., CA, 1000
Overbrook Foundation, The, NY, 6604
Overdeck Family Foundation, Inc., NY, 6605
Overhills Foundation, NY, 6606
Overlook International Foundation Inc., NY, 6607
Overly Foundation, Edith H., MA, 4201
Overture Foundation, WI, see 9848
Owen Family Foundation, Louis and Peaches, The, TX, 9075
Owen Foundation, Dian Graves, TX, 9076
Owen Trust, B. B., TX, 9077
Owenoke Foundation, The, CT, 1665
Owens Corning Foundation, Inc., OH, 7607
Owens Family Foundation, The, MA, 4202
Owens Foundation, Inc., William & Catherine, The, VA, 9503
Owens Foundation, The, IL, 3068
Owens Foundation, Thomas M. & Mary M., IL, see 3068
Owsley Brown Ii Cockayne Fund, Inc., KY, 3595
Owsley Foundation, Alvin & Lucy, TX, 9078
Oxford Area Foundation, The, PA, 8208
Oxley Foundation, Mary K., OK, 7784
Oxley Foundation, The, OK, 7785
Oxnard Foundation, CA, 1001

P & B Foundation, NC, 7280
P & M Charities, Inc., FL, see 2240
PACCAR Foundation, WA, 9698
Pace Foundation, Linda, TX, 9079
Pace Foundation, The, NY, see 5909
PACE, OH, see 7608
Pacific Forest & Watershed Lands Stewardship Council, CA, 1002
Pacific Life Foundation, CA, 1003
Pacific Mutual Charitable Foundation, CA, see 1003
Pacific Power/Rocky Mountain Power Foundation, OR, see 7877
Pacific Source Health Plan, OR, see 7878
Pacific Theatres Foundation, CA, 1004
Pacific Youth Foundation, CA, 1005
PacifiCorp Foundation For Learning, OR, see 7877
PacifiCorp Foundation, OR, 7877
PacificSource Charitable Foundation, Inc., OR, see 7878
PacificSource Foundation for Health Improvement, OR, 7878
Packard Foundation, David and Lucile, The, CA, 1006
Packard Humanities Institute, The, CA, 1007
Paducah Area Community Foundation, KY, see 3570
Padway Charitable Trust for the Arts and Education, Beatrix Finston, CA, 1008
Paestum Foundation, Inc., The, NY, 6608
Page Memorial Foundation, Carl Victor, The, CA, 1009
Pagel Foundation, Jack W., MN, see 4736
Pagel Foundation, MN, 4736
PAH Foundation, WA, 9699
Paiko Foundation, The, FL, 2255
Palace Head Foundation, Inc., MA, 4203
Palank Memorial Foundation, Inc., Paul, FL, 2256
Palestine Temple Charities Trust, RI, see 8438
Palestroni Foundation, Inc., Alfiero and Lucia, NJ, 5400
Palette Fund, Inc., The, NY, 6609
Paley Foundation, Inc., William S., NY, 6610
Palm Beach Community Trust Fund, NC, 7281
Palm Beach County Community Foundation, FL, see 2032
Palm Foundation, The, NY, 6611
Palmer Foundation, The, DC, 1937
Palmer Fund, Frank Loomis, CT, 1666
Paloheimo Foundation, TX, 9080
Palumbo Charitable Trust, A. J. & Sigismunda, PA, 8209
Pamphalon Foundation, Inc., FL, 2257

tion, The, NY, 6612
e Foundation, The, CA, 1010
, John C., PA, 8210
t, Thomas W., PA, 8211
oundation, The, NH, 5184
dation, Charles, WA, 9700
undation, NY, 6613
oundation Inc., CT, 1667
Scholarship Foundation, John & Mary, IA,
Charitable Foundation, Inc., Thomas Anthony,
4204
Foundation, Arthur M. and Martha R., MA, 4205
itas Foundation, CA, 1011
sol Community Foundation, Inc., NV, *see* 5138
sol Tahoe Community Foundation, NV, 5138
dee Foundation, Elsa U., MI, 4517
rdoe Foundation, Samuel P., MA, 4206
arents Advancing Choice in Education, OH, 7608
ariser Foundation, Inc., Paul S., FL, 2258
Parish Foundation, Suzanne D., MI, *see* 4518
Parish Foundation, Suzanne Upjohn Delano, MI, 4518
Park City Foundation, The, UT, 9341
Park Foundation, Chang K., NY, 6614
Park Foundation, Inc., NY, 6615
Park Foundation, The, OH, 7609
Park National Bank Foundation, The, OH, *see* 7610
Park National Corporation Foundation, OH, 7610
Parke County Community Foundation, Inc., IN, 3366
Parke Foundation, Jim and Shirley, NY, 6616
Parker Family Foundation, NJ, 5401
Parker Foundation, Mary E., The, DE, 1829
Parker Foundation, The, CA, 1012
Parker Foundation, Theodore Edson, The, MA, 4207
Parker-Hannifin Foundation, The, OH, 7611
Parkersburg Area Community Foundation, WV, 9789
Parks Foundation, Fred & Mabel R., TX, 9081
Parkview Foundation, NY, 6617
Parmer Family Foundation Inc., PA, 8212
Parmer Private Foundation, John C. & Carolyn Noonan, The, IL, 3069
Parnes Foundation Inc., E. & H., NJ, 5402
Parr Trust, Martha Sue, IL, 3070
Parrish Foundation, Charles Maxfield & Gloria F., UT, 9342
Parrish Foundation, Robert J. Harriet A. and David T., IN, 3367
Parrish Foundation, Steve and Diane, DE, 1830
Parsons Family Foundation, The, NY, 6618
Parsons Foundation, AZ, *see* 151
Parsons Foundation, Bob and Renee, The, AZ, 151
Parsons Foundation, Mary Morton, The, VA, 9504
Parsons Foundation, Ralph M., The, CA, 1013
Parsons Memorial Foundation, Ann, NY, 6619
Partners for Developing Futures, Inc., CA, 1014
Partnership Foundation, The, TX, 9082
Partridge Foundation, The, OH, 7612
Pasadena Community Foundation, CA, 1015
Pasadena Foundation, CA, *see* 1015
Pascale/Sykes Foundation, Inc., NJ, 5403
Pasculano Foundation, The, CT, 1668
Paso del Norte Health Foundation, TX, 9083
Pasquerilla Foundation, Frank J. & Sylvia T., PA, 8213
Pasquinelli Family Foundation, IL, 3071
Passport Foundation, CA, 1016
Pastega Family Foundation, Mario and Alma, OR, 7879
Patagonia.org, CA, 1017
Patch Foundation, The, MN, 4737
Patel Family Foundation, Inc., Drs. Kiran & Pallavi, FL, 2259
Patel Foundation, Dinesh and Kalpana, UT, 9343
Patel Foundation, Ravi and Naina, CA, 1018
Pathways in Education, Inc., CA, 1019
Patriarch Family Foundation, PA, 8214
Patron Saints Foundation, The, CA, 1020
Pattee Foundation, The, IL, 3072
Patten Charitable Trust, John L., RI, 8427
Patten Family Foundation, MA, 4208
Patterson Dental Foundation, MN, *see* 4738
Patterson Family Foundation, DE, 1831
Patterson Foundation, Cissy, The, SC, 8489
Patterson Foundation, MN, 4738
Patterson Foundation, Proctor, OH, 7613
Patterson Foundation, The, FL, 2260, 2261
Patterson Trust, Robert E. Leet & Clara Guthrie, CT, 1669
Patton Foundation, George W. & Mary B., TX, 9084
Patton Trust, Albert F., FL, 2262
Patton Trust, George William, TX, 9085
Paul Foundation, Inc., Josephine Bay Paul and C. Michael, NY, *see* 5652
Pauley Family Foundation, The, VA, 9505
Paulson Family Foundation, NY, 6620
Paulson, Jr. Foundation, Henry M. & Wendy J., IL, *see* 2707
Pay it Forward Foundation, The, CT, 1670
Payne Family Foundation Inc., L. Robert & Patricia L., CA, 1021
Payne Foundation, Frank E. Payne and Seba B., IL, 3073
Payne Foundation, Inc., David D. & Nona S., TX, 9086
Payne Fund, The, OH, 7614
PB Foundation, Inc., NY, 6621
PB&K Family Foundation, CO, 1474
PBHP, Inc., NY, 6622
PCLB Foundation, The, NY, *see* 5725
Peabody Charitable Fund, Amelia, MA, 4209
Peabody Foundation, Amelia, MA, 4210
Peabody Foundation, Inc., The, MA, 4211
Peabody Foundation, Mary K., IN, 3368
Peach Foundation, WA, 9701
Peacock Foundation, Inc., FL, 2263
Pearce Foundation, Inc., Dr. M. Lee, The, FL, 2264
Pearson-Rappaport Foundation, NY, 6623
Pechter Family Foundation, The, FL, 2265
Pechter Foundation, The, GA, 2526
Peck Foundation Milwaukee Ltd., WI, 9918
Peck Foundation, Ltd., Miriam & Bernard, WI, *see* 9918
Peco Foundation, NY, 6624
Pedas Family Foundation, Inc., James & Theodore, The, DC, 1938
Pediatric Epilepsy Research Foundation, TX, 9087
Peery Charitable Foundation, Louis S., The, UT, 9344
Peery Charitable Foundation, Louis Scowcroft, The, UT, *see* 9344
Peery Foundation, CA, 1022
Peierls Foundation, CO, 1475
Peirce Family Foundation, Inc., The, PA, 8215
Pelham Foundation, Jean T. and Heyward G., DE, 1832
Pell Family Foundation, CA, 1023
Pella Rolscreen Foundation, IA, 3473
Pelling Foundation Inc., Patricia G., GA, 2527
Pels Charitable Trust, Donald A., NY, 6625
Peltier Foundation, The, LA, 3658
Pema Foundation, Inc., CO, 1476
Pema Foundation, TX, 9088
PEMCO Foundation, Inc., WA, 9702
Penates Foundation, The, NH, 5185
Pendleton Charitable Trust, James B., WA, 9703
Penn Foundation, William, The, PA, 8216
Penn Treaty Special Services District, PA, 8217
Penney Company Fund, Inc., J. C., TX, 9089
Pennington Foundation, Irene W. & C. B., LA, 3659
Pennington Foundation, William N., NV, 5139
Penseco Foundation, PA, *see* 8218
Penske Foundation, Inc., MI, 4519
Penson Foundation, Shannon and Andrew S., NY, 6626
Pentair Foundation, The, MN, 4739
Pentecost Foundation, Joe D., MI, 4520
People's United Community Foundation, Inc., The, CT, 1671
Peoples Federal Savings Bank Charitable Foundation, MA, 4212
Peoples Security Charitable Foundation, PA, 8218
Peoria Area Community Foundation, IL, *see* 2763
Pepper Family Foundation, IL, 3074
Peppers Foundation, Ann, The, CA, 1024
Pepsi-Cola of Charlotte Foundation, Inc., CO, *see* 1426
PepsiCo Foundation, Inc., The, NY, 6627
Perdue Foundation, Inc., Arthur W., CT, 1672
Pere Foundation, Kors Le, The, DE, 1833
Perelman Education Foundation, Raymond & Ruth, PA, 8219
Perelman Family Foundation, NY, 6628
Perfect Moment Foundation, The, CA, 1025
Perforce Foundation, CA, 1026
Perkin Fund, The, MA, 4213
Perkins Charitable Foundation, The, OH, 7615
Perkins Foundation, B. F. & Rose H., WY, 9988
Perkins Foundation, Jean, CA, 1027
Perkins Foundation, Nancy Allison, IL, 3075
Perkins Memorial Fund, James J. and Mamie R., NC, 7282
Perkins-Prothro Foundation, TX, 9090
Perles Family Foundation, Claudia and Steven, FL, 2266
Perlman Family Foundation, Louis & Anita, IL, *see* 3076
Perlman Family Foundation, The, IL, 3076
Perls Foundation, The, MA, 4214
Permian Basin Area Foundation, TX, 9091
Perot Foundation, The, TX, 9092
Perot, Jr. Foundation, Sarah and Ross, The, TX, 9093
Perpetual Trust for Charitable Giving, MA, 4215
Perrigo Company Charitable Foundation, MI, 4521
Perrin Family Foundation, The, CT, 1673
Perrin Foundation Inc., NJ, 5404
Perritt Charitable Foundation, Richard A., IL, 3077
Perry Foundation, Inc., VA, 9506
Perry Foundation, Patricia and Douglas, VA, 9507
Pershing Charitable Trust, MO, 4952
Pershing Place Foundation, MO, 4953
Pershing Square Foundation, The, NY, 6629
Pertusati Chartitable Trust, Joseph & Evelyn, TX, 9094
Peters CBS Trust, G. Gorham, MA, 4216
Peters Foundation, Leon S., CA, 1028
Peters Foundation, Lovett & Ruth, OH, 7616
Peters Testementary Trust, G. Gorham, MA, *see* 4216
Petersen Foundation, Esper A., IL, 3078
Petersen Foundation, Margie & Robert E., CA, 1029
Peterson Family Foundation, Inc., VA, 9508
Peterson Foundation, Hal & Charlie, TX, 9095
Peterson Foundation, Mark and Nancy, The, UT, 9345
Peterson Foundation, Patricia Price, The, FL, 2267
Peterson Foundation, Peter G., NY, 6630
Peterson Foundation, Thomas F., OH, 7617
Peterson Memorial Fund, Chris & Mary L., OR, 7880
Petoskey-Harbor Springs Area Community Foundation, MI, 4522
Petrello Family Foundation, TX, 9096
Petrie Foundation, Carroll, NY, 6631
Petrie Foundation, Inc., Carroll and Milton, The, NY, 6632
Petro Kulynych Foundation, Inc., NC, *see* 7252
Petteys Memorial Foundation, Jack, CO, 1477
Pettit Foundation, Inc., Jane and Lloyd, WI, *see* 9919
Pettit Foundation, Jane Bradley, WI, 9919
Pettus Foundation, MO, 4954
Pettus, Jr. Foundation, James T., MO, *see* 4954
Petway Family Foundation Inc., FL, 2268
Pew Charitable Trusts, The, PA, 8220
Pfaffinger Foundation, CA, 1030
Pfau Foundation, Daniel and Susan, The, OH, 7618
Pfeiffer Family Foundation, DE, A
Pfeiffer Research Foundation, Gustavus and Louise, NJ, 5405
Pfeil Foundation Inc., The, DE, 1834
Pfizer Foundation, Inc., The, NY, 6633
Pfizer Patient Assistance Foundation, Inc., NY, 6634
Pfleger Foundation, George T., CA, 1031
Pfleger Foundation, Harriet E., The, CA, 1032
Pforzheimer Foundation, Inc., Carl and Lily, The, NY, 6635
Pfriem Foundation, Norma F., SC, 8490
PG&E Corporation Foundation, The, CA, 1033
PGE Foundation, OR, 7881
PGE-Enron Foundation, OR, *see* 7881
Pharmacy Network Foundation, Inc., The, NC, 7283
Phelps County Community Foundation, Inc., NE, 5075
Phelps Dodge Foundation, AZ, *see* 112
Phelps Family Foundation, CA, 1034
Phelps Trust, The, NY, *see* 6464
Phifer/Johnson Foundation, SC, 8491
Philadelphia Foundation, The, PA, 8221
Philadelphia Health Care Trust, PA, *see* 8239
Philanthropy International, CA, 1035
Philibosian Foundation, Stephen, The, CA, 1036
Philippe Foundation, Inc., NY, 6636
Philips Foundation, Jesse and Caryl, The, OH, 7619
Phillips Charitable Trust, Dr. & Mrs. Arthur William, PA, 8222

Phillips Family Foundation of Minnesota, Jay and Rose, The, MN, 4741
Phillips Family Foundation, Edward J. & Leslye, MN, 4740
Phillips Family Foundation, Inc., L. E., The, DE, 1835
Phillips Family Foundation, Samuel L., NC, 7284
Phillips Family Foundation, TX, 9097
Phillips Foundation, Edwin, MA, 4217
Phillips Foundation, Waite and Genevieve, NM, 5531
Phillips Memorial Charitable Trust, Stephen, MA, 4218
Phillips-Green Foundation, Inc., MA, 4219
Phillips-Van Heusen Foundation, Inc., NY, 6637
Phipps Foundation, Howard, NJ, 5406
PHM Foundation, The, TX, 9098
Phoenix Family Foundation, NJ, *see* 5259
Phoenixville Community Health Foundation, PA, 8223
Physicians New Orleans Foundation, LA, *see* 3652
Pick Charitable Trust, Melitta S., WI, 9920
Pick, Jr. Fund, Albert, IL, 3079
Pickens Foundation, T. Boone, The, TX, 9099
Picket Family Foundation Inc., NY, 6638
Pickett & Hatcher Educational Fund, Inc., GA, 2528
Picotte Family Foundation, John D., NY, 6639
Piece by Piece Productions Inc, NY, 6640
Piedmont Community Foundation, VA, 9509
Piedmont Natural Gas Foundation, NC, 7285
Pierce Charitable Trust, Harold Whitworth, The, MA, 4220
Pierce Family Charitable Foundation, The, IL, 3080
Pierce Family Foundation, IL, *see* 3080
Pierce Family Foundation, L. W., The, PA, *see* 8224
Pierce Family Foundation, Leo and Peggy, The, PA, 8224
Pikes Peak Community Foundation, CO, 1478
Pilchard Foundation, A. Franklin, IL, 3081
Pilgrim Foundation, The, PA, 8225
Pillsbury Foundation, Ed & H., MO, 4955
Pillsbury Foundation, Harriet, MO, 4956
Pillsbury Foundation, William, MO, *see* 4956
PIMCO Foundation, The, CA, 1037
Pincus Family Foundation, The, DE, 1836
Pincus Foundation, Claudio and Penny, NJ, 5407
Pindaros Foundation, Inc., The, NY, 6641
Pine River Foundation, The, MN, 4742
Pine Tree Foundation of New York, NY, 6642
Pine Tree Foundation, PA, 8226
Pinellas County Community Foundation, FL, 2269
Pinhook Foundation, Inc., LA, 3660
Pinkerton Foundation, The, NY, 6643
Pinon Foundation, TX, 9100
Pioneer Fund, The, CO, 1479
Pioneer Hi-Bred International, Inc. Foundation, IA, 3474
Piper Charitable Trust, Roy W., PA, 8227
Piper Charitable Trust, Virginia G., The, AZ, 152
Piper Foundation, Minnie Stevens, TX, 9101
Piper Jaffray Foundation, MN, 4743
Piqua Community Foundation, The, OH, 7620
Piqua-Miami County Foundation, OH, *see* 7569
Pisces Foundation, CA, 1038
Pitkin Foundation Inc., Winifred M. & George P., NJ, 5408
Pitney Bowes Employees Involvement Fund, Inc., The, CT, *see* 1674
Pitney Bowes Foundation, The, CT, 1674
Piton Foundation, The, CO, 1480
Piton Investment Fund, The, CO, 1481
Pitt Foundation, Inc., William H., The, CT, 1675
Pitt III Foundation, Inc., William H., The, CT, *see* 1675
Pitts Foundation, William I. H. and Lula E., GA, 2529
Pittsburgh Foundation, The, PA, 8228
Pittulloch Foundation, Inc., The, GA, 2530
Pivotal Foundation, AZ, 153
Placer Community Foundation, CA, 1039
Planet Heritage Foundation, Inc., DE, 1837
Plangere Foundation, Inc., FL, 2270
Plankenhorn Foundation Inc., Harry, PA, 8229
Planning and Art Resources for Communities Inc., NY, 6644
Plansoen Charitable Trust, Louis M., NC, 7286
Plant Memorial Fund, Inc., Henry B., NY, 6645
Plaster Foundation, Inc., Robert W., MO, 4957
Play 2 Dream Charitable Foundation, MA, 4221
Plaza De Panama Committee, CA, 1040
Pleiad Foundation, AL, 58
Pleroma, Inc., TX, 9102
Pletka Foundation, Kronhill, The, NY, 6646
Plitt Trust, Clarence Manger & Audrey Cordero, MD, 3862
PLM Foundation, NY, 6647
Plough Foundation, TN, 8615
Ploughshares Foundation, IL, 3082
Plum Beach Foundation, NY, 6648
Plum Creek Foundation, WA, 9704
Plumeri Foundation, Inc., Joe, NY, 6649
Plummer Charitable Foundation, Inc., Hellen I., NJ, 5409
Plymouth Rock Foundation, The, MA, 4222
PNC Bank Foundation, PA, *see* 8230
PNC Foundation, The, PA, 8230
PNM Foundation, Inc., NM, *see* 5532
PNM Resources Foundation, Inc., NM, 5532
Pocono Charitable Foundation, The, AZ, 154
Poe Charitable Trust, Parker, GA, 2531
Poepl Family Foundation, MN, 4744
Poetry Foundation, The, IL, 3083
Pohanka Family Foundation, John J., The, MD, 3863
Pohlad Family Foundation, Carl and Eloise, MN, 4745
Poindexter Charitable Foundation, John S. and Katherine R., GA, 2532
Point Gammon Foundation, NJ, 5410
Pokagon Fund, Inc., The, MI, 4523
Polaris Foundation, AZ, *see* 175
Polaris Foundation, The, MN, 4746
Polinger Family Foundation, Howard and Geraldine, MD, 3864
Polinger Foundation, Howard and Geraldine, MD, *see* 3864
Polk Bros. Foundation, Inc., IL, 3084
Polk County Community Foundation, Inc., The, NC, 7287
Polk Foundation, Ralph L. and Winifred E., MI, 4524
Pollock Foundation, TX, 9103
Pollock-Krasner Foundation, Inc., The, NY, 6650
Pollybill Foundation, Inc., WI, 9921
Polo Ralph Lauren Foundation, The, NY, 6651
Pomegranate Foundation, MA, 4223
Pomerleau Foundation Inc., Antonio B. and Rita M., VT, 9369
Pomeroy Foundation, William G., The, NY, 6652
Pond Foundation, C. Northrop and Alethea Marder, The, PA, 8231
Ponzio Family Foundation, The, CO, 1482
Ponzio Foundation, June and Craig, The, CO, *see* 1482
Poonai Charitable Foundation, Inc., Anila Sarswati and Parmanand Vijay, FL, 2271
Poor Richard's Charitable Trust, PA, 8232
Poorvu Family Foundation, William J. & Lia G., MA, 4224
Poorvu Foundation, William J. & Lia G., MA, *see* 4224
Pope Foundation, Generoso, The, NY, 6653
Pope Foundation, John William, NC, 7288
Pope Foundation, The, NY, *see* 6653
Pope Life Foundation, Lois, The, FL, 2272
Poplar Foundation, The, TN, 8616
Popplestone Foundation, The, MA, 4225
Popular Community Bank Foundation, IL, 3085
Porter County Community Foundation, Inc., IN, 3369
Porter Testamentary Trust, James Hyde, GA, 2533
Porticus North America Foundation, NY, 6654
Portland Foundation, The, IN, 3370
Portsmouth General Hospital Foundation, VA, 9510
Poses Family Foundation, The, NY, 6655
Posey Family Foundation, TX, 9104
Posner Foundation of Pittsburgh, PA, 8233
Posner Foundation, Inc., Gene & Ruth, WI, 9922
Poss Family Foundation, The, MA, 4226
Poss Kapor Familly Foundation, The, MA, *see* 4226
Post and Courier Foundation, SC, 8492
Post Family Foundation, Sandra and Lawrence, The, CA, 1041
Post Foundation, John A. and Margaret, NC, 7289
Potiker Family Foundation, CA, *see* 1042
Potiker Family Foundation, Hughes and Sheila, CA, 1042
Potishman Foundation, Leo, IL, 3086
Potomac Health Foundation, VA, 9511
Pott Foundation, Herman T. & Phenie R., MO, 4958
Potter Foundation, Justin & Valere, IL, 3087
Pottstown Area Health & Wellness Foundatio[n] 8234
Powell Foundation, The, TX, 9105
Powers Family Foundation, The, NY, 6656
Poweshiek Community Foundation, Greater, IA,
Poznanski Foundation, OR, 7882
PPG Industries Foundation, PA, 8235
Prairie Creek Partners Charitable Foundation, DE,
Prairie Foundation, The, TX, 9106
Praxair Foundation, Inc., CT, 1676
Precourt Foundation, The, CO, 1483
Predolin Foundation, Inc., Henry, WI, 9923
Preik Family Foundation, Inc., The, FL, 2273
Prentice Family Foundation, The, FL, 2274
Prentice Foundation, Inc., Abra, IL, 3088
Prentice Foundation, Inc., The, DE, 1839
Prentice Foundation, The, TX, 9107
Prentiss Foundation, Elisabeth Severance, The, OH, 7621
Presbyterian Village North Foundation, TX, 9108
Preservati Family Charitable Trust Foundation, The, WV, 9790
Presser Foundation, The, PA, 8236
Presto Foundation, The, DE, 1840
Preston Family Foundation, Raymond B., KY, 3596
Price Briggs Charitable Trust, Laura E., OH, 7622
Price Charitable Foundation, Tina & Steven, NY, 6657
Price Chopper's Golub Foundation, NY, 6658
Price Family Charitable Fund, The, CA, 1043
Price Family Foundation, Inc., The, NY, 6659
Price Family Foundation, John and Marcia, UT, 9346
Price Family Foundation, Julian, DE, 1841
Price Foundation, Inc., Louis and Harold, The, CO, 1484
Price Foundation, Inc., M. B., CA, 1044
Price Foundation, Inc., Michael F., NY, *see* 6659
Price Foundation, Sol & Helen, The, CA, *see* 1043
Price Foundation, T. Rowe, MD, 3865
Prichard School, Board of Trustees of the, WV, 9791
Prickett Fund, Lynn R. and Karl E., NC, 7290
Priddy Foundation, The, TX, 9109
Priem Family Foundation, The, CA, 1045
Prim Foundation, Wayne L., NV, 5140
Primerica Foundation Inc., The, GA, 2534
Prince Charitable Trust, Elizabeth, RI, *see* 8386
Prince Charitable Trusts, IL, 3089
Prince Foundation, Edgar and Elsa, MI, 4525
Prince Foundation, IL, 3090
Prince Foundation, MI, *see* 4525
Princeton Area Community Foundation, Inc., NJ, 5411
Princeton Area Foundation, Inc., The, NJ, *see* 5411
Princeton Regional Chamber of Commerce Foundation, Inc., NJ, 5412
Principal Financial Group Foundation, Inc., IA, 3476
Prins Foundation, Vivian G., NY, 6660
Prior Family Foundation, VI, 9378
Pritzker Charitable Distribution Fund, Colonel (IL) James N., IL, 3091
Pritzker Family Foundation, Anthony, The, IL, 3092
Pritzker Family Foundation, Margot & Thomas, IL, 3093
Pritzker Family Foundation, Robert and Mayari, IL, 3094
Pritzker Family Foundation, The, IL, 3095
Pritzker Family Fund, John and Lisa, The, CA, 1046
Pritzker Foundation, IL, 3096
Pritzker Foundation, Jay, The, TX, 9110
Pritzker Innovation Fund, TX, 9111
Pritzker Pucker Family Foundation, The, IL, 3097
Pritzker Traubert Family Foundation, The, IL, 3098
Proctor Charitable Foundation, Elizabeth Craig Weaver, TN, 8617
Proctor Foundation, Mattina R., MA, 4227
Professional Athletes Foundation, DC, 1939
Progress Charitable Foundation Delaware, DE, 1842
Progressive Insurance Foundation, The, OH, 7623
Project Home Again Foundation, NY, 6661
ProLogis Foundation, CO, 1485
Promethean Foundation, TN, 8618
Prometheus Foundation, NV, 5141
Promise Foundation, The, NY, A
Prophet Corporation Foundation, The, MN, *see* 4680
Propp Sons Fund, Inc., Morris and Anna, NY, 6662
Prospect Creek Foundation, MN, 4747
Prospect Hill Foundation, Inc., The, NY, 6663
Protective Life Foundation, AL, 59

FOU

Renewable Foundation, Inc., NJ, 5421
Renfield Foundation, Beatrice, NY, 6688
Renfield Foundation, Inc., Harold and Beatrice, NY, *see* 6688
Rennebohm Foundation, Inc., Oscar, The, WI, 9931
Renton Community Foundation, WA, 9715
Resch Foundation, Marion G., The, OH, 7629
Research Corporation for Science Advancement, AZ, 157
ResMed Foundation, CA, 1063
ResMed Sleep Disordered Breathing Foundation, CA, *see* 1063
Resnick Family Foundation, CA, *see* 1064
Resnick Foundation, Burton P. and Judith B., The, NY, 6689
Resnick Foundation, CA, 1064
Resnick Foundation, Inc., Ira M., The, NY, 6690
Resource Foundation, Inc., The, NY, 6691
Ressler Family Foundation, The, CA, 1065
Ressler/Gertz Foundation, The, CA, 1066
Retirement Research Foundation, The, IL, 3113
Reuss Memorial Trust, Allene, PA, 8247
Review Foundation, NY, 6692
Revs Institute for Automotive Research, Inc., The, FL, 2284
Revson Foundation, Inc., Charles H., NY, 6693
Rex Endowment, John, NC, 7295
Rexnord Foundation Inc., WI, 9932
Rey-Vaden Family Foundation, The, CA, 1067
Reyes Foundation, J. Christopher and Anne N., IL, 3114
Reyes Foundation, M. Jude & Lori W., IL, *see* 3239
Reynolds American Foundation, NC, 7296
Reynolds Charitable Trust, Kate B., NC, 7297
Reynolds Family Foundation, DE, 1848
Reynolds Family Foundation, NY, 6694
Reynolds Foundation, Alice Kleberg, TX, 9127
Reynolds Foundation, Donald W., NV, 5143
Reynolds Foundation, Gilmore & Golda, IN, 3376
Reynolds Foundation, Inc., Christopher, The, MA, 4238
Reynolds Foundation, Inc., Z. Smith, NC, 7298
Reynolds Foundation, J.B., MO, 4961
Reynolds Foundation, Marshall, DE, 1849
Reynolds Foundation, R. J., NC, *see* 7296
Reynolds Foundation, Richard S., VA, 9519
Reynolds III Foundation, Richard J. and Marie Mallouk, NC, 7299
RGK Foundation, TX, 9128
Rheuminations, Inc., NY, 6695
Rhoades Foundation, The, IL, 3115
Rhoades Fund, Otto L. and Hazel T., IL, *see* 3115
Rhoads Foundation, Ross R. & Sara G., NC, A
Rhoads,Jr. Family Environmental Fund, Jay,, PA, 8248
Rhode Island Community Foundation, The, RI, *see* 8429
Rhode Island Foundation, The, RI, 8429
Rhodebeck Charitable Trust, NY, A
Rhoden Charitable Foundation, Elmer C., MO, 4962
Rhodes Charitable Trust, Ann L. Rhodes and Carol Greene, TX, 9129
RHW Foundation, Inc., CO, *see* 1429
Rice Family Foundation, The, NY, 6696
Rice Family Foundation, The, VA, 9520
Rice Family Foundation, WA, 9716
Rice Foundation, Daniel F. and Ada L., IL, 3116
Rice Foundation, Ethel and Raymond F., KS, 3538
Rice Foundation, IL, *see* 3116
Rich Family Foundation, NY, 6697
Rich Foundation, Inc., The, GA, 2537
Rich Foundation, NY, *see* 6697
Richards 1997 Charitable Trust, Mary Lea Johnson, NY, 6698
Richards Charitable Foundation, Inc., W. Earl, AL, 62
Richards Family Foundation, Bruce and Avis, NY, 6699
Richards Family Foundation, GA, 2538
Richards Foundation, Inc., The, GA, 2539
Richards Private Foundation, Murray and Harriet, IL, 3117
Richards Scholarship Fund, Mabel Wilson, The, CA, 1068
Richards, Jr. Foundation for Charitable Giving, Roy, GA, *see* 2539
Richardson Charitable Trust, Anne S., TX, *see* 9131
Richardson Charitable Trust, H. Smith, NC, 7300
Richardson Foundation, Frank E. and Nancy M., NY, *see* 6700
Richardson Foundation, Inc., Smith, CT, 1679
Richardson Foundation, Sid W., TX, 9130
Richardson Foundation, The, NY, 6700
Richardson Fund, Anne S., TX, 9131
Richardson Irrevocable Trust, M. Valeria, WA, 9717
Richardson Testamentary Trust, Grace Jones, NC, 7301
Richardson Trust, Grace Jones, NC, *see* 7301
Richenthal Foundation, NY, 6701
Richland County Foundation of Mansfield, Ohio, The, OH, *see* 7630
Richland County Foundation, OH, 7630
Richman Family Foundation, NY, 6702
Richman Foundation, Fred & Rita, The, NY, *see* 6702
Richman Private Family Foundation, Richard and Ellen, CT, 1680
Richmond Children's Foundation, CA, *see* 1069
Richmond Community Foundation, CA, 1069
Richmond Community Foundation, Greater, VA, *see* 9416
Richmond Community Foundation, Inc., NC, 7302
Richmond County Savings Foundation, NY, 6703
Richmond Foundation Inc., Anita B. and Howard S., The, NY, 6704
Richmond Memorial Health Foundation, VA, 9521
Richter Memorial Fund, Paul K., RI, 8430
Rick L. and Vicki L .James Foundation Inc., IN, 3377
Ricketts Conservation Fund, CO, 1486
Rickey & Daughters Foundation, Dave, CA, 1070
Rickey Foundation, Brenda and Dave, CA, 1071
Ridgecliff Foundation Inc., OH, 7631
Ridgefield Foundation, The, NY, 6705
Riedman Foundation, The, NY, 6706
Rieger Charitable Foundation Trust, The, NY, 6707
Riepe Charitable Foundation, James S. & Gail P., MD, 3869
Riese Foundation, Dennis L., The, NY, 6708
Rifkin Family Foundation, IN, 3378
Riggio Foundation, The, NY, 6709
Riggs Benevolent Fund, AR, 196
Right Fork Foundation, CA, 1072
Righteous Persons Foundation, CA, 1073
Rigler Lawrence E. Deutsch Foundation, Lloyd, CA, 1074
Riley Family Foundation, NY, 6710
Riley Foundation, Mabel Louise, The, MA, 4239
Riley Foundation, The, MA, *see* 4239
Riley Foundation, The, MS, 4844
Riley Trust, George B., OH, 7632
Rimora Foundation, The, VA, 9522
Ring Foundation, CA, 1075
Rinker Foundation, Inc., Marshall and Vera Lea, FL, 2285
Rinker, Sr. Foundation, Inc., Marshall E., FL, 2286
Rinpoche International Charitable Foundation, Kangyur, NM, A
Riordan Family Foundation, Michael T., WI, 9933
Ripley County Community Foundation, Inc., IN, 3379
Ripple Foundation, The, NY, 6711
Risen Son Foundation, Inc., MS, 4845
Rispone Family Foundation, Edward L. & Phyllis M., The, LA, *see* 3662
Rispone Family Foundation, Edward L., The, LA, 3662
Ritter Charitable Trust, George W. & Mary F., OH, 7633
Ritter Foundation, May Ellen and Gerald, NY, 6712
Ritts Foundation, Herb, CA, 1076
Rivendell Stewards' Trust, CA, 1077
River Branch Foundation, FL, 2287
Rivera Foundation, Mariano, DE, 1850
Rivers Fund, Margaret, MN, 4752
Riverside Foundation Charitable Trust, The, PA, A
Riverside Foundation, Inc., FL, see 2288
Riverside Health Foundation, KS, 3539
Riverside Hospital Foundation Inc., FL, 2288
Riverstyx Foundation, WA, 9718
Riversville Foundation, The, NY, 6713
Rizavi Friedland Foundation, Inc., NY, *see* 6834
Rizzuto Foundation, Leandro P., The, NY, 6714
RJKB Family Charitable Foundation, Inc., FL, 2289
RJM Foundation, CA, 1078
RJM Foundation, The, PA, 8249
RLC Family Foundation, UT, 9348
Rmlow Foundation, CA, 1079
RNAV Foundation, NH, *see* 5174
RNB Foundation, Inc., NY, *see* 5665
RNR Foundation, Inc., MI, 4527
Roach Foundation Inc., The, TX, 9132
Roanoke-Chowan Foundation, Inc., NC, 7303
Robbins Family Foundation, The, CT, 1681
Robbins Foundation, Amy L., NY, *see* 6533
Robbins Foundation, Inc., CT, *see* 1681
Robbins Foundation, Jerome, NY, 6716
Robbins Foundation, Larry, NY, *see* 6715
Robbins Foundation, NY, 6715
Roberts & David Seltzer Charitable Trust, Lisa S., P, *see* 8232
Roberts Charitable Foundation, A.M., NY, 6717
Roberts Charitable Foundation, Elyse Meredith Rober and Raymond John, IL, 3118
Roberts Charitable Foundation, Gilroy & Lillian P., PA, 8250
Roberts Charitable Foundation, Margaret A., IL, 3119
Roberts Family Foundation, Inc, J. David and Kathleen A., FL, 2290
Roberts Family Foundation, MA, 4240
Roberts Family Foundation, Roy H. and Natalie C., IL, 3120
Roberts Foundation, Aileen K. and Brian L., The, PA, 8251
Roberts Foundation, Dora, IL, 3121
Roberts Foundation, Eric, The, CA, 1080
Roberts Foundation, Inc., Norman and Bettina, The, NJ, 5423
Roberts Foundation, Nora, NJ, 5422
Roberts Foundation, The, CA, 1081
Roberts, Jr. Trust, Percival, NC, 7304
Robertson Family Foundation, Inc., Blanche and Julian, The, NC, 7305
Robertson Foundation for Government Inc., NJ, 5424
Robertson Foundation, NY, 6718
Robertson Fund, Jeanne and Sanford, CA, 1082
Robertson Scholars Program, The, NY, 6719
Robina Foundation, MN, 4753
Robins Foundation, VA, 9523
Robins, Jr. Foundation, Ane Carter Robins and Walter R., The, VA, 9524
Robins, Kaplan, Miller & Csi Foundation, MN, 4754
Robinson Charitable Foundn, Velma Lee & John Harvey, TX, 9133
Robinson Charitable Trust, E
Robinson Charitable Trust, Hd & Lida, NE, 5076
Robinson Foundation for HearV, *see* 9785
see 396 sorders, Inc., CA,
Robinson Foundation, Inc., Jim a
6720 da, The, NY,
Robinson Foundation, The, OK, 77
Robinson Fund, Maurice R., IL, 312
Robinson Mountain Fund, E. O., KY,
Robinson Trust, C. J., FL, 2291
Robinson Worldwide Foundation, C. H.,
Robinson-Broadhurst Foundation, Inc., 20
Roblee Foundation, Joseph H. & Florence
Robson Foundation, Edward D. & Janet K., 963
Roche Foundation, The, CA, 1083
Rochester Area Community Foundation, NY, 0
Rochester Area Foundation, MN, 4755
Rochlin Foundation, Abraham & Sonia, NV, 51
Rock Foundation, The, CA, 1084
Rock Springs Foundation, The, MD, 3870
Rock, Paper, Scissors Foundation, Inc., CA, 1085
Rockdale Foundation Inc., The, GA, 2540
Rockdale Fund for Social Investment, Inc., GA, *see* 2
Rockefeller Brothers Fund, Inc., NY, 6723
Rockefeller Foundation, The, NY, 6724
Rockefeller Foundation, Winthrop, The, AR, 197
Rockefeller Fund, Inc., David, The, NY, 6725
Rockefeller Trust, Winthrop, AR, 198
Rockford Community Foundation, IL, *see* 2766
Rocking Moon Foundation, Inc., MD, 3871
Rockjensen Foundation, Inc., The, TX, 9134
Rockville Bank Community Foundation, Inc., CT, *see* 1682
Rockville Bank Foundation, Inc., CT, 1682
Rockwell Automation Charitable Corp., WI, 9934
Rockwell Collins Charitable Corporation, IA, 3477
Rockwell Fund, Inc., TX, 9135

Shapiro Foundation, Herman and Gwen, WI, 9945
Shapiro Foundation, Howard and Jackie, The, IL, 3153
Shapiro Foundation, Howard, IL, *see* 3153
Shapiro Foundation, Inc., Charles and M. R., IL, 3151
Shapiro Foundation, Inc., Fern G. Shapiro, Morris R. Shapiro, and Charles, IL, *see* 3151
Shapiro Foundation, The, CA, 1152
Shapiro-Silverberg Foundation, NY, 6838
Share Foundation, KS, *see* 3530
Share Trust, Charles Morton, OK, 7795
Shared Earth Foundation, The, MD, 3882
Sharf Fund, Jean S. & Frederic A., MA, 4268
Sharks Foundation, The, CA, 1153
Sharp Foundation, Evelyn, The, NY, 6839
Sharp Foundation, Inc., Ruth C. and Charles S., TX, 9167
Sharp Foundation, Peter Jay, The, NY, A
Sharpe Family Foundation, The, RI, 8437
Shasta Regional Community Foundation, CA, 1154
Shaughnessy Family Foundation, The, MO, 4969
Shaver Foundation, Alice, MA, 4269
Shaw "U.S." Foundation, The, HI, 2615
Shaw Family Endowment Fund, The, NY, 6840
Shaw Foundation, Arch W., MO, 4970
Shaw Foundation, Gardiner Howland, MA, 4270
Shaw Foundation, Harold W. & Mary Louise, The, CO, 1499
Shaw Foundation, Walden W. & Jean Young, The, IL, 3154
Shaw, William W., MO, *see* 4970
Shea Company Foundation, J.F., CA, 1155
Shea Family Foundation, Edmund and Mary, CA, 1156
Shea Family Foundation, PA, A
Shearwater Foundation Inc., VA, 9531
Sheba Foundation, The, IL, 3155
Sheehan Family Foundation, MA, 4271
Sheinberg Foundation, Eric P., CT, 1695
Shelden Fund, Elizabeth, Allan & Warren, MI, 4537
Sheldon Foundation, Inc., Ralph C., NY, 6841
Shell Companies Foundation, Inc., TX, *see* 9168
Shell Oil Company Foundation, TX, 9168
Shelter Hill Foundation, The, NY, 6842
Shelter Insurance Foundation, MO, 4971
Shelton Family Foundation, TX, 9169
Shelton Foundation, The, NC, 7310
Shen Family Foundation, The, NJ, 5450
Shenango Valley Foundation, PA, *see* 7994
Shepherd Foundation, NJ, 5451
Shepherds Hand, The, MI, 4538
Sheraton Foundation, Inc., The, MA, *see* 4284
Sheridan Family Foundation, Dr. Howard and Brenda, NJ, 5452
Sheridan Foundation, Inc., Thomas B. and Elizabeth M., The, MD, 3883
Sherman Charitable Foundation, Inc., Bruce & Cynthia, The, FL, 2318
Sherman Family Foundation, FL, 2319
Sherman Family Foundation, The, MO, 4972
Sherman Private Foundation, Betsy R. and George M., The, FL, *see* 2319
Sherwin-Williams Foundation, OH, 7661
Sherwood Foundation, The, NE, 5081
Sherwood Trust, WA, 9733
Shiebler Family Foundation, MN, 4762
Shield-Ayres Foundation, TX, 9170
Shields Foundation, Inc., George L., The, MD, 3884
Shiffick Charitable Foundation, Peggy and Bill, IL, 3156
SHIFT, FL, 2320
Shiley Foundation, The, CA, 1157
Shillman Foundation, The, CA, 1158
Shiloh Foundation, The, PA, 8283
Shin Foundation, Patrick N. C., The, HI, 2616
Shinn Foundation, Inc., George, TN, 8627
Shipley Family Foundation, Inc., The, MA, *see* 4272
Shipley Family Foundation, Walter V. and Judith L., The, NY, 6843
Shipley Foundation, Inc., MA, 4272
Shipman Charity, Daniel & Louise M., IL, 3157
Shippy Foundation, NY, 6844
Shire Philanthropic Foundation, CA, *see* 1249
Shirk Foundation, Russell and Betty, IL, 3158
Shirley Foundation, Jon and Mary, The, WA, 9734
Shiva Foundation, Susan Stein, NY, 6845
Shivers Cancer Foundation, TX, 9171
Shoemaker Foundation, Edwin J. & Ruth M., MI, 4539
Shoemaker Fund, Thomas H. and Mary Williams, The, PA, 8284
Shoolman Children's Foundation, Edith Glick, The, NY, 6846
Shoreland Foundation, The, NY, 6847
Shorenstein Foundation Inc., Lydia and Doug, DE, 1858
Shoresh Foundation, CA, 1159
Short, Jr. Trust, Shelton H., NC, 7311
Shortino Family Foundation, Leo M., The, CA, 1160
Shortino Foundation, The, CA, *see* 1160
Shott, Jr. Foundation Inc., Hugh I., WV, 9794
Shreiber Foundation, Gerald B., The, NJ, 5453
Shriners of Rhode Island Charities Trust, RI, 8438
SHS Foundation, The, NY, 6848
Shtesl Family Foundation, The, NY, 6849
Shubert Foundation, Inc., The, NY, 6850
Shulsky Foundation, The, NY, 6851
Shumaker Family Foundation, The, KS, 3546
Shumway Foundation, Helen and Ritter, RI, 8439
SI Bank & Trust Foundation, NY, *see* 6912
SICO Foundation, The, PA, *see* 8272
Sidell-Kagan Foundation, CA, 1161
Sidell-Kagan Scientific & Medical Research Foundation, CA, *see* 1161
Sidewalk Angels Foundation, NY, 6852
Sidgmore Family Foundation, MD, 3885
Sidhu-Singh Family Foundation, The, TX, 9172
Sidman Family Foundation, Inc., The, MA, 4273
Sidwell Family Foundation, Jeff and Jennie, The, OH, 7662
Sie Foundation, Anna and John J., The, CO, 1500
Siebel Foundation, Thomas and Stacey, The, CA, 1162
Sieben Foundation, Inc., MN, 4763
Siebens Charitable Foundation, Inc., Harold W., NY, 6853
Siebert Lutheran Foundation, Inc., WI, 9946
Siemens Foundation, NJ, 5454
Sierra Foundation Inc., NJ, 5455
Sierra Health Foundation, CA, 1163
Sierra Pacific Foundation, CA, 1164
Sigmund Foundation, Bill and Vi, MI, 4540
Silbermann Foundation, Inc., Rosanne H., The, NJ, 5456
Silberstein Foundation, Inc., William & Sylvia, The, NY, 6854
Silberstein Foundation, Stephen M., The, CA, 1165
Silicon Valley Community Foundation, CA, 1166
Silk Charitable Foundation, Fred F., OH, 7663
Silk Family Foundation, The, CA, 1167
Sills Family Foundation, VT, 9371
Silver Family Foundation, CT, 1696
Silver Family Foundation, Inc., The, NJ, 5457
Silver Foundation, Barbara, CT, *see* 1696
Silver Giving Foundation, The, CA, 1168
Silver Lining Foundation, The, CA, *see* 1168
Silver Mountain Foundation for the Arts, NJ, 5458
Silverman Family Foundation, Kenneth and Claudia, NJ, 5459
Silverman Foundation, Marty and Dorothy, NY, 6855
Silverstein Family Foundation, Inc., Raine & Stanley, The, NY, 6856
Silverton Foundation, TX, *see* 9235
Silverweed Foundation, Inc., NY, 6857
Silverwing Foundation, MI, 4541
Silvian Foundation, Inc., Slomo and Cindy, The, NY, 6858
Simkins Charitable Foundation, Leon J., FL, 2321
Simmons Charitable Foundation of Oklahoma, The, OK, 7796
Simmons Family Foundation, R. P., PA, 8285
Simmons Family Foundation, UT, 9351
Simmons Family Foundation, Virginia and L. E., The, TX, 9173
Simmons Foundation, Harold, TX, 9174
Simmons Foundation, The, TX, 9175
Simmons Mesothelioma Foundation, IL, 3159
Simms/Mann Family Foundation, The, CA, 1169
Simon Charitable Foundation Number One, Melvin and Bren, The, IN, 3387
Simon Charitable Foundation, David E. Simon & Jacqueline S., IN, 3385
Simon Charitable Foundation, Joshua Max, T 3386
Simon Charitable Foundation, Max, The, IN, se
Simon Family Charitable Foundation Trust, B. 8286
Simon Family Foundation, Herbert, The, IN, A
Simon Family Foundation, IL, *see* 3149
Simon Family Foundation, Ronald M., CA, *see* 11
Simon Family Foundation, The, IL, 3160
Simon Foundation for Education and Housing, CA,
Simon Foundation, Inc., William E. & Carol G., NY, 6859
Simon Foundation, Inc., William E., NY, 6859
Simon Foundation, Lucille Ellis, CA, 1170
Simon Foundation, Mildred, Herbert and Julian, MO, 4973
Simon Foundation, Todd and Betiana, The, NE, 5082
Simon Foundation-Florida, Sidney, Milton and Leoma, The, FL, 2322
Simon, Jr. Foundation, Cynthia L. & William E., The, NJ, 5460
Simon-Strauss Foundation, CA, 1172
Simone Foundation, Louise Manoogian, MI, *see* 4493
Simonian Foundation, Sam and Sylva, TX, 9176
Simons Foundation, Nick, The, NY, 6860
Simons Foundation, The, NY, 6861
Simonyi Fund for Arts and Sciences, Charles and Lisa, WA, 9735
Simonyi Fund for Arts and Sciences, Charles, WA, *see* 9735
Simple Actions Family Foundation, OR, 7889
Simplot Company Foundation, Inc., J. R., ID, 2643
Simpson Charitable Trust, TX, 9177
Simpson Family Foundation, Inc., NY, *see* 6691
Simpson Foundation, CA, *see* 1173
Simpson Foundation, The, NC, 7312
Simpson PSB Fund, CA, 1173
Sims Foundation, Inc., J. Marion, SC, 8497
Sims/Maes Foundation Inc., The, MA, 4274
Singer Family Foundation, CO, 1501
Singer Family Foundation, Joseph Singer & Ann, CO, *see* 1501
Singer Family Foundation, Paul, The, DE, 1859
Singer Foundation, Inc., Herbert & Nell, DE, 1860
Singer Foundation, Paul & Linda, The, DE, *see* 1859
Singer Foundation, Paul E., The, NY, 6862
Singgod Foundation, CA, *see* 1239
Singh Charitable Foundation, Inc., Raj & Neera, The, FL, 2323
Singhal Foundation, The, MA, *see* 3983
Singletary Foundation Inc., Lewis Hall and Mildred Sasser, GA, 2551
Sinsheimer Fund, Alexandrine and Alexander L., The, IL, 3161
Sinskey Foundation, Robert M., The, CA, 1174
Sioux Falls Area Community Foundation, SD, 8521
Siouxland Community Foundation, IA, 3480
Siouxland Foundation, IA, *see* 3480
Siragusa Foundation, The, IL, 3162
Sirius Fund, IL, 3163
Sirus Fund, The, NY, 6863
Sisler Foundation, Joe & Charlyne, NM, A
Sisler McFawn Foundation, The, OH, 7664
Sister Fund, The, NY, 6864
Sit Foundation, Eugene C. and Gail V., The, MN, 4764
Sit Investment Associates Foundation, MN, 4765
Sitchin Foundation Inc., NY, 6865
Sitt 1986 Charitable Trust, Joseph Jack, NY, 6866
Six Four Foundation, The, TX, 9178
Sixty Four Foundation, The, TX, *see* 9178
SJS Charitable Trust, NY, 6867
Skadden Foundation, NY, 6868
Skadden, Arps, Slate, Meagher & Flom Fellowship Foundation, NY, *see* 6868
Skelly Charitable Foundation, Gertrude E., The, FL, 2324
Skestos Family Foundation, OH, *see* 7501
Skilling and Andrews Foundation, MI, 4542
Skillman Foundation, The, MI, 4543
Skirball Foundation, NY, 6869
Skoll Foundation, The, CA, 1175
Skoll Global Threats Fund, CA, 1176
Sky View Foundation, OR, 7890

F

Spilker Foundation, Marc & Diane, NY, 6897
Spina Family Foundation, Stephanie H. & David A., MA, 4280
Spinal Muscular Atrophy Foundation, NY, 6898
Spingold Foundation, Inc., Nate B. and Frances, NY, see 6899
Spingold Foundation, Inc., The, NY, 6899
Spire Foundation, Inc., Nancy Woodson, WI, 9949
Spirit Foundation, The, NY, see 6570
Spirit Services, Inc., OH, A
Spitzer Charitable Trust, Bernard and Anne, NY, 6900
Spitzer Foundation, Arthur, CA, 1206
Spitzer Foundation, Inc., Bernard & Anne, The, NY, see 6900
Spoelhof Foundation, John and Judy, MI, 4545
Sprague Educational and Charitable Foundation, Seth, The, NY, 6901
Sprague Memorial Institute, Otho S. A., The, IL, 3172
Sprague, Jr. Foundation, Norman F., CA, 1207
Spray Foundation, Inc., The, KY, 3602
Spring Foundation, Inc., The, GA, 2555
Springbank Foundation, PA, 8293
Springcreek Foundation, The, CA, 1208
Springfield Foundation, The, OH, 7671
Springs Close Foundation, Inc., The, SC, 8504
Springs Foundation, Inc., SC, see 8504
Sprint Foundation, KS, 3549
Sprout Foundation, CO, 1505
Spunk Fund, Inc., NY, 6902
Spurlino Foundation, The, FL, 2330
Square D Foundation, IL, A
Square One Foundation, IL, 3173
SS Foundation, TX, 9196
SSB Charitable Foundation, CO, 1506
St. Agnes Catholic Education Foundation, MN, 4769
St. Anthony Foundation, NE, 5085
St. Croix Foundation, MN, see 4672
St. Croix Valley Foundation, WI, 9950
St. Faith's House Foundation, NY, 6903
St. George's Society of New York, NY, 6904
St. Giles Foundation, NY, 6905
St. Joe Community Foundation Inc., The, FL, 2331
St. John Foundation, Inc., Edward, MD, 3888
St. Jude Medical Foundation, MN, 4770
St. Louis Community Foundation, MO, see 4966
St. Marys Community Foundation, OH, 7672
St. Petersburg Times Fund, Inc., FL, 2332
St. Petersburg Times Scholarship Fund, FL, see 2332
ST2 Foundation, Inc., NJ, 5464
Stabler Foundation, Donald B. and Dorothy L., PA, 8294
Stabler Foundation, Donald B., The, PA, A
Stache Charitable Trust, Emil J., CA, 1209
Stackner Family Foundation, Inc., WI, 9951
Stackpole-Hall Foundation, PA, 8295
Stacy Foundation II, Festus & Helen, FL, 2334
Stacy Foundation, Inc., Festus and Helen, FL, 2333
Stadler Family Charitable Foundation, Inc., NJ, 5465
Stadtmauer Family Foundation, Inc., Marisa & Richard, NJ, 5466
Stainman Family Foundation, Inc., The, NY, 6906
Staley Family Foundation, CO, 1507
Stamps Family Charitable Foundation, Inc., MA, 4281
Stamps Foundation, Inc., James L., CA, 1210
Stange Charitable Trust, Mary G., MI, 4546
Stanislaus Community Foundation, CA, 1211
Stanley And Erika Tobin Foundation, CA, 1212
Stanley Family Foundation, CT, 1700
Stanley Foundation, Theodore & Vada, CT, see 1700
Stanton Foundation, Elizabeth and Oliver, The, NY, 6907
Stanton Foundation, Oliver & Elizabeth, The, NY, see 6907
Stanton Foundation, The, NY, 6908
Stanton Fund, Ruth and Frank, NY, see 6908
Staples Foundation for Learning, Inc., MA, see 4282
Staples Foundation, Inc., MA, 4282
Star Family Foundation, The, FL, 2335
Star Foundation, Stanley A., FL, see 2335
Star Foundation, TX, 9197
Starbucks Foundation, The, WA, 9742
Stardust Foundation, Inc., AZ, 164
Stare Fund, The, MA, 4283
Starfish Group, The, NY, 6909
Stark Community Foundation, OH, 7673
Stark County Foundation, Inc., The, OH, see 7673
Stark Foundation, Fran & Ray, The, CA, 1213
Stark Foundation, Nelda C. and H. J. Lutcher, TX, 9198
Stark Foundation, The, CA, see 1213
Starker Family Foundation Inc., The, NY, 6910
Starling Foundation, Dorothy Richard, TX, 9199
Starr Foundation, The, NY, 6911
Starwood Hotels and Resorts Worldwide Foundation, Inc., MA, 4284
Stasiak Private Foundation, John L., The, MD, 3889
State Auto Foundation, The, OH, 7674
State Employees' Credit Union Foundation, NC, 7321
State Farm Companies Foundation, IL, 3174
State Street Foundation, Inc., MA, 4285
Staten Island Foundation, The, NY, 6912
Statler Foundation, The, NY, 6913
Statter Foundation, Amy Plant, RI, 8441
Stauffer Charitable Trust, John, CA, 1214
Staunton Augusta Waynesboro Community Foundation, VA, see 9412
Staunton Farm Foundation, PA, 8296
Stavropoulos Family Foundation, Bill and Linda, FL, 2336
Steadley Memorial Trust, Kent D. & Mary L., RI, 8442
Steans Family Foundation, IL, 3175
Stearns Charitable Foundation, Inc., Anna B., MA, 4286
Stedman West Foundation, TX, 9200
Steel Dynamics Foundation, Inc., The, IN, 3389
Steel Family Foundation, Robert K., The, NY, 6914
Steelcase Foundation, MI, 4547
Steele Foundation, Inc., The, AZ, 165
Steele-Reese Foundation, The, NY, 6915
Steere Foundation, William & Lynda, CT, 1701
Stefanski Charitable Foundation, Ben S. & Gerome R., OH, see 7675
Stefanski Charitable Foundation, Marc A. and Rhonda L., The, OH, 7675
Stefansky Charitable Trust, Meir and Ruth, The, NY, 6916
Steffens 21st Century Foundation II, NY, 6917
Steigleder Charitable Trust, Bert L. and Patricia S., WI, 9952
Stein Family Foundation Inc., Joseph F., NY, 6918
Stein Family Foundation, Eugene and Marilyn, CA, 1215
Stein Family Foundation, FL, see 2337
Stein Foundation Inc., David A., FL, 2337
Stein Foundation Trust, Jay and Deanie, FL, 2338
Stein Foundation, Louis and Bessie, PA, 8297
Stein Memorial Foundation, Lazar and Sofia, The, NY, 6919
Stein/Bellet Foundation, Inc., PA, 8298
Steinberg 1992 Charitable Trust, Joseph S. & Diane H., NY, 6920
Steinberg Charitable Trust, Harold & Mimi, The, NY, 6921
Steinberg Family Fund, Inc., The, NY, 6922
Steinberg-Lalli Charitable Foundation, The, MA, 4287
Steiner Charitable Trust, David S. and Sylvia, The, NJ, 5467
Steinhardt Foundation, Judy and Michael, The, NY, 6923
Steiniger Charitable Foundation, Edward & Joan B., NY, 6924
Steinman Foundation, James Hale, PA, 8299
Steinman Foundation, John Frederick, PA, 8300
Steinmetz Foundation, CA, 1216
Steiro Foundation, Inc., The, NY, see 6918
Stemmons Foundation, TX, 9201
Stempel Foundation, Ernest E., NY, 6925
Stepanek Foundation Agency, Elaine F., MN, 4771
Stephens Charitable Foundation, Carol and Witt, AR, 203
Stephens Family Foundation, Harriet and Warren, AR, 204
Stephens Foundation, AL, 69
Stephens Foundation, Gerald D. & Helen M., IL, 3176
Stephenson Family Foundation, Charles and Peggy, The, OK, 7799
Stephenson Family Foundation, OK, see 7799
Stephenson Foundation, CA, 1217
Sterling Charitable Foundation, Donald T., The, CA, 1218
Sterling Family Foundation, TX, 9202
Sterling-Turner Foundation, TX, 9203
Stern Family Foundation Inc., Lawrence and R
PA, 8301
Stern Family Foundation, Alex, ND, 7360
Stern Family Foundation, Daniel and Nanna, Th
6926
Stern Family Foundation, The, CA, see 1219
Stern Family Foundation, The, NJ, 5468
Stern Family Foundation, Thomas D. & Denise R.,
6927
Stern Foundation for the Arts, Richard J., MO, 498
Stern Foundation, Bernice and Milton, NY, 6928
Stern Foundation, Inc., Gustav and Irene, FL, see 23
Stern Foundation, Inc., Steve and Bonnie, FL, 2339
Stern Foundation, Irvin, IL, 3177
Stern Foundation, Joyce C., The, NY, 6929
Stern Foundation, Marc and Eva, The, CA, 1219
Stern Memorial Trust, Sidney, TX, 9204
Sternberg Charitable Trust, NY, 6930
Sternberger Foundation, Inc., Sigmund, NC, see 7326
Sternlicht Family Foundation Inc., The, DE, 1861
Steuben County Community Foundation, IN, 3390
Stevens Charitable Foundation, Perry & Ruby, TX, 9205
Stevens Family Charitable Trust, TX, 9206
Stevens Foundation, Abbot and Dorothy H., The, MA, 4288
Stevens Foundation, Georgina G., CA, see 580
Stevens Foundation, Jess L. and Miriam B., OK, 7800
Stevens Foundation, Nathaniel & Elizabeth P., MA, 4289
Stevens Square Foundation, The, MN, 4772
Stevenson Family Charitable Trust, MA, 4290
Stevenson Foundation, Inc., Bruce and Mary, WA, 9743
Stevenson Foundation, Inc., Mary Hoyt, WA, see 9743
Steward Family Foundation, MO, 4981
Stewards Fund, The, NC, 7322
Stewardship Foundation, CA, 1220
Stewardship Foundation, The, WA, 9744
Stewart Education Foundation, AZ, 166
Stewart Educational Foundation, Donnell B. and Elizabeth Dee Shaw, AZ, see 166
Stewart Family Foundation, Sam & Diane, The, DE, 1862
Stewart Foundation, Genevieve McMillan-Reba, The, MA, 4291
Stewart Foundation, IL, 3178
Stewart Trust, Alexander and Margaret, DC, 1949
Stiefel Foundation, Ernst C., The, NY, 6931
Stifler Family Foundation, MA, 4292
Stiles-Nicholson Foundation, The, FL, 2340
Still Water Foundation, TX, 9207
Stiller Family Foundation, VT, 9372
Stine Family Foundation, IA, 3482
Stine Foundation, James M. and Margaret V., The, PA, 8302
Stip Charitable Remainder Unitrust, Milo, SD, A
Stock Foundation, Inc., K. C., WI, 9953
Stocker Foundation, The, OH, 7676
Stockman Family Foundation Trust, NY, 6932
Stoddard Charitable Trust, The, MA, 4293
Stoico/FIRSTFED Charitable Foundation, Robert F., MA, 4294
Stokely, Jr. Foundation, William B., The, TN, 8631
Stoller Family Foundation, OR, 7891
Stone Family Foundation, Inc., Michael and Karen, The, DE, 1863
Stone Family Foundation, OK, 7801
Stone Family Foundation, Roger and Susan, IL, 3179
Stone Foundation, Inc., The, WI, 9954
Stone Foundation, Irving I., OH, 7677
Stone Foundation, W. Clement & Jessie V., IL, 3180
Stone Pier Foundation, MN, 4773
Stone Trust, Georgia S., RI, 8443
Stoneleigh Foundation, PA, 8303
Stoneleigh Research and Education Center Serving Children and Youth, A., PA, see 8303
Stoneman Charitable Foundation, Inc., Anne and David, MA, see 4296
Stoneman Charitable Fund, James and Selma, MA, see 4295
Stoneman Charitable Fund, James M., MA, 4295
Stoneman Family Foundation, MA, 4296

Tartaglino-Richards Foundation, TX, 9221
Tartt Scholarship Fund, Hope Pierce, TX, 9222
Tateuchi Foundation, Atsuhiko and Ina Goodwin, The, WA, 9751
Tatuechi Foundation, WA, see 9751
Taub Foundation, Buddy, The, CA, 1240
Taub Foundation, Henry and Marilyn, The, NJ, 5477
Taub Foundation, Joseph & Arlene, NJ, 5478
Taube Family Foundation, CA, 1241
Tauber Family Foundation, Laszlo N., The, MD, 3893
Taubman Foundation for the Arts, VA, 9540
Taubman Foundation II, A. Alfred, MI, see 4552
Taubman Foundation, A. Alfred, The, MI, 4552
Taubman Foundation, Herman P. and Sophia, OK, 7804
Taubman Foundation, The, MI, 4553
Tauck Family Foundation, Inc., CT, 1706
Tauck Foundation, Inc., The, CT, see 1706
Taunton Female Charitable Association, MA, 4304
Tavitian Foundation Inc., NJ, 5479
Tawani Foundation, The, IL, see 3091
Taylor & Nancy Bryant Foundation, Jerry, FL, 2353
Taylor Charitable Trust, Jack DeLoss, WI, 9955
Taylor Family Foundation, Inc., Jack, FL, 2354
Taylor Family Foundation, Kenneth and Caroline, PA, 8311
Taylor Foundation, Crawford, The, MO, 4987
Taylor Foundation, Glen A., MN, 4777
Taylor Foundation, Patrick F., LA, 3669
Taylor Foundation, Robert and Jamie, IL, 3184
Taylor Memorial Trust, Charles H., MO, 4988
TBL Charitable Foundation, MA, 4305
TCF Bank Foundation, MN, see 4778
TCF Foundation, MN, 4778
TD Banknorth Charitable Foundation, ME, see 3710
TD Charitable Foundation, ME, 3710
TDC Foundation, The, CA, see 444
TE Connectivity Foundation, NY, 6966
Teach A Man To Fish Foundation, CA, 1242
Teach Foundation, SC, 8505
Teagle Foundation Incorporated, The, NY, 6967
Team Aerotek Foundation, Inc., MD, see 3719
TEAM Foundation, MN, 4779
TeamCFA Foundation, OR, 7893
Technical Training Foundation, MA, 4306
Tecovas Foundation, PA, 8312
Tecumseh Community Fund Foundation, MI, see 4485
Teel Family Foundation, Jim & Joyce, CA, 1243
Teferes Foundation, NY, 6968
Teichert Foundation, CA, 1244
Tekchand Foundation, CA, see 1294
Tektronix Foundation, OR, 7894
Tellabs Foundation, IL, 3185
Telluride Foundation, CO, 1512
Temple Foundation, David E. and Cassie L., The, OK, 7805
Temple Foundation, OK, see 7805
Temple Foundation, T. L. L., TX, 9223
Temple-Inland Foundation, TN, 8633
Templeton Foundation, Herbert A., OR, 7895
Templeton Foundation, John, PA, 8313
Templeton Foundation, Richard and Mary, NY, 6969
Ten Talents Foundation, MO, 4989
Ten-Ten Foundation, The, MO, 4990
Tenenbaum Foundation, AR, 206
Tenenblatt Foundation, William and Anna, CA, 1245
Tennessee Health Foundation, Inc., TN, 8634
Tensor Foundation, NY, 6970
Tepper Charitable Foundation, Inc., David, The, NJ, 5480
Terra Foundation for American Art, IL, 3186
Terra Nova Foundation, NY, 6971
Terry Charitable Foundation, Inc., R. B., NC, 7327
Terry Family Foundation, Mike and Mary, The, TX, 9224
Terry Family Foundation, Mike, The, TX, see 9224
Terry Foundation, The, TX, 9225
Terumah Foundation, Inc., NY, 6972
Tesuque Foundation, Inc., The, CA, 1246
Teubert Charitable Trust, James H. and Alice, The, WV, 9795
Teva Cares Foundation, PA, 8314
Texas Educational Association, The, MS, see 4810
Texas Flying Legends Museum, TX, 9226
Texas Instruments Foundation, TX, 9227
Texas Pioneer Arts Foundation, TX, see 8739
Texas Pioneer Foundation, TX, 9228
Textor Family Foundation, The, NY, 6973
Textron Charitable Trust, The, RI, 8446
TF Educational Foundation, CA, 1247
Thalheimer Foundation, Inc., Alvin and Fanny Blaustein, The, MD, 3894
Thank Heaven Foundation, TX, 9229
Tharpe Charitable Foundation, Inc., Max B., FL, 2355
Thatcher Foundation, CA, 1248
Thatcher Foundation, Inc., Samuel E. & Mary W., FL, 2356
Thaw Charitable Trust, Eugene V. & Clare E., NM, 5534
The Joseph D. and Lillie H. Jamail Foundation, TX, see 8929
Theobald Foundation, NY, 6974
Thewes Family Foundation, MI, 4554
Thiel Foundation, The, CA, 1249
Third Federal Foundation, OH, 7681
Thirteen Foundation, The, TX, 9230
Thirty Five Twenty, Inc., IN, see 3311
Thom and T-L Foundation, LeRoy, Jean, NE, 5089
Thomarie Foundation, The, AZ, 170
Thomas Charitable Trust, William and Helen, FL, 2357
Thomas Family Foundation, Billie and Gillis, TX, 9231
Thomas Foundation, Harold E. & Phyllis S., ID, 2645
Thomas Foundation, Inc., Joan and Lee, The, KY, see 3584
Thomas Foundation, The, TX, 9232, see 9231
Thome Memorial Foundation, Edward N. & Della L., IL, 3187
Thompson Charitable Foundation, Inc., Wade F. B., The, NY, see 6975
Thompson Charitable Foundation, The, TN, 8635
Thompson Educational Foundation, MI, 4555
Thompson Family Charitable Foundation Inc., The, FL, 2358
Thompson Family Foundation, Inc., The, NY, 6975
Thompson Family Foundation, Lucille S., TN, 8636
Thompson Foundation, Inc., The, AL, 70
Thompson Foundation, James and Angela, The, TX, see 9233
Thompson Foundation, Jim and Angela, TX, 9233
Thompson Foundation, Jon L. & Beverly A., RI, 8447
Thompson Foundation, MI, 4556
Thompson Foundation, The, WA, 9752
Thompson Foundation, William S. and Nancy E., The, CA, 1250
Thompson Trust, Thomas, MA, 4307
Thompson-Hartford Foundation, Inc., FL, 2359
Thompson-McCully Foundation, MI, see 4556
Thoresen Foundation, The, GA, 2557
Thorn, Jr. Foundation, Columbus W., MD, 3895
Thornburg Foundation, Garrett, NM, see 5535
Thornburg Foundation, NM, 5535
Thornburgh Family Foundation, The, FL, 2360
Thornedge Foundation, PA, 8315
Thornton Foundation, CA, 1251
Thornton Foundation, Charles, CA, see 1251
Thornton Foundation, Flora L., CA, 1252
Thornton Foundation, Laney, The, CA, 1253
Thornton Trust Venable Memorial Fund, FL, A
Thrasher Research Fund, UT, 9353
Three Guineas Fund, CA, 1254
Three Little Pigs Foundation, NY, 6976
Three Swallows Foundation, VA, 9541
Three Thirty Three Foundation Inc., VT, 9374
Thrive Foundation for Youth, CA, 1255
Thrivent Financial for Lutherans Foundation, WI, 9956
Thunder Bay Foundation, Inc., GA, 2558
Thurston County Community Foundation, Greater, WA, see 9605
Tianaderrah Foundation, The, NY, 6977
Tibstra Charitable Foundation, Thomas & Gertrude, NJ, A
Tickle Foundation, John D., The, VA, 9542
Tiffany & Co. Foundation, The, NY, 6978
Tiffin Charitable Foundation, The, OH, 7682
Tiger Baron Foundation, Inc., NY, 6979
Tiger Foundation, NY, 6980
Tijerina, Jr. Foundation, Raul, TX, 9234
Tikvah Fund, The, NY, 6981
Tilles Fund, The, MO, 4991
Tilles Nonsectarian Charity Fund, Rosalie, M
4991
Tillotson-Menlo Charitable Foundation, GA, 25
Time Warner Foundation, Inc., NY, 6982
Timken Company Charitable and Educational Fu
The, OH, 7683
Timken Company Charitable Trust, The, IL, 3188
Timken Company Educational Fund, Inc., The, OH
7683
Timken Foundation of Canton, OH, 7684
Tingari-Silverton Foundation, Inc., TX, 9235
Tinker Foundation Inc., The, NY, 6983
Tippit Charitable Trust, C. Carlisle and Margaret M., T
OH, 7685
Tipton County Foundation, Inc., IN, 3391
Tisch Family Foundation, Lizzie and Jonathan, The, NY
6984
Tisch Family Foundation, Steve, The, NY, 6985
Tisch Foundation, Inc., Alice M. & Thomas J., The, NY, 6986
Tisch Foundation, Inc., Andrew & Ann, The, NY, 6987
Tisch Foundation, Inc., James S. & Merryl H., The, NY, 6989
Tisch Foundation, Inc., Laurie M., The, NY, 6990
Tisch Foundation, Inc., NY, 6988
Tisch Foundation, Steve, The, NY, 6991
Tisch Foundation, Wilma S. and Laurence A., The, NY, 6992
Tishman Family Foundation, Dan and Sheryl, NY, 6993
Tishman Speyer Properties Foundation, Inc., NY, see 6896
Titmus Foundation, Inc., The, VA, 9543
Titus Foundation, C. W., OK, 7806
TJX Foundation, Inc., The, MA, 4308
TKF Foundation, MD, 3896
Toan-O'Brien Foundation, NM, 5536
Tober Foundation, Barbara and Donald, NY, 6994
Tobin Endowment, The, TX, 9236
Tocker Foundation, TX, 9237
Todd Charitable Foundation, Ruth D. and Wylie, MO, 4992
Tointon Family Foundation, The, CO, 1513
Toledo Community Foundation, Inc., OH, 7686
Toll Foundation, Bruce E. and Robbi S., The, PA, 8316
Toll Foundation, Bruce E., The, PA, see 8316
Toll Foundation, Robert and Jane, The, PA, 8317
Tollefson Family Foundation, Louise B. Blackman, FL, 2361
Tomar Foundation, Inc., NC, see 7306
Tombros Foundation, The, CT, 1707
Tomerlin Voelcker Fund, Max and Minnie, TX, 9238
Tomkat Charitable Trust, CA, 1256
TomKat Foundation, CA, 1257
Tomorrow Foundation, NY, 6995
Tomsich Foundation, OH, see 7625
Tooker Family Foundation, Gary and Diane, The, AZ, 171
Topeka Community Foundation, KS, 3552
Topfer Family Foundation, Morton & Angela, The, TX, see 9239
Topfer Family Foundation, TX, 9239
Torch Foundation, Jordan, PA, 8318
Toro Foundation, The, MN, 4780
Torrance Foundation, Mark & Susan, WA, 9753
Torrance Foundation, Mark, WA, see 9753
Torrey Foundation, CA, 1258
Tortora Family Foundation, NY, see 6996
Tortora Sillcox Family Foundation, NY, 6996
Tosa Foundation, CA, 1259
Toshiba America Foundation, NY, 6997
Total Depth Foundation, MN, 4781
Touchpoint Foundation, NJ, 5481
Toulmin Charitable Foundation III, V.B., OH, 7687
Tova Foundation, NY, 6998
Tow Charitable Trust, Inc., Leonard & Claire, The, CT, see 1708
Tow Foundation, Inc., The, CT, 1708
Towards Sustainability Foundation, MA, 4309
Towbes Foundation, The, CA, 1260
Tower Family Fund, Inc., NY, 6999
Tower Foundation, Peter and Elizabeth C., The, NY, 7000
Towerbrook Foundation, NY, 7001
Towle Family Foundation, MO, 4993

Van Eekeren Foundation, Donna, IL, 3202
Van Elslander Family Foundation, MI, 4569
Van Every Foundation, Philip L., NC, 7329
Van Houten Memorial Fund, Edward W. and Stella C., The, NC, 7330
Van Kampen Boyer Molinari Charitable Foundation, MI, 4570
Van Konynenburg Foundation, CA, 1282
van Loben Sels Foundation, CA, *see* 1283
van Loben Sels/RembeRock Foundation, CA, 1283
Van Noord Foundation, Andrew and Gladys, MI, 4571
Van Nuys Charities, J. B. & Emily, CA, 1284
Van Nuys Foundation, I. N. & Susanna H., CA, 1285
Van Sickle Foundation, Jack, NV, 5155
Van Vleet Foundation, FL, 2368
Van Voorhis Family Foundation, FL, 2369
Van Winter Charitable Foundation, Jerrold, MD, 3901
Vanberg Family Foundation, TX, 9247
Vance Charitable Foundation, Robert C., RI, 8450
Vander Maten Charitable Foundation, Larry D., MO, *see* 4989
Vanderbilt Trust, R. T., NC, 7331
VanderWeide Family Foundation, MI, 4572
VanderWeide Foundation, Robert & Cheri, MI, *see* 4572
Vanech Family Foundation, The, NJ, 5487
Vanguard Group Foundation, The, PA, 8327
Vanhoose Stewart Foundation, Inc., KY, 3604
Vanneck-Bailey Foundation, FL, 2370
Vatterott Family Foundation, Joan & John, The, FL, 2371
Vaughan Foundation, Inc., Susan, The, TX, 9248
Vaughan Foundation, MI, 4573
Vaughn Foundation, Jim M., IL, *see* 3203
Vaughn Foundation, The, IL, 3203
Veale Foundation, The, OH, 7694
Vectren Foundation, Inc., IN, 3394
Veden Charitable Trust, Frank W., MN, 4787
Vegesna Foundation, Raju, The, CA, 1286
Ventana Charitable Foundation, IL, 3204
Ventas Charitable Foundation, Inc., KY, 3605
Ventura County Community Foundation, CA, 1287
Verdoorn Family Foundation, Sid and Carol, MN, 4788
Vergara Trust, Lamar Bruni, TX, 9249
Veritas Foundation, MN, 4789
Verizon Foundation, NJ, 5489
Vermeer Charitable Foundation, IA, 3486
Vermilion Healthcare Foundation, IL, 3205
Vermont Community Foundation, VT, 9375
Vernon Foundation, Inc., Miles Hodsdon, The, NY, 7026
Versacare, Inc., CA, 1288
Vervane, Inc., CT, 1716
Vesper Foundation, OH, 7695
Vetlesen Foundation, G. Unger, The, NY, 7027
Vetter Foundation, NE, 5091
VF Foundation, The, NC, 7332
VHA Foundation, Inc., TX, 9250
VHA Health Foundation, Inc., The, TX, *see* 9250
VHIV, Inc., NY, 7028
Vibrant Village Foundation, The, OR, 7898
Vicente Foundation, Inc., Harriet and Esteban, The, NY, 7029
Vickar Charitable Foundation, L. Kerry, NC, *see* 7333
Vickar Family Foundation, Kerry & Simone, NC, 7333
Vicksburg Hospital Medical Foundation, MS, *see* 4848
Vicksburg Medical Foundation, MS, 4848
Vickter Foundation, David, The, CA, 1289
Victoria Foundation, Inc., NJ, 5490
Victory Foundation, DE, 1870
Vidalakis Family Foundation, CA, 1290
Vidda Foundation, The, NY, 7030
Viersen Family Foundation, Inc., Sam, OK, 7808
Viking Global Foundation Inc., CT, 1717
Vilcek Foundation, Inc., The, NY, 7031
Villa Banfi Foundation, The, NY, *see* 5641
Vince Club Family Foundation, The, IL, *see* 3097
Vincent Foundation, Inc., Thomas J., HI, 2619
Vincent Foundation, James L., The, MA, 4315
Vine and Branches Foundation, Inc., WI, 9960
Vinik Family Foundation, FL, 2372
Viola Fund, The, NY, 7032
Viragh Family Foundation, MD, 3902
Viragh Foundation, Inc., Skip, The, NV, 5156
Virginia Scrap Iron & Metal Co. Charitable Foundation, Inc., VA, *see* 9443
Viropharma Charitable Foundation, PA, 8328
Visiting Nurse Association of Chicago, IL, *see* 3206
Vista Hermosa, WA, 9756
Vital Projects Fund, Inc., NY, 7033
Vivint Giveback Foundation, The, UT, 9354
VNA Foundation, IL, 3206
Vodafone Americas Foundation, CO, 1519
Vodafone-US Foundation, CO, *see* 1519
Vogel Charities Inc., IA, 3487
Vogelstein Charitable Trust, John L., NY, *see* 7034
Vogelstein Foundation, John and Barbara, The, NY, 7034
Voice of Peace Foundation, Inc., IL, 3207
Voice of Peace, Inc., IL, *see* 3207
Volcker Family Foundation, Inc., The, NY, 7035
Volentine Family Foundation, CA, 1291
Volentine Foundation, Myatt W., CA, *see* 1291
Volgenau Charitable Foundation, The, VA, 9549
Vollintine Charitable Trust, Leona Stanford, IL, 3208
Vollmer Foundation, Inc., FL, 2373
Volo Non Valeo Foundation Inc., IN, 3395
Volpert Foundation, Barry and Teri, NY, 7036
von der Heyden Family Foundation, The, NY, 7037
von Hess Foundation, Richard C., The, PA, 8329
Von Voigtlander Foundation, Ted & Jane, MI, 4574
Vortex Foundation, OH, 7696
Voss Charitable Trust, Omer G. & Annabelle K., The, CA, *see* 1292
Voss Family Foundation, Omer G., The, CA, 1292
Voya Foundation, NY, 7038
Vradenburg Foundation, DC, 1954
Vranos Family Foundation, The, CT, 1718
Vucurevich Foundation, John T., SD, 8524
Vulcan Materials Company Foundation, AL, 73

W. I. H. Pitts Memorial Fund, FL, A
W.M. Foundation, MN, 4790
Wabash Valley Community Foundation, Inc., IN, 3396
Waccamaw Community Foundation, SC, 8507
Wachenheim Foundation, Sue and Edgar, NY, 7039
Wachovia Regional Foundation, PA, *see* 8333
Wachtell, Lipton, Rosen & Katz Foundation, NY, 7040
Waco Foundation, TX, 9251
Wade Family Charitable Foundation, CA, 1293
Wade Memorial Fund, Ellen Garretson, OH, 7697
Wadhwani Foundation, CA, 1294
Wadleigh Foundation, Inc., George C., MA, 4316
Wadleigh Home for Aged Men, Inc., George C., MA, *see* 4316
Wadsworth Golf Charities Foundation, OH, 7698
Waggoner Charitable Trust, Crystelle, TX, 9252
Waggoner Foundation, Don & Zelma, FL, 2374
Wagler Charitable Foundation, Phil, The, OH, 7699
Wagner Charitable Foundation, I.J. and Jeanne, The, UT, 9355
Wagner Family Foundation, Inc., The, NJ, 5491
Wagner Family Foundation, MA, 4317
Wagner Foundation, Ltd., R. H., WI, *see* 9961
Wagner Foundation, Ltd., The, WI, 9961
Wagner Foundation, Todd, TX, 9253
Waitt Family Foundation, CA, *see* 1295
Waitt Foundation, CA, 1295
Wal-Dot Foundation, TX, 9254
Wal-Mart Foundation, AR, *see* 210
Wal-Mart Foundation, Inc., The, AR, 210
Walbridge Fund, The, NY, 7041
Waldheim Charitable Foundation, Lesley A., The, MO, 4997
Waldorf Educational Foundation, The, PA, 8330
Waldron Charitable Foundation, Inc., Elbert H., Evelyn J. and Karen H., VA, 9550
Walentas Foundation, Ltd., NY, 7042
Walgreen Benefit Fund, IL, 3209
Walgreens Assistance, Inc., IL, 3210
Walker Area Community Foundation, AL, 74
Walker Charitable Foundation, Inc., Willard and Pat, AR, 209
Walker Charitable Trust, Jay P., IL, 3211
Walker Foundation, MS, 4849
Walker Foundation, Shaw and Betty, MI, 4575
Walker Foundation, Shaw, MI, *see* 4575
Walker Foundation, Stanley D. and Kay B., GA, 2567
Walker Foundation, W. E., MS, *see* 4849
Wall Foundation, Inc., Vance, NJ, 5492
Wallace Charitable Memorial Foundation, Inc. Alice, OH, 7700
Wallace Family Foundation, Edward W. Kane & J., The, MA, 4318
Wallace Foundation, Louise B., TN, 8642
Wallace Foundation, The, NY, 7043
Wallace Genetic Foundation, Inc., DC, 1955
Wallace Global Fund II, DC, 1956
Wallace Research Foundation, IA, 3488
Wallace-Reader's Digest Funds, NY, *see* 7043
Wallach Foundation, Mary and James G., NY, 7044
Wallach Foundation, Miriam G. and Ira D., NY, A
Wallerstein Foundation for Geriatric Life Improvemen NJ, 5493
Wallerstein Institute, Johanette, NJ, 5494
Wallestad Foundation, MN, 4791
Wallin Education Partners, MN, 4792
Wallin Foundation, MN, 4793
Walling Family Foundation, Halbert, TX, *see* 8749
Wallis Foundation, CA, 1296
Wallrath Educational Foundation, Richard, TX, 9255
Walmart Foundation, The, AR, *see* 210
Walsh Foundation, Mark A. & Lisa J., The, NY, 7045
Walsh Foundation, The, IL, 3212
Walsh Foundation, TX, 9256
Walter & Lorenz Foundation, Inc., ME, *see* 3711
Walter Christian Development Foundation, TX, 9257
Walter Corporation Foundation, Jim, FL, *see* 2375
Walter Family Trust, Byron L., IL, 3213
Walter Foundation, Inc., Otto and Fran, ME, 3711
Walter Foundation, Rosalind P., The, NY, 7046
Walter Foundation, The, FL, 2375
Walther Cancer Foundation, Inc., IN, 3397
Walther Cancer Institute Foundation, Inc., IN, *see* 3397
Walton Family Foundation, Inc., AR, 211
Wanek Family Foundation, Ltd., Todd & Karen, The, WI, 9962
Wanek Foundation, Ltd., Ronald & Joyce, The, WI, 9963
Wanek-Vogel Foundation, Ltd., The, WI, 9964
Wang Family Charitable Foundation, The, NY, 7047
Wang Foundation, The, MA, 4319
Wang International Foundation, Charles B., The, NJ, 5495
Wanzek Family Foundation, ND, 7361
Waraich Charitable Foundation, Riaz H., IL, 3214
Warburg Pincus Foundation, The, NY, 7048
Warburton Foundation, Ralph T. & Esther L., The, PA, 8331
Ward Charity Trust, Eugenie Phyllis, IL, 3215
Ward Foundation, A. Montgomery, IL, 3216
Ward Foundation, Louis L. & Adelaide C., MO, 4998
Ward Foundation, Michael and Kim, The, NY, 7049
Ward Foundation, Michael, The, NY, *see* 7049
Ward Foundation, MO, *see* 4998
Ward Heritage Foundation, Mamie McFaddin, TX, 9258
Wardlaw Charitable Trust, Edna, FL, 2376
Wardlaw Fund, Gertrude and William C., The, FL, 2377
Wardle Family Foundation, VA, 9551
Ware Foundation, The, FL, 2378
Ware Foundation, The, TX, 9259
Wareheim Foundation, E. C., MD, 3903
Warhol Foundation for the Visual Arts, Andy, The, NY, 7050
Warmenhoven Family Foundation, OH, 7701
Warnack Foundation, The, CA, 1297
Warnaco Foundation, The, NY, 7051
Warner Foundation, Inc., AL, 75
Warner Foundation, Inc., D. Michael, The, NC, *see* 7334
Warner Foundation, The, NC, 7334
Warner Foundation, The, NY, 7052
Warner Fund, Inc., Joseph Leroy and Ann C., The, NY, 7053
Warren and Beatrice W. Blanding Foundation, Riley J. & Lillian N., The, NY, 7054
Warren County Foundation, OH, 7702
Warren Foundation, Diane, The, CA, 1298
Warren Foundation, The, PA, *see* 7993
Warren Foundation, William K., The, OK, 7809
Warrington Foundation, The, OH, 7703
Warsh-Mott Legacy, CA, 1299
Washington County Charitable Trust, Mathias, The, MD, 3904

F

Whispering Fox Foundation, CO, 1522
Whitacre Family Foundation, TX, 9273
Whitaker Charitable Foundation, Lyndon C. and Mae M., MO, *see* 5001
Whitaker Foundation, MO, 5001
White Charitable Trust, Sherman White, Jr. and Virginia H., OH, 7714
White Family Foundation, Bruce and Beth, The, IN, 3405
White Family Foundation, Inc., Dean & Barbara, IN, 3406
White Foundation, Howard & Betty, The, CA, 1321
White Foundation, Thomas H., OH, *see* 7715
White Foundation, W. P. and H. B., IL, 3229
White Horse Youth Ranch, NV, 5158
White Lick Heritage Community Foundation, Inc., The, IN, *see* 3319
White Memorial Foundation, Bob, AR, 212
White No. 1 Trust, Thomas H., The, OH, 7715
White Trust, G. R., IL, 3230
White Trust, Melovee, TX, 9274
Whitefish Community Foundation, MT, 5019
Whitehall Foundation, Inc., FL, 2385
Whitehead Foundation, Joseph B., GA, 2571
Whitener Family Foundation, TX, 9275
Whiteside Scholarship Fund Trust, MN, 4805
Whiteside Scholarship Fund, Robert B. and Sophia, MN, *see* 4805
Whiting Foundation, Mrs. Giles, NY, 7079
Whiting Foundation, NY, *see* 7079
Whiting Foundation, The, MI, 4584
Whitley County Community Foundation, IN, 3407
Whitlock Foundation, W.W., VA, 9556
Whitman Institute, The, CA, 1322
Whitney Benefits, Inc., WY, 9998
Whitney Foundation, Helen Hay, The, NY, 7080
Whittier Foundation, CA, *see* 1323
Whittier Foundation, L. K., CA, 1323
Whittingham Family Foundation Inc., The, CT, 1720
Whitton-Spector Foundation, DE, 1874
Whitwell-Meyer Foundation, The, OK, 7813
Whole Planet Foundation, TX, 9276
Wiancko Charitable Foundation Inc., WA, 9761
Wichita Community Foundation, Greater, KS, *see* 3555
Wichita Community Foundation, KS, 3555
Wichita Falls Area Community Foundation, TX, 9277
Wickes Foundation, Harvey Randall, MI, 4585
Wicks Chapin Inc, NJ, 5500
Widener Memorial Foundation in Aid of Handicapped Children, PA, 8336
Widgeon Point Charitable Foundation, The, NY, 7081
Wieboldt Foundation, IL, 3231
Wiederhold Foundation, John T. and Jane A., CT, 1721
Wiegand Foundation, E. L., NV, 5159
Wiegand Morning Star Foundation, Inc., PA, 8337
Wiegers Family Foundation, The, NY, 7082
Wiener Foundation, Inc., Malcolm Hewitt, NY, 7083
Wiener, Jr. Foundation, William B., LA, 3670
Wiggins Foundation Inc., The, CT, 1722
Wight Foundation, Inc., The, NJ, 5501
Wilburforce Foundation, The, WA, 9762
Wilcox Family Foundation, CA, 1324
Wilcox Trust, George N., HI, 2621
Wildcat Foundation, The, TX, 9278
Wilderness Point Foundation, MA, 4323
Wildflower Foundation, FL, 2386
Wildflower Foundation, Inc., The, FL, 2387
Wildwood Foundation, The, NY, 7084
Wilemal Fund, IL, 3232
Wilf Family Foundation, NJ, 5502
Wilf Foundation, Inc., Z. S. & M., NJ, 5503
Wilf Foundation, Zygmunt & Audrey, NJ, 5504
Wilke Family Foundation, The, DE, 1875
Wilks Family Foundation, Harry T., OH, 7716
Wille Family Foundation, RI, 8451
Willett Charitable Foundation, William Gerald, The, VA, 9557
Willett Foundation, Harry L., CO, 1523
Williams Charitable Foundation, Ronald & Ann, CA, 1325
Williams Companies Foundation, Inc., The, OK, 7814
Williams Family Foundation of Georgia, Inc., GA, 2572
Williams Family Foundation, MI, 4586
Williams Family Foundation, Nell, IL, 3234
Williams Family Foundation, The, CO, 1524
Williams Family Foundation, Todd A., TX, 9279
Williams Foundation, C. K., The, PA, 8338
Williams Foundation, Edna Sproull, FL, 2388
Williams Foundation, Inc., Jesse Parker, GA, 2573
Williams Foundation, Sara & Evan, CA, 1326
Williams II Trust, Charles K., PA, 8339
Williams, Hobart W., IL, 3233
Williams, Jr. Family Foundation Inc., A. L., GA, 2575
Williams, Jr. Family Foundation, Inc., James M., GA, 2574
Williams-Corbett Foundation, CA, 1327
Williamsburg Community Foundation, VA, *see* 9559
Williamsburg Community Health Foundation, VA, 9558
Williamsburg Community Trust, Greater, VA, 9559
Williamsport-Lycoming Foundation, PA, *see* 8040
Willis Foundation, Hilda M., PA, 8340
Willits Foundation, The, NJ, 5505
Willmas Charitable Trust, MI, 4587
Willow Springs Charitable Trust, IL, 3235
Willumstad Family Charitable Trust, NY, 7085
Wilshire Charitable Foundation, OK, 7815
Wilson Charitable Foundation, Jasper L. & Jack Denton, IL, 3236
Wilson Charitable Trust "A", L.E., NC, 7337
Wilson Charitable Trust, Blair J., TN, 8645
Wilson Charitable Trust, Robert W., The, NY, 7086
Wilson Family Foundation, Edward M., PA, 8341
Wilson Family Foundation, Kemmons, The, TN, 8646
Wilson Family Foundation, The, NC, 7338
Wilson Foundation, Anne Potter, IL, 3237
Wilson Foundation, Huey and Angelina, LA, 3671
Wilson Foundation, Inc., Frances Wood, The, GA, 2576
Wilson Foundation, Inc., H. W., The, NY, 7087
Wilson Foundation, Marie C. and Joseph C., NY, 7088
Wilson Foundation, Ralph C., MI, 4588
Wilson Fund, Matilda R., MI, 4589
Wilson Public Trust, Ralph, TX, 9280
Wilson Sanitarium for Children of Baltimore City, Thomas, MD, 3909
Wilson Thornhill Foundation, CA, 1328
Wilson, Jr. Foundation, Janet H. and T. Henry, NC, *see* 7338
Windgate Charitable Foundation, Inc., AR, 213
Windhover Foundation, Inc., WI, 9968
Windie Foundation, CO, *see* 1525
Windmill Foundation, Inc., The, CT, 1723
Windmill Lane Foundation, The, NY, 7089
Windom, Judy, GA, *see* 2539
Windover Foundation, The, MA, 4324
Windreich Family Foundation Inc., CT, 1724
Windsong Trust, CA, 1329
Windsor Foundation Trust, FL, 2389
Wine and Art Educational Foundation, Jan and Mitsuko, The, CA, 1330
Wings of Freedom Foundation, CA, 1331
Winiarski Family Foundation, CA, 1332
Winkelried Family Foundation, The, NY, *see* 7090
Winkelried Foundation, Jon & Abby, The, NY, 7090
Winkler Family Foundation, TX, 9281
Winley Foundation, NY, 7091
Winn Family Foundation, TX, 9282
Winn-Dixie Foundation, Inc., FL, *see* 1996
Winnick Family Foundation, The, CA, 1333
Winnick Foundation, Gary and Karen, The, CA, *see* 1333
Winona Area Community Foundation, Greater, MN, *see* 4806
Winona Community Foundation, MN, 4806
WinShape Centre, Inc., GA, *see* 2577
WinShape Foundation, Inc., GA, 2577
Winslow Foundation, The, CO, 1525
Winslow Residuary Trust, W. R., NC, 7339
Winstar Institute, PA, 8342
Winston Foundation, Inc., Norman and Rosita, The, NY, *see* 7092
Winston Foundation, Inc., The, NY, 7092
Winston Hope Foundation, Inc., Harry, NY, 7093
Winston-Salem Foundation, The, NC, 7340
Winter Charitable Foundation, Inc., MA, *see* 4050
Winter Park Health Foundation, FL, 2390
Winter Park Memorial Hospital Association, Inc., FL, *see* 2390
Wintermann Foundation, David and Eula, TX, 9283
Winters Family Fund, The, NY, 7094
Wiregrass Foundation, AL, 77
Wirshup Family Foundation, CA, *see* 1159
Wirth Foundation Inc., Paul, John, Anton & Do 5095
Wischer Education Foundation, Irene S., TX, 92
Wisconsin Electric System Foundation, Inc., WI, 9969
Wisconsin Energy Corporation Foundation, Inc., V 9969
Wisconsin Power and Light Foundation, Inc., WI, s 9804
Wisconsin Public Service Foundation, WI, 9970
Wisdom Family Foundation, Inc, OK, 7816
Wise Foundation & Charitable Trust, Watson W., TX, s 9285
Wise Foundation, VA, 9560
Wise Foundation, Watson W., TX, 9285
Wiser Charitable Foundation Trust, Bob, The, VA, 9561
Wishes By Wyndham Foundation, NJ, 5506
Wishnick Foundation, Robert I., The, ID, 2646
Wishnick Foundation, William, The, ID, *see* 2646
Wiskemann Family Foundation, The, CA, *see* 908
Wismer Foundation, Joan M., The, PA, 8343
Witco Foundation, The, ID, *see* 2646
Witherbee Foundation, CA, 1334
Withington Foundation, Inc., PA, 8344
Witten Family Foundation, Richard & Elizabeth, NY, 7095
Witter Foundation, Dean, CA, 1335
WJS Foundation, Inc., NY, *see* 6843
WLC and SBC Family Foundation, NY, 7096
WLT Foundation, The, SC, 8508
Wockner Foundation, WA, 9763
Wodecroft Foundation, OH, 7717
Wohl Family Foundation, Inc., Diane & Howard, NY, 7097
Wohlers Family Foundation, IL, 3238
Wohlford Foundation, Mary, CA, 1336
Wohlgemuth Herschede Foundation, The, OH, 7718
Woldenberg Foundation, Dorothy & Malcolm, LA, *see* 3672
Woldenberg Foundation, The, LA, 3672
Wolf Creek Charitable Foundation, The, PA, 8345
Wolf Family Foundation, Randall A., CA, 1337
Wolf Foundation Inc., Melvin and Elaine, CO, 1526
Wolf Memorial Trust, George, DC, 1957
Wolf Mountain Foundation, CO, 1527
Wolfe Associates, OH, 7719
Wolfe Foundation, Betty K., The, FL, 2391
Wolfen Family Foundation, CA, 1338
Wolfensohn Family Foundation, NY, 7098
Wolff Family Foundation, Jean & Lewis, MI, 4590
Wolff Foundation, Cyvia and Melvyn, TX, 9286
Wolff Memorial Foundation, Pauline Sterne, TX, 9287
Wolfson Foundation, Louis E., MA, 4325
Wolfson, Sr. Foundation, Mitchell, FL, 2392
Wolk Foundation, Louis S. & Molly B., NY, 7099
Wollenberg Foundation, CA, 1339
Wollowick Family Foundation, FL, 2393
Wollowick Foundation, Inc., Rubin and Gladys, FL, *see* 2393
Wolohan Family Foundation, MI, 4591
Wolslager Foundation, The, TX, 9288
Wolstencroft Family Foundation, The, NY, 7100
Wolters Foundation, Kate and Richard, MI, 4592
Wolverine World Wide Foundation, MI, 4593
Woman's Christian Association, MN, *see* 4795
Women's Independence Scholarship Program, Inc., NC, 7341
Women's Project Foundation, OH, 7720
Womens Self Worth Foundation, CA, 1340
Wonderful Life Foundation, IL, 3239
Wong Foundation, Dsea, CA, 1341
Wong Foundation, Harry Chow & Nee-Chang Chock, HI, 2622
Wong Foundation, I. S., CA, 1342
Wonner Foundation, William Brown & Paul, The, CA, 1343
Wood Charitable Foundation, Inc., Clay and Louise, TX, *see* 9289
Wood Family Charitable Foundation, Inc., TX, 9289
Wood Family Foundation, WA, *see* 9695

F